standard catalog of

fourth edition

BASEBALL CARDS

the most comprehensive price guide ever published!

By the
Price Guide Editors
of Sports Collectors Digest

Edited by Bob Lemke

Special Consultants

John Brigandi
Dwight Chapin
Larry Fritsch
Dick Goddard
Don Harrison
Rob Lifson
Mark Macrae
Mike Mosier
John Spalding
Al Strumpf

Published by:

700 E. State Street • Iola, WI 54990-0001

Library of Congress Catalog Number: 88-80850

ISBN: 0-87341-322-9

Printed in the United States of America

ACKNOWLEDGEMENTS

Dozens of individuals have made countless valuable contributions which have been incorporated into the *Standard Catalog of Baseball Cards.* While all cannot be acknowledged, special appreciation is extended to the following principal contributors who have exhibited a special dedication by creating, revising or verifying listings and technical data, reviewing market valuations or loaning cards for photography.

Johnny Adams, Jr.
Ken Agona
(*Sports Cards Plus*)
Gary Agostino
Lisa Albano
Dan Albaugh
Mark Anker
Steve Applebaum
Bill Ballew
Chuck Baugh
(*Texas Rangers*)
John Beisiegel
Karen Bell
Dr. Charles E. Belles
Cathy Black
Mike Bodner
Bill Bossert
(*Mid-Atlantic Coin Exchange*)
Brian Boston
Mike Boyd
Jon Brecka
John Brigandi
(*Brigandi Coin Co.*)
Lou Brown
Dan Bruner
(*The Card King*)
Greg Bussineau
(*Superior Sports Cards*)
Billy Caldwell
(*Packman*)
Len Caprisecca
Tony Carrafiell
(*Delco Sports Cards*)
Brian Cataquet
Lee Champion
Dwight Chapin
Chriss Christiansen
Shane Cohen
(*Grand Slam Sports Collectibles*)
Rich Cole
Charles Conlon
Eric Cooper
(*All Star Cards*)
Bryan Couling
Bob Crabill
Clyde Cripe
Jim Cumpton
Robert Curtiss
Tom Daniels
(*T&J Sports Cards*)
James Davis
Tom Day
Dick DeCourcy
Ken Degnan
(*Georgia Music & Sports*)
Mike Del Gado
(*All American Sportscards*)
Larry Dluhy
(*Texas Trading Cards*)
John Dorsey
Curtis Earl
Mark Elliott
Joe Esposito
(*B&E Collectibles*)
Doak Ewing
Shirley Eross
(*Hobbyrama Sports by Eross*)
David Festberg
(*Baseball and Hobby Shop*)
Jay Finglass
Nick Flaviano
Jeff Fritsch
Larry Fritsch
Richard Galasso
Tom Galic
Tony Galovich
(*American Card Exchange*)
Frank Giffune
Richard Gilkeson
Gerald J. Glasser
Dick Goddard
Jack Goodman
Bill Goodwin
(*St. Louis Baseball Cards*)
Audre Gold
(*Au Sports Memorabilia*)
Keith David Goldfarb
(*K.Gold Sports*)
Howard Gordon
Mike Gordon
Bob Gray
Paul Green
Wayne Grove
(*First Base*)
Gerry Guenther
Don Guilbert
Tom Guilfoile
Julie Haddon
David, Joel & Walter Hall
(*Hall's Nostalgia*)
Gary Hamilton
Tom Harbin
Don Harrison
Rich Hawksley
Herbert Hecht
Bill Henderson
Kathy Henry
Steve Hershkowitz
Gregg Hitesman
Dennis Hollenbeck
Jack Horkan
Jim Horne
Ron Hosmer
Marvin Huck
Robert Jacobsen
Donn Jennings
David Jenkins
Scott Jensen
Jim Johnston
Stewart Jones
Larry Jordan
Judy Kay
(*Kay's Baseball Cards*)
Allan Kaye
Michael Keedy
Mark Kemmerle
Rick Keplinger
Kit Kiefer
John King
John Kitleson
(*Sports Collectibles*)
Bob Koehler
David Kohler
Michael Kott
(*Highland Mint*)
Steve Lacasse
Lee Lasseigne
Mark K. Larson
William Lawrence
Scott Lawson
Morley Leeking
Don Lepore
Rod Lethbridge
Howie Levy
(*Blue Chip Sportscard*)
Neil Lewis
Rob Lifson
Lew Lipset
Ken & Norman Liss
Jeff Litteral
Chuck Lobenthal
Mark MacRae
Ken Magee
Paul Marchant
Bill Mastro
Jay McCracken
Tony McLaughlin
Don McPherson
John Mehlin
Bill Mendel
Blake Meyer
(*Lone Star Sportcard Co.*)
Dick Millerd
Minnesota Sports Collectibles
Keith Mitchell
J.A. Monaco
Joe Morano
Brian Morris
Mike Mowery
Peter Mudavin
Mark Murphy
(*The Baseball Card "Kid"*)
Vincent Murray
David Musser
(*D.M.B.'s Baseball Cards*)
Frank Nagy
Joe Newman
Bill Nicolls
Chuck Nobriga
Mark Nochta
Wayne Nochta
Keith Olbermann
Joe Pasternack
(*Card Collectors Co.*)
Marty Perry
Tom Pfirrman
(*Baseball Card Corner*)
Dan Piepenbrok
(*Uneeda Hobbie*)
Stan Pietruska
(*Pro Sports Investments*)
Paul Pollard
Ed Ransom
Fred Rapoport
(*Yesterday's Heroes*)
Bob Richardson
Gavin Riley
Ron Ritzler
Mike Rodell
Mike Rogers
Chris Ronan
Tom Reid
Rocky Rosato
Alan Rosen
John Rumierz
Bob Rund
Jon Sands
(*Howard's Coin Shop*)
Kevin Savage
(*The Sports Gallery*)
Stephen Schauer
Dave Schwartz
(*Dave's Sportscards*)
Robert Scott
Corey Shanus
Dan Shedrick
Max Silberman
Barry Sloate
Joe Smith
Mark Soltan
John Spalding
Kevin Spears
Gene Speranza
David Spivack
Don Steinbach
Dan Stickney
Larry Stone
Doug Stultz
Jim Suckow
Joe Szeremet
Erik Teller
K.J. Terplak
Dick Tinsley
Bud Tompkins
(*Minnesota Connection*)
Scott Torrey
Rich Unruh
Jack Urban
Joe Valle
Pete Waldman
Eric Waller
Gary Walter
Ken Weimer
Dale Weselowski
Jeff T. Weis
E.C. Wharton-Tigar
Charles Williamson
Bill Wright
Kit Young
Ted Zanidakis

standard catalog of

BASEBALL CARDS

The most comprehensive price guide ever published

HOW TO USE THIS CATALOG

This catalog has been uniquely designed to serve the needs of all collectors, from beginning to advanced. It provides a comprehensive guide to more than 100 years of baseball card issues. The catalog is arranged so that even the most novice collector can consult it with confidence and ease.

The following explanations summarize the general practices used in preparing this catalog's listings. However, because of specialized requirements which may vary from card set to card set, these must not be considered ironclad. Where these standards have been set aside, appropriate notations are usually incorporated.

ARRANGEMENT

Because the most important feature in identifying, and pricing, a baseball card is its set of origin, the main body of this catalog, covering cards issued from 1886-date, has been alphabetically arranged according to the name by which the set is most popularly known to collectors or by which it can be most easily identified by a person examining a card.

Previous editions of this catalog have relied heavily upon card set identification numbers originated in the *American Card Catalog*. However, since that work was last updated more than 30 years ago its numbering system has become arcane and is of little use to the present generation of hobbyists. Where practical, sets which were listed in previous editions by their ACC designations have been reclassified alphabetically by a more readily identifiable signpost, such as manufacturer's name. Those sets continue to bear the ACC catalog number in the set heading and will be cross-referenced in the table of contents.

Those sets which were issued for more than one year are then listed chronologically, from earliest to most recent.

Within each set, the cards are listed by their designated card number, or in the absence of card numbers, alphabetically according to the last name of the player pictured. Listing numbers found in parenthesis indicate the number does not appear on the card. Certain cards which fall outside the parameters of the normal card numbering for a specific set may be found at the beginning or end of the listings for that set.

Listings are generally arranged in two major sections. The main body of the book lists major league baseball cards and related collectibles which were — prior to 1991 — originally issued as a premium with the purchase of another product or service. Following is a seperate section of the catalog which chronicles those issues which exclusively feature minor league players, draft pick issues and related collectibles.

IDENTIFICATION

While most modern baseball cards are well identified on front, back or both, as to date and issue, such has not always been the case. In general, the back of the card is more useful in identifying the set of origin than the front. The issuer or sponsor's name will usually appear on the back since, after all, baseball cards were first produced as a promotional item to stimulate sales of other products. As often as not, that issuer's name is the name by which the set is known to collectors and under which it will be found listed in this catalog.

As a special feature, each set listed in this catalog has been cross-indexed by its date of issue. This will allow identification in some difficult cases because a baseball card's general age, if not specific year of issue, can usually be fixed by studying the biological or statistical information on the back of the card. The last year mentioned in either the biography or stats is usually the year which preceded the year of issue.

PHOTOGRAPHS

A photograph of the front and back of at least one representative card from virtually every set listed in this catalog has been incorporated into the listings to aid in identification. (Persons who can provide sample cards for photography purposes for those sets which are mising photos in this volume are encouraged to contact the editor.)

Photographs have been printed in reduced size. The actual size of cards in each set is usually given in the introductory text preceding its listing. Cards which lack a specific mention of size should be presumed to be in the now-standard 2-1/2" x 3-1/2" format.

DATING

The dating of baseball cards by year of issue on the front or back of the card itself is a relatively new phenomenon. In most cases, to accurately determine a date of issue for an unidentified card, it must be studied for clues. As mentioned, the biography, career summary or statistics on the back of the card are the best way to pinpoint a year of issue. In most cases, the year of issue will be the year after the last season mentioned on the card.

Luckily for today's collector, earlier generations have done much of the research in determining year of issue for those cards which bear no clues. The painstaking task of matching players' listed and/or pictured team against their career records often allowed an issue date to be determined.

In some cases, particular card sets were issued over a period of more than one calendar year, but since they are collected together as a single set, their specific year of issue is not important. Such sets will be listed with their complete known range of issue years.

NUMBERING

While many baseball card issues as far back as the 1880s have contained card numbers assigned by the issuer to facilitate the collecting of a complete set the practice has by no means been universal. Even today, not every set bears card numbers.

Logically, those baseball cards which were numbered by their manufacturer are presented in that numerical order within the listings of this catalog. The many unnumbered issues, however, have been assigned catalog numbers to facilitate their universal identification within the hobby, especially when buying and selling by mail. In all cases, numbers which have been assigned, or which otherwise do not appear on the card through error or by design, are shown in this catalog within parentheses. In virtually all cases, unless a more natural system suggested itself by the unique matter of a particular set, the assignment of numbers by the cataloging staff has been done by alphabetical arrangement of the players' last names or the card's principal title.

Significant collectible variations of any particular card are noted within the listings by the application of a suffix letter within parentheses. In instances of variations, the suffix "a" is assigned to the variation which was created first, when it can be so identified.

NAMES

The identification of a player by full name on the front of his baseball card has been a common practice only since the 1920s. Prior to that, the player's last name and team were the usual information found on the card front.

As a standard practice, the listings in this volume present the player's name exactly as it appears on the front of the card. If the player's full name only appears on the back, rather than on the front of the card, the listing usually corresponds to that designation.

In cases where only the player's last name is given on the card, the cataloging staff has included the first name by which he was most often known for ease of identification.

Cards which contain misspelled first or last names, or even wrong initials, will usually have included in their listings the incorrect information, with a correction accompanying in parentheses. This extends, also, to cases where the name on the card does not correspond to the player actually pictured.

In some cases, to facilitate efficient presentations, to maintain ease of use for the reader, or to allow for proper computer sorting of data, a player's name or card title may be listed other than as it appears on the card.

GRADING

It is necessary that some sort of card grading standard be used so that buyer and seller (especially when dealing by mail) may reach an informed agreement on the value of a card.

Each card set's listings are generally priced in Krause Publications' price guides in three grades of preservation in which those cards are most commonly encountered in the daily buying and selling of the hobby marketplace.

Older cards (pre-1981) are listed in grades of Near Mint (NR MT), Excellent (EX) and Very Good (VG), reflecting the basic fact that few cards were able to survive for 25, 50 or even 100 years in close semblance to the condition of their issue.

The pricing of cards in these three conditions will allow readers to accurately price cards which fall in intermediate grades, such as EX-MT, or VG-EX.

More recent issues, which have been preserved in top condition in considerable number, are listed in the grades of Mint (MT), Near Mint and Excellent, reflective of the fact that there exists in the current market little or no demand for cards of the recent past in grades below Excellent.

In general, although grades below Very Good are not generally priced in price guides, close approximations of low-grade card values may be figured on the following formula: Good condition cards are valued at about 50 percent of VG price, with Fair cards about 50 percent of Good.

Cards in Poor condition have no market value except in the cases of the rarest and most expensive cards. In such cases, value has to be negotiated individually.

For the benefit of the reader, we present herewith the grading guide which was originally formulated by *Baseball Cards* (now *Sports Cards*) magazine and *Sports Collectors Digest* in 1981, and has been continually refined since that time.

These grading definitions have been used in the pricing of cards in this book, but they are by no means a universally-accepted grading standard.

The potential buyer of a baseball card should keep that in mind when encountering cards of nominally the same grade, but at a price which differs widely from that quoted in this book.

Ultimately, the collector himself must formulate his own personal grading standards in deciding whether cards available for purchase meet the needs of his own collection.

No collector is required to adhere to the grading standards presented herewith — or to any other published grading standards — but all are invited to do so. The editors of Krause Publications' sports books and price guides are eager to work toward the development of a standardized system of card grading that will be consistent with the realities of the hobby marketplace. Contact the editors.

Mint (MT): A perfect card. Well-centered, with parallel borders which appear equal to the naked eye. Four sharp, square corners. No creases, edge dents, surface scratches, paper flaws, loss of luster, yellowing or fading, regardless of age. No imperfectly printed card — out of register, badly cut or ink flawed — or card stained by contact with gum, wax or other substances can be considered truly Mint, even if new out of the pack. Generally, to be considered in Mint condition, a card's borders must exist in a ratio of 60/40 side to side and top to bottom.

Near Mint (NR MT): A nearly perfect card. At first glance, a Near Mint card appears perfect; upon closer examination, however, a minor flaw will be discovered. On well-centered cards, three of the four corners must be perfectly sharp; only one corner shows a minor imperfection upon close inspection. A slightly off-center card with one or more borders being noticeably unequal — but still present — would also fit this grade.

Excellent (EX): Corners are still fairly sharp with only moderate wear. Card borders may be off center. No creases. May have very minor gum, wax or product stains, front or back. Surfaces may show slight loss of luster from rubbing across other cards.

Very Good (VG): Show obvious handling. Corners rounded and/or perhaps showing minor creases. Other minor creases may be visible. Surfaces may exhibit loss of luster, but all printing is intact. May show major gum, wax or other packaging stains. No major creases, tape marks or extraneous markings or writing. Exhibits honest wear.

Good (G) (generally 50% of the VG price): A well-worn card, but exhibits no intentional damage or abuse. May have major or multiple creases. Corners rounded well beyond the border.

Fair (F) (generally 50% of the Good price): Shows excessive wear, along with damage or abuse. Will show all the wear characteristics of a Good card, along with such damage as thumb tack holes in or near margins, evidence of having been taped or pasted, perhaps small tears around the edges, or creases so heavy as to break the cardboard. Backs may show minor added pen or pencil writing, or be missing small bits of paper. Still, basically a complete card.

Poor (P): A card that has been tortured to death. Corners or other areas may be torn off. Card may have been trimmed, show holes from paper punch or have been used for BB gun practice. Front may have extraneous pen or pencil writing, or other defacement. Major portions of front or back design may be missing. Not a pretty sight.

In addition to these terms, collectors may encounter intermediate grades, such as VG-EX or EX-MT. These cards usually have characteristics of both the lower and higher grades, and are generally priced midway between those two values.

ROOKIE/FIRST CARD DESIGNATIONS

A player's name in *italic* type indicates a rookie card. An (FC) designation indicates a player's first card for that particular company. FCs will be found in major national regular-issue sets from 1981-94; generally Donruss, Fleer, Score, Topps and Upper Deck sets. They will also be located in the Donruss Rookies, Fleer Update, Topps Traded, Score Traded and Upper Deck Final Edition sets.

VALUATIONS

Values quoted in this book represent the current retail market at the time of compilation and are drawn from recommendations provided and verified through the editors' daily involvement in the publication of the hobby's leading advertising periodicals, as well as the input of specialized consultants, dealers and collectors.

It should be stressed, however, that this book is intended to serve only as an aid in evaluating cards. Actual market conditions are constantly changing. This is especially true of the cards of current players, whose on-field performance (and off-field exploits) during the course of a season can greatly affect the value of their cards — upwards or downwards.

Publication of this book is not intended as a solicitation to buy or sell the listed cards by the editors, publishers or contributors.

The values listed herein are retail prices — what a collector can expect to pay when buying a card from a dealer.

The wholesale price, that which a collector can expect to receive from a dealer when selling cards, will be significantly lower. Most dealers operate on a 100 percent mark-up, generally paying about 50 percent of a card's retail value. On some high-demand cards, dealers will pay up to 75 percent or even 100 percent or more of retail value, anticipating continued price increases. Conversely, for many low-demand cards, such as common players' cards of recent years, dealers may pay as little as 10 percent or even less of retail.

SETS

Collectors may note that the complete set prices for newer issues quoted in these listings are usually significantly lower than the total of the value of the individual cards which comprise the set.

This reflects two factors in the baseball card market. First, a seller is often willing to take a lower composite price for a complete set as a "volume discount" and to avoid inventorying a large number of common player or other lower-demand cards.

Second, to a degree, the value of common cards can be said to be inflated as a result of having a built-in overhead charge to justify the dealer's time in sorting cards, carrying them in stock and filling orders. This accounts for the fact that even brand new baseball cards, which cost the dealer around 1 cent each when bought in bulk, carry individual price tags of three to five cents or higher.

ERRORS/VARIATIONS

It is often hard for the beginning collector to understand that an error on a baseball card, in and of itself, does not usually add premium value to that card. It is usually only when the correcting of an error in the subsequent printing creates a variation that premium value attaches to an error.

Minor errors, such as wrong stats or personal data, misspellings, inconsistencies, etc. — usually affecting the back of the card — are very common, especially in recent years. Unless a corrected variation was also printed, these errors are not noted in the listings of this book because they are not generally perceived by collectors to have premium value.

On the other hand, major effort has been expended to include the most complete listings ever for collectible variation cards. Many scarce and valuable variations — dozens of them never before cataloged — are included in these listings because they are widely collected and often have significant premium value.

Beginning in the early 1990s, some card companies began production of their basic sets at more than one printing facility. This frequently resulted in numerous minor variations in photo cropping and back data presentation. Combined with a general decline in quality control from the mid-1980s through the early 1990s, which allowed unprecedented numbers of uncorrected error cards to be released, this caused a general softening of collector interest in errors and variations. Little attempt has been made to catalog the dozens, perhaps even hundreds of minor variations in such sets as 1991 Topps and Fleer due to the fact that there exists no premium value for such cards.

COUNTERFEITS/REPRINTS

As the value of baseball cards has risen in the past 10-20 years, certain cards and sets have become too expensive for the average collector to obtain. This, along with changes in the technology of color printing, has given rise to increasing numbers of counterfeit and reprint cards.

While both terms describe essentially the same thing — a modern day copy which attempts to duplicate as closely as possible an original baseball card — there are differences which are important to the collector.

Generally, a counterfeit is made with the intention of deceiving somebody into believing it is genuine, and thus paying large amounts of money for it. The counterfeiter takes every pain to try to make his fakes look as authentic as possible. In recent years, the 1963 Pete Rose, 1984 Donruss Don Mattingly and more than 100 superstar cards of the late 1960s-early 1990s have been counterfeited — all were quickly detected because of the differences in quality of printing and the cardboard on which they were printed.

A reprint, on the other hand, while it may have been made to look as close as possible to an original card, is made with the intention of allowing collectors to buy them as substitutes for cards they may never be otherwise able to afford. The big difference is that a reprint is generally marked as such, usually on the back of the card. In other cases, like the Topps 1952 reprint set and 1953-54 Archives issues, the replicas are printed in a size markedly different from the originals.

Collectors should be aware, however, that unscrupulous persons will sometimes cut off or otherwise obliterate the distinguishing word — "Reprint," "Copy," — or modern copyright date on the back of a reprint card in an attempt to pass it as genuine.

A collector's best defense against reprints and counterfeits is to acquire a knowledge of the look and feel of genuine baseball cards of various eras and issues.

The publishers of this catalog also publish the *SCD Sportscard Counterfeit Detector* book, listing more than 250 known counterfeit sportscards and providing details on identification of all known fakes. The book is available at card and hobby shops and many larger retail book outlets.

UNLISTED CARDS

Readers who have cards or sets which are not covered in this edition are invited to correspond with the editor for purposes of adding to the compilation work now in progress. Address: Bob Lemke, Standard Catalog of Baseball Cards, 700 E. State St., Iola, WI 54990.

Contributors will be acknowledged in future editions.

COLLECTORS ISSUES

There exists within the hobby a great body of cards known as "collectors issues" by virtue of their nature of having been produced solely for the hobby card market. These cards and sets are distinguished from "legitimate" issues in not having been created as a sales promotional item for another product or service — bubble gum, soda, snack cakes, dog food, cigarettes, gasoline, etc.

This distinction is no longer so easy to make since the early 1990s when many baseball card issues by even the major national companies began to be sold without an accompanying product.

Beginning with this edition, more resources will be devoted to cataloging collector issues, particularly those from the hobby's early years, which have now become collectible in their own right. Persons with access to complete checklists of such cards are encouraged to correspond with the editor for possible inclusion in future editions.

BASEBALL CARD HISTORY

In 1887 — more than 100 years ago — the first nationally-distributed baseball cards were issued by Goodwin & Co. of New York City. The 1 1/2" x 2 1/2" cards featured posed studio photographs glued to stiff cardboard. They were inserted into cigarette packages with such exotic brand names as Old Judge, Gypsy Queen and Dogs Head. Poses were formal, with artificial backgrounds and bare-handed players fielding balls suspended on strings to simulate action.

Then, as now, baseball cards were intended to stimulate product sales. What could be more American than using the diamond heroes of the national pastime to gain an edge on the competition? It is a tradition that has continued virtually unbroken for a century.

Following Goodwin's lead a year later, competitors began issuing baseball cards with their cigarettes, using full-color lithography to bring to life painted portraits of the era's top players.

After a few short years of intense competition, the cigarette industry's leading firms formed a monopoly and cornered the market. By the mid-1890s there was little competition, and no reason to issue baseball cards. The first great period of baseball card issues came to an end.

The importing of Turkish tobaccos in the years just prior to 1910 created a revolution in American smoking habits. With dozens of new firms entering the market, the idea of using baseball cards to boost sales was revived.

In the years from 1909-12, dozens of different sets of cards were produced to be given away in cigarette packages. There was a greater than ever variety in sizes, shapes and designs, from the extremely popular 1 1/2" x 2 5/8" color lithographed set of 500+ players which collectors call T206, to the large (5" x 8") Turkey Red premium cards given away to those sending in coupons found in cigarette packages.

There were double-folders, featuring two players on the same card, and triple-folders, which had two player portraits and an action scene. Gold ink and embossed designs were also tried to make competing companies' cards attractive and popular.

It was this era that saw the issue of the king of baseball cards, the T206 Honus Wagner card, worth as much as $400,000.

The zeal with which America's youngsters pursued their fathers, uncles and neighbors for cigarette cards in the years just prior to World War I convinced the nation's confectioners that baseball cards could also be used to boost candy sales.

While baseball cards had been produced by candy companies on a limited basis as far back as the 1880s, by the early 1920s the concept was being widely used in the industry. The highly competitive caramel business was a major force in this new marketing strategy, offering a baseball card in each nickel package of candy.

Not to be outdone, Cracker Jack began including baseball cards in each box. The 1914-15 Cracker Jack cards are important because they were the most popular of the candy cards to include players from a short-lived third major league, the Federal League.

Generally, candy cards of the era were not as colorful or well-printed as the earlier tobacco cards, due to the shortage of paper and ink-making ingredients caused by World War I.

The association of bubble gum and baseball cards is a phenomenon of only the past 60 years. In the early 1930s techniques were developed using rubber tree products to give chewing gum the elasticity necessary for blowing bubbles.

During this era the standard method of selling a slab of bubble gum and a baseball card in a colorfully wax-wrapped 1-cent package was developed. Bubble gum — and baseball card — production in this era was centered in Massachusetts, where National Chicle Co. (Cambridge) and Goudey Gum Co. (Boston) were headquartered.

Most bubble gum cards produced in the early 1930s featured a roughly square (about 2 1/2") format, with players depicted in colorful paintings. For the first time, considerable attention was paid to the backs of the cards, where biographical details, career highlights and past season statistics were presented.

In 1939, a new company entered the baseball card market — Gum Inc., of Philadelphia. Its "Play Ball" gum was the major supplier of baseball cards until 1941, when World War II caused a shortage of the materials necessary for both the production of bubble gum and the printing of baseball cards.

Three years after the end of World War II baseball cards returned on a national scale, with two companies competing for the bubble gum market. In Philadelphia, the former Gum Inc. reappeared on the market as Bowman Gum Inc.

Bowman's first baseball card set appeared in 1948, very similar in format to the cards which had existed prior to the war — black-and-white player photos on nearly square (2" x 2 1/2") cardboard. The 1948 Bowman effort was modest, with only 48 cards.

The following year, color was added to the photos. For 1950, Bowman replaced the retouched photos with original color paintings of players, many of which were repeated a year later in the 1951 issue. Also new for 1951 was a larger size card, 2" x 3 1/8".

Bowman had little national competition in this era. In 1948-49, Leaf Gum in Chicago produced a 98-card set that is the only bubble gum issue of the era to include a Joe DiMaggio card.

While Bowman dominated the post-war era through 1951, in that year Topps began production of its first baseball cards, issuing three different small sets of cards and serving warning that it was going to become a major force in the baseball card field.

In 1952, Brooklyn-based Topps entered the baseball card market in a big way. Not only was its 407-card set the largest single-year issue ever produced, but its 2 5/8" x 3 3/4" format was the largest-sized baseball card ever offered for over-the-counter sale.

Other innovations in Topps' premiere issue for 1952 included the first-ever use of team logos in card design, and on the back of the card, the first use of line statistics to document the player's previous-year and career performance.

By contrast, Bowman's set for 1952 remained in the smaller format, had 72 fewer cards and showed little change in design from 1951.

Just as clearly as Topps won the 1952 baseball card battle, Bowman came back in 1953 with what is often considered the finest baseball card set ever produced. For the first time ever, actual color photographs were reproduced on baseball cards in Bowman's 160-card set.

To allow the full impact of the new technology, there were no other design elements on the front of the card and Bowman adopted a larger format, 2 1/2" x 3 3/4".

And so the competition went for five years, with each company trying to gain an edge by signing players to exclusive contracts and cre-

ating new and exciting card designs each year. Gradually, Topps became the dominant force in the card market. In late 1955, Bowman admitted defeat and the company was sold to Topps.

Baseball cards entered a new era in 1957. After years of intense competition, Topps enjoyed a virtual monopoly that was rarely seriously challenged in the next 25 years. One such challenge in the opening years of the 1960s came from Post cereal, which from 1961-63 issued 200-card sets on the backs of its cereal boxes.

In 1957, Topps' baseball cards were issued in a new size — 2 1/2" x 3 1/2" — that would become the industry-wide standard that prevails to this day. It was also the year that Topps first used full-color photographs for its cards, rather than paintings or retouched black-and-white photos.

Another innovation in the 1957 set was the introduction of complete major/and or minor league statistics on the card backs. This feature quickly became a favorite with youngsters and provided fuel for endless schoolyard debates about whether one player was better than the other.

In the ensuing five years, major league baseball underwent monumental changes. In 1958, the Giants and Dodgers left New York for California. In 1961-62 expansion came to the major leagues, with new teams springing up from coast to coast and border to border. The Topps baseball cards of the era preserve those days when modern baseball was in its formative stages.

In 1963, for the first time in seven years, it looked as if there might once again be two baseball card issues to choose from. After three years of issuing "old-timers" card sets, Fleer issued a 66-card set of current players.

Topps took Fleer to court, where the validity of Topps' exclusive contracts with baseball players to appear on bubble gum cards was upheld. It was the last major challenge to Topps for nearly 20 years.

The 1960s offered baseball card collecting at its traditional finest. Youngsters would wait and worry through the long winter, watching candy-store shelves for the first appearance of the brightly colored 5-cent card packs in the spring.

A cry of "They're in!" could empty a playground in seconds as youngsters rushed to the corner store to see what design innovations Topps had come up with for the new year.

Then, periodically during the summer, new series would be released, offering a new challenge to complete. As the seasons wore down, fewer and fewer stores carried the few final series, and it became a struggle to complete the "high numbers" from a given year's set. But it was all part of the fun of buying baseball cards in the 1960s.

The early 1970s brought some important changes to the baseball card scene. The decade's first two Topps issues were stunning in that the traditional white border was dropped in favor of gray in 1970, and black in 1971.

In 1972, Topps' card design was absolutely psychedelic, with brightly colored frames around the player photos, and comic book typography popping out all over. The design for the 1973 cards was more traditional, but the photos were not.

Instead of close-up portraits or posed "action" shots, many cards in the 1973 Topps set featured actual game action photos. Unfortunately, too many of those photos made it hard to tell which player was which, and the set was roundly panned by collectors.

But most significantly, 1973 marked the last year in which baseball cards were issued by series through the course of the summer. On the positive side, this eliminated the traditional scarce "high numbers" produced toward the end of the season.

On the negative side, it meant players who had been traded in the pre-season could no longer be shown in their correct uniforms, and outstanding new players had to wait a full year before their rookie cards would debut.

This marketing change made a significant impact on the hobby and helped spur a tremendous growth period in the late 1970s. By offering all of the cards at once, Topps made it easy for baseball card dealers to offer complete sets early in the year.

Previously, collectors had to either assemble their sets by buying packs of cards, or wait until all series had been issued to buy a set from a dealer. It was in this era that many of today's top baseball card dealers got their start or made the switch to baseball cards a full-time business.

During this era, the first national competition to Topps' baseball card monopoly in many years was introduced. Hostess, a bakery products company, began distributing baseball cards printed on the bottoms of packages of its snack cakes, while the Kellogg's company distributed simulated 3-D cards in boxes of its cereals.

The eagerness with which collectors gobbled up these issues showed that the hobby was ready for a period of unprecedented growth.

The baseball card hobby literally boomed in 1981. A federal court broke Topps' monopoly on the issue of baseball cards with bubble gum, and Fleer, from Philadelphia, and Donruss, of Memphis, entered the field as the first meaningful competition in nearly 20 years.

That same year also marked a beginning of the resurgence in the number of regional baseball card issues. Over the next few years, dozens of such sets came onto the market, helping to boost sales of everything from snack cakes to soda pop and police public relations.

By 1984, more than half of the teams in the major leagues were issuing some type of baseball cards on a regional basis. The hobby had not enjoyed such diversity of issues since the mid-1950s.

While yet another court decision cost Fleer and Donruss the right to sell their baseball cards with bubble gum, both companies remained in the market and gained strength.

Topps' major contribution in this era was the introduction of annual "Traded" sets which offered cards of the year's new rookies as well as cards of traded players in their correct uniforms.

The mid-1980s showed continued strong growth in the number of active baseball card collectors, as well as the number of new baseball card issues. Topps, still the industry's leader, expanded the number and variety of its baseball issues with many different test issues and on-going specialty sets, including oversize cards, 3-D plastic cards, metal "cards" and much more.

After three years of over-production of its baseball card sets, Donruss, in 1984, significantly limited the number of cards printed, creating a situation in which demand exceeded supply, causing the value of Donruss cards to rise above Topps for the first time.

In 1984, Fleer followed Topps' lead and produced a season's-end "Update" set. Because the quantity of sets printed was extremely limited, and because it contains some of today's hottest young players, the 1984 Fleer Update set has become the most valuable baseball card issue produced in recent times.

In 1986, a fourth company joined the baseball card wars. Called "Sportflics," the cards were produced by a subsidiary of the Wrigley Gum Co., and featured three different photos on each card in a simulated 3-D effect.

For 1988, a fifth national baseball card set, called Score, entered the scene. A sixth national baseball card set, Upper Deck, was created in 1989.

The early 1990s saw another explosion in baseball card supply. While the number of major national card-producing licensors remained static, each company attempted to carve a niche in the market by creating separate brands to appeal to base-level collectors, intermediate hobbyists, and — especially — those interested in high-tech premium quality cards for which money was no object. This trend peaked in late 1993 with the introduction of Topps Finest brand cards, which by virtue of an extremely limited press run were selling for more than $20 a pack soon after issue.

Another phenomenon of the early 1990s was the creation of extremely low-production specialty cards to be inserted in card packages on a random basis. Often showcasing the card companies' latest technology, the insert cards often achieved significant premium value as collectors pursued them for their relative rarity. This spawned the hobby term "chase card" to designate these wax-pack prizes. It also spawned a lottery mentality on the part of many card buyers who spurned the contents of any pack which did not contain the high-value inserts.

GLOSSARY OF HOBBY TERMS

ACC: Acronym for the American Card Catalog. This catalog, written by Jefferson Burdick and published in 1960 by Nostalgia Press, uses numerical and alphabetical designations for identifying and cataloging card sets.

The letter used in the ACC designation refers to the generic type of card: B = blankets; D = bakery inserts, including bread; E = early candy and gum; F = food inserts; H = advertising; M = periodicals; N = 19th century U.S. tobacco; PC = postcards; R = recent candy and gum cards, 1930 to present; T = 20th century U.S. tobacco; UO = gas and oil inserts; V = Canadian candy; W = Exhibits, strip cards, team cards.

An optional hyphen and a one-, two- or three-digit number follows the letter prefix. The numbers represent the company or entity which issued the cards.

Action Packed: A football card manufacturer which produced its first set in 1989. The company has also done basketball and baseball sets, too.

Airbrushing: The touching up of a photo by an artist. Usually done on trading cards to show a player, who has changed teams, in his new uniform.

All-Star card: A special card identifying a player as a member of a National League, American League or Major League all-star team. Players shown on all-star cards may or may not be members of their league's official All-Star team. All-star cards can be part of a regular set or issued as an independent set. For several years, Topps has issued two different "glossy" sets of all-star cards on specially-coated stock.

Ask price: The price a dealer, investor or collector offers to sell his cards for.

Assorted: A term used in ads to indicate a lot of cards which may contain multiples of one or more cards. Lots which do not contain doubles are labeled "different."

Autographed card: A card that has actually been signed by the player pictured, as opposed to the facsimile signatures that are sometimes printed on cards as part of the design. The value of an autographed card is generally greater than that same card would be if it were unautographed.

Autograph guest: A current or former player or other celebrity who attends a card convention to sign autographs for fans. A fee, which can range from a few dollars to more than $30 for a player such as Joe DiMaggio, is usually charged for the autograph.

Baseball's Best: A season-end glossy set made by Donruss in 1988 and 1989. Also the name of a set made by Fleer in 1987 and 1988, and the name of a set of insert cards made by Baseball Cards magazine in 1989 and 1990.

Bazooka: A bubble gum-making subsidiary of Topps which made baseball cards from 1959-71 and again in 1988-1991.

Bid price: The price an investor, dealer, etc., offers to buy cards.

Big cards: The trade name for Topps' oversized, glossy-finish card issues produced from 1988-1990. The cards are reminiscent of Topps cards from the 1950s.

Blank-back: Usually used to refer to a card that has no printing on the back because of a manufacturing mistake. Cards that were intentionally issued without printing on the back are also known as blank-backed.

Blanket: An early 20th-century collectible consisting of a square piece of felt or other fabric which came wrapped around a package of cigarettes. Baseball players were one of the several subjects found on blankets. Most popular are the 5 1/4" x 5 1/4" B18 blankets from 1914, so-called because they were sometimes sewn together to form a blanket.

Blister pack: A blister pack is a method of card packaging in which cards are packaged in hard plastic on a cardboard backing, with three or four pockets of cards. Issued by Donruss (1987-present).

Book price: The retail selling price which appears in a price guide.

Borders: The portion of a card which surrounds the picture. Borders are usually white but are sometimes colored. The condition of a card's borders is one of the vital components in determining a card's grade.

Bowman: A very famous card company that made baseball cards from 1948-55, football cards from 1948-55, and basketball cards in 1948. Bowman was bought by Topps in 1956 and card production ceased. Topps revived the Bowman name in 1989 to date for a set of baseball cards.

Box-bottom cards: Cards printed on the bottom and/or sides of wax or foil boxes. Box-bottom cards are not considered to be part of the regular set and generally are not valuable unless kept intact as a panel.

Boxed set: A set of cards, usually consisting of either 33 or 44 cards, issued as a complete set and sold in its own box at a large chain or discount store. Boxed sets are usually made by one of the major manufacturers and contain cards of only the biggest names or hottest rookies.

Brick: A wrapped lot of cards, usually all from one year. See "starter set."

Burger King cards (BK): Cards issued in conjunction with Burger King products (1977-1987).

Buy price: The price which a dealer is willing to pay for cards or memorabilia. A dealer's buy price is usually quite a bit lower than that item's catalog or retail price.

Cabinet card: A large card from the late 19th or early 20th century, usually issued on heavy cardboard. The cards were often given away as premiums by tobacco companies, and were either photographs or reproductions of paintings. The name "cabinet" derives from how they were often displayed — inside curio cabinets.

Caption: The title on a card which identifies or describes the subject pictured, but may also be a line of dialogue. It generally appears under the illustration and/or on the back.

Card lot: A "lot" of cards is the same card, such as a 1988 Topps Don Mattingly card, sold in a lot or "grouping" of five, 10, 25, 50, 100 or whatever number of cards. A collector purchasing a "lot" or cards gets the cards at a discounted price, as opposed to buying a single card. Example: a single Mattingly card costs $1, but 100 Mattingly cards cost $75, or 75 cents each.

Card stock: The paper or cardboard that baseball cards are printed on.

Case: A sealed case containing wax boxes or other product units which card companies sell at wholesale to dealers or retail stores. For instance, a 1990 Topps "wax case" is made up of 20 "wax boxes."

Cello box: A retail display box of cello packs, usually, but not always, containing 24 packs.

Cello case: A wholesale unit of cello boxes, usually, but not always, containing 16 boxes.

Cello pack: A cellophane-wrapped pack of cards. A cello pack usually contains more cards than a wax pack. Depending on how the cards are packaged, the top and bottom card of a cello pack may or may not be easily visible through the cellophane. Many collectors will pay a premium for a cello pack with a card of a star player or hot rookie showing on the top or bottom.

Centering: The positioning of a card picture between its borders. A well-centered card has even borders, an important factor in grading a card.

Checklist: A list of every card in a particular set, usually with a space allowing the collector to check whether he has the card. A checklist can appear on a card, in a book or elsewhere. As a rule of thumb, checklists on cards are worth more if they're left unchecked.

Chipping: A card-grading term referring to a condition in which a portion of a card's dark-colored border is worn away. Chipping is a real problem, for instance, with 1953 and 1971 Topps cards, and more recent issues with colored borders.

Classic cards: Cards made by Game Time Ltd. to go with its Classic Baseball trivia game. The cards were first made in 1987 and are sold in sets. Several sets a year are produced.

Coin: A metal or plastic coin-sized disc which depicts a player. It can also refer to an actual coin or a coin-sized silver piece which commemorates an actual event.

Collation: The act of putting cards in order, usually numerical order.

Collectible: Something worth collecting. Baseball cards, programs, pennants, uniforms, and autographs are all examples of collectibles.

Collector issue: A set of cards produced primarily to be sold to collectors and not issued as a premium to be given away or sold with a commercial product. Collector issues fall into two categories: authorized (meaning the issue was made with the approval of professional sports and the players' association) or unauthorized (meaning the issue was made without approval).

Combination card: A single card which depicts two or more players, but is not a team card.

Common card: A card picturing a "common" or ordinary player — that is, not a star or superstar. "Commons" are the lowest-priced cards in a given series or set.

Condition: One of the major factors in determining the value of a card, this term applies to the wear and tear of a card.

Convention: Also known as a baseball card show or trading card show. A gathering of anywhere from one to 600 or more card dealers at a single location (convention center, hotel, school auditoriums or gymnasiums) for the purpose of buying, selling or trading cards. A convention is open to the public, and often times a fee is required to attend the show. Many conventions feature a player or several players to sign autographs.

Counterfeit card: A phony card made to look like a real card. Counterfeit cards have no collector value.

Crease: A bend mark in a card. usually due to mishandling. Creases substantially lower a card's grade and value.

CY: Cy Young Award.

Dealer: A person who buys, sells and trades baseball cards and other memorabilia for profit. A dealer may be full-time, part-time, own a shop, operate a mail-order business from his home, deal at baseball card shows on weekends or do any combination of the above.

Decollation: The act of putting cards in random order, usually for packaging.

Diamond King: A Donruss card featuring the artwork produced by Perez-Steele Galleries.

Die-cut card: A baseball card in which the player's outline has been partially separated from the background, enabling the card to be folded into a "stand-up" figure. Die-cut cards that have never been folded are worth more to collectors.

Ding: Slight damage to the corner or edge of a card.

Disc set: A set of disc-shaped cards, usually showing head-and-shoulder shots of players.

Distributor: Persons or organizations which buy cards directly from the card companies or from other dealers and resells them on a large scale. Sometimes distributors receive exclusive products, and thus are the only source of distribution for the product.

Donruss: A baseball-card manufacturer. Donruss began printing baseball cards in 1981.

Donruss Rookies (DR): A 56-card post-season set issued by Donruss which includes rookie players (1986-present). Sold exclusively through hobby dealers in a separate box.

Double-print: An individual card that, because of a particular printing configuration, appears twice on the same press sheet and is, therefore, twice as common as the other cards.

Doubles: A duplicate of a card in your collection. A card which, since you retain one for your set, can be traded or sold.

Drake's: An Ohio-based bakery that made baseball cards in 1950 and again from 1981-88.

Error card: A card that contains a mistake, including wrong photos, misspelled words, incorrect statistics, and so forth. Usually error cards have no extra value unless they have been corrected, resulting in a "variation" card.

Exclusive: When a company makes an agreement that a distributor is the only one selling the company's cards at the offering price.

Exhibit cards: Postcard-size cards picturing baseball players and other celebrities and sold in penny-arcade machines. Exhibit cards were produced from the 1920s to the 1960s.

Extended set: A term used to describe a late-season series of cards added on to and numbered after a regular set. Also known as an extended series, update set or traded set.

Facsimile autograph: A reproduced autograph. Facsimile autographs are often found on sports cards as part of the card's design.

Factory set: A complete set of cards collated and packaged by the card company. A factory set may or may not be packaged in a special box. Usually factory sets are sealed or have sealed inner packs as an added security measure. Factory sets with intact seals or inner packs command a slight premium over hand-collated sets.

Felt: A baseball item consisting of a felt pennant, usually with a photograph or likeness of the player attached. Felts were made in 1916 and again from 1936-37.

First card: The first card of a player in a national set. A first card may or may not be a player's rookie card; for instance, if a player appeared in a Fleer set one year and a Score set the next, the Fleer card would be that player's rookie card and his first Fleer card, while the Score card would be his first Score card but not his rookie card.

Flannel: A jersey made of a cotton or wool material. Most flannels were discontinued and replaced by knit jerseys in the early 1970s.

Fleer: A manufacturer of football, basketball and baseball cards. Fleer made baseball cards from 1959-63 and again from 1981 to the present.

Fleer Glossy Tin (FG): Limited-edition set produced by Fleer, which features the year's regular issue set in a high gloss finish and is sold in a tin box (1987-present). Fleer Update sets are also done in glossy style.

Fleer Update (FU): A 132-card post-season set from Fleer which includes players traded to other teams during the season, and rookies (1984-present). Sold exclusively through hobby dealers in its own separate box.

Foil: Foil-embossed stamp on a card.

Foil box: A retail display box of foil packs, usually, but not always, containing 36 packs.

Foil case: A wholesale unit of foil boxes, usually, but not always containing 24 boxes.

Foil pack: A pack of baseball cards packaged in a tamper-proof, shiny foil. Upper Deck packages its cards in foil packs.

Food set: A set either inserted in packages of food (hot dogs, cereal, popcorn, potato chips, candy, cookies, etc.) or offered as a send-in offer by a food company. Examples of food sets include Kahn's Wieners, Mother's Cookies, etc.

Full sheet: A full press sheet of cards that has never been cut; sometimes referred to as an "uncut" sheet. The number of cards on a sheet varies with the printing process, but most often contains 132 cards.

Gallery of Champions: Trade name for a set of miniature metallic reproductions of Topps cards made and sold by Topps from 1986-88. Gallery of Champions ingots were made in bronze, aluminum, silver and pewter.

Gloss: The amount of surface shine on a card. All baseball cards are made with some surface gloss. Cards that keep more of their gloss keep more of their value.

Glossy card: A card with a special, extra-shiny finish.

Glossy set: A set of glossy cards. Glossy sets can be either small and common (Topps' sendaway all-star sets) or large and scarce. Fleer, Topps, Score and Bowman have made glossy versions of their regular baseball card sets.

Goudey: A famous maker of baseball cards. The Goudey Gum Co. of Boston made baseball cards and non-sport cards from 1933-39.

Grade: The state of preservation of a card or piece of memorabilia. An item's value is based in large part on its grade (condition).

Grading service: A company that charges a fee to grade cards. Most grading services work like this: After a card is graded, it is placed in a tamper-proof plastic holder. A network of member-dealers then agrees to buy that card sight-unseen at that grade. Card grading services are a recent innovation, patterned after similar services in the coin collecting hobby.

Hall of Fame Postcard: A long-running series of postcards produced by several manufacturers and sold by the National Baseball Hall of Fame. Popular among autograph collectors.

Hall of Famer (HOFer): A member of the Baseball Hall of Fame in Cooperstown, N.Y., but also used to refer to a baseball card picturing a member of the Hall of Fame. Hall of Famer cards almost always command a premium over other cards.

Hand-collated set: A set assembled card-by-card by hand, usually by a collector or dealer putting the set together out of wax, cello or vending boxes.

Hartland: A statue produced by a Wisconsin plastics company in the late 1950s and early 1960s. Eighteen major league baseball players were models for Hartlands. The company also produced football player statues and a long line of Western and historical figures, horses and farm animals. Hartland baseball figures were reissued in 1989.

High numbers: A term usually used to describe the final series in a particular set of cards. High numbers were generally produced in smaller quantities than other series and are, therefore, scarcer and more valuable.

Hologram: The silvery, laser-etched trademark printed as an anti-counterfeiting device on Upper Deck cards. Also, the disc with a team logo inserted into Upper Deck packs.

Hoops: Trade name for the National Basketball Association's set of basketball cards, NBA Hoops.

In-action card: A card showing a ballplayer in action, as opposed to posed.

Insert: A collectible included inside a regular pack of baseball cards to boost sales. Inserts have included posters, baseball player stamps, coins, stickers, comic books, special cards, and tattoos.

Jell-O cards: Cards sold as premiums with Jell-O packages (1962-1963).

Jogo: A Canadian card manufacturer that has been producing card sets picturing players from the Canadian Football League (CFL) for the past decade.

Kellogg's: A cereal company which packaged three-dimensional baseball cards in its cereal from 1970-83, and also produced several football card sets.

Key cards: The most important cards in a set.

Last card: The final card issued of a ballplayer (or the final card of any particular set).

Layering: A term used in card grading to describe the separation of the layers of paper that make up the cardboard stock. Layering is a sign of wear that is first noticeable at the corners of the card.

Leaf: Donruss' parent firm. Donruss issued baseball cards in Canada under the Leaf name from 1985-88. Since 1990, the Leaf brand name has been used on a premium-quality issue from the company.

Legitimate issue: A licensed card set issued as a premium with a commercial product to increase sales; not a collector issue.

Letter of authenticity: A letter stating that a certain piece of memorabilia, such as a uniform, is authentic.

Limited edition: A term often used by makers of cards and memorabilia to indicate scarcity. A limited edition means just that — production of the item in question will be limited to a certain number. However, that number may be large or small.

Lithograph: An art print made by a specific process that results in a print of outstanding clarity. Most lithographs are limited editions — though, as always, some lithographs are more limited than others.

Logo sticker: A peel-off, adhesive-backed reproduction of a team's symbol. Logo stickers are packed in Fleer wax packs.

Mail-bid auction: A form of auction where all bids are sent in through the mail. The person who sends in the highest bid gets the merchandise.

Major set: A large, nationally-distributed set produced by a major card manufacturer, such as Topps, Fleer, Donruss, Score, Sportflics or Upper Deck.

Megalot: A card investor's term referring to a very large (normally 1,000 or more) group of cards of one player, purchased as an investment.

Memorabilia: Usually used in card collecting to refer to items other than cards which mark or commemorate a player and his career, a team or an event.

Mini: Small-size cards, sometimes miniature reproductions of regular cards (1975 Topps mini) and sometimes independent issues (1986-89 Topps Mini League Leaders).

Minor leaguer: A card depicting a player from the minor leagues. Minor league sets are a fast-growing segment of the hobby.

Miscut: A card that has been cut incorrectly from a press sheet during the manufacturing process and decreases in value as a result.

Mother's: An Oakland, Calif., cookie company which has issued high-quality, glossy-finish regional sets since 1983.

Multi-player card: A card picturing more than one player. Multi-player cards often show rookies or stars.

MVP: Most Valuable Player award winner.

Mylar: Trade name for a type of inert plastic used to make supplies for the protection of cards and memorabilia.

Nine-pocket sheet: The most common type of plastic sheet. A nine-pocket sheet is about the size of a sheet of typing paper and is designed to fit into a standard three-ring binder. The sheet has nine pockets to hold most normal-sized modern cards.

Non-sports card: A card picturing a subject other than sports. Non-sports cards have depicted movie stars, television shows, U.S. presidents, moments in history, entertainers and other subjects.

Notching: A card-grading term used to describe indentations along the edge of a card, sometimes caused by a rubber band. Notching decreases a card's value.

Obverse: The front of the card displaying the picture.

Off-center: A term used in card grading to describe a card that has uneven borders.

Old Judge: A brand of cigarettes which was popular in the late 1800s. Also the name given to the huge set of baseball cards issued as a premium with that brand of cigarettes. The cards, issued from 1887-90, carried advertisements for Old Judge cigarettes.

O-Pee-Chee: Topps' Canadian licensee. O-Pee-Chee makes and sells a baseball card set that resembles Topps' set but has fewer cards, and a hockey card set that resembles Topps but has more cards. O-Pee-Chee cards can sometimes be distinguished from Topps cards by the bilingual (French-English) backs.

Out of register: A term used to describe a printing error in which the various colors are not correctly superimposed upon one another, thereby decreasing the value of the card.

Panel: A strip of two or more uncut cards. Some card sets are issued in panels.

Panini: An international sticker manufacturer which came into the U.S. baseball sticker market in 1988 with a large and attractive set of baseball stickers. Panini also makes hockey, basketball and football stickers.

Parkhurst: A Canadian card manufacturer that produced NHL hockey sets in the 1950s and 1960s. Collectors often refer to Parkhurst cards as "Parkies." In 1952 the company issued a set of minor league baseball cards for its Frost-Ade brand soft drink. In recent years the brand name has been revitalized for use on premium-quality hockey card issues.

Perez-Steele: Usually used as a term to refer to an ongoing set of Hall of Fame postcards issued by the Perez-Steele Galleries of Fort Washington, Pa. The company has made a number of artistic card sets, including the Celebration and Greatest Moments sets. Popular with autograph collectors.

Phone auction: An auction where bids for baseball cards or other memorabilia are taken over the phone. The highest bidder gets the merchandise.

Pinnacle: A top-of-the-line brand name originated in 1992 from Score. In 1994 Score changed the name of its "umbrella" organization to Pinnacle Brands.

Plastic sheet: A polyethelyne or polyvinyl sheet designed to store baseball cards, the most common being the nine-pocket sheet (which fits today's standard-sized cards). The sheets have prepunched holes on the left side which allows them to be placed in a three-ring binder.

Play Ball: The name of baseball cards produced by Gum Inc. (1939-1941).

Police set: A regional card set made for a police department and given away to kids, usually one card at a time, to promote friendly relations. Police cards often carry a safety or anti-drug message on the back. Baseball, football, basketball and hockey police sets have been made of major league, minor league and college teams. Similar sets issued by fire departments are also generically called "police sets" or "safety sets."

Polyethylene: A type of plastic used to make card sheets and other collectors' supplies. Very flexible, but not as clear as other types of plastic. Safer than PVC for very long-term card storage.

Post: A cereal company which made baseball and football cards from 1960-63 and put them on the backs of its cereal boxes. Today the most valuable Post cards are uncut panels found on boxes. In 1990, the company returned with a baseball card set inserted into its cereal boxes.

PPD: Postage paid.

Premium: An extra. In terms of cards, this can either refer to a card inserted in a package of some other product or something extra inserted in a package of cards. "Premium" can also refer to the extra money a high-series or star card commands.

Pre-rookie: Term sometimes used to refer to any card of a player issued before his rookie card — a minor league card, for example, or a high school, college or Olympic team card.

Press run: The total number of any one set of cards printed.

Price guide: A periodical or book which contains checklists of cards, sets and other memorabilia and their values in varying conditions.

Price on request (P.O.R.): A dealer will advertise a card P.O.R. if he believes the card will fluctuate in price from the time he places his ad until the time the ad is seen by the public.

Pro Cards: A large and important maker of minor league cards. Pro Cards revolutionized the minor league card business in 1986 when it issued around 100 different minor league sets.

Promo card: A card made for promotional purposes. Promo cards generally have very limited distribution and can be quite valuable.

Proof card: A card made not to be sold but to test the card presses, the card design, photography, colors, paper, statistical accuracy and so forth.

Pro Set: A company which began making NFL-endorsed football cards in 1989.

Puzzle piece, poster piece: The back of a card containing a partial design which, when pieced together with corresponding pieces, forms a large picture or poster.

PVC: Shortened name of a chemical compound (polyvinyl chloride), sometimes used to make plastic sheets and other card collectors' supplies. PVC plastic is generally clearer and stiffer than other types of plastic sheets but may have a shorter safe life.

Rack box: A retail display box of rack packs. There are usually 24 rack packs to a rack box.

Rack case: A wholesale case of rack boxes. There are usually three or six rack boxes in a rack case.

Rack pack: A cellophane-wrapped pack of cards, usually having three compartments, designed to be hung from a peg in a retail store. Rack packs vary in the number of cards in each pack; also, some rack packs consist of nothing but cello-wrapped wax packs.

Rare: Difficult to obtain and limited in number. See "Scarce."

Rated Rookie (RR): A Donruss subset featuring young players the company thinks are the top rookie players from a particular year (1984-present).

Record Breaker card: A special Topps card found in a regular issue set which commemorates a record-breaking performance by a player from the previous season.

Regional set: A card set limited in distribution to one geographical area. Regional sets often depict players from one team.

Reprint: A reproduction of a previously-issued sports card or set. Generally produced to satisfy collector demand, they usually — but not always _ are labeled "reprint" and have little collector value.

Restored card: A card which has had "cosmetic surgery" — that is, a card which has had its imperfections fixed long after the card was issued. A card restorer can fix corners and restore gloss to card stock. Restored cards should be clearly labeled as such by whoever is selling them, and should be priced much less than unrestored cards in the same condition.

Reverse: The back of a card.

Reversed negative: A common error in which the picture negative is flip-flopped so the picture comes out backward, or reversed.

Rookie card: A player's first card issued by a major card producer in its regular annual set. It may or may not be issued during the player's actual rookie season. A rookie card is often a player's most valuable card.

ROY: Rookie of the Year.

SASE: A term used in hobby advertisements and elsewhere to indicate "self-addressed, stamped envelope."

Scarce: Not easily obtainable.

SCD: Sports Collectors Digest.

Score: Brand name of sports cards designed by Major League Marketing, manufactured by Optigraphics and distributed by Amurol. Score cards are distinguished by high-quality photos and graphics and full-color backs. Score issued its first baseball cards in 1988.

Score Select: Introduced in 1993 as a medium-price brand of sports cards.

Score Traded (ScTr): A 110-card post-season set issued by Score to include players traded during the season, as well as rookie players. Sold exclusively by hobby dealers in its own separate box.

Scuff: A rub or abrasion on a card which removes a portion of its gloss or printing. Scuffed cards are worth less than non-scuffed cards.

Second-year card: The second card of a player issued in the major sets. Usually, a second-year card is the most expensive card of a player, next to the rookie card.

Sell price: The price at which a dealer will sell cards. Generally much higher than his buy price.

Sepia: A dark reddish-brown coloration used in some card sets instead of traditional black-and-white.

Series: A group of cards that is part of a set and was issued at one time. The term is usually applied to Topps sets from 1952 through 1973, when sets were issued in various series.

Set: A complete run of cards, including one number of each card issued by a particular manufacturer in a particular year; for example, a 1985 Fleer set.

Short-print: A card that, for whatever reason, is not printed in as great a quantity as other cards in the set. The opposite of a double-print.

Skip-numbered: A set of cards not numbered in exact sequence, with some numbers missing. Some manufacturers have issued skip-numbered sets to trick collectors into buying more cards, looking for card numbers that didn't exist. Other sets became skip-numbered when one or more players were dropped from the set at the last minute and were not replaced.

SkyBox: A manufacturer of football and basketball cards.

Slab: Slang for the plastic holder in which cards graded by a grading service are encased. Graded cards are said to be "slabbed. "

Sleeve: A specially-designed plastic wrapper used to house and protect individual baseball cards.

Special card: A card in a set that depicts something other than a single player without mention of any special event that may involve that player; for example, a checklist card, All-Star card, team card or team leaders card.

Sportflics: Brand name of a baseball card made by Major League Marketing and Optigraphics and distributed by Amurol. Sportflics, which use an exclusive three-dimensional process to put several images on one card, were first made in 1986.

Stamp: An adhesive-backed paper which depicts a player. When the stamp, which can be an individual or a sheet of many stamps, is moistened, it can be attached to another surface or corresponding stamp album.

Standard size card: A card which measures 2 1/2" by 3 1/2" tall. In 1957, Topps baseball cards were produced in the 2 1/2" by 3 1/2" size, which set the standard for modern baseball cards.

Star card: A designation used to describe a player of better-than-average skill and performance who isn't of "superstar" caliber. The term "minor star" may also be used to differentiate between various levels of skill and popularity. In terms of value, star cards fall between commons and superstars.

Starter kit: A prepackaged kit for new collectors. Often it contains a binder and plastic sheets, individual card protectors, plastic holders, a book or magazine on collecting or a price guide, and cards.

Starter set: A less-than-complete set of cards meant to give beginning collectors a start towards completing a certain set.

Starting Lineup: A line of plastic action figures with accompanying cards produced by Kenner since 1988. Also, the trademark for a computer-based baseball game with cards produced by Parker Brothers.

Sticker: An adhesive-backed card. Stickers can either be card-size or smaller. Topps, Fleer and Panini have issued major sports sticker sets in the last several years. Stickers are not tremendously popular with collectors.

Stock: The cardboard on which a card is printed.

Subset: A set of cards with the same theme within a larger set. Examples: Donruss Diamond Kings are a "subset" of the Donruss set; or Topps All-Star cards are a subset of the Topps set.

Super card: A designation referring to the physical size of a card. Generally, any card larger than postcard size is referred to as a super.

Superstar card: A card picturing a player of Hall-of-Fame (current or future) caliber.

Tab: A portion of a card, usually perforated, which can be removed from the card without damaging the central part of the card.

Tattoos: Transfers showing ballplayers and/or team logos. Tattoos were a popular wax-pack premium in 1960s Topps wax packs; later Topps launched them as a stand-alone product, with little success.

Team card: A card picturing an entire team.

Team set: All the cards from a particular set showing members of a particular team. Team set collecting is becoming a very popular type of collecting.

Team-issued set: A set given away or sold by an individual team.

Test issue: A set of cards distributed on a limited basis to test its marketability. Topps has issued a variety of test products in the 1960s, 1970s and 1980s.

3-D card: Term used to refer to various types of cards and issues. A 3-D card may have a diffused background that lets the foreground image stand out (Kellogg's), multiple images (Sportflics) or a raised image (Topps 3-D).

Tiffany: Topps' name for its glossy version of its regular set. The first Tiffany set was issued in 1984.

Tin: Slang for a Fleer glossy set (1987-89), which are packaged in colorful, numbered tin boxes.

Tobacco cards: Cards issued in the late 19th and early 20th centuries as a premium with cigarettes or other tobacco products. The first tobacco cards were issued around 1886; the last tobacco baseball cards were issued with Red Man chewing tobacco in the mid-1950s.

Topps: The major figure in sports card making for the last 40 years, Topps began issuing sports card sets in 1951 and has issued them every year ever since. Topps also issues a number of auxiliary issues, including stickers, glossy all-star sets and glossy versions of regular sets.

Topps Traded (TT or TTR): A 132-card post-season set which includes players traded to other teams during the year, as well as rookie players (1981-present). They are sold exclusively through hobby dealers in their own separate box, although some of the 1989 sets were sold through major retail stores.

Traded set: An auxiliary set of cards issued toward the end of the season to reflect trades that were made after the printing of the regular set. Sometimes called "Update" sets, they also usually feature rookies not included in the regular set. The first stand-alone traded set was a baseball traded set issued by Topps in 1981.

Trimmed card: A card that has been cut down from its original size, greatly reducing its value.

Uncut sheet: A full press sheet of cards that has never been cut into individual cards.

Update set: See "Traded set."

Upper Deck: A California-based company which introduced a line of ultra-high-quality, expensive baseball cards in 1989 and has since been licensed to issue football, basketball and hockey cards, as well.

Upper Deck High Numbers (UDH): A 100-card set featuring players traded during the season, as well as rookie players. This set was sold through hobby dealers in Upper Deck foil packs, similar to the way cards before 1974 were released.

Variation: A card that exists in two different forms within the same set. A "variation" frequently occurs when an error card has been corrected. Some variations are worth more than others, based on the quantity of each variation produced.

Vending case: A wholesale package containing nothing but cards, originally intended to be used to fill card-vending machines. Most often a vending case contains 24 boxes of 500 cards each.

Vending set: A set put together from cards in vending boxes. Such sets will not have cards that exhibit wax or gum stains.

Want list: A collector's or dealer's list of items he is wishing to buy. Often, a collector will send a dealer a "want list," and the dealer will try to locate the items on the list.

Wax box: A retail box of wax packs. There are usually 36 wax packs in a wax box.

Wax case: A wholesale case of wax boxes. There are usually 20 wax boxes in a wax case. Often the term is shortened to "wax."

Wax pack: The basic unit of retail baseball card packaging. A specific number of baseball cards, packaged with a premium (bubble gum, puzzle pieces, logo stickers and so forth) in a wax-coated wrapper.

Wax stain: A condition caused by wax from the pack wrapper melting onto a card. Wax stains lower the value of a card, but can be removed by rubbing with a pair of pantyhose or using a commercial wax-removal solution.

Wrapper: What wax packs are packaged in. A collectible item in itself.

Wrong backs: A card with the wrong back (the player on the front does not match the biography/statistics on the back). Most collectors think these cards are damaged and are worth less than a correctly-printed card, although some collectors will pay premiums on superstars or rookies.

1976 A & P Brewers

The Aaron and Yount cards from this regional issue support the set price. The set was issued by the A & P grocery chain. Oversize - 5-7/8" x 9" - cards (actually printed on semi-gloss paper) were given out at the stores in 1976.

		NR MT	EX	VG
Complete set (16):		20.00	10.00	6.00
Common player:		.50	.25	.15
(1)	Henry Aaron	8.00	4.00	2.50
(2)	Pete Broberg	.50	.25	.15
(3)	Jim Colborn	.50	.25	.15
(4)	Mike Hegan	.50	.25	.15
(5)	Tim Johnson	.50	.25	.15
(6)	Von Joshua	.50	.25	.15
(7)	Sixto Lezcano	.50	.25	.15
(8)	Don Money	.50	.25	.15
(9)	Charlie Moore	.50	.25	.15
(10)	Darrell Porter	.50	.25	.15
(11)	George Scott	.50	.25	.15
(12)	Bill Sharp	.50	.25	.15
(13)	Jim Slaton	.50	.25	.15
(14)	Bill Travers	.50	.25	.15
(15)	Robin Yount	10.00	5.00	3.00
(16)	County Stadium	.50	.25	.15

1970 Action Cartridge

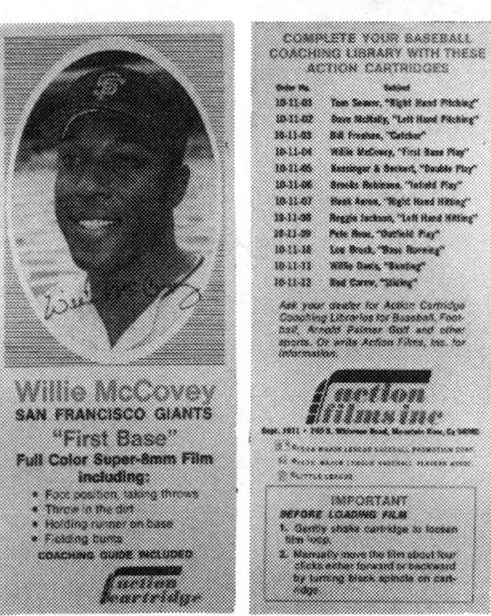

This set of boxes with baseball players' pictures on them was issued by Action Films Inc. of Mountain View, Calif., in 1970-71. The boxes, measuring 2-5/8" by 6" by 1" deep, contained 8mm film cartridges of various professional athletes demonstrating playing tips. The movie series include 12 baseball players. (Other sports represented were football, golf, tennis, hockey and skiing.) The movie cartridges are occasionally collected today, as are the boxes, which feature attractive, color player portraits. The photos appear inside an oval and include a facsimile autograph. The values listed are for complete boxes (without the movie cartridge).

		NR MT	EX	VG
Complete set (12):		350.00	175.00	100.00
Common player:		7.50	3.75	2.50
1	Tom Seaver	50.00	25.00	15.00
2	Dave McNally	7.50	3.75	2.25
3	Bill Freehan	9.00	4.50	2.75
4	Willie McCovey	30.00	15.00	9.00
5	Glenn Beckert, Don Kessinger	7.50	3.75	2.25
6	Brooks Robinson	40.00	20.00	12.00
7	Hank Aaron	75.00	37.00	22.00
8	Reggie Jackson	75.00	37.00	22.00
9	Pete Rose	65.00	32.00	19.50
10	Lou Brock	30.00	15.00	9.00
11	Willie Davis	7.50	3.75	2.25
12	Rod Carew	40.00	20.00	12.00

1988 Action Packed

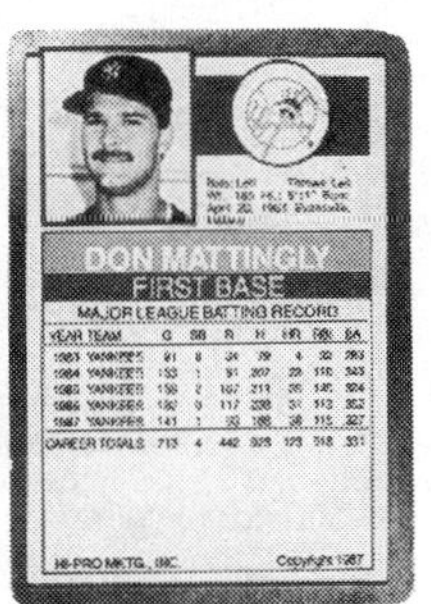

Action Packed released this test set in an effort to receive a license from Major League Baseball. The cards are styled like the Action Packed football issues on the card fronts. The flip sides are styled like Score baseball cards. The Ozzie Smith card is considered scarcer than the other five cards in the test set. Action Packed did not receive a license to produce baseball cards.

		MT	NR MT	EX
Complete set (6):		350.00	260.00	140.00
Common player:		40.00	30.00	15.00
(1)	Wade Boggs	90.00	67.00	36.00
(2)	Andre Dawson	50.00	37.00	20.00
(3)	Dwight Gooden	50.00	37.00	20.00
(4)	Carney Lansford	40.00	30.00	16.00
(5)	Don Mattingly	125.00	95.00	50.00
(6)	Ozzie Smith	90.00	67.00	36.00

1992 Action Packed Promos

This set was produced to preview Action Packed's All-Star Gallery card issue. The promo cards are identical in format to the regularly issued cards and use the same player photos. The only differences in the promos are found on the back, where the card number is missing from the lower-left corner and where a white "1992 Prototype" is overprinted on the gray background beneath the black career highlights. The promos were widely distributed at trade shows and to Action Packed's dealer network. The unnumbered promo cards are checklisted here alphabetically.

		MT	NR MT	EX
Complete set (5):		24.00	18.00	9.50
Common player:		4.00	3.00	1.50
(1)	Yogi Berra	8.00	6.00	3.25
(2)	Bob Gibson	4.00	3.00	1.50
(3)	Willie Mays	12.00	9.00	4.75
(4)	Warren Spahn	6.00	4.50	2.50
(5)	Willie Stargell	4.00	3.00	1.50

Values for recent cards and sets are listed in Mint (MT), Near Mint (NM), reflecting the fact that many cards from recent years have been preserved in top condition. Recent cards and sets in less than Excellent condition have little collector interest.

1992 Action Packed All-Star Gallery Series I

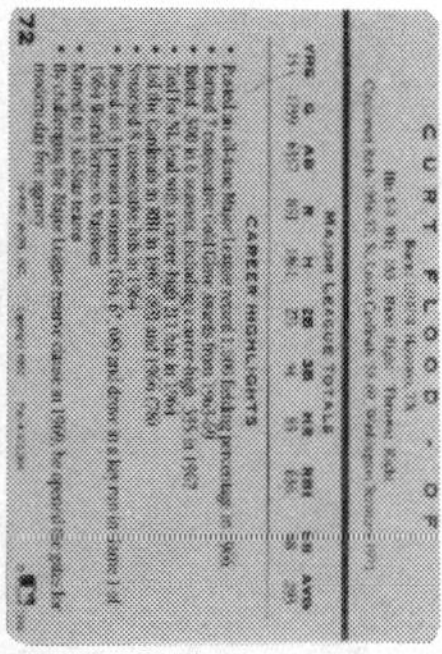

Action Packed, makers of a high quality, embossed style football card for several years, entered the baseball card field in 1992 with its 84-card All-Star Gallery, Series One. The cards feature former baseball greats, with 72 of the 84 cards in color and the remaining in sepia tone. Each foil pack of seven cards reportedly contained at least one Hall of Famer, and the company also made special 24K, gold leaf stamped cards of all of the HOFers that were randomly inserted in the packs.

		MT	NR MT	EX
Complete Set:		15.00	11.00	6.00
Common Player:		.15	.11	.06
1	Yogi Berra	.35	.25	.14
2	Lou Brock	.20	.15	.08
3	Bob Gibson	.25	.20	.10
4	Ferguson Jenkins	.20	.15	.08
5	Ralph Kiner	.20	.15	.08
6	Al Kaline	.30	.25	.12
7	Lou Boudreau	.20	.15	.08
8	Bobby Doerr	.20	.15	.08
9	Billy Herman	.20	.15	.08
10	Monte Irvin	.20	.15	.08
11	George Kell	.20	.15	.08
12	Robin Roberts	.20	.15	.08
13	Johnny Mize	.20	.15	.08
14	Willie Mays	.75	.60	.30
15	Enos Slaughter	.20	.15	.08
16	Warren Spahn	.30	.25	.12
17	Willie Stargell	.20	.15	.08
18	Billy Williams	.20	.15	.08
19	Vernon Law	.15	.11	.06
20	Virgil Trucks	.15	.11	.06
21	Mel Parnell	.15	.11	.06
22	Wally Moon	.15	.11	.06
23	Gene Woodling	.15	.11	.06
24	Richie Ashburn	.25	.20	.10
25	Mark Fidrych	.15	.11	.06
26	Elroy Face	.15	.11	.06
27	Larry Doby	.15	.11	.06
28	Dick Groat	.15	.11	.06
29	Cesar Cedeno	.15	.11	.06
30	Bob Horner	.15	.11	.06
31	Bobby Richardson	.15	.11	.06
32	Bobby Murcer	.15	.11	.06
33	Gil McDougald	.15	.11	.06
34	Roy White	.15	.11	.06
35	Bill Skowron	.20	.15	.08
36	Mickey Lolich	.15	.11	.06
37	Minnie Minoso	.15	.11	.06
38	Billy Pierce	.15	.11	.06
39	Ron Santo	.20	.15	.08
40	Sal Bando	.15	.11	.06
41	Ralph Branca	.15	.11	.06
42	Bert Campaneris	.15	.11	.06
43	Joe Garagiola	.25	.20	.10
44	Vida Blue	.15	.11	.06
45	Frank Crisetti	.15	.11	.06
46	Luis Tiant	.15	.11	.06
47	Maury Wills	.20	.15	.08
48	Sam McDowell	.15	.11	.06
49	Jimmy Piersall	.25	.20	.10
50	Jim Lonborg	.15	.11	.06
51	Don Newcombe	.20	.15	.08
52	Bobby Thomson	.20	.15	.08
53	Wilbur Wood	.15	.11	.06
54	Carl Erskine	.15	.11	.06
55	Chris Chambliss	.15	.11	.06
56	Dave Kingman	.15	.11	.06
57	Ken Holtzman	.15	.11	.06
58	Bud Harrelson	.15	.11	.06
59	Clem Labine	.15	.11	.06
60	Tony Oliva	.20	.15	.08
61	George Foster	.20	.15	.08
62	Bobby Bonds	.25	.20	.10
63	Harvey Haddix	.20	.15	.08
64	Steve Garvey	.20	.15	.08
65	Rocky Colavito	.25	.20	.10
66	Orlando Cepeda	.20	.15	.08
67	Ed Lopat	.15	.11	.06
68	Al Oliver	.15	.11	.06
69	Bill Mazeroski	.20	.15	.08
70	Al Rosen	.20	.15	.08
71	Bob Grich	.15	.11	.06
72	Curt Flood	.15	.11	.06
73	Willie Horton	.15	.11	.06

		MT	NR MT	EX
74	Rico Carty	.15	.11	.06
75	Davey Johnson	.15	.11	.06
76	Don Kessinger	.15	.11	.06
77	Frank J. Thomas	.15	.11	.06
78	Bobby Shantz	.20	.15	.08
79	Herb Score	.20	.15	.08
80	Boog Powell	.20	.15	.08
81	Rusty Staub	.20	.15	.08
82	Bill Madlock	.15	.11	.06
83	Manny Mota	.15	.11	.06
84	Bill White	.15	.11	.06

1992 Action Packed All-Star Gallery Series II

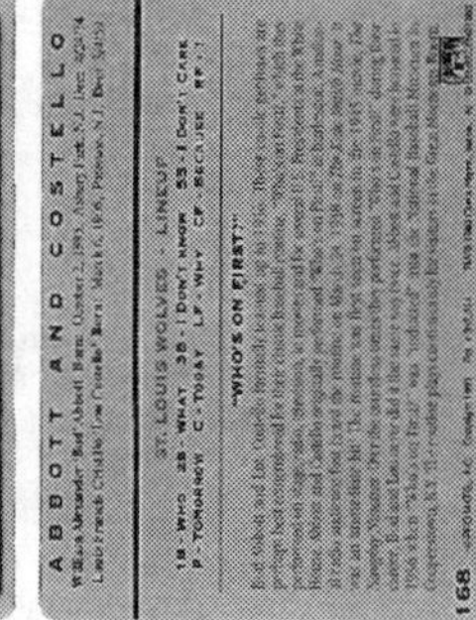

The Second Series of Action Packed All-Star Gallery was released in 1993, with cards numbered from 85 to 168. In a similar fashion to the First Series, Series Two features 52 cards in color, 31 in sepia tone and one as a colorized black and white. The series also includes two tongue-in-cheek cards - "Who's on First?" duo Bud Abbot and Lou Costello, and a card highlighting the TV and radio career of Bob Uecker.

		MT	NR MT	EX
Complete Set:		20.00	12.00	6.00
Common Player:		.15	.10	.05
85	Cy Young	.25	.20	.10
86	Honus Wagner	.25	.20	.10
87	Christy Mathewson	.25	.20	.10
88	Ty Cobb	.75	.60	.30
89	Eddie Collins	.20	.15	.08
90	Walter Johnson	.30	.25	.12
91	Tris Speaker	.25	.20	.10
92	Grover Alexander	.20	.15	.08
93	Edd Roush	.20	.15	.08
94	Babe Ruth	1.00	.70	.40
95	Rogers Hornsby	.35	.25	.14
96	Pie Traynor	.20	.15	.08
97	Lou Gehrig	.75	.60	.30
98	Mickey Cochrane	.20	.15	.08
99	Lefty Grove	.20	.15	.08
100	Jimmie Foxx	.25	.20	.10
101	Tony Lazzeri	.20	.15	.08
102	Mel Ott	.20	.15	.08
103	Carl Hubbell	.20	.15	.08
104	Al Lopez	.20	.15	.08
105	Lefty Gomez	.20	.15	.08
106	Dizzy Dean	.35	.25	.14
107	Hank Greenberg	.20	.15	.08
108	Joe Medwick	.20	.15	.08
109	Arky Vaughan	.20	.15	.08
110	Bob Feller	.25	.20	.10
111	Hal Newhouser	.20	.15	.08
112	Early Wynn	.20	.15	.08
113	Bob Lemon	.20	.15	.08
114	Red Schoendienst	.20	.15	.08
115	Satchel Paige	.35	.25	.14
116	Whitey Ford	.25	.20	.10
117	Eddie Mathews	.25	.20	.10
118	Harmon Killebrew	.25	.20	.10
119	Roberto Clemente	.60	.45	.25
120	Brooks Robinson	.40	.30	.15
121	Don Drysdale	.25	.20	.10
122	Luis Aparicio	.20	.15	.08
123	Willie McCovey	.20	.15	.08
124	Juan Marichal	.20	.15	.08
125	Gaylord Perry	.20	.15	.08
126	Catfish Hunter	.20	.15	.08
127	Jim Palmer	.25	.20	.10
128	Rod Carew	.25	.20	.10
129	Tom Seaver	.30	.25	.12
130	Rollie Fingers	.20	.15	.08
131	Joe Jackson	.75	.60	.30
132	Pepper Martin	.15	.11	.06
133	Joe Gordon	.15	.11	.06
134	Marty Marion	.15	.11	.06
135	Allie Reynolds	.15	.11	.06
136	Johnny Sain	.20	.15	.08
137	Gil Hodges	.25	.20	.10
138	Ted Kluszewski	.25	.20	.10
139	Nellie Fox	.25	.20	.10
140	Billy Martin	.20	.15	.08
141	Smoky Burgess	.15	.11	.06
142	Lew Burdette	.15	.11	.06
143	Joe Black	.15	.11	.06
144	Don Larsen	.20	.15	.08
145	Ken Boyer	.15	.11	.06
146	Johnny Callison	.15	.11	.06
147	Norm Cash	.20	.15	.08
148	Keith Hernandez	.15	.11	.06
149	Jim Kaat	.15	.11	.06
150	Bill Freehan	.15	.11	.06
151	Joe Torre	.15	.11	.06
152	Bob Uecker	.20	.15	.08
153	Dave McNally	.15	.11	.06
154	Denny McLain	.20	.15	.08
155	Dick Allen	.20	.15	.08
156	Jimmy Wynn	.15	.11	.06
157	Tommy John	.15	.11	.06
158	Paul Blair	.15	.11	.06
159	Reggie Smith	.15	.11	.06
160	Jerry Koosman	.15	.11	.06
161	Thurman Munson	.25	.20	.10
162	Graig Nettles	.15	.11	.06
163	Ron Cey	.15	.11	.06
164	Cecil Cooper	.15	.11	.06
165	Dave Parker	.20	.15	.08
166	Jim Rice	.15	.11	.06
167	Kent Tekulve	.15	.11	.06
168	Who's On First?	.25	.20	.10

1992 Action Packed Gold

Essentially identical to the regular-issue Action Packed All-Star Gallery cards, these premium inserts are specially numbered and highlighted with 24-karat gold detailing.

		MT	NR MT	EX
Complete set (65):		1400.	1000.	500.00
Common player:		20.00	15.00	8.00
	Series I			
1G	Yogi Berra	35.00	26.00	14.00
2G	Lou Brock	25.00	18.50	10.00
3G	Bob Gibson	25.00	18.50	10.00
4G	Ferguson Jenkins	20.00	15.00	8.00
5G	Ralph Kiner	20.00	15.00	8.00
6G	Al Kaline	35.00	26.00	14.00
7G	Lou Boudreau	20.00	15.00	8.00
8G	Bobby Doerr	20.00	15.00	8.00
9G	Billy Herman	20.00	15.00	8.00
10G	Monte Irvin	25.00	18.50	10.00
11G	George Kell	20.00	15.00	8.00
12G	Robin Roberts	25.00	18.50	10.00
13G	Johnny Mize	25.00	18.50	10.00
14G	Willie Mays	60.00	45.00	24.00
15G	Enos Slaughter	20.00	15.00	8.00
16G	Warren Spahn	30.00	22.00	12.00
17G	Willie Stargell	25.00	18.50	10.00
18G	Billy Williams	20.00	15.00	8.00
	Series II			
19G	Cy Young	30.00	22.00	12.00
20G	Honus Wagner	40.00	30.00	16.00
21G	Christy Mathewson	35.00	26.00	14.00
22G	Ty Cobb	45.00	34.00	18.00
23G	Eddie Collins	20.00	15.00	8.00
24G	Walter Johnson	35.00	26.00	14.00
25G	Tris Speaker	25.00	18.50	10.00
26G	Grover Alexander	25.00	18.50	10.00
27G	Edd Roush	20.00	15.00	8.00
28G	Babe Ruth	90.00	67.00	36.00
29G	Rogers Hornsby	25.00	18.50	10.00
30G	Pie Traynor	20.00	15.00	8.00
31G	Lou Gehrig	60.00	45.00	24.00
32G	Mickey Cochrane	25.00	18.50	10.00
33G	Lefty Grove	25.00	18.50	10.00
34G	Jimmie Foxx	30.00	22.00	12.00
35G	Tony Lazzeri	20.00	15.00	8.00
36G	Mel Ott	20.00	15.00	8.00
37G	Carl Hubbell	25.00	18.50	10.00
38G	Al Lopez	20.00	15.00	8.00
39G	Lefty Gomez	25.00	18.50	10.00
40G	Dizzy Dean	40.00	30.00	16.00
41G	Hank Greenberg	35.00	26.00	14.00
42G	Joe Medwick	20.00	15.00	8.00
43G	Arky Vaughan	20.00	15.00	8.00
44G	Bob Feller	25.00	18.50	10.00
45G	Hal Newhouser	20.00	15.00	8.00
46G	Early Wynn	20.00	15.00	8.00
47G	Bob Lemon	20.00	15.00	8.00
48G	Red Schoendienst	20.00	15.00	8.00
49G	Satchel Paige	45.00	34.00	18.00
50G	Whitey Ford	25.00	18.50	10.00
51G	Eddie Mathews	25.00	18.50	10.00
52G	Harmon Killebrew	25.00	18.50	10.00
53G	Roberto Clemente	45.00	34.00	18.00
54G	Brooks Robinson	25.00	18.50	10.00
55G	Don Drysdale	25.00	18.50	10.00
56G	Luis Aparicio	20.00	15.00	8.00
57G	Willie McCovey	25.00	18.50	10.00
58G	Juan Merichal	20.00	15.00	8.00
59G	Gaylord Perry	20.00	15.00	8.00
60G	Catfish Hunter	20.00	15.00	8.00
61G	Jim Palmer	25.00	18.50	10.00
62G	Rod Carew	25.00	18.50	10.00
63G	Tom Seaver	25.00	18.50	10.00
64G	Rollie Fingers	20.00	15.00	8.00
65G	Who's on First? (Bud Abbott, Lou Costello)	25.00	18.50	10.00

Values for recent cards and sets are listed in Mint (MT), Near Mint (NM), reflecting the fact that many cards from recent years have been preserved in top condition. Recent cards and sets in less than Excellent condition have little collector interest.

1993 Action Packed Tom Seaver Prototypes

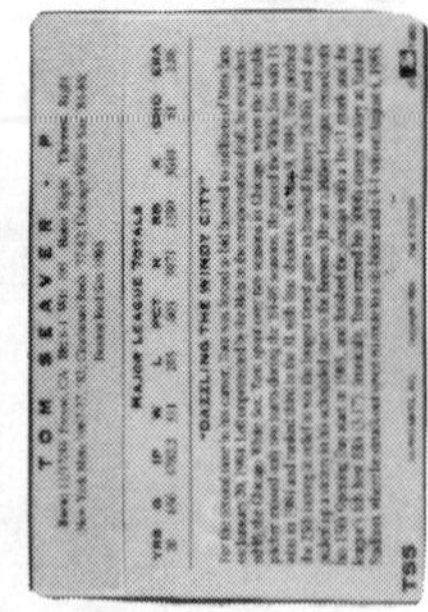

Tom Seaver's career was highlighted in this five-card promo set. Each card has an embossed front color photo surrounded by three gold pinstripes and a red border. Seaver's name is in red in a gold bar at bottom. Backs are printed in black and gold with a white undertype reading "1993 Prototype." Backs have biographical and career data, lifetime stats and a few sentences of career highlights. Cards have a "TS" prefix to the card number.

		MT	NR MT	EX
Complete set (5):		30.00	22.00	12.00
Common card:		5.00	3.75	2.00
1TS	The Franchise	5.00	3.75	2.00
2TS	Amazin' Mets	10.00	7.50	4.00
3TS	A Tearful Goodbye	5.00	3.75	2.00
4TS	Tom Terrific	10.00	7.50	4.00
5TS	Dazzling the Windy City	5.00	3.75	2.00

1983 Affiliated Food Rangers

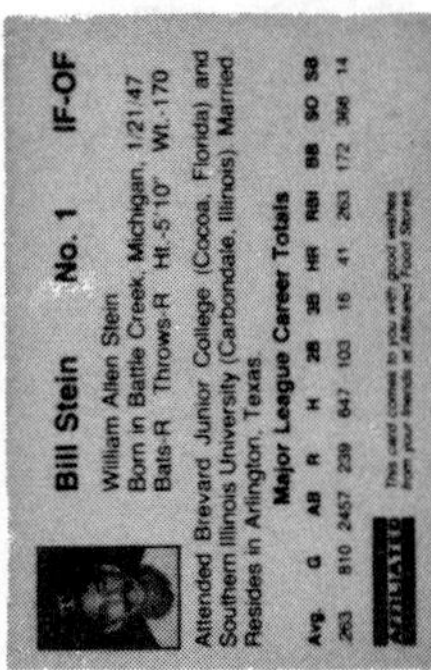

This 28-card set, featuring the Texas Rangers, was issued as a promotion by the Affiliated Food Stores chain of Arlington, Texas, late during the 1983 baseball season. Complete sets were given out free to youngsters 13 and under at the Sept. 3, 1983, Rangers game. The cards measure 2-3/8" by 3-1/2" and feature a full-color photo on the front. Also on the front, located inside a blue box, is the player's name, uniform number, and the words "1983 Rangers." The card backs contain a small player photo plus biographical and statistical information, along with the Affiliated logo and a brief promotional message. A total of 10,000 sets was reportedly printed. Cards are numbered by the players' uniform numbers in the checklist that follows.

		MT	NR MT	EX
Complete set (28):		6.00	4.50	2.50
Common player:		.25	.20	.10
1	Bill Stein	.25	.20	.10
2	Mike Richardt	.25	.20	.10
3	Wayne Tolleson	.25	.20	.10
5	Billy Sample	.25	.20	.10
6	Bobby Jones	.25	.20	.10
7	Bucky Dent	.35	.25	.14
8	Bobby Johnson	.25	.20	.10
9	Pete O'Brien	.25	.20	.10
10	Jim Sundberg	.25	.20	.10
11	Doug Rader	.30	.25	.12
12	Dave Hostetler	.25	.20	.10
14	Larry Biittner	.25	.20	.10
15	Larry Parrish	.25	.20	.10
17	Mickey Rivers	.25	.20	.10
21	Odell Jones	.25	.20	.10
24	Dave Schmidt	.25	.20	.10
25	Buddy Bell	.35	.25	.14
26	George Wright	.25	.20	.10
28	Frank Tanana	.25	.20	.10
29	John Butcher	.25	.20	.10
32	Jon Matlack	.25	.20	.10
40	Rick Honeycutt	.25	.20	.10
41	Dave Tobik	.25	.20	.10

44	Danny Darwin	.25	.20	.10
46	Jim Anderson	.25	.20	.10
48	Mike Smithson	.25	.20	.10
49	Charlie Hough	.45	.35	.20
----	Coaching Staff (Rich Donnelly, Glenn Ezell, Merv Rettenmund, Dick Such, Wayne Terwilliger)	.25	.20	.10

1990 Agfa Film

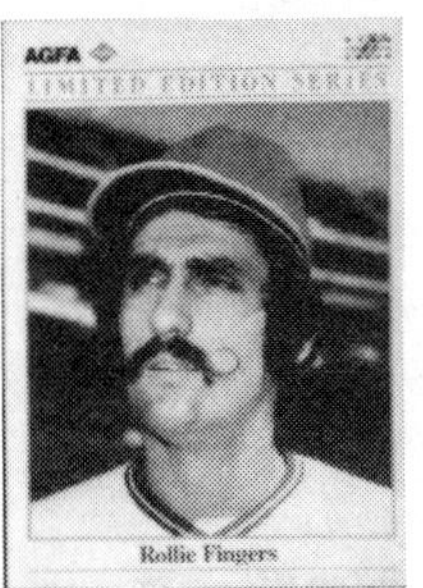

This "old-timers" set was distributed in three-card packs with the purchase of Agfa film. Produced by Michael Schecter Associates, whose logo appears on the back, the cards were not licensed by Major League Baseball, so team logos had to be eliminated from the photos. Cards have a white background with the film company's logos in the upper corners. Backs are in black-and-white and have full major league regular season and post-season stats.

		MT	NR MT	EX
Complete set (22):		18.00	13.50	7.25
Common player:		.50	.40	.20
1	Willie Mays	2.00	1.50	.80
2	Carl Yastrzemski	1.00	.70	.40
3	Harmon Killebrew	1.00	.70	.40
4	Joe Torre	.50	.40	.20
5	Al Kaline	1.50	1.25	.60
6	Hank Aaron	2.00	1.50	.80
7	Rod Carew	1.00	.70	.40
8	Roberto Clemente	2.00	1.50	.80
9	Luis Aparicio	.75	.60	.30
10	Roger Maris	1.00	.70	.40
11	Joe Morgan	.75	.60	.30
12	Maury Wills	.50	.40	.20
13	Brooks Robinson	1.50	1.25	.60
14	Tom Seaver	1.00	.70	.40
15	Steve Carlton	1.00	.70	.40
16	Whitey Ford	1.25	.90	.50
17	Jim Palmer	.75	.60	.30
18	Rollie Fingers	.75	.60	.30
19	Bruce Sutter	.50	.40	.20
20	Willie McCovey	1.00	.70	.40
21	Mike Schmidt	1.50	1.25	.60
22	Yogi Berra	1.50	1.25	.60

1970 Carl Aldana Orioles

Little is known about the distribution or origin of this 12-card regional set, which was available in 1970 in the Baltimore area. Measuring 3-1/4" by 2-1/8", the unnumbered cards picture members of the Baltimore Orioles and include two poses of Brooks Robinson. The cards feature line drawings of the players surrounded by a plain border. The player's last name appears below the portrait sketch. The set was named after Carl Aldana, who supplied the artwork for the cards.

		NR MT	EX	VG
Complete Set:		50.00	25.00	15.00
Common Player:		1.25	.60	.40
(1)	Mark Belanger	2.00	1.00	.60
(2)	Paul Blair	2.00	1.00	.60
(3)	Mike Cuellar	2.00	1.00	.60
(4)	Ellie Hendricks	1.25	.60	.40
(5)	Dave Johnson	3.00	1.50	.90
(6)	Dave McNally	2.25	1.25	.70
(7)	Jim Palmer	12.00	6.00	3.50
(8)	Boog Powell	3.00	1.50	.90
(9)	Brooks Robinson (diving - face showing)	12.00	6.00	3.50
(10)	Brooks Robinson (diving - back showing)	12.00	6.00	3.50
(11)	Frank Robinson	12.00	6.00	3.50
(12)	Earl Weaver	3.00	2.25	1.25

1990 All American Baseball Team

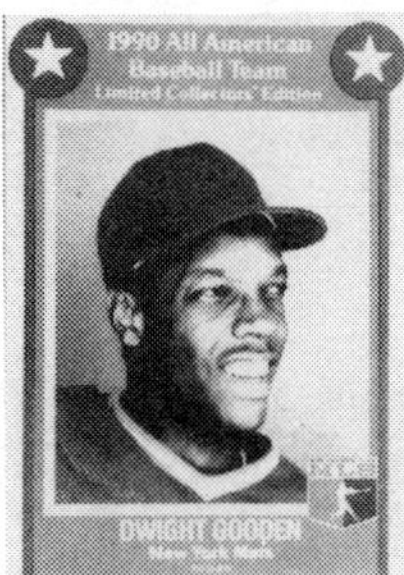

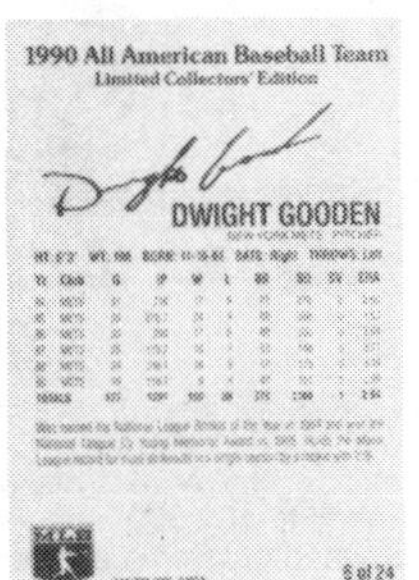

Produced by Mike Schecter Associates, this 24-card set includes many of the top players in the game. Team logos are airbrushed from the color photo on front, which is surrounded by a red, white and blue border and the MLB Players' Association logo. The backs are printed in blue on white stock, with a facsimile autograph appearing above the statistics.

		MT	NR MT	EX
Complete set (24):		25.00	18.50	10.00
Common player:		.50	.40	.20
1	George Brett	1.25	.90	.50
2	Mark McGwire	.75	.60	.30
3	Wade Boggs	1.25	.90	.50
4	Cal Ripken, Jr.	2.00	1.50	.80
5	Rickey Henderson	.95	.70	.40
6	Dwight Gooden	.75	.60	.30
7	Bo Jackson	.95	.70	.40
8	Roger Clemens	1.25	.90	.50
9	Orel Hershiser	.60	.45	.25
10	Ozzie Smith	.90	.70	.35
11	Don Mattingly	1.25	.90	.50
12	Kirby Puckett	.95	.70	.40
13	Robin Yount	1.25	.90	.50
14	Tony Gwynn	.75	.60	.30
15	Jose Canseco	1.25	.90	.50
16	Nolan Ryan	3.50	2.75	1.50
17	Ken Griffey, Jr.	3.50	2.75	1.50
18	Will Clark	1.25	.90	.50
19	Ryne Sandberg	2.00	1.50	.80
20	Kent Hrbek	.50	.40	.20
21	Carlton Fisk	.75	.60	.30
22	Paul Molitor	.95	.70	.40
23	Dave Winfield	1.25	.90	.50
24	Andre Dawson	.75	.60	.30

1887 Allen & Ginter World's Champions (N28)

Generally considered the first of the tobacco card issues, this 50-card set was titled "The World Champions" and included 10 baseball players and 40 other sports personalities such as John L. Sullivan and Buffalo Bill Cody. The 1-1/2" by 2-3/4" cards were inserted in boxes of Allen & Ginter cigarettes. The card fronts are color lithographs on white card stock, and are considered among the most attractive cards ever produced. All card backs have a complete checklist for this unnumbered set, which includes six eventual Hall of Famers (Cap Anson, John Clarkson, Charles Comiskey, Timothy Keefe, Mike Kelly and John Ward). Eight of the 10 players shown are from the National League and the other two from the American Association, then also considered a major league.

		NR MT	EX	VG
Complete set (10):		12000.	6000.	3500.
Common player:		475.00	240.00	140.00
(1)	Adrian C. Anson	2750.	1375.	825.00
(2)	Chas. W. Bennett	475.00	240.00	140.00
(3)	R.L. Caruthers	625.00	315.00	185.00
(4)	John Clarkson	1350.	675.00	400.00
(5)	Charles Comiskey	2000.	1000.	600.00
(6)	Capt. John Glasscock	475.00	240.00	140.00
(7)	Timothy Keefe	1650.	825.00	495.00
(8)	Mike Kelly	2500.	1250.	750.00
(9)	Joseph Mulvey	475.00	240.00	140.00
(10)	John M. Ward	1650.	825.00	495.00

1888 Allen & Ginter World's Champions (N29)

After their 1887 first series of tobacco cards proved a success, Allen & Ginter issued a second series of "World Champions" in 1888. Once again, 50 of these 1-1/2" by 2-3/4" color cards were produced, in virtually the same style as the year before. Only six baseball players are included in this set, with New York Giants catcher Buck Ewing the only player of note. The most obvious difference from the 1887 cards is the absence of the Allen & Ginter name on the card fronts. All six baseball players are from National League teams.

		NR MT	EX	VG
Complete set (6):		8000.	4000.	2400.
Common player:		1200.	600.00	275.00
(1)	Wm. Ewing	4000.	1500.	800.00
(2)	Jas. H. Fogarty (middle initial actually G.)	1200.	600.00	275.00
(3)	Charles H. Getzin (Getzein)	1200.	600.00	275.00
(4)	Geo. F. Miller	1200.	600.00	275.00
(5)	John Morrell (Morrill)	1200.	600.00	275.00
(6)	James Ryan	1200.	600.00	275.00

1910 All Star Base-Ball

Issued circa 1910, this rare 12-card set was issued by candy maker J.H. Dockman & Son. The cards, measuring approximately 1-7/8" by 3-3/8", were printed on the front and back of boxes of candy sold as "All Star Base-Ball Package." There are two players on each box - one on the front, the other on the back - but the cards consist of crude drawings that actually bear no resemblance to the player named below the drawing.

	NR MT	EX	VG
Complete set (16):	1200.	600.00	360.00
Common player:	60.00	30.00	15.00

(1)	Heinie Beckendorf	60.00	30.00	15.00
(2)	Roger Bresnahan	100.00	50.00	30.00
(3)	Al Burch	60.00	30.00	15.00
(4)	Frank Chance	150.00	75.00	45.00
(5)	Wid Conroy	60.00	30.00	15.00
(6)	Jack Coombs	60.00	30.00	15.00
(7)	George Gibson	60.00	30.00	15.00
(8)	Dick Hoblitzel	60.00	30.00	15.00
(9)	Johnny Kling	60.00	30.00	15.00
(10)	Frank LaPorte	60.00	30.00	15.00
(11)	Connie Mack	200.00	100.00	60.00
(12)	Christy Mathewson	300.00	150.00	90.00
(13)	Matty McIntyre	60.00	30.00	15.00
(14)	Jimmy Sheckard	60.00	30.00	15.00
(15)	Al Schweitzer	60.00	30.00	15.00
(16)	Harry Wolter	60.00	30.00	15.00

1971 Allstate Insurance

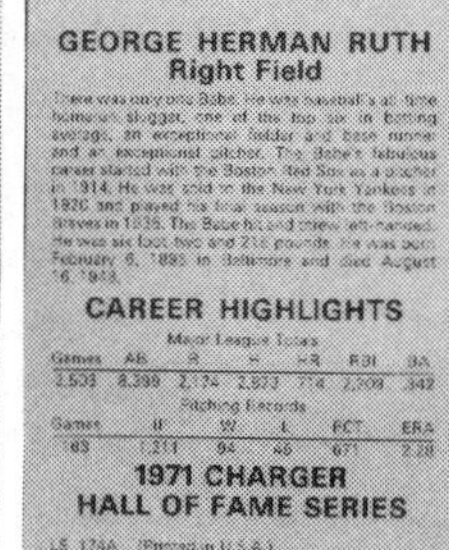

This 4-card series was distributed as part of an internal sales promotion for Allstate Insurance. Graphic artist Ray Lending, an Allstate employee, created the 2-1/2" by 3-1/4" cards in duo-tone black and green on white. Card fronts show the players in batting stance, with the player name in one of the upper corners and the "Hall of Fame Series" logo printed across the bottom of the card. The card backs carry the player's full name and position, followed by a brief career summary, biography, and Career Highlights chart listing major league totals. "1971 Charger" and "Hall of Fame Series" are printed at the bottom of the card back. 8,000 sets were distributed.

		NR MT	EX	VG
Complete set:		40.00	20.00	12.00
Common player:		10.00	5.00	3.00
(1)	Ty Cobb	10.00	5.00	3.00
(2)	Stan Musial	10.00	5.00	3.00
(3)	Babe Ruth	20.00	10.00	6.00
(4)	Ted Williams	10.00	5.00	3.00

1987 Allstate Insurance

This 6-card set was the second promotional series of baseball cards created by Allstate Insurance graphic artist Ray Lending for internal use by the company. Modeled after the famous "Diamond Stars" from the 1930s, this set features full-color player portraits of legendary sluggers. "Life Grand Slam" (the promotion theme) is printed beneath the player portrait and the player's name appears in an upper corner. Black and white backs provide personal information, player profiles and career highlights. 15,000 sets of the cards were distributed, although only a few filtered into the collecting hobby. Cards measure 2-3/4" by 3-5/8" in size. Full-color 22" x 28" reproductions of the cards in this set were produced in poster format.

		MT	NR MT	EX
Complete set:		30.00	15.00	8.00
Common player:		3.00	1.50	.80
(1)	Hank Aaron	6.00	4.50	2.50
(2)	Joe DiMaggio	9.00	6.75	3.50
(3)	Jimmie Foxx	3.00	2.25	1.25
(4)	Lou Gehrig	6.00	4.50	2.50
(5)	Babe Ruth	12.00	9.00	4.75
(6)	Ted Williams	6.00	4.50	2.50

1991 Alrak Griffey Gazette

Ken Griffey, Jr. was featured in a 1991 set of four cards entitled "Griffey Gazette" that was released by Alrak Enterprises. The card sets were limited to 100,000, and major league logos were airbrushed out from caps and uniforms.

		MT	NR MT	EX
Complete Set:		6.00	4.50	2.50
(1)	Crowd Pleaser (Ken Griffey, Jr.)	1.50	1.25	.60
(2)	Holdin On! (Ken Griffey, Jr.)	1.50	1.25	.60
(3)	24ct Gold Moment (Ken Griffey, Jr.)	1.50	1.25	.60
(4)	Next of Ken (Ken Griffey, Jr.) (with Ken Griffey, Sr.)	1.50	1.25	.60

1993 Alrak Ken Griffey, Jr.

Ken Griffey, Jr. was the subject of a four-card set released in 1993 by Alrak Enterprises. The set features Griffey in various poses and is highlighted with a 1992 All-Star MVP commemorative card. The cards are UV coated and gold foil stamped and limited to 24,000 sets. Additionally, the company also issued a Griffey Jr. Triple Play card in an oversized format (3-1/2" x 7-1/2") limited to 15,000.

		MT	NR MT	EX
Complete set (4):		6.00	4.50	2.50
Common card:		1.50	1.25	.60
(1)	Ken Griffey, Jr. (portrait)	1.50	1.25	.60
(2)	Ken Griffey, Jr. (batting)	1.50	1.25	.60
(3)	Ken Griffey, Jr. (throwing)	1.50	1.25	.60
(4)	Ken Griffey, Jr. (All-Star MVP)	1.50	1.25	.60

1908 American Caramel Co. (E91, Set A)

Issued by Philadelphia's American Caramel Company from 1908 through 1910, the E91 set of Base Ball Caramels is generally not popular with collectors because the color drawings show "generic" players, rather than actual major leaguers. In other words, the exact same drawing was used to depict two or three different players. For this reason, the set is sometimes referred to as "Fake Design". The player's name, position and team appear below the color drawing on the front of the card. The cards measure approximately 1-1/2" by 2-3/4" and were issued in three separate series. They can be differentiated by their backs, which checklist the cards. Set A backs list the Athletics in the upper left, the Giants in the upper right and the Cubs below. Set B backs list the Cubs and Athletics on top with the Giants below, and Set C backs list Pittsburg and Washington on top with Boston below. A line indicating the cards were "Manufactured Only by the American Caramel Co." appears at the bottom.

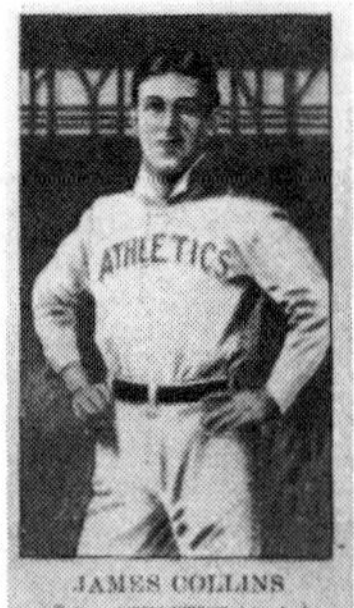

		NR MT	EX	VG
Complete set (33):		4000.	2000.	1200.
Common player:		65.00	32.00	19.50
(1)	Charles Bender	260.00	130.00	78.00
(2)	Roger Bresnahan	260.00	130.00	78.00
(3)	Albert Bridwell	65.00	32.00	19.50
(4)	Mordecai Brown	260.00	130.00	78.00
(5)	Frank Chance	325.00	162.00	97.00
(6)	James Collins	260.00	130.00	78.00
(7)	Harry Davis	65.00	32.00	19.50
(8)	Arthur Devlin	65.00	32.00	19.50
(9)	Michael Donlin	80.00	40.00	24.00
(10)	John Evers	260.00	130.00	78.00
(11)	Frederick L. Hartsel	65.00	32.00	19.50
(12)	John Kling	80.00	40.00	24.00
(13)	Christopher Matthewson (Mathewson)	450.00	225.00	135.00
(14)	Joseph McGinnity	260.00	130.00	78.00
(15)	John J McGraw	325.00	162.00	97.00
(16)	Daniel F Murphy	65.00	32.00	19.50
(17)	Simon Nicholls	65.00	32.00	19.50
(18)	Reuben Oldring	65.00	32.00	19.50
(19)	Orvill Overall (Orval)	65.00	32.00	19.50
(20)	Edward S. Plank	375.00	187.00	112.00
(21)	Edward Reulbach	65.00	32.00	19.50
(22)	James Scheckard (Sheckard)	65.00	32.00	19.50
(23)	Osee Schreckengost (Ossee)	65.00	32.00	19.50
(24)	Ralph O. Seybold	65.00	32.00	19.50
(25)	J. Bentley Seymour	65.00	32.00	19.50
(26)	Daniel Shay	65.00	32.00	19.50
(27)	Frank Shulte (Schulte)	65.00	32.00	19.50
(28)	James Slagle	65.00	32.00	19.50
(29)	Harry Steinfeldt	80.00	40.00	24.00
(30)	Luther H. Taylor	80.00	40.00	24.00
(31)	Fred Tenney	65.00	32.00	19.50
(32)	Joseph B. Tinker	260.00	130.00	78.00
(33)	George Edward Waddell	260.00	130.00	78.00

1909 American Caramel Co. (E91, Set B)

		NR MT	EX	VG
Complete set (33):		3900.	1950.	1150.
Common player:		65.00	32.00	19.50
(1)	James Archer	65.00	32.00	19.50
(2)	Frank Baker	260.00	130.00	78.00
(3)	John Barry	65.00	32.00	19.50
(4)	Charles Bender	325.00	160.00	95.00
(5)	Albert Bridwell	65.00	32.00	19.50
(6)	Mordecai Brown	260.00	130.00	78.00
(7)	Frank Chance	325.00	160.00	95.00
(8)	Edw. Collins	260.00	130.00	78.00
(9)	Harry Davis	65.00	32.00	19.50
(10)	Arthur Devlin	65.00	32.00	19.50
(11)	Michael Donlin	80.00	40.00	24.00
(12)	Larry Doyle	65.00	32.00	19.50
(13)	John Evers	260.00	130.00	78.00

(14)	Robt. Ganley	65.00	32.00	19.50
(15)	Frederick L. Hartsel	65.00	32.00	19.50
(16)	Arthur Hoffman (Hofman)	65.00	32.00	19.50
(17)	Harry Krause	65.00	32.00	19.50
(18)	Rich. W. Marquard	260.00	130.00	78.00
(19)	Christopher Matthewson (Mathewson)	450.00	225.00	135.00
(20)	John J. McGraw	325.00	160.00	95.00
(21)	J.T. Meyers	65.00	32.00	19.50
(22)	Dan Murphy	65.00	32.00	19.50
(23)	Jno. J. Murray	65.00	32.00	19.50
(24)	Orvill Overall (Orval)	65.00	32.00	19.50
(25)	Edward S. Plank	375.00	185.00	110.00
(26)	Edward Reulbach	65.00	32.00	19.50
(27)	James Scheckard (Sheckard)	65.00	32.00	19.50
(28)	J. Bentley Seymour	65.00	32.00	19.50
(29)	Harry Steinfeldt	80.00	40.00	24.00
(30)	Frank Shulte (Schulte)	65.00	32.00	19.50
(31)	Fred Tenney	65.00	32.00	19.50
(32)	Joseph B Tinker	260.00	130.00	78.00
(33)	Ira Thomas	65.00	32.00	19.50

1910 American Caramel Co. (E91, Set C)

Base Ball Caramels.

THIS CARD IS ONE OF A SET OF THIRTY-THREE BASE BALL PLAYERS, CONSISTING OF PITTSBURG, WASHINGTON AND BOSTON BASE BALL TEAMS, ONE OF WHICH IS WRAPPED WITH EVERY BASE BALL CARAMEL.

AMERICAN CARAMEL CO.

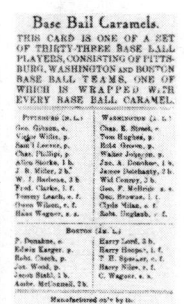

		NR MT	EX	VG
	Complete set (33):	3000.	1500.	900.00
	Common player:	65.00	32.00	19.50
(1)	W.J. Barbeau	65.00	32.00	19.50
(2)	Geo. Brown	65.00	32.00	19.50
(3)	Robt. Check (Charles Chech)	65.00	32.00	19.50
(4)	Fred Clarke	260.00	130.00	78.00
(5)	Wid Conroy	65.00	32.00	19.50
(6)	James Delehanty (Delahanty)	65.00	32.00	19.50
(7)	Jon A. Donohue (Donahue)	65.00	32.00	19.50
(8)	P. Donahue	65.00	32.00	19.50
(9)	Geo. Gibson	65.00	32.00	19.50
(10)	Robt. Groom	65.00	32.00	19.50
(11)	Harry Hooper	260.00	130.00	78.00
(12)	Tom Hughes	65.00	32.00	19.50
(13)	Walter Johnson	600.00	300.00	180.00
(14)	Edwin Karger	65.00	32.00	19.50
(15)	Tommy Leach	65.00	32.00	19.50
(16)	Sam'l Leever	65.00	32.00	19.50
(17)	Harry Lord	65.00	32.00	19.50
(18)	Geo. F. McBride	65.00	32.00	19.50
(19)	Ambr. McConnell	65.00	32.00	19.50
(20)	Clyde Milan	65.00	32.00	19.50
(21)	J.B. Miller	65.00	32.00	19.50
(22)	Harry Niles	65.00	32.00	19.50
(23)	Chas. Phillipi (Phillippe)	65.00	32.00	19.50
(24)	T.H. Speaker	425.00	210.00	125.00
(25)	Jacob Stahl	65.00	32.00	19.50
(26)	Chas. E. Street	65.00	32.00	19.50
(27)	Allen Storke	65.00	32.00	19.50
(28)	Robt. Unglaub	65.00	32.00	19.50
(29)	C. Wagner	65.00	32.00	19.50
(30)	Hans Wagner	600.00	300.00	180.00
(31)	Victor Willis	75.00	37.00	22.00
(32)	Owen Wilson	65.00	32.00	19.50
(33)	Jos. Wood	75.00	35.00	18.00

Grading Guide

Mint (MT): A perfect card. Well-centered with all corners sharp and square. No creases, stains, edge nicks, surface marks, yellowing or fading.

Near Mint (NM): A nearly perfect card. At first glance, a NM card appears to be perfect. May be slightly off-center. No surface marks, creases or loss of gloss.

Excellent (EX): Corners are still fairly sharp with only moderate wear. Borders may be off-center. No creases or stains on fronts or backs, but may show slight loss of surface luster.

Very Good (VG): Shows obvious handling. May have rounded corners, minor creases, major gum or wax stains. No major creases, tape marks, writing, etc.

Good (G): A well-worn card, but exhibits no intentional damage. May have major or multiple creases. Corners may be rounded well beyond card border.

1910 American Caramel die-cuts (E125)

Issued circa 1910 by the American Caramel Company, this set of die-cut cards is so rare that it wasn't even known to exist until the late 1960s. Apparently inserted in boxes of caramels, these cards, which are die-cut figures of baseball players, vary in size but are all relatively large - some measuring 7" high and 4" wide. Players from the Athletics, Red Sox, Giants and Pirates are known with a team checklist appearing on the back. According to the checklists, the set would be complete at 41 cards (including two separate poses of Honus Wagner), but to date only about 20 different cards have been found. The set is designated as E125.

		NR MT	EX	VG
	Complete set (41):	39000.	19500.	11500.
	Common player:	600.00	300.00	180.00
(1)	Babe Adams	600.00	300.00	180.00
(2)	Red Ames	600.00	300.00	180.00
(3)	Home Run Baker	1600.	800.00	480.00
(4)	Jack Barry	600.00	300.00	180.00
(5)	Chief Bender	1600.	800.00	480.00
(6)	Al Bridwell	600.00	300.00	180.00
(7)	Bobby Byrne	600.00	300.00	180.00
(8)	Bill Carrigan	600.00	300.00	180.00
(9)	Ed Cicotte	1200.	600.00	360.00
(10)	Fred Clark (Clarke)	1600.	800.00	480.00
(11)	Eddie Collins	2500.	1250.	750.00
(12)	Harry Davis	600.00	300.00	180.00
(13)	Art Devlin	600.00	300.00	180.00
(14)	Josh Devore	600.00	300.00	180.00
(15)	Larry Doyle	600.00	300.00	180.00
(16)	John Flynn	600.00	300.00	180.00
(17)	George Gibson	600.00	300.00	180.00
(18)	Topsy Hartsell (Hartsel)	600.00	300.00	180.00
(19)	Harry Hooper	1600.	800.00	480.00
(20)	Harry Krause	600.00	300.00	180.00
(21)	Tommy Leach	600.00	300.00	180.00
(22)	Harry Lord	600.00	300.00	180.00
(23)	Christy Mathewson	5000.	2500.	1500.
(24)	Amby McConnell	600.00	300.00	180.00
(25)	Fred Merkle	600.00	300.00	180.00
(26)	Dots Miller	600.00	300.00	180.00
(27)	Danny Murphy	600.00	300.00	180.00
(28)	Red Murray	600.00	300.00	180.00
(29)	Harry Niles	600.00	300.00	180.00
(30)	Rube Oldring	600.00	300.00	180.00
(31)	Eddie Plank	2500.	1250.	750.00
(32)	Cy Seymour	600.00	300.00	180.00
(33)	Tris Speaker	3200.	1600.	960.00
(34)	Jake Stahl	600.00	300.00	180.00
(35)	Ira Thomas	600.00	300.00	180.00
(36)	Heinie Wagner	600.00	300.00	180.00
(37)	Honus Wagner (batting)	5000.	2500.	1500.
(38)	Honus Wagner (throwing)	5000.	2500.	1500.
(39)	Art Wilson	600.00	300.00	180.00
(40)	Owen Wilson	600.00	300.00	180.00
(41)	Hooks Wiltse	600.00	300.00	180.00

1909 - 11 American Caramel Co. (E90-1)

The E90-1 set was issued by the American Caramel Co. from 1909 through 1911, with the bulk of the set being produced in the first year. The cards, which measure 1-1/2" by 2-3/4" in size and were issued with sticks of caramel candy, are color reproductions of actual photographs. The card backs state that 100 subjects are included in the set though more actually do exist. There are several levels of scarcity in the set, those levels being mostly determined by the year the cards were issued. Mitchell (Cincinnati), Clarke (Pittsburg), Graham, and Sweeney (Boston) are the most difficult cards in the set to obtain. For the collector's convenience, the players' first names have been added in the checklist that follows. The complete set price includes all variations.

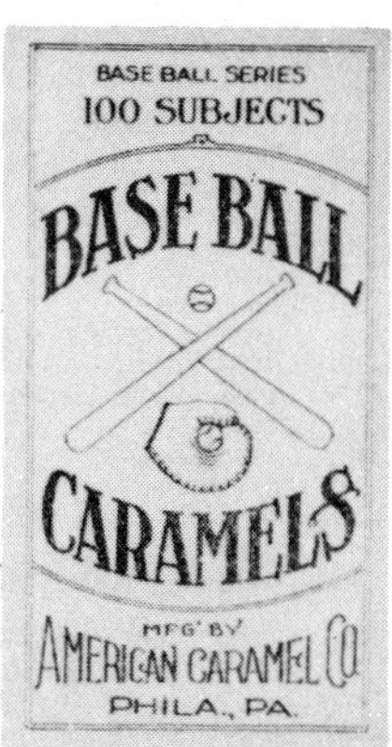

		NR MT	EX	VG
	Complete set (118):	70000.	35000.	21000.
	Common player:	125.00	62.00	37.00
(1)	Bill Bailey	125.00	62.00	37.00
(2)	Home Run Baker	550.00	275.00	165.00
(3)	Jack Barry	125.00	62.00	37.00
(4)	George Bell	125.00	62.00	37.00
(5)	Harry Bemis	225.00	112.00	67.00
(6)	Chief Bender	450.00	225.00	135.00
(7)	Bob Bescher	175.00	87.00	52.00
(8)	Cliff Blankenship	125.00	62.00	37.00
(9)	John Bliss	125.00	62.00	37.00
(10)	Bill Bradley	125.00	62.00	37.00
(11)	Kitty Bransfield ("P" on shirt)	125.00	62.00	37.00
(12)	Kitty Bransfield (no "P" on shirt)	175.00	87.00	52.00
(13)	Roger Bresnahan	500.00	250.00	150.00
(14)	Al Bridwell	125.00	62.00	37.00
(15)	Buster Brown (Boston)	125.00	62.00	37.00
(16)	Mordecai Brown (Chicago)	650.00	325.00	195.00
(17)	Donie Bush	125.00	62.00	37.00
(18)	John Butler	125.00	62.00	37.00
(19)	Howie Camnitz	125.00	62.00	37.00
(20)	Frank Chance	550.00	275.00	165.00
(21)	Hal Chase	150.00	75.00	45.00
(22a)	Fred Clarke (Philadelphia)	450.00	225.00	135.00
(22b)	Fred Clarke (Pittsburgh)	1500.	750.00	450.00
(23)	Wally Clement	175.00	87.00	52.00
(24)	Ty Cobb	4500.	2250.	1350.
(25)	Eddie Collins	550.00	275.00	165.00
(26)	Sam Crawford	500.00	250.00	150.00
(27)	Frank Corridon	125.00	62.00	37.00
(28)	Lou Criger	125.00	62.00	37.00
(29)	George Davis	125.00	62.00	37.00
(30)	Harry Davis	125.00	62.00	37.00
(31)	Ray Demmitt	375.00	187.00	112.00
(32)	Mike Donlin	125.00	62.00	37.00
(33)	Wild Bill Donovan	125.00	62.00	37.00
(34)	Red Dooin	125.00	62.00	37.00
(35)	Patsy Dougherty	225.00	112.00	67.00
(36)	Hugh Duffy	1800.	900.00	540.00
(37)	Jimmy Dygert	125.00	62.00	37.00
(38)	Rube Ellis	125.00	62.00	37.00
(39)	Clyde Engle	125.00	62.00	37.00
(40)	Art Fromme	450.00	225.00	135.00
(41)	George Gibson (back view)	600.00	300.00	180.00
(42)	George Gibson (front view)	125.00	62.00	37.00
(43)	Peaches Graham	2200.	1100.	660.00
(44)	Eddie Grant	125.00	62.00	37.00
(45)	Dolly Gray	125.00	62.00	37.00
(46)	Bob Groom	125.00	62.00	37.00
(47)	Charley Hall	125.00	62.00	37.00
(48)	Roy Hartzell (fielding)	125.00	62.00	37.00
(49)	Roy Hartzell (batting)	125.00	62.00	37.00
(50)	Heinie Heitmuller	125.00	62.00	37.00
(51)	Harry Howell (follow thru)	125.00	62.00	37.00
(52)	Harry Howell (windup)	175.00	87.00	52.00
(53)	Tex Irwin (Erwin)	125.00	62.00	37.00
(54)	Frank Isbell	125.00	62.00	37.00
(55)	Shoeless Joe Jackson	7500.	3750.	2250.
(56)	Hughie Jennings	500.00	250.00	150.00
(57)	Buck Jordon (Jordan)	125.00	62.00	37.00
(58)	Addie Joss (portrait)	500.00	250.00	150.00
(59)	Addie Joss (pitching)	1650.	825.00	495.00
(60)	Ed Karger	1650.	825.00	495.00
(61a)	Willie Keeler (portrait, pink background)	550.00	275.00	165.00
(61b)	Willie Keeler (portrait, red background)	1650.	825.00	495.00
(62)	Willie Keeler (throwing)	2000.	1000.	600.00
(63)	John Knight	125.00	62.00	37.00
(64)	Harry Krause	125.00	62.00	37.00
(65)	Nap Lajoie	775.00	387.00	232.00
(66)	Tommy Leach (throwing)	125.00	62.00	37.00
(67)	Tommy Leach (batting)	125.00	62.00	37.00
(68)	Sam Leever	125.00	62.00	37.00
(69)	Hans Lobert	1000.	500.00	300.00
(70)	Harry Lumley	125.00	62.00	37.00
(71)	Rube Marquard	500.00	250.00	150.00
(72)	Christy Matthewson (Mathewson)	1000.	500.00	300.00
(73)	Stuffy McInnes (McInnis)	125.00	62.00	37.00
(74)	Harry McIntyre	125.00	62.00	37.00
(75)	Larry McLean	225.00	112.00	67.00
(76)	George McQuillan	125.00	62.00	37.00
(77)	Dots Miller	125.00	62.00	37.00
(78)	Fred Mitchell (New York)	125.00	62.00	37.00

(79)	Mike Mitchell (Cincinnati)	10000.	5000.	3000.
(80)	George Mullin	125.00	62.00	37.00
(81)	Rebel Oakes	125.00	62.00	37.00
(82)	Paddy O'Connor	125.00	62.00	37.00
(83)	Charley O'Leary	125.00	62.00	37.00
(84)	Orval Overall	1000.	500.00	300.00
(85)	Jim Pastorius	125.00	62.00	37.00
(86)	Ed Phelps	125.00	62.00	37.00
(87)	Eddie Plank	900.00	450.00	270.00
(88)	Lew Richie	125.00	62.00	37.00
(89)	Germany Schaefer	125.00	62.00	37.00
(90)	Biff Schlitzer	175.00	87.00	52.00
(91)	Johnny Seigle (Siegle)	225.00	112.00	67.00
(92)	Dave Shean	175.00	87.00	52.00
(93)	Jimmy Sheckard	175.00	87.00	52.00
(94)	Tris Speaker	2000.	1000.	600.00
(95)	Jake Stahl	1650.	825.00	495.00
(96)	Oscar Stanage	125.00	62.00	37.00
(97)	George Stone (no hands visible)	125.00	62.00	37.00
(98)	George Stone (left hand visible)	125.00	62.00	37.00
(99)	George Stovall	125.00	62.00	37.00
(100)	Ed Summers	125.00	62.00	37.00
(101)	Bill Sweeney (Boston)	1800.	900.00	540.00
(102)	Jeff Sweeney (New York)	125.00	62.00	37.00
(103)	Jesse Tannehill (Chicago A.L.)	125.00	62.00	37.00
(104)	Lee Tannehill (Chicago N.L.)	125.00	62.00	37.00
(105)	Fred Tenney	125.00	62.00	37.00
(106)	Ira Thomas (Philadelphia)	125.00	62.00	37.00
(107)	Roy Thomas (Boston)	125.00	62.00	37.00
(108)	Joe Tinker	500.00	250.00	150.00
(109)	Bob Unglaub	125.00	62.00	37.00
(110)	Jerry Upp	125.00	62.00	37.00
(111)	Honus Wagner (batting)	1500.	750.00	450.00
(112)	Honus Wagner (throwing)	1500.	750.00	450.00
(113)	Bobby Wallace	400.00	200.00	120.00
(114)	Ed Walsh	1750.	875.00	525.00
(115)	Vic Willis	125.00	62.00	37.00
(116)	Hooks Wiltse	225.00	112.00	67.00
(117)	Cy Young (Cleveland)	900.00	450.00	270.00
(118)	Cy Young (Boston)	750.00	375.00	225.00

1910 American Caramel Co. Pirates (E90-2)

Closely related to the E90-1 American Caramel set, the E90-2 set consists of 11 cards featuring members of the 1909 champion Pittsburgh Pirates. The cards measure 1-1/2" by 2-3/4" and display a color lithograph on the front with a solid color background of either red, green blue or pink. The player's name and "Pittsburg" appear in blue capital letters in the border beneath the portrait. The backs are identical to those in the E90-1 set, depicting a drawing of a ball, glove and crossed bats with the words "Base Ball Caramels" and a reference to "100 Subjects." The set includes Hall of Famers Honus Wagner and Fred Clarke.

		NR MT	EX	VG
Complete set (11):		4250.	2125.	1275.
Common player:		225.00	112.00	67.00
(1)	Babe Adams	225.00	112.00	67.00
(2)	Fred Clarke	500.00	250.00	150.00
(3)	George Gibson	225.00	112.00	67.00
(4)	Ham Hyatt	225.00	112.00	67.00
(5)	Tommy Leach	225.00	112.00	67.00
(6)	Sam Leever	225.00	112.00	67.00
(7)	Nick Maddox	225.00	112.00	67.00
(8)	Dots Miller	225.00	112.00	67.00
(9)	Deacon Phillippe	225.00	112.00	67.00
(10)	Honus Wagner	2000.	1000.	600.00
(11)	Owen Wilson	225.00	112.00	67.00

1910 American Caramel Co. Cubs/Sox (E90-3)

CHICAGO
Schulte, r. f. Cubs

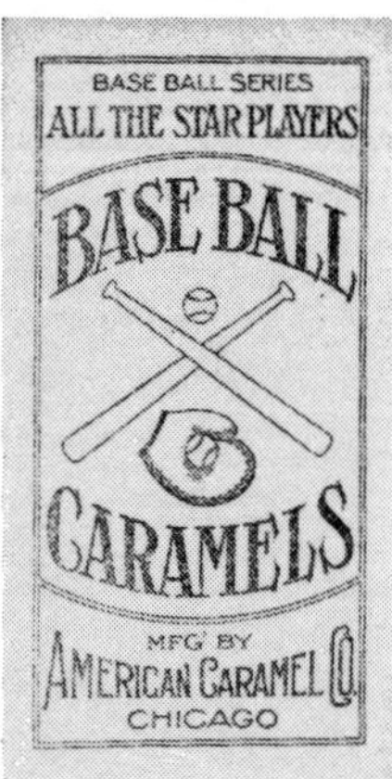
BASE BALL SERIES
ALL THE STAR PLAYERS
BASE BALL
CARAMELS
MFG BY
AMERICAN CARAMEL CO
CHICAGO

Similar in size (1-1/2" by 2-3/4") and style to the more popular E90-1 set, the E90-3 set was issued by the American Caramel Co. in 1910. The 20-card, color lithograph set includes 11 Chicago Cubs and nine White Sox. The fronts of the cards have a similar design to the E90-1 set, although different photos were used. The backs can be differentiated by two major changes: The bottom of the card indicates the American Caramel Co. of "Chicago," rather than Philadelphia, and the top of the card contains the phrase "All The Star Players," rather than "10 Subjects." The E90-3 cards are generally more than those in the E90-1 set.

		NR MT	EX	VG
Complete set (20):		6000.	3000.	1800.
Common player:		200.00	100.00	60.00
(1)	Jimmy Archer	200.00	100.00	60.00
(2)	Lena Blackburne	200.00	100.00	60.00
(3)	Mordecai Brown	600.00	300.00	180.00
(4)	Frank Chance	900.00	450.00	270.00
(5)	King Cole	200.00	100.00	60.00
(6)	Patsy Dougherty	200.00	100.00	60.00
(7)	Johnny Evers	600.00	300.00	180.00
(8)	Chick Gandil	300.00	150.00	90.00
(9)	Ed Hahn	200.00	100.00	60.00
(10)	Solly Hofman	200.00	100.00	60.00
(11)	Orval Overall	200.00	100.00	60.00
(12)	Fred Payne	200.00	100.00	60.00
(13)	Billy Purtell	200.00	100.00	60.00
(14)	Wildfire Schulte	200.00	100.00	60.00
(15)	Jimmy Sheckard	200.00	100.00	60.00
(16)	Frank Smith	200.00	100.00	60.00
(17)	Harry Steinfeldt	250.00	125.00	75.00
(18)	Joe Tinker	600.00	300.00	180.00
(19)	Ed Walsh	600.00	300.00	180.00
(20)	Rollie Zeider	200.00	100.00	60.00

1915 American Caramel (E106)

Chase, 1b. Buffalo Feds

This card is one of a set of forty-eight leading Baseball Players in the National, American and Federal Leagues. One card is given with every piece of Baseball Caramel manufactured by the AMERICAN CARAMEL CO. YORK PA. UNDER THE FAMOUS BRAND OF THE P. C. W.

This 48-card set, designated E106 by the American Card Catalog, was produced by the American Caramel Company of York, Pa., in 1915 and includes players from the National, American and Federal Leagues. The cards measure 1-1/2" by 2-3/4". The set is related to the E90-1 and E92 sets, from which the artwork is taken. The American Caramel cards, however, have a glossy coating, which makes them very susceptible to cracking. The backs of the cards advise that the card is "one of a set of forty-eight leading Baseball Players" and identifies the American Caramel Co. as the manufacturer.

		NR MT	EX	VG
Complete set (48):		28000.	14000.	8250.
Common player:		150.00	75.00	45.00
(1)	Jack Barry	150.00	75.00	45.00
(2)	Chief Bender (white hat)	400.00	200.00	120.00
(3)	Chief Bender (striped hat)	400.00	200.00	120.00
(4)	Bob Bescher	150.00	75.00	45.00
(5)	Roger Bresnahan	400.00	200.00	120.00
(6)	Al Bridwell	150.00	75.00	45.00
(7)	Donie Bush	150.00	75.00	45.00
(8)	Hal Chase (portrait)	250.00	125.00	75.00
(9)	Hal Chase (catching)	250.00	125.00	75.00
(10)	Ty Cobb (batting, facing front)	6000.	3000.	1200.
(11)	Ty Cobb (batting, facing to side)	6500.	3250.	2000.
(12)	Eddie Collins	350.00	175.00	105.00
(13)	Sam Crawford	350.00	175.00	105.00
(14)	Ray Demmitt	150.00	75.00	45.00
(15)	Wild Bill Donovan	150.00	75.00	45.00
(16)	Red Dooin	150.00	75.00	45.00
(17)	Mickey Doolan	150.00	75.00	45.00
(18)	Larry Doyle	150.00	75.00	45.00
(19)	Clyde Engle	150.00	75.00	45.00
(20)	Johnny Evers	350.00	175.00	105.00
(21)	Art Fromme	150.00	75.00	45.00
(22)	George Gibson (catching, back view)	150.00	75.00	45.00
(23)	George Gibson (catching, front view)	150.00	75.00	45.00
(24)	Roy Hartzell	150.00	75.00	45.00
(25)	Fred Jacklitsch	150.00	75.00	45.00
(26)	Hugh Jennings	350.00	175.00	105.00
(27)	Otto Knabe	150.00	75.00	45.00
(28)	Nap Lajoie	900.00	450.00	270.00
(29)	Hans Lobert	150.00	75.00	45.00
(30)	Rube Marquard	350.00	175.00	105.00
(31)	Christy Matthewson (Mathewson)	1000.	500.00	300.00
(32)	John McGraw	850.00	400.00	250.00
(33)	George McQuillan	150.00	75.00	45.00
(34)	Dots Miller	150.00	75.00	45.00
(35)	Danny Murphy	150.00	75.00	45.00
(36)	Rebel Oakes	150.00	75.00	45.00
(37)	Eddie Plank	900.00	425.00	255.00
(38)	Germany Schaefer	150.00	75.00	45.00
(39)	Tris Speaker	1000.	450.00	225.00
(40)	Oscar Stanage	150.00	75.00	45.00
(41)	George Stovall	150.00	75.00	45.00
(42)	Jeff Sweeney	150.00	75.00	45.00
(43)	Joe Tinker (portrait)	400.00	200.00	120.00
(44)	Joe Tinker (batting)	400.00	200.00	120.00
(45)	Honus Wagner (batting)	3000.	1250.	500.00
(46)	Honus Wagner (throwing)	3000.	1250.	500.00
(47)	Hooks Wiltse	150.00	75.00	45.00
(48)	Heinie Zimmerman	150.00	75.00	45.00

1921 American Carmel Series of 80 (E121)

DUFFY LEWIS
L. F. Washington Americans

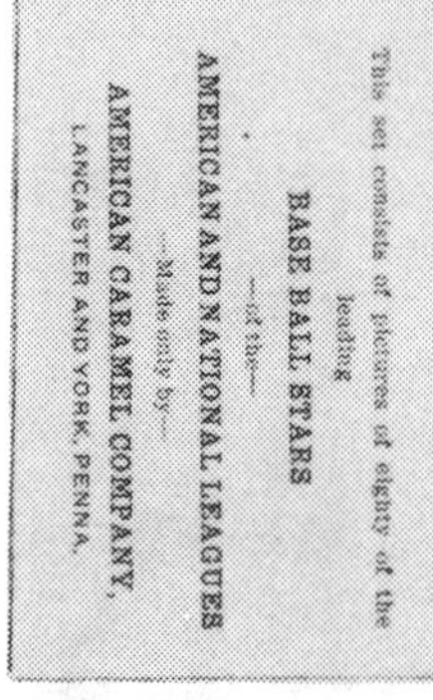
This set consists of pictures of eighty of the leading
BASE BALL STARS
—of the—
AMERICAN AND NATIONAL LEAGUES
—Made only by—
AMERICAN CARAMEL COMPANY,
LANCASTER AND YORK, PENNA.

Issued circa 1921, the E121 Series of 80 is designated as such because of the card reverses which indicate the player pictured is just one of 80 baseball stars in the set. The figure of 80 supplied by the American Caramel Co. is incorrect as over 100 different pictures do exist. The unnumbered cards, which measure 2" by 3-1/2", feature black and white photos. Two different backs exist for the Series of 80. The common back variation has the first line ending with the word "the," while the scarcer version ends with the word "eighty." The complete set price does not include the variations.

		NR MT	EX	VG
Complete set (121):		12750.	6375.	3825.
Commmon player:		30.00	15.00	9.00
(1)	G.C. Alexander (arms above head)	150.00	75.00	45.00
(2)	Grover Alexander	150.00	75.00	45.00
(3)	Jim Bagby	30.00	15.00	9.00
(4a)	J. Franklin Baker	150.00	75.00	45.00
(4b)	Frank Baker	150.00	75.00	45.00
(5)	Dave Bancroft (batting)	80.00	40.00	24.00
(6)	Dave Bancroft (leaping)	80.00	40.00	24.00
(7)	Ping Bodie	30.00	15.00	9.00
(8)	George Burns	30.00	15.00	9.00
(9)	Geo. J. Burns	30.00	15.00	9.00
(10)	Owen Bush	30.00	15.00	9.00
(11)	Max Carey (batting)	80.00	40.00	24.00
(12)	Max Carey (hands at hips)	80.00	40.00	24.00
(13)	Cecil Causey	30.00	15.00	9.00
(14)	Ty Cobb (throwing, looking front)	700.00	350.00	210.00
(15a)	Ty Cobb (throwing, looking right, Mgr. on front)	700.00	350.00	210.00
(15b)	Ty Cobb (throwing, looking right, Manager on front)	700.00	350.00	210.00
(16)	Eddie Collins	150.00	75.00	45.00
(17)	"Rip" Collins	30.00	15.00	9.00
(18)	Jake Daubert	50.00	25.00	15.00
(19)	George Dauss	30.00	15.00	9.00
(20)	Charles Deal (dark uniform)	30.00	15.00	9.00
(21)	Charles Deal (white uniform)	30.00	15.00	9.00
(22)	William Doak	30.00	15.00	9.00
(23)	Bill Donovan	30.00	15.00	9.00
(24)	"Phil" Douglas	50.00	25.00	15.00
(25a)	Johnny Evers (Manager)	80.00	40.00	24.00
(25b)	Johnny Evers (Mgr.)	80.00	40.00	24.00
(26)	Urban Faber (dark uniform)	80.00	40.00	24.00
(27)	Urban Faber (white uniform)	80.00	40.00	24.00
(28)	William Fewster (first name actually Wilson)	30.00	15.00	9.00
(29)	Eddie Foster	30.00	15.00	9.00
(30)	Frank Frisch	70.00	35.00	21.00
(31)	W.L. Gardner	30.00	15.00	9.00
(32a)	Alexander Gaston (no position on front)	30.00	15.00	9.00
(32b)	Alexander Gaston (position on front)	30.00	15.00	9.00
(33)	"Kid" Gleason	30.00	15.00	9.00
(34)	"Mike" Gonzalez	30.00	15.00	9.00
(35)	Hank Gowdy	30.00	15.00	9.00
(36)	John Graney	30.00	15.00	9.00
(37)	Tom Griffith	30.00	15.00	9.00
(38)	Heinie Groh	50.00	25.00	15.00
(39)	Harry Harper	30.00	15.00	9.00

(40)	Harry Heilman (Heilmann)	80.00	40.00	24.00
(41)	Walter Holke (portrait)	30.00	15.00	9.00
(42)	Walter Holke (throwing)	30.00	15.00	9.00
(43)	Charles Hollacher (Hollocher)	30.00	15.00	9.00
(44)	Harry Hooper	80.00	40.00	24.00
(45)	Rogers Hornsby	200.00	100.00	60.00
(46)	Waite Hoyt	80.00	40.00	24.00
(47)	Miller Huggins	80.00	40.00	24.00
(48)	Wm. C. Jacobson	30.00	15.00	9.00
(49)	Hugh Jennings	80.00	40.00	24.00
(50)	Walter Johnson (throwing)	275.00	137.00	82.00
(51)	Walter Johnson (hands at chest)	275.00	137.00	82.00
(52)	James Johnston	30.00	15.00	9.00
(53)	Joe Judge	30.00	15.00	9.00
(54)	George Kelly	80.00	40.00	24.00
(55)	Dick Kerr	30.00	15.00	9.00
(56)	P.J. Kilduff	30.00	15.00	9.00
(57a)	Bill Killifer (incorrect name)	50.00	25.00	15.00
(57b)	Bill Killefer (correct name)	50.00	25.00	15.00
(58)	John Lavan	30.00	15.00	9.00
(59)	"Nemo" Leibold	30.00	15.00	9.00
(60)	Duffy Lewis	50.00	25.00	15.00
(61)	Al. Mamaux	30.00	15.00	9.00
(62)	"Rabbit" Maranville	80.00	40.00	24.00
(63a)	Carl May (incorrect name)	80.00	40.00	24.00
(63b)	Carl Mays (correct name)	50.00	25.00	15.00
(64)	John McGraw	150.00	75.00	45.00
(65)	Jack McInnis	30.00	15.00	9.00
(66)	M.J. McNally	30.00	15.00	9.00
(67)	Emil Muesel (Photo actually Lou DeVormer)	50.00	25.00	15.00
(68)	R. Meusel	40.00	20.00	12.00
(69)	Clyde Milan	30.00	15.00	9.00
(70)	Elmer Miller	30.00	15.00	9.00
(71)	Otto Miller	30.00	15.00	9.00
(72)	Guy Morton	30.00	15.00	9.00
(73)	Eddie Murphy	30.00	15.00	9.00
(74)	"Hy" Myers	30.00	15.00	9.00
(75)	Arthur Nehf	30.00	15.00	9.00
(76)	Steve O'Neill	30.00	15.00	9.00
(77a)	Roger Peckinbaugh (incorrect name)	50.00	25.00	15.00
(77b)	Roger Peckinpaugh (correct name)	50.00	25.00	15.00
(78a)	Jeff Pfeffer (Brooklyn)	30.00	15.00	9.00
(78b)	Jeff Pfeffer (St. Louis)	30.00	15.00	9.00
(79)	Walter Pipp	40.00	20.00	12.00
(80)	Jack Quinn	30.00	15.00	9.00
(81)	John Rawlings	30.00	15.00	9.00
(82)	E.C. Rice	80.00	40.00	24.00
(83)	Eppa Rixey, Jr.	80.00	40.00	24.00
(84)	Robert Roth	30.00	15.00	9.00
(85a)	Ed. Roush (C.F.)	80.00	40.00	24.00
(85b)	Ed. Roush (L.F.)	70.00	35.00	21.00
(86a)	Babe Ruth	1500.	750.00	450.00
(86b)	"Babe" Ruth	1500.	750.00	450.00
(86c)	George Ruth	1500.	750.00	450.00
(87)	"Bill" Ryan	30.00	15.00	9.00
(88)	"Slim" Sallee (glove showing)	30.00	15.00	9.00
(89)	"Slim" Sallee (no glove showing)	30.00	15.00	9.00
(90)	Ray Schalk	80.00	40.00	24.00
(91)	Walter Schang	30.00	15.00	9.00
(92a)	Fred Schupp (name incorrect)	50.00	25.00	15.00
(92b)	Ferd Schupp (name correct)	50.00	25.00	15.00
(93)	Everett Scott	30.00	15.00	9.00
(94)	Hank Severeid	30.00	15.00	9.00
(95)	Robert Shawkey	50.00	25.00	15.00
(96a)	Pat Shea	50.00	25.00	15.00
(96b)	"Pat" Shea	30.00	15.00	9.00
(97)	George Sisler (batting)	70.00	35.00	21.00
(98)	George Sisler (throwing)	70.00	35.00	21.00
(99)	Earl Smith	30.00	15.00	9.00
(100)	Frank Snyder	30.00	15.00	9.00
(101a)	Tris Speaker (Mgr.)	200.00	100.00	60.00
(101b)	Tris Speaker (Manager - large projection)	200.00	100.00	60.00
(101c)	Tris Speaker (Manager - small projection)	200.00	100.00	60.00
(102)	Milton Stock	30.00	15.00	9.00
(103)	Amos Strunk	30.00	15.00	9.00
(104)	Zeb Terry	30.00	15.00	9.00
(105)	Chester Thomas	30.00	15.00	9.00
(106)	Fred Toney (trees in background)	30.00	15.00	9.00
(107)	Fred Toney (no trees in background)	30.00	15.00	9.00
(108)	George Tyler	30.00	15.00	9.00
(109)	Jim Vaughn (dark hat)	30.00	15.00	9.00
(110)	Jim Vaughn (white hat)	30.00	15.00	9.00
(111)	Bob Veach (glove in air)	30.00	15.00	9.00
(112)	Bob Veach (arms crossed)	30.00	15.00	9.00
(113)	Oscar Vitt	30.00	15.00	9.00
(114)	W. Wambsganss (photo actually Fred Coumbe)	50.00	25.00	15.00
(115)	Aaron Ward	30.00	15.00	9.00
(116)	Zach Wheat	150.00	75.00	45.00
(117)	George Whitted	30.00	15.00	9.00
(118)	Fred Williams	50.00	25.00	15.00
(119)	Ivy B. Wingo	30.00	15.00	9.00
(120)	Joe Wood	50.00	25.00	15.00
(121)	"Pep" Young	30.00	15.00	9.00

1922 American Carmel Series of 120 (E121)

Produced by the American Caramel Co. circa 1922, the E121 Series of 120 is labeled as such by the company's claim that the set contained 120 subjects. Identical in design to the E121 Series of 80 set except for the card backs, the cards measure 2" by 3-1/2" in size. Numerous variations are found in the set, most involving a change in the player's name, team or position. The complete set price does not include variations.

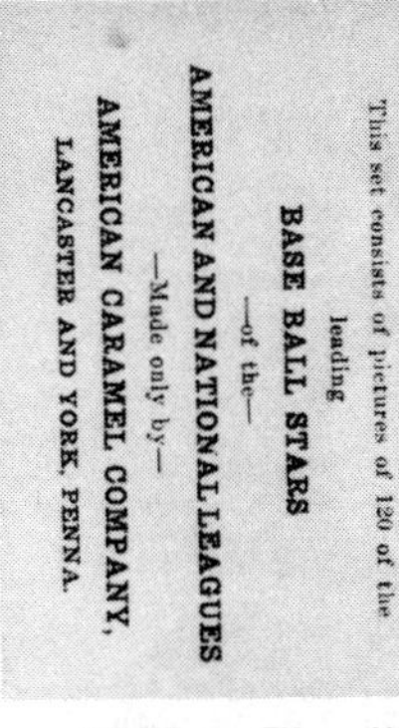
This set consists of pictures of 120 of the leading
BASE BALL STARS
—of the—
AMERICAN AND NATIONAL LEAGUES
—Made only by—
AMERICAN CARAMEL COMPANY,
LANCASTER AND YORK, PENNA.

		NR MT	EX	VG
	Complete set:	15000.	7500.	4500.
	Common player:	30.00	15.00	9.00
(1)	Chas. "Babe" Adams	30.00	15.00	9.00
(2)	G.C. Alexander	150.00	75.00	45.00
(3)	Jim Bagby	30.00	15.00	9.00
(4)	Dave Bancroft	100.00	50.00	30.00
(5)	Turner Barber	30.00	15.00	9.00
(6a)	Carlson Bigbee (correct name Carson L. Bigbee)	35.00	17.50	10.50
(6b)	Carlson L. Bigbee	30.00	15.00	9.00
(6c)	Corson L. Bigbee	35.00	17.50	10.50
(6d)	L. Bigbee	30.00	15.00	9.00
(7)	"Bullet Joe" Bush	30.00	15.00	9.00
(8)	Max Carey	100.00	50.00	30.00
(9)	Cecil Causey	30.00	15.00	9.00
(10)	Ty Cobb (batting)	700.00	350.00	210.00
(11)	Ty Cobb (throwing)	700.00	350.00	210.00
(12)	Eddie Collins	150.00	75.00	45.00
(13)	A. Wilbur Cooper	30.00	15.00	9.00
(14)	Stanley Coveleskie (Coveleski)	100.00	50.00	30.00
(15)	Dave Danforth	30.00	15.00	9.00
(16)	Jake Daubert	30.00	15.00	9.00
(17)	George Dauss	30.00	15.00	9.00
(18)	"Dixie" Davis	30.00	15.00	9.00
(19)	Lou DeVormer	30.00	15.00	9.00
(20)	William Doak	30.00	15.00	9.00
(21)	Phil Douglas	30.00	15.00	9.00
(22)	Urban Faber	100.00	50.00	30.00
(23)	Bib Falk (Bibb)	30.00	15.00	9.00
(24)	Wm. Fewster (first name actually Wilson)	30.00	15.00	9.00
(25)	Max Flack	30.00	15.00	9.00
(26)	Ira Falgstead (Flagstead)	30.00	15.00	9.00
(27)	Frank Frisch	150.00	75.00	45.00
(28)	W.L. Gardner	30.00	15.00	9.00
(29)	Alexander Gaston	30.00	15.00	9.00
(30)	E.P. Gharrity	30.00	15.00	9.00
(31)	George Gibson	30.00	15.00	9.00
(32)	Chas. "Whitey" Glazner	30.00	15.00	9.00
(33)	"Kid" Gleason	30.00	15.00	9.00
(34)	Hank Gowdy	30.00	15.00	9.00
(35)	John Graney	30.00	15.00	9.00
(36)	Tom Griffith	30.00	15.00	9.00
(37)	Chas. Grimm	35.00	17.50	10.50
(38)	Heine Groh	30.00	15.00	9.00
(39)	Jess Haines	100.00	50.00	30.00
(40)	Harry Harper	30.00	15.00	9.00
(41a)	Harry Heilman (name incorrect)	150.00	75.00	45.00
(41b)	Harry Heilmann (name correct)	100.00	50.00	30.00
(42)	Clarence Hodge	30.00	15.00	9.00
(43)	Walter Holke (portrait)	35.00	17.50	10.50
(44)	Walter Holke (throwing)	30.00	15.00	9.00
(45)	Charles Hollocher	30.00	15.00	9.00
(46)	Harry Hooper	100.00	50.00	30.00
(47a)	Rogers Hornsby (2B.)	200.00	100.00	60.00
(47b)	Rogers Hornsby (O.F.)	200.00	100.00	60.00
(48)	Waite Hoyt	100.00	50.00	30.00
(49)	Miller Huggins	100.00	50.00	30.00
(50)	Walter Johnson	400.00	200.00	120.00
(51)	Joe Judge	30.00	15.00	9.00
(52)	George Kelly	100.00	50.00	30.00
(53)	Dick Kerr	30.00	15.00	9.00
(54)	P.J. Kilduff	30.00	15.00	9.00
(55)	Bill Killifer (Killefer) (batting)	30.00	15.00	9.00
(56)	Bill Killifer (Killefer) (throwing)	30.00	15.00	9.00
(57)	John Lavan	30.00	15.00	9.00
(58)	Walter Mails	30.00	15.00	9.00
(59)	"Rabbit" Maranville	100.00	50.00	30.00
(60)	Elwood Martin	30.00	15.00	9.00
(61)	Carl Mays	35.00	17.50	10.50
(62)	John J. McGraw	125.00	62.00	37.00
(63)	Jack McInnis	30.00	15.00	9.00
(64)	M.J. McNally	30.00	15.00	9.00
(65)	Emil Meusel (photo actually Lou DeVormer)	30.00	15.00	9.00
(66)	R. Meusel	40.00	20.00	12.00
(67)	Clyde Milan	30.00	15.00	9.00
(68)	Elmer Miller	30.00	15.00	9.00
(69)	Otto Miller	30.00	15.00	9.00
(70)	Johnny Mostil	30.00	15.00	9.00
(71)	Eddie Mulligan	30.00	15.00	9.00
(72a)	Hy Myers	30.00	15.00	9.00
(72b)	"Hy" Myers	35.00	17.50	10.50
(73)	Earl Neale	40.00	20.00	12.00
(74)	Arthur Nehf	30.00	15.00	9.00
(75)	Leslie Nunamaker	30.00	15.00	9.00
(76)	Joe Oeschger	30.00	15.00	9.00
(77)	Chas. O'Leary	35.00	17.50	10.50
(78)	Steve O'Neill	30.00	15.00	9.00
(79)	D.B. Pratt	30.00	15.00	9.00
(80a)	John Rawlings (2B.)	30.00	15.00	9.00
(80b)	John Rawlings (Utl.)	30.00	15.00	9.00
(81)	E.S. Rice (intials actually E.C.)	100.00	50.00	30.00
(82)	Eppa J. Rixey	100.00	50.00	30.00
(83)	Eppa Rixey, Jr.	100.00	50.00	30.00
(84)	Wilbert Robinson	100.00	50.00	30.00
(85)	Tom Rogers	30.00	15.00	9.00
(86a)	Ed Rounnel	30.00	15.00	9.00
(86b)	Ed. Rommel	30.00	15.00	9.00
(87)	Ed Roush	100.00	50.00	30.00
(88)	"Muddy" Ruel	30.00	15.00	9.00
(89)	Walter Ruether	30.00	15.00	9.00
(90a)	Babe Ruth (photo montage)	1500.	750.00	450.00
(90b)	"Babe" Ruth (photo montage)	1500.	750.00	450.00
(91a)	Babe Ruth (holding bird)	1500.	750.00	450.00
(91b)	"Babe" Ruth (holding bird)	1500.	750.00	450.00
(92)	"Babe" Ruth (holding ball)	1500.	750.00	450.00
(93)	Bill Ryan	30.00	15.00	9.00
(94)	Ray Schalk (catching)	100.00	50.00	30.00
(95)	Ray Schalk (batting)	100.00	50.00	30.00
(96)	Wally Schang	35.00	17.50	10.50
(97)	Ferd Schupp	35.00	17.50	10.50
(98)	Everett Scott	30.00	15.00	9.00
(99)	Joe Sewell	150.00	75.00	45.00
(100)	Robert Shawkey	30.00	15.00	9.00
(101)	Pat Shea	30.00	15.00	9.00
(102)	Earl Sheely	30.00	15.00	9.00
(103)	Urban Schocker	30.00	15.00	9.00
(104)	George Sisler (batting)	150.00	75.00	45.00
(105)	George Sisler (throwing)	100.00	50.00	30.00
(106)	Earl Smith	30.00	15.00	9.00
(107)	Elmer Smith	30.00	15.00	9.00
(108)	Frank Snyder	30.00	15.00	9.00
(109)	Bill Southworth	30.00	15.00	9.00
(110a)	Tris Speaker (large projection)	200.00	100.00	60.00
(110b)	Tris Speaker (small projection)	200.00	100.00	60.00
(111a)	Milton Stock	35.00	17.50	10.50
(111b)	Milton J. Stock	30.00	15.00	9.00
(112)	Amos Strunk	30.00	15.00	9.00
(113)	Zeb Terry	30.00	15.00	9.00
(114)	Fred Toney	30.00	15.00	9.00
(115)	George Topocer (Toporcer)	30.00	15.00	9.00
(116)	Bob Veach	30.00	15.00	9.00
(117)	Oscar Vitt	30.00	15.00	9.00
(118)	Curtis Walker	30.00	15.00	9.00
(119)	W. Wambsganss (photo actually Fred Coumbe)	30.00	15.00	9.00
(120)	Aaron Ward	30.00	15.00	9.00
(121)	Zach Wheat	100.00	50.00	30.00
(122a)	George Whitted (Pittsburgh)	30.00	15.00	9.00
(122b)	George Whitted (Brooklyn)	30.00	15.00	9.00
(123)	Fred Williams	30.00	15.00	9.00
(124)	Ivy B. Wingo	30.00	15.00	9.00
(125)	Ross Young (Youngs)	150.00	75.00	45.00

1922 American Carmel Series of 80 (E122)

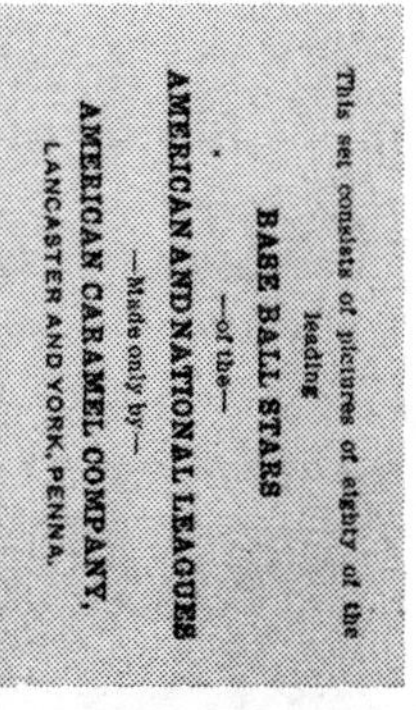
This set consists of pictures of eighty of the leading
BASE BALL STARS
—of the—
AMERICAN AND NATIONAL LEAGUES
—Made only by—
AMERICAN CARAMEL COMPANY,
LANCASTER AND YORK, PENNA.

Known as E122 in the American Card Catalog, this set is actually a subset of the E121 American Caramel set. The cards are nealy identical to E121's "Series of 80," except the player's name, position and team are printed inside a gray rectangle at the bottom of the card, and the photos have a more coarse appearance.

		NR MT	EX	VG
	Complete set:	7500.	3700.	2200.
	Common player:	40.00	20.00	12.00
(1)	Grover Alexander	175.00	87.00	52.00
(2)	Jim Bagby	40.00	20.00	12.00
(3)	J. Franklin Baker	150.00	75.00	45.00
(4)	Dave Bancroft	150.00	75.00	45.00
(5)	Ping Bodie	40.00	20.00	12.00
(6)	George Burns	40.00	20.00	12.00
(7)	Geo. J. Burns	40.00	20.00	12.00
(8)	Owen Bush	40.00	20.00	12.00
(9)	Max Carey	150.00	75.00	45.00
(10)	Cecil Causey	40.00	20.00	12.00
(11)	Ty Cobb	1000.	500.00	300.00
(12)	Eddie Collins	150.00	75.00	45.00
(13)	Jake Daubert	50.00	25.00	15.00
(14)	George Dauss	40.00	20.00	12.00
(15)	Charles Deal	40.00	20.00	12.00
(16)	William Doak	40.00	20.00	12.00
(17)	Bill Donovan	40.00	20.00	12.00
(18)	Johnny Evers	150.00	75.00	45.00
(19)	Urban Faber	150.00	75.00	45.00

(20)	Eddie Foster	40.00	20.00	12.00
(21)	W.L. Gardner	40.00	20.00	12.00
(22)	"Kid" Gleason	40.00	20.00	12.00
(23)	Hank Gowdy	40.00	20.00	12.00
(24)	John Graney	40.00	20.00	12.00
(25)	Tom Griffith	40.00	20.00	12.00
(26)	Harry Heilman (Heilmann)	150.00	75.00	45.00
(27)	Walter Holke	40.00	20.00	12.00
(28)	Charles Hollacher (Hollocher)	40.00	20.00	12.00
(29)	Harry Hooper	150.00	75.00	45.00
(30)	Rogers Hornsby	200.00	100.00	60.00
(31)	Wm. C. Jacobson	40.00	20.00	12.00
(32)	Walter Johnson	400.00	200.00	120.00
(33)	James Johnston	40.00	20.00	12.00
(34)	Joe Judge	40.00	20.00	12.00
(35)	George Kelly	150.00	75.00	45.00
(36)	Dick Kerr	40.00	20.00	12.00
(37)	P.J. Kilduff	40.00	20.00	12.00
(38)	Bill Killefer	40.00	20.00	12.00
(39)	John Lavan	40.00	20.00	12.00
(40)	Duffy Lewis	40.00	20.00	12.00
(41)	Perry Lipe	40.00	20.00	12.00
(42)	Al. Mamaux	40.00	20.00	12.00
(43)	"Rabbit" Maranville	150.00	75.00	45.00
(44)	Carl May (Mays)	60.00	30.00	18.00
(45)	John McGraw	150.00	75.00	45.00
(46)	Jack McInnis	40.00	20.00	12.00
(47)	Clyde Milan	40.00	20.00	12.00
(48)	Otto Miller	40.00	20.00	12.00
(49)	Guy Morton	40.00	20.00	12.00
(50)	Eddie Murphy	40.00	20.00	12.00
(51)	"Hy" Myers	40.00	20.00	12.00
(52)	Steve O'Neill	40.00	20.00	12.00
(53)	Roger Peckinbaugh (Peckinpaugh)	40.00	20.00	12.00
(54)	Jeff Pfeffer	40.00	20.00	12.00
(55)	Walter Pipp	75.00	37.00	22.00
(56)	E.C. Rice	150.00	75.00	45.00
(57)	Eppa Rixey, Jr.	150.00	75.00	45.00
(58)	Babe Ruth	1000.	500.00	300.00
(59)	"Slim" Sallee	40.00	20.00	12.00
(60)	Ray Schalk	150.00	75.00	45.00
(61)	Walter Schang	40.00	20.00	12.00
(62a)	Fred Schupp (name incorrect)	40.00	20.00	12.00
(62b)	Ferd Schupp (name correct)	40.00	20.00	12.00
(63)	Everett Scott	40.00	20.00	12.00
(64)	Hank Severeid	40.00	20.00	12.00
(65)	George Sisler (batting)	150.00	75.00	45.00
(66)	George Sisler (throwing)	150.00	75.00	45.00
(67)	Tris Speaker	200.00	100.00	60.00
(68)	Milton Stock	40.00	20.00	12.00
(69)	Amos Strunk	40.00	20.00	12.00
(70)	Chester Thomas	40.00	20.00	12.00
(71)	George Tyler	40.00	20.00	12.00
(72)	Jim Vaughn	40.00	20.00	12.00
(73)	Bob Veach	40.00	20.00	12.00
(74)	W. Wambsganss	60.00	30.00	18.00
(75)	Zach Wheat	150.00	75.00	45.00
(76)	Fred Williams	50.00	25.00	15.00
(77)	Ivy B. Wingo	40.00	20.00	12.00
(78)	Joe Wood	60.00	30.00	18.00
(79)	Pep Young	40.00	20.00	12.00

1922 American Carmel Series of 240 (E120)

JOHN (SHANO) COLLINS
UTILITY, BOSTON AMERICANS
BOSTON AMERICANS
"RED SOX"
MANAGER—HUGH DUFFY
HERB PENNOCK PITCHER
ELMER MYERS PITCHER
JACK QUINN PITCHER
BEN KARR PITCHER
HAROLD (MUDDY) RUEL CATCHER
AL WALTERS CATCHER
GEORGE BURNS FIRST B. AND O. F.
DERRILL PRATT SECOND BASE
CLARK PITTENGER THIRD BASE
JOE DUGAN INFIELD
NEMO LEIBOLD OUTFIELD
ELMER SMITH OUTFIELD
MIKE MENOSKY OUTFIELD
JOHN (SHANO) COLLINS UTILITY
JOE HARRIS INFIELD AND OUTFIELD
THIS PICTURE IS ONE OF A SERIES OF 240 PICTURES OF BASEBALL STARS—15 PLAYERS IN EACH OF THE 16 MAJOR LEAGUE TEAMS. WE SUPPLY HANDSOME BLANK ALBUMS TO HOLD 120 PICTURES—ONE FOR AMERICAN LEAGUE, ONE FOR NATIONAL LEAGUE—FOR 15 CENTS EACH POSTPAID.
AMERICAN CARAMEL CO.
LANCASTER, PA. YORK, PA.

One of the most popular of the "E" issues, the 1922 E120 set was produced by the American Caramel Co. in 1922 and distributed with sticks of caramel candy. The unnumbered cards measure 2" by 3-1/2" in size. Cards depicting players from the American League are printed in brown ink on yellow, while the National Leaguers are printed in green on a blue-green background. The card reverses carry team checklists Many of the E120 photos were used in other sets such as E121, W572, W573 and V61.

		NR MT	EX	VG
Complete set:		16000.	8000.	4800.
Common player:		40.00	20.00	12.00
(1)	Charles (Babe) Adams	40.00	20.00	12.00
(2)	Eddie Ainsmith	40.00	20.00	12.00
(3)	Vic Aldridge	40.00	20.00	12.00
(4)	Grover C. Alexander	150.00	75.00	45.00
(5)	Jim Bagby	40.00	20.00	12.00
(6)	Frank (Home Run) Baker	150.00	75.00	45.00
(7)	Dave (Beauty) Bancroft	100.00	50.00	30.00
(8)	Walt Barbare	40.00	20.00	12.00
(9)	Turner Barber	40.00	20.00	12.00
(10)	Jess Barnes	40.00	20.00	12.00
(11)	Clyde Barnhart	40.00	20.00	12.00
(12)	John Bassler	40.00	20.00	12.00
(13)	Will Bayne	40.00	20.00	12.00
(14)	Walter (Huck) Betts	40.00	20.00	12.00
(15)	Carson Bigbee	40.00	20.00	12.00
(16)	Lu Blue	40.00	20.00	12.00
(17)	Norman Boeckel	40.00	20.00	12.00
(18)	Sammy Bohne	40.00	20.00	12.00
(19)	George Burns	40.00	20.00	12.00
(20)	George Burns	40.00	20.00	12.00
(21)	"Bullet Joe" Bush	40.00	20.00	12.00
(22)	Leon Cadore	40.00	20.00	12.00
(23)	Marty Callaghan	40.00	20.00	12.00
(24)	Frank Calloway (Callaway)	40.00	20.00	12.00
(25)	Max Carey	100.00	50.00	30.00
(26)	Jimmy Caveney	40.00	20.00	12.00
(27)	Virgil Cheeves	40.00	20.00	12.00
(28)	Vern Clemons	40.00	20.00	12.00
(29)	Ty Cob (Cobb)	1000.	500.00	300.00
(30)	Bert Cole	40.00	20.00	12.00
(31)	Eddie Collins	150.00	75.00	45.00
(32)	John (Shano) Collins	40.00	20.00	12.00
(33)	T.P. (Pat) Collins	40.00	20.00	12.00
(34)	Wilbur Cooper	40.00	20.00	12.00
(35)	Harry Courtney	40.00	20.00	12.00
(36)	Stanley Coveleskie (Coveleski)	100.00	50.00	30.00
(37)	Elmer Cox	40.00	20.00	12.00
(38)	Sam Crane	40.00	20.00	12.00
(39)	Walton Cruise	40.00	20.00	12.00
(40)	Bill Cunningham	40.00	20.00	12.00
(41)	George Cutshaw	40.00	20.00	12.00
(42)	Dave Danforth	40.00	20.00	12.00
(43)	Jake Daubert	40.00	20.00	12.00
(44)	George Dauss	40.00	20.00	12.00
(45)	Frank (Dixie) Davis	40.00	20.00	12.00
(46)	Hank DeBerry	40.00	20.00	12.00
(47)	Albert (Lou) Devormer (DeVormer)	40.00	20.00	12.00
(48)	Bill Doak	40.00	20.00	12.00
(49)	Pete Donohue	40.00	20.00	12.00
(50)	"Shufflin" Phil Douglas	40.00	20.00	12.00
(51)	Joe Dugan	40.00	20.00	12.00
(52)	Louis (Pat) Duncan	40.00	20.00	12.00
(53)	Jimmy Dykes	40.00	20.00	12.00
(54)	Howard Ehmke	40.00	20.00	12.00
(55)	Frank Ellerbe	40.00	20.00	12.00
(56)	Urban (Red) Faber	100.00	50.00	30.00
(57)	Bib Falk (Bibb)	40.00	20.00	12.00
(58)	Dana Fillingim	40.00	20.00	12.00
(59)	Max Flack	40.00	20.00	12.00
(60)	Ira Flagstead	40.00	20.00	12.00
(61)	Art Fletcher	40.00	20.00	12.00
(62)	Horace Ford	40.00	20.00	12.00
(63)	Jack Fournier	40.00	20.00	12.00
(64)	Frank Frisch	150.00	75.00	45.00
(65)	Ollie Fuhrman	40.00	20.00	12.00
(66)	Clarance Galloway	40.00	20.00	12.00
(67)	Larry Gardner	40.00	20.00	12.00
(68)	Walter Gerber	40.00	20.00	12.00
(69)	Ed Gharrity	40.00	20.00	12.00
(70)	John Gillespie	40.00	20.00	12.00
(71)	Chas. (Whitey) Glazner	40.00	20.00	12.00
(72)	Johnny Gooch	40.00	20.00	12.00
(73)	Leon Goslin	100.00	50.00	30.00
(74)	Hank Gowdy	40.00	20.00	12.00
(75)	John Graney	40.00	20.00	12.00
(76)	Tom Griffith	40.00	20.00	12.00
(77)	Burleigh Grimes	100.00	50.00	30.00
(78)	Oscar Ray Grimes	40.00	20.00	12.00
(79)	Charlie Grimm	40.00	20.00	12.00
(80)	Heinie Groh	40.00	20.00	12.00
(81)	Jesse Haines	100.00	50.00	30.00
(82)	Earl Hamilton	40.00	20.00	12.00
(83)	Gene (Bubbles) Hargrave	40.00	20.00	12.00
(84)	Bryan Harris (Harriss)	40.00	20.00	12.00
(85)	Joe Harris	40.00	20.00	12.00
(86)	Stanley Harris	100.00	50.00	30.00
(87)	Chas. (Dowdy) Hartnett	150.00	75.00	45.00
(88)	Bob Hasty	40.00	20.00	12.00
(89)	Joe Hauser	40.00	20.00	12.00
(90)	Clif Heathcote (Cliff)	40.00	20.00	12.00
(91)	Harry Heilmann	100.00	50.00	30.00
(92)	Walter (Butch) Henline	40.00	20.00	12.00
(93)	Clarence (Shovel) Hodge	40.00	20.00	12.00
(94)	Walter Holke	40.00	20.00	12.00
(95)	Charles Hollocher	40.00	20.00	12.00
(96)	Harry Hooper	100.00	50.00	30.00
(97)	Rogers Hornsby	250.00	125.00	75.00
(98)	Waite Hoyt	100.00	50.00	30.00
(99)	Wilbur Hubbell (Wilbert)	40.00	20.00	12.00
(100)	Bernard (Bud) Hungling	40.00	20.00	12.00
(101)	Will Jacobson	40.00	20.00	12.00
(102)	Charlie Jamieson	40.00	20.00	12.00
(103)	Ernie Johnson	40.00	20.00	12.00
(104)	Sylvester Johnson	40.00	20.00	12.00
(105)	Walter Johnson	500.00	250.00	150.00
(106)	Jimmy Johnston	40.00	20.00	12.00
(107)	W.R. (Doc) Johnston	40.00	20.00	12.00
(108)	"Deacon" Sam Jones	40.00	20.00	12.00
(109)	Bob Jones	40.00	20.00	12.00
(110)	Percy Jones	40.00	20.00	12.00
(111)	Joe Judge	40.00	20.00	12.00
(112)	Ben Karr	40.00	20.00	12.00
(113)	Johnny Kelleher	40.00	20.00	12.00
(114)	George Kelly	100.00	50.00	30.00
(115)	Lee King	40.00	20.00	12.00
(116)	Wm (Larry) Kopff (Kopf)	40.00	20.00	12.00
(117)	Marty Krug	40.00	20.00	12.00
(118)	Johnny Lavan	40.00	20.00	12.00
(119)	Nemo Leibold	40.00	20.00	12.00
(120)	Roy Leslie	40.00	20.00	12.00
(121)	George Leverette (Leverett)	40.00	20.00	12.00
(122)	Adolfo Luque	40.00	20.00	12.00
(123)	Walter Mails	40.00	20.00	12.00
(124)	Al Mamaux	40.00	20.00	12.00
(125)	"Rabbit" Maranville	100.00	50.00	30.00
(126)	Cliff Markle	40.00	20.00	12.00
(127)	Richard (Rube) Marquard	150.00	75.00	45.00
(128)	Carl Mays	60.00	30.00	18.00
(129)	Hervey McClellan (Harvey)	40.00	20.00	12.00
(130)	Austin McHenry	40.00	20.00	12.00
(131)	"Stuffy" McInnis	40.00	20.00	12.00
(132)	Martin McManus	40.00	20.00	12.00
(133)	Mike McNally	40.00	20.00	12.00
(134)	Hugh McQuillan	40.00	20.00	12.00
(135)	Lee Meadows	40.00	20.00	12.00
(136)	Mike Menosky	40.00	20.00	12.00
(137)	Bob (Dutch) Meusel	60.00	30.00	18.00
(138)	Emil (Irish) Meusel	40.00	20.00	12.00
(139)	Clyde Milan	40.00	20.00	12.00
(140)	Edmund (Bing) Miller	40.00	20.00	12.00
(141)	Elmer Miller	40.00	20.00	12.00
(142)	Lawrence (Hack) Miller	40.00	20.00	12.00
(143)	Clarence Mitchell	40.00	20.00	12.00
(144)	George Mogridge	40.00	20.00	12.00
(145)	Roy Moore	40.00	20.00	12.00
(146)	John L. Mokan	40.00	20.00	12.00
(147)	John Morrison	40.00	20.00	12.00
(148)	Johnny Mostil	40.00	20.00	12.00
(149)	Elmer Myers	40.00	20.00	12.00
(150)	Hy Myers	40.00	20.00	12.00
(151)	Roliene Naylor (Roleine)	40.00	20.00	12.00
(152)	Earl (Greasy) Neale	60.00	30.00	18.00
(153)	Art Nehf	40.00	20.00	12.00
(154)	Les Nunamaker	40.00	20.00	12.00
(155)	Joe Oeschger	40.00	20.00	12.00
(156)	Bob O'Farrell	40.00	20.00	12.00
(157)	Ivan Olson	40.00	20.00	12.00
(158)	George O'Neil	40.00	20.00	12.00
(159)	Steve O'Neill	40.00	20.00	12.00
(160)	Frank Parkinson	40.00	20.00	12.00
(161)	Roger Peckinpaugh	40.00	20.00	12.00
(162)	Herb Pennock	100.00	50.00	30.00
(163)	Ralph (Cy) Perkins	40.00	20.00	12.00
(164)	Will Pertica	40.00	20.00	12.00
(165)	Jack Peters	40.00	20.00	12.00
(166)	Tom Phillips	40.00	20.00	12.00
(167)	Val Picinich	40.00	20.00	12.00
(168)	Herman Pillette	40.00	20.00	12.00
(169)	Ralph Pinelli	40.00	20.00	12.00
(170)	Wallie Pipp	50.00	25.00	15.00
(171)	Clark Pittenger (Clarke)	40.00	20.00	12.00
(172)	Raymond Powell	40.00	20.00	12.00
(173)	Derrill Pratt	40.00	20.00	12.00
(174)	Jack Quinn	40.00	20.00	12.00
(175)	Joe (Goldie) Rapp	40.00	20.00	12.00
(176)	John Rawlings	40.00	20.00	12.00
(177)	Walter (Dutch) Reuther (Ruether)	40.00	20.00	12.00
(178)	Sam Rice	100.00	50.00	30.00
(179)	Emory Rigney	40.00	20.00	12.00
(180)	Jimmy Ring	40.00	20.00	12.00
(181)	Eppa Rixey	100.00	50.00	30.00
(182)	Charles Robertson	40.00	20.00	12.00
(183)	Ed Rommel	40.00	20.00	12.00
(184)	Eddie Roush	100.00	50.00	30.00
(185)	Harold (Muddy) Ruel (Herold)	40.00	20.00	12.00
(186)	Babe Ruth	2000.	1000.	600.00
(187)	Ray Schalk	100.00	50.00	30.00
(188)	Wallie Schang	40.00	20.00	12.00
(189)	Ray Schmandt	40.00	20.00	12.00
(190)	Walter Schmidt	40.00	20.00	12.00
(191)	Joe Schultz	40.00	20.00	12.00
(192)	Everett Scott	40.00	20.00	12.00
(193)	Henry Severeid	40.00	20.00	12.00
(194)	Joe Sewell	125.00	62.00	37.00
(195)	Howard Shanks	40.00	20.00	12.00
(196)	Bob Shawkey	40.00	20.00	12.00
(197)	Earl Sheely	40.00	20.00	12.00
(198)	Will Sherdel	40.00	20.00	12.00
(199)	Ralph Shinners	40.00	20.00	12.00
(200)	Urban Shocker	40.00	20.00	12.00
(201)	Charles (Chick) Shorten	40.00	20.00	12.00
(202)	George Sisler	125.00	62.00	37.00
(203)	Earl Smith	40.00	20.00	12.00
(204)	Earl Smith	40.00	20.00	12.00
(205)	Elmer Smith	40.00	20.00	12.00
(206)	Jack Smith	40.00	20.00	12.00
(207)	Sherrod Smith	40.00	20.00	12.00
(208)	Colonel Snover	40.00	20.00	12.00
(209)	Frank Snyder	40.00	20.00	12.00
(210)	Al Sothoron	40.00	20.00	12.00
(211)	Bill Southworth	40.00	20.00	12.00
(212)	Tris Speaker	275.00	137.00	82.00
(213)	Arnold Statz	40.00	20.00	12.00
(214)	Milton Stock	40.00	20.00	12.00
(215)	Amos Strunk	40.00	20.00	12.00
(216)	Jim Tierney	40.00	20.00	12.00
(217)	John Tobin	40.00	20.00	12.00
(218)	Fred Toney	40.00	20.00	12.00
(219)	George Toporcer	40.00	20.00	12.00
(220)	Harold (Pie) Traynor	100.00	50.00	30.00
(221)	George Uhle	40.00	20.00	12.00
(222)	Elam Vangilder	40.00	20.00	12.00
(223)	Bob Veach	40.00	20.00	12.00
(224)	Clarence (Tillie) Walker	40.00	20.00	12.00
(225)	Curtis Walker	40.00	20.00	12.00
(226)	Al Walters	40.00	20.00	12.00
(227)	Bill Wambsganss	40.00	20.00	12.00
(228)	Aaron (Erin) Ward	40.00	20.00	12.00
(229)	John Watson	40.00	20.00	12.00
(230)	Frank Welch	40.00	20.00	12.00
(231)	Zach Wheat	125.00	62.00	37.00
(232)	Fred (Cy) Williams	40.00	20.00	12.00
(233)	Kenneth Williams	40.00	20.00	12.00
(234)	Ivy Wingo	40.00	20.00	12.00
(235)	Joe Wood	60.00	30.00	18.00
(236)	Lawrence Woodall	40.00	20.00	12.00
(237)	Russell Wrightstone	40.00	20.00	12.00
(238)	Everett Yaryan	40.00	20.00	12.00
(239)	Ross Young (Youngs)	125.00	62.00	37.00
(240)	J.T. Zachary	40.00	20.00	12.00

A player's name in italic type indicates a rookie card. An (FC) indicates a player's first card for that particular card company.

1927 American Carmel Series of 60 (E126)

This set consists of 60 of the most prominent baseball players in the country. We have made up an album which will hold the complete set. On receipt of 15 cents in stamps, we will send a blank album to any address in the United States.

Manufactured only by the
AMERICAN CARAMEL COMPANY
Lancaster, Pa.

Issued in 1927 by the American Caramel Company of Lancaster, Pa., this obscure 60-card set was one of the last of the caramel card issues. Measuring 2" by 3-1/4", the cards differ from most sets of the period because they are numbered. The back of each card includes an offer for an album to house the 60-card set which includes players from all 16 major league teams, but to date no such album has been found. The set has been given the designation E126.

		NR MT	EX	VG
Complete set (60):		10000.	5000.	3000.
Common player:		75.00	37.00	22.00
1	John Gooch	100.00	50.00	30.00
2	Clyde L. Barnhart	75.00	37.00	22.00
3	Joe Busch (Bush)	100.00	50.00	30.00
4	Lee Meadows	75.00	37.00	22.00
5	E.T. Cox	75.00	37.00	22.00
6	"Red" Faber	200.00	100.00	60.00
7	Aaron Ward	75.00	37.00	22.00
8	Ray Schalk	200.00	100.00	60.00
9	"Specks" Toporcer ("Specs")	75.00	37.00	22.00
10	Bill Southworth	75.00	37.00	22.00
11	Allen Sothoron	75.00	37.00	22.00
12	Will Sherdel	75.00	37.00	22.00
13	Grover Alexander	250.00	125.00	75.00
14	Jack Quinn	75.00	37.00	22.00
15	C. Galloway	75.00	37.00	22.00
16	"Eddie" Collins	275.00	137.00	82.00
17	"Ty" Cobb	1500.	750.00	450.00
18	Percy Jones	75.00	37.00	22.00
19	Chas. Grimm	100.00	50.00	30.00
20	"Bennie" Karr	75.00	37.00	22.00
21	Charlie Jamieson	75.00	37.00	22.00
22	Sherrod Smith	75.00	37.00	22.00
23	Virgil Cheeves	75.00	37.00	22.00
24	James Ring	75.00	37.00	22.00
25	"Muddy" Ruel	75.00	37.00	22.00
26	Joe Judge	75.00	37.00	22.00
27	Tris Speaker	400.00	200.00	120.00
28	Walter Johnson	600.00	300.00	180.00
29	E.C. "Sam" Rice	200.00	100.00	60.00
30	Hank DeBerry	75.00	37.00	22.00
31	Walter Henline	75.00	37.00	22.00
32	Max Carey	200.00	100.00	60.00
33	Arnold J. Statz	75.00	37.00	22.00
34	Emil Meusel	75.00	37.00	22.00
35	T.P. "Pat" Collins	75.00	37.00	22.00
36	Urban Shocker	75.00	37.00	22.00
37	Bob Shawkey	100.00	50.00	30.00
38	"Babe" Ruth	2700.	1350.	810.00
39	Bob Meusel	100.00	50.00	30.00
40	Alex Ferguson	75.00	37.00	22.00
41	"Stuffy" McInnis	75.00	37.00	22.00
42	"Cy" Williams	100.00	50.00	30.00
43	Russel Wrightstone (Russell)	75.00	37.00	22.00
44	John Tobin	75.00	37.00	22.00
45	Wm. C. Jacobson	75.00	37.00	22.00
46	Bryan "Slim" Harriss	75.00	37.00	22.00
47	Elam Vangilder	75.00	37.00	22.00
48	Ken Williams	75.00	37.00	22.00
49	Geo. R. Sisler	200.00	100.00	60.00
50	Ed Brown	75.00	37.00	22.00
51	Jack Smith	75.00	37.00	22.00
52	Dave Bancroft	200.00	100.00	60.00
53	Larry Woodall	75.00	37.00	22.00
54	Lu Blue	75.00	37.00	22.00
55	Johnny Bassler	75.00	37.00	22.00
56	"Jakie" May	75.00	37.00	22.00
57	Horace Ford	75.00	37.00	22.00
58	"Curt" Walker	75.00	37.00	22.00
59	"Artie" Nehf	75.00	37.00	22.00
60	Geo. Kelly	200.00	100.00	60.00

1962 American Tract Society

These full-color cards, which carry religious messages on the back, were issued in 1962 by the American Tract Society, an interdenominational, non-sectarian publisher of Christian literature in the

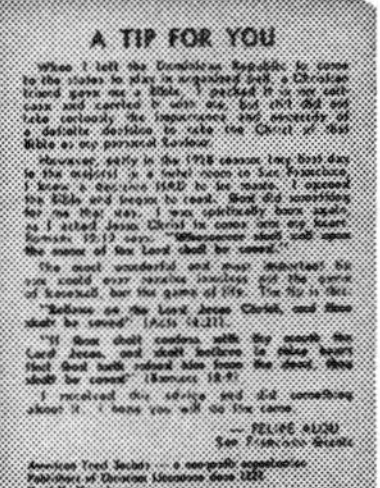

United States since 1825. Known as "Tracards", the cards measure 2-3/4" x 3-1/2" and feature color photographs on the fronts. The set includes religious scenes along with photos of various celebrities and sports stars, including baseball players Felipe Alou, Bobby Richardson, Jerry Kindall and Al Worthington. (There are two poses each of Alou and Kindall.) The backs carry rather lengthy, first-person religious testimonials from the players. The cards are numbered on the back in the lower right corner.

		NR MT	EX	VG
Complete set:		20.00	10.00	6.00
Common player:		4.00	2.00	1.25
43	Bobby Richardson	7.00	3.50	2.00
51a	Jerry Kindall (portrait to chest)	4.00	2.00	1.25
51b	Jerry Kindall (kneeling with bat)	4.00	2.00	1.25
52a	Felipe Alou (kneeling on one knee)	6.00	3.00	1.75
52b	Felipe Alou (batting, full length)	6.00	3.00	1.75
66	Al Worthington	4.00	2.00	1.25

1989 Ames 20/20 Club

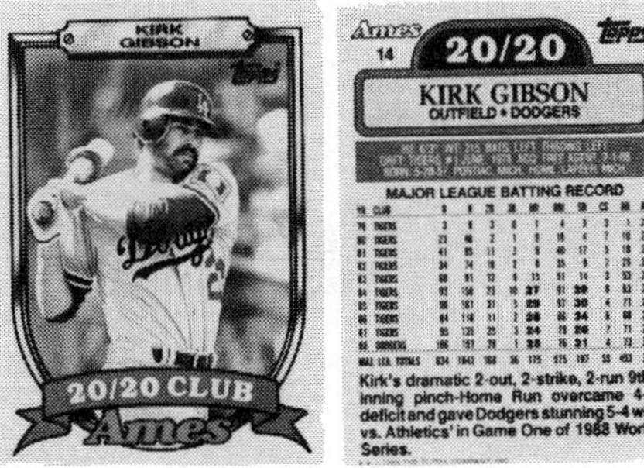

This 33-card set was produced by Topps for the Ames toy store chain. As its name implies, the special boxed set highlights members of the 20/20 club, players who have recorded 20 home runs and 20 stolen bases in the same season. The glossy cards feature action or posed photos on the front with the player's name at the top and "Ames 20/20 Club" along the bottom. The Topps logo appears in the upper right corner.

		MT	NR MT	EX
Complete set:		4.00	3.00	1.50
Common player:		.09	.07	.04
1	Jesse Barfield	.09	.07	.04
2	Kevin Bass	.09	.07	.04
3	Don Baylor	.09	.07	.04
4	George Bell	.12	.09	.05
5	Barry Bonds	.40	.30	.15
6	Phil Bradley	.09	.07	.04
7	Ellis Burks	.20	.15	.08
8	Jose Canseco	.70	.50	.30
9	Joe Carter	.20	.15	.08
10	Kal Daniels	.09	.07	.04
11	Eric Davis	.20	.15	.08
12	Mike Davis	.09	.07	.04
13	Andre Dawson	.12	.09	.05
14	Kirk Gibson	.09	.07	.04
15	Pedro Guerrero	.12	.09	.05
16	Rickey Henderson	.50	.40	.20
17	Bo Jackson	.60	.45	.25
18	Howard Johnson	.20	.15	.08
19	Jeffrey Leonard	.09	.07	.04
20	Kevin McReynolds	.12	.09	.05
21	Dale Murphy	.09	.07	.04
22	Dwayne Murphy	.09	.07	.04
23	Dave Parker	.12	.09	.05
24	Kirby Puckett	.50	.40	.20
25	Juan Samuel	.09	.07	.04
26	Ryne Sandberg	.20	.15	.08
27	Mike Schmidt	.80	.60	.30
28	Darryl Strawberry	.25	.20	.10
29	Alan Trammell	.09	.07	.04
30	Andy Van Slyke	.09	.07	.04
31	Devon White	.09	.07	.04
32	Dave Winfield	.12	.09	.05
33	Robin Yount	.30	.25	.12

1990 Ames All-Stars

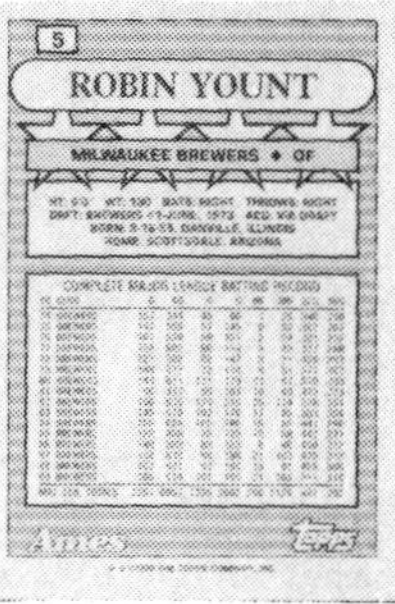

This 33-card set was the second consecutive issue produced by Topps for the Ames toy store chain. The cards measure 2-1/2" by 3-1/2" in size and feature baseball's top active hitters. Both the Ames and Topps logos appear on the cards.

		MT	NR MT	EX
Complete set:		4.00	3.00	1.50
Common player:		.10	.06	.03
1	Dave Winfield	.60	.45	.25
2	George Brett	.75	.60	.30
3	Jim Rice	.12	.09	.05
4	Dwight Evans	.12	.09	.05
5	Robin Yount	.60	.45	.25
6	Dave Parker	.40	.30	.15
7	Eddie Murray	.20	.15	.08
8	Keith Hernandez	.10	.08	.04
9	Andre Dawson	.20	.15	.08
10	Fred Lynn	.10	.08	.04
11	Dale Murphy	.20	.15	.08
12	Jack Clark	.10	.08	.04
13	Rickey Henderson	.50	.40	.20
14	Paul Molitor	.50	.40	.20
15	Cal Ripken	.75	.60	.30
16	Wade Boggs	.35	.25	.14
17	Tim Raines	.15	.11	.06
18	Don Mattingly	.40	.30	.15
19	Kent Hrbek	.10	.08	.04
20	Kirk Gibson	.10	.08	.04
21	Julio Franco	.10	.08	.04
22	George Bell	.10	.08	.04
23	Darryl Strawberry	.15	.11	.06
24	Kirby Puckett	.30	.25	.12
25	Juan Samuel	.10	.08	.04
26	Alvin Davis	.08	.06	.03
27	Joe Carter	.15	.11	.06
28	Eric Davis	.20	.15	.08
29	Jose Canseco	.50	.40	.20
30	Wally Joyner	.12	.09	.05
31	Will Clark	.50	.40	.20
32	Ruben Sierra	.25	.20	.10
33	Danny Tartabull	.15	.11	.06

1991 Arena Holograms

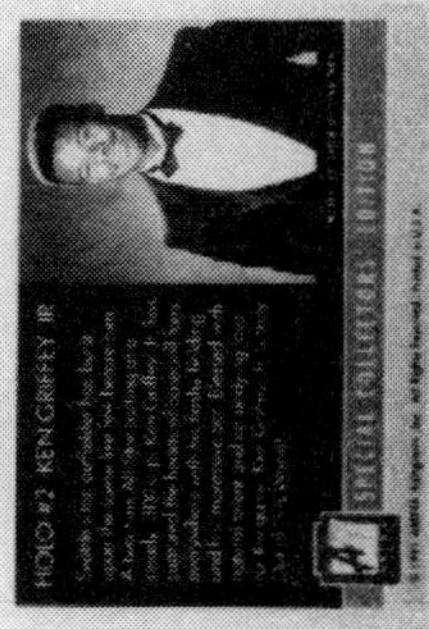

Superstars from four sports are featured in this hologram set. The cards were distributed through hobby dealers and are numbered on the back. The front of the card features the hologram, while the back features player information and a photo of the athlete in formal wear. The first five holograms were produced in an edition of 250,000 each, the Pat Falloon hologram was in an edition of 198,000.

		MT	NR MT	EX
Complete set:		12.00	9.00	4.75
Common player:		2.00	1.50	.80
1	Joe Montana	3.00	2.25	1.25
2	Ken Griffey, Jr.	3.00	2.25	1.25
3	Frank Thomas	3.00	3.00	1.50
4	Barry Sanders	3.00	2.25	1.25
5	David Robinson	2.00	1.50	.80
6	Pat Falloon	2.00	1.50	.80

Definitions for grading conditions are located in the Introduction of this price guide.

1955 Armour Coins

In 1955, Armour inserted a plastic "coin" in its packages of hot dogs. A raised profile of a ballplayer is on the front of each coin along with the player's name, position, birthplace and date, batting and throwing preference, and 1954 hitting or pitching record. The coins, which measure 1-1/2" in diameter and are unnumbered, came in a variety of colors, including the more common ones in aqua, dark blue, light green, orange, red and yellow. Scarcer colors are black, pale blue, lime green, very dark green, gold, pale orange, pink, silver, and tan. Scarce colors are double the value of the coins listed in the checklist that follows. Twenty-four different players are included in the set. Variations exist for Harvey Kuenn (letters in his name are condensed or spaced) and Mickey Mantle (name is spelled Mantle or incorrectly as Mantel). The complete set price includes the two variations.

		NR MT	EX	VG
Complete set:		1000.	500.00	300.00
Common player:		12.00	6.00	3.50
(1)	John "Johnny" Antonelli	15.00	7.50	4.50
(2)	Larry "Yogi" Berra	60.00	30.00	18.00
(3)	Delmar "Del" Crandall	15.00	7.50	4.50
(4)	Lawrence "Larry" Doby	18.00	9.00	5.50
(5)	James "Jim" Finigan	12.00	6.00	3.50
(6)	Edward "Whitey" Ford	60.00	30.00	18.00
(7)	James "Junior" Gilliam	20.00	10.00	6.00
(8)	Harvey "Kitten" Haddix	12.00	6.00	3.50
(9)	Ranson "Randy" Jackson (name actually Ransom)	20.00	10.00	6.00
(10)	Jack "Jackie" Jensen	18.00	9.00	5.50
(11)	Theodore "Ted" Kluszewski	24.00	12.00	7.25
(12a)	Harvey E. Kuenn (spaced letters in name)	25.00	12.50	7.50
(12b)	Harvey E. Kuenn (condensed letters in name)	40.00	20.00	12.00
(13a)	Charles "Mickey" Mantel (incorrect spelling)	150.00	75.00	45.00
(13b)	Charles "Mickey" Mantle (correct spelling)	400.00	200.00	125.00
(14)	Donald "Don" Mueller	20.00	10.00	6.00
(15)	Harold "Pee Wee" Reese	40.00	20.00	12.00
(16)	Allie P. Reynolds	18.00	9.00	5.50
(17)	Albert "Flip" Rosen	18.00	9.00	5.50
(18)	Curtis "Curt" Simmons	12.00	6.00	3.50
(19)	Edwin "Duke" Snider	60.00	30.00	18.00
(20)	Warren Spahn	40.00	20.00	12.00
(21)	Frank J. Thomas	35.00	17.50	10.50
(22)	Virgil "Fire" Trucks	12.00	6.00	3.50
(23)	Robert "Bob" Turley	18.00	9.00	5.50
(24)	James "Mickey" Vernon	12.00	6.00	3.50

1959 Armour Coins

After a three-year layoff, Armour again inserted plastic baseball "coins" into its hot dog packages. The coins retained their 1-1/2" size but did not include as much detailed information as in 1955. Missing from the coins' backs is information such as birthplace and date, team, and batting and throwing preference. The fronts contain the player's name and, unlike 1955, only the team nickname is given. The set consists of 20 coins which come in a myriad of colors. Common colors are navy blue, royal blue, dark green, orange, red, and pale yellow. Scarce colors are pale blue, cream, grey-green, pale green, dark or light pink, pale red, tan, and translucent coins of any color with or without multi-colored flecks in the plastic mix. Scarce colors are double the value listed for coins in the checklist. In 1959, Armour had a write-in offer of 10 coins for $1. The same 10 players were part of the write-in offer, accounting for why half of the coins in the set are much more plentiful than the other.

		NR MT	EX	VG
Complete set:		400.00	200.00	120.00
Common player:		10.00	5.00	3.00
(1)	Hank Aaron	45.00	22.00	13.50
(2)	John Antonelli	15.00	7.50	4.50
(3)	Richie Ashburn	25.00	12.50	7.50
(4)	Ernie Banks	45.00	22.00	13.50
(5)	Don Blasingame	10.00	5.00	3.00
(6)	Bob Cerv	10.00	5.00	3.00
(7)	Del Crandall	15.00	7.50	4.50
(8)	Whitey Ford	35.00	17.50	10.50
(9)	Nellie Fox	15.00	7.50	4.50
(10)	Jackie Jensen	30.00	15.00	9.00
(11)	Harvey Kuenn	15.00	7.50	4.50
(12)	Frank Malzone	10.00	5.00	3.00
(13)	Johnny Podres	15.00	7.50	4.50
(14)	Frank Robinson	25.00	12.50	7.50
(15)	Roy Sievers	10.00	5.00	3.00
(16)	Bob Skinner	10.00	5.00	3.00
(17)	Frank J. Thomas	15.00	7.50	4.50
(18)	Gus Triandos	10.00	5.00	3.00
(19)	Bob Turley	18.00	9.00	5.50
(20)	Mickey Vernon	15.00	7.50	4.50

1960 Armour Coins

The 1960 Armour coin issue is identical in number and style to the 1959 set. The unnumbered coins, which measure 1-1/2" in diameter, once again came in a variety of colors. Common colors for 1960 are dark blue, light blue, dark green, light green, red-orange, dark red, and light yellow. Scarce colors are aqua, grey-blue, cream, tan, and dark yellow. Scarce colors are double the value of the coins in the checklist. The Bud Daley coin is very scarce, although it is not exactly known why. Theories for the scarcity center on broken printing molds, contract disputes, and that the coin was only inserted in a test product that quickly proved to be unsuccessful. As in 1959, a mail-in offer for 10 free coins was made available by Armour. The set price for the 1960 Armour set does not include the three more difficult variations.

		NR MT	EX	VG
Complete set:		1200.	600.00	360.00
Common player:		7.00	3.50	2.00
(1a)	Hank Aaron (Braves)	45.00	22.00	13.50
(1b)	Hank Aaron (Milwaukee Braves)	75.00	37.00	22.00
(2)	Bob Allison	12.00	6.00	3.50
(3)	Ernie Banks	18.00	9.00	5.50
(4)	Ken Boyer	10.00	5.00	3.00
(5)	Rocky Colavito	15.00	7.50	4.50
(6)	Gene Conley	10.00	5.00	3.00
(7)	Del Crandall	10.00	5.00	3.00
(8)	Bud Daley	750.00	375.00	225.00
(9a)	Don Drysdale (L.A condensed)	20.00	10.00	6.00
(9b)	Don Drysdale (space between L. and A.)	25.00	12.50	7.50
(10)	Whitey Ford	20.00	10.00	6.00
(11)	Nellie Fox	15.00	7.50	4.50
(12)	Al Kaline	30.00	15.00	9.00
(13a)	Frank Malzone (Red Sox)	7.00	3.50	2.00
(13b)	Frank Malzone (Boston Red Sox)	25.00	12.50	7.50
(14)	Mickey Mantle	100.00	50.00	30.00
(15)	Ed Mathews	25.00	12.50	7.50
(16)	Willie Mays	45.00	22.00	13.50
(17)	Vada Pinson	10.00	5.00	3.00
(18)	Dick Stuart	10.00	5.00	3.00
(19)	Gus Triandos	7.00	3.50	2.00
(20)	Early Wynn	20.00	10.00	6.00

Grading Guide

Mint (MT): A perfect card. Well-centered with all corners sharp and square. No creases, stains, edge nicks, surface marks, yellowing or fading.

Near Mint (NM): A nearly perfect card. At first glance, a NM card appears to be perfect. May be slightly off-center. No surface marks, creases or loss of gloss.

Excellent (EX): Corners are still fairly sharp with only moderate wear. Borders may be off-center. No creases or stains on fronts or backs, but may show slight loss of surface luster.

Very Good (VG): Shows obvious handling. May have rounded corners, minor creases, major gum or wax stains. No major creases, tape marks, writing, etc.

Good (G): A well-worn card, but exhibits no intentional damage. May have major or multiple creases. Corners may be rounded well beyond card border.

1986 Ault Foods Blue Jays

The Ault Foods Blue Jays set is comprised of 24 full-color stickers. Designed to be placed in a special album, the stickers measure 2" by 3" in size. The attractive album measures 9" by 12" and is printed on glossy stock. While the stickers carry no information except for the player's last name and uniform number, the 20-page album contains extensive personal and statistical information about each of the 24 players.

		MT	NR MT	EX
Complete set (24):		30.00	37.00	20.00
Common player:		.60	.45	.25
Album:		5.00	3.75	2.00
1	Tony Fernandez	2.00	1.50	.80
5	Rance Mulliniks	.60	.45	.25
7	Damaso Garcia	.60	.45	.25
11	George Bell	3.00	2.25	1.25
12	Ernie Whitt	.60	.45	.25
13	Buck Martinez	.60	.45	.25
15	Lloyd Moseby	.95	.70	.40
16	Garth Iorg	.60	.45	.25
17	Kelly Gruber	2.00	1.50	.80
18	Jim Clancy	.75	.60	.30
22	Jimmy Key	1.00	.70	.40
23	Cecil Fielder	15.00	11.00	6.00
25	Steve Davis	.60	.45	.25
26	Willie Upshaw	.75	.60	.30
29	Jesse Barfield	.95	.70	.40
31	Jim Acker	.60	.45	.25
33	Doyle Alexander	.60	.45	.25
36	Bill Caudill	.60	.45	.25
37	Dave Stieb	2.00	1.50	.80
39	Don Gordon	.60	.45	.25
44	Cliff Johnson	.60	.45	.25
46	Gary Lavelle	.60	.45	.25
50	Tom Henke	1.25	.90	.50
53	Dennis Lamp	.60	.45	.25

1964 Aurovision Records

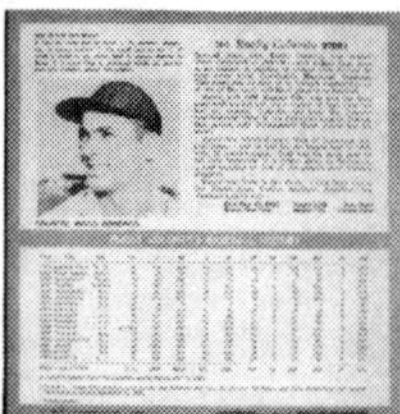

Never a candidate for the Billboard "Hot 100," this series of baseball picture records has been popular with collectors due to the high-quality photos on the front. On the grooved front side of the 6-3/4" x 6-3/4" plastic-laminated cardboard record is a color player photo with facsimile autograph, Sports Record trophy logo and 33-1/3 RPM notation. A color border surrounds the photo and is carried over to the unrecorded back side. There is another photo on back, along with a career summary and complete major and minor league stats and instructions for playing the record. In the bottom border is a 1962 copyright notice by Sports Champions Inc., and a notice that the Auravision Record is a product of Columbia Records. A hole at center of the record could be punched out for playing and the records featured a five-minute interview with the player by sportscaster Marty Glickman. Large quantities of the records made their way into the hobby as remainders. For early-1960s baseball items they remain reasonably priced today. The unnumbered records are checklisted here alphabetically.

		NR MT	EX	VG
	Complete set (16):	495.00	247.00	148.00
	Common player:	10.00	5.00	3.00
(1)	Bob Allison	10.00	5.00	3.00
(2)	Ernie Banks	45.00	22.00	13.50
(3)	Ken Boyer	20.00	10.00	6.00
(4)	Rocky Colavito	25.00	12.50	7.50
(5)	Don Drysdale	40.00	20.00	12.00
(6)	Whitey Ford	45.00	22.00	13.50
(7)	Jim Gentile	10.00	5.00	3.00
(8)	Al Kaline	40.00	20.00	12.00
(9)	Sandy Koufax	60.00	30.00	18.00
(10)	Mickey Mantle	145.00	75.00	45.00
(11)	Roger Maris	60.00	30.00	18.00
(12)	Willie Mays	60.00	30.00	18.00
(13)	Bill Mazeroski	25.00	12.50	7.50
(14)	Frank Robinson	40.00	20.00	12.00
(15)	Warren Spahn	40.00	20.00	12.00
(16)	Pete Ward	10.00	5.00	3.00

B

1914 B18 Blankets

These 5-1/4" flannels were issued in 1914 with several popular brands of tobacco. The flannels, whose American Card Catalog designation is B18, picked up the nickname blankets because many of the square pieces of cloth were sewn together to form pillow covers or bed spreads. Different color combinations on the flannels exist for all 10 teams included in the set. The complete set price in the checklist that follows does not include higher-priced variations.

		NR MT	EX	VG
	Complete Set:	4500.	2200.	1350.
	Common Player:	24.00	12.00	7.25
(1a)	Babe Adams (purple pennants)	48.00	24.00	14.50
(1b)	Babe Adams (red pennants)	55.00	27.00	16.50
(2a)	Sam Agnew (purple basepaths)	48.00	24.00	14.50
(2b)	Sam Agnew (red basepaths)	55.00	27.00	16.50
(3a)	Eddie Ainsmith (green pennants)	24.00	12.00	7.25
(3b)	Eddie Ainsmith (brown pennants)	24.00	12.00	7.25
(4a)	Jimmy Austin (purple basepaths)	48.00	24.00	14.50
(4b)	Jimmy Austin (red basepaths)	55.00	27.00	16.50
(5a)	Del Baker (white infield)	24.00	12.00	7.25
(5b)	Del Baker (brown infield)	90.00	45.00	27.00
(5c)	Del Baker (red infield)	275.00	137.00	82.00
(6a)	Johnny Bassler (purple pennants)	48.00	24.00	14.50
(6b)	Johnny Bassler (yellow pennants)	90.00	45.00	27.00
(7a)	Paddy Bauman (Baumann) (white infield)	24.00	12.00	7.25
(7b)	Paddy Bauman (Baumann) (brown infield)	90.00	45.00	27.00
(7c)	Paddy Bauman (Baumann) (red infield)	275.00	137.00	82.00
(8a)	Luke Boone (blue infield)	24.00	12.00	7.25
(8b)	Luke Boone (green infield)	24.00	12.00	7.25
(9a)	George Burns (brown basepaths)	24.00	12.00	7.25
(9b)	George Burns (green basepaths)	24.00	12.00	7.25
(10a)	Tioga George Burns (white infield)	24.00	12.00	7.25
(10b)	Tioga George Burns (brown infield)	90.00	45.00	27.00
(11a)	Max Carey (purple pennants)	90.00	45.00	27.00
(11b)	Max Carey (red pennants)	100.00	50.00	30.00
(12a)	Marty Cavanaugh (Kavanagh) (white infield)	24.00	12.00	7.25
(12b)	Marty Cavanaugh (Kavanagh) (brown infield)	125.00	62.00	37.00
(12c)	Marty Cavanaugh (Kavanagh) (red infield)	275.00	137.00	82.00
(12d)	Marty Kavanaugh (Kavanagh)	24.00	12.00	7.25
(13a)	Frank Chance (green infield)	48.00	24.00	14.50
(13b)	Frank Chance (brown pennants, blue infield)	48.00	24.00	14.50
(13c)	Frank Chance (yellow pennants, blue infield)	275.00	137.00	82.00
(14a)	Ray Chapman (purple pennants)	48.00	24.00	14.50
(14b)	Ray Chapman (yellow pennants)	90.00	45.00	27.00
(15a)	Ty Cobb (white infield)	275.00	137.00	82.00
(15b)	Ty Cobb (brown infield)	550.00	275.00	165.00
(15c)	Ty Cobb (red infield)	2500.	1250.	750.00
(16a)	King Cole (blue infield)	24.00	12.00	7.25
(16b)	King Cole (green infield)	24.00	12.00	7.25
(17a)	Joe Connolly (white infield)	24.00	12.00	7.25
(17b)	Joe Connolly (brown infield)	90.00	45.00	27.00
(18a)	Harry Coveleski (white infield)	24.00	12.00	7.25
(18b)	Harry Coveleski (brown infield)	90.00	45.00	27.00
(19a)	George Cutshaw (blue infield)	24.00	12.00	7.25
(19b)	George Cutshaw (green infield)	24.00	12.00	7.25
(20a)	Jake Daubert (blue infield)	30.00	15.00	9.00
(20b)	Jake Daubert (green infield)	30.00	15.00	9.00
(21a)	Ray Demmitt (white infield)	24.00	12.00	7.25
(21b)	Ray Demmitt (brown infield)	90.00	45.00	27.00
(22a)	Bill Doak (purple pennants)	48.00	24.00	14.50
(22b)	Bill Doak (yellow pennants)	90.00	45.00	27.00
(23a)	Cozy Dolan (purple pennants)	48.00	24.00	14.50
(23b)	Cozy Dolan (yellow pennants)	90.00	45.00	27.00
(24a)	Larry Doyle (brown basepaths)	30.00	15.00	9.00
(24b)	Larry Doyle (green basepaths)	30.00	15.00	9.00
(25a)	Art Fletcher (brown basepaths)	24.00	12.00	7.25
(25b)	Art Fletcher (green basepaths)	24.00	12.00	7.25
(26a)	Eddie Foster (brown pennants)	24.00	12.00	7.25
(26b)	Eddie Foster (green pennants)	24.00	12.00	7.25
(27a)	Del Gainor (white infield)	24.00	12.00	7.25
(27b)	Del Gainor (brown infield)	90.00	45.00	27.00
(28a)	Chick Gandil (brown pennants)	40.00	20.00	12.00
(28b)	Chick Gandil (green pennants)	40.00	20.00	12.00
(29a)	George Gibson (purple pennants)	48.00	24.00	14.50
(29b)	George Gibson (red pennants)	55.00	27.00	16.50
(30a)	Hank Gowdy (white infield)	24.00	12.00	7.25
(30b)	Hank Gowdy (brown infield)	90.00	45.00	27.00
(30c)	Hank Gowdy (red infield)	275.00	137.00	82.00
(31a)	Jack Graney (purple pennants)	48.00	24.00	14.50
(31b)	Jack Graney (yellow pennants)	90.00	45.00	27.00
(32a)	Eddie Grant (brown basepaths)	24.00	12.00	7.25
(32b)	Eddie Grant (green basepaths)	24.00	12.00	7.25
(33a)	Tommy Griffith (white infield, green pennants)	24.00	12.00	7.25
(33b)	Tommy Griffith (white infield, red pennants)	275.00	137.00	82.00
(33c)	Tommy Griffith (brown infield)	90.00	45.00	27.00
(33d)	Tommy Griffith (red infield)	275.00	137.00	82.00
(34a)	Earl Hamilton (purple basepaths)	48.00	24.00	14.50
(34b)	Earl Hamilton (red basepaths)	55.00	27.00	16.50
(35a)	Roy Hartzell (blue infield)	24.00	12.00	7.25
(35b)	Roy Hartzell (green infield)	24.00	12.00	7.25
(36a)	Miller Huggins (purple pennants)	90.00	45.00	27.00
(36b)	Miller Huggins (yellow pennants)	150.00	75.00	45.00
(37a)	John Hummel (brown infield)	24.00	12.00	7.25
(37b)	John Hummel (green infield)	24.00	12.00	7.25
(38a)	Ham Hyatt (purple pennants)	48.00	24.00	14.50
(38b)	Ham Hyatt (red pennants)	55.00	27.00	16.50
(39a)	Shoeless Joe Jackson (purple pennants)	1200.	600.00	350.00
(39b)	Shoeless Joe Jackson (yellow pennants)	1500.	750.00	450.00
(40a)	Bill James (white infield)	24.00	12.00	7.25
(40b)	Bill James (brown infield)	90.00	45.00	27.00
(41a)	Walter Johnson (brown pennants)	275.00	137.00	82.00
(41b)	Walter Johnson (green pennants)	275.00	137.00	82.00
(42a)	Ray Keating (blue infield)	24.00	12.00	7.25
(42b)	Ray Keating (green infield)	24.00	12.00	7.25
(43a)	Joe Kelley (Kelly) (purple pennants)	90.00	45.00	27.00
(43b)	Joe Kelley (Kelly) (red pennants)	100.00	50.00	30.00
(44a)	Ed Konetchy (purple pennants)	48.00	24.00	14.50
(44b)	Ed Konetchy (red pennants)	55.00	27.00	16.50
(45a)	Nemo Leibold (purple pennants)	48.00	24.00	14.50
(45b)	Nemo Leibold (yellow pennants)	90.00	45.00	27.00
(46a)	Fritz Maisel (blue infield)	24.00	12.00	7.25
(46b)	Fritz Maisel (green infield)	24.00	12.00	7.25
(47a)	Les Mann (white infield)	24.00	12.00	7.25
(47b)	Les Mann (brown infield)	90.00	45.00	27.00
(48a)	Rabbit Maranville (white infield)	55.00	27.00	16.50
(48b)	Rabbit Maranville (brown infield)	150.00	75.00	45.00
(48c)	Rabbit Maranville (red infield)	350.00	175.00	105.00
(49a)	Bill McAllister (McAllester) (purple pennants)	48.00	24.00	14.50
(49b)	Bill McAllister (McAllester) (red pennants)	55.00	27.00	16.50
(50a)	George McBride (brown pennants)	24.00	12.00	7.25
(50b)	George McBride (green pennants)	24.00	12.00	7.25
(51a)	Chief Meyers (brown basepaths)	24.00	12.00	7.25
(51b)	Chief Meyers (green basepaths)	24.00	12.00	7.25
(52a)	Clyde Milan (brown pennants)	24.00	12.00	7.25
(52b)	Clyde Milan (green pennants)	24.00	12.00	7.25
(53a)	Dots Miller (purple pennants)	48.00	24.00	14.50
(53b)	Dots Miller (yellow pennants)	90.00	45.00	27.00
(54a)	Otto Miller (blue infield)	24.00	12.00	7.25
(54b)	Otto Miller (green infield)	24.00	12.00	7.25
(55a)	Willie Mitchell (purple pennants)	48.00	24.00	14.50
(55b)	Willie Mitchell (yellow pennants)	90.00	45.00	27.00
(56a)	Danny Moeller (brown pennants)	24.00	12.00	7.25
(56b)	Danny Moeller (green pennants)	24.00	12.00	7.25
(57a)	Ray Morgan (brown pennants)	24.00	12.00	7.25
(57b)	Ray Morgan (green pennants)	24.00	12.00	7.25
(58a)	George Moriarty (white infield)	24.00	12.00	7.25
(58b)	George Moriarty (brown infield)	90.00	45.00	27.00
(58c)	George Moriarty (red infield)	275.00	137.00	82.00
(59a)	Mike Mowrey (purple pennants)	48.00	24.00	14.50
(59b)	Mike Mowrey (red pennants)	55.00	27.00	16.50
(60a)	Red Murray (brown basepaths)	24.00	12.00	7.25
(60b)	Red Murray (green basepaths)	24.00	12.00	7.25
(61a)	Ivy Olson (purple pennants)	48.00	24.00	14.50
(61b)	Ivy Olson (yellow pennants)	90.00	45.00	27.00
(62a)	Steve O'Neill (purple pennants)	48.00	24.00	14.50
(62b)	Steve O'Neill (red pennants)	90.00	45.00	27.00
(63a)	Marty O'Toole (purple pennants)	48.00	24.00	14.50
(63b)	Marty O'Toole (red pennants)	55.00	27.00	16.50
(64a)	Roger Peckinpaugh (blue infield)	30.00	15.00	9.00
(64b)	Roger Peckinpaugh (green infield)	30.00	15.00	9.00
(65a)	Hub Perdue (white infield)	24.00	12.00	7.25
(65b)	Hub Perdue (brown infield)	90.00	45.00	27.00
(65c)	Hub Purdue (red infield)	275.00	137.00	82.00
(66a)	Del Pratt (purple pennants)	48.00	24.00	14.50
(66b)	Del Pratt (yellow pennants)	55.00	27.00	16.50
(67a)	Hank Robinson (purple pennants)	48.00	24.00	14.50
(67b)	Hank Robinson (yellow pennants)	90.00	45.00	27.00
(68a)	Nap Rucker (blue infield)	24.00	12.00	7.25
(68b)	Nap Rucker (green infield)	24.00	12.00	7.25
(69a)	Slim Sallee (purple pennants)	48.00	24.00	14.50
(69b)	Slim Sallee (yellow pennants)	90.00	45.00	27.00
(70a)	Howard Shanks (brown pennants)	24.00	12.00	7.25
(70b)	Howard Shanks (green pennants)	24.00	12.00	7.25
(71a)	Burt Shotton (purple basepaths)	48.00	24.00	14.50
(71b)	Burt Shotton (red basepaths)	55.00	27.00	16.50
(72a)	Red Smith (blue infield)	24.00	12.00	7.25
(72b)	Red Smith (green infield)	24.00	12.00	7.25
(73a)	Fred Snodgrass (brown basepaths)	30.00	15.00	9.00
(73b)	Fred Snodgrass (green basepaths)	30.00	15.00	9.00
(74a)	Bill Steele (purple pennants)	48.00	24.00	14.50
74b	Bill Steele (yellow pennants)	90.00	45.00	27.00
(75a)	Casey Stengel (blue infield)	150.00	75.00	45.00
(75b)	Casey Stengel (green infield)	165.00	85.00	48.00
(76a)	Jeff Sweeney (blue infield)	24.00	12.00	7.25
(76b)	Jeff Sweeney (green infield)	24.00	12.00	7.25
(77a)	Jeff Tesreau (brown basepaths)	24.00	12.00	7.25
(77b)	Jeff Tesreau (green basepaths)	24.00	12.00	7.25
(78a)	Terry Turner (purple pennants)	48.00	24.00	14.50
(78b)	Terry Turner (yellow pennants)	90.00	45.00	27.00
(79a)	Lefty Tyler (white infield)	24.00	12.00	7.25
(79b)	Lefty Tyler (brown infield)	90.00	45.00	27.00
(79c)	Lefty Tyler (red infield)	275.00	137.00	82.00
(80a)	Jim Viox (purple pennants)	48.00	24.00	14.50
(80b)	Jim Viox (red pennants)	55.00	27.00	16.50
(81a)	Bull Wagner (blue infield)	24.00	12.00	7.25
(81b)	Bull Wagner (green infield)	24.00	12.00	7.25
(82a)	Bobby Wallace (purple basepaths)	90.00	45.00	27.00
(82b)	Bobby Wallace (red basepaths)	90.00	45.00	27.00
(83a)	Dee Walsh (purple basepaths)	48.00	24.00	14.50
(83b)	Dee Walsh (red basepaths)	55.00	27.00	16.50
(84a)	Jimmy Walsh (blue infield)	24.00	12.00	7.25
(84b)	Jimmy Walsh (green infield)	24.00	12.00	7.25
(85a)	Bert Whaling (white infield)	24.00	12.00	7.25
(85b)	Bert Whaling (brown infield)	90.00	45.00	27.00
(85c)	Bert Whaling (red infield)	275.00	137.00	82.00
(86a)	Zach Wheat (blue infield)	90.00	45.00	27.00
(86b)	Zach Wheat (green infield)	90.00	45.00	27.00
(87a)	Possum Whitted (purple pennants)	48.00	24.00	14.50
(87b)	Possum Whitted (yellow pennants)	90.00	45.00	27.00
(88a)	Gus Williams (purple basepaths)	48.00	24.00	14.50
(88b)	Gus Williams (red basepaths)	55.00	27.00	16.50
(89a)	Owen Wilson (purple pennants)	48.00	24.00	14.50
(89b)	Owen Wilson (yellow pennants)	90.00	45.00	27.00
(90a)	Hooks Wiltse (brown basepaths)	24.00	12.00	7.25
(90b)	Hooks Wiltse (green basepaths)	24.00	12.00	7.25

1916 BF2 Felt Pennants

Issued circa 1916, this unnumbered set consists of 97 felt pennants with a small black-and-white player photo glued to each one. The triangular pennants measure approximately 8-1/4" long, while the photos are 1-3/4" by 1-1/4" and appear to be identical to photos used for The Sporting News issues of the same period. The pennants list the player's name and team.

		NR MT	EX	VG
Complete Set:		7750.	3875.	2325.
Common Player:		45.00	22.00	13.50
(1)	Grover Alexander	125.00	62.00	37.00
(2)	Jimmy Archer	45.00	22.00	13.50
(3)	Home Run Baker	75.00	37.00	22.00
(4)	Dave Bancroft	75.00	37.00	22.00
(5)	Jack Barry	45.00	22.00	13.50
(6)	Chief Bender	75.00	37.00	22.00
(7)	Joe Benz	45.00	22.00	13.50
(8)	Mordecai Brown	75.00	37.00	22.00
(9)	George J. Burns	45.00	22.00	13.50
(10)	Donie Bush	45.00	22.00	13.50
(11)	Hick Cady	45.00	22.00	13.50
(12)	Max Carey	75.00	37.00	22.00
(13)	Ray Chapman	75.00	37.00	22.00
(14)	Ty Cobb	550.00	275.00	165.00
(15)	Eddie Collins	75.00	37.00	22.00
(16)	Shano Collins	45.00	22.00	13.50
(17)	Commy Comiskey	100.00	50.00	30.00
(18)	Harry Coveleskie (Coveleski)	45.00	22.00	13.50
(19)	Gavvy Cravath	45.00	22.00	13.50
(20)	Sam Crawford	75.00	37.00	22.00
(21)	Jake Daubert	45.00	22.00	13.50
(22)	Josh Devore	45.00	22.00	13.50
(23)	Red Dooin	45.00	22.00	13.50
(24)	Larry Doyle	45.00	22.00	13.50
(25)	Jean Dubuc	45.00	22.00	13.50
(26)	Johnny Evers	75.00	37.00	22.00
(27)	Red Faber	75.00	37.00	22.00
(28)	Eddie Foster	45.00	22.00	13.50
(29)	Del Gainer (Gainor)	45.00	22.00	13.50
(30)	Chick Gandil	75.00	37.00	22.00
(31)	Joe Gedeon	45.00	22.00	13.50
(32)	Hank Gowdy	45.00	22.00	13.50
(33)	Earl Hamilton	45.00	22.00	13.50
(34)	Claude Hendrix	45.00	22.00	13.50
(35)	Buck Herzog	45.00	22.00	13.50
(36)	Harry Hooper	75.00	37.00	22.00
(37)	Miller Huggins	75.00	37.00	22.00
(38)	Shoeless Joe Jackson	900.00	450.00	270.00
(39)	Seattle Bill James	45.00	22.00	13.50
(40)	Hugh Jennings	75.00	37.00	22.00
(41)	Walter Johnson	350.00	175.00	105.00
(42)	Fielder Jones	45.00	22.00	13.50
(43)	Joe Judge	45.00	22.00	13.50
(44)	Benny Kauff	45.00	22.00	13.50
(45)	Bill Killefer	45.00	22.00	13.50
(46)	Nap Lajoie	125.00	62.00	37.00
(47)	Jack Lapp	45.00	22.00	13.50
(48)	Doc Lavan	45.00	22.00	13.50
(49)	Jimmy Lavender	45.00	22.00	13.50
(50)	Dutch Leonard	45.00	22.00	13.50
(51)	Duffy Lewis	45.00	22.00	13.50
(52)	Hans Lobert	45.00	22.00	13.50
(53)	Fred Luderus	45.00	22.00	13.50
(54)	Connie Mack	100.00	50.00	30.00
(55)	Sherry Magee	45.00	22.00	13.50
(56)	Al Mamaux	45.00	22.00	13.50
(57)	Rabbit Maranville	75.00	37.00	22.00
(58)	Rube Marquard	75.00	37.00	22.00
(59)	George McBride	45.00	22.00	13.50
(60)	John McGraw	75.00	37.00	22.00
(61)	Stuffy McInnes (McInnis)	45.00	22.00	13.50
(62)	Fred Merkle	45.00	22.00	13.50
(63)	Chief Meyers	45.00	22.00	13.50
(64)	Clyde Milan	45.00	22.00	13.50
(65)	Otto Miller	45.00	22.00	13.50
(66)	Pat Moran	45.00	22.00	13.50
(67)	Ray Morgan	45.00	22.00	13.50
(68)	Guy Morton	45.00	22.00	13.50
(69)	Eddie Murphy	45.00	22.00	13.50
(70)	Rube Oldring	45.00	22.00	13.50
(71)	Dode Paskert	45.00	22.00	13.50
(72)	Wally Pipp	50.00	25.00	15.00
(73)	Pants Rowland	45.00	22.00	13.50
(74)	Nap Rucker	45.00	22.00	13.50
(75)	Dick Rudolph	45.00	22.00	13.50
(76)	Reb Russell	45.00	22.00	13.50
(77)	Vic Saier	45.00	22.00	13.50
(78)	Slim Sallee	45.00	22.00	13.50
(79)	Ray Schalk	75.00	37.00	22.00
(80)	Wally Schang	45.00	22.00	13.50
(81)	Wildfire Schulte	45.00	22.00	13.50
(82)	Jim Scott	45.00	22.00	13.50
(83)	George Sisler	75.00	37.00	22.00
(84)	George Stallings	45.00	22.00	13.50
(85)	Oscar Stanage	45.00	22.00	13.50
(86)	Jeff Tesreau	45.00	22.00	13.50
(87)	Joe Tinker	75.00	37.00	22.00
(88)	Lefty Tyler	45.00	22.00	13.50
(89)	Hippo Vaughn	45.00	22.00	13.50
(90)	Bobby Veach	45.00	22.00	13.50
(91)	Honus Wagner	325.00	162.00	97.00
(92)	Ed Walsh	75.00	37.00	22.00
(93)	Buck Weaver	80.00	40.00	24.00
(94)	Ivy Wingo	45.00	22.00	13.50
(95)	Joe Wood	45.00	22.00	13.50
(96)	Halph Young	45.00	22.00	13.50
(97)	Heinie Zimmerman	45.00	22.00	13.50

1936 - 37 BF3 Felt Pennants

The checklist for this obscure set of felt pennants issued circa 1936-1937 is not complete, and new examples are still being reported. The pennants do not carry any manufacturer's name and their method of distribution is not certain, although it is believed they were issued as a premium with candy

or gum. The pennants vary in size slightly but generally measure approximately 2-1/2" by 4-1/2" and were issued in various styles and colors, including red, yellow, white, blue, green, purple, black and brown. Most of the printing is white, although some pennants have been found with red or black printing, and the same pennant is often found in more than one color combination. The pennants feature both individual players and teams, including some minor league clubs. Advanced collectors have categorized the BF3 pennants into the following 11 design types, depending on what elements are included on the pennant: Type I: Player's name and figure. Type II: Player's name, team nickname and figure. Type III: Player's name and team nickname. Type IV: Team nickname and figure. Type V: Team nickname with emblem. Type VI: Team nickname only. Type VII: Player's name and team nickname on two-tailed pennant displayed inside the BF3 pennant. Type VIII: Player's name, year, and team nickname on ball. Type IX: Player's name, year on ball and team nickname. Type X: Team nickname and year. Type XI: Minor league and team.

		NR MT	EX	VG
Complete set:		4000.	2000.	1250.
Common pennant:		15.00	7.50	4.50
	Type I			
(1)	Luke Appling (batting)	25.00	12.50	7.50
(2)	Wally Berger (fielding)	15.00	7.50	4.50
(3)	Zeke Bonura (fielding ground ball)	15.00	7.50	4.50
(4)	Dolph Camilli (fielding)	15.00	7.50	4.50
(5)	Ben Chapman (batting)	15.00	7.50	4.50
(6)	Mickey Cochrane (catching)	25.00	12.50	7.50
(7)	Rip Collins (batting)	15.00	7.50	4.50
(8)	Joe Cronin (batting)	25.00	12.50	7.50
(9)	Kiki Cuyler (running)	25.00	12.50	7.50
(10)	Dizzy Dean (pitching)	40.00	20.00	12.50
(11)	Frank Demaree (batting)	15.00	7.50	4.50
(12)	Paul Derringer (pitching)	15.00	7.50	4.50
(13)	Bill Dickey (catching)	35.00	17.50	10.50
(14)	Jimmy Dykes (fielding)	15.00	7.50	4.50
(15)	Bob Feller (pitching)	35.00	17.50	10.50
(16)	Wes Ferrell (running)	15.00	7.50	4.50
(17)	Jimmy Foxx (batting)	35.00	17.50	10.50
(18)	Larry French (batting)	15.00	7.50	4.50
(19)	Franky Frisch (running)	25.00	12.50	7.50
(20)	Lou Gehrig (fielding at 1st base)	150.00	75.00	45.00
(21)	Charles Gehringer (running)	25.00	12.50	7.50
(22)	Lefty Gomez (pitching)	25.00	12.50	7.50
(23)	Goose Goslin (batting)	25.00	12.50	7.50
(24)	Hank Greenberg (fielding)	25.00	12.50	7.50
(25)	Charlie Grimm (running)	18.00	9.00	5.50
(26)	Lefty Grove (pitching)	25.00	12.50	7.50
(27)	Gabby Hartnett (catching)	25.00	12.50	7.50
(28)	Rollie Hemsley (catching)	15.00	7.50	4.50
(29)	Billy Herman (fielding at 1st base)	25.00	12.50	7.50
(30)	Frank Higgins (fielding)	15.00	7.50	4.50
(31)	Rogers Hornsby (batting)	25.00	12.50	7.50
(32)	Carl Hubbell (pitching)	25.00	12.50	7.50
(33)	Chuck Klein (throwing)	25.00	12.50	7.50
(34)	Tony Lazzeri (batting)	25.00	12.50	7.50
(35)	Hank Leiber (fielding ground ball)	15.00	7.50	4.50
(36)	Ernie Lombardi (catching)	25.00	12.50	7.50
(37)	Al Lopez (throwing)	25.00	12.50	7.50
(38)	Gus Mancuso (running)	15.00	7.50	4.50
(39)	Heinie Manush (batting)	25.00	12.50	7.50
(40)	Pepper Martin (batting)	18.00	9.00	5.50
(41)	Joe McCarthy (kneeling)	25.00	12.50	7.50
(42)	Wally Moses (running)	15.00	7.50	4.50
(43)	Van Mungo (standing)	15.00	7.50	4.50
(44)	Mel Ott (throwing)	35.00	17.50	10.50
(45)	Schoolboy Rowe (pitching)	18.00	9.00	5.50
(46)	Babe Ruth (batting)	250.00	125.00	75.00
(47)	George Selkirk (batting)	15.00	7.50	4.50
(48)	Luke Sewell (sliding)	15.00	7.50	4.50
(49)	Joe Stripp (batting)	15.00	7.50	4.50
(50)	Hal Trosky (fielding)	15.00	7.50	4.50
(51)	Floyd Vaughan (running, script signature)	25.00	12.50	7.50
(52)	Floyd Vaughan (running, not script signature)	25.00	12.50	7.50
(53)	Paul Waner (batting)	25.00	12.50	7.50
(54)	Lon Warneke (pitching)	15.00	7.50	4.50
(55)	Jimmy Wilson (fielding ground ball)	15.00	7.50	4.50
(56)	Joe Vosmik (running)	15.00	7.50	4.50
	Type II			
(1)	Luke Appling (batting)	25.00	12.50	7.50
(2)	Zeke Bonura (batting)	15.00	7.50	4.50
(3)	Dolph Camilli (batting)	15.00	7.50	4.50
(4)	Dizzy Dean (batting)	40.00	20.00	12.50
(5)	Frank Demaree (batting)	15.00	7.50	4.50
(6)	Bob Feller (pitching)	40.00	20.00	12.50
(7)	Wes Ferrell (throwing)	15.00	7.50	4.50
(8)	Frank Frisch (fielding)	25.00	12.50	7.50
(9)	Lou Gehrig (batting)	90.00	45.00	27.50
(10)	Lou Gehrig (fielding)	90.00	45.00	27.50
(11)	Hank Greenberg (throwing)	25.00	12.50	7.50
(12)	Charlie Grimm (fielding)	18.00	9.00	5.50
(13)	Charlie Grimm (throwing)	18.00	9.00	5.50
(14)	Lefty Grove (pitching)	25.00	12.50	7.50
(15)	Gabby Hartnett (batting)	25.00	12.50	7.50
(16)	Billy Herman (batting)	25.00	12.50	7.50
(17)	Tony Lazzeri (running)	25.00	12.50	7.50
(18)	Tony Lazzeri (throwing)	25.00	12.50	7.50
(19)	Hank Leiber (batting)	15.00	7.50	4.50
(20)	Ernie Lombardi (batting)	25.00	12.50	7.50
(21)	Ducky Medwick (batting)	25.00	12.50	7.50
(22)	Joe Stripp (batting)	15.00	7.50	4.50
(23)	Floyd Vaughan (batting)	25.00	12.50	7.50
(24)	Joe Vosmik (throwing)	15.00	7.50	4.50
(25)	Paul Waner (batting)	25.00	12.50	7.50
(26)	Lon Warneke (batting)	15.00	7.50	4.50
(27)	Lon Warneke (pitching)	15.00	7.50	4.50
	Type III			
(1)	Zeke Bonura	15.00	7.50	4.50
(2)	Dolph Camilli	15.00	7.50	4.50
(3)	Ben Chapman	15.00	7.50	4.50
(4)	Dizzy Dean	40.00	20.00	12.50
(5)	Bill Dickey	35.00	17.50	10.50
(6)	Joe DiMaggio (name in script)	150.00	75.00	45.00
(7)	Bob Feller (name in script)	35.00	17.50	10.50
(8)	Wes Ferrell	15.00	7.50	4.50
(9)	Lou Gehrig (name in script)	150.00	75.00	45.00
(10)	Charles Gehringer	25.00	12.50	7.50
(11)	Lefty Grove	25.00	12.50	7.50
(12)	Billy Herman (name in script)	25.00	12.50	7.50
(13)	Carl Hubbell	25.00	12.50	7.50
(14)	Chuck Klein	25.00	12.50	7.50
(15)	Tony Lazzeri	25.00	12.50	7.50
(16)	Al Lopez	25.00	12.50	7.50
(17)	Johnny Marcum	15.00	7.50	4.50
(18)	Pepper Martin	18.00	9.00	5.50
(19)	Van Lingo Mungo	15.00	7.50	4.50
(20)	Schoolboy Rowe	18.00	9.00	5.50
(21)	George Selkirk	15.00	7.50	4.50
(22)	Bill Terry	25.00	12.50	7.50
(23)	Hal Trosky	15.00	7.50	4.50
(24)	Floyd Vaughan	25.00	12.50	7.50
(25)	Lon Warneke	15.00	7.50	4.50
	Type IV			
(1)	Athletics (fielder)	15.00	7.50	4.50
(2)	Browns (catcher)	15.00	7.50	4.50
(3)	Cubs (batter)	15.00	7.50	4.50
(4)	Dodgers (batter)	15.00	7.50	4.50
(5)	Dodgers (fielder)	15.00	7.50	4.50
(6)	Giants (standing by base)	15.00	7.50	4.50
(7)	Giants (two players)	15.00	7.50	4.50
(8)	Phillies (pitcher)	15.00	7.50	4.50
(9)	Reds (batter)	15.00	7.50	4.50
(10)	Reds (pitcher)	15.00	7.50	4.50
(11)	White Sox (batter)	15.00	7.50	4.50
(12)	White Sox (catcher)	15.00	7.50	4.50
(13)	White Sox (pitcher)	15.00	7.50	4.50
(14)	Yankees (batter)	25.00	12.50	7.50
(15)	Yankees (fielding ball, from waist up)	25.00	12.50	7.50
	Type V			
(1)	Athletics (bat)	15.00	7.50	4.50
(2)	Athletics (elephant)	15.00	7.50	4.50
(3)	Bees (bee)	15.00	7.50	4.50
(4)	Browns (bat)	15.00	7.50	4.50
(5)	Cardinals (bat)	15.00	7.50	4.50
(6)	Cardinals (cardinal)	15.00	7.50	4.50
(7)	Cardinals (four birds flying)	15.00	7.50	4.50
(8)	Cubs (cub)	15.00	7.50	4.50
(9)	Cubs (cub's head)	15.00	7.50	4.50
(10)	Dodgers (ball, bat and glove)	15.00	7.50	4.50
(11)	Dodgers (ball)	15.00	7.50	4.50
(12)	Indians (Indian)	15.00	7.50	4.50
(13)	Indians (Indian's head)	15.00	7.50	4.50
(14)	Indians (Indian's head with hat)	15.00	7.50	4.50
(15)	Phillies (Liberty Bell)	15.00	7.50	4.50
(16)	Pirates (skull and crossbones)	15.00	7.50	4.50
(17)	Red Sox (ball and bat)	15.00	7.50	4.50
(18)	Red Sox (bat)	15.00	7.50	4.50
(19)	Reds (ball)	15.00	7.50	4.50
(20)	Senators (bat)	15.00	7.50	4.50
(21)	Senators (Capitol building)	15.00	7.50	4.50
(22)	Tigers (cap)	15.00	7.50	4.50
(23)	Tigers (tiger)	15.00	7.50	4.50
	Type VI			
(1)	Cardinals	15.00	7.50	4.50
(2)	Cubs	15.00	7.50	4.50
(3)	Dodgers	15.00	7.50	4.50
(4)	Giants	15.00	7.50	4.50
(5)	Indians	15.00	7.50	4.50
(6)	Phillies (Phillies on spine)	15.00	7.50	4.50
(7)	Pirates (Pirates on spine)	15.00	7.50	4.50
(8)	Pirates (no Pirates on spine)	15.00	7.50	4.50
(9)	Yankees	25.00	12.50	7.50
	Type VII			
(1)	Earl Grace	15.00	7.50	4.50
(2)	Al Lopez	25.00	12.50	7.50
	Type VIII			
(1)	Larry French	15.00	7.50	4.50
	Type IX			
(1)	Clay Bryant	15.00	7.50	4.50
(2)	Tex Carleton	15.00	7.50	4.50
(3)	Phil Cavaretta (Cavarretta)	15.00	7.50	4.50
(4)	Irving Cherry	15.00	7.50	4.50
(5)	Ripper Collins	15.00	7.50	4.50
(6)	Curt Davis	15.00	7.50	4.50
(7)	Vince DiMaggio	20.00	10.00	6.00
(8)	Frank Demaree	15.00	7.50	4.50
(9)	Wes Flowers	15.00	7.50	4.50
(10)	Larry French	15.00	7.50	4.50
(11)	Linus Frey	15.00	7.50	4.50
(12)	Augie Galan	15.00	7.50	4.50
(13)	Charlie Grimm	18.00	9.00	5.50

		NR MT	EX	VG
(14)	Stan Hack	15.00	7.50	4.50
(15)	Gabby Hartnett	25.00	12.50	7.50
(16)	Billy Herman	25.00	12.50	7.50
(17)	Walt Higbee	15.00	7.50	4.50
(18)	Billy Jurges	15.00	7.50	4.50
(19)	Andy Lotshaw	15.00	7.50	4.50
(20)	Henry Majeski	15.00	7.50	4.50
(21)	Joe Marty	15.00	7.50	4.50
(22)	Tony Piet	15.00	7.50	4.50
(23)	Chas. Root	15.00	7.50	4.50
(24)	Tuck Stainback	15.00	7.50	4.50
	Type X			
(1)	Yankees (1936 Champions)	25.00	12.50	7.50
	Type XI			
(1)	Barons (Southern Association)	15.00	7.50	4.50
(2)	Bears (International League)	15.00	7.50	4.50
(3)	Blues (American Association)	15.00	7.50	4.50
(4)	Brewers (American Association)	15.00	7.50	4.50
(5)	Chicks (Southern Association)	15.00	7.50	4.50
(6)	Colonels (American Association)	15.00	7.50	4.50
(7)	Giants (International League)	15.00	7.50	4.50
(8)	Maple Leafs (International League)	15.00	7.50	4.50
(9)	Millers (American Association)	15.00	7.50	4.50
(10)	Mud Hens (American Association)	15.00	7.50	4.50
(11)	Orioles (International League)	15.00	7.50	4.50
(12)	Red Birds (American Association)	15.00	7.50	4.50
(13)	Saints (American Association)	15.00	7.50	4.50
(14)	Smokies (Southern Association)	15.00	7.50	4.50
(15)	Travelers (Southern Association)	15.00	7.50	4.50

1949 Baas Cheri-Cola

Only five of these premium issues have ever been cataloged so it's unknown how many comprise a set. The 7-5/8" x 9-1/2" pictures feature black-and-white player photos on front, with the player's name printed in white script. On back, printed in red, is an ad for Baas Cheri-Cola Drink. The unnumbered pictures are checklisted in alphabetical order.

		NR MT	EX	VG
	Common player:	75.00	37.00	22.00
(1)	Bobby Doerr	100.00	50.00	30.00
(2)	Bob Feller	150.00	75.00	45.00
(3)	Ken Keltner	75.00	37.00	22.00
(4)	John Sain	75.00	37.00	22.00
(5)	Ted Williams	300.00	150.00	90.00

1948 Babe Ruth Story

The Philadelphia Gum Co., in 1948, created a card set about the movie "The Babe Ruth Story", which starred William Bendix and Claire Trevor. The set, whose American Card Catalog designation is R421, contains 28 black and white, numbered cards which measure 2" by 2-1/2". The Babe Ruth Story set was originally intended to consist of sixteen cards. Twelve additional cards (#'s 17-28) were added when Ruth died before the release of the film. The card backs include a offer for an autographed photo of William Bendix, starring as the Babe, for five Swell Bubble Gum wrappers and five cents.

		NR MT	EX	VG
	Complete Set:	1200.	600.00	360.00
	Common Player: 1-16	16.00	8.00	4.75
	Common Player: 17-28	55.00	27.00	16.50
1	"The Babe Ruth Story" In The Making	100.00	50.00	30.00
2	Bat Boy Becomes the Babe... William Bendix	16.00	8.00	4.75
3	Claire Hodgson...Claire Trevor	16.00	8.00	4.75
4	Babe Ruth and Claire Hodgson	16.00	8.00	4.75
5	Brother Matthias...Charles Bickford	16.00	8.00	4.75
6	Phil Conrad...Sam Levene	16.00	8.00	4.75
7	Night Club Singer...Gertrude Niesen	16.00	8.00	4.75
8	Baseball's Famous Deal...Jack Dunn (William Frawley)	16.00	8.00	4.75
9	Mr. & Mrs. Babe Ruth	16.00	8.00	4.75
10	Babe Ruth, Claire Ruth, and Brother Matthias	16.00	8.00	4.75
11	Babe Ruth and Miller Huggins (Fred Lightner)	16.00	8.00	4.75
12	Babe Ruth At Bed Of Ill Boy Johnny Sylvester (Gregory Marshall)	16.00	8.00	4.75
13	Sylvester Family Listening To Game	16.00	8.00	4.75
14	"When A Feller Needs a Friend" (With Dog At Police Station)	16.00	8.00	4.75
15	Dramatic Home Run	16.00	8.00	4.75
16	The Homer That Set the Record (#60)	16.00	8.00	4.75
17	"The Slap That Started Baseball's Famous Career"	55.00	27.00	16.50
18	The Babe Plays Santa Claus	55.00	27.00	16.50
19	Meeting Of Owner And Manager	55.00	27.00	16.50
20	"Broken Window Paid Off"	55.00	27.00	16.50
21	Babe In A Crowd Of Autograph Collectors	55.00	27.00	16.50
22	Charley Grimm And William Bendix	55.00	27.00	16.50
23	Ted Lyons And William Bendix	70.00	35.00	21.00
24	Lefty Gomez, William Bendix, And Bucky Harris	70.00	35.00	21.00
25	Babe Ruth and William Bendix	160.00	80.00	48.00
26	Babe Ruth And William Bendix	160.00	80.00	48.00
27	Babe Ruth And Claire Trevor	160.00	80.00	48.00
28	William Bendix, Babe Ruth, And Claire Trevor	160.00	80.00	48.00

1986 Baltimore Orioles Team Issue

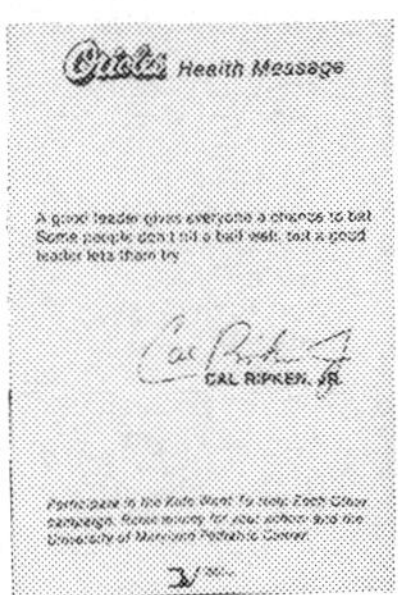

		MT	NR MT	EX
	Complete Set:	15.00	11.00	6.00
	Common Player:	.15	.11	.06
(1)	Don Aase	.15	.11	.06
(2a)	Mike Boddicker (message begins "I always...")	.20	.15	.08
(2b)	Mike Boddicker (message begins "They call...")	.20	.15	.08
(3)	Storm Davis	.20	.15	.08
(4a)	Rick Dempsey (message begins "I always...")	.15	.11	.06
(4b)	Rick Dempsey (message begins "In baseball...")	.15	.11	.06
(5)	Ken Dixon	.15	.11	.06
(6)	Jim Dwyer	.15	.11	.06
(7a)	Mike Flanagan (message begins "I know...")	.20	.15	.08
(7b)	Mike Flanagan (message begins "It's a...")	.20	.15	.08
(8)	Lee Lacy	.15	.11	.06
(9a)	Fred Lynn (message begins "I need...")	.35	.25	.14
(9b)	Fred Lynn (message begins "There are...")	.35	.25	.14
(10a)	Dennis Martinez	.60	.45	.25
(11)	Tippy Martinez	.15	.11	.06
(12)	Scott McGregor	.20	.15	.08
(13a)	Eddie Murray (message begins "Do you...")	1.25	.90	.50
(13b)	Eddie Murray (message begins "During my...")	1.25	.90	.50
(13c)	Eddie Murray (message begins "You can't...")	1.25	.90	.50
(14a)	Floyd Rayford (message begins "I always...")	.15	.11	.06
(14b)	Floyd Rayford (message begins "I had...")	.15	.11	.06
(15)	Cal Ripken, Jr. (message begins "A good...")	4.00	3.00	1.50
(15b)	Cal Ripken, Jr. (message begins "Drinking ...")	4.00	3.00	1.50
(15c)	Cal Ripken, Jr. (message begins "To hit...")	4.00	3.00	1.50
(16a)	Larry Sheets (message begins "As a...")	.15	.11	.06
(16b)	Larry Sheets (message begins "There is...")	.15	.11	.06
(17)	John Shelby	.15	.11	.06
(18)	Earl Weaver	.35	.25	.14
(19)	Alan Wiggins	.15	.11	.06
(20)	Mike Young	.15	.11	.06

1913 Tom Barker Game

Nearly identical in format to "The National Game" card set, this issue features a different back design of a red-and-white line art representation of a batter. Fronts of the round-cornered, 2-1/2" x 3-1/2" cards have a black-and-white player photo, or game action photo, along with two game scenarios used when playing the card game. There are nine action photos in the set. Player cards are checklisted here alphabetically.

		NR MT	EX	VG
	Complete set:	3000.	1500.	900.00
	Common player:	30.00	15.00	9.00
	Action Photo card:	15.00	7.50	4.50
(1)	Grover Alexander	100.00	50.00	30.00
(2)	Chief Bender	60.00	30.00	18.00
(3)	Bob Bescher	30.00	15.00	9.00
(4)	Joe Birmingham	30.00	15.00	9.00
(5)	Roger Bresnahan	60.00	30.00	18.00
(6)	Nixey Callahan	30.00	15.00	9.00
(7)	Bill Carrigan	30.00	15.00	9.00
(8)	Frank Chance	60.00	30.00	18.00
(9)	Hal Chase	45.00	22.00	13.50
(10)	Fred Clarke	60.00	30.00	18.00
(11)	Ty Cobb	600.00	300.00	180.00
(12)	Sam Crawford	60.00	30.00	18.00
(13)	Jake Daubert	30.00	15.00	9.00
(14)	Red Dooin	30.00	15.00	9.00
(15)	Johnny Evers	60.00	30.00	18.00
(16)	Vean Gregg	30.00	15.00	9.00
(17)	Clark Griffith	60.00	30.00	18.00
(18)	Dick Hoblitzel	30.00	15.00	9.00
(19)	Miller Huggins	60.00	30.00	18.00
(20)	Joe Jackson	800.00	400.00	240.00
(21)	Hughie Jennings	60.00	30.00	18.00
(22)	Walter Johnson	150.00	75.00	45.00
(23)	Ed Konetchy	30.00	15.00	9.00
(24)	Nap Lajoie	75.00	37.00	22.00
(25)	Connie Mack	75.00	37.00	22.00
(26)	Rube Marquard	60.00	30.00	18.00
(27)	Christy Mathewson	150.00	75.00	45.00
(28)	John McGraw	60.00	30.00	18.00
(29)	Chief Meyers	30.00	15.00	9.00
(30)	Clyde Milan	30.00	15.00	9.00
(31)	Marty O'Toole	30.00	15.00	9.00
(32)	Nap Rucker	30.00	15.00	9.00
(33)	Tris Speaker	100.00	50.00	30.00
(34)	George Stallings	30.00	15.00	9.00
(35)	Bill Sweeney	30.00	15.00	9.00
(36)	Joe Tinker	60.00	30.00	18.00
(37)	Honus Wagner	100.00	50.00	30.00
(38)	Ed Walsh	60.00	30.00	18.00
(39)	Zach Wheat	60.00	30.00	18.00
(40)	Ivy Wingo	30.00	15.00	9.00
(41)	Joe Wood	30.00	15.00	9.00
(42)	Cy Young	100.00	50.00	30.00
(43)	Rules card	40.00	20.00	12.00
(44)	Score card	40.00	20.00	12.00
(1A)	Batter swinging, looking forward	15.00	7.50	4.50
(2A)	Batter swinging, looking back	15.00	7.50	4.50
(3A)	Runner sliding, fielder at bag	15.00	7.50	4.50
(4A)	Runner sliding, umpire behind	15.00	7.50	4.50
(5A)	Runner sliding, hugging base	15.00	7.50	4.50
(6A)	Sliding into home, umpire at left	15.00	7.50	4.50
(7A)	Sliding into home, umpire at right	15.00	7.50	4.50
(8A)	Play at home, runner standing	15.00	7.50	4.50
(9A)	Runner looking backwards	15.00	7.50	4.50

A card number in parentheses () indicates the set is unnumbered.

1911 Baseball Bats

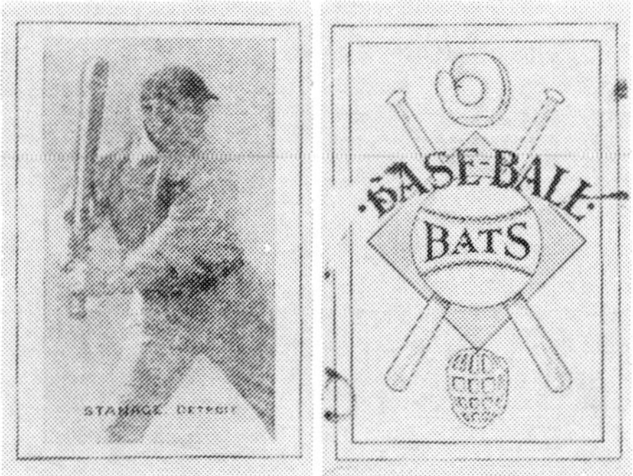

Issued circa 1911, cards in this rare 47-card issue were printed on the back panel of "Baseball Bats" penny candy. The cards themselves measure approximately 1-3/8" x 2-3/8" and feature a black-and-white player photo surrounded by an orange or white border player's name and team are printed in small, black capital letters near the bottom of the photo.

		NR MT	EX	VG
Complete Set:		8000.	4000.	2400.
Common Player:		100.00	50.00	30.00
(1)	Red Ames	100.00	50.00	30.00
(2)	Home Run Baker	175.00	87.00	52.00
(3)	Jack Barry	100.00	50.00	30.00
(4)	Ginger Beaumont	100.00	50.00	30.00
(5)	Chief Bender	175.00	87.00	52.00
(6)	Al Bridwell	100.00	50.00	30.00
(7)	Mordecai Brown	175.00	87.00	52.00
(8)	Bill Corrigan (Carrigan)	100.00	50.00	30.00
(9)	Frank Chance	175.00	87.00	52.00
(10)	Hal Chase	125.00	62.00	37.00
(11)	Ed Cicotte	125.00	62.00	37.00
(12)	Fred Clark (Clarke)	175.00	87.00	52.00
(13)	Ty Cobb	800.00	400.00	240.00
(14)	King Cole	100.00	50.00	30.00
(15)	Eddie Collins	200.00	100.00	60.00
(16)	Sam Crawford	175.00	87.00	52.00
(17)	Lou Criger	100.00	50.00	30.00
(18)	Harry Davis	100.00	50.00	30.00
(19)	Jim Delehanty	100.00	50.00	30.00
(20)	Art Devlin	100.00	50.00	30.00
(21)	Josh Devore	100.00	50.00	30.00
(22)	Wild Bill Donovan	100.00	50.00	30.00
(23)	Larry Doyle	110.00	55.00	33.00
(24)	Johnny Evers	175.00	87.00	52.00
(25)	John Flynn	100.00	50.00	30.00
(26)	George Gibson	175.00	87.00	52.00
(27)	Solly Hoffman (Hofman)	100.00	50.00	30.00
(28)	Walter Johnson	400.00	200.00	120.00
(29)	Johnny Kling	100.00	50.00	30.00
(30)	Nap Lajoie	250.00	125.00	75.00
(31)	Matty McIntyre	100.00	50.00	30.00
(32)	Fred Merkle	110.00	55.00	33.00
(33)	Tom Needham	100.00	50.00	30.00
(34)	Rube Oldring	100.00	50.00	30.00
(35)	Wildfire Schulte	100.00	50.00	30.00
(36)	Cy Seymour	100.00	50.00	30.00
(37)	Jimmy Sheckard	100.00	50.00	30.00
(38)	Tris Speaker	250.00	125.00	75.00
(39)	Oscar Stanage (batting - front view)	100.00	50.00	30.00
(40)	Oscar Stanage (batting - side view)	100.00	50.00	30.00
(41)	Ira Thomas	100.00	50.00	30.00
(42)	Joe Tinker	175.00	87.00	52.00
(43)	Heinie Wagner	100.00	50.00	30.00
(44)	Honus Wagner	400.00	200.00	120.00
(45)	Ed Walsh	175.00	87.00	52.00
(46)	Art Wilson	100.00	50.00	30.00
(47)	Owen Wilson	100.00	50.00	30.00

1988 Baseball Immortals

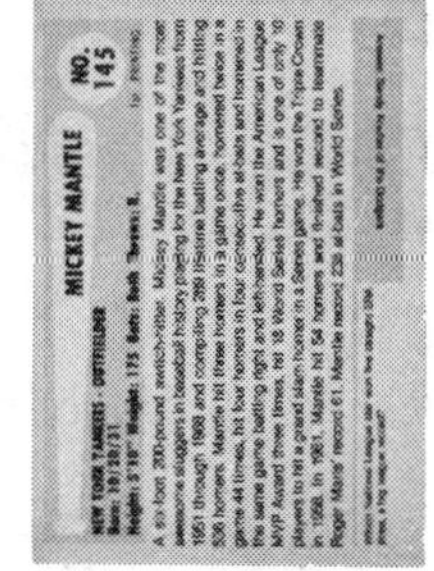

One of the most popular of the "collectors' issues," this set is produced with the permission of Major League Baseball by Renata Galasso Inc. and TCMA. The set features players in the Baseball Hall of Fame and was first issued in 1980. For several years thereafter the set was updated to include new inductees. The cards measure 2-1/2" by 3-1/2" and have colorful borders. The card fronts include the player's name, position and year of induction. The backs feature a short biography and a trivia question. The photos used are color; most players who were active before 1950 have colored black-and-white photos. The designation "first printing" appears on all cards issued in 1981 and after.

		MT	NR MT	EX
Complete Set:		18.00	13.50	7.25
Common Player:		.05	.04	.02
1	Babe Ruth	.35	.25	.14
2	Ty Cobb	.25	.20	.10
3	Walter Johnson	.10	.08	.04
4	Christy Mathewson	.10	.08	.04
5	Honus Wagner	.10	.08	.04
6	Morgan Bulkeley	.05	.04	.02
7	Ban Johnson	.05	.04	.02
8	Larry Lajoie	.07	.05	.03
9	Connie Mack	.07	.05	.03
10	John McGraw	.07	.05	.03
11	Tris Speaker	.07	.05	.03
12	George Wright	.05	.04	.02
13	Cy Young	.08	.06	.04
14	Grover Alexander	.07	.05	.03
15	Alexander Cartwright	.05	.04	.02
16	Henry Chadwick	.05	.04	.02
17	Cap Anson	.07	.05	.03
18	Eddie Collins	.07	.05	.03
19	Charles Comiskey	.05	.04	.02
20	Candy Cummings	.05	.04	.02
21	Buck Ewing	.05	.04	.02
22	Lou Gehrig	.25	.20	.10
23	Willie Keeler	.05	.04	.02
24	Hoss Radbourne	.05	.04	.02
25	George Sisler	.07	.05	.03
26	Albert Spalding	.05	.04	.02
27	Rogers Hornsby	.10	.08	.04
28	Judge Landis	.05	.04	.02
29	Roger Bresnahan	.05	.04	.02
30	Dan Brouthers	.05	.04	.02
31	Fred Clarke	.05	.04	.02
32	James Collins	.05	.04	.02
33	Ed Delahanty	.05	.04	.02
34	Hugh Duffy	.05	.04	.02
35	Hughie Jennings	.05	.04	.02
36	Mike "King" Kelly	.05	.04	.02
37	James O'Rourke	.05	.04	.02
38	Wilbert Robinson	.05	.04	.02
39	Jesse Burkett	.05	.04	.02
40	Frank Chance	.05	.04	.02
41	Jack Chesbro	.05	.04	.02
42	John Evers	.05	.04	.02
43	Clark Griffith	.05	.04	.02
44	Thomas McCarthy	.05	.04	.02
45	Joe McGinnity	.05	.04	.02
46	Eddie Plank	.05	.04	.02
47	Joe Tinker	.05	.04	.02
48	Rube Waddell	.05	.04	.02
49	Ed Walsh	.05	.04	.02
50	Mickey Cochrane	.07	.05	.03
51	Frankie Frisch	.05	.04	.02
52	Lefty Grove	.07	.05	.03
53	Carl Hubbell	.07	.05	.03
54	Herb Pennock	.05	.04	.02
55	Pie Traynor	.05	.04	.02
56	Three Finger Brown	.05	.04	.02
57	Charlie Gehringer	.07	.05	.03
58	Kid Nichols	.05	.04	.02
59	Jimmie Foxx	.10	.08	.04
60	Mel Ott	.07	.05	.03
61	Harry Heilmann	.05	.04	.02
62	Paul Waner	.05	.04	.02
63	Ed Barrow	.05	.04	.02
64	Chief Bender	.05	.04	.02
65	Tom Connolly	.05	.04	.02
66	Dizzy Dean	.10	.08	.04
67	Bill Klem	.05	.04	.02
68	Al Simmons	.05	.04	.02
69	Bobby Wallace	.05	.04	.02
70	Harry Wright	.05	.04	.02
71	Bill Dickey	.07	.05	.03
72	Rabbit Maranville	.05	.04	.02
73	Bill Terry	.07	.05	.03
74	Home Run Baker	.05	.04	.02
75	Joe DiMaggio	.15	.11	.06
76	Gabby Hartnett	.05	.04	.02
77	Ted Lyons	.05	.04	.02
78	Ray Schalk	.05	.04	.02
79	Dazzy Vance	.05	.04	.02
80	Joe Cronin	.07	.05	.03
81	Hank Greenberg	.07	.05	.03
82	Sam Crawford	.05	.04	.02
83	Joe McCarthy	.05	.04	.02
84	Zack Wheat	.05	.04	.02
85	Max Carey	.05	.04	.02
86	Billy Hamilton	.05	.04	.02
87	Bob Feller	.10	.08	.04
88	Bill McKechnie	.05	.04	.02
89	Jackie Robinson	.15	.11	.06
90	Edd Roush	.05	.04	.02
91	John Clarkson	.05	.04	.02
92	Elmer Flick	.05	.04	.02
93	Sam Rice	.05	.04	.02
94	Eppa Rixey	.05	.04	.02
95	Luke Appling	.05	.04	.02
96	Red Faber	.05	.04	.02
97	Burleigh Grimes	.05	.04	.02
98	Miller Huggins	.05	.04	.02
99	Tim Keefe	.05	.04	.02
100	Heinie Manush	.05	.04	.02
101	John Ward	.05	.04	.02
102	Pud Galvin	.05	.04	.02
103	Casey Stengel	.10	.08	.04
104	Ted Williams	.15	.11	.06
105	Branch Rickey	.05	.04	.02
106	Red Ruffing	.05	.04	.02
107	Lloyd Waner	.05	.04	.02
108	Kiki Cuyler	.05	.04	.02
109	Goose Goslin	.05	.04	.02
110	Joe (Ducky) Medwick	.05	.04	.02
111	Roy Campanella	.10	.08	.04
112	Stan Coveleski	.05	.04	.02
113	Waite Hoyt	.05	.04	.02
114	Stan Musial	.15	.11	.06
115	Lou Boudreau	.05	.04	.02
116	Earle Combs	.05	.04	.02
117	Ford Frick	.05	.04	.02
118	Jesse Haines	.05	.04	.02
119	Dave Bancroft	.05	.04	.02
120	Jake Beckley	.05	.04	.02
121	Chick Hafey	.05	.04	.02
122	Harry Hooper	.05	.04	.02
123	Joe Kelley	.05	.04	.02
124	Rube Marquard	.05	.04	.02
125	Satchel Paige	.07	.05	.03
126	George Weiss	.05	.04	.02
127	Yogi Berra	.10	.08	.04
128	Josh Gibson	.05	.04	.02
129	Lefty Gomez	.07	.05	.03
130	Will Harridge	.05	.04	.02
131	Sandy Koufax	.10	.08	.04
132	Buck Leonard	.05	.04	.02
133	Early Wynn	.05	.04	.02
134	Ross Youngs	.05	.04	.02
135	Roberto Clemente	.15	.11	.06
136	Billy Evans	.05	.04	.02
137	Monte Irvin	.05	.04	.02
138	George Kelly	.05	.04	.02
139	Warren Spahn	.10	.08	.04
140	Mickey Welch	.05	.04	.02
141	Cool Papa Bell	.05	.04	.02
142	Jim Bottomley	.05	.04	.02
143	Jocko Conlan	.05	.04	.02
144	Whitey Ford	.05	.04	.02
145	Mickey Mantle	.25	.20	.10
146	Sam Thompson	.05	.04	.02
147	Earl Averill	.05	.04	.02
148	Bucky Harris	.05	.04	.02
149	Billy Herman	.05	.04	.02
150	Judy Johnson	.05	.04	.02
151	Ralph Kiner	.07	.05	.03
152	Oscar Charleston	.05	.04	.02
153	Roger Connor	.05	.04	.02
154	Cal Hubbard	.05	.04	.02
155	Bob Lemon	.05	.04	.02
156	Fred Lindstrom	.05	.04	.02
157	Robin Roberts	.05	.04	.02
158	Ernie Banks	.07	.05	.03
159	Martin Dihigo	.05	.04	.02
160	John Henry Lloyd	.05	.04	.02
161	Al Lopez	.05	.04	.02
162	Amos Rusie	.05	.04	.02
163	Joe Sewell	.05	.04	.02
164	Addie Joss	.05	.04	.02
165	Larry MacPhail	.05	.04	.02
166	Eddie Mathews	.05	.04	.02
167	Warren Giles	.05	.04	.02
168	Willie Mays	.25	.20	.10
169	Hack Wilson	.05	.04	.02
170	Duke Snider	.10	.08	.04
171	Al Kaline	.07	.05	.03
172	Chuck Klein	.05	.04	.02
173	Tom Yawkey	.05	.04	.02
174	Bob Gibson	.07	.05	.03
175	Rube Foster	.05	.04	.02
176	Johnny Mize	.05	.04	.02
177	Hank Aaron	.25	.20	.10
178	Frank Robinson	.07	.05	.03
179	Happy Chandler	.05	.04	.02
180	Travis Jackson	.05	.04	.02
181	Brooks Robinson	.07	.05	.03
182	Juan Marichal	.05	.04	.02
183	George Kell	.05	.04	.02
184	Walter Alston	.05	.04	.02
185	Harmon Killebrew	.07	.05	.03
186	Luis Aparicio	.05	.04	.02
187	Don Drysdale	.07	.05	.03
188	Pee Wee Reese	.07	.05	.03
189	Rick Ferrell	.05	.04	.02
190	Willie McCovey	.07	.05	.03
191	Ernie Lombardi	.05	.04	.02
192	Bobby Doerr	.05	.04	.02
193	Arky Vaughan	.05	.04	.02
194	Enos Slaughter	.05	.04	.02
195	Lou Brock	.07	.05	.03
196	Hoyt Wilhelm	.05	.04	.02
197	Billy Williams	.05	.04	.02
198	"Catfish" Hunter	.05	.04	.02
199	Ray Dandridge	.05	.04	.02

1987 Baseball Super Stars Discs

Produced by Mike Schecter and Associates, the "Baseball Super Stars" disc set was released as part of a promotion for various brands of iced tea mixes in many parts of the country. Among the brands participating in the promotion were Acme, Alpha Beta, Bustelo, Key, King Kullen, Lady Lee, Our Own and Weis. The discs were issued in three-part folding panels with each disc measuring 2-1/2" in diameter. The disc fronts feature a full-color photo inside a bright yellow border. Two player discs were included

in each panel along with a coupon disc offering either an uncut press sheet of the set or a facsimile autographed ball.

		MT	NR MT	EX
Complete Panel Set:		10.00	7.50	4.00
Complete Singles Set:		5.00	3.75	2.00
Common Panel:		.25	.20	.10
Common Single Player:		.05	.04	.02
	Panel	1.00	.70	.40
1	Darryl Strawberry	.10	.08	.04
2	Roger Clemens	.40	.30	.15
	Panel	.35	.25	.14
3	Ron Darling	.05	.04	.02
4	Keith Hernandez	.10	.08	.04
	Panel	1.00	.70	.40
5	Tony Pena	.05	.04	.02
6	Don Mattingly	.70	.50	.30
	Panel	1.00	.70	.40
7	Eric Davis	.35	.25	.14
8	Gary Carter	.10	.08	.04
	Panel	.90	.60	.30
9	Dave Winfield	.25	.20	.10
10	Wally Joyner	.15	.11	.06
	Panel	1.00	.40	.20
11	Mike Schmidt	.50	.40	.20
12	Robby Thompson	.10	.08	.04
	Panel	1.00	.70	.40
13	Wade Boggs	.35	.25	.14
14	Cal Ripken Jr.	.50	.40	.20
	Panel	1.00	.70	.40
15	Dale Murphy	.25	.20	.10
16	Tony Gwynn	.15	.11	.06
	Panel	1.75	1.25	.70
17	Jose Canseco	.60	.45	.25
18	Rickey Henderson	.30	.25	.12
	Panel	.25	.20	.10
19	Lance Parrish	.08	.06	.03
20	Dave Righetti	.08	.06	.03

1988 Baseball Super Stars Discs

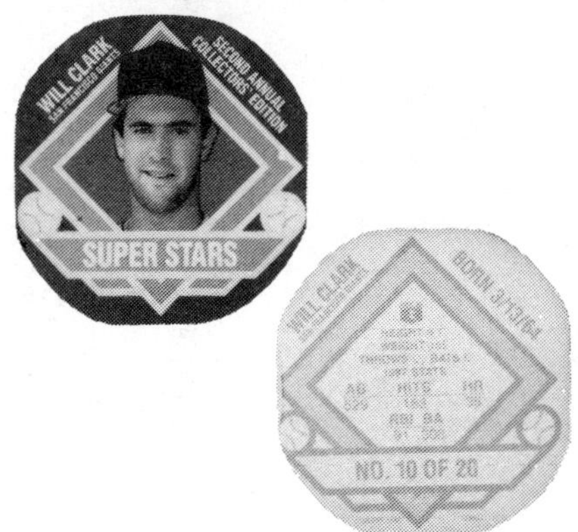

The "Second Annual Collector's Edition" of Baseball Super Stars Discs is very similar to the 1987 issue. A set of 20 discs (2-1/2" diameter) featuring full-color baseball player photos was inserted in specially marked cannisters of iced tea and fruit drinks. Each triple-fold insert consists of 2 player discs and one redemption card. Player discs are bright blue, yellow, red and green with a diamond design framing the player closeup. The player name appears upper left, the set logo appears upper right. Personalized disc series were issued for Tetley, Weis, Key Food and A&P supermarkets (untitled series were also sold at Lucky, Skaggs, Alpha Beta, Acme King Kullen, Laneco and Krasdale stores). The series name (i.e. Weis Winners) is printed below the player photo.

		MT	NR MT	EX
Complete Panel Set:		9.00	6.75	3.50
Complete Singles Set:		4.00	3.00	1.50
Common Panel:		.60	.45	.25
Common Single Player:		.05	.04	.02
	Panel	1.00	.70	.40
1	Wade Boggs	.40	.30	.15
2	Ellis Burks	.10	.08	.04
	Panel	1.00	.70	.40
3	Don Mattingly	.50	.40	.20
4	Mark McGwire	.25	.20	.10
	Panel	1.00	.50	.30
5	Matt Nokes	.10	.08	.04
6	Kirby Puckett	.40	.30	.15
	Panel	.60	.60	.30
7	Billy Ripken	.05	.04	.02
8	Kevin Seitzer	.05	.04	.02
	Panel	1.00	.70	.35
9	Roger Clemens	.30	.25	.12
10	Will Clark	.50	.40	.20
	Panel	.80	.60	.30
11	Vince Coleman	.10	.08	.04
12	Eric Davis	.20	.15	.08
	Panel	.70	.50	.30
13	Dave Magadan	.05	.04	.02
14	Dale Murphy	.25	.20	.10
	Panel	.80	.60	.30
15	Benito Santiago	.15	.11	.06
16	Mike Schmidt	.50	.40	.20
	Panel	.60	.45	.25
17	Darryl Strawberry	.10	.08	.04
18	Steve Bedrosian	.05	.04	.02
	Panel	.80	.60	.30
19	Dwight Gooden	.20	.15	.08
20	Fernando Valenzuela	.08	.06	.03

1990 Baseball Wit

This 108-card set was released in two printings. The first printing featured unnumbered cards and several errors. The second printing featured corrections and numbered cards. The set was available at several retail chains and feature trivia questions on the card backs. The set was dedicated to Little League baseball.

		MT	NR MT	EX
Complete Set:		8.00	6.00	3.25
Common Player:		.06	.05	.02
1	Orel Hershiser	.10	.08	.04
2	Tony Gwynn	.15	.11	.06
3	Mickey Mantle	.40	.30	.15
4	Willie Stargell	.15	.11	.06
5	Don Baylor	.10	.08	.04
6	Hank Aaron	.30	.25	.12
7	Don Larsen	.06	.05	.02
8	Lee Mazzilli	.06	.05	.02
9	Boog Powell	.06	.05	.02
10	Little League World Series	.06	.05	.02
11	Jose Canseco	.30	.25	.12
12	Mike Scott	.06	.05	.02
13	Bob Feller	.10	.08	.04
14	Ron Santo	.06	.05	.02
15	Mel Stottlemyre	.06	.05	.02
16	Shea Stadium	.06	.05	.02
17	Brooks Robinson	.10	.08	.04
18	Willie Mays	.30	.25	.12
19	Ernie Banks	.15	.11	.06
20	Keith Hernandez	.06	.05	.02
21	Bret Saberhagen	.06	.05	.02
22	Hall of Fame	.06	.05	.02
23	Luis Aparicio	.10	.08	.04
24	Yogi Berra	.15	.11	.06
25	Manny Mota	.06	.05	.02
26	Steve Garvey	.10	.08	.04
27	Bill Shea	.06	.05	.02
28	Fred Lynn	.06	.05	.02
29	Todd Worrell	.06	.05	.02
30	Roy Campanella	.15	.11	.06
31	Bob Gibson	.12	.09	.05
32	Gary Carter	.08	.06	.03
33	Jim Palmer	.15	.11	.06
34	Carl Yastrzemski	.12	.09	.05
35	Dwight Gooden	.10	.08	.04
36	Stan Musial	.20	.15	.08
37	Rickey Henderson	.25	.20	.10
38	Dale Murphy	.15	.11	.06
39	Mike Schmidt	.25	.20	.10
40	Gaylord Perry	.10	.08	.04
41	Ozzie Smith	.15	.11	.06
42	Reggie Jackson	.25	.20	.10
43	Steve Carlton	.15	.11	.06
44	Jim Perry	.06	.05	.02
45	Vince Coleman	.06	.05	.02
46	Tom Seaver	.20	.15	.08
47	Marty Marion	.06	.05	.02
48	Frank Robinson	.12	.09	.05
49	Joe DiMaggio	.35	.25	.14
50	Ted Williams	.30	.25	.12
51	Rollie Fingers	.12	.09	.05
52	Jackie Robinson	.30	.25	.12
53	Victor Raschi	.06	.05	.02
54	Johnny Bench	.20	.15	.08
55	Nolan Ryan	.40	.30	.15
56	Ty Cobb	.40	.30	.15
57	Harry Steinfeldt	.06	.05	.02
58	James O'Rourke	.06	.05	.02
59	John McGraw	.08	.06	.03
60	Candy Cummings	.06	.05	.02
61	Jimmie Foxx	.10	.08	.04
62	Walter Johnson	.10	.08	.04
63	1903 World Series	.06	.05	.02
64	Satchel Paige	.15	.11	.06
65	Bobby Wallace	.06	.05	.02
66	Cap Anson	.10	.08	.04
67	Hugh Duffy	.06	.05	.02
68	Buck Ewing	.06	.05	.02
69	Bobo Holloman	.06	.05	.02
70	Ed Delehanty (Delahanty)	.06	.05	.02
71	Dizzy Dean	.20	.15	.08
72	Tris Speaker	.15	.11	.06
73	Lou Gehrig	.40	.30	.15
74	Wee Willie Keeler	.06	.05	.02
75	Cal Hubbard	.06	.05	.02
76	Eddie Collins	.06	.05	.02
77	Chris Von Der Ahe	.06	.05	.02
78	Sam Crawford	.06	.05	.02
79	Cy Young	.15	.11	.06
80	Johnny Vander Meer	.06	.05	.02
81	Joey Jay	.06	.05	.02
82	Zack Wheat	.06	.05	.02
83	Jim Bottomley	.06	.05	.02
84	Honus Wagner	.20	.15	.08
85	Casey Stengel	.12	.09	.05
86	Babe Ruth	.50	.40	.20
87	John Lindemuth	.06	.05	.02
88	Max Carey	.06	.05	.02
89	Mordecai Brown	.06	.05	.02
90	1869 Red Stockings	.06	.05	.02
91	Rube Marquard	.06	.05	.02
92	Horse Radbourne	.06	.05	.02
93	Hack Wilson	.06	.05	.02
94	Lefty Grove	.08	.06	.03
95	Carl Hubbell	.08	.06	.03
96	A.J. Cartwright	.06	.05	.02
97	Rogers Hornsby	.15	.11	.06
98	Ernest Thayer	.06	.05	.02
99	Connie Mack	.12	.09	.05
100	1939 Centennial Celebration	.06	.05	.02
101	Branch Rickey	.10	.08	.04
102	Dan Brouthers	.06	.05	.02
103	First Baseball Uniform	.06	.05	.02
104	Christy Mathewson	.15	.11	.06
105	Joe Nuxhall	.06	.05	.02
106	1939 Centennial Celebration	.06	.05	.02
107	President Taft	.06	.05	.02
108	Abner Doubleday	.06	.05	.02

1934 Batter-Up

National Chicle's 192-card "Batter-Up" set was issued from 1934 through 1936. The blank-backed cards are die-cut, enabling collectors of the era to fold the top of the card over so that it could stand upright on its own support. The cards can be found in black and white or a variety of color tints. Card numbers 1-80 measure 2-3/8" by 3-1/4" in size, while the high-numbered cards (#'s 81-192) measure 1/4" smaller in width. The high-numbered cards are significantly more difficult to find than the lower numbers. The set's ACC designation is R318.

		NR MT	EX	VG
Complete Set (192):		20000.	10000.	6000.
Common Player: 1-80		60.00	30.00	18.00
Common Player: 81-192		100.00	50.00	30.00
1	Wally Berger	100.00	50.00	30.00
2	Ed Brandt	60.00	30.00	18.00
3	Al Lopez	100.00	50.00	30.00
4	Dick Bartell	60.00	30.00	18.00

5	Carl Hubbell	150.00	75.00	45.00
6	Bill Terry	150.00	75.00	45.00
7	Pepper Martin	60.00	30.00	18.00
8	Jim Bottomley	100.00	50.00	30.00
9	Tommy Bridges	60.00	30.00	18.00
10	Rick Ferrell	100.00	50.00	30.00
11	Ray Benge	60.00	30.00	18.00
12	Wes Ferrell	60.00	30.00	18.00
13	Bill Cissell	60.00	30.00	18.00
14	Pie Traynor	100.00	50.00	30.00
15	Roy Mahaffey	60.00	30.00	18.00
16	Chick Hafey	100.00	50.00	30.00
17	Lloyd Waner	100.00	50.00	30.00
18	Jack Burns	60.00	30.00	18.00
19	Buddy Myer	60.00	30.00	18.00
20	Bob Johnson	60.00	30.00	18.00
21	Arky Vaughn (Vaughan)	100.00	50.00	30.00
22	Red Rolfe	60.00	30.00	18.00
23	Lefty Gomez	185.00	92.00	55.00
24	Earl Averill	100.00	50.00	30.00
25	Mickey Cochrane	100.00	50.00	30.00
26	Van Mungo	60.00	30.00	18.00
27	Mel Ott	150.00	75.00	45.00
28	Jimmie Foxx	225.00	112.00	67.00
29	Jimmy Dykes	60.00	30.00	18.00
30	Bill Dickey	185.00	92.00	55.00
31	Lefty Grove	185.00	92.00	55.00
32	Joe Cronin	100.00	50.00	30.00
33	Frankie Frisch	150.00	75.00	45.00
34	Al Simmons	100.00	50.00	30.00
35	Rogers Hornsby	300.00	150.00	90.00
36	Ted Lyons	100.00	50.00	30.00
37	Rabbit Maranville	100.00	50.00	30.00
38	Jimmie Wilson	60.00	30.00	18.00
39	Willie Kamm	60.00	30.00	18.00
40	Bill Hallahan	60.00	30.00	18.00
41	Gus Suhr	60.00	30.00	18.00
42	Charlie Gehringer	185.00	92.00	55.00
43	Joe Heving	60.00	30.00	18.00
44	Adam Comorosky	60.00	30.00	18.00
45	Tony Lazzeri	100.00	50.00	30.00
46	Sam Leslie	60.00	30.00	18.00
47	Bob Smith	60.00	30.00	18.00
48	Willis Hudlin	60.00	30.00	18.00
49	Carl Reynolds	60.00	30.00	18.00
50	Fred Schulte	60.00	30.00	18.00
51	Cookie Lavagetto	60.00	30.00	18.00
52	Hal Schumacher	60.00	30.00	18.00
53	Doc Cramer	60.00	30.00	18.00
54	Si Johnson	60.00	30.00	18.00
55	Ollie Bejma	60.00	30.00	18.00
56	Sammy Byrd	60.00	30.00	18.00
57	Hank Greenberg	185.00	92.00	55.00
58	Bill Knickerbocker	60.00	30.00	18.00
59	Billy Urbanski	60.00	30.00	18.00
60	Ed Morgan	60.00	30.00	18.00
61	Eric McNair	60.00	30.00	18.00
62	Ben Chapman	60.00	30.00	18.00
63	Roy Johnson	60.00	30.00	18.00
64	"Dizzy" Dean	450.00	225.00	135.00
65	Zeke Bonura	60.00	30.00	18.00
66	Firpo Marberry	60.00	30.00	18.00
67	Gus Mancuso	60.00	30.00	18.00
68	Joe Vosmik	60.00	30.00	18.00
69	Earl Grace	60.00	30.00	18.00
70	Tony Piet	60.00	30.00	18.00
71	Rollie Hemsley	60.00	30.00	18.00
72	Fred Fitzsimmons	60.00	30.00	18.00
73	Hack Wilson	185.00	92.00	55.00
74	Chick Fullis	60.00	30.00	18.00
75	Fred Frankhouse	60.00	30.00	18.00
76	Ethan Allen	60.00	30.00	18.00
77	Heinie Manush	100.00	50.00	30.00
78	Rip Collins	60.00	30.00	18.00
79	Tony Cuccinello	60.00	30.00	18.00
80	Joe Kuhel	60.00	30.00	18.00
81	Thomas Bridges	100.00	50.00	30.00
82	Clinton Brown	100.00	50.00	30.00
83	Albert Blanche	100.00	50.00	30.00
84	"Boze" Berger	100.00	50.00	30.00
85	Goose Goslin	225.00	112.00	67.00
86	Vernon Gomez	450.00	225.00	135.00
87	Joe Glen (Glenn)	100.00	50.00	30.00
88	"Cy" Blanton	100.00	50.00	30.00
89	Tom Carey	100.00	50.00	30.00
90	Ralph Birkhofer	100.00	50.00	30.00
91	Frank Gabler	100.00	50.00	30.00
92	Dick Coffman	100.00	50.00	30.00
93	Ollie Bejma	100.00	50.00	30.00
94	Leroy Earl Parmalee	100.00	50.00	30.00
95	Carl Reynolds	100.00	50.00	30.00
96	Ben Cantwell	100.00	50.00	30.00
97	Curtis Davis	100.00	50.00	30.00
98	Wallace Moses, Billy Webb	100.00	50.00	30.00
99	Ray Benge	100.00	50.00	30.00
100	"Pie" Traynor	300.00	150.00	90.00
101	Phil. Cavarretta	100.00	50.00	30.00
102	"Pep" Young	100.00	50.00	30.00
103	Willis Hudlin	100.00	50.00	30.00
104	Mickey Haslin	100.00	50.00	30.00
105	Oswald Bluege	100.00	50.00	30.00
106	Paul Andrews	100.00	50.00	30.00
107	Edward A. Brandt	100.00	50.00	30.00
108	Dan Taylor	100.00	50.00	30.00
109	Thornton T. Lee	100.00	50.00	30.00
110	Hal Schumacher	100.00	50.00	30.00
111	Minter Hayes, Ted Lyons	450.00	225.00	135.00
112	Odell Hale	100.00	50.00	30.00
113	Earl Averill	225.00	112.00	67.00
114	Italo Chelini	100.00	50.00	30.00
115	Ivy Andrews, Jim Bottomley	450.00	225.00	135.00
116	Bill Walker	100.00	50.00	30.00
117	Bill Dickey	450.00	225.00	135.00
118	Gerald Walker	100.00	50.00	30.00
119	Ted Lyons	225.00	112.00	67.00
120	Elden Auker (Eldon)	100.00	50.00	30.00
121	Wild Bill Hallahan	100.00	50.00	30.00
122	Freddy Lindstrom	225.00	112.00	67.00
123	Oral C. Hildebrand	100.00	50.00	30.00
124	Luke Appling	225.00	112.00	67.00
125	"Pepper" Martin	125.00	62.00	37.00
126	Rick Ferrell	225.00	112.00	67.00
127	Ival Goodman	100.00	50.00	30.00
128	Joe Kuhel	100.00	50.00	30.00
129	Ernest Lombardi	225.00	112.00	67.00
130	Charles Gehringer	450.00	225.00	135.00
131	Van L. Mungo	100.00	50.00	30.00
132	Larry French	100.00	50.00	30.00
133	"Buddy" Myer	100.00	50.00	30.00
134	Mel Harder	100.00	50.00	30.00
135	Augie Galan	100.00	50.00	30.00
136	"Gabby" Hartnett	225.00	112.00	67.00
137	Stan Hack	100.00	50.00	30.00
138	Billy Herman	225.00	112.00	67.00
139	Bill Jurges	100.00	50.00	30.00
140	Bill Lee	100.00	50.00	30.00
141	"Zeke" Bonura	100.00	50.00	30.00
142	Tony Piet	100.00	50.00	30.00
143	Paul Dean	185.00	92.00	55.00
144	Jimmy Foxx	600.00	300.00	180.00
145	Joe Medwick	225.00	112.00	67.00
146	Rip Collins	100.00	50.00	30.00
147	Melo Almada	100.00	50.00	30.00
148	Allan Cooke	100.00	50.00	30.00
149	Moe Berg	185.00	92.00	55.00
150	Adolph Camilli	100.00	50.00	30.00
151	Oscar Melillo	100.00	50.00	30.00
152	Bruce Campbell	100.00	50.00	30.00
153	Lefty Grove	450.00	225.00	135.00
154	John Murphy	100.00	50.00	30.00
155	Luke Sewell	100.00	50.00	30.00
156	Leo Durocher	225.00	112.00	67.00
157	Lloyd Waner	225.00	112.00	67.00
158	Guy Bush	100.00	50.00	30.00
159	Jimmy Dykes	100.00	50.00	30.00
160	Steve O'Neill	100.00	50.00	30.00
161	Gen. Crowder	100.00	50.00	30.00
162	Joe Cascarella	100.00	50.00	30.00
163	"Bud" Hafey	100.00	50.00	30.00
164	"Gilly" Campbell	100.00	50.00	30.00
165	Ray Hayworth	100.00	50.00	30.00
166	Frank Demaree	100.00	50.00	30.00
167	John Babich	100.00	50.00	30.00
168	Marvin Owen	100.00	50.00	30.00
169	Ralph Kress	100.00	50.00	30.00
170	"Mule" Haas	100.00	50.00	30.00
171	Frank Higgins	100.00	50.00	30.00
172	Walter Berger	100.00	50.00	30.00
173	Frank Frisch	225.00	112.00	67.00
174	Wess Ferrell (Wes)	100.00	50.00	30.00
175	Pete Fox	100.00	50.00	30.00
176	John Vergez	100.00	50.00	30.00
177	William Rogell	100.00	50.00	30.00
178	"Don" Brennan	100.00	50.00	30.00
179	James Bottomley	225.00	112.00	67.00
180	Travis Jackson	225.00	112.00	67.00
181	Robert Rolfe	100.00	50.00	30.00
182	Frank Crosetti	225.00	112.00	67.00
183	Joe Cronin	225.00	112.00	67.00
184	"Schoolboy" Rowe	125.00	62.00	37.00
185	"Chuck" Klein	225.00	112.00	67.00
186	Lon Warneke	100.00	50.00	30.00
187	Gus Suhr	100.00	50.00	30.00
188	Ben Chapman	150.00	75.00	45.00
189	Clint. Brown	150.00	75.00	45.00
190	Paul Derringer	185.00	92.00	55.00
191	John Burns	225.00	112.00	67.00
192	John Broaca	350.00	175.00	100.00

1959 Bazooka

The 1959 Bazooka set, consisting of 23 full-color, unnumbered cards, was issued on boxes of Bazooka one-cent bubble gum. The individually wrapped pieces of Bazooka gum were produced by Topps Chewing Gum. The blank-backed cards measure 2-13/16" by 4-15/16" Nine cards were first issued, with 14 being added to the set later. The nine more plentiful cards are #'s 1, 5, 8, 9, 14, 15, 16, 17 and 22. Complete boxes would command 75 percent over the prices in the checklist that follows.

		NR MT	EX	VG
Complete Set:		8500.	4250.	2550.
Common Player:		125.00	62.00	37.00
(1a)	Hank Aaron (name in white)	650.00	325.00	195.00
(1b)	Hank Aaron (name in yellow)	650.00	325.00	195.00
(2)	Richie Ashburn	450.00	225.00	135.00
(3)	Ernie Banks	650.00	325.00	195.00
(4)	Ken Boyer	300.00	150.00	90.00
(5)	Orlando Cepeda	185.00	92.00	55.00
(6)	Bob Cerv	175.00	87.00	52.00
(7)	Rocco Colavito	500.00	250.00	150.00
(8)	Del Crandall	125.00	62.00	37.00
(9)	Jim Davenport	125.00	62.00	37.00
(10)	Don Drysdale	650.00	325.00	195.00
(11)	Nellie Fox	350.00	175.00	105.00
(12)	Jackie Jensen	250.00	125.00	75.00
(13)	Harvey Kuenn	250.00	125.00	75.00
(14)	Mickey Mantle	2000.	1000.	600.00
(15)	Willie Mays	525.00	262.00	157.00
(16)	Bill Mazeroski	150.00	75.00	45.00
(17)	Roy McMillan	125.00	62.00	37.00
(18)	Billy Pierce	175.00	87.00	52.00
(19)	Roy Sievers	175.00	87.00	52.00
(20)	Duke Snider	800.00	400.00	240.00
(21)	Gus Triandos	175.00	87.00	52.00
(22)	Bob Turley	125.00	62.00	37.00
(23)	Vic Wertz	150.00	75.00	45.00

1960 Bazooka

Three-card panels were found on the bottoms of Bazooka bubble gum boxes in 1960. The blank-backed set is comprised of 36 cards with the card number located at the bottom of each full-color card. The individual cards measure 1-13/16" by 2-3/4"; the panels measure 2-3/4" by 5-1/2" in size. Prices, in the checklist that follows, are given for complete panels and individual cards.

		NR MT	EX	VG
Complete Panel Set:		1800.	900.00	540.00
Complete Singles Set:		1200.	600.00	360.00
Common Player:		10.00	5.00	3.00
	Panel 1	100.00	50.00	30.00
1	Ernie Banks	50.00	25.00	15.00
2	Bud Daley	10.00	5.00	3.00
3	Wally Moon	10.00	5.00	3.00
	Panel 2	150.00	75.00	45.00
4	Hank Aaron	80.00	40.00	25.00
5	Milt Pappas	10.00	5.00	3.00
6	Dick Stuart	10.00	5.00	3.00
	Panel 3	250.00	125.00	75.00
7	Bob Clemente	100.00	50.00	30.00
8	Yogi Berra	50.00	25.00	15.00
9	Ken Boyer	10.00	5.00	3.00
	Panel 4	55.00	22.50	13.50
10	Orlando Cepeda	15.00	7.50	4.50
11	Gus Triandos	10.00	5.00	3.00
12	Frank Malzone	10.00	5.00	3.00
	Panel 5	135.00	67.50	40.00
13	Willie Mays	80.00	40.00	24.00
14	Camilo Pascual	10.00	5.00	3.00
15	Bob Cerv	10.00	5.00	3.00
	Panel 6	100.00	50.00	30.00
16	Vic Power	10.00	5.00	3.00
17	Larry Sherry	10.00	5.00	3.00
18	Al Kaline	50.00	25.00	15.00
	Panel 7	130.00	65.00	39.00
19	Warren Spahn	40.00	20.00	12.50
20	Harmon Killebrew	30.00	15.00	9.00
21	Jackie Jensen	15.00	7.50	4.50
	Panel 8	135.00	65.00	39.00
22	Luis Aparicio	25.00	12.50	7.50
23	Gil Hodges	30.00	15.00	9.00
24	Richie Ashburn	30.00	15.00	9.00
	Panel 9	100.00	50.00	30.00
25	Nellie Fox	25.00	12.50	7.50
26	Robin Roberts	30.00	15.00	9.00
27	Joe Cunningham	10.00	5.00	3.00
	Panel 10	135.00	65.00	39.00
28	Early Wynn	25.00	12.50	7.50
29	Frank Robinson	50.00	25.00	15.00
30	Rocky Colavito	20.00	10.00	6.00
	Panel 11	475.00	235.00	140.00
31	Mickey Mantle	300.00	150.00	90.00
32	Glen Hobbie	10.00	5.00	3.00
33	Roy McMillan	10.00	5.00	3.00

		NR MT	EX	VG
	Panel 12	45.00	22.50	13.50
34	Harvey Kuenn	10.00	5.00	3.00
35	Johnny Antonelli	10.00	5.00	3.00
36	Del Crandall	10.00	5.00	3.00

1961 Bazooka

Similar in design to the 1960 Bazooka set, the 1961 edition consists of 36 cards issued in panels of three on the bottom of Bazooka bubble gum boxes. The full-color cards, which measure 1-13/16" by 2-3/4" individually and 2-3/4" by 5-1/2" as panels, are numbered 1 through 36. The backs are blank.

		NR MT	EX	VG
	Complete Panel Set:	1500.	750.00	450.00
	Complete Singles Set:	750.00	375.00	225.00
	Common Player:	10.00	5.00	3.00
	Panel 1	475.00	235.00	140.00
1	Art Mahaffey	10.00	5.00	3.00
2	Mickey Mantle	300.00	150.00	90.00
3	Ron Santo	15.00	7.50	4.50
	Panel 2	125.00	62.50	37.50
4	Bud Daley	10.00	5.00	3.00
5	Roger Maris	80.00	40.00	24.00
6	Eddie Yost	10.00	5.00	3.00
	Panel 3	50.00	25.00	15.00
7	Minnie Minoso	15.00	7.50	4.50
8	Dick Groat	10.00	5.00	3.00
9	Frank Malzone	10.00	5.00	3.00
	Panel 4	75.00	35.00	21.00
10	Dick Donovan	10.00	5.00	3.00
11	Ed Mathews	30.00	15.00	9.00
12	Jim Lemon	10.00	5.00	3.00
	Panel 5	50.00	25.00	15.00
13	Chuck Estrada	10.00	5.00	3.00
14	Ken Boyer	10.00	5.00	3.00
15	Harvey Kuenn	10.00	5.00	3.00
	Panel 6	60.00	30.00	18.00
16	Ernie Broglio	10.00	5.00	3.00
17	Rocky Colavito	20.00	10.00	6.00
18	Ted Kluszewski	15.00	7.50	4.50
	Panel 7	250.00	125.00	75.00
19	Ernie Banks	75.00	38.00	23.00
20	Al Kaline	50.00	25.00	15.00
21	Ed Bailey	10.00	5.00	3.00
	Panel 8	125.00	62.50	37.50
22	Jim Perry	10.00	5.00	3.00
23	Willie Mays	80.00	40.00	24.00
24	Bill Mazeroski	15.00	7.50	4.50
	Panel 9	75.00	37.50	22.50
25	Gus Triandos	10.00	5.00	3.00
26	Don Drysdale	25.00	12.50	7.50
27	Frank Herrera	10.00	5.00	3.00
	Panel 10	80.00	40.00	24.00
28	Earl Battey	10.00	5.00	3.00
29	Warren Spahn	35.00	17.50	10.50
30	Gene Woodling	10.00	5.00	3.00
	Panel 11	75.00	37.50	22.50
31	Frank Robinson	35.00	17.50	10.50
32	Pete Runnels	10.00	5.00	3.00
33	Woodie Held	10.00	5.00	3.00
	Panel 12	55.00	27.50	16.50
34	Norm Larker	10.00	5.00	3.00
35	Luis Aparicio	20.00	10.00	6.00
36	Bill Tuttle	10.00	5.00	3.00

Grading Guide

Mint (MT): A perfect card. Well-centered with all corners sharp and square. No creases, stains, edge nicks, surface marks, yellowing or fading.

Near Mint (NM): A nearly perfect card. At first glance, a NM card appears to be perfect. May be slightly off-center. No surface marks, creases or loss of gloss.

Excellent (EX): Corners are still fairly sharp with only moderate wear. Borders may be off-center. No creases or stains on fronts or backs, but may show slight loss of surface luster.

Very Good (VG): Shows obvious handling. May have rounded corners, minor creases, major gum or wax stains. No major creases, tape marks, writing, etc.

Good (G): A well-worn card, but exhibits no intentional damage. May have major or multiple creases. Corners may be rounded well beyond card border.

1962 Bazooka

In 1962, Bazooka increased the size of its set to 45 full-color cards. The set is unnumbered and was issued in panels of three on the bottoms of bubble gum boxes. The individual cards measure 1-13/16" by 2-3/4" in size, whereas the panels are 2-3/4" by 5-1/2". In the checklist that follows the cards have been numbered alphabetically, using the name of the player who appears on the left end of the panel. Panel #s 1, 11 and 15 were issued in much shorter supply and command a higher price.

		NR MT	EX	VG
	Complete Panel Set:	5000.	2500.	1500.
	Complete Singles Set:	3150.	1575.	925.00
	Common Player:	10.00	5.00	3.00
	Panel 1	1075.	535.00	320.00
(1)	Bob Allison	150.00	75.00	45.00
(2)	Ed Mathews	350.00	175.00	105.00
(3)	Vada Pinson	150.00	75.00	45.00
	Panel 2	75.00	37.50	22.50
(4)	Earl Battey	10.00	5.00	3.00
(5)	Warren Spahn	30.00	15.00	9.00
(6)	Lee Thomas	10.00	5.00	3.00
	Panel 3	50.00	25.00	15.00
(7)	Orlando Cepeda	15.00	7.50	4.50
(8)	Woodie Held	10.00	5.00	3.00
(9)	Bob Aspromonte	10.00	5.00	3.00
	Panel 4	250.00	125.00	75.00
(10)	Dick Howser	10.00	5.00	3.00
(11)	Bob Clemente	100.00	50.00	30.00
(12)	Al Kaline	45.00	22.50	13.50
	Panel 5	165.00	82.50	50.00
(13)	Joey Jay	10.00	5.00	3.00
(14)	Roger Maris	75.00	37.50	22.50
(15)	Frank Howard	12.00	6.00	3.50
	Panel 6	150.00	75.00	45.00
(16)	Sandy Koufax	75.00	37.50	22.50
(17)	Jim Gentile	10.00	5.00	3.00
(18)	Johnny Callison	10.00	5.00	3.00
	Panel 7	45.00	22.50	13.50
(19)	Jim Landis	10.00	5.00	3.00
(20)	Ken Boyer	12.00	6.00	3.50
(21)	Chuck Schilling	10.00	5.00	3.00
	Panel 8	525.00	260.00	155.00
(22)	Art Mahaffey	10.00	5.00	3.00
(23)	Mickey Mantle	300.00	150.00	90.00
(24)	Dick Stuart	10.00	5.00	3.00
	Panel 9	110.00	55.00	33.00
(25)	Ken McBride	10.00	5.00	3.00
(26)	Frank Robinson	35.00	17.50	10.50
(27)	Gil Hodges	25.00	12.50	7.50
	Panel 10	200.00	100.00	60.00
(28)	Milt Pappas	10.00	5.00	3.00
(29)	Hank Aaron	100.00	50.00	30.00
(30)	Luis Aparicio	20.00	10.00	6.00
	Panel 11	1250.	625.00	375.00
(31)	Johnny Romano	150.00	75.00	45.00
(32)	Ernie Banks	500.00	250.00	150.00
(33)	Norm Siebern	150.00	75.00	45.00
	Panel 12	50.00	25.00	15.00
(34)	Ron Santo	15.00	7.50	4.50
(35)	Norm Cash	15.00	7.50	4.50
(36)	Jim Piersall	12.50	6.25	3.75
	Panel 13	190.00	95.00	55.00
(37)	Don Schwall	10.00	5.00	3.00
(38)	Willie Mays	100.00	50.00	30.00
(39)	Norm Larker	10.00	5.00	3.00
	Panel 14	125.00	62.50	37.50
(40)	Bill White	10.00	5.00	3.00
(41)	Whitey Ford	50.00	25.00	15.00
(42)	Rocky Colavito	20.00	10.00	6.00
	Panel 15	1050.	525.00	315.00
(43)	Don Zimmer	175.00	87.50	52.50
(44)	Harmon Killebrew	300.00	150.00	90.00
(45)	Gene Woodling	150.00	75.00	45.00

1963 Bazooka

The 1963 Bazooka issue reverted back to a 12-panel, 36-card set, but saw a change in the size of the cards. Individual cards measure 1-9/16" by 2-1/2", while panels are 2-1/2" by 4-11/16" in size. The card design was altered also, with the player's name, team and position situated in a white oval space at the bottom of the card. The full-color, blank-backed set is numbered 1-36. Five Bazooka All-Time Greats cards were inserted in each box of bubble gum.

		NR MT	EX	VG
	Complete Panel Set:	1750.	875.00	525.00
	Complete Singles Set:	1000.	500.00	300.00
	Common Player:	7.00	3.50	2.00
	Panel 1	575.00	275.00	170.00
1	Mickey Mantle (batting righty)	300.00	150.00	90.00
2	Bob Rodgers	7.00	3.50	2.00
3	Ernie Banks	50.00	25.00	15.00
	Panel 2	75.00	37.00	22.50
4	Norm Siebern	7.00	3.50	2.00
5	Warren Spahn (portrait)	30.00	15.00	9.00
6	Bill Mazeroski	15.00	7.50	4.50
	Panel 3	190.00	95.00	57.00
7	Harmon Killebrew (batting)	30.00	15.00	9.00
8	Dick Farrell (portrait)	7.00	3.50	2.00
9	Hank Aaron (glove in front)	80.00	40.00	24.00
	Panel 4	150.00	75.00	45.00
10	Dick Donovan	7.00	3.50	2.00
11	Jim Gentile (batting)	7.00	3.50	2.00
12	Willie Mays (bat in front)	80.00	40.00	24.00
	Panel 5	150.00	75.00	45.00
13	Camilo Pascual (hands at waist)	7.00	3.50	2.00
14	Roberto Clemente (portrait)	80.00	40.00	24.00
15	Johnny Callison (wearing pinstripe uniform)	7.00	3.50	2.00
	Panel 6	200.00	100.00	60.00
16	Carl Yastrzemski (kneeling)	75.00	37.50	22.50
17	Don Drysdale	45.00	22.50	13.50
18	Johnny Romano (portrait)	7.00	3.50	2.00
	Panel 7	30.00	15.00	9.00
19	Al Jackson	7.00	3.50	2.00
20	Ralph Terry	7.00	3.50	2.00
21	Bill Monbouquette	7.00	3.50	2.00
	Panel 8	115.00	57.50	35.00
22	Orlando Cepeda	15.00	7.50	4.50
23	Stan Musial	50.00	25.00	15.00
24	Floyd Robinson (no pinstripes on uniform)	7.00	3.50	2.00
	Panel 9	35.00	17.50	10.50
25	Chuck Hinton (batting)	7.00	3.50	2.00
26	Bob Purkey	7.00	3.50	2.00
27	Ken Hubbs	15.00	7.50	4.50
	Panel 10	80.00	40.00	24.00
28	Bill White	8.00	4.00	2.50
29	Ray Herbert	7.00	3.50	2.00
30	Brooks Robinson (glove in front)	35.00	17.50	10.50
	Panel 11	95.00	47.50	28.50
31	Frank Robinson (batting, uniform number doesn't show)	50.00	25.00	15.00
32	Lee Thomas	7.00	3.50	2.00
33	Rocky Colavito (Detroit)	18.00	9.00	5.50
	Panel 12	80.00	40.00	24.00
34	Al Kaline (kneeling)	35.00	17.50	10.50
35	Art Mahaffey	7.00	3.50	2.00
36	Tommy Davis (batting follow-through)	8.00	4.00	2.50

Grading Guide

Mint (MT): A perfect card. Well-centered with all corners sharp and square. No creases, stains, edge nicks, surface marks, yellowing or fading.

Near Mint (NM): A nearly perfect card. At first glance, a NM card appears to be perfect. May be slightly off-center. No surface marks, creases or loss of gloss.

Excellent (EX): Corners are still fairly sharp with only moderate wear. Borders may be off-center. No creases or stains on fronts or backs, but may show slight loss of surface luster.

Very Good (VG): Shows obvious handling. May have rounded corners, minor creases, major gum or wax stains. No major creases, tape marks, writing, etc.

Good (G): A well-worn card, but exhibits no intentional damage. May have major or multiple creases. Corners may be rounded well beyond card border.

1963 Bazooka All-Time Greats

Consisting of 41 cards, the Bazooka All-Time Greats set was issued as inserts (5 per box) in boxes of Bazooka bubble gum. A black and white head-shot of the player is placed inside a gold plaque within a white border. The card backs have black print on white and white and yellow and contain a brief biography of the player. The numbered cards measure 1-9/16" by 2-1/2" in size. The cards can be found with silver fronts instead of gold. The silver are worth double the values listed in the following checklist.

		NR MT	EX	VG
Complete Set:		350.00	175.00	100.00
Common Player:		7.50	3.75	2.25
1	Joe Tinker	7.50	3.75	2.25
2	Harry Heilmann	7.50	3.75	2.25
3	Jack Chesbro	7.50	3.75	2.25
4	Christy Mathewson	12.00	6.00	3.50
5	Herb Pennock	7.50	3.75	2.25
6	Cy Young	7.50	3.75	2.25
7	Ed Walsh	7.50	3.75	2.25
8	Nap Lajoie	7.50	3.75	2.25
9	Eddie Plank	7.50	3.75	2.25
10	Honus Wagner	12.00	6.00	3.50
11	Chief Bender	7.50	3.75	2.25
12	Walter Johnson	12.00	6.00	3.50
13	Three-Fingered Brown	7.50	3.75	2.25
14	Rabbit Maranville	7.50	3.75	2.25
15	Lou Gehrig	40.00	20.00	12.00
16	Ban Johnson	7.50	3.75	2.25
17	Babe Ruth	55.00	27.00	16.50
18	Connie Mack	7.50	3.75	2.25
19	Hank Greenberg	7.50	3.75	2.25
20	John McGraw	7.50	3.75	2.25
21	Johnny Evers	7.50	3.75	2.25
22	Al Simmons	7.50	3.75	2.25
23	Jimmy Collins	7.50	3.75	2.25
24	Tris Speaker	7.50	3.75	2.25
25	Frank Chance	7.50	3.75	2.25
26	Fred Clarke	7.50	3.75	2.25
27	Wilbert Robinson	7.50	3.75	2.25
28	Dazzy Vance	7.50	3.75	2.25
29	Grover Alexander	7.50	3.75	2.25
30	Kenesaw Landis	7.50	3.75	2.25
31	Willie Keeler	7.50	3.75	2.25
32	Rogers Hornsby	7.50	3.75	2.25
33	Hugh Duffy	7.50	3.75	2.25
34	Mickey Cochrane	7.50	3.75	2.25
35	Ty Cobb	40.00	20.00	12.00
36	Mel Ott	7.50	3.75	2.25
37	Clark Griffith	7.50	3.75	2.25
38	Ted Lyons	7.50	3.75	2.25
39	Cap Anson	7.50	3.75	2.25
40	Bill Dickey	7.50	3.75	2.25
41	Eddie Collins	7.50	3.75	2.25

1964 Bazooka

The 1964 Bazooka set is identical in design and size to the previous year's effort. However, different photographs were used from year to year by Topps, issuer of Bazooka bubble gum. The 1964 set consists of 36 full-color, blank-backed cards numbered 1 through 36. Individual cards measure 1-9/16" by 2-1/2"; three-card panels measure 2-1/2" by 4-11/16". Sheets of ten full-color baseball stamps were inserted in each box of bubble gum.

		NR MT	EX	VG
Complete Panel Set:		1450.	725.00	435.00
Complete Singles Set:		850.00	425.00	255.00
Common Player:		7.00	3.50	2.00
	Panel 1	350.00	175.00	100.00
1	Mickey Mantle (portrait)	200.00	100.00	60.00
2	Dick Groat	8.00	4.00	2.50
3	Steve Barber	7.00	3.50	2.00
	Panel 2	65.00	32.50	19.50
4	Ken McBride	7.00	3.50	2.00
5	Warren Spahn (head to waist shot)	30.00	15.00	9.00
6	Bob Friend	7.00	3.50	2.00
	Panel 3	175.00	87.50	52.50
7	Harmon Killebrew (portrait)	30.00	15.00	9.00
8	Dick Farrell (hands above head)	7.00	3.50	2.00
9	Hank Aaron (glove to left)	75.00	37.50	22.50
	Panel 4	125.00	62.50	37.50
10	Rich Rollins	7.00	3.50	2.00
11	Jim Gentile (portrait)	7.00	3.50	2.00
12	Willie Mays (looking to left)	75.00	37.50	22.50
	Panel 5	125.00	62.50	37.50
13	Camilo Pascual (pitching follow-through)	7.00	3.50	2.00
14	Roberto Clemente (throwing)	75.00	37.50	22.50
15	Johnny Callison (batting, screen showing)	7.00	3.50	2.00
	Panel 6	120.00	60.00	36.00
16	Carl Yastrzemski (batting)	45.00	22.50	13.50
17	Billy Williams (kneeling)	25.00	12.50	7.50
18	Johnny Romano (batting)	7.00	3.50	2.00
	Panel 7	70.00	35.00	21.00
19	Jim Maloney	7.00	3.50	2.00
20	Norm Cash	9.00	4.50	2.75
21	Willie McCovey	30.00	15.00	9.00
	Panel 8	30.00	15.00	9.00
22	Jim Fregosi (batting)	7.00	3.50	2.00
23	George Altman	7.00	3.50	2.00
24	Floyd Robinson (wearing pinstripe uniform)	7.00	3.50	2.00
	Panel 9	30.00	15.00	9.00
25	Chuck Hinton (portrait)	7.00	3.50	2.00
26	Ron Hunt (batting)	7.00	3.50	2.00
27	Gary Peters (pitching)	7.00	3.50	2.00
	Panel 10	75.00	37.50	22.50
28	Dick Ellsworth	7.00	3.50	2.00
29	Elston Howard (holding bat)	12.00	6.00	3.50
30	Brooks Robinson (kneeling with glove)	30.00	15.00	9.00
	Panel 11	180.00	90.00	54.00
31	Frank Robinson (uniforn number shows)	40.00	20.00	12.00
32	Sandy Koufax (glove in front)	60.00	30.00	18.00
33	Rocky Colavito (Kansas City)	15.00	7.50	4.50
	Panel 12	75.00	37.50	22.50
34	Al Kaline (holding two bats)	30.00	15.00	9.00
35	Ken Boyer (head to waist shot)	10.00	5.00	3.00
36	Tommy Davis (batting)	10.00	5.00	3.00

1964 Bazooka Stamps

Occasionally mislabeled "Topps Stamps," the 1964 Bazooka Stamps set was produced by Topps, but was found only in boxes of 1¢ Bazooka bubble gum. Issued in sheets of ten, 100 color stamps make up the set. Each stamp measures 1" by 1-1/2" in size. While the stamps are not individually numbered, the sheets are numbered one through ten. The stamps are commonly found as complete sheets of ten and are priced in that fashion in the checklist that follows.

		NR MT	EX	VG
Complete Sheet Set:		500.00	250.00	150.00
Common Sheet:		25.00	12.50	7.50
1	Max Alvis, Ed Charles, Dick Ellsworth, Jimmie Hall, Frank Malzone, Milt Pappas, Vada Pinson, Tony Taylor, Pete Ward, Bill White	25.00	12.50	7.50
2	Bob Aspromonte, Larry Jackson, Willie Mays, Al McBean, Bill Monbouquette, Bobby Richardson, Floyd Robinson, Frank Robinson, Norm Siebern, Don Zimmer	40.00	20.00	12.00
3	Ernie Banks, Roberto Clemente, Curt Flood, Jesse Gonder, Woody Held, Don Lock, Dave Nicholson, Joe Pepitone, Brooks Robinson, Carl Yastrzemski	60.00	30.00	18.00
4	Hank Aguirre, Jim Grant, Harmon Killebrew, Jim Maloney, Juan Marichal, Bill Mazeroski, Juan Pizarro, Boog Powell, Ed Roebuck, Ron Santo	40.00	20.00	12.00
5	Jim Bouton, Norm Cash, Orlando Cepeda, Tommy Harper, Chuck Hinton, Albie Pearson, Ron Perranoski, Dick Radatz, Johnny Romano, Carl Willey	30.00	15.00	9.00
6	Steve Barber, Jim Fregosi, Tony Gonzalez, Mickey Mantle, Jim O'Toole, Gary Peters, Rich Rollins, Warren Spahn, Dick Stuart, Joe Torre	125.00	62.00	37.00
7	Felipe Alou, George Altman, Ken Boyer, Rocky Colavito, Jim Davenport, Tommy Davis, Bill Freehan, Bob Friend, Ken Johnson, Billy Moran	30.00	15.00	9.00
8	Earl Battey, Ernie Broglio, Johnny Callison, Donn Clendenon, Don Drysdale, Jim Gentile, Elston Howard, Claude Osteen, Billy Williams, Hal Woodeshick	35.00	17.50	10.50
9	Hank Aaron, Jack Baldschun, Wayne Causey, Moe Drabowsky, Dick Groat, Frank Howard, Al Jackson, Jerry Lumpe, Ken McBride, Rusty Staub	40.00	20.00	12.00
10	Ray Culp, Vic Davalillo, Dick Farrell, Ron Hunt, Al Kaline, Sandy Koufax, Eddie Mathews, Willie McCovey, Camilo Pascual, Lee Thomas	50.00	25.00	15.00

1965 Bazooka

The 1965 Bazooka set is identical to the 1963 and 1964 sets. Different players were added each year and different photographs were used for those players being included again. Individual cards cut from the boxes measure 1-9/16" by 2-1/2". Complete three-card panels measure 2-1/2" by 4-11/16". Thirty-six full-color, blank-backed, num- bered cards comprise the set. Prices are given for individual cards and complete panels in the checklist that follows.

		NR MT	EX	VG
Complete Panel Set:		1200.	600.00	360.00
Complete Singles Set:		725.00	360.00	215.00
Common Player:		7.00	3.50	2.00
	Panel 1	300.00	150.00	90.00
1	Mickey Mantle (batting lefty)	200.00	100.00	60.00
2	Larry Jackson	7.00	3.50	2.00
3	Chuck Hinton	7.00	3.50	2.00
	Panel 2	30.00	15.00	9.00
4	Tony Oliva	10.00	5.00	3.00
5	Dean Chance	7.00	3.50	2.00
6	Jim O'Toole	7.00	3.50	2.00
	Panel 3	110.00	55.00	33.00
7	Harmon Killebrew (bat on shoulder)	25.00	12.50	7.50
8	Pete Ward	7.00	3.50	2.00
9	Hank Aaron (batting)	50.00	25.00	15.00
	Panel 4	100.00	50.00	30.00
10	Dick Radatz	7.00	3.50	2.00
11	Boog Powell	10.00	5.00	3.00
12	Willie Mays (looking down)	50.00	25.00	15.00
	Panel 5	100.00	50.00	30.00
13	Bob Veale	7.00	3.50	2.00
14	Roberto Clemente (batting)	50.00	25.00	15.00
15	Johnny Callison (batting, no screen in background)	7.00	3.50	2.00
	Panel 6	50.00	25.00	15.00
16	Joe Torre	7.00	3.50	2.00
17	Billy Williams (batting)	20.00	10.00	6.00
18	Bob Chance	7.00	3.50	2.00

	Panel 7	35.00	17.50	10.50
19	Bob Aspromonte	7.00	3.50	2.00
20	Joe Christopher	7.00	3.50	2.00
21	Jim Bunning	12.00	6.00	3.50
	Panel 8	80.00	40.00	24.00
22	Jim Fregosi (portrait)	7.00	3.50	2.00
23	Bob Gibson	25.00	12.50	7.50
24	Juan Marichal	20.00	10.00	6.00
	Panel 9	30.00	15.00	9.00
25	Dave Wickersham	7.00	3.50	2.00
26	Ron Hunt (throwing)	7.00	3.50	2.00
27	Gary Peters (portrait)	7.00	3.50	2.00
	Panel 10	85.00	42.50	25.00
28	Ron Santo	10.00	5.00	3.00
29	Elston Howard (with glove)	12.00	6.00	3.50
30	Brooks Robinson (portrait)	30.00	15.00	9.00
	Panel 11	130.00	65.00	39.00
31	Frank Robinson (portrait)	30.00	15.00	9.00
32	Sandy Koufax (hands over head)			
		45.00	22.50	13.50
33	Rocky Colavito (Cleveland)	14.00	7.00	4.25
	Panel 12	75.00	37.50	22.50
34	Al Kaline (portrait)	30.00	15.00	9.00
35	Ken Boyer (portrait)	10.00	5.00	3.00
36	Tommy Davis (fielding)	10.00	5.00	3.00
40	Tom Tresh	8.00	4.00	2.50
41	Tony Oliva	10.00	5.00	3.00
42	Don Drysdale	25.00	12.50	7.50
	Panel 15	25.00	12.50	7.50
43	Pete Richert	5.00	2.50	1.50
44	Bert Campaneris	8.00	4.00	2.50
45	Jim Maloney	5.00	2.50	1.50
	Panel 16	75.00	37.50	22.50
46	Al Kaline	30.00	15.00	9.00
47	Eddie Fisher	5.00	2.50	1.50
48	Billy Williams	20.00	10.00	6.00

1966 Bazooka

The 1966 Bazooka set was increased to 48 cards. Issued in panels of three on the bottoms of boxes of bubble gum, the full-color cards are blank-backed and numbered. Individual cards measure 1-9/16" by 2-1/2", whereas panels measure 2-1/2" by 4-11/16".

		NR MT	EX	VG
	Complete Panel Set:	1200.	600.00	360.00
	Complete Singles Set:	950.00	475.00	285.00
	Common Player:	5.00	2.50	1.50
	Panel 1	80.00	40.00	24.00
1	Sandy Koufax	50.00	25.00	15.00
2	Willie Horton	5.00	2.50	1.50
3	Frank Howard	8.00	4.00	2.50
	Panel 2	40.00	20.00	12.00
4	Richie Allen	8.00	4.00	2.25
5	Mel Stottlemyre	5.00	2.50	1.50
6	Tony Conigliaro	15.00	7.50	4.50
	Panel 3	280.00	140.00	84.00
7	Mickey Mantle	200.00	100.00	60.00
8	Leon Wagner	5.00	2.50	1.50
9	Ed Kranepool	5.00	2.50	1.50
	Panel 4	70.00	35.00	21.00
10	Juan Marichal	20.00	10.00	6.00
11	Harmon Killebrew	25.00	12.50	7.50
12	Johnny Callison	5.00	2.50	1.50
	Panel 5	55.00	27.00	16.50
13	Roy McMillan	5.00	2.50	1.50
14	Willie McCovey	25.00	12.50	7.50
15	Rocky Colavito	10.00	5.00	3.00
	Panel 6	90.00	45.00	27.00
16	Willie Mays	50.00	25.00	15.00
17	Sam McDowell	8.00	4.00	2.50
18	Vern Law	5.00	2.50	1.50
	Panel 7	55.00	27.00	16.50
19	Jim Fregosi	5.00	2.50	1.50
20	Ron Fairly	5.00	2.50	1.50
21	Bob Gibson	25.00	12.50	7.50
	Panel 8	75.00	37.50	22.50
22	Carl Yastrzemski	40.00	20.00	12.00
23	Bill White	8.00	4.00	2.50
24	Bob Aspromonte	5.00	2.50	1.50
	Panel 9	85.00	42.50	25.00
25	Dean Chance (California)	5.00	2.50	1.50
26	Roberto Clemente	50.00	25.00	15.00
27	Tony Cloninger	5.00	2.50	1.50
	Panel 10	85.00	42.50	25.00
28	Curt Blefary	5.00	2.50	1.50
29	Milt Pappas	5.00	2.50	1.50
30	Hank Aaron	50.00	25.00	15.00
	Panel 11	70.00	35.00	21.00
31	Jim Bunning	12.00	6.00	3.50
32	Frank Robinson (portrait)	30.00	15.00	9.00
33	Bill Skowron	8.00	4.00	2.50
	Panel 12	60.00	30.00	18.00
34	Brooks Robinson	30.00	15.00	9.00
35	Jim Wynn	5.00	2.50	1.50
36	Joe Torre	5.00	2.50	1.50
	Panel 13	125.00	62.50	37.50
37	Jim Grant	5.00	2.50	1.50
38	Pete Rose	75.00	37.50	22.50
39	Ron Santo	10.00	5.00	3.00
	Panel 14	60.00	30.00	18.00
40	Tom Tresh	8.00	4.00	2.50
41	Tony Oliva	10.00	5.00	3.00
42	Don Drysdale	25.00	12.50	7.50
	Panel 15	25.00	12.50	7.50
43	Pete Richert	5.00	2.50	1.50
44	Bert Campaneris	5.00	2.50	1.50
45	Jim Maloney	5.00	2.50	1.50
	Panel 16	80.00	40.00	24.00
46	Al Kaline	30.00	15.00	9.00
47	Matty Alou	5.00	2.50	1.50
48	Billy Williams	20.00	10.00	6.00

1967 Bazooka

The 1967 Bazooka set is identical in design to the Bazooka sets of 1964-1966. Issued in panels of three on the bottoms of bubble gum boxes, the set is made up of 48 full-color, blank-backed, numbered cards. Individual cards measure 1-9/16" by 2-1/2"; complete panels measure 2-1/2" by 4-11/16" in size.

		NR MT	EX	VG
	Complete Panel Set:	1200.	600.00	360.00
	Complete Singles Set:	850.00	425.00	255.00
	Common Player:	5.00	2.50	1.50
	Panel 1	25.00	12.50	7.50
1	Rick Reichardt	5.00	2.50	1.50
2	Tommy Agee	5.00	2.50	1.50
3	Frank Howard	8.00	4.00	2.50
	Panel 2	40.00	20.00	12.00
4	Richie Allen	8.00	4.00	2.25
5	Mel Stottlemyre	5.00	2.50	1.50
6	Tony Conigliaro	15.00	7.50	4.50
	Panel 3	295.00	145.00	85.00
7	Mickey Mantle	200.00	100.00	60.00
8	Leon Wagner	5.00	2.50	1.50
9	Gary Peters	5.00	2.50	1.50
	Panel 4	70.00	35.00	21.00
10	Juan Marichal	20.00	10.00	6.00
11	Harmon Killebrew	25.00	12.50	7.50
12	Johnny Callison	5.00	2.50	1.50
	65.00	32.50	19.50	
13	Denny McLain	12.00	6.00	3.50
14	Willie McCovey	25.00	12.50	7.50
15	Rocky Colavito	10.00	5.00	3.00
	Panel 6	80.00	40.00	24.00
16	Willie Mays	40.00	20.00	12.00
17	Sam McDowell	5.00	2.50	1.50
18	Jim Kaat	12.00	6.00	3.50
	Panel 7	50.00	25.00	15.00
19	Jim Fregosi	5.00	2.50	1.50
20	Ron Fairly	5.00	2.50	1.50
21	Bob Gibson	25.00	12.50	7.50
	Panel 8	70.00	35.00	21.00
22	Carl Yastrzemski	35.00	17.00	10.50
23	Bill White	8.00	4.00	2.25
24	Bob Aspromonte	5.00	2.50	1.50
	Panel 9	70.00	35.00	21.00
25	Dean Chance (Minnesota)	5.00	2.50	1.50
26	Roberto Clemente	40.00	20.00	12.00
27	Tony Cloninger	5.00	2.50	1.50
	Panel 10	70.00	35.00	21.00
28	Curt Blefary	5.00	2.50	1.50
29	Phil Regan	5.00	2.50	1.50
30	Hank Aaron	40.00	20.00	12.00
	Panel 11	60.00	30.00	18.00
31	Jim Bunning	12.00	6.00	3.50
32	Frank Robinson (batting)	25.00	12.50	7.50
33	Ken Boyer	8.00	4.00	2.25
	Panel 12	60.00	30.00	18.00
34	Brooks Robinson	30.00	15.00	9.00
35	Jim Wynn	5.00	2.50	1.50
36	Joe Torre	5.00	2.50	1.50
	Panel 13	105.00	52.50	31.50
37	Tommy Davis	5.00	2.50	1.50
38	Pete Rose	60.00	30.00	18.00
39	Ron Santo	10.00	5.00	3.00
	Panel 14	60.00	30.00	18.00
40	Tom Tresh	8.00	4.00	2.50
41	Tony Oliva	10.00	5.00	3.00
42	Don Drysdale	25.00	12.50	7.50
	Panel 15	25.00	12.50	7.50
43	Pete Richert	5.00	2.50	1.50
44	Bert Campaneris	5.00	2.50	1.50
45	Jim Maloney	5.00	2.50	1.50
	Panel 16	80.00	40.00	24.00
46	Al Kaline	30.00	15.00	9.00
47	Matty Alou	5.00	2.50	1.50
48	Billy Williams	20.00	10.00	6.00

1968 Bazooka

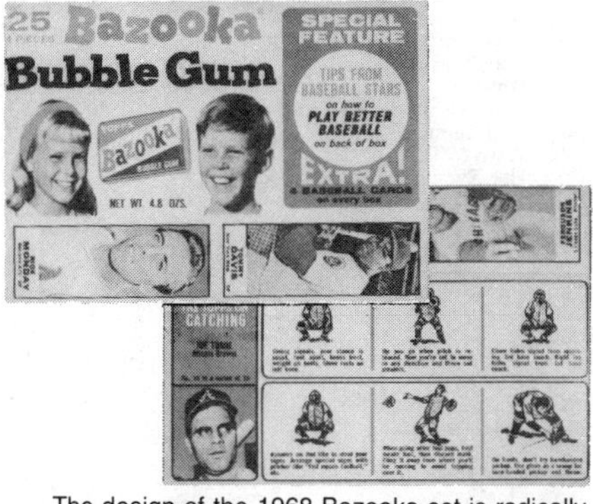

The design of the 1968 Bazooka set is radically different from previous years. The player cards are situated on the sides of the boxes with the box back containing "Tipps From The Topps." Four unnumbered player cards, measuring 1-1/4" by 3-1/8", are featured on each box. The box back includes a small player photo plus illustrated tips on various aspects of the game of baseball. The boxes are numbered 1-15 on the top panels. There are 56 different player cards in the set, with four of the cards (Agee, Drysdale, Rose, Santo) being used twice to round out the set of fifteen boxes.

		NR MT	EX	VG
	Complete Box Set:	2500.	1250.	750.00
	Complete Singles Set:	1500.	750.00	450.00
	Common Player:	5.00	2.50	1.50
	Box 1	200.00	100.00	60.00
1	Maury Wills (Bunting)	20.00	10.00	6.00
(1)	Clete Boyer	8.00	4.00	2.25
(2)	Paul Casanova	5.00	2.50	1.50
(3)	Al Kaline	30.00	15.00	9.00
(4)	Tom Seaver	70.00	35.00	21.00
	Box 2	115.00	57.50	35.00
2	Carl Yastrzemski (Batting)	40.00	20.00	12.00
(5)	Matty Alou	5.00	2.50	1.50
(6)	Bill Freehan	5.00	2.50	1.50
(7)	Catfish Hunter	20.00	10.00	6.00
(8)	Jim Lefebvre	5.00	2.50	1.50
	Box 3	95.00	47.50	28.50
3	Bert Campaneris (Stealing bases)			
		15.00	7.50	4.50
(9)	Bobby Knoop	5.00	2.50	1.50
(10)	Tim McCarver	12.00	6.00	3.50
(11)	Frank Robinson	25.00	12.50	7.50
(12)	Bob Veale	5.00	2.50	1.50
	Box 4	80.00	40.00	24.00
4	Maury Wills (Sliding)	20.00	10.00	6.00
(13)	Joe Azcue	5.00	2.50	1.50
(14)	Tony Conigliaro	15.00	7.50	4.50
(15)	Ken Holtzman	5.00	2.50	1.50
(16)	Bill White	8.00	4.00	2.25
	Box 5	135.00	67.50	40.00
5	Julian Javier (The Double Play)			
		15.00	7.50	4.50
(17)	Hank Aaron	40.00	20.00	12.00
(18)	Juan Marichal	20.00	10.00	6.00
(19)	Joe Pepitone	8.00	4.00	2.25
(20)	Rico Petrocelli	8.00	4.00	2.25
	Box 6	175.00	87.50	52.50
6	Orlando Cepeda (Playing 1st Base)			
		25.00	12.50	7.50
(21)	Tommie Agee	5.00	2.50	1.50
(22)	Don Drysdale	25.00	12.50	7.50
(23)	Pete Rose	50.00	25.00	15.00
(24)	Ron Santo	8.00	4.00	2.25
	Box 7	90.00	45.00	27.00
7	Bill Mazeroski (Playing 2nd Base)			
		20.00	10.00	6.00
(25)	Jim Bunning	12.00	6.00	3.50
(26)	Frank Howard	8.00	4.00	2.25
(27)	John Roseboro	9.00	4.50	2.75
(28)	George Scott	9.00	4.50	2.75
	Box 8	115.00	57.50	35.00
8	Brooks Robinson (Playing 3rd Base)			
		35.00	17.50	10.50
(29)	Tony Gonzalez	5.00	2.50	1.50
(30)	Willie Horton	5.00	2.50	1.50
(31)	Harmon Killebrew	25.00	12.50	7.50
(32)	Jim McGlothlin	5.00	2.50	1.50
	Box 9	90.00	45.00	27.00
9	Jim Fregosi (Playing Shortstop)			
		15.00	7.50	4.50
(33)	Max Alvis	5.00	2.50	1.50
(34)	Bob Gibson	20.00	10.00	6.00
(35)	Tony Oliva	10.00	6.00	3.50
(36)	Vada Pinson	10.00	6.00	3.50
	Box 10	75.00	37.50	22.50
10	Joe Torre (Catching)	15.00	7.50	4.50
(37)	Dean Chance	5.00	2.50	1.50
(38)	Tommy Davis	5.00	2.50	1.50
(39)	Ferguson Jenkins	20.00	10.00	6.00
(40)	Rick Monday	5.00	2.50	1.50
	Box 11	275.00	140.00	84.00
11	Jim Lonborg (Pitching)	15.00	7.50	4.50
(41)	Curt Flood	9.00	4.50	2.75
(42)	Joel Horlen	5.00	2.50	1.50
(43)	Mickey Mantle	150.00	75.00	45.00
(44)	Jim Wynn	5.00	2.50	1.50
	Box 12	120.00	60.00	36.00
12	Mike McCormick (Fielding the Pitcher's			

	Position)	15.00	7.50	4.50
(45)	Roberto Clemente	40.00	20.00	12.00
(46)	Al Downing	5.00	2.50	1.50
(47)	Don Mincher	5.00	2.50	1.50
(48)	Tony Perez	15.00	7.50	4.50
	Box 13	120.00	60.00	36.00
13	Frank Crosetti (Coaching)	15.00	7.50	4.50
(49)	Rod Carew	30.00	15.00	9.00
(50)	Willie McCovey	25.00	12.50	7.50
(51)	Ron Swoboda	5.00	2.50	1.50
(52)	Earl Wilson	5.00	2.50	1.50
	Box 14	120.00	60.00	36.00
14	Willie Mays (Playing the Outfield)	35.00	17.50	10.50
(53)	Richie Allen	8.00	4.00	2.25
(54)	Gary Peters	5.00	2.50	1.50
(55)	Rusty Staub	10.00	5.00	3.00
(56)	Billy Williams	20.00	10.00	6.00
	Box 15	175.00	87.50	52.50
15	Lou Brock (Base Running)	25.00	12.50	7.50
(57)	Tommie Agee	5.00	2.50	1.50
(58)	Don Drysdale	25.00	12.50	7.50
(59)	Pete Rose	50.00	25.00	15.00
(60)	Ron Santo	8.00	4.00	2.25

1969 - 70 Bazooka

Issued over a two-year span, the 1969-70 Bazooka set utilized the box bottom and sides. The box bottom, entitled "Baseball Extra," features an historic event in baseball. The bottom panels are numbered 1 through 12. Two "All-Time Great" cards were located on each side of the box. These cards are not numbered and have no distinct borders. Individual cards measure 1-1/4" by 3-1/8"; the "Baseball Extra" panels measure 3" by 6-1/4". The prices in the checklist that follows are for complete boxes only. Cards/panels cut from the boxes have a greatly reduced value - 25 per cent of the complete box prices for all cut pieces.

		NR MT	EX	VG
	Complete Box Set:	250.00	125.00	75.00
	Common Box:	25.00	12.50	7.50
1	No-Hit Duel By Toney And Vaughn (Mordecai Brown, Ty Cobb, Willie Keeler, Eddie Plank)	23.00	11.50	7.00
2	Alexander Conquers Yanks (Rogers Hornsby, Ban Johnson, Walter Johnson, Al Simmons)	20.00	10.00	6.00
3	Yanks Lazzeri Sets A.L. Hit Record (Hugh Duffy, Lou Gehrig, Tris Speaker, Joe Tinker)	23.00	11.50	7.00
4	Home Run Almost Hit Out Of Stadium (Grover Alexander, Chief Bender, Christy Mathewson, Cy Young)	20.00	10.00	6.00
5	Four Consecutive Homers By Gehrig (Frank Chance, Mickey Cochrane, John McGraw, Babe Ruth)	35.00	17.50	10.50
6	No-Hit Game By Walter Johnson (Johnny Evers, Walter Johnson, John McGraw, Cy Young)	20.00	10.00	6.00
7	Twelve RBI's By Bottomley (Ty Cobb, Eddie Collins, Johnny Evers, Lou Gehrig)	30.00	15.00	9.00
8	Ty Ties Record (Mickey Cochrane, Eddie Collins, Met Ott, Honus Wagner)	20.00	10.00	6.00
9	Babe Ruth Hits Three Homers In Game (Cap Anson, Jack Chesbro, Al Simmons, Tris Speaker)	30.00	15.00	9.00
10	Calls Shot In Series Game (Nap Lajoie, Connie Mack, Rabbit Maranville, Ed Walsh)	30.00	15.00	9.00
11	Ruth's 60th Homer Sets New Record (Frank Chance, Nap Lajoie, Mel Ott, Joe Tinker)	30.00	15.00	9.00
12	Double Shutout By Ed Reulbach (Rogers Hornsby, Rabbit Maranville, Christy Mathewson, Honus Wagner)	20.00	10.00	6.00

A player's name in italic type indicates a rookie card. An (FC) indicates a player's first card for that particular card company.

Values for recent cards and sets are listed in Mint (MT), Near Mint (NM), reflecting the fact that many cards from recent years have been preserved in top condition. Recent cards and sets in less than Excellent condition have little collector interest.

1971 Bazooka Unnumbered Set

This Bazooka set was issued in 1971, consisting of 36 full-color, blank-backed, unnumbered cards. Issued in panels of three on the bottoms of Bazooka bubble gum boxes, individual cards measure 2" by 2-5/8" whereas complete panels measure 2-5/8" by 5-5/16". In the checklist that follows, the cards have been numbered by panel using the name of the player who appears on the left portion of the panel.

		NR MT	EX	VG
	Complete Panel Set:	450.00	225.00	135.00
	Complete Singles Set:	400.00	200.00	120.00
	Common Player:	3.00	1.50	.90
	Panel 1	55.00	27.50	16.50
(1)	Tommie Agee	3.00	1.50	.90
(2)	Harmon Killebrew	15.00	7.50	4.50
(3)	Reggie Jackson	30.00	15.00	9.00
	Panel 2	40.00	20.00	12.00
(4)	Bert Campaneris	3.00	1.50	.90
(5)	Pete Rose	25.00	12.50	7.50
(6)	Orlando Cepeda	9.00	4.50	2.75
	Panel 3	35.00	17.50	10.50
(7)	Rico Carty	3.00	1.50	.90
(8)	Johnny Bench	25.00	12.50	7.50
(9)	Tommy Harper	3.00	1.50	.90
	Panel 4	45.00	22.50	13.50
(10)	Bill Freehan	3.00	1.50	.90
(11)	Roberto Clemente	30.00	15.00	9.00
(12)	Claude Osteen	3.00	1.50	.90
	Panel 5	25.00	12.50	7.50
(13)	Jim Fregosi	3.00	1.50	.90
(14)	Billy Williams	15.00	7.50	4.50
(15)	Dave McNally	3.00	1.50	.90
	Panel 6	55.00	27.50	16.50
(16)	Randy Hundley	3.00	1.50	.90
(17)	Willie Mays	30.00	15.00	9.00
(18)	Catfish Hunter	15.00	7.50	4.50
	Panel 7	30.00	15.00	9.00
(19)	Juan Marichal	15.00	7.50	4.50
(20)	Frank Howard	6.00	3.00	1.75
(21)	Bill Melton	3.00	1.50	.90
	Panel 8	55.00	27.50	16.50
(22)	Willie McCovey	20.00	10.50	6.00
(23)	Carl Yastrzemski	25.00	12.50	7.50
(24)	Clyde Wright	3.00	1.50	.90
	Panel 9	25.00	12.50	7.50
(25)	Jim Merritt	3.00	1.50	.90
(26)	Luis Aparicio	15.00	7.50	4.50
(27)	Bobby Murcer	3.00	1.50	.90
	Panel 10	12.00	6.00	3.50
(28)	Rico Petrocelli	3.00	1.50	.90
(29)	Sam McDowell	3.00	1.50	.90
(30)	Cito Gaston	5.00	2.50	1.50
	Panel 11	65.00	32.50	19.50
(31)	Brooks Robinson	20.00	10.00	6.00
(32)	Hank Aaron	30.00	15.00	9.00
(33)	Larry Dierker	3.00	1.50	.90
	Panel 12	35.00	17.50	10.50
(34)	Rusty Staub	6.00	3.00	1.75
(35)	Bob Gibson	20.00	10.00	6.00
(36)	Amos Otis	5.00	2.50	1.50

1971 Bazooka Numbered Set

The 1971 Bazooka numbered set is a proof set produced by the company after the unnumbered set was released. The set is comprised of 48 cards as opposed to the 36 cards which make up the unnumbered set. Issued in panels of three, the nine cards not found in the unnumbered set are #'s 1-3, 13-15 and 43-45. All other cards are identical to those found in the unnumbered set. The cards, which measure 2" by 2-5/8", contain full-color photos and are blank-backed.

		NR MT	EX	VG
	Complete Panel Set:	925.00	460.00	275.00
	Complete Singles Set:	750.00	375.00	225.00
	Common Player:	5.00	2.50	1.50
	Panel 1	95.00	47.50	28.50
1	Tim McCarver	10.00	5.00	3.00
2	Frank Robinson	45.00	23.00	13.50
3	Bill Mazeroski	10.00	5.00	3.00
	Panel 2	75.00	37.50	22.50
4	Willie McCovey	25.00	12.50	7.50
5	Carl Yastrzemski	30.00	15.00	9.00
6	Clyde Wright	5.00	2.50	1.50
	Panel 3	35.00	17.50	10.50
7	Jim Merritt	5.00	2.50	1.50
8	Luis Aparicio	20.00	10.00	12.00
9	Bobby Murcer	5.00	2.50	1.50
	Panel 4	20.00	10.00	6.00
10	Rico Petrocelli	5.00	2.50	1.50
11	Sam McDowell	5.00	2.50	1.50
12	Cito Gaston	8.00	4.00	2.25
	Panel 5	60.00	30.00	18.00
13	Ferguson Jenkins	20.00	10.00	6.00
14	Al Kaline	25.00	12.50	7.50
15	Ken Harrelson	5.00	2.50	1.50
	Panel 6	65.00	32.50	19.50
16	Tommie Agee	5.00	2.50	1.50
17	Harmon Killebrew	20.00	10.00	6.00
18	Reggie Jackson	30.00	15.00	9.00
	Panel 7	40.00	20.00	12.00
19	Juan Marichal	20.00	10.00	6.00
20	Frank Howard	8.00	4.00	2.25
21	Bill Melton	5.00	2.50	1.50
	Panel 8	120.00	60.00	36.00
22	Brooks Robinson	45.00	22.50	13.50
23	Hank Aaron	50.00	25.00	15.00
24	Larry Dierker	5.00	2.50	1.50
	Panel 9	35.00	17.50	10.50
25	Jim Fregosi	5.00	2.50	1.50
26	Billy Williams	20.00	10.00	6.00
27	Dave McNally	5.00	2.50	1.50
	Panel 10	45.00	22.50	13.50
28	Rico Carty	5.00	2.50	1.50
29	Johnny Bench	25.00	12.50	7.50
30	Tommy Harper	5.00	2.50	1.50
	Panel 11	60.00	30.00	18.00
31	Bert Campaneris	5.00	2.50	1.50
32	Pete Rose	35.00	17.50	10.50
33	Orlando Cepeda	10.00	5.00	3.00
	Panel 12	60.00	30.00	18.00
34	Maury Wills	10.00	5.00	3.00
35	Tom Seaver	30.00	15.00	9.00
36	Tony Oliva	10.00	5.00	3.00
	Panel 13	75.00	37.50	22.50
37	Bill Freehan	5.00	2.50	1.50
38	Roberto Clemente	50.00	25.00	15.00
39	Claude Osteen	5.00	2.50	1.50
	Panel 14	45.00	22.50	13.50
40	Rusty Staub	8.00	4.00	2.25
41	Bob Gibson	20.00	10.00	6.00
42	Amos Otis	8.00	4.00	2.25
	Pan 15	30.00	15.00	9.00
43	Jim Wynn	5.00	2.50	1.50
44	Rich Allen	10.00	5.00	3.00
45	Tony Conigliaro	10.00	5.00	3.00
	Panel 16	90.00	45.00	27.00
46	Randy Hundley	5.00	2.50	1.50
47	Willie Mays	50.00	25.00	15.00
48	Catfish Hunter	20.00	10.00	6.00

1988 Bazooka

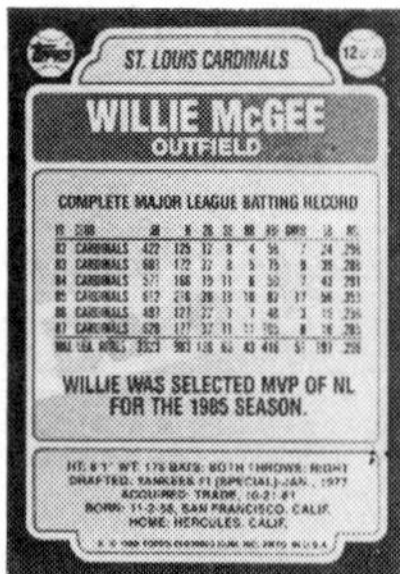

This 22-card set from Topps marks the first Bazooka issue since 1971. Full-color player photos are bordered in white, with the player name printed on a red, white and blue bubble gum box in the lower right corner. Flip sides are also red, white and blue, printed vertically. A large, but faint, Bazooka logo backs the Topps baseball logo team name, card number, player's name and position, followed by batting records, personal information and brief career highlights. Cards were sold inside specially marked 59¢ and 79¢ Bazooka gum and candy boxes, one card per box.

		MT	NR MT	EX
	Complete Set:	8.00	6.00	3.25
	Common Player:	.20	.15	.08
1	George Bell	.25	.20	.10
2	Wade Boggs	.70	.50	.30
3	Jose Canseco	.75	.55	.25
4	Roger Clemens	.75	.55	.25
5	Vince Coleman	.20	.15	.08
6	Eric Davis	.25	.20	.10
7	Tony Fernandez	.20	.15	.08
8	Dwight Gooden	.40	.30	.15
9	Tony Gwynn	.30	.25	.12
10	Wally Joyner	.30	.25	.12
11	Don Mattingly	1.50	1.25	.60
12	Willie McGee	.20	.15	.08
13	Mark McGwire	.40	.30	.15

		MT	NR MT	EX
14	Kirby Puckett	.50	.40	.20
15	Tim Raines	.25	.20	.10
16	Dave Righetti	.20	.15	.08
17	Cal Ripken	.75	.55	.25
18	Juan Samuel	.20	.15	.08
19	Ryne Sandberg	.75	.55	.25
20	Benny Santiago	.20	.15	.08
21	Darryl Strawberry	.45	.35	.15
22	Todd Worrell	.20	.15	.08

1989 Bazooka

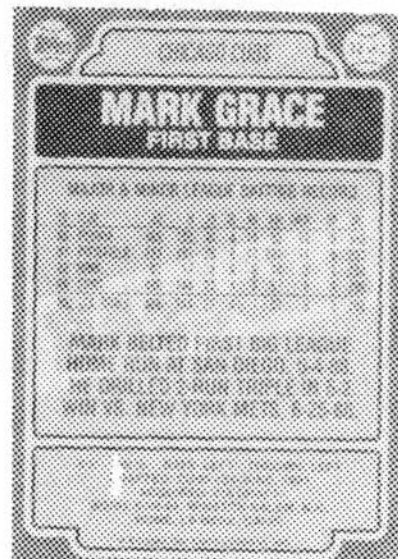

Topps produced this 22-card set in 1989 to be included (one card per box) in specially-marked boxes of its Bazooka brand bubblegum. The player photos have the words "Shining Star" along the top, while the player's name appears along the bottom of the card, along with the Topps Bazooka logo in the lower right corner. The cards are numbered alphabetically.

		MT	NR MT	EX
Complete Set:		5.00	3.75	2.00
Common Player:		.15	.11	.06
1	Tim Belcher	.15	.11	.06
2	Damon Berryhill	.15	.11	.06
3	Wade Boggs	.60	.45	.25
4	Jay Buhner	.15	.11	.06
5	Jose Canseco	.60	.45	.25
6	Vince Coleman	.15	.11	.06
7	Cecil Espy	.15	.11	.06
8	Dave Gallagher	.15	.11	.06
9	Ron Gant	.25	.20	.10
10	Kirk Gibson	.15	.11	.06
11	Paul Gibson	.15	.11	.06
12	Mark Grace	.35	.25	.12
13	Tony Gwynn	.25	.20	.10
14	Rickey Henderson	.30	.25	.12
15	Orel Hershiser	.25	.20	.10
16	Gregg Jefferies	.50	.40	.20
17	Ricky Jordan	.15	.11	.06
18	Chris Sabo	.15	.11	.06
19	Gary Sheffield	.35	.25	.12
20	Darryl Strawberry	.35	.25	.12
21	Frank Viola	.15	.11	.06
22	Walt Weiss	.15	.11	.06

1990 Bazooka

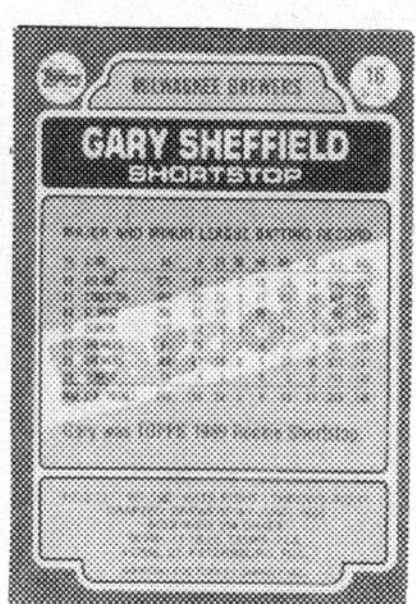

For the second consecutive year, Bazooka entitled its set "Shining Stars." Full color action and posed player shots are featured on the card fronts. The flip sides feature player statistics in a style much like the cards from the previous two Bazooka issues. Unlike the past two releases, the cards are not numbered alphabetically. The cards measure 2-1/2" by 3-1/2" in size and 22 cards complete the set.

		MT	NR MT	EX
Complete Set:		7.00	5.25	2.75
Common Player:		.15	.11	.06
1	Kevin Mitchell	.20	.15	.08
2	Robin Yount	.50	.40	.20
3	Mark Davis	.15	.11	.06
4	Bret Saberhagen	.15	.11	.06
5	Fred McGriff	.20	.15	.08
6	Tony Gwynn	.20	.15	.08
7	Kirby Puckett	.30	.25	.12
8	Vince Coleman	.15	.11	.06
9	Rickey Henderson	.30	.25	.12
10	Ben McDonald	.30	.25	.12
11	Gregg Olson	.15	.11	.06
12	Todd Zeile	.20	.15	.07
13	Carlos Martinez	.15	.11	.06
14	Gregg Jefferies	.25	.20	.10
15	Craig Worthington	.15	.11	.06
16	Gary Sheffield	.25	.20	.10
17	Greg Briley	.15	.11	.06
18	Ken Griffey,Jr.	2.00	1.50	.80
19	Jerome Walton	.15	.11	.06
20	Bob Geren	.15	.11	.06
21	Tom Gordon	.15	.11	.06
22	Jim Abbott	.25	.20	.10

1991 Bazooka

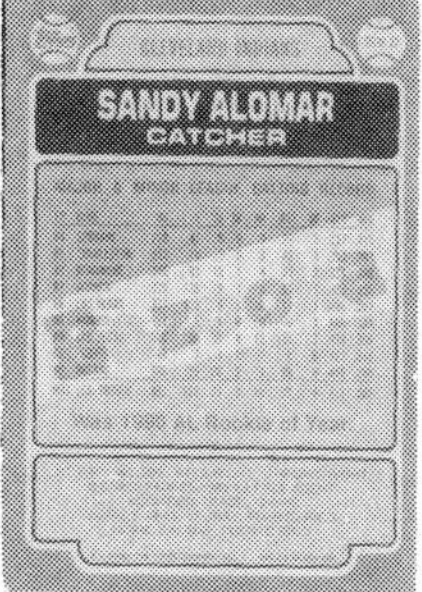

For the third consecutive year Bazooka entitled its set "Shining Stars." The cards are styled like the 1990 issue, but include the Topps "40th Anniversary" logo. The 1991 issue is considered much scarcer than the previous releases. The cards measure 2-1/2" by 3-1/2" in size and 22 cards complete the set.

		MT	NR MT	EX
Complete Set:		15.00	11.00	6.00
Common Player:		.30	.25	.12
1	Barry Bonds	.80	.60	.30
2	Rickey Henderson	.50	.40	.20
3	Bob Welch	.30	.25	.12
4	Doug Drabek	.30	.25	.12
5	Alex Fernandez	.40	.30	.15
6	Jose Offerman	.30	.25	.12
7	Frank Thomas	3.00	2.25	1.25
8	Cecil Fielder	.60	.45	.25
9	Ryne Sandberg	.75	.55	.25
10	George Brett	.45	.35	.15
11	Willie McGee	.30	.25	.12
12	Vince Coleman	.30	.25	.12
13	Hal Morris	.30	.25	.12
14	Delino DeShields	.30	.25	.12
15	Robin Ventura	.30	.25	.12
16	Jeff Huson	.30	.25	.12
17	Felix Jose	.30	.25	.12
18	Dave Justice	.45	.35	.15
19	Larry Walker	.30	.25	.12
20	Sandy Alomar, Jr.	.30	.25	.12
21	Kevin Appier	.30	.25	.12
22	Scott Radinsky	.30	.25	.12

1992 Bazooka

This set of 22 cards features miniature versions of the 1953 Topps Archives issue. The mini-cards are set against a blue background on front and back. Besides reproductions of issued 1953 Topps cards, these "Quadracards" include miniature versions of many of the special cards created for the Archives set. Cards feature the Bazooka logo on back, and were distributed in boxes of that bubble gum. They are readily available in complete set form.

		MT	NR MT	EX
Complete Set:		12.00	9.00	4.50
Common Player:		.50	.40	.20
1	Joe Adcock, Bob Lemon, Willie Mays, Vic Wertz	2.00	1.50	.75
2	Carl Furillo, Don Newcombe, Phil Rizzuto, Hank Sauer	.50	.40	.20
3	Ferris Fain, John Logan, Ed Mathews, Bobby Shantz	.50	.40	.20
4	Yogi Berra, Del Crandall, Howie Pollett, Gene Woodling	.50	.40	.20
5	Richie Ashburn, Leo Durocher, Allie Reynolds, Early Wynn	.50	.40	.20
6	Hank Aaron, Ray Boone, Luke Easter, Dick Williams	2.00	1.50	.75
7	Ralph Branca, Bob Feller, Rogers Hornsby, Bobby Thomson	.50	.40	.20
8	Jim Gilliam, Billy Martin, Orestes Minoso, Hal Newhouser	.50	.40	.20
9	Smoky Burgess, John Mize, Preacher Roe, Warren Spahn	.50	.40	.20
10	Monte Irvin, Bobo Newsom, Duke Snider, Wes Westrum	.50	.40	.20
11	Carl Erskine, Jackie Jensen, George Kell, Al Schoendienst	.50	.40	.20
12	Bill Bruton, Whitey Ford, Ed Lopat, Mickey Vernon	.50	.40	.20
13	Joe Black, Lew Burdette, Johnny Pesky, Enos Slaughter	.50	.40	.20
14	Gus Bell, Mike Garcia, Mel Parnell, Jackie Robinson	1.00	.75	.35
15	Alvin Dark, Dick Groat, Pee Wee Reese, John Sain	.50	.40	.20
16	Gil Hodges, Sal Maglie, Wilmer Mizell, Billy Pierce	.50	.40	.20
17	Nellie Fox, Ralph Kiner, Ted Kluszewski, Eddie Stanky	.50	.40	.20
18	Ewell Blackwell, Vern Law, Satchell Paige, Jim Wilson	.75	.55	.25
19	Lou Boudreau, Roy Face, Harvey Haddix, Bill Rigney	.50	.40	.20
20	Roy Campanella, Walt Dropo, Harvey Kuenn, Al Rosen	.50	.40	.20
21	Joe Garagiola, Robin Roberts, Casey Stengel, Hoyt Wilhelm	.50	.40	.20
22	John Antonelli, Bob Friend, Dixie Walker, Ted Williams	1.00	.75	.35

1958 Bell Brand Dodgers

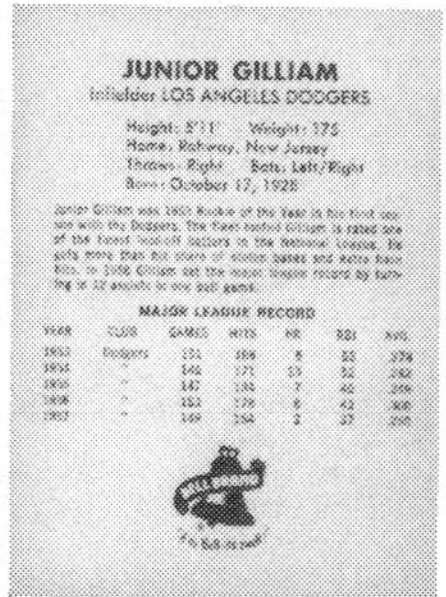

Celebrating the Dodgers first year of play in Los Angeles, Bell Brand inserted ten different unnumbered cards in their bags of potato chips and corn chips. The cards, which measure 3" by 4", have a sepia-colored photo inside a 1/4" green woodgrain border. The card backs feature statistical and biographical information and include the Bell Brand logo. Roy Campanella is included in the set despite a career-ending car wreck that prevented him from ever playing in Los Angeles.

		NR MT	EX	VG
Complete Set:		1200.	600.00	360.00
Common Player:		40.00	20.00	12.00
1	Roy Campanella	150.00	75.00	45.00
2	Gino Cimoli	125.00	62.00	37.00
3	Don Drysdale	100.00	50.00	30.00
4	Junior Gilliam	40.00	20.00	12.00
5	Gil Hodges	90.00	45.00	27.00
6	Sandy Koufax	150.00	75.00	45.00
7	Johnny Podres	125.00	62.00	37.00
8	Pee Wee Reese	100.00	50.00	30.00
9	Duke Snider	300.00	150.00	90.00
10	Don Zimmer	40.00	20.00	12.00

Definitions for grading conditions are located in the Introduction of this price guide.

Values for recent cards and sets are listed in Mint (MT), Near Mint (NM), reflecting the fact that many cards from recent years have been preserved in top condition. Recent cards and sets in less than Excellent condition have little collector interest.

1960 Bell Brand Dodgers

Bell Brand returned with a baseball card set in 1960 that was entirely different in style to their previous effort. The cards, which measure 2-1/2" by 3-1/2", feature beautiful, full-color photos. The backs carry a short player biography, the 1960 Dodgers home schedule, and the Bell Brand logo. Twenty different numbered cards were inserted in various size bags of potato chips and corn chips. Although sealed in cellophane, the cards were still subject to grease stains. Cards #'s 6, 12 and 18 are the scarcest in the set.

		NR MT	EX	VG
Complete Set:		750.00	375.00	225.00
Common Player:		22.00	11.00	6.50
1	Norm Larker	22.00	11.00	6.50
2	Duke Snider	95.00	47.00	28.00
3	Danny McDevitt	22.00	11.00	6.50
4	Jim Gilliam	35.00	17.50	10.50
5	Rip Repulski	20.00	10.00	6.00
6	Clem Labine	100.00	50.00	30.00
7	John Roseboro	22.00	11.00	6.50
8	Carl Furillo	35.00	17.50	10.50
9	Sandy Koufax	125.00	62.00	37.00
10	Joe Pignatano	22.00	11.00	6.50
11	Chuck Essegian	22.00	11.00	6.50
12	John Klippstein	80.00	40.00	24.00
13	Ed Roebuck	22.00	11.00	6.50
14	Don Demeter	22.00	11.00	6.50
15	Roger Craig	32.00	16.00	9.50
16	Stan Williams	22.00	11.00	6.50
17	Don Zimmer	28.00	14.00	8.50
18	Walter Alston	125.00	62.00	37.00
19	Johnny Podres	28.00	14.00	8.50
20	Maury Wills	35.00	17.50	10.50

1961 Bell Brand Dodgers

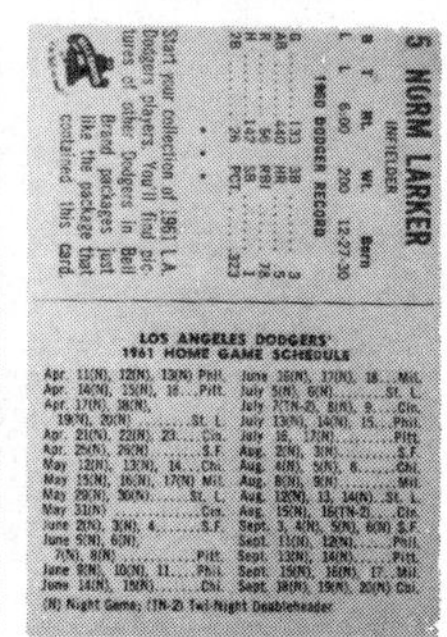

The 1961 Bell Brand set is identical in format to the previous year, although printed on thinner stock. Cards can be distinguished from the 1960 set by the 1961 schedule on the backs. The cards, which measure 2-7/16" by 3-1/2", are numbered by the player's uniform number. Twenty different cards were inserted into various size potato chip and corn chip packages, each card being sealed in a cellophane wrapper.

		NR MT	EX	VG
Complete Set:		550.00	275.00	165.00
Common Player:		18.00	9.00	5.50
3	Willie Davis	22.00	11.00	6.50
4	Duke Snider	60.00	30.00	18.00
5	Norm Larker	18.00	9.00	5.50
8	John Roseboro	18.00	9.00	5.50
9	Wally Moon	18.00	9.00	5.50
11	Bob Lillis	18.00	9.00	5.50
12	Tom Davis	18.00	9.00	5.50
14	Gil Hodges	45.00	22.00	13.50
16	Don Demeter	18.00	9.00	5.50
19	Jim Gilliam	22.00	11.00	6.50
22	John Podres	22.00	11.00	6.50
24	Walter Alston	45.00	22.00	13.50
30	Maury Wills	45.00	22.00	13.50
32	Sandy Koufax	120.00	60.00	36.00
34	Norm Sherry	18.00	9.00	5.50
37	Ed Roebuck	18.00	9.00	5.50
38	Roger Craig	30.00	15.00	9.00
40	Stan Williams	18.00	9.00	5.50
43	Charlie Neal	18.00	9.00	5.50
51	Larry Sherry	18.00	9.00	5.50

1962 Bell Brand Dodgers

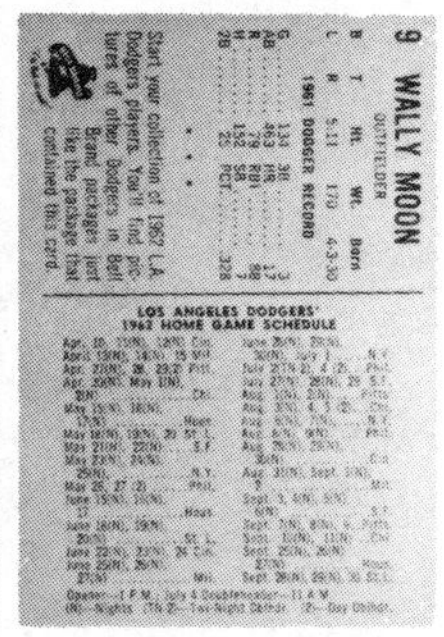

The 1962 Bell Brand set is identical in style to the previous two years and cards can be distinguished by the 1962 Dodgers schedule on the back. The set consists of 20 cards, each measuring 2-7/16" by 3- 1/2" and numbered by the player's uniform number. Printed on glossy stock, the 1962 set was less susceptible to grease stains.

		NR MT	EX	VG
Complete Set:		375.00	187.00	112.00
Common Player:		13.50	6.75	4.00
3	Willie Davis	17.00	8.50	5.00
4	Duke Snider	70.00	35.00	21.00
6	Ron Fairly	13.50	6.75	4.00
8	John Roseboro	13.50	6.75	4.00
9	Wally Moon	13.50	6.75	4.00
12	Tom Davis	13.50	6.75	4.00
16	Ron Perranoski	13.50	6.75	4.00
19	Jim Gilliam	17.00	8.50	5.00
20	Daryl Spencer	13.50	6.75	4.00
22	John Podres	17.00	8.50	5.00
24	Walter Alston	34.00	17.00	10.00
25	Frank Howard	17.00	8.50	5.00
30	Maury Wills	34.00	17.00	10.00
32	Sandy Koufax	90.00	45.00	27.00
34	Norm Sherry	13.50	6.75	4.00
37	Ed Roebuck	13.50	6.75	4.00
40	Stan Williams	13.50	6.75	4.00
51	Larry Sherry	13.50	6.75	4.00
53	Don Drysdale	60.00	30.00	18.00
56	Lee Walls	13.50	6.75	4.00

1992 Ben's Bakery Super Hitters Discs

Ben's Bakery, a small, eastern Canadian bakery, inserted promotional discs in its hot dog and hamburger buns in 1992. As in the case of 1991, which was the company's first year in the promotion, the 1992 set contained 20 different players, including many of the top stars in the country. Twenty of the game's top hitters, with a special emphasis on Blue Jays players, are featured in this regional issue by a small Eastern Canada bakery. The 2-3/4" diameter discs were packaged in the company's hot dog and hamburger buns. Fronts feature a color photo on which team logos have been airbrushed away. The bakery logo is flanked by a red "Super Hitters" in the white border at top. The player's name appears in white in an orange banner beneath the photo, with his team and position in blue at bottom. Backs are printed in black and include a few biographical details and 1991 stats, along with a card number and appropriate logos and copyright notices.

		MT	NR MT	EX
Complete Set (20):		40.00	30.00	16.00
Common Player:		1.00	.70	.40
1	Cecil Fielder	3.00	2.25	1.25
2	Joe Carter	1.50	1.25	.60
3	Roberto Alomar	2.00	1.50	.80
4	Devon White	1.00	.70	.40
5	Kelly Gruber	1.00	.70	.40
6	Cal Ripken, Jr.	5.00	3.75	2.00
7	Kirby Puckett	3.00	2.25	1.25
8	Paul Molitor	2.00	1.50	.80
9	Julio Franco	1.00	.70	.40
10	Ken Griffey, Jr.	7.00	5.25	2.75
11	Frank Thomas	7.00	5.25	2.75
12	Jose Canseco	3.00	2.25	1.25
13	Danny Tartabull	1.00	.70	.40
14	Terry Pendleton	1.00	.70	.40
15	Tony Gwynn	1.50	1.25	.60
16	Howard Johnson	1.00	.70	.40
17	Will Clark	2.50	2.00	1.00
18	Barry Bonds	4.00	3.00	1.50
19	Ryne Sandberg	5.00	3.75	2.00
20	Bobby Bonilla	1.00	.70	.40

1993 Ben's Bakery Super Pitchers Discs

An emphasis on Toronto's pitchers is noted in the checklist for this regional bakery issue. The 2-3/4" diameter discs were packed with hot dog and hamburger buns and follow a 1991 issue by the company featuring super hitters. A color player portrait at center has had the uniform logos airbrushed away. "Super Pitchers" in red flanks the bakery logo in the white border above the photo. The player's name appears in white in an orange banner beneath the photo, with his team and position in blue at bottom. Backs are printed in black and include minimal biographical data, a card number, 1992 stats and copyright information.

		MT	NR MT	EX
Complete Set (20):		16.00	12.00	6.50
Common Player:		.75	.60	.30
1	Dennis Eckersley	1.25	.90	.50
2	Chris Bosio	.75	.60	.30
3	Jack Morris	.75	.60	.30
4	Greg Maddux	1.50	1.25	.60
5	Dennis Martinez	.75	.60	.30
6	Tom Glavine	1.25	.90	.50
7	Doug Drabek	.75	.60	.30
8	John Smoltz	1.00	.70	.40
9	Randy Myers	.75	.60	.30
10	Jack McDowell	1.25	.90	.50
11	John Wetteland	.75	.60	.30
12	Roger Clemens	1.50	1.25	.60
13	Mike Mussina	1.00	.70	.40
14	Juan Guzman	.75	.60	.30
15	Jose Rijo	1.00	.70	.40
16	Tom Henke	.75	.60	.30
17	Gregg Olson	.75	.60	.30
18	Jim Abbott	1.25	.90	.50
19	Jimmy Key	.75	.60	.30
20	Rheal Cormier	1.00	.70	.40

1987 David Berg Hot Dogs Cubs

Changing sponsors from Gatorade to David Berg Pure Beef Hot Dogs, the Chicago Cubs handed out a 26-card set of baseball cards to fans attending the July 29th game at Wrigley Field. The cards are printed in full-color on white stock and measure 2-7/8" by 4-1/4" in size. The set is numbered by the players' uniform numbers. The card

backs contain player personal and statistical information, plus a full-color picture of a David Berg hot dog in a bun with all the garnishings. The set marked the sixth consecutive year the Cubs held a baseball card giveaway promotion.

		MT	NR MT	EX
Complete Set:		9.00	6.75	3.50
Common Player:		.15	.11	.06
1	Dave Martinez	.15	.11	.06
4	Gene Michael	.15	.11	.06
6	Keith Moreland	.15	.11	.06
7	Jody Davis	.15	.11	.06
8	Andre Dawson	1.00	.70	.40
10	Leon Durham	.20	.15	.08
11	Jim Sundberg	.15	.11	.06
12	Shawon Dunston	.60	.45	.25
19	Manny Trillo	.15	.11	.06
20	Bob Dernier	.15	.11	.06
21	Scott Sanderson	.15	.11	.06
22	Jerry Mumphrey	.15	.11	.06
23	Ryne Sandberg	4.00	3.00	1.50
24	Brian Dayett	.15	.11	.06
29	Chico Walker	.15	.11	.06
31	Greg Maddux	1.50	1.25	.60
33	Frank DiPino	.15	.11	.06
34	Steve Trout	.15	.11	.06
36	Gary Matthews	.20	.15	.08
37	Ed Lynch	.15	.11	.06
39	Ron Davis	.15	.11	.06
40	Rick Sutcliffe	.30	.25	.12
46	Lee Smith	.50	.40	.20
47	Dickie Noles	.15	.11	.06
49	Jamie Moyer	.15	.11	.06
----	The Coaching Staff (Johnny Oates, Jim Snyder, Herm Starrette, John Vukovich, Billy Williams)	.15	.11	.06

1988 David Berg Hot Dogs Cubs

This oversized (2-7/8" by 4-1/2") set of 26 cards was distributed to fans at Wrigley Field on August 24th. The set includes cards for the manager and coaching staff, as well as players. Full-color action photos are framed in red and blue on a white background. The backs feature small black and white player close-ups, colorful team logos, statistics and sponsor logos (David Berg Hot Dogs and Venture Store Restaurants). The numbers in the following checklist refer to players' uniforms.

		MT	NR MT	EX
Complete Set:		10.00	7.50	4.00
Common Player:		.15	.11	.06
2	Vance Law	.15	.11	.06
4	Don Zimmer	.15	.11	.06
7	Jody Davis	.15	.11	.06
8	Andre Dawson	1.00	.70	.40
9	Damon Berryhill	.15	.11	.06
12	Shawon Dunston	.45	.35	.20
17	Mark Grace	2.00	1.50	.80
18	Angel Salazar	.15	.11	.06
19	Manny Trillo	.15	.11	.06
21	Scott Sanderson	.20	.15	.08
22	Jerry Mumphrey	.15	.11	.06
23	Ryne Sandberg	4.00	3.00	1.50
24	Gary Varsho	.15	.11	.06
25	Rafael Palmeiro	1.25	.90	.50
28	Mitch Webster	.15	.11	.06
30	Darrin Jackson	.25	.20	.10
31	Greg Maddux	.90	.70	.35
32	Calvin Schiraldi	.15	.11	.06
33	Frank DiPino	.15	.11	.06
37	Pat Perry	.15	.11	.06
40	Rick Sutcliffe	.25	.20	.10
41	Jeff Pico	.15	.11	.06
45	Al Nipper	.15	.11	.06
49	Jamie Moyer	.15	.11	.06
50	Les Lancaster	.15	.11	.06
54	Rich Gossage	.30	.25	.12
----	The Coaching Staff (Joe Altobelli, Chuck Cottier, Larry Cox, Jose Martinez, Dick Pole)	.15	.11	.06

1951 Berk Ross

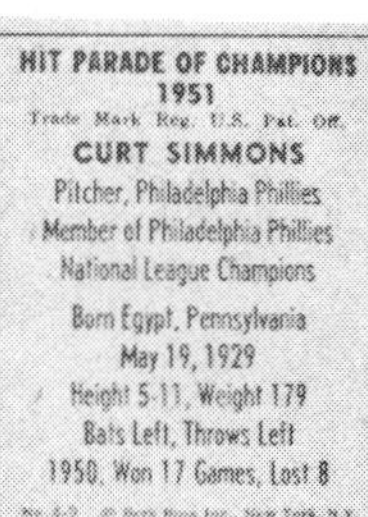
HIT PARADE OF CHAMPIONS
1951
Trade Mark Reg. U.S. Pat. Off.
CURT SIMMONS
Pitcher, Philadelphia Phillies
Member of Philadelphia Phillies
National League Champions
Born Egypt, Pennsylvania
May 19, 1929
Height 5-11, Weight 179
Bats Left, Throws Left
1950, Won 17 Games, Lost 8

Entitled "Hit Parade of Champions," the 1951 Berk Ross set features 72 stars of various sports. The cards, which measure 2-1/16" by 2-1/2" and have tinted color photographs, were issued in boxes containing two-card panels. The issue is divided into four subsets with the first ten players of each series being baseball players. Only the baseball players are listed in the checklist that follows. Complete panels are valued 50 per cent higher than the sum of the individual cards.

		NR MT	EX	VG
Complete Set (40):		1100.	550.00	325.00
Common Player:		12.00	6.00	3.50
1-1	Al Rosen	15.00	7.50	4.50
1-2	Bob Lemon	20.00	10.00	6.00
1-3	Phil Rizzuto	50.00	25.00	15.00
1-4	Hank Bauer	20.00	10.00	6.00
1-5	Billy Johnson	13.00	6.50	4.00
1-6	Jerry Coleman	13.00	6.50	4.00
1-7	Johnny Mize	30.00	15.00	9.00
1-8	Dom DiMaggio	30.00	15.00	9.00
1-9	Richie Ashburn	25.00	12.50	7.50
1-10	Del Ennis	13.00	6.50	4.00
2-1	Stan Musial	250.00	125.00	75.00
2-2	Warren Spahn	30.00	15.00	9.00
2-3	Tommy Henrich	15.00	7.50	4.50
2-4	Larry "Yogi" Berra	150.00	75.00	45.00
2-5	Joe DiMaggio	400.00	200.00	120.00
2-6	Bobby Brown	15.00	7.50	4.50
2-7	Granville Hamner	12.00	6.00	3.50
2-8	Willie Jones	12.00	6.00	3.50
2-9	Stanley Lopata	12.00	6.00	3.50
2-10	Mike Goliat	12.00	6.00	3.50
3-1	Ralph Kiner	25.00	12.50	7.50
3-2	Billy Goodman	12.00	6.00	3.50
3-3	Allie Reynolds	15.00	7.50	4.50
3-4	Vic Raschi	15.00	7.50	4.50
3-5	Joe Page	13.00	6.50	4.00
3-6	Eddie Lopat	13.00	6.50	4.00
3-7	Andy Seminick	12.00	6.00	3.50
3-8	Dick Sisler	12.00	6.00	3.50
3-9	Eddie Waitkus	12.00	6.00	3.50
3-10	Ken Heintzelman	12.00	6.00	3.50
4-1	Gene Woodling	15.00	7.50	4.50
4-2	Cliff Mapes	13.00	6.50	4.00
4-3	Fred Sanford	13.00	6.50	4.00
4-4	Tommy Bryne	13.00	6.50	4.00
4-5	Eddie (Whitey) Ford	125.00	62.00	37.00
4-6	Jim Konstanty	13.00	6.50	4.00
4-7	Russ Meyer	12.00	6.00	3.50
4-8	Robin Roberts	25.00	12.50	7.50
4-9	Curt Simmons	13.00	6.50	4.00
4-10	Sam Jethroe	15.00	7.50	4.50

Values quoted in this guide reflect the retail price of a card – the price a collector can expect to pay when buying a card from a dealer.
The wholesale price – that which a collector can expect to receive from a dealer when selling cards – will be significantly lower, depending on desirability and condition.

1952 Berk Ross

HIT PARADE OF CHAMPIONS
Trade Mark Reg. U.S. Pat. Off.
TED WILLIAMS
Outfielder, Boston Red Sox
Member of the American League
All-Star Team
Born San Diego, Calif.
October 30, 1918
Height 6-3, Weight 190
Throws Right, Bats Left
1951 Hit .318 in 148 games

Although the card size is different (2" by 3"), the style of the fronts and backs of the 1952 Berk Ross set is similar to the previous year's effort. Seventy-two unnumbered cards make up the set. Rizzuto is included twice in the set and the Blackwell and Fox cards have transposed backs. The cards were issued individually rather than as two-card panels like in 1951.

		NR MT	EX	VG
Complete Set (72):		3500.	1750.	1050.
Common Player:		12.00	6.00	3.50
(1)	Richie Ashburn	30.00	15.00	9.00
(2)	Hank Bauer	18.00	9.00	5.50
(3)	Larry "Yogi" Berra	115.00	57.00	34.00
(4)	Ewell Blackwell (photo actually Nelson Fox)	40.00	20.00	12.00
(5)	Bobby Brown	18.00	9.00	5.50
(6)	Jim Busby	12.00	6.00	3.50
(7)	Roy Campanella	125.00	62.00	37.00
(8)	Chico Carrasquel	12.00	6.00	3.50
(9)	Jerry Coleman	15.00	7.50	4.50
(10)	Joe Collins	15.00	7.50	4.50
(11)	Alvin Dark	15.00	7.50	4.50
(12)	Dom DiMaggio	18.00	9.00	5.50
(13)	Joe DiMaggio	725.00	362.00	217.00
(14)	Larry Doby	18.00	9.00	5.50
(15)	Bobby Doerr	30.00	15.00	9.00
(16)	Bob Elliot (Elliott)	12.00	6.00	3.50
(17)	Del Ennis	12.00	6.00	3.50
(18)	Ferris Fain	12.00	6.00	3.50
(19)	Bob Feller	75.00	37.00	22.00
(20)	Nelson Fox (photo actually Ewell Blackwell)	18.00	9.00	5.50
(21)	Ned Garver	12.00	6.00	3.50
(22)	Clint Hartung	12.00	6.00	3.50
(23)	Jim Hearn	12.00	6.00	3.50
(24)	Gil Hodges	50.00	25.00	15.00
(25)	Monte Irvin	30.00	15.00	9.00
(26)	Larry Jansen	12.00	6.00	3.50
(27)	George Kell	30.00	15.00	9.00
(28)	Sheldon Jones	12.00	6.00	3.50
(29)	Monte Kennedy	12.00	6.00	3.50
(30)	Ralph Kiner	30.00	15.00	9.00
(31)	Dave Koslo	12.00	6.00	3.50
(32)	Bob Kuzava	15.00	7.50	4.50
(33)	Bob Lemon	30.00	15.00	9.00
(34)	Whitey Lockman	12.00	6.00	3.50
(35)	Eddie Lopat	18.00	9.00	5.50
(36)	Sal Maglie	15.00	7.50	4.50
(37)	Mickey Mantle	1100.	550.00	330.00
(38)	Billy Martin	40.00	20.00	12.00
(39)	Willie Mays	400.00	200.00	120.00
(40)	Gil McDougal (McDougald)	18.00	9.00	5.50
(41)	Orestes Minoso	15.00	7.50	4.50
(42)	Johnny Mize	40.00	20.00	12.00
(43)	Tom Morgan	15.00	7.50	4.50
(44)	Don Mueller	12.00	6.00	3.50
(45)	Stan Musial	400.00	200.00	120.00
(46)	Don Newcombe	20.00	10.00	6.00
(47)	Ray Noble	12.00	6.00	3.50
(48)	Joe Ostrowski	15.00	7.50	4.50
(49)	Mel Parnell	12.00	6.00	3.50
(50)	Vic Raschi	18.00	9.00	5.50
(51)	Pee Wee Reese	55.00	27.00	16.50
(52)	Allie Reynolds	18.00	9.00	5.50
(53)	Bill Rigney	12.00	6.00	3.50
(54)	Phil Rizzuto (bunting)	55.00	27.00	16.50
(55)	Phil Rizzuto (swinging)	55.00	27.00	16.50
(56)	Robin Roberts	30.00	15.00	9.00
(57)	Eddie Robinson	12.00	6.00	3.50
(58)	Jackie Robinson	200.00	100.00	60.00
(59)	Elwin "Preacher" Roe	15.00	7.50	4.50
(60)	Johnny Sain	15.00	7.50	4.50
(61)	Albert "Red" Schoendienst	30.00	15.00	9.00
(62)	Duke Snider	125.00	62.00	37.00
(63)	George Spencer	12.00	6.00	3.50
(64)	Eddie Stanky	15.00	7.50	4.50
(65)	Henry Thompson	12.00	6.00	3.50
(66)	Bobby Thomson	18.00	9.00	5.50
(67)	Vic Wertz	12.00	6.00	3.50
(68)	Waldon Westlake	12.00	6.00	3.50
(69)	Wes Westrum	12.00	6.00	3.50
(70)	Ted Williams	400.00	200.00	120.00
(71)	Gene Woodling	18.00	9.00	5.50
(72)	Gus Zernial	12.00	6.00	3.50

1994 Big Apple 1969 Mets Discs

Big Apple Collector, Inc. released the "1969 World Champion Miracle Mets Commemorative Cap Sheet," which has likenesses of each of the 31 members of the squad captured in oil paintings by sports artist Ron Lewis. The player's likeness is centered in a 1-5/8" diameter round commemorative cap which is die cut but remains in place on the sheet. Each cap is gold foil accented, and each 11" x 14" sheet is produced in full color on 48-point card stock. The sheet has a suggested retail price of $39.95.

		MT	NR MT	EX
Complete Set:		35.00	26.00	14.00
Common Player:		.50	.40	.20
(1)	Gil Hodges	3.00	2.25	1.25
(2)	Rube Walker	.50	.40	.20
(3)	Yogi Berra	4.00	3.00	1.50
(4)	Joe Pignatano	.50	.40	.20
(5)	Ed Yost	.50	.40	.20
(6)	Tommie Agee	.75	.60	.30
(7)	Ken Boswell	.50	.40	.20
(8)	Don Cardwell	.50	.40	.20
(9)	Ed Charles	.65	.50	.25
(10)	Donn Clendenon	.65	.50	.25
(11)	Jack DiLauro	.50	.40	.20
(12)	Duffy Dyer	.50	.40	.20
(13)	Wayne Garrett	.50	.40	.20
(14)	Rod Gaspar	.50	.40	.20
(15)	Gary Gentry	.50	.40	.20
(16)	Jerry Grote	.50	.40	.20
(17)	Bud Harrelson	.75	.60	.30
(18)	Cleon Jones	.75	.60	.30
(19)	Cal Koonce	.65	.50	.25
(20)	Jerry Koosman	.65	.50	.25
(21)	Ed Kranepool	.65	.50	.25
(22)	J.C. Martin	.50	.40	.20
(23)	Jim McAndrew	.50	.40	.20
(24)	Tug McGraw	.65	.50	.25
(25)	Bob Pfeil	.50	.40	.20
(26)	Nolan Ryan	8.00	6.00	3.25
(27)	Tom Seaver	5.00	3.75	2.00
(28)	Art Shamsky	.65	.50	.25
(29)	Ron Swoboda	.65	.50	.25
(30)	Ron Taylor	.50	.40	.20
(31)	Al Weis	.65	.50	.25

1986 Big League Chew

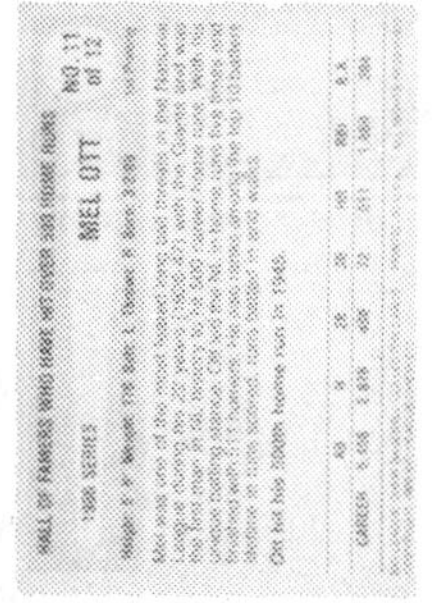

The 1986 Big Leauge Chew set consists of 12 cards featuring the players who have hit 500 or more career home runs. The cards, which measure 2-1/2" by 3-1/2", were inserted in specially marked packages of Big League Chew, the shredded bubble gum developed by former major leaguer Jim Bouton. The set is entitled "Home Run Legends" and was available through a write-in offer on the package. Recent-day players in the set are shown in color photos, while the older sluggers are pictured in black and white.

		MT	NR MT	EX
Complete Set:		6.00	4.50	2.50
Common Player:		.40	.30	.15
1	Hank Aaron	.60	.45	.25
2	Babe Ruth	1.00	.70	.40
3	Willie Mays	.60	.45	.25
4	Frank Robinson	.40	.30	.15
5	Harmon Killebrew	.40	.30	.15
6	Mickey Mantle	1.25	.90	.50
7	Jimmie Foxx	.40	.30	.15
8	Ted Williams	.70	.50	.30
9	Ernie Banks	.40	.30	.15
10	Eddie Mathews	.40	.30	.15
11	Mel Ott	.40	.30	.15
12	500-HR Group Card	.50	.40	.20

1956 Big League Stars Statues

While the plastic statues in this set are virtually identical to the set issued in 1955 by Dairy Queen, the packaging of the Big League Stars statues on a card with all the usual elements of a baseball card makes them more collectible. The DQ versions of the statues are white, while the Big League versions are bronze colored. The statues measure about 3" tall and were sold in a 4" x 5" cardboard and plastic blister pack for about 19 cents. The package features the player's name in a large banner near the top with his team printed below and line drawings of ballplayers in action around the statue. Backs have a player portrait photo with facsimile autograph, position, team, previous year and career stats and a career summary. A perforated tab at bottom can be pulled out to make a stand for the display. Most packages are found with the hole at top punched out to allow for hanging on a hook. Values listed here are for complete statue/package combinations. Statues alone sell for $25-50 for non-Hall of Famers, up to $200 for Mantle. Packages without the statue should be priced about one-third the values quoted here. The set is checklisted alphabetically.

		NR MT	EX	VG
Complete Set (18):		2100.	1000.	600.00
Common Player:		60.00	30.00	18.00
(1)	John Antonelli	60.00	30.00	18.00
(2)	Bob Avila	60.00	30.00	18.00
(3)	Yogi Berra	200.00	100.00	60.00
(4)	Roy Campanella	200.00	100.00	60.00
(5)	Larry Doby	60.00	30.00	18.00
(6)	Del Ennis	60.00	30.00	18.00
(7)	Jim Gilliam	75.00	37.00	22.00
(8)	Gil Hodges	125.00	62.00	37.00
(9)	Harvey Kuenn	60.00	30.00	18.00
(10)	Bob Lemon	90.00	45.00	27.00
(11)	Mickey Mantle	400.00	200.00	120.00
(12)	Ed Mathews	150.00	75.00	45.00
(13)	Minnie Minoso	75.00	37.00	22.00
(14)	Stan Musial	250.00	125.00	75.00
(15)	Pee Wee Reese	150.00	75.00	45.00
(16)	Al Rosen	60.00	30.00	18.00
(17)	Duke Snider	200.00	100.00	60.00
(18)	Mickey Vernon	60.00	30.00	18.00

Grading Guide

Mint (MT): A perfect card. Well-centered with all corners sharp and square. No creases, stains, edge nicks, surface marks, yellowing or fading.

Near Mint (NM): A nearly perfect card. At first glance, a NM card appears to be perfect. May be slightly off-center. No surface marks, creases or loss of gloss.

Excellent (EX): Corners are still fairly sharp with only moderate wear. Borders may be off-center. No creases or stains on fronts or backs, but may show slight loss of surface luster.

Very Good (VG): Shows obvious handling. May have rounded corners, minor creases, major gum or wax stains. No major creases, tape marks, writing, etc.

Good (G): A well-worn card, but exhibits no intentional damage. May have major or multiple creases. Corners may be rounded well beyond card border.

1991 Bleachers Frank Thomas

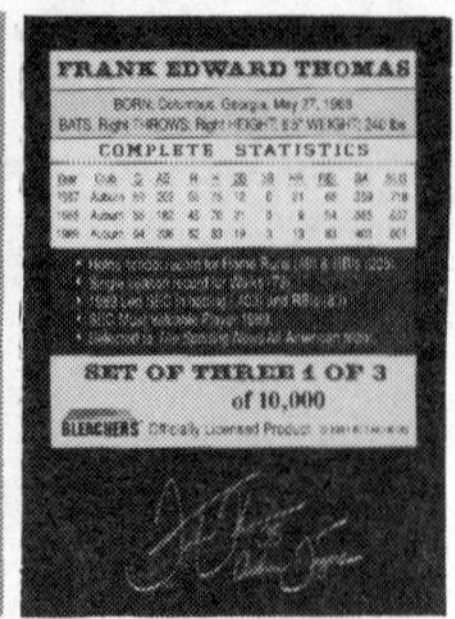

This limited edition three-card set features 23-karat gold cards. The photos feature Frank Thomas at different stages of his baseball career before the big leagues. Production was limited to 10,000 sets and 1,500 uncut strips. All are numbered and feature a gold facsimile autograph on the back.

		MT	NR MT	EX
Complete Set:		30.00	22.00	12.00
Common Player:		8.00	6.00	3.25
1	Frank Thomas (Auburn Tigers)	8.00	6.00	3.25
2	Frank Thomas (Sarasota White Sox)	8.00	6.00	3.25
3	Frank Thomas (Birmingham Barons)	8.00	6.00	3.25

1992 Bleachers Ken Griffey, Jr.

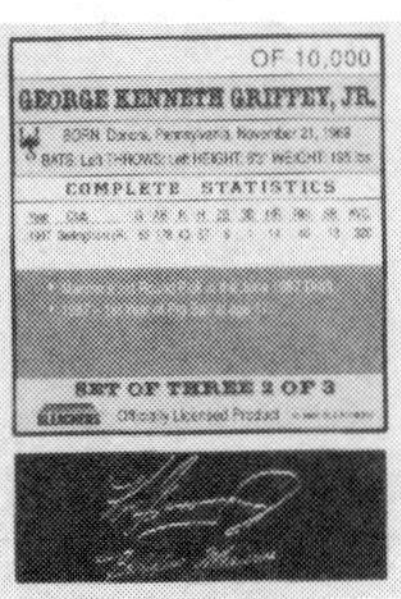

Young superstar Ken Griffey, Jr. is honored in this three-card set featuring him at different stages of his baseball career. The 23-karat gold cards feature full-color photos and a facsimile autograph on the back. Production was limited to 10,000 cut sets and 1,500 uncut strips.

		MT	NR MT	EX
Complete Set:		30.00	22.00	12.00
Common Player:		8.00	6.00	3.25
1	Ken Griffey, Jr. (Moeller High School)	8.00	6.00	3.25
2	Ken Griffey, Jr. (Bellingham Mariners)	8.00	6.00	3.25
3	Ken Griffey, Jr. (San Bernadino Spirit)	8.00	6.00	3.25

1992 Bleachers David Justice

Atlanta Brave slugger David Justice is the subject of this three card 23-karat gold set. The cards depict Justice at different stages of his baseball career. Like the other Bleachers issues, production was limited to 10,000 cut card sets and 1,500 uncut strips.

	MT	NR MT	EX
Complete Set:	25.00	18.00	9.00
Common Player:	7.00	5.25	2.75
1 David Justice (Durham Bulls)	7.00	5.25	2.75
2 David Justice (Greenville Braves)	7.00	5.25	2.75
3 David Justice (Richmond Braves)	7.00	5.25	2.75

1933 Blue Bird Babe Ruth

A small hoard of these cards appeared in the market in early 1994 making available a card which had previously been virtually unknown. Printed in black-and-white on thin card stock, the piece measures 3-7/8" x 5-7/8". The photo on front was used in modified form on several other early-1930s premium issues. The back offers balls and gloves available for redemption with soft drink bottle caps and cash.

	NR MT	EX	VG
Babe Ruth	2500.	1250.	750.00

1987 Boardwalk and Baseball

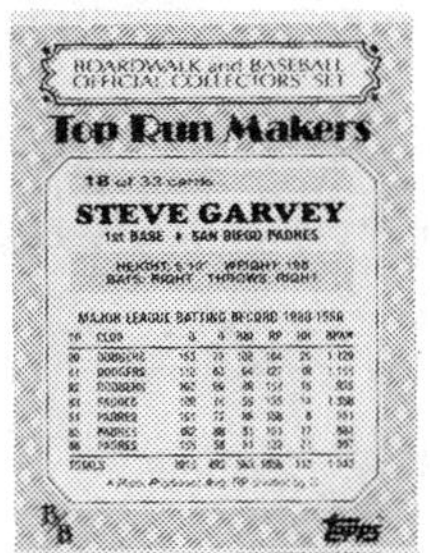

Created by Topps for distribution at the Boardwalk and Baseball theme park near Orlando, Fla., the cards are standard size with a thin, pink border circling a full-color photo. The backs are printed in black and light red, with the Topps and Boardwalk and Baseball (B/B) logos appearing at the bottom of the cards. There are 33-cards in the "Top Run Makers" boxed set, all hitters. A checklist appeared on the back panel of the box.

	MT	NR MT	EX
Complete Set:	6.00	4.50	2.50
Common Player:	.09	.07	.04
1 Mike Schmidt	.50	.40	.20
2 Eddie Murray	.35	.25	.14
3 Dale Murphy	.40	.30	.15
4 Dave Winfield	.30	.25	.12
5 Jim Rice	.20	.15	.08
6 Cecil Cooper	.12	.09	.05
7 Dwight Evans	.15	.11	.06
8 Rickey Henderson	.40	.30	.15
9 Robin Yount	.50	.40	.20
10 Andre Dawson	.25	.20	.10
11 Gary Carter	.35	.25	.14
12 Keith Hernandez	.20	.15	.08
13 George Brett	.50	.40	.20
14 Bill Buckner	.09	.07	.04
15 Tony Armas	.09	.07	.04
16 Harold Baines	.15	.11	.06
17 Don Baylor	.12	.09	.05
18 Steve Garvey	.35	.25	.14
19 Lance Parrish	.15	.11	.06
20 Dave Parker	.25	.20	.10
21 Buddy Bell	.09	.07	.04
22 Cal Ripken, Jr.	1.00	.70	.40
23 Bob Horner	.12	.09	.05
24 Tim Raines	.25	.20	.10
25 Jack Clark	.12	.09	.05
26 Leon Durham	.09	.07	.04
27 Pedro Guerrero	.12	.09	.05
28 Kent Hrbek	.15	.11	.06
29 Kirk Gibson	.20	.15	.08
30 Ryne Sandberg	1.00	.70	.40
31 Wade Boggs	.70	.50	.30
32 Don Mattingly	.90	.70	.35
33 Darryl Strawberry	.20	.15	.08

1955 - 60 Bill and Bob Braves Postcards

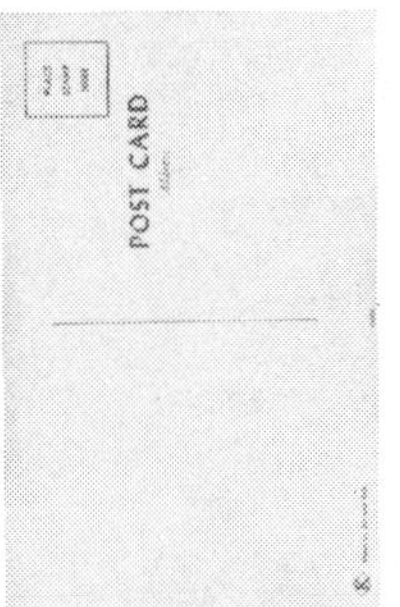

One of the most popular and scarce of the 1950s color postcard series is the run of Milwaukee Braves known as "Bill and Bobs". While some of the cards do carry a photo credit acknowledging the pair, and a few add a Bradenton, Fla., (spring training home of the Braves) address, little else is known about the issuer. The cards themselves appear to have been purchased by the players to honor photo and autograph requests. Several of the cards carry facsimile autographs pre-printed on the front. The cards feature crisp full-color photos on their borderless fronts. Postcard backs have a variety of printing including card numbers, photo credits, a Kodachrome logo and player name. Some cards are found with some of those elements, some with none. There is some question whether the Joe Torre card is actually a Bill and Bob product, because it is 1/16" narrower than the standard 3-1/2" x 5-1/2" format of the other cards, features the player with a Pepsi bottle in his hand and is rubber-stamped on back with a Pepsi bottler's address. The Torre card is usually collected along with the rest of the set.

	NR MT	EX	VG
Complete Set (20):	1200.	600.00	350.00
Common Player:	30.00	15.00	9.00
(1) Hank Aaron	400.00	200.00	120.00
(2) Joe Adcock (fielding)	60.00	30.00	18.00
(3) Joe Adcock (bat on shoulder)	50.00	25.00	15.00
(4) Joe Adcock (kneeling with two bats)	50.00	25.00	15.00
(5) Billy Bruton (kneeling)	60.00	30.00	18.00
(6) Billy Bruton (throwing)	75.00	37.00	22.00
(7) Bob Buhl	30.00	15.00	9.00
(8) Lou Burdette	30.00	15.00	9.00
(9) Gene Conley	30.00	15.00	9.00
(10) Wes Covington (kneeling with one bat)	50.00	25.00	15.00
(11) Wes Covington (kneeling with seven bats)	50.00	25.00	15.00
(12) Del Crandall (kneeling, one bat)	30.00	15.00	9.00
(13) Del Crandall (kneeling, two bats)	30.00	15.00	9.00
(14) Chuck Dressen	45.00	22.00	13.50
(15) Charlie Grimm	75.00	37.00	22.00
(16) Fred Haney	45.00	22.00	13.50
(17) Bob Keely	60.00	30.00	18.00
(18) Eddie Mathews	150.00	75.00	45.00
(19) Warren Spahn	125.00	62.00	37.00
(20) Frank Torre	75.00	37.00	22.00

1987 Bohemian Hearth Bread Padres

Bohemian Hearth Bread Company of San Diego issued a 22-card set highlighting the San Diego Padres. Produced in conjunction with Mike Schechter Associates, the cards are the standard 2-1/2" by 3-1/2" size. The card fronts contain a full-

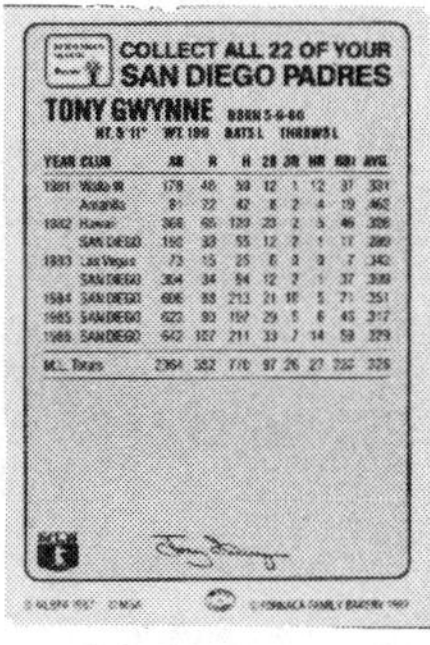

color photo encompassed by a yellow border. The Bohemian Hearth Bread logo is located in the upper left corner of the card. The card backs are printed in light brown ink on a cream color card stock and carry player personal and statistical information.

	MT	NR MT	EX
Complete Set:	50.00	37.50	20.00
Common Player:	.50	.40	.20
1 Garry Templeton	.90	.70	.35
4 Jose Cora	.50	.40	.20
5 Randy Ready	.50	.40	.20
6 Steve Garvey	5.00	3.75	2.00
7 Kevin Mitchell	6.00	4.50	2.50
8 John Kruk	8.00	6.00	3.25
9 Benito Santiago	6.00	4.50	2.50
10 Larry Bowa	1.00	.70	.40
11 Tim Flannery	.50	.40	.20
14 Carmelo Martinez	.50	.40	.20
16 Marvell Wynne	.50	.40	.20
19 Tony Gwynn	12.00	9.00	4.75
21 James Steels	.50	.40	.20
22 Stan Jefferson	.50	.40	.20
30 Eric Show	1.00	.70	.40
31 Ed Whitson	.90	.70	.35
34 Storm Davis	.90	.70	.35
37 Craig Lefferts	.80	.60	.30
40 Andy Hawkins	1.00	.70	.40
41 Lance McCullers	.50	.40	.20
43 Dave Dravecky	2.00	1.50	.80
54 Rich Gossage	3.00	2.25	1.25

1947 Bond Bread Jackie Robinson

The major league's first black player, Jackie Robinson, was featured in a 13-card set issued by Bond Bread in 1947. The cards, which measure 2-1/4" by 3-1/2", are black and white photos of Robinson in various action and portrait poses. The unnumbered cards bear three different backs which contain advertising for Bond Bread. Four of the 13 cards make use of a horizontal format. Card #6 in the checklist below is believed to have been issued in greater quantities and perhaps was a promotional card. The back of this card is the only one in the set containing a short biography of Robinson. The ACC designation for the set is D302.

	NR MT	EX	VG
Complete Set:	3750.	1850.	1100.
Common Player:	250.00	125.00	75.00
(1) Batting (awaiting pitch)	350.00	175.00	105.00
(2) Batting Follow-Thru (white shirtsleeves)	350.00	175.00	105.00
(3) Batting Follow-Thru (no shirtsleeves)	350.00	175.00	105.00
(4) Leaping (scoreboard in background)	350.00	175.00	105.00
(5) Leaping (no scoreboard)	350.00	175.00	105.00
(6) Portrait (facsimile autograph)	250.00	125.00	75.00
(7) Portrait (holding glove in air)	350.00	175.00	105.00
(8) Running (down the baseline)	350.00	175.00	105.00
(9) Running (about to catch ball)	350.00	175.00	105.00
(10) Sliding (umpire in picture)	350.00	175.00	105.00

(11)	Stretching For Throw (ball in glove)	350.00	175.00	105.00
(12)	Stretching For Throw (no ball visible)	350.00	175.00	105.00
(13)	Throwing (ball in hand)	350.00	175.00	105.00

1984 Borden's Reds Stickers

This regional set of eight Reds stickers was issued by Borden Dairy in the Cincinnati area in 1984. Originally issued in two perforated sheets of four stickers each, the individual stickers measure 2-1/2" by 3-7/8", while a full sheet measures 5-1/2" by 8". The colorful stickers feature a player photo surrounded by a bright red border with the Reds logo and the Borden logo in the corners. The backs display coupons for Borden dairy products. The set is numbered according to the players' uniform numbers.

		MT	NR MT	EX
Complete Panel Set:		18.00	20.00	10.00
Complete Singles Set:		12.00	13.50	7.25
Common Player:		.50	.40	.20
	Panel	4.00	3.00	1.50
2	Gary Redus	.50	.40	.20
20	Eddie Milner	.50	.40	.20
24	Tony Perez	1.00	.70	.40
46	Jeff Russell	.80	.60	.30
	Panel	14.00	15.00	8.00
16	Ron Oester	.50	.40	.20
36	Mario Soto	.60	.45	.25
39	Dave Parker	3.00	.70	.40
44	Eric Davis	8.00	11.00	6.00

1912 Boston Garter

If it weren't for the checklist printed on the back of the few known specimens, the extent of this extremely rare issue would be unknown. Many of the cards mentioned on the back have yet to be seen. Issued by the George Frost Company of Boston, and packed one card per box of a dozen garters, the approximately 4" x 8-1/4" cards are printed in color lithography on the front, and black-and-white on the back. Fronts have a picture of the player sitting in a chair, dressing in his uniform. The issuer's Boston-brand garter is prominently shown. A window in the background displays a cityscape. There was a card issued for one player on each of the 16 major league teams of the day.

		NR MT	EX	VG
Complete Set (16):		32500.	16000.	9500.
Common Player:		2000.	1000.	600.00
(1)	Christy Mathewson	4000.	2000.	1200.
(2)	Nap Rucker	2000.	1000.	600.00
(3)	Frank Chance	2500.	1250.	750.00
(4)	Charles Dooin	2000.	1000.	600.00
(5)	Johnny Kling	2000.	1000.	600.00
(6)	Roger Bresnahan	2500.	1250.	750.00
(7)	Bob Bescher	2000.	1000.	600.00
(8)	Fred Clarke	2500.	1250.	750.00
(9)	Hal Chase	2000.	1000.	600.00
(10)	Hugh Jennings	2500.	1250.	750.00
(11)	Eddie Collins	2500.	1250.	750.00
(12)	Tris Speaker	3000.	1500.	900.00
(13)	Frank LaPorte	2000.	1000.	600.00
(14)	Larry Lajoie	2750.	1375.	825.00
(15)	Ed Walsh	2500.	1250.	750.00
(16)	Walter Johnson	4000.	2000.	1200.

1913 Boston Garter

The second of what are presumed to have been three annual issue by the George Frost Co., Boston, contains 12 cards. The colorful lithograph fronts have a player picture in front of a ballpark diagram. A large Boston-brand garter appears at the bottom. Baseballs with the Boston Garter name appear in each upper corner. Black-and-white backs have a

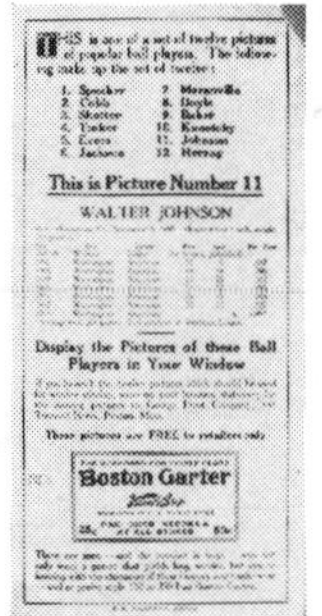

checklist for the set, career statistics for the player pictured and details on the cards' availability. Retailers received one card per box of dozen garters and could write to the company to complete the set. The 4" x 8-1/4" cards were intended to be displayed in shop windows.

		NR MT	EX	VG
Complete Set (12):		17000.	8500.	5000.
Common Player:		1000.	500.00	300.00
1	Tris Speaker	1800.	900.00	540.00
2	Ty Cobb	3000.	1500.	900.00
3	Burt Shotten (Shotton)	1000.	500.00	300.00
4	Joe Tinker	1500.	750.00	450.00
5	Johnny Evers	1500.	750.00	450.00
6	Joe Jackson	4000.	2000.	1200.
7	Rabbit Maranville	1500.	750.00	450.00
8	Larry Doyle	1000.	500.00	300.00
9	Frank Baker	1500.	750.00	450.00
10	Ed Konetchy	1000.	500.00	300.00
11	Walter Johnson	2500.	1250.	750.00
12	Buck Herzog	1000.	500.00	300.00

1914 Boston Garter

The 1914 date attributed to this 10-card set may or may not be accurate. Since the company's other two known issues can be reliably dated and were produced using the color lithographic process, it is presumed that the use of photographs would have come. Fronts of the approximately 4" x 8" cards feature a green duo-tone photo of the player. His last name appears in white script at the bottom, along with a baseball with the Boston Garter name. Backs have a checklist of the set and information on how retail store owners can send for additional cards to supplement those which were packaged one per box of a dozen garters.

		NR MT	EX	VG
Complete Set (10):		11000.	5500.	3300.
Common Player:		1000.	500.00	300.00
1	Christy Mathewson	2500.	1250.	750.00
2	Red Murray	1000.	500.00	300.00
3	Eddie Collins	1500.	750.00	450.00
4	Hugh Jennings	1500.	750.00	450.00
5	Hal Chase	1000.	500.00	300.00
6	Bob Bescher	1000.	500.00	300.00
7	Red Dooin	1000.	500.00	300.00
8	Larry Lajoie	1750.	875.00	525.00
9	Tris Speaker	2000.	1000.	600.00
10	Heinie Zimmerman	1000.	500.00	300.00

1948 Bowman

4 — JOHNNY MIZE
First Base—N. Y. Giants
Born: Demorest, Ga. Jan. 7, 1913
Bats: Left Throws: Right
Height: 6:02 Weight: 215
With a lifetime batting average of .328 he swings the heaviest bat in the National League. Tied with Ralph Kiner to lead all players with 51 home runs last year. He is the only National Leaguer who has 4 times hit 3 home runs in one game. He spent three years in the Navy. Married since 1937, he makes his home in Florida during the off season.
ASK FOR BLONY BUBBLE GUM
The Bubble Gum with the three different flavors
BOWMAN GUM, INC. Copyright 1948

Bowman Gum Co.'s premiere set was produced in 1948, making it one of the first major issues of the post-war period. Forty-eight black and white cards comprise the set, with each card measuring 2-1/16" by 2-1/2" in size. The card backs, printed in black ink on grey stock, include the card number and the player's name, team, position, and a short biography. Twelve cards (#'s 7, 8, 13, 16, 20, 22, 24, 26, 29, 30 and 34) were printed in short supply when they were removed from the 36-card printing sheet to make room for the set's high numbers (#'s 37-48). These 24 cards command a higher price than the remaining cards in the set.

		NR MT	EX	VG
Complete Set (48):		3300.	1600.	975.00
Common Player (1-36):		20.00	10.00	6.00
Common Player (37-48):		28.00	14.00	8.25
1	*Bob Elliott*	100.00	10.50	6.25
2	*Ewell Blackwell*	20.00	10.00	6.00
3	*Ralph Kiner*	135.00	67.50	40.00
4	Johnny Mize	110.00	55.00	33.00
5	Bob Feller	225.00	112.00	67.00
6	*Yogi Berra*	550.00	275.00	165.00
7	Pete Reiser	50.00	25.00	15.00
8	Phil Rizzuto	250.00	125.00	75.00
9	Walker Cooper	20.00	10.00	6.00
10	Buddy Rosar	20.00	10.00	6.00
11	Johnny Lindell	25.00	12.50	7.50
12	*Johnny Sain*	25.00	12.50	7.50
13	*Willard Marshall*	30.00	15.00	9.00
14	*Allie Reynolds*	40.00	20.00	12.00
15	Eddie Joost	20.00	10.00	6.00
16	Jack Lohrke	30.00	15.00	9.00
17	Enos Slaughter	90.00	45.00	27.00
18	*Warren Spahn*	325.00	160.00	95.00
19	Tommy Henrich	25.00	12.50	7.50
20	Buddy Kerr	30.00	15.00	9.00
21	*Ferris Fain*	20.00	10.00	6.00
22	Floyd (Bill) Bevens	40.00	20.00	12.00
23	Larry Jansen	20.00	10.00	6.00
24	Emil (Dutch) Leonard	30.00	15.00	9.00
25	Barney McCoskey (McCosky)	20.00	10.00	6.00
26	Frank Shea	40.00	20.00	12.00
27	Sid Gordon	20.00	10.00	6.00
28	Emil Verban	20.00	10.00	6.00
29	*Joe Page*	50.00	25.00	15.00
30	*Whitey Lockman*	30.00	15.00	9.00
31	Bill McCahan	20.00	10.00	6.00
32	*Bill Rigney*	20.00	10.00	6.00
33	Billy Johnson	25.00	12.50	7.50
34	Sheldon Jones	30.00	15.00	9.00
35	Snuffy Stirnweiss	25.00	12.50	7.50
36	*Stan Musial*	800.00	400.00	240.00
37	Clint Hartung	28.00	14.00	8.25
38	*Red Schoendienst*	150.00	75.00	45.00
39	Augie Galan	28.00	14.00	8.25
40	*Marty Marion*	55.00	27.50	16.50
41	Rex Barney	30.00	15.00	9.00
42	Ray Poat	28.00	14.00	8.25
43	Bruce Edwards	30.00	15.00	9.00
44	Johnny Wyrostek	28.00	14.00	8.25
45	Hank Sauer	28.00	14.00	8.25
46	Herman Wehmeier	28.00	14.00	8.25
47	*Bobby Thomson*	55.00	27.50	16.50
48	Dave Koslo	70.00	14.00	8.25

1949 Bowman

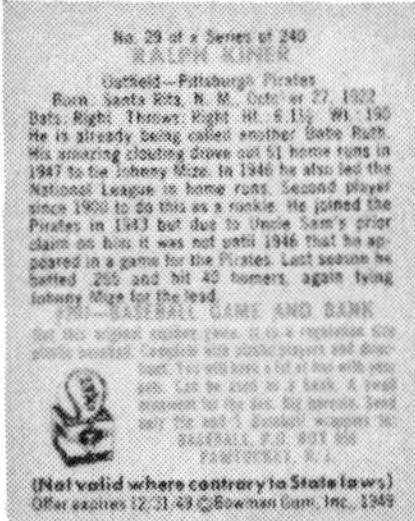

In 1949, Bowman increased the size of its issue to 240 numbered cards. The cards, which measure 2-1/16" by 2-1/2", are black and white photos overprinted with various pastel colors. Beginning with card #109 in the set, Bowman inserted the player's names on the card fronts. Twelve cards (#'s 4, 78, 83, 85, 88, 98, 109, 124, 127, 132 and 143), which were produced in the first four series of printings, were reprinted in the seventh series with either a card front or back modification. These variations are noted in the checklist that follows. Card #'s 1-3 and 5-73 can be found with either white or grey backs. The complete set of value in the following checklist does not include the higher priced variation cards.

		NR MT	EX	VG
Complete Set (240):		15000.	7500.	4500.
Common Player (1-36):		18.50	9.25	5.50
Common Player (37-73):		22.00	11.00	6.50
Common Player (74-144):		18.50	9.25	5.50
Common Player (145-240):		70.00	35.00	21.00
1	Vernon Bickford	100.00	20.00	5.50
2	"Whitey" Lockman	18.50	9.25	5.50
3	Bob Porterfield	22.00	11.00	6.50
4a	Jerry Priddy (no name on front)	18.50	9.25	5.50
4b	Jerry Priddy (name on front)	40.00	20.00	12.00
5	Hank Sauer	18.50	9.25	5.50
6	Phil Cavarretta	20.00	10.00	6.00

7	Joe Dobson	18.50	9.25	5.50
8	Murry Dickson	18.50	9.25	5.50
9	Ferris Fain	22.00	11.00	6.50
10	Ted Gray	18.50	9.25	5.50
11	Lou Boudreau (FC)	60.00	30.00	18.00
12	Cass Michaels	18.50	9.25	5.50
13	Bob Chesnes	18.50	9.25	5.50
14	*Curt Simmons*	30.00	15.00	9.00
15	*Ned Garver*	21.00	11.50	7.00
16	Al Kozar	18.50	9.25	5.50
17	Earl Torgeson	18.50	9.25	5.50
18	Bobby Thomson	30.00	15.00	9.00
19	*Bobby Brown*	60.00	30.00	18.00
20	Gene Hermanski	20.00	10.00	6.00
21	Frank Baumholtz	18.50	9.25	5.50
22	Harry "P-Nuts" Lowrey	18.50	9.25	5.50
23	Bobby Doerr (FC)	75.00	37.50	22.50
24	Stan Musial	550.00	275.00	165.00
25	Carl Scheib	18.50	9.25	5.50
26	George Kell (FC)	60.00	30.00	18.00
27	Bob Feller	150.00	75.00	45.00
28	Don Kolloway	18.50	9.25	5.50
29	Ralph Kiner	70.00	35.00	21.00
30	Andy Seminick	18.50	9.25	5.50
31	Dick Kokos	18.50	9.25	5.50
32	Eddie Yost	18.50	9.25	5.50
33	Warren Spahn	150.00	75.00	45.00
34	Dave Koslo	18.50	9.25	5.50
35	*Vic Raschi*	22.00	11.00	6.60
36	Pee Wee Reese (FC)	180.00	90.00	55.00
37	John Wyrostek	22.00	11.00	6.50
38	Emil Verban	22.00	11.00	6.50
39	Bill Goodman	22.00	11.00	6.50
40	"Red" Munger	22.00	11.00	6.50
41	Lou Brissie	22.00	11.00	6.50
42	"Hoot" Evers	22.00	11.00	6.50
43	Dale Mitchell	22.00	11.00	6.50
44	Dave Philley	22.00	11.00	6.50
45	Wally Westlake	22.00	11.00	6.50
46	*Robin Roberts*	275.00	137.00	82.00
47	Johnny Sain	24.00	12.00	7.20
48	Willard Marshall	22.00	11.00	6.50
49	Frank Shea	24.00	12.00	7.20
50	Jackie Robinson (FC)	900.00	450.00	275.00
51	Herman Wehmeier	22.00	11.00	6.50
52	Johnny Schmitz	22.00	11.00	6.50
53	Jack Kramer	22.00	11.00	6.50
54	Marty Marion	25.00	12.50	7.50
55	Eddie Joost	22.00	11.00	6.50
56	Pat Mullin	22.00	11.00	6.50
57	Gene Bearden	22.00	11.00	6.50
58	Bob Elliott	22.00	11.00	6.50
59	Jack Lohrke	22.00	11.00	6.50
60	Yogi Berra	350.00	175.00	105.00
61	Rex Barney	24.00	12.00	7.20
62	Grady Hatton	22.00	11.00	6.50
63	Andy Pafko	22.00	11.00	6.60
64	Dom DiMaggio (FC)	30.00	15.00	9.00
65	Enos Slaughter	60.00	30.00	18.00
66	Elmer Valo	22.00	11.00	6.50
67	Alvin Dark	24.00	12.00	7.20
68	Sheldon Jones	22.00	11.00	6.50
69	Tommy Henrich	25.00	12.50	7.50
70	*Carl Furillo*	75.00	37.50	22.50
71	Vern Stephens	22.00	11.00	6.50
72	Tommy Holmes	22.00	11.00	6.60
73	Billy Cox	24.00	12.00	7.20
74	Tom McBride	18.50	9.25	5.50
75	Eddie Mayo	18.50	9.25	5.50
76	Bill Nicholson	18.50	9.25	5.50
77	Ernie Bonham	18.50	9.25	5.50
78a	Sam Zoldak (no name on front)	18.50	9.25	5.50
78b	Sam Zoldak (name on front)	40.00	20.00	12.00
79	Ron Northey	18.50	9.25	5.50
80	Bill McCahan	18.50	9.25	5.50
81	Virgil "Red" Stallcup	18.50	9.25	5.50
82	Joe Page	24.00	12.00	7.20
83a	Bob Scheffing (no name on front)	18.50	9.25	5.50
83b	Bob Scheffing (name on front)	40.00	20.00	12.00
84	*Roy Campanella*	850.00	425.00	255.00
85a	Johnny Mize (no name on front)	65.00	32.50	19.50
85b	Johnny Mize (name on front)	125.00	62.00	37.00
86	Johnny Pesky	18.50	9.25	5.50
87	Randy Gumpert	18.50	9.25	5.50
88a	Bill Salkeld (no name on front)	18.50	9.25	5.50
88b	Bill Salkeld (name on front)	40.00	20.00	12.00
89	Mizell Platt	18.50	9.25	5.50
90	Gil Coan	18.50	9.25	5.50
91	Dick Wakefield	18.50	9.25	5.50
92	Willie Jones	18.50	9.25	5.50
93	Ed Stevens	18.50	9.25	5.50
94	*Mickey Vernon*	21.00	11.50	7.00
95	Howie Pollett	18.50	9.25	5.50
96	Taft Wright	18.50	9.25	5.50
97	Danny Litwhiler	18.50	9.25	5.50
98a	Phil Rizzuto (no name on front)	125.00	62.50	37.50
98b	Phil Rizzuto (name on front)	170.00	85.00	50.00
99	Frank Gustine	18.50	9.25	5.50
100	*Gil Hodges*	100.00	50.00	30.00
101	Sid Gordon	21.00	11.50	7.00
102	Stan Spence	18.50	9.25	5.50
103	Joe Tipton	18.50	9.25	5.50
104	Ed Stanky	21.00	11.50	7.00
105	Bill Kennedy	18.50	9.25	5.50
106	Jake Early	18.50	9.25	5.50
107	Eddie Lake	18.50	9.25	5.50
108	Ken Heintzelman	18.50	9.25	5.50
109a	Ed Fitz Gerald (script name on back)	18.50	9.25	5.50
109b	Ed Fitz Gerald (printed name on back)	40.00	20.00	12.00
110	*Early Wynn*	100.00	50.00	30.00
111	Red Schoendienst	65.00	32.50	19.50
112	Sam Chapman	18.50	9.25	5.50
113	Ray Lamanno	18.50	9.25	5.50
114	Allie Reynolds	25.00	12.50	7.50
115	Emil "Dutch" Leonard	18.50	9.25	5.50
116	Joe Hatten	22.00	11.00	6.50
117	Walker Cooper	18.50	9.25	5.50
118	Sam Mele	18.50	9.25	5.50
119	Floyd Baker	18.50	9.25	5.50
120	Cliff Fannin	18.50	9.25	5.50
121	Mark Christman	18.50	9.25	5.50
122	George Vico	18.50	9.25	5.50
123	Johnny Blatnick	18.50	9.25	5.50
124a	Danny Murtaugh (script name on back)	18.50	9.25	5.50
124b	Danny Murtaugh (printed name on back)	40.00	20.00	12.00
125	Ken Keltner	21.00	11.50	7.00
126a	Al Brazle (script name on back)	18.50	9.25	5.50
126b	Al Brazle (printed name on back)	40.00	20.00	12.00
127a	Henry Majeski (script name on back)	18.50	9.25	5.50
127b	Henry Majeski (printed name on back)	40.00	20.00	12.00
128	Johnny Vander Meer	21.00	11.50	7.00
129	Billy Johnson	24.00	12.00	7.20
130	Harry "The Hat" Walker	21.00	11.50	7.00
131	Paul Lehner	18.50	9.25	5.50
132a	Al Evans (script name on back)	18.50	9.25	5.50
132b	Al Evans (printed name on back)	40.00	20.00	12.00
133	Aaron Robinson	18.50	9.25	5.50
134	Hank Borowy	18.50	9.25	5.50
135	Stan Rojek	18.50	9.25	5.50
136	Hank Edwards	18.50	9.25	5.50
137	Ted Wilks	18.50	9.25	5.50
138	"Buddy" Rosar	18.50	9.25	5.50
139	Hank "Bow-Wow" Arft	18.50	9.25	5.50
140	Ray Scarborough	18.50	9.25	5.50
141	"Tony Lupien	18.50	9.25	5.50
142	Eddie Waitkus	18.50	9.25	5.50
143a	Bob Dillinger (script name on back)	18.50	9.25	5.50
143b	Bob Dillinger (printed name on back)	40.00	20.00	12.00
144	Mickey Haefner	18.50	9.25	5.50
145	"Blix" Donnelly	70.00	35.00	21.00
146	Mike McCormick	75.00	37.00	22.00
147	Elmer Singleton	70.00	35.00	21.00
148	Bob Swift	70.00	35.00	21.00
149	Roy Partee	80.00	40.00	24.00
150	Allie Clark	70.00	35.00	21.00
151	Mickey Harris	70.00	35.00	21.00
152	Clarence Maddern	70.00	35.00	21.00
153	Phil Masi	70.00	35.00	21.00
154	Clint Hartung	70.00	35.00	21.00
155	Mickey Guerra	70.00	35.00	21.00
156	Al Zarilla	70.00	35.00	21.00
157	Walt Masterson	70.00	35.00	21.00
158	Harry Brecheen	70.00	35.00	21.00
159	Glen Moulder	70.00	35.00	21.00
160	Jim Blackburn	70.00	35.00	21.00
161	"Jocko" Thompson	70.00	35.00	21.00
162	*Preacher Roe*	135.00	67.50	40.00
163	Clyde McCullough	70.00	35.00	21.00
164	*Vic Wertz*	70.00	35.00	21.00
165	"Snuffy" Stirnweiss	80.00	40.00	24.00
166	Mike Tresh	70.00	35.00	21.00
167	Boris "Babe" Martin	70.00	35.00	21.00
168	Doyle Lade	70.00	35.00	21.00
169	Jeff Heath	70.00	35.00	21.00
170	Bill Rigney	70.00	35.00	21.00
171	Dick Fowler	70.00	35.00	21.00
172	Eddie Pellagrini	70.00	35.00	21.00
173	Eddie Stewart	70.00	35.00	21.00
174	*Terry Moore*	80.00	40.00	24.00
175	Luke Appling (FC)	125.00	62.00	37.00
176	Ken Raffensberger	70.00	35.00	21.00
177	Stan Lopata	70.00	35.00	21.00
178	Tommy Brown	75.00	37.00	22.00
179	Hugh Casey	75.00	37.00	22.00
180	Connie Berry	70.00	35.00	21.00
181	Gus Niarhos	80.00	40.00	24.00
182	Hal Peck	70.00	35.00	21.00
183	Lou Stringer	70.00	35.00	21.00
184	Bob Chipman	70.00	35.00	21.00
185	Pete Reiser	75.00	37.00	22.00
186	"Buddy" Kerr	70.00	35.00	21.00
187	Phil Marchildon	70.00	35.00	21.00
188	Karl Drews	70.00	35.00	21.00
189	Earl Wooten	70.00	35.00	21.00
190	*Jim Hearn*	70.00	35.00	21.00
191	Joe Haynes	70.00	35.00	21.00
192	Harry Gumbert	70.00	35.00	21.00
193	Ken Trinkle	70.00	35.00	21.00
194	Ralph Branca	80.00	40.00	24.00
195	Eddie Bockman	70.00	35.00	21.00
196	Fred Hutchinson (FC)	70.00	35.00	21.00
197	Johnny Lindell	80.00	40.00	24.00
198	Steve Gromek	70.00	35.00	21.00
199	"Tex" Hughson	70.00	35.00	21.00
200	Jess Dobernic	70.00	35.00	21.00
201	Sibby Sisti	70.00	35.00	21.00
202	Larry Jansen	70.00	35.00	21.00
203	Barney McCosky	70.00	35.00	21.00
204	Bob Savage	70.00	35.00	21.00
205	Dick Sisler	70.00	35.00	21.00
206	Bruce Edwards	75.00	37.00	22.00
207	Johnny Hopp	70.00	35.00	21.00
208	"Dizzy" Trout	70.00	35.00	21.00
209	Charlie Keller	80.00	40.00	24.00
210	Joe Gordon	70.00	35.00	21.00
211	Dave "Boo" Ferris	70.00	35.00	21.00
212	Ralph Hamner	70.00	35.00	21.00
213	Charles "Red" Barrett	70.00	35.00	21.00
214	*Richie Ashburn*	550.00	275.00	165.00
215	Kirby Higbe	70.00	35.00	21.00
216	"Schoolboy" Rowe	75.00	37.00	22.00
217	Marino Pieretti	70.00	35.00	21.00
218	Dick Kryhoski	80.00	40.00	24.00
219	Virgil "Fire" Trucks (FC)	75.00	37.00	22.00
220	Johnny McCarthy	70.00	35.00	21.00
221	Bob Muncrief	70.00	35.00	21.00
222	Alex Kellner	70.00	35.00	21.00
223	Bob Hofman	70.00	35.00	21.00
224	*Satchel Paige* (FC)	1200.	600.00	350.00
225	*Gerry Coleman*	100.00	50.00	30.00
226	Duke Snider	1000.	500.00	300.00
227	Fritz Ostermueller	70.00	35.00	21.00
228	Jackie Mayo	70.00	35.00	21.00
229	Ed Lopat	100.00	50.00	30.00
230	Augie Galan	70.00	35.00	21.00
231	Earl Johnson	70.00	35.00	21.00
232	George McQuinn	80.00	40.00	24.00
233	Larry Doby (FC)	175.00	87.00	52.00
234	"Rip" Sewell	70.00	35.00	21.00
235	Jim Russell	70.00	35.00	21.00
236	Fred Sanford	80.00	40.00	24.00
237	Monte Kennedy	70.00	35.00	21.00
238	*Bob Lemon*	200.00	100.00	60.00
239	Frank McCormick	70.00	35.00	21.00
240	Norm "Babe" Young (Photo actually Bobby Young)	150.00	45.00	27.00

1950 Bowman

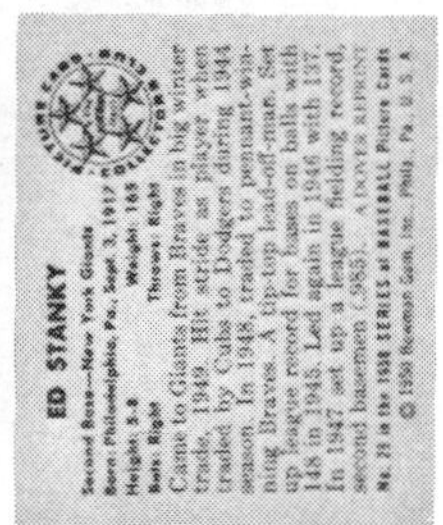

The quality of the 1950 Bowman issue showed a marked improvement over the company's previous efforts. The cards are beautiful color art reproductions of actual photographs and measure 2-1/16" by 2-1/2" in size. The card backs include the same type of information as found in the previous year's issue but are designed in a horizontal format. Cards found in the first two series of the set (#'s 1-72) are the scarcest in the issue. The backs of the final 72 cards in the set (#'s 181-252) can be found with or without the copyright line at the bottom of the card, the "without" version being the less common.

		NR MT	EX	VG
Complete Set (252):		9000.	4500.	2750.
Common Player (1-72):		45.00	22.00	13.50
Common Player (73-252):		18.00	9.00	5.50
1	Mel Parnell	200.00	27.50	5.50
2	Vern Stephens	45.00	22.00	13.50
3	Dom DiMaggio	75.00	37.50	22.50
4	Gus Zernial	45.00	22.00	13.50
5	Bob Kuzava	45.00	22.00	13.50
6	Bob Feller	200.00	100.00	60.00
7	Jim Hegan	45.00	22.00	13.50
8	George Kell	90.00	45.00	27.00
9	Vic Wertz	45.00	22.00	13.50
10	Tommy Henrich	55.00	27.00	16.50
11	Phil Rizzuto	165.00	82.00	49.00
12	Joe Page	55.00	27.00	16.50
13	Ferris Fain	45.00	22.00	13.50
14	Alex Kellner	45.00	22.00	13.50
15	Al Kozar	45.00	22.00	13.50
16	*Roy Sievers*	65.00	32.50	19.50
17	Sid Hudson	45.00	22.00	13.50
18	Eddie Robinson	45.00	22.00	13.50
19	Warren Spahn	200.00	100.00	60.00
20	Bob Elliott	45.00	22.00	13.50
21	Pee Wee Reese	225.00	112.50	67.50
22	Jackie Robinson	700.00	350.00	210.00
23	*Don Newcombe*	150.00	75.00	50.00
24	Johnny Schmitz	45.00	22.00	13.50
25	Hank Sauer	45.00	22.00	13.50
26	Grady Hatton	45.00	22.00	13.50
27	Herman Wehmeier	45.00	22.00	13.50
28	Bobby Thomson	75.00	37.50	22.50
29	Ed Stanky	45.00	22.00	13.50
30	Eddie Waitkus	45.00	22.00	13.50
31	*Del Ennis*	55.00	27.00	16.50
32	Robin Roberts	150.00	75.00	45.00
33	Ralph Kiner	125.00	62.50	37.50
34	Murry Dickson	45.00	22.00	13.50
35	Enos Slaughter	90.00	45.00	27.00
36	Eddie Kazak	45.00	22.00	13.50
37	Luke Appling	90.00	45.00	27.00
38	Bill Wight	45.00	22.00	13.50
39	Larry Doby	65.00	32.50	19.50
40	Bob Lemon	90.00	45.00	27.00
41	"Hoot" Evers	45.00	22.00	13.50
42	Art Houtteman	45.00	22.00	13.50
43	Bobby Doerr	90.00	45.00	27.00
44	Joe Dobson	45.00	22.00	13.50
45	Al Zarilla	45.00	22.00	13.50
46	Yogi Berra	375.00	185.00	110.00
47	Jerry Coleman	55.00	27.00	16.50
48	Lou Brissie	45.00	22.00	13.50
49	Elmer Valo	45.00	22.00	13.50
50	Dick Kokos	45.00	22.00	13.50

51	Ned Garver	45.00	22.00	13.50
52	Sam Mele	45.00	22.00	13.50
53	Clyde Vollmer	45.00	22.00	13.50
54	Gil Coan	45.00	22.00	13.50
55	"Buddy" Kerr	45.00	22.00	13.50
56	*Del Crandell* (Crandall)	55.00	27.00	16.50
57	Vernon Bickford	45.00	22.00	13.50
58	Carl Furillo	75.00	37.50	22.50
59	Ralph Branca	55.00	27.00	16.50
60	Andy Pafko	45.00	22.00	13.50
61	Bob Rush	45.00	22.00	13.50
62	Ted Kluszewski (FC)	70.00	35.00	21.00
63	Ewell Blackwell	45.00	22.00	13.50
64	Alvin Dark	45.00	22.00	13.50
65	Dave Koslo	45.00	22.00	13.50
66	Larry Jansen	45.00	22.00	13.50
67	Willie Jones	45.00	22.00	13.50
68	Curt Simmons	45.00	22.00	13.50
69	Wally Westlake	45.00	22.00	13.50
70	Bob Chesnes	45.00	22.00	13.50
71	Red Schoendienst	90.00	45.00	27.00
72	Howie Pollet	45.00	22.00	13.50
73	Willard Marshall	18.00	9.00	5.50
74	*Johnny Antonelli*	21.00	11.50	7.00
75	Roy Campanella	275.00	135.00	80.00
76	Rex Barney	20.00	10.00	6.00
77	Duke Snider	275.00	135.00	80.00
78	Mickey Owen	18.00	9.00	5.50
79	Johnny Vander Meer	18.00	9.00	5.50
80	Howard Fox	18.00	9.00	5.50
81	Ron Northey	18.00	9.00	5.50
82	"Whitey" Lockman	18.00	9.00	5.50
83	Sheldon Jones	18.00	9.00	5.50
84	Richie Ashburn	75.00	38.00	23.00
85	Ken Heintzelman	18.00	9.00	5.50
86	Stan Rojek	18.00	9.00	5.50
87	Bill Werle	18.00	9.00	5.50
88	Marty Marion	20.00	10.00	6.00
89	George Munger	18.00	9.00	5.50
90	Harry Brecheen	18.00	9.00	5.50
91	Cass Michaels	18.00	9.00	5.50
92	Hank Majeski	18.00	9.00	5.50
93	Gene Bearden	18.00	9.00	5.50
94	Lou Boudreau	50.00	25.00	15.00
95	Aaron Robinson	18.00	9.00	5.50
96	Virgil "Fire" Trucks	18.00	9.00	5.50
97	Maurice McDermott	18.00	9.00	5.50
98	Ted Williams (FC)	750.00	375.00	225.00
99	Billy Goodman	18.00	9.00	5.50
100	Vic Raschi	22.00	11.00	6.60
101	Bobby Brown	25.00	12.50	7.50
102	Billy Johnson	22.00	11.00	6.60
103	Eddie Joost	18.00	9.00	5.50
104	Sam Chapman	18.00	9.00	5.50
105	Bob Dillinger	18.00	9.00	5.50
106	Cliff Fannin	18.00	9.00	5.50
107	Sam Dente	18.00	9.00	5.50
108	Ray Scarborough	18.00	9.00	5.50
109	Sid Gordon	20.00	10.00	6.00
110	Tommy Holmes	18.00	9.00	5.50
111	Walker Cooper	18.00	9.00	5.50
112	Gil Hodges	70.00	35.00	21.00
113	Gene Hermanski	20.00	10.00	6.00
114	*Wayne Terwilliger*	21.00	11.50	7.00
115	Roy Smalley	18.00	9.00	5.50
116	Virgil "Red" Stallcup	18.00	9.00	5.50
117	Bill Rigney	18.00	9.00	5.50
118	Clint Hartung	18.00	9.00	5.50
119	Dick Sisler	18.00	9.00	5.50
120	Jocko Thompson	18.00	9.00	5.50
121	Andy Seminick	18.00	9.00	5.50
122	Johnny Hopp	18.00	9.00	5.50
123	Dino Restelli	18.00	9.00	5.50
124	Clyde McCullough	18.00	9.00	5.50
125	Del Rice	18.00	9.00	5.50
126	Al Brazle	18.00	9.00	5.50
127	Dave Philley	18.00	9.00	5.50
128	Phil Masi	18.00	9.00	5.50
129	Joe Gordon	21.00	11.50	7.00
130	Dale Mitchell	18.00	9.00	5.50
131	Steve Gromek	18.00	9.00	5.50
132	Mickey Vernon	18.00	9.00	5.50
133	Don Kolloway	18.00	9.00	5.50
134	"Dizzy" Trout	18.00	9.00	5.50
135	Pat Mullin	18.00	9.00	5.50
136	"Buddy" Rosar	18.00	9.00	5.50
137	Johnny Pesky	18.00	9.00	5.50
138	Allie Reynolds	40.00	20.00	12.00
139	Johnny Mize	55.00	27.00	16.50
140	Pete Suder	18.00	9.00	5.50
141	Joe Coleman	18.00	9.00	5.50
142	*Sherman Lollar*	22.00	11.00	6.60
143	Eddie Stewart	18.00	9.00	5.50
144	Al Evans	18.00	9.00	5.50
145	Jack Graham	18.00	9.00	5.50
146	Floyd Baker	18.00	9.00	5.50
147	*Mike Garcia*	25.00	12.50	7.50
148	Early Wynn	55.00	27.00	16.50
149	Bob Swift	18.00	9.00	5.50
150	George Vico	18.00	9.00	5.50
151	Fred Hutchinson	18.00	9.00	5.50
152	Ellis Kinder	18.00	9.00	5.50
153	Walt Masterson	18.00	9.00	5.50
154	Gus Niarhos	22.00	11.00	6.60
155	Frank "Spec" Shea	22.00	11.00	6.60
156	Fred Sanford	22.00	11.00	6.60
157	Mike Guerra	18.00	9.00	5.50
158	Paul Lehner	18.00	9.00	5.50
159	Joe Tipton	18.00	9.00	5.50
160	Mickey Harris	18.00	9.00	5.50
161	Sherry Robertson	18.00	9.00	5.50
162	Eddie Yost	18.00	9.00	5.50
163	Earl Torgeson	18.00	9.00	5.50
164	Sibby Sisti	18.00	9.00	5.50
165	Bruce Edwards	20.00	10.00	6.00
166	Joe Hatten	20.00	10.00	6.00
167	Preacher Roe	30.00	15.00	9.00
168	Bob Scheffing	18.00	9.00	5.50
169	Hank Edwards	18.00	9.00	5.50
170	Emil Leonard	18.00	9.00	5.50
171	Harry Gumbert	18.00	9.00	5.50
172	Harry Lowrey	18.00	9.00	5.50
173	Lloyd Merriman	18.00	9.00	5.50
174	*Henry Thompson*	18.00	9.00	5.50
175	Monte Kennedy	18.00	9.00	5.50
176	"Blix" Donnelly	18.00	9.00	5.50
177	Hank Borowy	18.00	9.00	5.50
178	Eddy Fitz Gerald	18.00	9.00	5.50
179	Charles Diering	18.00	9.00	5.50
180	Harry "The Hat" Walker	18.00	9.00	5.50
181	Marino Pieretti	18.00	9.00	5.50
182	Sam Zoldak	18.00	9.00	5.50
183	Mickey Haefner	18.00	9.00	5.50
184	Randy Gumpert	18.00	9.00	5.50
185	Howie Judson	18.00	9.00	5.50
186	Ken Keltner	20.00	10.00	6.00
187	Lou Stringer	18.00	9.00	5.50
188	Earl Johnson	18.00	9.00	5.50
189	Owen Friend	18.00	9.00	5.50
190	Ken Wood	18.00	9.00	5.50
191	Dick Starr	18.00	9.00	5.50
192	Bob Chipman	18.00	9.00	5.50
193	Pete Reiser	20.00	10.00	6.00
194	Billy Cox	20.00	10.00	6.00
195	Phil Cavarretta	18.00	9.00	5.50
196	Doyle Lade	18.00	9.00	5.50
197	Johnny Wyrostek	18.00	9.00	5.50
198	Danny Litwhiler	18.00	9.00	5.50
199	Jack Kramer	18.00	9.00	5.50
200	Kirby Higbe	18.00	9.00	5.50
201	Pete Castiglione	18.00	9.00	5.50
202	Cliff Chambers	18.00	9.00	5.50
203	Danny Murtaugh	18.00	9.00	5.50
204	Granny Hamner	18.00	9.00	5.50
205	Mike Goliat	18.00	9.00	5.50
206	Stan Lopata	18.00	9.00	5.50
207	Max Lanier	18.00	9.00	5.50
208	Jim Hearn	18.00	9.00	5.50
209	Johnny Lindell	18.00	9.00	5.50
210	Ted Gray	18.00	9.00	5.50
211	Charlie Keller	18.00	9.00	5.50
212	Gerry Priddy	18.00	9.00	5.50
213	Carl Scheib	18.00	9.00	5.50
214	Dick Fowler	18.00	9.00	5.50
215	Ed Lopat	22.00	11.00	6.60
216	Bob Porterfield	22.00	11.00	6.60
217	Casey Stengel (FC)	150.00	75.00	45.00
218	Cliff Mapes	22.00	11.00	6.60
219	*Hank Bauer*	70.00	35.00	20.00
220	Leo Durocher (FC)	70.00	35.00	21.00
221	Don Mueller	18.00	9.00	5.50
222	Bobby Morgan	20.00	10.00	6.00
223	Jimmy Russell	20.00	10.00	6.00
224	Jack Banta	20.00	10.00	6.00
225	Eddie Sawyer	18.00	9.00	5.50
226	*Jim Konstanty*	21.00	11.50	7.00
227	Bob Miller	18.00	9.00	5.50
228	Bill Nicholson	18.00	9.00	5.50
229	Frank Frisch	55.00	27.00	16.50
230	Bill Serena	18.00	9.00	5.50
231	Preston Ward	18.00	9.00	5.50
232	*Al Rosen*	50.00	25.00	15.00
233	Allie Clark	18.00	9.00	5.50
234	*Bobby Shantz*	25.00	12.50	7.50
235	Harold Gilbert	18.00	9.00	5.50
236	Bob Cain	18.00	9.00	5.50
237	Bill Salkeld	18.00	9.00	5.50
238	Nippy Jones	18.00	9.00	5.50
239	Bill Howerton	18.00	9.00	5.50
240	Eddie Lake	18.00	9.00	5.50
241	Neil Berry	18.00	9.00	5.50
242	Dick Kryhoski	18.00	9.00	5.50
243	Johnny Groth	18.00	9.00	5.50
244	Dale Coogan	18.00	9.00	5.50
245	Al Papai	18.00	9.00	5.50
246	*Walt Dropo*	25.00	12.50	7.50
247	*Irv Noren*	18.00	9.00	5.50
248	*Sam Jethroe*	21.00	11.50	7.00
249	"Snuffy" Stirnweiss	18.00	9.00	5.50
250	Ray Coleman	18.00	9.00	5.50
251	Les Moss	18.00	9.00	5.50
252	Billy DeMars	80.00	30.00	9.00

1951 Bowman

In 1951, Bowman increased the numbers of cards in its set for the third consecutive year when it issued 324 cards. The cards are, like 1950, color art reproductions of actual photographs but now measured 2-1/16" by 3-1/8" in size. The player's name is situated in a small, black box on the card front. Several of the card fronts are enlargements of the 1950 version. The high-numbered series of the set (#'s 253-324), which includes the rookie cards of Mantle and Mays, are the scarcest of the issue.

	NR MT	EX	VG
Complete Set (324):	21000.	10000.	6000.
Common Player (1-36):	22.00	11.00	6.50
Common Player (37-252):	15.00	7.50	4.50
Common Player (253-324):	55.00	27.00	16.50

1	*Whitey Ford*	1300.	575.00	300.00
2	Yogi Berra	350.00	175.00	105.00
3	Robin Roberts	80.00	40.00	25.00
4	Del Ennis	22.00	11.00	6.50
5	Dale Mitchell	22.00	11.00	6.50
6	Don Newcombe	35.00	17.50	10.50
7	Gil Hodges	75.00	37.50	22.50
8	Paul Lehner	22.00	11.00	6.50
9	Sam Chapman	22.00	11.00	6.50
10	Red Schoendienst	80.00	40.00	25.00
11	"Red" Munger	22.00	11.00	6.50
12	Hank Majeski	22.00	11.00	6.50
13	Ed Stanky	24.00	12.00	7.25
14	Alvin Dark	24.00	12.00	7.25
15	Johnny Pesky	22.00	11.00	6.50
16	Maurice McDermott	22.00	11.00	6.50
17	Pete Castiglione	22.00	11.00	6.50
18	Gil Coan	22.00	11.00	6.50
19	Sid Gordon	24.00	12.00	7.25
20	Del Crandall	22.00	11.00	6.50
21	"Snuffy" Stirnweiss	22.00	11.00	6.50
22	Hank Sauer	22.00	11.00	6.50
23	"Hoot" Evers	22.00	11.00	6.50
24	Ewell Blackwell	22.00	11.00	6.50
25	Vic Raschi	30.00	15.00	9.00
26	Phil Rizzuto	100.00	50.00	30.00
27	Jim Konstanty	22.00	11.00	6.50
28	Eddie Waitkus	22.00	11.00	6.50
29	Allie Clark	22.00	11.00	6.50
30	Bob Feller	125.00	62.00	37.00
31	Roy Campanella	260.00	130.00	78.00
32	Duke Snider	250.00	125.00	75.00
33	Bob Hooper	22.00	11.00	6.50
34	Marty Marion	25.00	12.50	7.50
35	Al Zarilla	22.00	11.00	6.50
36	Joe Dobson	22.00	11.00	6.50
37	Whitey Lockman	15.00	7.50	4.50
38	Al Evans	15.00	7.50	4.50
39	Ray Scarborough	15.00	7.50	4.50
40	*Gus Bell*	20.00	10.00	6.00
41	Eddie Yost	15.00	7.00	4.50
42	Vern Bickford	15.00	7.50	4.50
43	Billy DeMars	15.00	7.50	4.50
44	Roy Smalley	15.00	7.50	4.50
45	Art Houtteman	15.00	7.50	4.50
46	George Kell	65.00	32.50	19.50
47	Grady Hatton	15.00	7.50	4.50
48	Ken Raffensberger	15.00	7.50	4.50
49	Jerry Coleman	20.00	10.00	6.00
50	Johnny Mize	55.00	27.00	16.50
51	Andy Seminick	15.00	7.50	4.50
52	Dick Sisler	15.00	7.50	4.50
53	Bob Lemon	55.00	27.00	16.50
54	*Ray Boone*	20.00	10.00	6.00
55	Gene Hermanski	18.00	9.00	5.50
56	Ralph Branca	30.00	15.00	9.00
57	Alex Kellner	15.00	7.50	4.50
58	Enos Slaughter	55.00	27.00	16.50
59	Randy Gumpert	15.00	7.50	4.50
60	"Chico" Carrasquel	15.00	7.50	4.50
61	Jim Hearn	15.00	7.50	4.50
62	Lou Boudreau	55.00	27.00	16.50
63	Bob Dillinger	15.00	7.50	4.50
64	Bill Werle	15.00	7.50	4.50
65	Mickey Vernon	18.00	9.00	5.50
66	Bob Elliott	15.00	7.50	4.50
67	Roy Sievers	18.00	9.00	5.50
68	Dick Kokos	15.00	7.50	4.50
69	Johnny Schmitz	15.00	7.50	4.50
70	Ron Northey	15.00	7.50	4.50
71	Jerry Priddy	15.00	7.50	4.50
72	Lloyd Merriman	15.00	7.50	4.50
73	Tommy Byrne	20.00	10.00	6.00
74	Billy Johnson	20.00	10.00	6.00
75	Russ Meyer	15.00	7.50	4.50
76	Stan Lopata	15.00	7.50	4.50
77	Mike Goliat	15.00	7.50	4.50
78	Early Wynn	55.00	27.00	16.50
79	Jim Hegan	15.00	7.50	4.50
80	Pee Wee Reese	150.00	75.00	50.00
81	Carl Furillo	30.00	15.00	9.00
82	Joe Tipton	15.00	7.50	4.50
83	Carl Scheib	15.00	7.50	4.50
84	Barney McCosky	15.00	7.50	4.50
85	Eddie Kazak	15.00	7.50	4.50
86	Harry Brecheen	15.00	7.50	4.50
87	Floyd Baker	15.00	7.50	4.50
88	Eddie Robinson	15.00	7.50	4.50
89	Henry Thompson	15.00	7.50	4.50
90	Dave Koslo	15.00	7.50	4.50
91	Clyde Vollmer	15.00	7.50	4.50
92	Vern Stephens	15.00	7.50	4.50
93	Danny O'Connell	15.00	7.50	4.50
94	Clyde McCullough	15.00	7.50	4.50
95	Sherry Robertson	15.00	7.50	4.50
96	Sandy Consuegra	15.00	7.50	4.50
97	Bob Kuzava	15.00	7.50	4.50
98	Willard Marshall	15.00	7.50	4.50
99	Earl Torgeson	15.00	7.50	4.50
100	Sherman Lollar	15.00	7.50	4.50
101	Owen Friend	15.00	7.50	4.50
102	Emil "Dutch" Leonard	15.00	7.50	4.50
103	Andy Pafko	15.00	7.50	4.50
104	Virgil "Fire" Trucks	15.00	7.50	4.50
105	Don Kolloway	15.00	7.50	4.50

106	Pat Mullin	15.00	7.50	4.50
107	Johnny Wyrostek	15.00	7.50	4.50
108	Virgil Stallcup	15.00	7.50	4.50
109	Allie Reynolds	25.00	12.50	7.50
110	Bobby Brown	30.00	15.00	9.00
111	Curt Simmons	15.00	7.50	4.50
112	Willie Jones	15.00	7.50	4.50
113	Bill "Swish" Nicholson	15.00	7.50	4.50
114	Sam Zoldak	15.00	7.50	4.50
115	Steve Gromek	15.00	7.50	4.50
116	Bruce Edwards	18.00	9.00	5.50
117	Eddie Miksis	18.00	9.00	5.50
118	Preacher Roe	25.00	12.50	7.50
119	Eddie Joost	15.00	7.50	4.50
120	Joe Coleman	15.00	7.50	4.50
121	Gerry Staley	15.00	7.50	4.50
122	*Joe Garagiola*	125.00	62.50	37.50
123	Howie Judson	15.00	7.50	4.50
124	Gus Niarhos	15.00	7.50	4.50
125	Bill Rigney	15.00	7.50	4.50
126	Bobby Thomson	30.00	15.00	9.00
127	*Sal Maglie*	45.00	22.50	13.50
128	Ellis Kinder	15.00	7.50	4.50
129	Matt Batts	15.00	7.50	4.50
130	Tom Saffell	15.00	7.50	4.50
131	Cliff Chambers	15.00	7.50	4.50
132	Cass Michaels	15.00	7.50	4.50
133	Sam Dente	15.00	7.50	4.50
134	Warren Spahn	125.00	62.50	37.50
135	Walker Cooper	15.00	7.50	4.50
136	Ray Coleman	15.00	7.50	4.50
137	Dick Starr	15.00	7.50	4.50
138	Phil Cavarretta	15.00	7.50	4.50
139	Doyle Lade	15.00	7.50	4.50
140	Eddie Lake	15.00	7.50	4.50
141	Fred Hutchinson	18.00	9.00	5.50
142	Aaron Robinson	15.00	7.50	4.50
143	Ted Kluszewski	30.00	15.00	9.00
144	Herman Wehmeier	15.00	7.50	4.50
145	Fred Sanford	20.00	10.00	6.00
146	Johnny Hopp	20.00	10.00	6.00
147	Ken Heintzelman	15.00	7.50	4.50
148	Granny Hamner	15.00	7.50	4.50
149	"Bubba" Church	15.00	7.50	4.50
150	Mike Garcia	18.00	9.00	5.50
151	Larry Doby	20.00	10.00	6.00
152	Cal Abrams	18.00	9.00	5.50
153	Rex Barney	18.00	9.00	5.50
154	Pete Suder	15.00	7.50	4.50
155	Lou Brissie	15.00	7.50	4.50
156	Del Rice	15.00	7.50	4.50
157	Al Brazle	15.00	7.50	4.50
158	Chuck Diering	15.00	7.50	4.50
159	Eddie Stewart	15.00	7.50	4.50
160	Phil Masi	15.00	7.50	4.50
161	Wes Westrum	15.00	7.50	4.50
162	Larry Jansen	15.00	7.50	4.50
163	Monte Kennedy	15.00	7.50	4.50
164	Bill Wight	15.00	7.50	4.50
165	Ted Williams	650.00	325.00	195.00
166	Stan Rojek	15.00	7.50	4.50
167	Murry Dickson	15.00	7.50	4.50
168	Sam Mele	15.00	7.50	4.50
169	Sid Hudson	15.00	7.50	4.50
170	Sibby Sisti	15.00	7.50	4.50
171	Buddy Kerr	15.00	7.50	4.50
172	Ned Garver	15.00	7.50	4.50
173	Hank Arft	15.00	7.50	4.50
174	Mickey Owen	15.00	7.50	4.50
175	Wayne Terwilliger	15.00	7.50	4.50
176	Vic Wertz	15.00	7.50	4.50
177	Charlie Keller	15.00	7.50	4.50
178	Ted Gray	15.00	7.50	4.50
179	Danny Litwhiler	15.00	7.50	4.50
180	Howie Fox	15.00	7.50	4.50
181	Casey Stengel	110.00	55.00	33.00
182	Tom Ferrick	18.00	9.00	5.50
183	Hank Bauer	30.00	15.00	9.00
184	Eddie Sawyer	15.00	7.50	4.50
185	Jimmy Bloodworth	15.00	7.50	4.50
186	Richie Ashburn	55.00	27.00	16.50
187	Al Rosen	20.00	10.00	6.00
188	*Roberto Avila*	20.00	10.00	6.00
189	Erv Palica	18.00	9.00	5.50
190	Joe Hatten	18.00	9.00	5.50
191	Billy Hitchcock	15.00	7.50	4.50
192	Hank Wyse	15.00	7.50	4.50
193	Ted Wilks	15.00	7.50	4.50
194	Harry "Peanuts" Lowrey	15.00	7.50	4.50
195	Paul Richards	25.00	12.50	7.50
196	*Bill Pierce*	20.00	10.00	6.00
197	Bob Cain	15.00	7.50	4.50
198	*Monte Irvin*	100.00	50.00	30.00
199	Sheldon Jones	15.00	7.50	4.50
200	Jack Kramer	15.00	7.50	4.50
201	Steve O'Neill	15.00	7.50	4.50
202	Mike Guerra	15.00	7.50	4.50
203	*Vernon Law*	22.00	11.00	6.50
204	Vic Lombardi	15.00	7.50	4.50
205	Mickey Grasso	15.00	7.50	4.50
206	Connie Marrero	15.00	7.50	4.50
207	Billy Southworth	15.00	7.50	4.50
208	"Blix" Donnelly	15.00	7.50	4.50
209	Ken Wood	15.00	7.50	4.50
210	Les Moss	15.00	7.50	4.50
211	Hal Jeffcoat	15.00	7.50	4.50
212	Bob Rush	15.00	7.50	4.50
213	Neil Berry	15.00	7.50	4.50
214	Bob Swift	15.00	7.50	4.50
215	Kent Peterson	15.00	7.50	4.50
216	Connie Ryan	15.00	7.50	4.50
217	Joe Page	20.00	10.00	6.00
218	Ed Lopat	20.00	10.00	6.00
219	*Gene Woodling*	40.00	20.00	12.00
220	Bob Miller	15.00	7.50	4.50
221	Dick Whitman	15.00	7.50	4.50
222	Thurman Tucker	15.00	7.50	4.50
223	Johnny Vander Meer	15.00	7.50	4.50
224	Billy Cox	18.00	9.00	5.50
225	*Dan Bankhead*	20.00	10.00	6.00
226	Jimmy Dykes	18.00	9.00	4.50
227	Bobby Shantz	18.00	9.00	4.50
228	*Cloyd Boyer*	15.00	7.50	4.50
229	Bill Howerton	15.00	7.50	4.50
230	Max Lanier	15.00	7.50	4.50
231	Luis Aloma	15.00	7.50	4.50
232	*Nellie Fox*	125.00	67.00	37.00
233	Leo Durocher	65.00	32.00	19.50
234	Clint Hartung	15.00	7.50	4.50
235	Jack Lohrke	15.00	7.50	4.50
236	"Buddy" Rosar	15.00	7.50	4.50
237	Billy Goodman	15.00	7.50	4.50
238	Pete Reiser	18.00	9.00	5.50
239	Bill MacDonald	15.00	7.50	4.50
240	Joe Haynes	15.00	7.50	4.50
241	Irv Noren	15.00	7.50	4.50
242	Sam Jethroe	15.00	7.50	5.50
243	Johnny Antonelli	15.00	7.50	4.50
244	Cliff Fannin	15.00	7.50	4.50
245	John Berardino	22.00	11.00	6.50
246	Bill Serena	15.00	7.50	4.50
247	Bob Ramazotti	15.00	7.50	4.50
248	*Johnny Klippstein*	15.00	7.50	4.50
249	Johnny Groth	15.00	7.50	4.50
250	Hank Borowy	15.00	7.50	4.50
251	Willard Ramsdell	15.00	7.50	4.50
252	"Dixie" Howell	15.00	7.50	4.50
253	*Mickey Mantle*	8500.	4000.	2400.
254	*Jackie Jensen*	100.00	50.00	30.00
255	Milo Candini	55.00	27.00	16.50
256	Ken Silvestri	55.00	27.00	16.50
257	Birdie Tebbetts	55.00	27.00	16.50
258	*Luke Easter*	55.00	27.00	16.50
259	Charlie Dressen	70.00	35.00	21.00
260	*Carl Erskine*	90.00	45.00	27.00
261	Wally Moses	55.00	27.00	16.50
262	Gus Zernial	55.00	27.00	16.50
263	Howie Pollet	55.00	27.00	16.50
264	Don Richmond	55.00	27.00	16.50
265	*Steve Bilko*	55.00	27.00	16.50
266	Harry Dorish	55.00	27.00	16.50
267	Ken Holcombe	55.00	27.00	16.50
268	Don Mueller	55.00	27.00	16.50
269	Ray Noble	55.00	27.00	16.50
270	Willard Nixon	55.00	27.00	16.50
271	Tommy Wright	55.00	27.00	16.50
272	Billy Meyer	55.00	27.00	16.50
273	Danny Murtaugh	55.00	27.00	16.50
274	George Metkovich	55.00	27.00	16.50
275	Bucky Harris	90.00	45.00	27.00
276	Frank Quinn	55.00	27.00	16.50
277	Roy Hartsfield	55.00	27.00	16.50
278	Norman Roy	55.00	27.00	16.50
279	Jim Delsing	55.00	27.00	16.50
280	Frank Overmire	55.00	27.00	16.50
281	Al Widmar	55.00	27.00	16.50
282	Frank Frisch	90.00	45.00	27.00
283	Walt Dubiel	55.00	27.00	16.50
284	Gene Bearden	55.00	27.00	16.50
285	Johnny Lipon	55.00	27.00	16.50
286	Bob Usher	55.00	27.00	16.50
287	Jim Blackburn	55.00	27.00	16.50
288	Bobby Adams	55.00	27.00	16.50
289	Cliff Mapes	70.00	35.00	21.00
290	Bill Dickey (FC)	175.00	70.00	44.00
291	Tommy Henrich	70.00	35.00	20.00
292	Eddie Pellagrini	55.00	27.00	16.50
293	Ken Johnson	55.00	27.00	16.50
294	Jocko Thompson	55.00	27.00	16.50
295	Al Lopez	90.00	45.00	25.00
296	Bob Kennedy	55.00	27.00	16.50
297	Dave Philley	55.00	27.00	16.50
298	Joe Astroth	55.00	27.00	16.50
299	Clyde King	65.00	32.50	19.50
300	Hal Rice	55.00	27.00	16.50
301	Tommy Glaviano	55.00	27.00	16.50
302	Jim Busby	55.00	27.00	16.50
303	Marv Rotblatt	55.00	27.00	16.50
304	Allen Gettel	55.00	27.00	16.50
305	*Willie Mays*	3000.	1500.	750.00
306	*Jim Piersall*	100.00	50.00	30.00
307	Walt Masterson	55.00	27.00	16.50
308	Ted Beard	55.00	27.00	16.50
309	Mel Queen	55.00	27.00	16.50
310	Erv Dusak	55.00	27.00	16.50
311	Mickey Harris	55.00	27.00	16.50
312	*Gene Mauch*	65.00	32.50	19.50
313	Ray Mueller	55.00	27.00	16.50
314	Johnny Sain	65.00	32.50	19.50
315	Zack Taylor	55.00	27.00	16.50
316	Duane Pillette	55.00	27.00	16.50
317	*Smoky Burgess*	70.00	35.00	20.00
318	Warren Hacker	55.00	27.00	16.50
319	Red Rolfe	55.00	27.00	16.50
320	Hal White	55.00	27.00	16.50
321	Earl Johnson	55.00	27.00	16.50
322	Luke Sewell	55.00	27.00	16.50
323	*Joe Adcock*	100.00	50.00	30.00
324	Johnny Pramesa	110.00	30.00	18.00

Values quoted in this guide reflect the retail price of a card – the price a collector can expect to pay when buying a card from a dealer. The wholesale price – that which a collector can expect to receive from a dealer when selling cards – will be significantly lower, depending on desirability and condition.

Values for recent cards and sets are listed in Mint (MT), Near Mint (NM), reflecting the fact that many cards from recent years have been preserved in top condition. Recent cards and sets in less than Excellent condition have little collector interest.

1952 Bowman

MARTY MARION
Coach, Shortstop—St. Louis Browns
Born: Richburg, S. C., Dec. 1, 1917
Height: 6-2 Weight: 167
Bats: Right Throws: Right
"Mr. Shortstop" spent 11 seasons with the St. Louis Cardinals. In 1951 he was manager. Though his team was riddled with sickness and injuries, he brought it into a third-place finish. This year he joins the Browns as coach. Expects to continue playing at short.
No. 85 in the 1952 SERIES
BASEBALL
PICTURE CARDS

Bowman reverted back to a 252-card set in 1952, but retained the card size (2-1/16" by 3-1/8") employed the preceding year. The cards, which are color art reproductions of actual photographs, feature a facsimile autograph on the fronts.

		NR MT	EX	VG
	Complete Set (252):	9250.	4500.	2700.
	Common Player (1-36):	19.25	9.50	5.50
	Common Player (37-216):	18.00	9.00	5.50
	Common Player (217-252):	34.00	17.00	10.00
1	Yogi Berra	600.00	250.00	150.00
2	Bobby Thomson	27.00	13.50	8.00
3	Fred Hutchinson	19.25	9.50	5.50
4	Robin Roberts	60.00	30.00	18.00
5	*Minnie Minoso*	80.00	40.00	24.00
6	Virgil "Red" Stallcup	19.25	9.50	5.50
7	Mike Garcia	19.25	9.50	5.50
8	Pee Wee Reese	100.00	50.00	30.00
9	Vern Stephens	19.25	9.50	5.50
10	Bob Hooper	19.25	9.50	5.50
11	Ralph Kiner	60.00	30.00	18.00
12	Max Surkont	19.25	9.50	5.50
13	Cliff Mapes	19.25	9.50	5.50
14	Cliff Chambers	19.25	9.50	5.50
15	Sam Mele	19.25	9.50	5.50
16	Omar Lown	19.25	9.50	5.50
17	Ed Lopat	24.00	12.00	7.20
18	Don Mueller	19.25	9.50	5.50
19	Bob Cain	19.25	9.50	5.50
20	Willie Jones	19.25	9.50	5.50
21	Nellie Fox	40.00	20.00	12.00
22	Willard Ramsdell	19.25	9.50	5.50
23	Bob Lemon	55.00	27.00	16.50
24	Carl Furillo	30.00	15.00	9.00
25	Maurice McDermott	19.25	9.50	5.50
26	Eddie Joost	19.25	9.50	5.50
27	Joe Garagiola	65.00	32.00	19.50
28	Roy Hartsfield	19.25	9.50	5.50
29	Ned Garver	19.25	9.50	5.50
30	Red Schoendienst	60.00	30.00	18.00
31	Eddie Yost	19.25	9.50	5.50
32	Eddie Miksis	19.25	9.50	5.50
33	*Gil McDougald*	60.00	30.00	18.00
34	Al Dark	24.00	12.00	7.25
35	Granny Hamner	19.25	9.50	5.50
36	Cass Michaels	19.25	9.50	5.50
37	Vic Raschi	24.00	12.00	7.20
38	Whitey Lockman	18.00	9.00	5.50
39	Vic Wertz	18.00	9.00	5.50
40	"Bubba" Church	18.00	9.00	5.50
41	"Chico" Carrasquel	18.00	9.00	5.50
42	Johnny Wyrostek	18.00	9.00	5.50
43	Bob Feller	125.00	67.00	37.00
44	Roy Campanella	225.00	112.50	67.50
45	Johnny Pesky	18.00	9.00	5.50
46	Carl Scheib	18.00	9.00	5.50
47	Pete Castiglione	18.00	9.00	5.50
48	Vernon Bickford	18.00	9.00	5.50
49	Jim Hearn	18.00	9.00	5.50
50	Gerry Staley	18.00	9.00	5.50
51	Gil Coan	18.00	9.00	5.50
52	Phil Rizzuto	95.00	47.00	28.00
53	Richie Ashburn	50.00	25.00	15.00
54	Billy Pierce	20.00	10.00	6.00
55	Ken Raffensberger	18.00	9.00	5.50
56	Clyde King	22.00	11.00	6.50
57	Clyde Vollmer	18.00	9.00	5.50
58	Hank Majeski	18.00	9.00	5.50
59	Murry Dickson	18.00	9.00	5.50
60	Sid Gordon	20.00	10.00	6.00
61	Tommy Byrne	18.00	9.00	5.50
62	Joe Presko	18.00	9.00	5.50
63	Irv Noren	18.00	9.00	5.50
64	Roy Smalley	18.00	9.00	5.50
65	Hank Bauer	25.00	12.50	7.50
66	Sal Maglie	22.00	11.00	6.50
67	Johnny Groth	18.00	9.00	5.50
68	Jim Busby	18.00	9.00	5.50
69	Joe Adcock	20.00	10.00	6.00
70	Carl Erskine	24.00	12.00	7.20
71	Vernon Law	18.00	9.00	5.50
72	Earl Torgeson	18.00	9.00	5.50
73	Jerry Coleman	24.00	12.00	7.20
74	Wes Westrum	18.00	9.00	5.50
75	George Kell	50.00	25.00	15.00
76	Del Ennis	18.00	9.00	5.50
77	Eddie Robinson	18.00	9.00	5.50
78	Lloyd Merriman	18.00	9.00	5.50
79	Lou Brissie	18.00	9.00	5.50
80	Gil Hodges	80.00	40.00	25.00
81	Billy Goodman	18.00	9.00	5.50

82	Gus Zernial	18.00	9.00	5.50
83	Howie Pollet	18.00	9.00	5.50
84	Sam Jethroe	18.00	9.00	5.50
85	Marty Marion	20.00	10.00	6.00
86	Cal Abrams	22.00	11.00	6.50
87	Mickey Vernon	18.00	9.00	5.50
88	Bruce Edwards	18.00	9.00	5.50
89	Billy Hitchcock	18.00	9.00	5.50
90	Larry Jansen	18.00	9.00	5.50
91	Don Kolloway	18.00	9.00	5.50
92	Eddie Waitkus	18.00	9.00	5.50
93	Paul Richards	18.00	9.00	5.50
94	Luke Sewell	18.00	9.00	5.50
95	Luke Easter	18.00	9.00	5.50
96	Ralph Branca	24.00	12.00	7.20
97	Willard Marshall	18.00	9.00	5.50
98	Jimmy Dykes	18.00	9.00	5.50
99	Clyde McCullough	18.00	9.00	5.50
100	Sibby Sisti	18.00	9.00	5.50
101	Mickey Mantle	2600.	1250.	750.00
102	Peanuts Lowrey	18.00	9.00	5.50
103	Joe Haynes	18.00	9.00	5.50
104	Hal Jeffcoat	18.00	9.00	5.50
105	Bobby Brown	30.00	15.00	9.00
106	Randy Gumpert	18.00	9.00	5.50
107	Del Rice	18.00	9.00	5.50
108	George Metkovich	18.00	9.00	5.50
109	Tom Morgan	24.00	12.00	7.20
110	Max Lanier	18.00	9.00	5.50
111	"Hoot" Evers	18.00	9.00	5.50
112	"Smoky" Burgess	18.00	9.00	5.50
113	Al Zarilla	18.00	9.00	5.50
114	Frank Hiller	18.00	9.00	5.50
115	Larry Doby	25.00	12.50	7.50
116	Duke Snider	200.00	100.00	60.00
117	Bill Wight	18.00	9.00	5.50
118	Ray Murray	18.00	9.00	5.50
119	Bill Howerton	18.00	9.00	5.50
120	Chet Nichols	18.00	9.00	5.50
121	Al Corwin	18.00	9.00	5.50
122	Billy Johnson	18.00	9.00	5.50
123	Sid Hudson	18.00	9.00	5.50
124	Birdie Tebbetts	18.00	9.00	5.50
125	Howie Fox	18.00	9.00	5.50
126	Phil Cavarretta	18.00	9.00	5.50
127	Dick Sisler	18.00	9.00	5.50
128	Don Newcombe	25.00	12.50	7.50
129	Gus Niarhos	18.00	9.00	5.50
130	Allie Clark	18.00	9.00	5.50
131	Bob Swift	18.00	9.00	5.50
132	Dave Cole	18.00	9.00	5.50
133	Dick Kryhoski	18.00	9.00	5.50
134	Al Brazle	18.00	9.00	5.50
135	Mickey Harris	18.00	9.00	5.50
136	Gene Hermanski	18.00	9.00	5.50
137	Stan Rojek	18.00	9.00	5.50
138	Ted Wilks	18.00	9.00	5.50
139	Jerry Priddy	18.00	9.00	5.50
140	Ray Scarborough	18.00	9.00	5.50
141	Hank Edwards	18.00	9.00	5.50
142	Early Wynn	45.00	22.50	13.50
143	Sandy Consuegra	18.00	9.00	5.50
144	Joe Hatten	18.00	9.00	5.50
145	Johnny Mize	50.00	30.00	15.00
146	Leo Durocher	40.00	20.00	12.00
147	Marlin Stuart	18.00	9.00	5.50
148	Ken Heintzelman	18.00	9.00	5.50
149	Howie Judson	18.00	9.00	5.50
150	Herman Wehmeier	18.00	9.00	5.50
151	Al Rosen	20.00	10.00	6.00
152	Billy Cox	22.00	11.00	6.50
153	Fred Hatfield	18.00	9.00	5.50
154	Ferris Fain	18.00	9.00	5.50
155	Billy Meyer	18.00	9.00	5.50
156	Warren Spahn	90.00	45.00	27.00
157	Jim Delsing	18.00	9.00	5.50
158	Bucky Harris	40.00	20.00	12.00
159	Dutch Leonard	18.00	9.00	5.50
160	Eddie Stanky	20.00	10.00	6.00
161	Jackie Jensen	25.00	12.50	7.50
162	Monte Irvin	40.00	20.00	12.00
163	Johnny Lipon	18.00	9.00	5.50
164	Connie Ryan	18.00	9.00	5.50
165	Saul Rogovin	18.00	9.00	5.50
166	Bobby Adams	18.00	9.00	5.50
167	Bob Avila	20.00	10.00	6.00
168	Preacher Roe	25.00	12.50	7.50
169	Walt Dropo	18.00	9.00	5.50
170	Joe Astroth	18.00	9.00	5.50
171	Mel Queen	18.00	9.00	5.50
172	Ebba St. Claire	18.00	9.00	5.50
173	Gene Bearden	18.00	9.00	5.50
174	Mickey Grasso	18.00	9.00	5.50
175	Ransom Jackson	18.00	9.00	5.50
176	Harry Brecheen	18.00	9.00	5.50
177	Gene Woodling	20.00	10.00	6.00
178	Dave Williams	18.00	9.00	5.50
179	Pete Suder	18.00	9.00	5.50
180	Eddie Fitz Gerald	18.00	9.00	5.50
181	Joe Collins	24.00	12.00	7.20
182	Dave Koslo	18.00	9.00	5.50
183	Pat Mullin	18.00	9.00	5.50
184	Curt Simmons	18.00	9.00	5.50
185	Eddie Stewart	18.00	9.00	5.50
186	Frank Smith	18.00	9.00	5.50
187	Jim Hegan	18.00	9.00	5.50
188	Charlie Dressen	24.00	12.00	7.20
189	Jim Piersall	20.00	10.00	6.00
190	Dick Fowler	18.00	9.00	5.50
191	*Bob Friend*	20.00	10.00	6.00
192	John Cusick	18.00	9.00	5.50
193	Bobby Young	18.00	9.00	5.50
194	Bob Porterfield	18.00	9.00	5.50
195	Frank Baumholtz	18.00	9.00	5.50
196	Stan Musial	450.00	225.00	135.00
197	*Charlie Silvera*	24.00	12.00	7.20
198	Chuck Diering	18.00	9.00	5.50
199	Ted Gray	18.00	9.00	5.50
200	Ken Silvestri	18.00	9.00	5.50
201	Ray Coleman	18.00	9.00	5.50
202	Harry Perkowski	18.00	9.00	5.50
203	Steve Gromek	18.00	9.00	5.50
204	Andy Pafko	22.00	11.00	6.50
205	Walt Masterson	18.00	9.00	5.50
206	Elmer Valo	18.00	9.00	5.50
207	George Strickland	18.00	9.00	5.50
208	Walker Cooper	18.00	9.00	5.50
209	Dick Littlefield	18.00	9.00	5.50
210	Archie Wilson	18.00	9.00	5.50
211	Paul Minner	18.00	9.00	5.50
212	Solly Hemus	18.00	9.00	5.50
213	Monte Kennedy	18.00	9.00	5.50
214	Ray Boone	18.00	9.00	5.50
215	Sheldon Jones	18.00	9.00	5.50
216	Matt Batts	18.00	9.00	5.50
217	Casey Stengel	150.00	75.00	45.00
218	Willie Mays	1250.	625.00	375.00
219	Neil Berry	34.00	17.00	10.00
220	Russ Meyer	34.00	17.00	10.00
221	Lou Kretlow	34.00	17.00	10.00
222	"Dixie" Howell	34.00	17.00	10.00
223	*Harry Simpson*	35.00	17.50	10.50
224	Johnny Schmitz	36.00	18.00	10.75
225	Del Wilber	34.00	17.00	10.00
226	Alex Kellner	34.00	17.00	10.00
227	Clyde Sukeforth	34.00	17.00	10.00
228	Bob Chipman	34.00	17.00	10.00
229	Hank Arft	34.00	17.00	10.00
230	Frank Shea	34.00	17.00	10.00
231	*Dee Fondy*	34.00	17.00	10.00
232	Enos Slaughter	90.00	45.00	25.00
233	Bob Kuzava	40.00	20.00	12.00
234	Fred Fitzsimmons	34.00	17.00	10.00
235	Steve Souchock	34.00	17.00	10.00
236	Tommy Brown	34.00	17.00	10.00
237	Sherman Lollar	34.00	17.00	10.00
238	*Roy McMillan*	34.00	17.00	10.00
239	Dale Mitchell	34.00	17.00	10.00
240	*Billy Loes*	36.00	18.00	10.75
241	Mel Parnell	34.00	17.00	10.00
242	Everett Kell	34.00	17.00	10.00
243	"Red" Munger	34.00	17.00	10.00
244	*Lew Burdette*	70.00	35.00	21.00
245	George Schmees	34.00	17.00	10.00
246	Jerry Snyder	34.00	17.00	10.00
247	John Pramesa	34.00	17.00	10.00
248	Bill Werle	34.00	17.00	10.00
249	Henry Thompson	34.00	17.00	10.00
250	Ike Delock	34.00	17.00	10.00
251	Jack Lohrke	34.00	17.00	10.00
252	Frank Crosetti	125.00	45.00	20.00

1953 Bowman Color

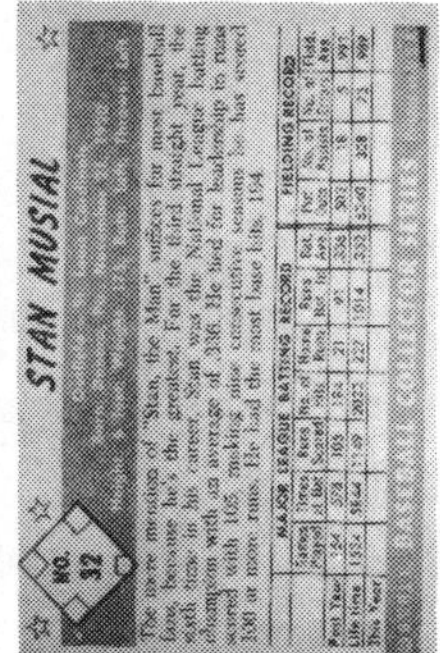

The first set of current major league players featuring actual color photographs, the 160-card 1953 Bowman Color set remains one of the most popular issues of the post-war era. The set is greatly appreciated for its uncluttered look; card fronts that contain no names, teams or facsimile autographs. Bowman increased the size of their cards to a 2-1/2" by 3-3/4" in order to better compete with Topps larger format. Bowman copied an idea from the 1952 Topps set and developed card backs that gave player career and previous-year statistics. The high-numbered cards (#s 113-160) are the scarcest of the set, with #s 113-128 being exceptionally difficult to find.

		NR MT	EX	VG
Complete Set (160):		10500.	5000.	3000.
Common Player (1-112):		25.00	12.50	7.50
Common Player (113-128):		50.00	25.00	15.00
Common Player (129-160):		35.00	17.50	10.50
1	Davey Williams	100.00	15.00	9.00
2	Vic Wertz	25.00	12.50	7.50
3	Sam Jethroe	25.00	12.50	7.50
4	Art Houtteman	25.00	12.50	7.50
5	Sid Gordon	32.00	16.00	9.50
6	Joe Ginsberg	25.00	12.50	7.50
7	Harry Chiti	25.00	12.50	7.50
8	Al Rosen	32.00	16.00	9.50
9	Phil Rizzuto	110.00	55.00	33.00
10	Richie Ashburn	75.00	37.00	22.00
11	Bobby Shantz	30.00	15.00	9.00
12	Carl Erskine	35.00	17.50	10.50
13	Gus Zernial	25.00	12.50	7.50
14	Billy Loes	35.00	17.50	10.50
15	Jim Busby	25.00	12.50	7.50
16	Bob Friend	25.00	12.50	7.50
17	Gerry Staley	25.00	12.50	7.50
18	Nellie Fox	65.00	32.50	19.50
19	Al Dark	30.00	15.00	9.00
20	Don Lenhardt	25.00	12.50	7.50
21	Joe Garagiola	60.00	30.00	18.00
22	Bob Porterfield	25.00	12.50	7.50
23	Herman Wehmeier	25.00	12.50	7.50
24	Jackie Jensen	35.00	17.50	10.50
25	"Hoot" Evers	25.00	12.50	7.50
26	Roy McMillan	25.00	12.50	7.50
27	Vic Raschi	35.00	17.50	10.50
28	"Smoky" Burgess	25.00	12.50	7.50
29	Roberto Avila	32.00	16.00	9.50
30	Phil Cavarretta	25.00	12.50	7.50
31	Jimmy Dykes	25.00	12.50	7.50
32	Stan Musial	500.00	250.00	150.00
33	Pee Wee Reese	450.00	225.00	135.00
34	Gil Coan	25.00	12.50	7.50
35	Maury McDermott	25.00	12.50	7.50
36	Minnie Minoso	35.00	17.50	10.50
37	Jim Wilson	25.00	12.50	7.50
38	Harry Byrd	25.00	12.50	7.50
39	Paul Richards	25.00	12.50	7.50
40	Larry Doby	35.00	17.50	10.50
41	Sammy White	25.00	12.50	7.50
42	Tommy Brown	25.00	12.50	7.50
43	Mike Garcia	25.00	12.50	7.50
44	Hank Bauer, Yogi Berra, Mickey Mantle	400.00	200.00	125.00
45	Walt Dropo	25.00	12.50	7.50
46	Roy Campanella	235.00	115.00	70.00
47	Ned Garver	25.00	12.50	7.50
48	Hank Sauer	25.00	12.50	7.50
49	Eddie Stanky	25.00	12.50	7.50
50	Lou Kretlow	25.00	12.50	7.50
51	Monte Irvin	50.00	25.00	15.00
52	Marty Marion	35.00	17.50	10.50
53	Del Rice	25.00	12.50	7.50
54	"Chico" Carrasquel	25.00	12.50	7.50
55	Leo Durocher	50.00	25.00	15.00
56	Bob Cain	25.00	12.50	7.50
57	Lou Boudreau	50.00	25.00	15.00
58	Willard Marshall	25.00	12.50	7.50
59	Mickey Mantle	2500.	1250.	750.00
60	Granny Hamner	25.00	12.50	7.50
61	George Kell	50.00	25.00	15.00
62	Ted Kluszewski	45.00	22.50	13.50
63	Gil McDougald	45.00	22.50	13.50
64	Curt Simmons	25.00	12.50	7.50
65	Robin Roberts	60.00	30.00	18.00
66	Mel Parnell	25.00	12.50	7.50
67	Mel Clark	25.00	12.50	7.50
68	Allie Reynolds	45.00	22.50	13.50
69	Charlie Grimm	25.00	12.50	7.50
70	Clint Courtney	25.00	12.50	7.50
71	Paul Minner	25.00	12.50	7.50
72	Ted Gray	25.00	12.50	7.50
73	Billy Pierce	32.00	16.00	9.50
74	Don Mueller	25.00	12.50	7.50
75	Saul Rogovin	25.00	12.50	7.50
76	Jim Hearn	25.00	12.50	7.50
77	Mickey Grasso	25.00	12.50	7.50
78	Carl Furillo	45.00	22.50	13.50
79	Ray Boone	25.00	12.50	7.50
80	Ralph Kiner	60.00	30.00	18.00
81	Enos Slaughter	60.00	30.00	18.00
82	Joe Astroth	25.00	12.50	7.50
83	Jack Daniels	25.00	12.50	7.50
84	Hank Bauer	45.00	22.50	13.50
85	Solly Hemus	25.00	12.50	7.50
86	Harry Simpson	25.00	12.50	7.50
87	Harry Perkowski	25.00	12.50	7.50
88	Joe Dobson	25.00	12.50	7.50
89	Sandalio Consuegra	25.00	12.50	7.50
90	Joe Nuxhall	25.00	12.50	7.50
91	Steve Souchock	25.00	12.50	7.50
92	Gil Hodges	100.00	50.00	30.00
93	Billy Martin, Phil Rizzuto	200.00	100.00	60.00
94	Bob Addis	25.00	12.50	7.50
95	Wally Moses	25.00	12.50	7.50
96	Sal Maglie	32.00	16.00	9.50
97	Eddie Mathews (FC)	175.00	87.50	52.50
98	Hector Rodriquez	25.00	12.50	7.50
99	Warren Spahn	175.00	87.50	52.50
100	Bill Wight	25.00	12.50	7.50
101	Red Schoendienst	80.00	40.00	25.00
102	Jim Hegan	25.00	12.50	7.50
103	Del Ennis	25.00	12.50	7.50
104	Luke Easter	25.00	12.50	7.50
105	Eddie Joost	25.00	12.50	7.50
106	Ken Raffensberger	25.00	12.50	7.50
107	Alex Kellner	25.00	12.50	7.50
108	Bobby Adams	25.00	12.50	7.50
109	Ken Wood	25.00	12.50	7.50
110	Bob Rush	25.00	12.50	7.50
111	Jim Dyck	25.00	12.50	7.50
112	Toby Atwell	25.00	12.50	7.50
113	Karl Drews	50.00	25.00	15.00
114	Bob Feller	250.00	125.00	75.00
115	Cloyd Boyer	50.00	25.00	15.00
116	Eddie Yost	50.00	25.00	15.00
117	Duke Snider	600.00	300.00	175.00
118	Billy Martin (FC)	225.00	112.50	67.50
119	Dale Mitchell	50.00	25.00	15.00
120	Marlin Stuart	50.00	25.00	15.00
121	Yogi Berra	450.00	225.00	135.00
122	Bill Serena	50.00	25.00	15.00
123	Johnny Lipon	50.00	25.00	15.00
124	Charlie Dressen	55.00	27.50	16.50
125	Fred Hatfield	50.00	25.00	15.00
126	Al Corwin	50.00	25.00	15.00
127	Dick Kryhoski	50.00	25.00	15.00
128	"Whitey" Lockman	50.00	25.00	15.00
129	Russ Meyer	45.00	22.50	13.50
130	Cass Michaels	35.00	17.50	10.50
131	Connie Ryan	35.00	17.50	10.50
132	Fred Hutchinson	35.00	17.50	10.50

No.	Player	NR MT	EX	VG
133	Willie Jones	35.00	17.50	10.50
134	Johnny Pesky	35.00	17.50	10.50
135	Bobby Morgan	45.00	22.50	13.50
136	Jim Bridewеser	50.00	25.00	15.00
137	Sam Dente	35.00	17.50	10.50
138	"Bubba" Church	35.00	17.50	10.50
139	Pete Runnels	35.00	17.50	10.50
140	Alpha Brazle	35.00	17.50	10.50
141	Frank "Spec" Shea	35.00	17.50	10.50
142	Larry Miggins	35.00	17.50	10.50
143	Al Lopez (FC)	50.00	25.00	15.00
144	Warren Hacker	35.00	17.50	10.50
145	George Shuba	45.00	22.50	13.50
146	Early Wynn	110.00	55.00	33.00
147	Clem Koshorek	35.00	17.50	10.50
148	Billy Goodman	35.00	17.50	10.50
149	Al Corwin	35.00	17.50	10.50
150	Carl Scheib	35.00	17.50	10.50
151	Joe Adcock	42.50	21.25	12.75
152	Clyde Vollmer	35.00	17.50	10.50
153	Whitey Ford	400.00	200.00	120.00
154	Omar "Turk" Lown	35.00	17.50	10.50
155	Allie Clark	35.00	17.50	10.50
156	Max Surkont	35.00	17.50	10.50
157	Sherman Lollar	35.00	17.50	10.50
158	Howard Fox	35.00	17.50	10.50
159	Mickey Vernon (Photo actually Floyd Baker)	35.00	17.50	10.50
160	Cal Abrams	90.00	20.00	12.00

1953 Bowman Black & White

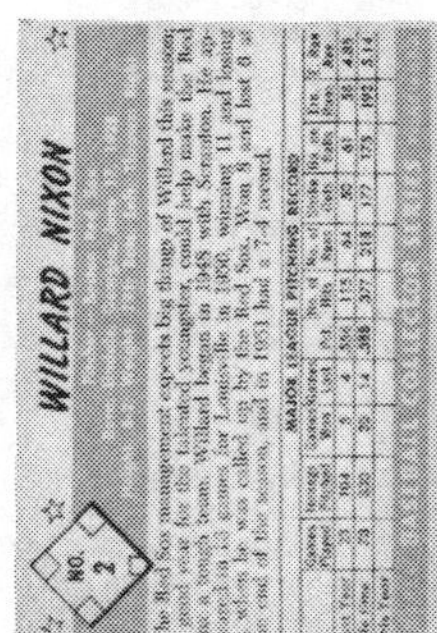

The 1953 Bowman Black and White set is similar in all respects to the 1953 Bowman Color set, except that it lacks color. Purportedly, high costs in producing the color series forced Bowman to issue the set in black and white. Sixty-four cards, which measure 2-1/2" by 3-3/4", comprise the set.

No.	Player	NR MT	EX	VG
	Complete Set (64):	2500.	1200.	700.00
	Common Player:	35.00	17.50	10.50
1	Gus Bell	110.00	35.00	12.00
2	Willard Nixon	35.00	17.50	10.50
3	Bill Rigney	35.00	17.50	10.50
4	Pat Mullin	35.00	17.50	10.50
5	Dee Fondy	35.00	17.50	10.50
6	Ray Murray	35.00	17.50	10.50
7	Andy Seminick	35.00	17.50	10.50
8	Pete Suder	35.00	17.50	10.50
9	Walt Masterson	35.00	17.50	10.50
10	Dick Sisler	35.00	17.50	10.50
11	Dick Gernert	35.00	17.50	10.50
12	Randy Jackson	35.00	17.50	10.50
13	Joe Tipton	35.00	17.50	10.50
14	Bill Nicholson	35.00	17.50	10.50
15	Johnny Mize	110.00	55.00	33.00
16	Stu Miller	35.00	17.50	10.50
17	Virgil Trucks	35.00	17.50	10.50
18	Billy Hoeft	35.00	17.50	10.50
19	Paul LaPalme	35.00	17.50	10.50
20	Eddie Robinson	35.00	17.50	10.50
21	Clarence "Bud" Podbielan	35.00	17.50	10.50
22	Matt Batts	35.00	17.50	10.50
23	Wilmer Mizell	37.50	18.75	11.25
24	Del Wilber	35.00	17.50	10.50
25	Johnny Sain	55.00	27.00	16.50
26	Preacher Roe	55.00	27.00	16.50
27	Bob Lemon	110.00	55.00	33.00
28	Hoyt Wilhelm (FC)	110.00	55.00	33.00
29	Sid Hudson	35.00	17.50	10.50
30	Walker Cooper	35.00	17.50	10.50
31	Gene Woodling	50.00	25.00	15.00
32	Rocky Bridges	35.00	17.50	10.50
33	Bob Kuzava	45.00	22.50	13.50
34	Ebba St. Clair (St. Claire)	35.00	17.50	10.50
35	Johnny Wyrostek	35.00	17.50	10.50
36	Jim Piersall	50.00	25.00	15.00
37	Hal Jeffcoat	35.00	17.50	10.50
38	Dave Cole	35.00	17.50	10.50
39	Casey Stengel	300.00	150.00	90.00
40	Larry Jansen	35.00	17.50	10.50
41	Bob Ramazotti	35.00	17.50	10.50
42	Howie Judson	35.00	17.50	10.50
43	Hal Bevan	35.00	17.50	10.50
44	Jim Delsing	35.00	17.50	10.50
45	Irv Noren	45.00	22.50	13.50
46	Bucky Harris	55.00	27.00	16.50
47	Jack Lohrke	35.00	17.50	10.50
48	Steve Ridzik	35.00	17.50	10.50
49	Floyd Baker	35.00	17.50	10.50
50	Emil "Dutch" Leonard	35.00	17.50	10.50
51	Lew Burdette	37.50	18.75	11.25
52	Ralph Branca	45.00	22.50	13.50
53	Morris Martin	35.00	17.50	10.50
54	Bill Miller	45.00	22.50	13.50
55	Don Johnson	35.00	17.50	10.50
56	Roy Smalley	35.00	17.50	10.50
57	Andy Pafko	35.00	17.50	10.50
58	Jim Konstanty	35.00	17.50	10.50
59	Duane Pillette	35.00	17.50	10.50
60	Billy Cox	40.00	20.00	12.00
61	Tom Gorman	45.00	22.50	13.50
62	Keith Thomas	35.00	17.50	10.50
63	Steve Gromek	35.00	17.50	10.50
64	Andy Hansen	50.00	17.50	10.50

1954 Bowman

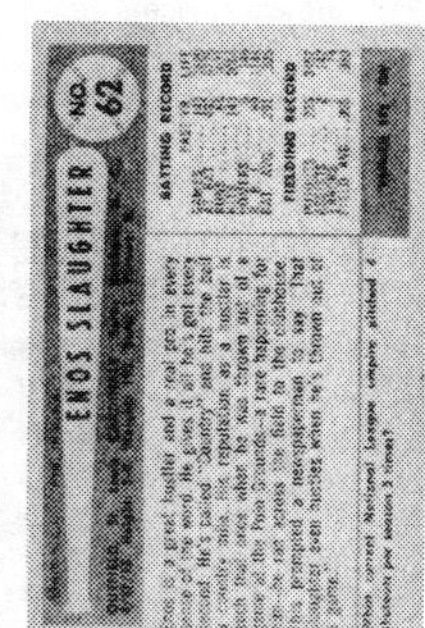

Bowman's 1954 set consists of 224 full-color cards that measure 2-1/2" by 3-3/4". It is believed that contractual problems caused the pulling of card #66 (Ted Williams) from the set, creating one of the most sought-after scarcities of the post-war era. The Williams card was replaced by Jim Piersall (who is also #210) in subsequent print runs. The set contains over 40 variations, most involving statistical errors on the card backs that were corrected. On most cards neither variation carries a premium value as both varieties appear to have been printed in equal amounts. The complete set price that follows does not include all variations or #66 Williams.

No.	Player	NR MT	EX	VG
	Complete Set (224):	4500.	2250.	1250.
	Common Player (1-112):	9.00	4.50	2.75
	Common Player (113-224):	12.00	6.00	3.50
1	Phil Rizzuto	150.00	75.00	45.00
2	Jack Jensen	12.00	6.00	3.50
3	Marion Fricano	9.00	4.50	2.75
4	Bob Hooper	9.00	4.50	2.75
5	Billy Hunter	9.00	4.50	2.75
6	Nellie Fox	30.00	15.00	9.00
7	Walter Dropo	9.00	4.50	2.75
8	Jim Busby	9.00	4.50	2.75
9	Dave Williams	9.00	4.50	2.75
10	Carl Erskine	12.00	6.00	3.50
11	Sid Gordon	10.00	5.00	3.00
12a	Roy McMillan (551/1290 At Bat)	9.00	4.50	2.75
12b	Roy McMillan (557/1296 At Bat)	9.00	4.50	2.75
13	Paul Minner	9.00	4.50	2.75
14	Gerald Staley	9.00	4.50	2.75
15	Richie Ashburn	35.00	17.50	10.50
16	Jim Wilson	9.00	4.50	2.75
17	Tom Gorman	15.00	7.50	4.50
18	"Hoot" Evers	9.00	4.50	2.75
19	Bobby Shantz	10.00	5.00	3.00
20	Artie Houtteman	9.00	4.50	2.75
21	Vic Wertz	9.00	4.50	2.75
22a	Sam Mele (213/1661 Putouts)	9.00	4.50	2.75
22b	Sam Mele (217/1665 Putouts)	9.00	4.50	2.75
23	*Harvey Kuenn*	35.00	17.50	10.50
24	Bob Porterfield	9.00	4.50	2.75
25a	Wes Westrum (1.000/.987 Field Avg.)	9.00	4.50	2.75
25b	Wes Westrum (.982/.986 Field Avg.)	9.00	4.50	2.75
26a	Billy Cox (1.000/.960 Field Avg.)	12.00	6.00	3.50
26b	Billy Cox (.972/.960 Field Avg.)	12.00	6.00	3.50
27	Dick Cole	9.00	4.50	2.75
28a	Jim Greengrass (Birthplace Addison, N.J.)	9.00	4.50	2.75
28b	Jim Greengrass (Birthplace Addison, N.Y.)	9.00	4.50	2.75
29	Johnny Klippstein	9.00	4.50	2.75
30	Del Rice	9.00	4.50	2.75
31	"Smoky" Burgess	9.00	4.50	2.75
32	Del Crandall	9.00	4.50	2.75
33a	Vic Raschi (no trade line)	12.00	6.00	3.50
33b	Vic Raschi (traded line)	30.00	15.00	9.00
34	Sammy White	9.00	4.50	2.75
35a	Eddie Joost (quiz answer is 8)	9.00	4.50	2.75
35b	Eddie Joost (quiz answer is 33)	9.00	4.50	2.75
36	George Strickland	9.00	4.50	2.75
37	Dick Kokos	9.00	4.50	2.75
38a	Minnie Minoso (.895/.961 Field Avg.)	12.00	6.00	3.60
38b	Minnie Minoso (.963/.963 Field Avg.)	12.00	6.00	3.60
39	Ned Garver	9.00	4.50	2.75
40	Gil Coan	9.00	4.50	2.75
41a	Alvin Dark (.986/.960 Field Avg.)	10.00	5.00	3.00
41b	Alvin Dark (.968/.960 Field Avg.)	10.00	5.00	3.00
42	Billy Loes	12.00	6.00	3.50
43a	Bob Friend (20 shutouts in quiz question)	9.00	4.50	2.75
43b	Bob Friend (16 shutouts in quiz question)	9.00	4.50	2.75
44	Harry Perkowski	9.00	4.50	2.75
45	Ralph Kiner	35.00	17.50	10.50
46	"Rip" Repulski	9.00	4.50	2.75
47a	Granny Hamner (.970/.953 Field Avg.)	9.00	4.50	2.75
47b	Granny Hamner (.953/.951 Field Avg.)	9.00	4.50	2.75
48	Jack Dittmer	9.00	4.50	2.75
49	Harry Byrd	15.00	7.50	4.50
50	George Kell	30.00	15.00	9.00
51	Alex Kellner	9.00	4.50	2.75
52	Joe Ginsberg	9.00	4.50	2.75
53a	Don Lenhardt (.969/.984 Field Avg.)	9.00	4.50	2.75
53b	Don Lenhardt (.966/.983 Field Avg.)	9.00	4.50	2.75
54	"Chico" Carrasquel	9.00	4.50	2.75
55	Jim Delsing	9.00	4.50	2.75
56	Maurice McDermott	9.00	4.50	2.75
57	Hoyt Wilhelm	35.00	17.50	10.50
58	Pee Wee Reese	65.00	32.00	19.50
59	Bob Schultz	9.00	4.50	2.75
60	Fred Baczewski	9.00	4.50	2.75
61a	Eddie Miksis (.954/.962 Field Avg.)	9.00	4.50	2.75
61b	Eddie Miksis (.954/.961 Field Avg.)	9.00	4.50	2.75
62	Enos Slaughter	40.00	20.00	12.00
63	Earl Torgeson	9.00	4.50	2.75
64	Eddie Mathews	60.00	30.00	18.00
65	Mickey Mantle	925.00	460.00	275.00
66a	Ted Williams	4250.	2000.	1200.
66b	Jimmy Piersall	100.00	50.00	30.00
67a	Carl Scheib (.306 Pct. with two lines under bio)	9.00	4.50	2.75
67b	Carl Scheib (.306 Pct. with one line under bio)	9.00	4.50	2.75
67c	Carl Scheib (.300 Pct.)	9.00	4.50	2.75
68	Bob Avila	10.00	5.00	3.00
69	Clinton Courtney	9.00	4.50	2.75
70	Willard Marshall	9.00	4.50	2.75
71	Ted Gray	9.00	4.50	2.75
72	Ed Yost	9.00	4.50	2.75
73	Don Mueller	9.00	4.50	2.75
74	Jim Gilliam (FC)	18.00	9.00	6.50
75	Max Surkont	9.00	4.50	2.75
76	Joe Nuxhall	9.00	4.50	2.75
77	Bob Rush	9.00	4.50	2.75
78	Sal Yvars	9.00	4.50	2.75
79	Curt Simmons	9.00	4.50	2.75
80a	Johnny Logan (106 Runs)	9.00	4.50	2.75
80b	Johnny Logan (100 Runs)	9.00	4.50	2.75
81a	Jerry Coleman (1.000/.975 Field Avg.)	15.00	7.50	4.50
81b	Jerry Coleman (.952/.975 Field Avg.)	15.00	7.50	4.50
82a	Bill Goodman (.965/.986 Field Avg.)	9.00	4.50	2.75
82b	Bill Goodman (.972/.985 Field Avg.)	9.00	4.50	2.75
83	Ray Murray	9.00	4.50	2.75
84	Larry Doby	12.00	6.00	3.50
85a	Jim Dyck (.926/.956 Field Avg.)	9.00	4.50	2.75
85b	Jim Dyck (.947/.960 Field Avg.)	9.00	4.50	2.75
86	Harry Dorish	9.00	4.50	2.75
87	Don Lund	9.00	4.50	2.75
88	Tommy Umphlett	9.00	4.50	2.75
89	Willie Mays	375.00	185.00	110.00
90	Roy Campanella	165.00	87.50	49.50
91	Cal Abrams	9.00	4.50	2.75
92	Ken Raffensberger	9.00	4.50	2.75
93a	Bill Serena (.983/.966 Field Avg.)	9.00	4.50	2.75
93b	Bill Serena (.977/.966 Field Avg.)	9.00	4.50	2.75
94a	Solly Hemus (476/1343 Assists)	9.00	4.50	2.75
94b	Solly Hemus (477/1343 Assists)	9.00	4.50	2.75
95	Robin Roberts	35.00	17.50	10.50
96	Joe Adcock	10.00	5.00	3.00
97	Gil McDougald	20.00	10.00	6.00
98	Ellis Kinder	9.00	4.50	2.75
99a	Peter Suder (.985/.974 Field Avg.)	9.00	4.50	2.75
99b	Peter Suder (.978/.974 Field Avg.)	9.00	4.50	2.75
100	Mike Garcia	9.00	4.50	2.75
101	*Don Larsen*	40.00	20.00	12.00
102	Bill Pierce	10.00	5.00	3.00
103a	Stephen Souchock (144/1192 Putouts)	9.00	4.50	2.75
103b	Stephen Souchock (147/1195 Putouts)	9.00	4.50	2.75
104	Frank Spec Shea	9.00	4.50	2.75
105a	Sal Maglie (quiz answer is 8)	10.00	5.00	3.00
105b	Sal Maglie (quiz answer is 1904)	10.00	5.00	3.00
106	Clem Labine	12.00	6.00	3.50
107	Paul LaPalme	9.00	4.50	2.75
108	Bobby Adams	9.00	4.50	2.75
109	Roy Smalley	9.00	4.50	2.75
110	Red Schoendienst	35.00	17.50	10.50
111	Murry Dickson	9.00	4.50	2.75
112	Andy Pafko	9.00	4.50	2.75
113	Allie Reynolds	20.00	10.00	6.00
114	Willard Nixon	12.00	6.00	3.50
115	Don Bollweg	12.00	6.00	3.50
116	Luke Easter	12.00	6.00	3.50
117	Dick Kryhoski	12.00	6.00	3.50
118	Bob Boyd	12.00	6.00	3.50
119	Fred Hatfield	12.00	6.00	3.50
120	Mel Hoderlein	12.00	6.00	3.50
121	Ray Katt	12.00	6.00	3.50
122	Carl Furillo	20.00	10.00	6.00
123	Toby Atwell	12.00	6.00	3.50
124a	Gus Bell (15/27 Errors)	12.00	6.00	3.50

124b	Gus Bell (11/26 Errors)	12.00	6.00	3.50
125	Warren Hacker	12.00	6.00	3.50
126	Cliff Chambers	12.00	6.00	3.50
127	Del Ennis	12.00	6.00	3.50
128	Ebba St. Claire	12.00	6.00	3.50
129	Hank Bauer	20.00	10.00	6.00
130	Milt Bolling	12.00	6.00	3.50
131	Joe Astroth	12.00	6.00	3.50
132	Bob Feller	100.00	50.00	30.00
133	Duane Pillette	12.00	6.00	3.50
134	Luis Aloma	12.00	6.00	3.50
135	Johnny Pesky	12.00	6.00	3.50
136	Clyde Vollmer	12.00	6.00	3.50
137	Al Corwin	12.00	6.00	3.50
138a	Gil Hodges (.993/.991 Field Avg.)	60.00	30.00	18.00
138b	Gil Hodges (.992/.991 Field Avg.)	45.00	22.50	13.50
139a	Preston Ward (.961/.992 Field Avg.)	12.00	6.00	3.50
139b	Preston Ward (.990/.992 Field Avg.)	12.00	6.00	3.50
140a	Saul Rogovin (7-12 Won/Lost with 2 Strikeouts)	12.00	6.00	3.50
140b	Saul Rogovin (7-12 Won/Lost with 62 Strikeouts)	12.00	6.00	3.50
140c	Saul Rogovin (8-12 Won/Lost)	12.00	6.00	3.50
141	Joe Garagiola	35.00	17.50	10.50
142	Al Brazle	12.00	6.00	3.50
143	Willie Jones	12.00	6.00	3.50
144	*Ernie Johnson*	15.00	7.50	4.50
145a	Billy Martin (.985/.983 Field Avg.)	35.00	17.50	10.50
145b	Billy Martin (.983/.982 Field Avg.)	45.00	22.50	13.50
146	Dick Gernert	12.00	6.00	3.50
147	Joe DeMaestri	12.00	6.00	3.50
148	Dale Mitchell	12.00	6.00	3.50
149	Bob Young	12.00	6.00	3.50
150	Cass Michaels	12.00	6.00	3.50
151	Pat Mullin	12.00	6.00	3.50
152	Mickey Vernon	12.00	6.00	3.50
153a	"Whitey" Lockman (100/331 Assists)	12.00	6.00	3.50
153b	"Whitey" Lockman (102/333 Assists)	12.00	6.00	3.50
154	Don Newcombe	27.50	13.50	8.25
155	*Frank J. Thomas*	12.00	6.00	3.50
156a	Rocky Bridges (320/467 Assists)	12.00	6.00	3.50
156b	Rocky Bridges (328/475 Assists)	12.00	6.00	3.50
157	Omar Lown	12.00	6.00	3.50
158	Stu Miller	12.00	6.00	3.50
159	John Lindell	12.00	6.00	3.50
160	Danny O'Connell	12.00	6.00	3.50
161	Yogi Berra	150.00	75.00	45.00
162	Ted Lepcio	12.00	6.00	3.50
163a	Dave Philley (152 Games, no traded line)	12.00	6.00	3.50
163b	Dave Philley (152 Games, traded line)	25.00	12.50	7.50
163c	Dave Philley (157 Games, traded line)	12.00	6.00	3.50
164	Early Wynn	45.00	22.50	13.50
165	Johnny Groth	12.00	6.00	3.50
166	Sandy Consuegra	12.00	6.00	3.50
167	Bill Hoeft	12.00	6.00	3.50
168	Edward Fitz Gerald	12.00	6.00	3.50
169	Larry Jansen	12.00	6.00	3.50
170	Duke Snider	175.00	87.00	52.00
171	Carlos Bernier	12.00	6.00	3.50
172	Andy Seminick	12.00	6.00	3.50
173	Dee Fondy	12.00	6.00	3.50
174a	Pete Castiglione (.966/.959 Field Avg.)	12.00	6.00	3.50
174b	Pete Castiglione (.970/.959 Field Avg.)	12.00	6.00	3.50
175	Mel Clark	12.00	6.00	3.50
176	Vernon Bickford	12.00	6.00	3.50
177	Whitey Ford	90.00	45.00	27.00
178	Del Wilber	12.00	6.00	3.50
179a	Morris Martin (44 ERA)	12.00	6.00	3.50
179b	Morris Martin (4.44 ERA)	12.00	6.00	3.50
180	Joe Tipton	12.00	6.00	3.50
181	Les Moss	12.00	6.00	3.50
182	Sherman Lollar	12.00	6.00	3.50
183	Matt Batts	12.00	6.00	3.50
184	Mickey Grasso	12.00	6.00	3.50
185a	*Daryl Spencer* (.941/.944 Field Avg.)	12.00	6.00	3.50
185b	*Daryl Spencer* (.933/.936 Field Avg.)	12.00	6.00	3.50
186	Russ Meyer	15.00	7.50	4.50
187	Vern Law	12.00	6.00	3.50
188	Frank Smith	12.00	6.00	3.50
189	Ransom Jackson	12.00	6.00	3.50
190	Joe Presko	12.00	6.00	3.50
191	Karl Drews	12.00	6.00	3.50
192	Lew Burdette	14.00	7.00	4.25
193	Eddie Robinson	18.00	9.00	5.50
194	Sid Hudson	12.00	6.00	3.50
195	Bob Cain	12.00	6.00	3.50
196	Bob Lemon	35.00	17.50	10.50
197	Lou Kretlow	12.00	6.00	3.50
198	Virgil Trucks	12.00	6.00	3.50
199	Steve Gromek	12.00	6.00	3.50
200	Connie Marrero	12.00	6.00	3.50
201	Bob Thomson	20.00	10.00	6.00
202	George Shuba	15.00	7.50	4.50
203	Vic Janowicz	15.00	7.50	4.50
204	Jack Collum	12.00	6.00	3.50
205	Hal Jeffcoat	12.00	6.00	3.50
206	Steve Bilko	12.00	6.00	3.50
207	Stan Lopata	12.00	6.00	3.50
208	Johnny Antonelli	12.00	6.00	3.50
209	Gene Woodling (photo reversed)	18.00	9.00	5.50
210	Jimmy Piersall	15.00	7.50	4.50
211	Jim Robertson	12.00	6.00	3.50
212a	Owen Friend (.964/.957 Field Avg.)	12.00	6.00	3.50
212b	Owen Friend (.967/.958 Field Avg.)	12.00	6.00	3.50
213	Dick Littlefield	12.00	6.00	3.50
214	Ferris Fain	12.00	6.00	3.50
215	Johnny Bucha	12.00	6.00	3.50
216a	Jerry Snyder (.988/.988 Field Avg.)	12.00	6.00	3.50
216b	Jerry Snyder (.968/.968 Field Avg.)	12.00	6.00	3.50
217a	Henry Thompson (.956/.951 Field Avg.)	12.00	6.00	3.50
217b	Henry Thompson (.958/.952 Field Avg.)	12.00	6.00	3.50
218	Preacher Roe	15.00	7.50	4.50
219	Hal Rice	12.00	6.00	3.50
220	Hobie Landrith	12.00	6.00	3.50
221	Frank Baumholtz	12.00	6.00	3.50
222	Memo Luna	12.00	6.00	3.50
223	Steve Ridzik	12.00	6.00	3.50
224	Billy Bruton	24.00	6.00	3.50

1955 Bowman

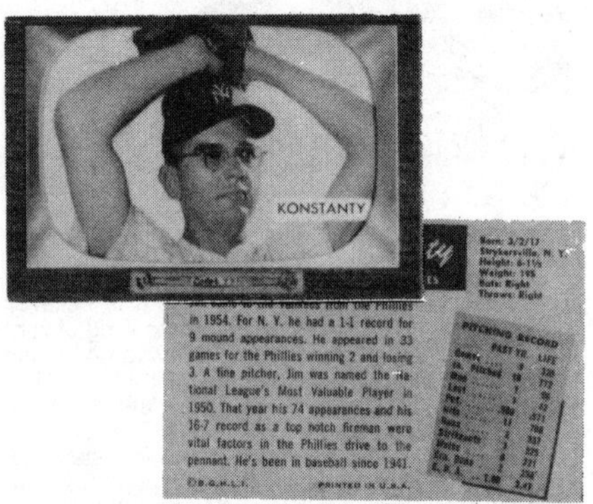

Bowman produced its final baseball card set in 1955, a popular issue which has player photographs placed inside a television set design. The set consists of 320 cards that measure 2-1/2" by 3-3/4" in size. High-numbered cards (#s 225-320) appear to have replaced certain low-numbered cards on the press sheets and are somewhat scarcer. The high series includes 31 umpire cards.

	NR MT	EX	VG
Complete Set (320):	5000.	2500.	1500.
Common Player (1-96):	7.00	3.50	2.00
Common Player (97-224):	5.00	2.50	1.50
Common Player (225-320):	15.00	7.50	4.50

		NR MT	EX	VG
1	Hoyt Wilhelm	80.00	20.00	12.00
2	Al Dark	10.00	5.00	3.00
3	Joe Coleman	7.00	3.50	2.00
4	Eddie Waitkus	7.00	3.50	2.00
5	Jim Robertson	7.00	3.50	2.00
6	Pete Suder	7.00	3.50	2.00
7	Gene Baker	7.00	3.50	2.00
8	Warren Hacker	7.00	3.50	2.00
9	Gil McDougald	15.00	7.50	4.50
10	Phil Rizzuto	35.00	17.50	10.50
11	Billy Bruton	7.00	3.50	2.00
12	Andy Pafko	7.00	3.50	2.00
13	Clyde Vollmer	7.00	3.50	2.00
14	Gus Keriazakos	7.00	3.50	2.00
15	*Frank Sullivan*	7.00	3.50	2.00
16	Jim Piersall	10.00	5.00	3.00
17	Del Ennis	7.00	3.50	2.00
18	Stan Lopata	7.00	3.50	2.00
19	Bobby Avila	10.00	5.00	3.00
20	Al Smith	7.00	3.50	2.00
21	Don Hoak (FC)	9.00	4.50	2.75
22	Roy Campanella	100.00	50.00	30.00
23	Al Kaline (FC)	90.00	45.00	27.00
24	Al Aber	7.00	3.50	2.00
25	Minnie Minoso	12.00	6.00	3.50
26	Virgil Trucks	7.00	3.50	2.00
27	Preston Ward	7.00	3.50	2.00
28	Dick Cole	7.00	3.50	2.00
29	Red Schoendienst	25.00	12.50	7.50
30	Bill Sarni	7.00	3.50	2.00
31	Johnny Temple	7.00	3.50	2.00
32	Wally Post	7.00	3.50	2.00
33	Nellie Fox	20.00	10.00	6.00
34	Clint Courtney	7.00	3.50	2.00
35	Bill Tuttle	7.00	3.50	2.00
36	Wayne Belardi	7.00	3.50	2.00
37	Pee Wee Reese	65.00	32.00	19.50
38	Early Wynn	25.00	12.50	7.50
39	Bob Darnell	12.00	6.00	3.50
40	Vic Wertz	7.00	3.50	2.00
41	Mel Clark	7.00	3.50	2.00
42	Bob Greenwood	7.00	3.50	2.00
43	Bob Buhl	7.00	3.50	2.00
44	Danny O'Connell	7.00	3.50	2.00
45	Tom Umphlett	7.00	3.50	2.00
46	Mickey Vernon	7.00	3.50	2.00
47	Sammy White	7.00	3.50	2.00
48a	Milt Bolling (Frank Bolling back)	10.00	5.00	3.00
48b	Milt Bolling (Milt Bolling back)	15.00	7.50	4.50
49	Jim Greengrass	7.00	3.50	2.00
50	Hobie Landrith	7.00	3.50	2.00
51	Elvin Tappe	7.00	3.50	2.00
52	Hal Rice	7.00	3.50	2.00
53	Alex Kellner	7.00	3.50	2.00
54	Don Bollweg	7.00	3.50	2.00
55	Cal Abrams	7.00	3.50	2.00
56	Billy Cox	10.00	5.00	3.00
57	Bob Friend	7.00	3.50	2.00
58	Frank J. Thomas	7.00	3.50	2.00
59	Whitey Ford	75.00	38.00	23.00
60	Enos Slaughter	30.00	15.00	9.00
61	Paul LaPalme	7.00	3.50	2.00
62	Royce Lint	7.00	3.50	2.00
63	Irv Noren	15.00	7.50	4.50
64	Curt Simmons	7.00	3.50	2.00
65	*Don Zimmer*	25.00	12.50	7.50
66	George Shuba	12.00	6.00	3.50
67	Don Larsen	18.00	9.00	5.50
68	*Elston Howard*	60.00	30.00	18.00
69	Bill Hunter	15.00	7.50	4.50
70	Lew Burdette	7.00	3.50	2.00
71	Dave Jolly	7.00	3.50	2.00
72	Chet Nichols	7.00	3.50	2.00
73	Eddie Yost	7.00	3.50	2.00
74	Jerry Snyder	7.00	3.50	2.00
75	Brooks Lawrence	7.00	3.50	2.00
76	Tom Poholsky	7.00	3.50	2.00
77	Jim McDonald	7.00	3.50	2.00
78	Gil Coan	7.00	3.50	2.00
79	Willie Miranda	7.00	3.50	2.00
80	Lou Limmer	7.00	3.50	2.00
81	Bob Morgan	7.00	3.50	2.00
82	Lee Walls	7.00	3.50	2.00
83	Max Surkont	7.00	3.50	2.00
84	George Freese	7.00	3.50	2.00
85	Cass Michaels	7.00	3.50	2.00
86	Ted Gray	7.00	3.50	2.00
87	Randy Jackson	7.00	3.50	2.00
88	Steve Bilko	7.00	3.50	2.00
89	Lou Boudreau	30.00	15.00	9.00
90	Art Ditmar	7.00	3.50	2.00
91	Dick Marlowe	7.00	3.50	2.00
92	George Zuverink	7.00	3.50	2.00
93	Andy Seminick	7.00	3.50	2.00
94	Hank Thompson	7.00	3.50	2.00
95	Sal Maglie	10.00	5.00	3.00
96	Ray Narleski	7.00	3.50	2.00
97	John Podres (FC)	15.00	7.50	4.50
98	Jim Gilliam	15.00	7.50	4.50
99	Jerry Coleman	15.00	7.50	4.50
100	Tom Morgan	15.00	7.50	4.50
101a	Don Johnson (Ernie Johnson (Braves) on front)	10.00	5.00	3.00
101b	Don Johnson (Don Johnson (Orioles) on front)	25.00	12.50	7.50
102	Bobby Thomson	10.00	5.00	3.00
103	Eddie Mathews	55.00	27.00	16.50
104	Bob Porterfield	5.00	2.50	1.50
105	Johnny Schmitz	5.00	2.50	1.50
106	Del Rice	5.00	2.50	1.50
107	Solly Hemus	5.00	2.50	1.50
108	Lou Kretlow	5.00	2.50	1.50
109	Vern Stephens	5.00	2.50	1.50
110	Bob Miller	5.00	2.50	1.50
111	Steve Ridzik	5.00	2.50	1.50
112	Granny Hamner	5.00	2.50	1.50
113	Bob Hall	5.00	2.50	1.50
114	Vic Janowicz	9.00	4.50	2.75
115	Roger Bowman	5.00	2.50	1.50
116	Sandy Consuegra	5.00	2.50	1.50
117	Johnny Groth	5.00	2.50	1.50
118	Bobby Adams	5.00	2.50	1.50
119	Joe Astroth	5.00	2.50	1.50
120	Ed Burtschy	5.00	2.50	1.50
121	Rufus Crawford	5.00	2.50	1.50
122	Al Corwin	5.00	2.50	1.50
123	Marv Grissom	5.00	2.50	1.50
124	Johnny Antonelli	5.00	2.50	1.50
125	Paul Giel	5.00	2.50	1.50
126	Billy Goodman	5.00	2.50	1.50
127	Hank Majeski	5.00	2.50	1.50
128	Mike Garcia	5.00	2.50	1.50
129	Hal Naragon	5.00	2.50	1.50
130	Richie Ashburn	20.00	10.00	6.00
131	Willard Marshall	5.00	2.50	1.50
132a	Harvey Kueen (misspelled last name)	10.00	5.00	3.00
132b	Harvey Kuenn (corrected)	35.00	17.50	10.50
133	Charles King	5.00	2.50	1.50
134	Bob Feller	55.00	27.00	16.50
135	Lloyd Merriman	5.00	2.50	1.50
136	Rocky Bridges	5.00	2.50	1.50
137	Bob Talbot	5.00	2.50	1.50
138	Davey Williams	5.00	2.50	1.50
139	Billy & Bobby Shantz	15.00	7.50	4.50
140	Bobby Shantz	10.00	5.00	3.00
141	Wes Westrum	5.00	2.50	1.50
142	Rudy Regalado	5.00	2.50	1.50
143	Don Newcombe	15.00	7.50	4.50
144	Art Houtteman	5.00	2.50	1.50
145	Bob Nieman	5.00	2.50	1.50
146	Don Liddle	5.00	2.50	1.50
147	Sam Mele	5.00	2.50	1.50
148	Bob Chakales	5.00	2.50	1.50
149	Cloyd Boyer	5.00	2.50	1.50
150	Bill Klaus	5.00	2.50	1.50
151	Jim Bridewieser	5.00	2.50	1.50
152	Johnny Klippstein	5.00	2.50	1.50
153	Eddie Robinson	15.00	7.50	4.50
154	*Frank Lary*	5.00	2.50	1.50
155	Gerry Staley	5.00	2.50	1.50
156	Jim Hughes	9.00	4.50	2.75
157a	Ernie Johnson (Don Johnson (Orioles) picture on front)	10.00	5.00	3.00
157b	Ernie Johnson (Ernie Johnson (Braves) picture on front)	25.00	12.50	7.50
158	Gil Hodges	40.00	20.00	12.00
159	Harry Byrd	5.00	2.50	1.50
160	Bill Skowron (FC)	18.00	9.00	5.50

161	Matt Batts	5.00	2.50	1.50
162	Charlie Maxwell (FC)	5.00	2.50	1.50
163	Sid Gordon	10.00	5.00	3.00
164	Toby Atwell	5.00	2.50	1.50
165	Maurice McDermott	5.00	2.50	1.50
166	Jim Busby	5.00	2.50	1.50
167	Bob Grim	15.00	7.50	4.50
168	Yogi Berra	90.00	45.00	27.00
169	Carl Furillo	20.00	10.00	6.00
170	Carl Erskine	12.00	6.00	3.50
171	Robin Roberts	30.00	15.00	9.00
172	Willie Jones	5.00	2.50	1.50
173	"Chico" Carrasquel	5.00	2.50	1.50
174	Sherman Lollar	5.00	2.50	1.50
175	Wilmer Shantz	5.00	2.50	1.50
176	Joe DeMaestri	5.00	2.50	1.50
177	Willard Nixon	5.00	2.50	1.50
178	Tom Brewer	5.00	2.50	1.50
179	Hank Aaron	200.00	100.00	60.00
180	Johnny Logan	5.00	2.50	1.50
181	Eddie Miksis	5.00	2.50	1.50
182	Bob Rush	5.00	2.50	1.50
183	Ray Katt	5.00	2.50	1.50
184	Willie Mays	200.00	100.00	60.00
185	Vic Raschi	5.00	2.50	1.50
186	Alex Grammas	5.00	2.50	1.50
187	Fred Hatfield	5.00	2.50	1.50
188	Ned Garver	5.00	2.50	1.50
189	Jack Collum	5.00	2.50	1.50
190	Fred Baczewski	5.00	2.50	1.50
191	Bob Lemon	25.00	12.50	7.50
192	George Strickland	5.00	2.50	1.50
193	Howie Judson	5.00	2.50	1.50
194	Joe Nuxhall	5.00	2.50	1.50
195a	Erv Palica (no traded line)	9.00	4.50	2.75
195b	Erv Palica (traded line)	18.00	9.00	5.50
196	Russ Meyer	12.00	6.00	7.25
197	Ralph Kiner	35.00	17.50	10.50
198	Dave Pope	5.00	2.50	1.50
199	Vernon Law	5.00	2.50	1.50
200	Dick Littlefield	5.00	2.50	1.50
201	Allie Reynolds	15.00	7.50	4.50
202	Mickey Mantle	550.00	275.00	165.00
203	Steve Gromek	5.00	2.50	1.50
204a	Frank Bolling (Milt Bolling back)	10.00	5.00	3.00
204b	Frank Bolling (Frank Bolling back)	15.00	7.50	4.50
205	"Rip" Repulski	5.00	2.50	1.50
206	Ralph Beard	5.00	2.50	1.50
207	Frank Shea	5.00	2.50	1.50
208	Ed Fitz Gerald	5.00	2.50	1.50
209	"Smoky" Burgess	5.00	2.50	1.50
210	Earl Torgeson	5.00	2.50	1.50
211	John "Sonny" Dixon	5.00	2.50	1.50
212	Jack Dittmer	5.00	2.50	1.50
213	George Kell	25.00	12.50	7.50
214	Billy Pierce	7.00	3.50	2.00
215	Bob Kuzava	5.00	2.50	1.50
216	Preacher Roe	7.00	3.50	2.00
217	Del Crandall	5.00	2.50	1.50
218	Joe Adcock	7.00	3.50	2.00
219	"Whitey" Lockman	5.00	2.50	1.50
220	Jim Hearn	5.00	2.50	1.50
221	Hector "Skinny" Brown	5.00	2.50	1.50
222	Russ Kemmerer	5.00	2.50	1.50
223	Hal Jeffcoat	5.00	2.50	1.50
224	Dee Fondy	5.00	2.50	1.50
225	Paul Richards	15.00	7.50	4.50
226	W.F. McKinley (umpire)	24.00	12.00	7.25
227	Frank Baumholtz	15.00	7.50	4.50
228	John M. Phillips	15.00	7.50	4.50
229	Jim Brosnan	15.00	7.50	4.50
230	Al Brazle	15.00	7.50	4.50
231	Jim Konstanty	25.00	12.50	7.50
232	Birdie Tebbetts	15.00	7.50	4.50
233	Bill Serena	15.00	7.50	4.50
234	Dick Bartell	15.00	7.50	4.50
235	J.A. Paparella (umpire)	24.00	12.00	7.25
236	Murry Dickson	15.00	7.50	4.50
237	Johnny Wyrostek	15.00	7.50	4.50
238	Eddie Stanky	22.00	11.00	6.50
239	Edwin A. Rommel (umpire)	24.00	12.00	7.25
240	Billy Loes	22.00	11.00	6.50
241	John Pesky	15.00	7.50	4.50
242	Ernie Banks (FC)	350.00	175.00	100.00
243	Gus Bell	15.00	7.50	4.50
244	Duane Pillette	15.00	7.50	4.50
245	Bill Miller	15.00	7.50	4.50
246	Hank Bauer	30.00	15.00	9.00
247	Dutch Leonard	15.00	7.50	4.50
248	Harry Dorish	15.00	7.50	4.50
249	Billy Gardner	15.00	7.50	4.50
250	Larry Napp (umpire)	24.00	12.00	7.25
251	Stan Jok	15.00	7.50	4.50
252	Roy Smalley	15.00	7.50	4.50
253	Jim Wilson	15.00	7.50	4.50
254	Bennett Flowers	15.00	7.50	4.50
255	Pete Runnels	15.00	7.50	4.50
256	Owen Friend	15.00	7.50	4.50
257	Tom Alston	15.00	7.50	4.50
258	John W. Stevens (umpire)	24.00	12.00	7.25
259	*Don Mossi*	15.00	7.50	4.50
260	Edwin H. Hurley (umpire)	24.00	12.00	7.25
261	Walt Moryn	22.00	11.00	6.50
262	Jim Lemon	15.00	7.50	4.50
263	Eddie Joost	15.00	7.50	4.50
264	Bill Henry	15.00	7.50	4.50
265	Al Barlick (umpire)	60.00	30.00	18.00
266	Mike Fornieles	15.00	7.50	4.50
267	George Honochick (umpire)	50.00	25.00	15.00
268	Roy Lee Hawes	15.00	7.50	4.50
269	Joe Amalfitano	15.00	7.50	4.50
270	Chico Fernandez	22.00	11.00	6.50
271	Bob Hooper	15.00	7.50	4.50
272	John Flaherty (umpire)	24.00	12.00	7.25
273	"Bubba" Church	15.00	7.50	4.50
274	Jim Delsing	15.00	7.50	4.50
275	William T. Grieve (umpire)	24.00	12.00	7.25
276	Ike Delock	15.00	7.50	4.50
277	Ed Runge (umpire)	24.00	12.00	7.25
278	*Charles Neal*	22.00	11.00	6.50
279	Hank Soar (umpire)	24.00	12.00	7.25
280	Clyde McCullough	15.00	7.50	4.50
281	Charles Berry (umpire)	24.00	12.00	7.25
282	Phil Cavarretta	15.00	7.50	4.50
283	Nestor Chylak (umpire)	24.00	12.00	7.25
284	William A. Jackowski (umpire)	24.00	12.00	7.25
285	Walt Dropo	15.00	7.50	4.50
286	Frank Secory (umpire)	24.00	12.00	7.25
287	Ron Mrozinski	15.00	7.50	4.50
288	Dick Smith	15.00	7.50	4.50
289	Art Gore (umpire)	24.00	12.00	7.25
290	Hershell Freeman	15.00	7.50	4.50
291	Frank Dascoli (umpire)	24.00	12.00	7.25
292	Marv Blaylock	15.00	7.50	4.50
293	Thomas D. Gorman (umpire)	24.00	12.00	7.25
294	Wally Moses	15.00	7.50	4.50
295	Lee Ballanfant (umpire)	24.00	12.00	7.25
296	*Bill Virdon*	30.00	15.00	9.00
297	"Dusty" Boggess (umpire)	24.00	12.00	7.25
298	Charlie Grimm	15.00	7.50	4.50
299	Lonnie Warneke (umpire)	24.00	12.00	7.25
300	Tommy Byrne	25.00	12.50	7.50
301	William Engeln (umpire)	24.00	12.00	7.25
302	*Frank Malzone*	30.00	15.00	9.00
303	Jocko Conlan (umpire)	75.00	37.00	22.00
304	Harry Chiti	15.00	7.50	4.50
305	Frank Umont (umpire)	24.00	12.00	7.25
306	Bob Cerv	25.00	12.50	7.50
307	"Babe" Pinelli (umpire)	24.00	12.00	7.25
308	Al Lopez	40.00	20.00	12.00
309	Hal Dixon (umpire)	24.00	12.00	7.25
310	Ken Lehman	22.00	11.00	6.50
311	Larry Goetz (umpire)	24.00	12.00	7.25
312	Bill Wight	15.00	7.50	4.50
313	Augie Donatelli (umpire)	24.00	12.00	7.25
314	Dale Mitchell	15.00	7.50	4.50
315	Cal Hubbard (umpire)	75.00	37.00	22.00
316	Marion Fricano	15.00	7.50	4.50
317	Bill Summers (umpire)	24.00	12.00	7.25
318	Sid Hudson	15.00	7.50	4.50
319	Al Schroll	15.00	7.50	4.50
320	George Susce, Jr.	40.00	10.00	6.00

1989 Bowman

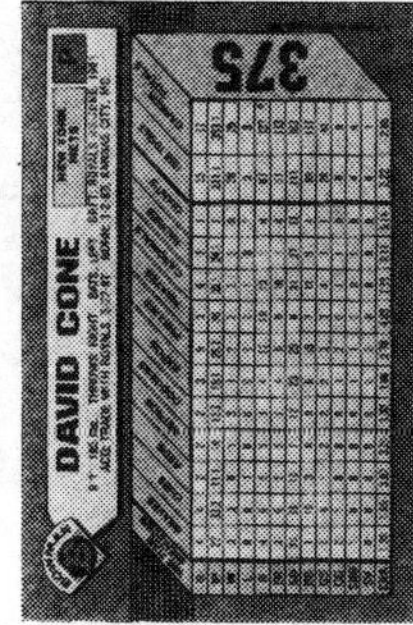

Topps, which purchased the Bowman Co. back in 1955, revived the Bowman name in 1989, issuing a 484-card set modeled after the 1953 Bowman cards. The cards are 2-1/2" by 3-3/4", slightly larger than a current standard-sized card. The fronts contain a full-color player photo, with facsimile autograph on the bottom and the Bowman logo in an upper corner. The unique card backs include a breakdown of the player's stats against each team in his league. A series of "Hot Rookie Stars" highlight the set. The cards were distributed in both wax packs and rack packs. Each pack included a special reproduction of a classic Bowman card with a sweepstakes on the back. The special cards said "reprint" on the front.

		MT	NR MT	EX
	Complete Set (484):	10.00	7.50	4.00
	Common Player:	.03	.02	.01
1	Oswald Peraza	.05	.04	.02
2	Brian Holton	.05	.04	.02
3	Jose Bautista	.05	.04	.02
4	*Pete Harnisch*	.20	.15	.08
5	Dave Schmidt	.03	.02	.01
6	Gregg Olson	.30	.25	.12
7	Jeff Ballard	.10	.08	.04
8	Bob Melvin	.03	.02	.01
9	Cal Ripken, Jr.	.40	.30	.15
10	Randy Milligan	.08	.06	.03
11	*Juan Bell*	.15	.11	.06
12	Billy Ripken	.05	.04	.02
13	Jim Trabor	.03	.02	.01
14	Pete Stanicek	.03	.02	.01
15	*Steve Finley*	.20	.15	.08
16	Larry Sheets	.03	.02	.01
17	Phil Bradley	.05	.04	.02
18	*Brady Anderson*	.30	.25	.12
19	Lee Smith	.03	.02	.01
20	Tom Fischer	.15	.11	.06
21	Mike Boddicker	.03	.02	.01
22	Rob Murphy	.03	.02	.01
23	Wes Gardner	.03	.02	.01
24	John Dopson	.10	.08	.04
25	Bob Stanley	.03	.02	.01
26	Roger Clemens	.35	.25	.14
27	Rich Gedman	.03	.02	.01
28	Marty Barrett	.03	.02	.01
29	Luis Rivera	.03	.02	.01
30	Jody Reed	.05	.04	.02
31	Nick Esasky	.05	.04	.02
32	Wade Boggs	.20	.15	.08
33	Jim Rice	.10	.08	.04
34	Mike Greenwell	.15	.11	.06
35	Dwight Evans	.15	.11	.06
36	Ellis Burks	.25	.20	.10
37	Chuck Finley	.05	.04	.02
38	Kirk McCaskill	.05	.04	.02
39	*Jim Abbott*	.60	.45	.25
40	*Bryan Harvey*	.35	.25	.14
41	Bert Blyleven	.08	.06	.03
42	Mike Witt	.03	.02	.01
43	Bob McClure	.03	.02	.01
44	Bill Schroeder	.03	.02	.01
45	Lance Parrish	.05	.04	.02
46	Dick Schofield	.03	.02	.01
47	Wally Joyner	.10	.08	.04
48	Jack Howell	.03	.02	.01
49	Johnny Ray	.03	.02	.01
50	Chili Davis	.05	.04	.02
51	Tony Armas	.03	.02	.01
52	Claudell Washington	.03	.02	.01
53	Brian Downing	.03	.02	.01
54	Devon White	.10	.08	.04
55	Bobby Thigpen	.08	.06	.03
56	Bill Long	.03	.02	.01
57	Jerry Reuss	.03	.02	.01
58	Shawn Hillegas	.03	.02	.01
59	Melido Perez	.10	.08	.04
60	Jeff Bittiger	.05	.04	.02
61	Jack McDowell	.25	.20	.10
62	Carlton Fisk	.10	.08	.04
63	Steve Lyons	.03	.02	.01
64	Ozzie Guillen	.05	.04	.02
65	*Robin Ventura*	1.25	.90	.50
66	Fred Manrique	.03	.02	.01
67	Dan Pasqua	.03	.02	.01
68	Ivan Calderon	.03	.02	.01
69	Ron Kittle	.03	.02	.01
70	Daryl Boston	.03	.02	.01
71	Dave Gallagher	.05	.04	.02
72	Harold Baines	.08	.06	.03
73	Charles Nagy	.20	.15	.08
74	John Farrell	.03	.02	.01
75	Kevin Wickander	.10	.08	.04
76	Greg Swindell	.15	.11	.06
77	Mike Walker	.15	.11	.06
78	Doug Jones	.05	.04	.02
79	Rich Yett	.03	.02	.01
80	Tom Candiotti	.03	.02	.01
81	Jesse Orosco	.03	.02	.01
82	Bud Black	.03	.02	.01
83	Andy Allanson	.03	.02	.01
84	Pete O'Brien	.05	.04	.02
85	Jerry Browne	.05	.04	.02
86	Brook Jacoby	.03	.02	.01
87	*Mark Lewis*	.25	.20	.10
88	Luis Aguayo	.03	.02	.01
89	Cory Snyder	.05	.04	.02
90	Oddibe McDowell	.05	.04	.02
91	Joe Carter	.25	.20	.10
92	Frank Tanana	.03	.02	.01
93	Jack Morris	.03	.02	.01
94	Doyle Alexander	.03	.02	.01
95	Steve Searcy	.08	.06	.03
96	Randy Bockus	.05	.04	.02
97	Jeff Robinson	.05	.04	.02
98	Mike Henneman	.05	.04	.02
99	Paul Gibson	.03	.02	.01
100	Frank Williams	.03	.02	.01
101	Matt Nokes	.05	.04	.02
102	Rico Brogna	.15	.11	.06
103	Lou Whitaker	.08	.06	.03
104	Al Pedrique	.03	.02	.01
105	Alan Trammell	.05	.04	.02
106	Chris Brown	.03	.02	.01
107	Pat Sheridan	.03	.02	.01
108	Gary Pettis	.03	.02	.01
109	Keith Moreland	.03	.02	.01
110	Mel Stottlemyre, Jr.	.15	.11	.06
111	Bret Saberhagen	.10	.08	.04
112	Floyd Bannister	.03	.02	.01
113	Jeff Montgomery	.05	.04	.02
114	Steve Farr	.05	.04	.02
115	Tom Gordon	.10	.08	.04
116	Charlie Leibrandt	.03	.02	.01
117	Mark Gubicza	.08	.06	.03
118	Mike MacFarlane	.03	.02	.01
119	Bob Boone	.05	.04	.02
120	Kurt Stillwell	.05	.04	.02
121	George Brett	.20	.15	.08
122	Frank White	.05	.04	.02
123	Kevin Seitzer	.08	.06	.03
124	Willie Wilson	.03	.02	.01
125	Pat Tabler	.03	.02	.01
126	Bo Jackson	.30	.25	.12
127	Hugh Walker	.20	.15	.08
128	Danny Tartabull	.05	.04	.02
129	Teddy Higuera	.08	.06	.03
130	Don August	.03	.02	.01
131	Juan Nieves	.03	.02	.01
132	Mike Birkbeck	.03	.02	.01
133	Dan Plesac	.05	.04	.02
134	Chris Bosio	.05	.04	.02
135	Bill Wegman	.03	.02	.01
136	Chuck Crim	.03	.02	.01
137	B.J. Surhoff	.05	.04	.02
138	Joey Meyer	.03	.02	.01
139	Dale Sveum	.03	.02	.01
140	Paul Molitor	.15	.11	.06
141	Jim Gantner	.03	.02	.01
142	Gary Sheffield	1.50	1.25	.60

No.	Player	MT	NM	EX
143	Greg Brock	.03	.02	.01
144	Robin Yount	.25	.20	.10
145	Glenn Braggs	.03	.02	.01
146	Rob Deer	.03	.02	.01
147	Fred Toliver	.03	.02	.01
148	Jeff Reardon	.03	.02	.01
149	Allan Anderson	.05	.04	.02
150	Frank Viola	.15	.11	.06
151	Shane Rawley	.03	.02	.01
152	Juan Berenguer	.03	.02	.01
153	Johnny Ard	.20	.15	.08
154	Tim Laudner	.03	.02	.01
155	Brian Harper	.03	.02	.01
156	Al Newman	.03	.02	.01
157	Kent Hrbek	.08	.06	.03
158	Gary Gaetti	.08	.06	.03
159	Wally Backman	.03	.02	.01
160	Gene Larkin	.03	.02	.01
161	Greg Gagne	.03	.02	.01
162	Kirby Puckett	.35	.25	.14
163	Danny Gladden	.03	.02	.01
164	Randy Bush	.03	.02	.01
165	Dave LaPoint	.03	.02	.01
166	Andy Hawkins	.03	.02	.01
167	Dave Righetti	.05	.04	.02
168	Lance McCullers	.03	.02	.01
169	Jimmy Jones	.03	.02	.01
170	Al Leiter	.03	.02	.01
171	John Candelaria	.03	.02	.01
172	Don Slaught	.03	.02	.01
173	Jamie Quirk	.03	.02	.01
174	Rafael Santana	.03	.02	.01
175	Mike Pagliarulo	.03	.02	.01
176	Don Mattingly	.20	.15	.08
177	Ken Phelps	.03	.02	.01
178	Steve Sax	.08	.06	.03
179	Dave Winfield	.20	.15	.08
180	Stan Jefferson	.03	.02	.01
181	Rickey Henderson	.25	.20	.10
182	Bob Brower	.03	.02	.01
183	Roberto Kelly	.10	.08	.04
184	Curt Young	.03	.02	.01
185	Gene Nelson	.03	.02	.01
186	Bob Welch	.03	.02	.01
187	Rick Honeycutt	.03	.02	.01
188	Dave Stewart	.08	.06	.03
189	Mike Moore	.08	.06	.03
190	Dennis Eckersley	.08	.06	.03
191	Eric Plunk	.03	.02	.01
192	Storm Davis	.03	.02	.01
193	Terry Steinbach	.10	.08	.04
194	Ron Hassey	.03	.02	.01
195	Stan Royer	.15	.11	.06
196	Walt Weiss	.15	.11	.06
197	Mark McGwire	.30	.25	.12
198	Carney Lansford	.08	.06	.03
199	Glenn Hubbard	.03	.02	.01
200	Dave Henderson	.05	.04	.02
201	Jose Canseco	.40	.30	.15
202	Dave Parker	.05	.04	.02
203	Scott Bankhead	.05	.04	.02
204	Tom Niedenfuer	.03	.02	.01
205	Mark Langston	.15	.11	.06
206	*Erik Hanson*	.25	.20	.10
207	Mike Jackson	.03	.02	.01
208	Dave Valle	.03	.02	.01
209	Scott Bradley	.03	.02	.01
210	Harold Reynolds	.08	.06	.03
211	*Tino Martinez*	.30	.25	.12
212	Rich Renteria	.03	.02	.01
213	Rey Quinones	.03	.02	.01
214	Jim Presley	.03	.02	.01
215	Alvin Davis	.10	.08	.04
216	Edgar Martinez	.10	.08	.04
217	Darnell Coles	.03	.02	.01
218	Jeffrey Leonard	.08	.06	.03
219	Jay Buhner	.15	.11	.06
220	*Ken Griffey, Jr.*	4.00	3.00	1.50
221	Drew Hall	.03	.02	.01
222	Bobby Witt	.03	.02	.01
223	Jamie Moyer	.03	.02	.01
224	Charlie Hough	.03	.02	.01
225	Nolan Ryan	.70	.50	.30
226	Jeff Russell	.05	.04	.02
227	Jim Sundberg	.03	.02	.01
228	Julio Franco	.15	.11	.06
229	Buddy Bell	.03	.02	.01
230	Scott Fletcher	.03	.02	.01
231	Jeff Kunkel	.03	.02	.01
232	Steve Buechele	.03	.02	.01
233	Monty Fariss	.12	.09	.05
234	Rick Leach	.03	.02	.01
235	Ruben Sierra	.30	.25	.12
236	Cecil Espy	.05	.04	.02
237	Rafael Palmeiro	.20	.15	.08
238	Pete Incaviglia	.03	.02	.01
239	Dave Steib	.05	.04	.02
240	Jeff Musselman	.03	.02	.01
241	Mike Flanagan	.03	.02	.01
242	Todd Stottlemyre	.10	.08	.04
243	Jimmy Key	.05	.04	.02
244	Tony Castillo	.10	.08	.04
245	Alex Sanchez	.05	.04	.02
246	Tom Henke	.03	.02	.01
247	John Cerutti	.03	.02	.01
248	Ernie Whitt	.03	.02	.01
249	Bob Brenly	.03	.02	.01
250	Rance Mulliniks	.03	.02	.01
251	Kelly Gruber	.10	.08	.04
252	Ed Sprague	.40	.30	.15
253	Fred McGriff	.35	.25	.14
254	Tony Fernandez	.08	.06	.03
255	Tom Lawless	.03	.02	.01
256	George Bell	.10	.08	.04
257	Jesse Barfield	.05	.04	.02
258	Sandy Alomar	.20	.15	.08
259	Ken Griffey	1.00	.70	.40
260	Cal Ripken, Jr.	.15	.11	.06
261	Mel Stottlemyre	.15	.11	.06
262	Zane Smith	.03	.02	.01
263	Charlie Puleo	.03	.02	.01
264	Derek Lilliquist	.15	.11	.06
265	Paul Assenmacher	.03	.02	.01
266	John Smoltz	.60	.45	.25
267	Tom Glavine	.40	.30	.15
268	Steve Avery	1.00	.70	.40
269	*Pete Smith*	.15	.11	.06
270	Jody Davis	.03	.02	.01
271	Bruce Benedict	.03	.02	.01
272	Andres Thomas	.03	.02	.01
273	Gerald Perry	.05	.04	.02
274	Ron Gant	.35	.25	.14
275	Darrell Evans	.03	.02	.01
276	Dale Murphy	.10	.08	.04
277	Dion James	.03	.02	.01
278	Lonnie Smith	.08	.06	.03
279	Geronimo Berroa	.05	.04	.02
280	Steve Wilson	.20	.15	.08
281	Rick Suctcliffe	.05	.04	.02
282	Kevin Coffman	.03	.02	.01
283	Mitch Williams	.10	.08	.04
284	Greg Maddux	.20	.15	.08
285	Paul Kilgus	.03	.02	.01
286	Mike Harkey	.10	.08	.04
287	Lloyd McClendon	.05	.04	.02
288	Damon Berryhill	.05	.04	.02
289	Ty Griffin	.10	.08	.04
290	Ryne Sandberg	.35	.25	.14
291	Mark Grace	.30	.25	.12
292	Curt Wilkerson	.03	.02	.01
293	Vance Law	.03	.02	.01
294	Shawon Dunston	.08	.06	.03
295	Jerome Walton	.08	.06	.03
296	Mitch Webster	.03	.02	.01
297	Dwight Smith	.08	.06	.03
298	Andre Dawson	.15	.11	.06
299	Jeff Sellers	.03	.02	.01
300	Jose Rijo	.05	.04	.02
301	John Franco	.05	.04	.02
302	Rick Mahler	.03	.02	.01
303	Ron Robinson	.03	.02	.01
304	Danny Jackson	.03	.02	.01
305	Rob Dibble	.08	.06	.03
306	Tom Browning	.03	.02	.01
307	Bo Diaz	.03	.02	.01
308	Manny Trillo	.03	.02	.01
309	Chris Sabo	.15	.11	.06
310	Ron Oester	.03	.02	.01
311	Barry Larkin	.15	.11	.06
312	Todd Benzinger	.05	.04	.02
313	Paul O'Neil	.05	.04	.02
314	Kal Daniels	.05	.04	.02
315	Joel Youngblood	.03	.02	.01
316	Eric Davis	.12	.09	.05
317	Dave Smith	.05	.04	.02
318	Mark Portugal	.03	.02	.01
319	Brian Meyer	.03	.02	.01
320	Jim Deshaies	.05	.04	.02
321	Juan Agosto	.03	.02	.01
322	Mike Scott	.10	.08	.04
323	Rick Rhoden	.03	.02	.01
324	Jim Clancy	.03	.02	.01
325	Larry Andersen	.03	.02	.01
326	Alex Trevino	.03	.02	.01
327	Alan Ashby	.03	.02	.01
328	Craig Reynolds	.03	.02	.01
329	Bill Doran	.03	.02	.01
330	Rafael Ramirez	.03	.02	.01
331	Glenn Davis	.10	.08	.04
332	Willie Ansley	.25	.20	.10
333	Gerald Young	.03	.02	.01
334	Cameron Drew	.10	.08	.04
335	Jay Howell	.05	.04	.02
336	Tim Belcher	.05	.04	.02
337	Fernando Valenzuela	.05	.04	.02
338	Ricky Horton	.03	.02	.01
339	Tim Leary	.03	.02	.01
340	Bill Bene	.15	.11	.06
341	Orel Hershiser	.08	.06	.03
342	Mike Scioscia	.05	.04	.02
343	Rick Dempsey	.03	.02	.01
344	Willie Randolph	.03	.02	.01
345	Alfredo Griffin	.03	.02	.01
346	Eddie Murray	.15	.11	.06
347	Mickey Hatcher	.03	.02	.01
348	Mike Sharperson	.03	.02	.01
349	John Shelby	.03	.02	.01
350	Mike Marshall	.03	.02	.01
351	Kirk Gibson	.05	.04	.02
352	Mike Davis	.03	.02	.01
353	Bryn Smith	.03	.02	.01
354	Pascual Perez	.03	.02	.01
355	Kevin Gross	.03	.02	.01
356	Andy McGaffigan	.03	.02	.01
357	Brian Holman	.05	.04	.02
358	Dave Wainhouse	.20	.15	.08
359	Denny Martinez	.03	.02	.01
360	Tim Burke	.03	.02	.01
361	Nelson Santovenia	.08	.06	.03
362	Tim Wallach	.05	.04	.02
363	Spike Owen	.03	.02	.01
364	Rex Hudler	.03	.02	.01
365	Andres Galarraga	.15	.11	.06
366	Otis Nixon	.03	.02	.01
367	Hubie Brooks	.03	.02	.01
368	Mike Aldrete	.03	.02	.01
369	Rock Raines	.08	.06	.03
370	Dave Martinez	.03	.02	.01
371	Bob Ojeda	.03	.02	.01
372	Ron Darling	.05	.04	.02
373	Wally Whitehurst	.08	.06	.03
374	Randy Myers	.05	.04	.02
375	David Cone	.10	.08	.04
376	Doc Gooden	.12	.09	.05
377	Sid Fernandez	.05	.04	.02
378	Dave Proctor	.20	.15	.08
379	Gary Carter	.03	.02	.01
380	Keith Miller	.05	.04	.02
381	Gregg Jefferies	.40	.30	.15
382	Tim Teufel	.03	.02	.01
383	Kevin Elster	.03	.02	.01
384	Dave Magadan	.03	.02	.01
385	Keith Hernandez	.05	.04	.02
386	Mookie Wilson	.05	.04	.02
387	Darryl Strawberry	.15	.11	.06
388	Kevin McReynolds	.10	.08	.04
389	Mark Carreon	.05	.04	.02
390	Jeff Parrett	.05	.04	.02
391	Mike Maddux	.03	.02	.01
392	Don Carman	.03	.02	.01
393	Bruce Ruffin	.03	.02	.01
394	Ken Howell	.03	.02	.01
395	Steve Bedrosian	.05	.04	.02
396	Floyd Youmans	.03	.02	.01
397	Larry McWilliams	.03	.02	.01
398	Pat Combs	.10	.08	.04
399	Steve Lake	.03	.02	.01
400	Dickie Thon	.03	.02	.01
401	Ricky Jordan	.12	.09	.05
402	Mike Schmidt	.30	.25	.12
403	Tom Herr	.03	.02	.01
404	Chris James	.03	.02	.01
405	Juan Samuel	.08	.06	.03
406	Von Hayes	.08	.06	.03
407	Ron Jones	.15	.11	.06
408	Curt Ford	.03	.02	.01
409	Bob Walk	.03	.02	.01
410	Jeff Robinson	.03	.02	.01
411	Jim Gott	.03	.02	.01
412	Scott Medvin	.03	.02	.01
413	John Smiley	.03	.02	.01
414	Bob Kipper	.03	.02	.01
415	Brian Fisher	.03	.02	.01
416	Doug Drabek	.03	.02	.01
417	Mike Lavalliere	.03	.02	.01
418	Ken Oberkfell	.03	.02	.01
419	Sid Bream	.03	.02	.01
420	Austin Manahan	.20	.15	.08
421	Jose Lind	.03	.02	.01
422	Bobby Bonilla	.12	.09	.05
423	Glenn Wilson	.03	.02	.01
424	Andy Van Slyke	.12	.09	.05
425	Gary Redus	.03	.02	.01
426	Barry Bonds	.50	.40	.20
427	Don Heinkel	.03	.02	.01
428	Ken Dayley	.03	.02	.01
429	Todd Worrell	.05	.04	.02
430	Brad DuVall	.20	.15	.08
431	Jose DeLeon	.03	.02	.01
432	Joe Magrane	.10	.08	.04
433	John Ericks	.20	.15	.08
434	Frank DiPino	.03	.02	.01
435	Tony Pena	.05	.04	.02
436	Ozzie Smith	.12	.09	.05
437	Terry Pendleton	.03	.02	.01
438	Jose Oquendo	.03	.02	.01
439	Tim Jones	.05	.04	.02
440	Pedro Guerrero	.10	.08	.04
441	Milt Thompson	.03	.02	.01
442	Willie McGee	.05	.04	.02
443	Vince Coleman	.05	.04	.02
444	Tom Brunansky	.05	.04	.02
445	Walt Terrell	.03	.02	.01
446	Eric Show	.03	.02	.01
447	Mark Davis	.10	.08	.04
448	Andy Benes	.40	.30	.15
449	Eddie Whitson	.03	.02	.01
450	Dennis Rasmussen	.03	.02	.01
451	Bruce Hurst	.03	.02	.01
452	Pat Clements	.03	.02	.01
453	Benito Santiago	.10	.08	.04
454	Sandy Alomar, Jr.	.30	.25	.12
455	Garry Templeton	.03	.02	.01
456	Jack Clark	.05	.04	.02
457	Tim Flannery	.03	.02	.01
458	Roberto Alomar	.80	.60	.30
459	Camelo Martinez	.03	.02	.01
460	John Kruk	.03	.02	.01
461	Tony Gwynn	.25	.20	.10
462	Jerald Clark	.05	.04	.02
463	Don Robinson	.03	.02	.01
464	Craig Lefferts	.03	.02	.01
465	Kelly Downs	.03	.02	.01
466	Rick Rueschel	.05	.04	.02
467	Scott Garrelts	.03	.02	.01
468	Wil Tejada	.03	.02	.01
469	Kirt Manwaring	.10	.08	.04
470	Terry Kennedy	.03	.02	.01
471	Jose Uribe	.03	.02	.01
472	Royce Clayton	.75	.60	.30
473	Robby Thompson	.05	.04	.02
474	Kevin Mitchell	.12	.09	.05
475	Ernie Riles	.03	.02	.01
476	Will Clark	.25	.20	.10
477	Donnell Nixon	.03	.02	.01
478	Candy Maldonado	.03	.02	.01
479	Tracy Jones	.03	.02	.01
480	Brett Butler	.05	.04	.02
481	Checklist	.05	.04	.02
482	Checklist	.05	.04	.02
483	Checklist	.05	.04	.02
484	Checklist	.05	.04	.02

Values for recent cards and sets are listed in Mint (MT), Near Mint (NM), reflecting the fact that many cards from recent years have been preserved in top condition. Recent cards and sets in less than Excellent condition have little collector interest.

1989 Bowman Inserts

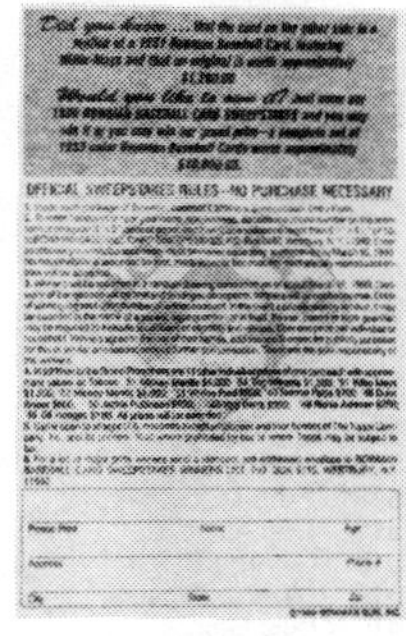

Bowman inserted sweepstakes cards in its 1989 packs. Each sweepstakes card features a reprint Bowman card on the front. The cards were by no means scarce.

		MT	NR MT	EX
Complete Set:		1.50	1.25	.60
Common Player:		.10	.08	.04
(1)	Richie Ashburn	.10	.08	.04
(2)	Yogi Berra	.20	.15	.08
(3)	Whitey Ford	.10	.08	.04
(4)	Gil Hodges	.10	.08	.04
(5)	Mickey Mantle (1951)	.25	.20	.10
(6)	Mickey Mantle (1953)	.25	.20	.10
(7)	Willie Mays	.25	.20	.10
(8)	Satchel Paige	.15	.11	.06
(9)	Jackie Robinson	.20	.15	.08
(10)	Duke Snider	.15	.11	.06
(11)	Ted Williams	.25	.20	.10

1990 Bowman

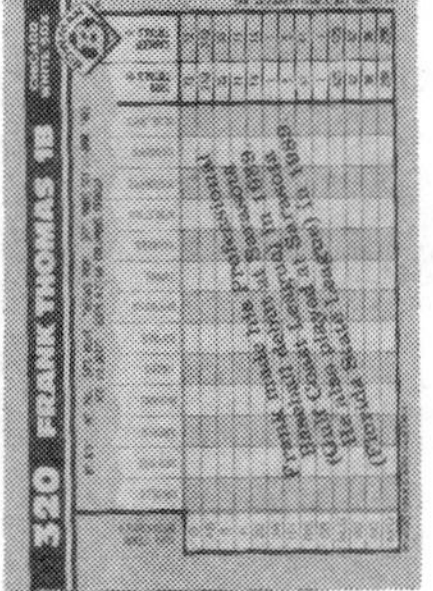

Bowman followed up its 1989 release with 528-card set in 1990. The 1990 cards follow the classic Bowman style featuring a full color photo bordered in white. The Bowman logo appears in the upper left corner. The player's team nickname and name appear on the bottom border of the card photo. Unlike the 1989 set, the 1990 cards measure 2-1/2" by 3-1/2" in size. The card backs are horizontal and display the player's statistics against the teams in his respective league. Included in the set are special insert cards that feature a reproduction of a painting of a modern-day superstar done in the style of the 1951 Bowman cards. The paintings were produced for Bowman by artist Craig Pursley. The card backs contain a sweepstakes offer with a chance to win a complete set of 11 lithographs made from these paintings.

		MT	NR MT	EX
Complete Set (528):		15.00	11.00	6.00
Common Player:		.05	.04	.02
1	*Tommy Greene*	.50	.40	.20
2	Tom Glavine	.25	.20	.10
3	Andy Nezelek	.08	.06	.03
4	Mike Stanton	.20	.15	.08
5	Rick Lueken	.08	.06	.03
6	Kent Mercker	.10	.08	.04
7	Derek Lilliquist	.06	.05	.02
8	Charlie Liebrandt	.05	.04	.02
9	Steve Avery	.60	.45	.25
10	John Smoltz	.25	.20	.10
11	Mark Lemke	.08	.06	.03
12	Lonnie Smith	.06	.05	.02
13	Oddibe McDowell	.05	.04	.02
14	Tyler Houston	.10	.08	.04
15	Jeff Blauser	.05	.04	.02
16	Ernie Whitt	.05	.04	.02
17	Alexis Infante	.10	.08	.04
18	Jim Presley	.06	.05	.02
19	Dale Murphy	.10	.08	.04
20	Nick Esasky	.06	.05	.02
21	Rick Sutcliffe	.06	.05	.02
22	Mike Bielecki	.06	.05	.02
23	Steve Wilson	.10	.08	.04
24	Kevin Blankenship	.10	.08	.04
25	Mitch Williams	.10	.08	.04
26	Dean Wilkins	.10	.08	.04
27	Greg Maddux	.20	.15	.08
28	Mike Harkey	.20	.15	.08
29	Mark Grace	.20	.15	.08
30	Ryne Sandberg	.50	.40	.20
31	Greg Smith	.20	.15	.08
32	Dwight Smith	.15	.11	.06
33	Damon Berryhill	.05	.04	.02
34	Earl Cunningham	.15	.11	.06
35	Jerome Walton	.08	.06	.03
36	Lloyd McClendon	.05	.04	.02
37	Ty Griffin	.20	.15	.08
38	Shawon Dunston	.10	.08	.04
39	Andre Dawson	.10	.08	.04
40	Luis Salazar	.05	.04	.02
41	Tim Layana	.20	.15	.08
42	Rob Dibble	.10	.08	.04
43	Tom Browning	.05	.04	.02
44	Danny Jackson	.05	.04	.02
45	Jose Rijo	.06	.05	.02
46	Scott Scudder	.20	.15	.08
47	Randy Myers	.06	.05	.02
48	Brian Lane	.15	.11	.06
49	Paul O'Neill	.05	.04	.02
50	Barry Larkin	.10	.08	.04
51	Reggie Jefferson	.40	.30	.15
52	Jeff Branson	.10	.08	.04
53	Chris Sabo	.08	.06	.03
54	Joe Oliver	.10	.08	.04
55	Todd Benzinger	.05	.04	.02
56	Rolando Roomes	.05	.04	.02
57	Hal Morris	.12	.09	.05
58	Eric Davis	.15	.11	.06
59	Scott Bryant	.20	.15	.08
60	Ken Griffey	.06	.05	.02
61	*Darryl Kile*	.75	.60	.30
62	Dave Smith	.05	.04	.02
63	Mark Portugal	.05	.04	.02
64	*Jeff Juden*	.35	.25	.14
65	Bill Gullickson	.05	.04	.02
66	Danny Darwin	.05	.04	.02
67	Larry Andersen	.05	.04	.02
68	Jose Cano	.10	.08	.04
69	Dan Schatzeder	.05	.04	.02
70	Jim Deshaies	.05	.04	.02
71	Mike Scott	.06	.05	.02
72	Gerald Young	.05	.04	.02
73	Ken Caminiti	.05	.04	.02
74	Ken Oberkfell	.05	.04	.02
75	Dave Rhode	.20	.15	.08
76	Bill Doran	.06	.05	.02
77	Andujar Cedeno	.20	.15	.08
78	Craig Biggio	.08	.06	.03
79	Karl Rhodes	.15	.11	.06
80	Glenn Davis	.10	.08	.04
81	Eric Anthony	.30	.25	.12
82	John Wetteland	.20	.15	.08
83	Jay Howell	.06	.05	.02
84	Orel Hershiser	.10	.08	.04
85	Tim Belcher	.08	.06	.03
86	Kiki Jones	.25	.20	.10
87	Mike Hartley	.20	.15	.08
88	Ramon Martinez	.30	.25	.12
89	Mike Scioscia	.06	.05	.02
90	Willie Randolph	.06	.05	.02
91	Juan Samuel	.06	.05	.02
92	Jose Offerman	.30	.25	.12
93	Dave Hansen	.30	.25	.12
94	Jeff Hamilton	.05	.04	.02
95	Alfredo Griffin	.05	.04	.02
96	Tom Goodwin	.35	.25	.14
97	Kirk Gibson	.06	.05	.02
98	Jose Vizcaino	.20	.15	.08
99	Kal Daniels	.06	.05	.02
100	Hubie Brooks	.06	.05	.02
101	Eddie Murray	.08	.06	.03
102	Dennis Boyd	.05	.04	.02
103	Tim Burke	.06	.05	.02
104	Bill Sampen	.20	.15	.08
105	Brett Gideon	.06	.05	.02
106	Mark Gardner	.20	.15	.08
107	Howard Farmer	.15	.11	.06
108	Mel Rojas	.15	.11	.06
109	Kevin Gross	.05	.04	.02
110	Dave Schmidt	.05	.04	.02
111	Denny Martinez	.06	.05	.02
112	Jerry Goff	.10	.08	.04
113	Andres Galarraga	.08	.06	.03
114	Tim Welch	.12	.09	.05
115	Marquis Grissom	.50	.40	.20
116	Spike Owen	.05	.04	.02
117	Larry Walker	.60	.45	.25
118	Rock Raines	.08	.06	.03
119	Delino DeShields	.40	.30	.15
120	Tom Foley	.05	.04	.02
121	Dave Martinez	.05	.04	.02
122	Frank Viola	.10	.08	.04
123	Julio Valera	.15	.11	.06
124	Alejandro Pena	.05	.04	.02
125	David Cone	.08	.06	.03
126	Doc Gooden	.20	.15	.08
127	Kevin Brown	.20	.15	.08
128	John Franco	.08	.06	.03
129	Terry Bross	.25	.20	.10
130	Blaine Beatty	.20	.15	.08
131	Sid Fernandez	.08	.06	.03
132	Mike Marshall	.05	.04	.02
133	Howard Johnson	.10	.08	.04
134	Jaime Roseboro	.20	.15	.08
135	Alan Zinter	.20	.15	.08
136	Keith Miller	.06	.05	.02
137	Kevin Elster	.05	.04	.02
138	Kevin McReynolds	.06	.05	.02
139	Barry Lyons	.05	.04	.02
140	Gregg Jefferies	.25	.20	.10
141	Darryl Strawberry	.25	.20	.10
142	Todd Hundley	.25	.20	.10
143	Scott Service	.15	.11	.06
144	Chuck Malone	.15	.11	.06
145	Steve Ontiveros	.05	.04	.02
146	Roger McDowell	.06	.05	.02
147	Ken Howell	.05	.04	.02
148	Pat Combs	.15	.11	.06
149	Jeff Parrett	.05	.04	.02
150	Chuck McElroy	.15	.11	.06
151	Jason Grimsley	.15	.11	.06
152	Len Dykstra	.08	.06	.03
153	Mickey Morandini	.15	.11	.06
154	John Kruk	.05	.04	.02
155	Dickie Thon	.05	.04	.02
156	Ricky Jordan	.10	.08	.04
157	Jeff Jackson	.10	.08	.04
158	Darren Daulton	.05	.04	.02
159	Tom Herr	.05	.04	.02
160	Von Hayes	.06	.05	.02
161	Dave Hollins	.50	.40	.20
162	Carmelo Martinez	.05	.04	.02
163	Bob Walk	.05	.04	.02
164	Doug Drabek	.08	.06	.03
165	Walt Terrell	.05	.04	.02
166	Bill Landrum	.05	.04	.02
167	Scott Ruskin	.08	.06	.03
168	Bob Patterson	.05	.04	.02
169	Bobby Bonilla	.10	.08	.04
170	Jose Lind	.05	.04	.02
171	Andy Van Slyke	.08	.06	.03
172	Mike LaValliere	.05	.04	.02
173	Willie Greene	.20	.15	.08
174	Jay Bell	.06	.05	.02
175	Sid Bream	.05	.04	.02
176	Tom Prince	.05	.04	.02
177	Wally Backman	.05	.04	.02
178	*Moises Alou*	.60	.45	.25
179	Steve Carter	.08	.06	.03
180	Gary Redus	.05	.04	.02
181	Barry Bonds	.40	.30	.15
182	Don Slaught	.05	.04	.02
183	Joe Magrane	.06	.05	.02
184	Bryn Smith	.05	.04	.02
185	Todd Worrell	.06	.05	.02
186	Jose Deleon	.05	.04	.02
187	Frank DiPino	.05	.04	.02
188	John Tudor	.05	.04	.02
189	Howard Hilton	.10	.08	.04
190	John Ericks	.10	.08	.04
191	Ken Dayley	.05	.04	.02
192	*Ray Lankford*	.75	.60	.30
193	Todd Zeile	.80	.60	.30
194	Willie McGee	.06	.05	.02
195	Ozzie Smith	.10	.08	.04
196	Milt Thompson	.05	.04	.02
197	Terry Pendleton	.05	.04	.02
198	Vince Coleman	.06	.05	.02
199	Paul Coleman	.25	.20	.10
200	Jose Oquendo	.05	.04	.02
201	Pedro Guerrero	.06	.05	.02
202	Tom Brunansky	.06	.05	.02
203	Roger Smithberg	.10	.08	.04
204	Eddie Whitson	.05	.04	.02
205	Dennis Rasmussen	.05	.04	.02
206	Craig Lefferts	.05	.04	.02
207	Andy Benes	.15	.11	.06
208	Bruce Hurst	.06	.05	.02
209	Eric Show	.05	.04	.02
210	Rafael Valdez	.10	.08	.04
211	Joey Cora	.05	.04	.02
212	Thomas Howard	.20	.15	.08
213	Rob Nelson	.05	.04	.02
214	Jack Clark	.06	.05	.02
215	Garry Templeton	.05	.04	.02
216	Fred Lynn	.05	.04	.02
217	Tony Gwynn	.08	.06	.03
218	Benny Santiago	.08	.06	.03
219	Mike Pagliarulo	.05	.04	.02
220	Joe Carter	.08	.06	.03
221	Roberto Alomar	.08	.06	.03
222	Bip Roberts	.05	.04	.02
223	Rick Reuschel	.05	.04	.02
224	Russ Swan	.20	.15	.08
225	Eric Gunderson	.20	.15	.08
226	Steve Bedrosian	.05	.04	.02
227	Mike Remlinger	.40	.30	.15
228	Scott Garrelts	.05	.04	.02
229	Ernie Camacho	.05	.04	.02
230	Andres Santana	.25	.20	.10
231	Will Clark	.35	.25	.14
232	Kevin Mitchell	.25	.20	.10
233	Robby Thompson	.05	.04	.02
234	Bill Bathe	.06	.05	.02
235	Tony Perezchica	.08	.06	.03
236	Gary Carter	.05	.04	.02
237	Brett Butler	.05	.04	.02
238	Matt Williams	.15	.11	.06
239	Ernie Riles	.05	.04	.02
240	Kevin Bass	.05	.04	.02
241	Terry Kennedy	.05	.04	.02
242	*Steve Hosey*	.20	.15	.08
243	*Ben McDonald*	.50	.40	.20
244	Jeff Ballard	.05	.04	.02
245	Joe Price	.05	.04	.02
246	Curt Schilling	.05	.04	.02
247	Pete Harnisch	.06	.05	.02
248	Mark Williamson	.05	.04	.02
249	Gregg Olson	.15	.11	.06
250	Chris Myers	.15	.11	.06
251	David Segui	.40	.30	.15
252	Joe Orsulak	.05	.04	.02
253	Craig Worthington	.05	.04	.02
254	Mickey Tettleton	.06	.05	.02
255	Cal Ripken, Jr.	.20	.15	.08
256	Billy Ripken	.05	.04	.02
257	Randy Milligan	.06	.05	.02
258	Brady Anderson	.05	.04	.02

259	Chris Hoiles	.40	.30	.15
260	Mike Devereaux	.05	.04	.02
261	Phil Bradley	.05	.04	.02
262	Leo Gomez	.30	.25	.12
263	Lee Smith	.06	.05	.02
264	Mike Rochford	.06	.05	.02
265	Jeff Reardon	.06	.05	.02
266	Wes Gardner	.05	.04	.02
267	Mike Boddicker	.05	.04	.02
268	Roger Clemens	.25	.20	.10
269	Rob Murphy	.05	.04	.02
270	Mickey Pina	.25	.20	.10
271	Tony Pena	.06	.05	.02
272	Jody Reed	.06	.05	.02
273	Kevin Romine	.05	.04	.02
274	Mike Greenwell	.08	.06	.03
275	*Mo Vaughn*	1.00	.75	.40
276	Danny Heep	.05	.04	.02
277	Scott Cooper	.40	.30	.15
278	Greg Blosser	.25	.20	.10
279	Dwight Evans	.06	.05	.02
280	Ellis Burks	.08	.06	.03
281	Wade Boggs	.10	.08	.04
282	Marty Barrett	.05	.04	.02
283	Kirk McCaskill	.06	.05	.02
284	Mark Langston	.06	.05	.02
285	Bert Blyleven	.06	.05	.02
286	Mike Fetters	.08	.06	.03
287	Kyle Abbott	.20	.15	.08
288	Jim Abbott	.10	.08	.04
289	Chuck Finley	.06	.05	.02
290	Gary DiSarcina	.15	.11	.06
291	Dick Schofield	.05	.04	.02
292	Devon White	.06	.05	.02
293	Bobby Rose	.15	.11	.06
294	Brian Downing	.05	.04	.02
295	Lance Parrish	.06	.05	.02
296	Jack Howell	.05	.04	.02
297	Claudell Washington	.05	.04	.02
298	John Orton	.06	.05	.02
299	Wally Joyner	.08	.06	.03
300	Lee Stevens	.30	.25	.12
301	Chili Davis	.05	.04	.02
302	Johnny Ray	.05	.04	.02
303	Greg Hibbard	.15	.11	.06
304	Eric King	.06	.05	.02
305	Jack McDowell	.08	.06	.03
306	Bobby Thigpen	.08	.06	.03
307	Adam Peterson	.05	.04	.02
308	Scott Radinsky	.20	.15	.08
309	Wayne Edwards	.06	.05	.02
310	Melido Perez	.06	.05	.02
311	Robin Ventura	.50	.40	.20
312	Sammy Sosa	.30	.25	.12
313	Dan Pasqua	.05	.04	.02
314	Carlton Fisk	.08	.06	.03
315	Ozzie Guillen	.08	.06	.03
316	Ivan Calderon	.08	.06	.03
317	Daryl Boston	.05	.04	.02
318	Craig Grebeck	.15	.11	.06
319	Scott Fletcher	.05	.04	.02
320	Frank Thomas	3.00	2.25	1.25
321	Steve Lyons	.05	.04	.02
322	Carlos Martinez	.10	.08	.04
323	Joe Skalski	.08	.06	.03
324	Tom Candiotti	.05	.04	.02
325	Greg Swindell	.06	.05	.02
326	Steve Olin	.15	.11	.06
327	Kevin Wickander	.08	.06	.03
328	Doug Jones	.06	.05	.02
329	Jeff Shaw	.10	.08	.04
330	Kevin Bearse	.10	.08	.04
331	Dion James	.05	.04	.02
332	Jerry Browne	.06	.05	.02
333	Albert Belle	.75	.60	.30
334	Felix Fermin	.05	.04	.02
335	Candy Maldonado	.06	.05	.02
336	Cory Snyder	.06	.05	.02
337	Sandy Alomar	.25	.20	.10
338	Mark Lewis	.12	.09	.05
339	*Carlos Baerga*	.75	.60	.30
340	Chris James	.05	.04	.02
341	Brook Jacoby	.06	.05	.02
342	Keith Hernandez	.06	.05	.02
343	Frank Tanana	.05	.04	.02
344	Scott Aldred	.15	.11	.06
345	Mike Henneman	.06	.05	.02
346	Steve Wapnick	.15	.11	.06
347	Greg Gohr	.15	.11	.06
348	Eric Stone	.15	.11	.06
349	Brian DuBois	.10	.08	.04
350	Kevin Ritz	.10	.08	.04
351	Rico Brogna	.10	.08	.04
352	Mike Heath	.05	.04	.02
353	Alan Trammell	.08	.06	.03
354	Chet Lemon	.06	.05	.02
355	Dave Bergman	.05	.04	.02
356	Lou Whitaker	.08	.06	.03
357	Cecil Fielder	.40	.30	.15
358	Milt Cuyler	.20	.15	.08
359	Tony Phillips	.06	.05	.02
360	*Travis Fryman*	1.50	1.25	.60
361	Ed Romero	.05	.04	.02
362	Lloyd Moseby	.06	.05	.02
363	Mark Gubicza	.08	.06	.03
364	Bret Saberhagen	.10	.08	.04
365	Tom Gordon	.15	.11	.06
366	Steve Farr	.05	.04	.02
367	Kevin Appier	.30	.25	.12
368	Storm Davis	.05	.04	.02
369	Mark Davis	.05	.04	.02
370	Jeff Montgomery	.06	.05	.02
371	Frank White	.06	.05	.02
372	Brent Mayne	.20	.15	.08
373	Bob Boone	.06	.05	.02
374	Jim Eisenreich	.05	.04	.02
375	Danny Tartabull	.08	.06	.03
376	Kurt Stillwell	.05	.04	.02
377	Bill Pecota	.05	.04	.02
378	Bo Jackson	.40	.30	.15
379	Bob Hamelin	.20	.15	.08
380	Kevin Seitzer	.08	.06	.03
381	Rey Palacios	.05	.04	.02
382	George Brett	.15	.11	.06
383	Gerald Perry	.05	.04	.02
384	Teddy Higuera	.08	.06	.03
385	Tom Filer	.05	.04	.02
386	Dan Plesac	.06	.05	.02
387	*Cal Eldred*	.60	.45	.25
388	Jaime Navarro	.06	.05	.02
389	Chris Bosio	.05	.04	.02
390	Randy Veres	.05	.04	.02
391	Gary Sheffield	.15	.11	.06
392	George Canale	.10	.08	.04
393	B.J. Surhoff	.06	.05	.02
394	Tim McIntosh	.15	.11	.06
395	Greg Brock	.05	.04	.02
396	Greg Vaughn	.25	.20	.10
397	Darryl Hamilton	.10	.08	.04
398	Dave Parker	.10	.08	.04
399	Paul Molitor	.08	.06	.03
400	Jim Gantner	.05	.04	.02
401	Rob Deer	.05	.04	.02
402	Billy Spiers	.15	.11	.06
403	Glenn Braggs	.06	.05	.02
404	Robin Yount	.20	.15	.08
405	Rick Aguilera	.05	.04	.02
406	Johnny Ard	.15	.11	.06
407	*Kevin Tapani*	.25	.20	.10
408	Park Pittman	.20	.15	.08
409	Allan Anderson	.05	.04	.02
410	Juan Berenguer	.05	.04	.02
411	Willie Banks	.40	.30	.15
412	Rich Yett	.05	.04	.02
413	Dave West	.08	.06	.03
414	Greg Gagne	.05	.04	.02
415	Chuck Knoblauch	.50	.40	.20
416	Randy Bush	.05	.04	.02
417	Gary Gaetti	.08	.06	.03
418	Kent Hrbek	.08	.06	.03
419	Al Newman	.05	.04	.02
420	Danny Gladden	.05	.04	.02
421	Paul Sorrento	.15	.11	.06
422	Derek Parks	.25	.20	.10
423	Scott Leius	.20	.15	.08
424	Kirby Puckett	.20	.15	.08
425	Willie Smith	.20	.15	.08
426	Dave Righetti	.08	.06	.03
427	Jeff Robinson	.05	.04	.02
428	Alan Mills	.20	.15	.08
429	Tim Leary	.05	.04	.02
430	Pascual Perez	.05	.04	.02
431	Alvaro Espinoza	.05	.04	.02
432	Dave Winfield	.12	.09	.05
433	Jesse Barfield	.06	.05	.02
434	Randy Velarde	.05	.04	.02
435	Rick Cerone	.05	.04	.02
436	Steve Balboni	.05	.04	.02
437	Mel Hall	.05	.04	.02
438	Bob Geren	.06	.05	.02
439	Bernie Williams	.40	.30	.15
440	Kevin Maas	.12	.09	.05
441	Mike Blowers	.15	.11	.06
442	Steve Sax	.08	.06	.03
443	Don Mattingly	.35	.25	.14
444	Roberto Kelly	.08	.06	.03
445	Mike Moore	.06	.05	.02
446	Reggie Harris	.15	.11	.06
447	Scott Sanderson	.05	.04	.02
448	Dave Otto	.05	.04	.02
449	Dave Stewart	.08	.06	.03
450	Rick Honeycutt	.05	.04	.02
451	Dennis Eckersley	.06	.05	.02
452	Carney Lansford	.06	.05	.02
453	Scott Hemond	.15	.11	.06
454	Mark McGwire	.20	.15	.08
455	Felix Jose	.15	.11	.06
456	Terry Steinbach	.06	.05	.02
457	Rickey Henderson	.25	.20	.10
458	Dave Henderson	.06	.05	.02
459	Mike Gallego	.05	.04	.02
460	Jose Canseco	.50	.40	.20
461	Walt Weiss	.06	.05	.02
462	Ken Phelps	.05	.04	.02
463	Darren Lewis	.40	.30	.15
464	Ron Hassey	.05	.04	.02
465	Roger Salkeld	.30	.25	.12
466	Scott Bankhead	.06	.05	.02
467	Keith Comstock	.05	.04	.02
468	Randy Johnson	.10	.08	.04
469	Erik Hanson	.10	.08	.04
470	Mike Schooler	.06	.05	.02
471	Gary Eave	.15	.11	.06
472	Jeffrey Leonard	.06	.05	.02
473	Dave Valle	.05	.04	.02
474	Omar Vizquel	.05	.04	.02
475	Pete O'Brien	.05	.04	.02
476	Henry Cotto	.05	.04	.02
477	Jay Buhner	.06	.05	.02
478	Harold Reynolds	.06	.05	.02
479	Alvin Davis	.08	.06	.03
480	Darnell Coles	.05	.04	.02
481	Ken Griffey, Jr.	1.75	1.25	.60
482	Greg Briley	.12	.09	.05
483	Scott Bradley	.05	.04	.02
484	Tino Martinez	.15	.11	.06
485	Jeff Russell	.06	.05	.02
486	Nolan Ryan	.50	.40	.20
487	Robb Nen	.20	.15	.08
488	Kevin Brown	.06	.05	.02
489	Brian Bohanon	.20	.15	.08
490	Ruben Sierra	.10	.07	.04
491	Pete Incaviglia	.06	.05	.02
492	*Juan Gonzalez*	2.50	2.00	1.00
493	Steve Buechele	.05	.04	.02
494	Scott Coolbaugh	.15	.11	.06
495	Geno Petralli	.05	.04	.02
496	Rafael Palmeiro	.10	.07	.04
497	Julio Franco	.08	.06	.03
498	Gary Pettis	.05	.04	.02
499	Donald Harris	.20	.15	.08
500	Monty Fariss	.20	.15	.08
501	Harold Baines	.08	.06	.03
502	Cecil Espy	.05	.04	.02
503	Jack Daugherty	.08	.06	.03
504	Willie Blair	.15	.11	.06
505	Dave Steib	.06	.05	.02
506	Tom Henke	.06	.05	.02
507	John Cerutti	.05	.04	.02
508	Paul Kilgus	.05	.04	.02
509	Jimmy Key	.06	.05	.02
510	*John Olerud*	1.25	.90	.50
511	Ed Sprague	.25	.20	.10
512	Manny Lee	.05	.04	.02
513	Fred McGriff	.08	.06	.03
514	Glenallen Hill	.10	.08	.04
515	George Bell	.08	.06	.03
516	Mookie Wilson	.06	.05	.02
517	Luis Sojo	.15	.11	.06
518	Nelson Liriano	.05	.04	.02
519	Kelly Gruber	.08	.06	.03
520	Greg Myers	.06	.05	.02
521	Pat Borders	.06	.05	.02
522	Junior Felix	.25	.20	.10
523	Eddie Zosky	.25	.20	.10
524	Tony Fernandez	.06	.05	.02
525	Checklist	.05	.04	.02
526	Checklist	.05	.04	.02
527	Checklist	.05	.04	.02
528	Checklist	.05	.04	.02

1990 Bowman Inserts

Bowman inserted sweepstakes cards in its 1990 packs, much like in 1989. This 11-card set features current players displayed in drawings by Craig Pursley.

		MT	NR MT	EX
Complete Set:		1.00	.70	.40
Common Player:		.06	.05	.02
(1)	Will Clark	.10	.08	.04
(2)	Mark Davis	.06	.05	.02
(3)	Dwight Gooden	.08	.06	.03
(4)	Bo Jackson	.08	.06	.03
(5)	Don Mattingly	.08	.06	.03
(6)	Kevin Mitchell	.08	.06	.03
(7)	Gregg Olson	.08	.06	.03
(8)	Nolan Ryan	.15	.11	.06
(9)	Bret Saberhagen	.08	.06	.03
(10)	Jerome Walton	.06	.05	.02
(11)	Robin Yount	.10	.08	.04

1991 Bowman

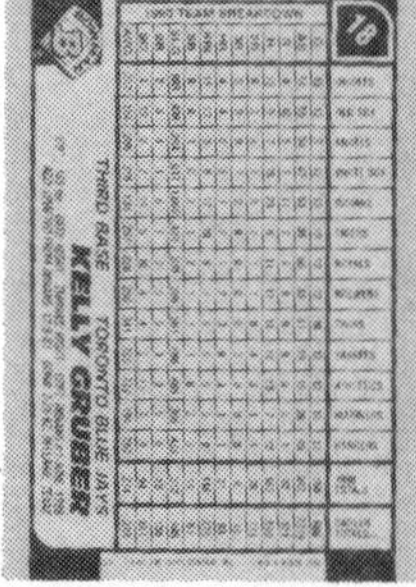

The 1991 Bowman set features 704 cards compared to 528 cards in the 1990 issue. The cards imitate the 1953 Bowman style. Special Rod Carew cards and gold foil-stamped cards are included. The set is numbered by teams. Like the 1989 and 1990 issues, the card backs feature a breakdown of performance against each other team in the league.

		MT	NR MT	EX
	Complete Set (704):	15.00	11.00	6.00
	Common Player:	.05	.04	.02
1	Rod Carew-I	.08	.06	.03
2	Rod Carew-II	.08	.06	.03
3	Rod Carew-III	.08	.06	.03
4	Rod Carew-IV	.08	.06	.03
5	Rod Carew-V	.08	.06	.03
6	Willie Fraser	.05	.04	.02
7	John Olerud	.30	.25	.12
8	William Suero	.10	.08	.04
9	Roberto Alomar	.20	.15	.08
10	Todd Stottlemyre	.06	.05	.02
11	Joe Carter	.12	.09	.05
12	*Steve Karsay*	.50	.40	.20
13	Mark Whiten	.20	.15	.08
14	Pat Borders	.05	.04	.02
15	Mike Timlin	.08	.06	.03
16	Tom Henke	.06	.05	.02
17	Eddie Zosky	.08	.06	.03
18	Kelly Gruber	.08	.06	.03
19	Jimmy Key	.06	.05	.02
20	Jerry Schunk	.12	.09	.05
21	Manny Lee	.05	.04	.02
22	Dave Steib	.08	.06	.03
23	Pat Hentgen	1.00	.70	.40
24	Glenallen Hill	.08	.06	.03
25	Rene Gonzales	.05	.04	.02
26	Ed Sprague	.15	.11	.06
27	Ken Dayley	.05	.04	.02
28	Pat Tabler	.05	.04	.02
29	*Denis Boucher*	.12	.09	.05
30	Devon White	.08	.06	.03
31	Dante Bichette	.08	.06	.03
32	Paul Molitor	.15	.11	.06
33	Greg Vaughn	.10	.08	.04
34	Dan Plesac	.05	.04	.02
35	Chris George	.08	.06	.03
36	Tim McIntosh	.08	.06	.03
37	Franklin Stubbs	.05	.04	.02
38	Bo Dodson	.08	.06	.03
39	Ron Robinson	.05	.04	.02
40	Ed Nunez	.05	.04	.02
41	Greg Brock	.05	.04	.02
42	Jaime Navarro	.06	.05	.02
43	Chris Bosio	.05	.04	.02
44	B.J. Surhoff	.06	.05	.02
45	Chris Johnson	.08	.06	.03
46	Willie Randolph	.06	.05	.02
47	Narciso Elvira	.10	.08	.04
48	Jim Gantner	.05	.04	.02
49	Kevin Brown	.05	.04	.02
50	Julio Machado	.05	.04	.02
51	Chuck Crim	.05	.04	.02
52	Gary Sheffield	.20	.15	.08
53	Angel Miranda	.10	.07	.04
54	Teddy Higuera	.06	.05	.02
55	Robin Yount	.10	.08	.04
56	Cal Eldred	.20	.15	.08
57	Sandy Alomar	.08	.06	.03
58	Greg Swindell	.06	.05	.02
59	Brook Jacoby	.06	.05	.02
60	Efrain Valdez	.08	.06	.03
61	Ever Magallanes	.10	.08	.04
62	Tom Candiotti	.05	.04	.02
63	Eric King	.05	.04	.02
64	Alex Cole	.05	.04	.02
65	Charles Nagy	.12	.09	.05
66	Mitch Webster	.05	.04	.02
67	Chris James	.05	.04	.02
68	Jim Thome	.50	.40	.20
69	Carlos Baerga	.25	.20	.10
70	Mark Lewis	.08	.06	.03
71	Jerry Browne	.05	.04	.02
72	Jesse Orosco	.05	.04	.02
73	Mike Huff	.06	.05	.02
74	Jose Escobar	.12	.09	.05
75	Jeff Manto	.06	.05	.02
76	*Turner Ward*	.15	.11	.06
77	Doug Jones	.05	.04	.02
78	*Bruce Egloff*	.12	.09	.05
79	Tim Costo	.20	.15	.08
80	Beau Allred	.06	.05	.02
81	Albert Belle	.30	.25	.12
82	John Farrell	.05	.04	.02
83	Glenn Davis	.08	.06	.03
84	Joe Orsulak	.05	.04	.02
85	Mark Williamson	.05	.04	.02
86	Ben McDonald	.12	.09	.05
87	Billy Ripken	.05	.04	.02
88	Leo Gomez	.08	.06	.03
89	Bob Melvin	.05	.04	.02
90	Jeff Robinson	.05	.04	.02
91	Jose Mesa	.05	.04	.02
92	Gregg Olson	.08	.06	.03
93	Mike Devereaux	.06	.05	.02
94	Luis Mercedes	.15	.11	.06
95	*Arthur Rhodes*	.20	.15	.08
96	Juan Bell	.05	.04	.02
97	Mike Mussina	1.25	.90	.50
98	Jeff Ballard	.05	.04	.02
99	Chris Hoiles	.12	.09	.05
100	Brady Anderson	.05	.04	.02
101	Bob Milacki	.05	.04	.02
102	David Segui	.06	.05	.02
103	Dwight Evans	.06	.05	.02
104	Cal Ripken, Jr.	.25	.20	.10
105	Mike Linskey	.12	.09	.05
106	*Jeff Tackett*	.12	.09	.05
107	Jeff Reardon	.08	.06	.03
108	Dana Kiecker	.05	.04	.02
109	Ellis Burks	.08	.06	.03
110	Dave Owen	.12	.09	.05
111	Danny Darwin	.05	.04	.02
112	Mo Vaughn	.50	.40	.20
113	Jeff McNeely	.25	.20	.10
114	Tom Bolton	.05	.04	.02
115	Greg Blosser	.12	.09	.05
116	Mike Greenwell	.10	.08	.04
117	*Phil Plantier*	.60	.45	.25
118	Roger Clemens	.20	.15	.08
119	John Marzano	.05	.04	.02
120	Jody Reed	.06	.05	.02
121	Scott Taylor	.12	.09	.05
122	Jack Clark	.06	.05	.02
123	Derek Livernois	.12	.09	.05
124	Tony Pena	.05	.04	.02
125	Tom Brunansky	.05	.04	.02
126	Carlos Quintana	.05	.04	.02
127	Tim Naehring	.10	.08	.04
128	Matt Young	.05	.04	.02
129	Wade Boggs	.12	.09	.05
130	Kevin Morton	.15	.11	.06
131	Pete Incaviglia	.05	.04	.02
132	Rob Deer	.05	.04	.02
133	Bill Gullickson	.05	.04	.02
134	Rico Brogna	.08	.06	.03
135	Lloyd Moseby	.05	.04	.02
136	Cecil Fielder	.15	.11	.06
137	Tony Phillips	.05	.04	.02
138	Mark Leiter	.05	.04	.02
139	John Cerutti	.05	.04	.02
140	Mickey Tettleton	.06	.05	.02
141	Milt Cuyler	.10	.08	.04
142	Greg Gohr	.10	.08	.04
143	Tony Bernazard	.05	.04	.02
144	Dan Gakeler	.12	.09	.05
145	Travis Fryman	.50	.40	.20
146	Dan Petry	.05	.04	.02
147	Scott Aldred	.08	.06	.03
148	John DeSilva	.10	.07	.04
149	Rusty Meacham	.12	.09	.05
150	Lou Whitaker	.06	.05	.02
151	Dave Haas	.06	.05	.02
152	Luis de los Santos	.05	.04	.02
153	Ivan Cruz	.10	.07	.04
154	Alan Trammell	.08	.06	.03
155	Pat Kelly	.10	.07	.04
156	Carl Everett	.35	.25	.14
157	Greg Cadaret	.05	.04	.02
158	Kevin Maas	.10	.07	.04
159	Jeff Johnson	.15	.11	.06
160	Willie Smith	.15	.11	.06
161	Gerald Williams	.20	.15	.08
162	Mike Humphreys	.12	.09	.05
163	Alvaro Espinoza	.05	.04	.02
164	Matt Nokes	.05	.04	.02
165	Wade Taylor	.12	.09	.05
166	Roberto Kelly	.08	.06	.03
167	John Habyan	.05	.04	.02
168	Steve Farr	.05	.04	.02
169	Jesse Barfield	.05	.04	.02
170	Steve Sax	.06	.05	.02
171	Jim Leyritz	.05	.04	.02
172	Robert Eenhoorn	.10	.07	.04
173	Bernie Williams	.15	.11	.06
174	Scott Lusader	.05	.04	.02
175	Torey Lovullo	.08	.06	.03
176	Chuck Cary	.05	.04	.02
177	Scott Sanderson	.05	.04	.02
178	Don Mattingly	.15	.11	.06
179	Mel Hall	.06	.05	.02
180	Juan Gonzalez	.75	.60	.30
181	Hensley Meulens	.08	.06	.03
182	Jose Offerman	.15	.11	.06
183	*Jeff Bagwell*	1.50	1.25	.60
184	Jeff Conine	.30	.25	.12
185	*Henry Rodriguez*	.35	.25	.14
186	Jimmie Reese	.15	.11	.06
187	Kyle Abbott	.10	.08	.04
188	Lance Parrish	.06	.05	.02
189	Rafael Montalvo	.12	.09	.05
190	Floyd Bannister	.05	.04	.02
191	Dick Schofield	.05	.04	.02
192	Scott Lewis	.12	.09	.05
193	Jeff Robinson	.05	.04	.02
194	Kent Anderson	.05	.04	.02
195	Wally Joyner	.10	.08	.04
196	Chuck Finley	.08	.06	.03
197	Luis Sojo	.05	.04	.02
198	Jeff Richardson	.08	.06	.03
199	Dave Parker	.08	.06	.03
200	Jim Abbott	.12	.09	.05
201	Junior Felix	.06	.05	.02
202	Mark Langston	.08	.06	.03
203	Tim Salmon	2.00	1.50	.80
204	Cliff Young	.08	.06	.03
205	Scott Bailes	.05	.04	.02
206	Bobby Rose	.06	.05	.02
207	Gary Gaetti	.06	.05	.02
208	Ruben Amaro	.12	.09	.05
209	Luis Polonia	.06	.05	.02
210	Dave Winfield	.15	.11	.06
211	Bryan Harvey	.06	.05	.02
212	Mike Moore	.05	.04	.02
213	Rickey Henderson	.15	.11	.06
214	Steve Chitren	.15	.11	.06
215	Bob Welch	.06	.05	.02
216	Terry Steinbach	.06	.05	.02
217	Ernie Riles	.05	.04	.02
218	Todd Van Poppel	.25	.20	.10
219	Mike Gallego	.05	.04	.02
220	Curt Young	.05	.04	.02
221	Todd Burns	.05	.04	.02
222	Vance Law	.05	.04	.02
223	Eric Show	.05	.04	.02
224	*Don Peters*	.10	.07	.04
225	Dave Stewart	.10	.08	.04
226	Dave Henderson	.06	.05	.02
227	Jose Canseco	.20	.15	.08
228	Walt Weiss	.06	.05	.02
229	Dann Howitt	.06	.05	.02
230	Willie Wilson	.05	.04	.02
231	Harold Baines	.06	.05	.02
232	Scott Hemond	.06	.05	.02
233	Joe Slusarski	.12	.09	.05
234	Mark McGwire	.15	.11	.06
235	*Kirk Dressendorfer*	.12	.09	.05
236	*Craig Paquette*	.20	.15	.08
237	Dennis Eckersley	.10	.08	.04
238	Dana Allison	.12	.09	.05
239	Scott Bradley	.05	.04	.02
240	Brian Holman	.06	.05	.02
241	Mike Schooler	.06	.05	.02
242	Rich Delucia	.12	.09	.05
243	Edgar Martinez	.08	.06	.03
244	Henry Cotto	.05	.04	.02
245	Omar Vizquel	.05	.04	.02
246	Ken Griffey, Jr.	.75	.60	.30
247	Jay Buhner	.06	.05	.02
248	Bill Krueger	.05	.04	.02
249	*Dave Fleming*	.40	.30	.15
250	*Patrick Lennon*	.15	.11	.06
251	Dave Valle	.05	.04	.02
252	Harold Reynolds	.06	.05	.02
253	Randy Johnson	.12	.09	.05
254	Scott Bankhead	.06	.05	.02
255	Ken Griffey	.08	.06	.03
256	Greg Briley	.05	.04	.02
257	Tino Martinez	.12	.09	.05
258	Alvin Davis	.06	.05	.02
259	Pete O'Brien	.05	.04	.02
260	Erik Hanson	.08	.06	.03
261	*Bret Boone*	.50	.40	.20
262	Roger Salkeld	.15	.11	.06
263	Dave Burba	.08	.06	.03
264	*Kerry Woodson*	.12	.09	.05
265	Julio Franco	.08	.06	.03
266	Dan Peltier	.10	.07	.04
267	Jeff Russell	.05	.04	.02
268	Steve Buechele	.06	.05	.02
269	Donald Harris	.12	.09	.05
270	Robb Nen	.10	.08	.04
271	Rich Gossage	.06	.05	.02
272	*Ivan Rodriguez*	.60	.45	.25
273	Jeff Huson	.06	.05	.02
274	Kevin Brown	.06	.05	.02
275	*Dan Smith*	.10	.07	.04
276	Gary Pettis	.05	.04	.02
277	Jack Daugherty	.05	.04	.02
278	Mike Jeffcoat	.05	.04	.02
279	Brad Arnsbarg	.06	.05	.02
280	Nolan Ryan	.50	.40	.20
281	Eric McCray	.10	.07	.04
282	Scott Chiamparino	.08	.06	.03
283	Ruben Sierra	.15	.11	.06
284	Geno Petralli	.05	.04	.02
285	Monty Fariss	.08	.06	.03
286	Rafael Palmeiro	.12	.09	.05
287	Bobb Witt	.06	.05	.02
288	Dean Palmer	.20	.15	.08
289	Tony Scruggs	.10	.07	.04
290	Kenny Rogers	.05	.04	.02
291	Bret Saberhagen	.08	.06	.03
292	*Brian McRae*	.25	.20	.10
293	Storm Davis	.05	.04	.02
294	Danny Tartabull	.08	.06	.03
295	David Howard	.12	.09	.05
296	Mike Boddicker	.06	.05	.02
297	Joel Johnston	.12	.09	.05
298	Tim Spehr	.15	.11	.06
299	Hector Wagner	.12	.09	.05
300	George Brett	.20	.15	.08
301	Mike Macfarlane	.06	.05	.02
302	Kirk Gibson	.06	.05	.02
303	Harvey Pulliam	.10	.07	.04
304	Jim Eisenreich	.05	.04	.02
305	Kevin Seitzer	.06	.05	.02
306	Mark Davis	.05	.04	.02
307	Kurt Stillwell	.05	.04	.02
308	Jeff Montgomery	.06	.05	.02
309	Kevin Appier	.06	.05	.02
310	Bob Hamelin	.20	.15	.08
311	Tom Gordon	.06	.05	.02
312	*Kerwin Moore*	.15	.11	.06
313	Hugh Walker	.12	.09	.05
314	Terry Shumpert	.05	.04	.02
315	Warren Cromartie	.05	.04	.02
316	Gary Thurman	.05	.04	.02
317	Steve Bedrosian	.05	.04	.02
318	Danny Gladden	.05	.04	.02
319	Jack Morris	.08	.06	.03
320	Kirby Puckett	.20	.15	.08
321	Kent Hrbek	.08	.06	.03
322	Kevin Tapani	.08	.06	.03
323	Denny Neagle	.12	.09	.05
324	Rich Garces	.12	.09	.05
325	Larry Casian	.10	.08	.04
326	Shane Mack	.08	.06	.03
327	Allan Anderson	.05	.04	.02
328	Junior Ortiz	.05	.04	.02
329	*Paul Abbott*	.10	.08	.04
330	Chuck Knoblauch	.20	.15	.08
331	Chili Davis	.08	.06	.03
332	*Todd Ritchie*	.15	.11	.06
333	Brian Harper	.06	.05	.02
334	Rick Aguilera	.06	.05	.02
335	Scott Erickson	.10	.07	.04
336	Pedro Munoz	.12	.09	.05
337	Scott Leuis	.10	.08	.04
338	Greg Gagne	.05	.04	.02
339	Mike Pagliarulo	.05	.04	.02
340	Terry Leach	.05	.04	.02
341	Willie Banks	.10	.08	.04
342	Bobby Thigpen	.06	.05	.02
343	*Roberto Hernandez*	.25	.20	.10
344	Melido Perez	.05	.04	.02
345	Carlton Fisk	.10	.08	.04
346	*Norberto Martin*	.12	.09	.05
347	*Johnny Ruffin*	.15	.11	.06
348	*Jeff Carter*	.10	.07	.04
349	Lance Johnson	.05	.04	.02
350	Sammy Sosa	.10	.08	.04

351	Alex Fernandez	.50	.40	.20
352	Jack McDowell	.10	.08	.04
353	Bob Wickman	.25	.20	.10
354	Wilson Alvarez	.40	.30	.15
355	Charlie Hough	.05	.04	.02
356	Ozzie Guillen	.06	.05	.02
357	Cory Snyder	.05	.04	.02
358	Robin Ventura	.15	.11	.06
359	Scott Fletcher	.05	.04	.02
360	Cesar Bernhardt	.12	.09	.05
361	Dan Pasqua	.05	.04	.02
362	Tim Raines	.08	.06	.03
363	Brian Drahman	.12	.09	.05
364	Wayne Edwards	.05	.04	.02
365	Scott Radinsky	.06	.05	.02
366	Frank Thomas	1.50	1.25	.60
367	Cecil Fielder	.10	.08	.04
368	Julio Franco	.10	.08	.04
369	Kelly Gruber	.08	.06	.03
370	Alan Trammell	.08	.06	.03
371	Rickey Henderson	.10	.08	.04
372	Jose Canseco	.10	.08	.04
373	Ellis Burks	.08	.06	.03
374	Lance Parrish	.06	.05	.02
375	Dave Parker	.08	.06	.03
376	Eddie Murray	.08	.06	.03
377	Ryne Sandberg	.12	.09	.05
378	Matt Williams	.10	.08	.04
379	Barry Larkin	.08	.06	.03
380	Barry Bonds	.35	.25	.14
381	Bobby Bonilla	.10	.08	.04
382	Darryl Strawberry	.08	.06	.03
383	Benny Santiago	.06	.05	.02
384	Don Robinson	.05	.04	.02
385	Paul Coleman	.10	.08	.04
386	Milt Thompson	.05	.04	.02
387	Lee Smith	.06	.05	.02
388	Ray Lankford	.15	.11	.06
389	Tom Pagnozzi	.06	.05	.02
390	Ken Hill	.06	.05	.02
391	Jamie Moyer	.05	.04	.02
392	*Greg Carmona*	.12	.09	.05
393	John Ericks	.10	.08	.04
394	Bob Tewksbury	.05	.04	.02
395	Jose Oquendo	.05	.04	.02
396	Rheal Cormier	.15	.11	.06
397	*Mike Milchin*	.12	.09	.05
398	Ozzie Smith	.15	.11	.06
399	Aaron Holbert	.15	.11	.06
400	Jose DeLeon	.05	.04	.02
401	Felix Jose	.08	.06	.03
402	Juan Agosto	.05	.04	.02
403	Pedro Guerrero	.08	.06	.03
404	Todd Zeile	.08	.06	.03
405	Gerald Perry	.05	.04	.02
406	Not issued			
407	Bryn Smith	.05	.04	.02
408	Bernard Gilkey	.20	.15	.08
409	Rex Hudler	.05	.04	.02
410a	Thomson/Branca	.10	.08	.04
410b	Donovan Osborne	.25	.20	.10
411	Lance Dickson	.15	.11	.06
412	Danny Jackson	.05	.04	.02
413	Jerome Walton	.06	.05	.02
414	Sean Cheetham	.10	.07	.04
415	Joe Girardi	.05	.04	.02
416	Ryne Sandberg	.20	.15	.08
417	Mike Harkey	.06	.05	.02
418	George Bell	.08	.06	.03
419	*Rick Wilkins*	.25	.20	.10
420	Earl Cunningham	.06	.05	.02
421	Heathcliff Slocumb	.12	.09	.05
422	Mike Bielecki	.05	.04	.02
423	*Jessie Hollins*	.12	.09	.05
424	Shawon Dunston	.06	.05	.02
425	Dave Smith	.05	.04	.02
426	Greg Maddux	.15	.11	.06
427	Jose Vizcaino	.05	.04	.02
428	Luis Salazar	.05	.04	.02
429	Andre Dawson	.10	.08	.04
430	Rick Sutcliffe	.05	.04	.02
431	Paul Assenmacher	.05	.04	.02
432	Erik Pappas	.12	.09	.05
433	Mark Grace	.10	.08	.04
434	Denny Martinez	.06	.05	.02
435	Marquis Grissom	.12	.09	.05
436	*Wil Cordero*	.35	.25	.14
437	Tim Wallach	.06	.05	.02
438	*Brian Barnes*	.15	.11	.06
439	Barry Jones	.05	.04	.02
440	Ivan Calderon	.08	.06	.03
441	*Stan Spencer*	.12	.09	.05
442	Larry Walker	.12	.09	.05
443	*Chris Haney*	.12	.09	.05
444	Hector Rivera	.12	.09	.05
445	Delino DeShields	.12	.09	.05
446	Andres Galarraga	.06	.05	.02
447	Gilberto Reyes	.06	.05	.02
448	Willie Greene	.10	.08	.04
449	Greg Colbrunn	.12	.09	.05
450	*Rondell White*	.75	.60	.30
451	Steve Frey	.06	.05	.02
452	*Shane Andrews*	.12	.09	.05
453	Mike Fitzgerald	.05	.04	.02
454	Spike Owen	.05	.04	.02
455	Dave Martinez	.05	.04	.02
456	Dennis Boyd	.05	.04	.02
457	Eric Bullock	.06	.05	.02
458	*Reid Cornelius*	.15	.11	.06
459	Chris Nabholz	.15	.11	.06
460	David Cone	.08	.06	.03
461	Hubie Brooks	.06	.05	.02
462	Sid Fernandez	.06	.05	.02
463	*Doug Simons*	.10	.08	.04
464	Howard Johnson	.10	.08	.04
465	Chris Donnels	.15	.11	.06
466	Anthony Young	.15	.11	.06
467	Todd Hundley	.12	.09	.05
468	Rick Cerone	.05	.04	.02
469	Kevin Elster	.05	.04	.02
470	Wally Whitehurst	.06	.05	.02
471	Vince Coleman	.08	.06	.03
472	Dwight Gooden	.08	.06	.03
473	Charlie O'Brien	.05	.04	.02
474	Jeromy Burnitz	.40	.30	.15
475	John Franco	.08	.06	.03
476	Daryl Boston	.05	.04	.02
477	Frank Viola	.08	.06	.03
478	D.J. Dozier	.10	.08	.04
479	Kevin McReynolds	.06	.05	.02
480	Tom Herr	.05	.04	.02
481	Gregg Jefferies	.08	.06	.03
482	Pete Schourek	.12	.09	.05
483	Ron Darling	.06	.05	.02
484	Dave Magadan	.06	.05	.02
485	*Andy Ashby*	.10	.08	.04
486	Dale Murphy	.08	.06	.03
487	Von Hayes	.06	.05	.02
488	*Kim Batiste*	.12	.09	.05
489	*Tony Longmire*	.12	.09	.05
490	Wally Backman	.05	.04	.02
491	Jeff Jackson	.08	.06	.03
492	Mickey Morandini	.08	.06	.03
493	Darrel Akerfelds	.05	.04	.02
494	Ricky Jordan	.06	.05	.02
495	Randy Ready	.05	.04	.02
496	Darrin Fletcher	.06	.05	.02
497	Chuck Malone	.05	.04	.02
498	Pat Combs	.06	.05	.02
499	Dickie Thon	.05	.04	.02
500	Roger McDowell	.06	.05	.02
501	Len Dykstra	.12	.09	.05
502	Joe Boever	.05	.04	.02
503	John Kruk	.08	.06	.03
504	Terry Mulholland	.06	.05	.02
505	Wes Chamberlain	.10	.07	.04
506	*Mike Lieberthal*	.15	.11	.06
507	Darren Daulton	.15	.11	.06
508	Charlie Hayes	.06	.05	.02
509	John Smiley	.06	.05	.02
510	Gary Varsho	.05	.04	.02
511	Curt Wilkerson	.05	.04	.02
512	*Orlando Merced*	.20	.15	.08
513	Barry Bonds	.35	.25	.14
514	Mike Lavalliere	.05	.04	.02
515	Doug Drabek	.06	.05	.02
516	Gary Redus	.05	.04	.02
517	*William Pennyfeather*	.10	.07	.04
518	Randy Tomlin	.06	.05	.02
519	*Mike Zimmerman*	.12	.09	.05
520	Jeff King	.06	.05	.02
521	*Kurt Miller*	.15	.11	.06
522	Jay Bell	.06	.05	.02
523	Bill Landrum	.05	.04	.02
524	Zane Smith	.05	.04	.02
525	Bobby Bonilla	.10	.08	.04
526	Bob Walk	.05	.04	.02
527	Austin Manahan	.08	.06	.03
528	*Joe Ausanio*	.12	.09	.05
529	Andy Van Slyke	.08	.06	.03
530	Jose Lind	.05	.04	.02
531	*Carlos Garcia*	.50	.40	.20
532	Don Slaught	.05	.04	.02
533	Colin Powell	.25	.20	.10
534	*Frank Bolick*	.25	.20	.10
535	*Gary Scott*	.10	.08	.04
536	Nikco Riesgo	.10	.08	.04
537	*Reggie Sanders*	.60	.45	.25
538	*Tim Howard*	.10	.08	.04
539	*Ryan Bowen*	.15	.11	.06
540	Eric Anthony	.08	.06	.03
541	Jim Deshaies	.05	.04	.02
542	Tom Nevers	.12	.09	.05
543	Ken Caminiti	.05	.04	.02
544	Karl Rhodes	.12	.09	.05
545	Xavier Hernandez	.08	.06	.03
546	Mike Scott	.06	.05	.02
547	Jeff Juden	.15	.11	.06
548	Darryl Kile	.08	.06	.03
549	Willie Ansley	.10	.08	.04
550	*Luis Gonzalez*	.35	.25	.14
551	*Mike Simms*	.15	.11	.06
552	Mark Portugal	.05	.04	.02
553	Jimmy Jones	.05	.04	.02
554	Jim Clancy	.05	.04	.02
555	Pete Harnisch	.06	.05	.02
556	Craig Biggio	.08	.06	.03
557	Eric Yelding	.05	.04	.02
558	Dave Rohde	.06	.05	.02
559	Casey Candaele	.05	.04	.02
560	Curt Schilling	.05	.04	.02
561	Steve Finley	.06	.05	.02
562	Javier Ortiz	.08	.06	.03
563	Andujar Cedeno	.20	.15	.08
564	Rafael Ramirez	.05	.04	.02
565	*Kenny Lofton*	1.00	.70	.40
566	Steve Avery	.15	.11	.06
567	Lonnie Smith	.05	.04	.02
568	Kent Mercker	.06	.05	.02
569	*Chipper Jones*	.75	.60	.30
570	Terry Pendleton	.06	.05	.02
571	Otis Nixon	.05	.04	.02
572	Juan Berenguer	.05	.04	.02
573	Charlie Leibrandt	.05	.04	.02
574	Dave Justice	.30	.25	.12
575	Keith Mitchell	.10	.08	.04
576	Tom Glavine	.15	.11	.06
577	Greg Olson	.05	.04	.02
578	Rafael Belliard	.05	.04	.02
579	Ben Rivera	.15	.11	.06
580	John Smoltz	.06	.05	.02
581	Tyler Houston	.05	.04	.02
582	*Mark Wohlers*	.15	.11	.06
583	Ron Gant	.12	.09	.05
584	Ramon Caraballo	.10	.08	.04
585	Sid Bream	.05	.04	.02
586	Jeff Treadway	.05	.04	.02
587	*Javier Lopez*	1.25	.90	.50
588	Deion Sanders	.20	.15	.08
589	Mike Heath	.05	.04	.02
590	*Ryan Klesko*	1.25	.90	.50
591	Bob Ojeda	.05	.04	.02
592	Alfredo Griffin	.05	.04	.02
593	*Raul Mondesi*	.50	.40	.20
594	Greg Smith	.05	.04	.02
595	Orel Hershiser	.08	.06	.03
596	Juan Samuel	.06	.05	.02
597	Brett Butler	.06	.05	.02
598	Gary Carter	.06	.05	.02
599	Stan Javier	.05	.04	.02
600	Kal Daniels	.08	.06	.03
601	*Jamie McAndrew*	.10	.07	.04
602	Mike Sharperson	.05	.04	.02
603	Jay Howell	.05	.04	.02
604	*Eric Karros*	.50	.40	.20
605	Tim Belcher	.06	.05	.02
606	Dan Opperman	.12	.09	.05
607	Lenny Harris	.05	.04	.02
608	Tom Goodwin	.10	.08	.04
609	Darryl Strawberry	.10	.08	.04
610	Ramon Martinez	.12	.09	.05
611	Kevin Gross	.05	.04	.02
612	Zakary Shinall	.12	.09	.05
613	Mike Scioscia	.05	.04	.02
614	Eddie Murray	.10	.07	.04
615	Ronnie Walden	.15	.11	.06
616	Will Clark	.20	.15	.08
617	Adam Hyzdu	.12	.09	.05
618	Matt Williams	.08	.06	.03
619	Don Robinson	.05	.04	.02
620	Jeff Brantley	.05	.04	.02
621	Greg Litton	.05	.04	.02
622	Steve Decker	.10	.08	.04
623	Robby Thompson	.06	.05	.02
624	*Mark Leonard*	.12	.09	.05
625	Kevin Bass	.05	.04	.02
626	Scott Garrelts	.05	.04	.02
627	Jose Uribe	.05	.04	.02
628	Eric Gunderson	.08	.06	.03
629	Steve Hosey	.10	.07	.04
630	Trevor Wilson	.06	.05	.02
631	Terry Kennedy	.05	.04	.02
632	Dave Righetti	.06	.05	.02
633	Kelly Downs	.05	.04	.02
634	Johnny Ard	.08	.06	.03
635	*Eric Christopherson*	.10	.07	.04
636	Kevin Mitchell	.10	.08	.04
637	John Burkett	.05	.04	.02
638	*Kevin Rogers*	.10	.07	.04
639	Bud Black	.05	.04	.02
640	Willie McGee	.06	.05	.02
641	Royce Clayton	.15	.11	.06
642	Tony Fernandez	.06	.05	.02
643	Ricky Bones	.12	.09	.05
644	Thomas Howard	.06	.05	.02
645	Dave Staton	.15	.11	.06
646	Jim Presley	.05	.04	.02
647	Tony Gwynn	.12	.09	.05
648	Marty Barrett	.05	.04	.02
649	Scott Coolbaugh	.06	.05	.02
650	Craig Lefferts	.05	.04	.02
651	Eddie Whitson	.05	.04	.02
652	Oscar Azocar	.05	.04	.02
653	Wes Gardner	.05	.04	.02
654	Bip Roberts	.06	.05	.02
655	*Robbie Beckett*	.15	.11	.06
656	Benny Santiago	.06	.05	.02
657	Greg W. Harris	.05	.04	.02
658	Jerald Clark	.06	.05	.02
659	Fred McGriff	.20	.15	.08
660	Larry Andersen	.05	.04	.02
661	Bruce Hurst	.06	.05	.02
662	Steve Martin	.12	.09	.05
663	Rafael Valdez	.06	.05	.02
664	*Paul Faries*	.10	.08	.04
665	Andy Benes	.08	.06	.03
666	Randy Myers	.06	.05	.02
667	Rob Dibble	.08	.06	.03
668	Glenn Sutko	.12	.09	.05
669	Glenn Braggs	.05	.04	.02
670	Billy Hatcher	.05	.04	.02
671	Joe Oliver	.05	.04	.02
672	Freddie Benavides	.12	.09	.05
673	Barry Larkin	.10	.08	.04
674	Chris Sabo	.08	.06	.03
675	Mariano Duncan	.05	.04	.02
676	*Chris Jones*	.10	.07	.04
677	*Gino Minutelli*	.12	.09	.05
678	Reggie Jefferson	.10	.07	.04
679	Jack Armstrong	.06	.05	.02
680	Chris Hammond	.15	.11	.06
681	Jose Rijo	.08	.06	.03
682	Bill Doran	.05	.04	.02
683	Terry Lee	.06	.05	.02
684	Tom Browning	.06	.05	.02
685	Paul O'Neill	.08	.06	.03
686	Eric Davis	.10	.08	.04
687	*Dan Wilson*	.15	.11	.06
688	Ted Power	.05	.04	.02
689	Tim Layana	.05	.04	.02
690	Norm Charlton	.06	.05	.02
691	Hal Morris	.10	.08	.04
692	Rickey Henderson	.10	.08	.04
693	*Sam Militello*	.20	.15	.08
694	*Matt Mieske*	.20	.15	.08
695	*Paul Russo*	.25	.20	.10
696	*Domingo Mota*	.12	.09	.05
697	*Todd Guggiana*	.12	.09	.05
698	Marc Newfield	.25	.20	.10
699	Checklist	.05	.04	.02
700	Checklist	.05	.04	.02
701	Checklist	.05	.04	.02
702	Checklist	.05	.04	.02
703	Checklist	.05	.04	.02
704	Checklist	.05	.04	.02

1992 Bowman

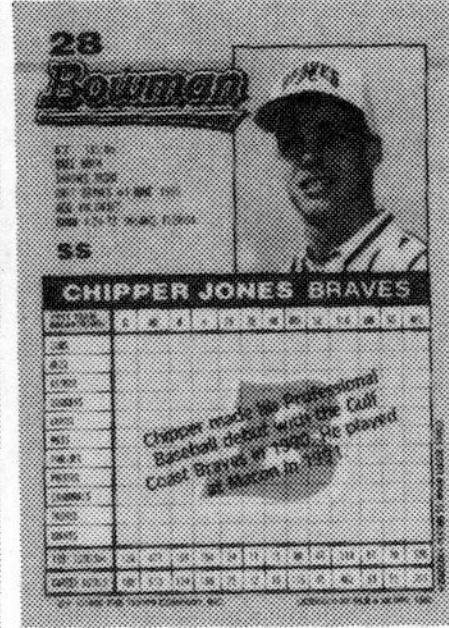

Topps introduced several changes with the release of its 1992 Bowman set. The 705-card set features 45 special insert cards stamped with gold foil. The cards are printed with a premium UV coated glossy card stock. Several players without major league experience are featured in the set. Included in this group are 1991 MVP's of the minor leagues and first round draft choices.

		MT	NR MT	EX
	Complete Set (704):	325.00	240.00	130.00
	Common Player:	.25	.20	.10
1	Ivan Rodriguez	1.50	1.25	.60
2	Kirk McCaskill	.25	.20	.10
3	Scott Livingstone	.40	.30	.15
4	*Salomon Torres*	3.00	2.25	1.25
5	Carlos Hernandez	.25	.20	.10
6	Dave Hollins	1.00	.75	.40
7	Scott Fletcher	.25	.20	.10
8	Jorge Fabregas	.40	.30	.15
9	Andujar Cedeno	.50	.40	.20
10	Howard Johnson	.25	.20	.10
11	Trevor Hoffman	.60	.45	.25
12	Roberto Kelly	.25	.20	.10
13	Gregg Jefferies	.75	.60	.30
14	Marquis Grissom	.75	.60	.30
15	Mike Ignasiak	.40	.30	.15
16	Jack Morris	.40	.30	.15
17	William Pennyfeather	.40	.30	.15
18	Todd Stottlemyre	.25	.20	.10
19	Chito Martinez	.25	.20	.10
20	Roberto Alomar	2.50	2.00	1.00
21	Sam Militello	.40	.30	.15
22	Hector Fajardo	.30	.25	.12
23	*Paul Quantrill*	.40	.30	.15
24	Chuck Knoblauch	.35	.25	.14
25	Reggie Jefferson	.35	.25	.14
26	Jeremy McGarity	.40	.30	.15
27	Jerome Walton	.25	.20	.10
28	Chipper Jones	5.00	3.75	2.00
29	*Brian Barber*	1.25	.90	.50
30	Ron Darling	.25	.20	.10
31	*Robert Petagine*	1.00	.70	.40
32	Chuck Finley	.25	.20	.10
33	Edgar Martinez	.40	.30	.15
34	Napolean Robinson	.40	.30	.15
35	Andy Van Slyke	.25	.20	.10
36	Bobby Thigpen	.25	.20	.10
37	Travis Fryman	3.50	2.75	1.50
38	Eric Christopherson	.40	.30	.15
39	Terry Mulholland	.25	.20	.10
40	Darryl Strawberry	.35	.25	.14
41	*Manny Alexander*	.50	.40	.20
42	*Tracey Sanders*	.60	.45	.25
43	Pete Incaviglia	.25	.20	.10
44	Kim Batiste	.40	.30	.15
45	Frank Rodriguez	2.00	1.50	.80
46	Greg Swindell	.25	.20	.10
47	Delino DeShields	.60	.45	.25
48	John Ericks	.25	.20	.10
49	Franklin Stubbs	.25	.20	.10
50	Tony Gwynn	.75	.60	.30
51	*Clifton Garrett*	.50	.40	.20
52	Mike Gardella	.30	.25	.12
53	Scott Erickson	.40	.30	.15
54	Gary Caballo	.40	.30	.15
55	Jose Oliva	.80	.60	.30
56	Brook Fordyce	.40	.30	.15
57	Mark Whiten	.30	.25	.12
58	Joe Slusarski	.25	.20	.10
59	*J.R. Phillips*	3.75	3.00	1.50
60	Barry Bonds	4.00	3.00	1.50
61	Bob Milacki	.25	.20	.10
62	Keith Mitchell	.40	.30	.15
63	Angel Miranda	.40	.30	.15
64	Raul Mondesi	10.00	7.50	4.00
65	Brian Koelling	.40	.30	.15
66	Brian McRae	.60	.45	.25
67	John Patterson	.30	.25	.12
68	John Wetteland	.25	.20	.10
69	Wilson Alvarez	1.50	1.25	.60
70	Wade Boggs	.90	.70	.35
71	Darryl Ratliff	.30	.25	.12
72	Jeff Jackson	.40	.30	.15
73	Jeremy Hernandez	.40	.30	.15
74	Darryl Hamilton	.25	.20	.10
75	Rafael Belliard	.25	.20	.10
76	Ricky Trilcek	.30	.25	.12
77	*Felipe Crespo*	.80	.60	.30
78	Carney Lansford	.25	.20	.10
79	Ryan Long	.60	.45	.25
80	Kirby Puckett	3.00	2.25	1.25
81	Earl Cunningham	.25	.20	.10
82	Pedro Martinez	1.50	1.25	.60
83	Scott Hatteberg	.50	.40	.20
84	Juan Gonzalez	10.00	7.50	4.00
85	Robert Nutting	.40	.30	.15
86	*Calvin Reese*	.60	.45	.25
87	Dave Silvestri	.40	.30	.15
88	*Scott Ruffcorn*	3.00	2.25	1.25
89	Rick Aguilera	.25	.20	.10
90	Cecil Fielder	1.25	.90	.50
91	Kirk Dressendorfer	.25	.20	.10
92	Jerry DiPoto	.40	.30	.15
93	Mike Felder	.25	.20	.10
94	Craig Paquette	.80	.60	.30
95	Elvin Paulino	.40	.30	.15
96	Donovan Osborne	2.00	1.50	.80
97	Hubie Brooks	.25	.20	.10
98	Derek Lowe	.40	.30	.15
99	David Zancanaro	.40	.30	.15
100	Ken Griffey, Jr.	10.00	7.50	4.00
101	Todd Hundley	.25	.20	.10
102	Mike Trombley	.60	.45	.25
103	*Ricky Gutierrez*	.80	.60	.30
104	Braulio Castillo	.40	.30	.15
105	Craig Lefferts	.25	.20	.10
106	Rick Sutcliffe	.25	.20	.10
107	Dean Palmer	1.00	.75	.40
108	Henry Rodriguez	2.50	2.00	1.00
109	Mark Clark	.40	.30	.15
110	Kenny Lofton	3.00	2.25	1.25
111	Mark Carreon	.25	.20	.10
112	*J.T. Bruett*	.40	.30	.15
113	Gerald Williams	.40	.30	.15
114	Frank Thomas	17.00	12.50	6.75
115	Kevin Reimer	.25	.20	.10
116	Sammy Sosa	1.00	.75	.40
117	Mickey Tettleton	.25	.20	.10
118	Reggie Sanders	1.50	1.25	.60
119	Trevor Wilson	.25	.20	.10
120	Cliff Brantley	.30	.25	.12
121	Spike Owen	.25	.20	.10
122	Jeff Montgomery	.25	.20	.10
123	Alex Sutherland	.30	.25	.12
124	Brien Taylor	2.50	2.00	1.00
125	Brian Williams	.60	.45	.25
126	Kevin Seitzer	.25	.20	.10
127	Carlos Delgado	16.00	12.00	6.50
128	Gary Scott	.25	.20	.10
129	Scott Cooper	1.50	1.25	.60
130	*Domingo Jean*	1.25	.90	.50
131	*Pat Mahomes*	.80	.60	.30
132	Mike Boddicker	.25	.20	.10
133	Roberto Hernandez	.80	.60	.30
134	Dave Valle	.25	.20	.10
135	Kurt Stillwell	.25	.20	.10
136	*Brad Pennington*	.50	.40	.20
137	Jermaine Swifton	.40	.30	.15
138	Ryan Hawblitzel	.50	.40	.20
139	Tito Navarro	.40	.30	.15
140	Sandy Alomar	.25	.20	.10
141	Todd Benzinger	.25	.20	.10
142	Danny Jackson	.25	.20	.10
143	*Melvin Nieves*	2.00	1.50	.80
144	Jim Campanis	.30	.25	.12
145	Luis Gonzalez	.40	.30	.15
146	Dave Doorneweerd	.40	.30	.15
147	Charlie Hayes	.40	.30	.15
148	Greg Maddux	1.00	.70	.40
149	Brian Harper	.25	.20	.10
150	Brent Miller	.40	.30	.15
151	Shawn Estes	.40	.30	.15
152	Mike Williams	.60	.45	.25
153	Charlie Hough	.25	.20	.10
154	Randy Myers	.25	.20	.10
155	*Kevin Young*	2.50	2.00	1.00
156	Rick Wilkins	1.00	.75	.40
157	Terry Schumpert	.25	.20	.10
158	Steve Karsay	3.50	2.75	1.50
159	Gary DiSarcina	.25	.20	.10
160	Deion Sanders	1.00	.70	.40
161	Tom Browning	.25	.20	.10
162	Dickie Thon	.25	.20	.10
163	Luis Mercedes	.40	.30	.15
164	Ricardo Ingram	.40	.30	.15
165	*Tavo Alavarez*	.60	.45	.25
166	Rickey Henderson	1.00	.70	.40
167	Jaime Navarro	.25	.20	.10
168	*Billy Ashley*	3.00	2.25	1.25
169	Phil Dauphin	.60	.45	.25
170	Ivan Cruz	.40	.30	.15
171	Harold Baines	.25	.20	.10
172	Bryan Harvey	.25	.20	.10
173	Alex Cole	.25	.20	.10
174	Curtis Shaw	.30	.25	.12
175	Matt Williams	1.00	.70	.40
176	Felix Jose	.30	.25	.12
177	Sam Horn	.25	.20	.10
178	Randy Johnson	.25	.20	.10
179	Ivan Calderon	.25	.20	.10
180	Steve Avery	2.00	1.50	.80
181	William Suero	.25	.20	.10
182	Bill Swift	.25	.20	.10
183	*Howard Battle*	.80	.60	.30
184	Ruben Amaro	.25	.20	.10
185	Jim Abbott	1.00	.70	.40
186	Mike Fitzgerald	.25	.20	.10
187	Bruce Hurst	.25	.20	.10
188	Jeff Juden	.60	.45	.25
189	Jeromy Burnitz	1.50	1.25	.60
190	Dave Burba	.25	.20	.10
191	Kevin Brown	.25	.20	.10
192	Patrick Lennon	.30	.25	.12
193	Jeffrey McNeely	.40	.30	.15
194	Wil Cordero	1.25	.90	.50
195	Chili Davis	.25	.20	.10
196	Milt Cuyler	.25	.20	.10
197	Von Hayes	.25	.20	.10
198	Todd Revening	.40	.30	.15
199	Joel Johnson	.25	.20	.10
200	Jeff Bagwell	3.00	2.25	1.25
201	Alex Fernandez	2.00	1.50	.80
202	Todd Jones	.40	.30	.15
203	Charles Nagy	.40	.30	.15
204	Tim Raines	.25	.20	.10
205	Kevin Maas	.25	.20	.10
206	Julio Franco	.25	.20	.10
207	Randy Velarde	.25	.20	.10
208	Lance Johnson	.25	.20	.10
209	Scott Leius	.25	.20	.10
210	Derek Lee	.40	.30	.15
211	Joe Sondrini	.30	.25	.12
212	Royce Clayton	1.50	1.25	.60
213	Chris George	.25	.20	.10
214	Gary Sheffield	1.25	.90	.50
215	Mark Gubicza	.25	.20	.10
216	Mike Moore	.25	.20	.10
217	Rick Huisman	.60	.45	.25
218	Jeff Russell	.25	.20	.10
219	D.J. Dozier	.25	.20	.10
220	Dave Martinez	.25	.20	.10
221	Al Newman	.25	.20	.10
222	Nolan Ryan	7.00	5.25	2.75
223	Teddy Higuera	.25	.20	.10
224	*Damon Buford*	.50	.40	.20
225	Ruben Sierra	.80	.60	.30
226	Tom Nevers	.30	.25	.12
227	Tommy Greene	.60	.45	.25
228	*Nigel Wilson*	3.00	2.25	1.25
229	John DeSilva	.40	.30	.15
230	Bobby Witt	.25	.20	.10
231	Greg Cadaret	.25	.20	.10
232	John VanderWal	.50	.40	.20
233	Jack Clark	.25	.20	.10
234	Bill Doran	.25	.20	.10
235	Bobby Bonilla	.50	.40	.20
236	Steve Olin	.25	.20	.10
237	Derek Bell	1.00	.75	.40
238	David Cone	.40	.30	.15
239	Victor Cole	.30	.25	.12
240	Rod Bolton	.60	.45	.25
241	Tom Pagnozzi	.25	.20	.10
242	Rob Dibble	.25	.20	.10
243	Michael Carter	.40	.30	.15
244	Don Peters	.30	.25	.12
245	Mike LaValliere	.25	.20	.10
246	Joe Perona	.30	.25	.12
247	Mitch Williams	.25	.20	.10
248	Jay Buhner	.50	.40	.20
249	Andy Benes	.40	.30	.15
250	*Alex Ochoa*	1.50	1.25	.60
251	Greg Blosser	.60	.45	.25
252	Jack Armstrong	.25	.20	.10
253	Juan Samuel	.25	.20	.10
254	Terry Pendleton	.40	.30	.15
255	Ramon Martinez	.40	.30	.15
256	Rico Brogna	.30	.25	.12
257	John Smiley	.25	.20	.10
258	Carl Everett	.60	.45	.25
259	Tim Salmon	20.00	15.00	8.00
260	Will Clark	1.50	1.25	.60
261	*Ugueth Urbina*	1.75	1.25	.80
262	Jason Wood	.30	.25	.12
263	Dave Magadan	.25	.20	.10
264	Dante Bichette	.50	.40	.20
265	Jose DeLeon	.25	.20	.10
266	*Mike Neill*	.60	.45	.25
267	Paul O'Neill	.25	.20	.10
268	Anthony Young	.25	.20	.10
269	Greg Harris	.25	.20	.10
270	Todd Van Poppel	.75	.60	.30
271	Pete Castellano	.60	.45	.25
272	Tony Phillips	.25	.20	.10
273	Mike Gallego	.25	.20	.10
274	*Steve Cooke*	1.00	.70	.40
275	Robin Ventura	1.25	.90	.50
276	Kevin Mitchell	.40	.30	.15
277	Doug Linton	.30	.25	.12
278	Robert Eenhorn	.30	.25	.12
279	*Gabe White*	2.00	1.50	.80
280	Dave Stewart	.25	.20	.10
281	Mo Sanford	.30	.25	.12
282	Greg Perschke	.30	.25	.12
283	Kevin Flora	.40	.30	.15
284	Jeff Williams	.30	.25	.12
285	Keith Miller	.25	.20	.10
286	Andy Ashby	.30	.25	.12
287	Doug Dascenzo	.25	.20	.10
288	Eric Karros	1.25	.90	.50
289	*Glenn Murray*	2.50	2.00	1.00
290	Troy Percival	.40	.30	.15
291	Orlando Merced	.50	.40	.20
292	Peter Hoy	.50	.40	.20
293	Tony Fernandez	.08	.06	.03
294	Juan Guzman	1.50	1.25	.60
295	Jesse Barfield	.25	.20	.10
296	Sid Fernandez	.08	.06	.03
297	Scott Cepicky	.80	.60	.30
298	Garret Anderson	.80	.60	.30
299	Cal Eldred	1.00	.75	.40
300	Ryne Sandberg	2.50	2.00	1.00
301	Jim Gantner	.25	.20	.10
302	Mariano Rivera	.80	.60	.30
303	Ron Lockett	.80	.60	.30
304	Jose Offerman	.08	.06	.03
305	Denny Martinez	.08	.06	.03
306	*Luis Ortiz*	.80	.60	.30
307	David Howard	.08	.06	.03
308	Russ Springer	.40	.30	.15
309	Chris Howard	.60	.45	.25
310	Kyle Abbott	.50	.40	.20
311	*Aaron Sele*	12.00	9.00	4.75
312	David Justice	2.50	2.00	1.00
313	Pete O'Brien	.25	.20	.10
314	Greg Hansell	.80	.60	.30
315	Dave Winfield	1.50	1.25	.60

316	Lance Dickson	.50	.40	.20
317	Eric King	.25	.20	.10
318	Vaughn Eshelman	.80	.60	.30
319	Tim Belcher	.08	.06	.03
320	Andres Galarraga	.08	.06	.03
321	Scott Bullett	.80	.60	.30
322	Doug Strange	.08	.06	.03
323	Jerald Clark	.08	.06	.03
324	Dave Righetti	.08	.06	.03
325	Greg Hibbard	.08	.06	.03
326	Eric Dillman	.80	.60	.30
327	Shane Reynolds	.80	.60	.30
328	Chris Hammond	.08	.06	.03
329	Albert Belle	4.00	3.00	1.50
330	*Rich Becker*	1.00	.70	.40
331	Eddie Williams	.08	.06	.03
332	Donald Harris	.08	.06	.03
333	Dave Smith	.08	.06	.03
334	Steve Fireovoid	.80	.60	.30
335	Steve Buechele	.25	.20	.10
336	Mike Schooler	.25	.20	.10
337	Kevin McReynolds	.08	.06	.03
338	Hensley Meulens	.08	.06	.03
339	*Benji Gil*	2.50	2.00	1.00
340	Don Mattingly	1.25	.90	.50
341	Alvin Davis	.25	.20	.10
342	Alan Mills	.25	.20	.10
343	Kelly Downs	.25	.20	.10
344	Leo Gomez	.40	.30	.15
345	*Tarrik Brock*	.60	.45	.25
346	Ryan Turner	1.75	1.25	.70
347	John Smoltz	.40	.30	.15
348	Bill Sampen	.25	.20	.10
349	Paul Byrd	.80	.60	.30
350	Mike Bordick	.40	.30	.15
351	Jose Lind	.08	.06	.03
352	David Wells	.25	.20	.10
353	Barry Larkin	.40	.30	.15
354	Bruce Ruffin	.25	.20	.10
355	Luis Rivera	.25	.20	.10
356	Sid Bream	.25	.20	.10
357	Julian Vasquez	.80	.60	.30
358	*Jason Bere*	8.50	6.50	3.50
359	Ben McDonald	.40	.30	.15
360	Scott Stahoviak	.80	.60	.30
361	Kirt Manwaring	.08	.06	.03
362	Jeff Johnson	.40	.30	.15
363	Rob Deer	.25	.20	.10
364	Tony Pena	.25	.20	.10
365	Melido Perez	.25	.20	.10
366	Clay Parker	.25	.20	.10
367	Dale Sveum	.25	.20	.10
368	Mike Scioscia	.25	.20	.10
369	Roger Salkeld	.50	.40	.20
370	Mike Stanley	.25	.20	.10
371	Jack McDowell	1.00	.70	.40
372	Tim Wallach	.25	.20	.10
373	Billy Ripken	.25	.20	.10
374	Mike Christopher	.80	.60	.30
375	Paul Molitor	1.25	.90	.50
376	Dave Stieb	.08	.06	.03
377	Pedro Guerrero	.40	.30	.15
378	Russ Swan	.25	.20	.10
379	Bob Ojeda	.25	.20	.10
380	Donn Pall	.25	.20	.10
381	Eddie Zosky	.40	.30	.15
382	Darnell Coles	.25	.20	.10
383	Tom Smith	.60	.45	.25
384	Mark McGwire	1.00	.75	.40
385	Gary Carter	.35	.25	.14
386	Rich Amarel	.40	.30	.15
387	Alan Embree	.60	.45	.25
388	Jonathan Hurst	.60	.45	.25
389	*Bobby Jones*	2.50	2.00	1.00
390	Rico Rossy	.60	.45	.25
391	Dan Smith	.60	.45	.25
392	Terry Steinbach	.08	.06	.03
393	Jon Farrell	.25	.20	.10
394	Dave Anderson	.25	.20	.10
395	Benito Santiago	.40	.30	.15
396	Mark Wohlers	.40	.30	.15
397	Mo Vaughn	2.00	1.50	.80
398	Randy Kramer	.40	.30	.15
399	*John Jaha*	1.75	1.25	.70
400	Cal Ripken, Jr.	3.00	2.25	1.25
401	Ryan Bowen	.60	.45	.25
402	Tim McIntosh	.25	.20	.10
403	Bernard Gilkey	.08	.06	.03
404	Junior Felix	.08	.06	.03
405	Cris Colon	.80	.60	.30
406	Marc Newfield	3.50	2.75	1.50
407	Bernie Williams	.40	.30	.15
408	Jay Howell	.25	.20	.10
409	Zane Smith	.25	.20	.10
410	Jeff Shaw	.25	.20	.10
411	Kerry Woodson	.08	.06	.03
412	Wes Chamberlain	.40	.30	.15
413	Dave Mulicki	.80	.60	.30
414	Benny Distefano	.08	.06	.03
415	Kevin Rogers	.80	.60	.30
416	Tim Naehring	.40	.30	.15
417	Clemente Nunez	.80	.60	.30
418	Luis Sojo	.25	.20	.10
419	Kevin Ritz	.25	.20	.10
420	Omar Oliveras	.25	.20	.10
421	Manuel Lee	.25	.20	.10
422	Julio Valera	.40	.30	.15
423	Omar Vizquel	.25	.20	.10
424	Darren Burton	.60	.45	.25
425	Mel Hall	.08	.06	.03
426	Dennis Powell	.25	.20	.10
427	Lee Stevens	.08	.06	.03
428	Glenn Davis	.08	.06	.03
429	Willie Greene	1.50	1.25	.60
430	Kevin Wickander	.08	.06	.03
431	Dennis Eckersley	.40	.30	.15
432	Joe Orsulak	.25	.20	.10
433	Eddie Murray	.08	.06	.03
434	Matt Stairs	.40	.30	.15
435	Wally Joyner	.40	.30	.15
436	Rondell White	7.50	5.75	3.00
437	Rob Mauer	.40	.30	.15
438	Joe Redfield	.60	.45	.25
439	Mark Lewis	.08	.06	.03
440	Darren Daulton	.40	.30	.15
441	Mike Henneman	.08	.06	.03
442	John Cangelosi	.25	.20	.10
443	*Vince Moore*	1.50	1.25	.60
444	John Wehner	.25	.20	.10
445	Kent Hrbek	.25	.20	.10
446	Mark McLemore	.25	.20	.10
447	Bill Wegman	.25	.20	.10
448	Robby Thompson	.25	.20	.10
449	Mark Anthony	.60	.45	.25
450	Archi Cianfrocco	.40	.30	.15
451	Johnny Ruffin	.50	.40	.20
452	Javier Lopez	12.00	9.00	4.75
453	Greg Gohr	.60	.45	.25
454	Tim Scott	.60	.45	.25
455	Stan Belinda	.08	.06	.03
456	Darrin Jackson	.08	.06	.03
457	Chris Gardner	.50	.40	.20
458	Esteban Beltre	.40	.30	.15
459	Phil Plantier	.60	.45	.25
460	Jim Thome	4.00	3.00	1.50
461	*Mike Piazza*	35.00	26.00	14.00
462	Matt Sinatro	.25	.20	.10
463	Scott Servais	.40	.30	.15
464	*Brian Jordan*	1.75	1.25	.70
465	Doug Drabek	.40	.30	.15
466	Carl Willis	.25	.20	.10
467	Bret Barbarie	.08	.06	.03
468	Hal Morris	.08	.06	.03
469	Steve Sax	.08	.06	.03
470	Jerry Willard	.25	.20	.10
471	Dan Wilson	.80	.60	.30
472	Chris Hoiles	.60	.45	.25
473	Rheal Cormier	.08	.06	.03
474	John Morris	.25	.20	.10
475	Jeff Reardon	.08	.06	.03
476	Mark Leiter	.25	.20	.10
477	Tom Gordon	.25	.20	.10
478	Kent Bottenfield	.60	.45	.25
479	Gene Larkin	.25	.20	.10
480	Dwight Gooden	.60	.45	.25
481	B.J. Surhoff	.40	.30	.15
482	Andy Stankiewicz	.40	.30	.15
483	Tino Martinez	.40	.30	.15
484	Craig Biggio	.50	.40	.20
485	Denny Neagle	.40	.30	.15
486	Rusty Meacham	.40	.30	.15
487	Kal Daniels	.08	.06	.03
488	Dave Henderson	.08	.06	.03
489	Tim Costo	.40	.30	.15
490	Doug Davis	.60	.45	.25
491	Frank Viola	.40	.30	.15
492	Cory Snyder	.08	.06	.03
493	Chris Martin	.60	.45	.25
494	Dion James	.25	.20	.10
495	Randy Tomlin	.08	.06	.03
496	Greg Vaughn	.40	.30	.15
497	Dennis Cook	.25	.20	.10
498	Rosario Rodriguez	.25	.20	.10
499	Dave Staton	.25	.20	.10
500	George Brett	1.50	1.25	.60
501	Brian Barnes	.08	.06	.03
502	Butch Henry	.08	.06	.03
503	Harold Reynolds	.08	.06	.03
504	*David Nied*	3.50	2.75	1.50
505	Lee Smith	.08	.06	.03
506	Steve Chitren	.25	.20	.10
507	Ken Hill	.40	.30	.15
508	Robbie Beckett	.60	.45	.25
509	Troy Afenir	.25	.20	.10
510	Kelly Gruber	.25	.20	.10
511	Bret Boone	1.00	.75	.40
512	Jeff Branson	.80	.60	.30
513	Mike Jackson	.25	.20	.10
514	Pete Harnisch	.08	.06	.03
515	Chad Kreuter	.25	.20	.10
516	Joe Vitko	.60	.45	.25
517	Orel Hershiser	.40	.30	.15
518	*John Doherty*	1.50	1.25	.60
519	Jay Bell	.40	.30	.15
520	Mark Langston	.40	.30	.15
521	Dann Howitt	.25	.20	.10
522	Bobby Reed	.40	.30	.15
523	Roberto Munoz	.60	.45	.25
524	Todd Ritchie	.25	.20	.10
525	Bip Roberts	.25	.20	.10
526	*Pat Listach*	1.00	.70	.40
527	Scott Brosius	.25	.20	.10
528	John Roper	.60	.45	.25
529	*Phil Hiatt*	3.00	2.25	1.25
530	Denny Walling	.25	.20	.10
531	Carlos Baerga	3.50	2.75	1.50
532	*Manny Ramirez*	17.00	12.50	6.75
533	Pat Clements	.25	.20	.10
534	Ron Gant	.50	.40	.20
535	Pat Kelly	.25	.20	.10
536	Billy Spiers	.25	.20	.10
537	Darren Reed	.40	.30	.15
538	Ken Caminiti	.25	.20	.10
539	*Butch Husky*	2.50	2.00	1.00
540	Matt Nokes	.25	.20	.10
541	John Kruk	.08	.06	.03
542	John Jaha (Foil)	2.50	2.00	1.00
543	Justin Thompson	.80	.60	.30
544	Steve Hosey	1.00	.75	.40
545	Joe Kmak	.40	.30	.15
546	John Franco	.25	.20	.10
547	Devon White	.25	.20	.10
548	Elston Hansen (Foil)	1.50	1.25	.60
549	Ryan Klesko	5.50	4.00	2.25
550	Danny Tartabull	.08	.06	.03
551	Frank Thomas (Foil)	45.00	34.00	18.00
552	Kevin Tapani	.08	.06	.03
553a	Willie Banks	.08	.06	.03
553b	Pat Clements	.08	.06	.03
554	*B.J. Wallace* (Foil)	4.00	3.00	1.50
555	Orlando Miller	.80	.60	.30
556	Mark Smith	1.00	.70	.40
557	Tim Wallach (Foil)	.80	.60	.30
558	Bill Gullickson	.08	.06	.03
559	Derek Bell (Foil)	1.50	1.25	.60
560	Joe Randa (Foil)	1.00	.70	.40
561	Frank Seminara	.40	.30	.15
562	Mark Gardner	.25	.20	.10
563	Rick Greene (Foil)	1.00	.70	.40
564	Gary Gaetti	.25	.20	.10
565	Ozzie Guillen	.25	.20	.10
566	Charles Nagy (Foil)	.50	.40	.20
567	Mike Milchin	.60	.45	.25
568	Ben Shelton (Foil)	.80	.60	.30
569	Chris Roberts (Foil)	2.00	1.50	.80
570	Ellis Burks	.25	.20	.10
571	Scott Scudder	.25	.20	.10
572	Jim Abbott (Foil)	1.50	1.25	.60
573	Joe Carter	1.50	1.25	.60
574	Steve Finley	.40	.30	.15
575	Jim Olander (Foil)	.60	.45	.25
576	Carlos Garcia	1.00	.70	.40
577	Greg Olson	.08	.06	.03
578	Greg Swindell (Foil)	.80	.60	.30
579	Matt Williams (Foil)	1.50	1.25	.60
580	Mark Grace	1.00	.70	.40
581	Howard House (Foil)	.90	.70	.35
582	Luis Polonia	.25	.20	.10
583	Erik Hanson	.08	.06	.03
584	Salomon Torres (Foil)	3.00	2.25	1.25
585	Carlton Fisk	.40	.30	.15
586	Bret Saberhagen	.40	.30	.15
587	*Chad McDonnell* (Foil)	1.50	1.25	.60
588	Jimmy Key	.25	.20	.10
589	Mike MacFarlane	.25	.20	.10
590	Barry Bonds (Foil)	6.00	4.50	2.50
591	Jamie McAndrew	.80	.60	.30
592	Shane Mack	.40	.30	.15
593	Kerwin Moore	.60	.45	.25
594	Joe Oliver	.25	.20	.10
595	Chris Sabo	.25	.20	.10
596	*Alex Gonzalez*	7.00	5.25	2.75
597	Brett Butler	.08	.06	.03
598	Mark Hutton	.60	.45	.25
599	Andy Benes (Foil)	.80	.60	.30
600	Jose Canseco	1.00	.70	.40
601	Darryl Kile	1.50	1.25	.60
602	Matt Stairs (Foil)	1.50	1.25	.60
603	Robert Butler (Foil)	1.00	.70	.40
604	Willie McGee	.08	.06	.03
605	Jack McDowell	1.50	1.25	.60
606	Tom Candiotti	.08	.06	.03
607	Ed Martel	.60	.45	.25
608	Matt Mieske (Foil)	.80	.60	.30
609	Darrin Fletcher	.08	.06	.03
610	Rafael Palmeiro	.08	.06	.03
611	Bill Swift (Foil)	.80	.60	.30
612	Mike Mussina	4.00	3.00	1.50
613	Vince Coleman	.08	.06	.03
614	Scott Cepicky (Foil)	.80	.60	.30
615	Mike Greenwell	.08	.06	.03
616	Kevin McGehee	.60	.45	.25
617	Jeffrey Hammonds (Foil)	9.00	6.75	3.50
618	Scott Taylor	.60	.45	.25
619	Dave Otto	.25	.20	.10
620	Mark McGwire (Foil)	1.50	1.25	.60
621	Kevin Tatar	.80	.60	.30
622	Steve Farr	.25	.20	.10
623	Ryan Klesko (Foil)	5.00	3.75	2.00
625	Andre Dawson	.60	.45	.25
626	Tino Martinez (Foil)	1.00	.75	.40
627	*Chad Curtis*	3.50	2.75	1.50
628	Mickey Morandini	.40	.30	.15
629	Gregg Olson (Foil)	.80	.60	.30
630	Lou Whitaker	.08	.06	.03
631	Arthur Rhodes	.60	.45	.25
632	Brandon Wilson	.80	.60	.30
633	*Lance Jennings*	.30	.25	.12
634	*Allen Watson*	2.50	2.00	1.00
635	Len Dykstra	1.00	.75	.40
636	Joe Girardi	.25	.20	.10
637	Kiki Hernandez (Foil)	1.00	.75	.40
638	Mike Hampton	.40	.30	.15
639	Al Osuna	.25	.20	.10
640	Kevin Appier	.40	.30	.15
641	Rick Helling (Foil)	3.00	2.25	1.25
642	Jody Reed	.25	.20	.10
643	Ray Lankford	.60	.45	.25
644	John Olerud	4.50	3.50	1.75
645	Paul Molitor (Foil)	4.00	3.00	1.50
646	Pat Borders	.25	.20	.10
647	Mike Morgan	.25	.20	.10
648	Larry Walker	1.00	.75	.40
649	Pete Castellano (Foil)	1.00	.75	.40
650	Fred McGriff	1.75	1.25	.70
651	Walt Weiss	.25	.20	.10
652	Calvin Murray (Foil)	3.50	2.75	1.50
653	Dave Nilsson	.60	.45	.25
654	Greg Pirkl	.80	.60	.30
655	Robin Ventura	2.75	2.00	1.00
656	Mark Portugal	.25	.20	.10
657	Roger McDowell	.25	.20	.10
658	Rick Hirtensteiner (Foil)	1.00	.75	.40
659	Glenallen Hill	.25	.20	.10
660	Greg Gagne	.25	.20	.10
661	Charles Johnson (Foil)	6.00	4.50	2.50
662	Brian Hunter	.40	.30	.15
663	Mark Lemke	.25	.20	.10
664	Tim Belcher (Foil)	1.00	.75	.40
665	Rich DeLucia	.25	.20	.10
666	Bob Walk	.25	.20	.10
667	Joe Carter (Foil)	3.00	2.25	1.25
668	Jose Guzman	.25	.20	.10
669	Otis Nixon	.25	.20	.10

670	Phil Nevin (Foil)	4.00	3.00	1.50
671	Eric Davis	.25	.20	.10
672	*Damion Easley*	1.50	1.25	.60
673	Will Clark (Foil)	2.50	2.00	1.00
674	Mark Kiefer	.30	.25	.12
675	Ozzie Smith	1.00	.70	.40
676	Manny Ramirez (Foil)	10.00	7.50	4.00
677	Gregg Olson	.25	.20	.10
678	*Cliff Floyd*	20.00	15.00	8.00
679	Duane Singleton	.50	.40	.20
680	Jose Rijo	.25	.20	.10
681	Willie Randolph	.25	.20	.10
682	Michael Tucker (Foil)	4.50	3.50	1.75
683	Darren Lewis	.25	.20	.10
684	Dale Murphy	.25	.20	.10
685	Mike Pagliarulo	.25	.20	.10
686	Paul Miller	.30	.25	.12
687	Mike Robertson	.40	.30	.15
688	Mike Devereaux	.25	.20	.10
689	Pedro Astacio	1.50	1.25	.60
690	Alan Trammell	.25	.20	.10
691	Roger Clemens	2.00	1.50	.80
692	Bud Black	.25	.20	.10
693	Turk Wendell	.50	.40	.20
694	Barry Larkin (Foil)	1.50	1.25	.60
695	Todd Zeile	.25	.20	.10
696	Pat Hentgen	4.00	3.00	1.50
697	*Eddie Taubensee*	.40	.30	.15
698	Guillermo Vasquez	.50	.40	.20
699	Tom Glavine	1.00	.70	.40
700	Robin Yount	2.00	1.50	.80
701	Checklist	.25	.20	.10
702	Checklist	.25	.20	.10
703	Checklist	.25	.20	.10
704	Checklist	.25	.20	.10
705	Checklist	.25	.20	.10

1993 Bowman

Bowman's 708-card 1993 set once again features a premium UV-coated glossy stock. There are also 48 special insert cards, with gold foil stamping, randomly inserted one per pack or two per jumbo pack. The foil cards, numbered 339-374 and 693-704, feature top prospects and rookie-of-the-year candidates, as do several regular cards in the set. Cards are standard size.

		MT	NR MT	EX
Complete Set (708):		120.00	90.00	47.50
Common Player:		.10	.07	.04
1	Glenn Davis	.10	.08	.04
2	*Hector Roa*	.25	.20	.10
3	*Ken Ryan*	.25	.20	.10
4	*Derek Wallace*	.35	.25	.14
5	Jorge Fabregas	.10	.08	.04
6	Joe Oliver	.10	.08	.04
7	Brandon Wilson	.25	.20	.10
8	*Mark Thompson*	.40	.30	.15
9	Tracy Sanders	.10	.08	.04
10	Rich Renteria	.10	.08	.04
11	Lou Whitaker	.10	.08	.04
12	*Brian Hunter*	.75	.60	.30
13	Joe Vitiello	.50	.40	.20
14	Eric Karros	.25	.20	.10
15	Joe Kmak	.10	.08	.04
16	Tavo Alvarez	.20	.15	.08
17	*Steve Dunn*	.30	.20	.12
18	Tony Fernandez	.10	.08	.04
19	Melido Perez	.10	.08	.04
20	Mike Lieberthal	.10	.08	.04
21	Terry Steinbach	.10	.08	.04
22	Stan Belinda	.10	.08	.04
23	Jay Buhner	.10	.08	.04
24	Allen Watson	.75	.60	.30
25	*Daryl Henderson*	.25	.20	.10
26	*Ray McDavid*	1.00	.70	.40
27	Shawn Green	1.00	.75	.40
28	Bud Black	.10	.08	.04
29	*Sherman Obando*	.35	.25	.14
30	*Mike Hostetler*	.10	.08	.04
31	*Nate Hinchey*	.50	.40	.20
32	Randy Myers	.10	.08	.04
33	*Brian Grebeck*	.20	.15	.08
34	John Roper	.10	.08	.04
35	Larry Thomas	.20	.15	.08
36	Alex Cole	.10	.08	.04
37	*Tom Kramer*	.40	.30	.15
38	*Matt Whisenant*	.25	.20	.10
39	*Chris Gomez*	.40	.30	.15
40	Luis Gonzalez	.10	.08	.04
41	Kevin Appier	.10	.08	.04

42	*Omar Daal*	.25	.20	.10
43	Duane Singleton	.10	.08	.04
44	Bill Risley	.10	.08	.04
45	*Pat Meares*	.40	.30	.15
46	Butch Huskey	.40	.30	.15
47	Bobby Munoz	.10	.08	.04
48	Juan Bell	.10	.08	.04
49	*Scott Lydy*	.40	.30	.15
50	Dennis Moeller	.10	.08	.04
51	Marc Newfield	1.25	.90	.50
52	*Tripp Croner*	.20	.15	.08
53	Kurt Miller	.10	.08	.04
54	Jim Pena	.10	.08	.04
55	Juan Guzman	.50	.40	.20
56	Matt Williams	.30	.25	.12
57	Harold Reynolds	.10	.08	.04
58	*Donnie Elliott*	.40	.30	.15
59	*Jon Shave*	.30	.25	.12
60	*Kevin Roberson*	1.00	.70	.40
61	*Hilly Hathaway*	.50	.40	.20
63	*Kerry Taylor*	.30	.25	.12
64	Ryan Hawblitzel	.10	.08	.04
65	Glenallen Hill	.10	.08	.04
66	*Ramon D. Martinez*	.30	.25	.12
67	Travis Fryman	.60	.45	.25
68	Tom Nevers	.10	.08	.04
69	Phil Hiatt	.60	.45	.25
70	Tim Wallach	.10	.08	.04
71	B.J. Surhoff	.10	.08	.04
72	Rondell White	1.50	1.25	.60
73	*Denny Hocking*	.20	.15	.08
74	*Mike Oquist*	.25	.20	.10
75	Paul O'Neill	.10	.08	.04
76	Willie Banks	.10	.08	.04
77	Bob Welch	.10	.08	.04
78	*Jose Sandoval*	.25	.20	.10
79	Bill Haselman	.10	.08	.04
80	Rheal Cormier	.10	.08	.04
81	Dean Palmer	.20	.15	.08
82	*Pat Gomez*	.25	.20	.10
83	Steve Karsay	1.00	.70	.40
84	*Carl Hanselman*	.20	.15	.08
85	*T.R. Lewis*	.40	.30	.15
86	Chipper Jones	1.00	.75	.40
87	Scott Hatteberg	.20	.15	.08
88	Greg Hibbard	.10	.08	.04
89	*Lance Painter*	.40	.30	.15
90	*Chad Mottola*	2.00	1.50	.80
91	Jason Bere	1.50	1.25	.60
92	Dante Bichette	.15	.11	.06
93	Sandy Alomar	.10	.08	.04
94	Carl Everett	.20	.15	.08
95	*Danny Bautista*	.50	.40	.20
96	Steve Finley	.10	.08	.04
97	David Cone	.10	.08	.04
98	Todd Hollandsworth	1.50	1.25	.60
99	Matt Mieske	.10	.08	.04
100	Larry Walker	.35	.25	.14
101	Shane Mack	.10	.08	.04
102	*Aaron Ledesma*	.20	.15	.08
103	*Andy Pettitte*	.60	.45	.25
104	Kevin Stocker	1.25	.90	.50
105	Mike Mobler	.20	.15	.08
106	Tony Menedez	.10	.08	.04
107	Derek Lowe	.10	.08	.04
108	Basil Shabazz	.30	.25	.12
109	Dan Smith	.10	.08	.04
110	*Scott Sanders*	.25	.20	.10
111	Todd Stottlemyre	.10	.08	.04
112	*Benji Sikonton*	.60	.45	.25
113	Rick Sutcliffe	.10	.08	.04
114	*Lee Heath*	.40	.30	.15
115	Jeff Russell	.10	.08	.04
116	*Dave Stevens*	.20	.15	.08
117	*Mark Holzemer*	.20	.15	.08
118	Tim Belcher	.10	.08	.04
119	Bobby Thigpen	.10	.08	.04
120	*Roger Bailey*	.20	.15	.08
121	*Tony Mitchell*	.25	.20	.10
122	Junior Felix	.10	.08	.04
123	*Rich Robertson*	.20	.15	.08
124	*Andy Cook*	.20	.15	.08
125	*Brian Bevil*	.25	.20	.10
126	Darryl Strawberry	.10	.08	.04
127	Cal Eldred	.15	.11	.06
128	Cliff Floyd	4.00	3.00	1.50
129	Alan Newman	.10	.08	.04
130	Howard Johnson	.10	.08	.04
131	Jim Abbott	.20	.15	.08
132	Chad McConnell	.40	.30	.15
133	*Miguel Jimenez*	.80	.60	.30
134	*Brett Backlund*	.75	.60	.30
135	*John Cummings*	.30	.25	.12
136	Brian Barber	.40	.30	.15
137	Rafael Palmeiro	.20	.15	.08
138	*Tim Worrell*	.30	.25	.12
139	*Jose Pett*	1.00	.75	.40
140	Barry Bonds	1.50	1.25	.60
141	Damon Buford	.10	.08	.04
142	Jeff Blauser	.10	.08	.04
143	Frankie Rodriguez	.50	.40	.20
144	Mike Morgan	.10	.08	.04
145	Gary DeSarcina	.10	.08	.04
146	Calvin Reese	.10	.08	.04
147	Johnny Ruffin	.10	.08	.04
148	David Nied	.60	.45	.25
149	Charles Nagy	.10	.08	.04
150	*Mike Myers*	.20	.15	.08
151	*Kenny Carlyle*	.20	.15	.08
152	Eric Anthony	.10	.08	.04
153	Jose Lind	.10	.08	.04
154	Pedro Martinez	.40	.30	.15
155	Mark Kiefer	.10	.08	.04
156	*Tim Laker*	.20	.15	.08
157	Pat Mahomes	.10	.08	.04
158	Bobby Bonilla	.10	.08	.04
159	Domingo Jean	.40	.30	.15
160	Darren Daulton	.10	.08	.04

161	Mark McGwire	.25	.20	.10
162	*Jason Kendall*	.60	.45	.25
163	Desi Relaford	.25	.20	.10
164	Ozzie Canseco	.10	.08	.04
165	Rick Helling	.75	.60	.30
166	*Steve Pegues*	.20	.15	.08
167	Paul Molitor	.50	.40	.20
168	*Larry Carter*	.20	.15	.08
169	Arthur Rhodes	.10	.08	.04
170	*Damon Hollins*	.40	.30	.15
171	Frank Viola	.10	.08	.04
172	*Steve Trachsel*	1.50	1.25	.60
173	*J.T. Snow*	.60	.45	.25
174	*Keith Gordon*	.20	.15	.08
175	Carlton Fisk	.10	.08	.04
176	*Jason Bates*	.20	.15	.08
177	*Mike Crosby*	.20	.15	.08
178	Benny Santiago	.10	.08	.04
179	Mike Moore	.10	.08	.04
180	Jeff Juden	.10	.08	.04
181	Darren Burton	.10	.08	.04
182	*Todd Williams*	.20	.15	.08
183	John Jaha	.15	.11	.06
184	*Mike Lansing*	.60	.45	.25
185	*Pedro Grifol*	.20	.15	.08
186	Vince Coleman	.10	.08	.04
187	Pat Kelly	.10	.08	.04
188	*Clemente Alvarez*	.20	.15	.08
189	Ron Darling	.10	.08	.04
190	Orlando Merced	.10	.08	.04
191	Chris Bosio	.10	.08	.04
192	*Steve Dixon*	.20	.15	.08
193	Doug Dascenzo	.10	.08	.04
194	*Ray Holbert*	.35	.25	.14
195	Howard Battle	.20	.15	.08
196	Willie McGee	.10	.08	.04
197	*John O'Donoghue*	.20	.15	.08
198	Steve Avery	.40	.30	.15
199	Greg Blosser	.20	.15	.08
200	Ryne Sandberg	.75	.60	.30
201	Joe Grahe	.10	.08	.04
202	Dan Wilson	.10	.08	.04
203	*Domingo Martinez*	.20	.15	.08
204	Andres Galarraga	.20	.15	.08
205	*Jamie Taylor*	.20	.15	.08
206	*Darrell Whitmore*	.75	.60	.30
207	*Ben Blomdahl*	.20	.15	.08
208	Doug Drabek	.10	.08	.04
209	Keith Miller	.10	.08	.04
210	Billy Ashley	.75	.60	.30
211	*Mike Farrell*	.20	.15	.08
212	John Wetteland	.10	.08	.04
213	Randy Tomlin	.10	.08	.04
214	Sid Fernandez	.10	.08	.04
215	*Quilvio Veras*	.60	.45	.25
216	Dave Hollins	.20	.15	.08
217	Mike Neill	.20	.15	.08
218	Andy Van Slyke	.10	.08	.04
219	Bret Boone	.20	.15	.08
220	Tom Pagnozzi	.10	.08	.04
221	*Mike Welch*	.20	.15	.08
222	Frank Seminara	.10	.08	.04
223	Ron Villone	.20	.15	.08
224	*D.J. Thielen*	.30	.25	.12
225	Cal Ripken, Jr.	1.00	.75	.40
226	*Pedro Borbon*	.20	.15	.08
227	Carlos Quintana	.10	.08	.04
228	*Tommy Shields*	.20	.15	.08
229	Tim Salmon	3.50	2.75	1.50
230	John Smiley	.10	.08	.04
231	Ellis Burks	.10	.08	.04
232	Pedro Castellano	.10	.08	.04
233	Paul Byrd	.10	.08	.04
234	Bryan Harvey	.10	.08	.04
235	Scott Livingstone	.10	.08	.04
236	*James Mouton*	2.00	1.50	.80
237	Joe Randa	.20	.15	.08
238	Pedro Astacio	.20	.15	.08
239	Darryl Hamilton	.10	.08	.04
240	*Joey Eischen*	.75	.60	.30
241	*Edgar Herrera*	.30	.25	.12
242	Doc Gooden	.10	.08	.04
243	Sam Militello	.10	.08	.04
244	*Ron Blazier*	.20	.15	.08
245	Ruben Sierra	.10	.08	.04
246	Al Martin	.50	.40	.20
247	Mike Felder	.10	.08	.04
248	Bob Tewksbury	.10	.08	.04
249	Craig Lefferts	.10	.08	.04
250	Luis Lopez	.10	.08	.04
251	Devon White	.10	.08	.04
252	Will Clark	.40	.30	.15
253	Mark Smith	.50	.40	.20
254	Terry Pendleton	.10	.08	.04
255	Aaron Sele	2.75	2.00	1.00
256	*Jose Viera*	.25	.20	.10
257	Damion Easley	.20	.15	.08
258	*Rod Lofton*	.20	.15	.08
259	*Chris Snopek*	.40	.30	.15
260	*Quinton McCracken*	.20	.15	.08
261	*Mike Matthews*	.30	.25	.12
262	*Hector Carrasco*	.40	.30	.15
263	Rick Greene	.20	.15	.08
264	*Chris Bolt*	.35	.25	.14
265	George Brett	.60	.45	.25
266	*Rick Gorecki*	.75	.60	.30
267	*Francisco Gamez*	.25	.20	.10
268	Marquis Grissom	.30	.25	.12
269	Kevin Tapani	.10	.08	.04
270	Ryan Thompson	.15	.11	.06
271	Gerald Williams	.10	.08	.04
272	*Paul Fletcher*	.25	.20	.10
273	Lance Blankenship	.10	.08	.04
274	*Marty Neff*	.25	.20	.10
275	Shawn Estes	.10	.08	.04
276	*Rene Arocha*	.50	.40	.20
277	*Scott Eyre*	.40	.30	.15
278	Phil Plantier	.10	.08	.04

279	*Paul Spoljaric*	1.00	.70	.40
280	Chris Gahbs	.15	.11	.06
281	Harold Baines	.10	.08	.04
282	*Jose Oliva*	.25	.20	.10
283	Matt Whiteside	.40	.30	.15
284	*Brant Brown*	.75	.60	.30
285	Russ Springer	.10	.08	.04
286	Chris Sabo	.10	.08	.04
287	Ozzie Guillen	.10	.08	.04
288	*Marcus Moore*	.40	.30	.15
289	Chad Ogea	.75	.60	.30
290	Walt Weiss	.10	.08	.04
291	Brian Edmondson	.10	.08	.04
292	Jimmy Gonzalez	.10	.08	.04
293	*Danny Hiceli*	.30	.25	.12
294	Jose Offerman	.10	.08	.04
295	Greg Vaughn	.10	.08	.04
296	Frank Bolick	.10	.08	.04
297	*Mike Maksudian*	.25	.20	.10
298	John Franco	.10	.08	.04
299	Danny Tartabull	.10	.08	.04
300	Len Dykstra	.25	.20	.10
301	Bobby Witt	.10	.08	.04
302	*Trey Beamon*	.75	.60	.30
303	Tino Martinez	.10	.08	.04
304	Aaron Holbert	.10	.08	.04
305	Juan Gonzalez	3.50	2.75	1.50
306	*Billy Hall*	.25	.20	.10
307	Duane Ward	.10	.08	.04
308	Rod Beck	.20	.15	.08
309	*Jose Mercedes*	.25	.20	.10
310	Otis Nixon	.10	.08	.04
311	*Gettys Glaze*	.25	.20	.10
312	Candy Maldonado	.10	.08	.04
313	Chad Curtis	.35	.25	.14
314	Tim Costo	.10	.08	.04
315	Mike Robertson	.10	.08	.04
316	Nigel Wilson	.75	.60	.30
317	*Greg McMichael*	.50	.40	.20
318	*Scott Pose*	.20	.15	.08
319	Ivan Cruz	.10	.08	.04
320	Greg Swindell	.10	.08	.04
321	Kevin McReynolds	.10	.08	.04
322	Tom Candiotti	.10	.08	.04
323	*Bob Wishnevski*	.20	.15	.08
324	Ken Hill	.10	.08	.04
325	Kirby Puckett	1.00	.75	.40
326	*Tim Bogar*	.20	.15	.08
327	Mariano Rivera	.10	.08	.04
328	Mitch Williams	.10	.08	.04
329	Craig Paquette	.20	.15	.08
330	Jay Bell	.10	.08	.04
331	*Jose Martinez*	.35	.25	.14
332	Rob Deer	.10	.08	.04
333	Brook Fordyce	.10	.08	.04
334	Matt Nokes	.10	.08	.04
335	Derek Lee	.10	.08	.04
336	*Paul Ellis*	.20	.15	.08
337	*Desi Wilson*	.40	.30	.15
338	Roberto Alomar	.75	.60	.30
339	Jim Tatum (Foil)	.20	.15	.08
340	J.T. Snow (Foil)	.60	.45	.25
341	Tim Salmon (Foil)	4.00	3.00	1.50
342	*Russ Davis* (Foil)	1.50	1.25	.60
343	Javier Lopez (Foil)	2.75	2.00	1.00
344	*Troy O'Leary* (Foil)	.60	.45	.25
345	*Marty Cordova* (Foil)	.60	.45	.25
346	*Bubba Smith* (Foil)	.35	.25	.14
347	Chipper Jones (Foil)	1.25	.90	.50
348	Jessie Hollins (Foil)	.20	.15	.08
349	Willie Greene (Foil)	.25	.20	.10
350	Mark Thompson (Foil)	.50	.40	.20
351	Nigel Wilson (Foil)	.75	.60	.30
352	Todd Jones (Foil)	.25	.20	.10
353	Raul Mondesi (Foil)	2.00	1.50	.80
354	Cliff Floyd (Foil)	4.00	3.00	1.50
355	Bobby Jones (Foil)	.80	.60	.30
356	Kevin Stocker (Foil)	1.50	1.25	.60
357	Midre Cummings (Foil)	1.50	1.25	.60
358	Allen Watson (Foil)	.75	.60	.30
359	Ray McDavid (Foil)	1.00	.70	.40
360	Steve Hosey (Foil)	.25	.20	.10
361	Brad Pennington (Foil)	.25	.20	.10
362	Frankie Rodriguez (Foil)	.60	.45	.25
363	Troy Percival (Foil)	.25	.20	.10
364	Jason Bere (Foil)	2.50	2.00	1.00
365	Manny Ramirez (Foil)	4.00	3.00	1.50
366	Justin Thompson (Foil)	.25	.20	.10
367	Joe Vitello (Foil)	.80	.60	.30
368	Tyrone Hill (Foil)	.75	.60	.30
369	David McCarty (Foil)	.50	.40	.20
370	Brien Taylor (Foil)	.75	.60	.30
371	Todd Van Poppel (Foil)	.40	.30	.15
372	Marc Newfield (Foil)	.75	.60	.30
373	*Terrell Lowery* (Foil)	1.00	.75	.40
374	Alex Gonzalez (Foil)	1.50	1.25	.60
375	Ken Griffey, Jr.	5.00	3.75	2.00
376	Donovan Osborne	.30	.25	.12
377	*Ritchie Moody*	.40	.30	.15
378	Shane Andrews	.40	.30	.15
379	Carlos Delgado	2.50	2.00	1.00
380	Bill Swift	.10	.08	.04
381	Leo Gomez	.10	.08	.04
382	Ron Gant	.25	.20	.10
383	Scott Fletcher	.10	.08	.04
384	*Matt Walbreck*	.40	.30	.15
385	Chuck Finley	.10	.08	.04
386	Kevin Mitchell	.10	.08	.04
387	Wilson Alvarez	.40	.30	.15
388	*John Burke*	.60	.45	.25
389	Alan Embree	.10	.08	.04
390	Trevor Hoffman	.10	.08	.04
391	Alan Trammell	.10	.08	.04
392	Todd Jones	.10	.08	.04
393	Felix Jose	.10	.08	.04
394	Orel Hershiser	.10	.08	.04
395	Pat Listach	.20	.15	.08
396	Gabe White	.50	.40	.20
397	*Dan Berafini*	.60	.45	.25
398	Todd Hundley	.10	.08	.04
399	Wade Boggs	.30	.25	.12
400	Tyler Green	.10	.08	.04
401	Mike Bordick	.10	.08	.04
402	Scott Bullett	.10	.08	.04
403	*Lagrande Russell*	.20	.15	.08
404	Ray Lankford	.10	.08	.04
405	Nolan Ryan	4.00	3.00	1.50
406	Robbie Beckett	.10	.08	.04
407	*Brent Bowers*	.20	.15	.08
408	*Adell Davenport*	.20	.15	.08
409	Brady Anderson	.10	.08	.04
410	Tom Glavine	.40	.30	.15
411	*Doug Hecker*	.40	.30	.15
412	Jose Guzman	.10	.08	.04
413	Luis Polonia	.10	.08	.04
414	Brian Williams	.10	.08	.04
415	Bo Jackson	.30	.25	.12
416	Eric Young	.15	.11	.06
417	Kenny Lofton	.50	.40	.20
418	Orestes Destrade	.10	.08	.04
419	Tony Phillips	.10	.08	.04
420	Jeff Bagwell	.50	.40	.20
421	Hark Gardner	.10	.08	.04
422	Brett Butler	.10	.08	.04
423	*Graeme Lloyd*	.15	.11	.06
424	Delino DeShields	.20	.15	.08
425	Scott Erickson	.10	.08	.04
426	Jeff Kent	.10	.08	.04
427	Jimmy Key	.10	.08	.04
428	Mickey Horandini	.10	.08	.04
429	*Marcos Arkas*	.50	.40	.20
430	Don Slaught	.10	.08	.04
431	Randy Johnson	.20	.15	.08
432	Omar Olivares	.10	.08	.04
433	Charlie Leibrandt	.10	.08	.04
434	Kurt Stillwell	.10	.08	.04
435	*Scott Brow*	.25	.20	.10
436	Robby Thompson	.10	.08	.04
437	Ben McDonald	.20	.15	.08
438	Deion Sanders	.30	.25	.12
439	Tony Pena	.10	.08	.04
440	Mark Grace	.20	.15	.08
441	Eduardo Perez	1.25	.60	.30
442	*Tim Pugh*	.30	.25	.12
443	Scott Ruffcorn	.60	.45	.25
444	*Jay Gainer*	.20	.15	.08
445	Albert Belle	.75	.60	.30
446	Bret Barberie	.10	.08	.04
447	Justin Mashore	.10	.08	.04
448	Pete Harnisch	.10	.08	.04
449	Greg Gagne	.10	.08	.04
450	Eric Davis	.10	.08	.04
451	Dave Mlicki	.10	.08	.04
452	Moises Alou	.20	.15	.08
453	Rick Aguilera	.10	.08	.04
454	Eddie Murray	.10	.08	.04
455	Bob Wickman	.20	.15	.08
456	Wes Chamberlain	.10	.08	.04
457	Brent Gates	.75	.60	.30
458	Paul Weber	.10	.08	.04
459	Mike Hampton	.10	.08	.04
460	Ozzie Smith	.40	.30	.15
461	Tom Henke	.10	.08	.04
462	Ricky Gutuerrez	.20	.15	.08
463	Jack Morris	.10	.08	.04
464	*Joel Chimelis*	.20	.15	.08
465	Gregg Olson	.10	.08	.04
466	Javier Lopez	2.50	2.00	1.00
467	Scott Cooper	.10	.08	.04
468	Willie Wilson	.10	.08	.04
469	Mark Langston	.10	.08	.04
470	Barry Larkin	.10	.08	.04
471	Rod Bolton	.10	.08	.04
472	Freddie Benavides	.10	.08	.04
473	*Ken Ramos*	.20	.15	.08
474	Chuck Carr	.10	.08	.04
475	Cecil Fielder	.40	.30	.15
476	Eddie Taubensee	.10	.08	.04
477	*Chris Eddy*	.25	.20	.10
478	Greg Hansell	.10	.08	.04
479	Kevin Reimer	.10	.08	.04
480	Denny Martinez	.10	.08	.04
481	Chuck Knoblauch	.20	.15	.08
482	Mike Draper	.10	.08	.04
483	Spike Owen	.10	.08	.04
484	Terry Mulholland	.10	.08	.04
485	Dennis Eckersley	.10	.08	.04
486	Blas Minor	.10	.08	.04
487	Dave Fleming	.15	.11	.06
488	Dan Cholonsky	.15	.11	.06
489	Ivan Rodriguez	.20	.15	.08
490	Gary Sheffield	.25	.20	.10
491	Ed Sprague	.10	.08	.04
492	Steve Hosey	.20	.15	.08
493	*Jimmy Haynes*	.50	.40	.20
494	John Smoltz	.10	.08	.04
495	Andre Dawson	.20	.15	.08
496	Rey Sanchez	.10	.08	.04
497	*Ty Van Durkleo*	.20	.15	.08
498	*Bobby Ayala*	.40	.30	.15
499	Tim Raines	.10	.08	.04
500	Charlie Hayes	.10	.08	.04
501	Paul Sorrento	.10	.08	.04
502	*Richie Lewis*	.30	.25	.12
503	*Jason Pfaff*	.25	.20	.10
504	Ken Caminiti	.10	.08	.04
505	Mike Macfarlane	.10	.08	.04
506	Jody Reed	.10	.08	.04
507	*Bobby Hughes*	.35	.25	.14
508	Wil Cordero	.10	.08	.04
509	*George Tsanis*	.20	.15	.08
510	Bret Saberhagen	.10	.08	.04
511	*Derek Jeter*	1.75	1.25	.70
512	Gene Schall	.50	.40	.20
513	Curtis Shan	.10	.08	.04
514	Steve Cooke	.20	.15	.08
515	Edgar Martinez	.10	.08	.04
516	Nike Milchin	.10	.08	.04
517	Billy Ripken	.10	.08	.04
518	Andy Benes	.10	.08	.04
519	*Juan de la Rosa*	.20	.15	.08
520	John Burkett	.10	.08	.04
521	Alex Ochoa	.40	.30	.15
522	*Tony Tarasco*	1.00	.75	.40
523	Luis Ortiz	.25	.20	.10
524	Rick Williams	.10	.08	.04
525	*Chris Turner*	.20	.15	.08
526	Rob Dibble	.10	.08	.04
527	Jack McDowell	.20	.15	.08
528	Daryl Boston	.10	.08	.04
529	*Bill Wertz*	.20	.15	.08
530	Charlie Hough	.10	.08	.04
531	Sean Bergman	.15	.11	.06
532	Doug Jones	.10	.08	.04
533	Jeff Montgomery	.10	.08	.04
534	*Roger Cedeno*	1.00	.70	.40
535	Robin Yount	.50	.40	.20
536	Mo Vaughn	.35	.25	.14
537	Brian Harper	.10	.08	.04
538	Juan Castillo	.10	.08	.04
539	Steve Farr	.10	.08	.04
540	John Kruk	.20	.15	.08
541	Troy Neel	.40	.30	.15
542	*Danny Clyburn*	.60	.45	.25
543	*Jim Converse*	.30	.25	.12
544	Gregg Jefferies	.10	.08	.04
545	Jose Canseco	.35	.25	.14
546	*Julio Bruno*	.25	.20	.10
547	Rob Butler	.20	.15	.08
548	Royce Clayton	.20	.15	.08
549	Chris Hoiles	.10	.08	.04
550	Greg Maddux	.40	.30	.15
551	*Joe Ciccarella*	.25	.20	.10
552	Ozzie Timmons	.25	.20	.10
553	Chili Davis	.10	.08	.04
554	Brian Koelling	.30	.25	.12
555	Frank Thomas	6.00	4.50	2.50
556	Vinny Castilla	.10	.08	.04
557	Reggie Jefferson	.10	.08	.04
558	Rob Natal	.10	.08	.04
559	Mike Henneman	.10	.08	.04
560	Craig Biggio	.10	.08	.04
561	*Billy Brewer*	.20	.15	.08
562	Dan Melendez	.20	.15	.08
563	*Kenny Felder*	.60	.45	.25
564	*Miguel Batista*	.50	.40	.20
565	Dave Winfield	.40	.30	.15
566	Al Shirley	.25	.20	.10
567	Robert Eenhoorn	.10	.08	.04
568	Mike Williams	.10	.08	.04
569	*Tanyon Sturtze*	.40	.30	.15
570	Tim Wakefield	.10	.08	.04
571	Greg Pirkl	.30	.25	.12
572	*Sean Lowe*	.40	.30	.15
573	*Terry Burows*	.25	.20	.10
574	*Kevin Higgins*	.30	.25	.12
575	Joe Carter	.30	.25	.12
576	Kevin Rogers	.10	.08	.04
577	Manny Alexander	.10	.08	.04
578	David Justice	.75	.60	.30
579	*Brian Conroy*	.30	.25	.12
580	*Jessie Hollins*	.20	.15	.08
581	*Ron Watson*	.20	.15	.08
582	Bip Roberts	.10	.08	.04
583	*Tom Urbani*	.20	.15	.08
584	*Jason Hutchins*	.30	.25	.12
585	Carlos Baerga	.80	.60	.30
586	Jeff Mutis	.25	.20	.10
587	Justin Thompson	.40	.30	.15
588	Orlando Miller	.40	.30	.15
589	Brian McRae	.10	.08	.04
590	Ramon Martinez	.10	.08	.04
591	Dave Nilsson	.10	.08	.04
592	*Jose Vidro*	.35	.25	.14
593	Rich Becker	.10	.08	.04
594	*Preston Wilson*	1.75	1.25	.70
595	Don Mattingly	.60	.45	.25
596	Tony Langmire	.10	.08	.04
597	Kevin Seitzer	.10	.08	.04
598	*Midre Cummings*	1.00	.75	.40
599	Omar Vizquel	.10	.08	.04
600	Lee Smith	.10	.08	.04
601	*David Hulse*	.40	.30	.15
602	*Darrell Sherman*	.20	.15	.08
603	Alex Gonzalez	1.75	1.25	.70
604	Geronimo Pena	.10	.08	.04
605	Mike Devereaux	.10	.08	.04
606	*Sterling Hitchcock*	.60	.45	.25
607	Mike Greenwell	.10	.08	.04
608	Steve Buechele	.10	.08	.04
609	Troy Percival	.10	.08	.04
610	Bobby Kelly	.10	.08	.04
611	*James Baldwin*	2.00	1.50	.80
612	Jerald Clark	.10	.08	.04
613	*Albie Lopez*	.75	.60	.30
614	Dave Magadan	.10	.08	.04
615	Mickey Tettleton	.10	.08	.04
616	*Sean Runyan*	.35	.25	.14
617	Bob Hamelin	.10	.08	.04
618	Raul Mondesi	2.00	1.50	.80
619	Tyrone Hill	.25	.20	.10
620	Darrin Fletcher	.10	.08	.04
621	Mike Trombley	.10	.08	.04
622	Jeromy Burnitz	.20	.15	.08
623	Bernie Williams	.10	.08	.04
624	*Mike Farmer*	.20	.15	.08
625	Rickey Henderson	.40	.30	.15
626	Carlos Garcia	.20	.15	.08
627	*Jeff Darwin*	.40	.30	.15
628	Todd Zeile	.10	.08	.04
629	Benji Gil	.60	.45	.25
630	Tony Gwynn	.40	.30	.15
631	*Aaron Small*	.25	.20	.10
632	*Joe Rosselli*	.30	.25	.12

633	Mike Mussina	.50	.40	.20
634	Ryan Klesko	1.50	1.25	.60
635	Roger Clemens	.60	.45	.25
636	Sammy Sosa	.20	.15	.08
637	*Orlando Palmeiro*	.20	.15	.08
638	Willie Greene	.10	.08	.04
639	George Bell	.10	.08	.04
640	*Garvin Alston*	.30	.25	.12
641	*Pete Janicki*	.40	.30	.15
642	*Chris Sheff*	.25	.20	.10
643	*Felipe Lira*	.40	.30	.15
644	Roberto Petagine	.50	.40	.20
645	Wally Joyner	.10	.08	.04
646	Mike Piazza	7.50	5.50	3.00
647	Jaime Navarro	.10	.08	.04
648	*Jeff Hartsock*	.25	.20	.10
649	David McCarty	.60	.45	.25
650	Bobby Jones	.75	.60	.30
651	Mark Hutton	.20	.15	.08
652	Kyle Abbott	.10	.08	.04
653	*Steve Cox*	.25	.20	.10
654	Jeff King	.10	.08	.04
655	Norm Charlton	.10	.08	.04
656	*Mike Gulan*	.30	.25	.12
657	Julio Franco	.10	.08	.04
658	*Cameron Cairncross*	.30	.25	.12
659	John Olerud	1.00	.75	.40
660	Salomon Torres	.90	.70	.35
661	Brad Pennington	.10	.08	.04
662	Melvin Nieves	.60	.45	.25
663	Ivan Calderon	.10	.08	.04
664	Turk Wendell	.10	.08	.04
665	Chris Pritchett	.15	.11	.06
666	Reggie Sanders	.20	.15	.08
667	Robin Ventura	.30	.25	.12
668	Joe Girardi	.10	.08	.04
669	Manny Ramirez	3.50	2.75	1.50
670	Jeff Conine	.10	.08	.04
671	Greg Gohr	.10	.08	.04
672	Andujar Cedeno	.10	.08	.04
673	*Les Norman*	.40	.30	.15
674	*Mike James*	.20	.15	.08
675	*Marshall Boze*	1.00	.75	.40
676	B.J. Wallace	.60	.45	.25
677	Kent Hrbek	.10	.08	.04
678	Jack Voight	.10	.08	.04
679	Brien Taylor	.60	.45	.25
680	Curt Schilling	.10	.08	.04
681	Todd Van Poppel	.30	.25	.12
682	Kevin Young	.15	.11	.06
683	Tommy Adams	.10	.08	.04
684	Bernard Gilkey	.10	.08	.04
685	Kevin Brown	.10	.08	.04
686	Fred McGriff	.50	.40	.20
687	Pat Borders	.10	.08	.04
688	Kirt Manwaring	.10	.08	.04
689	Sid Bream	.10	.08	.04
690	John Valentin	.10	.08	.04
691	*Steve Olsen*	.20	.15	.08
692	*Roberto Mejia*	1.50	1.25	.60
693	Carlos Delgado (Foil)	3.00	2.25	1.25
694	*Steve Gibralter* (Foil)	.50	.40	.20
695	Gary Mota (Foil)	.25	.20	.10
696	*Jose Malave* (Foil)	.90	.70	.35
697	*Larry Sutton* (Foil)	.50	.40	.20
698	*Dan Frye* (Foil)	.35	.25	.14
699	*Tim Clark* (Foil)	.60	.45	.25
700	*Brian Rupp* (Foil)	.50	.40	.20
701	Alou's (Foil)	.25	.20	.10
702	Bond's (Foil)	.75	.60	.30
703	Griffey's (Foil)	1.00	.75	.40
704	McRae's (Foil)	.25	.20	.10
705	Checklist 1	.10	.08	.04
706	Checklist 2	.10	.08	.04
707	Checklist 3	.10	.08	.04
708	Checklist 4	.10	.08	.04

1903 Breisch Williams Type I (E107)

W. GLEASON, 2 B, Phila., N.

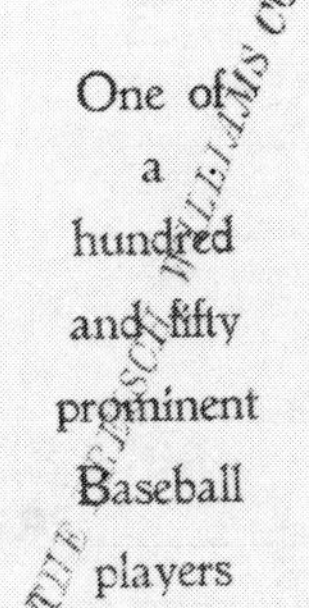

Identified by the American Card Catalog as E107, this circa 1903 set is very significant because it was the first major baseball card set since the days of the Old Judge issues in the 1880s, and it established the pattern for most of the tobacco and candy cards that were to follow over the next two decades. Measuring approximately 1-3/8" by 2-5/8", the cards feature black and white player photos with the name, position and team along the bottom. The back states simply "One of a hundred and fifty prominent Baseball players," although blank-backed varieties of this set are fairly common. Also found have been cards with a diagonal overprint stating "The Breisch-Williams Co." establishing the producer of the set. The Type I set consists of 147 different players although 11 additional variations can be found. The Type II cards are thicker than those in Type I and may have been cut from an advertising piece. The Keeler and Delehanty cards have captions different from those found in Type I. The 11 variations found in Type I are not included in the complete set price. Many of the photos were used in other sets, like T206 and M116 Sporting Life.

		NR MT	EX	VG
Complete Set:		35000.	17500.	10000.
Common Player:		200.00	100.00	60.00
(1a)	John Anderson (New York)	200.00	100.00	60.00
(1b)	John Anderson (St. Louis)	200.00	100.00	60.00
(2)	Jimmy Barret (Barrett)	200.00	100.00	60.00
(3)	Ginger Beaumont	200.00	100.00	60.00
(4)	Fred Beck	200.00	100.00	60.00
(5)	Jake Beckley	800.00	400.00	240.00
(6)	Harry Bemis	200.00	100.00	60.00
(7)	Chief Bender	675.00	337.00	202.00
(8)	Bill Bernhard	200.00	100.00	60.00
(9)	Harry Bey (Bay)	200.00	100.00	60.00
(10)	Bill Bradley	200.00	100.00	60.00
(11)	Fritz Buelow	200.00	100.00	60.00
(12)	Nixey Callahan	200.00	100.00	60.00
(13)	Scoops Carey	675.00	337.00	202.00
(14)	Charley Carr	200.00	100.00	60.00
(15)	Bill Carrick	200.00	100.00	60.00
(16)	Doc Casey	200.00	100.00	60.00
(17)	Frank Chance	675.00	337.00	202.00
(18)	Jack Chesbro	675.00	337.00	202.00
(19)	Boileryard Clark (Clarke)	200.00	100.00	60.00
(20)	Fred Clarke	800.00	400.00	240.00
(21)	Jimmy Collins	800.00	400.00	240.00
(22)	Duff Cooley	200.00	100.00	60.00
(23)	Tommy Corcoran	200.00	100.00	60.00
(24)	Bill Coughlan (Coughlin)	200.00	100.00	60.00
(25)	Lou Criger	200.00	100.00	60.00
(26)	Lave Cross	200.00	100.00	60.00
(27)	Monte Cross	200.00	100.00	60.00
(28)	Bill Dahlen	250.00	125.00	72.50
(29)	Tom Daly	200.00	100.00	60.00
(30)	George Davis	250.00	125.00	72.50
(31)	Harry Davis	200.00	100.00	60.00
(32)	Ed Delehanty (Delahanty)	950.00	475.00	285.00
(33)	Gene DeMont (DeMontreville)	200.00	100.00	60.00
(34a)	Pop Dillon (Detroit)	200.00	100.00	60.00
(34b)	Pop Dillon (Brooklyn)	200.00	100.00	60.00
(35)	Bill Dineen (Dinneen)	200.00	100.00	60.00
(36)	Jiggs Donahue	200.00	100.00	60.00
(37)	Mike Donlin	250.00	125.00	72.50
(38)	Patsy Donovan	200.00	100.00	60.00
(39)	Patsy Dougherty	200.00	100.00	60.00
(40)	Klondike Douglass	200.00	100.00	60.00
(41a)	Jack Doyle (Brooklyn)	200.00	100.00	60.00
(41b)	Jack Doyle (Philadelphia)	200.00	100.00	60.00
(42)	Lew Drill	200.00	100.00	60.00
(43)	Jack Dunn	200.00	100.00	60.00
(44a)	Kid Elberfield (Elberfeld) (Detroit)	200.00	100.00	60.00
(44b)	Kid Elberfield (Elberfeld) (no team designation)	200.00	100.00	60.00
(45)	Duke Farrell	200.00	100.00	60.00
(46)	Hobe Ferris	200.00	100.00	60.00
(47)	Elmer Flick	800.00	400.00	240.00
(48)	Buck Freeman	200.00	100.00	60.00
(49)	Bill Freil (Friel)	200.00	100.00	60.00
(50)	Dave Fultz	200.00	100.00	60.00
(51)	Ned Garvin	200.00	100.00	60.00
(52)	Billy Gilbert	200.00	100.00	60.00
(53)	Harry Gleason	200.00	100.00	60.00
(54a)	Kid Gleason (New York)	200.00	100.00	60.00
(54b)	Kid Gleason (Philadelphia)	200.00	100.00	60.00
(55)	John Gochnauer (Gochnaur)	200.00	100.00	60.00
(56)	Danny Green	200.00	100.00	60.00
(57)	Noodles Hahn	200.00	100.00	60.00
(58)	Bill Hallman	200.00	100.00	60.00
(59)	Ned Hanlon	200.00	100.00	60.00
(60)	Dick Harley	200.00	100.00	60.00
(61)	Jack Harper	200.00	100.00	60.00
(62)	Topsy Hartsell (Hartsel)	200.00	100.00	60.00
(63)	Emmet Heidrick	200.00	100.00	60.00
(64)	Charlie Hemphill	200.00	100.00	60.00
(65)	Weldon Henley	200.00	100.00	60.00
(66)	Piano Legs Hickman	200.00	100.00	60.00
(67)	Harry Howell	200.00	100.00	60.00
(68)	Frank Isabel (Isbell)	200.00	100.00	60.00
(69)	Fred Jacklitzch (Jacklitsch)	200.00	100.00	60.00
(70)	Fielder Jones (Chicago)	200.00	100.00	60.00
(71)	Charlie Jones (Boston)	200.00	100.00	60.00
(72)	Addie Joss	800.00	400.00	240.00
(73)	Mike Kahoe	200.00	100.00	60.00
(74)	Wee Willie Keeler	800.00	400.00	240.00
(75)	Joe Kelley	800.00	400.00	240.00
(76)	Brickyard Kennedy	200.00	100.00	60.00
(77)	Frank Kitson	200.00	100.00	60.00
(78a)	Malachi Kittredge (Boston)	200.00	100.00	60.00
(78b)	Malachi Kittredge (Washington)	200.00	100.00	60.00
(79)	Candy LaChance	200.00	100.00	60.00
(80)	Nap Lajoie	950.00	475.00	285.00
(81)	Tommy Leach	200.00	100.00	60.00
(82a)	Watty Lee (Washington)	200.00	100.00	60.00
(82b)	Watty Lee (Pittsburg)	200.00	100.00	60.00
(83)	Sam Leever	200.00	100.00	60.00
(84)	Herman Long	200.00	100.00	60.00
(85a)	Billy Lush (Detroit)	200.00	100.00	60.00
(85b)	Billy Lush (Cleveland)	200.00	100.00	60.00
(86)	Christy Mathewson	1850.	925.00	555.00
(87)	Sport McAllister	200.00	100.00	60.00
(88)	Jack McCarthy	200.00	100.00	60.00
(89)	Barry McCormick	200.00	100.00	60.00
(90)	Ed McFarland (Chicago)	200.00	100.00	60.00
(91)	Herm McFarland (New York)	200.00	100.00	60.00
(92)	Joe McGinnity	800.00	400.00	240.00
(93)	John McGraw	800.00	400.00	240.00
(94)	Deacon McGuire	200.00	100.00	60.00
(95)	Jock Menefee	200.00	100.00	60.00
(96)	Sam Mertes	200.00	100.00	60.00
(97)	Roscoe Miller	200.00	100.00	60.00
(98)	Fred Mitchell	200.00	100.00	60.00
(99)	Earl Moore	200.00	100.00	60.00
(100)	Danny Murphy	200.00	100.00	60.00
(101)	Jack O'Connor	200.00	100.00	60.00
(102)	Al Orth	200.00	100.00	60.00
(103)	Dick Padden	200.00	100.00	60.00
(104)	Freddy Parent	200.00	100.00	60.00
(105)	Roy Patterson	200.00	100.00	60.00
(106)	Heinie Peitz	200.00	100.00	60.00
(107)	Deacon Phillipi (Phillippe)	200.00	100.00	60.00
(108)	Wiley Piatt	200.00	100.00	60.00
(109)	Ollie Pickering	200.00	100.00	60.00
(110)	Eddie Plank	800.00	400.00	240.00
(111a)	Ed Poole (Cincinnati)	200.00	100.00	60.00
(111b)	Ed Poole (Brooklyn)	200.00	100.00	60.00
(112a)	Jack Powell (St. Louis)	200.00	100.00	60.00
(112b)	Jack Powell (New York)	200.00	100.00	60.00
(113)	Mike Powers	200.00	100.00	60.00
(114)	Claude Ritchie (Ritchey)	200.00	100.00	60.00
(115)	Jimmy Ryan	200.00	100.00	60.00
(116)	Ossee Schreckengost	200.00	100.00	60.00
(117)	Kip Selbach	200.00	100.00	60.00
(118)	Socks Seybold	200.00	100.00	60.00
(119)	Jimmy Sheckard	200.00	100.00	60.00
(120)	Ed Siever	200.00	100.00	60.00
(121)	Harry Smith	200.00	100.00	60.00
(122)	Tully Sparks	200.00	100.00	60.00
(123)	Jake Stahl	200.00	100.00	60.00
(124)	Harry Steinfeldt	200.00	100.00	60.00
(125)	Sammy Strang	200.00	100.00	60.00
(126)	Willie Sudhoff	200.00	100.00	60.00
(127)	Joe Sugden	200.00	100.00	60.00
(128)	Billy Sullivan	200.00	100.00	60.00
(129)	Jack Taylor	200.00	100.00	60.00
(130)	Fred Tenney	200.00	100.00	60.00
(131)	Ira Thomas	200.00	100.00	60.00
(132a)	Jack Thoney (Cleveland)	200.00	100.00	60.00
(132b)	Jack Thoney (New York)	200.00	100.00	60.00
(133)	Jack Townsend	200.00	100.00	60.00
(134)	George Van Haltren	200.00	100.00	60.00
(135)	Rube Waddell	800.00	400.00	240.00
(136)	Honus Wagner	2500.	1250.	725.00
(137)	Bobby Wallace	800.00	400.00	240.00
(138)	Jack Warner	200.00	100.00	60.00
(139)	Jimmy Wiggs	200.00	100.00	60.00
(140)	Jimmy Williams	200.00	100.00	60.00
(141)	Vic Willis	250.00	125.00	72.50
(142)	Snake Wiltse	200.00	100.00	60.00
(143)	George Winters (Winter)	200.00	100.00	60.00
(144)	Bob Wood	200.00	100.00	60.00
(145)	Joe Yeager	200.00	100.00	60.00
(146)	Cy Young	1600.	800.00	480.00
(147)	Chief Zimmer	200.00	100.00	60.00

1903 Breisch Williams Type II (E107)

DELAHANTY, Fielder, Wash.

		NR MT	EX	VG
Complete Set:		2300.	1150.	690.00
Common Player:		300.00	150.00	90.00
(1)	Ed Delehanty (Delahanty)	750.00	375.00	225.00
(2)	Jack Doyle	300.00	150.00	90.00
(3)	Wee Willie Keeler	750.00	375.00	225.00
(4)	Tommy Leach	300.00	150.00	90.00
(5)	Socks Seybold	300.00	150.00	90.00
(6)	Fred Tenney	300.00	150.00	90.00

1909 C.A. Briggs Co. (E97)

SULLIVAN, BOSTON AMER.

Measuring approximately 1-1/2" by 2-3/4", this 30-card set is nearly identical to several other candy issues of the same period. Designated as E97 in the American Card Catalog, the set was issued in 1909-1910 by C.A. Briggs Co., Lozenge Makers of Boston, Mass. The front of the card shows a tinted black and white player photo, with the player's last name, position and team printed below. The backs of the cards are printed in brown type and checklist the 30 players in the set alphabetically. The C.A. Briggs Co. name appears at the bottom. Black and white examples of this set have also been found on a thin paper stock with blank backs and are believed to be "proof cards." Four variations are also found in the set. The more expensive variations are not included in the complete set price.

		NR MT	EX	VG
Complete Set:		8500.	4250.	2500.
Common Player:		200.00	100.00	60.00
(1)	Jimmy Austin	200.00	100.00	60.00
(2)	Joe Birmingham	200.00	100.00	60.00
(3)	Bill Bradley	200.00	100.00	60.00
(4)	Kitty Bransfield	200.00	100.00	60.00
(5)	Howie Camnitz	200.00	100.00	60.00
(6)	Bill Carrigan	200.00	100.00	60.00
(7)	Harry Davis	200.00	100.00	60.00
(8)	Josh Devore	200.00	100.00	60.00
(9)	Mickey Doolan	200.00	100.00	60.00
(10)	Bull Durham	200.00	100.00	60.00
(11)	Jimmy Dygert	200.00	100.00	60.00
(12)	Topsy Hartsell (Hartsel)	200.00	100.00	60.00
(13)	Bill Heinchman (Hinchman)	200.00	100.00	60.00
(14)	Charlie Hemphill	200.00	100.00	60.00
(15)	Wee Willie Keeler	1000.	500.00	225.00
(16)	Joe Kelly (Kelley)	900.00	450.00	200.00
(17)	Red Kleinow	200.00	100.00	60.00
(18)	Rube Kroh	200.00	100.00	60.00
(19)	Matty McIntyre	200.00	100.00	60.00
(20)	Amby McConnell	200.00	100.00	60.00
(21)	Chief Meyers	200.00	100.00	60.00
(22)	Earl Moore	200.00	100.00	60.00
(23)	George Mullin	200.00	100.00	60.00
(24)	Red Murray	200.00	100.00	60.00
(25a)	Simon Nichols (Nicholls) (Philadelphia)	550.00	275.00	150.00
(25b)	Simon Nichols (Nicholls) (Cleveland)	200.00	100.00	60.00
(26)	Claude Rossman	200.00	100.00	60.00
(27)	Admiral Schlei	200.00	100.00	60.00
(28a)	Harry Steinfeld (name incorrect)	200.00	100.00	60.00
(28b)	Harry Steinfeldt (name correct)	550.00	275.00	150.00
(29a)	Dennis Sullivan (Chicago)	200.00	100.00	60.00
(29b)	Dennis Sullivan (Boston)	3500.	1500.	675.00
(30a)	Cy. Young (Cleveland)	1800.	900.00	400.00
(30b)	Cy. Young (Boston)	1500.	700.00	325.00

1954 Briggs Meats

The Briggs Meat set was issued over a two-year span (1953-54) and features 28 players from the Washington Senators and 12 from the New York City area baseball teams. The set was issued in two-card panels on hot dog packages sold in the Washington, D.C. vicinity. The color cards, which are blank-backed and measure 2-1/4" by 3-1/2", are printed on waxed cardboard. Pictures of the New York players can also be found on cards in the 1954 Dan-Dee Potato Chips and 1953-1955 Stahl-Meyer Franks sets. There is a slight difference in style between the Senators cards and those of the New York players. The white panel beneath the photo of the Washington players includes a facsimile autograph plus a few biographical details about the player. The New York players' cards have only the player's name and facsimile signature in that panel. Several of the Senators cards command a premium for scarcity.

		NR MT	EX	VG
Complete Set:		11750.	5750.	3300.
Common Player:		200.00	100.00	60.00
(1)	Hank Bauer	250.00	125.00	75.00
(2)	James Busby	200.00	100.00	60.00
(3)	Tommy Byrne	250.00	125.00	75.00
(4)	Gil Coan	200.00	100.00	60.00
(5)	John Dixon	200.00	100.00	60.00
(6)	Carl Erskine	250.00	125.00	75.00
(7)	Edward Fitzgerald (Fitz Gerald)	200.00	100.00	60.00
(8)	Newton Grasso	250.00	125.00	75.00
(9)	Melvin Hoderlein	200.00	100.00	60.00
(10)	Gil Hodges	350.00	175.00	100.00
(11)	Monte Irvin	250.00	125.00	75.00
(12)	Jackie Jensen	250.00	125.00	75.00
(13)	Whitey Lockman	200.00	100.00	60.00
(14)	Mickey Mantle	3000.	1500.	900.00
(15)	Conrado Marrero	200.00	100.00	60.00
(16)	Walter Masterson	250.00	125.00	75.00
(17)	Carmen Mauro	250.00	125.00	75.00
(18)	Willie Mays	2000.	1000.	600.00
(19)	Mickey McDermott	200.00	100.00	60.00
(20)	Gil McDougald	250.00	125.00	75.00
(21)	Julio Moreno	250.00	125.00	75.00
(22)	Don Mueller	200.00	100.00	60.00
(23)	Don Newcombe	250.00	125.00	75.00
(24)	Robert Oldis	200.00	100.00	60.00
(25)	Erwin Porterfield	200.00	100.00	60.00
(26)	Phil Rizzuto	400.00	200.00	120.00
(27)	James Runnels	200.00	100.00	60.00
(28)	John Schmitz	200.00	100.00	60.00
(29)	Angel Scull	200.00	100.00	60.00
(30)	Frank Shea	200.00	100.00	60.00
(31)	Albert Sima	250.00	125.00	75.00
(32)	Duke Snider	800.00	400.00	240.00
(33)	Charles Stobbs	200.00	100.00	60.00
(34)	Willard Terwilliger	200.00	100.00	60.00
(35)	Joe Tipton	200.00	100.00	60.00
(36)	Thomas Umphlett	200.00	100.00	60.00
(37)	Gene Verble	250.00	125.00	75.00
(38)	James Vernon	200.00	100.00	60.00
(39)	Clyde Volmer (Vollmer)	200.00	100.00	60.00
(40)	Edward Yost	200.00	100.00	60.00

1911 Brunners Bread (D304)

OTIS CRANDALL, N.Y. NAT'L

This unnumbered 25-card set, issued in 1911, is similar in design to the tobacco and candy company issues of the same period, but is different in size, measuring 1-3/4" by 2-1/2". The fronts of the cards feature a color lithograph with the player's name and team below in capital letters. The backs advertise various breads produced by the General Baking Company in the Buffalo, N.Y. area. The bottom of the back notes that "There are 25 subjects in this set/One with each loaf of the above breads."

		NR MT	EX	VG
Complete Set (25):		4250.	2500.	1500.
Common Player:		60.00	25.00	15.00
(1)	J. Frank Baker	150.00	75.00	45.00
(2)	Jack Barry	60.00	30.00	18.00
(3)	George Bell	60.00	30.00	18.00
(4)	Charles Bender	150.00	75.00	45.00
(5)	Frank Chance	150.00	75.00	45.00
(6)	Hal Chase	90.00	45.00	27.00
(7)	Ty Cobb	1100.	550.00	330.00
(8)	Eddie Collins	150.00	75.00	45.00
(9)	Otis Crandall	60.00	30.00	18.00
(10)	Sam Crawford	150.00	75.00	45.00
(11)	John Evers	150.00	75.00	45.00
(12)	Arthur Fletcher	60.00	30.00	18.00
(13)	Charles Herzog	60.00	30.00	18.00
(14)	M. Kelly	60.00	30.00	18.00
(15)	Napoleon Lajoie	200.00	100.00	60.00
(16)	Rube Marquard	150.00	75.00	45.00
(17)	Christy Mathewson	450.00	225.00	135.00
(18)	Fred Merkle	60.00	30.00	18.00
(19)	"Chief" Meyers	60.00	30.00	18.00
(20)	Marty O'Toole	60.00	30.00	18.00
(21)	Nap. Rucker	60.00	30.00	18.00
(22)	Arthur Shafer	60.00	30.00	18.00
(23)	Fred Tenny (Tenney)	60.00	30.00	18.00
(24)	Honus Wagner	750.00	375.00	225.00
(25)	Cy Young	450.00	225.00	135.00

1977 Burger King Yankees

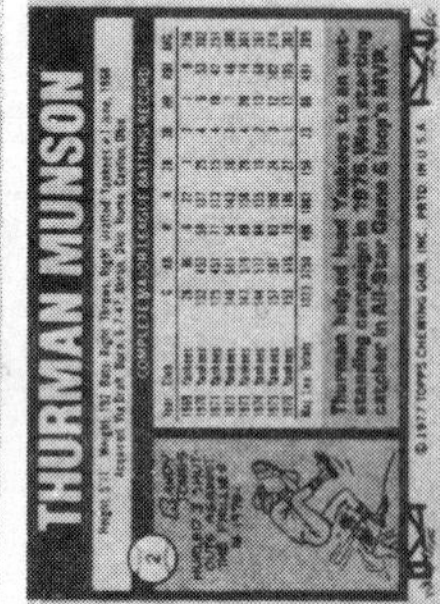

The first Topps-produced set for Burger King restaurants was issued in the New York area in 1977 and featured the A.L. champion New York Yankees. Twenty-two players plus an unnumbered checklist were issued at the beginning of the promotion with card #23 (Lou Piniella) being added to the set at a later date. The Piniella card was issued in limited quantities. The cards, numbered 1 through 23, are 2-1/2" by 3-1/2" in size and have fronts identical to the regular 1977 Topps set except for the following numbers: 2, 6, 7, 13, 14, 15, 17, 20 and 21. These cards feature different poses or major picture-cropping variations. It should be noted that very minor cropping variations between the regular Topps sets and the Burger King issues exist throughout the years the sets were produced.

		NR MT	EX	VG
Complete Set:		40.00	20.00	12.00
Common Player:		.30	.15	.09
1	Yankees Team (Billy Martin)	1.00	.50	.30
2	Thurman Munson	7.00	3.50	2.00
3	Fran Healy	.30	.15	.09
4	Catfish Hunter	2.00	1.00	.60
5	Ed Figueroa	.30	.15	.09
6	Don Gullett	.30	.15	.09
7	Mike Torrez	.30	.15	.09
8	Ken Holtzman	.30	.15	.09
9	Dick Tidrow	.30	.15	.09
10	Sparky Lyle	.50	.25	.15
11	Ron Guidry	.60	.30	.20
12	Chris Chambliss	.30	.15	.09
13	Willie Randolph	.60	.30	.20
14	Bucky Dent	.60	.30	.20
15	Graig Nettles	.75	.40	.25
16	Fred Stanley	.30	.15	.09
17	Reggie Jackson	8.00	4.00	2.50
18	Mickey Rivers	.30	.15	.09
19	Roy White	.50	.25	.15
20	Jim Wynn	.50	.25	.15
21	Paul Blair	.30	.15	.09
22	Carlos May	.30	.15	.09
23	Lou Piniella	20.00	10.00	6.00
----	Checklist	.10	.05	.03

1978 Burger King Astros

Burger King restaurants in the Houston area distributed a Topps-produced 23-card set showcasing the Astros in 1978. The cards are standard size (2-1/2" by 3-1/2") and are numbered 1 through 22. The checklist card is unnumbered. The card fronts are identical to the regular 1978 Topps set with the exception of card numbers 21 and 22, which have different poses. Although not noted in the following checklist, it should be remembered that very minor

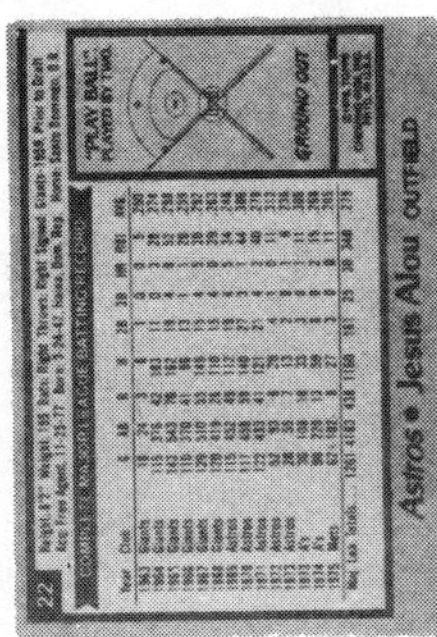

picture-cropping variations between the regular Topps issues and the 1977-1980 Burger King sets do exist.

		NR MT	EX	VG
Complete Set:		8.00	4.00	2.50
Common Player:		.35	.20	.11
1	Bill Virdon	.50	.25	.15
2	Joe Ferguson	.35	.20	.11
3	Ed Herrmann	.35	.20	.11
4	J.R. Richard	.60	.30	.20
5	Joe Niekro	.60	.30	.20
6	Floyd Bannister	.35	.20	.11
7	Joaquin Andujar	.35	.20	.11
8	Ken Forsch	.35	.20	.11
9	Mark Lemongello	.35	.20	.11
10	Joe Sambito	.35	.20	.11
11	Gene Pentz	.35	.20	.11
12	Bob Watson	.40	.20	.12
13	Julio Gonzalez	.35	.20	.11
14	Enos Cabell	.35	.20	.11
15	Roger Metzger	.35	.20	.11
16	Art Howe	.40	.20	.12
17	Jose Cruz	.50	.25	.15
18	Cesar Cedeno	.50	.25	.15
19	Terry Puhl	.35	.20	.11
20	Wilbur Howard	.35	.20	.11
21	Dave Bergman	.35	.20	.11
22	Jesus Alou	.50	.25	.15
----	Checklist	.04	.02	.01

1978 Burger King Rangers

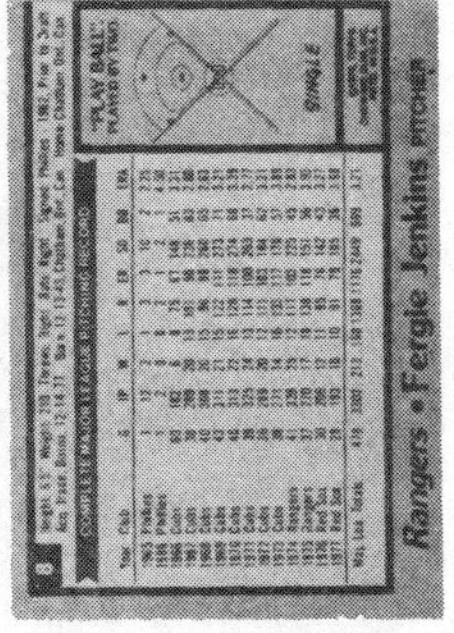

Issued by Burger King restaurants in the Dallas-Fort Worth area, this 23-card Topps-produced set features the Texas Rangers. The cards are standard size (2-1/2" by 3-1/2") and are identical in style to the regular 1978 Topps set with the following exceptions: #'s 5, 8, 10, 12, 17, 21 and 22. An unnumbered checklist card was included with the set.

		NR MT	EX	VG
Complete Set:		10.00	5.00	3.00
Common Player:		.35	.20	.11
1	Billy Hunter	.35	.20	.11
2	Jim Sundberg	.35	.20	.11
3	John Ellis	.35	.20	.11
4	Doyle Alexander	.35	.20	.11
5	Jon Matlack	.35	.20	.11
6	Dock Ellis	.35	.20	.11
7	George Medich	.35	.20	.11
8	Fergie Jenkins	2.50	1.25	.70
9	Len Barker	.35	.20	.11
10	Reggie Cleveland	.35	.20	.11
11	Mike Hargrove	.50	.25	.15
12	Bump Wills	.50	.25	.15
13	Toby Harrah	.50	.25	.15
14	Bert Campaneris	.50	.25	.15
15	Sandy Alomar	.50	.25	.15
16	Kurt Bevacqua	.35	.20	.11
17	Al Oliver	.90	.45	.25
18	Juan Beniquez	.35	.20	.11
19	Claudell Washington	.35	.20	.11
20	Richie Zisk	.35	.20	.11
21	John Lowenstein	.35	.20	.11
22	Bobby Thompson	.35	.20	.11
----	Checklist	.04	.02	.01

1978 Burger King Tigers

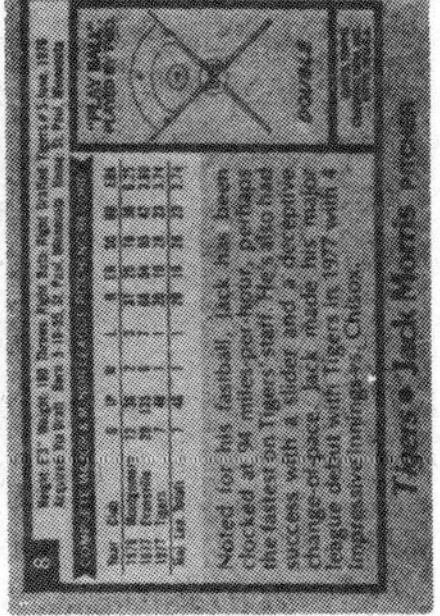

Rookie cards of Morris, Trammell and Whitaker make the Topps-produced 1978 Burger King Detroit Tigers issue the most popular of the BK sets. Twenty-two player cards and an unnumbered checklist make up the set which was issued in the Detroit area. The cards measure 2-1/2" by 3-1/2", and are identical to the regular 1978 Topps issue with the following exceptions - card #'s 6, 7, 8, 13, 15 and 16. Collectors are reminded that numerous minor picture-cropping variations between the regular Topps issues and the Burger King sets appear from the 1977 through 1980. These minor variations are not noted in the following checklist.

		NR MT	EX	VG
Complete Set:		45.00	22.00	13.50
Common Player:		.40	.20	.12
1	Ralph Houk	.50	.25	.15
2	Milt May	.40	.20	.12
3	John Wockenfuss	.40	.20	.12
4	Mark Fidrych	.90	.45	.25
5	Dave Rozema	.40	.20	.12
6	Jack Billingham	.40	.20	.12
7	Jim Slaton	.40	.20	.12
8	Jack Morris	10.00	5.00	3.00
9	John Hiller	.40	.20	.12
10	Steve Foucault	.40	.20	.12
11	Milt Wilcox	.40	.20	.12
12	Jason Thompson	.40	.20	.12
13	Lou Whitaker	15.00	7.50	4.50
14	Aurelio Rodriguez	.40	.20	.12
15	Alan Trammell	20.00	10.00	6.00
16	Steve Dillard	.40	.20	.12
17	Phil Mankowski	.40	.20	.12
18	Steve Kemp	.40	.20	.12
19	Ron LeFlore	.50	.25	.15
20	Tim Corcoran	.40	.20	.12
21	Mickey Stanley	.40	.20	.12
22	Rusty Staub	1.00	.50	.30
----	Checklist	.10	.05	.03

1978 Burger King Yankees

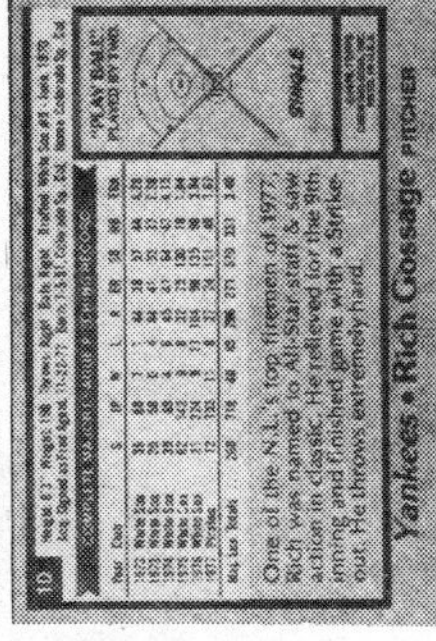

Produced by Topps for Burger King outlets in the New York area for the second year in a row, the 1978 Yankees set contains 22 cards plus an unnumbered checklist. The cards are numbered 1 through 22 and are the standard size of 2-1/2" by 3-1/2". The cards feature the same pictures found in the regular 1978 Topps set except for numbers 10, 11 and 16. Only those variations containing different poses or major picture-cropping differences are noted. Numerous minor picture-cropping variations, that are very insignificant in nature, exist between the regular Topps sets and the Burger King issues of 1977-1980.

		NR MT	EX	VG
Complete Set:		12.00	6.00	3.50
Common Player:		.30	.15	.09
1	Billy Martin	.80	.40	.25
2	Thurman Munson	3.00	1.50	.90
3	Cliff Johnson	.30	.15	.09
4	Ron Guidry	.40	.20	.12
5	Ed Figueroa	.30	.15	.09
6	Dick Tidrow	.30	.15	.09
7	Catfish Hunter	2.00	1.00	.60
8	Don Gullett	.30	.15	.09
9	Sparky Lyle	.50	.25	.15
10	Rich Gossage	.75	.40	.25
11	Rawly Eastwick	.30	.15	.09
12	Chris Chambliss	.30	.15	.09
13	Willie Randolph	.50	.25	.15
14	Graig Nettles	.50	.25	.15
15	Bucky Dent	.50	.25	.15
16	Jim Spencer	.30	.15	.09
17	Fred Stanley	.30	.15	.09
18	Lou Piniella	.60	.30	.20
19	Roy White	.50	.25	.15
20	Mickey Rivers	.30	.15	.09
21	Reggie Jackson	4.00	2.00	1.25
22	Paul Blair	.30	.15	.09
----	Checklist	.04	.02	.01

1979 Burger King Phillies

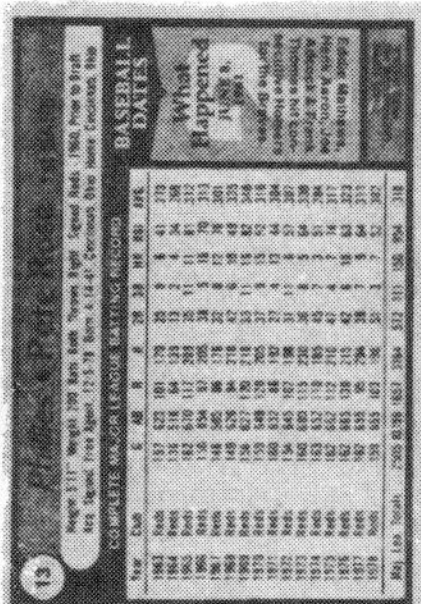

Twenty-two Philadelphia Phillies players are featured in the 1979 Burger King issue given out in the Philadelphia area. The Topps-produced set, whose cards measure 2-1/2" by 3-1/2", also includes an unnumbered checklist. The cards are identical to the regular 1979 Topps set except in seven instances. Card numbers 1, 11, 12, 13, 14, 17 and 22 have different poses. Very minor picture-cropping variations between the regular Topps issues and the Burger King sets can be found throughout the four years the cards were produced, but only those variations featuring major changes are noted in the following checklist.

		NR MT	EX	VG
Complete Set:		12.00	6.00	3.50
Common Player:		.20	.10	.06
1	Danny Ozark	.20	.10	.06
2	Bob Boone	.45	.25	.14
3	Tim McCarver	.40	.20	.12
4	Steve Carlton	3.00	1.50	.90
5	Larry Christenson	.20	.10	.06
6	Dick Ruthven	.20	.10	.06
7	Ron Reed	.20	.10	.06
8	Randy Lerch	.20	.10	.06
9	Warren Brusstar	.20	.10	.06
10	Tug McGraw	.30	.15	.09
11	Nino Espinosa	.20	.10	.06
12	Doug Bird	.20	.10	.06
13	Pete Rose	4.00	2.00	1.25
14	Manny Trillo	.40	.20	.12
15	Larry Bowa	.50	.25	.15
16	Mike Schmidt	4.00	2.00	1.25
17	Pete Mackanin	.20	.10	.06
18	Jose Cardenal	.20	.10	.06
19	Greg Luzinski	.40	.20	.12
20	Garry Maddox	.20	.10	.06
21	Bake McBride	.20	.10	.06
22	Greg Gross	.20	.10	.06
----	Checklist	.04	.02	.01

1979 Burger King Yankees

The New York Yankees were featured in a Topps-produced Burger King set for the third consecutive year in 1979. Once again, 22 numbered player cards and an unnumbered checklist made up the set. The cards, which measure 2-1/2" by 3-1/2", are identical to the 1979 Topps regular set except for card numbers 4, 8, 9 and 22 which included new poses. Only different poses or major picture-cropping variations between the regular Topps set and the Burger King issue are recognized in the checklist

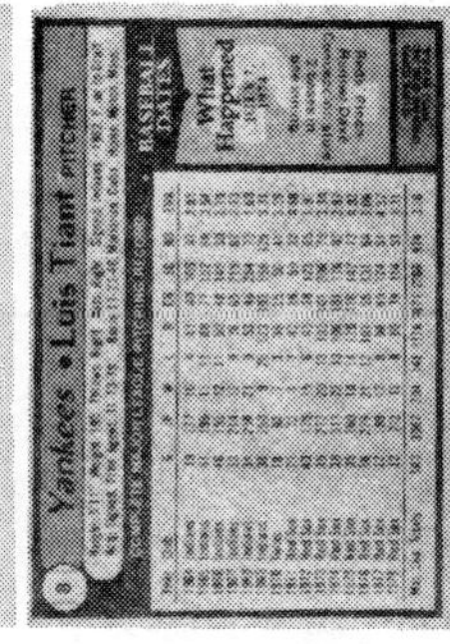

that follows. Numerous minor picture cropping variations between the regular Topps issue and the Burger King sets of 1977-1980 exist.

		NR MT	EX	VG
Complete Set:		12.00	6.00	3.50
Common Player:		.30	.15	.09
1	Yankees Team (Bob Lemon)	.50	.25	.15
2	Thurman Munson	2.00	1.00	.60
3	Cliff Johnson	.30	.15	.09
4	Ron Guidry	.50	.25	.15
5	Jay Johnstone	.40	.20	.12
6	Catfish Hunter	1.00	.50	.30
7	Jim Beattie	.30	.15	.09
8	Luis Tiant	.50	.25	.15
9	Tommy John	.75	.40	.25
10	Rich Gossage	.75	.40	.25
11	Ed Figueroa	.30	.15	.09
12	Chris Chambliss	.30	.15	.09
13	Willie Randolph	.50	.25	.15
14	Bucky Dent	.50	.25	.15
15	Graig Nettles	.50	.25	.15
16	Fred Stanley	.30	.15	.09
17	Jim Spencer	.30	.15	.09
18	Lou Piniella	.60	.30	.20
19	Roy White	.50	.25	.15
20	Mickey Rivers	.30	.15	.09
21	Reggie Jackson	3.00	1.50	.90
22	Juan Beniquez	.30	.15	.09
----	Checklist	.04	.02	.01

1980 Burger King Phillies

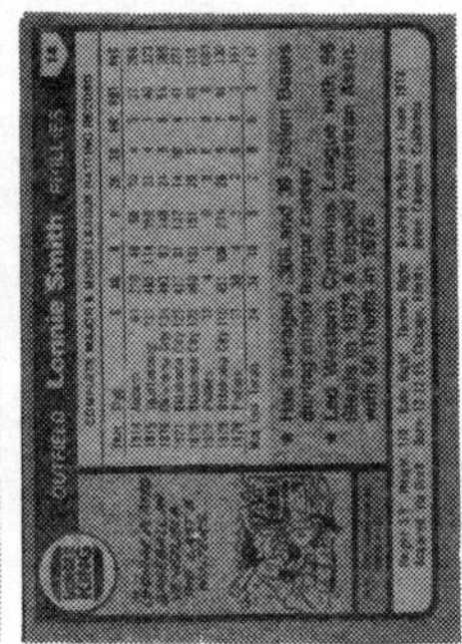

Philadelphia-area Burger King outlets issued a 23-card set featuring the Phillies for the second in a row in 1980. The Topps-produced set, whose cards measure 2-1/2" by 3-1/2", contains 22 player cards and an unnumbered checklist. The card fronts are identical in design to the regular 1980 Topps sets with the following exceptions - card numbers 1, 3, 8, 14 and 22 feature new poses. Collectors should note that very minor picture-cropping variations between the regular Topps issues and the Burger King sets exist in all years. Those minor differences are not noted in the checklist that follows. The 1980 Burger King sets were the first to include the Burger King logo on the card backs.

		NR MT	EX	VG
Complete Set:		10.00	5.00	3.00
Common Player:		.15	.08	.05
1	Dallas Green	.50	.25	.15
2	Bob Boone	.50	.25	.15
3	Keith Moreland	.30	.15	.09
4	Pete Rose	3.00	1.50	.90
5	Manny Trillo	.15	.08	.05
6	Mike Schmidt	3.00	1.50	.90
7	Larry Bowa	.25	.13	.08
8	John Vukovich	.15	.08	.05
9	Bake McBride	.15	.08	.05
10	Garry Maddox	.15	.08	.05
11	Greg Luzinski	.30	.15	.09
12	Greg Gross	.15	.08	.05
13	Del Unser	.15	.08	.05
14	Lonnie Smith	.50	.25	.15
15	Steve Carlton	1.75	.90	.50
16	Larry Christenson	.15	.08	.05
17	Nino Espinosa	.15	.08	.05
18	Randy Lerch	.15	.08	.05
19	Dick Ruthven	.15	.08	.05
20	Tug McGraw	.20	.10	.06
21	Ron Reed	.15	.08	.05
22	Kevin Saucier	.15	.08	.05
----	Checklist	.04	.02	.01

1980 Burger King Pitch, Hit & Run

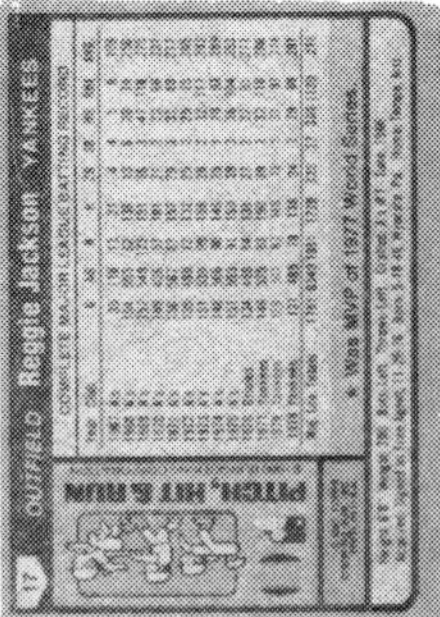

In 1980, Burger King issued, in conjunction with its "Pitch, Hit & Run" promotion, a Topps-produced 34-card set featuring pitchers (card #'s 1-11), hitters (#'s 12-22), and base stealers (#'s 23-33). The card fronts, which carry the Burger King logo, are identical in nature to the regular 1980 Topps set except for numbers 1, 4, 5, 7, 9, 10, 16, 17, 18, 22, 23, 27, 28, 29 and 30, which feature different poses. The cards, which are numbered 1 through 33, measure 2-1/2" by 3-1/2" in size. An unnumbered checklist was included with the set.

		NR MT	EX	VG
Complete Set:		28.00	14.00	8.50
Common Player:		.20	.10	.06
1	Vida Blue	.30	.15	.09
2	Steve Carlton	2.00	1.00	.60
3	Rollie Fingers	1.50	.70	.45
4	Ron Guidry	.30	.15	.09
5	Jerry Koosman	.30	.15	.09
6	Phil Niekro	.75	.40	.25
7	Jim Palmer	2.00	1.00	.60
8	J.R. Richard	.20	.10	.06
9	Nolan Ryan	8.00	4.00	2.50
10	Tom Seaver	2.00	1.00	.60
11	Bruce Sutter	.20	.10	.06
12	Don Baylor	.25	.13	.08
13	George Brett	2.00	1.00	.60
14	Rod Carew	2.00	1.00	.60
15	George Foster	.20	.10	.06
16	Keith Hernandez	.20	.10	.06
17	Reggie Jackson	2.25	1.25	.70
18	Fred Lynn	.50	.25	.15
19	Dave Parker	.50	.25	.15
20	Jim Rice	.60	.30	.20
21	Pete Rose	2.50	1.25	.70
22	Dave Winfield	2.00	1.00	.60
23	Bobby Bonds	.50	.25	.15
24	Enos Cabell	.20	.10	.06
25	Cesar Cedeno	.20	.10	.06
26	Julio Cruz	.20	.10	.06
27	Ron LeFlore	.20	.10	.06
28	Dave Lopes	.20	.10	.06
29	Omar Moreno	.20	.10	.06
30	Joe Morgan	1.50	.70	.45
31	Bill North	.20	.10	.06
32	Frank Taveras	.20	.10	.06
33	Willie Wilson	.20	.10	.06
----	Checklist	.04	.02	.01

1982 Burger King Braves

A set consisting of 27 "Collector Lids" featuring the Atlanta Braves was issued by Burger King restaurants in 1982. The lids, which measure 3-5/8" in diameter, were placed on a special Coca-Cola cup which listed the scores of the Braves' season-opening 13-game win streak. A black and white photo plus the player's name, position, height, weight, and 1981 statistics are found on the lid front. The unnumbered, blank-backed lids also contain logos for Burger King, Coca-Cola, and the Major League Baseball Players Association.

		MT	NR MT	EX
Complete Set:		40.00	30.00	16.00
Common Player:		1.00	.70	.40
(1)	Steve Bedrosian	2.00	1.50	.80
(2)	Bruce Benedict	1.00	.70	.40
(3)	Tommy Boggs	1.00	.70	.40
(4)	Brett Butler	2.50	2.00	1.00
(5)	Rick Camp	1.00	.70	.40
(6)	Chris Chambliss	1.00	.70	.40
(7)	Ken Dayley	1.00	.70	.40
(8)	Gene Garber	1.00	.70	.40
(9)	Preston Hanna	1.00	.70	.40
(10)	Terry Harper	1.00	.70	.40
(11)	Bob Horner	2.00	1.50	.80
(12)	Al Hrabosky	1.00	.70	.40
(13)	Glenn Hubbard	1.00	.70	.40
(14)	Randy Johnson	1.00	.70	.40
(15)	Rufino Linares	1.00	.70	.40
(16)	Rick Mahler	1.00	.70	.40
(17)	Larry McWilliams	1.00	.70	.40
(18)	Dale Murphy	12.00	9.00	4.75
(19)	Phil Niekro	5.00	3.75	2.00
(20)	Biff Pocoroba	1.00	.70	.40
(21)	Rafael Ramirez	1.00	.70	.40
(22)	Jerry Royster	1.00	.70	.40
(23)	Ken Smith	1.00	.70	.40
(24)	Bob Walk	1.00	.70	.40
(25)	Claudell Washington	1.00	.70	.40
(26)	Bob Watson	1.50	1.25	.60
(27)	Larry Whisenton	1.00	.70	.40

1982 Burger King Indians

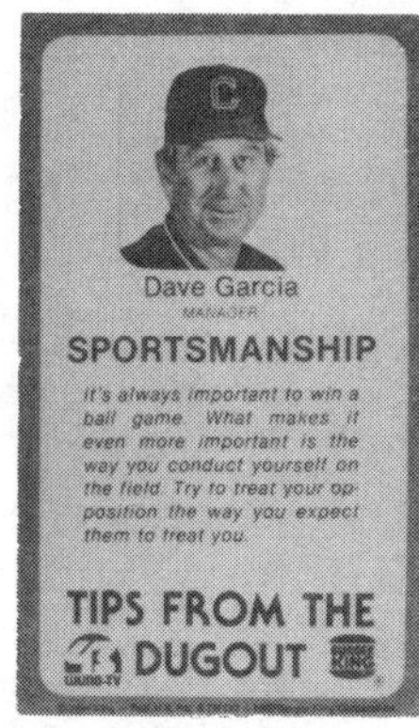

The 1982 Burger King Indians set was sponsored by WUAB-TV and Burger Kings in the Cleveland vicinity. The cards' green borders encompass a large yellow area which contains a black and white photo plus a baseball tip. Manager Dave Garcia and his four coaches provide the baseball hints. The cards, which measure 3" x 5", are unnumbered and blank-backed.

		MT	NR MT	EX
Complete Set:		8.00	6.00	3.25
Common Player:		.70	.50	.30
(1)	Dave Garcia (Be In The Game)	.70	.50	.30
(2)	Dave Garcia (Sportsmanship)	.70	.50	.30
(3)	Johnny Goryl (Rounding The Bases)	.70	.50	.30
(4)	Johnny Goryl (3rd Base Running)	.70	.50	.30
(5)	Tom McCraw (Follow Thru)	.70	.50	.30
(6)	Tom McCraw (Selecting A Bat)	.70	.50	.30
(7)	Tom McCraw (Watch The Ball)	.70	.50	.30
(8)	Mel Queen (Master One Pitch)	.70	.50	.30
(9)	Mel Queen (Warm Up)	.70	.50	.30
(10)	Dennis Sommers (Get Down On A Ground Ball)	.70	.50	.30
(11)	Dennis Sommers (Protect Your Fingers)	.70	.50	.30
(12)	Dennis Sommers (Tagging First Base)	.70	.50	.30

Values quoted in this guide reflect the retail price of a card – the price a collector can expect to pay when buying a card from a dealer. The wholesale price – that which a collector can expect to receive from a dealer when selling cards – will be significantly lower, depending on desirability and condition.

1986 Burger King

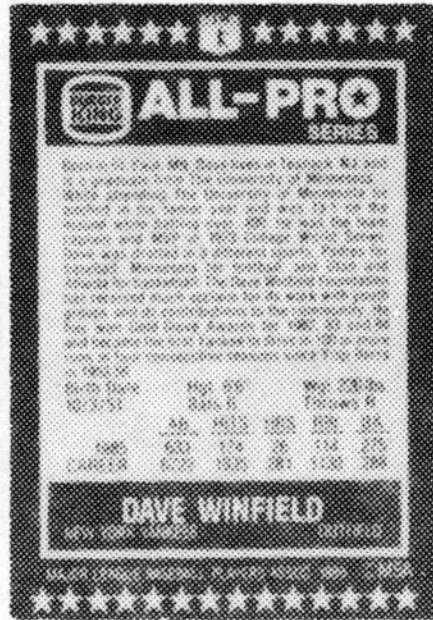

Burger King restaurants in the Pennsylvania and New Jersey areas issued a 20-card set entitled "All-Pro Series". The cards were issued with the purchase of a Whopper sandwich and came in folded panels of two cards each, along with a coupon card. The card fronts feature a color photo and contain the player's name, team and position plus the Burger King logo. Due to a licensing problem, the team insignias on the players' caps were airbrushed away. The card backs feature black print on white stock and contain brief biographical and statistical information.

		MT	NR MT	EX
Complete Panel Set:		12.00	9.00	4.75
Complete Singles Set:		6.00	4.50	2.50
Common Panel:		.75	.60	.30
Common Single Player:		.10	.08	.04
	Panel	1.50	.50	.30
1	Tony Pena	.10	.08	.04
2	Dave Winfield	.50	.40	.20
	Panel	1.50	1.50	.80
3	Fernando Valenzuela	.10	.08	.04
4	Pete Rose	.50	.40	.20
	Panel	2.50	1.25	.60
5	Mike Schmidt	.75	.60	.30
6	Steve Carlton	.50	.40	.20
	Panel	.75	.60	.30
7	Glenn Wilson	.10	.08	.04
8	Jim Rice	.20	.15	.08
	Panel	1.50	1.50	.75
9	Wade Boggs	.75	.60	.30
10	Juan Samuel	.10	.08	.04
	Panel	1.50	1.25	.60
11	Dale Murphy	.40	.30	.15
12	Reggie Jackson	.50	.40	.20
	Panel	1.25	.90	.50
13	Kirk Gibson	.20	.15	.08
14	Eddie Murray	.30	.25	.12
	Panel	2.00	1.25	.60
15	Cal Ripken, Jr.	.75	.60	.30
16	Willie McGee	.10	.08	.04
	Panel	1.50	1.25	.60
17	Dwight Gooden	.25	.20	.10
18	Steve Garvey	.20	.15	.08
	Panel	2.50	2.00	1.00
19	Don Mattingly	.75	.60	.30
20	George Brett	.75	.60	.30

1987 Burger King

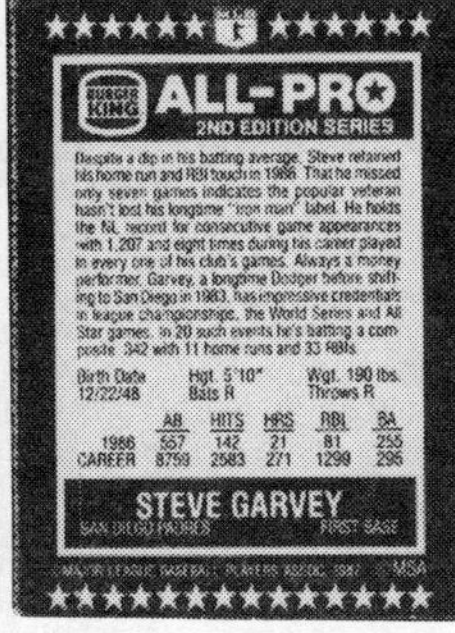

The 1987 Burger King "All-Pro 2nd Edition Series" set was part of a giveaway promotion at participating Burger King restaurants. The set is comprised of 20 players on ten different panels. The cards measure 2-1/2" by 3-1/2" each with a three-card panel (includes a coupon card) measuring 7-5/8" by 3-1/2". The card fronts feature a full-color photo and the Burger King logo surrounded by a blue stars-and-stripes border. The babcks contain black print on white stock and carry a brief player biography and 1986 career statistics. The set was produced by Mike Schecter Associates and, as with many MSA issues, all team insignias were airbrushed away.

		MT	NR MT	EX
Complete Panel Set:		8.00	6.00	3.25
Complete Singles Set:		4.00	3.00	1.50
Common Panel:		.25	.20	.10
Common Single Player:		.05	.04	.02
	Panel	1.25	.90	.50
1	Wade Boggs	.50	.40	.20
2	Gary Carter	.10	.08	.04
	Panel	1.00	.70	.40
3	Will Clark	.50	.40	.20
4	Roger Clemens	.20	.15	.08
	Panel	.50	.40	.20
5	Steve Garvey	.10	.08	.04
6	Ron Darling	.05	.04	.02
	Panel	.25	.20	.10
7	Pedro Guerrero	.05	.04	.02
8	Von Hayes	.05	.04	.02
	Panel	.60	.45	.25
9	Rickey Henderson	.25	.20	.10
10	Keith Hernandez	.05	.04	.02
	Panel	.60	.45	.25
11	Wally Joyner	.20	.15	.08
12	Mike Krukow	.05	.04	.02
	Panel	1.75	1.25	.70
13	Don Mattingly	.50	.40	.20
14	Ozzie Smith	.15	.11	.06
	Panel	.50	.40	.20
15	Tony Pena	.05	.04	.02
16	Jim Rice	.15	.11	.06
	Panel	1.50	1.15	.55
17	Ryne Sandberg	.50	.40	.20
18	Mike Schmidt	.40	.30	.15
	Panel	.50	.60	.30
19	Darryl Strawberry	.10	.08	.04
20	Fernando Valenzuela	.05	.04	.02

1933 Butter Cream

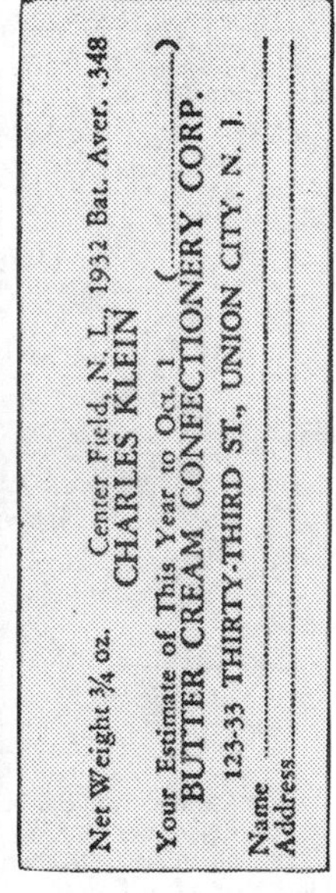

The 1933 Butter Cream set consists of 30 unnumbered, black and white cards which measure 1-1/4" by 3-1/2" in size. The card backs feature a contest sponsored by the Butter Cream Confectionary Corp. in which the collector was to estimate the players' statistics by a specific date. Two different backs are known: 1) Estimate through Sept. 1 and no company address, and 2) Estimate through Oct. 1 with the Butter Cream address. The ACC designation for the set is R306.

		NR MT	EX	VG
Complete Set:		13000.	6500.	3900.
Common Player:		300.00	150.00	90.00
(1)	Earl Averill	475.00	237.00	142.00
(2)	Ed. Brandt	300.00	150.00	90.00
(3)	Guy T. Bush	300.00	150.00	90.00
(4)	Gordon Cochrane	525.00	262.00	157.00
(5)	Joe Cronin	525.00	262.00	157.00
(6)	George Earnshaw	300.00	150.00	90.00
(7)	Wesley Ferrell	300.00	150.00	90.00
(8)	"Jimmy" E. Foxx	800.00	400.00	240.00
(9)	Frank C. Frisch	525.00	262.00	157.00
(10)	Charles M. Gelbert	300.00	150.00	90.00
(11)	"Lefty" Robert M. Grove	600.00	300.00	180.00
(12)	Leo Charles Hartnett	475.00	237.00	142.00
(13)	"Babe" Herman	300.00	150.00	90.00
(14)	Charles Klein	475.00	237.00	142.00
(15)	Ray Kremer	300.00	150.00	90.00
(16)	Fred C. Linstrom (Lindstrom)	475.00	237.00	142.00
(17)	Ted A. Lyons	475.00	237.00	142.00
(18)	"Pepper" John L. Martin	300.00	150.00	90.00
(19)	Robert O'Farrell	300.00	150.00	90.00
(20)	Ed. A. Rommel	300.00	150.00	90.00
(21)	Charles Root	300.00	150.00	90.00
(22)	Harold "Muddy" Ruel (Herold)	300.00	150.00	90.00
(23)	Babe Ruth	3000.	1500.	900.00
(24)	"Al" Simmons	475.00	237.00	142.00
(25)	"Bill" Terry	525.00	262.00	157.00
(26)	George E. Uhle	300.00	150.00	90.00
(27)	Lloyd J. Waner	475.00	237.00	142.00
(28)	Paul G. Waner	475.00	237.00	142.00
(29)	"Hack" Wilson	475.00	237.00	142.00
(30)	Glen. Wright	300.00	150.00	90.00

1934 Butterfinger (R310)

Cards in this 65-card set were available as a premium from Butterfinger and other candy products. The unnumbered cards measure approximately 7-3/4" by 9-3/4" and the heavy cardboard variety carry advertising for Butterfinger. The black-and-white cards feature a player photo with facsimile autograph surrounded by an off-white border. The cards are found on either paper or heavy cardboard stock, with the cardboard versions commanding a price about double that listed here.

		NR MT	EX	VG
Complete Set:		2500.	1000.	600.00
Common Player:		25.00	12.50	7.50
1	Earl Averill	50.00	25.00	15.00
2	Richard Bartell	25.00	12.50	7.50
3	Larry Benton	25.00	12.50	7.50
4	Walter Berger	25.00	12.50	7.50
5	Jim Bottomley	50.00	25.00	15.00
6	Ralph Boyle	25.00	12.50	7.50
7	Tex Carleton	25.00	12.50	7.50
8	Owen T. Carroll	25.00	12.50	7.50
9	Ben Chapman	25.00	12.50	7.50
10	Gordon "Mickey" Cochrane	50.00	25.00	15.00
11	James Collins	25.00	12.50	7.50
12	Joe Cronin	50.00	25.00	15.00
13	Alvin Crowder	25.00	12.50	7.50
14	Dizzy Dean	100.00	50.00	30.00
15	Paul Derringer	25.00	12.50	7.50
16	William Dickey	75.00	37.00	22.00
17	Leo Durocher	50.00	25.00	15.00
18	George Earnshaw	25.00	12.50	7.50
19	Richard Farrell	50.00	25.00	15.00
20	Lew Fonseca	25.00	12.50	7.50
21a	Jimmy Fox (name incorrect)	85.00	42.00	25.00
21b	Jimmy Foxx (name correct)	85.00	42.00	25.00
22	Benny Frey	25.00	12.50	7.50
23	Frankie Frisch	50.00	25.00	15.00
24	Lou Gehrig	335.00	167.00	100.00
25	Charles Gehringer	50.00	25.00	15.00
26	Vernon Gomez	50.00	25.00	15.00
27	Ray Grabowski	25.00	12.50	7.50
28	Robert Grove	50.00	25.00	15.00
29	George "Mule" Haas	25.00	12.50	7.50
30	"Chick" Hafey	50.00	25.00	15.00
31	Stanley Harris	50.00	25.00	15.00
32	J. Francis Hogan	25.00	12.50	7.50
33	Ed Holley	25.00	12.50	7.50
34	Rogers Hornsby	85.00	42.00	25.00
35	Waite Hoyt	50.00	25.00	15.00
36	Walter Johnson	95.00	47.00	28.00
37	Jim Jordan	25.00	12.50	7.50
38	Joe Kuhel	25.00	12.50	7.50
39	Hal Lee	25.00	12.50	7.50
40	Gus Mancuso	25.00	12.50	7.50
41	Henry Manush	50.00	25.00	15.00
42	Fred Marberry	25.00	12.50	7.50
43	Pepper Martin	35.00	17.50	10.50
44	Oscar Melillo	25.00	12.50	7.50
45	Johnny Moore	25.00	12.50	7.50
46	Joe Morrissey	25.00	12.50	7.50
47	Joe Mowrey	25.00	12.50	7.50
48	Bob O'Farrell	25.00	12.50	7.50
49	Melvin Ott	60.00	30.00	18.00
50	Monte Pearson	25.00	12.50	7.50
51	Carl Reynolds	25.00	12.50	7.50
52	Charles Ruffing	50.00	25.00	15.00
53	Babe Ruth	400.00	200.00	120.00
54	John "Blondy" Ryan	25.00	12.50	7.50
55	Al Simmons	50.00	25.00	15.00
56	Al Spohrer	25.00	12.50	7.50
57	Gus Suhr	25.00	12.50	7.50
58	Steve Swetonic	25.00	12.50	7.50
59	Dazzy Vance	50.00	25.00	15.00
60	Joe Vosmik	25.00	12.50	7.50
61	Lloyd Waner	50.00	25.00	15.00

62	Paul Waner	50.00	25.00	15.00
63	Sam West	25.00	12.50	7.50
64	Earl Whitehill	25.00	12.50	7.50
65	Jimmy Wilson	25.00	12.50	7.50

1985 CBS Radio Game of the Week

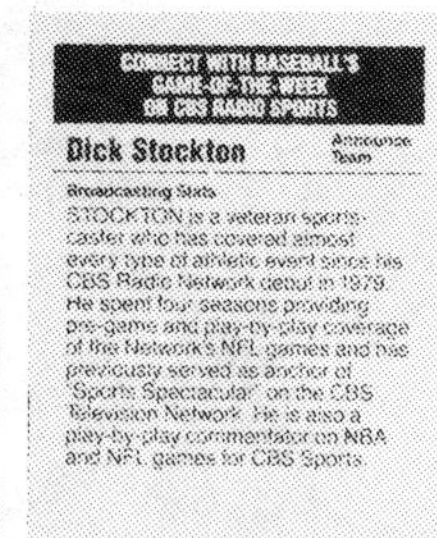

As part of a promotion for its radio Game of the Week broadcasts, CBS issued a six-card set in 1985 picturing network announcers, including former major leaguer Johnny Bench. The cards are the standard 2-1/2" by 3-1/2" and were sent to CBS affiliate stations only. The fronts of the full-color cards picture the announcers in CBS Radio Sports baseball-style uniforms.

		MT	NR MT	EX
Complete Set:		25.00	18.50	10.00
Common Player:		2.00	1.50	.80
(1)	Johnny Bench	10.00	7.50	4.00
(2)	Brent Musburger	5.00	3.75	2.00
(3)	Lindsey Nelson	4.00	3.00	1.50
(4)	John Rooney	2.00	1.50	.80
(5)	Dick Stockton	3.00	2.25	1.25
(6)	Bill White	5.00	3.75	2.00

1986 CBS Radio Game of the Week

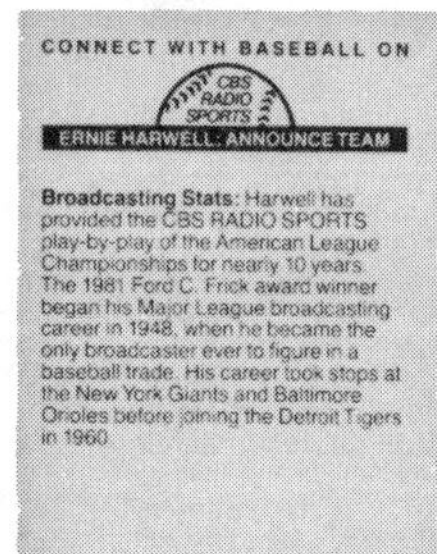

For the second consecutive year, CBS Radio Sports issued a five-card set featuring announcers used by the network for the Game of the Week and post-season broadcasts. The cards, which were included in a custom-designed wrapper, were sent to CBS radio affiliates as part of a promotion for the Game of the Week. The color cards measure 2-1/2" by 3-1/2" in size.

		MT	NR MT	EX
Complete Set:		20.00	15.00	8.00
Common Player:		2.00	1.50	.80
(1)	Sparky Anderson	8.00	6.00	3.25
(2)	Jack Buck	4.00	3.00	1.50
(3)	Howard David	2.00	1.50	.80
(4)	Ernie Harwell	6.00	4.50	2.50
(5)	Ted Robinson	2.00	1.50	.80

1985 Cain's Potato Chips Tigers

This 20-card set commemorating the 1984 World champion Tigers was issued by Cain's Potato Chips in the Michigan area in 1985. The yellow-bordered, unnumbered cards measure 2-3/4" in diameter and feature full-color oval photos inside a diamond. The word "Cain's" appears in the upper left corner, while the player's name appears in the lower left with his position directly below the photo. The words "1984 World Champions" are printed in the upper right corner. The backs include 1984 statistics. The cards were inserted in bags of potato chips.

		MT	NR MT	EX
Complete Set:		28.00	30.00	16.00
Common Player:		1.00	.70	.40
(1)	Doug Bair	1.00	.70	.40
(2)	Juan Berenguer	1.00	.70	.40
(3)	Dave Bergman	1.00	.70	.40
(4)	Tom Brookens	1.00	.70	.40
(5)	Marty Castillo	1.00	.70	.40
(6)	Darrell Evans	1.50	1.25	.60
(7)	Barbaro Garbey	1.00	.70	.40
(8)	Kirk Gibson	2.50	2.00	1.00
(9)	John Grubb	1.00	.70	.40
(10)	Willie Hernandez	1.00	.70	.40
(11)	Larry Herndon	1.00	.70	.40
(12)	Chet Lemon	1.25	.90	.50
(13)	Aurelio Lopez	1.00	.70	.40
(14)	Jack Morris	3.00	2.25	1.25
(15)	Lance Parrish	2.00	1.50	.80
(16)	Dan Petry	1.00	.70	.40
(17)	Bill Scherrer	1.00	.70	.40
(18)	Alan Trammell	5.00	3.75	2.00
(19)	Lou Whitaker	3.50	2.75	1.50
(20)	Milt Wilcox	1.00	.70	.40

1986 Cain's Potato Chips Tigers

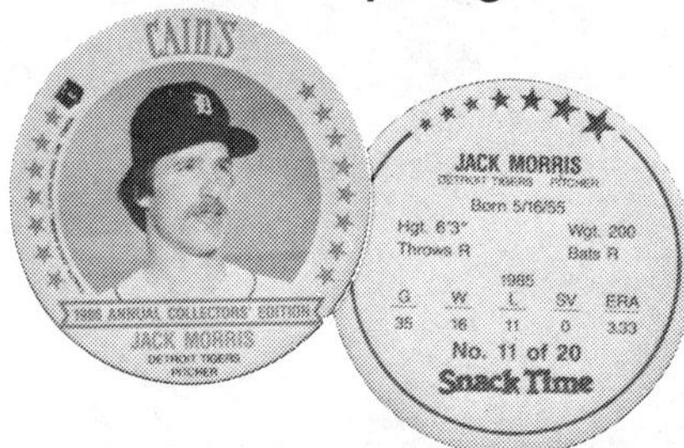

For the second year in a row, player discs of the Detroit Tigers were found in boxes of Cain's Potato Chips sold in the Detroit area. Twenty discs make up the set which is branded as a "1986 Annual Collectors' Edition." The discs, which measure 2-3/4" in diameter, have fronts which contain a color photo plus the player's name, team and position. The Cain's logo and the Major League Baseball Players Association's logo also appear. The backs, which display black print on white stock, contain player information plus the card number.

		MT	NR MT	EX
Complete Set:		27.00	20.00	11.00
Common Player:		1.00	.70	.40
1	Tom Brookens	1.00	.70	.40
2	Willie Hernandez	1.00	.70	.40
3	Dave Bergman	1.00	.70	.40
4	Lou Whitaker	3.50	2.75	1.50
5	Dave LaPoint	1.00	.70	.40
6	Lance Parrish	2.00	1.50	.80
7	Randy O'Neal	1.00	.70	.40
8	Nelson Simmons	1.00	.70	.40
9	Larry Herndon	1.00	.70	.40
10	Doug Flynn	1.00	.70	.40
11	Jack Morris	2.00	1.50	.80
12	Dan Petry	1.00	.70	.40
13	Walt Terrell	1.00	.70	.40
14	Chet Lemon	1.25	.90	.50
15	Frank Tanana	1.25	.90	.50
16	Kirk Gibson	2.50	2.00	1.00
17	Darrell Evans	1.50	1.25	.60
18	Dave Collins	1.00	.70	.40
19	John Grubb	1.00	.70	.40
20	Alan Trammell	4.00	3.00	1.50

A player's name in italic type indicates a rookie card. An (FC) indicates a player's first card for that particular card company.

1987 Cain's Potato Chips Tigers

Player discs of the Detroit Tigers were inserted in boxes of Cain's Potato Chips for the third consecutive year. The 1987 edition is made up of 20 round cards, each measuring 2-3/4" in diameter. The discs, which were packaged in a cellophane wrapper, feature a full-color photo surrounded by an orange border. The backs are printed in red on white stock. The set was produced by Mike Schecter and Associates.

		MT	NR MT	EX
Complete Set:		16.00	12.00	6.50
Common Player:		.60	.45	.25
1	Tom Brookens	.60	.45	.25
2	Darnell Coles	.60	.45	.25
3	Mike Heath	.60	.45	.25
4	Dave Bergman	.60	.45	.25
5	Dwight Lowry	.60	.45	.25
6	Darrell Evans	.90	.70	.35
7	Alan Trammell	2.75	2.00	1.00
8	Lou Whitaker	2.00	1.50	.80
9	Kirk Gibson	2.00	1.50	.80
10	Chet Lemon	.75	.60	.30
11	Larry Herndon	.60	.45	.25
12	John Grubb	.60	.45	.25
13	Willie Hernandez	.60	.45	.25
14	Jack Morris	1.50	1.25	.60
15	Dan Petry	.60	.45	.25
16	Walt Terrell	.60	.45	.25
17	Mark Thurmond	.60	.45	.25
18	Pat Sheridan	.60	.45	.25
19	Eric King	.60	.45	.25
20	Frank Tanana	.75	.60	.30

1950 Callahan Hall of Fame

These cards, which feature drawings of Hall of Famers, were produced from 1950 through 1956 and sold by the Baseball Hall of Fame in Cooperstown. The cards measure 1-3/4" by 2-1/2" and include a detailed player biography on the back. When introduced in 1950 the set included all members of the Hall of Fame up to that time, and then new cards were added each year as more players were elected. therefore, cards of players appearing in all previous editions are lesser in value than those players who appeared in just one or two years. When the set was discontinued in 1956 it consisted of 82 cards, which is now considered a complete set. The cards are not numbered and are listed here alphabetically.

		NR MT	EX	VG
Complete Set:		800.00	400.00	240.00
Common Player:		4.00	2.00	1.25
(1)	Grover Alexander	8.00	4.00	2.50
(2)	"Cap" Anson	8.00	4.00	2.50
(3)	J. Franklin "Home Run" Baker	9.25	4.75	2.75
(4)	Edward G. Barrow	9.25	4.75	2.75
(5a)	Charles "Chief" Bender (different biography)	9.25	4.75	2.75
(5b)	Charles "Chief" Bender (different biography)	9.25	4.75	2.75
(6)	Roger Bresnahan	4.00	2.00	1.25
(7)	Dan Brouthers	4.00	2.00	1.25
(8)	Mordecai Brown	4.00	2.00	1.25

(9)	Morgan G. Bulkeley	4.00	2.00	1.25
(10)	Jesse Burkett	4.00	2.00	1.25
(11)	Alexander Cartwright	4.00	2.00	1.25
(12)	Henry Chadwick	4.00	2.00	1.25
(13)	Frank Chance	4.00	2.00	1.25
(14)	Albert B. Chandler	40.00	20.00	12.00
(15)	Jack Chesbro	4.00	2.00	1.25
(16)	Fred Clarke	4.00	2.00	1.25
(17)	Ty Cobb	65.00	32.00	19.50
(18a)	Mickey Cochran (name incorrect)	20.00	10.00	6.00
(18b)	Mickey Cochrane (name correct)	8.00	4.00	2.50
(19a)	Eddie Collins (different biography)	8.00	4.00	2.50
(19b)	Eddie Collins (different biography)	8.00	4.00	2.50
(20)	Jimmie Collins	4.00	2.00	1.25
(21)	Charles A. Comiskey	4.00	2.00	1.25
(22)	Tom Connolly	9.25	4.75	2.75
(23)	"Candy" Cummings	4.00	2.00	1.25
(24)	Dizzy Dean	40.00	20.00	12.00
(25)	Ed Delahanty	4.00	2.00	1.25
(26a)	Bill Dickey (different biography)	40.00	20.00	12.00
(26b)	Bill Dickey (different biography)	40.00	20.00	12.00
(27)	Joe DiMaggio	135.00	67.00	40.00
(28)	Hugh Duffy	4.00	2.00	1.25
(29)	Johnny Evers	4.00	2.00	1.25
(30)	Buck Ewing	4.00	2.00	1.25
(31)	Jimmie Foxx	9.25	4.75	2.75
(32)	Frank Frisch	4.00	2.00	1.25
(33)	Lou Gehrig	65.00	32.00	19.50
(34)	Charles Gehringer	4.00	2.00	1.25
(35)	Clark Griffith	4.00	2.00	1.25
(36)	Lefty Grove	8.00	4.00	2.50
(37)	Leo "Gabby" Hartnett	9.25	4.75	2.75
(38)	Harry Heilmann	4.00	2.00	1.25
(39)	Rogers Hornsby	9.25	4.75	2.75
(40)	Carl Hubbell	8.00	4.00	2.50
(41)	Hughey Jennings	4.00	2.00	1.25
(42)	Ban Johnson	4.00	2.00	1.25
(43)	Walter Johnson	9.25	4.75	2.75
(44)	Willie Keeler	4.00	2.00	1.25
(45)	Mike Kelly	4.00	2.00	1.25
(46)	Bill Klem	9.25	4.75	2.75
(47)	Napoleon Lajoie	4.00	2.00	1.25
(48)	Kenesaw M. Landis	4.00	2.00	1.25
(49)	Ted Lyons	9.25	4.75	2.75
(50)	Connie Mack	9.25	4.75	2.75
(51)	Walter Maranville	9.25	4.75	2.75
(52)	Christy Mathewson	9.25	4.75	2.75
(53)	Tommy McCarthy	4.00	2.00	1.25
(54)	Joe McGinnity	4.00	2.00	1.25
(55)	John McGraw	8.00	4.00	2.50
(56)	Charles Nichols	4.00	2.00	1.25
(57)	Jim O'Rourke	4.00	2.00	1.25
(58)	Mel Ott	8.00	4.00	2.50
(59)	Herb Pennock	4.00	2.00	1.25
(60)	Eddie Plank	4.00	2.00	1.25
(61)	Charles Radbourne	4.00	2.00	1.25
(62)	Wilbert Robinson	4.00	2.00	1.25
(63)	Babe Ruth	100.00	50.00	30.00
(64)	Ray "Cracker" Schalk	9.25	4.75	2.75
(65)	Al Simmons	9.25	4.75	2.75
(66a)	George Sisler (different biography)	4.00	2.00	1.25
(66b)	George Sisler (different biography)	4.00	2.00	1.25
(67)	A. G. Spalding	4.00	2.00	1.25
(68)	Tris Speaker	4.00	2.00	1.25
(69)	Bill Terry	9.25	4.75	2.75
(70)	Joe Tinker	4.00	2.00	1.25
(71)	"Pie" Traynor	4.00	2.00	1.25
(72)	Clarence A. "Dizzy" Vance	9.25	4.75	2.75
(73)	Rube Waddell	4.00	2.00	1.25
(74)	Hans Wagner	40.00	20.00	12.00
(75)	Bobby Wallace	9.25	4.75	2.75
(76)	Ed Walsh	4.00	2.00	1.25
(77)	Paul Waner	8.00	4.00	2.50
(78)	George Wright	4.00	2.00	1.25
(79)	Harry Wright	9.25	4.75	2.75
(80)	Cy Young	9.25	4.75	2.75
(----a)	Museum Exterior View (different biography)	9.25	4.75	2.75
(----b)	Museum Exterior View (different biography)	9.25	4.75	2.75
(----a)	Museum Interior View (different biography)	9.25	4.75	2.75
(----b)	Museum Interior View (different biography)	9.25	4.75	2.75

1994 Capital Cards 1969 Mets Postcards

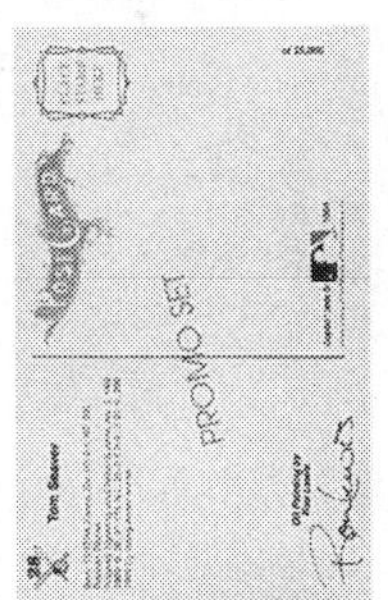

Capital Cards, produced a 32-card postcard set of members of the 1969 World Champion New York Mets from Ron Lewis paintings, limited to 25,000 sets. Capital Cards also produced 5,000 uncut sheets that are individually numbered and carried a suggested retail price of $99.95. The boxed postcard set retailed for $39.95. The cards could also be purchased with autographs.

		NR MT	EX	VG
Complete Set:		29.00	14.50	8.75
Common Player:		.50	.25	.15
1	Logo Card	.50	.25	.15
2	Gil Hodges	3.00	1.50	.90
3	Rube Walker	.50	.25	.15
4	Yogi Berra	4.00	2.00	1.25
5	Joe Pignatano	.50	.25	.15
6	Ed Yost	.50	.25	.15
7	Tommie Agee	.50	.25	.15
8	Ken Boswell	.50	.25	.15
9	Don Cardwell	.50	.25	.15
10	Ed Charles	.50	.25	.15
11	Donn Clendenon	.50	.25	.15
12	Jack DiLauro	.50	.25	.15
13	Duffy Dyer	.50	.25	.15
14	Wayne Garrett	.50	.25	.15
15	Rod Gaspar	.50	.25	.15
16	Gary Gentry	.50	.25	.15
17	Jerry Grote	.50	.25	.15
18	Bud Harrelson	.75	.40	.25
19	Cleon Jones	.90	.45	.25
20	Cal Koonce	.50	.25	.15
21	Jerry Koosman	.90	.45	.25
22	Ed Kranepool	.90	.45	.25
23	J.C. Martin	.50	.25	.15
24	Jim McAndrew	.50	.25	.15
25	Tug McGraw	.90	.45	.25
26	Bob Pfeil	.50	.25	.15
27	Nolan Ryan	6.00	3.00	1.75
28	Tom Seaver	4.00	2.00	1.25
29	Art Shamsky	.50	.25	.15
30	Ron Swoboda	.75	.40	.25
31	Ron Taylor	.50	.25	.15
32	Al Weis	.50	.25	.15

1989 Cap'n Crunch

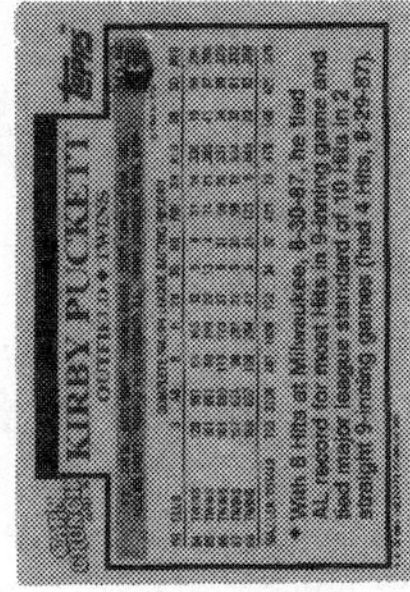

This 22-card set was produced by Topps for Cap'n Crunch cereal boxes. Two cards and a stick of gum were included in each cereal box while the offer was active. The fronts of these 2-1/2" by 3-1/2" cards feature red, white and blue borders. The card backs are horizontal and feature lifetime statistics. The set was not offered in any complete set deal.

		MT	NR MT	EX
Complete Set:		11.00	8.25	4.50
Common Player:		.50	.40	.20
1	Jose Canseco	.80	.60	.30
2	Kirk Gibson	.50	.40	.20
3	Orel Hershiser	.60	.45	.25
4	Frank Viola	.50	.40	.20
5	Tony Gwynn	.60	.45	.25
6	Cal Ripken	1.00	.70	.40
7	Darryl Strawberry	.60	.45	.25
8	Don Mattingly	.80	.60	.30
9	George Brett	.90	.70	.35
10	Andre Dawson	.60	.45	.25
11	Dale Murphy	.60	.45	.25
12	Alan Trammell	.60	.45	.25
13	Eric Davis	.60	.45	.25
14	Jack Clark	.50	.40	.20
15	Eddie Murray	.60	.45	.25
16	Mike Schmidt	1.00	.70	.40
17	Dwight Gooden	.60	.45	.25
18	Roger Clemens	.60	.45	.25
19	Will Clark	.70	.50	.30
20	Kirby Puckett	.70	.50	.30
21	Robin Yount	.90	.70	.35
22	Mark McGwire	.70	.50	.30

1955 Carling Beer Cleveland Indians

Apparently the first of a line of premium photos which extended into the early 1960s. Measuring 8-1/2" x 12" and printed in black-and-white on semi-gloss thin card stock, these photocards are blank-backed. The 1955 Carling photos are identifiable from the 1956 issue, with which they share a DBL prefix to the card number in the lower-right corner, by the phrase "Great Champions" appearing just under the player photo. It is unknown whether other 1955 Carlings may yet surface.

96A	Ralph Kiner	15.00	7.50	4.50
96B	Larry Doby	10.00	5.00	3.00

1956 Carling Beer Cleveland Indians

This set was sponsored by Carling Black Label Beer. The oversized (8-1/2" x 12") cards feature black-and-white posed photos with the player's name in a white strip and a Carling ad at the bottom of the card front. Backs are blank. Like the two cards known to have been issued in 1955, the 1956 set carries a DBL 96 series indication in the lower-right corner and lists brewery locations as Cleveland, St. Louis and Belleville, Ill. Unlike the '55 photocards, however, the first line under the player photo on the 1956 issue is "Premium Quality". Cards numbered DBL 96I and DBL 96J are unknown.

		NR MT	EX	VG
Complete Set (10):		75.00	37.00	22.00
Common Player:		5.00	2.50	1.50
96A	Al Smith	5.00	2.50	1.50
96B	Herb Score	10.00	5.00	3.00
96C	Al Rosen	7.00	3.50	2.00
96D	Mike Garcia	5.00	2.50	1.50
96E	Early Wynn	10.00	5.00	3.00
96F	Bob Feller	20.00	10.00	6.00
96G	Jim Hegan	5.00	2.50	1.50
96H	George Strickland	5.00	2.50	1.50
96K	Bob Lemon	10.00	5.00	3.00
96L	Art Houtteman	5.00	2.50	1.50

1957 Carling Beer Cleveland Indians

The fact that Kerby Farrell managed the Indians only in 1957 pinpoints the year of issue for those Carling Beer photocards which carry a DBL 179 series number in the lower-right corner. Following the black-and-white, blank-backed 8-1/2" x 12" format of earlier issues, the 1957 Carlings list on the bottom line breweries at Cleveland; Frankenmuth, Mich.; Natick, Mass., and, Belleville, Ill. Cards numbered DBL 179I and DBL 179J are currently unknown.

		NR MT	EX	VG
Complete Set (10):		75.00	37.00	22.00
Common Player:		5.00	2.50	1.50
179A	Vic Wertz	5.00	2.50	1.50
179B	Early Wynn	9.00	4.50	2.75
179C	Herb Score	7.50	3.75	2.25
179D	Bob Lemon	9.00	4.50	2.75
179E	Ray Narleski	5.00	2.50	1.50

179F	Jim Hegan	5.00	2.50	1.50
179G	Bob Avila	7.50	3.75	2.25
179H	Al Smith	5.00	2.50	1.50
179K	Kerby Farrell	5.00	2.50	1.50
179L	Rocky Colavito	25.00	12.50	7.50

1958 Carling Beer Cleveland Indians

Identical in format to earlier issues, the 1958 premium photos can be distinguished by the omission of the St. Louis address on the bottom line of type and the addition of Frankenmuth, Mich., and Natic, Mass., addresses. Cards in the 1958 series have numbers in the lower-right corner which begin with a DBL 2 or DBL 217 prefix.

		NR MT	EX	VG
Complete Set (10):		60.00	30.00	18.00
Common Player:		5.00	2.50	1.50
2	Vic Wertz	5.00	2.50	1.50
217	Minnie Minoso	9.00	4.50	2.75
217B	Gene Woodling	7.50	3.75	2.25
217C	Russ Nixon	5.00	2.50	1.50
217D	Bob Lemon	10.00	5.00	3.00
217E	Bobby Bragan	5.00	2.50	1.50
217F	Cal McLish	5.00	2.50	1.50
217G	Rocky Colavito	12.00	6.00	3.50
217H	Herb Score	9.00	4.50	2.75
217J	Chico Carrasquel	5.00	2.50	1.50

1959 Carling Beer Cleveland Indians

The appearance of Billy Martin among Carling photocards labeled with a DBL 266 prefix fixes the year of issue to 1959, the fiery second baseman's only year with the Tribe. Once again the 8-1/2" x 12" black-and-white, blank-backed cards follow the format of previous issues. Breweries listed on the bottom of the 1959 Carlings are Cleveland; Atlanta; Frankenmuth, Mich.; Natick, Mass.; Belleville, Ill., and, Tacoma, Wash.

		NR MT	EX	VG
Complete Set (6):		50.00	25.00	15.00
Common Player:		5.00	2.50	1.50
266A	Vic Power	6.00	3.00	1.75
266B	Minnie Minoso	9.00	4.50	2.75
266C	Herb Score	9.00	4.50	2.75
266D	Rocky Colavito	12.00	6.00	3.50
266E	Jimmy Piersall	9.00	4.50	2.75
266F	Billy Martin	15.00	7.50	4.50

1961 Carling Beer Cleveland Indians

Totally different player selection and the use of an LB prefix to the number in the lower-right corner define the 1961 issue from Carling Beer. Otherwise the photocards share the same 8-1/2" x 12" black-and-white format with earlier issues. The blank-backed cards of the 1961 issue list only a single brewery, Cleveland, at the bottom of the ad portion of the issues. The checklist here is arranged alphabetically. card. Cards numbered LB 420I and LB420J are unknown.

		NR MT	EX	VG
Complete Set (10):		48.00	24.00	14.00
Common Player:		5.00	2.50	1.50
420A	Jimmy Piersall	8.00	4.00	2.50
420B	Willie Kirkland	5.00	2.50	1.50
420C	Johnny Antonelli	5.00	2.50	1.50
420D	John Romano	5.00	2.50	1.50
420E	Woodie Held	5.00	2.50	1.50
420F	Tito Francona	5.00	2.50	1.50
420G	Jim Perry	7.50	3.75	2.25
420H	Bubba Phillips	5.00	2.50	1.50
420K	John Temple	5.00	2.50	1.50
420L	Vic Power	5.00	2.50	1.50

1992 Carl's Jr. Padres

For the fifth consecutive year the San Diego Padres issued a card set in conjunction with the Jr. Padres program. Carl's Jr., a fast food chain, began sponsoring the set in 1991. The set contains 25 cards and was available in either nine-card perforated sheets or precut. At 2-9/16" x 3-9/16" the cards are slightly larger than current standard. Player photos feature an All-Star Game logo in the lower-right corner. On the white border, the player's name and position are printed in dark blue beneath the photo. The team name is in light brown above the photo. On back, the player's stats, career highlights and biographical data are printed in dark blue. The unnumbered cards are checklisted here in alphabetical order.

		MT	NR MT	EX
Complete Set:		8.00	6.00	3.25
Common Player:		.25	.20	.10
(1)	Larry Anderson	.25	.20	.10
(2)	Oscar Azocar	.25	.20	.10
(3)	Andy Benes	.50	.40	.20
(4)	Dann Bilardello	.25	.20	.10
(5)	Jerald Clark	.35	.25	.14
(6)	Tony Fernandez	.35	.25	.14
(7)	Tony Gwynn	.75	.60	.30
(8)	Greg Harris	.25	.20	.10
(9)	Bruce Hurst	.25	.20	.10
(10)	Darrin Jackson	.35	.25	.14
(11)	Craig Lefferts	.25	.20	.10
(12)	Mike Maddux	.25	.20	.10
(13)	Fred McGriff	.75	.60	.30
(14)	Jose Melendez	.25	.20	.10
(15)	Randy Myers	.35	.25	.14
(16)	Greg Riddoch	.25	.20	.10
(17)	Rich Rodriguez	.25	.20	.10
(18)	Benito Santiago	.45	.35	.20
(19)	Gary Sheffield	.45	.35	.20
(20)	Craig Shipley	.35	.25	.14
(21)	Kurt Stillwell	.25	.20	.10
(22)	Tim Teufel	.25	.20	.10
(23)	Kevin Ward	.25	.20	.10
(24)	Ed Whitson	.25	.20	.10
(25)	All-Star logo	.25	.20	.10

1992 Carlson Travel 1982 Brewers

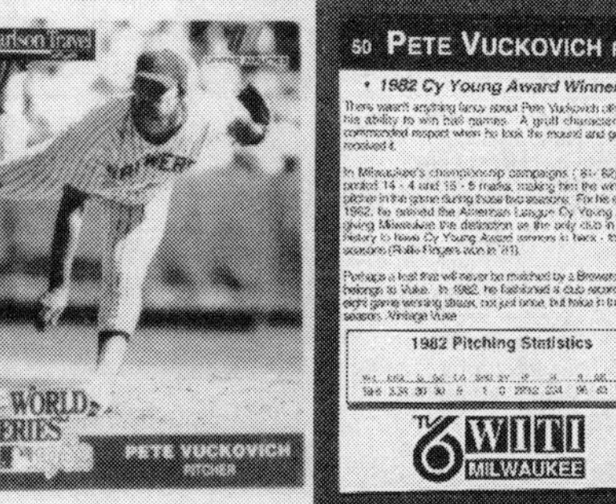

The Milwaukee Brewers' American League Championship season of 1982 was commemorated a decade later with this card set given away at a Brewers promotional date. The cards were sponsored by Carlson Travel and United Airlines, whose logos appear on the front of the cards, along with Channel 6 television, whose logo is on the back. Fronts feature game-action photos of the '82 Brewers, borderless at top and sides. Beneath the photo is a thin gold stripe, then a blue stripe with the player's name and position in white. A red, white and blue 1982 World Series logo appears in the lower-left corner. Backs are printed in blue on white, and include 1982 stats and a summary of the player's season. Player cards are numbered by uniform number in the upper-left.

		MT	NR MT	EX
Complete Set (31):		9.00	6.75	3.50
Common Player:		.25	.20	.10
4	Paul Molitor	1.00	.70	.40
5	Ned Yost	.25	.20	.10
7	Don Money	.35	.25	.14
10	Bob McClure	.25	.20	.10
11	Ed Romero	.25	.20	.10
13	Roy Howell	.25	.20	.10
15	Cecil Cooper	.50	.40	.20
16	Marshall Edwards	.25	.20	.10
17	Jim Gantner	.35	.25	.14
19	Robin Yount	2.00	1.50	.80
20	Gorman Thomas	.40	.30	.15
21	Don Sutton	.40	.30	.15
22	Charlie Moore	.25	.20	.10
23	Ted Simmons	.35	.25	.14
24	Ben Ogilvie	.40	.30	.15
27	Pete Ladd	.25	.20	.10
29	Mark Brouhard	.25	.20	.10
30	Moose Haas	.25	.20	.10
32	Harvey Kuenn	.35	.25	.14
33	Doc Medich	.25	.20	.10
34	Rollie Fingers	.75	.60	.30
41	Jim Slaton	.25	.20	.10
46	Jerry Augustine	.25	.20	.10
47	Dwight Bernard	.25	.20	.10
48	Mike Caldwell	.25	.20	.10
50	Pete Vuckovich	.35	.25	.14
----	Coaches (Pat Dobson, Larry Haney, Ron Hansen, Cal McLish, Harry Warner)	.25	.20	.10
----	Team card	.25	.20	.10
----	Bernie Brewer (mascot)	.25	.20	.10
----	Post-season Rally	.25	.20	.10
----	$50 travel coupon	.25	.20	.10

1964 Challenge the Yankees Game

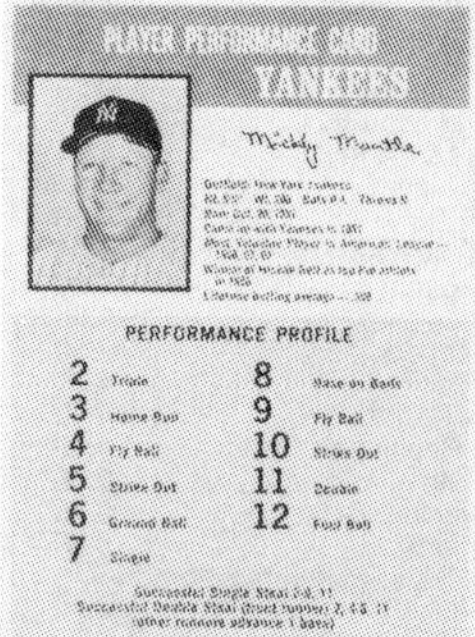

The 50 player cards in this set were part of a boxed dice baseball game produced by Hassenfeld Bros. of Pawtucket, R.I. The player cards are approximately 4" x 5-1/2" and blank-backed. They feature a small black-and-white photo, a facsimile autograph and a few biographical details and stats. Player selection is virtually the same for the games issued in 1964 and 1965, and the only way to distinguish cards from each year is to study the stats. Cards are unnumbered and are checklisted below in alphabetical order.

		NR MT	EX	VG
Complete Boxed Set:		550.00	275.00	165.00
Complete Card Set:		350.00	175.00	105.00
Common Player:		2.00	1.00	.60
(1)	Hank Aaron	50.00	25.00	15.00
(2)	Yogi Berra	30.00	15.00	9.00
(3)	Johnny Blanchard	4.00	2.00	1.25
(4)	Jim Bouton	7.00	3.50	2.00
(5)	Clete Boyer	6.00	3.00	1.75
(6)	Marshall Bridges	2.00	1.00	.60
(7)	Harry Bright	2.00	1.00	.60
(8)	Tom Cheney	2.00	1.00	.60
(9)	Del Crandall	2.00	1.00	.60
(10)	Al Downing	2.00	1.00	.60
(11)	Whitey Ford	15.00	7.50	4.50
(12)	Tito Francona	2.00	1.00	.60
(13)	Jake Gibbs	2.00	1.00	.60
(14)	Pedro Gonzalez	2.00	1.00	.60
(15)	Dick Groat	5.00	2.50	1.50
(16)	Steve Hamilton	2.00	1.00	.60
(17)	Elston Howard	6.00	3.00	1.75
(18)	Al Kaline	20.00	10.00	6.00
(19)	Tony Kubek	9.00	4.50	2.75
(20)	Phil Linz	2.00	1.00	.60
(21)	Hector Lopez	2.00	1.00	.60
(22)	Art Mahaffey	2.00	1.00	.60
(23)	Frank Malzone	2.00	1.00	.60
(24)	Mickey Mantle	100.00	50.00	30.00
(25)	Juan Marichal	12.00	6.00	3.50
(26)	Roger Maris	40.00	20.00	12.00
(27)	Eddie Mathews	15.00	7.50	4.50
(28)	Bill Mazeroski	9.00	4.50	2.75
(29)	Ken McBride	2.00	1.00	.60
(30)	Willie McCovey	12.00	6.00	3.50

(31)	Tom Metcalf	2.00	1.00	.60
(32)	Jim O'Toole	2.00	1.00	.60
(33)	Milt Pappas	2.00	1.00	.60
(34)	Joe Pepitone	6.00	3.00	1.75
(35)	Ron Perranoski	2.00	1.00	.60
(36)	Johnny Podres	9.00	4.50	2.75
(37)	Dick Radatz	2.00	1.00	.60
(38)	Hal Reniff	2.00	1.00	.60
(39)	Bobby Richardson	10.00	5.00	3.00
(40)	Rich Rollins	2.00	1.00	.60
(41)	Ron Santo	6.00	3.00	1.75
(42)	Moose Skowron	8.00	4.00	2.50
(43)	Duke Snider	15.00	7.50	4.50
(44)	Bill Stafford	2.00	1.00	.60
(45)	Ralph Terry	2.00	1.00	.60
(46)	Tom Tresh	4.00	2.00	1.25
(47)	Pete Ward	2.00	1.00	.60
(48)	Carl Warwick	2.00	1.00	.60
(49)	Stan Williams	2.00	1.00	.60
(50)	Carl Yastrzemski	50.00	25.00	15.00

1965 Challenge the Yankees Game

The 48 player cards in this set were part of a boxed dice baseball game produced by Hassenfeld Bros. of Pawtucket, R.I. The player cards are approximately 4" x 5-1/2" and blank-backed. They feature a small black-and-white photo, a facsimile autograph and a few biographical details and stats. Player selection is virtually the same for the games issued in 1964 and 1965, and the only way to distinguish cards from each year is to study the stats. Cards are unnumbered and are checklisted below in alphabetical order.

		NR MT	EX	VG
Complete Boxed Set:		600.00	300.00	180.00
Complete Card Set:		400.00	200.00	120.00
Common Player:		3.00	1.50	.90
(1)	Henry Aaron	45.00	22.00	13.50
(2)	Johnny Blanchard	3.00	1.50	.90
(3)	Jim Bouton	5.00	2.50	1.50
(4)	Clete Boyer	3.00	1.50	.90
(5)	Leon Carmel	3.00	1.50	.90
(6)	Joe Christopher	3.00	1.50	.90
(7)	Vic Davalillo	3.00	1.50	.90
(8)	Al Downing	3.00	1.50	.90
(9)	Whitey Ford	15.00	7.50	4.50
(10)	Bill Freehan	3.00	1.50	.90
(11)	Jim Gentile	3.00	1.50	.90
(12)	Jake Gibbs	3.00	1.50	.90
(13)	Pedro Gonzalez	3.00	1.50	.90
(14)	Dick Groat	5.00	2.50	1.50
(15)	Steve Hamilton	3.00	1.50	.90
(16)	Elston Howard	6.00	3.00	1.75
(17)	Al Kaline	15.00	7.50	4.50
(18)	Tony Kubek	6.00	3.00	1.75
(19)	Phil Linz	3.00	1.50	.90
(20)	Don Lock	3.00	1.50	.90
(21)	Art Mahaffey	3.00	1.50	.90
(22)	Frank Malzone	3.00	1.50	.90
(23)	Mickey Mantle	100.00	50.00	30.00
(24)	Juan Marichal	15.00	7.50	4.50
(25)	Roger Maris	30.00	15.00	9.00
(26)	Eddie Mathews	15.00	7.50	4.50
(27)	Bill Mazeroski	7.50	3.75	2.25
(28)	Ken McBride	3.00	1.50	.90
(29)	Tim McCarver	6.00	3.00	1.75
(30)	Willie McCovey	15.00	7.50	4.50
(31)	Tom Metcalf	3.00	1.50	.90
(32)	Pete Mikkelsen	3.00	1.50	.90
(33)	Jim O'Toole	3.00	1.50	.90
(34)	Milt Pappas	3.00	1.50	.90
(35)	Joe Pepitone	3.00	1.50	.90
(36)	Ron Perranoski	3.00	1.50	.90
(37)	Johnny Podres	7.50	3.75	2.25
(38)	Dick Radatz	3.00	1.50	.90
(39)	Pedro Ramos	3.00	1.50	.90
(40)	Hal Reniff	3.00	1.50	.90
(41)	Bobby Richardson	5.00	2.50	1.50
(42)	Rich Rollins	3.00	1.50	.90
(43)	Ron Santo	6.00	3.00	1.75
(44)	Bill Stafford	3.00	1.50	.90
(45)	Mel Stottlemyre	3.00	1.50	.90
(46)	Tom Tresh	3.00	1.50	.90
(47)	Pete Ward	3.00	1.50	.90
(48)	Carl Yaztrzemski	25.00	12.50	7.50

1987 Champion Phillies

This four card set is interesting in that the players are not identified on the card fronts or backs. The full-color cards, which measure 2-3/4" by 4-5/16", were produced by the Champion Spark Plug Co. as part of a contest held at participating Big A, Car Quest and Pep Boys auto parts stores. Entrants were advised to return the scratch-off coupon portion of the card for a chance to win a Blackbird Racer. Each card contains a scratch-off portion which may have contained an instant prize. Each card can be found with either a Big A, Car Quest or

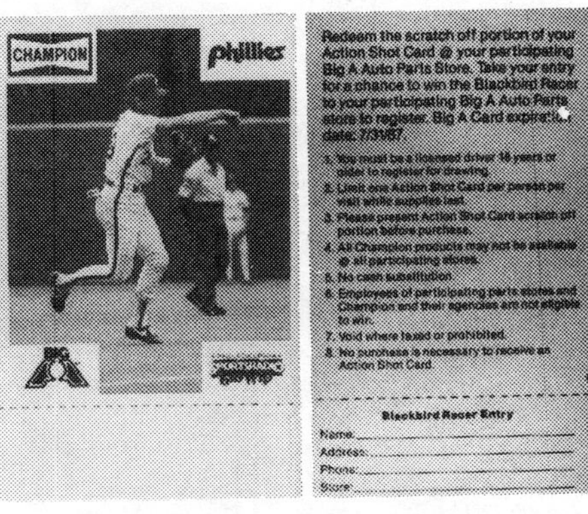

Pep Boys logo in the lower left corner on the card front. The contest was also sponsored in part by the Philadelphia Phillies and radio station WIP.

		MT	NR MT	EX
Complete Set:		15.00	15.00	8.00
Common Player:		1.00	.70	.40
(1)	Von Hayes (glove on knee)	2.00	1.50	.80
(2)	Steve Jeltz (#30 on uniform)	1.00	.70	.40
(3)	Juan Samuel (laying on base)	2.00	1.50	.80
(4)	Mike Schmidt (making throw)	12.00	9.00	4.75

1988 Chef Boyardee

This uncut sheet of 24 cards highlights 12 American and 12 National League players. Full-color player closeup photos are printed beneath a red, white and blue "1988 1st Annual Collector's Edition" header. The player name, team and position appear beneath his photo. Card backs are printed in blue ink on a red background and include biographical information, stats and career highlights including acquisition date and draft date/choice number. The set was produced by American Home Food Products for exclusive distribution via a mail-in offer involving proofs of purchase from the company's Chef Boyardee products.

		MT	NR MT	EX
Complete Uncut Sheet:		25.00	18.50	10.00
Complete Singles Set:		18.00	15.00	8.00
Common Single Player:		.50	.40	.20
1	Mark McGwire	1.00	.70	.40
2	Eric Davis	.75	.60	.30
3	Jack Morris	.50	.40	.20
4	George Bell	.60	.45	.25
5	Ozzie Smith	.75	.60	.30
6	Tony Gwynn	.75	.60	.30
7	Cal Ripken, Jr.	1.50	1.25	.60
8	Todd Worrell	.50	.40	.20
9	Larry Parrish	.50	.40	.20
10	Gary Carter	.70	.50	.30
11	Ryne Sandberg	1.50	1.25	.60
12	Keith Hernandez	.60	.45	.25
13	Kirby Puckett	1.00	.70	.40
14	Mike Schmidt	1.50	1.25	.60
15	Frank Viola	.50	.40	.20
16	Don Mattingly	1.50	1.25	.60
17	Dale Murphy	.70	.50	.30
18a	Andre Dawson (1987 team is Expos)	.75	.60	.30
18b	Andre Dawson (1987 team is Cubs)	.75	.60	.30
19	Mike Scott	.50	.40	.20
20	Rickey Henderson	1.00	.70	.40
21	Jim Rice	.75	.60	.30
22	Wade Boggs	1.00	.70	.40
23	Roger Clemens	1.00	.70	.40
24	Fernando Valenzuela	.60	.45	.25

A card number in parentheses () indicates the set is unnumbered.

1994 Churchs Chicken Hometown Stars

Produced by Pinnacle Brands for distribution in the fried chicken restaurant chain, the cards were distributed in packs of four with the purchase of a nine-piece family meal or were sold separately for 69 cents. Each foil pack contained three regular cards and one card with gold foil instead of regular printing on the player's name and "Hometown Stars." Every fourth pack contains one of 10 "Show Stoppers" Dufex-process chase cards. In standard 2-1/2" x 3-1/2", the cards featured full-bleed front action photos with the Churchs logo at lower-left and the player's name at lower-right. "Hometown Stars" is printed vertically at top-left. Backs have a portrait photo at left, a career summary and 1993 and career stats. Because the cards were licensed by the Major League Baseball Players Association, but not Major League Baseball, both the front and the back photos on each card have had the uniform logos airbrushed away.

		MT	NR MT	EX
Complete Set (28):		10.00	7.50	4.00
Complete Set (Gold) (28):		18.00	13.50	7.25
Common Player:		.25	.20	.10
Common Player (Gold):		.30	.25	.12
1	Brian McRae	.25	.20	.10
1a	Brian McRae (gold)	.30	.25	.12
2	Dwight Gooden	.35	.25	.14
2a	Dwight Gooden (gold)	.40	.30	.15
3	Ruben Sierra	.35	.25	.14
3a	Ruben Sierra (gold)	.40	.30	.15
4	Greg Maddux	.35	.25	.14
4a	Greg Maddux (gold)	.40	.30	.15
5	Kirby Puckett	.75	.60	.30
5a	Kirby Puckett (gold)	1.25	.90	.50
6	Jeff Bagwell	.35	.25	.14
6a	Jeff Bagwell (gold)	.40	.30	.15
7	Cal Ripken, Jr.	1.50	1.25	.60
7a	Cal Ripken, Jr. (gold)	2.00	1.50	.80
8	Lenny Dykstra	.35	.25	.14
8a	Lenny Dykstra (gold)	.40	.30	.15
9	Tim Salmon	1.25	.90	.50
9a	Tim Salmon (gold)	1.75	1.25	.70
10	Matt Williams	.35	.25	.14
10a	Matt Williams (gold)	.40	.30	.15
11	Roberto Alomar	.50	.40	.20
11a	Roberto Alomar (gold)	.75	.60	.30
12	Barry Larkin	.25	.20	.10
12a	Barry Larkin (gold)	.30	.25	.12
13	Roger Clemens	.35	.25	.14
13a	Roger Clemens (gold)	.40	.30	.15
14	Mike Piazza	1.00	.70	.40
14a	Mike Piazza (gold)	1.75	1.25	.70
15	Travis Fryman	.25	.20	.10
15a	Travis Fryman (gold)	.30	.25	.12
16	Ryne Sandberg	1.50	1.25	.60
16a	Ryne Sandberg (gold)	2.00	1.50	.80
17	Robin Ventura	.35	.25	.14
17a	Robin Ventura (gold)	.40	.30	.15
18	Gary Sheffield	.35	.25	.14
18a	Gary Sheffield (gold)	.40	.30	.15
19	Carlos Baerga	.50	.40	.20
19a	Carlos Baerga (gold)	.75	.60	.30
20	Jay Bell	.25	.20	.10
20a	Jay Bell (gold)	.30	.25	.12
21	Edgar Martinez	.25	.20	.10
21a	Edgar Martinez (gold)	.30	.25	.12
22	Phil Plantier	.25	.20	.10
22a	Phil Plantier (gold)	.30	.25	.12
23	Danny Tartabull	.25	.20	.10
23a	Danny Tartabull (gold)	.30	.25	.12
24	Marquis Grissom	.25	.20	.10
24a	Marquis Grissom (gold)	.30	.25	.12
25	Robin Yount	.75	.60	.30
25a	Robin Yount (gold)	1.00	.70	.40
26	Ozzie Smith	.50	.40	.20
26a	Ozzie Smith (gold)	.75	.60	.30
27	Ivan Rodriguez	.35	.25	.14
27a	Ivan Rodriguez (gold)	.40	.30	.15
28	Dante Bichette	.35	.25	.14
28a	Dante Bichette (gold)	.40	.30	.15

A player's name in italic type indicates a rookie card. An (FC) indicates a player's first card for that particular card company.

1994 Churchs Chicken Show Stoppers

Ten of baseball's top home-run hitters are featured in this insert set. Found approximately once every four packs in the four-card packs distributed by the fried chicken chain, the cards were produced by Pinnacle Brands using its foil-printing Dufex process. A player action photo is depicted inside a home-plate shaped frame at right. "Show Stoppers" is printed vertically at left in red and yellow tones. The background merges from green at left to purple at right, with the player's name in black in a yellow-to-red rainbow effect box beneath the photo. The Churchs logo is at bottom-left. On back is a portrait photo in a light blue box. There is a description of the player's home run prowess along with gold boxes showing his 1993 homers, slugging percentage and at bat/home run ratio. The border mirrors the front's green-to-purple effect. Because the cards are not licensed by Major League Baseball, the uniform logos have been removed from both the front and back photos.

		MT	NR MT	EX
Complete Set (10):		50.00	37.00	20.00
Common Player:		2.50	2.00	1.00
1	Juan Gonzalez	7.00	5.25	2.75
2	Barry Bonds	7.00	5.25	2.75
3	Ken Griffey, Jr.	9.00	6.75	3.50
4	David Justice	5.50	4.00	2.25
5	Frank Thomas	9.00	6.75	3.50
6	Fred McGriff	3.00	2.25	1.25
7	Albert Belle	3.00	2.25	1.25
8	Joe Carter	2.25	1.65	.90
9	Cecil Fielder	3.00	2.25	1.25
10	Mickey Tettleton	2.25	1.65	.90

1985 CIGNA Phillies

This 16-card set was sponsored by the CIGNA Corporation. Members of the Philadelphia Phillies are featured. The oversized cards feature full-color action photos on the front and player information and a safety tip on the card back.

		MT	NR MT	EX
Complete Set:		6.00	4.50	2.50
Common Player:		.20	.15	.08
1	Juan Samuel	.30	.25	.12
2	Von Hayes	.30	.25	.12
3	Ozzie Virgil	.20	.15	.08
4	Mike Schmidt	2.50	2.00	1.00
5	Greg Gross	.20	.15	.08
6	Tim Corcoran	.20	.15	.08
7	Jerry Koosman	.30	.25	.12
8	Jeff Stone	.20	.15	.08
9	Glenn Wilson	.20	.15	.08
10	Steve Jeltz	.20	.15	.08
11	Garry Maddox	.25	.20	.10
12	Steve Carlton	2.00	1.50	.80
13	John Denny	.20	.15	.08
14	Kevin Gross	.20	.15	.08
15	Shane Rawley	.20	.15	.08
16	Charlie Hudson	.20	.15	.08

1986 CIGNA Phillies

Styled like the 1985 issue, CIGNA once again released a 16-card set featuring the Philadelphia Phillies. The cards are numbered on the back.

		MT	NR MT	EX
Complete Set:		5.00	3.75	2.00
Common Player:		.20	.15	.08
1	Juan Samuel	.30	.25	.12
2	Don Carman	.20	.15	.08
3	Von Hayes	.30	.25	.12
4	Kent Tekulve	.20	.15	.08
5	Greg Gross	.20	.15	.08
6	Shane Rawley	.20	.15	.08
7	Darren Daulton	1.50	1.25	.60
8	Kevin Gross	.20	.15	.08
9	Steve Jeltz	.20	.15	.08
10	Mike Schmidt	2.50	2.00	1.00
11	Steve Bedrosian	.35	.25	.14
12	Gary Redus	.20	.15	.08
13	Charles Hudson	.20	.15	.08
14	John Russell	.20	.15	.08
15	Fred Toliver	.20	.15	.08
16	Glenn Wilson	.20	.15	.08

1985 Circle K

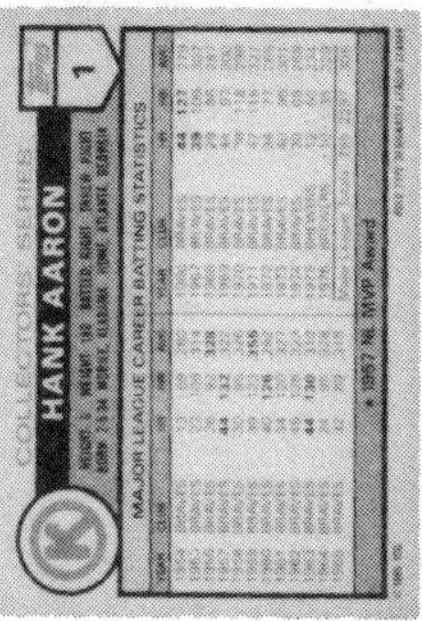

Produced by Topps for Circle K stores, this 33-card set is entitled "Baseball All Time Home Run Kings". The cards, which measure 2-1/2" by 3-1/2", are numbered on the back according to the player's position on the all-time career home run list. Joe DiMaggio, who ranked 31st, was not included in the set. The set is skip-numbered from 30 to 32. The glossy card fronts contain the player's name in the lower left corner and feature a color photo, although black and white photos were utilized for a few of the homer kings who played before 1960. The card backs have blue and red print on white stock and contain the player's career batting statistics. The set was issued with a specially designed box.

		MT	NR MT	EX
Complete Set:		8.00	6.00	3.25
Common Player:		.15	.11	.06
1	Hank Aaron	.60	.45	.25
2	Babe Ruth	2.00	1.50	.80
3	Willie Mays	.60	.45	.25
4	Frank Robinson	.25	.20	.10
5	Harmon Killebrew	.25	.20	.10
6	Mickey Mantle	2.00	1.50	.80
7	Jimmie Foxx	.25	.20	.10
8	Willie McCovey	.25	.20	.10
9	Ted Williams	.70	.50	.30
10	Ernie Banks	.35	.25	.14
11	Eddie Mathews	.25	.20	.10
12	Mel Ott	.20	.15	.08
13	Reggie Jackson	.40	.30	.15
14	Lou Gehrig	1.00	.70	.40
15	Stan Musial	.60	.45	.25
16	Willie Stargell	.20	.15	.08
17	Carl Yastrzemski	.50	.40	.20
18	Billy Williams	.20	.15	.08
19	Mike Schmidt	.50	.40	.20
20	Duke Snider	.40	.30	.15
21	Al Kaline	.35	.25	.14
22	Johnny Bench	.35	.25	.14
23	Frank Howard	.15	.11	.06
24	Orlando Cepeda	.15	.11	.06
25	Norm Cash	.20	.15	.08
26	Dave Kingman	.15	.11	.06
27	Rocky Colavito	.20	.15	.08
28	Tony Perez	.15	.11	.06
29	Gil Hodges	.20	.15	.08
30	Ralph Kiner	.20	.15	.08
32	Johnny Mize	.20	.15	.08
33	Yogi Berra	.35	.25	.14
34	Lee May	.15	.11	.06

1969 Citgo Coins

This 20-player set of small (about 1" in diameter) metal coins was issued by Citgo in 1969 to commemorate professional baseball's 100th anniversary. The brass-coated coins, susceptible to oxidation, display the player in a crude portrait with his name across the top. The backs honor the 100th anniversary of pro ball. The coins are unnumbered but are generally checklisted according to numbers that appear on a display card which was available from Citgo by mail.

		NR MT	EX	VG
Complete Set:		65.00	30.00	18.00
Common Player:		1.00	.50	.30
1	Denny McLain	2.00	1.00	.60
2	Dave McNally	1.00	.50	.30
3	Jim Lonborg	1.00	.50	.30
4	Harmon Killebrew	5.00	2.50	1.50
5	Mel Stottlemyre	1.00	.50	.30
6	Willie Horton	1.00	.50	.30
7	Jim Fregosi	1.50	.70	.45
8	Rico Petrocelli	1.00	.50	.30
9	Stan Bahnsen	1.00	.50	.30
10	Frank Howard	2.00	1.00	.60
11	Joe Torre	1.50	.70	.45
12	Jerry Koosman	1.00	.50	.30
13	Ron Santo	2.00	1.00	.60
14	Pete Rose	15.00	7.50	4.50
15	Rusty Staub	2.00	1.00	.60
16	Henry Aaron	18.00	9.00	5.50
17	Richie Allen	3.00	1.50	.90
18	Ron Swoboda	1.00	.50	.30
19	Willie McCovey	5.00	2.50	1.50
20	Jim Bunning	2.00	1.00	.60

1987 Classic Major League Baseball Game

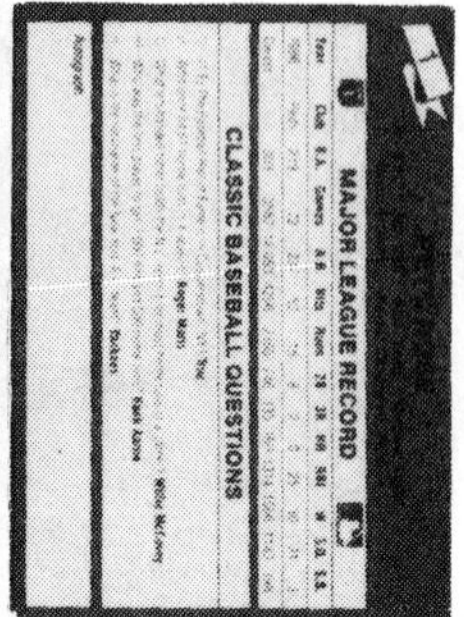

The "Classic Major League Baseball Board Game" set consists of 100 full-color cards which were used to play the game. Game participants were required to answer trivia questions found on the backs of the cards. The attractive cards measure 2-1/2" by 3-1/2" and are printed on glossy card stock. The card backs carry the player's career statistics besides the Classic Baseball Questions. The game was produced by Game Time, Ltd. of Marietta, Ga., and sold for $19.95 in most retail outlets.

		MT	NR MT	EX
Complete Set (100):		225.00	175.00	90.00
Common Player:		.10	.08	.04
1	Pete Rose	3.00	2.25	1.25
2	Len Dykstra	2.00	1.50	.80
3	Darryl Strawberry	4.00	3.00	1.50
4	Keith Hernandez	.20	.15	.08
5	Gary Carter	.30	.25	.12
6	Wally Joyner	1.00	.70	.40
7	Andres Thomas	.10	.08	.04
8	Pat Dodson	.10	.08	.04
9	Kirk Gibson	.30	.25	.12
10	Don Mattingly	4.00	3.00	1.50
11	Dave Winfield	1.00	.70	.40
12	Rickey Henderson	6.00	4.50	2.25
13	Dan Pasqua	.10	.08	.04
14	Don Baylor	.15	.11	.06
15	Bo Jackson	80.00	60.00	30.00
16	Pete Incaviglia	.20	.15	.08
17	Kevin Bass	.10	.08	.04
18	Barry Larkin	1.00	.70	.40
19	Dave Magadan	.80	.60	.30
20	Steve Sax	.20	.15	.08
21	Eric Davis	1.00	.70	.40
22	Mike Pagliarulo	.10	.08	.04
23	Fred Lynn	.20	.15	.08
24	Reggie Jackson	1.00	.70	.40
25	Larry Parrish	.10	.08	.04
26	Tony Gwynn	.80	.60	.30
27	Steve Garvey	.30	.20	.10
28	Glenn Davis	.10	.08	.04
29	Tim Raines	.25	.20	.10
30	Vince Coleman	.20	.15	.08
31	Willie McGee	.10	.08	.04
32	Ozzie Smith	.80	.60	.30
33	Dave Parker	.60	.45	.25
34	Tony Pena	.10	.08	.04
35	Ryne Sandberg	10.00	7.50	4.00
36	Brett Butler	.10	.08	.04
37	Dale Murphy	.50	.40	.20
38	Bob Horner	.10	.08	.04
39	Pedro Guerrero	.15	.11	.06
40	Brook Jacoby	.10	.08	.04
41	Carlton Fisk	.30	.25	.12

No.	Player	MT	NR MT	EX
42	Harold Baines	.15	.11	.06
43	Rob Deer	.10	.08	.04
44	Robin Yount	6.00	4.50	2.25
45	Paul Molitor	2.00	1.50	.80
46	Jose Canseco	30.00	22.50	11.25
47	George Brett	6.00	4.50	2.25
48	Jim Presley	.10	.08	.04
49	Rich Gedman	.10	.08	.04
50	Lance Parrish	.10	.08	.04
51	Eddie Murray	.50	.40	.20
52	Cal Ripken, Jr.	8.00	5.50	2.75
53	Kent Hrbek	.25	.20	.10
54	Gary Gaetti	.10	.08	.04
55	Kirby Puckett	6.00	4.50	2.25
56	George Bell	.20	.15	.08
57	Tony Fernandez	.20	.15	.08
58	Jesse Barfield	.10	.08	.04
59	Jim Rice	.40	.30	.15
60	Wade Boggs	2.00	1.50	.80
61	Marty Barrett	.10	.08	.04
62	Mike Schmidt	8.00	5.50	2.75
63	Von Hayes	.10	.08	.04
64	Jeff Leonard	.10	.08	.04
65	Chris Brown	.10	.08	.04
66	Dave Smith	.10	.08	.04
67	Mike Krukow	.10	.08	.04
68	Ron Guidry	.15	.11	.06
69	Rob Woodward (photo actually Pat Dodson)	.10	.08	.04
70	Rob Murphy	.10	.08	.04
71	Andres Galarraga	.25	.20	.10
72	Dwight Gooden	1.00	.70	.40
73	Bob Ojeda	.10	.08	.04
74	Sid Fernandez	.10	.08	.04
75	Jesse Orosco	.10	.08	.04
76	Roger McDowell	.10	.08	.04
77	John Tutor (Tudor)	.10	.08	.04
78	Tom Browning	.10	.08	.04
79	Rick Aguilera	.10	.08	.04
80	Lance McCullers	.10	.08	.04
81	Mike Scott	.10	.08	.04
82	Nolan Ryan	12.00	9.00	4.75
83	Bruce Hurst	.15	.11	.06
84	Roger Clemens	5.00	3.75	2.00
85	Oil Can Boyd	.10	.08	.04
86	Dave Righetti	.20	.15	.08
87	Dennis Rasmussen	.10	.08	.04
88	Bret Saberhagan (Saberhagen)	.20	.15	.08
89	Mark Langston	.20	.15	.08
90	Jack Morris	.15	.11	.06
91	Fernando Valenzuela	.15	.11	.06
92	Orel Hershiser	.30	.25	.12
93	Rick Honeycutt	.10	.08	.04
94	Jeff Reardon	.15	.11	.06
95	John Habyan	.10	.08	.04
96	Goose Gossage	.15	.11	.06
97	Todd Worrell	.20	.15	.08
98	Floyd Youmans	.10	.08	.04
99	Don Aase	.10	.08	.04
100	John Franco	.15	.11	.06

1987 Classic Travel Edition

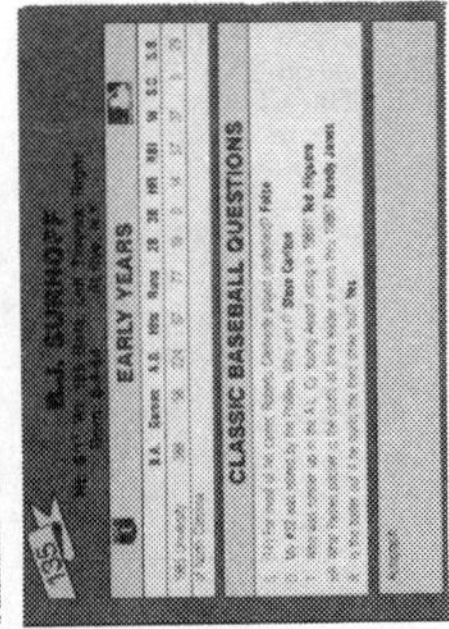

Game Time, Ltd. of Marietta, Ga., issued as an update to their Classic Baseball Board Game a 50-card set entitled "Travel Edition." The cards measure 2-1/2" by 3-1/2" and feature the same outstanding quality characteristic of the first release. Numbered from 101 to 150, the "Travel Edition" is an extension of the original set. Besides updating player trades and showcasing rookies, the set offers several highlights from the 1987 season, including Andre Dawson's beaning. All new trivia questions are contained on the card backs.

		MT	NR MT	EX
	Complete Set (50):	30.00	22.00	12.00
	Common Player:	.08	.06	.03
101	Mike Schmidt	2.00	1.50	.80
102	Eric Davis	1.00	.70	.40
103	Pete Rose	2.00	1.50	.80
104	Don Mattingly	2.00	1.50	.80
105	Wade Boggs	1.50	1.25	.60
106	Dale Murphy	.40	.30	.15
107	Glenn Davis	.08	.06	.03
108	Wally Joyner	2.00	1.50	.80
109	Bo Jackson	6.00	4.50	2.25
110	Cory Snyder	.08	.06	.03
111	Jim Lindeman	.08	.06	.03
112	Kirby Puckett	2.00	1.50	.80
113	Barry Bonds	8.00	5.50	2.25
114	Roger Clemens	2.00	1.50	.80
115	Oddibe McDowell	.08	.06	.03
116	Bret Saberhagen	.20	.15	.08
117	Joe Magrane	.08	.06	.03
118	Scott Fletcher	.08	.06	.03
119	Mark McLemore	.08	.06	.03
120	Who Me? (Joe Niekro)	.25	.20	.10
121	Mark McGwire	2.00	1.50	.80
122	Darryl Strawberry	1.50	1.25	.60
123	Mike Scott	.08	.06	.03
124	Andre Dawson	.40	.30	.15
125	Jose Canseco	4.00	3.00	1.50
126	Kevin McReynolds	.15	.11	.06
127	Joe Carter	.50	.40	.20
128	Casey Candaele	.08	.06	.03
129	Matt Nokes	.15	.11	.06
130	Kal Daniels	.15	.11	.06
131	Pete Incaviglia	.25	.20	.10
132	Benito Santiago	1.00	.70	.40
133	Barry Larkin	1.00	.70	.40
134	Gary Pettis	.08	.06	.03
135	B.J. Surhoff	.15	.11	.06
136	Juan Nieves	.08	.06	.03
137	Jim Deshaies	.08	.06	.03
138	Pete O'Brien	.08	.06	.03
139	Kevin Seitzer	.08	.06	.03
140	Devon White	.25	.20	.10
141	Rob Deer	.08	.06	.03
142	Kurt Stillwell	.08	.06	.03
143	Edwin Correa	.08	.06	.03
144	Dion James	.08	.06	.03
145	Danny Tartabull	.40	.30	.15
146	Jerry Browne	.08	.06	.03
147	Ted Higuera	.15	.11	.06
148	Jack Clark	.15	.11	.06
149	Ruben Sierra	2.00	1.50	.80
150	McGwire/Davis (Mark McGwire, Eric Davis)	1.50	1.25	.60

1988 Classic - Red

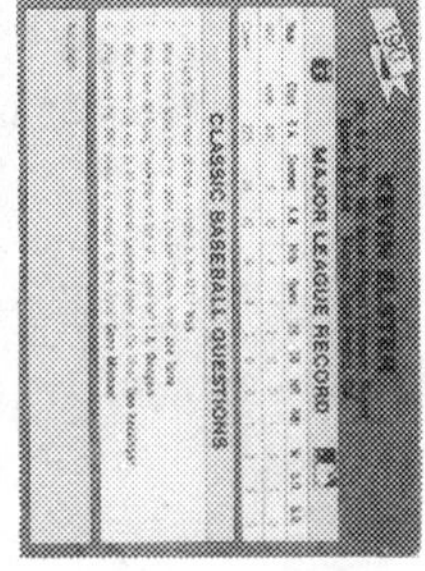

This 50-card set, numbered 151-200, was produced for use with the travel edition of Game Time's Classic Baseball Board Game. Special cards in the set include a McGwire/Mattingly, an instruction card with McGwire/Canseco and three different cards featuring Phil Niekro (in different uniforms). A follow-up to the first edition in 1987, the 1988 Red Series was designed for use with the 1988 Blue Series (#'s 201-250). Red Series card fronts have red borders, a yellow Classic logo in the upper left corner and a black and beige player banner beneath the photo. The card backs are printed in red and pink on white and include the player name, personal info, major league records, a baseball question and space for the player autograph. Classic card series sold via hobby dealers and retail toy stores nationwide. Game Time Ltd., the set's producer, was purchased by Scoreboard of Cherry Hill, N.J. in 1988.

		MT	NR MT	EX
	Complete Set (50):	16.00	12.00	6.50
	Common Player:	.08	.06	.03
151	Don Mattingly, Mark McGwire,	1.00	.70	.40
152	Don Mattingly	.75	.55	.25
153	Mark McGwire	.50	.40	.20
154	Eric Davis	.50	.40	.20
155	Wade Boggs	1.00	.70	.40
156	Dale Murphy	.50	.40	.20
157	Andre Dawson	.40	.30	.15
158	Roger Clemens	1.50	1.25	.60
159	Kevin Seitzer	.08	.06	.03
160	Benito Santiago	.08	.06	.03
161	Kal Daniels	.08	.06	.03
162	John Kruk	.20	.15	.08
163	Bill Ripken	.08	.06	.03
164	Kirby Puckett	.50	.40	.20
165	Jose Canseco	3.00	2.25	1.25
166	Matt Nokes	.15	.11	.06
167	Mike Schmidt	2.00	1.50	.80
168	Tim Raines	.25	.20	.10
169	Ryne Sandberg	2.00	1.50	.80
170	Dave Winfield	.50	.40	.20
171	Dwight Gooden	.50	.40	.20
172	Bret Saberhagen	.15	.11	.06
173	Willie McGee	.08	.06	.03
174	Jack Morris	.08	.06	.03
175	Jeff Leonard	.08	.06	.03
176	Cal Ripken, Jr.	3.00	2.25	1.25
177	Pete Incaviglia	.08	.06	.03
178	Devon White	.10	.08	.04
179	Nolan Ryan	5.00	3.75	2.00
180	Ruben Sierra	1.50	1.25	.60
181	Todd Worrell	.08	.06	.03
182	Glenn Davis	.08	.06	.03
183	Frank Viola	.15	.11	.06
184	Cory Snyder	.08	.06	.03
185	Tracy Jones	.08	.06	.03
186	Terry Steinbach	.15	.11	.06
187	Julio Franco	.15	.11	.06
188	Larry Sheets	.08	.06	.03
189	John Marzano	.08	.06	.03
190	Kevin Elster	.08	.06	.03
191	Vincente Palacios	.08	.06	.03
192	Kent Hrbek	.25	.20	.10
193	Eric Bell	.08	.06	.03
194	Kelly Downs	.08	.06	.03
195	Jose Lind	.10	.08	.04
196	Dave Stewart	.20	.15	.08
197	Jose Canseco, Mark McGwire	1.50	1.25	.60
198	Phil Niekro	.25	.20	.10
199	Phil Niekro	.25	.20	.10
200	Phil Niekro	.25	.20	.10

1988 Classic - Blue

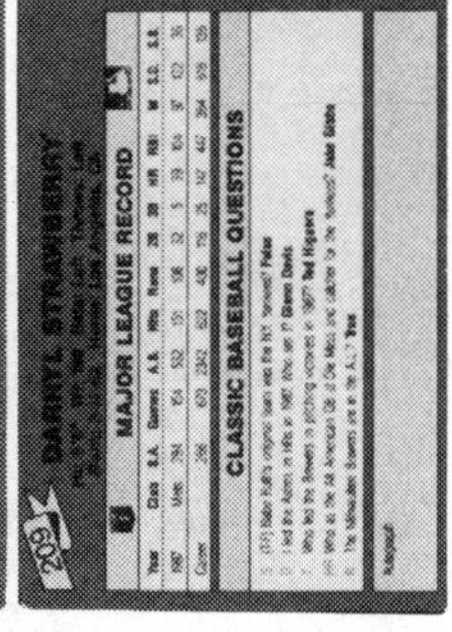

This 50-card set, numbered 201-250, was produced for use with the travel edition of Game Time's Classic Baseball Board Game. Two cards in the set feature two players: Davis/Murphy and McGwire/Mattingly. A follow-up to the first edition in 1987, the 1988 Blue was designed for use with the 1988 Red Series (151-200). Blue Series card fronts have blue borders, a yellow classic logo in the upper left corner and a black and beige player name banner beneath the photo. The card backs are printed in blue on white and include the player name, personal info, major league records, a baseball question and space for the player autograph. Classic card series are sold via hobby dealers and retail toy stores nationwide. Game Time Ltd., the set's producer, was purchased by Scoreboard of Cherry Hill, N.J. in 1988.

		MT	NR MT	EX
	Complete Set (50):	20.00	15.00	8.00
	Common Player:	.15	.11	.06
201	Davis/Murphy (Eric Davis, Dale Murphy)	.40	.30	.15
202	B.J. Surhoff	.15	.11	.06
203	John Kruk	.20	.15	.08
204	Sam Horn	.15	.11	.06
205	Jack Clark	.15	.11	.06
206	Wally Joyner	.40	.30	.15
207	Matt Nokes	.25	.20	.10
208	Bo Jackson	4.00	3.00	1.50
209	Darryl Strawberry	1.00	.70	.40
210	Ozzie Smith	.25	.20	.10
211	Don Mattingly	1.00	.70	.40
212	Mark McGwire	1.00	.70	.40
213	Eric Davis	.70	.50	.30
214	Wade Boggs	1.50	1.25	.60
215	Dale Murphy	.30	.25	.12
216	Andre Dawson	.30	.25	.12
217	Roger Clemens	1.00	.70	.40
218	Kevin Seitzer	.15	.11	.06
219	Benito Santiago	.25	.20	.10
220	Tony Gwynn	1.00	.70	.40
221	Mike Scott	.15	.11	.06
222	Steve Bedrosian	.15	.11	.06
223	Vince Coleman	.25	.20	.10
224	Rick Sutcliffe	.15	.11	.06
225	Will Clark	7.00	5.25	2.75
226	Pete Rose	1.50	1.25	.60
227	Mike Greenwell	.30	.25	.15
228	Ken Caminiti	.15	.11	.06
229	Ellis Burks	.50	.40	.20
230	Dave Magadan	.15	.11	.06
231	Alan Trammell	.30	.25	.12
232	Paul Molitor	.40	.30	.15
233	Gary Gaetti	.15	.11	.06
234	Rickey Henderson	1.25	.90	.50
235	Danny Tartabull	.60	.45	.25
236	Bobby Bonilla	1.00	.70	.40
237	Mike Dunne	.15	.11	.06
238	Al Leiter	.15	.11	.06
239	John Farrell	.15	.11	.06
240	Joe Magrane	.15	.11	.06

		MT	NR MT	EX
241	Mike Henneman	.15	.11	.06
242	George Bell	.25	.20	.10
243	Gregg Jefferies	.60	.45	.25
244	Jay Buhner	.40	.30	.15
245	Todd Benzinger	.15	.11	.06
246	Matt Williams	.80	.60	.30
247	McGwire/Mattingly (Don Mattingly, Mark McGwire no cardnumber on back)	1.00	.70	.40
248	George Brett	1.00	.70	.40
249	Jimmy Key	.15	.11	.06
250	Mark Langston	.20	.15	.08

1989 Classic

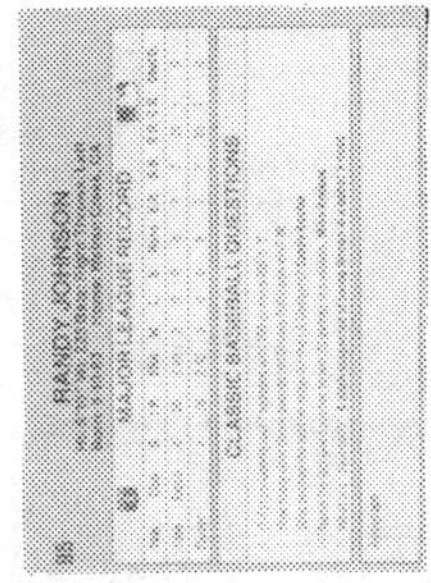

This 100-card set was released by The Score Board to accompany trivia board games. Fronts have a wide border which is pink at the top and blue at the bottom. Card backs are printed in blue. The player's name appears beneath the color photo. The flip side includes the card number in the upper left, personal information, and the player's major league record in a boxed area. Another boxed area below the record presents five trivia questions. The lower border of the flip side provides an autograph space. The Classic card series was sold by retail stores and hobby dealers nationwide.

		MT	NR MT	EX
Complete Set (100):		20.00	15.00	8.00
Common Player:		.08	.06	.03
1	Orel Hershiser	.30	.25	.12
2	Wade Boggs	.60	.45	.25
3	Jose Canseco	1.50	1.25	.60
4	Mark McGwire	.40	.30	.15
5	Don Mattingly	.60	.45	.25
6	Gregg Jefferies	.50	.40	.20
7	Dwight Gooden	.60	.45	.25
8	Darryl Strawberry	.40	.30	.15
9	Eric Davis	.40	.30	.15
10	Joey Meyer	.08	.06	.03
11	Joe Carter	.20	.15	.08
12	Paul Molitor	.40	.30	.15
13	Mark Grace	.30	.25	.12
14	Kurt Stillwell	.08	.06	.03
15	Kirby Puckett	.60	.45	.25
16	Keith Miller	.08	.06	.03
17	Glenn Davis	.08	.06	.03
18	Will Clark	.75	.55	.25
19	Cory Snyder	.08	.06	.03
20	Jose Lind	.08	.06	.03
21	Andres Thomas	.08	.06	.03
22	Dave Smith	.08	.06	.03
23	Mike Scott	.08	.06	.03
24	Kevin McReynolds	.08	.06	.03
25	B.J. Surhoff	.08	.06	.03
26	Mackey Sasser	.08	.06	.03
27	Chad Kreuter	.20	.15	.08
28	Hal Morris	.60	.45	.25
29	Wally Joyner	.20	.15	.08
30	Tony Gwynn	.40	.30	.15
31	Kevin Mitchell	.20	.15	.08
32	Dave Winfield	.40	.30	.15
33	Billy Bean	.08	.06	.03
34	Steve Bedrosian	.08	.06	.03
35	Ron Gant	.20	.15	.08
36	Len Dykstra	.20	.15	.08
37	Andre Dawson	.30	.25	.12
38	Brett Butler	.08	.06	.03
39	Rob Deer	.08	.06	.03
40	Tommy John	.20	.15	.08
41	Gary Gaetti	.15	.11	.06
42	Tim Raines	.20	.15	.08
43	George Bell	.20	.15	.08
44	Dwight Evans	.15	.11	.06
45	Denny Martinez	.15	.11	.06
46	Andres Galarraga	.20	.15	.08
47	George Brett	.50	.40	.20
48	Mike Schmidt	1.25	.90	.50
49	Dave Steib	.08	.06	.03
50	Rickey Henderson	.50	.40	.20
51	Craig Biggio	.40	.30	.15
52	Mark Lemke	.08	.06	.03
53	Chris Sabo	.40	.30	.15
54	Jeff Treadway	.08	.06	.03
55	Kent Hrbek	.15	.11	.06
56	Cal Ripken, Jr.	1.00	.70	.40
57	Tim Belcher	.08	.06	.03
58	Ozzie Smith	.40	.30	.15
59	Keith Hernandez	.08	.06	.03
60	Pedro Guerrero	.08	.06	.03
61	Greg Swindell	.08	.06	.03
62	Bret Saberhagen	.20	.15	.08
63	John Tudor	.08	.06	.03
64	Gary Carter	.15	.11	.06
65	Kevin Seitzer	.08	.06	.03
66	Jesse Barfield	.08	.06	.03
67	Luis Medina	.08	.06	.03
68	Walt Weiss	.20	.15	.08
69	Terry Steinbach	.08	.06	.03
70	Barry Larkin	.20	.15	.08
71	Pete Rose	.80	.60	.30
72	Luis Salazar	.08	.06	.03
73	Benito Santiago	.20	.15	.08
74	Kal Daniels	.08	.06	.03
75	Kevin Elster	.08	.06	.03
76	Rob Dibble	.25	.20	.10
77	Bobby Witt	.15	.11	.06
78	Steve Searcy	.08	.06	.03
79	Sandy Alomar	.15	.11	.06
80	Chili Davis	.20	.15	.08
81	Alvin Davis	.08	.06	.03
82	Charlie Leibrandt	.08	.06	.03
83	Robin Yount	.80	.60	.30
84	Mark Carreon	.08	.06	.03
85	Pascual Perez	.08	.06	.03
86	Dennis Rasmussen	.08	.06	.03
87	Ernie Riles	.08	.06	.03
88	Melido Perez	.08	.06	.03
89	Doug Jones	.08	.06	.03
90	Dennis Eckersley	.15	.11	.06
91	Bob Welch	.08	.06	.03
92	Bob Milacki	.08	.06	.03
93	Jeff Robinson	.08	.06	.03
94	Mike Henneman	.08	.06	.03
95	Randy Johnson	.40	.30	.15
96	Ron Jones	.08	.06	.03
97	Jack Armstrong	.08	.06	.03
98	Willie McGee	.08	.06	.03
99	Ryne Sandberg	.80	.60	.30
100	David Cone/ Danny Jackson	.70	.50	.25

A player's name in italic type indicates a rookie card. An (FC) indicates a player's first card for that particular card company.

1989 Classic Travel Update I

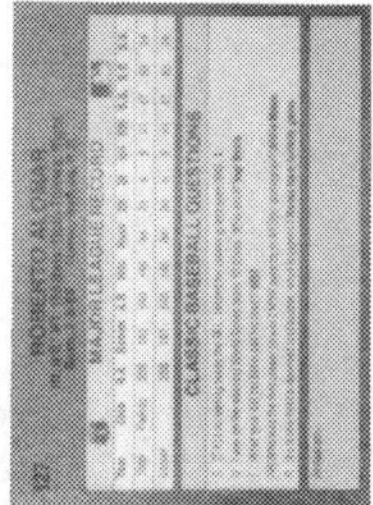

Sold only as a 50-card complete set under the official name of "Travel Update I," these cards are identical in format to the 1989 Classic 100-card set with the exception that the borders are orange at the top and maroon at the bottom. Backs are maroon. Like the Update I orange series, cards are numbered contiguously from 101-150.

		MT	NR MT	EX
Complete Set (50):		10.00	7.00	3.50
Common Player:		.08	.06	.03
101	Gary Sheffield	1.25	.90	.50
102	Wade Boggs	.80	.60	.30
103	Jose Canseco	.60	.40	.20
104	Mark McGwire	.60	.40	.20
105	Orel Hershiser	.20	.15	.08
106	Don Mattingly	1.25	.90	.50
107	Dwight Gooden	.50	.40	.20
108	Darryl Strawberry	.40	.30	.15
109	Eric Davis	.40	.30	.15
110	Bam Bam Meulens	.08	.06	.03
111	Andy Van Slyke	.15	.11	.06
112	Al Leiter	.08	.06	.03
113	Matt Nokes	.15	.11	.06
114	Mike Krukow	.08	.06	.03
115	Tony Fernandez	.15	.11	.06
116	Fred McGriff	.25	.20	.10
117	Barry Bonds	.80	.60	.20
118	Gerald Perry	.08	.06	.03
119	Roger Clemens	.30	.25	.12
120	Kirk Gibson	.12	.09	.05
121	Greg Maddux	.20	.15	.08
122	Bo Jackson	1.25	.90	.50
123	Danny Jackson	.08	.06	.03
124	Dale Murphy	.20	.15	.08
125	David Cone	.15	.11	.06
126	Tom Browning	.08	.06	.03
127	Roberto Alomar	1.00	.70	.40
128	Alan Trammell	.15	.11	.06
129	Rickey Jordan	.08	.06	.03
130	Ramon Martinez	.50	.40	.20
131	Ken Griffey, Jr.	5.00	3.75	2.00
132	Gregg Olson	.50	.40	.20
133	Carlos Quintana	.08	.06	.03
134	Dave West	.15	.11	.06
135	Cameron Drew	.08	.06	.03
136	Ted Higuera	.08	.06	.03
137	Sil Campusano	.08	.06	.03
138	Mark Gubicza	.15	.11	.06
139	Mike Boddicker	.08	.06	.03
140	Paul Gibson	.08	.06	.03
141	Jose Rijo	.20	.15	.08
142	John Costello	.08	.06	.03
143	Cecil Espy	.08	.06	.03
144	Frank Viola	.15	.11	.08
145	Erik Hanson	.30	.25	.12
146	Juan Samuel	.08	.06	.03
147	Harold Reynolds	.15	.11	.06
148	Joe Magrane	.08	.06	.03
149	Mike Greenwell	.15	.11	.06
150	Darryl Strawberry/ Will Clark	1.00	.70	.40

1989 Classic Travel Update II

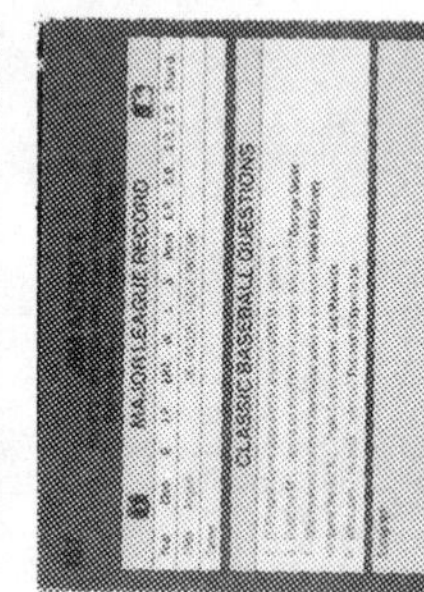

Numbered from 151-200, this 50-card set features rookies and traded players with their new teams. The cards are purple and gray and were sold as part of a board game with baseball trivia questions.

		MT	NR MT	EX
Complete Set (50):		10.00	7.50	4.00
Common Player:		.05	.04	.02
151	Jim Abbott	.50	.40	.20
152	Ellis Burks	.10	.08	.04
153	Mike Schmidt	1.00	.70	.30
154	Gregg Jefferies	.20	.15	.08
155	Mark Grace	.20	.15	.08
156	Jerome Walton	.05	.04	.02
157	Bo Jackson	1.00	.70	.40
158	Jack Clark	.05	.04	.02
159	Tom Glavine	.10	.08	.04
160	Eddie Murray	.15	.11	.06
161	John Dopson	.05	.04	.02
162	Ruben Sierra	.20	.15	.08
163	Rafael Palmeiro	.25	.20	.10
164	Nolan Ryan	1.50	1.25	.60
165	Barry Larkin	.20	.15	.08
166	Tommy Herr	.05	.04	.02
167	Roberto Kelly	.20	.15	.08
168	Glenn Davis	.05	.04	.02
169	Glenn Braggs	.05	.04	.02
170	Juan Bell	.05	.04	.02
171	Todd Burns	.05	.04	.02
172	Derek Lilliquist	.05	.04	.02
173	Orel Hershiser	.20	.15	.08
174	John Smoltz	.25	.20	.10
175	Ozzie Guillen/ Ellis Burks	.30	.25	.12
176	Kirby Puckett	.50	.40	.20
177	Robin Ventura	.75	.55	.25
178	Allan Anderson	.05	.04	.02
179	Steve Sax	.05	.04	.02
180	Will Clark	.75	.55	.25
181	Mike Devereaux	.05	.04	.02
182	Tom Gordon	.05	.04	.02
183	Rob Murphy	.05	.04	.02
184	Pete O'Brien	.05	.04	.02
185	Cris Carpenter	.05	.04	.02
186	Tom Brunansky	.05	.04	.02
187	Bob Boone	.15	.11	.06
188	Lou Whitaker	.10	.08	.04
189	Dwight Gooden	.20	.15	.08
190	Mark McGwire	.40	.30	.15
191	John Smiley	.05	.04	.02
192	Tommy Gregg	.05	.04	.02
193	Ken Griffey, Jr.	4.00	3.00	1.50
194	Bruce Hurst	.05	.04	.02
195	Greg Swindell	.10	.08	.04
196	Nelson Liriano	.05	.04	.02
197	Randy Myers	.05	.04	.02
198	Kevin Mitchell	.20	.15	.08
199	Dante Bichette	.10	.08	.04
200	Deion Sanders	.70	.50	.30

Values for recent cards and sets are listed in Mint (MT), Near Mint (NM), reflecting the fact that many cards from recent years have been preserved in top condition. Recent cards and sets in less than Excellent condition have little collector interest.

1990 Classic Baseball

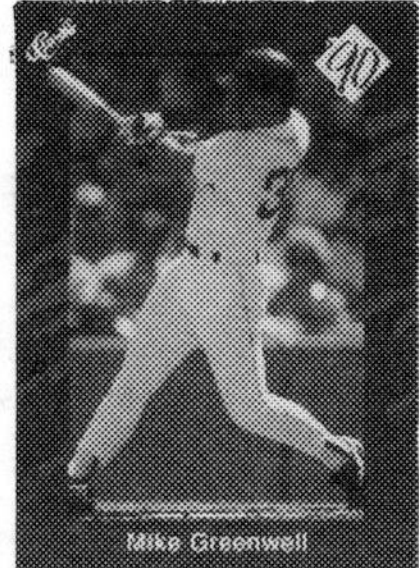

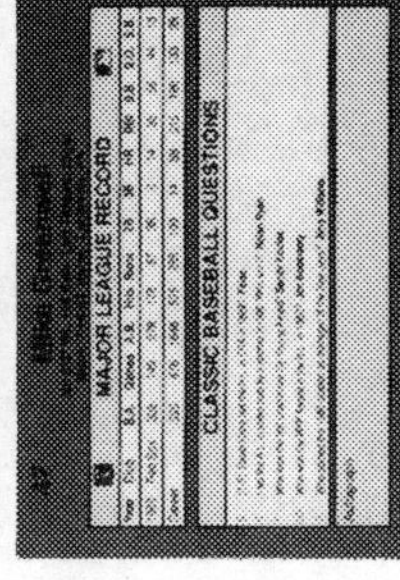

Classic Baseball returned in 1990 with another 150-card set. The cards were again sold as part of a baseball trivia game, and each game included a box designed to store all the cards in the set.

		MT	NR MT	EX
Complete Set (154):		15.00	11.00	6.00
Common Player:		.05	.04	.02
1	Nolan Ryan	2.00	1.50	.80
2	Bo Jackson	.50	.40	.20
3	Gregg Olson	.10	.08	.04
4	Tom Gordon	.05	.04	.02
5	Robin Ventura	.20	.15	.08
6	Will Clark	.50	.40	.20
7	Ruben Sierra	.20	.15	.08
8	Mark Grace	.25	.20	.10
9	Luis de los Santos	.05	.04	.02
10	Bernie Williams	.25	.20	.10
11	Eric Davis	.20	.15	.08
12	Carney Lansford	.05	.04	.02
13	John Smoltz	.10	.08	.04
14	Gary Sheffield	.25	.20	.10
15	Kent Merker	.25	.20	.10
16	Don Mattingly	.75	.55	.25
17	Tony Gwynn	.15	.11	.06
18	Ozzie Smith	.25	.20	.10
19	Fred McGriff	.25	.20	.10
20	Ken Griffey, Jr.	2.00	1.50	.80
21a	Deion Sanders ("Prime Time")	4.00	3.00	1.50
21b	Deion Sanders (Deion "Prime Time" Sanders)	.70	.50	.30
22	Jose Canseco	.40	.30	.15
23	Mitch Williams	.15	.11	.06
24	Cal Ripken, Jr.	.75	.55	.25
25	Bob Geren	.10	.08	.04
26	Wade Boggs	.50	.40	.20
27	Ryne Sandberg	.60	.45	.25
28	Kirby Puckett	.50	.40	.20
29	Mike Scott	.05	.04	.02
30	Dwight Smith	.05	.04	.02
31	Craig Worthington	.05	.04	.02
32	Ricky Jordan	.05	.04	.02
33	Darryl Strawberry	.25	.20	.10
34	Jerome Walton	.05	.04	.02
35	John Olerud	.70	.50	.30
36	Tom Glavine	.10	.08	.04
37	Rickey Henderson	.40	.30	.15
38	Rolando Roomes	.05	.04	.02
39	Mickey Tettleton	.10	.08	.04
40	Jim Abbott	.50	.40	.20
41	Dave Righetti	.05	.04	.02
42	Mike LaValliere	.05	.04	.02
43	Rob Dibble	.15	.11	.06
44	Pete Harnisch	.05	.04	.02
45	Jose Offerman	.20	.15	.08
46	Walt Weiss	.05	.04	.02
47	Mike Greenwell	.15	.11	.06
48	Barry Larkin	.15	.11	.06
49	Dave Gallagher	.05	.04	.02
50	Junior Felix	.05	.04	.02
51	Roger Clemens	.20	.15	.08
52	Lonnie Smith	.05	.04	.02
53	Jerry Browne	.05	.04	.02
54	Greg Briley	.05	.04	.02
55	Delino DeShields	.75	.55	.25
56	Carmelo Martinez	.05	.04	.02
57	Craig Biggio	.10	.08	.04
58	Dwight Gooden	.20	.15	.08
59a	Bo, Ruben, Mark (Bo Jackson)	2.00	1.50	.80
59a	Bo, Ruben, Mark (Ruben Sierra)	2.00	1.50	.80
59a	Bo, Ruben, Mark (Mark McGwire)	2.00	1.50	.80
59b	A.L. Fence Busters (Bo Jackson)	.60	.45	.25
59b	A.L. Fence Busters (Ruben Sierra)	.60	.45	.25
59b	A.L. Fence Busters (Mark McGwire)	.60	.45	.25
60	Greg Vaughn	.25	.20	.10
61	Roberto Alomar	.25	.20	.10
62	Steve Bedrosian	.05	.04	.02
63	Devon White	.10	.08	.04
64	Kevin Mitchell	.20	.15	.08
65	Marquis Grissom	.40	.30	.15
66	Brian Holman	.05	.04	.02
67	Julio Franco	.05	.04	.02
68	Dave West	.10	.08	.04
69	Harold Baines	.10	.08	.04
70	Eric Anthony	.30	.25	.12
71	Glenn Davis	.05	.04	.02
72	Mark Langston	.15	.11	.06
73	Matt Williams	.25	.20	.10
74	Rafael Palmeiro	.20	.15	.08
75	Pete Rose, Jr.	.20	.15	.08
76	Ramon Martinez	.15	.11	.06
77	Dwight Evans	.10	.08	.04
78	Mackey Sasser	.05	.04	.02
79	Mike Schooler	.05	.04	.02
80	Dennis Cook	.05	.04	.02
81	Orel Hershiser	.20	.15	.08
82	Barry Bonds	.50	.40	.20
83	Geronimo Berroa	.05	.04	.02
84	George Bell	.10	.08	.04
85	Andre Dawson	.20	.15	.08
86	John Franco	.05	.04	.02
87a	Clark/Gwynn (Will Clark)	3.00	2.25	1.25
87a	Clark/Gwynn (Tony Gwynn)	3.00	2.25	1.25
87b	N.L. Hit Kings (Will Clark)	.40	.30	.15
87b	N.L. Hit Kings (Tony Gwynn)	.40	.30	.15
88	Glenallen Hill	.05	.04	.02
89	Jeff Ballard	.05	.04	.02
90	Todd Zeile	.30	.25	.12
91	Frank Viola	.15	.11	.06
92	Ozzie Guillen	.10	.08	.04
93	Jeff Leonard	.05	.04	.02
94	Dave Smith	.05	.04	.02
95	Dave Parker	.20	.15	.08
96	Jose Gonzalez	.05	.04	.02
97	Dave Steib	.05	.04	.02
98	Charlie Hayes	.15	.11	.06
99	Jesse Barfield	.05	.04	.02
100	Joey Belle	1.00	.70	.40
101	Jeff Reardon	.05	.04	.02
102	Bruce Hurst	.05	.04	.02
103	Luis Medina	.05	.04	.02
104	Mike Moore	.05	.04	.02
105	Vince Coleman	.10	.08	.04
106	Alan Trammell	.15	.11	.06
107	Randy Myers	.05	.04	.02
108	Frank Tanana	.05	.04	.02
109	Craig Lefferts	.05	.04	.02
110	John Wetteland	.20	.15	.08
111	Chris Gwynn	.05	.04	.02
112	Mark Carreon	.05	.04	.02
113	Von Hayes	.05	.04	.02
114	Doug Jones	.05	.04	.02
115	Andres Galarraga	.10	.08	.04
116	Carlton Fisk	.20	.15	.08
117	Paul O'Neill	.05	.04	.02
118	Tim Raines	.10	.08	.04
119	Tom Brunansky	.05	.04	.02
120	Andy Benes	.35	.25	.14
121	Mark Portugal	.05	.04	.02
122	Willie Randolph	.05	.04	.02
123	Jeff Blauser	.05	.04	.02
124	Don August	.05	.04	.02
125	Chuck Cary	.05	.04	.02
126	John Smiley	.05	.04	.02
127	Terry Mullholland	.05	.04	.02
128	Harold Reynolds	.05	.04	.02
129	Hubie Brooks	.05	.04	.02
130	Ben McDonald	.30	.25	.12
131	Kevin Ritz	.05	.04	.02
132	Luis Quinones	.05	.04	.02
133 a	Bam Bam Muelens ((Muelens - error))	4.00	3.00	1.50
133 b	Bam Bam Meulens ((Meulens - correct))	.20	.15	.08
134	Bill Spiers	.05	.04	.02
135	Andy Hawkins	.05	.04	.02
136	Alvin Davis	.05	.04	.02
137	Lee Smith	.15	.11	.06
138	Joe Carter	.15	.11	.06
139	Bret Saberhagen	.10	.08	.04
140	Sammy Sosa	.30	.25	.12
141	Matt Nokes	.10	.08	.04
142	Bert Blyleven	.10	.08	.04
143	Bobby Bonilla	.25	.20	.10
144	Howard Johnson	.10	.08	.04
145	Joe Magrane	.05	.04	.02
146	Pedro Guerrero	.05	.04	.02
147	Robin Yount	.45	.35	.15
148	Dan Gladden	.05	.04	.02
149	Steve Sax	.05	.04	.02
150a	Clark/Mitchell (Will Clark)	1.00	.70	.40
150a	Clark/Mitchell (Kevin Mitchell)	1.00	.70	.40
150b	Bay Bombers (Will Clark)	.50	.40	.20
150b	Bay Bombers (Kevin Mitchell)	.50	.40	.20

1990 Classic Series II

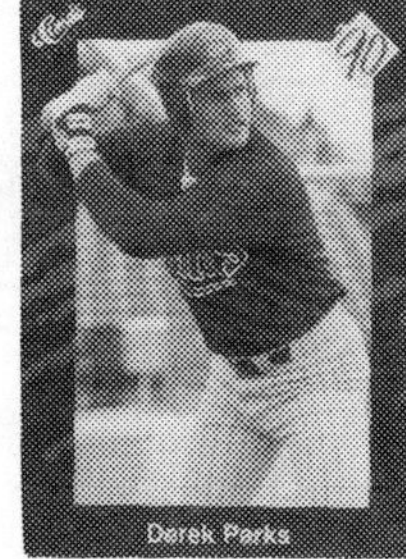

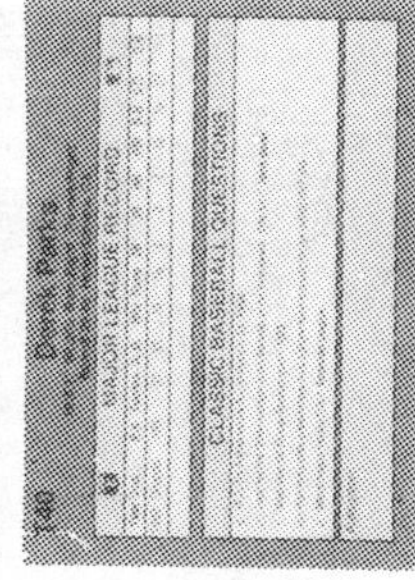

Like in previous years, Classic released a 50-card second series set for use with its baseball trivia game. Unlike the 1989 update set, the 1990 Classic Series II set is numbered 1-50 with a "T" designation accompanying the card number. The cards measure 2-1/2" by 3-1/2" and are designed after the original 1990 Classic cards. Series II cards have pink borders with a blue design, while the cards from the regular issue feature the opposite color combination. The cards are issued in a complete Series II set form.

		MT	NR MT	EX
Complete Set (50):		8.00	6.00	3.25
Common Player:		.05	.04	.02
1	Gregg Jefferies	.15	.11	.06
2	Steve Adkins	.05	.04	.02
3	Sandy Alomar, Jr.	.10	.08	.04
4	Steve Avery	.50	.40	.20
5	Mike Blowers	.20	.15	.08
6	George Brett	.50	.40	.20
7	Tom Browning	.05	.04	.02
8	Ellis Burks	.10	.08	.04
9	Joe Carter	.15	.11	.06
10	Jerald Clark	.05	.04	.02
11	"Hot Corners" (Matt Williams, Will Clark)	.40	.30	.15
12	Pat Combs	.05	.04	.02
13	Scott Cooper	.15	.11	.06
14	Mark Davis	.05	.04	.02
15	Storm Davis	.05	.04	.02
16	Larry Walker	.15	.11	.06
17	Brian DuBois	.05	.04	.02
18	Len Dykstra	.15	.11	.06
19	John Franco	.10	.08	.04
20	Kirk Gibson	.10	.08	.04
21	Juan Gonzalez	2.00	1.50	.80
22	Tommy Greene	.05	.04	.02
23	Kent Hrbek	.15	.11	.06
24	Mike Huff	.05	.04	.02
25	Bo Jackson	.70	.50	.30
26	Nolan Knows Bo (Bo Jackson, Nolan Ryan)	2.00	1.50	.80
27	Roberto Kelly	.10	.08	.04
28	Mark Langston	.10	.08	.04
29	Ray Lankford	.60	.45	.25
30	Kevin Maas	.20	.15	.08
31	Julio Machado	.05	.04	.02
32	Greg Maddux	.10	.08	.04
33	Mark McGwire	.20	.15	.08
34	Paul Molitor	.20	.15	.08
35	Hal Morris	.10	.08	.04
36	Dale Murphy	.25	.20	.10
37	Eddie Murray	.25	.20	.10
38	Jaime Navarro	.05	.04	.02
39	Dean Palmer	.40	.30	.15
40	Derek Parks	.05	.04	.02
41	Bobby Rose	.05	.04	.02
42	Wally Joyner	.15	.11	.06
43	Chris Sabo	.10	.08	.04
44	Benito Santiago	.10	.08	.04
45	Mike Stanton	.05	.04	.02
46	Terry Steinbach	.05	.04	.02
47	Dave Stewart	.10	.08	.04
48	Greg Swindell	.05	.04	.02
49	Jose Vizcaino	.05	.04	.02
----	"Royal Flush" (Bret Saberhagen, Mark Davis)	.25	.20	.10

1990 Classic Series III

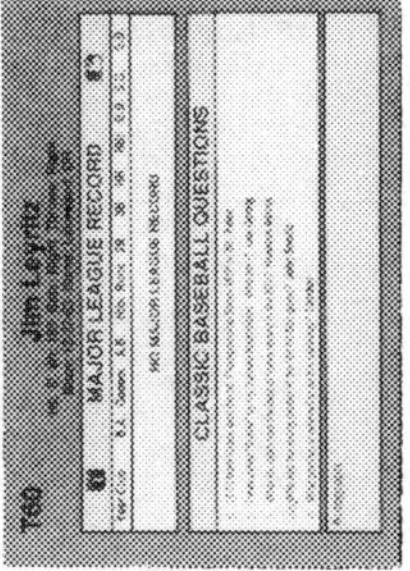

Classic's third series of 1990, features the same style as the previous two releases. The only major difference is the border color. Series III features yellow borders with blue accent. One hundred trivia playing cards are included in Series III. the cards are numbered 1T-100T. No card 51T or 57T exists. Two cards in the set are unnumbered. Like all other Classic issues, the cards are designed for use with the trivia board game.

		MT	NR MT	EX
Complete Set (100):		10.00	7.50	4.00
Common Player:		.05	.04	.02
1	Ken Griffey, Jr.	1.50	1.25	.60
2	John Tudor	.05	.04	.02
3	John Kruk	.10	.08	.04
4	Mark Gardner	.05	.04	.02
5	Scott Radinsky	.20	.15	.08
6	John Burkett	.20	.15	.08
7	Will Clark	.40	.30	.15
8	Gary Carter	.10	.08	.04
9	Ted Higuera	.05	.04	.02
10	Dave Parker	.20	.15	.08
11	Dante Bichette	.05	.04	.02
12	Don Mattingly	.50	.40	.20

13	Greg Harris	.05	.04	.02
14	David Hollins	.10	.08	.04
15	Matt Nokes	.10	.08	.04
16	Kevin Tapani	.05	.04	.02
17	Shane Mack	.05	.04	.02
18	Randy Myers	.05	.04	.02
19	Greg Olson	.05	.04	.02
20	Shawn Abner	.05	.04	.02
21	Jim Presley	.05	.04	.02
22	Randy Johnson	.10	.08	.04
23	Edgar Martinez	.05	.04	.02
24	Scott Coolbaugh	.05	.04	.02
25	Jeff Treadway	.05	.04	.02
26	Joe Klink	.05	.04	.02
27	Rickey Henderson	.30	.25	.12
28	Sam Horn	.05	.04	.02
29	Kurt Stillwell	.05	.04	.02
30	Andy Van Slyke	.10	.08	.04
31	Willie Banks	.20	.15	.08
32	Jose Canseco	.30	.25	.12
33	Felix Jose	.05	.04	.02
34	Candy Maldonado	.05	.04	.02
35	Carlos Baerga	.30	.25	.12
36	Keith Hernandez	.05	.04	.02
37	Frank Viola	.10	.08	.04
38	Pete O'Brien	.05	.04	.02
39	Pat Borders	.05	.04	.02
40	Mike Heath	.05	.04	.02
41	Kevin Brown	.05	.04	.02
42	Chris Bosio	.05	.04	.02
43	Shawn Boskie	.05	.04	.02
44	Carlos Quintana	.05	.04	.02
45	Juan Samuel	.05	.04	.02
46	Tim Layana	.05	.04	.02
47	Mike Harkey	.05	.04	.02
48	Gerald Perry	.05	.04	.02
49	Mike Witt	.05	.04	.02
50	Joe Orsulak	.05	.04	.02
51	(Not issued)			
52	Willie Blair	.10	.08	.04
53	Gene Larkin	.05	.04	.02
54	Jody Reed	.05	.04	.02
55	Jeff Reardon	.05	.04	.02
56	Kevin McReynolds	.05	.04	.02
57	(Not issued)			
58	Eric Yelding	.05	.04	.02
59	Fred Lynn	.05	.04	.02
60	Jim Leyritz	.05	.04	.02
61	John Orton	.05	.04	.02
62	Mike Lieberthal	.20	.15	.08
63	Mike Hartley	.05	.04	.02
64	Kal Daniels	.05	.04	.02
65	Terry Shumpert	.05	.04	.02
66	Sil Campusano	.05	.04	.02
67	Tony Pena	.05	.04	.02
68	Barry Bonds	.35	.25	.14
69	Oddibe McDowell	.05	.04	.02
70	Kelly Gruber	.05	.04	.02
71	Willie Randolph	.05	.04	.02
72	Rick Parker	.05	.04	.02
73	Bobby Bonilla	.20	.15	.08
74	Jack Armstrong	.05	.04	.02
75	Hubie Brooks	.05	.04	.02
76	Sandy Alomar, Jr.	.10	.08	.04
77	Ruben Sierra	.20	.15	.08
78	Erik Hanson	.08	.06	.03
79	Tony Phillips	.05	.04	.02
80	Rondell White	.25	.20	.10
81	Bobby Thigpen	.05	.04	.02
82	Ron Walden	.05	.04	.02
83	Don Peters	.20	.15	.08
84	#6 (Nolan Ryan)	1.00	.70	.40
85	Lance Dickson	.05	.04	.02
86	Ryne Sandberg	.40	.30	.15
87	Eric Christopherson	.05	.04	.02
88	Shane Andrews	.05	.04	.02
89	Marc Newfield	.60	.45	.25
90	Adam Hyzdu	.25	.20	.10
91	"Texas Heat" (Nolan Ryan, Reid Ryan)	2.00	1.50	.80
92	Chipper Jones	.50	.40	.20
93	Frank Thomas	3.00	2.25	1.25
94	Cecil Fielder	.25	.20	.10
95	Delino DeShields	.20	.15	.08
96	John Olerud	.20	.15	.08
97	Dave Justice	1.00	.70	.40
98	Joe Oliver	.10	.08	.04
99	Alex Fernandez	.40	.30	.15
100	Todd Hundley	.20	.15	.08
----	Mike Marshall (Game Instructions On Back)	.05	.04	.02
----	4 in 1 (Frank Viola, Nolan/Reid Ryan, Chipper Jones, Don Mattingly)	.30	.25	.12

1991 Classic

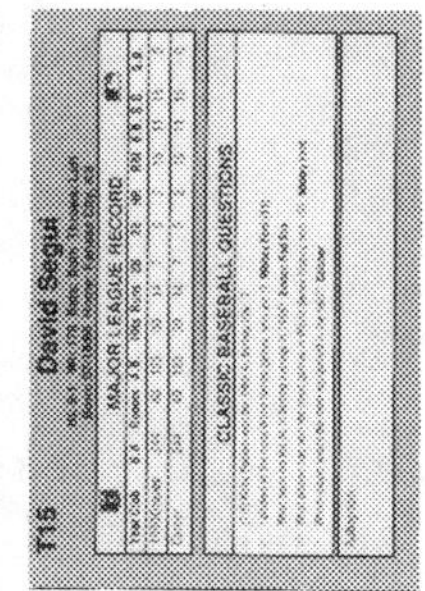

Top rookies and draft picks highlight this 99-card set from Classic. The cards come along with a board game and accessories designed for trivia game use. The card fronts feature fading blue borders with a touch of red. A "4-in-1" micro-player piece is included with each game set.

		MT	NR MT	EX
	Complete Set (99):	8.00	6.00	3.25
	Common Player:	.08	.06	.03
1	John Olerud	.20	.15	.08
2	Tino Martinez	.20	.15	.08
3	Ken Griffey,Jr.	1.00	.70	.40
4	Jeromy Burnitz	.25	.20	.10
5	Ron Gant	.15	.11	.06
6	Mike Benjamin	.08	.06	.03
7	Steve Decker	.10	.08	.04
8	Matt Williams	.10	.08	.04
9	Rafael Novoa	.08	.06	.03
10	Kevin Mitchell	.10	.08	.04
11	Dave Justice	.20	.15	.08
12	Leo Gomez	.20	.15	.08
13	Chris Hoiles	.20	.15	.08
14	Ben McDonald	.10	.08	.04
15	David Segui	.08	.06	.03
16	Anthony Telford	.25	.20	.10
17	Mike Mussina	.60	.45	.25
18	Roger Clemens	.20	.15	.08
19	Wade Boggs	.30	.25	.12
20	Tim Naehring	.10	.08	.04
21	Joe Carter	.10	.08	.04
22	Phil Plantier	.50	.40	.20
23	Rob Dibble	.08	.06	.03
24	Mo Vaughn	.50	.40	.20
25	Lee Stevens	.08	.06	.03
26	Chris Sabo	.10	.08	.04
27	Mark Grace	.15	.11	.06
28	Derrick May	.30	.25	.12
29	Ryne Sandberg	.30	.25	.12
30	Matt Stark	.08	.06	.03
31	Bobby Thigpen	.08	.06	.03
32	Frank Thomas	1.50	1.25	.60
33	Don Mattingly	.04	.11	.06
34	Eric Davis	.15	.11	.06
35	Reggie Jefferson	.20	.15	.08
36	Alex Cole	.08	.06	.03
37	Mark Lewis	.08	.06	.03
38	Tim Costo	.08	.06	.03
39	Sandy Alomar,Jr.	.10	.08	.04
40	Travis Fryman	.50	.40	.20
41	Cecil Fielder	.15	.11	.06
42	Milt Cuyler	.08	.06	.03
43	Andujar Cedeno	.20	.15	.08
44	Danny Darwin	.08	.06	.03
45	Randy Henis	.10	.08	.04
46	George Brett	.04	.08	.04
47	Jeff Conine	.20	.15	.08
48	Bo Jackson	.40	.30	.15
49	Brian McRae	.40	.30	.15
50	Brent Mayne	.20	.15	.08
51	Eddie Murray	.10	.08	.04
52	Ramon Martinez	.10	.08	.04
53	Jim Neidlinger	.10	.08	.04
54	Jim Poole	.10	.08	.04
55	Tim McIntosh	.08	.06	.03
56	Randy Veres	.08	.06	.03
57	Kirby Puckett	.30	.25	.12
58	Todd Ritchie	.08	.06	.03
59	Rich Garces	.08	.06	.03
60	Moises Alou	.12	.09	.05
61	Delino DeShields	.15	.11	.06
62	Oscar Azocar	.08	.06	.03
63	Kevin Maas	.10	.08	.04
64	Alan Mills	.08	.06	.03
65	John Franco	.08	.06	.03
66	Chris Jelic	.20	.15	.08
67	Dave Magadan	.08	.06	.03
68	Darryl Strawberry	.12	.09	.05
69	Hensley Meulens	.08	.06	.03
70	Juan Gonzalez	1.25	.90	.50
71	Reggie Harris	.08	.06	.03
72	Rickey Henderson	.20	.15	.08
73	Mark McGwire	.20	.15	.08
74	Willie McGee	.08	.06	.03
75	Todd Van Poppel	.75	.55	.25
76	Bob Welch	.08	.06	.03
77	"Future Aces" (Todd Van Poppel, Don Peters, David Zancanaro, Kirk Dressendorfer)	1.00	.70	.40
78	Lenny Dykstra	.15	.11	.06
79	Mickey Morandini	.20	.15	.08
80	Wes Chamberlain	.20	.15	.08
81	Barry Bonds	.30	.25	.12
82	Doug Drabek	.08	.06	.03
83	Randy Tomlin	.08	.06	.03
84	Scott Chiamparino	.08	.06	.03
85	Rafael Palmeiro	.15	.11	.06
86	Nolan Ryan	.50	.40	.20
87	Bobby Witt	.08	.06	.03
88	Fred McGriff	.15	.11	.06
89	Dave Steib	.08	.06	.03
90	Ed Sprague	.15	.11	.06
91	Vince Coleman	.08	.06	.03
92	Rod Brewer	.08	.06	.03
93	Bernard Gilkey	.35	.25	.14
94	Roberto Alomar	.20	.15	.08
95	Chuck Finley	.08	.06	.03
96	Dale Murphy	.20	.15	.08
97	Jose Rijo	.10	.08	.04
98	Hal Morris	.08	.06	.03
99	"Friendly Foes" (Dwight Gooden, Darryl Strawberry)	.15	.11	.06

1991 Classic Series II

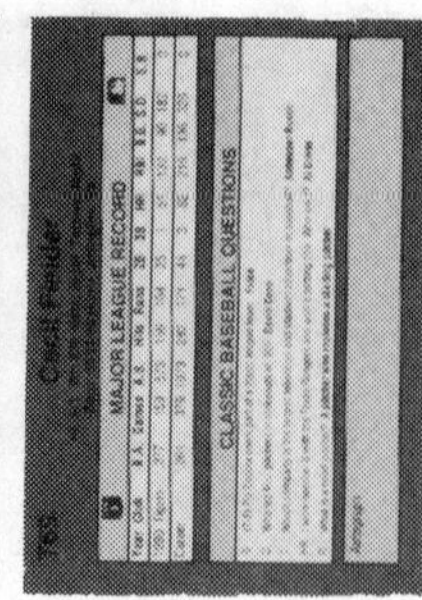

Classic released a 100-card second series in 1991 compared to a 50-card second series in 1990. The cards feature the same style as the first Classic series of 1991 with the exception of the border color. The first series featured blue borders, while Series II features maroon borders. The cards are designed for trivia game use. Series II includes several players with new teams and top rookies. Special Four-In-One, 300 Game Winner and Strikout Kings cards are included with each set.

		MT	NR MT	EX
	Complete Set (100):	8.00	6.00	3.25
	Common Player:	.08	.06	.03
1	Ken Griffey, Jr.	.80	.60	.30
2	Wilfredo Cordero	.25	.20	.10
3	Cal Ripken, Jr.	.40	.30	.15
4	D.J. Dozier	.15	.11	.06
5	Darrin Fletcher	.08	.06	.03
6	Glenn Davis	.08	.06	.03
7	Alex Fernandez	.10	.08	.04
8	Cory Snyder	.08	.06	.03
9	Tim Raines	.10	.08	.04
10	Greg Swindell	.08	.06	.03
11	Mark Lewis	.08	.06	.03
12	Rico Brogna	.20	.15	.08
13	Gary Sheffield	.15	.11	.06
14	Paul Molitor	.15	.11	.06
15	Kent Hrbek	.15	.11	.08
16	Scott Erickson	.20	.15	.08
17	Steve Sax	.08	.06	.03
18	Dennis Eckersley	.10	.08	.04
19	Jose Canseco	.25	.20	.10
20	Kirk Dressendorfer	.20	.15	.08
21	Ken Griffey,Sr.	.08	.06	.03
22	Erik Hanson	.10	.08	.04
23	Dan Peltier	.08	.06	.03
24	John Olerud	.10	.08	.04
25	Eddie Zosky	.15	.11	.06
26	Steve Avery	.20	.15	.08
27	John Smoltz	.10	.08	.04
28	Frank Thomas	1.00	.70	.40
29	Jerome Walton	.08	.06	.03
30	George Bell	.08	.06	.03
31	Jose Rijo	.08	.06	.03
32	Randy Myers	.08	.06	.03
33	Barry Larkin	.10	.08	.04
34	Eric Anthony	.08	.06	.03
35	Dave Hansen	.08	.06	.03
36	Eric Karros	.50	.40	.20
37	Jose Offerman	.08	.06	.03
38	Marquis Grissom	.10	.08	.04
39	Dwight Gooden	.15		.11
40	Gregg Jefferies	.10	.08	.04
41	Pat Combs	.08	.06	.03
42	Todd Zeile	.10	.08	.04
43	Benito Santiago	.10	.08	.04
44	Dave Staton	.08	.06	.03
45	Tony Fernandez	.08	.06	.03
46	Fred McGriff	.10	.08	.04
47	Jeff Brantley	.08	.06	.03
48	Junior Felix	.08	.06	.03
49	Jack Morris	.10	.08	.04
50	Chris George	.10	.08	.04
51	Henry Rodriguez	.25	.20	.10
52	Paul Marak	.10	.08	.04
53	Ryan Klesko	.50	.40	.20
54	Darren Lewis	.15	.11	.06
55	Lance Dickson	.08	.06	.03
56	Anthony Young	.08	.06	.03
57	Willie Banks	.10	.08	.04
58	Mike Bordick	.08	.06	.03
59	Roger Salkeld	.20	.15	.08
60	Steve Karsay	.20	.15	.08
61	Bernie Williams	.08	.06	.03
62	Mickey Tettleton	.10	.08	.04
63	Dave Justice	.15	.11	.06
64	Steve Decker	.08	.06	.03
65	Roger Clemens	.15	.11	.06
66	Phil Plantier	.10	.08	.04
67	Ryne Sandberg	.50	.40	.20
68	Sandy Alomar,Jr.	.10	.08	.04
69	Cecil Fielder	.15	.11	.06
70	George Brett	.50	.40	.20
71	Delino DeShields	.10	.08	.04
72	Dave Magadan	.08	.06	.03
73	Darryl Strawberry	.15	.11	.06
74	Juan Gonzalez	.30	.25	.12
75	Rickey Henderson	.20	.15	.08
76	Willie McGee	.08	.06	.03
77	Todd Van Poppel	.50	.40	.20

78	Barry Bonds	.30	.25	.12
79	Doug Drabek	.08	.06	.03
80	Nolan Ryan (300 games)	.40	.30	.15
81	Roberto Alomar	.15	.11	.06
82	Ivan Rodriguez	1.00	.70	.40
83	Dan Opperman	.08	.06	.03
84	Jeff Bagwell	.50	.40	.20
85	Braulio Castillo	.08	.06	.03
86	Doug Simons	.08	.06	.03
87	Wade Taylor	.15	.11	.06
88	Gary Scott	.08	.06	.03
89	Dave Stewart	.10	.08	.04
90	Mike Simms	.08	.06	.03
91	Luis Gonzalez	.25	.20	.10
92	Bobby Bonilla	.15	.11	.06
93	Tony Gwynn	.15	.11	.06
94	Will Clark	.25	.20	.10
95	Rich Rowland	.08	.06	.03
96	Alan Trammell	.15	.11	.06
97	"Strikeout Kings" (Nolan Ryan, Roger Clemens)	.40	.30	.15
98	Joe Carter	.15	.11	.06
99	Jack Clark	.08	.06	.03
100	Four-In-One	.25	.20	.10

1991 Classic Series III

Green borders highlight Classic's third series of cards for 1991. The set includes a gameboard and player cards featuring trivia questions on the back. Statistics, biographical information and card numbers are also found on the card backs.

		MT	NR MT	EX
	Complete Set (100):	8.00	6.00	3.25
	Common Player:	.06	.05	.02
1	Jim Abbott	.12	.09	.05
2	Craig Biggio	.06	.05	.02
3	Wade Boggs	.30	.25	.12
4	Bobby Bonilla	.15	.11	.06
5	Ivan Calderon	.06	.05	.02
6	Jose Canseco	.20	.15	.08
7	Andy Benes	.12	.09	.05
8	Wes Chamberlain	.12	.09	.05
9	Will Clark	.20	.15	.08
10	Royce Clayton	.20	.15	.08
11	Gerald Alexander	.06	.05	.02
12	Chili Davis	.08	.06	.03
13	Eric Davis	.12	.09	.05
14	Andre Dawson	.15	.11	.06
15	Rob Dibble	.06	.05	.02
16	Chris Donnels	.20	.15	.08
17	Scott Erickson	.12	.09	.05
18	Monty Fariss	.06	.05	.02
19	Ruben Amaro, Jr.	.25	.20	.10
20	Chuck Finley	.08	.06	.03
21	Carlton Fisk	.12	.09	.05
22	Carlos Baerga	.10	.08	.04
23	Ron Gant	.12	.09	.05
24	Dave Justice/ Ron Gant	.30	.25	.12
25	Mike Gardiner	.06	.05	.02
26	Tom Glavine	.10	.08	.04
27	Joe Grahe	.15	.11	.06
28	Derek Bell	.20	.15	.08
29	Mike Greenwell	.08	.06	.03
30	Ken Griffey, Jr.	.50	.40	.20
31	Leo Gomez	.06	.05	.02
32	Tom Goodwin	.15	.11	.06
33	Tony Gwynn	.12	.09	.05
34	Mel Hall	.06	.05	.02
35	Brian Harper	.08	.06	.03
36	Dave Henderson	.06	.05	.02
37	Albert Belle	.20	.15	.08
38	Orel Hershiser	.08	.06	.03
39	Brian Hunter	.12	.09	.05
40	Howard Johnson	.08	.06	.03
41	Felix Jose	.06	.05	.02
42	Wally Joyner	.10	.08	.04
43	Jeff Juden	.15	.11	.06
44	Pat Kelly	.12	.09	.05
45	Jimmy Key	.06	.05	.02
46	Chuck Knoblauch	.15	.11	.06
47	John Kruk	.12	.09	.05
48	Ray Lankford	.20	.15	.08
49	Ced Landrum	.06	.05	.02
50	Scott Livingstone	.12	.09	.05
51	Kevin Maas	.06	.05	.02
52	Greg Maddux	.08	.06	.03
53	Dennis Martinez	.06	.05	.02
54	Edgar Martinez	.06	.05	.02
55	Pedro Martinez	.08	.06	.03
56	Don Mattingly	.30	.25	.12
57	Orlando Merced	.30	.25	.12
58	Keith Mitchell	.10	.08	.04
59	Kevin Mitchell	.10	.08	.04
60	Paul Molitor	.12	.09	.05
61	Jack Morris	.08	.06	.03
62	Hal Morris	.06	.05	.02
63	Kevin Morton	.12	.09	.05
64	Pedro Munoz	.20	.15	.08
65	Eddie Murray	.15	.11	.06
66	Jack McDowell	.10	.08	.04
67	Jeff McNeely	.25	.20	.10
68	Brian McRae	.20	.15	.08
69	Kevin McReynolds	.06	.05	.02
70	Gregg Olson	.06	.05	.02
71	Rafael Palmeiro	.12	.09	.05
72	Dean Palmer	.12	.09	.05
73	Tony Phillips	.06	.05	.02
74	Kirby Puckett	.20	.15	.08
75	Carlos Quintana	.06	.05	.02
76	Pat Rice	.06	.05	.02
77	Cal Ripken, Jr.	.30	.25	.12
78	Ivan Rodriguez	1.00	.70	.40
79	Nolan Ryan	.50	.40	.20
80	Bret Saberhagen	.08	.06	.03
81	Tim Salmon	.75	.55	.25
82	Juan Samuel	.06	.05	.02
83	Ruben Sierra	.12	.09	.05
84	Heathcliff Slocumb	.06	.05	.02
85	Joe Slusarski	.12	.09	.05
86	John Smiley	.06	.05	.02
87	Dave Smith	.06	.05	.02
88	Ed Sprague	.08	.06	.03
89	Todd Stottlemyre	.06	.05	.02
90	Mike Timlin	.12	.09	.05
91	Greg Vaughn	.08	.06	.03
92	Frank Viola	.08	.06	.03
93	John Wehner	.08	.06	.03
94	Devon White	.08	.06	.03
95	Matt Williams	.15	.11	.06
96	Rick Wilkins	.15	.11	.06
97	Bernie Williams	.12	.09	.05
98	Starter & Stopper (Nolan Ryan, Goose Gossage)	.20	.15	.08
99	Gerald Williams	.30	.25	.12
----	4-In-1 (Bobby Bonilla, Will Clark, Cal Ripken Jr., Scott Erickson)	.20	.15	.08

1991 Classic Collector's Edition

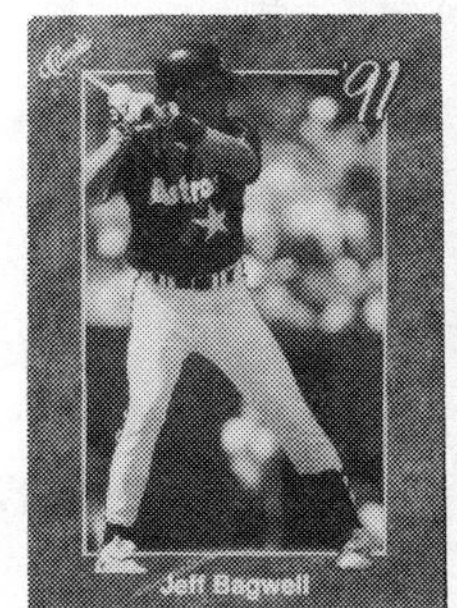

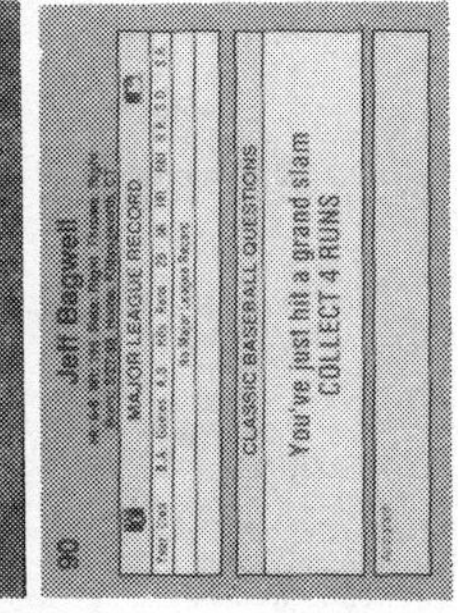

The Classic Collector's edition made its debut in 1991. This package includes a board game, trivia baseball cards, a baseball tips booklet and a certificate of authenticity. It is all packaged in an attractive collector's edition box. Each box is individually and sequentially numbered on the outside. This issue was limited with only 100,000 available. The card set features 200 trivia baseball cards. Mickey Morandini's card features a photo of Darren Daulton.

		MT	NR MT	EX
	Complete Set (200):	25.00	18.00	13.00
	Common Player:	.08	.06	.03
1	Frank Viola	.10	.08	.04
2	Tim Wallach	.08	.06	.03
3	Lou Whitaker	.10	.08	.04
4	Brett Butler	.08	.06	.03
5	Jim Abbott	.10	.08	.04
6	Jack Armstrong	.08	.06	.03
7	Craig Biggio	.08	.06	.03
8	Brian Barnes	.08	.06	.03
9	Dennis "Oil Can" Boyd	.08	.06	.03
10	Tom Browning	.08	.06	.03
11	Tom Brunansky	.08	.06	.03
12	Ellis Burks	.08	.06	.03
13	Harold Baines	.10	.08	.04
14	Kal Daniels	.08	.06	.03
15	Mark Davis	.08	.06	.03
16	Storm Davis	.08	.06	.03
17	Tom Glavine	.12	.09	.05
18	Mike Greenwell	.10	.08	.04
19	Kelly Gruber	.08	.06	.03
20	Mark Gubicza	.08	.06	.03
21	Pedro Guerrero	.08	.06	.03
22	Mike Harkey	.08	.06	.03
23	Orel Hershiser	.10	.08	.04
24	Ted Higuera	.08	.06	.03
25	Von Hayes	.08	.06	.03
26	Andre Dawson	.15	.11	.06
27	Shawon Dunston	.08	.06	.03
28	Roberto Kelly	.10	.08	.04
29	Joe Magrane	.08	.06	.03
30	Dennis Martinez	.10	.08	.04
31	Kevin McReynolds	.08	.06	.03
32	Matt Nokes	.10	.08	.04
33	Dan Plesac	.08	.06	.03
34	Dave Parker	.15	.11	.06
35	Randy Johnson	.10	.08	.04
36	Bret Saberhagen	.10	.08	.04
37	Mackey Sasser	.08	.06	.03
38	Mike Scott	.08	.06	.03
39	Ozzie Smith	.15	.11	.06
40	Kevin Seitzer	.08	.06	.03
41	Ruben Sierra	.12	.09	.05
42	Kevin Tapani	.08	.06	.03
43	Danny Tartabull	.12	.09	.05
44	Robby Thompson	.08	.06	.03
45	Andy Van Slyke	.12	.09	.05
46	Greg Vaughn	.12	.09	.05
47	Harold Reynolds	.10	.08	.04
48	Will Clark	.40	.30	.15
49	Gary Gaetti	.10	.08	.04
50	Joe Grahe	.08	.06	.03
51	Carlton Fisk	.20	.15	.08
52	Robin Ventura	.12	.09	.05
53	Ozzie Guillen	.10	.08	.04
54	Tom Candiotti	.08	.06	.03
55	Doug Jones	.08	.06	.03
56	Eric King	.08	.06	.03
57	Kirk Gibson	.12	.09	.05
58	Tim Costo	.08	.06	.03
59	Robin Yount	.25	.20	.10
60	Sammy Sosa	.20	.15	.08
61	Jesse Barfield	.08	.06	.03
62	Marc Newfield	.50	.40	.20
63	Jimmy Key	.08	.06	.03
64	Felix Jose	.08	.06	.03
65	Mark Whiten	.50	.40	.20
66	Tommy Greene	.08	.06	.03
67	Kent Mercker	.08	.06	.03
68	Greg Maddux	.10	.08	.04
69	Danny Jackson	.08	.06	.03
70	Reggie Sanders	.25	.20	.10
71	Eric Yelding	.08	.06	.03
72	Karl Rhodes	.20	.15	.08
73	Fernando Valenzuela	.10	.08	.04
74	Chris Nabholz	.10	.08	.04
75	Andres Galarraga	.10	.08	.04
76	Howard Johnson	.12	.09	.05
77	Hubie Brooks	.08	.06	.03
78	Terry Mulholland	.08	.06	.03
79	Paul Molitor	.15	.11	.06
80	Roger McDowell	.08	.06	.03
81	Darren Daulton	.10	.08	.04
82	Zane Smith	.08	.06	.03
83	Ray Lankford	.12	.09	.05
84	Bruce Hurst	.08	.06	.03
85	Andy Benes	.12	.09	.05
86	John Burkett	.10	.08	.04
87	Dave Righetti	.08	.06	.03
88	Steve Karsay	.40	.30	.15
89	D.J. Dozier	.40	.30	.15
90	Jeff Bagwell	.50	.40	.20
91	Joe Carter	.20	.15	.08
92	Wes Chamberlain	.12	.09	.05
93	Vince Coleman	.10	.08	.04
94	Pat Combs	.08	.06	.03
95	Jerome Walton	.08	.06	.03
96	Jeff Conine	.40	.30	.15
97	Alan Trammell	.15	.11	.06
98	Don Mattingly	.40	.30	.15
99	Ramon Martinez	.10	.08	.04
100	Dave Magadan	.08	.06	.03
101	Greg Swindell	.08	.06	.03
102	Dave Stewart	.10	.08	.04
103	Gary Sheffield	.15	.11	.06
104	George Bell	.10	.08	.04
105	Mark Grace	.15	.11	.06
106	Steve Sax	.08	.06	.03
107	Ryne Sandberg	.50	.40	.20
108	Chris Sabo	.10	.08	.04
109	Jose Rijo	.10	.08	.04
110	Cal Ripken, Jr.	.80	.60	.30
111	Kirby Puckett	.40	.30	.15
112	Eddie Murray	.20	.15	.08
113	Roberto Alomar	.30	.25	.12
114	Randy Myers	.08	.06	.03
115	Rafael Palmeiro	.15	.11	.06
116	John Olerud	.15	.11	.06
117	Gregg Jefferies	.12	.09	.05
118	Kent Hrbek	.12	.09	.05
119	Marquis Grissom	.12	.09	.05
120	Ken Griffey, Jr.	1.50	1.25	.60
121	Dwight Gooden	.20	.15	.08
122	Juan Gonzalez	.30	.25	.12
123	Ron Gant	.12	.09	.05
124	Travis Fryman	.12	.09	.05
125	John Franco	.08	.06	.03
126	Dennis Eckersley	.12	.09	.05
127	Cecil Fielder	.15	.11	.06
128	Phil Plantier	.50	.40	.20
129	Kevin Mitchell	.12	.09	.05
130	Kevin Maas	.08	.06	.03
131	Mark McGwire	.20	.15	.08
132	Ben McDonald	.10	.08	.04
133	Lenny Dykstra	.12	.09	.05
134	Delino DeShields	.12	.09	.05
135	Jose Canseco	.40	.30	.15
136	Eric Davis	.20	.15	.08
137	George Brett	.40	.30	.15
138	Steve Avery	.12	.09	.05
139	Eric Anthony	.10	.08	.04
140	Bobby Thigpen	.08	.06	.03
141	Ken Griffey, Sr.	.08	.06	.03
142	Barry Larkin	.12	.09	.05
143	Jeff Brantley	.08	.06	.03
144	Bobby Bonilla	.15	.11	.06
145	Jose Offerman	.08	.06	.03
146	Mike Mussina	.30	.25	.12
147	Erik Hanson	.10	.08	.04

148	Dale Murphy	.25	.20	.10
149	Roger Clemens	.30	.25	.12
150	Tino Martinez	.25	.20	.10
151	Todd Van Poppel	.75	.55	.25
152	Mo Vaughn	1.00	.70	.40
153	Derrick May	.20	.15	.08
154	Jack Clark	.08	.06	.03
155	Dave Hansen	.08	.06	.03
156	Tony Gwynn	.15	.11	.06
157	Brian McRae	.30	.25	.12
158	Matt Williams	.15	.11	.06
159	Kirk Dressendorfer	.30	.25	.12
160	Scott Erickson	.20	.15	.08
161	Tony Fernandez	.10	.08	.04
162	Willie McGee	.08	.06	.03
163	Fred McGriff	.12	.09	.05
164	Leo Gomez	.08	.06	.03
165	Bernard Gilkey	.30	.25	.12
166	Bobby Witt	.08	.06	.03
167	Doug Drabek	.08	.06	.03
168	Rob Dibble	.08	.06	.03
169	Glenn Davis	.08	.06	.03
170	Danny Darwin	.08	.06	.03
171	Eric Karros	.50	.40	.20
172	Eddie Zosky	.20	.15	.08
173	Todd Zeile	.12	.09	.05
174	Tim Raines	.12	.09	.05
175	Benito Santiago	.12	.09	.05
176	Dan Peltier	.20	.15	.08
177	Darryl Strawberry	.30	.25	.12
178	Hal Morris	.08	.06	.03
179	Hensley Meulens	.08	.06	.03
180	John Smoltz	.10	.08	.04
181	Frank Thomas	2.50	2.00	1.00
182	Dave Staton	.15	.11	.06
183	Scott Chiamparino	.08	.06	.03
184	Alex Fernandez	.30	.25	.12
185	Mark Lewis	.08	.06	.03
186	Bo Jackson	1.25	.90	.50
187	Mickey Morandini (photo actually Darren Daulton)	.30	.25	.12
188	Cory Snyder	.08	.06	.03
189	Rickey Henderson	.25	.20	.10
190	Junior Felix	.08	.06	.03
191	Milt Cuyler	.08	.06	.03
192	Wade Boggs	.30	.25	.12
193	"Justice Prevails" (David Justice)	.30	.25	.12
194	Sandy Alomar, Jr.	.12	.09	.05
195	Barry Bonds	.40	.30	.15
196	Nolan Ryan	1.00	.70	.40
197	Rico Brogna	.15	.11	.06
198	Steve Decker	.08	.06	.03
199	Bob Welch	.10	.08	.04
200	Andujar Cedeno	.12	.09	.05

1992 Classic Series I

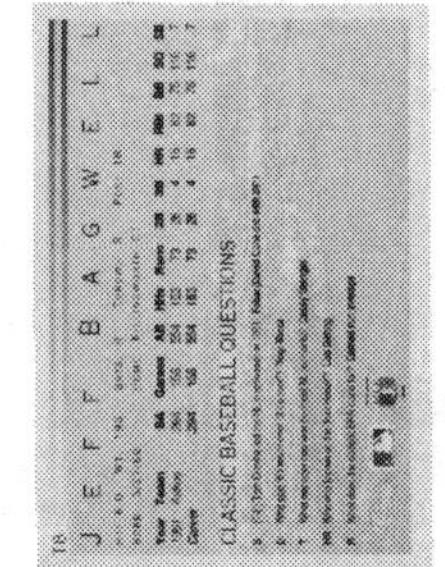

Classic introduced a new innovative design with the release of its 1992 set. The card fronts feature full-color photos bordered in white, while the flip sides feature statistics, biographical information and trivia questions accented by a fading stadium shot. The cards were released with a gameboard and are numbered on the back with a "T" prefix.

		MT	NR MT	EX
Complete Set (100):		8.00	6.00	3.25
Common Player:		.06	.05	.02
1	Jim Abbott	.12	.09	.05
2	Kyle Abbott	.10	.08	.04
3	Scott Aldred	.06	.05	.02
4	Roberto Alomar	.20	.15	.08
5	Wilson Alvarez	.08	.06	.03
6	Andy Ashby	.06	.05	.02
7	Steve Avery	.12	.09	.05
8	Jeff Bagwell	.12	.09	.05
9	Bret Barberie	.12	.09	.05
10	Kim Batiste	.10	.08	.04
11	Derek Bell	.10	.08	.04
12	Jay Bell	.10	.08	.04
13	Albert Belle	.15	.11	.06
14	Andy Benes	.10	.08	.04
15	Sean Berry	.08	.06	.03
16	Barry Bonds	.25	.20	.10
17	Ryan Bowen	.10	.08	.04
18	Trifecta (Alejandro Pena, Mark Wohlers, Kent Mercker)	.06	.05	.02
19	Scott Brosius	.06	.05	.02
20	Jay Buhner	.10	.08	.04
21	David Burba	.06	.05	.02
22	Jose Canseco	.25	.20	.10
23	Andujar Cedeno	.08	.06	.03
24	Will Clark	.25	.20	.10
25	Royce Clayton	.06	.05	.02
26	Roger Clemens	.20	.15	.08
27	David Cone	.08	.06	.03
28	Scott Cooper	.08	.06	.03
29	Chris Cron	.06	.05	.02
30	Len Dykstra	.10	.08	.04
31	Cal Eldred	.08	.06	.03
32	Hector Fajardo	.10	.08	.04
33	Cecil Fielder	.10	.08	.04
34	Dave Fleming	.10	.08	.04
35	Steve Foster	.06	.05	.02
36	Julio Franco	.06	.05	.02
37	Carlos Garcia	.06	.05	.02
38	Tom Glavine	.10	.08	.04
39	Tom Goodwin	.06	.05	.02
40	Ken Griffey, Jr.	.60	.45	.25
41	Chris Haney	.06	.05	.02
42	Bryan Harvey	.08	.06	.03
43	Rickey Henderson	.25	.20	.10
44	Carlos Hernandez	.06	.05	.02
45	Roberto Hernandez	.06	.05	.02
46	Brook Jacoby	.06	.05	.02
47	Howard Johnson	.10	.08	.04
48	Pat Kelly	.06	.05	.02
49	Darryl Kile	.08	.06	.03
50	Chuck Knoblauch	.12	.09	.05
51	Ray Lankford	.12	.09	.05
52	Mark Leiter	.06	.05	.02
53	Darren Lewis	.08	.06	.03
54	Scott Livingstone	.08	.06	.03
55	Shane Mack	.10	.08	.04
56	Chito Martinez	.20	.15	.08
57	Dennis Martinez	.06	.05	.02
58	Don Mattingly	.25	.20	.10
59	Paul McClellan	.06	.05	.02
60	Chuck McElroy	.06	.05	.02
61	Fred McGriff	.12	.09	.05
62	Orlando Merced	.10	.08	.04
63	Luis Mercedes	.08	.06	.03
64	Kevin Mitchell	.08	.06	.03
65	Hal Morris	.08	.06	.03
66	Jack Morris	.08	.06	.03
67	Mike Mussina	.12	.09	.05
68	Denny Neagle	.20	.15	.08
69	Tom Pagnozzi	.06	.05	.02
70	Terry Pendleton	.08	.06	.03
71	Phil Plantier	.10	.08	.04
72	Kirby Puckett	.15	.11	.06
73	Carlos Quintana	.06	.05	.02
74	Willie Randolph	.06	.05	.02
75	Arthur Rhodes	.08	.06	.03
76	Cal Ripken	.25	.20	.10
77	Ivan Rodriguez	.15	.11	.06
78	Nolan Ryan	.35	.25	.12
79	Ryne Sandberg	.25	.20	.10
80	Deion Sanders	.20	.15	.08
81	Reggie Sanders	.20	.15	.08
82	Mo Sanford	.15	.11	.06
83	Terry Shumpert	.06	.05	.02
84	Tim Spehr	.06	.05	.02
85	Lee Stevens	.06	.05	.02
86	Darryl Strawberry	.15	.11	.06
87	Kevin Tapani	.06	.05	.02
88	Danny Tartabull	.08	.06	.03
89	Frank Thomas	.80	.60	.30
90	Jim Thome	.20	.15	.08
91	Todd Van Poppel	.20	.15	.08
92	Andy Van Slyke	.08	.06	.03
93	John Wehner	.06	.05	.02
94	John Wetteland	.06	.05	.02
95	Devon White	.08	.06	.03
96	Brian Williams	.10	.08	.04
97	Mark Wohlers	.10	.08	.04
98	Robin Yount	.25	.20	.10
99	Eddie Zosky	.08	.06	.03
----	4-in-1 (Barry Bonds, Roger Clemens, Steve Avery, Nolan Ryan)	.12	.09	.05

1992 Classic Series II

The 100-cards in Classic's 1992 Series II came packaged with a gameboard and spinner. In a completely different format from Classic's other '92 issues, Series II features player photos bordered at left and right with red or blue color bars which fade toward top and bottom. The player's name is presented in a blue bar beneath the photo. Card backs have biographical data, previous-year and career statistics and five trivia questions, along with a color representation of the team's uniform. Cards, except the 4-In-1, are numbered with a "T" prefix.

		MT	NR MT	EX
Complete Set (100):		8.00	6.00	3.00
Common Player:		.06	.05	.02
1	Jim Abbott	.15	.11	.06
2	Jeff Bagwell	.12	.09	.05
3	Jose Canseco	.35	.25	.14
4	Julio Valera	.06	.05	.02
5	Scott Brosius	.06	.05	.02
6	Mark Langston	.10	.08	.04
7	Andy Stankiewicz	.06	.05	.02
8	Gary DiSarcina	.06	.05	.02
9	Pete Harnisch	.08	.06	.03
10	Mark McGwire	.20	.15	.08
11	Ricky Bones	.10	.08	.04
12	Steve Avery	.15	.11	.06
13	Deion Sanders	.25	.20	.10
14	Mike Mussina	.12	.09	.05
15	Dave Justice	.15	.11	.06
16	Pat Hentgen	.06	.05	.02
17	Tom Glavine	.12	.09	.05
18	Juan Guzman	.08	.06	.03
19	Ron Gant	.10	.08	.04
20	Kelly Gruber	.06	.05	.02
21	Eric Karros	.12	.09	.05
22	Derrick May	.08	.06	.03
23	Dave Hansen	.06	.05	.02
24	Andre Dawson	.12	.09	.05
25	Eric Davis	.15	.11	.06
26	Ozzie Smith	.15	.11	.06
27	Sammy Sosa	.10	.08	.04
28	Lee Smith	.10	.08	.04
29	Ryne Sandberg	.25	.20	.10
30	Robin Yount	.20	.15	.08
31	Matt Williams	.12	.09	.05
32	John Vander Wal	.06	.05	.02
33	Bill Swift	.06	.05	.02
34	Delino DeShields	.10	.08	.04
35	Royce Clayton	.06	.05	.02
36	Moises Alou	.08	.06	.03
37	Will Clark	.20	.15	.08
38	Darryl Strawberry	.20	.15	.08
39	Larry Walker	.10	.08	.04
40	Ramon Martinez	.06	.05	.02
41	Howard Johnson	.10	.08	.04
42	Tino Martinez	.06	.05	.02
43	Dwight Gooden	.15	.11	.06
44	Ken Griffey, Jr.	.45	.35	.20
45	David Cone	.08	.06	.03
46	Kenny Lofton	.06	.05	.02
47	Bobby Bonilla	.12	.09	.05
48	Carlos Baerga	.10	.08	.04
49	Don Mattingly	.25	.20	.10
50	Sandy Alomar, Jr.	.08	.06	.03
51	Lenny Dykstra	.12	.09	.05
52	Tony Gwynn	.15	.11	.06
53	Felix Jose	.06	.05	.02
54	Rick Sutcliffe	.06	.05	.02
55	Wes Chamberlain	.06	.05	.02
56	Cal Ripken, Jr.	.25	.20	.10
57	Kyle Abbott	.06	.05	.02
58	Leo Gomez	.06	.05	.02
59	Gary Sheffield	.12	.09	.05
60-	Anthony Young	.06	.05	.02
61-	Roger Clemens	.15	.11	.06
62-	Rafael Palmeiro	.15	.11	.06
63-	Wade Boggs	.20	.15	.08
64-	Andy Van Slyke	.12	.09	.05
65-	Ruben Sierra	.12	.09	.05
66-	Denny Neagle	.06	.05	.02
67-	Nolan Ryan	.45	.35	.20
68-	Doug Drabek	.08	.06	.03
69-	Ivan Rodriguez	.10	.08	.04
70-	Barry Bonds	.20	.15	.08
71-	Chuck Knoblauch	.10	.08	.04
72-	Reggie Sanders	.08	.06	.03
73-	Cecil Fielder	.15	.11	.06
74-	Barry Larkin	.12	.09	.05
75-	Scott Aldred	.06	.05	.02
76-	Rob Dibble	.06	.05	.02
77-	Brian McRae	.10	.08	.04
78-	Tim Belcher	.06	.05	.02
79-	George Brett	.25	.20	.10
80-	Frank Viola	.08	.06	.03
81-	Roberto Kelly	.08	.06	.03
82-	Jack McDowell	.10	.08	.04
83-	Mel Hall	.06	.05	.02
84-	Esteban Beltre	.15	.11	.06
85-	Robin Ventura	.12	.09	.05
86-	George Bell	.10	.08	.04
87-	Frank Thomas	.45	.35	.20
88-	John Smiley	.06	.05	.02
89-	Bobby Thigpen	.06	.05	.02
90-	Kirby Puckett	.20	.15	.08
91-	Kevin Mitchell	.08	.06	.03
92-	Peter Hoy	.15	.11	.06
93-	Russ Springer	.15	.11	.06
94-	Donovan Osborne	.06	.05	.02
95-	Dave Silvestri	.15	.11	.06
96-	Chad Curtis	.15	.11	.06
97-	Pat Mahomes	.06	.05	.02
98-	Danny Tartabull	.10	.08	.04
99-	John Doherty	.15	.11	.06
-----	4-In-1 (Ryne Sandberg, Mike Mussina, Reggie Sanders, Jose Canseco)	.20	.15	.08

Values quoted in this guide reflect the retail price of a card – the price a collector can expect to pay when buying a card from a dealer. The wholesale price – that which a collector can expect to receive from a dealer when selling cards – will be significantly lower, depending on desirability and condition.

1992 Classic Collector's Edition

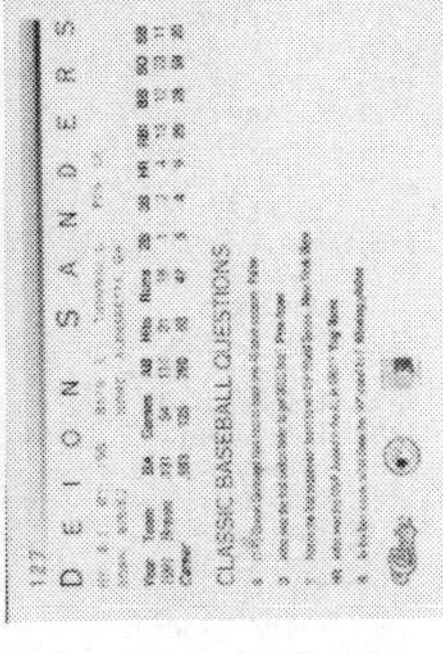

The second annual 200-card "Collector's Edition" set was packaged with a gameboard, spinner, generic player pieces a mechanical scoreboard and a book of tips from star players. The UV-coated card fronts feature color player photos against a deep purple border. The Classic logo, year of issue and player's name aare reversed out of the top and bottom borders. Card backs have a few biographical details, stats from the previous season and career totals, plus five trivia questions in case anyone actually decided to play the game.

		MT	NR MT	EX
Complete Set (200):		20.00	15.00	8.00
Common Player:		.06	.05	.02
1	Chuck Finley	.06	.05	.02
2	Craig Biggio	.08	.06	.03
3	Luis Gonzalez	.06	.05	.02
4	Pete Harnisch	.08	.06	.03
5	Jeff Juden	.06	.05	.02
6	Harold Baines	.08	.06	.03
7	Kirk Dressendorfer	.06	.05	.02
8	Dennis Eckersley	.10	.08	.04
9	Dave Henderson	.06	.05	.02
10	Dave Stewart	.10	.08	.04
11	Joe Carter	.15	.11	.06
12	Juan Guzman	.08	.06	.03
13	Dave Stieb	.06	.05	.02
14	Todd Stottlemyre	.06	.05	.02
15	Ron Gant	.12	.05	.02
16	Brian Hunter	.06	.05	.02
17	Dave Justice	.15	.11	.06
18	John Smoltz	.10	.08	.04
19	Mike Stanton	.06	.05	.02
20	Chris George	.06	.05	.02
21	Paul Molitor	.15	.11	.06
22	Omar Olivares	.06	.05	.02
23	Lee Smith	.08	.06	.03
24	Ozzie Smith	.15	.11	.06
25	Todd Zeile	.08	.06	.03
26	George Bell	.08	.06	.03
27	Andre Dawson	.15	.11	.06
28	Shawon Dunston	.06	.05	.02
29	Mark Grace	.12	.05	.02
30	Greg Maddux	.12	.05	.02
31	Dave Smith	.06	.05	.02
32	Brett Butler	.06	.05	.02
33	Orel Hershiser	.12	.05	.02
34	Eric Karros	.10	.08	.04
35	Ramon Martinez	.06	.05	.02
36	Jose Offerman	.06	.05	.02
37	Juan Samuel	.06	.05	.02
38	Delino DeShields	.12	.05	.02
39	Marquis Grissom	.08	.06	.03
40	Tim Wallach	.06	.05	.02
41	Eric Gunderson	.06	.05	.02
42	Willie McGee	.08	.06	.03
43	Dave Righetti	.06	.05	.02
44	Robby Thompson	.08	.06	.03
45	Matt Williams	.10	.08	.04
46	Sandy Alomar, Jr.	.08	.06	.03
47	Reggie Jefferson	.06	.05	.02
48	Mark Lewis	.06	.05	.02
49	Robin Ventura	.12	.05	.02
50	Tino Martinez	.06	.05	.02
51	Roberto Kelly	.08	.06	.03
52	Vince Coleman	.08	.06	.03
53	Dwight Gooden	.15	.11	.06
54	Todd Hundley	.06	.05	.02
55	Kevin Maas	.06	.05	.02
56	Wade Taylor	.06	.05	.02
57	Bryan Harvey	.08	.06	.03
58	Leo Gomez	.06	.05	.02
59	Ben McDonald	.08	.06	.03
60	Ricky Bones	.06	.05	.02
61	Tony Gwynn	.12	.05	.02
62	Benito Santiago	.10	.08	.04
63	Wes Chamberlain	.06	.05	.02
64	Tommy Greene	.06	.05	.02
65	Dale Murphy	.15	.11	.06
66	Steve Buechele	.06	.05	.02
67	Doug Drabek	.06	.05	.02
68	Joe Grahe	.06	.05	.02
69	Rafael Palmeiro	.15	.11	.06
70	Wade Boggs	.20	.15	.08
71	Ellis Burks	.08	.06	.03
72	Mike Greenwell	.08	.06	.03
73	Mo Vaughn	.12	.05	.02
74	Derek Bell	.06	.05	.02
75	Rob Dibble	.06	.05	.02
76	Barry Larkin	.12	.05	.02
77	Jose Rijo	.10	.08	.04
78	Doug Henry	.06	.05	.02
79	Chris Sabo	.08	.06	.03
80	Pedro Guerrero	.06	.05	.02
81	George Brett	.20	.15	.08
82	Tom Gordon	.06	.05	.02
83	Mark Gubicza	.06	.05	.02
84	Mark Whiten	.06	.05	.02
85	Brian McRae	.08	.06	.03
86	Danny Jackson	.06	.05	.02
87	Milt Cuyler	.06	.05	.02
88	Travis Fryman	.10	.08	.04
89	Mickey Tettleton	.10	.08	.04
90	Alan Trammell	.15	.11	.06
91	Lou Whitaker	.12	.05	.02
92	Chili Davis	.10	.08	.04
93	Scott Erickson	.06	.05	.02
94	Kent Hrbek	.12	.05	.02
95	Alex Fernandez	.08	.06	.03
96	Carlton Fisk	.12	.05	.02
97	Ramon Garcia	.06	.05	.02
98	Ozzie Guillen	.08	.06	.03
99	Tim Raines	.12	.05	.02
100	Bobby Thigpen	.06	.05	.02
101	Kirby Puckett	.15	.11	.06
102	Bernie Williams	.06	.05	.02
103	Dave Hansen	.06	.05	.02
104	Kevin Tapani	.06	.05	.02
105	Don Mattingly	.20	.15	.08
106	Frank Thomas	.50	.40	.20
107	Monty Fariss	.06	.05	.02
108	Bo Jackson	.45	.35	.20
109	Jim Abbott	.15	.11	.06
110	Jose Canseco	.25	.20	.10
111	Phil Plantier	.10	.08	.04
112	Brian Williams	.06	.05	.02
113	Mark Langston	.06	.05	.02
114	Wilson Alvarez	.06	.05	.02
115	Roberto Hernandez	.06	.05	.02
116	Darryl Kile	.08	.06	.03
117	Ryan Bowen	.15	.11	.06
118	Rickey Henderson	.15	.11	.06
119	Mark McGwire	.15	.11	.06
120	Devon White	.10	.08	.04
121	Roberto Alomar	.15	.11	.06
122	Kelly Gruber	.06	.05	.02
123	Eddie Zosky	.06	.05	.02
124	Tom Glavine	.08	.06	.03
125	Kal Daniels	.06	.05	.02
126	Cal Eldred	.06	.05	.02
127	Deion Sanders	.25	.20	.10
128	Robin Yount	.20	.15	.08
129	Cecil Fielder	.15	.11	.06
130	Ray Lankford	.08	.06	.03
131	Ryne Sandberg	.25	.20	.10
132	Darryl Strawberry	.20	.15	.08
133	Chris Haney	.06	.05	.02
134	Dennis Martinez	.06	.05	.02
135	Bryan Hickerson	.06	.05	.02
136	Will Clark	.15	.11	.06
137	Hal Morris	.06	.05	.02
138	Charles Nagy	.06	.05	.02
139	Jim Thome	.06	.05	.02
140	Albert Belle	.15	.11	.06
141	Reggie Sanders	.12	.05	.02
142	Scott Cooper	.10	.08	.04
143	David Cone	.06	.05	.02
144	Anthony Young	.06	.05	.02
145	Howard Johnson	.12	.05	.02
146	Arthur Rhodes	.08	.06	.03
147	Scott Aldred	.06	.05	.02
148	Mike Mussina	.10	.08	.04
149	Fred McGriff	.15	.11	.06
150	Andy Benes	.10	.08	.04
151	Ruben Sierra	.15	.11	.06
152	Len Dykstra	.15	.11	.06
153	Andy Van Slyke	.10	.08	.04
154	Orlando Merced	.06	.05	.02
155	Barry Bonds	.20	.15	.08
156	John Smiley	.06	.05	.02
157	Julio Franco	.06	.05	.02
158	Juan Gonzalez	.25	.20	.10
159	Ivan Rodriguez	.15	.11	.06
160	Willie Banks	.06	.05	.02
161	Eric Davis	.15	.11	.06
162	Eddie Murray	.15	.11	.06
163	Dave Fleming	.06	.05	.02
164	Wally Joyner	.15	.11	.06
165	Kevin Mitchell	.08	.06	.03
166	Ed Taubensee	.06	.05	.02
167	Danny Tartabull	.10	.08	.04
168	Ken Hill	.06	.05	.02
169	Willie Randolph	.06	.05	.02
170	Kevin McReynolds	.08	.06	.03
171	Gregg Jefferies	.12	.05	.02
172	Patrick Lennon	.06	.05	.02
173	Luis Mercedes	.06	.05	.02
174	Glenn Davis	.06	.05	.02
175	Bret Saberhagen	.08	.06	.03
176	Bobby Bonilla	.12	.05	.02
177	Kenny Lofton	.08	.06	.03
178	Jose Lind	.08	.06	.03
179	Royce Clayton	.06	.05	.02
180	Scott Scudder	.06	.05	.02
181	Chuck Knoblauch	.08	.06	.03
182	Terry Pendleton	.08	.06	.03
183	Nolan Ryan	.50	.40	.20
184	Rob Maurer	.06	.05	.02
185	Brian Bohanon	.06	.05	.02
186	Ken Griffey, Jr.	.50	.40	.20
187	Jeff Bagwell	.10	.08	.04
188	Steve Avery	.12	.05	.02
189	Roger Clemens	.15	.11	.06
190	Cal Ripken, Jr	.25	.20	.10
191	Kim Batiste	.06	.05	.02
192	Bip Roberts	.06	.05	.02
193	Greg Swindell	.06	.05	.02
194	Dave Winfield	.15	.11	.06
195	Steve Sax	.06	.05	.02
196	Frank Viola	.08	.06	.03
197	Mo Sanford	.06	.05	.02
198	Kyle Abbott	.06	.05	.02
199	Jack Morris	.08	.06	.03
200	Andy Ashby	.06	.05	.02

1993 Classic

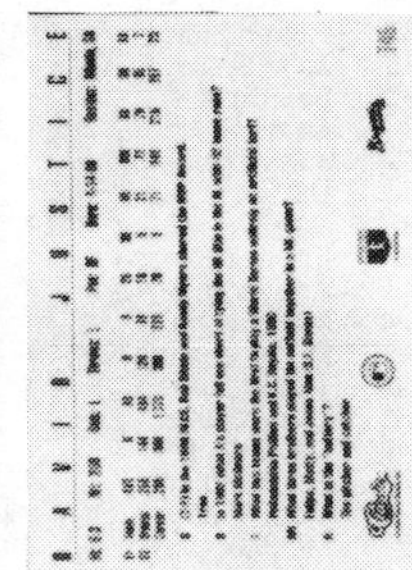

A 100-card travel edition of Classic's baseball trivia cards was produced for 1993. Cards feature game-action player photos with drak blue borders. A "Series 1993" logo appears in the upper-left corner of the photo. Backs have previous season and career stats along with five trivia questions. Cards are numbered in red with a "T" prefix.

		MT	NR MT	EX
Complete Set (100):		8.00	6.00	3.25
Common Player:		.10	.08	.04
1	Jim Abbott	.25	.20	.10
2	Roberto Alomar	.25	.20	.10
3	Moises Alou	.15	.11	.06
4	Brady Anderson	.15	.11	.06
5	Eric Anthony	.10	.08	.04
6	Alex Arias	.10	.08	.04
7	Pedro Astacio	.10	.08	.04
8	Steve Avery	.15	.11	.06
9	Carlos Baerga	.20	.15	.08
10	Jeff Bagwell	.15	.11	.06
11	George Bell	.10	.08	.04
12	Albert Belle	.15	.11	.06
13	Craig Biggio	.10	.08	.04
14	Barry Bonds	.35	.25	.14
15	Bobby Bonilla	.15	.11	.06
16	Mike Bordick	.10	.08	.04
17	George Brett	.50	.40	.20
18	Jose Canseco	.60	.45	.25
19	Joe Carter	.25	.20	.10
20	Royce Clayton	.10	.08	.04
21	Roger Clemens	.25	.20	.10
22	Greg Colbrunn	.10	.08	.04
23	David Cone	.10	.08	.04
24	Darren Daulton	.10	.08	.04
25	Delino DeShields	.15	.11	.06
26	Rob Dibble	.10	.08	.04
27	Dennis Eckersley	.15	.11	.06
28	Cal Eldred	.10	.08	.04
29	Scott Erickson	.10	.08	.04
30	Junior Felix	.10	.08	.04
31	Tony Fernandez	.10	.08	.04
32	Cecil Fielder	.25	.20	.10
33	Steve Finley	.10	.08	.04
34	Dave Fleming	.10	.08	.04
35	Travis Fryman	.15	.11	.06
36	Tom Glavine	.15	.11	.06
37	Juan Gonzalez	.45	.35	.20
38	Ken Griffey, Jr.	.90	.70	.35
39	Marquis Grissom	.15	.11	.06
40	Juan Guzman	.10	.08	.04
41	Tony Gwynn	.20	.15	.08
42	Rickey Henderson	.25	.20	.10
43	Felix Jose	.10	.08	.04
44	Wally Joyner	.15	.11	.06
45	David Justice	.25	.20	.10
46	Eric Karros	.15	.11	.06
47	Roberto Kelly	.15	.11	.06
48	Ryan Klesko	.35	.25	.14
49	Chuck Knoblauch	.15	.11	.06
50	John Kruk	.15	.11	.06
51	Ray Lankford	.15	.11	.06
52	Barry Larkin	.15	.11	.06
53	Pat Listach	.10	.08	.04
54	Kenny Lofton	.15	.11	.06
55	Shane Mack	.10	.08	.04
56	Greg Maddux	.15	.11	.06
57	Dave Magadan	.10	.08	.04
58	Edgar Martinez	.10	.08	.04
59	Don Mattingly	.40	.30	.15
60	Ben McDonald	.15	.11	.06
61	Jack McDowell	.15	.11	.06
62	Fred McGriff	.20	.15	.08
63	Mark McGwire	.20	.15	.08
64	Kevin McReynolds	.10	.08	.04
65	Sam Militello	.10	.08	.04
66	Paul Molitor	.20	.15	.08
67	Jeff Montgomery	.10	.08	.04
68	Jack Morris	.10	.08	.04
69	Eddie Murray	.20	.15	.08
70	Mike Mussina	.15	.11	.06

71	Otis Nixon	.10	.08	.04
72	Donovan Osborne	.10	.08	.04
73	Terry Pendleton	.15	.11	.06
74	Mike Piazza	.35	.25	.14
75	Kirby Puckett	.30	.25	.12
76	Cal Ripken, Jr.	.50	.40	.20
77	Bip Roberts	.10	.08	.04
78	Ivan Rodriguez	.10	.08	.04
79	Nolan Ryan	.90	.70	.35
80	Ryne Sandberg	.50	.40	.20
81	Deion Sanders	.25	.20	.10
82	Reggie Sanders	.10	.08	.04
83	Frank Seminara	.10	.08	.04
84	Gary Sheffield	.15	.11	.06
85	Ruben Sierra	.15	.11	.06
86	John Smiley	.10	.08	.04
87	Lee Smith	.10	.08	.04
88	Ozzie Smith	.20	.15	.08
89	John Smoltz	.10	.08	.04
90	Danny Tartabull	.10	.08	.04
91	Bob Tewksbury	.10	.08	.04
92	Frank Thomas	.90	.70	.35
93	Andy Van Slyke	.10	.08	.04
94	Mo Vaughn	.15	.11	.06
95	Robin Ventura	.15	.11	.06
96	Tim Wakefield	.10	.08	.04
97	Larry Walker	.10	.08	.04
98	Dave Winfield	.40	.30	.15
99	Robin Yount	.40	.30	.15
----	Mark McGwire, Sam Militello, Ryan Klesko, Greg Maddux	.20	.15	.08

1989 Cleveland Indians Team Set

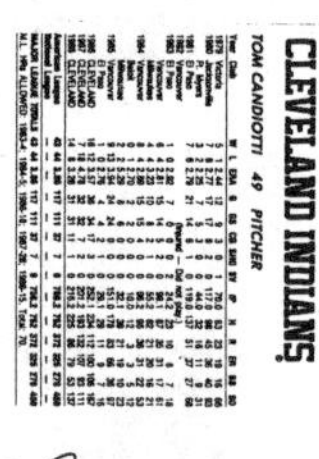

The Cleveland Indians released this oversized (2-3/4" by 4-1/2") 28-card set in 1989. The cards feature a full-color player photo on the front with the "Tribe" logo in the upper left corner. Card backs include major and minor league statistics and a facsimile autograph.

		MT	NR MT	EX
Complete Set:		5.00	3.75	2.00
Common Player:		.20	.15	.08
(1)	Doc Edwards	.20	.15	.08
(2)	Joel Skinner	.20	.15	.08
(3)	Andy Allanson	.20	.15	.08
(4)	Tom Candiotti	.20	.15	.08
(5)	Doug Jones	.20	.15	.08
(6)	Keith Atherton	.20	.15	.08
(7)	Rich Yett	.20	.15	.08
(8)	John Farrell	.20	.15	.08
(9)	Rod Nichols	.20	.15	.08
(10)	Joe Skalski	.30	.25	.12
(11)	Pete O'Brien	.30	.25	.12
(12)	Jerry Browne	.30	.25	.12
(13)	Brook Jacoby	.30	.25	.12
(14)	Felix Fermin	.20	.15	.08
(15)	Bud Black	.20	.15	.08
(16)	Brad Havens	.20	.15	.08
(17)	Greg Swindell	.40	.30	.15
(18)	Scott Bailes	.20	.15	.08
(19)	Jesse Orosco	.20	.15	.08
(20)	Oddibe McDowell	.30	.25	.12
(21)	Joe Carter	.50	.40	.20
(22)	Cory Snyder	.25	.20	.10
(23)	Louie Medina	.20	.15	.08
(24)	Dave Clark	.20	.15	.08
(25)	Brad Komminsk	.20	.15	.08
(26)	Luis Aguayo	.20	.15	.08
(27)	Pat Keedy	.20	.15	.08
(28)	Tribe Coaches	.20	.15	.08

1961 - 62 Cloverleaf Dairy Minnesota Twins

Although produced in both 1961 and 1962, these unnumbered cards picturing members of the Minnesota Twins are generally collected as one 32-card set. Measuring approximately 3-3/4" by 7-3/4", the cards were actually side panels from Cloverleaf Milk cartons. Complete cartons are valued at about twice the prices listed. The front of the card includes a player photo with name, position, personal data and year-by-year statistics appearing below. Printing on the cartons is in shades of green.

		NR MT	EX	VG
Complete Set (32):		1025.	500.00	300.00
Common Player:		30.00	15.00	9.00
(1)	Bernie Allen	30.00	15.00	9.00
(2)	George Banks	30.00	15.00	9.00
(3)	Earl Battey	35.00	17.50	10.50
(4)	Joe Bonikowski	30.00	15.00	9.00
(5)	Billy Gardner	30.00	15.00	9.00
(6)	Paul Giel	40.00	20.00	12.00
(7)	John Goryl	30.00	15.00	9.00
(8)	Lenny Green	30.00	15.00	9.00
(9)	Jim Kaat	50.00	25.00	15.00
(10)	Harmon Killebrew	200.00	100.00	60.00
(11)	Jack Kralick	30.00	15.00	9.00
(12)	Don Lee	30.00	15.00	9.00
(13)	Jim Lemon	30.00	15.00	9.00
(14)	Georges Maranda	30.00	15.00	9.00
(15)	Billy Martin	75.00	37.00	22.00
(16)	Orlando Martinez	30.00	15.00	9.00
(17)	Don Mincher	30.00	15.00	9.00
(18)	Ray Moore	30.00	15.00	9.00
(19)	Hal Naragon	30.00	15.00	9.00
(20)	Camilo Pascual	35.00	17.50	10.50
(21)	Vic Power	35.00	17.50	10.50
(22)	Pedro Ramos	30.00	15.00	9.00
(23)	Rich Rollins	30.00	15.00	9.00
(24)	Theodore Sadowski	30.00	15.00	9.00
(25)	Albert Stange	30.00	15.00	9.00
(26)	Dick Stigman	30.00	15.00	9.00
(27)	Chuck Stobbs	30.00	15.00	9.00
(28)	Bill Tuttle	30.00	15.00	9.00
(29)	Jose Valdivielso	30.00	15.00	9.00
(30)	Zoilo Versalles	35.00	17.50	10.50
(31)	Gerald Zimmerman	30.00	15.00	9.00
(32)	Manager and Coaches	30.00	15.00	9.00

1911 George Close Candy Co. (E94)

This 30-card set, issued in 1911, is nearly identical to several early candy and caramel sets of the same period. The set was issued by the George Close Candy Co. of Cambridge, Mass., however, many of the cards found contain no indication of who produced them. The cards measure 1-1/2" by 2-3/4" and feature tinted black and white player photos. The back of each card, printed in gray, carries a checklist of the 30 cards in the set. Eight different back variations are known to exist. One variation contains just the checklist without any advertising, while seven other variations include overprinted backs advertising various candy products manufactured by the George Close Company. The set carries the ACC designation E94.

		NR MT	EX	VG
Complete Set:		16000.	8000.	4800.
Common Player:		200.00	92.00	55.00
(1)	Jimmy Austin	200.00	100.00	60.00
(2)	Johnny Bates	200.00	100.00	60.00
(3)	Bob Bescher	200.00	100.00	60.00
(4)	Bobby Byrne	200.00	100.00	60.00
(5)	Frank Chance	500.00	250.00	150.00
(6)	Ed Cicotte	225.00	112.00	67.00
(7)	Ty Cobb	4500.	2250.	1350.
(8)	Sam Crawford	500.00	250.00	150.00
(9)	Harry Davis	200.00	100.00	60.00
(10)	Art Devlin	200.00	100.00	60.00
(11)	Josh Devore	200.00	100.00	60.00
(12)	Mickey Doolan	200.00	100.00	60.00
(13)	Patsy Dougherty	200.00	100.00	60.00
(14)	Johnny Evers	500.00	250.00	150.00
(15)	Eddie Grant	200.00	100.00	60.00
(16)	Hugh Jennings	500.00	250.00	150.00
(17)	Red Kleinow	200.00	100.00	60.00
(18)	Joe Lake	200.00	100.00	60.00
(19)	Nap Lajoie	800.00	400.00	240.00
(20)	Tommy Leach	200.00	100.00	60.00
(21)	Hans Lobert	200.00	100.00	60.00
(22)	Harry Lord	200.00	100.00	60.00
(23)	Sherry Magee	200.00	100.00	60.00
(24)	John McGraw	575.00	287.00	172.00
(25)	Earl Moore	200.00	100.00	60.00
(26)	Red Murray	200.00	100.00	60.00
(27)	Tris Speaker	900.00	450.00	270.00
(28)	Terry Turner	200.00	100.00	60.00
(29)	Honus Wagner	1500.	750.00	450.00
(30)	Cy Young	1000.	500.00	300.00

1988 CMC Don Mattingly

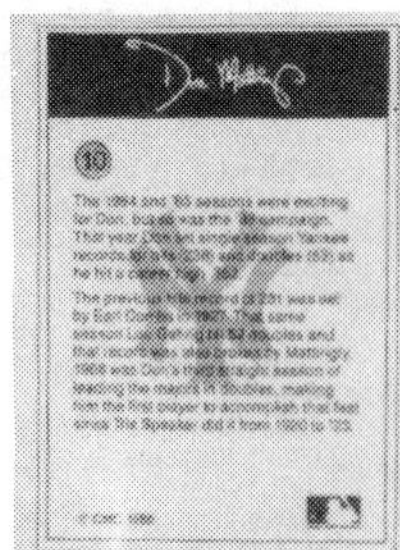

This collecting kit released by Collector's Marketing Corporation features a talking baseball card, a 20-card Don Mattingly set, an embossed collectors album and the Don Mattingly story. Each kit is numbered on the box.

	MT	NR MT	EX
Complete Set:	12.00	9.00	4.75
Common Player:	.60	.45	.25

1989 CMC Jose Canseco

This collecting kit from Collector's Marketing Corporation includes a talking baseball card, a 20-card Jose Canseco set, an embossed collectors album with plastic sheets and the Jose Canseco story. Each kit is numbered on the back of the box.

	MT	NR MT	EX
Complete Set:	12.00	9.00	4.75
Common Player:	.60	.45	.25

1989 CMC Mickey Mantle

A 20-card set honoring Mickey Mantle is among the items found in this collecting kit produced by Collectors Marketing Corporation. The cards were released along with a special album, a talking baseball card and a story about Mantle. The Yankee logo appears on the front and backs of the cards.

	MT	NR MT	EX
Complete Set:	12.00	9.00	4.75
Common Player:	.60	.45	.25

Grading Guide

Mint (MT): A perfect card. Well-centered with all corners sharp and square. No creases, stains, edge nicks, surface marks, yellowing or fading.

Near Mint (NM): A nearly perfect card. At first glance, a NM card appears to be perfect. May be slightly off-center. No surface marks, creases or loss of gloss.

Excellent (EX): Corners are still fairly sharp with only moderate wear. Borders may be off-center. No creases or stains on fronts or backs, but may show slight loss of surface luster.

Very Good (VG): Shows obvious handling. May have rounded corners, minor creases, major gum or wax stains. No major creases, tape marks, writing, etc.

Good (G): A well-worn card, but exhibits no intentional damage. May have major or multiple creases. Corners may be rounded well beyond card border.

1989 CMC Babe Ruth

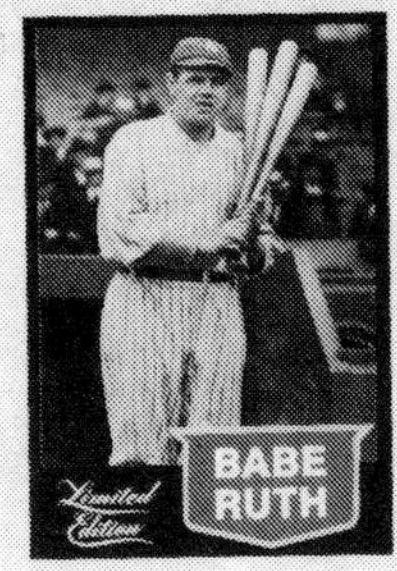

Produced by Collectors Marketing Corporation, this collecting kit features a 20-card set, an embossed collectors album, a talking baseball card and a story about Ruth. Each kit is numbered on the back of the collectors box and on the front display.

	MT	NR MT	EX
Complete Set:	12.00	9.00	4.75
Common Player:	.60	.45	.25

1952 Coca-Cola Playing Tips Test Cards

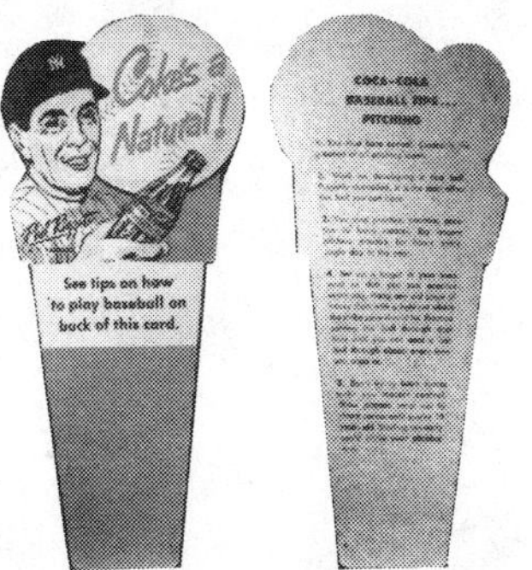

Apparently a regional issue to test the concept of baseball playing tips cards inserted into cartons of soda bottles, these test cards have a number of differences to the version which was more widely issued. The test cards are printed in black, red and yellow on the front, which features a drawing of the player with a bottle of Coke, along with his name in script and his team. Backs are printed in red on gray cardboard. The playing tips on back do not necessarily conform to the position of the player on front. Mays' card has a biography instead of playing tip. The cards are irregularly shaped, measuring about 3-1/2" at their widest point, and about 7-1/2" in length.

		NR MT	EX	VG
Complete Set (3):		4500.	2250.	1350.
(1)	Willie Mays	3500.	1750.	1000.
(2)	Phil Rizzuto	500.00	250.00	150.00
(3)	Phil Rizzuto	500.00	250.00	150.00

1952 Coca-Cola Playing Tips

While it was more widely distributed than the three test cards, the 10-card set of playing tips cards is still scarce today. Apparently only issued in the metropolitan New York region, the cards include only players from the Yankees, Giants and Dodgers. Fronts feature paintings of players in action, though the artwork bears little actual resemblance to the players named. The phrase "Coke is a natural" is in the background on pennants, panels, etc. The player's name, team and position are included in the picture. In the portion of the card meant to be inserted into the soda-bottle carton, the home schedule of the player's team for 1952 is presented. Printed on back are tips for playing the position of the pictured player. Cards are irregularly shaped, measuring about 3-1/2" at their widest point, and 7-1/2" in length. The unnumbered cards are checklisted here in alphabetical order.

		NR MT	EX	VG
Complete Set (10):		3750.	1850.	1100.
Common Player:		200.00	100.00	60.00
(1)	Hank Bauer	350.00	175.00	100.00
(2)	Carl Furillo	450.00	225.00	135.00
(3)	Gil Hodges	600.00	300.00	180.00
(4)	Ed Lopat	300.00	150.00	90.00
(5)	Gil McDougald	450.00	225.00	135.00
(6)	Don Mueller	200.00	100.00	60.00
(7)	Pee Wee Reese	600.00	300.00	180.00
(8)	Bobby Thomson (3B)	350.00	175.00	100.00
(9)	Bobby Thomson (hitting)	350.00	175.00	100.00
(10)	Wes Westrum	200.00	100.00	60.00

1981 Coca-Cola

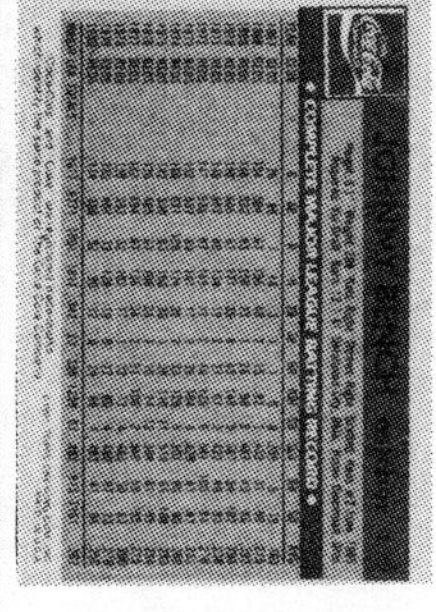

In 1981, Topps produced for Coca-Cola 12-card sets for 11 various American and National League teams. The sets include 11 player cards and one unnumbered header card. The card fronts, which measure 2-1/2" by 3-1/2", are identical in style to the 1981 Topps regular issue save for the Coca-Cola logo. The backs differ only from the '81 Topps regular set in that they are numbered 1-11 and carry the Coca-Cola trademark and copyright line. The backs of the header cards contain an offer for 132-card uncut sheets of 1981 Topps baseball cards.

		MT	NR MT	EX
Complete Set:		35.00	26.00	14.00
Common Player:		.06	.05	.02
	BOSTON RED SOX			
1	Tom Burgmeier	.06	.05	.02
2	Dennis Eckersley	.15	.11	.06
3	Dwight Evans	.20	.15	.08
4	Bob Stanley	.06	.05	.02
5	Glenn Hoffman	.06	.05	.02
6	Carney Lansford	.10	.08	.04
7	Frank Tanana	.10	.08	.04
8	Tony Perez	.20	.15	.08
9	Jim Rice	.80	.60	.30
10	Dave Stapleton	.06	.05	.02
11	Carl Yastrzemski	2.00	1.50	.80
----	Red Sox Header Card	.03	.02	.01
	CHICAGO CUBS			
1	Tim Blackwell	.06	.05	.02
2	Bill Buckner	.10	.11	.06
3	Ivan DeJesus	.06	.05	.02
4	Leon Durham	.08	.11	.06
5	Steve Henderson	.06	.05	.02
6	Mike Krukow	.06	.08	.04
7	Ken Reitz	.06	.05	.02
8	Rick Reuschel	.10	.11	.06
9	Scot Thompson	.06	.05	.02
10	Dick Tidrow	.06	.05	.02
11	Mike Tyson	.06	.05	.02
----	Cubs Header Card	.03	.02	.01
	CHICAGO WHITE SOX			
1	Britt Burns	.08	.08	.04
2	Todd Cruz	.06	.05	.02
3	Rich Dotson	.06	.15	.08
4	Jim Essian	.06	.05	.02
5	Ed Farmer	.06	.05	.02
6	Lamar Johnson	.06	.05	.02
7	Ron LeFlore	.10	.08	.04
8	Chet Lemon	.10	.08	.04
9	Bob Molinaro	.06	.05	.02
10	Jim Morrison	.06	.05	.02
11	Wayne Nordhagen	.06	.05	.02
----	White Sox Header Card	.03	.02	.01
	CINCINNATI REDS			
1	Johnny Bench	2.00	1.50	.80
2	Dave Collins	.10	.08	.04
3	Dave Concepcion	.15	.11	.06
4	Dan Driessen	.06	.08	.04
5	George Foster	.25	.20	.10
6	Ken Griffey	.15	.11	.06
7	Tom Hume	.06	.05	.02
8	Ray Knight	.10	.08	.04
9	Ron Oester	.06	.05	.02
10	Tom Seaver	2.00	.90	.50
11	Mario Soto	.10	.08	.04
----	Reds Header Card	.03	.02	.01
	DETROIT TIGERS			
1	Champ Summers	.06	.05	.02
2	Al Cowens	.06	.05	.02
3	Rich Hebner	.06	.05	.02
4	Steve Kemp	.06	.08	.04
5	Aurelio Lopez	.06	.05	.02
6	Jack Morris	.20	.25	.14
7	Lance Parrish	.15	.25	.14
8	Johnny Wockenfuss	.06	.05	.02
9	Alan Trammell	1.00	.70	.40
10	Lou Whitaker	.90	.70	.40
11	Kirk Gibson	.40	.70	.40
----	Tigers Header Card	.03	.02	.01
	HOUSTON ASTROS			
1	Alan Ashby	.06	.05	.02
2	Cesar Cedeno	.10	.11	.06
3	Jose Cruz	.10	.11	.06
4	Art Howe	.06	.05	.02
5	Rafael Landestoy	.06	.05	.02
6	Joe Niekro	.15	.11	.06
7	Terry Puhl	.06	.05	.02
8	J.R. Richard	.15	.11	.06
9	Nolan Ryan	8.00	6.00	3.25
10	Joe Sambito	.06	.05	.02
11	Don Sutton	.35	.25	.14
----	Astros Header Card	.03	.02	.01
	KANSAS CITY ROYALS			
1	Willie Aikens	.06	.05	.02
2	George Brett	2.00	1.25	.60
3	Larry Gura	.06	.05	.02
4	Dennis Leonard	.06	.05	.02
5	Hal McRae	.15	.11	.06
6	Amos Otis	.06	.08	.04
7	Dan Quisenberry	.15	.11	.06
8	U.L. Washington	.06	.05	.02
9	John Wathan	.06	.08	.04
10	Frank White	.10	.08	.04
11	Willie Wilson	.15	.11	.06
----	Royals Header Card	.03	.02	.01
	NEW YORK METS			
1	Neil Allen	.06	.05	.02
2	Doug Flynn	.06	.05	.02
3	Dave Kingman	.10	.11	.06
4	Randy Jones	.06	.05	.02
5	Pat Zachry	.06	.05	.02
6	Lee Mazzilli	.06	.08	.04
7	Rusty Staub	.15	.11	.06
8	Craig Swan	.06	.05	.02
9	Frank Taveras	.06	.05	.02
10	Alex Trevino	.06	.05	.02
11	Joel Youngblood	.06	.05	.02
----	Mets Header Card	.03	.02	.01
	PHILADELPHIA PHILLIES			
1	Bob Boone	.30	.25	.12
2	Larry Bowa	.15	.11	.06
3	Steve Carlton	2.00	.70	.40
4	Greg Luzinski	.15	.11	.06
5	Garry Maddox	.06	.08	.04
6	Bake McBride	.06	.05	.02
7	Tug McGraw	.10	.11	.06
8	Pete Rose	2.00	1.50	.80
9	Mike Schmidt	2.25	1.75	.90
10	Lonnie Smith	.15	.11	.06
11	Manny Trillo	.06	.05	.02
----	Phillies Header Card	.03	.02	.01
	PITTSBURGH PIRATES			
1	Jim Bibby	.06	.05	.02
2	John Candelaria	.10	.08	.04
3	Mike Easler	.06	.08	.04
4	Tim Foli	.06	.05	.02
5	Phil Garner	.06	.05	.02
6	Bill Madlock	.15	.11	.06
7	Omar Moreno	.06	.05	.02
8	Ed Ott	.06	.05	.02
9	Dave Parker	.35	.25	.14
10	Willie Stargell	1.50	.70	.40
11	Kent Tekulve	.06	.08	.04
----	Pirates Header Card	.03	.02	.01
	ST. LOUIS CARDINALS			
1	Bob Forsch	.06	.08	.04
2	George Hendrick	.06	.08	.04
3	Keith Hernandez	.10	.40	.20
4	Tom Herr	.10	.11	.06
5	Sixto Lezcano	.06	.05	.02
6	Ken Oberkfell	.06	.05	.02
7	Darrell Porter	.06	.08	.04
8	Tony Scott	.06	.05	.02
9	Lary Sorensen	.06	.05	.02
10	Bruce Sutter	.10	.11	.06
11	Garry Templeton	.10	.08	.04
----	Cardinals Header Card	.03	.02	.01

1982 Coca-Cola Brigham's Red Sox

Coca-Cola, in conjunction with Brigham's Ice Cream stores, issued a 23-card set in the Boston area featuring Red Sox players. The Topps-produced cards, which measure 2-1/2" by 3-1/2", are identical in style to the regular 1982 Topps set but

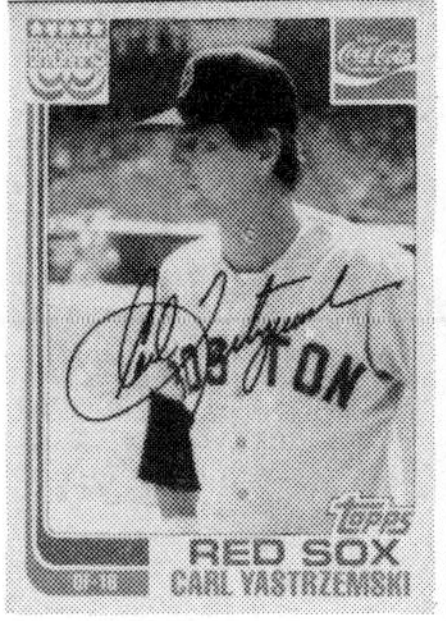
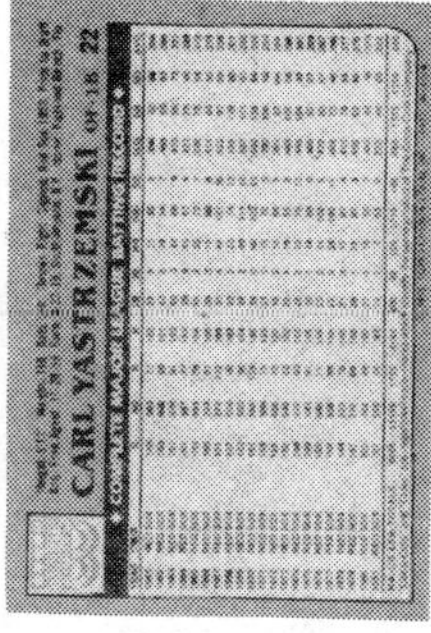

contain the Coca-Cola and Brigham's logos in the corners. The cards were distributed in three-card cello packs, including an unnumbered header card.

		MT	NR MT	EX
Complete Set:		7.00	5.25	2.75
Common Player:		.08	.06	.03
1	Gary Allenson	.08	.06	.03
2	Tom Burgmeier	.08	.06	.03
3	Mark Clear	.08	.06	.03
4	Steve Crawford	.08	.06	.03
5	Dennis Eckersley	1.00	.70	.40
6	Dwight Evans	.50	.40	.20
7	Rich Gedman	.10	.08	.04
8	Garry Hancock	.08	.06	.03
9	Glen Hoffman (Glenn)	.08	.06	.03
10	Carney Lansford	.10	.08	.04
11	Rick Miller	.08	.06	.03
12	Reid Nichols	.08	.06	.03
13	Bob Ojeda	.20	.15	.08
14	Tony Perez	.30	.25	.12
15	Chuck Rainey	.08	.06	.03
16	Jerry Remy	.08	.06	.03
17	Jim Rice	.60	.45	.25
18	Bob Stanley	.08	.06	.03
19	Dave Stapleton	.08	.06	.03
20	Mike Torrez	.08	.06	.03
21	John Tudor	.10	.08	.04
22	Carl Yastrzemski	3.00	2.25	1.25
----	Header Card	.05	.04	.02

1982 Coca-Cola Reds

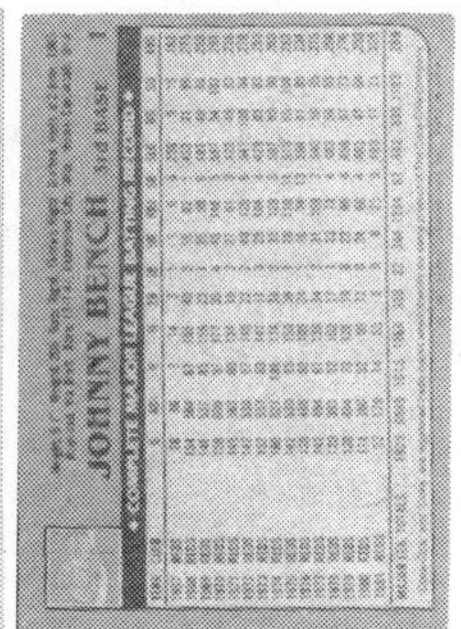

Produced by Topps for Coca-Cola, the set consists of 23 cards featuring the Cincinnati Reds and was distributed in the Cincinnati area. The cards, which are 2-1/2" by 3-1/2" in size, are identical in design to the regular 1982 Topps set but have a Coca-Cola logo on the front and red backs. An unnumbered header card is included in the set.

		MT	NR MT	EX
Complete Set:		9.00	6.75	3.50
Common Player:		.08	.06	.03
1	Johnny Bench	3.00	2.25	1.25
2	Bruce Berenyi	.08	.06	.03
3	Larry Biittner	.08	.06	.03
4	Cesar Cedeno	.15	.11	.06
5	Dave Concepcion	.15	.11	.06
6	Dan Driessen	.08	.06	.03
7	Greg Harris	.12	.09	.05
8	Paul Householder	.08	.06	.03
9	Tom Hume	.08	.06	.03
10	Clint Hurdle	.08	.06	.03
11	Jim Kern	.08	.06	.03
12	Wayne Krenchicki	.08	.06	.03
13	Rafael Landestoy	.08	.06	.03
14	Charlie Leibrandt	.15	.11	.06
15	Mike O'Berry	.08	.06	.03
16	Ron Oester	.08	.06	.03
17	Frank Pastore	.08	.06	.03
18	Joe Price	.08	.06	.03
19	Tom Seaver	3.00	2.25	1.25
20	Mario Soto	.15	.11	.06
21	Alex Trevino	.08	.06	.03
22	Mike Vail	.08	.06	.03
----	Header Card	.04	.03	.02

1985 Coca-Cola White Sox

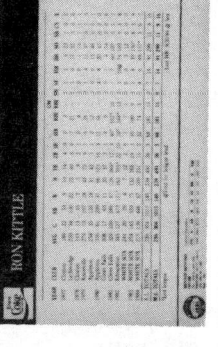

Featuring past and present White Sox players, the cards in this set were given out on Tuesday night home games. The cards, which measure 2-5/8" by 4-1/8", contain a color photo of a current Sox member. A red box at the bottom of the card carries the team logo, the player's name, uniform number and position, plus a small oval portrait of a past Sox player. The card backs contain the Coca-Cola logo and the lifetime hitting or pitching statistics for the current and past player. The set is numbered in the checklist that follows by the player's uniform number with the last three cards being unnumbered. Complete sets were available through a fan club offer found in White Sox programs.

		MT	NR MT	EX
Complete Set:		14.00	10.50	5.50
Common Player:		.25	.20	.10
O	Oscar Gamble (Zeke Bonura)	.25	.20	.10
1	Scott Fletcher (Luke Appling)	.40	.30	.15
3	Harold Baines (Bill Melton)	.80	.60	.30
5	Luis Salazar (Chico Carrasquel)	.25	.20	.10
7	Marc Hill (Sherm Lollar)	.25	.20	.10
8	Daryl Boston (Jim Landis)	.25	.20	.10
10	Tony LaRussa (Al Lopez)	.40	.30	.15
12	Julio Cruz (Nellie Fox)	.75	.60	.30
13	Ozzie Guillen (Luis Aparicio)	1.50	1.25	.60
17	Jerry Hairston (Smoky Burgess)	.40	.30	.15
20	Joe DeSa (Carlos May)	.25	.20	.10
22	Joel Skinner (J.C. Martin)	.25	.20	.10
23	Rudy Law (Bill Skowron)	.35	.25	.14
24	Floyd Bannister (Red Faber)	.35	.25	.14
29	Greg Walker (Dick Allen)	.40	.30	.15
30	Gene Nelson (Early Wynn)	.35	.25	.14
32	Tim Hulett (Pete Ward)	.25	.20	.10
34	Richard Dotson (Ed Walsh)	.35	.25	.14
37	Dan Spillner (Thornton Lee)	.25	.20	.10
40	Britt Burns (Gary Peters)	.25	.20	.10
41	Tom Seaver (Ted Lyons)	1.50	1.25	.60
42	Ron Kittle (Minnie Minoso)	.40	.30	.15
43	Bob James (Hoyt Wilhelm)	.40	.30	.15
44	Tom Paciorek (Eddie Collins)	.35	.25	.14
46	Tim Lollar (Billy Pierce)	.25	.20	.10
50	Juan Agosto (Wilbur Wood)	.25	.20	.10
72	Carlton Fisk (Ray Schalk)	1.50	1.25	.60
----	Comiskey Park, Ribbie and Roobarb (mascots), Nancy Faust (organist)	.50	.40	.20

1986 Coca-Cola White Sox

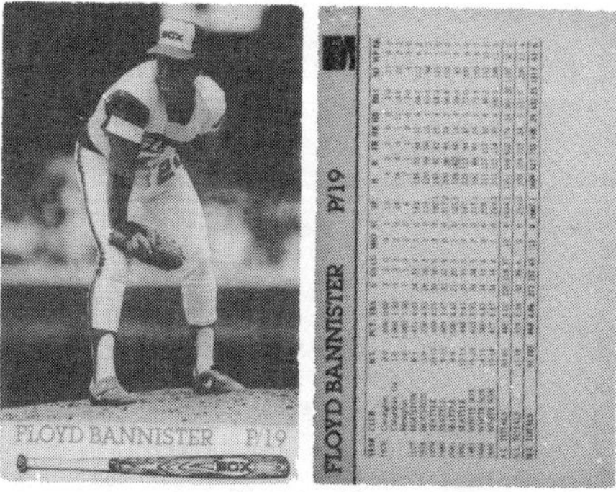

For the second year in a row, Coca-Cola, in conjunction with the Chicago White Sox, issued a 30-card set. As in 1985, cards were given out at the park on Tuesday night games. Full sets were again available through a fan club offer found in the White Sox program. The cards, which measure 2-5/8" by 4-1/8", feature 25 players plus other White Sox personnel. The card fronts feature a color photo (an action shot in most instances) and a white bar at the bottom. A black and white bat with "SOX" shown on the barrel is located within the white bar, along with the player's name, position and uniform number. The white and grey backs with black print include the Coca-Cola trademark. Lifetime statistics are shown on all player cards, but there is no personal information such as height, weight or age. The non-player cards are blank-backed save for the name and logo at the top. The cards in the checklist that follows are numbered by the players' uniform numbers, with the last five cards of the set being unnumbered.

		MT	NR MT	EX
Complete Set:		15.00	11.00	6.00
Common Player:		.25	.20	.10
1	Wayne Tolleson	.25	.20	.10
3	Harold Baines	.80	.60	.30
7	Marc Hill	.25	.20	.10
8	Daryl Boston	.25	.20	.10
12	Julio Cruz	.25	.20	.10
13	Ozzie Guillen	.40	.30	.15
17	Jerry Hairston	.25	.20	.10
19	Floyd Bannister	.25	.20	.10
20	Reid Nichols	.25	.20	.10
22	Joel Skinner	.25	.20	.10
24	Dave Schmidt	.25	.20	.10
26	Bobby Bonilla	2.50	2.00	1.00
29	Greg Walker	.30	.25	.12
30	Gene Nelson	.25	.20	.10
32	Tim Hulett	.25	.20	.10
33	Neil Allen	.25	.20	.10
34	Richard Dotson	.25	.20	.10
40	Joe Cowley	.25	.20	.10
41	Tom Seaver	2.00	1.50	.80
42	Ron Kittle	.35	.25	.14
43	Bob James	.25	.20	.10
44	John Cangelosi	.25	.20	.10
50	Juan Agosto	.25	.20	.10
52	Joel Davis	.25	.20	.10
72	Carlton Fisk	1.25	.90	.50
----	Ribbie & Roobarb (mascots)	.25	.20	.10
----	Nancy Faust (organist)	.25	.20	.10
----	Ken "Hawk" Harrelson	.30	.25	.12
----	Tony LaRussa	.35	.25	.12
----	Minnie Minoso	.40	.25	.12

1987 Coca-Cola Tigers

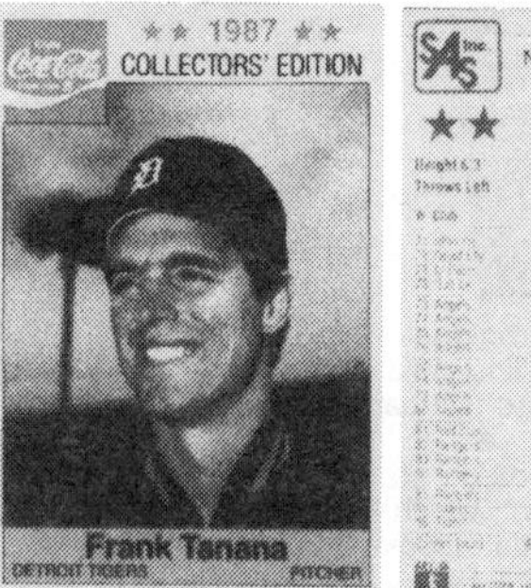
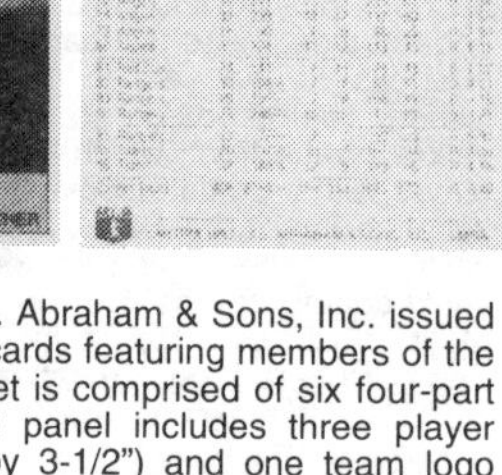

Coca-Cola and S. Abraham & Sons, Inc. issued a set of 18 baseball cards featuring members of the Detroit Tigers. The set is comprised of six four-part folding panels. Each panel includes three player cards (each 2-1/2" by 3-1/2") and one team logo card. A bright yellow border surrounds the full-color photo. The backs are designed on a vertical format and contain personal data and career statistics. The set was produced by Mike Schecter and Associates.

		MT	NR MT	EX
Complete Set:		6.00	4.50	2.50
Complete Singles Set:		2.00	1.50	.80
Common Panel:		.60	.45	.25
Common Single Player:		.05	.04	.02
	Panel	.95	.90	.50
1	Kirk Gibson	.30	.25	.12
2	Larry Herndon	.05	.04	.02
3	Walt Terrell	.10	.08	.04
	Panel	1.25	.90	.50
4	Alan Trammell	.50	.40	.20
5	Frank Tanana	.10	.08	.04
6	Pat Sheridan	.05	.04	.02
	Panel	.90	.70	.35
7	Jack Morris	.30	.25	.12
8	Mike Heath	.05	.04	.02
9	Dave Bergman	.05	.04	.02
	Panel	.60	.45	.25
10	Chet Lemon	.10	.08	.04
11	Dwight Lowry	.08	.06	.03
12	Dan Petry	.10	.08	.04
	Panel	.80	.60	.30
13	Darrell Evans	.20	.15	.08
14	Darnell Coles	.10	.08	.04
15	Willie Hernandez	.10	.08	.04
	Panel	1.00	.70	.40
16	Lou Whitaker	.30	.25	.12
17	Tom Brookens	.05	.04	.02
18	John Grubb	.05	.04	.02

The values quoted are intended to reflect the market price.

1987 Coca-Cola White Sox

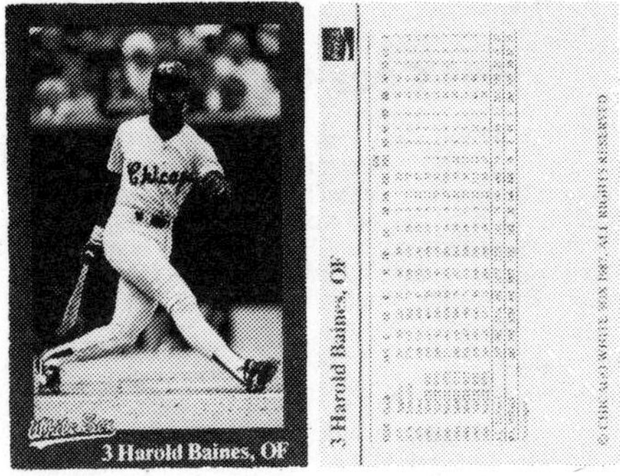

The Chicago White Sox Fan Club, in conjunction with Coca-Cola, offered members a set of 30 trading cards. For the $10 membership fee, fans received the set plus additional fan club gifts and privileges. The cards, which measure 2-5/8" by 4", feature full-color photos inside a blue and red border. The backs include the player's name, position, uniform number and statistics. The Coca-Cola logo is also included on the card backs.

		MT	NR MT	EX
Complete Set:		9.00	9.00	4.75
Common Player:		.25	.20	.10
1	Jerry Royster	.25	.20	.10
3	Harold Baines	.60	.45	.25
5	Ron Karkovice	.35	.25	.14
8	Daryl Boston	.25	.20	.10
10	Fred Manrique	.25	.20	.10
12	Steve Lyons	.25	.20	.10
13	Ozzie Guillen	.60	.45	.25
14	Russ Morman	.25	.20	.10
15	Donnie Hill	.25	.20	.10
16	Jim Fregosi	.30	.25	.12
17	Jerry Hairston	.25	.20	.10
19	Floyd Bannister	.25	.20	.10
21	Gary Redus	.30	.25	.12
22	Ivan Calderon	.30	.25	.12
25	Ron Hassey	.25	.20	.10
26	Jose DeLeon	.30	.25	.12
29	Greg Walker	.25	.20	.10
32	Tim Hulett	.25	.20	.10
33	Neil Allen	.25	.20	.10
34	Rich Dotson	.25	.20	.10
36	Ray Searage	.25	.20	.10
37	Bobby Thigpen	.30	.25	.12
40	Jim Winn	.25	.20	.10
43	Bob James	.25	.20	.10
50	Joel McKeon	.25	.20	.10
52	Joel Davis	.25	.20	.10
72	Carlton Fisk	.80	.60	.30
----	Ribbie & Roobarb (mascots)	.25	.20	.10
----	Nancy Faust (organist)	.25	.20	.10
----	Minnie Minoso	.30	.25	.12

1988 Coca-Cola Padres

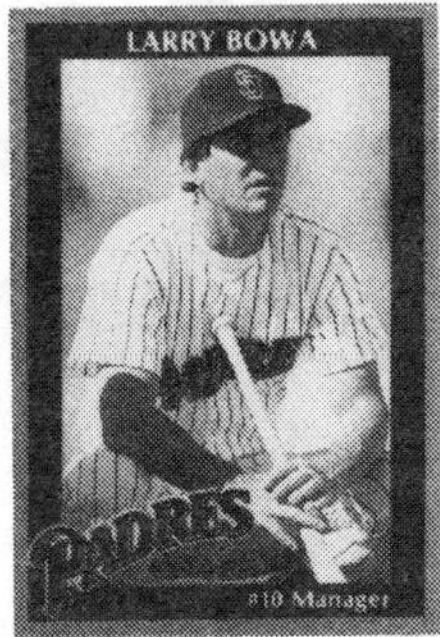

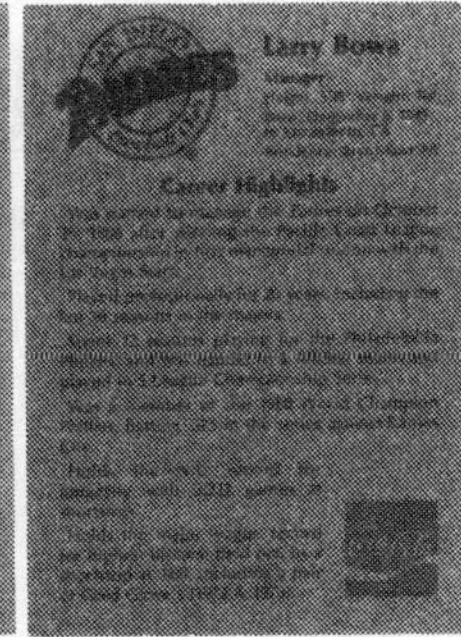

A 20-card team set sponsored by Coca-Cola was designed as part of the San Diego Padres Junior Fan Club promotion for 1988. This set was distributed as a nine-card starter sheet, with 11 additional single cards handed out during the team's home games. The standard-size cards feature full-color player photos framed by a black and orange border. The player's name is printed above the photo; uniform number and position appear lower right. A large Padres logo curves upward from the lower left corner. Card backs are brown on white and include the Padres logo upper left opposite the player's name and personal information. Career highlights and 1987 stats appear in the center of the card back above the Coca-Cola and Junior Padres Fan Club logos.

		MT	NR MT	EX
Complete Set:		30.00	25.00	13.00
Common Player:		.50	.40	.20
	Panel			
1	Garry Templeton	.75	.60	.30
5	Randy Ready	.50	.40	.20
10	Larry Bowa	.75	.60	.30
11	Tim Flannery	.50	.40	.20
35	Chris Brown	.50	.40	.20
45	Jimmy Jones	.50	.40	.20
48	Mark Davis	.50	.40	.20
55	Mark Grant	.50	.40	.20
----	20th Anniversary Logo Card	.10	.08	.04
	Singles			
7	Keith Moreland	1.00	.70	.40
8	John Kruk	3.00	1.75	.90
9	Benito Santiago	3.00	2.50	1.25
14	Carmelo Martinez	1.00	.70	.40
15	Jack McKeon	1.00	.70	.40
19	Tony Gwynn	8.00	7.50	4.00
22	Stan Jefferson	1.00	.70	.40
27	Mark Parent	1.00	1.50	.80
30	Eric Show	1.00	1.25	.60
31	Ed Whitson	1.00	.70	.40
41	Lance McCullers	1.00	.90	.50
51	Greg Booker	1.00	.70	.40

1988 Coca-Cola White Sox

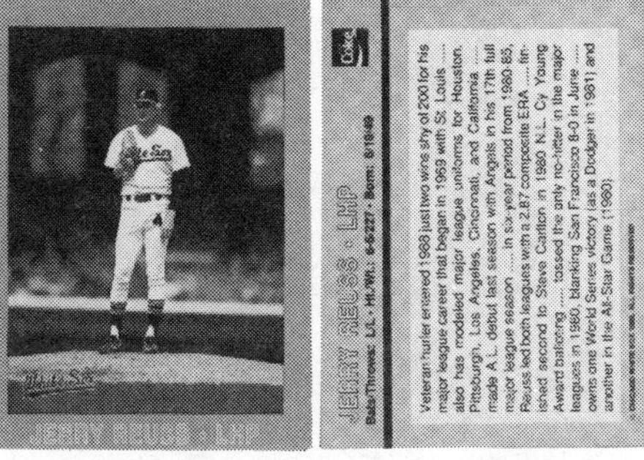

Part of a fan club membership package, this unnumbered 30-card set features full-color photos of 27 players, the team mascot, team organist and Comiskey Park. Cards have a bright red border, with the team logo in the lower left corner of the photo. A large player name fills the bottom border. Card backs are printed in black on grey and white and include player name, personal info and career summary. The set was included in the $10 membership package, with a portion of the cost going to the ChiSox Kids Charity.

		MT	NR MT	EX
Complete Set:		8.00	6.00	3.25
Common Player:		.20	.15	.08
(1)	Harold Baines	.50	.40	.20
(2)	Daryl Boston	.20	.15	.08
(3)	Ivan Calderon	.30	.25	.12
(4)	John Davis	.20	.15	.08
(5)	Jim Fregosi	.25	.20	.10
(6)	Carlton Fisk	.75	.60	.30
(7)	Ozzie Guillen	.40	.30	.15
(8)	Donnie Hill	.20	.15	.08
(9)	Rick Horton	.20	.15	.08
(10)	Lance Johnson	.40	.30	.15
(11)	Dave LaPoint	.20	.15	.08
(12)	Bill Long	.20	.15	.08
(13)	Steve Lyons	.20	.15	.08
(14)	Jack McDowell	.70	.50	.30
(15)	Fred Manrique	.20	.15	.08
(16)	Minnie Minoso	.30	.25	.12
(17)	Dan Pasqua	.30	.25	.12
(18)	John Pawlowski	.25	.20	.10
(19)	Melido Perez	.20	.15	.08
(20)	Billy Pierce	.25	.20	.10
(21)	Gary Redus	.20	.15	.08
(22)	Jerry Reuss	.25	.20	.10
(23)	Mark Salas	.20	.15	.08
(24)	Jose Segura	.20	.15	.08
(25)	Bobby Thigpen	.25	.20	.10
(26)	Greg Walker	.30	.25	.12
(27)	Kenny Williams	.30	.25	.12
(28)	Nancy Faust (organist)	.20	.15	.08
(29)	Ribbie & Roobarb (mascots)	.20	.15	.08
(30)	Comiskey Park	.40	.30	.15

1989 Coca-Cola Padres

This 20-card set is part of the Junior Padres Fan Club membership package. Members receive a 9-card starter set printed on one large perforated sheet. Additional cards are distributed to kids at specially designated games (free admission for kids). Card fronts feature an orange-and-brown double border, with a bright orange Padres logo printed lower left. Player uniform number and position are

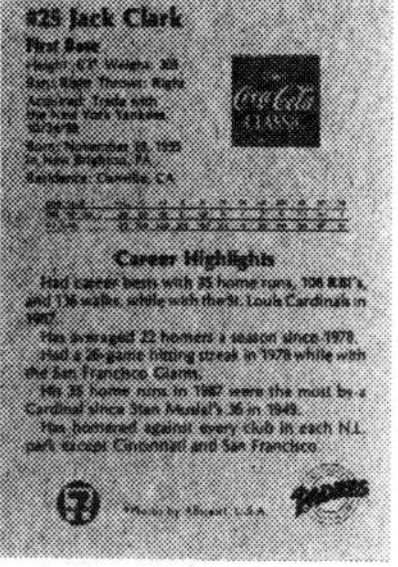

printed diagonally across the upper right corner, with the player's name in large block letters along the bottom border.

		MT	NR MT	EX
Complete Set:		26.00	22.00	12.00
Common Player:		.50	.40	.30
	Panel			
1	Garry Templeton	.70	.50	.30
5	Randy Ready	.50	.40	.20
12	Roberto Alomar	2.00	1.50	.80
14	Carmelo Martinez	.50	.40	.20
15	Jack McKeon	.50	.40	.20
30	Eric Show	.50	.40	.20
31	Ed Whitson	.50	.40	.20
43	Dennis Rasmussen	.50	.40	.20
----	Logo Card	.10	.08	.04
	Singles			
6	Luis Salazar	1.00	.70	.40
9	Benito Santiago	3.00	2.25	1.25
10	Leon Roberts	1.00	.70	.40
11	Tim Flannery	1.00	.70	.40
18	Chris James	1.00	1.50	.80
19	Tony Gwynn	8.00	6.00	3.25
25	Jack Clark	2.00	2.25	1.25
27	Mark Parent	1.00	1.50	.80
35	Walt Terrell	1.00	.70	.40
47	Bruce Hurst	1.50	1.50	.80
48	Mark Davis	1.50	2.25	1.25
55	Mark Grant	1.00	.70	.30

1989 Coca-Cola White Sox

For the fifth straight year, Coca-Cola sponsored a set of cards featuring the Chicago White Sox. The 30-card set was distributed to fans attending a special promotional day at Comiskey Park and was also available by mail to members of the ChiSox fan club. The fronts of the cards feature a red, white and blue color scheme and include a pair of crossed bats. "White Sox" appears along the top, while the name and position are in the lower right, and a pennant proclaiming "Chicago's American Pastime" is just below the photo. The horizontal backs include player biographies, other data, special facts about Comiskey Park and the Coca-Cola logo.

		MT	NR MT	EX
Complete Set:		7.00	5.25	2.75
Common Player:		.20	.15	.08
1	New Comiskey Park, 1991	.40	.30	.15
2	Comiskey Park	.40	.30	.15
3	Jeff Torborg	.20	.15	.08
4	Coaching Staff	.20	.15	.08
5	Harold Baines	.50	.40	.20
6	Daryl Boston	.20	.15	.08
7	Ivan Calderon	.30	.25	.12
8	Carlton Fisk	.60	.30	.15
9	Dave Gallagher	.20	.25	.12
10	Ozzie Guillen	.30	.25	.12
11	Shawn Hillegas	.20	.15	.08
12	Barry Jones	.30	.15	.08
13	Ron Karkovice	.20	.15	.08
14	Eric King	.25	.15	.08
15	Ron Kittle	.30	.25	.12
16	Bill Long	.20	.15	.08
17	Steve Lyons	.20	.15	.08

18	Donn Pall	.20	.15	.08
19	Dan Pasqua	.30	.25	.12
20	Ken Patterson	.20	.15	.08
21	Melido Perez	.25	.25	.12
22	Jerry Reuss	.25	.20	.10
23	Billy Jo Robidoux	.20	.15	.08
24	Steve Rosenberg	.20	.15	.08
25	Jeff Schaefer	.20	.20	.10
26	Bobby Thigpen	.25	.25	.14
27	Greg Walker	.20	.20	.10
28	Eddie Williams	.20	.20	.10
29	Nancy Faust, organist	.20	.15	.08
30	Minnie Minoso	.20	.15	.08

1990 Coca-Cola Garry Templeton

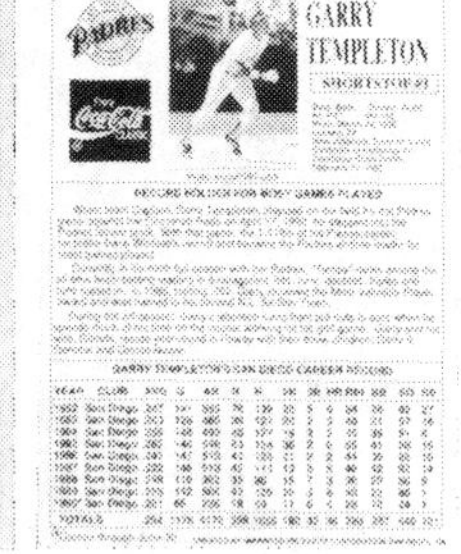

Coca-Cola, Vons stores and the San Diego Padres joined forces to release this special pin/baseball card collectible in honor of Garry Templeton becoming the club's all-time leader in games played. The card front features a full-color photo of Templeton and displays "Most Games Played" and "The Captain" in orange at the top of the photo. "Templeton" appears vertically in white along the left border. The Coca- Cola and Padre logos also appear on the card front. The bottom of the card features a perforated edge where the pin is attached as an extension of the card. The card back is printed in black and white and displays biographical information, career highlights and career statistics. The card was created by Imprinted Products Corporation of San Diego.

		MT	NR MT	EX
Complete Set:		1.50	1.25	.60
(1)	Most Games Played card (Garry Templeton)	.50	.40	.20
(2)	Most Games Played in (Garry Templeton)	1.00	.70	.40

1990 Coca-Cola Padres

This set was designed for members of the Junior Padres Club sponsored by Coca-Cola. Each member received an eight-card panel and then received two different single cards at every Junior Padres Club game attended. The card fronts feature full-color photos with the Padres logo in the upper right corner of the card. The backs feature statistics and career highlights. The cards are numbered by the player's uniform number.

		MT	NR MT	EX
Complete Set:		18.00	13.50	7.25
Common Player:		.35	.25	.14
	Panel			
10	Bip Roberts	.40	.30	.15
15	Jack McKeon	.35	.25	.14
30	Eric Show	.35	.25	.14
31	Ed Whitson	.35	.25	.14
40	Andy Benes	.90	.70	.35
43	Dennis Rasmussen	.35	.25	.14
55	Mark Grant	.35	.25	.14
----	Logo Card	.35	.25	.14
	Singles			
1	Garry Templeton	1.00	.70	.40
8	Fred Lynn	1.00	.70	.40
9	Benito Santiago	2.00	1.50	.80
11	Craig Lefferts	.80	.60	.30
12	Roberto Alomar	3.00	2.25	1.25
13	Mike Pagliarulo	1.00	.70	.40
17	Joe Carter	2.00	1.50	.80
19	Tony Gwynn	4.00	3.00	1.50
25	Jack Clark	.80	.60	.30
27	Mark Parent	.80	.60	.30
38	Calvin Schiraldi	.80	.60	.30
46	Greg Harris	.80	.70	.40
47	Bruce Hurst	.80	.60	.30

Definitions for grading conditions are located in the Introduction of this price guide.

1990 Coca-Cola Detroit Tigers

Once again utilizing the larger 2-7/8" x 4-1/4" format, this set was jointly sponsored by Coke and Kroger grocery stores and distributed at the July 14 game. Cards feature color action photos on front, surrounded by green borders. Backs have a black-and-white portrait photo, the appropriate logos and complete minor and major league stats. The player's uniform number appears in the upper-left corner.

		MT	NR MT	EX
Complete Set:		6.00	4.50	2.50
Common Player:		.15	.11	.06
(1)	Sparky Anderson	.25	.20	.10
(2)	Dave Bergman	.15	.11	.06
(3)	Brian DuBois	.15	.11	.06
(4)	Cecil Fielder	2.00	1.50	.80
(5)	Paul Gibson	.15	.11	.06
(6)	Jerry Don Gleaton	.15	.11	.06
(7)	Mike Heath	.15	.11	.06
(8)	Mike Henneman	.20	.15	.08
(9)	Tracy Jones	.15	.11	.06
(10)	Chet Lemon	.20	.15	.08
(11)	Urbano Lugo	.15	.11	.06
(12)	Jack Morris	.20	.15	.08
(13)	Lloyd Moseby	.15	.11	.06
(14)	Matt Nokes	.20	.15	.08
(15)	Edwin Nunez	.15	.11	.06
(16)	Dan Petry	.15	.11	.06
(17)	Tony Phillips	.20	.15	.08
(18)	Kevin Ritz	.15	.11	.06
(19)	Jeff Robinson	.15	.11	.06
(20)	Ed Romero	.15	.11	.06
(21)	Mark Salas	.15	.11	.06
(22)	Larry Sheets	.15	.11	.06
(23)	Frank Tanana	.20	.15	.08
(24)	Alan Trammell	.60	.45	.25
(25)	Gary Ward	.15	.11	.06
(26)	Lou Whitaker	.45	.35	.20
(27)	Ken Williams	.15	.11	.06
(28)	Coaches (Billy Consolo, Alex Grammas, Billy Muffet, Vada Pinson, Dick Tracewski)	.15	.11	.06

1990 Coca-Cola White Sox

An attractive "Comiskey Park 1910-1990" logo is featured on the front of each of the 30 cards in this set. The card fronts feature full-color photos with a thin white inner border. The cards are numbered according to uniform number, with the exception of four special cards including Top Prospect Frank Thomas. The horizontal card backs feature black print on white and gray stock. 1989 statistics and career highlights are provided. The set was made available nationally through hobby dealers. The 1990 set marks the sixth straight year that Coca-Cola sponsored a White Sox set.

		MT	NR MT	EX
Complete Set:		10.00	7.50	4.00
Common Player:		.15	.11	.06
1	Lance Johnson	.30	.25	.12
7	Scott Fletcher	.15	.11	.06
10	Jeff Torborg	.15	.11	.06
12	Steve Lyons	.15	.11	.06
13	Ozzie Guillen	.30	.25	.12
14	Craig Grebeck	.20	.15	.08
17	Dave Gallagher	.15	.11	.06
20	Ron Karkovice	.15	.11	.06
22	Ivan Calderon	.20	.15	.08
23	Robin Ventura	.60	.45	.25
24	Carlos Martinez	.15	.11	.06
25	Sammy Sosa	.30	.25	.12
27	Greg Hibbard	.15	.11	.06
29	Jack McDowell	.40	.30	.15
30	Donn Pall	.15	.11	.06
31	Scott Radinsky	.25	.20	.10
33	Melido Perez	.15	.11	.06
34	Ken Patterson	.15	.11	.06
36	Eric King	.15	.11	.06
37	Bobby Thigpen	.25	.20	.10
42	Ron Kittle	.20	.15	.08
44	Dan Pasqua	.30	.25	.12
45	Wayne Edwards	.15	.11	.06
50	Barry Jones	.15	.11	.06
52	Jerry Kutzler	.15	.11	.06
72	Carlton Fisk	.45	.35	.20
----	Top Prospect (Frank Thomas)	4.50	2.25	1.25
----	Coaches	.15	.11	.06
----	Captains-Guillen, Fisk	.20	.15	.08
----	Rookies	.20	.15	.08

1991 Coca-Cola Tigers

This 27-card set was sponsored by Coca-Cola and Kroger. The oversized cards feature color photos on the front along with the player's name vertically printed on the right border and the Tigers logo in the lower right corner. The backs are printed horizontally and feature statistics. The set is numbered according to uniform number.

		MT	NR MT	EX
Complete Set:		6.00	4.50	2.50
Common Player:		.20	.15	.08
1	Lou Whitaker	.40	.30	.15
3	Alan Trammell	.60	.45	.25
4	Tony Phillips	.25	.20	.10
10	Andy Allanson	.20	.15	.08
11	Sparky Anderson	.30	.25	.12
14	Dave Bergman	.20	.15	.08
15	Lloyd Moseby	.20	.15	.08
19	Jerry Don Gleaton	.20	.15	.08
20	Mickey Tettleton	.35	.25	.14
22	Milt Cuyler	.25	.20	.10
23	Mark Leiter	.20	.15	.08
24	Travis Fryman	.45	.35	.20
25	John Shelby	.20	.15	.08
26	Frank Tanana	.20	.15	.08
27	Mark Salas	.20	.15	.08
29	Pete Incaviglia	.25	.20	.10
31	Kevin Ritz	.25	.20	.10
35	Walt Terrell	.20	.15	.08
36	Bill Gullickson	.25	.20	.10
39	Mike Henneman	.25	.20	.10
44	Rob Deer	.20	.15	.08
45	Cecil Fielder	.90	.70	.35
46	Dan Petry	.20	.15	.08
48	Paul Gibson	.20	.15	.08
49	Steve Searcy	.20	.15	.08
55	John Cerutti	.20	.15	.08
----	Tigers Coaches (Billy Consolo, Jim Davenport, Alex Grammas, Billy Muffett, Vada Pinson, Dick Tracewski)	.20	.15	.08

1993 Coca-Cola Commanders of the Hill

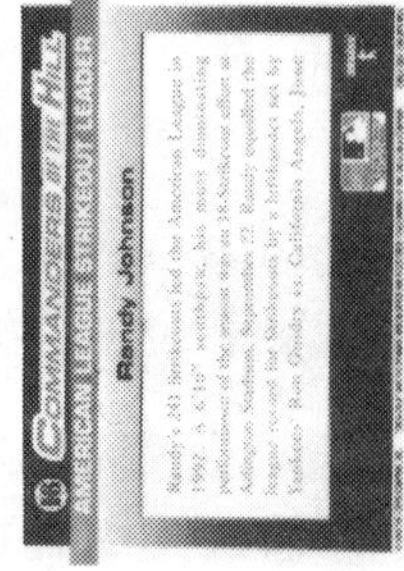

Coca-Cola and Topps teamed up to print a 30-card Commanders of the Hill set in 1993. The cards were available in five-card packages with soft-drink purchases on military bases at base exchange food court concessions. The set was divided into three areas: Cy Young Winners, Strikeout Leaders and Team ERA Leaders, with the National League player's names in yellow on a red background and the American League in red on yellow.

		MT	NR MT	EX
Complete Set:		12.50	9.50	5.00
Common Player:		.25	.20	.10
1	Dennis Eckersley	.75	.60	.30
2	Mike Mussina	.75	.60	.30
3	Roger Clemens	2.00	1.50	.80
4	Jim Abbott	.75	.60	.30
5	Jack McDowell	.75	.60	.30
6	Charles Nagy	.25	.20	.10
7	Bill Gullickson	.25	.20	.10
8	Kevin Appier	.25	.20	.10
9	Bill Wegman	.25	.20	.10
10	John Smiley	.25	.20	.10
11	Melido Perez	.25	.20	.10
12	Dave Stewart	.50	.40	.20
13	Dave Fleming	.25	.20	.10
14	Kevin Brown	.35	.25	.14
15	Juan Guzman	.35	.25	.14
16	Randy Johnson	.40	.30	.15
17	Greg Maddux	.75	.60	.30
18	Tom Glavine	.60	.45	.25
19	Greg Maddux	.75	.60	.30
20	Jose Rijo	.40	.30	.15
21	Pete Harnisch	.30	.25	.12
22	Tom Candiotti	.25	.20	.10
23	Denny Martinez	.30	.25	.12

24	Sid Fernandez	.25	.20	.10
25	Curt Schilling	.25	.20	.10
26	Doug Drabek	.25	.20	.10
27	Bob Tewksbury	.30	.25	.12
28	Andy Benes	.35	.25	.14
29	Bill Swift	.30	.25	.12
30	John Smoltz	.35	.25	.14

1909 Colgan's Chips (E254)

This unusual set of round cards, each measuring 1-1/2" in diameter, was issued over a three-year period from 1909 to 1911 by the Colgan Gum Company of Louisville, Ky. The cards were printed on paper and inserted in five-cent cannisters of Colgan's Mint Chips and Violet Chips. The broderless cards include a player portrait on the front along with the player's last name, team and league. The back identifies the set as "Stars of the Diamond" and carries advertising for Colgan's Gum. A total of 235 different players were pictures over the three-year period, but because of team changes and other variations, more than 300 different cards exist. The set, designated as E254, is closely related to the E270 Red Border and E270 Tin Tops sets of the same period. The complete set price does not include all variations.

		NR MT	EX	VG
Complete Set:		31500.	15750.	9450.
Common Player:		60.00	30.00	18.00
(1)	Ed Abbaticchio	60.00	30.00	18.00
(2)	Fred Abbott	60.00	30.00	18.00
(3a)	Bill Abstein (Pittsburg)	60.00	30.00	18.00
(3b)	Bill Abstein (Jersey City)	60.00	30.00	18.00
(4)	Babe Adams	60.00	30.00	18.00
(5)	Doc Adkins	60.00	30.00	18.00
(6)	Joe Agler	60.00	30.00	18.00
(7a)	Dave Altizer (Cincinnati)	60.00	30.00	18.00
(7b)	Dave Altizer (Minneapolis)	60.00	30.00	18.00
(8)	Nick Altrock	60.00	30.00	18.00
(9)	Red Ames	60.00	30.00	18.00
(10)	Jimmy Archer	60.00	30.00	18.00
(11a)	Jimmy Austin (New York)	60.00	30.00	18.00
(11b)	Jimmy Austin (St. Louis)	60.00	30.00	18.00
(12a)	Charlie Babb (Memphis)	60.00	30.00	18.00
(12b)	Charlie Babb (Norfolk)	60.00	30.00	18.00
(13)	Baerwald	60.00	30.00	18.00
(14)	Bill Bailey	60.00	30.00	18.00
(15)	Home Run Baker	150.00	75.00	45.00
(16)	Jack Barry	60.00	30.00	18.00
(17a)	Bill Bartley (curved letters)	60.00	30.00	18.00
(17b)	Bill Bartley (horizontal letters)	60.00	30.00	18.00
(18a)	Johnny Bates (Cincinnati)	60.00	30.00	18.00
(18b)	Johnny Bates (Philadelphia, black letters)	60.00	30.00	18.00
(18c)	Johnny Bates (Philadelphia, white letters)	60.00	30.00	18.00
(19)	Dick Bayless	60.00	30.00	18.00
(20a)	Ginger Beaumont (Boston)	60.00	30.00	18.00
(20b)	Ginger Beaumont (Chicago)	60.00	30.00	18.00
(20c)	Ginger Beaumont (St. Paul)	60.00	30.00	18.00
(21)	Beals Becker	60.00	30.00	18.00
(22)	George Bell	60.00	30.00	18.00
(23a)	Harry Bemis (Cleveland)	60.00	30.00	18.00
(23b)	Harry Bemis (Columbus)	60.00	30.00	18.00
(24a)	Heinie Berger (Cleveland)	60.00	30.00	18.00
(24b)	Heinie Berger (Columbus)	60.00	30.00	18.00
(25)	Bob Bescher	60.00	30.00	18.00
(26)	Beumiller	60.00	30.00	18.00
(27)	Joe Birmingham	60.00	30.00	18.00
(28)	Kitty Bransfield	60.00	30.00	18.00
(29)	Roger Bresnahan	150.00	75.00	45.00
(30)	Al Bridwell	60.00	30.00	18.00
(31)	Lew Brockett	60.00	30.00	18.00
(32)	Al Burch	60.00	30.00	18.00
(33a)	Burke (Ft. Wayne)	60.00	30.00	18.00
(33b)	Burke (Indianapolis)	60.00	30.00	18.00
(34)	Donie Bush	60.00	30.00	18.00
(35)	Bill Byers	60.00	30.00	18.00
(36)	Howie Cammitz (Camnitz)	60.00	30.00	18.00
(37a)	Charlie Carr (Indianapolis)	60.00	30.00	18.00
(37b)	Charlie Carr (Utica)	60.00	30.00	18.00
(38)	Frank Chance	175.00	87.00	52.00
(39)	Hal Chase	100.00	50.00	30.00
(40)	Bill Clancy (Clancey)	60.00	30.00	18.00
(41a)	Fred Clarke (Pittsburg)	150.00	75.00	45.00
(41b)	Fred Clarke (Pittsburgh)	150.00	75.00	45.00
(42)	Tommy Clarke (Cincinnati)	60.00	30.00	18.00
(43)	Bill Clymer	60.00	30.00	18.00
(44a)	Ty Cobb (no team on uniform)	1200.	600.00	250.00
(44b)	Ty Cobb (team name on uniform))	1500.	750.00	300.00
(45)	Eddie Collins	150.00	75.00	45.00
(46)	Bunk Congalton	60.00	30.00	18.00
(47)	Wid Conroy	60.00	30.00	18.00
(48)	Ernie Courtney	60.00	30.00	18.00
(49a)	Harry Coveleski (Cincinnati)	60.00	30.00	18.00
(49b)	Harry Coveleski (Chattanooga)	60.00	30.00	18.00
(50)	Doc Crandall	60.00	30.00	18.00
(51)	Gavvy Cravath	60.00	30.00	18.00
(52)	Dode Criss	60.00	30.00	18.00
(53)	Bill Dahlen	60.00	30.00	18.00
(54a)	Jake Daubert (Memphis)	60.00	30.00	18.00
(54b)	Jake Daubert (Brooklyn)	60.00	30.00	18.00
(55)	Harry Davis (Philadelphia)	60.00	30.00	18.00
(56)	Davis (St. Paul)	60.00	30.00	18.00
(57)	Frank Delahanty	60.00	30.00	18.00
(58a)	Ray Demmett (Demmitt) (New York)	60.00	30.00	18.00
(58b)	Ray Demmett (Demmitt) (Montreal)	60.00	30.00	18.00
(58c)	Ray Demmett (Demmitt) (St. Louis)	60.00	30.00	18.00
(59)	Art Devlin	60.00	30.00	18.00
(60)	Wild Bill Donovan	60.00	30.00	18.00
(61)	Mickey Doolin (Doolan)	60.00	30.00	18.00
(62)	Patsy Dougherty	60.00	30.00	18.00
(63)	Tom Downey	60.00	30.00	18.00
(64)	Larry Doyle	60.00	30.00	18.00
(65)	Jack Dunn	60.00	30.00	18.00
(66)	Dick Eagan (Egan)	60.00	30.00	18.00
(67a)	Kid Elberfield (Elberfeld) (Washington)	60.00	30.00	18.00
(67b)	Kid Elberfield (Elberfeld) (New York)	60.00	30.00	18.00
(68)	Rube Ellis	60.00	30.00	18.00
(69a)	Clyde Engle (New York)	60.00	30.00	18.00
(69b)	Clyde Engle (Boston)	60.00	30.00	18.00
(70a)	Steve Evans (curved letters)	60.00	30.00	18.00
(70b)	Steve Evans (horizontal letters)	60.00	30.00	18.00
(71)	Johnny Evers	150.00	75.00	45.00
(72)	Cecil Ferguson	60.00	30.00	18.00
(73)	Hobe Ferris	60.00	30.00	18.00
(74)	Field	60.00	30.00	18.00
(75)	Fitzgerald	60.00	30.00	18.00
(76a)	Patsy Flaherty (Kansas City)	60.00	30.00	18.00
(76b)	Patsy Flaherty (Atlanta)	60.00	30.00	18.00
(77)	Jack Flater	60.00	30.00	18.00
(78a)	Elmer Flick (Cleveland)	150.00	75.00	45.00
(78b)	Elmer Flick (Toledo)	150.00	75.00	45.00
(79a)	James Freck (Frick) (Baltimore)	60.00	30.00	18.00
(79b)	James Freck (Frick) (Toronto)	60.00	30.00	18.00
(80)	Jerry Freeman (photo actually Buck Freeman)	60.00	30.00	18.00
(81)	Art Froome (Fromme)	60.00	30.00	18.00
(82a)	Larry Gardner (Boston)	60.00	30.00	18.00
(82b)	Larry Gardner (New York)	60.00	30.00	18.00
(83)	Harry Gaspar	60.00	30.00	18.00
(84a)	Gus Getz	60.00	30.00	18.00
(84b)	Gus Getz	60.00	30.00	18.00
(85)	George Gibson	60.00	30.00	18.00
(86a)	Moose Grimshaw (Toronto)	60.00	30.00	18.00
(86b)	Moose Grimshaw (Louisville)	60.00	30.00	18.00
(87)	Ed Hahn	60.00	30.00	18.00
(88)	John Halla	60.00	30.00	18.00
(89)	Ed Hally (Holly)	60.00	30.00	18.00
(90)	Charlie Hanford	60.00	30.00	18.00
(91)	Topsy Hartsel	60.00	30.00	18.00
(92a)	Roy Hartzell (St. Louis)	60.00	30.00	18.00
(92b)	Roy Hartzell (New York)	60.00	30.00	18.00
(93)	Weldon Henley	60.00	30.00	18.00
(94)	Harry Hinchman	60.00	30.00	18.00
(95)	Solly Hofman	60.00	30.00	18.00
(96a)	Harry Hooper (Boston Na'l)	150.00	75.00	45.00
(96b)	Harry Hooper (Boston Am. L.)	150.00	75.00	45.00
(97)	Howard	60.00	30.00	18.00
(98a)	Hughes (no team name on uniform)	60.00	30.00	18.00
(98b)	Hughes (team name on uniform)	60.00	30.00	18.00
(99a)	Rudy Hulswilt (St. Louis, name incorrect)	60.00	30.00	18.00
(99b)	Rudy Hulswitt (St. Louis, name correct)	60.00	30.00	18.00
(99c)	Rudy Hulswitt (Chattanooga)	60.00	30.00	18.00
(100)	John Hummel	60.00	30.00	18.00
(101)	George Hunter	60.00	30.00	18.00
(102)	Shoeless Joe Jackson	3500.	1750.	1050.
(103)	Hugh Jennings	150.00	75.00	45.00
(104)	Davy Jones	60.00	30.00	18.00
(105)	Tom Jones	60.00	30.00	18.00
(106a)	Tim Jordon (Jordan) (Brooklyn)	60.00	30.00	18.00
(106b)	Tim Jordon (Jordan) (Atlanta)	60.00	30.00	18.00
(106c)	Tim Jordon (Jordan) (Louisville)	60.00	30.00	18.00
(107)	Addie Joss	200.00	100.00	60.00
(108)	Al Kaiser	60.00	30.00	18.00
(109)	Wee Wille Keeler	150.00	75.00	45.00
(110)	Joe Kelly (Kelley)	150.00	75.00	45.00
(111)	Bill Killefer	60.00	30.00	18.00
(112a)	Ed Killian (Detroit)	60.00	30.00	18.00
(112b)	Ed Killian (Toronto)	60.00	30.00	18.00
(113)	Johnny Kling	60.00	30.00	18.00
(114)	Otto Knabe	60.00	30.00	18.00
(115)	Jack Knight	60.00	30.00	18.00
(116)	Ed Konetchy	60.00	30.00	18.00
(117)	Rube Kroh	60.00	30.00	18.00
(118)	James Lafitte	60.00	30.00	18.00
(119)	Nap Lajoie	400.00	200.00	90.00
(120)	Lakoff	60.00	30.00	18.00
(121)	Frank Lange	60.00	30.00	18.00
(122a)	Frank LaPorte (St. Louis)	60.00	30.00	18.00
(122b)	Frank LaPorte (New York)	60.00	30.00	18.00
(123)	Tommy Leach	60.00	30.00	18.00
(124)	Jack Lelivelt	60.00	30.00	18.00
(125a)	Jack Lewis (Milwaukee)	60.00	30.00	18.00
(125b)	Jack Lewis (Indianapolis)	60.00	30.00	18.00
(126a)	Vive Lindaman (Boston)	60.00	30.00	18.00
(126b)	Vive Lindaman (Louisville)	60.00	30.00	18.00
(126c)	Vive Lindaman (Indianapolis)	60.00	30.00	18.00
(127)	Bris Lord	60.00	30.00	18.00
(128a)	Harry Lord (Boston)	60.00	30.00	18.00
(128b)	Harry Lord (Chicago)	60.00	30.00	18.00
(129a)	Bill Ludwig (Milwaukee)	60.00	30.00	18.00
(129b)	Bill Ludwig (St. Louis)	60.00	30.00	18.00
(130)	Madden	60.00	30.00	18.00
(131)	Nick Maddox	60.00	30.00	18.00
(132a)	Manser (Jersey City)	60.00	30.00	18.00
(132b)	Manser (Rochester)	60.00	30.00	18.00
(133)	Rube Marquard	150.00	75.00	45.00
(134)	Al Mattern	60.00	30.00	18.00
(135)	Bill Matthews	60.00	30.00	18.00
(136)	George McBride	60.00	30.00	18.00
(137)	McCathy	60.00	30.00	18.00
(138)	McConnell	60.00	30.00	18.00
(139)	Moose McCormick	60.00	30.00	18.00
(140)	Dan McGann	60.00	30.00	18.00
(141)	Jim McGinley	60.00	30.00	18.00
(142)	Iron Man McGinnity	150.00	75.00	45.00
(143a)	Matty McIntyre (Detroit)	60.00	30.00	18.00
(143b)	Matty McIntyre (Chicago)	60.00	30.00	18.00
(144)	Larry McLean	60.00	30.00	18.00
(145)	Fred Merkle	60.00	30.00	18.00
(146a)	Merritt (Buffalo)	60.00	30.00	18.00
(146b)	Merritt (Jersey City)	60.00	30.00	18.00
(147a)	Meyer (Newark, name correct)	60.00	30.00	18.00
(147b)	Meyers (Newark, name incorrect)	60.00	30.00	18.00
(148)	Chief Meyers (New York)	60.00	30.00	18.00
(149)	Clyde Milan	60.00	30.00	18.00
(150)	Dots Miller	60.00	30.00	18.00
(151)	Mike Mitchell	60.00	30.00	18.00
(152)	Moran	60.00	30.00	18.00
(153a)	Bill Moriarty (Louisville)	60.00	30.00	18.00
(153b)	Bill Moriarty (Omaha)	60.00	30.00	18.00
(154)	George Moriarty	60.00	30.00	18.00
(155a)	George Mullen (name incorrect)	60.00	30.00	18.00
(155b)	George Mullin (name correct)	60.00	30.00	18.00
(156a)	Simmy Murch (Chattanooga)	60.00	30.00	18.00
(156b)	Simmy Murch (Indianapolis)	60.00	30.00	18.00
(157)	Danny Murphy	60.00	30.00	18.00
(158a)	Red Murray (New York, white letters)	60.00	30.00	18.00
(158b)	Red Murray (New York, black letters)	60.00	30.00	18.00
(158c)	Red Murray (St. Paul)	60.00	30.00	18.00
(159)	Billy Nattress	60.00	30.00	18.00
(160a)	Red Nelson (St. Louis)	60.00	30.00	18.00
(160b)	Red Nelson (Toledo)	60.00	30.00	18.00
(161)	Rebel Oakes	60.00	30.00	18.00
(162)	Fred Odwell	60.00	30.00	18.00
(163)	O'Rourke	60.00	30.00	18.00
(164a)	Al Orth (New York)	60.00	30.00	18.00
(164b)	Al Orth (Indianapolis)	60.00	30.00	18.00
(165)	Fred Osborn	60.00	30.00	18.00
(166)	Orval Overall	60.00	30.00	18.00
(167)	Owens	60.00	30.00	18.00
(168)	Fred Parent	60.00	30.00	18.00
(169a)	Dode Paskert (Cincinnati)	60.00	30.00	18.00
(169b)	Dode Paskert (Philadelphia)	60.00	30.00	18.00
(170)	Heinie Peitz	60.00	30.00	18.00
(171)	Bob Peterson	60.00	30.00	18.00
(172)	Jake Pfeister	60.00	30.00	18.00
(173)	Deacon Phillipe (Phillippe)	60.00	30.00	18.00
(174a)	Ollie Pickering (Louisville)	60.00	30.00	18.00
(174b)	Ollie Pickering (Minneapolis)	60.00	30.00	18.00
(174c)	Ollie Pickering (Omaha)	60.00	30.00	18.00
(175a)	Billy Purtell (Chicago)	60.00	30.00	18.00
(175b)	Billy Purtell (Boston)	60.00	30.00	18.00
(176)	Bugs Raymond	60.00	30.00	18.00
(177)	Pat Regan (Ragan)	60.00	30.00	18.00
(178)	Barney Reilly	60.00	30.00	18.00
(179)	Duke Reilly (Reilley)	60.00	30.00	18.00
(180)	Ed Reulbach	60.00	30.00	18.00
(181)	Ritchery	60.00	30.00	18.00
(182)	Lou Ritter	60.00	30.00	18.00
(183)	Robinson	60.00	30.00	18.00
(184)	Rock	60.00	30.00	18.00
(185a)	Jack Rowan (Cincinnati)	60.00	30.00	18.00
(185b)	Jack Rowan (Philadelphia)	60.00	30.00	18.00
(186)	Nap Rucker	60.00	30.00	18.00
(187a)	Dick Rudolph (New York)	60.00	30.00	18.00
(187b)	Dick Rudolph (Toronto)	60.00	30.00	18.00
(188)	Ryan	60.00	30.00	18.00
(189)	Slim Sallee	60.00	30.00	18.00
(190a)	Bill Schardt (Birmingham)	60.00	30.00	18.00
(190b)	Bill Schardt (Milwaukee)	60.00	30.00	18.00
(191)	Jimmy Scheckard (Sheckard)	60.00	30.00	18.00
(192a)	George Schirm (Birmingham)	60.00	30.00	18.00
(192b)	George Schirm (Buffalo)	60.00	30.00	18.00
(193)	Larry Schlafly	60.00	30.00	18.00
(194)	Wildfire Schulte	60.00	30.00	18.00
(195a)	James Seabaugh (looking to left, photo actually Julius Weisman)	60.00	30.00	18.00
(195b)	James Seabaugh (looking straight ahead, correct photo)	60.00	30.00	18.00
(196)	Selby	60.00	30.00	18.00
(197a)	Cy Seymour (New York)	60.00	30.00	18.00
(197b)	Cy Seymour (Baltimore)	60.00	30.00	18.00
(198)	Hosea Siner	60.00	30.00	18.00
(199)	G. Smith	60.00	30.00	18.00
(200a)	Sid Smith (Atlanta)	60.00	30.00	18.00
(200b)	Sid Smith (Buffalo)	60.00	30.00	18.00
(201)	Fred Snodgrass	60.00	30.00	18.00
(202a)	Bob Spade (Cincinnati)	60.00	30.00	18.00
(202b)	Bob Spade (Newark)	60.00	30.00	18.00
(203a)	Tully Sparks (Philadelphia)	60.00	30.00	18.00
(203b)	Tully Sparks (Richmond)	60.00	30.00	18.00
(204a)	Tris Speaker (Boston Nat'l)	275.00	125.00	55.00
(204b)	Tris Speaker (Boston Am.)	275.00	125.00	55.00
(205)	Tubby Spencer	60.00	30.00	18.00
(206)	Jake Stahl	60.00	30.00	18.00
(207)	John Stansberry (Stansbury)	60.00	30.00	18.00
(208)	Harry Steinfeldt	35.00	17.50	10.50
(209)	George Stone	60.00	30.00	18.00
(210)	George Stovall	60.00	30.00	18.00
(211)	Gabby Street	60.00	30.00	18.00
(212a)	Sullivan (Louisville)	60.00	30.00	18.00
(212b)	Sullivan (Omaha)	60.00	30.00	18.00
(213)	Ed Summers	60.00	30.00	18.00
(214)	Lee Tannehill	60.00	30.00	18.00

(215)	Taylor	60.00	30.00	18.00
(216)	Joe Tinker	150.00	75.00	45.00
(217)	John Titus	60.00	30.00	18.00
(218)	Terry Turner	60.00	30.00	18.00
(219a)	Bob Unglaub (Washington)	60.00	30.00	18.00
(219b)	Bob Unglaub (Lincoln)	60.00	30.00	18.00
(220a)	Rube Waddell (St. Louis)	150.00	75.00	45.00
(220b)	Rube Waddell (Minneapolis)	150.00	75.00	45.00
(220c)	Rube Waddell (Newark)	150.00	75.00	45.00
(221a)	Honus Wagner (Pittsburg, curved letters)	900.00	400.00	150.00
(221b)	Honus Wagner (Pittsburg, horizontal letters)	900.00	400.00	150.00
(221c)	Honus Wagner (Pittsburgh)	900.00	400.00	150.00
(222)	Walker	60.00	30.00	18.00
(223)	Waller	60.00	30.00	18.00
(224)	Clarence Wauner (Wanner)	60.00	30.00	18.00
(225a)	Julius Wiesman (name incorrect)	60.00	30.00	18.00
(225b)	Julius Weisman (name correct)	60.00	30.00	18.00
(226)	Jack White (Buffalo)	60.00	30.00	18.00
(227)	Kirby White (Boston)	60.00	30.00	18.00
(228)	Ed Willett	60.00	30.00	18.00
(229a)	Otto Williams (Indianapolis)	60.00	30.00	18.00
(229b)	Otto Williams (Minneapolis)	60.00	30.00	18.00
(230)	Owen Wilson	60.00	30.00	18.00
(231)	Hooks Wiltse	60.00	30.00	18.00
(232a)	Orville Woodruff (Indianapolis)	60.00	30.00	18.00
(232b)	Orville Woodruff (Louisville)	60.00	30.00	18.00
(233)	Woods	60.00	30.00	18.00
(234)	Cy Young	500.00	250.00	135.00
(235)	Bill Zimmerman	60.00	30.00	18.00
(236)	Heinie Zimmerman	60.00	30.00	18.00

1912 Colgan's Chips Red Borders (E270)

This set, issued in 1912 by Colgan Gum Company of Louisville Ky., is very similar to the E254 Colgan's Chips set. Measuring 1-1/2" in diameter, these round, paper player photos were inserted in cannisters of Colgan's Mint and Violet Chips. They are differentiated from other similar issues by their distinctive red borders and by the back of the cards, which advises collectors to "Send 25 Box Tops" for a photo of the "World's Pennant Winning Team." The set is designated as the E270 Red Border set.

		NR MT	EX	VG
	Complete Set:	14000.	7000.	4200.
	Common Player:	90.00	37.00	22.00
(1)	Ed Abbaticchio	90.00	45.00	27.00
(2)	Fred Abbott	90.00	45.00	27.00
(3)	Babe Adams	90.00	45.00	27.00
(4)	Red Ames	90.00	45.00	27.00
(5)	Charlie Babb	90.00	45.00	27.00
(6)	Bill Bailey	90.00	45.00	27.00
(7)	Home Run Baker	200.00	100.00	60.00
(8)	Jack Barry	90.00	45.00	27.00
(9)	Johnny Bates	90.00	45.00	27.00
(10)	Dick Bayless	90.00	45.00	27.00
(11)	Beals Becker	90.00	45.00	27.00
(13)	Heinie Berger	90.00	45.00	27.00
(14)	Beumiller	90.00	45.00	27.00
(15)	Joe Birmingham	90.00	45.00	27.00
(16)	Kitty Bransfield	90.00	45.00	27.00
(17)	Roger Bresnahan	200.00	100.00	60.00
(18)	Lew Brockett	90.00	45.00	27.00
(19)	Al Burch	90.00	45.00	27.00
(20)	Donie Bush	90.00	45.00	27.00
(21)	Bill Byers	90.00	45.00	27.00
(22)	Howie Cammitz (Camnitz)	90.00	45.00	27.00
(23)	Charlie Carr	90.00	45.00	27.00
(24)	Frank Chance	200.00	100.00	60.00
(25)	Fred Clarke (Pittsburg)	200.00	100.00	60.00
(26)	Tommy Clarke (Cincinnati)	90.00	45.00	27.00
(27)	Bill Clymer	90.00	45.00	27.00
(28)	Ty Cobb	1500.	750.00	450.00
(29)	Eddie Collins	200.00	100.00	60.00
(30)	Wid Conroy	90.00	45.00	27.00
(31)	Harry Coveleski	90.00	45.00	27.00
(32)	Gavvy Cravath	90.00	45.00	27.00
(33)	Dode Criss	90.00	45.00	27.00
(34)	Harry Davis (Philadelphia)	90.00	45.00	27.00
(35)	Davis (St. Paul)	90.00	45.00	27.00
(36)	Frank Delahanty	90.00	45.00	27.00
(37)	Ray Demmett (Demmitt)	90.00	45.00	27.00
(38)	Art Devlin	90.00	45.00	27.00
(39)	Wild Bill Donovan	90.00	45.00	27.00
(40)	Mickey Doolan	90.00	45.00	27.00
(41)	Patsy Dougherty	90.00	45.00	27.00
(42)	Tom Downey	90.00	45.00	27.00
(43)	Larry Doyle	90.00	45.00	27.00
(44)	Jack Dunn	90.00	45.00	27.00
(45)	Dick Eagan (Egan)	90.00	45.00	27.00
(46)	Kid Elberfield (Elberfeld)	90.00	45.00	27.00
(47)	Rube Ellis	90.00	45.00	27.00
(48)	Steve Evans	90.00	45.00	27.00
(49)	Johnny Evers	200.00	100.00	60.00
(50)	Cecil Ferguson	90.00	45.00	27.00
(51)	Hobe Ferris	90.00	45.00	27.00
(52)	Fitzgerald	90.00	45.00	27.00
(53)	Fisher	90.00	45.00	27.00
(54)	Elmer Flick	200.00	100.00	60.00
(55)	James Freck (Frick)	90.00	45.00	27.00
(56)	Art Froome (Fromme)	90.00	45.00	27.00
(57)	Harry Gaspar	90.00	45.00	27.00
(58)	George Gibson	90.00	45.00	27.00
(59)	Moose Grimshaw	90.00	45.00	27.00
(60)	John Halla	90.00	45.00	27.00
(61)	Ed Hally (Holly)	90.00	45.00	27.00
(62)	Charlie Hanford	90.00	45.00	27.00
(63)	Topsy Hartsel	90.00	45.00	27.00
(64)	Roy Hartzell	90.00	45.00	27.00
(65)	Weldon Henley	90.00	45.00	27.00
(66)	Harry Hinchman	90.00	45.00	27.00
(67)	Solly Hofman	90.00	45.00	27.00
(68)	Harry Hooper	200.00	100.00	60.00
(69)	Howard	90.00	45.00	27.00
(70)	Hughes	90.00	45.00	27.00
(71)	Rudy Hulswitt	90.00	45.00	27.00
(72)	John Hummel	90.00	45.00	27.00
(73)	George Hunter	90.00	45.00	27.00
(74)	Hugh Jennings	200.00	100.00	60.00
(75)	Davy Jones	90.00	45.00	27.00
(76)	Tim Jordon (Jordan)	90.00	45.00	27.00
(77)	Bill Killefer	90.00	45.00	27.00
(78)	Ed Killian	90.00	45.00	27.00
(79)	Otto Knabe	90.00	45.00	27.00
(80)	Jack Knight	90.00	45.00	27.00
(81)	Ed Konetchy	90.00	45.00	27.00
(82)	Rube Kroh	90.00	45.00	27.00
(83)	LaCrosse (photo actually Bill Schardt)	90.00	45.00	27.00
(84)	Tommy Leach	90.00	45.00	27.00
(85)	Jack Lelivelt	90.00	45.00	27.00
(86)	Jack Lewis	90.00	45.00	27.00
(87)	Vive Lindaman	90.00	45.00	27.00
(88)	Bris Lord	90.00	45.00	27.00
(89)	Harry Lord	90.00	45.00	27.00
(90)	Bill Ludwig	90.00	45.00	27.00
(91)	Nick Maddox	90.00	45.00	27.00
(92)	Al Mattern	90.00	45.00	27.00
(93)	George McBride	90.00	45.00	27.00
(94)	McCathy	90.00	45.00	27.00
(95)	McConnell	90.00	45.00	27.00
(96)	Moose McCormick	90.00	45.00	27.00
(97)	Jim McGinley	90.00	45.00	27.00
(98)	Iron Man McGinnity	200.00	100.00	60.00
(99)	Matty McIntyre	90.00	45.00	27.00
(100)	Fred Merkle	90.00	45.00	27.00
(101)	Merritt	90.00	45.00	27.00
(102)	Chief Meyers	90.00	45.00	27.00
(103)	Clyde Milan	90.00	45.00	27.00
(104)	Dots Miller	90.00	45.00	27.00
(105)	Mike Mitchell	90.00	45.00	27.00
(106)	Bill Moriarty (Omaha)	90.00	45.00	27.00
(107)	George Moriarty (Detroit)	90.00	45.00	27.00
(108)	George Mullen	90.00	45.00	27.00
(109)	Simmy Murch	90.00	45.00	27.00
(110)	Danny Murphy	90.00	45.00	27.00
(111)	Red Murray	90.00	45.00	27.00
(112)	Red Nelson	90.00	45.00	27.00
(113)	Rebel Oakes	90.00	45.00	27.00
(114)	Orval Overall	90.00	45.00	27.00
(115)	Owens	90.00	45.00	27.00
(116)	Fred Parent	90.00	45.00	27.00
(117)	Dode Paskert	90.00	45.00	27.00
(118)	Heinie Peitz (Pietz)	90.00	45.00	27.00
(119)	Bob Peterson	90.00	45.00	27.00
(120)	Ollie Pickering	90.00	45.00	27.00
(121)	Bugs Raymond	90.00	45.00	27.00
(122)	Pat Regan (Ragan)	90.00	45.00	27.00
(123)	Robinson	90.00	45.00	27.00
(124)	Rock	90.00	45.00	27.00
(125)	Jack Rowan	90.00	45.00	27.00
(126)	Nap Rucker	90.00	45.00	27.00
(127)	Dick Rudolph	90.00	45.00	27.00
(128)	Slim Sallee	90.00	45.00	27.00
(129)	Jimmy Scheckard (Sheckard)	90.00	45.00	27.00
(130)	George Schirm	90.00	45.00	27.00
(131)	Wildfire Schulte	90.00	45.00	27.00
(132)	James Seabaugh	90.00	45.00	27.00
(133)	Selby	90.00	45.00	27.00
(134)	Hosea Siner	90.00	45.00	27.00
(135)	Sid Smith	90.00	45.00	27.00
(136)	Fred Snodgrass	90.00	45.00	27.00
(137)	Bob Spade	90.00	45.00	27.00
(138)	Tully Sparks	90.00	45.00	27.00
(139)	Tris Speaker	350.00	175.00	105.00
(140)	Tubby Spencer	90.00	45.00	27.00
(141)	George Stone	90.00	45.00	27.00
(142)	George Stovall	90.00	45.00	27.00
(143)	Gabby Street	90.00	45.00	27.00
(144)	Sullivan (Omaha)	90.00	45.00	27.00
(145)	John Sullivan (Louisville)	90.00	45.00	27.00
(146)	Ed Summers	90.00	45.00	27.00
(147)	Joe Tinker	200.00	100.00	60.00
(148)	John Titus	90.00	45.00	27.00
(149)	Rube Waddell	200.00	100.00	60.00
(150)	Walker	90.00	45.00	27.00
(151)	Waller	90.00	45.00	27.00
(152)	Julius Wiesman (Weisman)	90.00	45.00	27.00
(153)	Jack White	90.00	45.00	27.00
(154)	Otto Williams	90.00	45.00	27.00
(155)	Hooks Wiltse	90.00	45.00	27.00
(156)	Orville Woodruff	90.00	45.00	27.00
(157)	Woods	90.00	45.00	27.00
(158)	Cy Young	600.00	300.00	180.00
(159)	Heinie Zimmerman	90.00	45.00	27.00

1912 Colgan's Chips Tin Tops (E270)

Except for the backs, these round, paper cards (Measuring 1-1/2" in diameter) are identical to the E254 Colgan's Chips issue, and were inserted in tin cannisters of Colgan's Mint Chips and Violet Chips. The front contains a player portrait photo along with the player's last name, team and league. The back advises collectors to "Send 25 Tin Tops" and a two-cent stamp to receive a photo of the "World's Pennant Winning Team." The set carries the designation E270 Tin Tops.

		NR MT	EX	VG
	Complete Set:	18000.	9000.	5400.
	Common Player:	85.00	42.00	25.00
(1)	Doc Adkins	85.00	42.00	25.00
(2)	Whitey Alperman	85.00	42.00	25.00
(3a)	Red Ames (New York)	85.00	42.00	25.00
(3b)	Red Ames (Cincinnati)	85.00	42.00	25.00
(4a)	Tommy Atkins (Atlanta)	85.00	42.00	25.00
(4b)	Tommy Atkins (Ft. Wayne)	85.00	42.00	25.00
(5)	Jake Atz	85.00	42.00	25.00
(6)	Jimmy Austin	85.00	42.00	25.00
(7)	Home Run Baker	175.00	87.00	52.00
(8)	Johnny Bates	85.00	42.00	25.00
(9)	Beebe	85.00	42.00	25.00
(10)	Harry Bemis	85.00	42.00	25.00
(11)	Bob Bescher	85.00	42.00	25.00
(12)	Joe Birmingham	85.00	42.00	25.00
(13)	Roger Bresnahan	175.00	87.00	52.00
(14)	George Brown (Browne)	85.00	42.00	25.00
(15)	Al Burch	85.00	42.00	25.00
(16)	Burns	85.00	42.00	25.00
(17)	Donie Bush	85.00	42.00	25.00
(18)	Bobby Byrne	85.00	42.00	25.00
(19)	Nixey Callahan	85.00	42.00	25.00
(20)	Billy Campbell	85.00	42.00	25.00
(21)	Charlie Carr	85.00	42.00	25.00
(22)	Jay Cashion	85.00	42.00	25.00
(23)	Frank Chance	175.00	87.00	52.00
(24)	Hal Chase	110.00	55.00	33.00
(25)	Ed Cicotte	110.00	55.00	33.00
(26)	Clarke (Indianapolis)	85.00	42.00	25.00
(27)	Fred Clarke (Pittsburg)	175.00	87.00	52.00
(28)	Tommy Clarke (Cincinnati)	85.00	42.00	25.00
(29)	Clemons	85.00	42.00	25.00
(30)	Bill Clymer	85.00	42.00	25.00
(31)	Ty Cobb	1200.	600.00	360.00
(32)	Eddie Collins	175.00	87.00	52.00
(33a)	Bunk Congalton (Omaha)	85.00	42.00	25.00
(33b)	Bunk Congalton (Toledo)	85.00	42.00	25.00
(34)	Cook	85.00	42.00	25.00
(35)	Jack Coombs	85.00	42.00	25.00
(36)	Corcoran	85.00	42.00	25.00
(37)	Sam Crawford	175.00	87.00	52.00
(38)	Bert Daniels	85.00	42.00	25.00
(39)	Jake Daubert	85.00	42.00	25.00
(40a)	Josh Devore	85.00	42.00	25.00
(40b)	Josh Devore	85.00	42.00	25.00
(41)	Mike Donlin	85.00	42.00	25.00
(42)	Red Dooin	85.00	42.00	25.00
(43)	Mickey Doolan	85.00	42.00	25.00
(44)	Larry Doyle	85.00	42.00	25.00
(45)	Delos Drake	85.00	42.00	25.00
(46)	Kid Elberfield (Elberfeld)	85.00	42.00	25.00
(47)	Roy Ellam	85.00	42.00	25.00
(48)	Elliott	85.00	42.00	25.00
(49)	Rube Ellis	85.00	42.00	25.00
(50)	Elwert	85.00	42.00	25.00
(51)	Clyde Engle	85.00	42.00	25.00
(52)	Jimmy Esmond	85.00	42.00	25.00
(53)	Steve Evans	85.00	42.00	25.00
(54)	Johnny Evers	175.00	87.00	52.00
(55)	Hobe Ferris	85.00	42.00	25.00
(56)	Russ Ford	85.00	42.00	25.00
(57)	Ed Foster	85.00	42.00	25.00
(58)	Friel	85.00	42.00	25.00
(59)	John Frill	85.00	42.00	25.00
(60)	Art Froome (Fromme)	85.00	42.00	25.00
(61)	Gus Getz	85.00	42.00	25.00
(62)	George Gibson	85.00	42.00	25.00
(63)	Graham	85.00	42.00	25.00
(64a)	Eddie Grant (Cincinnati)	85.00	42.00	25.00
(64b)	Eddie Grant (New York)	85.00	42.00	25.00
(65)	Grief	85.00	42.00	25.00
(66)	Bob Grom (Groom)	85.00	42.00	25.00
(67)	Charlie Hanford	85.00	42.00	25.00
(68)	Topsy Hartsel	85.00	42.00	25.00
(69)	Harry Hinchman	85.00	42.00	25.00
(70)	Dick Hoblitzell	85.00	42.00	25.00
(71)	Happy Hogan (St. Louis)	85.00	42.00	25.00
(72)	Happy Hogan (San Francisco)	85.00	42.00	25.00
(73)	Harry Hooper	175.00	87.00	52.00
(74)	Miller Huggins	175.00	87.00	52.00
(75a)	Hughes (Milwaukee)	85.00	42.00	25.00

(75b)	Hughes (Rochester)	85.00	42.00	25.00
(76)	Rudy Hulswitt	85.00	42.00	25.00
(77)	John Hummel	85.00	42.00	25.00
(78)	Hugh Jennings	175.00	87.00	52.00
(79)	Pete Johns	85.00	42.00	25.00
(80)	Davy Jones	85.00	42.00	25.00
(81)	Tim Jordan	85.00	42.00	25.00
(82)	Bob Keefe	85.00	42.00	25.00
(83)	Wee Willie Keeler	175.00	87.00	52.00
(84)	Joe Kelly (Kelley)	175.00	87.00	52.00
(85)	Bill Killefer	85.00	42.00	25.00
(86)	Ed Killian	85.00	42.00	25.00
(87)	Klipfer	85.00	42.00	25.00
(88)	Otto Knabe	85.00	42.00	25.00
(89)	Jack Knight	85.00	42.00	25.00
(90)	Ed Konetchy	85.00	42.00	25.00
(91)	Paul Krichell	85.00	42.00	25.00
(92)	James Lafitte	85.00	42.00	25.00
(93)	Nap Lajoie	200.00	100.00	60.00
(94)	Frank Lange	85.00	42.00	25.00
(95)	Lee	85.00	42.00	25.00
(96)	Jack Lewis	85.00	42.00	25.00
(97)	Harry Lord	85.00	42.00	25.00
(98)	Johnny Lush	85.00	42.00	25.00
(99)	Madden	85.00	42.00	25.00
(100)	Nick Maddox	85.00	42.00	25.00
(101)	Sherry Magee	85.00	42.00	25.00
(102)	Manser	85.00	42.00	25.00
(103)	McAllister	85.00	42.00	25.00
(104)	McCathy	85.00	42.00	25.00
(105)	McConnell	85.00	42.00	25.00
(106)	Larry McLean	85.00	42.00	25.00
(107)	Fred Merkle	85.00	42.00	25.00
(108)	Chief Meyers	85.00	42.00	25.00
(109)	Miller (Columbus)	85.00	42.00	25.00
(110)	Dots Miller (Pittsburg)	85.00	42.00	25.00
(111)	Clarence Mitchell	85.00	42.00	25.00
(112)	Mike Mitchell	85.00	42.00	25.00
(113)	Roy Mitchell	85.00	42.00	25.00
(114)	Carlton Molesworth	85.00	42.00	25.00
(115)	Herbie Moran	85.00	42.00	25.00
(116)	George Moriarty	85.00	42.00	25.00
(117)	Danny Murphy	85.00	42.00	25.00
(118)	Jim Murray	85.00	42.00	25.00
(119)	Jake Northrop	85.00	42.00	25.00
(120)	Rube Oldring	85.00	42.00	25.00
(121)	Steve O'Neil (O'Neill)	85.00	42.00	25.00
(122)	O'Rourke	85.00	42.00	25.00
(123)	Larry Pape	85.00	42.00	25.00
(124)	Fred Parent	85.00	42.00	25.00
(125)	Perry	85.00	42.00	25.00
(126)	Billy Purtell	85.00	42.00	25.00
(127)	Bill Rariden	85.00	42.00	25.00
(128)	Morrie Rath	85.00	42.00	25.00
(129)	Dick Rudolph	85.00	42.00	25.00
(130)	Bud Ryan	85.00	42.00	25.00
(131)	Slim Sallee	85.00	42.00	25.00
(132)	Ray Schalk	85.00	42.00	25.00
(133)	Jimmy Scheckard (Sheckard)	85.00	42.00	25.00
(134)	Bob Shawkey	85.00	42.00	25.00
(135)	Skeeter Shelton	85.00	42.00	25.00
(136)	Smith (Montreal)	85.00	42.00	25.00
(137a)	Sid Smith (Atlanta)	85.00	42.00	25.00
(137b)	Sid Smith (Newark)	85.00	42.00	25.00
(138)	Fred Snodgrass	85.00	42.00	25.00
(139)	Tris Speaker	200.00	100.00	60.00
(140)	Jake Stahl	85.00	42.00	25.00
(141)	John Stansberry (Stansbury)	85.00	42.00	25.00
(142)	Amos Strunk	85.00	42.00	25.00
(143)	Sullivan	85.00	42.00	25.00
(144)	Harry Swacina	85.00	42.00	25.00
(145)	Bill Sweeney	85.00	42.00	25.00
(146)	Jeff Sweeney	85.00	42.00	25.00
(147)	Taylor	85.00	42.00	25.00
(148)	Jim Thorpe	2500.	1250.	750.00
(149)	Joe Tinker	175.00	87.00	52.00
(150)	John Titus	85.00	42.00	25.00
(151)	Terry Turner	85.00	42.00	25.00
(152)	Bob Unglaub	85.00	42.00	25.00
(153)	Viebahn	85.00	42.00	25.00
(154)	Rube Waddell	175.00	87.00	52.00
(155)	Honus Wagner	500.00	250.00	150.00
(156)	Bobby Wallace	175.00	87.00	52.00
(157)	Ed Walsh	175.00	87.00	52.00
(158)	Jack Warhop	85.00	42.00	25.00
(159)	Zach Wheat	175.00	87.00	52.00
(160)	Kaiser Wilhelm	85.00	42.00	25.00
(161)	Ed Willett	85.00	42.00	25.00
(162)	Owen Wilson	85.00	42.00	25.00
(163)	Hooks Wiltse	85.00	42.00	25.00
(164)	Joe Wood	85.00	42.00	25.00
(165)	Orville Woodruff	85.00	42.00	25.00
(166)	Joe Yeager	85.00	42.00	25.00
(167)	Bill Zimmerman	85.00	42.00	25.00

Grading Guide

Mint (MT): A perfect card. Well-centered with all corners sharp and square. No creases, stains, edge nicks, surface marks, yellowing or fading.

Near Mint (NM): A nearly perfect card. At first glance, a NM card appears to be perfect. May be slightly off-center. No surface marks, creases or loss of gloss.

Excellent (EX): Corners are still fairly sharp with only moderate wear. Borders may be off-center. No creases or stains on fronts or backs, but may show slight loss of surface luster.

Very Good (VG): Shows obvious handling. May have rounded corners, minor creases, major gum or wax stains. No major creases, tape marks, writing, etc.

Good (G): A well-worn card, but exhibits no intentional damage. May have major or multiple creases. Corners may be rounded well beyond card border.

1916 Collins-McCarthy (E135)

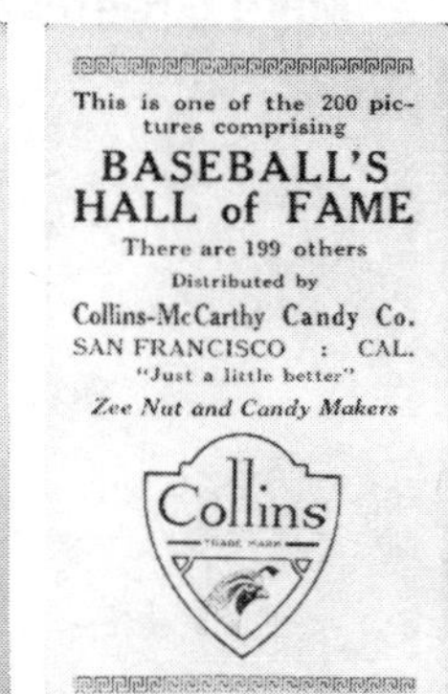

This is one of the 200 pictures comprising
BASEBALL'S
HALL of FAME
There are 199 others
Distributed by
Collins-McCarthy Candy Co.
SAN FRANCISCO : CAL.
"Just a little better"
Zee Nut and Candy Makers
Collins

Produced by the Collins-McCarthy Candy Co. of San Francisco, the 200-card, black and white set represents the company's only venture into issuing non-Pacific Coast League players. The cards, which are numbered alphabetically, measure 2" by 3-1/4" in size and are printed on think stock. Though the set is entitled "Baseball's Hall of Fame," many nondescript players appear in the issue. The complete set price does not include the more expensive variations.

		NR MT	EX	VG
	Complete Set:	24000.	12000.	7200.
	Common Player:	60.00	30.00	18.00
1	Sam Agnew	60.00	30.00	18.00
2	Grover Alexander	250.00	125.00	75.00
3	W.S. Alexander (W.E.)	60.00	30.00	18.00
4	Leon Ames	60.00	30.00	18.00
5	Fred Anderson	60.00	30.00	18.00
6	Ed Appleton	60.00	30.00	18.00
7	Jimmy Archer	60.00	30.00	18.00
8	Jimmy Austin	60.00	30.00	18.00
9	Jim Bagby	60.00	30.00	18.00
10	H.D. Baird	60.00	30.00	18.00
11	J. Franklin Baker	250.00	125.00	75.00
12	Dave Bancroft	250.00	125.00	75.00
13	Jack Barry	60.00	30.00	18.00
14	Joe Benz	60.00	30.00	18.00
15	Al Betzel	60.00	30.00	18.00
16	Ping Bodie	60.00	30.00	18.00
17	Joe Boehling	60.00	30.00	18.00
18	Eddie Burns	60.00	30.00	18.00
19	George Burns	60.00	30.00	18.00
20	Geo. J. Burns	60.00	30.00	18.00
21	Joe Bush	75.00	37.00	22.00
22	Owen Bush	60.00	30.00	18.00
23	Bobby Byrne	60.00	30.00	18.00
24	Forrest Cady	60.00	30.00	18.00
25	Max Carey	250.00	125.00	75.00
26	Ray Chapman	80.00	40.00	24.00
27	Larry Cheney	60.00	30.00	18.00
28	Eddie Cicotte	100.00	50.00	30.00
29	Tom Clarke	60.00	30.00	18.00
30	Ty Cobb	2000.	1000.	600.00
31	Eddie Collins	250.00	125.00	75.00
32	"Shauno" Collins (Shano)	60.00	30.00	18.00
33	Fred Coumbe	60.00	30.00	18.00
34	Harry Coveleskie (Coveleski)	60.00	30.00	18.00
35	Gavvy Cravath	60.00	30.00	18.00
36	Sam Crawford	250.00	125.00	75.00
37	Geo. Cutshaw	60.00	30.00	18.00
38	Jake Daubert	60.00	30.00	18.00
39	Geo. Dauss	60.00	30.00	18.00
40	Charles Deal	60.00	30.00	18.00
41	"Wheezer" Dell	60.00	30.00	18.00
42	William Doak	60.00	30.00	18.00
43	Bill Donovan	60.00	30.00	18.00
44	Larry Doyle	75.00	37.00	22.00
45	Johnny Evers	250.00	125.00	75.00
46	Urban Faber	250.00	125.00	75.00
47	"Hap" Felsch	80.00	40.00	24.00
48	Bill Fischer	60.00	30.00	18.00
49	Ray Fisher	60.00	30.00	18.00
50	Art Fletcher	60.00	30.00	18.00
51	Eddie Foster	60.00	30.00	18.00
52	Jacques Fournier	60.00	30.00	18.00
53	Del Gainer (Gainor)	60.00	30.00	18.00
54	Bert Gallia	60.00	30.00	18.00
55	"Chic" Gandil (Chick)	80.00	40.00	24.00
56	Larry Gardner	60.00	30.00	18.00
57	Joe Gedeon	60.00	30.00	18.00
58	Gus Getz	60.00	30.00	18.00
59	Frank Gilhooley	60.00	30.00	18.00
60	Wm. Gleason	60.00	30.00	18.00
61	M.A. Gonzales (Gonzalez)	60.00	30.00	18.00
62	Hank Gowdy	60.00	30.00	18.00
63	John Graney	60.00	30.00	18.00
64	Tom Griffith	60.00	30.00	18.00
65	Heinie Groh	75.00	37.00	22.00
66	Bob Groom	60.00	30.00	18.00
67	Louis Guisto	60.00	30.00	18.00
68	Earl Hamilton	60.00	30.00	18.00
69	Harry Harper	60.00	30.00	18.00
70	Grover Hartley	60.00	30.00	18.00
71	Harry Heilmann	250.00	125.00	75.00
72	Claude Hendrix	60.00	30.00	18.00
73	Olaf Henriksen	60.00	30.00	18.00
74	John Henry	60.00	30.00	18.00
75	"Buck" Herzog	60.00	30.00	18.00
76a	Hugh High (white stockings, photo actually Claude Williams)	250.00	125.00	75.00
76b	Hugh High (black stockings, correct photo)	80.00	40.00	24.00
77	Dick Hoblitzell	60.00	30.00	18.00
78	Walter Holke	60.00	30.00	18.00
79	Harry Hooper	250.00	125.00	75.00
80	Rogers Hornsby	400.00	200.00	120.00
81	Ivan Howard	60.00	30.00	18.00
82	Joe Jackson	5000.	2500.	1500.
83	Harold Janvrin	60.00	30.00	18.00
84	William James	60.00	30.00	18.00
85	C. Jamieson	60.00	30.00	18.00
86	Hugh Jennings	250.00	125.00	75.00
87	Walter Johnson	1000.	500.00	300.00
88	James Johnston	60.00	30.00	18.00
89	Fielder Jones	60.00	30.00	18.00
90a	Joe Judge (bat on right shoulder, photo actually Ray Morgan)	250.00	125.00	75.00
90b	Joe Judge (bat on left shoulder, correct photo)	80.00	40.00	24.00
91	Hans Lobert	60.00	30.00	18.00
92	Benny Kauff	60.00	30.00	18.00
93	Wm. Killefer Jr.	60.00	30.00	18.00
94	Ed. Konetchy	60.00	30.00	18.00
95	John Lavan	60.00	30.00	18.00
96	Jimmy Lavender	60.00	30.00	18.00
97	"Nemo" Leibold	60.00	30.00	18.00
98	H.B. Leonard	60.00	30.00	18.00
99	Duffy Lewis	75.00	37.00	22.00
100	Tom Long	60.00	30.00	18.00
101	Wm. Louden	60.00	30.00	18.00
102	Fred Luderus	60.00	30.00	18.00
103	Lee Magee	60.00	30.00	18.00
104	Sherwood Magee	60.00	30.00	18.00
105	Al Mamaux	60.00	30.00	18.00
106	Leslie Mann	60.00	30.00	18.00
107	"Rabbit" Maranville	250.00	125.00	75.00
108	Rube Marquard	250.00	125.00	75.00
109	Armando Marsans	60.00	30.00	18.00
110	J. Erskine Mayer	60.00	30.00	18.00
111	George McBride	60.00	30.00	18.00
112	Lew McCarty	60.00	30.00	18.00
113	John J. McGraw	275.00	137.00	82.00
114	Jack McInnis	60.00	30.00	18.00
115	Lee Meadows	60.00	30.00	18.00
116	Fred Merkle	75.00	37.00	22.00
117	"Chief" Meyers	60.00	30.00	18.00
118	Clyde Milan	60.00	30.00	18.00
119	Otto Miller	60.00	30.00	18.00
120	Clarence Mitchell	60.00	30.00	18.00
121a	Ray Morgan (bat on right shoulder, photo actually Joe Judge)	250.00	125.00	75.00
121b	Ray Morgan (bat on left shoulder, correct photo)	80.00	40.00	24.00
122	Guy Morton	60.00	30.00	18.00
123	"Mike" Mowrey	60.00	30.00	18.00
124	Elmer Myers	60.00	30.00	18.00
125	"Hy" Myers	60.00	30.00	18.00
126	A.E. Neale	80.00	40.00	24.00
127	Arthur Nehf	60.00	30.00	18.00
128	J.A. Niehoff	60.00	30.00	18.00
129	Steve O'Neill	60.00	30.00	18.00
130	"Dode" Paskert	60.00	30.00	18.00
131	Roger Peckinpaugh	75.00	37.00	22.00
132	"Pol" Perritt	60.00	30.00	18.00
133	"Jeff" Pfeffer	60.00	30.00	18.00
134	Walter Pipp	125.00	62.00	37.00
135	Derril Pratt (Derrill)	60.00	30.00	18.00
136	Bill Rariden	60.00	30.00	18.00
137	E.C. Rice	250.00	125.00	75.00
138	Wm. A. Ritter (Wm. H.)	60.00	30.00	18.00
139	Eppa Rixey	250.00	125.00	75.00
140	Davey Robertson	60.00	30.00	18.00
141	"Bob" Roth	60.00	30.00	18.00
142	Ed. Roush	250.00	125.00	75.00
143	Clarence Rowland	60.00	30.00	18.00
144	Dick Rudolph	60.00	30.00	18.00
145	William Rumler	60.00	30.00	18.00
146a	Reb Russell (pitching follow-thru, photo actually Mellie Wolfgang)	250.00	125.00	75.00
146b	Reb Russell (hands at side, correct photo)	800.00	400.00	240.00
147	"Babe" Ruth	3500.	1750.	1050.
148	Vic Saier	60.00	30.00	18.00
149	"Slim" Sallee	60.00	30.00	18.00
150	Ray Schalk	250.00	125.00	75.00
151	Walter Schang	60.00	30.00	18.00
152	Frank Schulte	60.00	30.00	18.00
153	Ferd Schupp	60.00	30.00	18.00
154	Everett Scott	60.00	30.00	18.00
155	Hank Severeid	60.00	30.00	18.00
156	Howard Shanks	60.00	30.00	18.00
157	Bob Shawkey	75.00	37.00	22.00
158	Jas. Sheckard	60.00	30.00	18.00
159	Ernie Shore	60.00	30.00	18.00
160	C.H. Shorten	60.00	30.00	18.00
161	Burt Shotton	60.00	30.00	18.00
162	Geo. Sisler	250.00	125.00	75.00
163	Elmer Smith	60.00	30.00	18.00
164	J. Carlisle Smith	60.00	30.00	18.00
165	Fred Snodgrass	60.00	30.00	18.00
166	Tris Speaker	375.00	187.00	112.00
167	Oscar Stanage	60.00	30.00	18.00
168	Charles Stengel	575.00	287.00	172.00
169	Milton Stock	60.00	30.00	18.00
170	Amos Strunk	60.00	30.00	18.00
171	"Zeb" Terry	60.00	30.00	18.00
172	"Jeff" Tesreau	60.00	30.00	18.00
173	Chester Thomas	60.00	30.00	18.00
174	Fred Toney	60.00	30.00	18.00
175	Terry Turner	60.00	30.00	18.00
176	George Tyler	60.00	30.00	18.00
177	Jim Vaughn	60.00	30.00	18.00
178	Bob Veach	60.00	30.00	18.00
179	Oscar Vitt	60.00	30.00	18.00

180	Hans Wagner	1750.	875.00	525.00
181	Clarence Walker	60.00	30.00	18.00
182	Jim Walsh	60.00	30.00	18.00
183	Al Walters	60.00	30.00	18.00
184	W. Wambsganss	80.00	40.00	24.00
185	Buck Weaver	100.00	50.00	30.00
186	Carl Weilman	60.00	30.00	18.00
187	Zack Wheat	250.00	125.00	75.00
188	Geo. Whitted	60.00	30.00	18.00
189	Joe Wilhoit	60.00	30.00	18.00
190a	Claude Williams (black stockings, photo actually Hugh High)	250.00	125.00	75.00
190b	Claude Williams (white stockings, correct photo)	100.00	50.00	30.00
191	Fred Williams	80.00	40.00	24.00
192	Art Wilson	60.00	30.00	18.00
193	Lawton Witt	60.00	30.00	18.00
194	Joe Wood	75.00	37.00	22.00
195	William Wortman	60.00	30.00	18.00
196	Steve Yerkes	60.00	30.00	18.00
197	Earl Yingling	60.00	30.00	18.00
198	"Pep" Young (photo actually Ralph Young)	60.00	30.00	18.00
199	Rollie Zeider	60.00	30.00	18.00
200	Henry Zimmerman	60.00	30.00	18.00

1989 Colla Jose Canseco Postcards

In 1989 California baseball photographer Barry Colla began a series of player postcard sets. Each set contains eight postcards of the player and is sold in a white paper envelope with the team logo. The postcards are identical in format, measuring 3-1/2" x 5-1/2". Fronts feature borderless color photos on a high-gloss stock. Backs are printed in black-and-white and feature a team logo at center. The player's name, uniform number, team and position are printed in the upper-left. A card number appears at top-center.

	MT	NR MT	EX
Complete Set (8):	6.00	4.50	2.50

1989 Colla Andre Dawson Postcards

	MT	NR MT	EX
Complete Set (8):	6.00	4.50	2.50

Values for recent cards and sets are listed in Mint (MT), Near Mint (NM), reflecting the fact that many cards from recent years have been preserved in top condition. Recent cards and sets in less than Excellent condition have little collector interest.

Values quoted in this guide reflect the retail price of a card – the price a collector can expect to pay when buying a card from a dealer. The wholesale price – that which a collector can expect to receive from a dealer when selling cards – will be significantly lower, depending on desirability and condition.

1989 Colla Mike Greenwell Postcards

	MT	NR MT	EX
Complete Set (8):	6.00	4.50	2.50

1989 Colla Don Mattingly Postcards

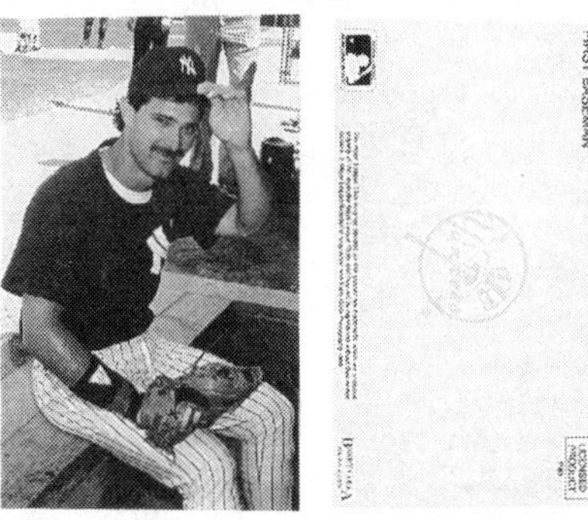

	MT	NR MT	EX
Complete Set (8):	6.00	4.50	2.50

1989 Colla Mark McGwire Postcards

	MT	NR MT	EX
Complete Set (8):	6.00	4.50	2.50

1989 Colla Kevin Mitchell Postcards

	MT	NR MT	EX
Complete Set (8):	6.00	4.50	2.50

1989 Colla Ozzie Smith Postcards

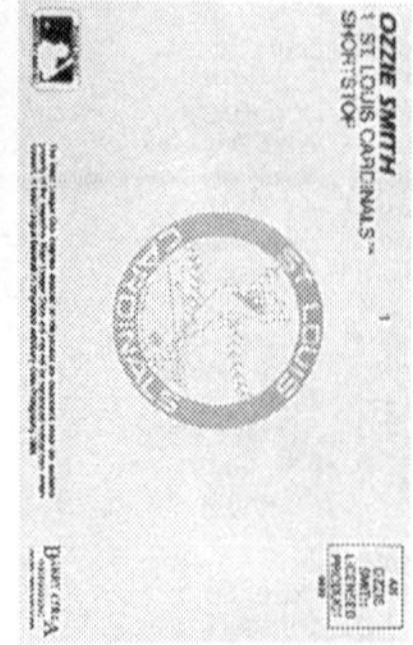

	MT	NR MT	EX
Complete Set (8):	6.00	4.50	2.50

1990 Colla Collection Promos

Each of the 12-card single-player sets produced by photographer Barry Colla in 1990 was preceded by a promo card. The promos feature the same borderless color photography as the issued cards. Backs have information on date and size of the limited-edition issues and ordering information printed in black and white. Checklist of the unnumbered cards is presented here in alphabetical order.

		MT	NR MT	EX
Complete Set (4):		12.00	9.00	4.75
Common Player:		3.00	2.25	1.25
(1)	Jose Canseco	3.00	2.25	1.25
(2)	Will Clark	3.00	2.25	1.25
(3)	Kevin Maas	3.00	2.25	1.25
(4)	Don Mattingly	3.00	2.25	1.25

1990 Colla Jose Canseco

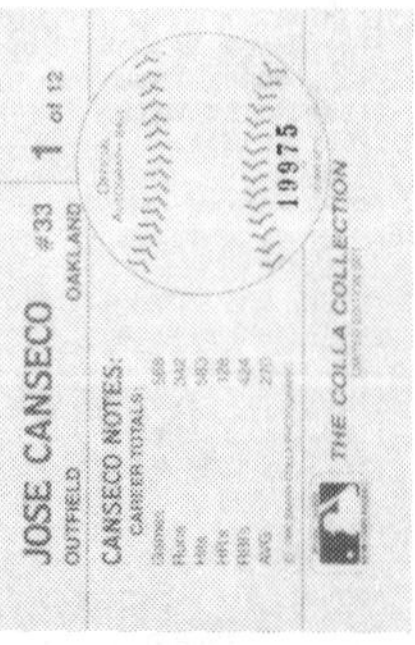

This 12-card set was released by photographer Barry Colla. The cards are borderless and feature full-color action and posed shots. 20,000 set were produced.

	MT	NR MT	EX
Complete Set:	12.00	9.00	4.75

A player's name in italic type indicates a rookie card. An (FC) indicates a player's first card for that particular card company.

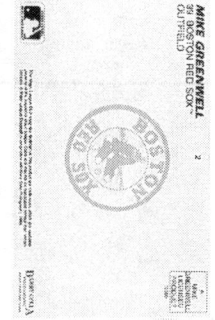

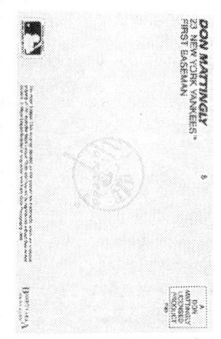

1990 Colla Will Clark

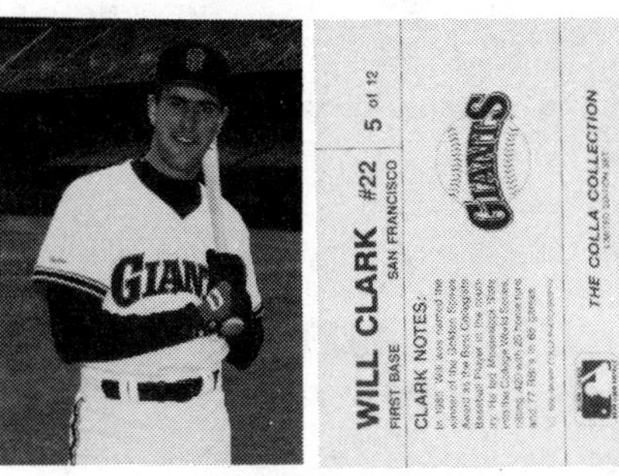

Notes about Will Clark are featured on the backs of the borderless photo cards in this 12-card set. The set was produced by Barry Colla and was sold in a special Will Clark box. Production was limited to 15,000.

	MT	NR MT	EX
Complete Set:	20.00	15.00	8.00

1990 Colla Kevin Maas

Yankee slugger Kevin Maas is the subject of this 12-card set. The set was produced by photographer Barry Colla and features borderless action and posed color photos. Production was limited to 7,500.

	MT	NR MT	EX
Complete Set:	10.00	7.50	4.00

1990 Colla Don Mattingly

This 12-card set showcases the photography of Barry Colla. The complete set is packaged in a special collectors box and production was limited to 15,000 sets.

	MT	NR MT	EX
Complete Set:	15.00	11.00	6.00

Values quoted in this guide reflect the retail price of a card – the price a collector can expect to pay when buying a card from a dealer. The wholesale price – that which a collector can expect to receive from a dealer when selling cards – will be significantly lower, depending on desirability and condition.

1990 Colla Will Clark Postcards

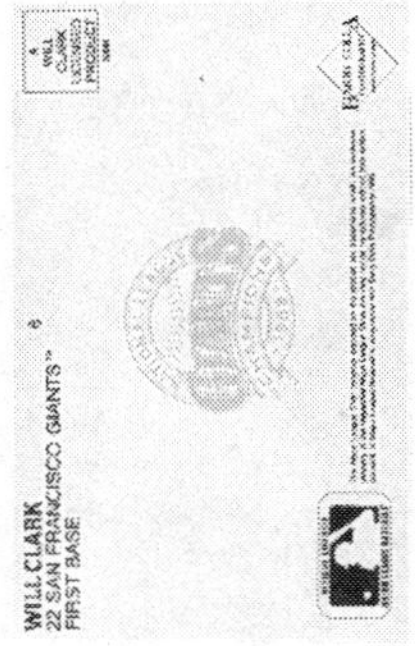

Barry Colla continued his series of single-player postcard sets with two additions in 1990. The basic format continued unchanged. The 3-1/2" x 5-1/2" card feature borderless color game-action and posed photos on a high-gloss stock. Black-and-white backs feature a team logo at center, a card number at top and, in the upper-left, the player's name, uniform number, team and position. Sets were sold in white paper envelopes with color team logos on the front.

	MT	NR MT	EX
Complete Set (8):	6.00	4.50	2.50

1991 Colla Collection Promos

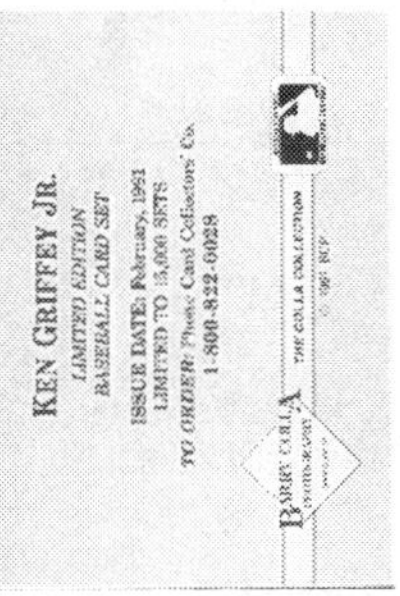

Each of the eight 12-card single-player sets produced by California photographer Barry Colla in 1991 was preceded by the issue of a promo card. Identical in format, the promos feature high quality borderless photos on glossy stock. Backs are printed in black-and-white and include information on the size and release date of the limited-edition set, along with ordering information and appropriate logos. The checklist of the unnumbered promo cards is presented here alphabetically.

		MT	NR MT	EX
Complete Set (8):		22.00	16.50	8.75
Common Player:		3.00	2.25	1.25
(1)	Roberto Alomar	3.00	2.25	1.25
(2)	Barry Bonds	4.00	3.00	1.50
(3)	Joe Carter	3.00	2.25	1.25
(4)	Dwight Gooden	3.00	2.25	1.25
(5)	Ken Griffey, Jr.	5.00	3.75	2.00
(6)	Dave Justice	3.50	2.75	1.50
(7)	Ryne Sandberg	3.50	2.75	1.50
(8)	Darryl Strawberry	3.00	2.25	1.25

1991 Colla Roberto Alomar

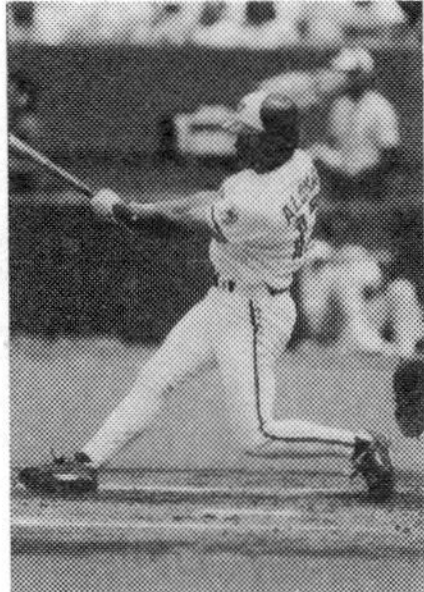

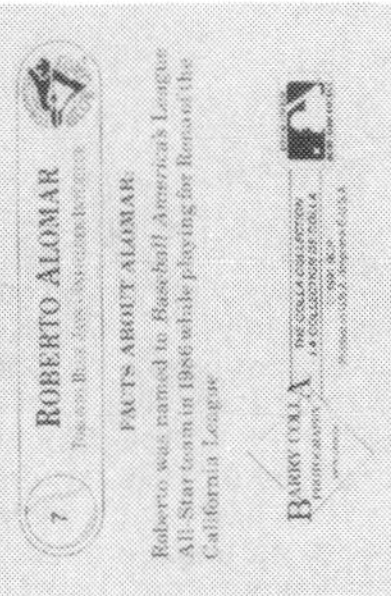

Blue Jay star Roberto Alomar is showcased in this 12-card set from Barry Colla. Production was limited to 7,500 sets and the cards feature Alomar in a variety of poses.

	MT	NR MT	EX
Complete Set:	15.00	11.00	6.00

1991 Colla Barry Bonds

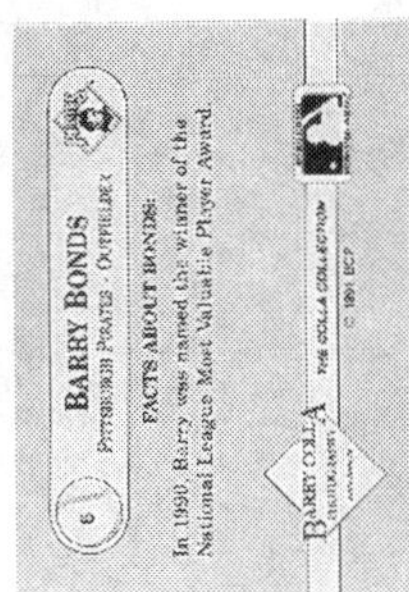

Barry Bonds was the subject of a 12-card set from The Colla Collection in 1991. The set consists of a dozen different poses of Bonds packed in a collector's box. The set was limited to 7,500, with the first card of each set numbered.

	MT	NR MT	EX
Complete Set:	15.00	11.00	6.00

1991 Colla Joe Carter

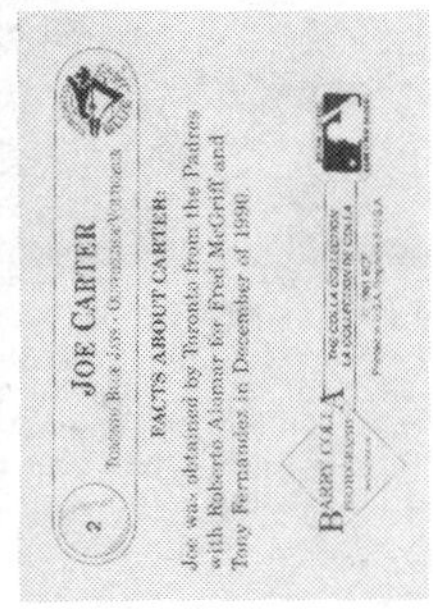

Joe Carter is the subject of this 12-card set by Barry Colla. Production was limited to 7,500 and the cards feature borderless full-color photos.

	MT	NR MT	EX
Complete Set:	10.00	7.50	4.00

1991 Colla Dwight Gooden

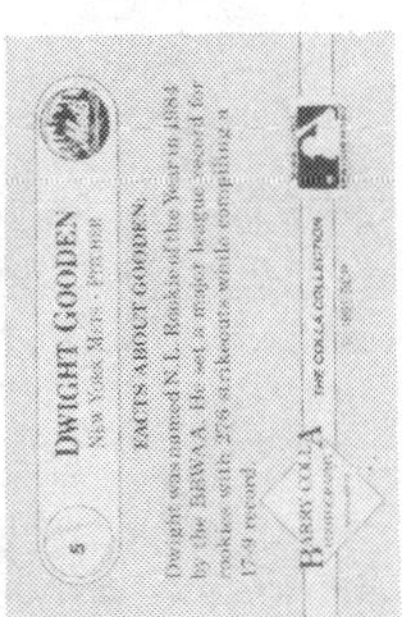

Production was limited to 15,000 sets of this 12-card issue. The backs of the cards feature facts about Gooden. The set was produced by photographer Barry Colla.

	MT	NR MT	EX
Complete Set:	10.00	7.50	4.00

The values quoted are intended to reflect the market price.

1991 Colla Ken Griffey, Jr.

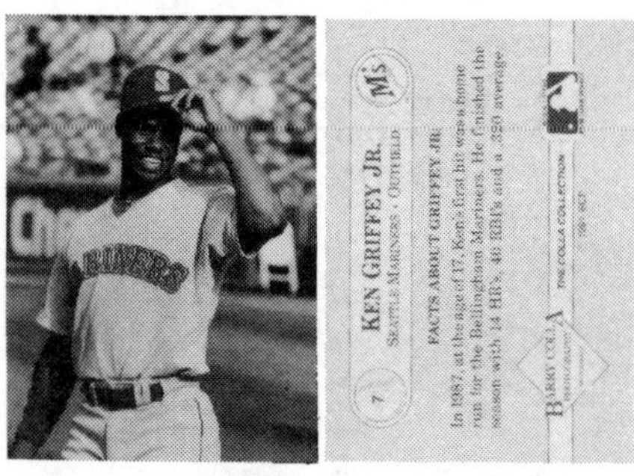

Like the Gooden set and others, only 15,000 sets were produced. The complete set features 12 cards. The set was produced by photographer Barry Colla. The backs of the cards are horizontal.

	MT	NR MT	EX
Complete Set:	25.00	18.50	10.00

1991 Colla David Justice

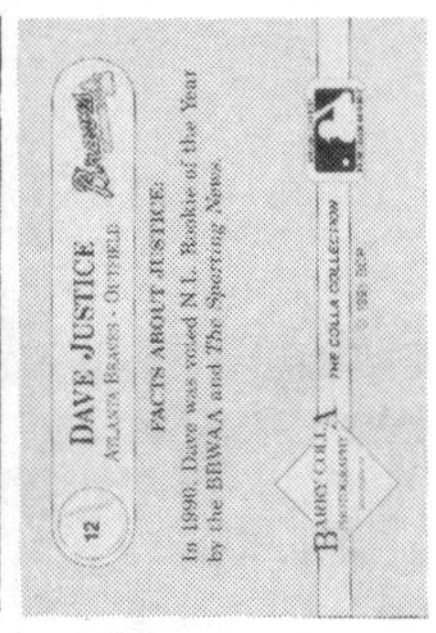

Colorful high gloss photos are featured in this 12-card set. 12 numbered cards and a title card make up the set. The set was produced by photographer Barry Colla and production was limited to 15,000 sets.

	MT	NR MT	EX
Complete Set:	12.00	9.00	4.75

1991 Colla Ryne Sandberg

Twelve numbered cards and a title card make up this 13-card set. The set was produced by Barry Colla and production was limited to 15,000 sets. The card backs are printed horizontally and feature statistics and facts about Sandberg.

	MT	NR MT	EX
Complete Set:	15.00	11.00	6.00

The values quoted are intended to reflect the market price.

Definitions for grading conditions are located in the Introduction of this price guide.

1991 Colla Darryl Strawberry

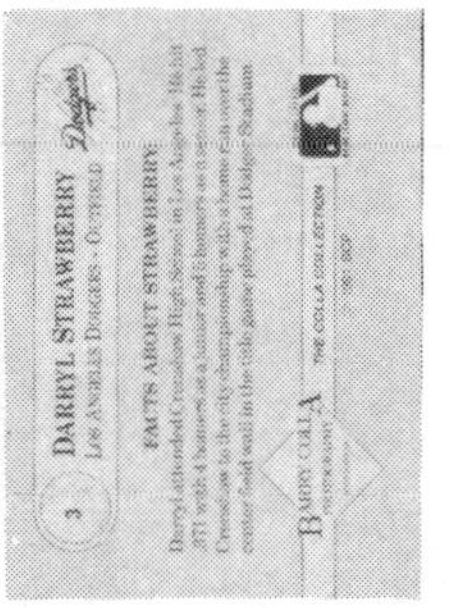

Dodger outfielder Darryl Strawberry is the subject of this 13-card set. The front of the cards feature full-color action and posed photos. The set was produced by photographer Barry Colla and production was limited to 15,000 sets.

	MT	NR MT	EX
Complete Set:	10.00	7.50	4.00

1991 Colla Ryne Sandberg Postcards

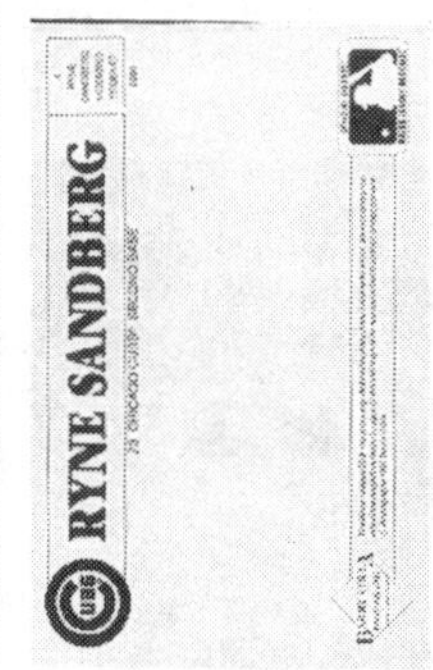

Only one single-player postcard set was produced by Barry Colla in 1991: Ryne Sandberg. The eight-card set, like the 1989-90 issues, features full-color game-action and posed photos presented on a borderless, high-gloss 3-1/2" x 5-1/2" format. Back design was changed for the 1991 issue. The team logo now appears in the upper-left corner with the player's name at top and his uniform number, team and position beneath. Sets were sold in a white paper envelope featuring a color Cubs logo.

	MT	NR MT	EX
Complete Set (8):	6.00	4.50	2.50

1992 Colla Collection Promos

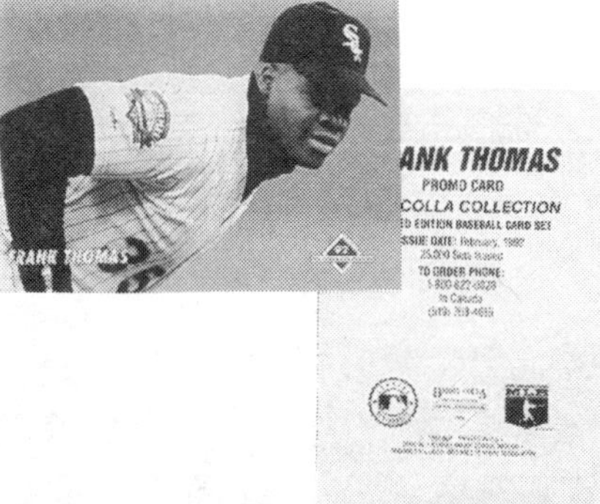

Each of the seven card sets produced by California photographer Barry Colla in 1992 was preceded by a promo card. In standard 2-1/2" x 3-1/2" size, the promos follow the format of the regular-issue cards with a borderless color photo on high-gloss stock. All of the card backs are printed in black-and-white and feature ordering information about the sets, expected release date and issue size and appropriate logos. Some promo cards feature checklists of all existing Colla Collection card sets. The unnumbered promo cards are checklisted here alphabetically.

		MT	NR MT	EX
Complete Set (7):		20.00	15.00	8.00
Common Player:		3.00	2.25	1.25
(1)	All-Star Set (Juan Guzman)	3.00	2.25	1.25
(2)	Steve Avery	3.00	2.25	1.25
(3)	Jeff Bagwell	3.00	2.25	1.25
(4)	Tony Gwynn	3.00	2.25	1.25
(5)	Mark McGwire	3.00	2.25	1.25
(6)	Frank Thomas	5.00	3.75	2.00
(7)	Nolan Ryan	5.00	3.75	2.00

1992 Colla All-Stars

The 1992 Colla All-Star set consists of 24 players from the All-Star game in San Diego that year, packaged in a collector's box. Limited to 25,000 sets, the first card in each set is numbered and collectors had the opportunity to win numbered and autographed Roberto Alomar cards.

		MT	NR MT	EX
Complete Set (24):		10.00	7.50	4.00
Common Player:		.25	.20	.10
1	Mark McGwire	.35	.25	.14
2	Will Clark	.40	.30	.15
3	Roberto Alomar	.40	.30	.15
4	Ryne Sandberg	1.00	.70	.40
5	Cal Ripken, Jr.	1.00	.70	.40
6	Ozzie Smith	.40	.30	.15
7	Wade Boggs	.40	.30	.15
8	Terry Pendleton	.25	.20	.10
9	Kirby Puckett	.40	.30	.15
10	Chuck Knoblauch	.35	.25	.14
11	Ken Griffey, Jr.	1.50	1.25	.60
12	Joe Carter	.25	.20	.10
13	Sandy Alomar, Jr.	.25	.20	.10
14	Benito Santiago	.25	.20	.10
15	Mike Mussina	.25	.20	.10
16	Fred McGriff	.35	.25	.14
17	Dennis Eckersley	.25	.20	.10
18	Tony Gwynn	.35	.25	.14
19	Roger Clemens	.35	.25	.14
20	Gary Sheffield	.35	.25	.14
21	Jose Canseco	.40	.30	.15
22	Barry Bonds	.40	.30	.15
23	Ivan Rodriguez	.35	.25	.14
24	Tony Fernandez	.25	.20	.10

1992 Colla Steve Avery

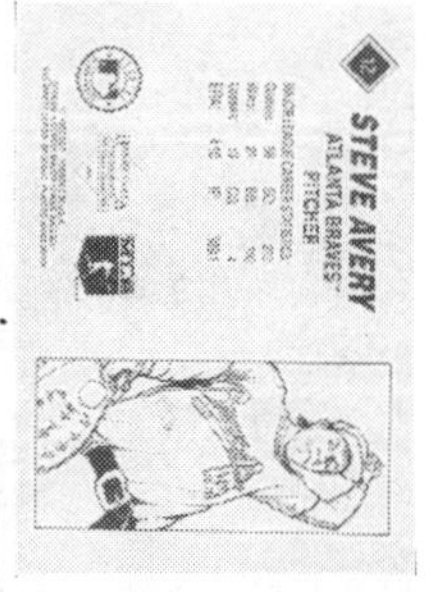

Produced in an edition of 7,500 sets, this 12-card set features the high-quality photography of Barry Colla on cards with a borderless, UV-coated front. Backs are printed in black-and-white and feature a cartoon and career note on the Braves' lefty. Card #1 is serially-numbered.

	MT	NR MT	EX
Complete Set:	10.00	7.50	4.00

1992 Colla Jeff Bagwell

National League Rookie of the Year Jeff Bagwell is featured in this 13-card set. 200 autographed cards were randomly inserted in sets. The set was produced by photographer Barry Colla. Production was 25,000 sets.

	MT	NR MT	EX
Complete Set:	10.00	7.50	4.00

1992 Colla Barry Bonds

This 12-card set showcases Pirate slugger Barry Bonds. Production was limited to 7,500 sets and it was produced by photographer Barry Colla.

	MT	NR MT	EX
Complete Set:	15.00	11.00	6.00

1992 Colla Tony Gwynn

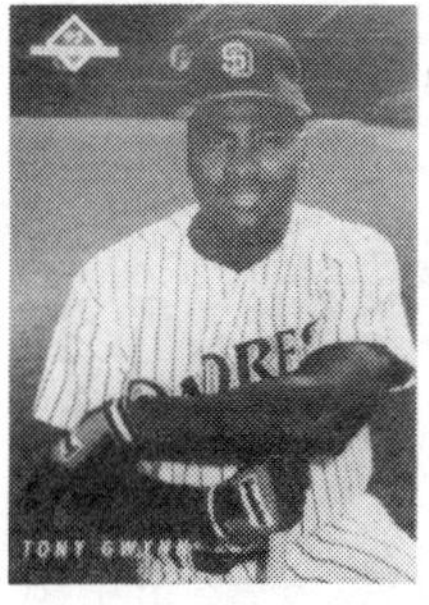
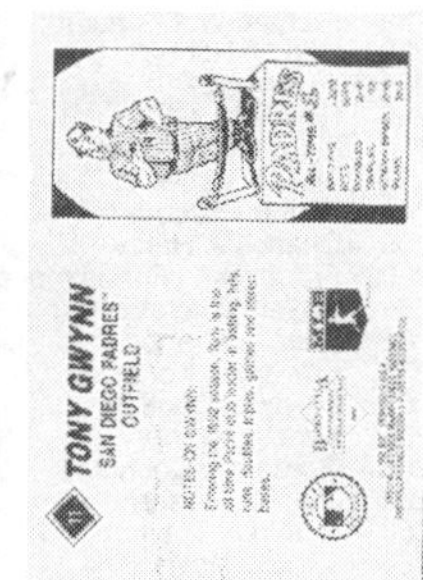

This 12-card boxed set was issued in an edition of 7,500, featuring posed and action shots of the Padres' star. Cards feature Barry Colla photography in a borderless, UV-coated format. Backs are printed in black-and-white and feature a cartoon and player note. The first card in the set is serially numbered.

	MT	NR MT	EX
Complete Set:	10.00	7.50	4.00

1992 Colla Mark McGwire

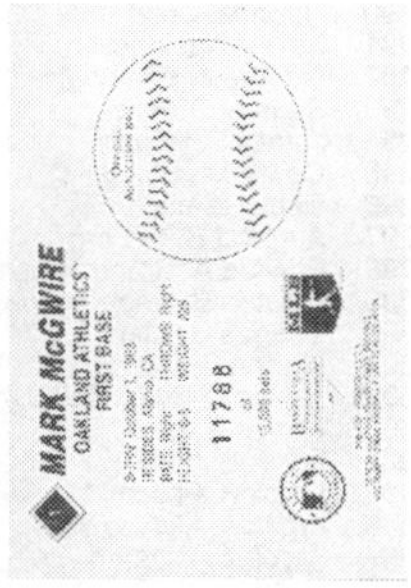

Twelve cards in a special collector's box comprise this limited-edition set honoring the A's first baseman. Produced to a total of 15,000 sets, the cards feature the borderless color photography of Barry Colla on a UV-coated stock. Backs have a cartoon and career note on McGwire. Card #1 in each set is serially numbered.

	MT	NR MT	EX
Complete Set:	10.00	7.50	4.00

1992 Colla Nolan Ryan

Nolan Ryan throwing a football is among the shots featured in this 12-card set from photographer Barry Colla. Production was limited to 25,000. The card fronts feature full-color borderless photos and the flip sides feature a cartoon and notes on Ryan.

	MT	NR MT	EX
Complete Set:	15.00	11.00	6.00

1992 Colla Frank Thomas

Cartoon drawings on the back of the cards are among the special features on the cards in this set from photographer Barry Colla. The complete set consists of 12 cards and production was limited to 25,000 sets. The card fronts feature borderless full-color photos, while the flip sides feature notes and a cartoon on Thomas.

	MT	NR MT	EX
Complete Set:	18.00	13.50	7.25

1993 Colla All-Stars

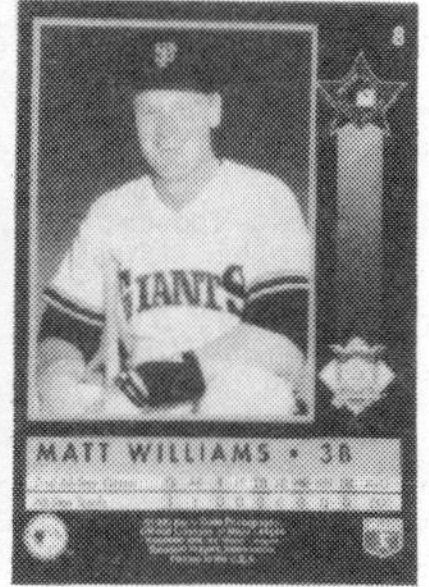

For the second year in 1993 California photographer Barry Colla produced a 24-card All-Star set commemorating the game played in Baltimore on July 13. The specially boxed collector's edition includes an unnumbered All-Star logo/checklist card. Cards feature black borders on the UV-coated front, featuring game-action or posed photos. Team logos are centered beneath the photo, with the player's name and position in white at bottom. Backs are also bordered in black and include another player color photo, league and All-Star logos and information and stats on prior All-Star Game appearances.

		MT	NR MT	EX
Complete Set (25):		11.00	8.25	4.50
Common Player:		.25	.20	.10
1	Roberto Alomar	.40	.30	.15
2	Barry Bonds	.75	.60	.30
3	Ken Griffey, Jr.	1.50	1.25	.60
4	John Kruk	.35	.25	.14
5	Kirby Puckett	.40	.30	.15
6	Darren Daulton	.25	.20	.10
7	Wade Boggs	.40	.30	.15
8	Matt Williams	.25	.20	.10
9	Cal Ripken, Jr.	1.00	.70	.40
10	Ryne Sandberg	1.00	.70	.40
11	Ivan Rodriguez	.35	.25	.14
12	Andy Van Slyke	.25	.20	.10
13	John Olerud	.35	.25	.14
14	Tom Glavine	.25	.20	.10
15	Juan Gonzalez	1.00	.70	.40
16	David Justice	.35	.25	.14
17	Mike Mussina	.25	.20	.10
18	Tony Gwynn	.35	.25	.14
19	Joe Carter	.25	.20	.10
20	Barry Larkin	.25	.20	.10
21	Brian Harper	.25	.20	.10
22	Ozzie Smith	.40	.30	.15
23	Mark McGwire	.35	.25	.14
24	Mike Piazza	1.25	.90	.50
----	Checklist	.05	.04	.02

1993 Colla Mike Piazza Postcards

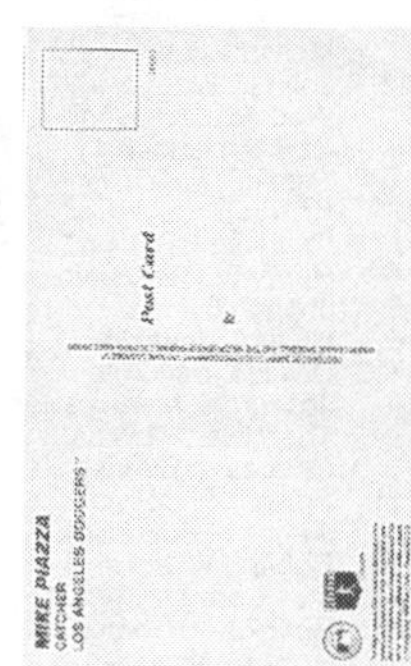

Following a one-year layoff, Barry Colla continued his single-player, eight-card postcard series in 1993 with a pair of sets. Like the earlier issues, the cards are 3-1/2" x 5-1/2" and feature high-gloss fronts with borderless game-action and posed photos. Black-and-white backs have a more traditional postcard format than earlier issues. The sets were sold in white paper envelopes with color team logos on front.

	MT	NR MT	EX
Complete Set (8):	6.00	4.50	2.50

1993 Colla Cal Ripken, Jr. Postcards

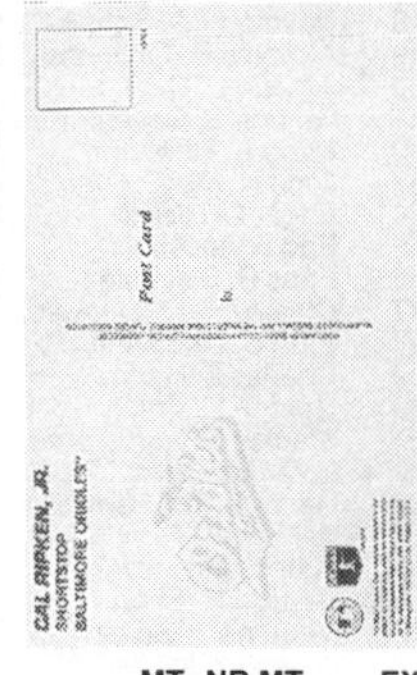

	MT	NR MT	EX
Complete Set (8):	6.00	4.50	2.50

A card number in parentheses () indicates the set is unnumbered.

1991 Conlon Collection

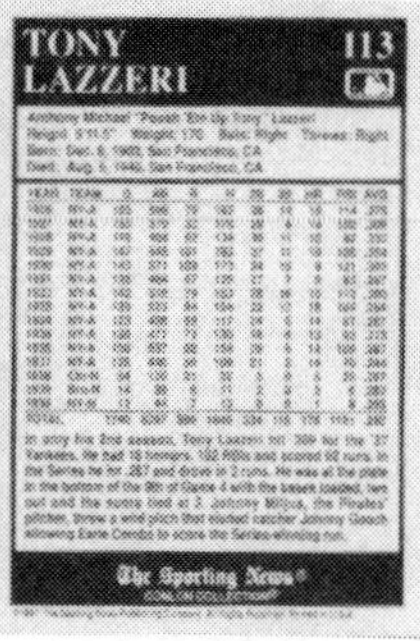

This 330-card set features the photography of Charles Martin Conlon, who was active from the before 1910 through the early 1940s. Black-and-white photos are set against black borders on the UV-coated card fronts. Megacards worked with The Sporting News, (owners of the Conlon photos) to release the set. Several subsets are featured such as Hall of Famers, 1927 New York Yankees, MVP's and more. The backs feature statistics and career highlights.

		MT	NR MT	EX
Complete Set (330):		30.00	22.50	11.00
Common Player:		.10	.08	.04
1	Rogers Hornsby	.15	.11	.06
2	James E. Foxx	.15	.11	.06
3	Jay H. Dean	.15	.11	.06
4	Walter J.V. Maranville	.15	.11	.06
5	Paul G. Waner	.15	.11	.06
6	Lloyd J. Waner	.15	.11	.06
7	Melvin T. Ott	.15	.11	.06
8	John P. Wagner	.15	.11	.06
9	Walter P. Johnson	.15	.11	.06
10	Carl O. Hubbell	.15	.11	.06
11	Frank F. Frisch	.15	.11	.06
12	Hazen S. Cuyler	.15	.11	.06
13	Charles H. Ruffing	.15	.11	.06
14	Henry B. Greenberg	.15	.11	.06
15	John J. Evers	.15	.11	.06
16	Hugh A. Jennings	.15	.11	.06
17	David J. Bancroft	.15	.11	.06
18	Joseph M. Medwick	.15	.11	.06
19	Theodore A. Lyons	.15	.11	.06
20	Charles A. Bender	.15	.11	.06
21	Edward T. Collins	.15	.11	.06
22	James L. Bottomley	.15	.11	.06
23	Robert M. Grove	.15	.11	.06
24	Max Carey	.15	.11	.06
25	Burleigh A. Grimes	.15	.11	.06
26	Ross M. Youngs	.15	.11	.06
27	Ernest N. Lombardi	.15	.11	.06
28	Joseph V. McCarthy	.15	.11	.06
29	Lewis R. Wilson	.15	.11	.06
30	Charles H. Klein	.15	.11	.06
31	Howard E. Averill Sr.	.15	.11	.06
32	Grover C. Alexander	.15	.11	.06
33	Charles J. Hafey	.15	.11	.06
34	William B. McKechnie	.15	.11	.06
35	Robert W.A. Feller	.15	.11	.06
36	Harold J. Traynor	.15	.11	.06
37	Charles D. Stengel	.15	.11	.06
38	Joseph F. Vaughan	.15	.11	.06
39	Eppa Rixey	.15	.11	.06
40	Joseph W. Sewell	.15	.11	.06
41	Urban C. Faber	.15	.11	.06
42	Travis C. Jackson	.15	.11	.06
43	Jesse J. Haines	.15	.11	.06
44	Tristram E. Speaker	.15	.11	.06
45	Cornelius Mack	.15	.11	.06
46	Cornelius Mack	.15	.11	.06
47	Cornelius Mack	.15	.11	.06
48	Raymond W. Schalk	.15	.11	.06
49	Aloysius H. Simmons	.15	.11	.06
50	Joseph E. Cronin	.15	.11	.06
51	Gordon S. Cochrane	.15	.11	.06
52	Harry E. Heilmann	.15	.11	.06
53	John R. Mize	.15	.11	.06
54	Edgar C. Rice	.15	.11	.06
55	Edd J. Roush	.15	.11	.06
56	Enos B. Slaughter	.15	.11	.06
57	Christopher Mathewson	.15	.11	.06
58	Fred C. Lindstrom	.15	.11	.06
59	Charles L. Hartnett	.15	.11	.06
60	George L. Kelly	.15	.11	.06
61	Stanley R. Harris	.15	.11	.06
62	Leon A. Goslin	.15	.11	.06
63	Henry E. Manush	.15	.11	.06
64	William H. Terry	.15	.11	.06
65	John J. McGraw	.15	.11	.06
66	George H. Sisler	.15	.11	.06
67	Vernon L. Gomez	.10	.08	.04
68	Joseph I. Judge	.10	.08	.04
69	Thomas J. Thevenow	.10	.08	.04
70	Charles M. Gelbert	.10	.08	.04
71	Minter C. Hayes	.10	.08	.04
72	Robert R. Fothergill	.10	.08	.04
73	Adam A. Comorosky	.10	.08	.04
74	Earl S. Smith	.10	.08	.04
75	Samuel D. Gray	.10	.08	.04
76	Peter W. Appleton	.10	.08	.04
77	Eugene Moore Jr.	.10	.08	.04
78	Arndt L. Jorgens	.10	.08	.04
79	William H. Knickerbocker	.10	.08	.04
80	Carl N. Reynolds	.10	.08	.04
81	Oscar D. Melillo	.10	.08	.04
82	John H. Burnett	.10	.08	.04
83	Alvin J. Powell	.10	.08	.04
84	John J. Murphy	.10	.08	.04
85	Leroy E. Parmelee	.10	.08	.04
86	James A. Ripple	.10	.08	.04
87	Gerald H. Walker	.10	.08	.04
88	George L. Earnshaw	.10	.08	.04
89	William H. Southworth	.10	.08	.04
90	Wallace Moses	.10	.08	.04
91	George E. Walberg	.10	.08	.04
92	James J. Dykes	.10	.08	.04
93	Charles H. Root	.10	.08	.04
94	John W. Cooney	.10	.08	.04
95	Charles J. Grimm	.10	.08	.04
96	Robert L. Johnson	.10	.08	.04
97	John W. Scott	.10	.08	.04
98	Raymond A. Radcliff	.10	.08	.04
99	Frederick R. Ostermueller	.10	.08	.04
100	Julian V. Wera	.10	.08	.04
101	Miller J. Huggins	.15	.11	.06
102	Raymond A. Morehart	.10	.08	.04
103	Bernard O. Bengough	.10	.08	.04
104	Walter H. Ruether	.10	.08	.04
105	Earle B. Combs	.15	.11	.06
106	Myles L. Thomas	.10	.08	.04
107	Benjamin E. Paschal	.10	.08	.04
108	Cedric M. Durst	.10	.08	.04
109	William W. Moore	.10	.08	.04
110	George H. Ruth	.50	.40	.20
111	Louis H. Gehrig	.50	.40	.20
112	Joseph A. Dugan	.10	.08	.04
113	Anthony M. Lazzeri	.15	.11	.06
114	Urban J. Shocker	.10	.08	.04
115	Waite C. Hoyt	.15	.11	.06
116	Charles T. O'Leary	.10	.08	.04
117	Arthur Fletcher	.10	.08	.04
118	Tharon L. Collins	.10	.08	.04
119	Joseph O. Giard	.10	.08	.04
120	Herbert J. Pennock	.15	.11	.06
121	Michael Gazella	.10	.08	.04
122	Robert W. Meusel	.10	.08	.04
123	George W. Pipgras	.10	.08	.04
124	John P. Grabowski	.10	.08	.04
125	Mark A. Koenig	.10	.08	.04
126	Stanley C. Hack	.10	.08	.04
127	Earl O. Whitehill	.10	.08	.04
128	William C. Lee	.10	.08	.04
129	Frank O. Mancuso	.10	.08	.04
130	Francis R. Blades	.10	.08	.04
131	John I. Burns	.10	.08	.04
132	Clinton H. Brown	.10	.08	.04
133	William J. Dietrich	.10	.08	.04
134	Darrell E. Blanton	.10	.08	.04
135	Harry B. Hooper	.15	.11	.06
136	Charles H. Shorten	.10	.08	.04
137	Clarence W. Walker	.10	.08	.04
138	George Foster	.10	.08	.04
139	John J. Barry	.10	.08	.04
140	Samuel P. Jones	.10	.08	.04
141	Ernest G. Shore	.10	.08	.04
142	Hubert B. Leonard	.10	.08	.04
143	Herbert J. Pennock	.15	.11	.06
144	Harold C. Janvrin	.10	.08	.04
145	George H. Ruth	.40	.30	.15
146	George E. Lewis	.10	.08	.04
147	William L. Gardner	.10	.08	.04
148	Richard C. Hoblitzel	.10	.08	.04
149	Lewis E. Scott	.10	.08	.04
150	Carl W. Mays	.10	.08	.04
151	John A. Niehoff	.10	.08	.04
152	Burton E. Shotton	.10	.08	.04
153	Leon K. Ames	.10	.08	.04
154	Fred Williams	.10	.08	.04
155	William W. Hinchman	.10	.08	.04
156	James R. Shawkey	.10	.08	.04
157	Walter C. Pipp	.10	.08	.04
158	George J. Burns	.10	.08	.04
159	Robert H. Veach	.10	.08	.04
160	Harold H. Chase	.10	.08	.04
161	Thomas L. Hughes	.10	.08	.04
162	Derrill B. Pratt	.10	.08	.04
163	Henry K. Groh	.10	.08	.04
164	Zachariah D. Wheat	.15	.11	.06
165	Francis J. O'Doul	.10	.08	.04
166	William E. Kamm	.10	.08	.04
167	Paul G. Waner	.15	.11	.06
168	Fred C. Snodgrass	.10	.08	.04
169	Floyd C. Herman	.10	.08	.04
170	Albert H. Bridwell	.10	.08	.04
171	John T. Meyers	.10	.08	.04
172	John B. Lobert	.10	.08	.04
173	Raymond B. Bressler	.10	.08	.04
174	Samuel P. Jones	.10	.08	.04
175	Robert A. O'Farrell	.10	.08	.04
176	George Toporcer	.10	.08	.04
177	George E. McNeely	.10	.08	.04
178	John H. Knott	.10	.08	.04
179	Clarence F. Mueller	.10	.08	.04
180	Thomas J.D. Bridges	.10	.08	.04
181	Lloyd A. Brown	.10	.08	.04
182	Lawrence J. Benton	.10	.08	.04
183	Max F. Bishop	.10	.08	.04
184	Morris Berg	.15	.11	.06
185	Ralph F. Perkins	.10	.08	.04
186	Stephen F. O'Neill	.10	.08	.04
187	Glenn C. Myatt	.10	.08	.04
188	Joseph A. Kuhel	.10	.08	.04
189	Martin J. McManus	.10	.08	.04
190	Charles F. Lucas	.10	.08	.04
191	John P. McInnis	.10	.08	.04
192	Edmund J. Miller	.10	.08	.04
193	James L. Sewell	.10	.08	.04
194	William H. Sherdel	.10	.08	.04
195	Harold J. Rhyne	.10	.08	.04
196	Guy T. Bush	.10	.08	.04
197	Ervin Fox	.10	.08	.04
198	Wesley C. Ferrell	.10	.08	.04
199	Roy C. Johnson	.10	.08	.04
200	William Wambsganss	.10	.08	.04
201	George H. Burns	.10	.08	.04
202	Clarence E. Mitchell	.10	.08	.04
203	Cornelius Ball	.10	.08	.04
204	John H. Neun	.10	.08	.04
205	Homer W. Summa	.10	.08	.04
206	Ernest K. Padgett	.10	.08	.04
207	Walter H. Holke	.10	.08	.04
208	Forrest G. Wright	.10	.08	.04
209	Henry M. Gowdy	.10	.08	.04
210	James W. Taylor	.10	.08	.04
211	Benjamin C. Cantwell	.10	.08	.04
212	Joseph F. Demaree	.10	.08	.04
213	Samuel P. Derringer	.10	.08	.04
214	William A. Hallahan	.10	.08	.04
215	Daniel K. MacFayden	.10	.08	.04
216	Harry F. Rice	.10	.08	.04
217	Robert Eldridge Smith	.10	.08	.04
218	Jackson R. Stephenson	.10	.08	.04
219	Perce L. Malone	.10	.08	.04
220	Henry B. Tate	.10	.08	.04
221	Joseph F. Vosmik	.10	.08	.04
222	George A. Watkins	.10	.08	.04
223	James Wilson	.10	.08	.04
224	George E. Uhle	.10	.08	.04
225	Melvin T. Ott	.15	.11	.06
226	Nicholas Altrock	.10	.08	.04
227	Charles H. Ruffing	.15	.11	.06
228	Joseph V.L. Krakauskas	.10	.08	.04
229	Walter A. Berger	.10	.08	.04
230	Norman L. Newsom	.10	.08	.04
231	Lonnie Warneke	.10	.08	.04
232	Frank E. Snyder	.10	.08	.04
233	Myril O. Hoag	.10	.08	.04
234	Baldomero M. Almada	.10	.08	.04
235	Ivy B. Wingo	.10	.08	.04
236	James P. Austin	.10	.08	.04
237	Henry J. Bonura	.10	.08	.04
238	Russell G. Wrightstone	.10	.08	.04
239	Alfred C. Todd	.10	.08	.04
240	Harold B. Warstler	.10	.08	.04
241	Samuel F. West	.10	.08	.04
242	Arthur C. Reinhart	.10	.08	.04
243	Walter C. Stewart	.10	.08	.04
244	John B. Gooch	.10	.08	.04
245	Eugene F. Hargrave	.10	.08	.04
246	George W. Harper	.10	.08	.04
247	George W. Connally	.10	.08	.04
248	Edgar G. Braxton	.10	.08	.04
249	Walter H. Schang	.10	.08	.04
250	Tyrus R. Cobb	.50	.40	.20
251	Rogers Hornsby	.15	.11	.06
252	Richard W. Marquard	.15	.11	.06
253	Carl O. Hubbell	.15	.11	.06
254	Joe Wood	.10	.08	.04
255	Robert M. Grove	.15	.11	.06
256	Lynwood T. Rowe	.10	.08	.04
257	Alvin F. Crowder	.10	.08	.04
258	Walter P. Johnson	.15	.11	.06
259	Charles J. Hafey	.15	.11	.06
260	Frederick L. Fitzsimmons	.10	.08	.04
261	William E. Webb	.10	.08	.04
262	Earle B. Combs	.15	.11	.06
263	Edward J. Konetchy	.10	.08	.04
264	Taylor L. Douthit	.10	.08	.04
265	Lloyd J. Waner	.15	.11	.06
266	Gordon S. Cochrane	.15	.11	.06
267	John O. Wilson	.10	.08	.04
268	Harold J. Traynor	.10	.08	.04
269	Virgil L. Davis	.10	.08	.04
270	Henry E. Manush	.15	.11	.06
271	Michael F. Higgins	.10	.08	.04
272	Adrian Joss	.15	.11	.06
273	Edward Augustine Walsh	.15	.11	.06
274	Johnny L.R. Martin	.10	.08	.04
275	Joseph W. Sewell	.15	.11	.06
276	Hubert B. Leonard	.10	.08	.04
277	Clifford C. Cravath	.10	.08	.04
278	Oral C. Hildebrand	.10	.08	.04
279	Remy P. Kremer	.10	.08	.04
280	Frank A. Pytlak	.10	.08	.04
281	Samuel D. Byrd	.10	.08	.04
282	Curtis B. Davis	.10	.08	.04
283	Lewis A. Fonseca	.10	.08	.04
284	Herold D. Ruel	.10	.08	.04
285	Julius J. Solters	.10	.08	.04
286	Fred W. Schulte	.10	.08	.04
287	John P. Quinn	.10	.08	.04
288	Arthur C. Whitney	.10	.08	.04
289	Jonathon T. Stone	.10	.08	.04
290	Hugh M. Critz	.10	.08	.04
291	Ira J. Flagstead	.10	.08	.04
292	George F. Grantham	.10	.08	.04
293	Samuel D. Hale	.10	.08	.04
294	James F. Hogan	.10	.08	.04
295	Oswald L. Bluege	.10	.08	.04
296	Debs Garms	.10	.08	.04
297	Augistaf B. Friberg	.10	.08	.04
298	Edward A. Brandt	.10	.08	.04
299	Ralston B. Hemsley	.10	.08	.04
300	Charles H. Klein	.15	.11	.06
301	Morton C. Cooper	.10	.08	.04
302	James L. Bottomley	.10	.08	.04
303	James E. Foxx	.15	.11	.06
304	Frank Schulte	.10	.08	.04
305	Frank F. Frisch	.15	.11	.06
306	Frank A. McCormick	.10	.08	.04
307	Jacob E. Daubert	.10	.08	.04
308	Roger T. Peckinpaugh	.10	.08	.04
309	George H. Burns	.10	.08	.04
310	Louis H. Gehrig	.40	.30	.15
311	Aloysius H. Simmons	.15	.11	.06
312	Edward T. Collins	.15	.11	.06
313	Charles L. Hartnett	.15	.11	.06

314	Joseph E. Cronin	.15	.11	.06
315	Paul G. Waner	.15	.11	.06
316	Robert A. O'Farrell	.10	.08	.04
317	Lawrence J. Doyle	.10	.08	.04
318	Lynford H. Lary	.10	.08	.04
319	Frank S. May	.10	.08	.04
320	Roy H. Spencer	.10	.08	.04
321	Samuel R. Coffman	.10	.08	.04
322	Peter J. Donohue	.10	.08	.04
323	George W. Haas	.10	.08	.04
324	Edward S. Farrell	.10	.08	.04
325	Charles F. Rhem	.10	.08	.04
326	Frederick Marberry	.10	.08	.04
327	Charles Martin Conlon	.10	.08	.04
328	Checklist 1-110	.10	.08	.04
329	Checklist 111-220	.10	.08	.04
330	Checklist 221-330	.10	.08	.04

1992 Conlon Collection

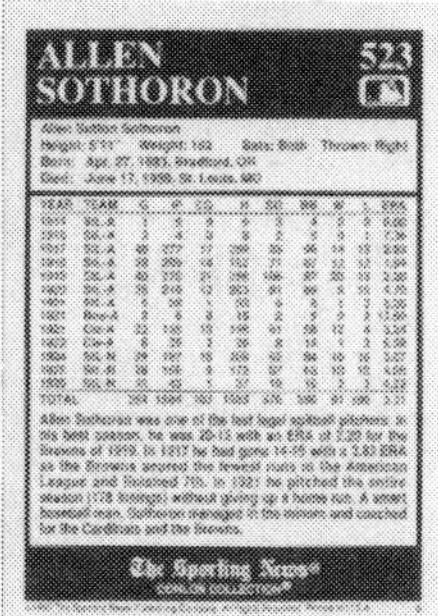

In their second season, the 330 cards of the Conlon Collection were numbered consecutively where the 1991 premiere issue ended. Cards 331-660 also maintained the high-gloss black-and-white format of the previous year. Many subsets within the issue carry special designations on the card fronts. Subsets included no-hitters, Triple Crown winners, "Great Stories," nicknames and more.

		MT	NR MT	EX
	Complete Set (330):	24.00	18.00	9.50
	Common Player:	.10	.08	.04
331	Christopher Mathewson	.15	.11	.06
332	George L. Wiltse	.10	.08	.04
333	George N. Rucker	.10	.08	.04
334	Leon K. Ames	.10	.08	.04
335	Charles A. Bender	.15	.11	.06
336	Joe Wood	.10	.08	.04
337	Edward Augstine Walsh	.15	.11	.06
338	George J. Mullin	.10	.08	.04
339	Earl A. Hamilton	.10	.08	.04
340	Charles M Tesreau	.10	.08	.04
341	James Scott	.10	.08	.04
342	Richard W. Marquard	.10	.08	.04
343	Claude R. Hendrix	.15	.11	.06
344	James S. Lavender	.10	.08	.04
345	Leslie A. Bush	.10	.08	.04
346	Hubert B. Leonard	.10	.08	.04
347	Fred A. Toney	.10	.08	.04
348	James L. Vaughn	.10	.08	.04
349	Ernest G. Koob	.10	.08	.04
350	Robert Groom	.10	.08	.04
351	Ernest G. Shore	.10	.08	.04
352	Horace O. Eller	.10	.08	.04
353	Walter P. Johnson	.15	.11	.06
354	Charles C. Robertson	.10	.08	.04
355	Jesse L. Barnes	.10	.08	.04
356	Samuel P. Jones	.10	.08	.04
357	Howard J. Ehmke	.10	.08	.04
358	Jesse J. Haines	.15	.11	.06
359	Theodore A. Lyons	.15	.11	.06
360	Carl O. Hubbell	.15	.11	.06
361	Wesley C. Ferrell	.10	.08	.04
362	Robert J. Burke	.10	.08	.04
363	Paul D. Dean	.10	.08	.04
364	Norman L. Newsom	.10	.08	.04
365	Lloyd V. Kennedy	.10	.08	.04
366	William J. Dietrich	.10	.08	.04
367	John S. Vander Meer	.10	.08	.04
368	John S. Vander Meer	.10	.08	.04
369	Montgomery M. Pearson	.10	.08	.04
370	Robert W.A. Feller	.15	.11	.06
371	Lonnie Warneke	.10	.08	.04
372	James A. Tobin	.10	.08	.04
373	Earl A. Moore	.10	.08	.04
374	William H. Dineen	.10	.08	.04
375	Malcolm W. Eason	.10	.08	.04
376	George A. Mogridge	.10	.08	.04
377	Clarence A. Vance	.15	.11	.06
378	James O. Carleton	.10	.08	.04
379	Clyde M. Shoun	.10	.08	.04
380	Franklin W. Hayes	.10	.08	.04
381	Benjamin R. Frey	.10	.08	.04
382	Henry W. Johnson	.10	.08	.04
383	Ralph Kress	.10	.08	.04
384	John T. Allen	.10	.08	.04
385	Harold A. Trosky Sr.	.10	.08	.04
386	Eugene E. Robertson	.10	.08	.04
387	Lemuel F. Young	.10	.08	.04
388	George A. Selkirk	.10	.08	.04
389	Edwin L. Wells	.10	.08	.04
390	James D. Weaver	.10	.08	.04
391	George H. McQuinn	.10	.08	.04
392	John B. Lobert	.10	.08	.04
393	Ernest E. Swanson	.10	.08	.04
394	Ernest A. Nevers	.10	.08	.04
395	James J. Levey	.10	.08	.04
396	Hugo F. Bezdek	.10	.08	.04
397	Walter E. French	.10	.08	.04
398	Charles F. Berry	.10	.08	.04
399	Franklin T. Grube	.10	.08	.04
400	Charles W. Dressen	.10	.08	.04
401	Alfred E. Neale	.10	.08	.04
402	Henry A. Vick	.10	.08	.04
403	James F. Thorpe	.50	.40	.20
404	Walter J. Gilbert	.10	.08	.04
405	John L. Urban	.10	.08	.04
406	Everett V. Purdy	.10	.08	.04
407	Albert O. Wright	.10	.08	.04
408	William M. Urbanski	.10	.08	.04
409	Charles W. Fischer	.10	.08	.04
410	John R. Warner	.10	.08	.04
411	Chalmer W. Cissell	.10	.08	.04
412	Mervin D.J. Shea	.10	.08	.04
413	Adolfo Luque	.10	.08	.04
414	John L. Bassler	.10	.08	.04
415	Arvel O. Hale	.10	.08	.04
416	Lawrence R. French	.10	.08	.04
417	William C. Walker	.10	.08	.04
418	Allen L. Cooke	.10	.08	.04
419	Philip J. Todt	.10	.08	.04
420	Ivy P. Andrews	.10	.08	.04
421	William J. Herman	.15	.11	.06
422	Tristram E. Speaker	.15	.11	.06
423	Aloysius H. Simmons	.15	.11	.06
424	Lewis R. Wilson	.15	.11	.06
425	Tyrus R. Cobb	.40	.30	.15
426	George H. Ruth	.50	.40	.20
427	Ernest N. Lombardi	.15	.11	.06
428	Jay H. Dean	.15	.11	.06
429	Lloyd J. Waner	.15	.11	.06
430	Henry B. Greenberg	.15	.11	.06
431	Robert M. Grove	.15	.11	.06
432	Gordon S. Cochrane	.15	.11	.06
433	Burleigh A. Grimes	.15	.11	.06
434	Harold J. Traynor	.15	.11	.06
435	John R. Mize	.15	.11	.06
436	Edgar C. Rice	.15	.11	.06
437	Leon A. Goslin	.15	.11	.06
438	Charles H. Klein	.15	.11	.06
439	Cornelius Mack	.15	.11	.06
440	James L. Bottomley	.15	.11	.06
441	Jackson R. Stephenson	.10	.08	.04
442	Kenneth R. Williams	.10	.08	.04
443	Charles B. Adams	.10	.08	.04
444	Joseph J. Jackson	.50	.40	.20
445	Harold Newhouser	.15	.11	.06
446	Wesley C. Ferrell	.10	.08	.04
447	Francis J. O'Doul	.10	.08	.04
448	Walter H. Schang	.10	.08	.04
449	Sherwood R. Magee	.10	.08	.04
450	Michael J. Donlin	.10	.08	.04
451	Roger M. Cramer	.10	.08	.04
452	Richard W. Bartell	.10	.08	.04
453	Earle T. Mack	.10	.08	.04
454	Walter G. Brown	.10	.08	.04
455	John A. Heving	.10	.08	.04
456	Percy L. Jones	.10	.08	.04
457	Theodore Blankenship	.10	.08	.04
458	Absalom H. Wingo	.10	.08	.04
459	Roger P. Bresnahan	.15	.11	.06
460	William J. Klem	.15	.11	.06
461	Charles L. Gehringer	.15	.11	.06
462	Stanley A. Coveleski	.15	.11	.06
463	Edward S. Plank	.15	.11	.06
464	Clark C.F. Griffith	.15	.11	.06
465	Herbert J. Pennock	.15	.11	.06
466	Earle B. Combs	.15	.11	.06
467	Robert P. Doerr	.15	.11	.06
468	Waite C. Hoyt	.15	.11	.06
469	Thomas H. Connolly	.15	.11	.06
470	Harry B. Hooper	.15	.11	.06
471	Richard B. Ferrell	.15	.11	.06
472	William G. Evans	.15	.11	.06
473	William J. Herman	.15	.11	.06
474	William M. Dickey	.15	.11	.06
475	Lucius B. Appling	.15	.11	.06
476	Ralph A. Pinelli	.10	.08	.04
477	Donald E. McNair	.10	.08	.04
478	John F. Blake	.10	.08	.04
479	Valentine J. Picinich	.10	.08	.04
480	Fred A. Heimach	.10	.08	.04
481	John G. Graney	.10	.08	.04
482	Ewell A. Russell	.10	.08	.04
483	Urban C. Faber	.15	.11	.06
484	Benjamin M. Kauff	.10	.08	.04
485	Clarence L. Rowland	.10	.08	.04
486	Robert H. Veach	.10	.08	.04
487	James C. Bagby	.10	.08	.04
488	William D. Perritt	.10	.08	.04
489	Charles L. Herzog	.10	.08	.04
490	Arthur Fletcher	.10	.08	.04
491	Walter H. Holke	.10	.08	.04
492	Arthur N. Nehr	.10	.08	.04
493	Lafayette F. Thompson	.10	.08	.04
494	James D. Welsh	.10	.08	.04
495	Oscar J. Vitt	.10	.08	.04
496	Owen T. Carroll	.10	.08	.04
497	James K. O'Dea	.10	.08	.04
498	Fredrick M. Frankhouse	.10	.08	.04
499	Jewel W. Ens	.10	.08	.04
500	Morris Arnovich	.10	.08	.04
501	Walter Gerber	.10	.08	.04
502	George W. Davis	.10	.08	.04
503	Charles S. Myer	.10	.08	.04
504	Samuel A. Leslie	.10	.08	.04
505	William C. Bolton	.10	.08	.04
506	Fred Walker	.10	.08	.04
507	John W. Smith	.10	.08	.04
508	Irving D. Hadley	.10	.08	.04
509	Clyde E. Crouse	.10	.08	.04
510	Joseph C. Glenn	.10	.08	.04
511	Clyde E. Kimsey	.10	.08	.04
512	Louis K. Finney	.10	.08	.04
513	Alfred V. Lawson	.10	.08	.04
514	Charles P. Fullis	.10	.08	.04
515	Earl H. Sheely	.10	.08	.04
516	George Gibson	.10	.08	.04
517	John J. Broaca	.10	.08	.04
518	Bibb A. Falk	.10	.08	.04
519	Frank O. Hurst	.10	.08	.04
520	Grover A. Hartley	.10	.08	.04
521	Donald H. Heffner	.10	.08	.04
522	Harvey L. Hendrick	.10	.08	.04
523	Allen S. Sothoron	.10	.08	.04
524	Anthony F. Piet	.10	.08	.04
525	Tyrus R. Cobb	.40	.30	.15
526	James E. Foxx	.15	.11	.06
527	Rogers Hornsby	.15	.11	.06
528	Napoleon LaJoie	.15	.11	.06
529	Louis H. Gehrig	.40	.30	.15
530	Henry Zimmerman	.10	.08	.04
531	Charles H. Klein	.15	.11	.06
532	Hugh Duffy	.15	.11	.06
533	Robert M. Grove	.15	.11	.06
534	Grover C. Alexander	.15	.11	.06
535	Amos W. Rusie	.15	.11	.06
536	Vernon L. Gomez	.15	.11	.06
537	William H. Walters	.10	.08	.04
538	Urban J. Hodapp	.10	.08	.04
539	Bruce D. Campbell	.10	.08	.04
540	Horace M. Lisenbee	.10	.08	.04
541	John F. Fournier	.10	.08	.04
542	James R. Tabor	.10	.08	.04
543	John H. Burnett	.10	.08	.04
544	Roy A. Hartzell	.10	.08	.04
545	Walter P. Gautreau	.10	.08	.04
546	Emil O. Yde	.10	.08	.04
547	Robert L. Johnson	.10	.08	.04
548	Joseph J. Hauser	.10	.08	.04
549	Edward M. Reulbach	.10	.08	.04
550	Baldomero M. Almada	.10	.08	.04
551	Gordon S. Cochrane	.15	.11	.06
552	Carl O. Hubbell	.15	.11	.06
553	Charles L. Gehringer	.15	.11	.06
554	Aloysius H. Simmons	.15	.11	.06
555	Mordecai P.C. Brown	.15	.11	.06
556	Hugh A. Jennings	.15	.11	.06
557	Norman A. Elberfeld	.10	.08	.04
558	Charles D. Stengel	.10	.08	.04
559	Alexander Schacht	.10	.08	.04
560	James E. Foxx	.15	.11	.06
561	George L. Kelly	.15	.11	.06
562	Lloyd J. Waner	.15	.11	.06
563	Paul G. Waner	.15	.11	.06
564	Walter P. Johnson	.15	.11	.06
565	John Franklin Baker	.15	.11	.06
566	Roy J. Hughes	.10	.08	.04
567	Lewis S. Riggs	.10	.08	.04
568	John H. Whitehead	.10	.08	.04
569	Elam R. Vangilder	.10	.08	.04
570	William A. Zitzmann	.10	.08	.04
571	Walter J. Schmidt	.10	.08	.04
572	John A. Tavener	.10	.08	.04
573	Joseph E. Genewich	.10	.08	.04
574	John A. Marcum	.10	.08	.04
575	Fred Hofmann	.10	.08	.04
576	Robert A. Rolfe	.10	.08	.04
577	Victor G. Sorrell	.10	.08	.04
578	Floyd J. Scott	.10	.08	.04
579	Alphonse Thomas	.10	.08	.04
580	Alfred J. Smith	.10	.08	.04
581	Walter J. Henline	.10	.08	.04
582	Edward T. Collins	.15	.11	.06
583	Earle B. Combs	.15	.11	.06
584	John J. McGraw	.15	.11	.06
585	Lewis R. Wilson	.15	.11	.06
586	Charles L. Hartnett	.15	.11	.06
587	Hazen S. Cuyler	.15	.11	.06
588	William H. Terry	.15	.11	.06
589	Joseph V. McCarthy	.15	.11	.06
590	Henry B. Greenberg	.15	.11	.06
591	Tristram E. Speaker	.15	.11	.06
592	William B. McKechnie	.15	.11	.06
593	Stanley R. Harris	.15	.11	.06
594	Herbert J. Pennock	.15	.11	.06
595	George H. Sisler	.15	.11	.06
596	Fred C. Lindstrom	.15	.11	.06
597	Howard E. Averill Sr.	.15	.11	.06
598	David J. Bancroft	.15	.11	.06
599	Cornelius Mack	.15	.11	.06
600	Joseph E. Cronin	.15	.11	.06
601	Kenneth L. Ash	.10	.08	.04
602	Alfred R. Spohrer	.10	.08	.04
603	Lee R. Mahaffey	.10	.08	.04
604	James F. O'Rourke	.10	.08	.04
605	Ulysses S.G. Stoner	.10	.08	.04
606	Frank H. Gabler	.10	.08	.04
607	Thomas F. Padden	.10	.08	.04
608	Charles A. Shires	.10	.08	.04
609	Sherrod M. Smith	.10	.08	.04
610	Philip Weintraub	.10	.08	.04
611	Russell Van Atta	.10	.08	.04
612	Joyner C. White	.10	.08	.04
613	Clifford G. Melton	.10	.08	.04
614	James J. Ring	.10	.08	.04
615	John H. Sand	.10	.08	.04
616	David D. Alexander	.10	.08	.04
617	Kent Greenfield	.10	.08	.04
618	Edwin H. Dyer	.10	.08	.04
619	William H. Sherdel	.10	.08	.04
620	Hubert M. Lanier	.10	.08	.04
621	Robert A. O'Farrell	.10	.08	.04
622	Rogers Hornsby	.15	.11	.06
623	William A. Beckman	.10	.08	.04
624	Morton C. Cooper	.10	.08	.04
625	William P. Delancey	.10	.08	.04
626	Martin W. Marion	.10	.08	.04

627	William H. Southworth	.10	.08	.04
628	John R. Mize	.15	.11	.06
629	Joseph M. Medwick	.15	.11	.06
630	Grover C. Alexander	.15	.11	.06
631	Paul D. Dean	.10	.08	.04
632	Herman S. Bell	.10	.08	.04
633	William W. Cooper	.10	.08	.04
634	Frank F. Frisch	.15	.11	.06
635	Jay H. Dean	.15	.11	.06
636	Donald J. Gutteridge	.10	.08	.04
637	Johnny L.R. Martin	.10	.08	.04
638	Edward J. Konetchy	.10	.08	.04
639	William A. Hallahan	.10	.08	.04
640	Lonnie Warneke	.10	.08	.04
641	Terry B. Moore	.10	.08	.04
642	Enos B. Slaughter	.15	.11	.06
643	Clarence F. Mueller	.10	.08	.04
644	George Toporcer	.10	.08	.04
645	James L. Bottomely	.15	.11	.06
646	Francis R. Blades	.10	.08	.04
647	Jesse J. Haines	.10	.08	.04
648	Andrew A. High	.10	.08	.04
649	Miller J. Huggins	.10	.08	.04
650	Ernesto R. Orsatti	.10	.08	.04
651	Lester R. Bell	.10	.08	.04
652	Charles E. Street	.10	.08	.04
653	Walter H. Roettger	.10	.08	.04
654	Sylvester W. Johnson	.10	.08	.04
655	Miguel A. Gonzalez	.10	.08	.04
656	James A. Collins	.15	.11	.06
657	Charles J. Hafey	.15	.11	.06
658	Checklist 331-440	.10	.08	.04
659	Checklist 441-550	.10	.08	.04
660	Checklist 551-660	.10	.08	.04

1993 Conlon Collection

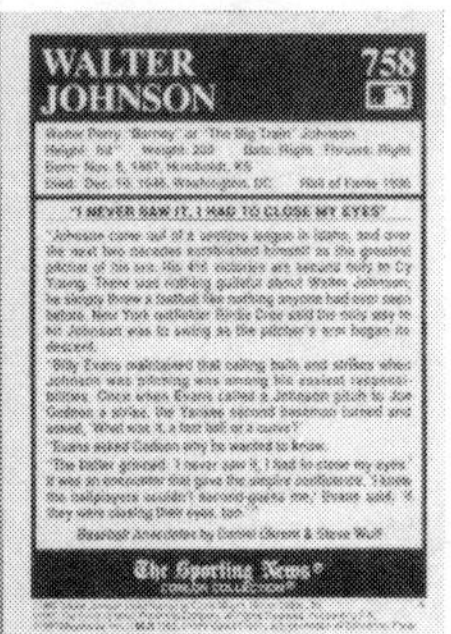

The third annual Conlon Collection issue of 330 cards is numbered 661-990, a continuation of the series produced in 1991-92. The format of black-and-white photos produced 50-90 years ago by Charles Martin Conlon and surrounded by a wide black border and UV coating was continued. As with earlier issues, card backs contain brief biographical data, a few stats and well-written career highlights. The 1993 set also featured many subsets arranged by topic, such as spitballers, native Americans, players who overcame handicaps, etc. One subset compared Nolan Ryan with star pitchers in baseball history and included a fantasy photo of Ryan shaking hands in the dugout with Walter Johnson (card #934).

		MT	NR MT	EX
Complete Set (330):		20.00	15.00	8.00
Common Player:		.10	.08	.04
661	William H. Terry	.15	.11	.06
662	Vernon L. Gomez	.15	.11	.06
663	George H. Ruth	.50	.40	.20
664	Frank F. Frisch	.15	.11	.06
665	Carl O. Hubbell	.15	.11	.06
666	Aloysius H. Simmons	.15	.11	.06
667	Charles L. Gehringer	.15	.11	.06
668	Howard E. Averill Sr.	.15	.11	.06
669	Robert M. Grove	.15	.11	.06
670	Harold J. Traynor	.15	.11	.06
671	Charles H. Klein	.15	.11	.06
672	Paul G. Waner	.15	.11	.06
673	Louis H. Gehrig	.40	.30	.15
674	Richard B. Ferrell	.15	.11	.06
675	Charles L. Hartnett	.15	.11	.06
676	Joseph E. Cronin	.15	.11	.06
677	Charles J. Hafey	.15	.11	.06
678	James J. Dykes	.10	.08	.04
679	Samuel F. West	.10	.08	.04
680	Johnny L.R. Martin	.10	.08	.04
681	Francis J. O'Doul	.10	.08	.04
682	Alvin F. Crowder	.10	.08	.04
683	James Wilson	.10	.08	.04
684	Richard W. Bartell	.10	.08	.04
685	William A. Hallahan	.10	.08	.04
686	Walter A. Berger	.10	.08	.04
687	Lonnie Warneke	.10	.08	.04
688	William B. Chapman	.10	.08	.04
689	Elwood G. English	.10	.08	.04
690	James H. Reese	.10	.08	.04
691	Roscoe A. Holm	.10	.08	.04
692	Charles D. Jamieson	.10	.08	.04
693	Jonathan T.W. Zachary	.10	.08	.04
694	John C. Ryan	.10	.08	.04
695	Earl J. Adams	.10	.08	.04
696	William E. Hunnefield	.10	.08	.04
697	Henry L. Meadows	.10	.08	.04
698	Thomas F. Carey	.10	.08	.04
699	John W. Rawlings	.10	.08	.04
700	Kenneth E. Holloway	.10	.08	.04
701	Lance C. Richbourg	.10	.08	.04
702	Raymond L. Fisher	.10	.08	.04
703	Edward Augustine Walsh	.15	.11	.06
704	Richard Rudolph	.10	.08	.04
705	Raymond B. Caldwell	.10	.08	.04
706	Burleigh A. Grimes	.15	.11	.06
707	Stanley A. Coveleski	.15	.11	.06
708	George A. Hildebrand	.10	.08	.04
709	John P. Quinn	.10	.08	.04
710	Urban C. Faber	.15	.11	.06
711	Urban J. Shocker	.10	.08	.04
712	Hubert B. Leonard	.10	.08	.04
713	Louis L. Koupal	.10	.08	.04
714	James C. Wasdell	.10	.08	.04
715	John H. Lindell	.10	.08	.04
716	Don W. Padgett	.10	.08	.04
717	Nelson T. Potter	.10	.08	.04
718	Lynwood T. Rowe	.10	.08	.04
719	David C. Danforth	.10	.08	.04
720	Claude W. Passeau	.10	.08	.04
721	Harry L. Kelley	.10	.08	.04
722	John T. Allen	.10	.08	.04
723	Thomas J.D. Bridges	.10	.08	.04
724	William C. Lee	.10	.08	.04
725	Fredrick M. Frankhouse	.10	.08	.04
726	John J. McCarthy	.10	.08	.04
727	Glen D. Russell	.10	.08	.04
728	Emory E. Rigney	.10	.08	.04
729	Howard S. Shanks	.10	.08	.04
730	Lucius B. Appling	.10	.08	.04
731	William J. Byron	.10	.08	.04
732	Earle B. Combs	.15	.11	.06
733	Henry B. Greenberg	.15	.11	.06
734	Walter W. Beck	.10	.08	.04
735	Hollis J. Thurston	.10	.08	.04
736	Lewis R. Wilson	.15	.11	.06
737	William A. McGowan	.10	.08	.04
738	Henry J. Bonura	.10	.08	.04
739	Thomas C. Baker	.10	.08	.04
740	William C. Jacobson	.10	.08	.04
741	Hazen S. Cuyler	.15	.11	.06
742	George F. Blaeholder	.10	.08	.04
743	Wilson D. Miles	.10	.08	.04
744	Lee E. Handley	.10	.08	.04
745	John F. Collins	.10	.08	.04
746	Wilfred P. Ryan	.10	.08	.04
747	Aaron L. Ward	.10	.08	.04
748	Montgomery M. Pearson	.10	.08	.04
749	Jacob W. Early	.10	.08	.04
750	William F. Atwood	.10	.08	.04
751	Mark A. Koenig	.10	.08	.04
752	John A. Hassett	.10	.08	.04
753	David J. Jones	.10	.08	.04
754	John P. Wagner	.15	.11	.06
755	William M. Dickey	.15	.11	.06
756	Albert M. Butcher	.10	.08	.04
757	Waite C. Hoyt	.15	.11	.06
758	Walter P. Johnson	.15	.11	.06
759	Howard J. Ehmke	.10	.08	.04
760	Norman L. Newsom	.10	.08	.04
761	Anthony M. Lazzeri	.15	.11	.06
762	Anthony M. Lazzeri	.15	.11	.06
763	Spurgeon F. Chandler	.15	.11	.06
764	Walter K. Higbe	.10	.08	.04
765	Paul R. Richards	.10	.08	.04
766	Rogers Hornsby	.15	.11	.06
767	Joseph F. Vosmik	.10	.08	.04
768	Jesse J. Haines	.15	.11	.06
769	William H. Walters	.10	.08	.04
770	Thomas D. Henrich	.10	.08	.04
771	James F. Thorpe	.40	.30	.15
772	Euel W. Moore	.10	.08	.04
773	Rudolph P. York	.10	.08	.04
774	Charles A. Bender	.15	.11	.06
775	John T. Meyers	.10	.08	.04
776	Robert L. Johnson	.10	.08	.04
777	Roy C. Johnson	.10	.08	.04
778	Richard T. Porter	.10	.08	.04
779	Ethan N. Allen	.10	.08	.04
780	Harry F. Sallee	.10	.08	.04
781	Roy C. Bell	.10	.08	.04
782	Arnold J. Statz	.10	.08	.04
783	Frank J. Henry	.10	.08	.04
784	Charles L. Woodall	.10	.08	.04
785	Philip E. Collins	.10	.08	.04
786	Joseph W. Sewell	.15	.11	.06
787	William J. Herman	.15	.11	.06
788	Rueben H. Oldring	.10	.08	.04
789	William H. Walker	.10	.08	.04
790	Joseph C. Schultz	.10	.08	.04
791	Fred E. Maguire	.10	.08	.04
792	Claude W. Willoughby	.10	.08	.04
793	James A. Ferguson	.10	.08	.04
794	John D. Morrison	.10	.08	.04
795	Tristram E. Speaker	.15	.11	.06
796	Tyrus R. Cobb	.40	.30	.15
797	Max Carey	.15	.11	.06
798	George H. Sisler	.15	.11	.06
799	Charles J. Hollocher	.10	.08	.04
800	James L. Vaughn	.10	.08	.04
801	Samuel P. Jones	.10	.08	.04
802	Harry B. Hooper	.15	.11	.06
803	Clifford C. Cravath	.10	.08	.04
804	Walter P. Johnson	.15	.11	.06
805	Jacob E. Daubert	.10	.08	.04
806	Jesse C. Milan	.10	.08	.04
807	Hugh A. McQuillan	.10	.08	.04
808	George F. Brickell	.10	.08	.04
809	Joseph V. Stripp	.10	.08	.04
810	Urban J. Hodapp	.10	.08	.04
811	John L. Vergez	.10	.08	.04
812	Linus R. Frey	.10	.08	.04
813	William W. Regan	.10	.08	.04
814	Norman R. Young	.10	.08	.04
815	Charles C. Robertson	.10	.08	.04
816	Walter F. Judnich	.10	.08	.04
817	Joseph B. Tinker	.15	.11	.06
818	John Evers	.15	.11	.06
819	Frank L. Chance	.15	.11	.06
820	John J. McGraw	.15	.11	.06
821	Charles J. Grimm	.10	.08	.04
822	Ted Lyons	.15	.11	.06
823	Joe McCarthy	.15	.11	.06
824	Connie Mack	.15	.11	.06
825	George Gibson	.10	.08	.04
826	Steve O'Neill	.10	.08	.04
827	Tristram E. Speaker	.15	.11	.06
828	William F. Carrigan	.10	.08	.04
829	Charles D. Stengel	.15	.11	.06
830	Miller J. Huggins	.15	.11	.06
831	William B. McKechnie	.15	.11	.06
832	Charles W. Dressen	.10	.08	.04
833	Charles E. Street	.10	.08	.04
834	Melvin T. Ott	.15	.11	.06
835	Frank F. Frisch	.15	.11	.06
836	George H. Sisler	.15	.11	.06
837	Napoleon LaJoie	.15	.11	.06
838	Tyrus R. Cobb	.40	.30	.15
839	William H. Southworth	.10	.08	.04
840	Clark C.F. Griffith	.15	.11	.06
841	William H. Terry	.15	.11	.06
842	Rogers Hornsby	.15	.11	.06
843	Joseph E. Cronin	.15	.11	.06
844	Alfonso R. Lopez	.15	.11	.06
845	Stanley R. Harris	.15	.11	.06
846	Wilbert Robinson	.15	.11	.06
847	Hugh A. Jennings	.15	.11	.06
848	James J. Dykes	.10	.08	.04
849	Roy J. Cullenbine	.10	.08	.04
850	Graham E. Moore	.10	.08	.04
851	John H. Rothrock	.10	.08	.04
852	William H. Lamar	.10	.08	.04
853	Monte Weaver	.10	.08	.04
854	Ival R. Goodman	.10	.08	.04
855	Henry L. Severeid	.10	.08	.04
856	Fred G. Haney	.10	.08	.04
857	Joseph B. Shaute	.10	.08	.04
858	Smead P. Jolley	.10	.08	.04
859	Edwin D. Williams	.10	.08	.04
860	Bernard O. Bengough	.10	.08	.04
861	Richard B. Ferrell	.15	.11	.06
862	Robert A. O'Farrell	.10	.08	.04
863	Virgil L. Davis	.10	.08	.04
864	Franklin W. Hayes	.10	.08	.04
865	Herold D. Ruel	.10	.08	.04
866	Gordon S. Cochrane	.15	.11	.06
867	John Kling	.10	.08	.04
868	Ivy B. Wingo	.10	.08	.04
869	William M. Dickey	.15	.11	.06
870	Frank E. Snyder	.10	.08	.04
871	Roger P. Bresnahan	.15	.11	.06
872	Walter H. Schang	.10	.08	.04
873	Alfonso R. Lopez	.15	.11	.06
874	James Wilson	.10	.08	.04
875	Valentine J. Picinich	.10	.08	.04
876	Stephen F. O'Neill	.10	.08	.04
877	Ernest N. Lombardi	.15	.11	.06
878	John L. Bassler	.10	.08	.04
879	Raymond W. Schalk	.15	.11	.06
880	Charles L. Hartnett	.15	.11	.06
881	Bruce D. Campbell	.10	.08	.04
882	Charles H. Ruffing	.15	.11	.06
883	Mordecai P.C. Brown	.15	.11	.06
884	Peter J. Archer	.10	.08	.04
885	David E. Keefe	.10	.08	.04
886	Nathan H. Andrews	.10	.08	.04
887	Edgar C. Rice	.15	.11	.06
888	George H. Ruth	.50	.40	.20
889	Charles J. Hafey	.15	.11	.06
890	Oscar D. Melillo	.10	.08	.04
891	Joe Wood	.10	.08	.04
892	John J. Evers	.15	.11	.06
893	George Toporcer	.10	.08	.04
894	Myril O. Hoag	.10	.08	.04
895	Robert G. Weiland	.10	.08	.04
896	Joseph A. Marty	.10	.08	.04
897	Sherwood R. Magee	.10	.08	.04
898	Daniel T. Taylor	.10	.08	.04
899	William E. Kamm	.10	.08	.04
900	Samuel J.T. Sheckard	.10	.08	.04
901	Sylvester W. Johnson	.10	.08	.04
902	Stephen R. Sundra	.10	.08	.04
903	Roger M. Cramer	.10	.08	.04
904	Hubert S. Pruett	.10	.08	.04
905	Russell A. Blackburne	.10	.08	.04
906	Eppa Rixey	.15	.11	.06
907	Leon A. Goslin	.15	.11	.06
908	George L. Kelly	.15	.11	.06
909	James L. Bottomley	.15	.11	.06
910	Christopher Mathewson	.15	.11	.06
911	Anthony M. Lazzeri	.15	.11	.06
912	John A. Mostil	.10	.08	.04
913	Robert P. Doerr	.15	.11	.06
914	Walter J.V. Maranville	.15	.11	.06
915	Harry E. Heilmann	.15	.11	.06
916	Rodrick J. Wallace	.15	.11	.06
917	James E. Foxx	.15	.11	.06
918	John R. Mize	.10	.08	.04
919	John N. Bentley	.10	.08	.04
920	Alexander Schacht	.10	.08	.04
921	Parke E. Coleman	.10	.08	.04
922	George H. Paskert	.10	.08	.04
923	Horace H. Ford	.10	.08	.04
924	Randolph E. Moore	.10	.08	.04
925	Milburn J. Shoffner	.10	.08	.04
926	Richard W. Siebert	.10	.08	.04
927	Anthony C. Kaufmann	.10	.08	.04
928	Jay H. Dean/ Nolan Ryan	.25	.20	.10
929	Clarence A. Vance/ Nolan Ryan	.25	.20	.10
930	Robert M. Grove/ Nolan Ryan	.25	.20	.10
931	George E. Waddell/ Nolan Ryan	.25	.20	.10

932	Grover C. Alexander/ Nolan Ryan	.25	.20	.10
933	Robert W.A. Feller/ Nolan Ryan	.25	.20	.10
934	Walter P. Johnson/ Nolan Ryan	.50	.40	.20
935	Theodore A. Lyons/ Nolan Ryan	.25	.20	.10
936	James C. Bagby	.10	.08	.04
937	Joseph Sugden	.10	.08	.04
938	Robert E. Grace	.10	.08	.04
939	John G. Heath	.10	.08	.04
940	Kenneth R. Williams	.10	.08	.04
941	Marvin J. Owen	.10	.08	.04
942	Cyril R. Weatherly	.10	.08	.04
943	Edward C. Morgan	.10	.08	.04
944	John C. Rizzo	.10	.08	.04
945	Archie R. McKain	.10	.08	.04
946	Robert M. Garbark	.10	.08	.04
947	John B. Osborn	.10	.08	.04
948	John S. Podgajny	.10	.08	.04
949	Joseph P. Evans	.10	.08	.04
950	George A. Rensa	.10	.08	.04
951	John H. Humphries	.10	.08	.04
952	Merritt P. Cain	.10	.08	.04
953	Roy E. Hansen	.10	.08	.04
954	John A. Niggeling	.10	.08	.04
955	Harold J. Wiltse	.10	.08	.04
956	Alejandro A.A.E. Carrasquel	.10	.08	.04
957	George A. Grant	.10	.08	.04
958	Philip W. Weinert	.10	.08	.04
959	Ervin B. Brame	.10	.08	.04
960	Raymond J. Harrell	.10	.08	.04
961	Edward K. Linke	.10	.08	.04
962	Samuel B. Gibson	.10	.08	.04
963	John C. Watwood	.10	.08	.04
964	James T. Prothro	.10	.08	.04
965	Julio G. Bonetti	.10	.08	.04
966	Howard R. Mills	.10	.08	.04
967	Clarence E. Galloway	.10	.08	.04
968	Harold J. Kelleher	.10	.08	.04
969	Elon C. Hogsett	.10	.08	.04
970	Edward B. Heusser	.10	.08	.04
971	Edward J. Baecht	.10	.08	.04
972	Otto H. Saltzgaver	.10	.08	.04
973	Leroy G. Herrmann	.10	.08	.04
974	Beveric B. Bean	.10	.08	.04
975	Harry Seibold	.10	.08	.04
976	Howard V. Keen	.10	.08	.04
977	William J. Barrett	.10	.08	.04
978	Patrick H. McNulty	.10	.08	.04
979	George E. Turbeville	.10	.08	.04
980	Edward D. Phillips	.10	.08	.04
981	Garland M. Buckeye	.10	.08	.04
982	Victor P. Frasier	.10	.08	.04
983	John G. Rhodes	.10	.08	.04
984	Emile D. Barnes	.10	.08	.04
985	James C. Edwards	.10	.08	.04
986	Herschel E. Bennett	.10	.08	.04
987	Carmen P. Hill	.10	.08	.04
988	Checklist 661-770	.10	.08	.04
989	Checklist 771-880	.10	.08	.04
990	Checklist 881-990	.10	.08	.04

1993 Conlon Color

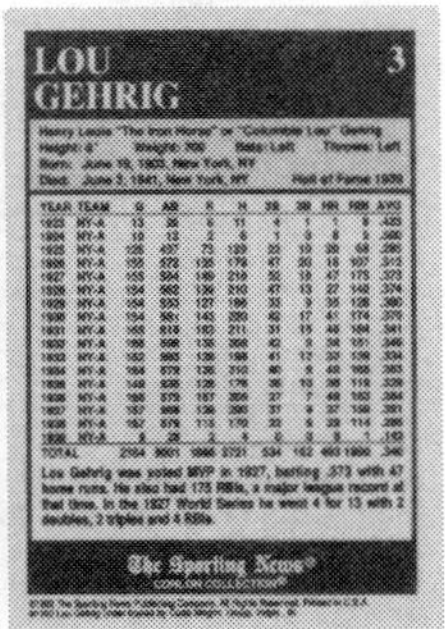

The cards in this 23-card set were previously released in black and white in either the 1991 or 1992 regular Conlon sets. The distribution of the color cards is unique. Cards 1-12 were issued as bonus cards in Megacards accessory items. 250,000 of cards 1-12 were produced. Cards 13-20 were randomly inserted in 1993 Conlon counter and blister packs. Only 100,000 of cards 13-20 were produced. Cards 21 and 22 were only available through a send-away offer and card 23 was available exclusively in the Seventh Edition SCD Baseball Card Price Guide. Only 60,000 of card number 23 were available.

	MT	NR MT	EX
Complete Set:	50.00	37.00	20.00
Common Player:	1.50	1.25	.60

1	Sunny Jim Bottomley	1.50	1.25	.60
2	Lefty Grove	1.50	1.25	.60
3	Lou Gehrig	4.00	3.00	1.50
4	Babe Ruth	5.00	3.75	2.00
5	Casey Stengel	2.00	1.50	.80
6	Rube Marquard	1.50	1.25	.60
7	Walter Johnson	2.00	1.50	.80
8	Lou Gehrig	3.00	2.25	1.25
9	Christy Mathewson	2.00	1.50	.80
10	Ty Cobb	3.00	2.25	1.25
11	Mel Ott	1.50	1.25	.60
12	Carl Hubbell	1.50	1.25	.60
13	Al Simmons	1.50	1.25	.60
14	Connie Mack	1.50	1.25	.60
15	Grover C. Alexander	1.50	1.25	.60
16	Jimmie Foxx	2.00	1.50	.80
17	Lloyd Waner	1.50	1.25	.60
18	Tris Speaker	3.00	2.25	1.25
19	Dizzy Dean	3.00	2.25	1.25
20	Rogers Hornsby	2.00	1.50	.80
21	Shoeless Joe Jackson	4.00	3.00	1.50
22	Jim Thorpe	4.00	3.00	1.50
23	Bob Feller	5.00	3.75	2.00

1994 Conlon Collection

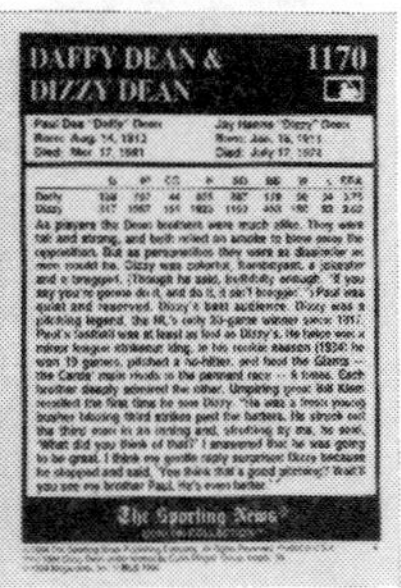

The production of "old-timers" cards based on the baseball photography of Charles M. Conlon from the 1910s through the 1930s continued into a fourth year in 1994 with another 330-card series, numbered 991-1320. Once again the format of previous years was continued. Subsets included the 1919 Chicago White Sox, major league brothers and action photos.

	MT	NR MT	EX
Complete Set (330):	20.00	15.00	8.00
Common Player:	.10	.08	.04

991	Johnny L.R. Martin	.10	.08	.04
992	Joseph W. Sewell	.15	.11	.06
993	Edd J. Roush	.15	.11	.06
994	Richard B. Ferrell	.15	.11	.06
995	John J. Broaca	.10	.08	.04
996	James L. Sewell	.10	.08	.04
997	Burleigh A. Grimes	.15	.11	.06
998	Lewis R. Wilson	.15	.11	.06
999	Robert M. Grove	.15	.11	.06
1000	Tyrus R. Cobb	.30	.25	.12
1001	John J. McGraw	.15	.11	.06
1002	Edward S. Plank	.15	.11	.06
1003	Samuel P. Jones	.10	.08	.04
1004	James L. Bottomley	.15	.11	.06
1005	Henry B. Greenberg	.15	.11	.06
1006	Lloyd J. Waner	.15	.11	.06
1007	William W. Moore	.10	.08	.04
1008	Lucius B. Appling	.15	.11	.06
1009	Harold Newhouser	.15	.11	.06
1010	Alfonso R. Lopez	.15	.11	.06
1011	Tyrus R. Cobb	.40	.30	.15
1012	Charles A. Nichols	.10	.08	.04
1013	Edward Augustine Walsh	.15	.11	.06
1014	Hugh Duffy	.15	.11	.06
1015	Richard W. Marquard	.15	.11	.06
1016	Adrian Joss	.15	.11	.06
1017	Rodrick J. Wallace	.15	.11	.06
1018	William H. Keeler	.15	.11	.06
1019	Jacob E. Daubert	.10	.08	.04
1020	Harry F. Sallee	.10	.08	.04
1021	Adolfo Luque	.10	.08	.04
1022	Ivy B. Wingo	.10	.08	.04
1023	Edd J. Roush	.15	.11	.06
1024	William A. Rariden	.10	.08	.04
1025	Sherwood R. Magee	.10	.08	.04
1026	Louis B. Duncan	.10	.08	.04
1027	Horace O. Eller	.10	.08	.04
1028	Alfred E. Neale	.10	.08	.04
1029	George D. Weaver	.10	.08	.04
1030	Joseph J. Jackson	.50	.40	.20
1031	Arnold Gandil	.10	.08	.04
1032	Charles A. Risberg	.10	.08	.04
1033	Raymond W. Schalk	.15	.11	.06
1034	Edward V. Cicotte	.10	.08	.04
1035	William H. James	.10	.08	.04
1036	Harry L. Leibold	.10	.08	.04
1037	Richard H. Kerr	.10	.08	.04
1038	William J. Gleason	.10	.08	.04
1039	Frederick W. McMullin	.10	.08	.04
1040	Edward T. Collins	.15	.11	.06
1041	Sox Pitchers (Lefty Williams, Bill James, Ed Cicotte, Dicky Kerr)	.10	.08	.04
1042	Sox Outfielders (Nemo Leibold, Happy Felsch, Shano Collins)	.10	.08	.04
1043	Kenneth F. Keltner	.10	.08	.04
1044	Charles F. Berry	.10	.08	.04
1045	Walter J. Lutzke	.10	.08	.04
1046	John C. Schulte	.10	.08	.04
1047	John V. Welch	.10	.08	.04
1048	Jack E. Russell	.10	.08	.04
1049	John J. Murray	.10	.08	.04
1050	Harold J. Traynor	.15	.11	.06
1051	Michael J. Donlin	.10	.08	.04
1052	Charles L. Hartnett	.15	.11	.06
1053	Anthony M. Lazzeri	.15	.11	.06
1054	Lawrence H. Miller	.10	.08	.04
1055	Clarence A. Vance	.15	.11	.06
1056	Williams F. Carrigan	.10	.08	.04
1057	John J. Murphy	.10	.08	.04
1058	Clifton E Heathcote	.10	.08	.04
1059	Joseph A. Dugan	.10	.08	.04
1060	Walter J.V. Maranville	.15	.11	.06
1061	Thomas D. Henrich	.10	.08	.04
1062	Leroy E. Parmelee	.10	.08	.04
1063	Vernon L. Gomez	.15	.11	.06
1064	Ernest N. Lombardi	.15	.11	.06
1065	David J. Bancroft	.15	.11	.06
1066	William B. McKechnie	.15	.11	.06
1067	John A. Hassett	.10	.08	.04
1068	Spurgeon F. Chandler	.10	.08	.04
1069	Roy J. Hughes	.10	.08	.04
1070	George A. Dauss	.10	.08	.04
1071	Joseph J. Hauser	.10	.08	.04
1072	Virgil L. Davis	.10	.08	.04
1073	Albert M. Butcher	.10	.08	.04
1074	Louis P. Chiozza	.10	.08	.04
1075	Center Field Bleachers	.10	.08	.04
1076	Charles L. Gehringer	.15	.11	.06
1077	Henry E. Manush	.15	.11	.06
1078	Charles H. Ruffing	.15	.11	.06
1079	Melvin L. Harder	.10	.08	.04
1080	George H. Ruth	.50	.40	.20
1081	William B. Chapman	.10	.08	.04
1082	Louis H. Gehrig	.40	.30	.15
1083	James E. Foxx	.15	.11	.06
1084	Aloysius H. Simmons	.15	.11	.06
1085	Joseph E. Cronin	.15	.11	.06
1086	William M. Dickey	.15	.11	.06
1087	Gordon S. Cochrane	.15	.11	.06
1088	Vernon L. Gomez	.15	.11	.06
1089	Howard E. Averill Sr.	.15	.11	.06
1090	Samuel F. West	.10	.08	.04
1091	Frank F. Frisch	.15	.11	.06
1092	William J. Herman	.15	.11	.06
1093	Harold J. Traynor	.15	.11	.06
1094	Joseph M. Medwick	.15	.11	.06
1095	Charles H. Klein	.15	.11	.06
1096	Hazen S. Cuyler	.15	.11	.06
1097	Melvin T. Ott	.15	.11	.06
1098	Walter T. Berger	.10	.08	.04
1099	Paul G. Waner	.15	.11	.06
1100	William H. Terry	.15	.11	.06
1101	Travis C. Jackson	.15	.11	.06
1102	Joseph F. Vaughan	.15	.11	.06
1103	Charles L. Hartnett	.15	.11	.06
1104	Alfonso R. Lopez	.15	.11	.06
1105	Carl O. Hubbell	.15	.11	.06
1106	Lonnie Warneke	.10	.08	.04
1107	Van L. Mungo	.10	.08	.04
1108	Johnny J.R. Martin	.10	.08	.04
1109	Jay H. Dean	.15	.11	.06
1110	Fredrick M. Frankhouse	.10	.08	.04
1111	Giullaedeau Spink Heydler	.10	.08	.04
1112	JG Taylor Spink/ Mrs. Spink	.10	.08	.04
1113	Hirchman and Keller	.10	.08	.04
1114	Victor E. Aldridge	.10	.08	.04
1115	Michael F. Higgins	.10	.08	.04
1116	Harold G. Carlson	.10	.08	.04
1117	Frederick L. Fitzsimmons	.10	.08	.04
1118	William H. Walters	.10	.08	.04
1119	Nicholas Altrock	.10	.08	.04
1120	Charles W. Dressen	.10	.08	.04
1121	Mark A. Koenig	.10	.08	.04
1122	Charles L. Gehringer	.15	.11	.06
1123	Lloyd V. Kennedy	.10	.08	.04
1124	Harlond B. Clift	.10	.08	.04
1125	Ernest G. Phelps	.10	.08	.04
1126	John R. Mize	.15	.11	.06
1127	Harold H. Schumacher	.10	.08	.04
1128	Ethan N. Allen	.10	.08	.04
1129	William A. Wambsganss	.10	.08	.04
1130	Frederick Leach	.10	.08	.04
1131	John W. Clancy	.10	.08	.04
1132	John F. Stewart	.10	.08	.04
1133	Wilbur L. Brubaker	.10	.08	.04
1134	Leslie Mann	.10	.08	.04
1135	Howard J. Ehmke	.10	.08	.04
1136	Aloysius H. Simmons	.15	.11	.06
1137	George L. Earnshaw	.10	.08	.04
1138	George W. Haas	.10	.08	.04
1139	Edmund J. Miller	.10	.08	.04
1140	Robert M. Grove	.15	.11	.06
1141	John P. Boley	.10	.08	.04
1142	Edward T. Collins Sr.	.15	.11	.06
1143	Walter E. French	.10	.08	.04
1144	Donald E. McNair	.10	.08	.04
1145	William D. Shores	.10	.08	.04
1146	Gordon S. Cochrane	.15	.11	.06
1147	Homer W. Summa	.10	.08	.04
1148	John P. Quinn	.10	.08	.04
1149	Max F. Bishop	.10	.08	.04
1150	James J. Dykes	.10	.08	.04
1151	George E. Walberg	.10	.08	.04
1152	James E. Foxx	.15	.11	.06
1153	George H. Burns	.10	.08	.04
1154	Roger M. Cramer	.10	.08	.04
1155	Samuel D. Hale	.10	.08	.04
1156	Edwin A. Rommel	.10	.08	.04
1157	Ralph F. Perkins	.10	.08	.04
1158	James J. Cronin	.15	.11	.06
1159	Cornelios Mack	.15	.11	.06
1160	Raymond C. Kolp	.10	.08	.04
1161	Clyde J. Manion	.10	.08	.04
1162	Franklin T. Grube	.10	.08	.04
1163	Stephen A. Swetonic	.10	.08	.04
1164	Joseph B. Tinker	.15	.11	.06
1165	John J. Evers	.15	.11	.06
1166	Frank L. Chance	.15	.11	.06
1167	Emerson Dickman	.10	.08	.04
1168	John T. Tobin	.10	.08	.04
1169	Wesley C. Ferrell	.10	.08	.04
1170	Jay H. Dean	.15	.11	.06
1171	Tony & Al Cuccinello	.10	.08	.04
1172	Harry & Stan Coveleski	.10	.08	.04

1173	Bob & Roy Johnson	.10	.08	.04
1174	Andy & Hugh High	.10	.08	.04
1175	Joe & Luke Sewell	.10	.08	.04
1176	John & Joe Heving	.10	.08	.04
1177	Ab & Ivy Wingo	.10	.08	.04
1178	Wade & Bill Killefer	.10	.08	.04
1179	Bubbles & Pinky Hargrave	.10	.08	.04
1180	Paul G. & Lloyd Waner	.10	.08	.04
1181	John S. Vander Meer	.10	.08	.04
1182	Joe G. Moore	.10	.08	.04
1183	Robert J. Burke	.10	.08	.04
1184	John F. Moore	.10	.08	.04
1185	John J. Egan	.10	.08	.04
1186	Thomas H. Connolly	.15	.11	.06
1187	Frank H. O'Loughlin	.10	.08	.04
1188	John E. Reardon	.10	.08	.04
1189	Charles B. Moran	.10	.08	.04
1190	William J. Klem	.15	.11	.06
1191	Albert D. Stark	.10	.08	.04
1192	Albert L. Orth	.10	.08	.04
1193	William E. Bransfield	.10	.08	.04
1194	Roy Van Graflan	.10	.08	.04
1195	Eugene F. Hart	.10	.08	.04
1196	John B. Conlan	.15	.11	.06
1197	Ralph A. Pinelli	.10	.08	.04
1198	John F. Sheridan	.10	.08	.04
1199	Richard F. Nallin	.10	.08	.04
1200	William H. Dineen	.10	.08	.04
1201	Henry F. O'Day	.10	.08	.04
1202	Charles Rigler	.10	.08	.04
1203	Robert D. Emslie	.10	.08	.04
1204	Charles H. Pfirman	.10	.08	.04
1205	Harry C. Geisel	.10	.08	.04
1206	Ernest C. Quigley	.10	.08	.04
1207	Emmett T. Ormsby	.10	.08	.04
1208	George A. Hildebrand	.10	.08	.04
1209	George J. Moriarty	.10	.08	.04
1210	William G. Evans	.10	.08	.04
1211	Clarence B. Owens	.10	.08	.04
1212	William A. McGowan	.15	.11	.06
1213	Walter K. Higbe	.10	.08	.04
1214	Taylor L. Douthit	.10	.08	.04
1215	Delmar D. Baker	.10	.08	.04
1216	Albert W. Demaree	.10	.08	.04
1217	Cornelius Mack	.15	.11	.06
1218	Napoleon Lajoie	.15	.11	.06
1219	John P. Wagner	.15	.11	.06
1220	Christopher Mathewson	.15	.11	.06
1221	Samuel E. Crawford	.15	.11	.06
1222	Tristram E. Speaker	.15	.11	.06
1223	Grover C. Alexander	.15	.11	.06
1224	Joseph E. Bowman	.10	.08	.04
1225	John D. Rigney	.10	.08	.04
1226	William E. Webb	.10	.08	.04
1227	Lloyd A. Moore	.10	.08	.04
1228	Bruce D. Campbell	.10	.08	.04
1229	Luzerne A. Blue	.10	.08	.04
1230	Mark A. Koenig	.10	.08	.04
1231	Walter H. Schang	.10	.08	.04
1232	Max Carey	.15	.11	.06
1233	Frank F. Frisch	.15	.11	.06
1234	Owen J. Bush	.10	.08	.04
1235	Goerge S. Davis	.10	.08	.04
1236	William G. Rogell	.10	.08	.04
1237	James A. Collins	.15	.11	.06
1238	Mauricel L. Burrus	.10	.08	.04
1239	Ernest E. Swanson	.10	.08	.04
1240	Elwood G. English	.10	.08	.04
1241	Joseph Harris	.10	.08	.04
1242	Harry H. McCurdy	.10	.08	.04
1243	Richard W. Bartell	.10	.08	.04
1244	Rupert L. Thompson	.10	.08	.04
1245	Charles B. Adams	.10	.08	.04
1246	Arthur N. Nehf	.10	.08	.04
1247	John G. Graney	.10	.08	.04
1248	Theodore A. Lyons	.15	.11	.06
1249	Louis H. Gehrig	.40	.30	.15
1250	Michael F. Welch	.15	.11	.06
1251	Urban C. Faber	.15	.11	.06
1252	Joseph J. McGinnity	.15	.11	.06
1253	Rogers Hornsby	.15	.11	.06
1254	Melvin T. Ott	.15	.11	.06
1255	Walter P. Johnson	.15	.11	.06
1256	Edgar C. Rice	.15	.11	.06
1257	James A. Tobin	.10	.08	.04
1258	Roger T. Peckinpaugh	.10	.08	.04
1259	George T. Stovall	.10	.08	.04
1260	Fredrick C. Merkle	.10	.08	.04
1261	Harry W. Collins	.10	.08	.04
1262	Henry C. Lind	.10	.08	.04
1263	George N. Rucker	.10	.08	.04
1264	Hollis J. Thurston	.10	.08	.04
1265	Alexander Metzler	.10	.08	.04
1266	Charles Martin Conlon	.10	.08	.04
1267	McCarty gets Magee	.10	.08	.04
1268	Sliding Home	.10	.08	.04
1269	Kauff safe at 3rd	.10	.08	.04
1270	Groh out at 3rd	.10	.08	.04
1271	Mollwitz out at the plate	.10	.08	.04
1272	Burns safe at home	.10	.08	.04
1273	Lee Magee out stealing 3rd	.10	.08	.04
1274	Killefer out at plate	.10	.08	.04
1275	John M. Warhop	.10	.08	.04
1276	Emil J. Leonard	.10	.08	.04
1277	Alvin F. Crowder	.10	.08	.04
1278	Chester P. Laabs	.10	.08	.04
1279	Leslie A. Bush	.10	.08	.04
1280	Raymond B. Bressler	.10	.08	.04
1281	Robret M. Brown	.10	.08	.04
1282	Bernard Deviveiros	.10	.08	.04
1283	Leslie W. Tietje	.10	.08	.04
1284	Charles Devens	.10	.08	.04
1285	Elliott A. Bigelow	.10	.08	.04
1286	John O. Dickshot	.10	.08	.04
1287	Charles L. Chatham	.10	.08	.04
1288	Walter E. Beall	.10	.08	.04
1289	Richard D. Attreau	.10	.08	.04
1290	Anthony V. Brief	.10	.08	.04
1291	James J. Gleason	.10	.08	.04
1292	Walter D. Shaner	.10	.08	.04
1293	Clifford R. Crawford	.10	.08	.04
1294	Manuel Salvo	.10	.08	.04
1295	Calvin L. Dorsett	.10	.08	.04
1296	Russell D. Peters	.10	.08	.04
1297	John D. Couch	.10	.08	.04
1298	Frank W. Ulrich	.10	.08	.04
1299	James M. Bivin	.10	.08	.04
1300	Paul E. Strand	.10	.08	.04
1301	John Y. Lanning	.10	.08	.04
1302	William R. Brenzel	.10	.08	.04
1303	Don Songer	.10	.08	.04
1304	Emil H. Levsen	.10	.08	.04
1305	Otto A. Bluege	.10	.08	.04
1306	Fabian S. Gaffke	.10	.08	.04
1307	Maurice J. Archdeacon	.10	.08	.04
1308	James B. Chaplin	.10	.08	.04
1309	Lawrence J. Rosenthal	.10	.08	.04
1310	William M. Bagwell	.10	.08	.04
1311	Ralph F. Dawson	.10	.08	.04
1312	John P.J. Sturm	.10	.08	.04
1313	Haskell C. Billings	.10	.08	.04
1314	Vernon S. Wilshere	.10	.08	.04
1315	Robert A. Asbjornson	.10	.08	.04
1316	Henry J. Steinbacher	.10	.08	.04
1317	Stanwood F. Baumgartner	.10	.08	.04
1318	Checklist 991-1100	.10	.08	.04
1319	Checklist 1101-1210	.10	.08	.04
1320	Checklist 1211-1320	.10	.08	.04

1991 Country Hearth Mariners

This 29-card set was limited and cards were inserted in loaves of bread and also given away at a Mariner home game. The card fronts feature full-color glossy photos, while the flip sides feature statistics.

		MT	NR MT	EX
	Complete Set:	15.00	11.00	6.00
	Common Player:	.25	.20	.10
1	Jim Lefebvre	.25	.20	.10
2	Jeff Schaefer	.25	.20	.10
3	Harold Reynolds	.35	.25	.14
4	Greg Briley	.25	.20	.10
5	Scott Bradley	.25	.20	.10
6	Dave Valle	.25	.20	.10
7	Edgar Martinez	.50	.40	.20
8	Pete O'Brien	.25	.20	.10
9	Omar Vizquel	.35	.25	.14
10	Tino Martinez	.30	.25	.12
11	Scott Bankhead	.25	.20	.10
12	Bill Swift	.35	.25	.14
13	Jay Buhner	.45	.35	.20
14	Alvin Davis	.25	.20	.10
15	Ken Griffey, Jr.	6.00	4.50	2.50
16	Tracy Jones	.25	.20	.10
17	Brent Knackert	.25	.20	.10
18	Henry Cotto	.25	.20	.10
19	Ken Griffey, Sr.	.50	.40	.20
20	Keith Comstock	.25	.20	.10
21	Brian Holman	.30	.25	.12
22	Russ Swan	.25	.20	.10
23	Mike Jackson	.25	.20	.10
24	Erik Hanson	.30	.25	.12
25	Mike Schooler	.30	.25	.12
26	Randy Johnson	.60	.45	.25
27	Rich DeLucia	.25	.20	.10
28	The Griffey's	2.50	2.00	1.00
29	Mascot	.25	.20	.10

1910 Coupon Cigarettes Type 1 (T213)

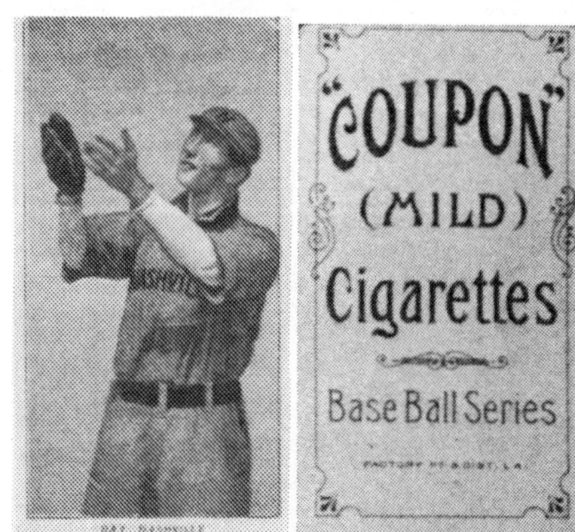

Because they feature the same photos used in the classic T206 tobacco set, some collectors fail to recognize the T213 Coupon set as a separate issue. Actually, the Coupon Cigarette cards make up three separate issues, produced from 1910 to 1919 and featuring a mix of players from the major leagues, the Federal League and the Southern League. While the fronts of the Coupon cards appear to be identical to the more popular T206 series, the backs clearly identify the cards as being a product of Coupon Cigarettes and allow the collector to easily differentiate between the three types. The Type I cards, produced in 1910, carry a general advertisement for Coupon "Mild" Cigarettes, while the Type II cards, issued from 1914 to 1916, contain the words "20 for 5 cents," and the Type III cards, issued in 1919, advertise "16 for 10 cts." Distribution of the Coupon cards was limited to the Louisiana area, making the set very obscure and difficult to checklist. Numerous variations further complicate the situation. To date, 68 different Type I cards have been found, 188 different Type II, and 69 Type III. Advanced collectors, however, speculate that more may exist. Type I cards are considered the rarest of the Coupon issues, and, because they were printed on a thinner stock, they are especially difficult to find in top condition. Although Type II cards are the most common, they were printed with a "glossy" coating, making them susceptible to cracking and creasing.

		NR MT	EX	VG
	Complete Set:	9000.	4500.	2750.
	Common Player:	80.00	40.00	24.00
(1)	Harry Bay	80.00	40.00	24.00
(2)	Beals Becker	80.00	40.00	24.00
(3)	Chief Bender	250.00	125.00	75.00
(4)	Bernhard	80.00	40.00	24.00
(5)	Ted Breitenstein	80.00	40.00	24.00
(6)	Bobby Byrne	80.00	40.00	24.00
(7)	Billy Campbell	80.00	40.00	24.00
(8)	Scoops Carey	250.00	125.00	75.00
(9)	Frank Chance	250.00	125.00	75.00
(10)	Chappy Charles	80.00	40.00	24.00
(11)	Hal Chase (portrait)	125.00	62.00	37.00
(12)	Hal Chase (throwing)	125.00	62.00	37.00
(13)	Ty Cobb	2000.	1000.	600.00
(14)	Bill Cranston	80.00	40.00	24.00
(15)	Birdie Cree	80.00	40.00	24.00
(16)	Wild Bill Donovan	80.00	40.00	24.00
(17)	Mickey Doolan	80.00	40.00	24.00
(18)	Jean Dubuc	80.00	40.00	24.00
(19)	Joe Dunn	80.00	40.00	24.00
(20)	Roy Ellam	80.00	40.00	24.00
(21)	Clyde Engle	80.00	40.00	24.00
(22)	Johnny Evers	250.00	125.00	75.00
(23)	Art Fletcher	80.00	40.00	24.00
(24)	Charlie Fritz	80.00	40.00	24.00
(25)	Ed Greminger	80.00	40.00	24.00
(26)	Bill Hart (Little Rock)	80.00	40.00	24.00
(27)	Jimmy Hart (Montgomery)	80.00	40.00	24.00
(28)	Topsy Hartsel	80.00	40.00	24.00
(29)	Gordon Hickman	80.00	40.00	24.00
(30)	Danny Hoffman	80.00	40.00	24.00
(31)	Harry Howell	80.00	40.00	24.00
(32)	Miller Huggins (hands at mouth)	250.00	125.00	75.00
(33)	Miller Huggins (portrait)	250.00	125.00	75.00
(34)	George Hunter	80.00	40.00	24.00
(35)	A.O. "Dutch" Jordan	80.00	40.00	24.00
(36)	Ed Killian	80.00	40.00	24.00
(37)	Otto Knabe	80.00	40.00	24.00
(38)	Frank LaPorte	80.00	40.00	24.00
(39)	Ed Lennox	80.00	40.00	24.00
(40)	Harry Lentz (Sentz)	80.00	40.00	24.00
(41)	Rube Marquard	250.00	125.00	75.00
(42)	Doc Marshall	80.00	40.00	24.00
(43)	Christy Mathewson	750.00	375.00	225.00
(44)	George McBride	80.00	40.00	24.00
(45)	Pryor McElveen	80.00	40.00	24.00
(46)	Matty McIntyre	80.00	40.00	24.00
(47)	Mike Mitchell	80.00	40.00	24.00
(48)	Carlton Molesworth	80.00	40.00	24.00
(49)	Mike Mowrey	80.00	40.00	24.00
(50)	Chief Myers (Meyers) (batting)	80.00	40.00	24.00
(51)	Chief Myers (Meyers) (fielding)	80.00	40.00	24.00
(52)	Dode Paskert	80.00	40.00	24.00
(53)	Hub Perdue	80.00	40.00	24.00
(54)	Arch Persons	80.00	40.00	24.00
(55)	Ed Reagan	80.00	40.00	24.00
(56)	Bob Rhoades (Rhoads)	80.00	40.00	24.00
(57)	Ike Rockenfeld	80.00	40.00	24.00
(58)	Claude Rossman	80.00	40.00	24.00
(59)	Boss Schmidt	80.00	40.00	24.00
(60)	Sid Smith	80.00	40.00	24.00
(61)	Charlie Starr	80.00	40.00	24.00
(62)	Gabby Street	80.00	40.00	24.00
(63)	Ed Summers	80.00	40.00	24.00
(64)	Jeff Sweeney	80.00	40.00	24.00
(65)	Ira Thomas	80.00	40.00	24.00
(66)	Woodie Thornton	80.00	40.00	24.00
(67)	Ed Willett	80.00	40.00	24.00
(68)	Owen Wilson	80.00	40.00	24.00

Values quoted in this guide reflect the retail price of a card – the price a collector can expect to pay when buying a card from a dealer. The wholesale price – that which a collector can expect to receive from a dealer when selling cards – will be significantly lower, depending on desirability and condition.

1914 Coupon Cigarettes Type 2 (T213)

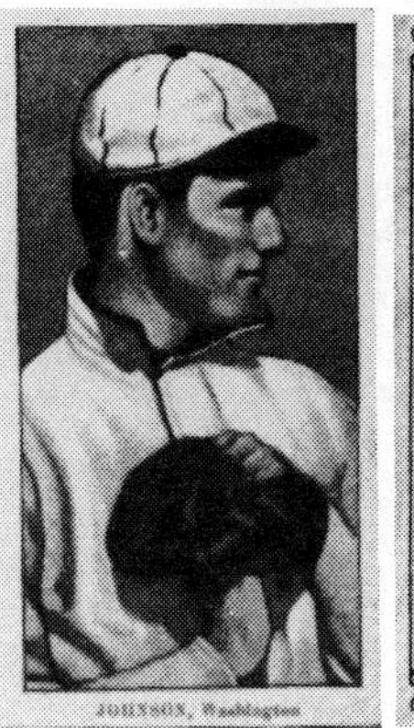

		NR MT	EX	VG
	Complete Set:	14000.	7000.	4200.
	Common Player:	75.00	37.00	22.00
(1a)	Red Ames (Cincinnati)	75.00	37.00	22.00
(1b)	Red Ames (St. Louis)	75.00	37.00	22.00
(2a)	Home Run Baker (Phila. Amer.)	175.00	87.00	52.00
(2b)	Home Run Baker (Philadelphia Amer.)	175.00	87.00	52.00
(2c)	Home Run Baker (New York)	175.00	87.00	52.00
(3)	Cy Barger	75.00	37.00	22.00
(4a)	Chief Bender (trees in background, Philadelphia Amer.)	175.00	87.00	52.00
(4b)	Chief Bender (trees in background, Baltimore)	175.00	87.00	52.00
(4c)	Chief Bender (trees in background, Philadelphia Nat.)	175.00	87.00	52.00
(5a)	Chief Bender (no trees in background, Philadelphia Amer.)	175.00	87.00	52.00
(5b)	Chief Bender (no trees in background, Baltimore)	175.00	87.00	52.00
(5c)	Chief Bender (no trees in background, Philadelphia Nat.)	175.00	87.00	52.00
(6)	Bill Bradley	75.00	37.00	22.00
(7a)	Roger Bresnahan (Chicago)	175.00	87.00	52.00
(7b)	Roger Bresnahan (Toledo)	175.00	87.00	52.00
(8a)	Al Bridwell (St. Louis)	75.00	37.00	22.00
(8b)	Al Bridwell (Nashville)	75.00	37.00	22.00
(9a)	Mordecai Brown (Chicago)	175.00	87.00	52.00
(9b)	Mordecai Brown (St. Louis)	175.00	87.00	52.00
(10)	Bobby Byrne	75.00	37.00	22.00
(11)	Howie Camnitz (arm at side)	75.00	37.00	22.00
(12a)	Howie Camnitz (Pittsburgh, hands above head)	75.00	37.00	22.00
(12b)	Howie Camnitz (Savannah, hands above head)	75.00	37.00	22.00
(13)	Billy Campbell	75.00	37.00	22.00
(14a)	Frank Chance (batting, New York)	175.00	87.00	52.00
(14b)	Frank Chance (Los Angeles, batting)	175.00	87.00	52.00
(15a)	Frank Chance (New York, portrait)	175.00	87.00	52.00
(15b)	Frank Chance (Los Angeles, portrait)	175.00	87.00	52.00
(16a)	Bill Chapelle (Brooklyn, "R" on shirt)	75.00	37.00	22.00
(16b)	Larry Chapelle (Chappel) (Cleveland, no "R" on shirt, photo actually Bill Chapelle)	75.00	37.00	22.00
(17a)	Hal Chase (Chicago, holding trophy)	90.00	45.00	27.00
(17b)	Hal Chase (Buffalo, holding trophy)	90.00	45.00	27.00
(18a)	Hal Chase (Chicago, portrait, blue background)	90.00	45.00	27.00
(18b)	Hal Chase (Buffalo, portrait, blue background)	90.00	45.00	27.00
(19a)	Hal Chase (Chicago, throwing)	90.00	45.00	27.00
(19b)	Hal Chase (Buffalo, throwing)	90.00	45.00	27.00
(20)	Ty Cobb (portrait)	900.00	450.00	270.00
(21)	Ty Cobb (with bat off shoulder)	900.00	450.00	270.00
(22a)	Eddie Collins (Philadelphia, "A" on shirt)	175.00	87.00	52.00
(22b)	Eddie Collins (Chicago, "A" on shirt)	175.00	87.00	52.00
(22c)	Eddie Collins (Chicago, no "A" on shirt)	175.00	87.00	52.00
(23a)	Doc Crandall (St. Louis Nat.)	75.00	37.00	22.00
(23b)	Doc Crandall (St. Louis Fed.)	75.00	37.00	22.00
(24)	Sam Crawford	175.00	87.00	52.00
(25)	Birdie Cree	75.00	37.00	22.00
(26a)	Harry Davis (Phila. Amer.)	75.00	37.00	22.00
(26b)	Harry Davis (Philadelphia Amer.)	75.00	37.00	22.00
(27a)	Ray Demmitt (New York)	75.00	37.00	22.00
27b	Ray Demmitt (Chicago)	75.00	37.00	22.00
(28a)	Josh Devore (Philadelphia)	75.00	37.00	22.00
(28b)	Josh Devore (Chillicothe)	75.00	37.00	22.00
(29a)	Mike Donlin (New York)	75.00	37.00	22.00
(29b)	Mike Donlin (.300 batter 7 years)	75.00	37.00	22.00
(30)	Wild Bill Donovan	75.00	37.00	22.00
(31a)	Mickey Doolan (Baltimore, batting)	75.00	37.00	22.00
(31b)	Mickey Doolan (Chicago, batting)	75.00	37.00	22.00
(32a)	Mickey Doolan (Baltimore, fielding)	75.00	37.00	22.00
(32b)	Mickey Doolan (Chicago, fielding)	75.00	37.00	22.00
(33)	Tom Downey	75.00	37.00	22.00
(34)	Larry Doyle (batting)	75.00	37.00	22.00
(35)	Larry Doyle (portrait)	75.00	37.00	22.00
(36)	Jean Dubuc	75.00	37.00	22.00
(37)	Jack Dunn	75.00	37.00	22.00
(38a)	Kid Elberfield (Elberfeld) (Brooklyn)	75.00	37.00	22.00
(38b)	Kid Elberfield (Elberfeld) (Chatanooga)	75.00	37.00	22.00
(39)	Steve Evans	75.00	37.00	22.00
(40)	Johnny Evers	175.00	87.00	52.00
(41)	Russ Ford	75.00	37.00	22.00
(42)	Art Fromme	75.00	37.00	22.00
(43a)	Chick Gandil (Washington)	90.00	45.00	27.00
(43b)	Chick Gandil (Cleveland)	90.00	45.00	27.00
(44)	Rube Geyer	75.00	37.00	22.00
(45)	Clark Griffith	175.00	87.00	52.00
(46)	Bob Groom	75.00	37.00	22.00
(47a)	Buck Herzog ("B" on shirt)	75.00	37.00	22.00
(47b)	Buck Herzog (no "B" on shirt)	75.00	37.00	22.00
(48a)	Dick Hoblitzell (Cincinnati)	75.00	37.00	22.00
(48b)	Dick Hoblitzell (Boston Nat.)	75.00	37.00	22.00
(48c)	Dick Hoblitzell (Boston Amer.)	75.00	37.00	22.00
(49a)	Solly Hofman	75.00	37.00	22.00
(49b)	Solly Hofmann (Hofman)	75.00	37.00	22.00
(50)	Miller Huggins (hands at mouth)	175.00	87.00	52.00
(51)	Miller Huggins (portrait)	175.00	87.00	52.00
(52a)	John Hummel (Brooklyn Nat.)	75.00	37.00	22.00
(52b)	John Hummel (Brooklyn)	75.00	37.00	22.00
(53)	Hughie Jennings (both hands showing)	175.00	87.00	52.00
(54)	Hughie Jennings (one hand showing)	175.00	87.00	52.00
(55)	Walter Johnson	750.00	375.00	225.00
(56a)	Tim Jordan (Toronto)	75.00	37.00	22.00
(56b)	Tim Jordan (Ft. Worth)	75.00	37.00	22.00
(57a)	Joe Kelley (New York)	175.00	87.00	52.00
(57b)	Joe Kelley (Toronto)	175.00	87.00	52.00
(58)	Otto Knabe	75.00	37.00	22.00
(59a)	Ed Konetchy (Pittsburgh Nat.)	75.00	37.00	22.00
(59b)	Ed Konetchy (Pittsburgh Fed.)	75.00	37.00	22.00
(59c)	Ed Konetchy (Boston)	75.00	37.00	22.00
(60)	Harry Krause	75.00	37.00	22.00
(61a)	Nap Lajoie (Phila. Amer.)	250.00	125.00	75.00
(61b)	Nap Lajoie (Philadelphia Amer.)	250.00	125.00	75.00
(61c)	Nap Lajoie (Cleveland)	250.00	125.00	75.00
(62a)	Tommy Leach (Chicago)	75.00	37.00	22.00
(62b)	Tommy Leach (Cincinnati)	75.00	37.00	22.00
(62c)	Tommy Leach (Rochester)	75.00	37.00	22.00
(63)	Ed Lennox	75.00	37.00	22.00
(64a)	Sherry Magee (Phila. Nat.)	75.00	37.00	22.00
(64b)	Sherry Magee (Philadelphia Nat.)	75.00	37.00	22.00
(64c)	Sherry Magee (Boston)	75.00	37.00	22.00
(65a)	Rube Marquard (New York, pitching, "NY" on shirt)	175.00	87.00	52.00
(65b)	Rube Marquard (Brooklyn, pitching, no "NY" on shirt)	175.00	87.00	52.00
(66a)	Rube Marquard (New York, portrait, "NY" on shirt)	175.00	87.00	52.00
(66b)	Rube Marquard (Brooklyn, portrait, no "NY" on shirt)	175.00	87.00	52.00
(67)	Christy Mathewson	750.00	375.00	225.00
(68)	John McGraw (glove at side)	175.00	87.00	52.00
(69)	John McGraw (portrait)	175.00	87.00	52.00
(70)	Larry McLean	75.00	37.00	22.00
(71a)	George McQuillan (Pittsburgh)	75.00	37.00	22.00
(71b)	George McQuillan (Phila. Nat.)	75.00	37.00	22.00
(72c)	George McQuillan (Philadelphia Nat.)	75.00	37.00	22.00
(73)	Fred Merkle	90.00	45.00	27.00
(74a)	Chief Meyers (New York, fielding)	75.00	37.00	22.00
(74b)	Chief Meyers (Brooklyn, fielding)	75.00	37.00	22.00
(75a)	Chief Meyers (New York, portrait)	75.00	37.00	22.00
(75b)	Chief Meyers (Brooklyn, portrait)	75.00	37.00	22.00
(76)	Dots Miller	75.00	37.00	22.00
(77)	Mike Mitchell	75.00	37.00	22.00
(78a)	Mike Mowrey (Pittsburgh Nat.)	75.00	37.00	22.00
(78b)	Mike Mowrey (Pittsburgh Fed.)	75.00	37.00	22.00
(78c)	Mike Mowrey (Brooklyn)	75.00	37.00	22.00
(79a)	George Mullin (Indianapolis)	75.00	37.00	22.00
(79b)	George Mullin (Newark)	75.00	37.00	22.00
(80)	Danny Murphy	75.00	37.00	22.00
(81a)	Red Murray (New York)	75.00	37.00	22.00
(81b)	Red Murray (Chicago)	75.00	37.00	22.00
(81c)	Red Murray (Kansas City)	75.00	37.00	22.00
(82)	Tom Needham	75.00	37.00	22.00
(83)	Rebel Oakes	75.00	37.00	22.00
(84a)	Rube Oldring (Phila. Amer.)	75.00	37.00	22.00
(84b)	Rube Oldring (Philadelphia Amer.)	75.00	37.00	22.00
(85a)	Dode Paskert (Phila. Nat.)	75.00	37.00	22.00
(85b)	Dode Paskert (Philadelphia Nat.)	75.00	37.00	22.00
(86)	Billy Purtell	75.00	37.00	22.00
(87a)	Jack Quinn (Baltimore)	75.00	37.00	22.00
(87b)	Jack Quinn (Vernon)	75.00	37.00	22.00
(88a)	Ed Reulbach (Brooklyn Nat.)	75.00	37.00	22.00
(88b)	Ed Reulbach (Brooklyn Fed.)	75.00	37.00	22.00
(88c)	Ed Reulbach (Pittsburgh)	75.00	37.00	22.00
(89a)	Nap Rucker (Brooklyn)	75.00	37.00	22.00
(89b)	Nap Rucker (Brooklyn Nat.)	75.00	37.00	22.00
(90)	Dick Rudolph	75.00	37.00	22.00
(91a)	Germany Schaefer (Washington, "W" on shirt)	75.00	37.00	22.00
(91b)	Germany Schaefer (K.C. Fed., "W" on shirt)	75.00	37.00	22.00
(91c)	Germany Schaefer (New York, no "W" on shirt)	75.00	37.00	22.00
(92)	Admiral Schlei (batting)	75.00	37.00	22.00
(93)	Admiral Schlei (portrait)	75.00	37.00	22.00
(94)	Boss Schmidt	75.00	37.00	22.00
(95)	Wildfire Schulte	75.00	37.00	22.00
(96)	Frank Smith	75.00	37.00	22.00
(97)	Tris Speaker	350.00	175.00	105.00
(98)	George Stovall	75.00	37.00	22.00
(99)	Gabby Street (catching)	75.00	37.00	22.00
(100)	Gabby Street (portrait)	75.00	37.00	22.00
(101)	Ed Summers	75.00	37.00	22.00
(102a)	Bill Sweeney (Boston)	75.00	37.00	22.00
(102b)	Bill Sweeney (Chicago)	75.00	37.00	22.00
(103a)	Jeff Sweeney (New York)	75.00	37.00	22.00
(103b)	Jeff Sweeney (Richmond)	75.00	37.00	22.00
(104a)	Ira Thomas (Phila. Amer.)	75.00	37.00	22.00
(104b)	Ira Thomas (Philadelphia Amer.)	75.00	37.00	22.00
(105a)	Joe Tinker (Chicago Fed., bat off shoulder)	175.00	87.00	52.00
(105b)	Joe Tinker (Chicago Nat., bat on shoulder)	175.00	87.00	52.00
(106a)	Joe Tinker (Chicago Fed., bat off shoulder)	175.00	87.00	52.00
(106b)	Joe Tinker (Chicago Nat., bat off shoulder)	175.00	87.00	52.00
(107)	Heinie Wagner	75.00	37.00	22.00
(108a)	Jack Warhop (New York, "NY" on shirt)	75.00	37.00	22.00
(108b)	Jack Warhop (St. Louis, no "NY" om shirt)	75.00	37.00	22.00
(109a)	Zach Wheat (Brooklyn)	175.00	87.00	52.00
(109b)	Zach Wheat (Brooklyn Nat.)	175.00	87.00	52.00
(110)	Kaiser Wilhelm	75.00	37.00	22.00
(111a)	Ed Willett (St. Louis)	75.00	37.00	22.00
(111b)	Ed Willett (Memphis)	75.00	37.00	22.00
(112)	Owen Wilson	75.00	37.00	22.00
(113a)	Hooks Wiltse (New York, pitching)	75.00	37.00	22.00
(113b)	Hooks Wiltse (Brooklyn, pitching)	75.00	37.00	22.00
(113c)	Hooks Wiltse (Jersey City, pitching)	75.00	37.00	22.00
(114a)	Hooks Wiltse (New York, portrait)	75.00	37.00	22.00
(114b)	Hooks Wiltse (Brooklyn, portrait)	75.00	37.00	22.00
(114c)	Hooks Wiltse (Jersey City, portrait)	75.00	37.00	22.00
(115)	Heinie Zimmerman	75.00	37.00	22.00

1919 Coupon Cigarettes Type 3 (T213)

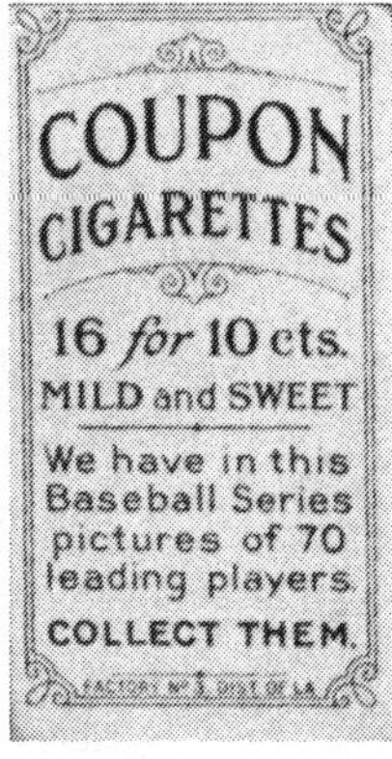

		NR MT	EX	VG
	Complete Set:	13750.	6875.	4100.
	Common Player:	120.00	60.00	36.00
(1)	Red Ames	120.00	60.00	36.00
(2)	Home Run Baker	275.00	137.00	82.00
(3)	Chief Bender (no trees in background)	275.00	137.00	82.00
(4)	Chief Bender (trees in background)	275.00	137.00	82.00
(5)	Roger Bresnahan	275.00	137.00	82.00
(6)	Al Bridwell	120.00	60.00	36.00
(7)	Miner Brown	275.00	137.00	82.00
(8)	Bobby Byrne	120.00	60.00	36.00
(9)	Frank Chance (batting)	275.00	137.00	82.00
(10)	Frank Chance (portrait)	275.00	137.00	82.00
(11)	Hal Chase (holding trophy)	135.00	67.00	40.00
(12)	Hal Chase (portrait)	135.00	67.00	40.00
(13)	Hal Chase (throwing)	135.00	67.00	40.00
(14)	Ty Cobb (batting)	2000.	1000.	600.00
(15)	Ty Cobb (portrait)	2000.	1000.	600.00
(16)	Eddie Collins	275.00	137.00	82.00
(17)	Sam Crawford	275.00	137.00	82.00
(18)	Harry Davis	120.00	60.00	36.00
(19)	Mike Donlin	120.00	60.00	36.00
(20)	Wild Bill Donovan	120.00	60.00	36.00
(21)	Mickey Doolan (batting)	120.00	60.00	36.00
(22)	Mickey Doolan (fielding)	120.00	60.00	36.00
(23)	Larry Doyle (batting)	120.00	60.00	36.00
(24)	Larry Doyle (portrait)	120.00	60.00	36.00
(25)	Jean Dubuc	120.00	60.00	36.00
(26)	Jack Dunn	120.00	60.00	36.00
(27)	Kid Elberfeld	120.00	60.00	36.00
(28)	Johnny Evers	275.00	137.00	82.00
(29)	Chick Gandil	135.00	67.00	40.00

(30)	Clark Griffith	275.00	137.00	82.00
(31)	Buck Herzog	120.00	60.00	36.00
(32)	Dick Hoblitzell	120.00	60.00	36.00
(33)	Miller Huggins (hands at mouth)	275.00	137.00	82.00
(34)	Miller Huggins (portrait)	275.00	137.00	82.00
(35)	John Hummel	120.00	60.00	36.00
(36)	Hughie Jennings (both hands showing)	275.00	137.00	82.00
(37)	Hughie Jennings (one hand showing)	275.00	137.00	82.00
(38)	Walter Johnson	800.00	400.00	240.00
(39)	Tim Jordan	120.00	60.00	36.00
(40)	Joe Kelley	275.00	137.00	82.00
(41)	Ed Konetchy	120.00	60.00	36.00
(42)	Larry Lajoie	275.00	137.00	82.00
(43)	Sherry Magee	125.00	62.00	37.00
(44)	Rube Marquard	275.00	137.00	82.00
(45)	Christy Mathewson	800.00	400.00	240.00
(47)	John McGraw (glove at side)	275.00	137.00	82.00
(48)	John McGraw (portrait)	275.00	137.00	82.00
(49)	George McQuillan	120.00	60.00	36.00
(50)	Fred Merkle	125.00	62.00	37.00
(51)	Dots Miller	120.00	60.00	36.00
(52)	Mike Mowrey	120.00	60.00	36.00
(53)	Chief Myers (Meyers) (Brooklyn)	120.00	60.00	36.00
(54)	Chief Myers (Meyers) (New Haven)	120.00	60.00	36.00
(55)	Dode Paskert	120.00	60.00	36.00
(56)	Jack Quinn	120.00	60.00	36.00
(57)	Ed Reulbach	120.00	60.00	36.00
(58)	Nap Rucker	120.00	60.00	36.00
(59)	Dick Rudolph	120.00	60.00	36.00
(60)	Herman Schaeffer (Schaefer)	120.00	60.00	36.00
(61)	Wildfire Schulte	120.00	60.00	36.00
(62)	Tris Speaker	450.00	225.00	135.00
(63)	Gabby Street (catching)	120.00	60.00	36.00
(64)	Gabby Street (portrait)	120.00	60.00	36.00
(65)	Jeff Sweeney	120.00	60.00	36.00
(66)	Ira Thomas	120.00	60.00	36.00
(67)	Joe Tinker	275.00	137.00	82.00
(68)	Zach Wheat	275.00	137.00	82.00
(69)	Geo. Wiltse	120.00	60.00	36.00
(70)	Heinie Zimmerman	120.00	60.00	36.00

1914 Cracker Jack

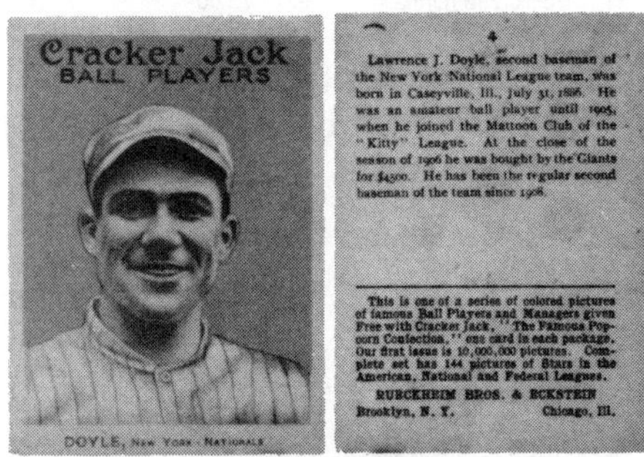

4

Lawrence J. Doyle, second baseman of the New York National League team, was born in Caseyville, Ill., July 31, 1886. He was an amateur ball player until 1905, when he joined the Mattoon Club of the "Kitty" League. At the close of the season of 1906 he was bought by the Giants for $4500. He has been the regular second baseman of the team since 1908.

This is one of a series of colored pictures of famous Ball Players and Managers given Free with Cracker Jack, "The Famous Popcorn Confection," one card in each package. Our first issue is 10,000,000 pictures. Complete set has 144 pictures of Stars in the American, National and Federal Leagues.

RUECKHEIM BROS. & ECKSTEIN
Brooklyn, N. Y. Chicago, Ill.

The 1914 Cracker Jack set, whose ACC designation is E145-1, is one of the most popular of the "E" card sets and features baseball stars from the American, National and Federal Leagues. The cards, which measure 2-1/4" by 3" and are printed on thin stock, were found in boxes of Cracker Jack. The 1914 issue consists of 144 cards with tinted color photographs on a red background. The numbered backs feature a short biography plus an advertisement. The advertising on the low-numbered cards in the set indicate that 10 million cards were issued, while the high-numbered cards boast that 15 million were printed.

		NR MT	EX	VG
Complete set (144):		70000.	25200.	15400.
Common player:		200.00	72.00	44.00
1	Otto Knabe	750.00	270.00	165.00
2	Home Run Baker	900.00	324.00	198.00
3	Joe Tinker	700.00	252.00	154.00
4	Larry Doyle	200.00	72.00	44.00
5	Ward Miller	200.00	72.00	44.00
6	Eddie Plank	1000.	360.00	220.00
7	Eddie Collins	650.00	234.00	143.00
8	Rube Oldring	200.00	72.00	44.00
9	Artie Hoffman (Hofman)	200.00	72.00	44.00
10	Stuffy McInnis	200.00	72.00	44.00
11	George Stovall	200.00	72.00	44.00
12	Connie Mack	700.00	252.00	154.00
13	Art Wilson	200.00	72.00	44.00
14	Sam Crawford	400.00	144.00	88.00
15	Reb Russell	200.00	72.00	44.00
16	Howie Camnitz	200.00	72.00	44.00
17a	Roger Bresnahan (no number on back)	600.00	216.00	132.00
17b	Roger Bresnahan (number on back)	600.00	216.00	132.00
18	Johnny Evers	550.00	198.00	121.00
19	Chief Bender	600.00	216.00	132.00
20	Cy Falkenberg	200.00	72.00	44.00
21	Heinie Zimmerman	200.00	72.00	44.00
22	Smoky Joe Wood	200.00	72.00	44.00
23	Charles Comiskey	600.00	216.00	132.00
24	George Mullen (Mullin)	200.00	72.00	44.00
25	Mike Simon	200.00	72.00	44.00
26	Jim Scott	200.00	72.00	44.00
27	Bill Carrigan	200.00	72.00	44.00
28	Jack Barry	200.00	72.00	44.00
29	Vean Gregg	200.00	72.00	44.00
30	Ty Cobb	6500.	2340.	1430.
31	Heinie Wagner	200.00	72.00	44.00
32	Mordecai Brown	500.00	180.00	110.00
33	Amos Strunk	200.00	72.00	44.00
34	Ira Thomas	200.00	72.00	44.00
35	Harry Hooper	550.00	198.00	121.00
36	Ed Walsh	600.00	216.00	132.00
37	Grover C. Alexander	800.00	288.00	176.00
38	Red Dooin	200.00	72.00	44.00
39	Chick Gandil	200.00	72.00	44.00
40	Jimmy Austin	200.00	72.00	44.00
41	Tommy Leach	200.00	72.00	44.00
42	Al Bridwell	200.00	72.00	44.00
43	Rube Marquard	550.00	198.00	121.00
44	Jeff Tesreau	200.00	72.00	44.00
45	Fred Luderus	200.00	72.00	44.00
46	Bob Groom	200.00	72.00	44.00
47	Josh Devore	200.00	72.00	44.00
48	Harry Lord	375.00	135.00	82.00
49	Dots Miller	200.00	72.00	44.00
50	John Hummell (Hummel)	200.00	72.00	44.00
51	Nap Rucker	200.00	72.00	44.00
52	Zach Wheat	550.00	198.00	121.00
53	Otto Miller	200.00	72.00	44.00
54	Marty O'Toole	200.00	72.00	44.00
55	Dick Hoblitzel (Hoblitzell)	200.00	72.00	44.00
56	Clyde Milan	200.00	72.00	44.00
57	Walter Johnson	2500.	900.00	550.00
58	Wally Schang	200.00	72.00	44.00
59	Doc Gessler	200.00	72.00	44.00
60	Rollie Zeider	500.00	180.00	110.00
61	Ray Schalk	500.00	180.00	110.00
62	Jay Cashion	500.00	180.00	110.00
63	Babe Adams	200.00	72.00	44.00
64	Jimmy Archer	200.00	72.00	44.00
65	Tris Speaker	1000.	360.00	220.00
66	Nap Lajoie	1250.	450.00	275.00
67	Doc Crandall	200.00	72.00	44.00
68	Honus Wagner	3000.	1080.	660.00
69	John McGraw	900.00	324.00	198.00
70	Fred Clarke	450.00	162.00	99.00
71	Chief Meyers	200.00	72.00	44.00
72	Joe Boehling	200.00	72.00	44.00
73	Max Carey	400.00	144.00	88.00
74	Frank Owens	200.00	72.00	44.00
75	Miller Huggins	500.00	180.00	110.00
76	Claude Hendrix	200.00	72.00	44.00
77	Hughie Jennings	550.00	198.00	121.00
78	Fred Merkle	200.00	72.00	44.00
79	Ping Bodie	200.00	72.00	44.00
80	Ed Reulbach	200.00	72.00	44.00
81	Jim Delehanty (Delahanty)	200.00	72.00	44.00
82	Gavvy Cravath	200.00	72.00	44.00
83	Russ Ford	200.00	72.00	44.00
84	Elmer Knetzer	200.00	72.00	44.00
85	Buck Herzog	200.00	72.00	44.00
86	Burt Shotten	200.00	72.00	44.00
87	Hick Cady	200.00	72.00	44.00
88	Christy Mathewson	2400.	864.00	528.00
89	Larry Cheney	200.00	72.00	44.00
90	Frank Smith	200.00	72.00	44.00
91	Roger Peckinpaugh	200.00	72.00	44.00
92	Al Demaree	200.00	72.00	44.00
93	Del Pratt	600.00	216.00	132.00
94	Eddie Cicotte	275.00	99.00	60.00
95	Ray Keating	200.00	72.00	44.00
96	Beals Becker	200.00	72.00	44.00
97	Rube Benton	200.00	72.00	44.00
98	Frank Laporte (LaPorte)	200.00	72.00	44.00
99	Frank Chance	1900.	684.00	418.00
100	Tom Seaton	200.00	72.00	44.00
101	Wildfire Schulte	200.00	72.00	44.00
102	Ray Fisher	200.00	72.00	44.00
103	Shoeless Joe Jackson	12000.	4320.	2640.
104	Vic Saier	200.00	72.00	44.00
105	Jimmy Lavender	200.00	72.00	44.00
106	Joe Birmingham	200.00	72.00	44.00
107	Tom Downey	200.00	72.00	44.00
108	Sherry Magee	200.00	72.00	44.00
109	Fred Blanding	200.00	72.00	44.00
110	Bob Bescher	200.00	72.00	44.00
111	Nixey Callahan	600.00	216.00	132.00
112	Jeff Sweeney	200.00	72.00	44.00
113	George Suggs	200.00	72.00	44.00
114	George Moriarity (Moriarty)	200.00	72.00	44.00
115	Ad Brennan	200.00	72.00	44.00
116	Rollie Zeider	200.00	72.00	44.00
117	Ted Easterly	200.00	72.00	44.00
118	Ed Konetchy	200.00	72.00	44.00
119	George Perring	200.00	72.00	44.00
120	Mickey Doolan	200.00	72.00	44.00
121	Hub Perdue	200.00	72.00	44.00
122	Donie Bush	200.00	72.00	44.00
123	Slim Sallee	200.00	72.00	44.00
124	Earle Moore (Earl)	200.00	72.00	44.00
125	Bert Niehoff	200.00	72.00	44.00
126	Walter Blair	200.00	72.00	44.00
127	Butch Schmidt	200.00	72.00	44.00
128	Steve Evans	200.00	72.00	44.00
129	Ray Caldwell	200.00	72.00	44.00
130	Ivy Wingo	200.00	72.00	44.00
131	George Baumgardner	200.00	72.00	44.00
132	Les Nunamaker	200.00	72.00	44.00
133	Branch Rickey	600.00	216.00	132.00
134	Armando Marsans	200.00	72.00	44.00
135	Bill Killifer (Killefer)	200.00	72.00	44.00
136	Rabbit Maranville	450.00	162.00	99.00
137	Bill Rariden	200.00	72.00	44.00
138	Hank Gowdy	200.00	72.00	44.00
139	Rebel Oakes	200.00	72.00	44.00
140	Danny Murphy	200.00	72.00	44.00
141	Cy Barger	200.00	72.00	44.00
142	Gene Packard	200.00	72.00	44.00
143	Jake Daubert	200.00	72.00	44.00
144	Jimmy Walsh	500.00	180.00	110.00

1915 Cracker Jack

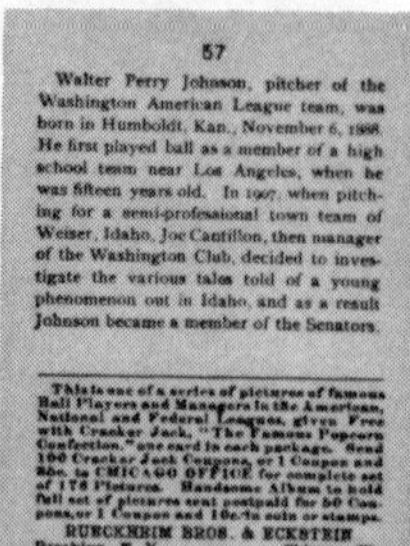

57

Walter Perry Johnson, pitcher of the Washington American League team, was born in Humboldt, Kan., November 6, 1888. He first played ball as a member of a high school team near Los Angeles, when he was fifteen years old. In 1907, when pitching for a semi-professional town team of Weiser, Idaho, Joe Cantillon, then manager of the Washington Club, decided to investigate the various tales told of a young phenomenon out in Idaho, and as a result Johnson became a member of the Senators.

This is one of a series of pictures of famous Ball Players and Managers in the American, National and Federal Leagues, given Free with Cracker Jack, "The Famous Popcorn Confection," one card in each package. Send 100 Cracker Jack Coupons, or 1 Coupon and 25c. to CHICAGO OFFICE for complete set of 176 Pictures. Handsome Album to hold full set of pictures sent postpaid for 50 Coupons, or 1 Coupon and 10c. in coin or stamps.

RUECKHEIM BROS. & ECKSTEIN
Brooklyn, N. Y. Chicago, Ill.

The 1915 Cracker Jack set (E145-2) is a reissue of the 1914 edition with some card additions and deletions, team designation changes, and new poses. A total of 176 cards comprise the set. The deletions involve card #'s 48, 60, 62, 99 and 111. Cards can be distinguished as either 1914 or 1915 by the backs. The advertising on the backs of the 1914 cards call the set complete at 144 pictures, while the 1915 version notes 176 pictures. A complete set and an album were available from the company.

		NR MT	EX	VG
Complete set (176):		60000.	33600.	20400.
Common player: 1-144		125.00	70.00	42.00
Common player: 145-176		160.00	90.00	54.00
1	Otto Knabe	500.00	225.00	100.00
2	Home Run Baker	700.00	390.00	290.00
3	Joe Tinker	600.00	336.00	204.00
4	Larry Doyle	125.00	70.00	42.00
5	Ward Miller	125.00	70.00	42.00
6	Eddie Plank	600.00	335.00	200.00
7	Eddie Collins	550.00	308.00	187.00
8	Rube Oldring	125.00	70.00	42.00
9	Artie Hoffman (Hofman)	125.00	70.00	42.00
10	Stuffy McInnis	125.00	70.00	42.00
11	George Stovall	125.00	70.00	42.00
12	Connie Mack	500.00	280.00	170.00
13	Art Wilson	125.00	70.00	42.00
14	Sam Crawford	450.00	252.00	153.00
15	Reb Russell	125.00	70.00	42.00
16	Howie Camnitz	125.00	70.00	42.00
17	Roger Bresnahan	500.00	280.00	170.00
18	Johnny Evers	500.00	280.00	170.00
19	Chief Bender	450.00	252.00	153.00
20	Cy Falkenberg	125.00	70.00	42.00
21	Heinie Zimmerman	125.00	70.00	42.00
22	Smoky Joe Wood	125.00	70.00	42.00
23	Charles Comiskey	500.00	280.00	170.00
24	George Mullen (Mullin)	125.00	70.00	42.00
25	Mike Simon	125.00	70.00	42.00
26	Jim Scott	125.00	70.00	42.00
27	Bill Carrigan	125.00	70.00	42.00
28	Jack Barry	125.00	70.00	42.00
29	Vean Gregg	125.00	70.00	42.00
30	Ty Cobb	5000.	2800.	1700.
31	Heinie Wagner	125.00	70.00	42.00
32	Mordecai Brown	450.00	252.00	153.00
33	Amos Strunk	125.00	70.00	42.00
34	Ira Thomas	125.00	70.00	42.00
35	Harry Hooper	450.00	252.00	153.00
36	Ed Walsh	450.00	252.00	153.00
37	Grover C. Alexander	600.00	335.00	200.00
38	Red Dooin	125.00	70.00	42.00
39	Chick Gandil	200.00	112.00	68.00
40	Jimmy Austin	125.00	70.00	42.00
41	Tommy Leach	125.00	70.00	42.00
42	Al Bridwell	125.00	70.00	42.00
43	Rube Marquard	450.00	250.00	150.00
44	Jeff Tesreau	125.00	70.00	42.00
45	Fred Luderus	125.00	70.00	42.00
46	Bob Groom	125.00	70.00	42.00
47	Josh Devore	125.00	70.00	42.00
48	Steve O'Neill	125.00	70.00	42.00
49	Dots Miller	125.00	70.00	42.00
50	John Hummell (Hummel)	125.00	70.00	42.00
51	Nap Rucker	125.00	70.00	42.00
52	Zach Wheat	500.00	280.00	170.00
53	Otto Miller	125.00	70.00	42.00
54	Marty O'Toole	125.00	70.00	42.00
55	Dick Hoblitzel (Hoblitzell)	125.00	70.00	42.00
56	Clyde Milan	125.00	70.00	42.00
57	Walter Johnson	1500.	840.00	510.00
58	Wally Schang	125.00	70.00	42.00
59	Doc Gessler	125.00	70.00	42.00
60	Oscar Dugey	125.00	70.00	42.00
61	Ray Schalk	400.00	224.00	136.00
62	Willie Mitchell	125.00	70.00	42.00
63	Babe Adams	125.00	70.00	42.00
64	Jimmy Archer	125.00	70.00	42.00
65	Tris Speaker	950.00	532.00	323.00
66	Nap Lajoie	600.00	335.00	200.00
67	Doc Crandall	125.00	70.00	42.00
68	Honus Wagner	2250.	1260.	765.00
69	John McGraw	600.00	335.00	200.00
70	Fred Clarke	400.00	224.00	136.00

71	Chief Meyers	125.00	70.00	42.00
72	Joe Boehling	125.00	70.00	42.00
73	Max Carey	375.00	210.00	127.00
74	Frank Owens	125.00	70.00	42.00
75	Miller Huggins	450.00	252.00	153.00
76	Claude Hendrix	125.00	70.00	42.00
77	Hughie Jennings	450.00	252.00	153.00
78	Fred Merkle	125.00	70.00	42.00
79	Ping Bodie	125.00	70.00	42.00
80	Ed Reulbach	125.00	70.00	42.00
81	Jim Delehanty (Delahanty)	125.00	70.00	42.00
82	Gavvy Cravath	125.00	70.00	42.00
83	Russ Ford	125.00	70.00	42.00
84	Elmer Knetzer	125.00	70.00	42.00
85	Buck Herzog	125.00	70.00	42.00
86	Burt Shotten	125.00	70.00	42.00
87	Hick Cady	125.00	70.00	42.00
88	Christy Mathewson	1500.	840.00	510.00
89	Larry Cheney	125.00	70.00	42.00
90	Frank Smith	125.00	70.00	42.00
91	Roger Peckinpaugh	125.00	70.00	42.00
92	Al Demaree	125.00	70.00	42.00
93	Del Pratt	125.00	70.00	42.00
94	Eddie Cicotte	200.00	110.00	68.00
95	Ray Keating	125.00	70.00	42.00
96	Beals Becker	125.00	70.00	42.00
97	Rube Benton	125.00	70.00	42.00
98	Frank Laporte (LaPorte)	125.00	70.00	42.00
99	Hal Chase	250.00	140.00	85.00
100	Tom Seaton	125.00	70.00	42.00
101	Wildfire Schulte	125.00	70.00	42.00
102	Ray Fisher	125.00	70.00	42.00
103	Shoeless Joe Jackson	7500.	4200.	2550.
104	Vic Saier	125.00	70.00	42.00
105	Jimmy Lavender	125.00	70.00	42.00
106	Joe Birmingham	125.00	70.00	42.00
107	Tom Downey	125.00	70.00	42.00
108	Sherry Magee	125.00	70.00	42.00
109	Fred Blanding	125.00	70.00	42.00
110	Bob Bescher	125.00	70.00	42.00
111	Herbie Moran	125.00	70.00	42.00
112	Jeff Sweeney	125.00	70.00	42.00
113	George Suggs	125.00	70.00	42.00
114	George Moriarity (Moriarty)	125.00	70.00	42.00
115	Ad Brennan	125.00	70.00	42.00
116	Rollie Zeider	125.00	70.00	42.00
117	Ted Easterly	125.00	70.00	42.00
118	Ed Konetchy	125.00	70.00	42.00
119	George Perring	125.00	70.00	42.00
120	Mickey Doolan	125.00	70.00	42.00
121	Hub Perdue	125.00	70.00	42.00
122	Donie Bush	125.00	70.00	42.00
123	Slim Sallee	125.00	70.00	42.00
124	Earle Moore (Earl)	125.00	70.00	42.00
125	Bert Niehoff	125.00	70.00	42.00
126	Walter Blair	125.00	70.00	42.00
127	Butch Schmidt	125.00	70.00	42.00
128	Steve Evans	125.00	70.00	42.00
129	Ray Caldwell	125.00	70.00	42.00
130	Ivy Wingo	125.00	70.00	42.00
131	George Baumgardner	125.00	70.00	42.00
132	Les Nunamaker	125.00	70.00	42.00
133	Branch Rickey	500.00	280.00	170.00
134	Armando Marsans	125.00	70.00	42.00
135	Bill Killifer (Killefer)	125.00	70.00	42.00
136	Rabbit Maranville	425.00	238.00	144.00
137	Bill Rariden	125.00	70.00	42.00
138	Hank Gowdy	125.00	70.00	42.00
139	Rebel Oakes	125.00	70.00	42.00
140	Danny Murphy	125.00	70.00	42.00
141	Cy Barger	125.00	70.00	42.00
142	Gene Packard	125.00	70.00	42.00
143	Jake Daubert	125.00	70.00	42.00
144	Jimmy Walsh	125.00	70.00	42.00
145	Ted Cather	160.00	90.00	54.00
146	Lefty Tyler	160.00	90.00	54.00
147	Lee Magee	160.00	90.00	54.00
148	Owen Wilson	160.00	90.00	54.00
149	Hal Janvrin	160.00	90.00	54.00
150	Doc Johnston	160.00	90.00	54.00
151	Possum Whitted	160.00	90.00	54.00
152	George McQuillen (McQuillan)	160.00	90.00	54.00
153	Bill James	160.00	90.00	54.00
154	Dick Rudolph	160.00	90.00	54.00
155	Joe Connolly	160.00	90.00	54.00
156	Jean Dubuc	160.00	90.00	54.00
157	George Kaiserling	160.00	90.00	54.00
158	Fritz Maisel	160.00	90.00	54.00
159	Heinie Groh	160.00	90.00	54.00
160	Benny Kauff	160.00	90.00	54.00
161	Edd Rousch (Roush)	400.00	224.00	136.00
162	George Stallings	160.00	90.00	54.00
163	Bert Whaling	160.00	90.00	54.00
164	Bob Shawkey	160.00	90.00	54.00
165	Eddie Murphy	160.00	90.00	54.00
166	Bullet Joe Bush	200.00	112.00	68.00
167	Clark Griffith	550.00	308.00	187.00
168	Vin Campbell	160.00	90.00	54.00
169	Ray Collins	160.00	90.00	54.00
170	Hans Lobert	160.00	90.00	54.00
171	Earl Hamilton	160.00	90.00	54.00
172	Erskine Mayer	160.00	90.00	54.00
173	Tilly Walker	160.00	90.00	54.00
174	Bobby Veach	160.00	90.00	54.00
175	Joe Benz	275.00	150.00	95.00
176	Hippo Vaughn	300.00	165.00	80.00

1982 Cracker Jack

The Topps-produced 1982 Cracker Jack set was issued to promote the first "Old Timers Baseball Classic, held in Washington, D.C. Sixteen cards comprise the set which was issued in two sheets of eight cards, plus an advertising card located in the center. The individual cards are 2-1/2" by 3-1/2" in

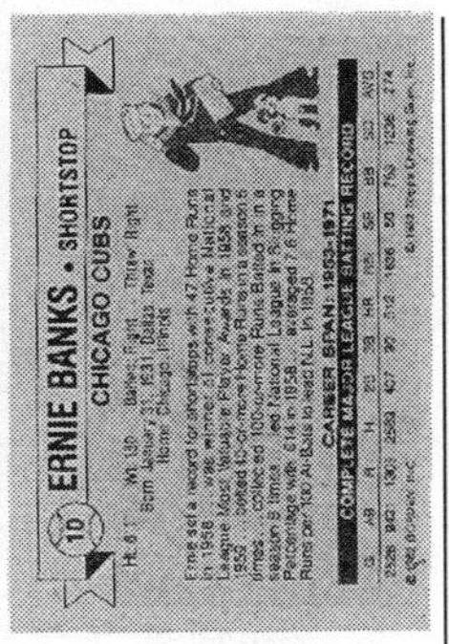

size with the complete sheets measuring 7-1/2" by 10-1/2". Card #'s 1-8 feature American League players with #'s 9-16 being former National League stars. The card fronts feature a full-color photo inside a Cracker Jack border. The backs contain the Cracker Jack logo plus a short player biography and his lifetime pitching or batting record. Complete sheets were available through a write-in offer.

		MT	NR MT	EX
Complete Panel Set:		9.00	6.75	3.50
Complete Singles Set:		4.00	3.00	1.50
Common Single Player:		.10	.08	.04
	Panel	5.00	3.75	2.00
1	Larry Doby	.10	.08	.04
2	Bob Feller	.25	.20	.10
3	Whitey Ford	.25	.20	.10
4	Al Kaline	.25	.20	.10
5	Harmon Killebrew	.15	.11	.06
6	Mickey Mantle	2.50	2.00	1.00
7	Tony Oliva	.10	.08	.04
8	Brooks Robinson	.25	.20	.10
	Panel	4.00	3.00	1.50
9	Hank Aaron	1.25	.90	.50
10	Ernie Banks	.35	.25	.14
11	Ralph Kiner	.15	.11	.06
12	Eddie Mathews	.25	.20	.10
13	Willie Mays	1.25	.90	.50
14	Robin Roberts	.25	.20	.10
15	Duke Snider	.25	.20	.10
16	Warren Spahn	.25	.20	.10
----	Advertising Card	.05	.02	.01

1991 Cracker Jack Topps I

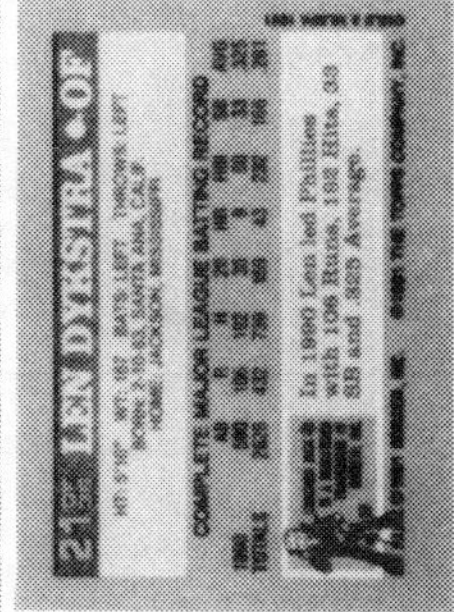

In their first issue in almost 10 years, Cracker Jack inserted miniature cards (1-1/4" x 1-3/4") as the toy surprise in packages of the famous snack. In 1991 the company produced two 36-card series, portraying many of the top stars in the game. The card fronts are identical to the corresponding regular issue Topps card, but the backs are significantly different because of the small amount of space available for statistics. The Cracker Jack sailor logo appears on the bright red backs, along with copyright information listing Borden, Cracker Jack's parent company.

		MT	NR MT	EX
Complete Set:		12.00	9.00	4.75
Common Player:		.25	.20	.10
1	Nolan Ryan	2.00	1.50	.80
2	Paul Molitor	.50	.40	.20
3	Tim Raines	.25	.20	.10
4	Frank Viola	.25	.20	.10
5	Sandy Alomar Jr.	.25	.20	.10
6	Ryne Sandberg	1.00	.70	.40
7	Don Mattingly	.75	.60	.30
8	Pedro Guerrero	.25	.20	.10
9	Jose Rijo	.25	.20	.10
10	Jose Canseco	.50	.40	.20
11	Dave Parker	.35	.25	.14
12	Doug Drabek	.25	.20	.10
13	Cal Ripken	1.00	.70	.40
14	Dave Justice	.30	.25	.12
15	George Brett	.60	.45	.25
16	Eric Davis	.25	.20	.10
17	Mark Langston	.25	.20	.10
18	Rickey Henderson	.50	.40	.20
19	Barry Bonds	.60	.45	.25
20	Kevin Maas	.25	.20	.10
21	Len Dykstra	.30	.25	.12
22	Roger Clemens	.35	.25	.14
23	Robin Yount	.45	.35	.20
24	Mark Grace	.30	.25	.12
25	Bo Jackson	.35	.25	.14
26	Tony Gwynn	.35	.25	.14
27	Mark McGwire	.35	.25	.14
28	Dwight Gooden	.30	.25	.12
29	Wade Boggs	.45	.35	.20
30	Kevin Mitchell	.25	.20	.10
31	Cecil Fielder	.40	.30	.15
32	Bobby Thigpen	.25	.20	.10
33	Benito Santiago	.25	.20	.10
34	Kirby Puckett	.45	.35	.20
35	Will Clark	.35	.25	.14
36	Ken Griffey Jr.	1.50	1.25	.60

1991 Cracker Jack Topps II

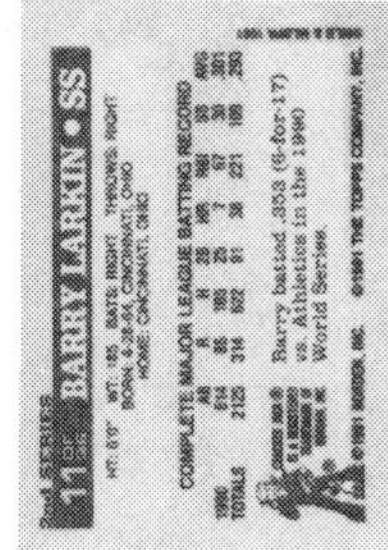

A second series of 36 micro cards was found in Cracker Jack boxes later in the 1991 season. Again numbered from 1-18, the 1-1/4" x 1-3/4" cards carry a "2nd Series" designation on the back above the card number. Like the first series, these cards replicate the front of the 1991 Topps issue and have modified back design which includes the "Sailor Jack" logo of the candy company. Because the Cracker Jack micro cards were not made available in any fashion other than one-per-box, they are difficult to find. Low collector demand has kept prices down.

		MT	NR MT	EX
Complete Set (36):		9.00	6.75	3.50
Common Player:		.25	.20	.10
1	Eddie Murray	.35	.25	.14
2	Carlton Fisk	.35	.25	.14
3	Eric Anthony	.25	.20	.10
4	Kelly Gruber	.25	.20	.10
5	Von Hayes	.25	.20	.10
6	Ben McDonald	.25	.20	.10
7	Andre Dawson	.35	.25	.14
8	Ellis Burks	.25	.20	.10
9	Matt Williams	.30	.25	.12
10	Dave Stewart	.25	.20	.10
11	Barry Larkin	.30	.25	.12
12	Chuck Finley	.25	.20	.10
13	Shane Mack	.25	.20	.10
14	Bret Saberhagen	.25	.20	.10
15	Bobby Bonilla	.30	.25	.12
16	Roberto Kelly	.25	.20	.10
17	Orel Hershiser	.30	.25	.12
18	Ruben Sierra	.30	.25	.12
19	Ron Gant	.30	.25	.12
20	Frank Thomas	1.50	1.25	.60
21	Tim Wallach	.25	.20	.10
22	Gregg Olson	.25	.20	.10
23	Shawon Dunston	.25	.20	.10
24	Kent Hrbek	.30	.25	.12
25	Ramon Martinez	.25	.20	.10
26	Alan Trammell	.30	.25	.12
27	Ozzie Smith	.35	.25	.14
28	Bob Welch	.25	.20	.10
29	Chris Sabo	.25	.20	.10
30	Steve Sax	.25	.20	.10
31	Bip Roberts	.25	.20	.10
32	Dave Steib	.25	.20	.10
33	Howard Johnson	.30	.25	.12
34	Mike Greenwell	.25	.20	.10
35	Delino DeShields	.30	.25	.12
36	Alex Fernandez	.25	.20	.10

1992 Cracker Jack Donruss I

In 1992, Cracker Jack turned to Donruss to produce the cards for the surprise in their packages. The first series of micro cards (1-1/4" x 1-3/4") was numbered 1-36 and featured many of the top play-

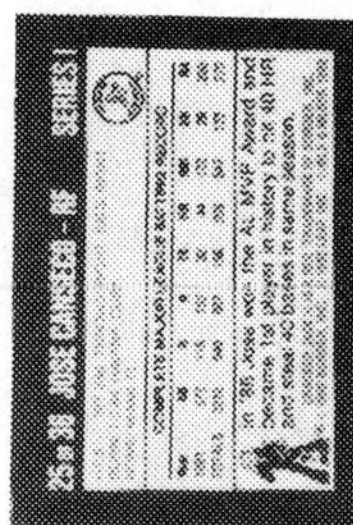

ers. The fronts of the cards are identical to the regular issue 1992 Donruss, but the backs have a different format and much less information because of the tiny space available. The backs have a blue border, with some spot red printing and the Cracker Jack sailor logo in the lower left corner.

		MT	NR MT	EX
Complete Set (36):		12.00	9.00	4.75
Common Player:		.25	.20	.10
1	Dennis Eckersley	.30	.25	.12
2	Jeff Bagwell	.25	.20	.10
3	Jim Abbott	.35	.25	.14
4	Steve Avery	.25	.20	.10
5	Kelly Gruber	.25	.20	.10
6	Ozzie Smith	.35	.25	.14
7	Lance Dickson	.25	.20	.10
8	Robin Yount	.50	.40	.20
9	Brett Butler	.25	.20	.10
10	Sandy Alomar Jr.	.25	.20	.10
11	Travis Fryman	.30	.25	.12
12	Ken Griffey, Jr.	1.00	.70	.40
13	Cal Ripken, Jr.	1.50	1.25	.60
14	Will Clark	.45	.35	.20
15	Nolan Ryan	2.00	1.50	.80
16	Tony Gwynn	.35	.25	.14
17	Roger Clemens	.35	.25	.14
18	Wes Chamberlain	.25	.20	.10
19	Barry Larkin	.30	.25	.12
20	Brian McRae	.25	.20	.10
21	Marquis Grissom	.25	.20	.10
22	Cecil Fielder	.35	.25	.14
23	Dwight Gooden	.35	.25	.14
24	Chuck Knoblauch	.30	.25	.12
25	Jose Canseco	.60	.45	.25
26	Terry Pendleton	.25	.20	.10
27	Ivan Rodriguez	.35	.25	.14
28	Ryne Sandberg	1.00	.70	.40
29	Kent Hrbek	.30	.25	.12
30	Ramon Martinez	.25	.20	.10
31	Todd Zeile	.25	.20	.10
32	Hal Morris	.25	.20	.10
33	Robin Ventura	.30	.25	.12
34	Doug Drabek	.25	.20	.10
35	Frank Thomas	1.50	1.25	.60
36	Don Mattingly	.60	.45	.25

1992 Cracker Jack Donruss II

The Second Series of the 1992 Crack Jack Donruss set is almost identical to the first series, with the only change being different players and red border on the back instead of blue. The micro cards are numbered 1-36, just as in the first series.

		MT	NR MT	EX
Complete Set (36):		8.00	6.00	3.25
Common Player:		.25	.20	.10
1	Craig Biggio	.30	.25	.12
2	Tom Glavine	.25	.20	.10
3	David Justice	.30	.25	.12
4	Lee Smith	.25	.20	.10
5	Mark Grace	.30	.25	.12
6	George Bell	.25	.20	.10
7	Darryl Strawberry	.30	.25	.12
8	Eric Davis	.25	.20	.10
9	Ivan Calderon	.25	.20	.10
10	Royce Clayton	.25	.20	.10
11	Matt Williams	.30	.25	.12
12	Fred McGriff	.30	.25	.12
13	Len Dykstra	.30	.25	.12
14	Barry Bonds	.45	.35	.20
15	Reggie Sanders	.30	.25	.12
16	Chris Sabo	.25	.20	.10
17	Howard Johnson	.25	.20	.10
18	Bobby Bonilla	.30	.25	.12
19	Rickey Henderson	.45	.35	.20
20	Mark Langston	.25	.20	.10
21	Joe Carter	.30	.25	.12
22	Paul Molitor	.40	.30	.15
23	Glenallen Hill	.25	.20	.10
24	Edgar Martinez	.30	.25	.12
25	Gregg Olson	.25	.20	.10
26	Ruben Sierra	.30	.25	.12
27	Julio Franco	.25	.20	.10
28	Phil Plantier	.30	.25	.12
29	Wade Boggs	.40	.30	.15
30	George Brett	.50	.40	.20
31	Alan Trammell	.30	.25	.12
32	Kirby Puckett	.45	.35	.20
33	Scott Erickson	.25	.20	.10
34	Matt Nokes	.25	.20	.10
35	Danny Tartabull	.30	.25	.12
36	Jack McDowell	.30	.25	.12

1993 Cracker Jack Anniversary

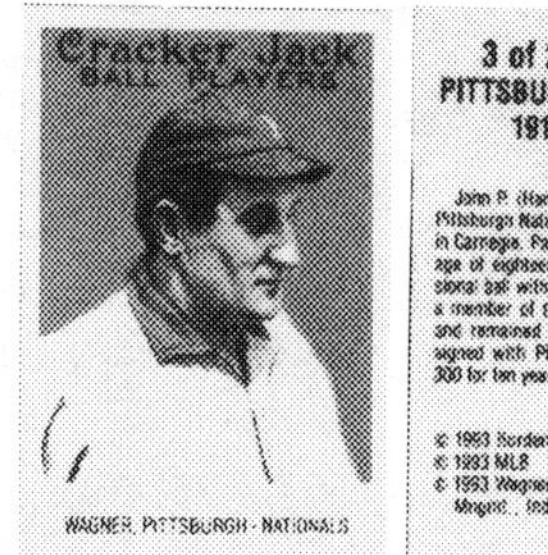

In 1993, as part of the company's 100th anniversary celebration, Cracker Jack issued a 24-card set of mini replicas of its famous 1915 cards. The cards, measuring 1-1/4" x 1-3/4", were included in specially-marked packages of the famous snack. The set, taken from the original 176-card Cracker Jack set, features Hall of Famers such as Cobb, Mathewson, Walter Johnson and others, plus the Joe Jackson card.

		MT	NR MT	EX
Complete Set:		10.00	7.50	4.00
Common Player:		.50	.40	.20
(1)	Ty Cobb	2.00	1.50	.80
(2)	Nap Lajoie	.50	.40	.20
(3)	Connie Mack	.50	.40	.20
(4)	Leslie Bush	.50	.40	.20
(5)	Tris Speaker	.50	.40	.20
(6)	Harry Hooper	.50	.40	.20
(7)	Eddie Collins	.50	.40	.20
(8)	Ed Walsh	.50	.40	.20
(9)	Joe Jackson	2.00	1.50	.80
(10)	Branch Rickey	.50	.40	.20
(11)	Walter Johnson	.75	.55	.30
(12)	Honus Wagner	.75	.55	.30
(13)	Fred Clarke	.50	.40	.20
(14)	Christy Mathewson	.60	.45	.25
(15)	John McGraw	.50	.40	.20
(16)	Johnny Evers	.50	.40	.20
(17)	Walter Maranville	.50	.40	.20
(18)	Zack Wheat	.50	.40	.20
(19)	Miller Huggins	.50	.40	.20
(20)	Grover Alexander	.50	.40	.20
(21)	Joe Tinker	.50	.40	.20
(22)	Mordecai Brown	.50	.40	.20
(23)	Eddie Plank	.50	.40	.20
(24)	Rube Marquard	.50	.40	.20

1980 - 83 Cramer Baseball Legends

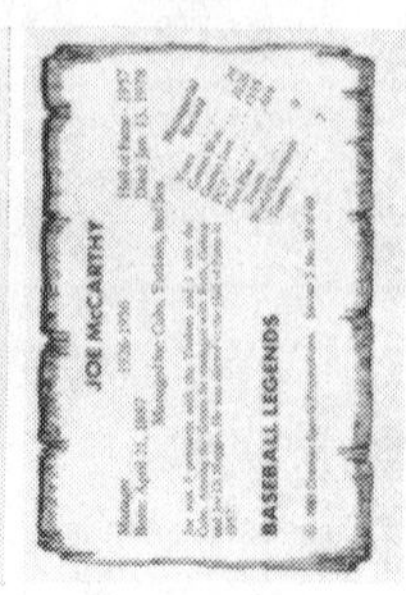

Consecutively numbered, this set was issued over a period of four years by Cramer Sports Promotions, the forerunner of today's Pacific card company. Sold in wax packs and measuring the standard 2-1/2" x 3-1/2", the cards have a sepia-toned photo on front with a black frame. In the background is a weathered wooden slat design with the player's name on a hanging board beneath. The borders are dull yellow. Backs are printed in brown and include a few personal data, career stats and a career summary. Cards 1-30 were issued in 1980; #31-60 in 1981; #61-90 in 1982 and #90-124 in 1983. Cards #121-124 were issued on the 1983 wax box.

		NR MT	EX	VG
Complete Set:		45.00	22.00	13.50
Common Player:		.25	.13	.08
1	Babe Ruth	4.00	2.00	1.25
2	Heinie Manush	.25	.13	.08
3	Rabbit Maranville	.25	.13	.08
4	Earl Averill	.25	.13	.08
5	Joe DiMaggio	3.00	1.50	.90
6	Mickey Mantle	3.00	1.50	.90
7	Hank Aaron	2.00	1.00	.60
8	Stan Musial	2.00	1.00	.60
9	Bill Terry	.25	.13	.08
10	Sandy Koufax	.45	.25	.14
11	Ernie Lombardi	.25	.13	.08
12	Dizzy Dean	.35	.20	.11
13	Lou Gehrig	3.00	1.50	.90
14	Walter Alston	.25	.13	.08
15	Jackie Robinson	.50	.25	.15
16	Jimmie Foxx	.25	.13	.08
17	Billy Southworth	.25	.13	.08
18	Honus Wagner	.35	.20	.11
19	Duke Snider	.35	.20	.11
20	Rogers Hornsby	.25	.13	.08
21	Paul Waner	.25	.13	.08
22	Luke Appling	.25	.13	.08
23	Billy Herman	.25	.13	.08
24	Lloyd Waner	.25	.13	.08
25	Fred Hutchinson	.25	.13	.08
26	Eddie Collins	.25	.13	.08
27	Lefty Grove	.25	.13	.08
28	Chuck Connors	.45	.25	.14
29	Lefty O'Doul	.25	.13	.08
30	Hank Greenberg	.25	.13	.08
31	Ty Cobb	3.00	1.50	.90
32	Enos Slaughter	.25	.13	.08
33	Ernie Banks	.45	.25	.14
34	Christy Mathewson	.35	.20	.11
35	Mel Ott	.25	.13	.08
36	Pie Traynor	.25	.13	.08
37	Clark Griffith	.25	.13	.08
38	Mickey Cochrane	.25	.13	.08
39	Joe Cronin	.25	.13	.08
40	Leo Durocher	.25	.13	.08
41	Frank Baker	.25	.13	.08
42	Joe Tinker	.25	.13	.08
43	John McGraw	.25	.13	.08
44	Bill Dickey	.25	.13	.08
45	Walter Johnson	.35	.20	.11
46	Frankie Frisch	.25	.13	.08
47	Casey Stengel	.25	.13	.08
48	Willie Mays	2.00	1.00	.60
49	Johnny Mize	.25	.13	.08
50	Roberto Clemente	2.00	1.00	.60
51	Burleigh Grimes	.25	.13	.08
52	Pee Wee Reese	.35	.20	.11
53	Bob Feller	.35	.20	.11
54	Brooks Robinson	.35	.20	.11
55	Sam Crawford	.25	.13	.08
56	Robin Roberts	.25	.13	.08
57	Warren Spahn	.25	.13	.08
58	Joe McCarthy	.25	.13	.08
59	Jocko Conlon	.25	.13	.08
60	Satchel Paige	.60	.30	.20
61	Ted Williams	2.00	1.00	.60
62	George Kelly	.25	.13	.08
63	Gil Hodges	.35	.20	.11
64	Jim Bottomley	.25	.13	.08
65	Al Kaline	.35	.20	.11
66	Harvey Kuenn	.25	.13	.08
67	Yogi Berra	.35	.20	.11
68	Nellie Fox	.25	.13	.08
69	Harmon Killebrew	.35	.20	.11
70	Edd Roush	.25	.13	.08
71	Mordecai Brown	.25	.13	.08
72	Gabby Hartnett	.25	.13	.08
73	Early Wynn	.25	.13	.08
74	Nap Lajoie	.25	.13	.08
75	Charlie Grimm	.25	.13	.08
76	Joe Garagiola	.35	.20	.11
77	Ted Lyons	.25	.13	.08
78	Mickey Vernon	.25	.13	.08
79	Lou Boudreau	.25	.13	.08
80	Al Dark	.25	.13	.08
81	Ralph Kiner	.25	.13	.08
82	Phil Rizzuto	.35	.20	.11
83	Stan Hack	.25	.13	.08
84	Frank Chance	.25	.13	.08
85	Ray Schalk	.25	.13	.08
86	Bill McKechnie	.25	.13	.08

87	Travis Jackson	.25	.13	.08
88	Pete Reiser	.25	.13	.08
89	Carl Hubbell	.25	.13	.08
90	Roy Campanella	.35	.20	.11
91	Cy Young	.35	.20	.11
92	Kiki Cuyler	.25	.13	.08
93	Chief Bender	.25	.13	.08
94	Richie Ashburn	.25	.13	.08
95	Riggs Stephenson	.25	.13	.08
96	Minnie Minoso	.25	.13	.08
97	Hack Wilson	.25	.13	.08
98	Al Lopez	.25	.13	.08
99	Willie Keeler	.25	.13	.08
100	Fred Lindstrom	.25	.13	.08
101	Roger Maris	.45	.25	.14
102	Roger Bresnahan	.25	.13	.08
103	Monty Stratton	.25	.13	.08
104	Goose Goslin	.25	.13	.08
105	Earle Combs	.25	.13	.08
106	Pepper Martin	.25	.13	.08
107	Joe Jackson	3.00	1.50	.90
108	George Sisler	.25	.13	.08
109	Red Ruffing	.25	.13	.08
110	Johnny Vander Meer	.25	.13	.08
111	Herb Pennock	.25	.13	.08
112	Chuck Klein	.25	.13	.08
113	Paul Derringer	.25	.13	.08
114	Addie Joss	.25	.13	.08
115	Bobby Thomson	.25	.13	.08
116	Chick Hafey	.25	.13	.08
117	Lefty Gomez	.25	.13	.08
118	George Kell	.25	.13	.08
119	Al Simmons	.25	.13	.08
120	Bob Lemon	.25	.13	.08
121	Hoyt Wilhelm	.25	.13	.08
122	Arky Vaughan	.25	.13	.08
123	Frank Robinson	.35	.20	.11
124	Grover Alexander	.25	.13	.08

1976 Crane Potato Chips

This unnumbered 70-card set of player discs was issued with Crane Potato Chips in 1976. The front of the discs are designed to look like a baseball with the player's portrait in the center and his name, position and team beneath.

		NR MT	EX	VG
Complete Set:		30.00	15.00	9.00
Common Player:		.10	.05	.03
(1)	Henry Aaron	2.25	1.25	.70
(2)	Johnny Bench	1.25	.60	.40
(3)	Vida Blue	.12	.06	.04
(4)	Larry Bowa	.12	.06	.04
(5)	Lou Brock	.60	.30	.20
(6)	Jeff Burroughs	.10	.05	.03
(7)	John Candelaria	.10	.05	.03
(8)	Jose Cardenal	.10	.05	.03
(9)	Rod Carew	.75	.40	.25
(10)	Steve Carlton	.75	.40	.25
(11)	Dave Cash	.10	.05	.03
(12)	Cesar Cedeno	.10	.05	.03
(13)	Ron Cey	.10	.05	.03
(14)	Carlton Fisk	.60	.30	.20
(15)	Tito Fuentes	.10	.05	.03
(16)	Steve Garvey	.70	.35	.20
(17)	Ken Griffey	.12	.06	.04
(18)	Don Gullett	.10	.05	.03
(19)	Willie Horton	.10	.05	.03
(20)	Al Hrabosky	.10	.05	.03
(21)	Catfish Hunter	.75	.40	.25
(22)	Reggie Jackson	1.75	.90	.50
(23)	Randy Jones	.10	.05	.03
(24)	Jim Kaat	.15	.08	.05
(25)	Don Kessinger	.10	.05	.03
(26)	Dave Kingman	.12	.06	.04
(27)	Jerry Koosman	.12	.06	.04
(28)	Mickey Lolich	.15	.08	.05
(29)	Greg Luzinski	.15	.08	.05
(30)	Fred Lynn	.20	.10	.06
(31)	Bill Madlock	.15	.08	.05
(32)	Carlos May	.10	.05	.03
(33)	John Mayberry	.10	.05	.03
(34)	Bake McBride	.10	.05	.03
(35)	Doc Medich	.10	.05	.03
(36)	Andy Messersmith	.10	.05	.03
(37)	Rick Monday	.10	.05	.03
(38)	John Montefusco	.10	.05	.03
(39)	Jerry Morales	.10	.05	.03
(40)	Joe Morgan	.75	.40	.25
(41)	Thurman Munson	.75	.40	.25
(42)	Bobby Murcer	.12	.06	.04
(43)	Al Oliver	.15	.08	.05
(44)	Jim Palmer	.75	.40	.25
(45)	Dave Parker	.20	.10	.06
(46)	Tony Perez	.35	.20	.11
(47)	Jerry Reuss	.10	.05	.03
(48)	Brooks Robinson	.75	.40	.25
(49)	Frank Robinson	.75	.40	.25
(50)	Steve Rogers	.10	.05	.03
(51)	Pete Rose	2.00	1.00	.60
(52)	Nolan Ryan	3.00	1.50	.90
(53)	Manny Sanguillen	.10	.05	.03
(54)	Mike Schmidt	1.75	.90	.50
(55)	Tom Seaver	1.25	.60	.40
(56)	Ted Simmons	.15	.08	.05
(57)	Reggie Smith	.12	.06	.04
(58)	Willie Stargell	.75	.40	.25
(59)	Rusty Staub	.15	.08	.05
(60)	Rennie Stennett	.10	.05	.03
(61)	Don Sutton	.20	.10	.06
(62)	Andy Thornton	.12	.06	.04
(63)	Luis Tiant	.15	.08	.05
(64)	Joe Torre	.12	.06	.04
(65)	Mike Tyson	.10	.05	.03
(66)	Bob Watson	.10	.05	.03
(67)	Wilbur Wood	.10	.05	.03
(68)	Jimmy Wynn	.10	.05	.03
(69)	Carl Yastrzemski	1.25	.60	.40
(70)	Richie Zisk	.10	.05	.03

1913 Cravats Felt Pennants

Little is known about this felt pennant issue, including the complete checklist. The name "Cravats" in the baseball above the player picture may represent the issuer, or describe the issue; the word "cravat" is an arcane term for a triangular piece of cloth. The pennants measure 4-1/8" across the top and are 9" long. Background colors are dark, with all printing in white. At center is a line art represntation of the player, with his name horizontally beneath and his team nickname vertically at bottom. At top is a bat and ball logo with the "Cravats" name. Most specimens are seen with a metal ring reinforcing the hole punched at top center. The known checklist points to 1913 as the most probably year of issue.

		NR MT	EX	VG
Common Player:		75.00	37.00	22.00
(1)	Eddie Ainsmith	75.00	37.00	22.00
(2)	Jack Coombs	75.00	37.00	22.00
(3)	Ed Konethy (Konetchy)	75.00	37.00	22.00
(4)	Stuffy McInnes (McInnis)	75.00	37.00	22.00
(5)	J.T. (Chief) Meyer (Meyers)	75.00	37.00	22.00
(6)	Jeff Tesreau	75.00	37.00	22.00

1909 Croft's Candy (E92)

Because they share the format and pictures with a handful of related issues (Croft's Cocoa, Dockman Gum, Nadja Caramels, etc.) this set shared the E92 designation in the old "American Card Catalog." It is more logical to present these sets as separate issues, based on the advertising which appears on the back. Fronts of the 1-1/2" x 2-3/4" cards feature a color lithograph of the player. His last name, position and team are printed in black the border below. Backs have a shield-shaped logo for Croft's Candy, a product of Croft & Allen Co., Philadelphia. Cards are unnumbered and the checklist is presented here alphabetically.

		NR MT	EX	VG
Complete Set:		15000.	7500.	4500.
Common Player:		150.00	75.00	45.00
(1)	Jack Barry	450.00	225.00	135.00
(2)	Harry Bemis	150.00	75.00	45.00
(3)	Chief Bender (striped cap)	700.00	350.00	210.00
(4)	Chief Bender (white cap)	450.00	225.00	135.00
(5)	Bill Bergen	150.00	75.00	45.00
(6)	Bob Bescher	150.00	75.00	45.00
(7)	Al Bridwell	150.00	75.00	45.00
(8)	Doc Casey	150.00	75.00	45.00
(9)	Frank Chance	450.00	225.00	135.00
(10)	Hal Chase	200.00	100.00	60.00
(11)	Ty Cobb	4500.	2250.	1350.
(12)	Eddie Collins	850.00	425.00	255.00
(13)	Sam Crawford	400.00	200.00	120.00
(14)	Harry Davis	150.00	75.00	45.00
(15)	Art Devlin	150.00	75.00	45.00
(16)	Wild Bill Donovan	150.00	75.00	45.00
(17)	Red Dooin	350.00	175.00	105.00
(18)	Mickey Doolan	150.00	75.00	45.00
(19)	Patsy Dougherty	150.00	75.00	45.00
(20)	Larry Doyle (throwing)	150.00	75.00	45.00
(21)	Larry Doyle (with bat)	150.00	75.00	45.00
(22)	Johnny Evers	1000.	500.00	300.00
(23)	George Gibson	150.00	75.00	45.00
(24)	Topsy Hartsel	150.00	75.00	45.00
(25)	Fred Jacklitsch	350.00	175.00	105.00
(26)	Hugh Jennings	400.00	200.00	120.00
(27)	Red Kleinow	150.00	75.00	45.00
(28)	Otto Knabe	350.00	175.00	105.00
(29)	Jack Knight	350.00	175.00	105.00
(30)	Nap Lajoie	700.00	350.00	210.00
(31)	Hans Lobert	150.00	75.00	45.00
(32)	Sherry Magee	150.00	75.00	45.00
(33)	Christy Matthewson (Mathewson)	1200.	600.00	360.00
(34)	John McGraw	550.00	275.00	165.00
(35)	Larry McLean	150.00	75.00	45.00
(36)	Dots Miller (batting)	150.00	75.00	45.00
(37)	Dots Miller (fielding)	350.00	175.00	105.00
(38)	Danny Murphy	150.00	75.00	45.00
(39)	Bil O'Hara	150.00	75.00	45.00
(40)	Germany Schaefer	150.00	75.00	45.00
(41)	Admiral Schlei	150.00	75.00	45.00
(42)	Boss Schmidt	150.00	75.00	45.00
(43)	Johnny Seigle (Siegle)	150.00	75.00	45.00
(44)	Dave Shean	150.00	75.00	45.00
(45)	Boss Smith (Schmidt)	150.00	75.00	45.00
(46)	Joe Tinker	450.00	225.00	135.00
(47)	Honus Wagner (batting)	1000.	500.00	300.00
(48)	Honus Wagner (throwing)	1000.	500.00	300.00
(49)	Cy Young	900.00	450.00	270.00
(50)	Heinie Zimmerman	150.00	75.00	45.00

1909 Croft's Cocoa (E92)

Like related issues once cataloged together as E92 (Croft's Candy, Dockman Gum, Nadja Caramels, etc.), these 1-1/2" x 2-3/4" cards feature a color player lithograph on front, which his name, position and team printed in the white border below. Backs have an ad for Crofts Swiss Milk Cocoa of Philadelphia. The checklist, presented here alphabetically, is identical to that of Croft's Candy.

		NR MT	EX	VG
Complete Set:		27500.	15000.	6500.
Common Player:		150.00	75.00	45.00
(1)	Jack Barry	450.00	225.00	135.00
(2)	Harry Bemis	150.00	75.00	45.00
(3)	Chief Bender (striped hat)	700.00	350.00	210.00
(4)	Chief Bender (white hat)	450.00	225.00	135.00
(5)	Bill Bergen	150.00	75.00	45.00
(6)	Bob Bescher	150.00	75.00	45.00
(7)	Al Bridwell	150.00	75.00	45.00
(8)	Doc Casey	150.00	75.00	45.00
(9)	Frank Chance	450.00	225.00	135.00
(10)	Hal Chase	200.00	100.00	60.00
(11)	Ty Cobb	4500.	2250.	1350.
(12)	Eddie Collins	850.00	425.00	255.00
(13)	Sam Crawford	400.00	200.00	120.00
(14)	Harry Davis	150.00	75.00	45.00
(15)	Art Devlin	150.00	75.00	45.00
(16)	Wild Bill Donovan	150.00	75.00	45.00

(17)	Red Dooin	350.00	175.00	105.00
(18)	Mickey Doolan	150.00	75.00	45.00
(19)	Patsy Dougherty	150.00	75.00	45.00
(20)	Larry Doyle (throwing)	150.00	75.00	45.00
(21)	Larry Doyle (with bat)	150.00	75.00	45.00
(22)	Johnny Evers	1000.	500.00	300.00
(23)	George Gibson	150.00	75.00	45.00
(24)	Topsy Hartsel	150.00	75.00	45.00
(25)	Fred Jacklitsch	350.00	175.00	105.00
(26)	Hugh Jennings	400.00	200.00	120.00
(27)	Red Kleinow	150.00	75.00	45.00
(28)	Otto Knabe	350.00	175.00	105.00
(29)	Jack Knight	350.00	175.00	105.00
(30)	Nap Lajoie	700.00	350.00	210.00
(31)	Hans Lobert	150.00	75.00	45.00
(32)	Sherry Magee	150.00	75.00	45.00
(33)	Christy Matthewson (Mathewson)	1200.	600.00	360.00
(34)	John McGraw	550.00	275.00	165.00
(35)	Larry McLean	150.00	75.00	45.00
(36)	Dots Miller (batting)	150.00	75.00	45.00
(37)	Dots Miller (fielding)	350.00	175.00	105.00
(38)	Danny Murphy	150.00	75.00	45.00
(39)	Bill O'Hara	150.00	75.00	45.00
(40)	Germany Schaefer	150.00	75.00	45.00
(41)	Admiral Schlei	150.00	75.00	45.00
(42)	Boss Schmidt	150.00	75.00	45.00
(43)	Johnny Seigle (Siegle)	150.00	75.00	45.00
(44)	Dave Shean	150.00	75.00	45.00
(45)	Boss Smith (Schmidt)	150.00	75.00	45.00
(46)	Joe Tinker	450.00	225.00	135.00
(47)	Honus Wagner (batting)	1000.	500.00	300.00
(48)	Honus Wagner (throwing)	1000.	500.00	300.00
(49)	Cy Young	900.00	450.00	270.00
(50)	Heinie Zimmerman	150.00	75.00	45.00

1991 Crown/Coke Orioles

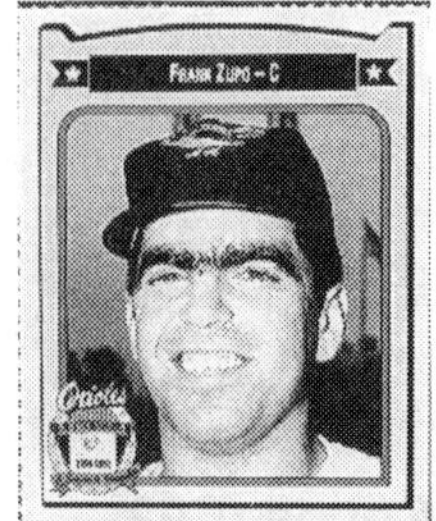

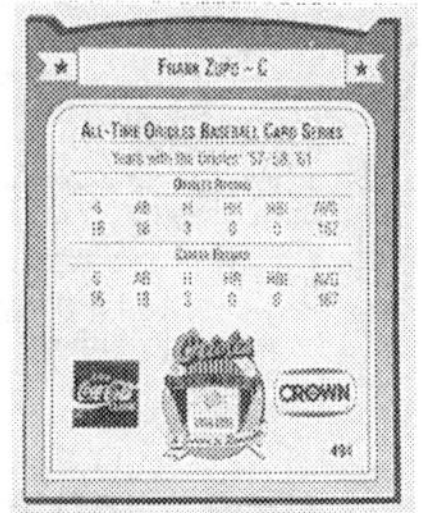

Claiming to include every player for the modern 1954-1991 Baltimore Orioles, this 501-card set was issued in four series. The first three series contain 120 cards each in a format of a dozen perforated cards on each of 10 sheets. Those series were given away at May 17, June 28 and Aug. 11 home games. The fourth series, 12 sheets of 12 cards each, including three blank cards was available only at participating Crown gas stations, which also sold the first three series following the give-away days at the ballpark. Cards measure 2-1/2" x 3-3/16" and are perforated on two, three or four sides, depending on their position on the 12-card sheet. All players are featured in sepia-toned head shots, virtually all in the uniform of the Orioles. Around the photos are borders of, successively, green, orange, black and white. The player's name and position appear in a black banner above the photo. In the lower-left corner is a 1954-1991 Memorial Stadium "Season to Remember" logo. That logo is repeated at bottom-center of the black-and-white backs, flanked by the logos of Coca-Cola and Crown. A card number appears in the lower-right. Most cards were numbered alphabetically. Backs also repeat the player's name and position in a white banner and include stats for the player's major league career and time with the Orioles.

		MT	NR MT	EX
Complete Set (501):		35.00	26.00	14.00
Common Player:		.10	.08	.04
1	Don Aase	.10	.08	.04
2	Cal Abrams	.10	.08	.04
3	Jerry Adair	.10	.08	.04
4	Bobby Adams	.10	.08	.04
5	Mike Adamson	.10	.08	.04
6	Jay Aldrich	.10	.08	.04
7	Bob Alexander	.10	.08	.04
8	Doyle Alexander	.10	.08	.04
9	Brady Anderson	.15	.11	.06
10	John Anderson	.10	.08	.04
11	Mike Anderson	.10	.08	.04
12	Luis Aparicio	.50	.40	.20
13	Tony Arnold	.10	.08	.04
14	Bobby Avila	.12	.09	.05
15	Benny Ayala	.10	.08	.04
16	Bob Bailor	.10	.08	.04
17	Frank Baker	.10	.08	.04
18	Jeff Ballard	.10	.08	.04
19	George Bamberger	.10	.08	.04
20	Steve Barber	.10	.08	.04
21	Ray "Buddy" Barker	.10	.08	.04
22	Ed Barnowski	.10	.08	.04
23	Jose Bautista	.10	.08	.04
24	Don Baylor	.15	.11	.06
25	Charlie Beamon	.10	.08	.04
26	Fred Beene	.10	.08	.04
27	Mark Belanger	.12	.09	.05
28	Eric Bell	.10	.08	.04
29	Juan Bell	.10	.08	.04
30	Juan Beniquez	.10	.08	.04
31	Neil Berry	.10	.08	.04
32	Frank Bertaina	.10	.08	.04
33	Fred Besana	.10	.08	.04
34	Vern Bickford	.10	.08	.04
35	Babe Birrer	.10	.08	.04
36	Paul Blair	.10	.08	.04
37	Curt Blefary	.10	.08	.04
38	Mike Blyzka	.10	.08	.04
39	Mike Boddicker	.10	.08	.04
40	Juan Bonilla	.10	.08	.04
41	Bob Bonner	.10	.08	.04
42	Dan Boone	.10	.08	.04
43	Rich Bordi	.10	.08	.04
44	Dave Boswell	.10	.08	.04
45	Sam Bowens	.10	.08	.04
46	Bob Boyd	.10	.08	.04
47	Gene Brabender	.10	.08	.04
48	Phil Bradley	.10	.08	.04
49	Jackie Brandt	.10	.08	.04
50	Marv Breeding	.10	.08	.04
51	Jim Brideweser	.10	.08	.04
52	Nellie Briles	.10	.08	.04
53	Dick Brown	.10	.08	.04
54	Hal Brown	.10	.08	.04
55	Larry Brown	.10	.08	.04
56	Mark Brown	.10	.08	.04
57	Marty Brown	.10	.08	.04
58	George Brunet	.10	.08	.04
59	Don Buford	.12	.09	.05
60	Al Bumbry	.10	.08	.04
61	Wally Bunker	.10	.08	.04
62	Leo Burke	.10	.08	.04
63	Rick Burleson	.10	.08	.04
64	Pete Burnside	.10	.08	.04
65	Jim Busby	.10	.08	.04
66	John Buzhardt	.10	.08	.04
67	Harry Byrd	.10	.08	.04
68	Enos Cabell	.10	.08	.04
69	Chico Carrasquel	.10	.08	.04
70	Camilo Carreon	.10	.08	.04
71	Foster Castleman	.10	.08	.04
72	Wayne Causey	.10	.08	.04
73	Art Ceccarelli	.10	.08	.04
74	Bob Chakales	.10	.08	.04
75	Tony Chevez	.10	.08	.04
76	Tom Chism	.10	.08	.04
77	Gino Cimoli	.10	.08	.04
78	Gil Coan	.10	.08	.04
79	Rich Coggins	.10	.08	.04
80	Joe Coleman	.10	.08	.04
81	Rip Coleman	.10	.08	.04
82	Fritz Connally	.10	.08	.04
83	Sandy Consuegra	.10	.08	.04
84	Doug Corbett	.10	.08	.04
85	Mark Corey	.10	.08	.04
86	Clint Courtney	.10	.08	.04
87	Billy Cox	.10	.08	.04
88	Dave Criscione	.10	.08	.04
89	Terry Crowley	.10	.08	.04
90	Todd Cruz	.10	.08	.04
91	Mike Cuellar	.15	.11	.06
92	Angie Dagres	.10	.08	.04
93	Clay Dalrymple	.10	.08	.04
94	Rich Dauer	.10	.08	.04
95	Jerry DaVanon	.10	.08	.04
96	Butch Davis	.10	.08	.04
97	Storm Davis	.10	.08	.04
98	Tommy Davis	.12	.09	.05
99	Doug DeCinces	.12	.09	.05
100	Luis DeLeon	.10	.08	.04
101	Ike Delock	.10	.08	.04
102	Rick Dempsey	.12	.09	.05
103	Mike Devereaux	.15	.11	.06
104	Chuck Diering	.10	.08	.04
105	Gordon Dillard	.10	.08	.04
106	Bill Dillman	.10	.08	.04
107	Mike Dimmel	.10	.08	.04
108	Ken Dixon	.10	.08	.04
109	Pat Dobson	.10	.08	.04
110	Tom Dodd	.10	.08	.04
111	Harry Dorish	.10	.08	.04
112	Moe Drabowsky	.10	.08	.04
113	Dick Drago	.10	.08	.04
114	Walt Dropo	.12	.09	.05
115	Tom Dukes	.10	.08	.04
116	Dave Duncan	.10	.08	.04
117	Ryne Duren	.12	.09	.05
118	Joe Durham	.10	.08	.04
119	Jim Dwyer	.10	.08	.04
120	Jim Dyck	.10	.08	.04
121	Mike Epstein	.10	.08	.04
122	Chuck Essegian	.10	.08	.04
123	Chuck Estrada	.10	.08	.04
124	Andy Etchebarren	.10	.08	.04
125	Hoot Evers	.10	.08	.04
126	Ed Farmer	.10	.08	.04
127	Chico Fernandez	.10	.08	.04
128	Don Ferrarese	.10	.08	.04
129	Jim Finigan	.10	.08	.04
130	Steve Finley	.12	.09	.05
131	Mike Fiore	.10	.08	.04
132	Eddie Fisher	.10	.08	.04
133	Jack Fisher	.10	.08	.04
134	Tom Fisher	.10	.08	.04
135	Mike Flanagan	.10	.08	.04
136	John Flinn	.10	.08	.04
137	Bobby Floyd	.10	.08	.04
138	Hank Foiles	.10	.08	.04
139	Dan Ford	.10	.08	.04
140	Dave Ford	.10	.08	.04
141	Mike Fornieles	.10	.08	.04
142	Howie Fox	.10	.08	.04
143	Tito Francona	.10	.08	.04
144	Joe Frazier	.10	.08	.04
145	Roger Freed	.10	.08	.04
146	Jim Fridley	.10	.08	.04
147	Jim Fuller	.10	.08	.04
148	Joe Gaines	.10	.08	.04
149	Vinicio "Chico" Garcia	.10	.08	.04
150	Kiko Garcia	.10	.08	.04
151	Billy Gardner	.10	.08	.04
152	Wayne Garland	.10	.08	.04
153	Tommy Gastall	.10	.08	.04
154	Jim Gentile	.12	.09	.05
155	Ken Gerhart	.10	.08	.04
156	Paul Gilliford	.10	.08	.04
157	Joe Ginsberg	.10	.08	.04
158	Leo Gomez	.10	.08	.04
159	Rene Gonzales	.10	.08	.04
160	Billy Goodman	.10	.08	.04
161	Dan Graham	.10	.08	.04
162	Ted Gray	.10	.08	.04
163	Gene Green	.10	.08	.04
164	Lenny Green	.10	.08	.04
165	Bobby Grich	.15	.11	.06
166	Mike Griffin	.10	.08	.04
167	Ross Grimsley	.10	.08	.04
168	Wayne Gross	.10	.08	.04
169	Glenn Gulliver	.10	.08	.04
170	Jackie Gutierrez	.10	.08	.04
171	John Habyan	.10	.08	.04
172	Harvey Haddix	.10	.08	.04
173	Bob Hale	.10	.08	.04
174	Dick Hall	.10	.08	.04
175	Bert Hamric	.10	.08	.04
176	Larry Haney	.10	.08	.04
177	Ron Hansen	.12	.09	.05
178	Jim Hardin	.10	.08	.04
179	Larry Harlow	.10	.08	.04
180	Pete Harnisch	.15	.11	.06
181	Tommy Harper	.12	.09	.05
182	Bob Harrison	.10	.08	.04
183	Roric Harrison	.10	.08	.04
184	Jack Harshman	.10	.08	.04
185	Mike Hart	.10	.08	.04
186	Paul Hartzell	.10	.08	.04
187	Grady Hatton	.10	.08	.04
188	Brad Havens	.10	.08	.04
189	Drungo Hazewood	.10	.08	.04
190	Jehosie Heard	.10	.08	.04
191	Mel Held	.10	.08	.04
192	Woodie Held	.10	.08	.04
193	Ellie Hendricks	.12	.09	.05
194	Leo Hernandez	.10	.08	.04
195	Whitey Herzog	.15	.11	.06
196	Kevin Hickey	.10	.08	.04
197	Billy Hoeft	.10	.08	.04
198	Chris Hoiles	.15	.11	.06
199	Fred Holdsworth	.10	.08	.04
200	Brian Holton	.10	.08	.04
201	Ken Holtzman	.10	.08	.04
202	Don Hood	.10	.08	.04
203	Sam Horn	.10	.08	.04
204	Art Houtteman	.10	.08	.04
205	Bruce Howard	.10	.08	.04
206	Rex Hudler	.10	.08	.04
207	Phil Huffman	.10	.08	.04
208	Keith Hughes	.10	.08	.04
209	Mark Huismann	.10	.08	.04
210	Tim Hulett	.10	.08	.04
211	Billy Hunter	.10	.08	.04
212	Dave Huppert	.10	.08	.04
213	Jim Hutto	.10	.08	.04
214	Dick Hyde	.10	.08	.04
215	Grant Jackson	.10	.08	.04
216	Lou Jackson	.10	.08	.04
217	Reggie Jackson	.50	.40	.20
218	Ron Jackson	.10	.08	.04
219	Jesse Jefferson	.10	.08	.04
220	Stan Jefferson	.10	.08	.04
221	Bob Johnson	.10	.08	.04
222	Connie Johnson	.10	.08	.04
223	Darrell Johnson	.10	.08	.04
224	Dave Johnson	.10	.08	.04
225	Davey Johnson	.12	.09	.05
226	David Johnson	.10	.08	.04
227	Don Johnson	.10	.08	.04
228	Ernie Johnson	.10	.08	.04
229	Gordon Jones	.10	.08	.04
230	Ricky Jones	.10	.08	.04
231	O'Dell Jones	.10	.08	.04
232	Sam Jones	.10	.08	.04
233	George Kell	.35	.25	.14
234	Frank Kellert	.10	.08	.04
235	Pat Kelly	.10	.08	.04
236	Bob Kennedy	.10	.08	.04
237	Terry Kennedy	.10	.08	.04
238	Joe Kerrigan	.10	.08	.04
239	Mike Kinnunen	.10	.08	.04
240	Willie Kirkland	.10	.08	.04
241	Ron Kittle	.10	.08	.04
242	Billy Klaus	.10	.08	.04
243	Ray Knight	.12	.09	.05
244	Darold Knowles	.10	.08	.04
245	Dick Kokos	.10	.08	.04
246	Brad Komminsk	.10	.08	.04
247	Dave Koslo	.10	.08	.04
248	Wayne Krenchicki	.10	.08	.04
249	Lou Kretlow	.10	.08	.04
250	Dick Kryhoski	.10	.08	.04
251	Bob Kuzava	.10	.08	.04
252	Lee Lacy	.10	.08	.04
253	Hobie Landrith	.10	.08	.04
254	Tito Landrum	.10	.08	.04
255	Don Larsen	.12	.09	.05
256	Charlie Lau	.12	.09	.05

257	Jim Lehew	.10	.08	.04
258	Ken Lehman	.10	.08	.04
259	Don Lenhardt	.10	.08	.04
260	Dave Leonhard	.10	.08	.04
261	Don Leppert	.10	.08	.04
262	Dick Littlefield	.10	.08	.04
263	Charlie Locke	.10	.08	.04
264	Whitey Lockman	.10	.08	.04
265	Billy Loes	.10	.08	.04
266	Ed Lopat	.10	.08	.04
267	Carlos Lopez	.10	.08	.04
268	Marcelino Lopez	.10	.08	.04
269	John Lowenstein	.10	.08	.04
270	Steve Luebber	.10	.08	.04
271	Dick Luebke	.10	.08	.04
272	Fred Lynn	.20	.15	.08
273	Bobby Mabe	.10	.08	.04
274	Elliott Maddox	.10	.08	.04
275	Hank Majeski	.10	.08	.04
276	Roger Marquis	.10	.08	.04
277	Freddie Marsh	.10	.08	.04
278	Jim Marshall	.10	.08	.04
279	Morrie Martin	.10	.08	.04
280	Dennis Martinez	.15	.11	.06
281	Tippy Martinez	.12	.09	.05
282	Tom Matchick	.10	.08	.04
283	Charlie Maxwell	.10	.08	.04
284	Dave May	.10	.08	.04
285	Lee May	.10	.08	.04
286	Rudy May	.10	.08	.04
287	Mike McCormick	.10	.08	.04
288	Ben McDonald	.15	.11	.06
289	Jim McDonald	.10	.08	.04
290	Scott McGregor	.12	.09	.05
291	Mickey McGuire	.10	.08	.04
292	Jeff McKnight	.10	.08	.04
293	Dave McNally	.12	.09	.05
294	Sam Mele	.10	.08	.04
295	Francisco Melendez	.10	.08	.04
296	Bob Melvin	.10	.08	.04
297	Jose Mesa	.10	.08	.04
298	Eddie Miksis	.10	.08	.04
299	Bob Milacki	.10	.08	.04
300	Bill Miller	.10	.08	.04
301	Dyar Miller	.10	.08	.04
302	John Miller	.10	.08	.04
303	Randy Miller	.10	.08	.04
304	Stu Miller	.10	.08	.04
305	Randy Milligan	.12	.09	.05
306	Paul Mirabella	.10	.08	.04
307	Willy Miranda	.10	.08	.04
308	John Mitchell	.10	.08	.04
309	Paul Mitchell	.10	.08	.04
310	Ron Moeller	.10	.08	.04
311	Bob Molinaro	.10	.08	.04
312	Ray Moore	.10	.08	.04
313	Andres Mora	.10	.08	.04
314	Jose Morales	.10	.08	.04
315	Keith Moreland	.10	.08	.04
316	Mike Morgan	.10	.08	.04
317	Dan Morogiello	.10	.08	.04
318	John Morris	.10	.08	.04
319	Les Moss	.10	.08	.04
320	Curt Motton	.10	.08	.04
321	Eddie Murray	.35	.25	.14
322	Ray Murray	.10	.08	.04
323	Tony Muser	.10	.08	.04
324	Buster Narum	.10	.08	.04
325	Bob Nelson	.10	.08	.04
326	Roger Nelson	.10	.08	.04
327	Carl Nichols	.10	.08	.04
328	Dave Nicholson	.10	.08	.04
329	Tom Niedenfuer	.10	.08	.04
330	Bob Nieman	.10	.08	.04
331	Donell Nixon	.10	.08	.04
332	Joe Nolan	.10	.08	.04
333	Dickie Noles	.10	.08	.04
334	Tim Nordbrook	.10	.08	.04
335	Jim Northrup	.10	.08	.04
336	Jack O'Connor	.10	.08	.04
337	Billy O'Dell	.10	.08	.04
338	John O'Donoghue	.10	.08	.04
339	Tom O'Malley	.10	.08	.04
340	Johnny Oates	.12	.09	.05
341	Chuck Oertel	.10	.08	.04
342	Bob Oliver	.10	.08	.04
343	Gregg Olson	.12	.09	.05
344	John Orsino	.10	.08	.04
345	Joe Orsulak	.15	.11	.06
346	John Pacella	.10	.08	.04
347	Dave Pagan	.10	.08	.04
348	Erv Palica	.10	.08	.04
349	Jim Palmer	.50	.40	.20
350	John Papa	.10	.08	.04
351	Milt Pappas	.10	.08	.04
352	Al Pardo	.10	.08	.04
353	Kelly Paris	.10	.08	.04
354	Mike Parrott	.10	.08	.04
355	Tom Patton	.10	.08	.04
356	Albie Pearson	.10	.08	.04
357	Orlando Pena	.10	.08	.04
358	Oswaldo Peraza	.10	.08	.04
359	Buddy Peterson	.10	.08	.04
360	Dave Philley	.10	.08	.04
361	Tom Phoebus	.10	.08	.04
362	Al Pilarcik	.10	.08	.04
363	Duane Pillette	.10	.08	.04
364	Lou Piniella	.12	.09	.05
365	Dave Pope	.10	.08	.04
366	Arnie Portocarrero	.10	.08	.04
367	Boog Powell	.35	.25	.14
368	Johnny Powers	.10	.08	.04
369	Carl Powis	.10	.08	.04
370	Joe Price	.10	.08	.04
371	Jim Pyburn	.10	.08	.04
372	Art Quirk	.10	.08	.04
373	Jamie Quirk	.10	.08	.04
374	Allan Ramirez	.10	.08	.04
375	Floyd Rayford	.10	.08	.04
376	Mike Reinbach	.10	.08	.04
377	Merv Rettenmund	.10	.08	.04
378	Bob Reynolds	.10	.08	.04
379	Del Rice	.10	.08	.04
380	Pete Richert	.10	.08	.04
381	Jeff Rineer	.10	.08	.04
382	Bill Ripken	.10	.08	.04
383	Cal Ripken	1.50	1.25	.60
384	Robin Roberts	.25	.20	.10
385	Brooks Robinson	1.00	.70	.40
386	Earl Robinson	.10	.08	.04
387	Eddie Robinson	.10	.08	.04
388	Frank Robinson	.50	.40	.20
389	Sergio Robles	.10	.08	.04
390	Aurelio Rodriguez	.10	.08	.04
391	Vic Rodriguez	.10	.08	.04
392	Gary Roenicke	.10	.08	.04
393	Saul Rogovin	.10	.08	.04
394	Wade Rowdon	.10	.08	.04
395	Ken Rowe	.10	.08	.04
396	Willie Royster	.10	.08	.04
397	Vic Roznovsky	.10	.08	.04
398	Ken Rudolph	.10	.08	.04
399	Lenn Sakata	.10	.08	.04
400	Chico Salmon	.10	.08	.04
401	Orlando Sanchez	.10	.08	.04
402	Bob Saverine	.10	.08	.04
403	Art Schallock	.10	.08	.04
404	Bill Scherrer	.10	.08	.04
405	Curt Schilling	.12	.09	.05
406	Dave Schmidt	.10	.08	.04
407	Johnny Schmitz	.10	.08	.04
408	Jeff Schneider	.10	.08	.04
409	Rick Schu	.10	.08	.04
410	Mickey Scott	.10	.08	.04
411	Kal Segrist	.10	.08	.04
412	David Segui	.10	.08	.04
413	Al Severinsen	.10	.08	.04
414	Larry Sheets	.10	.08	.04
415	John Shelby	.10	.08	.04
416	Barry Shetrone	.10	.08	.04
417	Tom Shopay	.10	.08	.04
418	Bill Short	.10	.08	.04
419	Norm Siebern	.10	.08	.04
420	Nelson Simmons	.10	.08	.04
421	Ken Singleton	.12	.09	.05
422	Doug Sisk	.10	.08	.04
423	Dave Skaggs	.10	.08	.04
424	Lou Sleater	.10	.08	.04
425	Al Smith	.10	.08	.04
426	Billy Smith	.10	.08	.04
427	Hal Smith	.10	.08	.04
428	"Texas" Mike Smith	.10	.08	.04
429	Nate Smith	.10	.08	.04
430	Nate Snell	.10	.08	.04
431	Russ Snyder	.10	.08	.04
432	Don Stanhouse	.10	.08	.04
433	Pete Stanicek	.10	.08	.04
434	Herm Starrette	.10	.08	.04
435	John Stefero	.10	.08	.04
436	Gene Stephens	.10	.08	.04
437	Vern Stephens	.10	.08	.04
438	Earl Stephenson	.10	.08	.04
439	Sammy Stewart	.10	.08	.04
440	Royle Stillman	.10	.08	.04
441	Wes Stock	.10	.08	.04
442	Tim Stoddard	.10	.08	.04
443	Dean Stone	.10	.08	.04
444	Jeff Stone	.10	.08	.04
445	Steve Stone	.12	.09	.05
446	Marlin Stuart	.10	.08	.04
447	Gordie Sundin	.10	.08	.04
448	Bill Swaggerty	.10	.08	.04
449	Willie Tasby	.10	.08	.04
450	Joe Taylor	.10	.08	.04
451	Dorn Taylor	.10	.08	.04
452	Anthony Telford	.10	.08	.04
453	Johnny Temple	.10	.08	.04
454	Mickey Tettleton	.15	.11	.06
455	Valmy Thomas	.10	.08	.04
456	Bobby Thomson	.15	.11	.06
457	Marv Thorneberry	.10	.08	.04
458	Mark Thurmond	.10	.08	.04
459	Jay Tibbs	.10	.08	.04
460	Mike Torrez	.10	.08	.04
461	Jim Traber	.10	.08	.04
462	Gus Triandos	.10	.08	.04
463	Paul "Dizzy" Trout	.10	.08	.04
464	Bob Turley	.10	.08	.04
465	Tom Underwood	.10	.08	.04
466	Fred Valentine	.10	.08	.04
467	Dave Van Gorder	.10	.08	.04
468	Dave Vineyard	.10	.08	.04
469	Ozzie Virgil	.10	.08	.04
470	Eddie Waitkus	.10	.08	.04
471	Greg Walker	.10	.08	.04
472	Jerry Walker	.10	.08	.04
473	Pete Ward	.10	.08	.04
474	Carl Warwick	.10	.08	.04
475	Ron Washington	.10	.08	.04
476	Eddie Watt	.10	.08	.04
477	Don Welchel	.10	.08	.04
478	George Werley	.10	.08	.04
479	Vic Wertz	.10	.08	.04
480	Wally Westlake	.10	.08	.04
481	Mickey Weston	.10	.08	.04
482	Alan Wiggins	.10	.08	.04
483	Bill Wight	.10	.08	.04
484	Hoyt Wilhelm	.25	.20	.10
485	Dallas Williams	.10	.08	.04
486	Dick Williams	.10	.08	.04
487	Earl Williams	.10	.08	.04
488	Mark Williamson	.10	.08	.04
489	Jim Wilson	.10	.08	.04
490	Gene Woodling	.10	.08	.04
491	Craig Worthington	.10	.08	.04
492	Bobby Young	.10	.08	.04
493	Mike Young	.10	.08	.04
494	Frank Zupo	.10	.08	.04
495	George Zuverink	.10	.08	.04
496	Glenn Davis	.10	.08	.04
497	Dwight Evans	.12	.09	.05
498	Dave Gallagher	.10	.08	.04
499	Paul Kilgus	.10	.08	.04
500	Jeff Robinson	.10	.08	.04
501	Ernie Whitt	.10	.08	.04

1992 Crown Orioles Action Standups

Crown Petroleum released a set of standup cards in 1992 of 12 Oriole greats, most retired, that was sold at Crown service stations in three series. In the second straight year that the company produced a card set, Crown issued the cards in three, four-card series. Cal Ripken and Tippy Martinez were the only active players portrayed in the set.

		MT	NR MT	EX
Complete Set:		16.00	12.00	6.50
Common Player:		.75	.60	.30
	Series I			
(1)	Frank Robinson	3.00	2.25	1.25
(2)	Brooks Robinson	3.00	2.25	1.25
(3)	Jim Palmer	3.00	2.25	1.25
(4)	Rick Dempsey	.75	.60	.30
	Series II			
(1)	Cal Ripken, Jr.	5.00	3.75	2.00
(2)	Tippy Martinez	.75	.60	.30
(3)	Bobby Grich	.75	.60	.30
(4)	Earl Weaver	1.50	1.25	.60
	Series III			
(1)	Boog Powell	1.50	1.25	.60
(2)	Paul Blair	.75	.60	.30
(3)	Terry Crowley	.75	.60	.30
(4)	Ken Singleton	.75	.60	.30

1911 Cullivan's Fireside Philadelphia A's

The 1911 T208 Fireside set, an 18-card Philadelphia Athletics set issued by the Thomas Cullivan Tobacco Company of Syracuse, N.Y., is among the rarest and most valuable of all 20th Century tobacco issues. Cullivan issued the set to commemorate the Athletics' 1910 Championship season, and, except for pitcher Jack Coombs, the checklist includes nearly all key members of the club, including manager Connie Mack. The cards are the standard size for tobacco issues, 1-1/2" by 2-5/8". The front of each card features a player portrait set against a colored background. The player's name and the word "Athletics" appear at the bottom, while "World's Champions 1910" is printed along the top. The backs of the cards advertise the set as the "Athletics Series" and advise that one card is included in each package of "Cullivan's Fireside Plain Scrap" tobacco. Collectors should be aware that the same checklist was used for a similar Athletics set issued by Rochester Baking/Williams Baking (D359) and also that blank-backed versions are also known to exist, but these are classified as E104 cards in the American Card Catalog.

		NR MT	EX	VG
Complete Set:		13000.	6500.	3900.
Common Player:		500.00	250.00	150.00
(1)	Home Run Baker	1500.	750.00	450.00
(2)	Jack Barry	500.00	250.00	150.00
(3)	Chief Bender	1500.	750.00	450.00
(4)	Eddie Collins	1500.	750.00	450.00
(5)	Harry Davis	500.00	250.00	150.00
(6)	Jimmy Dygert	500.00	250.00	150.00
(7)	Topsy Hartsel	500.00	250.00	150.00
(8)	Harry Krause	500.00	250.00	150.00

(9)	Jack Lapp	500.00	250.00	150.00
(10)	Paddy Livingstone (Livingston)	500.00	250.00	150.00
(11)	Bris Lord	500.00	250.00	150.00
(12)	Connie Mack	2000.	1000.	600.00
(13)	Cy Morgan	500.00	250.00	150.00
(14)	Danny Murphy	500.00	250.00	150.00
(15)	Rube Oldring	500.00	250.00	150.00
(16)	Eddie Plank	2000.	1000.	600.00
(17)	Amos Strunk	500.00	250.00	150.00
(18)	Ira Thomas	500.00	250.00	150.00'

D

1972 Daily Juice Co.

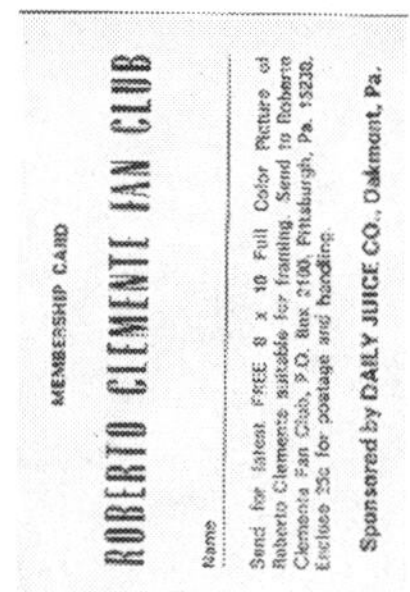

This one-card "set" was regionally issued to Roberto Clemente Fan Club members. Large numbers of the cards found their way into the hobby, including in uncut sheet form. The cards feature a full-color and black-and-white back. The card measures the standard 2-1/2" in width but is somewhat longer, at 3-3/4". This unnumbbered card remains about the least expensive baseball card that was issued during Clemente's lifetime.

	NR MT	EX	VG
Roberto Clemente	3.00	1.50	.90

1992 Dairy Queen Team USA

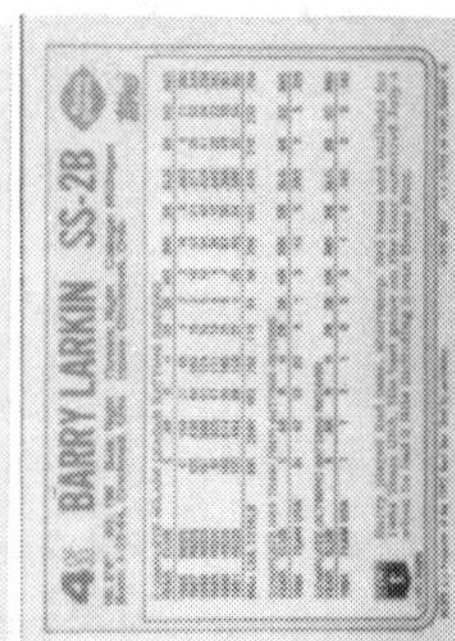

In 1992, in conjunction with the Dairy Queen Team USA Sundae-in-a-Helmet promotion, customers received a four-card pack of Team USA cards, part of a 33-card set manufactured by Topps for the company. Included in the set are 16 Team USA players from the 1984 and 1988 Olympics who have gone on to major league stardom. The set also has 15 Team USA Prospects, a 1988 Gold Medal team celebration card and a card of 1992 coach Ron Fraser. The front of the card features each player in their Team USA uniform and the backs include statistics from amateur, Team USA and professional competition.

		MT	NR MT	EX
Complete Set (33):		20.00	15.00	7.50
Common Player:		.25	.20	.10
1	Mark McGwire (1984)	2.00	1.50	.80
2	Will Clark (1984)	3.00	2.25	1.20
3	John Marzano (1984)	.25	.20	.10
4	Barry Larkin (1984)	1.00	.75	.40
5	Bobby Witt (1984)	.50	.40	.20
6	Scott Bankhead (1984)	.25	.20	.10
7	B.J. Surhoff (1984)	.50	.40	.20
8	Shane Mack (1984)	.75	.60	.30
9	Jim Abbott (1988)	1.50	1.25	.60
10	Ben McDonald (1988)	.50	.40	.20
11	Robin Ventura (1988)	1.00	.70	.40
12	Charles Nagy (1988)	.35	.25	.14
13	Andy Benes (1988)	.50	.40	.20
14	Joe Slusarski (1988)	.35	.25	.14
15	Ed Sprague (1988)	.35	.25	.14
16	Bret Barberie (1988)	.35	.25	.14
17	Gold Medal (1988)	.25	.20	.10
18	Jeff Granger (1992)	.25	.20	.10
19	John Dettmer (1992)	.25	.20	.10
20	Todd Greene (1992)	.25	.20	.10
21	Jeffrey Hammonds (1992)	.75	.60	.30
22	Dan Melendez (1992)	.25	.20	.10
23	Kennie Steenstra (1992)	.25	.20	.10
24	Todd Johnson (1992)	.25	.20	.10
25	Chris Roberts (1992)	.25	.20	.10
26	Steve Rodriguez (1992)	.25	.20	.10
27	Charles Johnson (1992)	.35	.25	.14
28	Chris Wimmer (1992)	.25	.20	.10
29	Tony Phillips (1992)	.35	.25	.14
30	Craig Wilson (1992)	.35	.25	.14
31	Jason Giambi (1992)	.35	.25	.14
32	Paul Shuey (1992)	.25	.20	.10
33	Ron Fraser (1992 coach)	.25	.20	.10

1954 Dan-Dee Potato Chips

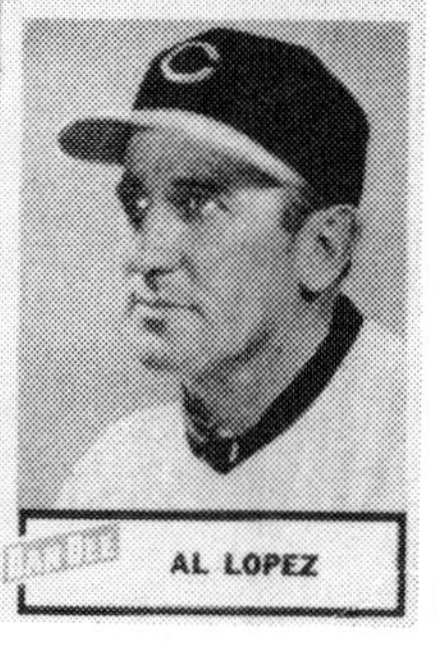

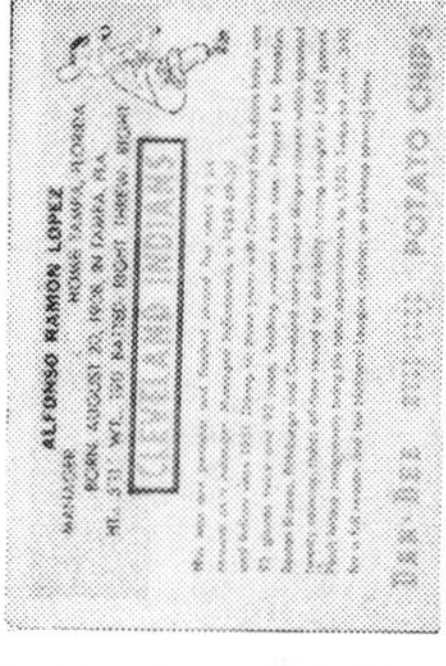

Issued in bags of potato chips, the cards in this 29-card set are commonly found with grease stains despite their waxed surface. The unnumbered cards, which measure 2-1/2" by 3-5/8", feature full-color photos. The card backs contain player statistical and biographical information. The set consists mostly of players from the Indians and Pirates. Photos of the Yankees players were also used for the Briggs Meats and Stahl-Meyer Franks sets. Cooper and Smith are the scarcest cards in the set.

		NR MT	EX	VG
Complete Set (29):		4500.	2250.	1350.
Common Player:		70.00	35.00	21.00
(1)	Bob Avila	70.00	35.00	21.00
(2)	Hank Bauer	87.50	44.00	26.00
(3)	Walker Cooper	400.00	200.00	120.00
(4)	Larry Doby	90.00	45.00	27.00
(5)	Luke Easter	70.00	35.00	21.00
(6)	Bob Feller	200.00	100.00	60.00
(7)	Bob Friend	70.00	35.00	21.00
(8)	Mike Garcia	70.00	35.00	21.00
(9)	Sid Gordon	70.00	35.00	21.00
(10)	Jim Hegan	70.00	35.00	21.00
(11)	Gil Hodges	150.00	75.00	45.00
(12)	Art Houtteman	70.00	35.00	21.00
(13)	Monte Irvin	100.00	50.00	30.00
(14)	Paul LaPalm (LaPalme)	70.00	35.00	21.00
(15)	Bob Lemon	110.00	55.00	33.00
(16)	Al Lopez	100.00	50.00	30.00
(17)	Mickey Mantle	1500.	650.00	350.00
(18)	Dale Mitchell	70.00	35.00	21.00
(19)	Phil Rizzuto	165.00	82.50	50.00
(20)	Curtis Roberts	70.00	35.00	21.00
(21)	Al Rosen	80.00	40.00	24.00
(22)	Red Schoendienst	110.00	55.00	33.00
(23)	Paul Smith	450.00	225.00	135.00
(24)	Duke Snider	240.00	120.00	72.00
(25)	George Strickland	70.00	35.00	21.00
(26)	Max Surkont	70.00	35.00	21.00
(27)	Frank J. Thomas	125.00	62.00	37.00
(28)	Wally Westlake	70.00	35.00	21.00
(29)	Early Wynn	110.00	55.00	33.00

Grading Guide

Mint (MT): A perfect card. Well-centered with all corners sharp and square. No creases, stains, edge nicks, surface marks, yellowing or fading.

Near Mint (NM): A nearly perfect card. At first glance, a NM card appears to be perfect. May be slightly off-center. No surface marks, creases or loss of gloss.

Excellent (EX): Corners are still fairly sharp with only moderate wear. Borders may be off-center. No creases or stains on fronts or backs, but may show slight loss of surface luster.

Very Good (VG): Shows obvious handling. May have rounded corners, minor creases, major gum or wax stains. No major creases, tape marks, writing, etc.

Good (G): A well-worn card, but exhibits no intentional damage. May have major or multiple creases. Corners may be rounded well beyond card border.

1910 Darby Chocolates (E271)

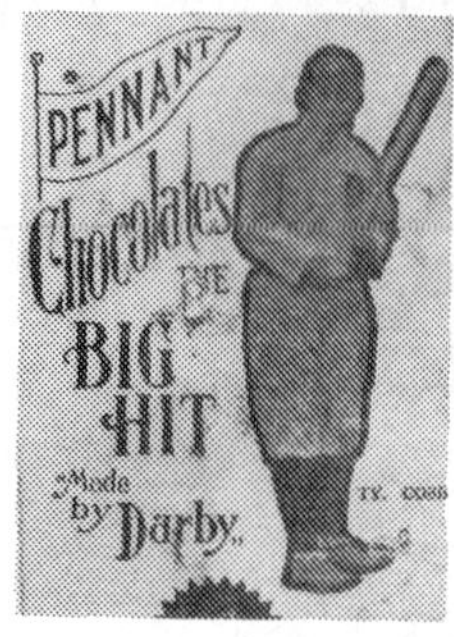

Designated as E271 by the ACC, the 1910 Darby Chocolates cards are among the rarest of all candy cards. The cards were printed on boxes of Darby's "Pennant" Chocolates, two players per box - one on the front of the box, the other on the back. The cards feature black and white player silhouettes outlined with a thick dark line. The cards are accented with orange or green tinting. Most of the 32 known examples of this set were not found until 1982, and there is speculation that the checklist is still not complete.

		NR MT	EX	VG
Complete Set:		35000.	17500.	10500.
Common Player:		400.00	200.00	120.00
(1)	Jimmy Archer	400.00	200.00	120.00
(2)	Chief Bender	800.00	400.00	240.00
(3)	"Bob" Bescher	400.00	200.00	120.00
(4)	Roger Bresnahan	800.00	400.00	240.00
(5)	Al Bridwell	400.00	200.00	120.00
(6)	Mordicai Brown (Mordecai)	800.00	400.00	240.00
(7)	"Eddie" Cicotte	650.00	325.00	195.00
(8)	Fred Clark (Clarke)	800.00	400.00	240.00
(9)	Ty. Cobb	2500.	1250.	750.00
(10)	King Cole	400.00	200.00	120.00
(11)	E. Collins	800.00	400.00	240.00
(12)	Wid Conroy	400.00	200.00	120.00
(13)	"Sam" Crawford	800.00	400.00	240.00
(14)	Bill Dahlin (Dahlen)	400.00	200.00	120.00
(15)	Bill Donovan	400.00	200.00	120.00
(16)	"Pat" Dougherty	400.00	200.00	120.00
(17)	Kid Elberfeld	400.00	200.00	120.00
(18)	"Johnny" Evers	800.00	400.00	240.00
(19)	Charlie Herzog	400.00	200.00	120.00
(20)	Walter Johnson	1500.	750.00	450.00
(21)	Ed Konetchy	400.00	200.00	120.00
(22)	Tommy Leach	400.00	200.00	120.00
(23)	Fred Luderous (Luderus)	400.00	200.00	120.00
(24)	"Mike" Mowery	400.00	200.00	120.00
(25)	Jack Powell	400.00	200.00	120.00
(26)	Slim Sallee	400.00	200.00	120.00
(27)	James Scheckard (Sheckard)	400.00	200.00	120.00
(28)	Walter Snodgrass	400.00	200.00	120.00
(29)	"Tris" Speaker	1000.	500.00	300.00
(30)	Charlie Suggs	400.00	200.00	120.00
(31)	Fred Tenney	400.00	200.00	120.00
(32)	"Hans" Wagner	2000.	1000.	600.00

1991 Jimmy Dean

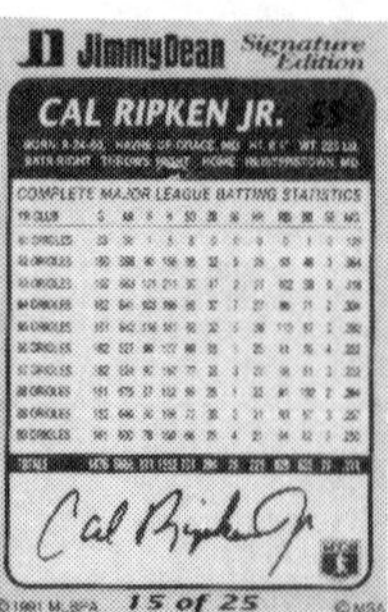

Baseball cards were inserted into packages of Jimmy Dean sausages in 1991. The complete set consists of 25 cards. Star players are featured in the set. Red and yellow borders surround fll-color player photos on the card fronts. No team logos appear on the cards. The card backs feature statistics, biographical information and a facsimile autograph. The set is entitled the "Signature Edition."

		MT	NR MT	EX
Complete Set:		12.00	9.00	4.75
Common Player:		.30	.25	.12
1	Will Clark	.60	.45	.25
2	Ken Griffey, Jr.	1.50	1.25	.60
3	Dale Murphy	.40	.30	.15
4	Barry Bonds	.40	.30	.15

5	Darryl Strawberry	.30	.25	.12
6	Ryne Sandberg	.70	.50	.30
7	Gary Sheffield	.40	.30	.15
8	Sandy Alomar, Jr.	.30	.25	.12
9	Frank Thomas	1.50	1.25	.60
10	Barry Larkin	.35	.25	.14
11	Kirby Puckett	.40	.30	.15
12	George Brett	.40	.30	.15
13	Kevin Mitchell	.30	.25	.12
14	Dave Justice	.60	.45	.25
15	Cal Ripken, Jr.	.70	.50	.30
16	Craig Biggio	.30	.25	.12
17	Rickey Henderson	.50	.40	.20
18	Roger Clemens	.50	.40	.20
19	Jose Canseco	.60	.45	.25
20	Ozzie Smith	.40	.30	.15
21	Cecil Fielder	.40	.30	.15
22	Dave Winfield	.40	.30	.15
23	Kevin Maas	.30	.25	.12
24	Nolan Ryan	1.50	1.25	.60
25	Dwight Gooden	.40	.30	.15

1992 Jimmy Dean

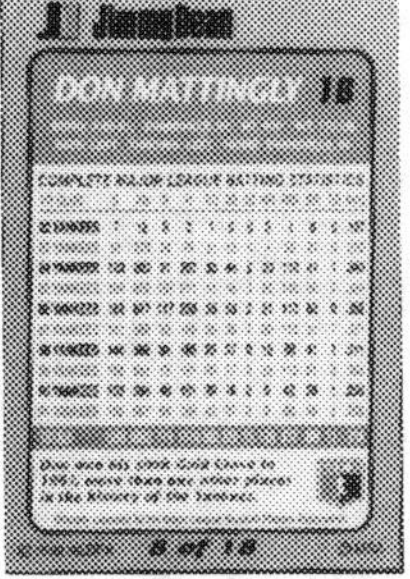

For the second year in a row, baseball cards were inserted into packages of Jimmy Dean sausage in 1992. Featuring 18 star players, the set portrays the player's name on a vertical panel at the left of the card, along with his team name and position. The Jimmy Dean logo appears in the lower right corner.

		MT	NR MT	EX
Complete Set (18):		9.00	6.75	3.50
Common Player:		.25	.20	.10
1	Jim Abbott	.35	.25	.14
2	Barry Bonds	.60	.45	.25
3	Jeff Bagwell	.30	.25	.12
4	Frank Thomas	1.50	1.25	.60
5	Steve Avery	.30	.25	.12
6	Chris Sabo	.25	.20	.10
7	Will Clark	.60	.45	.25
8	Don Mattingly	.60	.45	.25
9	Darryl Strawberry	.30	.25	.12
10	Roger Clemens	.35	.25	.14
11	Ken Griffey, Jr.	1.50	1.25	.60
12	Chuck Knoblauch	.35	.25	.14
13	Tony Gwynn	.35	.25	.14
14	Juan Gonzalez	.50	.40	.20
15	Cecil Fielder	.35	.25	.14
16	Bobby Bonilla	.30	.25	.12
17	Wes Chamberlain	.25	.20	.10
18	Ryne Sandberg	.70	.50	.30

1992 Jimmy Dean Living Legends

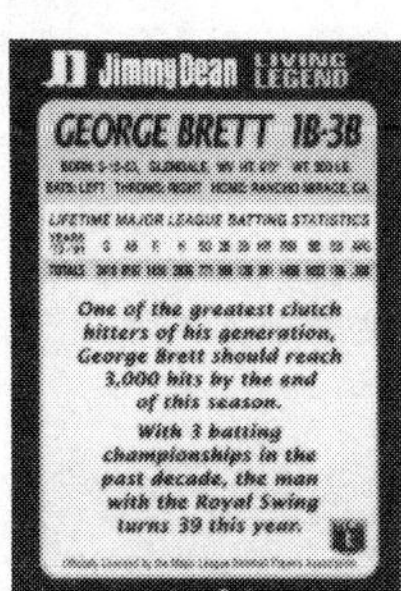

		MT	NR MT	EX
Complete Set (6):		20.00	15.00	8.00
Common Player:		3.00	2.25	1.25
1	George Brett	4.00	3.00	1.50
2	Carlton Fisk	3.00	2.25	1.25
3	Ozzie Smith	3.00	2.25	1.25
4	Robin Yount	4.00	3.00	1.50
5	Cal Ripken, Jr.	5.00	3.75	2.00
6	Nolan Ryan	6.00	4.50	2.50

A player's name in italic type indicates a rookie card. An (FC) indicates a player's first card for that particular card company.

1993 Jimmy Dean Rookie Cards

Jimmy Dean Foods issued a Rookie Stars baseball card set in 1993. The nine-card set featured promising rookies, with players highlighted against a marbelized background with color photos on both sides of the cards. The cards were distributed randomly in three-card sets in specially-marked packages of Jimmy Dean products.

		MT	NR MT	EX
Complete Set (9):		6.00	4.50	2.50
Common Player:		.25	.20	.10
(1)	Rich Amaral	.25	.20	.10
(2)	Vinny Castilla	.25	.20	.10
(3)	Jeff Conine	.50	.40	.20
(4)	Brent Gates	.35	.25	.14
(5)	Wayne Kirby	.25	.20	.10
(6)	Mike Lansing	.35	.25	.14
(7)	David Nied	.50	.40	.20
(8)	Mike Piazza	2.00	1.50	.80
(9)	Tim Salmon	2.00	1.50	.80

1933 DeLong

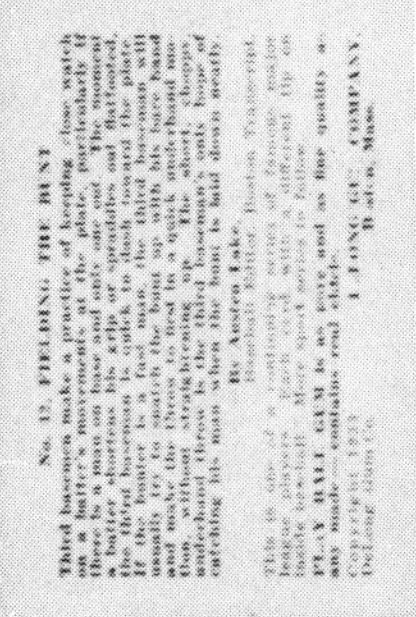

The DeLong Gum Company of Boston, Mass. was among the first to sell baseball cards with gum. It issued a set of 24 cards in 1933, the same year the Goudey Gum Co. issued its premiere set, making both companies pioneers in the field. The DeLong cards measure 2" by 3" and feature black and white player photos on a color background. The photos show the players in various action poses and positions them in the middle of a miniature stadium setting so that they appear to be giant in size. Most of the cards in the set are vertically designed, but a few are horizontal. The backs of the cards, written by Austen Lake, editor of the Boston Transcript, contain a series of sports tips to help youngsters become better ballplayers. Lake later wrote the tips that appeared on the backs of the Diamond Stars cards issued by National Chicle from 1934-1936. The ACC designation for this set is R333. The checklist below gives the players' names exactly as they appear on the fronts of the cards.

		NR MT	EX	VG
Complete Set (24):		10500.	5250.	3150.
Common Player:		225.00	112.00	67.00
1	"Marty" McManus	225.00	112.00	67.00
2	Al Simmons	275.00	137.00	75.00
3	Oscar Melillo	225.00	112.00	67.00
4	William (Bill) Terry	450.00	225.00	135.00
5	Charlie Gehringer	450.00	225.00	135.00
6	Gordon (Mickey) Cochrane	450.00	225.00	135.00
7	Lou Gehrig	3500.	1750.	1050.
8	Hazen S. (Kiki) Cuyler	335.00	167.00	100.00
9	Bill Urbanski	225.00	112.00	67.00
10	Frank J. (Lefty) O'Doul	225.00	112.00	67.00
11	Freddie Lindstrom	275.00	137.00	82.00
12	Harold (Pie) Traynor	335.00	167.00	100.00
13	"Rabbit" Maranville	335.00	167.00	100.00
14	Vernon "Lefty" Gomez	335.00	167.00	100.00
15	Riggs Stephenson	225.00	112.00	67.00
16	Lon Warneke	225.00	112.00	67.00
17	Pepper Martin	225.00	112.00	67.00
18	Jimmy Dykes	225.00	112.00	67.00
19	Chick Hafey	335.00	167.00	100.00
20	Joe Vosmik	225.00	112.00	67.00
21	Jimmy Foxx	600.00	300.00	175.00
22	Charles (Chuck) Klein	335.00	167.00	100.00
23	Robert (Lefty) Grove	500.00	250.00	150.00
24	"Goose" Goslin	335.00	167.00	100.00

1935 Al Demaree Die-cuts

Among the rarest of the 1930s gume cards are those issued by Dietz Gum Co., a Chicago confectioner, in packages of "Ball Players in Action Chewing Gum." The cards are so rare that the complete checklist may never be known. The set was cataloged as R304 in the American Card Catalog and is sometimes seen advertised as the Al Demaree die-cut issue. The cards feature photographic portraits of players set upon cartoon bodies drawn by former major league pitcher Demaree. The photo and artwork are generally in black-and-white, while the players on some teams have blue or red uniform details printed on. The cards can be folded to create a stand-up figure, but did not have a background to be cut or torn away, as is common with most die-cut baseball cards. Unfolded, the cards measure 6-1/2" long and from 1-5/8" to 1-3/4" wide, depending on pose.

		NR MT	EX	VG
Common Player:		250.00	125.00	75.00
4	Babe Ruth	7500.	3750.	2250.
6	Tony Lazzeri	500.00	250.00	150.00
7	Frank Crosetti	350.00	175.00	105.00
9	Lou Gehrig	5000.	2500.	1500.
11	Mule Haas	250.00	125.00	75.00
12	Evar Swenson	250.00	125.00	75.00
13	Marv Shea	250.00	125.00	75.00
14	Al Simmons (throwing)	500.00	250.00	150.00
15	Jack Hayes	250.00	125.00	75.00
16	Al Simmons (batting)	500.00	250.00	150.00
17	Jimmy Dykes	250.00	125.00	75.00
18	Luke Appling	500.00	250.00	150.00
19	Ted Lyons	500.00	250.00	150.00
20	Red Kress	250.00	125.00	75.00
21	Gee Walker	250.00	125.00	75.00
23	Mickey Cochrane (catching)	500.00	250.00	150.00
24	Mickey Cochrane (batting)	500.00	250.00	150.00
25	Pete Fox	250.00	125.00	75.00
26	Firpo Marberry	250.00	125.00	75.00
28	Mickey Owen	250.00	125.00	75.00
35	Joe Vosmik	250.00	125.00	75.00
41	Jack Burns	250.00	125.00	75.00
45	Ray Pepper	250.00	125.00	75.00
46	Bruce Campbel	250.00	125.00	75.00
48	Art Scharein	250.00	125.00	75.00
49	George Blaeholder	250.00	125.00	75.00
50	Rogers Hornsby	650.00	325.00	175.00
56	Dib Williams	250.00	125.00	75.00
57	Lou Finney	250.00	125.00	75.00
61	Ossie Bluege	250.00	125.00	75.00
64	Joe Cronin	500.00	250.00	150.00
66	Buddy Myer	250.00	125.00	75.00
67	Earl Whitehill	250.00	125.00	75.00
71	Ed Morgan	250.00	125.00	75.00
74	Carl Reynolds	250.00	125.00	75.00
76	Bill Cissell	250.00	125.00	75.00
77	Johnny Hodapp	250.00	125.00	75.00
78	Dusty Cooke	250.00	125.00	75.00
79	Lefty Grove	500.00	250.00	150.00
82	Gus Mancuso	250.00	125.00	75.00
83	Kiddo Davis	250.00	125.00	75.00
84	Blondy Ryan	250.00	125.00	75.00
86	Travis Jackson	500.00	250.00	150.00
89	Bill Terry	500.00	250.00	150.00
91	Tony Cuccinello	250.00	125.00	75.00
99	John Frederick	250.00	125.00	75.00
100	Sam Leslie	250.00	125.00	75.00
102	Mark Koenig	250.00	125.00	75.00
107	Syl Johnson	250.00	125.00	75.00
108	Jim Bottomley	500.00	250.00	150.00
112	Harvey Hendrick	250.00	125.00	75.00
115	Don Hurst	250.00	125.00	75.00
117	Prince Oana	250.00	125.00	75.00
121	Spud Davis	250.00	125.00	75.00
122	George Watkins	250.00	125.00	75.00
123	Frankie Frisch	500.00	250.00	150.00
125	Ripper Collins	250.00	125.00	75.00
126	Dizzy Dean	750.00	375.00	225.00

128	Joe Medwick	500.00	250.00	150.00
129	Leo Durocher	500.00	250.00	150.00
130	Ernie Orsatti	250.00	125.00	75.00
132	Shanty Hogan	250.00	125.00	75.00
137	Wally Berger	250.00	125.00	75.00
141	Gus Suhr	250.00	125.00	75.00
142	Earl Grace	250.00	125.00	75.00
152	Gabby Hartnett	500.00	250.00	150.00
154	Chuck Klein	500.00	250.00	150.00
158	Billy Herman	500.00	250.00	150.00
160	Charlie Grimm	250.00	125.00	75.00
162	Bill Klem	750.00	375.00	225.00
167	George Hildebrand	250.00	125.00	75.00
----	(All known specimens of cards below have had the tabs removed making it impossible to identify card numbers.)			
----	Willie Kamm	250.00	125.00	75.00
----	Jimmie Foxx	600.00	300.00	180.00
----	Pinky Higgins	250.00	125.00	75.00
----	Bob Johnson	250.00	125.00	75.00
----	Roy Mahaffey	250.00	125.00	75.00

1932 Charles Denby Cigars Cubs

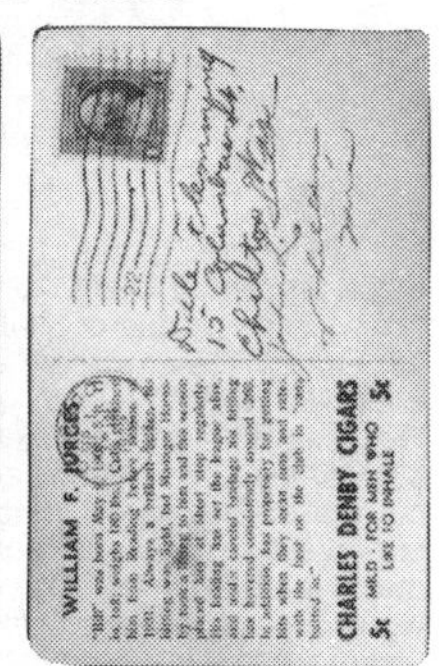

Actually a series of postcards, this Chicago Cubs set issued by the Charles Denby Company in 1932 is the last known tobacco issue produced before World War II. The cards are a standard postcard size (5-1/4" by 3-3/8") and feature a glossy black and white player photo with a facsimile autograph. In typical postcard style, the back of the card is divided in half, with a printed player profile on the left and room for the mailing address on the right. The back also includes an advertisement for Charles Denby Cigars, the mild five-cent cigar "for men who like to inhale". Only five different subjects have been reported to date, but there is speculation that more probably exist.

		NR MT	EX	VG
Complete Set:		500.00	250.00	150.00
Common Player:		80.00	40.00	24.00
(1)	Elwood English	80.00	40.00	24.00
(2)	Charles J. Grimm	110.00	55.00	33.00
(3)	William Herman	175.00	87.00	52.00
(4)	William F. Jurges	80.00	40.00	24.00
(5)	Lonnie Warneke	80.00	40.00	24.00

1991 Denny's Grand Slam

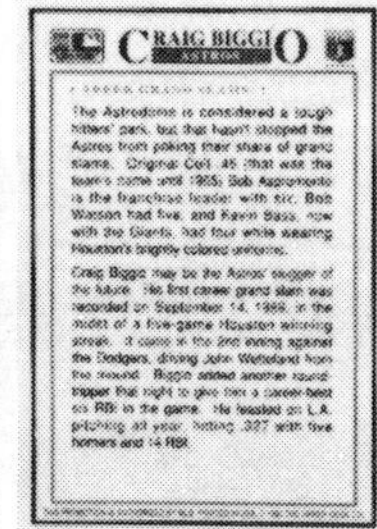

This 26-card set was produced by Upper Deck and features one player from each Major League team. One hologram card was distributed with the purchase of a Grand Slam meal. The cards are numbered on the front and are 3-D. The card backs describe grand slams hit by the featured player.

		MT	NR MT	EX
Complete Set:		50.00	37.00	20.00
Common Player:		1.50	1.25	.60
1	Ellis Burks	1.50	1.25	.60
2	Cecil Fielder	3.00	2.25	1.25
3	Will Clark	4.00	3.00	1.50
4	Eric Davis	2.00	1.50	.80
5	Dave Parker	2.00	1.50	.80
6	Kelly Gruber	1.50	1.25	.60
7	Kent Hrbek	2.00	1.50	.80
8	Don Mattingly	3.50	2.75	1.50
9	Brook Jacoby	1.50	1.25	.60
10	Mark McGwire	3.00	2.25	1.25
11	Howard Johnson	2.00	1.50	.80
12	Tim Wallach	1.50	1.25	.60
13	Ricky Jordan	1.50	1.25	.60
14	Andre Dawson	2.50	2.00	1.00
15	Eddie Murray	2.50	2.00	1.00
16	Danny Tartabull	1.50	1.25	.60
17	Bobby Bonilla	2.00	1.50	.80
18	Benito Santiago	1.50	1.25	.60
19	Alvin Davis	1.50	1.25	.60
20	Cal Ripken	5.00	3.75	2.00
21	Ruben Sierra	2.00	1.50	.80
22	Pedro Guererro	1.50	1.25	.60
23	Wally Joyner	1.50	1.25	.60
24	Craig Biggio	1.50	1.25	.60
25	Dave Justice	2.50	2.00	1.00
26	Tim Raines	1.50	1.25	.60

1992 Denny's Grand Slam

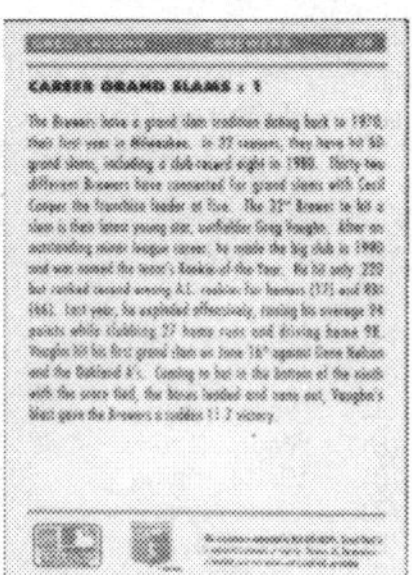

The second year of the Denny's Gland Slam promotion featured one power hitter from each major league team in 1992, portrayed on a hologram in front of a scene from his team's city. As in the first year, the cards were produced by Upper Deck and given away, one at a time, with a Denny's purchase during the middle of the summer. The set totals 26 cards.

		MT	NR MT	EX
Complete Set:		50.00	37.00	20.00
Common Player:		1.50	1.25	.60
1	Marquis Grissom	1.50	1.25	.60
2	Kem Caminiti	1.50	1.25	.60
3	Fred McGriff	2.50	2.00	1.00
4	Felix Jose	1.50	1.25	.60
5	Jack Clark	1.50	1.25	.60
6	Albert Belle	2.50	2.00	1.00
7	Sid Bream	1.50	1.25	.60
8	Robin Ventura	2.00	1.50	.80
9	Cal Ripken, Jr.	5.00	3.75	2.00
10	Ryne Sandberg	5.00	3.75	2.00
11	Paul O'Neill	1.50	1.25	.60
12	Luis Polonia	1.50	1.25	.60
13	Cecil Fielder	3.00	2.25	1.25
14	Kal Daniels	1.50	1.25	.60
15	Brian McRae	1.50	1.25	.60
16	Howard Johnson	1.50	1.25	.60
17	Greg Vaughn	1.50	1.25	.60
18	Dale Murphy	2.50	2.00	1.00
19	Kent Hrbek	2.00	1.50	.80
20	Barry Bonds	3.00	2.25	1.25
21	Matt Nokes	1.50	1.25	.60
22	Jose Canseco	3.00	2.25	1.25
23	Jay Buhner	1.50	1.25	.60
24	Will Clark	3.00	2.25	1.25
25	Ruben Sierra	2.00	1.50	.80
26	Joe Carter	2.00	1.50	.80

1993 Denny's Grand Slam Holograms

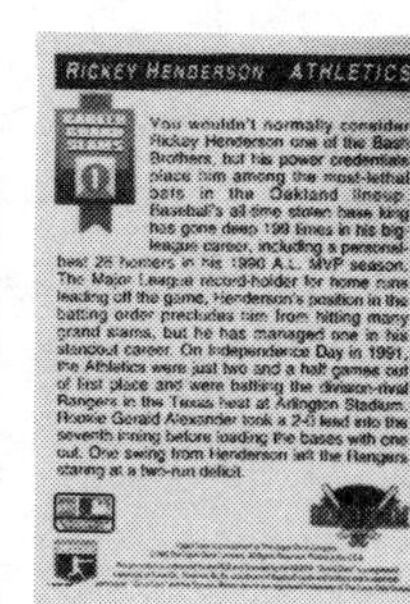

The 1993 Denny's Gland Slam set expanded to 28 cards with the addition of the Florida and Colorado expansion teams. The featured color photos of one grand slam slugger for each team superimposed over a hologram background. The reverse of each card gives anecdotes about the player's grand slams along with his career total. The cards were distributed at participating Denny's restaurants during mid-summer.

		MT	NR MT	EX
Complete Set:		50.00	37.00	20.00
Common Player:		1.50	1.25	.60
1	Chili Davis	1.50	1.25	.60
2	Eric Anthony	1.50	1.25	.60
3	Rickey Henderson	3.00	2.25	1.25
4	Joe Carter	2.00	1.50	.80
5	Terry Pendleton	1.50	1.25	.60
6	Robin Yount	4.00	3.00	1.50
7	Ray Lankford	2.00	1.50	.80
8	Ryne Sandberg	5.00	3.75	2.00
9	Darryl Strawberry	2.00	1.50	.80
10	Marquis Grissom	1.50	1.25	.60
11	Will Clark	3.00	2.25	1.25
12	Albert Belle	2.00	1.50	.80
13	Edgar Martinez	1.50	1.25	.60
14	Benito Santiago	1.50	1.25	.60
15	Eddie Murray	2.50	2.00	1.00
16	Cal Ripken, Jr.	5.00	3.75	2.00
17	Gary Sheffield	2.00	1.50	.80
18	Dave Hollins	2.00	1.50	.80
19	Andy Van Slyke	1.50	1.25	.60
20	Juan Gonzalez	3.00	2.25	1.25
21	John Valentin	1.50	1.25	.60
22	Joe Oliver	1.50	1.25	.60
23	Dante Bichette	2.00	1.50	.80
24	Wally Joyner	1.50	1.25	.60
25	Cecil Fielder	3.00	2.25	1.25
26	Kirby Puckett	4.00	3.00	1.50
27	Robin Ventura	2.00	1.50	.80
28	Danny Tartabull	1.50	1.25	.60

1909 Derby Cigars

Although there is no advertising on these cards to indicate their origin, it is generally accepted that this 1909 set was issued by Derby Cigars, a product of the American Tobacco Co. A dozen different subjects, all members of the New York Giants, have been found. Much uncertainty still surrounds this obscure set, but it is believed that the cards, which measure 1-3/4" by 2-3/4", were inserted in boxes of Derby "Little Cigars." The cards feature a player portrait inside an oval with the player's name and position at the bottom.

		NR MT	EX	VG
Complete Set:		800.00	400.00	250.00
Common Player:		40.00	20.00	12.00
(1)	Josh Devore	40.00	20.00	12.00
(2)	Larry Doyle	50.00	25.00	15.00
(3)	Art Fletcher	40.00	20.00	12.00
(4)	Buck Herzog	40.00	20.00	12.00
(5)	Rube Marquard	100.00	50.00	30.00
(6)	Christy Mathewson	225.00	112.00	67.00
(7)	Fred Merkle	50.00	25.00	15.00
(8)	Chief Meyers	40.00	20.00	12.00
(9)	Red Murray	40.00	20.00	12.00
(10)	John McGraw	100.00	50.00	30.00
(11)	Fred Snodgrass	40.00	20.00	12.00
(12)	Hooks Wiltse	40.00	20.00	12.00

1993 DiamondMarks Promos

In the same format as the regular-issue DiamondMark cards, these promos were produced to preview the concept for dealers and collectors. The promo cards feature different photos than those used on the issued version. The unnumbered cards are listed here alphabetically.

		MT	NR MT	EX
Complete Set (8):		100.00	75.00	40.00
Common Player:		15.00	11.00	6.00
(1)	Roberto Alomar	15.00	11.00	6.00
(2)	Will Clark	20.00	15.00	8.00
(3)	Dennis Eckersley	15.00	11.00	6.00
(4)	Ken Griffey, Jr.	35.00	26.00	14.00
(5)	Juan Gonzalez	20.00	15.00	8.00
(6)	Ryne Sandberg	25.00	18.50	10.00
(7)	Frank Thomas	35.00	26.00	14.00
(8)	Kirby Puckett	20.00	15.00	8.00

1993 DiamondMarks

While they look like baseball cards and were sold in foil packs like baseball cards, DaimondMarks were licensed as book marks. Issued by Barry Colla Productions, the 2-1/2" x 5" cards feature Barry Colla's trademark high-quality player photos on front and back. The UV-coated fronts feature black borders with the player's name in white above the photo and a color team logo beneath. Backs, also bordered in black, feature two color player photos in an open book design. There is a portrait photo on the left and a head-and-shoulders reproduction of the front photo at right. A bookmark with team lofo is incorporated in the design. The 120-card set is unnumbered and is arranged in the checklist below alphabetically within league and team.

		MT	NR MT	EX
Complete Set:		30.00	22.00	12.00
Common Player:		.25	.20	.10
	ATLANTA BRAVES			
(1)	Steve Avery	.50	.40	.20
(2)	Ron Gant	.50	.40	.20
(3)	Tom Glavine	.50	.40	.20
(4)	David Justice	1.00	.70	.40
(5)	Terry Pendleton	.25	.20	.10
(6)	Deion Sanders	1.00	.70	.40
(7)	John Smoltz	.50	.40	.20
	CHICAGO CUBS			
(8)	Mark Grace	.50	.40	.20
(9)	Randy Myers	.25	.20	.10
(10)	Ryne Sandberg	2.00	1.50	.80
(11)	Jose Vizcaino	.25	.20	.10
	CINCINNATI REDS			
(12)	Bobby Kelly	.25	.20	.10
(13)	Barry Larkin	.50	.40	.20
(14)	Kevin Mitchell	.25	.20	.10
(15)	Jose Rijo	.35	.25	.14
(16)	Reggie Sanders	.25	.20	.10
	COLORADO ROCKIES			
(17)	Dante Bichette	.25	.20	.10
(18)	Daryl Boston	.25	.20	.10
(19)	Andres Galarraga	.60	.45	.25
(20)	Charlie Hayes	.25	.20	.10
	FLORIDA MARLINS			
(21)	Orestes Destrade	.25	.20	.10
(22)	Dave Magadan	.25	.20	.10
(23)	Benito Santiago	.40	.30	.15
(24)	Walt Weiss	.25	.20	.10
	HOUSTON ASTROS			
(25)	Jeff Bagwell	.50	.40	.20
(26)	Craig Biggio	.50	.40	.20
(27)	Ken Caminiti	.25	.20	.10
(28)	Luis Gonzalez	.25	.20	.10
	LOS ANGELES DODGERS			
(29)	Brett Butler	.25	.20	.10
(30)	Eric Davis	.40	.30	.15
(31)	Orel Hershiser	.50	.40	.20
(32)	Eric Karros	.50	.40	.20
(33)	Ramon Martinez	.25	.20	.10
(34)	Mike Piazza	3.00	2.25	1.25
(35)	Darryl Strawberry	.50	.40	.20
	MONTREAL EXPOS			
(36)	Moises Alou	.25	.20	.10
(37)	Delino DeShields	.35	.25	.14
(38)	Marquis Grissom	.25	.20	.10
(39)	Dennis Martinez	.25	.20	.10
(40)	Larry Walker	.25	.20	.10
	NEW YORK METS			
(41)	Bobby Bonilla	.50	.40	.20
(42)	Dwight Gooden	.50	.40	.20
(43)	Howard Johnson	.50	.40	.20
(44)	Eddie Murray	.60	.45	.25
	PHILADELPHIA PHILLIES			
(45)	Darren Daulton	.25	.20	.10
(46)	Lenny Dykstra	.60	.45	.25
(47)	Dave Hollins	.25	.20	.10
(48)	John Kruk	.35	.25	.14
	PITTSBURGH PIRATES			
(49)	Jay Bell	.25	.20	.10
(50)	Al Martin	.25	.20	.10
(51)	Orlando Merced	.25	.20	.10
(52)	Andy Van Slyke	.25	.20	.10
	ST. LOUIS CARDINALS			
(53)	Gregg Jefferies	.35	.25	.14
(54)	Tom Pagnozzi	.25	.20	.10
(55)	Ozzie Smith	.60	.45	.25
(56)	Todd Zeile	.25	.20	.10
	SAN DIEGO PADRES			
(57)	Derek Bell	.25	.20	.10
(58)	Tony Gwynn	.50	.40	.20
(59)	Fred McGriff	.60	.45	.25
(60)	Gary Sheffield	.50	.40	.20
	SAN FRANCISCO GIANTS			
(61)	Barry Bonds	1.50	1.25	.60
(62)	John Burkett	.35	.25	.14
(63)	Will Clark	1.50	1.25	.60
(64)	Matt Williams	.60	.45	.25
	BALTIMORE ORIOLES			
(65)	Brady Anderson	.25	.20	.10
(66)	Mike Mussina	.50	.40	.20
(67)	Cal Ripken, Jr.	2.00	1.50	.80
	BOSTON RED SOX			
(68)	Roger Clemens	.50	.40	.20
(69)	Andre Dawson	.40	.30	.15
(70)	Mike Greenwell	.25	.20	.10
(71)	Mo Vaughn	.35	.25	.14
	DETROIT TIGERS			
(72)	Cecil Fielder	.60	.45	.25
(73)	Tony Phillips	.25	.20	.10
(74)	Mickey Tettleton	.25	.20	.10
(75)	Alan Trammell	.50	.40	.20
	CLEVELAND INDIANS			
(76)	Sandy Alomar Jr.	.25	.20	.10
(77)	Carlos Baerga	.50	.40	.20
(78)	Albert Belle	.50	.40	.20
(79)	Kenny Lofton	.35	.25	.14
	CHICAGO WHITE SOX			
(80)	Bo Jackson	.50	.40	.20
(81)	Frank Thomas	3.00	2.25	1.25
(82)	Robin Ventura	.40	.30	.15
	CALIFORNIA ANGELS			
(83)	Chad Curtis	.25	.20	.10
(84)	Gary DiSarcina	.25	.20	.10
(85)	Tim Salmon	2.00	1.50	.80
(86)	J.T. Snow	.25	.20	.10
	KANSAS CITY ROYALS			
(87)	George Brett	1.00	.70	.40
(88)	Wally Joyner	.25	.20	.10
(89)	Mike MacFarlane	.25	.20	.10
(90)	Brian McRae	.25	.20	.10
	MILWAUKEE BREWERS			
(91)	Darryl Hamilton	.25	.20	.10
(92)	Pat Listach	.25	.20	.10
(93)	B.J. Surhoff	.25	.20	.10
(94)	Robin Yount	1.00	.70	.40
	MINNESOTA TWINS			
(95)	Kent Hrbek	.50	.40	.20
(96)	Chuck Knoblauch	.35	.25	.14
(97)	Kirby Puckett	.60	.45	.25
(98)	Dave Winfield	.60	.45	.25
	NEW YORK YANKEES			
(99)	Wade Boggs	.50	.40	.20
(100)	Don Mattingly	.60	.45	.25
(101)	Danny Tartabull	.25	.20	.10
	OAKLAND ATHLETICS			
(102)	Dennis Eckersley	.35	.25	.14
(103)	Rickey Henderson	.60	.45	.25
(104)	Mark McGwire	.50	.40	.20
(105)	Ruben Sierra	.40	.30	.15
(106)	Terry Steinbach	.25	.20	.10
	SEATTLE MARINERS			
(107)	Ken Griffey, Jr.	3.00	2.25	1.25
(108)	Edgar Martinez	.25	.20	.10
(109)	Pete O'Brien	.25	.20	.10
(110)	David Valle	.25	.20	.10
	TEXAS RANGERS			
(111)	Jose Canseco	.60	.45	.25
(112)	Juan Gonzalez	1.50	1.25	.60
(113)	Ivan Rodriguez	.25	.20	.10
(114)	Nolan Ryan	3.00	2.25	1.25
	TORONTO BLUE JAYS			
(115)	Roberto Alomar	.60	.45	.25
(116)	Pat Borders	.25	.20	.10
(117)	Joe Carter	.35	.25	.14
(118)	Juan Guzman	.25	.20	.10
(119)	Paul Molitor	.50	.40	.20
(120)	Dave Stewart	.25	.20	.10

A card number in parentheses () indicates the set is unnumbered.

1993 DiamondMarks Inserts

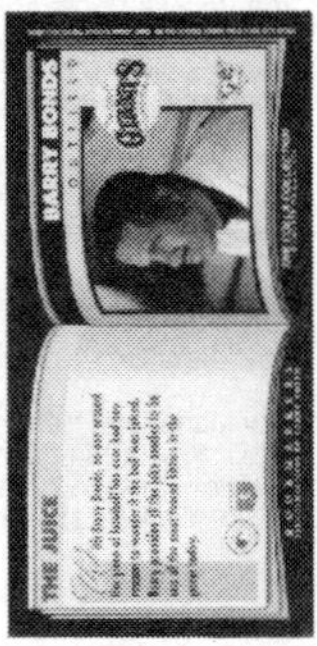

Randomly inserted into packs of DiamondMarks cards at the rate of one per 48-pack carton was a series of eight cards featuring the baseball artwork of Terry Smith. The inserts are the same 2-1/2" x 5" size as the regular issue and carry on with the basic black bordered design, though the inserts are UV-coated both front and back. Beneath the fantasy-design player art on the front is the player's name. On back the open book design is seen again, with a short player profile on the left and a Barry Colla photo portrait on the right, along with the appropriate team logo.

		MT	NR MT	EX
Complete Set:		100.00	75.00	40.00
Common Player:		15.00	11.00	6.00
(1)	Roberto Alomar	15.00	11.00	6.00
(2)	Barry Bonds	20.00	15.00	8.00
(3)	Ken Griffey, Jr.	25.00	18.50	10.00
(4)	David Justice	15.00	11.00	6.00
(5)	John Olerud	15.00	11.00	6.00
(6)	Nolan Ryan	30.00	22.00	12.00
(7)	Frank Thomas	20.00	15.00	8.00
(8)	Robin Yount	15.00	11.00	6.00

1934 - 36 Diamond Stars

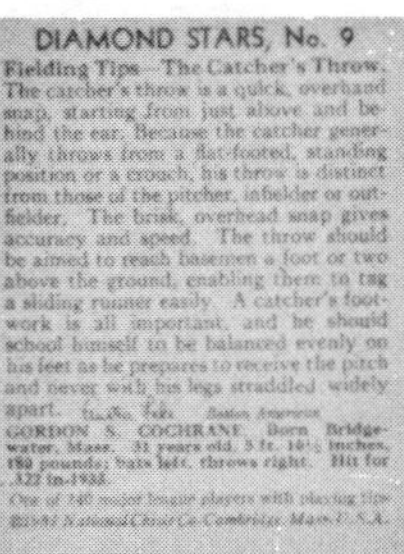

Issued from 1934 through 1936, the Diamond Stars set (ACC designation R327) consists of 108 cards. Produced by National Chicle, the numbered cards measure 2-3/8" by 2-7/8" and are color art reproductions of actual photographs. The year of issue can be determined by the player's statistics found on the reverse of the card. The backs feature either a player biography or a baseball playing tip. Some cards can be found with either green or blue printing on the backs. Artwork for 12 cards that were never issued was uncovered several years ago and a set featuring those cards was subsequently made available to the collecting public. The complete set price does not include the higher priced variations.

		NR MT	EX	VG
Complete Set:		20500.	10250.	6150.
Common Player: 1-31		100.00	50.00	30.00
Common Player: 32-72		75.00	37.00	22.00
Common Player: 73-84		75.00	37.00	22.00
Common Player: 85-96		70.00	35.00	21.00
Common Player: 97-108		350.00	175.00	105.00
1a	"Lefty" Grove (1934 green back)	1600.	800.00	480.00
1b	"Lefty" Grove (1935 green back)	1300.	650.00	390.00
2a	Al Simmons (1934 green back)	200.00	100.00	60.00
2b	Al Simmons (1935 green back)	200.00	100.00	60.00
2c	Al Simmons (1936 blue back)	225.00	112.00	67.00
3a	"Rabbit" Maranville (1934 green back)	100.00	50.00	30.00
3b	"Rabbit" Maranville (1935 green back)	100.00	50.00	30.00
4a	"Buddy" Myer (1934 green back)	90.00	45.00	27.00
4b	"Buddy" Myer (1935 green back)	90.00	45.00	27.00
4c	"Buddy" Myer (1936 blue back)	90.00	45.00	27.00
5a	Tom Bridges (1934 green back)	90.00	45.00	27.00
5b	Tom Bridges (1935 green back)	90.00	45.00	27.00
5c	Tom Bridges (1936 blue back)	90.00	45.00	27.00
6a	Max Bishop (1934 green back)	90.00	45.00	27.00
6b	Max Bishop (1935 green back)	90.00	45.00	27.00
7a	Lew Fonseca (1934 green back)	90.00	45.00	27.00
7b	Lew Fonseca (1935 green back)	90.00	45.00	27.00

8a	Joe Vosmik (1934 green back)	90.00	45.00	27.00
8b	Joe Vosmik (1935 green back)	90.00	45.00	27.00
8c	Joe Vosmik (1936 blue back)	90.00	45.00	27.00
9a	"Mickey" Cochrane (1934 green back)	225.00	112.00	67.00
9b	"Mickey" Cochrane (1935 green back)	225.00	112.00	67.00
9c	"Mickey" Cochrane (1936 blue back)	225.00	112.00	67.00
10a	Roy Mahaffey (1934 green back)	90.00	45.00	27.00
10b	Roy Mahaffey (1935 green back)	90.00	45.00	27.00
10c	Roy Mahaffey (1936 blue back)	90.00	45.00	27.00
11a	Bill Dickey (1934 green back)	275.00	137.00	82.00
11b	Bill Dickey (1935 green back)	275.00	137.00	82.00
12a	"Dixie" Walker (1934 green back)	90.00	45.00	27.00
12b	"Dixie" Walker (1935 green back)	90.00	45.00	27.00
12c	"Dixie" Walker (1936 blue back)	90.00	45.00	27.00
13a	George Blaeholder (1934 green back)	90.00	45.00	27.00
13b	George Blaeholder (1935 green back)	90.00	45.00	27.00
14a	Bill Terry (1934 green back)	110.00	55.00	33.00
14b	Bill Terry (1935 green back)	110.00	55.00	33.00
15a	Dick Bartell (1934 green back)	90.00	45.00	27.00
15b	Dick Bartell (1935 green back)	90.00	45.00	27.00
16a	Lloyd Waner (1934 green back)	125.00	62.00	37.00
16b	Lloyd Waner (1935 green back)	125.00	62.00	37.00
16c	Lloyd Waner (1936 blue back)	125.00	62.00	37.00
17a	Frankie Frisch (1934 green back)	110.00	55.00	33.00
17b	Frankie Frisch (1935 green back)	110.00	55.00	33.00
18a	"Chick" Hafey (1934 green back)	250.00	125.00	75.00
18b	"Chick" Hafey (1935 green back)	250.00	125.00	75.00
19a	Van Mungo (1934 green back)	90.00	45.00	27.00
19b	Van Mungo (1935 green back)	90.00	45.00	27.00
20a	"Shanty" Hogan (1934 green back)	90.00	45.00	27.00
20b	"Shanty" Hogan (1935 green back)	90.00	45.00	27.00
21a	Johnny Vergez (1934 green back)	90.00	45.00	27.00
21b	Johnny Vergez (1935 green back)	90.00	45.00	27.00
22a	Jimmy Wilson (1934 green back)	90.00	45.00	27.00
22b	Jimmy Wilson (1935 green back)	90.00	45.00	27.00
22c	Jimmy Wilson (1936 blue back)	90.00	45.00	27.00
23a	Bill Hallahan (1934 green back)	90.00	45.00	27.00
23b	Bill Hallahan (1935 green back)	90.00	45.00	27.00
24a	"Sparky" Adams (1934 green back)	90.00	45.00	27.00
24b	"Sparky" Adams (1935 green back)	90.00	45.00	27.00
25	Walter Berger	100.00	50.00	30.00
26a	"Pepper" Martin (1935 green back)	100.00	50.00	30.00
26b	"Pepper" Martin (1936 blue back)	100.00	50.00	30.00
27	"Pie" Traynor	225.00	112.00	67.00
28	"Al" Lopez	225.00	112.00	67.00
29	Robert Rolfe	90.00	45.00	27.00
30a	"Heinie" Manush (1935 green back)	125.00	62.00	37.00
30b	"Heinie" Manush (1936 blue back)	150.00	75.00	45.00
31a	"Kiki" Cuyler (1935 green back)	125.00	62.00	37.00
31b	"Kiki" Cuyler (1936 blue back)	125.00	62.00	37.00
32	Sam Rice	125.00	62.00	37.00
33	"Schoolboy" Rowe	90.00	45.00	27.00
34	Stanley Hack	90.00	45.00	27.00
35	Earle Averill	125.00	62.00	37.00
36a	Earnie Lombardi	200.00	100.00	60.00
36b	Ernie Lombardi	150.00	75.00	45.00
37	"Billie" Urbanski	70.00	35.00	21.00
38	Ben Chapman	90.00	45.00	27.00
39	Carl Hubbell	110.00	55.00	33.00
40	"Blondy" Ryan	70.00	35.00	21.00
41	Harvey Hendrick	70.00	35.00	21.00
42	Jimmy Dykes	90.00	45.00	27.00
43	Ted Lyons	100.00	50.00	30.00
44	Rogers Hornsby	395.00	197.00	118.00
45	"Jo Jo" White	70.00	35.00	21.00
46	"Red" Lucas	70.00	35.00	21.00
47	Cliff Bolton	70.00	35.00	21.00
48	"Rick" Ferrell	125.00	62.00	37.00
49	"Buck" Jordan	70.00	35.00	21.00
50	"Mel" Ott	275.00	137.00	82.00
51	John Whitehead	70.00	35.00	21.00
52	George Stainback	70.00	35.00	21.00
53	Oscar Melillo	70.00	35.00	21.00
54a	"Hank" Greenburg	400.00	200.00	120.00
54b	"Hank" Greenberg	250.00	125.00	75.00
55	Tony Cuccinello	70.00	35.00	21.00
56	"Gus" Suhr	70.00	35.00	21.00
57	"Cy" Blanton	70.00	35.00	21.00
58	Glenn Myatt	70.00	35.00	21.00
59	Jim Bottomley	125.00	62.00	37.00
60	Charley "Red" Ruffing	100.00	50.00	30.00
61	"Billie" Werber	70.00	35.00	21.00
62	Fred M. Frankhouse	70.00	35.00	21.00
63	"Stonewall" Jackson	125.00	62.00	37.00
64	Jimmie Foxx	350.00	175.00	105.00
65	"Zeke" Bonura	70.00	35.00	21.00
66	"Ducky" Medwick	100.00	50.00	30.00
67	Marvin Owen	70.00	35.00	21.00
68	"Sam" Leslie	70.00	35.00	21.00
69	Earl Grace	70.00	35.00	21.00
70	"Hal" Trosky	70.00	35.00	21.00
71	"Ossie" Bluege	70.00	35.00	21.00
72	"Tony" Piet	70.00	35.00	21.00
73a	"Fritz" Ostermueller (1935 green back)	75.00	37.00	22.00
73b	"Fritz" Ostermueller (1935 blue back)	75.00	37.00	22.00
73c	"Fritz" Ostermueller (1936 blue back)	75.00	37.00	22.00
74a	Tony Lazzeri (1935 green back)	125.00	62.00	37.00
74b	Tony Lazzeri (1935 blue back)	125.00	62.00	37.00
74c	Tony Lazzeri (1936 blue back)	125.00	62.00	37.00
75a	Irving Burns (1935 green back)	75.00	37.00	22.00
75b	Irving Burns (1935 blue back)	75.00	37.00	22.00
75c	Irving Burns (1936 blue back)	75.00	37.00	22.00
76a	Bill Rogell (1935 green back)	75.00	37.00	22.00
76b	Bill Rogell (1935 blue back)	75.00	37.00	22.00
76c	Bill Rogell (1936 blue back)	75.00	37.00	22.00
77a	Charlie Gehringer (1935 green back)	395.00	197.00	118.00
77b	Charlie Gehringer (1935 blue back)	395.00	197.00	118.00
77c	Charlie Gehringer (1936 blue back)	395.00	197.00	118.00
78a	Joe Kuhel (1935 green back)	75.00	37.00	22.00
78b	Joe Kuhel (1935 blue back)	75.00	37.00	22.00
78c	Joe Kuhel (1936 blue back)	75.00	37.00	22.00
79a	Willis Hudlin (1935 green back)	75.00	37.00	22.00
79b	Willis Hudlin (1935 blue back)	75.00	37.00	22.00
79c	Willis Hudlin (1936 blue back)	75.00	37.00	22.00
80a	Louis Chiozza (1935 green back)	75.00	37.00	22.00
80b	Louis Chiozza (1935 blue back)	75.00	37.00	22.00
80c	Louis Chiozza (1936 blue back)	75.00	37.00	22.00
81a	Bill DeLancey (1935 green back)	75.00	37.00	22.00
81b	Bill DeLancey (1935 blue back)	75.00	37.00	22.00
81c	Bill DeLancey (1936 blue back)	75.00	37.00	22.00
82a	John Babich (1935 green back)	100.00	50.00	30.00
82b	John Babich (1935 blue back)	100.00	50.00	30.00
82c	John Babich (1936 blue back)	100.00	50.00	30.00
83a	Paul Waner (1935 green back)	200.00	100.00	60.00
83b	Paul Waner (1935 blue back)	200.00	100.00	60.00
83c	Paul Waner (1936 blue back)	200.00	100.00	60.00
84a	Sam Byrd (1935 green back)	75.00	37.00	22.00
84b	Sam Byrd (1935 blue back)	75.00	37.00	22.00
84c	Sam Byrd (1936 blue back)	75.00	37.00	22.00
85	Julius Solters	125.00	62.00	37.00
86	Frank Crosetti	200.00	100.00	60.00
87	Steve O'Neil (O'Neill)	125.00	62.00	37.00
88	Geo. Selkirk	100.00	50.00	30.00
89	Joe Stripp	125.00	62.00	37.00
90	Ray Hayworth	125.00	62.00	37.00
91	Bucky Harris	150.00	75.00	45.00
92	Ethan Allen	125.00	62.00	37.00
93	Alvin Crowder	125.00	62.00	37.00
94	Wes Ferrell	125.00	62.00	37.00
95	Luke Appling	395.00	197.00	118.00
96	Lew Riggs	125.00	62.00	37.00
97	"Al" Lopez	500.00	250.00	150.00
98	"Schoolboy" Rowe	350.00	175.00	105.00
99	"Pie" Traynor	600.00	300.00	180.00
100	Earle Averill (Earl)	500.00	250.00	150.00
101	Dick Bartell	350.00	175.00	105.00
102	Van Mungo	350.00	175.00	105.00
103	Bill Dickey	800.00	400.00	240.00
104	Robert Rolfe	350.00	175.00	105.00
105	"Ernie" Lombardi	500.00	250.00	150.00
106	"Red" Lucas	350.00	175.00	105.00
107	Stanley Hack	350.00	175.00	105.00
108	Walter Berger	350.00	175.00	105.00

1924 Diaz Cigarettes

No. 121.
Fume Cigarros
TOMAS GUTIERREZ
La persona que nos entregue la colección completa de Pitchers consistente en 136 Postalitas Nos. 1 al 136, será gratificada con un lujoso Album que contiene los jugadores todos de las Ligas Nacional y Americana con las Postalitas ya impresas.
CIA CIGARRERA DIAZ, S. A
Finlay 66 (antes Zanja)
Habana.

Because they were printed in Cuba and feature only pitchers, the 1924 Diaz Cigarette cards are among the rarest and most intriguing of all tobacco issues. Produced in Havana for the Diaz brand, the black and white cards measure 1-3/4" by 2-1/2" and were printed on a glossy-type stock. The player's name and position are listed at the bottom of the card, while his team and league appear at the top. According to the card backs, printed in Spanish, the set consists of 136 cards - all major league pitchers. But to date only the cards checklisted here have been discovered.

		NR MT	EX	VG
	Common Player:	225.00	112.00	67.00
2	Waite C. Hoyt	400.00	200.00	120.00
12	Curtis Fullerton	225.00	112.00	67.00
14	George Walberg	225.00	112.00	67.00
40	A. Wilbur Cooper	225.00	112.00	67.00
51	Roy Meeker	225.00	112.00	67.00
58	Sam Gray	225.00	112.00	67.00
96	Philip B. Weinart	225.00	112.00	67.00
102	Howard	225.00	112.00	67.00
105	Hubert F. Pruett	225.00	112.00	67.00
121	Bert Cole	225.00	112.00	67.00
----	Harry Baldwin	225.00	112.00	67.00
----	Leslie J. Bush	225.00	112.00	67.00
----	Wm. Piercy	225.00	112.00	67.00
----	Arnold E. Stone	225.00	112.00	67.00

1992 Diet Pepsi All-Stars

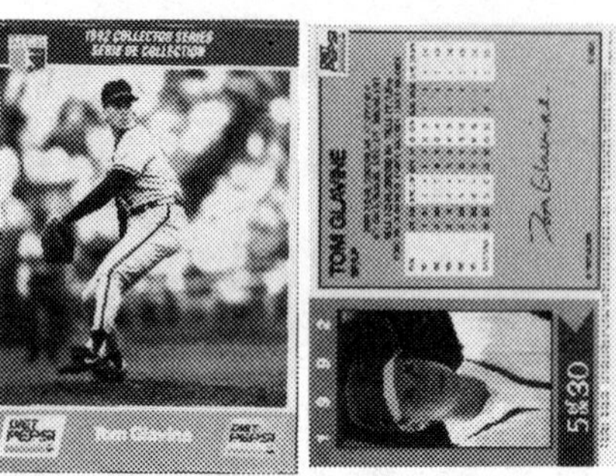

In 1992, Diet Pepsi issued an All-Star Baseball card set of 30 players which was only available in Canada. The cards were attached to two-liter bottles and issued with text in both French and English. Tom Glavine, featured on card #5, is shown as a right-handed pitcher as the negative for his card was reversed.

		MT	NR MT	EX
	Complete Set:	15.00	11.00	6.00
	Common Player:	.25	.20	.10
(1)	Dwight Gooden	.35	.25	.14
(2)	Howard Johnson	.25	.20	.10
(3)	Ryne Sandberg	2.00	1.50	.80
(4)	Barry Bonds	1.00	.70	.40
(5)	Ozzie Smith	.75	.60	.30
(6)	Tim Wallach	.25	.20	.10
(7)	Dennis Martinez	.25	.20	.10
(8)	Barry Larkin	.25	.20	.10
(9)	Tom Glavine	.25	.20	.10
(10)	Gary Carter	.25	.20	.10
(11)	Will Clark	.75	.60	.30
(12)	Cal Ripken, Jr.	2.00	1.50	.80
(13)	Roger Clemens	.65	.50	.25
(14)	Wade Boggs	.65	.50	.25
(15)	Jeff Reardon	.25	.20	.10
(16)	Sandy Alomar	.25	.20	.10
(17)	Cecil Fielder	.65	.50	.25
(18)	Jack Morris	.25	.20	.10
(19)	Kelly Gruber	.25	.20	.10
(20)	Roberto Alomar	1.00	.70	.40
(21)	Tom Henke	.25	.20	.10
(22)	Dave Winfield	1.00	.70	.40
(23)	Joe Carter	.40	.30	.15
(24)	Jose Canseco	.65	.50	.25
(25)	Rickey Henderson	.65	.50	.25
(26)	Kirby Puckett	1.00	.70	.40
(27)	Ken Griffey, Jr.	3.00	2.25	1.25
(28)	Dennis Eckersley	.25	.20	.10
(29)	Bryan Harvey	.25	.20	.10
(30)	Carlton Fisk	.50	.40	.20

1937 Dixie Lids

This unnumbered set of Dixie cup ice cream lids was issued in 1937 and consists of 24 different lids, although only six picture sports stars - four of whom are baseball stars. The lids are found in two different sizes, either 2-11/16" in diameter or 2-5/16" in diameter. The 1937 Dixie Lids were printed in black or dark red. The lids must have the small tab still intact to command top value.

		NR MT	EX	VG
	Complete Set:	400.00	200.00	120.00
	Common Player:	75.00	38.00	23.00
(1)	Charles Gehringer	110.00	55.00	33.00

(2)	Charles ("Gabby") Hartnett	110.00	55.00	33.00
(3)	Carl Hubbell	125.00	62.00	37.00
(4)	Joe Medwick	75.00	38.00	23.00

1937 Dixie Lids Premiums

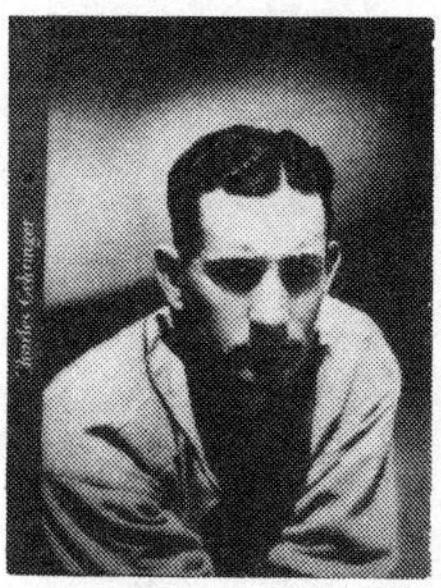

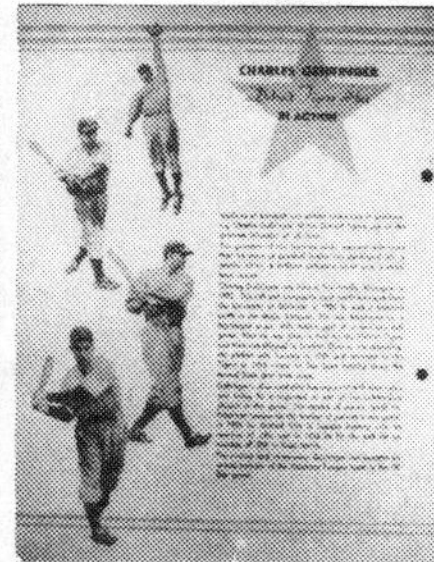

Issued as a premium offer in conjunction with the 1937 Dixie lids, this unnumbered set of color 8" by 10" pictures was printed on heavy paper and features the same subjects as the Dixie Lids set. The 1937 Dixie premiums have a distinctive dark green band along the left margin containing the player's name. The back has smaller photos of the player in action with a large star at the top and a player write-up.

		NR MT	EX	VG
Complete Set:		650.00	200.00	120.00
Common Player:		150.00	38.00	23.00
(1)	Charles Gehringer	175.00	87.00	52.00
(2)	Charles (Gabby) Hartnett	175.00	87.00	52.00
(3)	Carl Hubbell	200.00	100.00	60.00
(4)	Joe (Ducky) Medwick	150.00	75.00	45.00

1938 Dixie Lids

Similar to its set of the previous year, the 1938 Dixie Lids set is a 24-subject set that includes six sports stars - four of whom are baseball players. The lids are found in two sizes, either 2-11/16" in diameter or 2-5/16" in diameter. The 1938 Dixie lids are printed in blue ink. Dixie lids must have the small tab still intact to command top value.

		NR MT	EX	VG
Complete Set:		375.00	187.00	112.00
Common Player:		50.00	25.00	15.00
(1)	Bob Feller	110.00	55.00	33.00
(2)	Jimmie Foxx	110.00	55.00	33.00
(3)	Carl Hubbell	110.00	55.00	33.00
(4)	Wally Moses	50.00	25.00	15.00

1938 Dixie Lids Premiums

Issued in conjunction with the 1938 Dixie cup lids, this unnumbered set of 8" x 10" pictures contains the same subjects and is printed on surrounding the entire picture with the player's name to the left. The back contains smaller photos of the player in action with his name in script at the top and a short write-up.

		NR MT	EX	VG
Complete Set:		500.00	150.00	90.00
Common Player:		75.00	25.00	15.00
(1)	Bob Feller	150.00	75.00	45.00
(2)	Jimmy Foxx	150.00	75.00	45.00
(3)	Carl Hubbell	150.00	75.00	45.00
(4)	Wally Moses	75.00	37.00	22.00

1952 Dixie Lids

After a 14-year break, another Dixie lid set, featuring 24 baseball players, appeared in 1952. The unnumbered lids measure 2-11/16" in diameter and were printed with a blue tint. The Dixie lids of the 1950s can be distinguished from earlier issues because the bottom of the photo is squared off to accomodate the player's name. Dixie lids must contain the small tab to command top value.

		NR MT	EX	VG
Complete Set:		3500.	1750.	1050.
Common Player:		140.00	70.00	42.00
(1)	Richie Ashburn	200.00	100.00	60.00
(2)	Tommy Byrne	140.00	70.00	42.00
(3)	Chico Carrasquel	140.00	70.00	42.00
(4)	Pete Castiglione	140.00	70.00	42.00
(5)	Walker Cooper	140.00	70.00	42.00
(6)	Billy Cox	140.00	70.00	42.00
(7)	Ferris Fain	140.00	70.00	42.00
(8)	Bobby Feller	250.00	125.00	75.00
(9)	Nelson Fox	175.00	87.00	52.00
(10)	Monte Irvin	200.00	100.00	60.00
(11)	Ralph Kiner	200.00	100.00	60.00
(12)	Cass Michaels	140.00	70.00	42.00
(13)	Don Mueller	140.00	70.00	42.00
(14)	Mel Parnell	140.00	70.00	42.00
(15)	Allie Reynolds	175.00	87.00	52.00
(16)	Preacher Roe	175.00	87.00	52.00
(17)	Connie Ryan	140.00	70.00	42.00
(18)	Hank Sauer	140.00	70.00	42.00
(19)	Al Schoendienst	200.00	100.00	60.00
(20)	Andy Seminick	140.00	70.00	42.00
(21)	Bobby Shantz	150.00	75.00	45.00
(22)	Enos Slaughter	200.00	100.00	60.00
(23)	Virgil Trucks	140.00	70.00	42.00
(24)	Gene Woodling	150.00	75.00	45.00

1952 Dixie Lids Premiums

This unnumbered set of 24 player photos was issued as a premium in conjunction with the 1952 Dixie cup lids and features the same subjects. The player's team and facsimile autograph appear along the bottom of the 8" by 10" blank-backed photo, which was printed on heavy paper. The 1952 Dixie premiums show the player's 1951 season statistics in the lower right corner.

		NR MT	EX	VG
Complete Set:		600.00	300.00	180.00
Common Player:		30.00	15.00	9.00
(1)	Richie Ashburn	60.00	30.00	18.00
(2)	Tommy Byrne	30.00	15.00	9.00
(3)	Chico Carrasquel	30.00	15.00	9.00
(4)	Pete Castiglione	30.00	15.00	9.00
(5)	Walker Cooper	30.00	15.00	9.00
(6)	Billy Cox	30.00	15.00	9.00
(7)	Ferris Fain	30.00	15.00	9.00
(8)	Bob Feller	75.00	37.00	22.00
(9)	Nelson Fox	35.00	17.50	10.50
(10)	Monte Irvin	40.00	20.00	12.00
(11)	Ralph Kiner	45.00	22.00	13.50
(12)	Cass Michaels	30.00	15.00	9.00
(13)	Don Mueller	30.00	15.00	9.00
(14)	Mel Parnell	30.00	15.00	9.00
(15)	Allie Reynolds	35.00	17.50	10.50
(16)	Preacher Roe	35.00	17.50	10.50
(17)	Connie Ryan	30.00	15.00	9.00
(18)	Hank Sauer	30.00	15.00	9.00
(19)	Al Schoendienst	40.00	20.00	12.00
(20)	Andy Seminick	30.00	15.00	9.00
(21)	Bobby Shantz	35.00	17.50	10.50
(22)	Enos Slaughter	45.00	22.00	13.50
(23)	Virgil Trucks	30.00	15.00	9.00
(24)	Gene Woodling	35.00	17.50	10.50

1953 Dixie Lids

The 1953 Dixie Lids set again consists of 24 unnumbered players and is identical in design to the 1953 set. Each lid measures 2-11/16"in diameter and must include the small tab to command top value.

		NR MT	EX	VG
Complete Set:		1500.	750.00	450.00
Common Player:		35.00	17.50	10.50
(1)	Richie Ashburn	60.00	30.00	18.00
(2)	Chico Carrasquel	35.00	17.50	10.50
(3)	Billy Cox	35.00	17.50	10.50
(4)	Ferris Fain	35.00	17.50	10.50
(5)	Nelson Fox	50.00	25.00	15.00
(6a)	Sid Gordon (Boston)	70.00	35.00	21.00
(6b)	Sid Gordon (Milwaukee)	35.00	17.50	10.50
(7)	Warren Hacker	35.00	17.50	10.50
(8)	Monte Irvin	60.00	30.00	18.00
(9)	Jackie Jensen	40.00	20.00	12.00
(10a)	Ralph Kiner (Pittsburgh)	100.00	50.00	30.00
(10b)	Ralph Kiner (Chicago)	60.00	30.00	18.00
(11)	Ted Kluszewski	50.00	25.00	15.00
(12)	Bob Lemon	60.00	30.00	18.00
(13)	Don Mueller	35.00	17.50	10.50
(14)	Mel Parnell	35.00	17.50	10.50
(15)	Jerry Priddy	35.00	17.50	10.50
(16)	Allie Reynolds	40.00	20.00	12.00
(17)	Preacher Roe	40.00	20.00	12.00
(18)	Hank Sauer	35.00	17.50	10.50
(19)	Al Schoendienst	60.00	30.00	18.00
(20)	Bobby Shantz	40.00	20.00	12.00
(21)	Enos Slaughter	60.00	30.00	18.00
(22a)	Warren Spahn (Boston)	150.00	75.00	45.00
(22b)	Warren Spahn (Milwaukee)	75.00	37.00	22.00
(23a)	Virgil Trucks (Chicago)	75.00	37.00	22.00
(23b)	Virgil Trucks (St. Louis)	35.00	17.50	10.50
(24)	Gene Woodling	40.00	20.00	12.00

1953 Dixie Lids Premiums

This set of 24 8" by 10" photos was issued as a premium in conjunction with the 1953 Dixie Lids set and includes the same subjects. The player's team and facsimile autograph are at the bottom of the unnumbered, blank-backed photos. His 1952 season stats are shown in the lower right corner.

		NR MT	EX	VG
Complete Set:		750.00	350.00	210.00
Common Player:		30.00	10.00	6.00
(1)	Richie Ashburn	50.00	25.00	15.00
(2)	Chico Carrasquel	30.00	15.00	9.00

(3)	Billy Cox	30.00	15.00	9.00
(4)	Ferris Fain	30.00	15.00	9.00
(5)	Nelson Fox	40.00	20.00	12.00
(6)	Sid Gordon	30.00	15.00	9.00
(7)	Warren Hacker	30.00	15.00	9.00
(8)	Monte Irvin	50.00	25.00	15.00
(9)	Jack Jensen	35.00	17.50	10.50
(10)	Ralph Kiner	50.00	25.00	15.00
(11)	Ted Kluszewski	40.00	20.00	12.00
(12)	Bob Lemon	50.00	25.00	15.00
(13)	Don Mueller	30.00	15.00	9.00
(14)	Mel Parnell	30.00	15.00	9.00
(15)	Jerry Priddy	30.00	15.00	9.00
(16)	Allie Reynolds	35.00	17.50	10.50
(17)	Preacher Roe	35.00	17.50	10.50
(18)	Hank Sauer	30.00	15.00	9.00
(19)	Al Schoendienst	50.00	25.00	15.00
(20)	Bobby Shantz	30.00	15.00	9.00
(21)	Enos Slaughter	50.00	25.00	15.00
(22)	Warren Spahn	60.00	30.00	18.00
(23)	Virgil Trucks	30.00	15.00	9.00
(24)	Gene Woodling	35.00	17.50	10.50

1954 Dixie Lids

The 1954 Dixie Lids set consists of 18 players, and the lids are usually found with a gray tint. The lids usually measure 2-11/16" in diameter, although two other sizes also exist (2-1/4" in diameter and 3-3/16" in diameter), which are valued at about twice the prices listed. The 1953 Dixie Lids are similar to earlier issues, except they carry an offer for a "3-D Starviewer" around the outside edge. The small tabs must be attached to command top value. The lids are unnumbered.

		NR MT	EX	VG
Complete Set:		600.00	300.00	180.00
Common Player:		30.00	12.50	7.50
(1)	Richie Ashburn	50.00	25.00	15.00
(2)	Clint Courtney	30.00	15.00	9.00
(3)	Sid Gordon	30.00	15.00	9.00
(4)	Billy Hoeft	30.00	15.00	9.00
(5)	Monte Irvin	50.00	25.00	15.00
(6)	Jackie Jensen	35.00	17.50	10.50
(7)	Ralph Kiner	50.00	25.00	15.00
(8)	Ted Kluszewski	40.00	20.00	12.00
(9)	Gil McDougald	35.00	17.50	10.50
(10)	Minny Minoso	35.00	17.50	10.50
(11)	Danny O'Connell	30.00	15.00	9.00
(12)	Mel Parnell	30.00	15.00	9.00
(13)	Preacher Roe	35.00	17.50	10.50
(14)	Al Rosen	35.00	17.50	10.50
(15)	Al Schoendienst	50.00	25.00	15.00
(16)	Enos Slaughter	50.00	25.00	15.00
(17)	Gene Woodling	35.00	17.50	10.50
(18)	Gus Zernial	30.00	15.00	9.00

1909 Dockman & Sons Gum (E92)

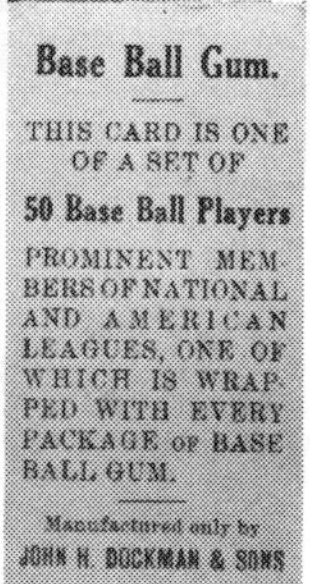
Base Ball Gum.

THIS CARD IS ONE OF A SET OF

50 Base Ball Players

PROMINENT MEMBERS OF NATIONAL AND AMERICAN LEAGUES, ONE OF WHICH IS WRAPPED WITH EVERY PACKAGE OF BASE BALL GUM.

Manufactured only by
JOHN H. DOCKMAN & SONS

Once cataloged as a part of the E92 compendium, the John Dockman & Sons Gum card issue differs from the Croft's Candy/Cocoa sets in that it has 10 fewer cards. Otherwise the format (1-1/2" x 2-3/4" and color litho player pictures are identical. Beneath the player picture on front is his last name, position and team. Backs, which describe the set as having 50 cards, are an ad for the gum company. Cards are checklisted here alphabetically. It is possible some of the "missing" 10 cards may yet surface.

		NR MT	EX	VG
Complete Set:		13500.	7500.	3000.
Common Player:		125.00	45.00	26.00
(1)	Harry Bemis	125.00	45.00	26.00
(2)	Chief Bender	375.00	135.00	80.00
(3)	Bill Bergen	125.00	45.00	26.00
(4)	Bob Bescher	125.00	45.00	26.00
(5)	Al Bridwell	125.00	45.00	26.00
(6)	Doc Casey	125.00	45.00	26.00
(7)	Frank Chance	375.00	135.00	80.00
(8)	Hal Chase	160.00	58.00	33.00
(9)	Sam Crawford	325.00	120.00	70.00
(10)	Harry Davis	125.00	45.00	26.00
(11)	Art Devlin	125.00	45.00	26.00
(12)	Wild Bill Donovan	125.00	45.00	26.00
(13)	Mickey Doolan	125.00	45.00	26.00
(14)	Patsy Dougherty	125.00	45.00	26.00
(15)	Larry Doyle (throwing)	125.00	45.00	26.00
(16)	Larry Doyle (with bat)	125.00	45.00	26.00
(17)	George Gibson	125.00	45.00	26.00
(18)	Topsy Hartsel	125.00	45.00	26.00
(19)	Hugh Jennings	350.00	126.00	73.00
(20)	Red Kleinow	125.00	45.00	26.00
(21)	Nap Lajoie	400.00	145.00	85.00
(22)	Hans Lobert	125.00	45.00	26.00
(23)	Sherry Magee	125.00	45.00	26.00
(24)	Christy Matthewson (Mathewson)	900.00	325.00	190.00
(25)	John McGraw	375.00	135.00	80.00
(26)	Larry McLean	125.00	45.00	26.00
(27)	Dots Miller	125.00	45.00	26.00
(28)	Danny Murphy	125.00	45.00	26.00
(29)	Bill O'Hara	125.00	45.00	26.00
(30)	Germany Schaefer	125.00	45.00	26.00
(31)	Admiral Schlei	125.00	45.00	26.00
(32)	Boss Schmidt	125.00	45.00	26.00
(33)	Johnny Seigle	125.00	45.00	26.00
(34)	Dave Shean	125.00	45.00	26.00
(35)	Boss Smith (Schmidt)	125.00	45.00	26.00
(36)	Joe Tinker	350.00	126.00	73.00
(37)	Honus Wagner (batting)	700.00	250.00	150.00
(38)	Honus Wagner (throwing)	700.00	250.00	150.00
(39)	Cy Young	600.00	215.00	125.00
(40)	Heinie Zimmerman	125.00	45.00	26.00

1988 Domino's Pizza Tigers

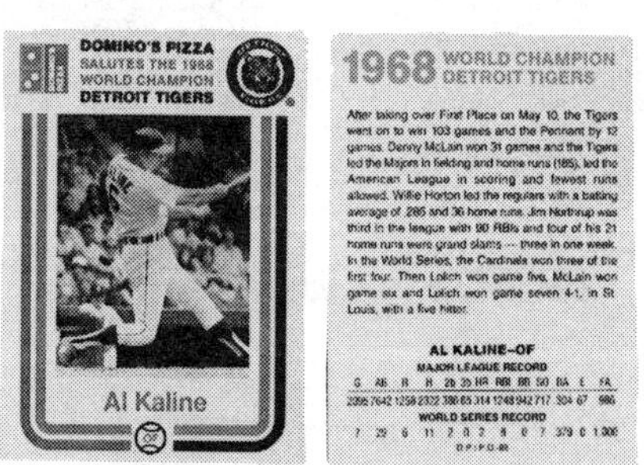

Domino's Pizza produced a 28-card set commemorating the 20th anniversary of the 1968 World Champion Detroit Tigers. The cards were given away at an Old Timers Game at Tiger Stadium in 1988. The cards, which measure 2-1/2" by 3-1/2", feature black and white photos semi-surrounded by a two-stripe band. The stripes on the card's left side are the same color (red and light blue) as the Domino's Pizza logo in the upper corner. The stripes on the card's right side match the colors of the Tigers logo (red and dark blue). The backs of all the cards (except for Ernie Harwell) contain a brief summary of the Tigers' 1968 season. Located at the bottom on the card backs are the players' major league records through 1968 plus their 1968 World Series statistics.

		MT	NR MT	EX
Complete Set:		9.00	6.75	3.50
Common Player:		.20	.15	.08
(1)	Gates Brown	.30	.25	.12
(2)	Norm Cash	.90	.70	.35
(3)	Wayne Comer	.20	.15	.08
(4)	Pat Dobson	.20	.15	.08
(5)	Bill Freehan	.60	.45	.25
(6)	John Hiller	.20	.25	.12
(7)	Ernie Harwell (announcer)	.30	.25	.12
(8)	Willie Horton	.40	.45	.25
(9)	Al Kaline	2.00	1.25	.60
(10)	Fred Lasher	.20	.15	.08
(11)	Mickey Lolich	.90	.70	.35
(12)	Tom Matchick	.20	.15	.08
(13)	Ed Mathews	1.50	.70	.40
(14)	Dick McAuliff (McAuliffe)	.40	.30	.15
(15)	Denny McLain	.80	.60	.30
(16)	Don McMahon	.20	.15	.08
(17)	Jim Northrup	.20	.30	.15
(18)	Ray Oyler	.20	.15	.08
(19)	Daryl Patterson	.20	.15	.08
(20)	Jim Price	.20	.15	.08
(21)	Joe Sparma	.20	.15	.08
(22)	Mickey Stanley	.20	.30	.15
(23)	Dick Tracewski	.20	.15	.08
(24)	Jon Warden	.20	.15	.08
(25)	Don Wert	.20	.15	.08
(26)	Earl Wilson	.20	.15	.08
(27)	Header Card	.20	.15	.08
(28)	Coupon Card	.20	.15	.08

1981 Donruss

ROLLIE FINGERS PITCHER

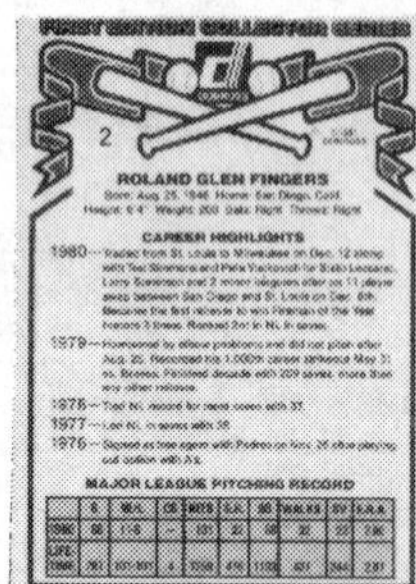

The Donruss Co. of Memphis, Tenn., produced its premiere baseball card issue in 1981 with a set that consisted of 600 numbered cards and five unnumbered checklists. The cards, which measure 2-1/2" by 3-1/2", are printed on thin stock. The card fronts contain the Donruss logo plus the year of issue. The card backs are designed on a vertical format and have black print on red and white. The set, entitled "First Edition Collector Series," contains nearly 40 variations, those being first-printing errors that were corrected in a subsequent print run. The cards were issued in gum wax packs, with hobby dealer sales being coordinated by TCMA of Amawalk, N.Y. The complete set price does not include the higher priced variations.

		MT	NR MT	EX
Complete Set (605):		60.00	45.00	24.00
Common Player:		.06	.05	.02
1	Ozzie Smith	3.00	2.25	1.25
2	Rollie Fingers	1.00	.70	.40
3	Rick Wise	.08	.06	.03
4	Gene Richards	.06	.05	.02
5	Alan Trammell	.80	.60	.30
6	Tom Brookens	.08	.06	.03
7a	Duffy Dyer (1980 Avg. .185)	1.00	.70	.40
7b	Duffy Dyer (1980 Avg. 185)	.10	.08	.04
8	Mark Fidrych	.08	.06	.03
9	Dave Rozema	.06	.05	.02
10	Ricky Peters	.06	.05	.02
11	Mike Schmidt	2.50	2.00	1.00
12	Willie Stargell	.80	.60	.30
13	Tim Foli	.06	.05	.02
14	Manny Sanguillen	.06	.05	.02
15	Grant Jackson	.06	.05	.02
16	Eddie Solomon	.06	.05	.02
17	Omar Moreno	.06	.05	.02
18	Joe Morgan	.60	.45	.25
19	Rafael Landestoy	.06	.05	.02
20	Bruce Bochy	.06	.05	.02
21	Joe Sambito	.06	.05	.02
22	Manny Trillo	.08	.06	.03
23a	*Dave Smith* (incomplete box around stats)	1.00	.70	.40
23b	*Dave Smith* (complete box around stats)	.30	.25	.12
24	Terry Puhl	.06	.05	.02
25	Bump Wills	.06	.05	.02
26a	John Ellis (Danny Walton photo - with bat)	1.25	.90	.50
26b	John Ellis (John Ellis photo - with glove)	.10	.08	.04
27	Jim Kern	.06	.05	.02
28	Richie Zisk	.08	.06	.03
29	John Mayberry	.08	.06	.03
30	Bob Davis	.06	.05	.02
31	Jackson Todd	.06	.05	.02
32	Al Woods	.06	.05	.02
33	Steve Carlton	1.75	1.25	.70
34	Lee Mazzilli	.08	.06	.03
35	John Stearns	.06	.05	.02
36	Roy Jackson	.06	.05	.02
37	Mike Scott	.15	.11	.06
38	Lamar Johnson	.06	.05	.02
39	Kevin Bell	.06	.05	.02
40	Ed Farmer	.06	.05	.02
41	Ross Baumgarten	.06	.05	.02
42	Leo Sutherland	.06	.05	.02
43	Dan Meyer	.06	.05	.02
44	Ron Reed	.06	.05	.02
45	Mario Mendoza	.06	.05	.02

46	Rick Honeycutt	.06	.05	.02
47	Glenn Abbott	.06	.05	.02
48	Leon Roberts	.06	.05	.02
49	Rod Carew	1.50	1.25	.60
50	Bert Campaneris	.10	.08	.04
51a	Tom Donahue (incorrect spelling)	1.00	.70	.40
51b	Tom Donohue (Donohue on front)	.10	.08	.04
52	Dave Frost	.06	.05	.02
53	Ed Halicki	.06	.05	.02
54	Dan Ford	.06	.05	.02
55	Garry Maddox	.10	.08	.04
56a	Steve Garvey (Surpassed 25 HR..)	1.75	1.25	.70
56b	Steve Garvey (Surpassed 21 HR..)	.60	.45	.25
57	Bill Russell	.08	.06	.03
58	Don Sutton	.30	.25	.12
59	Reggie Smith	.10	.08	.04
60	Rick Monday	.10	.08	.04
61	Ray Knight	.10	.08	.04
62	Johnny Bench	1.25	.90	.50
63	Mario Soto	.08	.06	.03
64	Doug Bair	.06	.05	.02
65	George Foster	.20	.15	.08
66	Jeff Burroughs	.08	.06	.03
67	Keith Hernandez	.20	.15	.08
68	Tom Herr	.10	.08	.04
69	Bob Forsch	.08	.06	.03
70	John Fulgham	.06	.05	.02
71a	Bobby Bonds (lifetime HR 986)	.30	.25	.12
71b	Bobby Bonds (lifetime HR 326)	.15	.11	.06
72a	Rennie Stennett ("...breaking broke leg..." on back)	1.00	.70	.40
72b	Rennie Stennett ("...breaking leg..." on back)	.10	.08	.04
73	Joe Strain	.06	.05	.02
74	Ed Whitson	.06	.05	.02
75	Tom Griffin	.06	.05	.02
76	Bill North	.06	.05	.02
77	Gene Garber	.06	.05	.02
78	Mike Hargrove	.06	.05	.02
79	Dave Rosello	.06	.05	.02
80	Ron Hassey	.06	.05	.02
81	Sid Monge	.06	.05	.02
82a	*Joe Charboneau* ("For some reason, Phillies..." on back)	1.00	.70	.40
82b	*Joe Charboneau* ("Phillies..." on back)	.12	.09	.05
83	Cecil Cooper	.15	.11	.06
84	Sal Bando	.10	.08	.04
85	Moose Haas	.06	.05	.02
86	Mike Caldwell	.06	.05	.02
87a	Larry Hisle ("...Twins with 28 RBI." on back)	1.00	.70	.40
87b	Larry Hisle ("...Twins with 28 HR" on back)	.10	.08	.04
88	Luis Gomez	.06	.05	.02
89	Larry Parrish	.10	.08	.04
90	Gary Carter	.50	.40	.20
91	*Bill Gullickson*	.15	.11	.06
92	Fred Norman	.06	.05	.02
93	Tommy Hutton	.06	.05	.02
94	Carl Yastrzemski	1.00	.70	.40
95	Glenn Hoffman	.06	.05	.02
96	Dennis Eckersley	2.00	1.50	.80
97a	Tom Burgmeier (Throws: Right)	1.00	.70	.40
97b	Tom Burgmeier (Throws: Left)	.10	.08	.04
98	Win Remmerswaal	.06	.05	.02
99	Bob Horner	.12	.09	.05
100	George Brett	4.00	3.00	1.50
101	Dave Chalk	.06	.05	.02
102	Dennis Leonard	.08	.06	.03
103	Renie Martin	.06	.05	.02
104	Amos Otis	.08	.06	.03
105	Graig Nettles	.15	.11	.06
106	Eric Soderholm	.06	.05	.02
107	Tommy John	.20	.15	.08
108	Tom Underwood	.06	.05	.02
109	Lou Piniella	.12	.09	.05
110	Mickey Klutts	.06	.05	.02
111	Bobby Murcer	.10	.08	.04
112	Eddie Murray	3.00	2.25	1.25
113	Rick Dempsey	.08	.06	.03
114	Scott McGregor	.08	.06	.03
115	Ken Singleton	.10	.08	.04
116	Gary Roenicke	.06	.05	.02
117	Dave Revering	.06	.05	.02
118	Mike Norris	.06	.05	.02
119	Rickey Henderson	10.00	7.50	4.00
120	Mike Heath	.06	.05	.02
121	Dave Cash	.06	.05	.02
122	Randy Jones	.08	.06	.03
123	Eric Rasmussen	.06	.05	.02
124	Jerry Mumphrey	.06	.05	.02
125	Richie Hebner	.06	.05	.02
126	Mark Wagner	.06	.05	.02
127	Jack Morris	.60	.45	.25
128	Dan Petry	.08	.06	.03
129	Bruce Robbins	.06	.05	.02
130	Champ Summers	.06	.05	.02
131a	Pete Rose ("see card 251" on back)	2.25	1.75	.90
131b	Pete Rose ("see card 371" on back)	1.25	.90	.50
132	Willie Stargell	.60	.45	.25
133	Ed Ott	.06	.05	.02
134	Jim Bibby	.06	.05	.02
135	Bert Blyleven	.12	.09	.05
136	Dave Parker	.45	.35	.20
137	Bill Robinson	.06	.05	.02
138	Enos Cabell	.06	.05	.02
139	Dave Bergman	.06	.05	.02
140	J R Richard	.10	.08	.04
141	Ken Forsch	.06	.05	.02
142	Larry Bowa	.15	.11	.06
143	Frank LaCorte (photo actually Randy Niemann)	.06	.05	.02
144	Dennis Walling	.06	.05	.02
145	Buddy Bell	.12	.09	.05
146	Fergie Jenkins	.50	.40	.20
147	Danny Darwin	.06	.05	.02
148	John Grubb	.06	.05	.02
149	Alfredo Griffin	.08	.06	.03
150	Jerry Garvin	.06	.05	.02
151	*Paul Mirabella* (FC)	.06	.05	.02
152	Rick Bosetti	.06	.05	.02
153	Dick Ruthven	.06	.05	.02
154	Frank Taveras	.06	.05	.02
155	Craig Swan	.06	.05	.02
156	*Jeff Reardon*	4.00	3.00	1.50
157	Steve Henderson	.06	.05	.02
158	Jim Morrison	.06	.05	.02
159	Glenn Borgmann	.06	.05	.02
160	*Lamarr Hoyt (LaMarr)*	.10	.08	.04
161	Rich Wortham	.06	.05	.02
162	Thad Bosley	.06	.05	.02
163	Julio Cruz	.06	.05	.02
164a	Del Unser (no 3B in stat heads)	1.00	.70	.40
164b	Del Unser (3B in stat heads)	.10	.08	.04
165	Jim Anderson	.06	.05	.02
166	Jim Beattie	.06	.05	.02
167	Shane Rawley	.06	.05	.02
168	Joe Simpson	.06	.05	.02
169	Rod Carew	1.50	1.25	.60
170	Fred Patek	.06	.05	.02
171	Frank Tanana	.10	.08	.04
172	Alfredo Martinez	.06	.05	.02
173	Chris Knapp	.06	.05	.02
174	Joe Rudi	.10	.08	.04
175	Greg Luzinski	.15	.11	.06
176	Steve Garvey	.50	.40	.20
177	Joe Ferguson	.06	.05	.02
178	Bob Welch	.60	.45	.25
179	Dusty Baker	.10	.08	.04
180	Rudy Law	.06	.05	.02
181	Dave Concepcion	.15	.11	.06
182	Johnny Bench	1.00	.70	.40
183	Mike LaCoss	.06	.05	.02
184	Ken Griffey	.12	.09	.05
185	Dave Collins	.08	.06	.03
186	Brian Asselstine	.06	.05	.02
187	Garry Templeton	.10	.08	.04
188	Mike Phillips	.06	.05	.02
189	Pete Vukovich	.08	.06	.03
190	John Urrea	.06	.05	.02
191	Tony Scott	.06	.05	.02
192	Darrell Evans	.12	.09	.05
193	Milt May	.06	.05	.02
194	Bob Knepper	.08	.06	.03
195	Randy Moffitt	.06	.05	.02
196	Larry Herndon	.08	.06	.03
197	Rick Camp	.06	.05	.02
198	Andre Thornton	.10	.08	.04
199	Tom Veryzer	.06	.05	.02
200	Gary Alexander	.06	.05	.02
201	Rick Waits	.06	.05	.02
202	Rick Manning	.06	.05	.02
203	Paul Molitor	3.00	2.25	1.25
204	Jim Gantner	.08	.06	.03
205	Paul Mitchell	.06	.05	.02
206	Reggie Cleveland	.06	.05	.02
207	Sixto Lezcano	.06	.05	.02
208	Bruce Benedict	.06	.05	.02
209	Rodney Scott	.06	.05	.02
210	John Tamargo	.06	.05	.02
211	Bill Lee	.08	.06	.03
212	Andre Dawson	1.75	1.25	.70
213	Rowland Office	.06	.05	.02
214	Carl Yastrzemski	1.25	.90	.50
215	Jerry Remy	.06	.05	.02
216	Mike Torrez	.08	.06	.03
217	Skip Lockwood	.06	.05	.02
218	Fred Lynn	.20	.15	.08
219	Chris Chambliss	.08	.06	.03
220	Willie Aikens	.06	.05	.02
221	John Wathan	.08	.06	.03
222	Dan Quisenberry	.15	.11	.06
223	Willie Wilson	.15	.11	.06
224	Clint Hurdle	.06	.05	.02
225	Bob Watson	.08	.06	.03
226	Jim Spencer	.06	.05	.02
227	Ron Guidry	.25	.20	.10
228	Reggie Jackson	4.00	3.00	1.50
229	Oscar Gamble	.08	.06	.03
230	Jeff Cox	.06	.05	.02
231	Luis Tiant	.12	.09	.05
232	Rich Dauer	.06	.05	.02
233	Dan Graham	.06	.05	.02
234	Mike Flanagan	.10	.08	.04
235	John Lowenstein	.06	.05	.02
236	Benny Ayala	.06	.05	.02
237	Wayne Gross	.06	.05	.02
238	Rick Langford	.06	.05	.02
239	Tony Armas	.10	.08	.04
240a	Bob Lacy (incorrect spelling)	1.00	.70	.40
240b	Bob Lacey (correct spelling)	.10	.08	.04
241	Gene Tenace	.08	.06	.03
242	Bob Shirley	.06	.05	.02
243	Gary Lucas	.08	.06	.03
244	Jerry Turner	.06	.05	.02
245	John Wockenfuss	.06	.05	.02
246	Stan Papi	.06	.05	.02
247	Milt Wilcox	.06	.05	.02
248	Dan Schatzeder	.06	.05	.02
249	Steve Kemp	.08	.06	.03
250	Jim Lentine	.06	.05	.02
251	Pete Rose	1.00	.70	.40
252	Bill Madlock	.12	.09	.05
253	Dale Berra	.06	.05	.02
254	Kent Tekulve	.08	.06	.03
255	Enrique Romo	.06	.05	.02
256	Mike Easler	.08	.06	.03
257	Chuck Tanner	.06	.05	.02
258	Art Howe	.06	.05	.02
259	Alan Ashby	.06	.05	.02
260	Nolan Ryan	8.00	6.00	3.25
261a	Vern Ruhle (Ken Forsch photo - head shot)	1.25	.90	.50
261b	Vern Ruhle (Vern Ruhle photo - waist to head shot)	.10	.08	.04
262	Bob Boone	.10	.08	.04
263	Cesar Cedeno	.12	.09	.05
264	Jeff Leonard	.06	.05	.02
265	Pat Putnam	.06	.05	.02
266	Jon Matlack	.08	.06	.03
267	Dave Rajsich	.06	.05	.02
268	Billy Sample	.06	.05	.02
269	*Damaso Garcia*	.10	.08	.04
270	Tom Buskey	.06	.05	.02
271	Joey McLaughlin	.06	.05	.02
272	Barry Bonnell	.06	.05	.02
273	Tug McGraw	.10	.08	.04
274	Mike Jorgensen	.06	.05	.02
275	Pat Zachry	.06	.05	.02
276	Neil Allen	.08	.06	.03
277	Joel Youngblood	.06	.05	.02
278	Greg Pryor	.06	.05	.02
279	*Britt Burns*	.10	.08	.04
280	*Rich Dotson*	.25	.20	.10
281	Chet Lemon	.08	.06	.03
282	Rusty Kuntz	.06	.05	.02
283	Ted Cox	.06	.05	.02
284	Sparky Lyle	.10	.08	.04
285	Larry Cox	.06	.05	.02
286	Floyd Bannister	.10	.08	.04
287	Byron McLaughlin	.06	.05	.02
288	Rodney Craig	.06	.05	.02
289	Bobby Grich	.10	.08	.04
290	Dickie Thon	.08	.06	.03
291	Mark Clear	.06	.05	.02
292	Dave Lemanczyk	.06	.05	.02
293	Jason Thompson	.06	.05	.02
294	Rick Miller	.06	.05	.02
295	Lonnie Smith	.08	.06	.03
296	Ron Cey	.12	.09	.05
297	Steve Yeager	.06	.05	.02
298	Bobby Castillo	.06	.05	.02
299	Manny Mota	.08	.06	.03
300	Jay Johnstone	.08	.06	.03
301	Dan Driessen	.08	.06	.03
302	Joe Nolan	.06	.05	.02
303	Paul Householder	.06	.05	.02
304	Harry Spilman	.06	.05	.02
305	Cesar Geronimo	.06	.05	.02
306a	Gary Mathews (Mathews on front)	1.25	.90	.50
306b	Gary Matthews (Matthews on front)	.10	.08	.04
307	Ken Reitz	.06	.05	.02
308	Ted Simmons	.12	.09	.05
309	John Littlefield	.06	.05	.02
310	George Frazier	.06	.05	.02
311	Dane Iorg	.06	.05	.02
312	Mike Ivie	.06	.05	.02
313	Dennis Littlejohn	.06	.05	.02
314	Gary LaVelle (Lavelle)	.06	.05	.02
315	Jack Clark	.25	.20	.10
316	Jim Wohlford	.06	.05	.02
317	Rick Matula	.06	.05	.02
318	Toby Harrah	.08	.06	.03
319a	Dwane Kuiper (Dwane on front)	1.00	.70	.40
319b	Duane Kuiper (Duane on front)	.10	.08	.04
320	Len Barker	.08	.06	.03
321	Victor Cruz	.06	.05	.02
322	Dell Alston	.06	.05	.02
323	Robin Yount	4.00	3.00	1.50
324	Charlie Moore	.06	.05	.02
325	Lary Sorensen	.06	.05	.02
326a	Gorman Thomas ("...30-HR mark 4th..." on back)	1.25	.90	.50
326b	Gorman Thomas ("...30-HR mark 3rd..." on back)	.10	.08	.04
327	Bob Rodgers	.08	.06	.03
328	Phil Niekro	.30	.25	.12
329	Chris Speier	.06	.05	.02
330a	Steve Rodgers (Rodgers on front)	1.00	.70	.40
330b	Steve Rogers (Rogers on front)	.10	.08	.04
331	Woodie Fryman	.08	.06	.03
332	Warren Cromartie	.06	.05	.02
333	Jerry White	.06	.05	.02
334	Tony Perez	.20	.15	.08
335	Carlton Fisk	1.75	1.25	.70
336	Dick Drago	.06	.05	.02
337	Steve Renko	.06	.05	.02
338	Jim Rice	.30	.25	.12
339	Jerry Royster	.06	.05	.02
340	Frank White	.10	.08	.04
341	Jamie Quirk	.06	.05	.02
342a	Paul Spittorff (Spittorff on front)	1.00	.70	.40
342b	Paul Splittorff (Splittorff on front)	.08	.06	.03
343	Marty Pattin	.06	.05	.02
344	Pete LaCock	.06	.05	.02
345	Willie Randolph	.10	.08	.04
346	Rick Cerone	.06	.05	.02
347	Rich Gossage	.20	.15	.08
348	Reggie Jackson	2.50	2.00	1.00
349	Ruppert Jones	.06	.05	.02
350	Dave McKay	.06	.05	.02
351	Yogi Berra	.15	.11	.06
352	Doug Decinces (DeCinces)	.10	.08	.04
353	Jim Palmer	.90	.70	.35
354	Tippy Martinez	.06	.05	.02
355	Al Bumbry	.08	.06	.03
356	Earl Weaver	.10	.08	.04
357a	Bob Picciolo (Bob on front)	1.00	.70	.40
357b	Rob Picciolo (Rob on front)	.10	.08	.04
358	Matt Keough	.06	.05	.02
359	Dwayne Murphy	.08	.06	.03
360	Brian Kingman	.06	.05	.02
361	Bill Fahey	.06	.05	.02
362	Steve Mura	.06	.05	.02
363	Dennis Kinney	.06	.05	.02
364	Dave Winfield	3.00	2.25	1.25

365 Lou Whitaker .40 .30 .15
366 Lance Parrish .20 .15 .08
367 Tim Corcoran .06 .05 .02
368 Pat Underwood .06 .05 .02
369 Al Cowens .06 .05 .02
370 Sparky Anderson .10 .08 .04
371 Pete Rose 1.50 1.25 .60
372 Phil Garner .08 .06 .03
373 Steve Nicosia .06 .05 .02
374 John Candelaria .10 .08 .04
375 Don Robinson .08 .06 .03
376 Lee Lacy .06 .05 .02
377 John Milner .06 .05 .02
378 Craig Reynolds .06 .05 .02
379a Luis Pujois (Pujois on front) 1.00 .70 .40
379b Luis Pujols (Pujols on front) .10 .08 .04
380 Joe Niekro .12 .09 .05
381 Joaquin Andujar .10 .08 .04
382 *Keith Moreland* .20 .15 .08
383 Jose Cruz .12 .09 .05
384 Bill Virdon .06 .05 .02
385 Jim Sundberg .08 .06 .03
386 Doc Medich .06 .05 .02
387 Al Oliver .15 .11 .06
388 Jim Norris .06 .05 .02
389 Bob Bailor .06 .05 .02
390 Ernie Whitt .08 .06 .03
391 Otto Velez .06 .05 .02
392 Roy Howell .06 .05 .02
393 *Bob Walk* .20 .15 .08
394 Doug Flynn .06 .05 .02
395 Pete Falcone .06 .05 .02
396 Tom Hausman .06 .05 .02
397 Elliott Maddox .06 .05 .02
398 Mike Squires .06 .05 .02
399 Marvis Foley .06 .05 .02
400 Steve Trout .06 .05 .02
401 Wayne Nordhagen .06 .05 .02
402 Tony Larussa (LaRussa) .08 .06 .03
403 Bruce Bochte .06 .05 .02
404 Bake McBride .06 .05 .02
405 Jerry Narron .06 .05 .02
406 Rob Dressler .06 .05 .02
407 Dave Heaverlo .06 .05 .02
408 Tom Paciorek .06 .05 .02
409 Carney Lansford .10 .08 .04
410 Brian Downing .10 .08 .04
411 Don Aase .06 .05 .02
412 Jim Barr .06 .05 .02
413 Don Baylor .12 .09 .05
414 Jim Fregosi .08 .06 .03
415 Dallas Green .08 .06 .03
416 Dave Lopes .10 .08 .04
417 Jerry Reuss .10 .08 .04
418 Rick Sutcliffe .20 .15 .08
419 Derrel Thomas .06 .05 .02
420 Tommy LaSorda (Lasorda) .10 .08 .04
421 *Charlie Leibrandt* .20 .15 .08
422 Tom Seaver 2.00 1.50 .80
423 Ron Oester .06 .05 .02
424 Junior Kennedy .06 .05 .02
425 Tom Seaver 2.00 1.50 .80
426 Bobby Cox .06 .05 .02
427 *Leon Durham* .20 .15 .08
428 Terry Kennedy .08 .06 .03
429 Silvio Martinez .06 .05 .02
430 George Hendrick .08 .06 .03
431 Red Schoendienst .15 .11 .06
432 John LeMaster .06 .05 .02
433 Vida Blue .12 .09 .05
434 John Montefusco .08 .06 .03
435 Terry Whitfield .06 .05 .02
436 Dave Bristol .06 .05 .02
437 Dale Murphy .90 .70 .35
438 Jerry Dybzinski .06 .05 .02
439 Jorge Orta .06 .05 .02
440 Wayne Garland .06 .05 .02
441 Miguel Dilone .06 .05 .02
442 Dave Garcia .06 .05 .02
443 Don Money .06 .05 .02
444a Buck Martinez (photo reversed) 1.00 .70 .40
444b Buck Martinez (photo correct) .10 .08 .04
445 Jerry Augustine .06 .05 .02
446 Ben Oglivie .08 .06 .03
447 Jim Slaton .06 .05 .02
448 Doyle Alexander .10 .08 .04
449 Tony Bernazard .06 .05 .02
450 Scott Sanderson .06 .05 .02
451 Dave Palmer .06 .05 .02
452 Stan Bahnsen .06 .05 .02
453 Dick Williams .06 .05 .02
454 Rick Burleson .08 .06 .03
455 Gary Allenson .06 .05 .02
456 Bob Stanley .06 .05 .02
457a *John Tudor* (lifetime W/L 9.7) 1.50 1.25 .60
457b *John Tudor* (lifetime W/L 9-7) .50 .40 .20
458 Dwight Evans .15 .11 .06
459 Glenn Hubbard .08 .06 .03
460 U L Washington .06 .05 .02
461 Larry Gura .06 .05 .02
462 Rich Gale .06 .05 .02
463 Hal McRae .10 .08 .04
464 Jim Frey .06 .05 .02
465 Bucky Dent .10 .08 .04
466 Dennis Werth .06 .05 .02
467 Ron Davis .08 .06 .03
468 Reggie Jackson 3.50 2.75 1.50
469 Bobby Brown .06 .05 .02
470 *Mike Davis* .10 .08 .04
471 Gaylord Perry .50 .40 .20
472 Mark Belanger .08 .06 .03
473 Jim Palmer .80 .60 .30
474 Sammy Stewart .06 .05 .02
475 Tim Stoddard .06 .05 .02
476 Steve Stone .08 .06 .03
477 Jeff Newman .06 .05 .02
478 Steve McCatty .06 .05 .02
479 Billy Martin .12 .09 .05
480 Mitchell Page .06 .05 .02
481 Steve Carlton (CY) .40 .30 .15
482 Bill Buckner .12 .09 .05
483a Ivan DeJesus (lifetime hits 702) 1.00 .70 .40
483b Ivan DeJesus (lifetime hits 642) .10 .08 .04
484 Cliff Johnson .06 .05 .02
485 Lenny Randle .06 .05 .02
486 Larry Milbourne .06 .05 .02
487 Roy Smalley .06 .05 .02
488 John Castino .06 .05 .02
489 Ron Jackson .06 .05 .02
490a Dave Roberts (1980 highlights begins "Showed pop...") 1.00 .70 .40
490b Dave Roberts (1980 highlights begins "Declared himself...") .10 .08 .04
491 George Brett (MVP) 2.50 2.00 1.00
492 Mike Cubbage .06 .05 .02
493 Rob Wilfong .06 .05 .02
494 Danny Goodwin .06 .05 .02
495 Jose Morales .06 .05 .02
496 Mickey Rivers .08 .06 .03
497 Mike Edwards .06 .05 .02
498 Mike Sadek .06 .05 .02
499 Lenn Sakata .06 .05 .02
500 Gene Michael .06 .05 .02
501 Dave Roberts .06 .05 .02
502 Steve Dillard .06 .05 .02
503 Jim Essian .06 .05 .02
504 Rance Mulliniks .06 .05 .02
505 Darrell Porter .08 .06 .03
506 Joe Torre .10 .08 .04
507 Terry Crowley .06 .05 .02
508 Bill Travers .06 .05 .02
509 Nelson Norman .06 .05 .02
510 Bob McClure .06 .05 .02
511 *Steve Howe* .10 .08 .04
512 Dave Rader .06 .05 .02
513 Mick Kelleher .06 .05 .02
514 Kiko Garcia .06 .05 .02
515 Larry Biittner .06 .05 .02
516a Willie Norwood (1980 highlights begins "Spent most...") 1.00 .70 .40
516b Willie Norwood (1980 highlights begins "Traded to...") .10 .08 .04
517 Bo Diaz .08 .06 .03
518 Juan Beniquez .06 .05 .02
519 Scot Thompson .06 .05 .02
520 Jim Tracy .06 .05 .02
521 Carlos Lezcano .06 .05 .02
522 Joe Amalfitano .06 .05 .02
523 Preston Hanna .06 .05 .02
524a Ray Burris (1980 highlights begins "Went on...") 1.00 .70 .40
524b Ray Burris (1980 highlights begins "Drafted by...") .10 .08 .04
525 Broderick Perkins .06 .05 .02
526 Mickey Hatcher .08 .06 .03
527 John Goryl .06 .05 .02
528 Dick Davis .06 .05 .02
529 Butch Wynegar .06 .05 .02
530 Sal Butera .06 .05 .02
531 Jerry Koosman .10 .08 .04
532a Jeff Zahn (Geoff) (1980 highlights begins "Was 2nd in...") 1.00 .70 .40
532b Jeff Zahn (Geoff) (1980 highlights begins "Signed a 3 year...") .10 .08 .04
533 Dennis Martinez .12 .09 .05
534 Gary Thomasson .06 .05 .02
535 Steve Macko .06 .05 .02
536 Jim Kaat .15 .11 .06
537 Best Hitters (George Brett, Rod Carew) 2.00 1.50 .80
538 *Tim Raines* 7.00 5.25 2.75
539 Keith Smith .06 .05 .02
540 Ken Macha .06 .05 .02
541 Burt Hooton .08 .06 .03
542 Butch Hobson .06 .05 .02
543 Bill Stein .06 .05 .02
544 Dave Stapleton .06 .05 .02
545 Bob Pate .06 .05 .02
546 Doug Corbett .06 .05 .02
547 Darrell Jackson .06 .05 .02
548 Pete Redfern .06 .05 .02
549 Roger Erickson .06 .05 .02
550 Al Hrabosky .08 .06 .03
551 Dick Tidrow .06 .05 .02
552 Dave Ford .06 .05 .02
553 Dave Kingman .12 .09 .05
554a Mike Vail (1980 highlights begins "After...") 1.00 .70 .40
554b Mike Vail (1980 highlights begins "Traded...") .10 .08 .04
555a Jerry Martin (1980 highlights begins "Overcame...") 1.00 .70 .40
555b Jerry Martin (1980 highlights begins "Traded...") .10 .08 .04
556a Jesus Figueroa (1980 highlights begins "Had...") 1.00 .70 .40
556b Jesus Figueroa (1980 highlights begins "Traded...") .10 .08 .04
557 Don Stanhouse .06 .05 .02
558 Barry Foote .06 .05 .02
559 Tim Blackwell .06 .05 .02
560 Bruce Sutter .15 .11 .06
561 Rick Reuschel .10 .08 .04
562 Lynn McGlothen .06 .05 .02
563a Bob Owchinko (1980 highlights begins "Traded...") 1.00 .70 .40
563b Bob Owchinko (1980 highlights begins "Involved...") .10 .08 .04
564 John Verhoeven .06 .05 .02
565 Ken Landreaux .06 .05 .02
566a Glen Adams (Glen on front) 1.00 .70 .40
566b Glenn Adams (Glenn on front) .10 .08 .04
567 Hosken Powell .06 .05 .02
568 Dick Noles .06 .05 .02
569 *Danny Ainge* 2.00 1.50 .80
570 Bobby Mattick .06 .05 .02
571 Joe LeFebvre (Lefebvre) .06 .05 .02
572 Bobby Clark .06 .05 .02
573 Dennis Lamp .06 .05 .02
574 Randy Lerch .06 .05 .02
575 *Mookie Wilson* .30 .25 .12
576 Ron LeFlore .08 .06 .03
577 Jim Dwyer .06 .05 .02
578 Bill Castro .06 .05 .02
579 Greg Minton .06 .05 .02
580 Mark Littell .06 .05 .02
581 Andy Hassler .06 .05 .02
582 Dave Stieb .40 .30 .15
583 Ken Oberkfell .06 .05 .02
584 Larry Bradford .06 .05 .02
585 Fred Stanley .06 .05 .02
586 Bill Caudill .06 .05 .02
587 Doug Capilla .06 .05 .02
588 George Riley .06 .05 .02
589 Willie Hernandez .10 .08 .04
590 Mike Schmidt (MVP) 1.00 .70 .40
591 Cy Young 1980 (Steve Stone) .08 .06 .03
592 Rick Sofield .06 .05 .02
593 Bombo Rivera .06 .05 .02
594 Gary Ward .08 .06 .03
595a Dave Edwards (1980 highlights begins "Sidelined...") 1.00 .70 .40
595b Dave Edwards (1980 highlights begins "Traded...") .10 .08 .04
596 Mike Proly .06 .05 .02
597 Tommy Boggs .06 .05 .02
598 Greg Gross .06 .05 .02
599 Elias Sosa .06 .05 .02
600 Pat Kelly .06 .05 .02
----a Checklist 1-120 (51 Tom Donohue) 2.00 1.50 .80
----b Checklist 1-120 (51 Tom Donahue) .10 .08 .04
---- Checklist 121-240 .06 .05 .02
----a Checklist 241-360 (306 Gary Mathews) .70 .50 .30
----b Checklist 241-360 (306 Gary Matthews) .10 .08 .04
----a Checklist 361-480 (379 Luis Pujois) .70 .50 .30
----b Checklist 361-480 (379 Luis Pujols) .10 .08 .04
----a Checklist 481-600 (566 Glen Adams) .70 .50 .30
----b Checklist 481-600 (566 Glenn Adams) .10 .08 .04

1982 Donruss

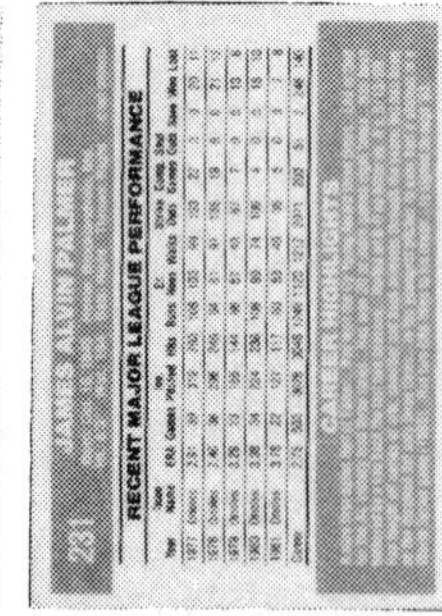

Using card stock thicker than the previous year, Donruss issued a 660-card set which includes 653 numbered cards and seven unnumbered checklists. The cards, which measure 2-1/2" by 3-1/2", were sold with puzzle pieces rather than gum as a result of a lawsuit by Topps. The puzzle pieces (three pieces on one card per pack) feature Babe Ruth. The first 26 cards of the set, entitled Diamond Kings, showcase the artwork of Dick Perez of Perez-Steele Galleries. The card fronts display the Donruss logo and the year of issue. The card backs have black and blue ink on white stock and include the player's career highlights. The complete set price does not include the higher priced variations.

	MT	NR MT	EX
Complete Set (660):	100.00	75.00	40.00
Common Player:	.06	.05	.02

1 Pete Rose (DK) 2.00 1.50 .80
2 Gary Carter (DK) .50 .40 .20
3 Steve Garvey (DK) .50 .40 .20
4 Vida Blue (DK) .12 .09 .05
5a Alan Trammel (DK name incorrect) 1.50 1.25 .60
5b Alan Trammell (DK COR) .40 .30 .15
6 Len Barker (DK) .08 .06 .03
7 Dwight Evans (DK) .15 .11 .06
8 Rod Carew (DK) .60 .45 .25
9 George Hendrick (DK) .08 .06 .03
10 Phil Niekro (DK) .30 .25 .12
11 Richie Zisk (DK) .08 .06 .03
12 Dave Parker (DK) .30 .25 .12
13 Nolan Ryan (DK) 4.00 3.00 1.50
14 Ivan DeJesus (DK) .08 .06 .03
15 George Brett (DK) 1.50 1.25 .60
16 Tom Seaver (DK) .80 .60 .30
17 Dave Kingman (DK) .15 .11 .06
18 Dave Winfield (DK) 1.50 1.25 .60

19	Mike Norris (DK)	.08	.06	.03
20	Carlton Fisk (DK)	.80	.60	.30
21	Ozzie Smith (DK)	.40	.30	.15
22	Roy Smalley (DK)	.08	.06	.03
23	Buddy Bell (DK)	.12	.09	.05
24	Ken Singleton (DK)	.10	.08	.04
25	John Mayberry (DK)	.08	.06	.03
26	Gorman Thomas (DK)	.10	.08	.04
27	Earl Weaver	.10	.08	.04
28	Rollie Fingers	.80	.60	.30
29	Sparky Anderson	.10	.08	.04
30	Dennis Eckersley	1.25	.90	.50
31	Dave Winfield	2.50	2.00	1.00
32	Burt Hooton	.08	.06	.03
33	Rick Waits	.06	.05	.02
34	George Brett	3.00	2.25	1.25
35	Steve McCatty	.06	.05	.02
36	Steve Rogers	.08	.06	.03
37	Bill Stein	.06	.05	.02
38	Steve Renko	.06	.05	.02
39	Mike Squires	.06	.05	.02
40	George Hendrick	.08	.06	.03
41	Bob Knepper	.08	.06	.03
42	Steve Carlton	1.00	.70	.40
43	Larry Biittner	.06	.05	.02
44	Chris Welsh	.06	.05	.02
45	Steve Nicosia	.06	.05	.02
46	Jack Clark	.25	.20	.10
47	Chris Chambliss	.08	.06	.03
48	Ivan DeJesus	.06	.05	.02
49	Lee Mazzilli	.08	.06	.03
50	Julio Cruz	.06	.05	.02
51	Pete Redfern	.06	.05	.02
52	Dave Stieb	.12	.09	.05
53	Doug Corbett	.06	.05	.02
54	*George Bell* (FC)	4.00	3.00	1.50
55	Joe Simpson	.06	.05	.02
56	Rusty Staub	.10	.08	.04
57	Hector Cruz	.06	.05	.02
58	Claudell Washington (FC)	.10	.08	.04
59	Enrique Romo	.06	.05	.02
60	Gary Lavelle	.06	.05	.02
61	Tim Flannery	.06	.05	.02
62	Joe Nolan	.06	.05	.02
63	Larry Bowa	.15	.11	.06
64	Sixto Lezcano	.06	.05	.02
65	Joe Sambito	.06	.05	.02
66	Bruce Kison	.06	.05	.02
67	Wayne Nordhagen	.06	.05	.02
68	Woodie Fryman	.08	.06	.03
69	Billy Sample	.06	.05	.02
70	Amos Otis	.08	.06	.03
71	Matt Keough	.06	.05	.02
72	Toby Harrah	.08	.06	.03
73	*Dave Righetti* (FC)	.60	.45	.25
74	Carl Yastrzemski	1.00	.70	.40
75	Bob Welch	.12	.09	.05
76a	Alan Trammel (ERR)	2.00	1.50	.80
76b	Alan Trammell (COR)	.60	.45	.25
77	Rick Dempsey	.08	.06	.03
78	Paul Molitor	3.00	2.25	1.25
79	Dennis Martinez	.08	.06	.03
80	Jim Slaton	.06	.05	.02
81	Champ Summers	.06	.05	.02
82	Carney Lansford	.08	.06	.03
83	Barry Foote	.06	.05	.02
84	Steve Garvey	.50	.40	.20
85	Rick Manning	.06	.05	.02
86	John Wathan	.08	.06	.03
87	Brian Kingman	.06	.05	.02
88	Andre Dawson	1.25	.90	.50
89	Jim Kern	.06	.05	.02
90	Bobby Grich	.10	.08	.04
91	Bob Forsch	.08	.06	.03
92	Art Howe	.06	.05	.02
93	Marty Bystrom	.06	.05	.02
94	Ozzie Smith	2.00	1.50	.80
95	Dave Parker	.30	.25	.12
96	Doyle Alexander	.10	.08	.04
97	Al Hrabosky	.08	.06	.03
98	Frank Taveras	.06	.05	.02
99	Tim Blackwell	.06	.05	.02
100	Floyd Bannister	.10	.08	.04
101	Alfredo Griffin	.08	.06	.03
102	Dave Engle	.06	.05	.02
103	Mario Soto	.08	.06	.03
104	Ross Baumgarten	.06	.05	.02
105	Ken Singleton	.10	.08	.04
106	Ted Simmons	.12	.09	.05
107	Jack Morris	.50	.40	.20
108	Bob Watson	.08	.06	.03
109	Dwight Evans	.15	.11	.06
110	Tom Lasorda	.10	.08	.04
111	Bert Blyleven	.12	.09	.05
112	Dan Quisenberry	.15	.11	.06
113	Rickey Henderson	4.00	3.00	1.50
114	Gary Carter	.70	.50	.30
115	Brian Downing	.10	.08	.04
116	Al Oliver	.15	.11	.06
117	LaMarr Hoyt	.06	.05	.02
118	Cesar Cedeno	.12	.09	.05
119	Keith Moreland	.10	.08	.04
120	Bob Shirley	.06	.05	.02
121	Terry Kennedy	.08	.06	.03
122	Frank Pastore	.06	.05	.02
123	Gene Garber	.06	.05	.02
124	Tony Pena (FC)	.25	.20	.10
125	Allen Ripley	.06	.05	.02
126	Randy Martz	.06	.05	.02
127	Richie Zisk	.08	.06	.03
128	Mike Scott	.15	.11	.06
129	Lloyd Moseby (FC)	.12	.09	.05
130	Rob Wilfong	.06	.05	.02
131	Tim Stoddard	.06	.05	.02
132	Gorman Thomas	.10	.08	.04
133	Dan Petry	.08	.06	.03
134	Bob Stanley	.06	.05	.02
135	Lou Piniella	.15	.11	.06
136	Pedro Guerrero (FC)	.30	.25	.12
137	Len Barker	.08	.06	.03
138	Richard Gale	.06	.05	.02
139	Wayne Gross	.06	.05	.02
140	*Tim Wallach* (FC)	2.00	1.50	.80
141	Gene Mauch	.08	.06	.03
142	Doc Medich	.06	.05	.02
143	Tony Bernazard	.06	.05	.02
144	Bill Virdon	.06	.05	.02
145	John Littlefield	.06	.05	.02
146	Dave Bergman	.06	.05	.02
147	Dick Davis	.06	.05	.02
148	Tom Seaver	1.50	1.25	.60
149	Matt Sinatro	.06	.05	.02
150	Chuck Tanner	.06	.05	.02
151	Leon Durham	.08	.06	.03
152	Gene Tenace	.08	.06	.03
153	Al Bumbry	.08	.06	.03
154	Mark Brouhard	.06	.05	.02
155	Rick Peters	.06	.05	.02
156	Jerry Remy	.06	.05	.02
157	Rick Reuschel	.10	.08	.04
158	Steve Howe	.08	.06	.03
159	Alan Bannister	.06	.05	.02
160	U L Washington	.06	.05	.02
161	Rick Langford	.06	.05	.02
162	Bill Gullickson	.08	.06	.03
163	Mark Wagner	.06	.05	.02
164	Geoff Zahn	.06	.05	.02
165	Ron LeFlore	.08	.06	.03
166	Dane Iorg	.06	.05	.02
167	Joe Niekro	.12	.09	.05
168	Pete Rose	1.50	1.25	.60
169	Dave Collins	.08	.06	.03
170	Rick Wise	.08	.06	.03
171	Jim Bibby	.06	.05	.02
172	Larry Herndon	.08	.06	.03
173	Bob Horner	.12	.09	.05
174	Steve Dillard	.06	.05	.02
175	Mookie Wilson	.12	.09	.05
176	Dan Meyer	.06	.05	.02
177	Fernando Arroyo	.06	.05	.02
178	Jackson Todd	.06	.05	.02
179	Darrell Jackson	.06	.05	.02
180	Al Woods	.06	.05	.02
181	Jim Anderson	.06	.05	.02
182	Dave Kingman	.12	.09	.05
183	Steve Henderson	.06	.05	.02
184	Brian Asselstine	.06	.05	.02
185	Rod Scurry	.06	.05	.02
186	Fred Breining	.06	.05	.02
187	Danny Boone	.06	.05	.02
188	Junior Kennedy	.06	.05	.02
189	Sparky Lyle	.10	.08	.04
190	Whitey Herzog	.08	.06	.03
191	Dave Smith	.10	.08	.04
192	Ed Ott	.06	.05	.02
193	Greg Luzinski	.15	.11	.06
194	Bill Lee	.08	.06	.03
195	Don Zimmer	.06	.05	.02
196	Hal McRae	.15	.11	.06
197	Mike Norris	.06	.05	.02
198	Duane Kuiper	.06	.05	.02
199	Rick Cerone	.06	.05	.02
200	Jim Rice	.30	.25	.12
201	Steve Yeager	.06	.05	.02
202	Tom Brookens	.06	.05	.02
203	Jose Morales	.06	.05	.02
204	Roy Howell	.06	.05	.02
205	Tippy Martinez	.06	.05	.02
206	Moose Haas	.06	.05	.02
207	Al Cowens	.06	.05	.02
208	Dave Stapleton	.06	.05	.02
209	Bucky Dent	.10	.08	.04
210	Ron Cey	.12	.09	.05
211	Jorge Orta	.06	.05	.02
212	Jamie Quirk	.06	.05	.02
213	Jeff Jones	.06	.05	.02
214	Tim Raines	1.50	1.25	.60
215	Jon Matlack	.08	.06	.03
216	Rod Carew	1.00	.70	.40
217	Jim Kaat	.15	.11	.06
218	Joe Pittman	.06	.05	.02
219	Larry Christenson	.06	.05	.02
220	Juan Bonilla	.06	.05	.02
221	Mike Easler	.08	.06	.03
222	Vida Blue	.12	.09	.05
223	Rick Camp	.06	.05	.02
224	Mike Jorgensen	.06	.05	.02
225	*Jody Davis* (FC)	.15	.11	.06
226	Mike Parrott	.06	.05	.02
227	Jim Clancy	.08	.06	.03
228	Hosken Powell	.06	.05	.02
229	Tom Hume	.06	.05	.02
230	Britt Burns	.06	.05	.02
231	Jim Palmer	.70	.50	.30
232	Bob Rodgers	.08	.06	.03
233	Milt Wilcox	.06	.05	.02
234	Dave Revering	.06	.05	.02
235	Mike Torrez	.08	.06	.03
236	Robert Castillo	.06	.05	.02
237	*Von Hayes* (FC)	.25	.20	.10
238	Renie Martin	.06	.05	.02
239	Dwayne Murphy	.08	.06	.03
240	Rodney Scott	.06	.05	.02
241	Fred Patek	.06	.05	.02
242	Mickey Rivers	.08	.06	.03
243	Steve Trout	.06	.05	.02
244	Jose Cruz	.12	.09	.05
245	Manny Trillo	.08	.06	.03
246	Lary Sorensen	.06	.05	.02
247	Dave Edwards	.06	.05	.02
248	Dan Driessen	.08	.06	.03
249	Tommy Boggs	.06	.05	.02
250	Dale Berra	.06	.05	.02
251	Ed Whitson	.06	.05	.02
252	*Lee Smith* (FC)	12.00	9.00	4.75
253	Tom Paciorek	.06	.05	.02
254	Pat Zachry	.06	.05	.02
255	Luis Leal	.06	.05	.02
256	John Castino	.06	.05	.02
257	Rich Dauer	.06	.05	.02
258	Cecil Cooper	.15	.11	.06
259	Dave Rozema	.06	.05	.02
260	John Tudor	.10	.08	.04
261	Jerry Mumphrey	.06	.05	.02
262	Jay Johnstone	.08	.06	.03
263	Bo Diaz	.08	.06	.03
264	Dennis Leonard	.08	.06	.03
265	Jim Spencer	.06	.05	.02
266	John Milner	.06	.05	.02
267	Don Aase	.06	.05	.02
268	Jim Sundberg	.08	.06	.03
269	Lamar Johnson	.06	.05	.02
270	Frank LaCorte	.06	.05	.02
271	Barry Evans	.06	.05	.02
272	Enos Cabell	.06	.05	.02
273	Del Unser	.06	.05	.02
274	George Foster	.20	.15	.08
275	*Brett Butler* (FC)	2.50	2.00	1.00
276	Lee Lacy	.06	.05	.02
277	Ken Reitz	.06	.05	.02
278	Keith Hernandez	.20	.15	.08
279	Doug DeCinces	.10	.08	.04
280	Charlie Moore	.06	.05	.02
281	Lance Parrish	.20	.15	.08
282	Ralph Houk	.08	.06	.03
283	Rich Gossage	.20	.15	.08
284	Jerry Reuss	.10	.08	.04
285	Mike Stanton	.06	.05	.02
286	Frank White	.10	.08	.04
287	Bob Owchinko	.06	.05	.02
288	Scott Sanderson	.06	.05	.02
289	Bump Wills	.06	.05	.02
290	Dave Frost	.06	.05	.02
291	Chet Lemon	.08	.06	.03
292	Tito Landrum	.06	.05	.02
293	Vern Ruhle	.06	.05	.02
294	Mike Schmidt	2.50	2.00	1.00
295	Sam Mejias	.06	.05	.02
296	Gary Lucas	.06	.05	.02
297	John Candelaria	.10	.08	.04
298	Jerry Martin	.06	.05	.02
299	Dale Murphy	.90	.70	.35
300	Mike Lum	.06	.05	.02
301	Tom Hausman	.06	.05	.02
302	Glenn Abbott	.06	.05	.02
303	Roger Erickson	.06	.05	.02
304	Otto Velez	.06	.05	.02
305	Danny Goodwin	.06	.05	.02
306	John Mayberry	.08	.06	.03
307	Lenny Randle	.06	.05	.02
308	Bob Bailor	.06	.05	.02
309	Jerry Morales	.06	.05	.02
310	Rufino Linares	.06	.05	.02
311	Kent Tekulve	.08	.06	.03
312	Joe Morgan	.50	.40	.20
313	John Urrea	.06	.05	.02
314	Paul Householder	.06	.05	.02
315	Garry Maddox	.10	.08	.04
316	Mike Ramsey	.06	.05	.02
317	Alan Ashby	.06	.05	.02
318	Bob Clark	.06	.05	.02
319	Tony LaRussa	.12	.09	.05
320	Charlie Lea	.08	.06	.03
321	Danny Darwin	.06	.05	.02
322	Cesar Geronimo	.06	.05	.02
323	Tom Underwood	.06	.05	.02
324	Andre Thornton	.10	.08	.04
325	Rudy May	.06	.05	.02
326	Frank Tanana	.10	.08	.04
327	Davey Lopes	.10	.08	.04
328	Richie Hebner	.06	.05	.02
329	Mike Flanagan	.10	.08	.04
330	Mike Caldwell	.06	.05	.02
331	Scott McGregor	.08	.06	.03
332	Jerry Augustine	.06	.05	.02
333	Stan Papi	.06	.05	.02
334	Rick Miller	.06	.05	.02
335	Graig Nettles	.15	.11	.06
336	Dusty Baker	.10	.08	.04
337	Dave Garcia	.06	.05	.02
338	Larry Gura	.06	.05	.02
339	Cliff Johnson	.06	.05	.02
340	Warren Cromartie	.06	.05	.02
341	Steve Comer	.06	.05	.02
342	Rick Burleson	.08	.06	.03
343	John Martin	.06	.05	.02
344	Craig Reynolds	.06	.05	.02
345	Mike Proly	.06	.05	.02
346	Ruppert Jones	.06	.05	.02
347	Omar Moreno	.06	.05	.02
348	Greg Minton	.06	.05	.02
349	*Rick Mahler* (FC)	.10	.08	.04
350	Alex Trevino	.06	.05	.02
351	Mike Krukow	.08	.06	.03
352a	Shane Rawley (Jim Anderson photo - shaking hands)	1.25	.90	.50
352b	Shane Rawley (correct photo - kneeling)	.15	.11	.06
353	Garth Iorg	.06	.05	.02
354	Pete Mackanin	.06	.05	.02
355	Paul Moskau	.06	.05	.02
356	Richard Dotson	.10	.08	.04
357	Steve Stone	.08	.06	.03
358	Larry Hisle	.08	.06	.03
359	Aurelio Lopez	.06	.05	.02
360	Oscar Gamble	.08	.06	.03
361	Tom Burgmeier	.06	.05	.02
362	Terry Forster	.08	.06	.03
363	Joe Charboneau	.08	.06	.03
364	Ken Brett	.08	.06	.03
365	Tony Armas	.10	.08	.04
366	Chris Speier	.06	.05	.02
367	Fred Lynn	.20	.15	.08
368	Buddy Bell	.12	.09	.05

369	Jim Essian	.06	.05	.02
370	Terry Puhl	.06	.05	.02
371	Greg Gross	.06	.05	.02
372	Bruce Sutter	.15	.11	.06
373	Joe Lefebvre	.06	.05	.02
374	Ray Knight	.10	.08	.04
375	Bruce Benedict	.06	.05	.02
376	Tim Foli	.06	.05	.02
377	Al Holland	.06	.05	.02
378	Ken Kravec	.06	.05	.02
379	Jeff Burroughs	.08	.06	.03
380	Pete Falcone	.06	.05	.02
381	Ernie Whitt	.08	.06	.03
382	Brad Havens	.06	.05	.02
383	Terry Crowley	.06	.05	.02
384	Don Money	.06	.05	.02
385	Dan Schatzeder	.06	.05	.02
386	Gary Allenson	.06	.05	.02
387	Yogi Berra	.15	.11	.06
388	Ken Landreaux	.06	.05	.02
389	Mike Hargrove	.06	.05	.02
390	Darryl Motley	.06	.05	.02
391	Dave McKay	.06	.05	.02
392	Stan Bahnsen	.06	.05	.02
393	Ken Forsch	.06	.05	.02
394	Mario Mendoza	.06	.05	.02
395	Jim Morrison	.06	.05	.02
396	Mike Ivie	.06	.05	.02
397	Broderick Perkins	.06	.05	.02
398	Darrell Evans	.15	.11	.06
399	Ron Reed	.06	.05	.02
400	Johnny Bench	.60	.45	.25
401	*Steve Bedrosian* (FC)	.50	.40	.20
402	Bill Robinson	.06	.05	.02
403	Bill Buckner	.12	.09	.05
404	Ken Oberkfell	.06	.05	.02
405	*Cal Ripken, Jr.*	45.00	34.00	18.00
406	Jim Gantner	.08	.06	.03
407	Kirk Gibson (FC)	.90	.70	.35
408	Tony Perez	.20	.15	.08
409	Tommy John	.20	.15	.08
410	*Dave Stewart* (FC)	3.50	2.75	1.50
411	Dan Spillner	.06	.05	.02
412	Willie Aikens	.06	.05	.02
413	Mike Heath	.06	.05	.02
414	Ray Burris	.06	.05	.02
415	Leon Roberts	.06	.05	.02
416	*Mike Witt* (FC)	.20	.15	.08
417	Bobby Molinaro	.06	.05	.02
418	Steve Braun	.06	.05	.02
419	Nolan Ryan	9.00	6.75	3.50
420	Tug McGraw	.12	.09	.05
421	Dave Concepcion	.12	.09	.05
422a	Juan Eichelberger (Gary Lucas photo - white player)	1.25	.90	.50
422b	Juan Eichelberger (correct photo - black player)	.08	.06	.03
423	Rick Rhoden	.10	.08	.04
424	Frank Robinson	.15	.11	.06
425	Eddie Miller	.06	.05	.02
426	Bill Caudill	.06	.05	.02
427	Doug Flynn	.06	.05	.02
428	Larry Anderson (Andersen)	.06	.05	.02
429	Al Williams	.06	.05	.02
430	Jerry Garvin	.06	.05	.02
431	Glenn Adams	.06	.05	.02
432	Barry Bonnell	.06	.05	.02
433	Jerry Narron	.06	.05	.02
434	John Stearns	.06	.05	.02
435	Mike Tyson	.06	.05	.02
436	Glenn Hubbard	.08	.06	.03
437	Eddie Solomon	.06	.05	.02
438	Jeff Leonard	.10	.08	.04
439	Randy Bass	.06	.05	.02
440	Mike LaCoss	.06	.05	.02
441	Gary Matthews	.10	.08	.04
442	Mark Littell	.06	.05	.02
443	Don Sutton	.30	.25	.12
444	John Harris	.06	.05	.02
445	Vada Pinson	.08	.06	.03
446	Elias Sosa	.06	.05	.02
447	Charlie Hough	.10	.08	.04
448	Willie Wilson	.15	.11	.06
449	Fred Stanley	.06	.05	.02
450	Tom Veryzer	.06	.05	.02
451	Ron Davis	.06	.05	.02
452	Mark Clear	.06	.05	.02
453	Bill Russell	.08	.06	.03
454	Lou Whitaker	.40	.30	.15
455	Dan Graham	.06	.05	.02
456	Reggie Cleveland	.06	.05	.02
457	Sammy Stewart	.06	.05	.02
458	Pete Vuckovich	.08	.06	.03
459	John Wockenfuss	.06	.05	.02
460	Glenn Hoffman	.06	.05	.02
461	Willie Randolph	.10	.08	.04
462	Fernando Valenzuela (FC)	.50	.40	.20
463	Ron Hassey	.06	.05	.02
464	Paul Splittorff	.06	.05	.02
465	Rob Picciolo	.06	.05	.02
466	Larry Parrish	.10	.08	.04
467	Johnny Grubb	.06	.05	.02
468	Dan Ford	.06	.05	.02
469	Silvio Martinez	.06	.05	.02
470	Kiko Garcia	.06	.05	.02
471	Bob Boone	.10	.08	.04
472	Luis Salazar	.08	.06	.03
473	Randy Niemann	.06	.05	.02
474	Tom Griffin	.06	.05	.02
475	Phil Niekro	.30	.25	.12
476	Hubie Brooks (FC)	.25	.20	.10
477	Dick Tidrow	.06	.05	.02
478	Jim Beattie	.06	.05	.02
479	Damaso Garcia	.06	.05	.02
480	Mickey Hatcher	.08	.06	.03
481	Joe Price	.06	.05	.02
482	Ed Farmer	.06	.05	.02
483	Eddie Murray	2.00	1.50	.80
484	Ben Oglivie	.08	.06	.03
485	Kevin Saucier	.06	.05	.02
486	Bobby Murcer	.10	.08	.04
487	Bill Campbell	.06	.05	.02
488	Reggie Smith	.10	.08	.04
489	Wayne Garland	.06	.05	.02
490	Jim Wright	.06	.05	.02
491	Billy Martin	.12	.09	.05
492	Jim Fanning	.06	.05	.02
493	Don Baylor	.12	.09	.05
494	Rick Honeycutt	.06	.05	.02
495	Carlton Fisk	1.50	1.25	.60
496	Denny Walling	.06	.05	.02
497	Bake McBride	.06	.05	.02
498	Darrell Porter	.08	.06	.03
499	Gene Richards	.06	.05	.02
500	Ron Oester	.06	.05	.02
501	*Ken Dayley* (FC)	.12	.09	.05
502	Jason Thompson	.06	.05	.02
503	Milt May	.12	.09	.05
504	Doug Bird	.06	.05	.02
505	Bruce Bochte	.06	.05	.02
506	Neil Allen	.06	.05	.02
507	Joey McLaughlin	.06	.05	.02
508	Butch Wynegar	.06	.05	.02
509	Gary Roenicke	.06	.05	.02
510	Robin Yount	3.00	2.25	1.25
511	Dave Tobik	.06	.05	.02
512	*Rich Gedman* (FC)	.15	.11	.06
513	*Gene Nelson* (FC)	.06	.05	.02
514	Rick Monday	.10	.08	.04
515	Miguel Dilone	.06	.05	.02
516	Clint Hurdle	.06	.05	.02
517	Jeff Newman	.06	.05	.02
518	Grant Jackson	.06	.05	.02
519	Andy Hassler	.06	.05	.02
520	Pat Putnam	.06	.05	.02
521	Greg Pryor	.06	.05	.02
522	Tony Scott	.06	.05	.02
523	Steve Mura	.06	.05	.02
524	Johnnie LeMaster	.06	.05	.02
525	Dick Ruthven	.06	.05	.02
526	John McNamara	.06	.05	.02
527	Larry McWilliams	.06	.05	.02
528	*Johnny Ray* (FC)	.10	.08	.04
529	*Pat Tabler* (FC)	.10	.08	.04
530	Tom Herr	.10	.08	.04
531a	San Diego Chicken (FC) (w/trademark symbol)	1.25	.90	.50
531b	San Diego Chicken (FC) (no trademark symbol)	.80	.60	.30
532	Sal Butera	.06	.05	.02
533	Mike Griffin	.06	.05	.02
534	Kelvin Moore	.06	.05	.02
535	Reggie Jackson	2.00	1.50	.80
536	Ed Romero	.06	.05	.02
537	Derrel Thomas	.06	.05	.02
538	Mike O'Berry	.06	.05	.02
539	Jack O'Connor	.06	.05	.02
540	*Bob Ojeda*	.50	.40	.20
541	Roy Lee Jackson	.06	.05	.02
542	Lynn Jones	.06	.05	.02
543	Gaylord Perry	.40	.30	.15
544a	Phil Garner (photo reversed)	1.25	.90	.50
544b	Phil Garner (photo correct)	.10	.08	.04
545	Garry Templeton	.10	.08	.04
546	Rafael Ramirez (FC)	.10	.08	.04
547	Jeff Reardon	1.25	.90	.50
548	Ron Guidry	.25	.20	.10
549	*Tim Laudner* (FC)	.12	.09	.05
550	John Henry Johnson	.06	.05	.02
551	Chris Bando	.06	.05	.02
552	Bobby Brown	.06	.05	.02
553	Larry Bradford	.06	.05	.02
554	*Scott Fletcher* (FC)	.40	.30	.15
555	Jerry Royster	.06	.05	.02
556	Shooty Babbitt	.06	.05	.02
557	*Kent Hrbek* (FC)	2.50	2.00	1.00
558	Yankee Winners (Ron Guidry, Tommy John)	.15	.11	.06
559	Mark Bomback	.06	.05	.02
560	Julio Valdez	.06	.05	.02
561	Buck Martinez	.06	.05	.02
562	*Mike Marshall* (FC)	.15	.11	.06
563	Rennie Stennett	.06	.05	.02
564	Steve Crawford	.06	.05	.02
565	Bob Babcock	.06	.05	.02
566	Johnny Podres	.08	.06	.03
567	Paul Serna	.06	.05	.02
568	Harold Baines (FC)	1.25	.90	.50
569	Dave LaRoche	.06	.05	.02
570	Lee May	.08	.06	.03
571	Gary Ward (FC)	.10	.08	.04
572	John Denny	.06	.05	.02
573	Roy Smalley	.06	.05	.02
574	*Bob Brenly* (FC)	.20	.15	.08
575	Bronx Bombers (Reggie Jackson, Dave Winfield)	2.00	1.50	.80
576	Luis Pujols	.06	.05	.02
577	Butch Hobson	.06	.05	.02
578	Harvey Kuenn	.08	.06	.03
579	Cal Ripken, Sr.	.08	.06	.03
580	Juan Berenguer	.08	.06	.03
581	Benny Ayala	.06	.05	.02
582	Vance Law (FC)	.08	.06	.03
583	*Rick Leach* (FC)	.12	.09	.05
584	George Frazier	.06	.05	.02
585	Phillies Finest (Pete Rose, Mike Schmidt)	.70	.50	.30
586	Joe Rudi	.10	.08	.04
587	Juan Beniquez	.06	.05	.02
588	*Luis DeLeon* (FC)	.08	.06	.03
589	Craig Swan	.06	.05	.02
590	Dave Chalk	.06	.05	.02
591	Billy Gardner	.06	.05	.02
592	Sal Bando	.08	.06	.03
593	Bert Campaneris	.10	.08	.04
594	Steve Kemp	.08	.06	.03
595a	Randy Lerch (Braves)	1.25	.90	.50
595b	Randy Lerch (Brewers)	.08	.06	.03
596	Bryan Clark	.06	.05	.02
597	Dave Ford	.06	.05	.02
598	Mike Scioscia (FC)	.20	.15	.08
599	John Lowenstein	.06	.05	.02
600	Rene Lachmann (Lachemann)	.06	.05	.02
601	Mick Kelleher	.06	.05	.02
602	Ron Jackson	.06	.05	.02
603	Jerry Koosman	.10	.08	.04
604	Dave Goltz	.08	.06	.03
605	Ellis Valentine	.06	.05	.02
606	Lonnie Smith	.08	.06	.03
607	Joaquin Andujar	.08	.06	.03
608	Garry Hancock	.06	.05	.02
609	Jerry Turner	.06	.05	.02
610	Bob Bonner	.06	.05	.02
611	Jim Dwyer	.06	.05	.02
612	Terry Bulling	.06	.05	.02
613	Joel Youngblood	.06	.05	.02
614	Larry Milbourne	.06	.05	.02
615	Phil Roof (Gene)	.06	.05	.02
616	Keith Drumright	.06	.05	.02
617	Dave Rosello	.06	.05	.02
618	Rickey Keeton	.06	.05	.02
619	Dennis Lamp	.06	.05	.02
620	Sid Monge	.06	.05	.02
621	Jerry White	.06	.05	.02
622	*Luis Aguayo* (FC)	.10	.08	.04
623	Jamie Easterly	.06	.05	.02
624	*Steve Sax* (FC)	2.00	1.50	.80
625	Dave Roberts	.06	.05	.02
626	Rick Bosetti	.06	.05	.02
627	*Terry Francona* (FC)	.10	.08	.04
628	Pride of the Reds (Johnny Bench, Tom Seaver)	.80	.60	.30
629	Paul Mirabella	.06	.05	.02
630	Rance Mulliniks	.06	.05	.02
631	Kevin Hickey	.06	.05	.02
632	Reid Nichols	.06	.05	.02
633	Dave Geisel	.06	.05	.02
634	Ken Griffey	.12	.09	.05
635	Bob Lemon	.10	.08	.04
636	Orlando Sanchez	.06	.05	.02
637	Bill Almon	.06	.05	.02
638	Danny Ainge	1.25	.90	.50
639	Willie Stargell	.40	.30	.15
640	Bob Sykes	.06	.05	.02
641	Ed Lynch	.06	.05	.02
642	John Ellis	.06	.05	.02
643	Fergie Jenkins	.15	.11	.06
644	Lenn Sakata	.06	.05	.02
645	Julio Gonzales	.06	.05	.02
646	Jesse Orosco (FC)	.10	.08	.04
647	Jerry Dybzinski	.06	.05	.02
648	Tommy Davis	.08	.06	.03
649	Ron Gardenhire	.06	.05	.02
650	Felipe Alou	.08	.06	.03
651	Harvey Haddix	.08	.06	.03
652	Willie Upshaw (FC)	.15	.11	.06
653	Bill Madlock	.12	.09	.05
----a	Checklist 1-26 DK (5 Trammel)	.70	.50	.30
----b	Checklist 1-26 DK (5 Trammell)	.08	.06	.03
----	Checklist 27-130	.06	.05	.02
----	Checklist 131-234	.06	.05	.02
----	Checklist 235-338	.06	.05	.02
----	Checklist 339-442	.06	.05	.02
----	Checklist 443-544	.06	.05	.02
----	Checklist 545-653	.06	.05	.02

1983 Donruss

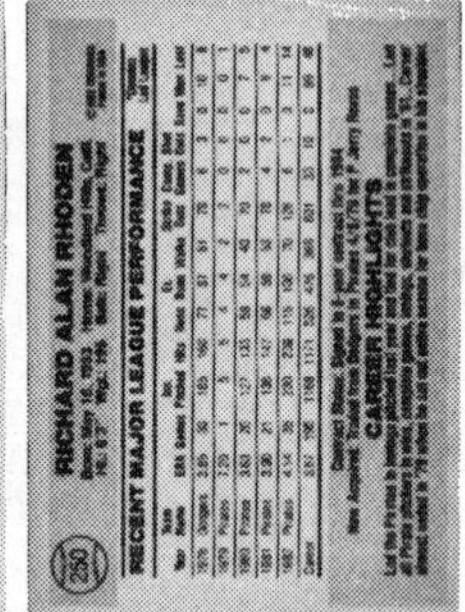

The 1983 Donruss set consists of 653 numbered cards plus seven unnumbered checklists. The cards, which measure 2-1/2" by 3-1/2", were issued with puzzle pieces (three pieces on one card per pack) that feature Ty Cobb. The first 26 cards in the set were once again the Diamond Kings series. The card fronts display the Donruss logo and the year of issue. The card backs have black print on yellow and white and include statistics, career highlights, and the player's contract status. (DK) in the checklist that follows indicates cards which belong to the Diamond Kings series.

		MT	NR MT	EX
	Complete Set (660):	125.00	94.00	50.00
	Common Player:	.06	.05	.02
1	Fernando Valenzuela (DK)	.20	.15	.08
2	Rollie Fingers (DK)	.20	.15	.08
3	Reggie Jackson (DK)	.60	.45	.25
4	Jim Palmer (DK)	.40	.30	.15

5	Jack Morris (DK)	.30	.25	.12
6	George Foster (DK)	.20	.15	.08
7	Jim Sundberg (DK)	.08	.06	.03
8	Willie Stargell (DK)	.40	.30	.15
9	Dave Stieb (DK)	.12	.09	.05
10	Joe Niekro (DK)	.12	.09	.05
11	Rickey Henderson (DK)	2.00	1.50	.80
12	Dale Murphy (DK)	.50	.40	.20
13	Toby Harrah (DK)	.08	.06	.03
14	Bill Buckner (DK)	.12	.09	.05
15	Willie Wilson (DK)	.15	.11	.06
16	Steve Carlton (DK)	.40	.30	.15
17	Ron Guidry (DK)	.15	.11	.06
18	Steve Rogers (DK)	.08	.06	.03
19	Kent Hrbek (DK)	.40	.30	.15
20	Keith Hernandez (DK)	.20	.15	.08
21	Floyd Bannister (DK)	.10	.08	.04
22	Johnny Bench (DK)	.60	.45	.25
23	Britt Burns (DK)	.08	.06	.03
24	Joe Morgan (DK)	.30	.25	.12
25	Carl Yastrzemski (DK)	.80	.60	.30
26	Terry Kennedy (DK)	.08	.06	.03
27	Gary Roenicke	.06	.05	.02
28	Dwight Bernard	.06	.05	.02
29	Pat Underwood	.06	.05	.02
30	Gary Allenson	.06	.05	.02
31	Ron Guidry	.25	.20	.10
32	Burt Hooton	.08	.06	.03
33	Chris Bando	.06	.05	.02
34	Vida Blue	.12	.09	.05
35	Rickey Henderson	3.00	2.25	1.25
36	Ray Burris	.06	.05	.02
37	John Butcher	.06	.05	.02
38	Don Aase	.06	.05	.02
39	Jerry Koosman	.10	.08	.04
40	Bruce Sutter	.15	.11	.06
41	Jose Cruz	.12	.09	.05
42	Pete Rose	1.50	1.25	.60
43	Cesar Cedeno	.12	.09	.05
44	Floyd Chiffer	.06	.05	.02
45	Larry McWilliams	.06	.05	.02
46	Alan Fowlkes	.06	.05	.02
47	Dale Murphy	.70	.50	.30
48	Doug Bird	.06	.05	.02
49	Hubie Brooks	.12	.09	.05
50	Floyd Bannister	.10	.08	.04
51	Jack O'Connor	.06	.05	.02
52	Steve Senteney	.06	.05	.02
53	*Gary Gaetti* (FC)	.80	.60	.30
54	Damaso Garcia	.06	.05	.02
55	Gene Nelson	.06	.05	.02
56	Mookie Wilson	.10	.08	.04
57	Allen Ripley	.06	.05	.02
58	Bob Horner	.12	.09	.05
59	Tony Pena	.10	.08	.04
60	Gary Lavelle	.06	.05	.02
61	Tim Lollar	.06	.05	.02
62	Frank Pastore	.06	.05	.02
63	Garry Maddox	.10	.08	.04
64	Bob Forsch	.08	.06	.03
65	Harry Spilman	.06	.05	.02
66	Geoff Zahn	.06	.05	.02
67	Salome Barojas	.06	.05	.02
68	David Palmer	.06	.05	.02
69	Charlie Hough	.10	.08	.04
70	Dan Quisenberry	.15	.11	.06
71	Tony Armas	.10	.08	.04
72	Rick Sutcliffe	.12	.09	.05
73	Steve Balboni (FC)	.08	.06	.03
74	Jerry Remy	.06	.05	.02
75	Mike Scioscia	.08	.06	.03
76	John Wockenfuss	.06	.05	.02
77	Jim Palmer	.80	.60	.30
78	Rollie Fingers	.60	.45	.25
79	Joe Nolan	.06	.05	.02
80	Pete Vuckovich	.08	.06	.03
81	Rick Leach	.06	.05	.02
82	Rick Miller	.06	.05	.02
83	Graig Nettles	.15	.11	.06
84	Ron Cey	.12	.09	.05
85	Miguel Dilone	.06	.05	.02
86	John Wathan	.08	.06	.03
87	Kelvin Moore	.06	.05	.02
88a	Byrn Smith (first name incorrect)	.70	.50	.30
88b	Bryn Smith (first name correct)	.08	.06	.03
89	Dave Hostetler	.06	.05	.02
90	Rod Carew	1.00	.70	.40
91	Lonnie Smith	.08	.06	.03
92	Bob Knepper	.08	.06	.03
93	Marty Bystrom	.06	.05	.02
94	Chris Welsh	.06	.05	.02
95	Jason Thompson	.06	.05	.02
96	Tom O'Malley	.06	.05	.02
97	Phil Niekro	.30	.25	.12
98	Neil Allen	.06	.05	.02
99	Bill Buckner	.12	.09	.05
100	*Ed Vande Berg* (FC)	.10	.08	.04
101	Jim Clancy	.08	.06	.03
102	Robert Castillo	.06	.05	.02
103	Bruce Berenyi	.06	.05	.02
104	Carlton Fisk	.80	.60	.30
105	Mike Flanagan	.10	.08	.04
106	Cecil Cooper	.15	.11	.06
107	Jack Morris	.80	.60	.30
108	Mike Morgan (FC)	.12	.09	.05
109	Luis Aponte	.06	.05	.02
110	Pedro Guerrero	.15	.11	.06
111	Len Barker	.08	.06	.03
112	Willie Wilson	.15	.11	.06
113	Dave Beard	.06	.05	.02
114	Mike Gates	.06	.05	.02
115	Reggie Jackson	1.50	1.25	.60
116	George Wright	.06	.05	.02
117	Vance Law	.08	.06	.03
118	Nolan Ryan	8.50	6.50	3.50
119	Mike Krukow	.08	.06	.03
120	Ozzie Smith	1.50	1.25	.60
121	Broderick Perkins	.06	.05	.02
122	Tom Seaver	1.50	1.25	.60
123	Chris Chambliss	.08	.06	.03
124	Chuck Tanner	.06	.05	.02
125	Johnnie LeMaster	.06	.05	.02
126	*Mel Hall* (FC)	.25	.20	.10
127	Bruce Bochte	.06	.05	.02
128	*Charlie Puleo* (FC)	.12	.09	.05
129	Luis Leal	.06	.05	.02
130	John Pacella	.06	.05	.02
131	Glenn Gulliver	.06	.05	.02
132	Don Money	.06	.05	.02
133	Dave Rozema	.06	.05	.02
134	Bruce Hurst (FC)	.25	.20	.10
135	Rudy May	.06	.05	.02
136	Tom LaSorda (Lasorda)	.10	.08	.04
137	Dan Spillner (photo actually Ed Whitson)	.06	.05	.02
138	Jerry Martin	.06	.05	.02
139	Mike Norris	.06	.05	.02
140	Al Oliver	.15	.11	.06
141	Daryl Sconiers	.06	.05	.02
142	Lamar Johnson	.06	.05	.02
143	Harold Baines	.15	.11	.06
144	Alan Ashby	.06	.05	.02
145	Garry Templeton	.10	.08	.04
146	Al Holland	.06	.05	.02
147	Bo Diaz	.08	.06	.03
148	Dave Concepcion	.12	.09	.05
149	Rick Camp	.06	.05	.02
150	Jim Morrison	.06	.05	.02
151	Randy Martz	.06	.05	.02
152	Keith Hernandez	.20	.15	.08
153	John Lowenstein	.06	.05	.02
154	Mike Caldwell	.06	.05	.02
155	Milt Wilcox	.06	.05	.02
156	Rich Gedman	.08	.06	.03
157	Rich Gossage	.20	.15	.08
158	Jerry Reuss	.10	.08	.04
159	Ron Hassey	.06	.05	.02
160	Larry Gura	.06	.05	.02
161	Dwayne Murphy	.08	.06	.03
162	Woodie Fryman	.08	.06	.03
163	Steve Comer	.06	.05	.02
164	Ken Forsch	.06	.05	.02
165	Dennis Lamp	.06	.05	.02
166	David Green	.06	.05	.02
167	Terry Puhl	.06	.05	.02
168	Mike Schmidt	2.00	1.50	.80
169	*Eddie Milner* (FC)	.10	.08	.04
170	John Curtis	.06	.05	.02
171	Don Robinson	.08	.06	.03
172	Richard Gale	.06	.05	.02
173	Steve Bedrosian	.12	.09	.05
174	Willie Hernandez	.08	.06	.03
175	Ron Gardenhire	.06	.05	.02
176	Jim Beattie	.06	.05	.02
177	Tim Laudner	.08	.06	.03
178	Buck Martinez	.06	.05	.02
179	Kent Hrbek	.80	.60	.30
180	Alfredo Griffin	.08	.06	.03
181	Larry Andersen	.06	.05	.02
182	Pete Falcone	.06	.05	.02
183	Jody Davis	.10	.08	.04
184	Glenn Hubbard	.08	.06	.03
185	Dale Berra	.06	.05	.02
186	Greg Minton	.06	.05	.02
187	Gary Lucas	.06	.05	.02
188	Dave Van Gorder	.06	.05	.02
189	Bob Dernier (FC)	.10	.08	.04
190	*Willie McGee* (FC)	3.00	2.25	1.25
191	Dickie Thon	.08	.06	.03
192	Bob Boone	.10	.08	.04
193	Britt Burns	.06	.05	.02
194	Jeff Reardon	.80	.60	.30
195	Jon Matlack	.08	.06	.03
196	*Don Slaught* (FC)	.20	.15	.08
197	Fred Stanley	.06	.05	.02
198	Rick Manning	.06	.05	.02
199	Dave Righetti	.25	.20	.10
200	Dave Stapleton	.06	.05	.02
201	Steve Yeager	.06	.05	.02
202	Enos Cabell	.06	.05	.02
203	Sammy Stewart	.06	.05	.02
204	Moose Haas	.06	.05	.02
205	Lenn Sakata	.06	.05	.02
206	Charlie Moore	.06	.05	.02
207	Alan Trammell	.40	.30	.15
208	Jim Rice	.30	.25	.12
209	Roy Smalley	.06	.05	.02
210	Bill Russell	.08	.06	.03
211	Andre Thornton	.10	.08	.04
212	Willie Aikens	.06	.05	.02
213	Dave McKay	.06	.05	.02
214	Tim Blackwell	.06	.05	.02
215	Buddy Bell	.12	.09	.05
216	Doug DeCinces	.10	.08	.04
217	Tom Herr	.10	.08	.04
218	Frank LaCorte	.06	.05	.02
219	Steve Carlton	1.00	.70	.40
220	Terry Kennedy	.08	.06	.03
221	Mike Easler	.08	.06	.03
222	Jack Clark	.25	.20	.10
223	Gene Garber	.06	.05	.02
224	Scott Holman	.06	.05	.02
225	Mike Proly	.06	.05	.02
226	Terry Bulling	.06	.05	.02
227	Jerry Garvin	.06	.05	.02
228	Ron Davis	.06	.05	.02
229	Tom Hume	.06	.05	.02
230	Marc Hill	.06	.05	.02
231	Dennis Martinez	.08	.06	.03
232	Jim Gantner	.08	.06	.03
233	Larry Pashnick	.06	.05	.02
234	Dave Collins	.08	.06	.03
235	Tom Burgmeier	.06	.05	.02
236	Ken Landreaux	.06	.05	.02
237	John Denny	.06	.05	.02
238	Hal McRae	.12	.09	.05
239	Matt Keough	.06	.05	.02
240	Doug Flynn	.06	.05	.02
241	Fred Lynn	.20	.15	.08
242	Billy Sample	.06	.05	.02
243	Tom Paciorek	.06	.05	.02
244	Joe Sambito	.06	.05	.02
245	Sid Monge	.06	.05	.02
246	Ken Oberkfell	.06	.05	.02
247	Joe Pittman (photo actually Juan Eichelberger)	.06	.05	.02
248	Mario Soto	.08	.06	.03
249	Claudell Washington	.08	.06	.03
250	Rick Rhoden	.10	.08	.04
251	Darrell Evans	.15	.11	.06
252	Steve Henderson	.06	.05	.02
253	Manny Castillo	.06	.05	.02
254	Craig Swan	.06	.05	.02
255	Joey McLaughlin	.06	.05	.02
256	Pete Redfern	.06	.05	.02
257	Ken Singleton	.10	.08	.04
258	Robin Yount	3.00	2.25	1.25
259	Elias Sosa	.06	.05	.02
260	Bob Ojeda	.12	.09	.05
261	Bobby Murcer	.10	.08	.04
262	*Candy Maldonado* (FC)	.40	.30	.15
263	Rick Waits	.06	.05	.02
264	Greg Pryor	.06	.05	.02
265	Bob Owchinko	.06	.05	.02
266	Chris Speier	.06	.05	.02
267	Bruce Kison	.06	.05	.02
268	Mark Wagner	.06	.05	.02
269	Steve Kemp	.10	.08	.04
270	Phil Garner	.08	.06	.03
271	Gene Richards	.06	.05	.02
272	Renie Martin	.06	.05	.02
273	Dave Roberts	.06	.05	.02
274	Dan Driessen	.08	.06	.03
275	Rufino Linares	.06	.05	.02
276	Lee Lacy	.06	.05	.02
277	*Ryne Sandberg* (FC)	40.00	30.00	16.00
278	Darrell Porter	.08	.06	.03
279	Cal Ripken, Jr.	15.00	11.00	6.00
280	Jamie Easterly	.06	.05	.02
281	Bill Fahey	.06	.05	.02
282	Glenn Hoffman	.06	.05	.02
283	Willie Randolph	.10	.08	.04
284	Fernando Valenzuela	.30	.25	.12
285	Alan Bannister	.06	.05	.02
286	Paul Splittorff	.06	.05	.02
287	Joe Rudi	.10	.08	.04
288	Bill Gullickson	.06	.05	.02
289	Danny Darwin	.06	.05	.02
290	Andy Hassler	.06	.05	.02
291	Ernesto Escarrega	.06	.05	.02
292	Steve Mura	.06	.05	.02
293	Tony Scott	.06	.05	.02
294	Manny Trillo	.08	.06	.03
295	Greg Harris (FC)	.08	.06	.03
296	Luis DeLeon	.06	.05	.02
297	Kent Tekulve	.08	.06	.03
298	Atlee Hammaker (FC)	.12	.09	.05
299	Bruce Benedict	.06	.05	.02
300	Fergie Jenkins	.20	.15	.08
301	Dave Kingman	.15	.11	.06
302	Bill Caudill	.06	.05	.02
303	John Castino	.06	.05	.02
304	Ernie Whitt	.08	.06	.03
305	Randy S. Johnson	.06	.05	.02
306	Garth Iorg	.06	.05	.02
307	Gaylord Perry	.40	.30	.15
308	Ed Lynch	.06	.05	.02
309	Keith Moreland	.08	.06	.03
310	Rafael Ramirez	.06	.05	.02
311	Bill Madlock	.12	.09	.05
312	Milt May	.06	.05	.02
313	John Montefusco	.06	.05	.02
314	Wayne Krenchicki	.06	.05	.02
315	George Vukovich	.06	.05	.02
316	Joaquin Andujar	.08	.06	.03
317	Craig Reynolds	.06	.05	.02
318	Rick Burleson	.08	.06	.03
319	Richard Dotson	.10	.08	.04
320	Steve Rogers	.08	.06	.03
321	Dave Schmidt (FC)	.10	.08	.04
322	*Bud Black* (FC)	.20	.15	.08
323	Jeff Burroughs	.08	.06	.03
324	Von Hayes	.15	.11	.06
325	Butch Wynegar	.06	.05	.02
326	Carl Yastrzemski	.80	.60	.30
327	Ron Roenicke	.06	.05	.02
328	*Howard Johnson* (FC)	2.50	2.00	1.00
329	Rick Dempsey	.08	.06	.03
330a	Jim Slaton (one yellow box on back)	.70	.50	.30
330b	Jim Slaton (two yellow boxes on back)	.08	.06	.03
331	Benny Ayala	.06	.05	.02
332	Ted Simmons	.12	.09	.05
333	Lou Whitaker	.40	.30	.15
334	Chuck Rainey	.06	.05	.02
335	Lou Piniella	.12	.09	.05
336	Steve Sax	.30	.25	.12
337	Toby Harrah	.08	.06	.03
338	George Brett	3.00	2.25	1.25
339	Davey Lopes	.10	.08	.04
340	Gary Carter	.40	.30	.15
341	John Grubb	.06	.05	.02
342	Tim Foli	.06	.05	.02
343	Jim Kaat	.15	.11	.06
344	Mike LaCoss	.06	.05	.02
345	Larry Christenson	.06	.05	.02
346	Juan Bonilla	.06	.05	.02
347	Omar Moreno	.06	.05	.02
348	Chili Davis (FC)	1.00	.75	.40
349	Tommy Boggs	.06	.05	.02
350	Rusty Staub	.10	.08	.04
351	Bump Wills	.06	.05	.02
352	Rick Sweet	.06	.05	.02

353	*Jim Gott* (FC)	.20	.15	.08
354	Terry Felton	.06	.05	.02
355	Jim Kern	.06	.05	.02
356	Bill Almon	.06	.05	.02
357	Tippy Martinez	.06	.05	.02
358	Roy Howell	.06	.05	.02
359	Dan Petry	.08	.06	.03
360	Jerry Mumphrey	.06	.05	.02
361	Mark Clear	.06	.05	.02
362	Mike Marshall	.12	.09	.05
363	Lary Sorensen	.06	.05	.02
364	Amos Otis	.08	.06	.03
365	Rick Langford	.06	.05	.02
366	Brad Mills	.06	.05	.02
367	Brian Downing	.10	.08	.04
368	Mike Richardt	.06	.05	.02
369	Aurelio Rodriguez	.08	.06	.03
370	Dave Smith	.08	.06	.03
371	Tug McGraw	.12	.09	.05
372	Doug Bair	.06	.05	.02
373	Ruppert Jones	.06	.05	.02
374	Alex Trevino	.06	.05	.02
375	Ken Dayley	.06	.05	.02
376	Rod Scurry	.06	.05	.02
377	Bob Brenly (FC)	.08	.06	.03
378	Scot Thompson	.06	.05	.02
379	Julio Cruz	.06	.05	.02
380	John Stearns	.06	.05	.02
381	Dale Murray	.06	.05	.02
382	*Frank Viola*	1.50	1.25	.60
383	Al Bumbry	.08	.06	.03
384	Ben Oglivie	.08	.06	.03
385	Dave Tobik	.06	.05	.02
386	Bob Stanley	.06	.05	.02
387	Andre Robertson	.06	.05	.02
388	Jorge Orta	.06	.05	.02
389	Ed Whitson	.06	.05	.02
390	Don Hood	.06	.05	.02
391	Tom Underwood	.06	.05	.02
392	Tim Wallach	.20	.15	.08
393	Steve Renko	.06	.05	.02
394	Mickey Rivers	.08	.06	.03
395	Greg Luzinski	.12	.09	.05
396	Art Howe	.06	.05	.02
397	Alan Wiggins	.06	.05	.02
398	Jim Barr	.06	.05	.02
399	Ivan DeJesus	.06	.05	.02
400	*Tom Lawless* (FC)	.08	.06	.03
401	Bob Walk	.08	.06	.03
402	Jimmy Smith	.06	.05	.02
403	Lee Smith	2.00	1.50	.80
404	George Hendrick	.08	.06	.03
405	Eddie Murray	.80	.60	.30
406	Marshall Edwards	.06	.05	.02
407	Lance Parrish	.35	.25	.14
408	Carney Lansford	.08	.06	.03
409	Dave Winfield	3.00	2.25	1.25
410	Bob Welch	.12	.09	.05
411	Larry Milbourne	.06	.05	.02
412	Dennis Leonard	.08	.06	.03
413	Dan Meyer	.06	.05	.02
414	Charlie Lea	.06	.05	.02
415	Rick Honeycutt	.06	.05	.02
416	Mike Witt	.15	.11	.06
417	Steve Trout	.06	.05	.02
418	Glenn Brummer	.06	.05	.02
419	Denny Walling	.06	.05	.02
420	Gary Matthews	.10	.08	.04
421	Charlie Liebrandt (Leibrandt)	.08	.06	.03
422	Juan Eichelberger	.06	.05	.02
423	*Matt Guante (Cecilio)* (FC)	.08	.06	.03
424	Bill Laskey	.06	.05	.02
425	Jerry Royster	.06	.05	.02
426	Dickie Noles	.06	.05	.02
427	George Foster	.15	.11	.06
428	*Mike Moore* (FC)	1.00	.70	.40
429	Gary Ward	.08	.06	.03
430	Barry Bonnell	.06	.05	.02
431	Ron Washington	.06	.05	.02
432	Rance Mulliniks	.06	.05	.02
433	Mike Stanton	.06	.05	.02
434	Jesse Orosco	.10	.08	.04
435	Larry Bowa	.12	.09	.05
436	Biff Pocoroba	.06	.05	.02
437	Johnny Ray	.12	.09	.05
438	Joe Morgan	.40	.30	.15
439	*Eric Show* (FC)	.30	.25	.12
440	Larry Biittner	.06	.05	.02
441	Greg Gross	.06	.05	.02
442	Gene Tenace	.08	.06	.03
443	Danny Heep	.06	.05	.02
444	Bobby Clark	.06	.05	.02
445	Kevin Hickey	.06	.05	.02
446	Scott Sanderson	.06	.05	.02
447	Frank Tanana	.10	.08	.04
448	Cesar Geronimo	.06	.05	.02
449	Jimmy Sexton	.06	.05	.02
450	Mike Hargrove	.06	.05	.02
451	Doyle Alexander	.10	.08	.04
452	Dwight Evans	.15	.11	.06
453	Terry Forster	.08	.06	.03
454	Tom Brookens	.06	.05	.02
455	Rich Dauer	.06	.05	.02
456	Rob Picciolo	.06	.05	.02
457	Terry Crowley	.06	.05	.02
458	Ned Yost	.06	.05	.02
459	Kirk Gibson	.40	.30	.15
460	Reid Nichols	.06	.05	.02
461	Oscar Gamble	.08	.06	.03
462	Dusty Baker	.10	.08	.04
463	Jack Perconte	.06	.05	.02
464	Frank White	.10	.08	.04
465	Mickey Klutts	.06	.05	.02
466	Warren Cromartie	.06	.05	.02
467	Larry Parrish	.10	.08	.04
468	Bobby Grich	.10	.08	.04
469	Dane Iorg	.06	.05	.02
470	Joe Niekro	.12	.09	.05
471	Ed Farmer	.06	.05	.02
472	Tim Flannery	.06	.05	.02
473	Dave Parker	.40	.30	.15
474	Jeff Leonard	.10	.08	.04
475	Al Hrabosky	.08	.06	.03
476	Ron Hodges	.06	.05	.02
477	Leon Durham	.08	.06	.03
478	Jim Essian	.06	.05	.02
479	Roy Lee Jackson	.06	.05	.02
480	Brad Havens	.06	.05	.02
481	Joe Price	.06	.05	.02
482	Tony Bernazard	.06	.05	.02
483	Scott McGregor	.08	.06	.03
484	Paul Molitor	1.50	1.25	.60
485	Mike Ivie	.06	.05	.02
486	Ken Griffey	.12	.09	.05
487	Dennis Eckersley	1.00	.70	.40
488	Steve Garvey	.40	.30	.15
489	Mike Fischlin	.06	.05	.02
490	U.L. Washington	.06	.05	.02
491	Steve McCatty	.06	.05	.02
492	Roy Johnson	.06	.05	.02
493	Don Baylor	.12	.09	.05
494	Bobby Johnson	.06	.05	.02
495	Mike Squires	.06	.05	.02
496	Bert Roberge	.06	.05	.02
497	Dick Ruthven	.06	.05	.02
498	Tito Landrum	.06	.05	.02
499	Sixto Lezcano	.06	.05	.02
500	Johnny Bench	1.00	.70	.40
501	Larry Whisenton	.06	.05	.02
502	Manny Sarmiento	.06	.05	.02
503	Fred Breining	.06	.05	.02
504	Bill Campbell	.06	.05	.02
505	Todd Cruz	.06	.05	.02
506	Bob Bailor	.06	.05	.02
507	Dave Stieb	.12	.09	.05
508	Al Williams	.06	.05	.02
509	Dan Ford	.06	.05	.02
510	Gorman Thomas	.10	.08	.04
511	Chet Lemon	.08	.06	.03
512	Mike Torrez	.08	.06	.03
513	Shane Rawley	.10	.08	.04
514	Mark Belanger	.08	.06	.03
515	Rodney Craig	.06	.05	.02
516	Onix Concepcion	.06	.05	.02
517	Mike Heath	.06	.05	.02
518	Andre Dawson	1.25	.90	.50
519	Luis Sanchez	.06	.05	.02
520	Terry Bogener	.06	.05	.02
521	Rudy Law	.06	.05	.02
522	Ray Knight	.10	.08	.04
523	Joe Lefebvre	.06	.05	.02
524	Jim Wohlford	.06	.05	.02
525	*Julio Franco* (FC)	5.00	3.75	2.00
526	Ron Oester	.06	.05	.02
527	Rick Mahler	.08	.06	.03
528	Steve Nicosia	.06	.05	.02
529	Junior Kennedy	.06	.05	.02
530a	Whitey Herzog (one yellow box on back)	.70	.50	.30
530b	Whitey Herzog (two yellow boxes on back)	.10	.08	.04
531a	Don Sutton (blue frame)	1.00	.70	.40
531b	Don Sutton (green frame)	.30	.25	.12
532	Mark Brouhard	.06	.05	.02
533a	Sparky Anderson (one yellow box on back)	.70	.50	.30
533b	Sparky Anderson (two yellow boxes on back)	.10	.08	.04
534	Roger LaFrancois	.06	.05	.02
535	George Frazier	.06	.05	.02
536	Tom Niedenfuer	.08	.06	.03
537	Ed Glynn	.06	.05	.02
538	Lee May	.08	.06	.03
539	Bob Kearney	.06	.05	.02
540	Tim Raines	.35	.25	.14
541	Paul Mirabella	.06	.05	.02
542	Luis Tiant	.12	.09	.05
543	Ron LeFlore	.08	.06	.03
544	*Dave LaPoint* (FC)	.12	.09	.05
545	Randy Moffitt	.06	.05	.02
546	Luis Aguayo	.06	.05	.02
547	Brad Lesley	.06	.05	.02
548	Luis Salazar	.06	.05	.02
549	John Candelaria	.10	.08	.04
550	Dave Bergman	.06	.05	.02
551	Bob Watson	.08	.06	.03
552	Pat Tabler	.06	.05	.02
553	Brent Gaff	.06	.05	.02
554	Al Cowens	.06	.05	.02
555	Tom Brunansky (FC)	.10	.08	.04
556	Lloyd Moseby	.06	.05	.02
557a	Pascual Perez (Twins)	.90	.70	.35
557b	Pascual Perez (Braves)	.15	.11	.06
558	Willie Upshaw	.08	.06	.03
559	Richie Zisk	.08	.06	.03
560	Pat Zachry	.06	.05	.02
561	Jay Johnstone	.08	.06	.03
562	Carlos Diaz	.06	.05	.02
563	John Tudor	.10	.08	.04
564	Frank Robinson	.12	.09	.05
565	Dave Edwards	.06	.05	.02
566	Paul Householder	.06	.05	.02
567	Ron Reed	.06	.05	.02
568	Mike Ramsey	.06	.05	.02
569	Kiko Garcia	.06	.05	.02
570	Tommy John	.20	.15	.08
571	Tony LaRussa	.12	.09	.05
572	Joel Youngblood	.06	.05	.02
573	*Wayne Tolleson* (FC)	.12	.09	.05
574	Keith Creel	.06	.05	.02
575	Billy Martin	.12	.09	.05
576	Jerry Dybzinski	.06	.05	.02
577	Rick Cerone	.06	.05	.02
578	Tony Perez	.20	.15	.08
579	*Greg Brock* (FC)	.20	.15	.08
580	Glen Wilson (Glenn)	.20	.15	.08
581	Tim Stoddard	.06	.05	.02
582	Bob McClure	.06	.05	.02
583	Jim Dwyer	.06	.05	.02
584	Ed Romero	.06	.05	.02
585	Larry Herndon	.08	.06	.03
586	*Wade Boggs* (FC)	25.00	18.50	10.00
587	Jay Howell (FC)	.15	.11	.06
588	Dave Stewart	.80	.60	.30
589	Bert Blyleven	.12	.09	.05
590	Dick Howser	.06	.05	.02
591	Wayne Gross	.06	.05	.02
592	Terry Francona	.06	.05	.02
593	Don Werner	.06	.05	.02
594	Bill Stein	.06	.05	.02
595	Jesse Barfield (FC)	.50	.40	.20
596	Bobby Molinaro	.06	.05	.02
597	Mike Vail	.06	.05	.02
598	*Tony Gwynn* (FC)	25.00	18.50	10.00
599	Gary Rajsich	.06	.05	.02
600	Jerry Ujdur	.06	.05	.02
601	Cliff Johnson	.06	.05	.02
602	Jerry White	.06	.05	.02
603	Bryan Clark	.06	.05	.02
604	Joe Ferguson	.06	.05	.02
605	Guy Sularz	.06	.05	.02
606a	Ozzie Virgil (FC) (green frame around photo)	.90	.70	.35
606b	Ozzie Virgil (FC) (orange frame around photo)	.08	.06	.03
607	Terry Harper (FC)	.06	.05	.02
608	Harvey Kuenn	.08	.06	.03
609	Jim Sundberg	.08	.06	.03
610	Willie Stargell	.40	.30	.15
611	Reggie Smith	.10	.08	.04
612	Rob Wilfong	.06	.05	.02
613	Niekro Brothers (Joe Niekro, Phil Niekro)	.15	.11	.06
614	Lee Elia	.06	.05	.02
615	Mickey Hatcher	.08	.06	.03
616	Jerry Hairston	.06	.05	.02
617	John Martin	.06	.05	.02
618	Wally Backman (FC)	.15	.11	.06
619	*Storm Davis* (FC)	.15	.11	.06
620	Alan Knicely	.06	.05	.02
621	John Stuper	.06	.05	.02
622	Matt Sinatro	.06	.05	.02
623	*Gene Petralli* (FC)	.15	.11	.06
624	Duane Walker	.06	.05	.02
625	Dick Williams	.06	.05	.02
626	Pat Corrales	.06	.05	.02
627	Vern Ruhle	.06	.05	.02
628	Joe Torre	.08	.06	.03
629	Anthony Johnson	.06	.05	.02
630	Steve Howe	.08	.06	.03
631	Gary Woods	.06	.05	.02
632	Lamarr Hoyt (LaMarr)	.06	.05	.02
633	Steve Swisher	.06	.05	.02
634	Terry Leach (FC)	.12	.09	.05
635	Jeff Newman	.06	.05	.02
636	Brett Butler	.10	.08	.04
637	Gary Gray	.06	.05	.02
638	Lee Mazzilli	.08	.06	.03
639a	Ron Jackson (A's)	6.00	4.50	2.50
639b	Ron Jackson (Angels - green frame around photo)	.90	.70	.35
639c	Ron Jackson (Angels - red frame around photo)	.20	.15	.08
640	Juan Beniquez	.06	.05	.02
641	Dave Rucker	.06	.05	.02
642	Luis Pujols	.06	.05	.02
643	Rick Monday	.10	.08	.04
644	Hosken Powell	.06	.05	.02
645	San Diego Chicken	.20	.15	.08
646	Dave Engle	.06	.05	.02
647	Dick Davis	.06	.05	.02
648	MVP's (Vida Blue, Joe Morgan, Frank Robinson)	.15	.11	.06
649	Al Chambers	.06	.05	.02
650	Jesus Vega	.06	.05	.02
651	Jeff Jones	.06	.05	.02
652	Marvis Foley	.06	.05	.02
653	Ty Cobb Puzzle	.06	.05	.02
----a	Dick Perez/DK Checklist (no word "Checklist" on back)	.70	.50	.30
----b	Dick Perez/DK Checklist (word "Checklist" on back)	.08	.06	.03
----	Checklist 27-130	.06	.05	.02
----	Checklist 131-234	.06	.05	.02
----	Checklist 235-338	.06	.05	.02
----	Checklist 339-442	.06	.05	.02
----	Checklist 443-546	.06	.05	.02
----	Checklist 547-653	.06	.05	.02

Grading Guide

Mint (MT): A perfect card. Well-centered with all corners sharp and square. No creases, stains, edge nicks, surface marks, yellowing or fading.

Near Mint (NM): A nearly perfect card. At first glance, a NM card appears to be perfect. May be slightly off-center. No surface marks, creases or loss of gloss.

Excellent (EX): Corners are still fairly sharp with only moderate wear. Borders may be off-center. No creases or stains on fronts or backs, but may show slight loss of surface luster.

Very Good (VG): Shows obvious handling. May have rounded corners, minor creases, major gum or wax stains. No major creases, tape marks, writing, etc.

Good (G): A well-worn card, but exhibits no intentional damage. May have major or multiple creases. Corners may be rounded well beyond card border.

1983 Donruss Action All-Stars

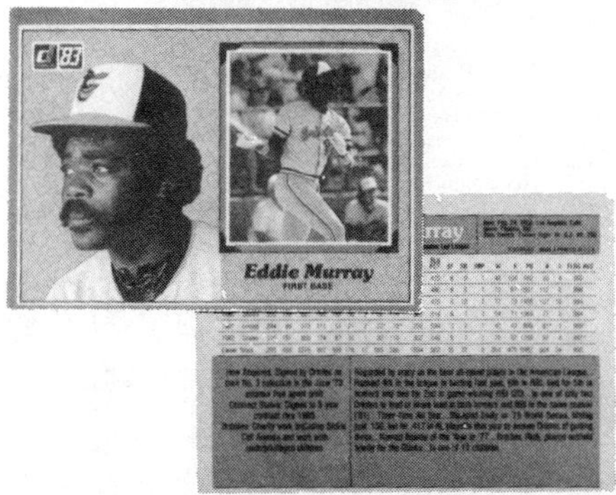

The cards in this 60-card set are designed on a horizontal format and contain a large close-up photo of the player on the left and a smaller action photo on the right. The cards, which measure 3-1/2" by 5", have deep red borders and contain the Donruss logo and the year of issue. The card backs have black print on red and white and contain various statistical and biographical information. The cards were sold with puzzle pieces (three pieces on one card per pack) that feature Mickey Mantle.

		MT	NR MT	EX
Complete Set:		12.00	9.00	4.75
Common Player:		.10	.08	.04
1	Eddie Murray	.30	.25	.12
2	Dwight Evans	.15	.11	.06
3a	Reggie Jackson (red covers part of statistics on back)	.60	.45	.25
3b	Reggie Jackson (red does not cover any statistics on back)	.60	.45	.25
4	Greg Luzinski	.15	.11	.06
5	Larry Herndon	.10	.08	.04
6	Al Oliver	.12	.09	.05
7	Bill Buckner	.10	.08	.04
8	Jason Thompson	.10	.08	.04
9	Andre Dawson	.40	.30	.15
10	Greg Minton	.10	.08	.04
11	Terry Kennedy	.10	.08	.04
12	Phil Niekro	.20	.15	.08
13	Willie Wilson	.12	.09	.05
14	Johnny Bench	.60	.45	.25
15	Ron Guidry	.15	.11	.06
16	Hal McRae	.15	.11	.06
17	Damaso Garcia	.10	.08	.04
18	Gary Ward	.10	.08	.04
19	Cecil Cooper	.12	.09	.05
20	Keith Hernandez	.15	.11	.06
21	Ron Cey	.12	.09	.05
22	Rickey Henderson	2.00	1.50	.80
23	Nolan Ryan	4.00	3.00	1.50
24	Steve Carlton	.40	.30	.15
25	John Stearns	.10	.08	.04
26	Jim Sundberg	.10	.08	.04
27	Joaquin Andujar	.10	.08	.04
28	Gaylord Perry	.25	.20	.10
29	Jack Clark	.15	.11	.06
30	Bill Madlock	.12	.09	.05
31	Pete Rose	.90	.70	.35
32	Mookie Wilson	.10	.08	.04
33	Rollie Fingers	.25	.20	.10
34	Lonnie Smith	.10	.08	.04
35	Tony Pena	.10	.08	.04
36	Dave Winfield	.40	.30	.15
37	Tim Lollar	.10	.08	.04
38	Rod Carew	.60	.45	.25
39	Toby Harrah	.10	.08	.04
40	Buddy Bell	.10	.08	.04
41	Bruce Sutter	.12	.09	.05
42	George Brett	2.00	1.50	.80
43	Carlton Fisk	.60	.45	.25
44	Carl Yastrzemski	1.50	1.25	.60
45	Dale Murphy	.40	.30	.15
46	Bob Horner	.12	.09	.05
47	Dave Concepcion	.12	.09	.05
48	Dave Stieb	.12	.09	.05
49	Kent Hrbek	.20	.15	.08
50	Lance Parrish	.15	.11	.06
51	Joe Niekro	.12	.09	.05
52	Cal Ripken, Jr.	2.50	2.00	1.00
53	Fernando Valenzuela	.12	.09	.05
54	Rickie Zisk	.10	.08	.04
55	Leon Durham	.10	.08	.04
56	Robin Yount	2.00	1.50	.80
57	Mike Schmidt	2.00	1.50	.80
58	Gary Carter	.15	.11	.06
59	Fred Lynn	.15	.11	.06
60	Checklist	.10	.08	.04

1983 Donruss Hall of Fame Heroes

The artwork of Dick Perez is featured in the 44-card Donruss Hall of Fame Heroes set issued in 1983. The standard-size cards (2-1/2" by 3-1/2") were available in wax packs that contained eight

cards plus a Mickey Mantle puzzle piece card (three pieces on one card per pack). The backs, which display red and blue print on white stock, contain a short player biograpical sketch derived from the Hall of Fame yearbook. The numbered set consists of 44 player cards, a Mantle puzzle card, and a checklist.

		MT	NR MT	EX
Complete Set:		8.00	6.00	3.25
Common Player:		.10	.08	.04
1	Ty Cobb	.70	.50	.30
2	Walter Johnson	.15	.11	.06
3	Christy Mathewson	.15	.11	.06
4	Josh Gibson	.10	.08	.04
5	Honus Wagner	.15	.11	.06
6	Jackie Robinson	.50	.40	.20
7	Mickey Mantle	1.00	.70	.40
8	Luke Appling	.10	.08	.04
9	Ted Williams	.70	.50	.30
10	Johnny Mize	.15	.11	.06
11	Satchel Paige	.15	.11	.06
12	Lou Boudreau	.10	.08	.04
13	Jimmie Foxx	.15	.11	.06
14	Duke Snider	.70	.50	.30
15	Monte Irvin	.15	.11	.06
16	Hank Greenberg	.15	.11	.06
17	Roberto Clemente	.50	.40	.20
18	Al Kaline	.50	.40	.20
19	Frank Robinson	.50	.40	.20
20	Joe Cronin	.10	.08	.04
21	Burleigh Grimes	.10	.08	.04
22	The Waner Brothers (Lloyd Waner, Paul Waner)	.10	.08	.04
23	Grover Alexander	.10	.08	.04
24	Yogi Berra	.50	.40	.20
25	James Bell	.10	.08	.04
26	Bill Dickey	.10	.08	.04
27	Cy Young	.15	.11	.06
28	Charlie Gehringer	.10	.08	.04
29	Dizzy Dean	.15	.11	.06
30	Bob Lemon	.10	.08	.04
31	Red Ruffing	.10	.08	.04
32	Stan Musial	.70	.50	.30
33	Carl Hubbell	.15	.11	.06
34	Hank Aaron	.70	.50	.30
35	John McGraw	.10	.08	.04
36	Bob Feller	.50	.40	.20
37	Casey Stengel	.15	.11	.06
38	Ralph Kiner	.15	.11	.06
39	Roy Campanella	.25	.20	.10
40	Mel Ott	.10	.08	.04
41	Robin Roberts	.15	.11	.06
42	Early Wynn	.10	.08	.04
43	Mickey Mantle Puzzle Card	.10	.08	.04
----	Checklist	.10	.07	.04

1984 Donruss

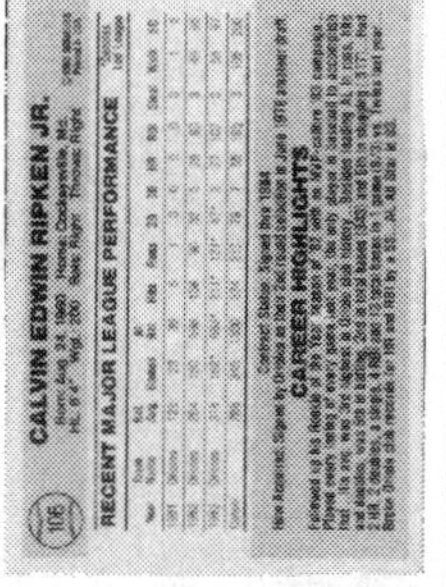

The 1984 Donruss set consists of 651 numbered cards, seven unnumbered checklists and two "Living Legends" cards (designated A and B). The A and B cards were issued only in wax packs and were not available to hobby dealers purchasing factory sets. The card fronts differ in style from the previous years, however the Donruss logo and year of issue are still included. The card backs have black print on green and white and are identical in format to the preceding year. The standard-size cards (2-1/2" by 3-1/2") were issued with a 63-piece puzzle of Duke Snider. A limited print run of the issue by Donruss has caused the set to escalate in price in recent years. The complete set price in the checklist that follows does not include the higher priced variations. Cards marked with (DK) or (RR) in the checklist refer to the Diamond Kings and Rated Rookies subsets. Each of the Diamond Kings cards and the DK checklist can be found in two varieties. The more common has Frank Steele's name misspelled "Steel" in the credit line at the bottom-right corner on the back. The error was later corrected.

		MT	NR MT	EX
Complete Set (660):		360.00	270.00	144.00
Common Player:		.12	.09	.05
A	Living Legends (Rollie Fingers) (Gaylord Perry)	5.00	3.75	2.00
B	Living Legends (Johnny Bench) (Carl Yastrzemski)	7.00	5.25	2.75
1a	Robin Yount (DK) (Steel)	3.00	2.25	1.25
1b	Robin Yount (DK) (Steele)	4.00	3.00	1.50
2a	Dave Concepcion (DK) (Steel)	.30	.25	.12
2b	Dave Concepcion (DK) (Steele)	.60	.45	.25
3a	Dwayne Murphy (DK) (Steel)	.25	.20	.10
3b	Dwayne Murphy (DK) (Steele)	.60	.45	.25
4a	John Castino (DK) (Steel)	.20	.15	.08
4b	John Castino (DK) (Steele)	.60	.45	.25
5a	Leon Durham (DK) (Steel)	.25	.20	.10
5b	Leon Durham (DK) (Steele)	.60	.45	.25
6a	Rusty Staub (DK) (Steel)	.30	.25	.12
6b	Rusty Staub (DK) (Steele)	.60	.45	.25
7a	Jack Clark (DK) (Steel)	.25	.20	.10
7b	Jack Clark (DK) (Steele)	.60	.45	.25
8a	Dave Dravecky (DK) (Steel)	.25	.20	.10
8b	Dave Dravecky (DK) (Steele)	.60	.45	.25
9a	Al Oliver (DK) (Steel)	.35	.25	.14
9b	Al Oliver (DK) (Steele)	.70	.50	.30
10a	Dave Righetti (DK) (Steel)	.25	.20	.10
10b	Dave Righetti (DK) (Steele)	.60	.45	.25
11a	Hal McRae (DK) (Steel)	.30	.25	.12
11b	Hal McRae (DK) (Steele)	.60	.45	.25
12a	Ray Knight (DK) (Steel)	.25	.20	.10
12b	Ray Knight (DK) (Steele)	.60	.45	.25
13a	Bruce Sutter (DK) (Steel)	.25	.20	.10
13b	Bruce Sutter (DK) (Steele)	.60	.45	.25
14a	Bob Horner (DK) (Steel)	.25	.20	.10
14b	Bob Horner (DK) (Steele)	.60	.45	.25
15a	Lance Parrish (DK) (Steel)	.25	.20	.10
15b	Lance Parrish (DK) (Steele)	.60	.45	.25
16a	Matt Young (DK) (Steel)	.25	.20	.10
16b	Matt Young (DK) (Steele)	.60	.45	.25
17a	Fred Lynn (DK) (Steel)	.35	.25	.14
17b	Fred Lynn (DK) (Steele)	.70	.50	.30
18a	Ron Kittle (FC) (DK) (Steel)	.25	.20	.10
18b	Ron Kittle (FC) (DK) (Steele)	.60	.45	.25
19a	Jim Clancy (DK) (Steel)	.25	.20	.10
19b	Jim Clancy (DK) (Steele)	.60	.45	.25
20a	Bill Madlock (DK) (Steel)	.30	.25	.12
20b	Bill Madlock (DK) (Steele)	.60	.45	.25
21a	Larry Parrish (DK) (Steel)	.25	.20	.10
21b	Larry Parrish (DK) (Steele)	.60	.45	.25
22a	Eddie Murray (DK) (Steel)	1.25	.90	.50
22b	Eddie Murray (DK) (Steele)	2.50	2.00	1.00
23a	Mike Schmidt (DK) (Steel)	4.00	3.00	1.50
23b	Mike Schmidt (DK) (Steele)	6.00	4.50	2.50
24a	Pedro Guerrero (DK) (Steel)	.25	.20	.10
24b	Pedro Guerrero (DK) (Steele)	.60	.45	.25
25a	Andre Thornton (DK) (Steel)	.25	.20	.10
25b	Andre Thornton (DK) (Steele)	.60	.45	.25
26a	Wade Boggs (DK) (Steel)	3.00	2.25	1.25
26b	Wade Boggs (DK) (Steele)	4.00	3.00	1.50
27	*Joel Skinner* (FC) (RR)	.12	.09	.05
28	Tom Dunbar (RR)	.12	.09	.05
29a	Mike Stenhouse (RR) (no number on back)	.15	.11	.06
29b	Mike Stenhouse (RR) (29 on back)	4.00	3.00	1.50
30a	*Ron Darling* (RR) (no number on back)	5.00	3.75	2.00
30b	*Ron Darling* (RR) 30 on back)	10.00	7.50	4.00
31	*Dion James* (FC) (RR)	.15	.11	.06
32	*Tony Fernandez* (RR)	6.00	4.50	2.50
33	Angel Salazar (RR)	.12	.09	.05
34	*Kevin McReynolds* (RR)	1.50	1.25	.60
35	*Dick Schofield* (RR)	.20	.15	.08
36	*Brad Komminsk* (FC) (RR)	.12	.09	.05
37	*Tim Teufel* (FC) (RR)	.30	.25	.12
38	Doug Frobel (RR)	.12	.09	.05
39	*Greg Gagne* (RR)	.60	.45	.25
40	Mike Fuentes (RR)	.12	.09	.05
41	*Joe Carter* (RR)	62.00	45.00	24.00
42	Mike Brown (RR)	.12	.09	.05
43	Mike Jeffcoat (RR)	.12	.09	.05
44	*Sid Fernandez* (FC) (RR)	4.00	3.00	1.50
45	Brian Dayett (RR)	.12	.09	.05
46	Chris Smith (RR)	.12	.09	.05
47	Eddie Murray	5.00	3.75	2.00
48	Robin Yount	10.00	7.50	4.00
49	Lance Parrish	.50	.40	.20
50	Jim Rice	.50	.40	.20
51	Dave Winfield	11.00	8.25	4.50
52	Fernando Valenzuela	.50	.40	.20
53	George Brett	12.00	9.00	4.75
54	Rickey Henderson	11.00	8.25	4.50
55	Gary Carter	1.00	.70	.40
56	Buddy Bell	.20	.15	.08
57	Reggie Jackson	6.00	4.50	2.50
58	Harold Baines	.25	.20	.10
59	Ozzie Smith	5.00	3.75	2.00
60	Nolan Ryan	30.00	22.00	12.00
61	Pete Rose	4.00	3.00	1.50
62	Ron Oester	.12	.09	.05
63	Steve Garvey	.75	.60	.30

64	Jason Thompson	.12	.09	.05
65	Jack Clark	.35	.25	.14
66	Dale Murphy	2.00	1.50	.80
67	Leon Durham	.12	.09	.05
68	*Darryl Strawberry*	15.00	11.00	6.00
69	Richie Zisk	.12	.09	.05
70	Kent Hrbek	.50	.40	.20
71	Dave Stieb	.25	.20	.10
72	Ken Schrom	.12	.09	.05
73	George Bell	1.25	.90	.50
74	John Moses	.15	.11	.06
75	Ed Lynch	.12	.09	.05
76	Chuck Rainey	.12	.09	.05
77	Biff Pocoroba	.12	.09	.05
78	Cecilio Guante	.12	.09	.05
79	Jim Barr	.12	.09	.05
80	Kurt Bevacqua	.12	.09	.05
81	Tom Foley	.12	.09	.05
82	Joe Lefebvre	.12	.09	.05
83	*Andy Van Slyke*	8.50	6.50	3.50
84	Bob Lillis	.12	.09	.05
85	Rick Adams	.12	.09	.05
86	Jerry Hairston	.12	.09	.05
87	Bob James	.12	.09	.05
88	Joe Altobelli	.12	.09	.05
89	Ed Romero	.12	.09	.05
90	John Grubb	.12	.09	.05
91	John Henry Johnson	.12	.09	.05
92	Juan Espino	.12	.09	.05
93	Candy Maldonado	.20	.15	.08
94	Andre Thornton	.20	.15	.08
95	Onix Concepcion	.12	.09	.05
96	*Don Hill* (FC)	.12	.09	.05
97	Andre Dawson	5.00	3.75	2.00
98	Frank Tanana	.15	.11	.06
99	*Curt Wilkerson* (FC)	.15	.11	.06
100	Larry Gura	.12	.09	.05
101	Dwayne Murphy	.12	.09	.05
102	Tom Brennan	.12	.09	.05
103	Dave Righetti	.40	.30	.15
104	Steve Sax	.30	.25	.12
105	Dan Petry	.12	.09	.05
106	Cal Ripken, Jr.	27.50	21.00	11.00
107	Paul Molitor	8.00	6.00	3.25
108	Fred Lynn	.35	.25	.14
109	Neil Allen	.12	.09	.05
110	Joe Niekro	.20	.15	.08
111	Steve Carlton	4.00	3.00	1.50
112	Terry Kennedy	.15	.11	.06
113	Bill Madlock	.20	.15	.08
114	Chili Davis	.15	.11	.06
115	Jim Gantner	.12	.09	.05
116	Tom Seaver	6.00	4.50	2.50
117	Bill Buckner	.20	.15	.08
118	Bill Caudill	.12	.09	.05
119	Jim Clancy	.15	.11	.06
120	John Castino	.12	.09	.05
121	Dave Concepcion	.20	.15	.08
122	Greg Luzinski	.20	.15	.08
123	Mike Boddicker (FC)	.20	.15	.08
124	Pete Ladd	.12	.09	.05
125	Juan Berenguer	.12	.09	.05
126	John Montefusco	.12	.09	.05
127	Ed Jurak	.12	.09	.05
128	Tom Niedenfuer	.12	.09	.05
129	Bert Blyleven	.30	.25	.12
130	Bud Black	.12	.09	.05
131	Gorman Heimueller	.12	.09	.05
132	Dan Schatzeder	.12	.09	.05
133	Ron Jackson	.12	.09	.05
134	*Tom Henke* (FC)	3.00	2.25	1.25
135	Kevin Hickey	.12	.09	.05
136	Mike Scott	.15	.11	.06
137	Bo Diaz	.12	.09	.05
138	Glenn Brummer	.12	.09	.05
139	Sid Monge	.12	.09	.05
140	Rich Gale	.12	.09	.05
141	Brett Butler	.15	.11	.06
142	Brian Harper	2.00	1.50	.80
143	John Rabb	.12	.09	.05
144	Gary Woods	.12	.09	.05
145	Pat Putnam	.12	.09	.05
146	*Jim Acker* (FC)	.15	.11	.06
147	Mickey Hatcher	.12	.09	.05
148	Todd Cruz	.12	.09	.05
149	Tom Tellmann	.12	.09	.05
150	John Wockenfuss	.12	.09	.05
151	Wade Boggs	15.00	11.00	6.00
152	Don Baylor	.20	.15	.08
153	Bob Welch	.20	.15	.08
154	Alan Bannister	.12	.09	.05
155	Willie Aikens	.12	.09	.05
156	Jeff Burroughs	.12	.09	.05
157	Bryan Little	.12	.09	.05
158	Bob Boone	.15	.11	.06
159	Dave Hostetler	.12	.09	.05
160	Jerry Dybzinski	.12	.09	.05
161	Mike Madden	.12	.09	.05
162	Luis DeLeon	.12	.09	.05
163	Willie Hernandez	.15	.11	.06
164	Frank Pastore	.12	.09	.05
165	Rick Camp	.12	.09	.05
166	Lee Mazzilli	.12	.09	.05
167	Scot Thompson	.12	.09	.05
168	Bob Forsch	.12	.09	.05
169	Mike Flanagan	.15	.11	.06
170	Rick Manning	.12	.09	.05
171	Chet Lemon	.12	.09	.05
172	Jerry Remy	.12	.09	.05
173	Ron Guidry	.35	.25	.14
174	Pedro Guerrero	.25	.20	.10
175	Willie Wilson	.25	.20	.10
176	Carney Lansford	.20	.15	.08
177	Al Oliver	.30	.25	.12
178	Jim Sundberg	.12	.09	.05
179	Bobby Grich	.20	.15	.08
180	Richard Dotson	.20	.15	.08
181	Joaquin Andujar	.12	.09	.05
182	Jose Cruz	.20	.15	.08
183	Mike Schmidt	15.00	11.00	6.00
184	*Gary Redus* (FC)	.30	.25	.12
185	Garry Templeton	.15	.11	.06
186	Tony Pena	.20	.15	.08
187	Greg Minton	.12	.09	.05
188	Phil Niekro	.50	.40	.20
189	Fergie Jenkins	.50	.40	.20
190	Mookie Wilson	.15	.11	.06
191	Jim Beattie	.12	.09	.05
192	Gary Ward	.12	.09	.05
193	Jesse Barfield	.20	.15	.08
194	Pete Filson	.12	.09	.05
195	Roy Lee Jackson	.12	.09	.05
196	Rick Sweet	.12	.09	.05
197	Jesse Orosco	.15	.11	.06
198	*Steve Lake* (FC)	.12	.09	.05
199	Ken Dayley	.12	.09	.05
200	Manny Sarmiento	.12	.09	.05
201	Mark Davis (FC)	.15	.11	.06
202	Tim Flannery	.12	.09	.05
203	Bill Scherrer	.12	.09	.05
204	Al Holland	.12	.09	.05
205	David Von Ohlen	.12	.09	.05
206	Mike LaCoss	.12	.09	.05
207	Juan Beniquez	.12	.09	.05
208	*Juan Agosto* (FC)	.12	.09	.05
209	Bobby Ramos	.12	.09	.05
210	Al Bumbry	.12	.09	.05
211	Mark Brouhard	.12	.09	.05
212	Howard Bailey	.12	.09	.05
213	Bruce Hurst	.20	.15	.08
214	Bob Shirley	.12	.09	.05
215	Pat Zachry	.12	.09	.05
216	Julio Franco	4.50	3.50	1.75
217	Mike Armstrong	.12	.09	.05
218	Dave Beard	.12	.09	.05
219	Steve Rogers	.12	.09	.05
220	John Butcher	.12	.09	.05
221	*Mike Smithson* (FC)	.12	.09	.05
222	Frank White	.20	.15	.08
223	Mike Heath	.12	.09	.05
224	Chris Bando	.12	.09	.05
225	Roy Smalley	.12	.09	.05
226	Dusty Baker	.20	.15	.08
227	Lou Whitaker	.60	.45	.25
228	John Lowenstein	.12	.09	.05
229	Ben Oglivie	.12	.09	.05
230	Doug DeCinces	.15	.11	.06
231	Lonnie Smith	.12	.09	.05
232	Ray Knight	.15	.11	.06
233	Gary Matthews	.20	.15	.08
234	Juan Bonilla	.12	.09	.05
235	Rod Scurry	.12	.09	.05
236	Atlee Hammaker	.12	.09	.05
237	Mike Caldwell	.12	.09	.05
238	Keith Hernandez	.40	.30	.15
239	Larry Bowa	.25	.20	.10
240	Tony Bernazard	.12	.09	.05
241	Damaso Garcia	.12	.09	.05
242	Tom Brunansky	.35	.25	.14
243	Dan Driessen	.12	.09	.05
244	Ron Kittle (FC)	.15	.11	.06
245	Tim Stoddard	.12	.09	.05
246	Bob L. Gibson	.12	.09	.05
247	Marty Castillo	.12	.09	.05
248	*Don Mattingly*	55.00	41.00	22.00
249	Jeff Newman	.12	.09	.05
250	*Alejandro Pena*	.60	.45	.25
251	Toby Harrah	.12	.09	.05
252	Cesar Geronimo	.12	.09	.05
253	Tom Underwood	.12	.09	.05
254	Doug Flynn	.12	.09	.05
255	Andy Hassler	.12	.09	.05
256	Odell Jones	.12	.09	.05
257	Rudy Law	.12	.09	.05
258	Harry Spilman	.12	.09	.05
259	Marty Bystrom	.12	.09	.05
260	Dave Rucker	.12	.09	.05
261	Ruppert Jones	.12	.09	.05
262	Jeff Jones	.12	.09	.05
263	*Gerald Perry* (FC)	.50	.40	.20
264	Gene Tenace	.12	.09	.05
265	Brad Wellman	.12	.09	.05
266	Dickie Noles	.12	.09	.05
267	Jamie Allen	.12	.09	.05
268	Jim Gott	.15	.11	.06
269	Ron Davis	.12	.09	.05
270	Benny Ayala	.12	.09	.05
271	Ned Yost	.12	.09	.05
272	Dave Rozema	.12	.09	.05
273	Dave Stapleton	.12	.09	.05
274	Lou Piniella	.20	.15	.08
275	Jose Morales	.12	.09	.05
276	Brod Perkins	.12	.09	.05
277	Butch Davis	.12	.09	.05
278	*Tony Phillips*	4.00	3.00	1.50
279	Jeff Reardon	.25	.20	.10
280	Ken Forsch	.12	.09	.05
281	*Pete O'Brien* (FC)	1.00	.70	.40
282	Tom Paciorek	.12	.09	.05
283	Frank LaCorte	.12	.09	.05
284	Tim Lollar	.12	.09	.05
285	Greg Gross	.12	.09	.05
286	Alex Trevino	.12	.09	.05
287	Gene Garber	.12	.09	.05
288	Dave Parker	.50	.40	.20
289	Lee Smith	3.00	2.25	1.25
290	Dave LaPoint	.15	.11	.06
291	*John Shelby* (FC)	.15	.11	.06
292	Charlie Moore	.12	.09	.05
293	Alan Trammell	.60	.45	.25
294	Tony Armas	.20	.15	.08
295	Shane Rawley	.20	.15	.08
296	Greg Brock	.15	.11	.06
297	Hal McRae	.20	.15	.08
298	Mike Davis	.12	.09	.05
299	Tim Raines	.80	.60	.30
300	Bucky Dent	.15	.11	.06
301	Tommy John	.35	.25	.14
302	Carlton Fisk	4.00	3.00	1.50
303	Darrell Porter	.12	.09	.05
304	Dickie Thon	.12	.09	.05
305	Garry Maddox	.12	.09	.05
306	Cesar Cedeno	.20	.15	.08
307	Gary Lucas	.12	.09	.05
308	Johnny Ray	.20	.15	.08
309	Andy McGaffigan	.12	.09	.05
310	Claudell Washington	.12	.09	.05
311	Ryne Sandberg	25.00	18.50	10.00
312	George Foster	.30	.25	.12
313	*Spike Owen* (FC)	.70	.50	.30
314	Gary Gaetti	.40	.30	.15
315	Willie Upshaw	.12	.09	.05
316	Al Williams	.12	.09	.05
317	Jorge Orta	.12	.09	.05
318	Orlando Mercado	.12	.09	.05
319	*Junior Ortiz* (FC)	.12	.09	.05
320	Mike Proly	.12	.09	.05
321	Randy S. Johnson	.12	.09	.05
322	Jim Morrison	.12	.09	.05
323	Max Venable	.12	.09	.05
324	Tony Gwynn	18.00	13.50	7.25
325	Duane Walker	.12	.09	.05
326	Ozzie Virgil	.12	.09	.05
327	Jeff Lahti	.12	.09	.05
328	*Bill Dawley* (FC)	.12	.09	.05
329	Rob Wilfong	.12	.09	.05
330	Marc Hill	.12	.09	.05
331	Ray Burris	.12	.09	.05
332	Allan Ramirez	.12	.09	.05
333	Chuck Porter	.12	.09	.05
334	Wayne Krenchicki	.12	.09	.05
335	Gary Allenson	.12	.09	.05
336	*Bob Meacham* (FC)	.12	.09	.05
337	Joe Beckwith	.12	.09	.05
338	Rick Sutcliffe	.25	.20	.10
339	*Mark Huismann* (FC)	.15	.11	.06
340	*Tim Conroy* (FC)	.15	.11	.06
341	Scott Sanderson	.12	.09	.05
342	Larry Biittner	.12	.09	.05
343	Dave Stewart	2.00	1.50	.80
344	Darryl Motley	.12	.09	.05
345	*Chris Codiroli* (FC)	.12	.09	.05
346	Rick Behenna	.12	.09	.05
347	Andre Robertson	.12	.09	.05
348	Mike Marshall	.25	.20	.10
349	Larry Herndon	.12	.09	.05
350	Rich Dauer	.12	.09	.05
351	Cecil Cooper	.25	.20	.10
352	Rod Carew	4.00	3.00	1.50
353	Willie McGee	.40	.30	.15
354	Phil Garner	.12	.09	.05
355	Joe Morgan	.60	.45	.25
356	Luis Salazar	.12	.09	.05
357	John Candelaria	.20	.15	.08
358	Bill Laskey	.12	.09	.05
359	Bob McClure	.12	.09	.05
360	Dave Kingman	.20	.15	.08
361	Ron Cey	.20	.15	.08
362	*Matt Young* (FC)	.15	.11	.06
363	Lloyd Moseby	.20	.15	.08
364	Frank Viola	2.00	1.50	.80
365	Eddie Milner	.12	.09	.05
366	Floyd Bannister	.20	.15	.08
367	Dan Ford	.12	.09	.05
368	Moose Haas	.12	.09	.05
369	Doug Bair	.12	.09	.05
370	*Ray Fontenot* (FC)	.12	.09	.05
371	Luis Aponte	.12	.09	.05
372	Jack Fimple	.12	.09	.05
373	*Neal Heaton* (FC)	.20	.15	.08
374	Greg Pryor	.12	.09	.05
375	Wayne Gross	.12	.09	.05
376	Charlie Lea	.12	.09	.05
377	Steve Lubratich	.12	.09	.05
378	Jon Matlack	.12	.09	.05
379	Julio Cruz	.12	.09	.05
380	John Mizerock	.12	.09	.05
381	*Kevin Gross* (FC)	.50	.40	.20
382	Mike Ramsey	.12	.09	.05
383	Doug Gwosdz	.12	.09	.05
384	Kelly Paris	.12	.09	.05
385	Pete Falcone	.12	.09	.05
386	Milt May	.12	.09	.05
387	Fred Breining	.12	.09	.05
388	*Craig Lefferts* (FC)	.25	.20	.10
389	Steve Henderson	.12	.09	.05
390	Randy Moffitt	.12	.09	.05
391	Ron Washington	.12	.09	.05
392	Gary Roenicke	.12	.09	.05
393	*Tom Candiotti* (FC)	1.00	.70	.40
394	Larry Pashnick	.12	.09	.05
395	Dwight Evans	.30	.25	.12
396	Goose Gossage	.40	.30	.15
397	Derrel Thomas	.12	.09	.05
398	Juan Eichelberger	.12	.09	.05
399	Leon Roberts	.12	.09	.05
400	Davey Lopes	.15	.11	.06
401	Bill Gullickson	.12	.09	.05
402	Geoff Zahn	.12	.09	.05
403	Billy Sample	.12	.09	.05
404	Mike Squires	.12	.09	.05
405	Craig Reynolds	.12	.09	.05
406	Eric Show	.15	.11	.06
407	John Denny	.12	.09	.05
408	Dann Bilardello	.12	.09	.05
409	Bruce Benedict	.12	.09	.05
410	Kent Tekulve	.12	.09	.05
411	Mel Hall	.20	.15	.08
412	John Stuper	.12	.09	.05
413	Rick Dempsey	.12	.09	.05
414	Don Sutton	1.00	.70	.40
415	Jack Morris	2.00	1.50	.80
416	John Tudor	.20	.15	.08
417	Willie Randolph	.20	.15	.08

418	Jerry Reuss	.15	.11	.06
419	Don Slaught	.12	.09	.05
420	Steve McCatty	.12	.09	.05
421	Tim Wallach	.25	.20	.10
422	Larry Parrish	.20	.15	.08
423	Brian Downing	.20	.15	.08
424	Britt Burns	.12	.09	.05
425	David Green	.12	.09	.05
426	Jerry Mumphrey	.12	.09	.05
427	Ivan DeJesus	.12	.09	.05
428	Mario Soto	.12	.09	.05
429	Gene Richards	.12	.09	.05
430	Dale Berra	.12	.09	.05
431	Darrell Evans	.25	.20	.10
432	Glenn Hubbard	.12	.09	.05
433	Jody Davis	.15	.11	.06
434	Danny Heep	.12	.09	.05
435	*Ed Nunez* (FC)	.12	.09	.05
436	Bobby Castillo	.12	.09	.05
437	Ernie Whitt	.12	.09	.05
438	Scott Ullger	.12	.09	.05
439	Doyle Alexander	.15	.11	.06
440	Domingo Ramos	.12	.09	.05
441	Craig Swan	.12	.09	.05
442	Warren Brusstar	.12	.09	.05
443	Len Barker	.12	.09	.05
444	Mike Easler	.12	.09	.05
445	Renie Martin	.12	.09	.05
446	*Dennis Rasmussen* (FC)	.70	.50	.30
447	Ted Power (FC)	.15	.11	.06
448	*Charlie Hudson* (FC)	.25	.20	.10
449	*Danny Cox* (FC)	.70	.50	.30
450	Kevin Bass (FC)	.15	.11	.06
451	Daryl Sconiers	.12	.09	.05
452	Scott Fletcher	.12	.09	.05
453	Bryn Smith	.12	.09	.05
454	Jim Dwyer	.12	.09	.05
455	Rob Picciolo	.12	.09	.05
456	Enos Cabell	.12	.09	.05
457	*Dennis Boyd* (FC)	.35	.25	.14
458	Butch Wynegar	.12	.09	.05
459	Burt Hooton	.12	.09	.05
460	Ron Hassey	.12	.09	.05
461	*Danny Jackson* (FC)	1.00	.70	.40
462	Bob Kearney	.12	.09	.05
463	Terry Francona	.12	.09	.05
464	Wayne Tolleson	.12	.09	.05
465	Mickey Rivers	.12	.09	.05
466	John Wathan	.12	.09	.05
467	Bill Almon	.12	.09	.05
468	George Vukovich	.12	.09	.05
469	Steve Kemp	.15	.11	.06
470	Ken Landreaux	.12	.09	.05
471	Milt Wilcox	.12	.09	.05
472	Tippy Martinez	.12	.09	.05
473	Ted Simmons	.20	.15	.08
474	Tim Foli	.12	.09	.05
475	George Hendrick	.12	.09	.05
476	Terry Puhl	.12	.09	.05
477	Von Hayes	.25	.20	.10
478	Bobby Brown	.12	.09	.05
479	Lee Lacy	.12	.09	.05
480	Joel Youngblood	.12	.09	.05
481	Jim Slaton	.12	.09	.05
482	*Mike Fitzgerald* (FC)	.20	.15	.08
483	Keith Moreland	.12	.09	.05
484	Ron Roenicke	.12	.09	.05
485	Luis Leal	.12	.09	.05
486	Bryan Oelkers	.12	.09	.05
487	Bruce Berenyi	.12	.09	.05
488	LaMarr Hoyt	.12	.09	.05
489	Joe Nolan	.12	.09	.05
490	Marshall Edwards	.12	.09	.05
491	*Mike Laga* (FC)	.12	.09	.05
492	Rick Cerone	.12	.09	.05
493	Mike Miller (Rick)	.12	.09	.05
494	Rick Honeycutt	.12	.09	.05
495	Mike Hargrove	.12	.09	.05
496	Joe Simpson	.12	.09	.05
497	*Keith Atherton* (FC)	.12	.09	.05
498	Chris Welsh	.12	.09	.05
499	Bruce Kison	.12	.09	.05
500	Bob Johnson	.12	.09	.05
501	Jerry Koosman	.15	.11	.06
502	Frank DiPino	.12	.09	.05
503	Tony Perez	.40	.30	.15
504	Ken Oberkfell	.12	.09	.05
505	*Mark Thurmond* (FC)	.12	.09	.05
506	Joe Price	.12	.09	.05
507	Pascual Perez	.15	.11	.06
508	*Marvell Wynne* (FC)	.12	.09	.05
509	Mike Krukow	.12	.09	.05
510	Dick Ruthven	.12	.09	.05
511	Al Cowens	.12	.09	.05
512	Cliff Johnson	.12	.09	.05
513	*Randy Bush* (FC)	.20	.15	.08
514	Sammy Stewart	.12	.09	.05
515	*Bill Schroeder* (FC)	.15	.11	.06
516	Aurelio Lopez	.12	.09	.05
517	Mike Brown	.12	.09	.05
518	Graig Nettles	.35	.25	.14
519	Dave Sax	.12	.09	.05
520	Gerry Willard	.12	.09	.05
521	Paul Splittorff	.12	.09	.05
522	Tom Burgmeier	.12	.09	.05
523	Chris Speier	.12	.09	.05
524	Bobby Clark	.12	.09	.05
525	George Wright	.12	.09	.05
526	Dennis Lamp	.12	.09	.05
527	Tony Scott	.12	.09	.05
528	Ed Whitson	.12	.09	.05
529	Ron Reed	.12	.09	.05
530	Charlie Puleo	.12	.09	.05
531	Jerry Royster	.12	.09	.05
532	Don Robinson	.12	.09	.05
533	Steve Trout	.12	.09	.05
534	Bruce Sutter	.30	.25	.12
535	Bob Horner	.20	.15	.08
536	Pat Tabler	.15	.11	.06
537	Chris Chambliss	.12	.09	.05
538	Bob Ojeda	.15	.11	.06
539	Alan Ashby	.12	.09	.05
540	Jay Johnstone	.12	.09	.05
541	Bob Dernier	.12	.09	.05
542	*Brook Jacoby* (FC)	1.50	1.25	.60
543	U.L. Washington	.12	.09	.05
544	Danny Darwin	.12	.09	.05
545	Kiko Garcia	.12	.09	.05
546	Vance Law	.12	.09	.05
547	Tug McGraw	.20	.15	.08
548	Dave Smith	.12	.09	.05
549	Len Matuszek	.12	.09	.05
550	Tom Hume	.12	.09	.05
551	Dave Dravecky	.15	.11	.06
552	Rick Rhoden	.15	.11	.06
553	Duane Kuiper	.12	.09	.05
554	Rusty Staub	.20	.15	.08
555	Bill Campbell	.12	.09	.05
556	Mike Torrez	.12	.09	.05
557	Dave Henderson (FC)	.25	.20	.10
558	Len Whitehouse	.12	.09	.05
559	Barry Bonnell	.12	.09	.05
560	Rick Lysander	.12	.09	.05
561	Garth Iorg	.12	.09	.05
562	Bryan Clark	.12	.09	.05
563	Brian Giles	.12	.09	.05
564	Vern Ruhle	.12	.09	.05
565	Steve Bedrosian	.20	.15	.08
566	Larry McWilliams	.12	.09	.05
567	Jeff Leonard	.15	.11	.06
568	Alan Wiggins	.12	.09	.05
569	*Jeff Russell* (FC)	.25	.20	.10
570	Salome Barojas	.12	.09	.05
571	Dane Iorg	.12	.09	.05
572	Bob Knepper	.15	.11	.06
573	Gary Lavelle	.12	.09	.05
574	Gorman Thomas	.15	.11	.06
575	Manny Trillo	.12	.09	.05
576	Jim Palmer	4.00	3.00	1.50
577	Dale Murray	.12	.09	.05
578	Tom Brookens	.12	.09	.05
579	Rich Gedman	.15	.11	.06
580	*Bill Doran* (FC)	.50	.40	.20
581	Steve Yeager	.12	.09	.05
582	Dan Spillner	.12	.09	.05
583	Dan Quisenberry	.15	.11	.06
584	Rance Mulliniks	.12	.09	.05
585	Storm Davis	.15	.11	.06
586	Dave Schmidt	.12	.09	.05
587	Bill Russell	.12	.09	.05
588	*Pat Sheridan* (FC)	.20	.15	.08
589	Rafael Ramirez	.12	.09	.05
590	Bud Anderson	.12	.09	.05
591	George Frazier	.12	.09	.05
592	*Lee Tunnell* (FC)	.12	.09	.05
593	Kirk Gibson	1.00	.70	.40
594	Scott McGregor	.12	.09	.05
595	Bob Bailor	.12	.09	.05
596	Tom Herr	.20	.15	.08
597	Luis Sanchez	.12	.09	.05
598	Dave Engle	.12	.09	.05
599	*Craig McMurtry* (FC)	.15	.11	.06
600	Carlos Diaz	.12	.09	.05
601	Tom O'Malley	.12	.09	.05
602	*Nick Esasky* (FC)	.25	.20	.10
603	Ron Hodges	.12	.09	.05
604	Ed Vande Berg	.12	.09	.05
605	Alfredo Griffin	.12	.09	.05
606	Glenn Hoffman	.12	.09	.05
607	Hubie Brooks	.20	.15	.08
608	Richard Barnes (photo actually Neal Heaton)	.12	.09	.05
609	*Greg Walker* (FC)	.20	.15	.08
610	Ken Singleton	.20	.15	.08
611	Mark Clear	.12	.09	.05
612	Buck Martinez	.12	.09	.05
613	Ken Griffey	.15	.11	.06
614	Reid Nichols	.12	.09	.05
615	*Doug Sisk* (FC)	.12	.09	.05
616	Bob Brenly	.12	.09	.05
617	Joey McLaughlin	.12	.09	.05
618	Glenn Wilson	.12	.09	.05
619	Bob Stoddard	.12	.09	.05
620	Len Sakata (Lenn)	.12	.09	.05
621	*Mike Young* (FC)	.15	.11	.06
622	John Stefero	.12	.09	.05
623	*Carmelo Martinez* (FC)	.15	.11	.06
624	Dave Bergman	.12	.09	.05
625	Runnin' Reds (David Green, Willie McGee, Lonnie Smith, Ozzie Smith)	.30	.25	.12
626	Rudy May	.12	.09	.05
627	Matt Keough	.12	.09	.05
628	*Jose DeLeon* (FC)	.50	.40	.20
629	Jim Essian	.12	.09	.05
630	*Darnell Coles* (FC)	.15	.11	.06
631	Mike Warren	.12	.09	.05
632	Del Crandall	.12	.09	.05
633	Dennis Martinez	.12	.09	.05
634	Mike Moore	.12	.09	.05
635	Lary Sorensen	.12	.09	.05
636	Ricky Nelson	.12	.09	.05
637	Omar Moreno	.12	.09	.05
638	Charlie Hough	.15	.11	.06
639	Dennis Eckersley	4.00	3.00	1.50
640	*Walt Terrell* (FC)	.20	.15	.08
641	Denny Walling	.12	.09	.05
642	*Dave Anderson* (FC)	.12	.09	.05
643	*Jose Oquendo* (FC)	.25	.20	.10
644	Bob Stanley	.12	.09	.05
645	Dave Geisel	.12	.09	.05
646	*Scott Garrelts* (FC)	.40	.30	.15
647	*Gary Pettis* (FC)	.40	.30	.15
648	Duke Snider Puzzle Card	.12	.09	.05
649	Johnnie LeMaster	.12	.09	.05
650	Dave Collins	.12	.09	.05
651	San Diego Chicken	.25	.20	.10

----a	Checklist 1-26 DK (Perez-Steel on back)	.12	.09	.05
----b	Checklist 1-26 DK (Perez-Steele on back)	.40	.30	.15
----	Checklist 27-130	.12	.09	.05
----	Checklist 131-234	.12	.09	.05
----	Checklist 235-338	.12	.09	.05
----	Checklist 339-442	.12	.09	.05
----	Checklist 443-546	.12	.09	.05
----	Checklist 547-651	.12	.09	.05

1984 Donruss Action All-Stars

Full-color photos on the card fronts and backs make the 1984 Donruss Action All-Stars set somewhat unusual. The fronts contain a large action photo plus the Donruss logo and year of issue inside a deep red border. The top half of the card backs feature a close-up photo with the bottom portion containing biographical and statistical information. The cards, which measure 3-1/2" by 5", were sold with Ted Williams puzzle pieces.

		MT	NR MT	EX
Complete Set:		7.50	5.75	3.00
Common Player:		.09	.07	.04
1	Gary Lavelle	.09	.07	.04
2	Willie McGee	.15	.11	.06
3	Tony Pena	.09	.07	.04
4	Lou Whitaker	.15	.11	.06
5	Robin Yount	.75	.60	.30
6	Doug DeCinces	.09	.07	.04
7	John Castino	.09	.07	.04
8	Terry Kennedy	.09	.07	.04
9	Rickey Henderson	.50	.40	.20
10	Bob Horner	.12	.09	.05
11	Harold Baines	.15	.11	.06
12	Buddy Bell	.09	.07	.04
13	Fernando Valenzuela	.12	.09	.05
14	Nolan Ryan	2.00	1.50	.80
15	Andre Thornton	.09	.07	.04
16	Gary Redus	.09	.07	.04
17	Pedro Guerrero	.12	.09	.05
18	Andre Dawson	.20	.15	.08
19	Dave Stieb	.12	.09	.05
20	Cal Ripken, Jr.	1.25	.90	.50
21	Ken Griffey	.12	.09	.05
22	Wade Boggs	.70	.50	.30
23	Keith Hernandez	.12	.09	.05
24	Steve Carlton	.30	.25	.12
25	Hal McRae	.12	.09	.05
26	John Lowenstein	.09	.07	.04
27	Fred Lynn	.15	.11	.06
28	Bill Buckner	.09	.07	.04
29	Chris Chambliss	.09	.07	.04
30	Richie Zisk	.09	.07	.04
31	Jack Clark	.15	.11	.06
32	George Hendrick	.09	.07	.04
33	Bill Madlock	.12	.09	.05
34	Lance Parrish	.15	.11	.06
35	Paul Molitor	.50	.40	.20
36	Reggie Jackson	.80	.60	.30
37	Kent Hrbek	.20	.15	.08
38	Steve Garvey	.20	.15	.08
39	Carney Lansford	.09	.07	.04
40	Dale Murphy	.30	.25	.12
41	Greg Luzinski	.12	.09	.05
42	Larry Parrish	.09	.07	.04
43	Ryne Sandberg	1.25	.90	.50
44	Dickie Thon	.09	.07	.04
45	Bert Blyleven	.12	.09	.05
46	Ron Oester	.09	.07	.04
47	Dusty Baker	.09	.07	.04
48	Steve Rogers	.09	.07	.04
49	Jim Clancy	.09	.07	.04
50	Eddie Murray	.25	.20	.10
51	Ron Guidry	.15	.11	.06
52	Jim Rice	.15	.11	.06
53	Tom Seaver	.30	.25	.12
54	Pete Rose	.30	.25	.12
55	George Brett	.75	.60	.30
56	Dan Quisenberry	.09	.07	.04
57	Mike Schmidt	.75	.60	.30
58	Ted Simmons	.12	.09	.05
59	Dave Righetti	.12	.09	.05
60	Checklist	.09	.07	.04

The values quoted are intended to reflect the market price.

1984 Donruss Champions

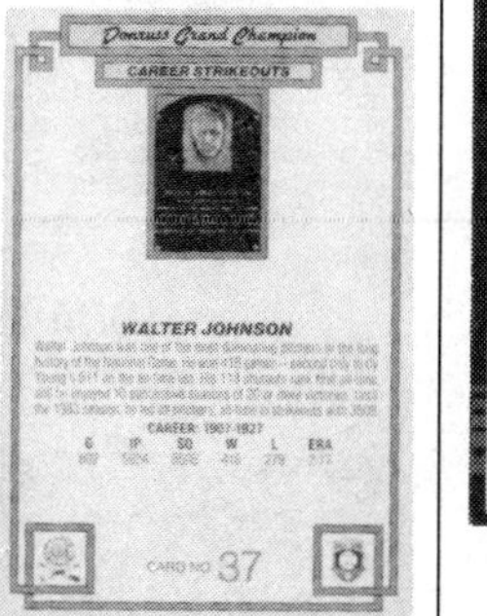

The 60-card Donruss Champions set includes ten Hall of Famers, forty-nine current players and one numbered checklist. The ten Hall of Famers' cards (called Grand Champions) feature the artwork of Dick Perez, while cards of the current players (called Champions) are color photos. The cards measure 3-1/2" by 5". The Grand Champions represent hallmarks of excellence in various statistical categories, while the Champions are the leaders among active players in each category. The ten Grand Champion cards are #'s 1, 8, 14, 20, 26, 31, 37, 43, 50 and 55. The cards were issued with Duke Snider puzzle pieces.

		MT	NR MT	EX
Complete Set:		7.00	5.25	2.75
Common Player:		.10	.08	.04
1	Babe Ruth	1.00	.70	.40
2	George Foster	.10	.08	.04
3	Dave Kingman	.10	.08	.04
4	Jim Rice	.10	.08	.04
5	Gorman Thomas	.10	.08	.04
6	Ben Oglivie	.10	.08	.04
7	Jeff Burroughs	.10	.08	.04
8	Hank Aaron	.75	.60	.30
9	Reggie Jackson	.30	.25	.12
10	Carl Yastrzemski	.35	.25	.14
11	Mike Schmidt	.50	.40	.20
12	Graig Nettles	.14	.11	.06
13	Greg Luzinski	.10	.08	.04
14	Ted Williams	.75	.60	.30
15	George Brett	.50	.40	.20
16	Wade Boggs	.50	.40	.20
17	Hal McRae	.10	.08	.04
18	Bill Buckner	.10	.08	.04
19	Eddie Murray	.25	.20	.10
20	Rogers Hornsby	.14	.11	.06
21	Rod Carew	.25	.20	.10
22	Bill Madlock	.10	.08	.04
23	Lonnie Smith	.10	.08	.04
24	Cecil Cooper	.10	.08	.04
25	Ken Griffey	.10	.08	.04
26	Ty Cobb	.50	.40	.20
27	Pete Rose	.40	.30	.15
28	Rusty Staub	.10	.08	.04
29	Tony Perez	.10	.08	.04
30	Al Oliver	.10	.08	.04
31	Cy Young	.14	.11	.06
32	Gaylord Perry	.10	.08	.04
33	Ferguson Jenkins	.10	.08	.04
34	Phil Niekro	.10	.08	.04
35	Jim Palmer	.20	.15	.08
36	Tommy John	.10	.08	.04
37	Walter Johnson	.20	.15	.08
38	Steve Carlton	.25	.20	.10
39	Nolan Ryan	.75	.60	.30
40	Tom Seaver	.35	.25	.14
41	Don Sutton	.14	.11	.06
42	Bert Blyleven	.10	.08	.04
43	Frank Robinson	.35	.25	.14
44	Joe Morgan	.25	.20	.10
45	Rollie Fingers	.14	.11	.06
46	Keith Hernandez	.10	.08	.04
47	Robin Yount	.50	.40	.20
48	Cal Ripken, Jr.	.50	.40	.20
49	Dale Murphy	.35	.25	.14
50	Mickey Mantle	1.00	.70	.40
51	Johnny Bench	.40	.30	.15
52	Carlton Fisk	.30	.25	.12
53	Tug McGraw	.10	.08	.04
54	Paul Molitor	.25	.20	.10
55	Carl Hubbell	.14	.11	.06
56	Steve Garvey	.15	.11	.06
57	Dave Parker	.14	.11	.06
58	Gary Carter	.15	.11	.06
59	Fred Lynn	.14	.11	.06
60	Checklist	.10	.08	.04

1985 Donruss

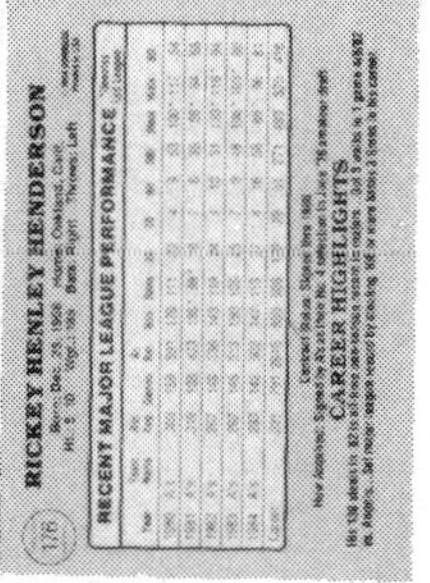

The black-bordered 1985 Donruss set includes 653 numbered cards and seven unnumbered checklists. Displaying the artwork of Dick Perez for the fourth consecutive year, card #'s 1-26 feature the Diamond Kings series. Donruss, realizing the hobby craze over rookie cards, included a Rated Rookies subset (card #'s 27-46). The cards, which are the standard size of 2-1/2" by 3-1/2", were issued with a Lou Gehrig puzzle. The backs of the cards have black print on yellow and white. The complete set price does not include the higher priced variations. (DK) and (RR) refer to the Diamond Kings and Rated Rookies subsets.

		MT	NR MT	EX
Complete Set (660):		200.00	150.00	80.00
Common Player:		.08	.06	.03
1	Ryne Sandberg (DK)	4.00	3.00	1.50
2	Doug DeCinces (DK)	.10	.08	.04
3	Rich Dotson (DK)	.12	.09	.05
4	Bert Blyleven (DK)	.15	.11	.06
5	Lou Whitaker (DK)	.30	.25	.12
6	Dan Quisenberry (DK)	.15	.11	.06
7	Don Mattingly (DK)	3.50	2.75	1.50
8	Carney Lansford (DK)	.10	.08	.04
9	Frank Tanana (DK)	.12	.09	.05
10	Willie Upshaw (DK)	.10	.08	.04
11	Claudell Washington (DK)	.10	.08	.04
12	Mike Marshall (DK)	.10	.08	.04
13	Joaquin Andujar (DK)	.10	.08	.04
14	Cal Ripken, Jr. (DK)	4.00	3.00	1.50
15	Jim Rice (DK)	.50	.40	.20
16	Don Sutton (DK)	.30	.25	.12
17	Frank Viola (DK)	.15	.11	.06
18	Alvin Davis (FC) (DK)	.10	.08	.04
19	Mario Soto (DK)	.10	.08	.04
20	Jose Cruz (DK)	.12	.09	.05
21	Charlie Lea (DK)	.10	.08	.04
22	Jesse Orosco (DK)	.10	.08	.04
23	Juan Samuel (FC) (DK)	.25	.20	.10
24	Tony Pena (DK)	.12	.09	.05
25	Tony Gwynn (DK)	1.75	1.25	.70
26	Bob Brenly (DK)	.10	.08	.04
27	*Danny Tartabull* (RR)	10.00	7.50	4.00
28	*Mike Bielecki* (FC) (RR)	.15	.11	.06
29	*Steve Lyons* (FC) (RR)	.20	.15	.08
30	*Jeff Reed* (FC) (RR)	.15	.11	.06
31	Tony Brewer (RR)	.08	.06	.03
32	*John Morris* (FC) (RR)	.08	.06	.03
33	*Daryl Boston* (FC) (RR)	.25	.20	.10
34	Alfonso Pulido (RR)	.08	.06	.03
35	*Steve Kiefer* (FC) (RR)	.08	.06	.03
36	*Larry Sheets* (FC) (RR)	.08	.06	.03
37	*Scott Bradley* (FC) (RR)	.08	.06	.03
38	*Calvin Schiraldi* (FC) (RR)	.08	.06	.03
39	*Shawon Dunston* (RR)	1.00	.70	.40
40	Charlie Mitchell (RR)	.08	.06	.03
41	*Billy Hatcher* (RR)	.60	.45	.25
42	Russ Stephans (RR)	.08	.06	.03
43	Alejandro Sanchez (RR)	.08	.06	.03
44	*Steve Jeltz* (FC) (RR)	.08	.06	.03
45	*Jim Traber* (FC) (RR)	.08	.06	.03
46	Doug Loman (RR)	.08	.06	.03
47	Eddie Murray	1.50	1.25	.60
48	Robin Yount	4.00	3.00	1.50
49	Lance Parrish	.30	.25	.12
50	Jim Rice	.30	.25	.12
51	Dave Winfield	4.50	3.50	1.75
52	Fernando Valenzuela	.35	.25	.14
53	George Brett	4.50	3.50	1.75
54	Dave Kingman	.15	.11	.06
55	Gary Carter	.40	.30	.15
56	Buddy Bell	.12	.09	.05
57	Reggie Jackson	.60	.45	.25
58	Harold Baines	.20	.15	.08
59	Ozzie Smith	1.50	1.25	.60
60	Nolan Ryan	10.00	7.50	4.00
61	Mike Schmidt	4.00	3.00	1.50
62	Dave Parker	.35	.25	.14
63	Tony Gwynn	5.00	3.75	2.00
64	Tony Pena	.12	.09	.05
65	Jack Clark	.25	.20	.10
66	Dale Murphy	.80	.60	.30
67	Ryne Sandberg	10.00	7.50	4.00
68	Keith Hernandez	.20	.15	.08
69	*Alvin Davis* (FC)	.25	.20	.10
70	Kent Hrbek	.30	.25	.12
71	Willie Upshaw	.10	.08	.04
72	Dave Engle	.08	.06	.03
73	Alfredo Griffin	.10	.08	.04
74a	Jack Perconte (last line of highlights begins "Batted .346...")	.10	.08	.04
74b	Jack Perconte (last line of highlights begins "Led the...")	1.25	.90	.50
75	Jesse Orosco	.10	.08	.04
76	Jody Davis	.12	.09	.05
77	Bob Horner	.12	.09	.05
78	Larry McWilliams	.08	.06	.03
79	Joel Youngblood	.08	.06	.03
80	Alan Wiggins	.08	.06	.03
81	Ron Oester	.08	.06	.03
82	Ozzie Virgil	.08	.06	.03
83	*Ricky Horton* (FC)	.10	.08	.04
84	Bill Doran	.12	.09	.05
85	Rod Carew	1.00	.70	.40
86	LaMarr Hoyt	.08	.06	.03
87	Tim Wallach	.15	.11	.06
88	Mike Flanagan	.12	.09	.05
89	Jim Sundberg	.10	.08	.04
90	Chet Lemon	.10	.08	.04
91	Bob Stanley	.08	.06	.03
92	Willie Randolph	.12	.09	.05
93	Bill Russell	.10	.08	.04
94	Julio Franco	1.50	1.25	.60
95	Dan Quisenberry	.12	.09	.05
96	Bill Caudill	.08	.06	.03
97	Bill Gullickson	.08	.06	.03
98	Danny Darwin	.08	.06	.03
99	Curtis Wilkerson	.08	.06	.03
100	Bud Black	.08	.06	.03
101	Tony Phillips	.40	.30	.15
102	Tony Bernazard	.08	.06	.03
103	Jay Howell	.10	.08	.04
104	Burt Hooton	.10	.08	.04
105	Milt Wilcox	.08	.06	.03
106	Rich Dauer	.08	.06	.03
107	Don Sutton	.35	.25	.14
108	Mike Witt	.15	.11	.06
109	Bruce Sutter	.15	.11	.06
110	Enos Cabell	.08	.06	.03
111	John Denny	.08	.06	.03
112	Dave Dravecky	.10	.08	.04
113	Marvell Wynne	.08	.06	.03
114	Johnnie LeMaster	.08	.06	.03
115	Chuck Porter	.08	.06	.03
116	John Gibbons	.08	.06	.03
117	Keith Moreland	.10	.08	.04
118	Darnell Coles	.12	.09	.05
119	Dennis Lamp	.08	.06	.03
120	Ron Davis	.08	.06	.03
121	Nick Esasky	.10	.08	.04
122	Vance Law	.10	.08	.04
123	Gary Roenicke	.08	.06	.03
124	Bill Schroeder	.08	.06	.03
125	Dave Rozema	.08	.06	.03
126	Bobby Meacham	.08	.06	.03
127	Marty Barrett (FC)	.25	.20	.10
128	*R.J. Reynolds* (FC)	.15	.11	.06
129	Ernie Camacho	.08	.06	.03
130	Jorge Orta	.08	.06	.03
131	Lary Sorensen	.08	.06	.03
132	Terry Francona	.08	.06	.03
133	Fred Lynn	.25	.20	.10
134	Bobby Jones	.08	.06	.03
135	Jerry Hairston	.08	.06	.03
136	Kevin Bass	.12	.09	.05
137	Garry Maddox	.08	.06	.03
138	Dave LaPoint	.10	.08	.04
139	Kevin McReynolds	.25	.20	.10
140	Wayne Krenchicki	.08	.06	.03
141	Rafael Ramirez	.08	.06	.03
142	Rod Scurry	.08	.06	.03
143	Greg Minton	.08	.06	.03
144	Tim Stoddard	.08	.06	.03
145	Steve Henderson	.08	.06	.03
146	George Bell	.70	.50	.30
147	Dave Meier	.08	.06	.03
148	Sammy Stewart	.08	.06	.03
149	Mark Brouhard	.08	.06	.03
150	Larry Herndon	.10	.08	.04
151	Oil Can Boyd	.10	.08	.04
152	Brian Dayett	.08	.06	.03
153	Tom Niedenfuer	.10	.08	.04
154	Brook Jacoby	.15	.11	.06
155	Onix Concepcion	.08	.06	.03
156	Tim Conroy	.08	.06	.03
157	*Joe Hesketh* (FC)	.15	.11	.06
158	Brian Downing	.12	.09	.05
159	Tommy Dunbar	.08	.06	.03
160	Marc Hill	.08	.06	.03
161	Phil Garner	.10	.08	.04
162	Jerry Davis	.08	.06	.03
163	Bill Campbell	.08	.06	.03
164	*John Franco* (FC)	.90	.70	.35
165	Len Barker	.10	.08	.04
166	*Benny Distefano* (FC)	.10	.08	.04
167	George Frazier	.08	.06	.03
168	Tito Landrum	.08	.06	.03
169	Cal Ripken, Jr.	10.00	7.50	4.00
170	Cecil Cooper	.15	.11	.06
171	Alan Trammell	.40	.30	.15
172	Wade Boggs	5.00	3.75	2.00
173	Don Baylor	.15	.11	.06
174	Pedro Guerrero	.15	.11	.06
175	Frank White	.12	.09	.05
176	Rickey Henderson	4.00	3.00	1.50
177	Charlie Lea	.08	.06	.03
178	Pete O'Brien	.20	.15	.08
179	Doug DeCinces	.12	.09	.05
180	Ron Kittle	.12	.09	.05
181	George Hendrick	.10	.08	.04
182	Joe Niekro	.12	.09	.05
183	Juan Samuel (FC)	.60	.45	.25
184	Mario Soto	.10	.08	.04
185	Goose Gossage	.25	.20	.10
186	Johnny Ray	.15	.11	.06
187	Bob Brenly	.08	.06	.03
188	Craig McMurtry	.08	.06	.03
189	Leon Durham	.10	.08	.04
190	*Dwight Gooden* (FC)	6.00	4.50	2.50
191	Barry Bonnell	.08	.06	.03
192	Tim Teufel	.12	.09	.05
193	Dave Stieb	.15	.11	.06
194	Mickey Hatcher	.08	.06	.03
195	Jesse Barfield	.15	.11	.06
196	Al Cowens	.08	.06	.03
197	Hubie Brooks	.12	.09	.05
198	Steve Trout	.08	.06	.03

199	Glenn Hubbard	.08	.06	.03
200	Bill Madlock	.15	.11	.06
201	*Jeff Robinson* (FC)	.10	.08	.04
202	Eric Show	.10	.08	.04
203	Dave Concepcion	.15	.11	.06
204	Ivan DeJesus	.08	.06	.03
205	Neil Allen	.08	.06	.03
206	Jerry Mumphrey	.08	.06	.03
207	Mike Brown	.08	.06	.03
208	Carlton Fisk	.40	.30	.15
209	Bryn Smith	.08	.06	.03
210	Tippy Martinez	.08	.06	.03
211	Dion James	.10	.08	.04
212	Willie Hernandez	.10	.08	.04
213	Mike Easler	.10	.08	.04
214	Ron Guidry	.10	.08	.04
215	Rick Honeycutt	.08	.06	.03
216	Brett Butler	.12	.09	.05
217	Larry Gura	.08	.06	.03
218	Ray Burris	.08	.06	.03
219	Steve Rogers	.10	.08	.04
220	Frank Tanana	.12	.09	.05
221	Ned Yost	.08	.06	.03
222	*Bret Saberhagen*	2.50	2.00	1.00
223	Mike Davis	.10	.08	.04
224	Bert Blyleven	.15	.11	.06
225	Steve Kemp	.10	.08	.04
226	Jerry Reuss	.10	.08	.04
227	Darrell Evans	.15	.11	.06
228	Wayne Gross	.08	.06	.03
229	Jim Gantner	.10	.08	.04
230	Bob Boone	.10	.08	.04
231	Lonnie Smith	.10	.08	.04
232	Frank DiPino	.08	.06	.03
233	Jerry Koosman	.12	.09	.05
234	Graig Nettles	.20	.15	.08
235	John Tudor	.12	.09	.05
236	John Rabb	.08	.06	.03
237	Rick Manning	.08	.06	.03
238	Mike Fitzgerald	.08	.06	.03
239	Gary Matthews	.12	.09	.05
240	*Jim Presley* (FC)	.10	.08	.04
241	Dave Collins	.10	.08	.04
242	Gary Gaetti	.30	.25	.12
243	Dann Bilardello	.08	.06	.03
244	Rudy Law	.08	.06	.03
245	John Lowenstein	.08	.06	.03
246	Tom Tellmann	.08	.06	.03
247	Howard Johnson	.50	.40	.20
248	Ray Fontenot	.08	.06	.03
249	Tony Armas	.12	.09	.05
250	Candy Maldonado	.12	.09	.05
251	*Mike Jeffcoat* (FC)	.10	.08	.04
252	Dane Iorg	.08	.06	.03
253	Bruce Bochte	.08	.06	.03
254	Pete Rose	1.75	1.25	.70
255	Don Aase	.08	.06	.03
256	George Wright	.08	.06	.03
257	Britt Burns	.08	.06	.03
258	Mike Scott	.20	.15	.08
259	Len Matuszek	.08	.06	.03
260	Dave Rucker	.08	.06	.03
261	Craig Lefferts	.10	.08	.04
262	*Jay Tibbs* (FC)	.08	.06	.03
263	Bruce Benedict	.08	.06	.03
264	Don Robinson	.10	.08	.04
265	Gary Lavelle	.08	.06	.03
266	Scott Sanderson	.08	.06	.03
267	Matt Young	.08	.06	.03
268	Ernie Whitt	.10	.08	.04
269	Houston Jimenez	.08	.06	.03
270	*Ken Dixon* (FC)	.12	.09	.05
271	Peter Ladd	.08	.06	.03
272	Juan Berenguer	.08	.06	.03
273	*Roger Clemens*	45.00	34.00	18.00
274	Rick Cerone	.08	.06	.03
275	Dave Anderson	.08	.06	.03
276	George Vukovich	.08	.06	.03
277	Greg Pryor	.08	.06	.03
278	Mike Warren	.08	.06	.03
279	Bob James	.08	.06	.03
280	Bobby Grich	.12	.09	.05
281	*Mike Mason* (FC)	.12	.09	.05
282	Ron Reed	.08	.06	.03
283	Alan Ashby	.08	.06	.03
284	Mark Thurmond	.08	.06	.03
285	Joe Lefebvre	.08	.06	.03
286	Ted Power	.08	.06	.03
287	Chris Chambliss	.10	.08	.04
288	Lee Tunnell	.08	.06	.03
289	Rich Bordi	.08	.06	.03
290	Glenn Brummer	.08	.06	.03
291	Mike Boddicker	.12	.09	.05
292	Rollie Fingers	.40	.30	.15
293	Lou Whitaker	.40	.30	.15
294	Dwight Evans	.15	.11	.06
295	Don Mattingly	6.00	4.50	2.50
296	Mike Marshall	.15	.11	.06
297	Willie Wilson	.15	.11	.06
298	Mike Heath	.08	.06	.03
299	Tim Raines	.50	.40	.20
300	Larry Parrish	.12	.09	.05
301	Geoff Zahn	.08	.06	.03
302	Rich Dotson	.12	.09	.05
303	David Green	.08	.06	.03
304	Jose Cruz	.12	.09	.05
305	Steve Carlton	1.25	.90	.50
306	Gary Redus	.10	.08	.04
307	Steve Garvey	.40	.30	.15
308	Jose DeLeon	.10	.08	.04
309	Randy Lerch	.08	.06	.03
310	Claudell Washington	.10	.08	.04
311	Lee Smith	1.00	.70	.40
312	Darryl Strawberry	1.75	1.25	.70
313	Jim Beattie	.08	.06	.03
314	John Butcher	.08	.06	.03
315	Damaso Garcia	.10	.08	.04
316	Mike Smithson	.08	.06	.03
317	Luis Leal	.08	.06	.03
318	Ken Phelps (FC)	.25	.20	.10
319	Wally Backman	.10	.08	.04
320	Ron Cey	.12	.09	.05
321	Brad Komminsk	.08	.06	.03
322	Jason Thompson	.08	.06	.03
323	*Frank Williams* (FC)	.08	.06	.03
324	Tim Lollar	.08	.06	.03
325	*Eric Davis*	6.00	4.50	2.50
326	Von Hayes	.12	.09	.05
327	Andy Van Slyke	1.00	.70	.40
328	Craig Reynolds	.08	.06	.03
329	Dick Schofield	.10	.08	.04
330	Scott Fletcher	.10	.08	.04
331	Jeff Reardon	.15	.11	.06
332	Rick Dempsey	.10	.08	.04
333	Ben Oglivie	.10	.08	.04
334	Dan Petry	.10	.08	.04
335	Jackie Gutierrez	.08	.06	.03
336	Dave Righetti	.10	.08	.04
337	Alejandro Pena	.10	.08	.04
338	Mel Hall	.10	.08	.04
339	Pat Sheridan	.08	.06	.03
340	Keith Atherton	.08	.06	.03
341	David Palmer	.08	.06	.03
342	Gary Ward	.10	.08	.04
343	Dave Stewart	.15	.11	.06
344	*Mark Gubicza* (FC)	.50	.40	.20
345	Carney Lansford	.12	.09	.05
346	Jerry Willard	.08	.06	.03
347	Ken Griffey	.12	.09	.05
348	*Franklin Stubbs* (FC)	.12	.09	.05
349	Aurelio Lopez	.08	.06	.03
350	Al Bumbry	.10	.08	.04
351	Charlie Moore	.08	.06	.03
352	Luis Sanchez	.08	.06	.03
353	Darrell Porter	.10	.08	.04
354	Bill Dawley	.08	.06	.03
355	Charlie Hudson	.10	.08	.04
356	Garry Templeton	.10	.08	.04
357	Cecilio Guante	.08	.06	.03
358	Jeff Leonard	.12	.09	.05
359	Paul Molitor	3.00	2.25	1.25
360	Ron Gardenhire	.08	.06	.03
361	Larry Bowa	.12	.09	.05
362	Bob Kearney	.08	.06	.03
363	Garth Iorg	.08	.06	.03
364	Tom Brunansky	.15	.11	.06
365	Brad Gulden	.08	.06	.03
366	Greg Walker	.12	.09	.05
367	Mike Young	.10	.08	.04
368	Rick Waits	.08	.06	.03
369	Doug Bair	.08	.06	.03
370	Bob Shirley	.08	.06	.03
371	Bob Ojeda	.12	.09	.05
372	Bob Welch	.15	.11	.06
373	Neal Heaton	.08	.06	.03
374	Danny Jackson (photo actually Steve Farr)	.80	.60	.30
375	Donnie Hill	.08	.06	.03
376	Mike Stenhouse	.08	.06	.03
377	Bruce Kison	.08	.06	.03
378	Wayne Tolleson	.08	.06	.03
379	Floyd Bannister	.12	.09	.05
380	Vern Ruhle	.08	.06	.03
381	Tim Corcoran	.08	.06	.03
382	Kurt Kepshire	.08	.06	.03
383	Bobby Brown	.08	.06	.03
384	Dave Van Gorder	.08	.06	.03
385	Rick Mahler	.08	.06	.03
386	Lee Mazzilli	.10	.08	.04
387	Bill Laskey	.08	.06	.03
388	Thad Bosley	.08	.06	.03
389	Al Chambers	.08	.06	.03
390	Tony Fernandez	.70	.50	.30
391	Ron Washington	.08	.06	.03
392	Bill Swaggerty	.08	.06	.03
393	Bob L. Gibson	.08	.06	.03
394	Marty Castillo	.08	.06	.03
395	Steve Crawford	.08	.06	.03
396	Clay Christiansen	.08	.06	.03
397	Bob Bailor	.08	.06	.03
398	Mike Hargrove	.08	.06	.03
399	Charlie Leibrandt	.10	.08	.04
400	Tom Burgmeier	.08	.06	.03
401	Razor Shines	.08	.06	.03
402	Rob Wilfong	.08	.06	.03
403	Tom Henke	.12	.09	.05
404	Al Jones	.08	.06	.03
405	Mike LaCoss	.08	.06	.03
406	Luis DeLeon	.08	.06	.03
407	Greg Gross	.08	.06	.03
408	Tom Hume	.08	.06	.03
409	Rick Camp	.08	.06	.03
410	Milt May	.08	.06	.03
411	*Henry Cotto* (FC)	.20	.15	.08
412	Dave Von Ohlen	.08	.06	.03
413	Scott McGregor	.10	.08	.04
414	Ted Simmons	.15	.11	.06
415	Jack Morris	.30	.25	.12
416	Bill Buckner	.15	.11	.06
417	Butch Wynegar	.08	.06	.03
418	Steve Sax	.25	.20	.10
419	Steve Balboni	.10	.08	.04
420	Dwayne Murphy	.10	.08	.04
421	Andre Dawson	1.75	1.25	.70
422	Charlie Hough	.10	.08	.04
423	Tommy John	.25	.20	.10
424a	Tom Seaver (Floyd Bannister photo, left-hander)	3.00	2.25	1.25
424b	Tom Seaver (correct photo)	30.00	22.00	12.00
425	Tom Herr	.12	.09	.05
426	Terry Puhl	.08	.06	.03
427	Al Holland	.08	.06	.03
428	Eddie Milner	.08	.06	.03
429	Terry Kennedy	.10	.08	.04
430	John Candelaria	.12	.09	.05
431	Manny Trillo	.10	.08	.04
432	Ken Oberkfell	.08	.06	.03
433	Rick Sutcliffe	.15	.11	.06
434	Ron Darling	.40	.30	.15
435	Spike Owen	.10	.08	.04
436	Frank Viola	.25	.20	.10
437	Lloyd Moseby	.12	.09	.05
438	*Kirby Puckett* (FC)	55.00	41.00	22.00
439	Jim Clancy	.10	.08	.04
440	Mike Moore	.08	.06	.03
441	Doug Sisk	.08	.06	.03
442	Dennis Eckersley	1.50	1.25	.60
443	Gerald Perry	.25	.20	.10
444	Dale Berra	.08	.06	.03
445	Dusty Baker	.10	.08	.04
446	Ed Whitson	.08	.06	.03
447	Cesar Cedeno	.12	.09	.05
448	*Rick Schu* (FC)	.08	.06	.03
449	Joaquin Andujar	.10	.08	.04
450	*Mark Bailey* (FC)	.12	.09	.05
451	*Ron Romanick* (FC)	.12	.09	.05
452	Julio Cruz	.08	.06	.03
453	Miguel Dilone	.08	.06	.03
454	Storm Davis	.12	.09	.05
455	Jaime Cocanower	.08	.06	.03
456	Barbaro Garbey	.12	.09	.05
457	Rich Gedman	.12	.09	.05
458	Phil Niekro	.30	.25	.12
459	Mike Scioscia	.10	.08	.04
460	Pat Tabler	.10	.08	.04
461	Darryl Motley	.08	.06	.03
462	Chris Codoroli (Codiroli)	.08	.06	.03
463	Doug Flynn	.08	.06	.03
464	Billy Sample	.08	.06	.03
465	Mickey Rivers	.10	.08	.04
466	John Wathan	.10	.08	.04
467	Bill Krueger	.08	.06	.03
468	Andre Thornton	.12	.09	.05
469	Rex Hudler	.12	.09	.05
470	*Sid Bream* (FC)	.80	.60	.30
471	Kirk Gibson	.40	.30	.15
472	John Shelby	.10	.08	.04
473	Moose Haas	.08	.06	.03
474	Doug Corbett	.08	.06	.03
475	Willie McGee	.35	.25	.14
476	Bob Knepper	.10	.08	.04
477	Kevin Gross	.12	.09	.05
478	Carmelo Martinez	.10	.08	.04
479	Kent Tekulve	.10	.08	.04
480	Chili Davis	.12	.09	.05
481	Bobby Clark	.08	.06	.03
482	Mookie Wilson	.12	.09	.05
483	Dave Owen	.08	.06	.03
484	Ed Nunez	.08	.06	.03
485	Rance Mulliniks	.08	.06	.03
486	Ken Schrom	.08	.06	.03
487	Jeff Russell	.08	.06	.03
488	Tom Paciorek	.08	.06	.03
489	Dan Ford	.08	.06	.03
490	Mike Caldwell	.08	.06	.03
491	Scottie Earl	.08	.06	.03
492	*Jose Rijo* (FC)	2.00	1.50	.80
493	Bruce Hurst	.15	.11	.06
494	Ken Landreaux	.08	.06	.03
495	Mike Fischlin	.08	.06	.03
496	Don Slaught	.08	.06	.03
497	Steve McCatty	.08	.06	.03
498	Gary Lucas	.08	.06	.03
499	Gary Pettis	.10	.08	.04
500	Marvis Foley	.08	.06	.03
501	Mike Squires	.08	.06	.03
502	*Jim Pankovitz* (FC)	.15	.11	.06
503	Luis Aguayo	.08	.06	.03
504	Ralph Citarella	.08	.06	.03
505	Bruce Bochy	.08	.06	.03
506	Bob Owchinko	.08	.06	.03
507	Pascual Perez	.10	.08	.04
508	Lee Lacy	.08	.06	.03
509	Atlee Hammaker	.08	.06	.03
510	Bob Dernier	.08	.06	.03
511	Ed Vande Berg	.08	.06	.03
512	Cliff Johnson	.08	.06	.03
513	Len Whitehouse	.08	.06	.03
514	Dennis Martinez	.10	.08	.04
515	Ed Romero	.08	.06	.03
516	Rusty Kuntz	.08	.06	.03
517	Rick Miller	.08	.06	.03
518	Dennis Rasmussen	.15	.11	.06
519	Steve Yeager	.08	.06	.03
520	Chris Bando	.08	.06	.03
521	U.L. Washington	.08	.06	.03
522	*Curt Young* (FC)	.15	.11	.06
523	Angel Salazar	.08	.06	.03
524	Curt Kaufman	.08	.06	.03
525	Odell Jones	.08	.06	.03
526	Juan Agosto	.08	.06	.03
527	Denny Walling	.08	.06	.03
528	Andy Hawkins (FC)	.20	.15	.08
529	Sixto Lezcano	.08	.06	.03
530	Skeeter Barnes	.08	.06	.03
531	Randy S. Johnson	.08	.06	.03
532	Jim Morrison	.08	.06	.03
533	Warren Brusstar	.08	.06	.03
534 a	*Jeff Pendleton* (error)	8.00	6.00	3.25
534b	*Terry Pendleton* (correct)	20.00	15.00	8.00
535	Vic Rodriguez	.08	.06	.03
536	Bob McClure	.08	.06	.03
537	Dave Bergman	.08	.06	.03
538	Mark Clear	.08	.06	.03
539	*Mike Pagliarulo* (FC)	1.00	.70	.40
540	Terry Whitfield	.08	.06	.03
541	Joe Beckwith	.08	.06	.03
542	Jeff Burroughs	.10	.08	.04
543	Dan Schatzeder	.08	.06	.03
544	Donnie Scott	.08	.06	.03
545	Jim Slaton	.08	.06	.03
546	Greg Luzinski	.12	.09	.05
547	*Mark Salas* (FC)	.08	.06	.03
548	Dave Smith	.10	.08	.04

No.	Player	MT	NR MT	EX
549	John Wockenfuss	.08	.06	.03
550	Frank Pastore	.08	.06	.03
551	Tim Flannery	.08	.06	.03
552	Rick Rhoden	.12	.09	.05
553	Mark Davis	.08	.06	.03
554	*Jeff Dedmon* (FC)	.15	.11	.06
555	Gary Woods	.08	.06	.03
556	Danny Heep	.08	.06	.03
557	*Mark Langston* (FC)	5.00	3.75	2.00
558	Darrell Brown	.08	.06	.03
559	*Jimmy Key*	5.00	3.75	2.00
560	Rick Lysander	.08	.06	.03
561	Doyle Alexander	.12	.09	.05
562	Mike Stanton	.08	.06	.03
563	Sid Fernandez	.50	.40	.20
564	Richie Hebner	.08	.06	.03
565	Alex Trevino	.08	.06	.03
566	Brian Harper	.08	.06	.03
567	*Dan Gladden* (FC)	.60	.45	.25
568	Luis Salazar	.08	.06	.03
569	Tom Foley	.08	.06	.03
570	Larry Andersen	.08	.06	.03
571	Danny Cox	.12	.09	.05
572	Joe Sambito	.08	.06	.03
573	Juan Beniquez	.08	.06	.03
574	Joel Skinner	.08	.06	.03
575	*Randy St. Claire* (FC)	.15	.11	.06
576	Floyd Rayford	.08	.06	.03
577	Roy Howell	.08	.06	.03
578	John Grubb	.08	.06	.03
579	Ed Jurak	.08	.06	.03
580	John Montefusco	.08	.06	.03
581	*Orel Hershiser*	2.50	2.00	1.00
582	*Tom Waddell* (FC)	.08	.06	.03
583	Mark Huismann	.08	.06	.03
584	Joe Morgan	.25	.20	.10
585	Jim Wohlford	.08	.06	.03
586	Dave Schmidt	.08	.06	.03
587	*Jeff Kunkel* (FC)	.12	.09	.05
588	Hal McRae	.12	.09	.05
589	Bill Almon	.08	.06	.03
590	Carmen Castillo (FC)	.10	.08	.04
591	Omar Moreno	.08	.06	.03
592	*Ken Howell* (FC)	.20	.15	.08
593	Tom Brookens	.08	.06	.03
594	Joe Nolan	.08	.06	.03
595	Willie Lozado	.08	.06	.03
596	*Tom Nieto* (FC)	.12	.09	.05
597	Walt Terrell	.10	.08	.04
598	Al Oliver	.15	.11	.06
599	Shane Rawley	.12	.09	.05
600	*Denny Gonzalez* (FC)	.10	.08	.04
601	*Mark Grant* (FC)	.15	.11	.06
602	Mike Armstrong	.08	.06	.03
603	George Foster	.15	.11	.06
604	Davey Lopes	.10	.08	.04
605	Salome Barojas	.08	.06	.03
606	Roy Lee Jackson	.08	.06	.03
607	Pete Filson	.08	.06	.03
608	Duane Walker	.08	.06	.03
609	Glenn Wilson	.10	.08	.04
610	*Rafael Santana* (FC)	.08	.06	.03
611	Roy Smith	.08	.06	.03
612	Ruppert Jones	.08	.06	.03
613	Joe Cowley (FC)	.08	.06	.03
614	*Al Nipper* (FC) (photo actually Mike Brown)	.20	.15	.08
615	Gene Nelson	.08	.06	.03
616	Joe Carter	13.00	9.75	5.25
617	Ray Knight	.12	.09	.05
618	Chuck Rainey	.08	.06	.03
619	Dan Driessen	.10	.08	.04
620	Daryl Sconiers	.08	.06	.03
621	Bill Stein	.08	.06	.03
622	Roy Smalley	.08	.06	.03
623	Ed Lynch	.08	.06	.03
624	*Jeff Stone* (FC)	.15	.11	.06
625	Bruce Berenyi	.08	.06	.03
626	Kelvin Chapman	.08	.06	.03
627	Joe Price	.08	.06	.03
628	Steve Bedrosian	.12	.09	.05
629	Vic Mata	.08	.06	.03
630	Mike Krukow	.10	.08	.04
631	*Phil Bradley* (FC)	.20	.15	.08
632	Jim Gott	.08	.06	.03
633	Randy Bush	.08	.06	.03
634	*Tom Browning* (FC)	.60	.45	.25
635	Lou Gehrig Puzzle Card	.08	.06	.03
636	Reid Nichols	.08	.06	.03
637	*Dan Pasqua* (FC)	.60	.45	.25
638	German Rivera	.08	.06	.03
639	*Don Schulze* (FC)	.10	.08	.04
640a	Mike Jones (last line of highlights begins "Was 11-7...")	.10	.08	.04
640b	Mike Jones (last line of highlights begins "Spent some ...")	1.25	.90	.50
641	Pete Rose	2.00	1.50	.80
642	*Wade Rowdon* (FC)	.10	.08	.04
643	Jerry Narron	.08	.06	.03
644	*Darrell Miller* (FC)	.08	.06	.03
645	*Tim Hulett* (FC)	.08	.06	.03
646	Andy McGaffigan	.08	.06	.03
647	Kurt Bevacqua	.08	.06	.03
648	*John Russell* (FC)	.20	.15	.08
649	*Ron Robinson* (FC)	.25	.20	.10
650	Donnie Moore (FC)	.08	.06	.03
651a	Two for the Title (Don Mattingly) (Dave Winfield) (yellow letters)	3.00	2.25	1.25
651b	Two for the Title (Don Mattingly) (Dave Winfield) (white letters)	6.00	4.50	2.50
652	Tim Laudner	.08	.06	.03
653	*Steve Farr* (FC)	.40	.30	.15
----	Checklist 1-26 DK	.08	.06	.03
----	Checklist 27-130	.08	.06	.03
----	Checklist 131-234	.08	.06	.03
----	Checklist 235-338	.08	.06	.03
----	Checklist 339-442	.08	.06	.03
----	Checklist 443-546	.08	.06	.03
----	Checklist 547-653	.08	.06	.03

1985 Donruss Action All-Stars

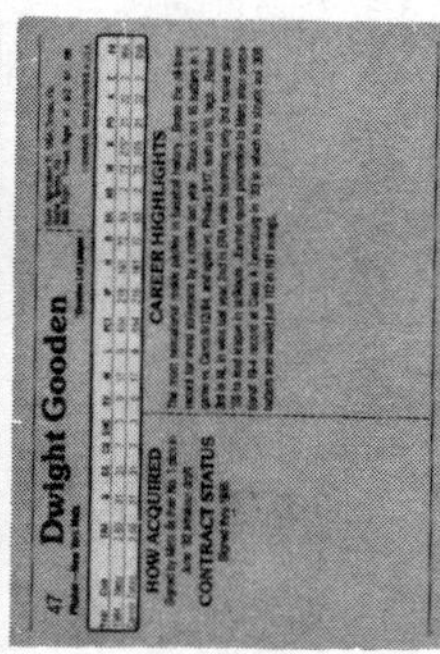

In 1985, Donruss issued an Action All-Stars set for the third consecutive year. The card fronts feature an action photo with an inset head-shot of the player inside a black border with grey boxes through it. The card backs have black print on blue and white and include statistical and biographical information. The cards were issued with a Lou Gehrig puzzle.

		MT	NR MT	EX
Complete Set:		8.00	6.00	3.25
Common Player:		.15	.11	.06
1	Tim Raines	.25	.20	.10
2	Jim Gantner	.15	.11	.06
3	Mario Soto	.15	.11	.06
4	Spike Owen	.15	.11	.06
5	Lloyd Moseby	.15	.11	.06
6	Damaso Garcia	.15	.11	.06
7	Cal Ripken, Jr.	2.00	1.50	.80
8	Dan Quisenberry	.15	.11	.06
9	Eddie Murray	.50	.40	.20
10	Tony Pena	.15	.11	.06
11	Buddy Bell	.15	.11	.06
12	Dave Winfield	.65	.50	.25
13	Ron Kittle	.15	.11	.06
14	Rich Gossage	.15	.11	.06
15	Dwight Evans	.15	.11	.06
16	Al Davis	.15	.11	.06
17	Mike Schmidt	1.00	.70	.40
18	Pascual Perez	.15	.11	.06
19	Tony Gwynn	.50	.40	.20
20	Nolan Ryan	3.00	2.25	1.25
21	Robin Yount	1.00	.70	.40
22	Mike Marshall	.15	.11	.06
23	Brett Butler	.15	.11	.06
24	Ryne Sandberg	2.00	1.50	.80
25	Dale Murphy	.40	.30	.15
26	George Brett	1.00	.70	.40
27	Jim Rice	.15	.11	.06
28	Ozzie Smith	.40	.30	.15
29	Larry Parrish	.15	.11	.06
30	Jack Clark	.15	.11	.06
31	Manny Trillo	.15	.11	.06
32	Dave Kingman	.15	.11	.06
33	Geoff Zahn	.15	.11	.06
34	Pedro Guerrero	.15	.11	.06
35	Dave Parker	.20	.15	.08
36	Rollie Fingers	.25	.20	.10
37	Fernando Valenzuela	.12	.09	.05
38	Wade Boggs	.60	.45	.25
39	Reggie Jackson	.60	.45	.25
40	Kent Hrbek	.20	.15	.08
41	Keith Hernandez	.15	.11	.06
42	Lou Whitaker	.15	.11	.06
43	Tom Herr	.15	.11	.06
44	Alan Trammell	.20	.15	.08
45	Butch Wynegar	.15	.11	.06
46	Leon Durham	.15	.11	.06
47	Dwight Gooden	.80	.60	.30
48	Don Mattingly	1.00	.70	.40
49	Phil Niekro	.20	.15	.08
50	Johnny Ray	.15	.11	.06
51	Doug DeCinces	.15	.11	.06
52	Willie Upshaw	.15	.11	.06
53	Lance Parrish	.15	.11	.06
54	Jody Davis	.15	.11	.06
55	Steve Carlton	.50	.40	.20
56	Juan Samuel	.15	.11	.06
57	Gary Carter	.25	.20	.10
58	Harold Baines	.15	.11	.06
59	Eric Show	.15	.11	.06
60	Checklist	.15	.11	.06

Values quoted in this guide reflect the retail price of a card – the price a collector can expect to pay when buying a card from a dealer. The wholesale price – that which a collector can expect to receive from a dealer when selling cards – will be significantly lower, depending on desirability and condition.

1985 Donruss Box Panels

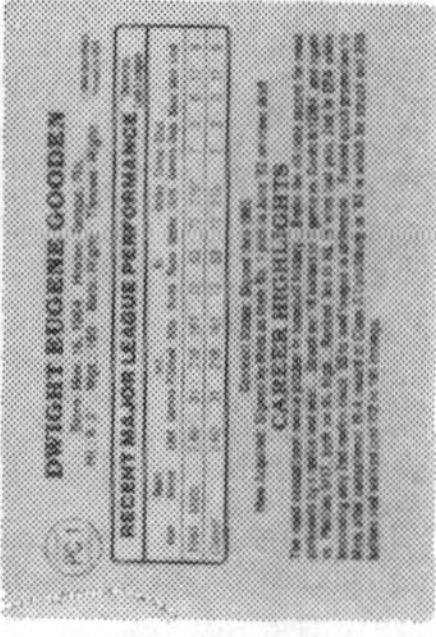

In 1985, Donruss placed on the bottoms of their wax pack boxes a four-card panel which included three player cards and a Lou Gehrig puzzle card. The player cards, numbered PC 1 through PC 3, have backs identical to the regular 1985 Donruss issue. The card fronts are identical in design to the regular issue, but carry different picture poses.

		MT	NR MT	EX
Complete Panel Set:		6.00	5.25	2.75
Complete Singles Set:		5.00	3.75	2.00
Common Single Player:		.10	.08	.04
	Panel	6.00	5.25	2.75
1	Dwight Gooden	2.00	1.50	.80
2	Ryne Sandberg	3.00	2.25	1.25
3	Ron Kittle	.10	.08	.04
----	Lou Gehrig Puzzle Card	.05	.04	.02

1985 Donruss Diamond Kings Supers

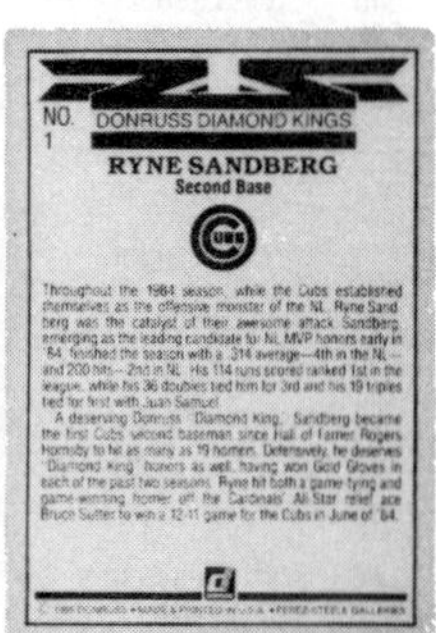

The 1985 Donruss Diamond Kings Supers are enlarged versions of the Diamond Kings card (#'s 1-26) in the regular 1985 Donruss set. The cards measure 4-15/16" by 6-3/4". The Diamond Kings series features the artwork of Dick Perez. Twenty-eight cards make up the set - 26 DK cards, an unnumbered checklist, and an unnumbered Dick Perez card. The back of the Perez card contains a brief history of Dick Perez and the Perez-Steele Galleries. The set could be obtained through a write-in offer found on the wrappers of the regular issue wax packs.

		MT	NR MT	EX
Complete Set:		15.00	11.00	6.00
Common Player:		.25	.20	.10
1	Ryne Sandberg	4.00	3.00	1.50
2	Doug DeCinces	.25	.20	.10
3	Richard Dotson	.25	.20	.10
4	Bert Blyleven	.25	.20	.10
5	Lou Whitaker	.30	.25	.12
6	Dan Quisenberry	.25	.20	.10
7	Don Mattingly	3.00	2.25	1.25
8	Carney Lansford	.25	.20	.10
9	Frank Tanana	.25	.20	.10
10	Willie Upshaw	.25	.20	.10
11	Claudell Washington	.25	.20	.10
12	Mike Marshall	.25	.20	.10
13	Joaquin Andujar	.25	.20	.10
14	Cal Ripken, Jr.	4.00	3.00	1.50
15	Jim Rice	.35	.25	.14
16	Don Sutton	.30	.25	.12
17	Frank Viola	.35	.25	.14
18	Alvin Davis	.25	.20	.10
19	Mario Soto	.25	.20	.10
20	Jose Cruz	.25	.20	.10
21	Charlie Lea	.25	.20	.10
22	Jesse Orosco	.25	.20	.10
23	Juan Samuel	.25	.20	.10
24	Tony Pena	.25	.20	.10
25	Tony Gwynn	.40	.30	.15
26	Bob Brenly	.25	.20	.10
----	Checklist, Dick Perez (DK artist)	.25	.09	.05

1985 Donruss Highlights

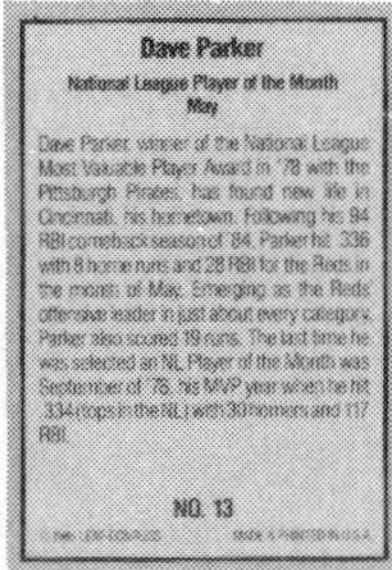

Designed in the style of the regular 1985 Donruss set, this issue features the Player of the Month in the major leagues plus highlight cards of special baseball events and milestones that occurred during the 1985 season. Fifty-six cards, including an unnumbered checklist, comprise the set which was available only through hobby dealers. The cards measure 2-1/2" by 3-1/2" and have glossy fronts. The last two cards in the set feature Donruss' picks for the A.L. and N.L. Rookies of the Year. The set was issued in a specially designed box.

		MT	NR MT	EX
	Complete Set:	26.00	19.50	10.50
	Common Player:	.12	.09	.05
1	Sets Opening Day Record (Tom Seaver)	.40	.30	.15
2	Establishes A.L. Save Mark (Rollie Fingers)	.15	.11	.06
3	A.L. Player of the Month - April (Mike Davis)	.12	.09	.05
4	A.L. Pitcher of the Month - April (Charlie Leibrandt)	.12	.09	.05
5	N.L. Player of the Month - April (Dale Murphy)	.40	.30	.15
6	N.L. Pitcher of the Month - April (Fernando Valenzuela)	.12	.09	.05
7	N.L. Shortstop Record (Larry Bowa)	.12	.09	.05
8	Joins Reds 2000 Hit Club (Dave Concepcion)	.12	.09	.05
9	Eldest Grand Slammer (Tony Perez)	.15	.11	.06
10	N.L. Career Run Leader (Pete Rose)	.90	.70	.35
11	A.L. Player of the Month - May (George Brett)	.90	.70	.35
12	A.L. Pitcher of the Month - May (Dave Stieb)	.12	.09	.05
13	N.L. Player of the Month - May (Dave Parker)	.20	.15	.08
14	N.L. Pitcher of the Month - May (Andy Hawkins)	.12	.09	.05
15	Records 11th Straight Win (Andy Hawkins)	.12	.09	.05
16	Two Homers In First Inning (Von Hayes)	.15	.11	.06
17	A.L. Player of the Month - June (Rickey Henderson)	.75	.60	.30
18	A.L. Pitcher of the Month - June (Jay Howell)	.12	.09	.05
19	N.L. Player of the Month - June (Pedro Guerrero)	.20	.15	.08
20	N.L. Pitcher of the Month - June (John Tudor)	.12	.09	.05
21	Marathon Game Iron Men (Gary Carter, Keith Hernandez)	.35	.25	.14
22	Records 4000th K (Nolan Ryan)	1.50	1.25	.60
23	All-Star Game MVP (LaMarr Hoyt)	.12	.09	.05
24	1st Ranger To Hit For Cycle (Oddibe McDowell)	.40	.30	.15
25	A.L. Player of the Month - July (George Brett)	.90	.70	.35
26	A.L. Pitcher of the Month - July (Bret Saberhagen)	.35	.25	.14
27	N.L. Player of the Month - July (Keith Hernandez)	.35	.25	.14
28	N.L. Pitcher of the Month - July (Fernando Valenzuela)	.12	.09	.05
29	Record Setting Base Stealers (Vince Coleman, Willie McGee)	.40	.30	.15
30	Notches 300th Career Win (Tom Seaver)	.35	.25	.14
31	Strokes 3000th Hit (Rod Carew)	.40	.30	.15
32	Establishes Met Record (Dwight Gooden)	.85	.60	.35
33	Achieves Strikeout Milestone (Dwight Gooden)	.85	.60	.35
34	Explodes For 9 RBI (Eddie Murray)	.40	.30	.15
35	A.L. Career Hbp Leader (Don Baylor)	.15	.11	.06
36	A.L. Player of the Month - August (Don Mattingly)	2.50	2.00	1.00
37	A.L. Pitcher of the Month - August (Dave Righetti)	.20	.15	.08
38	N.L. Player of the Month (Willie McGee)	.20	.15	.08
39	N.L. Pitcher of the Month - August (Shane Rawley)	.12	.09	.05
40	Ty-Breaking Hit (Pete Rose)	.90	.70	.35
41	Hits 3 Hrs Drives In 8 Runs (Andre Dawson)	.20	.15	.08
42	Sets Yankee Theft Mark (Rickey Henderson)	.75	.60	.30
43	20 Wins In Rookie Season (Tom Browning)	.35	.25	.14
44	Yankee Milestone For Hits (Don Mattingly)	2.50	2.00	1.00
45	A.L. Player of the Month - September (Don Mattingly)	2.50	2.00	1.00
46	A.L. Pitcher of the Month - September (Charlie Leibrandt)	.12	.09	.05
47	N.L. Player of the Month - September (Gary Carter)	.12	.09	.05
48	N.L. Pitcher of the Month - September (Dwight Gooden)	.85	.60	.35
49	Major League Record Setter (Wade Boggs)	2.00	1.50	.80
50	Hurls Shutout For 300th Win (Phil Niekro)	.30	.25	.12
51	Venerable HR King (Darrell Evans)	.15	.11	.06
52	N.L. Switch-hitting Record (Willie McGee)	.20	.15	.08
53	Equals DiMaggio Feat (Dave Winfield)	.45	.35	.20
54	Donruss N.L. Rookie of the Year (Vince Coleman)	1.50	1.25	.60
55	Donruss A.L. Rookie of the Year (Ozzie Guillen)	.50	.40	.20
----	Checklist	.20	.15	.08

1985 Donruss Sluggers of The Hall of Fame

In much the same manner as the first Bazooka cards were issued in 1959, this eight-player set from Donruss consists of cards which formed the bottom panel of a box of bubble gum. When cut off the box, cards measure 3-1/2" by 6-1/2", with blank backs. Players are pictured on the cards in paintings done by Dick Perez.

		MT	NR MT	EX
	Complete Set:	12.00	9.00	4.75
	Common Player:	.60	.45	.25
1	Babe Ruth	2.00	1.50	.80
2	Ted Williams	1.00	.70	.40
3	Lou Gehrig	1.75	1.25	.70
4	Johnny Mize	.60	.45	.25
5	Stan Musial	1.00	.70	.40
6	Mickey Mantle	3.00	2.25	1.25
7	Hank Aaron	2.00	1.50	.80
8	Frank Robinson	.90	.70	.35

1986 Donruss

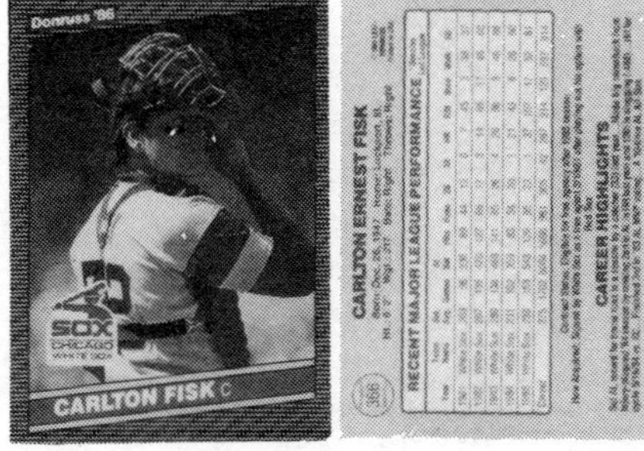

In 1986, Donruss issued a 660-card set which included 653 numbered cards and seven unnumbered checklists. The cards, which measure 2-1/2" by 3-1/2", have fronts that feature blue borders and backs that have black print on blue and white. For the fifth year in a row, the first 26 cards in the set are Diamond Kings. The Rated Rookies subset (card #'s 27-46) appears once again. The cards were distributed with a Hank Aaron puzzle. The complete set price does not include the higher priced variations. In the checklist that follows, (DK) and (RR) refer to the Diamond Kings and Rated Rookies series.

		MT	NR MT	EX
	Complete Set (660):	175.00	131.00	70.00
	Common Player:	.06	.05	.02
1	Kirk Gibson (DK)	.15	.11	.06
2	Goose Gossage (DK)	.20	.15	.08
3	Willie McGee (DK)	.15	.11	.06
4	George Bell (DK)	.15	.11	.06
5	Tony Armas (DK)	.10	.08	.04
6	Chili Davis (DK)	.10	.08	.04
7	Cecil Cooper (DK)	.12	.09	.05
8	Mike Boddicker (DK)	.10	.08	.04
9	Davey Lopes (DK)	.10	.08	.04
10	Bill Doran (DK)	.12	.09	.05
11	Bret Saberhagen (DK)	.25	.20	.10
12	Brett Butler (DK)	.10	.08	.04
13	Harold Baines (DK)	.15	.11	.06
14	Mike Davis (DK)	.10	.08	.04
15	Tony Perez (DK)	.15	.11	.06
16	Willie Randolph (DK)	.12	.09	.05
17	Bob Boone (DK)	.10	.08	.04
18	Orel Hershiser (DK)	.20	.15	.08
19	Johnny Ray (DK)	.12	.09	.05
20	Gary Ward (DK)	.10	.08	.04
21	Rick Mahler (DK)	.08	.06	.03
22	Phil Bradley (DK)	.10	.08	.04
23	Jerry Koosman (DK)	.12	.09	.05
24	Tom Brunansky (DK)	.15	.11	.06
25	Andre Dawson (DK)	.40	.30	.15
26	Dwight Gooden (DK)	.35	.25	.14
27	*Kal Daniels* (RR)	.15	.11	.06
28	*Fred McGriff* (RR)	35.00	26.00	14.00
29	*Cory Snyder* (RR)	.40	.30	.15
30	*Jose Guzman* (RR)	.75	.60	.30
31	*Ty Gainey* (FC) (RR)	.10	.08	.04
32	*Johnny Abrego* (FC) (RR)	.06	.05	.02
33a	*Andres Galarraga* (RR) (accent mark over e of Andres on back)	6.00	4.50	2.50
33b	*Andres Galarraga* (RR) (no accent mark)	6.00	4.50	2.50
34	*Dave Shipanoff* (FC) (RR)	.06	.05	.02
35	*Mark McLemore* (RR)	.40	.30	.15
36	*Marty Clary* (FC) (RR)	.08	.06	.03
37	*Paul O'Neill* (RR)	3.00	2.25	1.25
38	Danny Tartabull (RR)	1.75	1.25	.70
39	*Jose Canseco* (RR)	30.00	22.00	12.00
40	*Juan Nieves* (FC) (RR)	.10	.08	.04
41	*Lance McCullers* (FC) (RR)	.35	.25	.14
42	*Rick Surhoff* (FC) (RR)	.08	.06	.03
43	*Todd Worrell* (RR)	.40	.30	.15
44	Bob Kipper (FC) (RR)	.20	.15	.08
45	*John Habyan* (FC) (RR)	.15	.11	.06
46	*Mike Woodard* (FC) (RR)	.06	.05	.02
47	Mike Boddicker	.10	.08	.04
48	Robin Yount	2.00	1.50	.80
49	Lou Whitaker	.30	.25	.12
50	Dennis Boyd	.08	.06	.03
51	Rickey Henderson	2.00	1.50	.80
52	Mike Marshall	.15	.11	.06
53	George Brett	2.50	2.00	1.00
54	Dave Kingman	.15	.11	.06
55	Hubie Brooks	.10	.08	.04
56	*Oddibe McDowell* (FC)	.10	.08	.04
57	Doug DeCinces	.10	.08	.04
58	Britt Burns	.06	.05	.02
59	Ozzie Smith	1.00	.70	.40
60	Jose Cruz	.10	.08	.04
61	Mike Schmidt	2.00	1.50	.80
62	Pete Rose	1.00	.70	.40
63	Steve Garvey	.30	.25	.12
64	Tony Pena	.10	.08	.04
65	Chili Davis	.10	.08	.04
66	Dale Murphy	.35	.25	.14
67	Ryne Sandberg	4.50	3.50	1.75
68	Gary Carter	.35	.25	.14
69	Alvin Davis	.15	.11	.06
70	Kent Hrbek	.25	.20	.10
71	George Bell	.15	.11	.06
72	Kirby Puckett	10.00	7.50	4.00
73	Lloyd Moseby	.10	.08	.04
74	Bob Kearney	.06	.05	.02
75	Dwight Gooden	.80	.60	.30
76	Gary Matthews	.10	.08	.04
77	Rick Mahler	.06	.05	.02
78	Benny Distefano	.06	.05	.02
79	Jeff Leonard	.08	.06	.03
80	Kevin McReynolds	.30	.25	.12
81	Ron Oester	.06	.05	.02
82	John Russell	.06	.05	.02
83	Tommy Herr	.10	.08	.04
84	Jerry Mumphrey	.06	.05	.02
85	Ron Romanick	.06	.05	.02
86	Daryl Boston	.08	.06	.03
87	Andre Dawson	1.00	.70	.40
88	Eddie Murray	1.00	.70	.40
89	Dion James	.08	.06	.03
90	Chet Lemon	.08	.06	.03
91	Bob Stanley	.06	.05	.02
92	Willie Randolph	.10	.08	.04
93	Mike Scioscia	.08	.06	.03
94	Tom Waddell	.06	.05	.02
95	Danny Jackson	.30	.25	.12
96	Mike Davis	.08	.06	.03

97 Mike Fitzgerald .06 .05 .02
98 Gary Ward .08 .06 .03
99 Pete O'Brien .10 .08 .04
100 Bret Saberhagen .60 .45 .25
101 Alfredo Griffin .08 .06 .03
102 Brett Butler .08 .06 .03
103 Ron Guidry .12 .09 .05
104 Jerry Reuss .08 .06 .03
105 Jack Morris .25 .20 .10
106 Rick Dempsey .08 .06 .03
107 Ray Burris .06 .05 .02
108 Brian Downing .10 .08 .04
109 Willie McGee .15 .11 .06
110 Bill Doran .10 .08 .04
111 Kent Tekulve .08 .06 .03
112 Tony Gwynn 2.00 1.50 .80
113 Marvell Wynne .06 .05 .02
114 David Green .06 .05 .02
115 Jim Gantner .08 .06 .03
116 George Foster .15 .11 .06
117 Steve Trout .06 .05 .02
118 Mark Langston .30 .25 .12
119 Tony Fernandez .20 .15 .08
120 John Butcher .06 .05 .02
121 Ron Robinson .08 .06 .03
122 Dan Spillner .06 .05 .02
123 Mike Young .06 .05 .02
124 Paul Molitor 2.00 1.50 .80
125 Kirk Gibson .35 .25 .14
126 Ken Griffey .12 .09 .05
127 Tony Armas .08 .06 .03
128 *Mariano Duncan* (FC) .15 .11 .06
129 Mr. Clutch (Pat Tabler) .08 .06 .03
130 Frank White .10 .08 .04
131 Carney Lansford .10 .08 .04
132 Vance Law .08 .06 .03
133 Dick Schofield .06 .05 .02
134 Wayne Tolleson .06 .05 .02
135 Greg Walker .10 .08 .04
136 Denny Walling .06 .05 .02
137 Ozzie Virgil .06 .05 .02
138 Ricky Horton .08 .06 .03
139 LaMarr Hoyt .06 .05 .02
140 Wayne Krenchicki .06 .05 .02
141 Glenn Hubbard .06 .05 .02
142 Cecilio Guante .06 .05 .02
143 Mike Krukow .08 .06 .03
144 Lee Smith .10 .08 .04
145 Edwin Nunez .06 .05 .02
146 Dave Stieb .12 .09 .05
147 Mike Smithson .06 .05 .02
148 Ken Dixon .06 .05 .02
149 Danny Darwin .06 .05 .02
150 Chris Pittaro .06 .05 .02
151 Bill Buckner .12 .09 .05
152 Mike Pagliarulo .20 .15 .08
153 Bill Russell .08 .06 .03
154 Brook Jacoby .10 .08 .04
155 Pat Sheridan .06 .05 .02
156 *Mike Gallego* (FC) .15 .11 .06
157 Jim Wohlford .06 .05 .02
158 Gary Pettis .06 .05 .02
159 Toby Harrah .08 .06 .03
160 Richard Dotson .10 .08 .04
161 Bob Knepper .08 .06 .03
162 Dave Dravecky .08 .06 .03
163 Greg Gross .06 .05 .02
164 Eric Davis 1.50 1.25 .60
165 Gerald Perry .15 .11 .06
166 Rick Rhoden .10 .08 .04
167 Keith Moreland .08 .06 .03
168 Jack Clark .20 .15 .08
169 Storm Davis .10 .08 .04
170 Cecil Cooper .12 .09 .05
171 Alan Trammell .35 .25 .14
172 Roger Clemens 8.00 6.00 3.25
173 Don Mattingly 3.50 2.75 1.50
174 Pedro Guerrero .20 .15 .08
175 Willie Wilson .12 .09 .05
176 Dwayne Murphy .08 .06 .03
177 Tim Raines .40 .30 .15
178 Larry Parrish .10 .08 .04
179 Mike Witt .10 .08 .04
180 Harold Baines .15 .11 .06
181 *Vince Coleman* .35 .25 .14
182 *Jeff Heathcock* (FC) .10 .08 .04
183 Steve Carlton .60 .45 .25
184 Mario Soto .08 .06 .03
185 Goose Gossage .20 .15 .08
186 Johnny Ray .12 .09 .05
187 Dan Gladden .08 .06 .03
188 Bob Horner .12 .09 .05
189 Rick Sutcliffe .12 .09 .05
190 Keith Hernandez .20 .15 .08
191 Phil Bradley .20 .15 .08
192 Tom Brunansky .12 .09 .05
193 Jesse Barfield .20 .15 .08
194 Frank Viola .20 .15 .08
195 Willie Upshaw .08 .06 .03
196 Jim Beattie .06 .05 .02
197 Darryl Strawberry .75 .60 .30
198 Ron Cey .10 .08 .04
199 Steve Bedrosian .12 .09 .05
200 Steve Kemp .08 .06 .03
201 Manny Trillo .08 .06 .03
202 Garry Templeton .08 .06 .03
203 Dave Parker .25 .20 .10
204 John Denny .06 .05 .02
205 Terry Pendleton .15 .11 .06
206 Terry Puhl .06 .05 .02
207 Bobby Grich .10 .08 .04
208 *Ozzie Guillen* (FC) .90 .70 .35
209 Jeff Reardon .12 .09 .05
210 Cal Ripken, Jr. 5.00 3.75 2.00
211 Bill Schroeder .06 .05 .02
212 Dan Petry .08 .06 .03
213 Jim Rice .20 .15 .08
214 Dave Righetti .20 .15 .08
215 Fernando Valenzuela .35 .25 .14
216 Julio Franco .30 .25 .12
217 Darryl Motley .06 .05 .02
218 Dave Collins .08 .06 .03
219 Tim Wallach .12 .09 .05
220 George Wright .06 .05 .02
221 Tommy Dunbar .06 .05 .02
222 Steve Balboni .08 .06 .03
223 Jay Howell .08 .06 .03
224 Joe Carter 5.00 3.75 2.00
225 Ed Whitson .06 .05 .02
226 Orel Hershiser .30 .25 .12
227 Willie Hernandez .08 .06 .03
228 Lee Lacy .06 .05 .02
229 Rollie Fingers .20 .15 .08
230 Bob Boone .08 .06 .03
231 Joaquin Andujar .08 .06 .03
232 Craig Reynolds .06 .05 .02
233 Shane Rawley .10 .08 .04
234 Eric Show .08 .06 .03
235 Jose DeLeon .08 .06 .03
236 *Jose Uribe* (FC) .10 .08 .04
237 Moose Haas .06 .05 .02
238 Wally Backman .08 .06 .03
239 Dennis Eckersley .12 .09 .05
240 Mike Moore .06 .05 .02
241 Damaso Garcia .06 .05 .02
242 Tim Teufel .06 .05 .02
243 Dave Concepcion .12 .09 .05
244 Floyd Bannister .10 .08 .04
245 Fred Lynn .20 .15 .08
246 Charlie Moore .06 .05 .02
247 Walt Terrell .08 .06 .03
248 Dave Winfield 2.00 1.50 .80
249 Dwight Evans .12 .09 .05
250 *Dennis Powell* (FC) .10 .08 .04
251 Andre Thornton .10 .08 .04
252 Onix Concepcion .06 .05 .02
253 Mike Heath .06 .05 .02
254a David Palmer (2B on front) .06 .05 .02
254b David Palmer (P on front) 1.00 .70 .40
255 Donnie Moore .06 .05 .02
256 Curtis Wilkerson .06 .05 .02
257 Julio Cruz .06 .05 .02
258 Nolan Ryan 6.00 4.50 2.50
259 Jeff Stone .06 .05 .02
260a John Tudor (1981 Games is .18) .10 .08 .04
260b John Tudor (1981 Games is 18) 1.00 .70 .40
261 Mark Thurmond .06 .05 .02
262 Jay Tibbs .06 .05 .02
263 Rafael Ramirez .06 .05 .02
264 Larry McWilliams .06 .05 .02
265 Mark Davis .06 .05 .02
266 Bob Dernier .06 .05 .02
267 Matt Young .06 .05 .02
268 Jim Clancy .08 .06 .03
269 Mickey Hatcher .06 .05 .02
270 Sammy Stewart .06 .05 .02
271 Bob L. Gibson .06 .05 .02
272 Nelson Simmons .06 .05 .02
273 Rich Gedman .10 .08 .04
274 Butch Wynegar .06 .05 .02
275 Ken Howell .06 .05 .02
276 Mel Hall .08 .06 .03
277 Jim Sundberg .08 .06 .03
278 Chris Codiroli .06 .05 .02
279 *Herman Winningham* (FC) .15 .11 .06
280 Rod Carew .70 .50 .30
281 Don Slaught .06 .05 .02
282 Scott Fletcher .08 .06 .03
283 Bill Dawley .06 .05 .02
284 Andy Hawkins .06 .05 .02
285 Glenn Wilson .08 .06 .03
286 Nick Esasky .08 .06 .03
287 Claudell Washington .08 .06 .03
288 Lee Mazzilli .08 .06 .03
289 Jody Davis .10 .08 .04
290 Darrell Porter .08 .06 .03
291 Scott McGregor .08 .06 .03
292 Ted Simmons .12 .09 .05
293 Aurelio Lopez .06 .05 .02
294 Marty Barrett .10 .08 .04
295 Dale Berra .06 .05 .02
296 Greg Brock .08 .06 .03
297 Charlie Leibrandt .08 .06 .03
298 Bill Krueger .06 .05 .02
299 Bryn Smith .06 .05 .02
300 Burt Hooton .08 .06 .03
301 *Stu Cliburn* (FC) .06 .05 .02
302 Luis Salazar .06 .05 .02
303 Ken Dayley .06 .05 .02
304 Frank DiPino .06 .05 .02
305 Von Hayes .10 .08 .04
306a Gary Redus (1983 2B is .20) .08 .06 .03
306b Gary Redus (1983 2B is 20) 1.00 .70 .40
307 Craig Lefferts .06 .05 .02
308 Sam Khalifa .06 .05 .02
309 Scott Garrelts .06 .05 .02
310 Rick Cerone .06 .05 .02
311 Shawon Dunston .20 .15 .08
312 Howard Johnson .12 .09 .05
313 Jim Presley .06 .05 .02
314 Gary Gaetti .25 .20 .10
315 Luis Leal .06 .05 .02
316 Mark Salas .06 .05 .02
317 Bill Caudill .06 .05 .02
318 Dave Henderson .10 .08 .04
319 Rafael Santana .06 .05 .02
320 Leon Durham .08 .06 .03
321 Bruce Sutter .15 .11 .06
322 Jason Thompson .06 .05 .02
323 Bob Brenly .06 .05 .02
324 Carmelo Martinez .08 .06 .03
325 Eddie Milner .06 .05 .02
326 Juan Samuel .15 .11 .06
327 Tom Nieto .06 .05 .02
328 Dave Smith .08 .06 .03
329 *Urbano Lugo* (FC) .08 .06 .03
330 Joel Skinner .06 .05 .02
331 Bill Gullickson .06 .05 .02
332 Floyd Rayford .06 .05 .02
333 Ben Oglivie .08 .06 .03
334 Lance Parrish .30 .25 .12
335 Jackie Gutierrez .06 .05 .02
336 Dennis Rasmussen .12 .09 .05
337 Terry Whitfield .06 .05 .02
338 Neal Heaton .06 .05 .02
339 Jorge Orta .06 .05 .02
340 Donnie Hill .06 .05 .02
341 Joe Hesketh .06 .05 .02
342 Charlie Hough .10 .08 .04
343 Dave Rozema .06 .05 .02
344 Greg Pryor .06 .05 .02
345 *Mickey Tettleton* 3.00 2.25 1.25
346 George Vukovich .06 .05 .02
347 Don Baylor .12 .09 .05
348 Carlos Diaz .06 .05 .02
349 Barbaro Garbey .06 .05 .02
350 Larry Sheets .12 .09 .05
351 *Ted Higuera* (FC) .15 .11 .06
352 Juan Beniquez .06 .05 .02
353 Bob Forsch .08 .06 .03
354 Mark Bailey .06 .05 .02
355 Larry Andersen .06 .05 .02
356 Terry Kennedy .08 .06 .03
357 Don Robinson .08 .06 .03
358 Jim Gott .06 .05 .02
359 *Earnest Riles* (FC) .15 .11 .06
360 *John Christensen* (FC) .10 .08 .04
361 Ray Fontenot .06 .05 .02
362 Spike Owen .06 .05 .02
363 Jim Acker .06 .05 .02
364a Ron Davis (last line in highlights ends with "...in May.") .08 .06 .03
364b Ron Davis (last line in highlights ends with "...relievers (9).") 1.00 .70 .40
365 Tom Hume .06 .05 .02
366 Carlton Fisk .60 .45 .25
367 Nate Snell .06 .05 .02
368 Rick Manning .06 .05 .02
369 Darrell Evans .15 .11 .06
370 Ron Hassey .06 .05 .02
371 Wade Boggs 2.50 2.00 1.00
372 Rick Honeycutt .06 .05 .02
373 Chris Bando .06 .05 .02
374 Bud Black .06 .05 .02
375 Steve Henderson .06 .05 .02
376 Charlie Lea .06 .05 .02
377 Reggie Jackson 1.00 .70 .40
378 Dave Schmidt .06 .05 .02
379 Bob James .06 .05 .02
380 Glenn Davis (FC) .40 .30 .15
381 Tim Corcoran .06 .05 .02
382 Danny Cox .10 .08 .04
383 Tim Flannery .06 .05 .02
384 Tom Browning .20 .15 .08
385 Rick Camp .06 .05 .02
386 Jim Morrison .06 .05 .02
387 Dave LaPoint .08 .06 .03
388 Davey Lopes .08 .06 .03
389 Al Cowens .06 .05 .02
390 Doyle Alexander .10 .08 .04
391 Tim Laudner .06 .05 .02
392 Don Aase .06 .05 .02
393 Jaime Cocanower .06 .05 .02
394 Randy O'Neal (FC) .08 .06 .03
395 Mike Easler .08 .06 .03
396 Scott Bradley .06 .05 .02
397 Tom Niedenfuer .08 .06 .03
398 Jerry Willard .06 .05 .02
399 Lonnie Smith .08 .06 .03
400 Bruce Bochte .06 .05 .02
401 Terry Francona .06 .05 .02
402 Jim Slaton .06 .05 .02
403 Bill Stein .06 .05 .02
404 Tim Hulett .06 .05 .02
405 Alan Ashby .06 .05 .02
406 Tim Stoddard .06 .05 .02
407 Garry Maddox .08 .06 .03
408 Ted Power .06 .05 .02
409 Len Barker .08 .06 .03
410 Denny Gonzalez .06 .05 .02
411 George Frazier .06 .05 .02
412 Andy Van Slyke .15 .11 .06
413 Jim Dwyer .06 .05 .02
414 Paul Householder .06 .05 .02
415 Alejandro Sanchez .06 .05 .02
416 Steve Crawford .06 .05 .02
417 Dan Pasqua .15 .11 .06
418 Enos Cabell .06 .05 .02
419 Mike Jones .06 .05 .02
420 Steve Kiefer .06 .05 .02
421 *Tim Burke* (FC) .15 .11 .06
422 Mike Mason .06 .05 .02
423 Ruppert Jones .06 .05 .02
424 Jerry Hairston .06 .05 .02
425 Tito Landrum .06 .05 .02
426 Jeff Calhoun .06 .05 .02
427 *Don Carman* (FC) .08 .06 .03
428 Tony Perez .15 .11 .06
429 Jerry Davis .06 .05 .02
430 Bob Walk .06 .05 .02
431 Brad Wellman .06 .05 .02
432 Terry Forster .08 .06 .03
433 Billy Hatcher .10 .08 .04
434 Clint Hurdle .06 .05 .02
435 *Ivan Calderon* (FC) .50 .40 .20
436 Pete Filson .06 .05 .02
437 Tom Henke .08 .06 .03
438 Dave Engle .06 .05 .02
439 Tom Filer .06 .05 .02
440 Gorman Thomas .10 .08 .04
441 *Rick Aguilera* (FC) 1.25 .90 .50
442 Scott Sanderson .06 .05 .02
443 Jeff Dedmon .06 .05 .02
444 *Joe Orsulak* (FC) .15 .11 .06

445	Atlee Hammaker	.06	.05	.02
446	Jerry Royster	.06	.05	.02
447	Buddy Bell	.10	.08	.04
448	Dave Rucker	.06	.05	.02
449	Ivan DeJesus	.06	.05	.02
450	Jim Pankovits	.06	.05	.02
451	Jerry Narron	.06	.05	.02
452	Bryan Little	.06	.05	.02
453	Gary Lucas	.06	.05	.02
454	Dennis Martinez	.08	.06	.03
455	Ed Romero	.06	.05	.02
456	*Bob Melvin* (FC)	.12	.09	.05
457	Glenn Hoffman	.06	.05	.02
458	Bob Shirley	.06	.05	.02
459	Bob Welch	.12	.09	.05
460	Carmen Castillo	.06	.05	.02
461	Dave Leeper	.06	.05	.02
462	*Tim Birtsas* (FC)	.12	.09	.05
463	Randy St. Claire	.06	.05	.02
464	Chris Welsh	.06	.05	.02
465	Greg Harris	.06	.05	.02
466	Lynn Jones	.06	.05	.02
467	Dusty Baker	.08	.06	.03
468	Roy Smith	.06	.05	.02
469	Andre Robertson	.06	.05	.02
470	Ken Landreaux	.06	.05	.02
471	Dave Bergman	.06	.05	.02
472	Gary Roenicke	.06	.05	.02
473	Pete Vuckovich	.08	.06	.03
474	*Kirk McCaskill* (FC)	.40	.30	.15
475	Jeff Lahti	.06	.05	.02
476	Mike Scott	.20	.15	.08
477	*Darren Daulton* (FC)	5.00	3.75	2.00
478	Graig Nettles	.15	.11	.06
479	Bill Almon	.06	.05	.02
480	Greg Minton	.06	.05	.02
481	Randy Ready (FC)	.10	.08	.04
482	*Len Dykstra*	7.00	5.25	2.75
483	Thad Bosley	.06	.05	.02
484	*Harold Reynolds*	.40	.30	.15
485	Al Oliver	.12	.09	.05
486	Roy Smalley	.06	.05	.02
487	John Franco	.15	.11	.06
488	Juan Agosto	.06	.05	.02
489	Al Pardo	.06	.05	.02
490	*Bill Wegman* (FC)	.25	.20	.10
491	Frank Tanana	.10	.08	.04
492	*Brian Fisher* (FC)	.08	.06	.03
493	Mark Clear	.06	.05	.02
494	Len Matuszek	.06	.05	.02
495	Ramon Romero	.06	.05	.02
496	John Wathan	.08	.06	.03
497	Rob Picciolo	.06	.05	.02
498	U.L. Washington	.06	.05	.02
499	John Candelaria	.10	.08	.04
500	Duane Walker	.06	.05	.02
501	Gene Nelson	.06	.05	.02
502	John Mizerock	.06	.05	.02
503	Luis Aguayo	.06	.05	.02
504	Kurt Kepshire	.06	.05	.02
505	Ed Wojna	.06	.05	.02
506	Joe Price	.06	.05	.02
507	*Milt Thompson* (FC)	.30	.25	.12
508	Junior Ortiz	.06	.05	.02
509	Vida Blue	.10	.08	.04
510	Steve Engel	.06	.05	.02
511	Karl Best	.06	.05	.02
512	*Cecil Fielder*	24.00	18.00	9.50
513	Frank Eufemia	.06	.05	.02
514	Tippy Martinez	.06	.05	.02
515	*Billy Robidoux* (FC)	.10	.08	.04
516	Bill Scherrer	.06	.05	.02
517	Bruce Hurst	.12	.09	.05
518	Rich Bordi	.06	.05	.02
519	Steve Yeager	.06	.05	.02
520	Tony Bernazard	.06	.05	.02
521	Hal McRae	.10	.08	.04
522	Jose Rijo	.10	.08	.04
523	*Mitch Webster* (FC)	.08	.06	.03
524	*Jack Howell* (FC)	.08	.06	.03
525	Alan Bannister	.06	.05	.02
526	Ron Kittle	.10	.08	.04
527	Phil Garner	.08	.06	.03
528	Kurt Bevacqua	.06	.05	.02
529	Kevin Gross	.08	.06	.03
530	Bo Diaz	.08	.06	.03
531	Ken Oberkfell	.06	.05	.02
532	Rick Reuschel	.10	.08	.04
533	Ron Meridith	.06	.05	.02
534	Steve Braun	.06	.05	.02
535	Wayne Gross	.06	.05	.02
536	Ray Searage	.06	.05	.02
537	Tom Brookens	.06	.05	.02
538	Al Nipper	.06	.05	.02
539	Billy Sample	.06	.05	.02
540	Steve Sax	.20	.15	.08
541	Dan Quisenberry	.10	.08	.04
542	Tony Phillips	.06	.05	.02
543	*Floyd Youmans* (FC)	.20	.15	.08
544	*Steve Buechele* (FC)	.70	.50	.30
545	Craig Gerber	.06	.05	.02
546	Joe DeSa	.06	.05	.02
547	Brian Harper	.06	.05	.02
548	Kevin Bass	.10	.08	.04
549	Tom Foley	.06	.05	.02
550	Dave Van Gorder	.06	.05	.02
551	Bruce Bochy	.06	.05	.02
552	R.J. Reynolds	.08	.06	.03
553	*Chris Brown* (FC)	.20	.15	.08
554	Bruce Benedict	.06	.05	.02
555	Warren Brusstar	.06	.05	.02
556	Danny Heep	.06	.05	.02
557	Darnell Coles	.08	.06	.03
558	Greg Gagne	.08	.06	.03
559	Ernie Whitt	.08	.06	.03
560	Ron Washington	.06	.05	.02
561	Jimmy Key	.15	.11	.06
562	Billy Swift (FC)	.15	.11	.06
563	Ron Darling	.15	.11	.06
564	Dick Ruthven	.06	.05	.02
565	Zane Smith (FC)	.15	.11	.06
566	Sid Bream	.10	.08	.04
567a	Joel Youngblood (P on front)	.08	.06	.03
567b	Joel Youngblood (IF on front)	1.00	.70	.40
568	Mario Ramirez	.06	.05	.02
569	Tom Runnells	.06	.05	.02
570	Rick Schu	.06	.05	.02
571	Bill Campbell	.06	.05	.02
572	Dickie Thon	.08	.06	.03
573	Al Holland	.06	.05	.02
574	Reid Nichols	.06	.05	.02
575	Bert Roberge	.06	.05	.02
576	Mike Flanagan	.10	.08	.04
577	Tim Leary (FC)	.15	.11	.06
578	Mike Laga	.06	.05	.02
579	Steve Lyons	.06	.05	.02
580	Phil Niekro	.30	.25	.12
581	Gilberto Reyes	.06	.05	.02
582	Jamie Easterly	.06	.05	.02
583	Mark Gubicza	.12	.09	.05
584	*Stan Javier* (FC)	.15	.11	.06
585	Bill Laskey	.06	.05	.02
586	Jeff Russell	.06	.05	.02
587	Dickie Noles	.06	.05	.02
588	Steve Farr	.08	.06	.03
589	*Steve Ontiveros* (FC)	.15	.11	.06
590	Mike Hargrove	.06	.05	.02
591	Marty Bystrom	.06	.05	.02
592	Franklin Stubbs	.08	.06	.03
593	Larry Herndon	.08	.06	.03
594	Bill Swaggerty	.06	.05	.02
595	Carlos Ponce	.06	.05	.02
596	*Pat Perry* (FC)	.12	.09	.05
597	Ray Knight	.08	.06	.03
598	*Steve Lombardozzi* (FC)	.15	.11	.06
599	Brad Havens	.06	.05	.02
600	*Pat Clements* (FC)	.12	.09	.05
601	Joe Niekro	.12	.09	.05
602	Hank Aaron Puzzle Card	.06	.05	.02
603	*Dwayne Henry* (FC)	.10	.08	.04
604	Mookie Wilson	.10	.08	.04
605	Buddy Biancalana	.06	.05	.02
606	Rance Mulliniks	.06	.05	.02
607	Alan Wiggins	.06	.05	.02
608	Joe Cowley	.06	.05	.02
609a	Tom Seaver (green stripes around name COR)	1.00	.70	.40
609b	Tom seaver (yellow stripes around name ERR)	3.00	2.25	1.25
610	Neil Allen	.06	.05	.02
611	Don Sutton	.30	.25	.12
612	*Fred Toliver* (FC)	.15	.11	.06
613	Jay Baller	.06	.05	.02
614	Marc Sullivan	.06	.05	.02
615	John Grubb	.06	.05	.02
616	Bruce Kison	.06	.05	.02
617	Bill Madlock	.12	.09	.05
618	Chris Chambliss	.08	.06	.03
619	Dave Stewart	.12	.09	.05
620	Tim Lollar	.06	.05	.02
621	Gary Lavelle	.06	.05	.02
622	Charles Hudson	.06	.05	.02
623	*Joel Davis* (FC)	.08	.06	.03
624	*Joe Johnson* (FC)	.08	.06	.03
625	Sid Fernandez	.12	.09	.05
626	Dennis Lamp	.06	.05	.02
627	Terry Harper	.06	.05	.02
628	Jack Lazorko	.06	.05	.02
629	*Roger McDowell* (FC)	.30	.25	.12
630	Mark Funderburk	.06	.05	.02
631	Ed Lynch	.06	.05	.02
632	Rudy Law	.06	.05	.02
633	*Roger Mason* (FC)	.08	.06	.03
634	*Mike Felder* (FC)	.15	.11	.06
635	Ken Schrom	.06	.05	.02
636	Bob Ojeda	.08	.06	.03
637	Ed Vande Berg	.06	.05	.02
638	Bobby Meacham	.06	.05	.02
639	Cliff Johnson	.06	.05	.02
640	Garth Iorg	.06	.05	.02
641	Dan Driessen	.08	.06	.03
642	Mike Brown	.06	.05	.02
643	John Shelby	.06	.05	.02
644	Pete Rose (RB)	.50	.40	.20
645	Knuckle Brothers (Joe Niekro, Phil Niekro)	.15	.11	.06
646	Jesse Orosco	.08	.06	.03
647	*Billy Beane* (FC)	.06	.05	.02
648	Cesar Cedeno	.10	.08	.04
649	Bert Blyleven	.15	.11	.06
650	Max Venable	.06	.05	.02
651	Fleet Feet (Vince Coleman, Willie McGee)	.35	.25	.14
652	Calvin Schiraldi	.08	.06	.03
653	King of Kings (Pete Rose)	1.00	.70	.40
----	Checklist 1-26 DK	.06	.05	.02
----a	Checklist 27-130 (45 is Beane)	.08	.06	.03
----b	Checklist 27-130 (45 is Habyan)	.60	.45	.25
----	Checklist 131-234	.06	.05	.02
----	Checklist 235-338	.06	.05	.02
----	Checklist 339-442	.06	.05	.02
----	Checklist 443-546	.06	.05	.02
----	Checklist 547-653	.06	.05	.02

1986 Donruss All-Stars

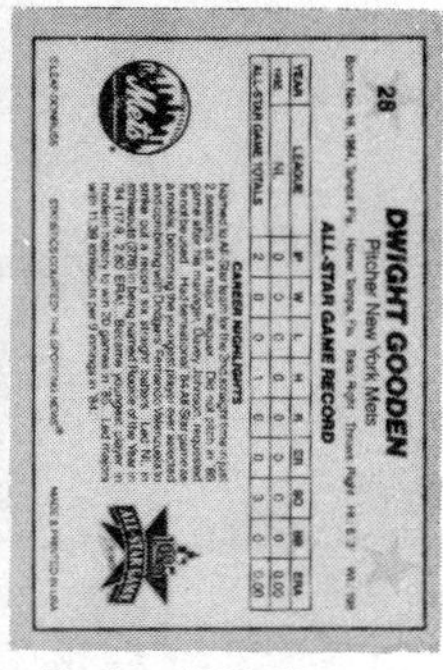

Issued in conjunction with the 1986 Donruss Pop-Ups set, the Donruss All-Stars set consists of 60 cards that measure 3-1/2" by 5". Fifty-nine players involved in the 1985 All-Star game plus an unnumbered checklist comprise the set. The card fronts have the same blue border found on the regular 1986 Donruss issue. Retail packs included one Pop-up card, three All-Star cards and one Hank Aaron puzzle card.

		MT	NR MT	EX
Complete Set:		8.00	6.00	3.25
Common Player:		.09	.07	.04
1	Tony Gwynn	.30	.25	.12
2	Tommy Herr	.09	.07	.04
3	Steve Garvey	.30	.25	.12
4	Dale Murphy	.40	.30	.15
5	Darryl Strawberry	.40	.30	.15
6	Graig Nettles	.12	.09	.05
7	Terry Kennedy	.09	.07	.04
8	Ozzie Smith	.30	.25	.12
9	LaMarr Hoyt	.09	.07	.04
10	Rickey Henderson	.75	.60	.30
11	Lou Whitaker	.25	.20	.10
12	George Brett	.75	.60	.30
13	Eddie Murray	.25	.20	.10
14	Cal Ripken, Jr.	1.00	.70	.40
15	Dave Winfield	.45	.35	.20
16	Jim Rice	.12	.09	.05
17	Carlton Fisk	.15	.11	.06
18	Jack Morris	.15	.11	.06
19	Jose Cruz	.09	.07	.04
20	Tim Raines	.25	.20	.10
21	Nolan Ryan	1.25	.90	.50
22	Tony Pena	.09	.07	.04
23	Jack Clark	.15	.11	.06
24	Dave Parker	.15	.11	.06
25	Tim Wallach	.12	.09	.05
26	Ozzie Virgil	.09	.07	.04
27	Fernando Valenzuela	.12	.09	.05
28	Dwight Gooden	.40	.30	.15
29	Glenn Wilson	.09	.07	.04
30	Garry Templeton	.09	.07	.04
31	Goose Gossage	.12	.09	.05
32	Ryne Sandberg	1.00	.70	.40
33	Jeff Reardon	.12	.09	.05
34	Pete Rose	.60	.45	.25
35	Scott Garrelts	.09	.07	.04
36	Willie McGee	.12	.09	.05
37	Ron Darling	.12	.09	.05
38	Dick Williams	.09	.07	.04
39	Paul Molitor	.35	.25	.14
40	Damaso Garcia	.09	.07	.04
41	Phil Bradley	.12	.09	.05
42	Dan Petry	.09	.07	.04
43	Willie Hernandez	.09	.07	.04
44	Tom Brunansky	.12	.09	.05
45	Alan Trammell	.20	.15	.08
46	Donnie Moore	.09	.07	.04
47	Wade Boggs	.60	.45	.25
48	Ernie Whitt	.09	.07	.04
49	Harold Baines	.15	.11	.06
50	Don Mattingly	1.00	.70	.40
51	Gary Ward	.09	.07	.04
52	Bert Blyleven	.12	.09	.05
53	Jimmy Key	.12	.09	.05
54	Cecil Cooper	.12	.09	.05
55	Dave Stieb	.12	.09	.05
56	Rich Gedman	.09	.07	.04
57	Jay Howell	.09	.07	.04
58	Sparky Anderson	.09	.07	.04
59	Minneapolis Metrodome	.09	.07	.04
----	Checklist	.09	.07	.04

1986 Donruss Box Panels

For the second year in a row, Donruss placed baseball cards on the bottom of their wax and cello pack boxes. The cards, which come four to a panel, are the standard 2-1/2" by 3-1/2" in size. With numbering that begins where Donruss left off in 1985, cards PC 4 through PC 6 were found on boxes of regular Donruss issue wax packs. Cards PC 7

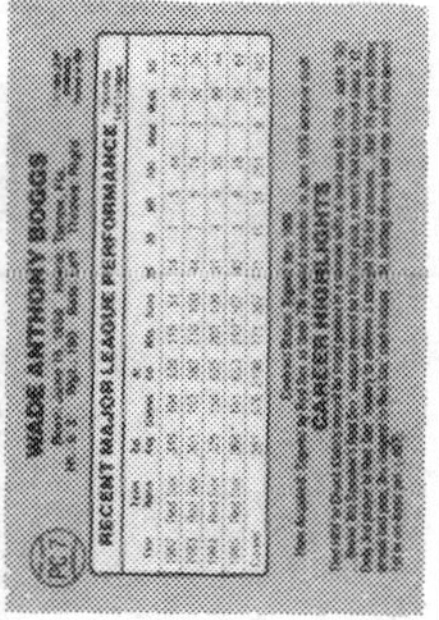

through PC 9 were found on boxes of the 1986 All-Star/Pop-up packs. An unnumbered Hank Aaron puzzle card was included on each box.

		MT	NR MT	EX
Complete Panel Set:		5.00	3.75	2.00
Complete Singles Set:		3.00	2.25	1.25
Common Single Player:		.15	.11	.06
	Panel	1.00	.70	.40
4	Kirk Gibson	.35	.25	.14
5	Willie Hernandez	.15	.11	.06
6	Doug DeCinces	.15	.11	.06
----	Aaron Puzzle Card	.04	.03	.02
	Panel	3.00	2.25	1.25
7	Wade Boggs	1.00	.70	.40
8	Lee Smith	.25	.11	.06
9	Cecil Cooper	.20	.15	.08
----	Aaron Puzzle Card	.04	.03	.02

1986 Donruss Diamond Kings Supers

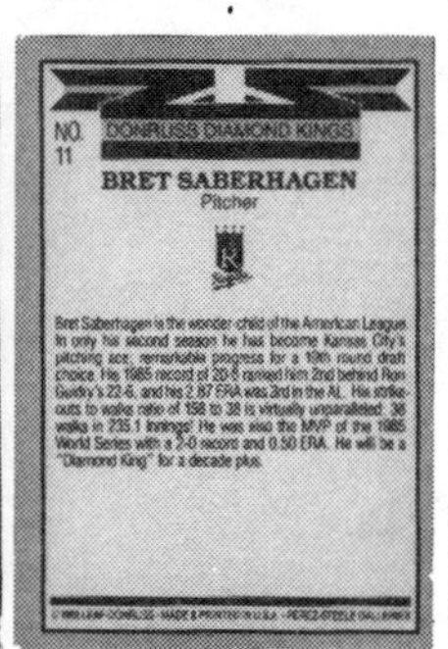

Donruss produced a set of giant-size Diamond Kings in 1986 for the second year in a row. The cards, which measure 4-11/6" by 6-3/4", are enlarged versions of the 26 Diamond Kings cards found in the regular 1986 Donruss set. Featuring the artwork of Dick Perez, the set consists of 28 cards - 26 DKs, an unnumbered checklist and an unnumbered Pete Rose "King of Kings" card.

		MT	NR MT	EX
Complete Set:		10.00	7.50	4.00
Common Player:		.20	.15	.08
1	Kirk Gibson	.50	.40	.20
2	Goose Gossage	.30	.25	.12
3	Willie McGee	.30	.25	.12
4	George Bell	.30	.25	.12
5	Tony Armas	.20	.15	.08
6	Chili Davis	.30	.25	.12
7	Cecil Cooper	.25	.20	.10
8	Mike Boddicker	.20	.15	.08
9	Davey Lopes	.20	.15	.08
10	Bill Doran	.25	.20	.10
11	Bret Saberhagen	.60	.45	.25
12	Brett Butler	.20	.15	.08
13	Harold Baines	.30	.25	.12
14	Mike Davis	.20	.15	.08
15	Tony Perez	.25	.20	.10
16	Willie Randolph	.25	.20	.10
18	Orel Hershiser	.70	.50	.30
19	Johnny Ray	.25	.20	.10
20	Gary Ward	.20	.15	.08
21	Rick Mahler	.20	.15	.08
22	Phil Bradley	.30	.25	.12
23	Jerry Koosman	.20	.15	.08
24	Tom Brunansky	.25	.20	.10
25	Andre Dawson	.60	.45	.25
26	Dwight Gooden	.90	.70	.35
----	Checklist, King of Kings (Pete Rose)	.15	.11	.06

The values quoted are intended to reflect the market price.

1986 Donruss Highlights

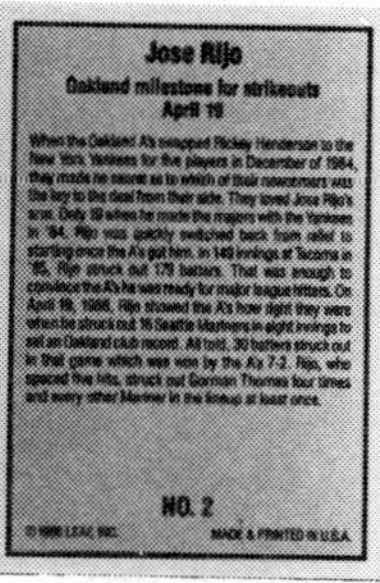

Donruss, for the second year in a row, issued a 56- card highlights set which featured cards of the A.L. and N.L. Player of the Month plus significant events that took place during the 1986 season. The cards, which measure 2-1/2" by 3-1/2" in size, are similar in design to the regular 1986 Donruss set but have a gold border instead of blue. A "Highlights" logo appears in the lower left corner of each card front. The card backs are designed on a vertical format and feature black print on a yellow background. As in 1985, the set includes Donruss' picks for the Rookies of the Year awards. A new feature was three cards honoring the 1986 Hall of Fame inductees. The set, available only through hobby dealers, was issued in a specially designed box.

		MT	NR MT	EX
Complete Set:		9.00	6.75	3.50
Common Player:		.10	.08	.04
1	Homers In First At-Bat (Will Clark)	2.00	1.50	.80
2	Oakland Milestone For Strikeouts (Jose Rijo)	.10	.08	.04
3	Royals' All-Time Hit Man (George Brett)	.25	.20	.10
4	Phillies RBI Leader (Mike Schmidt)	.30	.25	.12
5	KKKKKKKKKKKKKKKKKKK (Roger Clemens)	.50	.40	.20
6	A.L. Pitcher of the Month-April (Roger Clemens)	.25	.20	.10
7	A.L. Player of the Month-April (Kirby Puckett)	.50	.40	.20
8	N.L. Pitcher of the Month-April (Dwight Gooden)	.25	.20	.10
9	N.L. Player of the Month-April (Johnny Ray)	.10	.08	.04
10	Eclipses Mantle HR Record (Reggie Jackson)	.25	.20	.10
11	First Five Hit Game of Career (Wade Boggs)	.25	.20	.10
12	A.L. Pitcher of the Month-May (Don Aase)	.10	.08	.04
13	A.L. Player of the Month-May (Wade Boggs)	.25	.20	.10
14	N.L. Pitcher of the Month-May (Jeff Reardon)	.15	.11	.06
15	N.L. Player of the Month-May (Hubie Brooks)	.10	.08	.04
16	Notches 300th Career Win (Don Sutton)	.10	.08	.04
17	Starts Season 14-0 (Roger Clemens)	.25	.20	.10
18	A.L. Pitcher of the Month-June (Roger Clemens)	.25	.20	.10
19	A.L. Player of the Month-June (Kent Hrbek)	.10	.08	.04
20	N.L. Pitcher of the Month-June (Rick Rhoden)	.10	.08	.04
21	N.L. Player of the Month-June (Kevin Bass)	.10	.08	.04
22	Blasts 4 HRS in 1 Game (Bob Horner)	.10	.08	.04
23	Starting All Star Rookie (Wally Joyner)	.25	.20	.10
24	Starts 3rd Straight All Star Game (Darryl Strawberry)	.25	.20	.10
25	Ties All Star Game Record (Fernando Valenzuela)	.10	.08	.04
26	All Star Game MVP (Roger Clemens)	.25	.20	.10
27	A.L. Pitcher of the Month-July (Jack Morris)	.10	.08	.04
28	A.L. Player of the Month-July (Scott Fletcher)	.10	.08	.04
29	N.L. Pitcher of the Month-July (Todd Worrell)	.10	.08	.04
30	N.L. PLayer of the Month-July (Eric Davis)	.20	.15	.08
31	Records 3000th Strikeout (Bert Blyleven)	.15	.11	.06
32	1986 Hall of Fame Inductee (Bobby Doerr)	.15	.11	.06
33	1986 Hall of Fame Inductee (Ernie Lombardi)	.15	.11	.06
34	1986 Hall of Fame Inductee (Willie McCovey)	.20	.15	.08
35	Notches 4000th K (Steve Carlton)	.25	.20	.10
36	Surpasses DiMaggio Record (Mike Schmidt)	.30	.25	.12
37	Records 3rd "Quadruple Double" (Juan Samuel)	.10	.08	.04
38	A.L. Pitcher of the Month-August (Mike Witt)	.10	.08	.04
39	A.L. Player of the Month-August (Doug DeCinces)	.10	.08	.04
40	N.L. Pitcher of the Month-August (Bill Gullickson)	.10	.08	.04
41	N.L. Player of the Month-August (Dale Murphy)	.20	.15	.08
42	Sets Tribe Offensive Record (Joe Carter)	.25	.20	.10
43	Longest HR In Royals Stadium (Bo Jackson)	1.00	.70	.40
44	Majors 1st No-Hitter In 2 Years (Joe Cowley)	.10	.08	.04
45	Sets M.L. Strikeout Record (Jim Deshaies)	.10	.08	.04
46	No Hitter Clinches Division (Mike Scott)	.10	.08	.04
47	A.L. Pitcher of the Month-September (Bruce Hurst)	.10	.08	.04
48	A.L. Player of the Month-September (Don Mattingly)	.50	.40	.20
49	N.L. Pitcher of the Month-September (Mike Krukow)	.10	.08	.04
50	N.L. Player of the Month-September (Steve Sax)	.10	.08	.04
51	A.L. Record For Steals By A Rookie (John Cangelosi)	.10	.08	.04
52	Shatters M.L. Save Mark (Dave Righetti)	.10	.08	.04
53	Yankee Record For Hits & Doubles (Don Mattingly)	.50	.40	.20
54	Donruss N.L. Rookie of the Year (Todd Worrell)	.25	.20	.10
55	Donruss A.L. Rookie of the Year (Jose Canseco)	2.00	1.50	.80
56	Highlight Checklist	.10	.08	.04

1986 Donruss Pop-Ups

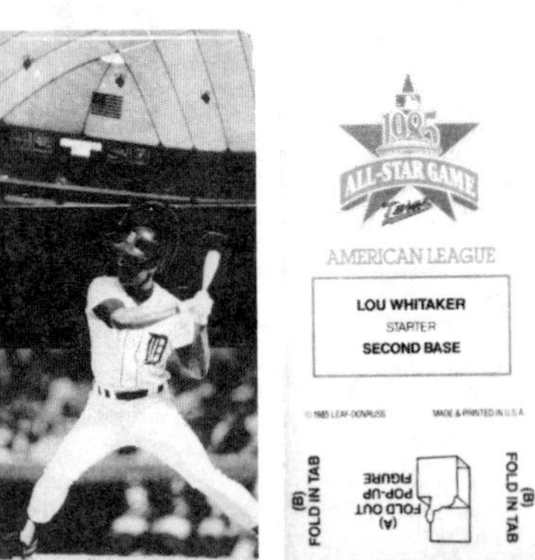

Issued in conjunction with the 1986 Donruss All-Stars set, the Donruss Pop-Ups (18 unnumbered cards) feature the 1985 All-Star Game starting lineups. The cards, which measure 2-1/2" by 5", are die-cut and fold out to form a three-dimensional stand-up card. The background for the cards is the Minneapolis Metrodome, site of the 1985 All-Star Game. Retail packs included one Pop-Up card, three All-Star cards and one Hank Aaron puzzle card.

		MT	NR MT	EX
Complete Set:		4.00	3.00	1.50
Common Player:		.20	.15	.08
(1)	George Brett	.60	.45	.25
(2)	Carlton Fisk	.30	.25	.12
(3)	Steve Garvey	.20	.15	.08
(4)	Tony Gwynn	.50	.40	.20
(5)	Rickey Henderson	.60	.45	.25
(6)	Tommy Herr	.20	.15	.08
(7)	LaMarr Hoyt	.20	.15	.08
(8)	Terry Kennedy	.20	.15	.08
(9)	Jack Morris	.20	.15	.08
(10)	Dale Murphy	.30	.25	.12
(11)	Eddie Murray	.30	.25	.12
(12)	Graig Nettles	.20	.15	.08
(13)	Jim Rice	.20	.15	.08
(14)	Cal Ripken, Jr.	.90	.70	.35
(15)	Ozzie Smith	.30	.25	.12
(16)	Darryl Strawberry	.40	.30	.15
(17)	Lou Whitaker	.30	.25	.12
(18)	Dave Winfield	.40	.30	.15

1986 Donruss Rookies

Entitled "The Rookies," this 56-card set includes the top 55 rookies of 1986 plus an unnumbered checklist. The cards, which measure 2-1/2" by 3-1/2", are similar to the format used for the 1986 Donruss regular issue, except that the borders are green rather than blue. Several of the rookies who had cards in the regular 1986 Donruss set appear again

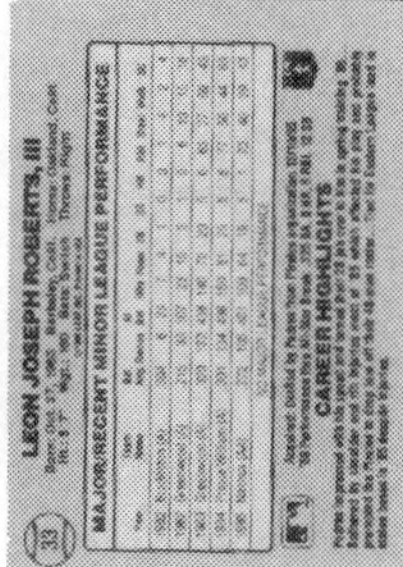

in "The Rookies" set. The sets, which were only available through hobby dealers, came in a specially designed box.

		MT	NR MT	EX
Complete Set (56):		45.00	34.00	18.00
Common Player:		.15	.11	.06
1	Wally Joyner	1.25	.90	.50
2	Tracy Jones (FC)	.15	.11	.06
3	Allan Anderson (FC)	.20	.15	.08
4	Ed Correa (FC)	.15	.11	.06
5	Reggie Williams	.15	.11	.06
6	Charlie Kerfeld (FC)	.15	.11	.06
7	Andres Galarraga	3.00	2.25	1.25
8	Bob Tewksbury (FC)	.80	.60	.30
9	Al Newman	.15	.11	.06
10	Andres Thomas (FC)	.15	.11	.06
11	Barry Bonds (FC)	16.00	12.00	6.50
12	Juan Nieves	.15	.11	.06
13	Mark Eichhorn (FC)	.25	.20	.10
14	Dan Plesac (FC)	.25	.20	.10
15	Cory Snyder	.40	.30	.15
16	Kelly Gruber	.25	.20	.10
17	Kevin Mitchell	1.50	1.25	.60
18	Steve Lombardozzi	.15	.11	.06
19	Mitch Williams	.50	.40	.20
20	John Cerutti (FC)	.25	.20	.10
21	Todd Worrell	.15	.11	.06
22	Jose Canseco	4.50	3.50	1.75
23	Pete Incaviglia (FC)	1.00	.70	.40
24	Jose Guzman	.25	.20	.10
25	Scott Bailes (FC)	.15	.11	.06
26	Greg Mathews (FC)	.15	.11	.06
27	Eric King (FC)	.20	.15	.08
28	Paul Assenmacher	.20	.15	.08
29	Jeff Sellers	.15	.11	.06
30	Bobby Bonilla	3.50	2.75	1.50
31	Doug Drabek (FC)	1.00	.70	.40
32	Will Clark (FC)	9.00	6.75	3.50
33	Bip Roberts	.60	.45	.25
34	Jim Deshaies (FC)	.25	.20	.10
35	Mike LaValliere (FC)	.40	.30	.15
36	Scott Bankhead (FC)	.20	.15	.08
37	Dale Sveum (FC)	.15	.11	.06
38	Bo Jackson (FC)	4.00	3.00	1.50
39	Rob Thompson (FC)	1.75	1.25	.70
40	Eric Plunk (FC)	.20	.15	.08
41	Bill Bathe	.15	.11	.06
42	John Kruk (FC)	4.00	3.00	1.50
43	Andy Allanson (FC)	.20	.15	.08
44	Mark Portugal	.15	.11	.06
45	Danny Tartabull	1.50	1.25	.60
46	Bob Kipper	.15	.11	.06
47	Gene Walter	.15	.11	.06
48	Rey Quinonez	.15	.11	.06
49	Bobby Witt (FC)	.30	.25	.12
50	Bill Mooneyham	.15	.11	.06
51	John Cangelosi (FC)	.15	.11	.06
52	Ruben Sierra	3.00	2.25	1.25
53	Rob Woodward	.15	.11	.06
54	Ed Hearn	.15	.11	.06
55	Joel McKeon	.15	.11	.06
56	Checklist 1-56	.05	.04	.02

1987 Donruss

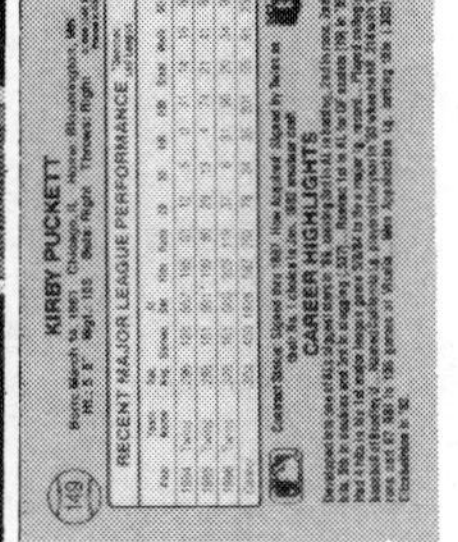

The 1987 Donruss set consists of 660 numbered cards, each measuring 2-1/2" by 3-1/2" in size. Full color photos are surrounded by a bold black border separated by two narrow bands of yellow which enclose a brown area filled with baseballs. The player's name, team and team logo appear on the card fronts along with the words "Donruss '87". The card backs are designed on a horizontal format and contain black print on a yellow and white background. The backs are very similar to those in previous years' sets. Backs of cards issued in wax and rack packs face to the left when turned over, while those issued in factory sets face to the right.

		MT	NR MT	EX
Complete Set (660):		55.00	41.00	22.00
Common Player:		.05	.04	.02
1	Wally Joyner (DK)	.25	.20	.10
2	Roger Clemens (DK)	.50	.40	.20
3	Dale Murphy (DK)	.12	.09	.05
4	Darryl Strawberry (DK)	.12	.09	.05
5	Ozzie Smith (DK)	.20	.15	.08
6	Jose Canseco (DK)	.40	.30	.15
7	Charlie Hough (DK)	.07	.05	.03
8	Brook Jacoby (DK)	.10	.08	.04
9	Fred Lynn (DK)	.12	.09	.05
10	Rick Rhoden (DK)	.10	.08	.04
11	Chris Brown (DK)	.10	.08	.04
12	Von Hayes (DK)	.10	.08	.04
13	Jack Morris (DK)	.10	.08	.04
14a	Kevin McReynolds (DK) (no yellow stripe on back)	1.25	.90	.50
14b	Kevin McReynolds (DK) (yellow stripe on back)	.20	.15	.08
15	George Brett (DK)	.60	.45	.25
16	Ted Higuera (DK)	.05	.04	.02
17	Hubie Brooks (DK)	.10	.08	.04
18	Mike Scott (DK)	.12	.09	.05
19	Kirby Puckett (DK)	.60	.45	.25
20	Dave Winfield (DK)	.25	.20	.10
21	Lloyd Moseby (DK)	.10	.08	.04
22a	Eric Davis (DK) (no yellow stripe on back)	1.00	.70	.40
22b	Eric Davis (DK) (yellow stripe on back)	.15	.11	.06
23	Jim Presley (DK)	.12	.09	.05
24	Keith Moreland (DK)	.07	.05	.03
25a	Greg Walker (DK) no yellow stripe on back)	.50	.40	.20
25b	Greg Walker (DK) (yellow stripe on back)	.10	.08	.04
26	Steve Sax (DK)	.12	.09	.05
27	Checklist 1-27	.05	.04	.02
28	*B.J. Surhoff* (RR)	.30	.25	.12
29	*Randy Myers* (RR)	.30	.25	.12
30	*Ken Gerhart* (FC) (RR)	.15	.11	.06
31	Benito Santiago (RR)	.40	.30	.15
32	*Greg Swindell* (RR)	.60	.45	.25
33	*Mike Birkbeck* (FC) (RR)	.20	.15	.08
34	*Terry Steinbach* (RR)	.40	.30	.15
35	*Bo Jackson* (RR)	3.00	2.25	1.25
36	*Greg Maddux* (RR)	7.00	5.25	2.75
37	*Jim Lindeman* (FC) (RR)	.15	.11	.06
38	*Devon White* (RR)	1.25	.90	.50
39	*Eric Bell* (FC) (RR)	.12	.09	.05
40	*Will Fraser* (FC) (RR)	.20	.15	.08
41	*Jerry Browne* (RR)	.25	.20	.10
42	*Chris James* (RR)	.20	.15	.08
43	*Rafael Palmeiro* (RR)	5.00	3.75	2.00
44	*Pat Dodson* (FC) (RR)	.12	.09	.05
45	*Duane Ward* (RR)	.80	.60	.30
46	*Mark McGwire* (RR)	3.50	2.75	1.50
47	*Bruce Fields* (FC) (RR) (Photo actually Darnell Coles)	.10	.08	.04
48	Eddie Murray	.50	.40	.20
49	Ted Higuera	.06	.05	.02
50	Kirk Gibson	.15	.11	.06
51	Oil Can Boyd	.07	.05	.03
52	Don Mattingly	1.00	.70	.40
53	Pedro Guerrero	.15	.11	.06
54	George Brett	1.00	.70	.40
55	Jose Rijo	.07	.05	.03
56	Tim Raines	.30	.25	.12
57	*Ed Correa*	.15	.11	.06
58	Mike Witt	.10	.08	.04
59	Greg Walker	.10	.08	.04
60	Ozzie Smith	.40	.30	.15
61	Glenn Davis	.06	.05	.02
62	Glenn Wilson	.07	.05	.03
63	Tom Browning	.10	.08	.04
64	Tony Gwynn	1.00	.70	.40
65	R.J. Reynolds	.07	.05	.03
66	*Will Clark*	6.00	4.50	2.50
67	Ozzie Virgil	.05	.04	.02
68	Rick Sutcliffe	.12	.09	.05
69	Gary Carter	.12	.09	.05
70	Mike Moore	.05	.04	.02
71	Bert Blyleven	.12	.09	.05
72	Tony Fernandez	.12	.09	.05
73	Kent Hrbek	.15	.11	.06
74	Lloyd Moseby	.10	.08	.04
75	Alvin Davis	.12	.09	.05
76	Keith Hernandez	.15	.11	.06
77	Ryne Sandberg	1.50	1.25	.60
78	Dale Murphy	.10	.08	.04
79	Sid Bream	.07	.05	.03
80	Chris Brown	.07	.05	.03
81	Steve Garvey	.20	.15	.08
82	Mario Soto	.07	.05	.03
83	Shane Rawley	.07	.05	.03
84	Willie McGee	.12	.09	.05
85	Jose Cruz	.10	.08	.04
86	Brian Downing	.07	.05	.03
87	Ozzie Guillen	.10	.08	.04
88	Hubie Brooks	.10	.08	.04
89	Cal Ripken, Jr.	1.25	.90	.50
90	Juan Nieves	.07	.05	.03
91	Lance Parrish	.06	.05	.02
92	Jim Rice	.12	.09	.05
93	Ron Guidry	.15	.11	.06
94	Fernando Valenzuela	.08	.06	.03
95	*Andy Allanson*	.15	.11	.06
96	Willie Wilson	.12	.09	.05
97	Jose Canseco	2.50	2.00	1.00
98	Jeff Reardon	.10	.08	.04
99	*Bobby Witt*	.20	.15	.08
100	Checklist 28-133	.05	.04	.02
101	Jose Guzman	.10	.08	.04
102	Steve Balboni	.07	.05	.03
103	Tony Phillips	.05	.04	.02
104	Brook Jacoby	.10	.08	.04
105	Dave Winfield	.60	.45	.25
106	Orel Hershiser	.15	.11	.06
107	Lou Whitaker	.25	.20	.10
108	Fred Lynn	.15	.11	.06
109	Bill Wegman	.07	.05	.03
110	Donnie Moore	.05	.04	.02
111	Jack Clark	.15	.11	.06
112	Bob Knepper	.07	.05	.03
113	Von Hayes	.10	.08	.04
114	*Bip Roberts*	.40	.30	.15
115	Tony Pena	.08	.06	.03
116	Scott Garrelts	.05	.04	.02
117	Paul Molitor	.75	.60	.30
118	Darryl Strawberry	.25	.20	.10
119	Shawon Dunston	.10	.08	.04
120	Jim Presley	.10	.08	.04
121	Jesse Barfield	.06	.05	.02
122	Gary Gaetti	.15	.11	.06
123	*Kurt Stillwell*	.15	.11	.06
124	Joel Davis	.05	.04	.02
125	Mike Boddicker	.07	.05	.03
126	Robin Yount	.75	.60	.30
127	Alan Trammell	.25	.20	.10
128	Dave Righetti	.15	.11	.06
129	Dwight Evans	.12	.09	.05
130	Mike Scioscia	.07	.05	.03
131	Julio Franco	.10	.08	.04
132	Bret Saberhagen	.12	.09	.05
133	Mike Davis	.07	.05	.03
134	Joe Hesketh	.05	.04	.02
135	*Wally Joyner*	.75	.60	.30
136	Don Slaught	.05	.04	.02
137	Daryl Boston	.05	.04	.02
138	Nolan Ryan	2.25	1.75	.90
139	Mike Schmidt	1.00	.70	.40
140	Tommy Herr	.10	.08	.04
141	Garry Templeton	.07	.05	.03
142	Kal Daniels	.20	.15	.08
143	Billy Sample	.05	.04	.02
144	Johnny Ray	.10	.08	.04
145	*Rob Thompson*	.75	.60	.30
146	Bob Dernier	.05	.04	.02
147	Danny Tartabull	.25	.20	.10
148	Ernie Whitt	.07	.05	.03
149	Kirby Puckett	2.00	1.50	.80
150	Mike Young	.05	.04	.02
151	Ernest Riles	.05	.04	.02
152	Frank Tanana	.07	.05	.03
153	Rich Gedman	.10	.08	.04
154	Willie Randolph	.10	.08	.04
155a	Bill Madlock (name in brown band)	.12	.09	.05
155b	Bill Madlock (name in red band)	.70	.50	.30
156a	Joe Carter (name in brown band)	.15	.11	.06
156b	Joe Carter (name in red band)	1.00	.70	.40
157	Danny Jackson	.15	.11	.06
158	Carney Lansford	.10	.08	.04
159	Bryn Smith	.05	.04	.02
160	Gary Pettis	.05	.04	.02
161	Oddibe McDowell	.10	.08	.04
162	*John Cangelosi*	.12	.09	.05
163	Mike Scott	.15	.11	.06
164	Eric Show	.07	.05	.03
165	Juan Samuel	.12	.09	.05
166	Nick Esasky	.07	.05	.03
167	Zane Smith	.07	.05	.03
168	Mike Brown	.05	.04	.02
169	Keith Moreland	.07	.05	.03
170	John Tudor	.10	.08	.04
171	Ken Dixon	.05	.04	.02
172	Jim Gantner	.07	.05	.03
173	Jack Morris	.15	.11	.06
174	Bruce Hurst	.10	.08	.04
175	Dennis Rasmussen	.10	.08	.04
176	Mike Marshall	.12	.09	.05
177	Dan Quisenberry	.07	.05	.03
178	Eric Plunk (FC)	.10	.08	.04
179	Tim Wallach	.12	.09	.05
180	Steve Buechele	.07	.05	.03
181	Don Sutton	.20	.15	.08
182	Dave Schmidt	.05	.04	.02
183	Terry Pendleton	.25	.20	.10
184	*Jim Deshaies*	.15	.11	.06
185	Steve Bedrosian	.12	.09	.05
186	Pete Rose	.60	.45	.25
187	Dave Dravecky	.07	.05	.03
188	Rick Reuschel	.10	.08	.04
189	Dan Gladden	.05	.04	.02
190	Rick Mahler	.05	.04	.02
191	Thad Bosley	.05	.04	.02
192	Ron Darling	.15	.11	.06
193	Matt Young	.05	.04	.02
194	Tom Brunansky	.10	.08	.04
195	Dave Stieb	.12	.09	.05
196	Frank Viola	.15	.11	.06
197	Tom Henke	.07	.05	.03
198	Karl Best	.05	.04	.02
199	Dwight Gooden	.25	.20	.10
200	Checklist 134-239	.05	.04	.02
201	Steve Trout	.05	.04	.02
202	Rafael Ramirez	.05	.04	.02
203	Bob Walk	.05	.04	.02
204	Roger Mason	.05	.04	.02
205	Terry Kennedy	.07	.05	.03
206	Ron Oester	.05	.04	.02
207	John Russell	.05	.04	.02

208	*Greg Mathews*	.10	.08	.04
209	Charlie Kerfeld	.10	.08	.04
210	Reggie Jackson	.35	.25	.14
211	Floyd Bannister	.10	.08	.04
212	Vance Law	.07	.05	.03
213	Rich Bordi	.05	.04	.02
214	*Dan Plesac*	.10	.08	.04
215	Dave Collins	.07	.05	.03
216	Bob Stanley	.05	.04	.02
217	Joe Niekro	.10	.08	.04
218	Tom Niedenfuer	.07	.05	.03
219	Brett Butler	.07	.05	.03
220	Charlie Leibrandt	.07	.05	.03
221	Steve Ontiveros	.05	.04	.02
222	Tim Burke	.05	.04	.02
223	Curtis Wilkerson	.05	.04	.02
224	*Pete Incaviglia*	.25	.20	.10
225	Lonnie Smith	.07	.05	.03
226	Chris Codiroli	.05	.04	.02
227	*Scott Bailes*	.08	.06	.03
228	Rickey Henderson	.60	.45	.25
229	Ken Howell	.05	.04	.02
230	Darnell Coles	.07	.05	.03
231	Don Aase	.05	.04	.02
232	Tim Leary	.07	.05	.03
233	Bob Boone	.07	.05	.03
234	Ricky Horton	.07	.05	.03
235	Mark Bailey	.05	.04	.02
236	Kevin Gross	.07	.05	.03
237	Lance McCullers	.07	.05	.03
238	Cecilio Guante	.05	.04	.02
239	Bob Melvin	.05	.04	.02
240	Billy Jo Robidoux	.05	.04	.02
241	Roger McDowell	.12	.09	.05
242	Leon Durham	.07	.05	.03
243	Ed Nunez	.05	.04	.02
244	Jimmy Key	.12	.09	.05
245	Mike Smithson	.05	.04	.02
246	Bo Diaz	.07	.05	.03
247	Carlton Fisk	.20	.15	.08
248	Larry Sheets	.08	.06	.03
249	*Juan Castillo* (FC)	.10	.08	.04
250	*Eric King*	.08	.06	.03
251	*Doug Drabek*	.75	.60	.30
252	Wade Boggs	.75	.60	.30
253	Mariano Duncan	.05	.04	.02
254	Pat Tabler	.07	.05	.03
255	Frank White	.10	.08	.04
256	Alfredo Griffin	.07	.05	.03
257	Floyd Youmans	.07	.05	.03
258	Rob Wilfong	.05	.04	.02
259	Pete O'Brien	.10	.08	.04
260	Tim Hulett	.05	.04	.02
261	Dickie Thon	.07	.05	.03
262	Darren Daulton	1.00	.70	.40
263	Vince Coleman	.12	.09	.05
264	Andy Hawkins	.05	.04	.02
265	Eric Davis	.30	.25	.12
266	*Andres Thomas*	.15	.11	.06
267	*Mike Diaz* (FC)	.15	.11	.06
268	Chili Davis	.07	.05	.03
269	Jody Davis	.07	.05	.03
270	Phil Bradley	.12	.09	.05
271	George Bell	.25	.20	.10
272	Keith Atherton	.05	.04	.02
273	Storm Davis	.10	.08	.04
274	Rob Deer (FC)	.10	.08	.04
275	Walt Terrell	.07	.05	.03
276	Roger Clemens	2.00	1.50	.80
277	Mike Easler	.07	.05	.03
278	Steve Sax	.15	.11	.06
279	Andre Thornton	.07	.05	.03
280	Jim Sundberg	.07	.05	.03
281	Bill Bathe	.05	.04	.02
282	Jay Tibbs	.05	.04	.02
283	Dick Schofield	.05	.04	.02
284	Mike Mason	.05	.04	.02
285	Jerry Hairston	.05	.04	.02
286	Bill Doran	.10	.08	.04
287	Tim Flannery	.05	.04	.02
288	Gary Redus	.05	.04	.02
289	John Franco	.10	.08	.04
290	*Paul Assenmacher*	.15	.11	.06
291	Joe Orsulak	.05	.04	.02
292	Lee Smith	.15	.11	.06
293	Mike Laga	.05	.04	.02
294	Rick Dempsey	.07	.05	.03
295	Mike Felder	.05	.04	.02
296	Tom Brookens	.05	.04	.02
297	Al Nipper	.05	.04	.02
298	Mike Pagliarulo	.10	.08	.04
299	Franklin Stubbs	.07	.05	.03
300	Checklist 240-345	.05	.04	.02
301	Steve Farr	.05	.04	.02
302	*Bill Mooneyham*	.10	.08	.04
303	Andres Galarraga	.60	.45	.25
304	Scott Fletcher	.07	.05	.03
305	Jack Howell	.07	.05	.03
306	*Russ Morman* (FC)	.10	.08	.04
307	Todd Worrell	.20	.15	.08
308	Dave Smith	.07	.05	.03
309	Jeff Stone	.05	.04	.02
310	Ron Robinson	.05	.04	.02
311	Bruce Bochy	.05	.04	.02
312	Jim Winn	.05	.04	.02
313	Mark Davis	.05	.04	.02
314	Jeff Dedmon	.05	.04	.02
315	*Jamie Moyer* (FC)	.07	.05	.03
316	Wally Backman	.07	.05	.03
317	Ken Phelps	.07	.05	.03
318	Steve Lombardozzi	.05	.04	.02
319	Rance Mulliniks	.05	.04	.02
320	Tim Laudner	.05	.04	.02
321	*Mark Eichhorn*	.07	.05	.03
322	*Lee Guetterman*	.07	.05	.03
323	Sid Fernandez	.12	.09	.05
324	Jerry Mumphrey	.05	.04	.02
325	David Palmer	.05	.04	.02
326	Bill Almon	.05	.04	.02
327	Candy Maldonado	.07	.05	.03
328	*John Kruk*	2.00	1.50	.80
329	John Denny	.05	.04	.02
330	Milt Thompson	.07	.05	.03
331	*Mike LaValliere*	.15	.11	.06
332	Alan Ashby	.05	.04	.02
333	Doug Corbett	.05	.04	.02
334	*Ron Karkovice* (FC)	.10	.08	.04
335	Mitch Webster	.07	.05	.03
336	Lee Lacy	.05	.04	.02
337	*Glenn Braggs* (FC)	.15	.11	.06
338	Dwight Lowry	.05	.04	.02
339	Don Baylor	.12	.09	.05
340	Brian Fisher	.07	.05	.03
341	*Reggie Williams*	.10	.08	.04
342	Tom Candiotti	.05	.04	.02
343	Rudy Law	.05	.04	.02
344	Curt Young	.07	.05	.03
345	Mike Fitzgerald	.05	.04	.02
346	*Ruben Sierra*	3.50	2.75	1.50
347	*Mitch Williams*	.35	.25	.14
348	Jorge Orta	.05	.04	.02
349	Mickey Tettleton	.10	.08	.04
350	Ernie Camacho	.05	.04	.02
351	Ron Kittle	.10	.08	.04
352	Ken Landreaux	.05	.04	.02
353	Chet Lemon	.07	.05	.03
354	John Shelby	.05	.04	.02
355	Mark Clear	.05	.04	.02
356	Doug DeCinces	.07	.05	.03
357	Ken Dayley	.05	.04	.02
358	Phil Garner	.05	.04	.02
359	Steve Jeltz	.05	.04	.02
360	Ed Whitson	.05	.04	.02
361	*Barry Bonds*	11.00	8.25	4.50
362	Vida Blue	.10	.08	.04
363	Cecil Cooper	.12	.09	.05
364	Bob Ojeda	.07	.05	.03
365	Dennis Eckersley	.20	.15	.08
366	Mike Morgan	.05	.04	.02
367	Willie Upshaw	.07	.05	.03
368	*Allan Anderson* (FC)	.10	.08	.04
369	Bill Gullickson	.07	.05	.03
370	*Bobby Thigpen* (FC)	.08	.06	.03
371	Juan Beniquez	.05	.04	.02
372	Charlie Moore	.05	.04	.02
373	Dan Petry	.07	.05	.03
374	Rod Scurry	.05	.04	.02
375	Tom Seaver	.40	.30	.15
376	Ed Vande Berg	.05	.04	.02
377	Tony Bernazard	.05	.04	.02
378	Greg Pryor	.05	.04	.02
379	Dwayne Murphy	.07	.05	.03
380	Andy McGaffigan	.05	.04	.02
381	Kirk McCaskill	.07	.05	.03
382	Greg Harris	.05	.04	.02
383	Rich Dotson	.07	.05	.03
384	Craig Reynolds	.05	.04	.02
385	Greg Gross	.05	.04	.02
386	Tito Landrum	.05	.04	.02
387	Craig Lefferts	.05	.04	.02
388	Dave Parker	.25	.20	.10
389	Bob Horner	.10	.08	.04
390	Pat Clements	.05	.04	.02
391	Jeff Leonard	.07	.05	.03
392	Chris Speier	.05	.04	.02
393	John Moses	.05	.04	.02
394	Garth Iorg	.05	.04	.02
395	Greg Gagne	.05	.04	.02
396	Nate Snell	.05	.04	.02
397	*Bryan Clutterbuck* (FC)	.10	.08	.04
398	Darrell Evans	.12	.09	.05
399	Steve Crawford	.05	.04	.02
400	Checklist 346-451	.05	.04	.02
401	*Phil Lombardi* (FC)	.10	.08	.04
402	Rick Honeycutt	.05	.04	.02
403	Ken Schrom	.05	.04	.02
404	Bud Black	.05	.04	.02
405	Donnie Hill	.05	.04	.02
406	Wayne Krenchicki	.05	.04	.02
407	*Chuck Finley* (FC)	.35	.25	.14
408	Toby Harrah	.07	.05	.03
409	Steve Lyons	.05	.04	.02
410	Kevin Bass	.10	.08	.04
411	Marvell Wynne	.05	.04	.02
412	Ron Roenicke	.05	.04	.02
413	*Tracy Jones*	.10	.08	.04
414	Gene Garber	.05	.04	.02
415	Mike Bielecki	.05	.04	.02
416	Frank DiPino	.05	.04	.02
417	Andy Van Slyke	.25	.20	.10
418	Jim Dwyer	.05	.04	.02
419	Ben Oglivie	.07	.05	.03
420	Dave Bergman	.05	.04	.02
421	Joe Sambito	.05	.04	.02
422	*Bob Tewksbury*	.20	.15	.08
423	Len Matuszek	.05	.04	.02
424	*Mike Kingery* (FC)	.07	.05	.03
425	Dave Kingman	.12	.09	.05
426	*Al Newman*	.07	.05	.03
427	Gary Ward	.07	.05	.03
428	Ruppert Jones	.05	.04	.02
429	Harold Baines	.15	.11	.06
430	Pat Perry	.05	.04	.02
431	Terry Puhl	.05	.04	.02
432	Don Carman	.07	.05	.03
433	Eddie Milner	.05	.04	.02
434	LaMarr Hoyt	.05	.04	.02
435	Rick Rhoden	.10	.08	.04
436	Jose Uribe	.07	.05	.03
437	Ken Oberkfell	.05	.04	.02
438	Ron Davis	.05	.04	.02
439	Jesse Orosco	.07	.05	.03
440	Scott Bradley	.05	.04	.02
441	Randy Bush	.05	.04	.02
442	*John Cerutti*	.10	.08	.04
443	Roy Smalley	.05	.04	.02
444	Kelly Gruber	.25	.20	.10
445	Bob Kearney	.05	.04	.02
446	*Ed Hearn*	.10	.08	.04
447	Scott Sanderson	.05	.04	.02
448	Bruce Benedict	.05	.04	.02
449	Junior Ortiz	.05	.04	.02
450	*Mike Aldrete*	.07	.05	.03
451	Kevin McReynolds	.15	.11	.06
452	*Rob Murphy* (FC)	.20	.15	.08
453	Kent Tekulve	.07	.05	.03
454	Curt Ford (FC)	.07	.05	.03
455	Davey Lopes	.07	.05	.03
456	Bobby Grich	.10	.08	.04
457	Jose DeLeon	.07	.05	.03
458	Andre Dawson	.30	.25	.12
459	Mike Flanagan	.07	.05	.03
460	*Joey Meyer* (FC)	.06	.05	.02
461	*Chuck Cary* (FC)	.05	.04	.02
462	Bill Buckner	.10	.08	.04
463	Bob Shirley	.05	.04	.02
464	*Jeff Hamilton* (FC)	.06	.05	.02
465	Phil Niekro	.15	.11	.06
466	Mark Gubicza	.12	.09	.05
467	Jerry Willard	.05	.04	.02
468	*Bob Sebra* (FC)	.05	.04	.02
469	Larry Parrish	.10	.08	.04
470	Charlie Hough	.07	.05	.03
471	Hal McRae	.10	.08	.04
472	*Dave Leiper* (FC)	.05	.04	.02
473	Mel Hall	.07	.05	.03
474	Dan Pasqua	.10	.08	.04
475	Bob Welch	.10	.08	.04
476	Johnny Grubb	.05	.04	.02
477	Jim Traber	.07	.05	.03
478	*Chris Bosio* (FC)	.40	.30	.15
479	Mark McLemore	.07	.05	.03
480	John Morris	.05	.04	.02
481	Billy Hatcher	.07	.05	.03
482	Dan Schatzeder	.05	.04	.02
483	Rich Gossage	.15	.11	.06
484	Jim Morrison	.05	.04	.02
485	Bob Brenly	.05	.04	.02
486	Bill Schroeder	.05	.04	.02
487	Mookie Wilson	.10	.08	.04
488	*Dave Martinez* (FC)	.15	.11	.06
489	Harold Reynolds	.10	.08	.04
490	Jeff Hearron	.05	.04	.02
491	Mickey Hatcher	.05	.04	.02
492	*Barry Larkin* (FC)	3.00	2.25	1.25
493	Bob James	.05	.04	.02
494	John Habyan	.05	.04	.02
495	*Jim Adduci* (FC)	.07	.05	.03
496	Mike Heath	.05	.04	.02
497	Tim Stoddard	.05	.04	.02
498	Tony Armas	.07	.05	.03
499	Dennis Powell	.05	.04	.02
500	Checklist 452-557	.05	.04	.02
501	Chris Bando	.05	.04	.02
502	*David Cone*	3.00	2.25	1.25
503	Jay Howell	.07	.05	.03
504	Tom Foley	.05	.04	.02
505	*Ray Chadwick* (FC)	.10	.08	.04
506	*Mike Loynd* (FC)	.15	.11	.06
507	Neil Allen	.05	.04	.02
508	Danny Darwin	.05	.04	.02
509	Rick Schu	.05	.04	.02
510	Jose Oquendo	.05	.04	.02
511	Gene Walter	.07	.05	.03
512	*Terry McGriff* (FC)	.12	.09	.05
513	Ken Griffey	.10	.08	.04
514	Benny Distefano	.05	.04	.02
515	*Terry Mulholland* (FC)	.80	.60	.30
516	Ed Lynch	.05	.04	.02
517	Bill Swift	.25	.20	.10
518	Manny Lee (FC)	.07	.05	.03
519	Andre David	.05	.04	.02
520	Scott McGregor	.07	.05	.03
521	Rick Manning	.05	.04	.02
522	Willie Hernandez	.07	.05	.03
523	Marty Barrett	.10	.08	.04
524	Wayne Tolleson	.05	.04	.02
525	*Jose Gonzalez* (FC)	.15	.11	.06
526	Cory Snyder	.12	.09	.05
527	Buddy Biancalana	.05	.04	.02
528	Moose Haas	.05	.04	.02
529	*Wilfredo Tejada* (FC)	.10	.08	.04
530	Stu Cliburn	.05	.04	.02
531	*Dale Mohorcic* (FC)	.07	.05	.03
532	Ron Hassey	.05	.04	.02
533	Ty Gainey	.05	.04	.02
534	Jerry Royster	.05	.04	.02
535	*Mike Maddux* (FC)	.10	.08	.04
536	Ted Power	.05	.04	.02
537	Ted Simmons	.12	.09	.05
538	*Rafael Belliard* (FC)	.12	.09	.05
539	Chico Walker	.05	.04	.02
540	Bob Forsch	.07	.05	.03
541	John Stefero	.05	.04	.02
542	*Dale Sveum*	.08	.06	.03
543	Mark Thurmond	.05	.04	.02
544	*Jeff Sellers*	.07	.05	.03
545	Joel Skinner	.05	.04	.02
546	Alex Trevino	.05	.04	.02
547	*Randy Kutcher* (FC)	.10	.08	.04
548	Joaquin Andujar	.07	.05	.03
549	*Casey Candaele* (FC)	.15	.11	.06
550	Jeff Russell	.05	.04	.02
551	John Candelaria	.10	.08	.04
552	Joe Cowley	.05	.04	.02
553	Danny Cox	.07	.05	.03
554	Denny Walling	.05	.04	.02
555	*Bruce Ruffin* (FC)	.20	.15	.08
556	Buddy Bell	.10	.08	.04
557	*Jimmy Jones* (FC)	.20	.15	.08
558	*Bobby Bonilla*	2.00	1.50	.80
559	Jeff Robinson	.07	.05	.03
560	Ed Olwine	.05	.04	.02
561	*Glenallen Hill* (FC)	.30	.25	.12

562	Lee Mazzilli	.07	.05	.03
563	Mike Brown	.05	.04	.02
564	George Frazier	.05	.04	.02
565	*Mike Sharperson* (FC)	.10	.08	.04
566	*Mark Portugal*	.10	.08	.04
567	Rick Leach	.05	.04	.02
568	Mark Langston	.12	.09	.05
569	Rafael Santana	.05	.04	.02
570	Manny Trillo	.07	.05	.03
571	Cliff Speck	.05	.04	.02
572	Bob Kipper	.05	.04	.02
573	*Kelly Downs* (FC)	.10	.08	.04
574	*Randy Asadoor* (FC)	.10	.08	.04
575	*Dave Magadan* (FC)	.40	.30	.15
576	*Marvin Freeman* (FC)	.12	.09	.05
577	Jeff Lahti	.05	.04	.02
578	Jeff Calhoun	.05	.04	.02
579	Gus Polidor (FC)	.07	.05	.03
580	Gene Nelson	.05	.04	.02
581	Tim Teufel	.05	.04	.02
582	Odell Jones	.05	.04	.02
583	Mark Ryal	.05	.04	.02
584	Randy O'Neal	.05	.04	.02
585	*Mike Greenwell* (FC)	1.25	.90	.50
586	Ray Knight	.07	.05	.03
587	*Ralph Bryant* (FC)	.12	.09	.05
588	Carmen Castillo	.05	.04	.02
589	Ed Wojna	.05	.04	.02
590	Stan Javier	.05	.04	.02
591	*Jeff Musselman* (FC)	.20	.15	.08
592	*Mike Stanley* (FC)	.75	.60	.30
593	Darrell Porter	.07	.05	.03
594	*Drew Hall* (FC)	.07	.05	.03
595	*Rob Nelson* (FC)	.10	.08	.04
596	Bryan Oelkers	.05	.04	.02
597	*Scott Nielsen* (FC)	.10	.08	.04
598	*Brian Holton* (FC)	.20	.15	.08
599	*Kevin Mitchell*	1.50	1.25	.60
600	Checklist 558-660	.05	.04	.02
601	Jackie Gutierrez	.05	.04	.02
602	*Barry Jones* (FC)	.12	.09	.05
603	Jerry Narron	.05	.04	.02
604	Steve Lake	.05	.04	.02
605	Jim Pankovits	.05	.04	.02
606	Ed Romero	.05	.04	.02
607	Dave LaPoint	.07	.05	.03
608	Don Robinson	.07	.05	.03
609	Mike Krukow	.07	.05	.03
610	*Dave Valle* (FC)	.12	.09	.05
611	Len Dykstra	.80	.60	.30
612	Roberto Clemente Puzzle Card	.05	.04	.02
613	Mike Trujillo (FC)	.05	.04	.02
614	Damaso Garcia	.05	.04	.02
615	Neal Heaton	.05	.04	.02
616	Juan Berenguer	.05	.04	.02
617	Steve Carlton	.25	.20	.10
618	Gary Lucas	.05	.04	.02
619	Geno Petralli	.05	.04	.02
620	Rick Aguilera	.20	.15	.08
621	Fred McGriff	4.00	3.00	1.50
622	Dave Henderson	.10	.08	.04
623	*Dave Clark* (FC)	.08	.06	.03
624	Angel Salazar	.05	.04	.02
625	Randy Hunt	.05	.04	.02
626	John Gibbons	.05	.04	.02
627	*Kevin Brown*	1.75	1.25	.70
628	Bill Dawley	.05	.04	.02
629	Aurelio Lopez	.05	.04	.02
630	Charlie Hudson	.05	.04	.02
631	Ray Soff	.05	.04	.02
632	*Ray Hayward* (FC)	.12	.09	.05
633	Spike Owen	.05	.04	.02
634	Glenn Hubbard	.05	.04	.02
635	*Kevin Elster* (FC)	.08	.06	.03
636	Mike LaCoss	.05	.04	.02
637	Dwayne Henry	.05	.04	.02
638	*Rey Quinones*	.07	.05	.03
639	Jim Clancy	.07	.05	.03
640	Larry Andersen	.05	.04	.02
641	Calvin Schiraldi	.05	.04	.02
642	*Stan Jefferson* (FC)	.15	.11	.06
643	Marc Sullivan	.05	.04	.02
644	Mark Grant	.05	.04	.02
645	Cliff Johnson	.05	.04	.02
646	Howard Johnson	.10	.08	.04
647	Dave Sax	.05	.04	.02
648	Dave Stewart	.10	.08	.04
649	Danny Heep	.05	.04	.02
650	Joe Johnson	.05	.04	.02
651	*Bob Brower* (FC)	.07	.05	.03
652	Rob Woodward	.07	.05	.03
653	John Mizerock	.05	.04	.02
654	*Tim Pyznarski* (FC)	.10	.08	.04
655	*Luis Aquino* (FC)	.10	.08	.04
656	Mickey Brantley (FC)	.10	.08	.04
657	Doyle Alexander	.07	.05	.03
658	Sammy Stewart	.05	.04	.02
659	Jim Acker	.05	.04	.02
660	Pete Ladd	.05	.04	.02

Values for recent cards and sets are listed in Mint (MT), Near Mint (NM), reflecting the fact that many cards from recent years have been preserved in top condition. Recent cards and sets in less than Excellent condition have little collector interest.

Values quoted in this guide reflect the retail price of a card – the price a collector can expect to pay when buying a card from a dealer. The wholesale price – that which a collector can expect to receive from a dealer when selling cards – will be significantly lower, depending on desirability and condition.

1987 Donruss All-Stars

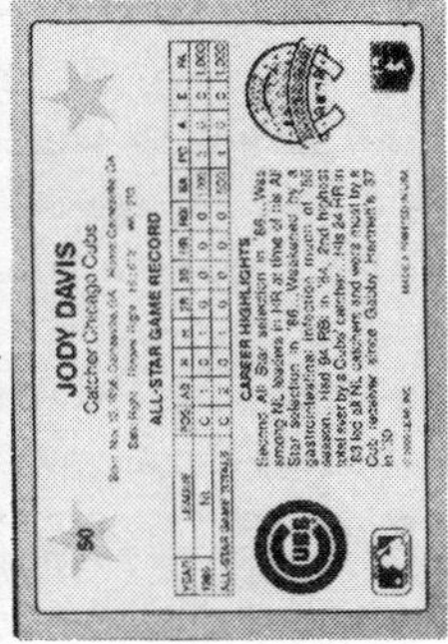

Issued in conjunction with the Donruss Pop-Ups set for the second consecutive year, the 1987 Donruss All-Stars set consists of 59 players (plus a checklist) who were selected to the 1986 All-Star Game. Measuring 3-1/2" by 5" in size, the card fronts feature black borders and American or National League logos. Included on the backs are the player's career highlights and All-Star Game statistics. Retail packs included one pop-Up card, three All-Star cards and one Roberto Clemente puzzle.

		MT	NR MT	EX
	Complete Set:	7.00	5.25	2.75
	Common Player:	.09	.07	.04
1	Wally Joyner	.25	.20	.10
2	Dave Winfield	.50	.40	.20
3	Lou Whitaker	.15	.11	.06
4	Kirby Puckett	.50	.40	.20
5	Cal Ripken, Jr.	1.00	.70	.40
6	Rickey Henderson	.50	.40	.20
7	Wade Boggs	.60	.45	.25
8	Roger Clemens	.35	.25	.14
9	Lance Parrish	.09	.07	.04
10	Dick Howser	.09	.07	.04
11	Keith Hernandez	.10	.08	.04
12	Darryl Strawberry	.25	.20	.10
13	Ryne Sandberg	1.00	.70	.40
14	Dale Murphy	.40	.30	.15
15	Ozzie Smith	.40	.30	.15
16	Tony Gwynn	.30	.25	.12
17	Mike Schmidt	.60	.45	.25
18	Dwight Gooden	.40	.30	.15
19	Gary Carter	.15	.11	.06
20	Whitey Herzog	.09	.07	.04
21	Jose Canseco	.90	.70	.35
22	John Franco	.09	.07	.04
23	Jesse Barfield	.12	.09	.05
24	Rick Rhoden	.09	.07	.04
25	Harold Baines	.15	.11	.06
26	Sid Fernandez	.12	.09	.05
27	George Brett	.60	.45	.25
28	Steve Sax	.15	.11	.06
29	Jim Presley	.12	.09	.05
30	Dave Smith	.09	.07	.04
31	Eddie Murray	.35	.25	.14
32	Mike Scott	.12	.09	.05
33	Don Mattingly	.90	.70	.35
34	Dave Parker	.25	.20	.10
35	Tony Fernandez	.15	.11	.06
36	Tim Raines	.25	.20	.10
37	Brook Jacoby	.12	.09	.05
38	Chili Davis	.09	.07	.04
39	Rich Gedman	.09	.07	.04
40	Kevin Bass	.09	.07	.04
41	Frank White	.09	.07	.04
42	Glenn Davis	.15	.11	.06
43	Willie Hernandez	.09	.07	.04
44	Chris Brown	.09	.07	.04
45	Jim Rice	.10	.08	.04
46	Tony Pena	.09	.07	.04
47	Don Aase	.09	.07	.04
48	Hubie Brooks	.09	.07	.04
49	Charlie Hough	.09	.07	.04
50	Jody Davis	.09	.07	.04
51	Mike Witt	.09	.07	.04
52	Jeff Reardon	.12	.09	.05
53	Ken Schrom	.09	.07	.04
54	Fernando Valenzuela	.10	.08	.04
55	Dave Righetti	.15	.11	.06
56	Shane Rawley	.09	.07	.04
57	Ted Higuera	.12	.09	.05
58	Mike Krukow	.09	.07	.04
59	Lloyd Moseby	.09	.07	.04
60	Checklist	.09	.07	.04

1987 Donruss Box Panels

Continuing with an idea they initiated in 1985, Donruss once again placed baseball cards on the bottoms of their retail boxes. The cards, which are 2-1/2" by 3-1/2" in size, come four to a panel with each panel containing an unnumbered Roberto Clemente puzzle card. With numbering that begins where Donruss left off in 1986, cards PC 10 through PC 12

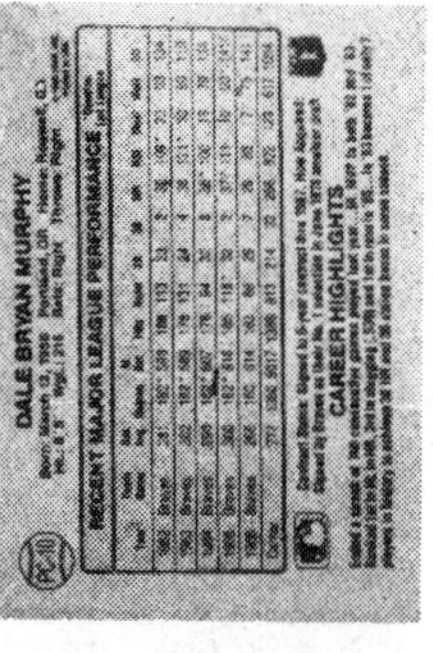

were found on boxes of Donruss regular issue wax packs. Cards PC 13 through PC 15 were located on boxes of the 1987 All-Star/Pop-Up packs.

		MT	NR MT	EX
	Complete Panel Set:	3.50	3.75	2.00
	Complete Singles Set:	3.00	2.25	1.25
	Common Single Player:	.15	.11	.06
	Panel	2.50	3.00	1.50
10	Dale Murphy	.35	.25	.14
11	Jeff Reardon	.20	.15	.08
12	Jose Canseco	2.00	1.50	.80
----	Roberto Clemente Puzzle Card	.04	.03	.02
	Panel	1.50	1.75	.90
13	Mike Scott	.20	.15	.08
14	Roger Clemens	1.00	.70	.40
15	Mike Krukow	.15	.11	.06
----	Roberto Clemente Puzzle Card	.04	.03	.02

1987 Donruss Diamond Kings Supers

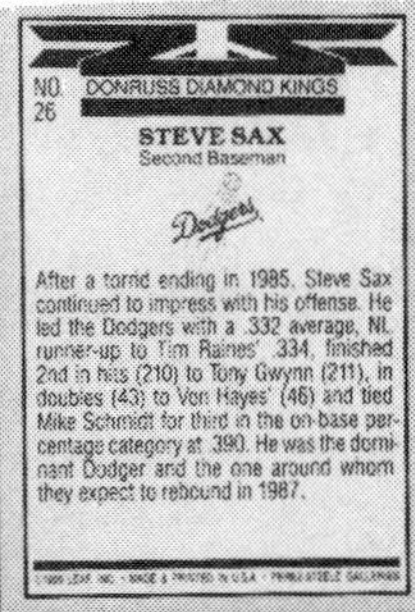

For a third straight baseball card season, Donruss produced a set of enlarged size Diamond Kings. The cards, which measure 4-11/16" by 6-3/4", are giant versions of the Diamond Kings subset found in the regular 1987 Donruss set. The 28-card set, which features the artwork of Dick Perez, contains 26 player cards, a checklist and a Roberto Clemente puzzle card. The set was available through a mail-in offer for $9.50 plus three wrappers.

		MT	NR MT	EX
	Complete Set:	10.00	9.00	4.75
	Common Player:	.20	.15	.08
1	Wally Joyner	.40	.30	.15
2	Roger Clemens	.90	.70	.35
3	Dale Murphy	.40	.30	.15
4	Darryl Strawberry	.60	.45	.25
5	Ozzie Smith	.60	.45	.25
6	Jose Canseco	2.00	1.50	.80
7	Charlie Hough	.20	.15	.08
8	Brook Jacoby	.20	.15	.08
9	Fred Lynn	.20	.15	.08
10	Rick Rhoden	.20	.15	.08
11	Chris Brown	.25	.20	.10
12	Von Hayes	.25	.20	.10
13	Jack Morris	.20	.15	.08
14	Kevin McReynolds	.35	.25	.14
15	George Brett	.70	.50	.30
16	Ted Higuera	.20	.15	.08
17	Hubie Brooks	.20	.15	.08
18	Mike Scott	.20	.15	.08
19	Kirby Puckett	.90	.70	.35
20	Dave Winfield	.50	.40	.20
21	Lloyd Moseby	.20	.15	.08
22	Eric Davis	.60	.45	.25
23	Jim Presley	.25	.20	.10
24	Keith Moreland	.20	.15	.08
25	Greg Walker	.20	.15	.08
26	Steve Sax	.30	.25	.12
27	Checklist	.15	.11	.06
----	Roberto Clemente Puzzle Card	.15	.11	.06

Regional interest may affect the value of a card.

1987 Donruss Highlights

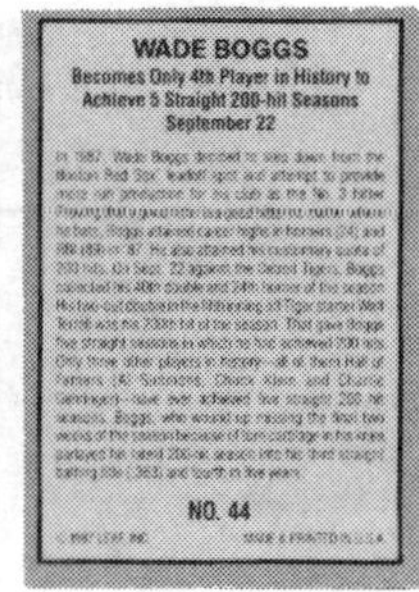

For a third consecutive year, Donruss produced a 56-card set which highlighted the special events of the 1987 baseball season. The cards, which measure 2-1/2" by 3-1/2", have a front design similar to the regular 1987 Donruss set. A blue border and the "Highlights" logo are the significant differences. The card backs feature black print on a white background and include the date the event took place plus the particulars about it. As in the past, the set includes Donruss' picks for the A.L. and N.L. Rookies of the Year. The set was issued in a specially designed box and was available only through hobby dealers.

		MT	NR MT	EX
	Complete Set:	6.00	6.00	3.25
	Common Player:	.10	.08	.04
1	First No-Hitter For Brewers (Juan Nieves)	.15	.11	.06
2	Hits 500th Homer (Mike Schmidt)	.40	.30	.15
3	N.L. Player of the Month - April (Eric Davis)	.25	.20	.10
4	N.L. Pitcher of the Month - April (Sid Fernandez)	.10	.08	.04
5	A.L. Player of the Month - April (Brian Downing)	.10	.08	.04
6	A.L. Pitcher of the Month - April (Bret Saberhagen)	.15	.11	.06
7	Free Agent Holdout Returns (Tim Raines)	.10	.08	.04
8	N.L. Player of the Month - May (Eric Davis)	.25	.20	.10
9	N.L. Pitcher of the Month - May (Steve Bedrosian)	.15	.11	.06
10	A.L. Player of the Month - May (Larry Parrish)	.10	.08	.04
11	A.L. Pitcher of the Month - May (Jim Clancy)	.10	.08	.04
12	N.L. Player of the Month - June (Tony Gwynn)	.30	.25	.12
13	N.L. Pitcher of the Month - June (Orel Hershiser)	.25	.20	.10
14	A.L. Player of the Month - June (Wade Boggs)	.50	.40	.20
15	A.L. Pitcher of the Month - June (Steve Ontiveros)	.10	.08	.04
16	All Star Game Hero (Tim Raines)	.25	.20	.10
17	Consecutive Game Homer Streak (Don Mattingly)	.75	.60	.30
18	1987 Hall of Fame Inductee (Jim "Catfish" Hunter)	.20	.15	.08
19	1987 Hall of Fame Inductee (Ray Dandridge)	.10	.08	.04
20	1987 Hall of Fame Inductee (Billy Williams)	.20	.15	.08
21	N.L. Player of the Month - July (Bo Diaz)	.10	.08	.04
22	N.L. Pitcher of the Month - July (Floyd Youmans)	.10	.08	.04
23	A.L. Player of the Month - July (Don Mattingly)	.75	.60	.30
24	A.L. Pitcher of the Month - July (Frank Viola)	.20	.15	.08
25	Strikes Out 4 Batters In 1 Inning (Bobby Witt)	.15	.11	.06
26	Ties A.L. 9-Inning Game Hit Mark (Kevin Seitzer)	.25	.20	.10
27	Sets Rookie Home Run Record (Mark McGwire)	.60	.45	.25
28	Sets Cubs' 1st Year Homer Mark (Andre Dawson)	.20	.15	.08
29	Hits In 39 Straight Games (Paul Molitor)	.15	.11	.06
30	Record Weekend (Kirby Puckett)	.35	.25	.14
31	N.L. Player of the Month - August (Andre Dawson)	.20	.15	.08
32	N.L. Pitcher of the Month - August (Doug Drabek)	.10	.08	.04
33	A.L. Player of the Month - August (Dwight Evans)	.15	.11	.06
34	A.L. Pitcher of the Month - August (Mark Langston)	.15	.11	.06
35	100 RBI In 1st 2 Major League Seasons (Wally Joyner)	.15	.11	.06
36	100 SB In 1st 3 Major League Seasons (Vince Coleman)	.20	.15	.08
37	Orioles' All Time Homer King (Eddie Murray)	.10	.08	.04
38	Ends Consecutive Innings Streak (Cal Ripken)	.30	.25	.12
39	Blue Jays Hit Record 10 Homers In 1 Game (Rob Ducey, Fred McGriff, Ernie Whitt)	.25	.20	.10
40	Equal A's RBI Marks (Jose Canseco, Mark McGwire)	1.00	.70	.40
41	Sets All-Time Catching Record (Bob Boone)	.10	.08	.04
42	Sets Mets' One-Season HR Mark (Darryl Strawberry)	.25	.20	.10
43	N.L.'s All-Time Switch Hit HR King (Howard Johnson)	.15	.11	.06
44	Five Straight 200-Hit Seasons (Wade Boggs)	.60	.45	.25
45	Eclipses Rookie Game Hitting Streak (Benito Santiago)	.25	.20	.10
46	Eclipses Jackson's A's HR Record (Mark McGwire)	.75	.60	.30
47	13th Rookie To Collect 200 Hits (Kevin Seitzer)	.25	.20	.10
48	Sets Slam Record (Don Mattingly)	.75	.60	.30
49	N.L. Player of the Month - September (Darryl Strawberry)	.25	.20	.10
50	N.L. Pitcher of the Month - September (Pascual Perez)	.10	.08	.04
51	A.L. Player of the Month - September (Alan Trammell)	.20	.15	.08
52	A.L. Pitcher of the Month - September (Doyle Alexander)	.10	.08	.04
53	Strikeout King - Again (Nolan Ryan)	1.00	.70	.40
54	Donruss A.L. Rookie of the Year (Mark McGwire)	.75	.60	.30
55	Donruss N.L. Rookie of the Year (Benito Santiago)	.25	.20	.10
56	Highlight Checklist	.10	.08	.04

1987 Donruss Opening Day

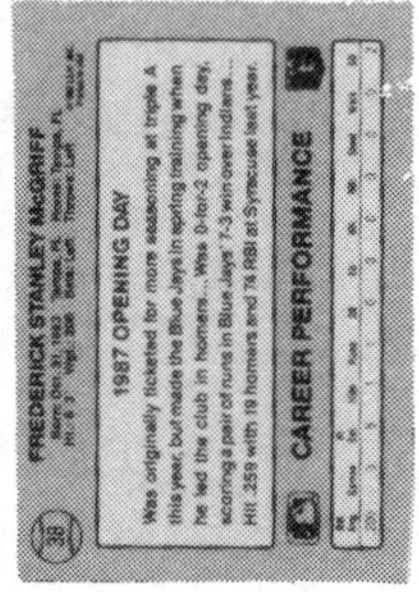

The Donruss Opening Day set includes all players in major league baseball's starting lineups on the opening day of the 1987 baseball season. Cards in the 272-piece set measure 2-1/2" by 3-1/2" and have a glossy coating. The card fronts are identical in design to the regular Donruss set, but new photos were utilized and the fronts contain maroon borders as opposed to black. The backs carry black printing on white and yellow and carry a brief player biography plus the player's career statistics. The set was packaged in a sturdy 15" by 5" by 2" box with a clear acetate lid.

		MT	NR MT	EX
	Complete Set:	15.00	18.50	10.00
	Common Player:	.05	.04	.02
1	Doug DeCinces	.07	.05	.03
2	Mike Witt	.12	.09	.05
3	George Hendrick	.07	.05	.03
4	Dick Schofield	.05	.04	.02
5	Devon White	.35	.25	.14
6	Butch Wynegar	.05	.04	.02
7	Wally Joyner	.50	.40	.20
8	Mark McLemore	.05	.04	.02
9	Brian Downing	.07	.05	.03
10	Gary Pettis	.05	.04	.02
11	Bill Doran	.07	.05	.03
12	Phil Garner	.05	.04	.02
13	Jose Cruz	.07	.05	.03
14	Kevin Bass	.07	.05	.03
15	Mike Scott	.12	.09	.05
16	Glenn Davis	.15	.11	.06
17	Alan Ashby	.05	.04	.02
18	Billy Hatcher	.07	.05	.03
19	Craig Reynolds	.05	.04	.02
20	Carney Lansford	.07	.05	.03
21	Mike Davis	.05	.04	.02
22	Reggie Jackson	.30	.25	.12
23	Mickey Tettleton	.07	.05	.03
24	Jose Canseco	2.00	1.50	.80
25	Rob Nelson	.05	.04	.02
26	Tony Phillips	.05	.04	.02
27	Dwayne Murphy	.05	.04	.02
28	Alfredo Griffin	.07	.05	.03
29	Curt Young	.05	.04	.02
30	Willie Upshaw	.05	.04	.02
31	Mike Sharperson	.05	.04	.02
32	Rance Mulliniks	.05	.04	.02
33	Ernie Whitt	.05	.04	.02
34	Jesse Barfield	.12	.09	.05
35	Tony Fernandez	.12	.09	.05
36	Lloyd Moseby	.07	.05	.03
37	Jimmy Key	.10	.08	.04
38	Fred McGriff	1.50	1.25	.60
39	George Bell	.25	.20	.10
40	Dale Murphy	.40	.30	.15
41	Rick Mahler	.05	.04	.02
42	Ken Griffey	.07	.05	.03
43	Andres Thomas	.10	.08	.04
44	Dion James	.05	.04	.02
45	Ozzie Virgil	.05	.04	.02
46	Ken Oberkfell	.05	.04	.02
47	Gary Roenicke	.05	.04	.02
48	Glenn Hubbard	.05	.04	.02
49	Bill Schroeder	.05	.04	.02
50	Greg Brock	.07	.05	.03
51	Billy Jo Robidoux	.05	.04	.02
52	Glenn Braggs	.12	.09	.05
53	Jim Gantner	.05	.04	.02
54	Paul Molitor	.35	.25	.14
55	Dale Sveum	.15	.11	.06
56	Ted Higuera	.12	.09	.05
57	Rob Deer	.07	.05	.03
58	Robin Yount	.35	.25	.14
59	Jim Lindeman	.10	.08	.04
60	Vince Coleman	.15	.11	.06
61	Tommy Herr	.07	.05	.03
62	Terry Pendleton	.07	.05	.03
63	John Tudor	.10	.08	.04
64	Tony Pena	.07	.05	.03
65	Ozzie Smith	.15	.11	.06
66	Tito Landrum	.05	.04	.02
67	Jack Clark	.15	.11	.06
68	Bob Dernier	.05	.04	.02
69	Rick Sutcliffe	.10	.08	.04
70	Andre Dawson	.20	.15	.08
71	Keith Moreland	.07	.05	.03
72	Jody Davis	.07	.05	.03
73	Brian Dayett	.05	.04	.02
74	Leon Durham	.07	.05	.03
75	Ryne Sandberg	.75	.60	.30
76	Shawon Dunston	.20	.15	.08
77	Mike Marshall	.10	.08	.04
78	Bill Madlock	.07	.05	.03
79	Orel Hershiser	.20	.15	.08
80	Mike Ramsey	.05	.04	.02
81	Ken Landreaux	.05	.04	.02
82	Mike Scioscia	.05	.04	.02
83	Franklin Stubbs	.07	.05	.03
84	Mariano Duncan	.05	.04	.02
85	Steve Sax	.15	.11	.06
86	Mitch Webster	.07	.05	.03
87	Reid Nichols	.05	.04	.02
88	Tim Wallach	.10	.08	.04
89	Floyd Youmans	.07	.05	.03
90	Andres Galarraga	.25	.20	.10
91	Hubie Brooks	.07	.05	.03
92	Jeff Reed	.05	.04	.02
93	Alonzo Powell	.05	.04	.02
94	Vance Law	.05	.04	.02
95	Bob Brenly	.05	.04	.02
96	Will Clark	2.50	2.00	1.00
97	Chili Davis	.07	.05	.03
98	Mike Krukow	.05	.04	.02
99	Jose Uribe	.05	.04	.02
100	Chris Brown	.07	.05	.03
101	Rob Thompson	.10	.08	.04
102	Candy Maldonado	.07	.05	.03
103	Jeff Leonard	.07	.05	.03
104	Tom Candiotti	.05	.04	.02
105	Chris Bando	.05	.04	.02
106	Cory Snyder	.10	.08	.04
107	Pat Tabler	.07	.05	.03
108	Andre Thornton	.07	.05	.03
109	Joe Carter	.25	.20	.10
110	Tony Bernazard	.05	.04	.02
111	Julio Franco	.10	.08	.04
112	Brook Jacoby	.10	.08	.04
113	Brett Butler	.07	.05	.03
114	Donnell Nixon	.05	.04	.02
115	Alvin Davis	.12	.09	.05
116	Mark Langston	.25	.20	.10
117	Harold Reynolds	.07	.05	.03
118	Ken Phelps	.05	.04	.02
119	Mike Kingery	.05	.04	.02
120	Dave Valle	.07	.05	.03
121	Rey Quinones	.07	.05	.03
122	Phil Bradley	.05	.04	.02
123	Jim Presley	.05	.04	.02
124	Keith Hernandez	.07	.05	.03
125	Kevin McReynolds	.12	.09	.05
126	Rafael Santana	.05	.04	.02
127	Bob Ojeda	.07	.05	.03
128	Darryl Strawberry	.30	.25	.12
129	Mookie Wilson	.07	.05	.03
130	Gary Carter	.15	.11	.06
131	Tim Teufel	.05	.04	.02
132	Howard Johnson	.20	.15	.08
133	Cal Ripken, Jr.	.75	.60	.30
134	Rick Burleson	.05	.04	.02
135	Fred Lynn	.12	.09	.05
136	Eddie Murray	.15	.11	.06
137	Ray Knight	.07	.05	.03
138	Alan Wiggins	.05	.04	.02
139	John Shelby	.05	.04	.02
140	Mike Boddicker	.07	.05	.03
141	Ken Gerhart	.07	.05	.03
142	Terry Kennedy	.07	.05	.03
143	Steve Garvey	.30	.25	.12
144	Marvell Wynne	.05	.04	.02
145	Kevin Mitchell	.60	.45	.25
146	Tony Gwynn	.35	.25	.14
147	Joey Cora	.10	.08	.04
148	Benito Santiago	.40	.30	.15
149	Eric Show	.07	.05	.03
150	Garry Templeton	.07	.05	.03
151	Carmelo Martinez	.05	.04	.02
152	Von Hayes	.10	.08	.04
153	Lance Parrish	.10	.08	.04
154	Milt Thompson	.07	.05	.03

155	Mike Easler	.05	.04	.02
156	Juan Samuel	.10	.08	.04
157	Steve Jeltz	.05	.04	.02
158	Glenn Wilson	.05	.04	.02
159	Shane Rawley	.07	.05	.03
160	Mike Schmidt	.40	.30	.15
161	Andy Van Slyke	.10	.08	.04
162	Johnny Ray	.07	.05	.03
163a	Barry Bonds (dark jersey, photo actually Johnny Ray)	125.00	94.00	50.00
163b	Barry Bonds (white jersey, correct photo)	.50	.40	.20
164	Junior Ortiz	.05	.04	.02
165	Rafael Belliard	.05	.04	.02
166	Bob Patterson	.05	.04	.02
167	Bobby Bonilla	.50	.40	.20
168	Sid Bream	.07	.05	.03
169	Jim Morrison	.05	.04	.02
170	Jerry Browne	.10	.08	.04
171	Scott Fletcher	.05	.04	.02
172	Ruben Sierra	.90	.70	.35
173	Larry Parrish	.07	.05	.03
174	Pete O'Brien	.07	.05	.03
175	Pete Incaviglia	.15	.11	.06
176	Don Slaught	.05	.04	.02
177	Oddibe McDowell	.10	.08	.04
178	Charlie Hough	.07	.05	.03
179	Steve Buechele	.05	.04	.02
180	Bob Stanley	.05	.04	.02
181	Wade Boggs	1.00	.70	.40
182	Jim Rice	.10	.08	.04
183	Bill Buckner	.07	.05	.03
184	Dwight Evans	.10	.08	.04
185	Spike Owen	.05	.04	.02
186	Don Baylor	.10	.08	.04
187	Marc Sullivan	.05	.04	.02
188	Marty Barrett	.07	.05	.03
189	Dave Henderson	.07	.05	.03
190	Bo Diaz	.05	.04	.02
191	Barry Larkin	.60	.45	.25
192	Kal Daniels	.25	.20	.10
193	Terry Francona	.05	.04	.02
194	Tom Browning	.07	.05	.03
195	Ron Oester	.05	.04	.02
196	Buddy Bell	.07	.05	.03
197	Eric Davis	.40	.30	.15
198	Dave Parker	.15	.11	.06
199	Steve Balboni	.05	.04	.02
200	Danny Tartabull	.30	.25	.12
201	Ed Hearn	.05	.04	.02
202	Buddy Biancalana	.05	.04	.02
203	Danny Jackson	.05	.04	.02
204	Frank White	.08	.06	.03
205	Bo Jackson	2.50	2.00	1.00
206	George Brett	.40	.30	.15
207	Kevin Seitzer	.30	.25	.12
208	Willie Wilson	.10	.08	.04
209	Orlando Mercado	.05	.04	.02
210	Darrell Evans	.07	.05	.03
211	Larry Herndon	.05	.04	.02
212	Jack Morris	.15	.11	.06
213	Chet Lemon	.07	.05	.03
214	Mike Heath	.05	.04	.02
215	Darnell Coles	.07	.05	.03
216	Alan Trammell	.20	.15	.08
217	Terry Harper	.05	.04	.02
218	Lou Whitaker	.15	.11	.06
219	Gary Gaetti	.15	.11	.06
220	Tom Nieto	.05	.04	.02
221	Kirby Puckett	.80	.60	.30
222	Tom Brunansky	.10	.08	.04
223	Greg Gagne	.05	.04	.02
224	Dan Gladden	.07	.05	.03
225	Mark Davidson	.07	.05	.03
226	Bert Blyleven	.10	.08	.04
227	Steve Lombardozzi	.05	.04	.02
228	Kent Hrbek	.15	.11	.06
229	Gary Redus	.05	.04	.02
230	Ivan Calderon	.10	.08	.04
231	Tim Hulett	.05	.04	.02
232	Carlton Fisk	.15	.11	.06
233	Greg Walker	.07	.05	.03
234	Ron Karkovice	.05	.04	.02
235	Ozzie Guillen	.07	.05	.03
236	Harold Baines	.12	.09	.05
237	Donnie Hill	.05	.04	.02
238	Rich Dotson	.07	.05	.03
239	Mike Pagliarulo	.10	.08	.04
240	Joel Skinner	.05	.04	.02
241	Don Mattingly	1.50	1.25	.60
242	Gary Ward	.05	.04	.02
243	Dave Winfield	.45	.35	.20
244	Dan Pasqua	.10	.08	.04
245	Wayne Tolleson	.05	.04	.02
246	Willie Randolph	.07	.05	.03
247	Dennis Rasmussen	.07	.05	.03
248	Rickey Henderson	.50	.40	.20
249	Angels Checklist	.05	.04	.02
250	Astros Checklist	.05	.04	.02
251	Athletics Checklist	.05	.04	.02
252	Blue Jays Checklist	.05	.04	.02
253	Braves Checklist	.05	.04	.02
254	Brewers Checklist	.05	.04	.02
255	Cardinals Checklist	.05	.04	.02
256	Dodgers Checklist	.05	.04	.02
257	Expos Checklist	.05	.04	.02
258	Giants Checklist	.05	.04	.02
259	Indians Checklist	.05	.04	.02
260	Mariners Checklist	.05	.04	.02
261	Orioles Checklist	.05	.04	.02
262	Padres Checklist	.05	.04	.02
263	Phillies Checklist	.05	.04	.02
264	Pirates Checklist	.05	.04	.02
265	Rangers Checklist	.05	.04	.02
266	Red Sox Checklist	.05	.04	.02
267	Reds Checklist	.05	.04	.02
268	Royals Checklist	.05	.04	.02
269	Tigers Checklist	.05	.04	.02
270	Twins Checklist	.05	.04	.02
271	White Sox/Cubs Checklist	.05	.04	.02
272	Yankees/Mets Checklist	.05	.04	.02

1987 Donruss Pop-Ups

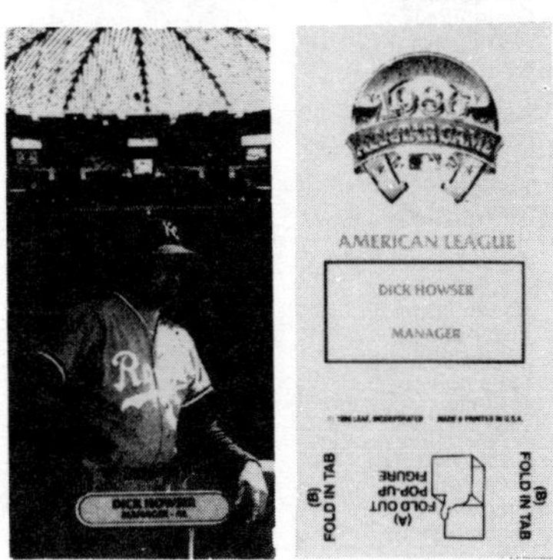

For the second straight year, Donruss released in con- junction with its All-Stars issue a set of cards designed to fold out to form a three-dimensional stand-up card. Consisting of 20 cards, as opposed to the previous year's 18, the 1987 Donruss Pop-Ups set contains players selected to the 1986 All-Star Game. Background for the 2-1/2" by 5" cards is the Houston Astrodome, site of the 1986 mid-summer classic. Retail packs included one Pop-Up card, three All-Star cards and one Roberto Clemente puzzle card.

		MT	NR MT	EX
Complete Set:		4.00	3.00	1.50
Common Player:		.20	.15	.08
(1)	Wade Boggs	.70	.50	.30
(2)	Gary Carter	.25	.20	.10
(3)	Roger Clemens	.80	.60	.30
(4)	Dwight Gooden	.60	.45	.25
(5)	Tony Gwynn	.50	.40	.20
(6)	Rickey Henderson	.75	.60	.30
(7)	Keith Hernandez	.25	.20	.10
(8)	Whitey Herzog	.20	.15	.08
(9)	Dick Howser	.20	.15	.08
(10)	Wally Joyner	.40	.30	.15
(11)	Dale Murphy	.60	.45	.25
(12)	Lance Parrish	.20	.15	.08
(13)	Kirby Puckett	.75	.60	.30
(14)	Cal Ripken, Jr.	1.00	.70	.40
(15)	Ryne Sandberg	1.00	.70	.40
(16)	Mike Schmidt	.90	.70	.35
(17)	Ozzie Smith	.30	.25	.12
(18)	Darryl Strawberry	.25	.20	.10
(19)	Lou Whitaker	.20	.15	.08
(20)	Dave Winfield	.50	.40	.20

1987 Donruss Rookies

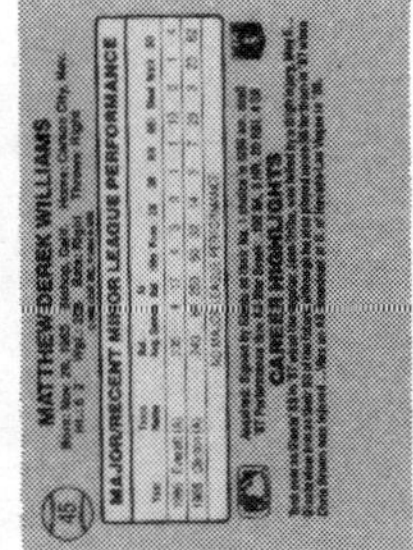

As they did in 1986, Donruss issued a 56-card set highlighting the major league's most promising rookies. The cards are the standard 2-1/2" by 3-1/2" size and are identical in design to the regular Donruss issue. The card fronts have green borders as opposed to the black found in the regular issue and carry the words "The Rookies" in the lower left portion of the card. The set came housed in a specially designed box and was available only through hobby dealers.

		MT	NR MT	EX
Complete Set (56):		20.00	15.00	8.00
Common Player:		.10	.08	.04
1	Mark McGwire	2.50	2.00	1.00
2	Eric Bell	.10	.08	.04
3	Mark Williamson (FC)	.10	.08	.04
4	Mike Greenwell	1.00	.70	.40
5	Ellis Burks	1.00	.70	.40
6	DeWayne Buice (FC)	.10	.08	.04
7	Mark Mclemore (McLemore)	.10	.08	.04
8	Devon White	.60	.45	.25
9	Willie Fraser	.15	.11	.06
10	Lester Lancaster (FC)	.15	.11	.06
11	Ken Williams (FC)	.10	.08	.04
12	Matt Nokes	.30	.25	.12
13	Jeff Robinson (FC)	.15	.11	.06
14	Bo Jackson	2.00	1.50	.80
15	Kevin Seitzer (FC)	.15	.11	.06
16	Billy Ripken (FC)	.15	.11	.06
17	B.J. Surhoff	.15	.11	.06
18	Chuck Crim (FC)	.10	.08	.04
19	Mike Birbeck	.10	.08	.04
20	Chris Bosio	.20	.15	.08
21	Les Straker (FC)	.10	.08	.04
22	Mark Davidson (FC)	.10	.08	.04
23	Gene Larkin (FC)	.20	.15	.08
24	Ken Gerhart	.10	.08	.04
25	Luis Polonia (FC)	.50	.40	.20
26	Terry Steinbach	.25	.20	.10
27	Mickey Brantley	.10	.08	.04
28	Mike Stanley	.30	.25	.12
29	Jerry Browne	.10	.08	.04
30	Todd Benzinger (FC)	.15	.11	.06
31	Fred McGriff	4.00	3.00	1.50
32	Mike Henneman (FC)	.35	.25	.14
33	Casey Candaele	.10	.08	.04
34	Dave Magadan	.20	.15	.08
35	David Cone	1.00	.70	.40
36	Mike Jackson (FC)	.20	.15	.08
37	John Mitchell (FC)	.10	.08	.04
38	Mike Dunne (FC)	.10	.08	.04
39	John Smiley	.60	.45	.25
40	Joe Magrane (FC)	.20	.15	.08
41	Jim Lindeman	.10	.08	.04
42	Shane Mack (FC)	.80	.60	.30
43	Stan Jefferson	.10	.08	.04
44	Benito Santiago	.25	.20	.10
45	Matt Williams (FC)	4.50	3.50	1.75
46	Dave Meads (FC)	.10	.08	.04
47	Rafael Palmeiro	4.50	3.50	1.75
48	Bill Long (FC)	.10	.08	.04
49	Bob Brower	.10	.08	.04
50	James Steels (FC)	.10	.08	.04
51	Paul Noce (FC)	.10	.08	.04
52	Greg Maddux	5.00	3.75	2.00
53	Jeff Musselman	.15	.11	.06
54	Brian Holton	.10	.08	.04
55	Chuck Jackson (FC)	.10	.08	.04
56	Checklist 1-56	.10	.08	.04

1988 Donruss

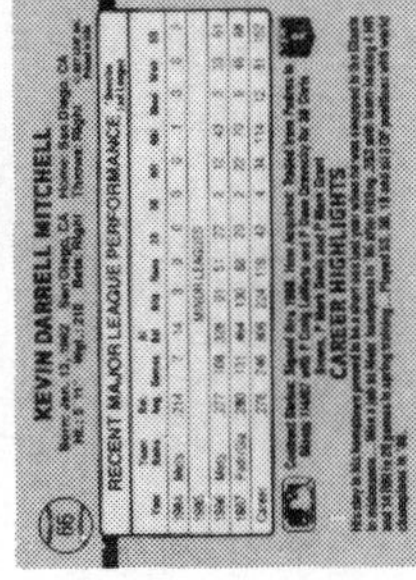

The 1988 Donruss set consists of 660 cards, each measuring 2-1/2" by 3-1/2" in size. The card fronts feature a full-color photo surrounded by a colorful border - alternating stripes of black, red, black, blue, black, blue, black, red and black (in that order) - separated by soft-focus edges and airbrushed fades. The player's name and position appear in a red band at the bottom of the card. The Donruss logo is situated in the upper left corner of the card, while the team logo is located in the lower right corner. For the seventh consecutive season, Donruss included a subset of "Diamond Kings" cards (#'s 1-27) in the issue. And for the fifth straight year, Donruss incorporated their highly popular "Rated Rookies" (card #'s 28-47) with the set.

		MT	NR MT	EX
Complete Set (660):		18.00	13.50	7.25
Common Player:		.05	.04	.02
1	Mark McGwire (DK)	.25	.20	.10
2	Tim Raines (DK)	.08	.06	.03
3	Benito Santiago (DK)	.08	.06	.03
4	Alan Trammell (DK)	.08	.06	.03
5	Danny Tartabull (DK)	.10	.08	.04
6	Ron Darling (DK)	.12	.09	.05
7	Paul Molitor (DK)	.15	.11	.06
8	Devon White (DK)	.10	.08	.04
9	Andre Dawson (DK)	.10	.08	.04
10	Julio Franco (DK)	.10	.08	.04
11	Scott Fletcher (DK)	.07	.05	.03
12	Tony Fernandez (DK)	.12	.09	.05
13	Shane Rawley (DK)	.07	.05	.03
14	Kal Daniels (DK)	.06	.05	.02
15	Jack Clark (DK)	.06	.05	.02
16	Dwight Evans (DK)	.08	.06	.03
17	Tommy John (DK)	.08	.06	.03
18	Andy Van Slyke (DK)	.10	.08	.04

19	Gary Gaetti (DK)	.06	.05	.02
20	Mark Langston (DK)	.06	.05	.02
21	Will Clark (DK)	.25	.20	.10
22	Glenn Hubbard (DK)	.07	.05	.03
23	Billy Hatcher (DK)	.07	.05	.03
24	Bob Welch (DK)	.10	.08	.04
25	Ivan Calderon (DK)	.10	.08	.04
26	Cal Ripken, Jr. (DK)	.35	.25	.14
27	Checklist 1-27	.05	.04	.02
28	*Mackey Sasser* (RR)	.10	.08	.04
29	*Jeff Treadway* (RR)	.10	.08	.04
30	*Mike Campbell* (FC) (RR)	.12	.09	.05
31	*Lance Johnson* (RR)	.50	.40	.20
32	*Nelson Liriano* (FC) (RR)	.08	.06	.03
33	Shawn Abner (FC) (RR)	.08	.06	.03
34	*Roberto Alomar* (RR)	3.50	2.75	1.50
35	*Shawn Hillegas* (FC) (RR)	.08	.06	.03
36	Joey Meyer (RR)	.06	.05	.02
37	Kevin Elster (RR)	.08	.06	.03
38	*Jose Lind* (RR)	.12	.09	.05
39	*Kirt Manwaring* (RR)	.15	.11	.06
40	*Mark Grace* (RR)	1.50	1.25	.60
41	*Jody Reed* (RR)	.20	.15	.08
42	*John Farrell* (FC) (RR)	.08	.06	.03
43	*Al Leiter* (RR)	.12	.09	.05
44	*Gary Thurman* (FC) (RR)	.08	.06	.03
45	*Vicente Palacios* (RR)	.10	.08	.04
46	*Eddie Williams* (FC) (RR)	.06	.05	.02
47	*Jack McDowell* (RR)	1.00	.75	.40
48	Ken Dixon	.05	.04	.02
49	Mike Birkbeck	.07	.05	.03
50	Eric King	.07	.05	.03
51	Roger Clemens	.50	.40	.20
52	Pat Clements	.05	.04	.02
53	Fernando Valenzuela	.06	.05	.02
54	Mark Gubicza	.12	.09	.05
55	Jay Howell	.07	.05	.03
56	Floyd Youmans	.05	.04	.02
57	Ed Correa	.05	.04	.02
58	*DeWayne Buice*	.15	.11	.06
59	Jose DeLeon	.07	.05	.03
60	Danny Cox	.07	.05	.03
61	Nolan Ryan	.60	.45	.25
62	Steve Bedrosian	.12	.09	.05
63	Tom Browning	.10	.08	.04
64	Mark Davis	.05	.04	.02
65	R.J. Reynolds	.05	.04	.02
66	Kevin Mitchell	.10	.08	.04
67	Ken Oberkfell	.05	.04	.02
68	Rick Sutcliffe	.10	.08	.04
69	Dwight Gooden	.10	.08	.04
70	Scott Bankhead	.07	.05	.03
71	Bert Blyleven	.12	.09	.05
72	Jimmy Key	.10	.08	.04
73	*Les Straker*	.15	.11	.06
74	Jim Clancy	.07	.05	.03
75	Mike Moore	.05	.04	.02
76	Ron Darling	.12	.09	.05
77	Ed Lynch	.05	.04	.02
78	Dale Murphy	.10	.08	.04
79	Doug Drabek	.07	.05	.03
80	Scott Garrelts	.05	.04	.02
81	Ed Whitson	.05	.04	.02
82	Rob Murphy	.07	.05	.03
83	Shane Rawley	.07	.05	.03
84	Greg Mathews	.07	.05	.03
85	Jim Deshaies	.07	.05	.03
86	Mike Witt	.07	.05	.03
87	Donnie Hill	.05	.04	.02
88	Jeff Reed	.05	.04	.02
89	Mike Boddicker	.07	.05	.03
90	Ted Higuera	.10	.08	.04
91	Walt Terrell	.07	.05	.03
92	Bob Stanley	.05	.04	.02
93	Dave Righetti	.15	.11	.06
94	Orel Hershiser	.08	.06	.03
95	Chris Bando	.05	.04	.02
96	Bret Saberhagen	.08	.06	.03
97	Curt Young	.07	.05	.03
98	Tim Burke	.05	.04	.02
99	Charlie Hough	.07	.05	.03
100a	Checklist 28-137	.05	.04	.02
100b	Checklist 28-133	.10	.08	.04
101	Bobby Witt	.10	.08	.04
102	George Brett	.40	.30	.15
103	Mickey Tettleton	.15	.11	.06
104	Scott Bailes	.07	.05	.03
105	Mike Pagliarulo	.10	.08	.04
106	Mike Scioscia	.07	.05	.03
107	Tom Brookens	.05	.04	.02
108	Ray Knight	.07	.05	.03
109	Dan Plesac	.10	.08	.04
110	Wally Joyner	.12	.09	.05
111	Bob Forsch	.07	.05	.03
112	Mike Scott	.12	.09	.05
113	Kevin Gross	.07	.05	.03
114	Benito Santiago	.10	.08	.04
115	Bob Kipper	.05	.04	.02
116	Mike Krukow	.07	.05	.03
117	Chris Bosio	.07	.05	.03
118	Sid Fernandez	.10	.08	.04
119	Jody Davis	.07	.05	.03
120	Mike Morgan	.05	.04	.02
121	Mark Eichhorn	.07	.05	.03
122	Jeff Reardon	.10	.08	.04
123	John Franco	.10	.08	.04
124	Richard Dotson	.07	.05	.03
125	Eric Bell	.05	.04	.02
126	Juan Nieves	.07	.05	.03
127	Jack Morris	.12	.09	.05
128	Rick Rhoden	.07	.05	.03
129	Rich Gedman	.07	.05	.03
130	Ken Howell	.05	.04	.02
131	Brook Jacoby	.10	.08	.04
132	Danny Jackson	.12	.09	.05
133	Gene Nelson	.05	.04	.02
134	Neal Heaton	.05	.04	.02
135	Willie Fraser	.05	.04	.02

136	Jose Guzman	.07	.05	.03
137	Ozzie Guillen	.07	.05	.03
138	Bob Knepper	.07	.05	.03
139	*Mike Jackson*	.20	.15	.08
140	*Joe Magrane*	.08	.06	.03
141	Jimmy Jones	.07	.05	.03
142	Ted Power	.05	.04	.02
143	Ozzie Virgil	.05	.04	.02
144	*Felix Fermin* (FC)	.08	.06	.03
145	Kelly Downs	.10	.08	.04
146	Shawon Dunston	.10	.08	.04
147	Scott Bradley	.05	.04	.02
148	Dave Stieb	.10	.08	.04
149	Frank Viola	.15	.11	.06
150	Terry Kennedy	.07	.05	.03
151	Bill Wegman	.05	.04	.02
152	*Matt Nokes*	.25	.20	.10
153	Wade Boggs	.25	.20	.10
154	Wayne Tolleson	.05	.04	.02
155	Mariano Duncan	.05	.04	.02
156	Julio Franco	.10	.08	.04
157	Charlie Leibrandt	.07	.05	.03
158	Terry Steinbach	.10	.08	.04
159	Mike Fitzgerald	.05	.04	.02
160	Jack Lazorko	.05	.04	.02
161	Mitch Williams	.07	.05	.03
162	Greg Walker	.07	.05	.03
163	Alan Ashby	.05	.04	.02
164	Tony Gwynn	.35	.25	.14
165	Bruce Ruffin	.07	.05	.03
166	Ron Robinson	.05	.04	.02
167	Zane Smith	.07	.05	.03
168	Junior Ortiz	.05	.04	.02
169	Jamie Moyer	.07	.05	.03
170	Tony Pena	.07	.05	.03
171	Cal Ripken	.50	.40	.20
172	B.J. Surhoff	.12	.09	.05
173	Lou Whitaker	.08	.06	.03
174	*Ellis Burks*	.35	.25	.14
175	Ron Guidry	.15	.11	.06
176	Steve Sax	.15	.11	.06
177	Danny Tartabull	.20	.15	.08
178	Carney Lansford	.10	.08	.04
179	Casey Candaele	.05	.04	.02
180	Scott Fletcher	.07	.05	.03
181	Mark McLemore	.05	.04	.02
182	Ivan Calderon	.10	.08	.04
183	Jack Clark	.15	.11	.06
184	Glenn Davis	.08	.06	.03
185	Luis Aguayo	.05	.04	.02
186	Bo Diaz	.07	.05	.03
187	Stan Jefferson	.07	.05	.03
188	Sid Bream	.07	.05	.03
189	Bob Brenly	.05	.04	.02
190	Dion James	.07	.05	.03
191	Leon Durham	.07	.05	.03
192	Jesse Orosco	.07	.05	.03
193	Alvin Davis	.12	.09	.05
194	Gary Gaetti	.12	.09	.05
195	Fred McGriff	.40	.30	.15
196	Steve Lombardozzi	.05	.04	.02
197	Rance Mulliniks	.05	.04	.02
198	Rey Quinones	.05	.04	.02
199	Gary Carter	.10	.08	.04
200a	Checklist 138-247	.05	.04	.02
200b	Checklist 134-239	.10	.08	.04
201	Keith Moreland	.07	.05	.03
202	Ken Griffey	.07	.05	.03
203	*Tommy Gregg* (FC)	.08	.06	.03
204	Will Clark	.30	.25	.12
205	John Kruk	.12	.09	.05
206	Buddy Bell	.07	.05	.03
207	Von Hayes	.07	.05	.03
208	Tommy Herr	.07	.05	.03
209	Craig Reynolds	.05	.04	.02
210	Gary Pettis	.05	.04	.02
211	Harold Baines	.12	.09	.05
212	Vance Law	.07	.05	.03
213	Ken Gerhart	.07	.05	.03
214	Jim Gantner	.05	.04	.02
215	Chet Lemon	.07	.05	.03
216	Dwight Evans	.12	.09	.05
217	Don Mattingly	.30	.25	.12
218	Franklin Stubbs	.07	.05	.03
219	Pat Tabler	.07	.05	.03
220	Bo Jackson	.30	.25	.12
221	Tony Phillips	.05	.04	.02
222	Tim Wallach	.10	.08	.04
223	Ruben Sierra	.30	.25	.12
224	Steve Buechele	.05	.04	.02
225	Frank White	.07	.05	.03
226	Alfredo Griffin	.07	.05	.03
227	Greg Swindell	.12	.09	.05
228	Willie Randolph	.07	.05	.03
229	Mike Marshall	.12	.09	.05
230	Alan Trammell	.08	.06	.03
231	Eddie Murray	.20	.15	.08
232	Dale Sveum	.07	.05	.03
233	Dick Schofield	.05	.04	.02
234	Jose Oquendo	.05	.04	.02
235	Bill Doran	.07	.05	.03
236	Milt Thompson	.05	.04	.02
237	Marvell Wynne	.05	.04	.02
238	Bobby Bonilla	.20	.15	.08
239	Chris Speier	.05	.04	.02
240	Glenn Braggs	.10	.08	.04
241	Wally Backman	.07	.05	.03
242	Ryne Sandberg	.40	.30	.15
243	Phil Bradley	.10	.08	.04
244	Kelly Gruber	.05	.04	.02
245	Tom Brunansky	.10	.08	.04
246	Ron Oester	.05	.04	.02
247	Bobby Thigpen	.10	.08	.04
248	Fred Lynn	.15	.11	.06
249	Paul Molitor	.15	.11	.06
250	Darrell Evans	.10	.08	.04
251	Gary Ward	.07	.05	.03
252	Bruce Hurst	.10	.08	.04

253	Bob Welch	.10	.08	.04
254	Joe Carter	.15	.11	.06
255	Willie Wilson	.10	.08	.04
256	Mark McGwire	.30	.25	.12
257	Mitch Webster	.07	.05	.03
258	Brian Downing	.07	.05	.03
259	Mike Stanley	.10	.08	.04
260	Carlton Fisk	.20	.15	.08
261	Billy Hatcher	.07	.05	.03
262	Glenn Wilson	.07	.05	.03
263	Ozzie Smith	.15	.11	.06
264	Randy Ready	.05	.04	.02
265	Kurt Stillwell	.10	.08	.04
266	David Palmer	.05	.04	.02
267	Mike Diaz	.07	.05	.03
268	Rob Thompson	.07	.05	.03
269	Andre Dawson	.20	.15	.08
270	Lee Guetterman	.05	.04	.02
271	Willie Upshaw	.07	.05	.03
272	Randy Bush	.05	.04	.02
273	Larry Sheets	.07	.05	.03
274	Rob Deer	.07	.05	.03
275	Kirk Gibson	.08	.06	.03
276	Marty Barrett	.07	.05	.03
277	Rickey Henderson	.20	.15	.08
278	Pedro Guerrero	.15	.11	.06
279	Brett Butler	.07	.05	.03
280	Kevin Seitzer	.08	.06	.03
281	Mike Davis	.07	.05	.03
282	Andres Galarraga	.15	.11	.06
283	Devon White	.12	.09	.05
284	Pete O'Brien	.07	.05	.03
285	Jerry Hairston	.05	.04	.02
286	Kevin Bass	.07	.05	.03
287	Carmelo Martinez	.07	.05	.03
288	Juan Samuel	.12	.09	.05
289	Kal Daniels	.06	.05	.02
290	Albert Hall	.05	.04	.02
291	Andy Van Slyke	.12	.09	.05
292	Lee Smith	.10	.08	.04
293	Vince Coleman	.08	.06	.03
294	Tom Niedenfuer	.07	.05	.03
295	Robin Yount	.30	.25	.12
296	*Jeff Robinson*	.08	.06	.03
297	*Todd Benzinger*	.10	.08	.04
298	Dave Winfield	.35	.25	.14
299	Mickey Hatcher	.05	.04	.02
300a	Checklist 248-357	.05	.04	.02
300b	Checklist 240-345	.10	.08	.04
301	Bud Black	.05	.04	.02
302	Jose Canseco	.30	.25	.12
303	Tom Foley	.05	.04	.02
304	Pete Incaviglia	.15	.11	.06
305	Bob Boone	.07	.05	.03
306	*Bill Long*	.08	.06	.03
307	Willie McGee	.12	.09	.05
308	*Ken Caminiti* (FC)	.40	.30	.15
309	Darren Daulton	.05	.04	.02
310	Tracy Jones	.12	.09	.05
311	Greg Booker	.07	.05	.03
312	Mike LaValliere	.07	.05	.03
313	Chili Davis	.07	.05	.03
314	Glenn Hubbard	.05	.04	.02
315	*Paul Noce*	.10	.08	.04
316	Keith Hernandez	.08	.06	.03
317	Mark Langston	.12	.09	.05
318	Keith Atherton	.05	.04	.02
319	Tony Fernandez	.12	.09	.05
320	Kent Hrbek	.15	.11	.06
321	John Cerutti	.07	.05	.03
322	Mike Kingery	.05	.04	.02
323	Dave Magadan	.12	.09	.05
324	Rafael Palmeiro	.40	.30	.15
325	Jeff Dedmon	.05	.04	.02
326	Barry Bonds	.50	.40	.20
327	Jeffrey Leonard	.07	.05	.03
328	Tim Flannery	.05	.04	.02
329	Dave Concepcion	.07	.05	.03
330	Mike Schmidt	.30	.25	.12
331	Bill Dawley	.05	.04	.02
332	Larry Andersen	.05	.04	.02
333	Jack Howell	.07	.05	.03
334	*Ken Williams*	.06	.05	.02
335	Bryn Smith	.05	.04	.02
336	*Billy Ripken*	.10	.08	.04
337	Greg Brock	.07	.05	.03
338	Mike Heath	.05	.04	.02
339	Mike Greenwell	.12	.09	.05
340	Claudell Washington	.07	.05	.03
341	Jose Gonzalez	.05	.04	.02
342	Mel Hall	.07	.05	.03
343	Jim Eisenreich	.07	.05	.03
344	Tony Bernazard	.05	.04	.02
345	Tim Raines	.08	.06	.03
346	Bob Brower	.07	.05	.03
347	Larry Parrish	.07	.05	.03
348	Thad Bosley	.05	.04	.02
349	Dennis Eckersley	.12	.09	.05
350	Cory Snyder	.06	.05	.02
351	Rick Cerone	.05	.04	.02
352	John Shelby	.05	.04	.02
353	Larry Herndon	.05	.04	.02
354	John Habyan	.05	.04	.02
355	*Chuck Crim*	.12	.09	.05
356	Gus Polidor	.05	.04	.02
357	Ken Dayley	.05	.04	.02
358	Danny Darwin	.05	.04	.02
359	Lance Parrish	.15	.11	.06
360	*James Steels*	.12	.09	.05
361	*Al Pedrique* (FC)	.15	.11	.06
362	Mike Aldrete	.07	.05	.03
363	Juan Castillo	.05	.04	.02
364	Len Dykstra	.15	.11	.06
365	Luis Quinones	.05	.04	.02
366	Jim Presley	.10	.08	.04
367	Lloyd Moseby	.07	.05	.03
368	Kirby Puckett	.50	.40	.20
369	Eric Davis	.12	.09	.05

370	Gary Redus	.05	.04	.02
371	Dave Schmidt	.05	.04	.02
372	Mark Clear	.05	.04	.02
373	Dave Bergman	.05	.04	.02
374	Charles Hudson	.05	.04	.02
375	Calvin Schiraldi	.05	.04	.02
376	Alex Trevino	.05	.04	.02
377	Tom Candiotti	.05	.04	.02
378	Steve Farr	.05	.04	.02
379	Mike Gallego	.05	.04	.02
380	Andy McGaffigan	.05	.04	.02
381	Kirk McCaskill	.07	.05	.03
382	Oddibe McDowell	.07	.05	.03
383	Floyd Bannister	.07	.05	.03
384	Denny Walling	.05	.04	.02
385	Don Carman	.07	.05	.03
386	Todd Worrell	.10	.08	.04
387	Eric Show	.07	.05	.03
388	Dave Parker	.08	.06	.03
389	Rick Mahler	.05	.04	.02
390	*Mike Dunne*	.08	.06	.03
391	Candy Maldonado	.07	.05	.03
392	Bob Dernier	.05	.04	.02
393	Dave Valle	.05	.04	.02
394	Ernie Whitt	.07	.05	.03
395	Juan Berenguer	.05	.04	.02
396	Mike Young	.05	.04	.02
397	Mike Felder	.05	.04	.02
398	Willie Hernandez	.07	.05	.03
399	Jim Rice	.08	.06	.03
400a	Checklist 358-467	.05	.04	.02
400b	Checklist 346-451	.10	.08	.04
401	Tommy John	.15	.11	.06
402	Brian Holton	.07	.05	.03
403	Carmen Castillo	.05	.04	.02
404	Jamie Quirk	.05	.04	.02
405	Dwayne Murphy	.07	.05	.03
406	*Jeff Parrett* (FC)	.08	.06	.03
407	Don Sutton	.20	.15	.08
408	Jerry Browne	.07	.05	.03
409	Jim Winn	.05	.04	.02
410	Dave Smith	.07	.05	.03
411	*Shane Mack*	.15	.11	.06
412	Greg Gross	.05	.04	.02
413	Nick Esasky	.07	.05	.03
414	Damaso Garcia	.05	.04	.02
415	Brian Fisher	.07	.05	.03
416	Brian Dayett	.05	.04	.02
417	Curt Ford	.05	.04	.02
418	*Mark Williamson*	.12	.09	.05
419	Bill Schroeder	.05	.04	.02
420	*Mike Henneman*	.25	.20	.10
421	*John Marzano* (FC)	.08	.06	.03
422	Ron Kittle	.07	.05	.03
423	Matt Young	.05	.04	.02
424	Steve Balboni	.07	.05	.03
425	*Luis Polonia*	.15	.11	.06
426	Randy St. Claire	.05	.04	.02
427	Greg Harris	.05	.04	.02
428	Johnny Ray	.07	.05	.03
429	Ray Searage	.05	.04	.02
430	Ricky Horton	.07	.05	.03
431	*Gerald Young* (FC)	.08	.06	.03
432	Rick Schu	.05	.04	.02
433	Paul O'Neill	.07	.05	.03
434	Rich Gossage	.15	.11	.06
435	John Cangelosi	.05	.04	.02
436	Mike LaCoss	.05	.04	.02
437	Gerald Perry	.10	.08	.04
438	Dave Martinez	.07	.05	.03
439	Darryl Strawberry	.15	.11	.06
440	John Moses	.05	.04	.02
441	Greg Gagne	.05	.04	.02
442	Jesse Barfield	.12	.09	.05
443	George Frazier	.05	.04	.02
444	Garth Iorg	.05	.04	.02
445	Ed Nunez	.05	.04	.02
446	Rick Aguilera	.05	.04	.02
447	Jerry Mumphrey	.05	.04	.02
448	Rafael Ramirez	.05	.04	.02
449	*John Smiley*	.10	.08	.04
450	Atlee Hammaker	.05	.04	.02
451	Lance McCullers	.07	.05	.03
452	Guy Hoffman (FC)	.07	.05	.03
453	Chris James	.12	.09	.05
454	Terry Pendleton	.10	.08	.04
455	*Dave Meads*	.15	.11	.06
456	Bill Buckner	.10	.08	.04
457	*John Pawlowski* (FC)	.10	.08	.04
458	Bob Sebra	.05	.04	.02
459	Jim Dwyer	.05	.04	.02
460	*Jay Aldrich* (FC)	.12	.09	.05
461	Frank Tanana	.07	.05	.03
462	Oil Can Boyd	.07	.05	.03
463	Dan Pasqua	.10	.08	.04
464	*Tim Crews* (FC)	.15	.11	.06
465	Andy Allanson	.07	.05	.03
466	*Bill Pecota* (FC)	.15	.11	.06
467	Steve Ontiveros	.05	.04	.02
468	Hubie Brooks	.10	.08	.04
469	*Paul Kilgus* (FC)	.15	.11	.06
470	Dale Mohorcic	.05	.04	.02
471	Dan Quisenberry	.07	.05	.03
472	Dave Stewart	.10	.08	.04
473	Dave Clark	.07	.05	.03
474	Joel Skinner	.05	.04	.02
475	Dave Anderson	.05	.04	.02
476	Dan Petry	.07	.05	.03
477	*Carl Nichols* (FC)	.12	.09	.05
478	Ernest Riles	.05	.04	.02
479	George Hendrick	.07	.05	.03
480	John Morris	.05	.04	.02
481	*Manny Hernandez* (FC)	.10	.08	.04
482	Jeff Stone	.05	.04	.02
483	Chris Brown	.07	.05	.03
484	Mike Bielecki	.05	.04	.02
485	Dave Dravecky	.07	.05	.03
486	Rick Manning	.05	.04	.02
487	Bill Almon	.05	.04	.02
488	Jim Sundberg	.07	.05	.03
489	Ken Phelps	.07	.05	.03
490	Tom Henke	.07	.05	.03
491	Dan Gladden	.05	.04	.02
492	Barry Larkin	.20	.15	.08
493	*Fred Manrique* (FC)	.06	.05	.02
494	Mike Griffin	.05	.04	.02
495	*Mark Knudson* (FC)	.10	.08	.04
496	Bill Madlock	.10	.08	.04
497	Tim Stoddard	.05	.04	.02
498	*Sam Horn* (FC)	.10	.08	.04
499	*Tracy Woodson* (FC)	.06	.05	.02
500a	Checklist 468-577	.05	.04	.02
500b	Checklist 452-557	.10	.08	.04
501	Ken Schrom	.05	.04	.02
502	Angel Salazar	.05	.04	.02
503	Eric Plunk	.05	.04	.02
504	Joe Hesketh	.05	.04	.02
505	Greg Minton	.05	.04	.02
506	Geno Petralli	.05	.04	.02
507	Bob James	.05	.04	.02
508	*Robbie Wine* (FC)	.12	.09	.05
509	Jeff Calhoun	.05	.04	.02
510	Steve Lake	.05	.04	.02
511	Mark Grant	.05	.04	.02
512	Frank Williams	.05	.04	.02
513	*Jeff Blauser* (FC)	.20	.15	.08
514	Bob Walk	.05	.04	.02
515	Craig Lefferts	.05	.04	.02
516	Manny Trillo	.07	.05	.03
517	Jerry Reed	.05	.04	.02
518	Rick Leach	.05	.04	.02
519	*Mark Davidson*	.12	.09	.05
520	*Jeff Ballard* (FC)	.08	.06	.03
521	*Dave Stapleton* (FC)	.10	.08	.04
522	Pat Sheridan	.05	.04	.02
523	Al Nipper	.05	.04	.02
524	Steve Trout	.05	.04	.02
525	Jeff Hamilton	.07	.05	.03
526	*Tommy Hinzo* (FC)	.15	.11	.06
527	Lonnie Smith	.07	.05	.03
528	*Greg Cadaret* (FC)	.08	.06	.03
529	Rob McClure (Bob)	.05	.04	.02
530	Chuck Finley	.10	.08	.04
531	Jeff Russell	.05	.04	.02
532	Steve Lyons	.05	.04	.02
533	Terry Puhl	.05	.04	.02
534	*Eric Nolte* (FC)	.15	.11	.06
535	Kent Tekulve	.07	.05	.03
536	*Pat Pacillo* (FC)	.15	.11	.06
537	Charlie Puleo	.05	.04	.02
538	*Tom Prince* (FC)	.15	.11	.06
539	Greg Maddux	.15	.11	.06
540	Jim Lindeman	.07	.05	.03
541	*Pete Stanicek* (FC)	.15	.11	.06
542	Steve Kiefer	.05	.04	.02
543	Jim Morrison	.05	.04	.02
544	Spike Owen	.05	.04	.02
545	*Jay Buhner* (FC)	.70	.50	.30
546	*Mike Devereaux*	.40	.30	.15
547	Jerry Don Gleaton	.05	.04	.02
548	Jose Rijo	.08	.06	.03
549	Dennis Martinez	.05	.04	.02
550	Mike Loynd	.05	.04	.02
551	Darrell Miller	.05	.04	.02
552	Dave LaPoint	.07	.05	.03
553	John Tudor	.10	.08	.04
554	*Rocky Childress* (FC)	.12	.09	.05
555	*Wally Ritchie* (FC)	.15	.11	.06
556	Terry McGriff	.05	.04	.02
557	Dave Leiper	.05	.04	.02
558	Jeff Robinson	.07	.05	.03
559	Jose Uribe	.05	.04	.02
560	Ted Simmons	.10	.08	.04
561	*Lester Lancaster*	.15	.11	.06
562	*Keith Miller* (FC)	.10	.08	.04
563	Harold Reynolds	.07	.05	.03
564	*Gene Larkin*	.10	.08	.04
565	Cecil Fielder	.25	.20	.10
566	Roy Smalley	.05	.04	.02
567	Duane Ward	.07	.05	.03
568	*Bill Wilkinson* (FC)	.15	.11	.06
569	Howard Johnson	.08	.06	.03
570	Frank DiPino	.05	.04	.02
571	*Pete Smith*	.20	.15	.08
572	Darnell Coles	.07	.05	.03
573	Don Robinson	.07	.05	.03
574	Rob Nelson	.05	.04	.02
575	Dennis Rasmussen	.10	.08	.04
576	Steve Jeltz (photo actually Juan Samuel)	.05	.04	.02
577	*Tom Pagnozzi*	.15	.11	.06
578	Ty Gainey	.05	.04	.02
579	Gary Lucas	.05	.04	.02
580	Ron Hassey	.05	.04	.02
581	Herm Winningham	.05	.04	.02
582	*Rene Gonzales* (FC)	.15	.11	.06
583	Brad Komminsk	.05	.04	.02
584	Doyle Alexander	.07	.05	.03
585	Jeff Sellers	.07	.05	.03
586	Bill Gullickson	.05	.04	.02
587	Tim Belcher (FC)	.10	.08	.04
588	*Doug Jones*	.25	.20	.10
589	*Melido Perez*	.30	.25	.12
590	Rick Honeycutt	.05	.04	.02
591	Pascual Perez	.07	.05	.03
592	Curt Wilkerson	.05	.04	.02
593	Steve Howe	.07	.05	.03
594	*John Davis* (FC)	.08	.06	.03
595	Storm Davis	.10	.08	.04
596	Sammy Stewart	.05	.04	.02
597	Neil Allen	.05	.04	.02
598	Alejandro Pena	.07	.05	.03
599	Mark Thurmond	.05	.04	.02
600a	Checklist 578-BC26	.05	.04	.02
600b	Checklist 558-660	.10	.08	.04
601	*Jose Mesa* (FC)	.10	.08	.04
602	*Don August* (FC)	.15	.11	.06
603	Terry Leach	.10	.08	.04
604	*Tom Newell* (FC)	.08	.06	.03
605	*Randall Byers* (FC)	.08	.06	.03
606	Jim Gott	.05	.04	.02
607	Harry Spilman	.05	.04	.02
608	John Candelaria	.07	.05	.03
609	*Mike Brumley* (FC)	.06	.05	.02
610	Mickey Brantley	.07	.05	.03
611	*Jose Nunez* (FC)	.08	.06	.03
612	Tom Nieto	.05	.04	.02
613	Rick Reuschel	.10	.08	.04
614	Lee Mazzilli	.12	.09	.05
615	*Scott Lusader* (FC)	.08	.06	.03
616	Bobby Meacham	.05	.04	.02
617	Kevin McReynolds	.15	.11	.06
618	Gene Garber	.05	.04	.02
619	*Barry Lyons* (FC)	.15	.11	.06
620	Randy Myers	.10	.08	.04
621	Donnie Moore	.05	.04	.02
622	Domingo Ramos	.05	.04	.02
623	Ed Romero	.05	.04	.02
624	*Greg Myers* (FC)	.10	.08	.04
625	Ripken Baseball Family (Billy Ripken, Cal Ripken, Jr., Cal Ripken, Sr.)	.15	.11	.06
626	Pat Perry	.05	.04	.02
627	Andres Thomas	.10	.08	.04
628	*Matt Williams*	2.00	1.50	.80
629	*Dave Hengel* (FC)	.08	.06	.03
630	Jeff Musselman	.07	.05	.03
631	Tim Laudner	.05	.04	.02
632	Bob Ojeda	.07	.05	.03
633	Rafael Santana	.05	.04	.02
634	*Wes Gardner* (FC)	.08	.06	.03
635	*Roberto Kelly* (FC)	1.25	.90	.50
636	Mike Flanagan	.12	.09	.05
637	*Jay Bell* (FC)	.50	.40	.20
638	Bob Melvin	.05	.04	.02
639	*Damon Berryhill* (FC)	.15	.11	.06
640	*David Wells* (FC)	.25	.20	.10
641	Stan Musial Puzzle Card	.05	.04	.02
642	Doug Sisk	.05	.04	.02
643	*Keith Hughes* (FC)	.08	.06	.03
644	*Tom Glavine* (FC)	2.50	2.00	1.00
645	Al Newman	.05	.04	.02
646	Scott Sanderson	.05	.04	.02
647	Scott Terry	.10	.08	.04
648	Tim Teufel	.12	.09	.05
649	Garry Templeton	.12	.09	.05
650	Manny Lee	.05	.04	.02
651	Roger McDowell	.10	.08	.04
652	Mookie Wilson	.15	.11	.06
653	David Cone	.60	.45	.25
654	*Ron Gant*	1.75	1.25	.70
655	Joe Price	.12	.09	.05
656	George Bell	.10	.08	.04
657	*Gregg Jefferies*	2.00	1.50	.80
658	*Todd Stottlemyre*	.40	.30	.15
659	*Geronimo Berroa*	.10	.08	.04
660	Jerry Royster	.12	.09	.05

1988 Donruss MVP

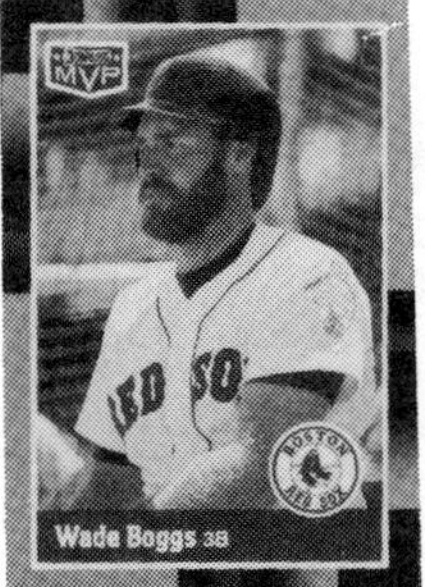

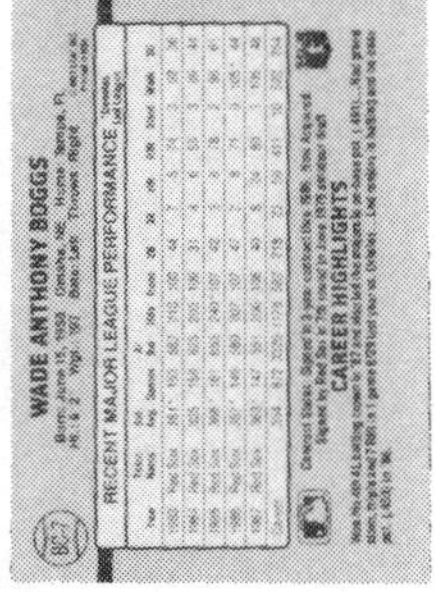

This 26-card set of standard-size player cards replaced the Donruss box-bottom cards in 1988. Instead of box-bottoms, the bonus cards (numbered BC-1 through BC-26) were randomly inserted in Donruss wax or rack packs. Cards feature the company's choice of Most Valuable Player for each major league team and are titled "Donruss MVP." The MVP cards were not included in the factory-collated sets. Card fronts carry the same basic red-blue-black flowing border design as the 1988 Donruss basic 660-card issue (with the exception of the Donruss MVP logo). Card backs are the same as the regular issue, except for the numbering system.

		MT	NR MT	EX
Complete Set (26):		7.00	5.25	2.75
Common Player:		.15	.11	.06
1	Cal Ripken, Jr.	.50	.40	.20
2	Eric Davis	.20	.15	.08
3	Paul Molitor	.35	.25	.14
4	Mike Schmidt	.35	.25	.14
5	Ivan Calderon	.15	.11	.06
6	Tony Gwynn	.30	.25	.12
7	Wade Boggs	.40	.30	.15
8	Andy Van Slyke	.15	.11	.06
9	Joe Carter	.25	.20	.10
10	Andre Dawson	.25	.20	.10
11	Alan Trammell	.25	.20	.10

12	Mike Scott	.15	.11	.06
13	Wally Joyner	.25	.20	.10
14	Dale Murphy	.35	.25	.14
15	Kirby Puckett	.40	.30	.15
16	Pedro Guerrero	.20	.15	.08
17	Kevin Seitzer	.20	.15	.08
18	Tim Raines	.25	.20	.10
19	George Bell	.25	.20	.10
20	Darryl Strawberry	.25	.20	.10
21	Don Mattingly	.50	.40	.20
22	Ozzie Smith	.30	.25	.12
23	Mark McGwire	.40	.30	.15
24	Will Clark	.50	.40	.20
25	Alvin Davis	.15	.11	.06
26	Ruben Sierra	.35	.25	.14

1988 Donruss All-Stars

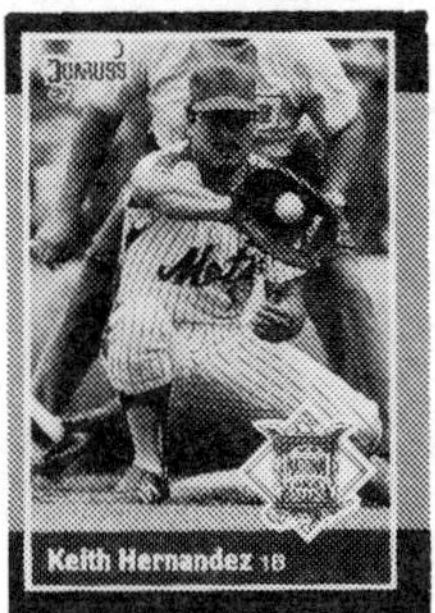

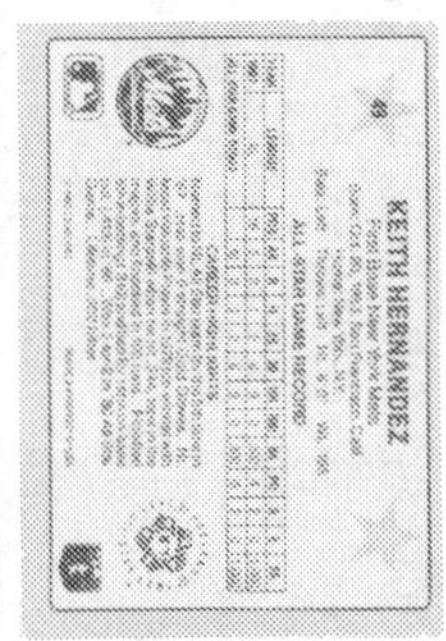

For the third consecutive year, this set of 64 cards featuring major league All-Stars was marketed in conjunction with Donruss Pop-Ups. The 1988 issue included a major change - the cards were reduced in size from 3-1/2" x 5" to a standard 2-1/2" x 3-1/2". The set features players from the 1987 All-Star Game starting lineup. Card fronts feature full-color photos, framed in blue, black and white, with a Donruss logo upper left. Player name and position appear in a red banner below the photo, along with the appropriate National or American League logo. All-Stars card backs include player stats and All-Star Game record. In 1988, All-Stars cards were distributed in individual packages containing three All-Stars, one Pop-Up and three Donruss puzzle pieces.

		MT	NR MT	EX
Complete Set:		5.00	5.25	2.75
Common Player:		.09	.07	.04
1	Don Mattingly	.90	.70	.35
2	Dave Winfield	.25	.20	.10
3	Willie Randolph	.09	.07	.04
4	Rickey Henderson	.50	.40	.20
5	Cal Ripken, Jr.	1.00	.70	.40
6	George Bell	.20	.15	.08
7	Wade Boggs	.80	.60	.30
8	Bret Saberhagen	.15	.11	.06
9	Terry Kennedy	.09	.07	.04
10	John McNamara	.09	.07	.04
11	Jay Howell	.09	.07	.04
12	Harold Baines	.12	.09	.05
13	Harold Reynolds	.09	.07	.04
14	Bruce Hurst	.09	.07	.04
15	Kirby Puckett	.50	.40	.20
16	Matt Nokes	.12	.09	.05
17	Pat Tabler	.09	.07	.04
18	Dan Plesac	.12	.09	.05
19	Mark McGwire	.60	.45	.25
20	Mike Witt	.09	.07	.04
21	Larry Parrish	.09	.07	.04
22	Alan Trammell	.20	.15	.08
23	Dwight Evans	.12	.09	.05
24	Jack Morris	.12	.09	.05
25	Tony Fernandez	.12	.09	.05
26	Mark Langston	.20	.15	.08
27	Kevin Seitzer	.12	.09	.05
28	Tom Henke	.09	.07	.04
29	Dave Righetti	.12	.09	.05
30	Oakland Coliseum	.09	.07	.04
31	Top Vote Getter (Wade Boggs)	.60	.45	.25
32	Checklist 1-32	.09	.07	.04
33	Jack Clark	.15	.11	.06
34	Darryl Strawberry	.20	.15	.08
35	Ryne Sandberg	1.00	.70	.40
36	Andre Dawson	.25	.20	.10
37	Ozzie Smith	.25	.20	.10
38	Eric Davis	.20	.15	.08
39	Mike Schmidt	.80	.60	.30
40	Mike Scott	.12	.09	.05
41	Gary Carter	.12	.09	.05
42	Davey Johnson	.09	.07	.04
43	Rick Sutcliffe	.12	.09	.05
44	Willie McGee	.12	.09	.05
45	Hubie Brooks	.09	.07	.04
46	Dale Murphy	.40	.30	.15
47	Bo Diaz	.09	.07	.04
48	Pedro Guerrero	.15	.11	.06
49	Keith Hernandez	.15	.11	.06
50	Ozzie Virgil	.09	.07	.04
51	Tony Gwynn	.25	.20	.10
52	Rick Reuschel	.12	.09	.05
53	John Franco	.12	.09	.05
54	Jeffrey Leonard	.09	.07	.04
55	Juan Samuel	.15	.11	.06
56	Orel Hershiser	.20	.15	.08
57	Tim Raines	.20	.15	.08
58	Sid Fernandez	.12	.09	.05
59	Tim Wallach	.12	.09	.05
60	Lee Smith	.09	.07	.04
61	Steve Bedrosian	.12	.09	.05
62	MVP (Tim Raines)	.20	.15	.08
63	Top Vote Getter (Ozzie Smith)	.15	.11	.06
64	Checklist 33-64	.09	.07	.04

1988 Donruss Baseball's Best

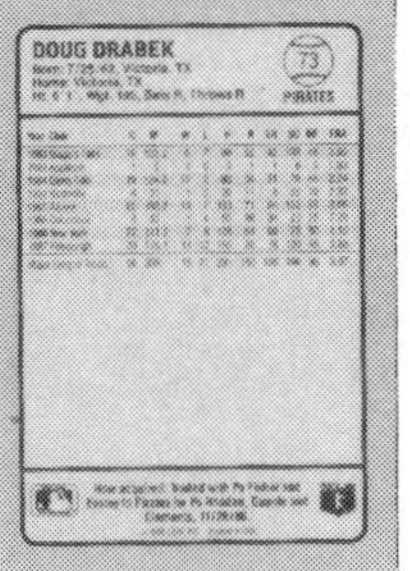

The design of this 336-card set (2-1/2" by 3-1/2") is similar to the regular 1988 Donruss issue with the exception of the borders which are orange, instead of blue. Full-color player photos are framed by the Donruss logo upper left, team logo lower right and a bright red and white player name that spans the bottom margin. The backs are black and white, framed by a yellow border, and include personal information, year-by-year stats and major league totals. This set was packaged in a bright red cardboard box (10" x 11" x 12") that contained six individually shrink-wrapped packs of 56 cards. Donruss marketed the set via retail chain outlets including Walgreens, Venture, Wall-Mart, Ben Frank- lin, Shopko, Super X, Target, McCrory's, Osco, Woolworth and J.C. Murphy.

		MT	NR MT	EX
Complete Set:		8.00	13.50	7.25
Common Player:		.05	.04	.02
1	Don Mattingly	.50	.40	.20
2	Ron Gant	.25	.20	.10
3	Bob Boone	.05	.04	.02
4	Mark Grace	.35	.25	.14
5	Andy Allanson	.05	.04	.02
6	Kal Daniels	.05	.04	.02
7	Floyd Bannister	.05	.04	.02
8	Alan Ashby	.05	.04	.02
9	Marty Barrett	.05	.04	.02
10	Tim Belcher	.05	.04	.02
11	Harold Baines	.07	.05	.03
12	Hubie Brooks	.05	.04	.02
13	Doyle Alexander	.05	.04	.02
14	Gary Carter	.09	.07	.04
15	Glenn Braggs	.05	.04	.02
16	Steve Bedrosian	.05	.04	.02
17	Barry Bonds	.50	.40	.20
18	Bert Blyleven	.07	.05	.03
19	Tom Brunansky	.05	.04	.02
20	John Candelaria	.05	.04	.02
21	Shawn Abner	.05	.04	.02
22	Jose Canseco	.45	.35	.20
23	Brett Butler	.05	.04	.02
24	Scott Bradley	.05	.04	.02
25	Ivan Calderon	.07	.05	.03
26	Rich Gossage	.07	.05	.03
27	Brian Downing	.05	.04	.02
28	Jim Rice	.10	.08	.04
29	Dion James	.05	.04	.02
30	Terry Kennedy	.05	.04	.02
31	George Bell	.07	.05	.03
32	Scott Fletcher	.05	.04	.02
33	Bobby Bonilla	.20	.15	.08
34	Tim Burke	.05	.04	.02
35	Darrell Evans	.07	.05	.03
36	Mike Davis	.05	.04	.02
37	Shawon Dunston	.07	.05	.03
38	Kevin Bass	.05	.04	.02
39	George Brett	.40	.30	.15
40	David Cone	.09	.07	.04
41	Ron Darling	.05	.04	.02
42	Roberto Alomar	.20	.15	.08
43	Dennis Eckersley	.10	.08	.04
44	Vince Coleman	.09	.07	.04
45	Sid Bream	.05	.04	.02
46	Gary Gaetti	.07	.05	.03
47	Phil Bradley	.05	.04	.02
48	Jim Clancy	.05	.04	.02
49	Jack Clark	.07	.05	.03
50	Mike Krukow	.05	.04	.02
51	Henry Cotto	.05	.04	.02
52	Rich Dotson	.05	.04	.02
53	Jim Gantner	.05	.04	.02
54	John Franco	.05	.04	.02
55	Pete Incaviglia	.07	.05	.03
56	Joe Carter	.10	.08	.04
57	Roger Clemens	.25	.20	.10
58	Gerald Perry	.05	.04	.02
59	Jack Howell	.05	.04	.02
60	Vance Law	.05	.04	.02
61	Jay Bell	.07	.05	.03
62	Eric Davis	.12	.09	.05
63	Gene Garber	.05	.04	.02
64	Glenn Davis	.05	.04	.02
65	Wade Boggs	.40	.30	.15
66	Kirk Gibson	.10	.08	.04
67	Carlton Fisk	.10	.08	.04
68	Casey Candaele	.05	.04	.02
69	Mike Heath	.05	.04	.02
70	Kevin Elster	.05	.04	.02
71	Greg Brock	.05	.04	.02
72	Don Carman	.05	.04	.02
73	Doug Drabek	.09	.07	.04
74	Greg Gagne	.07	.05	.03
75	Danny Cox	.05	.04	.02
76	Rickey Henderson	.30	.25	.12
77	Chris Brown	.05	.04	.02
78	Terry Steinbach	.05	.04	.02
79	Will Clark	.40	.30	.15
80	Mickey Brantley	.05	.04	.02
81	Ozzie Guillen	.07	.05	.03
82	Greg Maddux	.12	.09	.05
83	Kirk McCaskill	.05	.04	.02
84	Dwight Evans	.09	.07	.04
85	Ozzie Virgil	.05	.04	.02
86	Mike Morgan	.05	.04	.02
87	Tony Fernandez	.07	.05	.03
88	Jose Guzman	.05	.04	.02
89	Mike Dunne	.05	.04	.02
90	Andres Galarraga	.07	.05	.03
91	Mike Henneman	.05	.04	.02
92	Alfredo Griffin	.05	.04	.02
93	Rafael Palmeiro	.12	.09	.05
94	Jim Deshaies	.05	.04	.02
95	Mark Gubicza	.05	.04	.02
96	Dwight Gooden	.20	.15	.08
97	Howard Johnson	.10	.08	.04
98	Mark Davis	.05	.04	.02
99	Dave Stewart	.09	.07	.04
100	Joe Magrane	.05	.04	.02
101	Brian Fisher	.05	.04	.02
102	Kent Hrbek	.10	.08	.04
103	Kevin Gross	.05	.04	.02
104	Tom Henke	.05	.04	.02
105	Mike Pagliarulo	.05	.04	.02
106	Kelly Downs	.05	.04	.02
107	Alvin Davis	.05	.04	.02
108	Willie Randolph	.07	.05	.03
109	Rob Deer	.05	.04	.02
110	Bo Diaz	.05	.04	.02
111	Paul Kilgus	.05	.04	.02
112	Tom Candiotti	.05	.04	.02
113	Dale Murphy	.20	.15	.08
114	Rick Mahler	.05	.04	.02
115	Wally Joyner	.20	.15	.08
116	Ryne Sandberg	.25	.20	.10
117	John Farrell	.05	.04	.02
118	Nick Esasky	.05	.04	.02
119	Bo Jackson	.40	.30	.15
120	Bill Doran	.05	.04	.02
121	Ellis Burks	.15	.11	.06
122	Pedro Guerrero	.05	.04	.02
123	Dave LaPoint	.05	.04	.02
124	Neal Heaton	.05	.04	.02
125	Willie Hernandez	.05	.04	.02
126	Roger McDowell	.07	.05	.03
127	Ted Higuera	.05	.04	.02
128	Von Hayes	.07	.05	.03
129	Mike LaValliere	.05	.04	.02
130	Dan Gladden	.07	.05	.03
131	Willie McGee	.09	.07	.04
132	Al Lieter	.05	.04	.02
133	Mark Grant	.05	.04	.02
134	Bob Welch	.07	.05	.03
135	Dave Dravecky	.05	.04	.02
136	Mark Langston	.07	.05	.03
137	Dan Pasqua	.07	.05	.03
138	Rick Sutcliffe	.07	.05	.03
139	Dan Petry	.05	.04	.02
140	Rich Gedman	.05	.04	.02
141	Ken Griffey	.05	.04	.02
142	Eddie Murray	.10	.08	.04
143	Jimmy Key	.07	.05	.03
144	Dale Mohoric	.05	.04	.02
145	Jose Lind	.10	.08	.04
146	Dennis Martinez	.07	.05	.03
147	Chet Lemon	.05	.04	.02
148	Orel Hershiser	.10	.08	.04
149	Dave Martinez	.05	.04	.02
150	Billy Hatcher	.07	.05	.03
151	Charlie Leibrandt	.05	.04	.02
152	Keith Hernandez	.07	.05	.03
153	Kevin McReynolds	.07	.05	.03
154	Tony Gwynn	.15	.11	.06
155	Stan Javier	.05	.04	.02
156	Tony Pena	.05	.04	.02
157	Andy Van Slyke	.10	.08	.04
158	Gene Larkin	.07	.05	.03
159	Chris James	.05	.04	.02
160	Fred McGriff	.25	.20	.10
161	Rick Rhoden	.05	.04	.02
162	Scott Garrelts	.05	.04	.02
163	Mike Campbell	.05	.04	.02
164	Dave Righetti	.07	.05	.03
165	Paul Molitor	.15	.11	.06
166	Danny Jackson	.07	.05	.03
167	Pete O'Brien	.05	.04	.02
168	Julio Franco	.05	.04	.02
169	Mark McGwire	.35	.25	.14
170	Zane Smith	.05	.04	.02
171	Johnny Ray	.05	.04	.02
172	Lester Lancaster	.05	.04	.02
173	Mel Hall	.05	.04	.02

174	Tracy Jones	.05	.04	.02
175	Kevin Seitzer	.05	.04	.02
176	Bob Knepper	.05	.04	.02
177	Mike Greenwell	.15	.11	.06
178	Mike Marshall	.07	.05	.03
179	Melido Perez	.05	.04	.02
180	Tim Raines	.15	.11	.06
181	Jack Morris	.07	.05	.03
182	Darryl Strawberry	.25	.20	.10
183	Robin Yount	.35	.25	.14
184	Lance Parrish	.09	.07	.04
185	Darnell Coles	.05	.04	.02
186	Kirby Puckett	.30	.25	.12
187	Terry Pendleton	.07	.05	.03
188	Don Slaught	.05	.04	.02
189	Jimmy Jones	.05	.04	.02
190	Dave Parker	.15	.11	.06
191	Mike Aldrete	.05	.04	.02
192	Mike Moore	.05	.04	.02
193	Greg Walker	.05	.04	.02
194	Calvin Schiraldi	.05	.04	.02
195	Dick Schofield	.05	.04	.02
196	Jody Reed	.07	.05	.03
197	Pete Smith	.05	.04	.02
198	Cal Ripken, Jr.	.50	.40	.20
199	Lloyd Moseby	.05	.04	.02
200	Ruben Sierra	.15	.11	.06
201	R.J. Reynolds	.05	.04	.02
202	Bryn Smith	.05	.04	.02
203	Gary Pettis	.05	.04	.02
204	Steve Sax	.05	.04	.02
205	Frank DiPino	.05	.04	.02
206	Mike Scott	.05	.04	.02
207	Kurt Stillwell	.05	.04	.02
208	Mookie Wilson	.05	.04	.02
209	Lee Mazzilli	.05	.04	.02
210	Lance McCullers	.05	.04	.02
211	Rick Honeycutt	.05	.04	.02
212	John Tudor	.07	.05	.03
213	Jim Gott	.07	.05	.03
214	Frank Viola	.09	.07	.04
215	Juan Samuel	.07	.05	.03
216	Jesse Barfield	.05	.04	.02
217	Claudell Washington	.05	.04	.02
218	Rick Reuschel	.05	.04	.02
219	Jim Presley	.05	.04	.02
220	Tommy John	.12	.09	.05
221	Dan Plesac	.05	.04	.02
222	Barry Larkin	.10	.08	.04
223	Mike Stanley	.05	.04	.02
224	Cory Snyder	.07	.05	.03
225	Andre Dawson	.20	.15	.08
226	Ken Oberkfell	.05	.04	.02
227	Devon White	.09	.07	.04
228	Jamie Moyer	.05	.04	.02
229	Brook Jacoby	.07	.05	.03
230	Rob Murphy	.05	.04	.02
231	Bret Saberhagen	.10	.08	.04
232	Nolan Ryan	.50	.40	.20
233	Bruce Hurst	.07	.05	.03
234	Jesse Orosco	.05	.04	.02
235	Bobby Thigpen	.05	.04	.02
236	Pascual Perez	.05	.04	.02
237	Matt Nokes	.09	.07	.04
238	Bob Ojeda	.07	.05	.03
239	Joey Meyer	.05	.04	.02
240	Shane Rawley	.05	.04	.02
241	Jeff Robinson	.05	.04	.02
242	Jeff Reardon	.09	.07	.04
243	Ozzie Smith	.15	.11	.06
244	Dave Winfield	.35	.25	.14
245	John Kruk	.07	.05	.03
246	Carney Lansford	.05	.04	.02
247	Candy Maldonado	.05	.04	.02
248	Ken Phelps	.05	.04	.02
249	Ken Williams	.05	.04	.02
250	Al Nipper	.05	.04	.02
251	Mark McLemore	.05	.04	.02
252	Lee Smith	.07	.05	.03
253	Albert Hall	.05	.04	.02
254	Billy Ripken	.05	.04	.02
255	Kelly Gruber	.05	.04	.02
256	Charlie Hough	.07	.05	.03
257	John Smiley	.07	.05	.03
258	Tim Wallach	.10	.08	.04
259	Frank Tanana	.07	.05	.03
260	Mike Scioscia	.05	.04	.02
261	Damon Berryhill	.05	.04	.02
262	Dave Smith	.05	.04	.02
263	Willie Wilson	.07	.05	.03
264	Len Dykstra	.09	.07	.04
265	Randy Myers	.07	.05	.03
266	Keith Moreland	.05	.04	.02
267	Eric Plunk	.05	.04	.02
268	Todd Worrell	.05	.04	.02
269	Bob Walk	.05	.04	.02
270	Keith Atherton	.05	.04	.02
271	Mike Schmidt	.40	.30	.15
272	Mike Flanagan	.05	.04	.02
273	Rafael Santana	.05	.04	.02
274	Rob Thompson	.07	.05	.03
275	Rey Quinones	.05	.04	.02
276	Cecilio Guante	.05	.04	.02
277	B.J. Surhoff	.05	.04	.02
278	Chris Sabo	.10	.08	.04
279	Mitch Williams	.07	.05	.03
280	Greg Swindell	.07	.05	.03
281	Alan Trammell	.12	.09	.05
282	Storm Davis	.05	.04	.02
283	Chuck Finley	.07	.05	.03
284	Dave Stieb	.07	.05	.03
285	Scott Bailes	.05	.04	.02
286	Larry Sheets	.05	.04	.02
287	Danny Tartabull	.10	.08	.04
288	Checklist	.05	.04	.02
289	Todd Benzinger	.07	.05	.03
290	John Shelby	.05	.04	.02
291	Steve Lyons	.05	.04	.02
292	Mitch Webster	.05	.04	.02
293	Walt Terrell	.05	.04	.02
294	Pete Stanicek	.05	.04	.02
295	Chris Bosio	.07	.05	.03
296	Milt Thompson	.07	.05	.03
297	Fred Lynn	.12	.09	.05
298	Juan Berenguer	.05	.04	.02
299	Ken Dayley	.05	.04	.02
300	Joel Skinner	.05	.04	.02
301	Benito Santiago	.15	.11	.06
302	Ron Hassey	.05	.04	.02
303	Jose Uribe	.05	.04	.02
304	Harold Reynolds	.07	.05	.03
305	Dale Sveum	.05	.04	.02
306	Glenn Wilson	.05	.04	.02
307	Mike Witt	.05	.04	.02
308	Ron Robinson	.05	.04	.02
309	Denny Walling	.05	.04	.02
310	Joe Orsulak	.05	.04	.02
311	David Wells	.07	.05	.03
312	Steve Buechele	.05	.04	.02
313	Jose Oquendo	.05	.04	.02
314	Floyd Youmans	.05	.04	.02
315	Lou Whitaker	.10	.08	.04
316	Fernando Valenzuela	.07	.05	.03
317	Mike Boddicker	.05	.04	.02
318	Gerald Young	.05	.04	.02
319	Frank White	.07	.05	.03
320	Bill Wegman	.05	.04	.02
321	Tom Niedenfuer	.05	.04	.02
322	Ed Whitson	.05	.04	.02
323	Curt Young	.05	.04	.02
324	Greg Mathews	.05	.04	.02
325	Doug Jones	.07	.05	.03
326	Tommy Herr	.05	.04	.02
327	Kent Tekulve	.05	.04	.02
328	Rance Mulliniks	.05	.04	.02
329	Checklist	.05	.04	.02
330	Craig Lefferts	.05	.04	.02
331	Franklin Stubbs	.05	.04	.02
332	Rick Cerone	.05	.04	.02
333	Dave Schmidt	.05	.04	.02
334	Larry Parrish	.05	.04	.02
335	Tom Browning	.07	.05	.03
336	Checklist	.05	.04	.02

1988 Donruss Diamond Kings Supers

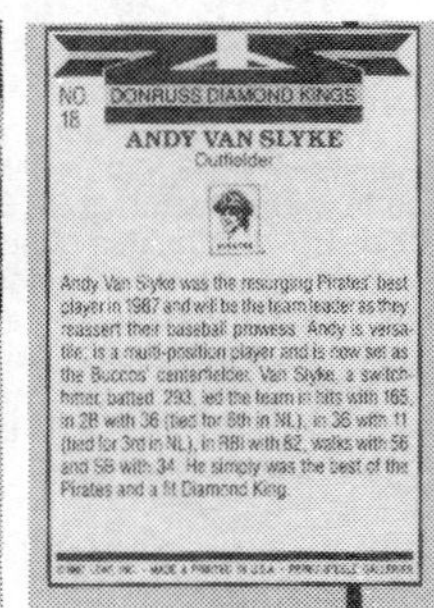

This 28-card set (including the checklist) marks the fourth edition of Donruss' super-size (5"x7") set. These cards, exact duplicates of the 1988 Diamond Kings that feature player portraits by Dick Perez, have a red, blue and black striped border. A gold Diamond Kings banner curves above the player portrait and a matching oval name banner is printed below. Each card features a large player closeup and a smaller full-figure inset on a split background that is white at the top and striped with multi-colors on the lower portion. Card backs are black and white with a blue border and contain the card number, DK logo, player name, team logo and a paragraph style career summary. A 12-piece Stan Musial puzzle was also included with the purchase of the super-size set which was marketed via a mail-in offer printed on Donruss wrappers.

		MT	NR MT	EX
Complete Set:		10.00	7.50	4.00
Common Player:		.20	.15	.08
1	Mark McGwire	.70	.50	.30
2	Tim Raines	.30	.25	.12
3	Benito Santiago	.30	.25	.12
4	Alan Trammell	.30	.25	.12
5	Danny Tartabull	.35	.25	.14
6	Ron Darling	.30	.25	.12
7	Paul Molitor	.50	.40	.20
8	Devon White	.35	.25	.14
9	Andre Dawson	.30	.25	.12
10	Julio Franco	.25	.20	.10
11	Scott Fletcher	.20	.15	.08
12	Tony Fernandez	.30	.25	.12
13	Shane Rawley	.20	.15	.08
14	Kal Daniels	.30	.25	.12
15	Jack Clark	.30	.25	.12
16	Dwight Evans	.25	.20	.10
17	Tommy John	.25	.20	.10
18	Andy Van Slyke	.25	.20	.10
19	Gary Gaetti	.30	.25	.12
20	Mark Langston	.35	.25	.14
21	Will Clark	1.75	1.25	.70
22	Glenn Hubbard	.20	.15	.08
23	Billy Hatcher	.20	.15	.08
24	Bob Welch	.20	.15	.08
25	Ivan Calderon	.20	.15	.08
26	Cal Ripken, Jr.	2.00	1.50	.80
27	Checklist	.20	.15	.08
641	Stan Musial Puzzle Card	.20	.15	.08

1988 Donruss Pop-Ups

Donruss introduced its Pop-Up cards in 1986. The first two annual issues featured 2-1/2" x 5" cards. In 1988, Donruss reduced the size of the Pop-Ups cards to a standard 2-1/2"x 3-1/2". The 1988 set includes 20 cards that fold out so that the upper portion of the player stands upright, giving a three-dimensional effect. Pop-ups feature players from the All-Star Game starting lineup. Card fronts feature full-color photos, with the player's name, team and position printed in black on a yellow banner near the bottom of the card front. As in previous issues, the card backs contain only the player's name, league and position. Pop-Ups were distributed in individual packages containing one Pop-Up, three puzzle pieces and three All-Star cards.

		MT	NR MT	EX
Complete Set:		3.00	3.00	1.50
Common Player:		.15	.11	.06
(1)	George Bell	.20	.15	.08
(2)	Wade Boggs	.50	.40	.20
(3)	Gary Carter	.20	.15	.08
(4)	Jack Clark	.20	.15	.08
(5)	Eric Davis	.20	.15	.08
(6)	Andre Dawson	.20	.15	.08
(7)	Rickey Henderson	.50	.40	.20
(8)	Davey Johnson	.15	.11	.06
(9)	Don Mattingly	.50	.40	.20
(10)	Terry Kennedy	.15	.11	.06
(11)	John McNamara	.15	.11	.06
(12)	Willie Randolph	.15	.11	.06
(13)	Cal Ripken, Jr.	.75	.60	.30
(14)	Bret Saberhagen	.35	.25	.14
(15)	Ryne Sandberg	.75	.60	.30
(16)	Mike Schmidt	.60	.45	.25
(17)	Mike Scott	.15	.11	.06
(18)	Ozzie Smith	.30	.25	.12
(19)	Darryl Strawberry	.25	.20	.10
(20)	Dave Winfield	.40	.30	.15

1988 Donruss Rookies

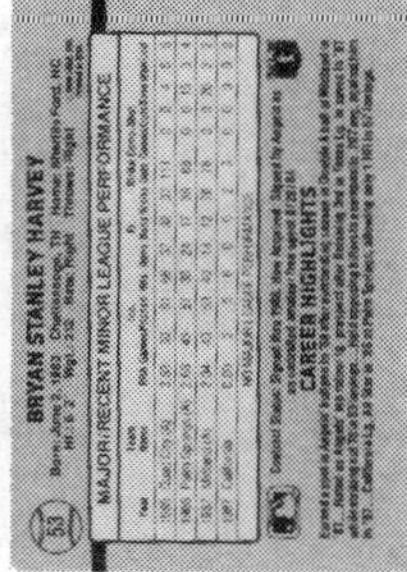

For the third consecutive year, Donruss issued this 56-card boxed set highlighting current rookies. The complete set includes a checklist and a 15-piece Stan Musial Diamond Kings puzzle. As in previous years, the set is similar to the company's basic issue, with the exception of the logo and border color. Card fronts feature red, green and black-striped borders, with a red-and-white player name printed in the lower left corner beneath the full-color photo. "The Rookies" logo is printed in red, white and black in the lower right corner. The card backs are printed in black on bright aqua and include personal data, recent performance stats and major league totals, as well as 1984-88 year-by-year minor league stats. The cards are the standard 2-1/2" by 3-1/2" size.

		MT	NR MT	EX
Complete Set (56):		20.00	15.00	8.00
Common Player:		.10	.08	.04
1	Mark Grace	2.50	2.00	1.00
2	Mike Campbell	.10	.08	.04
3	Todd Frowirth (FC)	.20	.15	.08
4	Dave Stapleton	.10	.08	.04
5	Shawn Abner	.10	.08	.04
6	Jose Cecena (FC)	.10	.08	.04
7	Dave Gallagher (FC)	.10	.08	.04
8	Mark Parent (FC)	.10	.08	.04
9	Cecil Espy (FC)	.15	.11	.06
10	Pete Smith	.10	.08	.04
11	Jay Buhner	1.25	.75	.40
12	Pat Borders (FC)	.40	.30	.15
13	Doug Jennings (FC)	.10	.08	.04
14	Brady Anderson (FC)	.90	.60	.30
15	Pete Stanicek	.15	.11	.06
16	Roberto Kelly	.75	.60	.30
17	Jeff Treadway	.10	.08	.04
18	Walt Weiss (FC)	.30	.25	.12
19	Paul Gibson (FC)	.15	.11	.06
20	Tim Crews	.10	.08	.04
21	Melido Perez	.15	.11	.06
22	Steve Peters (FC)	.10	.08	.04
23	Craig Worthington (FC)	.10	.08	.04
24	John Trautwein (FC)	.10	.08	.04
25	DeWayne Vaughn (FC)	.10	.08	.04
26	David Wells	.15	.11	.06
27	Al Leiter	.10	.08	.04
28	Tim Belcher	.20	.15	.08
29	Johnny Paredes (FC)	.10	.08	.04
30	Chris Sabo (FC)	.60	.45	.25
31	Damon Berryhill	.15	.11	.06
32	Randy Milligan	.25	.20	.10
33	Gary Thurman	.10	.08	.04
34	Kevin Elster	.10	.08	.04
35	Roberto Alomar	10.00	7.50	4.00
36	Edgar Martinez	1.00	.75	.40
37	Todd Stottlemyre	.40	.20	.10
38	Joey Meyer	.10	.08	.04
39	Carl Nichols	.10	.08	.04
40	Jack McDowell	2.00	1.50	.80
41	Jose Bautista (FC)	.20	.15	.08
42	Sil Campusano (FC)	.15	.11	.06
43	John Dopson (FC)	.20	.15	.08
44	Jody Reed	.35	.25	.14
45	Darrin Jackson (FC)	.30	.25	.12
46	Mike Capel (FC)	.10	.08	.04
47	Ron Gant	2.00	1.50	.80
48	John Davis	.10	.08	.04
49	Kevin Coffman (FC)	.10	.08	.04
50	Cris Carpenter (FC)	.20	.15	.08
51	Mackey Sasser	.10	.08	.04
52	Luis Alicea (FC)	.25	.20	.10
53	Bryan Harvey (FC)	1.75	1.25	.70
54	Steve Ellsworth (FC)	.10	.08	.04
55	Mike Macfarlane (FC)	.35	.20	.10
56	Checklist 1-56	.10	.08	.04

1988 Donruss Boston Red Sox Team Book

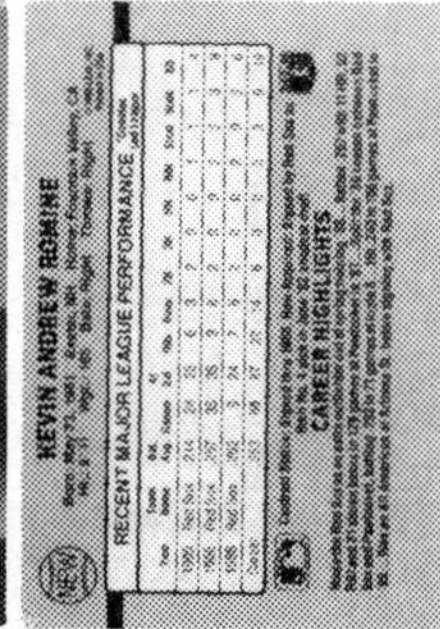

Three pages of nine cards each and a Stan Musial puzzle highlight this special team collection book. The cards feature the same design as the regular 1988 Donruss cards, but contain a 1988 copyright date instead of 1987 like the regular set. The cards are numbered like the regular issue with the exception of eight new cards which were produced especially for the Red Sox collection book. The book is commonly found complete with the cards and puzzle. The puzzle pieces are perforated for removal, but the card sheets are not.

		MT	NR MT	EX
Complete Set:		5.00	3.00	1.50
Common Player:		.08	.06	.03
N1	Brady Anderson	.50	.40	.20
N2	Rick Cerone	.08	.06	.03
N3	Steve Ellsworth	.08	.06	.03
N4	Dennis Lamp	.08	.06	.03
N5	Kevin Romine	.15	.11	.06
N6	Lee Smith	.40	.30	.15
N7	Mike Smithson	.08	.06	.03
N8	John Trautwein	.08	.06	.03
41	Jody Reed	.35	.25	.14
51	Roger Clemens	.80	.60	.30
92	Bob Stanley	.08	.06	.03
129	Rich Gedman	.08	.06	.03
153	Wade Boggs	.80	.60	.30
174	Ellis Burks	.75	.60	.30
216	Dwight Evans	.25	.20	.10
252	Bruce Hurst	.25	.20	.10
276	Marty Barrett	.12	.09	.05
297	Todd Benzinger	.15	.11	.06
339	Mike Greenwell	.90	.70	.35
399	Jim Rice	.20	.15	.08
421	John Marzano	.12	.09	.05
462	Oil Can Boyd	.12	.09	.05
498	Sam Horn	.20	.15	.08
544	Spike Owen	.12	.09	.05
585	Jeff Sellers	.08	.06	.03
623	Ed Romero	.08	.06	.03
634	Wes Gardner	.12	.09	.05

1988 Donruss Chicago Cubs Team Book

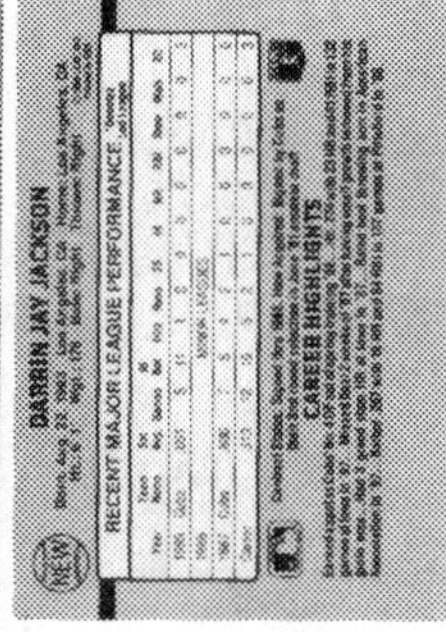

Primarily sold intact, the 1988 Donruss Chicago Cubs team book features three pages of cards and a fourth page featuring a Stan Musial puzzle. The inside cover provides space for autographs and the back inside cover provides team and ballpark history. The card fronts feature the design of the regular Donruss set. Eight "New" players are included in the team book. The cards have a 1988 copyright on the back in contrast with the 1987 copyright on the regular Donruss cards.

		MT	NR MT	EX
Complete Set:		5.00	3.75	2.00
Common Player:		.08	.06	.03
N1	Mike Bielecki	.20	.15	.08
N2	Rich Gossage	.20	.15	.08
N3	Drew Hall	.10	.08	.04
N4	Darrin Jackson	.30	.25	.12
N5	Vance Law	.08	.06	.03
N6	Al Nipper	.08	.06	.03
N7	Angel Salazar	.08	.06	.03
N8	Calvin Schiraldi	.08	.06	.03
40	Mark Grace	1.75	1.25	.70
68	Rick Sutcliffe	.15	.11	.06
119	Jody Davis	.08	.06	.03
146	Shawon Dunston	.35	.25	.14
169	Jamie Moyer	.08	.06	.03
191	Leon Durham	.08	.06	.03
242	Ryne Sandberg	.70	.50	.30
269	Andre Dawson	.40	.30	.15
315	Paul Noce	.08	.06	.03
324	Rafael Palmeiro	.70	.50	.30
438	Dave Martinez	.15	.11	.06
447	Jerry Mumphrey	.08	.06	.03
488	Jim Sundberg	.08	.06	.03
516	Manny Trillo	.10	.08	.04
539	Greg Maddux	.50	.40	.20
561	Les Lancaster	.08	.06	.03
570	Frank DiPino	.08	.06	.03
639	Damon Berryhill	.30	.25	.12
646	Scott Sanderson	.08	.06	.03

1988 Donruss New York Mets Team Book

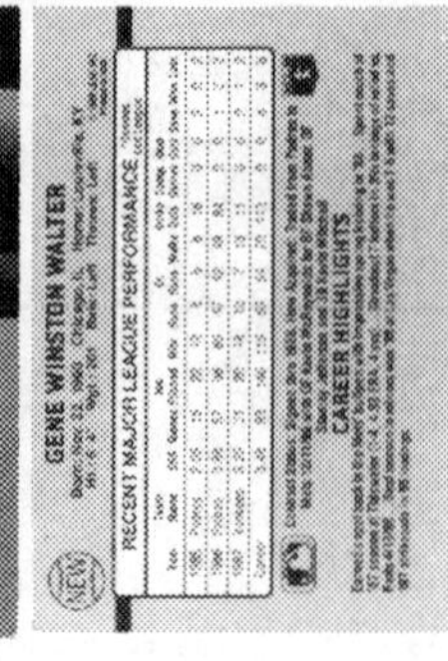

Distributed in book form, the 1988 Donruss New York Mets team book is still usually found intact. The team book features three pages of player cards, a full page featuring a perforated Stan Musial puzzle, space for autographs on the inside cover and team history information on the back inside cover. The outside covers of the Donruss team books are bright red. The player cards are the same as the regular Donruss issue with the exception of the copyright date. Three "New" Mets are featured in the team book.

		MT	NR MT	EX
Complete Set:		4.00	3.00	1.50
Common Player:		.08	.06	.03
N1	Jeff Innis	.15	.11	.06
N2	Mackey Sasser	.30	.25	.12
N3	Gene Walter	.08	.06	.03
37	Kevin Elster	.10	.08	.04
69	Dwight Gooden	.60	.45	.25
76	Ron Darling	.10	.08	.04
118	Sid Fernandez	.15	.11	.06
199	Gary Carter	.20	.15	.08
241	Wally Backman	.08	.06	.03
316	Keith Hernandez	.20	.15	.08
323	Dave Magadan	.30	.25	.12
364	Len Dykstra	.15	.11	.06
439	Darryl Strawberry	.70	.50	.30
446	Rick Aguilera	.10	.08	.04
562	Keith Miller	.10	.08	.04
569	Howard Johnson	.25	.20	.10
603	Terry Leach	.08	.06	.03
614	Lee Mazzilli	.08	.06	.03
617	Kevin McReynolds	.20	.15	.08
619	Barry Lyons	.08	.06	.03
620	Randy Myers	.20	.15	.08
632	Bob Ojeda	.08	.06	.03
648	Tim Teufel	.08	.06	.03
651	Roger McDowell	.15	.11	.06
652	Mookie Wilson	.10	.08	.04
653	David Cone	.30	.25	.12
657	Gregg Jefferies	2.00	1.50	.80

1988 Donruss New York Yankees Team Book

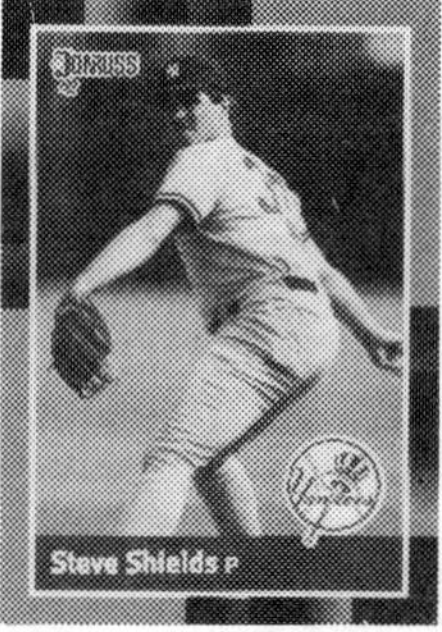

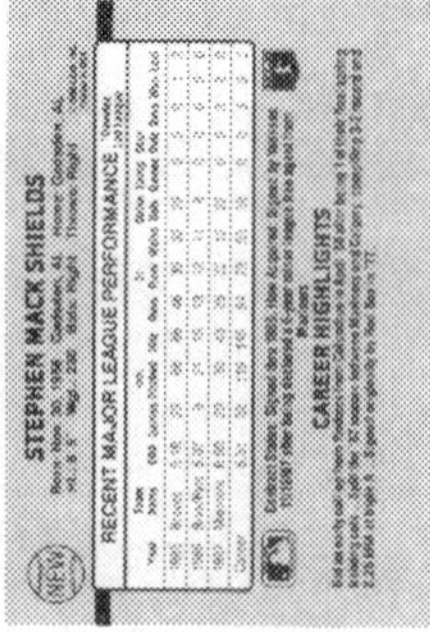

The 1988 Donruss New York Yankees team book includes the same features as the other team collection books. Three pages of cards, a Stan Musial puzzle, autograph space and team history information are provided. The team book is updated for 1988 trades. Nine "New" Yankees are included. The player cards are the same as the regular Donruss cards with the exception of the copyright dates. The team collection books are most often sold intact.

		MT	NR MT	EX
Complete Set:		5.00	3.75	2.00
Common Player:		.08	.06	.03
N1	John Candelaria	.10	.08	.04
N2	Jack Clark	.25	.20	.10
N3	Jose Cruz	.08	.06	.03
N4	Richard Dotson	.08	.06	.03
N5	Cecilio Guante	.08	.06	.03
N6	Lee Guetterman	.08	.06	.03
N7	Rafael Santana	.08	.06	.03
N8	Steve Shields	.08	.06	.03
N9	Don Slaught	.10	.08	.04
43	Al Leiter	.08	.06	.03
93	Dave Righetti	.15	.11	.06

105	Mike Pagliarulo	.10	.08	.04
128	Rick Rhoden	.08	.06	.03
175	Ron Guidry	.15	.11	.06
217	Don Mattingly	1.25	.90	.50
228	Willie Randolph	.15	.11	.06
251	Gary Ward	.08	.06	.03
277	Rickey Henderson	.70	.50	.30
278	Dave Winfield	.25	.20	.10
340	Claudell Washington	.08	.06	.03
374	Charles Hudson	.08	.06	.03
401	Tommy John	.15	.11	.06
474	Joel Skinner	.08	.06	.03
497	Tim Stoddard	.08	.06	.03
545	Jay Buhner	.30	.25	.12
616	Bobby Meacham	.08	.06	.03
635	Roberto Kelly	.90	.70	.35

1988 Donruss Oakland A's Team Book

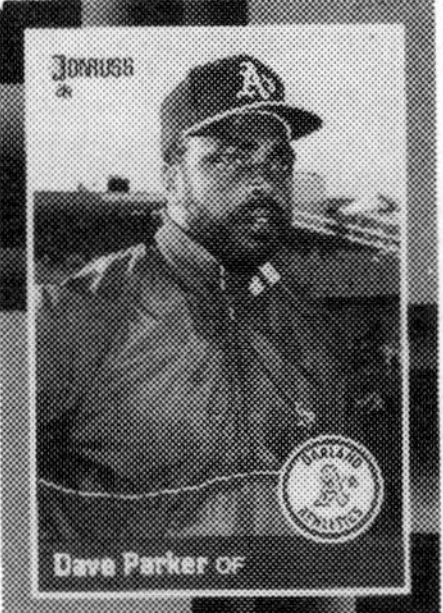

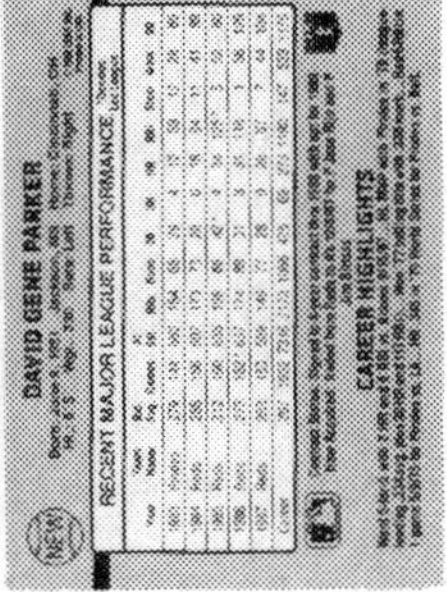

Eleven "New" players are among the featured cards in this unique collectible. The team book includes three pages of player cards, a Stan Musial puzzle, autograph space and team history information. The team books are most often sold intact. The player cards feature the same design as the regular Donruss cards.

		MT	NR MT	EX
Complete Set:		6.00	4.50	2.50
Common Player:		.08	.06	.03
N1	Don Baylor	.25	.20	.10
N2	Ron Hassey	.12	.09	.05
N3	Dave Henderson	.20	.15	.08
N4	Glenn Hubbard	.08	.06	.03
N5	Stan Javier	.10	.08	.04
N6	Doug Jennings	.20	.15	.08
N7	Edward Jurak	.08	.06	.03
N8	Dave Parker	.45	.35	.20
N9	Walt Weiss	.80	.60	.30
N10	Bob Welch	.30	.25	.12
N11	Matt Young	.08	.06	.03
97	Curt Young	.08	.06	.03
133	Gene Nelson	.08	.06	.03
158	Terry Steinbach	.20	.15	.08
178	Carney Lansford	.20	.15	.08
221	Tony Phillips	.08	.06	.03
256	Mark McGwire	.80	.60	.30
302	Jose Canseco	1.75	1.25	.70
349	Dennis Eckersley	.40	.30	.15
379	Mike Gallego	.08	.06	.03
425	Luis Polonia	.08	.06	.03
467	Steve Ontiveros	.08	.06	.03
472	Dave Stewart	.40	.30	.15
503	Eric Plunk	.08	.06	.03
528	Greg Cadaret	.08	.06	.03
590	Rick Honeycutt	.08	.06	.03
595	Storm Davis	.08	.06	.03

1989 Donruss

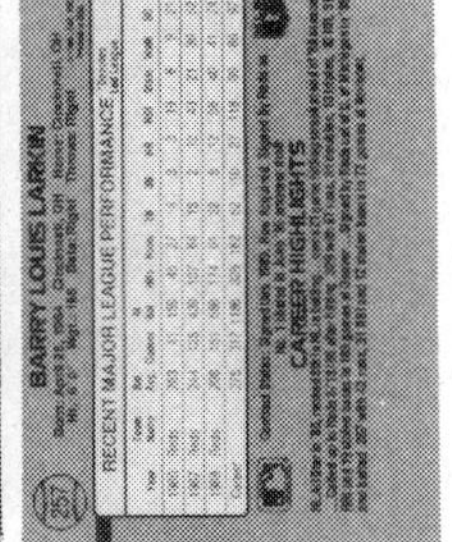

This basic annual issue consists of 660 standard-size (2-1/2" by 3-1/2") cards, including 26 Diamond Kings portrait cards and 20 Rated Rookies cards. Top and bottom borders of the cards are printed in a variety of colors that fade from dark to light (i.e. dark blue to light purple, bright red to pale yellow). A white-lettered player name is printed across the top margin. The team logo appears upper right and the Donruss logo lower left. A black stripe and thin white line make up the vertical side borders. The black outer stripe varnish that gives faintly visible filmstrip texture to the border. The backs (horizontal format) are printed in orange and black, similar to the 1988 design, with personal info, recent stats and major league totals. Team logo sticker cards (22 total) and Warren Spahn puzzle cards (63 total) are included in individual wax packs of cards.

		MT	NR MT	EX
Complete Set (660):		15.00	11.00	6.00
Common Player:		.04	.03	.02
1	Mike Greenwell (DK)	.08	.06	.03
2	Bobby Bonilla (DK)	.08	.06	.03
3	Pete Incaviglia (DK)	.08	.06	.03
4	Chris Sabo (DK)	.08	.06	.03
5	Robin Yount (DK)	.12	.09	.05
6	Tony Gwynn (DK)	.12	.09	.05
7	Carlton Fisk (DK)	.10	.08	.04
8	Cory Snyder (DK)	.08	.06	.03
9	David Cone (DK)	.08	.06	.03
10	Kevin Seitzer (DK)	.08	.06	.03
11	Rick Reuschel (DK)	.10	.08	.04
12	Johnny Ray (DK)	.10	.08	.04
13	Dave Schmidt (DK)	.08	.06	.03
14	Andres Galarraga (DK)	.15	.11	.06
15	Kirk Gibson (DK)	.08	.06	.03
16	Fred McGriff (DK)	.15	.11	.06
17	Mark Grace (DK)	.12	.09	.05
18	Jeff Robinson (DK)	.08	.06	.03
19	Vince Coleman (DK)	.06	.05	.02
20	Dave Henderson (DK)	.10	.08	.04
21	Harold Reynolds (DK)	.08	.06	.03
22	Gerald Perry (DK)	.10	.08	.04
23	Frank Viola (DK)	.08	.06	.03
24	Steve Bedrosian (DK)	.10	.08	.04
25	Glenn Davis (DK)	.08	.06	.03
26	Don Mattingly (DK)	.15	.11	.06
27	Checklist 1-27	.04	.03	.02
28	*Sandy Alomar, Jr.* (RR)	.15	.11	.06
29	*Steve Searcy* (FC) (RR)	.15	.11	.06
30	*Cameron Drew* (FC) (RR)	.15	.11	.06
31	*Gary Sheffield* (RR)	1.25	.90	.50
32	*Erik Hanson* (RR)	.40	.30	.15
33	*Ken Griffey, Jr.* (RR)	4.00	3.00	1.50
34	*Greg Harris* (RR)	.10	.08	.04
35	Gregg Jefferies (RR)	.50	.40	.20
36	*Luis Medina* (FC) (RR)	.08	.06	.03
37	*Carlos Quintana* (RR)	.12	.09	.05
38	*Felix Jose* (RR)	.25	.20	.10
39	*Cris Carpenter* (RR)	.10	.08	.04
40	*Ron Jones* (FC) (RR)	.10	.08	.04
41	*Dave West* (RR)	.12	.09	.05
42	*Randy Johnson* (RR)	.75	.60	.30
43	*Mike Harkey* (RR)	.15	.11	.06
44	*Pete Harnisch* (RR)	.25	.20	.10
45	*Tom Gordon* (RR)	.10	.08	.04
46	*Gregg Olson* (RR)	.25	.20	.10
47	*Alex Sanchez* (FC) (RR)	.15	.11	.06
48	Ruben Sierra	.35	.25	.14
49	Rafael Palmeiro	.25	.20	.10
50	Ron Gant	.25	.20	.10
51	Cal Ripken, Jr.	.40	.30	.15
52	Wally Joyner	.10	.08	.04
53	Gary Carter	.10	.08	.04
54	Andy Van Slyke	.08	.06	.03
55	Robin Yount	.25	.20	.10
56	Pete Incaviglia	.10	.08	.04
57	Greg Brock	.06	.05	.02
58	Melido Perez	.08	.06	.03
59	Craig Lefferts	.04	.03	.02
60	Gary Pettis	.04	.03	.02
61	Danny Tartabull	.15	.11	.06
62	Guillermo Hernandez	.06	.05	.02
63	Ozzie Smith	.12	.09	.05
64	Gary Gaetti	.12	.09	.05
65	Mark Davis	.04	.03	.02
66	Lee Smith	.08	.06	.03
67	Dennis Eckersley	.10	.08	.04
68	Wade Boggs	.25	.20	.10
69	Mike Scott	.10	.08	.04
70	Fred McGriff	.40	.30	.15
71	Tom Browning	.08	.06	.03
72	Claudell Washington	.06	.05	.02
73	Mel Hall	.06	.05	.02
74	Don Mattingly	.25	.20	.10
75	Steve Bedrosian	.08	.06	.03
76	Juan Samuel	.10	.08	.04
77	Mike Scioscia	.06	.05	.02
78	Dave Righetti	.12	.09	.05
79	Alfredo Griffin	.06	.05	.02
80	Eric Davis	.12	.09	.05
81	Juan Berenguer	.04	.03	.02
82	Todd Worrell	.08	.06	.03
83	Joe Carter	.15	.11	.06
84	Steve Sax	.12	.09	.05
85	Frank White	.06	.05	.02
86	John Kruk	.06	.05	.02
87	Rance Mulliniks	.04	.03	.02
88	Alan Ashby	.04	.03	.02
89	Charlie Leibrandt	.06	.05	.02
90	Frank Tanana	.06	.05	.02
91	Jose Canseco	.25	.20	.10
92	Barry Bonds	.60	.45	.25
93	Harold Reynolds	.06	.05	.02
94	Mark McLemore	.04	.03	.02
95	Mark McGwire	.30	.25	.12
96	Eddie Murray	.20	.15	.08
97	Tim Raines	.08	.06	.03
98	Rob Thompson	.06	.05	.02
99	Kevin McReynolds	.12	.09	.05
100	Checklist 28-137	.04	.03	.02
101	Carlton Fisk	.12	.09	.05
102	Dave Martinez	.06	.05	.02
103	Glenn Braggs	.06	.05	.02
104	Dale Murphy	.08	.06	.03
105	Ryne Sandberg	.40	.30	.15
106	Dennis Martinez	.06	.05	.02
107	Pete O'Brien	.06	.05	.02
108	Dick Schofield	.04	.03	.02
109	Henry Cotto	.04	.03	.02
110	Mike Marshall	.06	.05	.02
111	Keith Moreland	.06	.05	.02
112	Tom Brunansky	.10	.08	.04
113	Kelly Gruber	.04	.03	.02
114	Brook Jacoby	.08	.06	.03
115	*Keith Brown* (FC)	.08	.06	.03
116	Matt Nokes	.15	.11	.06
117	Keith Hernandez	.08	.06	.03
118	Bob Forsch	.06	.05	.02
119	Bert Blyleven	.10	.08	.04
120	Willie Wilson	.08	.06	.03
121	Tommy Gregg	.08	.06	.03
122	Jim Rice	.08	.06	.03
123	Bob Knepper	.06	.05	.02
124	Danny Jackson	.12	.09	.05
125	Eric Plunk	.04	.03	.02
126	Brian Fisher	.06	.05	.02
127	Mike Pagliarulo	.08	.06	.03
128	Tony Gwynn	.30	.25	.12
129	Lance McCullers	.06	.05	.02
130	Andres Galarraga	.15	.11	.06
131	Jose Uribe	.04	.03	.02
132	Kirk Gibson	.08	.06	.03
133	David Palmer	.04	.03	.02
134	R.J. Reynolds	.04	.03	.02
135	Greg Walker	.06	.05	.02
136	Kirk McCaskill	.06	.05	.02
137	Shawon Dunston	.08	.06	.03
138	Andy Allanson	.04	.03	.02
139	Rob Murphy	.04	.03	.02
140	Mike Aldrete	.06	.05	.02
141	Terry Kennedy	.06	.05	.02
142	Scott Fletcher	.06	.05	.02
143	Steve Balboni	.06	.05	.02
144	Bret Saberhagen	.12	.09	.05
145	Ozzie Virgil	.04	.03	.02
146	Dale Sveum	.06	.05	.02
147	Darryl Strawberry	.12	.09	.05
148	Harold Baines	.10	.08	.04
149	George Bell	.08	.06	.03
150	Dave Parker	.12	.09	.05
151	Bobby Bonilla	.12	.09	.05
152	Mookie Wilson	.06	.05	.02
153	Ted Power	.04	.03	.02
154	Nolan Ryan	.60	.45	.25
155	Jeff Reardon	.08	.06	.03
156	Tim Wallach	.08	.06	.03
157	Jamie Moyer	.04	.03	.02
158	Rich Gossage	.10	.08	.04
159	Dave Winfield	.25	.20	.10
160	Von Hayes	.08	.06	.03
161	Willie McGee	.10	.08	.04
162	Rich Gedman	.06	.05	.02
163	Tony Pena	.06	.05	.02
164	Mike Morgan	.04	.03	.02
165	Charlie Hough	.06	.05	.02
166	Mike Stanley	.10	.08	.04
167	Andre Dawson	.20	.15	.08
168	Joe Boever (FC)	.04	.03	.02
169	Pete Stanicek	.08	.06	.03
170	Bob Boone	.06	.05	.02
171	Ron Darling	.10	.08	.04
172	Bob Walk	.04	.03	.02
173	Rob Deer	.06	.05	.02
174	Steve Buechele	.04	.03	.02
175	Ted Higuera	.08	.06	.03
176	Ozzie Guillen	.06	.05	.02
177	Candy Maldonado	.06	.05	.02
178	Doyle Alexander	.06	.05	.02
179	Mark Gubicza	.10	.08	.04
180	Alan Trammell	.08	.06	.03
181	Vince Coleman	.15	.11	.06
182	Kirby Puckett	.30	.25	.12
183	Chris Brown	.06	.05	.02
184	Marty Barrett	.06	.05	.02
185	Stan Javier	.04	.03	.02
186	Mike Greenwell	.08	.06	.03
187	Billy Hatcher	.06	.05	.02
188	Jimmy Key	.08	.06	.03
189	Nick Esasky	.06	.05	.02
190	Don Slaught	.04	.03	.02
191	Cory Snyder	.08	.06	.03
192	John Candelaria	.06	.05	.02
193	Mike Schmidt	.40	.30	.15
194	Kevin Gross	.06	.05	.02
195	John Tudor	.08	.06	.03
196	Neil Allen	.04	.03	.02
197	Orel Hershiser	.08	.06	.03
198	Kal Daniels	.08	.06	.03
199	Kent Hrbek	.15	.11	.06
200	Checklist 138-247	.04	.03	.02
201	Joe Magrane	.08	.06	.03
202	Scott Bailes	.04	.03	.02
203	Tim Belcher	.10	.08	.04
204	George Brett	.30	.25	.12
205	Benito Santiago	.12	.09	.05
206	Tony Fernandez	.10	.08	.04
207	Gerald Young	.10	.08	.04
208	Bo Jackson	.25	.20	.10
209	Chet Lemon	.06	.05	.02
210	Storm Davis	.08	.06	.03
211	Doug Drabek	.06	.05	.02
212	Mickey Brantley (photo actually Nelson Simmons)	.04	.03	.02
213	Devon White	.08	.06	.03
214	Dave Stewart	.08	.06	.03
215	Dave Schmidt	.04	.03	.02
216	Bryn Smith	.04	.03	.02

217	Brett Butler	.06	.05	.02
218	Bob Ojeda	.06	.05	.02
219	*Steve Rosenberg* (FC)	.08	.06	.03
220	Hubie Brooks	.08	.06	.03
221	B.J. Surhoff	.08	.06	.03
222	Rick Mahler	.04	.03	.02
223	Rick Sutcliffe	.08	.06	.03
224	Neal Heaton	.04	.03	.02
225	Mitch Williams	.06	.05	.02
226	Chuck Finley	.08	.06	.03
227	Mark Langston	.10	.08	.04
228	Jesse Orosco	.06	.05	.02
229	Ed Whitson	.04	.03	.02
230	Terry Pendleton	.08	.06	.03
231	Lloyd Moseby	.06	.05	.02
232	Greg Swindell	.10	.08	.04
233	John Franco	.08	.06	.03
234	Jack Morris	.10	.08	.04
235	Howard Johnson	.08	.06	.03
236	Glenn Davis	.08	.06	.03
237	Frank Viola	.12	.09	.05
238	Kevin Seitzer	.06	.05	.02
239	Gerald Perry	.08	.06	.03
240	Dwight Evans	.10	.08	.04
241	Jim Deshaies	.04	.03	.02
242	Bo Diaz	.06	.05	.02
243	Carney Lansford	.06	.05	.02
244	Mike LaValliere	.06	.05	.02
245	Rickey Henderson	.20	.15	.08
246	Roberto Alomar	.80	.60	.30
247	Jimmy Jones	.04	.03	.02
248	Pascual Perez	.06	.05	.02
249	Will Clark	.35	.25	.14
250	Fernando Valenzuela	.08	.06	.03
251	Shane Rawley	.06	.05	.02
252	Sid Bream	.06	.05	.02
253	Steve Lyons	.04	.03	.02
254	Brian Downing	.06	.05	.02
255	Mark Grace	.20	.15	.08
256	Tom Candiotti	.04	.03	.02
257	Barry Larkin	.10	.08	.04
258	Mike Krukow	.06	.05	.02
259	Billy Ripken	.06	.05	.02
260	Cecilio Guante	.04	.03	.02
261	Scott Bradley	.04	.03	.02
262	Floyd Bannister	.06	.05	.02
263	Pete Smith	.08	.06	.03
264	Jim Gantner	.04	.03	.02
265	Roger McDowell	.08	.06	.03
266	Bobby Thigpen	.08	.06	.03
267	Jim Clancy	.06	.05	.02
268	Terry Steinbach	.08	.06	.03
269	Mike Dunne	.08	.06	.03
270	Dwight Gooden	.10	.08	.04
271	Mike Heath	.04	.03	.02
272	Dave Smith	.06	.05	.02
273	Keith Atherton	.04	.03	.02
274	Tim Burke	.04	.03	.02
275	Damon Berryhill	.12	.09	.05
276	Vance Law	.06	.05	.02
277	Rich Dotson	.06	.05	.02
278	Lance Parrish	.08	.06	.03
279	Denny Walling	.04	.03	.02
280	Roger Clemens	.30	.25	.12
281	Greg Mathews	.06	.05	.02
282	Tom Niedenfuer	.06	.05	.02
283	Paul Kilgus	.10	.08	.04
284	Jose Guzman	.08	.06	.03
285	Calvin Schiraldi	.04	.03	.02
286	Charlie Puleo	.04	.03	.02
287	Joe Orsulak	.04	.03	.02
288	Jack Howell	.06	.05	.02
289	Kevin Elster	.08	.06	.03
290	Jose Lind	.10	.08	.04
291	Paul Molitor	.25	.20	.10
292	Cecil Espy	.08	.06	.03
293	Bill Wegman	.04	.03	.02
294	Dan Pasqua	.08	.06	.03
295	Scott Garrelts	.04	.03	.02
296	Walt Terrell	.06	.05	.02
297	Ed Hearn	.04	.03	.02
298	Lou Whitaker	.08	.06	.03
299	Ken Dayley	.04	.03	.02
300	Checklist 248-357	.04	.03	.02
301	Tommy Herr	.06	.05	.02
302	Mike Brumley	.06	.05	.02
303	Ellis Burks	.10	.08	.04
304	Curt Young	.06	.05	.02
305	Jody Reed	.10	.08	.04
306	Bill Doran	.06	.05	.02
307	David Wells	.06	.05	.02
308	Ron Robinson	.04	.03	.02
309	Rafael Santana	.04	.03	.02
310	Julio Franco	.10	.08	.04
311	Jack Clark	.08	.06	.03
312	Chris James	.08	.06	.03
313	Milt Thompson	.04	.03	.02
314	John Shelby	.04	.03	.02
315	Al Leiter	.08	.06	.03
316	Mike Davis	.06	.05	.02
317	*Chris Sabo*	.25	.20	.10
318	Greg Gagne	.04	.03	.02
319	Jose Oquendo	.04	.03	.02
320	John Farrell	.10	.08	.04
321	Franklin Stubbs	.04	.03	.02
322	Kurt Stillwell	.06	.05	.02
323	Shawn Abner	.10	.08	.04
324	Mike Flanagan	.06	.05	.02
325	Kevin Bass	.06	.05	.02
326	Pat Tabler	.06	.05	.02
327	Mike Henneman	.08	.06	.03
328	Rick Honeycutt	.04	.03	.02
329	John Smiley	.10	.08	.04
330	Rey Quinones	.04	.03	.02
331	Johnny Ray	.06	.05	.02
332	Bob Welch	.08	.06	.03
333	Larry Sheets	.06	.05	.02
334	Jeff Parrett	.08	.06	.03
335	Rick Reuschel	.08	.06	.03
336	Randy Myers	.10	.08	.04
337	Ken Williams	.06	.05	.02
338	Andy McGaffigan	.04	.03	.02
339	Joey Meyer	.08	.06	.03
340	Dion James	.04	.03	.02
341	Les Lancaster	.06	.05	.02
342	Tom Foley	.04	.03	.02
343	Geno Petralli	.04	.03	.02
344	Dan Petry	.06	.05	.02
345	Alvin Davis	.06	.05	.02
346	Mickey Hatcher	.04	.03	.02
347	Marvell Wynne	.04	.03	.02
348	Danny Cox	.06	.05	.02
349	Dave Stieb	.08	.06	.03
350	Jay Bell	.06	.05	.02
351	Jeff Treadway	.10	.08	.04
352	Luis Salazar	.04	.03	.02
353	Len Dykstra	.15	.11	.06
354	Juan Agosto	.04	.03	.02
355	Gene Larkin	.10	.08	.04
356	Steve Farr	.04	.03	.02
357	Paul Assenmacher	.04	.03	.02
358	Todd Benzinger	.12	.09	.05
359	Larry Andersen	.04	.03	.02
360	Paul O'Neill	.04	.03	.02
361	Ron Hassey	.04	.03	.02
362	Jim Gott	.04	.03	.02
363	Ken Phelps	.06	.05	.02
364	Tim Flannery	.04	.03	.02
365	Randy Ready	.04	.03	.02
366	*Nelson Santovenia* (FC)	.08	.06	.03
367	Kelly Downs	.08	.06	.03
368	Danny Heep	.04	.03	.02
369	Phil Bradley	.08	.06	.03
370	Jeff Robinson	.06	.05	.02
371	Ivan Calderon	.06	.05	.02
372	Mike Witt	.06	.05	.02
373	Greg Maddux	.25	.20	.10
374	Carmen Castillo	.04	.03	.02
375	Jose Rijo	.06	.05	.02
376	Joe Price	.04	.03	.02
377	R.C. Gonzalez	.04	.03	.02
378	Oddibe McDowell	.06	.05	.02
379	Jim Presley	.06	.05	.02
380	Brad Wellman	.04	.03	.02
381	Tom Glavine	.25	.20	.10
382	Dan Plesac	.08	.06	.03
383	Wally Backman	.06	.05	.02
384	*Dave Gallagher*	.08	.06	.03
385	Tom Henke	.06	.05	.02
386	Luis Polonia	.06	.05	.02
387	Junior Ortiz	.04	.03	.02
388	David Cone	.12	.09	.05
389	Dave Bergman	.04	.03	.02
390	Danny Darwin	.04	.03	.02
391	Dan Gladden	.04	.03	.02
392	*John Dopson*	.08	.06	.03
393	Frank DiPino	.04	.03	.02
394	Al Nipper	.04	.03	.02
395	Willie Randolph	.06	.05	.02
396	Don Carman	.06	.05	.02
397	Scott Terry	.06	.05	.02
398	Rick Cerone	.04	.03	.02
399	Tom Pagnozzi	.06	.05	.02
400	Checklist 358-467	.04	.03	.02
401	Mickey Tettleton	.08	.06	.03
402	Curtis Wilkerson	.04	.03	.02
403	Jeff Russell	.04	.03	.02
404	Pat Perry	.04	.03	.02
405	*Jose Alvarez* (FC)	.06	.05	.02
406	Rick Schu	.04	.03	.02
407	*Sherman Corbett* (FC)	.08	.06	.03
408	Dave Magadan	.08	.06	.03
409	Bob Kipper	.04	.03	.02
410	Don August	.08	.06	.03
411	Bob Brower	.04	.03	.02
412	Chris Bosio	.04	.03	.02
413	Jerry Reuss	.06	.05	.02
414	Atlee Hammaker	.04	.03	.02
415	Jim Walewander (FC)	.06	.05	.02
416	*Mike Macfarlane*	.25	.20	.10
417	Pat Sheridan	.04	.03	.02
418	Pedro Guerrero	.08	.06	.03
419	Allan Anderson	.06	.05	.02
420	*Mark Parent*	.08	.06	.03
421	Bob Stanley	.04	.03	.02
422	Mike Gallego	.04	.03	.02
423	Bruce Hurst	.08	.06	.03
424	Dave Meads	.04	.03	.02
425	Jesse Barfield	.10	.08	.04
426	*Rob Dibble*	.15	.11	.06
427	Joel Skinner	.04	.03	.02
428	Ron Kittle	.06	.05	.02
429	Rick Rhoden	.08	.06	.03
430	Bob Dernier	.04	.03	.02
431	Steve Jeltz	.04	.03	.02
432	Rick Dempsey	.06	.05	.02
433	Roberto Kelly	.10	.08	.04
434	Dave Anderson	.04	.03	.02
435	Herm Winningham	.04	.03	.02
436	Al Newman	.04	.03	.02
437	Jose DeLeon	.06	.05	.02
438	Doug Jones	.10	.08	.04
439	Brian Holton	.06	.05	.02
440	Jeff Montgomery (FC)	.15	.11	.06
441	Dickie Thon	.04	.03	.02
442	Cecil Fielder	.25	.20	.10
443	*John Fishel* (FC)	.08	.06	.03
444	Jerry Don Gleaton	.04	.03	.02
445	*Paul Gibson*	.08	.06	.03
446	Walt Weiss	.08	.06	.03
447	Glenn Wilson	.06	.05	.02
448	Mike Moore	.04	.03	.02
449	Chili Davis	.06	.05	.02
450	Dave Henderson	.08	.06	.03
451	*Jose Bautista*	.06	.05	.02
452	Rex Hudler	.04	.03	.02
453	Bob Brenly	.04	.03	.02
454	Mackey Sasser	.06	.05	.02
455	Daryl Boston	.04	.03	.02
456	Mike Fitzgerald	.04	.03	.02
457	Jeffery Leonard	.06	.05	.02
458	Bruce Sutter	.08	.06	.03
459	Mitch Webster	.06	.05	.02
460	Joe Hesketh	.04	.03	.02
461	Bobby Witt	.08	.06	.03
462	Stew Cliburn	.04	.03	.02
463	Scott Bankhead	.04	.03	.02
464	*Ramon Martinez*	.40	.30	.15
465	Dave Leiper	.04	.03	.02
466	*Luis Alicea*	.10	.08	.04
467	John Cerutti	.06	.05	.02
468	Ron Washington	.04	.03	.02
469	Jeff Reed	.04	.03	.02
470	Jeff Robinson	.12	.09	.05
471	Sid Fernandez	.08	.06	.03
472	Terry Puhl	.04	.03	.02
473	Charlie Lea	.04	.03	.02
474	*Israel Sanchez* (FC)	.08	.06	.03
475	Bruce Benedict	.04	.03	.02
476	Oil Can Boyd	.06	.05	.02
477	Craig Reynolds	.04	.03	.02
478	Frank Williams	.04	.03	.02
479	Greg Cadaret	.06	.05	.02
480	*Randy Kramer* (FC)	.06	.05	.02
481	*Dave Eiland* (FC)	.06	.05	.02
482	Eric Show	.06	.05	.02
483	Garry Templeton	.06	.05	.02
484	Wallace Johnson (FC)	.04	.03	.02
485	Kevin Mitchell	.15	.11	.06
486	Tim Crews	.06	.05	.02
487	Mike Maddux	.04	.03	.02
488	Dave LaPoint	.06	.05	.02
489	Fred Manrique	.06	.05	.02
490	Greg Minton	.04	.03	.02
491	*Doug Dascenzo* (FC)	.08	.06	.03
492	Willie Upshaw	.06	.05	.02
493	*Jack Armstrong* (FC)	.10	.08	.04
494	Kirt Manwaring	.10	.08	.04
495	Jeff Ballard	.06	.05	.02
496	Jeff Kunkel	.04	.03	.02
497	Mike Campbell	.08	.06	.03
498	Gary Thurman	.10	.08	.04
499	Zane Smith	.06	.05	.02
500	Checklist 468-577	.04	.03	.02
501	Mike Birkbeck	.04	.03	.02
502	Terry Leach	.04	.03	.02
503	Shawn Hillegas	.06	.05	.02
504	Manny Lee	.04	.03	.02
505	*Doug Jennings*	.08	.06	.03
506	Ken Oberkfell	.04	.03	.02
507	Tim Teufel	.04	.03	.02
508	Tom Brookens	.04	.03	.02
509	Rafael Ramirez	.04	.03	.02
510	Fred Toliver	.04	.03	.02
511	*Brian Holman* (FC)	.12	.09	.05
512	Mike Bielecki	.04	.03	.02
513	*Jeff Pico* (FC)	.06	.05	.02
514	Charles Hudson	.04	.03	.02
515	Bruce Ruffin	.04	.03	.02
516	Larry McWilliams	.04	.03	.02
517	Jeff Sellers	.04	.03	.02
518	*John Costello* (FC)	.08	.06	.03
519	*Brady Anderson*	.40	.30	.15
520	Craig McMurtry	.04	.03	.02
521	Ray Hayward	.08	.06	.03
522	Drew Hall	.08	.06	.03
523	*Mark Lemke* (FC)	.10	.08	.04
524	*Oswald Peraza* (FC)	.08	.06	.03
525	*Bryan Harvey*	.40	.30	.15
526	Rick Aguilera	.04	.03	.02
527	Tom Prince	.06	.05	.02
528	Mark Clear	.04	.03	.02
529	Jerry Browne	.04	.03	.02
530	Juan Castillo	.04	.03	.02
531	Jack McDowell	.15	.11	.06
532	Chris Speier	.04	.03	.02
533	Darrell Evans	.08	.06	.03
534	Luis Aquino	.04	.03	.02
535	Eric King	.04	.03	.02
536	*Ken Hill* (FC)	.20	.15	.08
537	Randy Bush	.04	.03	.02
538	Shane Mack	.06	.05	.02
539	Tom Bolton (FC)	.06	.05	.02
540	Gene Nelson	.04	.03	.02
541	Wes Gardner	.06	.05	.02
542	Ken Caminiti	.06	.05	.02
543	Duane Ward	.04	.03	.02
544	*Norm Charlton* (FC)	.15	.11	.06
545	*Hal Morris* (FC)	.25	.20	.10
546	Rich Yett (FC)	.04	.03	.02
547	*Hensley Meulens* (FC)	.20	.15	.08
548	Greg Harris	.04	.03	.02
549	Darren Daulton	.04	.03	.02
550	Jeff Hamilton	.06	.05	.02
551	Luis Aguayo	.04	.03	.02
552	Tim Leary	.06	.05	.02
553	Ron Oester	.04	.03	.02
554	Steve Lombardozzi	.04	.03	.02
555	*Tim Jones* (FC)	.15	.11	.06
556	Bud Black	.04	.03	.02
557	Alejandro Pena	.04	.03	.02
558	*Jose DeJesus* (FC)	.15	.11	.06
559	Dennis Rasmussen	.08	.06	.03
560	*Pat Borders*	.12	.09	.05
561	*Craig Biggio* (FC)	.35	.25	.14
562	*Luis de los Santos* (FC)	.10	.08	.04
563	Fred Lynn	.10	.08	.04
564	*Todd Burns* (FC)	.08	.06	.03
565	Felix Fermin	.06	.05	.02
566	Darnell Coles	.06	.05	.02
567	Willie Fraser	.04	.03	.02
568	Glenn Hubbard	.04	.03	.02
569	*Craig Worthington*	.08	.06	.03
570	*Johnny Paredes*	.15	.11	.06

571	Don Robinson	.04	.03	.02
572	Barry Lyons	.08	.06	.03
573	Bill Long	.06	.05	.02
574	Tracy Jones	.10	.08	.04
575	Juan Nieves	.06	.05	.02
576	Andres Thomas	.06	.05	.02
577	*Rolando Roomes* (FC)	.06	.05	.02
578	Luis Rivera (FC)	.04	.03	.02
579	*Chad Kreuter* (FC)	.15	.11	.06
580	Tony Armas	.06	.05	.02
581	Jay Buhner	.12	.09	.05
582	Ricky Horton	.06	.05	.02
583	Andy Hawkins	.04	.03	.02
584	*Sil Campusano*	.06	.05	.02
585	Dave Clark	.06	.05	.02
586	*Van Snider* (FC)	.06	.05	.02
587	Todd Frohwirth (FC)	.06	.05	.02
588	Warren Spahn Puzzle Card	.04	.03	.02
589	*William Brennan* (FC)	.08	.06	.03
590	*German Gonzalez* (FC)	.06	.05	.02
591	Ernie Whitt	.06	.05	.02
592	Jeff Blauser	.08	.06	.03
593	Spike Owen	.04	.03	.02
594	Matt Williams	.40	.30	.15
595	Lloyd McClendon (FC)	.04	.03	.02
596	Steve Ontiveros	.04	.03	.02
597	*Scott Medvin* (FC)	.08	.06	.03
598	*Hipolito Pena* (FC)	.08	.06	.03
599	*Jerald Clark* (FC)	.15	.11	.06
600a	Checklist 578-BC26 (#635 is Kurt Schilling)	.15	.11	.06
600b	Checklist 578-BC26 (#635 is Curt Schilling)	.06	.05	.02
601	Carmelo Martinez	.04	.03	.02
602	Mike LaCoss	.04	.03	.02
603	Mike Devereaux	.15	.11	.06
604	*Alex Madrid* (FC)	.08	.06	.03
605	Gary Redus	.04	.03	.02
606	Lance Johnson	.06	.05	.02
607	*Terry Clark* (FC)	.15	.11	.06
608	Manny Trillo	.04	.03	.02
609	*Scott Jordan* (FC)	.08	.06	.03
610	Jay Howell	.06	.05	.02
611	*Francisco Melendez* (FC)	.06	.05	.02
612	Mike Boddicker	.06	.05	.02
613	Kevin Brown	.20	.15	.08
614	Dave Valle	.04	.03	.02
615	Tim Laudner	.04	.03	.02
616	*Andy Nezelek* (FC)	.06	.05	.02
617	Chuck Crim	.04	.03	.02
618	Jack Savage (FC)	.06	.05	.02
619	Adam Peterson (FC)	.06	.05	.02
620	Todd Stottlemyre	.15	.11	.06
621	*Lance Blankenship*	.10	.08	.04
622	*Miguel Garcia* (FC)	.06	.05	.02
623	Keith Miller	.06	.05	.02
624	*Ricky Jordan*	.10	.08	.04
625	Ernest Riles	.04	.03	.02
626	John Moses	.04	.03	.02
627	Nelson Liriano	.06	.05	.02
628	Mike Smithson	.04	.03	.02
629	Scott Sanderson	.04	.03	.02
630	Dale Mohorcic	.04	.03	.02
631	Marvin Freeman	.04	.03	.02
632	Mike Young	.04	.03	.02
633	Dennis Lamp	.04	.03	.02
634	*Dante Bichette*	.75	.60	.30
635	*Curt Schilling*	.35	.25	.14
636	*Scott May* (FC)	.08	.06	.03
637	*Mike Schooler*	.08	.06	.03
638	Rick Leach	.04	.03	.02
639	*Tom Lampkin* (FC)	.08	.06	.03
640	*Brian Meyer* (FC)	.06	.05	.02
641	Brian Harper	.04	.03	.02
642	*John Smoltz*	.75	.60	.30
643	Jose Canseco (40/40)	.15	.11	.06
644	Bill Schroeder	.04	.03	.02
645	*Edgar Martinez*	.20	.15	.08
646	*Dennis Cook*	.10	.08	.04
647	Barry Jones	.04	.03	.02
648	59 and Counting (Orel Hershiser)	.15	.11	.06
649	*Rod Nichols* (FC)	.15	.11	.06
650	Jody Davis	.06	.05	.02
651	*Bob Milacki*	.12	.09	.05
652	Mike Jackson	.06	.05	.02
653	*Derek Lilliquist*	.15	.11	.06
654	Paul Mirabella	.04	.03	.02
655	Mike Diaz	.06	.05	.02
656	Jeff Musselman	.06	.05	.02
657	Jerry Reed	.04	.03	.02
658	*Kevin Blankenship* (FC)	.08	.06	.03
659	Wayne Tolleson	.04	.03	.02
660	*Eric Hetzel* (FC)	.08	.06	.03

1989 Donruss MVP

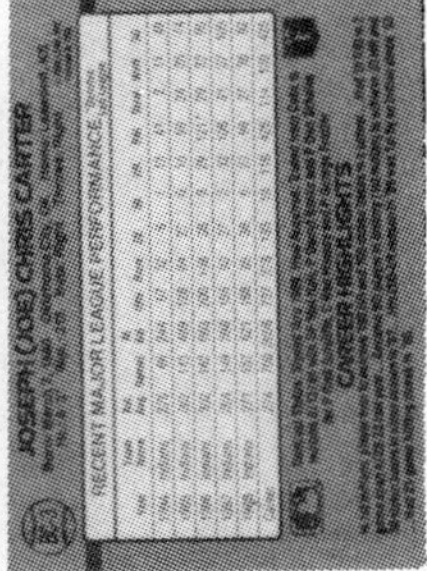

This 26-card set, numbered BC-1 through BC-26, was randomly packed in Donruss wax packs, but were not included in factory sets or other card packs. Players highlighted in this set are selected by Donruss, one player per team. MVP cards feature a variation of the design in the basic Donruss issue, with multi-color upper and lower borders and black side borders. The player name and Donruss '89 logos appear in the upper margin with the team logo appearing lower right. The "MVP" designation in large, bright letters serves as a backdrop for the full-color player photo. The cards measure 2-1/2" by 3-1/2" in size.

		MT	NR MT	EX
Complete Set (26):		3.00	.60	.30
Common Player:		.10	.03	.02
1	Kirby Puckett	.35	.25	.14
2	Mike Scott	.10	.08	.04
3	Joe Carter	.30	.25	.12
4	Orel Hershiser	.25	.20	.10
5	Jose Canseco	.75	.60	.30
6	Darryl Strawberry	.30	.25	.12
7	George Brett	.50	.40	.20
8	Andre Dawson	.25	.20	.10
9	Paul Molitor	.25	.20	.10
10	Andy Van Slyke	.15	.11	.06
11	Dave Winfield	.25	.20	.10
12	Kevin Gross	.10	.08	.04
13	Mike Greenwell	.30	.25	.12
14	Ozzie Smith	.30	.25	.12
15	Cal Ripken	.60	.45	.25
16	Andres Galarraga	.15	.11	.06
17	Alan Trammell	.25	.20	.10
18	Kal Daniels	.10	.08	.04
19	Fred McGriff	.25	.20	.10
20	Tony Gwynn	.10	.08	.04
21	Wally Joyner	.15	.11	.06
22	Will Clark	.30	.25	.12
23	Ozzie Guillen	.15	.11	.06
24	Gerald Perry	.10	.08	.04
25	Alvin Davis	.10	.08	.04
26	Ruben Sierra	.15	.11	.06

1989 Donruss Grand Slammers

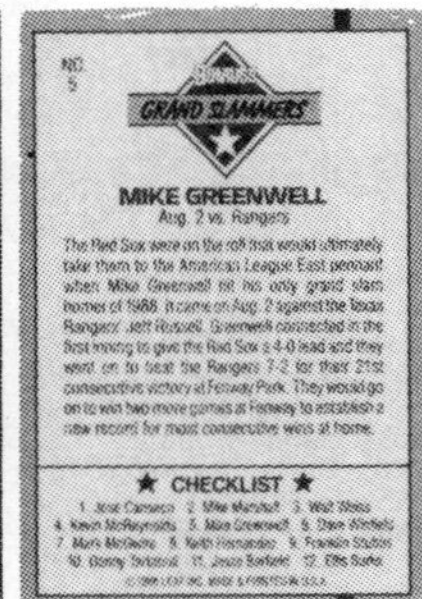

One card from this 12-card set was included in each Donruss cello pack. The complete insert set was included in factory sets. The featured players all hit grand slams in 1988. The 2-1/2" by 3-1/2" cards feature full color action photos. The card backs feature the story of the player's grand slam. Border variations on the front of the card have been discovered, but the prices are consistent with all forms of the cards.

		MT	NR MT	EX
Complete Set (12):		2.50	2.00	1.00
Common Player:		.12	.09	.05
1	Jose Canseco	.30	.25	.12
2	Mike Marshall	.12	.09	.05
3	Walt Weiss	.12	.09	.05
4	Kevin McReynolds	.15	.11	.06
5	Mike Greenwell	.25	.20	.10
6	Dave Winfield	.40	.30	.15
7	Mark McGwire	.30	.25	.12
8	Keith Hernandez	.15	.11	.06
9	Franklin Stubbs	.12	.09	.05
10	Danny Tartabull	.15	.11	.06
11	Jesse Barfield	.15	.11	.06
12	Ellis Burks	.15	.11	.06

1989 Donruss All-Stars

For the fourth consecutive year in conjunction with the Pop-Ups, Donruss featured a 64-card set with players from the 1988 All-Star Game. The card fronts include a red- to-gold fade or gold-to-red fade border and blue vertical side borders. The top border features the player's name and position along with the "Donruss 89" logo. Each full-color player photo is highlighted by a thin white line and includes a league logo in the lower right corner. Card backs reveal an

orange-gold border and black and white printing. The player's ID and personal information is displayed with a gold star on both sides. The star in the left corner includes the card number. 1988 All-Star game statistics and run totals follow along with a career highlights feature surrounded by the team, All-Star Game MLB, MLBPA, and Leaf Inc. logos. The All-Stars were distributed in wax packages containing five All-Stars, one Pop-Up, and one three-piece Warren Spahn puzzle card.

		MT	NR MT	EX
Complete Set:		9.00	6.75	3.50
Common Player:		.09	.07	.04
1	Mark McGwire	.50	.40	.20
2	Jose Canseco	1.00	.70	.40
3	Paul Molitor	.12	.09	.05
4	Rickey Henderson	.30	.25	.12
5	Cal Ripken, Jr.	.30	.25	.12
6	Dave Winfield	.20	.15	.08
7	Wade Boggs	.50	.40	.20
8	Frank Viola	.15	.11	.06
9	Terry Steinbach	.09	.07	.04
10	Tom Kelly	.09	.07	.04
11	George Brett	.12	.09	.05
12	Doyle Alexander	.09	.07	.04
13	Gary Gaetti	.12	.09	.05
14	Roger Clemens	.40	.30	.15
15	Mike Greenwell	.25	.20	.10
16	Dennis Eckersley	.12	.09	.05
17	Carney Lansford	.09	.07	.04
18	Mark Gubicza	.09	.07	.04
19	Tim Laudner	.09	.07	.04
20	Doug Jones	.09	.07	.04
21	Don Mattingly	1.00	.70	.40
22	Dan Plesac	.12	.09	.05
23	Kirby Puckett	.30	.25	.12
24	Jeff Reardon	.09	.07	.04
25	Johnny Ray	.09	.07	.04
26	Jeff Russell	.09	.07	.04
27	Harold Reynolds	.09	.07	.04
28	Dave Stieb	.09	.07	.04
29	Kurt Stillwell	.09	.07	.04
30	Jose Canseco	1.00	.70	.40
31	Terry Steinbach	.09	.07	.04
32	AL Checklist	.09	.07	.05
33	Will Clark	1.00	.70	.40
34	Darryl Strawberry	.60	.45	.25
35	Ryne Sandberg	.40	.30	.15
36	Andre Dawson	.20	.15	.08
37	Ozzie Smith	.20	.15	.08
38	Vince Coleman	.15	.11	.06
39	Bobby Bonilla	.15	.11	.06
40	Dwight Gooden	.40	.30	.15
41	Gary Carter	.10	.08	.04
42	Whitey Herzog	.09	.07	.05
43	Shawon Dunston	.09	.07	.05
44	David Cone	.12	.09	.05
45	Andres Galarraga	.09	.07	.04
46	Mark Davis	.09	.07	.04
47	Barry Larkin	.12	.09	.05
48	Kevin Gross	.09	.07	.04
49	Vance Law	.09	.07	.04
50	Orel Hershiser	.20	.15	.08
51	Willie McGee	.09	.07	.04
52	Danny Jackson	.09	.07	.04
53	Rafael Palmeiro	.20	.15	.08
54	Bob Knepper	.09	.07	.04
55	Lance Parrish	.09	.07	.04
56	Greg Maddux	.15	.11	.06
57	Gerald Perry	.09	.07	.04
58	Bob Walk	.09	.07	.04
59	Chris Sabo	.12	.09	.04
60	Todd Worrell	.09	.07	.04
61	Andy Van Slyke	.12	.09	.04
62	Ozzie Smith	.20	.15	.08
63	Riverfront Stadium	.09	.07	.04
64	NL Checklist	.09	.07	.04

1989 Donruss Baseball's Best

For the second consecutive year, Donruss issued a "Baseball's Best" set in 1989 to highlight the game's top players. The special 336-card set was packaged in a special box and was sold at various retail chains nationwide following the conclusion of the 1989 baseball season. The cards are styled

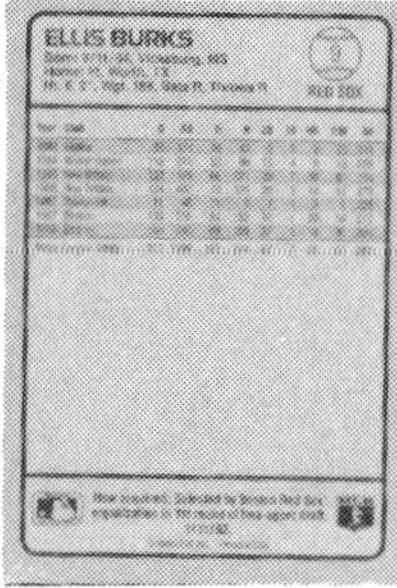

after the regular 1989 Donruss set with green borders and a glossy finish. The set included a Warren Spahn puzzle.

		MT	NR MT	EX
	Complete Set:	20.00	15.00	8.00
	Common Player:	.05	.04	.02
1	Don Mattingly	1.00	.70	.40
2	Tom Glavine	.15	.11	.06
3	Bert Blyleven	.08	.06	.03
4	Andre Dawson	.10	.08	.04
5	Pete O'Brien	.05	.04	.02
6	Eric Davis	.40	.30	.15
7	George Brett	.10	.08	.04
8	Glenn Davis	.10	.08	.04
9	Ellis Burks	.30	.25	.12
10	Kirk Gibson	.08	.06	.03
11	Carlton Fisk	.08	.06	.03
12	Andres Galarraga	.08	.06	.03
13	Alan Trammell	.06	.05	.02
14	Dwight Gooden	.30	.25	.12
15	Paul Molitor	.10	.08	.04
16	Roger McDowell	.05	.04	.02
17	Doug Drabek	.05	.04	.02
18	Kent Hrbek	.08	.06	.03
19	Vince Coleman	.08	.06	.03
20	Steve Sax	.08	.06	.03
21	Roberto Alomar	.30	.25	.12
22	Carney Lansford	.06	.05	.02
23	Will Clark	1.50	1.25	.60
24	Alvin Davis	.08	.06	.03
25	Bobby Thigpen	.08	.06	.03
26	Ryne Sandberg	.60	.45	.25
27	Devon White	.08	.06	.03
28	Mike Greenwell	.40	.30	.15
29	Dale Murphy	.10	.08	.04
30	Jeff Ballard	.10	.08	.04
31	Kelly Gruber	.08	.06	.03
32	Julio Franco	.15	.11	.06
33	Bobby Bonilla	.15	.11	.06
34	Tim Wallach	.05	.04	.02
35	Lou Whitaker	.07	.05	.03
36	Jay Howell	.07	.05	.03
37	Greg Maddux	.30	.25	.12
38	Bill Doran	.07	.05	.03
39	Danny Tartabull	.12	.09	.05
40	Darryl Strawberry	.50	.40	.20
41	Ron Darling	.10	.08	.06
42	Tony Gwynn	.30	.25	.12
43	Mark McGwire	.40	.30	.15
44	Ozzie Smith	.15	.11	.06
45	Andy Van Slyke	.12	.09	.05
46	Juan Berenguer	.05	.04	.02
47	Von Hayes	.08	.06	.03
48	Tony Fernandez	.12	.09	.05
49	Eric Plunk	.05	.04	.02
50	Ernest Riles	.05	.04	.02
51	Harold Reynolds	.07	.05	.03
52	Andy Hawkins	.06	.05	.02
53	Robin Yount	.35	.25	.14
54	Danny Jackson	.06	.05	.02
55	Nolan Ryan	1.25	.90	.50
56	Joe Carter	.12	.09	.05
57	Jose Canseco	1.00	.70	.40
58	Jody Davis	.05	.04	.02
59	Lance Parrish	.06	.05	.02
60	Mitch Williams	.15	.11	.06
61	Brook Jacoby	.06	.05	.02
62	Tom Browning	.10	.08	.06
63	Kurt Stillwell	.06	.05	.02
64	Rafael Ramirez	.05	.04	.02
65	Roger Clemens	.50	.40	.20
66	Mike Scioscia	.07	.05	.02
67	Dave Gallagher	.07	.05	.02
68	Mark Langston	.15	.11	.06
69	Chet Lemon	.06	.05	.02
70	Kevin McReynolds	.25	.20	.10
71	Rob Deer	.06	.05	.02
72	Tommy Herr	.07	.05	.03
73	Barry Bonds	.12	.09	.05
74	Frank Viola	.15	.11	.06
75	Pedro Guerrero	.15	.11	.06
76	Dave Righetti	.07	.05	.03
77	Bruce Hurst	.08	.06	.03
78	Rickey Henderson	.40	.30	.15
79	Robby Thompson	.08	.06	.03
80	Randy Johnson	.25	.20	.10
81	Harold Baines	.12	.09	.05
82	Calvin Schiraldi	.05	.04	.02
83	Kirk McCaskill	.05	.04	.02
84	Lee Smith	.07	.05	.03
85	John Smoltz	.25	.20	.10
86	Mickey Tettleton	.20	.15	.08
87	Jimmy Key	.08	.06	.03
88	Rafael Palmeiro	.10	.08	.04
89	Sid Bream	.05	.04	.02
90	Dennis Martinez	.05	.04	.02
91	Frank Tanana	.05	.04	.02
92	Eddie Murray	.15	.11	.06
93	Shawon Dunston	.15	.11	.06
94	Mike Scott	.10	.08	.04
95	Bret Saberhagen	.25	.20	.10
96	David Cone	.20	.15	.08
97	Kevin Elster	.05	.04	.02
98	Jack Clark	.20	.15	.08
99	Dave Stewart	.20	.15	.08
100	Jose Oquendo	.06	.05	.02
101	Jose Lind	.05	.04	.02
102	Gary Gaetti	.12	.09	.05
103	Ricky Jordan	.25	.20	.10
104	Fred McGriff	.50	.40	.20
105	Don Slaught	.05	.04	.02
106	Jose Uribe	.05	.04	.02
107	Jeffrey Leonard	.07	.05	.02
108	Lee Guetterman	.05	.04	.02
109	Chris Bosio	.08	.06	.03
110	Barry Larkin	.15	.11	.06
111	Ruben Sierra	.30	.25	.12
112	Greg Swindell	.12	.09	.05
113	Gary Sheffield	.40	.30	.15
114	Lonnie Smith	.10	.08	.04
115	Chili Davis	.08	.06	.03
116	Damon Berryhill	.08	.06	.03
117	Tom Candiotti	.05	.04	.02
118	Kal Daniels	.10	.08	.04
119	Mark Gubicza	.10	.08	.04
120	Jim Deshaies	.08	.06	.03
121	Dwight Evans	.10	.08	.04
122	Mike Morgan	.05	.04	.02
123	Dan Pasqua	.05	.04	.02
124	Bryn Smith	.07	.05	.03
125	Doyle Alexander	.07	.05	.03
126	Howard Johnson	.25	.20	.10
127	Chuck Crim	.07	.05	.03
128	Darren Daulton	.05	.04	.02
129	Jeff Robinson	.08	.06	.03
130	Kirby Puckett	.50	.40	.20
131	Joe Magrane	.10	.08	.04
132	Jesse Barfield	.07	.05	.03
133	Mark Davis (Photo actually Dave Leiper)	.25	.20	.10
134	Dennis Eckersley	.10	.08	.04
135	Mike Krukow	.05	.04	.02
136	Jay Buhner	.10	.08	.04
137	Ozzie Guillen	.08	.06	.03
138	Rick Sutcliffe	.12	.09	.05
139	Wally Joyner	.25	.20	.10
140	Wade Boggs	.60	.45	.25
141	Jeff Treadway	.08	.06	.05
142	Cal Ripken	.30	.25	.12
143	Dave Steib	.10	.08	.04
144	Pete Incaviglia	.07	.05	.03
145	Bob Walk	.05	.04	.02
146	Nelson Santovenia	.10	.08	.04
147	Mike Heath	.05	.04	.02
148	Willie Randolph	.08	.06	.03
149	Paul Kilgus	.05	.04	.02
150	Billy Hatcher	.07	.05	.03
151	Steve Farr	.05	.04	.02
152	Gregg Jefferies	.40	.30	.15
153	Randy Myers	.06	.05	.02
154	Garry Templeton	.06	.05	.02
155	Walt Weiss	.10	.08	.04
156	Terry Pendleton	.10	.08	.04
157	John Smiley	.08	.06	.03
158	Greg Gagne	.05	.04	.02
159	Lenny Dykstra	.08	.06	.03
160	Nelson Liriano	.05	.04	.02
161	Alvaro Espinoza	.10	.08	.04
162	Rick Reuschel	.08	.06	.03
163	Omar Vizquel	.15	.11	.06
164	Clay Parker	.15	.11	.06
165	Dan Plesac	.06	.05	.02
166	John Franco	.06	.05	.02
167	Scott Fletcher	.06	.05	.02
168	Cory Snyder	.12	.09	.05
169	Bo Jackson	1.00	.70	.40
170	Tommy Gregg	.08	.06	.03
171	Jim Abbott	.50	.40	.20
172	Jerome Walton	.50	.40	.20
173	Doug Jones	.06	.05	.02
174	Todd Benzinger	.08	.06	.03
175	Frank White	.08	.06	.03
176	Craig Biggio	.20	.15	.08
177	John Dopson	.10	.08	.06
178	Alfredo Griffin	.06	.05	.02
179	Melido Perez	.06	.05	.02
180	Tim Burke	.06	.05	.02
181	Matt Nokes	.10	.08	.04
182	Gary Carter	.10	.08	.04
183	Ted Higuera	.08	.06	.03
184	Ken Howell	.05	.04	.02
185	Rey Quinones	.05	.04	.02
186	Wally Backman	.07	.05	.03
187	Tom Brunansky	.07	.05	.03
188	Steve Balboni	.05	.04	.02
189	Marvell Wynne	.05	.04	.02
190	Dave Henderson	.08	.06	.03
191	Don Robinson	.05	.04	.02
192	Ken Griffey, Jr.	4.00	3.00	1.50
193	Ivan Calderon	.05	.04	.02
194	Mike Bielecki	.07	.05	.03
195	Johnny Ray	.07	.05	.03
196	Rob Murphy	.05	.04	.02
197	Andres Thomas	.05	.04	.02
198	Phil Bradley	.06	.05	.02
199	Junior Felix	.30	.25	.12
200	Jeff Russell	.08	.06	.03
201	Mike LaValliere	.05	.04	.02
202	Kevin Gross	.06	.05	.02
203	Keith Moreland	.06	.05	.02
204	Mike Marshall	.06	.05	.02
205	Dwight Smith	.30	.25	.12
206	Jim Clancy	.05	.04	.02
207	Kevin Seitzer	.10	.08	.04
208	Keith Hernandez	.10	.08	.04
209	Bob Ojeda	.06	.05	.02
210	Ed Whitson	.06	.05	.02
211	Tony Phillips	.06	.05	.02
212	Milt Thompson	.05	.04	.02
213	Randy Kramer	.05	.04	.02
214	Randy Bush	.05	.04	.02
215	Randy Ready	.05	.04	.02
216	Duane Ward	.05	.04	.02
217	Jimmy Jones	.05	.04	.02
218	Scott Garrelts	.08	.06	.03
219	Scott Bankhead	.10	.08	.04
220	Lance McCullers	.06	.05	.02
221	B.J. Surhoff	.06	.05	.02
222	Chris Sabo	.06	.05	.02
223	Steve Buechele	.06	.05	.02
224	Joel Skinner	.05	.04	.02
225	Orel Hershiser	.15	.11	.06
226	Derek Lilliquist	.10	.08	.06
227	Claudell Washington	.08	.06	.05
228	Lloyd McClendon	.10	.08	.04
229	Felix Fermin	.05	.04	.02
230	Paul O'Neill	.08	.06	.03
231	Charlie Leibrandt	.05	.04	.02
232	Dave Smith	.06	.05	.02
233	Bob Stanley	.05	.04	.02
234	Tim Belcher	.15	.11	.06
235	Eric King	.05	.04	.02
236	Spike Owen	.05	.04	.02
237	Mike Henneman	.05	.04	.02
238	Juan Samuel	.06	.05	.02
239	Greg Brock	.06	.05	.02
240	John Kruk	.06	.05	.02
241	Glenn Wilson	.06	.05	.02
242	Jeff Reardon	.06	.05	.02
243	Todd Worrell	.08	.06	.03
244	Dave LaPoint	.05	.04	.02
245	Walt Terrell	.05	.04	.02
246	Mike Moore	.08	.06	.03
247	Kelly Downs	.05	.04	.02
248	Dave Valle	.05	.04	.02
249	Ron Kittle	.06	.05	.04
250	Steve Wilson	.10	.08	.04
251	Dick Schofield	.05	.04	.02
252	Marty Barrett	.06	.05	.02
253	Dion James	.06	.05	.02
254	Bob Milacki	.10	.08	.04
255	Ernie Whitt	.06	.05	.02
256	Kevin Brown	.08	.06	.03
257	R.J. Reynolds	.05	.04	.02
258	Tim Raines	.10	.08	.04
259	Frank Williams	.05	.04	.02
260	Jose Gonzalez	.05	.04	.02
261	Mitch Webster	.05	.04	.02
262	Ken Caminiti	.07	.05	.03
263	Bob Boone	.07	.05	.03
264	Dave Magadan	.07	.05	.03
265	Rick Aguilera	.05	.04	.02
266	Chris James	.05	.04	.02
267	Bob Welch	.07	.05	.03
268	Ken Dayley	.05	.04	.02
269	Junior Ortiz	.05	.04	.02
270	Allan Anderson	.08	.06	.03
271	Steve Jeltz	.05	.04	.02
272	George Bell	.10	.08	.04
273	Roberto Kelly	.10	.08	.04
274	Brett Butler	.07	.05	.03
275	Mike Schooler	.07	.05	.02
276	Ken Phelps	.05	.04	.02
277	Glenn Braggs	.06	.05	.02
278	Jose Rijo	.06	.05	.02
279	Bobby Witt	.06	.05	.02
280	Jerry Browne	.06	.05	.02
281	Kevin Mitchell	.40	.30	.15
282	Craig Worthington	.15	.11	.06
283	Greg Minton	.05	.04	.02
284	Nick Esasky	.07	.05	.03
285	John Farrell	.05	.04	.02
286	Rick Mahler	.05	.04	.02
287	Tom Gordon	.40	.30	.15
288	Gerald Young	.05	.04	.02
289	Jody Reed	.08	.06	.03
290	Jeff Hamilton	.05	.04	.02
291	Gerald Perry	.05	.04	.02
292	Hubie Brooks	.05	.04	.02
293	Bo Diaz	.05	.04	.02
294	Terry Puhl	.05	.04	.02
295	Jim Gantner	.05	.04	.02
296	Jeff Parrett	.05	.04	.02
297	Mike Boddicker	.05	.04	.02
298	Dan Gladden	.05	.04	.02
299	Tony Pena	.07	.05	.03
300	Checklist	.05	.04	.02
301	Tom Henke	.05	.04	.02
302	Pascual Perez	.05	.04	.02
303	Steve Bedrosian	.05	.04	.02
304	Ken Hill	.10	.08	.04
305	Jerry Reuss	.07	.05	.03
306	Jim Eisenreich	.05	.04	.02
307	Jack Howell	.05	.04	.02
308	Rick Cerone	.05	.04	.02
309	Tim Leary	.05	.04	.02
310	Joe Orsulak	.05	.04	.02
311	Jim Dwyer	.05	.04	.02
312	Geno Petralli	.05	.04	.02
313	Rick Honeycutt	.05	.04	.02
314	Tom Foley	.05	.04	.02
315	Kenny Rogers	.10	.08	.04
316	Mike Flanagan	.06	.05	.02
317	Bryan Harvey	.06	.05	.02
318	Billy Ripken	.05	.04	.02
319	Jeff Montgomery	.05	.04	.02
320	Erik Hanson	.12	.09	.05
321	Brian Downing	.06	.05	.02

322	Gregg Olson	.40	.30	.15
323	Terry Steinbach	.12	.09	.05
324	Sammy Sosa	.40	.30	.15
325	Gene Harris	.05	.04	.02
326	Mike Devereaux	.10	.08	.04
327	Dennis Cook	.12	.09	.05
328	David Wells	.08	.06	.03
329	Checklist	.05	.04	.02
330	Kirt Manwaring	.10	.08	.04
331	Jim Presley	.05	.04	.02
332	Checklist	.05	.04	.02
333	Chuck Finley	.05	.04	.02
334	Rob Dibble	.08	.06	.03
335	Cecil Espy	.06	.05	.02
336	Dave Parker	.08	.06	.02

1989 Donruss Pop-Ups

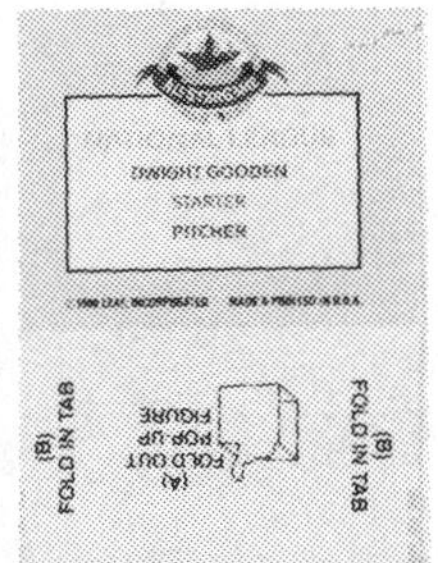

This set features the eighteen starters from the 1988 Major League All-Star game. The cards are designed with a perforated outline so each player can be popped out and made to stand upright. On the front side, each player's name, team, and position is featured in an orange-and-yellow rectangle below the borderless full-color photo. Each Pop-Up includes a unique double card, folded over and glued together on the back. The flip side features a red, white, and blue "Cincinnati Reds All-Star Game" logo at the top, a blue-lettered league designation, and the player's name and position in red. The lower portion of the flip side displays illustrated instructions for creating the base of the Pop-Up. The Pop-Ups were marketed in conjunction with All-Star and Warren Spahn Puzzle Cards.

		MT	NR MT	EX
Complete Set:		4.00	3.75	2.00
Common Player:		.20	.15	.08
(1)	Mark McGwire	.40	.30	.15
(2)	Jose Canseco	.60	.45	.25
(3)	Paul Molitor	.30	.25	.12
(4)	Rickey Henderson	.50	.40	.20
(5)	Cal Ripken, Jr.	.75	.60	.30
(6)	Dave Winfield	.40	.30	.15
(7)	Wade Boggs	.50	.40	.20
(8)	Frank Viola	.25	.20	.10
(9)	Terry Steinbach	.20	.15	.08
(10)	Tom Kelly	.20	.15	.08
(11)	Will Clark	.60	.45	.25
(12)	Darryl Strawberry	.25	.20	.10
(13)	Ryne Sandberg	.75	.60	.30
(14)	Andre Dawson	.35	.25	.14
(15)	Ozzie Smith	.30	.25	.12
(16)	Vince Coleman	.20	.15	.08
(17)	Bobby Bonilla	.30	.25	.12
(18)	Dwight Gooden	.30	.25	.12
(19)	Gary Carter	.20	.15	.08
(20)	Whitey Herzog	.20	.15	.08

1989 Donruss Rookies

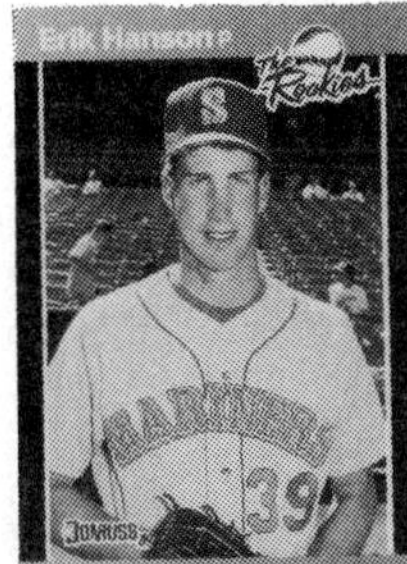

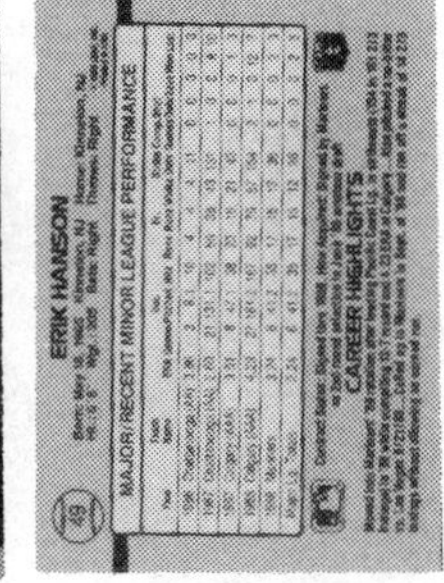

For the fourth straight year, Donruss issued a 56-card "Rookies" set in 1989. As in previous years, the set is similar in design to the regular Donruss set, except for a new "The Rookies" logo and a green and black border.

		MT	NR MT	EX
Complete Set (56):		15.00	11.00	6.00
Common Player:		.10	.08	.04
1	Gary Sheffield	1.75	1.25	.70
2	Gregg Jefferies	.50	.40	.20
3	Ken Griffey, Jr.	8.00	6.00	3.25
4	Tom Gordon	.12	.09	.05
5	Billy Spiers (FC)	.10	.08	.04
6	Deion Sanders (FC)	2.00	1.50	.80
7	Donn Pall (FC)	.20	.15	.08
8	Steve Carter (FC)	.20	.15	.08
9	Francisco Oliveras (FC)	.15	.11	.06
10	Steve Wilson (FC)	.20	.15	.08
11	Bob Geren (FC)	.20	.15	.08
12	Tony Castillo (FC)	.15	.11	.06
13	Kenny Rogers (FC)	.20	.15	.08
14	Carlos Martinez (FC)	.30	.25	.12
15	Edgar Martinez	.25	.20	.10
16	Jim Abbott (FC)	1.50	1.25	.60
17	Torey Lovullo (FC)	.20	.15	.08
18	Mark Carreon (FC)	.15	.11	.06
19	Geronimo Berroa	.10	.08	.04
20	Luis Medina	.10	.08	.04
21	Sandy Alomar, Jr.	.30	.25	.12
22	Bob Milacki	.10	.08	.04
23	Joe Girardi (FC)	.30	.25	.12
24	German Gonzalez	.10	.08	.04
25	Craig Worthington	.15	.11	.06
26	Jerome Walton (FC)	.12	.09	.05
27	Gary Wayne (FC)	.20	.15	.08
28	Tim Jones	.10	.08	.04
29	Dante Bichette	.50	.40	.20
30	Alexis Infante (FC)	.15	.11	.06
31	Ken Hill	.50	.40	.20
32	Dwight Smith (FC)	.12	.09	.05
33	Luis de los Santos	.10	.08	.04
34	Eric Yelding (FC)	.08	.06	.03
35	Gregg Olson	.40	.30	.15
36	Phil Stephenson (FC)	.15	.11	.06
37	Ken Patterson (FC)	.15	.11	.06
38	Rick Wrona (FC)	.15	.11	.06
39	Mike Brumley	.10	.08	.04
40	Cris Carpenter	.10	.08	.04
41	Jeff Brantley (FC)	.20	.15	.08
42	Ron Jones	.10	.08	.04
43	Randy Johnson	.75	.60	.30
44	Kevin Brown	.10	.08	.04
45	Ramon Martinez	.50	.40	.20
46	Greg Harris	.10	.08	.04
47	Steve Finley (FC)	.40	.30	.15
48	Randy Kramer	.10	.08	.04
49	Erik Hanson	.30	.25	.12
50	Matt Merullo (FC)	.15	.11	.06
51	Mike Devereaux	.15	.11	.06
52	Clay Parker (FC)	.15	.11	.06
53	Omar Vizquel (FC)	.20	.15	.08
54	Derek Lilliquist	.12	.09	.05
55	Junior Felix (FC)	.15	.11	.06
56	Checklist	.10	.08	.04

1989 Donruss Traded

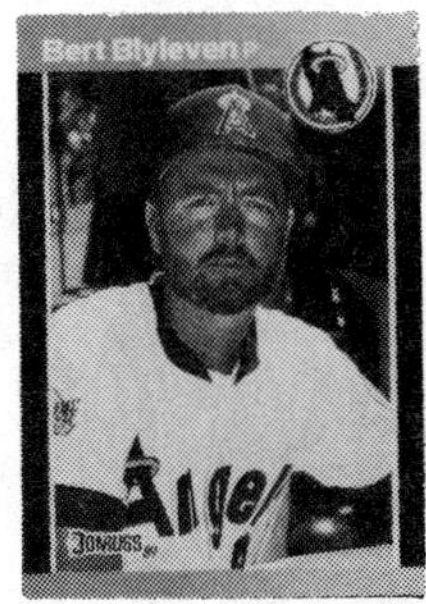

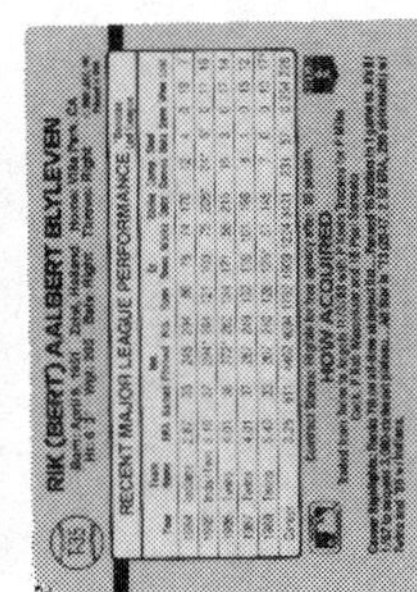

Donruss issued its first "Traded" set in 1989, releasing a 56-card boxed set designed in the same style as the regular 1989 Donruss set. The set included a Stan Musial puzzle card and a checklist.

		MT	NR MT	EX
Complete Set:		4.00	3.00	1.50
Common Player:		.06	.05	.02
1	Jeffrey Leonard	.08	.06	.03
2	Jack Clark	.15	.11	.06
3	Kevin Gross	.06	.05	.02
4	Tommy Herr	.08	.06	.03
5	Bob Boone	.10	.08	.04
6	Rafael Palmeiro	.30	.25	.12
7	John Dopson	.08	.06	.03
8	Willie Randolph	.08	.06	.03
9	Chris Brown	.06	.05	.02
10	Wally Backman	.06	.05	.02
11	Steve Ontiveros	.06	.05	.02
12	Eddie Murray	.30	.25	.12
13	Lance McCullers	.08	.06	.03
14	Spike Owen	.06	.05	.02
15	Rob Murphy	.06	.05	.02
16	Pete O'Brien	.08	.06	.03
17	Ken Williams	.06	.05	.02
18	Nick Esasky	.06	.05	.02
19	Nolan Ryan	1.50	1.25	.60
20	Brian Holton	.06	.05	.02
21	Mike Moore	.08	.06	.03
22	Joel Skinner	.06	.05	.02
23	Steve Sax	.15	.11	.06
24	Rick Mahler	.06	.05	.02
25	Mike Aldrete	.06	.05	.02
26	Jesse Orosco	.08	.06	.03
27	Dave LaPoint	.06	.05	.02
28	Walt Terrell	.08	.06	.03
29	Eddie Williams	.08	.06	.03
30	Mike Devereaux	.10	.08	.04
31	Julio Franco	.15	.11	.06
32	Jim Clancy	.06	.05	.02
33	Felix Fermin	.06	.05	.02
34	Curtis Wilkerson	.06	.05	.02
35	Bert Blyleven	.12	.09	.05
36	Mel Hall	.08	.06	.03
37	Eric King	.06	.05	.02
38	Mitch Williams	.12	.09	.05
39	Jamie Moyer	.06	.05	.02
40	Rick Rhoden	.08	.06	.03
41	Phil Bradley	.08	.06	.03
42	Paul Kilgus	.08	.06	.03
43	Milt Thompson	.06	.05	.02
44	Jerry Browne	.08	.06	.03
45	Bruce Hurst	.08	.06	.03
46	Claudell Washington	.08	.06	.03
47	Todd Benzinger	.12	.09	.05
48	Steve Balboni	.06	.05	.02
49	Oddibe McDowell	.08	.06	.03
50	Charles Hudson	.06	.05	.02
51	Ron Kittle	.08	.06	.03
52	Andy Hawkins	.06	.05	.02
53	Tom Brookens	.06	.05	.02
54	Tom Niedenfuer	.06	.05	.02
55	Jeff Parrett	.08	.06	.03
56	Checklist	.06	.05	.02

1990 Donruss Previews

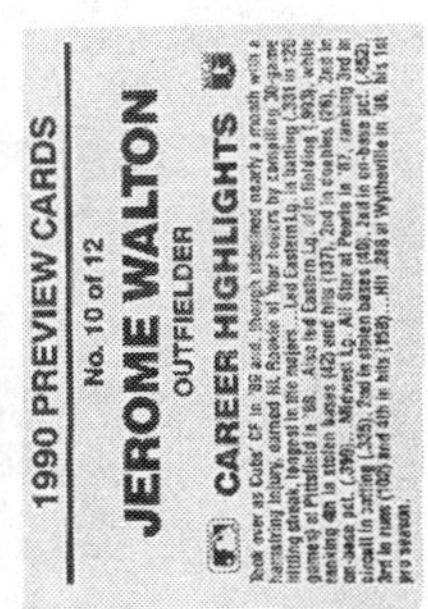

To introduce its 1990 baseball issue, Donruss sent two preview cards from a set of 12 to each member of its dealers' network. Though the photos are different than those used on the issued versions, the front format was the same, utilizing a bright red border flecked in black and white. Backs are printed in black on white and contain career highlights, but no stats. Issued at the dawn of the "promo card" craze, and succeeding the relatively valueless sample sheets used by most companies in earlier years, little value was attached to these preview cards initially. Today they are among the scarcest of the early-1990s promos.

		MT	NR MT	EX
Complete Set:		300.00	220.00	120.00
Common Player:		7.50	5.50	3.00
1	Todd Zeile	12.00	9.00	4.75
2	Ben McDonald	12.00	9.00	4.75
3	Bo Jackson	25.00	18.50	10.00
4	Will Clark	45.00	34.00	18.00
5	Dave Stewart	12.00	9.00	4.75
6	Kevin Mitchell	12.00	9.00	4.75
7	Nolan Ryan	150.00	110.00	60.00
8	Howard Johnson	12.00	9.00	4.75
9	Tony Gwynn	25.00	18.50	10.00
10	Jerome Walton	7.50	5.50	3.00
11	Wade Boggs	30.00	22.00	12.00
12	Kirby Puckett	30.00	22.00	12.00

1990 Donruss

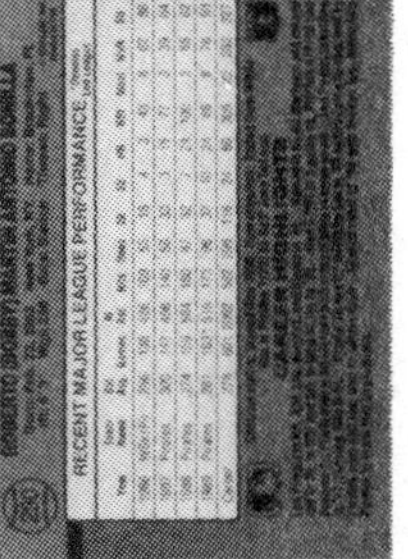

Donruss marked its 10th anniversary in the baseball card hobby with a 715-card set in 1990, up from previous 660-card sets. The standard-size cards feature bright red borders with the player's name in script at the top. The set includes 26 "Diamond Kings", 20 "Rated Rookies" and a Carl Yastrzemski puzzle. Each All-Star card back has two variations. The more common has the stats box headed "All-Star Performance". Slightly scarcer versions say "Recent Major League Performance", and are worth about twice the value of the correct version.

		MT	NR MT	EX
	Complete Set (716):	18.00	13.50	7.25
	Common Player:	.04	.03	.02
1	Bo Jackson (DK)	.20	.15	.08
2	Steve Sax (DK)	.12	.09	.05
3a	Ruben Sierra (DK) (no vertical black line at top-right on back)	1.00	.70	.40
3b	Ruben Sierra (DK) (vertical line at top-right on back)	.30	.25	.12
4	Ken Griffey, Jr. (DK)	.40	.30	.15
5	Mickey Tettleton (DK)	.12	.09	.05
6	Dave Stewart (DK)	.12	.09	.05
7	Jim Deshaies (DK)	.07	.05	.03
8	John Smoltz (DK)	.15	.11	.06
9	Mike Bielecki (DK)	.07	.05	.03
10a	Brian Downing (DK) (reversed negative)	1.00	.70	.40
10b	Brian Downing (DK) (corrected)	.25	.20	.10
11	Kevin Mitchell (DK)	.06	.05	.02
12	Kelly Gruber (DK)	.08	.06	.03
13	Joe Magrane (DK)	.08	.06	.03
14	John Franco (DK)	.08	.06	.03
15	Ozzie Guillen (DK)	.08	.06	.03
16	Lou Whitaker (DK)	.08	.06	.03
17	John Smiley (DK)	.08	.06	.03
18	Howard Johnson (DK)	.06	.05	.02
19	Willie Randolph (DK)	.08	.06	.03
20	Chris Bosio (DK)	.07	.05	.03
21	Tommy Herr (DK)	.07	.05	.03
22	Dan Gladden (DK)	.07	.05	.03
23	Ellis Burks (DK)	.08	.06	.03
24	Pete O'Brien (DK)	.08	.06	.03
25	Bryn Smith (DK)	.07	.05	.03
26	Ed Whitson (DK)	.07	.05	.03
27	Checklist 1-27	.04	.03	.02
28	*Robin Ventura* (RR)	.80	.60	.30
29	*Todd Zeile* (RR)	.20	.15	.08
30	Sandy Alomar, Jr. (RR)	.20	.15	.08
31	*Kent Mercker* (RR)	.10	.08	.04
32	*Ben McDonald* (RR)	.50	.40	.20
33a	*Juan Gonzalez* (RR) (reversed negative)	4.00	3.00	1.50
33b	*Juan Gonzalez* (RR) (corrected)	2.00	1.50	.80
34	*Eric Anthony* (RR)	.50	.40	.20
35	*Mike Fetters* (RR)	.20	.15	.08
36	*Marquis Grissom* (RR)	.60	.45	.25
37	*Greg Vaughn* (RR)	.30	.25	.12
38	*Brian Dubois* (FC) (RR)	.15	.11	.06
39	*Steve Avery* (RR)	.60	.45	.25
40	*Mark Gardner* (RR)	.20	.15	.08
41	*Andy Benes* (RR)	.40	.30	.15
42	*Delino DeShields* (RR)	.40	.30	.15
43	*Scott Coolbaugh* (RR)	.08	.06	.03
44	*Pat Combs* (RR)	.08	.06	.03
45	*Alex Sanchez* (RR)	.08	.06	.03
46	*Kelly Mann* (FC) (RR)	.08	.06	.03
47	*Julio Machado* (FC) (RR)	.08	.06	.03
48	Pete Incaviglia	.05	.04	.02
49	Shawon Dunston	.07	.05	.03
50	Jeff Treadway	.05	.04	.02
51	Jeff Ballard	.10	.08	.04
52	Claudell Washington	.08	.06	.03
53	Juan Samuel	.10	.08	.04
54	John Smiley	.08	.06	.03
55	Rob Deer	.06	.05	.02
56	Geno Petralli	.04	.03	.02
57	Chris Bosio	.10	.08	.04
58	Carlton Fisk	.12	.09	.05
59	Kirt Manwaring	.10	.08	.04
60	Chet Lemon	.06	.05	.02
61	Bo Jackson	.30	.25	.12
62	Doyle Alexander	.05	.04	.02
63	Pedro Guerrero	.12	.09	.05
64	Allan Anderson	.07	.05	.03
65	Greg Harris	.07	.05	.03
66	Mike Greenwell	.10	.08	.04
67	Walt Weiss	.08	.06	.03
68	Wade Boggs	.30	.25	.12
69	Jim Clancy	.04	.03	.02
70	*Junior Felix*	.08	.06	.03
71	Barry Larkin	.12	.09	.05
72	Dave LaPoint	.05	.04	.02
73	Joel Skinner	.04	.03	.02
74	Jesse Barfield	.08	.06	.03
75	Tommy Herr	.08	.06	.03
76	Ricky Jordan	.10	.08	.04
77	Eddie Murray	.15	.11	.06
78	Steve Sax	.10	.08	.04
79	Tim Belcher	.10	.08	.04
80	Danny Jackson	.06	.05	.02
81	Kent Hrbek	.10	.08	.04
82	Milt Thompson	.05	.04	.02
83	Brook Jacoby	.07	.05	.03
84	Mike Marshall	.08	.06	.03
85	Kevin Seitzer	.12	.09	.05
86	Tony Gwynn	.15	.11	.06
87	Dave Steib	.08	.06	.03
88	Dave Smith	.06	.05	.02
89	Bret Saberhagen	.08	.06	.03
90	Alan Trammell	.10	.08	.04
91	Tony Phillips	.05	.04	.02
92	Doug Drabek	.05	.04	.02
93	Jeffrey Leonard	.09	.07	.04
94	Wally Joyner	.15	.11	.06
95	Carney Lansford	.09	.07	.04
96	Cal Ripken, Jr.	.25	.20	.10
97	Andres Galarraga	.15	.11	.06
98	Kevin Mitchell	.10	.08	.04
99	Howard Johnson	.15	.11	.06
100a	Checklist 28-129	.04	.03	.02
100b	Checklist 28-125	.04	.03	.02
101	Melido Perez	.07	.05	.03
102	Spike Owen	.05	.04	.02
103	Paul Molitor	.20	.15	.08
104	Geronimo Berroa	.06	.05	.02
105	Ryne Sandberg	.25	.20	.10
106	Bryn Smith	.06	.05	.02
107	Steve Buechele	.04	.03	.02
108	Jim Abbott	.20	.15	.08
109	Alvin Davis	.10	.08	.04
110	Lee Smith	.05	.04	.02
111	Roberto Alomar	.50	.40	.20
112	Rick Reuschel	.09	.07	.04
113a	Kelly Gruber (Born 2/22)	.08	.06	.03
113b	Kelly Gruber (Born 2/26)	.25	.20	.10
114	Joe Carter	.09	.07	.04
115	Jose Rijo	.06	.05	.02
116	Greg Minton	.04	.03	.02
117	Bob Ojeda	.04	.03	.02
118	Glenn Davis	.08	.06	.03
119	Jeff Reardon	.05	.04	.02
120	Kurt Stillwell	.05	.04	.02
121	John Smoltz	.15	.11	.06
122	Dwight Evans	.08	.06	.03
123	Eric Yelding	.08	.06	.03
124	John Franco	.05	.04	.02
125	Jose Canseco	.20	.15	.08
126	Barry Bonds	.30	.25	.12
127	Lee Guetterman	.04	.03	.02
128	Jack Clark	.10	.08	.04
129	Dave Valle	.04	.03	.02
130	Hubie Brooks	.05	.04	.02
131	Ernest Riles	.04	.03	.02
132	Mike Morgan	.04	.03	.02
133	Steve Jeltz	.04	.03	.02
134	Jeff Robinson	.05	.04	.02
135	Ozzie Guillen	.05	.04	.02
136	Chili Davis	.06	.05	.02
137	Mitch Webster	.04	.03	.02
138	Jerry Browne	.06	.05	.02
139	Bo Diaz	.04	.03	.02
140	Robby Thompson	.07	.05	.03
141	Craig Worthington	.09	.07	.04
142	Julio Franco	.09	.07	.04
143	Brian Holman	.05	.04	.02
144	George Brett	.20	.15	.08
145	Tom Glavine	.15	.11	.06
146	Robin Yount	.20	.15	.08
147	Gary Carter	.06	.05	.02
148	Ron Kittle	.06	.05	.02
149	Tony Fernandez	.07	.05	.03
150	Dave Stewart	.07	.05	.03
151	Gary Gaetti	.07	.05	.03
152	Kevin Elster	.04	.03	.02
153	Gerald Perry	.05	.04	.02
154	Jesse Orosco	.05	.04	.02
155	Wally Backman	.05	.04	.02
156	Dennis Martinez	.05	.04	.02
157	Rick Sutcliffe	.08	.06	.03
158	Greg Maddux	.12	.09	.05
159	Andy Hawkins	.05	.04	.02
160	John Kruk	.05	.04	.02
161	Jose Oquendo	.05	.04	.02
162	John Dopson	.08	.06	.03
163	Joe Magrane	.08	.06	.03
164	Billy Ripken	.04	.03	.02
165	Fred Manrique	.04	.03	.02
166	Nolan Ryan	.40	.30	.15
167	Damon Berryhill	.06	.05	.02
168	Dale Murphy	.07	.05	.03
169	Mickey Tettleton	.08	.06	.03
170a	Kirk McCaskill (Born 4/19)	.06	.05	.02
170b	Kirk McCaskill (Born 4/9)	.25	.20	.10
171	Dwight Gooden	.08	.06	.03
172	Jose Lind	.04	.03	.02
173	B.J. Surhoff	.07	.05	.03
174	Ruben Sierra	.12	.09	.05
175	Dan Plesac	.08	.06	.03
176	Dan Pasqua	.05	.04	.02
177	Kelly Downs	.05	.04	.02
178	Matt Nokes	.08	.06	.03
179	Luis Aquino	.04	.03	.02
180	Frank Tanana	.04	.03	.02
181	Tony Pena	.07	.05	.03
182	Dan Gladden	.05	.04	.02
183	Bruce Hurst	.05	.04	.02
184	Roger Clemens	.20	.15	.08
185	Mark McGwire	.25	.20	.10
186	Rob Murphy	.04	.03	.02
187	Jim Deshaies	.06	.05	.02
188	Fred McGriff	.20	.15	.08
189	Rob Dibble	.06	.05	.02
190	Don Mattingly	.25	.20	.10
191	Felix Fermin	.04	.03	.02
192	Roberto Kelly	.08	.06	.03
193	Dennis Cook	.08	.06	.03
194	Darren Daulton	.04	.03	.02
195	Alfredo Griffin	.05	.04	.02
196	Eric Plunk	.05	.04	.02
197	Orel Hershiser	.20	.15	.08
198	Paul O'Neil	.07	.05	.03
199	Randy Bush	.04	.03	.02
200a	Checklist 130-231	.04	.03	.02
200b	Checklist 126-223	.04	.03	.02
201	Ozzie Smith	.10	.08	.04
202	Pete O'Brien	.06	.05	.02
203	Jay Howell	.06	.05	.02
204	Mark Gibicza	.08	.06	.03
205	Ed Whitson	.04	.03	.02
206	George Bell	.09	.07	.04
207	Mike Scott	.09	.07	.04
208	Charlie Leibrandt	.04	.03	.02
209	Mike Heath	.04	.03	.02
210	Dennis Eckersley	.09	.07	.04
211	Mike LaValliere	.04	.03	.02
212	Darnell Coles	.04	.03	.02
213	Lance Parrish	.07	.05	.03
214	Mike Moore	.07	.05	.03
215	*Steve Finley*	.20	.15	.08
216	Tim Raines	.09	.07	.04
217a	Scott Garrelts (Born 10/20)	.06	.05	.02
217b	Scott Garrelts (Born 10/30)	.25	.20	.10
218	Kevin McReynolds	.09	.07	.04
219	Dave Gallagher	.08	.06	.03
220	Tim Wallach	.08	.06	.03
221	Chuck Crim	.04	.03	.02
222	Lonnie Smith	.08	.06	.03
223	Andre Dawson	.12	.09	.05
224	Nelson Santovenia	.07	.05	.03
225	Rafael Palmeiro	.12	.09	.05
226	Devon White	.07	.05	.03
227	Harold Reynolds	.07	.05	.03
228	Ellis Burks	.15	.11	.06
229	Mark Parent	.04	.03	.02
230	Will Clark	.30	.25	.12
231	Jimmy Key	.08	.06	.03
232	John Farrell	.04	.03	.02
233	Eric Davis	.10	.08	.04
234	Johnny Ray	.05	.04	.02
235	Darryl Strawberry	.12	.09	.05
236	Bill Doran	.05	.04	.02
237	Greg Gagne	.05	.04	.02
238	Jim Eisenreich	.04	.03	.02
239	Tommy Gregg	.06	.05	.02
240	Marty Barrett	.05	.04	.02
241	Rafael Ramirez	.05	.04	.02
242	Chris Sabo	.10	.08	.04
243	Dave Henderson	.07	.05	.03
244	Andy Van Slyke	.07	.05	.03
245	Alvaro Espinoza	.05	.04	.02
246	Garry Templeton	.06	.05	.02
247	Gene Harris	.04	.03	.02
248	Kevin Gross	.05	.04	.02
249	Brett Butler	.09	.07	.04
250	Willie Randolph	.07	.05	.03
251	Roger McDowell	.05	.04	.02
252	Rafael Belliard	.04	.03	.02
253	Steve Rosenberg	.04	.03	.02
254	Jack Howell	.04	.03	.02
255	Marvell Wynne	.04	.03	.02
256	Tom Candiotti	.05	.04	.02
257	Todd Benzinger	.05	.04	.02
258	Don Robinson	.04	.03	.02
259	Phil Bradley	.08	.06	.03
260	Cecil Espy	.05	.04	.02
261	Scott Bankhead	.05	.04	.02
262	Frank White	.07	.05	.03
263	Andres Thomas	.05	.04	.02
264	Glenn Braggs	.05	.04	.02
265	David Cone	.10	.08	.04
266	Bobby Thigpen	.07	.05	.03
267	Nelson Liriano	.04	.03	.02
268	Terry Steinbach	.09	.07	.04
269	Kirby Puckett	.30	.25	.12
270	Gregg Jefferies	.25	.20	.10
271	Jeff Blauser	.05	.04	.02
272	Cory Snyder	.07	.05	.03
273	Roy Smith	.05	.04	.02
274	Tom Foley	.04	.03	.02
275	Mitch Williams	.09	.07	.04
276	Paul Kilgus	.04	.03	.02
277	Don Slaught	.04	.03	.02
278	Von Hayes	.08	.06	.03
279	Vince Coleman	.10	.08	.04
280	Mike Boddicker	.05	.04	.02
281	Ken Dayley	.04	.03	.02
282	Mike Devereaux	.07	.05	.03
283	*Kenny Rogers*	.09	.07	.04
284	Jeff Russell	.07	.05	.03
285	*Jerome Walton*	.08	.06	.03
286	Derek Lilliquist	.08	.06	.03
287	Joe Orsulak	.04	.03	.02
288	Dick Schofield	.04	.03	.02
289	Ron Darling	.09	.07	.04
290	Bobby Bonilla	.10	.08	.04
291	Jim Gantner	.05	.04	.02
292	Bobby Witt	.05	.04	.02
293	Greg Brock	.05	.04	.02
294	Ivan Calderon	.05	.04	.02
295	Steve Bedrosian	.06	.05	.02
296	Mike Henneman	.06	.05	.02
297	Tom Gordon	.08	.06	.03
298	Lou Whitaker	.08	.06	.03
299	Terry Pendleton	.07	.05	.03
300 a	Checklist 232-333	.04	.03	.02
300 b	Checklist 224-321	.04	.03	.02
301	Juan Berenguer	.04	.03	.02
302	Mark Davis	.09	.07	.04
303	Nick Esasky	.09	.07	.04
304	Rickey Henderson	.15	.11	.06
305	Rick Cerone	.04	.03	.02
306	Craig Biggio	.15	.11	.06
307	Duane Ward	.04	.03	.02
308	Tom Browning	.07	.05	.03
309	Walt Terrell	.05	.04	.02
310	Greg Swindell	.07	.05	.03
311	Dave Righetti	.07	.05	.03
312	Mike Maddux	.04	.03	.02
313	Len Dykstra	.15	.11	.06
314	Jose Gonzalez	.08	.06	.03
315	Steve Balboni	.04	.03	.02
316	Mike Scioscia	.07	.05	.03
317	Ron Oester	.04	.03	.02
318	*Gary Wayne*	.09	.07	.04
319	Todd Worrell	.06	.05	.02
320	Doug Jones	.05	.04	.02
321	Jeff Hamilton	.05	.04	.02
322	Danny Tartabull	.09	.07	.04

No.	Player			
323	Chris James	.05	.04	.02
324	Mike Flanagan	.05	.04	.02
325	Gerald Young	.05	.04	.02
326	Bob Boone	.09	.07	.04
327	Frank Williams	.04	.03	.02
328	Dave Parker	.09	.07	.04
329	Sid Bream	.04	.03	.02
330	Mike Schooler	.06	.05	.02
331	Bert Blyleven	.08	.06	.03
332	Bob Welch	.07	.05	.03
333	Bob Milacki	.06	.05	.02
334	Tim Burke	.05	.04	.02
335	Jose Uribe	.05	.04	.02
336	Randy Myers	.05	.04	.02
337	Eric King	.04	.03	.02
338	Mark Langston	.12	.09	.05
339	Ted Higuera	.08	.06	.03
340	Oddibe McDowell	.06	.05	.02
341	Lloyd McClendon	.07	.05	.03
342	Pascual Perez	.05	.04	.02
343	Kevin Brown	.08	.06	.03
344	Chuck Finley	.05	.04	.02
345	Erik Hanson	.09	.07	.04
346	Rich Gedman	.05	.04	.02
347	Bip Roberts	.10	.08	.04
348	Matt Williams	.15	.11	.06
349	Tom Henke	.05	.04	.02
350	Brad Komminsk	.05	.04	.02
351	Jeff Reed	.04	.03	.02
352	Brian Downing	.05	.04	.02
353	Frank Viola	.09	.07	.04
354	Terry Puhl	.05	.04	.02
355	Brian Harper	.05	.04	.02
356	Steve Farr	.05	.04	.02
357	Joe Boever	.05	.04	.02
358	Danny Heep	.04	.03	.02
359	Larry Andersen	.04	.03	.02
360	Rolando Roomes	.10	.08	.04
361	Mike Gallego	.05	.04	.02
362	Bob Kipper	.04	.03	.02
363	Clay Parker	.07	.05	.03
364	Mike Pagliarulo	.05	.04	.02
365	Ken Griffey, Jr.	1.50	1.25	.60
366	Rex Hudler	.04	.03	.02
367	Pat Sheridan	.04	.03	.02
368	Kirk Gibson	.09	.07	.04
369	Jeff Parrett	.05	.04	.02
370	Bob Walk	.05	.04	.02
371	Ken Patterson	.04	.03	.02
372	Bryan Harvey	.05	.04	.02
373	Mike Bielecki	.07	.05	.03
374	*Tom Magrann* (FC)	.12	.09	.05
375	Rick Mahler	.05	.04	.02
376	Craig Lefferts	.05	.04	.02
377	Gregg Olson	.20	.15	.08
378	Jamie Moyer	.04	.03	.02
379	Randy Johnson	.12	.09	.05
380	Jeff Montgomery	.06	.05	.02
381	Marty Clary	.06	.05	.02
382	*Bill Spiers*	.15	.11	.06
383	Dave Magadan	.06	.05	.02
384	*Greg Hibbard* (FC)	.10	.08	.04
385	Ernie Whitt	.05	.04	.02
386	Rick Honeycutt	.04	.03	.02
387	Dave West	.08	.06	.03
388	Keith Hernandez	.07	.05	.03
389	Jose Alvarez	.04	.03	.02
390	*Albert Belle* (FC)	1.00	.70	.40
391	Rick Aguilera	.05	.04	.02
392	Mike Fitzgerald	.04	.03	.02
393	*Dwight Smith*	.08	.06	.03
394	*Steve Wilson*	.09	.07	.04
395	*Bob Geren*	.08	.06	.03
396	Randy Ready	.04	.03	.02
397	Ken Hill	.07	.05	.03
398	Jody Reed	.05	.04	.02
399	Tom Brunansky	.07	.05	.03
400 a	Checklist 334-435	.04	.03	.02
400 b	Checklist 322-419	.04	.03	.02
401	Rene Gonzales	.04	.03	.02
402	Harold Baines	.09	.07	.04
403	Cecilio Guante	.04	.03	.02
404	Joe Girardi	.15	.11	.06
405 a	*Sergio Valdez* (FC) (black line crosses S in Sergio)	.25	.20	.10
405 b	Sergio Valdez (corrected)	.08	.06	.03
406	Mark Williamson	.04	.03	.02
407	Glenn Hoffman	.04	.03	.02
408	*Jeff Innis* (FC)	.10	.08	.04
409	Randy Kramer	.04	.03	.02
410	Charlie O'Brien (FC)	.04	.03	.02
411	Charlie Hough	.06	.05	.02
412	Gus Polidor	.04	.03	.02
413	Ron Karkovice	.04	.03	.02
414	Trevor Wilson (FC)	.07	.05	.03
415	*Kevin Ritz* (FC)	.10	.08	.04
416	Gary Thurman	.04	.03	.02
417	Jeff Robinson	.04	.03	.02
418	Scott Terry	.05	.04	.02
419	Tim Laudner	.04	.03	.02
420	Dennis Rasmussen	.04	.03	.02
421	Luis Rivera	.04	.03	.02
422	Jim Corsi (FC)	.07	.05	.03
423	Dennis Lamp	.04	.03	.02
424	Ken Caminiti	.06	.05	.02
425	David Wells	.06	.05	.02
426	Norm Charlton	.09	.07	.04
427	*Deion Sanders*	.40	.30	.15
428	Dion James	.05	.04	.02
429	Chuck Cary	.05	.04	.02
430	Ken Howell	.04	.03	.02
431	Steve Lake	.04	.03	.02
432	Kal Daniels	.09	.07	.04
433	Lance McCullers	.05	.04	.02
434	Lenny Harris (FC)	.10	.08	.04
435	*Scott Scudder* (FC)	.10	.08	.04
436	Gene Larkin	.04	.03	.02
437	Dan Quisenberry	.05	.04	.02
438	*Steve Olin* (FC)	.05	.04	.02
439	Mickey Hatcher	.05	.04	.02
440	Willie Wilson	.05	.04	.02
441	Mark Grant	.05	.04	.02
442	Mookie Wilson	.07	.05	.03
443	Alex Trevino	.04	.03	.02
444	Pat Tabler	.05	.04	.02
445	Dave Bergman	.04	.03	.02
446	Todd Burns	.05	.04	.02
447	R.J. Reynolds	.04	.03	.02
448	Jay Buhner	.08	.06	.03
449	*Lee Stevens* (FC)	.10	.08	.04
450	Ron Hassey	.04	.03	.02
451	Bob Melvin	.04	.03	.02
452	Dave Martinez	.05	.04	.02
453	*Greg Litton* (FC)	.08	.06	.03
454	Mark Carreon	.10	.08	.04
455	Scott Fletcher	.05	.04	.02
456	Otis Nixon	.04	.03	.02
457	*Tony Fossas* (FC)	.04	.03	.02
458	John Russell	.04	.03	.02
459	Paul Assenmacher	.04	.03	.02
460	Zane Smith	.04	.03	.02
461	*Jack Daugherty*	.08	.06	.03
462	*Rich Monteleone* (FC)	.08	.06	.03
463	Greg Briley (FC)	.08	.06	.03
464	Mike Smithson	.04	.03	.02
465	Benito Santiago	.09	.07	.04
466	*Jeff Brantley*	.10	.08	.04
467	Jose Nunez	.07	.05	.03
468	Scott Bailes	.04	.03	.02
469	Ken Griffey	.06	.05	.02
470	Bob McClure	.04	.03	.02
471	Mackey Sasser	.04	.03	.02
472	Glenn Wilson	.04	.03	.02
473	*Kevin Tapani*	.25	.20	.10
474	Bill Buckner	.05	.04	.02
475	Ron Gant	.20	.15	.08
476	Kevin Romine (FC)	.05	.04	.02
477	Juan Agosto	.04	.03	.02
478	Herm Winningham	.04	.03	.02
479	Storm Davis	.05	.04	.02
480	Jeff King (FC)	.09	.07	.04
481	*Kevin Mmahat* (FC)	.08	.06	.03
482	Carmelo Martinez	.05	.04	.02
483	*Omar Vizquel*	.10	.08	.04
484	Jim Dwyer	.04	.03	.02
485	Bob Knepper	.04	.03	.02
486	Dave Anderson	.04	.03	.02
487	Ron Jones	.09	.07	.04
488	Jay Bell	.05	.04	.02
489	*Sammy Sosa* (FC)	.60	.45	.25
490	*Kent Anderson* (FC)	.08	.06	.03
491	Domingo Ramos	.04	.03	.02
492	Dave Clark	.05	.04	.02
493	Tim Birtsas	.04	.03	.02
494	Ken Oberkfell	.04	.03	.02
495	Larry Sheets	.04	.03	.02
496	Jeff Kunkel	.04	.03	.02
497	Jim Presley	.04	.03	.02
498	Mike Macfarlane	.04	.03	.02
499	Pete Smith	.05	.04	.02
500 a	Checklist 436-537	.04	.03	.02
500 b	Checklist 420-517	.04	.03	.02
501	Gary Sheffield	.30	.25	.12
502	*Terry Bross* (FC)	.08	.06	.03
503	*Jerry Kutzler* (FC)	.06	.05	.02
504	Lloyd Moseby	.05	.04	.02
505	Curt Young	.04	.03	.02
506	Al Newman	.04	.03	.02
507	Keith Miller	.04	.03	.02
508	*Mike Stanton* (FC)	.20	.15	.08
509	Rich Yett	.04	.03	.02
510	*Tim Drummond* (FC)	.08	.06	.03
511	Joe Hesketh	.04	.03	.02
512	*Rick Wrona*	.10	.08	.04
513	Luis Salazar	.04	.03	.02
514	Hal Morris	.06	.05	.02
515	Terry Mullholland	.07	.05	.03
516	John Morris	.05	.04	.02
517	Carlos Quintana	.08	.06	.03
518	Frank DiPino	.04	.03	.02
519	Randy Milligan	.06	.05	.02
520	Chad Kreuter	.07	.05	.03
521	Mike Jeffcoat	.04	.03	.02
522	Mike Harkey	.10	.08	.04
523 a	Andy Nezelek (Born 1985)	.06	.05	.02
523 b	Andy Nezelek (Born 1965)	.25	.20	.10
524	Dave Schmidt	.04	.03	.02
525	Tony Armas	.04	.03	.02
526	Barry Lyons	.04	.03	.02
527	*Rick Reed* (FC)	.08	.06	.03
528	Jerry Reuss	.06	.05	.02
529	*Dean Palmer* (FC)	.75	.60	.30
530	*Jeff Peterek* (FC)	.06	.05	.02
531	*Carlos Martinez*	.08	.06	.03
532	Atlee Hammaker	.05	.04	.02
533	Mike Brumley	.04	.03	.02
534	Terry Leach	.04	.03	.02
535	*Doug Strange* (FC)	.08	.06	.03
536	Jose DeLeon	.05	.04	.02
537	Shane Rawley	.05	.04	.02
538	Joey Cora (FC)	.10	.08	.04
539	Eric Hetzel	.08	.06	.03
540	Gene Nelson	.04	.03	.02
541	Wes Gardner	.04	.03	.02
542	Mark Portugal	.04	.03	.02
543	Al Leiter	.05	.04	.02
544	Jack Armstrong	.04	.03	.02
545	Greg Cadaret	.04	.03	.02
546	Rod Nichols	.04	.03	.02
547	Luis Polonia	.05	.04	.02
548	Charlie Hayes (FC)	.20	.15	.08
549	Dickie Thon	.04	.03	.02
550	Tim Crews	.04	.03	.02
551	Dave Winfield	.20	.15	.08
552	Mike Davis	.04	.03	.02
553	Ron Robinson	.04	.03	.02
554	Carmen Castillo	.04	.03	.02
555	John Costello	.04	.03	.02
556	Bud Black	.04	.03	.02
557	Rick Dempsey	.04	.03	.02
558	Jim Acker	.04	.03	.02
559	Eric Show	.06	.05	.02
560	Pat Borders	.06	.05	.02
561	Danny Darwin	.04	.03	.02
562	*Rick Luecken* (FC)	.06	.05	.02
563	Edwin Nunez	.05	.04	.02
564	Felix Jose	.09	.07	.04
565	John Cangelosi	.04	.03	.02
566	Billy Swift	.04	.03	.02
567	Bill Schroeder	.04	.03	.02
568	Stan Javier	.04	.03	.02
569	Jim Traber	.04	.03	.02
570	Wallace Johnson	.04	.03	.02
571	Donell Nixon	.04	.03	.02
572	Sid Fernandez	.08	.06	.03
573	Lance Johnson	.09	.07	.04
574	Andy McGaffigan	.04	.03	.02
575	Mark Knudson	.04	.03	.02
576	*Tommy Greene* (FC)	.50	.40	.20
577	Mark Grace	.25	.20	.10
578	*Larry Walker* (FC)	.75	.60	.30
579	Mike Stanley	.04	.03	.02
580	Mike Witt	.05	.04	.02
581	Scott Bradley	.04	.03	.02
582	Greg Harris	.07	.05	.03
583	Kevin Hickey	.04	.03	.02
584	Lee Mazzilli	.04	.03	.02
585	Jeff Pico	.04	.03	.02
586	*Joe Oliver* (FC)	.12	.09	.05
587	Willie Fraser	.04	.03	.02
588	Puzzle Card	.04	.03	.02
589	Kevin Bass	.06	.05	.02
590	John Moses	.04	.03	.02
591	Tom Pagnozzi	.04	.03	.02
592	*Tony Castillo*	.05	.04	.02
593	Jerald Clark	.06	.05	.02
594	Dan Schatzeder	.04	.03	.02
595	Luis Quinones	.04	.03	.02
596	Pete Harnisch	.08	.06	.03
597	Gary Redus	.04	.03	.02
598	Mel Hall	.05	.04	.02
599	Rick Schu	.04	.03	.02
600a	Checklist 538-639	.04	.03	.02
600b	Checklist 518-617	.04	.03	.02
601	Mike Kingery	.04	.03	.02
602	Terry Kennedy	.04	.03	.02
603	Mike Sharperson	.06	.05	.02
604	Don Carman	.04	.03	.02
605	Jim Gott	.05	.04	.02
606	Donn Pall	.05	.04	.02
607	Rance Mulliniks	.04	.03	.02
608	Curt Wilkerson	.04	.03	.02
609	Mike Felder	.04	.03	.02
610	Guillermo Hernandez	.04	.03	.02
611	Candy Maldonado	.05	.04	.02
612	Mark Thurmond	.04	.03	.02
613	Rick Leach	.04	.03	.02
614	Jerry Reed	.04	.03	.02
615	Franklin Stubbs	.05	.04	.02
616	Billy Hatcher	.05	.04	.02
617	Don August	.05	.04	.02
618	Tim Teufel	.04	.03	.02
619	Shawn Hillegas	.04	.03	.02
620	Manny Lee	.04	.03	.02
621	Gary Ward	.05	.04	.02
622	*Mark Guthrie* (FC)	.08	.06	.03
623	Jeff Musselman	.05	.04	.02
624	Mark Lemke	.07	.05	.03
625	Fernando Valenzuela	.07	.05	.03
626	*Paul Sorrento* (FC)	.20	.15	.08
627	Glenallen Hill	.20	.15	.08
628	Les Lancaster	.05	.04	.02
629	Vance Law	.04	.03	.02
630	Randy Velarde (FC)	.10	.08	.04
631	Todd Frohwirth	.04	.03	.02
632	Willie McGee	.06	.05	.02
633	Oil Can Boyd	.06	.05	.02
634	Cris Carpenter	.09	.07	.04
635	Brian Holton	.04	.03	.02
636	Tracy Jones	.05	.04	.02
637	Terry Steinbach (AS)	.08	.06	.03
638	Brady Anderson	.09	.07	.04
639a	Jack Morris (black line crosses J of Jack)	.25	.20	.10
639b	Jack Morris (corrected)	.08	.06	.03
640	*Jaime Navarro* (FC)	.12	.09	.05
641	Darrin Jackson	.05	.04	.02
642	*Mike Dyer* (FC)	.10	.08	.04
643	Mike Schmidt	.30	.25	.12
644	Henry Cotto	.04	.03	.02
645	John Cerutti	.05	.04	.02
646	*Francisco Cabrera* (FC)	.06	.05	.02
647	Scott Sanderson	.05	.04	.02
648	Brian Meyer	.05	.04	.02
649	Ray Searage	.05	.04	.02
650	Bo Jackson (AS)	.15	.11	.06
651	Steve Lyons	.04	.03	.02
652	Mike LaCoss	.04	.03	.02
653	Ted Power	.04	.03	.02
654	Howard Johnson (AS)	.08	.06	.03
655	*Mauro Gozzo* (FC)	.08	.06	.03
656	*Mike Blowers* (FC)	.15	.11	.06
657	Paul Gibson	.05	.04	.02
658	Neal Heaton	.05	.04	.02
659a	Nolan Ryan 5,000 K's (King of Kings (#665) back)	2.50	2.00	1.00
659b	Nolan Ryan 5,000 K's (correct back)	.50	.40	.20
660a	Harold Baines (AS) (black line through star on front, Recent Major League Performance on back)	2.00	1.50	.80
660b	Harold Baines (AS) (black line through star on front, All-Star Game Performance on back)	3.00	2.25	1.25

660c	Harold Baines (AS) (black line behind star on front, Recent Major League Performance on back)	1.50	1.25	.60
660d	Harold Baines (AS) (black line behind star on front, All-Star Game Performance on back)	.10	.08	.04
661	Gary Pettis	.05	.04	.02
662	*Clint Zavaras* (FC)	.08	.06	.03
663	Rick Reuschel (AS)	.08	.06	.03
664	Alejandro Pena	.05	.04	.02
665a	Nolan Ryan (King of Kings) (5,000 K's (#659) back)	2.50	2.00	1.00
665b	Nolan Ryan (King of Kings) (correct back)	.50	.40	.20
665c	Nolan Ryan (King of Kings) (no number on back)	1.00	.70	.40
666	Ricky Horton	.04	.03	.02
667	Curt Schilling	.06	.05	.02
668	Bill Landrum (FC)	.05	.04	.02
669	Todd Stottlemyre	.05	.04	.02
670	Tim Leary	.05	.04	.02
671	*John Wetteland*	.30	.25	.12
672	Calvin Schiraldi	.04	.03	.02
673	Ruben Sierra (AS)	.09	.07	.04
674	Pedro Guerrero (AS)	.09	.07	.04
675	Ken Phelps	.04	.03	.02
676	Cal Ripken (AS)	.30	.25	.12
677	Denny Walling	.04	.03	.02
678	Goose Gossage	.04	.03	.02
679	*Gary Mielke* (FC)	.20	.15	.08
680	Bill Bathe	.04	.03	.02
681	Tom Lawless	.04	.03	.02
682	*Xavier Hernandez*	.20	.15	.08
683	Kirby Puckett (AS)	.20	.15	.08
684	Mariano Duncan	.05	.04	.02
685	Ramon Martinez	.10	.08	.04
686	Tim Jones	.05	.04	.02
687	Tom Filer	.04	.03	.02
688	Steve Lombardozzi	.04	.03	.02
689	*Bernie Williams* (FC)	.25	.20	.10
690	*Chip Hale* (FC)	.08	.06	.03
691	*Beau Allred* (FC)	.10	.08	.04
692	Ryne Sandberg (AS)	.25	.20	.10
693	*Jeff Huson* (FC)	.10	.08	.04
694	Curt Ford	.04	.03	.02
695	Eric Davis (AS)	.09	.07	.04
696	Scott Lusader	.05	.04	.02
697	Mark McGwire (AS)	.09	.07	.04
698	*Steve Cummings* (FC)	.05	.04	.02
699	*George Canale* (FC)	.05	.04	.02
700 a	Checklist 640-715/BC1-BC26	.04	.03	.02
700 b	Checklist 640-716/BC1-BC-26	.04	.03	.02
700 c	Checklist 618-716	.04	.03	.02
701	Julio Franco (AS)	.09	.07	.04
702	*Dave Johnson* (FC)	.10	.08	.04
703	Dave Stewart (AS)	.08	.06	.03
704	*Dave Justice* (FC)	1.25	.90	.50
705	Tony Gwynn (AS)	.15	.11	.06
706	Greg Myers	.06	.05	.02
707	Will Clark (AS)	.15	.11	.06
708	Benito Santiago (AS)	.08	.06	.03
709	Larry McWilliams	.04	.03	.02
710	Ozzie Smith (AS)	.08	.06	.03
711	*John Olerud* (FC)	1.50	1.25	.60
712	Wade Boggs (AS)	.09	.07	.04
713	*Gary Eave* (FC)	.06	.11	.06
714	Bob Tewksbury	.05	.04	.02
715	Kevin Mitchell (AS)	.09	.07	.04
716	A. Bartlett Giamatti	.35	.25	.14

1990 Donruss MVP

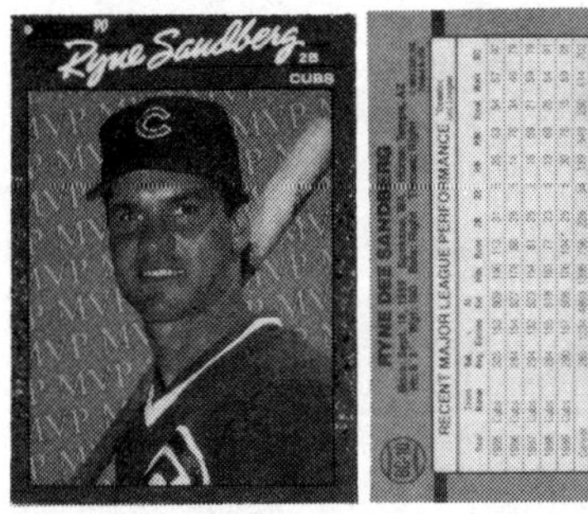

This special 26-card set includes one player from each Major League team. Numbered BC-1 (the "BC" stands for "Bonus Card") through BC-26, the cards from this set were randomly packed in 1990 Donruss wax packs and were not available in factory sets or other types of packaging. The red-bordered cards are similar in design to the regular 1990 Donruss set, except the player photos are set against a special background made up of the "MVP" logo.

		MT	NR MT	EX
Complete Set (26):		1.25	.90	.50
Common MVP:		.08	.06	.03
1	Bo Jackson	.30	.25	.12
2	Howard Johnson	.10	.08	.04
3	Dave Stewart	.08	.06	.03
4	Tony Gwynn	.15	.11	.06
5	Orel Hershiser	.10	.08	.04
6	Pedro Guerrero	.10	.08	.04
7	Tim Raines	.10	.08	.04
8	Kirby Puckett	.30	.25	.12
9	Alvin Davis	.08	.06	.03
10	Ryne Sandberg	.30	.25	.12
11	Kevin Mitchell	.20	.15	.08
12a	John Smoltz (photo of Tom Glavine)	2.00	1.50	.80
12b	John Smoltz (corrected)	.40	.30	.15
13	George Bell	.10	.08	.04
14	Julio Franco	.15	.11	.06
15	Paul Molitor	.20	.15	.08
16	Bobby Bonilla	.15	.11	.06
17	Mike Greenwell	.15	.11	.06
18	Cal Ripken	.30	.25	.12
19	Carlton Fisk	.12	.09	.05
20	Chili Davis	.08	.06	.03
21	Glenn Davis	.10	.08	.04
22	Steve Sax	.10	.08	.04
23	Eric Davis	.20	.15	.08
24	Greg Swindell	.08	.06	.03
25	Von Hayes	.08	.06	.03
26	Alan Trammell	.10	.08	.04

1990 Donruss Grand Slammers

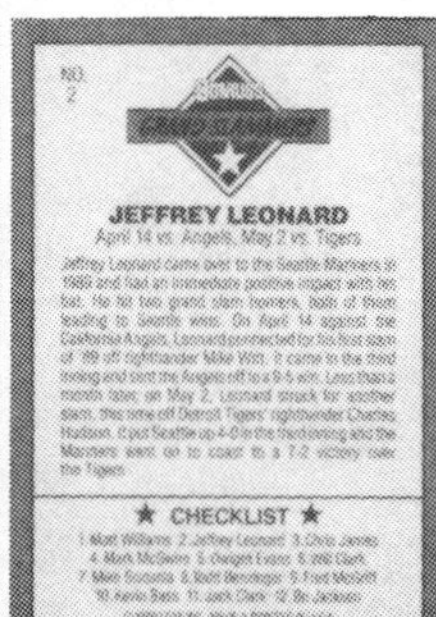

For the second consecutive year Donruss produced a set in honor of players who hit grand slams in the previous season. The cards are styled after the 1990 Donruss regular issue. The cards were inserted into 1990 Donruss factory sets, and one card per cello pack.

		MT	NR MT	EX
Complete Set (12):		2.00	1.50	.80
Common Player:		.10	.06	.03
1	Matt Williams	.25	.20	.10
2	Jeffrey Leonard	.12	.09	.05
3	Chris James	.12	.09	.05
4	Mark McGwire	.30	.25	.12
5	Dwight Evans	.15	.11	.06
6	Will Clark	.25	.15	.10
7	Mike Scioscia	.12	.09	.05
8	Todd Benzinger	.12	.09	.05
9	Fred McGriff	.40	.30	.15
10	Kevin Bass	.12	.09	.05
11	Jack Clark	.12	.09	.05
12	Bo Jackson	.25	.15	.10

1990 Donruss A.L. Best

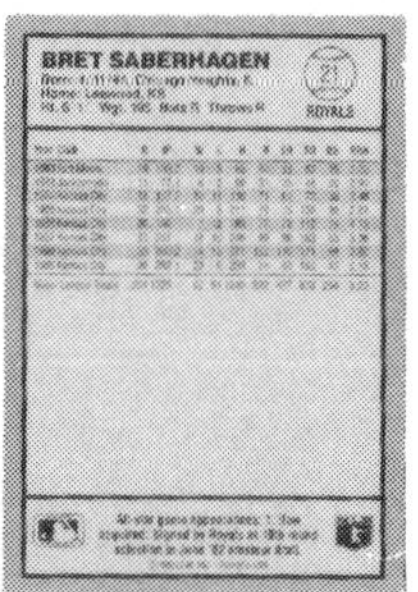

This 144-card set features the top players of the American League. The cards measure 2-1/2" by 3-1/2" and feature the same card front design as the regular Donruss set with the exception of having blue borders instead of red. The card backs feature a yellow frame with complete statistics and biogra- phical information provided. 1990 marks the first year that Donruss divided its baseball best issue into two sets designated by league.

		MT	NR MT	EX
Complete Set:		9.00	6.75	3.50
Common Player:		.04	.03	.02
1	Ken Griffey,Jr.	1.50	1.25	.60
2	Bob Milacki	.04	.03	.02
3	Mike Boddicker	.06	.05	.02
4	Bert Blyleven	.08	.06	.03
5	Carlton Fisk	.10	.08	.04
6	Greg Swindell	.06	.05	.02
7	Alan Trammell	.10	.08	.04
8	Mark Davis	.05	.04	.02
9	Chris Bosio	.04	.03	.02
10	Gary Gaetti	.10	.08	.04
11	Matt Nokes	.06	.05	.02
12	Dennis Eckersley	.10	.08	.04
13	Kevin Brown	.08	.06	.03
14	Tom Henke	.06	.05	.02
15	Mickey Tettleton	.08	.06	.03
16	Jody Reed	.08	.06	.03
17	Mark Langston	.08	.06	.03
18	Melido Perez	.06	.05	.02
19	John Farrell	.04	.03	.02
20	Tony Phillips	.04	.03	.02
21	Bret Saberhagen	.10	.08	.04
22	Robin Yount	.10	.08	.04
23	Kirby Puckett	.15	.11	.06
24	Steve Sax	.10	.08	.04
25	Dave Stewart	.10	.08	.04
26	Alvin Davis	.08	.06	.03
27	Geno Petralli	.04	.03	.02
28	Mookie Wilson	.05	.04	.02
29	Jeff Ballard	.04	.03	.02
30	Ellis Burks	.10	.08	.04
31	Wally Joyner	.08	.06	.03
32	Bobby Thigpen	.10	.08	.04
33	Keith Hernandez	.06	.05	.02
34	Jack Morris	.06	.05	.02
35	George Brett	.10	.08	.04
36	Dan Plesac	.08	.06	.03
37	Brian Harper	.05	.04	.02
38	Don Mattingly	.25	.20	.10
39	Dave Henderson	.08	.06	.03
40	Scott Bankhead	.06	.05	.02
41	Rafael Palmeiro	.10	.08	.04
42	Jimmy Key	.06	.05	.02
43	Gregg Olson	.10	.08	.04
44	Tony Pena	.06	.05	.02
45	Jack Howell	.04	.03	.02
46	Eric King	.04	.03	.02
47	Cory Snyder	.06	.05	.02
48	Frank Tanana	.04	.03	.02
49	Nolan Ryan	.60	.45	.25
50	Bob Boone	.06	.05	.02
51	Dave Parker	.10	.08	.04
52	Allan Anderson	.04	.03	.02
53	Tim Leary	.05	.04	.02
54	Mark McGwire	.25	.20	.10
55	Dave Valle	.04	.03	.02
56	Fred McGriff	.25	.20	.10
57	Cal Ripken	.15	.11	.06
58	Roger Clemens	.30	.25	.12
59	Lance Parrish	.08	.06	.03
60	Robin Ventura	.30	.25	.12
61	Doug Jones	.08	.06	.03
62	Lloyd Moseby	.06	.05	.02
63	Bo Jackson	.80	.60	.30
64	Paul Molitor	.08	.06	.03
65	Kent Hrbek	.08	.06	.03
66	Mel Hall	.04	.03	.02
67	Bob Welch	.10	.08	.04
68	Erik Hanson	.10	.08	.04
69	Harold Baines	.08	.06	.03
70	Junior Felix	.10	.08	.04
71	Craig Worthington	.06	.05	.02
72	Jeff Reardon	.08	.06	.03
73	Johnny Ray	.05	.04	.02
74	Ozzie Guillen	.10	.08	.04
75	Brook Jacoby	.08	.06	.03
76	Chet Lemon	.05	.04	.02
77	Mark Gubicza	.08	.06	.03
78	B.J. Surhoff	.08	.06	.03
79	Rick Aguilera	.05	.04	.02
80	Pascual Perez	.04	.03	.02
81	Jose Canseco	.70	.50	.30
82	Mike Schooler	.08	.06	.03
83	Jeff Huson	.12	.09	.05
84	Kelly Gruber	.15	.11	.06
85	Randy Milligan	.08	.06	.03
86	Wade Boggs	.35	.25	.14
87	Dave Winfield	.20	.15	.08
88	Scott Fletcher	.04	.03	.02
89	Tom Candiotti	.04	.03	.02
90	Mike Heath	.04	.03	.02
91	Kevin Seitzer	.08	.06	.03
92	Ted Higuera	.08	.06	.03
93	Kevin Tapani	.15	.11	.06
94	Roberto Kelly	.08	.06	.03
95	Walt Weiss	.06	.05	.02
96	Checklist	.04	.03	.02
97	Sandy Alomar	.30	.25	.12
98	Pete O'Brien	.05	.04	.02
99	Jeff Russell	.06	.05	.02
100	John Olerud	.50	.40	.20
101	Pete Harnisch	.05	.04	.02
102	Dwight Evans	.08	.06	.03
103	Chuck Finley	.08	.06	.03
104	Sammy Sosa	.25	.20	.10
105	Mike Henneman	.06	.05	.02
106	Kurt Stillwell	.06	.05	.02
107	Greg Vaughn	.30	.25	.12
108	Dan Gladden	.05	.04	.02
109	Jesse Barfield	.06	.05	.02
110	Willie Randolph	.06	.05	.02
111	Randy Johnson	.08	.06	.03
112	Julio Franco	.08	.06	.03
113	Tony Fernandez	.08	.06	.03
114	Ben McDonald	.50	.40	.20
115	Mike Greenwell	.20	.15	.08
116	Luis Polonia	.04	.03	.02
117	Carney Lansford	.06	.05	.02
118	Bud Black	.05	.04	.02
119	Lou Whitaker	.08	.06	.03
120	Jim Eisenreich	.04	.03	.02
121	Gary Sheffield	.25	.20	.10

122	Shane Mack	.08	.06	.03
123	Alvaro Espinoza	.04	.03	.02
124	Rickey Henderson	.40	.30	.15
125	Jeffrey Leonard	.05	.04	.02
126	Gary Pettis	.04	.03	.02
127	Dave Steib	.08	.06	.03
128	Danny Tartabull	.08	.06	.03
129	Joe Orsulak	.04	.03	.02
130	Tom Brunansky	.06	.05	.02
131	Dick Schofield	.04	.03	.02
132	Candy Maldonado	.06	.05	.02
133	Cecil Fielder	.30	.25	.12
134	Terry Shumpert	.20	.15	.08
135	Greg Gagne	.05	.04	.02
136	Dave Righetti	.08	.06	.03
137	Terry Steinbach	.06	.05	.02
138	Harold Reynolds	.08	.06	.03
139	George Bell	.08	.06	.03
140	Carlos Quintana	.06	.05	.02
141	Ivan Calderon	.08	.06	.03
142	Greg Brock	.04	.03	.02
143	Ruben Sierra	.15	.11	.06
144	Checklist	.04	.03	.02

1990 Donruss N.L. Best

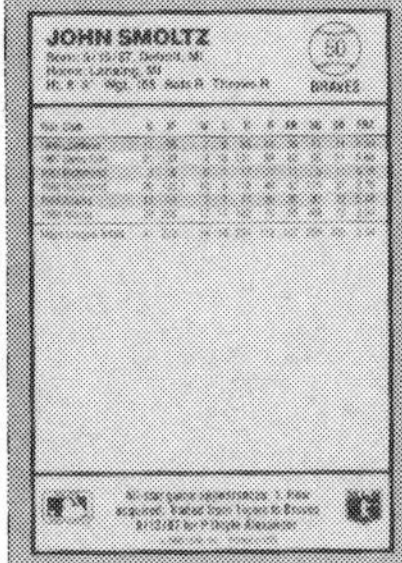

This 144-card set features the top players in the National League for 1990. The cards measure 2-1/2" by 3-1/2" and feature the same design as the regular Donruss cards. The only difference on the card fronts is the border color. The N.L. Best cards contain blue borders, while the regular cards featured red borders. Traded players are featured with their new teams. This set along with the A.L. Best set was available at select retail stores and within the hobby.

	MT	NR MT	EX
Complete Set:	9.00	6.75	3.50
Common Player:	.04	.03	.02

1	Eric Davis	.20	.15	.08
2	Tom Glavine	.10	.08	.04
3	Mike Bielecki	.05	.04	.02
4	Jim Deshaies	.05	.04	.02
5	Mike Scioscia	.05	.04	.02
6	Spike Owen	.05	.04	.02
7	Dwight Gooden	.20	.15	.08
8	Ricky Jordan	.08	.06	.03
9	Doug Drabek	.10	.08	.04
10	Bryn Smith	.04	.03	.02
11	Tony Gwynn	.10	.08	.04
12	John Burkett	.10	.08	.04
13	Nick Esasky	.06	.05	.02
14	Greg Maddux	.08	.06	.03
15	Joe Oliver	.08	.06	.03
16	Mike Scott	.08	.06	.03
17	Tim Belcher	.08	.06	.03
18	Kevin Gross	.06	.05	.02
19	Howard Johnson	.10	.08	.04
20	Darren Daulton	.06	.05	.02
21	John Smiley	.06	.05	.02
22	Ken Dayley	.05	.04	.02
23	Craig Lefferts	.05	.04	.02
24	Will Clark	.60	.45	.25
25	Greg Olson	.12	.09	.05
26	Ryne Sandberg	.50	.40	.20
27	Tom Browning	.06	.05	.02
28	Eric Anthony	.20	.15	.08
29	Juan Samuel	.06	.05	.02
30	Dennis Martinez	.06	.05	.02
31	Kevin Elster	.05	.04	.02
32	Tom Herr	.06	.05	.02
33	Sid Bream	.06	.05	.02
34	Terry Pendleton	.06	.05	.02
35	Roberto Alomar	.20	.15	.08
36	Kevin Bass	.06	.05	.02
37	Jim Presley	.06	.05	.02
38	Les Lancaster	.04	.03	.02
39	Paul O'Neill	.08	.06	.03
40	Dave Smith	.06	.05	.02
41	Kirk Gibson	.10	.08	.04
42	Tim Burke	.06	.05	.02
43	David Cone	.10	.08	.04
44	Ken Howell	.06	.05	.02
45	Barry Bonds	.20	.15	.08
46	Joe Magrane	.08	.06	.03
47	Andy Benes	.08	.06	.03
48	Gary Carter	.10	.08	.04
49	Pat Combs	.08	.06	.03
50	John Smoltz	.10	.08	.04
51	Mark Grace	.10	.08	.04
52	Barry Larkin	.10	.08	.04
53	Danny Darwin	.08	.06	.03
54	Orel Hershiser	.10	.08	.04
55	Tim Wallach	.08	.06	.03
56	Dave Magadan	.10	.08	.04
57	Roger McDowell	.08	.06	.03
58	Bill Landrum	.06	.05	.02
59	Jose DeLeon	.06	.05	.02
60	Bip Roberts	.06	.05	.02
61	Matt Williams	.10	.08	.04
62	Dale Murphy	.08	.06	.03
63	Dwight Smith	.08	.06	.03
64	Chris Sabo	.10	.08	.04
65	Glenn Davis	.10	.08	.04
66	Jay Howell	.06	.05	.02
67	Andres Galarraga	.08	.06	.03
68	Frank Viola	.10	.08	.04
69	John Kruk	.06	.05	.02
70	Bobby Bonilla	.15	.11	.06
71	Todd Zeile	.60	.45	.25
72	Joe Carter	.10	.08	.04
73	Robby Thompson	.06	.05	.02
74	Jeff Blauser	.04	.03	.02
75	Mitch Williams	.08	.06	.03
76	Rob Dibble	.10	.08	.04
77	Rafael Ramirez	.04	.03	.02
78	Eddie Murray	.10	.08	.04
79	Dave Martinez	.05	.04	.02
80	Darryl Strawberry	.50	.40	.20
81	Dickie Thon	.04	.03	.02
82	Jose Lind	.05	.04	.02
83	Ozzie Smith	.10	.08	.04
84	Bruce Hurst	.06	.05	.02
85	Kevin Mitchell	.20	.15	.08
86	Lonnie Smith	.05	.04	.02
87	Joe Girardi	.08	.06	.03
88	Randy Myers	.10	.08	.04
89	Craig Biggio	.08	.06	.03
90	Fernando Valenzuela	.06	.05	.02
91	Larry Walker	.20	.15	.08
92	John Franco	.10	.08	.04
93	Dennis Cook	.06	.05	.02
94	Bob Walk	.05	.04	.02
95	Pedro Guerrero	.08	.06	.03
96	Checklist	.04	.03	.02
97	Andre Dawson	.10	.08	.04
98	Ed Whitson	.06	.05	.02
99	Steve Bedrosian	.06	.05	.02
100	Oddibe McDowell	.06	.05	.02
101	Todd Benzinger	.06	.05	.02
102	Bill Doran	.08	.06	.03
103	Alfredo Griffin	.04	.03	.02
104	Tim Raines	.10	.08	.04
105	Sid Fernandez	.08	.06	.03
106	Charlie Hayes	.08	.06	.03
107	Mike LaValliere	.05	.04	.02
108	Jose Oquendo	.04	.03	.02
109	Jack Clark	.08	.06	.03
110	Scott Garrelts	.06	.05	.02
111	Ron Gant	.10	.08	.04
112	Shawon Dunston	.10	.08	.04
113	Mariano Duncan	.06	.05	.02
114	Eric Yelding	.10	.08	.04
115	Hubie Brooks	.08	.06	.03
116	Delino DeShields	.25	.20	.10
117	Gregg Jefferies	.20	.15	.08
118	Len Dykstra	.10	.08	.04
119	Andy Van Slyke	.10	.08	.04
120	Lee Smith	.08	.06	.03
121	Benito Santiago	.10	.08	.04
122	Jose Uribe	.04	.03	.02
123	Jeff Treadway	.05	.04	.02
124	Jerome Walton	.10	.08	.04
125	Billy Hatcher	.06	.05	.02
126	Ken Caminiti	.04	.03	.02
127	Kal Daniels	.08	.06	.03
128	Marquis Grissom	.30	.25	.12
129	Kevin McReynolds	.08	.06	.03
130	Wally Backman	.04	.03	.02
131	Willie McGee	.10	.08	.04
132	Terry Kennedy	.04	.03	.02
133	Garry Templeton	.04	.03	.02
134	Lloyd McClendon	.04	.03	.02
135	Daryl Boston	.04	.03	.02
136	Jay Bell	.08	.06	.03
137	Mike Pagliarulo	.06	.05	.02
138	Vince Coleman	.08	.06	.03
139	Brett Butler	.06	.05	.02
140	Von Hayes	.08	.06	.03
141	Ramon Martinez	.20	.15	.08
142	Jack Armstrong	.10	.08	.04
143	Franklin Stubbs	.05	.04	.02
144	Checklist	.04	.03	.02

1990 Donruss Diamond Kings Supers

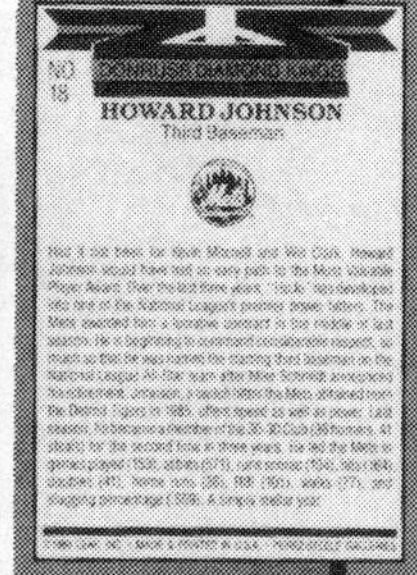

Donruss made this set available through a mail-in offer. Three wrappers, $10 and $2 for postage were necessary to obtain this set. The cards are exactly the same design as the regular Donruss Diamond Kings except they measure approximately 5" by 6-3/4" in size. The artwork of Dick Perez is featured.

	MT	NR MT	EX
Complete Set:	6.00	4.50	2.50
Common Player:	.10	.08	.04

1	Bo Jackson	1.25	.90	.50
2	Steve Sax	.15	.11	.06
3	Ruben Sierra	.35	.25	.14
4	Ken Griffey,Jr.	2.00	1.50	.80
5	Mickey Tettleton	.10	.08	.04
6	Dave Stewart	.20	.15	.08
7	Jim Deshaies	.10	.08	.04
8	John Smoltz	.20	.15	.08
9	Mike Bielecki	.10	.08	.04
10	Brian Downing	.10	.08	.04
11	Kevin Mitchell	.20	.15	.08
12	Kelly Gruber	.10	.08	.04
13	Joe Magrane	.15	.11	.06
14	John Franco	.15	.11	.06
15	Ozzie Guillen	.20	.15	.08
16	Lou Whitaker	.15	.11	.06
17	John Smiley	.10	.08	.04
18	Howard Johnson	.25	.20	.10
19	Willie Randolph	.10	.08	.04
20	Chris Bosio	.10	.08	.04
21	Tommy Herr	.10	.08	.04
22	Dan Gladden	.10	.08	.04
23	Ellis Burks	.20	.15	.08
24	Pete O'Brien	.10	.08	.04
25	Bryn Smith	.10	.08	.04
26	Ed Whitson	.10	.08	.04

1990 Donruss Learning Series

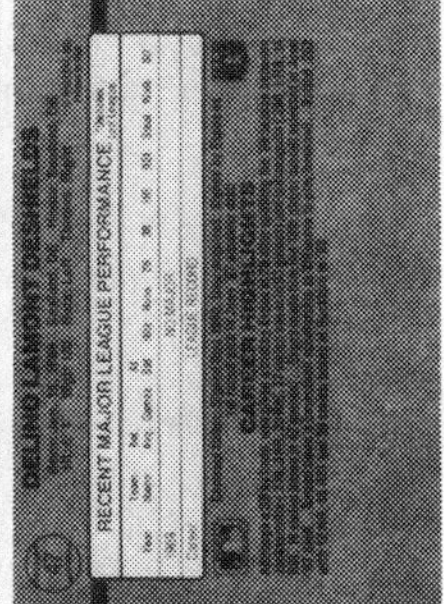

Cards from this 55-card set were released as a part of an educational package available to schools. The cards are styled like the regular-issue 1990 Donruss cards, but feature a special "learning series" logo on the front. The backs feature career highlights, statistics and card numbers. The cards were not released directly to the hobby.

	MT	NR MT	EX
Complete Set:	55.00	40.00	20.00
Common Player:	.40	.30	.15

1	George Brett (DK)	2.50	2.00	1.00
2	Kevin Mitchell	.60	.45	.25
3	Andy Van Slyke	.80	.60	.30
4	Benito Santiago	.60	.45	.25
5	Gary Carter	.80	.60	.30
6	Jose Canseco	5.00	3.75	2.00
7	Rickey Henderson	5.00	3.75	2.00
8	Ken Griffey,Jr.	10.00	7.50	4.00
9	Ozzie Smith	4.00	3.00	1.50
10	Dwight Gooden	3.00	2.25	1.25
11	Ryne Sandberg (DK)	8.00	6.00	3.25
12	Don Mattingly	6.00	4.50	2.50
13	Ozzie Guillen	.50	.40	.20
14	Dave Righetti	.40	.30	.15
15	Rick Dempsey	.40	.30	.15
16	Tom Herr	.40	.30	.15
17	Julio Franco	.40	.30	.15
18	Von Hayes	.40	.30	.15
19	Cal Ripken	8.00	6.00	3.25
20	Alan Trammell	.80	.60	.30
21	Wade Boggs	5.00	3.75	2.00
22	Glenn Davis	.40	.30	.15
23	Will Clark	6.00	4.50	2.50
24	Nolan Ryan	12.00	9.00	4.75
25	George Bell	.60	.45	.25
26	Cecil Fielder	2.00	1.50	.80
27	Gregg Olson	.40	.30	.15
28	Tim Wallach	.40	.30	.15
29	Ron Darling	.40	.30	.15
30	Kelly Gruber	.40	.30	.15
31	Shawn Boskie	.40	.30	.15
32	Mike Greenwell	.60	.45	.25
33	Dave Parker	.60	.45	.25
34	Joe Magrane	.40	.30	.15
35	Dave Stewart	.60	.45	.25
36	Kent Hrbek	.50	.40	.20
37	Robin Yount	3.00	2.25	1.25
38	Bo Jackson	1.50	1.25	.60
39	Fernando Valenzuela	.40	.30	.15

		MT	NR MT	EX
40	Sandy Alomar, Jr.	.50	.40	.20
41	Lance Parrish	.40	.30	.15
42	Candy Maldonado	.40	.30	.15
43	Mike LaValliere	.40	.30	.15
44	Jim Abbott	1.50	1.25	.60
45	Edgar Martinez	.60	.45	.25
46	Kirby Puckett	5.00	3.75	2.00
47	Delino DeShields	.80	.60	.30
48	Tony Gwynn	2.00	1.50	.80
49	Carlton Fisk	2.00	1.50	.80
50	Mike Scott	.40	.30	.15
51	Barry Larkin	1.50	1.25	.60
52	Andre Dawson	2.00	1.50	.80
53	Tom Glavine	.80	.60	.30
54	Tom Browning	.40	.30	.15
55	Checklist	.40	.30	.15

1990 Donruss Rookies

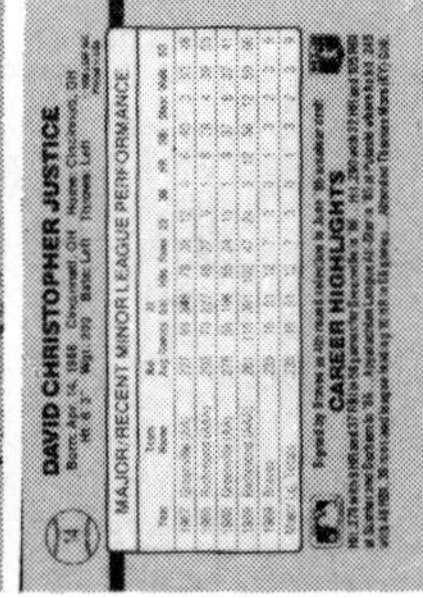

For the fifth straight year, Donruss issued a 56-card "Rookies" set in 1990. As in previous years, the set is similar in design to the regular Donruss set, except for a new "The Rookies" logo and green borders instead of red. The set is packaged in a special box and includes a special Carl Yastrzemski puzzle card.

		MT	NR MT	EX
Complete Set (56):		8.00	6.00	3.25
Common Player:		.10	.08	.04
1	Sandy Alomar	.15	.11	.06
2	John Olerud	1.50	1.25	.60
3	Pat Combs	.20	.15	.08
4	Brian Dubois	.10	.08	.04
5	Felix Jose	.12	.09	.05
6	Delino DeShields	.50	.40	.20
7	Mike Stanton	.10	.08	.04
8	Mike Munoz (FC)	.10	.08	.04
9	Craig Grebeck (FC)	.15	.11	.06
10	Joe Kraemer (FC)	.10	.08	.04
11	Jeff Huson	.10	.08	.04
12	Bill Sampen (FC)	.15	.11	.06
13	Brian Bohanon (FC)	.12	.09	.05
14	Dave Justice	1.25	.90	.50
15	Robin Ventura	.90	.70	.35
16	Greg Vaughn	.60	.45	.25
17	Wayne Edwards (FC)	.15	.11	.06
18	Shawn Boskie	.25	.20	.10
19	Carlos Baerga (FC)	1.50	1.25	.60
20	Mark Gardner	.20	.15	.08
21	Kevin Appier (FC)	.30	.25	.12
22	Mike Harkey	.20	.15	.08
23	Tim Layana (FC)	.20	.15	.08
24	Glenallen Hill	.20	.15	.08
25	Jerry Kutzler	.10	.08	.04
26	Mike Blowers	.15	.11	.06
27	Scott Ruskin (FC)	.25	.20	.10
28	Dana Kiecker (FC)	.15	.11	.06
29	Willie Blair (FC)	.10	.08	.04
30	Ben McDonald	.60	.45	.25
31	Todd Zeile	.40	.30	.15
32	Scott Coolbaugh	.12	.09	.05
33	Xavier Hernandez	.10	.08	.04
34	Mike Hartley (FC)	.15	.11	.06
35	Kevin Tapani	.30	.25	.12
36	Kevin Wickander (FC)	.10	.08	.04
37	Carlos Hernandez (FC)	.15	.11	.06
38	Brian Traxler (FC)	.20	.15	.08
39	Marty Brown (FC)	.10	.08	.04
40	Scott Radinsky (FC)	.25	.20	.10
41	Julio Machado	.15	.11	.06
42	Steve Avery	.80	.60	.30
43	Mark Lemke	.12	.09	.05
44	Alan Mills (FC)	.25	.20	.10
45	Marquis Grissom	.50	.40	.20
46	Greg Olson (FC)	.15	.11	.06
47	Dave Hollins (FC)	.80	.60	.30
48	Jerald Clark	.10	.08	.04
49	Eric Anthony	.20	.15	.08
50	Tim Drummond	.10	.08	.04
51	John Burkett (FC)	.40	.30	.15
52	Brent Knackert (FC)	.12	.09	.05
53	Jeff Shaw (FC)	.12	.09	.05
54	John Orton (FC)	.10	.08	.04
55	Terry Shumpert (FC)	.15	.11	.06
56	Checklist	.10	.08	.04

A player's name in italic type indicates a rookie card. An (FC) indicates a player's first card for that particular card company.

1991 Donruss Previews

Once again in late 1990 Donruss distributed individual cards from a 12-card preview issue to its dealer network as an introduction to its 1991 issue. Like the previous year's preview cards, the '91 samples utilized the format which would follow on the regular-issue cards, but the photos were different. This has helped create demand for these cards from superstar collectors. Backs are printed in black-and-white and have little more than a player name, card number and MLB logos.

		MT	NR MT	EX
Complete Set (12):		450.00	325.00	175.00
Common Player:		7.50	5.50	3.00
1	Dave Justice	35.00	26.00	14.00
2	Doug Drabek	12.00	9.00	4.75
3	Scott Chiamparino	7.50	5.50	3.00
4	Ken Griffey, Jr.	150.00	110.00	60.00
5	Bob Welch	9.00	6.75	3.50
6	Tino Martinez	15.00	11.00	6.00
7	Nolan Ryan	150.00	110.00	60.00
8	Dwight Gooden	15.00	11.00	6.00
9	Ryne Sandberg	45.00	34.00	18.00
10	Barry Bonds	45.00	34.00	18.00
11	Jose Canseco	45.00	36.00	18.00
12	Eddie Murray	25.00	18.50	10.00

1991 Donruss

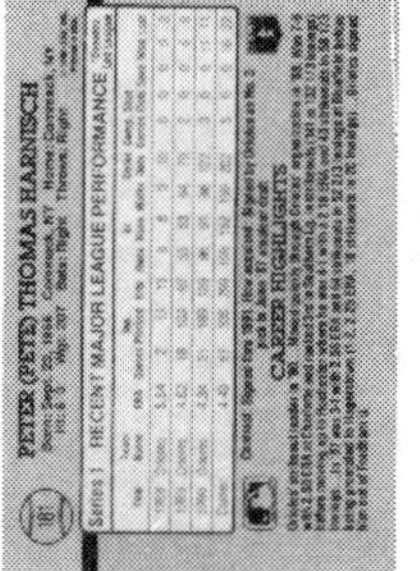

Donruss decided to use a two series format in 1991. The first series was released in December and the second in February. The 1991 design is somewhat reminiscent of the 1986 set. Blue borders are used. Limited edition cards including an autographed Ryne Sandberg card (5,000) were randomly inserted in wax packs. Other features of the set include 40 Rated Rookies, a "Legends Series," Elite Series, and another Diamond King subset. Collectors could also take part in Donruss' Instant Win promotion.

		MT	NR MT	EX
Complete Set (792):		18.00	13.50	7.25
Common Player:		.04	.03	.02
1	Dave Steib (DK)	.04	.03	.02
2	Craig Biggio (DK)	.05	.04	.02
3	Cecil Fielder (DK)	.12	.09	.05
4	Barry Bonds (DK)	.15	.11	.06
5	Barry Larkin (DK)	.06	.05	.02
6	Dave Parker (DK)	.05	.04	.02
7	Len Dykstra (DK)	.06	.05	.02
8	Bobby Thigpen (DK)	.05	.04	.02
9	Roger Clemens (DK)	.10	.08	.04
10	Ron Gant (DK)	.08	.06	.03
11	Delino DeShields (DK)	.08	.06	.03
12	Roberto Alomar (DK)	.10	.08	.04
13	Sandy Alomar (DK)	.06	.05	.02
14	Ryne Sandberg (DK)	.15	.11	.06
15	Ramon Martinez (DK)	.06	.05	.02
16	Edgar Martinez (DK)	.08	.06	.03
17	Dave Magadan (DK)	.04	.03	.02
18	Matt Williams (DK)	.12	.09	.05
19	Rafael Palmeiro (DK)	.05	.04	.02
20	Bob Welch (DK)	.06	.05	.02
21	Dave Righetti (DK)	.04	.03	.02
22	Brian Harper (DK)	.04	.03	.02
23	Gregg Olson (DK)	.05	.04	.02
24	Kurt Stillwell (DK)	.04	.03	.02
25	Pedro Guerrero (DK)	.05	.04	.02
26	Chuck Finley (DK)	.05	.04	.02
27	DK Checklist	.04	.03	.02
28	Tino Martinez (RR)	.10	.08	.04
29	Mark Lewis (RR)	.10	.08	.04
30	*Bernard Gilkey* (RR)	.20	.15	.08
31	Hensley Meulens (RR)	.08	.06	.03
32	*Derek Bell* (RR)	.40	.30	.15
33	Jose Offerman (RR)	.10	.08	.04
34	Terry Bross (RR)	.10	.08	.04
35	*Leo Gomez* (RR)	.12	.09	.05
36	Derrick May (RR)	.35	.25	.14
37	*Kevin Morton* (RR)	.10	.08	.04
38	Moises Alou (RR)	.35	.25	.14
39	*Julio Valera* (FC) (RR)	.06	.05	.02
40	Milt Cuyler (FC) (RR)	.10	.08	.04
41	*Phil Plantier* (RR)	.35	.25	.14
42	*Scott Chiamparino* (FC) (RR)	.08	.06	.03
43	*Ray Lankford* (RR)	.20	.15	.08
44	*Mickey Morandini* (FC) (RR)	.08	.06	.03
45	Dave Hansen (FC) (RR)	.10	.08	.04
46	*Kevin Belcher* (RR)	.15	.11	.06
47	Darrin Fletcher (FC) (RR)	.10	.08	.04
48	Steve Sax (AS)	.05	.04	.02
49	Ken Griffey,Jr. (AS)	.40	.30	.15
50	Jose Canseco (AS)	.12	.09	.05
51	Sandy Alomar (AS)	.10	.08	.04
52	Cal Ripken, Jr. (AS)	.15	.11	.06
53	Rickey Henderson (AS)	.15	.11	.06
54	Bob Welch (AS)	.05	.04	.02
55	Wade Boggs (AS)	.10	.08	.04
56	Mark McGwire (AS)	.10	.08	.04
57	Jack McDowell	.06	.05	.02
58	Jose Lind	.05	.04	.02
59	*Alex Fernandez*	.50	.40	.20
60	Pat Combs	.08	.06	.03
61	*Mike Walker* (FC)	.06	.05	.02
62	Juan Samuel	.05	.04	.02
63	Mike Blowers	.05	.04	.02
64	Mark Guthrie	.05	.04	.02
65	Mark Salas	.04	.03	.02
66	Tim Jones	.04	.03	.02
67	Tim Leary	.05	.04	.02
68	Andres Galarraga	.08	.06	.03
69	Bob Milacki	.05	.04	.02
70	Tim Belcher	.08	.06	.03
71	Todd Zeile	.06	.05	.02
72	Jerome Walton	.08	.06	.03
73	Kevin Seitzer	.06	.05	.02
74	Jerald Clark	.06	.05	.02
75	John Smoltz	.10	.08	.04
76	Mike Henneman	.05	.04	.02
77	Ken Griffey,Jr.	.75	.60	.30
78	Jim Abbott	.06	.05	.02
79	Gregg Jefferies	.15	.11	.06
80	Kevin Reimer (FC)	.08	.06	.03
81	Roger Clemens	.20	.15	.08
82	Mike Fitzgerald	.04	.03	.02
83	Bruce Hurst	.06	.05	.02
84	Eric Davis	.15	.11	.06
85	Paul Molitor	.15	.11	.06
86	Will Clark	.25	.20	.10
87	Mike Bielecki	.04	.03	.02
88	Bret Saberhagen	.10	.08	.04
89	Nolan Ryan	.35	.25	.14
90	Bobby Thigpen	.08	.06	.03
91	Dickie Thon	.04	.03	.02
92	Duane Ward	.04	.03	.02
93	Luis Polonia	.04	.03	.02
94	Terry Kennedy	.04	.03	.02
95	Kent Hrbek	.08	.06	.03
96	Danny Jackson	.06	.05	.02
97	Sid Fernandez	.08	.06	.03
98	Jimmy Key	.06	.05	.02
99	Franklin Stubbs	.05	.04	.02
100	Checklist	.04	.03	.02
101	R.J. Reynolds	.04	.03	.02
102	Dave Stewart	.08	.06	.03
103	Dan Pasqua	.05	.04	.02
104	Dan Plesac	.06	.05	.02
105	Mark McGwire	.15	.11	.06
106	John Farrell	.04	.03	.02
107	Don Mattingly	.20	.15	.08
108	Carlton Fisk	.10	.08	.04
109	Ken Oberkfell	.04	.03	.02
110	Darrel Akerfelds	.04	.03	.02
111	Gregg Olson	.08	.06	.03
112	Mike Scioscia	.06	.05	.02
113	Bryn Smith	.04	.03	.02
114	Bob Geren	.05	.04	.02
115	Tom Candiotti	.04	.03	.02
116	Kevin Tapani	.08	.06	.03
117	Jeff Treadway	.05	.04	.02
118	Alan Trammell	.08	.06	.03
119	Pete O'Brien	.04	.03	.02
120	Joel Skinner	.04	.03	.02
121	Mike LaValliere	.05	.04	.02
122	Dwight Evans	.08	.06	.03
123	Jody Reed	.08	.06	.03
124	Lee Guetterman	.04	.03	.02
125	Tim Burke	.05	.04	.02
126	Dave Johnson	.04	.03	.02
127	Fernando Valenzuela	.08	.06	.03
128	Jose DeLeon	.06	.05	.02
129	Andre Dawson	.10	.08	.04
130	Gerald Perry	.05	.04	.02
131	Greg Harris	.04	.03	.02
132	Tom Glavine	.15	.11	.06
133	Lance McCullers	.04	.03	.02
134	Randy Johnson	.08	.06	.03
135	Lance Parrish	.08	.06	.03
136	Mackey Sasser	.08	.06	.03
137	Geno Petralli	.04	.03	.02
138	Dennis Lamp	.04	.03	.02
139	Dennis Martinez	.06	.05	.02

140	Mike Pagliarulo	.05	.04	.02
141	Hal Morris	.10	.08	.04
142	Dave Parker	.10	.08	.04
143	Brett Butler	.06	.05	.02
144	Paul Assenmacher	.04	.03	.02
145	Mark Gubicza	.06	.05	.02
146	Charlie Hough	.05	.04	.02
147	Sammy Sosa	.15	.11	.06
148	Randy Ready	.04	.03	.02
149	Kelly Gruber	.08	.06	.03
150	Devon White	.06	.05	.02
151	Gary Carter	.08	.06	.03
152	Gene Larkin	.05	.04	.02
153	Chris Sabo	.08	.06	.03
154	David Cone	.08	.06	.03
155	Todd Stottlemyre	.06	.05	.02
156	Glenn Wilson	.05	.04	.02
157	Bob Walk	.05	.04	.02
158	Mike Gallego	.04	.03	.02
159	Greg Hibbard	.06	.05	.02
160	Chris Bosio	.05	.04	.02
161	Mike Moore	.06	.05	.02
162	Jerry Browne	.06	.05	.02
163	Steve Sax	.08	.06	.03
164	Melido Perez	.06	.05	.02
165	Danny Darwin	.05	.04	.02
166	Roger McDowell	.06	.05	.02
167	Bill Ripken	.04	.03	.02
168	Mike Sharperson	.05	.04	.02
169	Lee Smith	.08	.06	.03
170	Matt Nokes	.06	.05	.02
171	Jesse Orosco	.05	.04	.02
172	Rick Aguilera	.06	.05	.02
173	Jim Presley	.06	.05	.02
174	Lou Whitaker	.08	.06	.03
175	Harold Reynolds	.08	.06	.03
176	Brook Jacoby	.06	.05	.02
177	Wally Backman	.05	.04	.02
178	Wade Boggs	.10	.08	.04
179	Chuck Cary	.04	.03	.02
180	Tom Foley	.04	.03	.02
181	Pete Harnisch	.05	.04	.02
182	Mike Morgan	.05	.04	.02
183	Bob Tewksbury	.05	.04	.02
184	Joe Girardi	.06	.05	.02
185	Storm Davis	.05	.04	.02
186	Ed Whitson	.06	.05	.02
187	Steve Avery	.25	.20	.10
188	Lloyd Moseby	.06	.05	.02
189	Scott Bankhead	.06	.05	.02
190	Mark Langston	.08	.06	.03
191	Kevin McReynolds	.06	.05	.02
192	Julio Franco	.08	.06	.03
193	John Dopson	.05	.04	.02
194	Oil Can Boyd	.05	.04	.02
195	Bip Roberts	.06	.05	.02
196	Billy Hatcher	.06	.05	.02
197	Edgar Diaz (FC)	.08	.06	.03
198	Greg Litton	.05	.04	.02
199	Mark Grace	.08	.06	.03
200	Checklist	.04	.03	.02
201	George Brett	.15	.11	.06
202	Jeff Russell	.06	.05	.02
203	Ivan Calderon	.08	.06	.03
204	Ken Howell	.04	.03	.02
205	Tom Henke	.08	.06	.03
206	Bryan Harvey	.06	.05	.02
207	Steve Bedrosian	.08	.06	.03
208	Al Newman	.04	.03	.02
209	Randy Myers	.08	.06	.03
210	Daryl Boston	.04	.03	.02
211	Manny Lee	.06	.05	.02
212	Dave Smith	.06	.05	.02
213	Don Slaught	.04	.03	.02
214	Walt Weiss	.06	.05	.02
215	Donn Pall	.04	.03	.02
216	Jamie Navarro	.06	.05	.02
217	Willie Randolph	.06	.05	.02
218	Rudy Seanez (FC)	.08	.06	.03
219	*Jim Leyritz* (FC)	.08	.06	.03
220	Ron Karkovice	.05	.04	.02
221	Ken Caminiti	.05	.04	.02
222	Von Hayes	.08	.06	.03
223	Cal Ripken, Jr.	.25	.20	.10
224	Lenny Harris	.06	.05	.02
225	Milt Thompson	.05	.04	.02
226	Alvaro Espinoza	.05	.04	.02
227	Chris James	.06	.05	.02
228	Dan Gladden	.06	.05	.02
229	Jeff Blauser	.05	.04	.02
230	Mike Heath	.04	.03	.02
231	Omar Vizquel	.05	.04	.02
232	Doug Jones	.08	.06	.03
233	Jeff King	.06	.05	.02
234	Luis Rivera	.04	.03	.02
235	Ellis Burks	.08	.06	.03
236	Greg Cadaret	.04	.03	.02
237	Dave Martinez	.05	.04	.02
238	Mark Williamson	.04	.03	.02
239	Stan Javier	.05	.04	.02
240	Ozzie Smith	.10	.08	.04
241	*Shawn Boskie*	.06	.05	.02
242	Tom Gordon	.10	.08	.04
243	Tony Gwynn	.10	.08	.04
244	Tommy Gregg	.04	.03	.02
245	Jeff Robinson	.05	.04	.02
246	Keith Comstock	.04	.03	.02
247	Jack Howell	.05	.04	.02
248	Keith Miller	.05	.04	.02
249	Bobby Witt	.08	.06	.03
250	Rob Murphy	.04	.03	.02
251	Spike Owen	.06	.05	.02
252	Garry Templeton	.06	.05	.02
253	Glenn Braggs	.06	.05	.02
254	Ron Robinson	.06	.05	.02
255	Kevin Mitchell	.08	.06	.03
256	Les Lancaster	.04	.03	.02
257	*Mel Stottlemyre* (FC)	.10	.08	.04
258	Kenny Rogers	.06	.05	.02
259	Lance Johnson	.06	.05	.02
260	John Kruk	.06	.05	.02
261	Fred McGriff	.20	.15	.08
262	Dick Schofield	.04	.03	.02
263	Trevor Wilson	.05	.04	.02
264	David West	.05	.04	.02
265	Scott Scudder	.06	.05	.02
266	Dwight Gooden	.08	.06	.03
267	*Willie Blair* (FC)	.08	.06	.03
268	Mark Portugal	.04	.03	.02
269	Doug Drabek	.10	.08	.04
270	Dennis Eckersley	.10	.08	.04
271	Eric King	.05	.04	.02
272	Robin Yount	.15	.11	.06
273	Carney Lansford	.08	.06	.03
274	*Carlos Baerga*	.30	.25	.12
275	Dave Righetti	.08	.06	.03
276	Scott Fletcher	.04	.03	.02
277	Eric Yelding	.08	.06	.03
278	Charlie Hayes	.08	.06	.03
279	Jeff Ballard	.05	.04	.02
280	Orel Hershiser	.10	.08	.04
281	Jose Oquendo	.04	.03	.02
282	Mike Witt	.05	.04	.02
283	Mitch Webster	.04	.03	.02
284	Greg Gagne	.05	.04	.02
285	*Greg Olson*	.05	.04	.02
286	Tony Phillips	.05	.04	.02
287	Scott Bradley	.04	.03	.02
288	Cory Snyder	.08	.06	.03
289	Jay Bell	.06	.05	.02
290	Kevin Romine	.04	.03	.02
291	Jeff Robinson	.05	.04	.02
292	Steve Frey (FC)	.06	.05	.02
293	Craig Worthington	.05	.04	.02
294	Tim Crews	.04	.03	.02
295	Joe Magrane	.08	.06	.03
296	*Hector Villanueva* (FC)	.08	.06	.03
297	*Terry Shumpert*	.06	.05	.02
298	Joe Carter	.15	.11	.06
299	Kent Mercker	.10	.08	.04
300	Checklist	.04	.03	.02
301	Chet Lemon	.05	.04	.02
302	Mike Schooler	.08	.06	.03
303	Dante Bichette	.06	.05	.02
304	Kevin Elster	.05	.04	.02
305	Jeff Huson	.06	.05	.02
306	Greg Harris	.05	.04	.02
307	Marquis Grissom	.12	.09	.05
308	Calvin Schiraldi	.04	.03	.02
309	Mariano Duncan	.06	.05	.02
310	Bill Spiers	.06	.05	.02
311	Scott Garrelts	.06	.05	.02
312	Mitch Williams	.08	.06	.03
313	Mike Macfarlane	.05	.04	.02
314	Kevin Brown	.06	.05	.02
315	Robin Ventura	.15	.11	.06
316	Darren Daulton	.10	.08	.04
317	PUuat Borders	.06	.05	.02
318	Mark Eichhorn	.04	.03	.02
319	Jeff Brantley	.08	.06	.03
320	Shane Mack	.05	.04	.02
321	Rob Dibble	.06	.05	.02
322	John Franco	.06	.05	.02
323	Junior Felix	.08	.06	.03
324	Casey Candaele	.04	.03	.02
325	Bobby Bonilla	.10	.08	.04
326	Dave Henderson	.06	.05	.02
327	Wayne Edwards	.06	.05	.02
328	Mark Knudson	.04	.03	.02
329	Terry Steinbach	.06	.05	.02
330	*Colby Ward* (FC)	.06	.05	.02
331	*Oscar Azocar* (FC)	.08	.06	.03
332	*Scott Radinsky*	.15	.11	.06
333	Eric Anthony	.10	.08	.04
334	Steve Lake	.04	.03	.02
335	Bob Melvin	.04	.03	.02
336	Kal Daniels	.08	.06	.03
337	Tom Pagnozzi	.05	.04	.02
338	*Alan Mills*	.06	.05	.02
339	Steve Olin	.06	.05	.02
340	Juan Berenguer	.04	.03	.02
341	Francisco Cabrera	.06	.05	.02
342	Dave Bergman	.04	.03	.02
343	Henry Cotto	.04	.03	.02
344	Sergio Valdez	.08	.06	.03
345	Bob Patterson	.04	.03	.02
346	John Marzano	.05	.04	.02
347	*Dana Kiecker*	.08	.06	.03
348	Dion James	.04	.03	.02
349	Hubie Brooks	.08	.06	.03
350	Bill Landrum	.05	.04	.02
351	*Bill Sampen*	.08	.06	.03
352	Greg Briley	.05	.04	.02
353	Paul Gibson	.04	.03	.02
354	Dave Eiland	.04	.03	.02
355	Steve Finley	.06	.05	.02
356	Bob Boone	.06	.05	.02
357	Steve Buechele	.06	.05	.02
358	*Chris Hoiles* (FC)	.20	.15	.08
359	Larry Walker	.15	.11	.06
360	Frank DiPino	.04	.03	.02
361	Mark Grant	.04	.03	.02
362	Dave Magadan	.08	.06	.03
363	Robby Thompson	.06	.05	.02
364	Lonnie Smith	.05	.04	.02
365	Steve Farr	.05	.04	.02
366	Dave Valle	.05	.04	.02
367	*Tim Naehring* (FC)	.08	.06	.03
368	Jim Acker	.04	.03	.02
369	Jeff Reardon	.08	.06	.03
370	Tim Teufel	.04	.03	.02
371	Juan Gonzalez	.75	.60	.30
372	Luis Salazar	.04	.03	.02
373	Rick Honeycutt	.04	.03	.02
374	Greg Maddux	.10	.08	.04
375	Jose Uribe	.05	.04	.02
376	Donnie Hill	.04	.03	.02
377	Don Carman	.04	.03	.02
378	*Craig Grebeck*	.06	.05	.02
379	Willie Fraser	.05	.04	.02
380	Glenallen Hill	.08	.06	.03
381	Joe Oliver	.06	.05	.02
382	Randy Bush	.04	.03	.02
383	Alex Cole (FC)	.08	.06	.03
384	Norm Charlton	.08	.06	.03
385	Gene Nelson	.04	.03	.02
386	Checklist	.04	.03	.02
387	Rickey Henderson (MVP)	.15	.11	.06
388	Lance Parrish (MVP)	.05	.04	.02
389	Fred McGriff (MVP)	.15	.11	.06
390	Dave Parker (MVP)	.10	.08	.04
391	Candy Maldonado	.05	.04	.02
392	Ken Griffey,Jr. (MVP)	.40	.30	.15
393	Gregg Olson (MVP)	.10	.08	.04
394	Rafael Palmeiro (MVP)	.10	.08	.04
395	Roger Clemens (MVP)	.15	.11	.06
396	George Brett (MVP)	.10	.08	.04
397	Cecil Fielder (MVP)	.15	.11	.06
398	Brian Harper (MVP)	.05	.04	.02
399	Bobby Thigpen (MVP)	.06	.05	.02
400	Roberto Kelly (MVP)	.08	.06	.03
401	Danny Darwin (MVP)	.05	.04	.02
402	Dave Justice (MVP)	.25	.20	.10
403	Lee Smith (MVP)	.05	.04	.02
404	Ryne Sandberg (MVP)	.15	.11	.06
405	Eddie Murray (MVP)	.10	.08	.04
406	Tim Wallach (MVP)	.06	.05	.02
407	Kevin Mitchell (MVP)	.10	.08	.04
408	Darryl Strawberry (MVP)	.07	.05	.03
409	Joe Carter (MVP)	.08	.06	.03
410	Len Dykstra (MVP)	.08	.06	.03
411	Doug Drabek (MVP)	.06	.05	.02
412	Chris Sabo (MVP)	.08	.06	.03
413	*Paul Marak* (FC) (RR)	.06	.05	.02
414	Tim MCIntosh (FC) (RR)	.10	.08	.04
415	*Brian Barnes* (RR)	.10	.08	.04
416	*Eric Gunderson* (FC) (RR)	.08	.06	.03
417	*Mike Gardiner* (RR)	.10	.08	.04
418	Steve Carter (RR)	.08	.06	.03
419	*Gerald Alexander* (RR)	.15	.11	.06
420	*Rich Garces* (RR)	.10	.08	.04
421	*Chuck Knoblauch* (RR)	.20	.15	.08
422	*Scott Aldred* (RR)	.15	.11	.06
423	*Wes Chamberlain* (RR)	.20	.15	.08
424	*Lance Dickson* (RR)	.10	.08	.04
425	*Greg Colbrunn* (RR)	.15	.11	.06
426	*Rich Delucia* (FC) (RR)	.08	.06	.03
427	*Jeff Conine* (RR)	.35	.25	.14
428	*Steve Decker* (RR)	.10	.08	.04
429	*Turner Ward* (RR)	.12	.09	.05
430	*Mo Vaughn* (RR)	.50	.40	.20
431	*Steve Chitren* (RR)	.10	.08	.04
432	Mike Benjamin (FC) (RR)	.10	.08	.04
433	Ryne Sandberg (AS)	.10	.08	.04
434	Len Dykstra (AS)	.06	.05	.02
435	Andre Dawson (AS)	.10	.08	.04
436	Mike Scioscia (AS)	.06	.05	.02
437	Ozzie Smith (AS)	.10	.08	.04
438	Kevin Mitchell (AS)	.10	.08	.04
439	Jack Armstrong (AS)	.06	.05	.02
440	Chris Sabo (AS)	.08	.06	.03
441	Will Clark (AS)	.10	.08	.04
442	Mel Hall	.05	.04	.02
443	Mark Gardner	.06	.05	.02
444	Mike Devereaux	.06	.05	.02
445	Kirk Gibson	.06	.05	.02
446	Terry Pendleton	.08	.06	.03
447	Mike Harkey	.08	.06	.03
448	Jim Eisenreich	.04	.03	.02
449	Benito Santiago	.08	.06	.03
450	Oddibe McDowell	.04	.03	.02
451	Cecil Fielder	.20	.15	.08
452	Ken Griffey,Sr.	.08	.06	.03
453	Bert Blyleven	.06	.05	.02
454	Howard Johnson	.06	.05	.02
455	Monty Farris (FC)	.08	.06	.03
456	Tony Pena	.05	.04	.02
457	Tim Raines	.08	.06	.03
458	Dennis Rasmussen	.04	.03	.02
459	Luis Quinones	.04	.03	.02
460	B.J. Surhoff	.06	.05	.02
461	Ernest Riles	.04	.03	.02
462	Rick Sutcliffe	.06	.05	.02
463	Danny Tartabull	.10	.08	.04
464	Pete Incaviglia	.06	.05	.02
465	Carlos Martinez	.05	.04	.02
466	Ricky Jordan	.06	.05	.02
467	John Cerutti	.04	.03	.02
468	Dave Winfield	.12	.09	.05
469	Francisco Oliveras	.04	.03	.02
470	Roy Smith	.04	.03	.02
471	Barry Larkin	.12	.09	.05
472	Ron Darling	.06	.05	.02
473	David Wells	.06	.05	.02
474	Glenn Davis	.10	.08	.04
475	Neal Heaton	.04	.03	.02
476	Ron Hassey	.04	.03	.02
477	Frank Thomas (FC)	1.25	.90	.50
478	Greg Vaughn	.15	.11	.06
479	Todd Burns	.04	.03	.02
480	Candy Maldonado	.05	.04	.02
481	Dave LaPoint	.04	.03	.02
482	Alvin Davis	.08	.06	.03
483	Mike Scott	.06	.05	.02
484	Dale Murphy	.10	.08	.04
485	Ben McDonald	.10	.08	.04
486	Jay Howell	.06	.05	.02
487	Vince Coleman	.08	.06	.03
488	Alfredo Griffin	.05	.04	.02
489	Sandy Alomar	.08	.06	.03
490	Kirby Puckett	.15	.11	.06
491	Andres Thomas	.04	.03	.02
492	Jack Morris	.06	.05	.02
493	Matt Young	.04	.03	.02

494 Greg Myers .04 .03 .02
495 Barry Bonds .25 .20 .10
496 Scott Cooper (FC) .20 .15 .08
497 Dan Schatzeder .04 .03 .02
498 Jesse Barfield .06 .05 .02
499 Jerry Goff (FC) .05 .04 .02
500 Checklist .04 .03 .02
501 *Anthony Telford* (FC) .15 .11 .06
502 Eddie Murray .12 .09 .05
503 *Omar Olivares* (FC) .12 .09 .05
504 Ryne Sandberg .20 .15 .08
505 Jeff Montgomery .06 .05 .02
506 Mark Parent .04 .03 .02
507 Ron Gant .15 .11 .06
508 Frank Tanana .05 .04 .02
509 Jay Buhner .06 .05 .02
510 Max Venable .04 .03 .02
511 Wally Whitehurst .06 .05 .02
512 Gary Pettis .04 .03 .02
513 Tom Brunansky .06 .05 .02
514 Tim Wallach .08 .06 .03
515 Craig Lefferts .05 .04 .02
516 *Tim Layana* .10 .08 .04
517 Darryl Hamilton .08 .06 .03
518 Rick Reuschel .05 .04 .02
519 Steve Wilson .06 .05 .02
520 Kurt Stillwell .05 .04 .02
521 Rafael Palmeiro .12 .09 .05
522 Ken Patterson .04 .03 .02
523 Len Dykstra .12 .09 .05
524 Tony Fernandez .06 .05 .02
525 Kent Anderson .04 .03 .02
526 *Mark Leonard* (FC) .10 .08 .04
527 Allan Anderson .04 .03 .02
528 Tom Browning .06 .05 .02
529 Frank Viola .12 .09 .05
530 John Olerud .35 .25 .14
531 Juan Agosto .04 .03 .02
532 Zane Smith .06 .05 .02
533 Scott Sanderson .06 .05 .02
534 Barry Jones .05 .04 .02
535 Mike Felder .04 .03 .02
536 Jose Canseco .15 .11 .06
537 Felix Fermin .04 .03 .02
538 Roberto Kelly .08 .06 .03
539 Brian Holman .05 .04 .02
540 Mark Davidson .04 .03 .02
541 Terry Mulholland .06 .05 .02
542 Randy Milligan .06 .05 .02
543 Jose Gonzalez .04 .03 .02
544 *Craig Wilson* (FC) .06 .05 .02
545 Mike Hartley .04 .03 .02
546 Greg Swindell .06 .05 .02
547 Gary Gaetti .08 .06 .03
548 Dave Justice .50 .40 .20
549 Steve Searcy .04 .03 .02
550 Erik Hanson .06 .05 .02
551 Dave Stieb .08 .06 .03
552 Andy Van Slyke .08 .06 .03
553 Mike Greenwell .12 .09 .05
554 Kevin Maas .10 .08 .04
555 Delino Deshields .20 .15 .08
556 Curt Schilling .05 .04 .02
557 Ramon Martinez .08 .06 .03
558 Pedro Guerrero .08 .06 .03
559 Dwight Smith .05 .04 .02
560 Mark Davis .04 .03 .02
561 Shawn Abner .05 .04 .02
562 Charlie Leibrandt .05 .04 .02
563 John Shelby .04 .03 .02
564 Bill Swift .05 .04 .02
565 Mike Fetters .06 .05 .02
566 Alejandro Pena .05 .04 .02
567 Ruben Sierra .15 .11 .06
568 Calos Quintana .08 .06 .03
569 Kevin Gross .05 .04 .02
570 Derek Lilliquist .04 .03 .02
571 Jack Armstrong .06 .05 .02
572 Greg Brock .04 .03 .02
573 Mike Kingery .04 .03 .02
574 Greg Smith (FC) .06 .05 .02
575 *Brian McRae* (FC) .25 .20 .10
576 Jack Daugherty .05 .04 .02
577 Ozzie Guillen .06 .05 .02
578 Joe Boever .04 .03 .02
579 Luis Sojo .06 .05 .02
580 Chili Davis .06 .05 .02
581 Don Robinson .04 .03 .02
582 Brian Harper .06 .05 .02
583 Paul O'Neill .06 .05 .02
584 Bob Ojeda .05 .04 .02
585 Mookie Wilson .05 .04 .02
586 Rafael Ramirez .04 .03 .02
587 Gary Redus .04 .03 .02
588 Jamie Quirk .04 .03 .02
589 Shawn Hilligas .04 .03 .02
590 *Tom Edens* (FC) .08 .06 .03
591 Joe Klink (FC) .05 .04 .02
592 Charles Nagy (FC) .12 .09 .05
593 Eric Plunk .04 .03 .02
594 Tracy Jones .04 .03 .02
595 Craig Biggio .08 .06 .03
596 Jose DeJesus .06 .05 .02
597 Mickey Tettleton .08 .06 .03
598 Chris Gwynn .05 .04 .02
599 Rex Hudler .06 .05 .02
600 Checklist .04 .03 .02
601 Jim Gott .04 .03 .02
602 Jeff Manto (FC) .06 .05 .02
603 Nelson Liriano .04 .03 .02
604 Mark Lemke .06 .05 .02
605 Clay Parker .04 .03 .02
606 Edgar Martinez .08 .06 .03
607 *Mark Whiten* .25 .20 .10
608 Ted Power .04 .03 .02
609 Tom Bolton .05 .04 .02
610 Tom Herr .05 .04 .02
611 Andy Hawkins .04 .03 .02
612 Scott Ruskin .04 .03 .02
613 Ron Kittle .05 .04 .02
614 John Wetteland .06 .05 .02
615 *Mike Perez* (FC) .12 .09 .05
616 Dave Clark .04 .03 .02
617 Brent Mayne (FC) .12 .09 .05
618 Jack Clark .08 .06 .03
619 Marvin Freeman .04 .03 .02
620 Edwin Nunez .04 .03 .02
621 Russ Swan (FC) .08 .06 .03
622 Johnny Ray .04 .03 .02
623 Charlie O'Brien .04 .03 .02
624 *Joe Bitker* (FC) .06 .05 .02
625 Mike Marshall .04 .03 .02
626 Otis Nixon .05 .04 .02
627 Andy Benes .15 .11 .06
628 Ron Oester .04 .03 .02
629 Ted Higuera .06 .05 .02
630 Kevin Bass .05 .04 .02
631 Damon Berryhill .05 .04 .02
632 Bo Jackson .20 .15 .08
633 Brad Arnsberg .05 .04 .02
634 Jerry Willard .04 .03 .02
635 Tommy Greene .06 .05 .02
636 *Bob MacDonald* (FC) .05 .04 .02
637 Kirk McCaskill .05 .04 .02
638 John Burkett .05 .04 .02
639 *Paul Abbott* (FC) .06 .05 .02
640 Todd Benzinger .05 .04 .02
641 Todd Hundley (FC) .10 .08 .04
642 George Bell .10 .08 .04
643 *Javier Ortiz* (FC) .06 .05 .02
644 Sid Bream .05 .04 .02
645 Bob Welch .06 .05 .02
646 Phil Bradley .05 .04 .02
647 Bill Krueger .04 .03 .02
648 Rickey Henderson .12 .09 .05
649 Kevin Wickander .05 .04 .02
650 Steve Balboni .04 .03 .02
651 Gene Harris .05 .04 .02
652 Jim Deshaies .04 .03 .02
653 Jason Grimsley (FC) .06 .05 .02
654 Joe Orsulak .05 .04 .02
655 *Jimmy Poole* (FC) .06 .05 .02
656 Felix Jose .10 .08 .04
657 Dennis Cook .05 .04 .02
658 Tom Brookens .04 .03 .02
659 Junior Ortiz .04 .03 .02
660 Jeff Parrett .04 .03 .02
661 Jerry Don Gleaton .04 .03 .02
662 Brent Knackert .04 .03 .02
663 Rance Mulliniks .04 .03 .02
664 John Smiley .06 .05 .02
665 Larry Andersen .04 .03 .02
666 Willie McGee .08 .06 .03
667 *Chris Nabholz* (FC) .10 .08 .04
668 Brady Anderson .04 .03 .02
669 *Darren Holmes* (FC) .12 .09 .05
670 Ken Hill .06 .05 .02
671 Gary Varsho .04 .03 .02
672 Bill Pecota .05 .04 .02
673 Fred Lynn .05 .04 .02
674 Kevin D. Brown (FC) .10 .08 .04
675 Dan Petry .04 .03 .02
676 Mike Jackson .05 .04 .02
677 Wally Joyner .06 .05 .02
678 Danny Jackson .05 .04 .02
679 *Bill Haselman* (FC) .06 .05 .02
680 Mike Boddicker .06 .05 .02
681 *Mel Rojas* (FC) .12 .09 .05
682 Roberto Alomar .20 .15 .08
683 Dave Justice (R.O.Y.) .25 .20 .10
684 Chuck Crim .04 .03 .02
685 Matt Williams .12 .09 .05
686 Shawon Dunston .06 .05 .02
687 *Jeff Schulz* (FC) .08 .06 .03
688 *John Barfield* (FC) .08 .06 .03
689 Gerald Young .04 .03 .02
690 *Luis Gonzalez* (FC) .40 .30 .15
691 Frank Wills .05 .04 .02
692 Chuck Finley .08 .06 .03
693 Sandy Alomar (R.O.Y.) .06 .05 .02
694 Tim Drummond .05 .04 .02
695 Herm Winningham .04 .03 .02
696 Darryl Strawberry .10 .08 .04
697 Al Leiter .04 .03 .02
698 *Karl Rhodes* (FC) .08 .06 .03
699 Stan Belinda (FC) .08 .06 .03
700 Checklist .04 .03 .02
701 Lance Blankenship .04 .03 .02
702 Willie Stargell (Puzzle Card) .10 .08 .04
703 Jim Gantner .05 .04 .02
704 *Reggie Harris* (FC) .06 .05 .02
705 Rob Ducey .04 .03 .02
706 Tim Hulett .04 .03 .02
707 Atlee Hammaker .04 .03 .02
708 Xavier Hernandez .04 .03 .02
709 Chuck McElroy (FC) .08 .06 .03
710 John Mitchell .04 .03 .02
711 Carlos Hernandez .05 .04 .02
712 Geronimo Pena (FC) .10 .08 .04
713 *Jim Neidlinger* (FC) .06 .05 .02
714 John Orton .04 .03 .02
715 Terry Leach .04 .03 .02
716 Mike Stanton .06 .05 .02
717 Walt Terrell .04 .03 .02
718 Luis Aquino .05 .04 .02
719 Bud Black .05 .04 .02
720 Bob Kipper .04 .03 .02
721 *Jeff Gray* (FC) .08 .06 .03
722 Jose Rijo .08 .06 .03
723 Curt Young .04 .03 .02
724 Jose Vizcaino (FC) .08 .06 .03
725 *Randy Tomlin* (FC) .08 .06 .03
726 Junior Noboa .05 .04 .02
727 Bob Welch (Award Winner) .08 .06 .03
728 Gary Ward .04 .03 .02
729 Rob Deer .05 .04 .02
730 *David Segui* (FC) .08 .06 .03
731 Mark Carreon .04 .03 .02
732 Vicente Palacios .04 .03 .02
733 Sam Horn .05 .04 .02
734 *Howard Farmer* (FC) .08 .06 .03
735 Ken Dayley .04 .03 .02
736 Kelly Mann .08 .06 .03
737 *Joe Grahe* (FC) .12 .09 .05
738 Kelly Downs .04 .03 .02
739 *Jimmy Kremers* (FC) .06 .05 .02
740 Kevin Appier .12 .09 .05
741 Jeff Reed .04 .03 .02
742 Jose Rijo (World Series) .08 .06 .03
743 *Dave Rohde* (FC) .06 .05 .02
744 Dr. Dirt/ Mr. Clean (Len Dykstra, Dale Murphy)
.08 .06 .03
745 Paul Sorrento .06 .05 .02
746 Thomas Howard (FC) .06 .05 .02
747 *Matt Stark* (FC) .06 .05 .02
748 Harold Baines .08 .06 .03
749 Doug Dascenzo .05 .04 .02
750 Doug Drabek (Award Winner) .08 .06 .03
751 Gary Sheffield .15 .11 .06
752 *Terry Lee* (FC) .06 .05 .02
753 *Jim Vatcher* (FC) .08 .06 .03
754 Lee Stevens .12 .09 .05
755 Randy Veres (FC) .08 .06 .03
756 Bill Doran .06 .05 .02
757 Gary Wayne .04 .03 .02
758 *Pedro Munoz* (FC) .10 .08 .04
759 Chris Hammond (FC) .12 .09 .05
760 Checklist .04 .03 .02
761 Rickey Henderson (MVP) .12 .09 .05
762 Barry Bonds (MVP) .20 .15 .08
763 Billy Hatcher (World Series) .05 .04 .02
764 Julio Machado .05 .04 .02
765 Jose Mesa .05 .04 .02
766 Willie Randolph (World Series) .05 .04 .02
767 *Scott Erickson* (FC) .12 .09 .05
768 *Travis Fryman* (FC) .60 .45 .25
769 *Rich Rodriguez* (FC) .12 .09 .05
770 Checklist .04 .03 .02

1991 Donruss Highlights

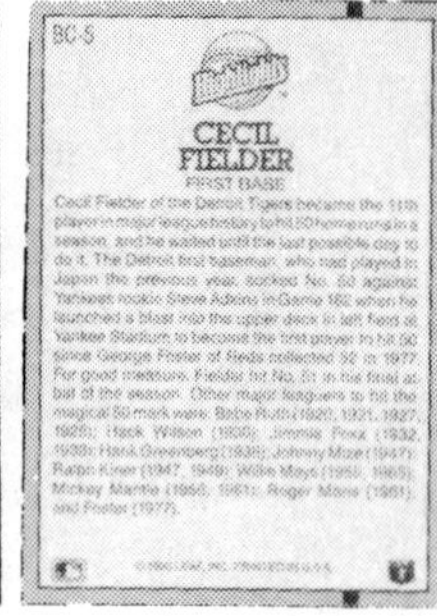

This 22-card subset features highlights from the 1990 season. The cards feature a "BC" designation along with the number and are styled after the 1991 regular issue Donruss Cards. Cards 1-10 feature blue borders due to their release with Series I cards. Cards 11-22 feature green borders and were released with Series II cards. A highlight logo appears on the front of the card. Each highlight is explained in depth on the card back.

	MT	NR MT	EX
Complete Set:	3.00	2.25	1.25
Common Player:	.10	.08	.04

1 Mark Langston/ Mike Witt (No-Hit Mariners)
.15 .11 .06
2 Randy Johnson (No-Hits Tigers) .15 .11 .06
3 Nolan Ryan (No-Hits A's) .40 .30 .15
4 Dave Stewart (No-Hits Blue Jays) .15 .11 .06
5 Cecil Fielder (50 Homer Club) .25 .20 .10
6 Carlton Fisk (Record Home Run) .20 .15 .08
7 Ryne Sandberg (Sets Fielding Records)
.20 .15 .08
8 Gary Carter (Breaks Catching Mark)
.15 .11 .06
9 Mark McGwire (Home Run Milestone)
.15 .11 .06
10 Bo Jackson (4 Consecutive HRs) .25 .20 .10
11 Fernando Valenzuela (No-Hits Cardinals)
.15 .11 .06
12 Andy Hawkins (No-Hits White Sox)
.10 .08 .04
13 Melido Perez (No-Hits Yankees) .10 .08 .04
14 Terry Mulholland (No-Hits Giants) .10 .08 .04
15 Nolan Ryan (300th Win) .40 .30 .15
16 Delino DeShields (4 Hits In Debut) .15 .11 .06
17 Cal Ripken (Errorless Games) .20 .15 .08
18 Eddie Murray (Switch Hit Homers) .15 .11 .06
19 George Brett (3 Decade Champ) .20 .15 .08
20 Bobby Thigpen (Shatters Save Mark)
.10 .08 .04
21 Dave Stieb (No-Hits Indians) .10 .08 .04
22 Willie McGee (NL Batting Champ) .10 .08 .04

A card number in parentheses () indicates the set is unnumbered.

1991 Donruss Grand Slammers

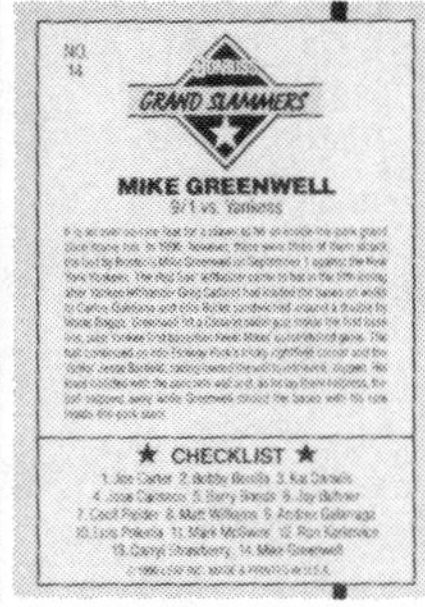

This 14-card set features players who hit grand slams in 1990. The cards are styled after the 1991 Donruss regular issue cards. The featured player is showcased with a star in the background. The set was included in factory sets and randomly in jumbo packs.

		MT	NR MT	EX
Complete Set (14):		2.50	2.00	1.00
Common Player:		.10	.08	.04
1	Joe Carter	.20	.15	.08
2	Bobby Bonilla	.20	.15	.08
3	Kal Daniels	.15	.11	.06
4	Jose Canseco	.30	.25	.12
5	Barry Bonds	.30	.25	.12
6	Jay Buhner	.15	.11	.06
7	Cecil Fielder	.30	.25	.12
8	Matt Williams	.20	.15	.08
9	Andres Galarraga	.10	.08	.04
10	Luis Polonia	.15	.11	.06
11	Mark McGwire	.20	.15	.08
12	Ron Karkovice	.10	.08	.04
13	Darryl Strawberry	.15	.11	.06
14	Mike Greenwell	.20	.15	.08

1991 Donruss Elite

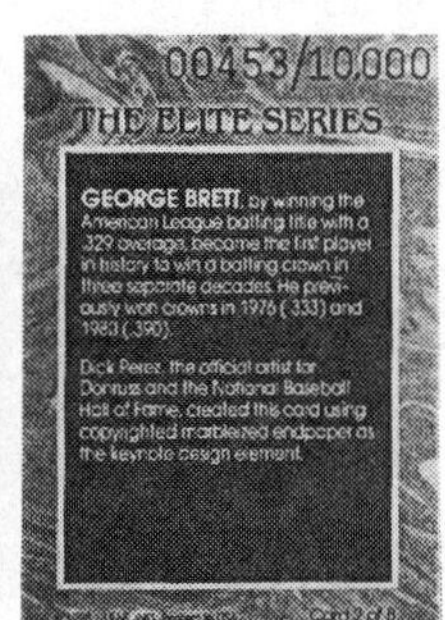

Donruss released a series of special inserts in 1991. Ten thousand of each Elite card was released, while 7,500 Legend cards and 5,000 Signature cards were issued. Cards were inserted in wax packs and feature marble borders. The Legend card features a Dick Perez drawing. Each card is designated with a serial number on the back.

		MT	NR MT	EX
Complete Set (10):		1400.	1000.	550.00
Common Player:		70.00	52.00	28.00
1	Barry Bonds	150.00	112.00	60.00
2	George Brett	125.00	94.00	50.00
3	Jose Canseco	90.00	67.00	36.00
4	Andre Dawson	70.00	52.00	28.00
5	Doug Drabek	70.00	52.00	28.00
6	Cecil Fielder	90.00	67.00	36.00
7	Rickey Henderson	80.00	60.00	32.00
8	Matt Williams	70.00	52.00	28.00
----	Nolan Ryan (Legend)	375.00	280.00	150.00
----	Ryne Sandberg (Signature)	400.00	300.00	160.00

Values for recent cards and sets are listed in Mint (MT), Near Mint (NM), reflecting the fact that many cards from recent years have been preserved in top condition. Recent cards and sets in less than Excellent condition have little collector interest.

Values quoted in this guide reflect the retail price of a card – the price a collector can expect to pay when buying a card from a dealer. The wholesale price – that which a collector can expect to receive from a dealer when selling cards – will be significantly lower, depending on desirability and condition.

1991 Donruss Rookies

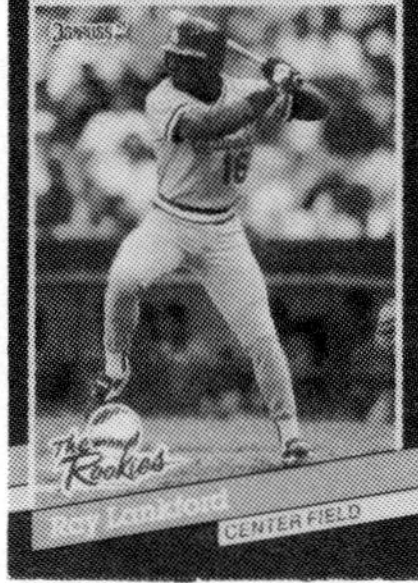

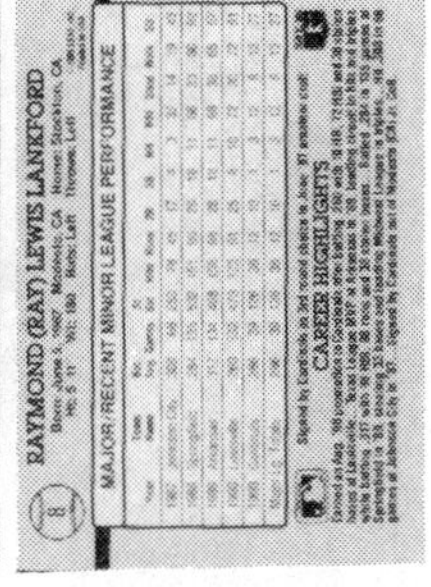

Red borders highlight the 1991 Donruss Rookies cards. This set marks the sixth year that Donruss has produced such an issue. Like in past years, "The Rookies" logo appears on the card fronts. The set is packaged in a special box and includes a Willie Stargell puzzle card.

		MT	NR MT	EX
Complete Set (56):		6.00	4.50	2.50
Common Player:		.10	.08	.04
1	Pat Kelly (FC)	.15	.11	.06
2	Rich DeLucia	.10	.08	.04
3	Wes Chamberlain	.20	.15	.08
4	Scott Leius (FC)	.10	.08	.04
5	Darryl Kile (FC)	.15	.11	.06
6	Milt Cuyler	.15	.11	.06
7	Todd Van Poppel (FC)	.30	.25	.12
8	Ray Lankford	.30	.25	.12
9	Brian Hunter (FC)	.20	.15	.08
10	Tony Perezchica	.10	.08	.04
11	Ced Landrum (FC)	.10	.08	.04
12	Dave Burba (FC)	.10	.08	.04
13	Ramon Garcia (FC)	.20	.15	.08
14	Ed Sprague (FC)	.15	.11	.06
15	Warren Newson (FC)	.15	.11	.06
16	Paul Faries (FC)	.10	.08	.04
17	Luis Gonzalez	.35	.25	.14
18	Charles Nagy	.15	.11	.06
19	Chris Hammond	.10	.08	.04
20	Frank Castillo (FC)	.25	.20	.10
21	Pedro Munoz	.20	.15	.08
22	Orlando Merced (FC)	.30	.25	.12
23	Jose Melendez (FC)	.10	.08	.04
24	Kirk Dressendorfer (FC)	.30	.25	.12
25	Heathcliff Slocumb (FC)	.10	.08	.04
26	Doug Simons (FC)	.10	.08	.04
27	Mike Timlin (FC)	.20	.15	.08
28	Jeff Fassero (FC)	.15	.11	.06
29	Mark Leiter (FC)	.10	.08	.04
30	Jeff Bagwell (FC)	1.00	.70	.40
31	Brian McRae	.35	.25	.14
32	Mark Whiten	.20	.15	.08
33	Ivan Rodriguez (FC)	1.00	.70	.40
34	Wade Taylor (FC)	.10	.08	.04
35	Darren Lewis (FC)	.35	.25	.14
36	Mo Vaughn	.50	.40	.20
37	Mike Remlinger (FC)	.10	.08	.04
38	Rick Wilkins (FC)	.20	.15	.08
39	Chuck Knoblauch	.40	.30	.15
40	Kevin Morton	.15	.11	.06
41	Carlos Rodriguez (FC)	.10	.08	.04
42	Mark Lewis	.20	.15	.08
43	Brent Mayne	.10	.08	.04
44	Chris Haney (FC)	.15	.11	.06
45	Denis Boucher (FC)	.15	.11	.06
46	Mike Gardiner	.10	.08	.04
47	Jeff Johnson (FC)	.15	.11	.06
48	Dean Palmer	.30	.25	.12
49	Chuck McElroy	.10	.08	.04
50	Chris Jones (FC)	.10	.08	.04
51	Scott Kamieniecki (FC)	.10	.08	.04
52	Al Osuna (FC)	.10	.08	.04
53	Rusty Meacham (FC)	.15	.11	.06
54	Chito Martinez (FC)	.25	.20	.10
55	Reggie Jefferson (FC)	.25	.20	.10
56	Checklist	.05	.04	.02

1992 Donruss Previews

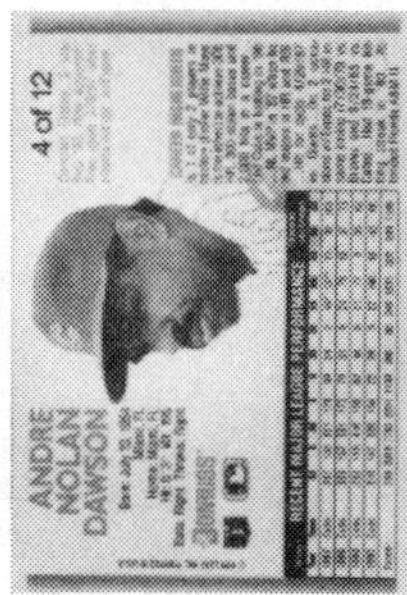

Four-card cello packs distributed to members of the Donruss dealers' network previewed the forthcoming 1992 baseball card issue. The preview cards have the same format, front and back photos as their counterparts in the regular set. Only the card number, the security underprinting, "Donruss Preview Card", and the stats, complete only through 1990, differ.

		MT	NR MT	EX
Complete Set (12):		400.00	300.00	160.00
Common Player:		20.00	15.00	8.00
1	Wade Boggs	40.00	30.00	16.00
2	Barry Bonds	40.00	30.00	16.00
3	Will Clark	40.00	30.00	16.00
4	Andre Dawson	20.00	15.00	8.00
5	Dennis Eckersley	20.00	15.00	8.00
6	Robin Ventura	30.00	22.00	12.00
7	Ken Griffey, Jr.	90.00	67.00	36.00
8	Kelly Gruber	20.00	15.00	8.00
9	Ryan Klesko (Rated Rookie)	50.00	37.00	20.00
10	Cal Ripken, Jr.	60.00	45.00	24.00
11	Nolan Ryan (Highlight)	75.00	56.00	30.00
12	Todd Van Poppel	20.00	15.00	8.00

1992 Donruss

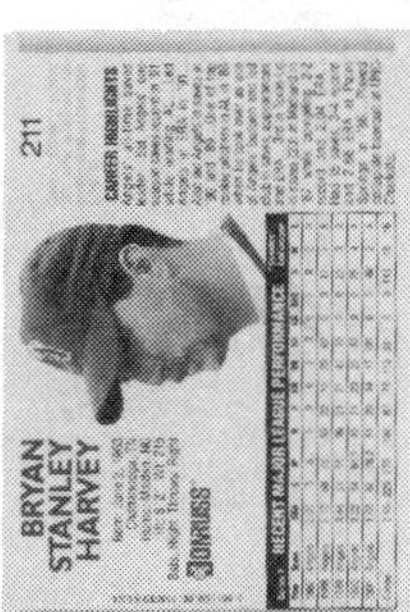

For the second consecutive year, Donruss chose to release its card set in two series. The 1992 cards feature improved stock, an anti-couterfeit feature and include both front and back photos. Once again Rated Rookies and All-Stars are included in the set. Special highlight cards also can be found in the 1992 Donruss set. Production was reduced in 1992 compared to 1988-1991.

		MT	NR MT	EX
Complete Set (784):		22.00	16.50	8.75
Common Player:		.05	.04	.02
1	*Mark Wohlers* (Rated Rookie)	.15	.11	.06
2	Wil Cordero (Rated Rookie)	.30	.25	.12
3	Kyle Abbott (Rated Rookie)	.08	.06	.03
4	*Dave Nilsson* (Rated Rookie)	.15	.11	.06
5	*Kenny Lofton* (Rated Rookie)	.40	.30	.15
6	*Luis Mercedes* (Rated Rookie)	.15	.11	.06
7	*Roger Salkeld* (Rated Rookie)	.15	.11	.06
8	Eddie Zosky (FC) (Rated Rookie)	.25	.20	.10
9	*Todd Van Poppel* (Rated Rookie)	.20	.15	.08
10	*Frank Seminara* (Rated Rookie)	.10	.08	.04
11	*Andy Ashby* (FC) (Rated Rookie)	.20	.15	.08
12	Reggie Jefferson (FC) (Rated Rookie)	.10	.08	.04
13	*Ryan Klesko* (Rated Rookie)	.50	.40	.20
14	*Carlos Garcia* (Rated Rookie)	.15	.11	.06
15	*John Ramos* (FC) (Rated Rookie)	.10	.08	.04
16	*Eric Karros* (Rated Rookie)	.25	.20	.10
17	*Pat Lennon* (FC) (Rated Rookie)	.10	.08	.04
18	*Eddie Taubensee* (Rated Rookie)	.10	.08	.04
19	*Roberto Hernandez* (Rated Rookie)	.10	.08	.04
20	D.J. Dozier (FC) (Rated Rookie)	.20	.15	.08
21	Dave Henderson (All-Star)	.10	.08	.04
22	Cal Ripken, Jr. (All-Star)	.20	.15	.08
23	Wade Boggs (All-Star)	.10	.08	.04
24	Ken Griffey, Jr. (All-Star)	.60	.45	.25
25	Jack Morris (All-Star)	.07	.05	.03
26	Danny Tartabull (All-Star)	.10	.08	.04
27	Cecil Fielder (All-Star)	.10	.07	.04
28	Roberto Alomar (All-Star)	.20	.15	.08
29	Sandy Alomar (All-Star)	.10	.08	.04
30	Rickey Henderson (All-Star)	.15	.11	.06
31	Ken Hill	.06	.05	.02
32	John Habyan	.05	.04	.02
33	Otis Nixon (Highlight)	.10	.08	.04
34	Tim Wallach	.08	.06	.03
35	Cal Ripken, Jr.	.30	.25	.12
36	Gary Carter	.08	.06	.03
37	Juan Agosto	.05	.04	.02
38	Doug Dascenzo	.05	.04	.02
39	Kirk Gibson	.08	.06	.03
40	Benito Santiago	.08	.06	.03
41	Otis Nixon	.06	.05	.02
42	Andy Allanson	.05	.04	.02
43	Brian Holman	.06	.05	.02
44	Dick Schofield	.05	.04	.02
45	Dave Magadan	.08	.06	.03
46	Rafael Palmeiro	.10	.08	.04
47	Jody Reed	.06	.05	.02
48	Ivan Calderon	.08	.06	.03
49	Greg Harris	.05	.04	.02
50	Chris Sabo	.08	.06	.03

51	Paul Molitor	.15	.11	.06
52	Robby Thompson	.06	.05	.02
53	Dave Smith	.05	.04	.02
54	Mark Davis	.05	.04	.02
55	Kevin Brown	.06	.05	.02
56	Donn Pall	.05	.04	.02
57	Len Dykstra	.15	.11	.06
58	Roberto Alomar	.25	.20	.10
59	Jeff Robinson	.05	.04	.02
60	Willie McGee	.08	.06	.03
61	Jay Buhner	.08	.06	.03
62	Mike Pagliarulo	.05	.04	.02
63	Paul O'Neill	.08	.06	.03
64	Hubie Brooks	.06	.05	.02
65	Kelly Gruber	.08	.06	.03
66	Ken Caminiti	.06	.05	.02
67	Gary Redus	.05	.04	.02
68	Harold Baines	.08	.06	.03
69	Charlie Hough	.06	.05	.02
70	B.J. Surhoff	.06	.05	.02
71	Walt Weiss	.06	.05	.02
72	Shawn Hillegas	.05	.04	.02
73	Roberto Kelly	.08	.06	.03
74	Jeff Ballard	.05	.04	.02
75	Craig Biggio	.08	.06	.03
76	Pat Combs	.06	.05	.02
77	Jeff Robinson	.05	.04	.02
78	Tim Belcher	.06	.05	.02
79	Cris Carpenter	.06	.05	.02
80	Checklist 1-79	.05	.04	.02
81	Steve Avery	.30	.25	.12
82	Chris James	.05	.04	.02
83	Brian Harper	.06	.05	.02
84	Charlie Leibrandt	.06	.05	.02
85	Mickey Tettleton	.08	.06	.03
86	Pete O'Brien	.06	.05	.02
87	Danny Darwin	.05	.04	.02
88	Bob Walk	.05	.04	.02
89	Jeff Reardon	.08	.06	.03
90	Bobby Rose	.08	.06	.03
91	Danny Jackson	.06	.05	.02
92	John Morris	.05	.04	.02
93	Bud Black	.06	.05	.02
94	Tommy Greene (Highlight)	.10	.08	.04
95	Rick Aguilera	.08	.06	.03
96	Gary Gaetti	.08	.06	.03
97	David Cone	.08	.06	.03
98	John Olerud	.25	.20	.10
99	Joel Skinner	.05	.04	.02
100	Jay Bell	.08	.06	.03
101	Bob Milacki	.05	.04	.02
102	Norm Charlton	.06	.05	.02
103	Chuck Crim	.05	.04	.02
104	Terry Steinbach	.06	.05	.02
105	Juan Samuel	.08	.06	.03
106	Steve Howe	.06	.05	.02
107	Rafael Belliard	.05	.04	.02
108	Joey Cora	.05	.04	.02
109	Tommy Greene	.08	.06	.03
110	Gregg Olson	.08	.06	.03
111	Frank Tanana	.06	.05	.02
112	Lee Smith	.08	.06	.03
113	Greg Harris	.05	.04	.02
114	Dwayne Henry	.05	.04	.02
115	Chili Davis	.08	.06	.03
116	Kent Mercker	.08	.06	.03
117	Brian Barnes	.08	.06	.03
118	Rich DeLucia	.06	.05	.02
119	Andre Dawson	.15	.11	.06
120	Carlos Baerga	.25	.20	.10
121	Mike LaValliere	.06	.05	.02
122	Jeff Gray	.06	.05	.02
123	Bruce Hurst	.08	.06	.03
124	Alvin Davis	.08	.06	.03
125	John Candelaria	.06	.05	.02
126	Matt Nokes	.08	.06	.03
127	George Bell	.10	.08	.04
128	Bret Saberhagen	.10	.08	.04
129	Jeff Russell	.08	.06	.03
130	Jim Abbott	.10	.08	.04
131	Bill Gullickson	.06	.05	.02
132	Todd Zeile	.15	.11	.06
133	Dave Winfield	.08	.06	.03
134	Wally Whitehurst	.06	.05	.02
135	Matt Williams	.12	.09	.05
136	Tom Browning	.08	.06	.03
137	Marquis Grissom	.15	.11	.06
138	Erik Hanson	.10	.08	.04
139	Rob Dibble	.08	.06	.03
140	Don August	.05	.04	.02
141	Tom Henke	.08	.06	.03
142	Dan Pasqua	.06	.05	.02
143	George Brett	.15	.11	.06
144	Jerald Clark	.06	.05	.02
145	Robin Ventura	.25	.20	.10
146	Dale Murphy	.08	.06	.03
147	Dennis Eckersley	.10	.08	.04
148	Eric Yelding	.05	.04	.02
149	Mario Diaz	.05	.04	.02
150	Casey Candaele	.05	.04	.02
151	Steve Olin	.06	.05	.02
152	Luis Salazar	.05	.04	.02
153	Kevin Maas	.08	.06	.03
154	Nolan Ryan (Highlight)	.40	.30	.15
155	Barry Jones	.05	.04	.02
156	Chris Hoiles	.15	.11	.06
157	Bobby Ojeda	.06	.05	.02
158	Pedro Guerrero	.08	.06	.03
159	Paul Assenmacher	.05	.04	.02
160	Checklist 80-157	.05	.04	.02
161	Mike Macfarlane	.06	.05	.02
162	Craig Lefferts	.06	.05	.02
163	*Brian Hunter*	.20	.15	.08
164	Alan Trammell	.10	.08	.04
165	Ken Griffey, Jr.	1.00	.75	.40
166	Lance Parrish	.08	.06	.03
167	Brian Downing	.05	.04	.02
168	John Barfield	.06	.05	.02
169	Jack Clark	.08	.06	.03
170	Chris Nabholz	.06	.05	.02
171	Tim Teufel	.05	.04	.02
172	Chris Hammond	.08	.06	.03
173	Robin Yount	.20	.15	.08
174	Dave Righetti	.08	.06	.03
175	Joe Girardi	.06	.05	.02
176	Mike Boddicker	.06	.05	.02
177	Dean Palmer	.20	.15	.08
178	Greg Hibbard	.06	.05	.02
179	Randy Ready	.05	.04	.02
180	Devon White	.08	.06	.03
181	Mark Eichhorn	.05	.04	.02
182	Mike Felder	.05	.04	.02
183	Joe Klink	.05	.04	.02
184	Steve Bedrosian	.06	.05	.02
185	Barry Larkin	.10	.08	.04
186	John Franco	.08	.06	.03
187	*Ed Sprague*	.15	.11	.06
188	Mark Portugal	.05	.04	.02
189	Jose Lind	.05	.04	.02
190	Bob Welch	.08	.06	.03
191	Alex Fernandez	.25	.20	.10
192	Gary Sheffield	.15	.11	.06
193	Rickey Henderson	.20	.15	.08
194	Rod Nichols	.05	.04	.02
195	*Scott Kamieniecki*	.15	.11	.06
196	Mike Flanagan	.05	.04	.02
197	Steve Finley	.08	.06	.03
198	Darren Daulton	.06	.05	.02
199	Leo Gomez	.15	.11	.06
200	Mike Morgan	.06	.05	.02
201	Bob Tewksbury	.05	.04	.02
202	Sid Bream	.08	.06	.03
203	Sandy Alomar	.08	.06	.03
204	Greg Gagne	.05	.04	.02
205	Juan Berenguer	.05	.04	.02
206	Cecil Fielder	.20	.15	.08
207	Randy Johnson	.08	.06	.03
208	Tony Pena	.06	.05	.02
209	Doug Drabek	.10	.08	.04
210	Wade Boggs	.20	.15	.08
211	Bryan Harvey	.08	.06	.03
212	Jose Vizcaino	.06	.05	.02
213	*Alonzo Powell* (FC)	.06	.05	.02
214	Will Clark	.20	.15	.08
215	Rickey Henderson (Highlight)	.10	.08	.04
216	Jack Morris	.08	.06	.03
217	Junior Felix	.06	.05	.02
218	Vince Coleman	.08	.06	.03
219	Jimmy Key	.08	.06	.03
220	Alex Cole	.08	.06	.03
221	Bill Landrum	.06	.05	.02
222	Randy Milligan	.08	.06	.03
223	Jose Rijo	.08	.06	.03
224	Greg Vaughn	.10	.08	.04
225	Dave Stewart	.08	.06	.03
226	Lenny Harris	.06	.05	.02
227	Scott Sanderson	.06	.05	.02
228	Jeff Blauser	.06	.05	.02
229	Ozzie Guillen	.08	.06	.03
230	John Kruk	.08	.06	.03
231	Bob Melvin	.05	.04	.02
232	Milt Cuyler	.15	.11	.06
233	Felix Jose	.15	.11	.06
234	Ellis Burks	.10	.08	.04
235	Pete Harnisch	.06	.05	.02
236	Kevin Tapani	.08	.06	.03
237	Terry Pendleton	.08	.06	.03
238	Mark Gardner	.08	.06	.03
239	Harold Reynolds	.06	.05	.02
240	Checklist 158-237	.05	.04	.02
241	Mike Harkey	.06	.05	.02
242	Felix Fermin	.05	.04	.02
243	Barry Bonds	.35	.25	.14
244	Roger Clemens	.20	.15	.08
245	Dennis Rasmussen	.05	.04	.02
246	Jose DeLeon	.06	.05	.02
247	Orel Hershiser	.10	.08	.04
248	Mel Hall	.06	.05	.02
249	*Rick Wilkins*	.25	.20	.10
250	Tom Gordon	.08	.06	.03
251	Kevin Reimer	.06	.05	.02
252	Luis Polonia	.06	.05	.02
253	Mike Henneman	.06	.05	.02
254	Tom Pagnozzi	.06	.05	.02
255	Chuck Finley	.10	.08	.04
256	Mackey Sasser	.05	.04	.02
257	John Burkett	.06	.05	.02
258	Hal Morris	.15	.11	.06
259	Larry Walker	.10	.08	.04
260	Billy Swift	.06	.05	.02
261	Joe Oliver	.06	.05	.02
262	Julio Machado	.05	.04	.02
263	Todd Stottlemyre	.08	.06	.03
264	Matt Merullo	.05	.04	.02
265	Brent Mayne	.08	.06	.03
266	Thomas Howard	.06	.05	.02
267	Lance Johnson	.06	.05	.02
268	Terry Mulholland	.08	.06	.03
269	Rick Honeycutt	.05	.04	.02
270	Luis Gonzalez	.10	.08	.04
271	Jose Guzman	.06	.05	.02
272	Jimmy Jones	.05	.04	.02
273	Mark Lewis	.10	.08	.04
274	Rene Gonzales	.05	.04	.02
275	*Jeff Johnson*	.15	.11	.06
276	Dennis Martinez (Highlight)	.10	.08	.04
277	Delino DeShields	.08	.06	.03
278	Sam Horn	.05	.04	.02
279	Kevin Gross	.06	.05	.02
280	Jose Oquendo	.05	.04	.02
281	Mark Grace	.15	.11	.06
282	Mark Gubicza	.08	.06	.03
283	Fred McGriff	.15	.11	.06
284	Ron Gant	.10	.08	.04
285	Lou Whitaker	.08	.06	.03
286	Edgar Martinez	.08	.06	.03
287	Ron Tingley	.05	.04	.02
288	Kevin McReynolds	.08	.06	.03
289	*Ivan Rodriguez*	.25	.20	.10
290	Mike Gardiner	.08	.06	.03
291	*Chris Haney*	.10	.08	.04
292	Darrin Jackson	.06	.05	.02
293	Bill Doran	.08	.06	.03
294	Ted Higuera	.08	.06	.03
295	Jeff Brantley	.08	.06	.03
296	Les Lancaster	.05	.04	.02
297	Jim Eisenreich	.05	.04	.02
298	Ruben Sierra	.08	.06	.03
299	Scott Radinsky	.08	.06	.03
300	Jose DeJesus	.08	.06	.03
301	*Mike Timlin*	.12	.09	.05
302	Luis Sojo	.08	.06	.03
303	Kelly Downs	.05	.04	.02
304	Scott Bankhead	.06	.05	.02
305	Pedro Munoz	.20	.15	.08
306	Scott Scudder	.06	.05	.02
307	Kevin Elster	.06	.05	.02
308	Duane Ward	.06	.05	.02
309	*Darryl Kile*	.15	.11	.06
310	Orlando Merced	.12	.09	.05
311	Dave Henderson	.10	.08	.04
312	Tim Raines	.10	.08	.04
313	Mark Lee (FC)	.06	.05	.02
314	Mike Gallego	.06	.05	.02
315	Charles Nagy	.10	.08	.04
316	Jesse Barfield	.08	.06	.03
317	Todd Frohwirth	.05	.04	.02
318	Al Osuna	.06	.05	.02
319	Darrin Fletcher	.06	.05	.02
320	Checklist 238-316	.05	.04	.02
321	David Segui	.10	.08	.04
322	Stan Javier	.05	.04	.02
323	Bryn Smith	.05	.04	.02
324	Jeff Treadway	.06	.05	.02
325	Mark Whiten	.15	.11	.06
326	Kent Hrbek	.08	.06	.03
327	David Justice	.35	.25	.14
328	Tony Phillips	.06	.05	.02
329	Rob Murphy	.05	.04	.02
330	Kevin Morton	.10	.08	.04
331	John Smiley	.08	.06	.03
332	Luis Rivera	.05	.04	.02
333	Wally Joyner	.15	.11	.06
334	*Heathcliff Slocumb*	.15	.11	.06
335	Rick Cerone	.05	.04	.02
336	*Mike Remlinger* (FC)	.08	.06	.03
337	Mike Moore	.06	.05	.02
338	Lloyd McClendon	.05	.04	.02
339	Al Newman	.05	.04	.02
340	Kirk McCaskill	.08	.06	.03
341	Howard Johnson	.06	.05	.02
342	Greg Myers	.05	.04	.02
343	Kal Daniels	.08	.06	.03
344	Bernie Williams	.10	.08	.04
345	Shane Mack	.10	.08	.04
346	Gary Thurman	.05	.04	.02
347	Dante Bichette	.06	.05	.02
348	Mark McGwire	.12	.09	.05
349	Travis Fryman	.25	.20	.10
350	Ray Lankford	.15	.11	.06
351	Mike Jeffcoat	.05	.04	.02
352	Jack McDowell	.10	.08	.04
353	Mitch Williams	.08	.06	.03
354	Mike Devereaux	.06	.05	.02
355	Andre Galarraga	.06	.05	.02
356	Henry Cotto	.05	.04	.02
357	Scott Bailes	.05	.04	.02
358	Jeff Bagwell	.30	.25	.12
359	Scott Leius	.08	.06	.03
360	Zane Smith	.06	.05	.02
361	Bill Pecota	.06	.05	.02
362	Tony Fernandez	.08	.06	.03
363	Glenn Braggs	.06	.05	.02
364	Bill Spiers	.06	.05	.02
365	Vicente Palacios	.05	.04	.02
366	Tim Burke	.06	.05	.02
367	Randy Tomlin	.06	.05	.02
368	Kenny Rogers	.06	.05	.02
369	Brett Butler	.08	.06	.03
370	Pat Kelly	.20	.15	.08
371	Bip Roberts	.06	.05	.02
372	Gregg Jefferies	.15	.11	.06
373	Kevin Bass	.06	.05	.02
374	Ron Karkovice	.05	.04	.02
375	Paul Gibson	.05	.04	.02
376	Bernard Gilkey	.10	.08	.04
377	Dave Gallagher	.06	.05	.02
378	Bill Wegman	.06	.05	.02
379	Pat Borders	.06	.05	.02
380	Ed Whitson	.06	.05	.02
381	Gilberto Reyes	.08	.06	.03
382	Russ Swan	.08	.06	.03
383	Andy Van Slyke	.08	.06	.03
384	Wes Chamberlain	.20	.15	.08
385	Steve Chitren	.08	.06	.03
386	Greg Olson	.06	.05	.02
387	Brian McRae	.10	.08	.04
388	Rich Rodriguez	.06	.05	.02
389	Steve Decker	.15	.11	.06
390	Chuck Knoblauch	.08	.06	.03
391	Bobby Witt	.06	.05	.02
392	Eddie Murray	.10	.08	.04
393	Juan Gonzalez	.80	.60	.30
394	Scott Ruskin	.05	.04	.02
395	Jay Howell	.06	.05	.02
396	Checklist 317-396	.05	.04	.02
397	Royce Clayton (Rated Rookie)	.20	.15	.08
398	*John Jaha* (Rated Rookie)	.15	.11	.06
399	Dan Wilson (FC) (Rated Rookie)	.15	.11	.06
400	*Archie Corbin* (Rated Rookie)	.10	.08	.04
401	*Barry Manuel* (Rated Rookie)	.08	.06	.03
402	Kim Batiste (FC) (Rated Rookie)	.10	.08	.04
403	*Pat Mahomes* (Rated Rookie)	.10	.08	.04
404	Dave Fleming (Rated Rookie)	.15	.11	.06

405	Jeff Juden (Rated Rookie)	.15	.11	.06
406	*Jim Thome* (Rated Rookie)	.40	.30	.15
407	Sam Militello (FC) (Rated Rookie)	.10	.08	.04
408	Jeff Nelson (FC) (Rated Rookie)	.10	.08	.04
409	Anthony Young (Rated Rookie)	.15	.11	.06
410	Tino Martinez (Rated Rookie)	.15	.11	.06
411	*Jeff Mutis* (FC) (Rated Rookie)	.08	.06	.03
412	*Rey Sanchez* (FC) (Rated Rookie)	.08	.06	.03
413	*Chris Gardner* (Rated Rookie)	.12	.09	.05
414	*John Vander Wal* (Rated Rookie)	.12	.09	.05
415	Reggie Sanders (Rated Rookie)	.15	.11	.06
416	*Brian Williams* (Rated Rookie)	.20	.15	.08
417	Mo Sanford (FC) (Rated Rookie)	.15	.11	.06
418	*David Weathers* (Rated Rookie)	.20	.15	.08
419	*Hector Fajardo* (Rated Rookie)	.10	.08	.04
420	*Steve Foster* (Rated Rookie)	.10	.08	.04
421	Lance Dickson (Rated Rookie)	.10	.08	.04
422	Andre Dawson (All-Star)	.10	.08	.04
423	Ozzie Smith (All-Star)	.10	.08	.04
424	Chris Sabo (All-Star)	.08	.06	.03
425	Tony Gwynn (All-Star)	.10	.08	.04
426	Tom Glavine (All-Star)	.10	.08	.04
427	Bobby Bonilla (All-Star)	.10	.08	.04
428	Will Clark (All-Star)	.15	.11	.06
429	Ryne Sandberg (All-Star)	.15	.11	.06
430	Benito Santiago (All-Star)	.08	.06	.03
431	Ivan Calderon (All-Star)	.08	.06	.03
432	Ozzie Smith	.08	.06	.03
433	Tim Leary	.05	.04	.02
434	Bret Saberhagen (Highlight)	.08	.06	.03
435	Mel Rojas	.06	.05	.02
436	Ben McDonald	.10	.08	.04
437	Tim Crews	.05	.04	.02
438	Rex Hudler	.05	.04	.02
439	Chico Walker	.05	.04	.02
440	Kurt Stillwell	.05	.04	.02
441	Tony Gwynn	.15	.11	.06
442	John Smoltz	.08	.06	.03
443	Lloyd Moseby	.05	.04	.02
444	Mike Schooler	.06	.05	.02
445	Joe Grahe	.06	.05	.02
446	Dwight Gooden	.10	.08	.04
447	Oil Can Boyd	.05	.04	.02
448	John Marzano	.05	.04	.02
449	Bret Barberie	.10	.08	.04
450	Mike Maddux	.05	.04	.02
451	Jeff Reed	.05	.04	.02
452	Dale Sveum	.05	.04	.02
453	Jose Uribe	.05	.04	.02
454	Bob Scanlan	.05	.04	.02
455	Kevin Appier	.08	.06	.03
456	Jeff Huson	.05	.04	.02
457	Ken Patterson	.05	.04	.02
458	Ricky Jordan	.08	.06	.03
459	Tom Candiotti	.06	.05	.02
460	Lee Stevens	.08	.06	.03
461	*Rod Beck* (FC)	.15	.11	.06
462	Dave Valle	.05	.04	.02
463	Scott Erickson	.25	.20	.10
464	Chris Jones	.06	.05	.02
465	Mark Carreon	.05	.04	.02
466	Rob Ducey	.05	.04	.02
467	Jim Corsi	.05	.04	.02
468	Jeff King	.05	.04	.02
469	Curt Young	.05	.04	.02
470	Bo Jackson	.15	.11	.06
471	Chris Bosio	.06	.05	.02
472	Jamie Quirk	.05	.04	.02
473	Jesse Orosco	.05	.04	.02
474	Alvaro Espinoza	.05	.04	.02
475	Joe Orsulak	.05	.04	.02
476	Checklist 397-477	.05	.04	.02
477	Gerald Young	.05	.04	.02
478	Wally Backman	.05	.04	.02
479	Juan Bell	.05	.04	.02
480	Mike Scioscia	.06	.05	.02
481	Omar Olivares	.06	.05	.02
482	Francisco Cabrera	.05	.04	.02
483	Greg Swindell	.08	.06	.03
484	Terry Leach	.05	.04	.02
485	Tommy Gregg	.05	.04	.02
486	Scott Aldred	.05	.04	.02
487	Greg Briley	.05	.04	.02
488	Phil Plantier	.20	.15	.08
489	Curtis Wilkerson	.05	.04	.02
490	Tom Brunansky	.06	.05	.02
491	Mike Fetters	.05	.04	.02
492	Frank Castillo	.08	.06	.03
493	Joe Boever	.05	.04	.02
494	Kirt Manwaring	.05	.04	.02
495	Wilson Alvarez (Highlight)	.06	.05	.02
496	Gene Larkin	.05	.04	.02
497	Gary DiSarcina	.06	.05	.02
498	Frank Viola	.08	.06	.03
499	Manuel Lee	.05	.04	.02
500	Albert Belle	.25	.20	.10
501	Stan Belinda	.05	.04	.02
502	Dwight Evans	.06	.05	.02
503	Eric Davis	.10	.08	.04
504	Darren Holmes	.05	.04	.02
505	Mike Bordick	.12	.09	.05
506	Dave Hansen	.06	.05	.02
507	Lee Guetterman	.05	.04	.02
508	*Keith Mitchell* (FC)	.15	.11	.06
509	Melido Perez	.05	.04	.02
510	Dickie Thon	.05	.04	.02
511	Mark Williamson	.05	.04	.02
512	Mark Salas	.05	.04	.02
513	Milt Thompson	.05	.04	.02
514	Mo Vaughn	.20	.15	.08
515	Jim Deshaies	.05	.04	.02
516	Rich Garces	.05	.04	.02
517	Lonnie Smith	.05	.04	.02
518	Spike Owen	.06	.05	.02
519	Tracy Jones	.05	.04	.02
520	Greg Maddux	.08	.06	.03
521	Carlos Martinez	.05	.04	.02
522	Neal Heaton	.05	.04	.02
523	Mike Greenwell	.08	.06	.03
524	Andy Benes	.08	.06	.03
525	Jeff Schaefer	.05	.04	.02
526	Mike Sharperson	.06	.05	.02
527	Wade Taylor	.06	.05	.02
528	Jerome Walton	.06	.05	.02
529	Storm Davis	.05	.04	.02
530	*Jose Hernandez*	.10	.08	.04
531	Mark Langston	.08	.06	.03
532	Rob Deer	.06	.05	.02
533	Geronimo Pena	.06	.05	.02
534	*Juan Guzman*	.12	.09	.05
535	Pete Schourek	.08	.06	.03
536	Todd Benzinger	.05	.04	.02
537	Billy Hatcher	.05	.04	.02
538	Tom Foley	.05	.04	.02
539	Dave Cochrane	.05	.04	.02
540	Mariano Duncan	.05	.04	.02
541	Edwin Nunez	.05	.04	.02
542	Rance Mulliniks	.05	.04	.02
543	Carlton Fisk	.10	.08	.04
544	Luis Aquino	.05	.04	.02
545	Ricky Bones	.08	.06	.03
546	Craig Grebeck	.05	.04	.02
547	Charlie Hayes	.06	.05	.02
548	Jose Canseco	.15	.11	.06
549	Andujar Cedeno	.10	.08	.04
550	Geno Petralli	.05	.04	.02
551	Javier Ortiz	.05	.04	.02
552	Rudy Seanez	.06	.05	.02
553	Rich Gedman	.05	.04	.02
554	Eric Plunk	.05	.04	.02
555	Nolan Ryan, Rich Gossage (Highlight)	.20	.15	.08
556	Checklist 478-555	.05	.04	.02
557	Greg Colbrunn	.06	.05	.02
558	*Chito Martinez* (FC)	.10	.08	.04
559	Darryl Strawberry	.10	.08	.04
560	Luis Alicea	.05	.04	.02
561	Dwight Smith	.06	.05	.02
562	Terry Shumpert	.05	.04	.02
563	Jim Vatcher	.05	.04	.02
564	Deion Sanders	.08	.06	.03
565	Walt Terrell	.05	.04	.02
566	Dave Burba	.05	.04	.02
567	Dave Howard	.05	.04	.02
568	Todd Hundley	.08	.06	.03
569	Jack Daugherty	.05	.04	.02
570	Scott Cooper	.10	.08	.04
571	Bill Sampen	.05	.04	.02
572	Jose Melendez	.10	.08	.04
573	Freddie Benavides	.05	.04	.02
574	Jim Gantner	.05	.04	.02
575	Trevor Wilson	.05	.04	.02
576	Ryne Sandberg	.20	.15	.08
577	Kevin Seitzer	.05	.04	.02
578	Gerald Alexander	.05	.04	.02
579	Mike Huff	.05	.04	.02
580	Von Hayes	.06	.05	.02
581	Derek Bell	.15	.11	.06
582	Mike Stanley	.05	.04	.02
583	Kevin Mitchell	.08	.06	.03
584	Mike Jackson	.05	.04	.02
585	Dan Gladden	.05	.04	.02
586	Ted Power	.05	.04	.02
587	Jeff Innis	.05	.04	.02
588	Bob MacDonald	.08	.06	.03
589	*Jose Tolentino* (FC)	.08	.06	.03
590	Bob Patterson	.05	.04	.02
591	*Scott Brosius* (FC)	.10	.08	.04
592	Frank Thomas	1.00	.70	.40
593	Darryl Hamilton	.08	.06	.03
594	Kirk Dressendorfer	.08	.06	.03
595	Jeff Shaw	.08	.06	.03
596	Don Mattingly	.12	.09	.05
597	Glenn Davis	.06	.05	.02
598	Andy Mota	.10	.08	.04
599	Jason Grimsley	.05	.04	.02
600	Jimmy Poole	.06	.05	.02
601	Jim Gott	.05	.04	.02
602	Stan Royer	.08	.06	.03
603	Marvin Freeman	.05	.04	.02
604	Denis Boucher	.08	.06	.03
605	Denny Neagle	.10	.08	.04
606	Mark Lemke	.06	.05	.02
607	Jerry Don Gleaton	.05	.04	.02
608	Brent Knackert	.05	.04	.02
609	Carlos Quintana	.05	.04	.02
610	Bobby Bonilla	.12	.09	.05
611	Joe Hesketh	.05	.04	.02
612	Daryl Boston	.05	.04	.02
613	Shawon Dunston	.08	.06	.03
614	Danny Cox	.05	.04	.02
615	Darren Lewis	.12	.09	.05
616	Alejandro Pena, Kent Mercker, Mark Wohlers, Kent Mercker, Mark Wohlers, (Highlight)	.10	.08	.04
617	Kirby Puckett	.15	.11	.06
618	Franklin Stubbs	.05	.04	.02
619	Chris Donnels	.10	.08	.04
620	David Wells	.05	.04	.02
621	Mike Aldrete	.05	.04	.02
622	Bob Kipper	.05	.04	.02
623	Anthony Telford	.05	.04	.02
624	Randy Myers	.05	.04	.02
625	Willie Randolph	.05	.04	.02
626	Joe Slusarski	.08	.06	.03
627	John Wetteland	.06	.05	.02
628	Greg Cadaret	.05	.04	.02
629	Tom Glavine	.10	.08	.04
630	Wilson Alvarez	.10	.08	.04
631	Wally Ritchie	.05	.04	.02
632	Mike Mussina	.25	.20	.10
633	Mark Leiter	.05	.04	.02
634	Gerald Perry	.05	.04	.02
635	Matt Young	.05	.04	.02
636	Checklist 556-635	.05	.04	.02
637	Scott Hemond	.05	.04	.02
638	David West	.05	.04	.02
639	Jim Clancy	.05	.04	.02
640	Doug Piatt (FC)	.10	.08	.04
641	Omar Vizquel	.05	.04	.02
642	Rick Sutcliffe	.08	.06	.03
643	Glenallen Hill	.08	.06	.03
644	Gary Varsho	.05	.04	.02
645	Tony Fossas	.05	.04	.02
646	Jack Howell	.05	.04	.02
647	*Jim Campanis* (FC)	.15	.11	.06
648	Chris Gwynn	.05	.04	.02
649	Jim Leyritz	.05	.04	.02
650	Chuck McElroy	.05	.04	.02
651	Sean Berry (FC)	.08	.06	.03
652	Donald Harris (FC)	.10	.08	.04
653	Don Slaught	.05	.04	.02
654	*Rusty Meacham*	.10	.08	.04
655	Scott Terry	.05	.04	.02
656	Ramon Martinez	.12	.09	.05
657	Keith Miller	.05	.04	.02
658	Ramon Garcia (FC)	.08	.06	.03
659	*Milt Hill* (FC)	.10	.08	.04
660	Steve Frey	.05	.04	.02
661	Bob McClure	.05	.04	.02
662	*Ced Landrum*	.08	.06	.03
663	*Doug Henry*	.10	.07	.04
664	Candy Maldonado	.05	.04	.02
665	Carl Willis	.05	.04	.02
666	Jeff Montgomery	.08	.06	.03
667	*Craig Shipley* (FC)	.10	.08	.04
668	*Warren Newson*	.08	.06	.03
669	Mickey Morandini	.08	.06	.03
670	Brook Jacoby	.05	.04	.02
671	*Ryan Bowen*	.10	.08	.04
672	Bill Krueger	.05	.04	.02
673	Rob Mallicoat	.05	.04	.02
674	Doug Jones	.05	.04	.02
675	Scott Livingstone	.10	.08	.04
676	Danny Tartabull	.10	.08	.04
677	Joe Carter (Highlight)	.08	.06	.03
678	Cecil Espy	.05	.04	.02
679	Randy Velarde	.05	.04	.02
680	Bruce Ruffin	.05	.04	.02
681	*Ted Wood*	.10	.08	.04
682	Dan Plesac	.05	.04	.02
683	Eric Bullock	.05	.04	.02
684	Junior Ortiz	.05	.04	.02
685	Dave Hollins	.06	.05	.02
686	Dennis Martinez	.08	.06	.03
687	Larry Andersen	.05	.04	.02
688	Doug Simons	.05	.04	.02
689	*Tim Spehr*	.08	.06	.03
690	*Calvin Jones* (FC)	.05	.04	.02
691	Mark Guthrie	.05	.04	.02
692	Alfredo Griffin	.05	.04	.02
693	Joe Carter	.12	.09	.05
694	*Terry Mathews* (FC)	.08	.06	.03
695	Pascual Perez	.05	.04	.02
696	Gene Nelson	.05	.04	.02
697	Gerald Williams	.15	.11	.06
698	*Chris Cron* (FC)	.15	.11	.06
699	Steve Buechele	.06	.05	.02
700	Paul McClellan (FC)	.08	.06	.03
701	Jim Lindeman	.05	.04	.02
702	Francisco Oliveras	.05	.04	.02
703	*Rob Maurer*	.10	.08	.04
704	*Pat Hentgen*	.25	.20	.10
705	Jaime Navarro	.06	.05	.02
706	*Mike Magnante* (FC)	.10	.08	.04
707	Nolan Ryan	.75	.60	.30
708	Bobby Thigpen	.08	.06	.03
709	John Cerutti	.05	.04	.02
710	Steve Wilson	.05	.04	.02
711	Hensley Meulens	.08	.06	.03
712	*Rheal Cormier* (FC)	.20	.15	.08
713	Scott Bradley	.05	.04	.02
714	Mitch Webster	.05	.04	.02
715	Roger Mason	.05	.04	.02
716	Checklist 636-716	.05	.04	.02
717	*Jeff Fassero*	.12	.09	.05
718	Cal Eldred	.12	.09	.05
719	Sid Fernandez	.08	.06	.03
720	*Bob Zupcic*	.08	.06	.03
721	Jose Offerman	.08	.06	.03
722	*Cliff Brantley*	.10	.07	.04
723	Ron Darling	.06	.05	.02
724	Dave Stieb	.06	.05	.02
725	Hector Villanueva	.06	.05	.02
726	Mike Hartley	.05	.04	.02
727	*Arthur Rhodes*	.15	.11	.06
728	Randy Bush	.05	.04	.02
729	Steve Sax	.08	.06	.03
730	Dave Otto	.05	.04	.02
731	*John Wehner*	.10	.08	.04
732	Dave Martinez	.05	.04	.02
733	*Ruben Amaro*	.10	.08	.04
734	Billy Ripken	.05	.04	.02
735	Steve Farr	.05	.04	.02
736	Shawn Abner	.05	.04	.02
737	*Gil Heredia* (FC)	.10	.08	.04
738	Ron Jones	.05	.04	.02
739	Tony Castillo	.05	.04	.02
740	Sammy Sosa	.08	.06	.03
741	Julio Franco	.08	.06	.03
742	Tim Naehring	.08	.06	.03
743	*Steve Wapnick* (FC)	.10	.08	.04
744	Craig Wilson	.08	.06	.03
745	*Darrin Chapin* (FC)	.08	.06	.03
746	*Chris George* (FC)	.08	.06	.03
747	Mike Simms	.08	.06	.03
748	Rosario Rodriguez	.08	.06	.03
749	Skeeter Barnes	.05	.04	.02
750	Roger McDowell	.05	.04	.02
751	Dann Howitt	.05	.04	.02
752	Paul Sorrento	.05	.04	.02
753	*Braulio Castillo* (FC)	.08	.06	.03
754	*Yorkis Perez* (FC)	.08	.06	.03
755	Willie Fraser	.05	.04	.02

756	*Jeremy Hernandez* (FC)	.10	.08	.04
757	Curt Schilling	.05	.04	.02
758	Steve Lyons	.05	.04	.02
759	Dave Anderson	.05	.04	.02
760	Willie Banks	.12	.09	.05
761	Mark Leonard	.05	.04	.02
762	Jack Armstrong	.06	.05	.02
763	Scott Servais	.08	.06	.03
764	Ray Stephens	.08	.06	.03
765	Junior Noboa	.05	.04	.02
766	*Jim Olander* (FC)	.10	.08	.04
767	Joe Magrane	.06	.05	.02
768	Lance Blankenship	.05	.04	.02
769	*Mike Humphreys* (FC)	.10	.08	.04
770	*Jarvis Brown* (FC)	.12	.09	.05
771	Damon Berryhill	.05	.04	.02
772	Alejandro Pena	.06	.05	.02
773	Jose Mesa	.05	.04	.02
774	*Gary Cooper* (FC)	.10	.08	.04
775	Carney Lansford	.06	.05	.02
776	Mike Bielecki	.05	.04	.02
777	Charlie O'Brien	.05	.04	.02
778	Carlos Hernandez	.05	.04	.02
779	Howard Farmer	.05	.04	.02
780	Mike Stanton	.05	.04	.02
781	Reggie Harris	.05	.04	.02
782	Xavier Hernandez	.05	.04	.02
783	*Bryan Hickerson* (FC)	.10	.08	.04
784	Checklist 717-BC8	.05	.04	.02

1992 Donruss Bonus Cards

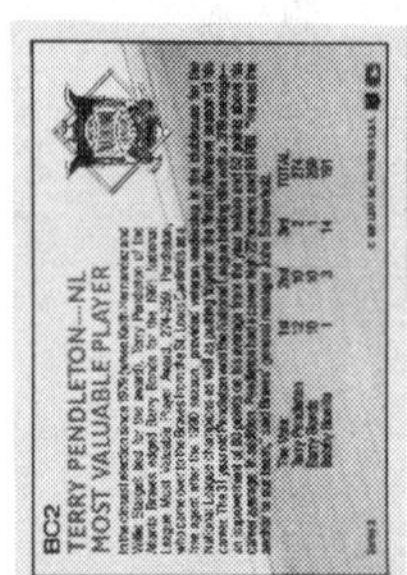

These eight bonus cards were randomly inserted in 1992 foil packs and are numbered with a BC prefix. Both leagues' MVPs, Cy Young and Rookie of the Year award winners are featured, as are logo cards for the new expansion teams, the Colorado Rockies and the Florida Marlins. Cards are standard size in a format similar to the regular issue.

		MT	NR MT	EX
	Complete Set (8):	1.50	1.25	.60
	Common Player:	.15	.11	.06
1	Cal Ripken, Jr. (MVP)	.50	.40	.20
2	Terry Pendleton (MVP)	.15	.11	.06
3	Roger Clemens (Cy Young)	.30	.25	.12
4	Tom Glavine (Cy Young)	.30	.25	.12
5	Chuck Knoblauch (Rookie of the Year)	.20	.15	.08
6	Jeff Bagwell (Rookie of the Year)	.50	.40	.20
7	Colorado Rockies	.50	.40	.20
8	Florida Marlins	.50	.40	.20

1992 Donruss Diamond Kings

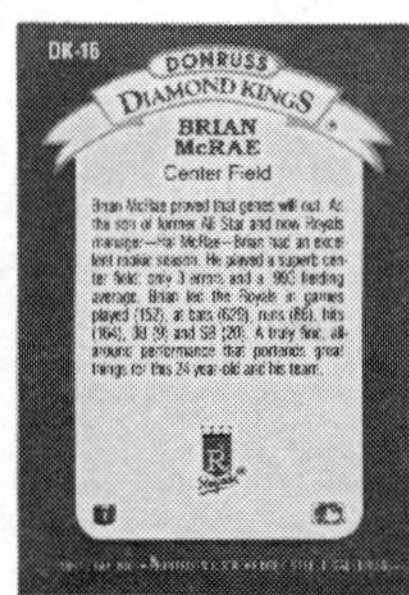

Donruss changed its Diamond Kings style and distribution in 1992. The cards still featured the art of Dick Perez, but quality was improved from past years. The cards were randomly inserted in foil packs. One player from each team is featured. Card numbers have a DK prefix.

		MT	NR MT	EX
	Complete Set (27):	28.00	21.00	11.00
	Common Player:	.75	.50	.25
1	Paul Molitor	2.50	2.00	1.00
2	Will Clark	2.50	1.50	.75
3	Joe Carter	2.50	2.00	1.00
4	Julio Franco	.75	.50	.25
5	Cal Ripken, Jr.	3.50	2.00	1.00
6	Dave Justice	3.00	2.00	1.00
7	George Bell	.75	.50	.25
8	Frank Thomas	9.00	6.00	3.00
9	Wade Boggs	1.00	.75	.40
10	Scott Sanderson	.75	.50	.25
11	Jeff Bagwell	2.50	2.00	1.00
12	John Kruk	1.00	.75	.40
13	Felix Jose	.75	.50	.25
14	Harold Baines	.75	.50	.25
15	Dwight Gooden	.75	.50	.25
16	Brian McRae	.75	.60	.30
17	Jay Bell	.75	.50	.25
18	Brett Butler	.75	.50	.25
19	Hal Morris	.75	.50	.25
20	Mark Langston	.75	.50	.25
21	Scott Erickson	.75	.50	.25
22	Randy Johnson	1.00	.60	.30
23	Greg Swindell	.75	.50	.25
24	Dennis Martinez	.75	.50	.25
25	Tony Phillips	.75	.50	.25
26	Fred McGriff	2.50	2.00	1.00
27	Checklist	.50	.30	.15

1992 Donruss Elite

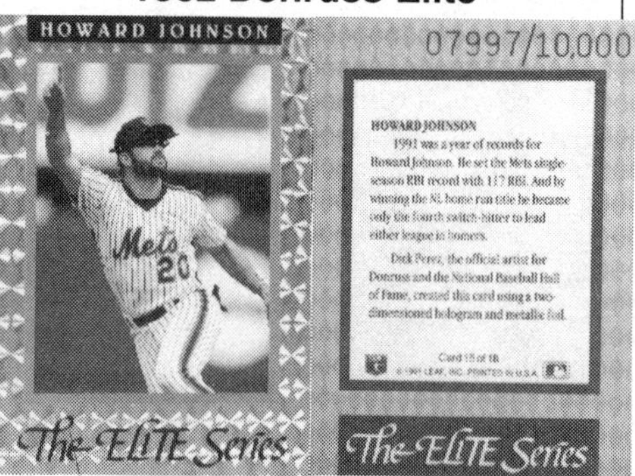

Donruss continued its Elite series in 1992 by inserting cards in foil packs. Each card was released in the same quantity as the 1991 cards - 10,000 Elite, 7,500 Legend and 5,000 Signature. The Elite cards, now featuring a prismatic border, are numbered as a continuation of the 1991 issue Rickey Henderson and Cal Ripken are the subjects of the Legend card and Signature card, respectively.

		MT	NR MT	EX
	Complete Set (12):	1100.	825.00	450.00
	Common Player:	25.00	18.00	10.00
9	Wade Boggs	40.00	30.00	15.00
10	Joe Carter	60.00	45.00	24.00
11	Will Clark	60.00	45.00	24.00
12	Dwight Gooden	35.00	26.00	14.00
13	Ken Griffey, Jr.	150.00	110.00	60.00
14	Tony Gwynn	35.00	26.00	14.00
15	Howard Johnson	30.00	22.00	12.00
16	Terry Pendleton	30.00	22.00	12.00
17	Kirby Puckett	90.00	67.00	36.00
18	Frank Thomas	200.00	150.00	80.00
----	Rickey Henderson (Legend)	125.00	90.00	45.00
----	Cal Ripken, Jr. (Signature)	400.00	300.00	120.00

1992 Donruss Rookies

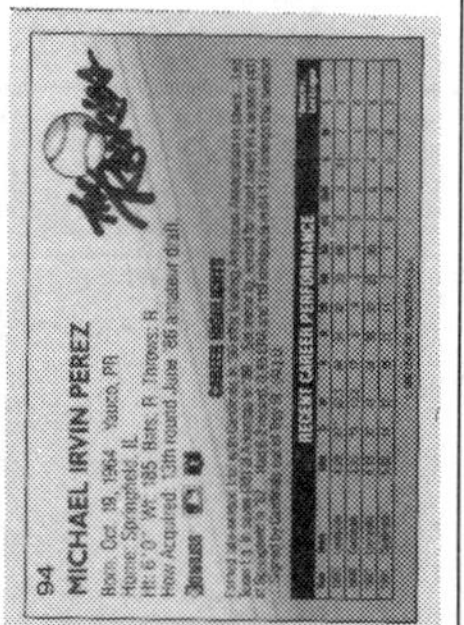

Donruss increased the size of its Rookies set in 1992 to include 132 cards. In the past the cards were released only in boxed set form, but the 1992 cards were available in packs. Special phenoms insert cards were randomly inserted into Rookies packs. The phenoms cards feature black borders, while the Rookies cards are styled after the regular 1992 Donruss issue. The cards are numbered alphabetically.

		MT	NR MT	EX
	Complete Set (132):	12.00	9.00	4.75
	Common Player:	.05	.04	.02
1	Kyle Abbott	.05	.04	.02
2	Troy Afenir	.05	.04	.02
3	Rich Amaral (FC)	.12	.09	.05
4	Ruben Amaro (FC)	.12	.09	.05
5	Billy Ashley (FC)	.25	.20	.10
6	Pedro Astacio (FC)	.25	.20	.10
7	Jim Austin (FC)	.05	.04	.02
8	Robert Ayrault (FC)	.10	.08	.04
9	Kevin Baez (FC)	.10	.08	.04
10	Estaban Beltre	.05	.04	.02
11	Brian Bohanon (FC)	.05	.04	.02
12	Kent Bottenfield (FC)	.12	.09	.05
13	Jeff Branson (FC)	.20	.15	.08
14	Brad Brink	.05	.04	.02
15	John Briscoe (FC)	.10	.08	.04
16	Doug Brocail (FC)	.10	.08	.04
17	Rico Brogna (FC)	.15	.11	.06
18	J.T. Bruett (FC)	.15	.11	.06
19	Jacob Brumfield	.12	.09	.05
20	Jim Bullinger (FC)	.12	.09	.05
21	Kevin Campbell (FC)	.05	.04	.02
22	Pedro Castellano (FC)	.20	.15	.08
23	Mike Christopher (FC)	.05	.04	.02
24	Archi Cianfrocco (FC)	.20	.15	.08
25	Mark Clark (FC)	.12	.09	.05
26	Craig Colbert (FC)	.05	.04	.02
27	Victor Cole (FC)	.12	.09	.05
28	Steve Cooke (FC)	.12	.09	.05
29	Tim Costo (FC)	.15	.11	.06
30	Chad Curtis (FC)	.60	.45	.25
31	Doug Davis (FC)	.10	.08	.04
32	Gary DiSarcina	.05	.04	.02
33	John Doherty (FC)	.10	.08	.04
34	Mike Draper (FC)	.20	.15	.08
35	Monty Fariss	.05	.04	.02
36	Bien Figueroa (FC)	.10	.08	.04
37	John Flaherty (FC)	.05	.04	.02
38	Tim Fortugno (FC)	.10	.08	.04
39	Eric Fox (FC)	.10	.08	.04
40	Jeff Frye (FC)	.10	.08	.04
41	Ramon Garcia (FC)	.12	.09	.05
42	Brent Gates (FC)	.25	.20	.10
43	Tom Goodwin (FC)	.10	.08	.04
44	Buddy Groom (FC)	.12	.09	.05
45	Jeff Grotewold (FC)	.20	.15	.08
46	Juan Guerrero (FC)	.20	.15	.08
47	Johnny Guzman (FC)	.10	.08	.04
48	Shawn Hare (FC)	.12	.09	.05
49	Ryan Hawblitzel (FC)	.20	.15	.08
50	Bert Heffernan (FC)	.05	.04	.02
51	Butch Henry (FC)	.10	.08	.04
52	Cesar Hernandez (FC)	.10	.08	.04
53	Vince Horsman (FC)	.10	.08	.04
54	Steve Hosey (FC)	.10	.08	.04
55	Pat Howell (FC)	.10	.08	.04
56	Peter Hoy (FC)	.10	.08	.04
57	Jon Hurst (FC)	.10	.08	.04
58	Mark Hutton (FC)	.15	.11	.06
59	Shawn Jeter (FC)	.20	.15	.08
60	Joel Johnston (FC)	.05	.04	.02
61	Jeff Kent (FC)	.50	.40	.20
62	Kurt Knudsen (FC)	.05	.04	.02
63	Kevin Koslofski (FC)	.20	.15	.08
64	Danny Leon (FC)	.10	.08	.04
65	Jesse Levis (FC)	.20	.15	.08
66	Tom Marsh (FC)	.10	.08	.04
67	Ed Martel (FC)	.10	.08	.04
68	Al Martin (FC)	.30	.25	.12
69	Pedro Martinez (FC)	.25	.20	.10
70	Derrick May	.10	.08	.04
71	Matt Maysey	.12	.09	.05
72	Russ McGinnis	.05	.04	.02
73	Tim McIntosh	.05	.04	.02
74	Jim McNamara (FC)	.05	.04	.02
75	Jeff McNeely (FC)	.30	.25	.12
76	Rusty Meacham	.05	.04	.02
77	Tony Melendez (FC)	.10	.08	.04
78	Henry Mercedes (FC)	.10	.08	.04
79	Paul Miller (FC)	.10	.08	.04
80	Joe Millette (FC)	.10	.08	.04
81	Blas Minor (FC)	.10	.08	.04
82	Dennis Moeller (FC)	.10	.08	.04
83	Raul Mondesi (FC)	.35	.25	.14
84	Rob Natal (FC)	.20	.15	.08
85	Troy Neel (FC)	.25	.20	.10
86	David Nied (FC)	.75	.60	.30
87	Jerry Nielsen (FC)	.20	.15	.08
88	Donovan Osborne (FC)	.25	.20	.10
89	John Patterson (FC)	.12	.09	.05
90	Roger Pavlik (FC)	.10	.08	.04
91	Dan Peltier (FC)	.10	.08	.04
92	Jim Pena (FC)	.10	.08	.04
93	William Pennyfeather (FC)	.10	.08	.04
94	Mike Perez	.10	.08	.04
95	Hipolito Pichardo (FC)	.20	.15	.08
96	Greg Pirkl (FC)	.05	.04	.02
97	Harvey Pulliam (FC)	.05	.04	.02
98	Manny Ramirez (FC)	1.50	1.25	.60
99	Pat Rapp (FC)	.12	.09	.05
100	Jeff Reboulet (FC)	.10	.08	.04
101	Darren Reed (FC)	.10	.08	.04
102	Shane Reynolds (FC)	.10	.08	.04
103	Bill Risley (FC)	.10	.08	.04
104	Ben Rivera (FC)	.10	.08	.04
105	Henry Rodriguez (FC)	.10	.08	.04
106	Rico Rossy (FC)	.10	.08	.04
107	Johnny Ruffin (FC)	.10	.08	.04
108	Steve Scarsone (FC)	.20	.15	.08
109	Tim Scott (FC)	.05	.04	.02
110	Steve Shifflett (FC)	.10	.08	.04
111	Dave Silvestri (FC)	.20	.15	.08
112	Matt Stairs (FC)	.05	.04	.02
113	William Suero (FC)	.05	.04	.02
114	Jeff Tackett (FC)	.10	.08	.04
115	Eddie Taubensee (FC)	.12	.09	.05
116	Rick Trlicek (FC)	.10	.08	.04
117	Scooter Tucker (FC)	.10	.08	.04
118	Shane Turner (FC)	.10	.08	.04

119	Julio Valera (FC)	.10	.08	.04
120	Paul Wagner (FC)	.10	.08	.04
121	Tim Wakefield (FC)	.20	.15	.08
122	Mike Walker (FC)	.05	.04	.02
123	Bruce Walton (FC)	.05	.04	.02
124	Lenny Webster	.05	.04	.02
125	Bob Wickman (FC)	.25	.20	.10
126	Mike Williams (FC)	.10	.08	.04
127	Kerry Woodson (FC)	.10	.08	.04
128	Eric Young (FC)	.12	.09	.05
129	Kevin Young (FC)	.25	.20	.10
130	Pete Young (FC)	.10	.08	.04
131	Checklist	.05	.04	.02
132	Checklist	.05	.04	.02

1992 Donruss Rookie Phenoms

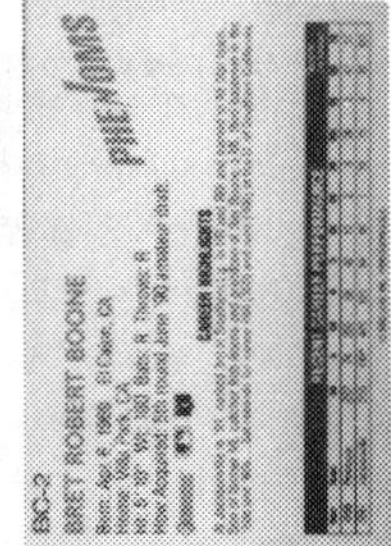

The first 12 cards in this insert set were available in Donruss Rookies foil packs. Cards 13-20 were found randomly packed in jumbo packs. Predominantly black on both front and back, the borders are highlighted with gold. A gold-foil "Phenoms" appears at top front.

		MT	NR MT	EX
Complete Set (20):		50.00	37.00	20.00
Common Player:		.50	.40	.20
1	Moises Alou	2.50	2.00	1.00
2	Bret Boone	1.50	1.25	.60
3	Jeff Conine	2.50	2.00	1.00
4	Dave Fleming	1.50	1.25	.60
5	Tyler Green	.75	.60	.30
6	Eric Karros	1.50	1.25	.60
7	Pat Listach	.75	.60	.30
8	Kenny Lofton	5.00	3.75	2.00
9	Mike Piazza	20.00	15.00	8.00
10	Tim Salmon	15.00	11.00	6.00
11	Andy Stankiewicz	.50	.40	.20
12	Dan Walters	.50	.40	.20
13	Ramon Caraballo	.60	.45	.25
14	Brian Jordan	2.00	1.50	.80
15	Ryan Klesko	7.50	5.50	3.00
16	Sam Militello	.75	.60	.30
17	Frank Seminara	.75	.60	.30
18	Salomon Torres	2.50	2.00	1.00
19	John Valentin	1.50	1.25	.60
20	Wil Cordero	1.50	1.25	.60

1992 Donruss Triple Play

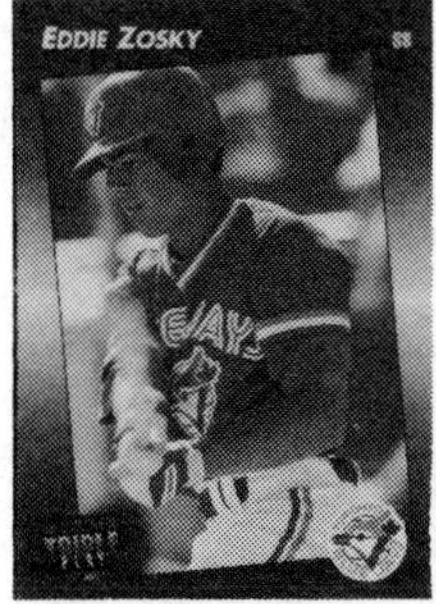

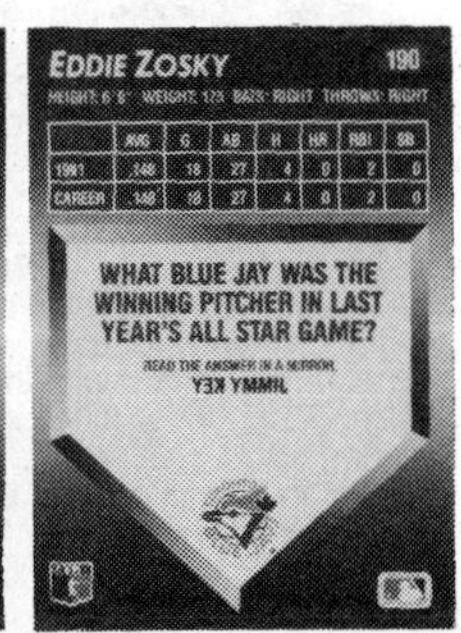

This 264-card set was released in wax pack form only by Donruss. The cards feature red borders and mark the first release of its kind by Donruss. Boyhood photos, mascots and ballparks are among the featured cards. This set was designed to give collectors an alternative product to the high end card sets. The cards are standard sized.

		MT	NR MT	EX
Complete Set (264):		12.00	9.00	4.75
Common Player:		.05	.04	.02
1	SkyDome	.05	.04	.02
2	Tom Foley	.05	.04	.02
3	Scott Erickson	.20	.15	.08
4	Matt Williams	.15	.11	.06
5	Dave Valle	.05	.04	.02
6	Andy Van Slyke (Little Hotshot)	.08	.06	.03
7	Tom Glavine	.15	.11	.06
8	Kevin Appier	.08	.06	.03
9	Pedro Guerrero	.08	.06	.03
10	Terry Steinbach	.06	.05	.02
11	Terry Mulholland	.06	.05	.02
12	Mike Boddicker	.05	.04	.02
13	Gregg Olson	.12	.09	.05
14	Tim Burke	.05	.04	.02
15	Candy Maldonado	.05	.04	.02
16	Orlando Merced	.15	.11	.06
17	Robin Ventura	.15	.10	.05
18	Eric Anthony	.10	.08	.04
19	Greg Maddux	.12	.09	.05
20	Erik Hanson	.06	.05	.02
21	Bob Ojeda	.05	.04	.02
22	Nolan Ryan	.40	.30	.15
23	Dave Righetti	.06	.05	.02
24	Reggie Jefferson	.20	.15	.08
25	Jody Reed	.06	.05	.02
26	Awesome Action (Steve Finley, Gary Carter)	.05	.04	.02
27	Chili Davis	.05	.04	.02
28	Hector Villanueva	.05	.04	.02
29	Cecil Fielder	.20	.15	.10
30	Hal Morris	.12	.09	.05
31	Barry Larkin	.15	.11	.06
32	Bobby Thigpen	.12	.09	.05
33	Andy Benes	.12	.09	.05
34	Harold Baines	.08	.06	.03
35	David Cone	.12	.09	.05
36	Mark Langston	.08	.06	.03
37	Bryan Harvey	.08	.06	.03
38	John Kruk	.12	.09	.05
39	Scott Sanderson	.05	.04	.02
40	Lonnie Smith	.06	.05	.02
41	Awesome Action (Rex Hudler)	.05	.04	.02
42	George Bell	.08	.06	.03
43	Steve Finley	.06	.05	.02
44	Mickey Tettleton	.08	.06	.03
45	Robby Thompson	.05	.04	.02
46	Pat Kelly	.10	.08	.04
47	Marquis Grissom	.12	.09	.05
48	Tony Pena	.05	.04	.02
49	Alex Cole	.05	.04	.02
50	Steve Buechele	.05	.04	.02
51	Ivan Rodriguez	.25	.15	.08
52	John Smiley	.05	.04	.02
53	Gary Sheffield	.20	.15	.08
54	Greg Olson	.08	.06	.03
55	Ramon Martinez	.08	.06	.03
56	B.J. Surhoff	.08	.06	.03
57	Bruce Hurst	.06	.05	.02
58	Todd Stottlemyre	.05	.04	.02
59	Brett Butler	.06	.05	.02
60	Glenn Davis	.10	.08	.04
61	Awesome Action (Glenn Braggs, Kirt Manwaring)	.05	.04	.02
62	Lee Smith	.08	.06	.03
63	Rickey Henderson	.15	.10	.05
64	Fun at the Ballpark (David Cone, Jeff Innis, John Franco)	.05	.04	.02
65	Rick Aguilera	.05	.04	.02
66	Kevin Elster	.05	.04	.02
67	Dwight Evans	.08	.06	.03
68	Andujar Cedeno	.15	.11	.06
69	Brian McRae	.15	.11	.06
70	Benito Santiago	.12	.09	.05
71	Randy Johnson	.06	.05	.02
72	Roberto Kelly	.12	.09	.05
73	Awesome Action (Juan Samuel)	.05	.04	.02
74	Alex Fernandez	.15	.11	.06
75	Felix Jose	.15	.11	.06
76	Brian Harper	.06	.05	.02
77	Scott Sanderson (Little Hotshot)	.05	.04	.02
78	Ken Caminiti	.06	.05	.02
79	Mo Vaughn	.15	.11	.06
80	Roger McDowell	.05	.04	.02
81	Robin Yount	.15	.11	.06
82	Dave Magadan	.06	.05	.02
83	Julio Franco	.12	.09	.05
84	Roberto Alomar	.25	.15	.06
85	Steve Avery	.20	.15	.08
86	Travis Fryman	.30	.25	.12
87	Fred McGriff	.15	.11	.06
88	Dave Stewart	.06	.05	.02
89	Larry Walker	.15	.11	.06
90	Chris Sabo	.15	.11	.06
91	Chuck Finley	.06	.05	.02
92	Dennis Martinez	.06	.05	.02
93	Jeff Johnson	.06	.05	.02
94	Lenny Dykstra	.15	.11	.06
95	Mark Whiten	.08	.06	.03
96	Wade Taylor	.08	.06	.03
97	Lance Dickson	.08	.06	.03
98	Kevin Tapani	.06	.05	.02
99	Awesome Action (Luis Polonia, Tony Phillips)	.05	.04	.02
100	Milt Cuyler	.05	.04	.02
101	Willie McGee	.05	.04	.02
102	Awesome Action (Tony Fernandez, Ryne Sandberg)	.05	.04	.02
103	Albert Belle	.25	.20	.10
104	Todd Hundley	.08	.06	.03
105	Ben McDonald	.15	.11	.06
106	Doug Drabek	.12	.09	.05
107	Tim Raines	.06	.05	.02
108	Joe Carter	.12	.09	.05
109	Reggie Sanders	.20	.15	.08
110	John Olerud	.25	.15	.06
111	Darren Lewis	.15	.11	.06
112	Juan Gonzalez	.75	.40	.20
113	Awesome Action (Andre Dawson)	.05	.04	.02
114	Mark Grace	.12	.09	.05
115	George Brett	.15	.11	.06
116	Barry Bonds	.30	.20	.10
117	Lou Whitaker	.06	.05	.02
118	Jose Oquendo	.05	.04	.02
119	Lee Stevens	.06	.05	.02
120	Phil Plantier	.15	.10	.05
121	Awesome Action (Matt Merullo, Devon White)	.05	.04	.02
122	Greg Vaughn	.12	.09	.05
123	Royce Clayton	.25	.20	.10
124	Bob Welch	.06	.05	.02
125	Juan Samuel	.05	.04	.02
126	Ron Gant	.20	.15	.08
127	Edgar Martinez	.08	.06	.03
128	Andy Ashby	.08	.06	.03
129	Jack McDowell	.08	.06	.03
130	Awesome Action (Dave Henderson, Jerry Browne)	.05	.04	.02
131	Leo Gomez	.12	.09	.05
132	Checklist 1-88	.05	.04	.02
133	Phillie Phanatic	.05	.04	.02
134	Bret Barbarie	.08	.06	.03
135	Kent Hrbek	.06	.05	.02
136	Hall Of Fame	.05	.04	.02
137	Omar Vizquel	.05	.04	.02
138	The Famous Chicken	.05	.04	.02
139	Terry Pendleton	.08	.06	.03
140	Jim Eisenreich	.05	.04	.02
141	Todd Zeile	.06	.05	.02
142	Todd Van Poppel	.20	.15	.08
143	Darren Daulton	.08	.06	.03
144	Mike Macfarlane	.05	.04	.02
145	Luis Mercedes	.20	.15	.08
146	Trevor Wilson	.05	.04	.02
147	Dave Steib	.05	.04	.02
148	Andy Van Slyke	.08	.06	.03
149	Carlton Fisk	.15	.11	.06
150	Craig Biggio	.08	.06	.03
151	Joe Girardi	.05	.04	.02
152	Ken Griffey, Jr.	.75	.50	.25
153	Jose Offerman	.08	.06	.03
154	Bobby Witt	.06	.05	.02
155	Will Clark	.20	.15	.08
156	Steve Olin	.08	.06	.03
157	Greg Harris	.05	.04	.02
158	Dale Murphy (Little Hotshot)	.08	.06	.03
159	Don Mattingly	.20	.15	.08
160	Shawon Dunston	.08	.06	.03
161	Bill Gullickson	.06	.05	.02
162	Paul O'Neill	.06	.05	.02
163	Norm Charlton	.06	.05	.02
164	Bo Jackson	.30	.25	.12
165	Tony Fernandez	.06	.05	.02
166	Dave Henderson	.06	.05	.02
167	Dwight Gooden	.15	.11	.06
168	Junior Felix	.06	.05	.02
169	Lance Parrish	.06	.05	.02
170	Pat Combs	.06	.05	.02
171	Chuck Knoblauch	.12	.09	.05
172	John Smoltz	.10	.08	.04
173	Wrigley Field	.05	.04	.02
174	Andre Dawson	.12	.09	.05
175	Pete Harnisch	.05	.04	.02
176	Alan Trammell	.08	.06	.03
177	Kirk Dressendorfer	.08	.06	.03
178	Matt Nokes	.06	.05	.02
179	Wil Cordero	.25	.20	.10
180	Scott Cooper	.08	.06	.03
181	Glenallen Hill	.06	.05	.02
182	John Franco	.06	.05	.02
183	Rafael Palmeiro	.12	.09	.05
184	Jay Bell	.06	.05	.02
185	Bill Wegman	.06	.05	.02
186	Deion Sanders	.15	.11	.06
187	Darryl Strawberry	.10	.08	.04
188	Jaime Navarro	.06	.05	.02
189	Darren Jackson	.06	.05	.02
190	Eddie Zosky	.06	.05	.02
191	Mike Scioscia	.05	.04	.02
192	Chito Martinez	.15	.11	.06
193	Awesome Action (Pat Kelly, Ron Tingley)	.05	.04	.02
194	Ray Lankford	.12	.09	.05
195	Dennis Eckersley	.10	.08	.04
196	Awesome Action (Ivan Calderon, Mike Maddux)	.05	.04	.02
197	Shane Mack	.06	.05	.02
198	Checklist 89-176	.05	.04	.02
199	Cal Ripken, Jr.	.25	.15	.08
200	Jeff Bagwell	.25	.15	.08
201	David Howard	.05	.04	.02
202	Kirby Puckett	.25	.15	.08
203	Harold Reynolds	.06	.05	.02
204	Jim Abbott	.12	.09	.05
205	Mark Lewis	.08	.06	.03
206	Frank Thomas	1.25	.90	.50
207	Rex Hudler	.05	.04	.02
208	Vince Coleman	.06	.05	.02
209	Delino DeShields	.10	.08	.04
210	Luis Gonzalez	.15	.11	.06
211	Wade Boggs	.12	.09	.05
212	Orel Hershiser	.08	.06	.03
213	Cal Eldred	.25	.20	.10
214	Jose Canseco	.10	.05	.02
215	Jose Guzman	.06	.05	.02
216	Roger Clemens	.20	.15	.08
217	Dave Justice	.30	.25	.14
218	Tony Phillips	.06	.05	.02
219	Tony Gwynn	.15	.10	.05
220	Mitch Williams	.06	.05	.02
221	Bill Sampen	.05	.04	.02
222	Billy Hatcher	.05	.04	.02
223	Gary Gaetti	.06	.05	.02
224	Tim Wallach	.06	.05	.02
225	Kevin Maas	.06	.05	.02
226	Kevin Brown	.06	.05	.02
227	Sandy Alomar	.15	.11	.06
228	John Habyan	.05	.04	.02
229	Ryne Sandberg	.20	.15	.08
230	Greg Gagne	.05	.04	.02
231	Autographs (Mark McGwire)	.05	.04	.02
232	Mike LaValliere	.05	.04	.02

233	Mark Gubicza	.05	.04	.02
234	Lance Parrish (Little Hotshot)	.06	.05	.02
235	Carlos Baerga	.25	.15	.08
236	Howard Johnson	.12	.09	.05
237	Mike Mussina	.30	.20	.10
238	Ruben Sierra	.10	.08	.04
239	Lance Johnson	.06	.05	.02
240	Devon White	.06	.05	.02
241	Dan Wilson	.25	.20	.10
242	Kelly Gruber	.12	.09	.05
243	Brett Butler (Little Hotshot)	.06	.05	.02
244	Ozzie Smith	.15	.11	.06
245	Chuck McElroy	.05	.04	.02
246	Shawn Boskie	.06	.05	.02
247	Mark Davis	.05	.04	.02
248	Bill Landrum	.05	.04	.02
249	Frank Tanana	.05	.04	.02
250	Darryl Hamilton	.08	.06	.03
251	Gary DiSarcina	.05	.04	.02
252	Mike Greenwell	.12	.09	.05
253	Cal Ripken, Jr. (Little Hotshot)	.25	.15	.06
254	Paul Molitor	.12	.09	.05
255	Tim Teufel	.05	.04	.02
256	Chris Hoiles	.35	.25	.14
257	Rob Dibble	.12	.09	.05
258	Sid Bream	.05	.04	.02
259	Chito Martinez	.08	.06	.03
260	Dale Murphy	.08	.06	.03
261	Greg Hibbard	.06	.05	.02
262	Mark McGwire	.15	.10	.05
263	Oriole Park	.05	.04	.02
264	Checklist 177-264	.05	.04	.02

1992 Donruss Triple Play Gallery of Stars

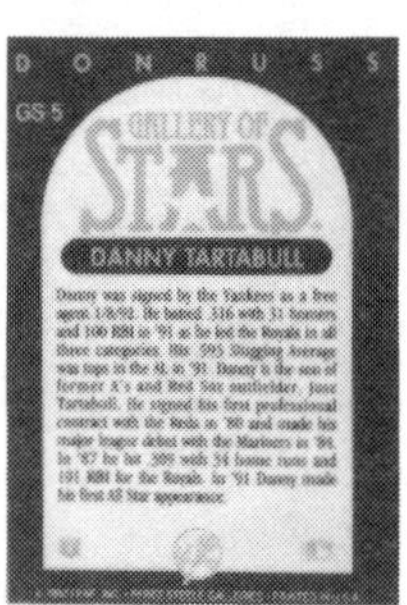

Two levels of scarcity are represented in this 12-card insert issue. Cards #1-6 (all cards have a GS prefix to the card number) feature in their new uniforms players who changed teams for 1993. Those inserts were found in the standard Triple Play foil packs and are somewhat more common than cards 7-12, which were found only in jumbo packs and which feature a better selection of established stars and rookies. All of the inserts feature the artwork of Dick Perez, with player portraits set against a colorful background. There is a red "Gallery of Stars" banner above the player, and a red cartouche below with the player's name. Silver-foil accents highlight the front design. Backs are red with a white "tombstone" containing a career summary. Logos are in gray.

		MT	NR MT	EX
Complete Set (12):		24.00	18.00	9.50
Common Player:		1.00	.70	.40
1	Bobby Bonilla	1.50	1.25	.60
2	Wally Joyner	1.50	1.25	.60
3	Jack Morris	1.00	.70	.40
4	Steve Sax	1.00	.70	.40
5	Danny Tartabull	1.50	1.25	.60
6	Frank Viola	1.00	.70	.40
7	Jeff Bagwell	2.00	1.50	.80
8	Ken Griffey, Jr.	7.00	5.25	2.75
9	David Justice	3.00	2.25	1.25
10	Ryan Klesko	4.00	3.00	1.50
11	Cal Ripken, Jr.	5.00	3.75	2.00
12	Frank Thomas	7.00	5.25	2.75

Grading Guide

Mint (MT): A perfect card. Well-centered with all corners sharp and square. No creases, stains, edge nicks, surface marks, yellowing or fading.

Near Mint (NM): A nearly perfect card. At first glance, a NM card appears to be perfect. May be slightly off-center. No surface marks, creases or loss of gloss.

Excellent (EX): Corners are still fairly sharp with only moderate wear. Borders may be off-center. No creases or stains on fronts or backs, but may show slight loss of surface luster.

Very Good (VG): Shows obvious handling. May have rounded corners, minor creases, major gum or wax stains. No major creases, tape marks, writing, etc.

Good (G): A well-worn card, but exhibits no intentional damage. May have major or multiple creases. Corners may be rounded well beyond card border.

1992 Donruss McDonald's

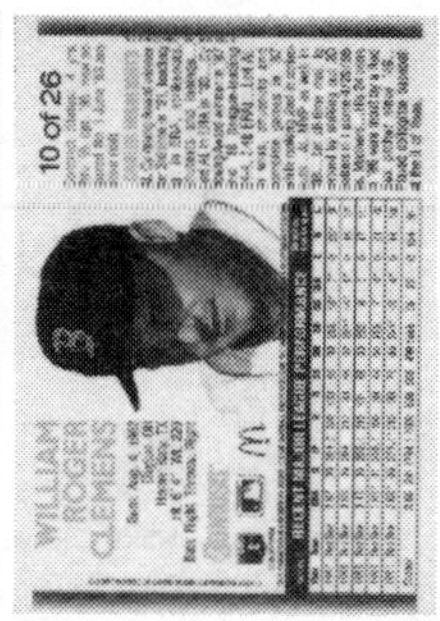

McDonald's restaurants in Ontario released a 26-card All-Star baseball card set in 1992 featuring many of the top players in the game. The cards were sold at Canadian McDonald's in packs of four with the purchase of a meal. Additionally, the company offered a six-card Toronto Blue Jays subset.

		MT	NR MT	EX
Complete Set (33):		20.00	15.00	8.00
Common Player:		.25	.20	.10
1	Cal Ripken, Jr.	.75	.60	.30
2	Frank Thomas	1.00	.75	.40
3	George Brett	.60	.45	.25
4	Roberto Kelly	.25	.20	.10
5	Nolan Ryan	1.00	.75	.40
6	Ryne Sandberg	.75	.60	.30
7	Darryl Strawberry	.35	.25	.14
8	Len Dykstra	.35	.25	.14
9	Fred McGriff	.35	.25	.14
10	Roger Clemens	.35	.25	.14
11	Sandy Alomar, Jr.	.25	.20	.10
12	Robin Yount	.60	.45	.25
13	Jose Canseco	.60	.45	.25
14	Jimmy Key	.25	.20	.10
15	Barry Larkin	.35	.25	.14
16	Don Mattingly	.60	.45	.25
17	Andy Van Slyke	.35	.25	.14
18	Will Clark	.50	.40	.20
19	Mark Langston	.25	.20	.10
20	Cecil Fielder	.50	.40	.20
21	Kirby Puckett	.50	.40	.20
22	Ken Griffey	.75	.60	.30
23	Dave Justice	.35	.25	.14
24	Jeff Bagwell	.35	.25	.14
25	Howard Johnson	.25	.20	.10
26	Ozzie Smith	.35	.25	.14
----	Checklist	.25	.20	.10
	Gold Blue Jays			
1	Roberto Alomar	.75	.60	.30
2	Joe Carter	.60	.45	.25
3	Kelly Gruber	.50	.40	.20
4	Jack Morris	.50	.40	.20
5	Tom Henke	.50	.40	.20
6	Devon White	.60	.45	.25

1992 Donruss Nolan Ryan Career Series

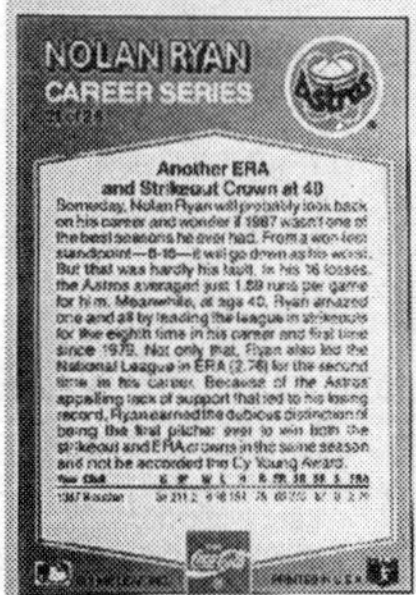

This 26-card set was issued in conjunction with Coca-Cola to honor Nolan Ryan's 26 major league seasons. One Nolan Ryan card was packaged with three regular 1992 Donruss cards in special 12-packs of Coke. Complete sets, in a black, red and gold box, were available through a mail-in offer. The 2-1/2" x 3-1/2" cards have a full-color photo on front, framed by a gold border. Ryan's name is printed in gold toward the bottom, above a blue bar which presents a team and year. The Coke logo is at upper right. On back there are details of Ryan's performance in the indicated year, the card number, and team and Coke logos.

		MT	NR MT	EX
Complete Set (26):		25.00	19.00	10.00
Common Card:		1.00	.70	.40
	NEW YORK METS			
1	1966 Breaking In (Nolan Ryan)	1.00	.70	.40
2	1968 Record-Setting Rookie (Nolan Ryan)	1.00	.70	.40
3	1969 World Champions (Nolan Ryan)	1.00	.70	.40
4	1970 Growing Pains (Nolan Ryan)	1.00	.70	.40
5	1971 Traded! (Nolan Ryan)	1.00	.70	.40
	CALIFORNIA ANGELS			
6	1972 Fitted For a Halo (Nolan Ryan)	1.00	.70	.40
7	1973 The First Two No-Nos and a Record (Nolan Ryan)	1.00	.70	.40
8	1974 No-Hitter No. 3/Another K Record (Nolan Ryan)	1.00	.70	.40
9	1975 Tying Koufax (Nolan Ryan)	1.00	.70	.40
10	1976 Back on Track (Nolan Ryan)	1.00	.70	.40
11	1977 Carrying the Load (Nolan Ryan)	1.00	.70	.40
12	1978 A Year of Injuries (Nolan Ryan)	1.00	.70	.40
13	1979 California Farewell (Nolan Ryan)	1.00	.70	.40
	HOUSTON ASTROS			
14	1980 Coming Home (Nolan Ryan)	1.00	.70	.40
15	1981 A Gusher in Houston (Nolan Ryan)	1.00	.70	.40
16	1982 Mounting 'Em Up (Nolan Ryan)	1.00	.70	.40
17	1983 Passing the Big Train (Nolan Ryan)	1.00	.70	.40
18	1984 Misleading Signs of Age (Nolan Ryan)	1.00	.70	.40
19	1985 Another Milestone/a New Contract (Nolan Ryan)	1.00	.70	.40
20	1986 The Elbow Flares Up Again (Nolan Ryan)	1.00	.70	.40
21	1987 Another ERA/Strikeout Crown at 40 (Nolan Ryan)	1.00	.70	.40
22	1988 Leaving Home Again (Nolan Ryan)	1.00	.70	.40
	TEXAS RANGERS			
23	1989 5,000 Strikeouts at Texas (Nolan Ryan)	1.00	.70	.40
24	1990 Win No. 300, No-hitter No. 6 (Nolan Ryan)	1.00	.70	.40
25	1991 No-hitter No. 7 (Nolan Ryan)	1.00	.70	.40
26	1992 Man of Records (Nolan Ryan)	1.00	.70	.40

1993 Donruss

Rated Rookies and a randomly inserted Diamond Kings subset once again are featured in the 1993 Donruss set. Series I of the set includes 396 cards. The card fronts feature white borders surrounding a full-color player photo. The player's name and position appear at the bottom of the photo along with a diamond featuring the team logo. The flip sides feature an additional photo, biographical information and career statistics. The cards are numbered on the back and the series the card appears in is given with the number. The cards are UV coated. Series II contains a subset of players labeled with an "Expansion Draft" headline over their Marlins or Rockies team logo on front, even though the player photos are in the uniform of their previous team.

		MT	NR MT	EX
Complete Set (792):		30.00	22.00	12.00
Common Player:		.05	.04	.02
1	Craig Lefferts	.05	.04	.02
2	Kent Mercker	.06	.05	.02
3	Phil Plantier	.10	.08	.04
4	*Alex Arias*	.15	.11	.06
5	Julio Valera	.08	.06	.03
6	Dan Wilson (FC)	.12	.09	.05
7	Frank Thomas	1.25	.90	.50
8	Eric Anthony	.08	.06	.03
9	Derek Lilliquist	.05	.04	.02
10	*Rafael Bournigal*	.12	.09	.05
11	*Manny Alexander* (Rated Rookie)	.12	.09	.05
12	Bret Barberie	.08	.06	.03
13	Mickey Tettleton	.08	.06	.03
14	Anthony Young	.08	.06	.03
15	Tim Spehr	.08	.06	.03

16	*Bob Ayrault*	.10	.08	.04
17	Bill Wegman	.06	.05	.02
18	Jay Bell	.08	.06	.03
19	Rick Aguilera	.08	.06	.03
20	Todd Zeile	.08	.06	.03
21	Steve Farr	.06	.05	.02
22	Andy Benes	.08	.06	.03
23	Lance Blankenship	.05	.04	.02
24	Ted Wood	.08	.06	.03
25	Omar Vizquel	.05	.04	.02
26	Steve Avery	.08	.06	.03
27	Brian Bohanon	.08	.06	.03
28	Rick Wilkins	.08	.06	.03
29	Devon White	.08	.06	.03
30	*Bobby Ayala* (FC)	.12	.09	.05
31	Leo Gomez	.08	.06	.03
32	Mike Simms	.08	.06	.03
33	Ellis Burks	.08	.06	.03
34	Steve Wilson	.05	.04	.02
35	Jim Abbott	.08	.06	.03
36	Tim Wallach	.06	.05	.02
37	Wilson Alvarez	.06	.05	.02
38	Daryl Boston	.05	.04	.02
39	Sandy Alomar, Jr.	.10	.08	.04
40	Mitch Williams	.08	.06	.03
41	Rico Brogna	.10	.08	.04
42	Gary Varsho	.05	.04	.02
43	Kevin Appier	.08	.06	.03
44	Eric Wedge (Rated Rookie)	.12	.09	.05
45	Dante Bichette	.05	.04	.02
46	Jose Oquendo	.05	.04	.02
47	*Mike Trombley*	.12	.09	.05
48	Dan Walters	.08	.06	.03
49	Gerald Williams	.08	.06	.03
50	Bud Black	.05	.04	.02
51	Bobby Witt	.06	.05	.02
52	Mark Davis	.05	.04	.02
53	*Shawn Barton*	.10	.07	.04
54	Paul Assenmacher	.05	.04	.02
55	Kevin Reimer	.06	.05	.02
56	*Billy Ashley* (Rated Rookie)	.30	.25	.12
57	Eddie Zosky	.08	.06	.03
58	Chris Sabo	.08	.06	.03
59	Billy Ripken	.05	.04	.02
60	*Scooter Tucker*	.12	.09	.05
61	*Tim Wakefield* (Rated Rookie)	.10	.08	.04
62	Mitch Webster	.05	.04	.02
63	Jack Clark	.06	.05	.02
64	Mark Gardner	.06	.05	.02
65	Lee Stevens	.06	.05	.02
66	Todd Hundley	.08	.06	.03
67	Bobby Thigpen	.08	.06	.03
68	Dave Hollins	.10	.08	.04
69	Jack Armstrong	.06	.05	.02
70	Alex Cole	.06	.05	.02
71	Mark Carreon	.05	.04	.02
72	Todd Worrell	.06	.05	.02
73	*Steve Shifflett*	.12	.09	.05
74	Jerald Clark	.06	.05	.02
75	Paul Molitor	.08	.06	.03
76	*Larry Carter*	.12	.09	.05
77	Rich Rowland (FC)	.10	.08	.04
78	Damon Berryhill	.06	.05	.02
79	Willie Banks	.08	.06	.03
80	Hector Villanueva	.06	.05	.02
81	Mike Gallego	.06	.05	.02
82	Tim Belcher	.06	.05	.02
83	Mike Bordick	.08	.06	.03
84	Criag Biggio	.08	.06	.03
85	Lance Parrish	.06	.05	.02
86	Brett Butler	.06	.05	.02
87	Mike Timlin	.06	.05	.02
88	Brian Barnes	.06	.05	.02
89	Brady Anderson	.08	.06	.03
90	D.J. Dozier	.08	.06	.03
91	Frank Viola	.08	.06	.03
92	Darren Daulton	.08	.06	.03
93	Chad Curtis	.15	.11	.06
94	Zane Smith	.05	.04	.02
95	George Bell	.08	.06	.03
96	Rex Hudler	.05	.04	.02
97	Mark Whiten	.08	.06	.03
98	Tim Teufel	.05	.04	.02
99	Kevin Ritz	.05	.04	.02
100	Jeff Brantley	.05	.04	.02
101	Jeff Conine	.08	.06	.03
102	*Vinny Castilla* (FC)	.15	.11	.06
103	Greg Vaughn	.08	.06	.03
104	Steve Buechele	.06	.05	.02
105	Darren Reed	.06	.05	.02
106	Bip Roberts	.08	.06	.03
107	John Habyan	.05	.04	.02
108	Scott Servais	.05	.04	.02
109	Walt Weiss	.05	.04	.02
110	*J.T. Snow* (Rated Rookie)	.30	.25	.12
111	Jay Buhner	.08	.06	.03
112	Darryl Strawberry	.08	.06	.03
113	*Roger Pavlik*	.12	.09	.05
114	Chris Nabholz	.06	.05	.02
115	Pat Borders	.06	.05	.02
116	*Pat Howell*	.12	.09	.05
117	Gregg Olson	.08	.06	.03
118	Curt Schilling	.08	.06	.03
119	Roger Clemens	.25	.20	.10
120	*Victor Cole*	.12	.09	.05
121	Gary DiSarcina	.05	.04	.02
122	Checklist 1-80	.05	.04	.02
123	Steve Sax	.08	.06	.03
124	Chuck Carr (FC)	.08	.06	.03
125	Mark Lewis	.08	.06	.03
126	Tony Gwynn	.08	.06	.03
127	Travis Fryman	.20	.15	.08
128	Dave Burba	.06	.05	.02
129	Wally Joyner	.08	.06	.03
130	John Smoltz	.08	.06	.03
131	Cal Eldred	.10	.07	.04
132	Checklist 81-159	.05	.04	.02
133	Arthur Rhodes	.10	.08	.04

134	Jeff Blauser	.06	.05	.02
135	Scott Cooper	.06	.05	.02
136	Doug Strange	.06	.05	.02
137	Luis Sojo	.06	.05	.02
138	*Jeff Branson*	.15	.11	.06
139	Alex Fernandez	.08	.06	.03
140	Ken Caminiti	.06	.05	.02
141	Charles Nagy	.08	.06	.03
142	Tom Candiotti	.06	.05	.02
143	Willie Green (Rated Rookie)	.12	.09	.05
144	John Vander Wal	.06	.05	.02
145	*Kurt Knudsen*	.10	.08	.04
146	John Franco	.06	.05	.02
147	*Eddie Pierce*	.12	.09	.05
148	Kim Batiste	.08	.06	.03
149	Darren Holmes	.05	.04	.02
150	*Steve Cooke*	.15	.11	.06
151	Terry Jorgensen	.08	.06	.03
152	*Mark Clark*	.12	.09	.05
153	Randy Velarde	.05	.04	.02
154	Greg Harris	.05	.04	.02
155	*Kevin Campbell*	.10	.08	.04
156	John Burkett	.06	.05	.02
157	Kevin Mitchell	.08	.06	.03
158	Deion Sanders	.10	.08	.04
159	Jose Canseco	.15	.11	.06
160	*Jeff Hartsock*	.12	.09	.05
161	*Tom Quinlan* (FC)	.15	.11	.06
162	*Tim Pugh* (FC)	.25	.20	.10
163	Glenn Davis	.08	.06	.03
164	*Shane Reynolds*	.12	.09	.05
165	Jody Reed	.06	.05	.02
166	Mike Sharperson	.06	.05	.02
167	Scott Lewis	.06	.05	.02
168	Dennis Martinez	.06	.05	.02
169	Scott Radinsky	.06	.05	.02
170	Dave Gallagher	.05	.04	.02
171	Jim Thome	.08	.06	.03
172	Terry Mulholland	.06	.05	.02
173	Milt Cuyler	.06	.05	.02
174	Bob Patterson	.05	.04	.02
175	Jeff Montgomery	.06	.05	.02
176	Tim Salmon (Rated Rookie)	1.25	.90	.50
177	Franklin Stubbs	.05	.04	.02
178	Donovan Osborne	.10	.08	.04
179	*Jeff Reboulet*	.10	.08	.04
180	*Jeremy Hernandez* (FC)	.15	.11	.06
181	Charlie Hayes	.06	.05	.02
182	Matt Williams	.08	.06	.03
183	Mike Raczka	.10	.07	.04
184	Francisco Cabrera	.05	.04	.02
185	Rich DeLucia	.05	.04	.02
186	Sammy Sosa	.06	.05	.02
187	Ivan Rodriguez	.12	.09	.05
188	Bret Boone (Rated Rookie)	.15	.11	.06
189	Juan Guzman	.12	.09	.05
190	Tom Browning	.06	.05	.02
191	Randy Milligan	.06	.05	.02
192	Steve Finley	.06	.05	.02
193	John Patterson (Rated Rookie)	.08	.06	.03
194	Kip Gross	.05	.04	.02
195	Tony Fossas	.05	.04	.02
196	Ivan Calderon	.08	.06	.03
197	Junior Felix	.06	.05	.02
198	Pete Schourek	.06	.05	.02
199	Craig Grebeck	.06	.05	.02
200	Juan Bell	.06	.05	.02
201	Glenallen Hill	.06	.05	.02
202	Danny Jackson	.06	.05	.02
203	John Kiely	.12	.09	.05
204	Bob Tewksbury	.08	.06	.03
205	*Kevin Koslofski* (FC)	.15	.11	.06
206	Craig Shipley	.08	.06	.03
207	John Jaha (FC)	.15	.11	.06
208	Royce Clayton	.10	.08	.04
209	Mike Piazza (Rated Rookie)	2.00	1.50	.80
210	Ron Gant	.08	.06	.03
211	Scott Erickson	.08	.06	.03
212	Doug Dascenzo	.05	.04	.02
213	Andy Stankiewicz (FC)	.12	.09	.05
214	Geronimo Berroa	.05	.04	.02
215	Dennis Eckersley	.08	.06	.03
216	Al Osuna	.05	.04	.02
217	Tino Martinez	.08	.06	.03
218	*Henry Rodriguez*	.12	.09	.05
219	Ed Sprague	.08	.06	.03
220	Ken Hill	.08	.06	.03
221	Chito Martinez	.08	.06	.03
222	Bret Saberhagen	.08	.06	.03
223	Mike Greenwell	.08	.06	.03
224	Mickey Morandini	.08	.06	.03
225	Chuck Finley	.08	.06	.03
226	Denny Neagle	.08	.06	.03
227	Kirk McCaskill	.06	.05	.02
228	Rheal Cormier	.08	.06	.03
229	Paul Sorrento	.08	.06	.03
230	Darrin Jackson	.06	.05	.02
231	Rob Deer	.06	.05	.02
232	Bill Swift	.06	.05	.02
233	Kevin McReynolds	.08	.06	.03
234	Terry Pendleton	.08	.06	.03
235	Dave Nilsson	.12	.09	.05
236	Chuck McElroy	.05	.04	.02
237	Derek Parks	.06	.05	.02
238	Norm Charlton	.08	.06	.03
239	Matt Nokes	.06	.05	.02
240	*Juan Guerrero*	.15	.11	.06
241	Jeff Parrett	.05	.04	.02
242	Ryan Thompson (Rated Rookie)	.25	.20	.10
243	Dave Fleming	.10	.08	.04
244	Dave Hansen	.05	.04	.02
245	Monty Fariss	.05	.04	.02
246	*Archi Cianfrocco*	.15	.11	.06
247	*Pat Hentgen* (FC)	.15	.11	.06
248	Bill Pecota	.05	.04	.02
249	Ben McDonald	.08	.06	.03
250	Cliff Brantley	.08	.06	.03
251	*John Valentin*	.15	.11	.06

252	Jeff King	.06	.05	.02
253	*Reggie Williams* (FC)	.15	.11	.06
254	Checklist 160-238	.05	.04	.02
255	Ozzie Guillen	.08	.06	.03
256	Mike Perez	.06	.05	.02
257	Thomas Howard	.06	.05	.02
258	Kurt Stillwell	.06	.05	.02
259	Mike Henneman	.06	.05	.02
260	Steve Decker	.06	.05	.02
261	Brent Mayne	.06	.05	.02
262	Otis Nixon	.08	.06	.03
263	*Mark Keifer* (FC)	.15	.11	.06
264	Checklist 239-317	.05	.04	.02
265	*Richie Lewis* (FC)	.15	.11	.06
266	*Pat Gomez*	.12	.09	.05
267	*Scott Taylor* (FC)	.15	.11	.06
268	Shawon Dunston	.06	.05	.02
269	Greg Myers	.05	.04	.02
270	Tim Costo	.10	.08	.04
271	Greg Hibbard	.06	.05	.02
272	Pete Harnisch	.06	.05	.02
273	*Dave Mlicki* (FC)	.12	.09	.05
274	Orel Hershiser	.08	.06	.03
275	Sean Berry (Rated Rookie)	.08	.06	.03
276	Doug Simons	.08	.06	.03
277	*John Doherty*	.10	.08	.04
278	Eddie Murray	.08	.06	.03
279	Chris Haney	.08	.06	.03
280	Stan Javier	.05	.04	.02
281	Jaime Navarro	.08	.06	.03
282	Orlando Merced	.08	.06	.03
283	Kent Hrbek	.08	.06	.03
284	Bernard Gilkey	.08	.06	.03
285	Russ Springer	.06	.05	.02
286	Mike Maddux	.05	.04	.02
287	*Eric Fox*	.12	.09	.05
288	Mark Leonard	.05	.04	.02
289	Tim Leary	.05	.04	.02
290	Brian Hunter	.08	.06	.03
291	Donald Harris	.08	.06	.03
292	Bob Scanlan	.05	.04	.02
293	Turner Ward	.08	.06	.03
294	Hal Morris	.08	.06	.03
295	Jimmy Poole	.08	.06	.03
296	Doug Jones	.06	.05	.02
297	Tony Pena	.06	.05	.02
298	Ramon Martinez	.08	.06	.03
299	*Tim Fortugno*	.12	.09	.05
300	Marquis Grissom	.10	.08	.04
301	Lance Johnson	.06	.05	.02
302	*Jeff Kent*	.15	.11	.06
303	Reggie Jefferson	.08	.06	.03
304	Wes Chamberlain	.08	.06	.03
305	*Shawn Hare*	.12	.09	.05
306	Mike LaValliere	.05	.04	.02
307	Gregg Jefferies	.08	.06	.03
308	*Troy Neel* (Rated Rookie)	.20	.15	.08
309	Pat Listach	.10	.08	.04
310	Geronimo Pena	.06	.05	.02
311	Pedro Munoz	.08	.06	.03
312	*Guillermo Velasquez*	.10	.08	.04
313	Roberto Kelly	.08	.06	.03
314	Mike Jackson	.05	.04	.02
315	Rickey Henderson	.12	.09	.05
316	Mark Lemke	.06	.05	.02
317	Erik Hanson	.08	.06	.03
318	Derrick May	.08	.06	.03
319	Geno Petralli	.05	.04	.02
320	Melvin Nieves (Rated Rookie)	.20	.15	.08
321	*Doug Linton* (FC)	.15	.11	.06
322	Rob Dibble	.08	.06	.03
323	Chris Hoiles	.10	.08	.04
324	Jimmy Jones	.05	.04	.02
325	Dave Staton (Rated Rookie)	.06	.05	.02
326	Pedro Martinez	.10	.08	.04
327	*Paul Quantrill*	.12	.09	.05
328	Greg Colbrunn	.05	.04	.02
329	*Hilly Hathaway*	.12	.09	.05
330	Jeff Innis	.06	.05	.02
331	Ron Karkovice	.06	.05	.02
332	*Keith Shepherd*	.12	.09	.05
333	*Alan Embree*	.12	.09	.05
334	*Paul Wagner*	.15	.11	.06
335	*Dave Haas* (FC)	.15	.11	.06
336	Ozzie Canseco	.10	.08	.04
337	Bill Sampen	.05	.04	.02
338	Rich Rodriguez	.05	.04	.02
339	Dean Palmer	.08	.06	.03
340	Greg Litton	.05	.04	.02
341	Jim Tatum (Rated Rookie)	.10	.07	.04
342	*Todd Haney*	.10	.08	.04
343	Larry Casian	.06	.05	.02
344	Ryne Sandberg	.25	.20	.10
345	*Sterling Hitchcock*	.30	.25	.12
346	Chris Hammond	.06	.05	.02
347	*Vince Horsman*	.12	.09	.05
348	*Butch Henry*	.12	.09	.05
349	Dann Howitt	.05	.04	.02
350	Roger McDowell	.05	.04	.02
351	Jack Morris	.08	.06	.03
352	Bill Krueger	.05	.04	.02
353	*Cris Colon*	.12	.09	.05
354	*Joe Vitko*	.12	.09	.05
355	Willie McGee	.08	.06	.03
356	Jay Baller	.06	.05	.02
357	Pat Mahomes	.10	.08	.04
358	Roger Mason	.05	.04	.02
359	*Jerry Nielsen*	.15	.11	.06
360	Tom Pagnozzi	.06	.05	.02
361	*Kevin Baez*	.15	.11	.06
362	*Tim Scott*	.15	.11	.06
363	*Domingo Martinez* (FC)	.20	.15	.08
364	Kirt Manwaring	.05	.04	.02
365	Rafael Palmeiro	.08	.06	.03
366	Ray Lankford	.12	.09	.05
367	Tim McIntosh	.08	.06	.03
368	*Jessie Hollins* (FC)	.15	.11	.06
369	Scott Leius	.06	.05	.02

370	Bill Doran	.05	.04	.02
371	*Sam Militello*	.10	.08	.04
372	Ryan Bowen	.08	.06	.03
373	Dave Henderson	.08	.06	.03
374	Dan Smith (FC) (Rated Rookie)	.12	.09	.05
375	*Steve Reed*	.12	.09	.05
376	Jose Offerman	.08	.06	.03
377	Kevin Brown	.08	.06	.03
378	Darrin Fletcher	.05	.04	.02
379	Duane Ward	.06	.05	.02
380	Wayne Kirby (FC) (Rated Rookie)	.12	.09	.05
381	*Steve Scarsone*	.15	.11	.06
382	Mariano Duncan	.06	.05	.02
383	*Ken Ryan* (FC)	.15	.11	.06
384	Lloyd McClendon	.05	.04	.02
385	Brian Holman	.05	.04	.02
386	Braulio Castillo	.08	.06	.03
387	*Danny Leon*	.12	.09	.05
388	Omar Olivares	.05	.04	.02
389	Kevin Wickander	.05	.04	.02
390	Fred McGriff	.20	.15	.08
391	Phil Clark (FC)	.12	.09	.05
392	Darren Lewis	.06	.05	.02
393	*Phil Hiatt*	.20	.15	.08
394	Mike Morgan	.06	.05	.02
395	Shane Mack	.08	.06	.03
396	Checklist 318-396	.05	.04	.02
397	David Segui	.05	.04	.02
398	Rafael Belliard	.05	.04	.02
399	Tim Naehring	.05	.04	.02
400	Frank Castillo	.05	.04	.02
401	Joe Grahe	.05	.04	.02
402	Reggie Sanders	.10	.08	.04
403	Roberto Hernandez	.05	.04	.02
404	Luis Gonzalez	.05	.04	.02
405	Carlos Baerga	.25	.20	.10
406	Carlos Hernandez	.05	.04	.02
407	Pedro Astacio (Rated Rookie)	.15	.11	.06
408	Mel Rojas	.05	.04	.02
409	Scott Livingstone	.05	.04	.02
410	Chico Walker	.05	.04	.02
411	Brian McRae	.05	.04	.02
412	Ben Rivera	.05	.04	.02
413	Ricky Bones	.05	.04	.02
414	Andy Van Slyke	.05	.04	.02
415	Chuck Knoblauch	.12	.09	.05
416	Luis Alicea	.05	.04	.02
417	Bob Wickman	.12	.09	.05
418	Doug Brocail	.05	.04	.02
419	Scott Brosius	.05	.04	.02
420	Rod Beck	.05	.04	.02
421	Edgar Martinez	.05	.04	.02
422	Ryan Klesko	.75	.60	.30
423	Nolan Ryan	.75	.60	.30
424	Rey Sanchez	.05	.04	.02
425	Roberto Alomar	.25	.20	.10
426	Barry Larkin	.10	.08	.04
427	Mike Mussina	.20	.15	.08
428	Jeff Bagwell	.15	.11	.06
429	Mo Vaughn	.10	.08	.04
430	Eric Karros	.10	.07	.04
431	John Orton	.05	.04	.02
432	Wil Cordero	.15	.11	.06
433	Jack McDowell	.08	.06	.03
434	Howard Johnson	.05	.04	.02
435	Albert Belle	.25	.20	.10
436	John Kruk	.05	.04	.02
437	Skeeter Barnes	.05	.04	.02
438	Don Slaught	.05	.04	.02
439	Rusty Meacham	.05	.04	.02
440	Tim Laker (Rated Rookie)	.12	.09	.05
441	Robin Yount	.10	.08	.04
442	Brian Jordan	.10	.07	.04
443	Kevin Tapani	.05	.04	.02
444	Gary Sheffield	.15	.11	.06
445	Rich Monteleone	.05	.04	.02
446	Will Clark	.15	.11	.06
447	Jerry Browne	.05	.04	.02
448	Jeff Treadway	.05	.04	.02
449	Mike Schooler	.05	.04	.02
450	Mike Harkey	.05	.04	.02
451	Julio Franco	.05	.04	.02
452	Kevin Young (Rated Rookie)	.12	.09	.05
453	Kelly Gruber	.05	.04	.02
454	Jose Rijo	.05	.04	.02
455	Mike Devereaux	.05	.04	.02
456	Andujar Cedeno	.08	.06	.03
457	Damion Easley (Rated Rookie)	.12	.09	.05
458	Kevin Gross	.05	.04	.02
459	Matt Young	.05	.04	.02
460	Matt Stairs	.05	.04	.02
461	Luis Polonia	.05	.04	.02
462	Dwight Gooden	.05	.04	.02
463	Warren Newson	.05	.04	.02
464	Jose DeLeon	.05	.04	.02
465	Jose Mesa	.05	.04	.02
466	Danny Cox	.05	.04	.02
467	Dan Gladden	.05	.04	.02
468	Gerald Perry	.05	.04	.02
469	Mike Boddicker	.05	.04	.02
470	Jeff Gardner	.05	.04	.02
471	Doug Henry	.05	.04	.02
472	Mike Benajmin	.05	.04	.02
473	Dan Peltier (Rated Rookie)	.05	.04	.02
474	Mike Stanton	.05	.04	.02
475	John Smiley	.05	.04	.02
476	Dwight Smith	.05	.04	.02
477	Jim Leyritz	.05	.04	.02
478	Dwayne Henry	.05	.04	.02
479	Mark McGwire	.10	.08	.04
480	Pete Incaviglia	.05	.04	.02
481	Dave Cochrane	.05	.04	.02
482	Eric Davis	.05	.04	.02
483	John Olerud	.25	.20	.10
484	Ken Bottenfield	.12	.09	.05
485	Mark McLemore	.05	.04	.02
486	Dave Magadan	.05	.04	.02
487	John Marzano	.05	.04	.02
488	Ruben Amaro	.05	.04	.02
489	Rob Ducey	.05	.04	.02
490	Stan Belinda	.05	.04	.02
491	Dan Pasqua	.05	.04	.02
492	Joe Magrane	.05	.04	.02
493	Brook Jacoby	.05	.04	.02
494	Gene Harris	.05	.04	.02
495	Mark Leiter	.05	.04	.02
496	Bryan Hickerson	.05	.04	.02
497	Tom Gordon	.05	.04	.02
498	Pete Smith	.05	.04	.02
499	Chris Bosio	.05	.04	.02
500	Shawn Boskie	.05	.04	.02
501	Dave West	.05	.04	.02
502	Milt Hill	.05	.04	.02
503	Pat Kelly	.05	.04	.02
504	Joe Boever	.05	.04	.02
505	Terry Steinbach	.05	.04	.02
506	Butch Huskey (Rated Rookie)	.15	.11	.06
507	David Valle	.05	.04	.02
508	Mike Scioscia	.05	.04	.02
509	Kenny Rogers	.05	.04	.02
510	Moises Alou	.05	.04	.02
511	David Wells	.05	.04	.02
512	Mackey Sasser	.05	.04	.02
513	Todd Frohwirth	.05	.04	.02
514	Ricky Jordan	.05	.04	.02
515	Mike Gardiner	.05	.04	.02
516	Gary Redus	.05	.04	.02
517	Gary Gaetti	.05	.04	.02
518	Checklist 397-476	.05	.04	.02
519	Carlton Fisk	.08	.06	.03
520	Ozzie Smith	.08	.06	.03
521	Rod Nichols	.05	.04	.02
522	Benito Santiago	.05	.04	.02
523	Bill Gullickson	.05	.04	.02
524	Robby Thompson	.05	.04	.02
525	Mike Macfarlane	.05	.04	.02
526	Sid Bream	.05	.04	.02
527	Darryl Hamilton	.05	.04	.02
528	Checklist 477-555	.05	.04	.02
529	Jeff Tackett	.05	.04	.02
530	Greg Olson	.05	.04	.02
531	Bob Zupcic	.08	.06	.03
532	Mark Grace	.08	.06	.03
533	Steve Frey	.05	.04	.02
534	Dave Martinez	.05	.04	.02
535	Robin Ventura	.12	.09	.05
536	Casey Candaele	.05	.04	.02
537	Kenny Lofton	.20	.15	.08
538	Jay Howell	.05	.04	.02
539	Fernando Ramsey (Rated Rookie)	.12	.09	.05
540	Larry Walker	.12	.09	.05
541	Cecil Fielder	.12	.09	.05
542	Lee Guetterman	.05	.04	.02
543	Keith Miller	.05	.04	.02
544	Lenny Dykstra	.05	.04	.02
545	B.J. Surhoff	.05	.04	.02
546	Bob Walk	.05	.04	.02
547	Brian Harper	.05	.04	.02
548	Lee Smith	.05	.04	.02
549	Danny Tartabull	.05	.04	.02
550	Frank Seminara	.05	.04	.02
551	Henry Mercedes	.05	.04	.02
552	Dave Righetti	.05	.04	.02
553	Ken Griffey, Jr.	1.00	.75	.40
554	Tom Glavine	.12	.09	.05
555	Juan Gonzalez	.75	.60	.30
556	Jim Bullinger	.05	.04	.02
557	Derek Bell	.05	.04	.02
558	Cesar Hernandez	.05	.04	.02
559	Cal Ripken, Jr.	.40	.30	.15
560	Eddie Taubensee	.05	.04	.02
561	John Flaherty	.05	.04	.02
562	Todd Benzinger	.05	.04	.02
563	Hubie Brooks	.05	.04	.02
564	Delino DeShields	.05	.04	.02
565	Tim Raines	.05	.04	.02
566	Sid Fernandez	.05	.04	.02
567	Steve Olin	.05	.04	.02
568	Tommy Greene	.05	.04	.02
569	Buddy Groom	.05	.04	.02
570	Randy Tomlin	.05	.04	.02
571	Hipolito Pichardo	.05	.04	.02
572	Rene Arocha (Rated Rookie)	.25	.20	.10
573	Mike Fetters	.05	.04	.02
574	Felix Jose	.05	.04	.02
575	Gene Larkin	.05	.04	.02
576	Bruce Hurst	.05	.04	.02
577	Bernie Williams	.05	.04	.02
578	Trevor Wilson	.05	.04	.02
579	Bob Welch	.05	.04	.02
580	Dave Justice	.25	.20	.10
581	Randy Johnson	.05	.04	.02
582	Jose Vizcaino	.05	.04	.02
583	Jeff Huson	.05	.04	.02
584	Rob Maurer (Rated Rookie)	.05	.04	.02
585	Todd Stottlemyre	.05	.04	.02
586	Joe Oliver	.05	.04	.02
587	Bob Milacki	.05	.04	.02
588	Rob Murphy	.05	.04	.02
589	Greg Pirkl (Rated Rookie)	.12	.09	.05
590	Lenny Harris	.05	.04	.02
591	Luis Rivera	.05	.04	.02
592	John Wetteland	.05	.04	.02
593	Mark Langston	.05	.04	.02
594	Bobby Bonilla	.05	.04	.02
595	Este Beltre	.05	.04	.02
596	Mike Hartley	.05	.04	.02
597	Felix Fermin	.05	.04	.02
598	Carlos Garcia	.05	.04	.02
599	Frank Tanana	.05	.04	.02
600	Pedro Guerrero	.05	.04	.02
601	Terry Shumpert	.05	.04	.02
602	Wally Whitehurst	.05	.04	.02
603	Kevin Seitzer	.05	.04	.02
604	Chris James	.05	.04	.02
605	Greg Gohr (Rated Rookie)	.05	.04	.02
606	Mark Wohlers	.05	.04	.02
607	Kirby Puckett	.25	.20	.10
608	Greg Maddux	.15	.11	.06
609	Don Mattingly	.15	.11	.06
610	Greg Cadaret	.05	.04	.02
611	Dave Stewart	.05	.04	.02
612	Mark Portugal	.05	.04	.02
613	Pete O'Brien	.05	.04	.02
614	Bobby Ojeda	.05	.04	.02
615	Joe Carter	.15	.11	.06
616	Pete Young	.05	.04	.02
617	Sam Horn	.05	.04	.02
618	Vince Coleman	.05	.04	.02
619	Wade Boggs	.05	.04	.02
620	*Todd Pratt*	.10	.07	.04
621	Ron Tingley	.05	.04	.02
622	Doug Drabek	.05	.04	.02
623	Scott Hemond	.05	.04	.02
624	Tim Jones	.05	.04	.02
625	Dennis Cook	.05	.04	.02
626	Jose Melendez	.05	.04	.02
627	Mike Munoz	.05	.04	.02
628	Jim Pena	.05	.04	.02
629	Gary Thurman	.05	.04	.02
630	Charlie Leibrandt	.05	.04	.02
631	Scott Fletcher	.05	.04	.02
632	Andre Dawson	.10	.08	.04
633	Greg Gagne	.05	.04	.02
634	Greg Swindell	.05	.04	.02
635	Kevin Maas	.05	.04	.02
636	Xavier Hernandez	.05	.04	.02
637	Ruben Sierra	.12	.09	.05
638	Dimitri Young (Rated Rookie)	.15	.11	.06
639	Harold Reynolds	.05	.04	.02
640	Tom Goodwin	.05	.04	.02
641	Todd Burns	.05	.04	.02
642	Jeff Fassero	.05	.04	.02
643	Dave Winfield	.15	.11	.06
644	Willie Randolph	.05	.04	.02
645	Luis Mercedes	.05	.04	.02
646	Dale Murphy	.05	.04	.02
647	Danny Darwin	.05	.04	.02
648	Dennis Moeller	.05	.04	.02
649	Chuck Crim	.05	.04	.02
650	Checklist 556-634	.05	.04	.02
651	Shawn Abner	.05	.04	.02
652	Tracy Woodson	.05	.04	.02
653	Scott Scudder	.05	.04	.02
654	Tom Lampkin	.05	.04	.02
655	Alan Trammell	.05	.04	.02
656	Cory Snyder	.05	.04	.02
657	Chris Gwynn	.05	.04	.02
658	Lonnie Smith	.05	.04	.02
659	Jim Austin	.05	.04	.02
660	Checklist 635-713	.05	.04	.02
661	Checklist (Tim Hulett)	.05	.04	.02
662	Marvin Freeman	.05	.04	.02
663	Greg Harris	.05	.04	.02
664	Heathcliff Slocumb	.05	.04	.02
665	Mike Butcher	.05	.04	.02
666	Steve Foster	.05	.04	.02
667	Donn Pall	.05	.04	.02
668	Darryl Kile	.05	.04	.02
669	Jesse Levis	.10	.08	.04
670	Jim Gott	.05	.04	.02
671	*Mark Hutton*	.10	.07	.04
672	Brian Drahman	.05	.04	.02
673	Chad Kreuter	.05	.04	.02
674	Tony Fernandez	.05	.04	.02
675	Jose Lind	.05	.04	.02
676	Kyle Abbott	.05	.04	.02
677	Dan Plesac	.05	.04	.02
678	Barry Bonds	.40	.30	.15
679	Chili Davis	.05	.04	.02
680	Stan Royer	.05	.04	.02
681	Scott Kamieniecki	.05	.04	.02
682	Carlos Martinez	.05	.04	.02
683	Mike Moore	.05	.04	.02
684	Candy Maldanado	.05	.04	.02
685	Jeff Nelson	.05	.04	.02
686	Lou Whitaker	.05	.04	.02
687	Jose Guzman	.05	.04	.02
688	Manuel Lee	.05	.04	.02
689	Bob MacDonald	.05	.04	.02
690	Scott Bankhead	.05	.04	.02
691	Alan Mills	.05	.04	.02
692	Brian Williams	.05	.04	.02
693	Tom Brunansky	.05	.04	.02
694	Lenny Webster	.05	.04	.02
695	Greg Briley	.05	.04	.02
696	Paul O'Neill	.05	.04	.02
697	Joey Cora	.05	.04	.02
698	Charlie O'Brien	.05	.04	.02
699	Junior Ortiz	.05	.04	.02
700	Ron Darling	.05	.04	.02
701	Tony Phillips	.05	.04	.02
702	William Pennyfeather	.05	.04	.02
703	Mark Gubicza	.05	.04	.02
704	Steve Hosey (Rated Rookie)	.12	.09	.05
705	Henry Cotto	.05	.04	.02
706	*David Hulse* (FC)	.20	.15	.08
707	Mike Pagliarulo	.05	.04	.02
708	Dave Stieb	.05	.04	.02
709	Melido Perez	.05	.04	.02
710	Jimmy Key	.05	.04	.02
711	Jeff Russell	.05	.04	.02
712	David Cone	.05	.04	.02
713	Russ Swan	.05	.04	.02
714	Mark Guthrie	.05	.04	.02
715	Checklist 714-792	.05	.04	.02
716	Al Martin (Rated Rookie)	.30	.25	.12
717	Randy Knorr	.05	.04	.02
718	Mike Stanley	.05	.04	.02
719	Rick Sutcliffe	.05	.04	.02
721	Chipper Jones (Rated Rookie)	.40	.30	.15
722	Jim Eisenreich	.05	.04	.02
723	Tom Henke	.05	.04	.02
724	Jeff Frye	.05	.04	.02

		MT	NR MT	EX
725	Harold Baines	.05	.04	.02
726	Scott Sanderson	.05	.04	.02
727	Tom Foley	.05	.04	.02
728	Bryan Harvey (Expansion Draft)	.05	.04	.02
729	Tom Edens	.05	.04	.02
730	Eric Young (Expansion Draft)	.12	.09	.05
731	Dave Weathers (Expansion Draft)	.05	.04	.02
732	Spike Owen	.05	.04	.02
733	Scott Aldred (Expansion Draft)	.05	.04	.02
734	Cris Carpenter (Expansion Draft)	.05	.04	.02
735	Dion James	.05	.04	.02
736	Joe Girardi (Expansion Draft)	.05	.04	.02
737	Nigel Wilson (Expansion Draft)	.20	.15	.08
738	Scott Chiamparino (Expansion Draft)	.05	.04	.02
739	Jeff Reardon	.05	.04	.02
740	Willie Blair (Expansion Draft)	.05	.04	.02
741	Jim Corsi (Expansion Draft)	.05	.04	.02
742	Ken Patterson	.05	.04	.02
743	Andy Ashby (Expansion Draft)	.05	.04	.02
744	Rob Natal (Expansion Draft)	.05	.04	.02
745	Kevin Bass	.05	.04	.02
746	Freddie Benavides (Expansion Draft)	.05	.04	.02
747	Chris Donnels (Expansion Draft)	.05	.04	.02
748	*Kerry Woodson*	.15	.11	.06
749	Calvin Jones (Expansion Draft)	.05	.04	.02
750	Gary Scott	.05	.04	.02
751	Joe Orsulak	.05	.04	.02
752	Armando Reynoso (Expansion Draft)	.05	.04	.02
753	Monty Farriss (Expansion Draft)	.05	.04	.02
754	Billy Hatcher	.05	.04	.02
755	Denis Boucher (Expansion Draft)	.05	.04	.02
756	Walt Weiss	.05	.04	.02
757	Mike Fitzgerald	.05	.04	.02
758	Rudy Seanez	.05	.04	.02
759	Bret Barberie (Expansion Draft)	.05	.04	.02
760	Mo Sanford (Expansion Draft)	.05	.04	.02
761	*Pedro Castellano,*	.12	.09	.05
762	Chuck Carr (Expansion Draft)	.05	.04	.02
763	Steve Howe	.05	.04	.02
764	Andres Galarraga	.05	.04	.02
765	Jeff Conine (Expansion Draft)	.05	.04	.02
766	Ted Power	.05	.04	.02
767	Butch Henry (Expansion Draft)	.05	.04	.02
768	Steve Decker (Expansion Draft)	.05	.04	.02
769	Storm Davis	.05	.04	.02
770	Vinny Castilla (Expansion Draft)	.05	.04	.02
771	Junior Felix (Expansion Draft)	.05	.04	.02
772	Walt Terrell	.05	.04	.02
773	Brad Ausmus (Expansion Draft)	.15	.11	.06
774	Jamie McAndrew (Expansion Draft)	.05	.04	.02
775	Milt Thompson	.05	.04	.02
776	Charlie Hayes (Expansion Draft)	.05	.04	.02
777	Jack Armstrong (Expansion Draft)	.05	.04	.02
778	Dennis Rasmussen	.05	.04	.02
779	Darren Holmes (Expansion Draft)	.05	.04	.02
780	*Alex Arias*	.12	.09	.05
781	Randy Bush	.05	.04	.02
782	Javier Lopez (Rated Rookie)	.75	.60	.30
783	Dante Bichette	.05	.04	.02
784	John Johnstone (Expansion Draft)	.15	.11	.06
785	Rene Gonzales	.05	.04	.02
786	Alex Cole (Expansion Draft)	.05	.04	.02
787	Jeromy Burnitz (Rated Rookie)	.15	.11	.06
788	Michael Huff	.05	.04	.02
789	Anthony Telford	.05	.04	.02
790	Jerald Clark (Expansion Draft)	.05	.04	.02
791	Joel Johnston	.05	.04	.02
792	David Nied (Rated Rookie)	.30	.25	.12

1993 Donruss Long Ball Leaders

Carrying a prefix of "LL" before the card number, these inserts were released in Series I (LL1-9) and Series II (LL10-18) jumbo packs.

		MT	NR MT	EX
Complete Set (18):		75.00	56.00	30.00
Common Player:		2.00	1.50	.80
1	Rob Deer	2.00	1.50	.80
2	Fred McGriff	6.00	4.50	2.50
3	Albert Belle	5.00	3.75	2.00
4	Mark McGwire	3.00	2.25	1.25
5	David Justice	5.00	3.75	2.00
6	Jose Canseco	3.00	2.25	1.25
7	Kent Hrbek	2.00	1.50	.80
8	Roberto Alomar	8.00	6.00	3.25
9	Ken Griffey, Jr.	14.00	10.50	5.50
10	Frank Thomas	20.00	15.00	8.00
11	Darryl Strawberry	2.00	1.50	.80
12	Felix Jose	2.00	1.50	.80
13	Cecil Fielder	3.50	2.75	1.50
14	Juan Gonzalez	14.00	10.50	5.50
15	Ryne Sandberg	4.00	3.00	1.50
16	Gary Sheffield	3.00	2.25	1.25
17	Jeff Bagwell	3.00	2.25	1.25
18	Larry Walker	2.00	1.50	.80

1993 Donruss MVP's

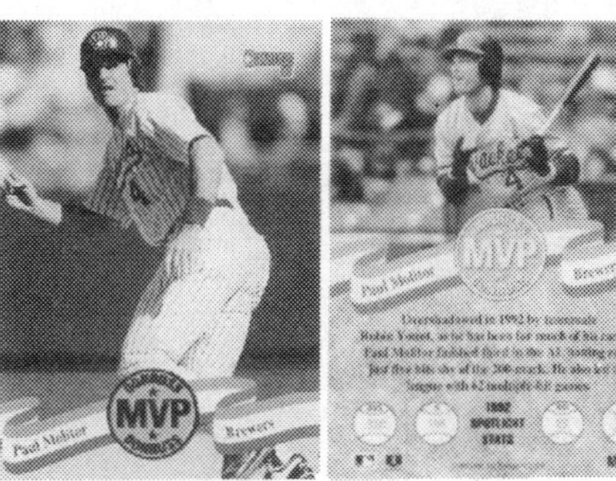

This 26-card set was inserted in jumbo packs of both Series I and Series II. Cards carry a MVP prefix to the card number.

		MT	NR MT	EX
Complete Set (26):		50.00	37.00	20.00
Common Player:		.75	.60	.30
1	Luis Polonia	.75	.60	.30
2	Frank Thomas	7.50	5.75	3.00
3	George Brett	2.50	2.00	1.00
4	Paul Molitor	2.50	2.00	1.00
5	Don Mattingly	2.00	1.50	.80
6	Roberto Alomar	3.00	2.25	1.25
7	Terry Pendleton	1.00	.70	.40
8	Eric Karros	1.25	.90	.50
9	Larry Walker	1.00	.70	.40
10	Eddie Murray	1.00	.70	.40
11	Darren Daulton	1.50	1.25	.60
12	Ray Lankford	1.00	.70	.40
13	Will Clark	2.00	1.50	.80
14	Cal Ripken, Jr.	3.00	2.25	1.25
15	Roger Clemens	2.50	2.00	1.00
16	Carlos Baerga	3.00	2.25	1.25
17	Cecil Fielder	2.00	1.50	.80
18	Kirby Puckett	3.50	2.75	1.50
19	Mark McGwire	1.00	.70	.40
20	Ken Griffey, Jr.	7.00	5.25	2.75
21	Juan Gonzalez	7.00	5.25	2.75
22	Ryne Sandberg	3.00	2.25	1.25
23	Bip Roberts	.75	.60	.30
24	Jeff Bagwell	2.00	1.50	.80
25	Barry Bonds	4.00	3.00	1.50
26	Gary Sheffield	1.50	1.25	.60

1993 Donruss Spirit of the Game

Series I and Series II foil and jumbo packs could be found with these cards randomly inserted. Several multi- player cards are included in the set. Card numbers bear an SG prefix.

		MT	NR MT	EX
Complete Set (20):		45.00	34.00	18.00
Common Player:		1.00	.70	.40
1	Turning Two (Dave Winfield, Mike Bordick)	1.50	1.25	.60
2	Play at the Plate (David Justice)	3.00	2.25	1.25
3	In There (Roberto Alomar)	4.00	3.00	1.50
4	Pumped (Dennis Eckersley)	2.00	1.50	.80
5	Dynamic Duo (Juan Gonzalez, Jose Canseco)	7.00	5.25	2.75
6	Gone (Frank Thomas, George Bell)	4.50	3.50	1.75
7	Safe or Out? (Wade Boggs)	2.00	1.50	.80
8	The Thrill (Will Clark)	4.00	3.00	1.50
9	Safe at Home (Damon Berryhill, Bip Roberts, Glenn Braggs)	1.00	.70	.40
10	Thirty X 31 (Cecil Fielder, Mickey Tettleton, Rob Deer)	2.00	1.50	.80
11	Bag Bandit (Kenny Lofton)	3.00	2.25	1.25
12	Back to Back (Fred McGriff, Gary Sheffield)	3.00	2.25	1.25
13	Range Rovers (Greg Gagne, Barry Larkin)	2.00	1.50	.80
14	The Ball Stops Here (Ryne Sandberg)	5.00	3.75	2.00
15	Over the Top (Carlos Baerga, Gary Gaetti)	3.00	2.25	1.25
16	At the Wall (Danny Tartabull)	1.00	.70	.40
17	Head First (Brady Anderson)	1.00	.70	.40
18	Big Hurt (Frank Thomas)	12.00	9.00	4.75
19	No-Hitter (Kevin Gross)	1.00	.70	.40
20	3,000 (Robin Yount)	3.50	2.75	1.50

1993 Donruss Diamond Kings

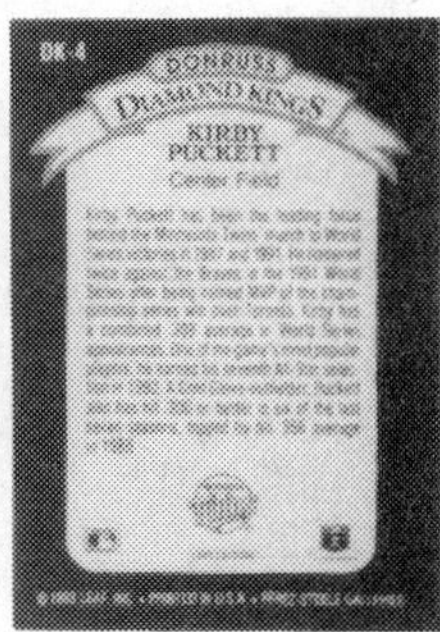

The traditional Donruss Diamond Kings cards were again used as an insert in Series I and Series II foil packs in 1993. The first 15 cards were found in Series I packs, while cards 16-31 were available in the second series packs.

		MT	NR MT	EX
Complete Set (31):		60.00	45.00	25.00
Common Player:		1.00	.70	.40
1	Ken Griffey, Jr.	8.00	6.00	3.25
2	Ryne Sandberg	5.00	3.75	2.00
3	Roger Clemens	5.00	3.75	2.00
4	Kirby Puckett	4.00	3.00	1.50
5	Bill Swift	1.25	.90	.50
6	Larry Walker	3.00	2.25	1.25
7	Juan Gonzalez	5.00	3.75	2.00
8	Wally Joyner	2.00	1.50	.80
9	Andy Van Slyke	2.00	1.50	.80
10	Robin Ventura	2.50	2.00	1.00
11	Bip Roberts	2.00	1.50	.80
12	Roberto Kelly	2.00	1.50	.80
13	Carlos Baerga	4.00	3.00	1.50
14	Orel Hershiser	2.00	1.50	.80
15	Cecil Fielder	3.00	2.25	1.25
16	Robin Yount	2.50	2.00	1.00
17	Darren Daulton	2.00	1.50	.80
18	Mark McGwire	4.00	3.00	1.50
19	Tom Glavine	2.50	2.00	1.00
20	Roberto Alomar	4.00	3.00	1.50
21	Gary Sheffield	4.00	3.00	1.50
22	Bob Tewksbury	2.00	1.50	.80
23	Brady Anderson	2.00	1.50	.80
24	Craig Biggio	2.00	1.50	.80
25	Eddie Murray	3.00	2.25	1.25
26	Luis Polonia	2.00	1.50	.80
27	Nigel Wilson	3.00	2.25	1.25
28	David Nied	3.00	2.25	1.25
29	Pat Listach	1.00	.70	.40
30	Eric Karros	2.25	1.75	.90
31	Checklist	1.00	.70	.40

A card number in parentheses () indicates the set is unnumbered.

1993 Donruss Masters of the Game

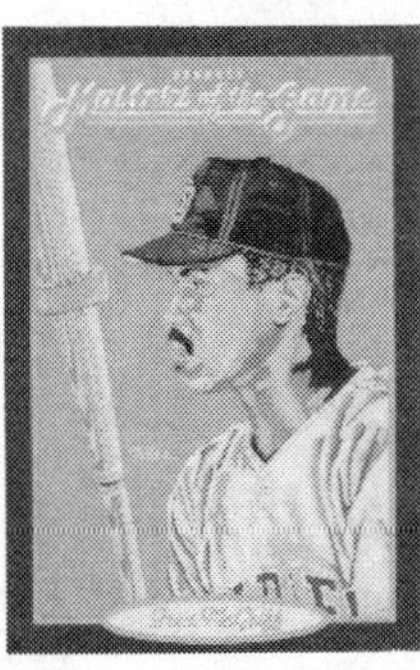

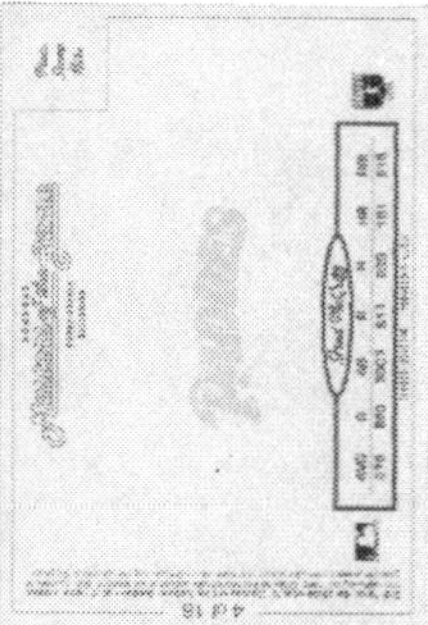

Donruss issued a series of 16 "Masters of the Game" art cards that were available only at WalMart stores. The oversized cards (3-1/2" by 5") feature the artwork of noted artist Dick Perez, creator of the Diamond Kings cards for the same company. The cards came issued one to a pack, along with a foil pack of 1993 Donruss cards for a retail price of about $2.96.

		MT	NR MT	EX
Complete Set:		50.00	37.00	20.00
Common Player:		2.00	1.50	.80
1	Frank Thomas	6.00	4.50	2.50
2	Nolan Ryan	6.00	4.50	2.50
3	Gary Sheffield	2.00	1.50	.80
4	Fred McGriff	3.00	2.25	1.25
5	Ryne Sandberg	5.00	3.75	2.00
6	Cal Ripken, Jr.	5.00	3.75	2.00
7	Jose Canseco	3.00	2.25	1.25
8	Ken Griffey, Jr.	6.00	4.50	2.50
9	Will Clark	4.00	3.00	1.50
10	Roberto Alomar	3.00	2.25	1.25
11	Juan Gonzalez	4.00	3.00	1.50
12	David Justice	2.50	2.00	1.00
13	Kirby Puckett	3.00	2.25	1.25
14	Barry Bonds	4.00	3.00	1.50
15	Robin Yount	4.00	3.00	1.50
16	Deion Sanders	3.00	2.25	1.25

1993 Donruss Elite

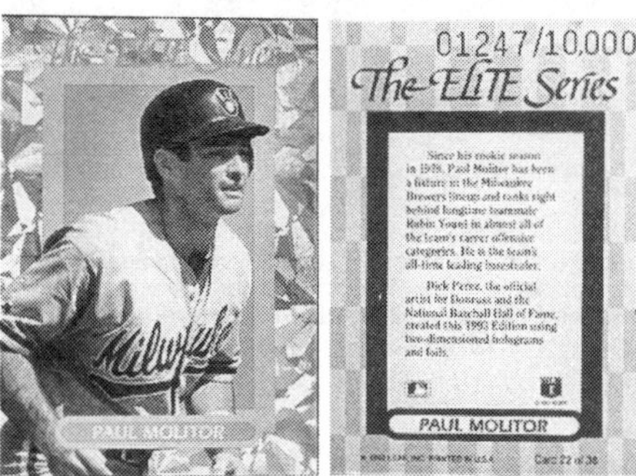

Continuing the card numbering from the 1992 Elite set, the Elite '93 inserts utilized a silver-foil front border look with blue back printing, as opposed to the gold/green scheme of the previous year. Each card is serial numbered as one of 10,000; this identified production number helping to make the Elites among the most valuable of insert cards.

		MT	NR MT	EX
Complete Set (20):		1400.	1050.	550.00
Common Player:		35.00	26.00	14.00
19	Fred McGriff	65.00	49.00	26.00
20	Ryne Sandberg	100.00	75.00	40.00
21	Eddie Murray	35.00	26.00	14.00
22	Paul Molitor	60.00	45.00	24.00
23	Barry Larkin	40.00	30.00	15.00
24	Don Mattingly	100.00	75.00	40.00
25	Dennis Eckersley	35.00	26.00	14.00
26	Roberto Alomar	90.00	67.00	36.00
27	Edgar Martinez	35.00	26.00	14.00
28	Gary Sheffield	40.00	30.00	16.00
29	Darren Daulton	40.00	30.00	15.00
30	Larry Walker	40.00	30.00	16.00
31	Barry Bonds	110.00	82.50	45.00
32	Andy Van Slyke	35.00	26.00	14.00
33	Mark McGwire	40.00	30.00	15.00
34	Cecil Fielder	40.00	30.00	15.00
35	Dave Winfield	60.00	45.00	24.00
36	Juan Gonzalez	150.00	110.00	60.00
----	Robin Yount (Legend)	150.00	115.00	45.00
----	Will Clark (Signature)	300.00	225.00	90.00

1993 Donruss Elite Supers

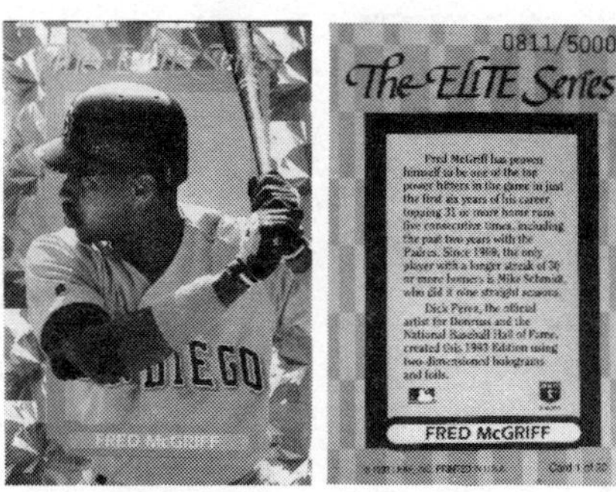

A Wal-Mart exclusive, Donruss produced super-size versions of its 1993 Elite inserts, added Nolan Ryan and Frank Thomas and a new card of Barry Bonds in his Giants uniform and packaged them one per shrink-wrapped box with Series I Donruss left-overs. Measuring 3-1/2" x 5" each card features a color player photo and prismatic borders on front. Backs are printed in blue and include a serial number identifying each of the cards from an edition of 5,000.

		MT	NR MT	EX
Complete Set (20):		350.00	262.00	140.00
Common Player:		6.00	4.50	2.50
1	Fred McGriff	15.00	11.00	6.00
2	Ryne Sandberg	30.00	22.00	12.00
3	Eddie Murray	8.00	6.00	3.25
4	Paul Molitor	25.00	18.50	10.00
5	Barry Larkin	10.00	7.50	4.00
6	Don Mattingly	25.00	18.50	10.00
7	Dennis Eckersley	8.00	6.00	3.25
8	Roberto Alomar	15.00	11.00	6.00
9	Edgar Martinez	6.00	4.50	2.50
10	Gary Sheffield	12.00	9.00	4.75
11	Darren Daulton	6.00	4.50	2.50
12	Larry Walker	6.00	4.50	2.50
13	Barry Bonds	35.00	26.00	14.00
14	Andy Van Slyke	6.00	4.50	2.50
15	Mark McGwire	12.00	9.00	4.75
16	Cecil Fielder	15.00	11.00	6.00
17	Dave Winfield	25.00	18.50	10.00
18	Juan Gonzalez	45.00	34.00	18.00
19	Frank Thomas	60.00	45.00	24.00
20	Nolan Ryan	60.00	45.00	24.00

1993 Donruss Elite Dominators

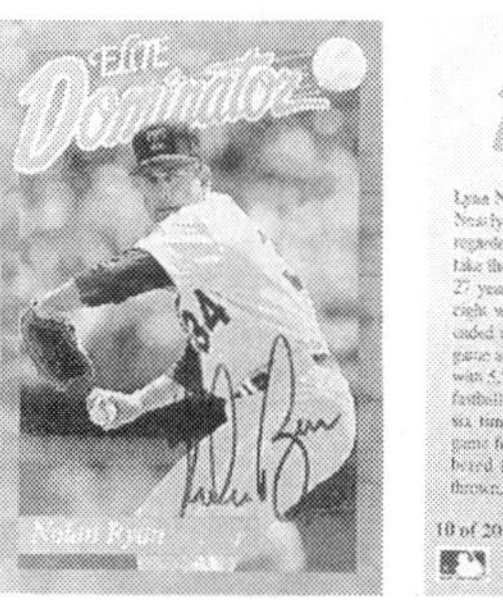

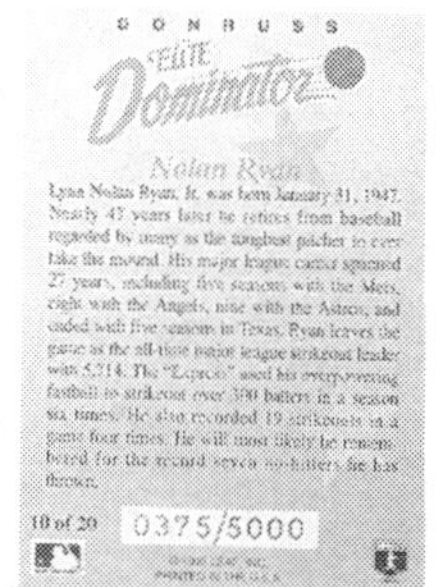

Created as a premium to move left-over boxes of its 1993 product on a home shopping network at $100 apiece, this special edition was produced in standard 2-1/2" x 3-1/2" size in a format similar to the 1991-93 Donruss Elite chase cards. Cards feature green prismatic borders, liberal use of foil stamping, etc. Only 5,000 of each card were produced, and each card is serially numbered on the back. Half of the cards of Nolan Ryan, Juan Gonzalez, Don Mattingly and Paul Molitor were personally autographed by the player.

		MT	NR MT	EX
Complete Set (20):		2200.	1650.	880.00
Common Player:		65.00	49.00	26.00
1	Ryne Sandberg	125.00	94.00	50.00
2	Fred McGriff	65.00	49.00	26.00
3	Greg Maddux	65.00	49.00	26.00
4	Ron Gant	65.00	49.00	26.00
5	Dave Justice	100.00	75.00	40.00
6	Don Mattingly	100.00	75.00	40.00
7	Tim Salmon	125.00	94.00	50.00
8	Mike Piazza	150.00	112.00	60.00
9	John Olerud	100.00	75.00	40.00
10	Nolan Ryan	275.00	206.00	110.00
11	Juan Gonzalez	175.00	131.00	70.00
12	Ken Griffey, Jr.	175.00	131.00	70.00
13	Frank Thomas	225.00	169.00	90.00
14	Tom Glavine	65.00	49.00	26.00
15	George Brett	125.00	94.00	50.00
16	Barry Bonds	125.00	94.00	50.00
17	Albert Belle	65.00	49.00	26.00
18	Paul Molitor	100.00	75.00	40.00
19	Cal Ripken, Jr.	150.00	112.00	60.00
20	Roberto Alomar	100.00	75.00	40.00
	Autographed cards			
6	Don Mattingly	250.00	187.00	100.00
10	Nolan Ryan	425.00	319.00	170.00
11	Juan Gonzalez	300.00	225.00	120.00
18	Paul Molitor	200.00	150.00	80.00

Values quoted in this guide reflect the retail price of a card – the price a collector can expect to pay when buying a card from a dealer. The wholesale price – that which a collector can expect to receive from a dealer when selling cards – will be significantly lower, depending on desirability and condition.

1993 Donruss 1992 Blue Jays Commemorative Set

Issued only as a special gold-boxed set, this 54-card series commemorates the Toronto Blue Jays 1992 World Championship. Each player on the Jays '92 roster has a card. There are also special cards recalling each game of the Series and a card of Skydome. The World Series highlights subset cards have a bunting design at top and a gold-foil World Series logo on front. Player cards feature borderless photos with the player's name and position in a blue color bar near bottom. A Blue Jays "Commemorative Set" logo is at lower-left. Backs have a player photo at top and a stat box at bottom with season, career and 1992 LCS and World Series numbers.

		MT	NR MT	EX
Complete Set (54):		9.00	6.75	3.50
Common Card:		.10	.08	.04
1	Checklist/Logo Card	.10	.08	.04
2	Roberto Alomar	.75	.60	.30
3	Derek Bell	.20	.15	.08
4	Pat Borders	.15	.11	.06
5	Joe Carter	.45	.35	.20
6	Alfredo Griffin	.10	.08	.04
7	Kelly Gruber	.10	.08	.04
8	Manuel Lee	.10	.08	.04
9	Candy Maldonado	.10	.08	.04
10	John Olerud	.60	.45	.25
11	Ed Sprague	.15	.11	.06
12	Pat Tabler	.10	.08	.04
13	Devon White	.30	.25	.12
14	Dave Winfield	.75	.60	.30
15	David Cone	.15	.11	.06
16	Mark Eichhorn	.10	.08	.04
17	Juan Guzman	.20	.15	.08
18	Tom Henke	.15	.11	.06
19	Jimmy Key	.15	.11	.06
20	Jack Morris	.25	.20	.10
21	Todd Stottlemyre	.15	.11	.06
22	Mike Timlin	.15	.11	.06
23	Duane Ward	.20	.15	.08
24	David Wells	.15	.11	.06
25	Randy Knorr	.10	.08	.04
26	Rance Mulliniks	.10	.08	.04
27	Tom Quinlan	.10	.08	.04
28	Cito Gaston	.25	.20	.10
29	Dave Steib	.20	.15	.08
30	Ken Dayley	.10	.08	.04
31	Turner Ward	.15	.11	.06
32	Eddie Zosky	.20	.15	.08
33	Pat Hentgen	.30	.25	.12
34	Al Leiter	.10	.08	.04
35	Doug Linton	.10	.08	.04
36	Bob MacDonald	.15	.11	.06
37	Rick Trlicek	.15	.11	.06
38	Domingo Martinez	.20	.15	.08
39	Mike Maksudian	.10	.08	.04
40	Rob Ducey	.10	.08	.04
41	Jeff Kent	.15	.11	.06
42	Greg Myers	.10	.08	.04
43	Dave Weathers	.10	.08	.04
44	Skydome	.10	.08	.04
45	Trophy Presentation (Jim Kaat, Cito Gaston, Paul Beeston / Bobby Brown)	.10	.08	.04
1WS	Series Opener	.10	.08	.04
2WS	Game 1 - Carter Homers in 4th	.10	.08	.04
3WS	Game 2 - Sprague's Game-Winning Pinch HR	.10	.08	.04
4WS	Game 3 - Maldonado Drives in Game-Winner	.10	.08	.04
5WS	Game 4 - Key's Win Puts Jays Up 3-1	.10	.08	.04
6WS	Game 5 - Olerud Scores Both Jays Runs	.10	.08	.04
7WS	Game 6 - Winfield's Double in 11th Wins	.10	.08	.04
8WS	Pat Border Series MVP	.10	.08	.04
9WS	World Champs Celebration	.10	.08	.04

1993 Donruss Triple Play

For the second year, Leaf-Donruss used the "Triple Play" brand name for its base-level card set aimed at the younger collector. The 264-card set was available in several types of retail packaging and included a number of special subsets, such as childhood photos (labeled LH - Little Hotshots in the

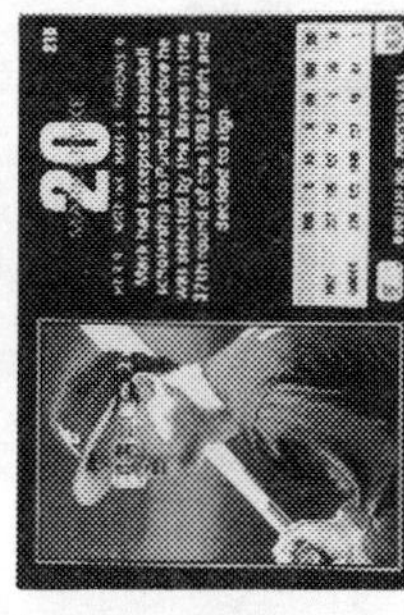

checklist) and insert sets. Checklist card #264 incorrectly show card #129, Joe Robbie Stadium, as #259. There is a second card, "Equipment," which also bears #129. An "Action Baseball" scratch-off game card was included in each foil pack.

		MT	NR MT	EX
Complete Set (264):		14.00	11.00	6.00
Common Player:		.05	.04	.02
1	Ken Griffey, Jr.	1.00	.75	.40
2	Roberto Alomar	.25	.20	.10
3	Cal Ripken, Jr.	.50	.40	.20
4	Eric Karros	.15	.11	.06
5	Cecil Fielder	.20	.15	.08
6	Gary Sheffield	.15	.11	.06
7	Darren Daulton	.10	.08	.04
8	Andy Van Slyke	.10	.08	.04
9	Dennis Eckersley	.07	.05	.03
10	Ryne Sandberg	.40	.30	.15
11	Mark Grace (Little Hotshots)	.35	.25	.14
12	Awesome Action #1 (Luis Polonia, Diego Segui)	.05	.04	.02
13	Mike Mussina	.07	.05	.03
14	Vince Coleman	.07	.05	.03
15	Rafael Belliard	.05	.04	.02
16	Ivan Rodriguez	.15	.11	.06
17	Eddie Taubensee	.05	.04	.02
18	Cal Eldred	.05	.04	.02
19	Rick Wilkins	.05	.04	.02
20	Edgar Martinez	.07	.05	.03
21	Brian McRae	.07	.05	.03
22	Darren Holmes	.05	.04	.02
23	Mark Whiten	.05	.04	.02
24	Todd Zeile	.07	.05	.03
25	Scott Cooper	.05	.04	.02
26	Frank Thomas	1.50	1.25	.60
27	Wil Cordero	.15	.11	.06
28	Juan Guzman	.05	.04	.02
29	Pedro Astacio	.05	.04	.02
30	Steve Avery	.10	.08	.04
31	Barry Larkin	.12	.09	.05
32	President Clinton	.25	.20	.10
33	Scott Erickson	.05	.04	.02
34	Mike Devereaux	.07	.05	.03
35	Tino Martinez	.05	.04	.02
36	Brent Mayne	.07	.05	.03
37	Tim Salmon	1.00	.75	.40
38	Dave Hollins	.07	.05	.03
39	Royce Clayton	.05	.04	.02
40	Shawon Dunston	.05	.04	.02
41	Eddie Murray	.10	.08	.04
42	Larry Walker	.07	.05	.03
43	Jeff Bagwell	.10	.08	.04
44	Milt Cuyler	.05	.04	.02
45	Mike Bordick	.05	.04	.02
46	Mike Greenwell	.07	.05	.03
47	Steve Sax	.05	.04	.02
48	Chuck Knoblauch	.10	.08	.04
49	Charles Nagy	.05	.04	.02
50	Tim Wakefield	.05	.04	.02
51	Tony Gwynn	.10	.08	.04
52	Rob Dibble	.05	.04	.02
53	Mickey Morandini	.05	.04	.02
54	Steve Hosey	.07	.05	.03
55	Mike Piazza	2.00	1.50	.80
56	Bill Wegman	.05	.04	.02
57	Kevin Maas	.05	.04	.02
58	Gary DiSarcina	.07	.05	.03
59	Travis Fryman	.10	.08	.04
60	Ruben Sierra	.15	.11	.06
61	Awesome Action #2 (Ken Caminiti)	.05	.04	.02
62	Brian Jordan	.10	.08	.04
63	Scott Chiamparino	.05	.04	.02
64	Awesome Action #3 (Mike Bordick, George Brett)	.10	.08	.04
65	Carlos Garcia	.07	.05	.03
66	Checklist 1-66	.05	.04	.02
67	John Smoltz	.07	.05	.03
68	Awesome Action #4 (Mark McGwire, Brian Harper)	.10	.08	.04
69	Kurt Stillwell	.05	.04	.02
70	Chad Curtis	.10	.08	.04
71	Rafael Palmeiro	.20	.15	.08
72	Kevin Young	.05	.04	.02
73	Glenn Davis	.05	.04	.02
74	Dennis Martinez	.07	.05	.03
75	Sam Militello	.05	.04	.02
76	Mike Morgan	.05	.04	.02
77	Frank Thomas (Little Hotshots)	.75	.60	.30
78	Staying Fit (Bip Roberts, Mike Devereaux)	.05	.04	.02
79	Steve Buechele	.05	.04	.02
80	Carlos Baerga	.10	.08	.04
81	Robby Thompson	.07	.05	.03
82	Kirk McCaskill	.05	.04	.02
83	Lee Smith	.07	.05	.03
84	Gary Scott	.05	.04	.02
85	Tony Pena	.05	.04	.02
86	Howard Johnson	.07	.05	.03
87	Mark McGwire	.15	.11	.06
88	Bip Roberts	.07	.05	.03
89	Devon White	.10	.08	.04
90	John Franco	.05	.04	.02
91	Tom Browning	.05	.04	.02
92	Mickey Tettleton	.10	.08	.04
93	Jeff Conine	.07	.05	.03
94	Albert Belle	.15	.11	.06
95	Fred McGriff	.12	.09	.05
96	Nolan Ryan	.75	.60	.30
97	Paul Molitor (Little Hotshots)	.25	.20	.10
98	Juan Bell	.05	.04	.02
99	Dave Fleming	.05	.04	.02
100	Craig Biggio	.07	.05	.03
101 a	Andy Stankiewicz (white name on front)	.05	.04	.02
101b	Andy Stankiewicz (red name on front)	.25	.20	.10
102	Delino DeShields	.10	.08	.04
103	Damion Easley	.07	.05	.03
104	Kevin McReynolds	.07	.05	.03
105	David Nied	.12	.09	.05
106	Rick Sutcliffe	.05	.04	.02
107	Will Clark	.20	.15	.08
108	Tim Raines	.12	.09	.05
109	Eric Anthony	.05	.04	.02
110	Mike LaValliere	.05	.04	.02
111	Dean Palmer	.07	.05	.03
112	Eric Davis	.12	.09	.05
113	Damon Berryhill	.05	.04	.02
114	Felix Jose	.05	.04	.02
115	Ozzie Guillen	.07	.05	.03
116	Pat Listach	.07	.05	.03
117	Tom Glavine	.07	.05	.03
118	Roger Clemens	.15	.11	.06
119	Dave Henderson	.05	.04	.02
120	Don Mattingly	.50	.40	.20
121	Orel Hershiser	.15	.11	.06
122	Ozzie Smith	.15	.11	.06
123	Joe Carter	.15	.11	.06
124	Bret Saberhagen	.07	.05	.03
125	Mitch Williams	.07	.05	.03
126	Jerald Clark	.05	.04	.02
127	Mile High Stadium	.05	.04	.02
128	Kent Hrbek	.10	.08	.04
129 a	Equipment (Curt Schilling, Mark Whiten)	.05	.04	.02
129 b	Joe Robbie Stadium	.05	.04	.02
130	Gregg Jefferies	.10	.08	.04
131	John Orton	.05	.04	.02
132	Checklist 67-132	.05	.04	.02
133	Bret Boone	.07	.05	.03
134	Pat Borders	.05	.04	.02
135	Gregg Olson	.05	.04	.02
136	Brett Butler	.07	.05	.03
137	Rob Deer	.05	.04	.02
138	Darrin Jackson	.07	.05	.03
139	John Kruk	.10	.08	.04
140	Jay Bell	.07	.05	.03
141	Bobby Witt	.05	.04	.02
142	New Cubs (Dan Plesac, Randy Myers, Jose Guzman)	.15	.11	.06
143	Wade Boggs (Little Hotshots)	.25	.20	.10
144	Awesome Action #5 (Kenny Lofton)	.05	.04	.02
145	Ben McDonald	.07	.05	.03
146	Dwight Gooden	.15	.11	.06
147	Terry Pendleton	.07	.05	.03
148	Julio Franco	.05	.04	.02
149	Ken Caminiti	.07	.05	.03
150	Greg Vaughn	.07	.05	.03
151	Sammy Sosa	.07	.05	.03
152	David Valle	.05	.04	.02
153	Wally Joyner	.12	.09	.05
154	Dante Bichette	.07	.05	.03
155	Mark Lewis	.05	.04	.02
156	Bob Tewksbury	.07	.05	.03
157	Billy Hatcher	.07	.05	.03
158	Jack McDowell	.10	.08	.04
159	Marquis Grissom	.07	.05	.03
160	Jack Morris	.07	.05	.03
161	Ramon Martinez	.05	.04	.02
162	Deion Sanders	.15	.11	.06
163	Tim Belcher	.05	.04	.02
164	Mascots	.10	.08	.04
165	Scott Leius	.05	.04	.02
166	Brady Anderson	.07	.05	.03
167	Randy Johnson	.07	.05	.03
168	Mark Gubicza	.05	.04	.02
169	Chuck Finley	.05	.04	.02
170	Terry Mulholland	.05	.04	.02
171	Matt Williams	.12	.09	.05
172	Dwight Smith	.05	.04	.02
173	Bobby Bonilla	.12	.09	.05
174	Ken Hill	.05	.04	.02
175	Doug Jones	.05	.04	.02
176	Tony Phillips	.05	.04	.02
177	Terry Steinbach	.07	.05	.03
178	Frank Viola	.07	.05	.03
179	Robin Ventura	.12	.09	.05
180	Shane Mack	.10	.08	.04
181	Kenny Lofton	.07	.05	.03
182	Jeff King	.05	.04	.02
183	Tim Teufel	.05	.04	.02
184	Chris Sabo	.07	.05	.03
185	Lenny Dykstra	.15	.11	.06
186	Trevor Wilson	.05	.04	.02
187	Darryl Strawberry	.15	.11	.06
188	Robin Yount	.35	.25	.14
189	Bob Wickman	.07	.05	.03
190	Luis Polonia	.07	.05	.03
191	Alan Trammell	.20	.15	.08
192	Bob Welch	.07	.05	.03
193	Awesome Action #6	.05	.04	.02
194	Tom Pagnozzi	.05	.04	.02
195	Bret Barberie	.05	.04	.02
196	Awesome Action #7 (Mike Scioscia)	.05	.04	.02
197	Randy Tomlin	.05	.04	.02
198	Checklist 133-198	.05	.04	.02
199	Ron Gant	.10	.08	.04
200	Awesome Action #8 (Roberto Alomar)	.10	.08	.04
201	Andy Benes	.07	.05	.03
202	Pepper	.05	.04	.02
203	Steve Finley	.07	.05	.03
204	Steve Olin	.05	.04	.02
205	Chris Hoiles	.07	.05	.03
206	John Wetteland	.05	.04	.02
207	Danny Tartabull	.07	.05	.03
208	Bernard Gilkey	.10	.08	.04
209	Tom Glavine (Little Hotshots)	.10	.08	.04
210	Benito Santiago	.10	.08	.04
211	Mark Grace	.12	.09	.05
212	Glenallen Hill	.05	.04	.02
213	Jeff Brantley	.05	.04	.02
214	George Brett	.50	.40	.20
215	Mark Lemke	.05	.04	.02
216	Ron Karkovice	.07	.05	.03
217	Tom Brunansky	.05	.04	.02
218	Todd Hundley	.05	.04	.02
219	Rickey Henderson	.25	.20	.10
220	Joe Oliver	.05	.04	.02
221	Juan Gonzalez	1.00	.75	.40
222	John Olerud	.15	.11	.06
223	Hal Morris	.07	.05	.03
224	Lou Whitaker	.10	.08	.04
225	Bryan Harvey	.07	.05	.03
226	Mike Gallego	.05	.04	.02
227	Willie McGee	.07	.05	.03
228	Jose Oquendo	.05	.04	.02
229	Darren Daulton (Little Hotshots)	.10	.08	.04
230	Curt Schilling	.05	.04	.02
231	Jay Buhner	.10	.08	.04
232	New Astros (Doug Drabek, Greg Swindell)	.05	.04	.02
233	Jaime Navarro	.05	.04	.02
234	Kevin Appier	.05	.04	.02
235	Mark Langston	.07	.05	.03
236	Jeff Montgomery	.05	.04	.02
237	Joe Girardi	.05	.04	.02
238	Ed Sprague	.05	.04	.02
239	Dan Walters	.05	.04	.02
240	Kevin Tapani	.05	.04	.02
241	Pete Harnisch	.07	.05	.03
242	Al Martin	.05	.04	.02
243	Jose Canseco	.25	.20	.10
244	Moises Alou	.10	.08	.04
245	Mark McGwire (Little Hotshots)	.15	.11	.06
246	Luis Rivera	.07	.05	.03
247	George Bell	.07	.05	.03
248	B.J. Surhoff	.05	.04	.02
249	David Justice	.12	.09	.05
250	Brian Harper	.07	.05	.03
251	Sandy Alomar, Jr.	.07	.05	.03
252	Kevin Brown	.05	.04	.02
253	New Dodgers (Tim Wallach, Jody Reed, Todd Worrell)	.05	.04	.02
254	Ray Lankford	.15	.11	.06
255	Derek Bell	.05	.04	.02
256	Joe Grahe	.05	.04	.02
257	Charlie Hayes	.07	.05	.03
258	New Yankees (Wade Boggs, Jim Abbott)	.25	.20	.10
259	Not issued			
260	Kirby Puckett	.35	.25	.14
261	Fun at the Ballpark (Jay Bell, Vince Coleman)	.05	.04	.02
262	Bill Swift	.07	.05	.03
263	Fun at the Ballpark (Roger McDowell)	.05	.04	.02
264	Checklist 199-264	.05	.04	.02

1993 Donruss Triple Play Gallery

The Gallery of Stars cards were found as random inserts in Triple Play jumbo packs. There are 10 cards in the set, featuring painted representations of the players.

		MT	NR MT	EX
Complete Set (10):		21.00	15.50	8.50
Common Player:		1.00	.70	.40
1	Barry Bonds	7.00	5.25	2.75
2	Andre Dawson	1.25	.90	.50
3	Wade Boggs	1.75	1.25	.70
4	Greg Maddux	2.00	1.50	.80
5	Dave Winfield	2.50	2.00	1.00
6	Paul Molitor	2.50	2.00	1.00
7	Jim Abbott	1.75	1.25	.70
8	J.T. Snow	1.50	1.25	.60
9	Benito Santiago	1.00	.70	.40
10	David Nied	2.50	2.00	1.00

Values for recent cards and sets are listed in Mint (MT), Near Mint (NM), reflecting the fact that many cards from recent years have been preserved in top condition. Recent cards and sets in less than Excellent condition have little collector interest.

1993 Donruss Triple Play League Leaders

These "double-headed" cards feature one player on each side. The six cards were random inserts in Triple Play retail packs and are currently the most popular of that brand's inserts.

		MT	NR MT	EX
Complete Set (6):		25.00	18.50	10.00
Common Player:		2.50	2.00	1.00
1	Barry Bonds/ Dennis Eckersley	7.50	5.75	3.00
2	Greg Maddux/ Dennis Eckersley	3.00	2.25	1.25
3	Eric Karros/ Pat Listach	2.50	2.00	1.00
4	Fred McGriff/ Juan Gonzalez	9.00	6.75	3.50
5	Darren Daulton/ Cecil Fielder	3.00	2.25	1.25
6	Gary Sheffield/ Edgar Martinez	2.50	2.00	1.00

1993 Donruss Triple Play Nicknames

Donruss marked its 10th anniversary in the baseball Popular nicknames of 10 of the game's top stars are featured in silver foil on this insert set found in Triple Play foil packs.

		MT	NR MT	EX
Complete Set (10):		30.00	22.00	12.00
Common Player:		1.00	.70	.40
1	Frank Thomas (Big Hurt)	8.00	6.00	3.25
2	Roger Clemens (Rocket)	3.00	2.25	1.25
3	Ryne Sandberg (Ryno)	3.50	2.75	1.50
4	Will Clark (Thrill)	2.50	2.00	1.00
5	Ken Griffey, Jr. (Junior)	7.00	5.25	2.75
6	Dwight Gooden (Doc)	1.00	.70	.40
7	Nolan Ryan (Express)	7.50	5.75	3.00
8	Deion Sanders (Prime Time)	2.00	1.50	.80
9	Ozzie Smith (Wizard)	2.00	1.50	.80
10	Fred McGriff (Crime Dog)	3.00	2.25	1.25

1993 Donruss Triple Play Action Baseball

These game folders were inserted in 1993 Triple Play foil packs at the rate of one per pack. Because collation of the folders was very bad, few collectors bothered to save them. Measuring 2-1/2" x 5", fronts have an action photo of an unnamed player. Printed over the bottom of the photo are two full-color team logos, with a white "Versus" between. At top is a silver panel with the Triple Play logo and "ActionBaseball". Inside the folder is a baseball diamond diagram, a three-inning scoreboard, rules for scoreboard, rules for playing the game and 32 scratch-off squares for playing. Backs are plain silver with Leaf and baseball logos, and a number designating the folder as "of 30."

		MT	NR MT	EX
Complete Set (30):		5.00	3.75	2.00
Common Player:		.10	.08	.04
1	Andy Van Slyke	.10	.08	.04
2	Bobby Bonilla	.10	.08	.04
3	Ozzie Smith	.20	.15	.08
4	Ryne Sandberg	.25	.20	.10
5	Darren Daulton	.10	.08	.04
6	Larry Walker	.10	.08	.04
7	Eric Karros	.20	.15	.08
8	Barry Larkin	.10	.08	.04
9	Deion Sanders	.20	.15	.08
10	Gary Sheffield	.10	.08	.04
11	Will Clark	.20	.15	.08
12	Jeff Bagwell	.10	.08	.04
13	Roberto Alomar	.15	.11	.06
14	Roger Clemens	.15	.11	.06
15	Cecil Fielder	.15	.11	.06
16	Robin Yount	.20	.15	.08
17	Cal Ripken, Jr.	.25	.20	.10
18	Carlos Baerga	.15	.11	.06
19	Don Mattingly	.15	.11	.06
20	Kirby Puckett	.20	.15	.08
21	Frank Thomas	.35	.25	.14
22	Juan Gonzalez	.20	.15	.08
23	Mark McGwire	.15	.11	.06
24	Ken Griffey, Jr.	.35	.25	.14
25	Wally Joyner	.15	.11	.06
26	Chad Curtis	.10	.08	.04
27	Batting glove	.10	.08	.04
28	Juan Guzman	.10	.08	.04
29	Dave Justice	.15	.11	.06
30	Joe Carter	.15	.11	.06

1994 Donruss Promos

To introduce both its regular 1994 issue and the "Special Edition" gold cards, Donruss produced this 12-card promo set for distribution to its dealer network. The promos are virtually identical in format to the regular cards except for the large gray diagonal overprint "Promotional Sample" on both front and back. Card numbers are also different on the promos.

		MT	NR MT	EX
Complete Set (12):		35.00	26.00	14.00
Common Player:		3.00	2.25	1.25
1	Barry Bonds	4.50	3.50	1.75
2	Darren Daulton	3.00	2.25	1.25
3	John Olerud	3.00	2.25	1.25
4	Frank Thomas	7.50	5.75	3.00
5	Mike Piazza	4.00	3.00	1.50
6	Tim Salmon	4.00	3.00	1.50
7	Ken Griffey, Jr.	6.00	4.50	2.50
8	Fred McGriff	3.00	2.25	1.25
9	Don Mattingly	4.50	3.50	1.75
10	Gary Sheffield	3.00	2.25	1.25
1G	Barry Bonds (Special Edition Gold)	6.00	4.50	2.50
4G	Frank Thomas (Special Edition Gold)	9.00	6.75	3.50

1994 Donruss

Donruss released its 1994 set in two series; each includes 330 cards, 50 Special Edition gold cards and several insert sets. The regular cards have full-bleed photos and are UV coated and foil stamped. Special Edition cards are gold-foil stamped on both sides and are included in each pack. Insert sets titled Spirit of the Game and Decade Dominators were produced in regular and super (3-1/2" x 5") formats. Other inserts were MVPs and Long Ball Leaders in regular size and super-size Award Winners. An Elite series of cards, continuing from previous years with #s 37-48, were also issued as inserts. A 10th Anniversary insert set featured 10 popular 1984 Donruss cards in gold-foil enhanced reprint versions.

		MT	NR MT	EX
Complete Set (660):		44.00	33.00	17.50
Complete Series 1 (330):		22.00	16.50	8.75
Complete Series 2 (330):		22.00	16.50	8.75
Common Player:		.05	.04	.02
1	Nolan Ryan (Career Salute 27 Years)	2.50	2.00	1.00
2	Mike Piazza	2.50	2.00	1.00
3	Moises Alou	.10	.08	.04
4	Ken Griffey, Jr.	2.50	2.00	1.00
5	Gary Sheffield	.15	.11	.06
6	Roberto Alomar	.40	.30	.15
7	John Kruk	.08	.06	.03
8	Gregg Olson	.05	.04	.02
9	Gregg Jefferies	.05	.04	.02
10	Tony Gwynn	.20	.15	.08
11	Chad Curtis	.10	.08	.04
12	Craig Biggio	.05	.04	.02
13	John Burkett	.05	.04	.02
14	Carlos Baerga	.40	.30	.15
15	Robin Yount	.35	.25	.14
16	Dennis Eckersley	.05	.04	.02
17	Dwight Gooden	.05	.04	.02
18	Ryne Sandberg	.50	.40	.20
19	Rickey Henderson	.15	.11	.06
20	Jack McDowell	.10	.08	.04
21	Jay Bell	.05	.04	.02
22	Kevin Brown	.05	.04	.02
23	Robin Ventura	.15	.11	.06
24	Paul Molitor	.30	.25	.12
25	David Justice	.30	.25	.12
26	Rafael Palmeiro	.10	.08	.04
27	Cecil Fielder	.15	.11	.06
28	Chuck Knoblauch	.05	.04	.02
29	Dave Hollins	.08	.06	.03
30	Jimmy Key	.05	.04	.02
31	Mark Langston	.05	.04	.02
32	Darryl Kile	.05	.04	.02
33	Ruben Sierra	.08	.06	.03
34	Ron Gant	.08	.06	.03
35	Ozzie Smith	.15	.11	.06
36	Wade Boggs	.15	.11	.06
37	Marquis Grissom	.10	.08	.04
38	Will Clark	.20	.15	.08
39	Kenny Lofton	.25	.20	.10
40	Cal Ripken, Jr.	.75	.60	.30
41	Steve Avery	.15	.11	.06
42	Mo Vaughn	.10	.08	.04
43	Brian McRae	.05	.04	.02
44	Mickey Tettleton	.05	.04	.02
45	Barry Larkin	.05	.04	.02
46	Charlie Hayes	.05	.04	.02
47	Kevin Appier	.05	.04	.02
48	Robby Thompson	.05	.04	.02
49	Juan Gonzalez	1.50	1.25	.60
50	Paul O'Neill	.05	.04	.02
51	Marcos Armas	.05	.04	.02
52	Mike Butcher	.05	.04	.02
53	Ken Caminiti	.05	.04	.02
54	Pat Borders	.05	.04	.02
55	Pedro Munoz	.05	.04	.02
56	Tim Belcher	.05	.04	.02
57	Paul Assenmacher	.05	.04	.02
58	Damon Berryhill	.05	.04	.02
59	Ricky Bones	.05	.04	.02
60	Rene Arocha	.10	.07	.04
61	Shawn Boskie	.05	.04	.02
62	Pedro Astacio	.05	.04	.02
63	Frank Bolick	.05	.04	.02
64	Bud Black	.05	.04	.02
65	Sandy Alomar, Jr.	.05	.04	.02
66	Rich Amaral	.05	.04	.02
67	Luis Aquino	.05	.04	.02
68	Kevin Baez	.05	.04	.02
69	Mike Devereaux	.05	.04	.02
70	Andy Ashby	.05	.04	.02
71	Larry Andersen	.05	.04	.02
72	Steve Cooke	.05	.04	.02
73	Mario Daiz	.05	.04	.02
74	Rob Deer	.05	.04	.02
75	Bobby Ayala	.05	.04	.02
76	Freddie Benavides	.05	.04	.02
77	Stan Belinda	.05	.04	.02

78	John Doherty	.05	.04	.02
79	Willie Banks	.05	.04	.02
80	Spike Owen	.05	.04	.02
81	Mike Bordick	.05	.04	.02
82	Chili Davis	.05	.04	.02
83	Luis Gonzalez	.05	.04	.02
84	Ed Sprague	.05	.04	.02
85	Jeff Reboulet	.05	.04	.02
86	Jason Bere	1.00	.70	.40
87	Mark Hutton	.05	.04	.02
88	Jeff Blauser	.05	.04	.02
89	Cal Eldred	.10	.07	.04
90	Bernard Gilkey	.05	.04	.02
91	Frank Castillo	.05	.04	.02
92	Jim Gott	.05	.04	.02
93	Greg Colbrunn	.05	.04	.02
94	Jeff Brantley	.05	.04	.02
95	Jeremy Hernandez	.05	.04	.02
96	Norm Charlton	.05	.04	.02
97	Alex Arias	.05	.04	.02
98	John Franco	.05	.04	.02
99	Chris Hoiles	.05	.04	.02
100	Brad Ausmus	.05	.04	.02
101	Wes Chamberlain	.05	.04	.02
102	Mark Dewey	.05	.04	.02
103	Benji Gil (Rated Rookie)	.15	.11	.06
104	John Dopson	.05	.04	.02
105	John Smiley	.05	.04	.02
106	David Nied	.15	.11	.06
107	George Brett (Career Salute 21 Years)	.75	.60	.30
108	Kirk Gibson	.05	.04	.02
109	Larry Casian	.05	.04	.02
110	Checklist (Ryne Sandberg 2,000 Hits)	.05	.04	.02
111	Brent Gates	.20	.15	.08
112	Damion Easley	.10	.08	.04
113	Pete Harnisch	.05	.04	.02
114	Danny Cox	.05	.04	.02
115	Kevin Tapani	.05	.04	.02
116	Roberto Hernandez	.05	.04	.02
117	Domingo Jean	.05	.04	.02
118	Sid Bream	.05	.04	.02
119	Doug Henry	.05	.04	.02
120	Omar Olivares	.05	.04	.02
121	Mike Harkey	.05	.04	.02
122	Carlos Hernandez	.05	.04	.02
123	Jeff Fassero	.15	.11	.06
124	Dave Burba	.05	.04	.02
125	Wayne Kirby	.05	.04	.02
126	John Cummings	.05	.04	.02
127	Bret Barberie	.05	.04	.02
128	Todd Hundley	.05	.04	.02
129	Tim Hulett	.05	.04	.02
130	Phil Clark	.05	.04	.02
131	Danny Jackson	.05	.04	.02
132	Tom Foley	.05	.04	.02
133	Donald Harris	.10	.08	.04
134	Scott Fletcher	.05	.04	.02
135	Johnny Ruffin (Rated Rookie)	.05	.04	.02
136	Jerald Clark	.05	.04	.02
137	Billy Brewer	.05	.04	.02
138	Dan Gladden	.05	.04	.02
139	Eddie Guardado	.05	.04	.02
140	Checklist (Cal Ripken, Jr. 2,000 Hits)	.05	.04	.02
141	Scott Hemond	.05	.04	.02
142	Steve Frey	.05	.04	.02
143	Xavier Hernandez	.05	.04	.02
144	Mark Eichhorn	.05	.04	.02
145	Ellis Burks	.05	.04	.02
146	Jim Leyritz	.05	.04	.02
147	Mark Lemke	.05	.04	.02
148	Pat Listach	.08	.06	.03
149	Donovan Osborne	.05	.04	.02
150	Glenallen Hill	.05	.04	.02
151	Orel Hershiser	.05	.04	.02
152	Darrin Fletcher	.05	.04	.02
153	Royce Clayton	.08	.06	.03
154	Derek Lilliquist	.05	.04	.02
155	Mike Felder	.05	.04	.02
156	Jeff Conine	.05	.04	.02
157	Ryan Thompson	.05	.04	.02
158	Ben McDonald	.10	.08	.04
159	Ricky Gutierrez	.05	.04	.02
160	Terry Mulholland	.05	.04	.02
161	Carlos Garcia	.10	.08	.04
162	Tom Henke	.05	.04	.02
163	Mike Greenwell	.05	.04	.02
164	Thomas Howard	.05	.04	.02
165	Joe Girardi	.05	.04	.02
166	Hubie Brooks	.05	.04	.02
167	Greg Gohr	.05	.04	.02
168	Chip Hale	.05	.04	.02
169	Rick Honeycutt	.05	.04	.02
170	Hilly Hathaway	.05	.04	.02
171	Todd Jones	.05	.04	.02
172	Tony Fernandez	.05	.04	.02
173	Bo Jackson	.20	.15	.08
174	Bobby Munoz	.05	.04	.02
175	Greg McMichael	.10	.07	.04
176	Graeme Lloyd	.08	.06	.03
177	Tom Pagnozzi	.05	.04	.02
178	Derrick May	.05	.04	.02
179	Pedro Martinez	.10	.07	.04
180	Ken Hill	.05	.04	.02
181	Bryan Hickerson	.05	.04	.02
182	Jose Mesa	.05	.04	.02
183	Dave Fleming	.05	.04	.02
184	Henry Cotto	.05	.04	.02
185	Jeff Kent	.05	.04	.02
186	Mark McLemore	.05	.04	.02
187	Trevor Hoffman	.15	.11	.06
188	Todd Pratt	.10	.07	.04
189	Blas Minor	.05	.04	.02
190	Charlie Leibrandt	.05	.04	.02
191	Tony Pena	.05	.04	.02
192	*Larry Luebbers*	.10	.07	.04
193	Greg Harris	.05	.04	.02
194	David Cone	.05	.04	.02
195	Bill Gullickson	.05	.04	.02
196	Brian Harper	.05	.04	.02
197	Steve Karsay (Rated Rookie)	.20	.15	.08
198	Greg Myers	.05	.04	.02
199	Mark Portugal	.05	.04	.02
200	Pat Hentgen	.25	.20	.10
201	Mike La Valliere	.05	.04	.02
202	Mike Stanley	.08	.06	.03
203	Kent Mercker	.05	.04	.02
204	Dave Nilsson	.05	.04	.02
205	Erik Pappas	.05	.04	.02
206	Mike Morgan	.05	.04	.02
207	Roger McDowell	.05	.04	.02
208	Mike Lansing	.10	.07	.04
209	Kirt Manwaring	.05	.04	.02
210	Randy Milligan	.05	.04	.02
211	Erik Hanson	.05	.04	.02
212	Orestes Destrade	.05	.04	.02
213	Mike Maddux	.05	.04	.02
214	Alan Mills	.05	.04	.02
215	Tim Mauser	.05	.04	.02
216	Ben Rivera	.05	.04	.02
217	Don Slaught	.05	.04	.02
218	Bob Patterson	.05	.04	.02
219	Carlos Quintana	.05	.04	.02
220	Checklist (Tim Raines 2,000 Hits)	.05	.04	.02
221	Hal Morris	.05	.04	.02
222	Darren Holmes	.05	.04	.02
223	Chris Gwynn	.05	.04	.02
224	Chad Kreuter	.05	.04	.02
225	Mike Hartley	.05	.04	.02
226	Scott Lydy	.05	.04	.02
227	Eduardo Perez	.35	.25	.14
228	Greg Swindell	.05	.04	.02
229	Al Leiter	.05	.04	.02
230	Scott Radinsky	.05	.04	.02
231	Bob Wickman	.05	.04	.02
232	Otis Nixon	.05	.04	.02
233	Kevin Reimer	.05	.04	.02
234	Geronimo Pena	.05	.04	.02
235	Kevin Roberson (Rated Rookie)	.12	.09	.05
236	Jody Reed	.05	.04	.02
237	Kirk Rueter (Rated Rookie)	.60	.45	.25
238	Willie McGee	.05	.04	.02
239	Charles Nagy	.05	.04	.02
240	Tim Leary	.05	.04	.02
241	Carl Everett	.05	.04	.02
242	Charlie O'Brien	.05	.04	.02
243	Mike Pagliarulo	.05	.04	.02
244	Kerry Taylor	.05	.04	.02
245	Kevin Stocker	.35	.25	.14
246	Joel Johnston	.05	.04	.02
247	Geno Petralli	.05	.04	.02
248	Jeff Russell	.05	.04	.02
249	Joe Oliver	.05	.04	.02
250	Robert Mejia	.30	.25	.12
251	Chris Haney	.05	.04	.02
252	Bill Krueger	.05	.04	.02
253	Shane Mack	.05	.04	.02
254	Terry Steinbach	.05	.04	.02
255	Luis Polonia	.05	.04	.02
256	Eddie Taubensee	.05	.04	.02
257	Dave Stewart	.05	.04	.02
258	Tim Raines	.05	.04	.02
259	Bernie Williams	.05	.04	.02
260	John Smoltz	.10	.08	.04
261	Kevin Seitzer	.05	.04	.02
262	Bob Tewksbury	.05	.04	.02
263	Bob Scanlan	.05	.04	.02
264	Henry Rodriguez	.05	.04	.02
265	Tim Scott	.05	.04	.02
266	Scott Sanderson	.05	.04	.02
267	Eric Plunk	.05	.04	.02
268	Edgar Martinez	.05	.04	.02
269	Charlie Hough	.05	.04	.02
270	Joe Orsulak	.05	.04	.02
271	Harold Reynolds	.05	.04	.02
272	Tim Teufel	.05	.04	.02
273	Bobby Thigpen	.05	.04	.02
274	Randy Tomlin	.05	.04	.02
275	Gary Redus	.05	.04	.02
276	Ken Ryan	.05	.04	.02
277	Tim Pugh	.05	.04	.02
278	Jayhawk Owens	.05	.04	.02
279	Phil Hiatt (Rated Rookie)	.12	.09	.05
280	Alan Trammell	.05	.04	.02
281	Dave McCarty (Rated Rookie)	.20	.15	.08
282	Bob Welch	.05	.04	.02
283	J.T. Snow	.20	.15	.08
284	Brian Williams	.05	.04	.02
285	Devon White	.05	.04	.02
286	Steve Sax	.05	.04	.02
287	Tony Tarasco	.30	.25	.12
288	Bill Spiers	.05	.04	.02
289	Allen Watson	.40	.30	.15
290	Checklist (Rickey Henderson 2,000 Hits)	.05	.04	.02
291	Joe Vizcaino	.05	.04	.02
292	Darryl Strawberry	.05	.04	.02
293	John Wetteland	.05	.04	.02
294	Bill Swift	.05	.04	.02
295	Jeff Treadway	.05	.04	.02
296	Tino Martinez	.05	.04	.02
297	Richie Lewis	.05	.04	.02
298	Bret Saberhagen	.05	.04	.02
299	Arthur Rhodes	.05	.04	.02
300	Guillermo Velasquez	.05	.04	.02
301	Milt Thompson	.05	.04	.02
302	Doug Strange	.05	.04	.02
303	Aaron Sele	.75	.60	.30
304	Bip Roberts	.05	.04	.02
305	Bruce Ruffin	.05	.04	.02
306	Jose Lind	.05	.04	.02
307	David Wells	.05	.04	.02
308	Bobby Witt	.05	.04	.02
309	Mark Wohlers	.05	.04	.02
310	B.J. Surhoff	.05	.04	.02
311	Mark Whiten	.08	.06	.03
312	Turk Wendell	.05	.04	.02
313	Raul Mondesi	.75	.60	.30
314	*Brian Turang*	.15	.11	.06
315	Chris Hammond	.05	.04	.02
316	Tim Bogar	.05	.04	.02
317	Brad Pennington	.05	.04	.02
318	Tim Worrell	.05	.04	.02
319	Mitch Williams	.05	.04	.02
320	Rondell White (Rated Rookie)	.50	.40	.20
321	Frank Viola	.05	.04	.02
322	Manny Ramirez (Rated Rookie)	1.25	.90	.50
323	Gary Wayne	.05	.04	.02
324	Mike Macfarlane	.05	.04	.02
325	Russ Springer	.05	.04	.02
326	Tim Wallach	.05	.04	.02
327	Salomon Torres (Rated Rookie)	.12	.09	.05
328	Omar Vizquel	.05	.04	.02
329	*Andy Tomberlin*	.10	.07	.04
330	Chris Sabo	.05	.04	.02
331	Mike Mussina	.25	.20	.10
332	Andy Benes	.05	.04	.02
333	Darren Daulton	.05	.04	.02
334	Orlando Merced	.05	.04	.02
335	Mark McGwire	.20	.15	.08
336	Dave Winfield	.15	.11	.06
337	Sammy Sosa	.07	.05	.03
338	Eric Karros	.10	.08	.04
339	Greg Vaughn	.08	.06	.03
340	Don Mattingly	.30	.25	.12
341	Frank Thomas	3.00	2.25	1.25
342	Fred McGriff	.20	.15	.08
343	Kirby Puckett	.60	.45	.25
344	Roberto Kelly	.05	.04	.02
345	Wally Joyner	.05	.04	.02
346	Andres Galarraga	.05	.04	.02
347	Bobby Bonilla	.08	.06	.03
348	Benito Santiago	.05	.04	.02
349	Barry Bonds	.75	.60	.30
350	Delino DeShields	.08	.06	.03
351	Albert Belle	.40	.30	.15
352	Randy Johnson	.05	.04	.02
353	Tim Salmon	1.25	.90	.50
354	John Olerud	.30	.25	.12
355	Dean Palmer	.05	.04	.02
356	Roger Clemens	.40	.30	.15
357	Jim Abbott	.08	.06	.03
358	Mark Grace	.05	.04	.02
359	Ozzie Guillen	.05	.04	.02
360	Lou Whitaker	.05	.04	.02
361	Jose Rijo	.05	.04	.02
362	Jeff Montgomery	.05	.04	.02
363	Chuck Finley	.05	.04	.02
364	Tom Glavine	.20	.15	.08
365	Jeff Bagwell	.25	.20	.10
366	Joe Carter	.20	.15	.08
367	Ray Lankford	.05	.04	.02
368	Ramon Martinez	.05	.04	.02
369	Jay Buhner	.05	.04	.02
370	Matt Williams	.05	.04	.02
371	Larry Walker	.08	.06	.03
372	Jose Canseco	.35	.25	.14
373	Len Dykstra	.10	.08	.04
374	Bryan Harvey	.05	.04	.02
375	Andy Van Slyke	.05	.04	.02
376	Ivan Rodriguez	.10	.08	.04
377	Kevin Mitchell	.06	.05	.02
378	Travis Fryman	.30	.25	.12
379	Duane Ward	.05	.04	.02
380	Greg Maddux	.35	.25	.14
381	Scott Servais	.05	.04	.02
382	Greg Olson	.05	.04	.02
383	Rey Sanchez	.05	.04	.02
384	Tom Kramer	.05	.04	.02
385	David Valle	.05	.04	.02
386	Eddie Murray	.10	.08	.04
387	Kevin Higgins	.05	.04	.02
388	Dan Wilson	.05	.04	.02
389	Todd Frohwirth	.05	.04	.02
390	Gerald Williams	.05	.04	.02
391	Hipolito Pichardo	.05	.04	.02
392	Pat Meares	.05	.04	.02
393	Luis Lopez	.05	.04	.02
394	Ricky Jordan	.05	.04	.02
395	Bob Walk	.05	.04	.02
396	Sid Fernandez	.05	.04	.02
397	Todd Worrell	.05	.04	.02
398	Darryl Hamilton	.05	.04	.02
399	Randy Myers	.05	.04	.02
400	Rod Brewer	.05	.04	.02
401	Lance Blankenship	.05	.04	.02
402	Steve Finley	.05	.04	.02
403	*Phil Leftwich*	.20	.15	.08
404	Juan Guzman	.10	.07	.04
405	Anthony Young	.05	.04	.02
406	Jeff Gardner	.05	.04	.02
407	Ryan Bowen	.05	.04	.02
408	Fernando Valenzuela	.05	.04	.02
409	David West	.05	.04	.02
410	Kenny Rogers	.05	.04	.02
411	Bob Zupcic	.05	.04	.02
412	Eric Young	.05	.04	.02
413	Bret Boone	.07	.05	.03
414	Danny Tartabull	.07	.05	.03
415	Bob MacDonald	.05	.04	.02
416	Ron Karkovice	.05	.04	.02
417	Scott Cooper	.05	.04	.02
418	Dante Bichette	.05	.04	.02
419	Tripp Cromer	.05	.04	.02
420	Billy Ashley	.25	.20	.10
421	Roger Smithberg	.05	.04	.02
422	Dennis Martinez	.05	.04	.02
423	Mike Blowers	.05	.04	.02
424	Darren Lewis	.05	.04	.02
425	Junior Ortiz	.05	.04	.02
426	Butch Huskey	.10	.07	.04
427	Jimmy Poole	.05	.04	.02

428	Walt Weiss	.05	.04	.02
429	Scott Bankhead	.05	.04	.02
430	Deion Sanders	.25	.20	.10
431	Scott Bullett	.07	.05	.03
432	Jeff Huson	.05	.04	.02
433	Tyler Green	.05	.04	.02
434	Billy Hatcher	.05	.04	.02
435	Bob Hamelin	.07	.05	.03
436	Reggie Sanders	.07	.05	.03
437	Scott Erickson	.07	.05	.03
438	Steve Reed	.05	.04	.02
439	Randy Velarde	.05	.04	.02
440	Checklist (Tony Gwtnn 2,000 Hits)	.05	.04	.02
441	Terry Leach	.05	.04	.02
442	Danny Bautista	.08	.06	.03
443	Kent Hrbek	.07	.05	.03
444	Rick Wilkins	.07	.05	.03
445	Tony Phillips	.05	.04	.02
446	Dion James	.05	.04	.02
447	Joey Cora	.05	.04	.02
448	Andre Dawson	.10	.08	.04
449	Pedro Castellano	.07	.05	.03
450	Tom Gordon	.05	.04	.02
451	Rob Dibble	.05	.04	.02
452	Ron Darling	.05	.04	.02
453	Chipper Jones	.35	.25	.14
454	Joe Grahe	.05	.04	.02
455	Domingo Cedeno	.08	.06	.03
456	Tom Edens	.05	.04	.02
457	Mitch Webster	.05	.04	.02
458	Jose Bautista	.05	.04	.02
459	Troy O'Leary	.05	.04	.02
460	Todd Zeile	.08	.06	.03
461	Sean Berry	.06	.05	.02
462	*Brad Holman*	.10	.08	.04
463	Dave Martinez	.05	.04	.02
464	Mark Lewis	.05	.04	.02
465	Paul Carey	.05	.04	.02
466	Jack Armstrong	.05	.04	.02
467	David Telgheder	.05	.04	.02
468	Gene Harris	.05	.04	.02
469	Danny Darwin	.05	.04	.02
470	Kim Batiste	.05	.04	.02
471	Tim Wakefield	.05	.04	.02
472	Craig Lefferts	.05	.04	.02
473	Jacob Brumfield	.05	.04	.02
474	Lance Painter	.06	.05	.02
475	Milt Cuyler	.05	.04	.02
476	Melido Perez	.05	.04	.02
477	Derek Parks	.07	.05	.03
478	Gary DiSarcina	.05	.04	.02
479	Steve Bedrosian	.05	.04	.02
480	Eric Anthony	.07	.05	.03
481	Julio Franco	.07	.05	.03
482	Tommy Greene	.06	.05	.02
483	Pat Kelly	.05	.04	.02
484	Nate Minchey (Rated Rookie)	.08	.06	.03
485	William Pennyfeather	.05	.04	.02
486	Harold Baines	.07	.05	.03
487	Howard Johnson	.10	.08	.04
488	Angel Miranda	.05	.04	.02
489	Scott Sanders	.05	.04	.02
490	Shawon Dunston	.07	.05	.03
491	Mel Rojas	.07	.05	.03
492	Jeff Nelson	.05	.04	.02
493	Archi Cianfrocco	.05	.04	.02
494	Al Martin	.05	.04	.02
495	Mike Gallego	.05	.04	.02
496	Mike Henneman	.05	.04	.02
497	Armando Reynoso	.05	.04	.02
498	Mickey Morandini	.05	.04	.02
499	Rick Renteria	.05	.04	.02
500	Rick Sutcliffe	.07	.05	.03
501	Bobby Jones (Rated Rookie)	.25	.20	.10
502	Gary Gaetti	.08	.06	.03
503	Rick Aguilera	.07	.05	.03
504	Todd Stottlemyre	.05	.04	.02
505	Mike Mohler	.05	.04	.02
506	Mike Stanton	.05	.04	.02
507	Jose Guzman	.05	.04	.02
508	Kevin Rogers	.05	.04	.02
509	Chuck Carr	.05	.04	.02
510	Chris Jones	.05	.04	.02
511	Brent Mayne	.05	.04	.02
512	Greg Harris	.05	.04	.02
513	Dave Henderson	.07	.05	.03
514	Eric Hillman	.05	.04	.02
515	Dan Peltier	.05	.04	.02
516	Craig Shipley	.05	.04	.02
517	John Valentin	.08	.06	.03
518	Wilson Alvarez	.07	.05	.03
519	Andujar Cedeno	.05	.04	.02
520	Troy Neel	.05	.04	.02
521	Tom Candiotti	.05	.04	.02
522	Matt Mieske	.05	.04	.02
523	Jim Thome	.25	.20	.10
524	Lou Frazier	.08	.06	.03
525	Mike Jackson	.05	.04	.02
526	Pedro Martinez	.05	.04	.02
527	Roger Pavlik	.05	.04	.02
528	Kent Bottenfield	.05	.04	.02
529	Felix Jose	.05	.04	.02
530	Mark Guthrie	.05	.04	.02
531	Steve Farr	.05	.04	.02
532	Craig Paquette	.05	.04	.02
533	Doug Jones	.05	.04	.02
534	Luis Alicea	.05	.04	.02
535	Cory Snyder	.05	.04	.02
536	Paul Sorrento	.05	.04	.02
537	Nigel Wilson	.12	.09	.05
538	Jeff King	.05	.04	.02
539	Willie Green	.07	.05	.03
540	Kirk McCaskill	.05	.04	.02
541	Al Osuna	.05	.04	.02
542	Greg Hibbard	.05	.04	.02
543	Brett Butler	.07	.05	.03
544	Jose Valentin	.05	.04	.02
545	Wil Cordero	.07	.05	.03
546	Chris Bosio	.05	.04	.02
547	Jamie Moyer	.05	.04	.02
548	Jim Eisenreich	.05	.04	.02
549	Vinny Castilla	.05	.04	.02
550	Checklist (Dave Winfield 3,000 Hits)	.05	.04	.02
551	John Roper	.08	.06	.03
552	Lance Johnson	.05	.04	.02
553	Scott Kamieniecki	.05	.04	.02
554	Mike Moore	.05	.04	.02
555	Steve Buechele	.05	.04	.02
556	Terry Pendleton	.08	.06	.03
557	Todd Van Poppel	.07	.05	.03
558	Rob Butler	.05	.04	.02
559	Zane Smith	.05	.04	.02
560	David Hulse	.05	.04	.02
561	Tim Costo	.05	.04	.02
562	John Habyan	.05	.04	.02
563	Terry Jorgensen	.05	.04	.02
564	Matt Nokes	.07	.05	.03
565	Kevin McReynolds	.07	.05	.03
566	Phil Plantier	.08	.06	.03
567	Chris Turner	.07	.05	.03
568	Carlos Delgado	.75	.60	.30
569	John Jaha	.05	.04	.02
570	Dwight Smith	.05	.04	.02
571	John Vander Wal	.05	.04	.02
572	Trevor Wilson	.05	.04	.02
573	Felix Fermin	.05	.04	.02
574	Marc Newfield (Rated Rookie)	.20	.15	.08
575	Jeromy Burnitz	.07	.05	.03
576	Leo Gomez	.05	.04	.02
577	Curt Schilling	.05	.04	.02
578	Kevin Young	.08	.06	.03
579	*Jerry Spradlin*	.10	.07	.04
580	Curt Leskanic	.05	.04	.02
581	Carl Willis	.05	.04	.02
582	Alex Fernandez	.07	.05	.03
583	Mark Holzemer	.05	.04	.02
584	Domingo Martinez	.07	.05	.03
585	Pete Smith	.05	.04	.02
586	Brian Jordan	.05	.04	.02
587	Kevin Gross	.05	.04	.02
588	J.R. Phillips (Rated Rookie)	.40	.30	.15
589	Chris Nabholz	.05	.04	.02
590	Bill Wertz	.05	.04	.02
591	Derek Bell	.07	.05	.03
592	Brady Anderson	.07	.05	.03
593	Matt Turner	.05	.04	.02
594	Pete Incaviglia	.07	.05	.03
595	Greg Gagne	.05	.04	.02
596	John Flaherty	.05	.04	.02
597	Scott Livingstone	.05	.04	.02
598	Rod Bolton	.05	.04	.02
599	Mike Perez	.05	.04	.02
600	Checklist (Roger Clemens 2,000 Strikeouts)	.05	.04	.02
601	Tony Castillo	.05	.04	.02
602	Henry Mercedes	.07	.05	.03
603	Mike Fetters	.05	.04	.02
604	Rod Beck	.07	.05	.03
605	Damon Buford	.05	.04	.02
606	Matt Whiteside	.05	.04	.02
607	Shawn Green	.05	.04	.02
608	Midre Cummings (Rated Rookie)	.25	.20	.10
609	Jeff McNeeley	.07	.05	.03
610	Danny Sheaffer	.05	.04	.02
611	Paul Wagner	.05	.04	.02
612	Torey Lovullo	.05	.04	.02
613	Javier Lopez	.75	.60	.30
614	Mariano Duncan	.05	.04	.02
615	Doug Brocail	.05	.04	.02
616	Dave Hansen	.05	.04	.02
617	Ryan Klesko	1.00	.75	.40
618	Eric Davis	.07	.05	.03
619	Scott Ruffcorn (Rated Rookie)	.25	.20	.10
620	Mike Trombley	.05	.04	.02
621	Jaime Navarro	.05	.04	.02
622	Rheal Cormier	.05	.04	.02
623	Jose Offerman	.05	.04	.02
624	David Segui	.05	.04	.02
625	Robb Nen (Rated Rookie)	.05	.04	.02
626	Dave Gallagher	.05	.04	.02
627	*Julian Tavarez*	.25	.20	.10
628	Chris Gomez	.20	.15	.08
629	Jeffrey Hammonds (Rated Rookie)	.75	.60	.30
630	Scott Brosius	.05	.04	.02
631	Willie Blair	.05	.04	.02
632	Doug Drabek	.07	.05	.03
633	Bill Wegman	.05	.04	.02
634	Jeff McKnight	.05	.04	.02
635	Rich Rodriguez	.05	.04	.02
636	Steve Trachsel	.05	.04	.02
637	Buddy Groom	.05	.04	.02
638	Sterling Hitchcock	.07	.05	.03
639	Chuck McElroy	.05	.04	.02
640	Rene Gonzales	.08	.06	.03
641	Dan Plesac	.05	.04	.02
642	Jeff Branson	.05	.04	.02
643	Darrell Whitmore	.07	.05	.03
644	Paul Quantrill	.05	.04	.02
645	Rich Rowland	.05	.04	.02
646	*Curtis Pride*	.50	.40	.20
647	Erik Plantenberg	.05	.04	.02
648	Albie Lopez	.07	.05	.03
649	*Rich Batchelor*	.10	.07	.04
650	Lee Smith	.08	.06	.03
651	Cliff Floyd	1.00	.75	.40
652	Pete Schourek	.05	.04	.02
653	Reggie Jefferson	.05	.04	.02
654	Bill Haselman	.05	.04	.02
655	Steve Hosey	.05	.04	.02
656	Mark Clark	.05	.04	.02
657	Mark Davis	.05	.04	.02
658	Dave Magadan	.05	.04	.02
659	Candy Maldonado	.05	.04	.02
660	Checklist (Mark Langston 2,0000 Strikeouts)	.05	.04	.02

1994 Donruss Decade Dominators

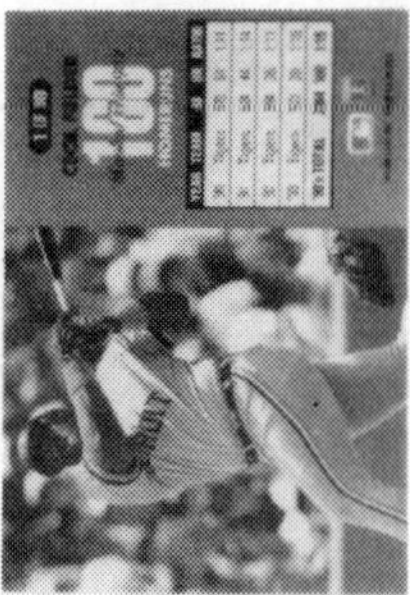

Donruss selected 10 top home run hitters (Series I) and 10 RBI leaders of the 1990s for this insert set. Cards were issued in all types of Series I and II packs. Full-bleed UV-coated cards were gold-foil enhanced on the front. Backs featured another full-color player photo and charted information on his 1990s home run or RBI output and ranking.

		MT	NR MT	EX
Complete Set (20):		55.00	41.00	22.00
Common Player:		1.50	1.25	.60
	Series I			
1	Cecil Fielder	2.50	2.00	1.00
2	Barry Bonds	5.00	3.50	2.00
3	Fred McGriff	3.00	2.25	1.25
4	Matt Williams	2.00	1.50	.80
5	Joe Carter	3.00	2.75	1.50
6	Juan Gonzalez	7.00	5.25	2.75
7	Jose Canseco	3.00	2.25	1.25
8	Ron Gant	1.50	1.25	.60
9	Ken Griffey, Jr.	9.00	6.75	3.50
10	Mark McGwire	1.50	1.25	.60
	Series II			
1	Tony Gwynn	2.00	2.00	1.00
2	Frank Thomas	9.00	7.50	4.00
3	Paul Molitor	3.00	2.25	1.25
4	Edgar Martinez	1.50	1.25	.60
5	Kirby Puckett	3.00	2.25	1.25
6	Ken Griffey, Jr.	9.00	6.75	3.50
7	Barry Bonds	5.00	3.75	2.00
8	Willie McGee	1.50	1.25	.60
9	Len Dykstra	2.00	1.50	.80
10	John Kruk	1.50	1.25	.60

1994 Donruss Decade Dominators Supers

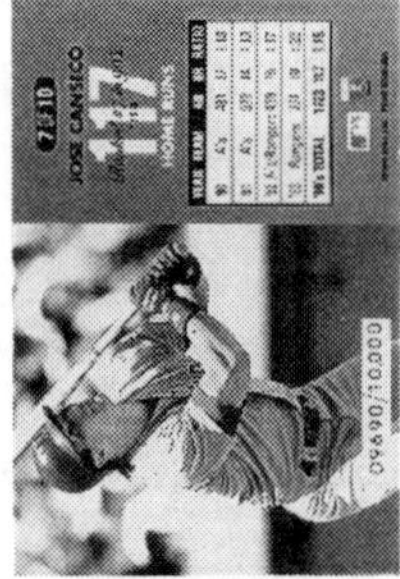

Super-size (3-1/2" x 5") versions of the 1994 Donruss Decade Dominators insert cards were produced as a premium, one card being packaged in a paper checklist envelope in each hobby box of Donruss foil packs. The supers are identical in format to the regular-size cards with the exception of a white serial number strip on the back, identifying each card's position with an edition of 10,000.

		MT	NR MT	EX
Complete Set (20):		70.00	52.00	28.00
Common Player:		4.00	3.00	1.50
	Series I			
1	Cecil Fielder	4.50	3.50	1.75
2	Barry Bonds	7.50	5.75	3.00
3	Fred McGriff	4.00	3.00	1.50
4	Matt Williams	4.00	3.00	1.50
5	Joe Carter	4.00	3.00	1.50
6	Juan Gonzalez	7.50	5.75	3.00
7	Jose Canseco	5.00	3.75	2.00
8	Ron Gant	4.00	3.00	1.50
9	Ken Griffey, Jr.	8.00	6.00	3.25
10	Mark McGwire	5.00	3.75	2.00
	Series II			
1	Tony Gwynn	3.50	2.75	1.50
2	Frank Thomas	8.00	6.00	3.25

3	Paul Molitor	5.00	3.75	2.00
4	Edgar Martinez	3.00	2.25	1.25
5	Kirby Puckett	5.00	3.75	2.00
6	Ken Griffey, Jr.	7.50	5.75	3.00
7	Barry Bonds	6.00	4.50	2.50
8	Willie McGee	3.00	2.25	1.25
9	Lenny Dykstra	3.50	2.75	1.50
10	John Kruk	3.50	2.75	1.50

1994 Donruss Elite

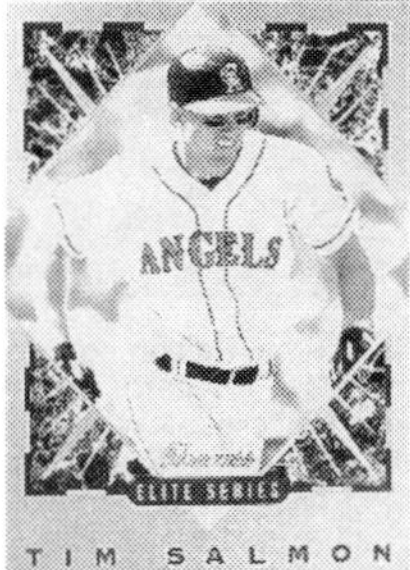

Donruss continues its popular Elite Series with 12 more players in 1994. The cards, numbered #37-48, were inserted in foil packs only. The cards feature the player in a diamond on the front; the back offers an opinion of why the player is considered an elite and is serially numbered from 1-10,000.

		MT	NR MT	EX
Complete Set (12):		650.00	490.00	260.00
Common Player:		30.00	22.00	12.00
37	Frank Thomas	140.00	105.00	55.00
38	Tony Gwynn	35.00	26.00	14.00
39	Tim Salmon	70.00	52.00	28.00
40	Albert Belle	50.00	35.00	18.00
41	John Kruk	30.00	22.00	12.00
42	Juan Gonzalez	80.00	60.00	32.00
43	John Olerud	35.00	26.00	14.00
44	Barry Bonds	70.00	52.00	28.00
45	Ken Griffey, Jr.	140.00	105.00	55.00
46	Mike Piazza	80.00	60.00	32.00
47	Jack McDowell	30.00	22.00	12.00
48	Andres Galarraga	35.00	26.00	14.00

1994 Donruss Diamond Kings

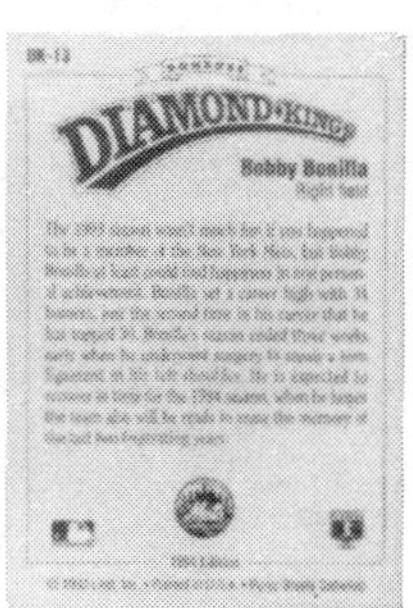

The artwork of Dick Perez is again featured on this insert set included in foil packs. Player art is set against garnish color backgrounds with a red-and-silver "Diamond Kings" foil logo above, and the player's name in script at bottom. Backs are printed in red on pale yellow and feature a 1993 season summary. Cards have a DK preface to the number. Cards #1-14 and #29, Dave Winfield, were included in Series I packs; cards #15-28 were found in Series II, along with the checklist card (#30), featuring a Dick Perez self-portrait.

		MT	NR MT	EX
Complete Set (30):		55.00	41.00	22.00
Common Player:		1.00	.75	.40
1	Barry Bonds	4.50	3.50	1.75
2	Mo Vaughn	2.50	2.00	1.00
3	Steve Avery	2.50	1.75	1.00
4	Tim Salmon	6.00	4.50	2.50
5	Rick Wilkins	1.50	1.25	.60
6	Brian Harper	1.00	.70	.40
7	Andres Galarraga	1.50	1.25	.60
8	Albert Belle	3.00	2.25	1.25
9	John Kruk	1.25	.90	.50
10	Ivan Rodriguez	1.00	.75	.40
11	Tony Gwynn	2.50	1.75	.90
12	Brian McRae	1.50	1.25	.60
13	Bobby Bonilla	1.00	.75	.40
14	Ken Griffey, Jr.	9.00	6.75	3.50
15	Mike Piazza	8.00	6.00	3.25
16	Don Mattingly	3.50	2.75	1.50
17	Barry Larkin	1.00	.75	.40
18	Ruben Sierra	1.00	.75	.40
19	Orlando Merced	1.00	.75	.40
20	Greg Vaughn	1.25	.90	.50
21	Gregg Jefferies	1.25	.90	.50
22	Cecil Fielder	1.75	1.25	.70
23	Moises Alou	1.25	.90	.50
24	John Olerud	3.00	2.25	1.25
25	Gary Sheffield	1.50	1.25	.60
26	Mike Mussina	2.50	2.00	1.00
27	Jeff Bagwell	2.50	2.00	1.00
28	Frank Thomas	10.00	7.50	4.00
29	Dave Winfield (King of Kings)	2.50	2.00	1.00
30	Dick Perez (Checklist)	1.00	.75	.40

1994 Donruss Diamond Kings Super

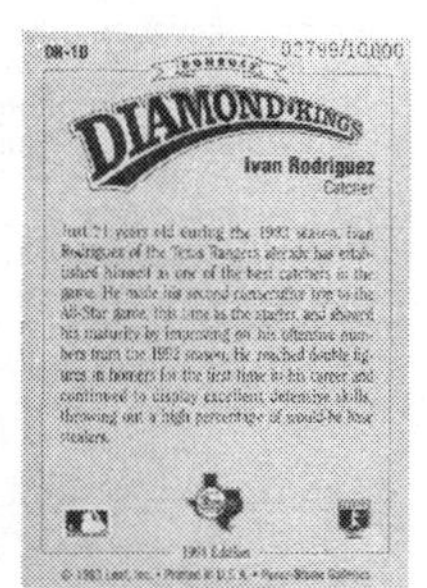

Each retail box of 1994 Donruss foil packs contains one super-size (4-7/8" x 6-13/16") version of the Diamond Kings insert set. Series I boxes offer cards #1-14, while 15-28 are found in Series II boxes. A 29th card, honoring Dave Winfield, was also produced. Super DKs are identical in format to the regular-size inserts, with the exception of a white serial number strip on the back which identifies the card in an edition of 10,000.

		MT	NR MT	EX
Complete Set (29):		95.00	71.00	38.00
Common Player:		3.00	2.25	1.25
1	Barry Bonds	6.00	4.50	2.50
2	Mo Vaughn	3.00	2.25	1.25
3	Steve Avery	3.00	2.25	1.25
4	Tim Salmon	6.00	4.50	2.50
5	Rick Wilkins	3.00	2.25	1.25
6	Brian Harper	3.00	2.25	1.25
7	Andres Galarraga	4.50	3.50	1.75
8	Albert Belle	3.75	2.75	1.50
9	John Kruk	3.75	2.75	1.50
10	Ivan Rodriguez	3.00	2.25	1.25
11	Tony Gwynn	3.50	2.75	1.50
12	Brian McRae	3.00	2.25	1.25
13	Bobby Bonilla	3.50	2.75	1.50
14	Ken Griffey, Jr.	7.50	5.75	3.00
15	Mike Piazza	6.00	4.50	2.50
16	Don Mattingly	4.00	3.00	1.50
17	Barry Larkin	3.00	2.25	1.25
18	Ruben Sierra	3.50	2.75	1.50
19	Orlando Merced	3.00	2.25	1.25
20	Greg Vaughn	3.00	2.25	1.25
21	Gregg Jefferies	3.50	2.75	1.50
22	Cecil Fielder	4.50	3.50	1.75
23	Moises Alou	3.50	2.75	1.50
24	John Olerud	3.75	2.75	1.50
25	Gary Sheffield	3.75	2.75	1.50
26	Mike Mussina	3.00	2.25	1.25
27	Jeff Bagwell	3.50	2.75	1.50
28	Frank Thomas	7.50	5.75	3.00
29	Dave Winfield	5.00	3.75	2.00

1994 Donruss MVPs

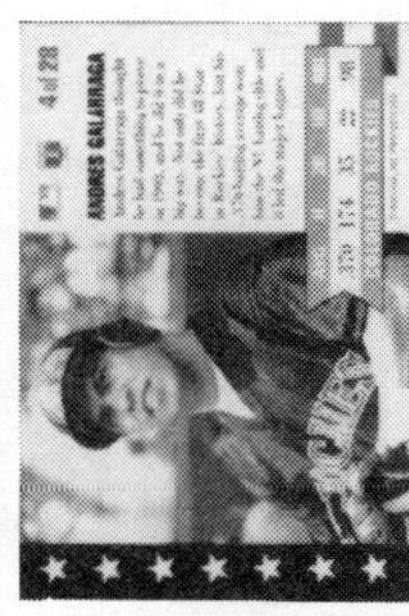

These 1994 Donruss insert cards were included in 1994 jumbo packs only. The fronts have a large metallic blue MVP logo, beneath which is a red stripe with the player's name and position in white. At the upper-left border are six vertical white stars. A gold-foil Donruss logo is at upper-right. Backs have a portrait photo bordered at left by a metallic blue strip with a row of seven vertical white stars. Stats for 1993 are in a red-and-white banner at bottom, and there is a short summary of why the player was selected as team MVP.

		MT	NR MT	EX
Complete Set (28):		30.00	22.00	12.00
Common Player:		.50	.40	.20
1	Dave Justice	1.00	.70	.40
2	Mark Grace	.50	.40	.20
3	Jose Rijo	.50	.40	.20
4	Andres Galarraga	.75	.60	.30
5	Bryan Harvey	.50	.40	.20
6	Jeff Bagwell	1.00	.70	.40
7	Mike Piazza	3.00	2.25	1.25
8	Moises Alou	.50	.40	.20
9	Bobby Bonilla	.50	.40	.20
10	Len Dykstra	.75	.60	.30
11	Jeff King	.50	.40	.20
12	Gregg Jefferies	.75	.60	.30
13	Tony Gwynn	1.00	.70	.40
14	Barry Bonds	3.00	2.25	1.25
15	Cal Ripken, Jr.	3.00	2.25	1.25
16	Mo Vaughn	1.00	.70	.40
17	Tim Salmon	2.00	1.50	.80
18	Frank Thomas	5.00	3.75	2.00
19	Albert Belle	1.50	1.25	.60
20	Cecil Fielder	1.50	1.25	.60
21	Wally Joyner	.75	.60	.30
22	Greg Vaughn	.75	.60	.30
23	Kirby Puckett	2.00	1.50	.80
24	Don Mattingly	2.00	1.50	.80
25	Ruben Sierra	.50	.40	.20
26	Ken Griffey, Jr.	5.00	3.75	2.00
27	Juan Gonzalez	3.00	2.25	1.25
28	John Olerud	1.25	.90	.50

1994 Donruss Award Winners Supers

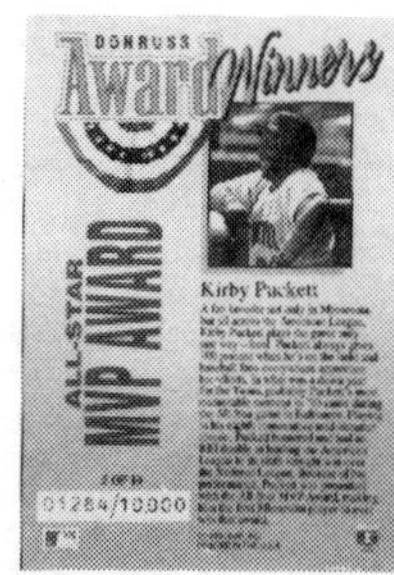

Major award winners of the 1993 season are honored in in this 10-card super-size (3-1/2" x 5") insert set. One card was packaged in each box of U.S. jumbo packs and in each Canadian foil-pack box. In the background abovre the player photo on front is a large "Donruss Award Winners" logo and bunting. The "Winners" is printed in blue foil. In a silver box at the bottom of the photo is the player's name and award. Rows of white stars at top and bottom complete the design. On a gold-tone background, the card backs have a second player photo, a description of his award winning performance and a white strip with a serial number identifying the card's place in an edition of 10,000.

		MT	NR MT	EX
Complete Set (10):		55.00	41.00	22.00
Common Player:		3.00	2.25	1.25
1	Barry Bonds (N.L. MVP)	6.00	4.50	2.50
2	Greg Maddux (N.L. Cy Young)	3.00	2.25	1.25
3	Mike Piazza (N.L. ROY)	6.00	4.50	2.50
4	Barry Bonds (N.L. HR Champ)	6.00	4.50	2.50
5	Kirby Puckett (All-Star MVP)	4.50	3.50	1.75
6	Frank Thomas (A.L. MVP)	12.00	9.00	4.75
7	Jack McDowell (A.L. Cy Young)	3.00	2.25	1.25
8	Tim Salmon (A.L. ROY)	5.00	3.75	2.00
9	Juan Gonzalez (A.L. HR Champ)	9.00	6.75	3.50
10	Paul Molitor (World Series MVP)	4.50	3.50	1.75

Values for recent cards and sets are listed in Mint (MT), Near Mint (NM), reflecting the fact that many cards from recent years have been preserved in top condition. Recent cards and sets in less than Excellent condition have little collector interest.

1994 Donruss Anniversary-1984

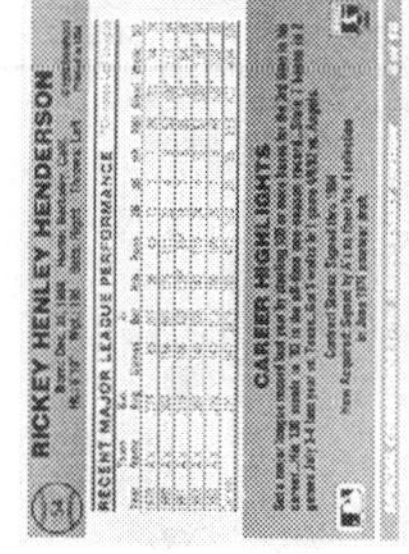

This set commemorates and features 10 of the most popular cards from Donruss' 1984 set. The cards, inserted in Series I hobby foil packs only, are "holographically enhanced" with foil stamping and UV coating.

		MT	NR MT	EX
Complete Set (10):		40.00	30.00	15.00
Common Player:		2.50	2.00	1.00
1	Joe Carter	5.00	3.75	2.00
2	Robin Yount	4.00	3.00	1.75
3	George Brett	6.00	4.50	2.50
4	Rickey Henderson	3.00	2.25	1.25
5	Nolan Ryan	12.00	9.00	4.75
6	Cal Ripken, Jr.	6.00	4.50	2.50
7	Wade Boggs	2.50	2.00	1.00
8	Don Mattingly	7.00	5.25	2.75
9	Ryne Sandberg	7.00	5.25	2.75
10	Tony Gwynn	3.00	2.25	1.25

A player's name in italic type indicates a rookie card. An (FC) indicates a player's first card for that particular card company.

1994 Donruss Long Ball Leaders

The "Tale of the Tape" for the 1993 season is chronicled in this 10-card series inserted into Series II hobby foil packs. Silver prismatic foil highlights the typography on the front of the card which includes the "Long Ball Leaders" logos (complete with embossed baseball), the player's last name and the distance of his blast. Cards backs have another player photo superimposed on the venue in which the home run was hit. The distance is repreated in silver over the ballpark photo. In a wide silver box at bottom are data about the home run.

		MT	NR MT	EX
Complete Set (10):		50.00	37.00	20.00
Common Player:		2.00	1.50	.80
1	Cecil Fielder	3.00	2.25	1.25
2	Dean Palmer	2.00	1.50	.80
3	Andres Galarraga	2.50	2.00	1.00
4	Bo Jackson	3.00	2.25	1.25
5	Ken Griffey, Jr.	15.00	11.00	6.00
6	Dave Justice	4.00	3.00	1.50
7	Mike Piazza	12.00	9.00	4.75
8	Frank Thomas	15.00	11.00	6.00
9	Barry Bonds	7.50	5.50	3.00
10	Juan Gonzalez	12.00	9.00	4.75

Values quoted in this guide reflect the retail price of a card – the price a collector can expect to pay when buying a card from a dealer. The wholesale price – that which a collector can expect to receive from a dealer when selling cards – will be significantly lower, depending on desirability and condition.

1994 Donruss Spirit of the Game

Ten players are featured in this 1994 Donruss insert set, packaged exclusively in retail boxes. Horizontal in format, fronts feature a color player action photo set against a gold-tone background which has the appearance of a multiple-exposure photo. The Donruss logo at upper-right and the bottom strip carrying the "Spirit of the Game" title are holographic foil. On back a player portrait photo is set against a backdrop of red, white and blue bunting. There is a short previous-season write-up at right. Cards #1-5 were included with Series I, cards 6-10 were in Series II packs.

		MT	NR MT	EX
Complete Set (10):		50.00	37.00	20.00
Common Player:		5.00	3.75	2.00
1	John Olerud	5.00	3.75	2.00
2	Barry Bonds	9.00	6.75	3.50
3	Ken Griffey, Jr.	15.00	11.00	6.00
4	Mike Piazza	9.00	6.75	3.50
5	Juan Gonzalez	10.00	7.50	4.00
6	Frank Thomas	15.00	11.00	6.00
7	Tim Salmon	6.00	4.50	2.50
8	Dave Justice	6.00	4.50	2.50
9	Don Mattingly	4.00	3.00	1.50
10	Len Dykstra	3.00	2.25	1.25

Values quoted in this guide reflect the retail price of a card – the price a collector can expect to pay when buying a card from a dealer. The wholesale price – that which a collector can expect to receive from a dealer when selling cards – will be significantly lower, depending on desirability and condition.

1994 Donruss Spirit of the Game Super

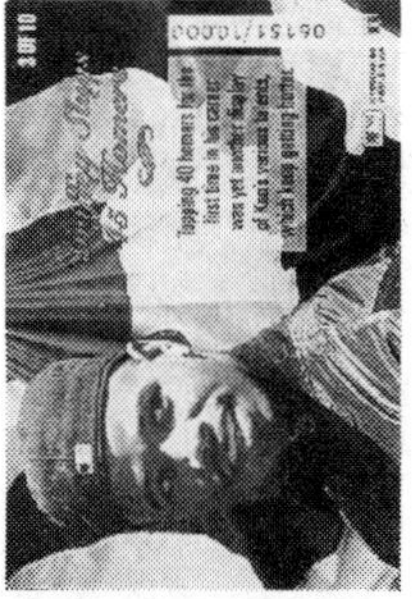

Virtually identical in format to the regular-size "Spirit of the game cards, these 3-1/2" x 5" versions have gold-foil, rather than holographic printing on the front, and have a serial number on back identifying it from an edition of 10,000. One Super card was inserted in each specially designated retail box.

		MT	NR MT	EX
Complete Set (10):		125.00	94.00	50.00
Common Player:		10.00	7.50	4.00
1	John Olerud	10.00	7.50	4.00
2	Barry Bonds	15.00	11.00	6.00
3	Ken Griffey, Jr.	22.00	16.50	8.75
4	Mike Piazza	18.00	13.50	7.25
5	Juan Gonzalez	20.00	15.00	8.00
6	Frank Thomas	25.00	18.50	10.00
7	Tim Salmon	16.00	12.00	6.50
8	David Justice	14.00	10.50	5.50
9	Don Mattingly	18.00	13.50	7.25
10	Lenny Dykstra	10.00	7.50	4.00

1994 Donruss Special Edition - Gold

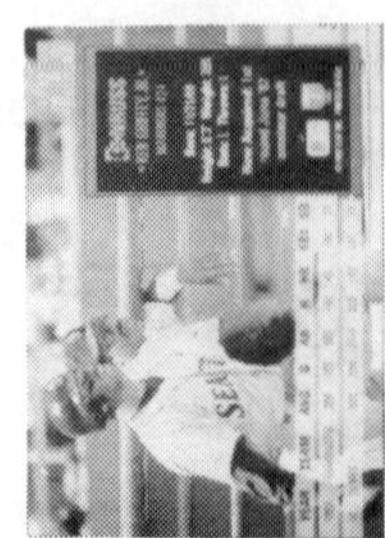

In 1994 Donruss added a Special Edition subset of 100 of the game's top players. Fifty cards each were included one or two per pack in all types of Donruss' Series I and II 1994 packaging. The cards have special gold-foil stamping on front in the area of the team logo and player name, and on back in a "Special Edition" number box in the upper-left corner.

		MT	NR MT	EX
Complete Set (100):		32.00	24.00	13.00
Common Player:		.25	.20	.10
1	Nolan Ryan	4.00	3.00	1.50
2	Mike Piazza	4.00	3.00	1.50
3	Moises Alou	.30	.25	.12
4	Ken Griffey, Jr.	6.00	4.50	2.50
5	Gary Sheffield	.35	.25	.14
6	Roberto Alomar	.60	.45	.25
7	John Kruk	.30	.25	.12
8	Gregg Olson	.25	.20	.10
9	Gregg Jefferies	.40	.30	.15
10	Tony Gwynn	.50	.40	.20
11	Chad Curtis	.30	.25	.12
12	Craig Biggio	.25	.20	.10
13	John Burkett	.25	.20	.10
14	Carlos Baerga	.75	.60	.30
15	Robin Yount	.75	.60	.30
16	Dennis Eckersley	.25	.20	.10
17	Dwight Gooden	.25	.20	.10
18	Ryne Sandberg	1.00	.70	.40
19	Rickey Henderson	.30	.25	.12
20	Jack McDowell	.30	.25	.12
21	Jay Bell	.25	.20	.10
22	Kevin Brown	.25	.20	.10
23	Robin Ventura	.40	.30	.15
24	Paul Molitor	.50	.40	.20
25	David Justice	.60	.45	.25
26	Rafael Palmeiro	.30	.25	.12
27	Cecil Fielder	.40	.30	.15
28	Chuck Knoblauch	.25	.20	.10
29	Dave Hollins	.30	.25	.12
30	Jimmy Key	.25	.20	.10
31	Mark Langston	.25	.20	.10
32	Darryl Kile	.25	.20	.10
33	Ruben Sierra	.35	.25	.14
34	Ron Gant	.30	.25	.12
35	Ozzie Smith	.35	.25	.14
36	Wade Boggs	.45	.35	.20
37	Marquis Grissom	.30	.25	.12
38	Will Clark	.60	.45	.25
39	Kenny Lofton	.35	.25	.14
40	Cal Ripken, Jr.	1.50	1.25	.60
41	Steve Avery	.30	.25	.12
42	Mo Vaughn	.25	.20	.10
43	Brian McRae	.25	.20	.10
44	Mickey Tettleton	.25	.20	.10
45	Barry Larkin	.25	.20	.10
46	Charlie Hayes	.25	.20	.10
47	Kevin Appier	.25	.20	.10
48	Robby Thompson	.25	.20	.10
49	Juan Gonzalez	3.00	2.25	1.25
50	Paul O'Neill	.25	.20	.10
331	Mike Mussina	.30	.25	.12
332	Andy Benes	.25	.20	.10
333	Darren Daulton	.25	.20	.10
334	Orlando Merced	.25	.20	.10
335	Mark McGwire	.30	.25	.12
336	Dave Winfield	.50	.40	.20
337	Sammy Sosa	.30	.25	.12
338	Eric Karros	.25	.20	.10
339	Greg Vaughn	.25	.20	.10
340	Don Mattingly	.75	.60	.30
341	Frank Thomas	4.00	3.00	1.50
342	Fred McGriff	.40	.30	.15
343	Kirby Puckett	1.00	.75	.40
344	Roberto Kelly	.25	.20	.10
345	Wally Joyner	.30	.25	.12
346	Andres Galarraga	.35	.25	.14
347	Bobby Bonilla	.25	.20	.10
348	Benito Santiago	.25	.20	.10
349	Barry Bonds	1.50	1.25	.60
350	Delino DeShields	.30	.25	.12
351	Albert Belle	.60	.45	.25
352	Randy Johnson	.30	.25	.12
353	Tim Salmon	2.00	1.50	.80
354	John Olerud	.40	.30	.15
355	Dean Palmer	.25	.20	.10
356	Roger Clemens	.35	.25	.14
357	Jim Abbott	.30	.25	.12

358	Mark Grace	.25	.20	.10
359	Ozzie Guillen	.25	.20	.10
360	Lou Whitaker	.25	.20	.10
361	Jose Rijo	.25	.20	.10
362	Jeff Montgomery	.25	.20	.10
363	Chuck Finley	.25	.20	.10
364	Tom Glavine	.25	.20	.10
365	Jeff Bagwell	.50	.40	.20
366	Joe Carter	.35	.25	.14
367	Ray Lankford	.25	.20	.10
368	Ramon Martinez	.25	.20	.10
369	Jay Buhner	.25	.20	.10
370	Matt Williams	.25	.20	.10
371	Larry Walker	.25	.20	.10
372	Jose Canseco	.50	.40	.20
373	Len Dykstra	.30	.25	.12
374	Bryan Harvey	.25	.20	.10
375	Andy Van Slyke	.25	.20	.10
376	Ivan Rodriguez	.25	.20	.10
377	Kevin Mitchell	.25	.20	.10
378	Travis Fryman	.25	.20	.10
379	Duane Ward	.25	.20	.10
380	Greg Maddux	.35	.25	.14

1994 Donruss Triple Play Promos

This 10-card set was given to dealers to preview the 1994 Donruss Triple Play issue. Cards are virtually identical to the regular-issue cards except for a large black "Promotional Sample" printed diagonally in black on both front and back. Cards are numbered as "X of 10" on the promos.

		MT	NR MT	EX
Complete Set (10):		35.00	26.00	14.00
Common Player:		3.00	2.25	1.25
1	Juan Gonzalez	6.00	4.50	2.50
2	Frank Thomas	7.50	5.75	3.00
3	Barry Bonds	5.00	3.75	2.00
4	Ken Griffey, Jr.	6.00	4.50	2.50
5	Paul Molitor	4.00	3.00	1.50
6	Mike Piazza	4.00	3.00	1.50
7	Tim Salmon	4.00	3.00	1.50
8	Lenny Dykstra	3.00	2.25	1.25
9	Don Mattingly	4.00	3.00	1.50
10	Greg Maddux	3.00	2.25	1.25

1994 Donruss Triple Play

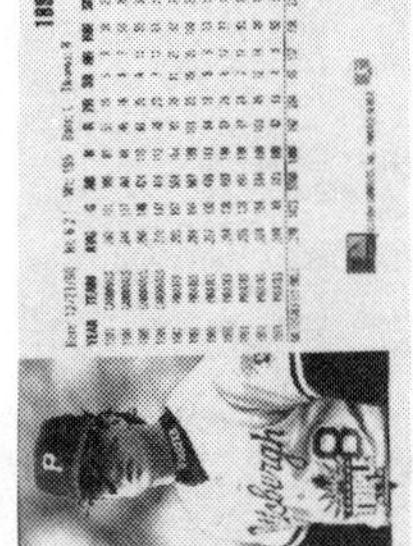

Triple Play cards returned for a third year in 1994, this time with a full-bleed design and issued in one series. According to company officials, production was less than 1994 Donruss Series I Baseball, which was roughly 17,500 20-box cases. In the regular issue 300-card set, 10 players from each team were featured, along with a 17-card Rookie Review subset. Three insert sets were included in both regular and jumbo packs; Nicknames (8), Bomb Squad (10), featuring top home run hitters and Medalists, a 15-card insert set with each card portraying the top three players in each league by position. Each card is horizontally designed with gold, silver and bronze foil.

		MT	NR MT	EX
Complete Set (300):		14.00	10.50	5.50
Common Player:		.05	.04	.02
1	Mike Bordick	.05	.04	.02
2	Dennis Eckersley	.06	.04	.02
3	Brent Gates	.05	.04	.02
4	Rickey Henderson	.05	.04	.02
5	Mark McGwire	.05	.04	.02
6	Troy Neel	.05	.04	.02
7	Craig Paquette	.05	.04	.02
8	Ruben Sierra	.05	.04	.02
9	Terry Steinbach	.05	.04	.02
10	Bobby Witt	.05	.04	.02
11	Chad Curtis	.05	.04	.02
12	Chili Davis	.05	.04	.02
13	Gary DiSarcina	.05	.04	.02
14	Damion Easley	.05	.04	.02
15	Chuck Finley	.05	.04	.02
16	Joe Grahe	.05	.04	.02
17	Mark Langston	.05	.04	.02
18	Eduardo Perez	.20	.15	.08
19	Tim Salmon	.60	.45	.25
20	J.T. Snow	.05	.04	.02
21	Jeff Bagwell	.05	.04	.02
22	Craig Biggio	.05	.04	.02
23	Ken Caminiti	.05	.04	.02
24	Andujar Cedeno	.05	.04	.02
25	Doug Drabek	.05	.04	.02
26	Steve Finley	.05	.04	.02
27	Luis Gonzalez	.05	.04	.02
28	Pete Harnisch	.05	.04	.02
29	Darryl Kile	.05	.04	.02
30	Mitch Williams	.05	.04	.02
31	Roberto Alomar	.30	.25	.12
32	Joe Carter	.15	.11	.06
33	Juan Guzman	.05	.04	.02
34	Pat Hentgen	.05	.04	.02
35	Paul Molitor	.20	.15	.08
36	John Olerud	.20	.15	.08
37	Ed Sprague	.05	.04	.02
38	Dave Stewart	.05	.04	.02
39	Duane Ward	.05	.04	.02
40	Devon White	.05	.04	.02
41	Steve Avery	.05	.04	.02
42	Jeff Blauser	.05	.04	.02
43	Ron Gant	.05	.04	.02
44	Tom Glavine	.05	.04	.02
45	David Justice	.25	.20	.10
46	Greg Maddux	.15	.11	.06
47	Fred McGriff	.10	.07	.04
48	Terry Pendleton	.05	.04	.02
49	Deion Sanders	.10	.07	.04
50	John Smoltz	.05	.04	.02
51	Ricky Bones	.05	.04	.02
52	Cal Eldred	.05	.04	.02
53	Darryl Hamilton	.05	.04	.02
54	John Jaha	.05	.04	.02
55	Pat Listach	.05	.04	.02
56	Jaime Navarro	.05	.04	.02
57	Dave Nilsson	.05	.04	.02
58	B.J. Surhoff	.05	.04	.02
59	Greg Vaughn	.05	.04	.02
60	Robin Yount	.10	.07	.04
61	Bernard Gilkey	.05	.04	.02
62	Gregg Jefferies	.05	.04	.02
63	Brian Jordan	.05	.04	.02
64	Ray Lankford	.05	.04	.02
65	Tom Pagnozzi	.05	.04	.02
66	Ozzie Smith	.20	.15	.08
67	Bob Tewksbury	.05	.04	.02
68	Allen Watson	.05	.04	.02
69	Mark Whiten	.05	.04	.02
70	Todd Zeile	.05	.04	.02
71	Steve Buechele	.05	.04	.02
72	Mark Grace	.05	.04	.02
73	Jose Guzman	.05	.04	.02
74	Derrick May	.05	.04	.02
75	Mike Morgan	.05	.04	.02
76	Randy Myers	.05	.04	.02
77	Ryne Sandberg	.35	.25	.14
78	Sammy Sosa	.05	.04	.02
79	Jose Vizcaino	.05	.04	.02
80	Rick Wilkins	.05	.04	.02
81	Pedro Astacio	.05	.04	.02
82	Brett Butler	.05	.04	.02
83	Delino DeShields	.05	.04	.02
84	Orel Hershiser	.05	.04	.02
85	Eric Karros	.05	.04	.02
86	Ramon Martinez	.05	.04	.02
87	Jose Offerman	.05	.04	.02
88	Mike Piazza	1.00	.75	.40
89	Darryl Strawberry	.05	.04	.02
90	Tim Wallach	.05	.04	.02
91	Moises Alou	.05	.04	.02
92	Wil Cordero	.05	.04	.02
93	Jeff Fassero	.05	.04	.02
94	Darrin Fletcher	.05	.04	.02
95	Marquis Grissom	.05	.04	.02
96	Ken Hill	.05	.04	.02
97	Mike Lansing	.05	.04	.02
98	Kirk Rueter	.50	.40	.20
99	Larry Walker	.05	.04	.02
100	John Wetteland	.05	.04	.02
101	Rod Beck	.05	.04	.02
102	Barry Bonds	.50	.40	.20
103	John Burkett	.05	.04	.02
104	Royce Clayton	.05	.04	.02
105	Darren Lewis	.05	.04	.02
106	Kirt Manwaring	.05	.04	.02
107	Willie McGee	.05	.04	.02
108	Bill Swift	.05	.04	.02
109	Robby Thompson	.05	.04	.02
110	Matt Williams	.05	.04	.02
111	Sandy Alomar Jr.	.05	.04	.02
112	Carlos Baerga	.25	.20	.10
113	Albert Belle	.25	.20	.10
114	Wayne Kirby	.05	.04	.02
115	Kenny Lofton	.15	.11	.06
116	Jose Mesa	.05	.04	.02
117	Eddie Murray	.08	.06	.03
118	Charles Nagy	.05	.04	.02
119	Paul Sorrento	.05	.04	.02
120	Jim Thome	.15	.11	.06
121	Rich Amaral	.05	.04	.02
122	Eric Anthony	.05	.04	.02
123	Mike Blowers	.05	.04	.02
124	Chris Bosio	.05	.04	.02
125	Jay Buhner	.05	.04	.02
126	Dave Fleming	.05	.04	.02
127	Ken Griffey, Jr.	1.00	.75	.40
128	Randy Johnson	.05	.04	.02
129	Edgar Martinez	.05	.04	.02
130	Tino Martinez	.05	.04	.02
131	Bret Barberie	.05	.04	.02
132	Ryan Bowen	.05	.04	.02
133	Chuck Carr	.05	.04	.02
134	Jeff Conine	.05	.04	.02
135	Orestes Destrade	.05	.04	.02
136	Chris Hammond	.05	.04	.02
137	Bryan Harvey	.05	.04	.02
138	Dave Magadan	.05	.04	.02
139	Benito Santiago	.05	.04	.02
140	Gary Sheffield	.05	.04	.02
141	Bobby Bonilla	.05	.04	.02
142	Jeromy Burnitz	.05	.04	.02
143	Dwight Gooden	.05	.04	.02
144	Todd Hundley	.05	.04	.02
145	Bobby Jones	.05	.04	.02
146	Jeff Kent	.05	.04	.02
147	Joe Orsulak	.05	.04	.02
148	Bret Saberhagen	.05	.04	.02
149	Pete Schourek	.05	.04	.02
150	Ryan Thompson	.05	.04	.02
151	Brady Anderson	.05	.04	.02
152	Harold Baines	.05	.04	.02
153	Mike Devereaux	.05	.04	.02
154	Chris Hoiles	.05	.04	.02
155	Ben McDonald	.05	.04	.02
156	Mark McLemore	.05	.04	.02
157	Mike Mussina	.05	.04	.02
158	Rafael Palmeiro	.05	.04	.02
159	Cal Ripken, Jr.	.35	.25	.14
160	Chris Sabo	.05	.04	.02
161	Brad Ausmus	.05	.04	.02
162	Derek Bell	.05	.04	.02
163	Andy Benes	.05	.04	.02
164	Doug Brocail	.05	.04	.02
165	Archi Cianfrocco	.05	.04	.02
166	Ricky Gutierrez	.05	.04	.02
167	Tony Gwynn	.10	.07	.04
168	Gene Harris	.05	.04	.02
169	Pedro Martinez	.05	.04	.02
170	Phil Plantier	.05	.04	.02
171	Darren Daulton	.05	.04	.02
172	Mariano Duncan	.05	.04	.02
173	Len Dykstra	.05	.04	.02
174	Tommy Greene	.05	.04	.02
175	Dave Hollins	.05	.04	.02
176	Danny Jackson	.05	.04	.02
177	John Kruk	.05	.04	.02
178	Terry Mulholland	.05	.04	.02
179	Curt Schilling	.05	.04	.02
180	Kevin Stocker	.25	.20	.10
181	Jay Bell	.05	.04	.02
182	Steve Cooke	.05	.04	.02
183	Carlos Garcia	.05	.04	.02
184	Joel Johnston	.05	.04	.02
185	Jeff King	.05	.04	.02
186	Al Martin	.05	.04	.02
187	Orlando Merced	.05	.04	.02
188	Don Slaught	.05	.04	.02
189	Andy Van Slyke	.05	.04	.02
190	Kevin Young	.05	.04	.02
191	Kevin Brown	.05	.04	.02
192	Jose Canseco	.15	.11	.06
193	Will Clark	.15	.11	.06
194	Juan Gonzalez	1.00	.75	.40
195	Tom Henke	.05	.04	.02
196	David Hulse	.05	.04	.02
197	Dean Palmer	.05	.04	.02
198	Roger Pavlik	.05	.04	.02
199	Ivan Rodriguez	.05	.04	.02
200	Kenny Rogers	.05	.04	.02
201	Roger Clemens	.20	.15	.08
202	Scott Cooper	.05	.04	.02
203	Andre Dawson	.05	.04	.02
204	Mike Greenwell	.05	.04	.02
205	Billy Hatcher	.05	.04	.02
206	Jeff Russell	.05	.04	.02
207	Aaron Sele	.40	.30	.15
208	John Valentin	.05	.04	.02
209	Mo Vaughn	.05	.04	.02
210	Frank Viola	.05	.04	.02
211	Rob Dibble	.05	.04	.02
212	Willie Greene	.05	.04	.02
213	Roberto Kelly	.05	.04	.02
214	Barry Larkin	.05	.04	.02
215	Kevin Mitchell	.05	.04	.02
216	Hal Morris	.05	.04	.02
217	Joe Oliver	.05	.04	.02
218	Jose Rijo	.05	.04	.02
219	Reggie Sanders	.05	.04	.02
220	John Smiley	.05	.04	.02
221	Dante Bichette	.05	.04	.02
222	Ellis Burke	.05	.04	.02
223	Andres Galarraga	.05	.04	.02
224	Joe Girardi	.05	.04	.02
225	Charlie Hayes	.05	.04	.02
226	Darren Holmes	.05	.04	.02
227	Howard Johnson	.05	.04	.02
228	Roberto Mejia	.15	.11	.06
229	David Nied	.05	.04	.02
230	Armando Reynoso	.05	.04	.02
231	Kevin Appier	.05	.04	.02
232	David Cone	.05	.04	.02

233	Greg Gagne	.05	.04	.02
234	Tom Gordon	.05	.04	.02
235	Felix Jose	.05	.04	.02
236	Wally Joyner	.05	.04	.02
237	Jose Lind	.05	.04	.02
238	Brian McRae	.05	.04	.02
239	Mike MacFarlane	.05	.04	.02
240	Jeff Montgomery	.05	.04	.02
241	Eric Davis	.05	.04	.02
242	John Doherty	.05	.04	.02
243	Cecil Fielder	.15	.11	.06
244	Travis Fryman	.20	.15	.08
245	Bill Gullickson	.05	.04	.02
246	Mike Henneman	.05	.04	.02
247	Tony Phillips	.05	.04	.02
248	Mickey Tettleton	.05	.04	.02
249	Alan Trammell	.05	.04	.02
250	Lou Whitaker	.05	.04	.02
251	Rick Aguilera	.05	.04	.02
252	Scott Erickson	.05	.04	.02
253	Kent Hrbek	.05	.04	.02
254	Chuck Knoblauch	.05	.04	.02
255	Shane Mack	.05	.04	.02
256	Dave McCarty	.10	.07	.04
257	Pat Meares	.05	.04	.02
258	Kirby Puckett	.40	.30	.15
259	Kevin Tapani	.05	.04	.02
260	Dave Winfield	.15	.11	.06
261	Wilson Alvarez	.05	.04	.02
262	Jason Bere	.25	.20	.10
263	Alex Fernandez	.08	.06	.03
264	Ozzie Guillen	.05	.04	.02
265	Roberto Hernandez	.05	.04	.02
266	Lance Johnson	.05	.04	.02
267	Jack McDowell	.10	.07	.04
268	Tim Raines	.05	.04	.02
269	Frank Thomas	1.50	1.25	.60
270	Robin Ventura	.10	.07	.04
271	Jim Abbott	.06	.05	.02
272	Wade Boggs	.10	.07	.04
273	Mike Gallego	.05	.04	.02
274	Pat Kelly	.05	.04	.02
275	Jimmy Key	.05	.04	.02
276	Don Mattingly	.25	.20	.10
277	Paul O'Neill	.05	.04	.02
278	Mike Stanley	.05	.04	.02
279	Danny Tartabull	.05	.04	.02
280	Bernie Williams	.05	.04	.02
281	Chipper Jones	.20	.15	.08
282	Ryan Klesko	.40	.30	.15
283	Javier Lopez	.50	.40	.20
284	Jeffrey Hammonds	.50	.40	.20
285	Jeff McNeely	.08	.06	.03
286	Manny Ramirez	.60	.45	.25
287	Billy Ashley	.10	.07	.04
288	Raul Mondesi	.20	.15	.08
289	Cliff Floyd	.75	.60	.30
290	Rondell White	.35	.25	.14
291	Steve Karsay	.25	.20	.10
292	Midre Cummings	.20	.15	.08
293	Salomon Torres	.25	.20	.10
294	J.R. Phillips	.25	.20	.10
295	Marc Newfield	.15	.11	.06
296	Carlos Delgado	.75	.60	.30
297	Butch Huskey	.10	.07	.04
298	Checklist	.05	.04	.02
299	Checklist	.05	.04	.02
300	Checklist	.05	.04	.02

1994 Donruss Triple Play Medalists

Statistical performance over the 1992-93 seasons was used to rank the players appearing in the Medalists insert set. Horizontal format cards have photos of the first, second and third place winners in appropriate boxes of gold, silver and bronze foil. "Medalists," the "medals" and "Triple Play 94" are embossed on the front. Backs have color action photos of each player along with team logos and a few stats.

		MT	NR MT	EX
Complete Set (15):		20.00	15.00	8.00
Common Player:		1.00	.75	.40
1	A.L. Catchers (Chris Hoiles, Mickey Tettleton, Brian Harper)	1.00	.75	.40
2	N.L. Catchers (Darren Daulton, Rick Wilkins, Kirt Manwaring)	1.00	.75	.40
3	A.L. First Basemen (Frank Thomas, Rafael Palmeiro, John Olerud)	5.00	3.75	2.00
4	N.L. First Basemen (Mark Grace, Fred McGriff, Jeff Bagwell)	2.50	2.00	1.00
5	A.L. Second Basemen (Roberto Alomar, Carlos Baerga, Lou Whitaker)	2.50	2.00	1.00
6	N.L. Second Basemen (Ryne Sandberg, Craig Biggio, Robby Thompson)	2.00	1.50	.80
7	A.L. Shortstops (Tony Fernandez, Cal Ripken, Jr., Alan Trammell)	2.50	2.00	1.00
8	N.L. Shortstops (Barry Larkin, Jay Bell, Jeff Blauser)	1.00	.75	.40
9	A.L. Third Basemen (Robin Ventura, Travis Fryman, Wade Boggs)	1.50	1.25	.60
10	N.L. Third Basemen (Terry Pendleton, Dave Hollins, Gary Sheffield)	1.50	1.25	.60
11	A.L. Outfielders (Ken Griffey, Jr., Kirby Puckett, Albert Belle)	5.00	3.75	2.00
12	N.L. Outfielders (Barry Bonds, Andy Van Slyke, Len Dykstra)	3.00	2.25	1.25
13	A.L. Starters (Jack McDowell, Kevin Brown, Randy Johnson)	1.25	.90	.50
14	N.L. Starters (Greg Maddux, Jose Rijo, Billy Swift)	1.50	1.25	.60
15	Designated Hitters (Paul Molitor, Dave Winfield, Harold Baines)	1.50	1.25	.60

1994 Donruss Triple Play Bomb Squad

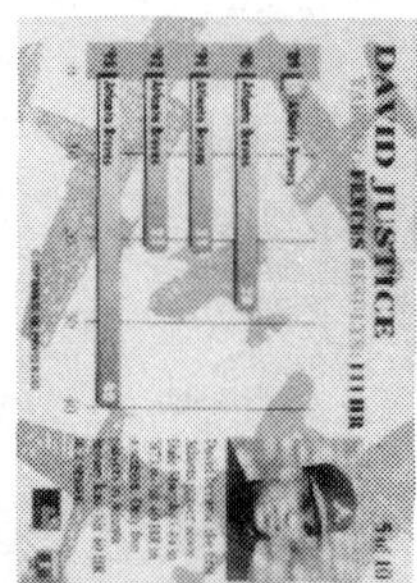

Ten of the top major league home runs hitters are included in this insert set. Fronts feature sepia-toned player photos within a wide brown frame. The Triple Play logo and player name are in gold foil, along with a large star-and-wings "Bomb Squad" logo at top. Backs have a white background with representations of vintage airplanes. A bar chart at left gives the player's home run totals by year. A small color portrait photo is at upper-right. Below are a few words about his homer history.

		MT	NR MT	EX
Complete Set (10):		25.00	18.00	10.00
Common Player:		1.00	.75	.40
1	Frank Thomas	7.00	5.25	2.75
2	Cecil Fielder	1.50	1.25	.60
3	Juan Gonzalez	5.00	3.75	2.00
4	Barry Bonds	3.50	2.75	1.50
5	David Justice	2.50	2.00	1.00
6	Fred McGriff	2.00	1.50	.80
7	Ron Gant	1.00	.75	.40
8	Ken Griffey, Jr.	5.00	3.75	2.00
9	Albert Belle	2.50	2.00	1.00
10	Matt Williams	1.00	.75	.40

The values quoted are intended to reflect the market price.

1994 Donruss Triple Play Nicknames

Eight of baseball's most colorful team nicknames are featured in this insert set. Fronts feature a background photo representative of the nickname, with the hometown above. A player photo is superimposed over that, with his name at top. At bottom the Triple Play and team logos are presented in gold foil. Backs have another player photo and a history of the team's nickname.

		MT	NR MT	EX
Complete Set (8):		25.00	18.00	10.00
Common Player:		1.50	1.25	.60
1	Cecil Fielder	2.50	2.00	1.00
2	Ryne Sandberg	4.00	3.00	1.50
3	Gary Sheffield	2.00	1.50	.80
4	Joe Carter	3.00	2.25	1.25
5	John Olerud	3.00	2.25	1.25
6	Cal Ripken, Jr.	6.00	4.50	2.50
7	Mark McGwire	2.00	1.50	.80
8	Gregg Jefferies	1.50	1.25	.60

1986 Dorman's Cheese

Found in specially-marked packages of Dorman's American Cheese Singles, the Dorman's set consists of ten two-card panels of baseball superstars. Labeled as a "Super Star Limited Edition" set, the panels measure 1-1/2" by 2" each and have a perforation line in the center. The fronts contain a color photo along with the Dorman's logo and the player's name, team and position. Due to a lack of proper licensing, all team insignias have been airbrushed from the players' caps. The backs of the cards contain brief player statistics.

		MT	NR MT	EX
Complete Panel Set:		20.00	15.00	8.00
Complete Singles Set:		8.00	6.00	3.25
Common Panel:		1.50	1.25	.60
Common Single Player:		.20	.15	.08
	Panel	2.00	1.50	.80
(1)	George Brett	.50	.40	.20
(2)	Jack Morris	.20	.15	.08
	Panel	2.50	1.50	.80
(3)	Gary Carter	.30	.25	.12
(4)	Cal Ripken, Jr.	.60	.45	.25
	Panel	2.00	1.50	.80
(5)	Dwight Gooden	.30	.25	.12
(6)	Kent Hrbek	.20	.15	.08
	Panel	3.00	1.50	.90
(7)	Rickey Henderson	.40	.30	.15
(8)	Mike Schmidt	.50	.40	.20
	Panel	2.00	1.50	.80
(9)	Keith Hernandez	.20	.15	.08
(10)	Dale Murphy	.30	.25	.12
	Panel	2.00	1.50	.80
(11)	Reggie Jackson	.40	.30	.15
(12)	Eddie Murray	.30	.25	.12
	Panel	3.00	3.00	1.50
(13)	Don Mattingly	.50	.40	.20
(14)	Ryne Sandberg	.60	.45	.25
	Panel	2.00	.90	.50
(15)	Willie McGee	.20	.15	.08
(16)	Robin Yount	.50	.40	.20
	Panel	2.00	1.75	.90
(17)	Rick Sutcliff (Sutcliffe)	.20	.15	.08
(18)	Wade Boggs	.50	.40	.20
	Panel	1.50	1.25	.60
(19)	Dave Winfield	.40	.30	.15
(20)	Jim Rice	.20	.15	.08

1953 - 55 Dormand Postcards

This mid-1950s issue features only selected players from the Yankees, Brooklyn Dodgers, White Sox and Philadelphia A's. Apparently produced on order by the players by Louis Dormand, a Long Island, N.Y., photographer, the cards were used to honor fan requests for photos and autographs. All of the cards have a facsimile autograph printed in front. Otherwise the fronts of these standard-size 3-1/2" x 5-1/2" postcards feature only sharp color photos with

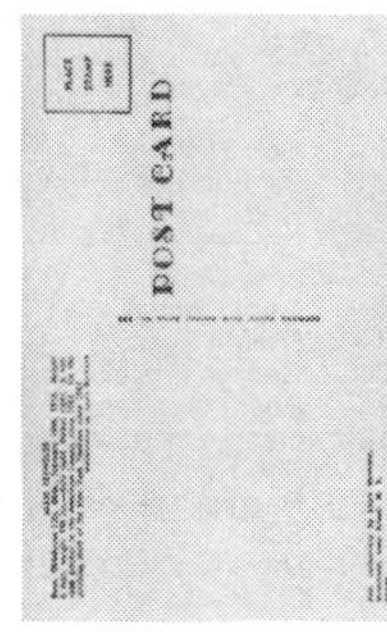

no border. Backs, printed in blue or green, feature a few player biographical and career details, one or two lines identifying the producer and usually a product and series numbers. Most have a Kodachrome logo. Some cards do not have all of these elements and several are found blank-backed. The Gil Hodges card is considerably scarcer than the others in the set, with those of Jim Konstanty, Elston Howard, and Casey Stengel also seldom seen. Besides the listed below in alphabetical order. standard-sized cards, there are oversize versions of Rizzuto's and Mantle's cards. A variation of Johnny Sain's card shows his Arkansas Chevrolet dealership in a photo above the player's picture. Players are listed alphabetically here. The complete set price includes only the standard-size cards.

		NR MT	EX	VG
Complete Set:		2400.	1200.	725.00
Common Player:		25.00	12.50	7.50
(1)	Hank Bauer	30.00	15.00	9.00
(2)	Yogi Berra	60.00	30.00	18.00
(3)	Don Bollweg	25.00	12.50	7.50
(4)	Roy Campanella	150.00	75.00	45.00
(5)	Chico Carrasquel	25.00	12.50	7.50
(6)	Jerry Coleman	25.00	12.50	7.50
(7)	Joe Collins (patch on sleeve)	30.00	15.00	9.00
(8)	Joe Collins (no patch on sleeve)	25.00	12.50	7.50
(9)	Frank Crosetti	40.00	20.00	12.00
(10)	Carl Erskine	50.00	25.00	15.00
(11)	Whitey Ford	50.00	25.00	15.00
(12)	Carl Furillo	60.00	30.00	18.00
(13)	Tom Gorman	25.00	12.50	7.50
(14)	Gil Hodges	400.00	200.00	120.00
(15)	Ralph Houk	25.00	12.50	7.50
(16)	Elston Howard	150.00	75.00	45.00
(17)	Jim Konstanty	125.00	62.00	37.00
(18)	Ed Lopat	25.00	12.50	7.50
(19)	Mickey Mantle (bat on shoulder)	200.00	100.00	60.00
(20)	Mickey Mantle (batting stance, 3-1/2" x 5-1/2")	100.00	50.00	30.00
(21)	Mickey Mantle (batting stance, 6" x 9")	250.00	125.00	75.00
(22)	Mickey Mantle (batting stance, 9" x 12")	250.00	125.00	75.00
(23)	Billy Martin	45.00	22.00	13.50
(24)	Jim McDonald	25.00	12.50	7.50
(25)	Gil McDougald (large autograph)	30.00	15.00	9.00
(26)	Gil McDougald (small autograph)	45.00	22.00	13.50
(27)	Bob Miller	25.00	12.50	7.50
(28)	Willie Miranda	25.00	12.50	7.50
(29)	Johnny Mize	75.00	37.00	22.00
(30)	Irv Noren	25.00	12.50	7.50
(31)	Billy Pierce	35.00	17.50	10.50
(32)	Pee Wee Reese	60.00	30.00	18.00
(33)	Allie Reynolds	25.00	12.50	7.50
(34)	Phil Rizzuto (autograph parallel to top)	45.00	22.00	13.50
(35)	Phil Rizzuto (autograph angles downward, 3-1/2" x 5-1/2")	45.00	22.00	13.50
(36)	Phil Rizzuto (autograph angles downward, 9" x 12")	150.00	75.00	45.00
(37)	Ed Robinson	40.00	20.00	12.00
(38)	Johnny Sain (beginning windup)	40.00	20.00	12.00
(39)	Johnny Sain (leg kick)	30.00	15.00	9.00
(40)	Johnny Sain (with auto dealership ad)	75.00	37.00	22.00
(41)	Ray Scarborough	25.00	12.50	7.50
(42)	Bobby Shantz	35.00	17.50	10.50
(43)	Charlie Silvera	25.00	12.50	7.50
(44)	Bill Skowron	45.00	22.00	13.50
(45)	Enos Slaughter	75.00	37.00	22.00
(46)	Casey Stengel	150.00	75.00	45.00
(47)	Gene Woodling	30.00	15.00	9.00

Values for recent cards and sets are listed in Mint (MT), Near Mint (NM), reflecting the fact that many cards from recent years have been preserved in top condition. Recent cards and sets in less than Excellent condition have little collector interest.

1941 Double Play

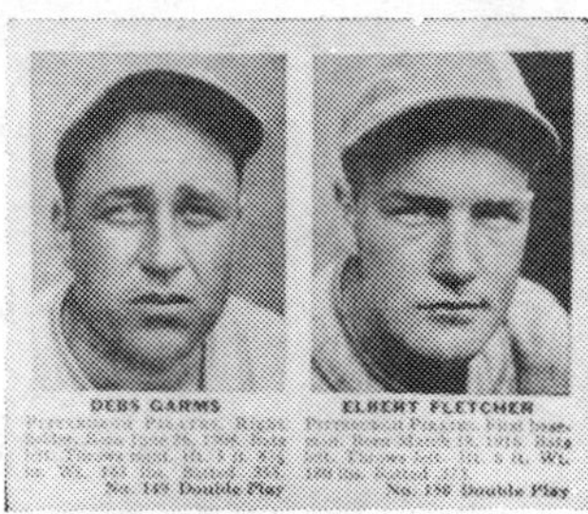

Issued by Gum, Inc., this set includes 75 numbered cards (two consecutive numbers per card) featuring 150 baseball players. The cards, which are blank-backed and measure 2-1/2" by 3-1/8", contain sepia-tone photos of two players. Action and portrait poses are found in the set, with card designs on either a vertical or horizontal format. The last fifty cards are the scarcest of the set. Cards cut to form two single cards have little value.

		NR MT	EX	VG
Complete Set:		6500.	3300.	2000.
Common Player: 1-100		38.50	19.00	11.50
Common Player: 101-150		55.00	27.00	16.50
1	Larry French			
2	Vance Page	75.00	38.50	23.00
3	Billy Herman			
4	Stanley Hack	55.00	27.00	16.50
5	Linus Frey			
6	John Vander Meer	50.00	25.00	15.00
7	Paul Derringer			
8	Bucky Walters	38.50	19.00	11.50
9	Frank McCormick			
10	Bill Werber	38.50	19.00	11.50
11	Jimmy Ripple			
12	Ernie Lombardi	65.00	32.00	19.50
13	Alex Kampouris			
14	John Wyatt	38.50	19.00	11.50
15	Mickey Owen			
16	Paul Waner	65.00	32.00	19.50
17	Harry Lavagetto			
18	Harold Reiser	50.00	25.00	15.00
19	Jimmy Wasdell			
20	Dolph Camilli	50.00	25.00	15.00
21	Dixie Walker			
22	Ducky Medwick	65.00	32.00	19.50
23	Harold Reese			
24	Kirby Higbe	250.00	125.00	75.00
25	Harry Danning			
26	Cliff Melton	38.50	19.00	11.50
27	Harry Gumbert			
28	Burgess Whitehead	38.50	19.00	11.50
29	Joe Orengo			
30	Joe Moore	38.50	19.00	11.50
31	Mel Ott			
32	Babe Young	100.00	50.00	30.00
33	Lee Handley			
34	Arky Vaughan	65.00	32.00	19.50
35	Bob Klinger			
36	Stanley Brown	38.50	19.00	11.50
37	Terry Moore			
38	Gus Mancuso	38.50	19.00	11.50
39	Johnny Mize			
40	Enos Slaughter	110.00	55.00	32.50
41	John Cooney			
42	Sibby Sisti	38.50	19.00	11.50
43	Max West			
44	Carvel Rowell	38.50	19.00	11.50
45	Dan Litwhiler			
46	Merrill May	38.50	19.00	11.50
47	Frank Hayes			
48	Al Brancato	38.50	19.00	11.50
49	Bob Johnson			
50	Bill Nagel	38.50	19.00	11.50
51	Buck Newsom			
52	Hank Greenberg	100.00	50.00	30.00
53	Barney McCosky			
54	Charley Gehringer	100.00	50.00	30.00
55	Pinky Higgins			
56	Dick Bartell	38.50	19.00	11.50
57	Ted Williams			
58	Jim Tabor	600.00	300.00	180.00
59	Joe Cronin			
60	Jimmy Foxx	200.00	100.00	60.00
61	Lefty Gomez			
62	Phil Rizzuto	300.00	150.00	90.00
63	Joe DiMaggio			
64	Charley Keller	750.00	375.00	220.00
65	Red Rolfe			
66	Bill Dickey	150.00	75.00	45.00
67	Joe Gordon			
68	Red Ruffing	80.00	40.00	24.00
69	Mike Tresh			
70	Luke Appling	65.00	32.00	19.50
71	Moose Solters			
72	John Rigney	38.50	19.00	11.50
73	Buddy Meyer			
74	Ben Chapman	38.50	19.00	11.50
75	Cecil Travis			
76	George Case	38.50	19.00	11.50
77	Joe Krakauskas			
78	Bob Feller	165.00	80.00	48.00
79	Ken Keltner			
80	Hal Trosky	38.50	19.00	11.50
81	Ted Williams			
82	Joe Cronin	700.00	350.00	210.00
83	Joe Gordon			
84	Charley Keller	50.00	25.00	15.00
85	Hank Greenberg			
86	Red Ruffing	100.00	50.00	30.00
87	Hal Trosky			
88	George Case	38.50	19.00	11.50
89	Mel Ott			
90	Burgess Whitehead	100.00	50.00	30.00
91	Harry Danning			
92	Harry Gumbert	38.50	19.00	11.50
93	Babe Young			
94	Cliff Melton	38.50	19.00	11.50
95	Jimmy Ripple			
96	Bucky Walters	38.50	19.00	11.50
97	Stanley Hack			
98	Bob Klinger	38.50	19.00	11.50
99	Johnny Mize			
100	Dan Litwhiler	65.00	32.00	19.50
101	Dominic Dallessandro			
102	Augie Galan	55.00	27.00	16.50
103	Bill Lee			
104	Phil Cavarretta	55.00	27.00	16.50
105	Lefty Grove			
106	Bobby Doerr	200.00	100.00	60.00
107	Frank Pytlak			
108	Dom DiMaggio	70.00	35.00	21.00
109	Gerald Priddy			
110	John Murphy	65.00	32.00	19.50
111	Tommy Henrich			
112	Marius Russo	80.00	40.00	24.00
113	Frank Crosetti			
114	John Sturm	80.00	40.00	24.00
115	Ival Goodman			
116	Myron McCormick	55.00	27.00	16.50
117	Eddie Joost			
118	Ernest Koy	55.00	27.00	16.50
119	Lloyd Waner			
120	Henry Majeski	80.00	40.00	24.00
121	Buddy Hassett			
122	Eugene Moore	55.00	27.00	16.50
123	Nick Etten			
124	John Rizzo	55.00	27.00	16.50
125	Sam Chapman			
126	Wally Moses	55.00	27.00	16.50
127	John Babich			
128	Richard Siebert	55.00	27.00	16.50
129	Nelson Potter			
130	Benny McCoy	55.00	27.00	16.50
131	Clarence Campbell			
132	Louis Boudreau	80.00	40.00	24.00
133	Rolly Hemsley			
134	Mel Harder	55.00	27.00	16.50
135	Gerald Walker			
136	Joe Heving	55.00	27.00	16.50
137	John Rucker			
138	Ace Adams	55.00	27.00	16.50
139	Morris Arnovich			
140	Carl Hubbell	135.00	65.00	39.00
141	Lew Riggs			
142	Leo Durocher	100.00	50.00	30.00
143	Fred Fitzsimmons			
144	Joe Vosmik	55.00	27.00	16.50
145	Frank Crespi			
146	Jim Brown	55.00	27.00	16.50
147	Don Heffner			
148	Harland Clift (Harlond)	55.00	27.00	16.50
149	Debs Garms			
150	Elbert Fletcher	80.00	40.00	24.00

1950 Drake's

Entitled "TV Baseball Series", the 1950 Drake's Bakeries set pictures 36 different players on a television screen format. The cards, which measure 2-1/2" by 2-1/2", contain black and white photos surrounded by a black border. The card backs carry a player biography plus an advertisement advising collectors to look for the cards in packages of Oatmeal or Jumble cookies. The ACC designation for the set is D358.

		NR MT	EX	VG
Complete Set:		5000.	3000.	1500.
Common Player:		50.00	25.00	15.00
1	Elwin "Preacher" Roe	100.00	50.00	30.00
2	Clint Hartung	50.00	25.00	15.00
3	Earl Torgeson	50.00	25.00	15.00
4	Leland "Lou" Brissie	50.00	25.00	15.00
5	Edwin "Duke" Snider	350.00	175.00	100.00
6	Roy Campanella	400.00	200.00	125.00
7	Sheldon "Available" Jones	50.00	25.00	15.00
8	Carroll "Whitey" Lockman	50.00	25.00	15.00

9	Bobby Thomson	80.00	40.00	25.00
10	Dick Sisler	50.00	25.00	15.00
11	Gil Hodges	200.00	100.00	60.00
12	Eddie Waitkus	50.00	25.00	15.00
13	Bobby Doerr	150.00	75.00	45.00
14	Warren Spahn	250.00	125.00	75.00
15	John "Buddy" Kerr	50.00	25.00	15.00
16	Sid Gordon	50.00	25.00	15.00
17	Willard Marshall	50.00	25.00	15.00
18	Carl Furillo	90.00	45.00	25.00
19	Harold "Pee Wee" Reese	300.00	150.00	90.00
20	Alvin Dark	70.00	35.00	20.00
21	Del Ennis	50.00	25.00	15.00
22	Ed Stanky	70.00	35.00	20.00
23	Tommy "Old Reliable" Henrich	90.00	45.00	25.00
24	Larry "Yogi" Berra	400.00	200.00	125.00
25	Phil "Scooter" Rizzuto	275.00	150.00	100.00
26	Jerry Coleman	70.00	35.00	20.00
27	Joe Page	70.00	35.00	20.00
28	Allie Reynolds	90.00	45.00	25.00
29	Ray Scarborough	50.00	25.00	15.00
30	George "Birdie" Tebbetts	50.00	25.00	15.00
31	Maurice "Lefty" McDermott	50.00	25.00	15.00
32	Johnny Pesky	70.00	35.00	20.00
33	Dom "Little Professor" DiMaggio	80.00	40.00	25.00
34	Vern "Junior" Stephens	50.00	25.00	15.00
35	Bob Elliott	50.00	25.00	15.00
36	Enos "Country" Slaughter	250.00	125.00	75.00

1981 Drake's

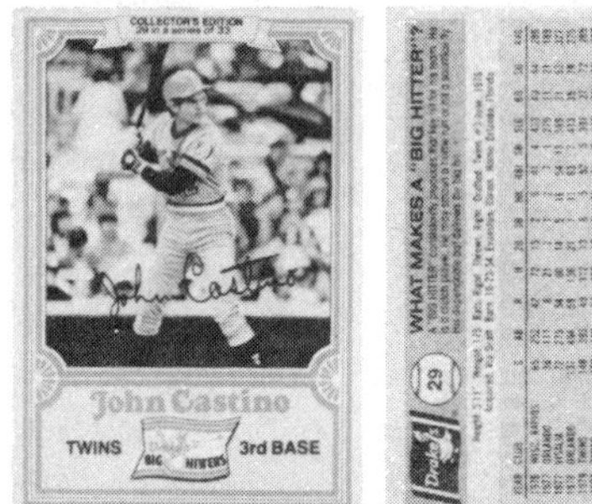

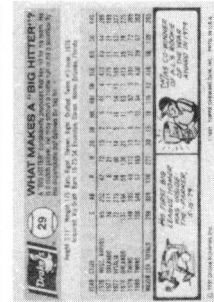

Producing their first baseball card set since 1950, Drake Bakeries, in conjunction with Topps, issued a 33-card set entitled "Big Hitters." The cards, which are the standard 2-1/2" by 3-1/2" in size, feature 19 American League and 14 National League sluggers. Full-color photos, containing a facsimile autograph, are positioned in red frames for A.L. players and blue frames for N.L. hitters. The player's name, team, position, and the Drake's logo are also included on the card fronts. The card backs, which are similar to the regular 1981 Topps issue, contain the card number (1-33), statistical and biographical information, and the Drake's logo.

		MT	NR MT	EX
Complete Set:		8.00	6.00	3.25
Common Player:		.12	.09	.05
1	Carl Yastrzemski	.70	.50	.30
2	Rod Carew	.60	.45	.25
3	Pete Rose	.90	.70	.35
4	Dave Parker	.25	.20	.10
5	George Brett	.70	.50	.30
6	Eddie Murray	.40	.30	.15
7	Mike Schmidt	1.00	.70	.40
8	Jim Rice	.25	.20	.10
9	Fred Lynn	.25	.20	.10
10	Reggie Jackson	.60	.45	.25
11	Steve Garvey	.45	.35	.20
12	Ken Singleton	.12	.09	.05
13	Bill Buckner	.12	.09	.05
14	Dave Winfield	.60	.45	.25
15	Jack Clark	.30	.25	.12
16	Cecil Cooper	.20	.15	.08
17	Bob Horner	.20	.15	.08
18	George Foster	.20	.15	.08
19	Dave Kingman	.20	.15	.08
20	Cesar Cedeno	.12	.09	.05
21	Joe Charboneau	.12	.09	.05
22	George Hendrick	.12	.09	.05
23	Gary Carter	.30	.25	.12
24	Al Oliver	.20	.15	.08
25	Bruce Bochte	.12	.09	.05
26	Jerry Mumphrey	.12	.09	.05
27	Steve Kemp	.12	.09	.05
28	Bob Watson	.12	.09	.05
29	John Castino	.12	.09	.05
30	Tony Armas	.12	.09	.05
31	John Mayberry	.12	.09	.05
32	Carlton Fisk	.30	.25	.12
33	Lee Mazzilli	.12	.09	.05

Values quoted in this guide reflect the retail price of a card – the price a collector can expect to pay when buying a card from a dealer. The wholesale price – that which a collector can expect to receive from a dealer when selling cards – will be significantly lower, depending on desirability and condition.

1982 Drake's

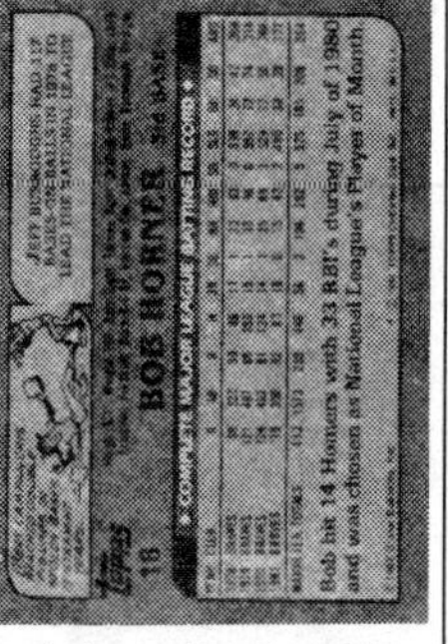

Drake Bakeries produced, in conjunction with Topps, a "2nd Annual Collectors' Edition" in 1982. Thirty-three standard-size cards (2-1/2" by 3-1/2") make up the set. Like the previous year, the set is entitled "Big Hitters" and is comprised of 19 American League players and 14 from the National League. The card fronts have a mounted photo appearance and contain a facsimile autograph. The player's name, team, position, and the Drake's logo also are located on the fronts. The card backs, other than being numbered 1-33 and containing a Drake's copyright line, are identical to the regular 1982 Topps issue.

		MT	NR MT	EX
Complete Set:		9.00	6.75	3.50
Common Player:		.12	.09	.05
1	Tony Armas	.12	.09	.05
2	Buddy Bell	.20	.15	.08
3	Johnny Bench	.50	.40	.20
4	George Brett	.70	.50	.30
5	Bill Buckner	.12	.09	.05
6	Rod Carew	.50	.40	.20
7	Gary Carter	.30	.25	.12
8	Jack Clark	.20	.15	.08
9	Cecil Cooper	.20	.15	.08
10	Jose Cruz	.12	.09	.05
11	Dwight Evans	.20	.15	.08
12	Carlton Fisk	.30	.25	.12
13	George Foster	.20	.15	.08
14	Steve Garvey	.35	.25	.14
15	Kirk Gibson	.30	.25	.12
16	Mike Hargrove	.12	.09	.05
17	George Hendrick	.12	.09	.05
18	Bob Horner	.20	.15	.08
19	Reggie Jackson	.60	.45	.25
20	Terry Kennedy	.12	.09	.05
21	Dave Kingman	.20	.15	.08
22	Greg Luzinski	.25	.20	.10
23	Bill Madlock	.20	.15	.08
24	John Mayberry	.12	.09	.05
25	Eddie Murray	.30	.25	.12
26	Graig Nettles	.20	.15	.08
27	Jim Rice	.20	.15	.08
28	Pete Rose	.90	.70	.35
29	Mike Schmidt	1.00	.70	.40
30	Ken Singleton	.12	.09	.05
31	Dave Winfield	.50	.40	.20
32	Butch Wynegar	.12	.09	.05
33	Richie Zisk	.12	.09	.05

Regional interest may affect the value of a card.

1983 Drake's

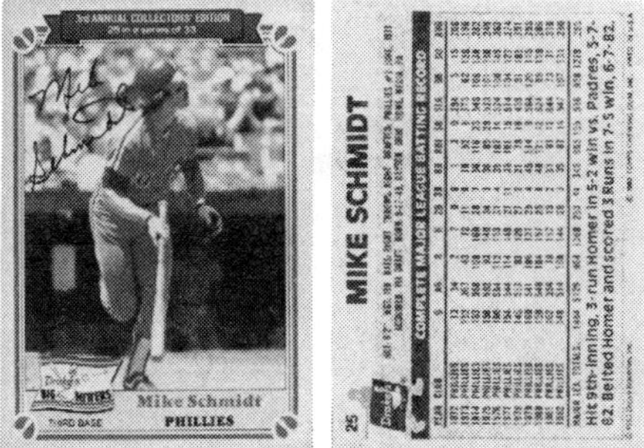

Seventeen American League and 16 National League "Big Hitters" make up the 33-card "3rd Annual Collectors' Edition" set issued by Drake Bakeries in 1983. The Topps-produced set contains 33 cards which measure 2-1/2" by 3-1/2" in size. The card fronts are somewhat similar in design to the previous year's set. The backs are identical to the 1983 Topps regular issue except for being numbered 1-33 and containing a Drake's logo and copyright line.

		MT	NR MT	EX
Complete Set:		7.00	5.25	2.75
Common Player:		.12	.09	.05
1	Don Baylor	.20	.15	.08
2	Bill Buckner	.12	.09	.05
3	Rod Carew	.50	.40	.20
4	Gary Carter	.30	.25	.12
5	Jack Clark	.20	.15	.08
6	Cecil Cooper	.20	.15	.08
7	Dwight Evans	.20	.15	.08
8	George Foster	.20	.15	.08
9	Pedro Guerrero	.20	.15	.08
10	George Hendrick	.12	.09	.05
11	Bob Horner	.20	.15	.08
12	Reggie Jackson	.60	.45	.25
13	Steve Kemp	.12	.09	.05
14	Dave Kingman	.20	.15	.08
15	Bill Madlock	.20	.15	.08
16	Gary Matthews	.12	.09	.05
17	Hal McRae	.20	.15	.08
18	Dale Murphy	.40	.30	.15
19	Eddie Murray	.30	.25	.12
20	Ben Oglivie	.12	.09	.05
21	Al Oliver	.20	.15	.08
22	Jim Rice	.20	.15	.08
23	Cal Ripken, Jr.	1.00	.70	.40
24	Pete Rose	.90	.70	.35
25	Mike Schmidt	1.00	.70	.40
26	Ken Singleton	.12	.09	.05
27	Gorman Thomas	.12	.09	.05
28	Jason Thompson	.12	.09	.05
29	Mookie Wilson	.12	.09	.05
30	Willie Wilson	.20	.15	.08
31	Dave Winfield	.50	.40	.20
32	Carl Yastrzemski	.40	.30	.15
33	Robin Yount	.60	.45	.25

A card number in parentheses () indicates the set is unnumbered.

1984 Drake's

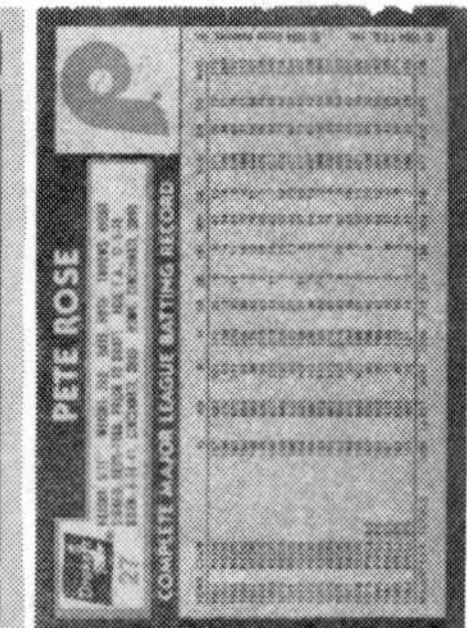

For the fourth year in a row, Drake Bakeries issued a 33-card "Big Hitters" set. The 1984 edition, produced again by Topps, includes 17 National League players and 16 from the American League. As in all previous years, the card fronts feature the player in a batting pose. The backs are identical to the 1984 Topps regular issue except for being numbered 1-33 and carrying the Drake's logo and copyright line. The cards are the standard size 2-1/2" by 3-1/2".

		MT	NR MT	EX
Complete Set:		9.00	6.75	3.50
Common Player:		.12	.09	.05
1	Don Baylor	.20	.15	.08
2	Wade Boggs	.90	.70	.35
3	George Brett	.70	.50	.30
4	Bill Buckner	.12	.09	.05
5	Rod Carew	.60	.45	.25
6	Gary Carter	.30	.25	.12
7	Ron Cey	.12	.09	.05
8	Cecil Cooper	.20	.15	.08
9	Andre Dawson	.30	.25	.12
10	Steve Garvey	.40	.30	.15
11	Pedro Guerrero	.20	.15	.08
12	George Hendrick	.12	.09	.05
13	Keith Hernandez	.20	.15	.08
14	Bob Horner	.20	.15	.08
15	Reggie Jackson	.60	.45	.25
16	Steve Kemp	.12	.09	.05
17	Ron Kittle	.12	.09	.05
18	Greg Luzinski	.20	.15	.08
19	Fred Lynn	.20	.15	.08
20	Bill Madlock	.20	.15	.08
21	Gary Matthews	.12	.09	.05
22	Dale Murphy	.60	.45	.25
23	Eddie Murray	.30	.25	.12
24	Al Oliver	.20	.15	.08
25	Jim Rice	.20	.15	.08
26	Cal Ripken, Jr.	1.00	.70	.40
27	Pete Rose	.90	.70	.35
28	Mike Schmidt	1.00	.70	.40
29	Darryl Strawberry	.60	.45	.25
30	Alan Trammell	.30	.25	.12
31	Mookie Wilson	.12	.09	.05
32	Dave Winfield	.60	.45	.25
33	Robin Yount	.40	.30	.15

1985 Drake's

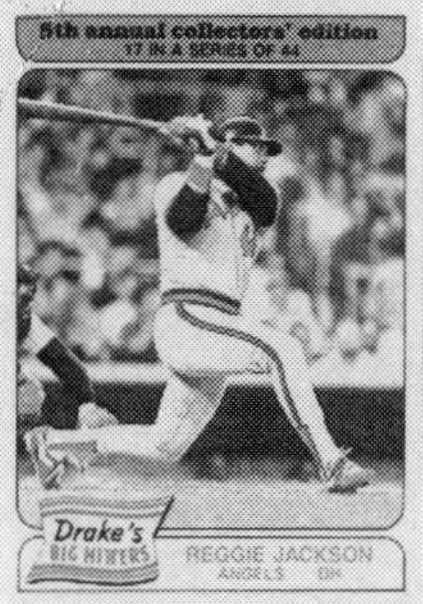

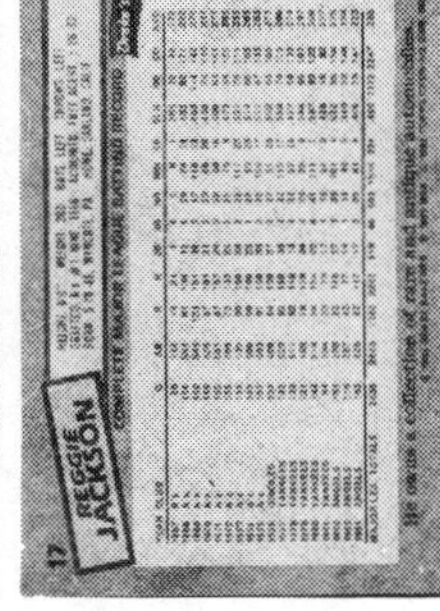

The "5th Annual Collectors' Edition" set produced by Topps for Drake Bakeries consists of 33 "Big Hitters" and 11 "Super Pitchers." The new "Super Pitchers" feature increased the set's size from the usual 33 cards to 44. The cards, which measure 2-1/2" by 3-1/2", show the player in either a batting or pitching pose. The backs differ only from the regular 1985 Topps issue in that they are numbered 1-44 and carry the Drake's logo.

		MT	NR MT	EX
Complete Set:		12.00	9.00	4.75
Commmon Player:		.12	.09	.05
1	Tony Armas	.12	.09	.05
2	Harold Baines	.20	.15	.08
3	Don Baylor	.20	.15	.08
4	George Brett	.70	.50	.30
5	Gary Carter	.45	.35	.20
6	Ron Cey	.12	.09	.05
7	Jose Cruz	.12	.09	.05
8	Alvin Davis	.12	.09	.05
9	Chili Davis	.25	.20	.10
10	Dwight Evans	.20	.15	.08
11	Steve Garvey	.45	.35	.20
12	Kirk Gibson	.35	.25	.14
13	Pedro Guerrero	.20	.15	.08
14	Tony Gwynn	.60	.45	.25
15	Keith Hernandez	.20	.15	.08
16	Kent Hrbek	.35	.25	.14
17	Reggie Jackson	.60	.45	.25
18	Gary Matthews	.12	.09	.05
19	Don Mattingly	.90	.70	.35
20	Dale Murphy	.70	.50	.30
21	Eddie Murray	.45	.35	.20
22	Dave Parker	.20	.15	.08
23	Lance Parrish	.20	.15	.08
24	Tim Raines	.35	.25	.14
25	Jim Rice	.20	.15	.08
26	Cal Ripken, Jr.	1.00	.70	.40
27	Juan Samuel	.25	.20	.10
28	Ryne Sandberg	1.00	.70	.40
29	Mike Schmidt	1.00	.70	.40
30	Darryl Strawberry	.45	.35	.20
31	Alan Trammell	.30	.25	.12
32	Dave Winfield	.50	.40	.20
33	Robin Yount	.40	.30	.15
34	Mike Boddicker	.12	.09	.05
35	Steve Carlton	.40	.30	.15
36	Dwight Gooden	.30	.25	.12
37	Willie Hernandez	.12	.09	.05
38	Mark Langston	.20	.15	.08
39	Dan Quisenberry	.12	.09	.05
40	Dave Righetti	.20	.15	.08
41	Tom Seaver	.60	.45	.25
42	Bob Stanley	.12	.09	.05
43	Rick Sutcliffe	.20	.15	.08
44	Bruce Sutter	.20	.15	.08

1986 Drake's

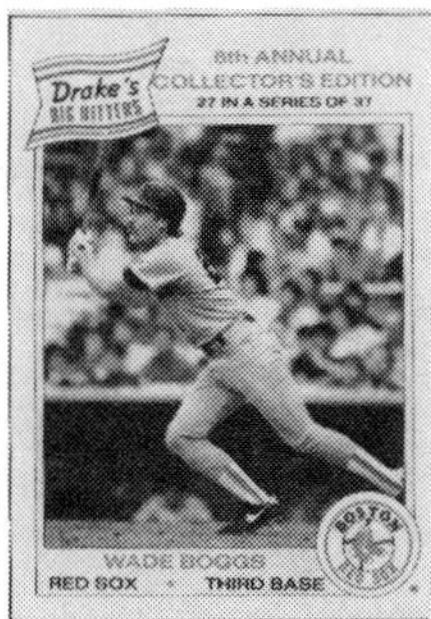

For the sixth year in a row, Drake Bakeries issued a baseball card set. Produced for Drake's by Topps in the past, the 1986 set was not and was available only by buying the actual products the cards were printed on. The cards, which measure 2-1/2" by 3-1/2", were issued in either two-, three-, or four-card panels. Fourteen panels, consisting of 37 different players, comprise the set. The players who make up the set are tabbed as either "Big Hitters" or "Super Pitchers." Logos of various Drake's products can be found on the panel backs. The value of the set is higher when collected in either panel or complete box form.

		MT	NR MT	EX
Complete Panel Set:		35.00	26.00	14.00
Complete Singles Set:		20.00	15.00	8.00
Common Panel:		1.75	1.25	.70
Common Single Player:		.20	.15	.08
	Panel	1.75	1.25	.70
1	Gary Carter	.50	.40	.20
2	Dwight Evans	.25	.20	.10
	Panel	2.00	1.50	.80
3	Reggie Jackson	.70	.50	.30
4	Dave Parker	.25	.20	.10
	Panel	1.75	1.25	.70
5	Rickey Henderson	.90	.70	.35
6	Pedro Guerrero	.30	.25	.12
	Panel	3.00	2.25	1.25
7	Don Mattingly	.90	.70	.35
8	Mike Marshall	.25	.20	.10
9	Keith Moreland	.20	.15	.08
	Panel	2.50	1.50	.80
10	Keith Hernandez	.25	.20	.10
11	Cal Ripken	1.00	.70	.40
	Panel	2.00	1.50	.80
12	Dale Murphy	.60	.45	.25
13	Jim Rice	.20	.15	.08
	Panel	2.25	1.75	.90
14	George Brett	.70	.50	.30
15	Tim Raines	.30	.25	.12
	Panel	1.75	1.50	.80
16	Darryl Strawberry	.40	.30	.15
17	Bill Buckner	.20	.15	.08
	Panel	3.50	2.75	1.50
18	Dave Winfield	.50	.40	.20
19	Ryne Sandberg	1.00	.70	.40
20	Steve Balboni	.20	.15	.08
21	Tom Herr	.20	.15	.08
	Panel	3.75	2.75	1.50
22	Pete Rose	.90	.70	.35
23	Willie McGee	.25	.20	.10
24	Harold Baines	.25	.20	.10
25	Eddie Murray	.40	.30	.15
	Panel	4.00	3.00	1.50
26	Mike Schmidt	1.00	.70	.40
27	Wade Boggs	.90	.70	.35
28	Kirk Gibson	.35	.25	.14
	Panel	2.00	1.50	.80
29	Bret Saberhagen	.35	.25	.14
30	John Tudor	.20	.15	.08
31	Orel Hershiser	.40	.30	.15
	Panel	3.00	2.25	1.25
32	Ron Guidry	.25	.20	.10
33	Nolan Ryan	2.00	1.50	.80
34	Dave Stieb	.25	.20	.10
	Panel	2.00	1.50	.80
35	Dwight Gooden	.50	.40	.20
36	Fernando Valenzuela	.25	.20	.10
37	Tom Browning	.25	.20	.10

1987 Drake's

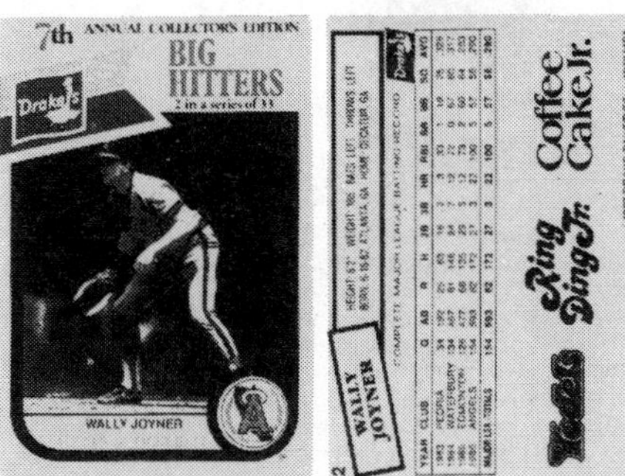

For the seventh consecutive season, Drake Bakeries produced a baseball card set. The cards, which measure 2-1/2" by 3-1/2", were included in either two-, three-, or four-card panels on boxes of various Drake's products distributed in the eastern United States. The set is comprised of 33 cards, with 25 players branded as "Big Hitters" and 8 as "Super Pitchers". The card fronts carry a full-color photo and the Drake's logo surrounded by a brown and yellow border. The backs contain the player's complete major league record.

		MT	NR MT	EX
Complete Panel Set:		30.00	22.00	12.00
Complete Singles Set:		20.00	15.00	8.00
Common Panel:		1.75	1.25	.70
Common Single Player:		.20	.15	.08
	Panel	2.00	1.50	.80
1	Darryl Strawberry	.40	.30	.15
2	Wally Joyner	.60	.45	.25
	Panel	3.75	2.75	1.50
3	Von Hayes	.25	.20	.10
4	Jose Canseco	1.75	1.25	.70
	Panel	3.00	2.25	1.25
5	Dave Winfield	.50	.40	.20
6	Cal Ripken, Jr.	1.00	.70	.40
	Panel	2.50	2.00	1.00
7	Keith Moreland	.20	.15	.08
8	Don Mattingly	.90	.70	.35
9	Willie McGee	.25	.20	.10
	Panel	1.75	1.50	.80
10	Keith Hernandez	.20	.15	.08
11	Tony Gwynn	.60	.45	.25
	Panel	4.50	3.25	1.75
12	Rickey Henderson	.90	.70	.35
13	Dale Murphy	.60	.45	.25
14	George Brett	.80	.60	.30
15	Jim Rice	.40	.30	.15
	Panel	4.00	3.00	1.50
16	Wade Boggs	.90	.70	.35
17	Kevin Bass	.20	.15	.08
18	Dave Parker	.25	.20	.10
19	Kirby Puckett	.60	.45	.25
	Panel	2.50	2.00	1.00
20	Gary Carter	.40	.30	.15
21	Ryne Sandberg	1.00	.70	.40
22	Harold Baines	.25	.20	.10
	Panel	2.75	2.00	1.00
23	Mike Schmidt	1.00	.70	.40
24	Eddie Murray	.40	.30	.15
25	Steve Sax	.25	.20	.10
	Panel	1.50	1.25	.60
26	Dwight Gooden	.40	.30	.15
27	Jack Morris	.25	.20	.10
	Panel	1.75	1.25	.60
28	Ron Darling	.25	.20	.10
29	Fernando Valenzuela	.35	.25	.14
30	John Tudor	.20	.15	.08
	Panel	5.00	2.75	2.00
31	Roger Clemens	.80	.60	.30
32	Nolan Ryan	2.00	1.50	.80
33	Mike Scott	.25	.20	.10

1988 Drake's

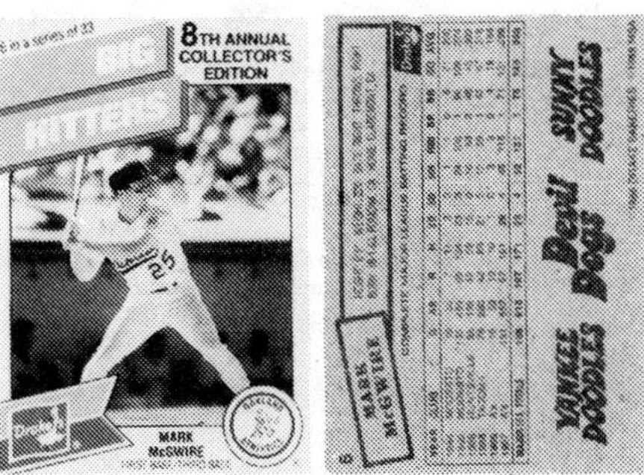

The 8th annual edition of this set includes 33 glossy full-color cards printed on cut-out panels of 2, 3 or 4 cards on Drake's dessert snack boxes. Card fronts have white borders with a large red and blue "Super Pitchers" (6 cards) or "Big Hitters" (27 cards) caption upper left, beside the "8th Annual Collector's Edition label. The Drake logo, player name and team logo are printed in black and include the card number, personal data, batting/pitching record and sponsor logos. Sets were available exclusively on 12 different Drake's packages. To complete the set, collectors had to purchase all 12 products.

		MT	NR MT	EX
Complete Panel Set:		30.00	22.00	12.00
Complete Singles Set:		20.00	15.00	8.00
Common Panel:		1.75	1.25	.70
Common Single Player:		.20	.15	.08
	Panel	2.50	2.00	1.00
1	Don Mattingly	.90	.70	.35
2	Tim Raines	.40	.30	.15
	Panel	2.50	2.00	1.00
3	Darryl Strawberry	.40	.30	.15
4	Wade Boggs	.90	.70	.35
	Panel	2.00	1.50	.80
5	Keith Hernandez	.25	.20	.10
6	Mark McGwire	.80	.60	.30
	Panel	3.00	2.25	1.25
7	Rickey Henderson	.80	.60	.30
8	Mike Schmidt	1.00	.70	.40
9	Dwight Evans	.25	.20	.10
	Panel	2.00	1.50	.80
10	Gary Carter	.40	.30	.15
11	Paul Molitor	.60	.45	.25
	Panel	2.75	2.00	1.00
12	Dave Winfield	.50	.40	.20
13	Alan Trammell	.35	.25	.14
14	Tony Gwynn	.50	.40	.20
	Panel	2.50	2.00	1.00
15	Dale Murphy	.60	.45	.25
16	Andre Dawson	.30	.25	.12
17	Von Hayes	.20	.15	.08
18	Willie Randolph	.20	.15	.08
	Panel	2.00	1.50	.80
19	Kirby Puckett	.50	.40	.20
20	Juan Samuel	.25	.20	.10
21	Eddie Murray	.40	.30	.15
	Panel	2.00	1.50	.80
22	George Bell	.35	.25	.14
23	Larry Sheets	.20	.15	.08
24	Eric Davis	.35	.25	.14

		MT	NR MT	EX
	Panel	4.00	3.00	1.50
25	Cal Ripken, Jr.	1.00	.70	.40
26	Pedro Guerrero	.25	.20	.10
27	Will Clark	1.00	.70	.40
	Panel	1.75	1.25	.70
28	Dwight Gooden	.50	.40	.20
29	Frank Viola	.25	.20	.10
	Panel	2.75	2.25	1.25
30	Roger Clemens	.60	.45	.25
31	Rick Sutcliffe	.20	.15	.08
32	Jack Morris	.25	.20	.10
33	John Tudor	.20	.15	.08

1989 Dubuque Braves

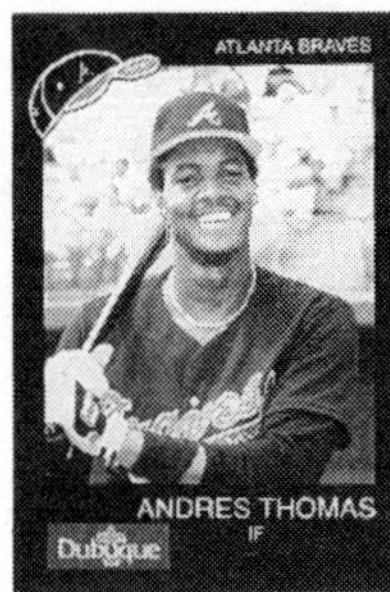

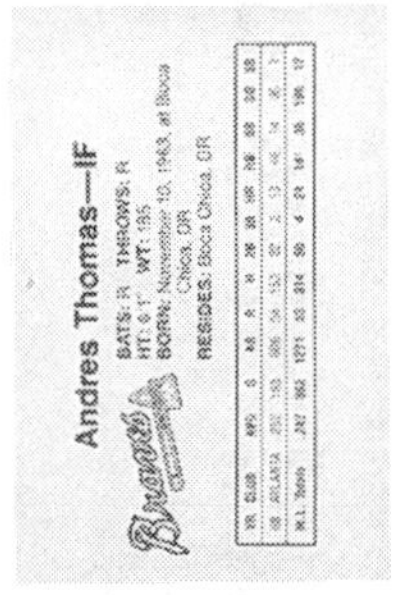

Given away on Sundays to correspond with player appearances at an autograph booth in the stadium, these 2-3/8" x 3-1/2" cards were sponsored by Braves hot dog concessionaire, Dubuque Meats. Cards have player photos centered within a dark blue border. A Braves cap is at upper-left, the hot dog company's logo at lower-left. The player's name, team and position are in white. Backs, printed in black on white, have the Braves logo, a few personal facts and figures and previous year/career stats. Because only 15,000 of each card were distributed over the course of the season, compilation of complete sets is extremely challenging. The checklist here is arranged in alphabetical order.

		MT	NR MT	EX
	Complete Set:	45.00	34.00	18.00
	Common Player:	1.00	.70	.40
(1)	Paul Assenmacher	1.00	.70	.40
(2)	Jim Acker	1.00	.70	.40
(3)	Jose Alvarez	1.00	.70	.40
(4)	Bruce Benedict	1.00	.70	.40
(5)	Jeff Blauser	1.50	1.25	.60
(6)	Joe Boever	1.00	.70	.40
(7)	Marty Clary	1.00	.70	.40
(8)	Bruce dal Canton	1.00	.70	.40
(9)	Jody Davis	1.00	.70	.40
(10)	Mark Eichhorn	1.00	.70	.40
(11)	Ron Gant	5.00	3.75	2.00
(12)	Tom Glavine	5.00	3.75	2.00
(13)	Tommy Gregg	1.00	.70	.40
(14)	Clarence Jones	1.00	.70	.40
(15)	Derek Lilliquist	1.00	.70	.40
(16)	Roy Majtyka	1.00	.70	.40
(17)	Oddibe McDowell	1.00	.70	.40
(18)	Dale Murphy	5.00	3.75	2.00
(19)	Russ Nixon	1.00	.70	.40
(20)	Gerald Perry	1.00	.70	.40
(21)	John Russell	1.00	.70	.40
(22)	Lonnie Smith	1.00	.70	.40
(23)	Pete Smith	1.00	.70	.40
(24)	John Smoltz	2.00	1.50	.80
(25)	Brian Snitker	1.00	.70	.40
(26)	Andres Thomas	1.00	.70	.40
(27)	Jeff Treadway	1.00	.70	.40
(28)	Jeff Wetherby	1.00	.70	.40
(29)	Ed Whited	1.00	.70	.40
(30)	Bobby Wine	1.00	.70	.40

1990 Dubuque Braves Team Photo Set

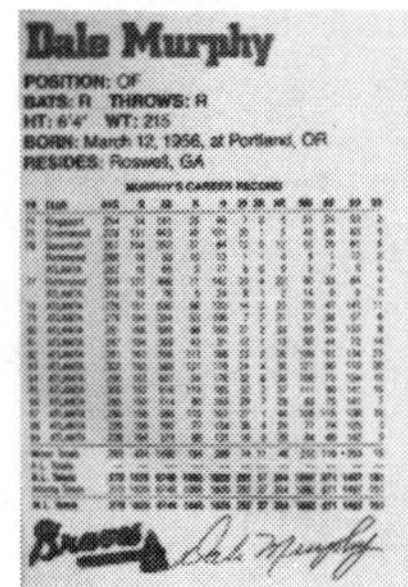

This three-panel team set was given away at an early-season game, commemorating the Braves 25th season in Atlanta. The sheet measures 11x28-1/2". The top panel is a team photo. The two lower panels contain 30 individual cards, 2-1/2x3-1/4", perforated to allow them to be separated. Backs are printed in red and blue. The perforated team set is much more common than the Dubuque cards given out a few at a time during Sunday home games. The checklist below is arranged according to uniform numbers which appear on the front of each card.

		MT	NR MT	EX
	Complete Set:	12.50	9.00	3.50
	Common Player:	.25	.20	.10
1	Oddibe McDowell	.25	.20	.10
2	Russ Nixon	.25	.20	.10
3	Dale Murphy	2.00	1.50	.60
4	Jeff Blauser	.25	.20	.10
5	Ron Gant	1.00	.75	.30
10	Greg Olson	.25	.20	.10
12	Ernie Whitt	.25	.20	.10
14	Andres Thomas	.25	.20	.10
15	Jeff Treadway	.25	.20	.10
16	Tommy Gregg	.25	.20	.10
17	Nick Esasky	.25	.20	.10
18	Jim Presley	.25	.20	.10
19	Francisco Cabrera	.25	.20	.10
20	Mark Lemke	.25	.20	.10
23	Dave Justice	2.00	1.50	.60
24	Derek Lilliquist	.25	.20	.10
25	Pete Smith	.25	.20	.10
27	Lonnie Smith	.25	.20	.10
29	John Smoltz	1.00	.75	.30
30	Mike Stanton	.25	.20	.10
36	Tony Castillo	.25	.20	.10
37	Joe Boever	.25	.20	.10
40	Charlie Kerfeld	.25	.20	.10
45	Charlie Leibrandt	.25	.20	.10
46	Dwayne Henry	.25	.20	.10
47	Tom Glavine	1.00	.75	.30
48	Marty Clary	.25	.20	.10
49	Rick Luecken	.25	.20	.10
58a	Joe Hesketh	.25	.20	.10
58b	Alexis Infante	.25	.20	.10

A player's name in italic type indicates a rookie card. An (FC) indicates a player's first card for that particular card company.

1990 Dubuque Braves

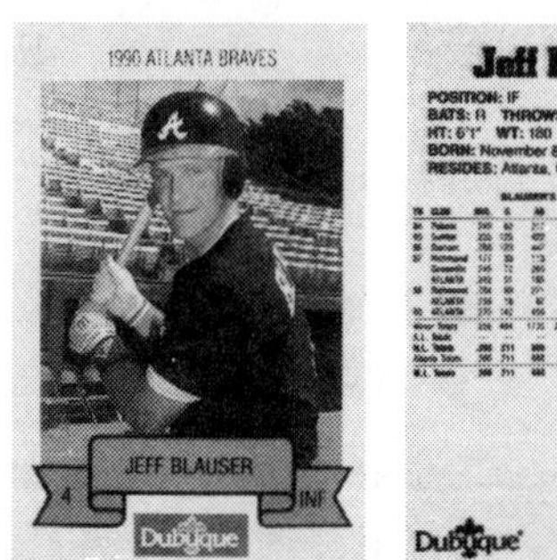

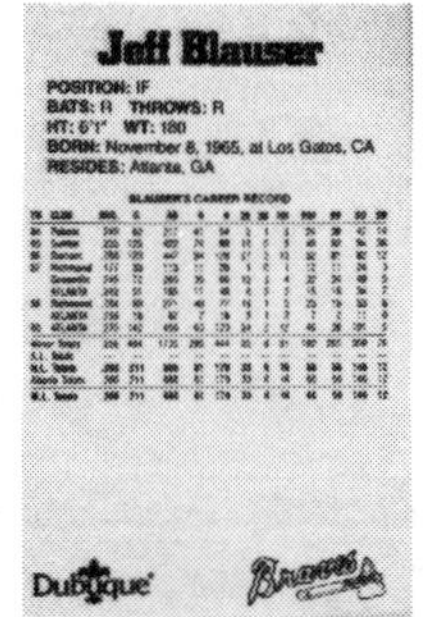

For a second season, the Braves hot dog vendor, Dubuque Meats, sponsored this season-long promotion. Up to four different player cards were given out at Sunday home games, corresponding with player appearances at an autograph booth. Some player cards were distributed more than once, while others, such as Dale Murphy, who was traded, were only given out one day. Players were added to the set right up through the final Sunday home game of the season. Complete sets are extremely difficult to assemble. The player photo on these 2-3/8" x3-1/2" cards have a white border. A red banner beneath the photo has the player's name, uniform number and position printed in black. Backs are printed in dark blue and feature full minor and major league stats. The checklist here is arranged alphabetically.

		MT	NR MT	EX
	Complete Set:	60.00	45.00	24.00
	Common Player:	1.00	.70	.40
(1)	Steve Avery	3.00	2.25	1.25
(2)	Jeff Blauser	1.50	1.25	.60
(3)	Joe Boever	1.00	.70	.40
(4)	Francisco Cabrera	1.00	.70	.40
(5)	Pat Corrales	1.00	.70	.40
(6)	Bobby Cox	1.00	.70	.40
(7)	Nick Esasky	1.00	.70	.40
(8)	Ron Gant	5.00	3.75	2.00
(9)	Tom Glavine	3.00	2.25	1.25
(10)	Mark Grant	1.00	.70	.40
(11)	Tommy Gregg	1.00	.70	.40
(12)	Dwayne Henry	1.00	.70	.40
(13)	Alexis Infante	1.00	.70	.40
(14)	Clarence Jones	1.00	.70	.40
(15)	Dave Justice	5.00	3.75	2.00
(16)	Jimmy Kremers	1.00	.70	.40
(17)	Charlie Leibrandt	1.00	.70	.40
(18)	Mark Lemke	1.00	.70	.40
(19)	Roy Majtyka	1.00	.70	.40
(20)	Leo Mazzone	1.00	.70	.40
(21)	Oddibe McDowell	1.00	.70	.40
(22)	Dale Murphy	5.00	3.75	2.00
(23)	Phil Niekro	5.00	3.75	2.00
(24)	Greg Olson	1.00	.70	.40
(25)	Jim Presley	1.00	.70	.40
(26)	Lonnie Smith	1.00	.70	.40
(27)	Pete Smith	1.00	.70	.40
(28)	John Smoltz	2.00	1.50	.80
(29)	Brian Snitker	1.00	.70	.40
(30)	Andres Thomas	1.00	.70	.40
(31)	Jeff Treadway	1.00	.70	.40
(32)	Ernie Whitt	1.00	.70	.40
(33)	Jimy Williams	1.00	.70	.40
(34)	Homer the Brave (mascot)	1.00	.70	.40
(35)	Rally (mascot)	1.00	.70	.40

The values quoted are intended to reflect the market price.

1991 Dubuque Braves Team Photo Set

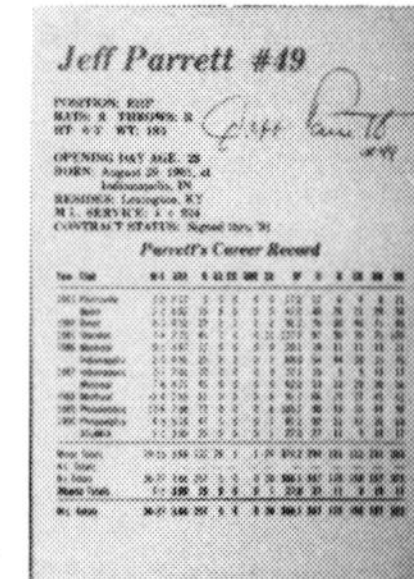

This team photo/player card triptych was an early season give-away. Each of the three fold-out panels measures about 9-1/2" x 10-1/2". The 30 individual player cards have perforated edges for easy removal from the sheet. The 2-1/8" x 3-1/8" cards have a player portrait photo at center, with blue diamond designs at the corners. A red box below the photo has the player's name and uniform number. Blue Braves and Dubuque logos appear at the lower corners of the white border. Backs are printed in red and blue and include full stats and a facsimile autograph, plus a few biographical details. The team sheet cards are considered much more common than the other Braves baseball card promotional giveaways, especially in complete sets. Cards are checklisted here alphabetically.

		MT	NR MT	EX
	Complete Set:	12.00	9.00	4.75
	Common Player:	.25	.20	.10
(1)	Steve Avery	.75	.60	.30
(2)	Rafael Belliard	.25	.20	.10
(3)	Juan Berenguer	.25	.20	.10
(4)	Jeff Blauser	.50	.40	.20
(5)	Sid Bream	.50	.40	.20
(6)	Francisco Cabrera	.35	.25	.14
(7)	Bobby Cox	.25	.20	.10
(8)	Nick Esasky	.25	.20	.10
(9)	Marvin Freeman	.25	.20	.10
(10)	Ron Gant	1.00	.70	.40
(11)	Tom Glavine	.65	.50	.25
(12)	Mark Grant	.25	.20	.10
(13)	Tommy Gregg	.25	.20	.10
(14)	Mike Heath	.25	.20	.10
(15)	Danny Heep	.25	.20	.10
(16)	David Justice	1.00	.70	.40
(17)	Charlie Leibrandt	.25	.20	.10
(18)	Mark Lemke	.35	.25	.14
(19)	Kent Mercker	.35	.25	.14
(20)	Otis Nixon	.35	.25	.14
(21)	Greg Olson	.25	.20	.10
(22)	Jeff Parrett	.25	.20	.10
(23)	Terry Pendleton	.65	.50	.25
(24)	Deion Sanders	.75	.60	.30
(25)	Doug Sisk	.25	.20	.10
(26)	Lonnie Smith	.25	.20	.10
(27)	Pete Smith	.25	.20	.10
(28)	John Smoltz	.35	.25	.14
(29)	Mike Stanton	.25	.20	.10
(30)	Jeff Treadway	.25	.20	.10

Values for recent cards and sets are listed in Mint (MT), Near Mint (NM), reflecting the fact that many cards from recent years have been preserved in top condition. Recent cards and sets in less than Excellent condition have little collector interest.

1991 Dubuque Braves

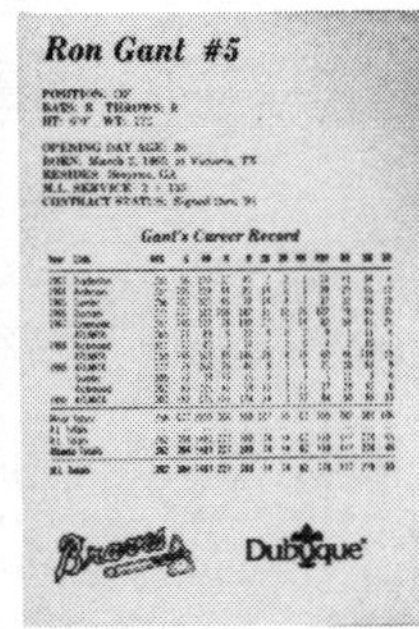

At each Sunday home game the Braves distributed some 15,000 of each of three to six player cards to kids under 14. The cards corresponded to appearances by those players at an autograph session. That method of distribution makes accumulation of complete sets very difficult. Sponsor of the set for the third straight year was the stadium's hot dog concessionaire, Dubuque Meats. Their logo appears in the upper-left corner of the player photo. At lower-right on the 2-1/4" x 3-1/2" cards is a baseball diamond figure with the team and player name and the year of issue. There is a white outer border on the card, with the photo framed in white-pinstriped dark blue. Backs are printed in dark blue, with logos, complete stats, biographical information and the player's uniform number. Cards are checklisted here in alphabetical order.

		MT	NR MT	EX
Complete Set:		60.00	45.00	24.00
Common Player:		1.00	.70	.40
(1)	Steve Avery	3.00	2.25	1.25
(2)	Jim Beauchamp	1.00	.70	.40
(3)	Mike Bell	1.00	.70	.40
(4)	Rafael Belliard	1.00	.70	.40
(5)	Juan Berenguer	1.00	.70	.40
(6)	Jeff Blauser	1.50	1.25	.60
(7)	Sid Bream	1.50	1.25	.60
(8)	Francisco Cabrera	1.00	.70	.40
(9)	Jim Clancy	1.00	.70	.40
(10)	Pat Corrales	1.00	.70	.40
(11)	Bobby Cox	1.00	.70	.40
(12)	Nick Esasky	1.00	.70	.40
(13)	Marvin Freeman	1.00	.70	.40
(14)	Ron Gant	5.00	3.75	2.00
(15)	Tom Glavine	3.00	2.25	1.25
(16)	Mark Grant	1.00	.70	.40
(17)	Tommy Gregg	1.00	.70	.40
(18)	Mike Heath	1.00	.70	.40
(19)	Brian Hunter	1.00	.70	.40
(20)	Clarence Jones	1.00	.70	.40
(21)	David Justice	5.00	3.75	2.00
(22)	Charlie Leibrandt	1.00	.70	.40
(23)	Mark Lemke	1.50	1.25	.60
(24)	Leo Mazzone	1.00	.70	.40
(25)	Kent Mercker	1.00	.70	.40
(26)	Keith Mitchell	1.00	.70	.40
(27)	Otis Nixon	1.50	1.25	.60
(28)	Greg Olson	1.00	.70	.40
(29)	Jeff Parrett	1.00	.70	.40
(30)	Terry Pendleton	2.50	2.00	1.00
(31)	Armando Reynoso	1.00	.70	.40
(32)	Deion Sanders	6.00	4.50	2.50
(33)	Lonnie Smith	1.00	.70	.40
(34)	Pete Smith	1.00	.70	.40
(35)	John Smoltz	2.00	1.50	.80
(36)	Mike Stanton	1.00	.70	.40
(37)	Jeff Treadway	1.00	.70	.40
(38)	Jimy Williams	1.00	.70	.40
(39)	Ned Yost	1.00	.70	.40
(40)	Homer the Brave (mascot)	1.00	.70	.40
(41)	Rally (mascot)	1.00	.70	.40

Grading Guide

Mint (MT): A perfect card. Well-centered with all corners sharp and square. No creases, stains, edge nicks, surface marks, yellowing or fading.

Near Mint (NM): A nearly perfect card. At first glance, a NM card appears to be perfect. May be slightly off-center. No surface marks, creases or loss of gloss.

Excellent (EX): Corners are still fairly sharp with only moderate wear. Borders may be off-center. No creases or stains on fronts or backs, but may show slight loss of surface luster.

Very Good (VG): Shows obvious handling. May have rounded corners, minor creases, major gum or wax stains. No major creases, tape marks, writing, etc.

Good (G): A well-worn card, but exhibits no intentional damage. May have major or multiple creases. Corners may be rounded well beyond card border.

1888 Duke Talk of the Diamond (N135)

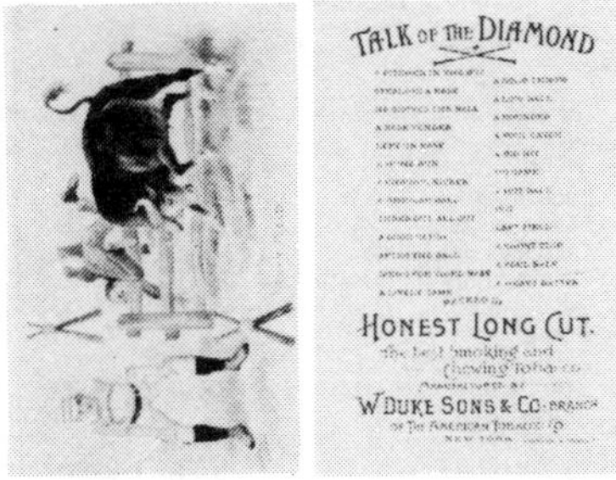

One of the more obscure 19th Century tobacco issues is a 25-card set issued by Honest Long Cut Tobacco in the late 1880's. Titled "Talk of the Diamond," the set features full-color cards measuring 4-1/8" by 2-1/2". Each card features a cartoon-like drawing illustrating a popular baseball term or expression. The left portion of the card pictures an unspecified player in a fielding position, and some of the artwork for that part of the set was borrowed from the more popular Buchner Gold Coin set (N284) issued about the same time. Because the "Talk of the Diamond" set does not feature individual players it has never really captured the attention of baseball card collectors. It does, however, hold interest as a novelty item of the period. It carries an N135 American Card Catalog designation.

		NR MT	EX	VG
Complete Set:		900.00	450.00	275.00
Common Card:		35.00	17.50	10.50
(1)	A Base Tender	35.00	17.50	10.50
(2)	A Big Hit	35.00	17.50	10.50
(3)	A Chronic Kicker	35.00	17.50	10.50
(4)	A Foul Balk	35.00	17.50	10.50
(5)	A Foul Catch	35.00	17.50	10.50
(6)	A Good Catch	35.00	17.50	10.50
(7)	A Good Throw	35.00	17.50	10.50
(8)	A Heavy Batter	35.00	17.50	10.50
(9)	A Home Run	35.00	17.50	10.50
(10)	A Hot Ball	35.00	17.50	10.50
(11)	A Low Ball	35.00	17.50	10.50
(12)	A Pitcher in the Box	35.00	17.50	10.50
(13)	A Regular Ball	35.00	17.50	10.50
(14)	A Rounder	35.00	17.50	10.50
(15)	A Short Stop	35.00	17.50	10.50
(16)	After the Ball	35.00	17.50	10.50
(17)	Going for Third Base	35.00	17.50	10.50
(18)	He Serves the Ball	35.00	17.50	10.50
(19)	Left Field	35.00	17.50	10.50
(20)	Left on Base	35.00	17.50	10.50
(21)	Lively Game	35.00	17.50	10.50
(22)	No Game	35.00	17.50	10.50
(23)	Out	35.00	17.50	10.50
(24)	Stealing a Base	35.00	17.50	10.50
(25)	Three out-All out	35.00	17.50	10.50

1992 Dunkin' Donuts Red Sox

The 1992 Boston Red Sox were the subject of a set of 30 cards, including cards of the manager and coaches. Co-sponsored by Dunkin Donuts and WVIT-TV and released in May in Connecticut, the set was sold as an uncut, perforated sheet of 30 cards, measuring about 9-1/2" x 10-3/4". Individual perforated cards could be removed from the sheet; they measure 2-1/8" x 3-1/8". Fronts have a player photo framed in black on a white background. In the border beneath the photo are the player's name, position, uniform number and sponsors' logos. Backs have complete major and minor league stats. The cards are checklisted here alphabetically.

		MT	NR MT	EX
Complete Set:		10.00	7.50	4.00
Common Player:		.25	.20	.10
(1)	Gary Allenson	.25	.20	.10
(2)	Wade Boggs	1.00	.70	.40
(3)	Tom Bolton	.25	.20	.10
(4)	Tom Brunansky	.25	.20	.10
(5)	Al Bumbry	.25	.20	.10
(6)	Ellis Burks	.50	.40	.20
(7)	Rick Burleson	.25	.20	.10
(8)	Jack Clark	.35	.25	.14
(9)	Roger Clemens	.90	.70	.35
(10)	Danny Darwin	.25	.20	.10
(11)	Tony Fossas	.25	.20	.10
(12)	Rich Gale	.25	.20	.10
(13)	Mike Gardiner	.25	.20	.10
(14)	Mike Greenwell	.60	.45	.25
(15)	Greg Harris	.30	.25	.12
(16)	Joe Hesketh	.25	.20	.10
(17)	Butch Hobson	.35	.25	.14
(18)	John Marzano	.25	.20	.10
(19)	Kevin Morton	.25	.20	.10
(20)	Tim Naehring	.25	.20	.10
(21)	Tony Pena	.35	.25	.14
(22)	Phil Plantier	.80	.60	.30
(23)	Carlos Quintana	.35	.25	.14
(24)	Jeff Reardon	.35	.25	.14
(25)	Jody Reed	.25	.20	.10
(26)	Luis Rivera	.25	.20	.10
(27)	Mo Vaughn	.60	.45	.25
(28)	Frank Viola	.50	.40	.20
(29)	Matt Young	.25	.20	.10
(30)	Don Zimmer	.35	.25	.14

Regional interest may affect the value of a card.

1993 Duracell Power Players

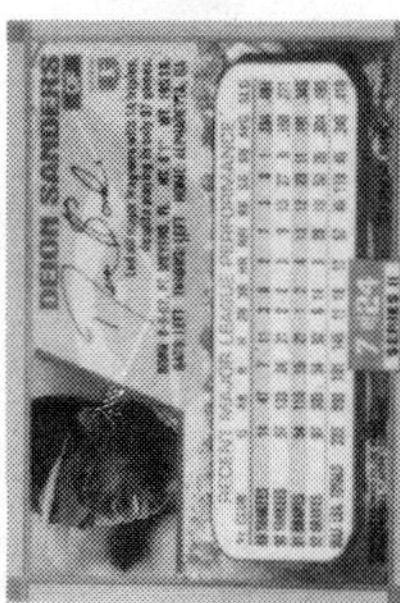

The Duracell battery company issued a 48-card set in 1993 that was presented in two 24-card series. The cards were available through the mail with proofs of purchase from selected Duracell products, with a six-set limit per household. The cards feature a Duracell battery at the top of the card, with a black and orange border surrounding a color photo of the player. The player's name is printed in yellow with team and position in white on top of a green background. Because the set was not licensed to use major league uniform logos, they were airbrushed off the photos. Backs have a player portrait photo, a facsimile autograph, recent stats and a few biographical and career details printed over a ballpark scene. Series I cards are number "X of 24;" Series II cards are so indicated beneath the card number.

		MT	NR MT	EX
Complete Set (48):		9.00	6.75	3.50
Common Player:		.10	.08	.04
	Series I			
1	Roger Clemens	.25	.20	.10
2	Frank Thomas	.75	.60	.30
3	Andre Dawson	.25	.20	.10
4	Orel Hershiser	.15	.11	.06
5	Kirby Puckett	.45	.35	.20
6	Edgar Martinez	.15	.11	.06
7	Craig Biggio	.10	.08	.04
8	Terry Pendleton	.10	.08	.04
9	Mark McGwire	.40	.30	.15
10	Dave Stewart	.10	.08	.04
11	Ozzie Smith	.25	.20	.10
12	Doug Drabek	.10	.08	.04
13	Dwight Gooden	.15	.11	.06
14	Tony Gwynn	.25	.20	.10
15	Carlos Baerga	.35	.25	.14
16	Robin Yount	.45	.35	.20
17	Barry Bonds	.45	.35	.20
18	Bip Roberts	.10	.08	.04
19	Don Mattingly	.45	.35	.20
20	Nolan Ryan	.75	.60	.30
21	Tom Glavine	.15	.11	.06
22	Will Clark	.40	.30	.15
23	Cecil Fielder	.40	.30	.15
24	Dave Winfield	.40	.30	.15
	Series II			
1	Cal Ripken, Jr.	.60	.45	.25
2	Melido Perez	.10	.08	.04
3	John Kruk	.15	.11	.06
4	Charlie Hayes	.10	.08	.04
5	George Brett	.45	.35	.20
6	Ruben Sierra	.15	.11	.06
7	Deion Sanders	.15	.11	.06
8	Andy Van Slyke	.10	.08	.04
9	Fred McGriff	.15	.11	.06
10	Benito Santiago	.10	.08	.04
11	Charles Nagy	.10	.08	.04
12	Greg Maddux	.15	.11	.06
13	Ryne Sandberg	.60	.45	.25
14	Dennis Martinez	.10	.08	.04
15	Ken Griffey, Jr.	.75	.60	.30
16	Jim Abbott	.15	.11	.06
17	Barry Larkin	.15	.11	.06
18	Gary Sheffield	.15	.11	.06
19	Jose Canseco	.45	.35	.20
20	Jack McDowell	.15	.11	.06
21	Darryl Strawberry	.15	.11	.06
22	Delino DeShields	.15	.11	.06
23	Dennis Eckersley	.15	.11	.06
24	Paul Molitor	.25	.20	.10

1910 E98 "Set of 30"

This set of 30 subjects was issued in 1910 and is closely related to several other early candy issues. that are nearly identical. The cards measure 1-1/2" x 2-3/4" and feature color lithograph player pictures. The backs, printed in brown, contain a checklist of the set but no advertising or other information indicating the manufacturer. The set was designated E98 by the "American Card Catalog." While the cards are unnumbered, they are listed here according to the numbers on the back checklist.

		NR MT	EX	VG
Complete Set (30):		20000.	10000.	5600.
Common Player:		150.00	75.00	45.00
(1)	Christy Mathewson	1500.	750.00	420.00
(2)	John McGraw	750.00	375.00	210.00
(3)	Johnny Kling	150.00	75.00	42.00
(4)	Frank Chance	700.00	350.00	196.00
(5)	Hans Wagner	2000.	1000.	560.00
(6)	Fred Clarke	650.00	325.00	182.00
(7)	Roger Bresnahan	650.00	325.00	182.00
(8)	Hal Chase	300.00	150.00	84.00
(9)	Russ Ford	150.00	75.00	42.00
(10)	Ty Cobb	5500.	2750.	1540.
(11)	Hughey Jennings	650.00	325.00	182.00
(12)	Chief Bender	650.00	325.00	182.00
(13)	Ed Walsh	700.00	350.00	196.00
(14)	Cy Young	1000.	500.00	280.00
(15)	Al Bridwell	150.00	75.00	42.00
(16)	Miner Brown	600.00	300.00	168.00
(17)	George Mullin	150.00	75.00	42.00
(18)	Chief Meyers	150.00	75.00	42.00
(19)	Hippo Vaughn	150.00	75.00	42.00
(20)	Red Dooin	150.00	75.00	42.00
(21)	Fred Tenny (Tenney)	150.00	75.00	42.00
(22)	Larry McLean	150.00	75.00	42.00
(23)	Nap Lajoie	800.00	400.00	230.00
(24)	Joe Tinker	650.00	325.00	182.00
(25)	Johnny Evers	650.00	325.00	182.00
(26)	Harry Davis	150.00	75.00	42.00
(27)	Eddie Collins	600.00	300.00	168.00
(28)	Bill Dahlen	150.00	75.00	42.00
(29)	Connie Mack	1000.	500.00	280.00
(30)	Jack Coombs	250.00	125.00	70.00

1909 E101 "Set of 50"

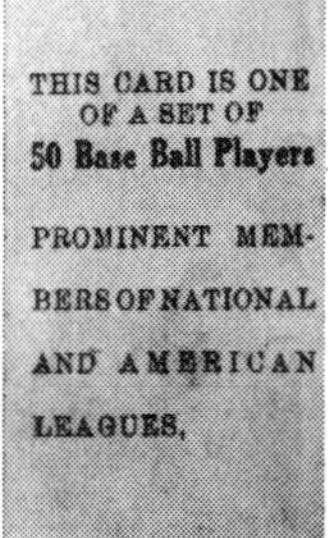

This 50-card set, issued in 1910, is closely related to the E92 set and is sometimes collected as part of that set. The fronts of the E101 cards are identical to the E92 set, but the back is an "anonymous" one, containing no advertising or any other information regarding the set's sponser. The backs read simply "This card is one of a set of 50 Base Ball Players/Prominent Members of National and American Leagues."

		NR MT	EX	VG
Complete Set (50):		16000.	8000.	4800.
Common Player:		150.00	75.00	45.00
(1)	Jack Barry	150.00	75.00	34.00
(2)	Harry Bemis	150.00	75.00	34.00
(3)	Chief Bender (white hat)	600.00	300.00	138.00
(4)	Chief Bender (striped hat)	600.00	300.00	138.00
(5)	Bill Bergen	150.00	75.00	34.00
(6)	Bob Bescher	150.00	75.00	34.00
(7)	Al Bridwell	150.00	75.00	34.00
(8)	Doc Casey	150.00	75.00	34.00
(9)	Frank Chance	600.00	300.00	138.00
(10)	Hal Chase	350.00	175.00	80.00
(11)	Ty Cobb	4500.	2250.	1035.
(12)	Eddie Collins	600.00	300.00	138.00
(13)	Sam Crawford	600.00	300.00	138.00
(14)	Harry Davis	150.00	75.00	34.00
(15)	Art Devlin	150.00	75.00	34.00
(16)	Wild Bill Donovan	150.00	75.00	34.00
(17)	Red Dooin	150.00	75.00	34.00
(18)	Mickey Doolan	150.00	75.00	34.00
(19)	Patsy Dougherty	150.00	75.00	34.00
(20)	Larry Doyle (with bat)	150.00	75.00	34.00
(21)	Larry Doyle (throwing)	150.00	75.00	34.00
(22)	Johnny Evers	600.00	300.00	138.00
(23)	George Gibson	150.00	75.00	34.00
(24)	Topsy Hartsel	150.00	75.00	34.00
(25)	Fred Jacklitsch	150.00	75.00	34.00
(26)	Hugh Jennings	550.00	275.00	126.00
(27)	Red Kleinow	150.00	75.00	34.00
(28)	Otto Knabe	150.00	75.00	34.00
(29)	Jack Knight	150.00	75.00	34.00
(30)	Nap Lajoie	800.00	400.00	185.00
(31)	Hans Lobert	150.00	75.00	34.00
(32)	Sherry Magee	150.00	75.00	34.00
(33)	Christy Matthewson (Mathewson)			
		1400.	700.00	322.00
(34)	John McGraw	600.00	300.00	140.00
(35)	Larry McLean	150.00	75.00	34.00
(36)	Dots Miller (batting)	150.00	75.00	34.00
(37)	Dots Miller (fielding)	150.00	75.00	34.00
(38)	Danny Murphy	150.00	75.00	34.00
(39)	Bill O'Hara	150.00	75.00	34.00
(40)	Germany Schaefer	150.00	75.00	34.00
(41)	Admiral Schlei	150.00	75.00	34.00
(42)	Boss Schmidt	150.00	75.00	34.00
(43)	Johnny Seigle	150.00	75.00	34.00
(44)	Dave Shean	150.00	75.00	34.00
(45)	Boss Smith (Schmidt)	150.00	75.00	34.00
(46)	Joe Tinker	600.00	300.00	138.00
(47)	Honus Wagner (batting)	1000.	500.00	230.00
(48)	Honus Wagner (throwing)	1000.	500.00	230.00
(49)	Cy Young	1000.	500.00	230.00
(50)	Heinie Zimmerman	150.00	75.00	34.00

The values quoted are intended to reflect the market price.

1908 E102 "Set of 25"

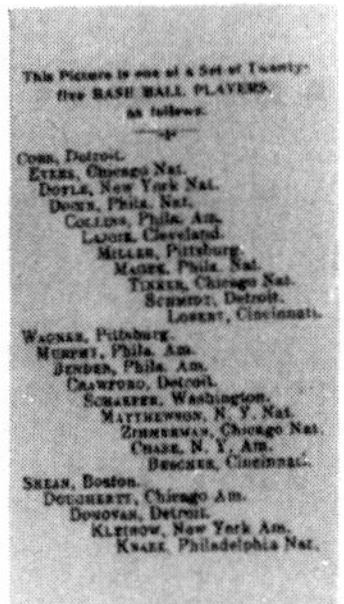

One of many similar early candy card sets, this set - designated as E102 in the American Card Catalog - was distributed around 1908, although the producer of the set is unknown. Measuring approximately 1-1/2" by 2-3/4", the set is almost identical in design to the E101 set and other closely related issues. The set consists of 25 players, which are checklisted on the back of the card. Four of the players have been found in two variations, resulting in 29 different cards. Because there is no advertising on the cards, the set can best be identified by the words - "This Picture is one of a Set of Twenty-five Base Ball Players, as follows" - which appears at the top of the back of each card.

		NR MT	EX	VG
Complete Set (29):		16500.	8250.	3950.
Common Player:		200.00	100.00	48.00
(1)	Chief Bender	600.00	300.00	144.00
(2)	Bob Bescher	200.00	100.00	48.00
(3)	Hal Chase	350.00	175.00	84.00
(4)	Ty Cobb	5500.	2750.	1320.
(5)	Eddie Collins	600.00	300.00	144.00
(6)	Sam Crawford	600.00	300.00	144.00
(7)	Wild Bill Donovan	200.00	100.00	48.00
(8)	Red Dooin	200.00	100.00	48.00
(9)	Patsy Dougherty	200.00	100.00	48.00
(10)	Larry Doyle (batting)	200.00	100.00	48.00
(11)	Larry Doyle (throwing)	200.00	100.00	48.00
(12)	Johnny Evers	600.00	300.00	144.00
(13)	Red Kleinow	200.00	100.00	48.00
(14)	Otto Knabe	200.00	100.00	48.00
(15)	Nap Lajoie	800.00	400.00	190.00
(16)	Hans Lobert	200.00	100.00	48.00
(17)	Sherry Magee	200.00	100.00	48.00
(18)	Christy Matthewson (Mathewson)			
		1500.	750.00	360.00
(19)	Dots Miller (batting)	200.00	100.00	48.00
(20)	Dots Miller (fielding)	1650.	825.00	395.00
(21)	Danny Murphy	200.00	100.00	48.00
(22)	Germany Schaefer	200.00	100.00	48.00
(23)	Boss Schmidt	200.00	100.00	48.00
(24)	Dave Shean	200.00	100.00	48.00
(25)	Boss Smith (Schmidt)	200.00	100.00	48.00
(26)	Joe Tinker	600.00	300.00	144.00
(27)	Honus Wagner (batting)	1500.	750.00	360.00
(28)	Honus Wagner (fielding)	1500.	750.00	360.00
(29)	Heinie Zimmerman	200.00	100.00	48.00

A player's name in italic type indicates a rookie card. An (FC) indicates a player's first card for that particular card company.

1966 East Hills Pirates

Stores in the East Hills Shopping Center, a large mall located in suburban Pittsburgh, distributed cards from this 25-card full-color set in 1966. The cards, which measure 3-1/4" by 4-1/4", are blank-backed and are numbered by the players' uniform numbers. The numbers appear in the lower right corners of the cards.

		NR MT	EX	VG
Complete Set (25):		160.00	80.00	48.00
Common Player:		5.00	2.50	1.50
3	Harry Walker	5.00	2.50	1.50
7	Bob Bailey	5.00	2.50	1.50
8	Willie Stargell	20.00	10.00	6.00
9	Bill Mazeroski	20.00	10.00	6.00
10	Jim Pagliaroni	5.00	2.50	1.50
11	Jose Pagan	5.00	2.50	1.50
12	Jerry May	5.00	2.50	1.50
14	Gene Alley	5.00	2.50	1.50
15	Manny Mota	7.00	3.50	2.00
16	Andy Rodgers	5.00	2.50	1.50
17	Donn Clendenon	5.00	2.50	1.50
18	Matty Alou	5.00	2.50	1.50
19	Pete Mikkelsen	5.00	2.50	1.50
20	Jesse Gonder	5.00	2.50	1.50
21	Roberto Clemente	50.00	25.00	15.00
22	Woody Fryman	5.00	2.50	1.50
24	Jerry Lynch	5.00	2.50	1.50
25	Tommie Sisk	5.00	2.50	1.50
26	Roy Face	8.00	4.00	2.50
28	Steve Blass	5.00	2.50	1.50
32	Vernon Law	8.00	4.00	2.50
34	Al McBean	5.00	2.50	1.50
39	Bob Veale	5.00	2.50	1.50
43	Don Cardwell	5.00	2.50	1.50
45	Gene Michael	7.00	3.50	2.00

Values for recent cards and sets are listed in Mint (MT), Near Mint (NM), reflecting the fact that many cards from recent years have been preserved in top condition. Recent cards and sets in less than Excellent condition have little collector interest.

1992 Eclipse Negro League

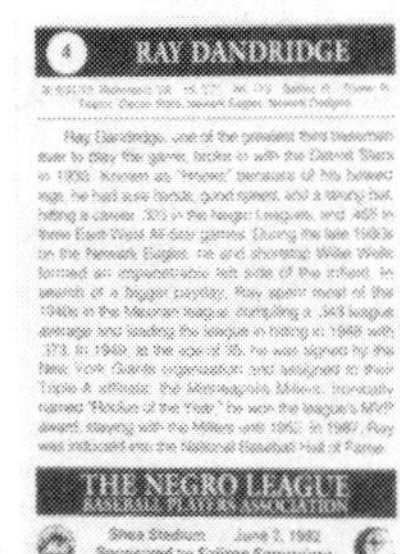

Four Negro League Baseball cards were handed out to the first 50,000 fans attending Negro League Baseball Players Association night on June 2. Cards feature the artwork of Paul Lee on front. Backs have a career summary and biographical details, along with the Mets and Eclipse logos.

		MT	NR MT	EX
Complete Set (4):		5.00	3.75	2.00
Common Player:		1.00	.70	.40
1	Monte Irvin	1.50	1.25	.60
2	"Buck" Leonard	1.00	.70	.40
3	Josh Gibson	2.00	1.50	.80
4	Ray Dandridge	1.00	.70	.40

The values quoted are intended to reflect the market price.

1990 Elite Senior League

This 126-card set features the players of the first Senior League season. Cards are printed on high quality stock and feature full-color photos. The card backs feature statistics. Earl Weaver and Mike Easler cards were distributed as promo cards.

		MT	NR MT	EX
Complete Set:		6.00	4.50	2.50
Common Player:		.04	.03	.02
1	Curt Flood	.08	.06	.03
2	Bob Tolan	.04	.03	.02
3	Dick Bosman	.04	.03	.02
4	Ivan DeJesus	.04	.03	.02
5	Dock Ellis	.04	.03	.02
6	Roy Howell	.04	.03	.02
7	Lamar Johnson	.04	.03	.02
8	Steve Kemp	.04	.03	.02
9	Ken Landreaux	.04	.03	.02
10	Randy Lerch	.04	.03	.02
11	Jon Matlack	.04	.03	.02
12	Gary Rajsich	.04	.03	.02
13	Lenny Randle	.04	.03	.02
14	Elias Sosa	.04	.03	.02
15	Ozzie Virgil	.04	.03	.02
16	Milt Wilcox	.04	.03	.02
17	Steve Henderson	.04	.03	.02
18	Ray Burris	.04	.03	.02
19	Mike Easler	.04	.03	.02
20	Juan Eichelberger	.04	.03	.02
21	Rollie Fingers	.50	.40	.20
22	Toby Harrah	.06	.05	.02
23	Randy Johnson	.04	.03	.02
24	Dave Kingman	.08	.06	.03
25	Lee Lacy	.04	.03	.02
26	Tito Landrum	.04	.03	.02
27	Paul Mirabella	.04	.03	.02
28	Mickey Rivers	.08	.06	.03
29	Rodney Scott	.04	.03	.02
30	Tim Stoddard	.04	.03	.02
31	Ron Washington	.04	.03	.02
32	Jerry White	.04	.03	.02
33	Dick Williams	.08	.06	.03
34	Clete Boyer	.08	.06	.03
35	Steve Dillard	.04	.03	.02
36	Garth Iorg	.04	.03	.02
37	Bruce Kison	.04	.03	.02
38	Wayne Krenchicki	.04	.03	.02
39	Ron LeFlore	.08	.06	.03
40	Tippy Martinez	.04	.03	.02
41	Omar Moreno	.04	.03	.02
42	Jim Morrison	.04	.03	.02
43	Graig Nettles	.10	.08	.04
44	Jim Nettles	.04	.03	.02
45	Wayne Nordhagen	.04	.03	.02
46	Al Oliver	.08	.06	.03
47	Jerry Royster	.04	.03	.02
48	Sammy Stewart	.04	.03	.02
49	Randy Bass	.04	.03	.02
50	Vida Blue	.08	.06	.03
51	Bruce Bochy	.04	.03	.02
52	Doug Corbett	.04	.03	.02
53	Jose Cruz	.04	.03	.02
54	Jamie Easterly	.04	.03	.02
55	Pete Falcone	.04	.03	.02
56	Bob Galasso	.04	.03	.02
57	Johnny Grubb	.04	.03	.02
58	Bake McBride	.04	.03	.02
59	Dyar Miller	.04	.03	.02
60	Tom Paciorek	.04	.03	.02
61	Ken Reitz	.04	.03	.02
62	U.L. Washington	.04	.03	.02
63	Alan Ashby	.04	.03	.02
64	Pat Dobson	.04	.03	.02
65	Doug Bird	.04	.03	.02
66	Marty Castillo	.04	.03	.02
67	Dan Driessen	.04	.03	.02
68	Wayne Garland	.04	.03	.02
69	Tim Ireland	.04	.03	.02
70	Ron Jackson	.04	.03	.02
71	Bobby Jones	.04	.03	.02
72	Dennis Leonard	.04	.03	.02
73	Rick Manning	.04	.03	.02
74	Amos Otis	.04	.03	.02
75	Pat Putnam	.04	.03	.02
76	Eric Rasmussen	.04	.03	.02
77	Paul Blair	.04	.03	.02
78	Bert Campaneris	.04	.03	.02
79	Cesar Cedeno	.08	.06	.03
80	Ed Figueroa	.04	.03	.02
81	Ross Grimsley	.04	.03	.02
82	George Hendrick	.04	.03	.02
83	Cliff Johnson	.04	.03	.02
84	Mike Kekich	.04	.03	.02
85	Rafael Landestoy	.04	.03	.02
86	Larry Milbourne	.04	.03	.02
87	Bobby Molinaro	.04	.03	.02
88	Sid Monge	.04	.03	.02
89	Rennie Stennett	.04	.03	.02
90	Derrell Thomas	.04	.03	.02
91	Earl Weaver	.15	.11	.06
92	Gary Allenson	.04	.03	.02
93	Pedro Borbon	.04	.03	.02
94	Al Bumbry	.08	.06	.03
95	Bill Campbell	.04	.03	.02
96	Bernie Carbo	.04	.03	.02
97	Ferguson Jenkins	.50	.40	.20
98	Pete LaCock	.04	.03	.02
99	Bill Lee	.06	.05	.02
100	Tommy McMillan	.04	.03	.02
101	Joe Pittman	.04	.03	.02
102	Gene Richards	.04	.03	.02
103	Leon Roberts	.04	.03	.02
104	Tony Scott	.04	.03	.02
105	Doug Simunic	.04	.03	.02
106	Rick Wise	.04	.03	.02
107	Willie Aikens	.04	.03	.02
108	Juan Beniquez	.04	.03	.02
109	Bobby Bonds	.10	.08	.04
110	Sergio Ferrer	.04	.03	.02
111	Chuck Ficks	.04	.03	.02
112	George Foster	.10	.08	.04
113	Dave Hilton	.04	.03	.02
114	Al Holland	.04	.03	.02
115	Clint Hurdle	.04	.03	.02
116	Bill Madlock	.10	.08	.04
117	Steve Ontiveros	.04	.03	.02
118	Roy Thomas	.04	.03	.02
119	Luis Tiant	.10	.08	.04
120	Walt Williams	.04	.03	.02
121	Vida Blue	.08	.06	.03
122	Bobby Bonds	.10	.08	.04
123	Rollie Fingers	.50	.40	.20
124	George Foster	.08	.06	.03
125	Fergie Jenkins	.50	.40	.20
126	Dave Kingman	.08	.06	.03

Definitions for grading conditions are located in the Introduction of this price guide.

1954 Esskay Hot Dogs Orioles

Measuring 2-1/4" by 3-1/2", the 1954 Esskay Hot Dogs set features the Baltimore Orioles. The unnumbered color cards were issued in panels of two on packages of hot dogs and are usually found with grease stains. The cards have waxed fronts with blank backs on a white stock. Complete boxes of Esskay Hot Dogs are scarce and command a price of 2-3 times greater than the single card values.

		NR MT	EX	VG
Complete Set (34):		4000.	2000.	1200.
Common Player:		125.00	62.00	37.00
(1)	Neil Berry	125.00	62.00	37.00
(2)	Michael Blyzka	125.00	62.00	37.00
(3)	Harry Brecheen	125.00	62.00	37.00
(4)	Gil Coan	125.00	62.00	37.00
(5)	Joe Coleman	125.00	62.00	37.00
(6)	Clinton Courtney	125.00	62.00	37.00
(7)	Charles E. Diering	125.00	62.00	37.00
(8)	Jimmie Dykes	140.00	70.00	42.00
(9)	Frank J. Fanovich	125.00	62.00	37.00
(10)	Howard Fox	125.00	62.00	37.00
(11)	Jim Fridley	125.00	62.00	37.00
(12)	Vinicio "Chico" Garcia	125.00	62.00	37.00
(13)	Jehosie Heard	400.00	200.00	120.00
(14)	Darrell Johnson	125.00	62.00	37.00
(15)	Bob Kennedy	125.00	62.00	37.00
(16)	Dick Kokos	125.00	62.00	37.00
(17)	Dave Koslo	125.00	62.00	37.00
(18)	Lou Kretlow	125.00	62.00	37.00
(19)	Richard D. Kryhoski	125.00	62.00	37.00
(20)	Don Larsen	140.00	70.00	42.00
(21)	Donald E. Lenhardt	125.00	62.00	37.00
(22)	Richard Littlefield	125.00	62.00	37.00
(23)	Sam Mele	125.00	62.00	37.00
(24)	Les Moss	125.00	62.00	37.00
(25)	Ray L. Murray	125.00	62.00	37.00
(26a)	"Bobo" Newsom (no stadium lights in background)	175.00	87.00	52.00
(26b)	"Bobo" Newson (stadium lights in background)	175.00	87.00	52.00
(27)	Tom Oliver	125.00	62.00	37.00
(28)	Duane Pillette	125.00	62.00	37.00
(29)	Francis M. Skaff	125.00	62.00	37.00
(30)	Marlin Stuart	125.00	62.00	37.00
(31)	Robert L. Turley	200.00	100.00	60.00
(32)	Eddie Waitkus	125.00	62.00	37.00
(33)	Vic Wertz	125.00	62.00	37.00
(34)	Robert G. Young	125.00	62.00	37.00

1955 Esskay Hot Dogs Orioles

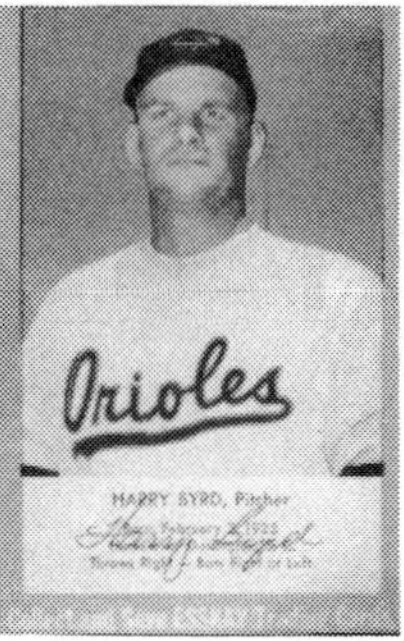

For the second consecutive year, Esskay Meats placed baseball cards of Orioles players on their boxes of hot dogs. The unnumbered, color cards measure 2-1/4" by 3-1/2" and can be distinguished from the previous year by their unwaxed fronts and gray backs. Many of the same photos from 1954 were used with only minor picture-cropping differences. For 1955, only one player card per box was printed. The space which was occupied by the second player card in 1954 carried a prize redemption coupon on 1955 boxes.

		NR MT	EX	VG
Complete Set (26):		2650.	1300.	790.00
Common Player:		125.00	62.00	37.00
(1)	Cal Abrams	125.00	62.00	37.00
(2)	Robert S. Alexander	125.00	62.00	37.00
(3)	Harry Byrd	125.00	62.00	37.00
(4)	Gil Coan	125.00	62.00	37.00
(5)	Joseph P. Coleman	125.00	62.00	37.00
(6)	William R. Cox	125.00	62.00	37.00
(7)	Charles E. Diering	125.00	62.00	37.00
(8)	Walter A. Evers	125.00	62.00	37.00
(9)	Don Johnson	125.00	62.00	37.00
(10)	Robert D. Kennedy	125.00	62.00	37.00
(11)	Lou Kretlow	125.00	62.00	37.00
(12)	Robert L. Kuzava	125.00	62.00	37.00
(13)	Fred Marsh	125.00	62.00	37.00
(14)	Charles Maxwell	125.00	62.00	37.00
(15)	Jimmie McDonald	125.00	62.00	37.00
(16)	Bill Miller	125.00	62.00	37.00
(17)	Willy Miranda	125.00	62.00	37.00
(18)	Raymond L. Moore	125.00	62.00	37.00
(19)	John Lester Moss	125.00	62.00	37.00
(20)	"Bobo" Newsom	140.00	70.00	42.00
(21)	Duane Pillette	125.00	62.00	37.00
(22)	Edward S. Waitkus	125.00	62.00	37.00
(23)	Harold W. Smith	125.00	62.00	37.00
(24)	Gus Triandos	125.00	62.00	37.00
(25)	Eugene R. Woodling	150.00	75.00	45.00
(26)	Robert G. Young	125.00	62.00	37.00

Values quoted in this guide reflect the retail price of a card – the price a collector can expect to pay when buying a card from a dealer. The wholesale price – that which a collector can expect to receive from a dealer when selling cards – will be significantly lower, depending on desirability and condition.

1949 Eureka Sportstamps

The commissioner of baseball, president of the National League and 198 N.L. players are included in this issue. The stamps were issued on team sheets measuring 7-1/2" x 10", with individual stamps measuring 1-1/2" x 2". An album issued with the set provided short player biographies. The stamps feature colorized posed player action photos. At bottom is a yellow strip with the player's name, stamp number and copyright line. Stamps are numbered alphabetically within teams.

		NR MT	EX	VG
Complete Set (200):		900.00	450.00	270.00
Common Player:		5.00	2.50	1.50
1	Albert B. (Happy) Chandler	7.50	3.75	2.25
2	Ford Frick	6.00	3.00	1.75
3	Billy Southworth	5.00	2.50	1.50
4	Johnny Antonelli	5.00	2.50	1.50
5	Red Barrett	5.00	2.50	1.50
6	Clint Conaster	5.00	2.50	1.50
7	Alvin Dark	5.00	2.50	1.50
8	Bob Elliott	5.00	2.50	1.50
9	Glenn Elliott	5.00	2.50	1.50
10	Elbie Fletcher	5.00	2.50	1.50
11	Bob Hall	5.00	2.50	1.50
12	Jeff Heath	5.00	2.50	1.50
13	Bobby Hogue	5.00	2.50	1.50
14	Tommy Holmes	5.00	2.50	1.50
15	Al Lakeman	5.00	2.50	1.50
16	Phil Masi	5.00	2.50	1.50
17	Nelson Potter	5.00	2.50	1.50
18	Pete Reiser	8.00	4.00	2.50
19	Rick Rickert	5.00	2.50	1.50
20	Connie Ryan	5.00	2.50	1.50
21	Jim Russell	5.00	2.50	1.50
22	Johnny Sain	9.00	4.50	2.75
23	Bill Salkeld	5.00	2.50	1.50
24	Sibby Sisti	5.00	2.50	1.50
25	Warren Spahn	25.00	12.50	7.50
26	Eddie Stanky	5.00	2.50	1.50
27	Bill Voiselle	5.00	2.50	1.50
28	Bert Shotton	9.00	4.50	2.75
29	Jack Banta	9.00	4.50	2.75
30	Rex Barney	9.00	4.50	2.75
31	Ralph Branca	12.00	6.00	3.50
32	Tommy Brown	9.00	4.50	2.75
33	Roy Campanella	35.00	17.50	10.50
34	Billy Cox	9.00	4.50	2.75
35	Bruce Edwards	9.00	4.50	2.75
36	Carl Furillo	15.00	7.50	4.50
37	Joe Hatten	9.00	4.50	2.75
38	Gene Hermanski	9.00	4.50	2.75
39	Gil Hodges	20.00	10.00	6.00
40	Johnny Jorgensen	9.00	4.50	2.75
41	Lefty Martin	9.00	4.50	2.75
42	Mike McCormick	9.00	4.50	2.75
43	Eddie Miksis	9.00	4.50	2.75
44	Paul Minner	9.00	4.50	2.75
45	Sam Narron	9.00	4.50	2.75
46	Don Newcombe	15.00	7.50	4.50
47	Jake Pitler	9.00	4.50	2.75
48	Pee Wee Reese	30.00	15.00	9.00
49	Jackie Robinson	50.00	25.00	15.00
50	Duke Snider	35.00	17.50	10.50
51	Dick Whitman	9.00	4.50	2.75
52	Forrest Burgess	5.00	2.50	1.50
53	Phil Cavaretta	5.00	2.50	1.50
54	Bob Chipman	5.00	2.50	1.50
55	Walter Dubiel	5.00	2.50	1.50
56	Hank Edwards	5.00	2.50	1.50
57	Frankie Gustine	5.00	2.50	1.50
58	Hal Jeffcoat	5.00	2.50	1.50
59	Emil Kush	5.00	2.50	1.50
60	Doyle Lade	5.00	2.50	1.50
61	Dutch Leonard	5.00	2.50	1.50
62	Peanuts Lowrey	5.00	2.50	1.50
63	Gene Mauch	7.50	3.75	2.25
64	Cal McLish	5.00	2.50	1.50
65	Rube Novotney	5.00	2.50	1.50
66	Andy Pafko	5.00	2.50	1.50
67	Bob Ramozzotti	5.00	2.50	1.50
68	Herman Reich	5.00	2.50	1.50
69	Bob Rush	5.00	2.50	1.50
70	Johnny Schmitz	5.00	2.50	1.50
71	Bob Scheffing	5.00	2.50	1.50
72	Roy Smalley	5.00	2.50	1.50
73	Emil Verban	5.00	2.50	1.50
74	Al Walker	5.00	2.50	1.50
75	Harry Walker	5.00	2.50	1.50
76	Bucky Walters	5.00	2.50	1.50
77	Bob Adams	5.00	2.50	1.50
78	Ewell Blackwell	5.00	2.50	1.50
79	Jimmy Bloodworth	5.00	2.50	1.50
80	Walker Cooper	5.00	2.50	1.50
81	Tony Cuccinello	5.00	2.50	1.50
82	Jess Dobernick	5.00	2.50	1.50
83	Eddie Erautt	5.00	2.50	1.50
84	Frank Fanovich	5.00	2.50	1.50
85	Howie Fox	5.00	2.50	1.50
86	Grady Hatton	5.00	2.50	1.50
87	Homer Howell	5.00	2.50	1.50
88	Ted Kluszewski	15.00	7.50	4.50
89	Danny Litwhiler	5.00	2.50	1.50
90	Everett Lively	5.00	2.50	1.50
91	Lloyd Merriman	5.00	2.50	1.50
92	Phil Page	5.00	2.50	1.50
93	Kent Peterson	5.00	2.50	1.50
94	Ken Raffensberger	5.00	2.50	1.50
95	Luke Sewell	5.00	2.50	1.50
96	Virgil Stallcup	5.00	2.50	1.50
97	Johnny Vander Meer	9.00	4.50	2.75
98	Herman Wehmeier	5.00	2.50	1.50
99	Johnny Wyrostek	5.00	2.50	1.50
100	Benny Zientara	5.00	2.50	1.50
101	Leo Durocher	12.00	6.00	3.50
102	Hank Behrman	5.00	2.50	1.50
103	Augie Galan	5.00	2.50	1.50
104	Sid Gordon	5.00	2.50	1.50
105	Bert Haas	5.00	2.50	1.50
106	Andy Hansen	5.00	2.50	1.50
107	Clint Hartung	5.00	2.50	1.50
108	Kirby Higbe	5.00	2.50	1.50
109	George Hausman	5.00	2.50	1.50
110	Larry Jansen	5.00	2.50	1.50
111	Sheldon Jones	5.00	2.50	1.50
112	Monte Kennedy	5.00	2.50	1.50
113	Buddy Kerr	5.00	2.50	1.50
114	Dave Koslo	5.00	2.50	1.50
115	Joe Lafata	5.00	2.50	1.50
116	Whitey Lockman	5.00	2.50	1.50
117	Jack Lohrke	5.00	2.50	1.50
118	Willard Marshall	5.00	2.50	1.50
119	Bill Milne	5.00	2.50	1.50
120	Johnny Mize	12.00	6.00	3.50
121	Don Mueller	5.00	2.50	1.50
122	Ray Mueller	5.00	2.50	1.50
123	Bill Rigney	5.00	2.50	1.50
124	Bobby Thomson	7.50	3.75	2.25
125	Sam Webb	5.00	2.50	1.50
126	Wesley Westrum	5.00	2.50	1.50
127	Eddie Sawyer	5.00	2.50	1.50
128	Richie Ashburn	12.00	6.00	3.50
129	Benny Bengough	5.00	2.50	1.50
130	Charlie Bicknell	5.00	2.50	1.50
131	Buddy Blattner	5.00	2.50	1.50
132	Hank Borowy	5.00	2.50	1.50
133	Ralph Caballero	5.00	2.50	1.50
134	Blix Donnelly	5.00	2.50	1.50
135	Del Ennis	5.00	2.50	1.50
136	Granville Hamner	5.00	2.50	1.50
137	Ken Heintzelman	5.00	2.50	1.50
138	Stan Hollmig	5.00	2.50	1.50
139	Willie Jones	5.00	2.50	1.50
140	Jim Konstanty	5.00	2.50	1.50
141	Stan Lopata	5.00	2.50	1.50
142	Jackie Mayo	5.00	2.50	1.50
143	Bill Nicholson	5.00	2.50	1.50
144	Robin Roberts	20.00	10.00	6.00
145	Schoolboy Rowe	5.00	2.50	1.50
146	Andy Seminick	5.00	2.50	1.50
147	Ken Silvestri	5.00	2.50	1.50
148	Curt Simmons	5.00	2.50	1.50
149	Dick Sisler	5.00	2.50	1.50
150	Ken Trinkle	5.00	2.50	1.50
151	Eddie Waitkus	5.00	2.50	1.50
152	Bill Meyer	5.00	2.50	1.50
153	Monte Basgall	5.00	2.50	1.50
154	Eddie Bockman	5.00	2.50	1.50
155	Ernie Bonham	5.00	2.50	1.50
156	Hugh Casey	5.00	2.50	1.50
157	Pete Castiglione	5.00	2.50	1.50
158	Cliff Chambers	5.00	2.50	1.50
159	Murry Dickson	5.00	2.50	1.50
160	Ed Fitz Gerald	5.00	2.50	1.50
161	Les Fleming	5.00	2.50	1.50
162	Hal Gregg	5.00	2.50	1.50
163	Goldie Holt	5.00	2.50	1.50
164	Johnny Hopp	5.00	2.50	1.50
165	Ralph Kiner	20.00	10.00	6.00
166	Vic Lombardi	5.00	2.50	1.50
167	Clyde McCullough	5.00	2.50	1.50
168	Danny Murtaugh	5.00	2.50	1.50
169	Bill Posedel	5.00	2.50	1.50
170	Elmer Riddle	5.00	2.50	1.50
171	Stan Rojek	5.00	2.50	1.50
172	Rip Sewell	5.00	2.50	1.50
173	Eddie Stevens	5.00	2.50	1.50
174	Dixie Walker	5.00	2.50	1.50
175	Bill Werle	5.00	2.50	1.50
176	Wally Westlake	5.00	2.50	1.50
177	Eddie Dyer	5.00	2.50	1.50
178	Bill Baker	5.00	2.50	1.50
179	Al Brazle	5.00	2.50	1.50
180	Harry Brecheen	5.00	2.50	1.50
181	Chuck Diering	5.00	2.50	1.50
182	Joe Garagiola	12.00	6.00	3.50
183	Tom Galviano	5.00	2.50	1.50
184	Jim Hearn	5.00	2.50	1.50
185	Ken Johnson	5.00	2.50	1.50
186	Nippy Jones	5.00	2.50	1.50
187	Ed Kazak	5.00	2.50	1.50
188	Lou Klein	5.00	2.50	1.50
189	Marty Marion	5.00	2.50	1.50
190	George Munger	5.00	2.50	1.50
191	Stan Musial	35.00	17.50	10.50
192	Spike Nelson	5.00	2.50	1.50
193	Howie Pollet	5.00	2.50	1.50
194	Bill Reeder	5.00	2.50	1.50
195	Del Rice	5.00	2.50	1.50
196	Ed Sauer	5.00	2.50	1.50
197	Red Schoendienst	20.00	10.00	6.00
198	Enos Slaughter	20.00	10.00	6.00
199	Ted Wilks	5.00	2.50	1.50
200	Ray Yochim	5.00	2.50	1.50

1921 Exhibits

The Exhibit Supply Company of Chicago issued the first in a long series of postcard-size baseball cards in 1921. The Exhibit cards commonly sold in "penny arcade" vending machines. The 1921 series consists of 64 cards and includes four players from each of the 16 major league teams. The cards feature black and white photos with the player's name printed in a fancy script. The player's position and team appear below the name in small, hand-lettered capital letters. American League is designated as "A.M.L.," which can help differentiate the 1921 series from future years. Some of the cards contain white borders while others do not. All have blank backs. There are various spelling errors in the picture legends.

		NR MT	EX	VG
Complete Set (64):		4000.	2000.	1200.
Common Player:		35.00	17.50	10.50
(1)	Chas. B. Adams	35.00	17.50	10.50
(2)	Grover C. Alexander	35.00	17.50	10.50
(3)	David Bancroft	90.00	45.00	27.00
(4)	Geo. J. Burns	35.00	17.50	10.50
(5)	Owen Bush	35.00	17.50	10.50
(6)	Max J. Carey	90.00	45.00	27.00
(7)	Ty Cobb	500.00	250.00	150.00
(8)	Eddie T. Collins	90.00	45.00	27.00
(9)	John Collins	35.00	17.50	10.50
(10)	Stanley Coveleskie (Coveleski)	90.00	45.00	27.00
(11)	Walton E. Cruse (Cruise)	35.00	17.50	10.50
(12)	Jacob E. Daubert	40.00	20.00	12.00
(13)	George Dauss	35.00	17.50	10.50
(14)	Charles A. Deal	35.00	17.50	10.50
(15)	Joe A. Dugan	45.00	22.00	13.50
(16)	James Dykes	40.00	20.00	12.00
(17)	U.C. "Red" Faber	90.00	45.00	27.00
(18)	J.F. Fournier	35.00	17.50	10.50
(19)	Frank F. Frisch	90.00	45.00	27.00
(20)	W.L. Gardner	35.00	17.50	10.50
(21)	H.M. "Hank" Gowdy	35.00	17.50	10.50
(22)	Burleigh Grimes	90.00	45.00	27.00
(23)	Heinie Groh	35.00	17.50	10.50
(24)	Jesse Haines	90.00	45.00	27.00
(25)	Sam Harris (Stanley)	90.00	45.00	27.00
(26)	Walter L. Holke	35.00	17.50	10.50
(27)	Charles J. Hollicher (Hollocher)	35.00	17.50	10.50
(28)	Rogers Hornsby	140.00	70.00	42.00
(29)	James H. Johnson (Johnston)	35.00	17.50	10.50
(30)	Walter P. Johnson	300.00	150.00	90.00
(31)	Sam P. Jones	35.00	17.50	10.50
(32)	Geo. L. Kelly	90.00	45.00	27.00
(33)	Dick Kerr	35.00	17.50	10.50
(34)	William L. Killifer	35.00	17.50	10.50
(35)	Ed Konetchy	35.00	17.50	10.50
(36)	John "Doc" Lavan	35.00	17.50	10.50
(37)	Walter J. Maranville	90.00	45.00	27.00
(38)	Carl W. Mays	40.00	20.00	12.00
(39)	J. "Stuffy" McInnis	35.00	17.50	10.50
(40)	Rollie C. Naylor	35.00	17.50	10.50
(41)	A. Earl Neale (Earle)	45.00	22.00	13.50
(42)	Ivan M. Olsen	35.00	17.50	10.50
(43)	S.F. "Steve" O'Neil (O'Neill)	35.00	17.50	10.50
(44)	Robert (Roger) Peckinpaugh	40.00	20.00	12.00
(45)	Ralph "Cy" Perkins	35.00	17.50	10.50
(46)	Raymond R. Powell	35.00	17.50	10.50
(47)	Joe "Goldie" Rapp	35.00	17.50	10.50
(48)	Edgar S. Rice	90.00	45.00	27.00
(49)	Jimmy Ring	35.00	17.50	10.50
(50)	Geo. H. "Babe" Ruth	950.00	475.00	285.00
(51)	Ray W. Schalk	90.00	45.00	27.00
(52)	Wallie Schang	35.00	17.50	10.50
(53)	Everett Scott	35.00	17.50	10.50
(54)	H.S. Shanks (photo actually Wally Schang)	35.00	17.50	10.50
(55)	Urban Shocker	35.00	17.50	10.50
(56)	Geo. J. Sisler	90.00	45.00	27.00
(57)	Tris Speaker	300.00	150.00	90.00

		NR MT	EX	VG
(58)	John Tobin	35.00	17.50	10.50
(59)	Robt. Veach	35.00	17.50	10.50
(60)	Zack D. Wheat	90.00	45.00	27.00
(61)	Geo. B. Whitted	35.00	17.50	10.50
(62)	Cy Williams	40.00	20.00	12.00
(63)	Kenneth R. Williams	40.00	20.00	12.00
(64)	Ivy B. Wingo	35.00	17.50	10.50

1922 Exhibits

The Exhibit Supply Company continued the same format in 1922 but doubled the number of cards in the series to 128, including eight players from each team. All but nine of the players who appeared in the 1921 series are pictured in the 1922 set, along with 74 new players. The cards again display black and white photos with blank backs. Some of the photos have white borders. The player's name appears in a plain script with the postition and team below in small capital letters. American League is designated as "A.L." Again, there are several spelling errors and incorrect player identifications. In early printings the Earl Smith card actually pictured Brad Kocher. Only the 74 new additions are included in the checklist that follows.

		NR MT	EX	VG
Complete Set (74):		2800.	1400.	840.00
Common Player:		45.00	22.00	13.50
(1)	J. Frank Baker	80.00	40.00	24.00
(2)	Jim Bagby	45.00	22.00	13.50
(3)	Walter Barbare	45.00	22.00	13.50
(4)	Turner Barber	45.00	22.00	13.50
(5)	John Bassler	45.00	22.00	13.50
(6)	Carlson L. Bigbee (Carson)	45.00	22.00	13.50
(7)	Sam Bohne	45.00	22.00	13.50
(8)	Geo. Burns	45.00	22.00	13.50
(9)	George Burns	45.00	22.00	13.50
(10)	Jeo Bush (Joe)	50.00	25.00	15.00
(11)	Leon Cadore	45.00	22.00	13.50
(12)	Jim Caveney	45.00	22.00	13.50
(13)	Wilbur Cooper	45.00	22.00	13.50
(14)	Dave Danforth	45.00	22.00	13.50
(15)	George Cutshaw	45.00	22.00	13.50
(16)	Bill Doak	45.00	22.00	13.50
(17)	Joe Dugan	55.00	27.00	16.50
(18)	Pat Duncan	45.00	22.00	13.50
(19)	Howard Emke (Ehmke)	45.00	22.00	13.50
(20)	Wm. Evans (umpire)	80.00	40.00	24.00
(21)	Bib Falk (Bibb)	45.00	22.00	13.50
(22)	Dana Fillingin (Fillingim)	45.00	22.00	13.50
(23)	Ira Flagstead	45.00	22.00	13.50
(24)	Art Fletcher	45.00	22.00	13.50
(25)	Wally Gerber	45.00	22.00	13.50
(26)	Ray Grimes	45.00	22.00	13.50
(27)	George Hildebrand (umpire)	45.00	22.00	13.50
(28)	Harry Heilman (Heilmann)	80.00	40.00	24.00
(29)	Wibur Hubbell (Wilbert)	45.00	22.00	13.50
(30)	Bill Jacobson	45.00	22.00	13.50
(31)	E.R. Johnson	45.00	22.00	13.50
(32)	Joe Judge	45.00	22.00	13.50
(33)	Bill Klem (umpire)	80.00	40.00	24.00
(34)	Harry Liebold (Leibold)	45.00	22.00	13.50
(35)	Walter Mails	45.00	22.00	13.50
(36)	Geo. Maisel	45.00	22.00	13.50
(37)	Lee Meadows	45.00	22.00	13.50
(38)	Clyde Milam (Milan)	45.00	22.00	13.50
(39)	Ed (Bing) Miller	45.00	22.00	13.50
(40)	Hack Miller	45.00	22.00	13.50
(41)	George Moriarty (umpire)	45.00	22.00	13.50
(42)	Robert Muesel (Meusel)	55.00	27.00	16.50
(43)	Harry Myers	45.00	22.00	13.50
(44)	Arthur Nehf	45.00	22.00	13.50
(45)	Joe Oeschger	45.00	22.00	13.50
(46)	Geo. O'Neil	45.00	22.00	13.50
(47)	Roger Peckinpaugh	50.00	25.00	15.00
(48)	Val Picinich	45.00	22.00	13.50
(49)	Bill Piercy	45.00	22.00	13.50
(50)	Derrill Pratt	45.00	22.00	13.50
(51)	Jack Quinn	45.00	22.00	13.50
(52)	Walter Reuther (Ruether)	45.00	22.00	13.50
(53)	Charles Rigler (umpire)	45.00	22.00	13.50
(54)	Eppa Rixey	80.00	40.00	24.00
(55)	Chas. Robertson	45.00	22.00	13.50
(56)	Everett Scott	45.00	22.00	13.50
(57)	Earl Sheely	45.00	22.00	13.50
(58)	Earl Smith (portrait)	45.00	22.00	13.50
(59)	Earl Smith (standing) (photo actually Brad Kocher)	45.00	22.00	13.50
(60)	Elmer Smith	45.00	22.00	13.50
(61)	Jack Smith (photo actually Jimmy Smith)	45.00	22.00	13.50
(62)	Sherrod Smith	45.00	22.00	13.50
(63)	Frank Snyder	45.00	22.00	13.50
(64)	Allan Sothoron	45.00	22.00	13.50
(65)	Arnold Statz	45.00	22.00	13.50
(66)	Milton Stock	45.00	22.00	13.50
(67)	James Tierney	45.00	22.00	13.50
(68)	George Toporcer	45.00	22.00	13.50
(69)	Clarence (Tilly) Walker	45.00	22.00	13.50
(70)	Curtis Walker	45.00	22.00	13.50
(71)	Aaron Ward	45.00	22.00	13.50
(72)	Joe Wood	50.00	25.00	15.00
(73)	Moses Yellowhorse	55.00	27.00	16.50
(74)	Ross Young (Youngs)	80.00	40.00	24.00

1922 Eastern Exhibit Supply Co.

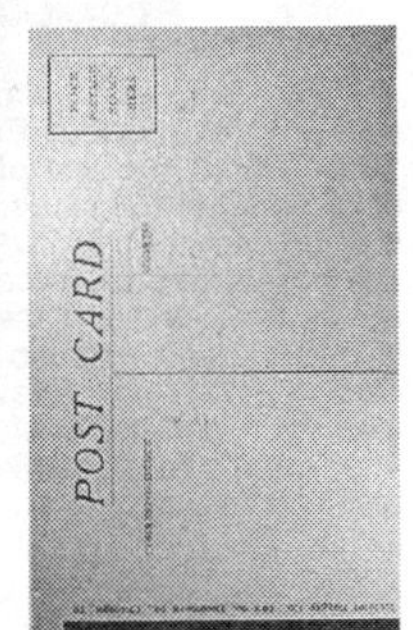

		NR MT	EX	VG
Complete Set (20):		2250.	1125.	675.00
Common Player:		45.00	22.00	13.50
(1)	Grover Alexander	90.00	45.00	27.00
(2)	Dave Bancroft	80.00	40.00	24.00
(3)	Jesse Barnes	45.00	22.00	13.50
(4)	Joe Bush	45.00	22.00	13.50
(5)	Ty Cobb	600.00	300.00	180.00
(6)	Eddie Collins	90.00	45.00	27.00
(7)	Urban Faber	80.00	40.00	24.00
(8)	Clarence Galloway	45.00	22.00	13.50
(9)	Heinie Groh	45.00	22.00	13.50
(10)	Harry Heilmann	80.00	40.00	24.00
(11)	Charlie Hollocher	45.00	22.00	13.50
(12)	Rogers Hornsby	90.00	45.00	27.00
(13)	Walter Johnson	125.00	62.00	37.00
(14)	Eddie Rommel	45.00	22.00	13.50
(15)	Babe Ruth	950.00	475.00	285.00
(16)	Ray Schalk	80.00	40.00	24.00
(17)	Wallie Schang	45.00	22.00	13.50
(18)	Tris Speaker	90.00	45.00	27.00
(19)	Zach Wheat	80.00	40.00	24.00
(20)	Kenneth Williams	45.00	22.00	13.50

1923 - 24 Exhibits

The Exhibit cards for 1923 and 1924 are generally collected as a single 128-card series. The format remained basically the same as the previous year, with black and white photos (some surrounded by a white border) and blank backs. The player's name is again shown in a plain script with the position and team printed below in a small, square-block type style. Many of the same photos were used from previous years, although some are cropped differently, and some players have new team designations, background changes, team emblems removed, borders added or taken away, and other minor changes. Fifty-eight new cards are featured, including 38 players pictured for the first time in an Exhibit set. Only the 58 new cards are included in the checklist that follows.

		NR MT	EX	VG
Complete Set (58):		3200.	1600.	950.00
Common Player:		50.00	25.00	15.00
(1)	Clyde Barnhart	50.00	25.00	15.00
(2)	Ray Blades	50.00	25.00	15.00
(3)	James Bottomley	90.00	45.00	27.00
(4)	George Burns	50.00	25.00	15.00
(5)	Dan Clark	50.00	25.00	15.00
(6)	Bill Doak	50.00	25.00	15.00
(7)	Joe Dugan	50.00	25.00	15.00
(8)	Howard J. Ehmke	50.00	25.00	15.00
(9)	Ira Flagstead	50.00	25.00	15.00
(10)	J.F. Fournier	50.00	25.00	15.00
(11)	Howard Freigan (Freigau)	50.00	25.00	15.00
(12)	C.E. Galloway	50.00	25.00	15.00
(13)	Joe Genewich	50.00	25.00	15.00
(14)	Mike Gonzales	50.00	25.00	15.00
(15)	H.M. "Hank" Gowdy	50.00	25.00	15.00
(16)	Charles Grimm	50.00	25.00	15.00
(17)	Heinie Groh	50.00	25.00	15.00
(18)	Chas. L. Harnett (Hartnett)	90.00	45.00	27.00
(19)	George Harper	50.00	25.00	15.00
(20)	Slim Harris (Harriss)	50.00	25.00	15.00
(21)	Clifton Heathcote	50.00	25.00	15.00
(22)	Andy High	50.00	25.00	15.00
(23)	Walter L. Holke	50.00	25.00	15.00
(24)	Charles D. Jamieson	50.00	25.00	15.00
(25)	Willie Kamm	50.00	25.00	15.00
(26)	Tony Kaufmann	50.00	25.00	15.00
(27)	Dudley Lee	50.00	25.00	15.00
(28)	Harry Liebold (Leibold)	50.00	25.00	15.00
(29)	Aldofo Luque	50.00	25.00	15.00
(30)	W.C. (Wid) Matthews	50.00	25.00	15.00
(31)	John J. McGraw	90.00	45.00	27.00
(32)	J. "Stuffy" McInnis	50.00	25.00	15.00
(33)	Johnny Morrison	50.00	25.00	15.00
(34)	John A. Mostil	50.00	25.00	15.00
(35)	J.F. O'Neill (should be S.F.)	50.00	25.00	15.00
(36)	Ernest Padgett	50.00	25.00	15.00
(37)	Val Picinich	50.00	25.00	15.00
(38)	Bill Piercy	50.00	25.00	15.00
(39)	Herman Pillette	50.00	25.00	15.00
(40)	Wallie Pipp	60.00	30.00	18.00
(41)	Raymond R. Powell	50.00	25.00	15.00
(42)	Del. Pratt	50.00	25.00	15.00
(43)	E.E. Rigney	50.00	25.00	15.00
(44)	Eddie Rommel	50.00	25.00	15.00
(45)	Geo. H. "Babe" Ruth	700.00	350.00	210.00
(46)	Muddy Ruel	50.00	25.00	15.00
(47)	J.H. Sand	50.00	25.00	15.00
(48)	Henry Severeid	50.00	25.00	15.00
(49)	Joseph Sewell	90.00	45.00	27.00
(50)	Al. Simmons	90.00	45.00	27.00
(51)	R.E. Smith	50.00	25.00	15.00
(52)	Sherrod Smith	50.00	25.00	15.00
(53)	Casey Stengel	200.00	100.00	60.00
(54)	J.R. Stevenson (Stephenson)	50.00	25.00	15.00
(55)	James Tierney	50.00	25.00	15.00
(56)	Robt. Veach	50.00	25.00	15.00
(57)	L. Woodall	50.00	25.00	15.00
(58)	Russell G. Wrighstone	50.00	25.00	15.00

1925 Exhibits

The 1925 series of Exhibits contains 128 unnumbered cards, each measuring 3-3/8" by 5-3/8". The player's name (in all capital letters), position and team (along with a line reading "Made in U.S.A.) are printed in a small white box in a lower corner of the card. Most of the photos are vertical, however a few are horizontal. There are several misspellings in the set, and the card of Robert Veach actually pictures Ernest Vache. The cards are listed here in alphabetical order.

		NR MT	EX	VG
Complete Set (128):		8250.	4000.	2400.
Common Player:		50.00	25.00	15.00
(1)	Sparky Adams	50.00	25.00	15.00
(2)	Grover C. Alexander	175.00	85.00	50.00
(3)	David Bancroft	85.00	42.00	25.00
(4)	Jesse Barnes	50.00	25.00	15.00
(5)	John Bassler	50.00	25.00	15.00
(6)	Lester Bell	50.00	25.00	15.00
(7)	Lawrence Benton	50.00	25.00	15.00
(8)	Carson Bigbee	50.00	25.00	15.00
(9)	Max Bishop	50.00	25.00	15.00
(10)	Raymond Blates (Blades)	50.00	25.00	15.00
(11)	Oswald Bluege	50.00	25.00	15.00
(12)	James Bottomly (Bottomley)	85.00	42.00	25.00
(13)	Raymond Bressler	50.00	25.00	15.00
(14)	John Brooks	50.00	25.00	15.00
(15)	Maurice Burrus	50.00	25.00	15.00
(16)	Max Carey	85.00	42.00	25.00
(17)	Tyrus Cobb	800.00	400.00	240.00
(18)	Eddie Collins	85.00	42.00	25.00
(19)	Stanley Coveleski	85.00	42.00	25.00
(20)	Hugh M. Critz	50.00	25.00	15.00
(21)	Hazen Cuyler	85.00	42.00	25.00
(22)	George Dauss	50.00	25.00	15.00
(23)	I.M. Davis	50.00	25.00	15.00
(24)	John H. DeBerry	50.00	25.00	15.00
(25)	Art Decatur	50.00	25.00	15.00
(26)	Peter Donohue	50.00	25.00	15.00
(27)	Charles Dressen	55.00	27.00	16.50
(28)	James J. Dykes	55.00	27.00	16.50
(29)	Howard Ehmke	50.00	25.00	15.00
(30)	Bib Falk (Bibb)	50.00	25.00	15.00
(31)	Wilson Fewster	50.00	25.00	15.00
(32)	Max Flack	50.00	25.00	15.00
(33)	Ira Flagstead	50.00	25.00	15.00
(34)	Jacques F. Fournier	50.00	25.00	15.00

(35)	Howard Freigau	50.00	25.00	15.00
(36)	Frank Frisch	85.00	42.00	25.00
(37)	Henry L. Gehrig	900.00	450.00	270.00
(38)	Joseph Genewich	50.00	25.00	15.00
(39)	Walter Gerber	50.00	25.00	15.00
(40)	Frank Gibson	50.00	25.00	15.00
(41)	Leon Goslin	85.00	42.00	25.00
(42)	George Grantham	50.00	25.00	15.00
(43)	Samuel Gray	50.00	25.00	15.00
(44)	Burleigh A. Grimes	85.00	42.00	25.00
(45)	Charles Grimm	55.00	27.00	16.50
(46)	Heine Groh (Heinie)	50.00	25.00	15.00
(47)	Samuel Hale	50.00	25.00	15.00
(48)	George Harper	50.00	25.00	15.00
(49)	David Harris	50.00	25.00	15.00
(50)	Stanley Harris	85.00	42.00	25.00
(51)	Leo Hartnett	85.00	42.00	25.00
(52)	Nelson Hawks	50.00	25.00	15.00
(53)	Harry Heilmann	85.00	42.00	25.00
(54)	Walter Henline	50.00	25.00	15.00
(55)	Walter Holke	50.00	25.00	15.00
(56)	Harry Hooper	85.00	42.00	25.00
(57)	Rogers Hornsby	175.00	85.00	50.00
(58)	Wilbur Hubbell	50.00	25.00	15.00
(59)	Travis C. Jackson	85.00	42.00	25.00
(60)	William Jacobson	50.00	25.00	15.00
(61)	Charles Jamieson	50.00	25.00	15.00
(62)	James H. Johnson (Johnston)	50.00	25.00	15.00
(63)	Walter Johnson	200.00	100.00	60.00
(64)	Joseph Judge	50.00	25.00	15.00
(65)	Willie Kamm	50.00	25.00	15.00
(66)	Ray Kremer	50.00	25.00	15.00
(67)	Walter Lutzke	50.00	25.00	15.00
(68)	Walter Maranville	85.00	42.00	25.00
(69)	John ("Stuffy") McInnes (McInnis)	50.00	25.00	15.00
(70)	Martin McManus	50.00	25.00	15.00
(71)	Earl McNeely	50.00	25.00	15.00
(72)	Emil Meusel	50.00	25.00	15.00
(73)	Edmund (Bing) Miller	50.00	25.00	15.00
(74)	John Mokan	50.00	25.00	15.00
(75)	Clarence Mueller	50.00	25.00	15.00
(76)	Robert W. Muesel (Meusel)	65.00	32.00	19.50
(77)	Glenn Myatt	50.00	25.00	15.00
(78)	Arthur Nehf	50.00	25.00	15.00
(79)	George O'Neil	50.00	25.00	15.00
(80)	Frank O'Rourke	50.00	25.00	15.00
(81)	Ralph Perkins	50.00	25.00	15.00
(82)	Valentine Picinich	50.00	25.00	15.00
(83)	Walter C. Pipp	65.00	32.00	19.50
(84)	John Quinn	50.00	25.00	15.00
(85)	Emory Rigney	50.00	25.00	15.00
(86)	Eppa Rixey	85.00	42.00	25.00
(87)	Edwin Rommel	50.00	25.00	15.00
(88)	Ed (Edd) Roush	85.00	42.00	25.00
(89)	Harold Ruel (Herold)	50.00	25.00	15.00
(90)	Charles Ruffing	85.00	42.00	25.00
(91)	George H. "Babe" Ruth	1100.	550.00	325.00
(92)	John Sand	50.00	25.00	15.00
(93)	Henry Severid (Severeid)	50.00	25.00	15.00
(94)	Joseph Sewell	85.00	42.00	25.00
(95)	Ray Shalk (Schalk)	85.00	42.00	25.00
(96)	Walter H. Shang (Schang)	50.00	25.00	15.00
(97)	J.R. Shawkey	55.00	27.00	16.50
(98)	Earl Sheely	50.00	25.00	15.00
(99)	William Sherdell (Sherdel)	50.00	25.00	15.00
(100)	Urban J. Shocker	50.00	25.00	15.00
(101)	George Sissler (Sisler)	85.00	42.00	25.00
(102)	Earl Smith	50.00	25.00	15.00
(103)	Sherrod Smith	50.00	25.00	15.00
(104)	Frank Snyder	50.00	25.00	15.00
(105)	Wm. H. Southworth	50.00	25.00	15.00
(106)	Tristram Speaker	100.00	50.00	30.00
(107)	Milton J. Stock	50.00	25.00	15.00
(108)	Homer Summa	50.00	25.00	15.00
(109)	William Terry	85.00	42.00	25.00
(110)	Hollis Thurston	50.00	25.00	15.00
(111)	John Tobin	50.00	25.00	15.00
(112)	Philip Todt	50.00	25.00	15.00
(113)	George Torporcer (Toporcer)	50.00	25.00	15.00
(114)	Harold Traynor	85.00	42.00	25.00
(115)	A.C. "Dazzy" Vance	85.00	42.00	25.00
(116)	Robert Veach	50.00	25.00	15.00
(117)	William Wambsganss	55.00	27.00	16.50
(118)	Aaron Ward	50.00	25.00	15.00
(119)	A.J. Weis	50.00	25.00	15.00
(120)	Frank Welch	50.00	25.00	15.00
(121)	Zack Wheat	85.00	42.00	25.00
(122)	Fred Williams	55.00	27.00	16.50
(123)	Kenneth Williams	55.00	27.00	16.50
(124)	Ernest Wingard	50.00	25.00	15.00
(125)	Ivy Wingo	50.00	25.00	15.00
(126)	Al Wings (Wingo)	50.00	25.00	15.00
(127)	Larry Woodall	50.00	25.00	15.00
(128)	Glen Wright (Glenn)	55.00	27.00	16.50

Grading Guide

Mint (MT): A perfect card. Well-centered with all corners sharp and square. No creases, stains, edge nicks, surface marks, yellowing or fading.

Near Mint (NM): A nearly perfect card. At first glance, a NM card appears to be perfect. May be slightly off-center. No surface marks, creases or loss of gloss.

Excellent (EX): Corners are still fairly sharp with only moderate wear. Borders may be off-center. No creases or stains on fronts or backs, but may show slight loss of surface luster.

Very Good (VG): Shows obvious handling. May have rounded corners, minor creases, major gum or wax stains. No major creases, tape marks, writing, etc.

Good (G): A well-worn card, but exhibits no intentional damage. May have major or multiple creases. Corners may be rounded well beyond card border.

1926 Exhibits

The 1926 Exhibit cards are the same size (3-3/8" by 5-3/8") as previous Exhibit issues but are easily distinguished because of their blue-gray color. The set consists of 128 cards, 91 of which are identical to the photos in the 1925 series. The 37 new photos do not include the boxed caption used in 1925. There are several errors in the 1926 set: The photos of Hunnefield and Thomas are transposed; Bischoff's card identifies him as playing for Boston, N.L. (rather than A.L.) and the photo of Galloway is reversed. The cards are unnumbered and are listed here alphabetically.

		NR MT	EX	VG
	Complete Set (128):	8250.	4125.	2475.
	Common Player:	50.00	25.00	15.00
(1)	Sparky Adams	50.00	25.00	15.00
(2)	David Bancroft	85.00	42.00	25.00
(3)	John Bassler	50.00	25.00	15.00
(4)	Lester Bell	50.00	25.00	15.00
(5)	John M. Bentley	50.00	25.00	15.00
(6)	Lawrence Benton	50.00	25.00	15.00
(7)	Carson Bigbee	50.00	25.00	15.00
(8)	George Bischoff	50.00	25.00	15.00
(9)	Max Bishop	50.00	25.00	15.00
(10)	J. Fred Blake	50.00	25.00	15.00
(11)	Ted Blankenship	50.00	25.00	15.00
(12)	Raymond Blates (Blades)	50.00	25.00	15.00
(13)	Lucerne A. Blue (Luzerne)	50.00	25.00	15.00
(14)	Oswald Bluege	50.00	25.00	15.00
(15)	James Bottomly (Bottomley)	85.00	42.00	25.00
(16)	Raymond Bressler	50.00	25.00	15.00
(17)	Geo. H. Burns	50.00	25.00	15.00
(18)	Maurice Burrus	50.00	25.00	15.00
(19)	John Butler	50.00	25.00	15.00
(20)	Max Carey	85.00	42.00	25.00
(21)	Tyrus Cobb	800.00	400.00	240.00
(22)	Eddie Collins	85.00	42.00	25.00
(23)	Patrick T. Collins	50.00	25.00	15.00
(24)	Earl B. Combs (Earle)	85.00	42.00	25.00
(25)	James E. Cooney	50.00	25.00	15.00
(26)	Stanley Coveleski	85.00	42.00	25.00
(27)	Hugh M. Critz	50.00	25.00	15.00
(28)	Hazen Cuyler	85.00	42.00	25.00
(29)	George Dauss	50.00	25.00	15.00
(30)	Peter Donohue	50.00	25.00	15.00
(31)	Charles Dressen	55.00	27.00	16.50
(32)	James J. Dykes	50.00	25.00	15.00
(33)	Bib Falk (Bibb)	50.00	25.00	15.00
(34)	Edward S. Farrell	50.00	25.00	15.00
(35)	Wilson Fewster	50.00	25.00	15.00
(36)	Ira Flagstead	50.00	25.00	15.00
(37)	Howard Freigau	50.00	25.00	15.00
(38)	Bernard Friberg	50.00	25.00	15.00
(39)	Frank Frisch	85.00	42.00	25.00
(40)	Jacques F. Furnier (Fournier)	50.00	25.00	15.00
(41)	Joseph Galloway (Clarence)	50.00	25.00	15.00
(42)	Henry L. Gehrig	900.00	450.00	270.00
(43)	Charles Gehringer	85.00	42.00	25.00
(44)	Joseph Genewich	50.00	25.00	15.00
(45)	Walter Gerber	50.00	25.00	15.00
(46)	Leon Goslin	85.00	42.00	25.00
(47)	George Grantham	50.00	25.00	15.00
(48)	Burleigh A. Grimes	85.00	42.00	25.00
(49)	Charles Grimm	50.00	25.00	15.00
(50)	Fred Haney	50.00	25.00	15.00
(51)	Wm. Hargrave	50.00	25.00	15.00
(52)	George Harper	50.00	25.00	15.00
(53)	Stanley Harris	85.00	42.00	25.00
(54)	Leo Hartnett	85.00	42.00	25.00
(55)	Joseph Hauser	55.00	27.00	16.50
(56)	C.E. Heathcote	50.00	25.00	15.00
(57)	Harry Heilmann	85.00	42.00	25.00
(58)	Walter Henline	50.00	25.00	15.00
(59)	Ramon Herrera	50.00	25.00	15.00
(60)	Andrew A. High	50.00	25.00	15.00
(61)	Rogers Hornsby	200.00	100.00	60.00
(62)	Clarence Huber	50.00	25.00	15.00
(63)	Wm. Hunnefield (photo actually Tommy Thomas)	50.00	25.00	15.00
(64)	William Jacobson	50.00	25.00	15.00
(65)	Walter Johnson	200.00	100.00	60.00
(66)	Joseph Judge	50.00	25.00	15.00
(67)	Willie Kamm	50.00	25.00	15.00
(68)	Ray Kremer	50.00	25.00	15.00
(69)	Anthony Lazzeri	85.00	42.00	25.00
(70)	Frederick Lindstrom	85.00	42.00	25.00
(71)	Walter Lutzke	50.00	25.00	15.00
(72)	John Makan (Mokan)	50.00	25.00	15.00
(73)	Walter Maranville	85.00	42.00	25.00
(74)	Martin McManus	50.00	25.00	15.00
(75)	Earl McNeely	50.00	25.00	15.00
(76)	Hugh A. McQuillan	50.00	25.00	15.00
(77)	Douglas McWeeny	50.00	25.00	15.00
(78)	Oscar Melillo	50.00	25.00	15.00
(79)	Edmund (Bind)(Bing) Miller	50.00	25.00	15.00
(80)	Clarence Mueller	50.00	25.00	15.00
(81)	Robert W. Muesel (Meusel)	65.00	32.00	19.50
(82)	Joseph W. Munson	50.00	25.00	15.00
(83)	Emil Musel (Meusel)	50.00	25.00	15.00
(84)	Glenn Myatt	50.00	25.00	15.00
(85)	Bernie F. Neis	50.00	25.00	15.00
(86)	Robert O'Farrell	50.00	25.00	15.00
(87)	George O'Neil	50.00	25.00	15.00
(88)	Frank O'Rourke	50.00	25.00	15.00
(89)	Ralph Perkins	50.00	25.00	15.00
(90)	Walter C. Pipp	65.00	32.00	19.50
(91)	Emory Rigney	50.00	25.00	15.00
(92)	James J. Ring	50.00	25.00	15.00
(93)	Eppa Rixey	85.00	42.00	25.00
(94)	Edwin Rommel	50.00	25.00	15.00
(95)	Ed. Roush	85.00	42.00	25.00
(96)	Harold Ruel (Herold)	50.00	25.00	15.00
(97)	Charles Ruffing	85.00	42.00	25.00
(98)	Geo. H. "Babe" Ruth	1100.	550.00	325.00
(99)	John Sand	50.00	25.00	15.00
(100)	Joseph Sewell	85.00	42.00	25.00
(101)	Ray Shalk (Schalk)	85.00	42.00	25.00
(102)	J.R. Shawkey	50.00	25.00	15.00
(103)	Earl Sheely	50.00	25.00	15.00
(104)	William Sherdell (Sherdel)	50.00	25.00	15.00
(105)	Urban J. Shocker	50.00	25.00	15.00
(106)	George Sissler (Sisler)	85.00	42.00	25.00
(107)	Earl Smith	50.00	25.00	15.00
(108)	Sherrod Smith	50.00	25.00	15.00
(109)	Frank Snyder	50.00	25.00	15.00
(110)	Tristram Speaker	125.00	62.00	37.00
(111)	Fred Spurgeon	50.00	25.00	15.00
(112)	Homer Summa	50.00	25.00	15.00
(113)	Edward Taylor	50.00	25.00	15.00
(114)	J. Taylor	50.00	25.00	15.00
(115)	William Terry	85.00	42.00	25.00
(116)	Hollis Thurston	50.00	25.00	15.00
(117)	Philip Todt	50.00	25.00	15.00
(118)	George Torporcer (Toporcer)	50.00	25.00	15.00
(119)	Harold Traynor	85.00	42.00	25.00
(120)	Wm. Wambsganss	50.00	25.00	15.00
(121)	John Warner	50.00	25.00	15.00
(122)	Zach Wheat	85.00	42.00	25.00
(123)	Kenneth Williams	65.00	32.00	19.50
(124)	Ernest Wingard	50.00	25.00	15.00
(125)	Fred Wingfield	50.00	25.00	15.00
(126)	Ivy Wingo	50.00	25.00	15.00
(127)	Glen Wright (Glenn)	65.00	32.00	19.50
(128)	Russell Wrightstone	50.00	25.00	15.00

1927 Exhibits

The Exhibit Supply Company issued a set of 64 cards in 1927, each measuring 3-3/8" by 5-3/8". The set can be identified from earlier issues by its light green tint. The player's name and team appear in capital letters in one lower corner, while "Ex. Sup. Co., Chgo." and "Made in U.S.A." appear in the other. All 64 photos used in the 1927 set were borrowed from previous issues, but 13 players are listed with new teams. There are several misspellings and other labeling errors in the set. The unnumbered cards are listed here in alphabetical order.

		NR MT	EX	VG
	Complete Set (64):	6000.	3000.	1800.
	Common Player:	50.00	25.00	15.00
(1)	Sparky Adams	50.00	25.00	15.00
(2)	Grover C. Alexander	115.00	57.00	34.00
(3)	David Bancroft	90.00	45.00	27.00
(4)	John Bassler	50.00	25.00	15.00
(5)	John M. Bentley (middle initial actually N.)	50.00	25.00	15.00
(6)	Fred Blankenship (Ted)	50.00	25.00	15.00
(7)	James Bottomly (Bottomley)	90.00	45.00	27.00
(8)	Raymond Bressler	50.00	25.00	15.00
(9)	Geo. H. Burns	50.00	25.00	15.00
(10)	John Buttler (Butler)	50.00	25.00	15.00
(11)	Tyrus Cobb	950.00	475.00	285.00
(12)	Eddie Collins	90.00	45.00	27.00
(13)	Hazen Cuyler	90.00	45.00	27.00

(14)	George Daus (Dauss)	50.00	25.00	15.00
(15)	A.R. Decatur	50.00	25.00	15.00
(16)	Wilson Fewster	50.00	25.00	15.00
(17)	Ira Flagstead	50.00	25.00	15.00
(18)	Henry L. Gehrig	950.00	475.00	285.00
(19)	Charles Gehringer	90.00	45.00	27.00
(20)	Joseph Genewich	50.00	25.00	15.00
(21)	Leon Goslin	90.00	45.00	27.00
(22)	Burleigh A. Grimes	90.00	45.00	27.00
(23)	Charles Grimm	50.00	25.00	15.00
(24)	Fred Haney	50.00	25.00	15.00
(25)	Wm. Hargrave	50.00	25.00	15.00
(26)	George Harper	50.00	25.00	15.00
(27)	Leo Hartnett	90.00	45.00	27.00
(28)	Clifton Heathcote	50.00	25.00	15.00
(29)	Harry Heilman (Heillmann)	90.00	45.00	27.00
(30)	Walter Henline	50.00	25.00	15.00
(31)	Andrew High	50.00	25.00	15.00
(32)	Rogers Hornsby	200.00	100.00	60.00
(33)	Wm. Hunnefield (photo actually Tommy Thomas)	50.00	25.00	15.00
(34)	Walter Johnson	250.00	125.00	75.00
(35)	Willie Kamm	50.00	25.00	15.00
(36)	Ray Kremer	50.00	25.00	15.00
(37)	Anthony Lazzeri	90.00	45.00	27.00
(38)	Fredrick Lindstrom (Frederick)	90.00	45.00	27.00
(39)	Walter Lutzke	50.00	25.00	15.00
(40)	John "Stuffy" McInnes (McInnis)	50.00	25.00	15.00
(41)	John Mokan	50.00	25.00	15.00
(42)	Robert W. Muesel (Meusel)	60.00	30.00	18.00
(43)	Glenn Myatt	50.00	25.00	15.00
(44)	Bernie Neis	50.00	25.00	15.00
(45)	Robert O'Farrell	50.00	25.00	15.00
(46)	Walter C. Pipp	80.00	40.00	24.00
(47)	Eppa Rixey	90.00	45.00	27.00
(48)	Harold Ruel (Herold)	50.00	25.00	15.00
(49)	Geo. H. "Babe" Ruth	1200.	600.00	360.00
(50)	Ray Schalk	90.00	45.00	27.00
(51)	George Sissler (Sisler)	90.00	45.00	27.00
(52)	Earl Smith	50.00	25.00	15.00
(53)	Wm. H. Southworth	50.00	25.00	15.00
(54)	Tristam Speaker (Tristram)	200.00	100.00	60.00
(55)	J. Taylor	50.00	25.00	15.00
(56)	Philip Todt	50.00	25.00	15.00
(57)	Harold Traynor	90.00	45.00	27.00
(58)	William Wambsganns (Wambsganss)	50.00	25.00	15.00
(59)	Zach Wheat	90.00	45.00	27.00
(60)	Kenneth Williams	50.00	25.00	15.00
(61)	Ernest Wingard	50.00	25.00	15.00
(62)	Fred Wingfield	50.00	25.00	15.00
(63)	Ivy Wingo	50.00	25.00	15.00
(64)	Russell Wrightstone	50.00	25.00	15.00

1928 Exhibits

The Exhibit Supply Company switched to a blue tint for the photos in its 64-card set in 1928. There are 36 new photos in the set, including 24 new players. Four players from the previous year are shown with new teams and 24 of the cards are identical to the 1927 series, except for the color of the card. Cards are found with either blank backs or postcard backs. The photos are captioned in the same style as the 1927 set. The set again includes some misspelling and incorrect labels. The cards are unnumbered and are listed here in alphabetical order.

		NR MT	EX	VG
Complete Set (64):		4750.	2375.	1425.
Common Player:		50.00	25.00	15.00
(1)	Grover C. Alexander	120.00	60.00	36.00
(2)	David Bancroft	90.00	45.00	27.00
(3)	Virgil Barnes	50.00	25.00	15.00
(4)	Francis R. Blades	50.00	25.00	15.00
(5)	L.A. Blue	50.00	25.00	15.00
(6)	Edward W. Brown	50.00	25.00	15.00
(7)	Max G. Carey	90.00	45.00	27.00
(8)	Chalmer W. Cissell	50.00	25.00	15.00
(9)	Gordon S. Cochrane	90.00	45.00	27.00
(10)	Pat Collins	50.00	25.00	15.00
(11)	Hugh M. Critz	50.00	25.00	15.00
(12)	Howard Ehmke	50.00	25.00	15.00
(13)	E. English	50.00	25.00	15.00
(14)	Bib Falk (Bibb)	50.00	25.00	15.00
(15)	Ira Flagstead	50.00	25.00	15.00
(16)	Robert Fothergill	50.00	25.00	15.00
(17)	Frank Frisch	90.00	45.00	27.00
(18)	Lou Gehrig	950.00	475.00	285.00
(19)	Leon Goslin	90.00	45.00	27.00
(20)	Eugene Hargrave	50.00	25.00	15.00
(21)	Charles R. Hargraves (Hargreaves)	50.00	25.00	15.00
(22)	Stanley Harris	90.00	45.00	27.00
(23)	Bryan "Slim" Harriss	50.00	25.00	15.00
(24)	Leo Hartnett	90.00	45.00	27.00
(25)	Joseph Hauser	50.00	25.00	15.00
(26)	Fred Hoffman (Hofmann)	50.00	25.00	15.00
(27)	J. Francis Hogan	50.00	25.00	15.00
(28)	Rogers Hornsby	200.00	100.00	60.00
(29)	Chas. Jamieson	50.00	25.00	15.00
(30)	Sam Jones	50.00	25.00	15.00
(31)	Ray Kremer	50.00	25.00	15.00
(32)	Fred Leach	50.00	25.00	15.00
(33)	Fredrick Lindstrom (Frederick)	90.00	45.00	27.00
(34)	Adolph Luque (Adolfo)	50.00	25.00	15.00
(35)	Theodore Lyons	90.00	45.00	27.00
(36)	Harry McCurdy	50.00	25.00	15.00
(37)	Glenn Myatt	50.00	25.00	15.00
(38)	John Ogden (photo actually Warren Ogden)	50.00	25.00	15.00
(39)	James Ring	50.00	25.00	15.00
(40)	A.C. Root (should be C.H.)	50.00	25.00	15.00
(41)	Edd. Roush	90.00	45.00	27.00
(42)	Harold Ruel (Herold)	50.00	25.00	15.00
(43)	Geo. H. "Babe" Ruth	1200.	600.00	360.00
(44)	Henry Sand	50.00	25.00	15.00
(45)	Joseph Sewell	90.00	45.00	27.00
(46)	Walter Shang (Schang)	50.00	25.00	15.00
(47)	Urban J. Shocker	50.00	25.00	15.00
(48)	Al. Simmons	90.00	45.00	27.00
(49)	Earl Smith	50.00	25.00	15.00
(50)	Robert Smith	50.00	25.00	15.00
(51)	Fred Schulte	50.00	25.00	15.00
(52)	Jack Tavener	50.00	25.00	15.00
(53)	J. Taylor	50.00	25.00	15.00
(54)	Philip Todt	50.00	25.00	15.00
(55)	Geo. Uhle	50.00	25.00	15.00
(56)	Arthur "Dazzy" Vance	90.00	45.00	27.00
(57)	Paul Waner	90.00	45.00	27.00
(58)	Earl G. Whitehill (middle intial actually O.)	50.00	25.00	15.00
(59)	Fred Williams	50.00	25.00	15.00
(60)	James Wilson	50.00	25.00	15.00
(61)	L.R. (Hack) Wilson	90.00	45.00	27.00
(62)	Lawrence Woodall	50.00	25.00	15.00
(63)	Glen Wright (Glenn)	50.00	25.00	15.00
(64)	William A. Zitzman (Zitzmann)	50.00	25.00	15.00

1929 "Anonymous" Exhibits

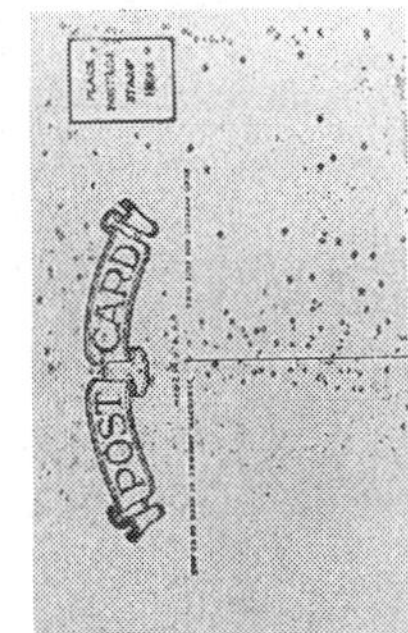

An early competitor to the Exhibit Supply Co., of Chicago, this Philadelphia-based company folded after just one year of production. Some card, indeed, can be found with the Eastern identification line blacked out and the identifier of Exhibit Supply printed below. Photos on the 3" x 5" cards are black-and-white.The cards have a postcard back and are unnumbered. They are checklisted here in alphabetical order. Probably issued in the Philadelphia area, these cards have a postcard back which includes the legend: "Not to be used in Exhibit machines." The fronts are borderless photos which generally have the player's name, team and league designation printed thereon. The Babe Ruth card is slightly different in that his name is in script, his position is given and there is no league designation. Cards can be found printed in yellow, red, and light or dark green, and it is possible that some or all players can be found in more than one color. Card size is about 3-3/8" x 5-3/8". The checklist below has been arranged alphabetically.

		NR MT	EX	VG
Complete Set (16):		2400.	1200.	720.00
Common Player:		40.00	20.00	12.00
(1)	Mickey Cochrane	75.00	37.00	22.00
(2)	Jimmy Foxx (Jimmie)	100.00	50.00	30.00
(3)	Lou Gehrig	800.00	400.00	240.00
(4)	Lefty Grove	75.00	37.00	22.00
(5)	George Haas	40.00	20.00	12.00
(6)	Rogers Hornsby	100.00	50.00	30.00
(7)	Chuck Klein	75.00	37.00	22.00
(8)	Bing Miller	40.00	20.00	12.00
(9)	Lefty O'Doul	55.00	27.00	16.50
(10)	Babe Ruth	950.00	475.00	285.00
(11)	Al Simmons	75.00	37.00	22.00
(12)	Pie Traynor	75.00	37.00	22.00
(13)	Dazzy Vance	75.00	37.00	22.00
(14)	Rube Walberg	40.00	20.00	12.00
(15)	Paul Waner	75.00	37.00	22.00
(16)	Hack Wilson	75.00	37.00	22.00

1929 - 30 Four-on-One Exhibits

Although the size of the card remained the same, the Exhibit Supply Company of Chicago began putting four player's pictures on each card in 1929 - a practice that would continue for the next decade. Known as "four-on-one" cards, the players are identified by name and team at the bottom of the photos, which are separated by borders. The 32 cards in the 1929-30 series have postcard backs and were printed in a wide range of color combinations including; black on orange, black on blue, brown on ornage, blue on green, black on red, black on white, blue on white, black on yellow, brown on white, brown on yellow and red on yellow. Most of the backs are uncolored, however, cards with a black on red front have been seen with red backs, and cards with blue on yellow fronts have been seen with yellow backs. There are numerous spelling and caption errors in the set, and the player identified as Babe Herman is actually Jesse Petty.

		NR MT	EX	VG
Complete Set (32):		2750.	1375.	825.00
Common Card:		45.00	22.00	13.50
(1)	Earl J. Adams, R. Bartell, Earl Sheely, Harold Traynor	60.00	30.00	18.00
(2)	Dale Alexander, C. Gehringer, G.F. McManus (should be M.J.), H.F. Rice	60.00	30.00	18.00
(3)	Grover C. Alexander, James Bottomly (Bottomley), Frank Frisch, James Wilson	90.00	45.00	27.00
(4)	Martin G. Autrey (Autry), Alex Metzler, Carl Reynolds, Alphonse Thomas	45.00	22.00	13.50
(5)	Earl Averill, B.A. Falk, K. Holloway, L. Sewell	60.00	30.00	18.00
(6)	David Bancroft, Del L. Bisonette (Bissonette), John H. DeBerry, Floyd C. Herman	60.00	30.00	18.00
(7)	C.E. Beck, Leo Hartnett, Rogers Hornsby, L.R. (Hack) Wilson	115.00	57.00	34.00
(8)	Ray Benge, Lester L. Sweetland, A.C. Whitney, Cy. Williams	45.00	22.00	13.50
(9)	Benny Bengough, Earl B. Coombs (Combs), Waite Hoyt, Anthony Lazzeri	65.00	32.00	19.50
(10)	L. Benton, Melvin Ott, Andrew Reese, William Terry	60.00	30.00	18.00
(11)	Max Bishop, James Dykes, Samuel Hale, Homer Summa	45.00	22.00	13.50
(12)	L.A. Blue, O. Melillo, F.O. Rourke (Frank O'Rourke), F. Schulte	45.00	22.00	13.50
(13)	Oswald Bluege, Leon Goslin, Joseph Judge, Harold Ruel	60.00	30.00	18.00
(14)	Chalmer W. Cissell, John W. Clancy, Willie Kamm, John L. Kerr	45.00	22.00	13.50
(15)	Gordon S. Cochrane, Jimmy Foxx, Robert M. Grove, George Haas	130.00	65.00	39.00
(16)	Pat Collins, Joe Dugan, Edward Farrel (Farrell), George Sisler	60.00	30.00	18.00
(17)	H.M. Critz, G.L. Kelly, V.J. Picinich, W.C. Walker	60.00	30.00	18.00
(18)	Nick Cullop, D'Arcy Flowers, Harvey Hendrick, Arthur "Dazzy" Vance	60.00	30.00	18.00
(19)	Hazen Cuyler, E. English, C.J. Grimm, C.H. Root	60.00	30.00	18.00
(20)	Taylor Douthit, Chas. M. Gilbert (Gelbert), Chas. J. Hafey, Fred G. Haney	60.00	30.00	18.00
(21)	Leo Durocher, Henry L. Gehrig, Mark Koenig, Geo. H. "Babe" Ruth	1250.	625.00	375.00
(22)	L.A. Fonseca, Carl Lind, J. Sewell, J. Tavener	60.00	30.00	18.00
(23)	H.E. Ford, C.F. Lucas, C.A. Pittenger, E.V. Purdy	45.00	22.00	13.50
(24)	Bernard Friberg, Donald Hurst, Frank O'Doul, Fresco Thompson	45.00	22.00	13.50
(25)	S. Gray, R. Kress, H. Manush, W.H. Shang	60.00	30.00	18.00
(26)	Charles R. Hargreaves, Ray Kremer, Lloyd Waner, Paul Waner	60.00	30.00	18.00
(27)	George Harper, Fred Maguire, Lance Richbourg, Robert Smith	45.00	22.00	13.50
(28)	Jack Hayes, Sam P. Jones, Chas. M. Myer, Sam Rice	60.00	30.00	18.00

(29) Harry E. Heilman (Heilmann), C.N. Richardson, M.J. Shea, G.E. Uhle 60.00 30.00 18.00
(30) J.A. Heving, R.R. Reeves (should be R.E.), J. Rothrock, C.H. Ruffing 60.00 30.00 18.00
(31) J.F. Hogan, T.C. Jackson, Fred Lindstrom, J.D. Welsh 60.00 30.00 18.00
(32) W.W. Regan, H. Rhyne, D. Taitt, P.J. Todt 45.00 22.00 13.50

1931 - 32 Four-on-One Exhibits

The 1931-1932 series issued by the Exhibit Company again consisted of 32 cards, each picturing four players. The series can be differentiated from the previous year by the coupon backs, which list various premiums available (including kazoos, toy pistols and other prizes). The cards again were printed in various color combinations, including; black on green, blue on green, black on orange, black on red, blue on white and black on yellow. There are numerous spelling and caption errors in the series. The Babe Herman/Jesse Petty error of the previous year was still not corrected, and the card of Rick Ferell not only misspells his name ("Farrel"), but also pictures the wrong player (Edward Farrell).

	NR MT	EX	VG
Complete Set (32):	3000.	1500.	900.00
Common Card:	50.00	25.00	15.00

(1) Earl J. Adams, James Bottomly (Bottomley), Frank Frisch, James Wilson 70.00 35.00 21.00
(2) Dale Alexander, C. Gehringer, G.F. McManus (should be M.J.), G.E. Uhle 70.00 35.00 21.00
(3) L.L. Appling (should be L.B.), Chalmer W. Cissell, Willie Kamm, Ted Lyons 70.00 35.00 21.00
(4) Buzz Arlett, Ray Benge, Chuck Klein, A.C. Whitney 70.00 35.00 21.00
(5) Earl Averill, B.A. Falk, L.A. Fonseca, L. Sewell 70.00 35.00 21.00
(6) Richard Bartell, Bernard Friberg, Donald Hurst, Harry McCurdy 50.00 25.00 15.00
(7) Walter Berger, Fred Maguire, Lance Richbourg, Earl Sheely 50.00 25.00 15.00
(8) Chas. Berry, Robt. Reeves, R.R. Reeves (should be R.E.), J. Rothrock 50.00 25.00 15.00
(9) Del L. Bisonette (Bissonette), Floyd C. Herman (photo - J. Petty), Jack Quinn, Glenn Wright 50.00 25.00 15.00
(10) L.A. Blue, Smead Jolley, Carl Reynolds, Henry Tate 50.00 25.00 15.00
(11) O. Bluege, Joe Judge, Chas. M. Myer, Sam Rice 70.00 35.00 21.00
(12) John Boley, James Dykes, E.J. Miller, Al. Simmons 70.00 35.00 21.00
(13) Gordon S. Chochrane, Jimmy Foxx, Robert M. Grove, George Haas 195.00 97.00 58.00
(14) Adam Comorosky, Gus Suhr, T.J. Thevenow, Harold Traynor 70.00 35.00 21.00
(15) Earl B. Coombs (Combs), W. Dickey, Anthony Lazzeri, H. Pennock 195.00 97.00 58.00
(16) H.M. Critz, J.F. Hogan, T.C. Jackson, Fred Lindstrom 70.00 35.00 21.00
(17) Joe Cronin, H. Manush, F. Marberry, Roy Spencer 70.00 35.00 21.00
(18) Nick Cullop, Les Durocher (Leo), Harry Heilmann, W.C. Walker 70.00 35.00 21.00
(19) Hazen Cuyler, E. English, C.J. Grimm, C.H. Root 70.00 35.00 21.00
(20) Taylor Douthit, Chas. M. Gilbert (Gelbert), Chas. J. Hafey, Bill Hallahan 50.00 25.00 15.00
(21) Richard Farrel (Ferrell) (photo actually Ed Farrell), S. Gray, R. Kress, W. Stewart 65.00 32.00 19.50
(22) W. Ferrell, J. Goldman, Hunnefield, Ed Morgan 50.00 25.00 15.00
(23) Fred Fitzsimmons, Robert O'Farrell, Melvin Ott, William Terry 70.00 35.00 21.00
(24) D'Arcy Flowers, Frank O'Doul, Fresco Thompson, Arthur "Dazzy" Vance 70.00 35.00 21.00
(25) H.E. Ford (should be H.H.), Gooch, C.F. Lucas, W. Roettger 50.00 25.00 15.00
(26) E. Funk, W. Hoyt, Mark Koenig, Wallie Schang 70.00 35.00 21.00
(27) Henry L. Gehrig, Lyn Lary, James Reese, Geo. H. "Babe" Ruth 900.00 450.00 275.00
(28) George Grantham, Ray Kremer, Lloyd Waner, Paul Waner 70.00 35.00 21.00
(29) Leon Goslin, O. Melillo, F.O. Rourke (Frank O'Rourke), F. Schulte 70.00 35.00 21.00
(30) Leo Hartnett, Rogers Hornsby, J.R. Stevenson (Stephenson), L.R. (Hack) Wilson 115.00 57.00 34.00
(31) D. MacFayden, H. Rhyne, Bill Sweeney, E.W. Webb 50.00 25.00 15.00
(32) Walter Maranville, Randolph Moore, Alfred Spohrer, J.T. Zachary 70.00 35.00 21.00

1933 Four-on-One Exhibits

The 1933 series of four-on-one Exhibits consists of 16 cards with blank backs. Color combinations include: blue on green, black on orange, black on red, blue on white and black on yellow. Most have a plain, white back, although the black on yellow cards are also found with a yellow back. Most of the pictures used are reprinted from previous series, and there are some spelling and caption errors, including the Richard Ferrell/Edward Farrel mixup from the previous year. Al Lopez is shown as "Vincent" Lopez.

	NR MT	EX	VG
Complete Set (16):	1900.	950.00	550.00
Common Card:	50.00	25.00	15.00

(1) Earl J. Adams, Frank Frisch, Chas. Gilbert (Gelbert), Bill Hallahan 70.00 35.00 21.00
(2) Earl Averill, W. Ferrell, Ed Morgan, L. Sewell 70.00 35.00 21.00
(3) Richard Bartell, Ray Benge, Donald Hurst, Chuck Klein 70.00 35.00 21.00
(4) Walter Berger, Walter Maranville, Alfred Spohrer, J.T. Zachary 70.00 35.00 21.00
(5) Charles Berry, L.A. Blue, Ted Lyons, Bob Seeds 70.00 35.00 21.00
(6) Chas. Berry, D. MacFayden, H. Rhyne, E.W. Webb 50.00 25.00 15.00
(7) Mickey Cochrane, Jimmy Foxx, Robert M. Grove, Al. Simmons 250.00 125.00 75.00
(8) H.M. Critz, Fred Fitzsimmons, Fred Lindstrom, Robert O'Farrell 70.00 35.00 21.00
(9) W. Dickey, Anthony Lazzeri, H. Pennock, George H. "Babe" Ruth 1000. 500.00 300.00
(10) Taylor Douthit, George Grantham, Chas. J. Hafey, C.F. Lucas 70.00 35.00 21.00
(11) E. English, C.J. Grimm, C.H. Root, J.R. Stevenson (Stephenson) 50.00 25.00 15.00
(12) Richard Farrel (Farrell) (photo actually Ed Farrell), Leon Goslin, S. Gray, O. Melillo 70.00 35.00 21.00
(13) C. Gehringer, "Muddy" Ruel, Jonathan Stone (first name - John, G.E. Uhle 70.00 35.00 21.00
(14) Joseph Judge, H. Manush, F. Marberry, Roy Spencer 70.00 35.00 21.00
(15) Vincent Lopez (Al), Frank O'Doul, Arthur "Dazzy" Vance, Glenn Wright 70.00 35.00 21.00
(16) Gus Suhr, Tom J. Thevenow, Lloyd Waner, Paul Waner 70.00 35.00 21.00

1934 Four-on-One Exhibits

This 16-card series issued by the Exhibit Co. in 1934 is again blank-backed and continues the four-on-one format. The 1934 series can be differentiated from previous years by the more subdued color combinations of the cards, which include lighter shades of blue, brown, green and violet - all printed on white card stock. Many new photos were also used in the 1934 series. Of the 64 players included, 25 appear for the first time and another 16 were given new poses. Spelling was improved, but Al Lopez is still identified as "Vincent."

	NR MT	EX	VG
Complete Set (16):	1750.	875.00	525.00
Common Card:	45.00	22.00	13.50

(1) Luke Appling, George Earnshaw, Al Simmons, Evar Swanson 60.00 30.00 18.00
(2) Earl Averill, W. Ferrell, Willie Kamm, Frank Pytlak 60.00 30.00 18.00
(3) Richard Bartell, Donald Hurst, Wesley Schulmerich, Jimmy Wilson 45.00 22.00 13.50
(4) Walter Berger, Ed Brandt, Frank Hogan, Bill Urbanski 45.00 22.00 13.50
(5) Jim Bottomley, Chas. J. Hafey, Botchi Lombardi, Tony Piet 60.00 30.00 18.00
(6) Irving Burns, Irving Hadley, Rollie Hemsley, O. Melillo 45.00 22.00 13.50
(7) Bill Cissell, Rick Ferrell, Lefty Grove, Roy Johnson 60.00 30.00 18.00
(8) Mickey Cochrane, C. Gehringer, Goose Goslin, Fred Marberry 90.00 45.00 27.00
(9) George Cramer (Roger), Jimmy Foxx, Frank Higgins, Slug Mahaffey 90.00 45.00 27.00
(10) Joe Cronin, Alvin Crowder, Joe Kuhel, H. Manush 60.00 30.00 18.00
(11) W. Dickey, Lou Gehrig, Vernon Gomez, Geo. H. "Babe" Ruth 1000. 500.00 300.00
(12) E. English, C.J. Grimm, Chas. Klein, Lon Warneke 60.00 30.00 18.00
(13) Frank Frisch, Bill Hallahan, Pepper Martin, John Rothrock 60.00 30.00 18.00
(14) Carl Hubbell, Mel Ott, Blondy Ryan, Bill Terry 90.00 45.00 27.00
(15) Leonard Koenecke, Sam Leslie, Vincent Lopez (Al), Glenn Wright 40.00 20.00 12.00
(16) T.J. Thevenow, Pie Traynor, Lloyd Waner, Paul Waner 85.00 42.00 25.00

Values for recent cards and sets are listed in Mint (MT), Near Mint (NM), reflecting the fact that many cards from recent years have been preserved in top condition. Recent cards and sets in less than Excellent condition have little collector interest.

Values quoted in this guide reflect the retail price of a card – the price a collector can expect to pay when buying a card from a dealer. The wholesale price – that which a collector can expect to receive from a dealer when selling cards – will be significantly lower, depending on desirability and condition.

1935 Four-on-One Exhibits

Continuing with the same four-on-one format, the Exhibit Supply Co. issued another 16-card series in 1935. All cards were printed in a slate-blue color with a plain, blank back. Seventeen of the players included in the 1935 series appear for the first time. While another 11 are shown with new poses. There are several spelling and caption errors. Babe Ruth appears in a regular Exhibit issue for the last time.

	NR MT	EX	VG
Complete Set (16):	2600.	1300.	775.00
Common Card:	40.00	20.00	12.00

(1) Earl Averill, Mel Harder, Willie Kamm, Hal Trosky 60.00 30.00 18.00
(2) Walter Berger, Ed Brandt, Frank Hogan, "Babe" Ruth 900.00 450.00 270.00
(3) Henry Bonura, Jimmy Dykes, Ted Lyons, Al Simmons 60.00 30.00 18.00
(4) Jimmy Bottomley, Paul Derringer, Chas. J. Hafey, Botchi Lombardi 85.00 42.00 25.00
(5) Irving Burns, Rollie Hemsley, O. Melillo, L.N. Newson 40.00 20.00 12.00
(6) Guy Bush, Pie Traynor, Floyd Vaughn (Vaughan), Paul Waner 85.00 42.00 25.00
(7) Mickey Cochrane, C. Gehringer, Goose Goslin, Linwood Rowe (Lynwood) 85.00 42.00 25.00
(8) Phil Collins, John "Blondy" Ryan, Geo. Watkins, Jimmy Wilson 40.00 20.00 12.00
(9) George Cramer (Roger), Jimmy Foxx, Bob Johnson, Slug Mahaffey 85.00 42.00 25.00
(10) Hughie Critz, Carl Hubbell, Mel Ott, Bill Terry 90.00 45.00 27.00
(11) Joe Cronin, Rick Ferrell, Lefty Grove, Billy Werber 85.00 42.00 25.00
(12) Tony Cuccinello (photo actually George Puccinelli), Vincent Lopez (Al), Van Mungo, Dan Taylor 50.00 25.00 15.00
(13) Jerome "Dizzy" Dean, Paul Dean, Frank Frisch, Pepper Martin 175.00 87.00 52.00
(14) W. Dickey, Lou Gehrig, Vernon Gomez, Tony Lazzeri 900.00 450.00 270.00
(15) C.J. Grimm, Gabby Hartnett, Chas. Klein, Lon Warneke 60.00 30.00 18.00
(16) H. Manush, Buddy Meyer (Myer), Fred Schulte, Earl Whitehill 60.00 30.00 18.00

1936 Four-on-One Exhibits

The 1936 series of four-on-one cards again consisted of 16 cards in either green or slate blue with plain, blank backs. The series can be differentiated from the previous year's Exhibit cards by the line "PTD. IN U.S.A." at the bottom. Of the 64 players pictured, 16 appear for the first time and another nine are shown in new poses. The series is again marred by several spelling and caption errors.

	NR MT	EX	VG
Complete Set (16):	1600.	800.00	475.00
Common Card:	45.00	22.00	13.50

No.	Players	NR MT	EX	VG
(1)	Paul Andrews, Harland Clift (Harlond), Rollie Hemsley, Sammy West	45.00	22.00	13.50
(2)	Luke Appling, Henry Bonura, Jimmy Dykes, Ted Lyons	55.00	27.00	16.50
(3)	Earl Averill, Mel Harder, Hal Trosky, Joe Vosmik	55.00	27.00	16.50
(4)	Walter Berger, Danny MacFayden, Bill Urbanski, Pinky Whitney	45.00	22.00	13.50
(5)	Charles Berry, Frank Higgins, Bob Johnson, Puccinelli	45.00	22.00	13.50
(6)	Ossie Bluege, Buddy Meyer (Myer), L.N. Newsom, Earl Whitehill	45.00	22.00	13.50
(7)	Stan. Bordagaray, Dutch Brandt, Fred Lindstrom, Van Mungo	55.00	27.00	16.50
(8)	Guy Bush, Pie Traynor, Floyd Vaughn (Vaughan), Paul Waner	75.00	37.00	22.00
(9)	Dolph Camilli, Curt Davis, Johnny Moore, Jimmy Wilson	45.00	22.00	13.50
(10)	Mickey Cochrane, C. Gehringer, Goose Goslin, Linwood Rowe	75.00	37.00	22.00
(11)	Joe Cronin, Rick Ferrell, Jimmy Foxx, Lefty Grove	95.00	47.00	28.00
(12)	Jerome "Dizzy" Dean, Paul Dean, Frank Frisch, Joe "Ducky" Medwick	175.00	87.00	52.00
(13)	Paul Derringer, Babe Herman, Alex Kampouris, Botchi Lombardi	55.00	27.00	16.50
(14)	Augie Galan, Gabby Hartnett, Billy Herman, Lon Warneke	55.00	27.00	16.50
(15)	Lou Gehrig, Vernon Gomez, Tony Lazzeri, Red Ruffing	800.00	400.00	240.00
(16)	Carl Hubbell, Gus Mancuso, Mel Ott, Bill Terry	65.00	33.00	20.00

1937 Four-on-One Exhibits

The 1937 four-on-one Exhibit cards were printed in either green or bright blue. The backs are again blank. The 1937 cards are difficult to distinguish from the 1936 series, because both contain the "PTD. IN U.S.A." line along the bottom. Of the 64 photos, 47 are re-issues from previous series.

	NR MT	EX	VG
Complete Set (16):	1775.	885.00	525.00
Common Card:	45.00	22.00	13.50

No.	Players	NR MT	EX	VG
(1)	Earl Averill, Bob Feller, Frank Pytlak, Hal Trosky	95.00	47.00	28.00
(2)	Luke Appling, Henry Bonura, Jimmy Dykes, Vernon Kennedy	60.00	30.00	18.00
(3)	Walter Berger, Alfonso Lopez, Danny MacFayden, Bill Urbanski	50.00	25.00	15.00
(4)	Cy Blanton, Gus Suhr, Floyd Vaughn (Vaughan), Paul Waner	60.00	30.00	18.00
(5)	Dolph Camilli, Johnny Moore, Wm. Walters, Pinky Whitney	45.00	22.00	13.50
(6)	Harland Clift (Harlond), Rollie Hemsley, Orval Hildebrand (Oral, Sammy West	45.00	22.00	13.50
(7)	Mickey Cochrane, C. Gehringer, Goose Goslin, Linwood Rowe	80.00	40.00	24.00
(8)	Joe Cronin, Rick Ferrell, Jimmy Foxx, Lefty Grove	95.00	47.00	28.00
(9)	Jerome "Dizzy" Dean, Stuart Martin, Joe "Ducky" Medwick, Lon Warneke	140.00	70.00	42.00
(10)	Paul Derringer, Botchi Lombardi, Lew Riggs, Phil Weintraub	60.00	30.00	18.00
(11)	Joe DiMaggio, Lou Gehrig, Vernon Gomez, Tony Lazzeri	1000.	500.00	300.00
(12)	E. English, Johnny Moore, Van Mungo, Gordon Phelps	45.00	22.00	13.50
(13)	Augie Galan, Gabby Hartnett, Billy Herman, Bill Lee	60.00	30.00	18.00
(14)	Carl Hubbell, Sam Leslie, Gus. Mancuso, Mel Ott	60.00	30.00	18.00
(15)	Bob Johnson, Harry Kelly (Kelley), Wallace Moses, Billy Weber	45.00	22.00	13.50
(16)	Joe Kuhel, Buddy Meyer (Myer), L.N. Newsom, Jonathan Stone	45.00	22.00	13.50

1938 Four-on-One Exhibits

The Exhibit Co. used its four-on-one format for the final time in 1938, issuing another 16-card series. the cards feature brown printing on white stock with the line "MADE IN U.S.A." appearing along the bottom. The backs are blank. Twelve players appeared for the first time and three others are shown in new poses. Again, there are several spelling and caption mistakes.

	NR MT	EX	VG
Complete Set (16):	1775.	875.00	525.00
Common Card:	45.00	22.00	13.50

No.	Players	NR MT	EX	VG
(1)	Luke Appling, Mike Kreevich, Ted Lyons, L. Sewell	60.00	30.00	18.00
(2)	Morris Arnovich, Chas. Klein, Wm. Walters, Pinky Whitney	60.00	30.00	18.00
(3)	Earl Averill, Bob Feller, Odell Hale, Hal Trosky	95.00	47.00	28.00
(4)	Beau Bell, Harland Clift (Harlond), L.N. Newsome, Sammy West	45.00	22.00	13.50
(5)	Cy Blanton, Gus Suhr, Floyd Vaughn (Vaughan), Paul Waner	60.00	30.00	18.00
(6)	Tom Bridges, C. Gehringer, Hank Greenberg, Rudy York	60.00	30.00	18.00
(7)	Dolph Camilli, Leo Durocher, Van Mungo, Gordon Phelps	50.00	25.00	15.00
(8)	Joe Cronin, Jimmy Foxx, Lefty Grove, Joe Vosmik	85.00	42.00	25.00
(9)	Tony Cuccinello (photo actually George Puccinell), Vince DiMaggio, Roy Johnson, Danny MacFayden	45.00	22.00	13.50
(10)	Jerome "Dizzy" Dean, Augie Galan, Gabby Hartnett, Billy Herman	125.00	62.00	37.00
(11)	Paul Derringer, Ival Goodman, Botchi Lombardi, Lew Riggs	60.00	30.00	18.00
(12)	W. Dickey, Joe DiMaggio, Lou Gehrig, Vernon Gomez	1000.	500.00	300.00
(13)	Rick Ferrell, W. Ferrell, Buddy Meyer (Myer), Jonathan Stone	60.00	30.00	18.00
(14)	Carl Hubbell, Hank Leiber, Mel Ott, Jim Ripple	75.00	37.00	22.00
(15)	Bob Johnson, Harry Kelly (Kelley), Wallace Moses, Billy Weber	45.00	22.00	13.50
(16)	Stuart Martin, Joe "Ducky" Medwick, Johnny Mize, Lon Warneke	60.00	30.00	18.00

1939 - 46 Salutation Exhibits

Referred to as "Exhibits" because they were issued by the Exhibit Supply Co. of Chicago, Ill., this group was produced over an 8-year span. They are frequently called "Salutations" because of the personalized greeting found on the card. The black and white cards, which measure 3-3/8" by 5-3/8", are unnumbered and blank-backed. Most exhibits were sold through vending machines for a penny. The complete set price includes all variations.

	NR MT	EX	VG
Complete Set:	4750.	2375.	1425.
Common Player:	5.00	2.50	1.50

No.	Player	NR MT	EX	VG
(1a)	Luke Appling ("Made In U.S.A." in left corner)	12.00	6.00	3.50
(1b)	Luke Appling ("Made In U.S.A." in right corner)	7.00	3.50	2.00
(2)	Earl Averill	375.00	175.00	100.00
(3)	Charles "Red" Barrett	5.00	2.50	1.50
(4)	Henry "Hank" Borowy	5.00	2.50	1.50
(5)	Lou Boudreau	8.00	4.00	2.50
(6)	Adolf Camilli	25.00	12.50	7.50
(7)	Phil Cavarretta	6.00	3.00	1.75
(8)	Harland Clift (Harlond)	12.00	6.00	3.50
(9)	Tony Cuccinello	25.00	12.50	7.50
(10)	Dizzy Dean	80.00	40.00	24.00
(11)	Paul Derringer	5.00	2.50	1.50
(12a)	Bill Dickey ("Made In U.S.A." in left corner)	25.00	12.50	7.50
(12b)	Bill Dickey ("Made In U.S.A." in right corner)	25.00	12.50	7.50
(13)	Joe DiMaggio	125.00	60.00	40.00
(14)	Bob Elliott	5.00	2.50	1.50
(15)	Bob Feller (portrait)	100.00	50.00	30.00
(16)	Bob Feller (pitching)	30.00	15.00	9.00
(17)	Dave Ferriss	5.00	2.50	1.50
(18)	Jimmy Foxx	100.00	50.00	30.00
(19)	Lou Gehrig	1000.	500.00	300.00
(20)	Charlie Gehringer	125.00	56.00	35.00
(21)	Vernon Gomez	180.00	90.00	55.00
(22a)	Joe Gordon (Cleveland)	25.00	12.50	7.50
(22b)	Joe Gordon (New York)	6.00	3.00	1.75
(23)	Hank Greenberg (Truly yours)	20.00	10.00	6.00
(24)	Hank Greenberg (Very truly yours)	80.00	40.00	24.00
(25)	Robert Grove	50.00	25.00	15.00
(26)	Gabby Hartnett	275.00	150.00	80.00
(27)	Buddy Hassett	15.00	7.50	4.50
(28a)	Jeff Heath (large projection)	25.00	12.50	7.50
(28b)	Jeff Heath (small projection)	5.00	2.50	1.50
(29)	Kirby Higbe	15.00	7.50	4.50
(30a)	Tommy Holmes (Yours truly)	5.00	2.50	1.50
(30b)	Tommy Holmes (Sincerely yours)	125.00	60.00	40.00
(31)	Carl Hubbell	25.00	12.50	7.50
(32)	Bob Johnson	15.00	7.50	4.50
(33)	Charles Keller	5.00	2.50	1.50
(34)	Ken Keltner	25.00	12.50	7.50
(35)	Chuck Klein	175.00	90.00	50.00
(36)	Mike Kreevich	80.00	40.00	24.00
(37)	Joe Kuhel	20.00	10.00	6.00
(38)	Bill Lee	20.00	10.00	6.00
(39)	Ernie Lombardi (Cordially)	200.00	100.00	60.00
(40)	Ernie Lombardi (Cordially yours)	8.00	4.00	2.50
(41a)	Martin Marion ("Made in U.S.A." in left corner)	6.00	3.00	1.75
(41b)	Martin Marion ("Made in U.S.A." in right corner)	6.00	3.00	1.75
(42)	Merrill May	20.00	10.00	6.00
(43a)	Frank McCormick ("Made In U.S.A." in left corner)	20.00	10.00	6.00
(43b)	Frank McCormick ("Made In U.S.A." in right corner)	6.00	3.00	1.75
(44a)	George McQuinn ("Made In U.S.A." in left corner)	20.00	10.00	6.00
(44b)	George McQuinn ("Made In U.S.A." in right corner)	6.00	3.00	1.75
(45)	Joe Medwick	30.00	15.00	9.00
(46a)	Johnny Mize ("Made In U.S.A." in left corner)	25.00	12.50	7.50
(46b)	Johnny Mize ("Made In U.S.A." in right corner)	15.00	7.50	4.50
(47)	Hugh Mulcahy	80.00	40.00	24.00
(48)	Hal Newhouser	7.50	3.75	2.25
(49)	Buck Newson (Newsom)	175.00	90.00	50.00
(50)	Louis (Buck) Newsom	5.00	2.50	1.50
(51a)	Mel Ott ("Made In U.S.A." in left corner)	50.00	25.00	15.00
(51b)	Mel Ott ("Made In U.S.A." in right corner)	25.00	12.50	7.50
(52a)	Andy Pafko ("C" on cap)	5.00	2.50	1.50
(52b)	Andy Pafko (plain cap)	5.00	2.50	1.50
(53)	Claude Passeau	6.00	3.00	1.75
(54a)	Howard Pollet ("Made In U.S.A." in left corner)	11.00	5.50	3.25
(54b)	Howard Pollet ("Made In U.S.A." in right corner)	5.00	2.50	1.50
(55a)	Pete Reiser ("Made In U.S.A." in left corner)	80.00	40.00	24.00
(55b)	Pete Reiser ("Made In U.S.A." in right corner)	5.00	2.50	1.50
(56)	Johnny Rizzo	90.00	45.00	27.00
(57)	Glenn Russell	90.00	45.00	27.00
(58)	George Stirnweiss	5.00	2.50	1.50
(59)	Cecil Travis	15.00	7.50	4.50
(60)	Paul Trout	5.00	2.50	1.50
(61)	Johnny Vander Meer	40.00	20.00	12.00
(62)	Arky Vaughn (Vaughan)	20.00	10.00	6.00
(63a)	Fred "Dixie" Walker ("D" on cap)	5.00	2.50	1.50
(63b)	Fred "Dixie" Walker ("D" blanked out)	50.00	25.00	15.00
(64)	"Bucky" Walters	5.00	2.50	1.50
(65)	Lon Warneke	6.50	3.25	2.00
(66)	Ted Williams (#9 shows)	350.00	175.00	105.00
(67)	Ted Williams (#9 not showing)	60.00	30.00	18.00
(68)	Rudy York	5.00	2.50	1.50

1961 Exhibits - Wrigley Field

Distributed at Chicago's Wrigley Field circa 1961, this 24-card set features members of the Baseball Hall of Fame. The cards measure 3-3/8" by 5-3/8" and include the player's full name along the bottom. They were printed on gray stock and have a postcard back. The set is unnumbered.

	NR MT	EX	VG
Complete Set:	325.00	162.00	97.00
Common Player:	4.00	2.00	1.25

No.	Player	NR MT	EX	VG
(1)	Grover Cleveland Alexander	6.00	3.00	1.75
(2)	Adrian Constantine Anson	6.00	3.00	1.75
(3)	John Franklin Baker	4.00	2.00	1.25
(4)	Roger Phillip Bresnahan	4.00	2.00	1.25
(5)	Mordecai Peter Brown	4.00	2.00	1.25
(6)	Frank Leroy Chance	5.00	2.50	1.50
(7)	Tyrus Raymond Cobb	50.00	25.00	15.00
(8)	Edward Trowbridge Collins	4.00	2.00	1.25

(9)	James J. Collins	4.00	2.00	1.25
(10)	John Joseph Evers	4.00	2.00	1.25
(11)	Henry Louis Gehrig	50.00	25.00	15.00
(12)	Clark C. Griffith	4.00	2.00	1.25
(13)	Walter Perry Johnson	10.00	5.00	3.00
(14)	Anthony Michael Lazzeri	4.00	2.00	1.25
(15)	James Walter Vincent Maranville	4.00	2.00	1.25
(16)	Christopher Mathewson	10.00	5.00	3.00
(17)	John Joseph McGraw	5.00	2.50	1.50
(18)	Melvin Thomass Ott	5.00	2.50	1.50
(19)	Herbert Jeffries Pennock	4.00	2.00	1.25
(20)	George Herman Ruth	70.00	35.00	21.00
(21)	Aloysius Harry Simmons	4.00	2.00	1.25
(22)	Tristram Speaker	12.00	6.00	3.50
(23)	Joseph B. Tinker	4.00	2.00	1.25
(24)	John Peter Wagner	10.00	5.00	3.00

Values for recent cards and sets are listed in Mint (MT), Near Mint (NM), reflecting the fact that many cards from recent years have been preserved in top condition. Recent cards and sets in less than Excellent condition have little collector interest.

1948 Baseball's Great Hall of Fame Exhibits

Titled "Baseball's Great Hall of Fame," this 32-player set features black and white player photos against a gray background. The photos are accented by Greek columns on either side with brief player information printed at the bottom. The blank-backed cards are unnumbered and are listed here alphabetically. The cards measure 3-3/8" by 5-3/8". Collectors should be aware that 24 of the cards in this set were reprinted on white stock in the mid-1970s.

		NR MT	EX	VG
Complete Set:		550.00	275.00	165.00
Common Player:		4.00	2.00	1.25
(1)	Grover Cleveland Alexander	7.00	3.50	2.00
(2)	Roger Bresnahan	4.00	2.00	1.25
(3)	Frank Chance	5.00	2.50	1.50
(4)	Jack Chesbro	4.00	2.00	1.25
(5)	Fred Clarke	4.00	2.00	1.25
(6)	Ty Cobb	50.00	25.00	15.00
(7)	Mickey Cochrane	5.00	2.50	1.50
(8)	Eddie Collins	4.00	2.00	1.25
(9)	Hugh Duffy	4.00	2.00	1.25
(10)	Johnny Evers	4.00	2.00	1.25
(11)	Frankie Frisch	4.00	2.00	1.25
(12)	Lou Gehrig	50.00	25.00	15.00
(13)	Clark Griffith	4.00	2.00	1.25
(14)	Robert "Lefty" Grove	6.00	3.00	1.75
(15)	Rogers Hornsby	10.00	5.00	3.00
(16)	Carl Hubbell	5.00	2.50	1.50
(17)	Hughie Jennings	4.00	2.00	1.25
(18)	Walter Johnson	15.00	7.50	4.50
(19)	Willie Keeler	4.00	2.00	1.25
(20)	Napolean Lajoie	7.00	3.50	2.00
(21)	Connie Mack	7.00	3.50	2.00
(22)	Christy Matthewson (Mathewson)	15.00	7.50	4.50
(23)	John J. McGraw	5.00	2.50	1.50
(24)	Eddie Plank	4.00	2.00	1.25
(25)	Babe Ruth (batting)	75.00	37.00	22.00
(26)	Babe Ruth (standing with bats)	200.00	100.00	60.00
(27)	George Sisler	5.00	2.50	1.50
(28)	Tris Speaker	7.00	3.50	2.00
(29)	Joe Tinker	4.00	2.00	1.25
(30)	Rube Waddell	4.00	2.00	1.25
(31)	Honus Wagner	15.00	7.50	4.50
(32)	Ed Walsh	4.00	2.00	1.25
(33)	Cy Young	9.00	4.50	2.75

1953 Canadian Exhibits

This Canadian-issued set consists of 64 cards and includes both major leaguers and player from the Montreal Royals of the International League. The cards are slightly smaller than the U.S. exhibit cards, measuring 3-1/4" by 5-1/4", and are numbered. The blank-backed cards were printed on gray stock. Card numbers 1-32 have a green or red tint, while card numbers 33-64 have a blue or reddish-brown tint.

		NR MT	EX	VG
Complete Set (64):		1400.	650.00	390.00
Common Player (1-32):		10.00	5.00	3.00
Common Player (33-64):		8.50	4.25	2.50
1	Preacher Roe	12.00	6.00	3.50
2	Luke Easter	10.00	5.00	3.00
3	Gene Bearden	10.00	5.00	3.00
4	Chico Carrasquel	10.00	5.00	3.00
5	Vic Raschi	12.00	6.00	3.50
6	Monty (Monte) Irvin	18.00	9.00	5.50
7	Henry Sauer	10.00	5.00	3.00
8	Ralph Branca	12.00	6.00	3.50
9	Ed Stanky	10.00	5.00	3.00
10	Sam Jethroe	10.00	5.00	3.00
11	Larry Doby	10.00	5.00	3.00
12	Hal Newhouser	18.00	9.00	5.50
13	Gil Hodges	25.00	12.50	7.50
14	Harry Brecheen	10.00	5.00	3.00
15	Ed Lopat	12.00	6.00	3.50
16	Don Newcombe	12.00	6.00	3.50
17	Bob Feller	35.00	17.50	10.50
18	Tommy Holmes	10.00	5.00	3.00
19	Jackie Robinson	110.00	55.00	33.00
20	Roy Campanella	110.00	55.00	33.00
21	Harold "Peewee" Reese	35.00	17.50	10.50
22	Ralph Kiner	22.00	11.00	6.50
23	Dom DiMaggio	12.00	6.00	3.50
24	Bobby Doerr	18.00	9.00	5.50
25	Phil Rizzuto	30.00	15.00	9.00
26	Bob Elliott	10.00	5.00	3.00
27	Tom Henrich	12.00	6.00	3.50
28	Joe DiMaggio	350.00	175.00	105.00
29	Harry Lowery (Lowrey)	10.00	5.00	3.00
30	Ted Williams	150.00	75.00	45.00
31	Bob Lemon	22.00	11.00	6.50
32	Warren Spahn	35.00	17.50	10.50
33	Don Hoak	12.00	6.00	3.50
34	Bob Alexander	10.00	5.00	3.00
35	John Simmons	10.00	5.00	3.00
36	Steve Lembo	10.00	5.00	3.00
37	Norman Larker	12.00	6.00	3.50
38	Bob Ludwick	10.00	5.00	3.00
39	Walter Moryn	12.00	6.00	3.50
40	Charlie Thompson	10.00	5.00	3.00
41	Ed Roebuck	12.00	6.00	3.50
42	Russell Rose	10.00	5.00	3.00
43	Edmundo (Sandy) Amoros	14.00	7.00	4.25
44	Bob Milliken	10.00	5.00	3.00
45	Art Fabbro	10.00	5.00	3.00
46	Spook Jacobs	10.00	5.00	3.00
47	Carmen Mauro	10.00	5.00	3.00
48	Walter Fiala	10.00	5.00	3.00
49	Rocky Nelson	10.00	5.00	3.00
50	Tom La Sorda (Lasorda)	80.00	40.00	24.00
51	Ronnie Lee	10.00	5.00	3.00
52	Hampton Coleman	10.00	5.00	3.00
53	Frank Marchio	10.00	5.00	3.00
54	William Sampson	10.00	5.00	3.00
55	Gil Mills	10.00	5.00	3.00
56	Al Ronning	10.00	5.00	3.00
57	Stan Musial	110.00	55.00	33.00
58	Walker Cooper	8.50	4.25	2.50
59	Mickey Vernon	8.50	4.25	2.50
60	Del Ennis	8.50	4.25	2.50
61	Walter Alston	35.00	17.50	10.50
62	Dick Sisler	8.50	4.25	2.50
63	Billy Goodman	8.50	4.25	2.50
64	Alex Kellner	8.50	4.25	2.50

Values quoted in this guide reflect the retail price of a card – the price a collector can expect to pay when buying a card from a dealer. The wholesale price – that which a collector can expect to receive from a dealer when selling cards – will be significantly lower, depending on desirability and condition.

1962 Statistic Back Exhibits

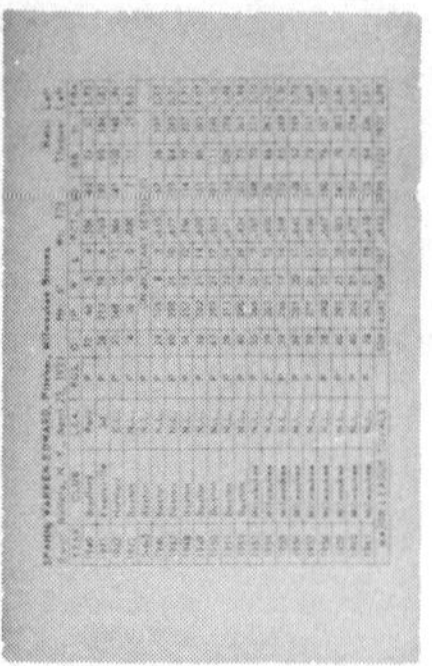

In 1962, the Exhibit Supply Co. added career statistics to the yearly set they produced. The black and white, unnumbered cards measure 3-3/8" by 5-3/8". The statistics found on the back are printed in black or red. The red backs are three times greater in value. The set is comprised of 32 cards.

		NR MT	EX	VG
Complete Set (32):		550.00	275.00	165.00
Common Player:		6.00	3.00	1.75
(1)	Hank Aaron	40.00	20.00	12.00
(2)	Luis Aparicio	15.00	7.50	4.50
(3)	Ernie Banks	25.00	12.50	7.50
(4)	Larry "Yogi" Berra	25.00	12.50	7.50
(5)	Ken Boyer	8.00	4.00	2.50
(6)	Lew Burdette	7.00	3.50	2.00
(7)	Norm Cash	7.00	3.50	2.00
(8)	Orlando Cepeda	10.00	5.00	3.00
(9)	Roberto Clemente	40.00	20.00	12.00
(10)	Rocky Colavito	15.00	7.50	4.50
(11)	Ed "Whitey" Ford	20.00	10.00	6.00
(12)	Nelson Fox	15.00	7.50	4.50
(13)	Tito Francona	6.00	3.00	1.75
(14)	Jim Gentile	6.00	3.00	1.75
(15)	Dick Groat	7.00	3.50	2.00
(16)	Don Hoak	7.00	3.50	2.00
(17)	Al Kaline	20.00	10.00	6.00
(18)	Harmon Killebrew	20.00	10.00	6.00
(19)	Sandy Koufax	35.00	17.50	10.50
(20)	Jim Landis	6.00	3.00	1.75
(21)	Art Mahaffey	6.00	3.00	1.75
(22)	Frank Malzone	6.00	3.00	1.75
(23)	Mickey Mantle	115.00	57.00	34.00
(24)	Roger Maris	20.00	10.00	6.00
(25)	Eddie Mathews	20.00	10.00	6.00
(26)	Willie Mays	40.00	20.00	12.00
(27)	Wally Moon	7.00	3.50	2.00
(28)	Stan Musial	40.00	20.00	12.00
(29)	Milt Pappas	6.00	3.00	1.75
(30)	Vada Pinson	8.00	4.00	2.50
(31)	Norm Siebern	6.00	3.00	1.75
(32)	Warren Spahn	20.00	10.00	6.00

1963 Statistic Back Exhibits

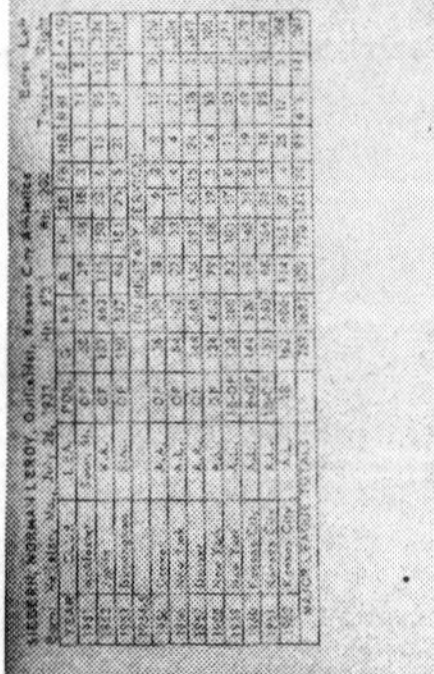

The Exhibit Supply Co. issued a 64-card set with career statistics on the backs of the cards in 1963. The unnumbered, black and white cards are printed on thick cardboard and measure 3-3/8" by 5-3/8" in size. The statistics on the back are printed in black.

		NR MT	EX	VG
Complete Set (64):		600.00	300.00	180.00
Common Player:		5.00	2.50	1.50
(1)	Hank Aaron	35.00	17.50	10.50
(2)	Luis Aparicio	15.00	7.50	4.50
(3)	Bob Aspromonte	5.00	2.50	1.50
(4)	Ernie Banks	20.00	10.00	6.00
(5)	Steve Barber	5.00	2.50	1.50
(6)	Earl Battey	5.00	2.50	1.50
(7)	Larry "Yogi" Berra	25.00	12.50	7.50

(8)	Ken Boyer	6.75	3.50	2.00
(9)	Lew Burdette	5.75	3.00	1.75
(10)	Johnny Callison	5.75	3.00	1.75
(11)	Norm Cash	5.75	3.00	1.75
(12)	Orlando Cepeda	10.00	5.00	3.00
(13)	Dean Chance	5.00	2.50	1.50
(14)	Tom Cheney	5.00	2.50	1.50
(15)	Roberto Clemente	35.00	17.50	10.50
(16)	Rocky Colavito	10.00	5.00	3.00
(17)	Choo Choo Coleman	5.00	2.50	1.50
(18)	Roger Craig	5.75	3.00	1.75
(19)	Joe Cunningham	5.00	2.50	1.50
(20)	Don Drysdale	15.00	7.50	4.50
(21)	Dick Farrell	5.00	2.50	1.50
(22)	Ed "Whitey" Ford	15.00	7.50	4.50
(23)	Nelson Fox	10.00	5.00	3.00
(24)	Tito Francona	5.00	2.50	1.50
(25)	Jim Gentile	5.00	2.50	1.50
(26)	Tony Gonzalez	5.00	2.50	1.50
(27)	Dick Groat	5.75	3.00	1.75
(28)	Ray Herbert	5.00	2.50	1.50
(29)	Chuck Hinton	5.00	2.50	1.50
(30)	Don Hoak	5.75	3.00	1.75
(31)	Frank Howard	6.75	3.50	2.00
(32)	Ken Hubbs	5.75	3.00	1.75
(33)	Joey Jay	5.00	2.50	1.50
(34)	Al Kaline	15.00	7.50	4.50
(35)	Harmon Killebrew	15.00	7.50	4.50
(36)	Sandy Koufax	25.00	12.50	7.50
(37)	Harvey Kuenn	6.75	3.50	2.00
(38)	Jim Landis	5.00	2.50	1.50
(39)	Art Mahaffey	5.00	2.50	1.50
(40)	Frank Malzone	5.00	2.50	1.50
(41)	Mickey Mantle	100.00	50.00	30.00
(42)	Roger Maris	15.00	7.50	4.50
(43)	Eddie Mathews	15.00	7.50	4.50
(44)	Willie Mays	35.00	17.50	10.50
(45)	Bill Mazeroski	6.75	3.50	2.00
(46)	Ken McBride	5.00	2.50	1.50
(47)	Wally Moon	5.75	3.00	1.75
(48)	Stan Musial	35.00	17.50	10.50
(49)	Charlie Neal	5.00	2.50	1.50
(50)	Bill O'Dell	5.00	2.50	1.50
(51)	Milt Pappas	5.75	3.00	1.75
(52)	Camilo Pascual	5.75	3.00	1.75
(53)	Jimmy Piersall	6.75	3.50	2.00
(54)	Vada Pinson	6.75	3.50	2.00
(55)	Brooks Robinson	25.00	12.50	7.50
(56)	Frankie Robinson	25.00	12.50	7.50
(57)	Pete Runnels	5.75	3.00	1.75
(58)	Ron Santo	6.75	3.50	2.00
(59)	Norm Siebern	5.00	2.50	1.50
(60)	Warren Spahn	20.00	10.00	6.00
(61)	Lee Thomas	5.00	2.50	1.50
(62)	Leon Wagner	5.00	2.50	1.50
(63)	Billy Williams	15.00	7.50	4.50
(64)	Maurice Wills	5.00	2.50	1.50

1947 - 66 Exhibits

Called "Exhibits" as they were produced by the Exhibit Supply Co. of Chicago, Ill., this group covers a span of twenty years. Each unnumbered, black and white card, printed on heavy stock, measures 3-3/8" by 5-3/8" and is blank-backed. The Exhibit Supply Co. issued new sets each year, with many players being repeated year after year. Other players appeared in only one or two years, thereby creating levels of scarcity. Many variations of the same basic pose are found in the group. Those cards are listed in the checklist that follows with an "a", "b", etc. following the assigned card number. The complete set includes all variations.

		NR MT	EX	VG
	Complete Set:	5000.	2500.	1500.
	Common Player:	5.75	3.00	1.75
(1)	Hank Aaron	30.00	15.00	9.00
(2a)	Joe Adcock (script signature)	5.75	3.00	1.75
(2b)	Joe Adcock (plain signature)	6.75	3.50	2.00
(3)	Max Alvis	25.00	12.50	7.50
(4)	Johnny Antonelli (Braves)	5.75	3.00	1.75
(5)	Johnny Antonelli (Giants)	6.75	3.50	2.00
(6)	Luis Aparicio (portrait)	9.50	4.75	2.75
(7)	Luis Aparicio (batting)	25.00	12.50	7.50
(8)	Luke Appling	9.50	4.75	2.75
(9a)	Ritchie Ashburn (Phillies, first name incorrect)	9.50	4.75	2.75
(9b)	Richie Ashburn (Phillies, first name correct)	10.00	5.00	3.00
(10)	Richie Ashburn (Cubs)	13.00	6.50	4.00
(11)	Bob Aspromonte	5.75	3.00	1.75
(12)	Toby Atwell	5.75	3.00	1.75
(13)	Ed Bailey (with cap)	6.75	3.50	2.00
(14)	Ed Bailey (no cap)	5.75	3.00	1.75
(15)	Gene Baker	5.75	3.00	1.75
(16a)	Ernie Banks (bat on shoulder, script signature)	25.00	12.50	7.50
(16b)	Ernie Banks (bat on shoulder, plain signature)	15.00	7.50	4.50
(17)	Ernie Banks (portrait)	25.00	12.50	7.50
(18)	Steve Barber	5.75	3.00	1.75
(19)	Earl Battey	6.75	3.50	2.00
(20)	Matt Batts	5.75	3.00	1.75
(21a)	Hank Bauer (N.Y. cap)	6.75	3.50	2.00
(21b)	Hank Bauer (plain cap)	9.50	4.75	2.75
(22)	Frank Baumholtz	5.75	3.00	1.75
(23)	Gene Bearden	5.75	3.00	1.75
(24)	Joe Beggs	12.00	6.00	3.50
(25)	Larry "Yogi" Berra	30.00	15.00	9.00
(26)	Yogi Berra	20.00	10.00	6.00
(27)	Steve Bilko	6.75	3.50	2.00
(28)	Ewell Blackwell (pitching)	9.50	4.75	2.75
(29)	Ewell Blackwell (portrait)	5.75	3.00	1.75
(30a)	Don Blasingame (St. Louis cap)	5.75	3.00	1.75
(30b)	Don Blasingame (plain cap)	8.00	4.00	2.50
(31)	Ken Boyer	9.50	4.75	2.75
(32)	Ralph Branca	9.50	4.75	2.75
(33)	Jackie Brandt	50.00	25.00	15.00
(34)	Harry Brecheen	5.75	3.00	1.75
(35)	Tom Brewer	12.00	6.00	3.50
(36)	Lou Brissie	6.75	3.50	2.00
(37)	Bill Bruton	5.75	3.00	1.75
(38)	Lew Burdette (pitching, side view)	5.75	3.00	1.75
(39)	Lew Burdette (pitching, front view)	8.00	4.00	2.50
(40)	Johnny Callison	9.50	4.75	2.75
(41)	Roy Campanella	20.00	10.00	6.00
(42)	Chico Carrasquel (portrait)	13.00	6.50	4.00
(43)	Chico Carrasquel (leaping)	5.75	3.00	1.75
(44)	George Case	12.00	6.00	3.50
(45)	Hugh Casey	6.75	3.50	2.00
(46)	Norm Cash	9.50	4.75	2.75
(47)	Orlando Cepeda (portrait)	10.00	5.00	3.00
(48)	Orlando Cepeda (batting)	10.00	5.00	3.00
(49a)	Bob Cerv (A's cap)	9.50	4.75	2.75
(49b)	Bob Cerv (plain cap)	16.00	8.00	4.75
(50)	Dean Chance	5.75	3.00	1.75
(51)	Spud Chandler	12.00	6.00	3.50
(52)	Tom Cheney	5.75	3.00	1.75
(53)	Bubba Church	6.75	3.50	2.00
(54)	Roberto Clemente	30.00	15.00	9.00
(55)	Rocky Colavito (portrait)	30.00	15.00	9.00
(56)	Rocky Colavito (batting)	9.50	4.75	2.75
(57)	Choo Choo Coleman	13.00	6.50	4.00
(58)	Gordy Coleman	25.00	12.50	7.50
(59)	Jerry Coleman	6.75	3.50	2.00
(60)	Mort Cooper	12.00	6.00	3.50
(61)	Walker Cooper	5.75	3.00	1.75
(62)	Roger Craig	12.00	6.00	3.50
(63)	Delmar Crandall	5.75	3.00	1.75
(64)	Joe Cunningham (batting)	30.00	15.00	9.00
(65)	Joe Cunningham (portrait)	9.50	4.75	2.75
(66)	Guy Curtwright (Curtright)	6.75	3.50	2.00
(67)	Bud Daley	35.00	17.50	10.50
(68a)	Alvin Dark (Braves)	9.50	4.75	2.75
(68b)	Alvin Dark (Giants)	6.75	3.50	2.00
(69)	Alvin Dark (Cubs)	9.50	4.75	2.75
(70)	Murray Dickson (Murry)	6.75	3.50	2.00
(71)	Bob Dillinger	9.50	4.75	2.75
(72)	Dom DiMaggio	18.00	9.00	5.50
(73)	Joe Dobson	9.50	4.75	2.75
(74)	Larry Doby	5.75	3.00	1.75
(75)	Bobby Doerr	12.00	6.00	3.50
(76)	Dick Donovan (plain cap)	9.50	4.75	2.75
(77)	Dick Donovan (Sox cap)	5.75	3.00	1.75
(78)	Walter Dropo	5.75	3.00	1.75
(79)	Don Drysdale (glove at waist)	30.00	15.00	9.00
(80)	Don Drysdale (portrait)	30.00	15.00	9.00
(81)	Luke Easter	6.75	3.50	2.00
(82)	Bruce Edwards	6.75	3.50	2.00
(83)	Del Ennis	5.75	3.00	1.75
(84)	Al Evans	6.00	3.00	1.75
(85)	Walter Evers	5.75	3.00	1.75
(86)	Ferris Fain (fielding)	9.50	4.75	2.75
(87)	Ferris Fain (portrait)	5.75	3.00	1.75
(88)	Dick Farrell	5.75	3.00	1.75
(89)	Ed "Whitey" Ford	25.00	12.50	7.50
(90)	Whitey Ford (pitching)	15.00	7.50	4.50
(91)	Whitey Ford (portrait)	60.00	30.00	17.50
(92)	Dick Fowler	9.50	4.75	2.75
(93)	Nelson Fox	6.75	3.50	2.00
(94)	Tito Francona	5.75	3.00	1.75
(95)	Bob Friend	5.75	3.00	1.75
(96)	Carl Furillo	10.00	5.00	3.00
(97)	Augie Galan	9.50	4.75	2.75
(98)	Jim Gentile	5.75	3.00	1.75
(99)	Tony Gonzalez	5.75	3.00	1.75
(100)	Billy Goodman (leaping)	5.75	3.00	1.75
(101)	Billy Goodman (batting)	9.50	4.75	2.75
(102)	Ted Greengrass (Jim)	5.75	3.00	1.75
(103)	Dick Groat	9.50	4.75	2.75
(104)	Steve Gromek	5.75	3.00	1.75
(105)	Johnny Groth	5.75	3.00	1.75
(106)	Orval Grove	13.00	6.50	4.00
(107a)	Frank Gustine (Pirates uniform)	6.75	3.50	2.00
(107b)	Frank Gustine (plain uniform)	6.75	3.50	2.00
(108)	Berthold Haas	13.00	6.50	4.00
(109)	Grady Hatton	6.75	3.50	2.00
(110)	Jim Hegan	5.75	3.00	1.75
(111)	Tom Henrich	9.50	4.75	2.75
(112)	Ray Herbert	25.00	12.50	7.50
(113)	Gene Hermanski	6.00	3.00	1.75
(114)	Whitey Herzog	9.50	4.75	2.75
(115)	Kirby Higbe	13.00	6.50	4.00
(116)	Chuck Hinton	5.75	3.00	1.75
(117)	Don Hoak	13.00	6.50	4.00
(118a)	Gil Hodges ("B" on cap)	12.00	6.00	3.50
(118b)	Gil Hodges ("LA" on cap)	10.00	5.00	3.00
(119)	Johnny Hopp	12.00	6.00	3.50
(120)	Elston Howard	9.50	4.75	2.75
(121)	Frank Howard	9.50	4.75	2.75
(122)	Ken Hubbs	35.00	17.50	10.50
(123)	Tex Hughson	12.00	6.00	3.50
(124)	Fred Hutchinson	6.00	3.00	1.75
(125)	Monty Irvin (Monte)	9.50	4.75	2.75
(126)	Joey Jay	5.75	3.00	1.75
(127)	Jackie Jensen	30.00	15.00	9.00
(128)	Sam Jethroe	6.75	3.50	2.00
(129)	Bill Johnson	6.75	3.50	2.00
(130)	Walter Judnich	12.00	6.00	3.50
(131)	Al Kaline (kneeling)	30.00	15.00	9.00
(132)	Al Kaline (portrait)	30.00	15.00	9.00
(133)	George Kell	9.50	4.75	2.75
(134)	Charley Keller	6.00	3.00	1.75
(135)	Alex Kellner	5.75	3.00	1.75
(136)	Kenn Keltner (Ken)	6.75	3.50	2.00
(137)	Harmon Killebrew (batting)	30.00	15.00	9.00
(138)	Harmon Killebrew (throwing)	30.00	15.00	9.00
(139)	Harmon Killibrew (Killebrew) (portrait)	30.00	15.00	9.00
(140)	Ellis Kinder	5.75	3.00	1.75
(141)	Ralph Kiner	9.50	4.75	2.75
(142)	Billy Klaus	25.00	12.50	7.50
(143)	Ted Kluzewski (Kluszewski) (batting)	9.50	4.75	2.75
(144a)	Ted Kluzewski (Kluszewski) (Pirates uniform)	9.50	4.75	2.75
(144b)	Ted Kluzewski (Kluszewski) (plain uniform)	13.00	6.50	4.00
(145)	Don Kolloway	9.50	4.75	2.75
(146)	Jim Konstanty	6.75	3.50	2.00
(147)	Sandy Koufax	25.00	12.50	7.50
(148)	Ed Kranepool	50.00	25.00	15.00
(149a)	Tony Kubek (light background)	9.50	4.75	2.75
(149b)	Tony Kubek (dark background)	6.75	3.50	2.00
(150a)	Harvey Kuenn ("D" on cap)	12.00	6.00	3.50
(150b)	Harvey Kuenn (plain cap)	13.00	6.50	4.00
(151)	Harvey Kuenn ("SF" on cap)	9.50	4.75	2.75
(152)	Kurowski (Whitey)	6.00	3.00	1.75
(153)	Eddie Lake	6.75	3.50	2.00
(154)	Jim Landis	5.75	3.00	1.75
(155)	Don Larsen	9.50	4.75	2.75
(156)	Bob Lemon (glove not visible)	9.50	4.75	2.75
(157)	Bob Lemon (glove partially visible)	30.00	15.00	9.00
(158)	Buddy Lewis	12.00	6.00	3.50
(159)	Johnny Lindell	25.00	12.50	7.50
(160)	Phil Linz	25.00	12.50	7.50
(161)	Don Lock	25.00	12.50	7.50
(162)	Whitey Lockman	5.75	3.00	1.75
(163)	Johnny Logan	5.75	3.00	1.75
(164)	Dale Long ("P" on cap)	5.75	3.00	1.75
(165)	Dale Long ("C" on cap)	9.50	4.75	2.75
(166)	Ed Lopat	6.75	3.50	2.00
(167a)	Harry Lowery (name misspelled)	6.75	3.50	2.00
(167b)	Harry Lowrey (name correct)	6.75	3.50	2.00
(168)	Sal Maglie	5.75	3.00	1.75
(169)	Art Mahaffey	6.75	3.50	2.00
(170)	Hank Majeski	5.75	3.00	1.75
(171)	Frank Malzone	5.75	3.00	1.75
(172)	Mickey Mantle (batting, pinstriped uniform)	100.00	50.00	30.00
(173a)	Mickey Mantle (batting, no pinstripes, first name outlined in white)	75.00	38.00	23.00
173b	Mickey Mantle (batting, no pinstripes, first name not outlined in white)	75.00	38.00	23.00
(174)	Mickey Mantle (portrait)	400.00	200.00	120.00
(175)	Martin Marion	9.50	4.75	2.75
(176)	Roger Maris	25.00	12.50	7.50
(177)	Willard Marshall	6.75	3.50	2.00
(178a)	Eddie Matthews (name incorrect)	12.00	6.00	3.50
(178b)	Eddie Mathews (name correct)	13.00	6.50	4.00
(179)	Ed Mayo	6.75	3.50	2.00
(180)	Willie Mays (batting)	30.00	15.00	9.00
(181)	Willie Mays (portrait)	35.00	17.50	10.50
(182)	Bill Mazeroski (portrait)	10.00	5.00	3.00
(183)	Bill Mazeroski (batting)	10.00	5.00	3.00
(184)	Ken McBride	5.75	3.00	1.75
(185a)	Barney McCaskey (McCosky)	13.00	6.50	4.00
(185b)	Barney McCoskey (McCosky)	90.00	45.00	27.00
(186)	Lindy McDaniel	5.75	3.00	1.75
(187)	Gil McDougald	9.50	4.75	2.75
(188)	Albert Mele	13.00	6.50	4.00
(189)	Sam Mele	6.75	3.50	2.00
(190)	Orestes Minoso ("C" on cap)	9.50	4.75	2.75
(191)	Orestes Minoso (Sox on cap)	5.75	3.00	1.75
(192)	Dale Mitchell	5.75	3.00	1.75
(193)	Wally Moon	9.50	4.75	2.75
(194)	Don Mueller	6.75	3.50	2.00
(195)	Stan Musial (kneeling)	25.00	12.50	7.50
(196)	Stan Musial (batting)	35.00	17.50	10.50
(197)	Charley Neal	18.00	9.00	5.50
(198)	Don Newcombe (shaking hands)	9.50	4.75	2.75
(199a)	Don Newcombe (Dodgers on jacket)	6.75	3.50	2.00
(199b)	Don Newcombe (plain jacket)	6.75	3.50	2.00
(200)	Hal Newhouser	9.50	4.75	2.75
(201)	Ron Northey	12.00	6.00	3.50
(202)	Bill O'Dell	5.75	3.00	1.75
(203)	Joe Page	12.00	6.00	3.50
(204)	Satchel Paige	40.00	20.00	12.00
(205)	Milt Pappas	5.75	3.00	1.75
(206)	Camilo Pascual	5.75	3.00	1.75
(207)	Albie Pearson	25.00	12.50	7.50

(215) John "Boog" Powell	35.00	17.50	10.50
(216) Vic Raschi	6.00	3.00	1.75
(217a) Harold "Peewee" Reese (fielding, ball partially visible)	15.00	7.50	4.50
(217b) Harold "Peewee" Reese (fielding, ball not visible)	15.00	7.50	4.50
(218) Del Rice	5.75	3.00	1.75
(219) Bobby Richardson	55.00	28.00	16.50
(220) Phil Rizzuto	15.00	7.50	4.50
(221a) Robin Roberts (script signature)	12.00	6.00	3.50
(221b) Robin Roberts (plain signature)	9.50	4.75	2.75
(222) Brooks Robinson	30.00	15.00	9.00
(223) Eddie Robinson	5.75	3.00	1.75
(224) Floyd Robinson	25.00	12.50	7.50
(225) Frankie Robinson	20.00	10.00	6.00
(226) Jackie Robinson	30.00	15.00	9.00
(227) Preacher Roe	9.50	4.75	2.75
(228) Bob Rogers (Rodgers)	25.00	12.50	7.50
(229) Richard Rollins	25.00	12.50	7.50
(230) Pete Runnels	12.00	6.00	3.50
(231) John Sain	6.75	3.50	2.00
(232) Ron Santo	9.50	4.75	2.75
(233) Henry Sauer	6.75	3.50	2.00
(234a) Carl Sawatski ("M" on cap)	5.75	3.00	1.75
(234b) Carl Sawatski ("P" on cap)	5.75	3.00	1.75
(234c) Carl Sawatski (plain cap)	13.00	6.50	4.00
(235) Johnny Schmitz	6.75	3.50	2.00
(236a) Red Schoendeinst (Schoendienst) (fielding, name in white)	9.50	4.75	2.75
(236b) Red Schoendeinst (Schoendienst) (fielding, name in red-brown)	10.00	5.00	3.00
(237) Red Schoendinst (Schoendienst) (batting)	9.50	4.75	2.75
(238a) Herb Score ("C" on cap)	6.75	3.50	2.00
(238b) Herb Score (plain cap)	12.00	6.00	3.50
(239) Andy Seminick	5.75	3.00	1.75
(240) Rip Sewell	9.50	4.75	2.75
(241) Norm Siebern	5.75	3.00	1.75
(242) Roy Sievers (batting)	6.75	3.50	2.00
(243a) Roy Sievers (portrait, "W" on cap, light background)	9.50	4.75	2.75
(243b) Roy Sievers (portrait, "W" on cap, dark background)	6.75	3.50	2.00
(243c) Roy Sievers (portrait, plain cap)	6.00	3.00	1.75
(244) Curt Simmons	6.75	3.50	2.00
(245) Dick Sisler	6.75	3.50	2.00
(246) Bill Skowron	9.50	4.75	2.75
(247) Bill "Moose" Skowron	55.00	28.00	16.50
(248) Enos Slaughter	9.50	4.75	2.75
(249a) Duke Snider ("B" on cap)	15.00	7.50	4.50
(249b) Duke Snider ("LA" on cap)	18.00	9.00	5.50
(250a) Warren Spahn ("B" on cap)	10.00	5.00	3.00
(250b) Warren Spahn ("M" on cap)	12.00	6.00	3.50
(251) Stanley Spence	13.00	6.50	4.00
(252) Ed Stanky (plain uniform)	6.75	3.50	2.00
(253) Ed Stanky (Giants uniform)	6.75	3.50	2.00
(254) Vern Stephens (batting)	6.75	3.50	2.00
(255) Vern Stephens (portrait)	6.75	3.50	2.00
(256) Ed Stewart	6.75	3.50	2.00
(257) Snuffy Stirnweiss	13.00	6.50	4.00
(258) George "Birdie" Tebbetts	12.00	6.00	3.50
(259) Frankie Thomas (photo actually Bob Skinner)	30.00	15.00	9.00
(260) Frank Thomas (portrait)	13.00	6.50	4.00
(261) Lee Thomas	5.75	3.00	1.75
(262) Bobby Thomson	9.50	4.75	2.75
(263a) Earl Torgeson (Braves uniform)	5.75	3.00	1.75
(263b) Earl Torgeson (plain uniform)	6.75	3.50	2.00
(264) Gus Triandos	9.50	4.75	2.75
(265) Virgil Trucks	5.75	3.00	1.75
(266) Johnny Vandermeer (VanderMeer)	13.00	6.50	4.00
(267) Emil Verban	9.50	4.75	2.75
(268) Mickey Vernon (throwing)	5.75	3.00	1.75
(269) Mickey Vernon (batting)	5.75	3.00	1.75
(270) Bill Voiselle	9.50	4.75	2.75
(271) Leon Wagner	5.75	3.00	1.75
(272a) Eddie Waitkus (throwing, Chicago uniform)	9.50	4.75	2.75
(272b) Eddie Waitkus (throwing, plain uniform)	6.75	3.50	2.00
(273) Eddie Waitkus (portrait)	13.00	6.50	4.00
(274) Dick Wakefield	6.75	3.50	2.00
(275) Harry Walker	9.50	4.75	2.75
(276) Bucky Walters	6.00	3.00	1.75
(277) Pete Ward	30.00	15.00	9.00
(278) Herman Wehmeier	6.75	3.50	2.00
(279) Vic Wertz (batting)	5.75	3.00	1.75
(280) Vic Wertz (portrait)	5.75	3.00	1.75
(281) Wally Westlake	6.75	3.50	2.00
(282) Wes Westrum	13.00	6.50	4.00
(283) Billy Williams	13.00	6.50	4.00
(284) Maurice Wills	12.00	6.00	3.50
(285a) Gene Woodling (script signature)	5.75	3.00	1.75
(285b) Gene Woodling (plain signature)	9.50	4.75	2.75
(286) Taffy Wright	6.75	3.50	2.00
(287) Carl Yastrazemski (Yastrzemski)	175.00	90.00	50.00
(288) Al Zarilla	6.75	3.50	2.00
(289a) Gus Zernial (script signature)	5.75	3.00	1.75
(289b) Gus Zernial (plain signature)	9.50	4.75	2.75
(290) Braves Team - 1948	35.00	17.50	10.50
(291) Dodgers Team - 1949	45.00	22.00	13.50
(292) Dodgers Team - 1952	45.00	22.00	13.50
(293) Dodgers Team - 1955	45.00	22.00	13.50
(294) Dodgers Team - 1956	45.00	22.00	13.50
(295) Giants Team - 1951	35.00	17.50	10.50
(296) Giants Team - 1954	35.00	17.50	10.50
(297) Indians Team - 1948	35.00	17.50	10.50
(298) Indians Team - 1954	35.00	17.50	10.50
(299) Phillies Team - 1950	35.00	17.50	10.50
(300) Yankees Team - 1949	60.00	30.00	18.00
(301) Yankees Team - 1950	60.00	30.00	18.00
(302) Yankees Team - 1951	60.00	30.00	18.00
(303) Yankees Team - 1952	60.00	30.00	18.00
(304) Yankees Team - 1955	60.00	30.00	18.00
(305) Yankees Team - 1956	60.00	30.00	18.00

1904 Fan Craze American League

One of the earliest 20th Century baseball card sets, this 1904 issue from the Fan Craze Company of Cincinnati was designed as a deck of playing cards and was intended to be used as a baseball table game. Separate sets were issued for the National League, which are printed in red, and the American League, which are blue. Both sets feature sepia-toned, black and white player portraits inside an oval with the player's name and team below. The top of the card indicates one of many various baseball plays, such as "Single," "Out at First," "Strike," "Stolen Base," etc. The unnumbered cards measure 2-1/2" by 3-1/2" and are identified as "An Artistic Constellation of Great Stars."

	NR MT	EX	VG
Complete Set:	5000.	2500.	1500.
Common Player:	60.00	30.00	18.00
(1) Nick Altrock	60.00	30.00	18.00
(2) Jim Barrett	60.00	30.00	18.00
(3) Harry Bay	60.00	30.00	18.00
(4) Albert Bender	175.00	87.00	52.00
(5) Bill Bernhardt	60.00	30.00	18.00
(6) W. Bradley	60.00	30.00	18.00
(7) Jack Chesbro	350.00	175.00	100.00
(8) Jimmy Collins	175.00	87.00	52.00
(9) Sam Crawford	175.00	87.00	52.00
(10) Lou Criger	60.00	30.00	18.00
(11) Lave Cross	60.00	30.00	18.00
(12) Monte Cross	60.00	30.00	18.00
(13) Harry Davis	60.00	30.00	18.00
(14) Bill Dinneen	60.00	30.00	18.00
(15) Pat Donovan	60.00	30.00	18.00
(16) Pat Dougherty	60.00	30.00	18.00
(17) Norman Elberfield (Elberfeld)	60.00	30.00	18.00
(18) Hoke Ferris (Hobe)	60.00	30.00	18.00
(19) Elmer Flick	175.00	87.00	52.00
(20) Buck Freeman	60.00	30.00	18.00
(21) Fred Glade	60.00	30.00	18.00
(22) Clark Griffith	175.00	87.00	52.00
(23) Charley Hickman	60.00	30.00	18.00
(24) Wm. Holmes	60.00	30.00	18.00
(25) Harry Howell	60.00	30.00	18.00
(26) Frank Isbel (Isbell)	60.00	30.00	18.00
(27) Albert Jacobson	60.00	30.00	18.00
(28) Ban Johnson	200.00	100.00	60.00
(29) Fielder Jones	60.00	30.00	18.00
(30) Adrian Joss	175.00	87.00	52.00
(31) Billy Keeler	250.00	125.00	75.00
(32) Napolean Lajoie	350.00	175.00	100.00
(33) Connie Mack	425.00	212.00	127.00
(34) Jimmy McAleer	60.00	30.00	18.00
(35) Jim McGuire	60.00	30.00	18.00
(36) Earl Moore	60.00	30.00	18.00
(37) George Mullen (Mullin)	60.00	30.00	18.00
(38) Billy Owen	60.00	30.00	18.00
(39) Fred Parent	60.00	30.00	18.00
(40) Case Patten	60.00	30.00	18.00
(41) Ed Plank	175.00	87.00	52.00
(42) Ossie Schreckengost	60.00	30.00	18.00
(43) Jake Stahl	60.00	30.00	18.00
(44) Fred Stone	60.00	30.00	18.00
(45) Wm. Sudhoff	60.00	30.00	18.00
(46) Roy Turner	60.00	30.00	18.00
(47) G.E. Waddell	175.00	87.00	52.00
(48) Bob Wallace	175.00	87.00	52.00
(49) G. Harris White	60.00	30.00	18.00
(50) Geo. Winters	60.00	30.00	18.00
(51) Cy Young	550.00	275.00	165.00

The values quoted are intended to reflect the market price.

1904 Fan Craze National League

Identical in size and format to the American League set, this series of unnumbered cards was issued by the Fan Craze Company of Cincinnati in 1904 and was designed like a decl of playing cards. The cards were intended to be used in playing a baseball table game. The National League cards are printed in red.

	NR MT	EX	VG
Complete Set:	4500.	2250.	1350.
Common Player:	60.00	30.00	18.00
(1) Leon Ames	60.00	30.00	18.00
(2) Clarence Beaumont	60.00	30.00	18.00
(3) Jake Beckley	200.00	100.00	60.00
(4) Billy Bergen	60.00	30.00	18.00
(5) Roger Bresnahan	200.00	100.00	60.00
(6) George Brown (Browne)	60.00	30.00	18.00
(7) Mordacai Brown	200.00	100.00	60.00
(8) Jas. Casey	60.00	30.00	18.00
(9) Frank Chance	200.00	100.00	60.00
(10) Fred Clarke	200.00	100.00	60.00
(11) Thos. Corcoran	60.00	30.00	18.00
(12) Bill Dahlen	60.00	30.00	18.00
(13) Mike Donlin	60.00	30.00	18.00
(14) Charley Dooin	60.00	30.00	18.00
(15) Mickey Doolin (Doolan)	60.00	30.00	18.00
(16) Hugh Duffy	200.00	100.00	60.00
(17) John E. Dunleavy	60.00	30.00	18.00
(18) Bob Ewing	60.00	30.00	18.00
(19) "Chick" Fraser	60.00	30.00	18.00
(20) J. Edward Hanlon	60.00	30.00	18.00
(21) G.E. Howard	60.00	30.00	18.00
(22) Miller Huggins	200.00	100.00	60.00
(23) Joseph Kelley	200.00	100.00	60.00
(24) John Kling	60.00	30.00	18.00
(25) Tommy Leach	60.00	30.00	18.00
(26) Harry Lumley	60.00	30.00	18.00
(27) Carl Lundgren	60.00	30.00	18.00
(28) Bill Maloney	60.00	30.00	18.00
(29) Dan McGann	60.00	30.00	18.00
(30) Joe McGinnity	200.00	100.00	60.00
(31) John J. McGraw	200.00	100.00	60.00
(32) Harry McIntire (McIntyre)	60.00	30.00	18.00
(33) Charley Nichols	60.00	30.00	18.00
(34) Mike O'Neil (O'Neill)	60.00	30.00	18.00
(35) Orville Overall (Orval)	60.00	30.00	18.00
(36) Frank Pfeffer	60.00	30.00	18.00
(37) Deacon Phillippe	60.00	30.00	18.00
(38) Charley Pittinger	60.00	30.00	18.00
(39) Harry C. Pulliam	60.00	30.00	18.00
(40) Claude Ritchey	60.00	30.00	18.00
(41) Ed Ruelbach (Reulbach)	60.00	30.00	18.00
(42) J. Bentley Seymour	60.00	30.00	18.00
(43) Jim Sheckard	60.00	30.00	18.00
(44) Jack Taylor	60.00	30.00	18.00
(45) Luther H. Taylor	75.00	37.00	22.00
(46) Fred Tenny (Tenney)	60.00	30.00	18.00
(47) Harry Theilman	60.00	30.00	18.00
(48) Roy Thomas	60.00	30.00	18.00
(49) Hans Wagner	600.00	300.00	180.00
(50) Jake Weimer	60.00	30.00	18.00
(51) Bob Wicker	60.00	30.00	18.00
(52) Victor Willis	60.00	30.00	18.00
(53) Lew Wiltsie	60.00	30.00	18.00
(54) Irving Young	60.00	30.00	18.00

Definitions for grading conditions are located in the Introduction of this price guide.

Values for recent cards and sets are listed in Mint (MT), Near Mint (NM), reflecting the fact that many cards from recent years have been preserved in top condition. Recent cards and sets in less than Excellent condition have little collector interest.

1922 Fans Cigarettes (T231)

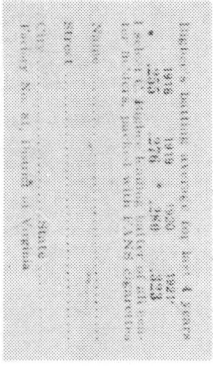

More mystery surrounds this obscure set, issued in 1922 by Fans Cigarettes, than any other tobacco issue. In fact, the only evidence of its existence until 1992 was a photocopy of a single card of Pittsburgh Pirates outfielder Carson Bigbee. Even the owner of the card is unknown. Assuming the photocopy is actual size, the card measures approximately 2-1/2" by 1-1/2" and is believed to be sepia-toned. Adding to the mystery is the number "85" which appears in the lower right corner on the front of the card. apparently indicating there were at least that many cards in the set. In 1992 card "61" was reported. The back of Bigbee's card displays his batting averages for each season from 1918 through 1921 and includes the line: "I select C. Bigbee leading batter of all center fielders, packed with FANS cigarettes." The statement is followed by blanks for a person to fill in his name and address, as if the card were some sort of "ballot." Although they have not received much publicity, these cards may be the rarest baseball cards in the hobby. As such, no value will be placed on the cards. American Card Catalog designation is T231.

		NR MT	EX	VG
Complete Set:				
61	Frank Baker			
85	Carson Bigbee			

1988 Fantastic Sam's

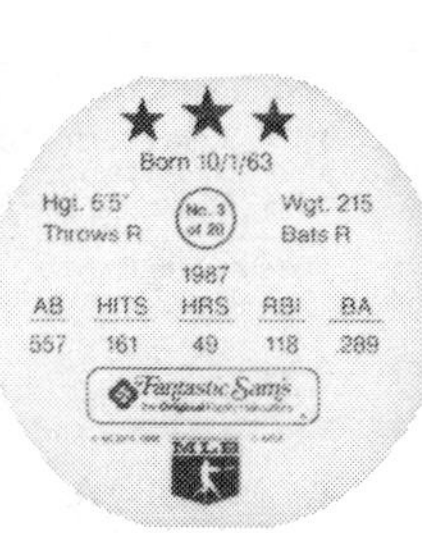

This set of 20 full-color player discs (2-1/2" diameter) was distributed during a Superstar Sweepstakes sponsored by Fantastic Sam's Family Haircutters' 1,800 stores nationwide. Each sweepstakes card consists of two connected discs (bright orange fronts, white backs) perforated for easy separation. One disc features the baseball player photo, the other carries the sweepstakes logo and a list of prizes. Player discs carry a Fantastic Sam's Baseball Superstars header curved above the photo, with his name, team and position printed in black. The disc backs are black and white and include personal info, card number and 1987 player stats. Sweepstakes discs list contest prizes (Grand Prize was 4 tickets to a 1988 Championship game) on the front and an entry form on the flipside. Below the prize list is a silver scratch-off rectangle which may reveal an instant prize.

		MT	NR MT	EX
Complete Set:		7.00	5.25	2.75
Common Player:		.20	.15	.08
1	Kirby Puckett	.75	.60	.30
2	George Brett	1.00	.70	.40
3	Mark McGwire	.60	.45	.25
4	Wally Joyner	.50	.40	.20
5	Paul Molitor	.60	.45	.25
6	Alan Trammell	.40	.30	.15
7	George Bell	.25	.20	.10
8	Wade Boggs	.90	.70	.35
9	Don Mattingly	.90	.70	.35
10	Julio Franco	.20	.15	.08
11	Ozzie Smith	.40	.30	.15
12	Will Clark	.75	.60	.30
13	Dale Murphy	.60	.45	.25
14	Eric Davis	.40	.30	.15
15	Andre Dawson	.40	.30	.15
16	Tim Raines	.30	.25	.12
17	Darryl Strawberry	.30	.25	.12
18	Tony Gwynn	.60	.45	.25
19	Mike Schmidt	1.00	.70	.40
20	Pedro Guerrero	.20	.15	.08

1987 Farmland Dairies Mets

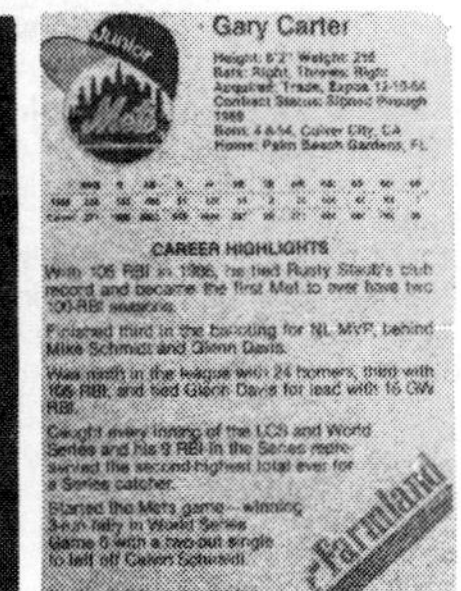

The New York Mets and Farmland Dairies produced a nine-card panel of baseball cards for members of the Junior Mets Club. Members of the club, kids 14 years of age and younger, received the perforated panel as part of a package featuring gifts and special privileges. The cards are the standard 2-1/2" by 3-1/2" with fronts containing a full-color photo encompassed by a blue border. The backs are designed on a vertical format and have player statistics and career highlights. The Farmland Dairies and Junior Mets Club logos are also carried on the card backs.

		MT	NR MT	EX
Complete Panel Set:		6.00	4.50	2.50
Complete Singles Set:		4.50	3.50	1.75
Common Single Player:		.25	.20	.10
1	Mookie Wilson	.25	.20	.10
4	Len Dykstra	.75	.60	.30
8	Gary Carter	.70	.50	.30
12	Ron Darling	.40	.30	.15
18	Darryl Strawberry	.40	.30	.15
19	Bob Ojeda	.25	.20	.10
22	Kevin McReynolds	.60	.45	.25
42	Roger McDowell	.35	.25	.14
----	Team Card	.25	.20	.10

1988 Farmland Dairies Mets

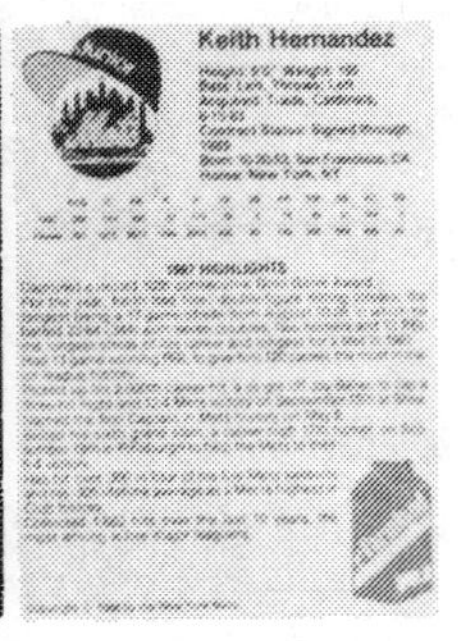

Part of the Junior Mets Fan Club membership package, this set of 9 standard size cards was printed on a single panel. Card fronts feature full-color action shots framed in orange and blue. A white player name runs across the top border, with a large team logo, uniform number and position printed below the photo. Card backs are blue on brown and include personal data, stats and 1987 season highlights. The set was offered to fans 14 years and younger for a $6 fan club membership fee, with a $1 discount for those who sent in two proofs of purchase from Farmland Dairies milk cartons.

		MT	NR MT	EX
Complete Panel Set:		6.00	4.50	2.50
Complete Singles Set:		4.50	3.50	1.75
Common Single Player:		.25	.20	.10
8	Gary Carter	.70	.50	.30
16	Dwight Gooden	1.00	.70	.40
17	Keith Hernandez	.40	.30	.15
18	Darryl Strawberry	.40	.30	.15
20	Howard Johnson	.70	.50	.30
21	Kevin Elster	.25	.20	.10
42	Roger McDowell	.25	.20	.10
48	Randy Myers	.35	.25	.14

1939 Father & Son Shoes Phillies

This 16-card set features members of the Phillies and A's and was distributed in the Philadelphia area in 1939 by Father & Son Shoes stores. The unnumbered black and white cards measure 3" by 4". The player's name, position and team appear below the photo, along with the line "Compliments of Fathers & Son Shoes." The backs are blank. The only player of note in the set is Hall of Famer Chuck Klein.

		NR MT	EX	VG
Complete Set:		600.00	362.00	217.00
Common Player:		35.00	17.50	10.50
(1)	Morrie Arnovich	35.00	17.50	10.50
(2)	Earl Brucker	35.00	17.50	10.50
(3)	George Caster	35.00	17.50	10.50
(4)	Spud Davis	35.00	17.50	10.50
(5)	Joe Gantenbein	35.00	17.50	10.50
(6)	Bob Johnson	45.00	22.00	13.50
(7)	Merrill May	35.00	17.50	10.50
(8)	Claude Passeau	35.00	17.50	10.50
(9)	Sam Chapman	35.00	17.50	10.50
(10)	Chuck Klein	150.00	75.00	45.00
(11)	Herschel Martin	35.00	17.50	10.50
(12)	Wally Moses	45.00	22.00	13.50
(13)	Hugh Mulcahy	35.00	17.50	10.50
(14)	Skeeter Newsome	35.00	17.50	10.50
(15)	George Scharien	35.00	17.50	10.50
(16)	Dick Siebert	35.00	17.50	10.50

1914 Fatima (T222)

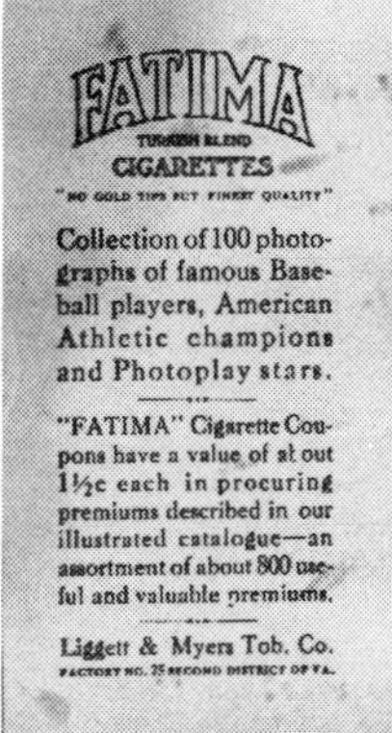
FATIMA
TURKISH BLEND
CIGARETTES
"NO GOLD TIPS BUT FINEST QUALITY"
Collection of 100 photographs of famous Base-ball players, American Athletic champions and Photoplay stars.
"FATIMA" Cigarette Coupons have a value of at out 1½c each in procuring premiums described in our illustrated catalogue—an assortment of about 800 useful and valuable premiums.
Liggett & Myers Tob. Co.

Unlike the typical 20th Century tobacco card issues, the T222 Fatima cards were glossy photographs on a thin paper stock and measure a larger 2-1/2" by 4-1/2". According to the back of the card, the set includes "100 photographs of famous Base-ball Players, American Athletic Champions and Photoplay stars," but apparently not all were issued. The baseball portion of the set appears to be complete at 52, while only four other athletes and four "photoplay" stars have been found. The set, issued in 1913, includes players from 13 of the 16 major league teams (all except the Red Sox, White Sox and Pirates.) The set features a mix of star and lesser-known players.

		NR MT	EX	VG
Complete Set:		9500.	7500.	4500.
Common Player:		150.00	75.00	45.00
(1)	Grover Alexander	600.00	300.00	180.00
(2)	Jimmy Archer	150.00	75.00	45.00
(3)	Jimmy Austin	150.00	75.00	45.00
(4)	Jack Barry	150.00	75.00	45.00
(5)	George Baumgardner	150.00	75.00	45.00
(6)	Rube Benton	150.00	75.00	45.00
(7)	Roger Bresnahan	400.00	200.00	120.00
(8)	Boardwalk Brown	150.00	75.00	45.00
(9)	George Burns	150.00	75.00	45.00
(10)	Bullet Joe Bush	160.00	80.00	48.00
(11)	George Chalmers	150.00	75.00	45.00
(12)	Frank Chance	450.00	225.00	135.00
(13)	Al Demaree	150.00	75.00	45.00
(14)	Art Fletcher	150.00	75.00	45.00
(15)	Earl Hamilton	150.00	75.00	45.00
(16)	John Henry	150.00	75.00	45.00
(17)	Byron Houck	150.00	75.00	45.00
(18)	Miller Huggins	400.00	200.00	120.00
(19)	Hughie Jennings	400.00	200.00	120.00
(20)	Walter Johnson	1500.	750.00	450.00
(21)	Ray Keating	150.00	75.00	45.00
(22)	Jack Lapp	150.00	75.00	45.00
(23)	Tommy Leach	150.00	75.00	45.00
(24)	Nemo Leibold	150.00	75.00	45.00
(25)	Jack Lelivelt	150.00	75.00	45.00
(26)	Hans Lobert	150.00	75.00	45.00
(27)	Lee Magee	150.00	75.00	45.00
(28)	Sherry Magee	150.00	75.00	45.00
(29)	Fritz Maisel	150.00	75.00	45.00
(30)	Rube Marquard	400.00	200.00	120.00
(31)	George McBride	150.00	75.00	45.00
(32)	Larry McLean	150.00	75.00	45.00
(33)	Stuffy McInnis	150.00	75.00	45.00
(34)	Ray Morgan	150.00	75.00	45.00
(35)	Eddie Murphy	150.00	75.00	45.00
(36)	Red Murray	150.00	75.00	45.00
(37)	Rube Oldring	150.00	75.00	45.00
(38)	Bill Orr	150.00	75.00	45.00
(39)	Hub Perdue	150.00	75.00	45.00
(40)	Art Phelan	150.00	75.00	45.00
(41)	Ed Reulbach	150.00	75.00	45.00
(42)	Vic Saier	150.00	75.00	45.00
(43)	Slim Sallee	150.00	75.00	45.00
(44)	Wally Schang	150.00	75.00	45.00
(45)	Wildfire Schulte	150.00	75.00	45.00
(46)	J.C. "Red" Smith	150.00	75.00	45.00
(47)	Amos Strunk	150.00	75.00	45.00
(48)	Bill Sweeney	150.00	75.00	45.00
(49)	Lefty Tyler	150.00	75.00	45.00
(50)	Ossie Vitt	150.00	75.00	45.00
(51)	Ivy Wingo	150.00	75.00	45.00
(52)	Heinie Zimmerman	150.00	75.00	45.00

1913 Fatima Team Cards (T200)

Issued by the Ligget & Myers Tobacco Co. in 1913 with Fatima brand cigarettes, the T200 set consists of eight National and eight American League team cards. The cards measure 2-5/8" by 4-3/4" and are glossy photographs on paper stock. Although it is unknown why, several of the cards are more difficult to obtain than others. The team cards feature 369 different players, managers and mascots. The card backs contain an offer for an enlarged copy (13" by 21") of a team card, minus the advertising on front, in exchange for 40 Fatima cigarette coupons. These large T200 premiums are very rare and have a value of 12-15 times greater than a common T200 card.

		NR MT	EX	VG
Complete Set:		8000.	4000.	2400.
Common Team:		300.00	150.00	90.00
(1)	Boston Nationals	475.00	237.00	142.00
(2)	Brooklyn Nationals	300.00	150.00	90.00
(3)	Chicago Nationals	300.00	150.00	90.00
(4)	Cincinnati Nationals	300.00	150.00	90.00
(5)	New York Nationals	350.00	175.00	105.00
(6)	Philadelphia Nationals	300.00	150.00	90.00
(7)	Pittsburgh Nationals	300.00	150.00	90.00
(8)	St. Louis Nationals	475.00	237.00	142.00
(9)	Boston Americans	275.00	137.00	83.00
(10)	Chicago Americans	375.00	187.00	112.00
(11)	Cleveland Americans	500.00	250.00	150.00
(12)	Detroit Americans	700.00	350.00	150.00
(13)	New York Americans	1200.	600.00	350.00
(14)	Philadelphia Americans	300.00	150.00	90.00
(15)	St. Louis Americans	1000.	500.00	300.00
(16)	Washington Americans	400.00	200.00	80.00

1951 Fischer Baking Labels

This set of end-labels from loaves of bread consists of 32 player photos, each measuring approximately 2-3/4" square. The labels include the player's name, team and position, along with a few words about him. The bakery's slogan "Bread For Energy" appears in a dark band along the bottom. The set, which is unnumbered, was distributed in the Northeast.

		NR MT	EX	VG
Complete Set (32):		2600.	1300.	800.00
Common Player:		90.00	45.00	27.00
(1)	Vern Bickford	90.00	45.00	27.00
(2)	Ralph Branca	100.00	50.00	30.00
(3)	Harry Brecheen	90.00	45.00	27.00
(4)	"Chico" Carrasquel	90.00	45.00	27.00
(5)	Cliff Chambers	90.00	45.00	27.00
(6)	"Hoot" Evers	90.00	45.00	27.00
(7)	Ned Garver	90.00	45.00	27.00
(8)	Billy Goodman	90.00	45.00	27.00
(9)	Gil Hodges	135.00	67.00	40.00
(10)	Larry Jansen	90.00	45.00	27.00
(11)	Willie Jones	90.00	45.00	27.00
(12)	Eddie Joost	90.00	45.00	27.00
(13)	George Kell	125.00	62.00	37.00
(14)	Alex Kellner	90.00	45.00	27.00
(15)	Ted Kluszewski	120.00	60.00	36.00
(16)	Jim Konstanty	90.00	45.00	27.00
(17)	Bob Lemon	125.00	62.00	37.00
(18)	Cass Michaels	90.00	45.00	27.00
(19)	Johnny Mize	125.00	62.00	37.00
(20)	Irv Noren	90.00	45.00	27.00
(21)	Joe Page	100.00	50.00	30.00
(22)	Andy Pafko	100.00	50.00	30.00
(23)	Mel Parnell	90.00	45.00	27.00
(24)	Johnny Sain	100.00	50.00	30.00
(25)	"Red" Schoendienst	120.00	60.00	36.00
(26)	Roy Sievers	90.00	45.00	27.00
(27)	Roy Smalley	90.00	45.00	27.00
(28)	Herman Wehmeier	90.00	45.00	27.00
(29)	Bill Werle	90.00	45.00	27.00
(30)	Wes Westrum	90.00	45.00	27.00
(31)	Early Wynn	125.00	62.00	37.00
(32)	Gus Zernial	90.00	45.00	27.00

1959 Fleer Ted Williams

1938 — First Spring Training

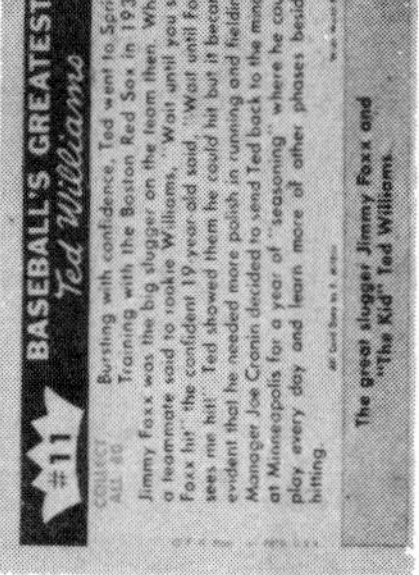

This 80-card 1959 Fleer set tells of the life of baseball great Ted Williams, from his childhood years up to 1958. The full-color cards measure 2-1/2" by 3-1/2" in size and make use of both horizontal and vertical formats. The card backs, all designed horizontally, contain a continuing biography of Williams. Card #68 was withdrawn from the set early in production and is scarce. Counterfeit cards of #68 have been produced and can be distinguished by a cross-hatch pattern which appears over the photo on the card fronts.

		NR MT	EX	VG
Complete Set:		1100.	550.00	325.00
Common Card:		8.00	4.00	2.50
1	The Early Years	30.00	12.50	7.50
2	Ted's Idol - Babe Ruth	40.00	20.00	12.00
3	Practice Makes Perfect	6.50	3.25	2.00
4	1934 - Ted Learns The Fine Points	6.50	3.25	2.00
5	Ted's Fame Spreads - 1935-36	6.50	3.25	2.00
6	Ted Turns Professional	6.50	3.25	2.00
7	1936 - From Mound To Plate	6.50	3.25	2.00
8	1937 - First Full Season	6.50	3.25	2.00
9	1937 - First Step To The Majors	6.50	3.25	2.00
10	1938 - Gunning As A Pastime	6.50	3.25	2.00
11	1938 - First Spring Training	6.50	3.25	2.00
12	1939 - Burning Up The Minors	6.50	3.25	2.00
13	1939 - Ted Shows He Will Stay	6.50	3.25	2.00
14	Outstanding Rookie of 1939	6.50	3.25	2.00
15	1940 - Williams Licks Sophomore Jinx	6.50	3.25	2.00
16	1941 - Williams' Greatest Year	6.50	3.25	2.00
17	1941 - How Ted Hit .400	6.50	3.25	2.00
18	1941 - All-Star Hero	6.50	3.25	2.00
19	1942 - Ted Wins Triple Crown	6.50	3.25	2.00
20	1942 - On To Naval Training	6.50	3.25	2.00
21	1943 - Honors For Williams	6.50	3.25	2.00
22	1944 - Ted Solos	6.50	3.25	2.00
23	1944 - Williams Wins His Wings	6.50	3.25	2.00
24	1945 - Sharpshooter	6.50	3.25	2.00
25	1945 - Ted Is Discharged	6.50	3.25	2.00
26	1946 - Off To A Flying Start	6.50	3.25	2.00
27	July 9, 1946 - One Man Show	6.50	3.25	2.00
28	July 14, 1946 - The Williams Shift	6.50	3.25	2.00
29	July 21, 1946, Ted Hits For The Cycle	6.50	3.25	2.00
30	1946 - Beating The Williams Shift	6.50	3.25	2.00
31	Oct. 1946 - Sox Lose The Series	6.50	3.25	2.00
32	1946 - Most Valuable Player	6.50	3.25	2.00
33	1947 - Another Triple Crown For Ted	6.50	3.25	2.00
34	1947 - Ted Sets Runs-Scored Record	6.50	3.25	2.00
35	1948 - The Sox Miss The Pennant	6.50	3.25	2.00
36	1948 - Banner Year For Ted	6.50	3.25	2.00
37	1949 - Sox Miss Out Again	6.50	3.25	2.00
38	1949 - Power Rampage	6.50	3.25	2.00
39	1950 - Great Start	6.50	3.25	2.00
40	July 11, 1950 - Ted Crashes Into Wall	6.50	3.25	2.00
41	1950 - Ted Recovers	6.50	3.25	2.00
42	1951 - Williams Slowed By Injury	6.50	3.25	2.00
43	1951 - Leads Outfielders In Double Plays	6.50	3.25	2.00
44	1952 - Back To The Marines	6.50	3.25	2.00
45	1952 - Farewell To Baseball?	6.50	3.25	2.00
46	1952 - Ready For Combat	6.50	3.25	2.00
47	1953 - Ted Crash Lands Jet	6.50	3.25	2.00
48	July 14, 1953 - Ted Returns	6.50	3.25	2.00
49	1953 - Smash Return	6.50	3.25	2.00
50	March 1954 - Spring Injury	6.50	3.25	2.00
51	May 16, 1954 - Ted Is Patched Up	6.50	3.25	2.00
52	1954 - Ted's Comeback	6.50	3.25	2.00
53	1954 - Ted's Comeback Is A Sucess	6.50	3.25	2.00
54	Dec. 1954, Fisherman Ted Hooks a Big One	6.50	3.25	2.00
55	1955 - Ted Decides Retirement Is "No Go"	6.50	3.25	2.00
56	1955 - 2,000th Major League Hit,)	6.50	3.25	2.00
58	1957 - Williams Hits .388	6.50	3.25	2.00
59	1957 - Hot September For Ted	6.50	3.25	2.00
60	1957 - More Records For Ted	6.50	3.25	2.00
61	1957 - Outfielder Ted	6.50	3.25	2.00
62	1958 - 6th Batting Title For Ted	6.50	3.25	2.00
63	Ted's All-Star Record	6.50	3.25	2.00
64	1958 - Daughter And Famous Daddy	6.50	3.25	2.00
65	August 30, 1958	6.50	3.25	2.00
66	1958 - Powerhouse	6.50	3.25	2.00
67	Two Famous Fisherman (with Sam Snead)	15.00	7.50	4.50
68	Jan. 23, 1959 - Ted Signs For 1959	750.00	375.00	220.00
69	A Future Ted Williams?	6.50	3.25	2.00
70	Ted Williams & Jim Thorpe	25.00	12.50	7.50
71	Ted's Hitting Fundamentals #1	6.50	3.25	2.00
72	Ted's Hitting Fundamentals #2	6.50	3.25	2.00
73	Ted's Hitting Fundamentals #3	6.50	3.25	2.00
74	Here's How!	6.50	3.25	2.00
75	Williams' Value To Red Sox (with Babe Ruth, Eddie Collins)	20.00	10.00	6.00
76	Ted's Remarkable "On Base" Record	6.50	3.25	2.00
77	Ted Relaxes	6.50	3.25	2.00
78	Honors For Williams	6.50	3.25	2.00
79	Where Ted Stands	6.50	3.25	2.00
80	Ted's Goals For 1959	15.00	4.00	2.50

Values quoted in this guide reflect the retail price of a card – the price a collector can expect to pay when buying a card from a dealer. The wholesale price – that which a collector can expect to receive from a dealer when selling cards – will be significantly lower, depending on desirability and condition.

The values quoted are intended to reflect the market price.

1960 Fleer

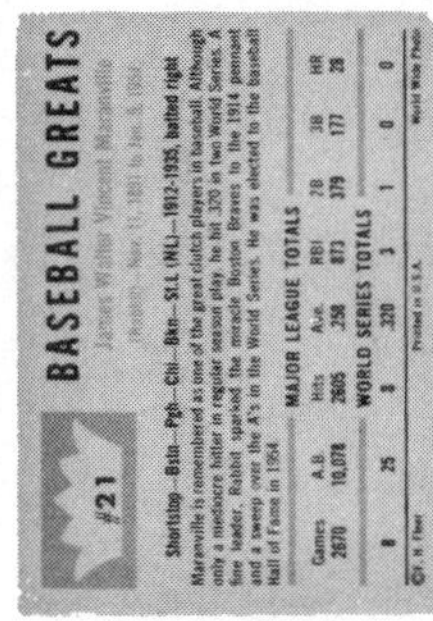

The 1960 Fleer Baseball Greats set consists of 78 cards of the game's top players from the past, plus a card of Ted Williams, who was in his final major league season. The cards are standard size (2-1/2" by 3-1/2") and feature color photos inside blue, green, red or yellow borders. The card backs carry a short player biography plus career hitting or pitching statistics. Unissued cards with a Pepper Martin back (#80), but with another player pictured on the front are in existence.

		NR MT	EX	VG
Complete Set (79):		425.00	200.00	120.00
Common Player:		3.00	1.50	.90
1	Nap Lajoie	10.00	5.00	3.00
2	Christy Mathewson	10.00	5.00	3.00
3	Babe Ruth	85.00	40.00	24.00
4	Carl Hubbell	3.00	1.50	.90
5	Grover Cleveland Alexander	5.00	2.50	1.50
6	Walter Johnson	10.00	5.00	3.00
7	Chief Bender	3.00	1.50	.90
8	Roger Bresnahan	3.00	1.50	.90
9	Mordecai Brown	3.00	1.50	.90
10	Tris Speaker	3.00	1.50	.90
11	Arky Vaughan	3.00	1.50	.90
12	Zack Wheat	3.00	1.50	.90
13	George Sisler	3.00	1.50	.90
14	Connie Mack	4.00	2.00	1.25
15	Clark Griffith	3.00	1.50	.90
16	Lou Boudreau	3.00	1.50	.90
17	Ernie Lombardi	3.00	1.50	.90
18	Heinie Manush	3.00	1.50	.90
19	Marty Marion	3.00	1.50	.90
20	Eddie Collins	3.00	1.50	.90
21	Rabbit Maranville	3.00	1.50	.90
22	Joe Medwick	3.00	1.50	.90
23	Ed Barrow	3.00	1.50	.90
24	Mickey Cochrane	3.00	1.50	.90
25	Jimmy Collins	3.00	1.50	.90
26	Bob Feller	7.00	3.50	2.00
27	Luke Appling	3.00	1.50	.90
28	Lou Gehrig	45.00	22.50	13.50
29	Gabby Hartnett	3.00	1.50	.90
30	Chuck Klein	3.00	1.50	.90
31	Tony Lazzeri	3.00	1.50	.90
32	Al Simmons	3.00	1.50	.90
33	Wilbert Robinson	3.00	1.50	.90
34	Sam Rice	3.00	1.50	.90
35	Herb Pennock	3.00	1.50	.90
36	Mel Ott	3.00	1.50	.90
37	Lefty O'Doul	3.00	1.50	.90
38	Johnny Mize	3.00	1.50	.90
39	Bing Miller	3.00	1.50	.90
40	Joe Tinker	3.00	1.50	.90
41	Frank Baker	3.00	1.50	.90
42	Ty Cobb	35.00	17.50	10.50
43	Paul Derringer	3.00	1.50	.90
44	Cap Anson	3.00	1.50	.90
45	Jim Bottomley	3.00	1.50	.90
46	Eddie Plank	3.00	1.50	.90
47	Cy Young	5.00	2.50	1.50
48	Hack Wilson	3.00	1.50	.90
49	Ed Walsh	3.00	1.50	.90
50	Frank Chance	3.00	1.50	.90
51	Dazzy Vance	3.00	1.50	.90
52	Bill Terry	3.00	1.50	.90
53	Jimmy Foxx	4.00	2.00	1.25
54	Lefty Gomez	3.00	1.50	.90
55	Branch Rickey	3.00	1.50	.90
56	Ray Schalk	3.00	1.50	.90
57	Johnny Evers	3.00	1.50	.90
58	Charlie Gehringer	3.00	1.50	.90
59	Burleigh Grimes	3.00	1.50	.90
60	Lefty Grove	3.00	1.50	.90
61	Rube Waddell	3.00	1.50	.90
62	Honus Wagner	10.00	5.00	3.00
63	Red Ruffing	3.00	1.50	.90
64	Judge Landis	3.00	1.50	.90
65	Harry Heilmann	3.00	1.50	.90
66	John McGraw	3.00	1.50	.90
67	Hughie Jennings	3.00	1.50	.90
68	Hal Newhouser	3.00	1.50	.90
69	Waite Hoyt	3.00	1.50	.90
70	Bobo Newsom	3.00	1.50	.90
71	Earl Averill	3.00	1.50	.90
72	Ted Williams	60.00	30.00	18.00
73	Warren Giles	3.00	1.50	.90
74	Ford Frick	3.00	1.50	.90
75	Ki Ki Cuyler	3.00	1.50	.90
76	Paul Waner	3.00	1.50	.90
77	Pie Traynor	3.00	1.50	.90
78	Lloyd Waner	3.00	1.50	.90
79	Ralph Kiner	3.00	1.50	.90

1961 - 62 Fleer

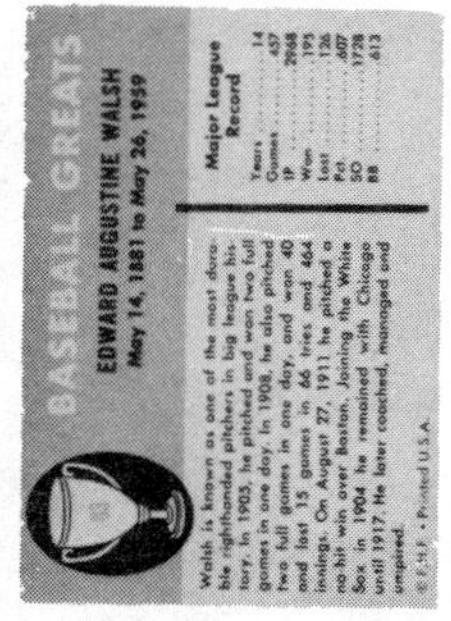

Over a two-year period, Fleer issued another set utilizing the Baseball Greats theme. The 154-card set was issued in two series and features a color player portrait against a color background. The player's name is located in a pennant set at the bottom of the card. The card backs feature orange and black on white stock and contain player biographical and statistical information. The cards measure 2-1/2" by 3-1/2" in size. The second series cards (#'s 89-154) were issued in 1962.

		NR MT	EX	VG
Complete Set (154):		1100.	500.00	300.00
Common Player (1-88):		4.00	2.00	1.25
Common Player (89-154):		10.00	5.00	3.00
1	Checklist (Frank Baker/Ty Cobb/Zach Wheat)	55.00	20.00	10.50
2	G.C. Alexander	6.00	3.00	1.75
3	Nick Altrock	4.00	2.00	1.25
4	Cap Anson	4.00	2.00	1.25
5	Earl Averill	4.00	2.00	1.25
6	Home Run Baker	4.00	2.00	1.25
7	Dave Bancroft	4.00	2.00	1.25
8	Chief Bender	4.00	2.00	1.25
9	Jim Bottomley	4.00	2.00	1.25
10	Roger Bresnahan	4.00	2.00	1.25
11	Mordecai Brown	4.00	2.00	1.25
12	Max Carey	4.00	2.00	1.25
13	Jack Chesbro	4.00	2.00	1.25
14	Ty Cobb	45.00	20.00	12.00
15	Mickey Cochrane	4.00	2.00	1.25
16	Eddie Collins	4.00	2.00	1.25
17	Earle Combs	4.00	2.00	1.25
18	Charles Comiskey	4.00	2.00	1.25
19	Ki Ki Cuyler	4.00	2.00	1.25
20	Paul Derringer	4.00	2.00	1.25
21	Howard Ehmke	4.00	2.00	1.25
22	Billy Evans	4.00	2.00	1.25
23	Johnny Evers	4.00	2.00	1.25
24	Red Faber	4.00	2.00	1.25
25	Bob Feller	6.00	3.00	1.75
26	Wes Ferrell	4.00	2.00	1.25
27	Lew Fonseca	4.00	2.00	1.25
28	Jimmy Foxx	6.00	3.00	1.75
29	Ford Frick	4.00	2.00	1.25
30	Frankie Frisch	4.00	2.00	1.25
31	Lou Gehrig	50.00	25.00	15.00
32	Charlie Gehringer	4.00	2.00	1.25
33	Warren Giles	4.00	2.00	1.25
34	Lefty Gomez	4.00	2.00	1.25
35	Goose Goslin	4.00	2.00	1.25
36	Clark Griffith	4.00	2.00	1.25
37	Burleigh Grimes	4.00	2.00	1.25
38	Lefty Grove	4.00	2.00	1.25
39	Chick Hafey	4.00	2.00	1.25
40	Jesse Haines	4.00	2.00	1.25
41	Gabby Hartnett	4.00	2.00	1.25
42	Harry Heilmann	4.00	2.00	1.25
43	Rogers Hornsby	4.00	2.00	1.25
44	Waite Hoyt	4.00	2.00	1.25
45	Carl Hubbell	4.00	2.00	1.25
46	Miller Huggins	4.00	2.00	1.25
47	Hughie Jennings	4.00	2.00	1.25
48	Ban Johnson	4.00	2.00	1.25
49	Walter Johnson	10.00	5.00	3.00
50	Ralph Kiner	4.00	2.00	1.25
51	Chuck Klein	4.00	2.00	1.25
52	Johnny Kling	4.00	2.00	1.25
53	Judge Landis	4.00	2.00	1.25
54	Tony Lazzeri	4.00	2.00	1.25
55	Ernie Lombardi	4.00	2.00	1.25
56	Dolf Luque	4.00	2.00	1.25
57	Heinie Manush	4.00	2.00	1.25
58	Marty Marion	4.00	2.00	1.25
59	Christy Mathewson	10.00	5.00	3.00
60	John McGraw	4.00	2.00	1.25
61	Joe Medwick	4.00	2.00	1.25
62	Bing Miller	4.00	2.00	1.25
63	Johnny Mize	4.00	2.00	1.25
64	Johnny Mostil	4.00	2.00	1.25
65	Art Nehf	4.00	2.00	1.25
66	Hal Newhouser	4.00	2.00	1.25
67	Bobo Newsom	4.00	2.00	1.25
68	Mel Ott	4.00	2.00	1.25
69	Allie Reynolds	4.00	2.00	1.25
70	Sam Rice	4.00	2.00	1.25
71	Eppa Rixey	4.00	2.00	1.25
72	Edd Roush	4.00	2.00	1.25
73	Schoolboy Rowe	4.00	2.00	1.25
74	Red Ruffing	4.00	2.00	1.25
75	Babe Ruth	85.00	40.00	24.00
76	Joe Sewell	4.00	2.00	1.25
77	Al Simmons	4.00	2.00	1.25
78	George Sisler	4.00	2.00	1.25
79	Tris Speaker	4.00	2.00	1.25
80	Fred Toney	4.00	2.00	1.25
81	Dazzy Vance	4.00	2.00	1.25
82	Jim Vaughn	4.00	2.00	1.25
83	Big Ed Walsh	4.00	2.00	1.25
84	Lloyd Waner	4.00	2.00	1.25
85	Paul Waner	4.00	2.00	1.25
86	Zach Wheat	4.00	2.00	1.25
87	Hack Wilson	4.00	2.00	1.25
88	Jimmy Wilson	4.00	2.00	1.25
89	Checklist (George Sisler/Pie Traynor)	35.00	17.50	10.50
90	Babe Adams	10.00	5.00	3.00
91	Dale Alexander	10.00	5.00	3.00
92	Jim Bagby	10.00	5.00	3.00
93	Ossie Bluege	10.00	5.00	3.00
94	Lou Boudreau	10.00	5.00	3.00
95	Tommy Bridges	10.00	5.00	3.00
96	Donnie Bush (Donie)	10.00	5.00	3.00
97	Dolph Camilli	10.00	5.00	3.00
98	Frank Chance	10.00	5.00	3.00
99	Jimmy Collins	10.00	5.00	3.00
100	Stanley Coveleskie (Coveleski)	10.00	5.00	3.00
101	Hughie Critz	10.00	5.00	3.00
102	General Crowder	10.00	5.00	3.00
103	Joe Dugan	10.00	5.00	3.00
104	Bibb Falk	10.00	5.00	3.00
105	Rick Ferrell	10.00	5.00	3.00
106	Art Fletcher	10.00	5.00	3.00
107	Dennis Galehouse	10.00	5.00	3.00
108	Chick Galloway	10.00	5.00	3.00
109	Mule Haas	10.00	5.00	3.00
110	Stan Hack	10.00	5.00	3.00
111	Bump Hadley	10.00	5.00	3.00
112	Billy Hamilton	10.00	5.00	3.00
113	Joe Hauser	10.00	5.00	3.00
114	Babe Herman	10.00	5.00	3.00
115	Travis Jackson	10.00	5.00	3.00
116	Eddie Joost	10.00	5.00	3.00
117	Addie Joss	10.00	5.00	3.00
118	Joe Judge	10.00	5.00	3.00
119	Joe Kuhel	10.00	5.00	3.00
120	Nap Lajoie	12.00	6.00	3.50
121	Dutch Leonard	10.00	5.00	3.00
122	Ted Lyons	10.00	5.00	3.00
123	Connie Mack	10.00	5.00	3.00
124	Rabbit Maranville	10.00	5.00	3.00
125	Fred Marberry	10.00	5.00	3.00
126	Iron Man McGinnity	10.00	5.00	3.00
127	Oscar Melillo	10.00	5.00	3.00
128	Ray Mueller	10.00	5.00	3.00
129	Kid Nichols	10.00	5.00	3.00
130	Lefty O'Doul	10.00	5.00	3.00
131	Bob O'Farrell	10.00	5.00	3.00
132	Roger Peckinpaugh	10.00	5.00	3.00
133	Herb Pennock	10.00	5.00	3.00
134	George Pipgras	10.00	5.00	3.00
135	Eddie Plank	10.00	5.00	3.00
136	Ray Schalk	10.00	5.00	3.00
137	Hal Schumacher	10.00	5.00	3.00
138	Luke Sewell	10.00	5.00	3.00
139	Bob Shawkey	10.00	5.00	3.00
140	Riggs Stephenson	10.00	5.00	3.00
141	Billy Sullivan	10.00	5.00	3.00
142	Bill Terry	10.00	5.00	3.00
143	Joe Tinker	10.00	5.00	3.00
144	Pie Traynor	10.00	5.00	3.00
145	George Uhle	10.00	5.00	3.00
146	Hal Troskey (Trosky)	10.00	5.00	3.00
147	Arky Vaughan	10.00	5.00	3.00
148	Johnny Vander Meer	10.00	5.00	3.00
149	Rube Waddell	10.00	5.00	3.00
150	Honus Wagner	35.00	17.50	10.50
151	Dixie Walker	10.00	5.00	3.00
152	Ted Williams	65.00	32.00	19.50
153	Cy Young	12.00	6.00	3.50
154	Ross Young (Youngs)	12.00	4.00	2.50

1963 Fleer

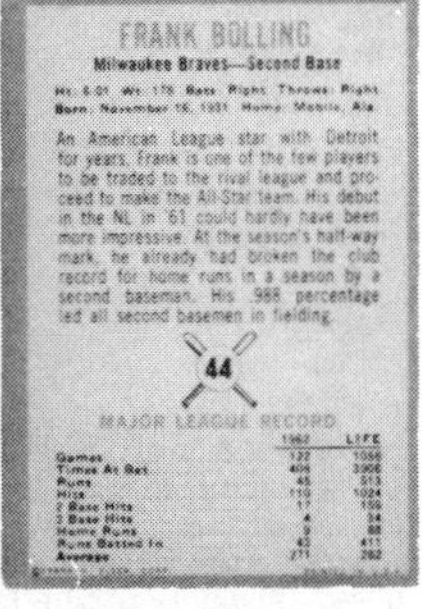

A lawsuit by Topps stopped Fleer's 1963 set at one series of 66 cards. Issued with a cookie rather than gum, the set features color photos of current players. The card backs include statistical information for 1962 and career plus a brief player biography. The cards, which measure 2-1/2" by 3-1/2", are numbered 1-66. An unnumbered checklist was issued with the set and is included in the complete set price in the checklist that follows. The checklist and #46 Adcock are scarce.

		NR MT	EX	VG
Complete Set (67):		1550.	775.00	450.00
Common Player:		12.00	6.00	3.50
1	Steve Barber	20.00	10.00	6.00
2	Ron Hansen	10.00	5.00	3.00
3	Milt Pappas	10.00	5.00	3.00
4	Brooks Robinson	65.00	32.00	19.50
5	Willie Mays	160.00	80.00	47.50
6	Lou Clinton	10.00	5.00	3.00
7	Bill Monbouquette	10.00	5.00	3.00
8	Carl Yastrzemski	90.00	45.00	27.00
9	Ray Herbert	10.00	5.00	3.00
10	Jim Landis	10.00	5.00	3.00
11	Dick Donovan	10.00	5.00	3.00
12	Tito Francona	10.00	5.00	3.00
13	Jerry Kindall	10.00	5.00	3.00
14	Frank Lary	10.00	5.00	3.00
15	Dick Howser	15.00	7.50	4.50
16	Jerry Lumpe	10.00	5.00	3.00
17	Norm Siebern	10.00	5.00	3.00
18	Don Lee	10.00	5.00	3.00
19	Albie Pearson	10.00	5.00	3.00
20	Bob Rodgers	10.00	5.00	3.00
21	Leon Wagner	10.00	5.00	3.00
22	Jim Kaat	18.00	9.00	5.50
23	Vic Power	10.00	5.00	3.00
24	Rich Rollins	10.00	5.00	3.00
25	Bobby Richardson	15.00	7.50	4.50
26	Ralph Terry	15.00	7.50	4.50
27	Tom Cheney	12.50	6.25	3.75
28	Chuck Cottier	10.00	5.00	3.00
29	Jimmy Piersall	10.00	5.00	3.00
30	Dave Stenhouse	10.00	5.00	3.00
31	Glen Hobbie	10.00	5.00	3.00
32	Ron Santo	20.00	10.00	6.00
33	Gene Freese	10.00	5.00	3.00
34	Vada Pinson	15.00	7.50	4.50
35	Bob Purkey	10.00	5.00	3.00
36	Joe Amalfitano	10.00	5.00	3.00
37	Bob Aspromonte	10.00	5.00	3.00
38	Dick Farrell	10.00	5.00	3.00
39	Al Spangler	10.00	5.00	3.00
40	Tommy Davis	10.00	5.00	3.00
41	Don Drysdale	40.00	20.00	12.00
42	Sandy Koufax	135.00	65.00	40.00
43	Maury Wills	60.00	30.00	18.00
44	Frank Bolling	10.00	5.00	3.00
45	Warren Spahn	50.00	20.00	12.00
46	Joe Adcock	150.00	75.00	45.00
47	Roger Craig	10.00	5.00	3.00
48	Al Jackson	10.00	5.00	3.00
49	Rod Kanehl	10.00	5.00	3.00
50	Ruben Amaro	10.00	5.00	3.00
51	John Callison	10.00	5.00	3.00
52	Clay Dalrymple	10.00	5.00	3.00
53	Don Demeter	10.00	5.00	3.00
54	Art Mahaffey	10.00	5.00	3.00
55	"Smoky" Burgess	10.00	5.00	3.00
56	Roberto Clemente	185.00	90.00	54.00
57	Elroy Face	10.00	5.00	3.00
58	Vernon Law	10.00	5.00	3.00
59	Bill Mazeroski	20.00	10.00	6.00
60	Ken Boyer	18.00	9.00	5.50
61	Bob Gibson	45.00	22.00	13.50
62	Gene Oliver	10.00	5.00	3.00
63	Bill White	15.00	7.50	4.50
64	Orlando Cepeda	20.00	10.00	6.00
65	Jimmy Davenport	10.00	5.00	3.00
66	Billy O'Dell	14.00	7.00	3.00
----	Checklist	450.00	225.00	135.00

1966 Fleer

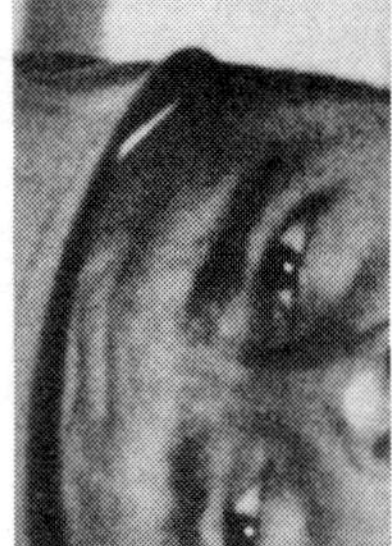

This seldom-seen issue was produced in the years when Fleer was locked out of the "regular" baseball card market. Standard 2-1/2" x 3-1/2" format cards are designed for playing a baseball match game. Backs have a portion of a black-and-white photo of Dodger pitcher Don Drysdale, which can be assembled in jigsaw puzzle fashion. Fronts are printed in red, blue, yellow and black, and numbered F1-F66. Because single cards have little collector appeal, the value of a set is considerably higher than the sum of the parts.

	NR MT	EX	VG
Complete Set (66):	350.00	175.00	100.00

1972 Fleer Famous Feats

This 40-card set by sports artist R.G. Laughlin is oversized, 2-1/2" x 4". It features the pen and ink work of the artist, with several colors added to the front. The backs are printed in blue on white card stock. The Major League Baseball logo appears on the front of the card, one of the few Laughlin issues to do so.

		NR MT	EX	VG
Complete Set (40):		25.00	11.50	3.10
Common Player:		.50	.23	.06
1	Joe McGinnity	.60	.30	.20
2	Rogers Hornsby	1.25	.55	.16
3	Christy Mathewson	1.25	.55	.16
4	Dazzy Vance	.60	.25	.08
5	Lou Gehrig	2.00	.90	.25
6	Jim Bottomley	.60	.25	.08
7	Johnny Evers	.60	.25	.08
8	Walter Johnson	1.25	.55	.16
9	Hack Wilson	.75	.35	.09
10	Wilbert Robinson	.60	.25	.08
11	Cy Young	1.00	.45	.13
12	Rudy York	.50	.23	.06
13	Grover C. Alexander	.75	.35	.09
14	Fred Toney, Hippo Vaughn	.50	.23	.06
15	Ty Cobb	2.00	.90	.25
16	Jimmie Foxx	1.25	.55	.16
17	Hub Leonard	.50	.23	.06
18	Eddie Collins	.60	.25	.08
19	Joe Oeschger, Leon Cadore	.50	.23	.06
20	Babe Ruth	3.00	1.35	.40
21	Honus Wagner	1.25	.55	.16
22	Red Rolfe	.50	.23	.06
23	Ed Walsh	.60	.25	.08
24	Paul Waner	.60	.25	.08
25	Mel Ott	1.00	.45	.13
26	Eddie Plank	.75	.35	.09
27	Sam Crawford	.60	.25	.08
28	Napoleon Lajoie	1.00	.45	.13
29	Ed Reulbach	.50	.23	.06
30	Pinky Higgins	.50	.23	.06
31	Bill Klem	.60	.25	.08
32	Tris Speaker	1.00	.45	.13
33	Hank Gowdy	.50	.23	.06
34	Lefty O'Doul	.50	.23	.06
35	Lloyd Waner	.60	.25	.08
36	Chuck Klein	.60	.25	.08
37	Deacon Phillippe	.50	.23	.06
38	Ed Delahanty	.60	.25	.08
39	Jack Chesbro	.60	.25	.08
40	Willie Keeler	.60	.30	.20

Grading Guide

Mint (MT): A perfect card. Well-centered with all corners sharp and square. No creases, stains, edge nicks, surface marks, yellowing or fading.

Near Mint (NM): A nearly perfect card. At first glance, a NM card appears to be perfect. May be slightly off-center. No surface marks, creases or loss of gloss.

Excellent (EX): Corners are still fairly sharp with only moderate wear. Borders may be off-center. No creases or stains on fronts or backs, but may show slight loss of surface luster.

Very Good (VG): Shows obvious handling. May have rounded corners, minor creases, major gum or wax stains. No major creases, tape marks, writing, etc.

Good (G): A well-worn card, but exhibits no intentional damage. May have major or multiple creases. Corners may be rounded well beyond card border.

1973 Fleer Wildest Days and Plays

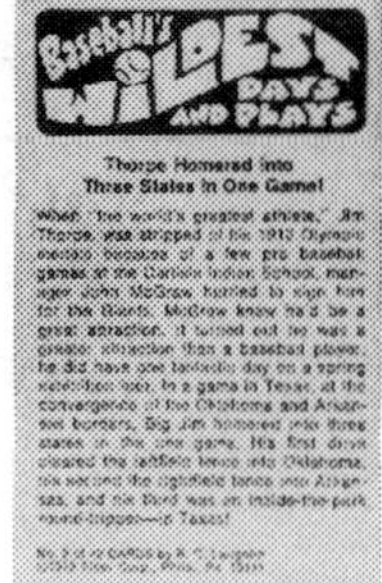

This 42-card set highlights unusual plays and happenings in baseball history, with the fronts featuring artwork by R.G. Laughlin. The cards are 2-1/2" x 4" and printed with color on the front and in red on the back.

		NR MT	EX	VG
Complete Set (42):		20.00	10.00	6.00
Common Player:		.50	.25	.15
1	Cubs and Phillies Score 49 Runs in Game	.50	.25	.15
2	Frank Chance Five HBP's in One Day	2.00	1.00	.60
3	Jim Thorpe Homered into 3 States	1.00	.50	.30
4	Eddie Gaedel Midget in Majors	1.00	.50	.30
5	Most Tied Game Ever	.50	.25	.15
6	Seven Errors in One Inning	.50	.25	.15
7	Four 20-Game Winners But No Pennant	.50	.25	.15
8	Dummy Hoy Umpires Signal Strikes	1.00	.50	.30
9	Fourteen Hits in One Inning	.50	.25	.15
10	Yankees Not Shut Out For Two Years	.50	.25	.15
11	Buck Weaver 17 Straight Fouls	1.00	.50	.30
12	George Sisler Greatest Thrill Was as a Pitcher	.60	.30	.20
13	Wrong-Way Baserunner	.50	.25	.15
14	Kiki Cuyler Sits Out Series	.60	.30	.20
15	Grounder Climbed Wall	.50	.25	.15
16	Gabby Street Washington Monument	.60	.30	.20
17	Mel Ott Ejected Twice	1.00	.50	.30
18	Shortest Pitching Career	.50	.25	.15
19	Three Homers in One Inning	.50	.25	.15
20	Bill Byron Singing Umpire	.50	.25	.15
21	Fred Clarke Walking Steal of Home	.60	.30	.20
22	Christy Mathewson 373rd Win Discovered	1.00	.50	.30
23	Hitting Through the Unglaub Arc	.50	.25	.15
24	Jim O'Rourke Catching at 52	.50	.25	.15
25	Fired for Striking Out in Series	.50	.25	.15
26	Eleven Run Inning on One Hit	.50	.25	.15
27	58 Innings in 3 Days	.50	.25	.15
28	Homer on Warm-Up Pitch	.50	.25	.15
29	Giants Win 26 Straight But Finish Fourth	.50	.25	.15
30	Player Who Stole First Base	.50	.25	.15
31	Ernie Shore Perfect Game in Relief	.60	.30	.20
32	Greatest Comeback	.50	.25	.15
33	All-Time Flash-In-The-Pan	.50	.25	.15
34	Pruett Fanned Ruth 19 out of 31	1.00	.50	.30
35	Fixed Batting Race Cobb/Lajoie	1.00	.50	.30
36	Wild-Pitch Rebound Play	.50	.25	.15
37	17 Straight Scoring Innings	.50	.25	.15
38	Wildest Opening Day	.50	.25	.15
39	Baseball's Strike One	.50	.25	.15
40	Opening Day No Hitter That Didn't Count	.50	.25	.15
41	Jimmie Foxx Six Straight Walks in One Game	1.00	.50	.30
42	Entire Team Hit and Scored in Inning	.50	.25	.15

1974 Fleer Baseball Firsts

This 42-card set from Fleer is titled "Baseball Firsts" and features several historical moments in baseball, as captured through the artwork of sports artist R.G. Laughlin. The cards are 2 1/2" by 4" and are numbered on the back, which is gray card stock with black printing. The set is not licensed by Major League Baseball.

		NR MT	EX	VG
Complete Set (42):		10.00	5.00	3.00
Common Player:		.25	.13	.08
1	Slide	.25	.13	.08
2	Spring Training	.25	.13	.08
3	Bunt	.25	.13	.08
4	Catcher's Mask	.25	.13	.08
5	Four Straight Homers (Lou Gehrig)	1.50	.70	.45

6	Radio Broadcast	.25	.13	.08
7	Numbered Uniforms	.25	.13	.08
8	Shin Guards	.25	.13	.08
9	Players Association	.25	.13	.08
10	Knuckleball	.25	.13	.08
11	Player With Glasses	.25	.13	.08
12	Baseball Cards	2.00	1.00	.60
13	Standardized Rules	.25	.13	.08
14	Grand Slam	.25	.13	.08
15	Player fined	.25	.13	.08
16	Presidential Opener	.25	.13	.08
17	Player Transaction	.25	.13	.08
18	All-Star Game	.25	.13	.08
19	Scoreboard	.25	.13	.08
20	Cork-center Ball	.25	.13	.08
21	Scorekeeping	.25	.13	.08
22	Domed Stadium	.25	.13	.08
23	Batting Helmet	.25	.13	.08
24	Fatality	.50	.25	.15
25	Unassisted Triple Play	.25	.13	.08
26	Home Run at Night	.25	.13	.08
27	Black Major Leaguer	.50	.25	.15
28	Pinch Hitter	.25	.13	.08
29	Million Dollar World Series	.25	.13	.08
30	Tarpaulin	.25	.13	.08
31	Team Initials	.25	.13	.08
32	Pennant Playoff	.25	.13	.08
33	Glove	.25	.13	.08
34	Curve Ball	.25	.13	.08
35	Night Game	.25	.13	.08
36	Admission Charge	.25	.13	.08
37	Farm System	.25	.13	.08
38	Telecast	.25	.13	.08
39	Commissioner	.25	.13	.08
40	.400 Hitter	.25	.13	.08
41	World Series	.25	.13	.08
42	Player Into Service	.25	.13	.08

1975 Fleer Pioneers of Baseball

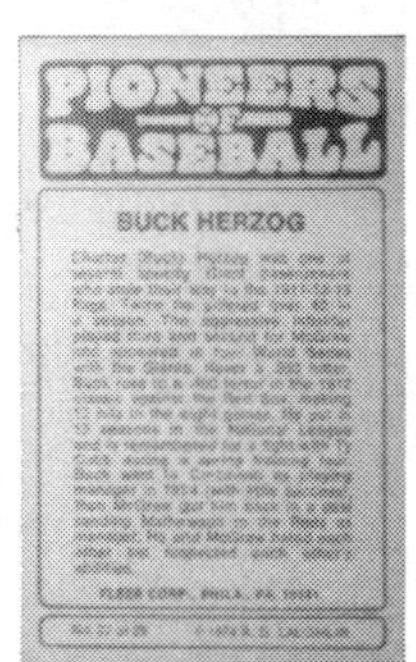

This 28-card set did not draw a great deal of interest in the hobby. The cards are slightly oversized and feature sepia-toned photographs of old baseball players. The backs feature information about the player and the card number. A "Pioneers of Baseball" banner appears at the top of the card back.

		NR MT	EX	VG
Complete Set:		15.00	7.50	4.50
Common Player:		.50	.25	.15
1	Cap Anson	.50	.25	.15
2	Harry Wright	.50	.25	.15
3	Buck Ewing	.50	.25	.15
4	A.G. Spalding	.50	.25	.15
5	Old Hoss Radbourn	.50	.25	.15
6	Dan Brouthers	.50	.25	.15
7	Roger Bresnahan	.50	.25	.15
8	Mike Kelly	.50	.25	.15
9	Ned Hanton	.50	.25	.15
10	Ed Delahanty	.50	.25	.15
11	Pud Galvin	.50	.25	.15
12	Amos Rusie	.50	.25	.15
13	Tommy McCarthy	.50	.25	.15
14	Ty Cobb	1.00	.50	.30
15	John McGraw	.50	.25	.15
16	Home Run Baker	.50	.25	.15
17	Johnny Evers	.50	.25	.15
18	Nap Lajoie	.50	.25	.15
19	Cy Young	.50	.25	.15
20	Eddie Collins	.50	.25	.15
21	John Glasscock	.50	.25	.15
22	Hal Chase	.50	.25	.15
23	Mordecai Brown	.50	.25	.15
24	Jake Daubert	.50	.25	.15
25	Mike Donlin	.50	.25	.15
26	John Clarkson	.50	.25	.15
27	Buck Herzog	.50	.25	.15
28	Art Nehf	.50	.25	.15

The values quoted are intended to reflect the market price.

1981 Fleer

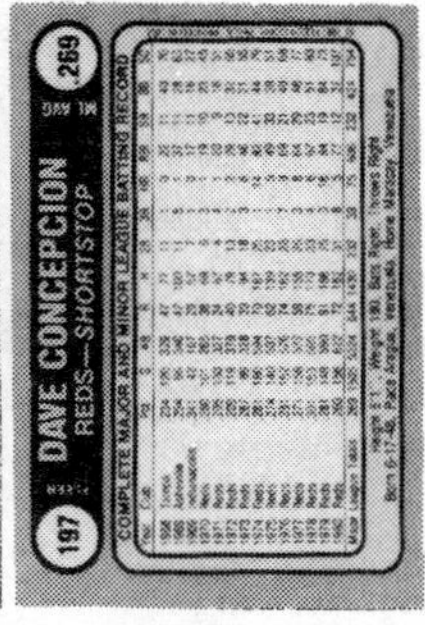

For the first time in 18 years, Fleer issued a baseball card set featuring current players. Fleer's 660-card effort included numerous errors in the first printing run which were subsequently corrected in additional runs. The cards, which measure 2-1/2" by 3-1/2", are numbered alphabetically by team. The card fronts feature a full-color photo inside a border which is color-coded by team. The card backs have black, grey and yellow ink on white stock and carry player statistical information. The player's batting average or earned run average is located in a circle in the upper right corner of the card. The complete set price in the checklist that follows does not include the higher priced variations.

		MT	NR MT	EX
Complete Set (660):		60.00	45.00	24.00
Common Player:		.06	.05	.02
1	Pete Rose	1.75	1.25	.70
2	Larry Bowa	.15	.11	.06
3	Manny Trillo	.08	.06	.03
4	Bob Boone	.10	.08	.04
5a	Mike schmidt (portrait)	2.00	1.50	.80
5b	Mike Schmidt (batting)	2.00	1.50	.80
6a	Steve carlton ("Lefty" on front)	1.00	.70	.40
6b	Steve carlton (Pitcher of the Year on front, date 1066 on back)	2.00	1.50	.80
6c	Steve Carlton (Pitcher of the Year on front, date 1966 on back)	3.00	2.25	1.25
7a	Tug McGraw (Game Saver on front)	.50	.40	.20
7b	Tug McGraw (Pitcher on front)	.12	.09	.05
8	Larry Christenson	.06	.05	.02
9	Bake McBride	.06	.05	.02
10	Greg Luzinski	.15	.11	.06
11	Ron Reed	.06	.05	.02
12	Dickie Noles	.06	.05	.02
13	*Keith Moreland*	.08	.06	.03
14	*Bob Walk*	.10	.08	.04
15	Lonnie Smith	.08	.06	.03
16	Dick Ruthven	.06	.05	.02
17	Sparky Lyle	.10	.08	.04
18	Greg Gross	.06	.05	.02
19	Garry Maddox	.10	.08	.04
20	Nino Espinosa	.06	.05	.02
21	George Vukovich	.06	.05	.02
22	John Vukovich	.06	.05	.02
23	Ramon Aviles	.06	.05	.02
24a	Kevin Saucier (Ken Saucier on back)	.15	.11	.06
24b	Kevin Saucier (Kevin Saucier on back)	.70	.50	.30
25	Randy Lerch	.06	.05	.02
26	Del Unser	.06	.05	.02
27	Tim McCarver	.15	.11	.06
28a	George Brett (batting)	4.00	3.00	1.50
28b	George brett (portrait)	1.00	.70	.40
29a	Willie Wilson (portrait)	.60	.45	.25
29b	Willie Wilson (batting)	.15	.11	.06
30	Paul Splittorff	.06	.05	.02
31	Dan Quisenberry	.15	.11	.06
32a	Amos Otis (batting)	.50	.40	.20
32b	Amos Otis (portrait)	.10	.08	.04
33	Steve Busby	.08	.06	.03
34	U.L. Washington	.06	.05	.02
35	Dave Chalk	.06	.05	.02
36	Darrell Porter	.08	.06	.03
37	Marty Pattin	.06	.05	.02
38	Larry Gura	.06	.05	.02
39	Renie Martin	.06	.05	.02
40	Rich Gale	.06	.05	.02
41a	Hal McRae (dark blue "Royals" on front)	.40	.30	.15
41b	Hal McRae (light blue "Royals" on front)	.10	.08	.04
42	Dennis Leonard	.08	.06	.03
43	Willie Aikens	.06	.05	.02
44	Frank White	.10	.08	.04
45	Clint Hurdle	.06	.05	.02
46	John Wathan	.08	.06	.03
47	Pete LaCock	.06	.05	.02
48	Rance Mulliniks	.06	.05	.02
49	Jeff Twitty	.06	.05	.02
50	Jamie Quirk	.06	.05	.02
51	Art Howe	.06	.05	.02
52	Ken Forsch	.06	.05	.02
53	Vern Ruhle	.06	.05	.02
54	Joe Niekro	.12	.09	.05
55	Frank LaCorte	.06	.05	.02
56	J.R. Richard	.10	.08	.04
57	Nolan Ryan	8.00	6.00	3.25
58	Enos Cabell	.06	.05	.02
59	Cesar Cedeno	.12	.09	.05
60	Jose Cruz	.12	.09	.05
61	Bill Virdon	.06	.05	.02
62	Terry Puhl	.06	.05	.02
63	Joaquin Andujar	.10	.08	.04
64	Alan Ashby	.06	.05	.02
65	Joe Sambito	.06	.05	.02
66	Denny Walling	.06	.05	.02
67	Jeff Leonard	.12	.09	.05
68	Luis Pujols	.06	.05	.02
69	Bruce Bochy	.06	.05	.02
70	Rafael Landestoy	.06	.05	.02
71	*Dave Smith*	.10	.08	.04
72	*Danny Heep*	.10	.08	.04
73	Julio Gonzalez	.06	.05	.02
74	Craig Reynolds	.06	.05	.02
75	Gary Woods	.06	.05	.02
76	Dave Bergman	.06	.05	.02
77	Randy Niemann	.06	.05	.02
78	Joe Morgan	.70	.50	.30
79a	Reggie Jackson (portrait)	4.00	3.00	1.50
79b	Reggie jackson (batting)	2.00	1.50	.80
80	Bucky Dent	.10	.08	.04
81	Tommy John	.20	.15	.08
82	Luis Tiant	.12	.09	.05
83	Rick Cerone	.06	.05	.02
84	Dick Howser	.06	.05	.02
85	Lou Piniella	.12	.09	.05
86	Ron Davis	.08	.06	.03
87a	Graig Nettles (Craig on back)	10.00	7.50	4.00
87b	Graig Nettles (Graig on back)	.30	.25	.12
88	Ron Guidry	.25	.20	.10
89	Rich Gossage	.20	.15	.08
90	Rudy May	.06	.05	.02
91	Gaylord Perry	.60	.45	.25
92	Eric Soderholm	.06	.05	.02
93	Bob Watson	.08	.06	.03
94	Bobby Murcer	.10	.08	.04
95	Bobby Brown	.06	.05	.02
96	Jim Spencer	.06	.05	.02
97	Tom Underwood	.06	.05	.02
98	Oscar Gamble	.08	.06	.03
99	Johnny Oates	.06	.05	.02
100	Fred Stanley	.06	.05	.02
101	Ruppert Jones	.06	.05	.02
102	Dennis Werth	.06	.05	.02
103	Joe Lefebvre	.06	.05	.02
104	Brian Doyle	.06	.05	.02
105	Aurelio Rodriguez	.08	.06	.03
106	Doug Bird	.06	.05	.02
107	Mike Griffin	.06	.05	.02
108	Tim Lollar	.06	.05	.02
109	Willie Randolph	.10	.08	.04
110	Steve Garvey	.40	.30	.15
111	Reggie Smith	.10	.08	.04
112	Don Sutton	.30	.25	.12
113	Burt Hooton	.08	.06	.03
114a	Davy Lopes (Davey) (no finger on back)	.10	.08	.04
114b	Davy Lopes (Davey) (small finger on back)	1.00	.70	.40
115	Dusty Baker	.10	.08	.04
116	Tom Lasorda	.10	.08	.04
117	Bill Russell	.08	.06	.03
118	Jerry Reuss	.10	.08	.04
119	Terry Forster	.08	.06	.03
120a	Bob Welch (Bob on back)	.60	.45	.25
120b	Bob Welch (Robert)	1.00	.70	.40
121	Don Stanhouse	.06	.05	.02
122	Rick Monday	.10	.08	.04
123	Derrel Thomas	.06	.05	.02
124	Joe Ferguson	.06	.05	.02
125	Rick Sutcliffe	.20	.15	.08
126a	Ron Cey (no finger on back)	.12	.09	.05
126b	Ron Cey (small finger on back)	1.00	.70	.40
127	Dave Goltz	.08	.06	.03
128	Jay Johnstone	.08	.06	.03
129	Steve Yeager	.06	.05	.02
130	Gary Weiss	.06	.05	.02
131	*Mike Scioscia*	.25	.20	.10
132	Vic Davalillo	.08	.06	.03
133	Doug Rau	.06	.05	.02
134	Pepe Frias	.06	.05	.02
135	Mickey Hatcher	.08	.06	.03
136	*Steve Howe*	.10	.08	.04
137	Robert Castillo	.06	.05	.02
138	Gary Thomasson	.06	.05	.02
139	Rudy Law	.06	.05	.02
140	*Fernand Valenzuela* (Fernando)	2.50	2.00	1.00
141	Manny Mota	.08	.06	.03
142	Gary Carter	.40	.30	.15
143	Steve Rogers	.08	.06	.03
144	Warren Cromartie	.06	.05	.02
145	Andre Dawson	2.00	1.50	.80
146	Larry Parrish	.10	.08	.04
147	Rowland Office	.06	.05	.02
148	Ellis Valentine	.06	.05	.02
149	Dick Williams	.06	.05	.02
150	*Bill Gullickson*	.15	.11	.06
151	Elias Sosa	.06	.05	.02
152	John Tamargo	.06	.05	.02
153	Chris Speier	.06	.05	.02
154	Ron LeFlore	.08	.06	.03
155	Rodney Scott	.06	.05	.02
156	Stan Bahnsen	.06	.05	.02
157	Bill Lee	.08	.06	.03
158	Fred Norman	.06	.05	.02
159	Woodie Fryman	.08	.06	.03
160	Dave Palmer	.06	.05	.02
161	Jerry White	.06	.05	.02
162	Roberto Ramos	.06	.05	.02
163	John D'Acquisto	.06	.05	.02
164	Tommy Hutton	.06	.05	.02
165	*Charlie Lea*	.12	.09	.05
166	Scott Sanderson	.06	.05	.02
167	Ken Macha	.06	.05	.02

168 Tony Bernazard .06 .05 .02
169 Jim Palmer 1.00 .70 .40
170 Steve Stone .08 .06 .03
171 Mike Flanagan .10 .08 .04
172 Al Bumbry .08 .06 .03
173 Doug DeCinces .10 .08 .04
174 Scott McGregor .08 .06 .03
175 Mark Belanger .08 .06 .03
176 Tim Stoddard .06 .05 .02
177a Rick Dempsey (no finger on front) .10 .08 .04
177b Rick Dempsey (small finger on front) 1.00 .70 .40
178 Earl Weaver .10 .08 .04
179 Tippy Martinez .06 .05 .02
180 Dennis Martinez .08 .06 .03
181 Sammy Stewart .06 .05 .02
182 Rich Dauer .06 .05 .02
183 Lee May .08 .06 .03
184 Eddie Murray 3.00 2.25 1.25
185 Benny Ayala .06 .05 .02
186 John Lowenstein .06 .05 .02
187 Gary Roenicke .06 .05 .02
188 Ken Singleton .10 .08 .04
189 Dan Graham .06 .05 .02
190 Terry Crowley .06 .05 .02
191 Kiko Garcia .06 .05 .02
192 Dave Ford .06 .05 .02
193 Mark Corey .06 .05 .02
194 Lenn Sakata .06 .05 .02
195 Doug DeCinces .10 .08 .04
196 Johnny Bench 1.00 .70 .40
197 Dave Concepcion .15 .11 .06
198 Ray Knight .10 .08 .04
199 Ken Griffey .12 .09 .05
200 Tom Seaver 2.00 1.50 .80
201 Dave Collins .08 .06 .03
202 George Foster .12 .09 .05
203 Junior Kennedy .06 .05 .02
204 Frank Pastore .06 .05 .02
205 Dan Driessen .08 .06 .03
206 Hector Cruz .06 .05 .02
207 Paul Moskau .06 .05 .02
208 *Charlie Leibrandt* .25 .20 .10
209 Harry Spilman .06 .05 .02
210 *Joe Price* .08 .06 .03
211 Tom Hume .06 .05 .02
212 Joe Nolan .06 .05 .02
213 Doug Bair .06 .05 .02
214 Mario Soto .08 .06 .03
215a Bill Bonham (no finger on back) .08 .06 .03
215b Bill Bonham (small finger on back) 1.00 .70 .40
216a George Foster (Slugger on front) .25 .20 .10
216b George Foster (Outfield on front) .20 .15 .08
217 Paul Householder .06 .05 .02
218 Ron Oester .06 .05 .02
219 Sam Mejias .06 .05 .02
220 Sheldon Burnside .06 .05 .02
221 Carl Yastrzemski 1.00 .70 .40
222 Jim Rice .50 .40 .20
223 Fred Lynn .20 .15 .08
224 Carlton Fisk .75 .60 .30
225 Rick Burleson .08 .06 .03
226 Dennis Eckersley 1.50 1.25 .60
227 Butch Hobson .06 .05 .02
228 Tom Burgmeier .06 .05 .02
229 Garry Hancock .06 .05 .02
230 Don Zimmer .06 .05 .02
231 Steve Renko .06 .05 .02
232 Dwight Evans .15 .11 .06
233 Mike Torrez .08 .06 .03
234 Bob Stanley .06 .05 .02
235 Jim Dwyer .06 .05 .02
236 Dave Stapleton .06 .05 .02
237 Glenn Hoffman .06 .05 .02
238 Jerry Remy .06 .05 .02
239 Dick Drago .06 .05 .02
240 Bill Campbell .06 .05 .02
241 Tony Perez .20 .15 .08
242 Phil Niekro .30 .25 .12
243 Dale Murphy .90 .70 .35
244 Bob Horner .12 .09 .05
245 Jeff Burroughs .08 .06 .03
246 Rick Camp .06 .05 .02
247 Bob Cox .06 .05 .02
248 Bruce Benedict .06 .05 .02
249 Gene Garber .06 .05 .02
250 Jerry Royster .06 .05 .02
251a Gary Matthews (no finger on back) .12 .09 .05
251b Gary Matthews (small finger on back) 1.00 .70 .40
252 Chris Chambliss .08 .06 .03
253 Luis Gomez .06 .05 .02
254 Bill Nahorodny .06 .05 .02
255 Doyle Alexander .10 .08 .04
256 Brian Asselstine .06 .05 .02
257 Biff Pocoroba .06 .05 .02
258 Mike Lum .06 .05 .02
259 Charlie Spikes .06 .05 .02
260 Glenn Hubbard .08 .06 .03
261 Tommy Boggs .06 .05 .02
262 Al Hrabosky .08 .06 .03
263 Rick Matula .06 .05 .02
264 Preston Hanna .06 .05 .02
265 Larry Bradford .06 .05 .02
266 *Rafael Ramirez* .08 .06 .03
267 Larry McWilliams .06 .05 .02
268 Rod Carew 1.50 1.25 .60
269 Bobby Grich .10 .08 .04
270 Carney Lansford .10 .08 .04
271 Don Baylor .12 .09 .05
272 Joe Rudi .10 .08 .04
273 Dan Ford .06 .05 .02
274 Jim Fregosi .08 .06 .03
275 Dave Frost .06 .05 .02
276 Frank Tanana .10 .08 .04
277 Dickie Thon .08 .06 .03
278 Jason Thompson .06 .05 .02
279 Rick Miller .06 .05 .02
280 Bert Campaneris .10 .08 .04
281 Tom Donohue .06 .05 .02
282 Brian Downing .10 .08 .04
283 Fred Patek .06 .05 .02
284 Bruce Kison .06 .05 .02
285 Dave LaRoche .06 .05 .02
286 Don Aase .06 .05 .02
287 Jim Barr .06 .05 .02
288 Alfredo Martinez .06 .05 .02
289 Larry Harlow .06 .05 .02
290 Andy Hassler .06 .05 .02
291 Dave Kingman .15 .11 .06
292 Bill Buckner .12 .09 .05
293 Rick Reuschel .10 .08 .04
294 Bruce Sutter .15 .11 .06
295 Jerry Martin .06 .05 .02
296 Scot Thompson .06 .05 .02
297 Ivan DeJesus .06 .05 .02
298 Steve Dillard .06 .05 .02
299 Dick Tidrow .06 .05 .02
300 Randy Martz .06 .05 .02
301 Lenny Randle .06 .05 .02
302 Lynn McGlothen .06 .05 .02
303 Cliff Johnson .06 .05 .02
304 Tim Blackwell .06 .05 .02
305 Dennis Lamp .06 .05 .02
306 Bill Caudill .06 .05 .02
307 Carlos Lezcano .06 .05 .02
308 Jim Tracy .06 .05 .02
309 Doug Capilla .06 .05 .02
310 Willie Hernandez .10 .08 .04
311 Mike Vail .06 .05 .02
312 Mike Krukow .08 .06 .03
313 Barry Foote .06 .05 .02
314 Larry Biittner .06 .05 .02
315 Mike Tyson .06 .05 .02
316 Lee Mazzilli .08 .06 .03
317 John Stearns .06 .05 .02
318 Alex Trevino .06 .05 .02
319 Craig Swan .06 .05 .02
320 Frank Taveras .06 .05 .02
321 Steve Henderson .06 .05 .02
322 Neil Allen .08 .06 .03
323 Mark Bomback .06 .05 .02
324 Mike Jorgensen .06 .05 .02
325 Joe Torre .08 .06 .03
326 Elliott Maddox .06 .05 .02
327 Pete Falcone .06 .05 .02
328 Ray Burris .06 .05 .02
329 Claudell Washington .08 .06 .03
330 Doug Flynn .06 .05 .02
331 Joel Youngblood .06 .05 .02
332 Bill Almon .06 .05 .02
333 Tom Hausman .06 .05 .02
334 Pat Zachry .06 .05 .02
335 *Jeff Reardon* 3.00 2.25 1.25
336 *Wally Backman* .35 .25 .14
337 Dan Norman .06 .05 .02
338 Jerry Morales .06 .05 .02
339 Ed Farmer .06 .05 .02
340 Bob Molinaro .06 .05 .02
341 Todd Cruz .06 .05 .02
342a *Britt Burns* (no finger on front) .20 .15 .08
342b *Britt Burns* (small finger on front) 1.00 .70 .40
343 Kevin Bell .06 .05 .02
344 Tony LaRussa .08 .06 .03
345 Steve Trout .06 .05 .02
346 *Harold Baines* 4.00 3.00 1.50
347 Richard Wortham .06 .05 .02
348 Wayne Nordhagen .06 .05 .02
349 Mike Squires .06 .05 .02
350 Lamar Johnson .06 .05 .02
351 Rickey Henderson 7.00 5.25 2.75
352 Francisco Barrios .06 .05 .02
353 Thad Bosley .06 .05 .02
354 Chet Lemon .08 .06 .03
355 Bruce Kimm .06 .05 .02
356 *Richard Dotson* .08 .06 .03
357 Jim Morrison .06 .05 .02
358 Mike Proly .06 .05 .02
359 Greg Pryor .06 .05 .02
360 Dave Parker .30 .25 .12
361 Omar Moreno .06 .05 .02
362a Kent Tekulve (1071 Waterbury on back) .15 .11 .06
362b Kent Tekulve (1971 Waterbury on back) .70 .50 .30
363 Willie Stargell .40 .30 .15
364 Phil Garner .08 .06 .03
365 Ed Ott .06 .05 .02
366 Don Robinson .08 .06 .03
367 Chuck Tanner .06 .05 .02
368 Jim Rooker .06 .05 .02
369 Dale Berra .06 .05 .02
370 Jim Bibby .06 .05 .02
371 Steve Nicosia .06 .05 .02
372 Mike Easler .08 .06 .03
373 Bill Robinson .06 .05 .02
374 Lee Lacy .06 .05 .02
375 John Candelaria .10 .08 .04
376 Manny Sanguillen .06 .05 .02
377 Rick Rhoden .10 .08 .04
378 Grant Jackson .06 .05 .02
379 Tim Foli .06 .05 .02
380 *Rod Scurry* .08 .06 .03
381 Bill Madlock .12 .09 .05
382a Kurt Bevacqua (photo reversed, backwards "P" on cap) .15 .11 .06
382b Kurt Bevacqua (correct photo) .70 .50 .30
383 Bert Blyleven .12 .09 .05
384 Eddie Solomon .06 .05 .02
385 Enrique Romo .06 .05 .02
386 John Milner .06 .05 .02
387 Mike Hargrove .06 .05 .02
388 Jorge Orta .06 .05 .02
389 Toby Harrah .08 .06 .03
390 Tom Veryzer .06 .05 .02
391 Miguel Dilone .06 .05 .02
392 Dan Spillner .06 .05 .02
393 Jack Brohamer .06 .05 .02
394 Wayne Garland .06 .05 .02
395 Sid Monge .06 .05 .02
396 Rick Waits .06 .05 .02
397 *Joe Charboneau* .10 .08 .04
398 Gary Alexander .06 .05 .02
399 Jerry Dybzinski .06 .05 .02
400 Mike Stanton .06 .05 .02
401 Mike Paxton .06 .05 .02
402 Gary Gray .06 .05 .02
403 Rick Manning .06 .05 .02
404 Bo Diaz .08 .06 .03
405 Ron Hassey .06 .05 .02
406 Ross Grimsley .06 .05 .02
407 Victor Cruz .06 .05 .02
408 Len Barker .08 .06 .03
409 Bob Bailor .06 .05 .02
410 Otto Velez .06 .05 .02
411 Ernie Whitt .08 .06 .03
412 Jim Clancy .08 .06 .03
413 Barry Bonnell .06 .05 .02
414 Dave Stieb .60 .45 .25
415 *Damaso Garcia* .10 .08 .04
416 John Mayberry .08 .06 .03
417 Roy Howell .06 .05 .02
418 *Dan Ainge* 4.00 3.00 1.50
419a Jesse Jefferson (Pirates on back) .10 .08 .04
419b Jesse Jefferson (Blue Jays on back) .50 .40 .20
420 Joey McLaughlin .06 .05 .02
421 *Lloyd Moseby* .10 .08 .04
422 Al Woods .06 .05 .02
423 Garth Iorg .06 .05 .02
424 Doug Ault .06 .05 .02
425 *Ken Schrom* .06 .05 .02
426 Mike Willis .06 .05 .02
427 Steve Braun .06 .05 .02
428 Bob Davis .06 .05 .02
429 Jerry Garvin .06 .05 .02
430 Alfredo Griffin .08 .06 .03
431 Bob Mattick .06 .05 .02
432 Vida Blue .12 .09 .05
433 Jack Clark .25 .20 .10
434 Willie McCovey .60 .45 .25
435 Mike Ivie .06 .05 .02
436a Darrel Evans (Darrel on front) .15 .11 .06
436b Darrell Evans (Darrell on front) .70 .50 .30
437 Terry Whitfield .06 .05 .02
438 Rennie Stennett .06 .05 .02
439 John Montefusco .08 .06 .03
440 Jim Wohlford .06 .05 .02
441 Bill North .06 .05 .02
442 Milt May .06 .05 .02
443 Max Venable .06 .05 .02
444 Ed Whitson .06 .05 .02
445 *Al Holland* .08 .06 .03
446 Randy Moffitt .06 .05 .02
447 Bob Knepper .08 .06 .03
448 Gary Lavelle .06 .05 .02
449 Greg Minton .06 .05 .02
450 Johnnie LeMaster .06 .05 .02
451 Larry Herndon .08 .06 .03
452 Rich Murray .06 .05 .02
453 Joe Pettini .06 .05 .02
454 Allen Ripley .06 .05 .02
455 Dennis Littlejohn .06 .05 .02
456 Tom Griffin .06 .05 .02
457 Alan Hargesheimer .06 .05 .02
458 Joe Strain .06 .05 .02
459 Steve Kemp .08 .06 .03
460 Sparky Anderson .10 .08 .04
461 Alan Trammell 1.00 .70 .40
462 Mark Fidrych .08 .06 .03
463 Lou Whitaker .40 .30 .15
464 Dave Rozema .06 .05 .02
465 Milt Wilcox .06 .05 .02
466 Champ Summers .06 .05 .02
467 Lance Parrish .20 .15 .08
468 Dan Petry .08 .06 .03
469 Pat Underwood .06 .05 .02
470 Rick Peters .06 .05 .02
471 Al Cowens .06 .05 .02
472 John Wockenfuss .06 .05 .02
473 Tom Brookens .08 .06 .03
474 Richie Hebner .06 .05 .02
475 Jack Morris 1.75 1.25 .70
476 Jim Lentine .06 .05 .02
477 Bruce Robbins .06 .05 .02
478 Mark Wagner .06 .05 .02
479 Tim Corcoran .06 .05 .02
480a Stan Papi (Pitcher on front) .15 .11 .06
480b Stan Papi (Shortstop on front) .70 .50 .30
481 *Kirk Gibson* 3.00 2.25 1.25
482 Dan Schatzeder .06 .05 .02
483 Amos Otis .70 .50 .30
484 Dave Winfield 3.00 2.25 1.25
485 Rollie Fingers 1.00 .70 .40
486 Gene Richards .06 .05 .02
487 Randy Jones .08 .06 .03
488 Ozzie Smith 2.00 1.50 .80
489 Gene Tenace .08 .06 .03
490 Bill Fahey .06 .05 .02
491 John Curtis .06 .05 .02
492 Dave Cash .06 .05 .02
493a Tim Flannery (photo reversed, batting righty) .15 .11 .06
493b Tim Flannery (photo correct, batting lefty) .70 .50 .30
494 Jerry Mumphrey .06 .05 .02
495 Bob Shirley .06 .05 .02

496	Steve Mura	.06	.05	.02
497	Eric Rasmussen	.06	.05	.02
498	Broderick Perkins	.06	.05	.02
499	Barry Evans	.06	.05	.02
500	Chuck Baker	.06	.05	.02
501	*Luis Salazar*	.15	.11	.06
502	Gary Lucas	.08	.06	.03
503	Mike Armstrong	.06	.05	.02
504	Jerry Turner	.06	.05	.02
505	Dennis Kinney	.06	.05	.02
506	Willy Montanez (Willie)	.06	.05	.02
507	Gorman Thomas	.10	.08	.04
508	Ben Oglivie	.08	.06	.03
509	Larry Hisle	.08	.06	.03
510	Sal Bando	.10	.08	.04
511	Robin Yount	4.00	3.00	1.50
512	Mike Caldwell	.06	.05	.02
513	Sixto Lezcano	.06	.05	.02
514a	Jerry Augustine (Billy Travers photo)	.15	.11	.06
514b	Billy Travers (correct name with photo)	.70	.50	.30
515	Paul Molitor	3.00	2.25	1.25
516	Moose Haas	.06	.05	.02
517	Bill Castro	.06	.05	.02
518	Jim Slaton	.06	.05	.02
519	Lary Sorensen	.06	.05	.02
520	Bob McClure	.06	.05	.02
521	Charlie Moore	.06	.05	.02
522	Jim Gantner	.08	.06	.03
523	Reggie Cleveland	.06	.05	.02
524	Don Money	.06	.05	.02
525	Billy Travers	.06	.05	.02
526	Buck Martinez	.06	.05	.02
527	Dick Davis	.06	.05	.02
528	Ted Simmons	.12	.09	.05
529	Garry Templeton	.10	.08	.04
530	Ken Reitz	.06	.05	.02
531	Tony Scott	.06	.05	.02
532	Ken Oberkfell	.06	.05	.02
533	Bob Sykes	.06	.05	.02
534	Keith Smith	.06	.05	.02
535	John Littlefield	.06	.05	.02
536	Jim Kaat	.15	.11	.06
537	Bob Forsch	.08	.06	.03
538	Mike Phillips	.06	.05	.02
539	*Terry Landrum*	.06	.05	.02
540	*Leon Durham*	.10	.08	.04
541	Terry Kennedy	.08	.06	.03
542	George Hendrick	.08	.06	.03
543	Dane Iorg	.06	.05	.02
544	Mark Littell (photo actually Jeff Little)	.06	.05	.02
545	Keith Hernandez	.40	.30	.15
546	Silvio Martinez	.06	.05	.02
547a	Pete Vuckovich (photo actually Don Hood)	.15	.11	.06
547b	Don Hood (correct name with photo)	.70	.50	.30
548	Bobby Bonds	.10	.08	.04
549	Mike Ramsey	.06	.05	.02
550	Tom Herr	.10	.08	.04
551	Roy Smalley	.06	.05	.02
552	Jerry Koosman	.10	.08	.04
553	Ken Landreaux	.06	.05	.02
554	John Castino	.06	.05	.02
555	Doug Corbett	.06	.05	.02
556	Bombo Rivera	.06	.05	.02
557	Ron Jackson	.06	.05	.02
558	Butch Wynegar	.06	.05	.02
559	Hosken Powell	.06	.05	.02
560	Pete Redfern	.06	.05	.02
561	Roger Erickson	.06	.05	.02
562	Glenn Adams	.06	.05	.02
563	Rick Sofield	.06	.05	.02
564	Geoff Zahn	.06	.05	.02
565	Pete Mackanin	.06	.05	.02
566	Mike Cubbage	.06	.05	.02
567	Darrell Jackson	.06	.05	.02
568	Dave Edwards	.06	.05	.02
569	Rob Wilfong	.06	.05	.02
570	Sal Butera	.06	.05	.02
571	Jose Morales	.06	.05	.02
572	Rick Langford	.06	.05	.02
573	Mike Norris	.06	.05	.02
574	Rickey Henderson	10.00	7.50	4.00
575	Tony Armas	.10	.08	.04
576	Dave Revering	.06	.05	.02
577	Jeff Newman	.06	.05	.02
578	Bob Lacey	.06	.05	.02
579	Brian Kingman (photo actually Alan Wirth)	.06	.05	.02
580	Mitchell Page	.06	.05	.02
581	Billy Martin	.12	.09	.05
582	Rob Picciolo	.06	.05	.02
583	Mike Heath	.06	.05	.02
584	Mickey Klutts	.06	.05	.02
585	Orlando Gonzalez	.06	.05	.02
586	*Mike Davis*	.12	.09	.05
587	Wayne Gross	.06	.05	.02
588	Matt Keough	.06	.05	.02
589	Steve McCatty	.06	.05	.02
590	Dwayne Murphy	.08	.06	.03
591	Mario Guerrero	.06	.05	.02
592	Dave McKay	.06	.05	.02
593	Jim Essian	.06	.05	.02
594	Dave Heaverlo	.06	.05	.02
595	Maury Wills	.10	.08	.04
596	Juan Beniquez	.06	.05	.02
597	Rodney Craig	.06	.05	.02
598	Jim Anderson	.06	.05	.02
599	Floyd Bannister	.10	.08	.04
600	Bruce Bochte	.06	.05	.02
601	Julio Cruz	.06	.05	.02
602	Ted Cox	.06	.05	.02
603	Dan Meyer	.06	.05	.02
604	Larry Cox	.06	.05	.02
605	Bill Stein	.06	.05	.02
606	Steve Garvey	.50	.40	.20
607	Dave Roberts	.06	.05	.02
608	Leon Roberts	.06	.05	.02
609	Reggie Walton	.06	.05	.02
610	Dave Edler	.06	.05	.02
611	Larry Milbourne	.06	.05	.02
612	Kim Allen	.06	.05	.02
613	Mario Mendoza	.06	.05	.02
614	Tom Paciorek	.06	.05	.02
615	Glenn Abbott	.06	.05	.02
616	Joe Simpson	.06	.05	.02
617	Mickey Rivers	.08	.06	.03
618	Jim Kern	.06	.05	.02
619	Jim Sundberg	.08	.06	.03
620	Richie Zisk	.08	.06	.03
621	Jon Matlack	.08	.06	.03
622	Fergie Jenkins	.50	.40	.20
623	Pat Corrales	.06	.05	.02
624	Ed Figueroa	.06	.05	.02
625	Buddy Bell	.12	.09	.05
626	Al Oliver	.15	.11	.06
627	Doc Medich	.06	.05	.02
628	Bump Wills	.06	.05	.02
629	Rusty Staub	.10	.08	.04
630	Pat Putnam	.06	.05	.02
631	John Grubb	.06	.05	.02
632	Danny Darwin	.06	.05	.02
633	Ken Clay	.06	.05	.02
634	Jim Norris	.06	.05	.02
635	John Butcher	.06	.05	.02
636	Dave Roberts	.06	.05	.02
637	Billy Sample	.06	.05	.02
638	Carl Yastrzemski	1.00	.70	.40
639	Cecil Cooper	.15	.11	.06
640	Mike Schmidt	2.00	1.50	.80
641a	Checklist 1-50 (41 Hal McRae)	.10	.08	.04
641b	Checklist 1-50 (41 Hal McRae Double Threat)	.40	.30	.15
642	Checklist 51-109	.06	.05	.02
643	Checklist 110-168	.06	.05	.02
644a	Checklist 169-220 (202 George Foster)	.10	.08	.04
644b	Checklist 169-220 (202 George Foster "Slugger")	.40	.30	.15
645a	Triple Threat (Larry Bowa, Pete Rose, Mike Schmidt) (no number on back)	2.00	1.50	.80
645b	Triple Threat (Larry Bowa, Pete Rose, Mike Schmidt)	2.00	1.50	.80
646	Checklist 221-267	.06	.05	.02
647	Checklist 268-315	.06	.05	.02
648	Checklist 316-359	.06	.05	.02
649	Checklist 360-408	.06	.05	.02
650	Reggie Jackson	3.25	2.50	1.25
651	Checklist 409-458	.06	.05	.02
652a	Checklist 459-509 (483 Aurelio Lopez)	.10	.08	.04
652b	Checklist 459-506 (no 483)	.40	.30	.15
653	Willie Wilson	1.00	.70	.40
654a	Checklist 507-550 (514 Jerry Augustine)	.10	.08	.04
654b	Checklist 507-550 (514 Billy Travers)	.40	.30	.15
655	George Brett	3.00	2.25	1.25
656	Checklist 551-593	.06	.05	.02
657	Tug McGraw	1.00	.70	.40
658	Checklist 594-637	.06	.05	.02
659a	Checklist 640-660 (last number on front is 551)	.10	.08	.04
659b	Checklist 640-660 (last number on front is 483)	.40	.30	.15
660a	Steve Carlton (date 1066 on back)	1.00	.70	.40
660b	Steve Carlton (date 1966 on back)	2.00	1.50	.80

1981 Fleer Star Stickers

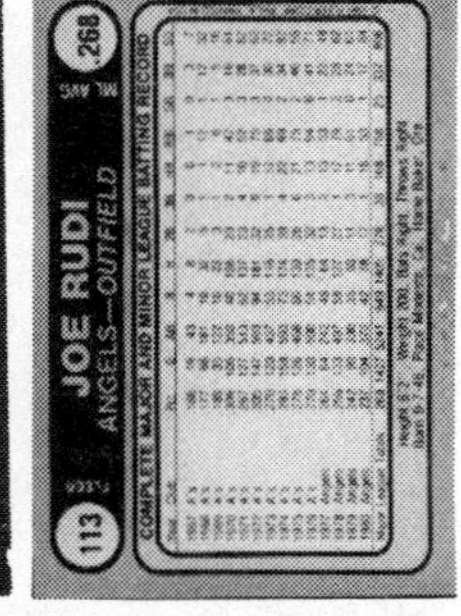

The 128-card 1981 Fleer Star Sticker set was designed for the card fronts to be peeled away from the cardboard backs. The card obverses feature color photos with blue and yellow trim. The card backs are identical in design to the regular 1981 Fleer set except for color and numbering. The set contains three unnumbered checklist cards whose fronts depict Reggie Jackson (#'s 1-42), George Brett (#'s 43-83) and Mike Schmidt (#'s 84-125). The cards, which are the standard 2-1/2" 3-1/2", were issued in gum wax packs.

		MT	NR MT	EX
Complete Set:		55.00	41.00	22.00
Common Player:		.10	.08	.04
1	Steve Garvey	1.00	.70	.40
2	Ron LeFlore	.10	.08	.04
3	Ron Cey	.25	.20	.10
4	Dave Revering	.10	.08	.04
5	Tony Armas	.15	.11	.06
6	Mike Norris	.10	.08	.04
7	Steve Kemp	.15	.11	.06
8	Bruce Bochte	.10	.08	.04
9	Mike Schmidt	6.00	4.50	2.50
10	Scott McGregor	.10	.08	.04
11	Buddy Bell	.20	.15	.08
12	Carney Lansford	.20	.15	.08
13	Carl Yastrzemski	5.00	3.75	2.00
14	Ben Oglivie	.10	.08	.04
15	Willie Stargell	5.00	3.75	2.00
16	Cecil Cooper	.15	.11	.06
17	Gene Richards	.10	.08	.04
18	Jim Kern	.10	.08	.04
19	Jerry Koosman	.15	.11	.06
20	Larry Bowa	.20	.15	.08
21	Kent Tekulve	.15	.11	.06
22	Dan Driessen	.10	.08	.04
23	Phil Niekro	1.00	.70	.40
24	Dan Quisenberry	.30	.25	.12
25	Dave Winfield	3.00	2.25	1.25
26	Dave Parker	1.00	.70	.40
27	Rick Langford	.10	.08	.04
28	Amos Otis	.15	.11	.06
29	Bill Buckner	.15	.11	.06
30	Al Bumbry	.10	.08	.04
31	Bake McBride	.10	.08	.04
32	Mickey Rivers	.10	.08	.04
33	Rick Burleson	.10	.08	.04
34	Dennis Eckersley	1.50	1.25	.60
35	Cesar Cedeno	.20	.15	.08
36	Enos Cabell	.10	.08	.04
37	Johnny Bench	5.00	3.75	2.00
38	Robin Yount	4.00	3.00	1.50
39	Mark Belanger	.10	.08	.04
40	Rod Carew	5.00	3.75	2.00
41	George Foster	.40	.30	.15
42	Lee Mazzilli	.15	.11	.06
43	Triple Threat (Larry Bowa, Pete Rose, Mike Schmidt)	3.00	2.25	1.25
44	J.R. Richard	.15	.11	.06
45	Lou Piniella	.30	.25	.12
46	Ken Landreaux	.10	.08	.04
47	Rollie Fingers	2.00	1.50	.80
48	Joaquin Andujar	.10	.08	.04
49	Tom Seaver	6.00	4.50	2.50
50	Bobby Grich	.20	.15	.08
51	Jon Matlack	.10	.08	.04
52	Jack Clark	.25	.20	.10
53	Jim Rice	.25	.20	.10
54	Rickey Henderson	8.00	6.00	3.25
55	Roy Smalley	.10	.08	.04
56	Mike Flanagan	.15	.11	.06
57	Steve Rogers	.10	.08	.04
58	Carlton Fisk	.60	.45	.25
59	Don Sutton	1.00	.70	.40
60	Ken Griffey	.50	.40	.20
61	Burt Hooton	.10	.08	.04
62	Dusty Baker	.20	.15	.08
63	Vida Blue	.25	.20	.10
64	Al Oliver	.30	.25	.12
65	Jim Bibby	.10	.08	.04
66	Tony Perez	.60	.45	.25
67	Davy Lopes (Davey)	.15	.11	.06
68	Bill Russell	.15	.11	.06
69	Larry Parrish	.20	.15	.08
70	Garry Maddox	.15	.11	.06
71	Phil Garner	.15	.11	.06
72	Graig Nettles	.35	.25	.14
73	Gary Carter	.60	.45	.25
74	Pete Rose	4.00	3.00	1.50
75	Greg Luzinski	.30	.25	.12
76	Ron Guidry	.25	.20	.10
77	Gorman Thomas	.15	.11	.06
78	Jose Cruz	.20	.15	.08
79	Bob Boone	.15	.11	.06
80	Bruce Sutter	.35	.25	.14
81	Chris Chambliss	.15	.11	.06
82	Paul Molitor	2.00	1.50	.80
83	Tug McGraw	.25	.20	.10
84	Ferguson Jenkins	1.00	.70	.40
85	Steve Carlton	4.00	3.00	1.50
86	Miguel Dilone	.10	.08	.04
87	Reggie Smith	.20	.15	.08
88	Rick Cerone	.10	.08	.04
89	Alan Trammell	1.00	.70	.40
90	Doug DeCinces	.20	.15	.08
91	Sparky Lyle	.15	.11	.06
92	Warren Cromartie	.10	.08	.04
93	Rick Reuschel	.25	.20	.10
94	Larry Hisle	.10	.08	.04
95	Paul Splittorff	.10	.08	.04
96	Manny Trillo	.10	.08	.04
97	Frank White	.20	.15	.08
98	Fred Lynn	.25	.20	.10
99	Bob Horner	.15	.11	.06
100	Omar Moreno	.10	.08	.04
101	Dave Concepcion	.20	.15	.08
102	Larry Gura	.10	.08	.04
103	Ken Singleton	.20	.15	.08
104	Steve Stone	.15	.11	.06
105	Richie Zisk	.10	.08	.04
106	Willie Wilson	.40	.30	.15
107	Willie Randolph	.20	.15	.08
108	Nolan Ryan	9.00	6.75	3.50
109	Joe Morgan	1.00	.70	.40
110	Bucky Dent	.20	.15	.08
111	Dave Kingman	.40	.30	.15
112	John Castino	.10	.08	.04
113	Joe Rudi	.20	.15	.08

114	Ed Farmer	.10	.08	.04
115	Reggie Jackson	6.00	4.50	2.50
116	George Brett	5.00	3.75	2.00
117	Eddie Murray	1.00	.70	.40
118	Rich Gossage	.25	.20	.10
119	Dale Murphy	1.00	.70	.40
120	Ted Simmons	.15	.11	.06
121	Tommy John	.25	.20	.10
122	Don Baylor	.50	.40	.20
123	Andre Dawson	1.00	.70	.40
124	Jim Palmer	4.00	3.00	1.50
125	Garry Templeton	.20	.15	.08
----	Reggie Jackson/Checklist 1-42	4.00	3.00	1.50
----	George Brett/Checklist 43-83	4.00	3.00	1.50
----	Mike Schmidt/Checklist 84-125	4.00	3.00	1.50

1982 Fleer

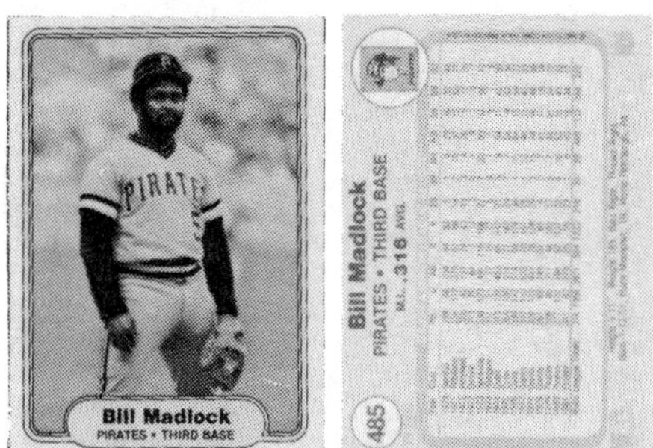

Fleer's 1982 set did not match the quality of the previous year's effort. Many of the photos in the set are blurred and have muddied backgrounds. The cards, which measure 2-1/2" by 3-1/2", feature color photos surrounded by a border frame which is color-coded by team. The card backs are blue, white, and yellow and contain the player's team logo plus the logos of Major League Baseball and the Major League Baseball Players Association. Due to a lawsuit by Topps, Fleer was forced to issue the set with team logo stickers rather than gum. The complete set price does not include the higher priced variations.

		MT	NR MT	EX
Complete Set (660):		100.00	75.00	40.00
Common Player:		.06	.05	.02
1	Dusty Baker	.10	.08	.04
2	Robert Castillo	.06	.05	.02
3	Ron Cey	.12	.09	.05
4	Terry Forster	.08	.06	.03
5	Steve Garvey	.30	.25	.12
6	Dave Goltz	.08	.06	.03
7	Pedro Guerrero (FC)	.10	.08	.04
8	Burt Hooton	.08	.06	.03
9	Steve Howe	.08	.06	.03
10	Jay Johnstone	.08	.06	.03
11	Ken Landreaux	.06	.05	.02
12	Davey Lopes	.10	.08	.04
13	*Mike Marshall* (FC)	.12	.09	.05
14	Bobby Mitchell	.06	.05	.02
15	Rick Monday	.10	.08	.04
16	*Tom Niedenfuer* (FC)	.08	.06	.03
17	*Ted Power* (FC)	.08	.06	.03
18	Jerry Reuss	.10	.08	.04
19	Ron Roenicke	.06	.05	.02
20	Bill Russell	.08	.06	.03
21	*Steve Sax* (FC)	1.00	.70	.40
22	Mike Scioscia	.08	.06	.03
23	Reggie Smith	.10	.08	.04
24	*Dave Stewart* (FC)	3.00	2.25	1.25
25	Rick Sutcliffe	.15	.11	.06
26	Derrel Thomas	.06	.05	.02
27	Fernando Valenzuela	.35	.25	.14
28	Bob Welch	.12	.09	.05
29	Steve Yeager	.06	.05	.02
30	Bobby Brown	.06	.05	.02
31	Rick Cerone	.06	.05	.02
32	Ron Davis	.06	.05	.02
33	Bucky Dent	.10	.08	.04
34	Barry Foote	.06	.05	.02
35	George Frazier	.06	.05	.02
36	Oscar Gamble	.08	.06	.03
37	Rich Gossage	.20	.15	.08
38	Ron Guidry	.25	.20	.10
39	Reggie Jackson	2.00	1.50	.80
40	Tommy John	.20	.15	.08
41	Rudy May	.06	.05	.02
42	Larry Milbourne	.06	.05	.02
43	Jerry Mumphrey	.06	.05	.02
44	Bobby Murcer	.10	.08	.04
45	*Gene Nelson*	.12	.09	.05
46	Graig Nettles	.15	.11	.06
47	Johnny Oates	.06	.05	.02
48	Lou Piniella	.12	.09	.05
49	Willie Randolph	.10	.08	.04
50	Rick Reuschel	.10	.08	.04
51	Dave Revering	.06	.05	.02
52	*Dave Righetti* (FC)	.60	.45	.25
53	Aurelio Rodriguez	.08	.06	.03
54	Bob Watson	.08	.06	.03
55	Dennis Werth	.06	.05	.02
56	Dave Winfield	2.50	2.00	1.00
57	Johnny Bench	.80	.60	.30
58	Bruce Berenyi	.06	.05	.02
59	Larry Biittner	.06	.05	.02
60	Scott Brown	.06	.05	.02
61	Dave Collins	.08	.06	.03
62	Geoff Combe	.06	.05	.02
63	Dave Concepcion	.12	.09	.05
64	Dan Driessen	.08	.06	.03
65	Joe Edelen	.06	.05	.02
66	George Foster	.20	.15	.08
67	Ken Griffey	.12	.09	.05
68	Paul Householder	.06	.05	.02
69	Tom Hume	.06	.05	.02
70	Junior Kennedy	.06	.05	.02
71	Ray Knight	.10	.08	.04
72	Mike LaCoss	.06	.05	.02
73	Rafael Landestoy	.06	.05	.02
74	Charlie Leibrandt	.10	.08	.04
75	Sam Mejias	.06	.05	.02
76	Paul Moskau	.06	.05	.02
77	Joe Nolan	.06	.05	.02
78	Mike O'Berry	.06	.05	.02
79	Ron Oester	.06	.05	.02
80	Frank Pastore	.06	.05	.02
81	Joe Price	.06	.05	.02
82	Tom Seaver	.90	.70	.35
83	Mario Soto	.08	.06	.03
84	Mike Vail	.06	.05	.02
85	Tony Armas	.10	.08	.04
86	Shooty Babitt	.06	.05	.02
87	Dave Beard	.06	.05	.02
88	Rick Bosetti	.06	.05	.02
89	Keith Drumright	.06	.05	.02
90	Wayne Gross	.06	.05	.02
91	Mike Heath	.06	.05	.02
92	Rickey Henderson	4.00	3.00	1.50
93	Cliff Johnson	.06	.05	.02
94	Jeff Jones	.06	.05	.02
95	Matt Keough	.06	.05	.02
96	Brian Kingman	.06	.05	.02
97	Mickey Klutts	.06	.05	.02
98	Rick Langford	.06	.05	.02
99	Steve McCatty	.06	.05	.02
100	Dave McKay	.06	.05	.02
101	Dwayne Murphy	.08	.06	.03
102	Jeff Newman	.06	.05	.02
103	Mike Norris	.06	.05	.02
104	Bob Owchinko	.06	.05	.02
105	Mitchell Page	.06	.05	.02
106	Rob Picciolo	.06	.05	.02
107	Jim Spencer	.06	.05	.02
108	Fred Stanley	.06	.05	.02
109	Tom Underwood	.06	.05	.02
110	Joaquin Andujar	.08	.06	.03
111	Steve Braun	.06	.05	.02
112	Bob Forsch	.08	.06	.03
113	George Hendrick	.08	.06	.03
114	Keith Hernandez	.20	.15	.08
115	Tom Herr	.10	.08	.04
116	Dane Iorg	.06	.05	.02
117	Jim Kaat	.15	.11	.06
118	Tito Landrum	.06	.05	.02
119	Sixto Lezcano	.06	.05	.02
120	Mark Littell	.06	.05	.02
121	John Martin	.06	.05	.02
122	Silvio Martinez	.06	.05	.02
123	Ken Oberkfell	.06	.05	.02
124	Darrell Porter	.08	.06	.03
125	Mike Ramsey	.06	.05	.02
126	Orlando Sanchez	.06	.05	.02
127	Bob Shirley	.06	.05	.02
128	Lary Sorensen	.06	.05	.02
129	Bruce Sutter	.15	.11	.06
130	Bob Sykes	.06	.05	.02
131	Garry Templeton	.10	.08	.04
132	Gene Tenace	.08	.06	.03
133	Jerry Augustine	.06	.05	.02
134	Sal Bando	.08	.06	.03
135	Mark Brouhard	.06	.05	.02
136	Mike Caldwell	.06	.05	.02
137	Reggie Cleveland	.06	.05	.02
138	Cecil Cooper	.15	.11	.06
139	Jamie Easterly	.06	.05	.02
140	Marshall Edwards	.06	.05	.02
141	Rollie Fingers	.50	.40	.20
142	Jim Gantner	.08	.06	.03
143	Moose Haas	.06	.05	.02
144	Larry Hisle	.08	.06	.03
145	Roy Howell	.06	.05	.02
146	Rickey Keeton	.06	.05	.02
147	Randy Lerch	.06	.05	.02
148	Paul Molitor	3.00	2.25	1.25
149	Don Money	.06	.05	.02
150	Charlie Moore	.06	.05	.02
151	Ben Oglivie	.08	.06	.03
152	Ted Simmons	.12	.09	.05
153	Jim Slaton	.06	.05	.02
154	Gorman Thomas	.10	.08	.04
155	Robin Yount	3.00	2.25	1.25
156	Pete Vukovich	.08	.06	.03
157	Benny Ayala	.06	.05	.02
158	Mark Belanger	.08	.06	.03
159	Al Bumbry	.08	.06	.03
160	Terry Crowley	.06	.05	.02
161	Rich Dauer	.06	.05	.02
162	Doug DeCinces	.10	.08	.04
163	Rick Dempsey	.08	.06	.03
164	Jim Dwyer	.06	.05	.02
165	Mike Flanagan	.10	.08	.04
166	Dave Ford	.06	.05	.02
167	Dan Graham	.06	.05	.02
168	Wayne Krenchicki	.06	.05	.02
169	John Lowenstein	.06	.05	.02
170	Dennis Martinez	.08	.06	.03
171	Tippy Martinez	.06	.05	.02
172	Scott McGregor	.08	.06	.03
173	Jose Morales	.06	.05	.02
174	Eddie Murray	.80	.60	.30
175	Jim Palmer	.60	.45	.25
176	*Cal Ripken, Jr.*	45.00	34.00	18.00
177	Gary Roenicke	.06	.05	.02
178	Lenn Sakata	.06	.05	.02
179	Ken Singleton	.10	.08	.04
180	Sammy Stewart	.06	.05	.02
181	Tim Stoddard	.06	.05	.02
182	Steve Stone	.08	.06	.03
183	Stan Bahnsen	.06	.05	.02
184	Ray Burris	.06	.05	.02
185	Gary Carter	.35	.25	.14
186	Warren Cromartie	.06	.05	.02
187	Andre Dawson	2.00	1.50	.80
188	*Terry Francona* (FC)	.08	.06	.03
189	Woodie Fryman	.08	.06	.03
190	Bill Gullickson	.08	.06	.03
191	Grant Jackson	.06	.05	.02
192	Wallace Johnson	.06	.05	.02
193	Charlie Lea	.06	.05	.02
194	Bill Lee	.08	.06	.03
195	Jerry Manuel	.06	.05	.02
196	Brad Mills	.06	.05	.02
197	John Milner	.06	.05	.02
198	Rowland Office	.06	.05	.02
199	David Palmer	.06	.05	.02
200	Larry Parrish	.10	.08	.04
201	Mike Phillips	.06	.05	.02
202	Tim Raines	1.50	1.25	.60
203	Bobby Ramos	.06	.05	.02
204	Jeff Reardon	1.00	.70	.40
205	Steve Rogers	.08	.06	.03
206	Scott Sanderson	.06	.05	.02
207	Rodney Scott (photo actually Tim Raines)	.10	.08	.04
208	Elias Sosa	.06	.05	.02
209	Chris Speier	.06	.05	.02
210	*Tim Wallach* (FC)	2.00	1.50	.80
211	Jerry White	.06	.05	.02
212	Alan Ashby	.06	.05	.02
213	Cesar Cedeno	.12	.09	.05
214	Jose Cruz	.12	.09	.05
215	Kiko Garcia	.06	.05	.02
216	Phil Garner	.08	.06	.03
217	Danny Heep	.06	.05	.02
218	Art Howe	.06	.05	.02
219	Bob Knepper	.08	.06	.03
220	Frank LaCorte	.06	.05	.02
221	Joe Niekro	.12	.09	.05
222	Joe Pittman	.06	.05	.02
223	Terry Puhl	.06	.05	.02
224	Luis Pujols	.06	.05	.02
225	Craig Reynolds	.06	.05	.02
226	J.R. Richard	.10	.08	.04
227	Dave Roberts	.06	.05	.02
228	Vern Ruhle	.06	.05	.02
229	Nolan Ryan	9.00	6.75	3.50
230	Joe Sambito	.06	.05	.02
231	Tony Scott	.06	.05	.02
232	Dave Smith	.10	.08	.04
233	Harry Spilman	.06	.05	.02
234	Don Sutton	.30	.25	.12
235	Dickie Thon	.08	.06	.03
236	Denny Walling	.06	.05	.02
237	Gary Woods	.06	.05	.02
238	*Luis Aguayo* (FC)	.08	.06	.03
239	Ramon Aviles	.06	.05	.02
240	Bob Boone	.10	.08	.04
241	Larry Bowa	.15	.11	.06
242	Warren Brusstar	.06	.05	.02
243	Steve Carlton	1.00	.70	.40
244	Larry Christenson	.06	.05	.02
245	Dick Davis	.06	.05	.02
246	Greg Gross	.06	.05	.02
247	Sparky Lyle	.10	.08	.04
248	Garry Maddox	.10	.08	.04
249	Gary Matthews	.10	.08	.04
250	Bake McBride	.06	.05	.02
251	Tug McGraw	.12	.09	.05
252	Keith Moreland	.10	.08	.04
253	Dickie Noles	.06	.05	.02
254	Mike Proly	.06	.05	.02
255	Ron Reed	.06	.05	.02
256	Pete Rose	1.00	.70	.40
257	Dick Ruthven	.06	.05	.02
258	Mike Schmidt	2.00	1.50	.80
259	Lonnie Smith	.08	.06	.03
260	Manny Trillo	.08	.06	.03
261	Del Unser	.06	.05	.02
262	George Vukovich	.06	.05	.02
263	Tom Brookens	.06	.05	.02
264	George Cappuzzello	.06	.05	.02
265	Marty Castillo	.06	.05	.02
266	Al Cowens	.06	.05	.02
267	Kirk Gibson	.40	.30	.15
268	Richie Hebner	.06	.05	.02
269	Ron Jackson	.06	.05	.02
270	Lynn Jones	.06	.05	.02
271	Steve Kemp	.08	.06	.03
272	*Rick Leach* (FC)	.12	.09	.05
273	Aurelio Lopez	.06	.05	.02
274	Jack Morris	.30	.25	.12
275	Kevin Saucier	.06	.05	.02
276	Lance Parrish	.20	.15	.08
277	Rick Peters	.06	.05	.02
278	Dan Petry	.08	.06	.03
279	David Rozema	.06	.05	.02
280	Stan Papi	.06	.05	.02
281	Dan Schatzeder	.06	.05	.02
282	Champ Summers	.06	.05	.02
283	Alan Trammell	.75	.60	.30
284	Lou Whitaker	.40	.30	.15
285	Milt Wilcox	.06	.05	.02
286	John Wockenfuss	.06	.05	.02
287	Gary Allenson	.06	.05	.02
288	Tom Burgmeier	.06	.05	.02
289	Bill Campbell	.06	.05	.02
290	Mark Clear	.06	.05	.02
291	Steve Crawford	.06	.05	.02

292 Dennis Eckersley 1.50 1.25 .60
293 Dwight Evans .15 .11 .06
294 *Rich Gedman* (FC) .25 .20 .10
295 Garry Hancock .06 .05 .02
296 Glenn Hoffman .06 .05 .02
297 Bruce Hurst (FC) .15 .11 .06
298 Carney Lansford .08 .06 .03
299 Rick Miller .06 .05 .02
300 Reid Nichols .06 .05 .02
301 *Bob Ojeda* (FC) .25 .20 .10
302 Tony Perez .20 .15 .08
303 Chuck Rainey .06 .05 .02
304 Jerry Remy .06 .05 .02
305 Jim Rice .25 .20 .10
306 Joe Rudi .10 .08 .04
307 Bob Stanley .06 .05 .02
308 Dave Stapleton .06 .05 .02
309 Frank Tanana .10 .08 .04
310 Mike Torrez .08 .06 .03
311 John Tudor (FC) .25 .20 .10
312 Carl Yastrzemski 1.00 .70 .40
313 Buddy Bell .12 .09 .05
314 Steve Comer .06 .05 .02
315 Danny Darwin .06 .05 .02
316 John Ellis .06 .05 .02
317 John Grubb .06 .05 .02
318 Rick Honeycutt .06 .05 .02
319 Charlie Hough .10 .08 .04
320 Fergie Jenkins .15 .11 .06
321 John Henry Johnson .06 .05 .02
322 Jim Kern .06 .05 .02
323 Jon Matlack .08 .06 .03
324 Doc Medich .06 .05 .02
325 Mario Mendoza .06 .05 .02
326 Al Oliver .15 .11 .06
327 Pat Putnam .06 .05 .02
328 Mickey Rivers .08 .06 .03
329 Leon Roberts .06 .05 .02
330 Billy Sample .06 .05 .02
331 Bill Stein .06 .05 .02
332 Jim Sundberg .08 .06 .03
333 Mark Wagner .06 .05 .02
334 Bump Wills .06 .05 .02
335 Bill Almon .06 .05 .02
336 Harold Baines .30 .25 .12
337 Ross Baumgarten .06 .05 .02
338 Tony Bernazard .06 .05 .02
339 Britt Burns .06 .05 .02
340 Richard Dotson .10 .08 .04
341 Jim Essian .06 .05 .02
342 Ed Farmer .06 .05 .02
343 Carlton Fisk 1.50 1.25 .60
344 Kevin Hickey .06 .05 .02
345 Lamarr Hoyt (LaMarr) .06 .05 .02
346 Lamar Johnson .06 .05 .02
347 Jerry Koosman .10 .08 .04
348 Rusty Kuntz .06 .05 .02
349 Dennis Lamp .06 .05 .02
350 Ron LeFlore .08 .06 .03
351 Chet Lemon .08 .06 .03
352 Greg Luzinski .15 .11 .06
353 Bob Molinaro .06 .05 .02
354 Jim Morrison .06 .05 .02
355 Wayne Nordhagen .06 .05 .02
356 Greg Pryor .06 .05 .02
357 Mike Squires .06 .05 .02
358 Steve Trout .06 .05 .02
359 Alan Bannister .06 .05 .02
360 Len Barker .08 .06 .03
361 Bert Blyleven .12 .09 .05
362 Joe Charboneau .08 .06 .03
363 John Denny .06 .05 .02
364 Bo Diaz .08 .06 .03
365 Miguel Dilone .06 .05 .02
366 Jerry Dybzinski .06 .05 .02
367 Wayne Garland .06 .05 .02
368 Mike Hargrove .06 .05 .02
369 Toby Harrah .08 .06 .03
370 Ron Hassey .06 .05 .02
371 *Von Hayes* (FC) .25 .20 .10
372 Pat Kelly .06 .05 .02
373 Duane Kuiper .06 .05 .02
374 Rick Manning .06 .05 .02
375 Sid Monge .06 .05 .02
376 Jorge Orta .06 .05 .02
377 Dave Rosello .06 .05 .02
378 Dan Spillner .06 .05 .02
379 Mike Stanton .06 .05 .02
380 Andre Thornton .10 .08 .04
381 Tom Veryzer .06 .05 .02
382 Rick Waits .06 .05 .02
383 Doyle Alexander .10 .08 .04
384 Vida Blue .12 .09 .05
385 Fred Breining .06 .05 .02
386 Enos Cabell .06 .05 .02
387 Jack Clark .15 .11 .06
388 Darrell Evans .15 .11 .06
389 Tom Griffin .06 .05 .02
390 Larry Herndon .08 .06 .03
391 Al Holland .06 .05 .02
392 Gary Lavelle .06 .05 .02
393 Johnnie LeMaster .06 .05 .02
394 Jerry Martin .06 .05 .02
395 Milt May .06 .05 .02
396 Greg Minton .06 .05 .02
397 Joe Morgan .50 .40 .20
398 Joe Pettini .06 .05 .02
399 Alan Ripley .06 .05 .02
400 Billy Smith .06 .05 .02
401 Rennie Stennett .06 .05 .02
402 Ed Whitson .06 .05 .02
403 Jim Wohlford .06 .05 .02
404 Willie Aikens .06 .05 .02
405 George Brett 3.00 2.25 1.25
406 Ken Brett .08 .06 .03
407 Dave Chalk .06 .05 .02
408 Rich Gale .06 .05 .02
409 Cesar Geronimo .06 .05 .02
410 Larry Gura .06 .05 .02
411 Clint Hurdle .06 .05 .02
412 Mike Jones .06 .05 .02
413 Dennis Leonard .08 .06 .03
414 Renie Martin .06 .05 .02
415 Lee May .08 .06 .03
416 Hal McRae .12 .09 .05
417 Darryl Motley .06 .05 .02
418 Rance Mulliniks .06 .05 .02
419 Amos Otis .08 .06 .03
420 *Ken Phelps* (FC) .10 .08 .04
421 Jamie Quirk .06 .05 .02
422 Dan Quisenberry .15 .11 .06
423 Paul Splittorff .06 .05 .02
424 U.L. Washington .06 .05 .02
425 John Wathan .08 .06 .03
426 Frank White .10 .08 .04
427 Willie Wilson .15 .11 .06
428 Brian Asselstine .06 .05 .02
429 Bruce Benedict .06 .05 .02
430 Tom Boggs .06 .05 .02
431 Larry Bradford .06 .05 .02
432 Rick Camp .06 .05 .02
433 Chris Chambliss .08 .06 .03
434 Gene Garber .06 .05 .02
435 Preston Hanna .06 .05 .02
436 Bob Horner .12 .09 .05
437 Glenn Hubbard .08 .06 .03
438a Al Hrabosky (All Hrabosky, 5'1" on back) 20.00 15.00 8.00
438b Al Hrabosky (Al Hrabosky, 5'1" on back) 1.25 .90 .50
438c Al Hrabosky (Al Hrabosky, 5'10" on back) .35 .25 .14
439 Rufino Linares .06 .05 .02
440 *Rick Mahler* (FC) .12 .09 .05
441 Ed Miller .06 .05 .02
442 John Montefusco .08 .06 .03
443 Dale Murphy .90 .70 .35
444 Phil Niekro .30 .25 .12
445 Gaylord Perry .40 .30 .15
446 Biff Pocoroba .06 .05 .02
447 Rafael Ramirez .08 .06 .03
448 Jerry Royster .06 .05 .02
449 Claudell Washington .08 .06 .03
450 Don Aase .06 .05 .02
451 Don Baylor .12 .09 .05
452 Juan Beniquez .06 .05 .02
453 Rick Burleson .08 .06 .03
454 Bert Campaneris .10 .08 .04
455 Rod Carew 1.00 .70 .40
456 Bob Clark .06 .05 .02
457 Brian Downing .10 .08 .04
458 Dan Ford .06 .05 .02
459 Ken Forsch .06 .05 .02
460 Dave Frost .06 .05 .02
461 Bobby Grich .10 .08 .04
462 Larry Harlow .06 .05 .02
463 John Harris .06 .05 .02
464 Andy Hassler .06 .05 .02
465 Butch Hobson .06 .05 .02
466 Jesse Jefferson .06 .05 .02
467 Bruce Kison .06 .05 .02
468 Fred Lynn .20 .15 .08
469 Angel Moreno .06 .05 .02
470 Ed Ott .06 .05 .02
471 Fred Patek .06 .05 .02
472 Steve Renko .06 .05 .02
473 *Mike Witt* (FC) .25 .20 .10
474 Geoff Zahn .06 .05 .02
475 Gary Alexander .06 .05 .02
476 Dale Berra .06 .05 .02
477 Kurt Bevacqua .06 .05 .02
478 Jim Bibby .06 .05 .02
479 John Candelaria .10 .08 .04
480 Victor Cruz .06 .05 .02
481 Mike Easler .08 .06 .03
482 Tim Foli .06 .05 .02
483 Lee Lacy .06 .05 .02
484 Vance Law (FC) .06 .05 .02
485 Bill Madlock .12 .09 .05
486 Willie Montanez .06 .05 .02
487 Omar Moreno .06 .05 .02
488 Steve Nicosia .06 .05 .02
489 Dave Parker .30 .25 .12
490 Tony Pena (FC) .25 .20 .10
491 Pascual Perez (FC) .15 .11 .06
492 *Johnny Ray* (FC) .10 .08 .04
493 Rick Rhoden .10 .08 .04
494 Bill Robinson .06 .05 .02
495 Don Robinson .08 .06 .03
496 Enrique Romo .06 .05 .02
497 Rod Scurry .06 .05 .02
498 Eddie Solomon .06 .05 .02
499 Willie Stargell .40 .30 .15
500 Kent Tekulve .08 .06 .03
501 Jason Thompson .06 .05 .02
502 Glenn Abbott .06 .05 .02
503 Jim Anderson .06 .05 .02
504 Floyd Bannister .10 .08 .04
505 Bruce Bochte .06 .05 .02
506 Jeff Burroughs .08 .06 .03
507 Bryan Clark .06 .05 .02
508 Ken Clay .06 .05 .02
509 Julio Cruz .06 .05 .02
510 Dick Drago .06 .05 .02
511 Gary Gray .06 .05 .02
512 Dan Meyer .06 .05 .02
513 Jerry Narron .06 .05 .02
514 Tom Paciorek .06 .05 .02
515 Casey Parsons .06 .05 .02
516 Lenny Randle .06 .05 .02
517 Shane Rawley .10 .08 .04
518 Joe Simpson .06 .05 .02
519 Richie Zisk .08 .06 .03
520 Neil Allen .06 .05 .02
521 Bob Bailor .06 .05 .02
522 Hubie Brooks (FC) .25 .20 .10
523 Mike Cubbage .06 .05 .02
524 Pete Falcone .06 .05 .02
525 Doug Flynn .06 .05 .02
526 Tom Hausman .06 .05 .02
527 Ron Hodges .06 .05 .02
528 Randy Jones .08 .06 .03
529 Mike Jorgensen .06 .05 .02
530 Dave Kingman .15 .11 .06
531 Ed Lynch .06 .05 .02
532 Mike Marshall .10 .08 .04
533 Lee Mazzilli .08 .06 .03
534 Dyar Miller .06 .05 .02
535 Mike Scott (FC) .20 .15 .08
536 Rusty Staub .10 .08 .04
537 John Stearns .06 .05 .02
538 Craig Swan .06 .05 .02
539 Frank Taveras .06 .05 .02
540 Alex Trevino .06 .05 .02
541 Ellis Valentine .06 .05 .02
542 Mookie Wilson (FC) .15 .11 .06
543 Joel Youngblood .06 .05 .02
544 Pat Zachry .06 .05 .02
545 Glenn Adams .06 .05 .02
546 Fernando Arroyo .06 .05 .02
547 John Verhoeven .06 .05 .02
548 Sal Butera .06 .05 .02
549 John Castino .06 .05 .02
550 Don Cooper .06 .05 .02
551 Doug Corbett .06 .05 .02
552 Dave Engle .06 .05 .02
553 Roger Erickson .06 .05 .02
554 Danny Goodwin .06 .05 .02
555a Darrell Jackson (black cap) 1.00 .70 .40
555b Darrell Jackson (red cap with emblem) .10 .08 .04
555c Darrell Jackson (red cap, no emblem) .25 .20 .10
556 Pete Mackanin .06 .05 .02
557 Jack O'Connor .06 .05 .02
558 Hosken Powell .06 .05 .02
559 Pete Redfern .06 .05 .02
560 Roy Smalley .06 .05 .02
561 Chuck Baker .06 .05 .02
562 Gary Ward .08 .06 .03
563 Rob Wilfong .06 .05 .02
564 Al Williams .06 .05 .02
565 Butch Wynegar .06 .05 .02
566 Randy Bass .06 .05 .02
567 Juan Bonilla .06 .05 .02
568 Danny Boone .06 .05 .02
569 John Curtis .06 .05 .02
570 Juan Eichelberger .06 .05 .02
571 Barry Evans .06 .05 .02
572 Tim Flannery .06 .05 .02
573 Ruppert Jones .06 .05 .02
574 Terry Kennedy .08 .06 .03
575 Joe Lefebvre .06 .05 .02
576a John Littlefield (pitching lefty) 200.00 150.00 80.00
576b John Littlefield (pitching righty) .08 .06 .03
577 Gary Lucas .06 .05 .02
578 Steve Mura .06 .05 .02
579 Broderick Perkins .06 .05 .02
580 Gene Richards .06 .05 .02
581 Luis Salazar .06 .05 .02
582 Ozzie Smith 1.75 1.25 .70
583 John Urrea .06 .05 .02
584 Chris Welsh .06 .05 .02
585 Rick Wise .08 .06 .03
586 Doug Bird .06 .05 .02
587 Tim Blackwell .06 .05 .02
588 Bobby Bonds .10 .08 .04
589 Bill Buckner .12 .09 .05
590 Bill Caudill .06 .05 .02
591 Hector Cruz .06 .05 .02
592 *Jody Davis* (FC) .10 .08 .04
593 Ivan DeJesus .06 .05 .02
594 Steve Dillard .06 .05 .02
595 Leon Durham .08 .06 .03
596 Rawly Eastwick .06 .05 .02
597 Steve Henderson .06 .05 .02
598 Mike Krukow .08 .06 .03
599 Mike Lum .06 .05 .02
600 Randy Martz .06 .05 .02
601 Jerry Morales .06 .05 .02
602 Ken Reitz .06 .05 .02
603a *Lee Smith* (Cubs logo reversed on back) 12.00 9.00 4.75
603b *Lee Smith* (corrected) 9.00 6.75 3.50
604 Dick Tidrow .06 .05 .02
605 Jim Tracy .06 .05 .02
606 Mike Tyson .06 .05 .02
607 Ty Waller .06 .05 .02
608 Danny Ainge 1.25 .90 .50
609 *Jorge Bell* (FC) 6.00 4.50 2.50
610 Mark Bomback .06 .05 .02
611 Barry Bonnell .06 .05 .02
612 Jim Clancy .08 .06 .03
613 Damaso Garcia .06 .05 .02
614 Jerry Garvin .06 .05 .02
615 Alfredo Griffin .08 .06 .03
616 Garth Iorg .06 .05 .02
617 Luis Leal .06 .05 .02
618 Ken Macha .06 .05 .02
619 John Mayberry .08 .06 .03
620 Joey McLaughlin .06 .05 .02
621 Lloyd Moseby .12 .09 .05
622 Dave Stieb .12 .09 .05
623 Jackson Todd .06 .05 .02
624 Willie Upshaw (FC) .08 .06 .03
625 Otto Velez .06 .05 .02
626 Ernie Whitt .08 .06 .03
627 Al Woods .06 .05 .02
628 1981 All-Star Game .08 .06 .03
629 All-Star Infielders (Bucky Dent, Frank White) .10 .08 .04
630 Big Red Machine (Dave Concepcion, Dan Driessen, George Foster) .15 .11 .06
631 Top N.L. Relief Pitcher (Bruce Sutter)

		.15	.11	.06
632	Steve & Carlton (Steve Carlton, Carlton Fisk)	.25	.20	.10
633	3000th Game, May 25, 1981 (Carl Yastrzemski)	.35	.25	.14
634	Dynamic Duo (Johnny Bench, Tom Seaver)	.30	.25	.12
635	West Meets East (Gary Carter, Fernando Valenzuela)	.30	.25	.12
636a	N.L. Strikeout King (Fernando Valenzuela) ("...led the National League...")	1.00	.70	.40
636b	N.L. Strikeout King (Fernando Valenzuela) ("... led the National League)	.50	.40	.20
637	Home Run King (Mike Schmidt)	.40	.30	.15
638	N.L. All-Stars (Gary Carter, Dave Parker)	.25	.20	.10
639	Perfect Game! (Len Barker, Bo Diaz)	.08	.06	.03
640	Pete Rose (Re-Pete, Pete Rose, Jr.)	1.50	1.25	.60
641	Phillies' Finest (Steve Carlton, Mike Schmidt, Lonnie Smith)	.50	.40	.20
642	Red Sox Reunion (Dwight Evans, Fred Lynn)	.15	.11	.06
643	Most Hits and Runs (Rickey Henderson)	2.00	1.50	.80
644	Most Saves 1981 A.L. (Rollie Fingers)	.15	.11	.06
645	Most 1981 Wins (Tom Seaver)	.25	.20	.10
646a	Yankee Powerhouse (Reggie Jackson, Dave Winfield) (comma after "outfielder" on back)	2.00	1.50	.80
646b	Yankee Powerhouse (Reggie Jackson) (no comma)	2.00	1.50	.80
646b	Yankee Powerhouse (Dave Winfield) (no comma)	2.00	1.50	.80
647	Checklist 1-56	.06	.05	.02
648	Checklist 57-109	.06	.05	.02
649	Checklist 110-156	.06	.05	.02
650	Checklist 157-211	.06	.05	.02
651	Checklist 212-262	.06	.05	.02
652	Checklist 263-312	.06	.05	.02
653	Checklist 313-358	.06	.05	.02
654	Checklist 359-403	.06	.05	.02
655	Checklist 404-449	.06	.05	.02
656	Checklist 450-501	.06	.05	.02
657	Checklist 502-544	.06	.05	.02
658	Checklist 545-585	.06	.05	.02
659	Checklist 586-627	.06	.05	.02
660	Checklist 628-646	.06	.05	.02

1982 Fleer Stamps

Issued by Fleer in 1982, this set consists of 242 player stamps, each measuring 2-1/2" by 1-13/16". Originally issued in perforated strips of 10, the full-color stamps are numbered in the lower left corner and were designed to be placed in an album. Six stamps feature two players each.

		MT	NR MT	EX
Complete Set:		12.00	9.00	4.75
Common Player:		.05	.02	.01
Stamp Album:		1.50	1.25	.60
1	Fernando Valenzuela	.15	.11	.06
2	Rick Monday	.05	.04	.02
3	Ron Cey	.06	.05	.02
4	Dusty Baker	.05	.04	.02
5	Burt Hooton	.05	.04	.02
6	Pedro Guerrero	.06	.05	.02
7	Jerry Reuss	.06	.05	.02
8	Bill Russell	.05	.04	.02
9	Steve Garvey	.20	.15	.08
10	Davey Lopes	.05	.04	.02
11	Tom Seaver	.25	.20	.10
12	George Foster	.08	.06	.03
13	Frank Pastore	.05	.04	.02
14	Dave Collins	.05	.04	.02
15	Dave Concepcion	.06	.05	.02
16	Ken Griffey	.08	.06	.03
17	Johnny Bench	.05	.04	.02
18	Ray Knight	.05	.04	.02
19	Mario Soto	.05	.04	.02
20	Ron Oester	.05	.04	.02
21	Ken Oberkfell	.05	.04	.02
22	Bob Forsch	.05	.04	.02
23	Keith Hernandez	.06	.05	.02
24	Dane Iorg	.05	.04	.02
25	George Hendrick	.05	.04	.02
26	Gene Tenace	.05	.04	.02
27	Garry Templeton	.06	.05	.02
28	Bruce Sutter	.08	.06	.03
29	Darrell Porter	.05	.04	.02
30	Tom Herr	.06	.05	.02
31	Tim Raines	.20	.15	.08
32	Chris Speier	.05	.04	.02
33	Warren Cromartie	.05	.04	.02
34	Larry Parrish	.05	.04	.02
35	Andre Dawson	.25	.20	.10
36	Steve Rogers	.05	.04	.02
37	Jeff Reardon	.08	.06	.03
38	Rodney Scott	.05	.04	.02
39	Gary Carter	.20	.15	.08
40	Scott Sanderson	.05	.04	.02
41	Cesar Cedeno	.06	.05	.02
42	Nolan Ryan	.50	.40	.20
43	Don Sutton	.12	.09	.05
44	Terry Puhl	.05	.04	.02
45	Joe Niekro	.06	.05	.02
46	Tony Scott	.05	.04	.02
47	Joe Sambito	.05	.04	.02
48	Art Howe	.05	.04	.02
49	Bob Knepper	.06	.05	.02
50	Jose Cruz	.05	.04	.02
51	Pete Rose	.40	.30	.15
52	Dick Ruthven	.05	.04	.02
53	Mike Schmidt	.30	.25	.12
54	Steve Carlton	.20	.15	.08
55	Tug McGraw	.08	.06	.03
56	Larry Bowa	.08	.06	.03
57	Garry Maddox	.05	.04	.02
58	Gary Matthews	.05	.04	.02
59	Manny Trillo	.05	.04	.02
60	Lonnie Smith	.05	.04	.02
61	Vida Blue	.08	.06	.03
62	Milt May	.05	.04	.02
63	Joe Morgan	.12	.09	.05
64	Enos Cabell	.05	.04	.02
65	Jack Clark	.10	.08	.04
66	Claudell Washington	.05	.04	.02
67	Gaylord Perry	.15	.11	.06
68	Phil Niekro	.15	.11	.06
69	Bob Horner	.08	.06	.03
70	Chris Chambliss	.05	.04	.02
71	Dave Parker	.12	.09	.05
72	Tony Pena	.06	.05	.02
73	Kent Tekulve	.05	.04	.02
74	Mike Easler	.05	.04	.02
75	Tim Foli	.05	.04	.02
76	Willie Stargell	.20	.15	.08
77	Bill Madlock	.06	.05	.02
78	Jim Bibby	.05	.04	.02
79	Omar Moreno	.05	.04	.02
80	Lee Lacy	.05	.04	.02
81	Hubie Brooks	.06	.05	.02
82	Rusty Staub	.06	.05	.02
83	Ellis Valentine	.05	.04	.02
84	Neil Allen	.05	.04	.02
85	Dave Kingman	.08	.06	.03
86	Mookie Wilson	.05	.04	.02
87	Doug Flynn	.05	.04	.02
88	Pat Zachry	.05	.04	.02
89	John Stearns	.05	.04	.02
90	Lee Mazzilli	.05	.04	.02
91	Ken Reitz	.05	.04	.02
92	Mike Krukow	.05	.04	.02
93	Jerry Morales	.05	.04	.02
94	Leon Durham	.06	.05	.02
95	Ivan DeJesus	.05	.04	.02
96	Bill Buckner	.06	.05	.02
97	Jim Tracy	.05	.04	.02
98	Steve Henderson	.05	.04	.02
99	Dick Tidrow	.05	.04	.02
100	Mike Tyson	.05	.04	.02
101	Ozzie Smith	.08	.06	.03
102	Ruppert Jones	.05	.04	.02
103	Broderick Perkins	.05	.04	.02
104	Gene Richrds	.05	.04	.02
105	Terry Kennedy	.05	.04	.02
106	Jim Bibby, Willie Stargell	.12	.09	.05
107	Larry Bowa, Pete Rose	.25	.20	.10
108	Warren Spahn, Fernando Valenzuela	.15	.11	.06
109	Dave Concepcion, Pete Rose	.25	.20	.10
110	Reggie Jackson, Dave Winfield	.20	.15	.08
111	Tom Lasorda, Fernando Valenzuela	.10	.08	.04
112	Reggie Jackson	.30	.25	.12
113	Dave Winfield	.20	.15	.08
114	Lou Piniella	.08	.06	.03
115	Tommy John	.10	.08	.04
116	Rich Gossage	.10	.08	.04
117	Ron Davis	.05	.04	.02
118	Rick Cerone	.05	.04	.02
119	Graig Nettles	.08	.06	.03
120	Ron Guidry	.08	.06	.03
121	Willie Randolph	.06	.05	.02
122	Dwayne Murphy	.05	.04	.02
123	Rickey Henderson	.25	.20	.10
124	Wayne Gross	.05	.04	.02
125	Mike Norris	.05	.04	.02
126	Rick Langford	.05	.04	.02
127	Jim Spencer	.05	.04	.02
128	Tony Armas	.05	.04	.02
129	Matt Keough	.05	.04	.02
130	Jeff Jones	.05	.04	.02
131	Steve McCatty	.05	.04	.02
132	Rollie Fingers	.10	.08	.04
133	Jim Gantner	.05	.04	.02
134	Gorman Thomas	.05	.04	.02
135	Robin Yount	.15	.11	.06
136	Paul Molitor	.10	.08	.04
137	Ted Simmons	.08	.06	.03
138	Ben Oglivie	.05	.04	.02
139	Moose Haas	.05	.04	.02
140	Cecil Cooper	.08	.06	.03
141	Pete Vuckovich	.05	.04	.02
142	Doug DeCinces	.05	.04	.02
143	Jim Palmer	.15	.11	.06
144	Steve Stone	.06	.05	.02
145	Mike Flanagan	.05	.04	.02
146	Rick Dempsey	.05	.04	.02
147	Al Bumbry	.05	.04	.02
148	Mark Belanger	.05	.04	.02
149	Scott McGregor	.05	.04	.02
150	Ken Singleton	.06	.05	.02
151	Eddie Murray	.25	.20	.10
152	Lance Parrish	.12	.09	.05
153	David Rozema	.05	.04	.02
154	Champ Summers	.05	.04	.02
155	Alan Trammell	.15	.11	.06
156	Lou Whitaker	.10	.08	.04
157	Milt Wilcox	.05	.04	.02
158	Kevin Saucier	.05	.04	.02
159	Jack Morris	.12	.09	.05
160	Steve Kemp	.05	.04	.02
161	Kirk Gibson	.12	.09	.05
162	Carl Yastrzemski	.35	.25	.14
163	Jim Rice	.12	.09	.05
164	Carney Lansford	.06	.05	.02
165	Dennis Eckersley	.06	.05	.02
166	Mike Torrez	.05	.04	.02
167	Dwight Evans	.08	.06	.03
168	Glenn Hoffman	.05	.04	.02
169	Bob Stanley	.05	.04	.02
170	Tony Perez	.08	.06	.03
171	Jerry Remy	.05	.04	.02
172	Buddy Bell	.06	.05	.02
173	Ferguson Jenkins	.08	.06	.03
174	Mickey Rivers	.05	.04	.02
175	Bump Wills	.05	.04	.02
176	Jon Matlack	.05	.04	.02
177	Steve Comer	.05	.04	.02
178	Al Oliver	.06	.05	.02
179	Bill Stein	.05	.04	.02
180	Pat Putnam	.05	.04	.02
181	Jim Sundberg	.05	.04	.02
182	Ron Leflore	.05	.04	.02
183	Carlton Fisk	.12	.09	.05
184	Harold Baines	.10	.08	.04
185	Bill Almon	.05	.04	.02
186	Richard Dotson	.05	.04	.02
187	Greg Luzinski	.08	.06	.03
188	Mike Squires	.05	.04	.02
189	Britt Burns	.05	.04	.02
190	Lamarr Hoyt	.05	.04	.02
191	Chet Lemon	.05	.04	.02
192	Joe Charboneau	.05	.04	.02
193	Toby Harrah	.05	.04	.02
194	John Denny	.05	.04	.02
195	Rick Manning	.05	.04	.02
196	Miguel Dilone	.05	.04	.02
197	Bo Diaz	.05	.04	.02
198	Mike Hargrove	.05	.04	.02
199	Bert Blyleven	.10	.08	.04
200	Len Barker	.05	.04	.02
201	Andre Thornton	.05	.04	.02
202	George Brett	.30	.25	.12
203	U.L. Washington	.05	.04	.02
204	Dan Quisenberry	.06	.05	.02
205	Larry Gura	.05	.04	.02
206	Willie Aikens	.05	.04	.02
207	Willie Wilson	.08	.06	.03
208	Dennis Leonard	.05	.04	.02
209	Frank White	.06	.05	.02
210	Hal McRae	.06	.05	.02
211	Amos Otis	.05	.04	.02
212	Don Aase	.05	.04	.02
213	Butch Hobson	.05	.04	.02
214	Fred Lynn	.10	.08	.04
215	Brian Downing	.05	.04	.02
216	Dan Ford	.05	.04	.02
217	Rod Carew	.25	.20	.10
218	Bobby Grich	.06	.05	.02
219	Rick Burleson	.05	.04	.02
220	Don Baylor	.10	.08	.04
221	Ken Forsch	.05	.04	.02
222	Bruce Bochte	.05	.04	.02
223	Richie Zisk	.05	.04	.02
224	Tom Paciorek	.05	.04	.02
225	Julio Cruz	.05	.04	.02
226	Jeff Burroughs	.05	.04	.02
227	Doug Corbett	.05	.04	.02
228	Roy Smalley	.05	.04	.02
229	Gary Ward	.05	.04	.02
230	John Castino	.05	.04	.02
231	Rob Wilfong	.05	.04	.02
232	Dave Stieb	.06	.05	.02
233	Otto Velez	.05	.04	.02
234	Damaso Garcia	.05	.04	.02
235	John Mayberry	.05	.04	.02
236	Alfredo Griffin	.06	.05	.02
237	Ted Williams, Carl Yastrzemski	.35	.25	.14
238	Rick Cerone, Graig Nettles	.05	.04	.02
239	Buddy Bell, George Brett	.15	.11	.06
240	Steve Carlton, Jim Kaat	.12	.09	.05
241	Steve Carlton, Dave Parker	.12	.09	.05
242	Ron Davis, Nolan Ryan	.10	.08	.04

Values quoted in this guide reflect the retail price of a card – the price a collector can expect to pay when buying a card from a dealer. The wholesale price – that which a collector can expect to receive from a dealer when selling cards – will be significantly lower, depending on desirability and condition.

1983 Fleer

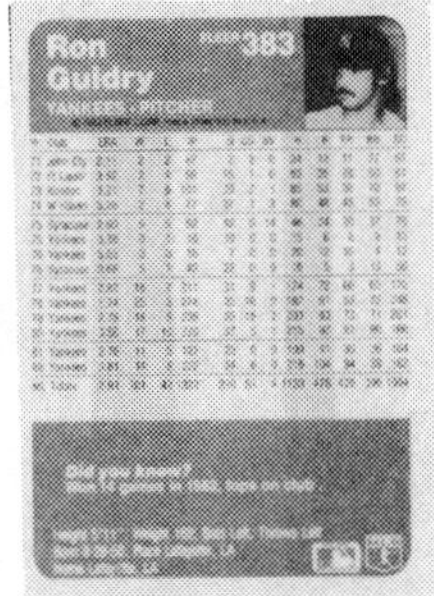

The 1983 Fleer set features color photos set inside a light brown border. The cards are the standard size of 2-1/2" by 3-1/2". A team logo is located at the card bottom and the word "Fleer" is found at the top. The card backs are designed on a vertical format and include a small black and white photo of the player along with biographical and statistical information. The reverses are done in two shades of brown on white stock. The set was issued with team logo stickers.

		MT	NR MT	EX
Complete Set (660):		125.00	94.00	50.00
Common Player:		.06	.05	.02
1	Joaquin Andujar	.08	.06	.03
2	Doug Bair	.06	.05	.02
3	Steve Braun	.06	.05	.02
4	Glenn Brummer	.06	.05	.02
5	Bob Forsch	.08	.06	.03
6	David Green	.06	.05	.02
7	George Hendrick	.08	.06	.03
8	Keith Hernandez	.15	.11	.06
9	Tom Herr	.10	.08	.04
10	Dane Iorg	.06	.05	.02
11	Jim Kaat	.15	.11	.06
12	Jeff Lahti	.06	.05	.02
13	Tito Landrum	.06	.05	.02
14	*Dave LaPoint* (FC)	.08	.06	.03
15	*Willie McGee*	2.00	1.50	.80
16	Steve Mura	.06	.05	.02
17	Ken Oberkfell	.06	.05	.02
18	Darrell Porter	.08	.06	.03
19	Mike Ramsey	.06	.05	.02
20	Gene Roof	.06	.05	.02
21	Lonnie Smith	.08	.06	.03
22	Ozzie Smith	1.50	1.25	.60
23	John Stuper	.06	.05	.02
24	Bruce Sutter	.15	.11	.06
25	Gene Tenace	.08	.06	.03
26	Jerry Augustine	.06	.05	.02
27	Dwight Bernard	.06	.05	.02
28	Mark Brouhard	.06	.05	.02
29	Mike Caldwell	.06	.05	.02
30	Cecil Cooper	.15	.11	.06
31	Jamie Easterly	.06	.05	.02
32	Marshall Edwards	.06	.05	.02
33	Rollie Fingers	.60	.45	.25
34	Jim Gantner	.08	.06	.03
35	Moose Haas	.06	.05	.02
36	Roy Howell	.06	.05	.02
37	Peter Ladd	.06	.05	.02
38	Bob McClure	.06	.05	.02
39	Doc Medich	.06	.05	.02
40	Paul Molitor	2.50	2.00	1.00
41	Don Money	.06	.05	.02
42	Charlie Moore	.06	.05	.02
43	Ben Oglivie	.08	.06	.03
44	Ed Romero	.06	.05	.02
45	Ted Simmons	.08	.06	.03
46	Jim Slaton	.06	.05	.02
47	Don Sutton	.30	.25	.12
48	Gorman Thomas	.06	.05	.02
49	Pete Vuckovich	.08	.06	.03
50	Ned Yost	.06	.05	.02
51	Robin Yount	3.00	2.25	1.25
52	Benny Ayala	.06	.05	.02
53	Bob Bonner	.06	.05	.02
54	Al Bumbry	.08	.06	.03
55	Terry Crowley	.06	.05	.02
56	*Storm Davis* (FC)	.10	.08	.04
57	Rich Dauer	.06	.05	.02
58	Rick Dempsey	.08	.06	.03
59	Jim Dwyer	.06	.05	.02
60	Mike Flanagan	.10	.08	.04
61	Dan Ford	.06	.05	.02
62	Glenn Gulliver	.06	.05	.02
63	John Lowenstein	.06	.05	.02
64	Dennis Martinez	.08	.06	.03
65	Tippy Martinez	.06	.05	.02
66	Scott McGregor	.08	.06	.03
67	Eddie Murray	1.00	.70	.40
68	Joe Nolan	.06	.05	.02
69	Jim Palmer	.50	.40	.20
70	Cal Ripken, Jr.	15.00	11.00	6.00
71	Gary Roenicke	.06	.05	.02
72	Lenn Sakata	.06	.05	.02
73	Ken Singleton	.10	.08	.04
74	Sammy Stewart	.06	.05	.02
75	Tim Stoddard	.06	.05	.02
76	Don Aase	.06	.05	.02
77	Don Baylor	.12	.09	.05
78	Juan Beniquez	.06	.05	.02
79	Bob Boone	.10	.08	.04
80	Rick Burleson	.08	.06	.03
81	Rod Carew	1.00	.70	.40
82	Bobby Clark	.06	.05	.02
83	Doug Corbett	.06	.05	.02
84	John Curtis	.06	.05	.02
85	Doug DeCinces	.10	.08	.04
86	Brian Downing	.10	.08	.04
87	Joe Ferguson	.06	.05	.02
88	Tim Foli	.06	.05	.02
89	Ken Forsch	.06	.05	.02
90	Dave Goltz	.08	.06	.03
91	Bobby Grich	.10	.08	.04
92	Andy Hassler	.06	.05	.02
93	Reggie Jackson	1.00	.70	.40
94	Ron Jackson	.06	.05	.02
95	Tommy John	.20	.15	.08
96	Bruce Kison	.06	.05	.02
97	Fred Lynn	.20	.15	.08
98	Ed Ott	.06	.05	.02
99	Steve Renko	.06	.05	.02
100	Luis Sanchez	.06	.05	.02
101	Rob Wilfong	.06	.05	.02
102	Mike Witt	.15	.11	.06
103	Geoff Zahn	.06	.05	.02
104	Willie Aikens	.06	.05	.02
105	Mike Armstrong	.06	.05	.02
106	Vida Blue	.12	.09	.05
107	*Bud Black*	.50	.40	.20
108	George Brett	3.00	2.25	1.25
109	Bill Castro	.06	.05	.02
110	Onix Concepcion	.06	.05	.02
111	Dave Frost	.06	.05	.02
112	Cesar Geronimo	.06	.05	.02
113	Larry Gura	.06	.05	.02
114	Steve Hammond	.06	.05	.02
115	Don Hood	.06	.05	.02
116	Dennis Leonard	.08	.06	.03
117	Jerry Martin	.06	.05	.02
118	Lee May	.08	.06	.03
119	Hal McRae	.12	.09	.05
120	Amos Otis	.08	.06	.03
121	Greg Pryor	.06	.05	.02
122	Dan Quisenberry	.15	.11	.06
123	*Don Slaught* (FC)	.20	.15	.08
124	Paul Splittorff	.06	.05	.02
125	U.L. Washington	.06	.05	.02
126	John Wathan	.08	.06	.03
127	Frank White	.10	.08	.04
128	Willie Wilson	.15	.11	.06
129	Steve Bedrosian (FC)	.10	.08	.04
130	Bruce Benedict	.06	.05	.02
131	Tommy Boggs	.06	.05	.02
132	Brett Butler (FC)	.12	.09	.05
133	Rick Camp	.06	.05	.02
134	Chris Chambliss	.08	.06	.03
135	Ken Dayley (FC)	.10	.08	.04
136	Gene Garber	.06	.05	.02
137	Terry Harper	.06	.05	.02
138	Bob Horner	.12	.09	.05
139	Glenn Hubbard	.08	.06	.03
140	Rufino Linares	.06	.05	.02
141	Rick Mahler	.08	.06	.03
142	Dale Murphy	.75	.60	.30
143	Phil Niekro	.30	.25	.12
144	Pascual Perez	.08	.06	.03
145	Biff Pocoroba	.06	.05	.02
146	Rafael Ramirez	.06	.05	.02
147	Jerry Royster	.06	.05	.02
148	Ken Smith	.06	.05	.02
149	Bob Walk	.08	.06	.03
150	Claudell Washington	.08	.06	.03
151	Bob Watson	.08	.06	.03
152	Larry Whisenton	.06	.05	.02
153	Porfirio Altamirano	.06	.05	.02
154	Marty Bystrom	.06	.05	.02
155	Steve Carlton	1.00	.70	.40
156	Larry Christenson	.06	.05	.02
157	Ivan DeJesus	.06	.05	.02
158	John Denny	.06	.05	.02
159	Bob Dernier (FC)	.06	.05	.02
160	Bo Diaz	.08	.06	.03
161	Ed Farmer	.06	.05	.02
162	Greg Gross	.06	.05	.02
163	Mike Krukow	.08	.06	.03
164	Garry Maddox	.10	.08	.04
165	Gary Matthews	.10	.08	.04
166	Tug McGraw	.12	.09	.05
167	Bob Molinaro	.06	.05	.02
168	Sid Monge	.06	.05	.02
169	Ron Reed	.06	.05	.02
170	Bill Robinson	.06	.05	.02
171	Pete Rose	1.50	1.25	.60
172	Dick Ruthven	.06	.05	.02
173	Mike Schmidt	1.75	1.25	.70
174	Manny Trillo	.08	.06	.03
175	Ozzie Virgil (FC)	.06	.05	.02
176	George Vukovich	.06	.05	.02
177	Gary Allenson	.06	.05	.02
178	Luis Aponte	.06	.05	.02
179	*Wade Boggs* (FC)	25.00	18.50	10.00
180	Tom Burgmeier	.06	.05	.02
181	Mark Clear	.06	.05	.02
182	Dennis Eckersley	.60	.45	.25
183	Dwight Evans	.15	.11	.06
184	Rich Gedman	.08	.06	.03
185	Glenn Hoffman	.06	.05	.02
186	Bruce Hurst	.10	.08	.04
187	Carney Lansford	.08	.06	.03
188	Rick Miller	.06	.05	.02
189	Reid Nichols	.06	.05	.02
190	Bob Ojeda	.12	.09	.05
191	Tony Perez	.20	.15	.08
192	Chuck Rainey	.06	.05	.02
193	Jerry Remy	.06	.05	.02
194	Jim Rice	.40	.30	.15
195	Bob Stanley	.06	.05	.02
196	Dave Stapleton	.06	.05	.02
197	Mike Torrez	.08	.06	.03
198	John Tudor	.10	.08	.04
199	Julio Valdez	.06	.05	.02
200	Carl Yastrzemski	1.00	.70	.40
201	Dusty Baker	.10	.08	.04
202	Joe Beckwith	.06	.05	.02
203	*Greg Brock* (FC)	.06	.05	.02
204	Ron Cey	.12	.09	.05
205	Terry Forster	.08	.06	.03
206	Steve Garvey	.35	.25	.14
207	Pedro Guerrero	.12	.09	.05
208	Burt Hooton	.08	.06	.03
209	Steve Howe	.08	.06	.03
210	Ken Landreaux	.06	.05	.02
211	Mike Marshall	.10	.08	.04
212	*Candy Maldonado*	.08	.06	.03
213	Rick Monday	.10	.08	.04
214	Tom Niedenfuer	.10	.08	.04
215	Jorge Orta	.06	.05	.02
216	Jerry Reuss	.10	.08	.04
217	Ron Roenicke	.06	.05	.02
218	Vicente Romo	.06	.05	.02
219	Bill Russell	.08	.06	.03
220	Steve Sax	.15	.11	.06
221	Mike Scioscia	.08	.06	.03
222	Dave Stewart	.60	.45	.25
223	Derrel Thomas	.06	.05	.02
224	Fernando Valenzuela	.10	.08	.04
225	Bob Welch	.12	.09	.05
226	Ricky Wright	.06	.05	.02
227	Steve Yeager	.06	.05	.02
228	Bill Almon	.06	.05	.02
229	Harold Baines	.15	.11	.06
230	Salome Barojas	.06	.05	.02
231	Tony Bernazard	.06	.05	.02
232	Britt Burns	.06	.05	.02
233	Richard Dotson	.10	.08	.04
234	Ernesto Escarrega	.06	.05	.02
235	Carlton Fisk	1.00	.70	.40
236	Jerry Hairston	.06	.05	.02
237	Kevin Hickey	.06	.05	.02
238	LaMarr Hoyt	.06	.05	.02
239	Steve Kemp	.10	.08	.04
240	Jim Kern	.06	.05	.02
241	*Ron Kittle* (FC)	.08	.06	.03
242	Jerry Koosman	.10	.08	.04
243	Dennis Lamp	.06	.05	.02
244	Rudy Law	.06	.05	.02
245	Vance Law	.08	.06	.03
246	Ron LeFlore	.08	.06	.03
247	Greg Luzinski	.12	.09	.05
248	Tom Paciorek	.06	.05	.02
249	Aurelio Rodriguez	.08	.06	.03
250	Mike Squires	.06	.05	.02
251	Steve Trout	.06	.05	.02
252	Jim Barr	.06	.05	.02
253	Dave Bergman	.06	.05	.02
254	Fred Breining	.06	.05	.02
255	Bob Brenly (FC)	.08	.06	.03
256	Jack Clark	.15	.11	.06
257	Chili Davis (FC)	.20	.15	.08
258	Darrell Evans	.15	.11	.06
259	Alan Fowlkes	.06	.05	.02
260	Rich Gale	.06	.05	.02
261	Atlee Hammaker (FC)	.06	.05	.02
262	Al Holland	.06	.05	.02
263	Duane Kuiper	.06	.05	.02
264	Bill Laskey	.06	.05	.02
265	Gary Lavelle	.06	.05	.02
266	Johnnie LeMaster	.06	.05	.02
267	Renie Martin	.06	.05	.02
268	Milt May	.06	.05	.02
269	Greg Minton	.06	.05	.02
270	Joe Morgan	.50	.40	.20
271	Tom O'Malley	.06	.05	.02
272	Reggie Smith	.10	.08	.04
273	Guy Sularz	.06	.05	.02
274	Champ Summers	.06	.05	.02
275	Max Venable	.06	.05	.02
276	Jim Wohlford	.06	.05	.02
277	Ray Burris	.06	.05	.02
278	Gary Carter	.35	.25	.14
279	Warren Cromartie	.06	.05	.02
280	Andre Dawson	1.25	.90	.50
281	Terry Francona	.06	.05	.02
282	Doug Flynn	.06	.05	.02
283	Woody Fryman	.08	.06	.03
284	Bill Gullickson	.06	.05	.02
285	Wallace Johnson	.06	.05	.02
286	Charlie Lea	.06	.05	.02
287	Randy Lerch	.06	.05	.02
288	Brad Mills	.06	.05	.02
289	Dan Norman	.06	.05	.02
290	Al Oliver	.15	.11	.06
291	David Palmer	.06	.05	.02
292	Tim Raines	.35	.25	.14
293	Jeff Reardon	.80	.60	.30
294	Steve Rogers	.08	.06	.03
295	Scott Sanderson	.06	.05	.02
296	Dan Schatzeder	.06	.05	.02
297	Bryn Smith	.08	.06	.03
298	Chris Speier	.06	.05	.02
299	Tim Wallach	.20	.15	.08
300	Jerry White	.06	.05	.02
301	Joel Youngblood	.06	.05	.02
302	Ross Baumgarten	.06	.05	.02
303	Dale Berra	.06	.05	.02
304	John Candelaria	.10	.08	.04
305	Dick Davis	.06	.05	.02
306	Mike Easler	.08	.06	.03
307	Richie Hebner	.06	.05	.02
308	Lee Lacy	.06	.05	.02
309	Bill Madlock	.12	.09	.05
310	Larry McWilliams	.06	.05	.02
311	John Milner	.06	.05	.02
312	Omar Moreno	.06	.05	.02
313	Jim Morrison	.06	.05	.02

314 Steve Nicosia .06 .05 .02
315 Dave Parker .30 .25 .12
316 Tony Pena .10 .08 .04
317 Johnny Ray .06 .05 .02
318 Rick Rhoden .10 .08 .04
319 Don Robinson .08 .06 .03
320 Enrique Romo .06 .05 .02
321 Manny Sarmiento .06 .05 .02
322 Rod Scurry .06 .05 .02
323 Jim Smith .06 .05 .02
324 Willie Stargell .40 .30 .15
325 Jason Thompson .06 .05 .02
326 Kent Tekulve .08 .06 .03
327a Tom Brookens (narrow (1/4") brown box at bottom on back) .30 .25 .12
327b Tom Brookens (wide (1-1/4") brown box at bottom on back) .08 .06 .03
328 Enos Cabell .06 .05 .02
329 Kirk Gibson .20 .15 .08
330 Larry Herndon .08 .06 .03
331 Mike Ivie .06 .05 .02
332 *Howard Johnson* 1.50 1.25 .60
333 Lynn Jones .06 .05 .02
334 Rick Leach .06 .05 .02
335 Chet Lemon .08 .06 .03
336 Jack Morris .40 .30 .15
337 Lance Parrish .10 .08 .04
338 Larry Pashnick .06 .05 .02
339 Dan Petry .08 .06 .03
340 Dave Rozema .06 .05 .02
341 Dave Rucker .06 .05 .02
342 Elias Sosa .06 .05 .02
343 Dave Tobik .06 .05 .02
344 Alan Trammell .60 .45 .25
345 Jerry Turner .06 .05 .02
346 Jerry Ujdur .06 .05 .02
347 Pat Underwood .06 .05 .02
348 Lou Whitaker .60 .45 .25
349 Milt Wilcox .06 .05 .02
350 *Glenn Wilson* (FC) .08 .06 .03
351 John Wockenfuss .06 .05 .02
352 Kurt Bevacqua .06 .05 .02
353 Juan Bonilla .06 .05 .02
354 Floyd Chiffer .06 .05 .02
355 Luis DeLeon .06 .05 .02
356 *Dave Dravecky* .30 .25 .12
357 Dave Edwards .06 .05 .02
358 Juan Eichelberger .06 .05 .02
359 Tim Flannery .06 .05 .02
360 *Tony Gwynn* (FC) 25.00 18.50 10.00
361 Ruppert Jones .06 .05 .02
362 Terry Kennedy .08 .06 .03
363 Joe Lefebvre .06 .05 .02
364 Sixto Lezcano .06 .05 .02
365 Tim Lollar .06 .05 .02
366 Gary Lucas .06 .05 .02
367 John Montefusco .06 .05 .02
368 Broderick Perkins .06 .05 .02
369 Joe Pittman .06 .05 .02
370 Gene Richards .06 .05 .02
371 Luis Salazar .06 .05 .02
372 *Eric Show* (FC) .08 .06 .03
373 Garry Templeton .10 .08 .04
374 Chris Welsh .06 .05 .02
375 Alan Wiggins .06 .05 .02
376 Rick Cerone .06 .05 .02
377 Dave Collins .08 .06 .03
378 Roger Erickson .06 .05 .02
379 George Frazier .06 .05 .02
380 Oscar Gamble .08 .06 .03
381 Goose Gossage .20 .15 .08
382 Ken Griffey .12 .09 .05
383 Ron Guidry .25 .20 .10
384 Dave LaRoche .06 .05 .02
385 Rudy May .06 .05 .02
386 John Mayberry .08 .06 .03
387 Lee Mazzilli .08 .06 .03
388 Mike Morgan (FC) .12 .09 .05
389 Jerry Mumphrey .06 .05 .02
390 Bobby Murcer .10 .08 .04
391 Graig Nettles .15 .11 .06
392 Lou Piniella .12 .09 .05
393 Willie Randolph .10 .08 .04
394 Shane Rawley .10 .08 .04
395 Dave Righetti .12 .09 .05
396 Andre Robertson .06 .05 .02
397 Roy Smalley .06 .05 .02
398 Dave Winfield 2.50 2.00 1.00
399 Butch Wynegar .06 .05 .02
400 Chris Bando .06 .05 .02
401 Alan Bannister .06 .05 .02
402 Len Barker .08 .06 .03
403 Tom Brennan .06 .05 .02
404 *Carmelo Castillo* (FC) .06 .05 .02
405 Miguel Dilone .06 .05 .02
406 Jerry Dybzinski .06 .05 .02
407 Mike Fischlin .06 .05 .02
408 Ed Glynn (photo actually Bud Anderson) .06 .05 .02
409 Mike Hargrove .06 .05 .02
410 Toby Harrah .08 .06 .03
411 Ron Hassey .06 .05 .02
412 Von Hayes .15 .11 .06
413 Rick Manning .06 .05 .02
414 Bake McBride .06 .05 .02
415 Larry Milbourne .06 .05 .02
416 Bill Nahorodny .06 .05 .02
417 Jack Perconte .06 .05 .02
418 Larry Sorensen .06 .05 .02
419 Dan Spillner .06 .05 .02
420 Rick Sutcliffe .12 .09 .05
421 Andre Thornton .10 .08 .04
422 Rick Waits .06 .05 .02
423 Eddie Whitson .06 .05 .02
424 Jesse Barfield (FC) .20 .15 .08
425 Barry Bonnell .06 .05 .02
426 Jim Clancy .08 .06 .03
427 Damaso Garcia .06 .05 .02
428 Jerry Garvin .06 .05 .02
429 Alfredo Griffin .08 .06 .03
430 Garth Iorg .06 .05 .02
431 Roy Lee Jackson .06 .05 .02
432 Luis Leal .06 .05 .02
433 Buck Martinez .06 .05 .02
434 Joey McLaughlin .06 .05 .02
435 Lloyd Moseby .12 .09 .05
436 Rance Mulliniks .06 .05 .02
437 Dale Murray .06 .05 .02
438 Wayne Nordhagen .06 .05 .02
439 *Gene Petralli* (FC) .08 .06 .03
440 Hosken Powell .06 .05 .02
441 Dave Stieb .12 .09 .05
442 Willie Upshaw .08 .06 .03
443 Ernie Whitt .08 .06 .03
444 Al Woods .06 .05 .02
445 Alan Ashby .06 .05 .02
446 Jose Cruz .12 .09 .05
447 Kiko Garcia .06 .05 .02
448 Phil Garner .08 .06 .03
449 Danny Heep .06 .05 .02
450 Art Howe .06 .05 .02
451 Bob Knepper .08 .06 .03
452 Alan Knicely .06 .05 .02
453 Ray Knight .10 .08 .04
454 Frank LaCorte .06 .05 .02
455 Mike LaCoss .06 .05 .02
456 Randy Moffitt .06 .05 .02
457 Joe Niekro .12 .09 .05
458 Terry Puhl .06 .05 .02
459 Luis Pujols .06 .05 .02
460 Craig Reynolds .06 .05 .02
461 Bert Roberge .06 .05 .02
462 Vern Ruhle .06 .05 .02
463 Nolan Ryan 8.00 6.00 3.25
464 Joe Sambito .06 .05 .02
465 Tony Scott .06 .05 .02
466 Dave Smith .08 .06 .03
467 Harry Spilman .06 .05 .02
468 Dickie Thon .08 .06 .03
469 Denny Walling .06 .05 .02
470 Larry Andersen .06 .05 .02
471 Floyd Bannister .10 .08 .04
472 Jim Beattie .06 .05 .02
473 Bruce Bochte .06 .05 .02
474 Manny Castillo .06 .05 .02
475 Bill Caudill .06 .05 .02
476 Bryan Clark .06 .05 .02
477 Al Cowens .06 .05 .02
478 Julio Cruz .06 .05 .02
479 Todd Cruz .06 .05 .02
480 Gary Gray .06 .05 .02
481 Dave Henderson (FC) .20 .15 .08
482 *Mike Moore* (FC) .50 .40 .20
483 Gaylord Perry .40 .30 .15
484 Dave Revering .06 .05 .02
485 Joe Simpson .06 .05 .02
486 Mike Stanton .06 .05 .02
487 Rick Sweet .06 .05 .02
488 *Ed Vande Berg* (FC) .06 .05 .02
489 Richie Zisk .08 .06 .03
490 Doug Bird .06 .05 .02
491 Larry Bowa .12 .09 .05
492 Bill Buckner .12 .09 .05
493 Bill Campbell .06 .05 .02
494 Jody Davis .10 .08 .04
495 Leon Durham .08 .06 .03
496 Steve Henderson .06 .05 .02
497 Willie Hernandez .08 .06 .03
498 Fergie Jenkins .15 .11 .06
499 Jay Johnstone .08 .06 .03
500 Junior Kennedy .06 .05 .02
501 Randy Martz .06 .05 .02
502 Jerry Morales .06 .05 .02
503 Keith Moreland .08 .06 .03
504 Dickie Noles .06 .05 .02
505 Mike Proly .06 .05 .02
506 Allen Ripley .06 .05 .02
507 *Ryne Sandberg* (FC) 30.00 22.00 12.00
508 Lee Smith 1.50 1.25 .60
509 Pat Tabler (FC) .08 .06 .03
510 Dick Tidrow .06 .05 .02
511 Bump Wills .06 .05 .02
512 Gary Woods .06 .05 .02
513 Tony Armas .10 .08 .04
514 Dave Beard .06 .05 .02
515 Jeff Burroughs .08 .06 .03
516 John D'Acquisto .06 .05 .02
517 Wayne Gross .06 .05 .02
518 Mike Heath .06 .05 .02
519 Rickey Henderson 3.00 2.25 1.25
520 Cliff Johnson .06 .05 .02
521 Matt Keough .06 .05 .02
522 Brian Kingman .06 .05 .02
523 Rick Langford .06 .05 .02
524 Davey Lopes .10 .08 .04
525 Steve McCatty .06 .05 .02
526 Dave McKay .06 .05 .02
527 Dan Meyer .06 .05 .02
528 Dwayne Murphy .08 .06 .03
529 Jeff Newman .06 .05 .02
530 Mike Norris .06 .05 .02
531 Bob Owchinko .06 .05 .02
532 Joe Rudi .10 .08 .04
533 Jimmy Sexton .06 .05 .02
534 Fred Stanley .06 .05 .02
535 Tom Underwood .06 .05 .02
536 Neil Allen .06 .05 .02
537 Wally Backman .08 .06 .03
538 Bob Bailor .06 .05 .02
539 Hubie Brooks .12 .09 .05
540 Carlos Diaz .06 .05 .02
541 Pete Falcone .06 .05 .02
542 George Foster .15 .11 .06
543 Ron Gardenhire .06 .05 .02
544 Brian Giles .06 .05 .02
545 Ron Hodges .06 .05 .02
546 Randy Jones .08 .06 .03
547 Mike Jorgensen .06 .05 .02
548 Dave Kingman .15 .11 .06
549 Ed Lynch .06 .05 .02
550 Jesse Orosco (FC) .08 .06 .03
551 Rick Ownbey .06 .05 .02
552 *Charlie Puleo* (FC) .06 .05 .02
553 Gary Rajsich .06 .05 .02
554 Mike Scott .10 .08 .04
555 Rusty Staub .10 .08 .04
556 John Stearns .06 .05 .02
557 Craig Swan .06 .05 .02
558 Ellis Valentine .06 .05 .02
559 Tom Veryzer .06 .05 .02
560 Mookie Wilson .10 .08 .04
561 Pat Zachry .06 .05 .02
562 Buddy Bell .12 .09 .05
563 John Butcher .06 .05 .02
564 Steve Comer .06 .05 .02
565 Danny Darwin .06 .05 .02
566 Bucky Dent .10 .08 .04
567 John Grubb .06 .05 .02
568 Rick Honeycutt .06 .05 .02
569 Dave Hostetler .06 .05 .02
570 Charlie Hough .10 .08 .04
571 Lamar Johnson .06 .05 .02
572 Jon Matlack .08 .06 .03
573 Paul Mirabella .06 .05 .02
574 Larry Parrish .10 .08 .04
575 Mike Richardt .06 .05 .02
576 Mickey Rivers .08 .06 .03
577 Billy Sample .06 .05 .02
578 *Dave Schmidt* (FC) .10 .08 .04
579 Bill Stein .06 .05 .02
580 Jim Sundberg .08 .06 .03
581 Frank Tanana .10 .08 .04
582 Mark Wagner .06 .05 .02
583 George Wright .06 .05 .02
584 Johnny Bench 1.00 .70 .40
585 Bruce Berenyi .06 .05 .02
586 Larry Biittner .06 .05 .02
587 Cesar Cedeno .12 .09 .05
588 Dave Concepcion .12 .09 .05
589 Dan Driessen .08 .06 .03
590 Greg Harris (FC) .08 .06 .03
591 Ben Hayes .06 .05 .02
592 Paul Householder .06 .05 .02
593 Tom Hume .06 .05 .02
594 Wayne Krenchicki .06 .05 .02
595 Rafael Landestoy .06 .05 .02
596 Charlie Leibrandt .08 .06 .03
597 *Eddie Milner* (FC) .06 .05 .02
598 Ron Oester .06 .05 .02
599 Frank Pastore .06 .05 .02
600 Joe Price .06 .05 .02
601 Tom Seaver 1.00 .70 .40
602 Bob Shirley .06 .05 .02
603 Mario Soto .08 .06 .03
604 Alex Trevino .06 .05 .02
605 Mike Vail .06 .05 .02
606 Duane Walker .06 .05 .02
607 Tom Brunansky (FC) .08 .06 .03
608 Bobby Castillo .06 .05 .02
609 John Castino .06 .05 .02
610 Ron Davis .06 .05 .02
611 Lenny Faedo .06 .05 .02
612 Terry Felton .06 .05 .02
613 *Gary Gaetti* .35 .25 .14
614 Mickey Hatcher .08 .06 .03
615 Brad Havens .06 .05 .02
616 Kent Hrbek .60 .45 .25
617 Randy S. Johnson .06 .05 .02
618 Tim Laudner (FC) .12 .09 .05
619 Jeff Little .06 .05 .02
620 Bob Mitchell .06 .05 .02
621 Jack O'Connor .06 .05 .02
622 John Pacella .06 .05 .02
623 Pete Redfern .06 .05 .02
624 Jesus Vega .06 .05 .02
625 *Frank Viola* 2.00 1.50 .80
626 Ron Washington .06 .05 .02
627 Gary Ward .08 .06 .03
628 Al Williams .06 .05 .02
629 Red Sox All-Stars (Mark Clear, Dennis Eckersley, Carl Yastrzemski) .25 .20 .10
630 300 Career Wins (Terry Bulling, Gaylord Perry) .15 .11 .06
631 Pride of Venezuela (Dave Concepcion, Manny Trillo) .10 .08 .04
632 All-Star Infielders (Buddy Bell, Robin Yount) .20 .15 .08
633 Mr. Vet & Mr. Rookie (Kent Hrbek, Dave Winfield) .25 .20 .10
634 Fountain of Youth (Pete Rose, Willie Stargell) .40 .30 .15
635 Big Chiefs (Toby Harrah, Andre Thornton) .08 .06 .03
636 "Smith Bros." (Lonnie Smith, Ozzie Smith) .10 .08 .04
637 Base Stealers' Threat (Gary Carter, Bo Diaz) .15 .11 .06
638 All-Star Catchers (Gary Carter, Carlton Fisk) .20 .15 .08
639 Rickey Henderson (IA) 2.00 1.50 .80
640 Home Run Threats (Reggie Jackson, Ben Oglivie) .25 .20 .10
641 Two Teams - Same Day (Joel Youngblood) .08 .06 .03
642 Last Perfect Game (Len Barker, Ron Hassey) .08 .06 .03
643 Blue (Vida Blue) .10 .08 .04
644 Black & (Bud Black) .10 .08 .04
645 Power (Reggie Jackson) .30 .25 .12
646 Speed & (Rickey Henderson) .30 .25 .12
647 Checklist 1-51 .06 .05 .02
648 Checklist 52-103 .06 .05 .02
649 Checklist 104-152 .06 .05 .02
650 Checklist 153-200 .06 .05 .02

		MT	NR MT	EX
651	Checklist 201-251	.06	.05	.02
652	Checklist 252-301	.06	.05	.02
653	Checklist 302-351	.06	.05	.02
654	Checklist 352-399	.06	.05	.02
655	Checklist 400-444	.06	.05	.02
656	Checklist 445-489	.06	.05	.02
657	Checklist 490-535	.06	.05	.02
658	Checklist 536-583	.06	.05	.02
659	Checklist 584-628	.06	.05	.02
660	Checklist 629-646	.06	.05	.02

1983 Fleer Stamps

The 1983 Fleer Stamp set consists of 288 stamps, including 224 player stamps and 64 team logo stamps. They were originally issued on four different sheets of 72 stamps each (checklisted below) and in "Vend-A-Stamp" dispensers of 18 stamps each. Sixteen different dispenser strips were needed to complete the set (strips 1-4 comprise Sheet 1; strips 5-8 comprise Sheet 2; strips 9-12 comprise Sheet 3; and strips 13-16 comprise Sheet 4.)

	MT	NR MT	EX
Complete Sheet Set:	7.00	5.25	2.75
Complete Vend-A-Stamp Set:	7.00	5.25	2.75
Common Sheet:	1.75	1.25	.70
Common Stamp Dispenser:	.25	.20	.10
Common Single Stamp:	.01	.01	

		MT	NR MT	EX
1	Sheet 1 (A's Logo, Angels Logo, Astros Logo, Cardinals Logo, Cubs Logo, Dodgers Logo, Expos Logo, Giants Logo, Indians Logo, Mets Logo, Orioles Logo, Phillies Logo, Pirates Logo, Red Sox Logo, Twins Logo, White Sox Logo, Neil Allen, Harold Baines, Buddy Bell, Dale Berra, Wade Boggs, George Brett, Bill Buckner, Jack Clark, Dave Concepcion, Warren Cromartie, Doug DeCinces, Luis DeLeon, Brian Downing, Dan Driessen, Mike Flanagan, Bob Forsch, Ken Forsch, Toby Harrah, Keith Hernandez, Steve Howe, Reggie Jackson, Ruppert Jones, Ray Knight, Gary Lavelle, Ron LeFlore, Davey Lopes, Lee Mazzilli, Bob McClure, Tug McGraw, Paul Molitor, Rick Monday, John Montefusco, Gaylord Perry, Dan Quisenberry, Ron Reed, Rick Rhoden, Ron Roenicke, Jerry Royster, Mike Schmidt, Roy Smalley, Reggie Smith, Mario Soto, Chris Speier, Willie Stargell, Rick Sutcliffe, Don Sutton, Craig Swan, Kent Tekulve, Dick Tidrow, Willie Upshaw, Fernando Valenzuela, U.L. Washington, Bump Wills, Dave Winfield, Robin Yount, Pat Zachry)	1.75	1.25	.70
2	Sheet 2 (Angels Logo, Astros Logo, Braves Logo, Cardinals Logo, Dodgers Logo, Expos Logo, Indians Logo, Mariners Logo, Mets Logo, Phillies Logo, Pirates Logo, Rangers Logo, Reds Logo, Royals Logo, Tigers Logo, Yankees Logo, Willie Aikens, Bob Bailor, Dusty Baker, Floyd Bannister, Len Barker, Hubie Brooks, Tom Brunansky, Chris Chambliss, Mark Clear, Andre Dawson, Bo Diaz, Dennis Eckersley, Rollie Fingers, George Foster, Goose Gossage, Ken Griffey, Ron Guidry, Rickey Henderson, Bob Horner, Lamarr Hoyt (LaMarr), Tom Hume, Garth Iorg, Tommy John, Sixto Lezcano, Fred Lynn, John Matlack (Jon), Scott McGregor, Eddie Milner, Greg Minton, Joe Morgan, Steve Mura, Dwayne Murphy, Ken Oberkfell, Ben Oglivie, Al Oliver, Jim Palmer, Lance Parrish, Larry Parrish, Lou Piniella, Tim Raines, Rafael Ramirez, Jeff Reardon, Jerry Reuss, Jim Rice, Pete Rose, Tom Seaver, Eric Show, Jim Sundberg, Bruce Sutter, Gorman Thomas, Jason Thompson, Tom Underwood, Mookie Wilson, Willie Wilson, John Wockenfuss, Carl Yastrzemski)	1.75	1.25	.70
3	Sheet 3 (A's Logo, Angels Logo, Blue Jays Logo, Braves Logo, Brewers Logo, Dodgers Logo, Giants Logo, Indians Logo, Mariners Logo, Orioles Logo, Padres Logo, Reds Logo, Royals Logo, Tigers Logo, Twins Logo, White Sox Logo, Alan Ashby, Dave Beard, Jim Beattie, Johnny Bench, Larry Biittner, Bob Boone, Rod Carew, Gary Carter, Bobby Castillo, Bill Caudill, Cecil Cooper, Mike Easler, Dwight Evans, Carlton Fisk, Gene Garber, Damaso Garcia, Larry Herndon, Al Holland, Burt Hooton, Art Howe, Kent Hrbek, Jerry Koosman, Duane Kuiper, Bill Laskey, Dennis Leonard, Garry Maddox, Bill Madlock, Rick Manning, Hal McRae, Keith Moreland, Jerry Mumphrey, Eddie Murray, Joe Niekro, Phil Niekro, Amos Otis, Darrell Porter, Johnny Ray, Mike Richardt, Cal Ripken, Jr, Steve Rogers, Nolan Ryan, Manny Sarmiento, Steve Sax, Ted Simmons, Ken Singleton, Bob Stanley, Rusty Staub, Dave Stieb, Dickie Thon, Andre Thornton, Manny Trillo, John Tudor, Ed Vande Berg, Bob Watson, Frank White, Milt Wilcox)	1.75	1.25	.70
4	Sheet 4 (Blue Jays Logo, Braves Logo, Brewers Logo, Cubs Logo, Expos Logo, Giants Logo, Padres Logo, Phillies Logo, Pirates Logo, Rangers Logo, Red Sox Logo, Reds Logo, Royals Logo, Twins Logo, White Sox Logo, Yankees Logo, Joaquin Andujar, Don Baylor, Vida Blue, Bruce Bochte, Larry Bowa, Al Bumbry, Jeff Burroughs, Enos Cabell, Steve Carlton, Cesar Cedeno, Rick Cerone, Ron Cey, Larry Christenson, Jim Clancy, Jose Cruz, Danny Darwin, Rich Dauer, Ron Davis, Ivan DeJesus, Leon Durham, Phil Garner, Steve Garvey, John Grubb, Atlee Hammaker, Mike Hargrove, Tom Herr, Ferguson Jenkins, Steve Kemp, Bruce Kison, Ken Landreaux, Carney Lansford, Charlie Lea, John Lowenstein, Greg Luzinski, Dennis Martinez, Tippy Martinez, Randy Martz, Gary Matthews, Milt May, Dale Murphy, Graig Nettles, Tom Paciorek, Dave Parker, Tony Pena, Hosken Powell, Willie Randolph, Lonnie Smith, Ozzie Smith, Dan Spillner, Ellis Valentine, Pete Vuckovich, Gary Ward, Claudell Washington, Lou Whitaker, Al Williams, Richie Zisk)	1.75	1.25	.70

1983 Fleer Stickers

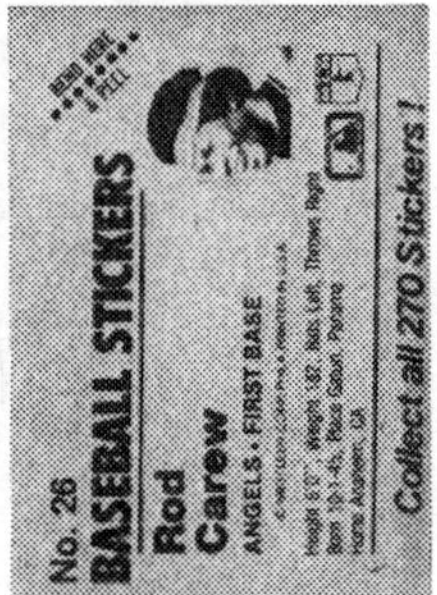

This 270-sticker set consists of both player stickers and team logo stickers, all measuring 1-13/16" by 2-1/2". The player stickers are numbered on the back. The front features a full-color photo surrounded by a blue border with two stars at the top. The 1983 Fleer stickers were issued in strips of ten player stickers plus two team logo stickers. The 26 logo stickers have been assigned numbers 271 through 296.

	MT	NR MT	EX
Complete Set:	18.00	13.50	7.25
Common Player:	.03	.02	.01

		MT	NR MT	EX
1	Bruce Sutter	.08	.06	.03
2	Willie McGee	.08	.06	.03
3	Darrell Porter	.03	.02	.01
4	Lonnie Smith	.03	.02	.01
5	Dane Iorg	.03	.02	.01
6	Keith Hernandez	.08	.06	.03
7	Joaquin Andujar	.04	.03	.02
8	Ken Oberkfell	.03	.02	.01
9	John Stuper	.03	.02	.01
10	Ozzie Smith	.10	.08	.04
11	Bob Forsch	.03	.02	.01
12	Jim Gantner	.03	.02	.01
13	Rollie Fingers	.10	.08	.04
14	Pete Vuckovich	.03	.02	.01
15	Ben Oglivie	.04	.03	.02
16	Don Sutton	.10	.08	.04
17	Bob McClure	.03	.02	.01
18	Robin Yount	.15	.11	.06
19	Paul Molitor	.10	.08	.04
20	Gorman Thomas	.06	.05	.02
21	Mike Caldwell	.03	.02	.01
22	Ted Simmons	.06	.05	.02
23	Cecil Cooper	.08	.06	.03
24	Steve Renko	.03	.02	.01
25	Tommy John	.08	.06	.03
26	Rod Carew	.25	.20	.10
27	Bruce Kison	.03	.02	.01
28	Ken Forsch	.03	.02	.01
29	Geoff Zahn	.03	.02	.01
30	Doug DiCinces	.06	.05	.02
31	Fred Lynn	.10	.08	.04
32	Reggie Jackson	.25	.20	.10
33	Don Baylor	.08	.06	.03
34	Bob Boone	.04	.03	.02
35	Brian Downing	.04	.03	.02
36	Goose Gossage	.08	.06	.03
37	Roy Smalley	.03	.02	.01
38	Graig Nettles	.06	.05	.02
39	Dave Winfield	.20	.15	.08
40	Lee Mazzilli	.04	.03	.02
41	Jerry Mumphrey	.03	.02	.01
42	Dave Collins	.03	.02	.01
43	Rick Cerone	.03	.02	.01
44	Willie Randolph	.06	.05	.02
45	Lou Piniella	.06	.05	.02
46	Ken Griffey	.06	.05	.02
47	Ron Guidry	.10	.08	.04
48	Jack Clark	.08	.06	.03
49	Reggie Smith	.06	.05	.02
50	Atlee Hammaker	.03	.02	.01
51	Fred Breining	.03	.02	.01
52	Gary Lavelle	.03	.02	.01
53	Chili Davis	.06	.05	.02
54	Greg Minton	.03	.02	.01
55	Joe Morgan	.12	.09	.05
56	Al Holland	.03	.02	.01
57	Bill Laskey	.03	.02	.01
58	Duane Kuiper	.03	.02	.01
59	Tom Burgmeier	.03	.02	.01
60	Carl Yastrzemski	.35	.25	.14
61	Mark Clear	.03	.02	.01
62	Mike Torrez	.03	.02	.01
63	Dennis Eckersley	.06	.05	.02
64	Wade Boggs	.75	.60	.30
65	Bob Stanley	.03	.02	.01
66	Jim Rice	.10	.08	.04
67	Carney Lansford	.06	.05	.02
68	Jerry Remy	.03	.02	.01
69	Dwight Evans	.08	.06	.03
70	John Candelaria	.06	.05	.02
71	Bill Madlock	.06	.05	.02
72	Dave Parker	.10	.08	.04
73	Kent Tekulve	.04	.03	.02
74	Tony Pena	.06	.05	.02
75	Manny Sarmiento	.03	.02	.01
76	Johnny Ray	.06	.05	.02
77	Dale Berra	.03	.02	.01
78	Lee Lacy	.03	.02	.01
79	Jason Thompson	.03	.02	.01
80	Mike Easler	.04	.03	.02
81	Willie Stargell	.20	.15	.08
82	Rick Camp	.03	.02	.01
83	Bob Watson	.03	.02	.01
84	Bob Horner	.08	.06	.03
85	Rafael Ramirez	.03	.02	.01
86	Chris Chambliss	.04	.03	.02
87	Gene Garber	.03	.02	.01
88	Claudell Washington	.04	.03	.02
89	Steve Bedrosian	.06	.05	.02
90	Dale Murphy	.30	.25	.12
91	Phil Niekro	.10	.08	.04
92	Jerry Royster	.03	.02	.01
93	Bob Walk	.03	.02	.01
94	Frank White	.06	.05	.02
95	Dennis Leonard	.03	.02	.01
96	Vida Blue	.06	.05	.02
97	U.L. Washington	.03	.02	.01
98	George Brett	.30	.25	.12
99	Amos Otis	.04	.03	.02
100	Dan Quisenberry	.06	.05	.02
101	Willie Aikens	.03	.02	.01
102	Hal McRae	.06	.05	.02
103	Larry Gura	.03	.02	.01
104	Willie Wilson	.06	.05	.02
105	Damaso Garcia	.03	.02	.01
106	Hosken Powell	.03	.02	.01
107	Joey McLaughlin	.03	.02	.01
108	Jim Clancy	.03	.02	.01
109	Barry Bonnell	.03	.02	.01
110	Garth Lorg	.03	.02	.01
111	Dave Stieb	.06	.05	.02
112	Fernando Valenzuela	.08	.06	.03
113	Steve Garvey	.10	.08	.04
114	Rick Monday	.04	.03	.02
115	Burt Hooton	.03	.02	.01
116	Bill Russell	.04	.03	.02
117	Pedro Guerrero	.06	.05	.02
118	Steve Sax	.08	.06	.03
119	Steve Howe	.04	.03	.02
120	Ken Landreaux	.03	.02	.01
121	Dusty Baker	.04	.03	.02
122	Ron Cey	.06	.05	.02
123	Jerry Reuss	.06	.05	.02
124	Bump Wills	.03	.02	.01
125	Keith Moreland	.06	.05	.02
126	Dick Tidrow	.03	.02	.01
127	Bill Campbell	.03	.02	.01
128	Larry Bowa	.06	.05	.02
129	Randy Martz	.03	.02	.01
130	Ferguson Jenkins	.06	.05	.02
131	Leon Durham	.04	.03	.02
132	Bill Buckner	.06	.05	.02
133	Ron Davis	.03	.02	.01
134	Jack O'Connor	.03	.02	.01
135	Kent Hrbek	.10	.08	.04
136	Gary Ward	.03	.02	.01
137	Al Williams	.03	.02	.01
138	Tom Brunansky	.06	.05	.02
139	Bobby Castillo	.03	.02	.01
140	Dusty Baker, Dale Murphy	.20	.15	.08
141	Nolan Ryan	.10	.08	.04
142	Lee Lacey (Lacy), Omar Moreno	.03	.02	.01
143	Al Oliver, Pete Rose	.40	.30	.15
144	Ricky Henderson	.25	.20	.10
145	Ray Knight, Pete Rose, Mike Schmidt	.40	.30	.15
146	Hal McRae, Ben Oglivie	.06	.05	.02
147	Tom Hume, Ray Knight	.04	.03	.02
148	Buddy Bell, Carlton Fisk	.06	.05	.02
149	Steve Kemp	.04	.03	.02
150	Rudy Law	.03	.02	.01
151	Ron LeFlore	.04	.03	.02
152	Jerry Koosman	.04	.03	.02
153	Carlton Fisk	.12	.09	.05
154	Salome Barojas	.03	.02	.01
155	Harold Baines	.10	.08	.04
156	Britt Burns	.03	.02	.01
157	Tom Paciorek	.03	.02	.01
158	Greg Luzinski	.06	.05	.02
159	LaMarr Hoyt	.03	.02	.01
160	George Wright	.03	.02	.01
161	Danny Darwin	.03	.02	.01
162	Lamar Johnson	.03	.02	.01
163	Charlie Hough	.04	.03	.02
164	Buddy Bell	.06	.05	.02
165	John Matlack (Jon)	.04	.03	.02
166	Billy Sample	.03	.02	.01
167	John Grubb	.03	.02	.01
168	Larry Parrish	.06	.05	.02
169	Ivan DeJesus	.03	.02	.01
170	Mike Schmidt	.30	.25	.12
171	Tug McGraw	.06	.05	.02

172	Ron Reed	.03	.02	.01
173	Garry Maddox	.04	.03	.02
174	Pete Rose	.40	.30	.15
175	Manny Trillo	.04	.03	.02
176	Steve Carlton	.20	.15	.08
177	Bo Diaz	.04	.03	.02
178	Gary Matthews	.04	.03	.02
179	Bill Caudill	.03	.02	.01
180	Ed Vande Berg	.03	.02	.01
181	Gaylord Perry	.12	.09	.05
182	Floyd Bannister	.04	.03	.02
183	Richie Zisk	.04	.03	.02
184	Al Cowens	.03	.02	.01
185	Bruce Bochte	.03	.02	.01
186	Jeff Burroughs	.04	.03	.02
187	Dave Beard	.03	.02	.01
188	Davey Lopes	.04	.03	.02
189	Dwayne Murphy	.04	.03	.02
190	Rick Langford	.03	.02	.01
191	Tom Underwood	.03	.02	.01
192	Rickey Henderson	.25	.20	.10
193	Mike Flanagan	.06	.05	.02
194	Scott McGregor	.04	.03	.02
195	Ken Singleton	.06	.05	.02
196	Rich Dauer	.03	.02	.01
197	John Lowenstein	.03	.02	.01
198	Cal Ripken, Jr.	.40	.30	.15
199	Dennis Martinez	.04	.03	.02
200	Jim Palmer	.15	.11	.06
201	Tippy Martinez	.03	.02	.01
202	Eddie Murray	.15	.11	.06
203	Al Bumbry	.03	.02	.01
204	Dickie Thon	.03	.02	.01
205	Phil Garner	.03	.02	.01
206	Jose Cruz	.04	.03	.02
207	Nolan Ryan	.15	.11	.06
208	Ray Knight	.04	.03	.02
209	Terry Puhl	.03	.02	.01
210	Joe Niekro	.06	.05	.02
211	Art Howe	.03	.02	.01
212	Alan Ashby	.03	.02	.01
213	Tom Hume	.03	.02	.01
214	Johnny Bench	.25	.20	.10
215	Larry Biittner	.03	.02	.01
216	Mario Soto	.04	.03	.02
217	Dan Driessen	.04	.03	.02
218	Tom Seaver	.20	.15	.08
219	Dave Concepcion	.06	.05	.02
220	Wayne Krenchicki	.03	.02	.01
221	Cesar Cedeno	.06	.05	.02
222	Ruppert Jones	.03	.02	.01
223	Terry Kennedy	.04	.03	.02
224	Luis DeLeon	.03	.02	.01
225	Eric Show	.04	.03	.02
226	Tim Flannery	.03	.02	.01
227	Garry Templeton	.04	.03	.02
228	Tim Lollar	.03	.02	.01
229	Sixto Lezcano	.03	.02	.01
230	Bob Bailor	.03	.02	.01
231	Craig Swan	.03	.02	.01
232	Dave Kingman	.06	.05	.02
233	Mookie Wilson	.04	.03	.02
234	John Stearns	.03	.02	.01
235	Ellis Valentine	.03	.02	.01
236	Neil Allen	.03	.02	.01
237	Pat Zachry	.03	.02	.01
238	Rusty Staub	.06	.05	.02
239	George Foster	.06	.05	.02
240	Rick Sutcliffe	.06	.05	.02
241	Andre Thornton	.04	.03	.02
242	Mike Hargrove	.03	.02	.01
243	Dan Spillner	.03	.02	.01
244	Lary Sorensen	.03	.02	.01
245	Len Barker	.03	.02	.01
246	Rick Manning	.03	.02	.01
247	Toby Harrah	.04	.03	.02
248	Milt Wilcox	.03	.02	.01
249	Lou Whitaker	.10	.08	.04
250	Tom Brookens	.03	.02	.01
251	Chet Lemon	.04	.03	.02
252	Jack Morris	.08	.06	.03
253	Alan Trammell	.15	.11	.06
254	John Wockenfuss	.03	.02	.01
255	Lance Parrish	.12	.09	.05
256	Larry Herndon	.03	.02	.01
257	Chris Speier	.03	.02	.01
258	Woody Fryman	.03	.02	.01
259	Scott Sanderson	.03	.02	.01
260	Steve Rogers	.03	.02	.01
261	Warren Cromartie	.03	.02	.01
262	Gary Carter	.20	.15	.08
263	Bill Gullickson	.03	.02	.01
264	Andre Dawson	.20	.15	.08
265	Tim Raines	.15	.11	.06
266	Charlie Lea	.03	.02	.01
267	Jeff Reardon	.06	.05	.02
268	Al Oliver	.06	.05	.02
269	George Hendrick	.04	.03	.02
270	John Montefusco	.03	.02	.01
(271)	A's Logo	.03	.02	.01
(272)	Angels Logo	.03	.02	.01
(273)	Astros Logo	.03	.02	.01
(274)	Blue Jays Logo	.03	.02	.01
(275)	Braves Logo	.03	.02	.01
(276)	Brewers Logo	.03	.02	.01
(277)	Cardinals Logo	.03	.02	.01
(278)	Cubs Logo	.03	.02	.01
(279)	Dodgers Logo	.03	.02	.01
(280)	Expos Logo	.03	.02	.01
(281)	Giants Logo	.03	.02	.01
(282)	Indians Logo	.03	.02	.01
(283)	Mariners Logo	.03	.02	.01
(284)	Mets Logo	.03	.02	.01
(285)	Orioles Logo	.03	.02	.01
(286)	Padres Logo	.03	.02	.01
(287)	Phillies Logo	.03	.02	.01
(288)	Pirates Logo	.03	.02	.01
(289)	Rangers Logo	.03	.02	.01
(290)	Red Sox Logo	.03	.02	.01
(291)	Reds Logo	.03	.02	.01
(292)	Royals Logo	.03	.02	.01
(293)	Tigers Logo	.03	.02	.01
(294)	Twins Logo	.03	.02	.01
(295)	Yankees Logo	.03	.02	.01
(296)	White Sox Logo	.03	.02	.01

1984 Fleer

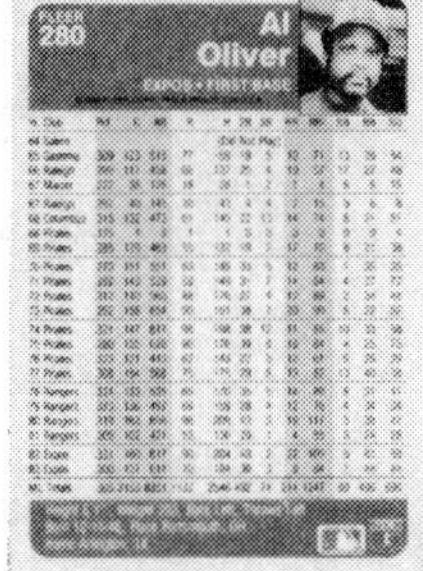

The 1984 Fleer set contained 660 cards for the fourth consecutive year. The cards, which measure 2-1/2" by 3-1/2", feature a color photo surrounded by four white borders and two blue stripes. The top stripe contains the word "Fleer" with the lower carrying the player's name. The card backs contain a small black and white photo of the player and are done in blue ink on white stock. The set was issued with team logo stickers.

		MT	NR MT	EX
Complete Set (660):		175.00	131.00	70.00
Common Player:		.08	.06	.03
1	Mike Boddicker (FC)	.10	.08	.04
2	Al Bumbry	.10	.08	.04
3	Todd Cruz	.08	.06	.03
4	Rich Dauer	.08	.06	.03
5	Storm Davis	.12	.09	.05
6	Rick Dempsey	.10	.08	.04
7	Jim Dwyer	.08	.06	.03
8	Mike Flanagan	.12	.09	.05
9	Dan Ford	.08	.06	.03
10	John Lowenstein	.08	.06	.03
11	Dennis Martinez	.10	.08	.04
12	Tippy Martinez	.08	.06	.03
13	Scott McGregor	.10	.08	.04
14	Eddie Murray	3.00	2.25	1.25
15	Joe Nolan	.08	.06	.03
16	Jim Palmer	1.75	1.25	.70
17	Cal Ripken, Jr.	18.00	13.50	7.25
18	Gary Roenicke	.08	.06	.03
19	Lenn Sakata	.08	.06	.03
20	*John Shelby* (FC)	.08	.06	.03
21	Ken Singleton	.12	.09	.05
22	Sammy Stewart	.08	.06	.03
23	Tim Stoddard	.08	.06	.03
24	Marty Bystrom	.08	.06	.03
25	Steve Carlton	3.50	2.75	1.50
26	Ivan DeJesus	.08	.06	.03
27	John Denny	.08	.06	.03
28	Bob Dernier	.08	.06	.03
29	Bo Diaz	.10	.08	.04
30	Kiko Garcia	.08	.06	.03
31	Greg Gross	.08	.06	.03
32	*Kevin Gross* (FC)	.08	.06	.03
33	Von Hayes	.08	.06	.03
34	Willie Hernandez	.12	.09	.05
35	Al Holland	.08	.06	.03
36	*Charles Hudson* (FC)	.08	.06	.03
37	Joe Lefebvre	.08	.06	.03
38	Sixto Lezcano	.08	.06	.03
39	Garry Maddox	.10	.08	.04
40	Gary Matthews	.12	.09	.05
41	Len Matuszek	.08	.06	.03
42	Tug McGraw	.12	.09	.05
43	Joe Morgan	.60	.45	.25
44	Tony Perez	.20	.15	.08
45	Ron Reed	.08	.06	.03
46	Pete Rose	3.00	2.25	1.25
47	*Juan Samuel*	.75	.60	.30
48	Mike Schmidt	9.00	6.75	3.50
49	Ozzie Virgil	.08	.06	.03
50	*Juan Agosto* (FC)	.08	.06	.03
51	Harold Baines	.25	.20	.10
52	Floyd Bannister	.08	.06	.03
53	Salome Barojas	.08	.06	.03
54	Britt Burns	.08	.06	.03
55	Julio Cruz	.08	.06	.03
56	Richard Dotson	.08	.06	.03
57	Jerry Dybzinski	.08	.06	.03
58	Carlton Fisk	2.75	2.00	1.00
59	Scott Fletcher (FC)	.15	.11	.06
60	Jerry Hairston	.08	.06	.03
61	Kevin Hickey	.08	.06	.03
62	Marc Hill	.08	.06	.03
63	LaMarr Hoyt	.08	.06	.03
64	Ron Kittle	.08	.06	.03
65	Jerry Koosman	.12	.09	.05
66	Dennis Lamp	.08	.06	.03
67	Rudy Law	.08	.06	.03
68	Vance Law	.10	.08	.04
69	Greg Luzinski	.12	.09	.05
70	Tom Paciorek	.08	.06	.03
71	Mike Squires	.08	.06	.03
72	Dick Tidrow	.08	.06	.03
73	*Greg Walker* (FC)	.08	.06	.03
74	Glenn Abbott	.08	.06	.03
75	Howard Bailey	.08	.06	.03
76	Doug Bair	.08	.06	.03
77	Juan Berenguer	.08	.06	.03
78	Tom Brookens	.08	.06	.03
79	Enos Cabell	.08	.06	.03
80	Kirk Gibson	1.00	.70	.40
81	John Grubb	.08	.06	.03
82	Larry Herndon	.08	.06	.03
83	Wayne Krenchicki	.08	.06	.03
84	Rick Leach	.08	.06	.03
85	Chet Lemon	.10	.08	.04
86	Aurelio Lopez	.08	.06	.03
87	Jack Morris	1.25	.90	.50
88	Lance Parrish	.15	.11	.06
89	Dan Petry	.08	.06	.03
90	Dave Rozema	.08	.06	.03
91	Alan Trammell	1.00	.70	.40
92	Lou Whitaker	1.00	.70	.40
93	Milt Wilcox	.08	.06	.03
94	Glenn Wilson	.08	.06	.03
95	John Wockenfuss	.08	.06	.03
96	Dusty Baker	.12	.09	.05
97	Joe Beckwith	.08	.06	.03
98	Greg Brock	.08	.06	.03
99	Jack Fimple	.08	.06	.03
100	Pedro Guerrero	.15	.11	.06
101	Rick Honeycutt	.08	.06	.03
102	Burt Hooton	.10	.08	.04
103	Steve Howe	.08	.06	.03
104	Ken Landreaux	.08	.06	.03
105	Mike Marshall	.08	.06	.03
106	Rick Monday	.10	.08	.04
107	Jose Morales	.08	.06	.03
108	Tom Niedenfuer	.10	.08	.04
109	*Alejandro Pena* (FC)	.10	.08	.04
110	Jerry Reuss	.12	.09	.05
111	Bill Russell	.10	.08	.04
112	Steve Sax	.20	.15	.08
113	Mike Scioscia	.10	.08	.04
114	Derrel Thomas	.08	.06	.03
115	Fernando Valenzuela	.15	.11	.06
116	Bob Welch	.15	.11	.06
117	Steve Yeager	.08	.06	.03
118	Pat Zachry	.08	.06	.03
119	Don Baylor	.15	.11	.06
120	Bert Campaneris	.12	.09	.05
121	Rick Cerone	.08	.06	.03
122	*Ray Fontenot* (FC)	.08	.06	.03
123	George Frazier	.08	.06	.03
124	Oscar Gamble	.10	.08	.04
125	Goose Gossage	.25	.20	.10
126	Ken Griffey	.12	.09	.05
127	Ron Guidry	.10	.08	.04
128	Jay Howell (FC)	.15	.11	.06
129	Steve Kemp	.10	.08	.04
130	Matt Keough	.08	.06	.03
131	*Don Mattingly* (FC)	32.00	24.00	13.00
132	John Montefusco	.08	.06	.03
133	Omar Moreno	.08	.06	.03
134	Dale Murray	.08	.06	.03
135	Graig Nettles	.20	.15	.08
136	Lou Piniella	.15	.11	.06
137	Willie Randolph	.12	.09	.05
138	Shane Rawley	.08	.06	.03
139	Dave Righetti	.20	.15	.08
140	Andre Robertson	.08	.06	.03
141	Bob Shirley	.08	.06	.03
142	Roy Smalley	.08	.06	.03
143	Dave Winfield	8.00	6.00	3.25
144	Butch Wynegar	.08	.06	.03
145	*Jim Acker* (FC)	.12	.09	.05
146	Doyle Alexander	.08	.06	.03
147	Jesse Barfield	.15	.11	.06
148	Jorge Bell	1.00	.70	.40
149	Barry Bonnell	.08	.06	.03
150	Jim Clancy	.10	.08	.04
151	Dave Collins	.10	.08	.04
152	*Tony Fernandez* (FC)	5.00	3.75	2.00
153	Damaso Garcia	.08	.06	.03
154	Dave Geisel	.08	.06	.03
155	Jim Gott (FC)	.10	.08	.04
156	Alfredo Griffin	.10	.08	.04
157	Garth Iorg	.08	.06	.03
158	Roy Lee Jackson	.08	.06	.03
159	Cliff Johnson	.08	.06	.03
160	Luis Leal	.08	.06	.03
161	Buck Martinez	.08	.06	.03
162	Joey McLaughlin	.08	.06	.03
163	Randy Moffitt	.08	.06	.03
164	Lloyd Moseby	.08	.06	.03
165	Rance Mulliniks	.08	.06	.03
166	Jorge Orta	.08	.06	.03
167	Dave Stieb	.15	.11	.06
168	Willie Upshaw	.08	.06	.03
169	Ernie Whitt	.08	.06	.03
170	Len Barker	.08	.06	.03
171	Steve Bedrosian	.08	.06	.03
172	Bruce Benedict	.08	.06	.03
173	Brett Butler	.20	.15	.08
174	Rick Camp	.08	.06	.03
175	Chris Chambliss	.08	.06	.03
176	Ken Dayley	.08	.06	.03
177	Pete Falcone	.08	.06	.03
178	Terry Forster	.10	.08	.04
179	Gene Garber	.08	.06	.03
180	Terry Harper	.08	.06	.03
181	Bob Horner	.12	.09	.05
182	Glenn Hubbard	.08	.06	.03
183	Randy S. Johnson	.08	.06	.03
184	*Craig McMurtry* (FC)	.08	.06	.03
185	Donnie Moore (FC)	.08	.06	.03
186	Dale Murphy	.75	.60	.30
187	Phil Niekro	.30	.25	.12

No.	Player			
188	Pascual Perez	.10	.08	.04
189	Biff Pocoroba	.08	.06	.03
190	Rafael Ramirez	.08	.06	.03
191	Jerry Royster	.08	.06	.03
192	Claudell Washington	.10	.08	.04
193	Bob Watson	.10	.08	.04
194	Jerry Augustine	.08	.06	.03
195	Mark Brouhard	.08	.06	.03
196	Mike Caldwell	.08	.06	.03
197	*Tom Candiotti*	1.00	.70	.40
198	Cecil Cooper	.15	.11	.06
199	Rollie Fingers	.25	.20	.10
200	Jim Gantner	.08	.06	.03
201	Bob L. Gibson	.08	.06	.03
202	Moose Haas	.08	.06	.03
203	Roy Howell	.08	.06	.03
204	Pete Ladd	.08	.06	.03
205	Rick Manning	.08	.06	.03
206	Bob McClure	.08	.06	.03
207	Paul Molitor	5.00	3.75	2.00
208	Don Money	.08	.06	.03
209	Charlie Moore	.08	.06	.03
210	Ben Oglivie	.10	.08	.04
211	Chuck Porter	.08	.06	.03
212	Ed Romero	.08	.06	.03
213	Ted Simmons	.15	.11	.06
214	Jim Slaton	.08	.06	.03
215	Don Sutton	.30	.25	.12
216	Tom Tellmann	.08	.06	.03
217	Pete Vuckovich	.10	.08	.04
218	Ned Yost	.08	.06	.03
219	Robin Yount	5.50	4.25	2.25
220	Alan Ashby	.08	.06	.03
221	Kevin Bass (FC)	.08	.06	.03
222	Jose Cruz	.08	.06	.03
223	*Bill Dawley* (FC)	.08	.06	.03
224	Frank DiPino	.08	.06	.03
225	*Bill Doran*	1.00	.70	.40
226	Phil Garner	.10	.08	.04
227	Art Howe	.08	.06	.03
228	Bob Knepper	.10	.08	.04
229	Ray Knight	.12	.09	.05
230	Frank LaCorte	.08	.06	.03
231	Mike LaCoss	.08	.06	.03
232	Mike Madden	.08	.06	.03
233	Jerry Mumphrey	.08	.06	.03
235	Terry Puhl	.08	.06	.03
236	Luis Pujols	.08	.06	.03
237	Craig Reynolds	.08	.06	.03
238	Vern Ruhle	.08	.06	.03
239	Nolan Ryan	20.00	15.00	8.00
240	Mike Scott	.20	.15	.08
241	Tony Scott	.08	.06	.03
242	Dave Smith	.08	.06	.03
243	Dickie Thon	.08	.06	.03
244	Denny Walling	.08	.06	.03
245	Dale Berra	.08	.06	.03
246	Jim Bibby	.08	.06	.03
247	John Candelaria	.12	.09	.05
248	*Jose DeLeon* (FC)	.20	.15	.08
249	Mike Easler	.08	.06	.03
250	Cecilio Guante (FC)	.08	.06	.03
251	Richie Hebner	.08	.06	.03
252	Lee Lacy	.08	.06	.03
253	Bill Madlock	.12	.09	.05
254	Milt May	.08	.06	.03
255	Lee Mazzilli	.08	.06	.03
256	Larry McWilliams	.08	.06	.03
257	Jim Morrison	.08	.06	.03
258	Dave Parker	.30	.25	.12
259	Tony Pena	.12	.09	.05
260	Johnny Ray	.08	.06	.03
261	Rick Rhoden	.12	.09	.05
262	Don Robinson	.10	.08	.04
263	Manny Sarmiento	.08	.06	.03
264	Rod Scurry	.08	.06	.03
265	Kent Tekulve	.10	.08	.04
266	Gene Tenace	.10	.08	.04
267	Jason Thompson	.08	.06	.03
268	*Lee Tunnell* (FC)	.08	.06	.03
269	*Marvell Wynne* (FC)	.08	.06	.03
270	Ray Burris	.08	.06	.03
271	Gary Carter	.40	.30	.15
272	Warren Cromartie	.08	.06	.03
273	Andre Dawson	3.00	2.25	1.25
274	Doug Flynn	.08	.06	.03
275	Terry Francona	.08	.06	.03
276	Bill Gullickson	.08	.06	.03
277	Bob James	.08	.06	.03
278	Charlie Lea	.08	.06	.03
279	Bryan Little	.08	.06	.03
280	Al Oliver	.20	.15	.08
281	Tim Raines	1.00	.70	.40
282	Bobby Ramos	.08	.06	.03
283	Jeff Reardon	.50	.40	.20
284	Steve Rogers	.10	.08	.04
285	Scott Sanderson	.08	.06	.03
286	Dan Schatzeder	.08	.06	.03
287	Bryn Smith	.08	.06	.03
288	Chris Speier	.08	.06	.03
289	Manny Trillo	.10	.08	.04
290	Mike Vail	.08	.06	.03
291	Tim Wallach	.15	.11	.06
292	Chris Welsh	.08	.06	.03
293	Jim Wohlford	.08	.06	.03
294	Kurt Bevacqua	.08	.06	.03
295	Juan Bonilla	.08	.06	.03
296	Bobby Brown	.08	.06	.03
297	Luis DeLeon	.08	.06	.03
298	Dave Dravecky	.10	.08	.04
299	Tim Flannery	.08	.06	.03
300	Steve Garvey	.50	.40	.20
301	Tony Gwynn	11.00	8.25	4.50
302	*Andy Hawkins* (FC)	.20	.15	.08
303	Ruppert Jones	.08	.06	.03
304	Terry Kennedy	.10	.08	.04
305	Tim Lollar	.08	.06	.03
306	Gary Lucas	.08	.06	.03
307	*Kevin McReynolds*	.75	.60	.30
308	Sid Monge	.08	.06	.03
309	Mario Ramirez	.08	.06	.03
310	Gene Richards	.08	.06	.03
311	Luis Salazar	.08	.06	.03
312	Eric Show	.12	.09	.05
313	Elias Sosa	.08	.06	.03
314	Garry Templeton	.12	.09	.05
315	*Mark Thurmond* (FC)	.10	.08	.04
316	Ed Whitson	.08	.06	.03
317	Alan Wiggins	.08	.06	.03
318	Neil Allen	.08	.06	.03
319	Joaquin Andujar	.10	.08	.04
320	Steve Braun	.08	.06	.03
321	Glenn Brummer	.08	.06	.03
322	Bob Forsch	.10	.08	.04
323	David Green	.08	.06	.03
324	George Hendrick	.10	.08	.04
325	Tom Herr	.12	.09	.05
326	Dane Iorg	.08	.06	.03
327	Jeff Lahti	.08	.06	.03
328	Dave LaPoint	.10	.08	.04
329	Willie McGee	.50	.40	.20
330	Ken Oberkfell	.08	.06	.03
331	Darrell Porter	.10	.08	.04
332	Jamie Quirk	.08	.06	.03
333	Mike Ramsey	.08	.06	.03
334	Floyd Rayford	.08	.06	.03
335	Lonnie Smith	.10	.08	.04
336	Ozzie Smith	1.50	1.25	.60
337	John Stuper	.08	.06	.03
338	Bruce Sutter	.20	.15	.08
339	*Andy Van Slyke* (FC)	6.00	4.50	2.50
340	Dave Von Ohlen	.08	.06	.03
341	Willie Aikens	.08	.06	.03
342	Mike Armstrong	.08	.06	.03
343	Bud Black	.10	.08	.04
344	George Brett	7.50	5.50	3.00
345	Onix Concepcion	.08	.06	.03
346	Keith Creel	.08	.06	.03
347	Larry Gura	.08	.06	.03
348	Don Hood	.08	.06	.03
349	Dennis Leonard	.10	.08	.04
350	Hal McRae	.12	.09	.05
351	Amos Otis	.12	.09	.05
352	Gaylord Perry	.60	.45	.25
353	Greg Pryor	.08	.06	.03
354	Dan Quisenberry	.12	.09	.05
355	Steve Renko	.08	.06	.03
356	Leon Roberts	.08	.06	.03
357	*Pat Sheridan* (FC)	.08	.06	.03
358	Joe Simpson	.08	.06	.03
359	Don Slaught	.08	.06	.03
360	Paul Splittorff	.08	.06	.03
361	U.L. Washington	.08	.06	.03
362	John Wathan	.10	.08	.04
363	Frank White	.12	.09	.05
364	Willie Wilson	.15	.11	.06
365	Jim Barr	.08	.06	.03
366	Dave Bergman	.08	.06	.03
367	Fred Breining	.08	.06	.03
368	Bob Brenly	.08	.06	.03
369	Jack Clark	.10	.08	.04
370	Chili Davis	.12	.09	.05
371	Mark Davis (FC)	.20	.15	.08
372	Darrell Evans	.15	.11	.06
373	Atlee Hammaker	.08	.06	.03
374	Mike Krukow	.10	.08	.04
375	Duane Kuiper	.08	.06	.03
376	Bill Laskey	.08	.06	.03
377	Gary Lavelle	.08	.06	.03
378	Johnnie LeMaster	.08	.06	.03
379	Jeff Leonard	.08	.06	.03
380	Randy Lerch	.08	.06	.03
381	Renie Martin	.08	.06	.03
382	Andy McGaffigan	.08	.06	.03
383	Greg Minton	.08	.06	.03
384	Tom O'Malley	.08	.06	.03
385	Max Venable	.08	.06	.03
386	Brad Wellman	.08	.06	.03
387	Joel Youngblood	.08	.06	.03
388	Gary Allenson	.08	.06	.03
389	Luis Aponte	.08	.06	.03
390	Tony Armas	.12	.09	.05
391	Doug Bird	.08	.06	.03
392	Wade Boggs	12.00	9.00	4.75
393	*Dennis Boyd* (FC)	.10	.08	.04
394	Mike Brown	.08	.06	.03
395	Mark Clear	.08	.06	.03
396	Dennis Eckersley	.15	.11	.06
397	Dwight Evans	.20	.15	.08
398	Rich Gedman	.10	.08	.04
399	Glenn Hoffman	.08	.06	.03
400	Bruce Hurst	.15	.11	.06
401	John Henry Johnson	.08	.06	.03
402	Ed Jurak	.08	.06	.03
403	Rick Miller	.08	.06	.03
404	Jeff Newman	.08	.06	.03
405	Reid Nichols	.08	.06	.03
406	Bob Ojeda	.12	.09	.05
407	Jerry Remy	.08	.06	.03
408	Jim Rice	.40	.30	.15
409	Bob Stanley	.08	.06	.03
410	Dave Stapleton	.08	.06	.03
411	John Tudor	.12	.09	.05
412	Carl Yastrzemski	.80	.60	.30
413	Buddy Bell	.12	.09	.05
414	Larry Biittner	.08	.06	.03
415	John Butcher	.08	.06	.03
416	Danny Darwin	.08	.06	.03
417	Bucky Dent	.12	.09	.05
418	Dave Hostetler	.08	.06	.03
419	Charlie Hough	.12	.09	.05
420	Bobby Johnson	.08	.06	.03
421	Odell Jones	.08	.06	.03
422	Jon Matlack	.10	.08	.04
423	*Pete O'Brien* (FC)	.30	.25	.12
424	Larry Parrish	.12	.09	.05
425	Mickey Rivers	.10	.08	.04
426	Billy Sample	.08	.06	.03
427	Dave Schmidt	.08	.06	.03
428	*Mike Smithson* (FC)	.08	.06	.03
429	Bill Stein	.08	.06	.03
430	Dave Stewart	.15	.11	.06
431	Jim Sundberg	.10	.08	.04
432	Frank Tanana	.12	.09	.05
433	Dave Tobik	.08	.06	.03
434	Wayne Tolleson (FC)	.08	.06	.03
435	George Wright	.08	.06	.03
436	Bill Almon	.08	.06	.03
437	*Keith Atherton* (FC)	.08	.06	.03
438	Dave Beard	.08	.06	.03
439	Tom Burgmeier	.08	.06	.03
440	Jeff Burroughs	.10	.08	.04
441	*Chris Codiroli* (FC)	.08	.06	.03
442	*Tim Conroy* (FC)	.08	.06	.03
443	Mike Davis	.08	.06	.03
444	Wayne Gross	.08	.06	.03
445	Garry Hancock	.08	.06	.03
446	Mike Heath	.08	.06	.03
447	Rickey Henderson	6.50	5.00	2.50
448	*Don Hill* (FC)	.08	.06	.03
449	Bob Kearney	.08	.06	.03
450	Bill Krueger	.08	.06	.03
451	Rick Langford	.08	.06	.03
452	Carney Lansford	.12	.09	.05
453	Davey Lopes	.10	.08	.04
454	Steve McCatty	.08	.06	.03
455	Dan Meyer	.08	.06	.03
456	Dwayne Murphy	.08	.06	.03
457	Mike Norris	.08	.06	.03
458	Ricky Peters	.08	.06	.03
459	*Tony Phillips* (FC)	2.50	2.00	1.00
460	Tom Underwood	.08	.06	.03
461	Mike Warren	.08	.06	.03
462	Johnny Bench	.80	.60	.30
463	Bruce Berenyi	.08	.06	.03
464	Dann Bilardello	.08	.06	.03
465	Cesar Cedeno	.12	.09	.05
466	Dave Concepcion	.15	.11	.06
467	Dan Driessen	.08	.06	.03
468	*Nick Esasky* (FC)	.08	.06	.03
469	Rich Gale	.08	.06	.03
470	Ben Hayes	.08	.06	.03
471	Paul Householder	.08	.06	.03
472	Tom Hume	.08	.06	.03
473	Alan Knicely	.08	.06	.03
474	Eddie Milner	.08	.06	.03
475	Ron Oester	.08	.06	.03
476	Kelly Paris	.08	.06	.03
477	Frank Pastore	.08	.06	.03
478	Ted Power	.10	.08	.04
479	Joe Price	.08	.06	.03
480	Charlie Puleo	.08	.06	.03
481	*Gary Redus* (FC)	.25	.20	.10
482	Bill Scherrer	.08	.06	.03
483	Mario Soto	.10	.08	.04
484	Alex Trevino	.08	.06	.03
485	Duane Walker	.08	.06	.03
486	Larry Bowa	.15	.11	.06
487	Warren Brusstar	.08	.06	.03
488	Bill Buckner	.15	.11	.06
489	Bill Campbell	.08	.06	.03
490	Ron Cey	.12	.09	.05
491	Jody Davis	.08	.06	.03
492	Leon Durham	.10	.08	.04
493	Mel Hall (FC)	.10	.08	.04
494	Fergie Jenkins	.20	.15	.08
495	Jay Johnstone	.10	.08	.04
496	*Craig Lefferts* (FC)	.20	.15	.08
497	*Carmelo Martinez* (FC)	.08	.06	.03
498	Jerry Morales	.08	.06	.03
499	Keith Moreland	.10	.08	.04
500	Dickie Noles	.08	.06	.03
501	Mike Proly	.08	.06	.03
502	Chuck Rainey	.08	.06	.03
503	Dick Ruthven	.08	.06	.03
504	Ryne Sandberg	18.00	13.50	7.25
505	Lee Smith	.15	.11	.06
506	Steve Trout	.08	.06	.03
507	Gary Woods	.08	.06	.03
508	Juan Beniquez	.08	.06	.03
509	Bob Boone	.10	.08	.04
510	Rick Burleson	.10	.08	.04
511	Rod Carew	1.25	.90	.50
512	Bobby Clark	.08	.06	.03
513	John Curtis	.08	.06	.03
514	Doug DeCinces	.12	.09	.05
515	Brian Downing	.12	.09	.05
516	Tim Foli	.08	.06	.03
517	Ken Forsch	.08	.06	.03
518	Bobby Grich	.12	.09	.05
519	Andy Hassler	.08	.06	.03
520	Reggie Jackson	1.50	1.25	.60
521	Ron Jackson	.08	.06	.03
522	Tommy John	.25	.20	.10
523	Bruce Kison	.08	.06	.03
524	Steve Lubratich	.08	.06	.03
525	Fred Lynn	.25	.20	.10
526	*Gary Pettis* (FC)	.08	.06	.03
527	Luis Sanchez	.08	.06	.03
528	Daryl Sconiers	.08	.06	.03
529	Ellis Valentine	.08	.06	.03
530	Rob Wilfong	.08	.06	.03
531	Mike Witt	.15	.11	.06
532	Geoff Zahn	.08	.06	.03
533	Bud Anderson	.08	.06	.03
534	Chris Bando	.08	.06	.03
535	Alan Bannister	.08	.06	.03
536	Bert Blyleven	.20	.15	.08
537	Tom Brennan	.08	.06	.03
538	Jamie Easterly	.08	.06	.03
539	Juan Eichelberger	.08	.06	.03
540	Jim Essian	.08	.06	.03
541	Mike Fischlin	.08	.06	.03
542	Julio Franco (FC)	2.00	1.50	.80

543	Mike Hargrove	.08	.06	.03
544	Toby Harrah	.10	.08	.04
545	Ron Hassey	.08	.06	.03
546	*Neal Heaton* (FC)	.15	.11	.06
547	Bake McBride	.08	.06	.03
548	Broderick Perkins	.08	.06	.03
549	Lary Sorensen	.08	.06	.03
550	Dan Spillner	.08	.06	.03
551	Rick Sutcliffe	.15	.11	.06
552	Pat Tabler	.10	.08	.04
553	Gorman Thomas	.10	.08	.04
554	Andre Thornton	.12	.09	.05
555	George Vukovich	.08	.06	.03
556	Darrell Brown	.08	.06	.03
557	Tom Brunansky	.20	.15	.08
558	*Randy Bush* (FC)	.15	.11	.06
559	Bobby Castillo	.08	.06	.03
560	John Castino	.08	.06	.03
561	Ron Davis	.08	.06	.03
562	Dave Engle	.08	.06	.03
563	Lenny Faedo	.08	.06	.03
564	Pete Filson	.08	.06	.03
565	Gary Gaetti	.30	.25	.12
566	Mickey Hatcher	.10	.08	.04
567	Kent Hrbek	.40	.30	.15
568	Rusty Kuntz	.08	.06	.03
569	Tim Laudner	.08	.06	.03
570	Rick Lysander	.08	.06	.03
571	Bobby Mitchell	.08	.06	.03
572	Ken Schrom	.08	.06	.03
573	Ray Smith	.08	.06	.03
574	*Tim Teufel* (FC)	.30	.25	.12
575	Frank Viola	1.00	.70	.40
576	Gary Ward	.10	.08	.04
577	Ron Washington	.08	.06	.03
578	Len Whitehouse	.08	.06	.03
579	Al Williams	.08	.06	.03
580	Bob Bailor	.08	.06	.03
581	Mark Bradley	.08	.06	.03
582	Hubie Brooks	.15	.11	.06
583	Carlos Diaz	.08	.06	.03
584	George Foster	.20	.15	.08
585	Brian Giles	.08	.06	.03
586	Danny Heep	.08	.06	.03
587	Keith Hernandez	.20	.15	.08
588	Ron Hodges	.08	.06	.03
589	Scott Holman	.08	.06	.03
590	Dave Kingman	.15	.11	.06
591	Ed Lynch	.08	.06	.03
592	*Jose Oquendo* (FC)	.15	.11	.06
593	Jesse Orosco	.10	.08	.04
594	*Junior Ortiz* (FC)	.10	.08	.04
595	Tom Seaver	4.00	3.00	1.50
596	*Doug Sisk* (FC)	.10	.08	.04
597	Rusty Staub	.12	.09	.05
598	John Stearns	.08	.06	.03
599	*Darryl Strawberry*	7.50	5.50	3.00
600	Craig Swan	.08	.06	.03
601	*Walt Terrell* (FC)	.12	.09	.05
602	Mike Torrez	.10	.08	.04
603	Mookie Wilson	.12	.09	.05
604	Jamie Allen	.08	.06	.03
605	Jim Beattie	.08	.06	.03
606	Tony Bernazard	.08	.06	.03
607	Manny Castillo	.08	.06	.03
608	Bill Caudill	.08	.06	.03
609	Bryan Clark	.08	.06	.03
610	Al Cowens	.08	.06	.03
611	Dave Henderson	.12	.09	.05
612	Steve Henderson	.08	.06	.03
613	Orlando Mercado	.08	.06	.03
614	Mike Moore	.10	.08	.04
615	Ricky Nelson	.08	.06	.03
616	*Spike Owen* (FC)	.20	.15	.08
617	Pat Putnam	.08	.06	.03
618	Ron Roenicke	.08	.06	.03
619	Mike Stanton	.08	.06	.03
620	Bob Stoddard	.08	.06	.03
621	Rick Sweet	.08	.06	.03
622	Roy Thomas	.08	.06	.03
623	Ed Vande Berg	.08	.06	.03
624	*Matt Young* (FC)	.15	.11	.06
625	Richie Zisk	.10	.08	.04
626	'83 All-Star Game Record Breaker (Fred Lynn)	.12	.09	.05
627	'83 All-Star Game Record Breaker (Manny Trillo)	.10	.08	.04
628	N.L. Iron Man (Steve Garvey)	.20	.15	.08
629	A.L. Batting Runner-Up (Rod Carew)	.25	.20	.10
630	A.L. Batting Champion (Wade Boggs)	1.00	.70	.40
631	Letting Go Of The Raines (Tim Raines)	.20	.15	.08
632	Double Trouble (Al Oliver)	.10	.08	.04
633	All-Star Second Base (Steve Sax)	.15	.11	.06
634	All-Star Shortstop (Dickie Thon)	.10	.08	.04
635	Ace Firemen (Tippy Martinez, Dan Quisenberry)	.10	.08	.04
636	Reds Reunited (Joe Morgan, Tony Perez, Pete Rose)	.50	.40	.20
637	Backstop Stars (Bob Boone, Lance Parrish)	.15	.11	.06
638	The Pine Tar Incident 7/24/83 (George Brett, Gaylord Perry)	.30	.25	.12
639	1983 No-Hitters (Bob Forsch, Dave Righetti, Mike Warren)	.10	.08	.04
640	Retiring Superstars (Johnny Bench, Carl Yastrzemski)	2.00	1.50	.80
641	Going Out In Style (Gaylord Perry)	.15	.11	.06
642	300 Club & Strikeout Record (Steve Carlton)	.20	.15	.08
643	The Managers (Joe Altobelli, Paul Owens)	.10	.08	.04
644	The MVP (Rick Dempsey)	.10	.08	.04
645	The Rookie Winner (Mike Boddicker)	.12	.09	.05
646	The Clincher (Scott McGregor)	.10	.08	.04
647	Checklist: Orioles/Royals (Joe Altobelli)	.08	.06	.03
648	Checklist: Phillies/Giants (Paul Owens)	.08	.06	.03
649	Checklist: White Sox/Red Sox (Tony LaRussa)	.08	.06	.03
650	Checklist: Tigers/Rangers (Sparky Anderson)	.08	.06	.03
651	Checklist: Dodgers/A's (Tom Lasorda)	.08	.06	.03
652	Checklist: Yankees/Reds (Billy Martin)	.08	.06	.03
653	Checklist: Blue Jays/Cubs (Bobby Cox)	.08	.06	.03
654	Checklist: Braves/Angels (Joe Torre)	.08	.06	.03
655	Checklist: Brewers/Indians (Rene Lachemann)	.08	.06	.03
656	Checklist: Astros/Twins (Bob Lillis)	.08	.06	.03
657	Checklist: Pirates/Mets (Chuck Tanner)	.08	.06	.03
658	Checklist: Expos/Mariners (Bill Virdon)	.08	.06	.03
659	Checklist: Padres/Specials (Dick Williams)	.08	.06	.03
660	Checklist: Cardinals/Specials (Whitey Herzog)	.08	.06	.03

1984 Fleer Update

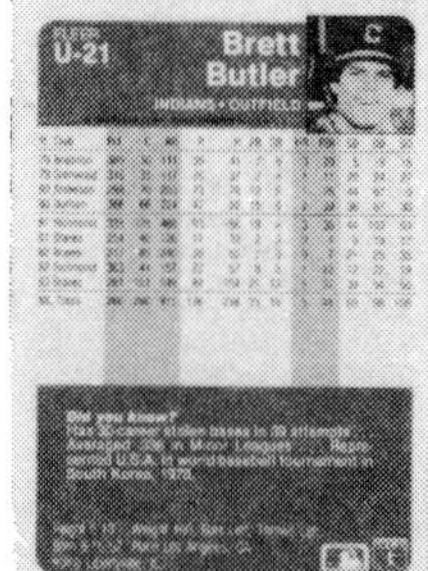

Following the lead of Topps, Fleer issued near the end of the baseball season a 132-card set to update player trades and include rookies not depicted in the regular issue. The cards, which measure 2-1/2" by 3-1/2", are identical in design to the regular issue but are numbered U-1 through U-132. Available to the collecting public only through hobby dealers, the set was printed in limited quantities and has escalated in price quite rapidly the past several years. The set was issued with team logo stickers in a specially designed box.

		MT	NR MT	EX
	Complete Set (132):	850.00	637.00	340.00
	Common Player:	.25	.20	.10
1	Willie Aikens	.25	.20	.10
2	Luis Aponte	.25	.20	.10
3	Mark Bailey (FC)	.25	.20	.10
4	Bob Bailor	.25	.20	.10
5	Dusty Baker	.25	.20	.10
6	Steve Balboni (FC)	.25	.20	.10
7	Alan Bannister	.25	.20	.10
8	Marty Barrett (FC)	.25	.20	.10
9	Dave Beard	.25	.20	.10
10	Joe Beckwith	.25	.20	.10
11	Dave Bergman	.25	.20	.10
12	Tony Bernazard	.25	.20	.10
13	Bruce Bochte	.25	.20	.10
14	Barry Bonnell	.25	.20	.10
15	Phil Bradley (FC)	.25	.20	.10
16	Fred Breining	.25	.20	.10
17	Mike Brown	.25	.20	.10
18	Bill Buckner	.50	.40	.20
19	Ray Burris	.25	.20	.10
20	John Butcher	.25	.20	.10
21	Brett Butler	.30	.25	.12
22	Enos Cabell	.25	.20	.10
23	Bill Campbell	.25	.20	.10
24	Bill Caudill	.25	.20	.10
25	Bobby Clark	.25	.20	.10
26	Bryan Clark	.25	.20	.10
27	Roger Clemens (FC)	400.00	300.00	160.00
28	Jaime Cocanower	.25	.20	.10
29	Ron Darling (FC)	7.00	5.25	2.75
30	Alvin Davis (FC)	.25	.20	.10
31	Bob Dernier	.25	.20	.10
32	Carlos Diaz	.25	.20	.10
33	Mike Easler	.25	.20	.10
34	Dennis Eckersley	10.00	7.50	4.00
35	Jim Essian	.25	.20	.10
36	Darrell Evans	.60	.45	.25
37	Mike Fitzgerald (FC)	.25	.20	.10
38	Tim Foli	.25	.20	.10
39	John Franco (FC)	6.00	4.50	2.50
40	George Frazier	.25	.20	.10
41	Rich Gale	.25	.20	.10
42	Barbaro Garbey	.25	.20	.10
43	Dwight Gooden (FC)	50.00	37.00	20.00
44	Goose Gossage	.50	.40	.20
45	Wayne Gross	.25	.20	.10
46	Mark Gubicza (FC)	3.00	2.25	1.25
47	Jackie Gutierrez	.25	.20	.10
48	Toby Harrah	.25	.20	.10
49	Ron Hassey	.25	.20	.10
50	Richie Hebner	.25	.20	.10
51	Willie Hernandez	.25	.20	.10
52	Ed Hodge	.25	.20	.10
53	Ricky Horton (FC)	.25	.20	.10
54	Art Howe	.25	.20	.10
55	Dane Iorg	.25	.20	.10
56	Brook Jacoby (FC)	2.00	1.50	.80
57	Dion James (FC)	.25	.20	.10
58	Mike Jeffcoat (FC)	.25	.20	.10
59	Ruppert Jones	.25	.20	.10
60	Bob Kearney	.25	.20	.10
61	Jimmy Key (FC)	20.00	15.00	8.00
62	Dave Kingman	.25	.20	.10
63	Brad Komminsk (FC)	.25	.20	.10
64	Jerry Koosman	.50	.40	.20
65	Wayne Krenchicki	.25	.20	.10
66	Rusty Kuntz	.25	.20	.10
67	Frank LaCorte	.25	.20	.10
68	Dennis Lamp	.25	.20	.10
69	Tito Landrum	.25	.20	.10
70	Mark Langston (FC)	25.00	18.50	10.00
71	Rick Leach	.25	.20	.10
72	Craig Lefferts (FC)	.25	.20	.10
73	Gary Lucas	.25	.20	.10
74	Jerry Martin	.25	.20	.10
75	Carmelo Martinez	.25	.20	.10
76	Mike Mason (FC)	.25	.20	.10
77	Gary Matthews	.25	.20	.10
78	Andy McGaffigan	.25	.20	.10
79	Joey McLaughlin	.25	.20	.10
80	Joe Morgan	6.00	4.50	2.50
81	Darryl Motley	.25	.20	.10
82	Graig Nettles	1.00	.70	.40
83	Phil Niekro	4.00	3.00	1.50
84	Ken Oberkfell	.25	.20	.10
85	Al Oliver	.80	.60	.30
86	Jorge Orta	.25	.20	.10
87	Amos Otis	.25	.20	.10
88	Bob Owchinko	.25	.20	.10
89	Dave Parker	4.00	3.00	1.50
90	Jack Perconte	.25	.20	.10
91	Tony Perez	7.00	5.25	2.75
92	Gerald Perry (FC)	1.00	.70	.40
93	Kirby Puckett (FC)	400.00	300.00	160.00
94	Shane Rawley	.25	.20	.10
95	Floyd Rayford	.25	.20	.10
96	Ron Reed	.25	.20	.10
97	R.J. Reynolds (FC)	.25	.20	.10
98	Gene Richards	.25	.20	.10
99	Jose Rijo (FC)	25.00	18.50	10.00
100	Jeff Robinson (FC)	.25	.20	.10
101	Ron Romanick (FC)	.25	.20	.10
102	Pete Rose	30.00	22.00	12.00
103	Bret Saberhagen (FC)	25.00	18.50	10.00
104	Scott Sanderson	.25	.20	.10
105	Dick Schofield (FC)	.25	.20	.10
106	Tom Seaver	25.00	18.50	10.00
107	Jim Slaton	.25	.20	.10
108	Mike Smithson	.25	.20	.10
109	Lary Sorensen	.25	.20	.10
110	Tim Stoddard	.25	.20	.10
111	Jeff Stone (FC)	.25	.20	.10
112	Champ Summers	.25	.20	.10
113	Jim Sundberg	.25	.20	.10
114	Rick Sutcliffe	.80	.60	.30
115	Craig Swan	.25	.20	.10
116	Derrel Thomas	.25	.20	.10
117	Gorman Thomas	.25	.20	.10
118	Alex Trevino	.25	.20	.10
119	Manny Trillo	.25	.20	.10
120	John Tudor	.25	.20	.10
121	Tom Underwood	.25	.20	.10
122	Mike Vail	.25	.20	.10
123	Tom Waddell (FC)	.25	.20	.10
124	Gary Ward	.25	.20	.10
125	Terry Whitfield	.25	.20	.10
126	Curtis Wilkerson	.25	.20	.10
127	Frank Williams (FC)	.25	.20	.10
128	Glenn Wilson	.25	.20	.10
129	John Wockenfuss	.25	.20	.10
130	Ned Yost	.25	.20	.10
131	Mike Young (FC)	.25	.20	.10
132	Checklist 1-132	.25	.20	.10

1984 Fleer Stickers

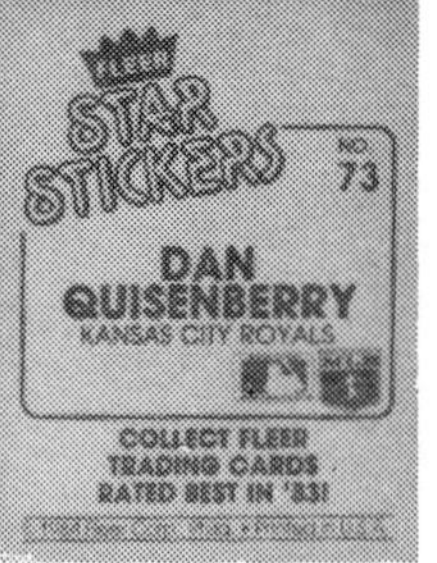

This 126-sticker set was designed to be housed in a special collector's album that was organized according to various league leader categories, resulting in some players being pictured on more than one sticker. Each full-color sticker measures 2-1/2" by 1-15/16" and is framed with a beige border. The stickers, which were sold in packs of six, are numbered on the back.

	MT	NR MT	EX
Complete Set:	12.00	9.00	4.75
Common Player:	.03	.02	.01
Sticker Album:	1.00	.70	.40

No.	Player	MT	NR MT	EX
1	Dickie Thon	.03	.02	.01
2	Ken Landreaux	.03	.02	.01
3	Darrell Evans	.06	.05	.02
4	Harold Baines	.10	.08	.04
5	Dave Winfield	.20	.15	.08
6	Bill Madlock	.06	.05	.02
7	Lonnie Smith	.03	.02	.01
8	Jose Cruz	.04	.03	.02
9	George Hendrick	.04	.03	.02
10	Ray Knight	.04	.03	.02
11	Wade Boggs	.40	.30	.15
12	Rod Carew	.25	.20	.10
13	Lou Whitaker	.10	.08	.04
14	Alan Trammell	.15	.11	.06
15	Cal Ripken, Jr.	.50	.40	.20
16	Mike Schmidt	.40	.30	.15
17	Dale Murphy	.30	.25	.12
18	Andre Dawson	.15	.11	.06
19	Pedro Guerrero	.12	.09	.05
20	Jim Rice	.20	.15	.08
21	Tony Armas	.03	.02	.01
22	Ron Kittle	.04	.03	.02
23	Eddie Murray	.25	.20	.10
24	Jose Cruz	.04	.03	.02
25	Andre Dawson	.15	.11	.06
26	Rafael Ramirez	.03	.02	.01
27	Al Oliver	.06	.05	.02
28	Wade Boggs	.40	.30	.15
29	Cal Ripken, Jr.	.50	.40	.20
30	Lou Whitaker	.10	.08	.04
31	Cecil Cooper	.08	.06	.03
32	Dale Murphy	.30	.25	.12
33	Andre Dawson	.15	.11	.06
34	Pedro Guerrero	.12	.09	.05
35	Mike Schmidt	.40	.30	.15
36	George Brett	.30	.25	.12
37	Jim Rice	.20	.15	.08
38	Eddie Murray	.25	.20	.10
39	Carlton Fisk	.12	.09	.05
40	Rusty Staub	.06	.05	.02
41	Duane Walker	.03	.02	.01
42	Steve Braun	.03	.02	.01
43	Kurt Bevacqua	.03	.02	.01
44	Hal McRae	.06	.05	.02
45	Don Baylor	.10	.08	.04
46	Ken Singleton	.06	.05	.02
47	Greg Luzinski	.08	.06	.03
48	Mike Schmidt	.40	.30	.15
49	Keith Hernandez	.15	.11	.06
50	Dale Murphy	.30	.25	.12
51	Tim Raines	.20	.15	.08
52	Wade Boggs	.40	.30	.15
53	Rickey Henderson	.25	.20	.10
54	Rod Carew	.25	.20	.10
55	Ken Singleton	.06	.05	.02
56	John Denny	.03	.02	.01
57	John Candelaria	.04	.03	.02
58	Larry McWilliams	.03	.02	.01
59	Pascual Perez	.04	.03	.02
60	Jesse Orosco	.04	.03	.02
61	Moose Haas	.03	.02	.01
62	Richard Dotson	.04	.03	.02
63	Mike Flanagan	.04	.03	.02
64	Scott McGregor	.04	.03	.02
65	Atlee Hammaker	.03	.02	.01
66	Rick Honeycutt	.03	.02	.01
67	Lee Smith	.06	.05	.02
68	Al Holland	.03	.02	.01
69	Greg Minton	.03	.02	.01
70	Bruce Sutter	.08	.06	.03
71	Jeff Reardon	.08	.06	.03
72	Frank DiPino	.03	.02	.01
73	Dan Quisenberry	.06	.05	.02
74	Bob Stanley	.03	.02	.01
75	Ron Davis	.03	.02	.01
76	Bill Caudill	.03	.02	.01
77	Peter Ladd	.03	.02	.01
78	Steve Carlton	.20	.15	.08
79	Mario Soto	.04	.03	.02
80	Larry McWilliams	.03	.02	.01
81	Fernando Valenzuela	.15	.11	.06
82	Nolan Ryan	.75	.55	.30
83	Jack Morris	.12	.09	.05
84	Floyd Bannister	.04	.03	.02
85	Dave Stieb	.06	.05	.02
86	Dave Righetti	.12	.09	.05
87	Rick Sutcliffe	.08	.06	.03
88	Tim Raines	.20	.15	.08
89	Alan Wiggins	.03	.02	.01
90	Steve Sax	.10	.08	.04
91	Mookie Wilson	.04	.03	.02
92	Rickey Henderson	.25	.20	.10
93	Rudy Law	.03	.02	.01
94	Willie Wilson	.08	.06	.03
95	Julio Cruz	.03	.02	.01
96	Johnny Bench	.30	.25	.12
97	Carl Yastrzemski	.35	.25	.14
98	Gaylord Perry	.15	.11	.06
99	Pete Rose	.40	.30	.15
100	Joe Morgan	.12	.09	.05
101	Steve Carlton	.20	.15	.08
102	Jim Palmer	.15	.11	.06
103	Rod Carew	.25	.20	.10
104	Darryl Strawberry	.20	.15	.08
105	Craig McMurtry	.03	.02	.01
106	Mel Hall	.03	.02	.01
107	Lee Tunnell	.03	.02	.01
108	Bill Dawley	.03	.02	.01
109	Ron Kittle	.04	.03	.02
110	Mike Boddicker	.04	.03	.02
111	Julio Franco	.08	.06	.03
112	Daryl Sconiers	.03	.02	.01
113	Neal Heaton	.03	.02	.01
114	John Shelby	.03	.02	.01
115	Rick Dempsey	.03	.02	.01
116	John Lowenstein	.03	.02	.01
117	Jim Dwyer	.03	.02	.01
118	Bo Diaz	.03	.02	.01
119	Pete Rose	.40	.30	.15
120	Joe Morgan	.20	.15	.08
121	Gary Matthews	.04	.03	.02
122	Garry Maddox	.04	.03	.02
123	Paul Owens	.03	.02	.01
124	Tom Lasorda	.06	.05	.02
125	Joe Altobelli	.03	.02	.01
126	Tony LaRussa	.03	.02	.01

1985 Fleer

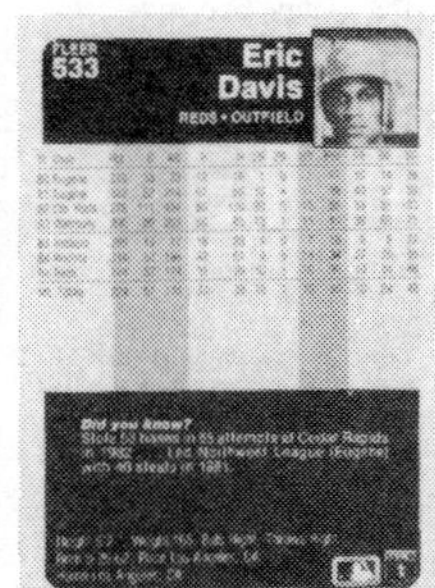

The 1985 Fleer set consists of 660 cards, each measuring 2-1/2" by 3-1/2" in size. The card fronts feature a color photo plus the player's team logo and the word "Fleer." The photos have a color-coded frame which corresponds to the player's team. A grey border surrounds the color-coded frame. The card backs are similar in design to the previous two years, but have two shades of red and black ink on white stock. For the fourth consecutive year, Fleer included special cards and team checklists in the set. Also incorporated in a set for the first time were ten "Major League Prospect" cards, each featuring two rookie hopefuls. The set was issued with team logo stickers.

	MT	NR MT	EX
Complete Set (660):	190.00	142.00	76.00
Common Player:	.06	.05	.02

No.	Player	MT	NR MT	EX
1	Doug Bair	.06	.05	.02
2	Juan Berenguer	.06	.05	.02
3	Dave Bergman	.06	.05	.02
4	Tom Brookens	.06	.05	.02
5	Marty Castillo	.06	.05	.02
6	Darrell Evans	.12	.09	.05
7	Barbaro Garbey	.12	.09	.05
8	Kirk Gibson	.20	.15	.08
9	John Grubb	.06	.05	.02
10	Willie Hernandez	.08	.06	.03
11	Larry Herndon	.08	.06	.03
12	Howard Johnson	.40	.30	.15
13	Ruppert Jones	.06	.05	.02
14	Rusty Kuntz	.06	.05	.02
15	Chet Lemon	.08	.06	.03
16	Aurelio Lopez	.06	.05	.02
17	Sid Monge	.06	.05	.02
18	Jack Morris	.20	.15	.08
19	Lance Parrish	.10	.08	.04
20	Dan Petry	.08	.06	.03
21	Dave Rozema	.06	.05	.02
22	Bill Scherrer	.06	.05	.02
23	Alan Trammell	.50	.40	.20
24	Lou Whitaker	.50	.40	.20
25	Milt Wilcox	.06	.05	.02
26	Kurt Bevacqua	.06	.05	.02
27	*Greg Booker* (FC)	.06	.05	.02
28	Bobby Brown	.06	.05	.02
29	Luis DeLeon	.06	.05	.02
30	Dave Dravecky	.08	.06	.03
31	Tim Flannery	.06	.05	.02
32	Steve Garvey	.35	.25	.14
33	Goose Gossage	.20	.15	.08
34	Tony Gwynn	5.00	3.75	2.00
35	Greg Harris	.06	.05	.02
36	Andy Hawkins	.08	.06	.03
37	Terry Kennedy	.08	.06	.03
38	Craig Lefferts	.08	.06	.03
39	Tim Lollar	.06	.05	.02
40	Carmelo Martinez	.08	.06	.03
41	Kevin McReynolds	.25	.20	.10
42	Graig Nettles	.15	.11	.06
43	Luis Salazar	.06	.05	.02
44	Eric Show	.08	.06	.03
45	Garry Templeton	.08	.06	.03
46	Mark Thurmond	.06	.05	.02
47	Ed Whitson	.06	.05	.02
48	Alan Wiggins	.06	.05	.02
49	Rich Bordi	.06	.05	.02
50	Larry Bowa	.12	.09	.05
51	Warren Brusstar	.06	.05	.02
52	Ron Cey	.10	.08	.04
53	*Henry Cotto* (FC)	.08	.06	.03
54	Jody Davis	.10	.08	.04
55	Bob Dernier	.06	.05	.02
56	Leon Durham	.08	.06	.03
57	Dennis Eckersley	1.25	.90	.50
58	George Frazier	.06	.05	.02
59	Richie Hebner	.06	.05	.02
60	Dave Lopes	.08	.06	.03
61	Gary Matthews	.10	.08	.04
62	Keith Moreland	.08	.06	.03
63	Rick Reuschel	.10	.08	.04
64	Dick Ruthven	.06	.05	.02
65	Ryne Sandberg	8.00	6.00	3.25
66	Scott Sanderson	.06	.05	.02
67	Lee Smith	.10	.08	.04
68	Tim Stoddard	.06	.05	.02
69	Rick Sutcliffe	.12	.09	.05
70	Steve Trout	.06	.05	.02
71	Gary Woods	.06	.05	.02
72	Wally Backman	.08	.06	.03
73	Bruce Berenyi	.06	.05	.02
74	Hubie Brooks	.10	.08	.04
75	Kelvin Chapman	.06	.05	.02
76	Ron Darling	.30	.25	.12
77	Sid Fernandez (FC)	.25	.20	.10
78	Mike Fitzgerald	.08	.06	.03
79	George Foster	.15	.11	.06
80	Brent Gaff	.06	.05	.02
81	Ron Gardenhire	.06	.05	.02
82	*Dwight Gooden*	6.50	5.00	2.50
83	Tom Gorman	.06	.05	.02
84	Danny Heep	.06	.05	.02
85	Keith Hernandez	.15	.11	.06
86	Ray Knight	.10	.08	.04
87	Ed Lynch	.06	.05	.02
88	Jose Oquendo	.08	.06	.03
89	Jesse Orosco	.08	.06	.03
90	*Rafael Santana* (FC)	.06	.05	.02
91	Doug Sisk	.06	.05	.02
92	Rusty Staub	.12	.09	.05
93	Darryl Strawberry	1.75	1.25	.70
94	Walt Terrell	.08	.06	.03
95	Mookie Wilson	.10	.08	.04
96	Jim Acker	.06	.05	.02
97	Willie Aikens	.06	.05	.02
98	Doyle Alexander	.10	.08	.04
99	Jesse Barfield	.15	.11	.06
100	George Bell	.20	.15	.08
101	Jim Clancy	.08	.06	.03
102	Dave Collins	.08	.06	.03
103	Tony Fernandez	.25	.20	.10
104	Damaso Garcia	.06	.05	.02
105	Jim Gott	.06	.05	.02
106	Alfredo Griffin	.08	.06	.03
107	Garth Iorg	.06	.05	.02
108	Roy Lee Jackson	.06	.05	.02
109	Cliff Johnson	.06	.05	.02
110	*Jimmy Key*	5.00	3.75	2.00
111	Dennis Lamp	.06	.05	.02
112	Rick Leach	.06	.05	.02
113	Luis Leal	.06	.05	.02
114	Buck Martinez	.06	.05	.02
115	Lloyd Moseby	.10	.08	.04
116	Rance Mulliniks	.06	.05	.02
117	Dave Stieb	.12	.09	.05
118	Willie Upshaw	.08	.06	.03
119	Ernie Whitt	.08	.06	.03
120	Mike Armstrong	.06	.05	.02
121	Don Baylor	.12	.09	.05
122	Marty Bystrom	.06	.05	.02
123	Rick Cerone	.06	.05	.02
124	Joe Cowley (FC)	.06	.05	.02
125	Brian Dayett (FC)	.06	.05	.02
126	Tim Foli	.06	.05	.02
127	Ray Fontenot	.06	.05	.02
128	Ken Griffey	.10	.08	.04
129	Ron Guidry	.25	.20	.10
130	Toby Harrah	.08	.06	.03
131	Jay Howell	.08	.06	.03
132	Steve Kemp	.08	.06	.03
133	Don Mattingly	8.00	6.00	3.25
134	Bobby Meacham	.06	.05	.02
135	John Montefusco	.06	.05	.02
136	Omar Moreno	.06	.05	.02
137	Dale Murray	.06	.05	.02
138	Phil Niekro	.25	.20	.10
139	*Mike Pagliarulo*	.20	.15	.08
140	Willie Randolph	.10	.08	.04
141	Dennis Rasmussen (FC)	.15	.11	.06
142	Dave Righetti	.20	.15	.08
143	*Jose Rijo*	3.50	2.75	1.50
144	Andre Robertson	.06	.05	.02
145	Bob Shirley	.06	.05	.02
146	Dave Winfield	4.00	3.00	1.50
147	Butch Wynegar	.06	.05	.02
148	Gary Allenson	.06	.05	.02
149	Tony Armas	.10	.08	.04
150	Marty Barrett	.20	.15	.08
151	Wade Boggs	4.00	3.00	1.50
152	Dennis Boyd	.10	.08	.04
153	Bill Buckner	.12	.09	.05
154	Mark Clear	.06	.05	.02
155	*Roger Clemens*	48.00	36.00	19.00
156	Steve Crawford	.06	.05	.02
157	Mike Easler	.08	.06	.03
158	Dwight Evans	.12	.09	.05
159	Rich Gedman	.10	.08	.04
160	Jackie Gutierrez	.06	.05	.02
161	Bruce Hurst	.12	.09	.05
162	John Henry Johnson	.06	.05	.02
163	Rick Miller	.06	.05	.02
164	Reid Nichols	.06	.05	.02

165 *Al Nipper* (FC) .08 .06 .03
166 Bob Ojeda .10 .08 .04
167 Jerry Remy .06 .05 .02
168 Jim Rice .20 .15 .08
169 Bob Stanley .06 .05 .02
170 Mike Boddicker .10 .08 .04
171 Al Bumbry .08 .06 .03
172 Todd Cruz .06 .05 .02
173 Rich Dauer .06 .05 .02
174 Storm Davis .10 .08 .04
175 Rick Dempsey .08 .06 .03
176 Jim Dwyer .06 .05 .02
177 Mike Flanagan .10 .08 .04
178 Dan Ford .06 .05 .02
179 Wayne Gross .06 .05 .02
180 John Lowenstein .06 .05 .02
181 Dennis Martinez .08 .06 .03
182 Tippy Martinez .06 .05 .02
183 Scott McGregor .08 .06 .03
184 Eddie Murray 1.75 1.25 .70
185 Joe Nolan .06 .05 .02
186 Floyd Rayford .06 .05 .02
187 Cal Ripken, Jr. 10.00 7.50 4.00
188 Gary Roenicke .06 .05 .02
189 Lenn Sakata .06 .05 .02
190 John Shelby .08 .06 .03
191 Ken Singleton .08 .06 .03
192 Sammy Stewart .06 .05 .02
193 Bill Swaggerty .06 .05 .02
194 Tom Underwood .06 .05 .02
195 Mike Young .12 .09 .05
196 Steve Balboni .08 .06 .03
197 Joe Beckwith .06 .05 .02
198 Bud Black .06 .05 .02
199 George Brett 4.00 3.00 1.50
200 Onix Concepcion .06 .05 .02
201 *Mark Gubicza* .80 .60 .30
202 Larry Gura .06 .05 .02
203 Mark Huismann (FC) .06 .05 .02
204 Dane Iorg .06 .05 .02
205 Danny Jackson (FC) .15 .11 .06
206 Charlie Leibrandt .08 .06 .03
207 Hal McRae .10 .08 .04
208 Darryl Motley .06 .05 .02
209 Jorge Orta .06 .05 .02
210 Greg Pryor .06 .05 .02
211 Dan Quisenberry .10 .08 .04
212 *Bret Saberhagen* 2.50 2.00 1.00
213 Pat Sheridan .06 .05 .02
214 Don Slaught .06 .05 .02
215 U.L. Washington .06 .05 .02
216 John Wathan .08 .06 .03
217 Frank White .10 .08 .04
218 Willie Wilson .12 .09 .05
219 Neil Allen .06 .05 .02
220 Joaquin Andujar .08 .06 .03
221 Steve Braun .06 .05 .02
222 Danny Cox (FC) .20 .15 .08
223 Bob Forsch .08 .06 .03
224 David Green .06 .05 .02
225 George Hendrick .08 .06 .03
226 Tom Herr .10 .08 .04
227 *Ricky Horton* .06 .05 .02
228 Art Howe .06 .05 .02
229 Mike Jorgensen .06 .05 .02
230 Kurt Kepshire .06 .05 .02
231 Jeff Lahti .06 .05 .02
232 Tito Landrum .06 .05 .02
233 Dave LaPoint .08 .06 .03
234 Willie McGee .30 .25 .12
235 *Tom Nieto* (FC) .06 .05 .02
236 *Terry Pendleton* (FC) 7.00 5.25 2.75
237 Darrell Porter .08 .06 .03
238 Dave Rucker .06 .05 .02
239 Lonnie Smith .08 .06 .03
240 Ozzie Smith 2.00 1.50 .80
241 Bruce Sutter .12 .09 .05
242 Andy Van Slyke 1.50 1.25 .60
243 Dave Von Ohlen .06 .05 .02
244 Larry Andersen .06 .05 .02
245 Bill Campbell .06 .05 .02
246 Steve Carlton 1.50 1.25 .60
247 Tim Corcoran .06 .05 .02
248 Ivan DeJesus .06 .05 .02
249 John Denny .06 .05 .02
250 Bo Diaz .08 .06 .03
251 Greg Gross .06 .05 .02
252 Kevin Gross .10 .08 .04
253 Von Hayes .12 .09 .05
254 Al Holland .06 .05 .02
255 Charles Hudson .08 .06 .03
256 Jerry Koosman .10 .08 .04
257 Joe Lefebvre .06 .05 .02
258 Sixto Lezcano .06 .05 .02
259 Garry Maddox .10 .08 .04
260 Len Matuszek .06 .05 .02
261 Tug McGraw .10 .08 .04
262 Al Oliver .12 .09 .05
263 Shane Rawley .10 .08 .04
264 Juan Samuel .20 .15 .08
265 Mike Schmidt 5.00 3.75 2.00
266 *Jeff Stone* .06 .05 .02
267 Ozzie Virgil .06 .05 .02
268 Glenn Wilson .08 .06 .03
269 John Wockenfuss .06 .05 .02
270 Darrell Brown .06 .05 .02
271 Tom Brunansky .12 .09 .05
272 Randy Bush .06 .05 .02
273 John Butcher .06 .05 .02
274 Bobby Castillo .06 .05 .02
275 Ron Davis .06 .05 .02
276 Dave Engle .06 .05 .02
277 Pete Filson .06 .05 .02
278 Gary Gaetti .25 .20 .10
279 Mickey Hatcher .06 .05 .02
280 Ed Hodge .06 .05 .02
281 Kent Hrbek .25 .20 .10
282 Houston Jimenez .06 .05 .02
283 Tim Laudner .06 .05 .02
284 Rick Lysander .06 .05 .02
285 Dave Meier .06 .05 .02
286 *Kirby Puckett* 55.00 41.00 22.00
287 Pat Putnam .06 .05 .02
288 Ken Schrom .06 .05 .02
289 Mike Smithson .06 .05 .02
290 Tim Teufel .08 .06 .03
291 Frank Viola .20 .15 .08
292 Ron Washington .06 .05 .02
293 Don Aase .06 .05 .02
294 Juan Beniquez .06 .05 .02
295 Bob Boone .08 .06 .03
296 Mike Brown .06 .05 .02
297 Rod Carew 1.50 1.25 .60
298 Doug Corbett .06 .05 .02
299 Doug DeCinces .10 .08 .04
300 Brian Downing .10 .08 .04
301 Ken Forsch .06 .05 .02
302 Bobby Grich .10 .08 .04
303 Reggie Jackson 2.00 1.50 .80
304 Tommy John .20 .15 .08
305 Curt Kaufman .06 .05 .02
306 Bruce Kison .06 .05 .02
307 Fred Lynn .20 .15 .08
308 Gary Pettis .08 .06 .03
309 *Ron Romanick* .06 .05 .02
310 Luis Sanchez .06 .05 .02
311 Dick Schofield .12 .09 .05
312 Daryl Sconiers .06 .05 .02
313 Jim Slaton .06 .05 .02
314 Derrel Thomas .06 .05 .02
315 Rob Wilfong .06 .05 .02
316 Mike Witt .12 .09 .05
317 Geoff Zahn .06 .05 .02
318 Len Barker .08 .06 .03
319 Steve Bedrosian .12 .09 .05
320 Bruce Benedict .06 .05 .02
321 Rick Camp .06 .05 .02
322 Chris Chambliss .08 .06 .03
323 *Jeff Dedmon* (FC) .06 .05 .02
324 Terry Forster .08 .06 .03
325 Gene Garber .06 .05 .02
326 *Albert Hall* (FC) .06 .05 .02
327 Terry Harper .06 .05 .02
328 Bob Horner .12 .09 .05
329 Glenn Hubbard .06 .05 .02
330 Randy S. Johnson .06 .05 .02
331 Brad Komminsk .06 .05 .02
332 Rick Mahler .06 .05 .02
333 Craig McMurtry .06 .05 .02
334 Donnie Moore .06 .05 .02
335 Dale Murphy .50 .40 .20
336 Ken Oberkfell .06 .05 .02
337 Pascual Perez .08 .06 .03
338 Gerald Perry .15 .11 .06
339 Rafael Ramirez .06 .05 .02
340 Jerry Royster .06 .05 .02
341 Alex Trevino .06 .05 .02
342 Claudell Washington .08 .06 .03
343 Alan Ashby .06 .05 .02
344 *Mark Bailey* .06 .05 .02
345 Kevin Bass .06 .05 .02
346 Enos Cabell .06 .05 .02
347 Jose Cruz .10 .08 .04
348 Bill Dawley .06 .05 .02
349 Frank DiPino .06 .05 .02
350 Bill Doran .12 .09 .05
351 Phil Garner .08 .06 .03
352 Bob Knepper .08 .06 .03
353 Mike LaCoss .06 .05 .02
354 Jerry Mumphrey .06 .05 .02
355 Joe Niekro .10 .08 .04
356 Terry Puhl .06 .05 .02
357 Craig Reynolds .06 .05 .02
358 Vern Ruhle .06 .05 .02
359 Nolan Ryan 10.00 7.50 4.00
360 Joe Sambito .06 .05 .02
361 Mike Scott .15 .11 .06
362 Dave Smith .08 .06 .03
363 *Julio Solano* (FC) .06 .05 .02
364 Dickie Thon .08 .06 .03
365 Denny Walling .06 .05 .02
366 Dave Anderson .06 .05 .02
367 Bob Bailor .06 .05 .02
368 Greg Brock .08 .06 .03
369 Carlos Diaz .06 .05 .02
370 Pedro Guerrero .10 .08 .04
371 *Orel Hershiser* 2.50 2.00 1.00
372 Rick Honeycutt .06 .05 .02
373 Burt Hooton .08 .06 .03
374 *Ken Howell* (FC) .15 .11 .06
375 Ken Landreaux .08 .06 .03
376 Candy Maldonado .10 .08 .04
377 Mike Marshall .08 .06 .03
378 Tom Niedenfuer .08 .06 .03
379 Alejandro Pena .08 .06 .03
380 Jerry Reuss .08 .06 .03
381 *R.J. Reynolds* .06 .05 .02
382 German Rivera .06 .05 .02
383 Bill Russell .08 .06 .03
384 Steve Sax .10 .08 .04
385 Mike Scioscia .08 .06 .03
386 *Franklin Stubbs* (FC) .06 .05 .02
387 Fernando Valenzuela .10 .08 .04
388 Bob Welch .12 .09 .05
389 Terry Whitfield .06 .05 .02
390 Steve Yeager .06 .05 .02
391 Pat Zachry .06 .05 .02
392 Fred Breining .06 .05 .02
393 Gary Carter .35 .25 .14
394 Andre Dawson 2.00 1.50 .80
395 Miguel Dilone .06 .05 .02
396 Dan Driessen .08 .06 .03
397 Doug Flynn .06 .05 .02
398 Terry Francona .06 .05 .02
399 Bill Gullickson .06 .05 .02
400 Bob James .06 .05 .02
401 Charlie Lea .06 .05 .02
402 Bryan Little .06 .05 .02
403 Gary Lucas .06 .05 .02
404 David Palmer .06 .05 .02
405 Tim Raines .35 .25 .14
406 Mike Ramsey .06 .05 .02
407 Jeff Reardon .12 .09 .05
408 Steve Rogers .08 .06 .03
409 Dan Schatzeder .06 .05 .02
410 Bryn Smith .06 .05 .02
411 Mike Stenhouse .06 .05 .02
412 Tim Wallach .12 .09 .05
413 Jim Wohlford .06 .05 .02
414 Bill Almon .06 .05 .02
415 Keith Atherton .06 .05 .02
416 Bruce Bochte .06 .05 .02
417 Tom Burgmeier .06 .05 .02
418 Ray Burris .06 .05 .02
419 Bill Caudill .06 .05 .02
420 Chris Codiroli .06 .05 .02
421 Tim Conroy .06 .05 .02
422 Mike Davis .08 .06 .03
423 Jim Essian .06 .05 .02
424 Mike Heath .06 .05 .02
425 Rickey Henderson 4.00 3.00 1.50
426 Donnie Hill .06 .05 .02
427 Dave Kingman .15 .11 .06
428 Bill Krueger .06 .05 .02
429 Carney Lansford .10 .08 .04
430 Steve McCatty .06 .05 .02
431 Joe Morgan .40 .30 .15
432 Dwayne Murphy .08 .06 .03
433 Tony Phillips .30 .25 .12
434 Lary Sorensen .06 .05 .02
435 Mike Warren .06 .05 .02
436 *Curt Young* (FC) .10 .08 .04
437 Luis Aponte .06 .05 .02
438 Chris Bando .06 .05 .02
439 Tony Bernazard .06 .05 .02
440 Bert Blyleven .15 .11 .06
441 Brett Butler .10 .08 .04
442 Ernie Camacho .06 .05 .02
443 Joe Carter 14.00 10.50 5.50
444 Carmelo Castillo .06 .05 .02
445 Jamie Easterly .06 .05 .02
446 *Steve Farr* .40 .30 .15
447 Mike Fischlin .06 .05 .02
448 Julio Franco .60 .45 .25
449 Mel Hall .08 .06 .03
450 Mike Hargrove .06 .05 .02
451 Neal Heaton .06 .05 .02
452 Brook Jacoby .10 .08 .04
453 *Mike Jeffcoat* .08 .06 .03
454 *Don Schulze* (FC) .06 .05 .02
455 Roy Smith .06 .05 .02
456 Pat Tabler .08 .06 .03
457 Andre Thornton .10 .08 .04
458 George Vukovich .06 .05 .02
459 Tom Waddell .06 .05 .02
460 Jerry Willard .06 .05 .02
461 Dale Berra .06 .05 .02
462 John Candelaria .10 .08 .04
463 Jose DeLeon .08 .06 .03
464 Doug Frobel .06 .05 .02
465 Cecilio Guante .06 .05 .02
466 Brian Harper .06 .05 .02
467 Lee Lacy .06 .05 .02
468 Bill Madlock .12 .09 .05
469 Lee Mazzilli .08 .06 .03
470 Larry McWilliams .06 .05 .02
471 Jim Morrison .06 .05 .02
472 Tony Pena .10 .08 .04
473 Johnny Ray .06 .05 .02
474 Rick Rhoden .10 .08 .04
475 Don Robinson .08 .06 .03
476 Rod Scurry .06 .05 .02
477 Kent Tekulve .08 .06 .03
478 Jason Thompson .06 .05 .02
479 John Tudor .10 .08 .04
480 Lee Tunnell .06 .05 .02
481 Marvell Wynne .06 .05 .02
482 Salome Barojas .06 .05 .02
483 Dave Beard .06 .05 .02
484 Jim Beattie .06 .05 .02
485 Barry Bonnell .06 .05 .02
486 *Phil Bradley* .10 .08 .04
487 Al Cowens .06 .05 .02
488 *Alvin Davis* .10 .08 .04
489 Dave Henderson .15 .11 .06
490 Steve Henderson .06 .05 .02
491 Bob Kearney .06 .05 .02
492 *Mark Langston* 4.00 3.00 1.50
493 Larry Milbourne .06 .05 .02
494 Paul Mirabella .06 .05 .02
495 Mike Moore .20 .15 .08
496 Edwin Nunez (FC) .08 .06 .03
497 Spike Owen .08 .06 .03
498 Jack Perconte .06 .05 .02
499 Ken Phelps .10 .08 .04
500 *Jim Presley* (FC) .06 .05 .02
501 Mike Stanton .06 .05 .02
502 Bob Stoddard .06 .05 .02
503 Gorman Thomas .06 .05 .02
504 Ed Vande Berg .06 .05 .02
505 Matt Young .06 .05 .02
506 Juan Agosto .06 .05 .02
507 Harold Baines .15 .11 .06
508 Floyd Bannister .10 .08 .04
509 Britt Burns .06 .05 .02
510 Julio Cruz .06 .05 .02
511 Richard Dotson .10 .08 .04
512 Jerry Dybzinski .06 .05 .02
513 Carlton Fisk 1.00 .70 .40
514 Scott Fletcher .08 .06 .03
515 Jerry Hairston .06 .05 .02
516 Marc Hill .06 .05 .02
517 LaMarr Hoyt .06 .05 .02
518 Ron Kittle .06 .05 .02

519	Rudy Law	.06	.05	.02
520	Vance Law	.08	.06	.03
521	Greg Luzinski	.10	.08	.04
522	Gene Nelson	.06	.05	.02
523	Tom Paciorek	.06	.05	.02
524	Ron Reed	.06	.05	.02
525	Bert Roberge	.06	.05	.02
526	Tom Seaver	1.25	.90	.50
527	Roy Smalley	.06	.05	.02
528	Dan Spillner	.06	.05	.02
529	Mike Squires	.06	.05	.02
530	Greg Walker	.06	.05	.02
531	Cesar Cedeno	.10	.08	.04
532	Dave Concepcion	.12	.09	.05
533	*Eric Davis* (FC)	6.00	4.50	2.50
534	Nick Esasky	.08	.06	.03
535	Tom Foley	.06	.05	.02
536	*John Franco*	.75	.60	.30
537	Brad Gulden	.06	.05	.02
538	Tom Hume	.06	.05	.02
539	Wayne Krenchicki	.06	.05	.02
540	Andy McGaffigan	.06	.05	.02
541	Eddie Milner	.06	.05	.02
542	Ron Oester	.06	.05	.02
543	Bob Owchinko	.06	.05	.02
544	Dave Parker	.25	.20	.10
545	Frank Pastore	.06	.05	.02
546	Tony Perez	.15	.11	.06
547	Ted Power	.06	.05	.02
548	Joe Price	.06	.05	.02
549	Gary Redus	.08	.06	.03
550	Pete Rose	2.00	1.50	.80
551	Jeff Russell (FC)	.10	.08	.04
552	Mario Soto	.08	.06	.03
553	*Jay Tibbs* (FC)	.15	.11	.06
554	Duane Walker	.06	.05	.02
555	Alan Bannister	.06	.05	.02
556	Buddy Bell	.12	.09	.05
557	Danny Darwin	.06	.05	.02
558	Charlie Hough	.08	.06	.03
559	Bobby Jones	.06	.05	.02
560	Odell Jones	.06	.05	.02
561	*Jeff Kunkel* (FC)	.06	.05	.02
562	*Mike Mason*	.06	.05	.02
563	Pete O'Brien	.12	.09	.05
564	Larry Parrish	.10	.08	.04
565	Mickey Rivers	.08	.06	.03
566	Billy Sample	.06	.05	.02
567	Dave Schmidt	.06	.05	.02
568	Donnie Scott	.06	.05	.02
569	Dave Stewart	.12	.09	.05
570	Frank Tanana	.10	.08	.04
571	Wayne Tolleson	.06	.05	.02
572	Gary Ward	.08	.06	.03
573	Curtis Wilkerson	.08	.06	.03
574	George Wright	.06	.05	.02
575	Ned Yost	.06	.05	.02
576	Mark Brouhard	.06	.05	.02
577	Mike Caldwell	.06	.05	.02
578	Bobby Clark	.06	.05	.02
579	Jaime Cocanower	.06	.05	.02
580	Cecil Cooper	.15	.11	.06
581	Rollie Fingers	.20	.15	.08
582	Jim Gantner	.06	.05	.02
583	Moose Haas	.06	.05	.02
584	Dion James	.06	.05	.02
585	Pete Ladd	.06	.05	.02
586	Rick Manning	.06	.05	.02
587	Bob McClure	.06	.05	.02
588	Paul Molitor	3.00	2.25	1.25
589	Charlie Moore	.06	.05	.02
590	Ben Oglivie	.08	.06	.03
591	Chuck Porter	.06	.05	.02
592	*Randy Ready* (FC)	.08	.06	.03
593	Ed Romero	.06	.05	.02
594	Bill Schroeder (FC)	.06	.05	.02
595	Ray Searage	.06	.05	.02
596	Ted Simmons	.12	.09	.05
597	Jim Sundberg	.08	.06	.03
598	Don Sutton	.30	.25	.12
599	Tom Tellmann	.06	.05	.02
600	Rick Waits	.06	.05	.02
601	Robin Yount	4.00	3.00	1.50
602	Dusty Baker	.08	.06	.03
603	Bob Brenly	.06	.05	.02
604	Jack Clark	.10	.08	.04
605	Chili Davis	.20	.15	.08
606	Mark Davis	.06	.05	.02
607	*Dan Gladden* (FC)	.50	.40	.20
608	Atlee Hammaker	.06	.05	.02
609	Mike Krukow	.08	.06	.03
610	Duane Kuiper	.06	.05	.02
611	Bob Lacey	.06	.05	.02
612	Bill Laskey	.06	.05	.02
613	Gary Lavelle	.06	.05	.02
614	Johnnie LeMaster	.06	.05	.02
615	Jeff Leonard	.06	.05	.02
616	Randy Lerch	.06	.05	.02
617	Greg Minton	.06	.05	.02
618	Steve Nicosia	.06	.05	.02
619	Gene Richards	.06	.05	.02
620	*Jeff Robinson*	.10	.08	.04
621	Scot Thompson	.06	.05	.02
622	Manny Trillo	.08	.06	.03
623	Brad Wellman	.06	.05	.02
624	*Frank Williams*	.15	.11	.06
625	Joel Youngblood	.06	.05	.02
626	Cal Ripken (IA)	3.50	2.75	1.50
627	Mike Schmidt (IA)	1.50	1.25	.60
628	Giving the Signs (Sparky Anderson)	.08	.06	.03
629	A.L. Pitcher's Nightmare (Rickey Henderson, Dave Winfield)	1.00	.70	.40
630	N.L. Pitcher's Nightmare (Ryne Sandberg, Mike Schmidt)	2.00	1.50	.80
631	N.L. All-Stars (Gary Carter, Steve Garvey, Ozzie Smith, Darryl Strawberry)	.25	.20	.10
632	All-Star Game Winning Battery (Gary Carter, Charlie Lea)	.12	.09	.05
633	N.L. Pennant Clinchers (Steve Garvey, Goose Gossage)	.20	.15	.08
634	N.L. Rookie Phenoms (Dwight Gooden, Juan Samuel)	.25	.20	.10
635	Toronto's Big Guns (Willie Upshaw)	.08	.06	.03
636	Toronto's Big Guns (Lloyd Moseby)	.08	.06	.03
637	Holland (Al Holland)	.08	.06	.03
638	Tunnell (Lee Tunnell)	.08	.06	.03
639	Reggie Jackson (IA)	.75	.60	.30
640	Pete Rose (IA)	.75	.60	.30
641	Father & Son (Cal Ripken, Jr., Cal Ripken, Sr.)	3.00	2.25	1.25
642	Cubs Team	.08	.06	.03
643	1984's Two Perfect Games & One No-Hitter (Jack Morris, David Palmer, Mike Witt)	.15	.11	.06
644	Major League Prospect (Willie Lozado, Vic Mata)	.06	.05	.02
645	Major League Prospect (*Kelly Gruber*, Randy O'Neal)	.25	.20	.10
646	Major League Prospect (*Jose Roman* (FC), Joel Skinner)	.06	.05	.02
647	Major League Prospect (*Steve Kiefer* (FC), Danny Tartabull)	7.50	5.75	3.00
648	Major League Prospect (*Rob Deer*, Alejandro Sanchez)	.25	.20	.10
649	Major League Prospect (*Shawon Dunston*, Bill Hatcher)	1.00	.70	.40
650	Major League Prospect (*Mike Bielecki* (FC), Ron Robinson)	.15	.11	.06
651	Major League Prospect (*Zane Smith*, Paul Zuvella)	.30	.25	.12
652	Major League Prospect (*Glenn Davis*, Joe Hesketh)	.20	.15	.08
653	Major League Prospect (*Steve Jeltz* (FC), John Russell)	.10	.08	.04
654	Checklist 1-95	.06	.05	.02
655	Checklist 96-195	.06	.05	.02
656	Checklist 196-292	.06	.05	.02
657	Checklist 293-391	.06	.05	.02
658	Checklist 392-481	.06	.05	.02
659	Checklist 482-575	.06	.05	.02
660	Checklist 576-660	.06	.05	.02

1985 Fleer Update

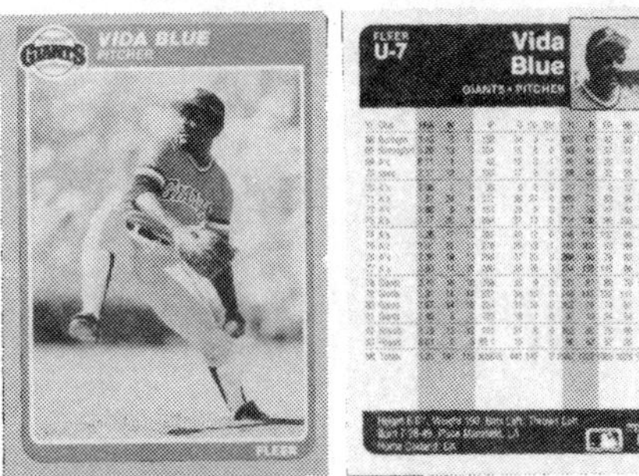

For the second straight year, Fleer issued a 132-card update set. The cards, which measure 2-1/2" by 3-1/2", portray players on their new teams and also includes rookies not depicted in the regular issue. The cards are identical in design to the 1985 Fleer set but are numbered U-1 through U-132. The set was issued with team logo stickers in a specially designed box and was available only through hobby dealers.

		MT	NR MT	EX
	Complete Set (132):	30.00	22.00	12.00
	Common Player:	.10	.08	.04
1	Don Aase	.10	.08	.04
2	Bill Almon	.10	.08	.04
3	Dusty Baker	.15	.11	.06
4	Dale Berra	.10	.08	.04
5	Karl Best (FC)	.10	.08	.04
6	Tim Birtsas (FC)	.10	.08	.04
7	Vida Blue	.20	.15	.08
8	Rich Bordi	.10	.08	.04
9	Daryl Boston (FC)	.20	.15	.08
10	Hubie Brooks	.20	.15	.08
11	Chris Brown (FC)	.10	.08	.04
12	Tom Browning (FC)	.35	.25	.14
13	Al Bumbry	.10	.08	.04
14	Tim Burke (FC)	.10	.08	.04
15	Ray Burris	.10	.08	.04
16	Jeff Burroughs	.15	.11	.06
17	Ivan Calderon (FC)	.15	.11	.06
18	Jeff Calhoun	.10	.08	.04
19	Bill Campbell	.10	.08	.04
20	Don Carman (FC)	.10	.08	.04
21	Gary Carter	.60	.45	.25
22	Bobby Castillo	.10	.08	.04
23	Bill Caudill	.10	.08	.04
24	Rick Cerone	.10	.08	.04
25	Jack Clark	.20	.15	.08
26	Pat Clements (FC)	.10	.08	.04
27	Stewart Cliburn (FC)	.10	.08	.04
28	Vince Coleman (FC)	.75	.60	.30
29	Dave Collins	.15	.11	.06
30	Fritz Connally	.10	.08	.04
31	Henry Cotto (FC)	.10	.08	.04
32	Danny Darwin	.10	.08	.04
33	Darren Daulton (FC)	20.00	15.00	8.00
34	Jerry Davis	.10	.08	.04
35	Brian Dayett	.10	.08	.04
36	Ken Dixon (FC)	.10	.08	.04
37	Tommy Dunbar	.10	.08	.04
38	Mariano Duncan (FC)	.80	.60	.30
39	Bob Fallon	.10	.08	.04
40	Brian Fisher (FC)	.15	.11	.06
41	Mike Fitzgerald	.10	.08	.04
42	Ray Fontenot	.10	.08	.04
43	Greg Gagne (FC)	.50	.40	.20
44	Oscar Gamble	.10	.08	.04
45	Jim Gott	.10	.08	.04
46	David Green	.10	.08	.04
47	Alfredo Griffin	.15	.11	.06
48	Ozzie Guillen (FC)	1.75	1.25	.70
49	Toby Harrah	.15	.11	.06
50	Ron Hassey	.10	.08	.04
51	Rickey Henderson	4.00	3.00	1.50
52	Steve Henderson	.10	.08	.04
53	George Hendrick	.15	.11	.06
54	Teddy Higuera (FC)	.15	.11	.06
55	Al Holland	.10	.08	.04
56	Burt Hooton	.15	.11	.06
57	Jay Howell	.15	.11	.06
58	LaMarr Hoyt	.10	.08	.04
59	Tim Hulett (FC)	.10	.08	.04
60	Bob James	.10	.08	.04
61	Cliff Johnson	.10	.08	.04
62	Howard Johnson	.90	.70	.35
63	Ruppert Jones	.10	.08	.04
64	Steve Kemp	.15	.11	.06
65	Bruce Kison	.10	.08	.04
66	Mike LaCoss	.10	.08	.04
67	Lee Lacy	.10	.08	.04
68	Dave LaPoint	.10	.08	.04
69	Gary Lavelle	.10	.08	.04
70	Vance Law	.10	.08	.04
71	Manny Lee (FC)	.10	.08	.04
72	Sixto Lezcano	.10	.08	.04
73	Tim Lollar	.10	.08	.04
74	Urbano Lugo (FC)	.10	.08	.04
75	Fred Lynn	.30	.25	.12
76	Steve Lyons (FC)	.15	.11	.06
77	Mickey Mahler	.10	.08	.04
78	Ron Mathis (FC)	.10	.08	.04
79	Len Matuszek	.10	.08	.04
80	Oddibe McDowell (FC)	.15	.11	.06
81	Roger McDowell (FC)	.50	.40	.20
82	Donnie Moore	.10	.08	.04
83	Ron Musselman	.10	.08	.04
84	Al Oliver	.25	.20	.10
85	Joe Orsulak (FC)	.20	.15	.08
86	Dan Pasqua (FC)	.60	.45	.25
87	Chris Pittaro (FC)	.10	.08	.04
88	Rick Reuschel	.10	.08	.04
89	Earnie Riles (FC)	.10	.08	.04
90	Jerry Royster	.10	.08	.04
91	Dave Rozema	.10	.08	.04
92	Dave Rucker	.10	.08	.04
93	Vern Ruhle	.10	.08	.04
94	Mark Salas (FC)	.10	.08	.04
95	Luis Salazar	.10	.08	.04
96	Joe Sambito	.10	.08	.04
97	Billy Sample	.10	.08	.04
98	Alex Sanchez	.10	.08	.04
99	Calvin Schiraldi (FC)	.25	.20	.10
100	Rick Schu (FC)	.10	.08	.04
101	Larry Sheets (FC)	.10	.08	.04
102	Ron Shepherd	.10	.08	.04
103	Nelson Simmons (FC)	.10	.08	.04
104	Don Slaught	.10	.08	.04
105	Roy Smalley	.10	.08	.04
106	Lonnie Smith	.15	.11	.06
107	Nate Snell (FC)	.10	.08	.04
108	Lary Sorensen	.10	.08	.04
109	Chris Speier	.10	.08	.04
110	Mike Stenhouse	.10	.08	.04
111	Tim Stoddard	.10	.08	.04
112	John Stuper	.10	.08	.04
113	Jim Sundberg	.10	.08	.04
114	Bruce Sutter	.15	.11	.06
115	Don Sutton	.60	.45	.25
116	Bruce Tanner (FC)	.10	.08	.04
117	Kent Tekulve	.10	.08	.04
118	Walt Terrell	.10	.08	.04
119	Mickey Tettleton (FC)	8.00	6.00	3.25
120	Rich Thompson	.10	.08	.04
121	Louis Thornton (FC)	.10	.08	.04
122	Alex Trevino	.10	.08	.04
123	John Tudor	.30	.25	.12
124	Jose Uribe (FC)	.10	.08	.04
125	Dave Valle (FC)	.20	.15	.08
126	Dave Von Ohlen	.10	.08	.04
127	Curt Wardle	.10	.08	.04
128	U.L. Washington	.10	.08	.04
129	Ed Whitson	.10	.08	.04
130	Herm Winningham (FC)	.10	.08	.04
131	Rich Yett (FC)	.10	.08	.04
132	Checklist	.10	.08	.04

Values quoted in this guide reflect the retail price of a card – the price a collector can expect to pay when buying a card from a dealer. The wholesale price – that which a collector can expect to receive from a dealer when selling cards – will be significantly lower, depending on desirability and condition.

1985 Fleer Stickers

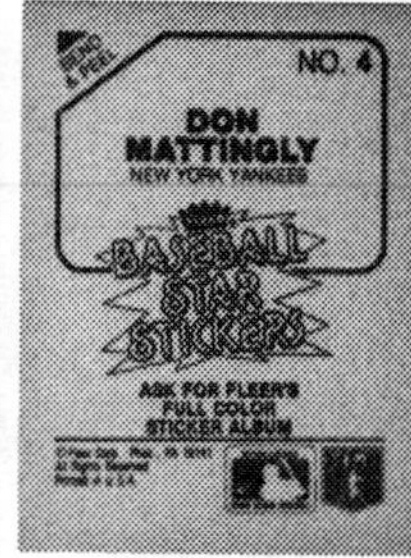

The 1985 Fleer sticker set consists of 126 player stickers, each measuring 2-1/2" by 1-15/16". Numbered on the back, the stickers were designed to be put in a special album.

		MT	NR MT	EX
Complete Set:		15.00	11.00	6.00
Common Player:		.03	.02	.01
Sticker Album:		1.00	.70	.40
1	Pete Rose	.40	.30	.15
2	Pete Rose	.30	.25	.12
3	Pete Rose	.30	.25	.12
4	Don Mattingly	.90	.70	.35
5	Dave Winfield	.20	.15	.08
6	Wade Boggs	.50	.40	.20
7	Buddy Bell	.06	.05	.02
8	Tony Gwynn	.25	.20	.10
9	Lee Lacy	.03	.02	.01
10	Chili Davis	.06	.05	.02
11	Ryne Sandberg	.75	.60	.30
12	Tony Armas	.04	.03	.02
13	Jim Rice	.20	.15	.08
14	Dave Kingman	.06	.05	.02
15	Alvin Davis	.12	.09	.05
16	Gary Carter	.20	.15	.08
17	Mike Schmidt	.40	.30	.15
18	Dale Murphy	.30	.25	.12
19	Ron Cey	.06	.05	.02
20	Eddie Murray	.25	.20	.10
21	Harold Baines	.10	.08	.04
22	Kirk Gibson	.15	.11	.06
23	Jim Rice	.20	.15	.08
24	Gary Matthews	.06	.05	.02
25	Keith Hernandez	.15	.11	.06
26	Gary Carter	.20	.15	.08
27	George Hendrick	.04	.03	.02
28	Tony Armas	.04	.03	.02
29	Dave Kingman	.06	.05	.02
30	Dwayne Murphy	.04	.03	.02
31	Lance Parrish	.12	.09	.05
32	Andre Thornton	.04	.03	.02
33	Dale Murphy	.30	.25	.12
34	Mike Schmidt	.40	.30	.15
35	Gary Carter	.20	.15	.08
36	Darryl Strawberry	.30	.25	.12
37	Don Mattingly	.90	.70	.35
38	Larry Parrish	.04	.03	.02
39	George Bell	.20	.15	.08
40	Dwight Evans	.06	.05	.02
41	Cal Ripken, Jr.	.75	.60	.30
42	Tim Raines	.20	.15	.08
43	Johnny Ray	.06	.05	.02
44	Juan Samuel	.08	.06	.03
45	Ryne Sandberg	.75	.60	.30
46	Mike Easler	.04	.03	.02
47	Andre Thornton	.04	.03	.02
48	Dave Kingman	.06	.05	.02
49	Don Baylor	.08	.06	.03
50	Rusty Staub	.06	.05	.02
51	Steve Braun	.03	.02	.01
52	Kevin Bass	.06	.05	.02
53	Greg Gross	.03	.02	.01
54	Rickey Henderson	.25	.20	.10
55	Dave Collins	.03	.02	.01
56	Brett Butler	.04	.03	.02
57	Gary Pettis	.04	.03	.02
58	Tim Raines	.20	.15	.08
59	Juan Samuel	.08	.06	.03
60	Alan Wiggins	.03	.02	.01
61	Lonnie Smith	.03	.02	.01
62	Eddie Murray	.25	.20	.10
63	Eddie Murray	.25	.20	.10
64	Eddie Murray	.25	.20	.10
65	Eddie Murray	.25	.20	.10
66	Eddie Murray	.25	.20	.10
67	Eddie Murray	.25	.20	.10
68	Tom Seaver	.20	.15	.08
69	Tom Seaver	.20	.15	.08
70	Tom Seaver	.20	.15	.08
71	Tom Seaver	.20	.15	.08
72	Tom Seaver	.20	.15	.08
73	Tom Seaver	.20	.15	.08
74	Mike Schmidt	.30	.25	.12
75	Mike Schmidt	.30	.25	.12
76	Mike Schmidt	.30	.25	.12
77	Mike Schmidt	.30	.25	.12
78	Mike Schmidt	.30	.25	.12
79	Mike Schmidt	.30	.25	.12
80	Mike Boddicker	.04	.03	.02
81	Bert Blyleven	.08	.06	.03
82	Jack Morris	.12	.09	.05
83	Dan Petry	.04	.03	.02
84	Frank Viola	.06	.05	.02
85	Joaquin Andujar	.04	.03	.02
86	Mario Soto	.04	.03	.02
87	Dwight Gooden	.60	.45	.25
88	Joe Niekro	.06	.05	.02
89	Rick Sutcliffe	.08	.06	.03
90	Mike Boddicker	.04	.03	.02
91	Dave Stieb	.06	.05	.02
92	Bert Blyleven	.08	.06	.03
93	Phil Niekro	.12	.09	.05
94	Alejandro Pena	.03	.02	.01
95	Dwight Gooden	.30	.25	.12
96	Orel Hershiser	.15	.11	.06
97	Rick Rhoden	.04	.03	.02
98	John Candelaria	.04	.03	.02
99	Dan Quisenberry	.06	.05	.02
100	Bil Caudill	.03	.02	.01
101	Willie Hernandez	.04	.03	.02
102	Dave Righetti	.10	.08	.04
103	Ron Davis	.03	.02	.01
104	Bruce Sutter	.08	.06	.03
105	Lee Smith	.06	.05	.02
106	Jesse Orosco	.04	.03	.02
107	Al Holland	.03	.02	.01
108	Goose Gossage	.08	.06	.03
109	Mark Langston	.10	.08	.04
110	Dave Stieb	.06	.05	.02
111	Mike Witt	.06	.05	.02
112	Bert Blyleven	.08	.06	.03
113	Dwight Gooden	.30	.25	.12
114	Fernando Valenzuela	.15	.11	.06
115	Nolan Ryan	.15	.11	.06
116	Mario Soto	.04	.03	.02
117	Ron Darling	.08	.06	.03
118	Dan Gladden	.04	.03	.02
119	Jeff Stone	.04	.03	.02
120	John Franco	.06	.05	.02
121	Barbaro Garbey	.03	.02	.01
122	Kirby Puckett	.20	.15	.08
123	Roger Clemens	.60	.45	.25
124	Bret Saberhagen	.20	.15	.08
125	Sparky Anderson	.03	.02	.01
126	Dick Williams	.03	.02	.01

1985 Fleer Limited Edition

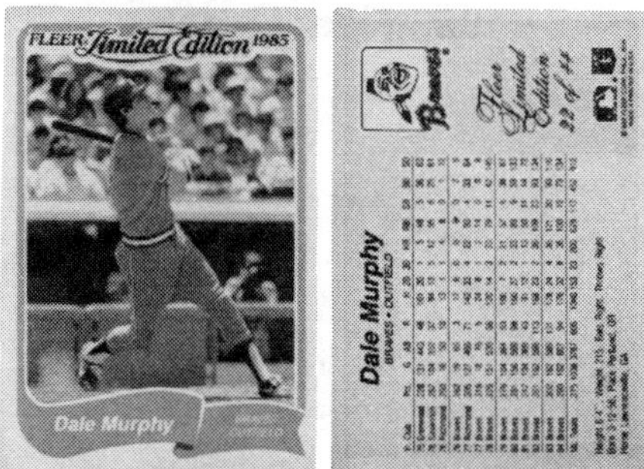

The 1985 Fleer Limited Edition 44-card set was distributed through McCrory's, J.J. Newbury, McClellan, Kress, YDC, and Green stores. The cards, which are the standard 2-1/2" by 3-1/2" size, have full-color photos inside a red and yellow frame. The card backs are set in black type against two different shades of yellow and contain the player's personal and statistical information. The set was issued in a specially designed box which carried the complete checklist for the set on the back. Six team logo stickers were also included with the set.

		MT	NR MT	EX
Complete Set:		6.00	4.50	2.50
Common Player:		.05	.04	.02
1	Buddy Bell	.07	.05	.03
2	Bert Blyleven	.10	.08	.04
3	Wade Boggs	.70	.50	.30
4	George Brett	.70	.50	.30
5	Rod Carew	.30	.25	.12
6	Steve Carlton	.25	.20	.10
7	Alvin Davis	.05	.04	.02
8	Andre Dawson	.15	.11	.06
9	Steve Garvey	.25	.20	.10
10	Goose Gossage	.07	.05	.03
11	Tony Gwynn	.20	.15	.08
12	Keith Hernandez	.07	.05	.03
13	Kent Hrbek	.15	.11	.06
14	Reggie Jackson	.30	.25	.12
15	Dave Kingman	.05	.04	.02
16	Ron Kittle	.05	.04	.02
17	Mark Langston	.10	.08	.04
18	Jeff Leonard	.05	.04	.02
19	Bill Madlock	.07	.05	.03
20	Don Mattingly	.70	.50	.30
21	Jack Morris	.15	.11	.06
22	Dale Murphy	.30	.25	.12
23	Eddie Murray	.25	.20	.10
24	Tony Pena	.07	.05	.03
25	Dan Quisenberry	.07	.05	.03
26	Tim Raines	.15	.11	.06
27	Jim Rice	.25	.20	.10
28	Cal Ripken, Jr.	.70	.50	.30
29	Pete Rose	.60	.45	.25
30	Nolan Ryan	1.25	.90	.50
31	Ryne Sandberg	.70	.50	.30
32	Steve Sax	.15	.11	.06
33	Mike Schmidt	.70	.50	.30
34	Tom Seaver	.50	.40	.20
35	Ozzie Smith	.20	.15	.08
36	Mario Soto	.05	.04	.02
37	Dave Stieb	.10	.08	.04
38	Darryl Strawberry	.30	.25	.12
39	Rick Sutcliffe	.10	.08	.04
40	Alan Trammell	.15	.11	.06
41	Willie Upshaw	.05	.04	.02
42	Fernando Valenzuela	.07	.05	.03
43	Dave Winfield	.25	.20	.10
44	Robin Yount	.70	.50	.30

1986 Fleer

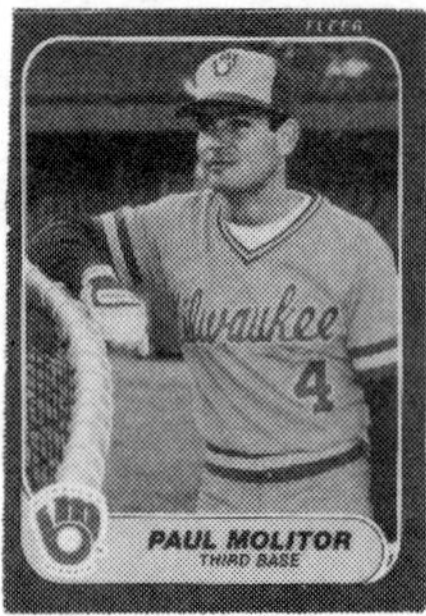

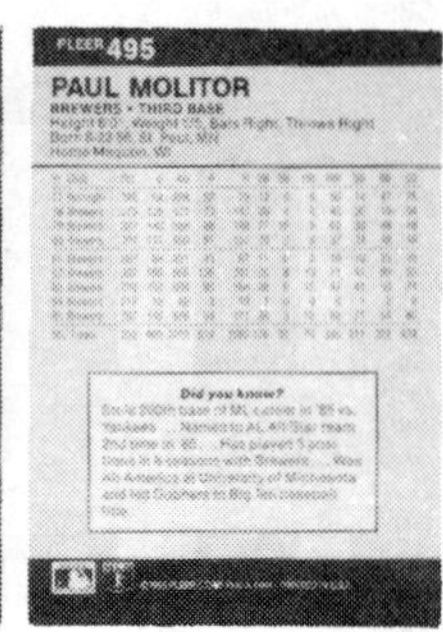

The 1986 Fleer set contains 660 color photos, with each card measuring 2-1/2" by 3-1/2" in size. The card fronts include the word "Fleer," the player's team logo, and a player picture enclosed by a dark blue border. The card reverses are minus the black and white photo that was included in past Fleer efforts. Player biographical and statistical information appear in black and yellow ink on white stock. As in 1985, Fleer devoted ten cards, entitled "Major League Prospects," to twenty promising rookie players. The 1986 set, as in the previous four years was issued with team logo stickers.

		MT	NR MT	EX
Complete Set (660):		125.00	94.00	50.00
Common Player:		.06	.05	.02
1	Steve Balboni	.08	.06	.03
2	Joe Beckwith	.06	.05	.02
3	Buddy Biancalana	.06	.05	.02
4	Bud Black	.06	.05	.02
5	George Brett	2.25	1.75	.90
6	Onix Concepcion	.06	.05	.02
7	Steve Farr	.08	.06	.03
8	Mark Gubicza	.12	.09	.05
9	Dane Iorg	.06	.05	.02
10	Danny Jackson	.20	.15	.08
11	Lynn Jones	.06	.05	.02
12	Mike Jones	.06	.05	.02
13	Charlie Leibrandt	.08	.06	.03
14	Hal McRae	.10	.08	.04
15	Omar Moreno	.06	.05	.02
16	Darryl Motley	.06	.05	.02
17	Jorge Orta	.06	.05	.02
18	Dan Quisenberry	.08	.06	.03
19	Bret Saberhagen	.40	.30	.15
20	Pat Sheridan	.06	.05	.02
21	Lonnie Smith	.08	.06	.03
22	Jim Sundberg	.08	.06	.03
23	John Wathan	.08	.06	.03
24	Frank White	.10	.08	.04
25	Willie Wilson	.12	.09	.05
26	Joaquin Andujar	.08	.06	.03
27	Steve Braun	.06	.05	.02
28	Bill Campbell	.06	.05	.02
29	Cesar Cedeno	.10	.08	.04
30	Jack Clark	.20	.15	.08
31	*Vince Coleman*	.30	.25	.12
32	Danny Cox	.10	.08	.04
33	Ken Dayley	.06	.05	.02
34	Ivan DeJesus	.06	.05	.02
35	Bob Forsch	.08	.06	.03
36	Brian Harper	.06	.05	.02
37	Tom Herr	.10	.08	.04
38	Ricky Horton	.08	.06	.03
39	Kurt Kepshire	.06	.05	.02
40	Jeff Lahti	.06	.05	.02
41	Tito Landrum	.06	.05	.02
42	Willie McGee	.15	.11	.06
43	Tom Nieto	.06	.05	.02
44	Terry Pendleton	1.00	.70	.40
45	Darrell Porter	.08	.06	.03
46	Ozzie Smith	1.00	.70	.40
47	John Tudor	.10	.08	.04
48	Andy Van Slyke	.60	.45	.25
49	*Todd Worrell* (FC)	.40	.30	.15
50	Jim Acker	.06	.05	.02
51	Doyle Alexander	.10	.08	.04
52	Jesse Barfield	.20	.15	.08
53	George Bell	.15	.11	.06
54	Jeff Burroughs	.08	.06	.03
55	Bill Caudill	.06	.05	.02
56	Jim Clancy	.08	.06	.03
57	Tony Fernandez	.20	.15	.08
58	Tom Filer	.06	.05	.02
59	Damaso Garcia	.06	.05	.02
60	Tom Henke (FC)	.15	.11	.06

61	Garth Iorg	.06	.05	.02
62	Cliff Johnson	.06	.05	.02
63	Jimmy Key	.50	.40	.20
64	Dennis Lamp	.06	.05	.02
65	Gary Lavelle	.06	.05	.02
66	Buck Martinez	.06	.05	.02
67	Lloyd Moseby	.10	.08	.04
68	Rance Mulliniks	.06	.05	.02
69	Al Oliver	.10	.08	.04
70	Dave Stieb	.12	.09	.05
71	Louis Thornton	.06	.05	.02
72	Willie Upshaw	.08	.06	.03
73	Ernie Whitt	.08	.06	.03
74	*Rick Aguilera* (FC)	1.00	.70	.40
75	Wally Backman	.08	.06	.03
76	Gary Carter	.25	.20	.10
77	Ron Darling	.15	.11	.06
78	*Len Dykstra*	7.00	5.25	2.75
79	Sid Fernandez	.12	.09	.05
80	George Foster	.15	.11	.06
81	Dwight Gooden	1.50	1.25	.60
82	Tom Gorman	.06	.05	.02
83	Danny Heep	.06	.05	.02
84	Keith Hernandez	.15	.11	.06
85	Howard Johnson	.20	.15	.08
86	Ray Knight	.08	.06	.03
87	Terry Leach	.08	.06	.03
88	Ed Lynch	.06	.05	.02
89	*Roger McDowell* (FC)	.40	.30	.15
90	Jesse Orosco	.08	.06	.03
91	Tom Paciorek	.06	.05	.02
92	Ronn Reynolds	.06	.05	.02
93	Rafael Santana	.06	.05	.02
94	Doug Sisk	.06	.05	.02
95	Rusty Staub	.10	.08	.04
96	Darryl Strawberry	.90	.70	.35
97	Mookie Wilson	.10	.08	.04
98	Neil Allen	.06	.05	.02
99	Don Baylor	.12	.09	.05
100	Dale Berra	.06	.05	.02
101	Rich Bordi	.06	.05	.02
102	Marty Bystrom	.06	.05	.02
103	Joe Cowley	.06	.05	.02
104	*Brian Fisher*	.08	.06	.03
105	Ken Griffey	.10	.08	.04
106	Ron Guidry	.20	.15	.08
107	Ron Hassey	.06	.05	.02
108	Rickey Henderson	2.00	1.50	.80
109	Don Mattingly	2.50	2.00	1.00
110	Bobby Meacham	.06	.05	.02
111	John Montefusco	.06	.05	.02
112	Phil Niekro	.25	.20	.10
113	Mike Pagliarulo	.20	.15	.08
114	Dan Pasqua	.08	.06	.03
115	Willie Randolph	.10	.08	.04
116	Dave Righetti	.08	.06	.03
117	Andre Robertson	.06	.05	.02
118	Billy Sample	.06	.05	.02
119	Bob Shirley	.06	.05	.02
120	Ed Whitson	.06	.05	.02
121	Dave Winfield	1.50	1.25	.60
122	Butch Wynegar	.06	.05	.02
123	Dave Anderson	.06	.05	.02
124	Bob Bailor	.06	.05	.02
125	Greg Brock	.08	.06	.03
126	Enos Cabell	.06	.05	.02
127	Bobby Castillo	.06	.05	.02
128	Carlos Diaz	.06	.05	.02
129	*Mariano Duncan*	.15	.11	.06
130	Pedro Guerrero	.08	.06	.03
131	Orel Hershiser	.30	.25	.12
132	Rick Honeycutt	.06	.05	.02
133	Ken Howell	.06	.05	.02
134	Ken Landreaux	.06	.05	.02
135	Bill Madlock	.12	.09	.05
136	Candy Maldonado	.10	.08	.04
137	Mike Marshall	.15	.11	.06
138	Len Matuszek	.06	.05	.02
139	Tom Niedenfuer	.08	.06	.03
140	Alejandro Pena	.08	.06	.03
141	Jerry Reuss	.08	.06	.03
142	Bill Russell	.08	.06	.03
143	Steve Sax	.10	.08	.04
144	Mike Scioscia	.08	.06	.03
145	Fernando Valenzuela	.10	.08	.04
146	Bob Welch	.12	.09	.05
147	Terry Whitfield	.06	.05	.02
148	Juan Beniquez	.06	.05	.02
149	Bob Boone	.08	.06	.03
150	John Candelaria	.10	.08	.04
151	Rod Carew	.70	.50	.30
152	*Stewart Cliburn* (FC)	.08	.06	.03
153	Doug DeCinces	.10	.08	.04
154	Brian Downing	.08	.06	.03
155	Ken Forsch	.06	.05	.02
156	Craig Gerber	.06	.05	.02
157	Bobby Grich	.10	.08	.04
158	George Hendrick	.08	.06	.03
159	Al Holland	.06	.05	.02
160	Reggie Jackson	1.25	.90	.50
161	Ruppert Jones	.06	.05	.02
162	*Urbano Lugo*	.08	.06	.03
163	*Kirk McCaskill* (FC)	.35	.25	.14
164	Donnie Moore	.06	.05	.02
165	Gary Pettis	.06	.05	.02
166	Ron Romanick	.06	.05	.02
167	Dick Schofield	.06	.05	.02
168	Daryl Sconiers	.06	.05	.02
169	Jim Slaton	.06	.05	.02
170	Don Sutton	.25	.20	.10
171	Mike Witt	.10	.08	.04
172	Buddy Bell	.10	.08	.04
173	Tom Browning	.30	.25	.12
174	Dave Concepcion	.12	.09	.05
175	Eric Davis	1.00	.70	.40
176	Bo Diaz	.08	.06	.03
177	Nick Esasky	.08	.06	.03
178	John Franco	.12	.09	.05
179	Tom Hume	.06	.05	.02
180	Wayne Krenchicki	.06	.05	.02
181	Andy McGaffigan	.06	.05	.02
182	Eddie Milner	.06	.05	.02
183	Ron Oester	.06	.05	.02
184	Dave Parker	.20	.15	.08
185	Frank Pastore	.06	.05	.02
186	Tony Perez	.15	.11	.06
187	Ted Power	.08	.06	.03
188	Joe Price	.06	.05	.02
189	Gary Redus	.06	.05	.02
190	Ron Robinson	.08	.06	.03
191	Pete Rose	.70	.50	.30
192	Mario Soto	.08	.06	.03
193	John Stuper	.06	.05	.02
194	Jay Tibbs	.06	.05	.02
195	Dave Van Gorder	.06	.05	.02
196	Max Venable	.06	.05	.02
197	Juan Agosto	.06	.05	.02
198	Harold Baines	.15	.11	.06
199	Floyd Bannister	.10	.08	.04
200	Britt Burns	.06	.05	.02
201	Julio Cruz	.06	.05	.02
202	*Joel Davis* (FC)	.08	.06	.03
203	Richard Dotson	.10	.08	.04
204	Carlton Fisk	.50	.40	.20
205	Scott Fletcher	.08	.06	.03
206	*Ozzie Guillen*	.80	.60	.30
207	Jerry Hairston	.06	.05	.02
208	Tim Hulett	.08	.06	.03
209	Bob James	.06	.05	.02
210	Ron Kittle	.10	.08	.04
211	Rudy Law	.06	.05	.02
212	Bryan Little	.06	.05	.02
213	Gene Nelson	.06	.05	.02
214	Reid Nichols	.06	.05	.02
215	Luis Salazar	.06	.05	.02
216	Tom Seaver	1.00	.70	.40
217	Dan Spillner	.06	.05	.02
218	Bruce Tanner	.06	.05	.02
219	Greg Walker	.10	.08	.04
220	Dave Wehrmeister	.06	.05	.02
221	Juan Berenguer	.06	.05	.02
222	Dave Bergman	.06	.05	.02
223	Tom Brookens	.06	.05	.02
224	Darrell Evans	.12	.09	.05
225	Barbaro Garbey	.06	.05	.02
226	Kirk Gibson	.15	.11	.06
227	John Grubb	.06	.05	.02
228	Willie Hernandez	.08	.06	.03
229	Larry Herndon	.08	.06	.03
230	Chet Lemon	.08	.06	.03
231	Aurelio Lopez	.06	.05	.02
232	Jack Morris	.12	.09	.05
233	Randy O'Neal	.06	.05	.02
234	Lance Parrish	.08	.06	.03
235	Dan Petry	.08	.06	.03
236	Alex Sanchez	.06	.05	.02
237	Bill Scherrer	.06	.05	.02
238	Nelson Simmons	.06	.05	.02
239	Frank Tanana	.10	.08	.04
240	Walt Terrell	.08	.06	.03
241	Alan Trammell	.30	.25	.12
242	Lou Whitaker	.30	.25	.12
243	Milt Wilcox	.06	.05	.02
244	Hubie Brooks	.10	.08	.04
245	*Tim Burke* (FC)	.15	.11	.06
246	Andre Dawson	.30	.25	.12
247	Mike Fitzgerald	.06	.05	.02
248	Terry Francona	.06	.05	.02
249	Bill Gullickson	.06	.05	.02
250	Joe Hesketh	.06	.05	.02
251	Bill Laskey	.06	.05	.02
252	Vance Law	.08	.06	.03
253	Charlie Lea	.06	.05	.02
254	Gary Lucas	.06	.05	.02
255	David Palmer	.06	.05	.02
256	Tim Raines	.35	.25	.14
257	Jeff Reardon	.20	.15	.08
258	Bert Roberge	.06	.05	.02
259	Dan Schatzeder	.06	.05	.02
260	Bryn Smith	.06	.05	.02
261	Randy St. Claire (FC)	.08	.06	.03
262	Scot Thompson	.06	.05	.02
263	Tim Wallach	.12	.09	.05
264	U.L. Washington	.06	.05	.02
265	*Mitch Webster* (FC)	.08	.06	.03
266	*Herm Winningham*	.06	.05	.02
267	*Floyd Youmans* (FC)	.06	.05	.02
268	Don Aase	.06	.05	.02
269	Mike Boddicker	.08	.06	.03
270	Rich Dauer	.06	.05	.02
271	Storm Davis	.10	.08	.04
272	Rick Dempsey	.08	.06	.03
273	Ken Dixon	.06	.05	.02
274	Jim Dwyer	.06	.05	.02
275	Mike Flanagan	.10	.08	.04
276	Wayne Gross	.06	.05	.02
277	Lee Lacy	.06	.05	.02
278	Fred Lynn	.10	.08	.04
279	Tippy Martinez	.06	.05	.02
280	Dennis Martinez	.08	.06	.03
281	Scott McGregor	.08	.06	.03
282	Eddie Murray	1.00	.70	.40
283	Floyd Rayford	.06	.05	.02
284	Cal Ripken, Jr.	5.00	3.75	2.00
285	Gary Roenicke	.06	.05	.02
286	Larry Sheets	.08	.06	.03
287	John Shelby	.06	.05	.02
288	Nate Snell	.06	.05	.02
289	Sammy Stewart	.06	.05	.02
290	Alan Wiggins	.06	.05	.02
291	Mike Young	.06	.05	.02
292	Alan Ashby	.06	.05	.02
293	Mark Bailey	.06	.05	.02
294	Kevin Bass	.10	.08	.04
295	Jeff Calhoun	.06	.05	.02
296	Jose Cruz	.10	.08	.04
297	Glenn Davis	.10	.08	.04
298	Bill Dawley	.06	.05	.02
299	Frank DiPino	.06	.05	.02
300	Bill Doran	.10	.08	.04
301	Phil Garner	.08	.06	.03
302	*Jeff Heathcock* (FC)	.06	.05	.02
303	*Charlie Kerfeld* (FC)	.06	.05	.02
304	Bob Knepper	.08	.06	.03
305	Ron Mathis	.06	.05	.02
306	Jerry Mumphrey	.06	.05	.02
307	Jim Pankovits	.06	.05	.02
308	Terry Puhl	.06	.05	.02
309	Craig Reynolds	.06	.05	.02
310	Nolan Ryan	6.00	4.50	2.50
311	Mike Scott	.15	.11	.06
312	Dave Smith	.08	.06	.03
313	Dickie Thon	.08	.06	.03
314	Denny Walling	.06	.05	.02
315	Kurt Bevacqua	.06	.05	.02
316	Al Bumbry	.06	.05	.02
317	Jerry Davis	.06	.05	.02
318	Luis DeLeon	.06	.05	.02
319	Dave Dravecky	.08	.06	.03
320	Tim Flannery	.06	.05	.02
321	Steve Garvey	.30	.25	.12
322	Goose Gossage	.20	.15	.08
323	Tony Gwynn	2.75	2.00	1.00
324	Andy Hawkins	.06	.05	.02
325	LaMarr Hoyt	.06	.05	.02
326	Roy Lee Jackson	.06	.05	.02
327	Terry Kennedy	.08	.06	.03
328	Craig Lefferts	.06	.05	.02
329	Carmelo Martinez	.08	.06	.03
330	*Lance McCullers* (FC)	.25	.20	.10
331	Kevin McReynolds	.12	.09	.05
332	Graig Nettles	.15	.11	.06
333	Jerry Royster	.06	.05	.02
334	Eric Show	.08	.06	.03
335	Tim Stoddard	.06	.05	.02
336	Garry Templeton	.08	.06	.03
337	Mark Thurmond	.06	.05	.02
338	Ed Wojna	.06	.05	.02
339	Tony Armas	.08	.06	.03
340	Marty Barrett	.10	.08	.04
341	Wade Boggs	2.25	1.75	.90
342	Dennis Boyd	.08	.06	.03
343	Bill Buckner	.12	.09	.05
344	Mark Clear	.06	.05	.02
345	Roger Clemens	9.00	6.75	3.50
346	Steve Crawford	.06	.05	.02
347	Mike Easler	.08	.06	.03
348	Dwight Evans	.12	.09	.05
349	Rich Gedman	.10	.08	.04
350	Jackie Gutierrez	.06	.05	.02
351	Glenn Hoffman	.06	.05	.02
352	Bruce Hurst	.12	.09	.05
353	Bruce Kison	.06	.05	.02
354	Tim Lollar	.06	.05	.02
355	Steve Lyons	.08	.06	.03
356	Al Nipper	.08	.06	.03
357	Bob Ojeda	.08	.06	.03
358	Jim Rice	.12	.09	.05
359	Bob Stanley	.06	.05	.02
360	Mike Trujillo	.06	.05	.02
361	Thad Bosley	.06	.05	.02
362	Warren Brusstar	.06	.05	.02
363	Ron Cey	.10	.08	.04
364	Jody Davis	.10	.08	.04
365	Bob Dernier	.06	.05	.02
366	Shawon Dunston	.15	.11	.06
367	Leon Durham	.08	.06	.03
368	Dennis Eckersley	.20	.15	.08
369	Ray Fontenot	.06	.05	.02
370	George Frazier	.06	.05	.02
371	Bill Hatcher	.10	.08	.04
372	Dave Lopes	.08	.06	.03
373	Gary Matthews	.10	.08	.04
374	Ron Meredith	.06	.05	.02
375	Keith Moreland	.08	.06	.03
376	Reggie Patterson	.06	.05	.02
377	Dick Ruthven	.06	.05	.02
378	Ryne Sandberg	4.00	3.00	1.50
379	Scott Sanderson	.06	.05	.02
380	Lee Smith	.50	.40	.20
381	Lary Sorensen	.06	.05	.02
382	Chris Speier	.06	.05	.02
383	Rick Sutcliffe	.12	.09	.05
384	Steve Trout	.06	.05	.02
385	Gary Woods	.06	.05	.02
386	Bert Blyleven	.15	.11	.06
387	Tom Brunansky	.12	.09	.05
388	Randy Bush	.06	.05	.02
389	John Butcher	.06	.05	.02
390	Ron Davis	.06	.05	.02
391	Dave Engle	.06	.05	.02
392	Frank Eufemia	.06	.05	.02
393	Pete Filson	.06	.05	.02
394	Gary Gaetti	.20	.15	.08
395	Greg Gagne	.10	.08	.04
396	Mickey Hatcher	.06	.05	.02
397	Kent Hrbek	.20	.15	.08
398	Tim Laudner	.06	.05	.02
399	Rick Lysander	.06	.05	.02
400	Dave Meier	.06	.05	.02
401	Kirby Puckett	10.00	7.50	4.00
402	Mark Salas	.08	.06	.03
403	Ken Schrom	.06	.05	.02
404	Roy Smalley	.06	.05	.02
405	Mike Smithson	.06	.05	.02
406	Mike Stenhouse	.06	.05	.02
407	Tim Teufel	.06	.05	.02
408	Frank Viola	.15	.11	.06
409	Ron Washington	.06	.05	.02
410	Keith Atherton	.06	.05	.02
411	Dusty Baker	.08	.06	.03
412	*Tim Birtsas*	.06	.05	.02
413	Bruce Bochte	.06	.05	.02
414	Chris Codiroli	.06	.05	.02

No.	Player	MT	NR MT	EX
415	Dave Collins	.08	.06	.03
416	Mike Davis	.08	.06	.03
417	Alfredo Griffin	.08	.06	.03
418	Mike Heath	.06	.05	.02
419	Steve Henderson	.06	.05	.02
420	Donnie Hill	.06	.05	.02
421	Jay Howell	.08	.06	.03
422	Tommy John	.20	.15	.08
423	Dave Kingman	.15	.11	.06
424	Bill Krueger	.06	.05	.02
425	Rick Langford	.06	.05	.02
426	Carney Lansford	.10	.08	.04
427	Steve McCatty	.06	.05	.02
428	Dwayne Murphy	.06	.05	.02
429	*Steve Ontiveros* (FC)	.06	.05	.02
430	Tony Phillips	.06	.05	.02
431	Jose Rijo	.25	.20	.10
432	*Mickey Tettleton*	3.50	2.75	1.50
433	Luis Aguayo	.06	.05	.02
434	Larry Andersen	.06	.05	.02
435	Steve Carlton	.60	.45	.25
436	*Don Carman*	.10	.08	.04
437	Tim Corcoran	.06	.05	.02
438	*Darren Daulton*	5.00	3.75	2.00
439	John Denny	.06	.05	.02
440	Tom Foley	.06	.05	.02
441	Greg Gross	.06	.05	.02
442	Kevin Gross	.08	.06	.03
443	Von Hayes	.10	.08	.04
444	Charles Hudson	.06	.05	.02
445	Garry Maddox	.08	.06	.03
446	Shane Rawley	.10	.08	.04
447	Dave Rucker	.06	.05	.02
448	John Russell	.06	.05	.02
449	Juan Samuel	.12	.09	.05
450	Mike Schmidt	2.00	1.50	.80
451	Rick Schu	.08	.06	.03
452	Dave Shipanoff	.06	.05	.02
453	Dave Stewart	.12	.09	.05
454	Jeff Stone	.06	.05	.02
455	Kent Tekulve	.08	.06	.03
456	Ozzie Virgil	.06	.05	.02
457	Glenn Wilson	.08	.06	.03
458	Jim Beattie	.06	.05	.02
459	Karl Best	.06	.05	.02
460	Barry Bonnell	.06	.05	.02
461	Phil Bradley	.08	.06	.03
462	*Ivan Calderon*	.08	.06	.03
463	Al Cowens	.06	.05	.02
464	Alvin Davis	.06	.05	.02
465	Dave Henderson	.10	.08	.04
466	Bob Kearney	.06	.05	.02
467	Mark Langston	.30	.25	.12
468	Bob Long	.06	.05	.02
469	Mike Moore	.06	.05	.02
470	Edwin Nunez	.06	.05	.02
471	Spike Owen	.06	.05	.02
472	Jack Perconte	.06	.05	.02
473	Jim Presley	.06	.05	.02
474	Donnie Scott	.06	.05	.02
475	Bill Swift (FC)	.12	.09	.05
476	Danny Tartabull	1.50	1.25	.60
477	Gorman Thomas	.06	.05	.02
478	Roy Thomas	.06	.05	.02
479	Ed Vande Berg	.06	.05	.02
480	Frank Wills	.06	.05	.02
481	Matt Young	.06	.05	.02
482	Ray Burris	.06	.05	.02
483	Jaime Cocanower	.06	.05	.02
484	Cecil Cooper	.12	.09	.05
485	Danny Darwin	.06	.05	.02
486	Rollie Fingers	.20	.15	.08
487	Jim Gantner	.08	.06	.03
488	Bob L. Gibson	.06	.05	.02
489	Moose Haas	.06	.05	.02
490	*Teddy Higuera*	.10	.08	.04
491	Paul Householder	.06	.05	.02
492	Pete Ladd	.06	.05	.02
493	Rick Manning	.06	.05	.02
494	Bob McClure	.06	.05	.02
495	Paul Molitor	1.75	1.25	.70
496	Charlie Moore	.06	.05	.02
497	Ben Oglivie	.08	.06	.03
498	Randy Ready	.06	.05	.02
499	*Earnie Riles*	.08	.06	.03
500	Ed Romero	.06	.05	.02
501	Bill Schroeder	.06	.05	.02
502	Ray Searage	.06	.05	.02
503	Ted Simmons	.12	.09	.05
504	Pete Vuckovich	.08	.06	.03
505	Rick Waits	.06	.05	.02
506	Robin Yount	2.00	1.50	.80
507	Len Barker	.08	.06	.03
508	Steve Bedrosian	.12	.09	.05
509	Bruce Benedict	.06	.05	.02
510	Rick Camp	.06	.05	.02
511	Rick Cerone	.06	.05	.02
512	Chris Chambliss	.08	.06	.03
513	Jeff Dedmon	.06	.05	.02
514	Terry Forster	.08	.06	.03
515	Gene Garber	.06	.05	.02
516	Terry Harper	.06	.05	.02
517	Bob Horner	.12	.09	.05
518	Glenn Hubbard	.06	.05	.02
519	*Joe Johnson* (FC)	.06	.05	.02
520	Brad Komminsk	.06	.05	.02
521	Rick Mahler	.06	.05	.02
522	Dale Murphy	.30	.25	.12
523	Ken Oberkfell	.06	.05	.02
524	Pascual Perez	.08	.06	.03
525	Gerald Perry	.12	.09	.05
526	Rafael Ramirez	.06	.05	.02
527	*Steve Shields* (FC)	.12	.09	.05
528	Zane Smith	.10	.08	.04
529	Bruce Sutter	.12	.09	.05
530	*Milt Thompson* (FC)	.15	.11	.06
531	Claudell Washington	.08	.06	.03
532	Paul Zuvella	.06	.05	.02
533	Vida Blue	.10	.08	.04
534	Bob Brenly	.06	.05	.02
535	*Chris Brown*	.06	.05	.02
536	Chili Davis	.10	.08	.04
537	Mark Davis	.06	.05	.02
538	Rob Deer	.12	.09	.05
539	Dan Driessen	.08	.06	.03
540	Scott Garrelts	.08	.06	.03
541	Dan Gladden	.08	.06	.03
542	Jim Gott	.06	.05	.02
543	David Green	.06	.05	.02
544	Atlee Hammaker	.06	.05	.02
545	Mike Jeffcoat	.06	.05	.02
546	Mike Krukow	.08	.06	.03
547	Dave LaPoint	.08	.06	.03
548	Jeff Leonard	.08	.06	.03
549	Greg Minton	.06	.05	.02
550	Alex Trevino	.06	.05	.02
551	Manny Trillo	.08	.06	.03
552	*Jose Uribe*	.06	.05	.02
553	Brad Wellman	.06	.05	.02
554	Frank Williams	.06	.05	.02
555	Joel Youngblood	.06	.05	.02
556	Alan Bannister	.06	.05	.02
557	Glenn Brummer	.06	.05	.02
558	*Steve Buechele* (FC)	.20	.15	.08
559	*Jose Guzman* (FC)	.10	.08	.04
560	Toby Harrah	.08	.06	.03
561	Greg Harris	.06	.05	.02
562	*Dwayne Henry* (FC)	.10	.08	.04
563	Burt Hooton	.08	.06	.03
564	Charlie Hough	.08	.06	.03
565	Mike Mason	.06	.05	.02
566	*Oddibe McDowell*	.10	.08	.04
567	Dickie Noles	.06	.05	.02
568	Pete O'Brien	.10	.08	.04
569	Larry Parrish	.10	.08	.04
570	Dave Rozema	.06	.05	.02
571	Dave Schmidt	.06	.05	.02
572	Don Slaught	.06	.05	.02
573	Wayne Tolleson	.06	.05	.02
574	Duane Walker	.06	.05	.02
575	Gary Ward	.08	.06	.03
576	Chris Welsh	.06	.05	.02
577	Curtis Wilkerson	.06	.05	.02
578	George Wright	.06	.05	.02
579	Chris Bando	.06	.05	.02
580	Tony Bernazard	.06	.05	.02
581	Brett Butler	.08	.06	.03
582	Ernie Camacho	.06	.05	.02
583	Joe Carter	3.50	2.75	1.50
584	Carmello Castillo (Carmelo)	.06	.05	.02
585	Jamie Easterly	.06	.05	.02
586	Julio Franco	.10	.08	.04
587	Mel Hall	.08	.06	.03
588	Mike Hargrove	.06	.05	.02
589	Neal Heaton	.06	.05	.02
590	Brook Jacoby	.10	.08	.04
591	*Otis Nixon* (FC)	.60	.45	.25
592	Jerry Reed	.06	.05	.02
593	Vern Ruhle	.06	.05	.02
594	Pat Tabler	.08	.06	.03
595	Rich Thompson	.06	.05	.02
596	Andre Thornton	.08	.06	.03
597	Dave Von Ohlen	.06	.05	.02
598	George Vukovich	.06	.05	.02
599	Tom Waddell	.06	.05	.02
600	Curt Wardle	.06	.05	.02
601	Jerry Willard	.06	.05	.02
602	Bill Almon	.06	.05	.02
603	Mike Bielecki	.08	.06	.03
604	Sid Bream	.10	.08	.04
605	Mike Brown	.06	.05	.02
606	*Pat Clements*	.12	.09	.05
607	Jose DeLeon	.08	.06	.03
608	Denny Gonzalez	.06	.05	.02
609	Cecilio Guante	.06	.05	.02
610	Steve Kemp	.08	.06	.03
611	Sam Khalifa	.06	.05	.02
612	Lee Mazzilli	.08	.06	.03
613	Larry McWilliams	.06	.05	.02
614	Jim Morrison	.06	.05	.02
615	*Joe Orsulak*	.25	.20	.10
616	Tony Pena	.10	.08	.04
617	Johnny Ray	.10	.08	.04
618	Rick Reuschel	.10	.08	.04
619	R.J. Reynolds	.08	.06	.03
620	Rick Rhoden	.10	.08	.04
621	Don Robinson	.08	.06	.03
622	Jason Thompson	.06	.05	.02
623	Lee Tunnell	.06	.05	.02
624	Jim Winn	.06	.05	.02
625	Marvell Wynne	.06	.05	.02
626	Dwight Gooden (IA)	.40	.30	.15
627	Don Mattingly (IA)	1.25	.90	.50
628	Pete Rose (4,192 hits)	.50	.40	.20
629	Rod Carew (3,000 Hits)	.50	.40	.20
630	Phil Niekro (300 Wins, Tom Seaver)	.15	.11	.06
631	Ouch! (Don Baylor)	.08	.06	.03
632	Instant Offense (Tim Raines, Darryl Strawberry)	.25	.20	.10
633	Shortstops Supreme (Cal Ripken, Jr., Alan Trammell)	1.00	.70	.40
634	Boggs & "Hero" (Wade Boggs, George Brett)	1.00	.70	.40
635	Braves Dynamic Duo (Bob Horner, Dale Murphy)	.30	.25	.12
636	Cardinal Ignitors (Vince Coleman, Willie McGee)	.25	.20	.10
637	Terror on the Basepaths (Vince Coleman)	.15	.11	.06
638	Charlie Hustle & Dr. K (Dwight Gooden, Pete Rose)	.70	.50	.30
639	1984 and 1985 A.L. Batting Champs (Wade Boggs, Don Mattingly)	1.00	.70	.40
640	N.L. West Sluggers (Steve Garvey, Dale Murphy, Dave Parker)	.30	.25	.12
641	Staff Aces (Dwight Gooden, Fernando Valenzuela)	.40	.30	.15
642	Blue Jay Stoppers (Jimmy Key, Dave Stieb)	.10	.08	.04
643	A.L. All-Star Backstops (Carlton Fisk, Rich Gedman)	.10	.08	.04
644	Major League Prospect (*Benito Santiago*, Gene Walter)	1.50	1.25	.60
645	Major League Prospect (*Colin Ward* (FC), Mike Woodard)	.10	.08	.04
646	Major League Prospect (*Kal Daniels*, Paul O'Neill)	2.00	1.50	.80
647	Major League Prospect (*Andres Galarraga*, Fred Toliver)	5.00	3.75	2.00
648	Major League Prospect (*Curt Ford* (FC), Bob Kipper)	.25	.20	.10
649	Major League Prospect (*Jose Canseco*, Eric Plunk)	22.00	16.50	8.75
650	Major League Prospect (*Mark McLemore*, Gus Polidor)	.40	.30	.15
651	Major League Prospect (*Mickey Brantley* (FC), Rob Woodward)	.15	.11	.06
652	Major League Prospect (*Mark Funderburk* (FC), Billy Joe Robidoux)	.10	.08	.04
653	Major League Prospect (*Cecil Fielder*, Cory Snyder)	20.00	15.00	8.00
654	Checklist 1-97	.06	.05	.02
655	Checklist 98-196	.06	.05	.02
656	Checklist 197-291	.06	.05	.02
657	Checklist 292-385	.06	.05	.02
658	Checklist 386-482	.06	.05	.02
659	Checklist 483-578	.06	.05	.02
660	Checklist 579-660	.06	.05	.02

1986 Fleer All Stars

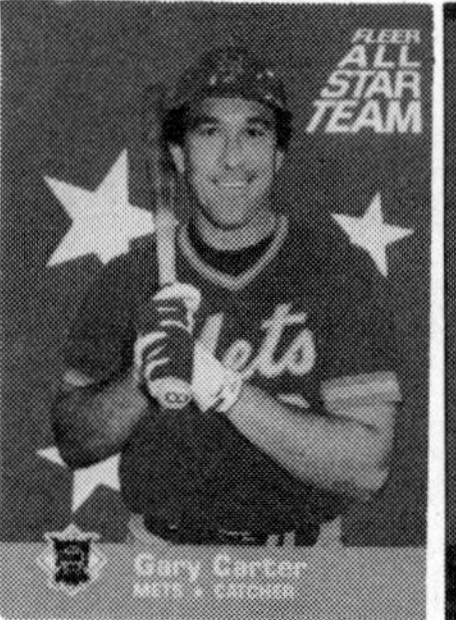

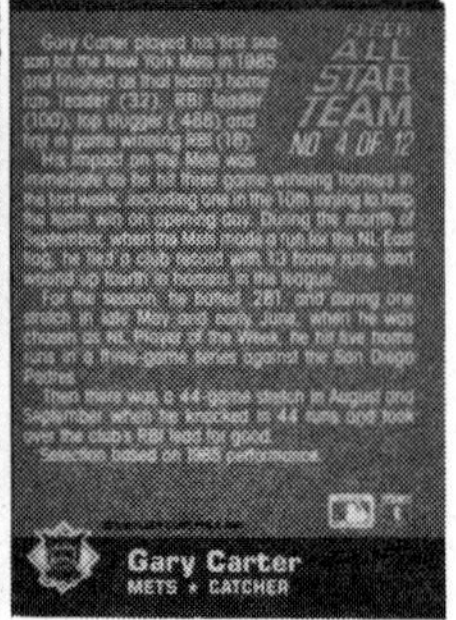

Fleer's choices for a major league All-Star team make up this 12-card set. The cards, which measure 2-1/2" by 3-1/2", were randomly inserted in 35¢ wax packs and 59¢ cello packs. The card fronts have a color photo set against a bright red background for A.L. players or a bright blue background for N.L. players. The card backs feature the player's career highlights set in white type against a red and blue background.

		MT	NR MT	EX
Complete Set (12):		22.00	16.50	8.75
Common Player:		.25	.20	.10
1	Don Mattingly	5.00	3.75	2.00
2	Tom Herr	.25	.20	.10
3	George Brett	5.00	3.75	2.00
4	Gary Carter	.75	.60	.30
5	Cal Ripken, Jr.	8.00	6.00	3.25
6	Dave Parker	.75	.60	.30
7	Rickey Henderson	3.00	2.25	1.25
8	Pedro Guerrero	.25	.20	.10
9	Dan Quisenberry	.30	.25	.12
10	Dwight Gooden	.75	.60	.30
11	Gorman Thomas	.25	.20	.10
12	John Tudor	.25	.20	.10

A player's name in italic type indicates a rookie card. An (FC) indicates a player's first card for that particular card company.

Grading Guide

Mint (MT): A perfect card. Well-centered with all corners sharp and square. No creases, stains, edge nicks, surface marks, yellowing or fading.

Near Mint (NM): A nearly perfect card. At first glance, a NM card appears to be perfect. May be slightly off-center. No surface marks, creases or loss of gloss.

Excellent (EX): Corners are still fairly sharp with only moderate wear. Borders may be off-center. No creases or stains on fronts or backs, but may show slight loss of surface luster.

Very Good (VG): Shows obvious handling. May have rounded corners, minor creases, major gum or wax stains. No major creases, tape marks, writing, etc.

Good (G): A well-worn card, but exhibits no intentional damage. May have major or multiple creases. Corners may be rounded well beyond card border.

1986 Fleer Future Hall Of Famers

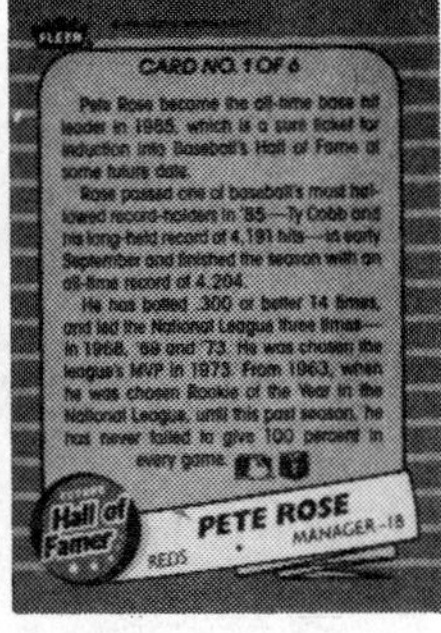

The 1986 Fleer Future Hall of Famers set is comprised of six players Fleer felt would gain eventual entrance into the Baseball Hall of Fame. The cards are the standard 2-1/2" by 3-1/2" in size and were randomly inserted in three-pack cello packs. The card fronts feature a player photo set against a blue background with horizontal light blue stripes. The card backs are printed in black on a blue background and feature player highlights in paragraph form.

		MT	NR MT	EX
Complete Set (6):		15.00	11.00	6.00
Common Player:		1.75	1.25	.70
1	Pete Rose	2.00	1.50	.80
2	Steve Carlton	1.75	1.25	.70
3	Tom Seaver	1.75	1.25	.70
4	Rod Carew	1.75	1.25	.70
5	Nolan Ryan	9.00	6.75	3.50
6	Reggie Jackson	1.75	1.25	.70

1986 Fleer Box Panels

Picking up on a Donruss idea, Fleer issued eight cards in panels of four on the bottoms of the wax and cello pack boxes. The cards are numbered C-1 through C-8 and are 2-1/2" by 3-1/2", with a complete panel measuring 5" by 7-1/8" in size. Included in the eight cards are six player cards and two team logo/checklist cards.

		MT	NR MT	EX
Complete Panel Set:		3.50	2.75	1.50
Complete Singles Set:		1.75	1.25	.70
Common Single Player:		.20	.15	.08
	Panel	2.50	2.00	1.00
1	Royals Logo/Checklist	.05	.04	.02
2	George Brett	.90	.70	.35
3	Ozzie Guillen	.20	.15	.08
4	Dale Murphy	.40	.30	.15
	Panel	1.50	1.25	.60
5	Cardinals Logo/Checklist	.05	.04	.02
6	Tom Browning	.20	.15	.08
7	Gary Carter	.35	.25	.14
8	Carlton Fisk	.35	.25	.14

Values quoted in this guide reflect the retail price of a card – the price a collector can expect to pay when buying a card from a dealer. The wholesale price – that which a collector can expect to receive from a dealer when selling cards – will be significantly lower, depending on desirability and condition.

Values for recent cards and sets are listed in Mint (MT), Near Mint (NM), reflecting the fact that many cards from recent years have been preserved in top condition. Recent cards and sets in less than Excellent condition have little collector interest.

1986 Fleer Update

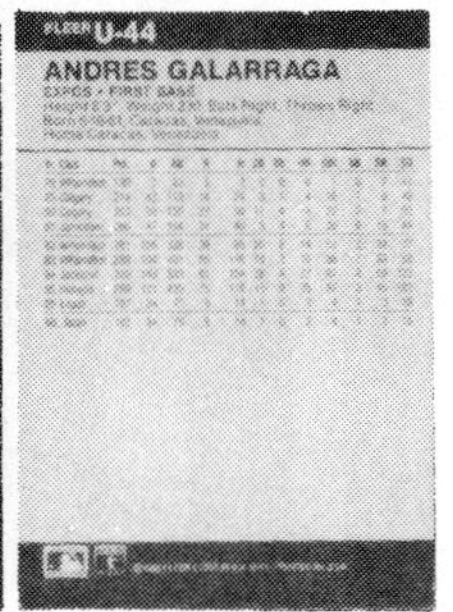

Issued near the end of the baseball season, the 1986 Fleer Update set consists of 132 cards numbered U-1 through U-132. The cards, which measure 2-1/2" by 3-1/2" in size, are identical in design to the regular 1986 Fleer set. The purpose of the set is to update player trades and include new players not depicted in the regular issue. The set was issued with team logo stickers in a specially designed box and was available only through hobby dealers.

		MT	NR MT	EX
Complete Set (132):		30.00	22.00	12.00
Common Player:		.08	.06	.03
1	Mike Aldrete (FC)	.08	.06	.03
2	Andy Allanson (FC)	.08	.06	.03
3	Neil Allen	.08	.06	.03
4	Joaquin Andujar	.08	.06	.03
5	Paul Assenmacher (FC)	.20	.15	.08
6	Scott Bailes (FC)	.08	.06	.03
7	Jay Baller (FC)	.08	.06	.03
8	Scott Bankhead (FC)	.20	.15	.08
9	Bill Bathe (FC)	.08	.06	.03
10	Don Baylor	.15	.11	.06
11	Billy Beane (FC)	.08	.06	.03
12	Steve Bedrosian	.15	.11	.06
13	Juan Beniquez	.08	.06	.03
14	Barry Bonds (FC)	15.00	11.00	6.00
15	Bobby Bonilla (FC)	3.00	2.25	1.25
16	Rich Bordi	.08	.06	.03
17	Bill Campbell	.08	.06	.03
18	Tom Candiotti	.08	.06	.03
19	John Cangelosi (FC)	.08	.06	.03
20	Jose Canseco	4.00	3.00	1.50
21	Chuck Cary (FC)	.08	.06	.03
22	Juan Castillo (FC)	.08	.06	.03
23	Rick Cerone	.08	.06	.03
24	John Cerutti (FC)	.10	.08	.04
25	Will Clark (FC)	7.50	6.00	3.25
26	Mark Clear	.08	.06	.03
27	Darnell Coles (FC)	.15	.11	.06
28	Dave Collins	.10	.08	.04
29	Tim Conroy	.08	.06	.03
30	Ed Correa (FC)	.08	.06	.03
31	Joe Cowley	.08	.06	.03
32	Bill Dawley	.08	.06	.03
33	Rob Deer	.08	.06	.03
34	John Denny	.08	.06	.03
35	Jim DeShaies	.25	.20	.10
36	Doug Drabek (FC)	1.00	.75	.40
37	Mike Easler	.12	.09	.05
38	Mark Eichhorn (FC)	.12	.09	.05
39	Dave Engle	.08	.06	.03
40	Mike Fischlin	.08	.06	.03
41	Scott Fletcher	.15	.11	.06
42	Terry Forster	.12	.09	.05
43	Terry Francona	.08	.06	.03
44	Andres Galarraga	2.50	2.00	1.00
45	Lee Guetterman (FC)	.20	.15	.08
46	Bill Gullickson	.08	.06	.03
47	Jackie Gutierrez	.08	.06	.03
48	Moose Haas	.08	.06	.03
49	Billy Hatcher	.15	.11	.06
50	Mike Heath	.08	.06	.03
51	Guy Hoffman (FC)	.08	.06	.03
52	Tom Hume	.08	.06	.03
53	Pete Incaviglia (FC)	1.00	.70	.40
54	Dane Iorg	.08	.06	.03
55	Chris James (FC)	.08	.06	.03
56	Stan Javier (FC)	.12	.09	.05
57	Tommy John	.20	.15	.08
58	Tracy Jones (FC)	.08	.06	.03
59	Wally Joyner (FC)	1.50	1.25	.60
60	Wayne Krenchicki	.08	.06	.03
61	John Kruk (FC)	2.00	1.50	.80
62	Mike LaCoss	.08	.06	.03
63	Pete Ladd	.08	.06	.03
64	Dave LaPoint	.08	.06	.03
65	Mike LaValliere (FC)	.20	.15	.08
66	Rudy Law	.08	.06	.03
67	Dennis Leonard	.10	.08	.04
68	Steve Lombardozzi (FC)	.08	.06	.03
69	Aurelio Lopez	.08	.06	.03
70	Mickey Mahler	.08	.06	.03
71	Candy Maldonado	.08	.06	.03
72	Roger Mason (FC)	.10	.08	.04
73	Greg Mathews (FC)	.10	.08	.04
74	Andy McGaffigan	.08	.06	.03
75	Joel McKeon (FC)	.08	.06	.03
76	Kevin Mitchell (FC)	1.50	1.25	.60
77	Bill Mooneyham (FC)	.08	.06	.03
78	Omar Moreno	.08	.06	.03
79	Jerry Mumphrey	.08	.06	.03
80	Al Newman (FC)	.12	.09	.05
81	Phil Niekro	.25	.20	.10
82	Randy Niemann	.08	.06	.03
83	Juan Nieves (FC)	.08	.06	.03
84	Bob Ojeda	.12	.09	.05
85	Rick Ownbey	.08	.06	.03
86	Tom Paciorek	.08	.06	.03
87	David Palmer	.08	.06	.03
88	Jeff Parrett (FC)	.08	.06	.03
89	Pat Perry (FC)	.08	.06	.03
90	Dan Plesac (FC)	.12	.09	.05
91	Darrell Porter	.12	.09	.05
92	Luis Quinones (FC)	.08	.06	.03
93	Rey Quinonez (FC)	.08	.06	.03
94	Gary Redus	.10	.08	.04
95	Jeff Reed (FC)	.08	.06	.03
96	Bip Roberts (FC)	.60	.45	.25
97	Billy Joe Robidoux	.12	.09	.05
98	Gary Roenicke	.08	.06	.03
99	Ron Roenicke	.08	.06	.03
100	Angel Salazar	.08	.06	.03
101	Joe Sambito	.08	.06	.03
102	Billy Sample	.08	.06	.03
103	Dave Schmidt	.08	.06	.03
104	Ken Schrom	.08	.06	.03
105	Ruben Sierra (FC)	5.00	3.75	2.00
106	Ted Simmons	.20	.15	.08
107	Sammy Stewart	.08	.06	.03
108	Kurt Stillwell (FC)	.08	.06	.03
109	Dale Sveum (FC)	.08	.06	.03
110	Tim Teufel	.08	.06	.03
111	Bob Tewksbury (FC)	.75	.60	.30
112	Andres Thomas (FC)	.08	.06	.03
113	Jason Thompson	.08	.06	.03
114	Milt Thompson	.12	.09	.05
115	Rob Thompson (FC)	1.50	1.25	.60
116	Jay Tibbs	.08	.06	.03
117	Fred Toliver	.12	.09	.05
118	Wayne Tolleson	.08	.06	.03
119	Alex Trevino	.08	.06	.03
120	Manny Trillo	.10	.08	.04
121	Ed Vande Berg	.08	.06	.03
122	Ozzie Virgil	.08	.06	.03
123	Tony Walker (FC)	.08	.06	.03
124	Gene Walter	.12	.09	.05
125	Duane Ward (FC)	1.00	.70	.40
126	Jerry Willard	.08	.06	.03
127	Mitch Williams (FC)	.40	.30	.15
128	Reggie Williams (FC)	.08	.06	.03
129	Bobby Witt (FC)	.30	.25	.12
130	Marvell Wynne	.08	.06	.03
131	Steve Yeager	.08	.06	.03
132	Checklist	.08	.06	.03

1986 Fleer Baseball's Best

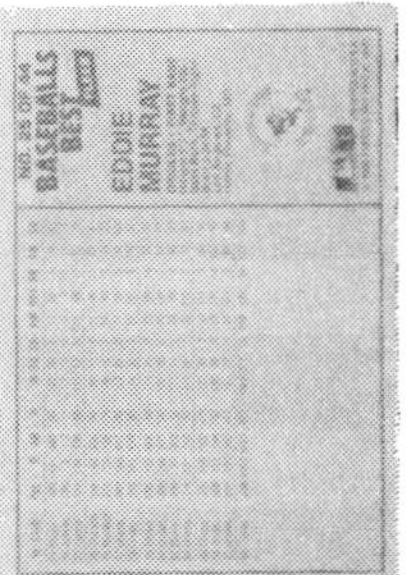

The 1986 Fleer Baseball's Best set consists of 44 cards and was produced for the McCrory's store chain and their affiliated stores. Subtitled "Sluggers vs. Pitchers," the set contains 22 each of the game's best hitters and pitchers. The cards, which measure 2-1/2" by 3-1/2", have color photos depicting an action pose. The backs are done in blue and red ink on white stock and carry the player's personal and statistical information. The sets were issued in a specially designed box with six team logo stickers.

		MT	NR MT	EX
Complete Set:		5.00	3.75	2.00
Common Player:		.05	.04	.02
1	Bert Blyleven	.10	.08	.04
2	Wade Boggs	.70	.50	.30
3	George Brett	.70	.50	.30
4	Tom Browning	.15	.11	.06
5	Jose Canseco	2.00	1.50	.80
6	Will Clark	1.50	1.25	.60
7	Roger Clemens	.70	.50	.30
8	Alvin Davis	.10	.08	.04
9	Julio Franco	.10	.08	.04
10	Kirk Gibson	.20	.15	.08
11	Dwight Gooden	.50	.40	.20
12	Goose Gossage	.12	.09	.05
13	Pedro Guerrero	.15	.11	.06
14	Ron Guidry	.12	.09	.05
15	Tony Gwynn	.25	.20	.10
16	Orel Hershiser	.20	.15	.08
17	Kent Hrbek	.15	.11	.06
18	Reggie Jackson	.50	.40	.20
19	Wally Joyner	.50	.40	.20
20	Charlie Leibrandt	.05	.04	.02
21	Don Mattingly	.70	.50	.30

22	Willie McGee	.12	.09	.05
23	Jack Morris	.15	.11	.06
24	Dale Murphy	.30	.25	.12
25	Eddie Murray	.25	.20	.10
26	Jeff Reardon	.07	.05	.03
27	Rick Reuschel	.07	.05	.03
28	Cal Ripken, Jr	.80	.60	.30
29	Pete Rose	.60	.45	.25
30	Nolan Ryan	1.75	1.25	.70
31	Bret Saberhagen	.15	.11	.06
32	Ryne Sandberg	.80	.60	.30
33	Mike Schmidt	.50	.40	.20
34	Tom Seaver	.25	.20	.10
35	Bryn Smith	.05	.04	.02
36	Mario Soto	.05	.04	.02
37	Dave Stieb	.10	.08	.04
38	Darryl Strawberry	.35	.25	.14
39	Rick Sutcliffe	.10	.08	.04
40	John Tudor	.10	.08	.04
41	Fernando Valenzuela	.20	.15	.08
42	Bobby Witt	.15	.11	.06
43	Mike Witt	.07	.05	.03
44	Robin Yount	.35	.25	.14

1986 Fleer League Leaders

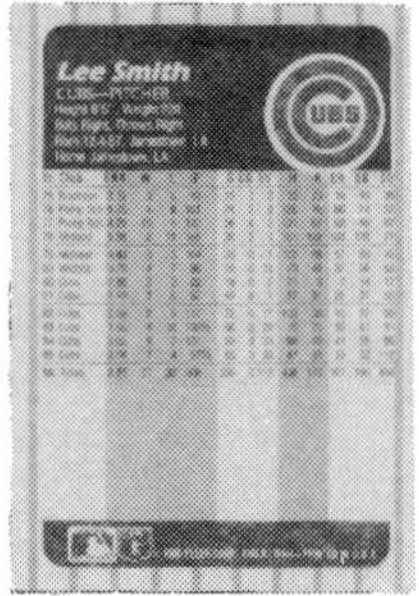

Fleer's 1986 "League Leaders" set features 44 of the game's top players and was issued through the Walgreens drug store chain. The card fronts contain a color photo and feature the player's name, team and postition in a blue band near the bottom of the card. The words "League Leaders" appear in a red band at the top of the card. The background for the card fronts is alternating blue and white stripes. The card backs are printed in blue, red and white and carry the player's statistical information and team logo. The cards are the standard 2-1/2" by 3-1/2" size. The set was issued in a special cardboard box, along with six team logo stickers.

		MT	NR MT	EX
Complete Set (44):		5.00	3.75	2.00
Common Player:		.05	.04	.02
1	Wade Boggs	.60	.45	.25
2	George Brett	.60	.45	.25
3	Jose Canseco	2.00	1.50	.80
4	Rod Carew	.30	.25	.12
5	Gary Carter	.25	.20	.10
6	Jack Clark	.12	.09	.05
7	Vince Coleman	.30	.25	.12
8	Jose Cruz	.05	.04	.02
9	Alvin Davis	.10	.08	.04
10	Mariano Duncan	.05	.04	.02
11	Leon Durham	.05	.04	.02
12	Carlton Fisk	.25	.20	.10
13	Julio Franco	.10	.08	.04
14	Scott Garrelts	.05	.04	.02
15	Steve Garvey	.25	.20	.10
16	Dwight Gooden	.40	.30	.15
17	Ozzie Guillen	.10	.08	.04
18	Willie Hernandez	.05	.04	.02
19	Bob Horner	.07	.05	.03
20	Kent Hrbek	.15	.11	.06
21	Charlie Leibrandt	.05	.04	.02
22	Don Mattingly	.60	.45	.25
23	Oddibe McDowell	.12	.09	.05
24	Willie McGee	.10	.08	.04
25	Keith Moreland	.05	.04	.02
26	Lloyd Moseby	.07	.05	.03
27	Dale Murphy	.30	.25	.12
28	Phil Niekro	.15	.11	.06
29	Joe Orsulak	.05	.04	.02
30	Dave Parker	.25	.20	.10
31	Lance Parrish	.15	.11	.06
32	Kirby Puckett	.70	.50	.30
33	Tim Raines	.25	.20	.10
34	Earnie Riles	.07	.05	.03
35	Cal Ripken, Jr.	.80	.60	.30
36	Pete Rose	.60	.45	.25
37	Bret Saberhagen	.15	.11	.06
38	Juan Samuel	.10	.08	.04
39	Ryne Sandberg	.80	.60	.30
40	Tom Seaver	.25	.20	.10
41	Lee Smith	.07	.05	.03
42	Ozzie Smith	.12	.09	.05
43	Dave Stieb	.10	.08	.04
44	Robin Yount	.35	.25	.14

1986 Fleer Limited Edition

Produced for the McCrory's store chain and their affiliates for the second year in a row, the 1986 Fleer Limited Edition set contains 44 cards. The cards, which are the standard 2-1/2" by 3-1/2" size, have color photos enclosed by green, red and yellow trim. The card backs carry black print on two shades of red. The set was issued in a special cardboard box, along with six team logo stickers.

		MT	NR MT	EX
Complete Set:		5.00	3.75	2.00
Common Player:		.05	.04	.02
1	Doyle Alexander	.05	.04	.02
2	Joaquin Andujar	.05	.04	.02
3	Harold Baines	.12	.09	.05
4	Wade Boggs	.70	.50	.30
5	Phil Bradley	.05	.04	.02
6	George Brett	.70	.50	.30
7	Hubie Brooks	.07	.05	.03
8	Chris Brown	.05	.04	.02
9	Tom Brunansky	.05	.04	.02
10	Gary Carter	.25	.20	.10
11	Vince Coleman	.25	.20	.10
12	Cecil Cooper	.07	.05	.03
13	Jose Cruz	.05	.04	.02
14	Mike Davis	.05	.04	.02
15	Carlton Fisk	.15	.11	.06
16	Julio Franco	.07	.05	.03
17	Damaso Garcia	.05	.04	.02
18	Rich Gedman	.05	.04	.02
19	Kirk Gibson	.20	.15	.08
20	Dwight Gooden	.40	.30	.15
21	Pedro Guerrero	.07	.05	.03
22	Tony Gwynn	.25	.20	.10
23	Rickey Henderson	.50	.40	.20
24	Orel Hershiser	.20	.15	.08
25	LaMarr Hoyt	.05	.04	.02
26	Reggie Jackson	.30	.25	.12
27	Don Mattingly	.70	.50	.30
28	Oddibe McDowell	.05	.04	.02
29	Willie McGee	.10	.08	.04
30	Paul Molitor	.20	.15	.08
31	Dale Murphy	.30	.25	.12
32	Eddie Murray	.25	.20	.10
33	Dave Parker	.20	.15	.08
34	Tony Pena	.05	.04	.02
35	Jeff Reardon	.05	.04	.02
36	Cal Ripken, Jr.	.80	.60	.30
37	Pete Rose	.60	.45	.25
38	Bret Saberhagen	.15	.11	.06
39	Juan Samuel	.07	.05	.03
40	Ryne Sandberg	.80	.60	.30
41	Mike Schmidt	.75	.60	.30
42	Lee Smith	.07	.05	.03
43	Don Sutton	.12	.09	.05
44	Lou Whitaker	.15	.11	.06

1986 Fleer Mini

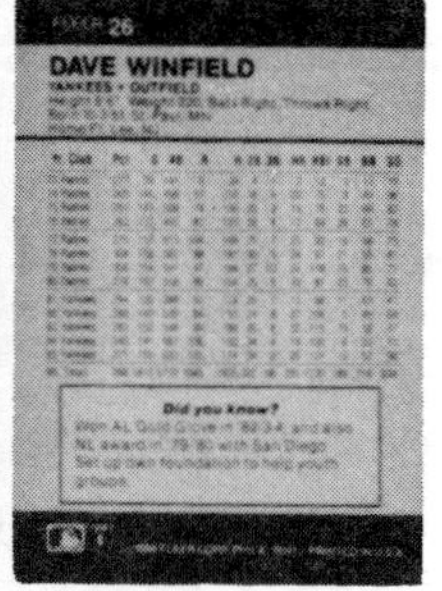

Fleer's 1986 "Classic Miniatures" set contains 120 cards that measure 1-13/16" by 2-9/16" in size. The design of the high-gloss cards is identical to the regular 1986 Fleer set but the player photos are entirely different. The set, which was issued in a specially designed box along with 18 team logo stickers, was available to the collecting public only through hobby dealers.

		MT	NR MT	EX
Complete Set:		12.00	9.00	4.75
Common Player:		.05	.04	.02
1	George Brett	.80	.60	.30
2	Dan Quisenberry	.07	.05	.03
3	Bret Saberhagen	.15	.11	.06
4	Lonnie Smith	.05	.04	.02
5	Willie Wilson	.10	.08	.04
6	Jack Clark	.12	.09	.05
7	Vince Coleman	.25	.20	.10
8	Tom Herr	.07	.05	.03
9	Willie McGee	.10	.08	.04
10	Ozzie Smith	.12	.09	.05
11	John Tudor	.07	.05	.03
12	Jesse Barfield	.12	.09	.05
13	George Bell	.20	.15	.08
14	Tony Fernandez	.10	.08	.04
15	Damaso Garcia	.05	.04	.02
16	Dave Stieb	.07	.05	.03
17	Gary Carter	.20	.15	.08
18	Ron Darling	.10	.08	.04
19	Dwight Gooden	.30	.25	.12
20	Keith Hernandez	.10	.08	.04
21	Darryl Strawberry	.25	.20	.10
22	Ron Guidry	.15	.11	.06
23	Rickey Henderson	.60	.45	.25
24	Don Mattingly	.90	.70	.35
25	Dave Righetti	.12	.09	.05
26	Dave Winfield	.45	.35	.20
27	Mariano Duncan	.07	.05	.03
28	Pedro Guerrero	.12	.09	.05
29	Bill Madlock	.10	.08	.04
30	Mike Marshall	.10	.08	.04
31	Fernando Valenzuela	.10	.08	.04
32	Reggie Jackson	.30	.25	.12
33	Gary Pettis	.05	.04	.02
34	Ron Romanick	.05	.04	.02
35	Don Sutton	.12	.09	.05
36	Mike Witt	.07	.05	.03
37	Buddy Bell	.07	.05	.03
38	Tom Browning	.10	.08	.04
39	Dave Parker	.12	.09	.05
40	Pete Rose	.60	.45	.25
41	Mario Soto	.05	.04	.02
42	Harold Baines	.12	.09	.05
43	Carlton Fisk	.15	.11	.06
44	Ozzie Guillen	.12	.09	.05
45	Ron Kittle	.07	.05	.03
46	Tom Seaver	.20	.15	.08
47	Kirk Gibson	.20	.15	.08
48	Jack Morris	.15	.11	.06
49	Lance Parrish	.15	.11	.06
50	Alan Trammell	.20	.15	.08
51	Lou Whitaker	.15	.11	.06
52	Hubie Brooks	.07	.05	.03
53	Andre Dawson	.15	.11	.06
54	Tim Raines	.20	.15	.08
55	Bryn Smith	.05	.04	.02
56	Tim Wallach	.10	.08	.04
57	Mike Boddicker	.05	.04	.02
58	Eddie Murray	.25	.20	.10
59	Cal Ripken, Jr.	1.00	.70	.40
60	John Shelby	.05	.04	.02
61	Mike Young	.05	.04	.02
62	Jose Cruz	.07	.05	.03
63	Glenn Davis	.15	.11	.06
64	Phil Garner	.05	.04	.02
65	Nolan Ryan	2.00	1.50	.80
66	Mike Scott	.12	.09	.05
67	Steve Garvey	.20	.15	.08
68	Goose Gossage	.12	.09	.05
69	Tony Gwynn	.25	.20	.10
70	Andy Hawkins	.05	.04	.02
71	Garry Templeton	.05	.04	.02
72	Wade Boggs	.80	.60	.30
73	Roger Clemens	.80	.60	.30
74	Dwight Evans	.12	.09	.05
75	Rich Gedman	.05	.04	.02
76	Jim Rice	.20	.15	.08
77	Shawon Dunston	.10	.08	.04
78	Leon Durham	.05	.04	.02
79	Keith Moreland	.05	.04	.02
80	Ryne Sandberg	1.00	.70	.40
81	Rick Sutcliffe	.10	.08	.04
82	Bert Blyleven	.12	.09	.05
83	Tom Brunansky	.10	.08	.04
84	Kent Hrbek	.15	.11	.06
85	Kirby Puckett	.70	.50	.30
86	Bruce Bochte	.05	.04	.02
87	Jose Canseco	1.00	.70	.40
88	Mike Davis	.05	.04	.02
89	Jay Howell	.07	.05	.03
90	Dwayne Murphy	.05	.04	.02
91	Steve Carlton	.20	.15	.08
92	Von Hayes	.10	.08	.04
93	Juan Samuel	.12	.09	.05
94	Mike Schmidt	.50	.40	.20
95	Glenn Wilson	.05	.04	.02
96	Phil Bradley	.10	.08	.04
97	Alvin Davis	.10	.08	.04
98	Jim Presley	.10	.08	.04
99	Danny Tartabull	.15	.11	.06
100	Cecil Cooper	.10	.08	.04
101	Paul Molitor	.12	.09	.05
102	Earnie Riles	.07	.05	.03
103	Robin Yount	.45	.35	.20
104	Bob Horner	.10	.08	.04
105	Dale Murphy	.30	.25	.12
106	Bruce Sutter	.10	.08	.04
107	Claudell Washington	.05	.04	.02
108	Chris Brown	.12	.09	.05
109	Chili Davis	.05	.04	.02
110	Scott Garrelts	.05	.04	.02
111	Oddibe McDowell	.12	.09	.05
112	Pete O'Brien	.07	.05	.03
113	Gary Ward	.05	.04	.02
114	Brett Butler	.05	.04	.02

115	Julio Franco	.10	.08	.04
116	Brook Jacoby	.10	.08	.04
117	Mike Brown	.05	.04	.02
118	Joe Orsulak	.05	.04	.02
119	Tony Pena	.07	.05	.03
120	R.J. Reynolds	.05	.04	.02

1986 Fleer Star Stickers

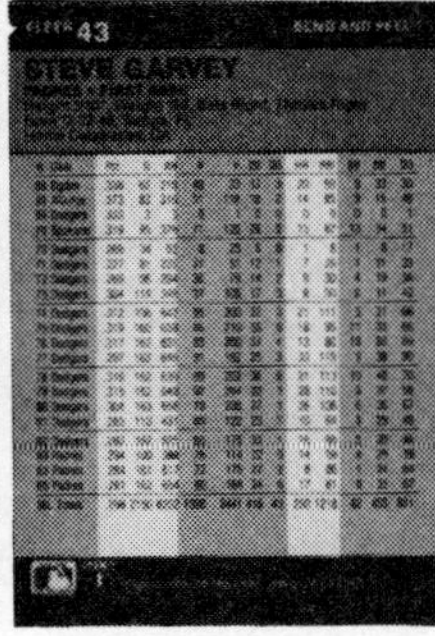

After a five-year layoff, Fleer once again produced a Star Sticker set. The cards, which measure 2-1/2" by 3-1/2", have color photos inside dark maroon borders. The card backs are identical to the 1986 regular issue except for the 1-132 numbering system and blue ink instead of yellow. The words "Bend and Peel" are found in the upper right corner of the card backs. Card #132 is a multi-player card featuring Dwight Gooden and Dale Murphy on the front and a complete checklist for the set on the reverse. The cards were sold in wax packs with team logo stickers.

		MT	NR MT	EX
Complete Set:		30.00	22.00	12.00
Common Player:		.05	.04	.02
1	Harold Baines	.20	.15	.08
2	Jesse Barfield	.20	.15	.08
3	Don Baylor	.12	.09	.05
4	Juan Beniquez	.05	.04	.02
5	Tim Birtsas	.08	.06	.03
6	Bert Blyleven	.15	.11	.06
7	Bruce Bochte	.05	.04	.02
8	Wade Boggs	1.00	.70	.40
9	Dennis Boyd	.12	.09	.05
10	Phil Bradley	.05	.04	.02
11	George Brett	1.00	.70	.40
12	Hubie Brooks	.10	.08	.04
13	Chris Brown	.05	.04	.02
14	Tom Browning	.10	.08	.04
15	Tom Brunansky	.05	.04	.02
16	Bill Buckner	.10	.08	.04
17	Britt Burns	.05	.04	.02
18	Brett Butler	.08	.06	.03
19	Jose Canseco	1.00	.70	.40
20	Rod Carew	.40	.30	.15
21	Steve Carlton	.40	.30	.15
22	Don Carman	.05	.04	.02
23	Gary Carter	.25	.20	.10
24	Jack Clark	.10	.08	.04
25	Vince Coleman	.25	.20	.10
26	Cecil Cooper	.10	.08	.04
27	Jose Cruz	.10	.08	.04
28	Ron Darling	.20	.15	.08
29	Alvin Davis	.05	.04	.02
30	Jody Davis	.05	.04	.02
31	Mike Davis	.05	.04	.02
32	Andre Dawson	.25	.20	.10
33	Mariano Duncan	.10	.08	.04
34	Shawon Dunston	.10	.08	.04
35	Leon Durham	.05	.04	.02
36	Darrell Evans	.10	.08	.04
37	Tony Fernandez	.10	.08	.04
38	Carlton Fisk	.20	.15	.08
39	John Franco	.10	.08	.04
40	Julio Franco	.10	.08	.04
41	Damaso Garcia	.05	.04	.02
42	Scott Garrelts	.05	.04	.02
43	Steve Garvey	.25	.20	.10
44	Rich Gedman	.05	.04	.02
45	Kirk Gibson	.25	.20	.10
46	Dwight Gooden	.50	.40	.20
47	Pedro Guerrero	.10	.08	.04
48	Ron Guidry	.10	.08	.04
49	Ozzie Guillen	.15	.11	.06
50	Tony Gwynn	.25	.20	.10
51	Andy Hawkins	.08	.06	.03
52	Von Hayes	.10	.08	.04
53	Rickey Henderson	.50	.40	.20
54	Tom Henke	.05	.04	.02
55	Keith Hernandez	.10	.08	.04
56	Willie Hernandez	.05	.04	.02
57	Tom Herr	.05	.04	.02
58	Orel Hershiser	.20	.15	.08
59	Teddy Higuera	.05	.04	.02
60	Bob Horner	.10	.08	.04
61	Charlie Hough	.08	.06	.03
62	Jay Howell	.08	.06	.03
63	LaMarr Hoyt	.05	.04	.02
64	Kent Hrbek	.20	.15	.08
65	Reggie Jackson	.50	.40	.20
66	Bob James	.05	.04	.02
67	Dave Kingman	.05	.04	.02
68	Ron Kittle	.05	.04	.02
69	Charlie Leibrandt	.05	.04	.02
70	Fred Lynn	.25	.20	.10
71	Mike Marshall	.05	.04	.02
72	Don Mattingly	1.00	.70	.40
73	Oddibe McDowell	.10	.08	.04
74	Willie McGee	.10	.08	.04
75	Scott McGregor	.05	.04	.02
76	Paul Molitor	.20	.15	.08
77	Donnie Moore	.05	.04	.02
78	Keith Moreland	.05	.04	.02
79	Jack Morris	.10	.08	.04
80	Dale Murphy	.40	.30	.15
81	Eddie Murray	.25	.20	.10
82	Phil Niekro	.25	.20	.10
83	Joe Orsulak	.10	.08	.04
84	Dave Parker	.25	.20	.10
85	Lance Parrish	.10	.08	.04
86	Larry Parrish	.05	.04	.02
87	Tony Pena	.10	.08	.04
88	Gary Pettis	.05	.04	.02
89	Jim Presley	.05	.04	.02
90	Kirby Puckett	.90	.70	.35
91	Dan Quisenberry	.10	.08	.04
92	Tim Raines	.20	.15	.08
93	Johnny Ray	.05	.04	.02
94	Jeff Reardon	.10	.08	.04
95	Rick Reuschel	.05	.04	.02
96	Jim Rice	.15	.11	.06
97	Dave Righetti	.10	.08	.04
98	Earnie Riles	.05	.04	.02
99	Cal Ripken, Jr.	1.00	.70	.40
100	Ron Romanick	.05	.04	.02
101	Pete Rose	.70	.50	.30
102	Nolan Ryan	2.00	1.50	.80
103	Bret Saberhagen	.20	.15	.08
104	Mark Salas	.05	.04	.02
105	Juan Samuel	.10	.08	.04
106	Ryne Sandberg	1.00	.70	.40
107	Mike Schmidt	.90	.70	.35
108	Mike Scott	.10	.08	.04
109	Tom Seaver	.30	.25	.12
110	Bryn Smith	.05	.04	.02
111	Dave Smith	.05	.04	.02
112	Lee Smith	.10	.08	.04
113	Ozzie Smith	.25	.20	.10
114	Mario Soto	.05	.04	.02
115	Dave Stieb	.10	.08	.04
116	Darryl Strawberry	.50	.40	.20
117	Bruce Sutter	.10	.08	.04
118	Garry Templeton	.05	.04	.02
119	Gorman Thomas	.05	.04	.02
120	Andre Thornton	.05	.04	.02
121	Alan Trammell	.20	.15	.08
122	John Tudor	.05	.04	.02
123	Fernando Valenzuela	.20	.15	.08
124	Frank Viola	.20	.15	.08
125	Gary Ward	.05	.04	.02
126	Lou Whitaker	.20	.15	.08
127	Frank White	.05	.04	.02
128	Glenn Wilson	.05	.04	.02
129	Willie Wilson	.10	.08	.04
130	Dave Winfield	.40	.30	.15
131	Robin Yount	.35	.25	.14
132	Dwight Gooden, Dale Murphy/Checklist	.50	.40	.20

1986 Fleer Star Stickers Box Panels

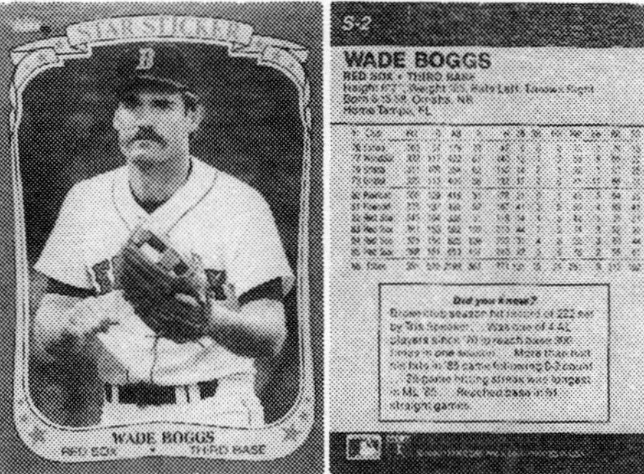

Four cards, numbered S-1 through S-4, were placed on the bottoms of 1986 Fleer Star Stickers wax pack boxes. The cards are nearly identical in format to the regular issue sticker cards. Individual cards measure 2-1/2" by 3-1/2" in size, while a complete panel of four measures 5" by 7-1/8".

		MT	NR MT	EX
Complete Panel Set:		2.00	1.50	.80
Complete Singles Set:		1.00	.70	.40
Common Single Player:		.30	.25	.12
1	Dodgers Logo	.05	.04	.02
2	Wade Boggs	1.00	.70	.40
3	Steve Garvey	.30	.25	.12
4	Dave Winfield	.50	.40	.20

1987 Fleer

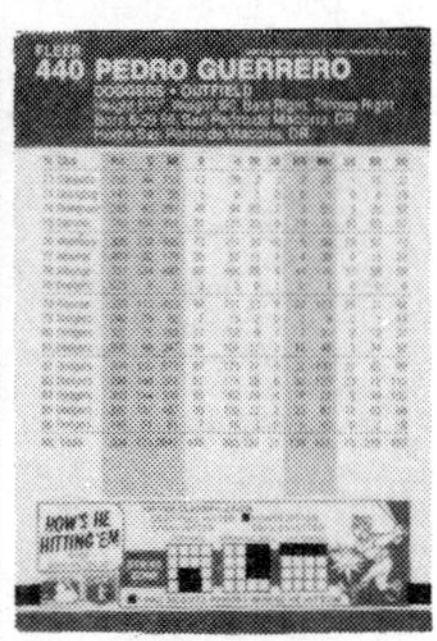

The 1987 Fleer set consists of 660 cards, each measuring 2-1/2" by 3-1/2". The card fronts feature an attractive blue and white border. The player's name and position appears in the upper left corner of the card. The player's team logo is located in the lower right corner. The card backs are done in blue, red and white and contain an innovative "Pro Scouts Report" feature which lists the hitter's or pitcher's batting and pitching strengths. For the third year in a row, Fleer included its "Major League Prospects" subset. Fleer produced a glossy- finish Collectors Edition set which came housed in a specially-designed tin box. It was speculated that 100,000 of the glossy sets were produced. After experiencing a dramatic drop in price during 1987, the glossy set now sells for only a few dollars more than the regular issue.

		MT	NR MT	EX
Complete Set (660):		90.00	67.00	36.00
Common Player:		.06	.05	.02
1	Rick Aguilera	.06	.05	.02
2	Richard Anderson	.06	.05	.02
3	Wally Backman	.08	.06	.03
4	Gary Carter	.15	.11	.06
5	Ron Darling	.15	.11	.06
6	Len Dykstra	.75	.60	.30
7	*Kevin Elster*	.10	.08	.04
8	Sid Fernandez	.12	.09	.05
9	Dwight Gooden	.35	.25	.14
10	*Ed Hearn* (FC)	.06	.05	.02
11	Danny Heep	.06	.05	.02
12	Keith Hernandez	.10	.08	.04
13	Howard Johnson	.10	.08	.04
14	Ray Knight	.08	.06	.03
15	Lee Mazzilli	.06	.05	.02
16	Roger McDowell	.12	.09	.05
17	*Kevin Mitchell*	1.25	.90	.50
18	Randy Niemann	.06	.05	.02
19	Bob Ojeda	.08	.06	.03
20	Jesse Orosco	.08	.06	.03
21	Rafael Santana	.06	.05	.02
22	Doug Sisk	.06	.05	.02
23	Darryl Strawberry	.40	.30	.15
24	Tim Teufel	.06	.05	.02
25	Mookie Wilson	.10	.08	.04
26	Tony Armas	.08	.06	.03
27	Marty Barrett	.10	.08	.04
28	Don Baylor	.12	.09	.05
29	Wade Boggs	1.50	1.25	.60
30	Oil Can Boyd	.08	.06	.03
31	Bill Buckner	.10	.08	.04
32	Roger Clemens	3.00	2.25	1.25
33	Steve Crawford	.06	.05	.02
34	Dwight Evans	.12	.09	.05
35	Rich Gedman	.10	.08	.04
36	Dave Henderson	.10	.08	.04
37	Bruce Hurst	.10	.08	.04
38	Tim Lollar	.06	.05	.02
39	Al Nipper	.06	.05	.02
40	Spike Owen	.06	.05	.02
41	Jim Rice	.20	.15	.08
42	Ed Romero	.06	.05	.02
43	Joe Sambito	.06	.05	.02
44	Calvin Schiraldi	.06	.05	.02
45	Tom Seaver	1.00	.70	.40
46	*Jeff Sellers* (FC)	.06	.05	.02
47	Bob Stanley	.06	.05	.02
48	Sammy Stewart	.06	.05	.02
49	Larry Andersen	.06	.05	.02
50	Alan Ashby	.06	.05	.02
51	Kevin Bass	.10	.08	.04
52	Jeff Calhoun	.06	.05	.02
53	Jose Cruz	.10	.08	.04
54	Danny Darwin	.06	.05	.02
55	Glenn Davis	.08	.06	.03
56	*Jim Deshaies*	.25	.20	.10
57	Bill Doran	.10	.08	.04
58	Phil Garner	.06	.05	.02
59	Billy Hatcher	.08	.06	.03
60	Charlie Kerfeld	.06	.05	.02
61	Bob Knepper	.08	.06	.03
62	Dave Lopes	.08	.06	.03
63	Aurelio Lopez	.06	.05	.02
64	Jim Pankovits	.06	.05	.02
65	Terry Puhl	.06	.05	.02
66	Craig Reynolds	.06	.05	.02
67	Nolan Ryan	4.00	3.00	1.50
68	Mike Scott	.15	.11	.06
69	Dave Smith	.06	.05	.02

70	Dickie Thon	.06	.05	.02
71	Tony Walker	.06	.05	.02
72	Denny Walling	.06	.05	.02
73	Bob Boone	.08	.06	.03
74	Rick Burleson	.08	.06	.03
75	John Candelaria	.06	.05	.02
76	Doug Corbett	.06	.05	.02
77	Doug DeCinces	.08	.06	.03
78	Brian Downing	.08	.06	.03
79	*Chuck Finley* (FC)	1.50	1.25	.60
80	Terry Forster	.08	.06	.03
81	Bobby Grich	.10	.08	.04
82	George Hendrick	.08	.06	.03
83	Jack Howell (FC)	.10	.08	.04
84	Reggie Jackson	1.00	.70	.40
85	Ruppert Jones	.06	.05	.02
86	*Wally Joyner*	1.75	1.25	.70
87	Gary Lucas	.06	.05	.02
88	Kirk McCaskill	.08	.06	.03
89	Donnie Moore	.06	.05	.02
90	Gary Pettis	.06	.05	.02
91	Vern Ruhle	.06	.05	.02
92	Dick Schofield	.06	.05	.02
93	Don Sutton	.15	.11	.06
94	Rob Wilfong	.06	.05	.02
95	Mike Witt	.10	.08	.04
96	*Doug Drabek*	1.00	.70	.40
97	Mike Easler	.08	.06	.03
98	Mike Fischlin	.06	.05	.02
99	Brian Fisher	.08	.06	.03
100	Ron Guidry	.15	.11	.06
101	Rickey Henderson	1.50	1.25	.60
102	Tommy John	.10	.08	.04
103	Ron Kittle	.06	.05	.02
104	Don Mattingly	1.75	1.25	.70
105	Bobby Meacham	.06	.05	.02
106	Joe Niekro	.10	.08	.04
107	Mike Pagliarulo	.10	.08	.04
108	Dan Pasqua	.10	.08	.04
109	Willie Randolph	.10	.08	.04
110	Dennis Rasmussen	.10	.08	.04
111	Dave Righetti	.15	.11	.06
112	Gary Roenicke	.06	.05	.02
113	Rod Scurry	.06	.05	.02
114	Bob Shirley	.06	.05	.02
115	Joel Skinner	.06	.05	.02
116	Tim Stoddard	.06	.05	.02
117	*Bob Tewksbury*	1.00	.70	.40
118	Wayne Tolleson	.06	.05	.02
119	Claudell Washington	.06	.05	.02
120	Dave Winfield	1.00	.70	.40
121	Steve Buechele	.08	.06	.03
122	*Ed Correa*	.06	.05	.02
123	Scott Fletcher	.08	.06	.03
124	Jose Guzman	.10	.08	.04
125	Toby Harrah	.08	.06	.03
126	Greg Harris	.06	.05	.02
127	Charlie Hough	.08	.06	.03
128	*Pete Incaviglia*	1.50	1.25	.60
129	Mike Mason	.06	.05	.02
130	Oddibe McDowell	.10	.08	.04
131	*Dale Mohorcic* (FC)	.06	.05	.02
132	Pete O'Brien	.10	.08	.04
133	Tom Paciorek	.06	.05	.02
134	Larry Parrish	.08	.06	.03
135	Geno Petralli	.06	.05	.02
136	Darrell Porter	.08	.06	.03
137	Jeff Russell	.06	.05	.02
138	*Ruben Sierra*	7.50	5.75	3.00
139	Don Slaught	.06	.05	.02
140	Gary Ward	.08	.06	.03
141	Curtis Wilkerson	.06	.05	.02
142	*Mitch Williams*	.60	.45	.25
143	*Bobby Witt*	.40	.30	.15
144	Dave Bergman	.06	.05	.02
145	Tom Brookens	.06	.05	.02
146	Bill Campbell	.06	.05	.02
147	*Chuck Cary*	.10	.08	.04
148	Darnell Coles	.08	.06	.03
149	Dave Collins	.08	.06	.03
150	Darrell Evans	.12	.09	.05
151	Kirk Gibson	.15	.11	.06
152	John Grubb	.06	.05	.02
153	Willie Hernandez	.08	.06	.03
154	Larry Herndon	.08	.06	.03
155	*Eric King*	.10	.08	.04
156	Chet Lemon	.08	.06	.03
157	Dwight Lowry	.06	.05	.02
158	Jack Morris	.15	.11	.06
159	Randy O'Neal	.06	.05	.02
160	Lance Parrish	.08	.06	.03
161	Dan Petry	.08	.06	.03
162	Pat Sheridan	.06	.05	.02
163	Jim Slaton	.06	.05	.02
164	Frank Tanana	.08	.06	.03
165	Walt Terrell	.08	.06	.03
166	Mark Thurmond	.06	.05	.02
167	Alan Trammell	.25	.20	.10
168	Lou Whitaker	.25	.20	.10
169	Luis Aguayo	.06	.05	.02
170	Steve Bedrosian	.06	.05	.02
171	Don Carman	.06	.05	.02
172	Darren Daulton	1.50	1.25	.60
173	Greg Gross	.06	.05	.02
174	Kevin Gross	.08	.06	.03
175	Von Hayes	.10	.08	.04
176	Charles Hudson	.06	.05	.02
177	Tom Hume	.06	.05	.02
178	Steve Jeltz	.06	.05	.02
179	*Mike Maddux* (FC)	.20	.15	.08
180	Shane Rawley	.08	.06	.03
181	Gary Redus	.06	.05	.02
182	Ron Roenicke	.06	.05	.02
183	*Bruce Ruffin* (FC)	.06	.05	.02
184	John Russell	.06	.05	.02
185	Juan Samuel	.12	.09	.05
186	Dan Schatzeder	.06	.05	.02
187	Mike Schmidt	1.75	1.25	.70
188	Rick Schu	.06	.05	.02
189	Jeff Stone	.06	.05	.02
190	Kent Tekulve	.08	.06	.03
191	Milt Thompson	.08	.06	.03
192	Glenn Wilson	.08	.06	.03
193	Buddy Bell	.10	.08	.04
194	Tom Browning	.10	.08	.04
195	Sal Butera	.06	.05	.02
196	Dave Concepcion	.12	.09	.05
197	Kal Daniels	.06	.05	.02
198	Eric Davis	.50	.40	.20
199	John Denny	.06	.05	.02
200	Bo Diaz	.08	.06	.03
201	Nick Esasky	.08	.06	.03
202	John Franco	.10	.08	.04
203	Bill Gullickson	.06	.05	.02
204	*Barry Larkin*	5.00	3.75	2.00
205	Eddie Milner	.06	.05	.02
206	*Rob Murphy* (FC)	.20	.15	.08
207	Ron Oester	.06	.05	.02
208	Dave Parker	.20	.15	.08
209	Tony Perez	.15	.11	.06
210	Ted Power	.06	.05	.02
211	Joe Price	.06	.05	.02
212	Ron Robinson	.06	.05	.02
213	Pete Rose	.60	.45	.25
214	Mario Soto	.08	.06	.03
215	*Kurt Stillwell*	.06	.05	.02
216	Max Venable	.06	.05	.02
217	Chris Welsh	.06	.05	.02
218	*Carl Willis* (FC)	.06	.05	.02
219	Jesse Barfield	.15	.11	.06
220	George Bell	.25	.20	.10
221	Bill Caudill	.06	.05	.02
222	*John Cerutti*	.06	.05	.02
223	Jim Clancy	.08	.06	.03
224	*Mark Eichhorn*	.15	.11	.06
225	Tony Fernandez	.20	.15	.08
226	Damaso Garcia	.06	.05	.02
227	Kelly Gruber	.20	.15	.08
228	Tom Henke	.08	.06	.03
229	Garth Iorg	.06	.05	.02
230	Cliff Johnson	.06	.05	.02
231	Joe Johnson	.06	.05	.02
232	Jimmy Key	.25	.20	.10
233	Dennis Lamp	.06	.05	.02
234	Rick Leach	.06	.05	.02
235	Buck Martinez	.06	.05	.02
236	Lloyd Moseby	.06	.05	.02
237	Rance Mulliniks	.06	.05	.02
238	Dave Stieb	.12	.09	.05
239	Willie Upshaw	.08	.06	.03
240	Ernie Whitt	.08	.06	.03
241	*Andy Allanson*	.06	.05	.02
242	*Scott Bailes*	.06	.05	.02
243	Chris Bando	.06	.05	.02
244	Tony Bernazard	.06	.05	.02
245	John Butcher	.06	.05	.02
246	Brett Butler	.08	.06	.03
247	Ernie Camacho	.06	.05	.02
248	Tom Candiotti	.06	.05	.02
249	Joe Carter	2.00	1.50	.80
250	Carmen Castillo	.06	.05	.02
251	Julio Franco	.10	.08	.04
252	Mel Hall	.08	.06	.03
253	Brook Jacoby	.10	.08	.04
254	Phil Niekro	.20	.15	.08
255	Otis Nixon	.20	.15	.08
256	Dickie Noles	.06	.05	.02
257	Bryan Oelkers	.06	.05	.02
258	Ken Schrom	.06	.05	.02
259	Don Schulze	.06	.05	.02
260	Cory Snyder	.15	.11	.06
261	Pat Tabler	.08	.06	.03
262	Andre Thornton	.08	.06	.03
263	*Rich Yett* (FC)	.06	.05	.02
264	*Mike Aldrete*	.10	.08	.04
265	Juan Berenguer	.06	.05	.02
266	Vida Blue	.10	.08	.04
267	Bob Brenly	.06	.05	.02
268	Chris Brown	.08	.06	.03
269	*Will Clark*	20.00	15.00	8.00
270	Chili Davis	.08	.06	.03
271	Mark Davis	.06	.05	.02
272	*Kelly Downs* (FC)	.12	.09	.05
273	Scott Garrelts	.06	.05	.02
274	Dan Gladden	.06	.05	.02
275	Mike Krukow	.08	.06	.03
276	*Randy Kutcher* (FC)	.06	.05	.02
277	Mike LaCoss	.06	.05	.02
278	Jeff Leonard	.08	.06	.03
279	Candy Maldonado	.08	.06	.03
280	Roger Mason	.06	.05	.02
281	Bob Melvin (FC)	.06	.05	.02
282	Greg Minton	.06	.05	.02
283	Jeff Robinson	.08	.06	.03
284	Harry Spilman	.06	.05	.02
285	*Rob Thompson*	2.00	1.50	.80
286	Jose Uribe	.06	.05	.02
287	Frank Williams	.06	.05	.02
288	Joel Youngblood	.06	.05	.02
289	Jack Clark	.08	.06	.03
290	Vince Coleman	.10	.08	.04
291	Tim Conroy	.06	.05	.02
292	Danny Cox	.08	.06	.03
293	Ken Dayley	.06	.05	.02
294	Curt Ford	.06	.05	.02
295	Bob Forsch	.06	.05	.02
296	Tom Herr	.10	.08	.04
297	Ricky Horton	.08	.06	.03
298	Clint Hurdle	.06	.05	.02
299	Jeff Lahti	.06	.05	.02
300	Steve Lake	.06	.05	.02
301	Tito Landrum	.06	.05	.02
302	*Mike LaValliere*	.25	.20	.10
303	*Greg Mathews* (FC)	.20	.15	.08
304	Willie McGee	.12	.09	.05
305	Jose Oquendo	.06	.05	.02
306	Terry Pendleton	.50	.40	.20
307	Pat Perry	.08	.06	.03
308	Ozzie Smith	.80	.60	.30
309	Ray Soff	.06	.05	.02
310	John Tudor	.10	.08	.04
311	Andy Van Slyke	.50	.40	.20
312	Todd Worrell	.20	.15	.08
313	Dann Bilardello	.06	.05	.02
314	Hubie Brooks	.10	.08	.04
315	Tim Burke	.06	.05	.02
316	Andre Dawson	.75	.60	.30
317	Mike Fitzgerald	.06	.05	.02
318	Tom Foley	.06	.05	.02
319	Andres Galarraga	1.00	.70	.40
320	Joe Hesketh	.06	.05	.02
321	Wallace Johnson	.06	.05	.02
322	Wayne Krenchicki	.06	.05	.02
323	Vance Law	.06	.05	.02
324	Dennis Martinez	.08	.06	.03
325	Bob McClure	.06	.05	.02
326	Andy McGaffigan	.06	.05	.02
327	*Al Newman*	.08	.06	.03
328	Tim Raines	.30	.25	.12
329	Jeff Reardon	.10	.08	.04
330	*Luis Rivera* (FC)	.10	.08	.04
331	*Bob Sebra* (FC)	.06	.05	.02
332	Bryn Smith	.06	.05	.02
333	Jay Tibbs	.06	.05	.02
334	Tim Wallach	.12	.09	.05
335	Mitch Webster	.08	.06	.03
336	Jim Wohlford	.06	.05	.02
337	Floyd Youmans	.08	.06	.03
338	*Chris Bosio* (FC)	.70	.50	.30
339	*Glenn Braggs* (FC)	.10	.08	.04
340	Rick Cerone	.06	.05	.02
341	Mark Clear	.06	.05	.02
342	*Bryan Clutterbuck* (FC)	.06	.05	.02
343	Cecil Cooper	.12	.09	.05
344	Rob Deer	.10	.08	.04
345	Jim Gantner	.08	.06	.03
346	Ted Higuera	.06	.05	.02
347	John Henry Johnson	.06	.05	.02
348	Tim Leary (FC)	.08	.06	.03
349	Rick Manning	.06	.05	.02
350	Paul Molitor	1.00	.70	.40
351	Charlie Moore	.06	.05	.02
352	Juan Nieves	.10	.08	.04
353	Ben Oglivie	.08	.06	.03
354	*Dan Plesac*	.12	.09	.05
355	Ernest Riles	.06	.05	.02
356	Billy Joe Robidoux	.06	.05	.02
357	Bill Schroeder	.06	.05	.02
358	*Dale Sveum*	.08	.06	.03
359	Gorman Thomas	.06	.05	.02
360	Bill Wegman (FC)	.10	.08	.04
361	Robin Yount	1.25	.90	.50
362	Steve Balboni	.08	.06	.03
363	*Scott Bankhead*	.08	.06	.03
364	Buddy Biancalana	.06	.05	.02
365	Bud Black	.06	.05	.02
366	George Brett	1.25	.90	.50
367	Steve Farr	.06	.05	.02
368	Mark Gubicza	.12	.09	.05
369	*Bo Jackson*	7.00	5.25	2.75
370	Danny Jackson	.15	.11	.06
371	*Mike Kingery*	.06	.05	.02
372	Rudy Law	.06	.05	.02
373	Charlie Leibrandt	.08	.06	.03
374	Dennis Leonard	.08	.06	.03
375	Hal McRae	.10	.08	.04
376	Jorge Orta	.06	.05	.02
377	Jamie Quirk	.06	.05	.02
378	Dan Quisenberry	.08	.06	.03
379	Bret Saberhagen	.20	.15	.08
380	Angel Salazar	.06	.05	.02
381	Lonnie Smith	.08	.06	.03
382	Jim Sundberg	.08	.06	.03
383	Frank White	.10	.08	.04
384	Willie Wilson	.12	.09	.05
385	Joaquin Andujar	.08	.06	.03
386	Doug Bair	.06	.05	.02
387	Dusty Baker	.08	.06	.03
388	Bruce Bochte	.06	.05	.02
389	Jose Canseco	5.00	3.75	2.00
390	Chris Codiroli	.06	.05	.02
391	Mike Davis	.08	.06	.03
392	Alfredo Griffin	.08	.06	.03
393	Moose Haas	.06	.05	.02
394	Donnie Hill	.06	.05	.02
395	Jay Howell	.08	.06	.03
396	Dave Kingman	.12	.09	.05
397	Carney Lansford	.10	.08	.04
398	*David Leiper* (FC)	.10	.08	.04
399	*Bill Mooneyham*	.10	.08	.04
400	Dwayne Murphy	.08	.06	.03
401	Steve Ontiveros	.06	.05	.02
402	Tony Phillips	.06	.05	.02
403	Eric Plunk	.08	.06	.03
404	Jose Rijo	.25	.20	.10
405	*Terry Steinbach* (FC)	.60	.45	.25
406	Dave Stewart	.25	.20	.10
407	Mickey Tettleton	.60	.45	.25
408	Dave Von Ohlen	.06	.05	.02
409	Jerry Willard	.06	.05	.02
410	Curt Young	.08	.06	.03
411	Bruce Bochy	.06	.05	.02
412	Dave Dravecky	.08	.06	.03
413	Tim Flannery	.06	.05	.02
414	Steve Garvey	.25	.20	.10
415	Goose Gossage	.15	.11	.06
416	Tony Gwynn	1.50	1.25	.60
417	Andy Hawkins	.06	.05	.02
418	LaMarr Hoyt	.06	.05	.02
419	Terry Kennedy	.08	.06	.03
420	*John Kruk*	5.00	3.75	2.00
421	Dave LaPoint	.06	.05	.02
422	Craig Lefferts	.06	.05	.02
423	Carmelo Martinez	.06	.05	.02

424	Lance McCullers	.06	.05	.02
425	Kevin McReynolds	.15	.11	.06
426	Graig Nettles	.12	.09	.05
427	*Bip Roberts*	.75	.60	.30
428	Jerry Royster	.06	.05	.02
429	Benito Santiago	.40	.30	.15
430	Eric Show	.08	.06	.03
431	Bob Stoddard	.06	.05	.02
432	Garry Templeton	.08	.06	.03
433	Gene Walter	.06	.05	.02
434	Ed Whitson	.06	.05	.02
435	Marvell Wynne	.06	.05	.02
436	Dave Anderson	.06	.05	.02
437	Greg Brock	.06	.05	.02
438	Enos Cabell	.06	.05	.02
439	Mariano Duncan	.06	.05	.02
440	Pedro Guerrero	.15	.11	.06
441	Orel Hershiser	.25	.20	.10
442	Rick Honeycutt	.06	.05	.02
443	Ken Howell	.06	.05	.02
444	Ken Landreaux	.06	.05	.02
445	Bill Madlock	.12	.09	.05
446	Mike Marshall	.12	.09	.05
447	Len Matuszek	.06	.05	.02
448	Tom Niedenfuer	.06	.05	.02
449	Alejandro Pena	.08	.06	.03
450	Dennis Powell (FC)	.06	.05	.02
451	Jerry Reuss	.08	.06	.03
452	Bill Russell	.08	.06	.03
453	Steve Sax	.15	.11	.06
454	Mike Scioscia	.08	.06	.03
455	Franklin Stubbs	.08	.06	.03
456	Alex Trevino	.06	.05	.02
457	Fernando Valenzuela	.10	.08	.04
458	Ed Vande Berg	.06	.05	.02
459	Bob Welch	.10	.08	.04
460	*Reggie Williams*	.06	.05	.02
461	Don Aase	.06	.05	.02
462	Juan Beniquez	.06	.05	.02
463	Mike Boddicker	.08	.06	.03
464	Juan Bonilla	.06	.05	.02
465	Rich Bordi	.06	.05	.02
466	Storm Davis	.10	.08	.04
467	Rick Dempsey	.08	.06	.03
468	Ken Dixon	.06	.05	.02
469	Jim Dwyer	.06	.05	.02
470	Mike Flanagan	.08	.06	.03
471	Jackie Gutierrez	.06	.05	.02
472	Brad Havens	.06	.05	.02
473	Lee Lacy	.06	.05	.02
474	Fred Lynn	.15	.11	.06
475	Scott McGregor	.08	.06	.03
476	Eddie Murray	.75	.60	.30
477	Tom O'Malley	.06	.05	.02
478	Cal Ripken, Jr.	3.00	2.25	1.25
479	Larry Sheets	.08	.06	.03
480	John Shelby	.06	.05	.02
481	Nate Snell	.06	.05	.02
482	Jim Traber (FC)	.06	.05	.02
483	Mike Young	.06	.05	.02
484	Neil Allen	.06	.05	.02
485	Harold Baines	.15	.11	.06
486	Floyd Bannister	.06	.05	.02
487	Daryl Boston	.06	.05	.02
488	Ivan Calderon	.06	.05	.02
489	*John Cangelosi*	.12	.09	.05
490	Steve Carlton	.40	.30	.15
491	Joe Cowley	.06	.05	.02
492	Julio Cruz	.06	.05	.02
493	Bill Dawley	.06	.05	.02
494	Jose DeLeon	.08	.06	.03
495	Richard Dotson	.08	.06	.03
496	Carlton Fisk	.60	.45	.25
497	Ozzie Guillen	.10	.08	.04
498	Jerry Hairston	.06	.05	.02
499	Ron Hassey	.06	.05	.02
500	Tim Hulett	.06	.05	.02
501	Bob James	.06	.05	.02
502	Steve Lyons	.06	.05	.02
503	*Joel McKeon*	.06	.05	.02
504	Gene Nelson	.06	.05	.02
505	Dave Schmidt	.06	.05	.02
506	Ray Searage	.06	.05	.02
507	*Bobby Thigpen* (FC)	.20	.15	.08
508	Greg Walker	.06	.05	.02
509	Jim Acker	.06	.05	.02
510	Doyle Alexander	.08	.06	.03
511	*Paul Assenmacher*	.15	.11	.06
512	Bruce Benedict	.06	.05	.02
513	Chris Chambliss	.08	.06	.03
514	Jeff Dedmon	.06	.05	.02
515	Gene Garber	.06	.05	.02
516	Ken Griffey	.10	.08	.04
517	Terry Harper	.06	.05	.02
518	Bob Horner	.10	.08	.04
519	Glenn Hubbard	.06	.05	.02
520	Rick Mahler	.06	.05	.02
521	Omar Moreno	.06	.05	.02
522	Dale Murphy	.25	.20	.10
523	Ken Oberkfell	.06	.05	.02
524	Ed Olwine	.06	.05	.02
525	David Palmer	.06	.05	.02
526	Rafael Ramirez	.06	.05	.02
527	Billy Sample	.06	.05	.02
528	Ted Simmons	.12	.09	.05
529	Zane Smith	.08	.06	.03
530	Bruce Sutter	.12	.09	.05
531	*Andres Thomas*	.06	.05	.02
532	Ozzie Virgil	.06	.05	.02
533	*Allan Anderson* (FC)	.06	.05	.02
534	Keith Atherton	.06	.05	.02
535	Billy Beane	.06	.05	.02
536	Bert Blyleven	.12	.09	.05
537	Tom Brunansky	.10	.08	.04
538	Randy Bush	.06	.05	.02
539	George Frazier	.06	.05	.02
540	Gary Gaetti	.15	.11	.06
541	Greg Gagne	.06	.05	.02
542	Mickey Hatcher	.06	.05	.02
543	Neal Heaton	.06	.05	.02
544	Kent Hrbek	.15	.11	.06
545	Roy Lee Jackson	.06	.05	.02
546	Tim Laudner	.06	.05	.02
547	Steve Lombardozzi	.06	.05	.02
548	*Mark Portugal*	1.00	.70	.40
549	Kirby Puckett	4.00	3.00	1.50
550	Jeff Reed	.06	.05	.02
551	Mark Salas	.06	.05	.02
552	Roy Smalley	.06	.05	.02
553	Mike Smithson	.06	.05	.02
554	Frank Viola	.25	.20	.10
555	Thad Bosley	.06	.05	.02
556	Ron Cey	.10	.08	.04
557	Jody Davis	.08	.06	.03
558	Ron Davis	.06	.05	.02
559	Bob Dernier	.06	.05	.02
560	Frank DiPino	.06	.05	.02
561	Shawon Dunston	.15	.11	.06
562	Leon Durham	.08	.06	.03
563	Dennis Eckersley	.40	.30	.15
564	Terry Francona	.06	.05	.02
565	Dave Gumpert	.06	.05	.02
566	Guy Hoffman	.08	.06	.03
567	Ed Lynch	.06	.05	.02
568	Gary Matthews	.10	.08	.04
569	Keith Moreland	.08	.06	.03
570	*Jamie Moyer* (FC)	.06	.05	.02
571	Jerry Mumphrey	.06	.05	.02
572	Ryne Sandberg	3.00	2.25	1.25
573	Scott Sanderson	.06	.05	.02
574	Lee Smith	.10	.08	.04
575	Chris Speier	.06	.05	.02
576	Rick Sutcliffe	.12	.09	.05
577	Manny Trillo	.08	.06	.03
578	Steve Trout	.06	.05	.02
579	Karl Best	.06	.05	.02
580	Scott Bradley (FC)	.08	.06	.03
581	Phil Bradley	.12	.09	.05
582	Mickey Brantley	.08	.06	.03
583	Mike Brown	.06	.05	.02
584	Alvin Davis	.06	.05	.02
585	*Lee Guetterman* (FC)	.15	.11	.06
586	Mark Huismann	.06	.05	.02
587	Bob Kearney	.06	.05	.02
588	Pete Ladd	.06	.05	.02
589	Mark Langston	.30	.25	.12
590	Mike Moore	.06	.05	.02
591	Mike Morgan	.06	.05	.02
592	John Moses	.06	.05	.02
593	Ken Phelps	.08	.06	.03
594	Jim Presley	.10	.08	.04
595	*Rey Quinonez (Quinones)*	.06	.05	.02
596	Harold Reynolds	.15	.11	.06
597	Billy Swift	.30	.25	.12
598	Danny Tartabull	.50	.40	.20
599	Steve Yeager	.06	.05	.02
600	Matt Young	.06	.05	.02
601	Bill Almon	.06	.05	.02
602	*Rafael Belliard* (FC)	.12	.09	.05
603	Mike Bielecki	.06	.05	.02
604	*Barry Bonds*	35.00	26.00	14.00
605	*Bobby Bonilla*	4.50	3.50	1.75
606	Sid Bream	.08	.06	.03
607	Mike Brown	.06	.05	.02
608	Pat Clements	.06	.05	.02
609	*Mike Diaz* (FC)	.06	.05	.02
610	Cecilio Guante	.06	.05	.02
611	*Barry Jones* (FC)	.06	.05	.02
612	Bob Kipper	.06	.05	.02
613	Larry McWilliams	.06	.05	.02
614	Jim Morrison	.06	.05	.02
615	Joe Orsulak	.06	.05	.02
616	Junior Ortiz	.06	.05	.02
617	Tony Pena	.08	.06	.03
618	Johnny Ray	.06	.05	.02
619	Rick Reuschel	.06	.05	.02
620	R.J. Reynolds	.06	.05	.02
621	Rick Rhoden	.10	.08	.04
622	Don Robinson	.08	.06	.03
623	Bob Walk	.06	.05	.02
624	Jim Winn	.06	.05	.02
625	Youthful Power (Jose Canseco, Pete Incaviglia)	.70	.50	.30
626	300 Game Winners (Phil Niekro, Don Sutton)	.12	.09	.05
627	A.L. Firemen (Don Aase, Dave Righetti)	.08	.06	.03
628	Rookie All-Stars (Jose Canseco, Wally Joyner)	.75	.60	.30
629	Magic Mets (Gary Carter, Dwight Gooden, Keith Hernandez, Darryl Strawberry)	.15	.11	.06
630	N.L. Best Righties (Mike Krukow, Mike Scott)	.08	.06	.03
631	Sensational Southpaws (John Franco, Fernando Valenzuela)	.10	.08	.04
632	Count 'Em (Bob Horner)	.08	.06	.03
633	A.L. Pitcher's Nightmare (Jose Canseco, Kirby Puckett, Jim Rice)	.70	.50	.30
634	All Star Battery (Gary Carter, Roger Clemens)	.40	.30	.15
635	4,000 Strikeouts (Steve Carlton)	.12	.09	.05
636	Big Bats At First Sack (Glenn Davis, Eddie Murray)	.20	.15	.08
637	On Base (Wade Boggs, Keith Hernandez)	.35	.25	.14
638	Sluggers From Left Side (Don Mattingly, Darryl Strawberry)	.75	.60	.30
639	Former MVP's (Dave Parker, Ryne Sandberg)	.12	.09	.05
640	Dr. K. & Super K (Roger Clemens, Dwight Gooden)	.50	.40	.20
641	A.L. West Stoppers (Charlie Hough, Mike Witt)	.08	.06	.03
642	Doubles & Triples (Tim Raines, Juan Samuel)	.12	.09	.05
643	Outfielders With Punch (Harold Baines, Jesse Barfield)	.10	.08	.04
644	Major League Prospects (*Dave Clark* (FC), Greg Swindell)	1.00	.70	.40
645	Major League Prospects (*Ron Karkovice*, Russ Morman)	.25	.20	.10
646	Major League Prospects (*Willie Fraser*, Devon White)	2.50	2.00	1.00
647	Major League Prospects (*Jerry Browne* (FC), Mike Stanley)	1.25	.90	.50
648	Major League Prospects (*Phil Lombardi* (FC), Dave Magadan)	.75	.60	.30
649	Major League Prospects (*Ralph Bryant* (FC), Jose Gonzalez)	.20	.15	.08
650	Major League Prospects (*Randy Asadoor* (FC), Jimmy Jones)	.20	.15	.08
651	Major League Prospects (*Marvin Freeman*, Tracy Jones)	.25	.20	.10
652	Major League Prospects (*Kevin Seitzer*, John Stefero)	.25	.20	.10
653	Major League Prospects (*Steve Fireovid* (FC), Rob Nelson)	.10	.08	.04
654	Checklist 1-95	.06	.05	.02
655	Checklist 96-192	.06	.05	.02
656	Checklist 193-288	.06	.05	.02
657	Checklist 289-384	.06	.05	.02
658	Checklist 385-483	.06	.05	.02
659	Checklist 484-578	.06	.05	.02
660	Checklist 579-660	.06	.05	.02

1987 Fleer All Stars

As in 1986, Fleer All Star Team cards were randomly inserted in Fleer wax and cello packs. Twelve cards, each measuring the standard 2-1/2" by 3-1/2", comprise the set. The card fronts feature a full-color player photo set against a gray background for American League players and a black background for National Leaguers. Card backs are printed in black, red and white and feature a lengthy player biography. Fleer's choices for a major league All-Star team is once again the theme for the set.

		MT	NR MT	EX
Complete Set (12):		18.00	13.50	7.25
Common Player:		.30	.20	.10
1	Don Mattingly	3.00	1.50	.80
2	Gary Carter	1.00	.70	.40
3	Tony Fernandez	.40	.30	.15
4	Steve Sax	.30	.20	.10
5	Kirby Puckett	6.00	4.00	2.00
6	Mike Schmidt	3.00	1.50	.80
7	Mike Easler	.30	.20	.10
8	Todd Worrell	.30	.20	.10
9	George Bell	.60	.45	.25
10	Fernando Valenzuela	.30	.20	.10
11	Roger Clemens	5.00	3.00	1.50
12	Tim Raines	1.00	.70	.40

1987 Fleer Headliners

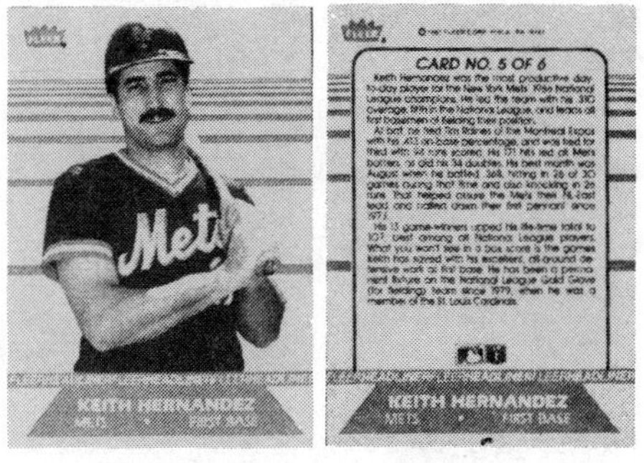

A continuation of the 1986 Future Hall of Famers idea, Fleer encountered legal problems with using the Hall of Fame name and abated them by entitling the set "Headliners." The cards, which are the standard 2-1/2" by 3-1/2" size, were randomly inserted in three-pack cello packs. Card fronts feature a player photo set against a beige background with bright red stripes. The card backs are printed in black, red and gray and offer a brief biography with an emphasis on the player's performance during the 1986 season.

		MT	NR MT	EX
Complete Set (6):		4.00	3.00	1.50
Common Player:		.30	.25	.12
1	Wade Boggs	1.50	1.25	.60
2	Jose Canseco	1.50	1.25	.60
3	Dwight Gooden	.40	.30	.15
4	Rickey Henderson	1.50	1.25	.60
5	Keith Hernandez	.30	.25	.12
6	Jim Rice	.30	.25	.12

A card number in parentheses () indicates the set is unnumbered.

1987 Fleer '86 World Series

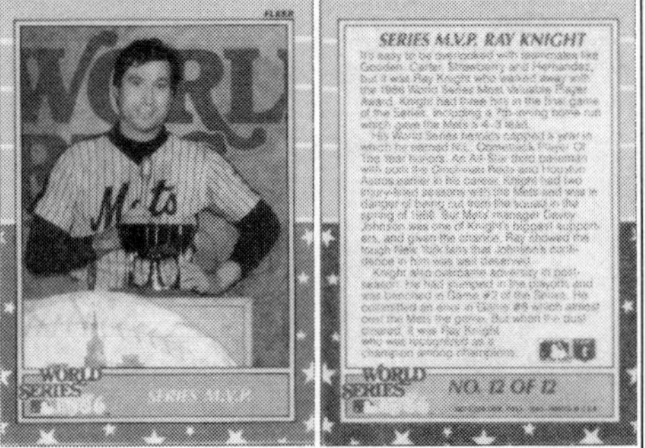

Fleer issued a set of 12 cards highlighting the 1986 World Series between the Boston Red Sox and New York Mets. The sets were available only with Fleer factory-packaged sets of 660 regular issue cards. The cards, which are the standard 2-1/2" by 3-1/2" size, have either horizontal or vertical formats. The fronts are bordered in red, white and blue stars and stripes with a thin gold frame around the photo. The backs are printed in red and blue ink on white stock and include information regarding the photo on the card fronts.

		MT	NR MT	EX
Complete Set (12):		2.00	1.50	.80
Common Player:		.25	.20	.10
1	Left-Hand Finesse Beats Mets (Bruce Hurst)	.25	.20	.10
2	Wade Boggs, Keith Hernandez	.50	.40	.20
3	Roger Clemens	1.50	1.25	.60
4	Gary Carter	.50	.40	.20
5	Ron Darling	.25	.20	.10
6	.433 Series Batting Average (Marty Barrett)	.25	.20	.10
7	Dwight Gooden	.50	.40	.20
8	Strategy At Work	.25	.20	.10
9	Dewey! (Dwight Evans)	.25	.20	.10
10	One Strike From Boston Victory (Dave Henderson, Spike Owen)	.25	.20	.10
11	Ray Knight, Darryl Strawberry	.25	.20	.10
12	Series M.V.P. (Ray Knight)	.25	.20	.10

1987 Fleer Box Panels

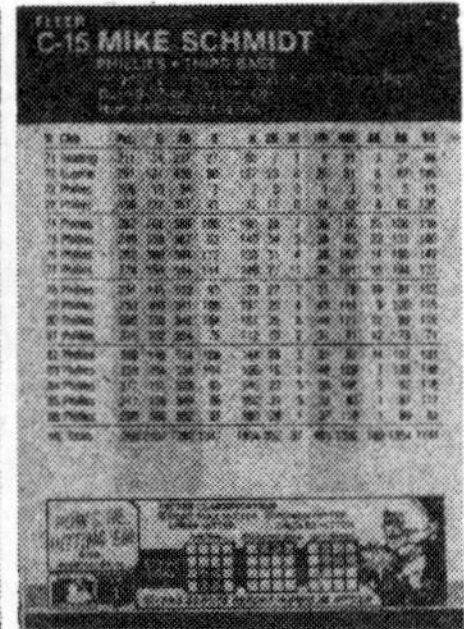

For the second straight year, Fleer produced a special set of cards designed to stimulate sales of their wax and cello pack boxes. In 1987, Fleer issued 16 cards in panels of four on the bottoms of retail boxes. The cards are numbered C-1 through C-16 and are 2-1/2" by 3-1/2" in size. The cards have the same design as the regular issue set with the player photos and card numbers being different.

		MT	NR MT	EX
Complete Panel Set:		8.00	6.00	3.25
Complete Singles Set:		3.50	2.75	1.50
Common Panel:		2.25	1.75	.90
Common Single Player:		.20	.15	.08
	Panel	2.50	2.00	1.00
1	Mets Logo	.05	.04	.02
6	Keith Hernandez	.15	.11	.06
8	Dale Murphy	.60	.45	.25
14	Ryne Sandberg	.80	.60	.30
	Panel	2.25	1.75	.90
2	Jesse Barfield	.20	.15	.08
3	George Brett	.80	.60	.30
5	Red Sox Logo	.05	.04	.02
11	Kirby Puckett	.75	.60	.30
	Panel	2.75	2.00	1.00
4	Dwight Gooden	.40	.30	.15
9	Astros Logo	.05	.04	.02
10	Dave Parker	.25	.20	.10
15	Mike Schmidt	.80	.60	.30
	Panel	2.75	2.00	1.00
7	Wally Joyner	.40	.30	.15
12	Dave Righetti	.20	.15	.08
13	Angels Logo	.05	.04	.02
16	Robin Yount	.80	.60	.30

1987 Fleer Update

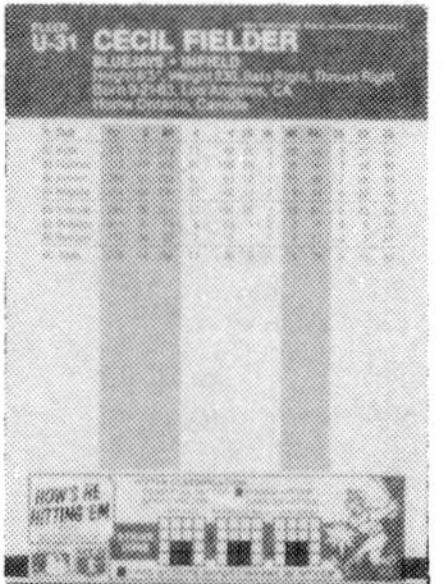

Fleer followed suit on a Topps idea in 1984 and began producing "Update" sets. The 1987 edition brings the regular Fleer set to date by including traded players and hot rookies. The cards measure 2-1/2" by 3-1/2" and are housed in a specially designed box with 25 team logo stickers. As a companion to the glossy-coated Fleer Collectors Edition set, Fleer produced a special edition Update set it its own tin box. Values of the glossy-coated cards are only a few dollars more than the regular Update cards.

		MT	NR MT	EX
Complete Set (132):		15.00	11.00	6.00
Common Player:		.06	.05	.02
1	Scott Bankhead	.08	.06	.03
2	Eric Bell (FC)	.06	.05	.02
3	Juan Beniquez	.06	.05	.02
4	Juan Berenguer	.06	.05	.02
5	Mike Birkbeck (FC)	.06	.05	.02
6	Randy Bockus (FC)	.06	.05	.02
7	Rod Booker (FC)	.06	.05	.02
8	Thad Bosley	.06	.05	.02
9	Greg Brock	.06	.05	.02
10	Bob Brower (FC)	.06	.05	.02
11	Chris Brown	.06	.05	.02
12	Jerry Browne	.06	.05	.02
13	Ralph Bryant	.06	.05	.02
14	DeWayne Buice (FC)	.06	.05	.02
15	Ellis Burks (FC)	.60	.45	.25
16	Casey Candaele (FC)	.10	.08	.04
17	Steve Carlton	.40	.30	.15
18	Juan Castillo	.06	.05	.02
19	Chuck Crim (FC)	.10	.08	.04
20	Mark Davidson (FC)	.10	.08	.04
21	Mark Davis	.06	.05	.02
22	Storm Davis	.06	.05	.02
23	Bill Dawley	.06	.05	.02
24	Andre Dawson	.40	.30	.15
25	Brian Dayett	.06	.05	.02
26	Rick Dempsey	.06	.05	.02
27	Ken Dowell (FC)	.06	.05	.02
28	Dave Dravecky	.08	.06	.03
29	Mike Dunne (FC)	.10	.08	.04
30	Dennis Eckersley	.30	.25	.12
31	Cecil Fielder	1.00	.70	.40
32	Brian Fisher	.10	.08	.04
33	Willie Fraser	.10	.08	.04
34	Ken Gerhart (FC)	.06	.05	.02
35	Jim Gott	.06	.05	.02
36	Dan Gladden	.06	.05	.02
37	Mike Greenwell (FC)	.80	.60	.30
38	Cecilio Guante	.06	.05	.02
39	Albert Hall	.06	.05	.02
40	Atlee Hammaker	.06	.05	.02
41	Mickey Hatcher	.06	.05	.02
42	Mike Heath	.06	.05	.02
43	Neal Heaton	.06	.05	.02
44	Mike Henneman (FC)	.30	.25	.12
45	Guy Hoffman	.06	.05	.02
46	Charles Hudson	.06	.05	.02
47	Chuck Jackson (FC)	.06	.05	.02
48	Mike Jackson (FC)	.06	.05	.02
49	Reggie Jackson	.60	.45	.25
50	Chris James	.06	.05	.02
51	Dion James	.06	.05	.02
52	Stan Javier	.06	.05	.02
53	Stan Jefferson (FC)	.06	.05	.02
54	Jimmy Jones	.10	.08	.04
55	Tracy Jones	.10	.08	.04
56	Terry Kennedy	.08	.06	.03
57	Mike Kingery	.06	.05	.02
58	Ray Knight	.10	.08	.04
59	Gene Larkin (FC)	.30	.25	.12
60	Mike LaValliere	.06	.05	.02
61	Jack Lazorko (FC)	.06	.05	.02
62	Terry Leach	.06	.05	.02
63	Rick Leach	.06	.05	.02
64	Craig Lefferts	.06	.05	.02
65	Jim Lindeman (FC)	.06	.05	.02
66	Bill Long (FC)	.06	.05	.02
67	Mike Loynd (FC)	.06	.05	.02
68	Greg Maddux (FC)	4.00	3.00	1.50
69	Bill Madlock	.15	.11	.06
70	Dave Magadan	.80	.60	.30
71	Joe Magrane (FC)	.60	.45	.25
72	Fred Manrique (FC)	.06	.05	.02
73	Mike Mason	.06	.05	.02
74	Lloyd McClendon (FC)	.06	.05	.02
75	Fred McGriff (FC)	4.00	3.00	1.50
76	Mark McGwire (FC)	4.00	3.00	1.50
77	Mark McLemore	.06	.05	.02
78	Kevin McReynolds	.08	.06	.03
79	Dave Meads (FC)	.06	.05	.02
80	Greg Minton	.06	.05	.02
81	John Mitchell (FC)	.06	.05	.02
82	Kevin Mitchell	.60	.45	.25
83	John Morris	.06	.05	.02
84	Jeff Musselman (FC)	.15	.11	.06
85	Randy Myers (FC)	.40	.30	.15
86	Gene Nelson	.06	.05	.02
87	Joe Niekro	.10	.08	.04
88	Tom Nieto	.06	.05	.02
89	Reid Nichols	.06	.05	.02
90	Matt Nokes (FC)	.40	.30	.15
91	Dickie Noles	.06	.05	.02
92	Edwin Nunez	.06	.05	.02
93	Jose Nunez (FC)	.06	.05	.02
94	Paul O'Neill	.50	.40	.20
95	Jim Paciorek (FC)	.06	.05	.02
96	Lance Parrish	.08	.06	.03
97	Bill Pecota (FC)	.08	.06	.03
98	Tony Pena	.08	.06	.03
99	Luis Polonia (FC)	.40	.30	.15
100	Randy Ready	.06	.05	.02
101	Jeff Reardon	.08	.06	.03
102	Gary Redus	.08	.06	.03
103	Rick Rhoden	.10	.08	.04
104	Wally Ritchie (FC)	.06	.05	.02
105	Jeff Robinson (FC)	.08	.06	.03
106	Mark Salas	.06	.05	.02
107	Dave Schmidt	.06	.05	.02
108	Kevin Seitzer	.06	.05	.02
109	John Shelby	.06	.05	.02
110	John Smiley (FC)	.30	.25	.12
111	Lary Sorenson	.06	.05	.02
112	Chris Speier	.06	.05	.02
113	Randy St. Claire	.06	.05	.02
114	Jim Sundberg	.08	.06	.03
115	B.J. Surhoff (FC)	.20	.15	.08
116	Greg Swindell	.40	.30	.15
117	Danny Tartabull	.40	.30	.15
118	Dorn Taylor (FC)	.06	.05	.02
119	Lee Tunnell	.06	.05	.02
120	Ed Vande Berg	.06	.05	.02
121	Andy Van Slyke	.20	.15	.08
122	Gary Ward	.06	.05	.02
123	Devon White	.50	.40	.20
124	Alan Wiggins	.06	.05	.02
125	Bill Wilkinson (FC)	.06	.05	.02
126	Jim Winn	.06	.05	.02
127	Frank Williams	.06	.05	.02
128	Ken Williams (FC)	.06	.05	.02
129	Matt Williams (FC)	4.00	3.00	1.50
130	Herm Winningham	.06	.05	.02
131	Matt Young	.06	.05	.02
132	Checklist 1-132	.06	.05	.02

1987 Fleer Baseball's Award Winners

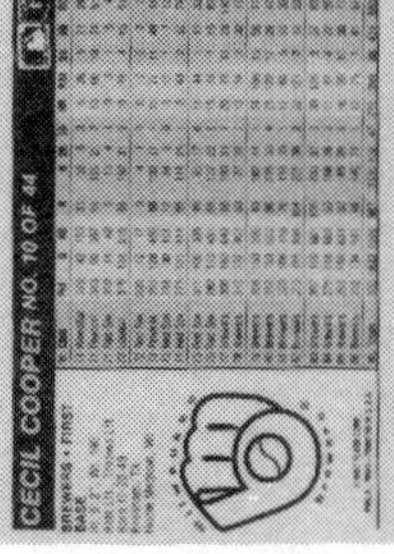

The 1987 Fleer Award Winners boxed set was prepared by Fleer for distribution by 7-Eleven stores. The cards, which measure 2-1/2" by 3-1/2", feature players who have won various major league awards during their careers. The card fronts contain full-color photos surrounded by a yellow border. The name of the award the player won is printed at the bottom of the card in an oval-shaped band designed to resemble a metal nameplate on a trophy. Card backs, printed in black, yellow and white, include lifetime major and minor league statistics along with typical personal information. Each boxed set contained six team logo stickers.

		MT	NR MT	EX
Complete Set:		5.00	3.75	2.00
Common Player:		.05	.04	.02
1	Marty Barrett	.07	.05	.03
2	George Bell	.20	.15	.08
3	Bert Blyleven	.10	.08	.04
4	Bob Boone	.05	.04	.02
5	John Candelaria	.05	.04	.02
6	Jose Canseco	1.00	.70	.40
7	Gary Carter	.25	.20	.10
8	Joe Carter	.25	.20	.10
9	Roger Clemens	.50	.40	.20
10	Cecil Cooper	.10	.08	.04
11	Eric Davis	.30	.25	.12
12	Tony Fernandez	.10	.08	.04
13	Scott Fletcher	.05	.04	.02
14	Bob Forsch	.05	.04	.02
15	Dwight Gooden	.25	.20	.10
16	Ron Guidry	.12	.09	.05
17	Ozzie Guillen	.07	.05	.03
18	Bill Gullickson	.05	.04	.02
19	Tony Gwynn	.25	.20	.10
20	Bob Knepper	.05	.04	.02
21	Ray Knight	.05	.04	.02
22	Mark Langston	.20	.15	.08
23	Candy Maldonado	.05	.04	.02
24	Don Mattingly	.90	.70	.35
25	Roger McDowell	.07	.05	.03
26	Dale Murphy	.30	.25	.12
27	Dave Parker	.12	.09	.05
28	Lance Parrish	.15	.11	.06
29	Gary Pettis	.05	.04	.02
30	Kirby Puckett	.70	.50	.30
31	Johnny Ray	.07	.05	.03
32	Dave Righetti	.12	.09	.05
33	Cal Ripken, Jr.	1.00	.70	.40
34	Bret Saberhagen	.15	.11	.06
35	Ryne Sandberg	1.00	.70	.40
36	Mike Schmidt	.40	.30	.15
37	Mike Scott	.12	.09	.05
38	Ozzie Smith	.12	.09	.05
39	Robbie Thompson	.10	.08	.04
40	Fernando Valenzuela	.20	.15	.08
41	Mitch Webster	.05	.04	.02
42	Frank White	.07	.05	.03
43	Mike Witt	.07	.05	.03
44	Todd Worrell	.15	.11	.06

1987 Fleer Baseball All Stars

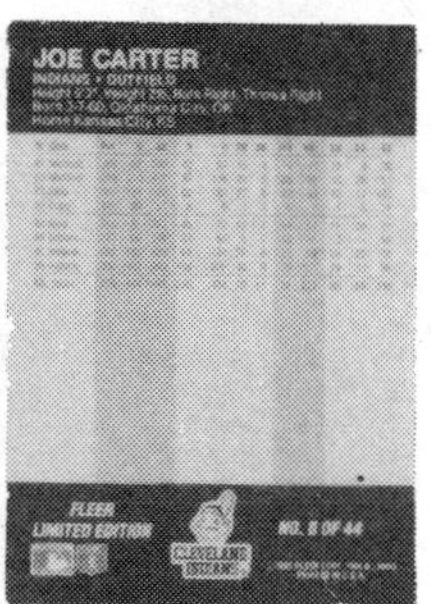

Produced by Fleer for exclusive distribution through Ben Franklin stores, the "Baseball All Stars" set is comprised of 44 cards which are the standard 2-1/2" by 3-1/2" size. The cards have full-color photos surrounded by a bright red border with white pinstripes at the top and bottom. The card backs are printed in blue, white and dark red and include complete major and minor league statistics. The set was issued in a special cardboard box.

		MT	NR MT	EX
Complete Set:		5.00	4.00	2.00
Common Player:		.05	.04	.02
1	Harold Baines	.05	.04	.02
2	Jesse Barfield	.12	.09	.05
3	Wade Boggs	.60	.45	.25
4	Dennis "Oil Can" Boyd	.05	.04	.02
5	Scott Bradley	.05	.04	.02
6	Jose Canseco	1.00	.70	.40
7	Gary Carter	.25	.20	.10
8	Joe Carter	.25	.20	.10
9	Mark Clear	.05	.04	.02
10	Roger Clemens	.50	.40	.20
11	Jose Cruz	.05	.04	.02
12	Chili Davis	.07	.05	.03
13	Jody Davis	.05	.04	.02
14	Rob Deer	.05	.04	.02
15	Brian Downing	.05	.04	.02
16	Sid Fernandez	.07	.05	.03
17	John Franco	.07	.05	.03
18	Andres Galarraga	.15	.11	.06
19	Dwight Gooden	.25	.20	.10
20	Tony Gwynn	.25	.20	.10
21	Charlie Hough	.05	.04	.02
22	Bruce Hurst	.05	.04	.02
23	Wally Joyner	.30	.25	.12
24	Carney Lansford	.05	.04	.02
25	Fred Lynn	.12	.09	.05
26	Don Mattingly	.90	.70	.35
27	Willie McGee	.05	.04	.02
28	Jack Morris	.15	.11	.06
29	Dale Murphy	.30	.25	.12
30	Bob Ojeda	.07	.05	.03
31	Tony Pena	.07	.05	.03
32	Kirby Puckett	.70	.50	.30
33	Dan Quisenberry	.07	.05	.03
34	Tim Raines	.25	.20	.10
35	Willie Randolph	.07	.05	.03
36	Cal Ripken, Jr.	1.00	.70	.40
37	Pete Rose	.50	.40	.20
38	Nolan Ryan	1.50	1.25	.60
39	Juan Samuel	.05	.04	.02
40	Mike Schmidt	.40	.30	.15
41	Ozzie Smith	.12	.09	.05
42	Andres Thomas	.05	.04	.02
43	Fernando Valenzuela	.20	.15	.08
44	Mike Witt	.07	.05	.03

1987 Fleer Baseball's Best

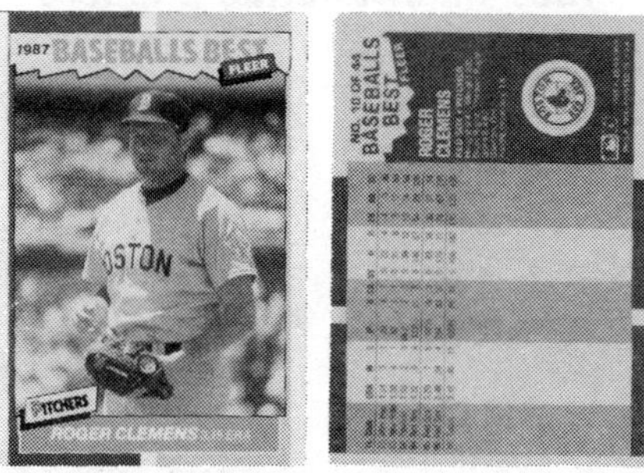

For a second straight baseball card season, Fleer produced for McCrory's stores and their affiliates a 44-card "Baseball's Best" set. Subtitled "Sluggers vs. Pitchers," 28 everyday players and 16 pitchers are featured. The card design is nearly identical to the previous year's effort. The cards, which measure 2-1/2" by 3-1/2", were housed in a specially designed box along with six team logo stickers.

		MT	NR MT	EX
Complete Set:		5.00	3.75	2.00
Common Player:		.05	.04	.02
1	Kevin Bass	.07	.05	.03
2	Jesse Barfield	.12	.09	.05
3	George Bell	.20	.15	.08
4	Wade Boggs	.60	.45	.25
5	Sid Bream	.05	.04	.02
6	George Brett	.60	.45	.25
7	Ivan Calderon	.10	.08	.04
8	Jose Canseco	1.00	.70	.40
9	Jack Clark	.12	.09	.05
10	Roger Clemens	.50	.40	.20
11	Eric Davis	.25	.20	.10
12	Andre Dawson	.15	.11	.06
13	Sid Fernandez	.07	.05	.03
14	John Franco	.07	.05	.03
15	Dwight Gooden	.25	.20	.10
16	Pedro Guerrero	.15	.11	.06
17	Tony Gwynn	.25	.20	.10
18	Rickey Henderson	.30	.25	.12
19	Tom Henke	.05	.04	.02
20	Ted Higuera	.10	.08	.04
21	Pete Incaviglia	.15	.11	.06
22	Wally Joyner	.20	.15	.08
23	Jeff Leonard	.05	.04	.02
24	Joe Magrane	.15	.11	.06
25	Don Mattingly	.90	.70	.35
26	Mark McGwire	.60	.45	.25
27	Jack Morris	.15	.11	.06
28	Dale Murphy	.40	.30	.15
29	Dave Parker	.12	.09	.05
30	Ken Phelps	.05	.04	.02
31	Kirby Puckett	.75	.60	.30
32	Tim Raines	.25	.20	.10
33	Jeff Reardon	.10	.08	.04
34	Dave Righetti	.12	.09	.05
35	Cal Ripken, Jr.	1.00	.70	.40
36	Bret Saberhagen	.15	.11	.06
37	Mike Schmidt	.60	.45	.25
38	Mike Scott	.12	.09	.05
39	Kevin Seitzer	.20	.15	.08
40	Darryl Strawberry	.40	.30	.15
41	Rick Sutcliffe	.10	.08	.04
42	Pat Tabler	.05	.04	.02
43	Fernando Valenzuela	.10	.08	.04
44	Mike Witt	.07	.05	.03

Definitions for grading conditions are located in the Introduction of this price guide.

1987 Fleer Baseball's Exciting Stars

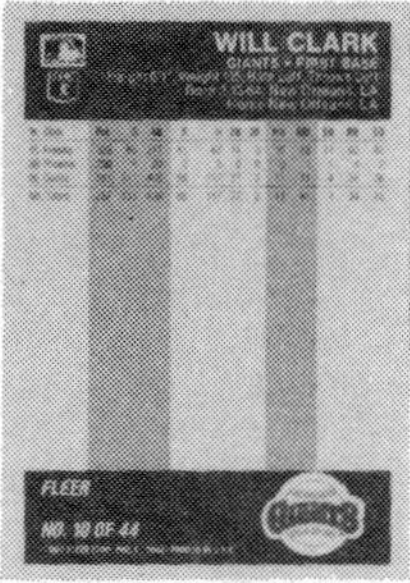

Another entry into the Fleer lineup of individual boxed sets, the "Baseball's Exciting Stars" set was produced by Fleer for Cumberland Farms stores. The card fronts feature a red, white and blue border with the words "Exciting Stars" printed in yellow at the top. The backs are printed in red and blue and carry complete major and minor league statistics. Included with the boxed set of 44 cards were six team logo stickers.

		MT	NR MT	EX
Complete Set:		5.00	3.75	2.00
Common Player:		.05	.04	.02
1	Don Aase	.05	.04	.02
2	Rick Aguilera	.07	.05	.03
3	Jesse Barfield	.12	.09	.05
4	Wade Boggs	.60	.45	.25
5	Dennis "Oil Can" Boyd	.05	.04	.02
6	Sid Bream	.07	.05	.03
7	Jose Canseco	1.00	.70	.40
8	Steve Carlton	.25	.20	.10
9	Gary Carter	.25	.20	.10
10	Will Clark	1.00	.70	.40
11	Roger Clemens	.40	.30	.15
12	Danny Cox	.07	.05	.03
13	Alvin Davis	.10	.08	.04
14	Eric Davis	.25	.20	.10
15	Rob Deer	.07	.05	.03
16	Brian Downing	.05	.04	.02
17	Gene Garber	.05	.04	.02
18	Steve Garvey	.25	.20	.10
19	Dwight Gooden	.25	.20	.10
20	Mark Gubicza	.10	.08	.04
21	Mel Hall	.05	.04	.02
22	Terry Harper	.05	.04	.02
23	Von Hayes	.10	.08	.04
24	Rickey Henderson	.60	.45	.25
25	Tom Henke	.05	.04	.02
26	Willie Hernandez	.05	.04	.02
27	Ted Higuera	.10	.08	.04
28	Rick Honeycutt	.05	.04	.02
29	Kent Hrbek	.15	.11	.06
30	Wally Joyner	.20	.15	.08
31	Charlie Kerfeld	.05	.04	.02
32	Fred Lynn	.12	.09	.05
33	Don Mattingly	.80	.60	.30
34	Tim Raines	.25	.20	.10
35	Dennis Rasmussen	.07	.05	.03
36	Johnny Ray	.07	.05	.03
37	Jim Rice	.20	.15	.08
38	Pete Rose	.50	.40	.20
39	Lee Smith	.07	.05	.03
40	Cory Snyder	.10	.08	.04
41	Darryl Strawberry	.40	.30	.15
42	Kent Tekulve	.05	.04	.02
43	Willie Wilson	.10	.08	.04
44	Bobby Witt	.12	.09	.05

1987 Fleer Baseball's Game Winners

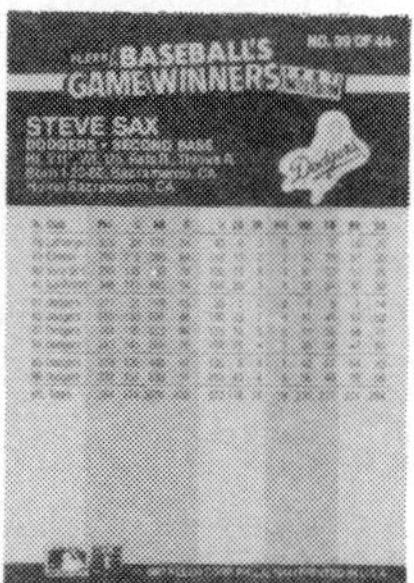

The 1987 Fleer "Baseball's Game Winners" boxed set of 44 cards was produced for distribution through Bi-Mart Discount Drug, Pay'n-Save, Mott's 5 & 10, M.E. Moses, and Winn's stores. The cards, which measure 2-1/2" by 3-1/2", have a light blue border with the player's name and game winning RBI or games won statistics in a yellow oval band at the top of the card. Below the full-color player photo is the name of the set in blue, yellow and red. Included with the boxed set were six team logo stickers.

		MT	NR MT	EX
Complete Set:		5.00	3.75	2.00
Common Player:		.05	.04	.02
1	Harold Baines	.10	.08	.04
2	Don Baylor	.10	.08	.04
3	George Bell	.20	.15	.08
4	Tony Bernazard	.05	.04	.02
5	Wade Boggs	.60	.45	.25
6	George Brett	.60	.45	.25
7	Hubie Brooks	.07	.05	.03
8	Jose Canseco	1.00	.70	.40
9	Gary Carter	.20	.15	.08
10	Roger Clemens	.40	.30	.15
11	Eric Davis	.25	.20	.10
12	Glenn Davis	.15	.11	.06
13	Shawon Dunston	.07	.05	.03
14	Mark Eichhorn	.10	.08	.04
15	Gary Gaetti	.12	.09	.05
16	Steve Garvey	.25	.20	.10
17	Kirk Gibson	.20	.15	.08
18	Dwight Gooden	.25	.20	.10
19	Von Hayes	.07	.05	.03
20	Willie Hernandez	.07	.05	.03
21	Ted Higuera	.10	.08	.04
22	Wally Joyner	.35	.25	.14
23	Bob Knepper	.05	.04	.02
24	Mike Krukow	.05	.04	.02
25	Jeff Leonard	.05	.04	.02
26	Don Mattingly	.90	.70	.35
27	Kirk McCaskill	.07	.05	.03
28	Kevin McReynolds	.12	.09	.05
29	Jim Morrison	.05	.04	.02
30	Dale Murphy	.30	.25	.12
31	Pete O'Brien	.07	.05	.03
32	Bob Ojeda	.07	.05	.03
33	Larry Parrish	.05	.04	.02
34	Ken Phelps	.05	.04	.02
35	Dennis Rasmussen	.07	.05	.03
36	Ernest Riles	.07	.05	.03
37	Cal Ripken, Jr.	1.00	.70	.40
38	Ron Robinson	.05	.04	.02
39	Steve Sax	.15	.11	.06
40	Mike Schmidt	.50	.40	.20
41	John Tudor	.07	.05	.03
42	Fernando Valenzuela	.10	.08	.04
43	Mike Witt	.07	.05	.03
44	Curt Young	.05	.04	.02

1987 Fleer Baseball's Hottest Stars

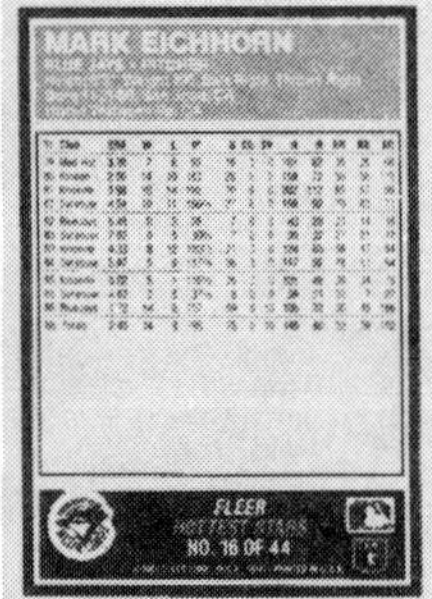

The "Baseball's Hottest Stars" 44-card set was produced by Fleer for the Revco Drug Store chain. Measuring the standard 2-1/2" by 3-1/2", the cards feature full-color photos surrounded by a red, white and blue border. The player's name, position and team appear in a blue band at the bottom of the card. Card backs are printed in red, white and black and contain the player's lifetime professional statistics. The set was housed in a special cardboard box with six team logo stickers.

		MT	NR MT	EX
Complete Set:		5.00	3.75	2.00
Common Player:		.05	.04	.02
1	Joaquin Andujar	.05	.04	.02
2	Harold Baines	.10	.08	.04
3	Kevin Bass	.07	.05	.03
4	Don Baylor	.10	.08	.04
5	Barry Bonds	1.00	.70	.40
6	George Brett	.60	.45	.25
7	Tom Brunansky	.10	.08	.04
8	Brett Butler	.05	.04	.02
9	Jose Canseco	1.00	.70	.40
10	Roger Clemens	.50	.40	.20
11	Ron Darling	.10	.08	.04
12	Eric Davis	.25	.20	.10
13	Andre Dawson	.15	.11	.06
14	Doug DeCinces	.05	.04	.02
15	Leon Durham	.07	.05	.03
16	Mark Eichhorn	.10	.08	.04
17	Scott Garrelts	.05	.04	.02
18	Dwight Gooden	.25	.20	.10
19	Dave Henderson	.05	.04	.02
20	Rickey Henderson	.50	.40	.20
21	Keith Hernandez	.07	.05	.03
22	Ted Higuera	.10	.08	.04
23	Bob Horner	.07	.05	.03
24	Pete Incaviglia	.20	.15	.08
25	Wally Joyner	.30	.25	.12
26	Mark Langston	.07	.05	.03
27	Don Mattingly	.90	.70	.35
28	Dale Murphy	.30	.25	.12
29	Kirk McCaskill	.07	.05	.03
30	Willie McGee	.10	.08	.04
31	Dave Righetti	.07	.05	.03
32	Pete Rose	.40	.30	.15
33	Bruce Ruffin	.05	.04	.02
34	Steve Sax	.07	.05	.03
35	Mike Schmidt	.45	.35	.20
36	Larry Sheets	.05	.04	.02
37	Eric Show	.07	.05	.03
38	Dave Smith	.05	.04	.02
39	Cory Snyder	.07	.05	.03
40	Frank Tanana	.05	.04	.02
41	Alan Trammell	.20	.15	.08
42	Reggie Williams	.05	.04	.02
43	Mookie Wilson	.05	.04	.02
44	Todd Worrell	.15	.11	.06

1987 Fleer League Leaders

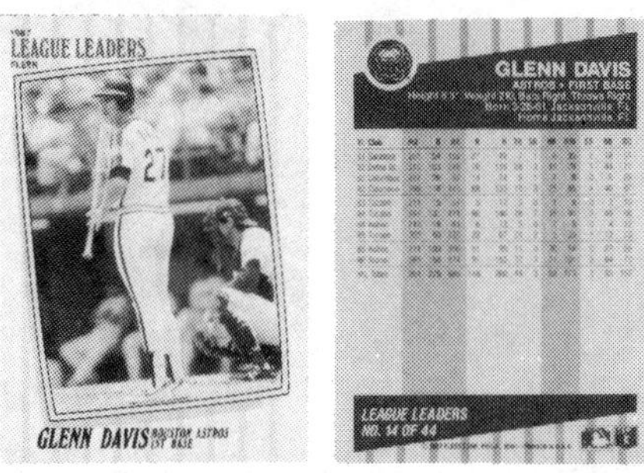

For the second year in a row, Fleer produced a 44- card "League Leaders" set for Walgreens. The card fronts feature a border style which is identical to that used in 1986. However, an elliptical shaped full-color player photo is placed diagonally on the front. "1987 Fleer League Leaders" appears in the upper left corner of the front although nowhere on the card does it state in which pitching, hitting or fielding department was the player a league leader. The card backs are printed in red and blue on white stock. The cards in the boxed set are the standard 2-1/2" by 3-1/2" size.

		MT	NR MT	EX
Complete Set (44):		5.00	3.75	2.00
Common Player:		.05	.04	.02
1	Jesse Barfield	.12	.09	.05
2	Mike Boddicker	.07	.05	.03
3	Wade Boggs	.60	.45	.25
4	Phil Bradley	.10	.08	.04
5	George Brett	.60	.45	.25
6	Hubie Brooks	.07	.05	.03
7	Chris Brown	.07	.05	.03
8	Jose Canseco	.70	.50	.30
9	Joe Carter	.20	.15	.08
10	Roger Clemens	.40	.30	.15
11	Vince Coleman	.15	.11	.06
12	Joe Cowley	.05	.04	.02
13	Kal Daniels	.10	.08	.04
14	Glenn Davis	.07	.05	.03
15	Jody Davis	.07	.05	.03
16	Darrell Evans	.07	.05	.03
17	Dwight Evans	.10	.08	.04
18	John Franco	.07	.05	.03
19	Julio Franco	.10	.08	.04
20	Dwight Gooden	.25	.20	.10
21	Goose Gossage	.12	.09	.05
22	Tom Herr	.07	.05	.03
23	Ted Higuera	.10	.08	.04
24	Bob Horner	.07	.05	.03
25	Pete Incaviglia	.20	.15	.08
26	Wally Joyner	.30	.25	.12
27	Dave Kingman	.10	.08	.04
28	Don Mattingly	.90	.70	.35
29	Willie McGee	.10	.08	.04
30	Donnie Moore	.05	.04	.02
31	Keith Moreland	.05	.04	.02
32	Eddie Murray	.25	.20	.10
33	Mike Pagliarulo	.10	.08	.04
34	Larry Parrish	.05	.04	.02
35	Tony Pena	.07	.05	.03
36	Kirby Puckett	.50	.40	.20
37	Pete Rose	.50	.40	.20
38	Juan Samuel	.12	.09	.05
39	Ryne Sandberg	1.00	.70	.40
40	Mike Schmidt	.40	.30	.15
41	Darryl Strawberry	.40	.30	.15
42	Greg Walker	.07	.05	.03
43	Bob Welch	.07	.05	.03
44	Todd Worrell	.12	.09	.05

1987 Fleer Limited Edition

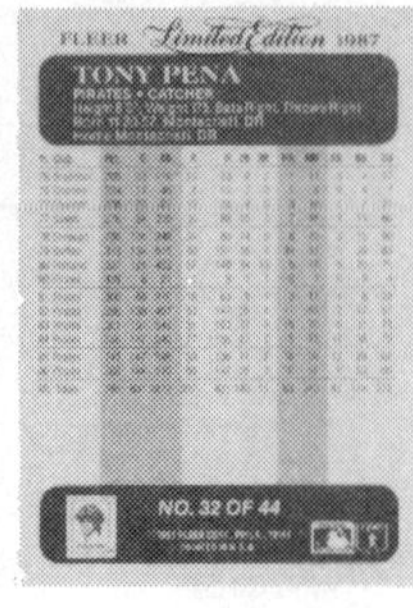

For the third straight year, Fleer produced a Limited Edition set for the McCrory's store chain and their affiliates. The cards are the standard 2-1/2" by 3-1/2" size and feature light blue borders at the top and bottom and a diagonal red and white border running along both sides. The set was issued in a specially prepared cardboard box, along with six team logo stickers.

		MT	NR MT	EX
Complete Set:		5.00	3.75	2.00
Common Player:		.05	.04	.02
1	Floyd Bannister	.05	.04	.02
2	Marty Barrett	.07	.05	.03
3	Steve Bedrosian	.10	.08	.04
4	George Bell	.20	.15	.08
5	George Brett	.70	.50	.30
6	Jose Canseco	1.00	.70	.40
7	Joe Carter	.12	.09	.05
8	Will Clark	1.00	.70	.40
9	Roger Clemens	.40	.30	.15
10	Vince Coleman	.07	.05	.03
11	Glenn Davis	.07	.05	.03
12	Mike Davis	.05	.04	.02
13	Len Dykstra	.15	.11	.06
14	John Franco	.07	.05	.03
15	Julio Franco	.10	.08	.04
16	Steve Garvey	.25	.20	.10
17	Kirk Gibson	.20	.15	.08
18	Dwight Gooden	.25	.20	.10
19	Tony Gwynn	.25	.20	.10
20	Keith Hernandez	.10	.08	.04
21	Teddy Higuera	.07	.05	.03
22	Kent Hrbek	.15	.11	.06
23	Wally Joyner	.30	.25	.12
24	Mike Krukow	.05	.04	.02
25	Mike Marshall	.05	.04	.02
26	Don Mattingly	.90	.70	.35
27	Oddibe McDowell	.10	.08	.04
28	Jack Morris	.15	.11	.06
29	Lloyd Moseby	.07	.05	.03
30	Dale Murphy	.30	.25	.12
31	Eddie Murray	.25	.20	.10
32	Tony Pena	.07	.05	.03
33	Jim Presley	.05	.04	.02
34	Jeff Reardon	.10	.08	.04
35	Jim Rice	.10	.08	.04
36	Pete Rose	.40	.30	.15
37	Mike Schmidt	.40	.30	.15
38	Mike Scott	.12	.09	.05
39	Lee Smith	.10	.08	.04
40	Lonnie Smith	.05	.04	.02
41	Gary Ward	.05	.04	.02
42	Dave Winfield	.40	.30	.15
43	Todd Worrell	.12	.09	.05
44	Robin Yount	.60	.45	.25

The values quoted are intended to reflect the market price.

1987 Fleer Mini

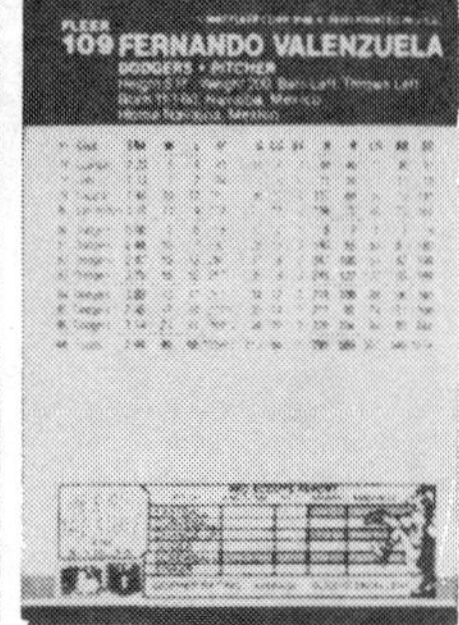

Continuing with an idea originated the previous year, the Fleer "Classic Miniatures" set consists of 120 cards that measure 1-13/16" by 2-9/16" in size. The cards are identical in design to the regular issue set produced by Fleer, but use completely different photos. The set was issued in a specially prepared collectors box along with 18 team logo stickers. The Fleer Mini set was available only through hobby dealers.

		MT	NR MT	EX
Complete Set:		5.00	6.75	3.50
Common Player:		.05	.04	.02
1	Don Aase	.05	.04	.02
2	Joaquin Andujar	.05	.04	.02
3	Harold Baines	.12	.09	.05
4	Jesse Barfield	.05	.04	.02
5	Kevin Bass	.05	.04	.02
6	Don Baylor	.10	.08	.04
7	George Bell	.20	.15	.08
8	Tony Bernazard	.05	.04	.02
9	Bert Blyleven	.12	.09	.05
10	Wade Boggs	.60	.45	.25
11	Phil Bradley	.10	.08	.04
12	Sid Bream	.05	.04	.02
13	George Brett	.60	.45	.25
14	Hubie Brooks	.07	.05	.03
15	Chris Brown	.07	.05	.03
16	Tom Candiotti	.05	.04	.02
17	Jose Canseco	1.00	.70	.40
18	Gary Carter	.20	.15	.08
19	Joe Carter	.12	.09	.05
20	Roger Clemens	.60	.45	.25
21	Vince Coleman	.15	.11	.06
22	Cecil Cooper	.10	.08	.04
23	Ron Darling	.10	.08	.04
24	Alvin Davis	.10	.08	.04
25	Chili Davis	.05	.04	.02
26	Eric Davis	.20	.15	.08
27	Glenn Davis	.15	.11	.06
28	Mike Davis	.05	.04	.02
29	Doug DeCinces	.05	.04	.02
30	Rob Deer	.07	.05	.03
31	Jim Deshaies	.10	.08	.04
32	Bo Diaz	.05	.04	.02
33	Richard Dotson	.07	.05	.03
34	Brian Downing	.05	.04	.02
35	Shawon Dunston	.07	.05	.03
36	Mark Eichhorn	.10	.08	.04
37	Dwight Evans	.12	.09	.05
38	Tony Fernandez	.10	.08	.04
39	Julio Franco	.10	.08	.04
40	Gary Gaetti	.12	.09	.05
41	Andres Galarraga	.15	.11	.06
42	Scott Garrelts	.05	.04	.02
43	Steve Garvey	.20	.15	.08
44	Kirk Gibson	.20	.15	.08
45	Dwight Gooden	.25	.20	.10
46	Ken Griffey	.07	.05	.03
47	Mark Gubicza	.10	.08	.04
48	Ozzie Guillen	.07	.05	.03
49	Bill Gullickson	.05	.04	.02
50	Tony Gwynn	.25	.20	.10
51	Von Hayes	.10	.08	.04
52	Rickey Henderson	.60	.45	.25
53	Keith Hernandez	.15	.11	.06
54	Willie Hernandez	.05	.04	.02
55	Ted Higuera	.10	.08	.04
56	Charlie Hough	.05	.04	.02
57	Kent Hrbek	.15	.11	.06
58	Pete Incaviglia	.10	.08	.04
59	Wally Joyner	.20	.15	.08
60	Bob Knepper	.07	.05	.03
61	Mike Krukow	.05	.04	.02
62	Mark Langston	.10	.08	.04
63	Carney Lansford	.07	.05	.03
64	Jim Lindeman	.12	.09	.05
65	Bill Madlock	.10	.08	.04
66	Don Mattingly	.80	.60	.30
67	Kirk McCaskill	.05	.04	.02
68	Lance McCullers	.10	.08	.04
69	Keith Moreland	.05	.04	.02
70	Jack Morris	.15	.11	.06
71	Jim Morrison	.05	.04	.02
72	Lloyd Moseby	.07	.05	.03
73	Jerry Mumphrey	.05	.04	.02
74	Dale Murphy	.30	.25	.12
75	Eddie Murray	.25	.20	.10
76	Pete O'Brien	.07	.05	.03
77	Bob Ojeda	.07	.05	.03
78	Jesse Orosco	.05	.04	.02
79	Dan Pasqua	.10	.08	.04
80	Dave Parker	.12	.09	.05
81	Larry Parrish	.05	.04	.02
82	Jim Presley	.05	.04	.02
83	Kirby Puckett	.60	.45	.25
84	Dan Quisenberry	.07	.05	.03
85	Tim Raines	.20	.15	.08
86	Dennis Rasmussen	.07	.05	.03
87	Johnny Ray	.07	.05	.03
88	Jeff Reardon	.07	.05	.03
89	Jim Rice	.20	.15	.08
90	Dave Righetti	.12	.09	.05
91	Earnest Riles	.05	.04	.02
92	Cal Ripken, Jr.	.80	.60	.30
93	Ron Robinson	.05	.04	.02
94	Juan Samuel	.12	.09	.05
95	Ryne Sandberg	.80	.60	.30
96	Steve Sax	.15	.11	.06
97	Mike Schmidt	.40	.30	.15
98	Ken Schrom	.05	.04	.02
99	Mike Scott	.12	.09	.05
100	Ruben Sierra	.50	.40	.20
101	Lee Smith	.07	.05	.03
102	Ozzie Smith	.12	.09	.05
103	Cory Snyder	.10	.08	.04
104	Kent Tekulve	.05	.04	.02
105	Andres Thomas	.10	.08	.04
106	Rob Thompson	.10	.08	.04
107	Alan Trammell	.20	.15	.08
108	John Tudor	.07	.05	.03
109	Fernando Valenzuela	.10	.08	.04
110	Greg Walker	.07	.05	.03
111	Mitch Webster	.05	.04	.02
112	Lou Whitaker	.15	.11	.06
113	Frank White	.07	.05	.03
114	Reggie Williams	.05	.04	.02
115	Glenn Wilson	.05	.04	.02
116	Willie Wilson	.10	.08	.04
117	Dave Winfield	.35	.25	.14
118	Mike Witt	.07	.05	.03
119	Todd Worrell	.12	.09	.05
120	Floyd Youmans	.05	.04	.02

1987 Fleer Baseball Record Setters

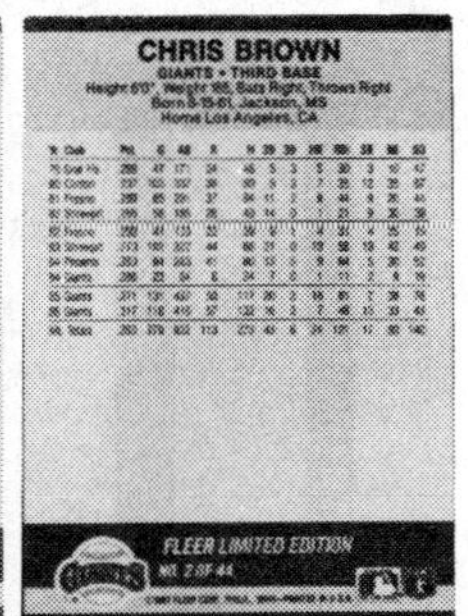

Produced by Fleer for the Eckerd Drug chain, the 1987 Fleer Record Setters set contains 44 cards that measure the standard 2-1/2" by 3-1/2" size. Although the set is titled "Record Setters," the actual records the players have set is not specified anywhere on the cards. Given that several players included in the set were young prospects, a better title for those cards might have been "Possible Record Setters". The set came housed in a special cardboard box with six team logo stickers.

		MT	NR MT	EX
Complete Set:		5.00	3.75	2.00
Common Player:		.05	.04	.02
1	George Brett	.60	.45	.25
2	Chris Brown	.07	.05	.03
3	Jose Canseco	1.00	.70	.40
4	Roger Clemens	.40	.30	.15
5	Alvin Davis	.10	.08	.04
6	Shawon Dunston	.07	.05	.03
7	Tony Fernandez	.10	.08	.04
8	Carlton Fisk	.12	.09	.05
9	Gary Gaetti	.10	.08	.04
10	Gene Garber	.05	.04	.02
11	Rich Gedman	.05	.04	.02
12	Dwight Gooden	.25	.20	.10
13	Ozzie Guillen	.07	.05	.03
14	Bill Gullickson	.05	.04	.02
15	Billy Hatcher	.07	.05	.03
16	Orel Hershiser	.20	.15	.08
17	Wally Joyner	.35	.25	.14
18	Ray Knight	.05	.04	.02
19	Craig Lefferts	.05	.04	.02
20	Don Mattingly	.90	.70	.35
21	Kevin Mitchell	.30	.25	.12
22	Lloyd Moseby	.07	.05	.03
23	Dale Murphy	.30	.25	.12
24	Eddie Murray	.25	.20	.10
25	Phil Niekro	.15	.11	.06
26	Ben Oglivie	.05	.04	.02
27	Jesse Orosco	.05	.04	.02
28	Joe Orsulak	.05	.04	.02
29	Larry Parrish	.05	.04	.02
30	Tim Raines	.25	.20	.10
31	Shane Rawley	.07	.05	.03
32	Dave Righetti	.12	.09	.05
33	Pete Rose	.40	.30	.15
34	Steve Sax	.15	.11	.06
35	Mike Schmidt	.40	.30	.15
36	Mike Scott	.12	.09	.05
37	Don Sutton	.12	.09	.05
38	Alan Trammell	.20	.15	.08
39	John Tudor	.10	.08	.04
40	Gary Ward	.05	.04	.02
41	Lou Whitaker	.15	.11	.06
42	Willie Wilson	.10	.08	.04
43	Todd Worrell	.15	.11	.06
44	Floyd Youmans	.10	.08	.04

Values quoted in this guide reflect the retail price of a card – the price a collector can expect to pay when buying a card from a dealer. The wholesale price – that which a collector can expect to receive from a dealer when selling cards – will be significantly lower, depending on desirability and condition.

Values for recent cards and sets are listed in Mint (MT), Near Mint (NM), reflecting the fact that many cards from recent years have been preserved in top condition. Recent cards and sets in less than Excellent condition have little collector interest.

1987 Fleer Star Stickers

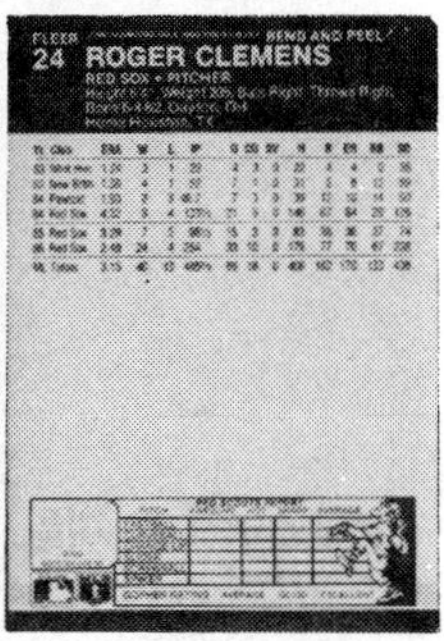

The 1987 Fleer Star Stickers set contains 132 cards which become stickers if the back is bent and peeled off. As in the previous year, the card backs are identical, save the numbering system, to the regular issue cards. The cards measure 2-1/2" by 3-1/2" and were sold in wax packs with team logo stickers. The fronts have a green border with a red and white banner wrapped across the upper left corner and the sides. The backs are printed in green and yellow.

		MT	NR MT	EX
Complete Set:		20.00	15.00	8.00
Common Player:		.05	.04	.02
1	Don Aase	.05	.04	.02
2	Harold Baines	.20	.15	.08
3	Floyd Bannister	.08	.06	.03
4	Jesse Barfield	.08	.06	.03
5	Marty Barrett	.10	.08	.04
6	Kevin Bass	.10	.08	.04
7	Don Baylor	.12	.09	.05
8	Steve Bedrosian	.15	.11	.06
9	George Bell	.35	.25	.14
10	Bert Blyleven	.15	.11	.06
11	Mike Boddicker	.08	.06	.03
12	Wade Boggs	.80	.60	.30
13	Phil Bradley	.08	.06	.03
14	Sid Bream	.08	.06	.03
15	George Brett	.70	.50	.30
16	Hubie Brooks	.10	.08	.04
17	Tom Brunansky	.15	.11	.06
18	Tom Candiotti	.05	.04	.02
19	Jose Canseco	1.00	.70	.40
20	Gary Carter	.40	.30	.15
21	Joe Carter	.20	.15	.08
22	Will Clark	1.00	.70	.40
23	Mark Clear	.05	.04	.02
24	Roger Clemens	.90	.70	.35
25	Vince Coleman	.25	.20	.10
26	Jose Cruz	.10	.08	.04
27	Ron Darling	.20	.15	.08
28	Alvin Davis	.08	.06	.03
29	Chili Davis	.10	.08	.04
30	Eric Davis	.20	.15	.08
31	Glenn Davis	.08	.06	.03
32	Mike Davis	.05	.04	.02
33	Andre Dawson	.25	.20	.10
34	Doug DeCinces	.08	.06	.03
35	Brian Downing	.08	.06	.03
36	Shawon Dunston	.12	.09	.05
37	Mark Eichhorn	.12	.09	.05
38	Dwight Evans	.15	.11	.06
39	Tony Fernandez	.15	.11	.06
40	Bob Forsch	.05	.04	.02
41	John Franco	.10	.08	.04
42	Julio Franco	.12	.09	.05
43	Gary Gaetti	.20	.15	.08
44	Gene Garber	.05	.04	.02
45	Scott Garrelts	.05	.04	.02
46	Steve Garvey	.40	.30	.15
47	Kirk Gibson	.30	.25	.12
48	Dwight Gooden	.40	.30	.15
49	Ken Griffey	.10	.08	.04
50	Ozzie Guillen	.10	.08	.04
51	Bill Gullickson	.05	.04	.02
52	Tony Gwynn	.25	.20	.10
53	Mel Hall	.08	.06	.03
54	Greg Harris	.05	.04	.02
55	Von Hayes	.12	.09	.05
56	Rickey Henderson	.80	.60	.30
57	Tom Henke	.10	.08	.04
58	Keith Hernandez	.15	.11	.06
59	Willie Hernandez	.05	.04	.02
60	Ted Higuera	.10	.08	.04
61	Bob Horner	.12	.09	.05
62	Charlie Hough	.08	.06	.03
63	Jay Howell	.08	.06	.03
64	Kent Hrbek	.30	.25	.12
65	Bruce Hurst	.12	.09	.05
66	Pete Incaviglia	.20	.15	.08
67	Bob James	.05	.04	.02
68	Wally Joyner	.30	.25	.12
69	Mike Krukow	.05	.04	.02
70	Mark Langston	.15	.11	.06
71	Carney Lansford	.08	.06	.03
72	Fred Lynn	.25	.20	.10
73	Bill Madlock	.12	.09	.05
74	Don Mattingly	.90	.70	.35
75	Kirk McCaskill	.05	.04	.02
76	Lance McCullers	.12	.09	.05
77	Oddibe McDowell	.15	.11	.06
78	Paul Molitor	.40	.30	.15

79	Keith Moreland	.08	.06	.03
80	Jack Morris	.25	.20	.10
81	Jim Morrison	.05	.04	.02
82	Jerry Mumphrey	.05	.04	.02
83	Dale Murphy	.70	.50	.30
84	Eddie Murray	.50	.40	.20
85	Ben Oglivie	.05	.04	.02
86	Bob Ojeda	.10	.08	.04
87	Jesse Orosco	.08	.06	.03
88	Dave Parker	.25	.20	.10
89	Larry Parrish	.08	.06	.03
90	Tony Pena	.10	.08	.04
91	Jim Presley	.15	.11	.06
92	Kirby Puckett	.70	.50	.30
93	Dan Quisenberry	.12	.09	.05
94	Tim Raines	.35	.25	.14
95	Dennis Rasmussen	.10	.08	.04
96	Shane Rawley	.08	.06	.03
97	Johnny Ray	.10	.08	.04
98	Jeff Reardon	.10	.08	.04
99	Jim Rice	.20	.15	.08
100	Dave Righetti	.20	.15	.08
101	Cal Ripken, Jr.	1.00	.70	.40
102	Pete Rose	.60	.45	.25
103	Nolan Ryan	2.00	1.50	.80
104	Juan Samuel	.15	.11	.06
105	Ryne Sandberg	1.00	.70	.40
106	Steve Sax	.20	.15	.08
107	Mike Schmidt	1.00	.70	.40
108	Mike Scott	.15	.11	.06
109	Dave Smith	.05	.04	.02
110	Lee Smith	.10	.08	.04
111	Lonnie Smith	.05	.04	.02
112	Ozzie Smith	.20	.15	.08
113	Cory Snyder	.10	.08	.04
114	Darryl Strawberry	.40	.30	.15
115	Don Sutton	.25	.20	.10
116	Kent Tekulve	.08	.06	.03
117	Gorman Thomas	.08	.06	.03
118	Alan Trammell	.30	.25	.12
119	John Tudor	.12	.09	.05
120	Fernando Valenzuela	.12	.09	.05
121	Bob Welch	.12	.09	.05
122	Lou Whitaker	.25	.20	.10
123	Frank White	.10	.08	.04
124	Reggie Williams	.05	.04	.02
125	Willie Wilson	.08	.06	.03
126	Dave Winfield	.40	.30	.15
127	Mike Witt	.10	.08	.04
128	Todd Worrell	.25	.20	.10
129	Curt Young	.08	.06	.03
130	Robin Yount	.60	.45	.25
131	Jose Canseco, Don Mattingly/Checklist	1.00	.70	.40
132	Eric Davis, Bo Jackson/Checklist	.75	.60	.30

1987 Fleer Star Sticker Box Panels

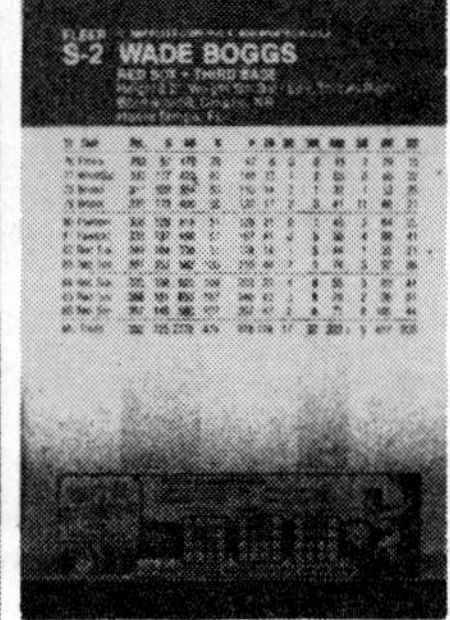

Fleer issued on the bottoms of their Fleer Star Stickers wax pack boxes six player cards plus two team logo/checklist cards. The cards, which measure 2-1/2" by 3-1/2", are numbered S-1 through S-8. The cards are identical in design to the Star Stickers.

		MT	NR MT	EX
Complete Panel Set:		6.00	4.50	2.50
Complete Singles Set:		3.25	2.50	1.25
Common Single Player:		.10	.08	.04
	Panel	5.00	3.75	2.00
2	Wade Boggs	1.00	.70	.40
3	Bert Blyleven	.20	.15	.08
6	Phillies Logo	.05	.04	.02
8	Don Mattingly	1.00	.70	.40
	Panel	1.00	.70	.40
1	Tigers Logo	.05	.04	.02
4	Jose Cruz	.15	.11	.06
5	Glenn Davis	.10	.08	.04
7	Bob Horner	.10	.08	.04

1988 Fleer

A clean, uncluttered look was the trademark of the 660-card 1988 Fleer set. The cards, which are the standard 2-1/2" by 3-1/2", feature blue and red diagonal lines set inside a white border. The player name and position are located on a slant in the upper left corner of the card. The player's team logo appears in the upper right corner. Below the player photo a blue and red band with the word "Fleer" appears. The backs of the cards include the card number, player personal information, and career statistics, plus a new feature called "At Their Best." This feature graphically shows a player's pitching or hitting statistics for home and road games and how he fared during day games as opposed to night contests. The set includes 19 special cards (#'s 622-640) and 12 "Major League Prospects" cards (#'s 641-653).

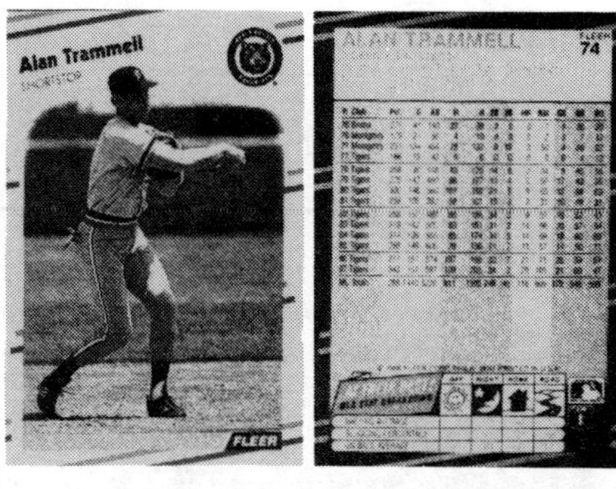

		MT	NR MT	EX
Complete Set (660):		35.00	27.00	13.50
Common Player:		.06	.05	.02
1	Keith Atherton	.06	.05	.02
2	Don Baylor	.10	.08	.04
3	Juan Berenguer	.06	.05	.02
4	Bert Blyleven	.12	.09	.05
5	Tom Brunansky	.10	.08	.04
6	Randy Bush	.06	.05	.02
7	Steve Carlton	.35	.25	.14
8	*Mark Davidson* (FC)	.12	.09	.05
9	George Frazier	.06	.05	.02
10	Gary Gaetti	.15	.11	.06
11	Greg Gagne	.06	.05	.02
12	Dan Gladden	.06	.05	.02
13	Kent Hrbek	.15	.11	.06
14	*Gene Larkin*	.12	.09	.05
15	Tim Laudner	.06	.05	.02
16	Steve Lombardozzi	.06	.05	.02
17	Al Newman	.06	.05	.02
18	Joe Niekro	.08	.06	.03
19	Kirby Puckett	.60	.45	.25
20	Jeff Reardon	.10	.08	.04
21a	Dan Schatzader (incorrect spelling)	.20	.15	.08
21b	Dan Schatzeder (correct spelling)	.06	.05	.02
22	Roy Smalley	.06	.05	.02
23	Mike Smithson	.06	.05	.02
24	*Les Straker* (FC)	.06	.05	.02
25	Frank Viola	.15	.11	.06
26	Jack Clark	.08	.06	.03
27	Vince Coleman	.10	.08	.04
28	Danny Cox	.08	.06	.03
29	Bill Dawley	.06	.05	.02
30	Ken Dayley	.06	.05	.02
31	Doug DeCinces	.08	.06	.03
32	Curt Ford	.06	.05	.02
33	Bob Forsch	.08	.06	.03
34	David Green	.06	.05	.02
35	Tom Herr	.08	.06	.03
36	Ricky Horton	.08	.06	.03
37	*Lance Johnson* (FC)	.75	.60	.30
38	Steve Lake	.06	.05	.02
39	Jim Lindeman	.10	.08	.04
40	*Joe Magrane*	.10	.08	.04
41	Greg Mathews	.08	.06	.03
42	Willie McGee	.12	.09	.05
43	John Morris	.06	.05	.02
44	Jose Oquendo	.06	.05	.02
45	Tony Pena	.08	.06	.03
46	Terry Pendleton	.20	.15	.08
47	Ozzie Smith	.25	.20	.10
48	John Tudor	.10	.08	.04
49	Lee Tunnell	.06	.05	.02
50	Todd Worrell	.10	.08	.04
51	Doyle Alexander	.08	.06	.03
52	Dave Bergman	.06	.05	.02
53	Tom Brookens	.06	.05	.02
54	Darrell Evans	.10	.08	.04
55	Kirk Gibson	.08	.06	.03
56	Mike Heath	.06	.05	.02
57	*Mike Henneman*	.25	.20	.10
58	Willie Hernandez	.08	.06	.03
59	Larry Herndon	.06	.05	.02
60	Eric King	.08	.06	.03
61	Chet Lemon	.08	.06	.03
62	*Scott Lusader* (FC)	.06	.05	.02
63	Bill Madlock	.10	.08	.04
64	Jack Morris	.20	.15	.08
65	Jim Morrison	.06	.05	.02
66	*Matt Nokes*	.25	.20	.10
67	Dan Petry	.08	.06	.03
68a	*Jeff Robinson* (Born 12-13-60 on back)	.30	.25	.12
68b	*Jeff Robinson* (Born 12/14/61 on back)	.15	.11	.06
69	Pat Sheridan	.06	.05	.02
70	Nate Snell	.06	.05	.02
71	Frank Tanana	.08	.06	.03
72	Walt Terrell	.08	.06	.03
73	Mark Thurmond	.06	.05	.02
74	Alan Trammell	.10	.08	.04
75	Lou Whitaker	.10	.08	.04
76	Mike Aldrete	.08	.06	.03
77	Bob Brenly	.06	.05	.02
78	Will Clark	1.00	.70	.40
79	Chili Davis	.08	.06	.03
80	Kelly Downs	.10	.08	.04
81	Dave Dravecky	.08	.06	.03
82	Scott Garrelts	.06	.05	.02
83	Atlee Hammaker	.06	.05	.02
84	Dave Henderson	.10	.08	.04
85	Mike Krukow	.08	.06	.03
86	Mike LaCoss	.06	.05	.02
87	Craig Lefferts	.06	.05	.02
88	Jeff Leonard	.08	.06	.03
89	Candy Maldonado	.08	.06	.03
90	Ed Milner	.06	.05	.02
91	Bob Melvin	.06	.05	.02
92	Kevin Mitchell	.20	.15	.08
93	*Jon Perlman* (FC)	.06	.05	.02
94	Rick Reuschel	.10	.08	.04
95	Don Robinson	.08	.06	.03
96	Chris Speier	.06	.05	.02
97	Harry Spilman	.06	.05	.02
98	Robbie Thompson	.10	.08	.04
99	Jose Uribe	.06	.05	.02
100	*Mark Wasinger* (FC)	.06	.05	.02
101	*Matt Williams*	5.00	3.75	2.00
102	Jesse Barfield	.15	.11	.06
103	George Bell	.10	.08	.04
104	Juan Beniquez	.06	.05	.02
105	John Cerutti	.08	.06	.03
106	Jim Clancy	.08	.06	.03
107	*Rob Ducey* (FC)	.06	.05	.02
108	Mark Eichhorn	.08	.06	.03
109	Tony Fernandez	.12	.09	.05
110	Cecil Fielder	.75	.60	.30
111	Kelly Gruber	.08	.06	.03
112	Tom Henke	.08	.06	.03
113	Garth Iorg (Iorg)	.06	.05	.02
114	Jimmy Key	.10	.08	.04
115	Rick Leach	.06	.05	.02
116	Manny Lee	.08	.06	.03
117	*Nelson Liriano* (FC)	.06	.05	.02
118	*Fred McGriff*	2.50	2.00	1.00
119	Lloyd Moseby	.08	.06	.03
120	Rance Mulliniks	.06	.05	.02
121	Jeff Musselman	.06	.05	.02
122	*Jose Nunez*	.06	.05	.02
123	Dave Stieb	.10	.08	.04
124	Willie Upshaw	.08	.06	.03
125	Duane Ward (FC)	.08	.06	.03
126	Ernie Whitt	.08	.06	.03
127	Rick Aguilera	.06	.05	.02
128	Wally Backman	.08	.06	.03
129	*Mark Carreon* (FC)	.12	.09	.05
130	Gary Carter	.10	.08	.04
131	David Cone (FC)	.75	.60	.30
132	Ron Darling	.12	.09	.05
133	Len Dykstra	.25	.20	.10
134	Sid Fernandez	.10	.08	.04
135	Dwight Gooden	.12	.09	.05
136	Keith Hernandez	.08	.06	.03
137	*Gregg Jefferies* (FC)	5.00	3.75	2.00
138	Howard Johnson	.10	.08	.04
139	Terry Leach	.06	.05	.02
140	*Barry Lyons* (FC)	.06	.05	.02
141	Dave Magadan	.10	.08	.04
142	Roger McDowell	.10	.08	.04
143	Kevin McReynolds	.15	.11	.06
144	*Keith Miller* (FC)	.06	.05	.02
145	*John Mitchell* (FC)	.06	.05	.02
146	Randy Myers	.15	.11	.06
147	Bob Ojeda	.08	.06	.03
148	Jesse Orosco	.08	.06	.03
149	Rafael Santana	.06	.05	.02
150	Doug Sisk	.06	.05	.02
151	Darryl Strawberry	.15	.11	.06
152	Tim Teufel	.06	.05	.02
153	Gene Walter	.06	.05	.02
154	Mookie Wilson	.08	.06	.03
155	*Jay Aldrich* (FC)	.06	.05	.02
156	Chris Bosio	.08	.06	.03
157	Glenn Braggs	.10	.08	.04
158	Greg Brock	.08	.06	.03
159	Juan Castillo	.06	.05	.02
160	Mark Clear	.06	.05	.02
161	Cecil Cooper	.10	.08	.04
162	*Chuck Crim*	.12	.09	.05
163	Rob Deer	.08	.06	.03
164	Mike Felder	.06	.05	.02
165	Jim Gantner	.06	.05	.02
166	Ted Higuera	.10	.08	.04
167	Steve Kiefer	.06	.05	.02
168	Rick Manning	.06	.05	.02
169	Paul Molitor	.40	.30	.15
170	Juan Nieves	.08	.06	.03
171	Dan Plesac	.10	.08	.04
172	Earnest Riles	.06	.05	.02
173	Bill Schroeder	.06	.05	.02
174	*Steve Stanicek* (FC)	.06	.05	.02
175	B.J. Surhoff	.10	.08	.04
176	Dale Sveum	.08	.06	.03
177	Bill Wegman	.06	.05	.02
178	Robin Yount	.60	.45	.25
179	Hubie Brooks	.10	.08	.04
180	Tim Burke	.06	.05	.02
181	Casey Candaele	.06	.05	.02
182	Mike Fitzgerald	.06	.05	.02
183	Tom Foley	.06	.05	.02
184	Andres Galarraga	.20	.15	.08
185	Neal Heaton	.06	.05	.02
186	Wallace Johnson	.06	.05	.02
187	Vance Law	.08	.06	.03
188	Dennis Martinez	.08	.06	.03

189	Bob McClure	.06	.05	.02
190	Andy McGaffigan	.06	.05	.02
191	Reid Nichols	.06	.05	.02
192	Pascual Perez	.08	.06	.03
193	Tim Raines	.10	.08	.04
194	Jeff Reed	.06	.05	.02
195	Bob Sebra	.06	.05	.02
196	Bryn Smith	.06	.05	.02
197	Randy St. Claire	.06	.05	.02
198	Tim Wallach	.10	.08	.04
199	Mitch Webster	.08	.06	.03
200	Herm Winningham	.06	.05	.02
201	Floyd Youmans	.06	.05	.02
202	*Brad Arnsberg* (FC)	.08	.06	.03
203	Rick Cerone	.06	.05	.02
204	Pat Clements	.06	.05	.02
205	Henry Cotto	.06	.05	.02
206	Mike Easler	.08	.06	.03
207	Ron Guidry	.15	.11	.06
208	Bill Gullickson	.06	.05	.02
209	Rickey Henderson	.60	.45	.25
210	Charles Hudson	.06	.05	.02
211	Tommy John	.15	.11	.06
212	*Roberto Kelly* (FC)	1.50	1.25	.60
213	Ron Kittle	.08	.06	.03
214	Don Mattingly	.60	.45	.25
215	Bobby Meacham	.06	.05	.02
216	Mike Pagliarulo	.10	.08	.04
217	Dan Pasqua	.10	.08	.04
218	Willie Randolph	.08	.06	.03
219	Rick Rhoden	.08	.06	.03
220	Dave Righetti	.15	.11	.06
221	Jerry Royster	.06	.05	.02
222	Tim Stoddard	.06	.05	.02
223	Wayne Tolleson	.06	.05	.02
224	Gary Ward	.08	.06	.03
225	Claudell Washington	.08	.06	.03
226	Dave Winfield	.50	.40	.20
227	Buddy Bell	.08	.06	.03
228	Tom Browning	.10	.08	.04
229	Dave Concepcion	.08	.06	.03
230	Kal Daniels	.08	.06	.03
231	Eric Davis	.15	.11	.06
232	Bo Diaz	.08	.06	.03
233	Nick Esasky	.08	.06	.03
234	John Franco	.10	.08	.04
235	Guy Hoffman	.06	.05	.02
236	Tom Hume	.06	.05	.02
237	Tracy Jones	.12	.09	.05
238	*Bill Landrum* (FC)	.10	.08	.04
239	Barry Larkin	.20	.15	.08
240	Terry McGriff (FC)	.06	.05	.02
241	Rob Murphy	.08	.06	.03
242	Ron Oester	.06	.05	.02
243	Dave Parker	.10	.08	.04
244	Pat Perry	.06	.05	.02
245	Ted Power	.06	.05	.02
246	Dennis Rasmussen	.10	.08	.04
247	Ron Robinson	.06	.05	.02
248	Kurt Stillwell	.10	.08	.04
249	*Jeff Treadway* (FC)	.12	.09	.05
250	Frank Williams	.06	.05	.02
251	Steve Balboni	.08	.06	.03
252	Bud Black	.06	.05	.02
253	Thad Bosley	.06	.05	.02
254	George Brett	.75	.60	.30
255	*John Davis* (FC)	.06	.05	.02
256	Steve Farr	.06	.05	.02
257	Gene Garber	.06	.05	.02
258	Jerry Gleaton	.06	.05	.02
259	Mark Gubicza	.12	.09	.05
260	Bo Jackson	.90	.70	.35
261	Danny Jackson	.12	.09	.05
262	*Ross Jones* (FC)	.06	.05	.02
263	Charlie Leibrandt	.06	.05	.02
264	*Bill Pecota*	.06	.05	.02
265	*Melido Perez*	.15	.11	.06
266	Jamie Quirk	.06	.05	.02
267	Dan Quisenberry	.08	.06	.03
268	Bret Saberhagen	.15	.11	.06
269	Angel Salazar	.06	.05	.02
270	Kevin Seitzer	.08	.06	.03
271	Danny Tartabull	.30	.25	.12
272	*Gary Thurman* (FC)	.08	.06	.03
273	Frank White	.08	.06	.03
274	Willie Wilson	.10	.08	.04
275	Tony Bernazard	.06	.05	.02
276	Jose Canseco	1.00	.70	.40
277	Mike Davis	.08	.06	.03
278	Storm Davis	.10	.08	.04
279	Dennis Eckersley	.12	.09	.05
280	Alfredo Griffin	.08	.06	.03
281	Rick Honeycutt	.06	.05	.02
282	Jay Howell	.08	.06	.03
283	Reggie Jackson	.50	.40	.20
284	Dennis Lamp	.06	.05	.02
285	Carney Lansford	.10	.08	.04
286	Mark McGwire	1.25	.90	.50
287	Dwayne Murphy	.08	.06	.03
288	Gene Nelson	.06	.05	.02
289	Steve Ontiveros	.06	.05	.02
290	Tony Phillips	.06	.05	.02
291	Eric Plunk	.06	.05	.02
292	*Luis Polonia*	.25	.20	.10
293	*Rick Rodriguez* (FC)	.06	.05	.02
294	Terry Steinbach	.10	.08	.04
295	Dave Stewart	.10	.08	.04
296	Curt Young	.08	.06	.03
297	Luis Aguayo	.06	.05	.02
298	Steve Bedrosian	.12	.09	.05
299	Jeff Calhoun	.06	.05	.02
300	Don Carman	.08	.06	.03
301	*Todd Frohwirth* (FC)	.20	.15	.08
302	Greg Gross	.06	.05	.02
303	Kevin Gross	.08	.06	.03
304	Von Hayes	.08	.06	.03
305	*Keith Hughes* (FC)	.06	.05	.02
306	*Mike Jackson*	.06	.05	.02
307	Chris James	.20	.15	.08
308	Steve Jeltz	.06	.05	.02
309	Mike Maddux	.07	.05	.03
310	Lance Parrish	.15	.11	.06
311	Shane Rawley	.08	.06	.03
312	*Wally Ritchie*	.06	.05	.02
313	Bruce Ruffin	.08	.06	.03
314	Juan Samuel	.12	.09	.05
315	Mike Schmidt	.50	.40	.20
316	Rick Schu	.06	.05	.02
317	Jeff Stone	.06	.05	.02
318	Kent Tekulve	.08	.06	.03
319	Milt Thompson	.06	.05	.02
320	Glenn Wilson	.08	.06	.03
321	Rafael Belliard	.06	.05	.02
322	Barry Bonds	2.00	1.50	.80
323	Bobby Bonilla	.35	.25	.14
324	Sid Bream	.08	.06	.03
325	John Cangelosi	.06	.05	.02
326	Mike Diaz	.08	.06	.03
327	Doug Drabek	.08	.06	.03
328	*Mike Dunne*	.08	.06	.03
329	Brian Fisher	.08	.06	.03
330	*Brett Gideon* (FC)	.06	.05	.02
331	Terry Harper	.06	.05	.02
332	Bob Kipper	.06	.05	.02
333	Mike LaValliere	.08	.06	.03
334	*Jose Lind* (FC)	.30	.25	.12
335	Junior Ortiz	.06	.05	.02
336	*Vicente Palacios* (FC)	.12	.09	.05
337	*Bob Patterson* (FC)	.12	.09	.05
338	*Al Pedrique* (FC)	.06	.05	.02
339	R.J. Reynolds	.06	.05	.02
340	*John Smiley*	.20	.15	.08
341	Andy Van Slyke	.20	.15	.08
342	Bob Walk	.06	.05	.02
343	Marty Barrett	.08	.06	.03
344	*Todd Benzinger* (FC)	.12	.09	.05
345	Wade Boggs	.35	.25	.14
346	*Tom Bolton* (FC)	.06	.05	.02
347	Oil Can Boyd	.08	.06	.03
348	*Ellis Burks*	1.50	1.25	.60
349	Roger Clemens	.75	.60	.30
350	Steve Crawford	.06	.05	.02
351	Dwight Evans	.12	.09	.05
352	*Wes Gardner* (FC)	.08	.06	.03
353	Rich Gedman	.08	.06	.03
354	Mike Greenwell	.30	.25	.12
355	*Sam Horn* (FC)	.12	.09	.05
356	Bruce Hurst	.10	.08	.04
357	*John Marzano* (FC)	.08	.06	.03
358	Al Nipper	.06	.05	.02
359	Spike Owen	.06	.05	.02
360	*Jody Reed* (FC)	.15	.11	.06
361	Jim Rice	.10	.08	.04
362	Ed Romero	.06	.05	.02
363	Kevin Romine (FC)	.08	.06	.03
364	Joe Sambito	.06	.05	.02
365	Calvin Schiraldi	.06	.05	.02
366	Jeff Sellers	.08	.06	.03
367	Bob Stanley	.06	.05	.02
368	Scott Bankhead	.06	.05	.02
369	Phil Bradley	.10	.08	.04
370	Scott Bradley	.06	.05	.02
371	Mickey Brantley	.06	.05	.02
372	*Mike Campbell* (FC)	.06	.05	.02
373	Alvin Davis	.06	.05	.02
374	Lee Guetterman	.06	.05	.02
375	*Dave Hengel* (FC)	.06	.05	.02
376	Mike Kingery	.06	.05	.02
377	Mark Langston	.12	.09	.05
378	*Edgar Martinez*	1.25	.90	.50
379	Mike Moore	.06	.05	.02
380	Mike Morgan	.06	.05	.02
381	John Moses	.06	.05	.02
382	*Donnell Nixon* (FC)	.06	.05	.02
383	Edwin Nunez	.06	.05	.02
384	Ken Phelps	.08	.06	.03
385	Jim Presley	.10	.08	.04
386	Rey Quinones	.06	.05	.02
387	Jerry Reed	.06	.05	.02
388	Harold Reynolds	.08	.06	.03
389	Dave Valle	.08	.06	.03
390	*Bill Wilkinson*	.06	.05	.02
391	Harold Baines	.12	.09	.05
392	Floyd Bannister	.08	.06	.03
393	Daryl Boston	.06	.05	.02
394	Ivan Calderon	.08	.06	.03
395	Jose DeLeon	.08	.06	.03
396	Richard Dotson	.08	.06	.03
397	Carlton Fisk	.15	.11	.06
398	Ozzie Guillen	.08	.06	.03
399	Ron Hassey	.06	.05	.02
400	Donnie Hill	.06	.05	.02
401	Bob James	.06	.05	.02
402	Dave LaPoint	.08	.06	.03
403	*Bill Lindsey* (FC)	.06	.05	.02
404	*Bill Long* (FC)	.06	.05	.02
405	Steve Lyons	.06	.05	.02
406	*Fred Manrique*	.06	.05	.02
407	*Jack McDowell*	2.50	2.00	1.00
408	Gary Redus	.06	.05	.02
409	Ray Searage	.06	.05	.02
410	Bobby Thigpen	.06	.05	.02
411	Greg Walker	.08	.06	.03
412	*Kenny Williams*	.06	.05	.02
413	Jim Winn	.06	.05	.02
414	Jody Davis	.08	.06	.03
415	Andre Dawson	.20	.15	.08
416	Brian Dayett	.06	.05	.02
417	Bob Dernier	.06	.05	.02
418	Frank DiPino	.06	.05	.02
419	Shawon Dunston	.10	.08	.04
420	Leon Durham	.08	.06	.03
421	*Les Lancaster* (FC)	.10	.08	.04
422	Ed Lynch	.06	.05	.02
423	Greg Maddux	1.50	1.25	.60
424	Dave Martinez (FC)	.07	.05	.03
425a	Keith Moreland (bunting, photo actually Jody Davis)	3.00	2.25	1.25
425b	Keith Moreland (standing upright, correct photo)	.08	.06	.03
426	Jamie Moyer	.08	.06	.03
427	Jerry Mumphrey	.06	.05	.02
428	*Paul Noce* (FC)	.06	.05	.02
429	Rafael Palmeiro (FC)	1.75	1.25	.70
430	Wade Rowdon (FC)	.06	.05	.02
431	Ryne Sandberg	1.00	.70	.40
432	Scott Sanderson	.06	.05	.02
433	Lee Smith	.10	.08	.04
434	Jim Sundberg	.08	.06	.03
435	Rick Sutcliffe	.10	.08	.04
436	Manny Trillo	.08	.06	.03
437	Juan Agosto	.06	.05	.02
438	Larry Andersen	.06	.05	.02
439	Alan Ashby	.06	.05	.02
440	Kevin Bass	.08	.06	.03
441	*Ken Caminiti*	.75	.60	.30
442	*Rocky Childress* (FC)	.06	.05	.02
443	Jose Cruz	.08	.06	.03
444	Danny Darwin	.06	.05	.02
445	Glenn Davis	.06	.05	.02
446	Jim Deshaies	.08	.06	.03
447	Bill Doran	.08	.06	.03
448	Ty Gainey	.06	.05	.02
449	Billy Hatcher	.08	.06	.03
450	Jeff Heathcock	.06	.05	.02
451	Bob Knepper	.08	.06	.03
452	*Rob Mallicoat* (FC)	.06	.05	.02
453	*Dave Meads*	.06	.05	.02
454	Craig Reynolds	.06	.05	.02
455	Nolan Ryan	1.50	1.25	.60
456	Mike Scott	.12	.09	.05
457	Dave Smith	.08	.06	.03
458	Denny Walling	.06	.05	.02
459	*Robbie Wine* (FC)	.06	.05	.02
460	*Gerald Young* (FC)	.06	.05	.02
461	Bob Brower	.08	.06	.03
462a	Jerry Browne (white player, photo actually Bob Brower)	3.50	2.75	1.50
462b	Jerry Browne (black player, correct photo)	.08	.06	.03
463	Steve Buechele	.06	.05	.02
464	Edwin Correa	.06	.05	.02
465	*Cecil Espy* (FC)	.15	.11	.06
466	Scott Fletcher	.08	.06	.03
467	Jose Guzman	.08	.06	.03
468	Greg Harris	.06	.05	.02
469	Charlie Hough	.08	.06	.03
470	Pete Incaviglia	.10	.08	.04
471	*Paul Kilgus* (FC)	.06	.05	.02
472	Mike Loynd	.08	.06	.03
473	Oddibe McDowell	.08	.06	.03
474	Dale Mohorcic	.06	.05	.02
475	Pete O'Brien	.08	.06	.03
476	Larry Parrish	.08	.06	.03
477	Geno Petralli	.06	.05	.02
478	Jeff Russell	.06	.05	.02
479	Ruben Sierra	1.00	.70	.40
480	Mike Stanley	.12	.09	.05
481	Curtis Wilkerson	.06	.05	.02
482	Mitch Williams	.08	.06	.03
483	Bobby Witt	.10	.08	.04
484	Tony Armas	.08	.06	.03
485	Bob Boone	.08	.06	.03
486	Bill Buckner	.10	.08	.04
487	*DeWayne Buice*	.06	.05	.02
488	Brian Downing	.08	.06	.03
489	Chuck Finley	.06	.05	.02
490	Willie Fraser	.06	.05	.02
491	Jack Howell	.08	.06	.03
492	Ruppert Jones	.06	.05	.02
493	Wally Joyner	.15	.11	.06
494	Jack Lazorko	.06	.05	.02
495	Gary Lucas	.06	.05	.02
496	Kirk McCaskill	.08	.06	.03
497	Mark McLemore	.06	.05	.02
498	Darrell Miller	.06	.05	.02
499	Greg Minton	.06	.05	.02
500	Donnie Moore	.06	.05	.02
501	Gus Polidor	.06	.05	.02
502	Johnny Ray	.08	.06	.03
503	Mark Ryal (FC)	.06	.05	.02
504	Dick Schofield	.06	.05	.02
505	Don Sutton	.12	.09	.05
506	Devon White	.15	.11	.06
507	Mike Witt	.08	.06	.03
508	Dave Anderson	.06	.05	.02
509	Tim Belcher (FC)	.20	.15	.08
510	Ralph Bryant	.06	.05	.02
511	*Tim Crews* (FC)	.15	.11	.06
512	*Mike Devereaux* (FC)	1.25	.90	.50
513	Mariano Duncan	.06	.05	.02
514	Pedro Guerrero	.15	.11	.06
515	Jeff Hamilton (FC)	.12	.09	.05
516	Mickey Hatcher	.06	.05	.02
517	Brad Havens	.06	.05	.02
518	Orel Hershiser	.10	.08	.04
519	*Shawn Hillegas* (FC)	.06	.05	.02
520	Ken Howell	.06	.05	.02
521	Tim Leary	.08	.06	.03
522	Mike Marshall	.12	.09	.05
523	Steve Sax	.15	.11	.06
524	Mike Scioscia	.08	.06	.03
525	Mike Sharperson (FC)	.06	.05	.02
526	John Shelby	.06	.05	.02
527	Franklin Stubbs	.08	.06	.03
528	Fernando Valenzuela	.08	.06	.03
529	Bob Welch	.10	.08	.04
530	Matt Young	.06	.05	.02
531	Jim Acker	.06	.05	.02
532	Paul Assenmacher	.06	.05	.02
533	*Jeff Blauser* (FC)	.75	.60	.30
534	*Joe Boever* (FC)	.08	.06	.03
535	Martin Clary (FC)	.06	.05	.02
536	*Kevin Coffman* (FC)	.06	.05	.02

537	Jeff Dedmon	.06	.05	.02
538	*Ron Gant*	3.00	2.25	1.25
539	*Tom Glavine* (FC)	7.50	5.75	3.00
540	Ken Griffey	.08	.06	.03
541	Al Hall	.06	.05	.02
542	Glenn Hubbard	.06	.05	.02
543	Dion James	.08	.06	.03
544	Dale Murphy	.12	.09	.05
545	Ken Oberkfell	.06	.05	.02
546	David Palmer	.06	.05	.02
547	Gerald Perry	.10	.08	.04
548	Charlie Puleo	.06	.05	.02
549	Ted Simmons	.10	.08	.04
550	Zane Smith	.08	.06	.03
551	Andres Thomas	.08	.06	.03
552	Ozzie Virgil	.06	.05	.02
553	Don Aase	.06	.05	.02
554	*Jeff Ballard* (FC)	.06	.05	.02
555	Eric Bell	.08	.06	.03
556	Mike Boddicker	.08	.06	.03
557	Ken Dixon	.06	.05	.02
558	Jim Dwyer	.06	.05	.02
559	Ken Gerhart	.08	.06	.03
560	*Rene Gonzales* (FC)	.06	.05	.02
561	Mike Griffin	.06	.05	.02
562	John Hayban (Habyan)	.06	.05	.02
563	Terry Kennedy	.08	.06	.03
564	Ray Knight	.08	.06	.03
565	Lee Lacy	.06	.05	.02
566	Fred Lynn	.15	.11	.06
567	Eddie Murray	.35	.25	.14
568	Tom Niedenfuer	.08	.06	.03
569	*Bill Ripken* (FC)	.12	.09	.05
570	Cal Ripken, Jr.	1.00	.70	.40
571	Dave Schmidt	.06	.05	.02
572	Larry Sheets	.08	.06	.03
573	*Pete Stanicek* (FC)	.06	.05	.02
574	*Mark Williamson* (FC)	.06	.05	.02
575	Mike Young	.06	.05	.02
576	Shawn Abner (FC)	.08	.06	.03
577	Greg Booker	.06	.05	.02
578	Chris Brown	.08	.06	.03
579	*Keith Comstock* (FC)	.06	.05	.02
580	*Joey Cora* (FC)	.20	.15	.08
581	Mark Davis	.06	.05	.02
582	Tim Flannery	.06	.05	.02
583	Goose Gossage	.15	.11	.06
584	Mark Grant	.06	.05	.02
585	Tony Gwynn	.50	.40	.20
586	Andy Hawkins	.06	.05	.02
587	Stan Jefferson	.10	.08	.04
588	Jimmy Jones	.08	.06	.03
589	John Kruk	.10	.08	.04
590	*Shane Mack* (FC)	.50	.40	.20
591	Carmelo Martinez	.08	.06	.03
592	Lance McCullers	.08	.06	.03
593	*Eric Nolte* (FC)	.06	.05	.02
594	Randy Ready	.06	.05	.02
595	Luis Salazar	.06	.05	.02
596	Benito Santiago	.20	.15	.08
597	Eric Show	.08	.06	.03
598	Garry Templeton	.08	.06	.03
599	Ed Whitson	.06	.05	.02
600	Scott Bailes	.08	.06	.03
601	Chris Bando	.06	.05	.02
602	*Jay Bell*	1.00	.75	.40
603	Brett Butler	.08	.06	.03
604	Tom Candiotti	.06	.05	.02
605	Joe Carter	.50	.40	.20
606	Carmen Castillo	.06	.05	.02
607	*Brian Dorsett* (FC)	.06	.05	.02
608	*John Farrell* (FC)	.06	.05	.02
609	Julio Franco	.10	.08	.04
610	Mel Hall	.08	.06	.03
611	*Tommy Hinzo* (FC)	.06	.05	.02
612	Brook Jacoby	.10	.08	.04
613	*Doug Jones* (FC)	.40	.30	.15
614	Ken Schrom	.06	.05	.02
615	Cory Snyder	.08	.06	.03
616	Sammy Stewart	.06	.05	.02
617	Greg Swindell	.25	.20	.10
618	Pat Tabler	.08	.06	.03
619	Ed Vande Berg	.06	.05	.02
620	*Eddie Williams* (FC)	.06	.05	.02
621	Rich Yett	.06	.05	.02
622	Slugging Sophomores (Wally Joyner, Cory Snyder)	.35	.25	.14
623	Dominican Dynamite (George Bell, Pedro Guerrero)	.12	.09	.05
624	Oakland's Power Team (Jose Canseco, Mark McGwire)	.50	.40	.20
625	Classic Relief (Dan Plesac, Dave Righetti)	.08	.06	.03
626	All Star Righties (Jack Morris, Bret Saberhagen, Mike Witt)	.10	.08	.04
627	Game Closers (Steve Bedrosian, John Franco)	.08	.06	.03
628	Masters of the Double Play (Ryne Sandberg, Ozzie Smith)	.35	.25	.14
629	Rookie Record Setter (Mark McGwire)	.35	.25	.14
630	Changing the Guard in Boston (Todd Benzinger, Ellis Burks, Mike Greenwell)	.25	.20	.10
631	N.L. Batting Champs (Tony Gwynn, Tim Raines)	.20	.15	.08
632	Pitching Magic (Orel Hershiser, Mike Scott)	.12	.09	.05
633	Big Bats At First (Mark McGwire, Pat Tabler)	.20	.15	.08
634	Hitting King and the Thief (Tony Gwynn, Vince Coleman)	.12	.09	.05
635	A.L. Slugging Shortstops (Tony Fernandez, Cal Ripken, Jr., Alan Trammell)	.15	.11	.06
636	Tried and True Sluggers (Gary Carter, Mike Schmidt)	.25	.20	.10
637	Crunch Time (Eric Davis, Darryl Strawberry)	.12	.09	.05
638	A.L. All Stars (Matt Nokes, Kirby Puckett)	.20	.15	.08
639	N.L. All Stars (Keith Hernandez, Dale Murphy)	.15	.11	.06
640	The "O's" Brothers (Bill Ripken, Cal Ripken, Jr.)	.25	.20	.10
641	Major League Prospects (*Mark Grace*, Darrin Jackson)	5.00	3.75	2.00
642	Major League Prospects (*Damon Berryhill* (FC), Jeff Montgomery)	1.25	.90	.50
643	Major League Prospects (*Felix Fermin* (FC), Jessie Reid)	.20	.15	.08
644	Major League Prospects (*Greg Myers*, Greg Tabor)	.20	.15	.08
645	Major League Prospects (*Jim Eppard* (FC), Joey Meyer)	.20	.15	.08
646	Major League Prospects (*Adam Peterson* (FC), Randy Velarde)	.20	.15	.08
647	Major League Prospects (*Chris Gwynn*, Peter Smith)	.25	.20	.10
648	Major League Prospects (*Greg Jelks* (FC), Tom Newell)	.25	.20	.10
649	Major League Prospects (*Mario Diaz* (FC), Clay Parker)	.25	.20	.10
650	Major League Prospects (*Jack Savage* (FC), Todd Simmons)	.25	.20	.10
651	Major League Prospects (*John Burkett*, Kirt Manwaring)	2.50	2.00	1.00
652	Major League Prospects (*Dave Otto* (FC), Walt Weiss)	.40	.30	.15
653	Major League Prospects (*Randell Byers (Randall)* (FC), Jeff King)	.40	.30	.15
654a	Checklist 1-101 (21 is Schatzader)	.10	.08	.04
654b	Checklist 1-101 (21 is Schatzeder)	.06	.05	.02
655	Checklist 102-201	.06	.05	.02
656	Checklist 202-296	.06	.05	.02
657	Checklist 297-390	.06	.05	.02
658	Checklist 391-483	.06	.05	.02
659	Checklist 484-575	.06	.05	.02
660	Checklist 576-660	.06	.05	.02

1988 Fleer All Stars

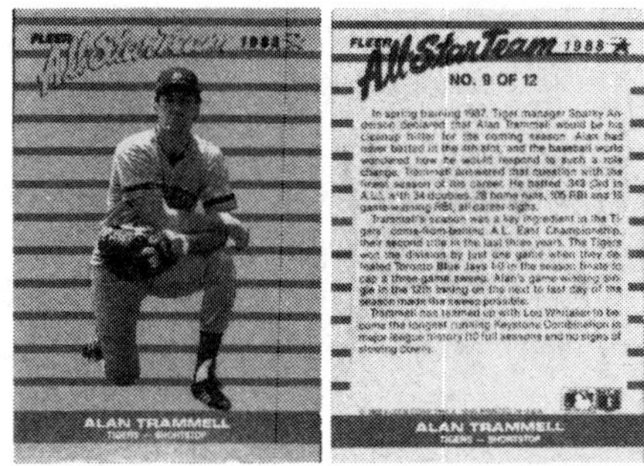

For the third consecutive year, Fleer randomly inserted All Star Team cards in their wax and cello packs. Twelve cards make up the set, each card measuring 2-1/2" by 3-1/2" in size. Players chosen for the set are Fleer's choices for a major league All-Star team.

		MT	NR MT	EX
Complete Set (12):		8.00	6.00	3.00
Common Player:		.25	.15	.10
1	Matt Nokes	.40	.30	.15
2	Tom Henke	.25	.20	.10
3	Ted Higuera	.25	.20	.10
4	Roger Clemens	3.00	2.25	1.25
5	George Bell	.40	.30	.15
6	Andre Dawson	.60	.45	.25
7	Eric Davis	.40	.30	.15
8	Wade Boggs	1.00	.70	.40
9	Alan Trammell	.60	.45	.25
10	Juan Samuel	.25	.20	.10
11	Jack Clark	.25	.20	.10
12	Paul Molitor	1.00	.70	.40

1988 Fleer Headliners

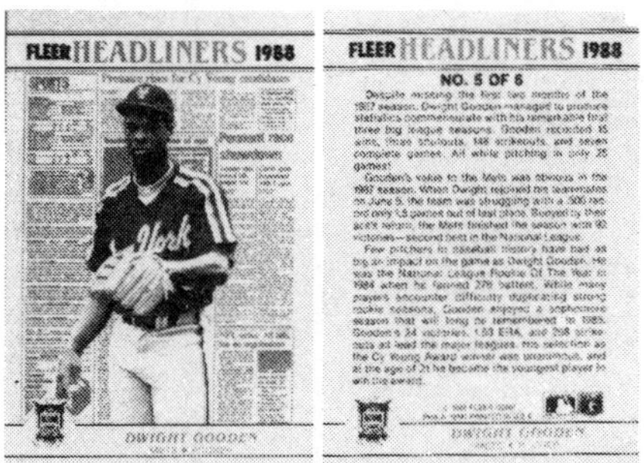

This six-card special set was inserted in Fleer three-packs, sold by retail outlets and hobby dealers nationwide. The card fronts feature crisp full-color player cut-outs printed on a grey and white USA Today-style sports page. "Fleer Headliners 1988" is printed in black and red on a white banner across the top of the card, both front and back. A similar white banner across the card bottom bears the black and white National or American League logo and a red player/team name. Card backs are black on grey with red accents and include the card number and a three-paragraph career summary.

		MT	NR MT	EX
Complete Set (6):		5.00	3.00	1.50
Common Player:		.50	.30	.15
1	Don Mattingly	2.00	1.50	.80
2	Mark McGwire	1.50	1.00	.50
3	Jack Morris	.50	.30	.15
4	Darryl Strawberry	.60	.40	.20
5	Dwight Gooden	.60	.40	.20
6	Tim Raines	.60	.40	.20

1988 Fleer '87 World Series

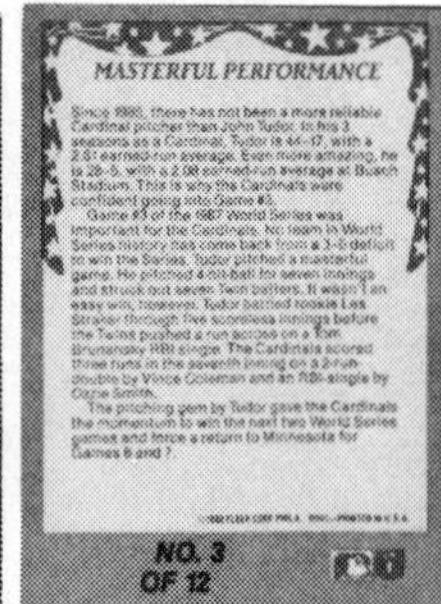

Highlights of the 1987 Series are captured in this full-color insert set found only in Fleer's regular 660-card factory sealed sets. This second World Series edition by Fleer features cards framed in red, with a blue and white starred bunting draped over the upper edges of the photo and a brief photo caption printed on a yellow band across the lower border. Numbered card backs are red, white and blue and include a description of the action pictured on the front, with stats for the Series.

		MT	NR MT	EX
Complete Set (12):		2.50	1.50	.75
Common Player:		.20	.12	.06
1	"Grand" Hero In Game 1 (Dan Gladden)	.30	.25	.12
2	The Cardinals "Bush" Whacked (Randy Bush, Tony Pena)	.30	.25	.12
3	Masterful Performance Turns Momentum (John Tudor)	.30	.25	.12
4	Ozzie Smith	.75	.50	.25
5	Throw Smoke! (Tony Pena, Todd Worrell)	.35	.25	.14
6	Cardinal Attack - Disruptive Speed (Vince Coleman)	.20	.12	.06
7	Herr's Wallop (Dan Driessen, Tom Herr)	.20	.12	.06
8	Kirby Puckett	1.00	.70	.40
9	Kent Hrbek	.30	.25	.12
10	Rich Hacker (coach, Tom Herr, Lee Weyer (umpire))	.20	.12	.06
11	Game 7's Play At The Plate (Don Baylor, Dave Phillips (umpire))	.30	.25	.12
12	Frank Viola	.35	.25	.14

1988 Fleer Box Panels

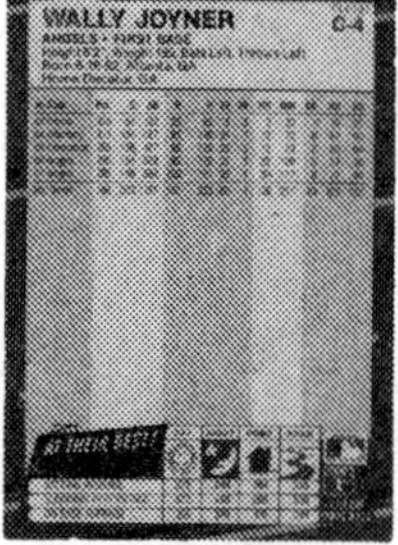

Fleer's third annual box-bottom issue once again included 16 full-color trading cards printed on the bottoms of four different wax and cello pack retail display boxes. Each box contains three player cards and one team logo card. Player cards follow the same design as the basic 1988 Fleer issue - full-color player photo, name upper left, team logo upper right, Fleer logo lower right. Card fronts feature a blue and red striped border, with a thin white line framing the photo. Card backs are printed in blue and red and include personal information and statistics. Standard- size, the cards are numbered C-1 through C-16.

		MT	NR MT	EX
Complete Panel Set:		6.25	4.75	2.50
Complete Singles Set:		2.50	2.00	1.00
Common Panel:		1.25	.90	.50
Common Single Player:		.15	.11	.06
	Panel	2.00	1.50	.80
1	Cardinals Logo	.05	.04	.02
11	Mike Schmidt	.60	.45	.25
14	Dave Stewart	.15	.11	.06
15	Tim Wallach	.20	.15	.08
	Panel	2.50	1.50	.80
2	Dwight Evans	.15	.11	.06
8	Shane Rawley	.15	.11	.06
10	Ryne Sandberg	1.00	.70	.40
13	Tigers Logo	.05	.04	.02
	Panel	2.75	2.00	1.00
3	Andres Galarraga	.40	.30	.15
6	Dale Murphy	.60	.45	.25
9	Giants Logo	.05	.04	.02
12	Kevin Seitzer	.25	.20	.10
	Panel	2.25	1.75	.90
4	Wally Joyner	.20	.15	.08
5	Twins Logo	.05	.04	.02
7	Kirby Puckett	.70	.50	.30
16	Todd Worrell	.10	.08	.04

1988 Fleer Update

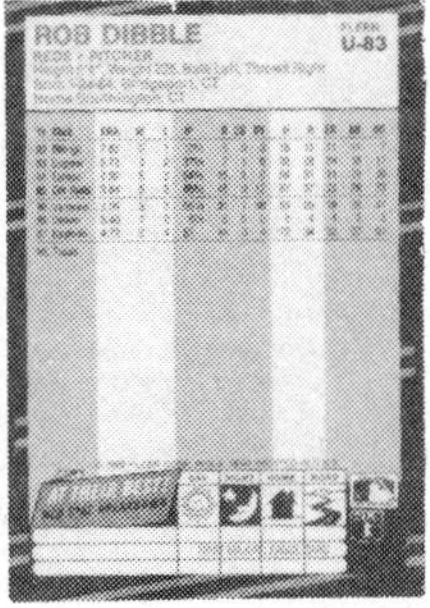

This 132-card update set (numbered U-1 through U-132 and 2-1/2" by 3-1/2") features traded veterans and rookies in a mixture of full-color action shots and close-ups, framed by white borders with red and blue stripes. Player name and position appear upper left, printed on an upward slant leading into the team logo, upper right. A bright stripe in a variety of colors (blue, red, green, yellow) edges the bottom of the photo and leads into the Fleer logo at lower right. The backs are red, white and blue-grey and include personal info, along with yearly and "At Their Best" (day, night, home, road) stats charts. The set was packaged in white cardboard boxes with red and blue stripes. A glossy-coated edition of the update set was issued in its own in box and is valued at two times greater than the regular issue.

		MT	NR MT	EX
Complete Set (132):		13.00	11.00	6.00
Common Player:		.06	.05	.02
1	Jose Bautista (FC)	.06	.05	.02
2	Joe Orsulak	.06	.05	.02
3	Doug Sisk	.06	.05	.02
4	Craig Worthington (FC)	.08	.06	.03
5	Mike Boddicker	.08	.06	.03
6	Rick Cerone	.06	.05	.02
7	Larry Parrish	.08	.06	.03
8	Lee Smith	.20	.15	.08
9	Mike Smithson	.06	.05	.02
10	John Trautwein (FC)	.06	.05	.02
11	Sherman Corbett (FC)	.06	.05	.02
12	Chili Davis	.10	.08	.04
13	Jim Eppard	.08	.06	.03
14	Bryan Harvey (FC)	1.50	1.25	.60
15	John Davis	.08	.06	.03
16	Dave Gallagher (FC)	.10	.08	.04
17	Ricky Horton	.08	.06	.03
18	Dan Pasqua	.10	.08	.04
19	Melido Perez	.08	.06	.03
20	Jose Segura (FC)	.06	.05	.02
21	Andy Allanson	.08	.06	.03
22	Jon Perlman	.06	.05	.02
23	Domingo Ramos	.06	.05	.02
24	Rick Rodriguez	.08	.06	.03
25	Willie Upshaw	.10	.08	.04
26	Paul Gibson (FC)	.08	.06	.03
27	Don Heinkel (FC)	.06	.05	.02
28	Ray Knight	.08	.06	.03
29	Gary Pettis	.08	.06	.03
30	Luis Salazar	.06	.05	.02
31	Mike MacFarlane	.40	.30	.15
32	Jeff Montgomery	.35	.25	.14
33	Ted Power	.06	.05	.02
34	Israel Sanchez (FC)	.06	.05	.02
35	Kurt Stillwell	.06	.05	.02
36	Pat Tabler	.06	.05	.02
37	Don August (FC)	.06	.05	.02
38	Darryl Hamilton (FC)	.40	.30	.15
39	Jeff Leonard	.08	.06	.03
40	Joey Meyer	.06	.05	.02
41	Allan Anderson	.10	.08	.04
42	Brian Harper	.06	.05	.02
43	Tom Herr	.10	.08	.04
44	Charlie Lea	.06	.05	.02
45	John Moses	.06	.05	.02
46	John Candelaria	.10	.08	.04
47	Jack Clark	.08	.06	.03
48	Richard Dotson	.06	.05	.02
49	Al Leiter (FC)	.06	.05	.02
50	Rafael Santana	.06	.05	.02
51	Don Slaught	.06	.05	.02
52	Todd Burns (FC)	.06	.05	.02
53	Dave Henderson	.10	.08	.04
54	Doug Jennings (FC)	.06	.05	.02
55	Dave Parker	.12	.09	.05
56	Walt Weiss	.20	.15	.08
57	Bob Welch	.10	.08	.04
58	Henry Cotto	.06	.05	.02
59	Marion Diaz (Mario)	.06	.05	.02
60	Mike Jackson	.06	.05	.02
61	Bill Swift	.15	.11	.06
62	Jose Cecena (FC)	.06	.05	.02
63	Ray Hayward (FC)	.06	.05	.02
64	Jim Steels (FC)	.06	.05	.02
65	Pat Borders (FC)	.20	.15	.08
66	Sil Campusano (FC)	.08	.06	.03
67	Mike Flanagan	.06	.05	.02
68	Todd Stottlemyre (FC)	.15	.11	.06
69	David Wells (FC)	.15	.11	.06
70	Jose Alvarez (FC)	.06	.05	.02
71	Paul Runge	.06	.05	.02
72	Cesar Jimenez (FC) (German)	.06	.05	.02
73	Pete Smith	.20	.15	.08
74	John Smoltz (FC)	4.00	3.00	1.50
75	Damon Berryhill	.10	.08	.04
76	Goose Gossage	.10	.08	.04
77	Mark Grace	2.50	2.00	1.00
78	Darrin Jackson	.15	.11	.06
79	Vance Law	.06	.05	.02
80	Jeff Pico (FC)	.06	.05	.02
81	Gary Varsho (FC)	.06	.05	.02
82	Tim Birtsas	.06	.05	.02
83	Rob Dibble (FC)	.25	.20	.10
84	Danny Jackson	.15	.11	.06
85	Paul O'Neill	.15	.11	.06
86	Jose Rijo	.15	.11	.06
87	Chris Sabo (FC)	.80	.60	.30
88	John Fishel (FC)	.06	.05	.02
89	Craig Biggio (FC)	1.50	1.25	.60
90	Terry Puhl	.06	.05	.02
91	Rafael Ramirez	.06	.05	.02
92	Louie Meadows (FC)	.06	.05	.02
93	Kirk Gibson	.20	.15	.08
94	Alfredo Griffin	.08	.06	.03
95	Jay Howell	.08	.06	.03
96	Jesse Orosco	.06	.05	.02
97	Alejandro Pena	.06	.05	.02
98	Tracy Woodson (FC)	.06	.05	.02
99	John Dopson (FC)	.06	.05	.02
100	Brian Holman (FC)	.10	.08	.04
101	Rex Hudler (FC)	.08	.06	.03
102	Jeff Parrett (FC)	.06	.05	.02
103	Nelson Santovenia (FC)	.06	.05	.02
104	Kevin Elster	.06	.05	.02
105	Jeff Innis (FC)	.06	.05	.02
106	Mackey Sasser (FC)	.06	.05	.02
107	Phil Bradley	.06	.05	.02
108	Danny Clay (FC)	.06	.05	.02
109	Greg Harris	.06	.05	.02
110	Ricky Jordan (FC)	.06	.05	.02
111	David Palmer	.06	.05	.02
112	Jim Gott	.06	.05	.02
113	Tommy Gregg (FC) (photo actually Randy Milligan)	.10	.08	.04
114	Barry Jones	.06	.05	.02
115	Randy Milligan (FC)	.10	.08	.04
116	Luis Alicea (FC)	.10	.08	.04
117	Tom Brunansky	.06	.05	.02
118	John Costello (FC)	.10	.08	.04
119	Jose DeLeon	.08	.06	.03
120	Bob Horner	.10	.08	.04
121	Scott Terry (FC)	.06	.05	.02
122	Roberto Alomar (FC)	12.00	9.00	4.75
123	Dave Leiper	.06	.05	.02
124	Keith Moreland	.06	.05	.02
125	Mark Parent (FC)	.06	.05	.02
126	Dennis Rasmussen	.10	.08	.04
127	Randy Bockus	.06	.05	.02
128	Brett Butler	.10	.08	.04
129	Donell Nixon	.06	.05	.02
130	Earnest Riles	.06	.05	.02
131	Roger Samuels (FC)	.06	.05	.02
132	Checklist	.06	.05	.02

1988 Fleer Award Winners

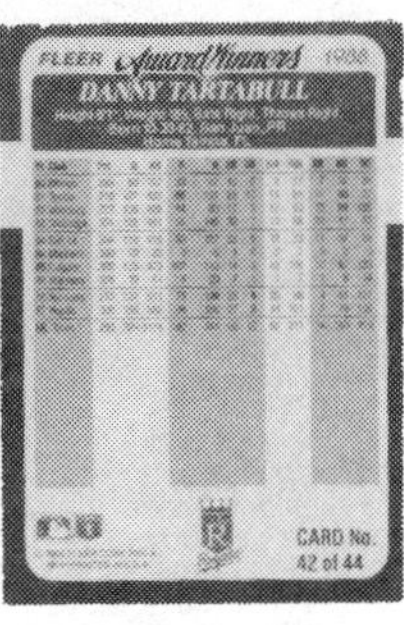

This limited edition 44-card boxed set of 1987 award-winning player cards also includes six team logo sticker cards. Red, white, blue and yellow bands border the sharp, full-color player photos printed below a "Fleer Award Winners 1988" banner. The player's name and award are printed beneath the photo. Flip sides are red, white and blue and list personal information, career data, team logo and card number. This set was sold exclusively at 7-11 stores nationwide.

		MT	NR MT	EX
Complete Set:		5.00	3.75	2.00
Common Player:		.05	.04	.02
1	Steve Bedrosian	.10	.08	.04
2	George Bell	.20	.15	.08
3	Wade Boggs	.70	.50	.30
4	Jose Canseco	.70	.50	.30
5	Will Clark	.60	.45	.25
6	Roger Clemens	.40	.30	.15
7	Kal Daniels	.10	.08	.04
8	Eric Davis	.25	.20	.10
9	Andre Dawson	.15	.11	.06
10	Mike Dunne	.10	.08	.04
11	Dwight Evans	.10	.08	.04
12	Carlton Fisk	.15	.11	.06
13	Julio Franco	.07	.05	.03
14	Dwight Gooden	.20	.15	.08
15	Pedro Guerrero	.15	.11	.06
16	Tony Gwynn	.25	.20	.10
17	Orel Hershiser	.20	.15	.08
18	Tom Henke	.05	.04	.02
19	Ted Higuera	.10	.08	.04
20	Charlie Hough	.05	.04	.02
21	Wally Joyner	.20	.15	.08
22	Jimmy Key	.07	.05	.03
23	Don Mattingly	.70	.50	.30
24	Mark McGwire	.50	.40	.20
25	Paul Molitor	.12	.09	.05
26	Jack Morris	.12	.09	.05
27	Dale Murphy	.30	.25	.12
28	Terry Pendleton	.05	.04	.02
29	Kirby Puckett	.70	.50	.30
30	Tim Raines	.25	.20	.10
31	Jeff Reardon	.07	.05	.03
32	Harold Reynolds	.05	.04	.02
33	Dave Righetti	.12	.09	.05
34	Benito Santiago	.15	.11	.06
35	Mike Schmidt	.40	.30	.15
36	Mike Scott	.10	.08	.04
37	Kevin Seitzer	.20	.15	.08
38	Larry Sheets	.07	.05	.03
39	Ozzie Smith	.25	.20	.10
40	Darryl Strawberry	.40	.30	.15
41	Rick Sutcliffe	.10	.08	.04
42	Danny Tartabull	.12	.09	.05
43	Alan Trammell	.15	.11	.06
44	Tim Wallach	.10	.08	.04

1988 Fleer Baseball All Stars

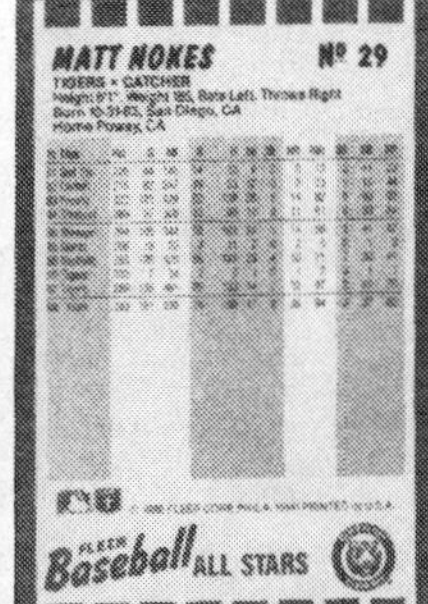

This limited edition 44-card boxed set features excellent photography of major league All-Stars. The standard-size cards feature a sporty bright blue- and yellow- striped background. The player name is printed in white across the upper left front corner. "Fleer Baseball 88 All Stars" appears on a yellow band beneath the photo. Card backs feature a blue- and white-striped design with a yellow highlighted section at the top that contains the player name, card number, team, position and personal data, followed by lifetime career stats. Fleer All Stars are cello-wrapped in blue and yellow striped boxes with checklist backs. The set includes six team logo sticker cards that feature black and white aerial shots of major league ballparks. The set was marketed exclusively by Ben Franklin stores.

		MT	NR MT	EX
Complete Set:		5.00	3.75	2.00
Common Player:		.05	.04	.02
1	George Bell	.20	.15	.08
2	Wade Boggs	.70	.50	.30
3	Bobby Bonilla	.12	.09	.05
4	George Brett	.70	.50	.30
5	Jose Canseco	.70	.50	.30
6	Jack Clark	.15	.11	.06
7	Will Clark	.70	.50	.30
8	Roger Clemens	.40	.30	.15
9	Eric Davis	.20	.15	.08
10	Andre Dawson	.15	.11	.06
11	Julio Franco	.07	.05	.03
12	Dwight Gooden	.20	.15	.08
13	Tony Gwynn	.25	.20	.10
14	Orel Hershiser	.20	.15	.08
15	Teddy Higuera	.10	.08	.04
16	Charlie Hough	.05	.04	.02
17	Kent Hrbek	.15	.11	.06
18	Bruce Hurst	.10	.08	.04
19	Wally Joyner	.20	.15	.08
20	Mark Langston	.10	.08	.04
21	Dave LaPoint	.05	.04	.02
22	Candy Maldonado	.05	.04	.02
23	Don Mattingly	.70	.50	.30
24	Roger McDowell	.07	.05	.03
25	Mark McGwire	.50	.40	.20
26	Jack Morris	.12	.09	.05
27	Dale Murphy	.30	.25	.12
28	Eddie Murray	.20	.15	.08
29	Matt Nokes	.15	.11	.06
30	Kirby Puckett	.70	.50	.30
31	Tim Raines	.25	.20	.10
32	Willie Randolph	.07	.05	.03
33	Jeff Reardon	.07	.05	.03
34	Nolan Ryan	1.50	1.25	.60
35	Juan Samuel	.10	.08	.04
36	Mike Schmidt	.40	.30	.15
37	Mike Scott	.10	.08	.04
38	Kevin Seitzer	.20	.15	.08
39	Ozzie Smith	.25	.20	.10
40	Darryl Strawberry	.40	.30	.15
41	Rick Sutcliffe	.10	.08	.04
42	Alan Trammell	.15	.11	.06
43	Tim Wallach	.10	.08	.04
44	Dave Winfield	.30	.25	.12

1988 Fleer Baseball MVP

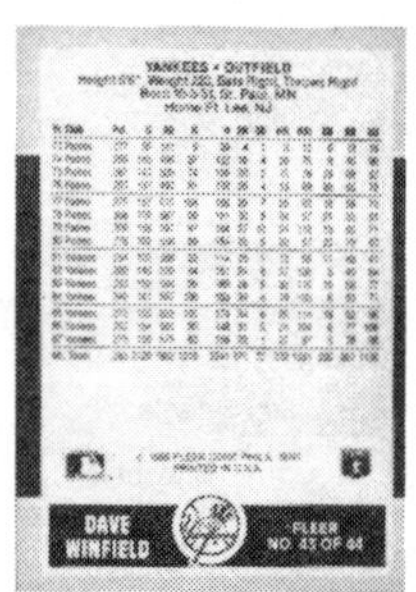

This boxed set of 44 standard-size cards and six team logo stickers was produced by Fleer for exclusive distribution at Toys "R" Us stores. This premiere edition features full-color player photos framed by a yellow and blue border. The player's name is printed in red below and to the left of the photo; team and position are printed in black in the lower right corner. The "Fleer Baseball MVP" logo appears bottom center. Card backs are yellow and blue on a white background. The player's team, position and personal data are followed by stats, logo and a blue banner bearing the player's name, team logo and card number. The six sticker cards feature black and white stadium photos on the backs.

		MT	NR MT	EX
Complete Set:		5.00	3.75	2.00
Common Player:		.05	.04	.02
1	George Bell	.20	.15	.08
2	Wade Boggs	.80	.60	.30
3	Jose Canseco	.80	.60	.30
4	Ivan Calderon	.07	.05	.03
5	Will Clark	.80	.60	.30
6	Roger Clemens	.40	.30	.15
7	Vince Coleman	.15	.11	.06
8	Eric Davis	.20	.15	.08
9	Andre Dawson	.15	.11	.06
10	Dave Dravecky	.05	.04	.02
11	Mike Dunne	.10	.08	.04
12	Dwight Evans	.10	.08	.04
13	Sid Fernandez	.07	.05	.03
14	Tony Fernandez	.10	.08	.04
15	Julio Franco	.07	.05	.03
16	Dwight Gooden	.20	.15	.08
17	Tony Gwynn	.25	.20	.10
18	Ted Higuera	.10	.08	.04
19	Charlie Hough	.05	.04	.02
20	Wally Joyner	.15	.11	.06
21	Mark Langston	.10	.08	.04
22	Don Mattingly	.80	.60	.30
23	Mark McGwire	.50	.40	.20
24	Jack Morris	.12	.09	.05
25	Dale Murphy	.30	.25	.12
26	Kirby Puckett	.50	.40	.20
27	Tim Raines	.25	.20	.10
28	Willie Randolph	.07	.05	.03
29	Ryne Sandberg	.80	.60	.30
30	Benito Santiago	.25	.20	.10
31	Mike Schmidt	.40	.30	.15
32	Mike Scott	.10	.08	.04
33	Kevin Seitzer	.10	.08	.04
34	Larry Sheets	.07	.05	.03
35	Ozzie Smith	.25	.20	.10
36	Dave Stewart	.10	.08	.04
37	Darryl Strawberry	.40	.30	.15
38	Rick Sutcliffe	.10	.08	.04
39	Alan Trammell	.15	.11	.06
40	Fernando Valenzuela	.10	.08	.04
41	Frank Viola	.12	.09	.05
42	Tim Wallach	.10	.08	.04
43	Dave Winfield	.20	.15	.08
44	Robin Yount	.80	.60	.30

1988 Fleer Baseball's Best

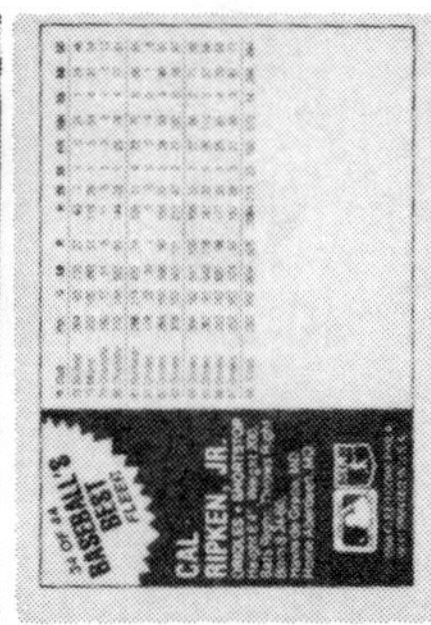

This boxed set of 44 standard-size cards (2-1/2" by 3-1/2") and six team logo stickers is the third annual issue from Fleer highlighting the best major league sluggers and pitchers. Five additional player cards were printed on retail display box bottoms, along with a checklist logo card (numbered C-1 through C-6). Full-color player photos are framed by a green border that fades to yellow. A red (slugger) or blue (pitcher) player name is printed beneath the photo. The card backs are printed in green on a white background with yellow highlights. Card number, player name and personal info appear in a green vertical box on the left-hand side of the card back with a yellow cartoon-style team logo overprinted across a stats chart on the right. This set was produced by Fleer for exclusive distribution by McCrory's stores (McCrory, McClellan, J.J. Newberry, H.L. Green, TG&Y).

		MT	NR MT	EX
Complete Set:		5.00	3.75	2.00
Common Player:		.05	.04	.02
1	George Bell	.20	.15	.08
2	Wade Boggs	.80	.60	.30
3	Bobby Bonilla	.12	.09	.05
4	Tom Brunansky	.10	.08	.04
5	Ellis Burks	.40	.30	.15
6	Jose Canseco	.80	.60	.30
7	Joe Carter	.12	.09	.05
8	Will Clark	.80	.60	.30
9	Roger Clemens	.40	.30	.15
10	Eric Davis	.20	.15	.08
11	Glenn Davis	.07	.05	.03
12	Andre Dawson	.15	.11	.06
13	Dennis Eckersley	.07	.05	.03
14	Andres Galarraga	.15	.11	.06
15	Dwight Gooden	.20	.15	.08
16	Pedro Guerrero	.15	.11	.06
17	Tony Gwynn	.25	.20	.10
18	Orel Hershiser	.20	.15	.08
19	Ted Higuera	.10	.08	.04
20	Pete Incaviglia	.07	.05	.03
21	Danny Jackson	.10	.08	.04
22	Doug Jennings	.07	.05	.03
23	Mark Langston	.10	.08	.04
24	Dave LaPoint	.05	.04	.02
25	Mike LaValliere	.07	.05	.03
26	Don Mattingly	.80	.60	.30
27	Mark McGwire	.50	.40	.20
28	Dale Murphy	.30	.25	.12
29	Ken Phelps	.05	.04	.02
30	Kirby Puckett	.60	.45	.25
31	Johnny Ray	.05	.04	.02
32	Jeff Reardon	.07	.05	.03
33	Dave Righetti	.12	.09	.05
34	Cal Ripkin, Jr. (Ripken)	.80	.60	.30
35	Chris Sabo	.40	.30	.15
36	Mike Schmidt	.40	.30	.15
37	Mike Scott	.10	.08	.04
38	Kevin Seitzer	.15	.11	.06
39	Dave Stewart	.10	.08	.04
40	Darryl Strawberry	.40	.30	.15
41	Greg Swindell	.10	.08	.04
42	Frank Tanana	.05	.04	.02
43	Dave Winfield	.40	.30	.15
44	Todd Worrell	.10	.08	.04

1988 Fleer Baseball's Best Box Panel

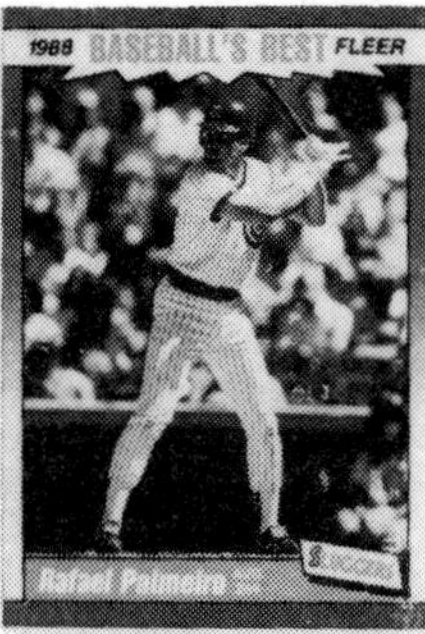

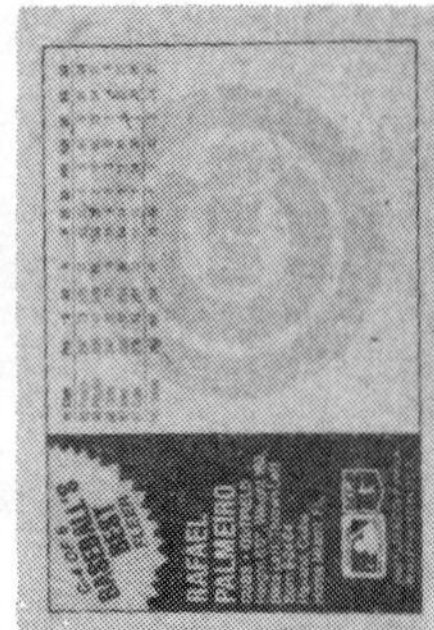

Six cards were placed on the bottoms of retail boxes of the Fleer 44-card Baseball's Best boxed sets in 1988. The cards, which measure 2-1/2" by 3-1/2", are identical in design to cards found in the 44-card set. The cards are numbered C-1 through C-6 and were produced by Fleer for distribution by McCrory stores and its affiliates.

		MT	NR MT	EX
Complete Panel Set:		1.50	1.25	.60
Complete Singles Set:		.90	.70	.35
Common Single Player:		.15	.11	.06
1	Ron Darling	.20	.15	.08
2	Rickey Henderson	.60	.45	.25
3	Carney Lansford	.15	.11	.06
4	Rafael Palmeiro	.40	.30	.15
5	Frank Viola	.20	.15	.08
6	Twins Logo	.05	.04	.02

1988 Fleer Baseball's Exciting Stars

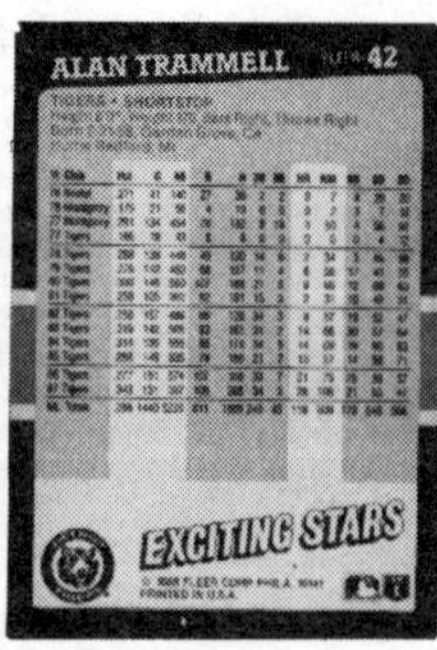

This 44-card limited-edition boxed set showcases star major leaguers. Player photos are slanted upwards to the right, framed by a blue border with a red and white bar stripe across the middle. The player's name is printed in white above the photo. "Baseball's Exciting Stars" is printed in red and yellow across the bottom margin, following the upward slant of the photo. Fleer's logo appears lower right intersecting a white baseball bearing the number "88". Card backs are numbered and printed in red, white and blue. The set was packaged in a checklist box, with six team logo sticker cards featuring black and white stadium photos on the flip sides. Exciting Stars was distributed via Cumberland Farm stores throughout the northeastern U.S. and Florida.

		MT	NR MT	EX
Complete Set (44):		5.00	3.75	2.00
Common Player:		.05	.04	.02
1	Harold Baines	.10	.08	.04
2	Kevin Bass	.07	.05	.03
3	George Bell	.20	.15	.08
4	Wade Boggs	.80	.60	.30
5	Mickey Brantley	.05	.04	.02
6	Sid Bream	.05	.04	.02

7	Jose Canseco	.80	.60	.30
8	Jack Clark	.07	.05	.03
9	Will Clark	.80	.60	.30
10	Roger Clemens	.40	.30	.15
11	Vince Coleman	.15	.11	.06
12	Eric Davis	.20	.15	.08
13	Andre Dawson	.15	.11	.06
14	Julio Franco	.07	.05	.03
15	Dwight Gooden	.20	.15	.08
16	Mike Greenwell	.40	.30	.15
17	Tony Gwynn	.25	.20	.10
18	Von Hayes	.07	.05	.03
19	Tom Henke	.05	.04	.02
20	Orel Hershiser	.20	.15	.08
21	Teddy Higuera	.10	.08	.04
22	Brook Jacoby	.07	.05	.03
23	Wally Joyner	.20	.15	.08
24	Jimmy Key	.07	.05	.03
25	Don Mattingly	.80	.60	.30
26	Mark McGwire	.50	.40	.20
27	Jack Morris	.12	.09	.05
28	Dale Murphy	.30	.25	.12
29	Matt Nokes	.15	.11	.06
30	Kirby Puckett	.70	.50	.30
31	Tim Raines	.25	.20	.10
32	Ryne Sandberg	.80	.60	.30
33	Benito Santiago	.25	.20	.10
34	Mike Schmidt	.40	.30	.15
35	Mike Scott	.10	.08	.04
36	Kevin Seitzer	.15	.11	.06
37	Larry Sheets	.07	.05	.03
38	Ruben Sierra	.20	.15	.08
39	Darryl Strawberry	.40	.30	.15
40	Ozzie Smith	.25	.20	.10
41	Danny Tartabull	.10	.08	.04
42	Alan Trammell	.15	.11	.06
43	Fernando Valenzuela	.10	.08	.04
44	Devon White	.20	.15	.08

1988 Fleer Baseball's Hottest Stars

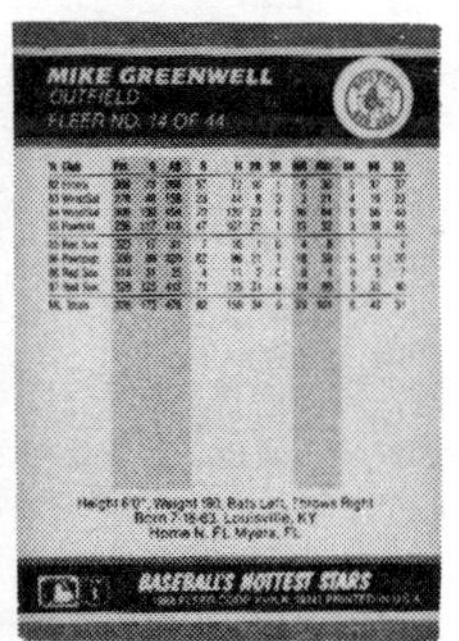

This boxed set of 44 standard-size player cards and six team logo sticker cards was produced by Fleer for exclusive distribution at Revco drug stores nation-wide. Card fronts feature full-color photos of players representing every major league team. Photos are framed in red, orange and yellow, with a blue and white player name printed across the bottom of the card front. A flaming baseball logo bearing the words "Hottest Stars" appears in the lower left corner of the player photo. Card backs are red, white and blue. The player's name, position, card number and team togo are printed across the top section, followed by a stats box, personal data, batting and throwing preferences. The set also includes a six team logo sticker cards with flipside stadium photos in black and white.

		MT	NR MT	EX
Complete Set (44):		5.00	3.75	2.00
Common Player:		.05	.04	.02
1	George Bell	.12	.09	.05
2	Wade Boggs	.80	.60	.30
3	Bobby Bonilla	.20	.15	.08
4	George Brett	.70	.50	.30
5	Jose Canseco	.80	.60	.30
6	Will Clark	.80	.60	.30
7	Roger Clemens	.40	.30	.15
8	Eric Davis	.20	.15	.08
9	Andre Dawson	.15	.11	.06
10	Tony Fernandez	.10	.08	.04
11	Julio Franco	.07	.05	.03
12	Gary Gaetti	.10	.08	.04
13	Dwight Gooden	.20	.15	.08
14	Mike Greenwell	.40	.30	.15
15	Tony Gwynn	.25	.20	.10
16	Rickey Henderson	.50	.40	.20
17	Keith Hernandez	.07	.05	.03
18	Tom Herr	.07	.05	.03
19	Orel Hershiser	.20	.15	.08
20	Ted Higuera	.10	.08	.04
21	Wally Joyner	.20	.15	.08
22	Jimmy Key	.07	.05	.03
23	Mark Langston	.10	.08	.04
24	Don Mattingly	.80	.60	.30
25	Jack McDowell	.35	.25	.14
26	Mark McGwire	.50	.40	.20
27	Kevin Mitchell	.20	.15	.08
28	Jack Morris	.12	.09	.05
29	Dale Murphy	.30	.25	.12
30	Kirby Puckett	.50	.40	.20
31	Tim Raines	.25	.20	.10
32	Shane Rawley	.05	.04	.02
33	Benito Santiago	.25	.20	.10
34	Mike Schmidt	.40	.30	.15
35	Mike Scott	.10	.08	.04
36	Kevin Seitzer	.15	.11	.06
37	Larry Sheets	.07	.05	.03
38	Ruben Sierra	.50	.40	.20
39	Dave Smith	.05	.04	.02
40	Ozzie Smith	.30	.25	.12
41	Darryl Strawberry	.40	.30	.15
42	Rick Sutcliffe	.10	.08	.04
43	Pat Tabler	.05	.04	.02
44	Alan Trammell	.15	.11	.06

1988 Fleer League Leaders

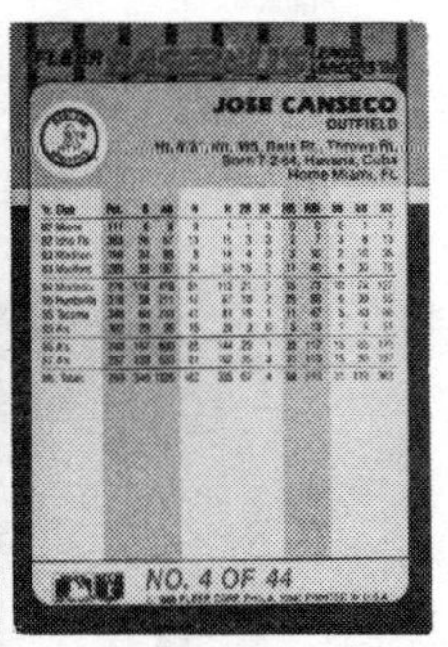

This 44-card boxed set is the third annual limited edition set from Fleer highlighting leading players. The 1988 edition contains the same type of information, front and back, as the previous sets, with a new color scheme and design. Card fronts have bright blue borders, solid on the lower portion, striped on the upper, with a gold bar separating the two sections. "Fleer's Baseball's League Leaders '88" headlines the card face. The full-color player photo is centered above a yellow player name banner. The numbered card backs are blue, pink and white, and contain player stats and personal notes. Six team logo sticker cards, with flipside black and white photos of ballparks, accompany this set which was marketed exclusively by Walgreen drug stores.

		MT	NR MT	EX
Complete Set (44):		5.00	3.75	2.00
Common Player:		.05	.04	.02
1	George Bell	.20	.15	.08
2	Wade Boggs	.80	.60	.30
3	Ivan Calderon	.07	.05	.03
4	Jose Canseco	.80	.60	.30
5	Will Clark	.80	.60	.30
6	Roger Clemens	.40	.30	.15
7	Vince Coleman	.15	.11	.06
8	Eric Davis	.20	.15	.08
9	Andre Dawson	.15	.11	.06
10	Bill Doran	.07	.05	.03
11	Dwight Evans	.10	.08	.04
12	Julio Franco	.07	.05	.03
13	Gary Gaetti	.10	.08	.04
14	Andres Galarraga	.15	.11	.06
15	Dwight Gooden	.20	.15	.08
16	Tony Gwynn	.25	.20	.10
17	Tom Henke	.05	.04	.02
18	Keith Hernandez	.07	.05	.03
19	Orel Hershiser	.20	.15	.08
20	Ted Higuera	.10	.08	.04
21	Kent Hrbek	.15	.11	.06
22	Wally Joyner	.20	.15	.08
23	Jimmy Key	.07	.05	.03
24	Mark Langston	.10	.08	.04
25	Don Mattingly	.80	.60	.30
26	Mark McGwire	.50	.40	.20
27	Paul Molitor	.25	.20	.10
28	Jack Morris	.12	.09	.05
29	Dale Murphy	.30	.25	.12
30	Kirby Puckett	.50	.40	.20
31	Tim Raines	.25	.20	.10
32	Rick Rueschel	.07	.05	.03
33	Bret Saberhagen	.15	.11	.06
34	Benito Santiago	.25	.20	.10
35	Mike Schmidt	.40	.30	.15
36	Mike Scott	.10	.08	.04
37	Kevin Seitzer	.15	.11	.06
38	Larry Sheets	.07	.05	.03
39	Ruben Sierra	.50	.40	.20
40	Darryl Strawberry	.40	.30	.15
41	Rick Sutcliffe	.10	.08	.04
42	Alan Trammell	.15	.11	.06
43	Andy Van Slyke	.10	.08	.04
44	Todd Worrell	.10	.08	.04

1988 Fleer Mini

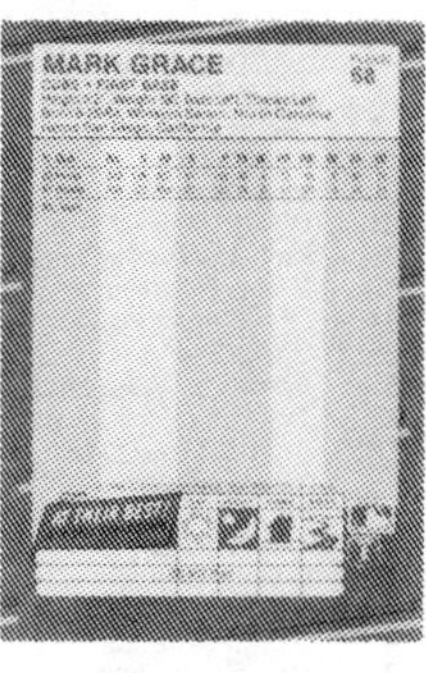

This third annual issue of miniatures (1-7/8" by 2-5/8") includes 120 high-gloss cards featuring new photos, not copies from the regular issue, although the card designs are identical. Card fronts have white borders, with red and blue striping and a bright color band beneath the photo leading to a blue Fleet logo lower right. The player name is printed upper left; the full-color team logo appears upper right. Card backs are red, white and blue and include personal data, yearly career stats and a stats breakdown of batting average, slugging percentage and on-base average, listed for day, night, home and road games. Card backs are numbered in alphabetical order by teams which are also listed alphabetically. The set includes 18 team logo stickers with black and white aerial stadium photos on the flip sides.

		MT	NR MT	EX
Complete Set (120):		10.00	7.50	4.00
Common Player:		.05	.04	.02
1	Eddie Murray	.25	.20	.10
2	Dave Schmidt	.05	.04	.02
3	Larry Sheets	.07	.05	.03
4	Wade Boggs	.70	.50	.30
5	Roger Clemens	.80	.60	.30
6	Dwight Evans	.12	.09	.05
7	Mike Greenwell	.40	.30	.15
8	Sam Horn	.07	.05	.03
9	Lee Smith	.07	.05	.03
10	Brian Downing	.05	.04	.02
11	Wally Joyner	.15	.11	.06
12	Devon White	.10	.08	.04
13	Mike Witt	.07	.05	.03
14	Ivan Calderon	.07	.05	.03
15	Ozzie Guillen	.07	.05	.03
16	Jack McDowell	.50	.40	.20
17	Kenny Williams	.05	.04	.02
18	Joe Carter	.20	.15	.08
19	Julio Franco	.10	.08	.04
20	Pat Tabler	.05	.04	.02
21	Doyle Alexander	.05	.04	.02
22	Jack Morris	.15	.11	.06
23	Matt Nokes	.15	.11	.06
24	Walt Terrell	.05	.04	.02
25	Alan Trammell	.20	.15	.08
26	Bret Saberhagen	.15	.11	.06
27	Kevin Seitzer	.07	.05	.03
28	Danny Tartabull	.15	.11	.06
29	Gary Thurman	.07	.05	.03
30	Ted Higuera	.10	.08	.04
31	Paul Molitor			
32	Dan Plesac	.10	.08	.04
33	Robin Yount	.45	.35	.20
34	Gary Gaetti	.12	.09	.05
35	Kent Hrbek	.15	.11	.06
36	Kirby Puckett	.50	.40	.20
37	Jeff Reardon	.07	.05	.03
38	Frank Viola	.12	.09	.05
39	Jack Clark	.12	.09	.05
40	Rickey Henderson	.80	.60	.30
41	Don Mattingly	.80	.60	.30
42	Willie Randolph	.05	.04	.02
43	Dave Righetti	.12	.09	.05
44	Dave Winfield	.40	.30	.15
45	Jose Canseco	.80	.60	.30
46	Mark McGwire	.40	.30	.15
47	Dave Parker	.12	.09	.05
48	Dave Stewart	.07	.05	.03
49	Walt Weiss	.35	.25	.14
50	Bob Welch	.07	.05	.03
51	Mickey Brantley	.05	.04	.02
52	Mark Langston	.10	.08	.04
53	Harold Reynolds	.07	.05	.03
54	Scott Fletcher	.05	.04	.02
55	Charlie Hough	.05	.04	.02
56	Pete Incaviglia	.12	.09	.05
57	Larry Parrish	.05	.04	.02
58	Ruben Sierra	.20	.15	.08
59	George Bell	.20	.15	.08
60	Mark Eichhorn	.05	.04	.02
61	Tony Fernandez	.10	.08	.04
62	Tom Henke	.05	.04	.02
63	Jimmy Key	.07	.05	.03
64	Dion James	.05	.04	.02
65	Dale Murphy	.30	.25	.12
66	Zane Smith	.05	.04	.02
67	Andre Dawson	.15	.11	.06
68	Mark Grace	.80	.60	.30
69	Jerry Mumphrey	.05	.04	.02
70	Ryne Sandberg	1.00	.70	.40
71	Rick Sutcliffe	.10	.08	.04
72	Kal Daniels	.12	.09	.05
73	Eric Davis	.20	.15	.08
74	John Franco	.07	.05	.03

75	Ron Robinson	.05	.04	.02
76	Jeff Treadway	.10	.08	.04
77	Kevin Bass	.07	.05	.03
78	Glenn Davis	.10	.08	.04
79	Nolan Ryan	1.00	.70	.40
80	Mike Scott	.12	.09	.05
81	Dave Smith	.05	.04	.02
82	Kirk Gibson	.20	.15	.08
83	Pedro Guerrero	.12	.09	.05
84	Orel Hershiser	.20	.15	.08
85	Steve Sax	.10	.08	.04
86	Fernando Valenzuela	.10	.08	.04
87	Tim Burke	.05	.04	.02
88	Andres Galarraga	.15	.11	.06
89	Neal Heaton	.05	.04	.02
90	Tim Raines	.20	.15	.08
91	Tim Wallach	.10	.08	.04
92	Dwight Gooden	.25	.20	.10
93	Keith Hernandez	.15	.11	.06
94	Gregg Jefferies	.70	.50	.30
95	Howard Johnson	.10	.08	.04
96	Roger McDowell	.05	.04	.02
97	Darryl Strawberry	.40	.30	.15
98	Steve Bedrosian	.10	.08	.04
99	Von Hayes	.10	.08	.04
100	Shane Rawley	.05	.04	.02
101	Juan Samuel	.12	.09	.05
102	Mike Schmidt	.40	.30	.15
103	Bobby Bonilla	.30	.25	.12
104	Mike Dunne	.07	.05	.03
105	Andy Van Slyke	.10	.08	.04
106	Vince Coleman	.15	.11	.06
107	Bob Horner	.07	.05	.03
108	Willie McGee	.10	.08	.04
109	Ozzie Smith	.25	.20	.10
110	John Tudor	.07	.05	.03
111	Todd Worrell	.10	.08	.04
112	Tony Gwynn	.25	.20	.10
113	John Kruk	.20	.15	.08
114	Lance McCullers	.05	.04	.02
115	Benito Santiago	.15	.11	.06
116	Will Clark	.60	.45	.25
117	Jeff Leonard	.05	.04	.02
118	Candy Maldonado	.05	.04	.02
119	Kirt Manwaring	.07	.05	.03
120	Don Robinson	.05	.04	.02

1988 Fleer Record Setters

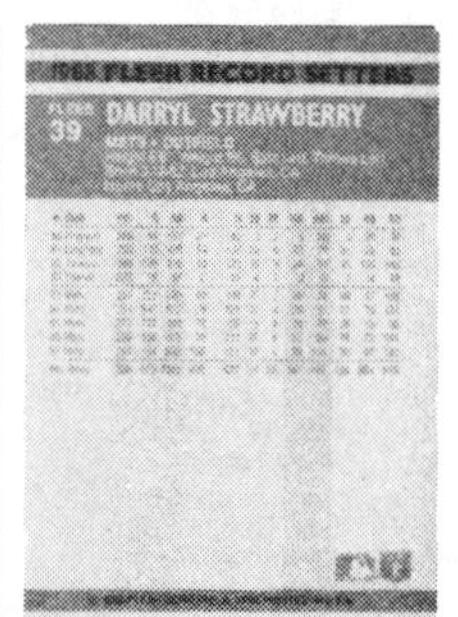

For the second consecutive year, Fleer Corp. issued this special limited-edition 44-card set for exclusive distribution by Eckerd Drug stores. Cards are standard size with red and blue borders framing the full-color player photos. A "1988 Fleer Record Setters" headline is printed on a yellow strip above the player's photo. The player's photo. The player's name, team and position appear beneath the pose. Card backs list personal information and career stats in red and blue ink on a white background. Each 44-card set comes cello-wrapped in a checklist box that contains six additional cards with peel-off team logo stickers. The sticker cards feature black and white aerial photos of major league ballparks, along with stadium statistics such as field size, seating capacity and date of the first game played.

		MT	NR MT	EX
Complete Set (44):		5.00	3.75	2.00
Common Player:		.05	.04	.02
1	Jesse Barfield	.10	.08	.04
2	George Bell	.20	.15	.08
3	Wade Boggs	.80	.60	.30
4	Jose Canseco	.80	.60	.30
5	Jack Clark	.07	.05	.03
6	Will Clark	.80	.60	.30
7	Roger Clemens	.40	.30	.15
8	Alvin Davis	.05	.04	.02
9	Eric Davis	.20	.15	.08
10	Andre Dawson	.15	.11	.06
11	Mike Dunne	.05	.04	.02
12	John Franco	.07	.05	.03
13	Julio Franco	.07	.05	.03
14	Dwight Gooden	.20	.15	.08
15	Mark Gubicza	.07	.05	.03
16	Ozzie Guillen	.07	.05	.03
17	Tony Gwynn	.25	.20	.10
18	Orel Hershiser	.20	.15	.08
19	Teddy Higuera	.10	.08	.04
20	Howard Johnson	.12	.09	.05
21	Wally Joyner	.20	.15	.08
22	Jimmy Key	.07	.05	.03
23	Jeff Leonard	.05	.04	.02
24	Don Mattingly	.80	.60	.30
25	Mark McGwire	.50	.40	.20
26	Jack Morris	.12	.09	.05
27	Dale Murphy	.30	.25	.12
28	Larry Parrish	.05	.04	.02
29	Kirby Puckett	.65	.50	.25
30	Tim Raines	.25	.20	.10
31	Harold Reynolds	.07	.05	.03
32	Dave Righetti	.12	.09	.05
33	Cal Ripken, Jr.	.80	.60	.30
34	Benito Santiago	.25	.20	.10
35	Mike Schmidt	.70	.50	.30
36	Mike Scott	.10	.08	.04
37	Kevin Seitzer	.10	.08	.04
38	Ozzie Smith	.25	.20	.10
39	Darryl Strawberry	.40	.30	.15
40	Rick Sutcliffe	.10	.08	.04
41	Alan Trammell	.15	.11	.06
42	Frank Viola	.12	.09	.05
43	Mitch Williams	.05	.04	.02
44	Todd Worrell	.10	.08	.04

1988 Fleer Star Stickers

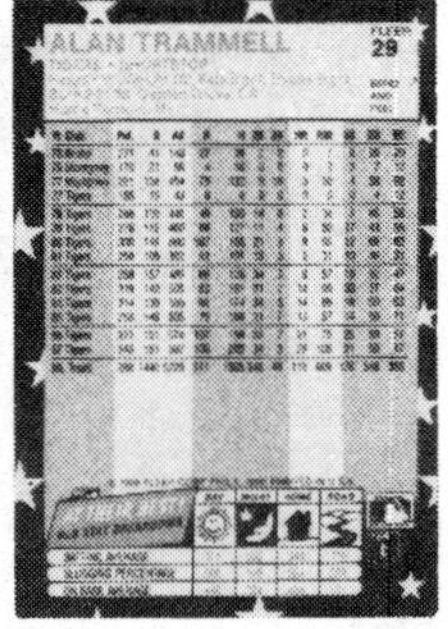

This set of 132 standard-size sticker cards (including a checklist card) features exclusive player photos, different from those in the Fleer regular issue. Card fronts have light gray borders sprinkled with multi-colored stars. The "Fleer Star Stickers" logo appears upper left, player names are printed beneath the photos. Card backs are printed in red, gray and black on white and include personal data and a breakdown of pitching and batting stats into day, night, home and road categories. Cards were marketed in two different display boxes that feature six players and two team logos from Fleer's 1988 Limited Edition box-bottom set.

		MT	NR MT	EX
Complete Set (132):		20.00	15.00	8.00
Common Player:		.05	.04	.02
1	Mike Boddicker	.08	.06	.03
2	Eddie Murray	.50	.40	.20
3	Cal Ripken, Jr.	1.00	.70	.40
4	Larry Sheets	.05	.04	.02
5	Wade Boggs	.80	.60	.30
6	Ellis Burks	.30	.25	.12
7	Roger Clemens	.70	.50	.30
8	Dwight Evans	.15	.11	.06
9	Mike Greenwell	.40	.30	.15
10	Bruce Hurst	.12	.09	.05
11	Brian Downing	.08	.06	.03
12	Wally Joyner	.25	.20	.10
13	Mike Witt	.10	.08	.04
14	Ivan Calderon	.12	.09	.05
15	Jose DeLeon	.05	.04	.02
16	Ozzie Guillen	.15	.11	.06
17	Bobby Thigpen	.10	.08	.04
18	Joe Carter	.20	.15	.08
19	Julio Franco	.12	.09	.05
20	Brook Jacoby	.12	.09	.05
21	Cory Snyder	.05	.04	.02
22	Pat Tabler	.10	.08	.04
23	Doyle Alexander	.08	.06	.03
24	Kirk Gibson	.30	.25	.12
25	Mike Henneman	.20	.15	.08
26	Jack Morris	.25	.20	.10
27	Matt Nokes	.15	.11	.06
28	Walt Terrell	.05	.04	.02
29	Alan Trammell	.30	.25	.12
30	George Brett	.80	.60	.30
31	Charlie Leibrandt	.05	.04	.02
32	Bret Saberhagen	.25	.20	.10
33	Kevin Seitzer	.07	.05	.03
34	Danny Tartabull	.25	.20	.10
35	Frank White	.10	.08	.04
36	Rob Deer	.10	.08	.04
37	Ted Higuera	.07	.05	.03
38	Paul Molitor	.35	.25	.14
39	Dan Plesac	.12	.09	.05
40	Robin Yount	.50	.40	.20
41	Bert Blyleven	.15	.11	.06
42	Tom Brunansky	.07	.05	.03
43	Gary Gaetti	.20	.15	.08
44	Kent Hrbek	.30	.25	.12
45	Kirby Puckett	.65	.50	.25
46	Jeff Reardon	.10	.08	.04
47	Frank Viola	.15	.11	.06
48	Don Mattingly	.90	.70	.35
49	Mike Pagliarulo	.12	.09	.05
50	Willie Randolph	.08	.06	.03
51	Rick Rhoden	.08	.06	.03
52	Dave Righetti	.20	.15	.08
53	Dave Winfield	.40	.30	.15
54	Jose Canseco	1.00	.70	.40
55	Carney Lansford	.08	.06	.03
56	Mark McGwire	.60	.45	.25
57	Dave Stewart	.12	.09	.05
58	Curt Young	.08	.06	.03
59	Alvin Davis	.05	.04	.02
60	Mark Langston	.15	.11	.06
61	Ken Phelps	.05	.04	.02
62	Harold Reynolds	.10	.08	.04
63	Scott Fletcher	.05	.04	.02
64	Charlie Hough	.08	.06	.03
65	Pete Incaviglia	.10	.08	.04
66	Oddibe McDowell	.10	.08	.04
67	Pete O'Brien	.10	.08	.04
68	Larry Parrish	.08	.06	.03
69	Ruben Sierra	.25	.20	.10
70	Jesse Barfield	.07	.05	.03
71	George Bell	.25	.20	.10
72	Tony Fernandez	.12	.09	.05
73	Tom Henke	.10	.08	.04
74	Jimmy Key	.12	.09	.05
75	Lloyd Moseby	.05	.04	.02
76	Dion James	.05	.04	.02
77	Dale Murphy	.35	.25	.14
78	Zane Smith	.08	.06	.03
79	Andre Dawson	.25	.20	.10
80	Ryne Sandberg	1.00	.70	.40
81	Rick Sutcliffe	.15	.11	.06
82	Kal Daniels	.10	.08	.04
83	Eric Davis	.15	.11	.06
84	John Franco	.10	.08	.04
85	Kevin Bass	.10	.08	.04
86	Glenn Davis	.10	.08	.04
87	Bill Doran	.10	.08	.04
88	Nolan Ryan	1.50	1.25	.60
89	Mike Scott	.15	.11	.06
90	Dave Smith	.05	.04	.02
91	Pedro Guerrero	.07	.05	.03
92	Orel Hershiser	.15	.11	.06
93	Steve Sax	.07	.05	.03
94	Fernando Valenzuela	.10	.08	.04
95	Tim Burke	.05	.04	.02
96	Andres Galarraga	.20	.15	.08
97	Tim Raines	.25	.20	.10
98	Tim Wallach	.12	.09	.05
99	Mitch Webster	.05	.04	.02
100	Ron Darling	.10	.08	.04
101	Sid Fernandez	.10	.08	.04
102	Dwight Gooden	.35	.25	.14
103	Keith Hernandez	.10	.08	.04
104	Howard Johnson	.12	.09	.05
105	Roger McDowell	.10	.08	.04
106	Darryl Strawberry	.40	.30	.15
107	Steve Bedrosian	.12	.09	.05
108	Von Hayes	.12	.09	.05
109	Shane Rawley	.08	.06	.03
110	Juan Samuel	.15	.11	.06
111	Mike Schmidt	.70	.50	.30
112	Milt Thompson	.05	.04	.02
113	Sid Bream	.08	.06	.03
114	Bobby Bonilla	.35	.25	.14
115	Mike Dunne	.15	.11	.06
116	Andy Van Slyke	.12	.09	.05
117	Vince Coleman	.12	.09	.05
118	Willie McGee	.15	.11	.06
119	Terry Pendleton	.10	.08	.04
120	Ozzie Smith	.25	.20	.10
121	John Tudor	.12	.09	.05
122	Todd Worrell	.20	.15	.08
123	Tony Gwynn	.25	.20	.10
124	John Kruk	.20	.15	.08
125	Benito Santiago	.15	.11	.06
126	Will Clark	.70	.50	.30
127	Dave Dravecky	.05	.04	.02
128	Jeff Leonard	.05	.04	.02
129	Candy Maldonado	.05	.04	.02
130	Rick Rueschel	.10	.08	.04
131	Don Robinson	.05	.04	.02
132	Checklist	.05	.04	.02

1988 Fleer Star Stickers Box Panels

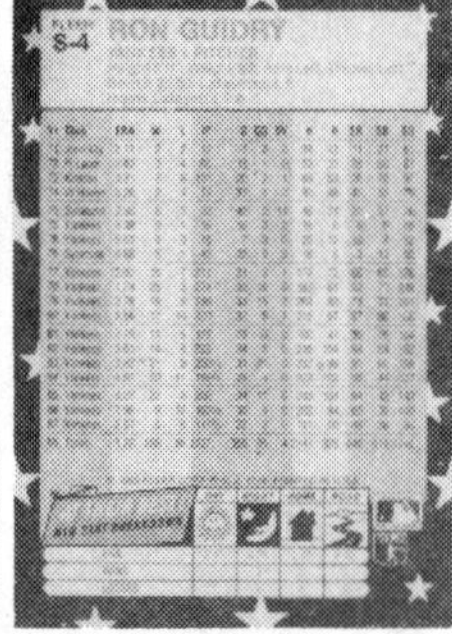

This set of eight box-bottom cards was printed on two different retail display boxes. Six players and two team logo sticker cards are included in the set, three player photos and one team photo per box. The full-color player photos are exclusively limited to the Fleer Star Sticker set. The cards, which measure 2-1/2" by 3-1/2", have a light gray border sprinkled with multi-color stars. The backs are printed in navy blue and red.

		MT	NR MT	EX
Complete Panel Set:		3.50	2.75	1.50
Complete Singles Set:		1.75	1.25	.70
Common Singles Player:		.15	.11	.06
	Panel	2.50	2.00	1.00
1	Eric Davis, Mark McGwire	.70	.50	.30
3	Kevin Mitchell	.25	.20	.10
5	Rickey Henderson	.50	.40	.20
7	Tigers Logo	.05	.04	.02
	Panel	1.00	.70	.40
2	Gary Carter	.35	.25	.14
4	Ron Guidry	.15	.11	.06
6	Don Baylor	.15	.11	.06
8	Giants Logo	.05	.04	.02

1988 Fleer Superstars

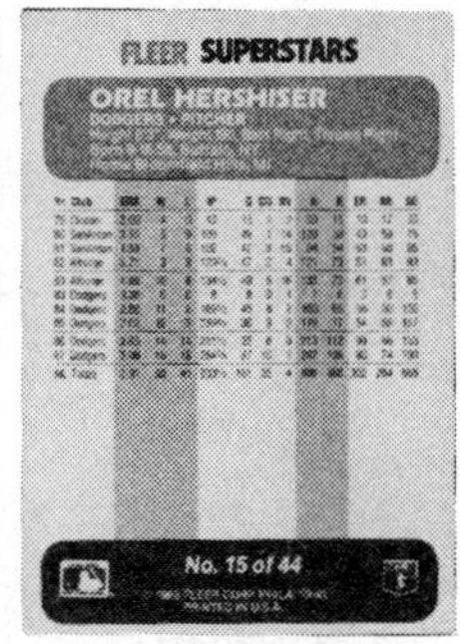

This is the fourth edition of Fleer's 44-card boxed set produced for distribution by McCrory's (1985-87 issues were simply titled "Fleer Limited Edition"). The Superstars standard-size card set features full-color player photos framed by red, white and blue striped top and bottom borders. "Fleer 1988" is printed in an elongated yellow oval banner above the photo. A pale yellow rectangle below the photo carries the player's name and team logo. Card fronts have a semi-glossy slightly textured finish. Card backs are red and blue on white and include card numbers, personal data and statistics. Six team logo sticker cards are also included in this set which was marketed in red, white and blue boxes with checklist backs. Boxed sets were sold exclusively at McCrory's stores and its affiliates.

		MT	NR MT	EX
Complete Set (44):		5.00	4.50	2.50
Common Player:		.05	.04	.02
1	Steve Bedrosian	.10	.08	.04
2	George Bell	.10	.08	.04
3	Wade Boggs	.80	.60	.30
4	Barry Bonds	.80	.60	.30
5	Jose Canseco	.80	.60	.30
6	Joe Carter	.20	.15	.08
7	Jack Clark	.10	.08	.04
8	Will Clark	.70	.50	.30
9	Roger Clemens	.40	.30	.15
10	Alvin Davis	.10	.08	.04
11	Eric Davis	.20	.15	.08
12	Glenn Davis	.05	.04	.02
13	Andre Dawson	.15	.11	.06
14	Dwight Gooden	.20	.15	.08
15	Orel Hershiser	.20	.15	.08
16	Teddy Higuera	.05	.04	.02
17	Kent Hrbek	.15	.11	.06
18	Wally Joyner	.15	.11	.06
19	Jimmy Key	.07	.05	.03
20	John Kruk	.20	.15	.08
21	Jeff Leonard	.05	.04	.02
22	Don Mattingly	.80	.60	.30
23	Mark McGwire	.50	.40	.20
24	Kevin McReynolds	.12	.09	.05
25	Dale Murphy	.30	.25	.12
26	Matt Nokes	.15	.11	.06
27	Terry Pendleton	.05	.04	.02
28	Kirby Puckett	.50	.40	.20
29	Tim Raines	.25	.20	.10
30	Rick Rhoden	.07	.05	.03
31	Cal Ripken, Jr.	.80	.60	.30
32	Benito Santiago	.15	.11	.06
33	Mike Schmidt	.40	.30	.15
34	Mike Scott	.10	.08	.04
35	Kevin Seitzer	.10	.08	.04
36	Ruben Sierra	.25	.20	.10
37	Cory Snyder	.07	.05	.03
38	Darryl Strawberry	.40	.30	.15
39	Rick Sutcliffe	.10	.08	.04
40	Danny Tartabull	.12	.09	.05
41	Alan Trammell	.15	.11	.06
42	Ken Williams	.07	.05	.03
43	Mike Witt	.07	.05	.03
44	Robin Yount	.50	.40	.20

The values quoted are intended to reflect the market price.

1989 Fleer

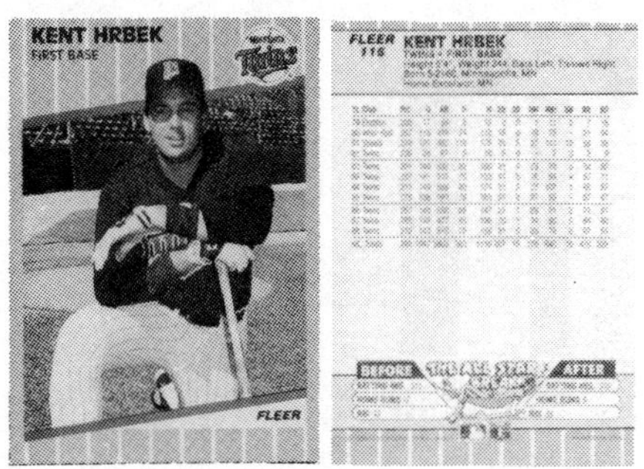

This set includes 660 standard-size cards and was issued with 45 team logo stickers. Individual card fronts feature a grey and white striped background with full-color player photos framed by a bright line of color that slants upward to the right. The set also includes two subsets: 15 Major League Prospects and 12 SuperStar Specials. A special bonus set of 12 All-Star Team cards was randomly inserted in individual wax packs of 15 cards. The last seven cards in the set are checklists, with players listed alphabetically by teams.

		MT	NR MT	EX
Complete Set (660):		18.00	12.00	6.00
Common Player:		.05	.04	.02
1	Don Baylor	.10	.08	.04
2	*Lance Blankenship* (FC)	.10	.08	.04
3	*Todd Burns*	.08	.06	.03
4	Greg Cadaret (FC)	.07	.05	.03
5	Jose Canseco	.25	.20	.10
6	Storm Davis	.10	.08	.04
7	Dennis Eckersley	.12	.09	.05
8	Mike Gallego (FC)	.05	.04	.02
9	Ron Hassey	.05	.04	.02
10	Dave Henderson	.10	.08	.04
11	Rick Honeycutt	.05	.04	.02
12	Glenn Hubbard	.05	.04	.02
13	Stan Javier	.05	.04	.02
14	*Doug Jennings*	.08	.06	.03
15	*Felix Jose* (FC)	.40	.30	.15
16	Carney Lansford	.07	.05	.03
17	Mark McGwire	.40	.30	.15
18	Gene Nelson	.05	.04	.02
19	Dave Parker	.12	.09	.05
20	Eric Plunk	.05	.04	.02
21	Luis Polonia	.07	.05	.03
22	Terry Steinbach	.10	.08	.04
23	Dave Stewart	.10	.08	.04
24	Walt Weiss	.10	.08	.04
25	Bob Welch	.10	.08	.04
26	Curt Young	.07	.05	.03
27	Rick Aguilera	.05	.04	.02
28	Wally Backman	.07	.05	.03
29	Mark Carreon	.07	.05	.03
30	Gary Carter	.08	.06	.03
31	David Cone	.15	.11	.06
32	Ron Darling	.12	.09	.05
33	Len Dykstra	.15	.11	.06
34	Kevin Elster	.10	.08	.04
35	Sid Fernandez	.10	.08	.04
36	Dwight Gooden	.12	.09	.05
37	Keith Hernandez	.08	.06	.03
38	Gregg Jefferies	.40	.30	.15
39	Howard Johnson	.08	.06	.03
40	Terry Leach	.05	.04	.02
41	Dave Magadan	.10	.08	.04
42	Bob McClure	.05	.04	.02
43	Roger McDowell	.10	.08	.04
44	Kevin McReynolds	.15	.11	.06
45	Keith Miller	.10	.08	.04
46	Randy Myers	.10	.08	.04
47	Bob Ojeda	.07	.05	.03
48	Mackey Sasser	.07	.05	.03
49	Darryl Strawberry	.15	.11	.06
50	Tim Teufel	.05	.04	.02
51	*Dave West* (FC)	.12	.09	.05
52	Mookie Wilson	.07	.05	.03
53	Dave Anderson	.05	.04	.02
54	Tim Belcher	.10	.08	.04
55	Mike Davis	.07	.05	.03
56	Mike Devereaux	.15	.11	.06
57	Kirk Gibson	.08	.06	.03
58	Alfredo Griffin	.07	.05	.03
59	Chris Gwynn	.12	.09	.05
60	Jeff Hamilton	.07	.05	.03
61a	Danny Heep (Home: San Antonio, TX)	.70	.50	.30
61b	Danny Heep (Home: Lake Hills, TX)	.05	.04	.02
62	Orel Hershiser	.08	.06	.03
63	Brian Holton (FC)	.07	.05	.03
64	Jay Howell	.07	.05	.03
65	Tim Leary	.07	.05	.03
66	Mike Marshall	.12	.09	.05
67	*Ramon Martinez*	.50	.40	.20
68	Jesse Orosco	.07	.05	.03
69	Alejandro Pena	.07	.05	.03
70	Steve Sax	.15	.11	.06
71	Mike Scioscia	.07	.05	.03
72	Mike Sharperson	.05	.04	.02
73	John Shelby	.05	.04	.02
74	Franklin Stubbs	.05	.04	.02
75	John Tudor	.10	.08	.04
76	Fernando Valenzuela	.08	.06	.03
77	Tracy Woodson	.10	.08	.04
78	Marty Barrett	.07	.05	.03
79	Todd Benzinger	.12	.09	.05
80	Mike Boddicker	.07	.05	.03
81	Wade Boggs	.25	.20	.10
82	"Oil Can" Boyd	.07	.05	.03
83	Ellis Burks	.10	.08	.04
84	Rick Cerone	.05	.04	.02
85	Roger Clemens	.40	.30	.15
86	*Steve Curry* (FC)	.06	.05	.02
87	Dwight Evans	.10	.08	.04
88	Wes Gardner	.07	.05	.03
89	Rich Gedman	.07	.05	.03
90	Mike Greenwell	.08	.06	.03
91	Bruce Hurst	.10	.08	.04
92	Dennis Lamp	.05	.04	.02
93	Spike Owen	.05	.04	.02
94	Larry Parrish	.07	.05	.03
95	*Carlos Quintana* (FC)	.12	.09	.05
96	Jody Reed	.12	.09	.05
97	Jim Rice	.08	.06	.03
98a	Kevin Romine (batting follow-thru, photo actually Randy Kutcher)	.50	.40	.20
98b	Kevin Romine (arms crossed on chest, correct photo)	.60	.45	.25
99	Lee Smith	.10	.08	.04
100	Mike Smithson	.05	.04	.02
101	Bob Stanley	.05	.04	.02
102	Allan Anderson	.07	.05	.03
103	Keith Atherton	.05	.04	.02
104	Juan Berenguer	.05	.04	.02
105	Bert Blyleven	.12	.09	.05
106	*Eric Bullock* (FC)	.15	.11	.06
107	Randy Bush	.05	.04	.02
108	John Christensen (FC)	.05	.04	.02
109	Mark Davidson	.07	.05	.03
110	Gary Gaetti	.15	.11	.06
111	Greg Gagne	.05	.04	.02
112	Dan Gladden	.05	.04	.02
113	*German Gonzalez* (FC)	.06	.05	.02
114	Brian Harper	.05	.04	.02
115	Tom Herr	.07	.05	.03
116	Kent Hrbek	.08	.06	.03
117	Gene Larkin	.10	.08	.04
118	Tim Laudner	.05	.04	.02
119	Charlie Lea	.05	.04	.02
120	Steve Lombardozzi	.05	.04	.02
121a	John Moses (Home: Phoenix, AZ)	.25	.20	.10
121b	John Moses (Home: Tempe, AZ)	.05	.04	.02
122	Al Newman	.05	.04	.02
123	Mark Portugal	.05	.04	.02
124	Kirby Puckett	.35	.25	.14
125	Jeff Reardon	.10	.08	.04
126	Fred Toliver	.05	.04	.02
127	Frank Viola	.15	.11	.06
128	Doyle Alexander	.07	.05	.03
129	Dave Bergman	.05	.04	.02
130a	Tom Brookens (Mike Heath stats on back)	2.25	1.75	.90
130b	Tom Brookens (correct stats on back)	.30	.25	.12
131	*Paul Gibson*	.05	.04	.02
132a	Mike Heath (Tom Brookens stats on back)	2.25	1.75	.90
132b	Mike Heath (correct stats on back)	.30	.25	.12
133	*Don Heinkel*	.15	.11	.06
134	Mike Henneman	.10	.08	.04
135	Guillermo Hernandez	.07	.05	.03
136	Eric King	.05	.04	.02
137	Chet Lemon	.07	.05	.03
138	Fred Lynn	.10	.08	.04
139	Jack Morris	.15	.11	.06
140	Matt Nokes	.10	.08	.04
141	Gary Pettis	.05	.04	.02
142	Ted Power	.05	.04	.02
143	Jeff Robinson	.12	.09	.05
144	Luis Salazar	.05	.04	.02
145	*Steve Searcy* (FC)	.10	.08	.04
146	Pat Sheridan	.05	.04	.02
147	Frank Tanana	.07	.05	.03
148	Alan Trammell	.08	.06	.03
149	Walt Terrell	.07	.05	.03
150	Jim Walewander (FC)	.07	.05	.03
151	Lou Whitaker	.08	.06	.03
152	Tim Birtsas	.05	.04	.02
153	Tom Browning	.10	.08	.04
154	*Keith Brown* (FC)	.06	.05	.02
155	*Norm Charlton* (FC)	.30	.25	.12
156	Dave Concepcion	.10	.08	.04
157	Kal Daniels	.15	.11	.06
158	Eric Davis	.12	.09	.05
159	Bo Diaz	.07	.05	.03
160	*Rob Dibble*	.25	.20	.10
161	Nick Esasky	.07	.05	.03
162	John Franco	.10	.08	.04
163	Danny Jackson	.15	.11	.06
164	Barry Larkin	.15	.11	.06
165	Rob Murphy	.05	.04	.02
166	Paul O'Neill	.05	.04	.02
167	Jeff Reed	.05	.04	.02
168	Jose Rijo	.07	.05	.03
169	Ron Robinson	.05	.04	.02
170	*Chris Sabo*	.40	.30	.15
171	*Candy Sierra* (FC)	.15	.11	.06
172	*Van Snider* (FC)	.08	.06	.03
173	Jeff Treadway	.12	.09	.05
174	Frank Williams	.05	.04	.02
175	Herm Winningham	.05	.04	.02
176	Jim Adduci (FC)	.05	.04	.02
177	Don August	.10	.08	.04
178	Mike Birkbeck	.05	.04	.02
179	Chris Bosio	.05	.04	.02
180	Glenn Braggs	.07	.05	.03
181	Greg Brock	.07	.05	.03
182	Mark Clear	.05	.04	.02

183	Chuck Crim	.05	.04	.02
184	Rob Deer	.07	.05	.03
185	Tom Filer	.05	.04	.02
186	Jim Gantner	.05	.04	.02
187	*Darryl Hamilton*	.30	.25	.12
188	Ted Higuera	.10	.08	.04
189	Odell Jones	.05	.04	.02
190	Jeffrey Leonard	.07	.05	.03
191	Joey Meyer	.10	.08	.04
192	Paul Mirabella	.05	.04	.02
193	Paul Molitor	.25	.20	.10
194	Charlie O'Brien (FC)	.07	.05	.03
195	Dan Plesac	.10	.08	.04
196	*Gary Sheffield*	1.25	.90	.50
197	B.J. Surhoff	.10	.08	.04
198	Dale Sveum	.07	.05	.03
199	Bill Wegman	.05	.04	.02
200	Robin Yount	.25	.20	.10
201	Rafael Belliard	.05	.04	.02
202	Barry Bonds	.60	.45	.25
203	Bobby Bonilla	.12	.09	.05
204	Sid Bream	.07	.05	.03
205	Benny Distefano (FC)	.05	.04	.02
206	Doug Drabek	.07	.05	.03
207	Mike Dunne	.10	.08	.04
208	Felix Fermin	.07	.05	.03
209	Brian Fisher	.07	.05	.03
210	Jim Gott	.05	.04	.02
211	Bob Kipper	.05	.04	.02
212	Dave LaPoint	.07	.05	.03
213	Mike LaValliere	.07	.05	.03
214	Jose Lind	.10	.08	.04
215	Junior Ortiz	.05	.04	.02
216	Vicente Palacios	.07	.05	.03
217	Tom Prince (FC)	.10	.08	.04
218	Gary Redus	.05	.04	.02
219	R.J. Reynolds	.05	.04	.02
220	Jeff Robinson	.07	.05	.03
221	John Smiley	.12	.09	.05
222	Andy Van Slyke	.12	.09	.05
223	Bob Walk	.05	.04	.02
224	Glenn Wilson	.07	.05	.03
225	Jesse Barfield	.10	.08	.04
226	George Bell	.10	.08	.04
227	*Pat Borders*	.30	.25	.12
228	John Cerutti	.07	.05	.03
229	Jim Clancy	.07	.05	.03
230	Mark Eichhorn	.07	.05	.03
231	Tony Fernandez	.12	.09	.05
232	Cecil Fielder	.25	.20	.10
233	Mike Flanagan	.07	.05	.03
234	Kelly Gruber	.05	.04	.02
235	Tom Henke	.07	.05	.03
236	Jimmy Key	.10	.08	.04
237	Rick Leach	.05	.04	.02
238	Manny Lee	.05	.04	.02
239	Nelson Liriano	.07	.05	.03
240	Fred McGriff	.35	.25	.14
241	Lloyd Moseby	.07	.05	.03
242	Rance Mulliniks	.05	.04	.02
243	Jeff Musselman	.07	.05	.03
244	Dave Stieb	.10	.08	.04
245	Todd Stottlemyre (FC)	.10	.08	.04
246	Duane Ward	.05	.04	.02
247	David Wells	.10	.08	.04
248	Ernie Whitt	.07	.05	.03
249	Luis Aguayo	.05	.04	.02
250a	Neil Allen (Home: Sarasota, FL)	.25	.20	.10
250b	Neil Allen (Home: Syosset, NY)	.05	.04	.02
251	John Candelaria	.07	.05	.03
252	Jack Clark	.15	.11	.06
253	Richard Dotson	.07	.05	.03
254	Rickey Henderson	.35	.25	.14
255	Tommy John	.12	.09	.05
256	Roberto Kelly	.20	.15	.08
257	Al Leiter	.15	.11	.06
258	Don Mattingly	.35	.25	.14
259	Dale Mohorcic	.05	.04	.02
260	*Hal Morris* (FC)	.50	.40	.20
261	Scott Nielsen (FC)	.10	.08	.04
262	Mike Pagliarulo	.10	.08	.04
263	*Hipolito Pena* (FC)	.15	.11	.06
264	Ken Phelps	.07	.05	.03
265	Willie Randolph	.07	.05	.03
266	Rick Rhoden	.07	.05	.03
267	Dave Righetti	.12	.09	.05
268	Rafael Santana	.05	.04	.02
269	Steve Shields (FC)	.07	.05	.03
270	Joel Skinner	.05	.04	.02
271	Don Slaught	.05	.04	.02
272	Claudell Washington	.07	.05	.03
273	Gary Ward	.07	.05	.03
274	Dave Winfield	.30	.25	.12
275	Luis Aquino (FC)	.05	.04	.02
276	Floyd Bannister	.07	.05	.03
277	George Brett	.25	.20	.10
278	Bill Buckner	.10	.08	.04
279	*Nick Capra* (FC)	.15	.11	.06
280	*Jose DeJesus* (FC)	.15	.11	.06
281	Steve Farr	.05	.04	.02
282	Jerry Gleaton	.05	.04	.02
283	Mark Gubicza	.10	.08	.04
284	*Tom Gordon*	.30	.25	.12
285	Bo Jackson	.35	.25	.14
286	Charlie Leibrandt	.07	.05	.03
287	*Mike Macfarlane*	.20	.15	.08
288	Jeff Montgomery	.12	.09	.05
289	Bill Pecota	.07	.05	.03
290	Jamie Quirk	.05	.04	.02
291	Bret Saberhagen	.15	.11	.06
292	Kevin Seitzer	.06	.05	.02
293	Kurt Stillwell	.07	.05	.03
294	Pat Tabler	.07	.05	.03
295	Danny Tartabull	.20	.15	.08
296	Gary Thurman	.12	.09	.05
297	Frank White	.07	.05	.03
298	Willie Wilson	.10	.08	.04
299	Roberto Alomar	.75	.60	.30
300	*Sandy Alomar, Jr.* (FC)	.40	.30	.15
301	Chris Brown	.07	.05	.03
302	Mike Brumley (FC)	.07	.05	.03
303	Mark Davis	.05	.04	.02
304	Mark Grant	.05	.04	.02
305	Tony Gwynn	.35	.25	.14
306	*Greg Harris* (FC)	.10	.08	.04
307	Andy Hawkins	.05	.04	.02
308	Jimmy Jones	.05	.04	.02
309	John Kruk	.12	.09	.05
310	Dave Leiper	.05	.04	.02
311	Carmelo Martinez	.05	.04	.02
312	Lance McCullers	.07	.05	.03
313	Keith Moreland	.07	.05	.03
314	Dennis Rasmussen	.10	.08	.04
315	Randy Ready	.05	.04	.02
316	Benito Santiago	.15	.11	.06
317	Eric Show	.07	.05	.03
318	Todd Simmons	.10	.08	.04
319	Garry Templeton	.07	.05	.03
320	Dickie Thon	.05	.04	.02
321	Ed Whitson	.05	.04	.02
322	Marvell Wynne	.05	.04	.02
323	Mike Aldrete	.07	.05	.03
324	Brett Butler	.07	.05	.03
325	Will Clark	.40	.30	.15
326	Kelly Downs	.10	.08	.04
327	Dave Dravecky	.07	.05	.03
328	Scott Garrelts	.05	.04	.02
329	Atlee Hammaker	.05	.04	.02
330	*Charlie Hayes* (FC)	.60	.45	.25
331	Mike Krukow	.07	.05	.03
332	Craig Lefferts	.05	.04	.02
333	Candy Maldonado	.07	.05	.03
334	Kirt Manwaring	.10	.08	.04
335	Bob Melvin	.05	.04	.02
336	Kevin Mitchell	.10	.08	.04
337	Donell Nixon	.05	.04	.02
338	*Tony Perezchica* (FC)	.15	.11	.06
339	Joe Price	.05	.04	.02
340	Rick Reuschel	.10	.08	.04
341	Earnest Riles	.05	.04	.02
342	Don Robinson	.05	.04	.02
343	Chris Speier	.05	.04	.02
344	Robby Thompson	.07	.05	.03
345	Jose Uribe	.05	.04	.02
346	Matt Williams	.30	.25	.12
347	*Trevor Wilson* (FC)	.15	.11	.06
348	Juan Agosto	.05	.04	.02
349	Larry Andersen	.05	.04	.02
350a	Alan Ashby ("Throws Rig")	.50	.40	.20
350b	Alan Ashby ("Throws Right")	.05	.04	.02
351	Kevin Bass	.07	.05	.03
352	Buddy Bell	.07	.05	.03
353	*Craig Biggio*	.60	.45	.25
354	Danny Darwin	.05	.04	.02
355	Glenn Davis	.06	.05	.02
356	Jim Deshaies	.05	.04	.02
357	Bill Doran	.07	.05	.03
358	*John Fishel*	.20	.15	.08
359	Billy Hatcher	.07	.05	.03
360	Bob Knepper	.07	.05	.03
361	*Louie Meadows*	.15	.11	.06
362	Dave Meads	.05	.04	.02
363	Jim Pankovits	.05	.04	.02
364	Terry Puhl	.05	.04	.02
365	Rafael Ramirez	.05	.04	.02
366	Craig Reynolds	.05	.04	.02
367	Mike Scott	.12	.09	.05
368	Nolan Ryan	.50	.40	.20
369	Dave Smith	.07	.05	.03
370	Gerald Young	.12	.09	.05
371	Hubie Brooks	.10	.08	.04
372	Tim Burke	.05	.04	.02
373	*John Dopson*	.10	.08	.04
374	Mike Fitzgerald	.05	.04	.02
375	Tom Foley	.05	.04	.02
376	Andres Galarraga	.15	.11	.06
377	Neal Heaton	.05	.04	.02
378	Joe Hesketh	.05	.04	.02
379	*Brian Holman*	.10	.08	.04
380	Rex Hudler	.05	.04	.02
381	*Randy Johnson* (FC)	.75	.60	.30
382	Wallace Johnson	.05	.04	.02
383	Tracy Jones	.10	.08	.04
384	Dave Martinez	.07	.05	.03
385	Dennis Martinez	.07	.05	.03
386	Andy McGaffigan	.05	.04	.02
387	Otis Nixon	.05	.04	.02
388	*Johnny Paredes* (FC)	.12	.09	.05
389	Jeff Parrett	.10	.08	.04
390	Pascual Perez	.07	.05	.03
391	Tim Raines	.08	.06	.03
392	Luis Rivera	.05	.04	.02
393	*Nelson Santovenia*	.15	.11	.06
394	Bryn Smith	.05	.04	.02
395	Tim Wallach	.10	.08	.04
396	Andy Allanson	.05	.04	.02
397	*Rod Allen*	.15	.11	.06
398	Scott Bailes	.05	.04	.02
399	Tom Candiotti	.05	.04	.02
400	Joe Carter	.20	.15	.08
401	Carmen Castillo	.05	.04	.02
402	Dave Clark	.07	.05	.03
403	John Farrell	.10	.08	.04
404	Julio Franco	.10	.08	.04
405	Don Gordon	.05	.04	.02
406	Mel Hall	.07	.05	.03
407	Brad Havens	.05	.04	.02
408	Brook Jacoby	.10	.08	.04
409	Doug Jones	.12	.09	.05
410	*Jeff Kaiser* (FC)	.15	.11	.06
411	*Luis Medina* (FC)	.06	.05	.02
412	Cory Snyder	.15	.11	.06
413	Greg Swindell	.12	.09	.05
414	*Ron Tingley* (FC)	.15	.11	.06
415	Willie Upshaw	.07	.05	.03
416	Ron Washington	.05	.04	.02
417	Rich Yett	.05	.04	.02
418	Damon Berryhill	.12	.09	.05
419	Mike Bielecki	.05	.04	.02
420	*Doug Dascenzo* (FC)	.08	.06	.03
421	Jody Davis	.07	.05	.03
422	Andre Dawson	.20	.15	.08
423	Frank DiPino	.05	.04	.02
424	Shawon Dunston	.10	.08	.04
425	"Goose" Gossage	.12	.09	.05
426	Mark Grace	.40	.30	.15
427	*Mike Harkey* (FC)	.15	.11	.06
428	Darrin Jackson	.07	.05	.03
429	Les Lancaster	.07	.05	.03
430	Vance Law	.07	.05	.03
431	Greg Maddux	.20	.15	.08
432	Jamie Moyer	.05	.04	.02
433	Al Nipper	.05	.04	.02
434	Rafael Palmeiro	.30	.25	.12
435	Pat Perry	.05	.04	.02
436	*Jeff Pico*	.05	.04	.02
437	Ryne Sandberg	.40	.30	.15
438	Calvin Schiraldi	.05	.04	.02
439	Rick Sutcliffe	.10	.08	.04
440	Manny Trillo	.05	.04	.02
441	*Gary Varsho*	.08	.06	.03
442	Mitch Webster	.07	.05	.03
443	*Luis Alicea*	.15	.11	.06
444	Tom Brunansky	.12	.09	.05
445	Vince Coleman	.15	.11	.06
446	*John Costello*	.15	.11	.06
447	Danny Cox	.07	.05	.03
448	Ken Dayley	.05	.04	.02
449	Jose DeLeon	.07	.05	.03
450	Curt Ford	.05	.04	.02
451	Pedro Guerrero	.15	.11	.06
452	Bob Horner	.10	.08	.04
453	*Tim Jones* (FC)	.15	.11	.06
454	Steve Lake	.05	.04	.02
455	Joe Magrane	.10	.08	.04
456	Greg Mathews	.07	.05	.03
457	Willie McGee	.12	.09	.05
458	Larry McWilliams	.05	.04	.02
459	Jose Oquendo	.05	.04	.02
460	Tony Pena	.07	.05	.03
461	Terry Pendleton	.10	.08	.04
462	*Steve Peters* (FC)	.15	.11	.06
463	Ozzie Smith	.15	.11	.06
464	Scott Terry	.08	.06	.03
465	Denny Walling	.05	.04	.02
466	Todd Worrell	.10	.08	.04
467	Tony Armas	.07	.05	.03
468	*Dante Bichette*	.40	.30	.15
469	Bob Boone	.07	.05	.03
470	*Terry Clark* (FC)	.05	.04	.02
471	Stew Cliburn (FC)	.05	.04	.02
472	*Mike Cook* (FC)	.05	.04	.02
473	*Sherman Corbett*	.05	.04	.02
474	Chili Davis	.07	.05	.03
475	Brian Downing	.07	.05	.03
476	Jim Eppard	.07	.05	.03
477	Chuck Finley	.05	.04	.02
478	Willie Fraser	.05	.04	.02
479	*Bryan Harvey*	.30	.25	.12
480	Jack Howell	.07	.05	.03
481	Wally Joyner	.10	.08	.04
482	Jack Lazorko	.05	.04	.02
483	Kirk McCaskill	.07	.05	.03
484	Mark McLemore	.05	.04	.02
485	Greg Minton	.05	.04	.02
486	Dan Petry	.07	.05	.03
487	Johnny Ray	.07	.05	.03
488	Dick Schofield	.05	.04	.02
489	Devon White	.12	.09	.05
490	Mike Witt	.07	.05	.03
491	Harold Baines	.12	.09	.05
492	Daryl Boston	.05	.04	.02
493	Ivan Calderon	.07	.05	.03
494	Mike Diaz	.07	.05	.03
495	Carlton Fisk	.20	.15	.08
496	*Dave Gallagher*	.15	.11	.06
497	Ozzie Guillen	.07	.05	.03
498	Shawn Hillegas	.07	.05	.03
499	Lance Johnson	.07	.05	.03
500	Barry Jones	.05	.04	.02
501	Bill Long	.07	.05	.03
502	Steve Lyons	.05	.04	.02
503	Fred Manrique	.07	.05	.03
504	Jack McDowell	.15	.11	.06
505	*Donn Pall*	.15	.11	.06
506	Kelly Paris	.05	.04	.02
507	Dan Pasqua	.10	.08	.04
508	*Ken Patterson*	.15	.11	.06
509	Melido Perez	.10	.08	.04
510	Jerry Reuss	.07	.05	.03
511	Mark Salas	.05	.04	.02
512	Bobby Thigpen	.10	.08	.04
513	Mike Woodard	.05	.04	.02
514	Bob Brower	.05	.04	.02
515	Steve Buechele	.05	.04	.02
516	*Jose Cecena*	.15	.11	.06
517	Cecil Espy	.07	.05	.03
518	Scott Fletcher	.07	.05	.03
519	Cecilio Guante	.05	.04	.02
520	Jose Guzman	.10	.08	.04
521	Ray Hayward	.05	.04	.02
522	Charlie Hough	.07	.05	.03
523	Pete Incaviglia	.12	.09	.05
524	Mike Jeffcoat	.05	.04	.02
525	Paul Kilgus	.10	.08	.04
526	*Chad Kreuter* (FC)	.15	.11	.06
527	Jeff Kunkel	.05	.04	.02
528	Oddibe McDowell	.07	.05	.03
529	Pete O'Brien	.07	.05	.03
530	Geno Petralli	.05	.04	.02
531	Jeff Russell	.05	.04	.02
532	Ruben Sierra	.35	.25	.14
533	Mike Stanley	.05	.04	.02
534	Ed Vande Berg	.05	.04	.02

535	Curtis Wilkerson	.05	.04	.02
536	Mitch Williams	.07	.05	.03
537	Bobby Witt	.10	.08	.04
538	Steve Balboni	.07	.05	.03
539	Scott Bankhead	.05	.04	.02
540	Scott Bradley	.05	.04	.02
541	Mickey Brantley	.05	.04	.02
542	Jay Buhner	.15	.11	.06
543	Mike Campbell	.10	.08	.04
544	Darnell Coles	.07	.05	.03
545	Henry Cotto	.05	.04	.02
546	Alvin Davis	.12	.09	.05
547	Mario Diaz	.07	.05	.03
548	*Ken Griffey, Jr.* (FC)	7.00	5.25	2.75
549	*Erik Hanson* (FC)	.20	.15	.08
550	Mike Jackson	.07	.05	.03
551	Mark Langston	.10	.08	.04
552	Edgar Martinez	.15	.11	.06
553	*Bill McGuire* (FC)	.05	.04	.02
554	Mike Moore	.05	.04	.02
555	Jim Presley	.07	.05	.03
556	Rey Quinones	.05	.04	.02
557	Jerry Reed	.05	.04	.02
558	Harold Reynolds	.07	.05	.03
559	*Mike Schooler* (FC)	.10	.08	.04
560	Bill Swift	.05	.04	.02
561	Dave Valle	.05	.04	.02
562	Steve Bedrosian	.10	.08	.04
563	Phil Bradley	.10	.08	.04
564	Don Carman	.07	.05	.03
565	Bob Dernier	.05	.04	.02
566	Marvin Freeman	.05	.04	.02
567	Todd Frohwirth	.07	.05	.03
568	Greg Gross	.05	.04	.02
569	Kevin Gross	.07	.05	.03
570	Greg Harris	.05	.04	.02
571	Von Hayes	.10	.08	.04
572	Chris James	.10	.08	.04
573	Steve Jeltz	.05	.04	.02
574	*Ron Jones* (FC)	.05	.04	.02
575	*Ricky Jordan*	.10	.08	.04
576	Mike Maddux	.05	.04	.02
577	David Palmer	.05	.04	.02
578	Lance Parrish	.15	.11	.06
579	Shane Rawley	.07	.05	.03
580	Bruce Ruffin	.05	.04	.02
581	Juan Samuel	.12	.09	.05
582	Mike Schmidt	.35	.25	.14
583	Kent Tekulve	.07	.05	.03
584	Milt Thompson	.05	.04	.02
585	*Jose Alvarez*	.05	.04	.02
586	Paul Assenmacher	.05	.04	.02
587	Bruce Benedict	.05	.04	.02
588	Jeff Blauser	.10	.08	.04
589	*Terry Blocker* (FC)	.05	.04	.02
590	Ron Gant	.25	.20	.10
591	Tom Glavine	.40	.30	.15
592	Tommy Gregg	.10	.08	.04
593	Albert Hall	.05	.04	.02
594	Dion James	.05	.04	.02
595	Rick Mahler	.05	.04	.02
596	Dale Murphy	.10	.08	.04
597	Gerald Perry	.10	.08	.04
598	Charlie Puleo	.05	.04	.02
599	Ted Simmons	.10	.08	.04
600	Pete Smith	.10	.08	.04
601	Zane Smith	.07	.05	.03
602	*John Smoltz*	.80	.60	.30
603	Bruce Sutter	.10	.08	.04
604	Andres Thomas	.07	.05	.03
605	Ozzie Virgil	.05	.04	.02
606	*Brady Anderson* (FC)	.50	.40	.20
607	Jeff Ballard	.07	.05	.03
608	*Jose Bautista*	.08	.06	.03
609	Ken Gerhart	.07	.05	.03
610	Terry Kennedy	.07	.05	.03
611	Eddie Murray	.30	.25	.12
612	Carl Nichols (FC)	.05	.04	.02
613	Tom Niedenfuer	.07	.05	.03
614	Joe Orsulak	.05	.04	.02
615	*Oswaldo Peraza (Oswald)* (FC)	.15	.11	.06
616a	Bill Ripken (vulgarity on bat knob)	8.00	6.00	3.25
616b	Bill Ripken (scribble over vulgarity)	10.00	7.50	4.00
616c	Bill Ripken (black box over vulgarity)	.10	.08	.04
616d	Bill Ripken (vulgarity whited out)	30.00	22.00	12.00
617	Cal Ripken, Jr.	.40	.30	.15
618	Dave Schmidt	.05	.04	.02
619	Rick Schu	.05	.04	.02
620	Larry Sheets	.07	.05	.03
621	Doug Sisk	.05	.04	.02
622	Pete Stanicek	.05	.04	.02
623	Mickey Tettleton	.15	.11	.06
624	Jay Tibbs	.05	.04	.02
625	Jim Traber	.07	.05	.03
626	Mark Williamson	.07	.05	.03
627	*Craig Worthington*	.20	.15	.08
628	Speed and Power (Jose Canseco)	.20	.15	.08
629	Pitcher Perfect (Tom Browning)	.10	.08	.04
630	Like Father Like Sons (Roberto Alomar, Sandy Alomar, Jr.)	.50	.40	.20
631	N.L. All-Stars (Will Clark, Rafael Palmeiro)	.40	.30	.15
632	Homeruns Coast to Coast (Will Clark, Darryl Strawberry)	.25	.20	.10
633	Hot Corner's Hot Hitters (Wade Boggs, Carney Lansford)	.10	.08	.04
634	Triple A's (Jose Canseco, Mark McGwire, Terry Steinbach)	.30	.25	.12
635	Dual Heat (Mark Davis, Dwight Gooden)	.20	.15	.08
636	N.L. Pitching Power (David Cone, Danny Jackson)	.10	.07	.04
637	Cannon Arms (Bobby Bonilla, Chris Sabo)	.15	.11	.06
638	Double Trouble (Andres Galarraga, Gerald Perry)	.10	.08	.04
639	Power Center (Eric Davis, Kirby Puckett)	.15	.11	.06
640	Major League Prospects (*Cameron Drew* (FC), Steve Wilson)	.15	.11	.06
641	Major League Prospects (Kevin Brown, Kevin Reimer)	.50	.40	.20
642	Major League Prospects (*Jerald Clark* (FC), Brad Pounders)	.20	.15	.08
643	Major League Prospects (*Mike Capel* (FC), Drew Hall)	.15	.11	.06
644	Major League Prospects (*Joe Girardi*, Rolando Roomes)	.35	.25	.14
645	Major League Prospects (*Marty Brown* (FC), Lenny Harris)	.12	.09	.05
646	Major League Prospects (*Luis de los Santos* (FC), Jim Campbell)	.12	.09	.05
647	Major League Prospects (*Miguel Garcia* (FC), Randy Kramer)	.12	.09	.05
648	Major League Prospects (*Torey Lovullo* (FC), Robert Palacios)	.15	.11	.06
649	Major League Prospects (*Jim Corsi*, Bob Milacki)	.12	.09	.05
650	Major League Prospects (*Grady Hall* (FC), Mike Rochford)	.12	.09	.05
651	Major League Prospects (*Vance Lovelace* (FC), Terry Taylor)	.12	.09	.05
652	Major League Prospects (*Dennis Cook* (FC), Ken Hill)	.50	.40	.20
653	Major League Prospects (*Scott Service* (FC), Shane Turner)	.12	.09	.05
654	Checklist 1-101	.05	.04	.02
655	Checklist 102-200	.05	.04	.02
656	Checklist 201-298	.05	.04	.02
657	Checklist 299-395	.05	.04	.02
658	Checklist 396-490	.05	.04	.02
659	Checklist 491-584	.05	.04	.02
660	Checklist 585-660	.05	.04	.02

1989 Fleer All Stars

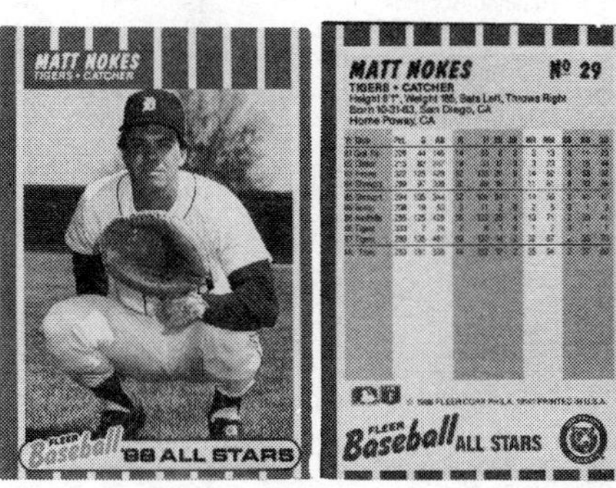

This special 12-card set represents Fleer's choices for its 1989 Major League All-Star Team. For the fourth consecutive year, Fleer inserted the special cards randomly inside their regular 1989 wax and cello packs. The cards feature two player photos set against a green background with the "1989 Fleer All Star Team" logo bannered across the top, and the player's name, position and team in the lower left corner. The backs contain a several-paragraph player profile.

		MT	NR MT	EX
	Complete Set (12):	4.00	3.00	1.50
	Common Player:	.15	.10	.05
1	Bobby Bonilla	.50	.40	.20
2	Jose Canseco	1.00	.70	.40
3	Will Clark	.90	.70	.35
4	Dennis Eckersley	.40	.30	.15
5	Julio Franco	.15	.11	.06
6	Mike Greenwell	.25	.20	.10
7	Orel Hershiser	.15	.11	.06
8	Paul Molitor	.90	.70	.35
9	Mike Scioscia	.15	.11	.06
10	Darryl Strawberry	.40	.30	.15
11	Alan Trammell	.25	.20	.10
12	Frank Viola	.25	.20	.10

Grading Guide

Mint (MT): A perfect card. Well-centered with all corners sharp and square. No creases, stains, edge nicks, surface marks, yellowing or fading.

Near Mint (NM): A nearly perfect card. At first glance, a NM card appears to be perfect. May be slightly off-center. No surface marks, creases or loss of gloss.

Excellent (EX): Corners are still fairly sharp with only moderate wear. Borders may be off-center. No creases or stains on fronts or backs, but may show slight loss of surface luster.

Very Good (VG): Shows obvious handling. May have rounded corners, minor creases, major gum or wax stains. No major creases, tape marks, writing, etc.

Good (G): A well-worn card, but exhibits no intentional damage. May have major or multiple creases. Corners may be rounded well beyond card border.

1989 Fleer For The Record

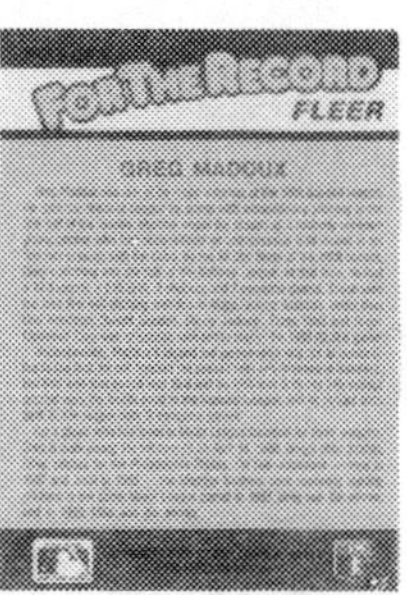

Fleer's "For the Record" set features six players and their achievements from 1988. Fronts of the standard 2-1/2" by 3-1/2" cards feature a full color photo of the player set against a red background. The words "For the Record" appear in blue script at the top of the card and the players name on the bottom, printed in white type. Card backs are grey and describe individual accomplishments. The cards were distributed randomly in rack packs.

		MT	NR MT	EX
	Complete Set (6):	4.00	3.00	1.50
	Common Player:	.25	.15	.10
1	Wade Boggs	1.00	.70	.40
2	Roger Clemens	1.00	.70	.40
3	Andres Galarraga	.80	.60	.30
4	Kirk Gibson	.25	.20	.10
5	Greg Maddux	.80	.60	.30
6	Don Mattingly	1.00	.70	.40

The values quoted are intended to reflect the market price.

1989 Fleer World Series

This 12-card set, which depicts highlights of the 1988 World Series, was included as a special subset with the regular factory-collated Fleer set. It was not available as individual cards in wax packs, cello packs or any other form.

		MT	NR MT	EX
	Complete Set (12):	2.50	2.00	1.00
	Common Player:	.15	.11	.06
1	Dodgers' Secret Weapon (Mickey Hatcher)	.15	.11	.06
2	Rookie Starts Series (Tim Belcher)	.15	.11	.06
3	Jose Canseco	.40	.30	.15
4	Dramatic Comeback (Mike Scioscia)	.15	.11	.06
5	Kirk Gibson	.30	.25	.12
6	Orel Hershiser	.30	.25	.12
7	One Swing, Three RBI's (Mike Marshall)	.25	.20	.10
8	Mark McGwire	.40	.30	.15
9	Sax's Speed Wins Game 4 (Steve Sax)	.15	.11	.06
10	Series Caps Award-Winning Year (Walt Weiss)	.15	.11	.06
11	Orel Hershiser	.25	.20	.10
12	Dodger Blue, World Champs	.25	.20	.10

1989 Fleer Box Panels

For the fourth consecutive year, Fleer issued a series of cards on the bottom panels of its regular 1989 wax pack boxes. The 28-card set includes 20 players and eight team logo cards, all designed in the identical style of the regular 1989 Fleer set. The box-bottom cards were randomly printed, four cards (three player cards and one team logo) on each bottom panel. The cards were numbered from C-1 to C-28.

		MT	NR MT	EX
Complete Panel Set:		6.00	4.50	2.50
Complete Singles Set:		3.00	2.25	1.25
Common Single Player:		.15	.11	.06
1	Mets Logo	.05	.04	.02
2	Wade Boggs	.40	.30	.15
3	George Brett	.40	.30	.15
4	Jose Canseco	.50	.40	.20
5	A's Logo	.05	.04	.02
6	Will Clark	.40	.30	.15
7	David Cone	.25	.20	.10
8	Andres Galarraga	.25	.20	.10
9	Dodgers Logo	.05	.04	.02
10	Kirk Gibson	.15	.11	.06
11	Mike Greenwell	.25	.20	.10
12	Tony Gwynn	.25	.20	.10
13	Tigers Logo	.05	.04	.02
14	Orel Hershiser	.20	.15	.08
15	Danny Jackson	.15	.11	.06
16	Wally Joyner	.25	.20	.10
17	Red Sox Logo	.05	.04	.02
18	Yankees Logo	.05	.04	.02
19	Fred McGriff	.30	.25	.12
20	Kirby Puckett	.35	.25	.12
21	Chris Sabo	.15	.11	.06
22	Kevin Seitzer	.15	.11	.06
23	Pirates Logo	.05	.04	.02
24	Astros Logo	.05	.04	.02
25	Darryl Strawberry	.30	.25	.12
26	Alan Trammell	.20	.15	.08
27	Andy Van Slyke	.20	.15	.07
28	Frank Viola	.20	.15	.08

1989 Fleer Update

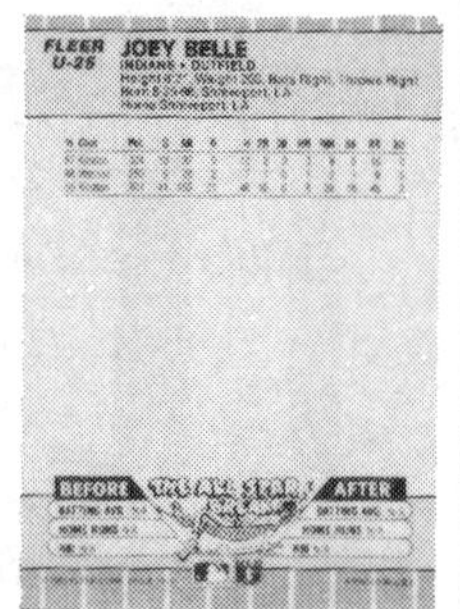

Fleer produced its sixth consecutive "Update" set in 1989 to supplement the company's regular set. As in the past, the set consisted of 132 cards (numbered U-1 through U-132) that were sold by hobby dealers in special collector's boxes.

		MT	NR MT	EX
Complete Set (132):		10.00	7.50	4.00
Common Player:		.06	.05	.02
1	Phil Bradley	.06	.05	.02
2	Mike Devereaux	.25	.20	.10
3	Steve Finley (FC)	.25	.20	.10
4	Kevin Hickey	.06	.05	.02
5	Brian Holton	.06	.05	.02
6	Bob Milacki	.20	.15	.08
7	Randy Milligan	.10	.08	.04
8	John Dopson	.15	.11	.06
9	Nick Esasky	.10	.08	.04
10	Rob Murphy	.06	.05	.02
11	Jim Abbott (FC)	1.25	.90	.50
12	Bert Blyleven	.06	.05	.02
13	Jeff Manto (FC)	.08	.06	.03
14	Bob McClure	.06	.05	.02
15	Lance Parrish	.06	.05	.02
16	Lee Stevens (FC)	.06	.05	.02
17	Claudell Washington	.06	.05	.02
18	Mark Davis	.06	.05	.02
19	Eric King	.06	.05	.02
20	Ron Kittle	.06	.05	.02
21	Matt Merullo (FC)	.15	.11	.06
22	Steve Rosenberg (FC)	.08	.06	.03
23	Robin Ventura (FC)	2.00	1.50	.80
24	Keith Atherton	.06	.05	.02
25	Albert Belle (FC)	4.00	3.00	1.50
26	Jerry Browne	.06	.05	.02
27	Felix Fermin	.06	.05	.02
28	Brad Komminsk	.06	.05	.02
29	Pete O'Brien	.06	.05	.02
30	Mike Brumley	.06	.05	.02
31	Tracy Jones	.06	.05	.02
32	Mike Schwabe (FC)	.06	.05	.02
33	Gary Ward	.06	.05	.02
34	Frank Williams	.06	.05	.02
35	Kevin Appier (FC)	.90	.70	.35
36	Bob Boone	.06	.05	.02
37	Luis de los Santos	.06	.05	.02
38	Jim Eisenreich (FC)	.06	.05	.02
39	Jaime Navarro (FC)	.35	.25	.14
40	Bill Spiers (FC)	.06	.05	.02
41	Greg Vaughn (FC)	.90	.70	.35
42	Randy Veres (FC)	.06	.05	.02
43	Wally Backman	.06	.05	.02
44	Shane Rawley	.06	.05	.02
45	Steve Balboni	.06	.05	.02
46	Jesse Barfield	.06	.05	.02
47	Alvaro Espinoza (FC)	.06	.05	.02
48	Bob Geren (FC)	.20	.15	.08
49	Mel Hall	.06	.05	.02
50	Andy Hawkins	.06	.05	.02
51	Hensley Meulens (FC)	.06	.05	.02
52	Steve Sax	.10	.08	.04
53	Deion Sanders (FC)	2.50	2.00	1.00
54	Rickey Henderson	.20	.15	.08
55	Mike Moore	.10	.08	.04
56	Tony Phillips	.06	.05	.02
57	Greg Briley	.10	.08	.04
58	Gene Harris	.10	.08	.04
59	Randy Johnson	.75	.60	.30
60	Jeffrey Leonard	.06	.05	.02
61	Dennis Powell	.06	.05	.02
62	Omar Vizquel (FC)	.20	.15	.08
63	Kevin Brown	.08	.06	.03
64	Julio Franco	.08	.06	.03
65	Jamie Moyer	.06	.05	.02
66	Rafael Palmeiro	.15	.11	.06
67	Nolan Ryan	1.75	1.25	.70
68	Francisco Cabrera (FC)	.20	.15	.08
69	Junior Felix (FC)	.20	.15	.08
70	Al Leiter	.06	.05	.02
71	Alex Sanchez (FC)	.06	.05	.02
72	Geronimo Berroa (FC)	.06	.05	.02
73	Derek Lilliquist (FC)	.06	.05	.02
74	Lonnie Smith	.10	.08	.04
75	Jeff Treadway	.06	.05	.02
76	Paul Kilgus	.06	.05	.02
77	Lloyd McClendon	.15	.11	.06
78	Scott Sanderson	.06	.05	.02
79	Dwight Smith (FC)	.10	.08	.04
80	Jerome Walton (FC)	.06	.05	.02
81	Mitch Williams	.15	.11	.06
82	Steve Wilson	.08	.06	.03
83	Todd Benzinger	.06	.05	.02
84	Ken Griffey	.10	.08	.04
85	Rick Mahler	.06	.05	.02
86	Rolando Roomes	.15	.11	.06
87	Scott Scudder (FC)	.10	.08	.04
88	Jim Clancy	.06	.05	.02
89	Rick Rhoden	.06	.05	.02
90	Dan Schatzeder	.06	.05	.02
91	Mike Morgan	.06	.05	.02
92	Eddie Murray	.20	.15	.08
93	Willie Randolph	.06	.05	.02
94	Ray Searage	.06	.05	.02
95	Mike Aldrete	.06	.05	.02
96	Kevin Gross	.06	.05	.02
97	Mark Langston	.15	.11	.06
98	Spike Owen	.06	.05	.02
99	Zane Smith	.06	.05	.02
100	Don Aase	.06	.05	.02
101	Barry Lyons	.06	.05	.02
102	Juan Samuel	.06	.05	.02
103	Wally Whitehurst (FC)	.10	.08	.04
104	Dennis Cook	.15	.11	.06
105	Len Dykstra	.20	.15	.08
106	Charlie Hayes (FC)	.50	.40	.20
107	Tommy Herr	.06	.05	.02
108	Ken Howell	.06	.05	.02
109	John Kruk	.15	.11	.06
110	Roger McDowell	.06	.05	.02
111	Terry Mulholland (FC)	.10	.08	.04
112	Jeff Parrett	.06	.05	.02
113	Neal Heaton	.06	.05	.02
114	Jeff King	.10	.08	.04
115	Randy Kramer	.06	.05	.02
116	Bill Landrum	.06	.05	.02
117	Cris Carpenter (FC)	.06	.05	.02
118	Frank DiPino	.06	.05	.02
119	Ken Hill	.15	.11	.06
120	Dan Quisenberry	.06	.05	.02
121	Milt Thompson	.06	.05	.02
122	Todd Zeile (FC)	.80	.60	.30
123	Jack Clark	.10	.08	.04
124	Bruce Hurst	.06	.05	.02
125	Mark Parent	.06	.05	.02
126	Bip Roberts	.06	.05	.02
127	Jeff Brantley (FC)	.15	.11	.06
128	Terry Kennedy	.06	.05	.02
129	Mike LaCoss	.06	.05	.02
130	Greg Litton (FC)	.08	.06	.03
131	Mike Schmidt	.60	.45	.25
132	Checklist	.06	.05	.02

Regional interest may affect the value of a card.

1989 Fleer Baseball All Stars

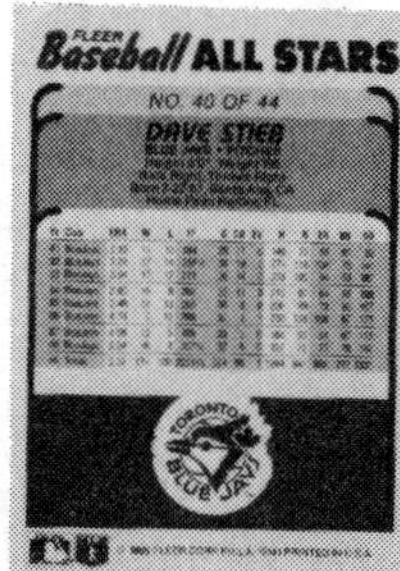

This specially-boxed set was produced by Fleer for the Ben Franklin store chain. The full-color player photos are surrounded by a border of pink and yellow vertical bands. "Fleer Baseball All-Stars" appears along the top in red, white and blue. The set was sold in a box with a checklist on the back.

		MT	NR MT	EX
Complete Set (44):		4.00	3.00	1.50
Common Player:		.10	.06	.03
1	Doyle Alexander	.10	.08	.04
2	George Bell	.12	.09	.05
3	Wade Boggs	.50	.40	.20
4	Bobby Bonilla	.15	.11	.06
5	Jose Canseco	.50	.40	.20
6	Will Clark	.40	.30	.15
7	Roger Clemens	.30	.25	.12
8	Vince Coleman	.15	.11	.06
9	David Cone	.15	.11	.06
10	Mark Davis	.10	.08	.04
11	Andre Dawson	.15	.11	.06
12	Dennis Eckersley	.15	.11	.06
13	Andres Galarraga	.15	.11	.06
14	Kirk Gibson	.12	.09	.05
15	Dwight Gooden	.30	.25	.12
16	Mike Greenwell	.25	.20	.10
17	Mark Gubicza	.10	.08	.04
18	Ozzie Guillen	.10	.08	.04
19	Tony Gwynn	.20	.15	.08
20	Rickey Henderson	.25	.20	.10
21	Orel Hershiser	.20	.15	.08
22	Danny Jackson	.10	.08	.04
23	Doug Jones	.10	.08	.04
24	Ricky Jordan	.10	.08	.04
25	Bob Knepper	.10	.08	.04
26	Barry Larkin	.20	.15	.08
27	Vance Law	.10	.08	.04
28	Don Mattingly	.50	.40	.20
29	Mark McGwire	.40	.30	.15
30	Paul Molitor	.40	.30	.15
31	Gerald Perry	.10	.08	.04
32	Kirby Puckett	.40	.30	.15
33	Johnny Ray	.10	.08	.04
34	Harold Reynolds	.10	.08	.04
35	Cal Ripken, Jr.	.50	.40	.20
36	Don Robinson	.10	.08	.04
37	Ruben Sierra	.30	.25	.12
38	Dave Smith	.10	.08	.04
39	Darryl Strawberry	.30	.25	.12
40	Dave Steib	.10	.08	.04
41	Alan Trammell	.15	.11	.06
42	Andy Van Slyke	.15	.11	.06
43	Frank Viola	.12	.09	.05
44	Dave Winfield	.25	.20	.10

1989 Fleer Baseball MVP

Filled with superstars, this 44-card boxed set was produced by Fleer in 1989 for the Toys "R" Us chain. The fronts of the cards are designed in a yellow and green color scheme and include a "Fleer Baseball MVP" logo above the color player photo. The backs are printed in shades of green and yellow and include biographical notes and stats. The set was issued in a special box with a checklist on the back.

		MT	NR MT	EX
Complete Set (44):		3.75	2.75	1.50
Common Player:		.05	.04	.02
1	Steve Bedrosian	.05	.04	.02
2	George Bell	.10	.08	.04
3	Wade Boggs	.70	.50	.30
4	George Brett	.70	.50	.30
5	Hubie Brooks	.05	.04	.02
6	Jose Canseco	.90	.70	.35
7	Will Clark	.70	.50	.30
8	Roger Clemens	.30	.25	.12
9	Eric Davis	.20	.15	.08
10	Glenn Davis	.07	.05	.03
11	Andre Dawson	.12	.09	.05
12	Andres Galarraga	.12	.09	.05
13	Kirk Gibson	.10	.08	.04
14	Dwight Gooden	.20	.15	.08
15	Mark Grace	.20	.15	.08
16	Mike Greenwell	.15	.11	.06
17	Tony Gwynn	.20	.15	.08
18	Bryan Harvey	.10	.08	.04
19	Orel Hershiser	.15	.11	.06
20	Ted Higuera	.07	.05	.03

21	Danny Jackson	.05	.04	.02
22	Mike Jackson	.05	.04	.02
23	Doug Jones	.05	.04	.02
24	Greg Maddux	.15	.11	.06
25	Mike Marshall	.05	.04	.02
26	Don Mattingly	.70	.50	.30
27	Fred McGriff	.30	.25	.12
28	Mark McGwire	.50	.40	.20
29	Kevin McReynolds	.10	.08	.04
30	Jack Morris	.05	.04	.02
31	Gerald Perry	.05	.04	.02
32	Kirby Puckett	.50	.40	.20
33	Chris Sabo	.10	.08	.04
34	Mike Scott	.07	.05	.03
35	Ruben Sierra	.25	.20	.10
36	Darryl Strawberry	.25	.20	.10
37	Danny Tartabull	.09	.07	.04
38	Bobby Thigpen	.07	.05	.03
39	Alan Trammell	.15	.11	.06
40	Andy Van Slyke	.12	.09	.05
41	Frank Viola	.10	.08	.04
42	Walt Weiss	.15	.11	.06
43	Dave Winfield	.25	.20	.10
44	Todd Worrell	.07	.05	.03

1989 Fleer Baseball's Exciting Stars

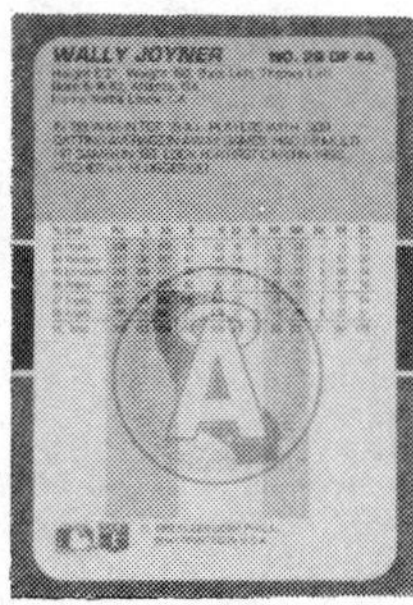

Sold exclusively in Cumberland Farm stores, this 44-card boxed set pictures the game's top stars. The card fronts feature a color player photo surrounded by a blue border with "Baseball's Exciting Stars" along the top. The cards were were numbered alphabetically and packed in a special box with a complete checklist on the back.

		MT	NR MT	EX
	Complete Set (44):	3.50	2.75	1.50
	Common Player:	.05	.04	.02
1	Harold Baines	.07	.05	.03
2	Wade Boggs	.70	.50	.30
3	Jose Canseco	.90	.70	.35
4	Joe Carter	.12	.09	.05
5	Will Clark	.70	.50	.30
6	Roger Clemens	.30	.25	.12
7	Vince Coleman	.15	.11	.06
8	David Cone	.15	.11	.06
9	Eric Davis	.20	.15	.08
10	Glenn Davis	.05	.04	.02
11	Andre Dawson	.12	.09	.05
12	Dwight Evans	.09	.07	.04
13	Andres Galarraga	.12	.09	.05
14	Kirk Gibson	.12	.09	.05
15	Dwight Gooden	.30	.25	.12
16	Jim Gott	.05	.04	.02
17	Mark Grace	.20	.15	.08
18	Mike Greenwell	.20	.15	.08
19	Mark Gibicza	.07	.05	.03
20	Tony Gwynn	.25	.20	.10
21	Rickey Henderson	.40	.30	.15
22	Tom Henke	.05	.04	.02
23	Mike Henneman	.05	.04	.02
24	Orel Hershiser	.20	.15	.08
25	Danny Jackson	.05	.04	.02
26	Gregg Jefferies	.20	.15	.08
27	Ricky Jordan	.05	.04	.02
28	Wally Joyner	.15	.11	.06
29	Mark Langston	.15	.11	.06
30	Tim Leary	.05	.04	.02
31	Don Mattingly	.70	.50	.30
32	Mark McGwire	.60	.45	.25
33	Dale Murphy	.15	.11	.06
34	Kirby Puckett	.60	.45	.25
35	Chris Sabo	.10	.08	.04
36	Kevin Seitzer	.05	.04	.02
37	Ruben Sierra	.20	.15	.08
38	Ozzie Smith	.15	.11	.06
39	Dave Stewart	.07	.05	.03
40	Darryl Strawberry	.20	.15	.08
41	Alan Trammell	.15	.11	.06
42	Frank Viola	.15	.11	.06
43	Dave Winfield	.40	.30	.15
44	Robin Yount	.45	.35	.20

1989 Fleer Heroes of Baseball

This 44-card boxed set was produced by Fleer for the Woolworth store chain. The fronts of the cards are designed in a red and blue color scheme

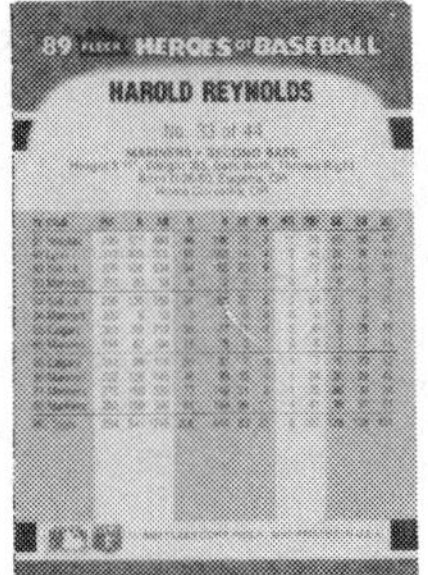

and feature full-color photos that fade into a soft focus on all edges. "Fleer Heroes of Baseball" appears just above the player's name, team and position at the bottom of the card. The set is numbered alphabetically and was packaged in a special box with a checklist on the back.

		MT	NR MT	EX
	Complete Set (44):	4.50	3.50	1.75
	Common Player:	.05	.04	.02
1	George Bell	.12	.09	.05
2	Wade Boggs	.70	.50	.30
3	Barry Bonds	.80	.60	.30
4	Tom Brunansky	.08	.06	.03
5	Jose Canseco	.90	.70	.35
6	Joe Carter	.20	.15	.08
7	Will Clark	.60	.45	.25
8	Roger Clemens	.30	.25	.12
9	David Cone	.15	.11	.06
10	Eric Davis	.15	.11	.06
11	Glenn Davis	.05	.04	.02
12	Andre Dawson	.12	.09	.05
13	Dennis Eckersley	.12	.09	.05
14	John Franco	.05	.04	.02
15	Gary Gaetti	.12	.09	.05
16	Andres Galarraga	.15	.11	.06
17	Kirk Gibson	.12	.09	.05
18	Dwight Gooden	.15	.11	.06
19	Mike Greenwell	.20	.15	.08
20	Tony Gwynn	.25	.20	.10
21	Bryan Harvey	.07	.05	.03
22	Orel Hershiser	.15	.11	.06
23	Ted Higuera	.05	.04	.02
24	Danny Jackson	.05	.04	.02
25	Ricky Jordan	.05	.04	.02
26	Don Mattingly	.70	.50	.30
27	Fred McGriff	.30	.25	.12
28	Mark McGwire	.60	.45	.25
29	Kevin McReynolds	.15	.11	.06
30	Gerald Perry	.05	.04	.02
31	Kirby Puckett	.50	.40	.20
32	Johnny Ray	.05	.04	.02
33	Harold Reynolds	.05	.04	.02
34	Cal Ripken, Jr.	.90	.70	.35
35	Ryne Sandberg	.90	.70	.35
36	Kevin Seitzer	.05	.04	.02
37	Ruben Sierra	.20	.15	.08
38	Darryl Strawberry	.20	.15	.08
39	Bobby Thigpen	.05	.04	.02
40	Alan Trammell	.12	.09	.05
41	Andy Van Slyke	.10	.08	.04
42	Frank Viola	.10	.08	.04
43	Dave Winfield	.40	.30	.15
44	Robin Yount	.40	.30	.15

1989 Fleer League Leaders

Another of the various small, boxed sets issued by Fleer, the 44-card "League Leaders" set was produced for Walgreen stores. The standard-size cards feature color photos on the front surrounded by a red border with "Fleer League Leaders" across the top. The player's name, team and position appear in a yellow band at the bottom. The backs include player stats and data and the team logo. The cards are numbered alphabetically and packaged in a special box that includes the full checklist on the back.

		MT	NR MT	EX
	Complete Set (44):	4.00	3.00	1.50
	Common Player:	.05	.04	.02
1	Allan Anderson	.05	.04	.02
2	Wade Boggs	.70	.50	.30
3	Jose Canseco	.90	.70	.35
4	Will Clark	.60	.45	.25
5	Roger Clemens	.30	.25	.12
6	Vince Coleman	.15	.11	.06
7	David Cone	.15	.11	.06
8	Kal Daniels	.05	.04	.02
9	Chili Davis	.05	.04	.02
10	Eric Davis	.20	.15	.08
11	Glenn Davis	.05	.04	.02
12	Andre Dawson	.12	.09	.05
13	John Franco	.05	.04	.02
14	Andres Galarraga	.12	.09	.05
15	Kirk Gibson	.12	.09	.05
16	Dwight Gooden	.30	.25	.12
17	Mark Grace	.30	.25	.12
18	Mike Greenwell	.20	.15	.07
19	Tony Gwynn	.25	.20	.10
20	Orel Hershiser	.15	.11	.06
21	Pete Incaviglia	.10	.08	.04
22	Danny Jackson	.05	.04	.02
23	Gregg Jefferies	.30	.25	.12
24	Joe Magrane	.05	.04	.02
25	Don Mattingly	.70	.50	.30
26	Fred McGriff	.30	.25	.12
27	Mark McGwire	.60	.45	.25
28	Dale Murphy	.15	.11	.06
29	Dan Plesac	.05	.04	.02
30	Kirby Puckett	.40	.30	.15
31	Harold Reynolds	.12	.09	.05
32	Cal Ripken, Jr.	.70	.50	.30
33	Jeff Robinson	.05	.04	.02
34	Mike Scott	.12	.09	.05
35	Ozzie Smith	.15	.09	.05
36	Dave Stewart	.07	.05	.03
37	Darryl Strawberry	.30	.25	.12
38	Greg Swindell	.09	.07	.04
39	Bobby Thigpen	.05	.04	.02
40	Alan Trammell	.12	.09	.05
41	Andy Van Slyke	.12	.09	.05
42	Frank Viola	.12	.09	.05
43	Dave Winfield	.30	.25	.12
44	Robin Yount	.30	.25	.12

1989 Fleer Superstars

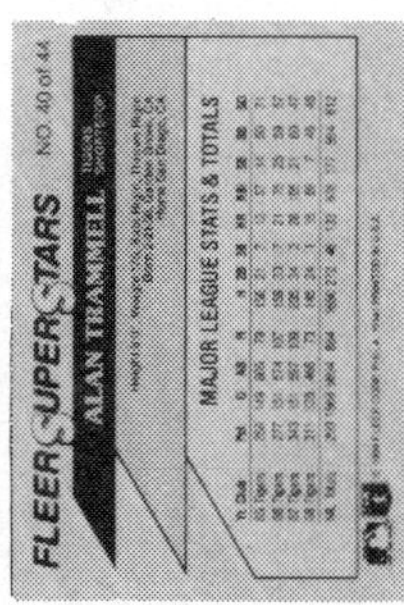

This 44-card boxed set was produced by Fleer for the McCrory store chain. The cards are the standard 2-1/2" by 3-1/2" and the full-color player photos are outlined in red with a tan-and-white striped border. The player's name, position and team logo appear at the bottom of the card. The backs carry yellow and white stripes and include the Fleer "SuperStars" logo, player stats and biographical information. The cards are numbered alphabetically and packaged in a special box that includes a checklist on the back.

		MT	NR MT	EX
	Complete Set (44):	4.00	3.00	1.50
	Common Player:	.05	.04	.02
1	Roberto Alomar	.30	.25	.12
2	Harold Baines	.12	.09	.05
3	Tim Belcher	.07	.05	.03
4	Wade Boggs	.70	.50	.30
5	George Brett	.70	.50	.30
6	Jose Canseco	.90	.70	.35
7	Gary Carter	.05	.04	.02
8	Will Clark	.70	.50	.30
9	Roger Clemens	.30	.25	.12
10	Kal Daniels	.05	.04	.02
11	Eric Davis	.20	.15	.08
12	Andre Dawson	.12	.09	.05
13	Tony Fernandez	.09	.07	.04
14	Scott Fletcher	.05	.04	.02
15	Andres Galarraga	.15	.11	.06
16	Kirk Gibson	.15	.11	.06
17	Dwight Gooden	.20	.15	.08
18	Jim Gott	.05	.04	.02
19	Mark Grace	.20	.15	.08
20	Mike Greenwell	.20	.15	.08
21	Tony Gwynn	.25	.20	.10
22	Rickey Henderson	.30	.25	.12
23	Orel Hershiser	.15	.11	.06
24	Ted Higuera	.05	.04	.02
25	Gregg Jefferies	.20	.15	.08
26	Wally Joyner	.15	.11	.06

27	Mark Langston	.15	.11	.06
28	Greg Maddux	.20	.15	.08
29	Don Mattingly	.70	.50	.30
30	Fred McGriff	.30	.25	.12
31	Mark McGwire	.40	.30	.15
32	Dan Plesac	.05	.04	.02
33	Kirby Puckett	.60	.45	.25
34	Jeff Reardon	.05	.04	.02
35	Chris Sabo	.07	.05	.03
36	Mike Schmidt	.50	.40	.20
37	Mike Scott	.07	.05	.03
38	Cory Snyder	.05	.04	.02
39	Darryl Strawberry	.20	.15	.08
40	Alan Trammell	.12	.09	.05
41	Frank Viola	.10	.08	.04
42	Walt Weiss	.10	.08	.04
43	Dave Winfield	.40	.30	.15
44	Todd Worrell	.05	.04	.02

1990 Fleer

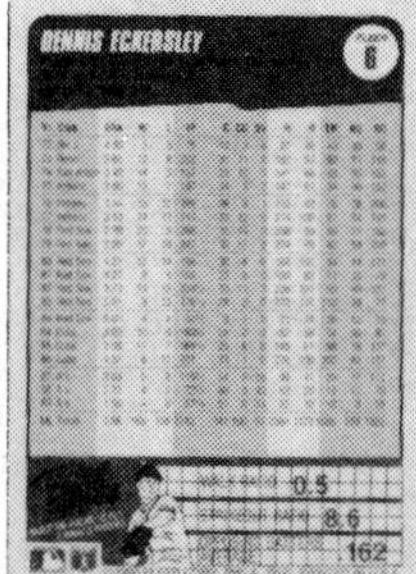

Fleer's 1990 set, its 10th consecutive baseball card offering, again consisted of 660 cards numbered by team. The front of the cards feature mostly action photos surrounded by one of several different color bands and a white border. The "Fleer '90" logo appears in the upper left corner, while the team logo is the upper right. The player's name and position are printed in a flowing banner below the photo. The set includes various special cards, including a series of "Major League Prospects," Players of the Decade, team checklist cards and a series of multi-player cards. The backs include complete career stats, player data, and a special "Vital Signs" section showing on-base percentage, slugging percentage, etc. for batters; and strikeout and walk ratios, opposing batting averages, etc. for pitchers.

		MT	NR MT	EX
Complete Set (660):		18.00	13.50	7.25
Common Player:		.05	.04	.02
1	Lance Blankenship	.07	.05	.03
2	Todd Burns	.06	.05	.02
3	Jose Canseco	.25	.20	.10
4	Jim Corsi	.09	.07	.04
5	Storm Davis	.06	.05	.02
6	Dennis Eckersley	.12	.09	.05
7	Mike Gallego	.06	.05	.02
8	Ron Hassey	.05	.04	.02
9	Dave Henderson	.10	.08	.06
10	Rickey Henderson	.20	.15	.08
11	Rick Honeycutt	.05	.04	.02
12	Stan Javier	.05	.04	.02
13	Felix Jose	.20	.15	.08
14	Carney Lansford	.07	.05	.03
15	Mark McGwire	.25	.20	.10
16	Mike Moore	.10	.08	.04
17	Gene Nelson	.05	.04	.02
18	Dave Parker	.12	.09	.05
19	Tony Phillips	.05	.04	.02
20	Terry Steinbach	.10	.08	.06
21	Dave Stewart	.10	.08	.06
22	Walt Weiss	.10	.08	.06
23	Bob Welch	.06	.05	.03
24	Curt Young	.05	.04	.02
25	Paul Assenmacher	.05	.04	.02
26	Damon Berryhill	.10	.08	.04
27	Mike Bielecki	.10	.08	.04
28	Kevin Blankenship	.07	.05	.03
29	Andre Dawson	.12	.09	.05
30	Shawon Dunston	.09	.07	.04
31	Joe Girardi	.12	.09	.05
32	Mark Grace	.25	.20	.10
33	Mike Harkey	.12	.09	.05
34	Paul Kilgus	.05	.04	.02
35	Les Lancaster	.06	.05	.02
36	Vance Law	.05	.04	.02
37	Greg Maddux	.10	.08	.04
38	Lloyd McClendon	.10	.08	.04
39	Jeff Pico	.05	.04	.02
40	Ryne Sandberg	.35	.25	.14
41	Scott Sanderson	.05	.04	.02
42	Dwight Smith	.10	.07	.04
43	Rick Sutcliffe	.08	.06	.03
44	*Jerome Walton*	.05	.04	.02
45	Mitch Webster	.05	.04	.02
46	Curt Wilkerson	.05	.04	.02
47	*Dean Wilkins* (FC)	.05	.04	.02
48	Mitch Williams	.08	.06	.03
49	Steve Wilson	.08	.06	.03
50	Steve Bedrosian	.06	.05	.02
51	*Mike Benjamin* (FC)	.15	.11	.06
52	*Jeff Brantley*	.10	.08	.04
53	Brett Butler	.07	.05	.03
54	Will Clark	.40	.30	.15
55	Kelly Downs	.05	.04	.02
56	Scott Garrelts	.09	.07	.04
57	Atlee Hammaker	.05	.04	.02
58	Terry Kennedy	.05	.04	.02
59	Mike LaCoss	.05	.04	.02
60	Craig Lefferts	.06	.05	.02
61	*Greg Litton*	.10	.08	.04
62	Candy Maldonado	.06	.05	.02
63	Kirt Manwaring	.09	.07	.04
64	*Randy McCament* (FC)	.05	.04	.02
65	Kevin Mitchell	.20	.15	.08
66	Donell Nixon	.05	.04	.02
67	Ken Oberkfell	.05	.04	.02
68	Rick Reuschel	.09	.07	.04
69	Ernest Riles	.05	.04	.02
70	Don Robinson	.05	.04	.02
71	Pat Sheridan	.05	.04	.02
72	Chris Speier	.05	.04	.02
73	Robby Thompson	.07	.05	.03
74	Jose Uribe	.06	.05	.02
75	Matt Williams	.20	.15	.08
76	George Bell	.08	.06	.03
77	Pat Borders	.07	.05	.03
78	John Cerutti	.05	.04	.02
79	*Junior Felix*	.12	.09	.05
80	Tony Fernandez	.09	.07	.04
81	Mike Flanagan	.05	.04	.02
82	*Mauro Gozzo* (FC)	.05	.04	.02
83	Kelly Gruber	.07	.05	.03
84	Tom Henke	.05	.04	.02
85	Jimmy Key	.07	.05	.03
86	Manny Lee	.05	.04	.02
87	Nelson Liriano	.05	.04	.02
88	Lee Mazzilli	.05	.04	.02
89	Fred McGriff	.25	.20	.10
90	Lloyd Moseby	.06	.05	.02
91	Rance Mulliniks	.05	.04	.02
92	Alex Sanchez	.08	.06	.03
93	Dave Steib	.09	.07	.05
94	Todd Stottlemyre	.09	.07	.05
95	Duane Ward	.05	.04	.02
96	David Wells	.05	.04	.02
97	Ernie Whitt	.06	.05	.02
98	Frank Wills	.05	.04	.02
99	Mookie Wilson	.09	.07	.04
100	*Kevin Appier* (FC)	.25	.20	.10
101	Luis Aquino	.05	.04	.02
102	Bob Boone	.07	.05	.03
103	George Brett	.25	.20	.10
104	Jose DeJesus	.08	.06	.03
105	Luis de los Santos	.08	.06	.03
106	Jim Eisenreich	.05	.04	.02
107	Steve Farr	.05	.04	.02
108	Tom Gordon	.25	.20	.10
109	Mark Gubicza	.09	.07	.04
110	Bo Jackson	.35	.25	.14
111	Terry Leach	.05	.04	.02
112	Charlie Leibrandt	.05	.04	.02
113	*Rick Luecken*	.08	.06	.03
114	Mike Macfarlane	.05	.04	.02
115	Jeff Montgomery	.06	.05	.03
116	Bret Saberhagen	.10	.08	.04
117	Kevin Seitzer	.10	.08	.04
118	Kurt Stillwell	.06	.05	.02
119	Pat Tabler	.05	.04	.02
121	Gary Thurman	.05	.04	.02
122	Frank White	.07	.05	.03
123	Willie Wilson	.06	.05	.03
124	*Matt Winters* (FC)	.05	.04	.02
125	Jim Abbott	.20	.15	.08
126	Tony Armas	.05	.04	.02
127	Dante Bichette	.09	.07	.04
128	Bert Blyleven	.09	.07	.04
129	Chili Davis	.06	.05	.02
130	Brian Downing	.06	.05	.02
131	*Mike Fetters*	.10	.07	.04
132	Chuck Finley	.06	.05	.02
133	Willie Fraser	.05	.04	.02
134	Bryan Harvey	.05	.04	.02
135	Jack Howell	.05	.04	.02
136	Wally Joyner	.10	.08	.04
137	*Jeff Manto*	.10	.08	.04
138	Kirk McCaskill	.06	.05	.02
139	Bob McClure	.05	.04	.02
140	Greg Minton	.05	.04	.02
141	Lance Parrish	.07	.05	.02
142	Dan Petry	.05	.04	.02
143	Johnny Ray	.05	.04	.02
144	Dick Schofield	.06	.05	.02
145	*Lee Stevens*	.10	.07	.04
146	Claudell Washington	.06	.05	.02
147	Devon White	.08	.06	.03
148	Mike Witt	.06	.05	.02
149	Roberto Alomar	.30	.25	.12
150	Sandy Alomar, Jr.	.10	.07	.04
151	Andy Benes (FC)	.30	.25	.12
152	Jack Clark	.06	.05	.02
153	Pat Clements	.05	.04	.02
154	Joey Cora	.15	.11	.06
155	Mark Davis	.09	.07	.04
156	Mark Grant	.05	.04	.02
157	Tony Gwynn	.25	.20	.10
158	Greg Harris	.10	.08	.04
159	Bruce Hurst	.06	.05	.02
160	Darrin Jackson	.05	.04	.02
161	Chris James	.06	.05	.02
162	Carmelo Martinez	.06	.05	.02
163	Mike Pagliarulo	.06	.05	.02
164	Mark Parent	.05	.04	.02
165	Dennis Rasmussen	.05	.04	.02
166	Bip Roberts	.08	.06	.03
167	Benito Santiago	.12	.09	.05
168	Calvin Schiraldi	.05	.04	.02
169	Eric Show	.06	.05	.02
170	Garry Templeton	.06	.05	.02
171	Ed Whitson	.06	.05	.02
172	Brady Anderson	.07	.05	.03
173	Jeff Ballard	.07	.05	.03
174	Phil Bradley	.07	.05	.03
175	Mike Devereaux	.07	.05	.03
176	*Steve Finley*	.10	.07	.04
177	Pete Harnisch (FC)	.10	.08	.04
178	Kevin Hickey	.10	.08	.04
179	Brian Holton	.05	.04	.02
180	*Ben McDonald*	.50	.40	.20
181	Bob Melvin	.05	.04	.02
182	Bob Milacki	.07	.05	.03
183	Randy Milligan	.06	.05	.02
184	Gregg Olson (FC)	.10	.07	.04
185	Joe Orsulak	.05	.04	.02
186	Bill Ripken	.05	.04	.02
187	Cal Ripken, Jr.	.35	.25	.14
188	Dave Schmidt	.05	.04	.02
189	Larry Sheets	.05	.04	.02
190	Mickey Tettleton	.08	.06	.03
191	Mark Thurmond	.05	.04	.02
192	Jay Tibbs	.05	.04	.02
193	Jim Traber	.05	.04	.02
194	Mark Williamson	.05	.04	.02
195	Craig Worthington	.08	.06	.03
196	Don Aase	.05	.04	.02
197	*Blaine Beatty*	.08	.06	.03
198	Mark Carreon	.10	.08	.04
199	Gary Carter	.06	.05	.02
200	David Cone	.10	.08	.04
201	Ron Darling	.07	.05	.03
202	Kevin Elster	.05	.04	.02
203	Sid Fernandez	.09	.07	.04
204	Dwight Gooden	.10	.07	.04
205	Keith Hernandez	.06	.05	.02
206	*Jeff Innis*	.08	.06	.03
207	Gregg Jefferies	.20	.15	.08
208	Howard Johnson	.08	.06	.03
209	Barry Lyons	.05	.04	.02
210	Dave Magadan	.06	.05	.02
211	Kevin McReynolds	.07	.05	.03
212	Jeff Musselman	.05	.04	.02
213	Randy Myers	.06	.05	.02
214	Bob Ojeda	.06	.05	.02
215	Juan Samuel	.06	.05	.02
216	Mackey Sasser	.05	.04	.02
217	Darryl Strawberry	.10	.07	.04
218	Tim Teufel	.05	.04	.02
219	Frank Viola	.10	.08	.04
220	Juan Agosto	.05	.04	.02
221	Larry Anderson	.05	.04	.02
222	*Eric Anthony* (FC)	.50	.40	.20
223	Kevin Bass	.08	.06	.03
224	Craig Biggio	.10	.08	.04
225	Ken Caminiti	.06	.05	.02
226	Jim Clancy	.05	.04	.02
227	Danny Darwin	.05	.04	.02
228	Glenn Davis	.09	.07	.04
229	Jim Deshaies	.07	.05	.02
230	Bill Doran	.06	.05	.02
231	Bob Forsch	.05	.04	.02
233	Terry Puhl	.05	.04	.02
234	Rafael Ramirez	.05	.04	.02
235	Rick Rhoden	.05	.04	.02
236	Dan Schatzeder	.05	.04	.02
237	Mike Scott	.08	.06	.03
238	Dave Smith	.06	.05	.02
239	Alex Trevino	.05	.04	.02
240	Glenn Wilson	.05	.04	.02
241	Gerald Young	.05	.04	.02
242	Tom Brunansky	.07	.05	.03
243	Cris Carpenter	.10	.08	.04
244	*Alex Cole* (FC)	.20	.15	.08
245	Vince Coleman	.10	.08	.04
246	John Costello	.05	.04	.02
247	Ken Dayley	.05	.04	.02
248	Jose DeLeon	.06	.05	.02
249	Frank DiPino	.05	.04	.02
250	Pedro Guerrero	.09	.07	.04
251	Ken Hill	.09	.07	.04
252	Joe Magrane	.09	.07	.04
253	Willie McGee	.06	.05	.02
254	John Morris	.05	.04	.02
255	Jose Oquendo	.06	.05	.02
256	Tony Pena	.06	.05	.02
257	Terry Pendleton	.06	.05	.02
258	Ted Power	.05	.04	.02
259	Dan Quisenberry	.05	.04	.02
260	Ozzie Smith	.09	.07	.04
261	Scott Terry	.06	.05	.02
262	Milt Thompson	.05	.04	.02
263	Denny Walling	.05	.04	.02
264	Todd Worrell	.06	.05	.02
265	*Todd Zeile*	.50	.40	.20
266	Marty Barrett	.05	.04	.02
267	Mike Boddicker	.05	.04	.02
268	Wade Boggs	.40	.30	.15
269	Ellis Burks	.35	.25	.12
270	Rick Cerone	.05	.04	.02
271	Roger Clemens	.25	.20	.10
272	John Dopson	.06	.05	.02
273	Nick Esasky	.07	.05	.03
274	Dwight Evans	.09	.07	.05
275	Wes Gardner	.05	.04	.02
276	Rich Gedman	.05	.04	.02
277	Mike Greenwell	.20	.15	.08
278	Danny Heep	.05	.04	.02
279	Eric Hetzel	.10	.08	.04
280	Dennis Lamp	.05	.04	.02
281	Rob Murphy	.05	.04	.02
282	Joe Price	.05	.04	.02
283	Carlos Quintana	.10	.07	.04
284	Jody Reed	.06	.05	.02
285	Luis Rivera	.05	.04	.02
286	Kevin Romine	.05	.04	.02
287	Lee Smith	.05	.04	.02
288	Mike Smithson	.05	.04	.02

289	Bob Stanley	.05	.04	.02
290	Harold Baines	.09	.07	.04
291	Kevin Brown	.09	.07	.04
292	Steve Buechele	.05	.04	.02
293	*Scott Coolbaugh* (FC)	.05	.04	.02
294	*Jack Daugherty* (FC)	.05	.04	.02
295	Cecil Espy	.06	.05	.02
296	Julio Franco	.07	.05	.03
297	*Juan Gonzalez* (FC)	2.00	1.50	.80
298	Cecilio Guante	.05	.04	.02
299	Drew Hall	.05	.04	.02
300	Charlie Hough	.06	.05	.02
301	Pete Incaviglia	.08	.06	.03
302	Mike Jeffcoat	.05	.04	.02
303	Chad Kreuter	.08	.06	.03
304	Jeff Kunkel	.05	.04	.02
305	Rick Leach	.05	.04	.02
306	Fred Manrique	.05	.04	.02
307	Jamie Moyer	.06	.05	.02
308	Rafael Palmeiro	.07	.05	.02
309	Geno Petralli	.05	.04	.02
310	Kevin Reimer	.10	.08	.06
311	*Kenny Rogers* (FC)	.20	.15	.08
312	Jeff Russell	.06	.05	.02
313	Nolan Ryan	.60	.45	.25
314	Ruben Sierra	.12	.09	.05
315	Bobby Witt	.05	.04	.02
316	Chris Bosio	.07	.05	.02
317	Glenn Braggs	.07	.05	.02
318	Greg Brock	.05	.04	.02
319	Chuck Crim	.05	.04	.02
320	Rob Deer	.06	.05	.02
321	Mike Felder	.05	.04	.02
322	Tom Filer	.05	.04	.02
323	*Tony Fossas* (FC)	.05	.04	.02
324	Jim Gantner	.05	.04	.02
325	Darryl Hamilton	.08	.06	.03
326	Ted Higuera	.08	.06	.03
327	Mark Knudson (FC)	.10	.08	.04
328	Bill Krueger	.05	.04	.02
329	*Tim McIntosh* (FC)	.05	.04	.02
330	Paul Molitor	.15	.11	.06
331	*Jaime Navarro*	.15	.11	.06
332	Charlie O'Brien	.05	.04	.02
333	*Jeff Peterek* (FC)	.05	.04	.02
334	Dan Plesac	.07	.05	.03
335	Jerry Reuss	.06	.05	.02
336	Gary Sheffield	.25	.20	.10
337	*Bill Spiers*	.10	.08	.04
338	B.J. Surhoff	.07	.05	.02
339	*Greg Vaughn*	.40	.30	.15
340	Robin Yount	.20	.15	.08
341	Hubie Brooks	.06	.05	.02
342	Tim Burke	.06	.05	.02
343	Mike Fitzgerald	.05	.04	.02
344	Tom Foley	.05	.04	.02
345	Andres Galarraga	.15	.11	.06
346	Damaso Garcia	.05	.04	.02
347	*Marquis Grissom* (FC)	.50	.40	.20
348	Kevin Gross	.06	.05	.02
349	Joe Hesketh	.05	.04	.02
350	*Jeff Huson*	.10	.07	.04
351	Wallace Johnson	.05	.04	.02
352	Mark Langston	.10	.07	.04
353	Dave Martinez	.06	.05	.02
354	Dennis Martinez	.06	.05	.02
355	Andy McGaffigan	.05	.04	.02
356	Otis Nixon	.05	.04	.02
357	Spike Owen	.05	.04	.02
358	Pascual Perez	.06	.05	.02
359	Tim Raines	.10	.08	.04
360	Nelson Santovenia	.10	.08	.04
361	Bryn Smith	.06	.05	.02
362	Zane Smith	.05	.04	.02
363	*Larry Walker*	.75	.60	.30
364	Tim Wallach	.06	.05	.02
365	Rick Aguilera	.05	.04	.02
366	Allan Anderson	.06	.05	.02
367	Wally Backman	.06	.05	.02
368	Doug Baker (FC)	.05	.04	.02
369	Juan Berenguer	.05	.04	.02
370	Randy Bush	.05	.04	.02
371	Carmen Castillo	.05	.04	.02
372	*Mike Dyer* (FC)	.05	.04	.02
373	Gary Gaetti	.07	.05	.03
374	Greg Gagne	.05	.04	.02
375	Dan Gladden	.05	.04	.02
376	German Gonzalez	.05	.04	.02
377	Brian Harper	.06	.05	.02
378	Kent Hrbek	.10	.08	.04
379	Gene Larkin	.05	.04	.02
380	Tim Laudner	.05	.04	.02
381	John Moses	.05	.04	.02
382	Al Newman	.05	.04	.02
383	Kirby Puckett	.40	.30	.15
384	Shane Rawley	.06	.05	.02
385	Jeff Reardon	.06	.05	.02
386	Roy Smith	.05	.04	.02
387	*Gary Wayne* (FC)	.05	.04	.02
388	Dave West	.10	.07	.04
389	Tim Belcher	.12	.09	.05
390	Tim Crews	.05	.04	.02
391	Mike Davis	.05	.04	.02
392	Rick Dempsey	.05	.04	.02
393	Kirk Gibson	.09	.07	.04
394	Jose Gonzalez	.05	.04	.02
395	Alfredo Griffin	.06	.05	.02
396	Jeff Hamilton	.06	.05	.02
397	Lenny Harris	.10	.08	.06
398	Mickey Hatcher	.05	.04	.02
399	Orel Hershiser	.12	.09	.05
400	Jay Howell	.06	.05	.02
401	Mike Marshall	.06	.05	.02
402	Ramon Martinez	.20	.15	.08
403	Mike Morgan	.05	.04	.02
404	Eddie Murray	.10	.08	.04
405	Alejandro Pena	.05	.04	.02
406	Willie Randolph	.08	.06	.03

407	Mike Scioscia	.06	.05	.02
408	Ray Searage	.05	.04	.02
409	Fernando Valenzuela	.07	.05	.03
410	*Jose Vizcaino* (FC)	.25	.20	.10
411	*John Wetteland* (FC)	.25	.20	.10
412	Jack Armstrong	.05	.04	.02
413	Todd Benzinger	.07	.05	.03
414	Tim Birtsas	.05	.04	.02
415	Tom Browning	.07	.05	.03
416	Norm Charlton	.08	.06	.03
417	Eric Davis	.08	.06	.03
418	Rob Dibble	.10	.07	.04
419	John Franco	.07	.05	.03
420	Ken Griffey, Sr.	.07	.05	.03
421	*Chris Hammond* (FC)	.25	.20	.10
422	Danny Jackson	.06	.05	.02
423	Barry Larkin	.15	.11	.06
424	Tim Leary	.06	.05	.02
425	Rick Mahler	.05	.04	.02
426	*Joe Oliver*	.10	.07	.04
427	Paul O'Neill	.07	.05	.03
428	Luis Quinones	.05	.04	.02
429	Jeff Reed	.05	.04	.02
430	Jose Rijo	.07	.05	.03
431	Ron Robinson	.05	.04	.02
432	Rolando Roomes	.10	.08	.04
433	Chris Sabo	.08	.06	.03
434	*Scott Scudder*	.10	.07	.04
435	Herm Winningham	.05	.04	.02
436	Steve Balboni	.05	.04	.02
437	Jesse Barfield	.08	.06	.03
438	*Mike Blowers*	.20	.15	.08
439	Tom Brookens	.05	.04	.02
440	Greg Cadaret	.05	.04	.02
441	Alvaro Espinoza	.10	.07	.04
442	*Bob Geren*	.10	.07	.04
443	Lee Guetterman	.05	.04	.02
444	Mel Hall	.06	.05	.02
445	Andy Hawkins	.06	.05	.02
446	Roberto Kelly	.10	.07	.04
447	Don Mattingly	.35	.25	.14
448	Lance McCullers	.05	.04	.02
449	Hensley Meulens	.08	.06	.03
450	Dale Mohorcic	.05	.04	.02
451	Clay Parker	.10	.07	.04
452	Eric Plunk	.05	.04	.02
453	Dave Righetti	.07	.05	.03
454	*Deion Sanders*	.30	.25	.12
455	Steve Sax	.07	.05	.03
456	Don Slaught	.05	.04	.02
457	Walt Terrell	.05	.04	.02
458	Dave Winfield	.15	.11	.06
459	Jay Bell	.05	.04	.02
460	Rafael Belliard	.05	.04	.02
461	Barry Bonds	.40	.30	.15
462	Bobby Bonilla	.10	.08	.04
463	Sid Bream	.05	.04	.02
464	Benny Distefano	.06	.05	.02
465	Doug Drabek	.06	.05	.02
466	Jim Gott	.06	.05	.02
467	Billy Hatcher	.06	.05	.02
468	Neal Heaton	.06	.05	.02
469	Jeff King	.10	.07	.04
470	Bob Kipper	.05	.04	.02
471	Randy Kramer	.05	.04	.02
472	Bill Landrum	.06	.05	.02
473	Mike LaValliere	.06	.05	.02
474	Jose Lind	.06	.05	.02
475	Junior Ortiz	.05	.04	.02
476	Gary Redus	.05	.04	.02
477	*Rick Reed* (FC)	.05	.04	.02
478	R.J. Reynolds	.05	.04	.02
479	Jeff Robinson	.05	.04	.02
480	John Smiley	.07	.05	.03
481	Andy Van Slyke	.09	.07	.04
482	Bob Walk	.06	.05	.04
483	Andy Allanson	.05	.04	.02
484	Scott Bailes	.05	.04	.02
485	*Albert Belle*	1.50	1.25	.60
486	Bud Black	.05	.04	.02
487	Jerry Browne	.07	.05	.03
488	Tom Candiotti	.05	.04	.02
489	Joe Carter	.12	.09	.05
490	David Clark	.06	.05	.02
491	John Farrell	.06	.05	.02
492	Felix Fermin	.05	.04	.02
493	Brook Jacoby	.06	.05	.02
494	Dion James	.06	.05	.02
495	Doug Jones	.06	.05	.02
496	Brad Komminsk	.05	.04	.02
497	Rod Nichols	.05	.04	.02
498	Pete O'Brien	.07	.05	.03
499	*Steve Olin* (FC)	.15	.11	.06
500	Jesse Orosco	.05	.04	.02
501	Joel Skinner	.05	.04	.02
502	Cory Snyder	.09	.07	.04
503	Greg Swindell	.10	.08	.04
504	Rich Yett	.05	.04	.02
505	Scott Bankhead	.07	.05	.03
506	Scott Bradley	.05	.04	.02
507	Greg Briley	.15	.11	.06
508	Jay Buhner	.07	.05	.03
509	Darnell Coles	.05	.04	.02
510	Keith Comstock	.05	.04	.02
511	Henry Cotto	.05	.04	.02
512	Alvin Davis	.12	.09	.05
513	Ken Griffey, Jr.	2.00	1.50	.80
514	Erik Hanson	.10	.07	.04
515	Gene Harris	.15	.11	.06
516	Brian Holman	.07	.05	.03
517	Mike Jackson	.05	.04	.02
518	Randy Johnson	.15	.11	.06
519	Jeffrey Leonard	.08	.06	.03
520	Edgar Martinez	.10	.08	.04
521	Dennis Powell	.05	.04	.02
522	Jim Presley	.06	.05	.02
523	Jerry Reed	.05	.04	.02
524	Harold Reynolds	.07	.05	.03

525	Mike Schooler	.06	.05	.04
526	Bill Swift	.05	.04	.02
527	David Valle	.05	.04	.02
528	*Omar Vizquel*	.20	.15	.08
529	Ivan Calderon	.06	.05	.02
530	Carlton Fisk	.10	.08	.04
531	Scott Fletcher	.06	.05	.02
532	Dave Gallagher	.09	.07	.04
533	Ozzie Guillen	.07	.05	.03
534	*Greg Hibbard* (FC)	.20	.15	.08
535	Shawn Hillegas	.05	.04	.02
536	Lance Johnson	.07	.05	.03
537	Eric King	.05	.04	.02
538	Ron Kittle	.07	.05	.02
539	Steve Lyons	.05	.04	.02
540	Carlos Martinez	.10	.07	.04
541	*Tom McCarthy* (FC)	.10	.07	.04
542	*Matt Merullo*	.08	.06	.03
543	Donn Pall	.05	.04	.02
544	Dan Pasqua	.06	.05	.02
545	Ken Patterson	.06	.05	.02
546	Melido Perez	.07	.05	.03
547	Steve Rosenberg	.07	.05	.03
548	*Sammy Sosa* (FC)	.50	.40	.20
549	Bobby Thigpen	.07	.05	.03
550	Robin Ventura	.60	.45	.25
551	Greg Walker	.06	.05	.02
552	Don Carman	.05	.04	.02
553	*Pat Combs* (FC)	.10	.08	.04
554	Dennis Cook	.10	.07	.04
555	Darren Daulton	.05	.04	.02
556	Len Dykstra	.15	.11	.06
557	Curt Ford	.05	.04	.02
558	Charlie Hayes	.10	.08	.04
559	Von Hayes	.07	.05	.03
560	Tom Herr	.06	.05	.02
561	Ken Howell	.05	.04	.02
562	Steve Jeltz	.05	.04	.02
563	Ron Jones	.08	.06	.03
564	Ricky Jordan	.10	.07	.04
565	John Kruk	.07	.05	.03
566	Steve Lake	.05	.04	.02
567	Roger McDowell	.06	.05	.02
568	Terry Mulholland	.05	.04	.02
569	Dwayne Murphy	.05	.04	.02
570	Jeff Parrett	.06	.05	.02
571	Randy Ready	.05	.04	.02
572	Bruce Ruffin	.05	.04	.02
573	Dickie Thon	.05	.04	.02
574	Jose Alvarez	.05	.04	.02
575	Geronimo Berroa	.06	.05	.03
576	Jeff Blauser	.05	.04	.02
577	Joe Boever	.07	.05	.03
578	Marty Clary	.05	.04	.02
579	Jody Davis	.05	.04	.02
580	Mark Eichhorn	.05	.04	.02
581	Darrell Evans	.06	.05	.02
582	Ron Gant	.06	.05	.02
583	Tom Glavine	.09	.07	.04
584	*Tommy Greene* (FC)	.25	.20	.10
585	Tommy Gregg	.10	.07	.04
586	*Dave Justice*	1.50	1.25	.60
587	Mark Lemke (FC)	.10	.08	.04
588	Derek Lilliquist	.10	.08	.04
589	Oddibe McDowell	.07	.05	.03
590	*Kent Mercker* (FC)	.35	.25	.14
591	Dale Murphy	.10	.07	.04
592	Gerald Perry	.06	.05	.02
593	Lonnie Smith	.06	.05	.02
594	Pete Smith	.07	.05	.03
595	John Smoltz	.15	.11	.06
596	*Mike Stanton* (FC)	.30	.25	.12
597	Andres Thomas	.06	.05	.02
598	Jeff Treadway	.06	.05	.02
599	Doyle Alexander	.06	.05	.02
600	Dave Bergman	.05	.04	.02
601	*Brian Dubois*	.12	.09	.05
602	Paul Gibson	.06	.05	.02
603	Mike Heath	.05	.04	.02
604	Mike Henneman	.07	.05	.03
605	Guillermo Hernandez	.05	.04	.02
606	*Shawn Holman* (FC)	.05	.04	.02
607	Tracy Jones	.09	.07	.04
608	Chet Lemon	.06	.05	.02
609	Fred Lynn	.06	.05	.02
610	Jack Morris	.07	.05	.02
611	Matt Nokes	.10	.08	.04
612	Gary Pettis	.05	.04	.02
613	*Kevin Ritz*	.12	.09	.05
614	Jeff Robinson	.07	.05	.03
615	Steve Searcy	.10	.08	.04
616	Frank Tanana	.06	.05	.02
617	Alan Trammell	.09	.07	.04
618	Gary Ward	.05	.04	.02
619	Lou Whitaker	.09	.07	.04
620	Frank Williams	.05	.04	.02
621a	Players of the Decade - 1980 (George Brett) (... 10 .390 hitting ...)	2.25	1.75	.90
621b	Players of the Decade - 1980 (George Brett)	.50	.40	.20
622	Players Of The Decade - 1981 (Fernando Valenzuela)	.20	.15	.08
623	Players Of The Decade - 1982 (Dale Murphy)	.25	.20	.10
624a	Players of the Decade - 1983 (Cal Ripkin, Jr.) (Ripkin)	3.00	2.25	1.25
624b	Players of the Decade - 1983 (Cal Ripken, Jr.)	.25	.20	.10
625	Players of the Decade - 1984 (Ryne Sandberg)	.25	.20	.10
626	Players of the Decade - 1985 (Don Mattingly)	.60	.45	.25
627	Players of the Decade - 1986 (Roger Clemens)	.25	.20	.10
628	Players of the Decade - 1987 (George Bell)	.20	.15	.08
629	Players of the Decade - 1988 (Jose Canseco)	.60	.45	.25

#	Card	MT	NR MT	EX
630a	Players of the Decade - 1989 (Will Clark) (total bases 32)	1.50	1.25	.60
630b	Players of the Decade - 1989 (Will Clark) (total bases 321)	.60	.45	.25
631	Game Savers (Mark Davis/Mitch Williams)	.10	.08	.04
632	Boston Igniters (Wade Boggs/Mike Greenwell)	.10	.08	.04
633	Starter & Stopper (Mark Gubicza/Jeff Russell)	.10	.08	.04
634	League's Best Shortstops (Tony Fernandez/Cal Ripken, Jr.)	.10	.08	.04
635	Human Dynamos (Kirby Puckett/Bo Jackson)	.10	.08	.04
636	300 Strikeout Club (Nolan Ryan/Mike Scott)	.10	.08	.04
637	The Dymanic Duo (Will Clark/Kevin Mitchell)	.10	.08	.04
638	A.L. All-Stars (Don Mattingly/Mark McGwire)	.10	.08	.04
639	N.L. East Rivals (Howard Johnson/Ryne Sandberg)	.10	.08	.04
640	Major League Prospects (*Rudy Seanez* (FC), Colin Charland)	.15	.11	.06
641	Major League Prospects (*George Canale*, Kevin Maas)	.15	.11	.06
642	Major League Prospects (*Kelly Mann* (FC), Dave Hansen)	.30	.25	.12
643	Major League Prospects (*Greg Smith* (FC), Stu Tate)	.15	.11	.06
644	Major League Prospects (*Tom Drees* (FC), Dan Howitt)	.15	.11	.06
645	Major League Prospects (*Mike Roesler* (FC), Derrick May)	.50	.40	.20
646	Major League Prospects (*Scott Hemond*, Mark Gardner)	.15	.11	.06
647	Major League Prospects (*John Orton* (FC), Scott Leuis)	.25	.20	.10
648	Major League Prospects (*Rich Monteleone* (FC), Dana Williams)	.15	.11	.06
649	Major League Prospects (*Mike Huff* (FC), Steve Frey)	.25	.20	.10
650	Major League Prospects (*Chuck McElroy* (FC), Moises Alou)	.75	.60	.30
651	Major League Prospects (*Bobby Rose* (FC), Mike Hartley)	.15	.11	.06
652	Major League Prospects (*Matt Kinzer* (FC), Wayne Edwards)	.20	.15	.08
653	Major League Prospects (*Delino DeShields*, Jason Grimsley)	.60	.45	.25
654	Athletics, Cubs, Giants & Blue Jays (Checklist)	.05	.04	.02
655	Royals, Angels, Padres & Orioles (Checklist)	.05	.04	.02
656	Mets, Astros, Cardinals & Red Sox (Checklist)	.05	.04	.02
657	Rangers, Brewers, Expos & Twins (Checklist)	.05	.04	.02
658	Dodgers, Reds, Yankees & Pirates (Checklist)	.05	.04	.02
659	Indians, Mariners, White Sox & Phillies (Checklist)	.05	.04	.02
660	Braves, Tigers & Special Cards (Checklist)	.05	.04	.02

A player's name in italic type indicates a rookie card. An (FC) indicates a player's first card for that particular card company.

1990 Fleer All-Stars

The top players at each position, as selected by Fleer, are featured in this 12-card set. The cards were inserted in cello packs and some wax packs. The cards measure 2-1/2" by 3-1/2" and feature a unique two-photo format on the card fronts.

	MT	NR MT	EX
Complete Set (12):	5.00	4.00	2.00
Common Player:	.20	.15	.08

#	Player	MT	NR MT	EX
1	Harold Baines	.25	.20	.10
2	Will Clark	.80	.60	.30
3	Mark Davis	.20	.15	.08
4	Howard Johnson	.30	.25	.12
5	Joe Magrane	.25	.20	.10
6	Kevin Mitchell	.25	.15	.10
7	Kirby Puckett	1.00	.70	.40
8	Cal Ripken	1.50	1.00	.50
9	Ryne Sandberg	1.50	1.00	.50
10	Mike Scott	.20	.15	.08
11	Ruben Sierra	.35	.25	.14
12	Mickey Tettleton	.20	.15	.08

1990 Fleer League Standouts

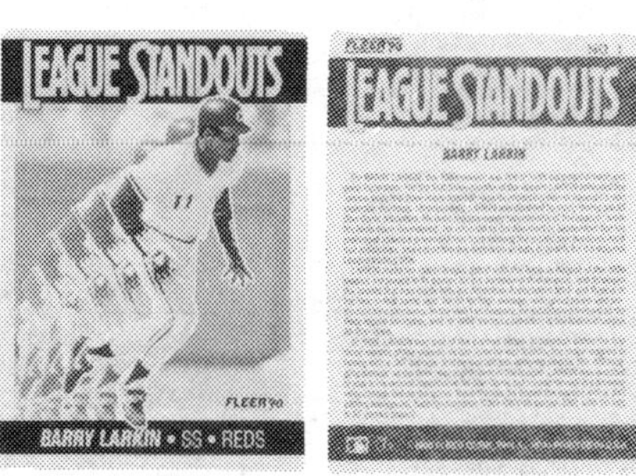

Fleer's "League Standouts" set features six of baseball's top players. The cards were distributed randomly in Fleer three-packs. The card fronts feature full color photos with a six dimensional effect. An attractive black and gold frame borders the photo. The card backs are yellow and describe the player's individual accomplishments. The cards measure 2-1/2" by 3-1/2" in size.

	MT	NR MT	EX
Complete Set (6):	4.00	3.00	1.50
Common Player:	.50	.40	.20

#	Player	MT	NR MT	EX
1	Barry Larkin	.50	.40	.20
2	Mark Grace	.60	.45	.25
3	Don Mattingly	1.00	.70	.40
4	Darryl Strawberry	.50	.40	.20
5	Jose Canseco	1.25	.90	.50
6	Wade Boggs	.75	.60	.30

The values quoted are intended to reflect the market price.

1990 Fleer World Series

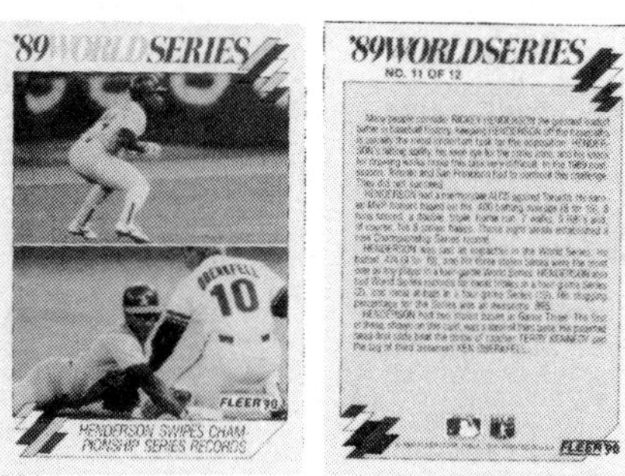

This 12-card set, which depicts highlights of the 1989 World Series, was included as a special subset with the regular factory-collated Fleer set. Ironically, single World Series cards were discovered in cello and three-packs. This was not intended to happen. Fronts of the 2-1/2" by 3-1/2" cards feature full-color photos set against a white background with a red and blue "'89 World Series" banner. The card backs are pink and white and describe the events of the 1989 Fall Classic.

	MT	NR MT	EX
Complete Set (12):	2.50	1.50	.75
Common Player:	.10	.06	.03

#	Card	MT	NR MT	EX
1	The Final Piece To The Puzzle (Mike Moore)	.20	.15	.08
2	Kevin Mitchell	.20	.15	.08
3	Game Two's Crushing Blow	.20	.15	.08
4	Will Clark	.75	.60	.30
5	Jose Canseco	.75	.60	.30
6	Great leather In The Field	.20	.15	.08
7	Game One And A's Break Out On Top	.20	.15	.08
8	Dave Stewart	.25	.20	.10
9	Parker's Bat Produces Power (Dave Parker)	.20	.15	.08
10	World Series Record Book Game 3	.20	.15	.08
11	Rickey Henderson	.30	.25	.12
12	Oakland A's - Baseball's Best In '89	.25	.20	.10

Values for recent cards and sets are listed in Mint (MT), Near Mint (NM), reflecting the fact that many cards from recent years have been preserved in top condition. Recent cards and sets in less than Excellent condition have little collector interest.

1990 Fleer Box Panels

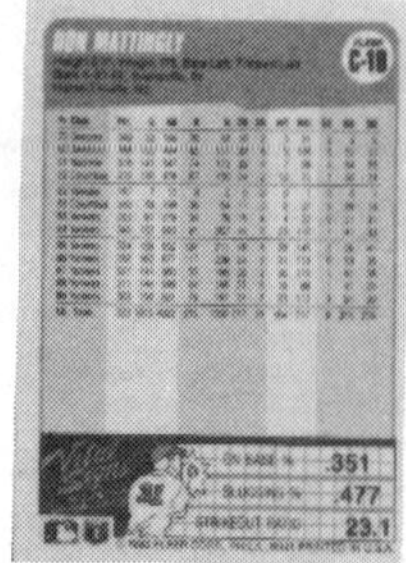

For the fifth consecutive year, Fleer issued a series of cards on the bottom panels of its regular 1990 wax pack boxes. This 28-card set features both players and team logo cards. The cards were numbered C-1 to C-28.

	MT	NR MT	EX
Complete Set (28):	5.00	3.75	2.00
Common Player:	.05	.04	.02

#	Player	MT	NR MT	EX
1	Giants Logo	.05	.04	.02
2	Tim Belcher	.06	.05	.02
3	Roger Clemens	.35	.25	.14
4	Eric Davis	.20	.15	.08
5	Glenn Davis	.10	.08	.04
6	Cubs Logo	.05	.04	.02
7	Jon Franco	.06	.05	.02
8	Mike Greenwell	.20	.15	.08
9	Athletics Logo	.05	.04	.02
10	Ken Griffey, Jr.	1.50	1.25	.60
11	Pedro Guerrero	.05	.04	.02
12	Tony Gwynn	.20	.15	.08
13	Blue Jays Logo	.05	.04	.02
14	Orel Hershiser	.20	.15	.08
15	Bo Jackson	.50	.40	.20
16	Howard Johnson	.15	.11	.06
17	Mets Logo	.05	.04	.02
18	Cardinals Logo	.05	.04	.02
19	Don Mattingly	.60	.45	.25
20	Mark McGwire	.40	.30	.15
21	Kevin Mitchell	.15	.11	.06
22	Kirby Puckett	.35	.25	.14
23	Royals Logo	.05	.04	.02
24	Orioles Logo	.05	.04	.02
25	Ruben Sierra	.30	.25	.12
26	Dave Stewart	.20	.15	.08
27	Jerome Walton	.05	.04	.02
28	Robin Yount	.25	.20	.10

1990 Fleer Update

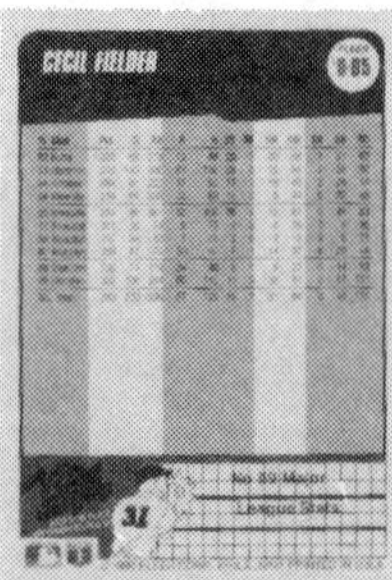

Fleer produced its seventh consecutive "Update" set in 1990 to supplement the company's regular set. As in the past, the set consists of 132 cards (numbered U-1 through U-132) that were sold by hobby dealers in special collectors boxes. The cards are designed in the exact same style as the regular issue. A special Nolan Ryan commemorative card is included in the 1990 Fleer Update set.

	MT	NR MT	EX
Complete Set (132):	8.00	6.00	3.25
Common Player:	.06	.05	.02

#	Player	MT	NR MT	EX
1	Steve Avery (FC)	.75	.60	.30
2	Francisco Cabrera	.10	.08	.04
3	Nick Esasky	.06	.05	.02
4	Jim Kremers (FC)	.06	.05	.02
5	Greg Olson (FC)	.10	.08	.04
6	Jim Presley	.06	.05	.02
7	Shawn Boskie (FC)	.10	.07	.04
8	Joe Kraemer (FC)	.06	.05	.02
9	Luis Salazar	.06	.05	.02
10	Hector Villanueva (FC)	.10	.08	.04
11	Glenn Braggs	.06	.05	.02
12	Mariano Duncan	.06	.05	.02
13	Billy Hatcher	.06	.05	.02
14	Tim Layana (FC)	.10	.08	.04
15	Hal Morris	.40	.30	.15

16	Javier Ortiz (FC)	.10	.07	.04
17	Dave Rohde (FC)	.15	.11	.06
18	Eric Yelding (FC)	.10	.08	.04
19	Hubie Brooks	.08	.06	.03
20	Kal Daniels	.08	.06	.03
21	Dave Hansen	.15	.11	.06
22	Mike Hartley	.15	.11	.06
23	Stan Javier	.06	.05	.02
24	Jose Offerman (FC)	.15	.11	.06
25	Juan Samuel	.06	.05	.02
26	Dennis Boyd	.06	.05	.02
27	Delino DeShields	.40	.30	.15
28	Steve Frey	.12	.09	.05
29	Mark Gardner	.15	.11	.06
30	Chris Nabholz (FC)	.20	.15	.08
31	Bill Sampen (FC)	.15	.11	.06
32	Dave Schmidt	.06	.05	.02
33	Daryl Boston	.06	.05	.02
34	Chuck Carr (FC)	.35	.25	.14
35	John Franco	.08	.06	.03
36	Todd Hundley (FC)	.25	.20	.10
37	Julio Machado (FC)	.06	.05	.02
38	Alejandro Pena	.06	.05	.02
39	Darren Reed (FC)	.06	.05	.02
40	Kelvin Torve (FC)	.06	.05	.02
41	Darrel Akerfelds (FC)	.06	.05	.02
42	Jose DeJesus	.10	.08	.04
43	Dave Hollins (FC)	.75	.60	.30
44	Carmelo Martinez	.06	.05	.02
45	Brad Moore (FC)	.06	.05	.02
46	Dale Murphy	.30	.25	.12
47	Wally Backman	.06	.05	.02
48	Stan Belinda (FC)	.10	.07	.04
49	Bob Patterson	.06	.05	.02
50	Ted Power	.06	.05	.02
51	Don Slaught	.06	.05	.02
52	Geronimo Pena (FC)	.25	.20	.10
53	Lee Smith	.08	.06	.03
54	John Tudor	.06	.05	.02
55	Joe Carter	.25	.20	.10
56	Tom Howard (FC)	.10	.07	.04
57	Craig Lefferts	.06	.05	.02
58	Rafael Valdez (FC)	.10	.08	.04
59	Dave Anderson	.06	.05	.02
60	Kevin Bass	.06	.05	.02
61	John Burkett	.50	.40	.20
62	Gary Carter	.10	.08	.04
63	Rick Parker (FC)	.10	.08	.04
64	Trevor Wilson	.10	.08	.04
65	Chris Hoiles (FC)	.25	.20	.10
66	Tim Hulett	.06	.05	.02
67	Dave Johnson (FC)	.10	.08	.04
68	Curt Schilling (FC)	.30	.25	.12
69	David Segui (FC)	.10	.08	.04
70	Tom Brunansky	.08	.06	.03
71	Greg Harris	.06	.05	.02
72	Dana Kiecker (FC)	.12	.09	.05
73	Tim Naehring (FC)	.20	.15	.08
74	Tony Pena	.06	.05	.02
75	Jeff Reardon	.08	.06	.03
76	Jerry Reed	.06	.05	.02
77	Mark Eichhorn	.06	.05	.02
78	Mark Langston	.08	.06	.03
79	John Orton	.12	.09	.05
80	Luis Polonia	.06	.05	.02
81	Dave Winfield	.20	.15	.08
82	Cliff Young (FC)	.10	.08	.04
83	Wayne Edwards	.10	.08	.04
84	Alex Fernandez (FC)	1.50	1.25	.60
85	Craig Grebeck (FC)	.15	.11	.06
86	Scott Radinsky (FC)	.12	.09	.05
87	Frank Thomas (FC)	4.00	3.00	1.50
88	Beau Allred (FC)	.10	.08	.04
89	Sandy Alomar, Jr.	.15	.11	.06
90	Carlos Baerga (FC)	1.25	.90	.50
91	Kevin Bearse (FC)	.10	.08	.04
92	Chris James	.06	.05	.02
93	Candy Maldonado	.06	.05	.02
94	Jeff Manto	.12	.09	.05
95	Cecil Fielder	.25	.20	.10
96	Travis Fryman (FC)	1.50	1.25	.60
97	Lloyd Moseby	.06	.05	.02
98	Edwin Nunez	.06	.05	.02
99	Tony Phillips	.06	.05	.02
100	Larry Sheets	.06	.05	.02
101	Mark Davis	.06	.05	.02
102	Storm Davis	.06	.05	.02
103	Gerald Perry	.06	.05	.02
104	Terry Shumpert	.10	.08	.04
105	Edgar Diaz (FC)	.06	.05	.02
106	Dave Parker	.20	.15	.08
107	Tim Drummond (FC)	.10	.08	.04
108	Junior Ortiz	.06	.05	.02
109	Park Pittman (FC)	.10	.08	.04
110	Kevin Tapani (FC)	.25	.20	.10
111	Oscar Azocar (FC)	.15	.11	.06
112	Jim Leyritz (FC)	.15	.11	.06
113	Kevin Maas	.15	.11	.06
114	Alan Mills (FC)	.12	.09	.05
115	Matt Nokes	.06	.05	.02
116	Pascual Perez	.06	.05	.02
117	Ozzie Canseco (FC)	.10	.08	.04
118	Scott Sanderson	.06	.05	.02
119	Tino Martinez (FC)	.12	.09	.05
120	Jeff Schaefer (FC)	.10	.08	.04
121	Matt Young	.06	.05	.02
122	Brian Bohanon (FC)	.10	.08	.04
123	Jeff Huson	.15	.11	.06
124	Ramon Manon (FC)	.10	.08	.04
125	Gary Mielke (FC)	.10	.08	.04
126	Willie Blair (FC)	.15	.11	.06
127	Glenallen Hill (FC)	.10	.08	.04
128	John Olerud (FC)	1.50	1.25	.60
129	Luis Sojo (FC)	.15	.11	.06
130	Mark Whiten (FC)	.70	.50	.30
131	Three Decades of No Hitters (Nolan Ryan)	.70	.50	.30
132	Checklist	.06	.05	.02

1990 Fleer Award Winners

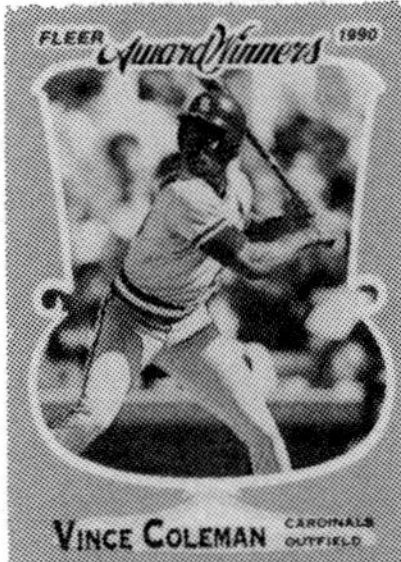

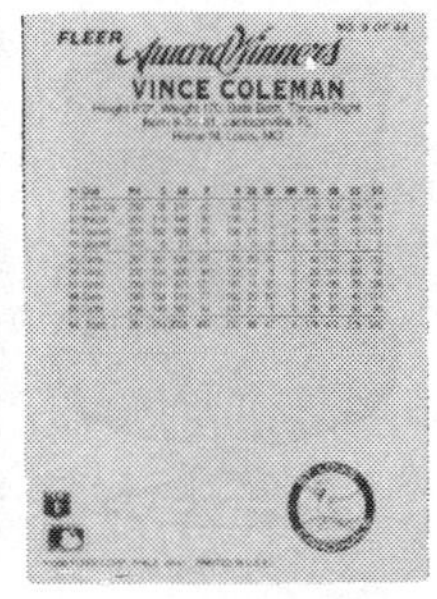

Hill's Department Stores and 7-Eleven Outlets are exclusively carrying the 1990 Fleer "Award Winners." This 44-card boxed set includes baseball's statistical leaders of 1989, six special cards that feature peel-off team logo stickers and a baseball trivia quiz. The card fronts feature a full-color player photo framed by a winner's cup design and a blue border. The card backs showcase player statistics in blue on a yellow and white background. The cards measure 2-1/2" by 3-1/2" in size. A complete checklist is provided on the back of each box. The checklist incorrectly lists Bob Boone's team as the Angels.

		MT	NR MT	EX
Complete Set (44):		3.50	2.75	1.50
Common Player:		.05	.04	.02
1	Jeff Ballard	.05	.04	.02
2	Tim Belcher	.08	.06	.03
3	Bert Blyleven	.08	.06	.03
4	Wade Boggs	.40	.30	.15
5	Bob Boone	.05	.04	.02
6	Jose Canseco	.50	.40	.20
7	Will Clark	.40	.30	.15
8	Jack Clark	.05	.04	.02
9	Vince Coleman	.05	.04	.02
10	Ron Darling	.05	.04	.02
11	Eric Davis	.10	.08	.04
12	Jose DeLeon	.05	.04	.02
13	Tony Fernandez	.05	.04	.02
14	Carlton Fisk	.10	.08	.04
15	Scott Garrelts	.05	.04	.02
16	Tom Gordon	.05	.04	.02
17	Ken Griffey,Jr.	1.75	1.25	.70
18	Von Hayes	.05	.04	.02
19	Rickey Henderson	.30	.25	.12
20	Bo Jackson	.40	.30	.15
21	Howard Johnson	.15	.11	.06
22	Don Mattingly	.40	.30	.15
23	Fred McGriff	.25	.20	.10
24	Kevin Mitchell	.10	.08	.04
25	Gregg Olson	.05	.04	.02
26	Gary Pettis	.05	.04	.02
27	Kirby Puckett	.40	.30	.15
28	Harold Reynolds	.05	.04	.02
29	Jeff Russell	.05	.04	.02
30	Nolan Ryan	.70	.50	.30
31	Bret Saberhagen	.10	.08	.04
32	Ryne Sandberg	.40	.30	.15
33	Benito Santiago	.10	.08	.04
34	Mike Scott	.05	.04	.02
35	Ruben Sierra	.15	.11	.06
36	Lonnie Smith	.05	.04	.02
37	Ozzie Smith	.15	.11	.06
38	Dave Stewart	.10	.08	.04
39	Greg Swindell	.05	.04	.02
40	Andy Van Slyke	.08	.06	.03
41	Tim Wallach	.05	.04	.02
42	Jerome Walton	.05	.04	.02
43	Mitch Williams	.08	.06	.03
44	Robin Yount	.30	.25	.12

1990 Fleer Baseball All Stars

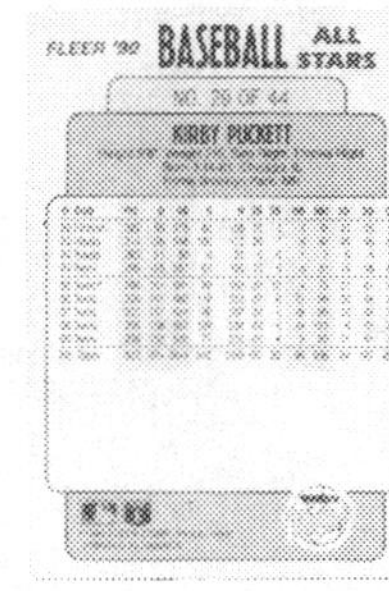

Sold exclusively in Ben Franklin stores, this 44-card boxed set showcases the game's top players. The card fronts feature a full color player photo surrounded by a tan border. The flip side contains individual player statistics and data printed in red and black. The cards measure 2-1/2" by 3-1/2" in size and are packed in a special box with a complete checklist on the back. Like other Fleer boxed sets, the cards are numbered alphabetically.

		MT	NR MT	EX
Complete Set (44):		4.00	3.00	1.50
Common Player:		.05	.04	.02
1	Wade Boggs	.60	.45	.25
2	Bobby Bonilla	.20	.15	.08
3	Tim Burke	.05	.04	.02
4	Jose Canseco	.60	.45	.25
5	Will Clark	.60	.45	.25
6	Eric Davis	.10	.08	.04
7	Glenn Davis	.05	.04	.02
8	Julio Franco	.05	.04	.02
9	Tony Fernandez	.05	.04	.02
10	Gary Gaetti	.05	.04	.02
11	Scott Garrelts	.05	.04	.02
12	Mark Grace	.20	.15	.08
13	Mike Greenwell	.20	.15	.08
14	Ken Griffey,Jr.	1.75	1.25	.70
15	Mark Gubicza	.05	.04	.02
16	Pedro Guerrero	.05	.04	.02
17	Von Hayes	.05	.04	.02
18	Orel Hershiser	.10	.08	.04
19	Bruce Hurst	.05	.04	.02
20	Bo Jackson	.60	.45	.25
21	Howard Johnson	.10	.08	.04
22	Doug Jones	.05	.04	.02
23	Barry Larkin	.10	.08	.04
24	Don Mattingly	.60	.45	.25
25	Mark McGwire	.40	.30	.15
26	Kevin McReynolds	.05	.04	.02
27	Kevin Mitchell	.10	.08	.04
28	Dan Plesac	.05	.04	.02
29	Kirby Puckett	.60	.45	.25
30	Cal Ripken,Jr.	.60	.45	.25
31	Bret Saberhagen	.10	.08	.04
32	Ryne Sandberg	.60	.45	.25
33	Steve Sax	.10	.08	.04
34	Ruben Sierra	.15	.11	.06
35	Ozzie Smith	.10	.08	.04
36	John Smoltz	.10	.08	.04
37	Darryl Strawberry	.20	.15	.08
38	Terry Steinbach	.05	.04	.02
39	Dave Stewart	.10	.08	.04
40	Bobby Thigpen	.05	.04	.02
41	Alan Trammell	.10	.08	.04
42	Devon White	.05	.04	.02
43	Mitch Williams	.05	.04	.02
44	Robin Yount	.40	.30	.15

1990 Fleer Baseball MVP

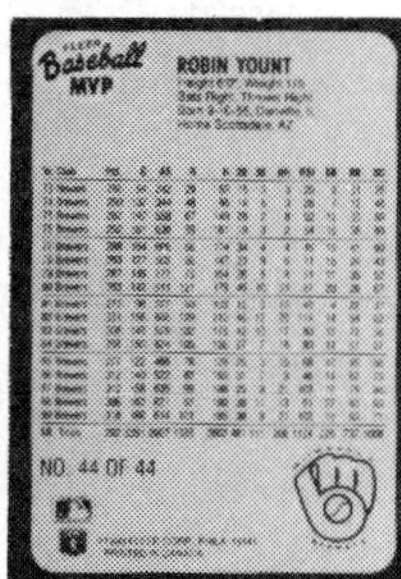

This 44-card boxed set was produced by Fleer for the Toys "R" Us chain. Card fronts are designed with graduating black-to-white borders, surrounding a color photo of each player. Card backs contain individual player data and career statistics. The back of each box carries a checklist of all the players in the set. Six peel-off team logo stickers featuring a baseball trivia quiz on the back are also included with each set. The cards are 2-1/2" by 3-1/2" in size and are numbered alphabetically.

		MT	NR MT	EX
Complete Set (44):		4.00	3.00	1.50
Common Player:		.05	.04	.02
1	George Bell	.10	.08	.04
2	Bert Blyleven	.10	.08	.04
3	Wade Boggs	.60	.45	.25
4	Bobby Bonilla	.15	.11	.06
5	George Brett	.60	.45	.25
6	Jose Canseco	.70	.50	.30
7	Will Clark	.40	.30	.15
8	Roger Clemens	.30	.25	.12
9	Eric Davis	.60	.45	.25
10	Glenn Davis	.05	.04	.02
11	Tony Fernandez	.10	.08	.04
12	Dwight Gooden	.25	.20	.10
13	Mike Greenwell	.20	.15	.08
14	Ken Griffey, Jr.	.15	.11	.06
15	Pedro Guerrero	.05	.04	.02

16	Tony Gwynn	.15	.11	.06
17	Rickey Henderson	.40	.30	.15
18	Tom Herr	.05	.04	.02
19	Orel Hershiser	.10	.08	.04
20	Kent Hrbek	.05	.04	.02
21	Bo Jackson	.40	.30	.15
22	Howard Johnson	.15	.11	.06
23	Don Mattingly	.60	.45	.25
24	Fred McGriff	.25	.20	.10
25	Mark McGwire	.40	.30	.15
26	Kevin Mitchell	.10	.08	.04
27	Paul Molitor	.40	.30	.15
28	Dale Murphy	.30	.25	.12
29	Kirby Puckett	.40	.30	.15
30	Tim Raines	.10	.08	.04
31	Cal Ripken, Jr.	.60	.45	.25
32	Bret Saberhagen	.10	.08	.04
33	Ryne Sandberg	.60	.45	.25
34	Ruben Sierra	.15	.11	.06
35	Dwight Smith	.05	.04	.02
36	Ozzie Smith	.20	.15	.08
37	Darryl Strawberry	.20	.15	.08
38	Dave Stewart	.10	.08	.04
39	Greg Swindell	.05	.04	.02
40	Bobby Thigpen	.05	.04	.02
41	Alan Trammell	.10	.08	.04
42	Jerome Walton	.05	.04	.02
43	Mitch Williams	.08	.06	.03
44	Robin Yount	.35	.25	.14

1990 Fleer League Leaders

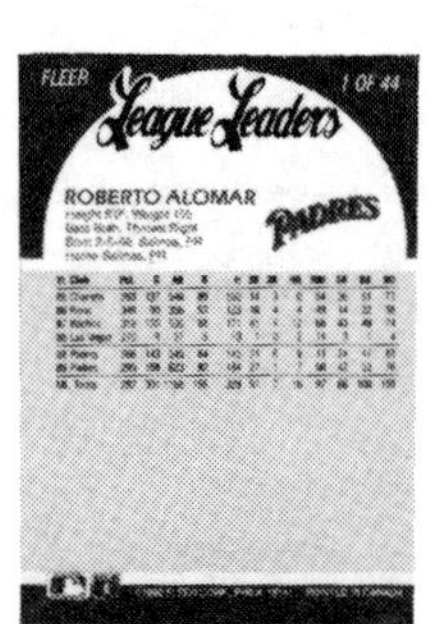

For the fifth consecutive year Fleer released a "League Leaders" trading card set. The set includes 44 top Major League players and features six special cards containing peel-off team logos and a baseball trivia quiz. Card number 42 (Jerome Walton) pictures a player other than Walton. The cards measure 2-1/2" by 3-1/2" in size. The card fronts display a full-color photo bordered by a blue frame. The card backs feature complete statistics. The cards are numbered alphabetically and a complete checklist is displayed on the back of the card box. The set is available at Walgreen Drug Stores.

		MT	NR MT	EX
Complete Set (44):		4.00	3.00	1.50
Common Player:		.05	.04	.02
1	Roberto Alomar	.35	.25	.14
2	Tim Belcher	.08	.06	.03
3	George Bell	.10	.08	.04
4	Wade Boggs	.50	.40	.20
5	Jose Canseco	.60	.45	.25
6	Will Clark	.50	.40	.20
7	David Cone	.08	.06	.03
8	Eric Davis	.10	.08	.04
9	Glenn Davis	.05	.04	.02
10	Nick Esasky	.05	.04	.02
11	Dennis Eckersley	.10	.08	.04
12	Mark Grace	.15	.11	.06
13	Mike Greenwell	.15	.11	.06
14	Ken Griffey, Jr.	1.50	1.25	.60
15	Mark Gubicza	.05	.04	.02
16	Pedro Guerrero	.05	.04	.02
17	Tony Gwynn	.15	.11	.06
18	Rickey Henderson	.40	.30	.15
19	Bo Jackson	.40	.30	.15
20	Doug Jones	.05	.04	.02
21	Ricky Jordan	.05	.04	.02
22	Barry Larkin	.15	.11	.06
23	Don Mattingly	.60	.45	.25
24	Fred McGriff	.25	.20	.10
25	Mark McGwire	.40	.30	.15
26	Kevin Mitchell	.10	.08	.04
27	Jack Morris	.05	.04	.02
28	Gregg Olson	.05	.04	.02
29	Dan Plesac	.05	.04	.02
30	Kirby Puckett	.40	.30	.15
31	Nolan Ryan	.90	.70	.35
32	Bret Saberhagen	.10	.08	.04
33	Ryne Sandberg	.60	.45	.25
34	Steve Sax	.10	.08	.04
35	Mike Scott	.05	.04	.02
36	Ruben Sierra	.15	.11	.06
37	Lonnie Smith	.05	.04	.02
38	Darryl Strawberry	.15	.11	.06
39	Bobby Thigpen	.05	.04	.02
40	Andy Van Slyke	.10	.08	.04
41	Tim Wallach	.05	.04	.02
42	Jerome Walton	.05	.04	.02
43	Devon White	.05	.04	.02
44	Robin Yount	.35	.25	.14

1990 Fleer Soaring Stars

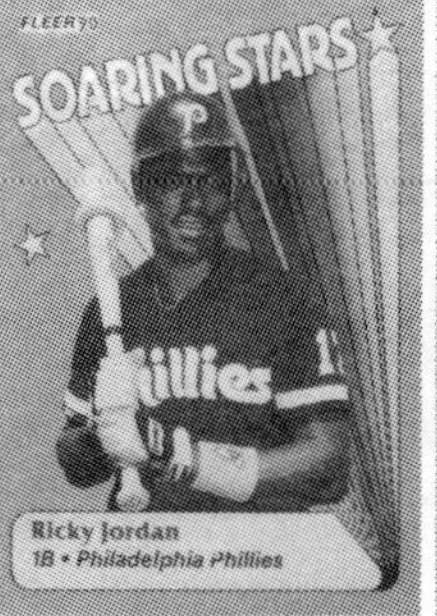

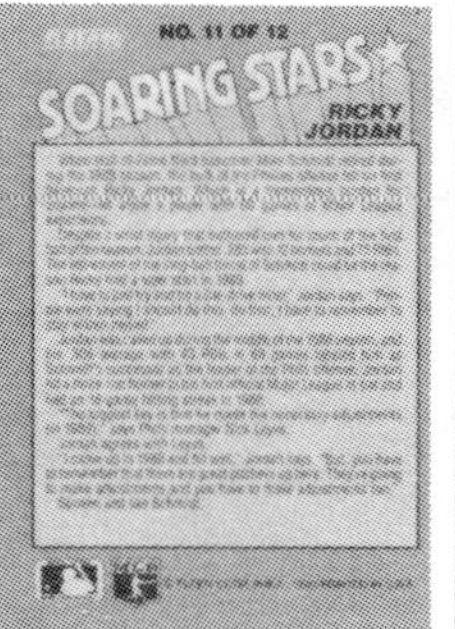

Cards from this 12-card set could be found in 1990 Fleer jumbo cello packs. The cards are styled with a cartoon flavor, featuring astronomical graphics surrounding the player. The card backs feature information about the promising young player.

		MT	NR MT	EX
Complete Set (12):		11.00	8.25	4.25
Common Player:		.20	.15	.08
1	Todd Zeile	.40	.30	.15
2	Mike Stanton	.20	.15	.08
3	Larry Walker	1.50	1.25	.60
4	Robin Ventura	2.00	1.50	.80
5	Scott Coolbaugh	.20	.15	.08
6	Ken Griffey,Jr.	8.00	6.00	3.25
7	Tom Gordon	.20	.15	.08
8	Jerome Walton	.20	.15	.08
9	Junior Felix	.20	.15	.08
10	Jim Abbott	.75	.60	.30
11	Ricky Jordan	.20	.15	.08
12	Dwight Smith	.20	.15	.08

1991 Fleer

Fleer expanded its 1991 set to include 720 cards. The cards feature yellow boders surrounding full-color action photos. The player's name appears above the photo, while the team and position is displayed below. The "Fleer 91" logo appears in the lower right corner of the photo. The card backs feature a circular player photo, biographical information, complete statistics, and career highlights. Five special Super Star cards are among the cards in the regular set. Once again the cards are numbered alphabetically within team. Because Fleer used more than one printer, many minor variations in photo cropping and typography can be found. The most notable are included in the checklist here.

		MT	NR MT	EX
Complete Set (720):		15.00	11.00	6.00
Common Player:		.05	.04	.02
1	*Troy Afenir* (FC)	.10	.08	.04
2	Harold Baines	.08	.06	.03
3	Lance Blankenship	.06	.05	.02
4	Todd Burns	.05	.04	.02
5	Jose Canseco	.15	.11	.06
6	Dennis Eckersley	.10	.08	.04
7	Mike Gallego	.05	.04	.02
8	Ron Hassey	.05	.04	.02
9	Dave Henderson	.08	.06	.03
10	Rickey Henderson	.15	.11	.06
11	Rick Honeycutt	.05	.04	.02
12	Doug Jennings	.06	.05	.02
13	*Joe Klink* (FC)	.10	.08	.04
14	Carney Lansford	.08	.06	.03
15	*Darren Lewis* (FC)	.20	.15	.08
16	Willie McGee	.08	.06	.03
17a	Mark McGwire	.20	.15	.08
17b	Mark McGwire (seven-line career summary)	.20	.15	.08
18	Mike Moore	.06	.05	.02
19	Gene Nelson	.05	.04	.02
20	Dave Otto	.05	.04	.02
21	Jamie Quirk	.05	.04	.02
22	Willie Randolph	.06	.05	.02
23	Scott Sanderson	.06	.05	.02
24	Terry Steinbach	.06	.05	.02
25	Dave Stewart	.10	.08	.04
26	Walt Weiss	.06	.05	.02
27	Bob Welch	.08	.06	.03
28	Curt Young	.05	.04	.02
29	Wally Backman	.05	.04	.02
30	*Stan Belinda*	.10	.08	.04
31	Jay Bell	.06	.05	.02
32	Rafael Belliard	.05	.04	.02
33	Barry Bonds	.25	.20	.10
34	Bobby Bonilla	.12	.09	.05
35	Sid Bream	.06	.05	.02
36	Doug Drabek	.10	.08	.04
37	*Carlos Garcia* (FC)	.60	.45	.25
38	Neal Heaton	.06	.05	.02
39	Jeff King	.08	.06	.03
40	Bob Kipper	.05	.04	.02
41	Bill Landrum	.06	.05	.02
42	Mike LaValliere	.06	.05	.02
43	Jose Lind	.06	.05	.02
44	Carmelo Martinez	.05	.04	.02
45	Bob Patterson	.05	.04	.02
46	Ted Power	.05	.04	.02
47	Gary Redus	.05	.04	.02
48	R.J. Reynolds	.05	.04	.02
49	Don Slaught	.05	.04	.02
50	John Smiley	.05	.04	.02
51	Zane Smith	.06	.05	.02
52	*Randy Tomlin* (FC)	.10	.08	.04
53	Andy Van Slyke	.08	.06	.03
54	Bob Walk	.05	.04	.02
55	Jack Armstrong	.08	.06	.03
56	Todd Benzinger	.06	.05	.02
57	Glenn Braggs	.06	.05	.02
58	Keith Brown	.06	.05	.02
59	Tom Browning	.06	.05	.02
60	Norm Charlton	.08	.06	.03
61	Eric Davis	.10	.07	.04
62	Rob Dibble	.10	.08	.04
63	Bill Doran	.08	.06	.03
64	Mariano Duncan	.06	.05	.02
65	Chris Hammond	.06	.05	.02
66	Billy Hatcher	.06	.05	.02
67	Danny Jackson	.06	.05	.02
68	Barry Larkin	.10	.08	.04
69	*Tim Layana*	.10	.08	.04
70	*Terry Lee* (FC)	.15	.11	.06
71	Rick Mahler	.05	.04	.02
72	Hal Morris	.15	.11	.06
73	Randy Myers	.08	.06	.03
74	Ron Oester	.05	.04	.02
75	Joe Oliver	.08	.06	.03
76	Paul O'Neill	.06	.05	.02
77	Luis Quinones	.05	.04	.02
78	Jeff Reed	.05	.04	.02
79	Jose Rijo	.08	.06	.03
80	Chris Sabo	.08	.06	.03
81	Scott Scudder	.06	.05	.02
82	Herm Winningham	.05	.04	.02
83	Larry Andersen	.05	.04	.02
84	Marty Barrett	.05	.04	.02
85	Mike Boddicker	.06	.05	.02
86	Wade Boggs	.12	.09	.05
87	Tom Bolton	.05	.04	.02
88	Tom Brunansky	.06	.05	.02
89	Ellis Burks	.15	.11	.06
90	Roger Clemens	.20	.15	.08
91	Scott Cooper (FC)	.20	.15	.08
92	John Dopson	.05	.04	.02
93	Dwight Evans	.06	.05	.02
94	Wes Gardner	.05	.04	.02
95	*Jeff Gray* (FC)	.10	.08	.04
96	Mike Greenwell	.10	.08	.04
97	Greg Harris	.05	.04	.02
98	*Daryl Irvine* (FC)	.08	.06	.03
99	*Dana Kiecker*	.10	.08	.04
100	Randy Kutcher	.05	.04	.02
101	Dennis Lamp	.05	.04	.02
102	Mike Marshall	.05	.04	.02
103	John Marzano	.05	.04	.02
104	Rob Murphy	.05	.04	.02
105a	*Tim Naehring* (seven-line career summary)	.08	.06	.03
105b	*Tim Naehring* (nine-line career summary)	.08	.06	.03
106	Tony Pena	.06	.05	.02
107	*Phil Plantier* (FC)	.50	.40	.20
108	Carlos Quintana	.06	.05	.02
109	Jeff Reardon	.06	.05	.02
110	Jerry Reed	.05	.04	.02
111	Jody Reed	.06	.05	.02
112	Luis Rivera	.05	.04	.02
113a	Kevin Romine (one-line career summary)	.05	.04	.02
113b	Kevin Romine (two-line career summary)	.05	.04	.02
114	Phil Bradley	.06	.05	.02
115	Ivan Calderon	.06	.05	.02
116	Wayne Edwards	.05	.04	.02
117	*Alex Fernandez*	.25	.20	.10
118	Carlton Fisk	.10	.08	.04
119	Scott Fletcher	.05	.04	.02
120	*Craig Grebeck*	.08	.06	.03
121	Ozzie Guillen	.08	.06	.03
122	Greg Hibbard	.06	.05	.02
123	Lance Johnson	.06	.05	.02
124	Barry Jones	.05	.04	.02
125a	Ron Karkovice (two-line career summary)	.05	.04	.02
125b	Ron Karkovice (one-line career summary)	.04	.03	.02
126	Eric King	.05	.04	.02
127	Steve Lyons	.05	.04	.02
128	Carlos Martinez	.06	.05	.02
129	Jack McDowell	.06	.05	.02
130	Donn Pall	.05	.04	.02
131	Dan Pasqua	.05	.04	.02

132 Ken Patterson .05 .04 .02
133 Melido Perez .06 .05 .02
134 Adam Peterson .05 .04 .02
135 *Scott Radinsky* .08 .06 .03
136 Sammy Sosa .15 .11 .06
137 Bobby Thigpen .08 .06 .03
138 Frank Thomas 1.25 .90 .50
139 Robin Ventura .20 .15 .08
140 Daryl Boston .05 .04 .02
141 *Chuck Carr* .20 .15 .08
142 Mark Carreon .05 .04 .02
143 David Cone .06 .05 .02
144 Ron Darling .06 .05 .02
145 Kevin Elster .05 .04 .02
146 Sid Fernandez .06 .05 .02
147 John Franco .08 .06 .03
148 Dwight Gooden .10 .07 .04
149 Tom Herr .06 .05 .02
150 *Todd Hundley* .08 .06 .03
151 Gregg Jefferies .10 .08 .04
152 Howard Johnson .08 .06 .03
153 Dave Magadan .08 .06 .03
154 Kevin McReynolds .08 .06 .03
155 Keith Miller .06 .05 .02
156 Bob Ojeda .05 .04 .02
157 Tom O'Malley .05 .04 .02
158 Alejandro Pena .05 .04 .02
159 *Darren Reed* .08 .06 .03
160 Mackey Sasser .06 .05 .02
161 Darryl Strawberry .10 .08 .04
162 Tim Teufel .05 .04 .02
163 Kelvin Torve .08 .06 .03
164 Julio Valera .10 .08 .04
165 Frank Viola .12 .09 .05
166 Wally Whitehurst .05 .04 .02
167 Jim Acker .05 .04 .02
168 *Derek Bell* (FC) .35 .25 .14
169 George Bell .08 .06 .03
170 *Willie Blair* .08 .06 .03
171 Pat Borders .06 .05 .02
172 John Cerutti .05 .04 .02
173 Junior Felix .06 .05 .02
174 Tony Fernandez .08 .06 .03
175 Kelly Gruber .05 .04 .02
176 Tom Henke .06 .05 .02
177 Glenallen Hill .08 .06 .03
178 Jimmy Key .06 .05 .02
179 Manny Lee .05 .04 .02
180 Fred McGriff .20 .15 .08
181 Rance Mulliniks .05 .04 .02
182 Greg Myers .05 .04 .02
183 John Olerud .30 .25 .12
184 Luis Sojo .08 .06 .03
185 Dave Steib .08 .06 .03
186 Todd Stottlemyre .06 .05 .02
187 Duane Ward .05 .04 .02
188 David Wells .05 .04 .02
189 *Mark Whiten* .15 .11 .06
190 Ken Williams .05 .04 .02
191 Frank Wills .05 .04 .02
192 Mookie Wilson .05 .04 .02
193 Don Aase .05 .04 .02
194 Tim Belcher .08 .06 .03
195 Hubie Brooks .08 .06 .03
196 Dennis Cook .06 .05 .02
197 Tim Crews .05 .04 .02
198 Kal Daniels .06 .05 .02
199 Kirk Gibson .08 .06 .03
200 Jim Gott .05 .04 .02
201 Alfredo Griffin .05 .04 .02
202 Chris Gwynn .06 .05 .02
203 Dave Hansen .08 .06 .03
204 Lenny Harris .06 .05 .02
205 Mike Hartley .10 .08 .04
206 Mickey Hatcher .05 .04 .02
207 *Carlos Hernandez* (FC) .10 .08 .04
208 Orel Hershiser .10 .08 .04
209 Jay Howell .06 .05 .02
210 Mike Huff .10 .08 .04
211 Stan Javier .05 .04 .02
212 Ramon Martinez .08 .06 .03
213 Mike Morgan .05 .04 .02
214 Eddie Murray .08 .06 .03
215 *Jim Neidlinger* (FC) .08 .06 .03
216 Jose Offerman .10 .08 .04
217 *Jim Poole* (FC) .06 .05 .02
218 Juan Samuel .06 .05 .02
219 Mike Scioscia .06 .05 .02
220 Ray Searage .05 .04 .02
221 Mike Sharperson .06 .05 .02
222 Fernando Valenzuela .06 .05 .02
223 Jose Vizcaino .10 .08 .04
224 Mike Aldrete .05 .04 .02
225 *Scott Anderson* (FC) .10 .08 .04
226 Dennis Boyd .06 .05 .02
227 Tim Burke .06 .05 .02
228 Delino DeShields .15 .11 .06
229 Mike Fitzgerald .05 .04 .02
230 Tom Foley .05 .04 .02
231 Steve Frey .05 .04 .02
232 Andres Galarraga .08 .06 .03
233 Mark Gardner .10 .08 .04
234 Marquis Grissom (FC) .20 .15 .08
235 Kevin Gross .06 .05 .02
236 Drew Hall .05 .04 .02
237 Dave Martinez .06 .05 .02
238 Dennis Martinez .06 .05 .02
239 Dale Mohorcic .05 .04 .02
240 *Chris Nabholz* .08 .06 .03
241 Otis Nixon .05 .04 .02
242 Junior Noboa (FC) .08 .06 .03
243 Spike Owen .06 .05 .02
244 Tim Raines .08 .06 .03
245 *Mel Rojas* (FC) .12 .09 .05
246 *Scott Ruskin* (FC) .08 .06 .03
247 *Bill Sampen* .06 .05 .02
248 Nelson Santovenia .05 .04 .02
249 Dave Schmidt .05 .04 .02
250 Larry Walker .15 .11 .06
251 Tim Wallach .08 .06 .03
252 Dave Anderson .05 .04 .02
253 Kevin Bass .06 .05 .02
254 Steve Bedrosian .06 .05 .02
255 Jeff Brantley .08 .06 .03
256 John Burkett .08 .06 .03
257 Brett Butler .06 .05 .02
258 Gary Carter .08 .06 .03
259 Will Clark .25 .20 .10
260 *Steve Decker* (FC) .10 .08 .04
261 Kelly Downs .05 .04 .02
262 Scott Garrelts .06 .05 .02
263 Terry Kennedy .05 .04 .02
264 Mike LaCoss .05 .04 .02
265 *Mark Leonard* (FC) .10 .08 .04
266 Greg Litton .06 .05 .02
267 Kevin Mitchell .08 .06 .03
268 Randy O'Neal (FC) .05 .04 .02
269 *Rick Parker* .06 .05 .02
270 Rick Reuschel .06 .05 .02
271 Ernest Riles .05 .04 .02
272 Don Robinson .05 .04 .02
273 Robby Thompson .06 .05 .02
274 Mark Thurmond .05 .04 .02
275 Jose Uribe .05 .04 .02
276 Matt Williams .15 .11 .06
277 Trevor Wilson .06 .05 .02
278 *Gerald Alexander* (FC) .15 .11 .06
279 Brad Arnsberg .06 .05 .02
280 *Kevin Belcher* (FC) .15 .11 .06
281 *Joe Bitker* (FC) .08 .06 .03
282 Kevin Brown .06 .05 .02
283 Steve Buechele .05 .04 .02
284 Jack Daugherty .06 .05 .02
285 Julio Franco .10 .08 .04
286 Juan Gonzalez .70 .50 .30
287 *Bill Haselman* (FC) .15 .11 .06
288 Charlie Hough .05 .04 .02
289 Jeff Huson .06 .05 .02
290 Pete Incaviglia .06 .05 .02
291 Mike Jeffcoat .05 .04 .02
292 Jeff Kunkel .05 .04 .02
293 Gary Mielke .08 .06 .03
294 Jamie Moyer .05 .04 .02
295 Rafael Palmeiro .08 .06 .03
296 Geno Petralli .05 .04 .02
297 Gary Pettis .06 .05 .02
298 Kevin Reimer .10 .08 .04
299 Kenny Rogers .06 .05 .02
300 Jeff Russell .06 .05 .02
301 John Russell .05 .04 .02
302 Nolan Ryan .40 .30 .15
303 Ruben Sierra .12 .09 .05
304 Bobby Witt .08 .06 .03
305 Jim Abbott .08 .06 .03
306 Kent Anderson (FC) .06 .05 .02
307 Dante Bichette .06 .05 .02
308 Bert Blyleven .08 .06 .03
309 Chili Davis .06 .05 .02
310 Brian Downing .05 .04 .02
311 Mark Eichhorn .05 .04 .02
312 Mike Fetters .08 .06 .03
313 Chuck Finley .08 .06 .03
314 Willie Fraser .05 .04 .02
315 Bryan Harvey .06 .05 .02
316 Donnie Hill .05 .04 .02
317 Wally Joyner .10 .08 .04
318 Mark Langston .10 .08 .04
319 Kirk McCaskill .06 .05 .02
320 John Orton .06 .05 .02
321 Lance Parrish .08 .06 .03
322 Luis Polonia .05 .04 .02
323 Johnny Ray .05 .04 .02
324 Bobby Rose .06 .05 .02
325 Dick Schofield .05 .04 .02
326 Rick Schu .05 .04 .02
327a Lee Stevens (six-line career summary)
.10 .08 .04
327b Lee Stevens (seven-line career summary)
.10 .08 .04
328 Devon White .06 .05 .02
329 Dave Winfield .12 .09 .05
330 *Cliff Young* .15 .11 .06
331 Dave Bergman .05 .04 .02
332 *Phil Clark* (FC) .12 .09 .05
333 Darnell Coles .05 .04 .02
334 Milt Cuyler (FC) .08 .06 .03
335 Cecil Fielder .15 .11 .06
336 *Travis Fryman* .50 .40 .20
337 Paul Gibson .05 .04 .02
338 Jerry Don Gleaton .05 .04 .02
339 Mike Heath .05 .04 .02
340 Mike Henneman .06 .05 .02
341 Chet Lemon .06 .05 .02
342 Lance McCullers .05 .04 .02
343 Jack Morris .08 .06 .03
344 lloyd Moseby .06 .05 .02
345 Edwin Nunez .05 .04 .02
346 Clay Parker .05 .04 .02
347 Dan Petry .05 .04 .02
348 Tony Phillips .06 .05 .02
349 Jeff Robinson .06 .05 .02
350 Mark Salas .05 .04 .02
351 *Mike Schwabe* .06 .05 .02
352 Larry Sheets .05 .04 .02
353 John Shelby .05 .04 .02
354 Frank Tanana .06 .05 .02
355 Alan Trammell .08 .06 .03
356 Gary Ward .05 .04 .02
357 Lou Whitaker .08 .06 .03
358 Beau Allred .06 .05 .02
359 Sandy Alomar,Jr. .08 .06 .03
360 *Carlos Baerga* .25 .20 .10
361 *Kevin Bearse* .06 .05 .02
362 Tom Brookens .05 .04 .02
363 Jerry Browne .06 .05 .02
364 Tom Candiotti .05 .04 .02
365 Alex Cole .06 .05 .02
366 John Farrell .05 .04 .02
367 Felix Fermin .05 .04 .02
368 Keith Hernandez .08 .06 .03
369 Brook Jacoby .08 .06 .03
370 Chris James .06 .05 .02
371 Dion James .05 .04 .02
372 Doug Jones .08 .06 .03
373 Candy Maldonado .08 .06 .03
374 Steve Olin .06 .05 .02
375 Jesse Orosco .05 .04 .02
376 Rudy Seanez .06 .05 .02
377 Joel Skinner .05 .04 .02
378 Cory Snyder .08 .06 .03
379 Greg Swindell .06 .05 .02
380 Sergio Valdez (FC) .08 .06 .03
381 *Mike Walker* (FC) .06 .05 .02
382 *Colby Ward* (FC) .06 .05 .02
383 *Turner Ward* .15 .11 .06
384 Mitch Webster .05 .04 .02
385 Kevin Wickander (FC) .06 .05 .02
386 Darrel Akerfelds .06 .05 .02
387 Joe Boever .05 .04 .02
388a Rod Booker (no 1981 stats) .05 .04 .02
388b Rod Booker (1981 stats included) .10 .08 .04
389 Sil Campusano .05 .04 .02
390 Don Carman .05 .04 .02
391 *Wes Chamberlain* (FC) .20 .15 .08
392 Pat Combs .06 .05 .02
393 Darren Daulton .06 .05 .02
394 Jose DeJesus .06 .05 .02
395 Len Dykstra .10 .08 .04
396 Jason Grimsley .06 .05 .02
397 Charlie Hayes .08 .06 .03
398 Von Hayes .08 .06 .03
399 *Dave Hollins* .25 .20 .10
400 Ken Howell .06 .05 .02
401 Ricky Jordan .10 .08 .04
402 John Kruk .06 .05 .02
403 Steve Lake .05 .04 .02
404 *Chuck Malone* (FC) .08 .06 .03
405 Roger McDowell .08 .06 .03
406 Chuck McElroy .08 .06 .03
407 *Mickey Morandini* (FC) .08 .06 .03
408 Terry Mulholland .06 .05 .02
409 Dale Murphy .10 .08 .04
410 Randy Ready .05 .04 .02
411 Bruce Ruffin .05 .04 .02
412 Dickie Thon .05 .04 .02
413 Paul Assenmacher .05 .04 .02
414 Damon Berryhill .06 .05 .02
415 Mike Bielecki .06 .05 .02
416 *Shawn Boskie* .08 .06 .03
417 Dave Clark .05 .04 .02
418 Doug Dascenzo .05 .04 .02
419a Andre Dawson (no 1976 stats) .10 .08 .04
419b Andre Dawson (1976 stats included)
.10 .08 .04
420 Shawon Dunston .10 .08 .04
421 Joe Girardi .06 .05 .02
422 Mark Grace .10 .08 .04
423 Mike Harkey .08 .06 .03
424 Les Lancaster .05 .04 .02
425 Bill Long .05 .04 .02
426 Greg Maddux .15 .11 .06
427 Derrick May .20 .15 .08
428 Jeff Pico .05 .04 .02
429 Domingo Ramos .05 .04 .02
430 Luis Salazar .05 .04 .02
431 Ryne Sandberg .20 .15 .08
432 Dwight Smith .06 .05 .02
433 Greg Smith .08 .06 .03
434 Rick Sutcliffe .08 .06 .03
435 Gary Varsho .05 .04 .02
436 *Hector Villanueva* .08 .06 .03
437 Jerome Walton .08 .06 .03
438 Curtis Wilkerson .05 .04 .02
439 Mitch Williams .08 .06 .03
440 Steve Wilson .06 .05 .02
441 Marvell Wynne .05 .04 .02
442 Scott Bankhead .06 .05 .02
443 Scott Bradley .05 .04 .02
444 Greg Briley .06 .05 .02
445 Mike Brumley .05 .04 .02
446 Jay Buhner .06 .05 .02
447 *Dave Burba* (FC) .10 .08 .04
448 Henry Cotto .05 .04 .02
449 Alvin Davis .08 .06 .03
450 Ken Griffey, Jr. 1.00 .75 .40
451 Erik Hanson .12 .09 .05
452 Gene Harris .05 .04 .02
453 Brian Holman .06 .05 .02
454 Mike Jackson .06 .05 .02
455 Randy Johnson .10 .08 .04
456 Jeffrey Leonard .06 .05 .02
457 Edgar Martinez .06 .05 .02
458 Tino Martinez .10 .08 .04
459 Pete O'Brien .05 .04 .02
460 Harold Reynolds .08 .06 .03
461 Mike Schooler .08 .06 .03
462 Bill Swift .06 .05 .02
463 David Valle .05 .04 .02
464 Omar Vizquel .06 .05 .02
465 Matt Young .06 .05 .02
466 Brady Anderson .05 .04 .02
467 Jeff Ballard .06 .05 .02
468 Juan Bell (FC) .08 .06 .03
469a Mike Devereaux ("six" last word in career summary top line) .06 .05 .02
469b Mike Devereaux ("runs" last word in career summary top line) .06 .05 .02
470 Steve Finley .06 .05 .02
471 Dave Gallagher .05 .04 .02
472 *Leo Gomez* (FC) .10 .08 .04
473 Rene Gonzales .05 .04 .02
474 Pete Harnisch .06 .05 .02
475 Kevin Hickey .05 .04 .02
476 *Chris Hoiles* .10 .08 .04

477	Sam Horn	.06	.05	.02
478	Tim Hulett	.05	.04	.02
479	Dave Johnson	.05	.04	.02
480	Ron Kittle	.08	.06	.03
481	Ben McDonald	.10	.08	.04
482	Bob Melvin	.05	.04	.02
483	Bob Milacki	.06	.05	.02
484	Randy Milligan	.06	.05	.02
485	*John Mitchell* (FC)	.06	.05	.02
486	Gregg Olson	.08	.06	.03
487	Joe Orsulak	.05	.04	.02
488	Joe Price	.05	.04	.02
489	Bill Ripken	.05	.04	.02
490	Cal Ripken, Jr.	.20	.15	.08
491	Curt Schilling	.06	.05	.02
492	*David Segui*	.06	.05	.02
493	*Anthony Telford* (FC)	.06	.05	.02
494	Mickey Tettleton	.06	.05	.02
495	Mark Williamson	.05	.04	.02
496	Craig Worthington	.06	.05	.02
497	Juan Agosto	.05	.04	.02
498	Eric Anthony	.08	.06	.03
499	Craig Biggio	.08	.06	.03
500	Ken Caminiti	.06	.05	.02
501	Casey Candaele	.05	.04	.02
502	*Andujar Cedeno*	.30	.25	.12
503	Danny Darwin	.06	.05	.02
504	Mark Davidson	.05	.04	.02
505	Glenn Davis	.05	.04	.02
506	Jim Deshaies	.06	.05	.02
507	*Luis Gonzalez*	.35	.25	.14
508	Bill Gullickson	.05	.04	.02
509	Xavier Hernandez (FC)	.08	.06	.03
510	Brian Meyer	.06	.05	.02
511	Ken Oberkfell	.05	.04	.02
512	Mark Portugal	.05	.04	.02
513	Rafael Ramirez	.05	.04	.02
514	*Karl Rhodes* (FC)	.08	.06	.03
515	Mike Scott	.08	.06	.03
516	*Mike Simms*	.10	.08	.04
517	Dave Smith	.06	.05	.02
518	Franklin Stubbs	.06	.05	.02
519	Glenn Wilson	.06	.05	.02
520	Eric Yelding	.10	.08	.04
521	Gerald Young	.05	.04	.02
522	Shawn Abner	.05	.04	.02
523	Roberto Alomar	.15	.11	.06
524	Andy Benes	.10	.08	.04
525	Joe Carter	.10	.08	.04
526	Jack Clark	.08	.06	.03
527	Joey Cora	.06	.05	.02
528	*Paul Faries* (FC)	.06	.05	.02
529	Tony Gwynn	.15	.11	.06
530	Atlee Hammaker	.05	.04	.02
531	Greg Harris	.06	.05	.02
532	*Thomas Howard*	.06	.05	.02
533	Bruce Hurst	.06	.05	.02
534	Craig Lefferts	.06	.05	.02
535	Derek Lilliquist	.06	.05	.02
536	Fred Lynn	.06	.05	.02
537	Mike Pagliarulo	.06	.05	.02
538	Mark Parent	.05	.04	.02
539	Dennis Rasmussen	.05	.04	.02
540	Bip Roberts	.08	.06	.03
541	*Richard Rodriguez* (FC)	.06	.05	.02
542	Benito Santiago	.10	.08	.04
543	Calvin Schiraldi	.05	.04	.02
544	Eric Show	.06	.05	.02
545	Phil Stephenson	.05	.04	.02
546	Garry Templeton	.06	.05	.02
547	Ed Whitson	.06	.05	.02
548	Eddie Williams	.05	.04	.02
549	Kevin Appier	.10	.08	.04
550	Luis Aquino	.05	.04	.02
551	Bob Boone	.08	.06	.03
552	George Brett	.15	.11	.06
553	*Jeff Conine*	.30	.25	.12
554	Steve Crawford	.05	.04	.02
555	Mark Davis	.06	.05	.02
556	Storm Davis	.06	.05	.02
557	Jim Eisenreich	.06	.05	.02
558	Steve Farr	.05	.04	.02
559	Tom Gordon	.10	.08	.04
560	Mark Gubicza	.08	.06	.03
561	Bo Jackson	.20	.15	.08
562	Mike Macfarlane	.05	.04	.02
563	*Brian McRae* (FC)	.25	.20	.10
564	Jeff Montgomery	.06	.05	.02
565	Bill Pecota	.05	.04	.02
566	Gerald Perry	.06	.05	.02
567	Bret Saberhagen	.10	.08	.04
568	*Jeff Schulz* (FC)	.08	.06	.03
569	Kevin Seitzer	.08	.06	.03
570	*Terry Shumpert*	.06	.05	.02
571	Kurt Stillwell	.06	.05	.02
572	Danny Tartabull	.08	.06	.03
573	Gary Thurman	.05	.04	.02
574	Frank White	.06	.05	.02
575	Willie Wilson	.06	.05	.02
576	Chris Bosio	.06	.05	.02
577	Greg Brock	.06	.05	.02
578	George Canale	.06	.05	.02
579	Chuck Crim	.05	.04	.02
580	Rob Deer	.06	.05	.02
581	*Edgar Diaz*	.06	.05	.02
582	*Tom Edens* (FC)	.08	.06	.03
583	Mike Felder	.05	.04	.02
584	Jim Gantner	.06	.05	.02
585	Darryl Hamilton	.06	.05	.02
586	Ted Higuera	.08	.06	.03
587	Mark Knudson	.05	.04	.02
588	Bill Krueger	.05	.04	.02
589	Tim McIntosh	.08	.06	.03
590	Paul Mirabella	.05	.04	.02
591	Paul Molitor	.10	.08	.04
592	Jaime Navarro	.08	.06	.03
593	Dave Parker	.12	.09	.05
594	Dan Plesac	.06	.05	.02
595	Ron Robinson	.06	.05	.02
596	Gary Sheffield	.15	.11	.06
597	Bill Spiers	.06	.05	.02
598	B.J. Surhoff	.06	.05	.02
599	Greg Vaughn	.12	.09	.05
600	Randy Veres	.05	.04	.02
601	Robin Yount	.15	.11	.06
602a	Rick Aguilera (five-line career summary)	.06	.05	.02
602b	Rick Aguilera (four-line career summary)	.06	.05	.02
603	Allan Anderson	.05	.04	.02
604	Juan Berenguer	.05	.04	.02
605	Randy Bush	.05	.04	.02
606	Carmen Castillo	.05	.04	.02
607	Tim Drummond	.06	.05	.02
608	*Scott Erickson*	.08	.06	.03
609	Gary Gaetti	.08	.06	.03
610	Greg Gagne	.06	.05	.02
611	Dan Gladden	.06	.05	.02
612	Mark Guthrie (FC)	.06	.05	.02
613	Brian Harper	.06	.05	.02
614	Kent Hrbek	.08	.06	.03
615	Gene Larkin	.06	.05	.02
616	Terry Leach	.05	.04	.02
617	Nelson Liriano	.05	.04	.02
618	Shane Mack	.06	.05	.02
619	John Moses	.05	.04	.02
620	*Pedro Munoz*	.10	.08	.04
621	Al Newman	.05	.04	.02
622	Junior Ortiz	.05	.04	.02
623	Kirby Puckett	.15	.11	.06
624	Roy Smith	.05	.04	.02
625	Kevin Tapani	.10	.08	.04
626	Gary Wayne	.05	.04	.02
627	David West	.06	.05	.02
628	Cris Carpenter	.06	.05	.02
629	Vince Coleman	.08	.06	.03
630	Ken Dayley	.06	.05	.02
631	Jose DeLeon	.06	.05	.02
632	Frank DiPino	.05	.04	.02
633	*Bernard Gilkey*	.25	.20	.10
634	Pedro Guerrero	.08	.06	.03
635	Ken Hill	.06	.05	.02
636	Felix Jose	.08	.06	.03
637	*Ray Lankford*	.25	.20	.10
638	Joe Magrane	.08	.06	.03
639	Tom Niedenfuer	.05	.04	.02
640	Jose Oquendo	.05	.04	.02
641	Tom Pagnozzi	.05	.04	.02
642	Terry Pendleton	.06	.05	.02
643	*Mike Perez* (FC)	.12	.09	.05
644	Bryn Smith	.05	.04	.02
645	Lee Smith	.08	.06	.03
646	Ozzie Smith	.10	.08	.04
647	Scott Terry	.05	.04	.02
648	Bob Tewksbury	.05	.04	.02
649	Milt Thompson	.05	.04	.02
650	John Tudor	.06	.05	.02
651	Denny Walling	.05	.04	.02
652	*Craig Wilson* (FC)	.06	.05	.02
653	Todd Worrell	.06	.05	.02
654	Todd Zeile	.08	.06	.03
655	*Oscar Azocar*	.06	.05	.02
656	Steve Balboni	.05	.04	.02
657	Jesse Barfield	.08	.06	.03
658	Greg Cadaret	.05	.04	.02
659	Chuck Cary	.05	.04	.02
660	Rick Cerone	.05	.04	.02
661	Dave Eiland (FC)	.06	.05	.02
662a	Alvaro Espinoza (no 1979-80 stats)	.06	.05	.02
662b	Alvaro Espinoza (1979-80 stats included)	.06	.05	.02
663	Bob Geren	.06	.05	.02
664	Lee Guetterman	.05	.04	.02
665	Mel Hall	.06	.05	.02
666a	Andy Hawkins (no 1978 stats)	.06	.05	.02
666b	Andy Hawkins (1978 stats included)	.06	.05	.02
667	Jimmy Jones	.05	.04	.02
668	Roberto Kelly	.10	.08	.04
669	Dave LaPoint	.05	.04	.02
670	Tim Leary	.06	.05	.02
671	*Jim Leyritz*	.06	.05	.02
672	Kevin Maas	.06	.05	.02
673	Don Mattingly	.20	.15	.08
674	Matt Nokes	.06	.05	.02
675	Pascual Perez	.06	.05	.02
676	Eric Plunk	.05	.04	.02
677	Dave Righetti	.08	.06	.03
678	Jeff Robinson	.05	.04	.02
679	Steve Sax	.10	.08	.04
680	Mike Witt	.06	.05	.02
681	Steve Avery	.20	.15	.08
682	Mike Bell	.10	.08	.04
683	Jeff Blauser	.06	.05	.02
684	Francisco Cabrera	.10	.08	.04
685	Tony Castillo (FC)	.08	.06	.03
686	Marty Clary	.05	.04	.02
687	Nick Esasky	.08	.06	.03
688	Ron Gant	.10	.07	.04
689	Tom Glavine	.15	.11	.06
690	Mark Grant	.05	.04	.02
691	Tommy Gregg	.06	.05	.02
692	Dwayne Henry	.05	.04	.02
693	Dave Justice	.40	.30	.15
694	*Jimmy Kremers*	.08	.06	.03
695	Charlie Leibrandt	.06	.05	.02
696	Mark Lemke	.06	.05	.02
697	Oddibe McDowell	.06	.05	.02
698	*Greg Olson*	.08	.06	.03
699	Jeff Parrett	.06	.05	.02
700	Jim Presley	.06	.05	.02
701	*Victor Rosario* (FC)	.05	.04	.02
702	Lonnie Smith	.06	.05	.02
703	Pete Smith	.06	.05	.02
704	John Smoltz	.08	.06	.03
705	Mike Stanton	.08	.06	.03
706	Andres Thomas	.05	.04	.02
707	Jeff Treadway	.06	.05	.02
708	*Jim Vatcher* (FC)	.05	.04	.02
709	Home Run Kings (Ryne Sandberg, Cecil Fielder)	.15	.11	.06
710	Second Generation Superstars (Barry Bonds, Ken Griffey, Jr.)	.50	.40	.20
711	NLCS Team Leaders (Bobby Bonilla, Barry Larkin)	.15	.11	.06
712	Top Game Savers (Bobby Thigpen, John Franco)	.10	.08	.04
713	Chicago's 100 Club (Andre Dawson, Ryne Sandberg)	.15	.11	.06
714	Checklists (Athletics, Pirates, Reds, Red Sox)	.05	.04	.02
715	Checklists (White Sox, Mets Blue Jays, Dodgers)	.05	.04	.02
716	Checklists (Expos, Giants, Rangers, Angels)	.05	.04	.02
717	Checklists (Tigers, Indians, Phillies, Cubs)	.05	.04	.02
718	Checklists (Mariners, Orioles, Astros, Padres)	.05	.04	.02
719	Checklists (Royals, Brewers, Twins, Cardinals)	.05	.04	.02
720	Checklists (Yankees, Braves, Super Stars)	.05	.04	.02

A player's name in italic type indicates a rookie card. An (FC) indicates a player's first card for that particular card company.

1991 Fleer All Stars

Three player photos are featured on each card in this special insert set. An action shot and portrait close-up are featured on the front, while a full-figure pose is showcased on the back. The cards are horizontal and were inserted into 1991 Fleer cello packs.

		MT	NR MT	EX
Complete Set (10):		18.00	13.50	7.25
Common Player:		.60	.45	.25
1	Ryne Sandberg	2.50	2.00	1.00
2	Barry Larkin	.60	.45	.25
3	Matt Williams	.60	.45	.25
4	Cecil Fielder	1.50	1.00	.50
5	Barry Bonds	2.50	2.00	1.00
6	Rickey Henderson	1.00	.75	.40
7	Ken Griffey, Jr.	6.00	4.00	2.00
8	Jose Canseco	1.00	.75	.40
9	Benito Santiago	.60	.45	.25
10	Roger Clemens	1.50	1.00	.50

1991 Fleer ProVisions

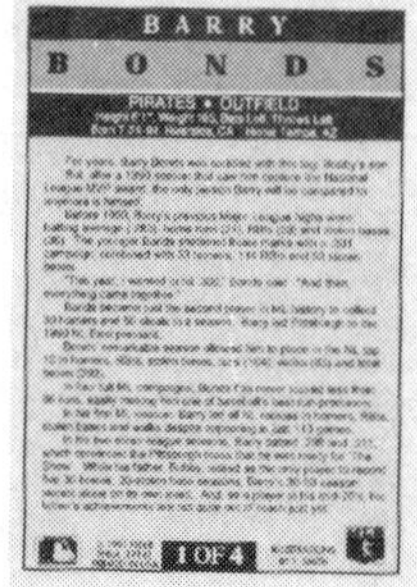

The illustrations of artist Terry Smith are showcased in this special set. Twelve fantasy portraits were produced for cards inserted into rack packs. Four other ProVision cards were inserted into factory sets. The rack pack cards feature black borders, while the factory set cards have white borders. Information on the card backs supports the manner in which Smith painted each player. Factory insert ProVisions are indicated by an "F" suffix in the checklist here.

		MT	NR MT	EX
Complete Set (12):		4.00	3.00	1.50
Common Player:		.15	.10	.05
Complete Factory Set (4):		3.00	2.25	1.25
Common Player:		.40	.30	.15
1	Kirby Puckett	.40	.30	.15
2	Will Clark	.60	.45	.25
3	Ruben Sierra	.20	.15	.08
4	Mark McGwire	.20	.15	.08
5	Bo Jackson	.50	.40	.20
6	Jose Canseco	.50	.40	.20
7	Dwight Gooden	.25	.20	.10
8	Mike Greenwell	.25	.20	.10
9	Roger Clemens	.40	.30	.15
10	Eric Davis	.25	.20	.10
11	Don Mattingly	.75	.60	.30
12	Darryl Strawberry	.25	.20	.10
1F	Barry Bonds	1.00	.75	.40
2F	Rickey Henderson	.50	.40	.20
3F	Ryne Sandberg	1.00	.70	.40
4F	Dave Stewart	.40	.30	.15

1991 Fleer World Series

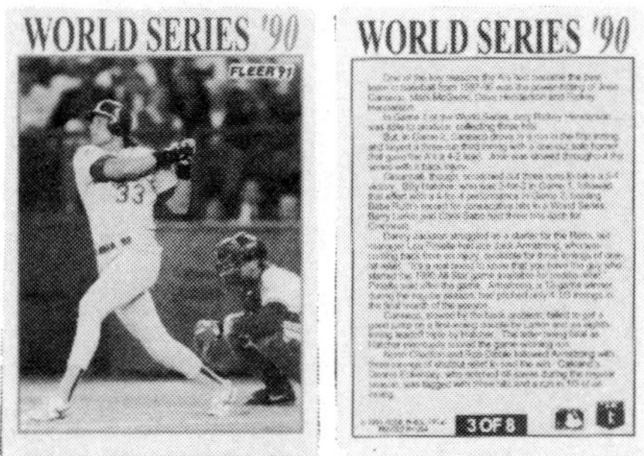

Once again Fleer released a set in honor of the World Series from the previous season. The 1991 issue features only eight cards compared to twelve in 1990. The cards feature white borders surrounding full-color action shots from the 1990 Fall Classic. The card backs feature an overview of the World Series action.

		MT	NR MT	EX
Complete Set (8):		1.50	1.00	.50
Common Player:		.20	.15	.08
1	Eric Davis	.25	.20	.10
2	Billy Hatcher	.20	.15	.08
3	Jose Canseco	.35	.25	.14
4	Rickey Henderson	.35	.25	.14
5	Chris Sabo/Carney Lansford	.20	.15	.08
6	Dave Stewart	.25	.20	.10
7	Jose Rijo	.25	.20	.10
8	Reds Celebrate	.20	.15	.08

1991 Fleer Box Panels

Unlike past box panel sets, the 1991 Fleer box panels feature a theme; 1990 no-hitters are celebrated on the three different boxes. The cards feature blank backs and are numbered in order of no-hitter on the front. A team logo was included on each box. The card fronts are styled after the 1991 Fleer cards. A special no-hitter logo appears in the lower left corner.

		MT	NR MT	EX
Complete Set (10):		1.50	1.25	.60
Common Player:		.10	.08	.04
1	Mark Langston/Mike Witt	.10	.08	.04
2	Randy Johnson	.10	.08	.04
3	Nolan Ryan	.80	.60	.30
4	Dave Stewart	.15	.11	.06
5	Fernando Valenzuela	.10	.08	.04
6	Andy Hawkins	.10	.08	.04
7	Melido Perez	.10	.08	.04
8	Terry Mulholland	.10	.08	.04
9	Dave Steib	.10	.08	.04
----	Team Logos	.05	.04	.02

1991 Fleer Update

Fleer produced its eighth consecutive "Update" set in 1991 to supplement the company's regular set. As in the past, the set consists of 132 cards that were sold by hobby dealers in special collectors boxes. The cards are designed in the same style as the regular Fleer issue.

		MT	NR MT	EX
Complete Set (132):		6.00	4.50	2.50
Common Player:		.06	.05	.02
1	Glenn Davis	.06	.05	.02
2	Dwight Evans	.08	.06	.03
3	Jose Mesa (FC)	.08	.06	.03
4	Jack Clark	.12	.09	.05
5	Danny Darwin	.06	.05	.02
6	Steve Lyons	.06	.05	.02
7	Mo Vaughn (FC)	.35	.25	.14
8	Floyd Bannister	.06	.05	.02
9	Gary Gaetti	.08	.06	.03
10	Dave Parker	.35	.25	.14
11	Joey Cora	.06	.05	.02
12	Charlie Hough	.06	.05	.02
13	Matt Merullo	.08	.06	.03
14	Warren Newson (FC)	.10	.08	.04
15	Tim Raines	.15	.11	.06
16	Albert Belle	.30	.25	.12
17	Glenallen Hill	.08	.06	.03
18	Shawn Hillegas	.06	.05	.02
19	Mark Lewis (FC)	.15	.11	.06
20	Charles Nagy (FC)	.25	.20	.10
21	Mark Whiten	.20	.15	.08
22	John Cerutti	.06	.05	.02
23	Rob Deer	.06	.05	.02
24	Mickey Tettleton	.08	.06	.03
25	Warren Cromartie	.06	.05	.02
26	Kirk Gibson	.08	.06	.03
27	David Howard (FC)	.15	.11	.06
28	Brent Mayne (FC)	.25	.20	.10
29	Dante Bichette	.06	.05	.02
30	Mark Lee (FC)	.08	.06	.03
31	Julio Machado	.06	.05	.02
32	Edwin Nunez	.06	.05	.02
33	Willie Randolph	.08	.06	.03
34	Franklin Stubbs	.06	.05	.02
35	Bill Wegman	.06	.05	.02
36	Chili Davis	.08	.06	.03
37	Chuck Knoblauch (FC)	.50	.40	.20
38	Scott Leius	.15	.11	.06
39	Jack Morris	.10	.08	.04
40	Mike Pagliarulo	.06	.05	.02
41	Lenny Webster (FC)	.06	.05	.02
42	John Habyan (FC)	.12	.09	.05
43	Steve Howe	.08	.06	.03
44	Jeff Johnson (FC)	.10	.08	.04
45	Scott Kamieniecki (FC)	.10	.08	.04
46	Pat Kelly (FC)	.25	.20	.10
47	Hensley Meulens	.12	.09	.05
48	Wade Taylor (FC)	.20	.15	.08
49	Bernie Williams (FC)	.20	.15	.08
50	Kirk Dressendorfer (FC)	.20	.15	.08
51	Ernest Riles	.06	.05	.02
52	Rich DeLucia (FC)	.08	.06	.03
53	Tracy Jones	.06	.05	.02
54	Bill Krueger	.06	.05	.02
55	Alonzo Powell (FC)	.06	.05	.02
56	Jeff Schaefer	.06	.05	.02
57	Russ Swan (FC)	.06	.05	.02
58	John Barfield (FC)	.06	.05	.02
59	Rich Gossage	.08	.06	.03
60	Jose Guzman	.06	.05	.02
61	Dean Palmer (FC)	.40	.30	.15
62	Ivan Rodriguez (FC)	1.00	.70	.40
63	Roberto Alomar	.25	.20	.10
64	Tom Candiotti	.06	.05	.02
65	Joe Carter	.15	.11	.06
66	Ed Sprague (FC)	.20	.15	.08
67	Pat Tabler	.06	.05	.02
68	Mike Timlin (FC)	.20	.15	.08
69	Devon White	.08	.06	.03
70	Rafael Belliard	.06	.05	.02
71	Juan Berenguer	.06	.05	.02
72	Sid Bream	.08	.06	.03
73	Marvin Freeman	.06	.05	.02
74	Kent Mercker	.08	.06	.03
75	Otis Nixon	.06	.05	.02
76	Terry Pendleton	.08	.06	.03
77	George Bell	.10	.08	.04
78	Danny Jackson	.06	.05	.02
79	Chuck McElroy	.06	.05	.02
80	Gary Scott (FC)	.06	.05	.02
81	Heathcliff Slocumb (FC)	.15	.11	.06
82	Dave Smith	.06	.05	.02
83	Rick Wilkins (FC)	.30	.25	.12
84	Freddie Benavides (FC)	.20	.15	.08
85	Ted Power	.06	.05	.02
86	Mo Sanford (FC)	.30	.25	.12
87	Jeff Bagwell (FC)	1.50	1.25	.60
88	Steve Finley	.08	.06	.03
89	Pete Harnisch	.08	.06	.03
90	Darryl Kile (FC)	.20	.15	.08
91	Brett Butler	.08	.06	.03
92	John Candelaria	.06	.05	.02
93	Gary Carter	.08	.06	.03
94	Kevin Gross	.06	.05	.02
95	Bob Ojeda	.06	.05	.02
96	Darryl Strawberry	.30	.25	.12
97	Ivan Calderon	.08	.06	.03
98	Ron Hassey	.06	.05	.02
99	Gilberto Reyes	.08	.06	.03
100	Hubie Brooks	.08	.06	.03
101	Rick Cerone	.06	.05	.02
102	Vince Coleman	.08	.06	.03
103	Jeff Innis	.08	.06	.03
104	Pete Schourek (FC)	.20	.15	.08
105	Andy Ashby (FC)	.12	.09	.05
106	Wally Backman	.06	.05	.02
107	Darrin Fletcher (FC)	.12	.09	.05
108	Tommy Greene	.08	.06	.03
109	John Morris	.06	.05	.02
110	Mitch Williams	.08	.06	.03
111	Lloyd McClendon	.06	.05	.02
112	Orlando Merced (FC)	.40	.30	.15
113	Vicente Palacios	.06	.05	.02
114	Gary Varsho	.06	.05	.02
115	John Wehner (FC)	.15	.11	.06
116	Rex Hudler	.06	.05	.02
117	Tim Jones	.06	.05	.02
118	Geronimo Pena (FC)	.15	.11	.06
119	Gerald Perry	.06	.05	.02
120	Larry Andersen	.06	.05	.02
121	Jerald Clark	.06	.05	.02
122	Scott Coolbaugh	.08	.06	.03
123	Tony Fernandez	.08	.06	.03
124	Darrin Jackson	.06	.05	.02
125	Fred McGriff	.15	.11	.06
126	Jose Mota (FC)	.06	.05	.02
127	Tim Teufel	.06	.05	.02
128	Bud Black	.06	.05	.02
129	Mike Felder	.06	.05	.02
130	Willie McGee	.08	.06	.03
131	Dave Righetti	.08	.06	.03
132	Checklist	.06	.05	.02

1991 Fleer Ultra

This 400-card set was originally going to be called the Elite set, but Fleer chose to use the Ultra label. The card fronts feature gray borders surrounding full-color action photos. The backs feature three player photos and statistics. Hot Prospects and Great Performers are among the special cards featured within the set. This set is the premier release for Fleer Ultra.

		MT	NR MT	EX
Complete Set (400):		30.00	22.00	12.00
Common Player:		.06	.05	.02
1	Steve Avery	.90	.70	.35
2	Jeff Blauser	.06	.05	.02
3	Francisco Cabrera	.08	.06	.03
4	Ron Gant	.25	.20	.10
5	Tom Glavine	.50	.40	.20
6	Tommy Gregg	.06	.05	.02
7	Dave Justice	1.25	.90	.50
8	Oddibe McDowell	.06	.05	.02
9	Greg Olson	.08	.06	.03
10	Terry Pendleton	.15	.11	.06
11	Lonnie Smith	.06	.05	.02
12	John Smoltz	.15	.11	.06
13	Jeff Treadway	.06	.05	.02
14	Glenn Davis	.10	.08	.04
15	Mike Devereaux	.08	.06	.03
16	Leo Gomez	.15	.11	.06
17	Chris Hoiles	.35	.25	.14
18	Dave Johnson	.06	.05	.02
19	Ben McDonald	.35	.25	.14
20	Randy Milligan	.08	.06	.03
21	Gregg Olson	.10	.08	.04
22	Joe Orsulak	.06	.05	.02
23	Bill Ripken	.06	.05	.02

24	Cal Ripken, Jr.	.60	.45	.25
25	David Segui	.15	.11	.06
26	Craig Worthington	.08	.06	.03
27	Wade Boggs	.25	.20	.10
28	Tom Bolton	.06	.05	.02
29	Tom Brunansky	.08	.06	.03
30	Ellis Burks	.12	.09	.05
31	Roger Clemens	.50	.40	.20
32	Mike Greenwell	.15	.11	.06
33	Greg Harris	.06	.05	.02
34	Daryl Irvine	.15	.11	.06
35	Mike Marshall	.06	.05	.02
36	Tim Naehring	.15	.11	.06
37	Tony Pena	.06	.05	.02
38	Phil Plantier	1.00	.75	.40
39	Carlos Quintana	.08	.06	.03
40	Jeff Reardon	.08	.06	.03
41	Jody Reed	.06	.05	.02
42	Luis Rivera	.06	.05	.02
43	Jim Abbott	.20	.15	.08
44	Chuck Finley	.15	.11	.06
45	Bryan Harvey	.08	.06	.03
46	Donnie Hill	.06	.05	.02
47	Jack Howell	.06	.05	.02
48	Wally Joyner	.15	.11	.06
49	Mark Langston	.12	.09	.05
50	Kirk McCaskill	.06	.05	.02
51	Lance Parrish	.08	.06	.03
52	Dick Schofield	.06	.05	.02
53	Lee Stevens	.15	.11	.06
54	Dave Winfield	.35	.25	.14
55	George Bell	.12	.09	.05
56	Damon Berryhill	.06	.05	.02
57	Mike Bielecki	.06	.05	.02
58	Andre Dawson	.20	.15	.08
59	Shawon Dunston	.10	.08	.04
60	Joe Girardi	.06	.05	.02
61	Mark Grace	.15	.11	.06
62	Mike Harkey	.08	.06	.03
63	Les Lancaster	.06	.05	.02
64	Greg Maddux	.30	.25	.12
65	Derrick May	.40	.30	.15
66	Ryne Sandberg	.60	.45	.25
67	Luis Salazar	.06	.05	.02
68	Dwight Smith	.06	.05	.02
69	Hector Villanueva	.08	.06	.03
70	Jerome Walton	.12	.09	.05
71	Mitch Williams	.08	.06	.03
72	Carlton Fisk	.20	.15	.08
73	Scott Fletcher	.06	.05	.02
74	Ozzie Guillen	.10	.08	.04
75	Greg Hibbard	.08	.06	.03
76	Lance Johnson	.06	.05	.02
77	Steve Lyons	.06	.05	.02
78	Jack McDowell	.12	.09	.05
79	Dan Pasqua	.06	.05	.02
80	Melido Perez	.06	.05	.02
81	Tim Raines	.10	.08	.04
82	Sammy Sosa	.60	.45	.25
83	Cory Snyder	.06	.05	.02
84	Bobby Thigpen	.08	.06	.03
85	Frank Thomas	6.00	4.50	2.50
86	Robin Ventura	.80	.60	.30
87	Todd Benzinger	.06	.05	.02
88	Glenn Braggs	.06	.05	.02
89	Tom Browning	.08	.06	.03
90	Norm Charlton	.08	.06	.03
91	Eric Davis	.15	.11	.06
92	Rob Dibble	.10	.08	.04
93	Bill Doran	.08	.06	.03
94	Mariano Duncan	.06	.05	.02
95	Billy Hatcher	.06	.05	.02
96	Barry Larkin	.15	.11	.06
97	Randy Myers	.08	.06	.03
98	Hal Morris	.20	.15	.08
99	Joe Oliver	.06	.05	.02
100	Paul O'Neill	.08	.06	.03
101	Jeff Reed	.06	.05	.02
102	Jose Rijo	.08	.06	.03
103	Chris Sabo	.10	.08	.04
104	Beau Allred	.06	.05	.02
105	Sandy Alomar,Jr.	.10	.08	.04
106	Carlos Baerga	1.25	.90	.50
107	Albert Belle	1.25	.90	.50
108	Jerry Browne	.06	.05	.02
109	Tom Candiotti	.06	.05	.02
110	Alex Cole	.06	.05	.02
111	John Farrell	.06	.05	.02
112	Felix Fermin	.06	.05	.02
113	Brook Jacoby	.06	.05	.02
114	Chris James	.06	.05	.02
115	Doug Jones	.06	.05	.02
116	Steve Olin	.06	.05	.02
117	Greg Swindell	.08	.06	.03
118	Turner Ward	.20	.15	.08
119	Mitch Webster	.06	.05	.02
120	Dave Bergman	.06	.05	.02
121	Cecil Fielder	.40	.30	.15
122	Travis Fryman	2.50	2.00	1.00
123	Mike Henneman	.08	.06	.03
124	Lloyd Moseby	.06	.05	.02
125	Dan Petry	.06	.05	.02
126	Tony Phillips	.06	.05	.02
127	Mark Salas	.06	.05	.02
128	Frank Tanana	.06	.05	.02
129	Alan Trammell	.15	.11	.06
130	Lou Whitaker	.08	.06	.03
131	Eric Anthony	.10	.08	.04
132	Craig Biggio	.15	.11	.06
133	Ken Caminiti	.08	.06	.03
134	Casey Candaele	.06	.05	.02
135	Andujar Cedeno	.50	.40	.20
136	Mark Davidson	.06	.05	.02
137	Jim Deshaies	.06	.05	.02
138	Mark Portugal	.06	.05	.02
139	Rafael Ramirez	.06	.05	.02
140	Mike Scott	.08	.06	.03
141	Eric Yelding	.06	.05	.02
142	Gerald Young	.06	.05	.02
143	Kevin Appier	.10	.08	.04
144	George Brett	.35	.25	.14
145	Jeff Conine	.40	.30	.15
146	Jim Eisenreich	.06	.05	.02
147	Tom Gordon	.10	.08	.04
148	Mark Gubicza	.08	.06	.03
149	Bo Jackson	.40	.30	.15
150	Brent Mayne	.15	.11	.06
151	Mike Macfarlane	.06	.05	.02
152	Brian McRae	.50	.40	.20
153	Jeff Montgomery	.08	.06	.03
154	Bret Saberhagen	.10	.08	.04
155	Kevin Seitzer	.06	.05	.02
156	Terry Shumpert	.06	.05	.02
157	Kurt Stillwell	.06	.05	.02
158	Danny Tartabull	.15	.11	.06
159	Tim Belcher	.08	.06	.03
160	Kal Daniels	.10	.08	.04
161	Alfredo Griffin	.06	.05	.02
162	Lenny Harris	.06	.05	.02
163	Jay Howell	.06	.05	.02
164	Ramon Martinez	.15	.11	.06
165	Mike Morgan	.06	.05	.02
166	Eddie Murray	.20	.15	.08
167	Jose Offerman	.15	.11	.06
168	Juan Samuel	.08	.06	.03
169	Mike Scioscia	.08	.06	.03
170	Mike Sharperson	.06	.05	.02
171	Darryl Strawberry	.15	.11	.06
172	Greg Brock	.06	.05	.02
173	Chuck Crim	.06	.05	.02
174	Jim Gantner	.08	.06	.03
175	Ted Higuera	.08	.06	.03
176	Mark Knudson	.06	.05	.02
177	Tim McIntosh	.08	.06	.03
178	Paul Molitor	.25	.20	.10
179	Dan Plesac	.06	.05	.02
180	Gary Sheffield	.50	.40	.20
181	Bill Spiers	.06	.05	.02
182	B.J. Surhoff	.06	.05	.02
183	Greg Vaughn	.20	.15	.08
184	Robin Yount	.25	.20	.10
185	Rick Aguilera	.08	.06	.03
186	Greg Gagne	.06	.05	.02
187	Dan Gladden	.06	.05	.02
188	Brian Harper	.06	.05	.02
189	Kent Hrbek	.08	.06	.03
190	Gene Larkin	.06	.05	.02
191	Shane Mack	.08	.06	.03
192	Pedro Munoz	.10	.07	.04
193	Al Newman	.06	.05	.02
194	Junior Ortiz	.06	.05	.02
195	Kirby Puckett	.75	.60	.30
196	Kevin Tapani	.08	.06	.03
197	Dennis Boyd	.06	.05	.02
198	Tim Burke	.06	.05	.02
199	Ivan Calderon	.08	.06	.03
200	Delino DeShields	.25	.20	.10
201	Mike Fitzgerald	.06	.05	.02
202	Steve Frey	.06	.05	.02
203	Andres Galarraga	.08	.06	.03
204	Marquis Grissom	.40	.30	.15
205	Dave Martinez	.06	.05	.02
206	Dennis Martinez	.08	.06	.03
207	Junior Noboa	.06	.05	.02
208	Spike Owen	.06	.05	.02
209	Scott Ruskin	.06	.05	.02
210	Tim Wallach	.08	.06	.03
211	Daryl Boston	.06	.05	.02
212	Vince Coleman	.10	.08	.04
213	David Cone	.10	.08	.04
214	Ron Darling	.08	.06	.03
215	Kevin Elster	.06	.05	.02
216	Sid Fernandez	.08	.06	.03
217	John Franco	.08	.06	.03
218	Dwight Gooden	.10	.07	.04
219	Tom Herr	.06	.05	.02
220	Todd Hundley	.15	.11	.06
221	Gregg Jefferies	.15	.11	.06
222	Howard Johnson	.10	.07	.04
223	Dave Magadan	.10	.08	.04
224	Kevin McReynolds	.10	.08	.04
225	Keith Miller	.06	.05	.02
226	Mackey Sasser	.06	.05	.02
227	Frank Viola	.10	.08	.04
228	Jesse Barfield	.08	.06	.03
229	Greg Cadaret	.06	.05	.02
230	Alvaro Espinoza	.06	.05	.02
231	Bob Geren	.06	.05	.02
232	Lee Guetterman	.06	.05	.02
233	Mel Hall	.08	.06	.03
234	Andy Hawkins	.06	.05	.02
235	Roberto Kelly	.10	.08	.04
236	Tim Leary	.06	.05	.02
237	Jim Leyritz	.06	.05	.02
238	Kevin Maas	.08	.06	.03
239	Don Mattingly	.40	.30	.15
240	Hensley Meulens	.10	.08	.04
241	Eric Plunk	.06	.05	.02
242	Steve Sax	.08	.06	.03
243	Todd Burns	.06	.05	.02
244	Jose Canseco	.40	.30	.15
245	Dennis Eckersley	.10	.08	.04
246	Mike Gallego	.06	.05	.02
247	Dave Henderson	.10	.08	.04
248	Rickey Henderson	.30	.25	.12
249	Rick Honeycutt	.06	.05	.02
250	Carney Lansford	.08	.06	.03
251	Mark McGwire	.25	.20	.10
252	Mike Moore	.06	.05	.02
253	Terry Steinbach	.06	.05	.02
254	Dave Stewart	.10	.08	.04
255	Walt Weiss	.06	.05	.02
256	Bob Welch	.08	.06	.03
257	Curt Young	.06	.05	.02
258	Wes Chamberlain	.20	.15	.08
259	Pat Combs	.08	.06	.03
260	Darren Daulton	.06	.05	.02
261	Jose DeJesus	.06	.05	.02
262	Len Dykstra	.15	.11	.06
263	Charlie Hayes	.08	.06	.03
264	Von Hayes	.08	.06	.03
265	Ken Howell	.06	.05	.02
266	John Kruk	.08	.06	.03
267	Roger McDowell	.08	.06	.03
268	Mickey Morandini	.15	.11	.06
269	Terry Mulholland	.08	.06	.03
270	Dale Murphy	.10	.08	.04
271	Randy Ready	.06	.05	.02
272	Dickie Thon	.06	.05	.02
273	Stan Belinda	.06	.05	.02
274	Jay Bell	.08	.06	.03
275	Barry Bonds	.75	.60	.30
276	Bobby Bonilla	.25	.20	.10
277	Doug Drabek	.10	.08	.04
278	Carlos Garcia	.75	.60	.30
279	Neal Heaton	.06	.05	.02
280	Jeff King	.08	.06	.03
281	Bill Landrum	.06	.05	.02
282	Mike LaValliere	.06	.05	.02
283	Jose Lind	.06	.05	.02
284	Orlando Merced	.50	.40	.20
285	Gary Redus	.06	.05	.02
286	Don Slaught	.06	.05	.02
287	Andy Van Slyke	.10	.08	.04
288	Jose DeLeon	.06	.05	.02
289	Pedro Guerrero	.10	.08	.04
290	Ray Lankford	.50	.40	.20
291	Joe Magrane	.08	.06	.03
292	Jose Oquendo	.06	.05	.02
293	Tom Pagnozzi	.06	.05	.02
294	Bryn Smith	.06	.05	.02
295	Lee Smith	.08	.06	.03
296	Ozzie Smith	.20	.15	.08
297	Milt Thompson	.06	.05	.02
298	Craig Wilson	.12	.09	.05
299	Todd Zeile	.20	.15	.08
300	Shawn Abner	.06	.05	.02
301	Andy Benes	.12	.09	.05
302	Paul Faries	.12	.09	.05
303	Tony Gwynn	.20	.15	.08
304	Greg Harris	.06	.05	.02
305	Thomas Howard	.10	.08	.04
306	Bruce Hurst	.08	.06	.03
307	Craig Lefferts	.06	.05	.02
308	Fred McGriff	.50	.40	.20
309	Dennis Rasmussen	.06	.05	.02
310	Bip Roberts	.08	.06	.03
311	Benito Santiago	.10	.08	.04
312	Garry Templeton	.06	.05	.02
313	Ed Whitson	.06	.05	.02
314	Dave Anderson	.06	.05	.02
315	Kevin Bass	.06	.05	.02
316	Jeff Brantley	.06	.05	.02
317	John Burkett	.08	.06	.03
318	Will Clark	.40	.30	.15
319	Steve Decker	.20	.15	.08
320	Scott Garrelts	.06	.05	.02
321	Terry Kennedy	.06	.05	.02
322	Mark Leonard	.12	.09	.05
323	Darren Lewis	.20	.15	.08
324	Greg Litton	.06	.05	.02
325	Willie McGee	.10	.08	.04
326	Kevin Mitchell	.15	.11	.06
327	Don Robinson	.06	.05	.02
328	Andres Santana	.15	.11	.06
329	Robby Thompson	.06	.05	.02
330	Jose Uribe	.06	.05	.02
331	Matt Williams	.25	.20	.10
332	Scott Bradley	.06	.05	.02
334	Alvin Davis	.08	.06	.03
335	Ken Griffey, Sr.	.08	.06	.03
336	Ken Griffey, Jr.	3.50	2.75	1.50
337	Erik Hanson	.10	.08	.04
338	Brian Holman	.06	.05	.02
339	Randy Johnson	.08	.06	.03
340	Edgar Martinez	.08	.06	.03
341	Tino Martinez	.10	.07	.04
342	Pete O'Brien	.06	.05	.02
343	Harold Reynolds	.08	.06	.03
344	David Valle	.06	.05	.02
345	Omar Vizquel	.06	.05	.02
346	Brad Arnsberg	.06	.05	.02
347	Kevin Brown	.06	.05	.02
348	Julio Franco	.10	.08	.04
349	Jeff Huson	.06	.05	.02
350	Rafael Palmeiro	.20	.15	.08
351	Geno Petralli	.06	.05	.02
352	Gary Pettis	.06	.05	.02
353	Kenny Rogers	.06	.05	.02
354	Jeff Russell	.06	.05	.02
355	Nolan Ryan	1.50	1.25	.60
356	Ruben Sierra	.25	.20	.10
357	Bobby Witt	.08	.06	.03
358	Roberto Alomar	1.25	.90	.50
359	Pat Borders	.06	.05	.02
360	Joe Carter	.30	.25	.12
361	Kelly Gruber	.08	.06	.03
362	Tom Henke	.08	.06	.03
363	Glenallen Hill	.08	.06	.03
364	Jimmy Key	.08	.06	.03
365	Manny Lee	.06	.05	.02
366	Rance Mulliniks	.06	.05	.02
367	John Olerud	1.25	.90	.50
368	Dave Stieb	.08	.06	.03
369	Duane Ward	.06	.05	.02
370	David Wells	.06	.05	.02
371	Mark Whiten	.15	.11	.06
372	Mookie Wilson	.06	.05	.02
373	Willie Banks	.20	.15	.08
374	Steve Carter	.06	.05	.02
375	Scott Chiamparino	.10	.08	.04
376	Steve Chitren	.10	.08	.04
377	Darrin Fletcher	.10	.08	.04
378	Rich Garces	.10	.08	.04

#	Player	MT	NR MT	EX
379	Reggie Jefferson	.20	.15	.08
380	Eric Karros	.75	.60	.30
381	Pat Kelly	.30	.25	.12
382	Chuck Knoblauch	.40	.30	.15
383	Denny Neagle	.20	.15	.08
384	Dan Opperman	.10	.07	.04
385	John Ramos	.10	.08	.04
386	Henry Rodriguez	.35	.25	.14
387	Mo Vaughn	1.50	1.25	.60
388	Gerald Williams	.40	.30	.15
389	Mike York	.20	.15	.08
390	Eddie Zosky	.12	.09	.05
391	Great Performer (Barry Bonds)	.30	.25	.12
392	Great Performer (Cecil Fielder)	.20	.15	.08
393	Great Performer (Rickey Henderson)	.20	.15	.08
394	Great Performer (Dave Justice)	.30	.25	.12
395	Great Performer (Nolan Ryan)	.60	.45	.25
396	Great Performer (Bobby Thigpen)	.10	.08	.04
397	Checklist	.06	.05	.02
398	Checklist	.06	.05	.02
399	Checklist	.06	.05	.02
400	Checklist	.06	.05	.02

1991 Fleer Ultra Gold

A three dimensional effect is presented on the front of the Fleer Ultra Gold cards. The flip sides feature career information. The cards are numbered on the back. The Puckett and Sandberg cards feature incorrect historical information on the backs.

		MT	NR MT	EX
Complete Set (10):		9.00	6.00	3.00
Common Player:		.40	.30	.15
1	Barry Bonds	1.50	.90	.50
2	Will Clark	1.25	.90	.50
3	Doug Drabek	.40	.30	.15
4	Ken Griffey, Jr.	4.00	3.00	1.50
5	Rickey Henderson	.75	.60	.30
6	Bo Jackson	1.00	.75	.40
7	Ramon Martinez	.40	.30	.15
8	Kirby Puckett	1.25	.90	.50
9	Chris Sabo	.40	.30	.15
10	Ryne Sandberg	1.50	1.25	.60

1991 Fleer Ultra Update

This 120-card set was produced as a supplement to the premier Fleer Ultra set. The cards feature the same style as the regular Fleer Ultra cards. The 4-photo Ultra look is featured on each card. The cards were sold in full color, shrinkwrapped boxes.

		MT	NR MT	EX
Complete Set (120):		75.00	56.00	30.00
Common Player:		.15	.11	.06
1	Dwight Evans	.15	.11	.06
2	Chito Martinez	.25	.20	.10
3	Bob Melvin	.15	.11	.06
4	Mike Mussina	8.00	6.00	3.25
5	Jack Clark	.15	.11	.06
6	Dana Kiecker	.15	.11	.06
7	Steve Lyons	.15	.11	.06
8	Gary Gaetti	.15	.11	.06
9	Dave Gallagher	.15	.11	.06
10	Dave Parker	.25	.20	.10
11	Luis Polonia	.15	.11	.06
12	Luis Sojo	.15	.11	.06
13	Wilson Alvarez	5.00	3.75	2.00
14	Alex Fernandez	7.00	5.25	2.75
15	Craig Grebeck	.15	.11	.06
16	Ron Karkovice	.15	.11	.06
17	Warren Newson	.15	.11	.06
18	Scott Radinsky	.15	.11	.06
19	Glenallen Hill	.15	.11	.06
20	Charles Nagy	1.50	1.25	.60
21	Mark Whiten	1.25	.90	.50
22	Milt Cuyler	.15	.11	.06
23	Paul Gibson	.15	.11	.06
24	Mickey Tettleton	.40	.30	.15
25	Todd Benzinger	.15	.11	.06
26	Storm Davis	.15	.11	.06
27	Kirk Gibson	.15	.11	.06
28	Bill Pecota	.15	.11	.06
29	Gary Thurman	.15	.11	.06
30	Darryl Hamilton	.35	.25	.14
31	Jaime Navarro	.15	.11	.06
32	Willie Randolph	.15	.11	.06
33	Bill Wegman	.15	.11	.06
34	Randy Bush	.15	.11	.06
35	Chili Davis	.15	.11	.06
36	Scott Erickson	.40	.30	.15
37	Chuck Knoblauch	1.50	1.25	.60
38	Scott Leius	.15	.11	.06
39	Jack Morris	.20	.15	.08
40	John Habyan	.15	.11	.06
41	Pat Kelly	.60	.45	.25
42	Matt Nokes	.15	.11	.06
43	Scott Sanderson	.15	.11	.06
44	Bernie Williams	1.50	1.25	.60
45	Harold Baines	.20	.15	.08
46	Brook Jacoby	.15	.11	.06
47	Ernest Riles	.15	.11	.06
48	Willie Wilson	.15	.11	.06
49	Jay Buhner	.75	.60	.30
50	Rich DeLucia	.15	.11	.06
51	Mike Jackson	.15	.11	.06
52	Bill Krueger	.15	.11	.06
53	Bill Swift	.15	.11	.06
54	Brian Downing	.15	.11	.06
55	Juan Gonzalez	35.00	26.00	14.00
56	Dean Palmer	5.00	3.75	2.00
57	Kevin Reimer	.15	.11	.06
58	Ivan Rodriguez	4.50	3.50	1.75
59	Tom Candiotti	.15	.11	.06
60	Juan Guzman	3.50	2.75	1.50
61	Bob MacDonald	.15	.11	.06
62	Greg Myers	.15	.11	.06
63	Ed Sprague	.40	.30	.15
64	Devon White	.30	.25	.12
65	Rafael Belliard	.15	.11	.06
66	Juan Berenguer	.15	.11	.06
67	Brian Hunter	.35	.25	.14
68	Kent Mercker	.35	.25	.14
69	Otis Nixon	.15	.11	.06
70	Danny Jackson	.15	.11	.06
71	Chuck McElroy	.15	.11	.06
72	Gary Scott	.15	.11	.06
73	Heathcliff Slocumb	.15	.11	.06
74	Chico Walker	.15	.11	.06
75	Rick Wilkins	2.00	1.50	.80
76	Chris Hammond	.50	.40	.20
77	Luis Quinones	.15	.11	.06
78	Herm Winningham	.15	.11	.06
79	Jeff Bagwell	12.00	9.00	4.75
80	Jim Corsi	.15	.11	.06
81	Steve Finley	.15	.11	.06
82	Luis Gonzalez	2.50	2.00	1.00
83	Pete Harnisch	.15	.11	.06
84	Darryl Kile	3.00	2.25	1.25
85	Brett Butler	.15	.11	.06
86	Gary Carter	.20	.15	.08
87	Tim Crews	.15	.11	.06
88	Orel Hershiser	.15	.11	.06
89	Bob Ojeda	.15	.11	.06
90	Bret Barberie	.50	.40	.20
91	Barry Jones	.15	.11	.06
92	Gilberto Reyes	.15	.11	.06
93	Larry Walker	3.00	2.25	1.25
94	Hubie Brooks	.15	.11	.06
95	Tim Burke	.15	.11	.06
96	Rick Cerone	.15	.11	.06
97	Jeff Innis	.15	.11	.06
98	Wally Backman	.15	.11	.06
99	Tommy Greene	1.50	1.25	.60
100	Ricky Jordan	.15	.11	.06
101	Mitch Williams	.15	.11	.06
102	John Smiley	.15	.11	.06
103	Randy Tomlin	.40	.30	.15
104	Gary Varsho	.15	.11	.06
105	Cris Carpenter	.15	.11	.06
106	Ken Hill	1.00	.75	.40
107	Felix Jose	.20	.15	.08
108	*Omar Oliveras*	.20	.15	.08
109	Gerald Perry	.15	.11	.06
110	Jerald Clark	.15	.11	.06
111	Tony Fernandez	.15	.11	.06
112	Darrin Jackson	.15	.11	.06
113	Mike Maddux	.15	.11	.06
114	Tim Teufel	.15	.11	.06
115	Bud Black	.15	.11	.06
116	Kelly Downs	.15	.11	.06
117	Mike Felder	.15	.11	.06
118	Willie McGee	.15	.11	.06
119	Trevor Wilson	.15	.11	.06
120	Checklist	.15	.11	.06

A player's name in italic type indicates a rookie card. An (FC) indicates a player's first card for that particular card company.

1992 Fleer

For the second consecutive year, Fleer produced a 720-card set. The standard card fronts feature full-color action photos bordered in blue with the player's name, position and team logo on the right border. The backs feature another full-color action photo, biographical information and statistics. A special twelve card Roger Clemens subset is also included in the 1992 Fleer set. Three more Clemens cards are available through a mail-in offer, and 2,000 Roger Clemens autographed cards were inserted in 1992 packs. Once again the cards are numbered according to team. Subsets in the issue included Major League Propects (#652-680), Record Setters (#681-687), League Leaders (#688-697), Superstar Specials (#698-707) and ProVisions (#708-713), which for the first time were part of the regular numbered set rather tham limited edition insert cards.

		MT	NR MT	EX
Complete Set (720):		20.00	15.00	8.00
Common Player:		.04	.03	.02
1	Brady Anderson	.04	.03	.02
2	Jose Bautista	.04	.03	.02
3	Juan Bell	.06	.05	.02
4	Glenn Davis	.08	.06	.03
5	Mike Devereaux	.05	.04	.02
6	Dwight Evans	.08	.06	.03
7	Mike Flanagan	.04	.03	.02
8	Leo Gomez	.15	.11	.06
9	Chris Hoiles	.10	.08	.04
10	Sam Horn	.05	.04	.02
11	Tim Hulett	.04	.03	.02
12	Dave Johnson	.04	.03	.02
13	*Chito Martinez* (FC)	.20	.15	.08
14	Ben McDonald	.10	.08	.04
15	Bob Melvin	.04	.03	.02
16	*Luis Mercedes* (FC)	.15	.11	.06
17	Jose Mesa	.05	.04	.02
18	Bob Milacki	.05	.04	.02
19	Randy Milligan	.06	.05	.02
20	Mike Mussina	.40	.30	.15
21	Gregg Olson	.08	.06	.03
22	Joe Orsulak	.04	.03	.02
23	Jim Poole	.05	.04	.02
24	*Arthur Rhodes*	.20	.15	.08
25	Billy Ripken	.04	.03	.02
26	Cal Ripken, Jr.	.30	.25	.12
27	David Segui	.08	.06	.03
28	Roy Smith	.04	.03	.02
29	Anthony Telford	.04	.03	.02
30	Mark Williamson	.04	.03	.02
31	Craig Worthington	.06	.05	.02
32	Wade Boggs	.15	.11	.06
33	Tom Bolton	.04	.03	.02
34	Tom Brunansky	.05	.04	.02
35	Ellis Burks	.08	.06	.03
36	Jack Clark	.08	.06	.03
37	Roger Clemens	.15	.11	.06
38	Danny Darwin	.04	.03	.02
39	Mike Greenwell	.08	.06	.03
40	Joe Hesketh	.04	.03	.02
41	Daryl Irvine	.05	.04	.02
42	Dennis Lamp	.04	.03	.02
43	Tony Pena	.05	.04	.02
44	Phil Plantier	.25	.20	.10
45	Carlos Quintana	.06	.05	.02
46	Jeff Reardon	.08	.06	.03
47	Jody Reed	.05	.04	.02
48	Luis Rivera	.04	.03	.02
49	Mo Vaughn	.30	.25	.12
50	Jim Abbott	.10	.08	.04
51	Kyle Abbott	.08	.06	.03
52	*Ruben Amaro, Jr.* (FC)	.15	.11	.06
53	Scott Bailes	.04	.03	.02
54	*Chris Beasley*	.12	.09	.05
55	Mark Eichhorn	.04	.03	.02
56	Mike Fetters	.04	.03	.02
57	Chuck Finley	.08	.06	.03
58	Gary Gaetti	.08	.06	.03
59	Dave Gallagher	.05	.04	.02
60	Donnie Hill	.04	.03	.02
61	Bryan Harvey	.06	.05	.02
62	Wally Joyner	.10	.08	.04
63	Mark Langston	.10	.08	.04
64	Kirk McCaskill	.05	.04	.02
65	John Orton	.04	.03	.02
66	Lance Parrish	.06	.05	.02
67	Luis Polonia	.05	.04	.02
68	Bobby Rose	.05	.04	.02
69	Dick Schofield	.04	.03	.02
70	Luis Sojo	.05	.04	.02
71	Lee Stevens	.08	.06	.03
72	Dave Winfield	.12	.09	.05
73	Cliff Young	.06	.05	.02
74	Wilson Alvarez	.08	.06	.03
75	*Esteban Beltre*	.20	.15	.08
76	Joey Cora	.04	.03	.02
77	*Brian Drahman* (FC)	.15	.11	.06
78	Alex Fernandez	.15	.11	.06
79	Carlton Fisk	.10	.08	.04
80	Scott Fletcher	.04	.03	.02
81	Craig Grebeck	.04	.03	.02
82	Ozzie Guillen	.06	.05	.02
83	Greg Hibbard	.06	.05	.02
84	Charlie Hough	.05	.04	.02
85	Mike Huff	.05	.04	.02
86	Bo Jackson	.40	.30	.15
87	Lance Johnson	.04	.03	.02
88	Ron Karkovice	.04	.03	.02
89	Jack McDowell	.08	.06	.03
90	Matt Merullo	.04	.03	.02
91	*Warren Newson*	.15	.11	.06
92	Donn Pall	.04	.03	.02

93	Dan Pasqua	.05	.04	.02
94	Ken Patterson	.04	.03	.02
95	Melido Perez	.05	.04	.02
96	Scott Radinsky	.04	.03	.02
97	Tim Raines	.10	.08	.04
98	Sammy Sosa	.08	.06	.03
99	Bobby Thigpen	.08	.06	.03
100	Frank Thomas	1.00	.70	.40
101	Robin Ventura	.20	.15	.08
102	Mike Aldrete	.04	.03	.02
103	Sandy Alomar, Jr.	.10	.08	.04
104	Carlos Baerga	.15	.11	.06
105	Albert Belle	.15	.11	.06
106	Willie Blair	.05	.04	.02
107	Jerry Browne	.04	.03	.02
108	Alex Cole	.06	.05	.02
109	Felix Fermin	.04	.03	.02
110	Glenallen Hill	.06	.05	.02
111	Shawn Hillegas	.04	.03	.02
112	Chris James	.05	.04	.02
113	Reggie Jefferson (FC)	.20	.15	.08
114	Doug Jones	.05	.04	.02
115	Eric King	.04	.03	.02
116	Mark Lewis	.15	.11	.06
117	Carlos Martinez	.05	.04	.02
118	Charles Nagy	.08	.06	.03
119	Rod Nichols	.04	.03	.02
120	Steve Olin	.04	.03	.02
121	Jesse Orosco	.04	.03	.02
122	Rudy Seanez	.04	.03	.02
123	Joel Skinner	.04	.03	.02
124	Greg Swindell	.08	.06	.03
125	*Jim Thome* (FC)	.20	.15	.08
126	Mark Whiten	.10	.08	.04
127	Scott Aldred	.10	.08	.04
128	Andy Allanson	.04	.03	.02
129	John Cerutti	.04	.03	.02
130	Milt Cuyler	.10	.08	.04
131	*Mike Dalton* (FC)	.15	.11	.06
132	Rob Deer	.05	.04	.02
133	Cecil Fielder	.15	.11	.06
134	Travis Fryman	.25	.20	.10
135	*Dan Gakeler* (FC)	.15	.11	.06
136	Paul Gibson	.04	.03	.02
137	Bill Gullickson	.05	.04	.02
138	Mike Henneman	.05	.04	.02
139	Pete Incaviglia	.05	.04	.02
140	*Mark Leiter* (FC)	.12	.09	.05
141	*Scott Livingstone* (FC)	.20	.15	.08
142	Lloyd Moseby	.04	.03	.02
143	Tony Phillips	.05	.04	.02
144	Mark Salas	.04	.03	.02
145	Frank Tanana	.05	.04	.02
146	Walt Terrell	.04	.03	.02
147	Mickey Tettleton	.06	.05	.02
148	Alan Trammell	.10	.08	.04
149	Lou Whitaker	.08	.06	.03
150	Kevin Appier	.06	.05	.02
151	Luis Aquino	.04	.03	.02
152	Todd Benzinger	.05	.04	.02
153	Mike Boddicker	.05	.04	.02
154	George Brett	.15	.11	.06
155	Storm Davis	.05	.04	.02
156	Jim Eisenreich	.04	.03	.02
157	Kirk Gibson	.08	.06	.03
158	Tom Gordon	.06	.05	.02
159	Mark Gubicza	.06	.05	.02
160	*David Howard* (FC)	.20	.15	.08
161	Mike Macfarlane	.05	.04	.02
162	Brent Mayne	.05	.04	.02
163	Brian McRae	.25	.20	.10
164	Jeff Montgomery	.05	.04	.02
165	Bill Pecota	.04	.03	.02
166	*Harvey Pulliam* (FC)	.15	.11	.06
167	Bret Saberhagen	.08	.06	.03
168	Kevin Seitzer	.05	.04	.02
169	Terry Shumpert	.05	.04	.02
170	Kurt Stillwell	.05	.04	.02
171	Danny Tartabull	.08	.06	.03
172	Gary Thurman	.04	.03	.02
173	Dante Bichette	.05	.04	.02
174	Kevin Brown	.04	.03	.02
175	Chuck Crim	.04	.03	.02
176	Jim Gantner	.05	.04	.02
177	Darryl Hamilton	.05	.04	.02
178	Ted Higuera	.06	.05	.02
179	Darren Holmes	.04	.03	.02
180	Mark Lee	.04	.03	.02
181	Julio Machado	.04	.03	.02
182	Paul Molitor	.15	.11	.06
183	Jaime Navarro	.06	.05	.02
184	Edwin Nunez	.04	.03	.02
185	Dan Plesac	.05	.04	.02
186	Willie Randolph	.05	.04	.02
187	Ron Robinson	.04	.03	.02
188	Gary Sheffield	.20	.15	.08
189	Bill Spiers	.05	.04	.02
190	B.J. Surhoff	.05	.04	.02
191	Dale Sveum	.04	.03	.02
192	Greg Vaughn	.08	.06	.03
193	Bill Wegman	.05	.04	.02
194	Robin Yount	.15	.11	.06
195	Rick Aguilera	.05	.04	.02
196	Allan Anderson	.04	.03	.02
197	Steve Bedrosian	.04	.03	.02
198	Randy Bush	.04	.03	.02
199	Larry Casian (FC)	.05	.04	.02
200	Chili Davis	.06	.05	.02
201	Scott Erickson	.20	.15	.08
202	Greg Gagne	.04	.03	.02
203	Dan Gladden	.04	.03	.02
204	Brian Harper	.05	.04	.02
205	Kent Hrbek	.06	.05	.02
206	Chuck Knoblauch	.15	.11	.06
207	Gene Larkin	.04	.03	.02
208	Terry Leach	.04	.03	.02
209	Scott Leius	.10	.08	.04
210	Shane Mack	.08	.06	.03
211	Jack Morris	.08	.06	.03
212	Pedro Munoz (FC)	.20	.15	.08
213	*Denny Neagle* (FC)	.20	.15	.08
214	Al Newman	.04	.03	.02
215	Junior Ortiz	.04	.03	.02
216	Mike Pagliarulo	.04	.03	.02
217	Kirby Puckett	.15	.11	.06
218	Paul Sorrento	.06	.05	.02
219	Kevin Tapani	.08	.06	.03
220	Lenny Webster	.06	.05	.02
221	Jesse Barfield	.06	.05	.02
222	Greg Cadaret	.04	.03	.02
223	Dave Eiland	.04	.03	.02
224	Alvaro Espinoza	.04	.03	.02
225	Steve Farr	.05	.04	.02
226	Bob Geren	.04	.03	.02
227	Lee Guetterman	.04	.03	.02
228	John Habyan	.04	.03	.02
229	Mel Hall	.06	.05	.02
230	Steve Howe	.06	.05	.02
231	*Mike Humphreys* (FC)	.20	.15	.08
232	*Scott Kamieniecki*	.15	.11	.06
233	Pat Kelly	.15	.11	.06
234	Roberto Kelly	.08	.06	.03
235	Tim Leary	.04	.03	.02
236	Kevin Maas	.15	.11	.06
237	Don Mattingly	.30	.25	.12
238	Hensley Meulens	.08	.06	.03
239	Matt Nokes	.06	.05	.02
240	Pascual Perez	.05	.04	.02
241	Eric Plunk	.04	.03	.02
242	*John Ramos* (FC)	.15	.11	.06
243	Scott Sanderson	.05	.04	.02
244	Steve Sax	.06	.05	.02
245	*Wade Taylor*	.15	.11	.06
246	Randy Velarde	.04	.03	.02
247	Bernie Williams	.20	.15	.08
248	Troy Afenir	.05	.04	.02
249	Harold Baines	.08	.06	.03
250	Lance Blankenship	.04	.03	.02
251	*Mike Bordick* (FC)	.10	.08	.04
252	Jose Canseco	.15	.11	.06
253	Steve Chitren	.06	.05	.02
254	Ron Darling	.06	.05	.02
255	Dennis Eckersley	.07	.05	.03
256	Mike Gallego	.04	.03	.02
257	Dave Henderson	.08	.06	.03
258	Rickey Henderson	.20	.15	.08
259	Rick Honeycutt	.04	.03	.02
260	Brook Jacoby	.06	.05	.02
261	Carney Lansford	.06	.05	.02
262	Mark McGwire	.15	.11	.06
263	Mike Moore	.05	.04	.02
264	Gene Nelson	.04	.03	.02
265	Jamie Quirk	.04	.03	.02
266	*Joe Slusarski* (FC)	.15	.11	.06
267	Terry Steinbach	.06	.05	.02
268	Dave Stewart	.08	.06	.03
269	Todd Van Poppel (FC)	.15	.11	.06
270	Walt Weiss	.06	.05	.02
271	Bob Welch	.06	.05	.02
272	Curt Young	.04	.03	.02
273	Scott Bradley	.04	.03	.02
274	Greg Briley	.04	.03	.02
275	Jay Buhner	.06	.05	.02
276	Henry Cotto	.04	.03	.02
277	Alvin Davis	.06	.05	.02
278	Rich DeLucia	.06	.05	.02
279	Ken Griffey, Jr.	1.00	.75	.40
280	Erik Hanson	.08	.06	.03
281	Brian Holman	.05	.04	.02
282	Mike Jackson	.04	.03	.02
283	Randy Johnson	.08	.06	.03
284	Tracy Jones	.04	.03	.02
285	Bill Krueger	.04	.03	.02
286	Edgar Martinez	.06	.05	.02
287	Tino Martinez	.10	.08	.04
288	Rob Murphy	.04	.03	.02
289	Pete O'Brien	.04	.03	.02
290	Alonzo Powell	.06	.05	.02
291	Harold Reynolds	.06	.05	.02
292	Mike Schooler	.05	.04	.02
293	Russ Swan	.04	.03	.02
294	Bill Swift	.04	.03	.02
295	Dave Valle	.04	.03	.02
296	Omar Vizquel	.04	.03	.02
297	Gerald Alexander	.05	.04	.02
298	Brad Arnsberg	.05	.04	.02
299	Kevin Brown	.05	.04	.02
300	Jack Daugherty	.04	.03	.02
301	Mario Diaz	.04	.03	.02
302	Brian Downing	.05	.04	.02
303	Julio Franco	.08	.06	.03
304	Juan Gonzalez	.70	.50	.30
305	Rich Gossage	.05	.04	.02
306	Jose Guzman	.05	.04	.02
307	*Jose Hernandez*	.15	.11	.06
308	Jeff Huson	.05	.04	.02
309	Mike Jeffcoat	.04	.03	.02
310	*Terry Mathews* (FC)	.20	.15	.08
311	Rafael Palmeiro	.10	.08	.04
312	Dean Palmer	.20	.15	.08
313	Geno Petralli	.04	.03	.02
314	Gary Pettis	.04	.03	.02
315	Kevin Reimer	.05	.04	.02
316	*Ivan Rodriguez*	.25	.20	.10
317	Kenny Rogers	.05	.04	.02
318	*Wayne Rosenthal*	.10	.08	.04
319	Jeff Russell	.05	.04	.02
320	Nolan Ryan	.35	.25	.14
321	Ruben Sierra	.12	.09	.05
322	Jim Acker	.04	.03	.02
323	Roberto Alomar	.15	.11	.06
324	Derek Bell	.25	.20	.10
325	Pat Borders	.05	.04	.02
326	Tom Candiotti	.05	.04	.02
327	Joe Carter	.10	.07	.04
328	Rob Ducey	.05	.04	.02
329	Kelly Gruber	.08	.06	.03
330	*Juan Guzman*	.25	.20	.10
331	Tom Henke	.06	.05	.02
332	Jimmy Key	.06	.05	.02
333	Manny Lee	.05	.04	.02
334	Al Leiter	.04	.03	.02
335	*Bob MacDonald* (FC)	.10	.08	.04
336	Candy Maldonado	.05	.04	.02
337	Rance Mulliniks	.04	.03	.02
338	Greg Myers	.05	.04	.02
339	John Olerud	.30	.25	.12
340	*Ed Sprague*	.10	.08	.04
341	Dave Stieb	.08	.06	.03
342	Todd Stottlemyre	.05	.04	.02
343	*Mike Timlin*	.15	.11	.06
344	Duane Ward	.05	.04	.02
345	David Wells	.05	.04	.02
346	Devon White	.08	.06	.03
347	Mookie Wilson	.04	.03	.02
348	Eddie Zosky	.08	.06	.03
349	Steve Avery	.20	.15	.08
350	Mike Bell (FC)	.08	.06	.03
351	Rafael Belliard	.04	.03	.02
352	Juan Berenguer	.04	.03	.02
353	Jeff Blauser	.05	.04	.02
354	Sid Bream	.05	.04	.02
355	Francisco Cabrera	.05	.04	.02
356	Marvin Freeman	.04	.03	.02
357	Ron Gant	.10	.07	.04
358	Tom Glavine	.15	.11	.06
359	*Brian Hunter* (FC)	.10	.07	.04
360	Dave Justice	.30	.25	.12
361	Charlie Leibrandt	.04	.03	.02
362	Mark Lemke	.05	.04	.02
363	Kent Mercker	.05	.04	.02
364	*Keith Mitchell* (FC)	.10	.07	.04
365	Greg Olson	.05	.04	.02
366	Terry Pendleton	.08	.06	.03
367	*Armando Reynoso* (FC)	.15	.11	.06
368	Deion Sanders	.15	.11	.06
369	Lonnie Smith	.04	.03	.02
370	Pete Smith	.04	.03	.02
371	John Smoltz	.10	.08	.04
372	Mike Stanton	.05	.04	.02
373	Jeff Treadway	.05	.04	.02
374	*Mark Wohlers* (FC)	.15	.11	.06
375	Paul Assenmacher	.04	.03	.02
376	George Bell	.08	.06	.03
377	Shawn Boskie	.06	.05	.02
378	*Frank Castillo* (FC)	.15	.11	.06
379	Andre Dawson	.12	.09	.05
380	Shawon Dunston	.08	.06	.03
381	Mark Grace	.08	.06	.03
382	Mike Harkey	.05	.04	.02
383	Danny Jackson	.05	.04	.02
384	Les Lancaster	.04	.03	.02
385	*Cedric Landrum* (FC)	.15	.11	.06
386	Greg Maddux	.06	.05	.02
387	Derrick May	.15	.11	.06
388	Chuck McElroy	.04	.03	.02
389	Ryne Sandberg	.20	.15	.08
390	*Heathcliff Slocumb*	.10	.08	.04
391	Dave Smith	.05	.04	.02
392	Dwight Smith	.05	.04	.02
393	Rick Sutcliffe	.05	.04	.02
394	Hector Villanueva	.06	.05	.02
395	*Chico Walker* (FC)	.10	.08	.04
396	Jerome Walton	.06	.05	.02
397	*Rick Wilkins*	.15	.11	.06
398	Jack Armstrong	.06	.05	.02
399	*Freddie Benavides*	.10	.08	.04
400	Glenn Braggs	.05	.04	.02
401	Tom Browning	.06	.05	.02
402	Norm Charlton	.06	.05	.02
403	Eric Davis	.10	.07	.04
404	Rob Dibble	.08	.06	.03
405	Bill Doran	.05	.04	.02
406	Mariano Duncan	.05	.04	.02
407	*Kip Gross*	.10	.08	.04
408	Chris Hammond	.06	.05	.02
409	Billy Hatcher	.04	.03	.02
410	*Chris Jones* (FC)	.15	.11	.06
411	Barry Larkin	.10	.08	.04
412	Hal Morris	.10	.08	.04
413	Randy Myers	.05	.04	.02
414	Joe Oliver	.05	.04	.02
415	Paul O'Neill	.06	.05	.02
416	Ted Power	.04	.03	.02
417	Luis Quinones	.04	.03	.02
418	Jeff Reed	.04	.03	.02
419	Jose Rijo	.08	.06	.03
420	Chris Sabo	.08	.06	.03
421	Reggie Sanders (FC)	.15	.11	.06
422	Scott Scudder	.05	.04	.02
423	Glenn Sutko	.05	.04	.02
424	Eric Anthony	.08	.06	.03
425	*Jeff Bagwell*	.30	.25	.12
426	Craig Biggio	.08	.06	.03
427	Ken Caminiti	.05	.04	.02
428	Casey Candaele	.04	.03	.02
429	Mike Capel	.04	.03	.02
430	Andujar Cedeno	.15	.11	.06
431	Jim Corsi	.04	.03	.02
432	Mark Davidson	.04	.03	.02
433	Steve Finley	.06	.05	.02
434	Luis Gonzalez	.20	.15	.08
435	Pete Harnisch	.06	.05	.02
436	Dwayne Henry	.04	.03	.02
437	Xavier Hernandez	.04	.03	.02
438	Jimmy Jones	.04	.03	.02
439	*Darryl Kile*	.10	.08	.04
440	*Rob Mallicoat* (FC)	.15	.11	.06
441	*Andy Mota* (FC)	.15	.11	.06
442	Al Osuna	.05	.04	.02
443	Mark Portugal	.04	.03	.02
444	*Scott Servais* (FC)	.10	.08	.04
445	Mike Simms	.10	.08	.04
446	Gerald Young	.04	.03	.02

No.	Player	MT	NR MT	EX
447	Tim Belcher	.06	.05	.02
448	Brett Butler	.08	.06	.03
449	John Candelaria	.04	.03	.02
450	Gary Carter	.08	.06	.03
451	Dennis Cook	.04	.03	.02
452	Tim Crews	.04	.03	.02
453	Kal Daniels	.08	.06	.03
454	Jim Gott	.04	.03	.02
455	Alfredo Griffin	.04	.03	.02
456	Kevin Gross	.04	.03	.02
457	Chris Gwynn	.04	.03	.02
458	Lenny Harris	.05	.04	.02
459	Orel Hershiser	.08	.06	.03
460	Jay Howell	.05	.04	.02
461	Stan Javier	.04	.03	.02
462	Eric Karros (FC)	.20	.15	.08
463	Ramon Martinez	.12	.09	.05
464	Roger McDowell	.05	.04	.02
465	Mike Morgan	.05	.04	.02
466	Eddie Murray	.10	.07	.04
467	Jose Offerman	.12	.09	.05
468	Bob Ojeda	.05	.04	.02
469	Juan Samuel	.06	.05	.02
470	Mike Scioscia	.06	.05	.02
471	Darryl Strawberry	.10	.07	.04
472	*Bret Barberie* (FC)	.15	.11	.06
473	Brian Barnes	.06	.05	.02
474	Eric Bullock	.04	.03	.02
475	Ivan Calderon	.08	.06	.03
476	Delino DeShields	.08	.06	.03
477	*Jeff Fassero* (FC)	.10	.08	.04
478	Mike Fitzgerald	.04	.03	.02
479	Steve Frey	.04	.03	.02
480	Andres Galarraga	.06	.05	.02
481	Mark Gardner	.06	.05	.02
482	Marquis Grissom	.12	.09	.05
483	*Chris Haney* (FC)	.20	.15	.08
484	Barry Jones	.04	.03	.02
485	Dave Martinez	.05	.04	.02
486	Dennis Martinez	.08	.06	.03
487	Chris Nabholz	.06	.05	.02
488	Spike Owen	.04	.03	.02
489	Gilberto Reyes	.05	.04	.02
490	Mel Rojas	.05	.04	.02
491	Scott Ruskin	.05	.04	.02
492	Bill Sampen	.05	.04	.02
493	Larry Walker	.10	.08	.04
494	Tim Wallach	.08	.06	.03
495	Daryl Boston	.04	.03	.02
496	Hubie Brooks	.06	.05	.02
497	Tim Burke	.05	.04	.02
498	Mark Carreon	.04	.03	.02
499	Tony Castillo	.04	.03	.02
500	Vince Coleman	.08	.06	.03
501	David Cone	.08	.06	.03
502	Kevin Elster	.04	.03	.02
503	Sid Fernandez	.06	.05	.02
504	John Franco	.06	.05	.02
505	Dwight Gooden	.12	.09	.05
506	Todd Hundley	.12	.09	.05
507	Jeff Innis	.04	.03	.02
508	Gregg Jefferies	.12	.09	.05
509	Howard Johnson	.07	.05	.03
510	Dave Magadan	.06	.05	.02
511	*Terry McDaniel* (FC)	.20	.15	.08
512	Kevin McReynolds	.08	.06	.03
513	Keith Miller	.04	.03	.02
514	Charlie O'Brien	.04	.03	.02
515	Mackey Sasser	.04	.03	.02
516	*Pete Schourek*	.10	.08	.04
517	Julio Valera	.06	.05	.02
518	Frank Viola	.10	.08	.04
519	Wally Whitehurst	.05	.04	.02
520	*Anthony Young* (FC)	.20	.15	.08
521	*Andy Ashby*	.10	.08	.04
522	*Kim Batiste* (FC)	.10	.08	.04
523	Joe Boever	.04	.03	.02
524	Wes Chamberlain	.20	.15	.08
525	Pat Combs	.05	.04	.02
526	Danny Cox	.04	.03	.02
527	Darren Daulton	.05	.04	.02
528	Jose DeJesus	.05	.04	.02
529	Len Dykstra	.08	.06	.03
530	Darrin Fletcher	.05	.04	.02
531	Tommy Greene	.06	.05	.02
532	Jason Grimsley	.05	.04	.02
533	Charlie Hayes	.05	.04	.02
534	Von Hayes	.06	.05	.02
535	Dave Hollins	.08	.06	.03
536	Ricky Jordan	.08	.06	.03
537	John Kruk	.06	.05	.02
538	Jim Lindeman	.04	.03	.02
539	Mickey Morandini	.08	.06	.03
540	Terry Mulholland	.06	.05	.02
541	Dale Murphy	.12	.09	.05
542	Randy Ready	.04	.03	.02
543	Wally Ritchie	.04	.03	.02
544	Bruce Ruffin	.04	.03	.02
545	Steve Searcy	.04	.03	.02
546	Dickie Thon	.04	.03	.02
547	Mitch Williams	.08	.06	.03
548	Stan Belinda	.04	.03	.02
549	Jay Bell	.06	.05	.02
550	Barry Bonds	.15	.11	.06
551	Bobby Bonilla	.12	.09	.05
552	Steve Buechele	.05	.04	.02
553	Doug Drabek	.08	.06	.03
554	Neal Heaton	.04	.03	.02
555	Jeff King	.05	.04	.02
556	Bob Kipper	.04	.03	.02
557	Bill Landrum	.04	.03	.02
558	Mike LaValliere	.05	.04	.02
559	Jose Lind	.04	.03	.02
560	Lloyd McClendon	.04	.03	.02
561	Orlando Merced	.25	.20	.10
562	Bob Patterson	.04	.03	.02
563	*Joe Redfield* (FC)	.10	.08	.04
564	Gary Redus	.04	.03	.02

No.	Player	MT	NR MT	EX
565	Rosario Rodriguez	.04	.03	.02
566	Don Slaught	.04	.03	.02
567	John Smiley	.06	.05	.02
568	Zane Smith	.05	.04	.02
569	Randy Tomlin	.08	.06	.03
570	Andy Van Slyke	.06	.05	.02
571	Gary Varsho	.04	.03	.02
572	Bob Walk	.04	.03	.02
573	*John Wehner* (FC)	.25	.20	.10
574	Juan Agosto	.04	.03	.02
575	Cris Carpenter	.05	.04	.02
576	Jose DeLeon	.05	.04	.02
577	Rich Gedman	.04	.03	.02
578	Bernard Gilkey	.10	.08	.04
579	Pedro Guerrero	.08	.06	.03
580	Ken Hill	.05	.04	.02
581	Rex Hudler	.04	.03	.02
582	Felix Jose	.10	.08	.04
583	Ray Lankford	.15	.11	.06
584	Omar Olivares	.06	.05	.02
585	Jose Oquendo	.04	.03	.02
586	Tom Pagnozzi	.05	.04	.02
587	Geronimo Pena	.05	.04	.02
588	Mike Perez	.05	.04	.02
589	Gerald Perry	.04	.03	.02
590	Bryn Smith	.04	.03	.02
591	Lee Smith	.06	.05	.02
592	Ozzie Smith	.12	.09	.05
593	Scott Terry	.04	.03	.02
594	Bob Tewksbury	.04	.03	.02
595	Milt Thompson	.04	.03	.02
596	Todd Zeile	.12	.09	.05
597	Larry Andersen	.04	.03	.02
598	Oscar Azocar	.04	.03	.02
599	Andy Benes	.10	.08	.04
600	*Ricky Bones* (FC)	.10	.08	.04
601	Jerald Clark	.05	.04	.02
602	Pat Clements	.04	.03	.02
603	Paul Faries	.06	.05	.02
604	Tony Fernandez	.06	.05	.02
605	Tony Gwynn	.12	.09	.05
606	Greg Harris	.05	.04	.02
607	Thomas Howard	.05	.04	.02
608	Bruce Hurst	.06	.05	.02
609	Darrin Jackson	.04	.03	.02
610	Tom Lampkin	.04	.03	.02
611	Craig Lefferts	.04	.03	.02
612	*Jim Lewis*	.10	.07	.04
613	Mike Maddux	.04	.03	.02
614	Fred McGriff	.15	.11	.06
615	*Jose Melendez* (FC)	.20	.15	.08
616	*Jose Mota*	.15	.11	.06
617	Dennis Rasmussen	.04	.03	.02
618	Bip Roberts	.06	.05	.02
619	Rich Rodriguez	.04	.03	.02
620	Benito Santiago	.08	.06	.03
621	*Craig Shipley* (FC)	.10	.08	.04
622	Tim Teufel	.04	.03	.02
623	*Kevin Ward* (FC)	.15	.11	.06
624	Ed Whitson	.05	.04	.02
625	Dave Anderson	.04	.03	.02
626	Kevin Bass	.05	.04	.02
627	*Rod Beck* (FC)	.10	.08	.04
628	Bud Black	.05	.04	.02
629	Jeff Brantley	.05	.04	.02
630	John Burkett	.05	.04	.02
631	Will Clark	.25	.20	.10
632	Royce Clayton (FC)	.15	.11	.06
633	Steve Decker	.10	.08	.04
634	Kelly Downs	.04	.03	.02
635	Mike Felder	.04	.03	.02
636	Scott Garrelts	.04	.03	.02
637	Eric Gunderson	.08	.06	.03
638	*Bryan Hickerson* (FC)	.12	.09	.05
639	Darren Lewis	.15	.11	.06
640	Greg Litton	.04	.03	.02
641	Kirt Manwaring	.06	.05	.02
642	*Paul McClellan* (FC)	.10	.08	.04
643	Willie McGee	.08	.06	.03
644	Kevin Mitchell	.12	.09	.05
645	Francisco Olivares	.04	.03	.02
646	*Mike Remlinger* (FC)	.10	.08	.04
647	Dave Righetti	.06	.05	.02
648	Robby Thompson	.05	.04	.02
649	Jose Uribe	.04	.03	.02
650	Matt Williams	.12	.09	.05
651	Trevor Wilson	.06	.05	.02
652	Tom Goodwin (FC) (Prospects)	.25	.20	.10
653	Terry Bross (FC) (Prospects)	.08	.06	.03
654	*Mike Christopher* (Prospects)	.12	.09	.05
655	*Kenny Lofton* (Prospects)	.50	.40	.20
656	*Chris Cron* (FC) (Prospects)	.20	.15	.08
657	Willie Banks (FC) (Prospects)	.25	.20	.10
658	*Pat Rice* (Prospects)	.12	.09	.05
659a	*Rob Mauer* (FC) (Prospects, last name misspelled)	1.00	.70	.40
659b	*Rob Maurer* (FC) (Prospects, corrected)	.12	.09	.05
660	Don Harris (FC) (Prospects)	.12	.09	.05
661	*Henry Rodriguez* (Prospects)	.25	.20	.10
662	*Cliff Brantley* (Prospects)	.12	.09	.05
663	*Mike Linskey* (FC) (Prospects)	.20	.15	.08
664	Gary Disarcina (FC) (Prospects)	.08	.06	.03
665	*Gil Heredia* (Prospects)	.12	.09	.05
666	*Vinny Castilla* (FC) (Prospects)	.12	.09	.05
667	Paul Abbott (FC) (Prospects)	.08	.06	.03
668	Monty Fariss (FC) (Prospects)	.08	.06	.03
669	*Jarvis Brown* (FC) (Prospects)	.10	.08	.04
670	*Wayne Kirby* (Prospects)	.25	.20	.10
671	*Scott Brosius* (Prospects)	.15	.11	.06
672	Bob Hamelin (Prospects)	.15	.11	.06
673	*Joel Johnston* (FC) (Prospects)	.20	.15	.08
674	*Tim Spehr* (FC) (Prospects)	.15	.11	.06
675	*Jeff Gardner* (FC) (Prospects)	.15	.11	.06
676	*Rico Rossy* (FC) (Prospects)	.20	.15	.08
677	*Roberto Hernandez* (Prospects)	.20	.15	.08
678	*Ted Wood* (Prospects)	.12	.09	.05
679	Cal Eldred (FC) (Prospects)	.15	.11	.06

No.	Player	MT	NR MT	EX
680	Sean Berry (FC) (Prospects)	.08	.06	.03
681	Rickey Henderson (Stolen Base Record)	.15	.11	.06
682	Nolan Ryan (Record 7th No-hitter)	.20	.15	.08
683	Dennis Martinez (Perfect Game)	.05	.04	.02
684	Wilson Alvarez (Rookie No-hitter)	.05	.04	.02
685	Joe Carter (3 100 RBI Seasons)	.06	.05	.02
686	Dave Winfield (400 Home Runs)	.10	.08	.04
687	David Cone (Ties NL Record Strikeouts)	.06	.05	.02
688	Jose Canseco (League Leaders)	.15	.11	.06
689	Howard Johnson (League Leaders)	.06	.05	.02
690	Julio Franco (League Leaders)	.08	.06	.03
691	Terry Pendleton (League Leaders)	.08	.06	.03
692	Cecil Fielder (League Leaders)	.10	.08	.04
693	Scott Erickson (League Leaders)	.10	.08	.04
694	Tom Glavine (League Leaders)	.08	.06	.03
695	Dennis Martinez (League Leaders)	.05	.04	.02
696	Bryan Harvey (League Leaders)	.05	.04	.02
697	Lee Smith (League Leaders)	.05	.04	.02
698	Super Siblings (Roberto & Sandy Alomar)	.08	.06	.03
699	The Indispensables (Bobby Bonilla/Will Clark)	.10	.08	.04
700	Teamwork (Mark Wohlers/Kent Mercker/ Alejandro Pena)	.06	.05	.02
701	Tiger Tandems (Chris Jones/Bo Jackson/Gregg Olson/Frank Thomas)	.20	.15	.08
702	The Ignitors (Paul Molitor/Brett Butler)	.06	.05	.02
703	The Indispensables II (Cal Ripken, Jr./Joe Carter)	.15	.11	.06
704	Power Packs (Barry Larkin/Kirby Puckett)	.10	.08	.04
705	Today and Tomorrow (Mo Vaughn/Cecil Fielder)	.15	.11	.06
706	Teenage Sensations (Ramon Martinez/Ozzie Guillen)	.08	.06	.03
707	Designated Hitters (Harold Baines/Wade Boggs)	.08	.06	.03
708	Robin Yount (ProVision)	.20	.15	.08
709	Ken Griffey, Jr. (ProVision)	1.00	.75	.40
710	Nolan Ryan (ProVision)	.80	.60	.30
711	Cal Ripken, Jr. (ProVision)	.25	.20	.10
712	Frank Thomas (ProVision)	1.00	.70	.40
713	Dave Justice (ProVision)	.40	.30	.15
714	Checklist 1-101	.04	.03	.02
715	Checklist 102-194	.04	.03	.02
716	Checklist 195-296	.04	.03	.02
717	Checklist 297-397	.04	.03	.02
718	Checklist 398-494	.04	.03	.02
719	Checklist 495-596	.04	.03	.02
720 a	Checklist 597-720 (659 Rob Mauer)	.04	.03	.02
720 b	Checklist 597-720 (659 Rob Maurer)	.04	.03	.02

1992 Fleer All-Stars

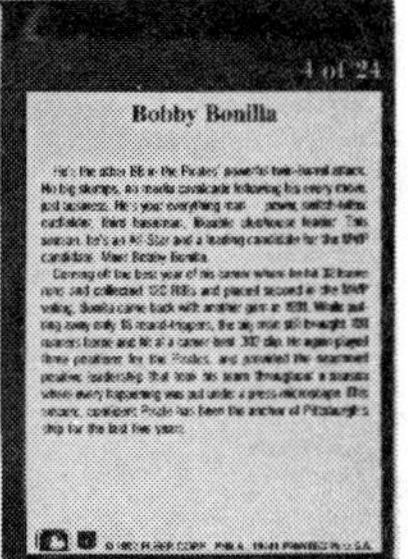

Black borders with gold highlights are featured on these special wax pack insert cards. The fronts feature glossy action photos with a portrait photo inset. The card backs feature career highlights and are numbered.

		MT	NR MT	EX
	Complete Set (24):	30.00	22.00	12.00
	Common Player:	.40	.30	.15
1	Felix Jose	.40	.30	.15
2	Tony Gwynn	1.50	1.25	.60
3	Barry Bonds	2.00	1.50	.80
4	Bobby Bonilla	1.00	.75	.40
5	Mike LaValliere	.40	.30	.15
6	Tom Glavine	.60	.45	.25
7	Ramon Martinez	.40	.30	.15
8	Lee Smith	.40	.30	.15
9	Mickey Tettleton	.50	.40	.20
10	Scott Erickson	.50	.40	.20
11	Frank Thomas	9.00	6.00	3.25
12	Danny Tartabull	.75	.60	.30
13	Will Clark	2.00	1.50	.80
14	Ryne Sandberg	3.00	2.00	1.00
15	Terry Pendleton	.60	.45	.25
16	Barry Larkin	.60	.45	.25
17	Rafael Palmeiro	.80	.60	.30
18	Julio Franco	.40	.30	.15
19	Robin Ventura	1.75	1.25	.70
20	Cal Ripken, Jr.	3.00	2.25	1.25

21	Joe Carter	1.00	.70	.40
22	Kirby Puckett	2.00	1.50	.80
23	Ken Griffey, Jr.	7.50	5.00	2.50
24	Jose Canseco	1.50	1.00	.50

1992 Fleer Roger Clemens

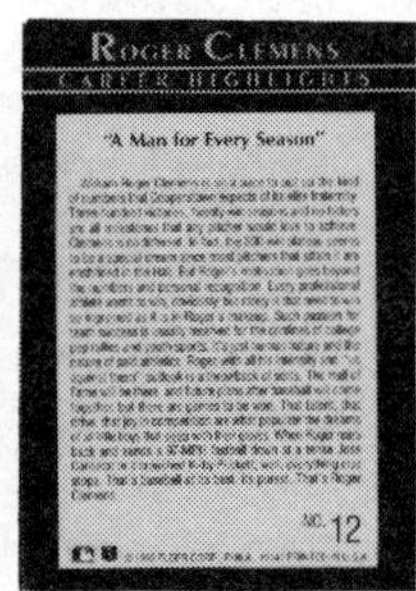

This 15-card set honors the career highlights of Roger Clemens. The initial 12 cards from the set were inserted in 1992 Fleer wax packs. A limited number of autographed cards were inserted as well. The additional three cards from the set were available through a mail-in offer. The card fronts feature black borders with metallic gold type. The flip side is yellow with black borders. Various career highlights are featured on the backs of the different cards.

		MT	NR MT	EX
Complete Set (15):		12.00	9.00	4.75
Common Card:		1.00	.60	.30
Autographed Card:		75.00	55.00	30.00
1	Quiet Storm	1.00	.75	.40
2	Courted by the Mets and Twins	1.00	.75	.40
3	The Show	1.00	.75	.40
4	A Rocket Launched	1.00	.75	.40
5	Time of Trial	1.00	.75	.40
6	Break Through	1.00	.75	.40
7	Play it Again Roger	1.00	.75	.40
8	Business as Usual	1.00	.75	.40
9	Heee's Back	1.00	.75	.40
10	Blood, Sweat and Tears	1.00	.75	.45
11	Prime of Life	1.00	.75	.40
12	Man for Every Season	1.00	.75	.40
13	Cooperstown Bound	1.00	.75	.40
14	The Heat of the Moment	1.00	.75	.40
15	Final Words	1.00	.75	.40

1992 Fleer Lumber Co.

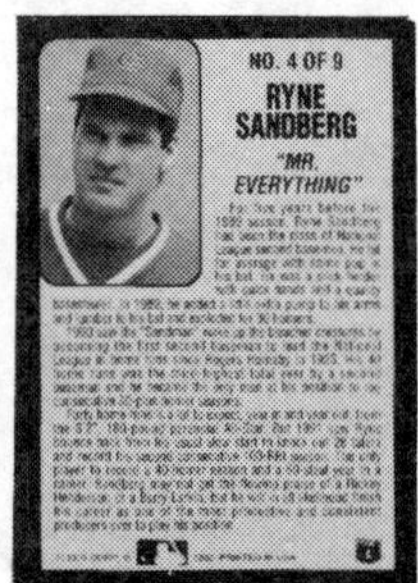

Baseball's top power hitters at each position are featured in this nine-card set. The card fronts feature full-color action photos bordered in black. "The Lumber Co." appears along the right border in the shape of a baseball bat. The card backs feature posed player photos and career highlights. The set was included only in factory sets released to the hobby trade.

		MT	NR MT	EX
Complete Set (9):		14.00	10.50	5.50
Common Player:		1.00	.60	.30
1	Cecil Fielder	1.50	1.25	.60
2	Mickey Tettleton	1.00	.60	.30
3	Darryl Strawberry	1.00	.75	.40
4	Ryne Sandberg	4.00	3.00	1.50
5	Jose Canseco	2.00	1.50	.75
6	Matt Williams	1.50	.90	.50
7	Cal Ripken, Jr.	4.00	3.00	1.50
8	Barry Bonds	4.50	3.50	1.75
9	Ron Gant	1.00	.75	.40

The values quoted are intended to reflect the market price.

1992 Fleer Rookie Sensations

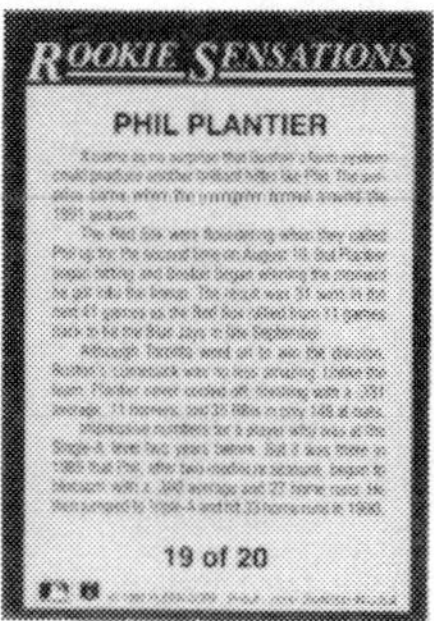

This 20-card set features the top rookies of 1991 and rookie prospects from 1992. The card fronts feature blue borders with "Rookie Sensations" in gold along the top border. A name plate is featured below the photo and also includes the team. The flip sides feature background information on the player. The cards were randomly inserted in 1992 Fleer cello packs. This issue saw very high prices when initially released then suffered long-term declines as the hobby became inundated with more and more insert sets.

		MT	NR MT	EX
Complete Set (20):		80.00	60.00	32.00
Common Player:		1.00	.70	.40
1	Frank Thomas	35.00	26.00	14.00
2	Todd Van Poppel	2.00	1.50	.80
3	Orlando Merced	2.50	2.00	1.00
4	Jeff Bagwell	12.00	9.00	4.75
5	Jeff Fassero	2.50	2.00	1.00
6	Darren Lewis	2.50	1.50	.75
7	Milt Cuyler	1.00	.70	.40
8	Mike Timlin	1.00	.70	.40
9	Brian McRae	2.50	1.50	.75
10	Chuck Knoblauch	3.50	2.75	1.50
11	Rich DeLucia	1.00	.70	.40
12	Ivan Rodriguez	6.00	4.50	2.50
13	Juan Guzman	5.00	3.75	2.00
14	Steve Chitren	1.00	.70	.40
15	Mark Wohlers	1.50	1.25	.60
16	Wes Chamberlain	1.00	.75	.40
17	Ray Lankford	5.00	3.00	1.50
18	Chito Martinez	1.00	.70	.40
19	Phil Plantier	8.00	6.00	3.25
20	Scott Leius	1.25	.90	.50

Values quoted in this guide reflect the retail price of a card – the price a collector can expect to pay when buying a card from a dealer. The wholesale price – that which a collector can expect to receive from a dealer when selling cards – will be significantly lower, depending on desirability and condition.

1992 Fleer Smoke 'N Heat

This 12-card set of top pitchers was included in factory sets designated for sale within the general retail trade. Card numbers have an S prefix.

		MT	NR MT	EX
Complete Set (12):		10.00	7.50	4.00
Common Player:		.50	.40	.20
1	Lee Smith	.50	.40	.20
2	Jack McDowell	1.25	.90	.50
3	David Cone	.50	.40	.20
4	Roger Clemens	2.50	2.00	1.00
5	Nolan Ryan	6.00	4.50	2.50
6	Scott Erickson	.50	.40	.20
7	Tom Glavine	.90	.70	.35
8	Dwight Gooden	.75	.60	.30
9	Andy Benes	.60	.45	.25
10	Steve Avery	1.00	.75	.40
11	Randy Johnson	1.00	.75	.40
12	Jim Abbott	1.00	.70	.40

1992 Fleer Team Leaders

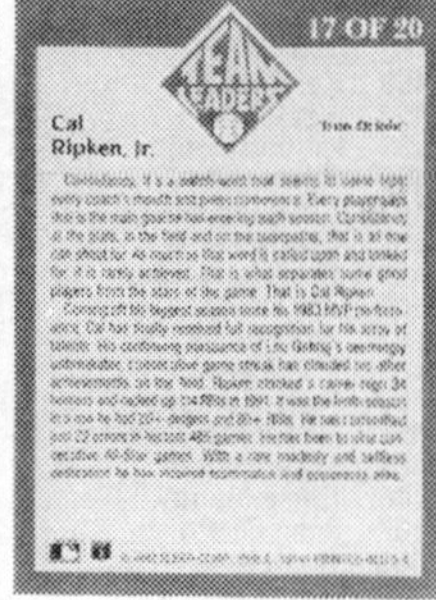

White and green borders highlight this insert set from Fleer. The card fronts also feature a special gold-foil "team leaders" logo beneath the full-color player photo. The card backs feature player information. The cards were randomly inserted in 1992 Fleer rack packs.

		MT	NR MT	EX
Complete Set (20):		34.00	25.00	13.50
Common Player:		.50	.40	.20
1	Don Mattingly	2.50	2.00	1.00
2	Howard Johnson	.60	.45	.25
3	Chris Sabo	.50	.40	.20
4	Carlton Fisk	.75	.60	.30
5	Kirby Puckett	3.00	2.25	1.25
6	Cecil Fielder	1.00	.75	.40
7	Tony Gwynn	1.50	1.25	.60
8	Will Clark	2.00	1.50	.80
9	Bobby Bonilla	1.00	.75	.40
10	Len Dykstra	1.00	.75	.40
11	Tom Glavine	1.50	1.25	.60
12	Rafael Palmeiro	1.00	.75	.40
13	Wade Boggs	1.50	1.25	.60
14	Joe Carter	1.00	.75	.40
15	Ken Griffey, Jr.	8.00	6.00	3.25
16	Darryl Strawberry	.50	.40	.20
17	Cal Ripken, Jr.	3.00	2.25	1.25
18	Danny Tartabull	.60	.45	.25
19	Jose Canseco	1.50	1.25	.60
20	Andre Dawson	.75	.60	.30

1992 Fleer Update

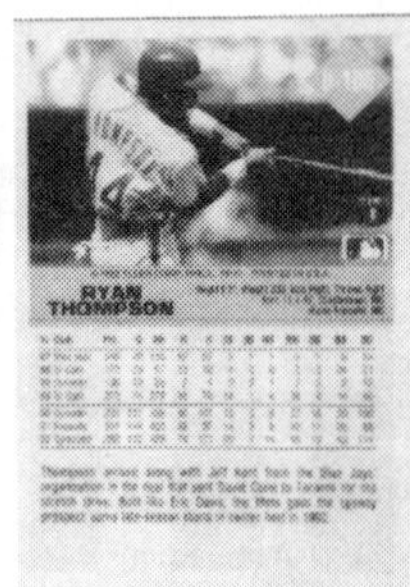

This 132-card set was released in boxed set form and features traded players, free agents and top rookies from 1992. The cards are styled after the regular 1992 Fleer and are numbered alphabetically according to team. This set marks the ninth year that Fleer has released an update set. The set includes four black-bordered "Headliner" cards.

		MT	NR MT	EX
Complete Set (136):		150.00	115.00	60.00
Common Player:		.20	.15	.08
H1	1992 All-Star Game MVP (Ken Griffey, Jr.)	25.00	20.00	10.00
H2	3000 Career Hits (Robin Yount)	7.00	5.25	2.75
H3	Major League Career Saves Record (Jeff Reardon)	1.00	.70	.40
H4	Record RBI Performance (Cecil Fielder)	4.00	3.00	1.50
1	Todd Frohwirth	.20	.15	.08
2	Alan Mills	.20	.15	.08
3	Rick Sutcliffe	.20	.15	.08
4	John Valentin (FC)	2.00	1.50	.80
5	Frank Viola	.20	.15	.08
6	Bob Zupcic (FC)	1.25	.90	.50
7	Mike Butcher (FC)	.20	.15	.08
8	Chad Curtis (FC)	4.00	3.00	1.50
9	Damion Easley (FC)	2.00	1.50	.80
10	Tim Salmon (FC)	38.00	28.00	15.00
11	Julio Valera	.20	.15	.08
12	George Bell	.20	.15	.08
13	Roberto Hernandez (FC)	.50	.40	.20
14	Shawn Jeter (FC)	.70	.50	.30
15	Thomas Howard	.20	.15	.08

16	Jesse Levis (FC)	.50	.40	.20
17	Kenny Lofton	12.00	9.00	4.75
18	Paul Sorrento	.20	.15	.08
19	Rico Brogna (FC)	.35	.25	.14
20	John Doherty (FC)	.20	.15	.08
21	Dan Gladden	.20	.15	.08
22	Buddy Groom (FC)	.35	.25	.14
23	Shawn Hare (FC)	.35	.25	.14
24	John Kiely (FC)	.40	.30	.15
25	Kurt Knudsen (FC)	.30	.25	.12
26	Gregg Jefferies	.30	.25	.12
27	Wally Joyner	.30	.25	.12
28	Kevin Koslofski (FC)	.40	.30	.15
29	Kevin McReynolds	.20	.15	.08
30	Rusty Meacham	.20	.15	.08
31	Keith Miller	.20	.15	.08
32	Hipolito Pichardo (FC)	.70	.50	.30
33	James Austin (FC)	.20	.15	.08
34	Scott Fletcher	.20	.15	.08
35	John Jaha (FC)	1.50	1.25	.60
36	Pat Listach (FC)	2.00	1.50	.80
37	Dave Nilsson (FC)	2.00	1.50	.80
38	Kevin Seitzer	.20	.15	.08
39	Tom Edens	.20	.15	.08
40	Pat Mahomes (FC)	1.00	.70	.40
41	John Smiley	.20	.15	.08
42	Charlie Hayes	.75	.60	.30
43	Sam Militello (FC)	1.50	1.25	.60
44	Andy Stankiewicz (FC)	.60	.45	.25
45	Danny Tartabull	.20	.15	.08
46	Bob Wickman (FC)	3.00	2.25	1.25
47	Jerry Browne	.20	.15	.08
48	Kevin Campbell (FC)	.20	.15	.08
49	Vince Horsman (FC)	.20	.15	.08
50	Troy Neel (FC)	3.50	2.75	1.50
51	Ruben Sierra	1.00	.70	.40
52	Bruce Walton (FC)	.20	.15	.08
53	Willie Wilson	.20	.15	.08
54	Bret Boone (FC)	3.50	2.75	1.50
55	Dave Fleming (FC)	2.50	2.00	1.00
56	Kevin Mitchell	.20	.15	.08
57	Jeff Nelson (FC)	.20	.15	.08
58	Shane Turner (FC)	.50	.40	.20
59	Jose Canseco	1.50	1.25	.60
60	Jeff Frye (FC)	.30	.25	.12
61	Damilo Leon (FC)	.40	.30	.15
62	Roger Pavlik (FC)	.60	.45	.25
63	David Cone	.20	.15	.08
64	Pat Hentgen (FC)	7.00	5.25	2.75
65	Randy Knorr (FC)	.20	.15	.08
66	Jack Morris	.20	.15	.08
67	Dave Winfield	2.50	2.00	1.00
68	David Nied (FC)	7.00	5.25	2.75
69	Otis Nixon	.20	.15	.08
70	Alejandro Pena	.20	.15	.08
71	Jeff Reardon	.20	.15	.08
72	Alex Arias (FC)	.60	.45	.25
73	Jim Bullinger (FC)	.30	.25	.12
74	Mike Morgan	.20	.15	.08
75	Rey Sanchez (FC)	.20	.15	.08
76	Bob Scanlan	.20	.15	.08
77	Sammy Sosa	2.00	1.50	.80
78	Scott Bankhead	.20	.15	.08
79	Tim Belcher	.20	.15	.08
80	Steve Foster (FC)	.40	.30	.15
81	Willie Greene (FC)	2.00	1.50	.80
82	Bip Roberts	.20	.15	.08
83	Scott Ruskin	.20	.15	.08
84	Greg Swindell	.20	.15	.08
85	Juan Guerrero (FC)	.40	.30	.15
86	Butch Henry (FC)	.30	.25	.12
87	Doug Jones	.20	.15	.08
88	Brian Williams (FC)	1.00	.70	.40
89	Tom Candiotti	.20	.15	.08
90	Eric Davis	.50	.40	.20
91	Carlos Hernandez (FC)	.20	.15	.08
92	Mike Piazza (FC)	75.00	56.00	30.00
93	Mike Sharperson	.20	.15	.08
94	Eric Young (FC)	3.00	2.25	1.25
95	Moises Alou	3.00	2.25	1.25
96	Greg Colbrunn	.20	.15	.08
97	Wil Cordero (FC)	3.00	2.25	1.25
98	Ken Hill	.20	.15	.08
99	John Vander Wal (FC)	.40	.30	.15
100	John Wetteland	.20	.15	.08
101	Bobby Bonilla	.75	.60	.30
102	Eric Hilman (FC)	.60	.45	.25
103	Pat Howell (FC)	.60	.45	.25
104	Jeff Kent (FC)	3.00	2.25	1.25
105	Dick Schofield	.20	.15	.08
106	Ryan Thompson (FC)	1.25	.90	.50
107	Chico Walker	.20	.15	.08
108	Juan Bell	.20	.15	.08
109	Mariano Duncan	.20	.15	.08
110	Jeff Grotewold (FC)	.70	.50	.30
111	Ben Rivera (FC)	.35	.25	.14
112	Curt Schilling	.20	.15	.08
113	Victor Cole (FC)	.70	.50	.30
114	Al Martin (FC)	4.00	3.00	1.50
115	Roger Mason	.20	.15	.08
116	Blas Minor (FC)	.70	.50	.30
117	Tim Wakefield (FC)	1.50	1.25	.60
118	Mark Clark (FC)	.35	.25	.14
119	Rheal Cormier (FC)	.40	.30	.15
120	Donovan Osborne (FC)	2.00	1.50	.80
121	Todd Worrell	.20	.15	.08
122	Jeremy Hernandez (FC)	.30	.25	.12
123	Randy Myers	.20	.15	.08
124	Frank Seminara (FC)	.30	.25	.12
125	Gary Sheffield	2.50	2.00	1.00
126	Dan Walters (FC)	.30	.25	.12
127	Steve Hosey (FC)	1.00	.70	.40
128	Mike Jackson	.20	.15	.08
129	Jim Pena (FC)	.70	.50	.30
130	Cory Snyder	.20	.15	.08
131	Bill Swift	.20	.15	.08
132	Checklist	.20	.15	.08

1992 Fleer Ultra

Fleer released its second consecutive Ultra set in 1992. The card fronts feature full-color action photos with a marble accent at the card bottom. The flip sides are horizontal with two additional player photos. Many insert sets were randomly included in foil packs as premiums. These included rookie, All-Star and award winners, among others. A two-card Tony Gwynn send-away set was also available through an offer from Fleer. For $1 and 10 Ultra wrappers, collectors could receive the Gwynn cards. The set is numbered by team; cards #1-300 comprise Series I, cards #301-600 are Series II.

		MT	NR MT	EX
	Complete Set (600):	40.00	30.00	16.00
	Common Player:	.12	.09	.05
1	Glenn Davis	.12	.09	.05
2	Mike Devereaux	.15	.11	.06
3	Dwight Evans	.12	.09	.05
4	Leo Gomez	.30	.25	.12
5	Chris Hoiles	.30	.25	.12
6	Sam Horn	.12	.09	.05
7	Chito Martinez	.15	.11	.06
8	Randy Milligan	.12	.09	.05
9	Mike Mussina	1.75	1.25	.70
10	Billy Ripken	.12	.09	.05
11	Cal Ripken, Jr.	1.00	.70	.40
12	Tom Brunansky	.12	.09	.05
13	Ellis Burks	.15	.11	.06
14	Jack Clark	.12	.09	.05
15	Roger Clemens	.75	.60	.30
16	Mike Greenwell	.12	.09	.05
17	Joe Hesketh	.12	.09	.05
18	Tony Pena	.12	.09	.05
19	Carlos Quintana	.12	.09	.05
20	Jeff Reardon	.12	.09	.05
21	Jody Reed	.12	.09	.05
22	Luis Rivera	.12	.09	.05
23	Mo Vaughn	1.00	.70	.40
24	Gary DiSarcina	.12	.09	.05
25	Chuck Finley	.15	.11	.06
26	Gary Gaetti	.12	.09	.05
27	Bryan Harvey	.15	.11	.06
28	Lance Parrish	.12	.09	.05
29	Luis Polonia	.12	.09	.05
30	Dick Schofield	.12	.09	.05
31	Luis Sojo	.12	.09	.05
32	Wilson Alvarez	.12	.09	.05
33	Carlton Fisk	.15	.11	.06
34	Craig Grebeck	.12	.09	.05
35	Ozzie Guillen	.12	.09	.05
36	Greg Hibbard	.12	.09	.05
37	Charlie Hough	.12	.09	.05
38	Lance Johnson	.12	.09	.05
39	Ron Karkovice	.12	.09	.05
40	Jack McDowell	.15	.11	.06
41	Donn Pall	.12	.09	.05
42	Melido Perez	.12	.09	.05
43	Tim Raines	.15	.11	.06
44	Frank Thomas	5.00	3.75	2.00
45	Sandy Alomar, Jr.	.15	.11	.06
46	Carlos Baerga	.75	.60	.30
47	Albert Belle	1.00	.70	.40
48	Jerry Browne	.12	.09	.05
49	Felix Fermin	.12	.09	.05
50	Reggie Jefferson	.15	.11	.06
51	Mark Lewis	.20	.15	.08
52	Carlos Martinez	.12	.09	.05
53	Steve Olin	.12	.09	.05
54	Jim Thome	.50	.40	.20
55	Mark Whiten	.25	.20	.10
56	Dave Bergman	.12	.09	.05
57	Milt Cuyler	.12	.09	.05
58	Rob Deer	.12	.09	.05
59	Cecil Fielder	.50	.40	.20
60	Travis Fryman	1.50	1.25	.60
61	Scott Livingstone	.15	.11	.06
62	Tony Phillips	.15	.11	.06
63	Mickey Tettleton	.15	.11	.06
64	Alan Trammell	.15	.11	.06
65	Lou Whitaker	.15	.11	.06
66	Kevin Appier	.15	.11	.06
67	Mike Boddicker	.12	.09	.05
68	George Brett	.40	.30	.15
69	Jim Eisenreich	.12	.09	.05
70	Mark Gubicza	.12	.09	.05
71	David Howard	.12	.09	.05
72	Joel Johnston	.12	.09	.05
73	Mike Macfarlane	.12	.09	.05
74	Brent Mayne	.12	.09	.05
75	Brian McRae	.30	.25	.12
76	Jeff Montgomery	.12	.09	.05
77	Terry Shumpert	.15	.11	.06
78	Don August	.12	.09	.05
79	Dante Bichette	.12	.09	.05
80	Ted Higuera	.12	.09	.05
81	Paul Molitor	.30	.25	.12
82	Jamie Navarro	.15	.11	.06
83	Gary Sheffield	.50	.40	.20
84	Bill Spiers	.12	.09	.05
85	B.J. Surhoff	.12	.09	.05
86	Greg Vaughn	.25	.20	.10
87	Robin Yount	.40	.30	.15
88	Rick Aguilera	.12	.09	.05
89	Chili Davis	.12	.09	.05
90	Scott Erickson	.15	.11	.06
91	Brian Harper	.12	.09	.05
92	Kent Hrbek	.12	.09	.05
93	Chuck Knoblauch	.25	.20	.10
94	Scott Leius	.12	.09	.05
95	Shane Mack	.15	.11	.06
96	Mike Pagliarulo	.12	.09	.05
97	Kirby Puckett	1.00	.70	.40
98	Kevin Tapani	.12	.09	.05
99	Jesse Barfield	.12	.09	.05
100	Alvaro Espinoza	.12	.09	.05
101	Mel Hall	.12	.09	.05
102	Pat Kelly	.12	.09	.05
103	Roberto Kelly	.10	.08	.04
104	Kevin Maas	.12	.09	.05
105	Don Mattingly	.50	.40	.20
106	Hensley Meulens	.12	.09	.05
107	Matt Nokes	.12	.09	.05
108	Steve Sax	.15	.11	.06
109	Harold Baines	.15	.11	.06
110	Jose Canseco	.40	.30	.15
111	Ron Darling	.12	.09	.05
112	Mike Gallego	.12	.09	.05
113	Dave Henderson	.12	.09	.05
114	Rickey Henderson	.40	.30	.15
115	Mark McGwire	.50	.40	.20
116	Terry Steinbach	.12	.09	.05
117	Dave Stewart	.15	.11	.06
118	Todd Van Poppel	.50	.40	.20
119	Bob Welch	.12	.09	.05
120	Greg Briley	.12	.09	.05
121	Jay Buhner	.12	.09	.05
122	Rich DeLucia	.12	.09	.05
123	Ken Griffey, Jr.	5.00	3.75	2.00
124	Erik Hanson	.12	.09	.05
125	Randy Johnson	.12	.09	.05
126	Edgar Martinez	.15	.11	.06
127	Tino Martinez	.15	.11	.06
128	Pete O'Brien	.12	.09	.05
129	Harold Reynolds	.12	.09	.05
130	Dave Valle	.12	.09	.05
131	Julio Franco	.15	.11	.06
132	Juan Gonzalez	4.00	3.00	1.50
133	Jeff Huson	.12	.09	.05
134	Mike Jeffcoat	.12	.09	.05
135	Terry Mathews	.12	.09	.05
136	Rafael Palmeiro	.20	.15	.08
137	Dean Palmer	.40	.30	.15
138	Geno Petralli	.12	.09	.05
139	Ivan Rodriguez	.40	.30	.15
140	Jeff Russell	.12	.09	.05
141	Nolan Ryan	3.00	2.25	1.25
142	Ruben Sierra	.25	.20	.10
143	Roberto Alomar	.75	.60	.30
144	Pat Borders	.12	.09	.05
145	Joe Carter	.40	.30	.15
146	Kelly Gruber	.12	.09	.05
147	Jimmy Key	.12	.09	.05
148	Manny Lee	.12	.09	.05
149	Rance Mulliniks	.12	.09	.05
150	Greg Myers	.12	.09	.05
151	John Olerud	1.00	.75	.40
152	Dave Stieb	.12	.09	.05
153	Todd Stottlemyre	.12	.09	.05
154	Duane Ward	.12	.09	.05
155	Devon White	.12	.09	.05
156	Eddie Zosky	.15	.11	.06
157	Steve Avery	.50	.40	.20
158	Rafael Belliard	.12	.09	.05
159	Jeff Blauser	.12	.09	.05
160	Sid Bream	.12	.09	.05
161	Ron Gant	.25	.20	.10
162	Tom Glavine	.50	.40	.20
163	Brian Hunter	.30	.25	.12
164	Dave Justice	1.00	.70	.40
165	Mark Lemke	.12	.09	.05
166	Greg Olson	.12	.09	.05
167	Terry Pendleton	.15	.11	.06
168	Lonnie Smith	.12	.09	.05
169	John Smoltz	.15	.11	.06
170	Mike Stanton	.12	.09	.05
171	Jeff Treadway	.12	.09	.05
172	Paul Assenmacher	.12	.09	.05
173	George Bell	.15	.11	.06
174	Shawon Dunston	.12	.09	.05
175	Mark Grace	.30	.25	.12
176	Danny Jackson	.12	.09	.05
177	Les Lancaster	.12	.09	.05
178	Greg Maddux	.15	.11	.06
179	Luis Salazar	.12	.09	.05
180	Rey Sanchez	.15	.11	.06
181	Ryne Sandberg	1.00	.70	.40
182	Jose Vizcaino	.12	.09	.05
183	Chico Walker	.12	.09	.05
184	Jerome Walton	.12	.09	.05
185	Glenn Braggs	.12	.09	.05
186	Tom Browning	.12	.09	.05
187	Rob Dibble	.15	.11	.06
188	Bill Doran	.12	.09	.05
189	Chris Hammond	.15	.11	.06
190	Billy Hatcher	.12	.09	.05
191	Barry Larkin	.30	.25	.12
192	Hal Morris	.15	.11	.06
193	Joe Oliver	.12	.09	.05

194	Paul O'Neill	.12	.09	.05
195	Jeff Reed	.12	.09	.05
196	Jose Rijo	.12	.09	.05
197	Chris Sabo	.15	.11	.06
198	Jeff Bagwell	1.00	.75	.40
199	Craig Biggio	.15	.11	.06
200	Ken Caminiti	.12	.09	.05
201	Andujar Cedeno	.15	.11	.06
202	Steve Finley	.15	.11	.06
203	Luis Gonzalez	.15	.11	.06
204	Pete Harnisch	.15	.11	.06
205	Xavier Hernandez	.12	.09	.05
206	Darryl Kile	.12	.09	.05
207	Al Osuna	.12	.09	.05
208	Curt Schilling	.12	.09	.05
209	Brett Butler	.12	.09	.05
210	Kal Daniels	.12	.09	.05
211	Lenny Harris	.12	.09	.05
212	Stan Javier	.12	.09	.05
213	Ramon Martinez	.15	.11	.06
214	Roger McDowell	.12	.09	.05
215	Jose Offerman	.12	.09	.05
216	Juan Samuel	.12	.09	.05
217	Mike Scioscia	.12	.09	.05
218	Mike Sharperson	.12	.09	.05
219	Darryl Strawberry	.20	.15	.08
220	Delino DeShields	.20	.15	.08
221	Tom Foley	.12	.09	.05
222	Steve Frey	.12	.09	.05
223	Dennis Martinez	.12	.09	.05
224	Spike Owen	.12	.09	.05
225	Gilberto Reyes	.12	.09	.05
226	Tim Wallach	.12	.09	.05
227	Daryl Boston	.12	.09	.05
228	Tim Burke	.12	.09	.05
229	Vince Coleman	.12	.09	.05
230	David Cone	.15	.11	.06
231	Kevin Elster	.12	.09	.05
232	Dwight Gooden	.15	.11	.06
233	Todd Hundley	.15	.11	.06
234	Jeff Innis	.12	.09	.05
235	Howard Johnson	.15	.11	.06
236	Dave Magadan	.12	.09	.05
237	Mackey Sasser	.12	.09	.05
238	Anthony Young	.15	.11	.06
239	Wes Chamberlain	.15	.11	.06
240	Darren Daulton	.15	.11	.06
241	Len Dykstra	.20	.15	.08
242	Tommy Greene	.12	.09	.05
243	Charlie Hayes	.12	.09	.05
244	Dave Hollins	.20	.15	.08
245	Ricky Jordan	.15	.11	.06
246	John Kruk	.15	.11	.06
247	Mickey Morandini	.15	.11	.06
248	Terry Mulholland	.12	.09	.05
249	Dale Murphy	.12	.09	.05
250	Jay Bell	.15	.11	.06
251	Barry Bonds	1.50	1.25	.60
252	Steve Buechele	.12	.09	.05
253	Doug Drabek	.15	.11	.06
254	Mike LaValliere	.12	.09	.05
255	Jose Lind	.12	.09	.05
256	Lloyd McClendon	.12	.09	.05
257	Orlando Merced	.30	.25	.12
258	Don Slaught	.12	.09	.05
259	John Smiley	.12	.09	.05
260	Zane Smith	.12	.09	.05
261	Randy Tomlin	.15	.11	.06
262	Andy Van Slyke	.15	.11	.06
263	Pedro Guererro	.15	.11	.06
264	Felix Jose	.12	.09	.05
265	Ray Lankford	.40	.30	.15
266	Omar Olivares	.12	.09	.05
267	Jose Oquendo	.12	.09	.05
268	Tom Pagnozzi	.12	.09	.05
269	Bryn Smith	.12	.09	.05
270	Lee Smith	.12	.09	.05
271	Ozzie Smith	.40	.30	.15
272	Milt Thompson	.12	.09	.05
273	Todd Zeile	.12	.09	.05
274	Andy Benes	.15	.11	.06
275	Jerald Clark	.12	.09	.05
276	Tony Fernandez	.12	.09	.05
277	Tony Gwynn	.40	.30	.15
278	Greg Harris	.12	.09	.05
279	Thomas Howard	.12	.09	.05
280	Bruce Hurst	.12	.09	.05
281	Mike Maddux	.12	.09	.05
282	Fred McGriff	.50	.40	.20
283	Benito Santiago	.15	.11	.06
284	Kevin Bass	.12	.09	.05
285	Jeff Brantley	.12	.09	.05
286	John Burkett	.12	.09	.05
287	Will Clark	.75	.60	.30
288	Royce Clayton	.60	.45	.25
289	Steve Decker	.12	.09	.05
290	Kelly Downs	.12	.09	.05
291	Mike Felder	.12	.09	.05
292	Darren Lewis	.15	.11	.06
293	Kirt Manwaring	.12	.09	.05
294	Willie McGee	.12	.09	.05
295	Robby Thompson	.12	.09	.05
296	Matt Williams	.40	.30	.15
297	Trevor Wilson	.12	.09	.05
298	Checklist 1-108 (Sandy Alomar, Jr.)	.10	.08	.04
299	Checklist 109-208 (Rey Sanchez)	.10	.08	.04
300	Checklist 209-300 (Nolan Ryan)	.15	.11	.06
301	Brady Anderson	.20	.15	.08
302	Todd Frohwirth	.12	.09	.05
303	Ben McDonald	.30	.25	.12
304	Mark McLemore	.12	.09	.05
305	Jose Mesa	.12	.09	.05
306	Bob Milacki	.12	.09	.05
307	Gregg Olson	.20	.15	.08
308	David Segui	.12	.09	.05
309	Rick Sutcliffe	.20	.15	.08
310	Jeff Tackett	.20	.15	.08
311	Wade Boggs	.30	.25	.12
312	Scott Cooper	.20	.15	.08
313	John Flaherty	.15	.11	.06
314	Wayne Housie	.20	.15	.08
315	Peter Hoy	.20	.15	.08
316	John Marzano	.12	.09	.05
317	Tim Naehring	.20	.15	.08
318	Phil Plantier	.60	.45	.25
319	Frank Viola	.15	.11	.06
320	Matt Young	.12	.09	.05
321	Jim Abbott	.30	.25	.12
322	Hubie Brooks	.12	.09	.05
323	*Chad Curtis*	1.00	.75	.40
324	Alvin Davis	.12	.09	.05
325	Junior Felix	.20	.15	.08
326	Von Hayes	.12	.09	.05
327	Mark Langston	.15	.11	.06
328	Scott Lewis	.12	.09	.05
329	Don Robinson	.12	.09	.05
330	Bobby Rose	.12	.09	.05
331	Lee Stevens	.12	.09	.05
332	George Bell	.15	.11	.06
333	Esteban Beltre	.12	.09	.05
334	Joey Cora	.12	.09	.05
335	Alex Fernandez	.40	.30	.15
336	Roberto Hernandez	.15	.11	.06
337	Mike Huff	.12	.09	.05
338	Kirk McCaskill	.12	.09	.05
339	Dan Pasqua	.12	.09	.05
340	Scott Radinsky	.12	.09	.05
341	Steve Sax	.20	.15	.08
342	Bobby Thigpen	.30	.25	.12
343	Robin Ventura	.60	.45	.25
344	Jack Armstrong	.12	.09	.05
345	Alex Cole	.12	.09	.05
346	Dennis Cook	.12	.09	.05
347	Glenallen Hill	.12	.09	.05
348	Thomas Howard	.12	.09	.05
349	Brook Jacoby	.12	.09	.05
350	Kenny Lofton	1.25	.90	.50
351	Charles Nagy	.20	.15	.08
352	Rod Nichols	.12	.09	.05
353	Junior Ortiz	.12	.09	.05
354	Dave Otto	.12	.09	.05
355	Tony Perezchica	.12	.09	.05
356	Scott Scudder	.12	.09	.05
357	Paul Sorrento	.12	.09	.05
358	Skeeter Barnes	.12	.09	.05
359	Mark Carreon	.12	.09	.05
360	John Doherty	.12	.09	.05
361	Dan Gladden	.12	.09	.05
362	Bill Gullickson	.20	.15	.08
363	Shawn Hare	.15	.11	.06
364	Mike Henneman	.20	.15	.08
365	Chad Kreuter	.12	.09	.05
366	Mark Leiter	.12	.09	.05
367	Mike Munoz	.12	.09	.05
368	Kevin Ritz	.12	.09	.05
369	Mark Davis	.12	.09	.05
370	Tom Gordon	.12	.09	.05
371	Chris Gwynn	.12	.09	.05
372	Gregg Jefferies	.25	.20	.10
373	Wally Joyner	.15	.11	.06
374	Kevin McReynolds	.15	.11	.06
375	Keith Miller	.12	.09	.05
376	Rico Rossy	.15	.11	.06
377	Curtis Wilkerson	.12	.09	.05
378	Ricky Bones	.12	.09	.05
379	Chris Bosio	.12	.09	.05
380	Cal Eldred	.75	.60	.30
381	Scott Fletcher	.12	.09	.05
382	Jim Gantner	.12	.09	.05
383	Darryl Hamilton	.12	.09	.05
384	Doug Henry	.25	.20	.10
385	Pat Listach	.50	.40	.20
386	Tim McIntosh	.12	.09	.05
387	Edwin Nunez	.12	.09	.05
388	Dan Plesac	.12	.09	.05
389	Kevin Seitzer	.12	.09	.05
390	Franklin Stubbs	.12	.09	.05
391	William Suero	.15	.11	.06
392	Bill Wegman	.12	.09	.05
393	Willie Banks	.12	.09	.05
394	Jarvis Brown	.15	.11	.06
395	Greg Gagne	.12	.09	.05
396	Mark Guthrie	.12	.09	.05
397	Bill Krueger	.12	.09	.05
398	Pat Mahomes	.50	.40	.20
399	Pedro Munoz	.15	.11	.06
400	John Smiley	.12	.09	.05
401	Gary Wayne	.12	.09	.05
402	Lenny Webster	.12	.09	.05
403	Carl Willis	.12	.09	.05
404	Greg Cadaret	.12	.09	.05
405	Steve Farr	.12	.09	.05
406	Mike Gallego	.12	.09	.05
407	Charlie Hayes	.12	.09	.05
408	Steve Howe	.12	.09	.05
409	Dion James	.12	.09	.05
410	Jeff Johnson	.12	.09	.05
411	Tim Leary	.12	.09	.05
412	Jim Leyritz	.12	.09	.05
413	Melido Perez	.12	.09	.05
414	Scott Sanderson	.12	.09	.05
415	Andy Stankiewicz	.35	.25	.14
416	Mike Stanley	.12	.09	.05
417	Danny Tartabull	.15	.11	.06
418	Lance Blankenship	.12	.09	.05
419	Mike Bordick	.12	.09	.05
420	Scott Brosius	.12	.09	.05
421	Dennis Eckersley	.15	.11	.06
422	Scott Hemond	.12	.09	.05
423	Carney Lansford	.12	.09	.05
424	Henry Mercedes	.15	.11	.06
425	Mike Moore	.12	.09	.05
426	Gene Nelson	.12	.09	.05
427	Randy Ready	.12	.09	.05
428	Bruce Walton	.12	.09	.05
429	Willie Wilson	.12	.09	.05
430	Rich Amaral	.12	.09	.05
431	Dave Cochrane	.12	.09	.05
432	Henry Cotto	.12	.09	.05
433	Calvin Jones	.20	.15	.08
434	Kevin Mitchell	.25	.20	.10
435	Clay Parker	.12	.09	.05
436	Omar Vizquel	.12	.09	.05
437	Floyd Bannister	.12	.09	.05
438	Kevin Brown	.12	.09	.05
439	John Cangelosi	.12	.09	.05
440	Brian Downing	.12	.09	.05
441	Monty Fariss	.12	.09	.05
442	Jose Guzman	.12	.09	.05
443	Donald Harris	.15	.11	.06
444	Kevin Reimer	.12	.09	.05
445	Kenny Rogers	.12	.09	.05
446	Wayne Rosenthal	.12	.09	.05
447	Dickie Thon	.12	.09	.05
448	Derek Bell	.40	.30	.15
449	Juan Guzman	.75	.60	.30
450	Tom Henke	.12	.09	.05
451	Candy Maldonado	.12	.09	.05
452	Jack Morris	.20	.15	.08
453	David Wells	.12	.09	.05
454	Dave Winfield	.50	.40	.20
455	Juan Berenguer	.12	.09	.05
456	Damon Berryhill	.12	.09	.05
457	Mike Bielecki	.12	.09	.05
458	Marvin Freeman	.12	.09	.05
459	Charlie Leibrandt	.12	.09	.05
460	Kent Mercker	.12	.09	.05
461	Otis Nixon	.15	.11	.06
462	Alejandro Pena	.12	.09	.05
463	Ben Rivera	.15	.11	.06
464	Deion Sanders	.50	.40	.20
465	Mark Wohlers	.30	.25	.12
466	Shawn Boskie	.12	.09	.05
467	Frank Castillo	.12	.09	.05
468	Andre Dawson	.15	.11	.06
469	Joe Girardi	.12	.09	.05
470	Chuck McElroy	.12	.09	.05
471	Mike Morgan	.12	.09	.05
472	Ken Patterson	.12	.09	.05
473	Bob Scanlan	.12	.09	.05
474	Gary Scott	.25	.20	.10
475	Dave Smith	.12	.09	.05
476	Sammy Sosa	.50	.40	.20
477	Hector Villanueva	.12	.09	.05
478	Scott Bankhead	.12	.09	.05
479	Tim Belcher	.12	.09	.05
480	Freddie Benavides	.15	.11	.06
481	Jacob Brumfield	.15	.11	.06
482	Norm Charlton	.15	.11	.06
483	Dwayne Henry	.12	.09	.05
484	Dave Martinez	.12	.09	.05
485	Bip Roberts	.15	.11	.06
486	Reggie Sanders	.60	.45	.25
487	Greg Swindell	.15	.11	.06
488	Ryan Bowen	.15	.11	.06
489	Casey Candaele	.12	.09	.05
490	Juan Guerrero	.15	.11	.06
491	Pete Incaviglia	.12	.09	.05
492	Jeff Juden	.15	.11	.06
493	Rob Murphy	.12	.09	.05
494	Mark Portugal	.12	.09	.05
495	Rafael Ramirez	.12	.09	.05
496	Scott Servais	.12	.09	.05
497	Ed Taubensee	.15	.11	.06
498	Brian Williams	.20	.15	.08
499	Todd Benzinger	.12	.09	.05
500	John Candelaria	.12	.09	.05
501	Tom Candiotti	.12	.09	.05
502	Tim Crews	.12	.09	.05
503	Eric Davis	.20	.15	.08
504	Jim Gott	.12	.09	.05
505	Dave Hansen	.12	.09	.05
506	Carlos Hernandez	.12	.09	.05
507	Orel Hershiser	.12	.09	.05
508	Eric Karros	.75	.60	.30
509	Bob Ojeda	.12	.09	.05
510	Steve Wilson	.12	.09	.05
511	Moises Alou	.15	.11	.06
512	Bret Barberie	.20	.15	.08
513	Ivan Calderon	.25	.20	.10
514	Gary Carter	.25	.20	.10
515	Archi Cianfrocco	.25	.20	.10
516	Jeff Fassero	.12	.09	.05
517	Darrin Fletcher	.12	.09	.05
518	Marquis Grissom	.30	.25	.12
519	Chris Haney	.15	.11	.06
520	Ken Hill	.15	.11	.06
521	Chris Nabholz	.12	.09	.05
522	Bill Sampen	.12	.09	.05
523	John VanderWal	.15	.11	.06
524	David Wainhouse	.25	.20	.10
525	Larry Walker	.35	.25	.14
526	John Wetteland	.15	.11	.06
527	Bobby Bonilla	.20	.15	.08
528	Sid Fernandez	.15	.11	.06
529	John Franco	.12	.09	.05
530	Dave Gallagher	.12	.09	.05
531	Paul Gibson	.12	.09	.05
532	Eddie Murray	.25	.20	.10
533	Junior Noboa	.12	.09	.05
534	Charlie O'Brien	.12	.09	.05
535	Bill Pecota	.12	.09	.05
536	Willie Randolph	.12	.09	.05
537	Bret Saberhagen	.12	.09	.05
538	Dick Schofield	.12	.09	.05
539	Pete Schourek	.12	.09	.05
540	Ruben Amaro	.20	.15	.08
541	Andy Ashby	.12	.09	.05
542	Kim Batiste	.15	.11	.06
543	Cliff Brantley	.15	.11	.06
544	Mariano Duncan	.12	.09	.05
545	Jeff Grotewold	.15	.11	.06

546	Barry Jones	.12	.09	.05
547	Julio Peguero	.15	.11	.06
548	Curt Schilling	.12	.09	.05
549	Mitch Williams	.20	.15	.08
550	Stan Belinda	.12	.09	.05
551	Scott Bullett	.20	.15	.08
552	Cecil Espy	.12	.09	.05
553	Jeff King	.12	.09	.05
554	Roger Mason	.12	.09	.05
555	Paul Miller	.15	.11	.06
556	Denny Neagle	.15	.11	.06
557	Vocente Palacios	.12	.09	.05
558	Bob Patterson	.12	.09	.05
559	Tom Prince	.12	.09	.05
560	Gary Redus	.12	.09	.05
561	Gary Varsho	.12	.09	.05
562	Juan Agosto	.12	.09	.05
563	Cris Carpenter	.12	.09	.05
564	Mark Clark	.15	.11	.06
565	Jose DeLeon	.12	.09	.05
566	Rich Gedman	.12	.09	.05
567	Bernard Gilkey	.15	.11	.06
568	Rex Hudler	.12	.09	.05
569	Tim Jones	.12	.09	.05
570	Donovan Osborne	.25	.20	.10
571	Mike Perez	.12	.09	.05
572	Gerald Perry	.12	.09	.05
573	Bob Tewksbury	.15	.11	.06
574	Todd Worrell	.12	.09	.05
575	Dave Eiland	.12	.09	.05
576	Jeremy Hernandez	.15	.11	.06
577	Craig Lefferts	.12	.09	.05
578	Jose Melendez	.12	.09	.05
579	Randy Myers	.12	.09	.05
580	Gary Pettis	.12	.09	.05
581	Rich Rodriguez	.12	.09	.05
582	Gary Sheffield	.50	.40	.20
583	Craig Shipley	.12	.09	.05
584	Kurt Stillwell	.12	.09	.05
585	Tim Teufel	.12	.09	.05
586	*Rod Beck*	.50	.40	.20
587	Dave Burba	.12	.09	.05
588	Craig Colbert	.15	.11	.06
589	Bryan Hickerson	.12	.09	.05
590	Mike Jackson	.12	.09	.05
591	Mark Leonard	.12	.09	.05
592	Jim McNamara	.15	.11	.06
593	John Patterson	.20	.15	.08
594	Dave Righetti	.12	.09	.05
595	Cory Snyder	.12	.09	.05
596	Bill Swift	.15	.11	.06
597	Ted Wood	.15	.11	.06
598	Checklist 301-403 (Scott Sanderson)	.10	.08	.04
599	Checklist 404-498 (Junior Ortiz)	.10	.08	.04
600	Checklist 499-600 (Mike Morgan)	.10	.08	.04

1992 Fleer Ultra Award Winners

The 25 cards in this insert issue were randomly packaged with Series I Ultra. One of the Cal Ripken cards (#21) can be found with a photo made from a reversed negative, as well as with the proper orientation. Neither version carries a premium.

		MT	NR MT	EX
	Complete Set (25):	50.00	30.00	20.00
	Common Player:	1.00	.60	.30
1	Jack Morris	1.00	.70	.40
2	Chuck Knoblauch	1.25	.90	.50
3	Jeff Bagwell	4.00	3.00	1.50
4	Terry Pendleton	1.00	.70	.40
5	Cal Ripken, Jr.	5.00	3.75	2.00
6	Roger Clemens	3.00	2.25	1.25
7	Tom Glavine	2.50	2.00	1.00
8	Tom Pagnozzi	1.00	.70	.40
9	Ozzie Smith	2.50	2.00	1.00
10	Andy Van Slyke	1.00	.70	.40
11	Barry Bonds	5.00	3.75	2.00
12	Tony Gwynn	2.50	2.00	1.00
13	Matt Williams	2.00	1.50	.80
14	Will Clark	3.50	2.75	1.50
15	Robin Ventura	2.50	2.00	1.00
16	Mark Langston	1.00	.70	.40
18	Devon White	1.00	.70	.40
19	Don Mattingly	3.00	2.25	1.25
20	Roberto Alomar	4.00	3.00	1.50
21a	Cal Ripken, Jr. (reversed negative)	5.00	3.75	2.00
21b	Cal Ripken, Jr. (correct)	5.00	3.75	2.00
22	Ken Griffey, Jr.	10.00	7.50	4.00
23	Kirby Puckett	5.00	3.75	2.00
24	Greg Maddux	2.50	2.00	1.00
25	Ryne Sandberg	5.00	3.75	2.00

1992 Fleer Ultra All-Rookies

The 10 promising rookies in this set could be found on special cards inserted in Ultra Series II foil packs.

		MT	NR MT	EX
	Complete Set (10):	15.00	12.00	6.00
	Common Player:	.60	.40	.20
1	Eric Karros	3.50	2.50	1.25
2	Andy Stankiewicz	.60	.40	.20
3	Gary DiSarcina	.60	.40	.20
4	Archi Cianfrocco	1.00	.60	.30
5	Jim McNamara	.60	.40	.20
6	Chad Curtis	4.50	3.00	1.50
7	Kenny Lofton	7.50	5.00	2.50
8	Reggie Sanders	3.00	2.00	1.00
9	Pat Mahomes	.90	.70	.35
10	Donovan Osborne	.90	.70	.35

A player's name in italic type indicates a rookie card. An (FC) indicates a player's first card for that particular card company.

1992 Fleer Ultra All-Stars

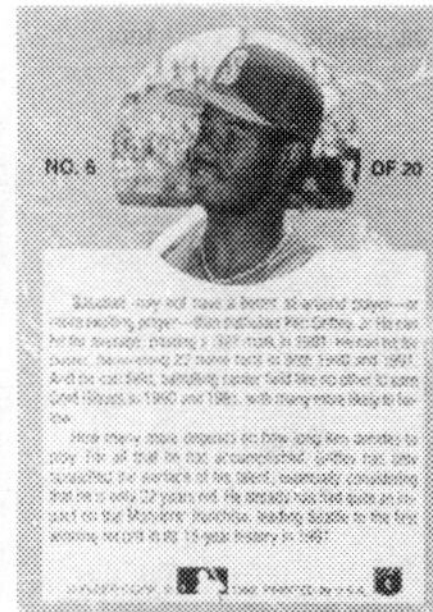

An All-Star team from each league, with two pitchers, could be assembled by collecting these inserts from Ultra Series II foil packs.

		MT	NR MT	EX
	Complete Set (20):	28.00	16.00	8.00
	Common Player:	.60	.40	.20
1	Mark McGwire	1.00	.75	.40
2	Roberto Alomar	2.00	1.50	.75
3	Cal Ripken, Jr.	3.50	2.50	1.25
4	Wade Boggs	1.25	.75	.40
5	Mickey Tettleton	.60	.40	.20
6	Ken Griffey, Jr.	9.00	6.00	3.00
7	Tom Glavine	.60	.40	.20
8	Kirby Puckett	3.00	2.00	1.00
9	Frank Thomas	11.00	6.00	3.00
10	Jack McDowell	.90	.70	.35
11	Will Clark	2.50	1.50	.75
12	Ryne Sandberg	3.50	2.50	1.25
13	Barry Larkin	.90	.70	.35
14	Gary Sheffield	1.00	.75	.40
15	Tom Pagnozzi	.60	.40	.20
16	Barry Bonds	3.00	2.25	1.20
17	Deion Sanders	1.75	1.25	.60
18	Darryl Strawberry	.75	.60	.30
19	David Cone	.60	.40	.20
20	Tom Glavine	.90	.70	.35

Values for recent cards and sets are listed in Mint (MT), Near Mint (NM), reflecting the fact that many cards from recent years have been preserved in top condition. Recent cards and sets in less than Excellent condition have little collector interest.

1992 Fleer Ultra Tony Gwynn

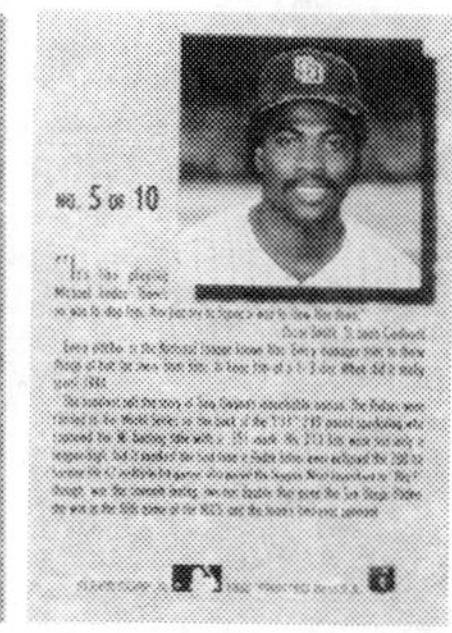

This 12-card subset of Ultra's spokesman features 10 cards which were available as inserts in Series I foil packs, plus two cards labeled "Special No. 1" and "Special No. 2" which could only be obtained in a send-away offer. Some 2,000 of these cards carry a "certified" Gwynn autograph.

		MT	NR MT	EX
	Complete Set (12):	12.00	8.00	4.00
	Common Card:	1.00	.60	.30
	Autograph:	90.00	70.00	35.00
	INSERT CARDS			
1	Tony Gwynn (leaping at outfield wall)	1.00	.75	.40
2	Tony Gwynn (batting in brown warm-up jersey)	1.00	.75	.40
3	Tony Gwynn (catching fly, glove over head)	1.00	.75	.40
4	Tony Gwynn (follow-through of swing)	1.00	.75	.40
5	Tony Gwynn (leading off first base)	1.00	.75	.40
6	Tony Gwynn (Silver Slugger/Gold Glove)	1.00	.75	.40
7	Tony Gwynn (bunting)	1.00	.75	.40
8	Tony Gwynn (swinging)	1.00	.75	.40
9	Tony Gwynn (leaving batter's box)	1.00	.75	.40
10	Tony Gwynn (batting, wearing sun glasses)	1.00	.75	.40
	SEND-AWAY CARDS			
1	Tony Gwynn (batting)	1.00	.75	.40
2	Tony Gwynn (fielding)	1.00	.75	.40

1992 Fleer 7-Eleven

The 1992 Performer Collection was a combined effort from Fleer and 7-11. Customers at 7-11 stores received a packet of five cards with gasoline purchases to build the 24-card set of major stars. The cards are standard size, with virtually the identical design to the regular issue Fleer set of 1992, with only the addition of "The Performer" logo on the lower corner of the card.

		MT	NR MT	EX
	Complete Set (24):	6.00	4.50	2.50
	Common Player:	.15	.11	.06
1	Nolan Ryan	1.00	.70	.40
2	Frank Thomas	1.00	.70	.40
3	Ryne Sandberg	.50	.40	.20
4	Ken Griffey, Jr.	.75	.60	.30
5	Cal Ripken, Jr.	.50	.40	.20
6	Roger Clemens	.30	.25	.12
7	Cecil Fielder	.30	.25	.12
8	Dave Justice	.20	.15	.08
9	Wade Boggs	.40	.30	.15
10	Tony Gwynn	.20	.15	.08
11	Kirby Puckett	.25	.20	.10
12	Darryl Strawberry	.20	.15	.08
13	Jose Canseco	.45	.35	.20
14	Barry Larkin	.15	.11	.06
15	Terry Pendleton	.15	.11	.06
16	Don Mattingly	.40	.30	.15
17	Rickey Henderson	.35	.25	.14
18	Ruben Sierra	.20	.15	.08

19	Jeff Bagwell	.20	.15	.08
20	Tom Glavine	.15	.11	.06
21	Ramon Martinez	.15	.11	.06
22	Will Clark	.40	.30	.15
23	Barry Bonds	.40	.30	.15
24	Roberto Alomar	.25	.20	.10

1993 Fleer

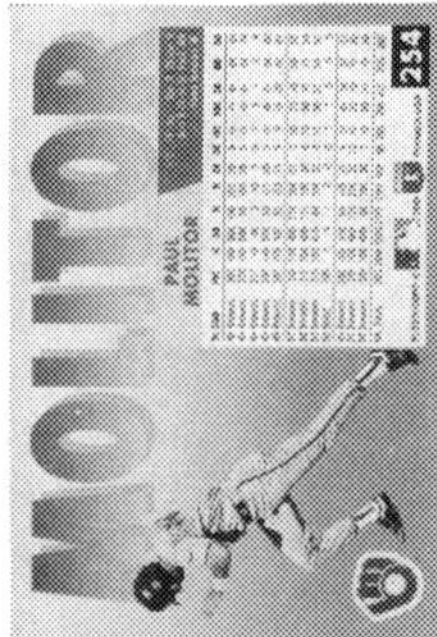

The card fronts feature silver borders with the player's name, team and position in a banner along the left side of the card. The Fleer logo appears in the lower right corner. The backs feature an action photo of the player with his name in bold behind him. A box featuring biographical information, statistics and player information is located to the right of the action photo. The cards are numbered alphabetically by team. The basic Fleer issue for 1993 was issued in two series of 360 cards each. The 720-card set included a number of subsets and could be found in many different types of packaging with an unprecedented number of inserts sets to spice up each offering.

		MT	NR MT	EX
	Complete Set (720):	30.00	22.00	12.00
	Common Player:	.04	.03	.02
1	Steve Avery	.15	.11	.06
2	Sid Bream	.04	.03	.02
3	Ron Gant	.08	.06	.03
4	Tom Glavine	.15	.11	.06
5	Brian Hunter	.08	.06	.03
6	Ryan Klesko (FC)	.35	.25	.14
7	Charlie Leibrandt	.04	.03	.02
8	Kent Mercker	.04	.03	.02
9	*David Nied* (FC)	.40	.30	.15
10	Otis Nixon	.06	.05	.02
11	Greg Olson	.04	.03	.02
12	Terry Pendleton	.08	.06	.03
13	Deion Sanders	.15	.11	.06
14	John Smoltz	.08	.06	.03
15	Mike Stanton	.04	.03	.02
16	Mark Wohlers	.08	.06	.03
17	Paul Assenmacher	.04	.03	.02
18	Steve Buechele	.04	.03	.02
19	Shawon Dunston	.06	.05	.02
20	Mark Grace	.08	.06	.03
21	Derrick May	.10	.08	.04
22	Chuck McElroy	.04	.03	.02
23	Mike Morgan	.06	.05	.02
24	Rey Sanchez	.10	.08	.04
25	Ryne Sandberg	.25	.20	.10
26	Bob Scanlan	.04	.03	.02
27	Sammy Sosa	.06	.05	.02
28	Rick Wilkins	.06	.05	.02
29	*Bobby Ayala* (FC)	.15	.11	.06
30	Tim Belcher	.06	.05	.02
31	*Jeff Branson* (FC)	.12	.09	.05
32	Norm Charlton	.08	.06	.03
33	*Steve Foster* (FC)	.12	.09	.05
34	Willie Greene (FC)	.12	.09	.05
35	Chris Hammond	.06	.05	.02
36	Milt Hill (FC)	.10	.08	.04
37	Hal Morris	.06	.05	.02
38	Joe Oliver	.06	.05	.02
39	Paul O'Neill	.06	.05	.02
40	*Tim Pugh* (FC)	.12	.09	.05
41	Jose Rijo	.08	.06	.03
42	Bip Roberts	.08	.06	.03
43	Chris Sabo	.08	.06	.03
44	Reggie Sanders	.15	.11	.06
45	Eric Anthony	.08	.06	.03
46	Jeff Bagwell	.20	.12	.05
47	Craig Biggio	.08	.06	.03
48	Joe Boever	.04	.03	.02
49	Casey Candaele	.04	.03	.02
50	Steve Finley	.06	.05	.02
51	Luis Gonzalez	.08	.06	.03
52	Pete Harnisch	.08	.06	.03
53	Xavier Hernandez	.04	.03	.02
54	Doug Jones	.05	.04	.02
55	Eddie Taubensee	.08	.06	.03
56	Brian Williams	.08	.06	.03
57	*Pedro Astacio*	.12	.09	.05
58	Todd Benzinger	.04	.03	.02
59	Brett Butler	.06	.05	.02
60	Tom Candiotti	.06	.05	.02
61	Lenny Harris	.04	.03	.02
62	Carlos Hernandez	.08	.06	.03
63	Orel Hershiser	.08	.06	.03
64	Eric Karros	.15	.11	.06
65	Ramon Martinez	.08	.06	.03
66	Jose Offerman	.06	.05	.02
67	Mike Scioscia	.04	.03	.02
68	Mike Sharperson	.04	.03	.02
69	*Eric Young*	.15	.11	.06
70	Moises Alou	.08	.06	.03
71	Ivan Calderon	.08	.06	.03
72	*Archi Cianfrocco*	.15	.11	.06
73	Wil Cordero	.10	.08	.04
74	Delino DeShields	.08	.06	.03
75	Mark Gardner	.05	.04	.02
76	Ken Hill	.08	.06	.03
77	*Tim Laker*	.15	.11	.06
78	Chris Nabholz	.06	.05	.02
79	Mel Rojas	.04	.03	.02
80	*John Vander Wal*	.12	.09	.05
81	Larry Walker	.10	.08	.04
82	Tim Wallach	.06	.05	.02
83	John Wetteland	.08	.06	.03
84	Bobby Bonilla	.12	.09	.05
85	Daryl Boston	.04	.03	.02
86	Sid Fernandez	.08	.06	.03
87	*Eric Hillman* (FC)	.12	.09	.05
88	Todd Hundley	.08	.06	.03
89	Howard Johnson	.08	.06	.03
90	*Jeff Kent*	.15	.11	.06
91	Eddie Murray	.10	.08	.04
92	Bill Pecota	.04	.03	.02
93	Bret Saberhagen	.08	.06	.03
94	Dick Schofield	.04	.03	.02
95	Pete Schourek	.04	.03	.02
96	Anthony Young	.06	.05	.02
97	Ruben Amaro Jr.	.06	.05	.02
98	Juan Bell	.06	.05	.02
99	Wes Chamberlain	.06	.05	.02
100	Darren Daulton	.08	.06	.03
101	Mariano Duncan	.04	.03	.02
102	Mike Hartley	.04	.03	.02
103	Ricky Jordan	.06	.05	.02
104	John Kruk	.08	.06	.03
105	Mickey Morandini	.08	.06	.03
106	Terry Mulholland	.06	.05	.02
107	*Ben Rivera* (FC)	.12	.09	.05
108	Curt Schilling	.08	.06	.03
109	*Keith Shepherd*	.08	.06	.03
110	Stan Belinda	.05	.04	.02
111	Jay Bell	.06	.05	.02
112	Barry Bonds	.25	.20	.10
113	Jeff King	.05	.04	.02
114	Mike LaValliere	.04	.03	.02
115	Jose Lind	.04	.03	.02
116	Roger Mason	.04	.03	.02
117	Orlando Merced	.06	.05	.02
118	Bob Patterson	.04	.03	.02
119	Don Slaught	.04	.03	.02
120	Zane Smith	.05	.04	.02
121	Randy Tomlin	.06	.05	.02
122	Andy Van Slyke	.08	.06	.03
123	*Tim Wakefield*	.06	.05	.05
124	Rheal Cormier	.08	.06	.03
125	Bernard Gilkey	.08	.06	.03
126	Felix Jose	.08	.06	.03
127	Ray Lankford	.12	.09	.05
128	Bob McClure	.04	.03	.02
129	Donovan Osborne	.10	.08	.04
130	Tom Pagnozzi	.06	.05	.02
131	Geronimo Pena	.06	.05	.02
132	Mike Perez	.06	.05	.02
133	Lee Smith	.06	.05	.02
134	Bob Tewksbury	.06	.05	.02
135	Todd Worrell	.06	.05	.02
136	Todd Zeile	.08	.06	.03
137	Jerald Clark	.05	.04	.02
138	Tony Gwynn	.12	.09	.05
139	Greg Harris	.05	.04	.02
140	Jeremy Hernandez	.05	.04	.02
141	Darrin Jackson	.05	.04	.02
142	Mike Maddux	.04	.03	.02
143	Fred McGriff	.15	.11	.06
144	Jose Melendez	.08	.06	.03
145	Rich Rodriguez	.04	.03	.02
146	Frank Seminara	.08	.06	.03
147	Gary Sheffield	.12	.09	.05
148	Kurt Stillwell	.05	.04	.02
149	*Dan Walters*	.10	.08	.04
150	Rod Beck	.06	.05	.02
151	Bud Black	.04	.03	.02
152	Jeff Brantley	.05	.04	.02
153	John Burkett	.05	.04	.02
154	Will Clark	.15	.11	.06
155	Royce Clayton	.08	.06	.03
156	Mike Jackson	.04	.03	.02
157	Darren Lewis	.08	.06	.03
158	Kirt Manwaring	.05	.04	.02
159	Willie McGee	.06	.05	.02
160	Cory Snyder	.06	.05	.02
161	Bill Swift	.06	.05	.02
162	Trevor Wilson	.05	.04	.02
163	Brady Anderson	.10	.08	.04
164	Glenn Davis	.06	.05	.02
165	Mike Devereaux	.08	.06	.03
166	Todd Frohwirth	.04	.03	.02
167	Leo Gomez	.06	.05	.02
168	Chris Hoiles	.08	.06	.03
169	Ben McDonald	.08	.06	.03
170	Randy Milligan	.04	.03	.02
171	Alan Mills	.04	.03	.02
172	Mike Mussina	.25	.20	.10
173	Gregg Olson	.08	.06	.03
174	Arthur Rhodes	.10	.08	.04
175	David Segui	.05	.04	.02
176	Ellis Burks	.08	.06	.03
177	Roger Clemens	.15	.11	.06
178	Scott Cooper	.08	.06	.03
179	Danny Darwin	.04	.03	.02
180	Tony Fossas	.04	.03	.02
181	*Paul Quantrill*	.08	.06	.03
182	Jody Reed	.05	.04	.02
183	*John Valentin*	.15	.11	.06
184	Mo Vaughn	.10	.07	.04
185	Frank Viola	.08	.06	.03
186	Bob Zupcic	.08	.06	.03
187	Jim Abbott	.08	.06	.03
188	Gary DiSarcina	.04	.03	.02
189	*Damion Easley*	.15	.11	.06
190	Junior Felix	.06	.05	.02
191	Chuck Finley	.06	.05	.02
192	Joe Grahe	.06	.05	.02
193	Bryan Harvey	.06	.05	.02
194	Mark Langston	.08	.06	.03
195	John Orton	.04	.03	.02
196	Luis Polonia	.05	.04	.02
197	*Tim Salmon*	1.50	.90	.60
198	Luis Sojo	.05	.04	.02
199	Wilson Alvarez	.05	.04	.02
200	George Bell	.08	.06	.03
201	Alex Fernandez	.08	.06	.03
202	Craig Grebeck	.04	.03	.02
203	Ozzie Guillen	.06	.05	.02
204	Lance Johnson	.06	.05	.02
205	Ron Karkovice	.04	.03	.02
206	Kirk McCaskill	.05	.04	.02
207	Jack McDowell	.10	.08	.04
208	Scott Radinsky	.04	.03	.02
209	Tim Raines	.08	.06	.03
210	Frank Thomas	1.00	.75	.40
211	Robin Ventura	.12	.09	.05
212	Sandy Alomar Jr.	.08	.06	.03
213	Carlos Baerga	.25	.20	.10
214	Dennis Cook	.04	.03	.02
215	Thomas Howard	.06	.05	.02
216	Mark Lewis	.08	.06	.03
217	Derek Lilliquist	.04	.03	.02
218	Kenny Lofton	.20	.12	.06
219	Charles Nagy	.15	.11	.06
220	Steve Olin	.06	.05	.02
221	Paul Sorrento	.06	.05	.02
222	Jim Thome	.10	.08	.04
223	Mark Whiten	.10	.08	.04
224	Milt Cuyler	.06	.05	.02
225	Rob Deer	.06	.05	.02
226	*John Doherty*	.12	.09	.05
227	Cecil Fielder	.12	.09	.05
228	Travis Fryman	.20	.12	.06
229	Mike Henneman	.06	.05	.02
230	*John Kiely*	.12	.09	.05
231	*Kurt Knudsen*	.12	.09	.05
232	Scott Livingstone	.10	.08	.04
233	Tony Phillips	.08	.06	.03
234	Mickey Tettleton	.08	.06	.03
235	Kevin Appier	.08	.06	.03
236	George Brett	.12	.09	.05
237	Tom Gordon	.05	.04	.02
238	Gregg Jefferies	.10	.08	.04
239	Wally Joyner	.08	.06	.03
240	*Kevin Koslofski*	.12	.09	.05
241	Mike Macfarlane	.05	.04	.02
242	Brian McRae	.08	.06	.03
243	Rusty Meacham	.08	.06	.03
244	Keith Miller	.06	.05	.02
245	Jeff Montgomery	.06	.05	.02
246	*Hipolito Pichardo*	.10	.08	.04
247	Ricky Bones	.08	.06	.03
248	Cal Eldred	.15	.11	.06
249	Mike Fetters	.05	.04	.02
250	Darryl Hamilton	.08	.06	.03
251	Doug Henry	.06	.05	.02
252	John Jaha (FC)	.15	.11	.06
253	Pat Listach	.10	.08	.04
254	Paul Molitor	.12	.09	.05
255	Jaime Navarro	.08	.06	.03
256	Kevin Seitzer	.06	.05	.02
257	B.J. Surhoff	.06	.05	.02
258	Greg Vaughn	.06	.05	.02
259	Bill Wegman	.06	.05	.02
260	Robin Yount	.15	.11	.06
261	Rick Aguilera	.08	.06	.03
262	Chili Davis	.06	.05	.02
263	Scott Erickson	.06	.05	.02
264	Greg Gagne	.05	.04	.02
265	Mark Guthrie	.04	.03	.02
266	Brian Harper	.08	.06	.03
267	Kent Hrbek	.08	.06	.03
268	Terry Jorgensen	.08	.06	.03
269	Gene Larkin	.04	.03	.02
270	Scott Leius	.06	.05	.02
271	Pat Mahomes	.15	.11	.06
272	Pedro Munoz	.10	.08	.04
273	Kirby Puckett	.20	.12	.06
274	Kevin Tapani	.08	.06	.03
275	Carl Willis	.04	.03	.02
276	Steve Farr	.05	.04	.02
277	John Habyan	.04	.03	.02
278	Mel Hall	.06	.05	.02
279	Charlie Hayes	.06	.05	.02
280	Pat Kelly	.06	.05	.02
281	Don Mattingly	.12	.09	.05
282	Sam Militello	.08	.06	.03
283	Matt Nokes	.06	.05	.02
284	Melido Perez	.06	.05	.02
285	Andy Stankiewicz	.10	.08	.04
286	Danny Tartabull	.08	.06	.03
287	Randy Velarde	.04	.03	.02
288	Bob Wickman	.10	.07	.04
289	Bernie Williams	.10	.08	.04
290	Lance Blankenship	.05	.04	.02
291	Mike Bordick	.08	.06	.03
292	Jerry Browne	.04	.03	.02
293	Dennis Eckersley	.10	.08	.04
294	Rickey Henderson	.15	.11	.06
295	*Vince Horsman*	.12	.09	.05
296	Mark McGwire	.10	.08	.04
297	Jeff Parrett	.04	.03	.02
298	Ruben Sierra	.10	.08	.04
299	Terry Steinbach	.06	.05	.02
300	Walt Weiss	.05	.04	.02

301	Bob Welch	.06	.05	.02
302	Willie Wilson	.06	.05	.02
303	Bobby Witt	.06	.05	.02
304	*Bret Boone*	.15	.11	.06
305	Jay Buhner	.06	.05	.02
306	Dave Fleming	.08	.06	.03
307	Ken Griffey, Jr.	.75	.60	.30
308	Erik Hanson	.06	.05	.02
309	Edgar Martinez	.12	.09	.05
310	Tino Martinez	.08	.06	.03
311	Jeff Nelson	.12	.09	.05
312	Dennis Powell	.04	.03	.02
313	Mike Schooler	.05	.04	.02
314	Russ Swan	.04	.03	.02
315	Dave Valle	.04	.03	.02
316	Omar Vizquel	.04	.03	.02
317	Kevin Brown	.08	.06	.03
318	Todd Burns	.04	.03	.02
319	Jose Canseco	.10	.08	.04
320	Julio Franco	.08	.06	.03
321	*Jeff Frye* (FC)	.12	.09	.05
322	Juan Gonzalez	.60	.45	.25
323	Jose Guzman	.06	.05	.02
324	Jeff Huson	.05	.04	.02
325	Dean Palmer	.08	.06	.03
326	Kevin Reimer	.06	.05	.02
327	Ivan Rodriguez	.15	.11	.06
328	Kenny Rogers	.04	.03	.02
329	Dan Smith (FC)	.08	.06	.03
330	Roberto Alomar	.25	.20	.10
331	Derek Bell	.12	.09	.05
332	Pat Borders	.06	.05	.02
333	Joe Carter	.12	.09	.05
334	Kelly Gruber	.08	.06	.03
335	Tom Henke	.08	.06	.03
336	Jimmy Key	.08	.06	.03
337	Manuel Lee	.05	.04	.02
338	Candy Maldonado	.06	.05	.02
339	John Olerud	.25	.15	.08
340	Todd Stottlemyre	.05	.04	.02
341	Duane Ward	.05	.04	.02
342	Devon White	.08	.06	.03
343	Dave Winfield	.15	.11	.06
344	Edgar Martinez (League Leaders)	.08	.06	.03
345	Cecil Fielder (League Leaders)	.10	.08	.04
346	Kenny Lofton (League Leaders)	.10	.07	.04
347	Jack Morris (League Leaders)	.07	.05	.03
348	Roger Clemens (League Leaders)	.12	.09	.05
349	Fred McGriff (Round Trippers)	.12	.09	.05
350	Barry Bonds (Round Trippers)	.15	.11	.06
351	Gary Sheffield (Round Trippers)	.12	.09	.05
352	Darren Daulton (Round Trippers)	.08	.06	.03
353	Dave Hollins (Round Trippers)	.08	.06	.03
354	Brothers In Blue (Pedro Martinez, Ramon Martinez)	.12	.09	.05
355	Power Packs (Ivan Rodriguez, Kirby Puckett)	.15	.11	.06
356	Triple Threats (Ryne Sandberg, Gary Sheffield)	.15	.11	.06
357	Infield Trifecta (Roberto Alomar, Chuck Knoblauch, Carlos Baerga)	.15	.11	.06
358	Checklist	.04	.03	.02
359	Checklist	.04	.03	.02
360	Checklist	.04	.03	.02
361	Rafael Belliard	.05	.04	.02
362	Damon Berryhill	.05	.04	.02
363	Mike Bielecki	.05	.04	.02
364	Jeff Blauser	.05	.04	.02
365	Francisco Cabrera	.05	.04	.02
366	Marvin Freeman	.05	.04	.02
367	Dave Justice	.25	.15	.10
368	Mark Lemke	.06	.05	.02
369	Alejandro Pena	.06	.05	.02
370	Jeff Reardon	.05	.04	.02
371	Lonnie Smith	.06	.05	.02
372	Pete Smith	.06	.05	.02
373	Shawn Boskie	.05	.04	.02
374	Jim Bullinger	.05	.04	.02
375	Frank Castillo	.05	.04	.02
376	Doug Dascenzo	.06	.05	.02
377	Andre Dawson	.08	.06	.03
378	Mike Harkey	.06	.05	.02
379	Greg Hibbard	.05	.04	.02
380	Greg Maddux	.12	.09	.05
381	Ken Patterson	.05	.04	.02
382	Jeff Robinson	.05	.04	.02
383	Luis Salazar	.04	.03	.02
384	Dwight Smith	.06	.05	.02
385	Jose Vizcaino	.05	.04	.02
386	Scott Bankhead	.06	.05	.02
387	Tom Browning	.06	.05	.02
388	Darnell Coles	.06	.05	.02
389	Rob Dibble	.05	.04	.02
390	Bill Doran	.05	.04	.02
391	Dwayne Henry	.06	.05	.02
392	Cesar Hernandez	.07	.05	.02
393	Roberto Kelly	.08	.06	.03
394	Barry Larkin	.10	.08	.04
395	Dave Martinez	.05	.04	.02
396	Kevin Mitchell	.06	.05	.02
397	Jeff Reed	.06	.05	.02
398	Scott Ruskin	.05	.04	.02
399	Greg Swindell	.06	.05	.02
400	Dan Wilson	.08	.06	.03
401	Andy Ashby	.06	.05	.02
402	Freddie Benavides	.05	.04	.02
403	Dante Bichette	.06	.05	.02
404	Willie Blair	.05	.04	.02
405	Denis Boucher	.06	.05	.02
406	Vinny Castilla	.06	.05	.02
407	Braulio Castillo	.06	.05	.02
408	Alex Cole	.06	.05	.02
409	Andres Galarraga	.08	.06	.03
410	Joe Girardi	.05	.04	.02
411	Butch Henry	.05	.04	.02
412	Darren Holmes	.05	.04	.02
413	Calvin Jones	.06	.05	.02
414	*Steve Reed*	.10	.07	.04
415	Kevin Ritz	.05	.04	.02
416	*Jim Tatum*	.15	.11	.06
417	Jack Armstrong	.05	.04	.02
418	Bret Barberie	.05	.04	.02
419	Ryan Bowen	.06	.05	.02
420	Cris Carpenter	.06	.05	.02
421	Chuck Carr	.06	.05	.02
422	Scott Chiamparino	.06	.05	.02
423	Jeff Conine	.08	.06	.03
424	Jim Corsi	.06	.05	.02
425	Steve Decker	.05	.04	.02
426	Chris Donnels	.06	.05	.02
427	Monty Fariss	.06	.05	.02
428	Bob Natal	.06	.05	.02
429	*Pat Rapp*	.08	.06	.03
430	Dave Weathers	.06	.05	.02
431	*Nigel Wilson*	.60	.40	.20
432	Ken Caminiti	.05	.04	.02
433	Andujar Cedeno	.06	.05	.02
434	Tom Edens	.06	.05	.02
435	Juan Guerrero	.06	.05	.02
436	Pete Incaviglia	.06	.05	.02
437	Jimmy Jones	.05	.04	.02
438	Darryl Kile	.05	.04	.02
439	Rob Murphy	.05	.04	.02
440	Al Osuna	.04	.03	.02
441	Mark Portugal	.04	.03	.02
442	Scott Servais	.04	.03	.02
443	John Candelaria	.04	.03	.02
444	Tim Crews	.04	.03	.02
445	Eric Davis	.06	.05	.02
446	Tom Goodwin	.06	.05	.02
447	Jim Gott	.05	.04	.02
448	Kevin Gross	.05	.04	.02
449	Dave Hansen	.05	.04	.02
450	Jay Howell	.06	.05	.02
451	Roger McDowell	.05	.04	.02
452	Bob Ojeda	.05	.04	.02
453	Henry Rodriguez	.06	.05	.02
454	Darryl Strawberry	.08	.06	.03
455	Mitch Webster	.06	.05	.02
456	Steve Wilson	.04	.03	.02
457	Brian Barnes	.05	.04	.02
458	Sean Berry	.08	.06	.03
459	Jeff Fassero	.06	.05	.02
460	Darrin Fletcher	.05	.04	.02
461	Marquis Grissom	.10	.08	.04
462	Dennis Martinez	.06	.05	.02
463	Spike Owen	.05	.04	.02
464	Matt Stairs	.05	.04	.02
465	Sergio Valdez	.06	.05	.02
466	Kevin Bass	.05	.04	.02
467	Vince Coleman	.05	.04	.02
468	Mark Dewey	.05	.04	.02
469	Kevin Elster	.05	.04	.02
470	Tony Fernandez	.06	.05	.02
471	John Franco	.05	.04	.02
472	Dave Gallagher	.05	.04	.02
473	Paul Gibson	.06	.05	.02
474	Dwight Gooden	.08	.06	.03
475	Lee Guetterman	.05	.04	.02
476	Jeff Innis	.05	.04	.02
477	Dave Magadan	.06	.05	.02
478	Charlie O'Brien	.06	.05	.02
479	Willie Randolph	.06	.05	.02
480	Mackey Sasser	.06	.05	.02
481	Ryan Thompson	.20	.15	.08
482	Chico Walker	.06	.05	.02
483	Kyle Abbott	.05	.04	.02
484	Bob Ayrault	.06	.05	.02
485	Kim Batiste	.06	.05	.02
486	Cliff Brantley	.06	.05	.02
487	Jose DeLeon	.05	.04	.02
488	Len Dykstra	.10	.08	.04
489	Tommy Greene	.08	.06	.03
490	Jeff Grotewold	.06	.05	.02
491	Dave Hollins	.10	.08	.04
492	Danny Jackson	.05	.04	.02
493	Stan Javier	.05	.04	.02
494	Tom Marsh	.05	.04	.02
495	Greg Matthews	.05	.04	.02
496	Dale Murphy	.05	.04	.02
497	*Todd Pratt*	.15	.11	.06
498	Mitch Williams	.05	.04	.02
499	Danny Cox	.05	.04	.02
500	Doug Drabek	.05	.04	.02
501	Carlos Garcia	.12	.09	.05
502	Lloyd McClendon	.05	.04	.02
503	Denny Neagle	.05	.04	.02
504	Gary Redus	.05	.04	.02
505	Bob Walk	.05	.04	.02
506	John Wehner	.05	.04	.02
507	Luis Alicea	.05	.04	.02
508	Mark Clark	.05	.04	.02
509	Pedro Guerrero	.05	.04	.02
510	Rex Hudler	.05	.04	.02
511	Brian Jordan	.10	.07	.04
512	Omar Olivares	.05	.04	.02
513	Jose Oquendo	.05	.04	.02
514	Gerald Perry	.05	.04	.02
515	Bryn Smith	.05	.04	.02
516	Craig Wilson	.05	.04	.02
517	Tracy Woodson	.05	.04	.02
518	Larry Anderson	.05	.04	.02
519	Andy Benes	.05	.04	.02
520	Jim Deshaies	.05	.04	.02
521	Bruce Hurst	.05	.04	.02
522	Randy Myers	.05	.04	.02
523	Benito Santiago	.05	.04	.02
524	Tim Scott	.05	.04	.02
525	Tim Teufel	.05	.04	.02
526	Mike Benjamin	.05	.04	.02
527	Dave Burba	.05	.04	.02
528	Craig Colbert	.05	.04	.02
529	Mike Felder	.05	.04	.02
530	Bryan Hickerson	.05	.04	.02
531	Chris James	.05	.04	.02
532	Mark Leonard	.05	.04	.02
533	Greg Litton	.05	.04	.02
534	Francisco Oliveras	.05	.04	.02
535	John Patterson	.05	.04	.02
536	Jim Pena	.05	.04	.02
537	Dave Righetti	.05	.04	.02
538	Robby Thompson	.05	.04	.02
539	Jose Uribe	.05	.04	.02
540	Matt Williams	.05	.04	.02
541	Storm Davis	.05	.04	.02
542	Sam Horn	.05	.04	.02
543	Tim Hulett	.05	.04	.02
544	Craig Lefferts	.05	.04	.02
545	Chito Martinez	.05	.04	.02
546	Mark McLemore	.05	.04	.02
547	Luis Mercedes	.05	.04	.02
548	Bob Milacki	.05	.04	.02
549	Joe Orsulak	.05	.04	.02
550	Billy Ripken	.05	.04	.02
551	Cal Ripken, Jr.	.20	.15	.08
552	Rick Sutcliffe	.05	.04	.02
553	Jeff Tackett	.05	.04	.02
554	Wade Boggs	.10	.08	.04
555	Tom Brunansky	.05	.04	.02
556	Jack Clark	.05	.04	.02
557	John Dopson	.05	.04	.02
558	Mike Gardiner	.05	.04	.02
559	Mike Greenwell	.05	.04	.02
560	Greg Harris	.05	.04	.02
561	Billy Hatcher	.05	.04	.02
562	Joe Hesketh	.05	.04	.02
563	Tony Pena	.05	.04	.02
564	Phil Plantier	.05	.04	.02
565	Luis Riveria	.05	.04	.02
566	Herm Winningham	.05	.04	.02
567	Matt Young	.05	.04	.02
568	Bert Blyleven	.05	.04	.02
569	Mike Butcher	.05	.04	.02
570	Chuck Crim	.05	.04	.02
571	*Chad Curtis*	.12	.09	.05
572	Tim Fortugno	.05	.04	.02
573	Steve Frey	.05	.04	.02
574	Gary Gaetti	.05	.04	.02
575	Scott Lewis	.05	.04	.02
576	Lee Stevens	.05	.04	.02
577	Ron Tingley	.05	.04	.02
578	Julio Valera	.05	.04	.02
579	Shawn Abner	.05	.04	.02
580	Joey Cora	.05	.04	.02
581	Chris Cron	.05	.04	.02
582	Carlton Fisk	.05	.04	.02
583	Roberto Hernandez	.05	.04	.02
584	Charlie Hough	.05	.04	.02
585	Terry leach	.05	.04	.02
586	Donn Pall	.05	.04	.02
587	Dan Pasqua	.05	.04	.02
588	Steve Sax	.05	.04	.02
589	Bobby Thigpen	.05	.04	.02
590	Albert Belle	.10	.08	.04
591	Felix Fermin	.05	.04	.02
592	Glenallen Hill	.05	.04	.02
593	Brook Jacoby	.05	.04	.02
594	Reggie Jefferson	.05	.04	.02
595	Carlos Martinez	.05	.04	.02
596	Jose Mesa	.05	.04	.02
597	Rod Nichols	.05	.04	.02
598	Junior Ortiz	.05	.04	.02
599	Eric Plunk	.05	.04	.02
600	Ted Power	.05	.04	.02
601	Scott Scudder	.05	.04	.02
602	Kevin Wickander	.05	.04	.02
603	Skeeter Barnes	.05	.04	.02
604	Mark Carreon	.05	.04	.02
605	Dan Gladden	.05	.04	.02
606	Bill Gullickson	.05	.04	.02
607	Chad Kreuter	.05	.04	.02
608	Mark Leiter	.05	.04	.02
609	Mike Munoz	.05	.04	.02
610	Rich Rowland	.05	.04	.02
611	Frank Tanana	.05	.04	.02
612	Walt Terrell	.05	.04	.02
613	Alan Trammell	.05	.04	.02
614	Lou Whitaker	.05	.04	.02
615	Luis Aquino	.05	.04	.02
616	Mike Boddicker	.05	.04	.02
617	Jim Eisenreich	.05	.04	.02
618	Mark Gubicza	.05	.04	.02
619	David Howard	.05	.04	.02
620	Mike Magnante	.05	.04	.02
621	Brent Mayne	.05	.04	.02
622	Kevin McReynolds	.05	.04	.02
623	*Eddie Pierce*	.10	.07	.04
624	Bill Sampen	.05	.04	.02
625	Steve Shifflett	.05	.04	.02
626	Gary Thurman	.05	.04	.02
627	Curtis Wikerson	.05	.04	.02
628	Chris Bosio	.05	.04	.02
629	Scott Fletcher	.05	.04	.02
630	Jim Gantner	.05	.04	.02
631	Dave Nilsson	.05	.04	.02
632	Jesse Orosco	.05	.04	.02
633	Dan Plesac	.05	.04	.02
634	Ron Robinson	.05	.04	.02
635	Bill Spiers	.05	.04	.02
636	Franklin Stubbs	.05	.04	.02
637	Willie Banks	.05	.04	.02
638	Randy Bush	.05	.04	.02
639	Chuck Knoblauch	.10	.07	.04
640	Shane Mack	.05	.04	.02
641	Mike Pagliarulo	.05	.04	.02
642	Jeff Reboulet	.05	.04	.02
643	John Smiley	.05	.04	.02
644	*Mike Trombley*	.08	.06	.03
645	Gary Wayne	.05	.04	.02
646	Lenny Webster	.05	.04	.02
647	Tim Burke	.05	.04	.02
648	Mike Gallego	.05	.04	.02

649	Dion James	.05	.04	.02
650	Jeff Johnson	.05	.04	.02
651	Scott Kamieniecki	.05	.04	.02
652	Kevin Maas	.05	.04	.02
653	Rich Monteleone	.05	.04	.02
654	Jerry Nielsen	.05	.04	.02
655	Scott Sanderson	.05	.04	.02
656	Mike Stanley	.05	.04	.02
657	Gerald Williams	.05	.04	.02
658	Curt Young	.05	.04	.02
659	Harold Baines	.05	.04	.02
660	Kevin Campbell	.05	.04	.02
661	Ron Darling	.05	.04	.02
662	Kelly Downs	.05	.04	.02
663	Eric Fox	.05	.04	.02
664	Dave Henderson	.05	.04	.02
665	Rick Honeycutt	.05	.04	.02
666	Mike Moore	.05	.04	.02
667	Jamie Quirk	.05	.04	.02
668	Jeff Russell	.05	.04	.02
669	Dave Stewart	.05	.04	.02
670	Greg Briley	.05	.04	.02
671	Dave Cochrane	.05	.04	.02
672	Henry Cotto	.05	.04	.02
673	Rich DeLucia	.05	.04	.02
674	Brian Fisher	.05	.04	.02
675	Mark Grant	.05	.04	.02
676	Randy Johnson	.05	.04	.02
677	Tim Leary	.05	.04	.02
678	Pete O'Brien	.05	.04	.02
679	Lance Parrish	.05	.04	.02
680	Harold Reynolds	.05	.04	.02
681	Shane Turner	.05	.04	.02
682	Jack Daugherty	.05	.04	.02
683	*David Hulse*	.15	.11	.06
684	Terry Mathews	.05	.04	.02
685	Al Newman	.05	.04	.02
686	Edwin Nunez	.05	.04	.02
687	Rafael Palmeiro	.10	.08	.04
688	Roger Pavlik	.05	.04	.02
689	Geno Petralli	.05	.04	.02
690	Nolan Ryan	.60	.45	.25
691	David Cone	.05	.04	.02
692	Alfredo Griffin	.05	.04	.02
693	Juan Guzman	.12	.09	.05
694	Pat Hentgen	.15	.11	.06
695	Randy Knorr	.05	.04	.02
696	Bob MacDonald	.05	.04	.02
697	Jack Morris	.05	.04	.02
698	Ed Sprague	.05	.04	.02
699	Dave Stieb	.05	.04	.02
700	Pat Tabler	.05	.04	.02
701	Mike Timlin	.05	.04	.02
702	David Wells	.05	.04	.02
703	Eddie Zosky	.05	.04	.02
704	Gary Sheffield (League Leaders)	.10	.08	.04
705	Darren Daulton (League Leaders)	.08	.06	.03
706	Marquis Grissom (League Leaders)	.08	.06	.03
707	Greg Maddux (League Leaders)	.08	.06	.03
708	Bill Swift (League Leaders)	.05	.04	.02
709	Juan Gonzalez (Round Trippers)	.50	.30	.15
710	Mark McGwire (Round Trippers)	.10	.08	.04
711	Cecil Fielder (Round Trippers)	.10	.08	.04
712	Albert Belle (Round Trippers)	.12	.09	.05
713	Joe Carter (Round Trippers)	.10	.08	.04
714	Power Brokers (Frank Thomas, Cecil Fielder)	.35	.25	.14
715	Unsung Heroes (Larry Walker, Darren Daulton)	.10	.08	.04
716	Hot Corner Hammers (Edgar Martinez, Robin Ventura)	.10	.08	.04
717	Start to Finish (Roger Clemens, Dennis Eckersley)	.10	.08	.04
718	Checklist	.05	.04	.02
719	Checklist	.05	.04	.02
720	Checklist	.05	.04	.02

The values quoted are intended to reflect the market price.

1993 Fleer Golden Moments I

This three-card insert set was available in Series I wax packs. Fronts feature black borders with gold-foil baseballs in the corners. The palyer's name appears in a "Golden Moments" banner at the bottom of the photo. Backs have a portrait photo of the player at top-center and a white box with information on the highlight. The cards are not numbered and are checklisted here alphabetically.

		MT	NR MT	EX
	Complete Set (3):	5.00	3.75	2.00
	Common Player:	.75	.60	.30
(1)	George Brett	3.00	2.25	1.20
(2)	Mickey Morandini	.75	.60	.30
(3)	Dave Winfield	2.00	1.50	.80

1993 Fleer Golden Moments II

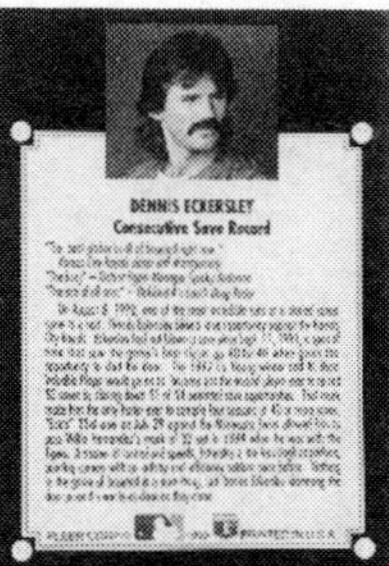

A second three-card series of "Golden Moments" was randomly inserted into Fleer Series II wax packs.

		MT	NR MT	EX
	Complete Set (3):	7.00	5.50	3.00
	Common Player:	.75	.60	.30
(1)	Dennis Eckersley	.75	.60	.30
(2)	Bip Roberts	.75	.60	.30
(3)	Frank Thomas/Juan Gonzalez	6.00	4.50	2.25

1993 Fleer Major League Prospects I

Yet another way to package currently hot rookies and future prospects to increase sales of the base product, there were 18 insert cards found in Series I wax packs.

		MT	NR MT	EX
	Complete Set (18):	25.00	18.50	10.00
	Common Player:	.75	.60	.30
1	Melvin Nieves	3.00	2.25	1.25
2	Sterling Hitchcock	1.50	1.25	.60
3	Tim Costo	1.00	.70	.40
4	Manny Alexander	.75	.60	.30
5	Alan Embree	.75	.60	.30
6	Kevin Young	2.00	1.50	.80
7	J.T. Snow	2.00	1.50	.80
8	Russ Springer	.75	.60	.30
9	Billy Ashley	4.00	3.00	1.50
10	Kevin Rogers	.75	.60	.30
11	Steve Hosey	2.00	1.50	.80
12	Eric Wedge	.75	.60	.30
13	Mike Piazza	15.00	11.00	6.00
14	Jesse Levis	.75	.60	.30
15	Rico Brogna	.75	.60	.30
16	Alex Arias	.75	.60	.30
17	Rod Brewer	.75	.60	.30
18	Troy Neel	1.00	.70	.40

1993 Fleer Major League Prospects II

Series II wax packs could be found with a second series of 18 potential future stars. Most of the players in the second series were still a few seasons away from everyday play in the majors.

		MT	NR MT	EX
	Complete Set (18):	16.00	12.00	6.50
	Common Player:	.75	.60	.30
1	Scooter Tucker	.75	.60	.30
2	Kerry Woodson	.75	.60	.30
3	Greg Colbrunn	.75	.60	.30
4	Pedro Martinez	1.50	1.25	.60
5	Dave Silvestri	.75	.60	.30
6	Kent Bottenfield	.75	.60	.30
7	Rafael Bournigal	.75	.60	.30
8	J.T. Bruett	.75	.60	.30
9	Dave Mlicki	.75	.60	.30
10	Paul Wagner	.75	.60	.30
11	Mike Williams	.75	.60	.30
12	Henry Mercedes	.75	.60	.30
13	Scott Taylor	.75	.60	.30
14	Dennis Moeller	.75	.60	.30
15	Javy Lopez	6.00	4.50	2.50
16	Steve Cooke	.75	.60	.30
17	Pete Young	.75	.60	.30
18	Ken Ryan	.75	.60	.30

1993 Fleer All-Stars

Attractive horizontal-format All-Star cards comprised another of the many 1993 Fleer insert issues. Twelve cards of National League All-Stars were included in Series I wax packs, while a dozen American League All-Stars were found in Series II packs. They are among the more popular and valuable of the '93 Fleer inserts.

		MT	NR MT	EX
	Complete Set AL (12):	30.00	20.00	10.00
	Complete Set NL (12):	16.00	10.00	6.00
	Common Player:	.75	.60	.30
	AL ALL-STARS			
1	Frank Thomas	10.00	7.50	4.00
2	Roberto Alomar	4.00	3.00	1.50
3	Edgar Martinez	1.00	.75	.40
4	Pat Listach	.75	.60	.30
5	Cecil Fielder	1.75	1.25	.70
6	Juan Gonzalez	8.00	6.00	3.25
7	Ken Griffey, Jr.	9.00	6.75	3.50
8	Joe Carter	3.00	2.25	1.20
9	Kirby Puckett	4.00	3.00	1.50
10	Brian Harper	.75	.60	.30
11	Dave Fleming	.75	.60	.30
12	Jack McDowell	2.00	1.50	.80
	NL ALL-STARS			
1	Fred McGriff	3.00	2.25	1.20
2	Delino DeShields	1.00	.75	.40
3	Gary Sheffield	1.50	1.00	.60
4	Barry Larkin	1.00	.75	.40
5	Felix Jose	1.00	.75	.40
6	Larry Walker	1.50	1.00	.60
7	Barry Bonds	4.50	3.50	1.75
8	Andy Van Slyke	2.00	1.50	.80
9	Darren Daulton	1.50	1.00	.60
10	Greg Maddux	2.50	2.00	1.00
11	Tom Glavine	2.00	1.50	.80
12	Lee Smith	2.00	1.50	.80

1993 Fleer ProVisions I

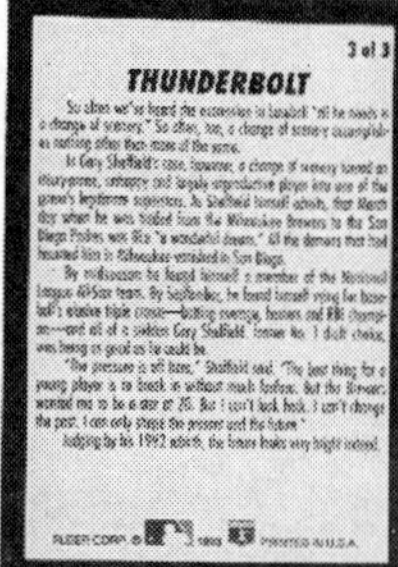

This three-card insert set in Series I wax packs features the baseball art of Wayne Still. Black-bordered fronts feature a player-fantasy painting at center, with the player's name gold-foil stamped beneath. Backs are also bordered in black and have a white box with a career summary.

		MT	NR MT	EX
Complete Set (3):		6.00	4.00	2.00
Common Player:		.75	.60	.30
1	Roberto Alomar	4.00	3.00	1.50
2	Dennis Eckersley	.75	.60	.30
3	Gary Sheffield	1.75	1.25	.70

1993 Fleer ProVisions II

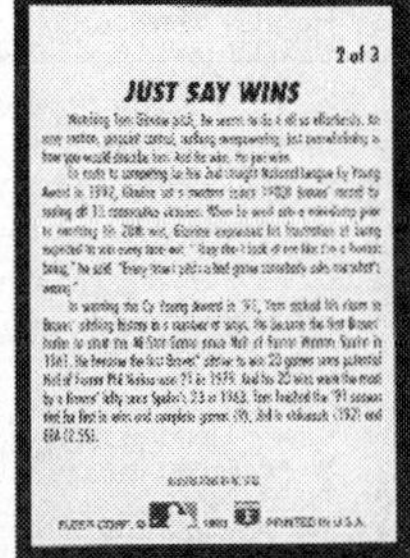

A second series of three cards based on Wayne Still's artwork was randomly inserted in Series II wax packs.

		MT	NR MT	EX
Complete Set (3):		4.00	3.00	1.50
Common Player:		.75	.60	.30
1	Andy Van Slyke	.75	.60	.30
2	Tom Glavine	1.75	1.25	.70
3	Cecil Fielder	2.00	1.50	.80

1993 Fleer Tom Glavine Career Highlights

This 15-card insert set spotlighted the career highlights of Fleer's 1993 spokesman, Tom Glavine. Twelve cards were available in Series I and Series II packs; cards #13-15 could be obtained only via a special mail offer. A limited number of certified autograph cards were also inserted into packs. Cards #1-4 and 7-10 can each be found with two variations of the writeups on the back. The versions found in Series II packaging are the "correct" backs. Neither version carries a premium value.

		MT	NR MT	EX
Complete Set (15):		6.00	4.50	2.25
Common Card:		.50	.40	.20
Autographed Card:		60.00	45.00	22.50
1	Tom Glavine	.50	.40	.20
2	Tom Glavine	.50	.40	.20
3	Tom Glavine	.50	.40	.20
4	Tom Glavine	.50	.40	.20
5	Tom Glavine	.50	.40	.20
6	Tom Glavine	.50	.40	.20
7	Tom Glavine	.50	.40	.20
8	Tom Glavine	.50	.40	.20
9	Tom Glavine	.50	.40	.20
10	Tom Glavine	.50	.40	.20
11	Tom Glavine	.50	.40	.20
12	Tom Glavine	.50	.40	.20
13	Tom Glavine	.50	.40	.20
14	Tom Glavine	.50	.40	.20
15	Tom Glavine	.50	.40	.20

1993 Fleer Rookie Sensations I

Ten rookie sensations - some of whom had not been true rookies for several seasons - were featured in this insert issue which was packaged exclusively in Series I cello packs. Card fronts have a player photo set against a silver background and

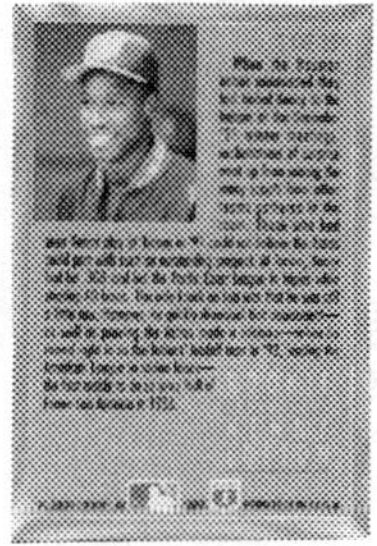

surrounded by a blue border. The player's name and other front printing are in gold foil. Backs are also printed in silver with a blue border. There is a player portrait photo and career summary.

		MT	NR MT	EX
Complete Set (10):		28.00	21.00	11.00
Common Player:		1.00	.70	.40
1	Kenny Lofton	8.00	6.00	3.25
2	Cal Eldred	4.50	3.50	1.75
3	Pat Listach	2.50	2.00	1.00
4	Roberto Hernandez	1.25	.90	.50
5	Dave Fleming	4.00	3.00	1.50
6	Eric Karros	5.00	3.75	2.00
7	Reggie Sanders	4.50	3.50	1.75
8	Derrick May	3.00	2.25	1.25
9	Mike Perez	2.00	1.50	.80
10	Donovan Osborne	3.00	2.25	1.25

1993 Fleer Rookie Sensations II

A second, less formidable line-up, of 10 young players was randomly inserted in Series II cello packs. Format was the same as Series I cards.

		MT	NR MT	EX
Complete Set (10):		18.00	13.50	7.25
Common Player:		1.00	.70	.40
1	Moises Alou	3.50	2.75	1.50
2	Pedro Astacio	3.00	2.25	1.25
3	Jim Austin	2.50	2.00	1.00
4	Chad Curtis	7.00	5.25	2.75
5	Gary DiSarcina	2.50	2.00	1.00
6	Scott Livingstone	2.00	1.50	.80
7	Sam Militello	1.50	1.25	.60
8	Arthur Rhodes	1.50	1.25	.60
9	Tim Wakefield	2.00	1.50	.80
10	Bob Zupcic	1.25	.90	.50

1993 Fleer AL Team Leaders

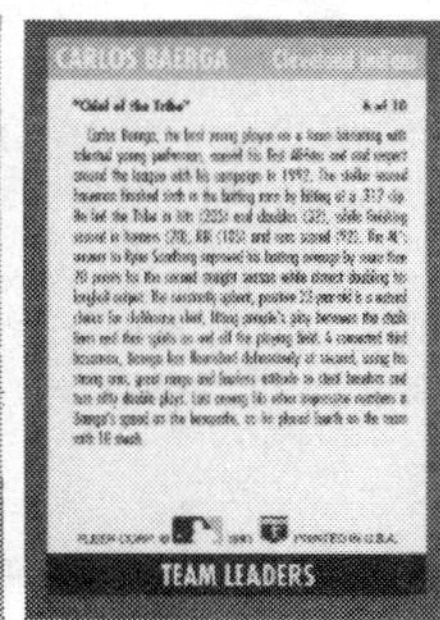

This 10-card insert issue was exclusive to Series I rack packs. Fronts have a portrait photo, with a small action photo superimposed. At the side is a red-and-blue bar with the player's name and "Team Leaders" printed vertically. On back is a career summary. Card borders are a light metallic green and both sides of the card are UV coated.

		MT	NR MT	EX
Complete Set (10):		25.00	18.00	10.00
Common Player:		.75	.60	.30
1	Kirby Puckett	3.00	2.25	1.25
2	Mark McGwire	1.25	.90	.50
3	Pat Listach	1.00	.70	.40
4	Roger Clemens	3.00	2.25	1.25
5	Frank Thomas	10.00	7.50	4.00
6	Carlos Baerga	2.50	2.00	1.00
7	Brady Anderson	.75	.60	.30
8	Juan Gonzalez	6.00	4.50	2.50
9	Roberto Alomar	3.00	2.25	1.25
10	Ken Griffey, Jr.	10.00	7.50	4.00

1993 Fleer NL Team Leaders

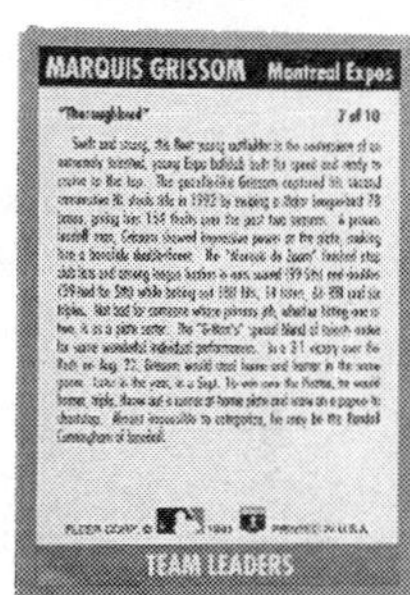

This 10-card insert issue was exclusive to Series II rack packs. Format is similar to the American League cards issued with Series I.

		MT	NR MT	EX
Complete Set (10):		10.00	7.50	4.00
Common Player:		.75	.60	.30
1	Will Clark	2.00	1.50	.80
2	Terry Pendleton	.75	.60	.30
3	Ray Lankford	.90	.70	.35
4	Eric Karros	1.00	.70	.40
5	Gary Sheffield	1.50	1.25	.60
6	Ryne Sandberg	4.00	3.00	1.50
7	Marquis Grissom	1.25	.90	.50
8	John Kruk	.75	.60	.30
9	Jeff Bagwell	3.00	2.25	1.25
10	Andy Van Slyke	.75	.60	.30

The values quoted are intended to reflect the market price.

1993 Fleer Ultra

The first series of 300 cards retains Fleer's successful features from 1992, including additional gold foil stamping, UV coating, and team color-coded marbled bars on the fronts. The backs feature a dimensionalized ballpark background, which creates a 3-D effect, stats and two photos, a portrait and an action shot. Dennis Eckersley is featured in a limited-edition "Career Highlights" set and has personally autographed more than 2,000 of his cards, to be randomly inserted into both series' packs. A 10-card Home Run Kings subset and 25-card Ultra Awards Winners subset were also randomly inserted in packs. These subsets' card have gold foil on both sides. Ultra Rookies cards are included in both series. Ultra's second series has three limited-edition subsets: Ultra All-Stars, Ultra All-Rookie Team, and Strikeout Kings, plus cards featuring Colorado Rockies and Florida Marlins players.

		MT	NR MT	EX
Complete Set (650):		35.00	26.00	14.00
Complete Series 1 (300):		15.00	11.00	6.00
Complete Series 2 (350):		20.00	15.00	8.00
Common Player:		.10	.08	.04
1	Steve Avery	.60	.45	.25
2	Rafael Belliard	.10	.08	.04
3	Damon Berryhill	.10	.08	.04
4	Sid Bream	.10	.08	.04
5	Ron Gant	.15	.11	.06
6	Tom Glavine	.30	.25	.12
7	Ryan Klesko	1.50	1.25	.60
8	Mark Lemke	.10	.08	.04
9	Javier Lopez	1.75	1.25	.70
10	Greg Olson	.10	.08	.04
11	Terry Pendleton	.10	.08	.04
12	Deion Sanders	.30	.25	.12
13	Mike Stanton	.10	.08	.04
14	Paul Assenmacher	.10	.08	.04
15	Steve Buechele	.10	.08	.04
16	Frank Castillo	.10	.08	.04
17	Shawon Dunston	.10	.08	.04
18	Mark Grace	.20	.15	.08
19	Derrick May	.10	.08	.04
20	Chuck McElroy	.10	.08	.04
21	Mike Morgan	.10	.08	.04
22	Bob Scanlan	.10	.08	.04
23	Dwight Smith	.10	.08	.04
24	Sammy Sosa	.10	.08	.04
25	Rick Wilkins	.10	.08	.04
26	Tim Belcher	.10	.08	.04
27	Jeff Branson	.10	.08	.04
28	Bill Doran	.10	.08	.04
29	Chris Hammond	.10	.08	.04
30	Barry Larkin	.20	.15	.08
31	Hal Morris	.10	.08	.04
32	Joe Oliver	.10	.08	.04
33	Jose Rijo	.10	.08	.04
34	Bip Roberts	.10	.08	.04
35	Chris Sabo	.10	.08	.04
36	Reggie Sanders	.15	.11	.06
37	Craig Biggio	.10	.08	.04
38	Ken Caminiti	.10	.08	.04
39	Steve Finley	.10	.08	.04
40	Luis Gonzalez	.12	.09	.05
41	Juan Guerrero	.10	.08	.04
42	Pete Harnisch	.10	.08	.04
43	Xavier Hernandez	.10	.08	.04
44	Doug Jones	.10	.08	.04
45	Al Osuna	.10	.08	.04
46	Eddie Taubensee	.10	.08	.04
47	Scooter Tucker	.10	.08	.04
48	Brian Williams	.10	.08	.04
49	Pedro Astacio	.15	.11	.06
50	Rafael Bourmigal	.15	.11	.06
51	Brett Butler	.10	.08	.04
52	Tom Candiotti	.10	.08	.04
53	Eric Davis	.10	.08	.04
54	Lenny Harris	.10	.08	.04
55	Orel Hershiser	.10	.08	.04
56	Eric Karros	.15	.11	.06
57	Pedro Martinez	.25	.20	.10
58	Roger McDowell	.10	.08	.04
59	Jose Offerman	.10	.08	.04
60	Mike Piazza	5.00	3.75	2.00
61	Moises Alou	.15	.11	.06
62	Kent Bottenfield	.10	.08	.04
63	Archi Cianfrocco	.10	.08	.04
64	Greg Colbrunn	.10	.08	.04
65	Wil Cordero	.25	.20	.10
66	Delino DeShields	.20	.15	.08
67	Darrin Fletcher	.10	.08	.04
68	Ken Hill	.10	.08	.04
69	Chris Nabholz	.10	.08	.04
70	Mel Rojas	.10	.08	.04
71	Larry Walker	.20	.15	.08
72	Sid Fernandez	.10	.08	.04
73	John Franco	.10	.08	.04
74	Dave Gallagher	.10	.08	.04
75	Todd Hundley	.10	.08	.04
76	Howard Johnson	.10	.08	.04
77	Jeff Kent	.40	.30	.15
78	Eddie Murray	.15	.11	.06
79	Bret Saberhagen	.10	.08	.04
80	Chico Walker	.10	.08	.04
81	Anthony Young	.10	.08	.04
82	Kyle Abbott	.10	.08	.04
83	Ruben Amaro Jr.	.12	.09	.05
84	Juan Bell	.10	.08	.04
85	Wes Chamberlain	.10	.08	.04
86	Darren Daulton	.20	.15	.08
87	Mariano Duncan	.10	.08	.04
88	Dave Hollins	.20	.15	.08
89	Ricky Jordan	.10	.08	.04
90	John Kruk	.20	.15	.08
91	Mickey Morandini	.10	.08	.04
92	Terry Mulholland	.10	.08	.04
93	Ben Rivera	.10	.08	.04
94	Mike Williams	.15	.11	.06
95	Stan Belinda	.10	.08	.04
96	Jay Bell	.10	.08	.04
97	Jeff King	.10	.08	.04
98	Mike LaValliere	.10	.08	.04
99	Lloyd McClendon	.10	.08	.04
100	Orlando Merced	.10	.08	.04
101	Zane Smith	.10	.08	.04
102	Randy Tomlin	.10	.08	.04
103	Andy Van Slyke	.10	.08	.04
104	Tim Wakefield	.12	.09	.05
105	John Wehner	.10	.08	.04
106	Bernard Gilkey	.10	.08	.04
107	Brian Jordan	.15	.11	.06
108	Ray Lankford	.20	.15	.08
109	Donovan Osborne	.20	.15	.08
110	Tom Pagnozzi	.10	.08	.04
111	Mike Perez	.10	.08	.04
112	Lee Smith	.10	.08	.04
113	Ozzie Smith	.30	.25	.12
114	Bob Tewksbury	.10	.08	.04
115	Todd Zeile	.10	.08	.04
116	Andy Benes	.15	.11	.06
117	Greg Harris	.10	.08	.04
118	Darrin Jackson	.10	.08	.04
119	Fred McGriff	.40	.25	.12
120	Rich Rodriguez	.10	.08	.04
121	Frank Seminara	.10	.08	.04
122	Gary Sheffield	.20	.15	.08
123	Craig Shipley	.10	.08	.04
124	Kurt Stillwell	.10	.08	.04
125	Dan Walters	.10	.08	.04
126	Rod Beck	.10	.08	.04
127	Mike Benjamin	.10	.08	.04
128	Jeff Brantley	.10	.08	.04
129	John Burkett	.10	.08	.04
130	Will Clark	.40	.30	.20
131	Royce Clayton	.15	.11	.06
132	Steve Hosey	.15	.11	.06
133	Mike Jackson	.10	.08	.04
134	Darren Lewis	.10	.08	.04
135	Kirt Manwaring	.10	.08	.04
136	Bill Swift	.10	.08	.04
137	Robby Thompson	.10	.08	.04
138	Brady Anderson	.15	.11	.06
139	Glenn Davis	.10	.08	.04
140	Leo Gomez	.10	.08	.04
141	Chito Martinez	.10	.08	.04
142	Ben McDonald	.10	.08	.04
143	Alan Mills	.10	.08	.04
144	Mike Mussina	.80	.60	.30
145	Gregg Olson	.10	.08	.04
146	David Segui	.10	.08	.04
147	Jeff Tackett	.10	.08	.04
148	Jack Clark	.10	.08	.04
149	Scott Cooper	.10	.08	.04
150	Danny Darwin	.10	.08	.04
151	John Dopson	.10	.08	.04
152	Mike Greenwell	.10	.08	.04
153	Tim Naehring	.10	.08	.04
154	Tony Pena	.10	.08	.04
155	Paul Quantrill	.10	.08	.04
156	Mo Vaughn	.40	.30	.15
157	Frank Viola	.10	.08	.04
158	Bob Zupcic	.10	.08	.04
159	Chad Curtis	.20	.15	.08
160	Gary Discarcina	.10	.08	.04
161	Damion Easley	.20	.15	.08
162	Chuck Finley	.10	.08	.04
163	Tim Fortugno	.10	.08	.04
164	Rene Gonzales	.10	.08	.04
165	Joe Grahe	.10	.08	.04
166	Mark Langston	.10	.08	.04
167	John Orton	.10	.08	.04
168	Luis Polonia	.10	.08	.04
169	Julio Valera	.10	.08	.04
170	Wilson Alvarez	.20	.15	.08
171	George Bell	.10	.08	.04
172	Joey Cora	.10	.08	.04
173	Alex Fernandez	.20	.15	.08
174	Lance Johnson	.10	.08	.04
175	Ron Karkovice	.10	.08	.04
176	Jack McDowell	.20	.15	.08
177	Scott Radinsky	.10	.08	.04
178	Tim Raines	.10	.08	.04
179	Steve Sax	.10	.08	.04
180	Bobby Thigpen	.10	.08	.04
181	Frank Thomas	3.00	2.25	1.25
182	Sandy Alomar Jr.	.10	.08	.04
183	Carlos Baerga	.70	.40	.20
184	Felix Fermin	.10	.08	.04
185	Thomas Howard	.10	.08	.04
186	Mark Lewis	.10	.08	.04
187	Derek Lilliquist	.10	.08	.04
188	Carlos Martinez	.10	.08	.04
189	Charles Nagy	.15	.11	.06
190	Scott Scudder	.10	.08	.04
191	Paul Sorrento	.10	.08	.04
192	Jim Thome	.60	.45	.25
193	Mark Whiten	.12	.09	.05
194	Milt Cuyler	.10	.08	.04
195	Rob Deer	.10	.08	.04
196	John Doherty	.10	.08	.04
197	Travis Fryman	.60	.45	.25
198	Dan Gladden	.10	.08	.04
199	Mike Henneman	.10	.08	.04
200	John Kiely	.10	.08	.04
201	Chad Kreuter	.10	.08	.04
202	Scott Livingstone	.10	.08	.04
203	Tony Phillips	.10	.08	.04
204	Alan Trammell	.10	.08	.04
205	Mike Boddicker	.10	.08	.04
206	George Brett	.60	.45	.25
207	Tom Gordon	.10	.08	.04
208	Mark Gubicza	.10	.08	.04
209	Gregg Jefferies	.20	.15	.08
210	Wally Joyner	.10	.08	.04
211	Kevin Koslofski	.10	.08	.04
212	Brent Mayne	.10	.08	.04
213	Brian McRae	.10	.08	.04
214	Kevin McReynolds	.10	.08	.04
215	Rusty Meacham	.10	.08	.04
216	Steve Shifflett	.10	.08	.04
217	James Austin	.10	.08	.04
218	Cal Eldred	.15	.11	.06
219	Darryl Hamilton	.10	.08	.04
220	Doug Henry	.10	.08	.04
221	John Jaha	.12	.09	.05
222	Dave Nilsson	.12	.09	.05
223	Jesse Orosco	.10	.08	.04
224	B.J. Surhoff	.10	.08	.04
225	Greg Vaughn	.15	.11	.06
226	Bill Wegman	.10	.08	.04
227	Robin Yount	.40	.30	.15
228	Rick Aguilera	.10	.08	.04
229	J.T. Bruett	.10	.08	.04
230	Scott Erickson	.10	.08	.04
231	Kent Hrbek	.10	.08	.04
232	Terry Jorgensen	.10	.08	.04
233	Scott Leius	.10	.08	.04
234	Pat Mahomes	.15	.11	.06
235	Pedro Munoz	.20	.15	.08
236	Kirby Puckett	.60	.45	.25
237	Kevin Tapani	.15	.11	.06
238	Lenny Webster	.10	.08	.04
239	Carl Willis	.10	.08	.04
240	Mike Gallego	.10	.08	.04
241	John Habyan	.10	.08	.04
242	Pat Kelly	.10	.08	.04
243	Kevin Maas	.10	.08	.04
244	Don Mattingly	.50	.40	.20
245	Hensley Meulens	.10	.08	.04
246	Sam Militello	.15	.11	.06
247	Matt Nokes	.10	.08	.04
248	Melido Perez	.10	.08	.04
249	Andy Stankiewicz	.10	.08	.04
250	Randy Velarde	.10	.08	.04
251	Bob Wickman	.20	.15	.08
252	Bernie Williams	.10	.08	.04
253	Lance Blankenship	.10	.08	.04
254	Mike Bordick	.10	.08	.04
255	Jerry Browne	.10	.08	.04
256	Ron Darling	.10	.08	.04
257	Dennis Eckersley	.15	.11	.06
258	Rickey Henderson	.30	.25	.12
259	Vince Horsman	.10	.08	.04
260	Troy Neel	.30	.25	.12
261	Jeff Parrett	.10	.08	.04
262	Terry Steinbach	.10	.08	.04
263	Bob Welch	.10	.08	.04
264	Bobby Witt	.10	.08	.04
265	Rich Amaral	.10	.08	.04
266	Bret Boone	.20	.15	.08
267	Jay Buhner	.10	.08	.04
268	Dave Fleming	.15	.11	.06
269	Randy Johnson	.15	.11	.06
270	Edgar Martinez	.10	.08	.04
271	Mike Schooler	.10	.08	.04
272	Russ Swan	.10	.08	.04
273	Dave Valle	.10	.08	.04
274	Omar Vizquel	.10	.08	.04
275	Kerry Woodson	.10	.08	.04
276	Kevin Brown	.10	.08	.04
277	Julio Franco	.10	.08	.04
278	Jeff Frye	.10	.08	.04
279	Juan Gonzalez	2.50	2.00	1.00
280	Jeff Huson	.10	.08	.04
281	Rafael Palmeiro	.15	.11	.06
282	Dean Palmer	.20	.15	.08
283	Roger Pavlik	.10	.08	.04
284	Ivan Rodriguez	.20	.15	.08
285	Kenny Rogers	.10	.08	.04
286	Derek Bell	.10	.08	.04
287	Pat Borders	.10	.08	.04
288	Joe Carter	.30	.25	.12
289	Bob MacDonald	.10	.08	.04
290	Jack Morris	.10	.08	.04
291	John Olerud	.75	.60	.30
292	Ed Sprague	.20	.15	.08
293	Todd Stottlemyre	.10	.08	.04
294	Mike Timlin	.10	.08	.04
295	Duane Ward	.10	.08	.04
296	David Wells	.10	.08	.04
297	Devon White	.10	.08	.04
298	Checklist	.10	.08	.04
299	Checklist	.10	.08	.04
300	Checklist	.10	.08	.04
301	Steve Bedrosian	.10	.08	.04
302	Jeff Blauser	.10	.08	.04
303	Francisco Cabrera	.10	.08	.04
304	Marvin Freeman	.10	.08	.04
305	Brian Hunter	.10	.08	.04
306	Dave Justice	.75	.60	.30
307	Greg Maddux	.40	.30	.15
308	*Greg McMichael*	.30	.25	.12
309	Kent Mercker	.10	.08	.04
310	Otis Nixon	.10	.08	.04
311	Pete Smith	.10	.08	.04
312	John Smoltz	.20	.15	.08
313	Jose Guzman	.10	.08	.04
314	Mike Harkey	.10	.08	.04
315	Greg Hibbard	.10	.08	.04
316	Candy Maldonado	.10	.08	.04
317	Randy Myers	.10	.08	.04
318	Dan Plesac	.10	.08	.04
319	Rey Sanchez	.10	.08	.04
320	Ryne Sandberg	.75	.60	.30
321	*Tommy Shields*	.15	.11	.06
322	Jose Vizcaino	.10	.08	.04
323	*Matt Walbeck*	.25	.20	.10
324	Willie Wilson	.10	.08	.04
325	Tom Browning	.10	.08	.04
326	Tim Costo	.15	.11	.06
327	Rob Dibble	.10	.08	.04
328	Steve Foster	.10	.08	.04
329	Roberto Kelly	.12	.09	.05
330	Randy Milligan	.10	.08	.04
331	Kevin Mitchell	.12	.09	.05
332	*Tim Pugh*	.25	.20	.10
333	Jeff Reardon	.10	.08	.04
334	*John Roper*	.20	.15	.08
335	Juan Samuel	.10	.08	.04
336	John Smiley	.10	.08	.04
337	San Wilson	.10	.08	.04
338	Scott Aldred	.10	.08	.04
339	Andy Ashby	.10	.08	.04
340	Freddie Benavides	.10	.08	.04
341	Dante Bichette	.10	.08	.04
342	Willie Blair	.10	.08	.04
343	Daryl Boston	.10	.08	.04
344	*Vinny Castilla*	.15	.11	.06
345	Jerald Clark	.10	.08	.04
346	Alex Cole	.10	.08	.04
347	Andres Galarraga	.10	.08	.04
348	Joe Girardi	.10	.08	.04

349	*Ryan Hawblitzel*	.15	.11	.06
350	Charlie Hayes	.10	.08	.04
351	Butch Henry	.10	.08	.04
352	Darren Holmes	.10	.08	.04
353	Dale Murphy	.10	.08	.04
354	David Nied	.40	.30	.15
355	Jeff Parrett	.10	.08	.04
356	*Steve Reed*	.20	.15	.08
357	Bruce Ruffin	.10	.08	.04
358	*Danny Sheaffer*	.15	.11	.06
359	Bryn Smith	.10	.08	.04
360	*Jim Tatum*	.15	.11	.06
361	Eric Young	.15	.11	.06
362	Gerald Young	.10	.08	.04
363	Luis Aquino	.10	.08	.04
364	*Alex Arias*	.10	.08	.04
365	Jack Armstrong	.10	.08	.04
366	Bret Barberie	.10	.08	.04
367	Ryan Bowen	.10	.08	.04
368	Greg Briley	.10	.08	.04
369	Cris Carpenter	.10	.08	.04
370	Chuck Carr	.10	.08	.04
371	*Jeff Conine*	.15	.11	.06
372	Steve Decker	.10	.08	.04
373	Orestes Destrade	.10	.08	.04
374	Monty Fariss	.10	.08	.04
375	Junior Felix	.10	.08	.04
376	Chris Hammond	.10	.08	.04
377	Bryan Harvey	.10	.08	.04
378	*Trevor Hoffman*	.15	.11	.06
379	Charlie Hough	.10	.08	.04
380	Joe Klink	.10	.08	.04
381	*Richie Lewis*	.20	.15	.08
382	Dave Magadan	.10	.08	.04
383	Bob McClure	.10	.08	.04
384	*Scott Pose*	.20	.15	.08
385	*Rich Renteria*	.15	.11	.06
386	Benito Santiago	.10	.08	.04
387	Walt Weiss	.10	.08	.04
388	Nigel Wilson	1.00	.70	.40
389	Eric Anthony	.10	.08	.04
390	Jeff Bagwell	.50	.40	.20
391	Andujar Cedeno	.10	.08	.04
392	Doug Drabek	.10	.08	.04
393	Darryl Kile	.10	.08	.04
394	Mark Portugal	.10	.08	.04
395	Karl Rhodes	.10	.08	.04
396	Scott Servais	.10	.08	.04
397	Greg Swindell	.10	.08	.04
398	Tom Goodwin	.10	.08	.04
399	Kevin Gross	.10	.08	.04
400	Carlos Hernandez	.10	.08	.04
401	Ramon Martinez	.10	.08	.04
402	Raul Mondesi	1.50	1.25	.60
403	Jody Reed	.10	.08	.04
404	Mike Sharperson	.10	.08	.04
405	Cory Snyder	.10	.08	.04
406	Darryl Strawberry	.10	.08	.04
407	*Rick Trlicek*	.15	.11	.06
408	Tim Wallach	.10	.08	.04
409	Todd Worrell	.10	.08	.04
410	Tavo Alvarez	.15	.11	.06
411	*Sean Berry*	.15	.11	.06
412	*Frank Bolick*	.15	.11	.06
413	Cliff Floyd	2.00	1.50	.80
414	Mike Gardiner	.10	.08	.04
415	Marquis Grissom	.20	.15	.08
416	*Tim Laker*	.20	.15	.08
417	*Mike Lansing*	.40	.30	.15
418	Dennis Martinez	.10	.08	.04
419	John Vander Wal	.10	.08	.04
420	John Wetteland	.10	.08	.04
421	Rondell White	1.25	.90	.50
422	Bobby Bonilla	.15	.11	.06
423	Jeromy Burnitz	.20	.15	.08
424	*Vince Burnitz*	.15	.11	.06
425	*Mike Draper*	.15	.11	.06
426	Tony Fernandez	.10	.08	.04
427	Dwight Gooden	.10	.08	.04
428	Jeff Innis	.10	.08	.04
429	Bobby Jones	.40	.30	.15
430	Mike Maddux	.10	.08	.04
431	Charlie O'Brien	.10	.08	.04
432	Joe Orsulak	.10	.08	.04
433	Pete Schourek	.10	.08	.04
434	Frank Tanana	.10	.08	.04
435	*Ryan Thompson*	.20	.15	.08
436	Kim Batiste	.10	.08	.04
437	Mark Davis	.10	.08	.04
438	Jose DeLeon	.10	.08	.04
439	Len Dykstra	.20	.15	.08
440	Jim Eisenreich	.10	.08	.04
441	Tommy Greene	.10	.08	.04
442	Pete Incaviglia	.10	.08	.04
443	Danny Jackson	.10	.08	.04
444	Todd Pratt	.10	.08	.04
445	Curt Schilling	.10	.08	.04
446	Milt Thompson	.10	.08	.04
447	David West	.10	.08	.04
448	Mitch Williams	.10	.08	.04
449	Steve Cooke	.20	.15	.08
450	Carlos Garcia	.15	.11	.06
451	Al Martin	.30	.25	.12
452	*Blas Minor*	.15	.11	.06
453	Dennis Moeller	.15	.11	.06
454	Denny Neagle	.10	.08	.04
455	Don Slaught	.10	.08	.04
456	Lonnie Smith	.10	.08	.04
457	Paul Wagner	.15	.11	.06
458	Bob Walk	.10	.08	.04
459	Kevin Young	.20	.15	.08
460	*Rene Arocha*	.40	.30	.15
461	Brian Barber	.20	.15	.08
462	Rheal Cormier	.10	.08	.04
463	Gregg Jefferies	.15	.11	.06
464	Joe Magrane	.10	.08	.04
465	Omar Olivares	.10	.08	.04
466	Geronimo Pena	.10	.08	.04
467	Allen Watson	.50	.40	.20
468	Mark Whiten	.15	.11	.06
469	Derek Bell	.25	.20	.10
470	Phil Clark	.10	.08	.04
471	*Pat Gomez*	.20	.15	.08
472	Tony Gwynn	.30	.25	.12
473	Jeremy Hernandez	.10	.08	.04
474	Bruce Hurst	.10	.08	.04
475	Phil Plantier	.25	.20	.10
476	*Scott Sanders*	.25	.20	.10
477	*Tim Scott*	.15	.11	.06
478	*Darrell Sherman*	.15	.11	.06
479	Guillermo Velasquez	.15	.11	.06
480	*Tim Worrell*	.20	.15	.08
481	Todd Benzinger	.10	.08	.04
482	Bud Black	.10	.08	.04
483	Barry Bonds	1.00	.70	.40
484	Dave Burba	.10	.08	.04
485	Bryan Hickerson	.10	.08	.04
486	Dave Martinez	.10	.08	.04
487	Willie McGee	.10	.08	.04
488	Jeff Reed	.10	.08	.04
489	Kevin Rogers	.15	.11	.06
490	Matt Williams	.15	.11	.06
491	Trevor Wilson	.10	.08	.04
492	Harold Baines	.10	.08	.04
493	Mike Devereaux	.10	.08	.04
494	Todd Frohwirth	.10	.08	.04
495	Chris Hoiles	.10	.08	.04
496	Luis Mercedes	.15	.11	.06
497	*Sherman Obando*	.30	.25	.12
498	*Brad Pennington*	.15	.11	.06
499	Harold Reynolds	.10	.08	.04
500	Arthur Rhodes	.15	.11	.06
501	Cal Ripken, Jr.	.75	.60	.30
502	Rick Sutcliffe	.10	.08	.04
503	Fernando Valenzuela	.10	.08	.04
504	Mark Williamson	.10	.08	.04
505	Scott Bankhead	.10	.08	.04
506	Greg Blosser	.15	.11	.06
507	Ivan Calderon	.10	.08	.04
508	Roger Clemens	.60	.45	.25
509	Andre Clemens	.10	.08	.04
510	Scott Fletcher	.10	.08	.04
511	Greg Harris	.10	.08	.04
512	Billy Hatcher	.10	.08	.04
513	Bob Melvin	.10	.08	.04
514	Carlos Quintana	.10	.08	.04
515	Luis Rivera	.10	.08	.04
516	Jeff Russell	.10	.08	.04
517	*Ken Ryan*	.30	.25	.12
518	Chili Davis	.10	.08	.04
519	*Jim Edmonds*	.30	.25	.12
520	Gary Gaetti	.10	.08	.04
521	Torey Lovullo	.10	.08	.04
522	*Tony Percival*	.15	.11	.06
523	Tim Salmon	2.50	2.00	1.00
524	Scott Sanderson	.10	.08	.04
525	*J.T. Snow*	.50	.40	.20
526	Jerome Walton	.10	.08	.04
527	Jason Bere	1.50	1.25	.60
528	*Rod Bolton*	.15	.11	.06
529	Ellis Burks	.10	.08	.04
530	Carlton Fisk	.10	.08	.04
531	Craig Grebeck	.10	.08	.04
532	Ozzie Guillen	.10	.08	.04
533	Roberto Hernandez	.10	.08	.04
534	Bo Jackson	.25	.20	.10
535	Kirk McCaskill	.10	.08	.04
536	Dave Stieb	.10	.08	.04
537	Robin Ventura	.35	.20	.10
538	Albert Belle	.70	.50	.25
539	Mike Bielecki	.10	.08	.04
540	Glenallen Hill	.10	.08	.04
541	Reggie Jefferson	.10	.08	.04
542	Kenny Lofton	.40	.30	.15
543	*Jeff Mutis*	.15	.11	.06
544	Junior Ortiz	.10	.08	.04
545	Manny Ramirez	3.00	2.25	1.25
546	Jeff Treadway	.10	.08	.04
547	Kevin Wickander	.10	.08	.04
548	Cecil Fielder	.35	.20	.10
549	Kirk Gibson	.10	.08	.04
550	*Greg Gohr*	.15	.11	.06
551	David Haas	.10	.08	.04
552	Bill Krueger	.10	.08	.04
553	Mike Moore	.10	.08	.04
554	Mickey Tettleton	.10	.08	.04
555	Lou Whitaker	.10	.08	.04
556	Kevin Appier	.10	.08	.04
557	*Billy Brewer*	.15	.11	.06
558	David Cone	.10	.08	.04
559	Greg Gagne	.10	.08	.04
560	Mark Gardner	.10	.08	.04
561	Phil Hiatt	.15	.11	.06
562	Felix Jose	.10	.08	.04
563	Jose Lind	.10	.08	.04
564	Mike Macfarlane	.10	.08	.04
565	Keith Miller	.10	.08	.04
566	Jeff Montgomery	.10	.08	.04
567	Hipolito Pechardo	.10	.08	.04
568	Ricky Bones	.10	.08	.04
569	Tom Brunansky	.10	.08	.04
570	*Joe Kmak*	.15	.11	.06
571	Pat Listach	.15	.11	.06
572	*Graeme Lloyd*	.15	.11	.06
573	*Carlos Maldonado*	.15	.11	.06
574	Josias Manzanillo	.15	.11	.06
575	Matt Mieske	.15	.11	.06
576	Kevin Reimer	.10	.08	.04
577	Bill Spiers	.10	.08	.04
578	Dickie Thon	.10	.08	.04
579	Willie Banks	.10	.08	.04
580	Jim Deshaies	.10	.08	.04
581	Mark Guthrie	.10	.08	.04
582	Brian Harper	.10	.08	.04
583	Chuck Knoblauch	.15	.11	.06
584	Gene Larkin	.10	.08	.04
585	Shane Mack	.10	.08	.04
586	David McCarty	.30	.25	.12
587	Mike Pagliarulo	.10	.08	.04
588	Mike Trombley	.10	.08	.04
589	Dave Winfield	.40	.30	.15
590	Jim Abbott	.20	.15	.08
591	Wade Boggs	.25	.20	.10
592	*Russ Davis*	.75	.60	.30
593	Steve Farr	.10	.08	.04
594	Steve Howe	.10	.08	.04
595	*Mike Humphreys*	.15	.11	.06
596	Jimmy Key	.10	.08	.04
597	Jim Leyritz	.10	.08	.04
598	*Bobby Munoz*	.15	.11	.06
599	Paul O'Neill	.10	.08	.04
600	Spike Owen	.10	.08	.04
601	Mike Stanley	.10	.08	.04
602	Danny Tartabull	.10	.08	.04
603	Scott Brosius	.10	.08	.04
604	Storm Davis	.10	.08	.04
605	Eric Fox	.10	.08	.04
606	Goose Gossage	.10	.08	.04
607	Scott Hammond	.10	.08	.04
608	Dave Henderson	.10	.08	.04
609	Mark McGwire	.20	.15	.08
610	*Mike Mohler*	.15	.11	.06
611	Edwin Nunez	.10	.08	.04
612	Kevin Seitzer	.10	.08	.04
613	Ruben Sierra	.15	.11	.06
614	Chris Bosio	.10	.08	.04
615	Norm Charlton	.10	.08	.04
616	*Jim Converse*	.25	.20	.10
617	*John Cummings*	.25	.20	.10
618	Mike Felder	.10	.08	.04
619	Ken Griffey, Jr.	3.00	2.25	1.25
620	*Mike Hampton*	.15	.11	.06
621	Erik Hanson	.10	.08	.04
622	Bill Haselman	.10	.08	.04
623	Tino Martinez	.10	.08	.04
624	Lee Tinsley	.15	.11	.06
625	*Fernando Vina*	.25	.20	.10
626	*David Wainhouse*	.15	.11	.06
627	Jose Canseco	.35	.25	.14
628	Benji Gil	.50	.40	.20
629	Tom Henke	.10	.08	.04
630	*David Hulse*	.60	.45	.25
631	Manuel Lee	.10	.08	.04
632	Craig Lefferts	.10	.08	.04
633	*Robb Nen*	.15	.11	.06
634	Gary Redus	.10	.08	.04
635	Bill Ripken	.10	.08	.04
636	Nolan Ryan	2.50	2.00	1.00
637	Dan Smith	.10	.08	.04
638	*Matt Whiteside*	.20	.15	.08
639	Roberto Alomar	.90	.70	.35
640	Juan Guzman	.20	.15	.08
641	Pat Hentgen	.60	.45	.25
642	Darrin Jackson	.10	.08	.04
643	Randy Knorr	.10	.08	.04
644	*Domingo Martinez*	.20	.15	.08
645	Paul Molitor	.30	.25	.12
646	Dick Schofield	.10	.08	.04
647	Dave Stewart	.10	.08	.04
648	Checklist	.10	.08	.04
649	Checklist	.10	.08	.04
650	Checklist	.10	.08	.04

1993 Fleer Ultra All-Rookies

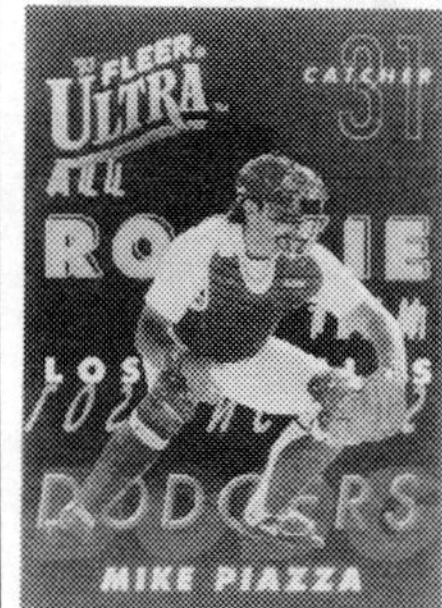

These insert cards are foil stamped on both sides and were randomly inserted into 1994 Series II packs. The cards have black fronts, with six different colors of type. The player's uniform number and position are located in the upper right-hand corner. The player's name and Ultra logo are gold-foil stamped. Backs have a black background on which are a player photo and a career summary.

		MT	NR MT	EX
Complete Set (10):		25.00	19.00	10.00
Common Player:		1.00	.70	.40
1	Rene Arocha	1.25	.90	.50
2	Jeff Conine	2.50	2.00	1.00
3	Phil Hiatt	1.25	.90	.50
4	Mike Lansing	1.25	.90	.50
5	Al Martin	1.50	1.25	.60
6	David Nied	2.00	1.50	.80
7	Mike Piazza	12.00	9.00	4.75
8	Tim Salmon	7.00	5.25	2.75
9	J.T. Snow	1.50	1.25	.60
10	Kevin Young	1.00	.70	.40

1993 Fleer Ultra All-Stars

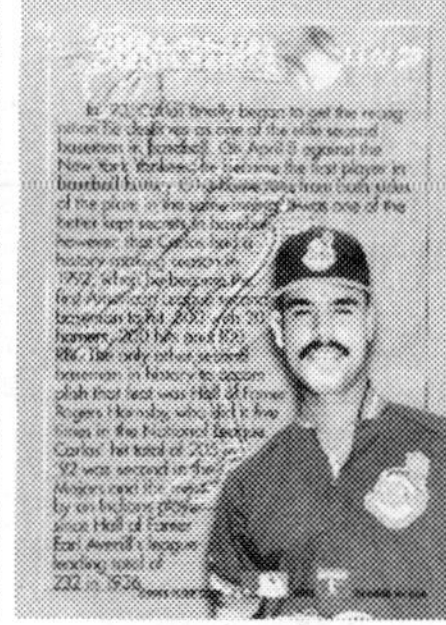

This 20-card set features 10 of the top players from each league. Cards were randomly inserted into Series II packs and are foil stamped on both sides.

		MT	NR MT	EX
Complete Set (20):		40.00	30.00	16.00
Common Player:		1.00	.75	.40
1	Darren Daulton	2.00	1.50	.80
2	Will Clark	3.00	2.25	1.20
3	Ryne Sandberg	5.00	3.75	2.00
4	Barry Larkin	1.25	.95	.50
5	Gary Sheffield	1.50	1.25	.60
6	Barry Bonds	5.00	3.75	2.00
7	Ray Lankford	1.00	.75	.40
8	Larry Walker	1.00	.75	.40
9	Greg Maddux	2.00	1.50	.75
10	Lee Smith	1.00	.75	.40
11	Ivan Rodriguez	1.50	1.25	.60
12	Mark McGwire	1.50	1.25	.60
13	Carlos Baerga	3.00	2.25	1.20
14	Cal Ripken, Jr.	6.00	4.50	2.25
15	Edgar Martinez	1.00	.75	.40
16	Juan Gonzalez	8.00	6.00	3.25
17	Ken Griffey, Jr.	12.00	9.00	4.75
18	Kirby Puckett	5.00	3.75	2.00
19	Frank Thomas	14.00	10.50	5.50
20	Mike Mussina	3.00	2.25	1.25

1993 Fleer Ultra Award Winners

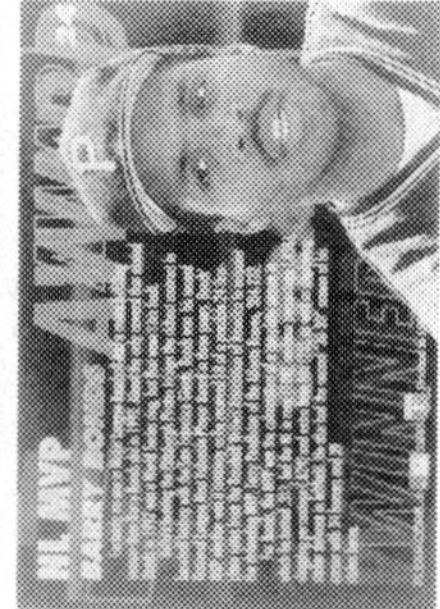

This 25-card insert set features 18 Top Glove players (nine from each league), two rookies of the year, three MVPs (both leagues and World Series), both Cy Young Award winners and one Player of the Year. All cards are UV coated and foil stamped on both sides and were found Series I packs. Fronts have a black background with "Fleer Ultra Award Winners" splashed around in trendy colors. The Ultra logo, player's name and his award are spelled out in gold foil. The horizontally arranged backs have much the same elements, plus a summary of the season's performance which led to the award. There is a close-up player photo, as well.

		MT	NR MT	EX
Complete Set (25):		50.00	35.00	20.00
Common Player:		1.00	.75	.40
1	Greg Maddux	2.00	1.50	.75
2	Tom Pagnozzi	1.00	.75	.40
3	Mark Grace	1.25	.90	.50
4	Jose Lind	1.00	.75	.40
5	Terry Pendleton	1.00	.75	.40
6	Ozzie Smith	2.00	1.50	.75
7	Barry Bonds	5.00	3.75	2.00
8	Andy Van Slyke	1.25	.90	.50
9	Larry Walker	1.00	.75	.40
10	Mark Langston	1.00	.75	.40
11	Ivan Rodriguez	1.50	1.25	.60
12	Don Mattingly	5.00	3.75	2.00
13	Roberto Alomar	4.00	3.00	1.50
14	Robin Ventura	2.00	1.50	.75
15	Cal Ripken, Jr.	6.00	4.50	2.25
16	Ken Griffey, Jr.	12.00	9.00	4.75
17	Kirby Puckett	5.00	3.75	2.00
18	Devon White	1.25	.90	.50
19	Pat Listach	1.00	.75	.40
20	Eric Karros	1.25	.90	.50
21	Pat Borders	1.00	.75	.40
22	Greg Maddux	2.00	1.50	.80
23	Dennis Eckersley	2.00	1.50	.60
24	Barry Bonds	5.00	3.75	2.00
25	Gary Sheffield	1.50	1.25	.60

1993 Fleer Ultra Dennis Eckersley

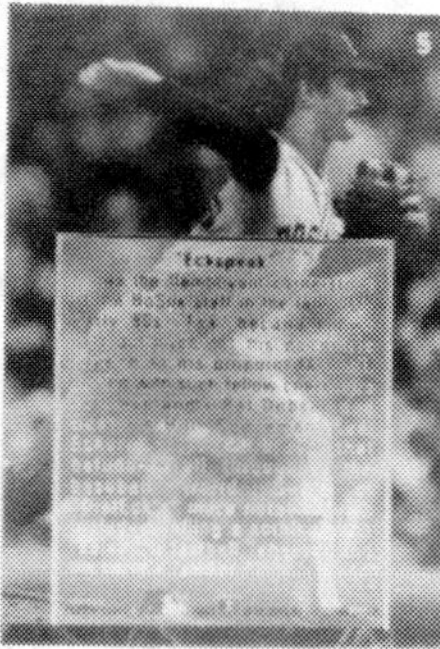

This 10-card, limited-edition "Career Highlights" subset commemorates Dennis Eckersley's illustrious career. Cards, which are UV coated and silver foil-stamped on both sides, were randomly inserted into both series' packs. Eckersley autographed more than 2,000 of the cards, which were also randomly inserted into packs. By sending in 10 Fleer Ultra wrappers plus $1, collectors could receive two additional Eckersley cards which were not available in regualr packs. Card fronts have a color action photo, the background of which has been colorized into shades of purple. A black marble strip at bottom has the city name and years he was with the team in silver foil. A large black marble box in one corner has the "Dennis Eckersley Career Highlights" logo in silver foil. On back, a purple box is dropped out of a color photo, and silver-foil typography describes some phrase of Eck's career.

		MT	NR MT	EX
Complete Set (12):		7.50	5.50	3.00
Common Card:		.75	.60	.30
Autographed Card:		75.00	55.00	30.00
1	"Perfection" (A's 1987-92)	.75	.60	.30
2	"The Kid" (Indians 1975-77)	.75	.60	.30
3	"The Warrior" (Indians 1975-77)	.75	.60	.30
4	"Beantown Blazer" (Red Sox 1978-84)	.75	.60	.30
5	"Eckspeak" (Red Sox 1978-84)	.75	.60	.30
6	"Down to Earth" (Red Sox 1978-84)	.75	.60	.30
7	"Wrigley Bound" (Cubs 1984-86)	.75	.60	.30
8	"No Relief" (A's 1987-92)	.75	.60	.30
9	"In Control" (A's 1987-92)	.75	.60	.30
10	"Simply the Best" (A's 1987-92)	.75	.60	.30
11	"Reign of Perfection" (A's 1987-92)	.75	.60	.30
12	"Leaving His Mark" (A's 1987-92)	.75	.60	.30

Regional interest may affect the value of a card.

1993 Fleer Ultra Home Run Kings

This 10-card subset features top home run kings. Cards, which are UV coated and have gold foil stamping on both sides, were inserts in Series I packs.

		MT	NR MT	EX
Complete Set (10):		30.00	22.50	12.00
Common Player:		2.00	1.50	.80
1	Juan Gonzalez	10.00	7.50	4.00
2	Mark McGwire	2.50	2.00	1.00
3	Cecil Fielder	2.50	2.00	1.00
4	Fred McGriff	3.00	2.25	1.20
5	Albert Belle	3.00	2.25	1.25
6	Barry Bonds	5.00	3.75	2.00
7	Joe Carter	3.00	2.25	1.20
8	Gary Sheffield	2.00	1.50	.80
9	Darren Daulton	2.00	1.50	.80
10	Dave Hollins	2.00	1.50	.80

1993 Fleer Ultra Performers

A 10-card Ultra Performers subset of Fleer Ultra baseball cards was offered directly to collectors in 1993. The subset, available only by mail, was limited to 150,000 sets. The cards featured gold-foil stamping and UV coating on both sides and a six-photo design, including five on the front of the card. Each card was identified on the back by set serial number jet-printed in black in a strip at bottom.

		MT	NR MT	EX
Complete Set (10):		18.00	13.50	7.25
Common Player:		1.00	.75	.40
1	Barry Bonds	4.00	3.00	1.50
2	Juan Gonzalez	4.00	3.00	1.50
3	Ken Griffey, Jr.	7.00	5.25	2.75
4	Eric Karros	1.25	.90	.50
5	Pat Listach	1.00	.75	.40
6	Greg Maddux	1.50	1.00	.60
7	David Nied	1.50	1.25	.60
8	Gary Sheffield	1.50	1.25	.60
9	J.T. Snow	1.00	.75	.40
10	Frank Thomas	7.50	5.50	3.00

1993 Fleer Ultra Strikeout Kings

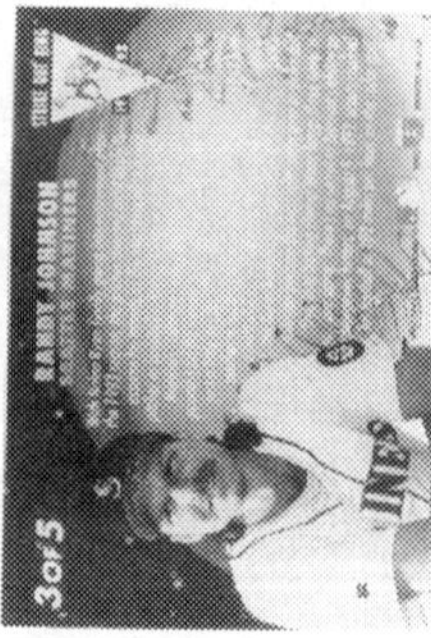

Five of baseball's top strikeout pitchers are featured in this second-series Ultra insert set. Cards are UV coated and foil stamped on both sides. Each card front has a picture of a pitcher winding up to throw. A baseball is in the background, with the pitcher in the forefront.

		MT	NR MT	EX
Complete Set (5):		15.00	11.25	6.00
Common Player:		1.00	.75	.40
1	Roger Clemens	4.00	3.00	1.50
2	Juan Guzman	2.00	1.50	.80
3	Randy Johnson	2.00	1.50	.80
4	Nolan Ryan	10.00	7.50	4.00
5	John Smoltz	1.00	.75	.40

A player's name in italic type indicates a rookie card. An (FC) indicates a player's first card for that particular card company.

1993 Fleer Final Edition

This 310-card set was sold as a complete set in its own box. Cards have the prefix F included with their card numbers. The set also includes 10 Diamond Tribute cards, which are numbered DT1-DT10.

		MT	NR MT	EX
Complete Set (310):		20.00	15.00	8.00
Common Player:		.05	.04	.02
1	Steve Bedrosian	.05	.04	.02
2	Jay Howell	.05	.04	.02
3	Greg Maddux	.15	.11	.06
4	*Greg McMichael*	.25	.20	.10
5	*Tony Tarasco*	.40	.30	.15
6	Jose Bautista	.05	.04	.02
7	Jose Guzman	.05	.04	.02
8	Greg Hibbard	.05	.04	.02
9	Candy Maldonado	.05	.04	.02
10	Randy Myers	.05	.04	.02
11	*Matt Walbeck*	.10	.08	.04
12	Turk Wendell	.05	.04	.02
13	Willie Nelson	.05	.04	.02
14	Greg Cadaret	.05	.04	.02
15	Roberto Kelly	.05	.04	.02
16	Randy Milligan	.05	.04	.02
17	Kevin Mitchell	.05	.04	.02
18	Jeff Reardon	.05	.04	.02
19	John Roper	.05	.04	.02
20	John Smiley	.05	.04	.02
21	Andy Ashby	.05	.04	.02
22	Dante Bichette	.05	.04	.02
23	Willie Blair	.05	.04	.02
24	Pedro Castellano	.05	.04	.02
25	Vinny Castilla	.05	.04	.02
26	Jerald Clark	.05	.04	.02
27	Alex Cole	.05	.04	.02
28	*Scott Fredrickson*	.20	.15	.08
29	*Jay Gainer*	.20	.15	.08
30	Andres Galarraga	.15	.11	.06
31	Joe Girardi	.05	.04	.02
32	Ryan Hawblitzel	.05	.04	.02
33	Charlie Hayes	.05	.04	.02
34	Darren Holmes	.05	.04	.02
35	Chris Jones	.05	.04	.02
36	David Nied	.40	.30	.15
37	*J. Owens*	.20	.15	.08
38	*Lance Painter*	.10	.08	.04
39	Jeff Parrett	.05	.04	.02
40	Steve Reed	.05	.04	.02
41	Armando Reynoso	.05	.04	.02
42	Bruce Ruffin	.05	.04	.02
43	*Danny Sheaffer*	.10	.08	.04
44	Keith Shepherd	.05	.04	.02
45	Jim Tatum	.05	.04	.02
46	Gary Wayne	.05	.04	.02
47	Eric Young	.10	.08	.04
48	Luis Aquino	.05	.04	.02
49	Alex Arias	.05	.04	.02
50	Jack Armstrong	.05	.04	.02
51	Bret Barberie	.05	.04	.02
52	Geronimo Berroa	.05	.04	.02
53	Ryan Bowen	.05	.04	.02
54	Greg Briley	.05	.04	.02
55	Chris Carpenter	.05	.04	.02
56	Chuck Carr	.05	.04	.02
57	Jeff Conine	.05	.04	.02
58	Jim Corsi	.05	.04	.02
59	Orestes Destrade	.05	.04	.02
60	Junior Felix	.05	.04	.02
61	Chris Hammond	.05	.04	.02
62	Bryan Harvey	.05	.04	.02
63	Charlie Hough	.05	.04	.02
64	Joe Klink	.05	.04	.02
65	*Richie Lewis*	.20	.15	.08
66	*Mitch Lyden*	.15	.11	.06
67	Bob Natal	.05	.04	.02
68	*Scott Pose*	.10	.08	.04
69	Rich Renteria	.05	.04	.02
70	Benito Santiago	.05	.04	.02
71	Gary Sheffield	.10	.08	.04
72	*Matt Turner*	.15	.11	.06
73	Walt Weiss	.05	.04	.02
74	*Darrell Whitmore*	.30	.25	.12
75	Nigel Wilson	.50	.40	.20
76	Kevin Bass	.05	.04	.02
77	Doug Drabek	.05	.04	.02
78	Tom Edens	.05	.04	.02
79	Chris James	.05	.04	.02
80	Greg Swindell	.05	.04	.02
81	*Omar Daal*	.10	.08	.04
82	Raul Mondesi	.05	.04	.02
83	Jody Reed	.05	.04	.02
84	Cory Snyder	.05	.04	.02
85	Rick Trlicek	.05	.04	.02
86	Tim Wallach	.05	.04	.02
87	Todd Worrell	.05	.04	.02
88	Tavo Alvarez	.10	.08	.04
89	Frank Bolick	.05	.04	.02
90	Kent Bottenfield	.05	.04	.02
91	Greg Colbrynn	.05	.04	.02
92	Cliff Floyd	1.75	1.25	.70
93	*Lou Frazier*	.15	.11	.06
94	Mike Gardiner	.05	.04	.02
95	*Mike Lansing*	.15	.11	.06
96	Bill Risley	.05	.04	.02
97	Jeff Shaw	.05	.04	.02
98	Kevin Baez	.05	.04	.02
99	*Tim Bogar*	.10	.08	.04
100	Jeromy Burnitz	.10	.08	.04
101	Mike Draper	.10	.08	.04
102	Darrin Jackson	.05	.04	.02
103	Mike Maddux	.05	.04	.02
104	Joe Orsulak	.05	.04	.02
105	Doug Saunders	.10	.08	.04
106	Frank Tanana	.05	.04	.02
107	Dave Telgheder	.15	.11	.06
108	Larry Anderson	.05	.04	.02
109	Jim Eisenreich	.05	.04	.02
110	Pete Incaviglia	.05	.04	.02
111	Danny Jackson	.05	.04	.02
112	David West	.05	.04	.02
113	Al Martin	.20	.15	.08
114	Blas Minor	.05	.04	.02
115	Dennis Moeller	.05	.04	.02
116	Will Pennyfeather	.05	.04	.02
117	Rich Robertson	.05	.04	.02
118	Ben Shelton	.05	.04	.02
119	Lonnie Smith	.05	.04	.02
120	Freddie Toliver	.05	.04	.02
121	Paul Wagner	.05	.04	.02
122	Kevin Young	.15	.11	.06
123	*Rene Arocha*	.30	.25	.12
124	Greg Jefferies	.10	.08	.04
125	Paul Kilgus	.05	.04	.02
126	Les Lancaster	.05	.04	.02
127	Joe Magrane	.05	.04	.02
128	Rob Murphy	.05	.04	.02
129	Erik Pappas	.05	.04	.02
130	Stan Royer	.05	.04	.02
131	Ozzie Smith	.15	.11	.06
132	Tom Urbani	.05	.04	.02
133	Mark Whiten	.05	.04	.02
134	Derek Bell	.05	.04	.02
135	Doug Brocall	.05	.04	.02
136	Phil Clark	.05	.04	.02
137	*Mark Ettles*	.10	.08	.04
138	Jeff Gardner	.05	.04	.02
139	*Pat Gomez*	.10	.08	.04
140	Ricky Gutierrez	.10	.08	.04
141	Gene Harris	.05	.04	.02
142	*Kevin Higgins*	.15	.11	.06
143	Trevor Hoffman	.05	.04	.02
144	Phil Plantier	.10	.08	.04
145	*Kerry Taylor*	.10	.08	.04
146	Guillermo Velasquez	.05	.04	.02
147	Wally Whitehurst	.05	.04	.02
148	*Tim Worrell*	.10	.08	.04
149	Todd Benzinger	.05	.04	.02
150	Barry Bonds	.50	.40	.20
151	Greg Brummett	.05	.04	.02
152	Mark Carreon	.05	.04	.02
153	Dave Martinez	.05	.04	.02
154	Jeff Reed	.05	.04	.02
155	Kevin Rogers	.05	.04	.02
156	Harold Baines	.05	.04	.02
157	Damon Buford	.05	.04	.02
158	*Paul Carey*	.15	.11	.06
159	Jeffrey Hammonds	.75	.60	.30
160	Jaime Moyer	.05	.04	.02
161	*Sherman Obando*	.15	.11	.06
162	*John O'Donoghue*	.15	.11	.06
163	Brad Pennington	.05	.04	.02
164	Jim Poole	.05	.04	.02
165	Harold Reynolds	.05	.04	.02
166	Fernando Valenzuela	.05	.04	.02
167	*Jack Voight*	.15	.11	.06
168	Mark Williamson	.05	.04	.02
169	Scott Bankhead	.05	.04	.02
170	Greg Blosser	.05	.04	.02
171	*Jim Byrd*	.10	.08	.04
172	Ivan Calderon	.05	.04	.02
173	Andre Dawson	.05	.04	.02
174	Scott Fletcher	.05	.04	.02
175	Jose Melendez	.05	.04	.02
176	Carlos Quintana	.05	.04	.02
177	Jeff Russell	.05	.04	.02
178	Aaron Sele	.75	.60	.30
179	*Rod Correia*	.10	.08	.04
180	Chili Davis	.05	.04	.02
181	*Jim Edmonds*	.20	.15	.08
182	Rene Gonzales	.05	.04	.02
183	*Hilly Hathaway*	.15	.11	.06
184	Torey Lovullo	.05	.04	.02
185	Greg Myers	.05	.04	.02
186	Gene Nelson	.05	.04	.02
187	Troy Percival	.05	.04	.02
188	Scott Sanderson	.05	.04	.02
189	*Darryl Scott*	.15	.11	.06
190	*J.T. Snow*	.60	.45	.25
191	Russ Springer	.05	.04	.02
192	Jason Bere	1.00	.70	.40
193	Rodney Bolton	.05	.04	.02
194	Ellis Burks	.05	.04	.02
195	Bo Jackson	.15	.11	.06
196	Mike LaValliere	.05	.04	.02
197	Scott Ruffcorn	.25	.20	.10
198	*Jeff Schwartz*	.10	.08	.04
199	Jerry DiPoto	.05	.04	.02
200	Alvaro Espinoza	.05	.04	.02
201	Wayne Kirby	.05	.04	.02
202	*Tom Kramer*	.10	.08	.04
203	Jesse Levis	.05	.04	.02
204	Manny Rodriguez	.75	.60	.30
205	Jeff Treadway	.05	.04	.02
206	*Bill Wertz*	.10	.08	.04
207	Cliff Young	.05	.04	.02
208	Matt Young	.05	.04	.02
209	Kirk Gibson	.05	.04	.02
210	Greg Gohr	.05	.04	.02
211	Bill Krueger	.05	.04	.02
212	Bob MacDonald	.05	.04	.02
213	Mike Moore	.05	.04	.02
214	David Wells	.05	.04	.02
215	*Billy Brewer*	.10	.08	.04
216	David Cone	.05	.04	.02
217	Greg Gagne	.05	.04	.02
218	Mark Gardner	.05	.04	.02
219	Chis Haney	.05	.04	.02
220	Phil Hiatt	.20	.15	.08
221	Jose Lind	.05	.04	.02
222	Juan Bell	.05	.04	.02
223	Tom Brunansky	.05	.04	.02
224	Mike Ignasiak	.05	.04	.02
225	Joe Knak	.05	.04	.02
226	Tom Lampkin	.05	.04	.02
227	*Graeme Lloyd*	.10	.08	.04
228	Carlos Maldonado	.05	.04	.02
229	Matt Mieske	.05	.04	.02
230	Angel Miranda	.05	.04	.02
231	*Troy O'Leary*	.25	.20	.10
232	Kevin Reimer	.05	.04	.02
233	Larry Casian	.05	.04	.02
234	Jim Deshaies	.05	.04	.02
235	*Eddie Guardado*	.15	.11	.06
236	Chip Hale	.05	.04	.02
237	*Mike Maksudian*	.25	.20	.10
238	David McCarty	.25	.20	.10
239	*Pat Meares*	.10	.08	.04
240	*George Tsamis*	.10	.08	.04
241	Dave Winfield	.15	.11	.06
242	Jim Abbott	.10	.08	.04
243	Wade Boggs	.10	.08	.04
244	*Andy Cook*	.10	.08	.04
245	*Russ Davis*	.40	.30	.15
246	Mike Humphreys	.05	.04	.02
247	Jimmy Key	.05	.04	.02
248	Jim Leyritz	.05	.04	.02
249	Bobby Munoz	.05	.04	.02
250	Paul O'Neill	.05	.04	.02
251	Spike Owen	.05	.04	.02
252	Dave Silvestri	.05	.04	.02
253	*Marcos Armas*	.25	.20	.10
254	Brent Gates	.20	.15	.08
255	Goose Gossage	.05	.04	02
256	*Scott Lydy*	.25	.20	.10
257	Henry Mercedes	.05	.04	.02
258	*Mike Mohler*	.10	.08	.04
259	Troy Neel	.25	.20	.10
260	Edwin Nunez	.05	.04	.02
261	Craig Paquette	.10	.08	.04
262	Kevin Seitzer	.05	.04	.02
263	Rich Amaral	.05	.04	.02
264	Mike Blowers	.05	.04	.02
265	Chris Bosio	.05	.04	.02
266	Norm Charlton	.05	.04	.02
267	*Jim Converse*	.10	.08	.04
268	*John Cummings*	.10	.08	.04
269	Mike Felder	.05	.04	.02
270	Mike Hampton	.05	.04	.02
271	Bill Haselman	.05	.04	.02
272	Dwayne Henry	.05	.04	.02
273	Greg Litton	.05	.04	.02
274	Mackey Sasser	.05	.04	.02
275	Lee Tinsley	.05	.04	.02
276	David Wainhouse	.05	.04	.02
277	*Jeff Bronkey*	.10	.08	.04
278	Benji Gil	.15	.11	.06
279	Tom Henke	.05	.04	.02
280	Charlie Leibrandt	.05	.04	.02
281	Robb Nen	.05	.04	.02
282	Bill Ripken	.05	.04	.02
283	*Jon Shave*	.10	.08	.04
284	Doug Strange	.05	.04	.02
285	*Matt Whiteside*	.10	.08	.04
286	*Scott Brow*	.15	.11	.06
287	*Willie Canate*	.15	.11	.06
288	Tony Castillo	.05	.04	.02
289	*Domingo Cedeno*	.10	.08	.04
290	Darnell Coles	.05	.04	.02
291	Danny Cox	.05	.04	.02
292	Mark Eichhorn	.05	.04	.02
293	Tony Fernandez	.05	.04	.02
294	Al Leiter	.05	.04	.02
295	Paul Molitor	.30	.25	.12
296	Dave Stewart	.05	.04	.02
297	*Woody Williams*	.15	.11	.06
298	Checklist	.05	.04	.02
299	Checklist	.05	.04	.02
300	Checklist	.05	.04	.02
1DT	Wade Boggs	.50	.40	.20
2DT	George Brett	.50	.40	.20
3DT	Andre Dawson	.20	.15	.08
4DT	Carlton Fisk	.20	.15	.08
5DT	Paul Molitor	.40	.30	.15
6DT	Nolan Ryan	1.50	1.00	.60
7DT	Lee Smith	.20	.15	.08
8DT	Ozzie Smith	.40	.30	.15
9DT	Dave Winfield	.50	.40	.20
10DT	Robin Yount	.50	.40	.20

1993 Fleer Flair

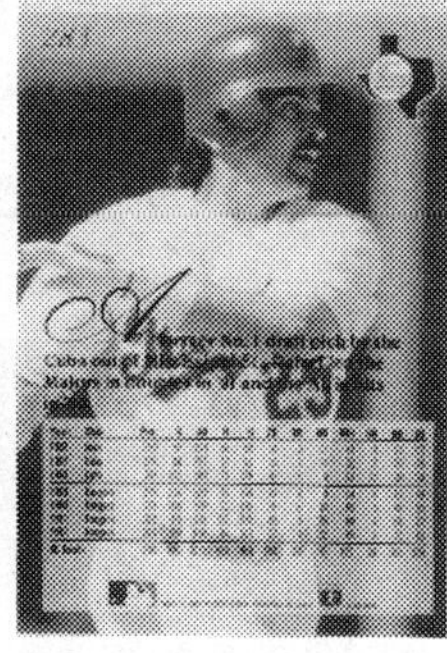

Designed as Fleer's super-premium card brand, this 300-card set contains extra-thick cards which feature gold stamping and UV coating front and back. Portrait and action photos are combined in a high-tech front picture and there is a muted photo on the back, as well.

		MT	NR MT	EX
Complete Set (300):		110.00	82.50	45.00
Common Player:		.25	.15	.08
1	Steve Avery	1.00	.70	.40
2	Jeff Blauser	.25	.15	.08
3	Ron Gant	.35	.25	.14
4	Tom Glavine	1.00	.70	.40
5	Dave Justice	2.00	1.50	.80
6	Mark Lemke	.25	.15	.08
7	Greg Maddux	.75	.60	.30
8	Fred McGriff	1.25	.90	.50
9	Terry Pendleton	.35	.25	.14
10	Deion Sanders	.75	.60	.30
11	John Smoltz	.40	.30	.15
12	Mike Stanton	.25	.15	.08
13	Steve Buechele	.25	.15	.08
14	Mark Grace	.50	.30	.15
15	Greg Hibbard	.25	.15	.08
16	Derrick May	.35	.25	.14
17	Chuck McElroy	.25	.15	.08
18	Mike Morgan	.25	.15	.08
19	Randy Myers	.25	.15	.08
20	Ryne Sandberg	2.50	2.00	1.00
21	Dwight Smith	.25	.15	.08
22	Sammy Sosa	.60	.45	.25
23	Jose Vizcaino	.25	.15	.08
24	Tim Belcher	.25	.15	.08
25	Rob Dibble	.25	.15	.08
26	Roberto Kelly	.30	.25	.12
27	Barry Larkin	.35	.25	.14
28	Kevin Mitchell	.25	.15	.08
29	Hal Morris	.25	.15	.08
30	Joe Oliver	.25	.15	.08
31	Jose Rijo	.25	.15	.08
32	Bip Roberts	.25	.15	.08
33	Chris Sabo	.25	.15	.08
34	Reggie Sanders	.60	.45	.25
35	Dante Bichette	.25	.15	.08
36	Willie Blair	.25	.15	.08
37	Jerald Clark	.25	.15	.08
38	Alex Cole	.25	.15	.08
39	Andres Galarraga	.50	.30	.15
40	Joe Girardi	.25	.15	.08
41	Charlie Hayes	.25	.15	.08
42	Chris Jones	.25	.15	.08
43	David Nied	1.50	1.25	.60
44	Eric Young	.50	.40	.20
45	Alex Arias	.25	.15	.08
46	Jack Armstrong	.25	.15	.08
47	Bret Barberie	.25	.15	.08
48	Chuck Carr	.40	.30	.15
49	Jeff Conine	.50	.40	.20
50	Orestes Destrade	.25	.15	.08
51	Chris Hammond	.25	.15	.08
52	Bryan Harvey	.25	.15	.08
53	Benito Santiago	.25	.15	.08
54	Gary Sheffield	.90	.70	.35
55	Walt Weiss	.25	.15	.08
56	Eric Anthony	.25	.15	.08
57	Jeff Bagwell	1.50	1.25	.60
58	Craig Biggio	.25	.15	.08
59	Ken Caminiti	.25	.15	.08
60	Andujar Cedeno	.40	.30	.15
61	Doug Drabek	.25	.15	.08
62	Steve Finley	.25	.15	.08
63	Luis Gonzalez	.35	.20	.10
64	Pete Harnisch	.25	.15	.08
65	Doug Jones	.25	.15	.08
66	Darryl Kile	.25	.15	.08
67	Greg Swindell	.25	.15	.08
68	Brett Butler	.25	.15	.08
69	Jim Gott	.25	.15	.08
70	Orel Hershiser	.25	.15	.08
71	Eric Karros	.75	.60	.30
72	Pedro Martinez	.50	.30	.15
73	Ramon Martinez	.25	.15	.08
74	Roger McDowell	.25	.15	.08
75	Mike Piazza	12.00	9.00	4.75
76	Jody Reed	.25	.15	.08
77	Tim Wallach	.25	.15	.08
78	Moises Alou	1.00	.75	.40
79	Greg Colbrunn	.25	.15	.08
80	Wil Cordero	.40	.30	.15
81	Delino DeShields	.50	.40	.20
82	Jeff Fassero	.25	.15	.08
83	Marquis Grissom	.80	.60	.30
84	Ken Hill	.25	.15	.08
85	*Mike Lansing*	1.00	.75	.40
86	Dennis Martinez	.25	.15	.08
87	Larry Walker	.60	.45	.25
88	John Wetteland	.25	.15	.08
89	Bobby Bonilla	.50	.30	.15
90	Vince Coleman	.25	.15	.08
91	Dwight Gooden	.25	.15	.08
92	Todd Hundley	.25	.15	.08
93	Howard Johnson	.25	.15	.08
94	Eddie Murray	.50	.30	.15
95	Joe Orsulak	.25	.15	.08
96	Bret Saberhagen	.25	.15	.08
97	Darren Daulton	.40	.30	.15
98	Mariano Duncan	.25	.15	.08
99	Len Dykstra	.60	.45	.25
100	Jim Eisenreich	.25	.15	.08
101	Tommy Greene	.35	.20	.10
102	Dave Hollins	.50	.40	.20
103	Pete Incaviglia	.25	.15	.08
104	Danny Jackson	.25	.15	.08
105	John Kruk	.40	.30	.15
106	Terry Mulholland	.25	.15	.08
107	Curt Schilling	.25	.15	.08
108	Mitch Williams	.25	.15	.08
109	Stan Belinda	.25	.15	.08
110	Jay Bell	.25	.15	.08
111	Steve Cooke	.25	.15	.08
112	Carlos Garcia	.90	.70	.35
113	Jeff King	.25	.15	.08
114	Al Martin	.50	.30	.15
115	Orlando Merced	.25	.15	.08
116	Don Slaught	.25	.15	.08
117	Andy Van Slyke	.35	.25	.14
118	Tim Wakefield	.25	.15	.08
119	*Rene Arocha*	.90	.70	.35
120	Bernard Gilkey	.40	.30	.15
121	Greg Jefferies	.50	.30	.15
122	Ray Lankford	.30	.25	.12
123	Donovan Osborne	.25	.15	.08
124	Tom Pagnozzi	.25	.15	.08
125	Erik Pappas	.25	.15	.08
126	Geronimo Pena	.25	.15	.08
127	Lee Smith	.25	.15	.08
128	Ozzie Smith	1.00	.70	.40
129	Bob Tewksbury	.25	.15	8.00
130	Mark Whiten	.40	.30	.15
131	Derek Bell	.35	.25	.14
132	Andy Benes	.25	.15	.08
133	Tony Gwynn	1.00	.75	.40
134	Gene Harris	.25	.15	.08
135	Trevor Hoffman	.25	.15	.08
136	Phil Plantier	1.00	.70	.40
137	Rod Beck	.25	.15	.08
138	Barry Bonds	4.00	3.00	1.50
139	John Burkett	.25	.15	.08
140	Will Clark	1.00	.75	.40
141	Royce Clayton	.40	.30	.15
142	Mike Jackson	.25	.15	.08
143	Darren Lewis	.25	.15	.08
144	Kirt Manwaring	.25	.15	.08
145	Willie McGee	.25	.15	.08
146	Bill Swift	.25	.15	.08
147	Robby Thompson	.25	.15	.08
148	Matt Williams	.75	.60	.30
149	Brady Anderson	.25	.15	.08
150	Mike Devereaux	.25	.15	.08
151	Chris Hoiles	.25	.15	.08
152	Ben McDonald	.25	.15	.08
153	Mark McLemore	.25	.15	.08
154	Mike Mussina	1.50	1.25	.60
155	Gregg Olson	.25	.15	.08
156	Harold Reynolds	.25	.15	.08
157	Cal Ripken Jr.	2.50	2.00	1.00
158	Rick Sutcliffe	.25	.15	.08
159	Fernando Valenzuela	.25	.15	.08
160	Roger Clemens	1.50	1.25	.60
161	Scott Cooper	.25	.15	.08
162	Andre Dawson	.75	.60	.30
163	Scott Fletcher	.25	.15	.08
164	Mike Greenwell	.25	.15	.08
165	Greg Harris	.25	.15	.08
166	Billy Hatcher	.25	.15	.08
167	Jeff Russell	.25	.15	.08
168	Mo Vaughn	1.00	.75	.40
169	Frank Viola	.25	.15	.08
170	Chad Curtis	.60	.45	.25
171	Chili Davis	.25	.15	.08
172	Gary DiSarcina	.25	.15	.08
173	Damion Easley	.50	.40	.20
174	Chuck Finley	.25	.15	.08
175	Mark Langston	.25	.15	.08
176	Luis Polonia	.25	.15	.08
177	Tim Salmon	7.00	5.25	2.75
178	Scott Sanderson	.25	.15	.08
179	*J.T. Snow*	1.00	.75	.40
180	Wilson Alvarez	.35	.20	.10
181	Ellis Burks	.25	.15	.08
182	Joey Cora	.25	.15	.08
183	Alex Fernandez	.50	.30	.15
184	Ozzie Guillen	.25	.15	.08
185	Roberto Hernandez	.25	.15	.08
186	Bo Jackson	1.00	.75	.40
187	Lance Johnson	.25	.15	.08
188	Jack McDowell	.60	.45	.25
189	Frank Thomas	9.00	6.75	3.50
190	Robin Ventura	1.00	.70	.40
191	Carlos Baerga	1.50	1.25	.60
192	Albert Belle	1.75	1.25	.70
193	Wayne Kirby	.25	.15	.08
194	Derek Lilliquist	.25	.15	.08
195	Kenny Lofton	.90	.70	.35
196	Carlos Martinez	.25	.15	.08
197	Jose Mesa	.25	.15	.08
198	Eric Plunk	.25	.15	.08
199	Paul Sorrento	.25	.15	.08
200	John Doherty	.25	.15	.08
201	Cecil Fielder	1.00	.70	.40
202	Travis Fryman	1.75	1.25	.70
203	Kirk Gibson	.25	.15	.08
204	Mike Henneman	.25	.15	.08
205	Chad Kreuter	.25	.15	.08
206	Scott Livingstone	.25	.15	.08
207	Tony Phillips	.25	.15	.08
208	Mickey Tettleton	.25	.15	.08
209	Alan Trammell	.25	.15	.08
210	David Wells	.25	.15	.08
211	Lou Whitaker	.25	.15	.08
212	Kevin Appier	.25	.15	.08
213	George Brett	2.00	1.50	.80
214	David Cone	.25	.15	.08
215	Tom Gordon	.25	.15	.08
216	Phil Hiatt	.60	.45	.25
217	Felix Jose	.25	.15	.08
218	Wally Joyner	.25	.15	.08
219	Jose Lind	.25	.15	.08
220	Mike Macfarlane	.25	.15	.08
221	Brian McRae	.25	.15	.08
222	Jeff Montgomery	.25	.15	.08
223	Cal Eldred	.50	.30	.15
224	Darryl Hamilton	.25	.15	.08
225	John Jaha	.75	.60	.30
226	Pat Listach	.40	.30	.15
227	*Graeme Lloyd*	.35	.25	.14
228	Kevin Reimer	.25	.15	.08
229	Bill Spiers	.25	.15	.08
230	B.J. Surhoff	.25	.15	.08
231	Greg Vaughn	.40	.30	.15
232	Robin Yount	2.00	1.50	.80
233	Rick Aguilera	.25	.15	.08
234	Jim Deshaies	.25	.15	.08
235	Brian Harper	.25	.15	.08
236	Kent Hrbek	.25	.15	.08
237	Chuck Knoblauch	.40	.30	.15
238	Shane Mack	.25	.15	.08
239	David McCarty	.75	.60	.30
240	Pedro Munoz	.25	.15	.08
241	Mike Pagliarulo	.25	.15	.08
242	Kirby Puckett	2.00	1.50	.80
243	Dave Winfield	1.00	.70	.40
244	Jim Abbott	.40	.30	.15
245	Wade Boggs	.75	.60	.30
246	Pat Kelly	.25	.15	.08
247	Jimmy Key	.25	.15	.08
248	Jim Leyritz	.25	.15	.08
249	Don Mattingly	2.00	1.50	.80
250	Matt Nokes	.25	.15	.08
251	Paul O'Neill	.25	.15	.08
252	Mike Stanley	.25	.15	.08
253	Danny Tartabull	.25	.15	.08
254	Bob Wickman	.50	.40	.20
255	Bernie Williams	.25	.15	.08
256	Mike Bordick	.25	.15	.08
257	Dennis Eckersley	.25	.15	.08
258	Brent Gates	1.50	1.25	.60
259	Goose Gossage	.25	.15	.08
260	Rickey Henderson	1.00	.70	.40
261	Mark McGwire	.50	.30	.15
262	Ruben Sierra	.50	.40	.20
263	Terry Steinbach	.25	.15	.08
264	Bob Welch	.25	.15	.08
265	Bobby Witt	.25	.15	.08
266	Rich Amaral	.25	.15	.08
267	Chris Bosio	.25	.15	.08
268	Jay Buhner	.25	.15	.08
269	Norm Charlton	.25	.15	.08
270	Ken Griffey, Jr.	10.00	7.50	4.00
271	Erik Hanson	.25	.15	.08
272	Randy Johnson	.50	.40	.20
273	Edgar Martinez	.25	.15	.08
274	Tino Martinez	.25	.15	.08
275	Dave Valle	.25	.15	.08
276	Omar Vizquel	.25	.15	.08
277	Kevin Brown	.25	.15	.08
278	Jose Canseco	.75	.60	.30
279	Julio Franco	.25	.15	.08
280	Juan Gonzalez	7.00	5.25	2.75
281	Tom Henke	.25	.15	.08
282	David Hulse	.25	.15	.08
283	Rafael Palmeiro	.60	.45	.25
284	Dean Palmer	.40	.30	.15
285	Ivan Rodriguez	1.00	.75	.40
286	Nolan Ryan	6.00	4.50	2.50
287	Roberto Alomar	1.50	1.25	.60
288	Pat Borders	.25	.15	.08
289	Joe Carter	1.00	.75	.40
290	Juan Guzman	.75	.60	.30
291	Pat Hentgen	1.00	.75	.40
292	Paul Molitor	1.50	1.25	.60
293	John Olerud	2.00	1.50	.80
294	Ed Sprague	.25	.15	.08
295	Dave Stewart	.25	.15	.08
296	Duane Ward	.25	.15	.08
297	Devon White	.25	.15	.08
298	Checklist	.25	.15	.08
299	Checklist	.25	.15	.08
300	Checklist	.25	.15	.08

Values for recent cards and sets are listed in Mint (MT), Near Mint (NM), reflecting the fact that many cards from recent years have been preserved in top condition. Recent cards and sets in less than Excellent condition have little collector interest.

Values quoted in this guide reflect the retail price of a card – the price a collector can expect to pay when buying a card from a dealer. The wholesale price – that which a collector can expect to receive from a dealer when selling cards – will be significantly lower, depending on desirability and condition.

1993 Fleer Flair Wave of the Future

Twenty of the game's top prospects were featured in this insert issue randomly packaged in Flair packs. Cards #19-20, Darrell Whitmore and Nigel Wilson, were printed with each other's back; no corrected version was made.

		MT	NR MT	EX
Complete Set (20):		95.00	71.00	38.00
Common Player:		3.00	2.25	1.25
1	Jason Bere	8.00	6.00	3.25
2	Jeremy Burnitz	4.00	3.00	1.50
3	Russ Davis	5.00	3.75	2.00
4	Jim Edmonds	3.00	2.25	1.25
5	Cliff Floyd	15.00	11.00	6.00
6	Jeffrey Hammonds	8.00	6.00	3.25
7	Trevor Hoffman	3.00	2.25	1.25
8	Domingo Jean	4.00	3.00	1.50
9	David McCarty	3.50	2.75	1.50
10	Bobby Munoz	3.00	2.25	1.25
11	Brad Pennington	3.00	2.25	1.25
12	Mike Piazza	15.00	11.00	6.00
13	Manny Ramirez	9.00	6.75	3.50
14	John Roper	3.00	2.25	1.25
15	Tim Salmon	8.00	6.00	3.25
16	Aaron Sele	8.00	6.00	3.25
17	Allen Watson	5.00	3.75	2.00
18	Rondell White	6.00	4.50	2.50
19	Darell Whitmore	5.00	3.75	2.00
20	Nigel Wilson	5.00	3.75	2.00

1993 Fleer Atlantic

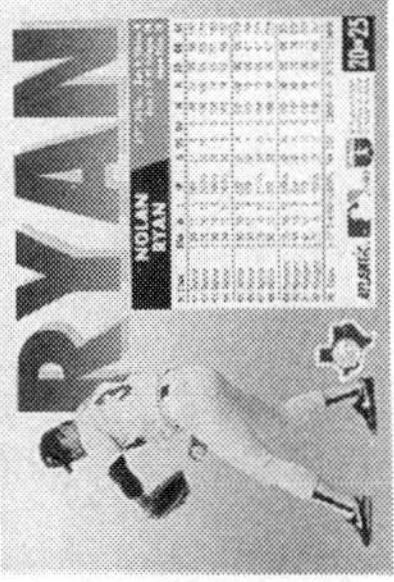

The Atlantic Collectors Edition set of 1993 featured 24 of the top players in the game (plus one checklist) portrayed in a style matching the regular-issue Fleer set, with the addition of the Atlantic logo and a gold border. The cards were given away five at a time with gasoline purchases at gas stations in New York and Pennsylvania during the summer.

		MT	NR MT	EX
Complete Set (25):		9.00	6.75	3.50
Common Player:		.25	.20	.10
1	Roberto Alomar	.50	.40	.20
2	Barry Bonds	1.00	.70	.40
3	Bobby Bonilla	.25	.20	.10
4	Will Clark	.75	.60	.30
5	Roger Clemens	.50	.40	.20
6	Darren Daulton	.25	.20	.10
7	Dennis Eckersley	.25	.20	.10
8	Cecil Fielder	.50	.40	.20
9	Tom Glavine	.25	.20	.10
10	Juan Gonzalez	.90	.70	.35
11	Ken Griffey Jr.	1.50	1.25	.60
12	John Kruk	.25	.20	.10
13	Greg Maddux	.25	.20	.10
14	Don Mattingly	1.00	.70	.40
15	Fred McGriff	.50	.40	.20
16	Mark McGwire	.90	.70	.35
17	Terry Pendleton	.25	.20	.10
18	Kirby Puckett	.90	.70	.35
19	Cal Ripken Jr.	1.00	.70	.40
20	Nolan Ryan	2.00	1.50	.80
21	Ryne Sandberg	1.00	.70	.40
22	Gary Sheffield	.25	.20	.10
23	Frank Thomas	1.50	1.25	.60
24	Andy Van Slyke	.25	.20	.10
25	Checklist	.05	.04	.02

1993 Fleer Fruit of the Loom

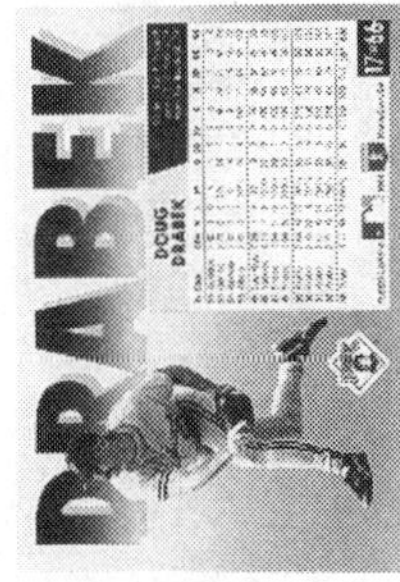

Fruit of the Loom and Fleer combined to create a 66-card baseball set in 1993 that featured many of the top players in the game. The cards, with the same design as the regular issue Fleer cards for 1993, also display the Fruit of the Loom logo in the upper left corner. Three cards were inserted in specially marked packages of the company's products.

		MT	NR MT	EX
Complete Set (66):		80.00	60.00	32.00
Common Player:		1.00	.70	.40
1	Roberto Alomar	2.00	1.50	.80
2	Brady Anderson	1.00	.70	.40
3	Jeff Bagwell	1.50	1.25	.60
4	Albert Belle	1.50	1.25	.60
5	Craig Biggio	1.25	.90	.50
6	Barry Bonds	4.00	3.00	1.50
7	George Brett	6.00	4.50	2.50
8	Brett Butler	1.00	.70	.40
9	Jose Canseco	3.00	2.25	1.25
10	Joe Carter	2.00	1.50	.80
11	Will Clark	3.00	2.25	1.25
12	Roger Clemens	1.50	1.25	.60
13	Darren Daulton	1.25	.90	.50
14	Andre Dawson	1.50	1.25	.60
15	Delino DeShields	1.25	.90	.50
16	Rob Dibble	1.00	.70	.40
17	Doug Drabek	1.00	.70	.40
18	Dennis Eckersley	1.25	.90	.50
19	Cecil Fielder	1.50	1.25	.60
20	Travis Fryman	1.25	.90	.50
21	Tom Glavine	1.25	.90	.50
22	Juan Gonzalez	4.00	3.00	1.50
23	Dwight Gooden	1.25	.90	.50
24	Mark Grace	1.25	.90	.50
25	Ken Griffey, Jr.	6.00	4.50	2.50
26	Marquis Grissom	1.50	1.25	.60
27	Juan Guzman	1.00	.70	.40
28	Tony Gwynn	1.50	1.25	.60
29	Rickey Henderson	2.00	1.50	.80
30	David Justice	1.25	.90	.50
31	Eric Karros	1.25	.90	.50
32	Chuck Knoblauch	1.25	.90	.50
33	John Kruk	1.25	.90	.50
34	Ray Lankford	1.25	.90	.50
35	Barry Larkin	1.25	.90	.50
36	Pat Listach	1.00	.70	.40
37	Kenny Lofton	1.25	.90	.50
38	Shane Mack	1.00	.70	.40
39	Greg Maddux	1.25	.90	.50
40	Dennis Martinez	1.00	.70	.40
41	Edgar Martinez	1.00	.70	.40
42	Ramon Martinez	1.00	.70	.40
43	Don Mattingly	2.50	2.00	1.00
44	Jack McDowell	1.25	.90	.50
45	Fred McGriff	1.50	1.25	.60
46	Mark McGwire	1.50	1.25	.60
47	Jeff Montgomery	1.00	.70	.40
48	Eddie Murray	1.25	.90	.50
49	Charles Nagy	1.00	.70	.40
50	Tom Pagnozzi	1.00	.70	.40
51	Terry Pendleton	1.00	.70	.40
52	Kirby Puckett	2.50	2.00	1.00
53	Jose Rijo	1.00	.70	.40
54	Cal Ripken, Jr.	5.00	3.75	2.00
55	Nolan Ryan	6.00	4.50	2.50
56	Ryne Sandberg	5.00	3.75	2.00
57	Gary Sheffield	1.25	.90	.50
58	Bill Swift	1.00	.70	.40
59	Danny Tartabull	1.00	.70	.40
60	Mickey Tettleton	1.00	.70	.40
61	Frank Thomas	6.00	4.50	2.50
62	Andy Van Slyke	1.00	.70	.40
63	Robin Ventura	1.25	.90	.50
64	Larry Walker	1.00	.70	.40
65	Robin Yount	3.00	2.25	1.25
66	Checklist	.10	.08	.04

A player's name in italic type indicates a rookie card. An (FC) indicates a player's first card for that particular card company.

1994 Fleer

Fleer's 720-card 1994 set, released in one series, includes another 204 insert cards to be pusued by collectors. Every pack includes one of the cards, randomly inserted form among the 12 insert sets the company produced. Regular cards have action photos on front, with a team logo in one of the lower corners. The player's name and position is stamped in gold foil around the logo. On back, another color player photo is overprinted with color boxes and player data and stats, leaving a clear image of the player's face, 1-1/2" x 1-3/4" in size. Cards are UV coated on both sides. Insert sets are: Rookie Sensations (20 cards), Lumber Company (10), Smoke N' Heat (12), Team Leaders (28), League Leaders (28), Fleer Award Winners (6), Major League Prospects (35), ProVisions (9), American League All-Stars (25), National League All-Stars (25), Golden Moments (10), and Tim Salmon, Rookie of the Year (12). Salmon has autographed more than 2,000 cards. Three additional Salmon cards not available in regular card packs were available only through a mail-in program with Fleer. Collectors could receive the cards by cards by sending 10 wrappers and $1.50 to the company.

		MT	NR MT	EX
Complete Set (720):		35.00	26.00	14.00
Common Player:		.05	.04	.02
1	Brady Anderson	.05	.04	.02
2	Harold Baines	.05	.04	.02
3	Mike Devereaux	.05	.04	.02
4	Todd Frohwirth	.05	.04	.02
5	Jeffrey Hammonds	.75	.60	.30
6	Chris Hoiles	.05	.04	.02
7	Tim Hulett	.05	.04	.02
8	Ben McDonald	.05	.04	.02
9	Mark McLemore	.05	.04	.02
10	Alan Mills	.05	.04	.02
11	Jamie Moyer	.05	.04	.02
12	Mike Mussina	.20	.15	.08
13	Gregg Olson	.05	.04	.02
14	Mike Pagliarulo	.05	.04	.02
15	Brad Pennington	.05	.04	.02
16	Jim Poole	.05	.04	.02
17	Harold Reynolds	.05	.04	.02
18	Arthur Rhodes	.05	.04	.02
19	Cal Ripken, Jr.	.35	.25	.14
20	David Segui	.05	.04	.02
21	Rick Sutcliffe	.05	.04	.02
22	Fernando Valenzuela	.05	.04	.02
23	Jack Voigt	.05	.04	.02
24	Mark Williamson	.05	.04	.02
25	Scott Bankhead	.05	.04	.02
26	Roger Clemens	.20	.15	.08
27	Scott Cooper	.05	.04	.02
28	Danny Darwin	.05	.04	.02
29	Andre Dawson	.05	.04	.02
30	Rob Deer	.05	.04	.02
31	John Dopson	.05	.04	.02
32	Scott Fletcher	.05	.04	.02
33	Mike Greenwell	.05	.04	.02
34	Greg Harris	.05	.04	.02
35	Billy Hatcher	.05	.04	.02
36	Bob Melvin	.05	.04	.02
37	Tony Pena	.05	.04	.02
38	Paul Quantrill	.05	.04	.02
39	Carlos Quintana	.05	.04	.02
40	Ernest Riles	.05	.04	.02
41	Jeff Russell	.05	.04	.02
42	Ken Ryan	.05	.04	.02
43	Aaron Sele	.60	.45	.25
44	John Valentin	.05	.04	.02
45	Mo Vaughn	.15	.11	.06
46	Frank Viola	.05	.04	.02
47	Bob Zupcic	.05	.04	.02
48	Mike Butcher	.05	.04	.02
49	Rod Correia	.05	.04	.02
50	Chad Curtis	.15	.11	.06
51	Chili Davis	.05	.04	.02
52	Gary DiSarcina	.05	.04	.02
53	Damion Easley	.10	.07	.04
54	Jim Edmonds	.05	.04	.02
55	Chuck Finley	.05	.04	.02
56	Steve Frey	.05	.04	.02
57	Rene Gonzales	.05	.04	.02
58	Joe Grahe	.05	.04	.02
59	Hilly Hathaway	.05	.04	.02
60	Stan Javier	.05	.04	.02
61	Mark Langston	.05	.04	.02

62	Phil Leftwich	.05	.04	.02
63	Torey Lovullo	.05	.04	.02
64	Joe Magrane	.05	.04	.02
65	Greg Myers	.05	.04	.02
66	Ken Patterson	.05	.04	.02
67	Eduardo Perez	.05	.04	.02
68	Luis Polonia	.05	.04	.02
69	Tim Salmon	.75	.60	.30
70	J.T. Snow	.20	.15	.08
71	Ron Tingley	.05	.04	.02
72	Julio Valera	.05	.04	.02
73	Wilson Alvarez	.05	.04	.02
74	Tim Belcher	.05	.04	.02
75	George Bell	.05	.04	.02
76	Jason Bere	.75	.60	.30
77	Rod Bolton	.05	.04	.02
78	Ellis Burks	.05	.04	.02
79	Joey Cora	.05	.04	.02
80	Alex Fernandez	.05	.04	.02
81	Craig Grebeck	.05	.04	.02
82	Ozzie Guillen	.05	.04	.02
83	Roberto Hernandez	.05	.04	.02
84	Bo Jackson	.15	.11	.06
85	Lance Johnson	.05	.04	.02
86	Ron Karkovice	.05	.04	.02
87	Mike LaValliere	.05	.04	.02
88	Kirk McCaskill	.05	.04	.02
89	Jack McDowell	.10	.07	.04
90	Warren Newson	.05	.04	.02
91	Dan Pasqua	.05	.04	.02
92	Scott Radinsky	.05	.04	.02
93	Tim Raines	.05	.04	.02
94	Steve Sax	.05	.04	.02
95	Jeff Schwarz	.05	.04	.02
96	Frank Thomas	1.50	1.25	.60
97	Robin Ventura	.15	.11	.06
98	Sandy Alomar, Jr.	.05	.04	.02
99	Carlos Baerga	.25	.20	.10
100	Albert Belle	.25	.20	.10
101	Mark Clark	.05	.04	.02
102	Jerry DiPoto	.05	.04	.02
103	Alvaro Espinoza	.05	.04	.02
104	Felix Fermin	.05	.04	.02
105	Jeremy Hernandez	.05	.04	.02
106	Reggie Jefferson	.05	.04	.02
107	Wayne Kirby	.05	.04	.02
108	Tom Kramer	.05	.04	.02
109	Mark Lewis	.05	.04	.02
110	Derek Lilliquist	.05	.04	.02
111	Kenny Lofton	.15	.11	.06
112	Candy Maldonado	.05	.04	.02
113	Jose Mesa	.05	.04	.02
114	Jeff Mutis	.05	.04	.02
115	Charles Nagy	.05	.04	.02
116	Bob Ojeda	.05	.04	.02
117	Junior Ortiz	.05	.04	.02
118	Eric Plunk	.05	.04	.02
119	Manny Ramirez	.75	.60	.30
120	Paul Sorrento	.05	.04	.02
121	Jim Thome	.20	.15	.08
122	Jeff Treadway	.05	.04	.02
123	Bill Wertz	.05	.04	.02
124	Skeeter Barnes	.05	.04	.02
125	Milt Cuyler	.05	.04	.02
126	Eric Davis	.05	.04	.02
127	John Doherty	.05	.04	.02
128	Cecil Fielder	.10	.08	.04
129	Travis Fryman	.25	.20	.10
130	Kirk Gibson	.05	.04	.02
131	Dan Gladden	.05	.04	.02
132	Greg Gohr	.05	.04	.02
133	Chris Gomez	.05	.04	.02
134	Bill Gullickson	.05	.04	.02
135	Mike Henneman	.05	.04	.02
136	Kurt Knudsen	.05	.04	.02
137	Chad Kreuter	.05	.04	.02
138	Bill Krueger	.05	.04	.02
139	Scott Livingstone	.05	.04	.02
140	Bob MacDonald	.05	.04	.02
141	Mike Moore	.05	.04	.02
142	Tony Phillips	.05	.04	.02
143	Mickey Tettleton	.05	.04	.02
144	Alan Trammell	.05	.04	.02
145	David Wells	.05	.04	.02
146	Lou Whitaker	.05	.04	.02
147	Kevin Appier	.05	.04	.02
148	Stan Belinda	.05	.04	.02
149	George Brett	.35	.25	.14
150	Billy Brewer	.05	.04	.02
151	Hubie Brooks	.05	.04	.02
152	David Cone	.05	.04	.02
153	Gary Gaetti	.05	.04	.02
154	Greg Gagne	.05	.04	.02
155	Tom Gordon	.05	.04	.02
156	Mark Gubicza	.05	.04	.02
157	Chris Gwynn	.05	.04	.02
158	John Habyan	.05	.04	.02
159	Chris Haney	.05	.04	.02
160	Phil Hiatt	.10	.07	.04
161	Felix Jose	.05	.04	.02
162	Wally Joyner	.05	.04	.02
163	Jose Lind	.05	.04	.02
164	Mike Macfarlane	.05	.04	.02
165	Mike Magnante	.05	.04	.02
166	Brent Mayne	.05	.04	.02
167	Brian McRae	.05	.04	.02
168	Kevin McReynolds	.05	.04	.02
169	Keith Miller	.05	.04	.02
170	Jeff Montgomery	.05	.04	.02
171	Hipolito Pichardo	.05	.04	.02
172	Rico Rossy	.05	.04	.02
173	Juan Bell	.05	.04	.02
174	Ricky Bones	.05	.04	.02
175	Cal Eldred	.10	.08	.04
176	Mike Fetters	.05	.04	.02
177	Darryl Hamilton	.05	.04	.02
178	Doug Henry	.05	.04	.02
179	Mike Ignasiak	.05	.04	.02
180	John Jaha	.08	.06	.03
181	Pat Listach	.08	.06	.03
182	Graeme Lloyd	.08	.06	.03
183	Matt Mieske	.10	.08	.04
184	Angel Miranda	.05	.04	.02
185	Jaime Navarro	.05	.04	.02
186	Dave Nilsson	.05	.04	.02
187	Troy O'Leary	.05	.04	.02
188	Jesse Orosco	.05	.04	.02
189	Kevin Reimer	.05	.04	.02
190	Kevin Seitzer	.05	.04	.02
191	Bill Spiers	.05	.04	.02
192	B.J. Surhoff	.05	.04	.02
193	Dickie Thon	.05	.04	.02
194	Jose Valentin	.05	.04	.02
195	Greg Vaughn	.05	.04	.02
196	Bill Wegman	.05	.04	.02
197	Robin Yount	.20	.15	.08
198	Rick Aguilera	.05	.04	.02
199	Willie Banks	.05	.04	.02
200	Bernardo Brito	.05	.04	.02
201	Larry Casian	.05	.04	.02
202	Scott Erickson	.05	.04	.02
203	Eddie Guardado	.05	.04	.02
204	Mark Guthrie	.05	.04	.02
205	Chip Hale	.05	.04	.02
206	Brian Harper	.05	.04	.02
207	Mike Hartley	.05	.04	.02
208	Kent Hrbek	.05	.04	.02
209	Terry Jorgensen	.05	.04	.02
210	Chuck Knoblauch	.05	.04	.02
211	Gene Larkin	.05	.04	.02
212	Shane Mack	.05	.04	.02
213	David McCarty	.10	.07	.04
214	Pat Meares	.05	.04	.02
215	Pedro Munoz	.05	.04	.02
216	Derek Parks	.05	.04	.02
217	Kirby Puckett	.40	.30	.15
218	Jeff Reboulet	.05	.04	.02
219	Kevin Tapani	.05	.04	.02
220	Mike Trombley	.05	.04	.02
221	George Tsamis	.05	.04	.02
222	Carl Willis	.05	.04	.02
223	Dave Winfield	.20	.15	.08
224	Jim Abbott	.05	.04	.02
225	Paul Assenmacher	.05	.04	.02
226	Wade Boggs	.10	.07	.04
227	Russ Davis	.15	.11	.06
228	Steve Farr	.05	.04	.02
229	Mike Gallego	.05	.04	.02
230	Paul Gibson	.05	.04	.02
231	Steve Howe	.05	.04	.02
232	Dion James	.05	.04	.02
233	Domingo Jean	.10	.07	.04
234	Scott Kamieniecki	.05	.04	.02
235	Pat Kelly	.05	.04	.02
236	Jimmy Key	.05	.04	.02
237	Jim Leyritz	.05	.04	.02
238	Kevin Maas	.05	.04	.02
239	Don Mattingly	.20	.15	.08
240	Rich Monteleone	.05	.04	.02
241	Bobby Munoz	.05	.04	.02
242	Matt Nokes	.05	.04	.02
243	Paul O'Neill	.05	.04	.02
244	Spike Owen	.05	.04	.02
245	Melido Perez	.05	.04	.02
246	Lee Smith	.05	.04	.02
247	Mike Stanley	.05	.04	.02
248	Danny Tartabull	.05	.04	.02
249	Randy Velarde	.05	.04	.02
250	Bob Wickman	.05	.04	.02
251	Bernie Williams	.05	.04	.02
252	Mike Aldrete	.05	.04	.02
253	Marcos Armas	.10	.07	.04
254	Lance Blankenship	.05	.04	.02
255	Mike Bordick	.05	.04	.02
256	Scott Brosius	.05	.04	.02
257	Jerry Browne	.05	.04	.02
258	Ron Darling	.05	.04	.02
259	Kelly Downs	.05	.04	.02
260	Dennis Eckersley	.05	.04	.02
261	Brent Gates	.15	.11	.06
262	Goose Gossage	.05	.04	.02
263	Scott Hemond	.05	.04	.02
264	Dave Henderson	.05	.04	.02
265	Rick Honeycutt	.05	.04	.02
266	Vince Horsman	.05	.04	.02
267	Scott Lydy	.05	.04	.02
268	Mark McGwire	.10	.08	.04
269	Mike Mohler	.05	.04	.02
270	Troy Neel	.10	.07	.04
271	Edwin Nunez	.05	.04	.02
272	Craig Paquette	.05	.04	.02
273	Ruben Sierra	.08	.06	.03
274	Terry Steinbach	.05	.04	.02
275	Todd Van Poppel	.08	.06	.03
276	Bob Welch	.05	.04	.02
277	Bobby Witt	.05	.04	.02
278	Rich Amaral	.05	.04	.02
279	Mike Blowers	.05	.04	.02
280	Bret Boone	.08	.06	.03
281	Chris Bosio	.05	.04	.02
282	Jay Buhner	.05	.04	.02
283	Norm Charlton	.05	.04	.02
284	Mike Felder	.05	.04	.02
285	Dave Fleming	.05	.04	.02
286	Ken Griffey, Jr.	1.50	1.25	.60
287	Erik Hanson	.05	.04	.02
288	Bill Haselman	.05	.04	.02
289	*Brad Holman*	.10	.07	.04
290	Randy Johnson	.08	.06	.03
291	Tim Leary	.05	.04	.02
292	Greg Litton	.05	.04	.02
293	Dave Magadan	.05	.04	.02
294	Edgar Martinez	.05	.04	.02
295	Tino Martinez	.05	.04	.02
296	Jeff Nelson	.05	.04	.02
297	*Erik Plantenberg*	.10	.07	.04
298	Mackey Sasser	.05	.04	.02
299	*Brian Turang*	.15	.11	.06
300	Dave Valle	.05	.04	.02
301	Omar Vizquel	.05	.04	.02
302	Brian Bohanon	.05	.04	.02
303	Kevin Brown	.05	.04	.02
304	Jose Canseco	.15	.11	.06
305	Mario Diaz	.05	.04	.02
306	Julio Franco	.05	.04	.02
307	Juan Gonzalez	1.00	.75	.40
308	Tom Henke	.05	.04	.02
309	David Hulse	.10	.07	.04
310	Manuel Lee	.05	.04	.02
311	Craig Lefferts	.05	.04	.02
312	Charlie Leibrandt	.05	.04	.02
313	Rafael Palmeiro	.10	.08	.04
314	Dean Palmer	.05	.04	.02
315	Roger Pavlik	.05	.04	.02
316	Dan Peltier	.10	.07	.04
317	Geno Petralli	.05	.04	.02
318	Gary Redus	.05	.04	.02
319	Ivan Rodriguez	.10	.08	.04
320	Kenny Rogers	.05	.04	.02
321	Nolan Ryan	1.25	.90	.50
322	Doug Strange	.05	.04	.02
323	Matt Whiteside	.05	.04	.02
324	Roberto Alomar	.35	.25	.14
325	Pat Borders	.05	.04	.02
326	Joe Carter	.15	.11	.06
327	Tony Castillo	.05	.04	.02
328	Darnell Coles	.05	.04	.02
329	Danny Cox	.05	.04	.02
330	Mark Eichhorn	.05	.04	.02
331	Tony Fernandez	.05	.04	.02
332	Alfredo Griffin	.05	.04	.02
333	Juan Guzman	.10	.07	.04
334	Rickey Henderson	.15	.11	.06
335	Pat Hentgen	.20	.15	.08
336	Randy Knorr	.05	.04	.02
337	Al Leiter	.05	.04	.02
338	Paul Molitor	.30	.25	.12
339	Jack Morris	.05	.04	.02
340	John Olerud	.25	.20	.10
341	Dick Schofield	.05	.04	.02
342	Ed Sprague	.05	.04	.02
343	Dave Stewart	.05	.04	.02
344	Todd Stottlemyre	.05	.04	.02
345	Mike Timlin	.05	.04	.02
346	Duane Ward	.05	.04	.02
347	Turner Ward	.05	.04	.02
348	Devon White	.05	.04	.02
349	Woody Williams	.05	.04	.02
350	Steve Avery	.15	.11	.06
351	Steve Bedrosian	.05	.04	.02
352	Rafael Belliard	.05	.04	.02
353	Damon Berryhill	.05	.04	.02
354	Jeff Blauser	.05	.04	.02
355	Sid Bream	.05	.04	.02
356	Francisco Cabrera	.05	.04	.02
357	Marvin Freeman	.05	.04	.02
358	Ron Gant	.08	.06	.03
359	Tom Glavine	.15	.11	.06
360	Jay Howell	.05	.04	.02
361	Dave Justice	.25	.20	.10
362	Ryan Klesko	.40	.30	.15
363	Mark Lemke	.05	.04	.02
364	Javier Lopez	.40	.30	.15
365	Greg Maddux	.15	.11	.06
366	Fred McGriff	.20	.15	.08
367	Greg McMichael	.10	.07	.04
368	Kent Mercker	.05	.04	.02
369	Otis Nixon	.05	.04	.02
370	Greg Olson	.05	.04	.02
371	Bill Pecota	.05	.04	.02
372	Terry Pendleton	.05	.04	.02
373	Deion Sanders	.10	.08	.04
374	Pete Smith	.05	.04	.02
375	John Smoltz	.10	.08	.04
376	Mike Stanton	.05	.04	.02
377	Tony Tarasco	.25	.20	.10
378	Mark Wohlers	.05	.04	.02
379	Jose Bautista	.05	.04	.02
380	Shawn Boskie	.05	.04	.02
381	Steve Buechele	.05	.04	.02
382	Frank Castillo	.05	.04	.02
383	Mark Grace	.10	.08	.04
384	Jose Guzman	.05	.04	.02
385	Mike Harkey	.05	.04	.02
386	Greg Hibbard	.05	.04	.02
387	Glenallen Hill	.05	.04	.02
388	Steve Lake	.05	.04	.02
389	Derrick May	.05	.04	.02
390	Chuck McElroy	.05	.04	.02
391	Mike Morgan	.05	.04	.02
392	Randy Myers	.05	.04	.02
393	Dan Plesac	.05	.04	.02
394	Kevin Roberson	.10	.07	.04
395	Rey Sanchez	.05	.04	.02
396	Ryne Sandberg	.40	.30	.15
397	Bob Scanlan	.05	.04	.02
398	Dwight Smith	.05	.04	.02
399	Sammy Sosa	.10	.08	.04
400	Jose Vizcaino	.05	.04	.02
401	Rick Wilkins	.05	.04	.02
402	Willie Wilson	.05	.04	.02
403	Eric Yelding	.05	.04	.02
404	Bobby Ayala	.05	.04	.02
405	Jeff Branson	.05	.04	.02
406	Tom Browning	.05	.04	.02
407	Jacob Brumfield	.05	.04	.02
408	Tim Costo	.15	.11	.06
409	Rob Dibble	.05	.04	.02
410	Willie Greene	.05	.04	.02
411	Thomas Howard	.05	.04	.02
412	Roberto Kelly	.05	.04	.02
413	Bill Landrum	.05	.04	.02
414	Barry Larkin	.05	.04	.02
415	*Larry Luebbers*	.15	.11	.06

416 Kevin Mitchell .05 .04 .02
417 Hal Morris .05 .04 .02
418 Joe Oliver .05 .04 .02
419 Tim Pugh .05 .04 .02
420 Jeff Reardon .05 .04 .02
421 Jose Rijo .05 .04 .02
422 Bip Roberts .05 .04 .02
423 John Roper .05 .04 .02
424 Johnny Ruffin .05 .04 .02
425 Chris Sabo .05 .04 .02
426 Juan Samuel .05 .04 .02
427 Reggie Sanders .10 .08 .04
428 Scott Service .05 .04 .02
429 John Smiley .05 .04 .02
430 *Jerry Spradlin* .10 .07 .04
431 Kevin Wickander .05 .04 .02
432 Freddie Benavides .05 .04 .02
433 Dante Bichette .05 .04 .02
434 Willie Blair .05 .04 .02
435 Daryl Boston .05 .04 .02
436 Kent Bottenfield .05 .04 .02
437 Vinny Castilla .05 .04 .02
438 Jerald Clark .05 .04 .02
439 Alex Cole .05 .04 .02
440 Andres Galarraga .05 .04 .02
441 Joe Girardi .05 .04 .02
442 Greg Harris .05 .04 .02
443 Charlie Hayes .05 .04 .02
444 Darren Holmes .05 .04 .02
445 Chris Jones .05 .04 .02
446 Roberto Mejia .20 .15 .08
447 David Nied .10 .07 .04
448 J. Owens .05 .04 .02
449 Jeff Parrett .05 .04 .02
450 Steve Reed .05 .04 .02
451 Armando Reynoso .05 .04 .02
452 Bruce Ruffin .05 .04 .02
453 Mo Sanford .05 .04 .02
454 Danny Sheaffer .05 .04 .02
455 Jim Tatum .10 .07 .04
456 Gary Wayne .05 .04 .02
457 Eric Young .10 .08 .04
458 Luis Aquino .05 .04 .02
459 Alex Arias .05 .04 .02
460 Jack Armstrong .05 .04 .02
461 Bret Barberie .05 .04 .02
462 Ryan Bowen .05 .04 .02
463 Chuck Carr .05 .04 .02
464 Jeff Conine .05 .04 .02
465 Henry Cotto .05 .04 .02
466 Orestes Destrade .05 .04 .02
467 Chris Hammond .05 .04 .02
468 Bryan Harvey .05 .04 .02
469 Charlie Hough .05 .04 .02
470 Joe Klink .05 .04 .02
471 Richie Lewis .05 .04 .02
472 *Bob Natal* .10 .08 .04
473 *Pat Rapp* .15 .11 .06
474 *Rich Renteria* .10 .07 .04
475 Rich Rodriguez .05 .04 .02
476 Benito Santiago .05 .04 .02
477 Gary Sheffield .10 .07 .04
478 Matt Turner .05 .04 .02
479 David Weathers .05 .04 .02
480 Walt Weiss .05 .04 .02
481 Darrell Whitmore .10 .07 .04
482 Eric Anthony .05 .04 .02
483 Jeff Bagwell .15 .11 .06
484 Kevin Bass .05 .04 .02
485 Craig Biggio .05 .04 .02
486 Ken Caminiti .05 .04 .02
487 Andujar Cedeno .05 .04 .02
488 Chris Donnels .05 .04 .02
489 Doug Drabek .05 .04 .02
490 Steve Finley .05 .04 .02
491 Luis Gonzalez .05 .04 .02
492 Pete Harnisch .05 .04 .02
493 Xavier Hernandez .05 .04 .02
494 Doug Jones .05 .04 .02
495 Todd Jones .05 .04 .02
496 Darryl Kile .05 .04 .02
497 Al Osuna .05 .04 .02
498 Mark Portugal .05 .04 .02
499 Scott Servais .05 .04 .02
500 Greg Swindell .05 .04 .02
501 Eddie Taubensee .05 .04 .02
502 Jose Uribe .05 .04 .02
503 Brian Williams .05 .04 .02
504 Billy Ashley .12 .09 .05
505 Pedro Astacio .15 .11 .06
506 Brett Butler .05 .04 .02
507 Tom Candiotti .05 .04 .02
508 Omar Daal .05 .04 .02
509 Jim Gott .05 .04 .02
510 Kevin Gross .05 .04 .02
511 Dave Hansen .05 .04 .02
512 Carlos Hernandez .05 .04 .02
513 Orel Hershiser .05 .04 .02
514 Eric Karros .10 .07 .04
515 Pedro Martinez .10 .07 .04
516 Ramon Martinez .05 .04 .02
517 Roger McDowell .05 .04 .02
518 Raul Mondesi 1.00 .75 .40
519 Jose Offerman .05 .04 .02
520 Mike Piazza 1.25 .90 .50
521 Jody Reed .05 .04 .02
522 Henry Rodriguez .05 .04 .02
523 Mike Sharperson .05 .04 .02
524 Cory Snyder .05 .04 .02
525 Darryl Strawberry .05 .04 .02
526 Rick Trlicek .05 .04 .02
527 Tim Wallach .05 .04 .02
528 Mitch Webster .05 .04 .02
529 Steve Wilson .05 .04 .02
530 Todd Worrell .05 .04 .02
531 Moises Alou .10 .08 .04
532 Brian Barnes .05 .04 .02
533 Sean Berry .05 .04 .02
534 Greg Colbrunn .05 .04 .02
535 Delino DeShields .08 .06 .03
536 Jeff Fassero .08 .06 .03
537 Darrin Fletcher .05 .04 .02
538 Cliff Floyd 1.00 .75 .40
539 Lou Frazier .05 .04 .02
540 Marquis Grissom .10 .08 .04
541 Butch Henry .05 .04 .02
542 Ken Hill .05 .04 .02
543 Mike Lansing .10 .07 .04
544 *Brian Looney* .20 .15 .08
545 Dennis Martinez .05 .04 .02
546 Chris Nabholz .05 .04 .02
547 Randy Ready .05 .04 .02
548 Mel Rojas .05 .04 .02
549 Kirk Rueter .40 .30 .15
550 Tim Scott .05 .04 .02
551 Jeff Shaw .05 .04 .02
552 Tim Spehr .05 .04 .02
553 John VanderWal .05 .04 .02
554 Larry Walker .08 .06 .03
555 John Wetteland .05 .04 .02
556 Rondell White .40 .30 .15
557 Tim Bogar .08 .06 .03
558 Bobby Bonilla .06 .05 .02
559 Jeremy Burnitz .05 .04 .02
560 Sid Fernandez .05 .04 .02
561 John Franco .05 .04 .02
562 Dave Gallagher .05 .04 .02
563 Dwight Gooden .05 .04 .02
564 Eric Hillman .05 .04 .02
565 Todd Hundley .05 .04 .02
566 Jeff Innis .05 .04 .02
567 Darrin Jackson .05 .04 .02
568 Howard Johnson .05 .04 .02
569 Bobby Jones .05 .04 .02
570 Jeff Kent .05 .04 .02
571 Mike Maddux .05 .04 .02
572 Jeff McKnight .05 .04 .02
573 Eddie Murray .08 .06 .03
574 Charlie O'Brien .05 .04 .02
575 Joe Orsulak .05 .04 .02
576 Bret Saberhagen .05 .04 .02
577 Pete Schourek .05 .04 .02
578 Dave Telgheder .05 .04 .02
579 Ryan Thompson .05 .04 .02
580 Anthony Young .05 .04 .02
581 Ruben Amaro .05 .04 .02
582 Larry Andersen .05 .04 .02
583 Kim Batiste .05 .04 .02
584 Wes Chamberlain .05 .04 .02
585 Darren Daulton .08 .06 .03
586 Mariano Duncan .05 .04 .02
587 Len Dykstra .10 .07 .04
588 Jim Eisenreich .05 .04 .02
589 Tommy Greene .05 .04 .02
590 Dave Hollins .08 .06 .03
591 Pete Incaviglia .05 .04 .02
592 Danny Jackson .05 .04 .02
593 Ricky Jordan .05 .04 .02
594 John Kruk .08 .06 .03
595 Roger Mason .05 .04 .02
596 Mickey Morandini .05 .04 .02
597 Terry Mulholland .05 .04 .02
598 Todd Pratt .05 .04 .02
599 Ben Rivera .05 .04 .02
600 Curt Schilling .05 .04 .02
601 Kevin Stocker .40 .30 .15
602 Milt Thompson .05 .04 .02
603 David West .05 .04 .02
604 Mitch Williams .05 .04 .02
605 Jay Bell .05 .04 .02
606 Dave Clark .05 .04 .02
607 Steve Cooke .05 .04 .02
608 Tom Foley .05 .04 .02
609 Carlos Garcia .10 .07 .04
610 Joel Johnston .05 .04 .02
611 Jeff King .05 .04 .02
612 Al Martin .10 .07 .04
613 Lloyd McClendon .05 .04 .02
614 Orlando Merced .05 .04 .02
615 Blas Minor .10 .07 .04
616 Denny Neagle .05 .04 .02
617 *Mark Petkovsek* .10 .07 .04
618 Tom Prince .05 .04 .02
619 Don Slaught .05 .04 .02
620 Zane Smith .05 .04 .02
621 Randy Tomlin .05 .04 .02
622 Andy Van Slyke .05 .04 .02
623 Paul Wagner .05 .04 .02
624 Tim Wakefield .05 .04 .02
625 Bob Walk .05 .04 .02
626 Kevin Young .10 .07 .04
627 Luis Alicea .05 .04 .02
628 Rene Arocha .10 .07 .04
629 Rod Brewer .05 .04 .02
630 Rheal Cormier .05 .04 .02
631 Bernard Gilkey .08 .06 .03
632 Lee Guetterman .05 .04 .02
633 Gregg Jefferies .06 .05 .02
634 Brian Jordan .05 .04 .02
635 Les Lancaster .05 .04 .02
636 Ray Lankford .05 .04 .02
637 Rob Murphy .05 .04 .02
638 Omar Olivares .05 .04 .02
639 Jose Oquendo .05 .04 .02
640 Donovan Osborne .05 .04 .02
641 Tom Pagnozzi .05 .04 .02
642 Erik Pappas .05 .04 .02
643 Geronimo Pena .05 .04 .02
644 Mike Perez .05 .04 .02
645 Gerald Perry .05 .04 .02
646 Ozzie Smith .15 .11 .06
647 Bob Tewksbury .05 .04 .02
648 Allen Watson .15 .11 .06
649 Mark Whiten .08 .06 .03
650 Tracy Woodson .08 .06 .03
651 Todd Zeile .05 .04 .02
652 Andy Ashby .05 .04 .02
653 Brad Ausmus .05 .04 .02
654 Billy Bean .05 .04 .02
655 Derek Bell .05 .04 .02
656 Andy Benes .05 .04 .02
657 Doug Brocail .05 .04 .02
658 Jarvis Brown .05 .04 .02
659 Archi Cianfrocco .05 .04 .02
660 Phil Clark .05 .04 .02
661 Mark Davis .05 .04 .02
662 Jeff Gardner .05 .04 .02
663 Pat Gomez .05 .04 .02
664 Ricky Gutierrez .05 .04 .02
665 Tony Gwynn .15 .11 .06
666 Gene Harris .05 .04 .02
667 Kevin Higgins .05 .04 .02
668 Trevor Hoffman .05 .04 .02
669 Pedro Martinez .10 .07 .04
670 Tim Mauser .05 .04 .02
671 Melvin Nieves .10 .08 .04
672 Phil Plantier .05 .04 .02
673 Frank Seminara .05 .04 .02
674 Craig Shipley .05 .04 .02
675 Kerry Taylor .05 .04 .02
676 Tim Teufel .05 .04 .02
677 Guillermo Velasquez .05 .04 .02
678 Wally Whitehurst .05 .04 .02
679 Tim Worrell .08 .06 .03
680 Rod Beck .05 .04 .02
681 Mike Benjamin .05 .04 .02
682 Todd Benzinger .05 .04 .02
683 Bud Black .05 .04 .02
684 Barry Bonds .50 .40 .20
685 Jeff Brantley .05 .04 .02
686 Dave Burba .05 .04 .02
687 John Burkett .05 .04 .02
688 Mark Carreon .05 .04 .02
689 Will Clark .15 .11 .06
690 Royce Clayton .08 .06 .03
691 Bryan Hickerson .05 .04 .02
692 Mike Jackson .05 .04 .02
693 Darren Lewis .05 .04 .02
694 Kirt Manwaring .05 .04 .02
695 Dave Martinez .05 .04 .02
696 Willie McGee .05 .04 .02
697 John Patterson .05 .04 .02
698 Jeff Reed .05 .04 .02
699 Kevin Rogers .05 .04 .02
700 Scott Sanderson .05 .04 .02
701 Steve Scarsone .05 .04 .02
702 Billy Swift .05 .04 .02
703 Robby Thompson .05 .04 .02
704 Matt Williams .10 .08 .04
705 Trevor Wilson .05 .04 .02
706 "Brave New World" (Fred McGriff, Ron Gant, Dave Justice) .05 .04 .02
707 "1-2 Punch" (Paul Molitor, John Olerud) .15 .11 .06
708 "American Heat" (Mike Mussina, Jack McDowell) .05 .04 .02
709 "Together Again" (Lou Whitaker, Alan Trammell) .05 .04 .02
710 "Lone Star Lumber" (Rafael Palmeiro, Juan Gonzalez) .40 .30 .15
711 "Batmen" (Brett Butler, Tony Gwynn) .05 .04 .02
712 "Twin Peaks" (Kirby Puckett, Chuck Knoblauch) .05 .04 .02
713 "Back to Back" (Mike Piazza, Eric Karros) .50 .40 .20
714 Checklist .05 .04 .02
715 Checklist .05 .04 .02
716 Checklist .05 .04 .02
717 Checklist .05 .04 .02
718 Checklist .05 .04 .02
719 Checklist .05 .04 .02
720 Checklist .05 .04 .02

1994 Fleer Rookie Sensations

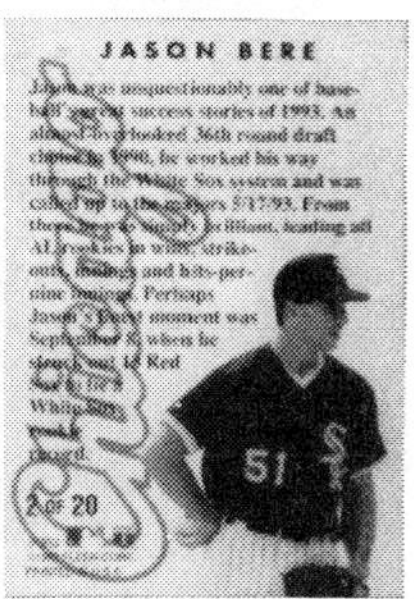

This 20-card insert set features the top rookies from 1993. Both Rookie of the Year award winners, Tim Salmon and Mike Piazza, are included. This insert was available only in 21-card jumbo packs, with stated odds of finding a Rookie Seasations card of one in four packs. Full-bleed fronts have a pair player photos - one highlighted by a neon outline - superimposed on a graduated background approximating the team colors. Team uniform logo details appear vertically at the right or left side. The player's name is gold-foil stamped in a banner at bottom. The Rookie Sensations and Fleer logos are also gold-imprinted. On back, the team uniform logo is repeated on a white background, along with another player photo and a short write-up.

		MT	NR MT	EX
Complete Set (20):		45.00	34.00	18.00
Common Player:		1.00	.70	.40
1	Rene Arocha	1.00	.70	.40
2	Jason Bere	5.00	3.75	2.00
3	Jeromy Burnitz	1.50	1.25	.60
4	Chuck Carr	1.25	.90	.50
5	Jeff Conine	2.00	1.50	.80
6	Steve Cooke	1.00	.75	.40
7	Cliff Floyd	5.00	3.75	2.00
8	Jeffrey Hammonds	2.75	2.00	1.00
9	Wayne Kirby	1.00	.70	.40
10	Mike Lansing	1.25	.90	.50
11	Al Martin	1.50	1.25	.60
12	Greg McMichael	1.00	.70	.40
13	Troy Neel	1.50	1.25	.60
14	Mike Piazza	10.00	7.50	4.00
15	Armando Reynoso	1.00	.70	.40
16	Kirk Rueter	3.50	2.75	1.50
17	Tim Salmon	6.00	4.50	2.50
18	Aaron Sele	3.00	2.25	1.25
19	J.T. Snow	1.50	1.25	.60
20	Kevin Stocker	1.50	1.25	.60

1994 Fleer Lumber Co.

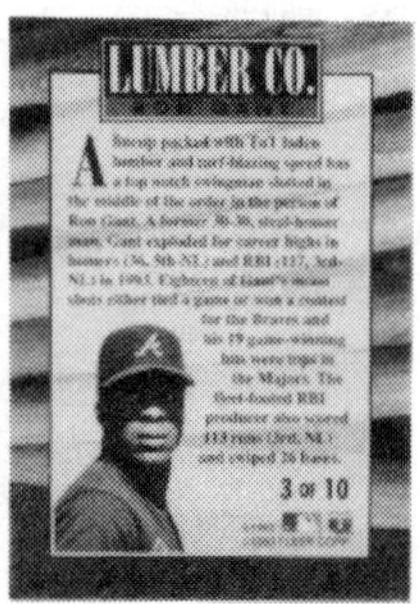

This 10-card insert set features the major leagues' top home run hitters. Inserted only in 21-card jumbo packs, odds of finding one were given as one per five packs. Card fronts feature player action photos against a background resembling the label area of a baseball bat. On back is a background photo of a row of bats on the dirt. A player write-up and close-up photo complete the design. Cards are UV coated on both sides.

		MT	NR MT	EX
Complete Set (10):		18.00	13.50	7.25
Common Player:		1.00	.75	.40
1	Albert Belle	1.50	1.25	.60
2	Barry Bonds	3.50	2.75	1.50
3	Ron Gant	1.00	.75	.40
4	Juan Gonzalez	4.50	3.50	1.75
5	Ken Griffey, Jr.	6.00	4.50	2.50
6	Dave Justice	1.50	1.25	.60
7	Fred McGriff	1.50	1.25	.60
8	Rafael Palmeiro	1.00	.75	.40
9	Frank Thomas	6.00	4.50	2.50
10	Matt Williams	1.00	.75	.40

The values quoted are intended to reflect the market price.

1994 Fleer Smoke N' Heat

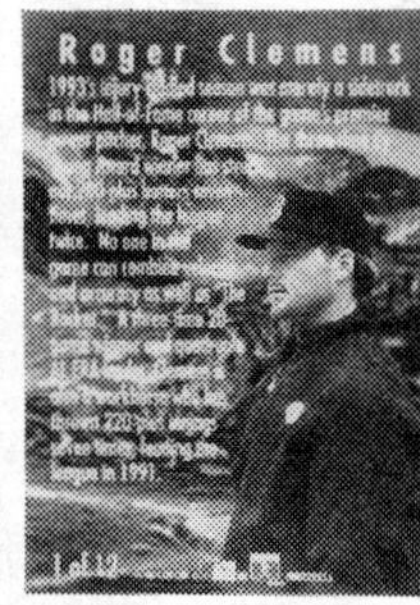

Among the scarcest of the '94 Fleer inserts, available at a stated rate of one per 30 packs, these feature 10 of the top strikeout pitchers in the major leagues. "Metallized" card fronts have a player photo set against an infernal background with large letters, "Smoke 'N Heat". The player's name is in gold foil at bottom. Backs have a similar choatic hot-red background, a player photo and career summary.

		MT	NR MT	EX
Complete Set (12):		90.00	67.00	36.00
Common Player:		4.00	3.00	1.50
1	Roger Clemens	15.00	11.00	6.00
2	David Cone	4.00	3.00	1.50
3	Juan Guzman	4.00	3.00	1.50
4	Pete Harnisch	4.00	3.00	1.50
5	Randy Johnson	6.00	4.50	2.50
6	Mark Langston	4.00	3.00	1.50
7	Greg Maddux	10.00	7.50	4.00
8	Mike Mussina	18.00	13.50	7.25
9	Jose Rijo	4.00	3.00	1.50
10	Nolan Ryan	42.00	32.00	17.00
11	Curt Schilling	4.00	3.00	1.50
12	John Smoltz	4.00	3.00	1.50

1994 Fleer Team Leaders

A player from each major league team has been chosen for this 28-card insert set. Fronts feature a team logo against a backgound of graduated team colors. Player portrait and action photos are superimposed. At bottom is the player name, team and position, all in gold foil. Backs have a team logo and player photo set against a white background, with a short write-up justifying the player's selection as a "Team Leader." Odds of finding one of these inserts were given as one in eight packs.

		MT	NR MT	EX
Complete Set (28):		27.00	21.00	11.00
Common Player:		.50	.40	.20
1	Cal Ripken, Jr.	1.50	1.25	.60
2	Mo Vaughn	.50	.40	.20
3	Tim Salmon	2.50	2.00	1.00
4	Frank Thomas	4.50	3.50	1.75
5	Carlos Baerga	1.50	1.25	.60
6	Cecil Fielder	1.00	.70	.40
7	Brian McRae	.50	.40	.20
8	Greg Vaughn	.50	.40	.20
9	Kirby Puckett	1.50	1.25	.60
10	Don Mattingly	1.25	.90	.50
11	Mark McGwire	.75	.60	.30
12	Ken Griffey, Jr.	5.00	3.75	2.00
13	Juan Gonzalez	3.50	2.75	1.50
14	Paul Molitor	.90	.70	.35
15	Dave Justice	1.25	.90	.50
16	Ryne Sandberg	1.50	1.25	.60
17	Barry Larkin	.60	.45	.25
18	Andres Galarraga	.50	.40	.20
19	Gary Sheffield	.60	.45	.25
20	Jeff Bagwell	1.00	.70	.40
21	Mike Piazza	4.50	3.50	1.75
22	Marquis Grissom	.75	.60	.30
23	Bobby Bonilla	.50	.40	.20
24	Len Dykstra	.50	.40	.20
25	Jay Bell	.50	.40	.20
26	Gregg Jefferies	.60	.45	.25
27	Tony Gwynn	.75	.60	.30
28	Will Clark	1.00	.75	.40

1994 Fleer League Leaders

Twelve players who led the major leagues in various statistical categories in 1993 are featured in this insert set. Cards are UV coated and have gold-foil stamping on both sides. Within a light metallic green border, card fronts feature a color action photo superimposed over a similar photo in black-and-white. The category in which the player led his league is printed down the right border. Other printing is gold-foil. On back is a color photo and details of the league-leading performance. Cards are UV coated on each side. Stated odds of finding a League Leaders card were one per 17 packs.

		MT	NR MT	EX
Complete Set (12):		10.00	7.50	4.00
Common Player:		.25	.20	.10
1	John Olerud	1.00	.70	.40
2	Albert Belle	1.25	.90	.50
3	Rafael Palmeiro	.50	.40	.20
4	Kenny Lofton	.75	.60	.30
5	Jack McDowell	.35	.25	.14
6	Kevin Appier	.25	.20	.10
7	Andres Galarraga	.35	.25	.14
8	Barry Bonds	2.50	2.00	1.00
9	Len Dykstra	.60	.45	.25
10	Chuck Carr	.25	.20	.10
11	Tom Glavine	1.00	.70	.40
12	Greg Maddux	1.00	.70	.40

1994 Fleer Award Winners

The 1993 MVP, Cy Young and Rookie of the Year award winners from both leagues are featured in this six-card insert set. Cards are UV coated on both sides. Three different croppings of the same player action photo are featured on the front, with the player's name and other printing in gold foil. Backs have a player potrait and short summary of his previous season's perormance. According to the company, odds of finding one of these horozontal-format inserts were one in 37 packs.

		MT	NR MT	EX
Complete Set (6):		15.00	11.00	6.00
Common Player:		1.00	.70	.40
1	Frank Thomas	6.00	4.50	2.50
2	Barry Bonds	2.00	1.50	.80
3	Jack McDowell	1.00	.70	.40
4	Greg Maddux	1.50	1.25	.60
5	Tim Salmon	3.00	2.25	1.25
6	Mike Piazza	4.50	3.50	1.75

1994 Fleer Major League Prospects

Thirty-five of the game promising young stars are featured in this insert set. A light green metallic border frames a player photo, with his team logo lightly printed over the background. Most of the printing is gold-foil stamped. Backs have a player photo against a pinstriped background. A light blue box contains career details. Given odds of finding a "Major League Prospects" cards are one in six packs.

	MT	NR MT	EX
Complete Set (35):	22.00	16.50	8.75
Common Player:	.25	.20	.10

1	Kurt Abbott	.60	.45	.25
2	Brian Anderson	.40	.30	.15
3	Rich Aude	.75	.60	.30
4	Cory Bailey	.50	.40	.20
5	Danny Bautista	.50	.40	.20
6	Marty Cordova	.50	.40	.20
7	Tripp Cromer	.25	.20	.10
8	Midre Cummings	1.50	1.25	.60
9	Carlos Delgado	2.00	1.50	.80
10	Steve Dreyer	.75	.60	.30
11	Steve Dunn	.25	.20	.10
12	Jeff Granger	1.00	.70	.40
13	Tyrone Hill	.50	.40	.20
14	Denny Hocking	.40	.30	.15
15	John Hope	.25	.20	.10
16	Butch Huskey	.40	.30	.15
17	Miguel Jimenez	.60	.45	.25
18	Chipper Jones	1.25	.90	.50
19	Steve Karsay	1.00	.70	.40
20	Mike Kelly	.60	.45	.25
21	Mike Lieberthal	.25	.20	.10
22	Albie Lopez	.50	.40	.20
23	Jeff McNeely	.50	.40	.20
24	Dan Miceli	.40	.30	.15
25	Nate Minchey	.40	.30	.15
26	Marc Newfield	1.00	.75	.40
27	Darren Oliver	.25	.20	.10
28	Luis Ortiz	.40	.30	.15
29	Curtis Pride	.60	.45	.25
30	Roger Salkeld	.75	.60	.30
31	Scott Sanders	.40	.30	.15
32	Dave Staton	.40	.30	.15
33	Salomon Torres	.60	.45	.25
34	Steve Trachsel	1.25	.90	.50
35	Chris Turner	.35	.25	.14

1994 Fleer All-Stars

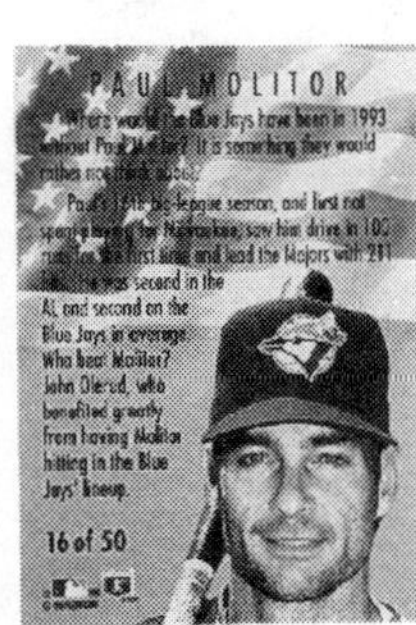

Each league's 25 representatives for the 1993 All-Star Game are featured in this insert set. Fronts have a player action photo with a rippling American flag in the top half of the background. The '93 All-Star logo is featured at the bottom, along with a gold-foil impression of the player's name. The flag motif is repeated at top of the card back, along with a player potrait photo set against a red (American League) or blue (National League) background. The player's name, career summary and card number are printed in black. Odds of finding one of the 50 All-Star inserts are one in every two 15-card foil packs.

		MT	NR MT	EX
Complete Set (50):		20.00	15.00	8.00
Common Player:		.25	.20	.10
1	Roberto Alomar	.75	.60	.30
2	Carlos Baerga	.75	.60	.30
3	Albert Belle	.75	.60	.30
4	Wade Boggs	.40	.30	.15
5	Joe Carter	.50	.40	.20
6	Scott Cooper	.25	.20	.10
7	Cecil Fielder	.40	.30	.15
8	Travis Fryman	.50	.40	.20
9	Juan Gonzalez	1.50	1.25	.60
10	Ken Griffey, Jr.	4.00	3.00	1.50
11	Pat Hentgen	.25	.20	.10
12	Randy Johnson	.35	.25	.14
13	Jimmy Key	.25	.20	.10
14	Mark Langston	.25	.20	.10
15	Jack McDowell	.30	.25	.12
16	Paul Molitor	.50	.40	.20
17	Jeff Montgomery	.25	.20	.10
18	Mike Mussina	.50	.40	.20
19	John Olerud	.75	.60	.30
20	Kirby Puckett	1.00	.75	.40
21	Cal Ripken, Jr.	1.00	.75	.40
22	Ivan Rodriguez	.35	.25	.14
23	Frank Thomas	4.00	3.00	1.50
24	Greg Vaughn	.25	.20	.10
25	Duane Ward	.25	.20	.10
26	Steve Avery	.50	.40	.20
27	Rod Beck	.25	.20	.10
28	Jay Bell	.25	.20	.10
29	Andy Benes	.25	.20	.10
30	Jeff Blauser	.25	.20	.10
31	Barry Bonds	1.00	.75	.40
32	Bobby Bonilla	.30	.25	.12
33	John Burkett	.25	.20	.10
34	Darren Daulton	.30	.25	.12
35	Andres Galarraga	.30	.25	.12
36	Tom Glavine	.40	.30	.15
37	Mark Grace	.35	.25	.14
38	Marquis Grissom	.35	.25	.14
39	Tony Gwynn	.40	.30	.15
40	Bryan Harvey	.25	.20	.10
41	Dave Hollins	.25	.20	.10
42	Dave Justice	.60	.45	.25
43	Darryl Kile	.25	.20	.10
44	John Kruk	.30	.25	.12
45	Barry Larkin	.30	.25	.12
46	Terry Mulholland	.25	.20	.10
47	Mike Piazza	2.00	1.50	.80
48	Ryne Sandberg	.75	.60	.30
49	Gary Sheffield	.40	.30	.15
50	John Smoltz	.30	.25	.12

1994 Fleer Tim Salmon A.L. Rookie of the Year

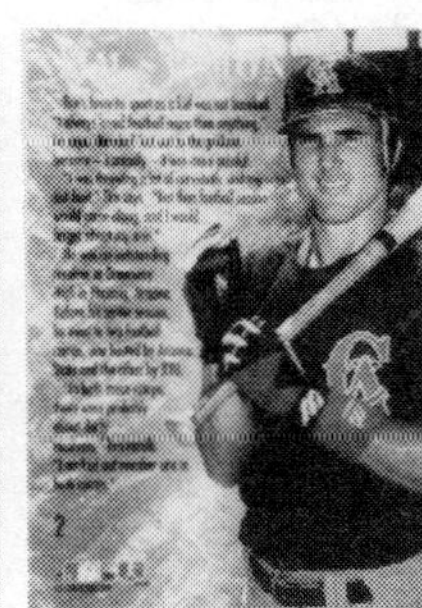

The popular Angels Rookie of the Year is featured in a 15-card set produced in what Fleer terms "metallized" format. The first 12 cards in the set were inserted into foil packs at the rate of about one card per box. Three additional cards could be obtained by sending $1.50 and 10 '94 Fleer wrappers to a mail-in offer. On both front and back, the cards have a color player photo set against a metallic-image background.

		MT	NR MT	EX
Complete Set (15):		50.00	37.00	20.00
Common Card:		5.00	3.75	2.00
1	Tim Salmon	5.00	3.75	2.00
2	Tim Salmon	5.00	3.75	2.00
3	Tim Salmon	5.00	3.75	2.00
4	Tim Salmon	5.00	3.75	2.00
5	Tim Salmon	5.00	3.75	2.00
6	Tim Salmon	5.00	3.75	2.00
7	Tim Salmon	5.00	3.75	2.00
8	Tim Salmon	5.00	3.75	2.00
9	Tim Salmon	5.00	3.75	2.00
10	Tim Salmon	5.00	3.75	2.00
11	Tim Salmon	5.00	3.75	2.00
12	Tim Salmon	5.00	3.75	2.00
13	Tim Salmon	5.00	3.75	2.00
14	Tim Salmon	5.00	3.75	2.00
15	Tim Salmon	5.00	3.75	2.00

1994 Fleer Golden Moments

Ten highlights from the 1993 Major League baseball season are commemorated in this insert set. Each of the cards has a title which summarizes the historical moment. These inserts were available exclusively in Fleer cards packaged for large retail outlets.

		MT	NR MT	EX
Complete Set (10):		18.00	13.50	7.25
Common Player:		.50	.40	.20
1	"Four in One" (Mark Whiten)	.50	.40	.20
2	"Left and Right" (Carlos Baerga)	2.00	1.50	.80
3	"3,000 Hit Club" (Dave Winfield)	1.50	1.25	.60
4	"Eight Straight" (Ken Griffey, Jr.)	5.00	3.75	2.00
5	"Triumphant Return" (Bo Jackson)	1.50	1.25	.60
6	"Farewell to Baseball" (George Brett)	2.50	2.00	1.00
7	"Farewell to Baseball" (Nolan Ryan)	4.00	3.00	1.50
8	"Thirty Times Six" (Fred McGriff)	1.50	1.25	.60
9	"Enters 5th Dimension" (Frank Thomas)	6.00	4.50	2.50
10	"The No-Hit Parade" (Chris Bosio, Jim Abbott, Darryl Kile)	.50	.40	.20

1994 Fleer Golden Moments Super

Super-size (3-1/2" x 5") versions of the Golden Moments insert set of 10 were included in hobby cases at the rate of one set, in a specially-printed folder, per 20-box case. Each card carries a serial number designating its position in an edition of 10,000.

		MT	NR MT	EX
Complete Set (10):		75.00	56.00	30.00
Common Player:		5.00	3.75	2.00
1	"Four in One" (Mark Whiten)	5.00	3.75	2.00
2	"Left and Right" (Carlos Baerga)	7.50	5.50	3.00
3	"3,000 Hit Club" (Dave Winfield)	7.50	5.50	3.00
4	"Eight Straight" (Ken Griffey, Jr.)	15.00	11.00	6.00
5	"Triumphant Return" (Bo Jackson)	7.50	5.50	3.00
6	"Farewell to Baseball" (George Brett)	10.00	7.50	4.00
7	"Farewell to Baseball" (Nolan Ryan)	12.50	9.50	5.00
8	"Thirty Times Six" (Fred McGriff)	7.50	5.50	3.00
9	"Enters 5th Dimension" (Frank Thomas)	15.00	11.00	6.00
10	"The No-Hit Parade" (Chris Bosio, Jim Abbott, Darryl Kile)	5.00	3.75	2.00

1994 Fleer ProVisions

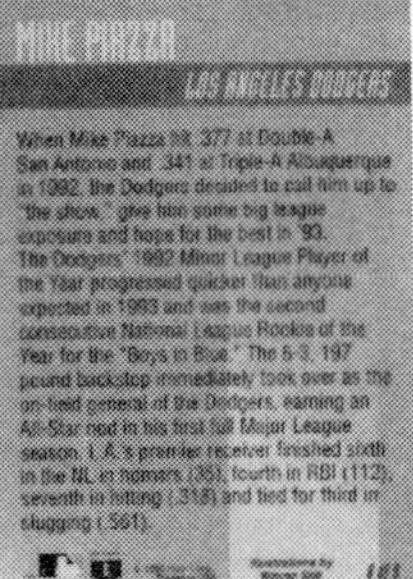

Nine players are featured in this ProVisions insert set. Cards feature the fantasy artwork of Wayne Still in a format that produces one large image when all nine cards are properly arranged. Besides the art, card fronts feature the player's name in gold-foil. Backs have a background in several shades of red, with the player's name and team at the top in white. A short career summary is printed in black. Cards are UV coated on both sides. Odds of finding this particular insert in a pack are one in 12.

		MT	NR MT	EX
Complete Set (9):		6.00	4.50	2.50
Common Player:		.40	.30	.15
1	Darren Daulton	.40	.30	.15
2	John Olerud	1.00	.70	.40
3	Matt Williams	.40	.30	.15
4	Carlos Baerga	1.00	.75	.40
5	Ozzie Smith	.50	.40	.20
6	Juan Gonzalez	2.00	1.50	.80
7	Jack McDowell	.40	.30	.15
8	Mike Piazza	2.50	2.00	1.00
9	Tony Gwynn	.50	.40	.20

1994 Fleer Ultra

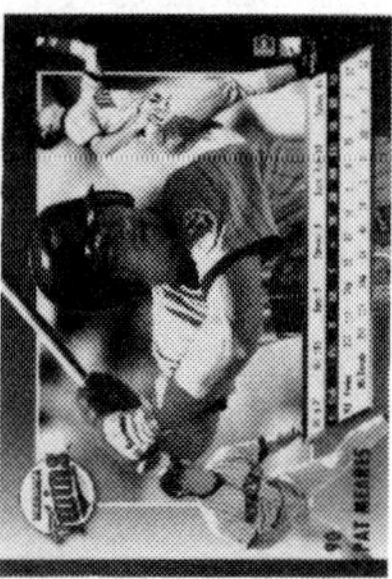

Issued in two series of 300 cards each, Fleer Ultra for 1994 represented a new highwater mark in production values for a mid-priced brand. Each side of the basic cards is UV coated and gold-foil embossed. Fronts feature full-bleed action photos. At bottom the player name, team, position and Fleer Ultra logo appear in gold foil above a gold-foil strip. Some rookie cards are specially designated with a large gold "ROOKIE" above the Ultra logo. Backs feature a basic background that is team color coordinated. Three more player action photos are featured on the back, along with a team logo and a modicum of stats and personal data. There is a gold stripe along the left edge and the player's name and card number appear in gold in the lower-left corner. The set featured seven types of insert cards, packaged one per pack.

	MT	NR MT	EX
Complete Set (600):	55.00	41.00	22.00
Complete Series 1 (300):	27.50	21.00	11.00
Complete Series 2 (300):	27.50	21.00	11.00
Common Player:	.10	.08	.04

#	Player	MT	NR MT	EX
1	Jeffrey Hammonds	.60	.45	.25
2	Chris Hoiles	.10	.08	.04
3	Ben McDonald	.10	.08	.04
4	Mark McLemore	.10	.08	.04
5	Alan Mills	.10	.08	.04
6	Jamie Moyer	.10	.08	.04
7	Brad Pennington	.10	.08	.04
8	Jim Poole	.10	.08	.04
9	Cal Ripken, Jr.	.75	.60	.30
10	Jack Voigt	.10	.08	.04
11	Roger Clemens	.40	.30	.15
12	Danny Darwin	.10	.08	.04
13	Andre Dawson	.10	.08	.04
14	Scott Fletcher	.10	.08	.04
15	Greg Harris	.10	.08	.04
16	Billy Hatcher	.10	.08	.04
17	Jeff Russell	.10	.08	.04
18	Aaron Sele	1.00	.75	.40
19	Mo Vaughn	.15	.11	.06
20	Mike Butcher	.10	.08	.04
21	Rod Correia	.10	.08	.04
22	Steve Frey	.10	.08	.04
23	*Phil Leftwich*	.25	.20	.10
24	Torey Lovullo	.10	.08	.04
25	Ken Patterson	.10	.08	.04
26	Eduardo Perez	.40	.30	.15
27	Tim Salmon	1.50	1.25	.60
28	J.T. Snow	.40	.30	.15
29	Chris Turner	.10	.08	.04
30	Wilson Alvarez	.10	.08	.04
31	Jason Bere	1.00	.75	.40
32	Joey Cora	.10	.08	.04
33	Alex Fernandez	.15	.11	.06
34	Roberto Hernandez	.10	.08	.04
35	Lance Johnson	.10	.08	.04
36	Ron Karkovice	.10	.08	.04
37	Kirk McCaskill	.10	.08	.04
38	Jeff Schwarz	.10	.08	.04
39	Frank Thomas	3.00	2.25	1.25
40	Sandy Alomar Jr.	.10	.08	.04
41	Albert Belle	.50	.40	.20
42	Felix Fermin	.10	.08	.04
43	Wayne Kirby	.10	.08	.04
44	Tom Kramer	.10	.08	.04
45	Kenny Lofton	.25	.20	.10
46	Jose Mesa	.10	.08	.04
47	Eric Plunk	.10	.08	.04
48	Paul Sorrento	.10	.08	.04
49	Jim Thome	.40	.30	.15
50	Bill Wertz	.10	.08	.04
51	John Doherty	.10	.08	.04
52	Cecil Fielder	.25	.20	.10
53	Travis Fryman	.25	.20	.10
54	Chris Gomez	.25	.20	.10
55	Mike Henneman	.10	.08	.04
56	Chad Kreuter	.10	.08	.04
57	Bob MacDonald	.10	.08	.04
58	Mike Moore	.10	.08	.04
59	Tony Phillips	.10	.08	.04
60	Lou Whitaker	.10	.08	.04
61	Kevin Appier	.12	.09	.05
62	Greg Gagne	.10	.08	.04
63	Chris Gwynn	.10	.08	.04
64	Bob Hamelin	.12	.09	.05
65	Chris Haney	.10	.08	.04
66	Phil Hiatt	.15	.11	.06
67	Felix Jose	.10	.08	.04
68	Jose Lind	.10	.08	.04
69	Mike Macfarlane	.10	.08	.04
70	Jeff Montgomery	.10	.08	.04
71	Hipolito Pichardo	.10	.08	.04
72	Juan Bell	.10	.08	.04
73	Cal Eldred	.12	.09	.05
74	Darryl Hamilton	.10	.08	.04
75	Doug Henry	.10	.08	.04
76	Mike Ignasiak	.10	.08	.04
77	John Jaha	.12	.09	.05
78	Graeme Lloyd	.10	.08	.04
79	Angel Miranda	.10	.08	.04
80	Dave Nilsson	.12	.09	.05
81	Troy O'Leary	.12	.09	.05
82	Kevin Reimer	.10	.08	.04
83	Willie Banks	.10	.08	.04
84	Larry Casian	.10	.08	.04
85	Scott Erickson	.10	.08	.04
86	Eddie Guardado	.10	.08	.04
87	Kent Hrbek	.10	.08	.04
88	Terry Jorgensen	.10	.08	.04
89	Chuck Knoblauch	.10	.08	.04
90	Pat Meares	.10	.08	.04
91	Mike Trombley	.10	.08	.04
92	Dave Winfield	.30	.25	.12
93	Wade Boggs	.20	.15	.08
94	Scott Kamieniecki	.10	.08	.04
95	Pat Kelly	.10	.08	.04
96	Jimmy Key	.10	.08	.04
97	Jim Leyritz	.10	.08	.04
98	Bobby Munoz	.10	.08	.04
99	Paul O'Neill	.10	.08	.04
100	Melido Perez	.10	.08	.04
101	Mike Stanley	.10	.08	.04
102	Danny Tartabull	.10	.08	.04
103	Bernie Williams	.10	.08	.04
104	*Kurt Abbott*	.25	.20	.10
105	Mike Bordick	.10	.08	.04
106	Ron Darling	.10	.08	.04
107	Brent Gates	.35	.25	.14
108	Miguel Jimenez	.10	.08	.04
109	Steve Karsay	.60	.45	.25
110	Scott Lydy	.10	.08	.04
111	Mark McGwire	.20	.15	.08
112	Troy Neel	.12	.09	.05
113	Craig Paquette	.10	.08	.04
114	Bob Welch	.10	.08	.04
115	Bobby Witt	.10	.08	.04
116	Rich Amaral	.10	.08	.04
117	Mike Blowers	.10	.08	.04
118	Jay Buhner	.10	.08	.04
119	Dave Fleming	.12	.09	.05
120	Ken Griffey, Jr.	3.00	2.25	1.25
121	Tino Martinez	.10	.08	.04
122	Marc Newfield	.40	.30	.15
123	Ted Power	.10	.08	.04
124	Mackey Sasser	.10	.08	.04
125	Omar Vizquel	.10	.08	.04
126	Kevin Brown	.10	.08	.04
127	Juan Gonzalez	2.50	2.00	1.00
128	Tom Henke	.10	.08	.04
129	David Hulse	.12	.09	.05
130	Dean Palmer	.12	.09	.05
131	Roger Pavlik	.10	.08	.04
132	Ivan Rodriguez	.10	.08	.04
133	Kenny Rogers	.10	.08	.04
134	Doug Strange	.10	.08	.04
135	Pat Borders	.10	.08	.04
136	Joe Carter	.35	.25	.14
137	Darnell Coles	.10	.08	.04
138	Pat Hentgen	.20	.15	.08
139	Al Leiter	.10	.08	.04
140	Paul Molitor	.30	.25	.12
141	John Olerud	.40	.30	.15
142	Ed Sprague	.10	.08	.04
143	Dave Stewart	.10	.08	.04
144	Mike Timlin	.10	.08	.04
145	Duane Ward	.10	.08	.04
146	Devon White	.10	.08	.04
147	Steve Avery	.30	.25	.12
148	Steve Bedrosian	.10	.08	.04
149	Damon Berryhill	.10	.08	.04
150	Jeff Blauser	.10	.08	.04
151	Tom Glavine	.30	.25	.12
152	Chipper Jones	.40	.30	.15
153	Mark Lemke	.10	.08	.04
154	Fred McGriff	.30	.25	.12
155	Greg McMichael	.15	.11	.06
156	Deion Sanders	.25	.20	.10
157	John Smoltz	.10	.08	.04
158	Mark Wohlers	.10	.08	.04
159	Jose Bautista	.10	.08	.04
160	Steve Buechele	.10	.08	.04
161	Mike Harkey	.10	.08	.04
162	Greg Hibbard	.10	.08	.04
163	Chuck McElroy	.10	.08	.04
164	Mike Morgan	.10	.08	.04
165	Kevin Roberson	.40	.30	.15
166	Ryne Sandberg	.60	.45	.25
167	Jose Vizcaino	.10	.08	.04
168	Rick Wilkins	.10	.08	.04
169	Willie Wilson	.10	.08	.04
170	Willie Greene	.12	.09	.05
171	Roberto Kelly	.10	.08	.04
172	Larry Luebbers	.20	.15	.08
173	Kevin Mitchell	.12	.09	.05
174	Joe Oliver	.10	.08	.04
175	John Roper	.10	.08	.04
176	Johnny Ruffin	.10	.08	.04
177	Reggie Sanders	.12	.09	.05
178	John Smiley	.10	.08	.04
179	Jerry Spradlin	.15	.11	.06
180	Freddie Benavides	.10	.08	.04
181	Dante Bichette	.10	.08	.04
182	Willie Blair	.10	.08	.04
183	Kent Bottenfield	.10	.08	.04
184	Jerald Clark	.10	.08	.04
185	Joe Girardi	.10	.08	.04
186	Roberto Mejia	.25	.20	.10
187	Steve Reed	.10	.08	.04
188	Armando Reynoso	.10	.08	.04
189	Bruce Ruffin	.10	.08	.04
190	Eric Young	.10	.08	.04
191	Luis Aquino	.10	.08	.04
192	Bret Barberie	.10	.08	.04
193	Ryan Bowen	.10	.08	.04
194	Chuck Carr	.10	.08	.04
195	Orestes Destrade	.10	.08	.04
196	Richie Lewis	.10	.08	.04
197	Dave Magadan	.10	.08	.04
198	Bob Natal	.10	.08	.04
199	Gary Sheffield	.15	.11	.06
200	Matt Turner	.10	.08	.04
201	Darrell Whitmore	.12	.09	.05
202	Eric Anthony	.10	.08	.04
203	Jeff Bagwell	.20	.15	.08
204	Andujar Cedeno	.12	.09	.05
205	Luis Gonzalez	.10	.08	.04
206	Xavier Hernandez	.10	.08	.04
207	Doug Jones	.10	.08	.04
208	Darryl Kile	.10	.08	.04
209	Scott Servais	.10	.08	.04
210	Greg Swindell	.10	.08	.04
211	Brian Williams	.10	.08	.04
212	Pedro Astacio	.12	.09	.05
213	Brett Butler	.10	.08	.04
214	Omar Daal	.10	.08	.04
215	Jim Gott	.10	.08	.04
216	Raul Mondesi	1.00	.75	.40
217	Jose Offerman	.10	.08	.04
218	Mike Piazza	2.50	2.00	1.00
219	Cory Snyder	.10	.08	.04
220	Tim Wallach	.10	.08	.04
221	Todd Worrell	.10	.08	.04
222	Moises Alou	.12	.09	.05
223	Sean Berry	.10	.08	.04
224	Wil Cordero	.10	.08	.04
225	Jeff Fassero	.10	.08	.04
226	Darrin Fletcher	.10	.08	.04
227	Cliff Floyd	1.50	1.25	.60
228	Marquis Grissom	.12	.09	.05
229	Ken Hill	.10	.08	.04
230	Mike Lansing	.10	.08	.04
231	Kirk Rueter	.75	.60	.30
232	John Wetteland	.10	.08	.04
233	Rondell White	.50	.40	.20
234	Tim Bogar	.10	.08	.04
235	Jeromy Burnitz	.10	.08	.04
236	Dwight Gooden	.10	.08	.04
237	Todd Hundley	.10	.08	.04
238	Jeff Kent	.10	.08	.04
239	Josias Manzanillo	.10	.08	.04
240	Joe Orsulak	.10	.08	.04
241	Ryan Thompson	.10	.08	.04
242	Kim Batiste	.10	.08	.04
243	Darren Daulton	.12	.09	.05
244	Tommy Greene	.10	.08	.04
245	Dave Hollins	.10	.08	.04
246	Pete Incaviglia	.10	.08	.04
247	Danny Jackson	.10	.08	.04
248	Ricky Jordan	.10	.08	.04
249	John Kruk	.10	.08	.04
250	Mickey Morandini	.10	.08	.04
251	Terry Mulholland	.10	.08	.04
252	Ben Rivera	.10	.08	.04
253	Kevin Stocker	.75	.60	.30
254	Jay Bell	.10	.08	.04
255	Steve Cooke	.10	.08	.04
256	Jeff King	.10	.08	.04
257	Al Martin	.10	.08	.04
258	Danny Miceli	.10	.08	.04
259	Blas Minor	.10	.08	.04
260	Don Slaught	.10	.08	.04
261	Paul Wagner	.10	.08	.04
262	Tim Wakefield	.10	.08	.04
263	Kevin Young	.12	.09	.05
264	Rene Arocha	.12	.09	.05
265	*Richard Batchelor*	.20	.15	.08
266	Gregg Jefferies	.10	.08	.04
267	Brian Jordan	.10	.08	.04
268	Jose Oquendo	.10	.08	.04
269	Donovan Osborne	.10	.08	.04
270	Erik Pappas	.10	.08	.04
271	Mike Perez	.10	.08	.04
272	Bob Tewksbury	.10	.08	.04
273	Mark Whiten	.10	.08	.04
274	Todd Zeile	.10	.08	.04
275	Andy Ashby	.10	.08	.04
276	Brad Ausmus	.10	.08	.04
277	Phil Clark	.10	.08	.04
278	Jeff Gardner	.10	.08	.04
279	Ricky Gutierrez	.10	.08	.04
280	Tony Gwynn	.25	.20	.10
281	Tim Mauser	.10	.08	.04
282	Scott Sanders	.10	.08	.04
283	Frank Seminara	.10	.08	.04
284	Wally Whitehurst	.10	.08	.04
285	Rod Beck	.10	.08	.04
286	Barry Bonds	1.00	.75	.40
287	Dave Burba	.10	.08	.04
288	Mark Carreon	.10	.08	.04
289	Royce Clayton	.12	.09	.05
290	Mike Jackson	.10	.08	.04
291	Darren Lewis	.10	.08	.04
292	Kirt Manwaring	.10	.08	.04
293	Dave Martinez	.10	.08	.04
294	Billy Swift	.10	.08	.04
295	Salomon Torres	.20	.15	.08
296	Matt Williams	.10	.08	.04
297	Checklist 1-103 (Joe Orsulak)	.10	.08	.04
298	Checklist 104-201 (Pete Incaviglia)	.10	.08	.04
299	Checklist 202-300 (Todd Hundley)	.10	.08	.04
300	Checklist - Inserts (John Doherty)	.10	.08	.04
301	Brady Anderson	.10	.08	.04

302 Harold Baines .10 .08 .04
303 Damon Buford .10 .08 .04
304 Mike Devereaux .10 .08 .04
305 Sid Fernandez .10 .08 .04
306 Rick Krivda .10 .08 .04
307 Mike Mussina .20 .15 .08
308 Rafael Palmeiro .15 .11 .06
309 Chris Sabo .10 .08 .04
310 Lee Smith .10 .08 .04
311 *Gregg Zaun* .15 .11 .06
312 Scott Cooper .10 .08 .04
313 Mike Greenwell .10 .08 .04
314 Tim Naehring .12 .09 .05
315 Otis Nixon .12 .09 .05
316 Paul Quantrill .10 .08 .04
317 John Valentin .10 .08 .04
318 Dave Valle .10 .08 .04
319 Frank Viola .10 .08 .04
320 Brian Anderson .10 .08 .04
321 *Garret Anderson* .15 .11 .06
322 Chad Curtis .12 .09 .05
323 Chili Davis .10 .08 .04
324 Gary DiSarcina .10 .08 .04
325 Damion Easley .12 .09 .05
326 Jim Edmonds .10 .08 .04
327 Chuck Finley .10 .08 .04
328 Joe Grahe .10 .08 .04
329 Bo Jackson .20 .15 .08
330 Mark Langston .10 .08 .04
331 Harold Reynolds .10 .08 .04
332 James Baldwin .50 .40 .20
333 *Ray Durham* .15 .11 .06
334 Julio Franco .10 .08 .04
335 Craig Grebeck .10 .08 .04
336 Ozzie Guillen .10 .08 .04
337 Joe Hall .10 .08 .04
338 Darrin Jackson .10 .08 .04
339 Jack McDowell .12 .09 .05
340 Tim Raines .10 .08 .04
341 Robin Ventura .20 .15 .08
342 Carlos Baerga .40 .30 .15
343 Derek Lilliquist .10 .08 .04
344 Dennis Martinez .10 .08 .04
345 Jack Morris .10 .08 .04
346 Eddie Murray .12 .09 .05
347 Chris Nabholz .10 .08 .04
348 Charles Nagy .10 .08 .04
349 Chad Ogea .10 .08 .04
350 Manny Ramirez 1.00 .70 .40
351 Omar Vizquel .10 .08 .04
352 Danny Bautista .10 .08 .04
353 Tim Belcher .10 .08 .04
354 Eric Davis .10 .08 .04
355 Rick Greene .10 .08 .04
356 Mickey Tettleton .10 .08 .04
357 Alan Trammell .12 .09 .05
358 David Wells .10 .08 .04
359 Stan Belinda .10 .08 .04
360 Vince Coleman .10 .08 .04
361 David Cone .10 .08 .04
362 Gary Gaetti .10 .08 .04
363 Tom Gordon .10 .08 .04
364 Dave Henderson .10 .08 .04
365 Wally Joyner .10 .08 .04
366 Brent Mayne .10 .08 .04
367 Brian McRae .10 .08 .04
368 Michael Tucker .15 .11 .06
369 Ricky Bones .10 .08 .04
370 Brian Harper .10 .08 .04
371 Tyrone Hill .20 .15 .08
372 Mark Kiefer .10 .08 .04
373 Pat Listach .12 .09 .05
374 *Mike Matheny* .12 .09 .05
375 *Jose Mercedes* .12 .09 .05
376 Kevin Seitzer .10 .08 .04
377 B.J. Surhoff .10 .08 .04
378 Greg Vaughn .12 .09 .05
379 Turner Ward .10 .08 .04
380 *Wes Weger* .15 .11 .06
381 Bill Wegman .10 .08 .04
382 Rick Aguilera .10 .08 .04
383 Rich Becker .10 .08 .04
384 Steve Dunn .10 .08 .04
385 *Keith Garagozzo* .15 .11 .06
386 *LaTroy Hawkins* .15 .11 .06
387 Shane Mack .10 .08 .04
388 David McCarty .15 .11 .06
389 Pedro Munoz .10 .08 .04
390 *Derek Parks* .20 .15 .08
391 Kirby Puckett .35 .25 .14
392 Kevin Tapani .10 .08 .04
393 Matt Walbeck .25 .20 .10
394 Jim Abbott .10 .08 .04
395 Mike Gallego .10 .08 .04
396 Xavier Hernandez .10 .08 .04
397 Don Mattingly .25 .20 .10
398 Terry Mulholland .10 .08 .04
399 Matt Nokes .10 .08 .04
400 Luis Polonia .10 .08 .04
401 Bob Wickman .10 .08 .04
402 Mark Acre .10 .08 .04
403 Geronimo Berroa .15 .11 .06
404 *Fausto Cruz* .20 .15 .08
405 Dennis Eckersley .12 .09 .05
406 Rickey Henderson .20 .15 .08
407 Stan Javier .10 .08 .04
408 *Carlos Reyes* .15 .11 .06
409 Ruben Sierra .12 .09 .05
410 Terry Steinbach .10 .08 .04
411 Bill Taylor .10 .08 .04
412 Todd Van Poppel .12 .09 .05
413 Eric Anthony .10 .08 .04
414 Bobby Ayala .10 .08 .04
415 Chris Bosio .10 .08 .04
416 Darren Bragg .10 .08 .04
417 Tim Davis .10 .08 .04
418 Randy Johnson .10 .08 .04
419 Kevin King .10 .08 .04
420 *Anthony Manahan* .20 .15 .08
421 Edgar Martinez .10 .08 .04
422 Keith Mitchell .10 .08 .04
423 *Mac Suzuki* .15 .11 .06
424 Dan Wilson .10 .08 .04
425 *Duff Brumley* .15 .11 .06
426 Jose Canseco .20 .15 .08
427 Will Clark .20 .15 .08
428 Steve Dreyer .10 .08 .04
429 Rick Helling .10 .08 .04
430 James Hurst .10 .08 .04
431 Chris James .10 .08 .04
432 Darren Oliver .10 .08 .04
433 Matt Whiteside .10 .08 .04
434 Roberto Alomar .40 .30 .15
435 Scott Brow .12 .09 .05
436 *Domingo Cedeno* .20 .15 .08
437 Carlos Delgado 1.00 .70 .40
438 Alex Gonzalez 1.00 .70 .40
439 Juan Guzman .12 .09 .05
440 Paul Spoljaric .10 .08 .04
441 Todd Stottlemyre .10 .08 .04
442 Woody Williams .10 .08 .04
443 David Justice .30 .25 .12
444 Mike Kelly .15 .11 .06
445 Ryan Klesko .25 .20 .10
446 Javier Lopez .75 .60 .30
447 Greg Maddux .25 .20 .10
448 Kent Mercker .10 .08 .04
449 Charlie O'Brien .10 .08 .04
450 Terry Pendleton .10 .08 .04
451 Mike Stanton .10 .08 .04
452 Tony Tarasco .25 .20 .10
453 *Terrell Wade* .20 .15 .08
454 Shawon Dunston .10 .08 .04
455 Mark Grace .12 .09 .05
456 Jose Guzman .10 .08 .04
457 Jose Hernandez .10 .08 .04
458 Glenallen Hill .10 .08 .04
459 Blaise Ilsley .10 .08 .04
460 *Brooks Kieschnick* 1.50 1.25 .60
461 Derrick May .10 .08 .04
462 Randy Myers .10 .08 .04
463 Karl Rhodes .10 .08 .04
464 Sammy Sosa .10 .08 .04
465 *Steve Trachsel* .35 .25 .14
466 *Eddie Zambrano* .15 .11 .06
467 Bret Boone .10 .08 .04
468 Tom Browning .10 .08 .04
469 *Hector Carrasco* .25 .20 .10
470 Rob Dibble .10 .08 .04
471 Erik Hanson .10 .08 .04
472 Thomas Howard .10 .08 .04
473 Kevin Jarvis .10 .08 .04
474 Barry Larkin .10 .08 .04
475 Hal Morris .10 .08 .04
476 Jose Rijo .10 .08 .04
477 John Burke .10 .08 .04
478 Ellis Burks .10 .08 .04
479 Marvin Freeman .10 .08 .04
480 Andres Galarraga .10 .08 .04
481 Greg Harris .10 .08 .04
482 Charlie Hayes .10 .08 .04
483 Darren Holmes .10 .08 .04
484 Howard Johnson .10 .08 .04
485 *Marcus Moore* .15 .11 .06
486 David Nied .25 .20 .10
487 Mark Thompson .10 .08 .04
488 Walt Weiss .10 .08 .04
489 Kurt Abbott .10 .08 .04
490 Matias Carrillo .12 .09 .05
491 Jeff Conine .10 .08 .04
492 Chris Hammond .10 .08 .04
493 Bryan Harvey .10 .08 .04
494 Charlie Hough .10 .08 .04
495 *Yorkis Perez* .20 .15 .08
496 Pat Rapp .15 .11 .06
497 Benito Santiago .10 .08 .04
498 David Weathers .10 .08 .04
499 Craig Biggio .10 .08 .04
500 Ken Caminiti .10 .08 .04
501 Doug Drabek .10 .08 .04
502 *Tony Eusebio* .20 .15 .08
503 Steve Finley .10 .08 .04
504 Pete Harnisch .10 .08 .04
505 Brian Hunter .10 .08 .04
506 Domingo Jean .10 .08 .04
507 Todd Jones .10 .08 .04
508 *Orlando Miller* .20 .15 .08
509 James Mouton .20 .15 .08
510 Roberto Petagine .10 .08 .04
511 Shane Reynolds .10 .08 .04
512 Mitch Williams .10 .08 .04
513 Billy Ashley .25 .20 .10
514 Tom Candiotti .10 .08 .04
515 Delino DeShields .10 .08 .04
516 *Darren Dreifort* .50 .40 .20
517 Kevin Gross .10 .08 .04
518 Orel Hershiser .10 .08 .04
519 Eric Karros .10 .08 .04
520 Ramon Martinez .10 .08 .04
521 *Chan Ho Park* .75 .60 .30
522 Henry Rodriguez .20 .15 .08
523 Joey Eischen .12 .09 .05
524 Rod Henderson .10 .08 .04
525 Pedro Martinez .10 .08 .04
526 Mel Rojas .12 .09 .05
527 Larry Walker .12 .09 .05
528 *Gabe White* .25 .20 .10
529 Bobby Bonilla .12 .09 .05
530 Jonathan Hurst .10 .08 .04
531 Bobby Jones .25 .20 .10
532 Kevin McReynolds .10 .08 .04
533 *Bill Pulsipher* .15 .11 .06
534 Bret Saberhagen .10 .08 .04
535 Pete Smith .10 .08 .04
536 *Kelly Stinnett* .15 .11 .06
537 Dave Telgheder .10 .08 .04
538 *Quilvio Veras* .15 .11 .06
539 Jose Vizcaino .10 .08 .04
540 Pete Walker .10 .08 .04
541 Ricky Bottalico .10 .08 .04
542 Wes Chamberlain .10 .08 .04
543 Mariano Duncan .10 .08 .04
544 Len Dykstra .15 .11 .06
545 Jim Eisenreich .10 .08 .04
546 *Phil Geisler* .20 .15 .08
547 Wayne Gomes .12 .09 .05
548 Doug Jones .10 .08 .04
549 Jeff Juden .10 .08 .04
550 Mike Lieberthal .10 .08 .04
551 *Tony Longmire* .30 .25 .12
552 Tom Marsh .12 .09 .05
553 Bobby Munoz .15 .11 .06
554 Curt Schilling .10 .08 .04
555 Carlos Garcia .12 .09 .05
556 *Ravelo Manzanillo* .20 .15 .08
557 Orlando Merced .10 .08 .04
558 *Will Pennyfeather* .20 .15 .08
559 Andy Van Slyke .10 .08 .04
560 Rick White .10 .08 .04
561 Luis Alicea .12 .09 .05
562 *Brian Barber* .20 .15 .08
563 *Clint Davis* .20 .15 .08
564 Bernard Gilkey .10 .08 .04
565 Ray Lankford .12 .09 .05
566 Tom Pagnozzi .10 .08 .04
567 Ozzie Smith .20 .15 .08
568 Rick Sutcliffe .10 .08 .04
569 Allen Watson .25 .20 .10
570 Dmitri Young .25 .20 .10
571 Derek Bell .10 .08 .04
572 Andy Benes .10 .08 .04
573 Archi Cianfrocco .10 .08 .04
574 Joey Hamilton .10 .08 .04
575 Gene Harris .10 .08 .04
576 Trevor Hoffman .12 .09 .05
577 *Tim Hyers* .15 .11 .06
578 *Brian Johnson* .20 .15 .08
579 *Keith Lockhart* .25 .20 .10
580 Pedro Martinez .10 .08 .04
581 Ray McDavid .15 .11 .06
582 Phil Plantier .15 .11 .06
583 Bip Roberts .10 .08 .04
584 *A.J. Sager* .20 .15 .08
585 Dave Staton .10 .08 .04
586 Todd Benzinger .10 .08 .04
587 John Burkett .10 .08 .04
588 Bryan Hickerson .10 .08 .04
589 Willie McGee .10 .08 .04
590 John Patterson .10 .08 .04
591 Mark Portugal .10 .08 .04
592 Kevin Rogers .10 .08 .04
593 *Joe Rosselli* .15 .11 .06
594 Steve Soderstrom .15 .11 .06
595 Robby Thompson .10 .08 .04
596 125th Anniversary Card .15 .11 .06
597 Checklist .10 .08 .04
598 Checklist .10 .08 .04
599 Checklist .10 .08 .04
600 Checklist .10 .08 .04

1994 Fleer Ultra All-Rookie Team

A stylized sunrise landscape is the background for this insert set featuring top rookies and inserted into Ultra Series II packs at the rate of about one per 10.

		MT	NR MT	EX
Complete Set (10):		25.00	18.00	10.00
Common Player:		1.00	.75	.40
1	Carlos Delgado	3.00	2.25	1.25
2	Cliff Floyd	5.00	3.75	2.00
3	Alex Gonzalez	3.00	2.25	1.25
4	Jeffrey Hammonds	3.50	2.75	1.50
5	Ryan Klesko	5.00	3.75	2.00
6	Javier Lopez	5.00	3.75	2.00
7	Raul Mondesi	4.00	3.00	1.50
8	James Mouton	1.50	1.25	.60
9	Chan Ho Park	1.50	1.25	.60
10	Dave Staton	1.00	.75	.40

A card number in parentheses () indicates the set is unnumbered.

1994 Fleer Ultra All-Stars

Fleer's opinion of the top 20 players in 1994 are featured in this most common of the Series II Ultra insert sets. Silver-foil highlights enchance the chase cards, found, according ot stated odds, once per three packs, on average.

		MT	NR MT	EX
Complete Set (20):		25.00	18.00	10.00
Common Player:		.50	.40	.20
1	Chris Hoiles	.50	.40	.20
2	Frank Thomas	5.00	3.75	2.00
3	Roberto Alomar	1.50	1.25	.60
4	Cal Ripken, Jr.	1.50	1.25	.60
5	Robin Ventura	1.00	.75	.40
6	Albert Belle	1.50	1.25	.60
7	Juan Gonzalez	3.00	2.25	1.25
8	Ken Griffey, Jr.	3.50	2.75	1.50
9	John Olerud	1.25	.90	.50
10	Jack McDowell	.50	.40	.20
11	Mike Piazza	3.50	2.75	1.50
12	Fred McGriff	1.25	.90	.50
13	Ryne Sandberg	1.50	1.25	.60
14	Jay Bell	.50	.40	.20
15	Matt Williams	.60	.45	.25
16	Barry Bonds	2.50	2.00	1.00
17	Len Dykstra	.75	.60	.30
18	Dave Justice	1.50	1.25	.60
19	Tom Glavine	.75	.60	.30
20	Greg Maddux	1.00	.75	.40

1994 Fleer Ultra Award Winners

The most common of the Fleer Ultra insert sets for 1994 is the 25-card "Award Winners." Horizontal format cards feature front and back background with a gold-embossed look. A player action photo appears on the front. A gold-foil seal on the front has a symbolic player representation flanked by the pictured player's name and award. A gold Fleer Ultra logo is at top. Backs have a player portrait photo and a write-up about the award. The name of the award and the player's name appear in gold foil at the top. Stated odds of finding an Award Winners card were one in three packs.

		MT	NR MT	EX
Complete Set (25):		24.00	18.00	9.50
Common Player:		.40	.30	.15
1	Ivan Rodriguez	.50	.40	.20
2	Don Mattingly	1.00	.75	.40
3	Roberto Alomar	1.25	.90	.50
4	Robin Ventura	.75	.60	.30
5	Omar Vizquel	.40	.30	.15
6	Ken Griffey, Jr.	4.00	3.00	1.50
7	Kenny Lofton	.75	.60	.30
8	Devon White	.50	.40	.20
9	Mark Langston	.40	.30	.15
10	Kirt Manwaring	.40	.30	.15
11	Mark Grace	.60	.45	.25
12	Robby Thompson	.50	.40	.20
13	Matt Williams	.60	.45	.25
14	Jay Bell	.40	.30	.15
15	Barry Bonds	2.50	2.00	1.00
16	Marquis Grissom	.60	.45	.25
17	Larry Walker	.60	.45	.25
18	Greg Maddux	.75	.60	.30
19	Frank Thomas	5.00	3.75	2.00
20	Barry Bonds	2.50	2.00	1.00
21	Paul Molitor	1.25	.90	.50
22	Jack McDowell	.60	.45	.25
23	Greg Maddux	.75	.60	.30
24	Tim Salmon	2.50	2.00	1.00
25	Mike Piazza	4.00	3.00	1.50

1994 Fleer Ultra Career Achievement Awards

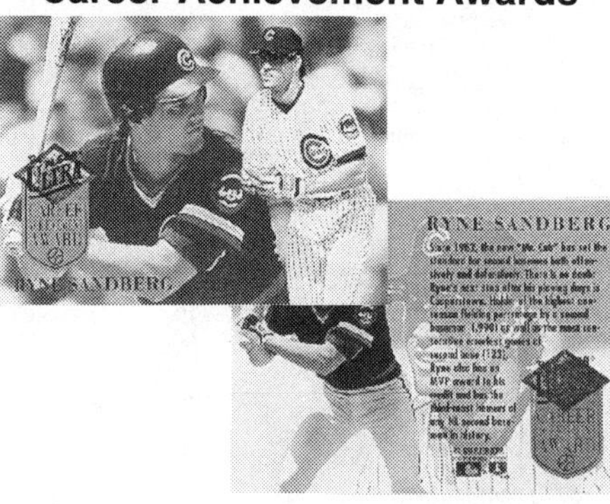

The outstanding careers of five of baseball's top veteran stars are recognized in this chase set, inserted on average once every 21 packs of Ultra Series II. The gold-highlighted horizontal fronts combine a current color photo with a background single-tint photo from the player's earlier days.

		MT	NR MT	EX
Complete Set (5):		20.00	15.00	8.00
Common Player:		3.00	2.25	1.25
1	Joe Carter	4.00	3.00	1.50
2	Paul Molitor	4.00	3.00	1.50
3	Cal Ripken, Jr.	6.00	4.50	2.50
4	Ryne Sandberg	6.00	4.50	2.50
5	Dave Winfield	3.50	2.75	1.50

1994 Fleer Ultra Firemen

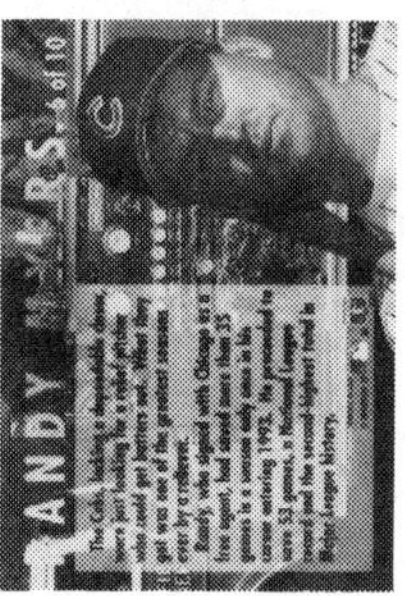

Ten of the major leagues' leading relief pitchers are featured in this Ultra insert set. Cards have an action photo of the player superimposed over a background photo of a fire truck. A shield at top, in gold foil, has a smoke-eater's helmet, stylized flames and proclaims the player an "Ultra Fireman." The company logo and player name appear in gold foil at bottom. Backs are horizontal in format and feature the pumper's control panel in the background photo. The player name appears in large gold-foil letters at top. A color player portrait photo appears on one side, with a description of his relief role and successes in a whitened box. Fireman cards are found, on average, once per 11 packs, according to stated odds.

		MT	NR MT	EX
Complete Set (10):		8.00	6.00	3.25
Common Player:		.75	.60	.30
1	Jeff Montgomery	1.00	.75	.40
2	Duane Ward	.75	.60	.30
3	Tom Henke	.75	.60	.30
4	Roberto Hernandez	1.00	.75	.40
5	Dennis Eckersley	1.25	.90	.50
6	Randy Myers	.75	.60	.30
7	Rod Beck	.75	.60	.30
8	Bryan Harvey	1.00	.75	.40
9	John Wetteland	.75	.60	.30
10	Mitch Williams	.75	.60	.30

The values quoted are intended to reflect the market price.

1994 Fleer Ultra Hitting Machines

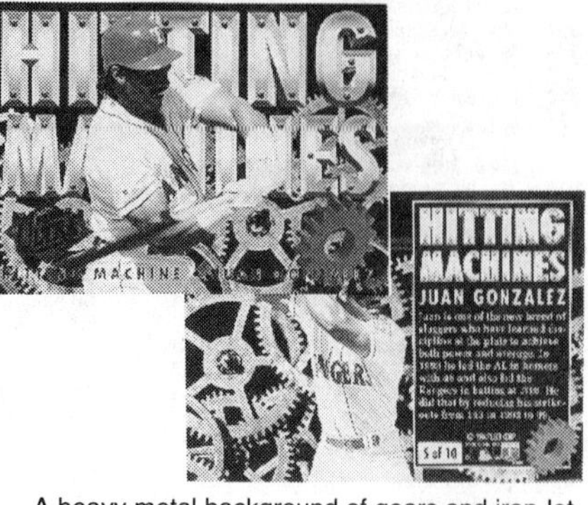

A heavy metal background of gears and iron-letter logo is featured in this insert set honoring the game's top hitters. The cards turn up about once in every five packs of Ultra Series II.

		MT	NR MT	EX
Complete Set (10):		15.00	11.00	6.00
Common Player:		.75	.60	.30
1	Roberto Alomar	1.25	.90	.50
2	Carlos Baerga	1.25	.90	.50
3	Barry Bonds	2.00	1.50	.80
4	Andres Galarraga	.75	.60	.30
5	Juan Gonzalez	3.00	2.25	1.25
6	Tony Gwynn	1.00	.75	.40
7	Paul Molitor	1.00	.75	.40
8	John Olerud	1.25	.90	.50
9	Mike Piazza	3.50	2.75	1.50
10	Frank Thomas	5.00	3.75	2.00

Values quoted in this guide reflect the retail price of a card – the price a collector can expect to pay when buying a card from a dealer. The wholesale price – that which a collector can expect to receive from a dealer when selling cards – will be significantly lower, depending on desirability and condition.

1994 Fleer Ultra Home Run Kings

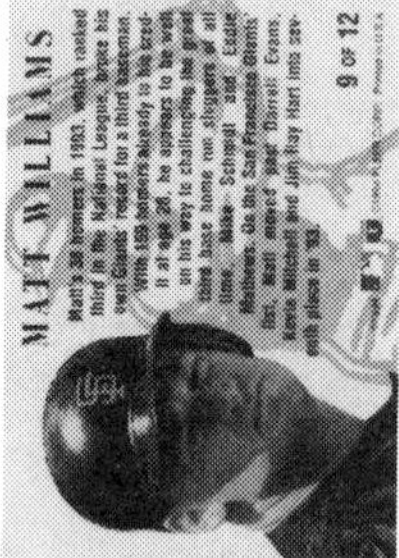

One of two high-end inserts sets in '94 Ultra is the 12-card "Home Run Kings" found exclusively in 14-card foil packs, on an average of once per 36-pack box. Featuring the technology Fleer calls "etched metallization," the cards have a black background with a red and blue foil representation of a batter. An action photo of a player taking a mighty cut or starting his home-run trot is featured. A large gold-foil "Home Run King" crown-and-shield device are in an upper corner, while the Ultra logo and player name are in gold foil at bottom. Backs have a white background with the red and blue batter symbol. The player's name appears in gold foil at the top, along with a portrait photo and a summary of his home run prowess.

		MT	NR MT	EX
Complete Set (12):		100.00	75.00	40.00
Common Player:		3.00	2.25	1.25
1	Juan Gonzalez	17.50	13.00	7.00
2	Ken Griffey, Jr.	25.00	18.00	10.00
3	Frank Thomas	25.00	18.50	10.00
4	Albert Belle	7.50	5.50	3.00
5	Rafael Palmeiro	4.00	3.00	1.50
6	Joe Carter	5.00	3.75	2.00
7	Barry Bonds	14.00	10.50	5.50
8	David Justice	7.50	5.50	3.00
9	Matt Williams	3.50	2.75	1.50
10	Fred McGriff	5.00	3.75	2.00
11	Ron Gant	3.00	2.25	1.25
12	Mike Piazza	18.00	13.50	7.25

1994 Fleer Ultra On-Base Leaders

One of the lesser-known, but most valuable, stats - on-base percentage - is featured in this subset found exclusively in 17-card packs, at the rate of about one per 37 packs. The fronts feature color photos against a stat-filled printed-foil background.

		MT	NR MT	EX
Complete Set (12):		70.00	52.00	28.00
Common Player:		2.50	2.00	1.00
1	Roberto Alomar	6.00	4.50	2.50
2	Barry Bonds	10.00	7.50	4.00
3	Len Dykstra	4.50	3.50	1.75
4	Andres Galarraga	3.00	2.25	1.25
5	Mark Grace	3.50	2.75	1.50
6	Ken Griffey, Jr.	18.00	13.50	7.25
7	Gregg Jefferies	3.00	2.25	1.25
8	Orlando Merced	2.50	2.00	1.00
9	Paul Molitor	5.00	3.75	2.00
10	John Olerud	6.00	4.50	2.50
11	Tony Phillips	2.50	2.00	1.00
12	Frank Thomas	18.00	13.50	7.25

1994 Fleer Ultra RBI Kings

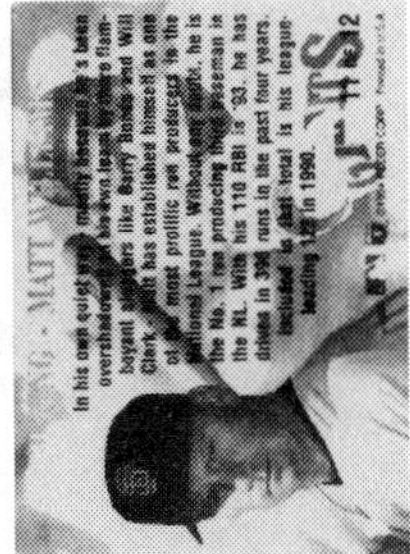

Exclusive to the 19-card jumbo packs of Fleer Ultra are a series of 12 "RBI Kings" insert cards, found, according to stated odds, one per 36 packs. The horizontal-format card front uses Fleer's "etched metallized" technology to produce a sepia-toned background action photo, in front of which is a color player photo. An Ultra logo appears in gold foil in an upper corner while a fancy shield-and-scroll "RBI King" logo and the player's name are in gold at the bottom. Backs repeat the basic front motif and include a color player portrait photo, his name in gold foil and a paragraph justifying his selection as an RBI King.

		MT	NR MT	EX
Complete Set (12):		100.00	75.00	40.00
Common Player:		2.50	2.00	1.00
1	Albert Belle	7.00	5.25	2.75
2	Frank Thomas	20.00	15.00	8.00
3	Joe Carter	5.00	3.75	2.00
4	Juan Gonzalez	15.00	11.00	6.00
5	Cecil Fielder	4.00	3.00	1.50
6	Carlos Baerga	6.00	4.50	2.50
7	Barry Bonds	10.00	7.50	4.00
8	David Justice	7.00	5.25	2.75
9	Ron Gant	3.00	2.25	1.25
10	Mike Piazza	15.00	11.00	6.00
11	Matt Williams	4.00	3.00	1.50
12	Darren Daulton	2.50	2.00	1.00

1994 Fleer Ultra League Leaders

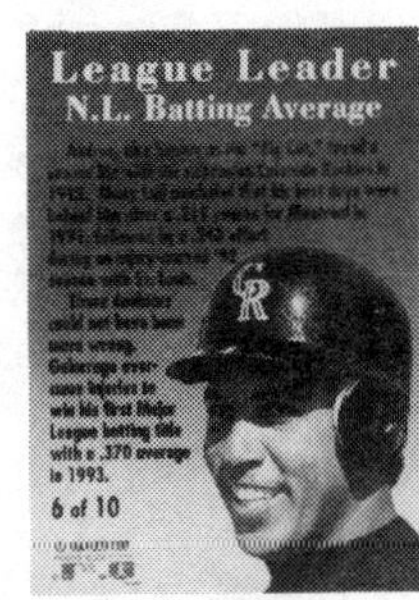

Arguably the least attractive of the '94 Fleer Ultra inserts are the 10 "League Leaders." Fronts feature a full-bleed action photo on which the bottom has been re-colored to a team hue giving the effect of teal, purple and magenta miasmas rising from the turf. An Ultra logo appear in gold foil in an upper corner, with the player's name in gold foil at about the dividing line between the natural color and colorized portions of the photo. A large "League Leader" appears in the bottom half of the photo, with the category led printed in the lower-left. Backs repeat the team color at top, fading to white at the bottom. In gold foil are "League Leader" and the category. A portrait-type player photo appears at bottom. Several paragraphs detail the league leading performance of the previous season. Stated odds of finding a League Leaders insert are one

		MT	NR MT	EX
Complete Set (10):		7.00	5.25	2.75
Common Player:		.50	.40	.20
1	John Olerud	1.50	1.25	.60
2	Rafael Palmeiro	.75	.60	.30
3	Kenny Lofton	.75	.60	.30
4	Jack McDowell	.60	.45	.25
5	Randy Johnson	.50	.40	.20
6	Andres Galarraga	.50	.40	.20
7	Len Dykstra	.75	.60	.30
8	Chuck Carr	.50	.40	.20
9	Tom Glavine	1.00	.75	.40
10	Jose Rijo	.50	.40	.20

Definitions for grading conditions are located in the Introduction of this price guide.

1994 Fleer Ultra Phillies Finest

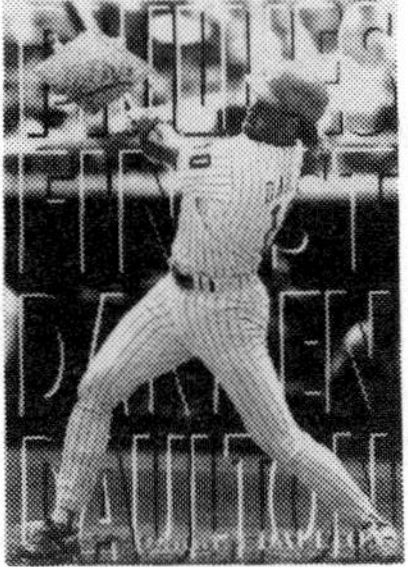

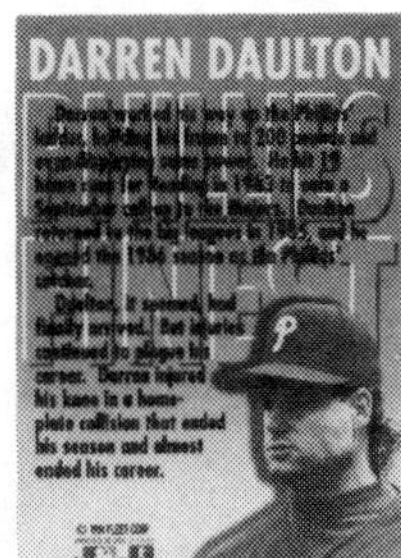

As a tribute ot two of Fleer's home-team heroes, the Philadelphia-based card company created an Ultra insert set featuring 22 cards each of "Phillies Finest," John Kruk and Darren Daulton. Twenty of the cards were issued as Series I and II inserts, about one in every eight packs, while four were available only by a mail-in offer. Fronts feature action photos with large block letters popping out of the background. The Ultra logo and player name appear in gold foil. Backs have portrait photos and career summaries, with the player's name and card number in gold foil. Daulton and Kruk each autographed 1,000 of the inserts. Stated odds of finding the autographed cards were one in 11,000 packs.

		MT	NR MT	EX
Complete Set (24):		24.00	18.00	9.50
Common Player:		1.50	1.25	.60
Autographed Card:		75.00	56.00	30.00
1	Darren Daulton (standing, holding glove, mask)	1.50	1.25	.60
2	Darren Daulton (batting follow-through)	1.50	1.25	.60
3	Darren Daulton (blocking runner at plate)	1.50	1.25	.60
4	Darren Daulton (starting for first base)	1.50	1.25	.60
5	Darren Daulton	1.50	1.25	.60
6	Darren Daulton	1.50	1.25	.60
7	Darren Daulton	1.50	1.25	.60
8	Darren Daulton	1.50	1.25	.60
9	Darren Daulton	1.50	1.25	.60
10	Darren Daulton	1.50	1.25	.60
1M	Darren Daulton (throwing)	1.50	1.25	.60
3M	Darren Daulton	1.50	1.25	.60
6	John Kruk	1.50	1.25	.60
7	John Kruk (fielding)	1.50	1.25	.60
8	John Kruk (batting follow-through)	1.50	1.25	.60
9	John Kruk (limbering up with bat)	1.50	1.25	.60
10	John Kruk (running bases)	1.50	1.25	.60
16	John Kruk	1.50	1.25	.60
17	John Kruk	1.50	1.25	.60
18	John Kruk	1.50	1.25	.60
19	John Kruk	1.50	1.25	.60
20	John Kruk	1.50	1.25	.60
2M	John Kruk (waiting to field)	1.50	1.25	.60
4M	John Kruk	1.50	1.25	.60

1994 Fleer Ultra Rising Stars

An outer space background printed on metallic foil sets this chase set apart from most of the rest of the Ultra Series II inserts. The silver-foil enhanced cards of projected superstars of tomorrow are found on average once every 37 packs.

		MT	NR MT	EX
Complete Set (10):		60.00	45.00	24.00
Common Player:		2.50	2.00	1.00
1	Carlos Baerga	5.00	3.75	2.00
2	Jeff Bagwell	4.50	3.50	1.75
3	Albert Belle	6.00	4.50	2.50
4	Cliff Floyd	10.00	7.50	4.00
5	Travis Fryman	3.50	2.75	1.50
6	Marquis Grissom	3.00	2.25	1.25
7	Kenny Lofton	4.50	3.50	1.75
8	John Olerud	7.50	5.50	3.00
9	Mike Piazza	14.00	10.50	5.50
10	Frank Thomas	18.00	13.50	7.25

The values quoted are intended to reflect the market price.

1994 Fleer Ultra Second Year Standouts

Approximately once every 11 packs, the Ultra insert find is a "Second Year Standout" card. Ten of the game's sophomore stars are featured. Fronts feature a pair of action photos against a team-color background. Gold-foil highlights are the Ultra logo, the player's name and a "Second Year Standout" shield. The shield and player name are repeated in gold foil on the back, as is the team color background. There is a player portrait photo at bottom and a summary of the player's 1993 season.

		MT	NR MT	EX
Complete Set (10):		18.00	13.50	7.25
Common Player:		1.00	.75	.40
1	Jason Bere	2.50	2.00	1.00
2	Brent Gates	1.50	1.25	.60
3	Jeffrey Hammonds	4.00	3.00	1.50
4	Tim Salmon	4.50	3.50	1.75
5	Aaron Sele	3.00	2.25	1.25
6	Chuck Carr	1.00	.75	.40
7	Jeff Conine	1.50	1.25	.60
8	Greg McMichael	1.00	.75	.40
9	Mike Piazza	9.00	6.75	3.50
10	Kevin Stocker	1.50	1.25	.60

Values for recent cards and sets are listed in Mint (MT), Near Mint (NM), reflecting the fact that many cards from recent years have been preserved in top condition. Recent cards and sets in less than Excellent condition have little collector interest.

1994 Fleer Ultra Strikeout Kings

A gold-foil "Strikeout Kings" crown-and-shield logo is featured on the front of this chase set. Cards are found on average once per seven packs.

		MT	NR MT	EX
Complete Set (5):		8.00	6.00	3.25
Common Player:		1.00	.75	.40
1	Randy Johnson	2.00	1.50	.80
2	Mark Langston	1.50	1.25	.60
3	Greg Maddux	4.00	3.00	1.50
4	Jose Rijo	1.00	.75	.40
5	John Smoltz	1.50	1.25	.60

1994 Fleer Atlantic

Five-card packs of this special Fleer set were given away with an eight-gallon premium gasoline purchase at Pennsylvania and New York Atlantic/Sunoco stations between June 1 and July 6. Many of the cards suffered damaged borders from the packaging process. Cards are in the basic 1994 Fleer format, though the name and position around the team logo at top are in white on these cards, rather than gold-foil. Different front and back photos are used in this set. Backs include the gas station logos at bottom.

		MT	NR MT	EX
Complete Set (25):		9.00	6.75	3.50
Common Player:		.25	.20	.10
1	Roberto Alomar	.40	.30	.15
2	Carlos Baerga	.35	.25	.14
3	Jeff Bagwell	.25	.20	.10
4	Jay Bell	.25	.20	.10
5	Barry Bonds	.60	.45	.25
6	Joe Carter	.35	.25	.14
7	Roger Clemens	.35	.25	.14
8	Darren Daulton	.25	.20	.10
9	Lenny Dykstra	.35	.25	.14
10	Cecil Fielder	.40	.30	.15
11	Tom Glavine	.30	.25	.12
12	Juan Gonzalez	.60	.45	.25
13	Ken Griffey, Jr.	1.25	.90	.50
14	David Justice	.40	.30	.15
15	John Kruk	.30	.25	.12
16	Greg Maddux	.30	.25	.12
17	Don Mattingly	.60	.45	.25
18	Jack McDowell	.25	.20	.10
19	John Olerud	.35	.25	.14
20	Mike Piazza	.45	.35	.20
21	Kirby Puckett	.50	.40	.20
22	Tim Salmon	.35	.25	.14
23	Frank Thomas	1.25	.90	.50
24	Andy Van Slyke	.25	.20	.10
25	Checklist	.05	.04	.02

Values for recent cards and sets are listed in Mint (MT), Near Mint (NM), reflecting the fact that many cards from recent years have been preserved in top condition. Recent cards and sets in less than Excellent condition have little collector interest.

1962 Ford Detroit Tigers Postcards

Because baseball card collectors have to compete with auto memorabilia hobbyists for these scarce cards, they are among the most valuable postcard issues of the early 1960s. In standard 3-1/2" x 5-1/2" postcard format, the full-color cards feature photos taken on a golf course of players posed in front of various new Fords. White backs have a name, position and team, with a box for a stamp. Probably given out in conjunction with autograph appearances at car dealers (they are frequntly found autographed), the set lacks some of the team's biggest stars (Al Kaline, Norm Cash), and includes coaches and even trainer Jack Homel. Probably because of lack of demand, the coaches' and trainer's cards are the scarcest to find today. The unnumbered cards are checklisted here alphabetically.

		NR MT	EX	VG
Complete Set (16):		950.00	475.00	275.00
Common Player:		60.00	30.00	18.00
(1)	Hank Aguirre	60.00	30.00	18.00
(2)	Steve Boros	80.00	40.00	24.00
(3)	Dick Brown	60.00	30.00	18.00
(4)	Phil Cavaretta	90.00	45.00	27.00
(5)	Rocky Colavito	125.00	62.00	37.00
(6)	Jim Bunning	95.00	47.00	28.00
(7)	Terry Fox	60.00	30.00	18.00
(8)	Purn Goldy	60.00	30.00	18.00
(9)	Jack Homel	90.00	45.00	27.00
(10)	Ron Kline	60.00	30.00	18.00
(11)	Don Mossi	60.00	30.00	18.00
(12)	George Myatt	80.00	40.00	24.00
(13)	Ron Nischwitz	60.00	30.00	18.00
(14)	Larry Osborne	60.00	30.00	18.00
(15)	Mike Roarke	90.00	45.00	27.00
(16)	Phil Regan	60.00	30.00	18.00

1887 Four Base Hits

Although the exact origin of this set is still in doubt, the Four Base Hits cards are among the rarest and most sought after of all 19th century tobacco issues. There is some speculation that the cards, measuring 2-1/4" by 3-7/8", were produced by Charles Gross & Co. because of their similarity to the Kalamazoo Bats issues, but there is also some evidence to support the theory that they were issued by August Beck & Co., producer of the Yum Yum set. The Four Base Hits cards feature sepia-toned photos with the player's name and position below the picture, and the words "Smoke Four Base Hits. Four For 10 Cents." along the bottom. The card labeled "Daily" is a double error. The name should have been spelled "Daly," but the card actually pictures Billy Sunday. Because new discoveries continue to surface for this issue, no complete-set value is listed.

		NR MT	EX	VG
Common Player:		2000.	1000.	600.00
(1)	John Clarkson	3500.	1750.	1050.
(2)	Tido Daily (Daly)	2000.	1000.	600.00
(3)	Pat Deasley	2000.	1000.	600.00
(4)	Buck Ewing	3500.	1750.	1050.
(5)	Pete Gillespie	2000.	1000.	600.00
(6)	Frank Hankinson	2000.	1000.	600.00
(7)	King Kelly	4000.	2000.	1200.
(8)	Al Mays	2000.	1000.	600.00
(9)	Jim Mutrie	2000.	1000.	600.00
(10)	Chief Roseman	2000.	1000.	600.00
(11)	Marty Sullivan	2000.	1000.	600.00
(12)	Rip Van Haltren	2000.	1000.	600.00
(13)	Monte Ward	3500.	1750.	1050.
(14)	Mickey Welch	3500.	1750.	1050.

The values quoted are intended to reflect the market price.

1963 French Bauer Milk Caps

This regional set of cardboard milk bottle caps was issued in the Cincinnati area in 1963 and features 30 members of the Cincinnati Reds. The unnumbered, blank-backed cards are approximately 1-1/4" in diameter and feature rather crude drawings of the players with their names in script alongside the artwork and the words "Visit Beautiful Crosley Field/See The Reds in Action" along the outside. An album was issued to house the set.

		NR MT	EX	VG
Complete Set:		550.00	275.00	165.00
Common Player:		5.00	2.50	1.50
Album:		100.00	50.00	10.00
(1)	Don Blasingame	5.00	2.50	1.50
(2)	Leo Cardenas	5.00	2.50	1.50
(3)	Gordon Coleman	5.00	2.50	1.50
(4)	Wm. O. DeWitt	5.00	2.50	1.50
(5)	John Edwards	5.00	2.50	1.50
(6)	Jesse Gonder	5.00	2.50	1.50
(7)	Tommy Harper	5.00	2.50	1.50
(8)	Bill Henry	5.00	2.50	1.50
(9)	Fred Hutchinson	8.00	4.00	2.50
(10)	Joey Jay	5.00	2.50	1.50
(11)	Eddie Kasko	5.00	2.50	1.50
(12)	Marty Keough	5.00	2.50	1.50
(13)	Jim Maloney	8.00	4.00	2.50
(14)	Joe Nuxhall	8.00	4.00	2.50
(15)	Reggie Otero	5.00	2.50	1.50
(16)	Jim O'Toole	5.00	2.50	1.50
(17)	Jim Owens	5.00	2.50	1.50
(18)	Vada Pinson	18.00	9.00	5.50
(19)	Bob Purkey	5.00	2.50	1.50
(20)	Frank Robinson	80.00	40.00	24.00
(21)	Dr. Richard Rohde	5.00	2.50	1.50
(22)	Pete Rose	200.00	100.00	60.00
(23)	Ray Shore	5.00	2.50	1.50
(24)	Dick Sisler	5.00	2.50	1.50
(25)	Bob Skinner	5.00	2.50	1.50
(26)	John Tsitorius	5.00	2.50	1.50
(27)	Jim Turner	5.00	2.50	1.50
(28)	Ken Walters	5.00	2.50	1.50
(29)	Al Worthington	5.00	2.50	1.50
(30)	Dom Zanni	5.00	2.50	1.50

1987 French/Bray Orioles

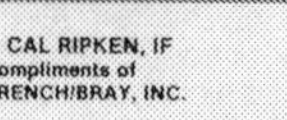

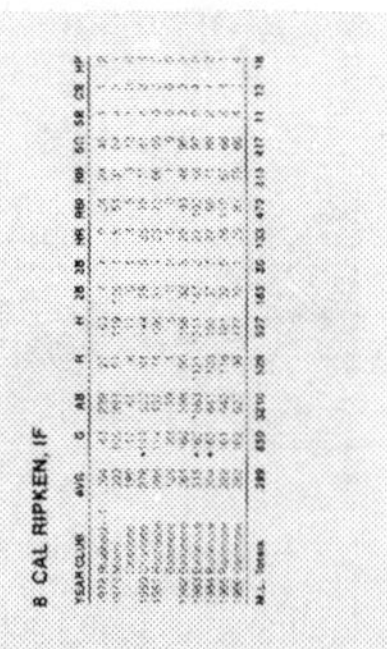

The Baltimore Orioles and French Bray, Inc. issued a baseball card set to be handed out to fans in attendance at Memorial Stadium on July 26th. Thirty perforated, detachable cards were printed within a three-panel fold-out piece measuring 9-1/2" by 11-1/4". The card fronts feature full-color player photos surrounded by an orange border. The French/Bray logo appears on the card front. The backs are of simple design, containing only the player's name, uniform number, position and professional record.

		MT	NR MT	EX
Complete Set:		10.00	7.50	4.00
Common Player:		.15	.11	.06
2	Alan Wiggins	.15	.11	.06
3	Bill Ripken	.15	.11	.06
6	Floyd Rayford	.15	.11	.06
7	Cal Ripken, Sr.	.15	.11	.06
8	Cal Ripken, Jr.	4.00	3.00	1.50
9	Jim Dwyer	.15	.11	.06
10	Terry Crowley	.15	.11	.06
15	Terry Kennedy	.20	.15	.08
16	Scott McGregor	.20	.15	.08
18	Larry Sheets	.15	.11	.06
19	Fred Lynn	.50	.40	.20
20	Frank Robinson	.80	.60	.30
24	Dave Schmidt	.15	.11	.06
25	Ray Knight	.20	.15	.08
27	Lee Lacy	.15	.11	.06
31	Mark Wiley	.15	.11	.06
32	Mark Williamson	.30	.25	.12
33	Eddie Murray	1.50	1.25	.60
38	Ken Gerhart	.15	.11	.06
39	Ken Dixon	.15	.11	.06
40	Jimmy Williams	.15	.11	.06
42	Mike Griffin	.15	.11	.06
43	Mike Young	.15	.11	.06
44	Elrod Hendricks	.15	.11	.06
45	Eric Bell	.15	.11	.06
46	Mike Flanagan	.25	.20	.10
49	Tom Niedenfuer	.15	.11	.06
52	Mike Boddicker	.25	.20	.10
54	John Habyan	.15	.11	.06
57	Tony Arnold	.15	.11	.06

1988 French/Bray Orioles

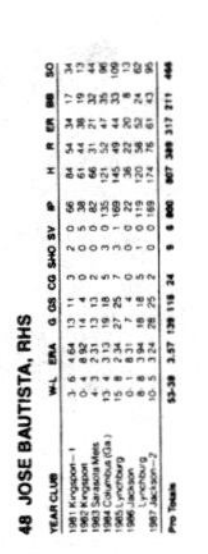

French-Bray sponsored a full-color brochure that was distributed to fans during an in-stadium promotion. A blue and orange front cover features inset photos of the Orioles in action on the upper left in a filmstrip motif. To the right is the Orioles logo and their 1988 slogan, "You Gotta Be There" above a baseball glove and ball. The 3-panel foldout measures approximately 9-1/2" by 11-1/4" and includes a team photo on the inside cover, with two perforated pages of individual cards featuring players, coaches and the team manager. Individual cards measure 2-1/4" by 3-1/8", with close-ups framed in white with an orange accent line. The player name and sponsor logo are printed beneath the photo. The black and white backs are numbered by player uniform and provide career stats. Additional copies of the brochure were made available from the Orioles Baseball Store following the free giveaway.

		MT	NR MT	EX
Complete Set:		8.00	6.00	3.25
Common Player:		.15	.11	.06
2	Don Buford	.25	.20	.10
6	Joe Orsulak	.25	.20	.10
7	Bill Ripken	.15	.11	.06
8	Cal Ripken, Jr.	3.00	2.25	1.25
9	Jim Dwyer	.15	.11	.06
10	Terry Crowley	.15	.11	.06
12	Mike Morgan	.25	.20	.10
14	Mickey Tettleton	1.50	1.25	.60
15	Terry Kennedy	.20	.15	.08
17	Pete Stanicek	.15	.11	.06
18	Larry Sheets	.15	.11	.06
19	Fred Lynn	.50	.40	.20
20	Frank Robinson	.80	.60	.30
23	Ozzie Peraza	.15	.11	.06
24	Dave Schmidt	.15	.11	.06
25	Rich Schu	.15	.11	.06
28	Jim Traber	.15	.11	.06
31	Herm Starrette	.15	.11	.06
33	Eddie Murray	1.50	1.25	.60
34	Jeff Ballard	.15	.11	.06
38	Ken Gerhart	.15	.11	.06
40	Minnie Mendoza	.15	.11	.06
41	Don Aase	.15	.11	.06
44	Elrod Hendricks	.15	.11	.06
47	John Hart	.15	.11	.06
48	Jose Bautista	.15	.11	.06
49	Tom Niedenfuer	.15	.11	.06
52	Mike Boddicker	.25	.20	.10
53	Jay Tibbs	.15	.11	.06
88	Rene Gonzales	.25	.20	.10

1989 French/Bray Orioles

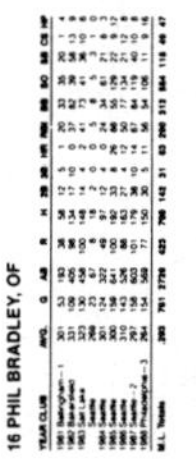

This 32-card Baltimore Orioles team set was co-sponsored by French-Bray and the Wilcox Walter Furlong Paper Co., and was distributed as an in-stadium promotion to fans attending the May 12, 1989, Orioles game. Smaller than standard size, the cards measure 2-1/4" by 3" and feature a full-color player photo with number, name and position below. The backs, done in black and white, include brief player data and complete major and minor league stats.

		MT	NR MT	EX
Complete Set:		8.00	6.00	3.25
Common Player:		.15	.11	.06
3	Bill Ripken	.15	.11	.06
6	Joe Orsulak	.15	.11	.06
7	Cal Ripken, Sr.	.15	.11	.06
8	Cal Ripken, Jr.	2.50	2.00	1.00
9	Brady Anderson	.90	.70	.35
10	Steve Finley	.80	.60	.30
11	Craig Worthington	.15	.11	.06
12	Mike Devereaux	.25	.20	.10
14	Mickey Tettleton	.50	.40	.20
15	Randy Milligan	.25	.20	.10
16	Phil Bradley	.15	.11	.06
18	Bob Milacki	.20	.15	.08
19	Larry Sheets	.15	.11	.06
20	Frank Robinson	.80	.60	.30
21	Mark Thurmond	.15	.11	.06
23	Kevin Hickey	.15	.11	.06
24	Dave Schmidt	.15	.11	.06
28	Jim Traber	.15	.11	.06
29	Jeff Ballard	.15	.11	.06
30	Gregg Olson	1.00	.70	.40
31	Al Jackson	.15	.11	.06
32	Mark Williamson	.15	.11	.06
36	Bob Melvin	.15	.11	.06
37	Brian Holton	.15	.11	.06
40	Tom McCraw	.15	.11	.06
42	Pete Harnisch	.35	.25	.14
43	Fransisco Melendez	.15	.11	.06
44	Elrod Hendricks	.15	.11	.06
46	Johnny Oates	.15	.11	.06
48	Jose Bautista	.15	.11	.06
88	Rene Gonzales	.15	.11	.06

1992 French's Mustard

In 1992 French's Mustard gave away a promotional card with the purchase of its mustard products, with each of 18 cards displaying photographs of two players. The cards, which have team insignias airbrushed out, feature a green border color photos and the player's statistics on the back.

		MT	NR MT	EX
Complete Set:		8.00	6.00	3.25
Common Card:		.25	.20	.10
1	Jeff Bagwell, Chuck Knoblauch	.50	.40	.20
2	Roger Clemens, Tom Glavine	.60	.45	.25
3	Julio Franco, Terry Pendleton	.35	.25	.14
4	Howard Johnson, Jose Canseco	.75	.60	.30
5	John Smiley, Scott Erickson	.35	.25	.14
6	Bryan Harvey, Lee Smith	.35	.25	.14
7	Kirby Puckett, Barry Bonds	1.00	.70	.40
8	Robin Ventura, Matt Williams	.75	.60	.30
9	Tony Pena, Tom Pagnozzi	.25	.20	.10
10	Benito Santiago, Sandy Alomar, Jr.	.25	.20	.10
11	Don Mattingly, Will Clark	1.50	1.25	.60
12	Ryne Sandberg, Roberto Alomar	1.50	1.25	.60
13	Cal Ripken, Jr., Ozzie Smith	1.50	1.25	.60
14	Ken Griffey, Jr., Dave Justice	2.00	1.50	.80
15	Joe Carter, Tony Gwynn	.50	.40	.20
16	Rickey Henderson, Darryl Strawberry	.60	.45	.25
17	Wade Boggs, Chris Sabo	.50	.40	.20
18	Jack Morris, Steve Avery	.40	.30	.15

1928 Fro-joy

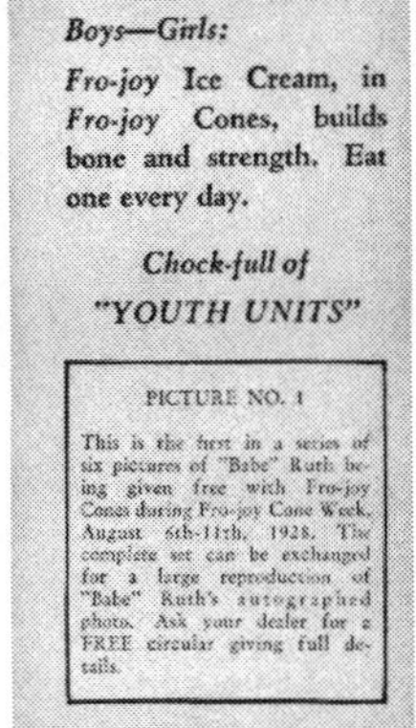

Capitalizing on the extreme popularity of Babe Ruth, this six-card set was given away with Fro-joy Cones during the August 6-11, 1928 Fro-joy Cone Week. The cards, which measure 2-1/16" by 4" in size, contain black and white photos designed on either a horizontal or vertical format. The card fronts also contain a caption with a few sentences explaining the photo. The card backs contain advertising for Fro-joy Ice Cream and Cones. Uncut sheets along with a large-format action photo of Ruth were available in a mail-in redemption offer. Virtually all uncut sheets offered in the market today, and all color Fro-joy cards are recent counterfeits.

		NR MT	EX	VG
Complete Set:		750.00	375.00	225.00
Common Card:		100.00	50.00	30.00
Uncut sheet with premium photo		2500.	1250.	750.00
1	George Herman ("Babe") Ruth	125.00	62.00	37.00
2	Look Out, Mr. Pitcher!	125.00	62.00	37.00
3	"Babe" Ruth's Grip!	100.00	50.00	30.00
4	Ruth is a Crack Fielder	125.00	62.00	37.00
5	Bang! The Babe Lines Out!	125.00	62.00	37.00
6	When The "Babe" Comes Home	125.00	62.00	37.00

1985 Fun Food Buttons

Fun Foods of Little Silver, N.J. issued a set of 133 full-color metal pins in 1985. The buttons, which are 1-1/4" in diameter and have a "safety pin" back, have bright borders which correspond to the player's team colors. The button backs are numbered and contain the player's 1984 batting or earned run average. The buttons were available as complete sets through hobby dealers and were also distributed in packs (three buttons per pack) through retail stores.

		MT	NR MT	EX
Complete Set:		25.00	18.50	10.00
Common Player:		.10	.08	.04
1	Dave Winfield	.40	.30	.15
2	Lance Parrish	.25	.20	.10
3	Gary Carter	.35	.25	.14
4	Pete Rose	.80	.60	.30
5	Jim Rice	.20	.15	.08
6	George Brett	.75	.60	.30
7	Fernando Valenzuela	.15	.11	.06
8	Darryl Strawberry	.25	.20	.10
9	Steve Garvey	.35	.25	.14
10	Rollie Fingers	.20	.15	.08
11	Mike Schmidt	1.25	.90	.50
12	Kent Tekulve	.10	.08	.04
13	Ryne Sandberg	.75	.60	.30
14	Bruce Sutter	.15	.11	.06
15	Tom Seaver	.30	.25	.12
16	Reggie Jackson	.70	.50	.30
17	Rickey Henderson	.50	.40	.20
18	Mark Langston	.35	.25	.14
19	Jack Clark	.20	.15	.08
20	Willie Randolph	.15	.11	.06
21	Kirk Gibson	.30	.25	.12
22	Andre Dawson	.30	.25	.12
23	Dave Concepcion	.15	.11	.06
24	Tony Armas	.10	.08	.04
25	Dan Quisenberry	.10	.08	.04
26	Pedro Guerrero	.25	.20	.10
27	Dwight Gooden	.30	.25	.12
28	Tony Gwynn	.40	.30	.15
29	Robin Yount	.70	.50	.30
30	Steve Carlton	1.00	.70	.40
31	Bill Madlock	.15	.11	.06
32	Rick Sutcliffe	.15	.11	.06
33	Willie McGee	.20	.15	.08
34	Greg Luzinski	.15	.11	.06
35	Rod Carew	.40	.30	.15
36	Dave Kingman	.15	.11	.06
37	Alvin Davis	.15	.11	.06
38	Chili Davis	.25	.20	.10
39	Don Baylor	.15	.11	.06
40	Alan Trammell	.35	.25	.14
41	Tim Raines	.35	.25	.14
42	Cesar Cedeno	.15	.11	.06
43	Wade Boggs	.60	.45	.25
44	Frank White	.15	.11	.06
45	Steve Sax	.25	.20	.10
46	George Foster	.15	.11	.06
47	Terry Kennedy	.10	.08	.04
48	Cecil Cooper	.15	.11	.06
49	John Denny	.10	.08	.04
50	John Candelaria	.10	.08	.04
51	Jody Davis	.10	.08	.04
52	George Hendrick	.10	.08	.04
53	Ron Kittle	.15	.11	.06
54	Fred Lynn	.20	.15	.08
55	Carney Lansford	.10	.08	.04
56	Gorman Thomas	.10	.08	.04
57	Manny Trillo	.10	.08	.04
58	Steve Kemp	.10	.08	.04
59	Jack Morris	.20	.15	.08
60	Dan Petry	.10	.08	.04
61	Mario Soto	.10	.08	.04
62	Dwight Evans	.20	.15	.08
63	Hal McRae	.10	.08	.04
64	Mike Marshall	.15	.11	.06
65	Mookie Wilson	.15	.11	.06
66	Graig Nettles	.15	.11	.06
67	Ben Oglivie	.10	.08	.04
68	Juan Samuel	.20	.15	.08
69	Johnny Ray	.15	.11	.06
70	Gary Matthews	.15	.11	.06
71	Ozzie Smith	.20	.15	.08
72	Carlton Fisk	.40	.30	.15
73	Doug DeCinces	.10	.08	.04
74	Joe Morgan	.60	.45	.25
75	Dave Stieb	.15	.11	.06
76	Buddy Bell	.15	.11	.06
77	Don Mattingly	.90	.70	.35
78	Lou Whitaker	.25	.20	.10
79	Willie Hernandez	.10	.08	.04
80	Dave Parker	.20	.15	.08
81	Bob Stanley	.10	.08	.04
82	Willie Wilson	.15	.11	.06
83	Orel Hershiser	.30	.25	.12
84	Rusty Staub	.15	.11	.06
85	Goose Gossage	.20	.15	.08
86	Don Sutton	.25	.20	.10
87	Al Holland	.10	.08	.04
88	Tony Pena	.15	.11	.06
89	Ron Cey	.15	.11	.06
90	Joaquin Andujar	.10	.08	.04
91	LaMarr Hoyt	.10	.08	.04
92	Tommy John	.20	.15	.08
93	Dwayne Murphy	.10	.08	.04
94	Willie Upshaw	.10	.08	.04
95	Gary Ward	.10	.08	.04
96	Ron Guidry	.20	.15	.08
97	Chet Lemon	.10	.08	.04
98	Aurelio Lopez	.10	.08	.04
99	Tony Perez	.20	.15	.08
100	Bill Buckner	.15	.11	.06
101	Mike Hargrove	.10	.08	.04
102	Scott McGregor	.10	.08	.04
103	Dale Murphy	.60	.45	.25
104	Keith Hernandez	.20	.15	.08
105	Paul Molitor	.45	.35	.20
106	Bert Blyleven	.15	.11	.06
107	Leon Durham	.10	.08	.04
108	Lee Smith	.15	.11	.06
109	Nolan Ryan	2.00	1.50	.80
110	Harold Baines	.15	.11	.06
111	Kent Hrbek	.25	.20	.10
112	Ron Davis	.10	.08	.04
113	George Bell	.30	.25	.12
114	Charlie Hough	.10	.08	.04
115	Phil Niekro	.25	.20	.10
116	Dave Righetti	.20	.15	.08
117	Darrell Evans	.15	.11	.06
118	Cal Ripken, Jr.	.75	.60	.30
119	Eddie Murray	.45	.35	.20
120	Storm Davis	.10	.08	.04
121	Mike Boddicker	.10	.08	.04
122	Bob Horner	.15	.11	.06
123	Chris Chambliss	.10	.08	.04
124	Ted Simmons	.15	.11	.06
125	Andre Thornton	.15	.11	.06
126	Larry Bowa	.15	.11	.06
127	Bob Dernier	.10	.08	.04
128	Joe Niekro	.15	.11	.06
129	Jose Cruz	.15	.11	.06
130	Tom Brunansky	.10	.08	.04
131	Gary Gaetti	.25	.20	.10
132	Lloyd Moseby	.15	.11	.06
133	Frank Tanana	.10	.08	.04

1888 G & B Chewing Gum (E223)

This set, issued with G&B Chewing Gum, is the first baseball card issued with candy or gum and the only 19th Century candy issue. The cards in the G&B set are small, measuring just 1" by 2-1/8". The cards are very similar in design to the August Beck Yum Yum issue (N403) and many of the photos appear have been to borrowed from that set. The player's name and position appear in thin capital letters below the photo, followed by either "National League" or "American League" (actually referring to the American Association). At the very bottom of the card, the manufacturer, "G&B N.Y." is indicated. (Some of the "National League" cards also include the words "Chewing Gum" after the league designation.) The set has been assigned the ACC number E223.

		NR MT	EX	VG
Complete Set:		80000.	40000.	25000.
Common Player:		750.00	250.00	150.00
(1)	Cap Anson	7500.	3750.	2250.
(2)	Fido Baldwin (bat at side)	750.00	375.00	225.00
(3)	Fido Baldwin (portrait)	1500.	750.00	450.00
(4)	Lady Baldwin (Detroit)	750.00	375.00	225.00
(5)	Stephen Brady	1500.	750.00	450.00
(6)	Bill Brown (portrait)	1500.	750.00	450.00
(7)	Bill Brown (standing)	750.00	375.00	225.00
(8)	Charles Buffington (Buffinton)	750.00	375.00	225.00
(9)	Thomas Burns	1500.	750.00	450.00
(10)	John Clarkson	3000.	1500.	900.00
(11)	John Coleman	1500.	750.00	450.00
(12)	Commy Comiskey	3000.	1500.	900.00
(13)	Roger Connor (batting)	1500.	750.00	450.00
(14)	Roger Connor (portrait)	3000.	1500.	900.00
(15)	Con Daily	1500.	750.00	450.00
(16)	Tom Deasley	1500.	750.00	450.00
(17)	Dude Esterbrook	1500.	750.00	450.00
(18)	Buck Ewing (batting)	1500.	750.00	450.00
(19)	Buck Ewing (portrait)	3000.	1500.	900.00
(20)	Charlie Ferguson	750.00	375.00	225.00
(21)	Silver Flint	1500.	750.00	450.00
(22)	Charlie Getzein	750.00	375.00	225.00
(23)	Will Gleason	750.00	375.00	225.00
(24)	Frank Hankinson	1500.	750.00	450.00
(25)	Pete Hotaling	750.00	375.00	225.00
(26)	Spud Johnson	750.00	375.00	225.00
(27)	Tim Keefe (batting)	1500.	750.00	450.00
(28)	Tim Keefe (throwing)	1500.	750.00	450.00
(29)	Tim Keefe (portrait)	3000.	1500.	900.00
(30)	King Kelly (batting)	1500.	750.00	450.00
(31)	King Kelly (standing by urn)	3500.	1750.	1050.
(32)	Gus Krock	1500.	750.00	450.00
(33)	Connie Mack	3500.	1750.	1050.
(34)	Doggie Miller	750.00	375.00	225.00
(35)	Honest John Morrill	750.00	375.00	225.00
(36)	James Mutrie	1500.	750.00	450.00
(37)	Little Nick Nicoll (Nicol)	1500.	750.00	450.00
(38)	Tip O'Neill	1500.	750.00	450.00
(39)	Orator Jim O'Rourke	3000.	1500.	900.00
(40)	Fred Pfeffer	750.00	375.00	225.00
(41)	Henry Porter	750.00	375.00	225.00
(42)	Danny Richardson (batting)	750.00	375.00	225.00
(43)	Danny Richardson (portrait)	1500.	750.00	450.00
(44)	Chief Roseman	1500.	750.00	450.00
(45)	Jimmy Ryan (portrait)	1500.	750.00	450.00
(46)	Jimmy Ryan (throwing)	750.00	375.00	225.00
(47)	Little Bill Sowders (throwing)	750.00	375.00	225.00
(48)	Marty Sullivan	1500.	750.00	450.00
(49)	Billy Sunday (fielding)	1500.	750.00	450.00
(50)	Billy Sunday (portrait)	3000.	1500.	900.00
(51)	Ezra Sutton	750.00	375.00	225.00
(52)	Silent Mike Tiernan (batting)	750.00	375.00	225.00
(53)	Silent Mike Tiernan (portrait)	1500.	750.00	450.00
(54)	Big Sam Thompson	1500.	750.00	450.00
(55)	Larry Twitchell	1500.	750.00	450.00
(56)	Rip Van Haltren	1500.	750.00	450.00
(57)	Monte Ward	3000.	1500.	900.00
(58)	Smiling Mickey Welch (pitching)	1500.	750.00	450.00
(59)	Smiling Mickey Welch (portrait)	3000.	1500.	900.00
(60)	Curt Welsh (Welch)	1500.	750.00	450.00
(61)	Grasshopper Whitney	1500.	750.00	450.00
(62)	Pete Wood	750.00	375.00	225.00

1983 Gardner's Brewers

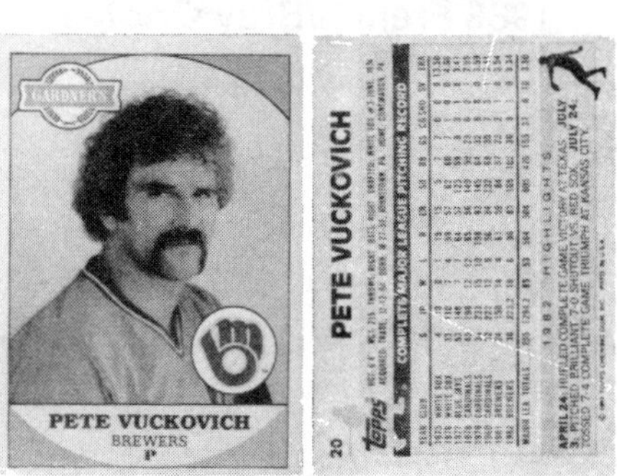

Topps produced in 1983 for Gardner's Bakery of Madison, Wisconsin, a 22-card set featuring the American League champion Milwaukee Brewers. The cards, which measure 2-1/2" by 3-1/2", have colorful fronts which contain the player's name, team and position plus the Brewers and Gardner's logos. The card backs are identical to the regular Topps issue but are numbered 1-22. The cards were inserted in specially marked packages of Gardner's bread products and were susceptible to grease stains.

		MT	NR MT	EX
Complete Set:		15.00	11.00	6.00
Common Player:		.50	.40	.20
1	Harvey Kuenn	.70	.50	.30
2	Dwight Bernard	.50	.40	.20
3	Mark Brouhard	.50	.40	.20
4	Mike Caldwell	.50	.40	.20
5	Cecil Cooper	1.25	.90	.50
6	Marshall Edwards	.50	.40	.20
7	Rollie Fingers	2.00	1.50	.80
8	Jim Gantner	.50	.40	.20
9	Moose Haas	.50	.40	.20
10	Bob McClure	.50	.40	.20
11	Paul Molitor	4.00	3.00	1.50
12	Don Money	.50	.40	.20
13	Charlie Moore	.50	.40	.20
14	Ben Oglivie	.50	.40	.20
15	Ed Romero	.50	.40	.20
16	Ted Simmons	.50	.40	.20
17	Jim Slaton	.50	.40	.20
18	Don Sutton	1.00	.70	.40
19	Gorman Thomas	.50	.40	.20
20	Pete Vuckovich	.50	.40	.20
21	Ned Yost	.50	.40	.20
22	Robin Yount	7.00	5.25	2.75

The values quoted are intended to reflect the market price.

1984 Gardner's Brewers

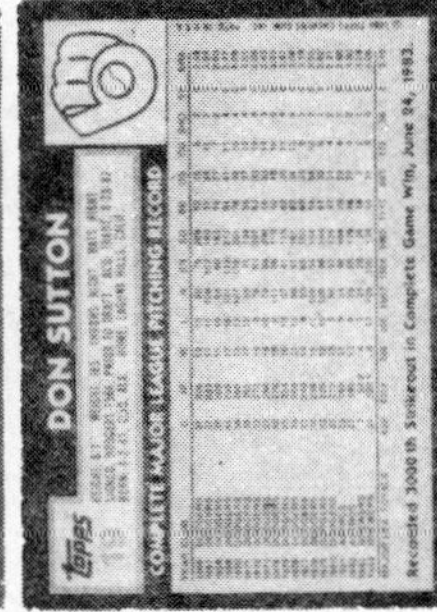

For the second straight year, Gardner's Bakery inserted baseball cards featuring the Milwaukee Brewers with their bread products. The 22-card set, entitled "1984 Series II," have multi-colored fronts that include the Brewers and Gardner's logos. The card backs are identical to the regular 1984 Topps issue except for the 1-22 numbering system. The Topps-produced cards are the standard 2-1/2" by 3-1/2" size. The cards are sometimes found with grease stains, resulting from contact with the bread.

		MT	NR MT	EX
Complete Set:		15.00	11.00	6.00
Common Player:		.50	.40	.20
1	Rene Lachemann	.50	.40	.20
2	Mark Brouhard	.50	.40	.20
3	Mike Caldwell	.50	.40	.20
4	Bobby Clark	.50	.40	.20
5	Cecil Cooper	1.00	.70	.40
6	Rollie Fingers	2.00	1.50	.80
7	Jim Gantner	.50	.40	.20
8	Moose Haas	.50	.40	.20
9	Roy Howell	.50	.40	.20
10	Pete Ladd	.50	.40	.20
11	Rick Manning	.50	.40	.20
12	Bob McClure	.50	.40	.20
13	Paul Molitor	3.00	2.25	1.25
14	Charlie Moore	.50	.40	.20
15	Ben Oglivie	.50	.40	.20
16	Ed Romero	.50	.40	.20
17	Ted Simmons	.50	.40	.20
18	Jim Sundberg	.50	.40	.20
19	Don Sutton	1.00	.70	.40
20	Tom Tellmann	.50	.40	.20
21	Pete Vuckovich	.50	.40	.20
22	Robin Yount	5.00	3.75	2.00

1985 Gardner's Brewers

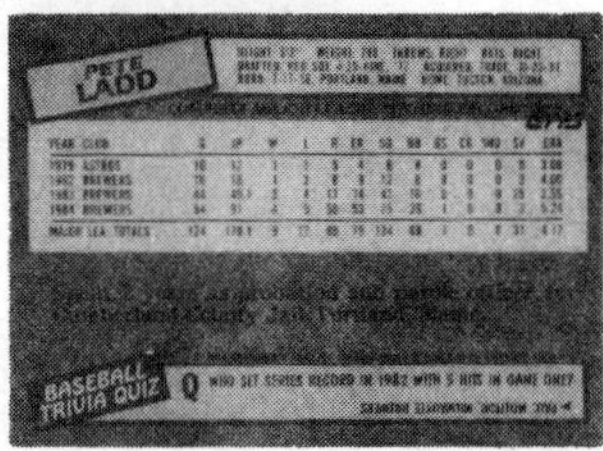

Gardner's Bakery issued a 22-card set featuring the Milwaukee Brewers for the third consecutive year in 1985. The set was produced by Topps and is designed in a horizontal format. The card fronts feature color photos inside blue, red and yellow frames. The player's name and position are placed in orange boxes to the right of the photo and are accompanied by the Brewers and Gardner's logos. The card backs are identical in design to the regular 1985 Topps set but are blue rather than green and are numbered 1-22. The cards, which were inserted in specially marked bread products, are often found with grease stains.

		MT	NR MT	EX
Complete Set:		12.00	9.00	4.75
Common Player:		.35	.25	.14
1	George Bamberger	.35	.25	.14
2	Mark Brouhard	.35	.25	.14
3	Bob Clark	.35	.25	.14
4	Jaime Cocanower	.35	.25	.14
5	Cecil Cooper	.90	.70	.35
6	Rollie Fingers	1.25	.90	.50
7	Jim Gantner	.35	.25	.14
8	Moose Haas	.35	.25	.14
9	Dion James	.35	.25	.14
10	Pete Ladd	.35	.25	.14
11	Rick Manning	.35	.25	.14
12	Bob McClure	.35	.25	.14
13	Paul Molitor	2.50	2.00	1.00
14	Charlie Moore	.35	.25	.14
15	Ben Oglivie	.35	.25	.14
16	Chuck Porter	.35	.25	.14
17	Ed Romero	.35	.25	.14
18	Bill Schroeder	.35	.25	.14
19	Ted Simmons	.35	.25	.14
20	Tom Tellmann	.35	.25	.14
21	Pete Vuckovich	.35	.25	.14
22	Robin Yount	4.00	3.00	1.50

1989 Gardner's Brewers

Returning after a three-year hiatus, Gardner's Bread of Madison, Wis., issued a 15-card Milwaukee Brewers set in 1989. The blue and white-bordered cards are the standard size and feature posed portrait photos with all Brewer logos airbrushed from the players' caps. The Gardner's logo appears at the top of the card, while the player's name is below the photo. The set, which was produced in conjunction with Mike Schechter Associates, was issued with loaves of bread or packages of buns, one card per package.

		MT	NR MT	EX
Complete Set:		4.00	3.00	1.50
Common Player:		.10	.08	.04
1	Paul Molitor	1.00	.70	.40
2	Robin Yount	2.00	1.50	.80
3	Jim Gantner	.10	.08	.04
4	Rob Deer	.10	.08	.04
5	B.J. Surhoff	.25	.20	.10
6	Dale Sveum	.10	.08	.04
7	Ted Higuera	.25	.20	.10
8	Dan Plesac	.25	.20	.10
9	Bill Wegman	.15	.11	.06
10	Juan Nieves	.15	.11	.06
11	Greg Brock	.10	.08	.04
12	Glenn Braggs	.10	.08	.04
13	Joey Meyer	.10	.08	.04
14	Ernest Riles	.10	.08	.04
15	Don August	.10	.08	.04

1986 Gatorade Cubs

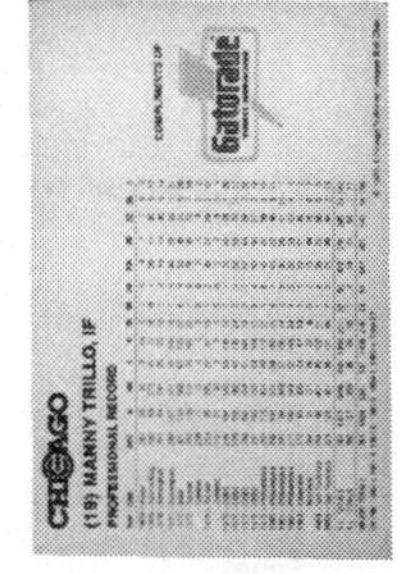

Gatorade sponsored this 28-card set which was given away at the July 17, 1986 Cubs game. The cards measure 2-7/8" by 4-1/4" and feature color photos set inside red and white frames. The Cubs logo appears at the top of the card in blue and red. The card backs include statistical information and the Gatorade logo. This set marked the fifth consecutive year the Cubs had held a baseball card giveaway promotion.

		MT	NR MT	EX
Complete Set:		8.00	6.00	3.25
Common Player:		.10	.08	.04
4	Gene Michael	.10	.08	.04
6	Keith Moreland	.30	.25	.12
7	Jody Davis	.30	.25	.12
10	Leon Durham	.30	.25	.12
11	Ron Cey	.30	.25	.12
12	Shawon Dunston	1.25	.90	.50
15	Davey Lopes	.25	.20	.10
16	Terry Francona	.10	.08	.04
18	Steve Christmas	.10	.08	.04
19	Manny Trillo	.15	.11	.06
20	Bob Dernier	.10	.08	.04
21	Scott Sanderson	.15	.11	.06
22	Jerry Mumphrey	.10	.08	.04
23	Ryne Sandberg	3.00	2.25	1.25
27	Thad Bosley	.10	.08	.04
28	Chris Speier	.10	.08	.04
29	Steve Lake	.10	.08	.04
31	Ray Fontenot	.10	.08	.04
34	Steve Trout	.20	.15	.08
36	Gary Matthews	.30	.25	.12
39	George Frazier	.10	.08	.04
40	Rick Sutcliffe	.50	.40	.20
43	Dennis Eckersley	.90	.70	.35
46	Lee Smith	.60	.45	.25
48	Jay Baller	.15	.11	.06
49	Jamie Moyer	.25	.20	.10
50	Guy Hoffman	.10	.08	.04
----	The Coaching Staff (Ruben Amaro, Billy Connors, Johnny Oates, John Vuckovich, Billy Williams)	.15	.11	.06

The values quoted are intended to reflect the market price.

1987 Gatorade Indians

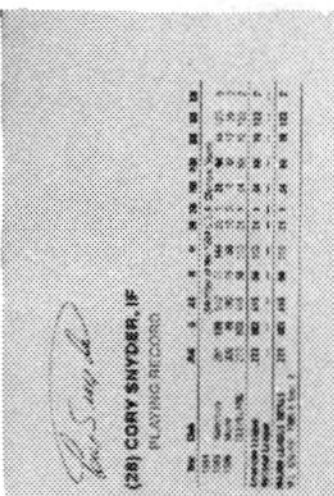

For the second year in a row, the Cleveland Indians gave out a perforated set of baseball cards to fans attending the Team Photo/Baseball Card Day promotion. Sponsored by Gatorade, the individual cards measure 2-1/2" by 3-1/8". The fronts contain a full-color photo surrounded by a red frame inside a white border. The player's name, uniform number and the Gatorade logo are also on the fronts. The card backs are printed in black, blue and red and carry a facsimile autograph and the player's playing record.

		MT	NR MT	EX
Complete Set:		7.00	5.25	2.75
Common Player:		.10	.08	.04
2	Brett Butler	.20	.15	.08
4	Tony Bernazard	.10	.08	.04
6	Andy Allanson	.10	.08	.04
7	Pat Corrales	.10	.08	.04
8	Carmen Castillo	.10	.08	.04
10	Pat Tabler	.10	.08	.04
11	Jamie Easterly	.10	.08	.04
12	Dave Clark	.10	.08	.04
13	Ernie Camacho	.10	.08	.04
14	Julio Franco	.40	.30	.15
17	Junior Noboa	.10	.08	.04
18	Ken Schrom	.10	.08	.04
20	Otis Nixon	.25	.20	.10
21	Greg Swindell	.40	.30	.15
22	Frank Wills	.10	.08	.04
23	Chris Bando	.10	.08	.04
24	Rick Dempsey	.15	.11	.06
26	Brook Jacoby	.30	.25	.12
27	Mel Hall	.15	.11	.06
28	Cory Snyder	.30	.25	.12
29	Andre Thornton	.30	.25	.12
30	Joe Carter	.80	.60	.30
35	Phil Niekro	.40	.30	.15
36	Ed Vande Berg	.10	.08	.04
42	Rich Yett	.10	.08	.04
43	Scott Bailes	.10	.08	.04
46	Doug Jones	.25	.20	.10
49	Tom Candiotti	.20	.15	.08
54	Tom Waddell	.10	.08	.04
----	Manager and Coaching Staff (Jack Aker, Bobby Bonds, Pat Corrales, Doc Edwards, Johnny Goryl)	.10	.08	.04

A card number in parentheses () indicates the set is unnumbered.

1988 Gatorade Indians

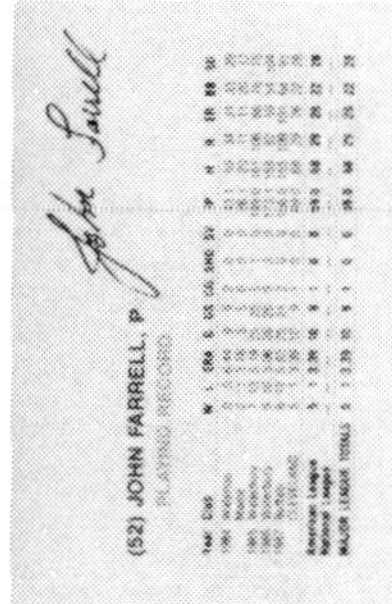

This 3-panel foldout was sponsored by Gatorade for distribution during an in-stadium giveaway. The white cover includes four game day photos. One panel of the 9-1/2" by 11-1/4" glossy full-color brochure features a team photo (with checklist), two panels consist of 30 perforated baseball cards (2-1/4" by 3") featuring team members. Posed close-up photos are framed in red on a white background. The player's name and uniform number are printed below the photo. The card backs are printed in red, blue and black on white. A facsimile autograph appears at the top right portion of the card back, opposite the player uniform number, name and position. Both major and minor league stats are listed.

		MT	NR MT	EX
Complete Set:		5.00	3.75	2.00
Common Player:		.10	.08	.04
2	Tom Spencer	.10	.08	.04
6	Andy Allanson	.10	.08	.04
7	Luis Issac	.10	.08	.04
8	Carmen Castillo	.10	.08	.04
9	Charlie Manuel	.10	.08	.04
10	Pat Tabler	.10	.08	.04
11	Doug Jones	.30	.25	.12
14	Julio Franco	.40	.30	.15
15	Ron Washington	.10	.08	.04
16	Jay Bell	.60	.45	.25
17	Bill Laskey	.10	.08	.04
20	Willie Upshaw	.20	.15	.08
21	Greg Swindell	.80	.60	.30
23	Chris Bando	.10	.08	.04
25	Dave Clark	.10	.08	.04
26	Brook Jacoby	.15	.11	.06
27	Mel Hall	.10	.08	.04
28	Cory Snyder	.20	.15	.08
30	Joe Carter	.80	.60	.30
31	Dan Schatzeder	.10	.08	.04
32	Doc Edwards	.10	.08	.04
33	Ron Kittle	.10	.08	.04
35	Mark Wiley	.10	.08	.04
42	Rich Yett	.10	.08	.04
43	Scott Bailes	.10	.08	.04
45	Johnny Goryl	.10	.08	.04
47	Jeff Kaiser	.10	.08	.04
49	Tom Candiotti	.10	.08	.04
50	Jeff Dedmon	.10	.08	.04
52	John Farrell	.10	.08	.04

1914 General Baking Co. (D303)

COMPLIMENTS OF
GENERAL
BAKING CO.
UNTIL SEPTEMBER 1ST.
WRAPPED IN
STAR BREAD
FRENCH BREAD
LITTLE GENERAL
BREAD

Issued in 1914 by the General Baking Company, these unnumbered cards measure 1-1/2" by 2-3/4". The player photos and fronts of the cards are identical to the E106 set, but the D303 cards are easily identified by the advertisement for General Baking on the back.

		NR MT	EX	VG
Complete Set (51):		10000.	5000.	3000.
Common Player:		100.00	50.00	30.00
(1)	Jack Barry	100.00	50.00	30.00
(2)	Chief Bender (blue background)	250.00	125.00	75.00
(3)	Chief Bender (green background)	250.00	125.00	75.00
(4)	Bob Bescher (New York)	100.00	50.00	30.00
(5)	Bob Bescher (St. Louis)	100.00	50.00	30.00
(6)	Roger Bresnahan	250.00	125.00	75.00
(7)	Al Bridwell	100.00	50.00	30.00
(8)	Donie Bush	100.00	50.00	30.00
(9)	Hal Chase (catching)	125.00	62.00	37.00
(10)	Hal Chase (portrait)	125.00	62.00	37.00
(11)	Ty Cobb (batting, front view)	1250.	625.00	375.00
(12)	Ty Cobb (batting, side view)	1250.	625.00	375.00
(13)	Eddie Collins	250.00	125.00	75.00
(14)	Sam Crawford	250.00	125.00	75.00
(15)	Ray Demmitt	100.00	50.00	30.00
(16)	Wild Bill Donovan	100.00	50.00	30.00
(17)	Red Dooin	100.00	50.00	30.00
(18)	Mickey Doolan	100.00	50.00	30.00
(19)	Larry Doyle	100.00	50.00	30.00
(20)	Clyde Engle	100.00	50.00	30.00
(21)	Johnny Evers	250.00	125.00	75.00
(22)	Art Fromme	100.00	50.00	30.00
(23)	George Gibson (catching, back view)	100.00	50.00	30.00
(24)	George Gibson (catching, front view)	100.00	50.00	30.00
(25)	Roy Hartzell	100.00	50.00	30.00
(26)	Fred Jacklitsch	100.00	50.00	30.00
(27)	Hugh Jennings	250.00	125.00	75.00
(28)	Otto Knabe	100.00	50.00	30.00
(29)	Nap Lajoie	375.00	187.00	112.00
(30)	Hans Lobert	100.00	50.00	30.00
(31)	Rube Marquard	250.00	125.00	75.00
(32)	Christy Mathewson	750.00	375.00	225.00
(33)	John McGraw	250.00	125.00	75.00
(34)	George McQuillan	100.00	50.00	30.00
(35)	Dots Miller	100.00	50.00	30.00
(36)	Danny Murphy	100.00	50.00	30.00
(37)	Rebel Oakes	100.00	50.00	30.00
(38)	Eddie Plank (no position on front)	250.00	125.00	75.00
(39)	Eddie Plank (position on front)	250.00	125.00	75.00
(40)	Germany Schaefer	100.00	50.00	30.00
(41)	Boss Smith (Schmidt)	100.00	50.00	30.00
(42)	Tris Speaker	300.00	150.00	90.00
(43)	Oscar Stanage	100.00	50.00	30.00
(44)	George Stovall	100.00	50.00	30.00
(45)	Jeff Sweeney	100.00	50.00	30.00
(46)	Joe Tinker (batting)	250.00	125.00	75.00
(47)	Joe Tinker (portrait)	250.00	125.00	75.00
(48)	Honus Wagner (batting)	750.00	375.00	225.00
(49)	Honus Wagner (throwing)	750.00	375.00	225.00
(50)	Hooks Wiltse	100.00	50.00	30.00
(51)	Heinie Zimmerman	100.00	50.00	30.00

1985 General Mills Stickers

General Mills of Canada inserted a panel of two baseball stickers, in a cellophane wrapper, in each box of Cheerios in 1985. The full-color sticker panels, which measure 2-3/8" by 3-3/4" in size, feature 30 popular players. The stickers are blank-backed and unnumbered and contain the player's name, team and position in both English and French. The General Mills logo appears at the top of each sticker. Curiously, all team insignias on the players' uniforms and hats have been airbrushed off.

		MT	NR MT	EX
Complete Set:		15.00	11.00	6.00
Common Panel:		.60	.45	.25
	Panel	.80	.60	.30
(1)	Gary Carter			
(2)	Tom Brunansky			
	Panel	.80	.60	.30
(3)	Gary Carter			
(4)	Dave Stieb			
	Panel	.80	.60	.30
(5)	Andre Dawson			
(6)	Alvin Davis			
	Panel	.90	.70	.35
(7)	Steve Garvey			
(8)	George Bell			
	Panel	.80	.60	.30
(9)	Steve Garvey			
(10)	Jim Rice			
	Panel	.80	.60	.30
(11)	Jeff Leonard			
(12)	Eddie Murray			
	Panel	1.50	1.25	.60
(13)	Dale Murphy			
(14)	Robin Yount			
	Panel	.80	.60	.30
(15)	Terry Puhl			
(16)	Reggie Jackson			
	Panel	.60	.45	.25
(17)	Johnny Ray			
(18)	Lou Whitaker			
	Panel	.80	.60	.30
(19)	Ryne Sandberg			
(20)	Mike Hargrove			
	Panel	1.75	1.25	.70
(21)	Mike Schmidt			
(22)	George Brett			
	Panel	1.25	.90	.50
(23)	Ozzie Smith			
(24)	Dave Winfield			
	Panel	.70	.50	.30
(25)	Mario Soto			
(26)	Carlton Fisk			
	Panel	.70	.50	.30
(27)	Fernando Valenzuela			
(28)	Dwayne Murphy			

1986 General Mills Booklets

In 1986, General Mills of Canada inserted six different "Baseball Players Booklets" in specially marked boxes of Cheerios. Ten different players are featured in each booklet, with statistics for the 1985 season being in both English and French. The booklet, when opened fully, measures 3-3/4" by 15". Also included in the booklet is a contest sponsored by Petro-Canada service stations to win a day with a major league player at his 1987 spring training site in Florida. Team insignias have been airbrushed off the players' uniforms and caps.

		MT	NR MT	EX
Complete Set:		12.50	9.50	5.00
Common Booklet:		1.25	.90	.50
1	A.L. East (Wade Boggs, Kirk Gibson, Rickey Henderson, Don Mattingly, Jack Morris, Lance Parrish, Jim Rice, Dave Righetti, Cal Ripken, Lou Whitaker)	3.75	2.75	1.50
2	A.L. West (Harold Baines, Phil Bradley, George Brett, Carlton Fisk, Ozzie Guillen, Kent Hrbek, Reggie Jackson, Dan Quisenberry, Bret Saberhagen, Frank White)	2.00	1.50	.80
3	Toronto Blue Jays (Jesse Barfield, George Bell, Bill Caudill, Tony Fernandez, Damaso Garcia, Lloyd Moseby, Rance Mulliniks, Dave Stieb, Willie Upshaw, Ernie Whitt)	1.25	.90	.50
4	N.L. East (Gary Carter, Jack Clark, George Foster, Dwight Gooden, Gary Matthews, Willie McGee, Ryne Sandberg, Mike Schmidt, Lee Smith, Ozzie Smith)	3.25	2.50	1.25
5	N.L. West (Dave Concepcion, Pedro Guerrero, Terry Kennedy, Dale Murphy, Graig Nettles, Dave Parker, Tony Perez, Steve Sax, Bruce Sutter, Fernando Valenzuela)	1.50	1.25	.60
6	Montreal Expos (Hubie Brooks, Andre Dawson, Mike Fitzgerald, Vance Law, Tim Raines, Jeff Reardon, Bryn Smith, Jason Thompson, Tim Wallach, Mitch Webster)	1.25	.90	.50

Grading Guide

Mint (MT): A perfect card. Well-centered with all corners sharp and square. No creases, stains, edge nicks, surface marks, yellowing or fading.

Near Mint (NM): A nearly perfect card. At first glance, a NM card appears to be perfect. May be slightly off-center. No surface marks, creases or loss of gloss.

Excellent (EX): Corners are still fairly sharp with only moderate wear. Borders may be off-center. No creases or stains on fronts or backs, but may show slight loss of surface luster.

Very Good (VG): Shows obvious handling. May have rounded corners, minor creases, major gum or wax stains. No major creases, tape marks, writing, etc.

Good (G): A well-worn card, but exhibits no intentional damage. May have major or multiple creases. Corners may be rounded well beyond card border.

1987 General Mills Booklets

For a second straight year, General Mills of Canada inserted one of six different "Baseball SuperStars Booklets" in specially marked boxes of Cheerios and Honey Nut Cheerios cereal. Each booklet contains ten full-color photos for a total of 60 players. The booklets, when completely unfolded, measure 15" by 3-3/4". Written in both English and French, the set was produced by Mike Schecter and Associates. All team insignias have been airbrushed away.

	MT	NR MT	EX
Complete Set:	12.50	9.50	5.00
Common Booklet:	1.25	.90	.50

		MT	NR MT	EX
1	Toronto Blue Jays (Jesse Barfield, George Bell, Tony Fernandez, Kelly Gruber, Tom Henke, Jimmy Key, Lloyd Moseby, Dave Stieb, Willie Upshaw, Ernie Whitt)	1.25	.90	.50
2	A.L. East (Wade Boggs, Roger Clemens, Kirk Gibson, Rickey Henderson, Don Mattingly, Jack Morris, Eddie Murray, Pat Tabler, Dave Winfield, Robin Yount)	3.75	2.75	1.50
3	A.L. West (Phil Bradley, George Brett, Jose Canseco, Carlton Fisk, Reggie Jackson, Wally Joyner, Kirk McCaskill, Larry Parrish, Kirby Puckett, Dan Quisenberry)	3.50	2.75	1.50
4	Montreal Expos (Hubie Brooks, Mike Fitzgerald, Andres Galarraga, Vance Law, Andy McGaffigan, Bryn Smith, Jason Thompson, Tim Wallach, Mitch Webster, Floyd Youmans)	1.25	.90	.50
5	N.L. East (Gary Carter, Dwight Gooden, Keith Hernandez, Willie McGee, Tim Raines, R.J. Reynolds, Ryne Sandberg, Mike Schmidt, Ozzie Smith, Darryl Strawberry)	3.25	2.50	1.25
6	N.L. West (Kevin Bass, Chili Davis, Bill Doran, Pedro Guerrero, Tony Gwynn, Dale Murphy, Dave Parker, Steve Sax, Mike Scott, Fernando Valenzuela)	2.00	1.50	.80

1953 Glendale Hot Dogs Tigers

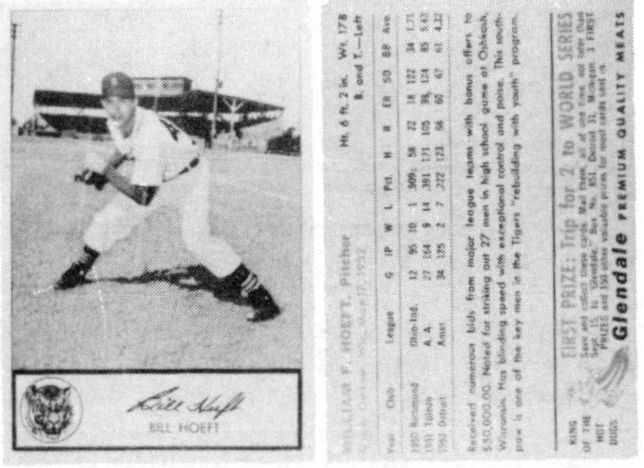

Glendale Meats issued these unnumbered, full-color cards (2-5/8" by 3-3/4") in packages of hot dogs. Featuring Detroit Tigers players, the card fronts contain a player picture plus the player's name, a facsimile autograph, and the Tigers logo. The card reverses carry player statistical and biographical information plus an offer for a trip for two to the World Series. Collectors were advised to mail all the cards they had saved to Glendale Meats. The World Series trip plus 150 other prizes were to be given to the individuals sending in the most cards. As with most cards issued with food products, quality-condition cards are tough to find because of the cards' susceptibilty to stains. The Houtteman card is extremely scarce.

		NR MT	EX	VG
Complete Set (28):		6400.	3200.	1900.
Common Player:		150.00	75.00	45.00
(1)	Matt Batts	150.00	75.00	45.00
(2)	Johnny Bucha	150.00	75.00	45.00
(3)	Frank Carswell	150.00	75.00	45.00
(4)	Jim Delsing	150.00	75.00	45.00
(5)	Walt Dropo	150.00	75.00	45.00
(6)	Hal Erickson	150.00	75.00	45.00
(7)	Paul Foytack	150.00	75.00	45.00
(8)	Owen Friend	175.00	87.00	52.00
(9)	Ned Garver	150.00	75.00	45.00
(10)	Joe Ginsberg	400.00	200.00	120.00
(11)	Ted Gray	150.00	75.00	45.00
(12)	Fred Hatfield	150.00	75.00	45.00
(13)	Ray Herbert	175.00	87.00	52.00
(14)	Bill Hitchcock	150.00	75.00	45.00
(15)	Bill Hoeft	325.00	162.00	97.00
(16)	Art Houtteman	2600.	1300.	780.00
(17)	Milt Jordan	225.00	112.00	67.00
(18)	Harvey Kuenn	375.00	187.00	112.00
(19)	Don Lund	150.00	75.00	45.00
(20)	Dave Madison	150.00	75.00	45.00
(21)	Dick Marlowe	150.00	75.00	45.00
(22)	Pat Mullin	150.00	75.00	45.00
(23)	Bob Neiman	150.00	75.00	45.00
(24)	Johnny Pesky	175.00	87.00	52.00
(25)	Jerry Priddy	150.00	75.00	45.00
(26)	Steve Souchock	150.00	75.00	45.00
(27)	Russ Sullivan	150.00	75.00	45.00
(28)	Bill Wight	225.00	112.00	67.00

1969 Globe Imports

Largely ignored by collectors for more than 20 years, this issue has little to offer any but the most avid superstar collector. Printed in black-and-white on very thin white cardboard, with blank backs, the cards measure 1-5/8" x 2-1/4". Rather muddy player action photos are at center of each card, with the player's name reversed out of a black strip at the bottom. Single cards are never seen, but since the complete set is very inexpensive it should not deter the superstar collector from acquisition.

		NR MT	EX	VG
Complete Set (52):		3.00	1.50	.90
Common Player:		.05	.03	.02
	HEARTS			
J	Al Kaline	.40	.20	.12
Q	Gene Alley	.05		
K	Rusty Staub	.10	.05	.03
A	Willie Mays	.50	.25	.15
2	Chris Short	.05	.03	.02
3	Tony Conigliaro	.10	.05	.03
4	Bill Freehan	.05	.03	.02
5	Willie McCovey	.25	.13	.08
6	Joel Horlen	.05	.03	.02
7	Ernie Banks	.40	.20	.12
8	Jim Wynn	.05	.03	.02
9	Brooks Robinson	.40	.20	.12
10	Orlando Cepeda	.25	.13	.08
	CLUBS			
J	Max Alvis	.05	.03	.02
Q	Ron Swoboda	.05	.03	.02
K	Johnny Callison	.05	.03	.02
A	Richie Allen	.10	.05	.03
2	Reggie Smith	.05	.03	.02
3	Jerry Koosman	.05	.03	.02
4	Tony Oliva	.10	.05	.03
5	Bud Harrelson	.05	.03	.02
6	Rick Reichardt	.05	.03	.02
7	Billy Williams	.25	.13	.08
8	Pete Rose	.40	.20	.12
9	Jim Maloney	.05	.03	.02
10	Tim McCarver	.10	.05	.03
	DIAMONDS			
J	Bob Aspromonte	.05	.03	.02
Q	Lou Brock	.25	.13	.08
K	Jim Lonborg	.05	.03	.02
A	Bob Gibson	.25	.13	.08
2	Paul Casanova	.05	.03	.02
3	Juan Marichal	.25	.13	.08
4	Jim Fregosi	.05	.03	.02
5	Earl Wilson	.05	.03	.02
6	Tony Horton	.05	.03	.02
7	Harmon Killebrew	.25	.13	.08
8	Tom Seaver	.25	.13	.08
9	Curt Flood	.10	.05	.03
10	Frank Robinson	.40	.20	.12
	SPADES			
J	Ron Santo	.10	.05	.03
Q	Al Ferrara	.05	.03	.02
K	Clete Boyer	.05	.03	.02
A	Ken Harrelson	.05	.03	.02
2	Denny McLain	.10	.05	.03
3	Rick Monday	.05	.03	.02
4	Richie Allen	.10	.05	.03
5	Mel Stottlemyre	.05	.03	.02
6	Tommy John	.10	.05	.03
7	Don Mincher	.05	.03	.02
8	Chico Cardenas	.05	.03	.02
9	Willie Davis	.05	.03	.02
10	Bert Campaneris	.05	.03	.02

1887 Gold Coin (Buchner) (N284)

Issued circa 1887, the N284 issue was produced by D. Buchner & Company for its Gold Coin brand of chewing tobacco. Actually, the series was not comprised only of baseball players - actors, jockeys, firemen and policemen were also included. The cards, which measure 1-3/4" by 3", are color drawings. The set is not a popular one among collectors as the drawings do not in all cases represent the players designated on the cards. In most instances, players at a given position share the same drawing depicted on the card front. Three different card backs are found, all advising collectors to save the valuable chewing tobacco wrappers. Wrappers could be redeemed for various prizes.

		NR MT	EX	VG
Complete Set (143):		20000.	10000.	6000.
Common Player:		115.00	57.00	34.00
(1)	Ed Andrews (hands at neck)	115.00	57.00	34.00
(2)	Andrews (hands waist high)	140.00	70.00	42.00
(3)	Cap Anson (hands outstretched)	625.00	312.00	187.00
(4)	Cap Anson (left hand on hip)	700.00	350.00	210.00
(5)	Tug Arundel	115.00	57.00	34.00
(6)	Sam Barkley (Pittsburgh)	115.00	57.00	34.00
(7)	Sam Barkley (St. Louis)	160.00	80.00	48.00
(8)	Charley Bassett	115.00	57.00	34.00
(9)	Charlie Bastian	115.00	57.00	34.00
(10)	Ed Beecher	115.00	57.00	34.00
(11)	Charlie Bennett	115.00	57.00	34.00
(12)	Handsome Henry Boyle	140.00	70.00	42.00
(13)	Dan Brouthers (hands outstretched)	275.00	137.00	82.00
(14)	Dan Brouthers (with bat)	325.00	162.00	97.00
(15)	Tom Brown	115.00	57.00	34.00
(16)	Jack Burdock	115.00	57.00	34.00
(17)	Oyster Burns (Baltimore)	140.00	70.00	42.00
(18)	Tom Burns (Chicago)	115.00	57.00	34.00
(19)	Doc Bushong	160.00	80.00	48.00
(20)	John Cahill	140.00	70.00	42.00
(21)	Cliff Carroll (Washington)	115.00	57.00	34.00
(22)	Fred Carroll (Pittsburgh)	115.00	57.00	34.00
(23)	Parisian Bob Carruthers (Caruthers)	190.00	95.00	57.00
(24)	Dan Casey	160.00	80.00	48.00
(25)	John Clarkson (ball at chest)	275.00	137.00	82.00
(26)	John Clarkson (arm outstretched)	325.00	162.00	97.00
(27)	Jack Clements	115.00	57.00	34.00
(28)	John Coleman	115.00	57.00	34.00
(29)	Charles Comiskey	625.00	312.00	187.00
(30)	Roger Connor (hands outstretched)	275.00	137.00	82.00
(31)	Roger Connor (hands outstretched, face level)	325.00	162.00	97.00
(32)	Corbett	140.00	70.00	42.00
(33)	Sam Craig (Crane)	140.00	70.00	42.00
(34)	Sam Crane	140.00	70.00	42.00
(35)	Crowley	140.00	70.00	42.00
(36)	Ed Cushmann (Cushman)	140.00	70.00	42.00
(37)	Ed Dailey (Daily)	115.00	57.00	34.00
(38)	Con Daley (Daily)	115.00	57.00	34.00
(39)	Pat Deasley	140.00	70.00	42.00
(40)	Jerry Denny (hands on knees)	115.00	57.00	34.00
(41)	Jerry Denny (hands on thighs)	140.00	70.00	42.00
(42)	Jim Donnelly	115.00	57.00	34.00
(43)	Jim Donohue (Donahue)	140.00	70.00	42.00
(44)	Mike Dorgan (right field)	115.00	57.00	34.00
(45)	Mike Dorgan (batter)	140.00	70.00	42.00
(46)	Sure Shot Dunlap	115.00	57.00	34.00
(47)	Dude Esterbrook	140.00	70.00	42.00
(48)	Buck Ewing (ready to tag)	275.00	137.00	82.00
(49)	Buck Ewing (hands at neck)	325.00	162.00	97.00
(50)	Sid Farrar	115.00	57.00	34.00
(51)	Jack Farrell (ready to tag)	115.00	57.00	34.00
(52)	Jack Farrell (hands at knees)	140.00	70.00	42.00

		NR MT	EX	VG
(53)	Charlie Ferguson	115.00	57.00	34.00
(54)	Silver Flint	115.00	57.00	34.00
(55)	Jim Fogerty (Fogarty)	115.00	57.00	34.00
(56)	Tom Forster	140.00	70.00	42.00
(57)	Dave Foutz	190.00	95.00	57.00
(58)	Chris Fulmer	140.00	70.00	42.00
(59)	Joe Gerhardt	140.00	70.00	42.00
(60)	Charlie Getzein	115.00	57.00	34.00
(61)	Pete Gillespie (left field)	115.00	57.00	34.00
(62)	Pete Gillespie (batter)	140.00	70.00	42.00
(63)	Barney Gilligan	115.00	57.00	34.00
(64)	Pebbly Jack Glasscock (fielding grounder)	140.00	70.00	42.00
(65)	Pebbly Jack Glasscock (hands on knees)	160.00	80.00	48.00
(66)	Will Gleason	160.00	80.00	48.00
(67)	Piano Legs Gore	115.00	57.00	34.00
(68)	Frank Hankinson	140.00	70.00	42.00
(69)	Ned Hanlon	115.00	57.00	34.00
(70)	Hart	140.00	70.00	42.00
(71)	Egyptian Healy	115.00	57.00	34.00
(72)	Paul Hines (centre field)	115.00	57.00	34.00
(73)	Paul Hines (batter)	140.00	70.00	42.00
(74)	Joe Hornung	115.00	57.00	34.00
(75)	Cutrate Irwin	115.00	57.00	34.00
(76)	Dick Johnston	115.00	57.00	34.00
(77)	Tim Keefe (right arm outstretched)	275.00	137.00	82.00
(78)	Tim Keefe (arm outstretched)	325.00	162.00	97.00
(79)	King Kelly (right field)	325.00	162.00	97.00
(80)	King Kelly (catcher)	350.00	175.00	105.00
(81)	Kennedy	140.00	70.00	42.00
(82)	Matt Kilroy	140.00	70.00	42.00
(83)	Arlie Latham	190.00	95.00	57.00
(84)	Jimmy Manning	115.00	57.00	34.00
(85)	Bill McClellan	140.00	70.00	42.00
(86)	Jim McCormick	140.00	70.00	42.00
(87)	Jack McGeachy	115.00	57.00	34.00
(88)	Jumbo McGinnis	160.00	80.00	48.00
(89)	George Meyers (Myers)	140.00	70.00	42.00
(90)	Doggie Miller	115.00	57.00	34.00
(91)	Honest John Morrill (hands outstretched)	115.00	57.00	34.00
(92)	Honest John Morrill (hands at neck)	140.00	70.00	42.00
(93)	Tom Morrissy (Morrissey)	140.00	70.00	42.00
(94)	Joe Mulvey (hands on knees)	115.00	57.00	34.00
(95)	Joe Mulvey (hands above head)	140.00	70.00	42.00
(96)	Al Myers	115.00	57.00	34.00
(97)	Candy Nelson	140.00	70.00	42.00
(98)	Little Nick Nichol	160.00	80.00	48.00
(99)	Billy O'Brien	115.00	57.00	34.00
(100)	Tip O'Neil (O'Neill)	190.00	95.00	57.00
(101)	Orator Jim O'Rourke (hands cupped)	275.00	137.00	82.00
(102)	Orator Jim O'Rourke (hands on thighs)	325.00	162.00	97.00
(103)	Dave Orr	140.00	70.00	42.00
(104)	Jimmy Peoples	115.00	57.00	34.00
(105)	Fred Pfeffer	115.00	57.00	34.00
(106)	Bill Phillips	115.00	57.00	34.00
(107)	Mark Polhemus	115.00	57.00	34.00
(108)	Henry Porter	115.00	57.00	34.00
(109)	Blondie Purcell	140.00	70.00	42.00
(110)	Old Hoss Radbourn (hands at chest)	275.00	137.00	82.00
(111)	Old Hoss Radbourn (hands above waist)	325.00	162.00	97.00
(112)	Danny Richardson (New York, hands at knees)	115.00	57.00	34.00
(113)	Danny Richardson (New York, foot on base)	140.00	70.00	42.00
(114)	Hardy Richardson (Detroit, hands at right shoulder)	115.00	57.00	34.00
(115)	Hardy Richardson (Detroit, hands above head)	140.00	70.00	42.00
(116)	Yank Robinson	160.00	80.00	48.00
(117)	George Rooks	140.00	70.00	42.00
(118)	Chief Rosemann (Roseman)	140.00	70.00	42.00
(119)	Jimmy Ryan	140.00	70.00	42.00
(120)	Emmett Seery (hands at right shoulder)	115.00	57.00	34.00
(121)	Emmett Seery (hands outstretched)	140.00	70.00	42.00
(122)	Otto Shomberg (Schomberg)	115.00	57.00	34.00
(123)	Pap Smith	115.00	57.00	34.00
(124)	Joe Strauss	140.00	70.00	42.00
(125)	Danny Sullivan	160.00	80.00	48.00
(126)	Marty Sullivan	115.00	57.00	34.00
(127)	Billy Sunday	160.00	80.00	48.00
(128)	Ezra Sutton	115.00	57.00	34.00
(129)	Big Sam Thompson (hand at belt)	275.00	137.00	82.00
(130)	Big Sam Thompson (hands chest high)	325.00	162.00	97.00
(131)	Chris Von Der Ahe	625.00	312.00	187.00
(132)	Monte Ward (fielding grounder)	275.00	137.00	82.00
(133)	Monte Ward (hands by knee)	325.00	162.00	97.00
(134)	Monte Ward (hands on knees)	325.00	162.00	97.00
(135)	Curt Welch	160.00	80.00	48.00
(136)	Deacon White	140.00	70.00	42.00
(137)	Art Whitney (Pittsburgh)	115.00	57.00	34.00
(138)	Grasshopper Whitney (Washington)	115.00	57.00	34.00
(139)	Ned Williamson (fielding grounder)	160.00	80.00	48.00
(140)	Ned Williamson (hands at chest)	190.00	95.00	57.00
(141)	Medoc Wise	115.00	57.00	34.00
(142)	Dandy Wood (hands at right shoulder)	115.00	57.00	34.00
(143)	Dandy Wood (stealing base)	140.00	70.00	42.00

Regional interest may affect the value of a card.

1934 Gold Medal Flour

This set of 12 unnumbered, blank-backed cards was issued by Gold Medal Flour to commemorate the 1934 World Series. The cards, which measure 3-1/4" by 5-3/8", feature members of the Detroit Tigers and the St. Louis Cardinals, who were participants in the '34 World Series.

		NR MT	EX	VG
Complete Set (12):		675.00	335.00	200.00
Common Player:		40.00	20.00	12.00
(1)	Tommy Bridges	40.00	20.00	12.00
(2)	Mickey Cochrane	75.00	37.00	22.00
(3)	Dizzy Dean	150.00	75.00	45.00
(4)	Paul Dean	55.00	27.00	16.50
(5)	Frank Frisch	75.00	37.00	22.00
(6)	"Goose" Goslin	75.00	37.00	22.00
(7)	William Hallahan	40.00	20.00	12.00
(8)	Fred Marberry	40.00	20.00	12.00
(9)	John "Pepper" Martin	50.00	25.00	15.00
(10)	Joe Medwick	75.00	37.00	22.00
(11)	William Rogell	40.00	20.00	12.00
(12)	"Jo Jo" White	40.00	20.00	12.00

1961 Golden Press

23

John J. McGraw

1891-1906 Baltimore, New York NL

John McGraw was a brilliant third baseman, compiling a .334 lifetime batting average while leading the original Baltimore Orioles to pennants in 1894-1895-1896. However, he is better known as the manager of the New York Giants. From 1902 to 1931 McGraw's Giants won ten pennants and three World Series championships. Moreover, McGraw developed such great players as Christy Mathewson, Mel Ott, Bill Terry and Frankie Frisch, all of whom became major league managers themselves.

Lifetime Record 16 yrs.

G	AB	R	H	HR	RBI	SB	PCT
1082	3919	1019	1307	–	–	444	.334

Elected to Hall of Fame 1937

The 1961 Golden Press set features 33 players, all enshrined in the Baseball Hall of Fame. The full color cards measure 2-1/2" by 3-1/2" and came in a booklet with perforations so that they could be easily removed. Full books with the cards intact would command 50 percent over the set price in the checklist that follows. Card numbers 1-3 and 28-33 are slightly higher in price as they were located on the book's front and back covers, making them more susceptible to scuffing and wear.

		NR MT	EX	VG
Complete Set (33):		150.00	75.00	45.00
Complete Set in Book:		175.00	85.00	50.00
Common Player:		3.00	1.50	.90
1	Mel Ott	3.00	1.50	.90
2	Grover Cleveland Alexander	3.00	1.50	.90
3	Babe Ruth	25.00	12.50	7.50
4	Hank Greenberg	3.00	1.50	.90
5	Bill Terry	3.00	1.50	.90
6	Carl Hubbell	3.00	1.50	.90
7	Rogers Hornsby	4.00	2.00	1.25
8	Dizzy Dean	5.00	2.50	1.50
9	Joe DiMaggio	16.00	8.00	4.75
10	Charlie Gehringer	3.00	1.50	.90
11	Gabby Hartnett	3.00	1.50	.90
12	Mickey Cochrane	3.00	1.50	.90
13	George Sisler	3.00	1.50	.90
14	Joe Cronin	3.00	1.50	.90
15	Pie Traynor	3.00	1.50	.90
16	Lou Gehrig	16.00	8.00	4.75
17	Lefty Grove	3.00	1.50	.90
18	Chief Bender	3.00	1.50	.90
19	Frankie Frisch	3.00	1.50	.90
20	Al Simmons	3.00	1.50	.90
21	Home Run Baker	3.00	1.50	.90
22	Jimmy Foxx	4.00	2.00	1.25
23	John McGraw	3.00	1.50	.90
24	Christy Mathewson	6.00	3.00	1.75
25	Ty Cobb	16.00	8.00	4.75
26	Dazzy Vance	3.00	1.50	.90
27	Bill Dickey	3.00	1.50	.90
28	Eddie Collins	3.00	1.50	.90
29	Walter Johnson	6.00	3.00	1.75
30	Tris Speaker	4.00	2.00	1.25
31	Nap Lajoie	3.00	1.50	.90
32	Honus Wagner	6.00	3.00	1.75
33	Cy Young	6.00	3.00	1.75

1888 Goodwin Champions (N162)

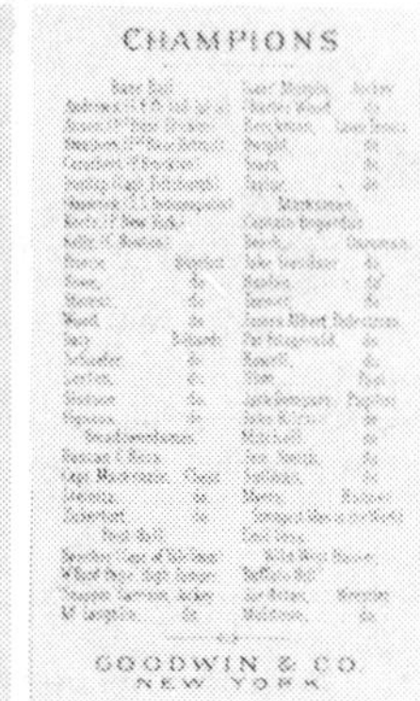

Issued in 1888 by New York's Goodwin & Co., the 50-card "Champions" set includes eight baseball players - seven from the National League and one from the American Association. The full-color cards, which measure 1-1/2" by 2-5/8", were inserted in packages of Old Judge and Gypsy Queen Cigarettes. A small ad for the cards lists all 50 subjects of the "Champions" set, which also included popular billiards players, bicyclists, marksmen, pugilists, runners, wrestlers, college football stars, weightlifters, and Wild West star Buffalo Bill Cody. Four of the eight baseball players in the set (Anson, Kelly, Keefe and Brouthers) are Hall of Famers. The cards feature very attractive player portraits, making the "Champions" set among the most beautiful of all the 19th Century tobacco inserts.

		NR MT	EX	VG
Complete Set (8):		12000.	5000.	3000.
Common Player:		600.00	260.00	150.00
(1)	Ed Andrews	600.00	260.00	150.00
(2)	Cap Anson	4500.	1935.	1125.
(3)	Dan Brouthers	2000.	860.00	500.00
(4)	Parisian Bob Caruthers	750.00	320.00	187.00
(5)	Sure Shot Dunlap	600.00	260.00	150.00
(6)	Pebbly Jack Glasscock	800.00	345.00	200.00
(7)	Tim Keefe	1800.	775.00	450.00
(8)	King Kelly	2500.	1075.	625.00

The values quoted are intended to reflect the market price.

1933 Goudey

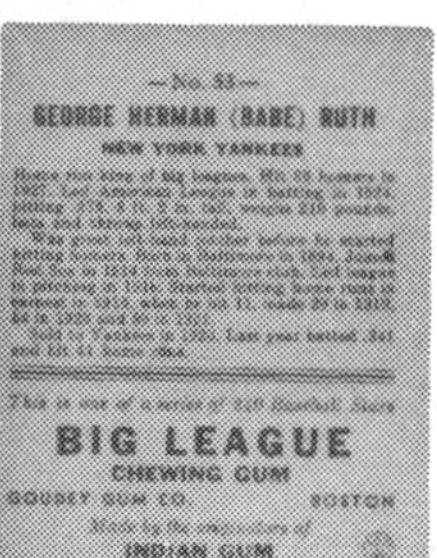

Goudey Gum Co.'s first baseball card issue was their 240-card effort in 1933. The cards are color art reproductions of either portrait or action photos. The numbered cards measure 2-3/8" by 2-7/8" in size and carry a short player biography on the reverses. Card #106 (Napoleon Lajoie) is listed in the set though it was not actually issued until 1934. The card is very scarce and is unique in that it carries a 1934 design obverse and a 1933 reverse. The ACC designation for the set is R319.

		NR MT	EX	VG
Complete Set:		78000.	32000.	14500.
Common Player (1-40):		130.00	52.00	25.00
Common Player (41-44):		75.00	30.00	14.00
Common Player (45-52):		130.00	52.00	25.00
Common Player (53-240):		75.00	30.00	14.00
1	Benny Bengough	1200.	400.00	75.00
2	Arthur (Dazzy) Vance	435.00	174.00	83.00
3	Hugh Critz	130.00	52.00	25.00
4	Henry "Heinie" Schuble	130.00	52.00	25.00
5	Floyd (Babe) Herman	175.00	70.00	33.00
6a	Jimmy Dykes (age is 26 in bio)	200.00	80.00	38.00
6b	Jimmy Dykes (age is 36 in bio)	175.00	70.00	33.00
7	Ted Lyons	225.00	90.00	43.00
8	Roy Johnson	130.00	52.00	25.00
9	Dave Harris	130.00	52.00	25.00
10	Glenn Myatt	130.00	52.00	25.00
11	Billy Rogell	130.00	52.00	25.00
12	George Pipgras	130.00	52.00	25.00
13	Lafayette Thompson	130.00	52.00	25.00
14	Henry Johnson	130.00	52.00	25.00
15	Victor Sorrell	130.00	52.00	25.00
16	George Blaeholder	130.00	52.00	25.00
17	Watson Clark	130.00	52.00	25.00
18	Herold (Muddy) Ruel	130.00	52.00	25.00
19	Bill Dickey	550.00	220.00	104.00
20	Bill Terry	400.00	160.00	76.00
21	Phil Collins	130.00	52.00	25.00
22	Harold (Pie) Traynor	350.00	140.00	66.00
23	Hazen (Ki-Ki) Cuyler	350.00	140.00	66.00
24	Horace Ford	130.00	52.00	25.00
25	Paul Waner	350.00	140.00	66.00
26	Chalmer Cissell	130.00	52.00	25.00
27	George Connally	130.00	52.00	25.00
28	Dick Bartell	130.00	52.00	25.00
29	Jimmy Foxx	650.00	260.00	123.00
30	Frank Hogan	130.00	52.00	25.00
31	Tony Lazzeri	350.00	140.00	66.00
32	John (Bud) Clancy	130.00	52.00	25.00
33	Ralph Kress	130.00	52.00	25.00
34	Bob O'Farrell	130.00	52.00	25.00
35	Al Simmons	450.00	180.00	85.00
36	Tommy Thevenow	130.00	52.00	25.00
37	Jimmy Wilson	130.00	52.00	25.00
38	Fred Brickell	130.00	52.00	25.00
39	Mark Koenig	130.00	52.00	25.00
40	Taylor Douthit	130.00	52.00	25.00
41	Gus Mancuso	75.00	30.00	14.00
42	Eddie Collins	200.00	80.00	38.00
43	Lew Fonseca	85.00	34.00	16.00
44	Jim Bottomley	200.00	80.00	38.00
45	Larry Benton	130.00	52.00	25.00
46	Ethan Allen	130.00	52.00	25.00
47	Henry "Heinie" Manush	300.00	120.00	57.00
48	Marty McManus	130.00	52.00	25.00
49	Frank Frisch	350.00	140.00	66.00
50	Ed Brandt	130.00	52.00	25.00
51	Charlie Grimm	150.00	60.00	28.00
52	Andy Cohen	130.00	52.00	25.00
53	George Herman (Babe) Ruth	6000.	2850.	1350.
54	Ray Kremer	75.00	30.00	14.00
55	Perce (Pat) Malone	75.00	30.00	14.00
56	Charlie Ruffing	220.00	88.00	42.00
57	Earl Clark	75.00	30.00	14.00
58	Frank (Lefty) O'Doul	90.00	36.00	17.00
59	Edmund (Bing) Miller	75.00	30.00	14.00
60	Waite Hoyt	175.00	70.00	33.00
61	Max Bishop	75.00	30.00	14.00
62	"Pepper" Martin	100.00	40.00	19.00
63	Joe Cronin	225.00	90.00	43.00
64	Burleigh Grimes	200.00	80.00	38.00
65	Milton Gaston	75.00	30.00	14.00
66	George Grantham	75.00	30.00	14.00
67	Guy Bush	75.00	30.00	14.00
68	Horace Lisenbee	75.00	30.00	14.00
69	Randy Moore	75.00	30.00	14.00
70	Floyd (Pete) Scott	75.00	30.00	14.00
71	Robert J. Burke	75.00	30.00	14.00
72	Owen Carroll	75.00	30.00	14.00
73	Jesse Haines	175.00	70.00	33.00
74	Eppa Rixey	175.00	70.00	33.00
75	Willie Kamm	75.00	30.00	14.00
76	Gordon (Mickey) Cochrane	250.00	100.00	47.00
77	Adam Comorosky	75.00	30.00	14.00
78	Jack Quinn	75.00	30.00	14.00
79	Urban (Red) Faber	190.00	76.00	36.00
80	Clyde Manion	75.00	30.00	14.00
81	Sam Jones	75.00	30.00	14.00
82	Dibrell Williams	75.00	30.00	14.00
83	Pete Jablonowski	130.00	52.00	25.00
84	Glenn Spencer	75.00	30.00	14.00
85	John Henry "Heinie" Sand	75.00	30.00	14.00
86	Phil Todt	75.00	30.00	14.00
87	Frank O'Rourke	75.00	30.00	14.00
88	Russell Rollings	75.00	30.00	14.00
89	Tris Speaker	400.00	160.00	76.00
90	Jess Petty	75.00	30.00	14.00
91	Tom Zachary	75.00	30.00	14.00
92	Lou Gehrig	4000.	1500.	850.00
93	John Welch	75.00	30.00	14.00
94	Bill Walker	75.00	30.00	14.00
95	Alvin Crowder	75.00	30.00	14.00
96	Willis Hudlin	75.00	30.00	14.00
97	Joe Morrissey	75.00	30.00	14.00
98	Walter Berger	75.00	30.00	14.00
99	Tony Cuccinello	75.00	30.00	14.00
100	George Uhle	90.00	36.00	17.00
101	Richard Coffman	75.00	30.00	14.00
102	Travis C. Jackson	200.00	80.00	38.00
103	Earl Combs (Earle)	175.00	70.00	33.00
104	Fred Marberry	75.00	30.00	14.00
105	Bernie Friberg	75.00	30.00	14.00
106	Napoleon (Larry) Lajoie	34500.	15000.	9000.
107	Henry (Heinie) Manush	190.00	76.00	36.00
108	Joe Kuhel	75.00	30.00	14.00
109	Joe Cronin	190.00	76.00	36.00
110	Leon "Goose" Goslin	190.00	76.00	36.00
111	Monte Weaver	75.00	30.00	14.00
112	Fred Schulte	75.00	30.00	14.00
113	Oswald Bluege	75.00	30.00	14.00
114	Luke Sewell	75.00	30.00	14.00
115	Cliff Heathcote	75.00	30.00	14.00
116	Eddie Morgan	75.00	30.00	14.00
117	Walter (Rabbit) Maranville	200.00	80.00	38.00
118	Valentine J. (Val) Picinich	75.00	30.00	14.00
119	Rogers Hornsby	450.00	180.00	85.00
120	Carl Reynolds	75.00	30.00	14.00
121	Walter Stewart	75.00	30.00	14.00
122	Alvin Crowder	75.00	30.00	14.00
123	Jack Russell	75.00	30.00	14.00
124	Earl Whitehill	75.00	30.00	14.00
125	Bill Terry	300.00	120.00	57.00
126	Joe Moore	75.00	30.00	14.00
127	Melvin Ott	325.00	130.00	62.00
128	Charles (Chuck) Klein	225.00	90.00	43.00
129	Harold Schumacher	90.00	36.00	17.00
130	Fred Fitzsimmons	75.00	30.00	14.00
131	Fred Frankhouse	75.00	30.00	14.00
132	Jim Elliott	75.00	30.00	14.00
133	Fred Lindstrom	175.00	70.00	33.00
134	Edgar (Sam) Rice	175.00	70.00	33.00
135	Elwood (Woody) English	75.00	30.00	14.00
136	Flint Rhem	75.00	30.00	14.00
137	Fred (Red) Lucas	75.00	30.00	14.00
138	Herb Pennock	190.00	76.00	36.00
139	Ben Cantwell	75.00	30.00	14.00
140	Irving (Bump) Hadley	75.00	30.00	14.00
141	Ray Benge	75.00	30.00	14.00
142	Paul Richards	100.00	40.00	19.00
143	Glenn Wright	90.00	36.00	17.00
144	George Herman (Babe) Ruth	4500.	2200.	1275.
145	George Walberg	75.00	30.00	14.00
146	Walter Stewart	75.00	30.00	14.00
147	Leo Durocher	200.00	80.00	38.00
148	Eddie Farrell	75.00	30.00	14.00
149	George Herman (Babe) Ruth	5500.	2750.	1300.
150	Ray Kolp	75.00	30.00	14.00
151	D'Arcy (Jake) Flowers	75.00	30.00	14.00
152	James (Zack) Taylor	75.00	30.00	14.00
153	Charles (Buddy) Myer	75.00	30.00	14.00
154	Jimmy Foxx	500.00	200.00	95.00
155	Joe Judge	75.00	30.00	14.00
156	Danny Macfayden (MacFayden)	90.00	36.00	17.00
157	Sam Byrd	90.00	36.00	17.00
158	Morris (Moe) Berg	175.00	70.00	33.00
159	Oswald Bluege	75.00	30.00	14.00
160	Lou Gehrig	4000.	2100.	1000.
161	Al Spohrer	75.00	30.00	14.00
162	Leo Mangum	75.00	30.00	14.00
163	Luke Sewell	75.00	30.00	14.00
164	Lloyd Waner	175.00	70.00	33.00
165	Joe Sewell	175.00	70.00	33.00
166	Sam West	75.00	30.00	14.00
167a	Jack Russell (name on two lines)	75.00	30.00	14.00
167b	Jack Russell (name on one line)	225.00	90.00	43.00
168a	Leon (Goose) Goslin (name on one line)	190.00	76.00	36.00
168b	Leon (Goose) Goslin (name on two lines)	350.00	140.00	66.00
169	Al Thomas	75.00	30.00	14.00
170	Harry McCurdy	75.00	30.00	14.00
171	Charley Jamieson	75.00	30.00	14.00
172	Billy Hargrave	75.00	30.00	14.00
173	Roscoe Holm	75.00	30.00	14.00
174	Warren (Curley) Ogden	75.00	30.00	14.00
175	Dan Howley	75.00	30.00	14.00
176	John Ogden	75.00	30.00	14.00
177	Walter French	75.00	30.00	14.00
178	Jackie Warner	75.00	30.00	14.00
179	Fred Leach	75.00	30.00	14.00
180	Eddie Moore	75.00	30.00	14.00
181	George Herman (Babe) Ruth	5500.	2200.	1500.
182	Andy High	75.00	30.00	14.00
183	George Walberg	75.00	30.00	14.00
184	Charley Berry	75.00	30.00	14.00
185	Bob Smith	75.00	30.00	14.00
186	John Schulte	75.00	30.00	14.00
187	Henry (Heinie) Manush	175.00	70.00	33.00
188	Rogers Hornsby	450.00	180.00	85.00
189	Joe Cronin	190.00	76.00	36.00
190	Fred Schulte	75.00	30.00	14.00
191	Ben Chapman	100.00	40.00	19.00
192	Walter Brown	100.00	40.00	19.00
193	Lynford Lary	90.00	36.00	17.00
194	Earl Averill	190.00	76.00	36.00
195	Evar Swanson	75.00	30.00	14.00
196	Leroy Mahaffey	75.00	30.00	14.00
197	Richard (Rick) Ferrell	175.00	70.00	33.00
198	Irving (Jack) Burns	75.00	30.00	14.00
199	Tom Bridges	70.00	28.00	13.50
200	Bill Hallahan	75.00	30.00	14.00
201	Ernie Orsatti	75.00	30.00	14.00
202	Charles Leo (Gabby) Hartnett	175.00	70.00	33.00
203	Lonnie Warneke	75.00	30.00	14.00
204	Jackson Riggs Stephenson	100.00	40.00	19.00
205	Henry (Heinie) Meine	75.00	30.00	14.00
206	Gus Suhr	75.00	30.00	14.00
207	Melvin Ott	400.00	160.00	76.00
208	Byrne (Bernie) James	75.00	30.00	14.00
209	Adolfo Luque	75.00	30.00	14.00
210	Virgil Davis	75.00	30.00	14.00
211	Lewis (Hack) Wilson	300.00	120.00	57.00
212	Billy Urbanski	75.00	30.00	14.00
213	Earl Adams	75.00	30.00	14.00
214	John Kerr	75.00	30.00	14.00
215	Russell Van Atta	90.00	36.00	17.00
216	Vernon Gomez	350.00	140.00	66.00
217	Frank Crosetti	190.00	76.00	36.00
218	Wesley Ferrell	90.00	36.00	17.00
219	George (Mule) Haas	75.00	30.00	14.00
220	Robert (Lefty) Grove	575.00	230.00	109.00
221	Dale Alexander	75.00	30.00	14.00
222	Charley Gehringer	300.00	120.00	57.00
223	Jerome (Dizzy) Dean	700.00	280.00	133.00
224	Frank Demaree	75.00	30.00	14.00
225	Bill Jurges	75.00	30.00	14.00
226	Charley Root	90.00	36.00	17.00
227	Bill Herman	200.00	80.00	38.00
228	Tony Piet	75.00	30.00	14.00
229	Floyd Vaughan	225.00	90.00	43.00
230	Carl Hubbell	300.00	120.00	57.00
231	Joe Moore	75.00	30.00	14.00
232	Frank (Lefty) O'Doul	100.00	40.00	19.00
233	Johnny Vergez	75.00	30.00	14.00
234	Carl Hubbell	300.00	120.00	57.00
235	Fred Fitzsimmons	75.00	30.00	14.00
236	George Davis	75.00	30.00	14.00
237	Gus Mancuso	75.00	30.00	14.00
238	Hugh Critz	75.00	30.00	14.00
239	Leroy Parmelee	90.00	36.00	17.00
240	Harold Schumacher	350.00	90.00	17.00

1934 Goudey

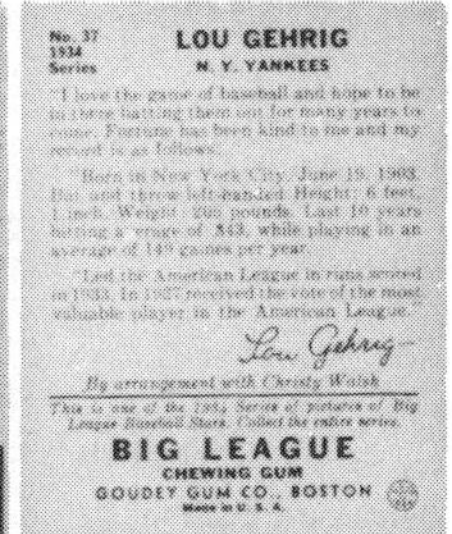

The 1934 Goudey set contains 96 cards (2-3/8" by 2-7/8") that feature color art reproductions of actual photographs. The card fronts have two different designs; one featuring a small head-shot photo of Lou Gehrig with the words "Lou Gehrig says..." inside a blue band, while the other design carries a "Chuck Klein says..." and also has his photo. The card backs contain a short player biography that appears to have been written by Gehrig or Klein. The ACC designation for the set is R320.

		NR MT	EX	VG
Complete Set:		21000.	8400.	3990.
Common Player (1-48):		70.00	28.00	13.50
Common Player (49-72):		85.00	34.00	16.00
Common Player (73-96):		250.00	100.00	47.00
1	Jimmy Foxx	1450.	700.00	170.00
2	Gordon (Mickey) Cochrane	250.00	100.00	47.00
3	Charlie Grimm	70.00	28.00	13.50
4	Elwood (Woody) English	70.00	28.00	13.50
5	Ed Brandt	70.00	28.00	13.50
6	Jerome (Dizzy) Dean	800.00	320.00	152.00
7	Leo Durocher	200.00	80.00	38.00
8	Tony Piet	70.00	28.00	13.50
9	Ben Chapman	85.00	34.00	16.00
10	Charles (Chuck) Klein	225.00	90.00	43.00
11	Paul Waner	200.00	80.00	38.00
12	Carl Hubbell	250.00	100.00	47.00
13	Frank Frisch	225.00	90.00	43.00
14	Willie Kamm	70.00	28.00	13.50
15	Alvin Crowder	70.00	28.00	13.50
16	Joe Kuhel	70.00	28.00	13.50
17	Hugh Critz	70.00	28.00	13.50
18	Henry (Heinie) Manush	200.00	80.00	38.00
19	Robert (Lefty) Grove	450.00	180.00	85.00
20	Frank Hogan	70.00	28.00	13.50
21	Bill Terry	250.00	100.00	47.00
22	Floyd Vaughan	200.00	80.00	38.00
23	Charley Gehringer	110.00	44.00	21.00
24	Ray Benge	70.00	28.00	13.50
25	Roger Cramer	70.00	28.00	13.50
26	Gerald Walker	70.00	28.00	13.50
27	Luke Appling	225.00	90.00	43.00
28	Ed. Coleman	70.00	28.00	13.50
29	Larry French	70.00	28.00	13.50
30	Julius Solters	70.00	28.00	13.50
31	Baxter Jordan	70.00	28.00	13.50
32	John (Blondy) Ryan	70.00	28.00	13.50
33	Frank (Don) Hurst	70.00	28.00	13.50
34	Charles (Chick) Hafey	200.00	80.00	38.00
35	Ernie Lombardi	200.00	80.00	38.00
36	Walter (Huck) Betts	70.00	28.00	13.50
37	Lou Gehrig	3500.	1750.	800.00
38	Oral Hildebrand	70.00	28.00	13.50
39	Fred Walker	70.00	28.00	13.50
40	John Stone	70.00	28.00	13.50
41	George Earnshaw	70.00	28.00	13.50
42	John Allen	85.00	34.00	16.00
43	Dick Porter	70.00	28.00	13.50
44	Tom Bridges	70.00	28.00	13.50
45	Oscar Melillo	70.00	28.00	13.50
46	Joe Stripp	70.00	28.00	13.50
47	John Frederick	70.00	28.00	13.50
48	James (Tex) Carleton	70.00	28.00	13.50
49	Sam Leslie	85.00	34.00	16.00
50	Walter Beck	85.00	34.00	16.00
51	Jim (Rip) Collins	85.00	34.00	16.00
52	Herman Bell	85.00	34.00	16.00
53	George Watkins	85.00	34.00	16.00
54	Wesley Schulmerich	85.00	34.00	16.00

55	Ed Holley	85.00	34.00	16.00
56	Mark Koenig	85.00	34.00	16.00
57	Bill Swift	85.00	34.00	16.00
58	Earl Grace	85.00	34.00	16.00
59	Joe Mowry	85.00	34.00	16.00
60	Lynn Nelson	85.00	34.00	16.00
61	Lou Gehrig	3250.	1650.	900.00
62	Henry Greenberg	450.00	180.00	85.00
63	Minter Hayes	85.00	34.00	16.00
64	Frank Grube	85.00	34.00	16.00
65	Cliff Bolton	85.00	34.00	16.00
66	Mel Harder	85.00	34.00	16.00
67	Bob Weiland	85.00	34.00	16.00
68	Bob Johnson	85.00	34.00	16.00
69	John Marcum	85.00	34.00	16.00
70	Ervin (Pete) Fox	85.00	34.00	16.00
71	Lyle Tinning	85.00	34.00	16.00
72	Arndt Jorgens	85.00	34.00	16.00
73	Ed Wells	250.00	100.00	47.00
74	Bob Boken	250.00	100.00	47.00
75	Bill Werber	250.00	100.00	47.00
76	Hal Trosky	250.00	100.00	47.00
77	Joe Vosmik	250.00	100.00	47.00
78	Frank (Pinkey) Higgins	250.00	100.00	47.00
79	Eddie Durham	250.00	100.00	47.00
80	Marty McManus	250.00	100.00	47.00
81	Bob Brown	250.00	100.00	47.00
82	Bill Hallahan	250.00	100.00	47.00
83	Jim Mooney	250.00	100.00	47.00
84	Paul Derringer	300.00	120.00	57.00
85	Adam Comorosky	250.00	100.00	47.00
86	Lloyd Johnson	250.00	100.00	47.00
87	George Darrow	250.00	100.00	47.00
88	Homer Peel	250.00	100.00	47.00
89	Linus Frey	250.00	100.00	47.00
90	Hazen (Ki-Ki) Cuyler	500.00	200.00	95.00
91	Dolph Camilli	250.00	100.00	47.00
92	Steve Larkin	250.00	100.00	47.00
93	Fred Ostermueller	250.00	100.00	47.00
94	Robert A. (Red) Rolfe	350.00	140.00	66.00
95	Myril Hoag	300.00	120.00	57.00
96	Jim DeShong	400.00	160.00	76.00

1934 Goudey Premiums (R309-1)

Consisting of just four unnumbered cards, this set of black and white photos was printed on heavy cardboard and issued as a premium by the Goudey Gum Co. in 1934. The cards measure 5-1/2" by 8-5/16" and were accented with a gold, picture-frame border and an easel on the back.

		NR MT	EX	VG
Complete Set:		4250.	2100.	1250.
Common Card:		800.00	400.00	240.00
(1)	American League All-Stars of 1933	800.00	400.00	240.00
(2)	National League All-Stars of 1933	800.00	400.00	240.00
(3)	"Worlds Champions 1933" (New York Giants)	1000.	500.00	300.00
(4)	George Herman (Babe) Ruth	1800.	900.00	540.00

1934 Goudey Thum Movies (R342)

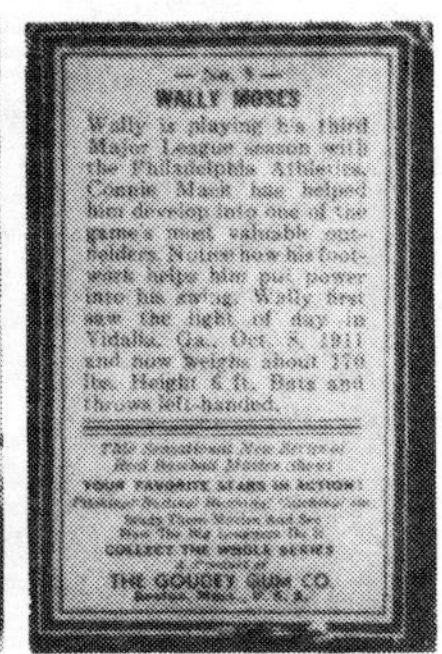

Assigned the American Card Catalog number R342, these 2" by 3" booklets are similar to the "Big League Baseball Movies" (R326) issued by Goudey circa 1937. The "Thum Movies" set consists of 13 players. The booklets are numbered on the top of the back page.

		NR MT	EX	VG
Complete Set:		1350.	650.00	400.00
Common Player:		55.00	27.00	16.50
1	John Irving Burns	55.00	27.00	16.50
2	Joe Vosmik	55.00	27.00	16.50
3	Mel Ott	140.00	70.00	42.00
4	Joe DiMaggio	450.00	225.00	135.00
5	Wally Moses	55.00	27.00	16.50
6	Van Lingle Mungo	55.00	27.00	16.50
7	Luke Appling	75.00	37.00	22.00
8	Bob Feller	140.00	70.00	42.00
9	Paul Derringer	55.00	27.00	16.50
10	Paul Waner	75.00	37.00	22.00
11	Joe Medwick	75.00	37.00	22.00
12	James Emory Foxx	140.00	70.00	42.00
13	Wally Berger	55.00	27.00	16.50

1935 Goudey

The 1935 Goudey set features four players from the same team on one card. Thirty-six card fronts make up the set with numerous front/back combinations existing. The card backs form nine different puzzles: 1) Tigers Team, 2) Chuck Klein, 3) Frankie Frisch, 4) Mickey Cochrane, 5) Joe Cronin, 6) Jimmy Foxx, 7) Al Simmons, 8) Indians Team, and 9) Senators Team. The cards, which measure 2-3/8" by 2-7/8", have an ACC designation of R321.

		NR MT	EX	VG
Complete Set (36):		5500.	2750.	1650.
Common Player:		70.00	35.00	21.00
(1)	Sparky Adams, Jim Bottomley, Adam Comorosky, Tony Piet	100.00	50.00	30.00
(2)	Ethan Allen, Fred Brickell, Bubber Jonnard, Hack Wilson	100.00	50.00	30.00
(3)	Johnny Allen, Jimmie Deshong (DeShong), Red Rolfe, Dixie Walker	70.00	35.00	21.00
(4)	Luke Appling, Jimmie Dykes, George Earnshaw, Luke Sewell	100.00	50.00	30.00
(5)	Earl Averill, Oral Hildebrand, Willie Kamm, Hal Trosky	175.00	87.00	52.00
(6)	Dick Bartell, Hughie Critz, Gus Mancuso, Mel Ott	125.00	62.00	37.00
(7)	Ray Benge, Fred Fitzsimmons, Mark Koenig, Tom Zachary	70.00	35.00	21.00
(8)	Larry Benton, Ben Cantwell, Flint Rhem, Al Spohrer	70.00	35.00	21.00
(9)	Charlie Berry, Bobby Burke, Red Kress, Dazzy Vance	100.00	50.00	30.00
(10)	Max Bishop, Bill Cissell, Joe Cronin, Carl Reynolds	125.00	62.00	37.00
(11)	George Blaeholder, Dick Coffman, Oscar Melillo, Sammy West	70.00	35.00	21.00
(12)	Cy Blanton, Babe Herman, Tom Padden, Gus Suhr	70.00	35.00	21.00
(13)	Zeke Bonura, Mule Haas, Jackie Hayes, Ted Lyons	100.00	50.00	30.00
(14)	Jim Bottomley, Adam Comorosky, Willis Hudlin, Glenn Myatt	100.00	50.00	30.00
(15)	Ed Brandt, Fred Frankhouse, Shanty Hogan, Gene Moore	350.00	175.00	105.00
(16)	Ed Brandt, Rabbit Maranville, Marty McManus, Babe Ruth	1900.	950.00	570.00
(17)	Tommy Bridges, Mickey Cochrane, Charlie Gehringer, Billy Rogell	175.00	87.00	52.00
(18)	Jack Burns, Frank Grube, Rollie Hemsley, Bob Weiland	70.00	35.00	21.00
(19)	Guy Bush, Waite Hoyt, Lloyd Waner, Paul Waner	150.00	75.00	45.00
(20)	Sammy Byrd, Danny MacFayden, Pepper Martin, Bob O'Farrell	70.00	35.00	21.00
(21)	Gilly Campbell, Ival Goodman, Alex Kampouris, Billy Meyers (Myers)	70.00	35.00	21.00
(22)	Tex Carleton, Dizzy Dean, Frankie Frisch, Ernie Orsatti	375.00	187.00	112.00
(23)	Watty Clark, Lonny Frey, Sam Leslie, Joe Stripp	70.00	35.00	21.00
(24)	Mickey Cochrane, Willie Kamm, Muddy Ruel, Al Simmons	150.00	75.00	45.00
(25)	Ed Coleman, Doc Cramer, Bob Johnson, Johnny Marcum	70.00	35.00	21.00
(26)	General Crowder, Goose Goslin, Firpo Marberry, Heinie Schuble	100.00	50.00	30.00
(27)	Kiki Cuyler, Woody English, Burleigh Grimes, Chuck Klein	70.00	35.00	21.00
(28)	Bill Dickey, Tony Lazzeri, Pat Malone, Red Ruffing	275.00	137.00	82.00
(29)	Rick Ferrell, Wes Ferrell, Fritz Ostermueller, Bill Werber	100.00	50.00	30.00
(30)	Pete Fox, Hank Greenberg, Schoolboy Rowe, Gee Walker	150.00	75.00	45.00
(31)	Jimmie Foxx, Pinky Higgins, Roy Mahaffey, Dib Williams	275.00	137.00	82.00
(32)	Bump Hadley, Lyn Lary, Heinie Manush, Monte Weaver	100.00	50.00	30.00
(33)	Mel Harder, Bill Knickerbocker, Lefty Stewart, Joe Vosmik	70.00	35.00	21.00
(34)	Travis Jackson, Gus Mancuso, Hal Schumacher, Bill Terry	175.00	87.00	52.00
(35)	Joe Kuhel, Buddy Meyer (Myer), John Stone, Earl Whitehill	70.00	35.00	21.00
(36)	Red Lucas, Tommy Thevenow, Pie Traynor, Glenn Wright	100.00	50.00	30.00

1935 Goudey Premiums (R309-2)

The 18 glossy, black-and-white photos in this set, issued as a premium by Goudey in 1935, measure 5-1/2" by 9", and were printed on thin paper. The unnumbered set includes three team photos and 15 players, whose names are written in script in the "wide pen" style by Goudey in other issues.

		NR MT	EX	VG
Complete Set:		2400.	1200.	725.00
Common Player:		110.00	55.00	33.00
(1)	Elden Auker	110.00	55.00	33.00
(2)	Johnny Babich	110.00	55.00	33.00
(3)	Dick Bartell	110.00	55.00	33.00
(4)	Lester R. Bell	110.00	55.00	33.00
(5)	Wally Berger	110.00	55.00	33.00
(6)	Mickey Cochrane	200.00	100.00	60.00
(7)	Ervin Fox	110.00	55.00	33.00
(8)	Vernon Gomez	200.00	100.00	60.00
(9)	Leon "Goose" Goslin	200.00	100.00	60.00
(10)	Hank Greenberg	200.00	100.00	60.00
(11)	Oscar Melillo	110.00	55.00	33.00
(12)	Mel Ott	200.00	100.00	60.00
(13)	Schoolboy Rowe	110.00	55.00	33.00
(14)	Vito Tamulis	110.00	55.00	33.00
(15)	Gerald Walker	110.00	55.00	33.00
(16)	Boston Red Sox	120.00	60.00	35.00
(17)	Cleveland Indians	120.00	60.00	35.00
(18)	Washington Senators	120.00	60.00	35.00

1936 Goudey

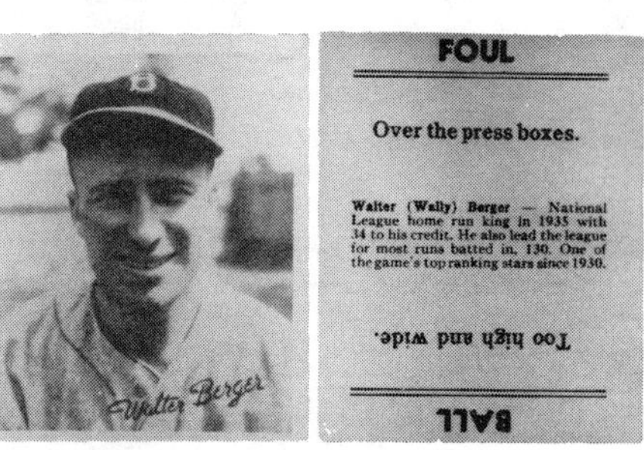

The 1936 Goudey set consists of 25 black and white cards, each measuring 2-3/8" by 2-7/8". A facsimile autograph is positioned on the card fronts. The card backs contain a brief player biography and were to be used by collectors to play a baseball game. Different game situations (out, single, double, etc.) are given on each card. Numerous front/back exist in the set. The ACC designation for the set is R322.

		NR MT	EX	VG
Complete Set:		2000.	1000.	600.00
Common Player:		50.00	25.00	15.00
(1)	Walter Berger	55.00	22.00	13.50
(2)	Henry Bonura	50.00	25.00	15.00
(3)	Stan Bordagaray	50.00	25.00	15.00
(4)	Bill Brubaker	50.00	25.00	15.00
(5)	Dolph Camilli	55.00	27.00	16.50
(6)	Clydell Castleman	50.00	25.00	15.00
(7)	"Mickey" Cochrane	175.00	87.00	52.00
(8)	Joe Coscarart	50.00	25.00	15.00
(9)	Frank Crosetti	90.00	45.00	27.00
(10)	"Kiki" Cuyler	125.00	62.00	37.00
(11)	Paul Derringer	55.00	27.00	16.50
(12)	Jimmy Dykes	55.00	27.00	16.50
(13)	"Rick" Ferrell	125.00	62.00	37.00
(14)	"Lefty" Gomez	225.00	110.00	65.00
(15)	Hank Greenberg	300.00	150.00	90.00
(16)	"Bucky" Harris	125.00	62.00	37.00
(17)	"Rolly" Hemsley	50.00	25.00	15.00
(18)	Frank Higgins	50.00	25.00	15.00
(19)	Oral Hildebrand	50.00	25.00	15.00
(20)	"Chuck" Klein	150.00	75.00	45.00
(21)	"Pepper" Martin	75.00	37.00	22.00
(22)	"Buck" Newsom	55.00	27.00	16.50
(23)	Joe Vosmik	50.00	25.00	15.00
(24)	Paul Waner	150.00	75.00	45.00
(25)	Bill Werber	50.00	25.00	15.00

1936 Goudey "Wide Pen" Premiums (R314)

Issued in 1936 by the Goudey Gum Company, these cards are known in the hobby as "Wide Pens" because of the distinctive, thick style of writing used for the facsimilie autographs. The black and white, unnumbered cards measure 3-1/4" by 5-1/2" and are found in several different types. Some cards have borders, while others do not. Some cards are found both with and without a "Litho USA" line along the bottom. Some cards in the set are found on a creamy paper stock. The set includes both major leaguers and players from the Canadian minor league teams in Montreal and Toronto. The cards were originally available as an in-store premium. Some players can be found in two or more poses. The set's American Card Catalog designation is R314. It is possible other poses or players may yet be discovered.

		NR MT	EX	VG
Complete Set:		3250.	1600.	950.00
Common Player:		15.00	7.50	4.50
(1)	Ethan Allen	15.00	7.50	4.50
(2)	Mel Almada	15.00	7.50	4.50
(3)	"Luke" Appling	25.00	12.50	7.50
(4)	Earl Averill	22.00	11.00	6.50
(5 a)	Dick Bartell (portrait)	15.00	7.50	4.50
(5b)	Dick Bartell (sliding)	15.00	7.50	4.50
(6)	Buddy Bates	15.00	7.50	4.50
(7)	Walter Berger	18.00	9.00	5.50
(8)	Del Bisonette	15.00	7.50	4.50
(9)	Geo. Blaeholder	15.00	7.50	4.50
(10)	Lincoln Blakely	15.00	7.50	4.50
(11)	"Cy" Blanton	15.00	7.50	4.50
(12)	"Cliff" Bolton	15.00	7.50	4.50
(13)	Zeke Bonura	15.00	7.50	4.50
(14)	Isaac J. Boone	15.00	7.50	4.50
(15)	Stan Bordagaray	15.00	7.50	4.50
(16)	Tommy Bridges	15.00	7.50	4.50
(17)	Bill Brubaker	15.00	7.50	4.50
(18)	John H. Burnett	15.00	7.50	4.50
(19)	Sam Byrd	15.00	7.50	4.50
(20)	Dolph Camilli	15.00	7.50	4.50
(21a)	Clydell Castleman (pitching)	15.00	7.50	4.50
(21b)	Clydell Castleman (portrait)	15.00	7.50	4.50
(22)	"Phil" Cavaretta (Cavarretta)	18.00	9.00	5.50
(23)	Leon Chagnan	15.00	7.50	4.50
(24)	Ben Chapman, Bill Werber	25.00	12.50	7.50
(25)	Herman Clifton	15.00	7.50	4.50
(26)	Mickey Cochrane	30.00	15.00	9.00
(27)	Earl Coombs (Earle Combs)	22.00	11.00	6.50
(28)	Joe Coscarart	15.00	7.50	4.50
(29)	Roger "Doc" Cramer	15.00	7.50	4.50
(30)	Joe Cronin	22.00	11.00	6.50
(31)	Frank Crosetti	18.00	9.00	5.50
(32)	Tony Cuccinello	15.00	7.50	4.50
(33)	"Kiki" Cuyler	22.00	11.00	6.50
(34)	Curt Davis	15.00	7.50	4.50
(35)	Virgil Davis	15.00	7.50	4.50
(36)	Paul Derringer	15.00	7.50	4.50
(37)	Bill Dickey	30.00	15.00	9.00
(38)	"Joe" DiMaggio	90.00	45.00	24.00
(39)	Joe DiMaggio, Joe McCarthy	150.00	75.00	45.00
(40)	"Bobby" Doerr	22.00	11.00	6.50
(41)	Gus Dugas	15.00	7.50	4.50
(42)	Jimmy Dykes	15.00	7.50	4.50
(43)	Henry Erickson	15.00	7.50	4.50
(44)	"Bob" Feller	40.00	20.00	12.00
(45)	Rick Ferrell	22.00	11.00	6.50
(46)	Wes Ferrell	15.00	7.50	4.50
(47)	Rick Ferrell, Wes Ferrell	35.00	17.50	10.50
(48)	Lou Finney	15.00	7.50	4.50
(49)	"Elbie" Fletcher	15.00	7.50	4.50
(50)	Erwin "Pete" Fox	15.00	7.50	4.50
(51)	"Jimmie Foxx	30.00	15.00	9.00
(52)	Tony Freitas	15.00	7.50	4.50
(53)	Lonnie Frey	15.00	7.50	4.50
(54)	Frankie Frisch	30.00	15.00	9.00
(55)	Art Funk	15.00	7.50	4.50
(56)	"Augie" Galan	15.00	7.50	4.50
(57)	Charles Gehringer	30.00	15.00	9.00
(58)	Charlie Gelbert	15.00	7.50	4.50
(59)	"Lefty" Gomez	24.00	12.00	7.25
(60)	"Goose" Goslin	22.00	11.00	6.50
(61)	Earl Grace	15.00	7.50	4.50
(62)	George Granger	15.00	7.50	4.50
(63)	Hank Greenberg	30.00	15.00	9.00
(64)	"Mule" Haas	15.00	7.50	4.50
(65)	Odell Hale	15.00	7.50	4.50
(66)	Bill Hallahan	15.00	7.50	4.50
(67)	"Mel" Harder	15.00	7.50	4.50
(68)	"Bucky" Harris	22.00	11.00	6.50
(69)	"Gabby" Hartnett	25.00	12.50	7.50
(70)	Ray Hayworth	15.00	7.50	4.50
(71)	Tommy Heath	15.00	7.50	4.50
(72)	"Rollie" Hemsley	15.00	7.50	4.50
(73)	Phil Hensick	15.00	7.50	4.50
(74)	Babe Herman	18.00	9.00	5.50
(75)	LeRoy Herman	15.00	7.50	4.50
(76)	Frank Higgins	15.00	7.50	4.50
(77)	Oral Hildebrand	15.00	7.50	4.50
(78)	Myril Hoag	15.00	7.50	4.50
(79)	Alex Hooks	15.00	7.50	4.50
(80)	Waite Hoyt	22.00	11.00	6.50
(81)	Carl Hubbell	30.00	15.00	9.00
(82)	Willis Hudlin	15.00	7.50	4.50
(83)	Woody Jensen	15.00	7.50	4.50
(84)	Bob Johnson	15.00	7.50	4.50
(85)	Henry Johnson	15.00	7.50	4.50
(86)	"Buck" Jordan	15.00	7.50	4.50
(87)	Alex Kampouris	15.00	7.50	4.50
(88)	Hal King	15.00	7.50	4.50
(89)	"Chuck" Klein	25.00	12.50	7.50
(90)	Bill Knickerbocker	15.00	7.50	4.50
(91)	Joe Kuhel	15.00	7.50	4.50
(92)	Lyn Lary	15.00	7.50	4.50
(93)	Harry Lavagetto	15.00	7.50	4.50
(94)	Sam Leslie	15.00	7.50	4.50
(95)	Freddie Lindstrom	22.00	11.00	6.50
(96)	Ernie Lombardi	22.00	11.00	6.50
(97)	"Al" Lopez	22.00	11.00	6.50
(98)	Charles S. Lucas	15.00	7.50	4.50
(99)	Dan MacFayden	15.00	7.50	4.50
(100)	Heinie Manush	22.00	11.00	6.50
(101)	John Marcum	15.00	7.50	4.50
(102)	"Pepper" Martin	18.00	9.00	5.50
(103)	Eric McNair	15.00	7.50	4.50
(104)	"Ducky" Medwick	22.00	11.00	6.50
(105)	Edward S. Miller	15.00	7.50	4.50
(106)	Gene Moore	15.00	7.50	4.50
(107)	Randy Moore	15.00	7.50	4.50
(108)	Terry Moore	18.00	9.00	5.50
(109)	Jake Mooty	15.00	7.50	4.50
(110)	Guy Moreau	15.00	7.50	4.50
(111)	Edward Moriarty	15.00	7.50	4.50
(112)	"Wally" Moses	15.00	7.50	4.50
(113)	George Murray	15.00	7.50	4.50
(114)	Glenn Myatt	15.00	7.50	4.50
(115)	"Buddy" Myer	15.00	7.50	4.50
(116)	Lauri Myllykargos	15.00	7.50	4.50
(117)	"Buck" Newsom	15.00	7.50	4.50
(118)	Francis J. Nicholas	15.00	7.50	4.50
(119)	Pat Nutticomb	15.00	7.50	4.50
(120)	Bill O'Brien	15.00	7.50	4.50
(121)	Thomas Oliver	15.00	7.50	4.50
(122)	Steve O'Neill	15.00	7.50	4.50
(123)	Steve O'Neill, Frank Pytlak	25.00	12.50	7.50
(124)	Fred Ostermueller	15.00	7.50	4.50
(125)	Marvin Owen	15.00	7.50	4.50
(126)	Tommy Padden	15.00	7.50	4.50
(127)	Andy Pattison	15.00	7.50	4.50
(128)	Ray Pepper	15.00	7.50	4.50
(129)	Tony Piet	15.00	7.50	4.50
(130)	Cup Polli	15.00	7.50	4.50
(131)	Harlan Pool	15.00	7.50	4.50
(132)	Walter Purcey	15.00	7.50	4.50
(133)	"Rabbit" Pytlak	15.00	7.50	4.50
(134)	"Rip" Radcliff	15.00	7.50	4.50
(135)	Bobby Reis	15.00	7.50	4.50
(136)	Bill Rhiel	15.00	7.50	4.50
(137)	"Lew" Riggs	15.00	7.50	4.50
(138)	Bill Rogell	15.00	7.50	4.50
(139)	"Red" Rolfe	15.00	7.50	4.50
(140)	"Schoolboy" Rowe	15.00	7.50	4.50
(141)	Ben Sankey	15.00	7.50	4.50
(142)	Les Scarcella	15.00	7.50	4.50
(143)	Al Schacht	15.00	7.50	4.50
(144)	Bob Seeds	15.00	7.50	4.50
(145)	"Luke" Sewell	15.00	7.50	4.50
(146)	Frank Shaughnessy	15.00	7.50	4.50
(147)	Al Simmons	22.00	11.00	6.50
(148)	Harry Smythe	15.00	7.50	4.50
(149)	Julius Solters	15.00	7.50	4.50
(150)	John Stone	15.00	7.50	4.50
(151)	Gus Suhr	15.00	7.50	4.50
(152)	Joe Sullivan	15.00	7.50	4.50
(153)	Bill Swift	15.00	7.50	4.50
(154)	Vito Tamulis	15.00	7.50	4.50
(155)	Ben Tate	15.00	7.50	4.50
(156)	Dan Taylor	15.00	7.50	4.50
(157)	Fresco Thompson	15.00	7.50	4.50
(158)	Cecil Travis	15.00	7.50	4.50
(159)	Hal Trosky	15.00	7.50	4.50
(160)	"Bill" Urbanski	15.00	7.50	4.50
(161)	Russ Van Atta	15.00	7.50	4.50
(162)	"Arky" Vaughan	25.00	12.50	7.50
(163)	Joe Vosmik	15.00	7.50	4.50
(164)	Gerald Walker	15.00	7.50	4.50
(165)	"Buck" Walter (Bucky)	15.00	7.50	4.50
(166)	Lloyd Waner	25.00	12.50	7.50
(167)	Paul Waner	25.00	12.50	7.50
(168)	"Lon" Warneke	15.00	7.50	4.50
(169)	"Rabbit" Warstler	15.00	7.50	4.50
(170)	Tom Webb	15.00	7.50	4.50
(171)	Bill Werber	15.00	7.50	4.50
(172)	"Jo Jo" White	15.00	7.50	4.50
(173)	Burgess Whitehead	15.00	7.50	4.50
(174)	John Whitehead	15.00	7.50	4.50
(175)	Earl Whitehill	15.00	7.50	4.50
(176)	Charles Wilson	15.00	7.50	4.50
(177)	Francis Wistert	15.00	7.50	4.50
(178)	Whitlow Wyatt	15.00	7.50	4.50

1937 Goudey Baseball Movies (R326)

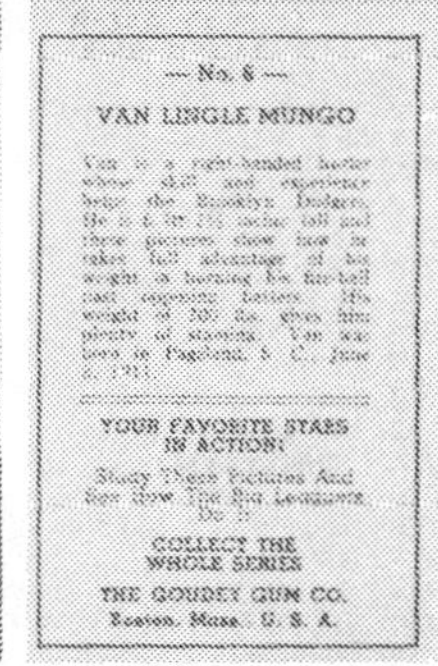

Issued circa 1937, this set of "flip movies" was comprised of small (2" by 3") booklets whose pages produced a movie effect when flipped rapidly, similar to a penny arcade novelty popular at the time. There are 13 players in the set, each movie having two cleary labeled parts. The cover of the booklets identify the set as "Big League Baseball Movies." Issued by Goudey, they carry the American Card Catalog designation R326.

		NR MT	EX	VG
Complete Set (26):		2600.	1300.	800.00
Common Player:		45.00	22.00	13.50
1a	John Irving Burns (Part 1)	45.00	22.00	13.50
1b	John Irving Burns (Part 2)	45.00	22.00	13.50
2a	Joe Vosmik (Part 1)	45.00	22.00	13.50
2b	Joe Vosmik (Part 2)	45.00	22.00	13.50
3a	Mel Ott (Part 1)	100.00	50.00	30.00
3b	Mel Ott (Part 2)	100.00	50.00	30.00
4a	Joe DiMaggio (Part 1, Joe DiMaggio cover photo)	450.00	225.00	135.00
4aa	Joe DiMaggio (Part 1, Vince DiMaggio cover photo)	350.00	175.00	105.00
4b	Joe DiMaggio (Part 2, Joe DiMaggio cover photo)	450.00	225.00	135.00
4bb	Joe DiMaggio (Part 2, Vince DiMaggio cover photo)	350.00	175.00	105.00
5a	Wally Moses (Part 1)	45.00	22.00	13.50
5b	Wally Moses (Part 2)	45.00	22.00	13.50
6a	Van Lingle Mungo (Part 1)	45.00	22.00	13.50
6b	Van Lingle Mungo (Part 2)	45.00	22.00	13.50
7a	Luke Appling (Part 1)	70.00	35.00	21.00
7b	Luke Appling (Part 2)	70.00	35.00	21.00
8a	Bob Feller (Part 1)	150.00	75.00	45.00
8b	Bob Feller (Part 2)	150.00	75.00	45.00
9a	Paul Derringer (Part 1)	45.00	22.00	13.50
9b	Paul Derringer (Part 2)	45.00	22.00	13.50
10a	Paul Waner (Part 1)	70.00	35.00	21.00
10b	Paul Waner (Part 2)	70.00	35.00	21.00
11a	Joe Medwick (Part 1)	70.00	35.00	21.00
11b	Joe Medwick (Part 2)	70.00	35.00	21.00
12a	James Emory Foxx (Part 1)	150.00	75.00	45.00
12b	James Emory Foxx (Part 2)	150.00	75.00	45.00
13a	Wally Berger (Part 1)	45.00	22.00	13.50
13b	Wally Berger (Part 2)	45.00	22.00	13.50

The values quoted are intended to reflect the market price.

1938 Goudey

Sometimes referred to as the Goudey Heads-Up set, this issue begins numbering (#241) where the 1933 Goudey set left off. On the card fronts, a photo is used for the player's head with the body being a cartoon drawing. Twenty-four different players are pictured twice in the set. Card #'s 241-264 feature plain backgrounds on the card fronts. Card #'s 265-288 contain the same basic design and photo but include small drawings and comments within the background. The card backs contain player statistical and biographical information. The ACC designation for the issue is R323.

	NR MT	EX	VG
Complete Set:	16500.	7095.	4125.
Common Player (241-264):	125.00	54.00	31.00
Common Player (265-288):	140.00	60.00	35.00
241 Charlie Gehringer	500.00	215.00	125.00
242 Ervin Fox	125.00	54.00	31.00
243 Joe Kuhel	125.00	54.00	31.00
244 Frank DeMaree	125.00	54.00	31.00
245 Frank Pytlak	125.00	54.00	31.00
246 Ernie Lombardi	225.00	97.00	56.00
247 Joe Vosmik	125.00	54.00	31.00
248 Dick Bartell	125.00	54.00	31.00
249 Jimmy Foxx	550.00	236.00	137.00
250 Joe DiMaggio	4000.	2100.	1100.
251 Bump Hadley	125.00	54.00	31.00
252 Zeke Bonura	125.00	54.00	31.00
253 Hank Greenberg	450.00	193.00	112.00
254 Van Lingle Mungo	140.00	60.00	35.00
255 Julius Solters	125.00	54.00	31.00
256 Vernon Kennedy	125.00	54.00	31.00
257 Al Lopez	225.00	97.00	56.00
258 Bobby Doerr	300.00	129.00	75.00
259 Bill Werber	125.00	54.00	31.00
260 Rudy York	140.00	60.00	35.00
261 Rip Radcliff	125.00	54.00	31.00
262 Joe Ducky Medwick	350.00	150.00	87.00
263 Marvin Owen	125.00	54.00	31.00
264 Bob Feller	800.00	344.00	200.00
265 Charlie Gehringer	450.00	193.00	112.00
266 Ervin Fox	140.00	60.00	35.00
267 Joe Kuhel	140.00	60.00	35.00
268 Frank DeMaree	140.00	60.00	35.00
269 Frank Pytlak	140.00	60.00	35.00
270 Ernie Lombardi	275.00	118.00	69.00
271 Joe Vosmik	140.00	60.00	35.00
272 Dick Bartell	140.00	60.00	35.00
273 Jimmy Foxx	600.00	258.00	150.00
274 Joe DiMaggio	4500.	2200.	1200.
275 Bump Hadley	140.00	60.00	35.00
276 Zeke Bonura	140.00	60.00	35.00
277 Hank Greenberg	500.00	215.00	125.00
278 Van Lingle Mungo	140.00	60.00	35.00
279 Julius Solters	140.00	60.00	35.00
280 Vernon Kennedy	140.00	60.00	35.00
281 Al Lopez	250.00	107.00	62.00
282 Bobby Doerr	350.00	150.00	87.00
283 Bill Werber	140.00	60.00	35.00
284 Rudy York	140.00	60.00	35.00
285 Rip Radcliff	140.00	60.00	35.00
286 Joe Ducky Medwick	400.00	172.00	100.00
287 Marvin Owen	140.00	60.00	35.00
288 Bob Feller	900.00	387.00	225.00

1939 Goudey Premiums (R303-A)

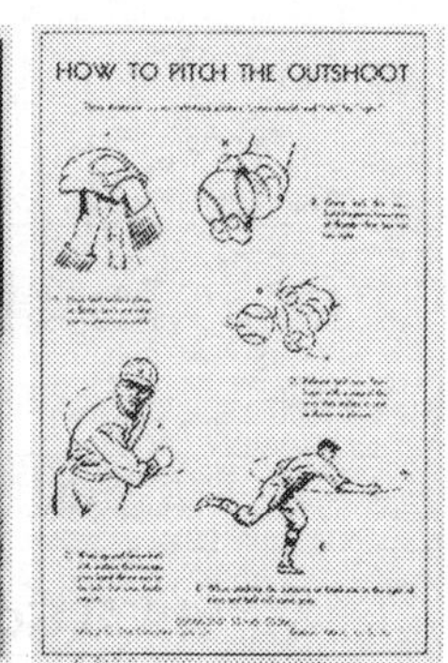

Although this unnumbered set of paper premiums has the name "Diamond Stars Gum" on the back, it is not related to National Chicle's Diamond Stars card sets. Rather, this 48-player set was a premium issued by the Goudey Gum Company. Each premium photo measures 6-3/16" by 4" and is printed in a brown-toned sepia. The front of the photo includes a facsimile autograph, while the back contains drawings that illustrate various baseball tips.

	NR MT	EX	VG
Complete Set (48):	2000.	1000.	600.00
Common Player:	25.00	12.50	7.50
(1) Luke Appling	45.00	22.00	13.50
(2) Earl Averill	45.00	22.00	13.50
(3) Wally Berger	30.00	15.00	9.00
(4) Darrell Blanton	25.00	12.50	7.50
(5) Zeke Bonura	25.00	12.50	7.50
(6) Mace Brown	25.00	12.50	7.50
(7) George Case	25.00	12.50	7.50
(8) Ben Chapman	30.00	15.00	9.00
(9) Joe Cronin	45.00	22.00	13.50
(10) Frank Crosetti	35.00	17.50	10.50
(11) Paul Derringer	25.00	12.50	7.50
(12) Bill Dickey	75.00	37.00	22.00
(13) Joe DiMaggio	275.00	137.00	82.00
(14) Bob Feller	80.00	40.00	24.00
(15) Jimmy Foxx	80.00	40.00	24.00
(16) Charles Gehringer	45.00	22.00	13.50
(17) Lefty Gomez	45.00	22.00	13.50
(18) Ival Goodman	25.00	12.50	7.50
(19) Joe Gordon	25.00	12.50	7.50
(20) Hank Greenberg	50.00	25.00	15.00
(21) Buddy Hassett	25.00	12.50	7.50
(22) Jeff Heath	25.00	12.50	7.50
(23) Tom Henrich	25.00	12.50	7.50
(24) Billy Herman	40.00	20.00	12.00
(25) Frank Higgins	25.00	12.50	7.50
(26) Fred Hutchinson	30.00	15.00	9.00
(27) Bob Johnson	25.00	12.50	7.50
(28) Ken Keltner	25.00	12.50	7.50
(29) Mike Kreevich	25.00	12.50	7.50
(30) Ernie Lombardi	45.00	22.00	13.50
(31) Gus Mancuso	25.00	12.50	7.50
(32) Eric McNair	25.00	12.50	7.50
(33) Van Mungo	25.00	12.50	7.50
(34) Buck Newsom	25.00	12.50	7.50
(35) Mel Ott	35.00	17.50	10.50
(36) Marvin Owen	25.00	12.50	7.50
(37) Frank Pytlak	25.00	12.50	7.50
(38) Woodrow Rich	25.00	12.50	7.50
(39) Charley Root	25.00	12.50	7.50
(40) Al Simmons	45.00	22.00	13.50
(41) James Tabor	25.00	12.50	7.50
(42) Cecil Travis	25.00	12.50	7.50
(43) Hal Trosky	25.00	12.50	7.50
(44) Arky Vaughan	45.00	22.00	13.50
(45) Joe Vosmik	25.00	12.50	7.50
(46) Lon Warneke	25.00	12.50	7.50
(47) Ted Williams	350.00	175.00	105.00
(48) Rudy York	25.00	12.50	7.50

1939 Goudey Premiums (R303-B)

Although larger (7-5/16" by 4-3/4"), the photos in this 24-player set are identical to those in the R303-A set of the same year, and the format of the set is unchanges. The set, designated as R303-B, can be found in both black and white sepia.

	NR MT	EX	VG
Complete Set (24):	1000.	500.00	300.00
Common Player:	20.00	10.00	6.00
(1) Luke Appling	40.00	20.00	12.00
(2) George Case	20.00	10.00	6.00
(3) Ben Chapman	22.00	11.00	6.50
(4) Joe Cronin	40.00	20.00	12.00
(5) Bill Dickey	50.00	25.00	15.00
(6) Joe DiMaggio	300.00	150.00	90.00
(7) Bob Feller	60.00	30.00	18.00
(8) Jimmy Foxx	60.00	30.00	18.00
(9) Lefty Gomez	40.00	20.00	12.00
(10) Ival Goodman	20.00	10.00	6.00
(11) Joe Gordon	20.00	10.00	6.00
(12) Hank Greenberg	40.00	20.00	12.00
(13) Jeff Heath	20.00	10.00	6.00
(14) Billy Herman	35.00	17.50	10.50
(15) Frank Higgins	20.00	10.00	6.00
(16) Ken Keltner	22.00	11.00	6.50
(17) Mike Kreevich	20.00	10.00	6.00
(18) Ernie Lombardi	35.00	17.50	10.50
(19) Gus Mancuso	20.00	10.00	6.00
(20) Mel Ott	40.00	20.00	12.00
(21) Al Simmons	40.00	20.00	12.00
(22) Arky Vaughan	40.00	20.00	12.00
(23) Joe Vosmik	20.00	10.00	6.00
(24) Rudy York	20.00	10.00	6.00

1941 Goudey

Goudey Gum Co.'s last set was issued in 1941. The cards, which measure 2-3/8" by 2-7/8" in size, contain black and white photos set against blue, green, red or yellow backgrounds. The player's name, team and position plus the card number are situated in a box at the bottom of the card. The card reverses are blank. The ACC designation for the set is R324.

	NR MT	EX	VG
Complete Set (33):	2600.	1300.	825.00
Common Player:	50.00	25.00	15.00
1 Hugh Mulcahy	100.00	50.00	30.00
2 Harlond Clift	50.00	25.00	15.00
3 Louis Chiozza	50.00	25.00	15.00
4 Warren (Buddy) Rosar	50.00	25.00	15.00
5 George McQuinn	50.00	25.00	15.00
6 Emerson Dickman	50.00	25.00	15.00
7 Wayne Ambler	50.00	25.00	15.00
8 Bob Muncrief	50.00	25.00	15.00
9 Bill Dietrich	50.00	25.00	15.00
10 Taft Wright	50.00	25.00	15.00
11 Don Heffner	50.00	25.00	15.00
12 Fritz Ostermueller	50.00	25.00	15.00
13 Frank Hayes	50.00	25.00	15.00
14 John (Jack) Kramer	50.00	25.00	15.00
15 Dario Lodigiani	50.00	25.00	15.00
16 George Case	50.00	25.00	15.00
17 Vito Tamulis	50.00	25.00	15.00
18 Whitlow Wyatt	50.00	25.00	15.00
19 Bill Posedel	50.00	25.00	15.00
20 Carl Hubbell	175.00	90.00	50.00
21 Harold Warstler	175.00	90.00	50.00
22 Joe Sullivan	250.00	125.00	70.00
23 Norman (Babe) Young	175.00	90.00	50.00
24 Stanley Andrews	250.00	125.00	70.00
25 Morris Arnovich	175.00	90.00	50.00
26 Elburt Fletcher	50.00	25.00	15.00
27 Bill Crouch	60.00	30.00	18.00
28 Al Todd	50.00	25.00	15.00
29 Debs Garms	50.00	25.00	15.00
30 Jim Tobin	50.00	25.00	15.00
31 Chester Ross	50.00	25.00	15.00
32 George Coffman	60.00	30.00	18.00
33 Mel Ott	275.00	150.00	80.00

1955 Robert Gould All Stars

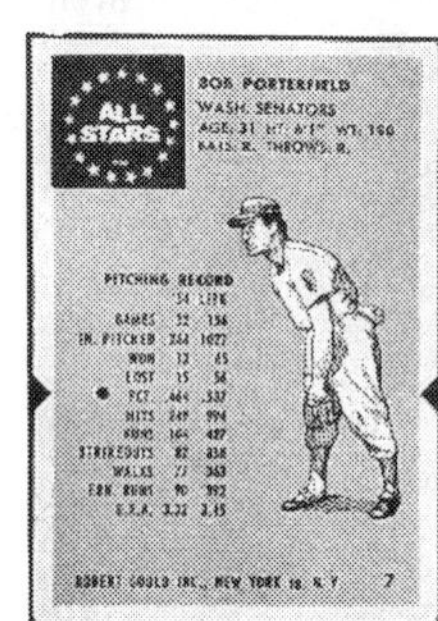

One of several issues of miniature plastic player statues issued in the mid-Fifties was the All-Stars series by Robert Gould Inc. of New York. The white plastic statues, which sold for about a quarter, came rubber-banded to a baseball card. The card measures 2-1/2" x 3-1/2" with a white border. A rather crude black-and-white line drawing of the player is set against a green background. There are a few biographical details and 1954 and lifetime stats. An "All Stars" logo is in an upper corner, while the card number is at lower-right. The cards are blank-backed. All cards have a pair of notches at the sides and a punch hole to hold the rubber band. Prices shown here are for the cards alone. Cards which retain the statues are valued from two to four times higher.

	NR MT	EX	VG
Complete Set (28):	1500.	750.00	450.00
Common Player:	50.00	25.00	15.00
1 Willie Mays	275.00	137.00	82.00
2 Gus Zernial	50.00	25.00	15.00
3 Red Schoendienst	80.00	40.00	24.00
4 Chico Carrasquel	50.00	25.00	15.00
5 Jim Hegan	50.00	25.00	15.00
6 Curt Simmons	50.00	25.00	15.00
7 Bob Porterfield	50.00	25.00	15.00
8 Jim Busby	50.00	25.00	15.00
9 Don Mueller	50.00	25.00	15.00
10 Ted Kluszewski	75.00	37.00	22.00
11 Ray Boone	50.00	25.00	15.00
12 Smoky Burgess	50.00	25.00	15.00
13 Bob Rush	50.00	25.00	15.00
14 Early Wynn	75.00	37.00	22.00
15 Bill Bruton	50.00	25.00	15.00
16 Gus Bell	50.00	25.00	15.00
17 Jim Finigan	50.00	25.00	15.00
18 Ganny Hamner	50.00	25.00	15.00
19 Hank Thompson	50.00	25.00	15.00
20 Joe Coleman	50.00	25.00	15.00
21 Don Newcombe	60.00	30.00	18.00

22	Richie Ashburn	75.00	37.00	22.00
23	Bobby Thomson	60.00	30.00	18.00
24	Sid Gordon	50.00	25.00	15.00
25	Gerry Coleman	50.00	25.00	15.00
26	Ernie Banks	225.00	112.00	67.00
27	Billy Pierce	50.00	25.00	15.00
28	Mel Parnell	50.00	25.00	15.00

1981 Granny Goose Potato Chips A's

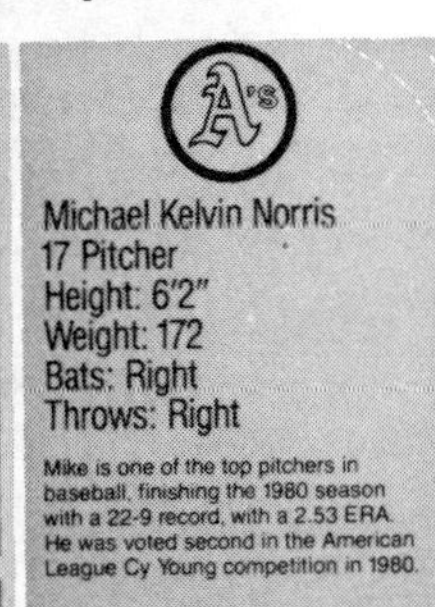

The 1981 Granny Goose set features the Oakland A's. The cards, which measure 2-1/2" by 3-1/2" in size, were issued in bags of potato chips and are sometimes found with grease stains. The cards have full color fronts with the print done in the team's green and yellow colors. The backs contain the A's logo and a short player biography. The Revering card was withdrawn from the set shortly after he was traded and is in shorter supply than the rest of the cards in the set. The cards are numbered in the checklist that follows by the player's uniform number.

		MT	NR MT	EX
Complete Set (15):		100.00	75.00	40.00
Common Player:		2.00	1.50	.80
1	Billy Martin	10.00	7.50	4.00
2	Mike Heath	2.00	1.50	.80
5	Jeff Newman	2.00	1.50	.80
6	Mitchell Page	2.00	1.50	.80
8	Rob Picciolo	2.00	1.50	.80
10	Wayne Gross	2.00	1.50	.80
13	Dave Revering	45.00	34.00	18.00
17	Mike Norris	2.00	1.50	.80
20	Tony Armas	4.00	3.00	1.50
21	Dwayne Murphy	2.00	1.50	.80
22	Rick Langford	2.00	1.50	.80
27	Matt Keough	2.00	1.50	.80
35	Rickey Henderson	30.00	22.00	12.00
39	Dave McKay	2.00	1.50	.80
54	Steve McCatty	2.00	1.50	.80

1982 Granny Goose Potato Chips A's

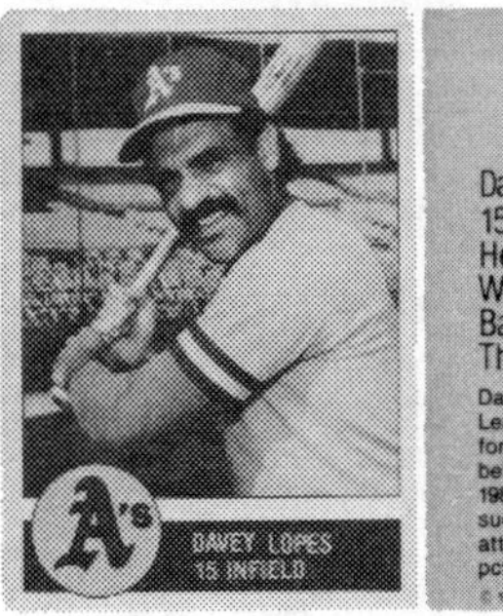

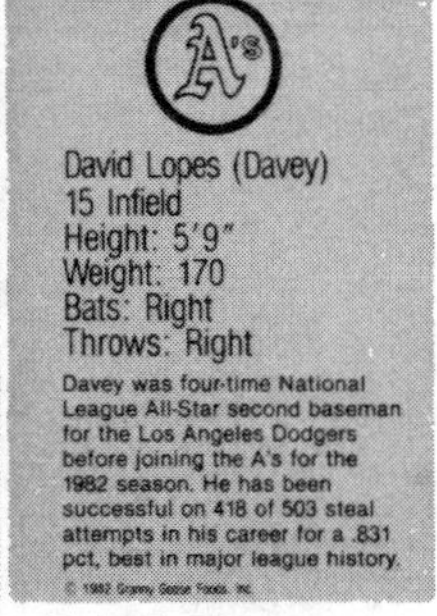

Granny Goose repeated its promotion from the previous year and issued another set featuring the Oakland A's. The cards, which measure 2-1/2" by 3-1/2", were distributed in two fashions - in bags of potato chips and at Fan Appreciation Day at Oakland-Alameda Coliseum. The cards are identical in design to the 1981 set and can be distinguished from it by the date on the copyright on the bottom of the card reverse. The cards are numbered in the checklist that follows by the player's uniform number.

		MT	NR MT	EX
Complete Set (15):		15.00	11.00	6.00
Common Player:		.40	.30	.15
1	Billy Martin	2.00	1.50	.80
2	Mike Heath	.40	.30	.15
5	Jeff Newman	.40	.30	.15
8	Rob Picciolo	.40	.30	.15
10	Wayne Gross	.40	.30	.15
11	Fred Stanley	.40	.30	.15
15	Davey Lopes	.80	.60	.30
17	Mike Norris	.40	.30	.15
20	Tony Armas	1.00	.70	.40
21	Dwayne Murphy	.40	.30	.15
22	Rick Langford	.40	.30	.15
27	Matt Keough	.40	.30	.15
35	Rickey Henderson	12.00	9.00	4.75
44	Cliff Johnson, Jr.	.40	.30	.15
54	Steve McCatty	.40	.30	.15

1982 Granny Goose Signature Set

Wayne Dale Gross
10 Infield
Height: 6'2"
Weight: 205
Bats: Left
Throws: Right
Wayne was the A's regular third baseman during the season. He had 3 game-winning RBI's for the A's in 1981.

© 1982 Granny Goose Foods, Inc.

The cards from this very scarce 15-card set are identical to the regular Granny Goose cards, but contain a facsimile autograph on the front. The cards were initially intended as special prize-redemption inserts from Granny Goose potato chips, but were never released in any quantity.

		MT	NR MT	EX
Complete Set (15):		175.00	125.00	70.00
Common Player:		5.00	3.75	2.00
1	Billy Martin	20.00	15.00	8.00
2	Mike Heath	5.00	3.75	2.00
5	Jeff Newman	5.00	3.75	2.00
8	Rob Picciolo	5.00	3.75	2.00
10	Wayne Gross	5.00	3.75	2.00
11	Fred Stanley	5.00	3.75	2.00
15	Davey Lopes	10.00	7.50	4.00
17	Mike Norris	5.00	3.75	2.00
20	Tony Armas	5.00	3.75	2.00
21	Dwayne Murphy	5.00	3.75	2.00
22	Rick Langford	5.00	3.75	2.00
27	Matt Keough	5.00	3.75	2.00
35	Rickey Henderson	30.00	22.00	12.00
44	Cliff Johnson, Jr.	5.00	3.75	2.00
54	Steve McCatty	5.00	3.75	2.00

1983 Granny Goose Potato Chips A's

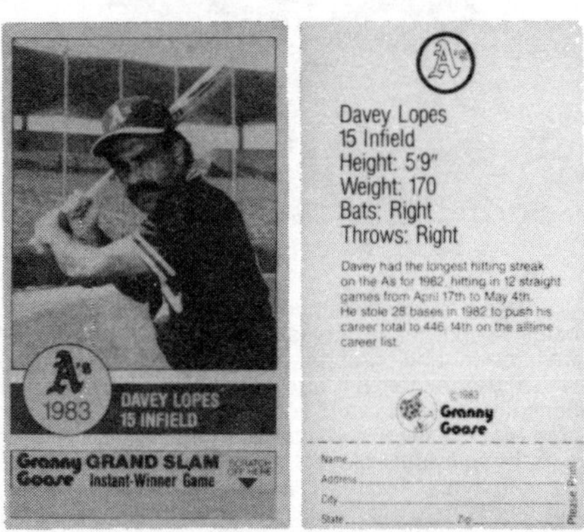

For the third consecutive year, Granny Goose issued a set of baseball cards featuring the Oakland A's. The cards were issued with or without a detachable coupon found at the bottom of each card. Issued in bags of potato chips were the coupon cards, which contain a scratch-off section offering prizes. The cards without the coupon section were given away to fans at Oakland-Alameda Coliseum on July 3, 1983. Cards with the detachable coupon command a 50 per cent premium over the couponless variety. The cards in the following checklist are numbered by the player's uniform number.

		MT	NR MT	EX
Complete Set:		15.00	11.00	6.00
Common Player:		.40	.30	.15
2	Mike Heath	.40	.30	.15
4	Carney Lansford	.60	.45	.25
10	Wayne Gross	.40	.30	.15
14	Steve Boros	.40	.30	.15
15	Davey Lopes	.80	.60	.30
16	Mike Davis	.40	.30	.15
17	Mike Norris	.40	.30	.15
21	Dwayne Murphy	.40	.30	.15
22	Rick Langford	.40	.30	.15
27	Matt Keough	.40	.30	.15
31	Tom Underwood	.40	.30	.15
33	Dave Beard	.40	.30	.15
35	Rickey Henderson	10.00	7.50	4.00
39	Tom Burgmeier	.40	.30	.15
54	Steve McCatty	.40	.30	.15

1969 Greiner Tires Pittsburgh Pirates

One of the scarcer of the many Pirates regionals of the late 1960s is this eight-card issue. Printed on heavy paper in black-and-white, the 5" x 7" cards are blank-backed and unnumbered. They are checklisted here alphabetically. Some sources say the Matty Alou card is scarcer than the rest of the set.

		NR MT	EX	VG
Complete Set (8):		125.00	62.50	37.50
Common Player:		9.00	4.50	2.75
(1)	Gene Alley	9.00	4.50	2.75
(2)	Matty Alou	15.00	7.50	4.50
(3)	Steve Blass	9.00	4.50	2.75
(4)	Roberto Clemente	60.00	30.00	18.00
(5)	Jerry May	9.00	4.50	2.75
(6)	Bill Mazeroski	24.00	12.00	7.25
(7)	Larry Shepard	9.00	4.50	2.75
(8)	Willie Stargell	24.00	12.00	7.25

1887 Gypsy Queens

The 1887 Gypsy Queen set is very closely related to the N172 Old Judge set and employs the same poses.The Gypsy Queens are easily identified by the words "Gypsy Queen" along the top of the cards. A line near the bottom lists the player's name, position and team, followed by an 1887 copyright line and words "Cigarettes" and "Goodwin & Co. N.Y." Although the checklist is still considered incomplete, 133 different poses have been discovered so far. Collectors should be aware that the Gypsy Queens were issued in two distinct sizes, the more common version measuring 1-1/2" by 2-1/2" (same as Old Judge) and a larger size measuring 2" by 3-1/2" which are considered extremely rare. The large Gypsy Queens are identical in format to the smaller size.

	NR MT	EX	VG
Complete Set:	99000.	50000.	20000.
Common Player:	350.00	150.00	50.00

(1)	Tug Arundel	350.00	150.00	50.00
(2)	Fido Baldwin	350.00	150.00	50.00
(3)	Samuel Barkley (fielding)	350.00	150.00	50.00
(4)	Samuel Barkley (tagging player)	350.00	150.00	50.00
(5)	Handsome Boyle	350.00	150.00	50.00
(6)	Dan Brouthers (looking at ball)	1000.	500.00	190.00
(7)	Dan Brouthers (looking to right)	1000.	500.00	190.00
(8a)	California Brown (New York, throwing, large size)	4500.	2000.	900.00
(8b)	California Brown (New York, throwing, small size)	350.00	150.00	50.00
(9)	California Brown (New York, wearing mask)	350.00	150.00	50.00
(10)	Thomas Brown (Pittsburg, catching)	350.00	150.00	50.00
(11)	Thomas Brown (Pittsburg, with bat)	350.00	150.00	50.00
(12)	Black Jack Burdock	350.00	150.00	50.00
(13)	Watch Burnham	350.00	150.00	50.00
(14)	Doc Bushong	350.00	150.00	50.00
(15)	Patsy Cahill	350.00	150.00	50.00
(16)	Frederick Carroll	350.00	150.00	50.00
(17)	Parisian Bob Caruthers	350.00	150.00	50.00
(18)	Jack Clements (hands on knees)	350.00	150.00	50.00
(19)	Jack Clements (with bat)	350.00	150.00	50.00
(20)	John Coleman	350.00	150.00	50.00
(21)	Commy Comiskey	1000.	500.00	190.00
(22a)	Roger Connor (large size)	7000.	3000.	1250.
(22b)	Roger Connor (small size)	1000.	500.00	190.00
(23)	Dick Conway	350.00	150.00	50.00
(24)	Larry Corcoran	350.00	150.00	50.00
(25)	Samuel Crane (fielding)	350.00	150.00	50.00
(26)	Samuel Crane (with bat)	350.00	150.00	50.00
(27)	Edward Dailey	350.00	150.00	50.00
(28)	Abner Dalrymple	350.00	150.00	50.00
(29)	Dell Darling	350.00	150.00	50.00
(30)	Pat Dealey (bat at side)	350.00	150.00	50.00
(31)	Pat Dealey (bat on right shoulder)	350.00	150.00	50.00
(32)	Jerry Denny (catching)	350.00	150.00	50.00
(33)	Jerry Denny (with bat)	350.00	150.00	50.00
(34)	Jim Donnelly	350.00	150.00	50.00
(35)	Mike Dorgan	350.00	150.00	50.00
(36)	Buck Ewing (large size)	7000.	3000.	1250.
(37)	Buck Ewing (small size)	1000.	500.00	190.00
(38)	Jack Farrell (bat at side)	350.00	150.00	50.00
(39)	Jack Farrell (bat in air)	350.00	150.00	50.00
(40)	Jack Farrell (fielding)	350.00	150.00	50.00
(41)	Jack Farrell (hands on thighs)	350.00	150.00	50.00
(42)	Charlie Ferguson (hands at chest)	350.00	150.00	50.00
(43)	Charlie Ferguson (tagging player)	350.00	150.00	50.00
(44)	Charlie Ferguson (with bat)	350.00	150.00	50.00
(45)	Jocko Fields (catching)	350.00	150.00	50.00
(46)	Jocko Fields (throwing)	350.00	150.00	50.00
(47)	Dave Foutz	350.00	150.00	50.00
(48)	Honest John Gaffney	350.00	150.00	50.00
(49)	Pud Galvin (with bat)	1000.	500.00	190.00
(50)	Pud Galvin (without bat)	1000.	500.00	190.00
(51)	Emil Geiss (hands above waist)	350.00	150.00	50.00
(52)	Emil Geiss (right hand extended)	350.00	150.00	50.00
(53)	Barney Gilligan	350.00	150.00	50.00
(54)	Pebbly Jack Glasscock (hands on knees)	350.00	150.00	50.00
(55)	Pebbly Jack Glasscock (throwing)	350.00	150.00	50.00
(56)	Pebbly Jack Glasscock (with bat)	350.00	150.00	50.00
(57)	Will Gleason	350.00	150.00	50.00
(58)	Piano Legs Gore (fielding)	350.00	150.00	50.00
(59)	Piano Legs Gore (hand at head level)	350.00	150.00	50.00
(60)	Ed Greer	350.00	150.00	50.00
(61)	Tom Gunning (stooping to catch low ball on left)	350.00	150.00	50.00
(62)	Tom Gunning (bending, hands by right knee)	350.00	150.00	50.00
(63)	Ned Hanlon (catching)	350.00	150.00	50.00
(64)	Ned Hanlon (with bat)	350.00	150.00	50.00
(65)	Pa Harkins (hands above waist)	350.00	150.00	50.00
(66)	Pa Harkins (throwing)	350.00	150.00	50.00
(67)	Egyptian Healey	350.00	150.00	50.00
(68)	Paul Hines	350.00	150.00	50.00
(69)	Joe Hornung	350.00	150.00	50.00
(70)	Nat Hudson	350.00	150.00	50.00
(71)	Cutrate Irwin	350.00	150.00	50.00
(72)	Dick Johnston (catching)	350.00	150.00	50.00
(73)	Dick Johnston (with bat)	350.00	150.00	50.00
(74a)	Tim Keefe (pitching, hands at chest, large size)	7000.	3000.	1250.
(74b)	Tim Keefe (pitching, hands at chest, small size)	1000.	500.00	190.00
(75)	Tim Keefe (pitching, hands above waist, facing front)	1000.	500.00	190.00
(76)	Tim Keefe (right hand extended at head level)	1000.	500.00	190.00
(77)	Tim Keefe (with bat)	1000.	500.00	190.00
(78)	King Kelly (catching)	1200.	550.00	200.00
(79)	King Kelly (portrait)	1200.	550.00	200.00
(80a)	King Kelly (with bat, lg. size)	7000.	3000.	1250.
(80b)	King Kelly (with bat, sm. size)	1200.	550.00	200.00
(81)	Rudy Kemmler	350.00	150.00	50.00
(82)	Bill Krieg (catching)	350.00	150.00	50.00
(83)	Bill Krieg (with bat)	350.00	150.00	50.00
(84)	Arlie Latham	350.00	150.00	50.00
(85)	Mike Mattimore (hands above head)	350.00	150.00	50.00
(86)	Mike Mattimore (hands at neck)	350.00	150.00	50.00
(87)	Tommy McCarthy (catching)	1000.	500.00	190.00
(88)	Tommy McCarthy (with bat)	1000.	500.00	190.00
(89)	Bill McClellan	350.00	150.00	50.00
(90)	Jim McCormick	350.00	150.00	50.00
(91)	Jack McGeachy	350.00	150.00	50.00
(92)	Deacon McGuire	350.00	150.00	50.00
(93)	George Myers (Indianapolis, stooping)	350.00	150.00	50.00
(94)	George Myers (Indianapolis, with bat)	350.00	150.00	50.00
(95)	Al Myers (Washington)	350.00	150.00	50.00
(96)	Little Nick Nicol	350.00	150.00	50.00
(97)	Hank O'Day (ball in hand)	350.00	150.00	50.00
(98)	Hank O'Day (with bat)	350.00	150.00	50.00
(99)	Tip O'Neill	350.00	150.00	50.00
(100)	George Pinkney	350.00	150.00	50.00
(101)	Hardy Richardson (Detroit)	350.00	150.00	50.00
(102)	Danny Richardson (New York, large size)	4500.	2000.	900.00
(103)	Danny Richardson (New York, small size)	350.00	150.00	50.00
(104)	Yank Robinson	350.00	150.00	50.00
(105)	Jack Rowe	350.00	150.00	50.00
(106)	Emmett Seery (arms folded)	350.00	150.00	50.00
(107)	Emmett Seery (ball in hands)	350.00	150.00	50.00
(108)	Emmett Seery (catching)	350.00	150.00	50.00
(109)	George Shoch	350.00	150.00	50.00
(110)	Otto Shomberg (Schomberg)	350.00	150.00	50.00
(111)	Pap Smith	350.00	150.00	50.00
(112)	Cannonball Stemmyer (Stemmeyer) (pitching)	350.00	150.00	50.00
(113)	Cannonball Stemmyer (Stemmeyer) (with bat)	350.00	150.00	50.00
(114)	Ezra Sutton (with bat)	350.00	150.00	50.00
(115)	Big Sam Thompson (arms folded)	1000.	500.00	190.00
(116)	Big Sam Thompson (bat at side)	1000.	500.00	190.00
(117)	Big Sam Thompson (swinging at ball)	1000.	500.00	190.00
(118)	Silent Mike Tiernan (lg. size)	4500.	2000.	900.00
(119)	Stephen Toole	350.00	150.00	50.00
(120)	Larry Twitchell (hands by chest)	350.00	150.00	50.00
(121)	Larry Twitchell (right hand extended)	350.00	150.00	50.00
(122)	Chris Von Der Ahe	350.00	150.00	50.00
(123)	Monte Ward (large size)	7000.	3000.	1250.
(124)	Curt Welch	350.00	150.00	50.00
(125)	Art Whitney (Pittsburg, bending)	350.00	150.00	50.00
(126)	Art Whitney (Pittsburg, with bat)	350.00	150.00	50.00
(127)	Grasshopper Whitney (Washington)	350.00	150.00	50.00
(128)	Medoc Wise	350.00	150.00	50.00
(129)	George "Dandy" Wood	350.00	150.00	50.00

1888 Joseph Hall Cabinets

These fourteen cabinet-size (6-1/2" by 4-1/2") cards feature team photos taken by Joseph Hall, a well-known photographer of the day. The cards, which are extremely rare, all have Hall's name beneath the photo and some include his Brooklyn address. The team is identified in large capital letters with the individual players identified in smaller type on both sides. Fourteen teams are known to date, but others may also exist, and Hall may have produced similar team cabinets in other years as well.

		NR MT	EX	VG
Complete Set (14):		90000.	45000.	27000.
Common Team:		6500.	3250.	2000.
(1)	Athletic Ball Club, 1888	6150.	3750.	2300.
(2)	Boston Ball Club, 1888	14750.	9000.	550.00
(3)	Brooklyn Ball Club, 1888	5350.	3250.	2000.
(4)	Chicago Ball Club, 1888	8200.	5000.	3000.
(5)	Cincinnati Ball Club, 1888	5350.	3250.	2000.
(6)	Cleveland Ball Club, 1888	5350.	3250.	2000.
(7)	Detroit Ball Club, 1888	6550.	4000.	2500.
(8)	Indianapolis Ball Club, 1888	5350.	3250.	2000.
(9)	Kansas City Ball Club, 1888	5350.	3250.	2000.
(10)	Louisville Ball Club, 1888	5350.	3250.	2000.
(11)	New York Ball Club, 1888 (wearing baseball uniforms)	8200.	5000.	3000.
(12)	New York Ball Club, 1888 (wearing tuxedos)	8200.	5000.	3000.
(13)	St. Louis Baseball Club, 1888	6150.	3750.	2300.
(14)	Washington Baseball Club, 1888	10250.	6250.	4000.

1911 Helmar Stamps (T332)

In an interesting departure from the traditional tobacco cards of the period, Helmar Cigarettes in 1911 issued a series of small major league baseball player "stamps." The stamps, each measuring approximately 1-1/8" by 1-3/8", feature a black and white player portrait surrounded by a colorful, ornate frame. The stamps were originally issued in a 2" by 2-1/2" glassine envelope which advertised the Helmar brand and promoted "Philately - the Popular European Rage." To date, 181 different player stamps have been found. The set includes as many as 50 different frame designs are also known to exist. The Helmar stamp set has been assigned a T332 designation by the American Card Catalog.

		NR MT	EX	VG
Complete Set:		10000.	5000.	3000.
Common Player:		35.00	17.50	10.50
(1)	Babe Adams	35.00	17.50	10.50
(2)	Red Ames	35.00	17.50	10.50
(3)	Jimmy Archer	35.00	17.50	10.50
(4)	Jimmy Austin	35.00	17.50	10.50
(5)	Home Run Baker	95.00	47.00	28.00
(6)	Neal Ball	35.00	17.50	10.50
(7)	Cy Barger	35.00	17.50	10.50
(8)	Jack Barry	35.00	17.50	10.50
(9)	Johnny Bates	35.00	17.50	10.50
(10)	Fred Beck	35.00	17.50	10.50
(11)	Beals Becker	35.00	17.50	10.50
(12)	George Bell	35.00	17.50	10.50
(13)	Chief Bender	95.00	47.00	28.00
(14)	Bob Bescher	35.00	17.50	10.50
(15)	Joe Birmingham	35.00	17.50	10.50
(16)	John Bliss	35.00	17.50	10.50
(17)	Bruno Block	35.00	17.50	10.50
(18)	Ping Bodie	35.00	17.50	10.50
(19)	Roger Bresnahan	95.00	47.00	28.00
(20)	Al Bridwell	35.00	17.50	10.50
(21)	Lew Brockett	35.00	17.50	10.50
(22)	Mordecai Brown	95.00	47.00	28.00
(23)	Bill Burns	35.00	17.50	10.50
(24)	Donie Bush	35.00	17.50	10.50
(25)	Bobby Byrne	35.00	17.50	10.50
(26)	Nixey Callahan	35.00	17.50	10.50
(27)	Howie Camnitz	35.00	17.50	10.50
(28)	Max Carey	95.00	47.00	28.00
(29)	Bill Carrigan	35.00	17.50	10.50
(30)	Frank Chance	95.00	47.00	28.00
(31)	Hal Chase	50.00	25.00	15.00
(32)	Ed Cicotte	50.00	25.00	15.00
(33)	Fred Clarke	95.00	47.00	28.00
(34)	Tommy Clarke	35.00	17.50	10.50
(35)	Ty Cobb	700.00	350.00	210.00
(36)	King Cole	35.00	17.50	10.50
(37)	Eddie Collins (Philadelphia)	95.00	47.00	28.00
(38)	Shano Collins (Chicago)	35.00	17.50	10.50
(39)	Wid Conroy	35.00	17.50	10.50
(40)	Doc Crandall	35.00	17.50	10.50
(41)	Sam Crawford	95.00	47.00	28.00
(42)	Birdie Cree	35.00	17.50	10.50
(43)	Bill Dahlen	35.00	17.50	10.50
(44)	Jake Daubert	35.00	17.50	10.50
(45)	Harry Davis	35.00	17.50	10.50
(46)	Jim Delahanty	35.00	17.50	10.50
(47)	Art Devlin	35.00	17.50	10.50
(48)	Josh Devore	35.00	17.50	10.50
(49)	Mike Donlin	35.00	17.50	10.50
(50)	Wild Bill Donovan	35.00	17.50	10.50
(51)	Red Dooin	35.00	17.50	10.50
(52)	Mickey Doolan	35.00	17.50	10.50
(53)	Patsy Dougherty	35.00	17.50	10.50
(54)	Tom Downey	35.00	17.50	10.50
(55)	Larry Doyle	35.00	17.50	10.50
(56)	Louis Drucke	35.00	17.50	10.50
(57)	Clyde Engle	35.00	17.50	10.50
(58)	Tex Erwin	35.00	17.50	10.50
(59)	Steve Evans	35.00	17.50	10.50
(60)	Johnny Evers	95.00	47.00	28.00
(61)	Jack Ferry	35.00	17.50	10.50
(62)	Ray Fisher	35.00	17.50	10.50
(63)	Art Fletcher	35.00	17.50	10.50
(64)	Russ Ford	35.00	17.50	10.50
(65)	Art Fromme	35.00	17.50	10.50
(66)	Earl Gardner	35.00	17.50	10.50
(67)	Harry Gaspar	35.00	17.50	10.50
(68)	George Gibson	35.00	17.50	10.50
(69)	Roy Golden	35.00	17.50	10.50

(70)	Hank Gowdy	35.00	17.50	10.50
(71)	Peaches Graham	35.00	17.50	10.50
(72)	Eddie Grant	45.00	22.00	13.50
(73)	Dolly Gray	35.00	17.50	10.50
(74)	Clark Griffith	95.00	47.00	28.00
(75)	Bob Groom	35.00	17.50	10.50
(76)	Bob Harmon	35.00	17.50	10.50
(77)	Grover Hartley	35.00	17.50	10.50
(78)	Arnold Hauser	35.00	17.50	10.50
(79)	Buck Herzog	35.00	17.50	10.50
(80)	Dick Hoblitzell	35.00	17.50	10.50
(81)	Solly Hoffman (Hofman)	35.00	17.50	10.50
(82)	Miller Huggins	95.00	47.00	28.00
(83)	Long Tom Hughes	35.00	17.50	10.50
(84)	John Hummel	35.00	17.50	10.50
(85)	Hughie Jennings	95.00	47.00	28.00
(86)	Walter Johnson	400.00	200.00	120.00
(87)	Davy Jones	35.00	17.50	10.50
(88)	Johnny Kling	35.00	17.50	10.50
(89)	Otto Knabe	35.00	17.50	10.50
(90)	Jack Knight	35.00	17.50	10.50
(91)	Ed Konetchy	35.00	17.50	10.50
(92)	Harry Krause	35.00	17.50	10.50
(93)	Nap Lajoie	125.00	62.00	37.00
(94)	Joe Lake	35.00	17.50	10.50
(95)	Frank LaPorte	35.00	17.50	10.50
(96)	Tommy Leach	35.00	17.50	10.50
(97)	Lefty Leifield	35.00	17.50	10.50
(98)	Ed Lennox	35.00	17.50	10.50
(99)	Paddy Livingston	35.00	17.50	10.50
(100)	Hans Lobert	35.00	17.50	10.50
(101)	Harry Lord	35.00	17.50	10.50
(102)	Fred Luderas (Luderus)	35.00	17.50	10.50
(103)	Sherry Magee	35.00	17.50	10.50
(104)	Rube Marquard	95.00	47.00	28.00
(105)	Christy Mathewson	400.00	200.00	120.00
(106)	Al Mattern	35.00	17.50	10.50
(107)	George McBride	35.00	17.50	10.50
(108)	Amby McConnell	35.00	17.50	10.50
(109)	John McGraw	75.00	37.00	22.00
(110)	Harry McIntire (McIntyre)	35.00	17.50	10.50
(111)	Matty McIntyre	35.00	17.50	10.50
(112)	Larry McLean	35.00	17.50	10.50
(113)	Fred Merkle	35.00	17.50	10.50
(114)	Chief Meyers	35.00	17.50	10.50
(115)	Clyde Milan	35.00	17.50	10.50
(116)	Dots Miller	35.00	17.50	10.50
(117)	Mike Mitchell	35.00	17.50	10.50
(118)	Earl Moore	35.00	17.50	10.50
(119)	Pat Moran	35.00	17.50	10.50
(120)	George Moriarty	35.00	17.50	10.50
(121)	Mike Mowrey	35.00	17.50	10.50
(122)	George Mullin	35.00	17.50	10.50
(123)	Danny Murphy	35.00	17.50	10.50
(124)	Red Murray	35.00	17.50	10.50
(125)	Tom Needham	35.00	17.50	10.50
(126)	Rebel Oakes	35.00	17.50	10.50
(127)	Rube Oldring	35.00	17.50	10.50
(128)	Marty O'Toole	35.00	17.50	10.50
(129)	Fred Parent	35.00	17.50	10.50
(130)	Dode Paskert	35.00	17.50	10.50
(131)	Barney Pelty	35.00	17.50	10.50
(132)	Eddie Phelps	35.00	17.50	10.50
(133)	Jack Powell	35.00	17.50	10.50
(134)	Jack Quinn	35.00	17.50	10.50
(135)	Ed Reulbach	35.00	17.50	10.50
(136)	Lew Richie	35.00	17.50	10.50
(137)	Reggie Richter	35.00	17.50	10.50
(138)	Jack Rowan	35.00	17.50	10.50
(139)	Nap Rucker	35.00	17.50	10.50
(140)	Slim Sallee	35.00	17.50	10.50
(141)	Doc Scanlan	35.00	17.50	10.50
(142)	Germany Schaefer	35.00	17.50	10.50
(143)	Boss Schmidt	35.00	17.50	10.50
(144)	Wildfire Schulte	35.00	17.50	10.50
(145)	Jim Scott	35.00	17.50	10.50
(146)	Tillie Shafer	35.00	17.50	10.50
(147)	Dave Shean	35.00	17.50	10.50
(148)	Jimmy Sheckard	35.00	17.50	10.50
(149)	Mike Simon	35.00	17.50	10.50
(150)	Fred Snodgrass	35.00	17.50	10.50
(151)	Tris Speaker	200.00	100.00	60.00
(152)	Oscar Stanage	35.00	17.50	10.50
(153)	Bill Steele	35.00	17.50	10.50
(154)	Harry Stovall	35.00	17.50	10.50
(155)	Gabby Street	35.00	17.50	10.50
(156)	George Suggs	35.00	17.50	10.50
(157)	Billy Sullivan	35.00	17.50	10.50
(158)	Bill Sweeney	35.00	17.50	10.50
(159)	Jeff Sweeney	35.00	17.50	10.50
(160)	Lee Tannehill	35.00	17.50	10.50
(161)	Ira Thomas	35.00	17.50	10.50
(162)	Joe Tinker	95.00	47.00	28.00
(163)	John Titus	35.00	17.50	10.50
(164)	Fred Toney	35.00	17.50	10.50
(165)	Terry Turner	35.00	17.50	10.50
(166)	Hippo Vaughn	35.00	17.50	10.50
(167)	Heinie Wagner	35.00	17.50	10.50
(168)	Bobby Wallace	95.00	47.00	28.00
(169)	Ed Walsh	75.00	37.00	22.00
(170)	Jack Warhop	35.00	17.50	10.50
(171)	Zach Wheat	95.00	47.00	28.00
(172)	Doc White	35.00	17.50	10.50
(173)	Ed Willett	35.00	17.50	10.50
(174)	Art Wilson (New York)	35.00	17.50	10.50
(175)	Owen Wilson (Pittsburgh)	35.00	17.50	10.50
(176)	Hooks Wiltse	35.00	17.50	10.50
(177)	Harry Wolter	35.00	17.50	10.50
(178)	Harry Wolverton	35.00	17.50	10.50
(179)	Cy Young	500.00	250.00	150.00
(180)	Irv Young	35.00	17.50	10.50

A player's name in italic type indicates a rookie card. An (FC) indicates a player's first card for that particular card company.

1888 S.F. Hess (N338-2)

The most popular of the S.F. Hess & Co. issues, this 21-card set was issued in 1889 and pictures 16 players from the New York Giants, two New York Mets players, two from St. Louis and one from Detroit. The cards measure 2-3/4" by 1-1/2" and feature sepia-toned photographs, most of which are enclosed in ovals with a dark background. The player's name is printed in capital letters just beneath the photo, and the S.F. Hess & Co. logo appears at the bottom (without using the Creole Cigarette brand name).

		NR MT	EX	VG
Complete Set:		19000.	9500.	5700.
Common Player:		750.00	375.00	225.00
(1)	Bill Brown	750.00	375.00	225.00
(2)	Roger Conner (Connor)	1800.	900.00	550.00
(3)	Ed Crane	750.00	375.00	225.00
(4)	Buck Ewing	1800.	900.00	550.00
(5)	Elmer Foster	750.00	375.00	225.00
(6)	Wm. George	750.00	375.00	225.00
(7)	Joe Gerhardt	750.00	375.00	225.00
(8)	Chas. Getzein	750.00	375.00	225.00
(9)	Geo. Gore	750.00	375.00	225.00
(10)	Gil Hatfield	750.00	375.00	225.00
(11)	Tim Keefe	1800.	900.00	550.00
(12)	Arlie Latham	750.00	375.00	225.00
(13)	Pat Murphy	750.00	375.00	225.00
(14)	Jim Mutrie	750.00	375.00	225.00
(15)	Dave Orr	750.00	375.00	225.00
(16)	Danny Richardson	750.00	375.00	225.00
(17)	Mike Slattery	750.00	375.00	225.00
(18)	Silent Mike Tiernan	750.00	375.00	225.00
(19)	Lidell Titcomb	750.00	375.00	225.00
(20)	Johnny Ward	1800.	900.00	550.00
(21)	Curt Welch	750.00	375.00	225.00
(22)	Mickey Welch	1800.	900.00	550.00
(23)	Arthur Whitney	750.00	375.00	225.00

Regional interest may affect the value of a card.

1993 Highland Mint Mint-Card

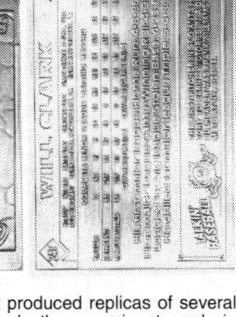

The Highland Mint produced replicas of several Topps rookie cards and other prominent cards in bronze and silver. Limited to 1,000 in silver and 5,000 in bronze, the company produced cards of many current stars along with a replica of Brooks Robinson's 1957 rookie card. The cards carried a suggested retail price of $235 for the silver and $50 for the bronze. Cards measure 2-1/2" x 3-1/2" and are 1/10" thick. Each Mint-Card has a serial number engraved on the edge and is sold in a heavy lucite holder, packaged with a certificate of authenticity in a plastic book-style folder. Besides baseball card replicas, the company also produced football and hockey Mint-Cards.

		MT	NR MT	EX
Complete Set, Silver (17):		4000.	3000.	1600.
Complete Set, Bronze (17):		850.00	637.00	340.00
Common Player, Silver:		235.00	176.00	94.00
Common Player, Bronze:		50.00	37.00	20.00
(1a)	Brooks Robinson (1957, silver)	235.00	176.00	94.00
(1b)	Brooks Robinson (1957, bronze)	50.00	37.00	20.00
(2a)	Dave Winfield (1974, silver)	235.00	176.00	94.00
(2b)	Dave Winfield (1974, bronze)	50.00	37.00	20.00
(3a)	George Brett (1975, silver)	295.00	221.00	118.00
(3b)	George Brett (1975, bronze)	50.00	37.00	20.00
(4a)	Robin Yount (1975, silver)	235.00	176.00	94.00
(4b)	Robin Yount (1975, bronze)	50.00	37.00	20.00
(5a)	Ozzie Smith (1979, silver)	235.00	176.00	94.00
(5b)	Ozzie Smnith (1979, bronze)	50.00	37.00	20.00
(6a)	Don Mattingly (1984, silver)	235.00	176.00	94.00
(6b)	Don Mattingly (1984, bronze)	50.00	37.00	20.00
(7a)	Roger Clemens (1985, silver)	235.00	176.00	94.00
(7b)	Roger Clemens (1985, bronze)	50.00	37.00	20.00
(8a)	Kirby Puckett (1985, silver)	235.00	176.00	94.00
(8b)	Kirby Puckett (1985, bronze)	50.00	37.00	20.00
(9a)	Barry Bonds (1986, silver)	235.00	176.00	94.00
(9b)	Barry Bonds (1986, bronze)	50.00	37.00	20.00
(10a)	Will Clark (1986, silver)	235.00	176.00	94.00
(10b)	Will Clark (1986, bronze)	50.00	37.00	20.00
(11a)	Roberto Alomar (1988, silver)	235.00	176.00	94.00
(11b)	Roberto Alomar (1988, bronze)	50.00	37.00	20.00
(12a)	Juan Gonzalez (1990, silver)	235.00	176.00	94.00
(12b)	Juan Gonzalez (1990, bronze)	50.00	37.00	20.00
(13a)	Ken Griffey, Jr. (1992, silver)	235.00	176.00	94.00
(13b)	Ken Griffey, Jr. (1992, bronze)	50.00	37.00	20.00
(14a)	Cal Ripken, Jr. (1992, silver)	235.00	176.00	94.00
(14b)	Cal Ripken, Jr. (1992, bronze)	50.00	37.00	20.00
(15a)	Nolan Ryan (1992, silver)	700.00	525.00	280.00
(15b)	Nolan Ryan (1992, bronze)	145.00	109.00	58.00
(16a)	Ryne Sandberg (1992, silver)	235.00	176.00	94.00
(16b)	Ryne Sandberg (1992, bronze)	50.00	37.00	20.00
(17a)	Frank Thomas (1992, silver)	235.00	176.00	94.00
(17b)	Frank Thomas (1992, bronze)	50.00	37.00	20.00

1994 Highland Mint Mint-Cards

In 1994 the Highland Mint continued its production of Mint-Cards, licensed metal replicas of Topps baseball, football and hockey cards. Production of baseball players in the series was reduced to 750 in silver and halved to 2,500 in bronze. Suggested retail prices remained at $235 and $50, respectively. Once again cards were produced in the same 2-1/2" x 3-1/2" format as original Topps cards and were minted to a thickness of 1/10", with a serial number engraved on the edge. Mint-cards were sold in a heavy lucite holder, packaed with a certificate of authenticity in a plastic book-style holder.

		MT	NR MT	EX
Complete Set, Silver:		1700.	1250.	675.00
Complete Set, Bronze:		375.00	280.00	150.00
Common Player, Silver:		235.00	175.00	95.00
Common Player, Bronze:		50.00	37.00	20.00
(1a)	Ernie Banks (1954, silver)	235.00	175.00	95.00
(1b)	Ernie Banks (1954, bronze)	50.00	37.00	20.00
(2a)	Carl Yastrzemski (1960, silver)	235.00	175.00	95.00
(2b)	Carl Yastrzemski (1960, bronze)	50.00	37.00	20.00
(3a)	Mike Schmidt (1974, silver)	235.00	175.00	95.00
(3b)	Mike Schmidt (1974, bronze)	50.00	37.00	20.00
(4a)	Paul Molitor (1979, silver)	235.00	175.00	90.00
(4b)	Paul Molitor (1979, bronze)	50.00	37.00	20.00
(5a)	Deion Sanders (1989, silver)	235.00	175.00	95.00
(5b)	Deion Sanders (1989, bronze)	50.00	37.00	20.00
(6a)	Dave Justice (1990, silver)	235.00	175.00	90.00
(6b)	Dave Justice (1990, bronze)	50.00	37.00	20.00
(7a)	Mike Piazza (1992, silver)	235.00	175.00	95.00
(7b)	Mike Piazza (1992, bronze)	50.00	37.00	20.00
(8a)	Tim Salmon (1993, silver)	235.00	175.00	95.00
(8b)	Tim Salmon (1993, bronze)	50.00	37.00	20.00

1989 Hills Team MVP's

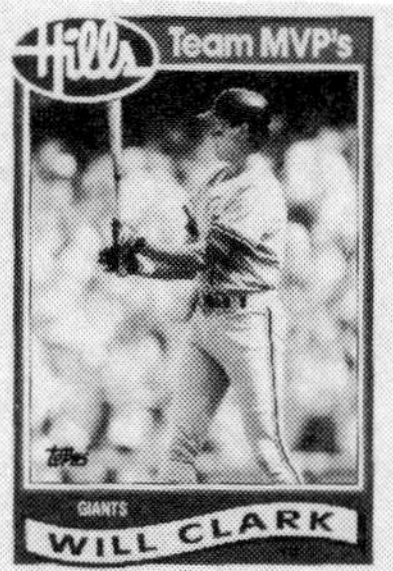

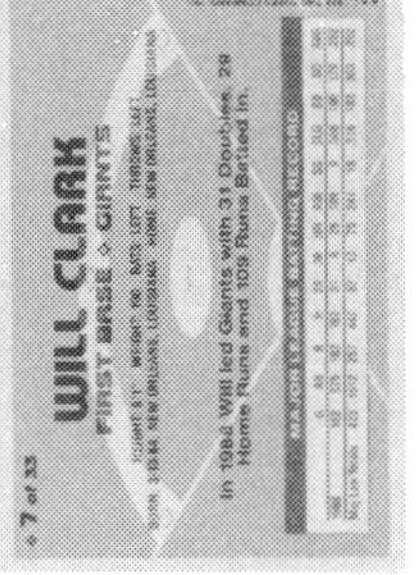

This high-gloss, 33-card boxed set of superstars was produced by Topps for the Hills department store chain. The words "Hills Team MVP's" appear above the player photos, while the player's name and team are printed below. The front of the card carries a red, white and blue color scheme with yellow and gold accents. The horizontal backs include player data set against a green playing field background.

		MT	NR MT	EX
Complete Set (33):		5.00	3.75	2.00
Common Player:		.05	.04	.02
1	Harold Baines	.05	.04	.02
2	Wade Boggs	.30	.25	.12
3	George Brett	.30	.25	.12
4	Tom Brunansky	.05	.04	.02
5	Jose Canseco	.35	.25	.14
6	Joe Carter	.15	.11	.06
7	Will Clark	.35	.25	.14
8	Roger Clemens	.15	.11	.06
9	Dave Cone	.05	.04	.02
10	Glenn Davis	.05	.04	.02
11	Andre Dawson	.09	.07	.04
12	Dennis Eckersley	.09	.07	.04
13	Andres Galarraga	.10	.08	.04
14	Kirk Gibson	.06	.05	.02
15	Mike Greenwell	.10	.08	.04
16	Tony Gwynn	.15	.11	.06
17	Orel Hershiser	.09	.07	.04
18	Danny Jackson	.05	.04	.02
19	Mark Langston	.09	.07	.04
20	Fred McGriff	.20	.15	.08
21	Dale Murphy	.25	.20	.10
22	Eddie Murray	.25	.20	.10
23	Kirby Puckett	.30	.25	.12
24	Johnny Ray	.05	.04	.02
25	Juan Samuel	.05	.04	.02
26	Ruben Sierra	.15	.11	.06
27	Dave Stewart	.05	.04	.02
28	Darryl Strawberry	.10	.08	.04
29	Allan Trammell	.15	.11	.06
30	Andy Van Slyke	.05	.04	.02
31	Frank Viola	.06	.05	.02
32	Dave Winfield	.30	.25	.12
33	Robin Yount	.35	.25	.14

1990 Hills Hit Men

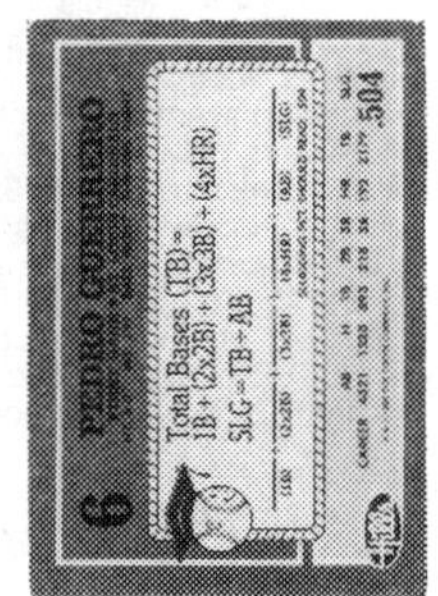

The 33 slugging percentage leaders are featured in this high-gloss set. The cards were produced by Topps for the Hills department store chain. The card fronts feature "Hit Men" in a bat design above the photo. The player's name appears on a band below the photo. The horizontal backs feature a breakdown of the player's slugging percentage and also display career statistics.

		MT	NR MT	EX
Complete Set (33):		5.00	3.75	2.00
Common Player:		.05	.04	.02
1	Eric Davis	.10	.08	.04
2	Will Clark	.25	.20	.10
3	Don Mattingly	.20	.15	.08
4	Darryl Strawberry	.10	.08	.04
5	Kevin Mitchell	.10	.08	.04
6	Pedro Guerrero	.05	.04	.02
7	Jose Canseco	.30	.25	.12
8	Jim Rice	.05	.04	.02
9	Danny Tartabull	.09	.07	.04
10	George Brett	.30	.25	.12
11	Kent Hrbek	.10	.08	.04
12	George Bell	.09	.07	.04
13	Eddie Murray	.15	.11	.06
14	Fred Lynn	.05	.04	.02
15	Andre Dawson	.15	.11	.06
16	Dale Murphy	.15	.11	.06
17	Dave Winfield	.20	.15	.08
18	Jack Clark	.05	.04	.02
19	Wade Boggs	.25	.20	.10
20	Ruben Sierra	.15	.11	.06
21	Dave Parker	.10	.08	.04
22	Glenn Davis	.05	.04	.02
23	Dwight Evans	.05	.04	.02
24	Jesse Barfield	.05	.04	.02
25	Kirk Gibson	.06	.05	.02
26	Alvin Davis	.05	.04	.02
27	Kirby Puckett	.20	.15	.08
28	Joe Carter	.15	.11	.06
29	Carlton Fisk	.15	.11	.06
30	Harold Baines	.05	.04	.02
31	Andres Galarraga	.10	.08	.04
32	Cal Ripken, Jr.	.35	.25	.14
33	Howard Johnson	.08	.06	.03

1958 Hires Root Beer Test Set

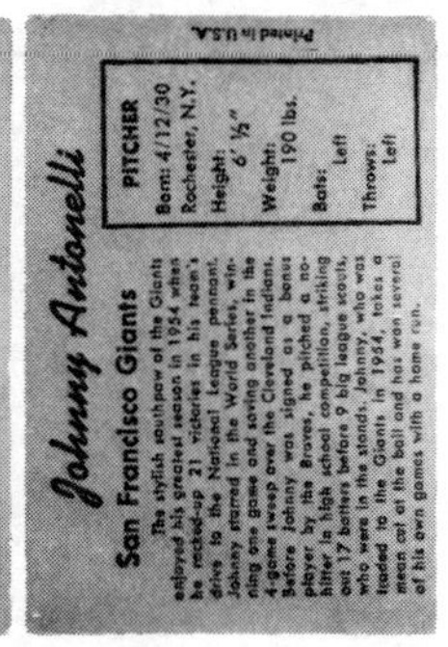

Among the scarcest of the regional issues of the late 1950s is the eight-card test issue which preceded the Hires Root Beer set of 66 cards. Probably issued in a very limited area in the Northeast, the test cards differ from the regular issue in that they have sepia-toned, rather than color pictures, which are set against plain yellow or orange backgrounds (much like the 1958 Topps), instead of viewed through a knothole. Like the regular Hires cards, the 2-5/16" by 3-1/2" cards were issued with an attached wedge-shaped tab of like size. The tab offered membership in Hires baseball fan club, and served to hold the card into the carton of bottled root beer with which it was given away. Values quoted here are for cards with tabs. Cards without tabs would be valued approximately 50 per cent lower.

		NR MT	EX	VG
Complete Set (8):		1500.	750.00	450.00
Common Player:		140.00	70.00	42.00
(1)	Johnny Antonelli	165.00	82.00	49.00
(2)	Jim Busby	140.00	70.00	42.00
(3)	Chico Fernandez	140.00	70.00	42.00
(4)	Bob Friend	165.00	82.00	49.00
(5)	Vern Law	165.00	82.00	49.00
(6)	Stan Lopata	140.00	70.00	42.00
(7)	Willie Mays	600.00	300.00	180.00
(8)	Al Pilarcik	140.00	70.00	42.00

Regional interest may affect the value of a card.

1958 Hires Root Beer

Like most baseball cards issued with a tab in the 1950s, the Hires cards are extremely scarce today in their original form. The basic card was attached to a wedge-shaped tab that served the dual purpose of offering a fan club membership and of holding the card into the cardboard carton of soda bottles with which it was distributed. The card itself measures 2-5/16" by 3-1/2". The tab extends for another 3-1/2". Numbering of the Hires set begins at 10 and goes through 76, with card #69 never issued, making a set complete at 66 cards. Values given below are for cards with tabs. Cards without tabs would be valued approximately 50 per cent lower.

		NR MT	EX	VG
Complete Set:		2400.	1200.	720.00
Common Player:		35.00	17.50	10.50
10	Richie Ashburn	150.00	75.00	45.00
11	Chico Carrasquel	35.00	17.50	10.50
12	Dave Philley	35.00	17.50	10.50
13	Don Newcombe	40.00	20.00	12.00
14	Wally Post	35.00	17.50	10.50
15	Rip Repulski	35.00	17.50	10.50
16	Chico Fernandez	35.00	17.50	10.50
17	Larry Doby	40.00	20.00	12.00
18	Hector Brown	35.00	17.50	10.50
19	Danny O'Connell	35.00	17.50	10.50
20	Granny Hamner	35.00	17.50	10.50
21	Dick Groat	35.00	17.50	10.50
22	Ray Narleski	35.00	17.50	10.50
23	Pee Wee Reese	125.00	62.00	37.00
24	Bob Friend	35.00	17.50	10.50
25	Willie Mays	300.00	150.00	90.00
26	Bob Nieman	35.00	17.50	10.50
27	Frank J. Thomas	35.00	17.50	10.50
28	Curt Simmons	35.00	17.50	10.50
29	Stan Lopata	35.00	17.50	10.50
30	Bob Skinner	35.00	17.50	10.50
31	Ron Kline	35.00	17.50	10.50
32	Willie Miranda	35.00	17.50	10.50
33	Bob Avila	35.00	17.50	10.50
34	Clem Labine	35.00	17.50	10.50
35	Ray Jablonski	35.00	17.50	10.50
36	Bill Mazeroski	45.00	22.00	13.50
37	Billy Gardner	35.00	17.50	10.50
38	Pete Runnels	35.00	17.50	10.50
39	Jack Sanford	35.00	17.50	10.50
40	Dave Sisler	35.00	17.50	10.50
41	Don Zimmer	35.00	17.50	10.50
42	Johnny Podres	40.00	20.00	12.00
43	Dick Farrell	35.00	17.50	10.50
44	Hank Aaron	300.00	150.00	90.00
45	Bill Virdon	35.00	17.50	10.50
46	Bobby Thomson	40.00	20.00	12.00
47	Willard Nixon	35.00	17.50	10.50
48	Billy Loes	35.00	17.50	10.50
49	Hank Sauer	35.00	17.50	10.50
50	Johnny Antonelli	35.00	17.50	10.50
51	Daryl Spencer	35.00	17.50	10.50
52	Ken Lehman	35.00	17.50	10.50
53	Sammy White	35.00	17.50	10.50
54	Charley Neal	35.00	17.50	10.50
55	Don Drysdale	100.00	50.00	30.00
56	Jack Jensen	40.00	20.00	12.00
57	Ray Katt	35.00	17.50	10.50
58	Franklin Sullivan	35.00	17.50	10.50
59	Roy Face	35.00	17.50	10.50
60	Willie Jones	35.00	17.50	10.50
61	Duke Snider	150.00	75.00	45.00
62	Whitey Lockman	35.00	17.50	10.50
63	Gino Cimoli	35.00	17.50	10.50
64	Marv Grissom	35.00	17.50	10.50
65	Gene Baker	35.00	17.50	10.50
66	George Zuverink	35.00	17.50	10.50
67	Ted Kluszewski	45.00	22.00	13.50
68	Jim Busby	35.00	17.50	10.50
69	Not Issued	35.00	17.50	10.50
70	Curt Barclay	35.00	17.50	10.50
71	Hank Foiles	35.00	17.50	10.50
72	Gene Stephens	35.00	17.50	10.50
73	Al Worthington	35.00	17.50	10.50
74	Al Walker	35.00	17.50	10.50
75	Bob Boyd	35.00	17.50	10.50
76	Al Pilarcik	35.00	17.50	10.50

1992 Holoprisms

The Holoprism set actually consists of two 4-card hologram sets of Rookies of the Year Jeff Bagwell and Chuck Knoblauch. Each player set was packaged in a special plastic case. The production was limited to 250,000 of each set. Each set is numbered and contains a letter of authenticity.

	MT	NR MT	EX
Complete Bagwell Set (4):	6.00	4.50	2.50
Complete Knoblauch Set (4):	6.00	4.50	2.50
Jeff Bagwell (1-4)	1.50	1.25	.60
Chuck Knoblauch (1-4)	1.50	1.25	.60

Values quoted in this guide reflect the retail price of a card – the price a collector can expect to pay when buying a card from a dealer. The wholesale price – that which a collector can expect to receive from a dealer when selling cards – will be significantly lower, depending on desirability and condition.

Values for recent cards and sets are listed in Mint (MT), Near Mint (NM), reflecting the fact that many cards from recent years have been preserved in top condition. Recent cards and sets in less than Excellent condition have little collector interest.

1989 Holsum Bakeries Superstars Discs

		MT	NR MT	EX
Complete Set (20):		12.00	9.00	4.75
Common Player:		.40	.30	.15
1	Wally Joyner	.40	.30	.15
2	Wade Boggs	1.00	.70	.40
3	Ozzie Smith	.80	.60	.30
4	Don Mattingly	1.50	1.25	.60
5	Jose Canseco	2.00	1.50	.80
6	Tony Gwynn	.70	.50	.30
7	Eric Davis	.60	.45	.25
8	Kirby Puckett	1.00	.70	.40
9	Kevin Seitzer	.40	.30	.15
10	Darryl Strawberry	.60	.45	.25
11	Gregg Jefferies	.75	.60	.30
12	Mark Grace	.70	.50	.30
13	Matt Nokes	.40	.30	.15
14	Mark McGwire	.80	.60	.30
15	Don Mattingly	1.50	1.25	.60
16	Roger Clemens	.70	.50	.30
17	Frank Viola	.50	.40	.20
18	Orel Hershiser	.50	.40	.20
19	Dave Cone	.40	.30	.15
20	Kirk Gibson	.40	.30	.15

1990 Holsum Bakeries Superstars Discs

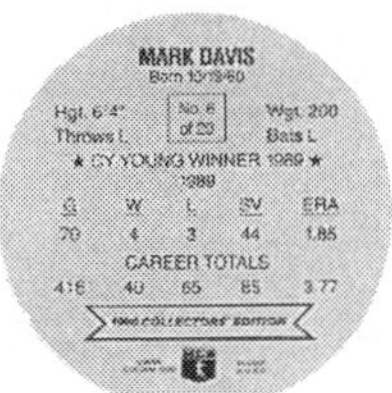

Players in this disc set are featured in round portrait photos on which uniform logos have been painted over for lack of a license from Major League Baseball (the set is licensed by the players' union and bears their logo on back. Most of the front border on these 2-3/4" diameter discs is in red, with yellow stars and white baseballs around the portrait and the bakery's logo at top. A yellow banner beneath the photo has the "Superstars" logo. At bottom, in the white portion of the border, the player's name is presented in red, with his team and position in blue. Backs are printed in blue and include 1989 and career stats, a few biographical details, the card number and appropriate copyrights.

		MT	NR MT	EX
Complete Set (20):		11.00	8.25	4.50
Common Player:		.50	.40	.20
1	George Bell	.50	.40	.20
2	Tim Raines	.50	.40	.20
3	Tom Henke	.50	.40	.20
4	Andres Galarraga	.65	.50	.25
5	Bret Saberhagen	.50	.40	.20
6	Mark Davis	.50	.40	.20
7	Robin Yount	1.00	.70	.40
8	Rickey Henderson	.75	.60	.30
9	Kevin Mitchell	.60	.45	.25
10	Howard Johnson	.60	.45	.25
11	Will Clark	.75	.60	.30
12	Orel Hershiser	.50	.40	.20
13	Fred McGriff	.65	.50	.25
14	Dave Stewart	.50	.40	.20
15	Vince Coleman	.50	.40	.20
16	Steve Sax	.50	.40	.20
17	Kirby Puckett	.75	.60	.30
18	Tony Gwynn	.75	.60	.30
19	Jerome Walton	.50	.40	.20

Definitions for grading conditions are located in the Introduction of this price guide.

1991 Holsum Bakeries Superstars Discs

		MT	NR MT	EX
Complete Set (20):		15.00	11.00	6.00
Common Player:		.50	.40	.20
1	Darryl Strawberry	.60	.45	.25
2	Eric Davis	.60	.45	.25
3	Tim Wallach	.50	.40	.20
4	Kevin Mitchell	.60	.45	.25
5	Tony Gwynn	.75	.60	.30
6	Ryne Sandberg	1.50	1.25	.60
7	Doug Drabek	.50	.40	.20
8	Randy Myers	.50	.40	.20
9	Ken Griffey, Jr.	2.50	2.00	1.00
10	Alan Trammell	.65	.50	.25
11	Ken Griffey, Sr.	.50	.40	.20
12	Rickey Henderson	.75	.60	.30
13	Roger Clemens	.60	.45	.25
14	Bob Welch	.50	.40	.20
15	Kelly Gruber	.50	.40	.20
16	Mark McGwire	.65	.50	.25
17	Cecil Fielder	.65	.50	.25
18	Dave Steib	.50	.40	.20
19	Nolan Ryan	2.50	2.00	1.00
20	Cal Ripken, Jr.	1.50	1.25	.60

1959 Home Run Derby

This 20-card unnumbered set was produced by American Motors to publicize the Home Run Derby television program. The cards measure approximately 3-1/4" by 5-1/4" and feature black and white player photos on black-backed white stock. The player name and team are printed beneath the photo. This set was reprinted (and marked as such) in 1988 by Card Collectors' Company of New York.

		NR MT	EX	VG
Complete Set (20):		4000.	2000.	1200.
Common Player:		100.00	50.00	30.00
(1)	Hank Aaron	450.00	225.00	135.00
(2)	Bob Allison	100.00	50.00	30.00
(3)	Ernie Banks	300.00	150.00	90.00
(4)	Ken Boyer	150.00	75.00	45.00
(5)	Bob Cerv	100.00	50.00	30.00
(6)	Rocky Colavito	225.00	112.00	67.00
(7)	Gil Hodges	225.00	112.00	67.00
(8)	Jackie Jensen	150.00	75.00	45.00
(9)	Al Kaline	300.00	150.00	90.00
(10)	Harmon Killebrew	275.00	137.00	82.00
(11)	Jim Lemon	100.00	50.00	30.00
(12)	Mickey Mantle	1200.	600.00	360.00
(13)	Ed Mathews	275.00	137.00	82.00
(14)	Willie Mays	450.00	225.00	135.00
(15)	Wally Post	100.00	50.00	30.00
(16)	Frank Robinson	275.00	137.00	82.00
(17)	Mark Scott (host)	150.00	75.00	45.00
(18)	Duke Snider	400.00	200.00	120.00
(19)	Dick Stuart	125.00	62.00	37.00
(20)	Gus Triandos	100.00	50.00	30.00

1991 Homers Cookies

One card was inserted in each box of Homers Cookies. The cards measure 2 1/2" by 3 1/2" and feature sepia-toned photos. The card backs feature

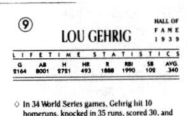

lifetime statistics and career highlights. The cards are also numbered on the back and a checklist is featured on the back of each card.

		MT	NR MT	EX
Complete Set (9):		8.00	6.00	3.25
Common Player:		.50		.40
1	Babe Ruth	1.50	1.25	.60
2	Satchel Paige	1.00	.70	.40
3	Lefty Gomez	.50	.40	.20
4	Ty Cobb	1.25	.90	.50
5	Cy Young	.50	.40	.20
6	Bob Feller	.50	.40	.20
7	Roberto Clemente	1.00	.70	.40
8	Dizzy Dean	.75	.60	.30
9	Lou Gehrig	1.25	.90	.50

1947 Homogenized Bond Bread

Issued by Homogenized Bond Bread in 1947, this set consists of 48 unnumbered black and white cards, each measuring 2-1/4" by 3-1/2". Of the 48 cards, 44 are baseball players; four picture boxers. The cards are usually found with rounded corners, although cards with square corners are also known to exist. The set contains both portrait and action photos, and features the player's facsimile autograph on the front. In the 1980s a large quantity of half the cards in the set was uncovered in New York, creating a great disparity of supply between the 22 cards found in the hoard and the rest of the set. Current pricing reflects that fact.

		NR MT	EX	VG
Complete Set (44):		750.00	375.00	225.00
Common Player:		6.00	3.00	1.75
(1)	Rex Barney	6.00	3.00	1.75
(2)	Yogi Berra	55.00	27.00	16.50
(3)	Ewell Blackwell	4.00	2.00	1.25
(4)	Lou Boudreau	10.00	5.00	3.00
(5)	Ralph Branca	10.00	5.00	3.00
(6)	Harry Brecheen	4.00	2.00	1.25
(7)	Dom DiMaggio	10.00	5.00	3.00
(8)	Joe DiMaggio	150.00	75.00	45.00
(9)	Bobbie Doerr (Bobby)	10.00	5.00	3.00
(10)	Bruce Edwards	6.00	3.00	1.75
(11)	Bob Elliott	4.00	2.00	1.25
(12)	Del Ennis	4.00	2.00	1.25
(13)	Bob Feller	15.00	7.50	4.50
(14)	Carl Furillo	10.00	5.00	3.00
(15)	Cid Gordon (Sid)	6.00	3.00	1.75
(16)	Joe Gordon	4.00	2.00	1.25
(17)	Joe Hatten	6.00	3.00	1.75
(18)	Gil Hodges	35.00	17.50	10.50
(19)	Tommy Holmes	4.00	2.00	1.25
(20)	Larry Janson (Jansen)	6.00	3.00	1.75
(21)	Sheldon Jones	6.00	3.00	1.75
(22)	Edwin Joost	6.00	3.00	1.75
(23)	Charlie Keller	10.00	5.00	3.00
(24)	Ken Keltner	4.00	2.00	1.25
(25)	Buddy Kerr	6.00	3.00	1.75
(26)	Ralph Kiner	12.00	6.00	3.50
(27)	John Lindell	6.00	3.00	1.75
(28)	Whitey Lockman	6.00	3.00	1.75
(29)	Willard Marshall	6.00	3.00	1.75

(30)	Johnny Mize	8.00	4.00	2.50
(31)	Stan Musial	60.00	30.00	18.00
(32)	Andy Pafko	4.00	2.00	1.25
(33)	Johnny Pesky	4.00	2.00	1.25
(34)	Pee Wee Reese	55.00	27.00	16.50
(35)	Phil Rizzuto	15.00	7.50	4.50
(36)	Aaron Robinson	4.00	2.00	1.25
(37)	Jackie Robinson	55.00	27.00	16.50
(38)	John Sain	6.00	3.00	1.75
(39)	Enos Slaughter	8.00	4.00	2.50
(40)	Vern Stephens	4.00	2.00	1.25
(41)	George Tebbetts	6.00	3.00	1.75
(42)	Bob Thomson	10.00	5.00	3.00
(43)	Johnny Vandermeer (VanderMeer)	10.00	5.00	3.00
(44)	Ted Williams	50.00	25.00	15.00

1893 Honest (Duke) Cabinets (N142)

These color cabinet cards, which measure 6" x 9-1/2", were produced by W.H. Duke sometime between 1893 and 1895. The player name is centered at the bottom of the card front. The brand name "Honest" is located in the lower left corner with the words "New York" in the lower right corner. Three cyclists are also part of the set.

		NR MT	EX	VG
Complete Set (4):		12000.	6000.	3500.
Common Player:		3000.	1500.	900.00
(1)	G.S. Davis	3000.	1500.	900.00
(2)	E.J. Delahanty	4000.	2000.	1250.
(3)	W.M. Nash	3000.	1500.	900.00
(4)	W. Robinson	4000.	2000.	1250.

1975 Hostess

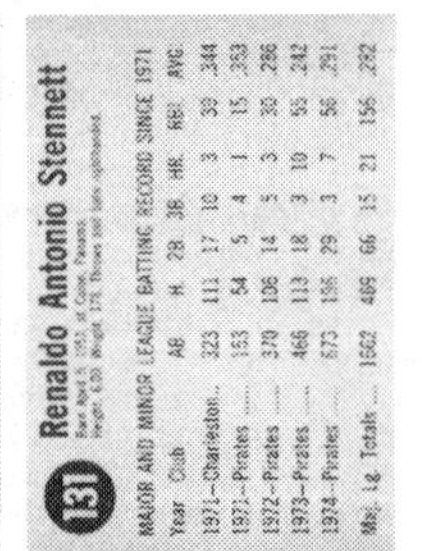

The first of what would become five annual issues, the 1975 Hostess set consists of 50 three-card panels which formed the bottom of boxes of family-size snack cake products. Unlike many similar issues, the Hostess cards do not share common borders, so it was possible to cut them neatly and evenly from the box. Well-cut single cards measure 2-1/4" by 3-1/4", while a three-card panel measures 7-1/4" by 3-1/4". Because some of the panels were issued on packages of less popular snack cakes, they are somewhat scarcer today. Since the hobby was quite well-developed when the Hostess cards were first issued, there is no lack of complete panels. Even unused complete boxes are available today. Some of the photos in this issue also appear on Topps cards of the era.

		NR MT	EX	VG
Complete Panel Set:		400.00	200.00	120.00
Complete Singles Set:		200.00	100.00	60.00
Common Panel:		2.50	1.25	.70
Common Single Player:		.40	.20	.12
	Panel 1	4.00	2.00	1.25
1	Bobby Tolan	.40	.20	.12
2	Cookie Rojas	.40	.20	.12
3	Darrell Evans	.60	.30	.20
	Panel 2	7.00	3.50	2.00
4	Sal Bando	.50	.25	.15
5	Joe Morgan	2.00	1.00	.60
6	Mickey Lolich	.75	.40	.25
	Panel 3	5.50	2.75	1.50
7	Don Sutton	1.50	.70	.45
8	Bill Melton	.40	.20	.12
9	Tim Foli	.40	.20	.12
	Panel 4	4.50	2.25	1.25
10	Joe Lahoud	.40	.20	.12
11a	Bert Hooten (incorrect spelling)	1.50	.70	.45
11b	Burt Hooton (correct spelling)	1.50	.70	.45
12	Paul Blair	.40	.20	.12
	Panel 5	3.50	1.75	1.00
13	Jim Barr	.40	.20	.12
14	Toby Harrah	.50	.25	.15
15	John Milner	.40	.20	.12
	Panel 6	4.50	2.75	1.25
16	Ken Holtzman	.50	.25	.15
17	Cesar Cedeno	.50	.25	.15
18	Dwight Evans	.65	.35	.20
	Panel 7	8.50	4.25	2.50
19	Willie McCovey	3.00	1.50	.90
20	Tony Oliva	.70	.35	.20
21	Manny Sanguillen	.40	.20	.12
	Panel 8	8.50	4.25	2.50
22	Mickey Rivers	.50	.25	.15
23	Lou Brock	3.00	1.50	.90
24	Craig Nettles	.70	.35	.20
	Panel 9	4.00	2.00	1.25
25	Jimmy Wynn	.50	.25	.15
26	George Scott	.50	.25	.15
27	Greg Luzinski	.70	.35	.20
	Panel 10	20.00	10.00	6.00
28	Bert Campaneris	.50	.25	.15
29	Pete Rose	8.00	4.00	2.50
30	Buddy Bell	.50	.25	.15
	Panel 11	3.00	1.50	.90
31	Gary Matthews	.50	.25	.15
32	Fred Patek	.40	.20	.12
33	Mike Lum	.40	.20	.12
	Panel 12	3.50	1.75	1.00
34	Ellie Rodriguez	.40	.20	.12
35	Milt May	.40	.20	.12
36	Willie Horton	.50	.25	.15
	Panel 13	12.00	6.00	3.50
37	Dave Winfield	4.50	2.25	1.25
38	Tom Grieve	.40	.20	.12
39	Barry Foote	.40	.20	.12
	Panel 14	3.50	1.75	1.00
40	Joe Rudi	.50	.25	.15
41	Bake McBride	.40	.20	.12
42	Mike Cuellar	.50	.25	.15
	Panel 15	3.50	1.75	1.00
43	Garry Maddox	.50	.25	.15
44	Carlos May	.40	.20	.12
45	Bud Harrelson	.40	.20	.12
	Panel 16	16.50	8.25	5.00
46	Dave Chalk	.40	.20	.12
47	Dave Concepcion	.50	.25	.15
48	Carl Yastrzemski	6.50	3.25	2.00
	Panel 17	7.00	3.50	2.00
49	Steve Garvey	2.00	1.00	.60
50	Amos Otis	.50	.25	.15
51	Rickey Reuschel	.50	.25	.15
	Panel 18	4.50	2.25	1.25
52	Rollie Fingers	2.00	1.00	.60
53	Bob Watson	.40	.20	.12
54	John Ellis	.40	.20	.12
	Panel 19	12.00	6.00	3.50
55	Bob Bailey	.40	.20	.12
56	Rod Carew	4.00	2.00	1.25
57	Richie Hebner	.40	.20	.12
	Panel 20	25.00	12.50	7.50
58	Nolan Ryan	10.00	5.00	3.00
59	Reggie Smith	.50	.25	.15
60	Joe Coleman	.40	.20	.12
	Panel 21	14.00	7.00	4.25
61	Ron Cey	.50	.25	.15
62	Darrell Porter	.50	.25	.15
63	Steve Carlton	4.00	2.00	1.25
	Panel 22	3.50	1.75	1.00
64	Gene Tenace	.40	.20	.12
65	Jose Cardenal	.40	.20	.12
66	Bill Lee	.40	.20	.12
	Panel 23	3.50	1.75	1.00
67	Dave Lopes	.50	.25	.15
68	Wilbur Wood	.50	.25	.15
69	Steve Renko	.40	.20	.12
	Panel 24	4.00	2.00	1.25
70	Joe Torre	.65	.35	.20
71	Ted Sizemore	.40	.20	.12
72	Bobby Grich	.50	.25	.15
	Panel 25	13.00	6.50	3.75
73	Chris Speier	.40	.20	.12
74	Bert Blyleven	.70	.35	.20
75	Tom Seaver	3.00	1.50	.90
	Panel 26	3.50	1.75	1.00
76	Nate Colbert	.40	.20	.12
77	Don Kessinger	.40	.20	.12
78	George Medich	.40	.20	.12
	Panel 27	35.00	17.50	10.50
79	Andy Messersmith	.70	.35	.20
80	Robin Yount	20.00	10.00	6.00
81	Al Oliver	.90	.45	.25
	Panel 28	18.00	9.00	5.50
82	Bill Singer	.50	.25	.15
83	Johnny Bench	4.50	2.25	1.25
84	Gaylord Perry	2.00	1.00	.60
	Panel 29	5.00	2.50	1.50
85	Dave Kingman	.60	.30	.20
86	Ed Herrmann	.50	.25	.15
87	Ralph Garr	.60	.30	.20
	Panel 30	22.00	11.00	6.50
88	Reggie Jackson	7.00	3.50	2.00
89a	Doug Radar (incorrect spelling)	2.00	1.00	.60
89b	Doug Rader (correct spelling)	2.00	1.00	.60
90	Elliott Maddox	.50	.25	.15
	Panel 31	3.50	1.75	1.00
91	Bill Russell	.60	.30	.20
92	John Mayberry	.50	.25	.15
93	Dave Cash	.50	.25	.15
	Panel 32	5.00	2.50	1.50
94	Jeff Burroughs	.60	.30	.20
95	Ted Simmons	.65	.35	.20
96	Joe Decker	.50	.25	.15
	Panel 33	11.00	5.50	3.25
97	Bill Buckner	1.00	.50	.30
98	Bobby Darwin	.50	.25	.15
99	Phil Niekro	2.00	1.00	.60
	Panel 34	4.00	2.00	1.25
100	Mike Sundberg (Jim)	.50	.25	.15
101	Greg Gross	.40	.20	.12
102	Luis Tiant	.70	.35	.20
	Panel 35	3.50	1.75	1.00
103	Glenn Beckert	.40	.20	.12
104	Hal McRae	.50	.25	.15
105	Mike Jorgensen	.40	.20	.12
	Panel 36	3.50	1.75	1.00
106	Mike Hargrove	.40	.20	.12
107	Don Gullett	.40	.20	.12
108	Tito Fuentes	.40	.20	.12
	Panel 37	6.00	3.00	1.75
109	John Grubb	.40	.20	.12
110	Jim Kaat	.90	.45	.25
111	Felix Millan	.40	.20	.12
	Panel 38	3.50	1.75	1.00
112	Don Money	.40	.20	.12
113	Rick Monday	.50	.25	.15
114	Dick Bosman	.40	.20	.12
	Panel 39	6.00	3.00	1.75
115	Roger Metzger	.40	.20	.12
116	Fergie Jenkins	.90	.45	.25
117	Dusty Baker	.60	.30	.20
	Panel 40	11.00	5.50	3.25
118	Billy Champion	.50	.25	.15
119	Bob Gibson	3.50	1.75	1.00
120	Bill Freehan	.65	.35	.20
	Panel 41	2.50	1.25	.70
121	Cesar Geronimo	.40	.20	.12
122	Jorge Orta	.40	.20	.12
123	Cleon Jones	.40	.20	.12
	Panel 42	12.00	6.00	3.50
124	Steve Busby	.40	.20	.12
125a	Bill Madlock (Pitcher)	2.00	1.00	.60
125b	Bill Madlock (Third Base)	2.00	1.00	.60
126	Jim Palmer	2.00	1.00	.60
	Panel 43	5.50	2.25	1.25
127	Tony Perez	.90	.45	.25
128	Larry Hisle	.40	.20	.12
129	Rusty Staub	.70	.35	.20
	Panel 44	19.00	9.50	5.75
130	Hank Aaron	9.00	4.50	2.75
131	Rennie Stennett	.50	.25	.15
132	Rico Petrocelli	.60	.30	.20
	Panel 45	18.00	9.00	5.50
133	Mike Schmidt	6.00	3.00	1.75
134	Sparky Lyle	.50	.25	.15
135	Willie Stargell	3.00	1.50	.90
	Panel 46	10.00	5.00	3.00
136	Ken Henderson	.40	.20	.12
137	Willie Montanez	.40	.20	.12
138	Thurman Munson	2.50	1.25	.70
	Panel 47	3.50	1.75	1.00
139	Richie Zisk	.40	.20	.12
140	George Hendricks (Hendrick)	.50	.25	.15
141	Bobby Murcer	.50	.25	.15
	Panel 48	13.00	6.50	4.00
142	Lee May	.50	.25	.15
143	Carlton Fisk	1.00	.50	.30
144	Brooks Robinson	3.50	1.75	1.00
	Panel 49	4.00	2.00	1.25
145	Bobby Bonds	.50	.25	.15
146	Gary Sutherland	.40	.20	.12
147	Oscar Gamble	.40	.20	.12
	Panel 50	7.00	3.50	2.00
148	Catfish Hunter	2.50	1.25	.70
149	Tug McGraw	.50	.25	.15
150	Dave McNally	.50	.25	.15

1975 Hostess Twinkies

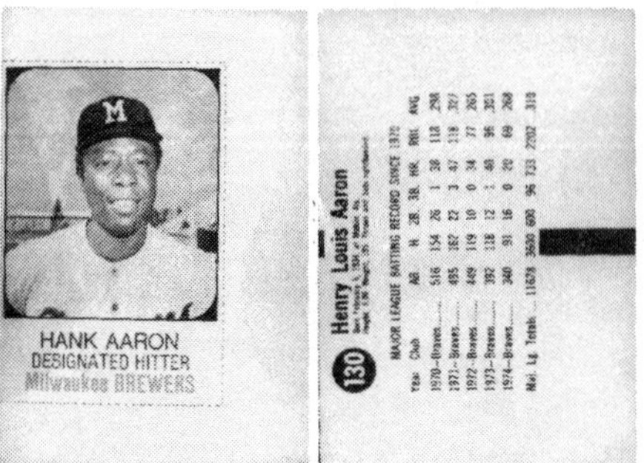

Believed to have been issued only in the Western states, and on a limited basis at that, the 1975 Hostess Twinkie set features 60 of the cards from the "regular" Hostess set of that year. The cards were issued one per pack with the popular snack cake. Card #'s 1-36 are a direct pick-up from the Hostess set, while the remaining 24 cards in the set were selected from the more popular names in the remainder of the Hostess issue - with an emphasis on West Coast players. Thus, after card #36, the '75

Twinkie cards are skip-numbered from 40-136. In identical 2-1/4" by 3-1/4" size, the Twinkie cards differ from the Hostess issue only in the presence of small black bars at top and bottom center of the back of the card. Values quoted are for full bottom panels.

		NR MT	EX	VG
Complete Set (136):		200.00	100.00	60.00
Common Player:		.90	.45	.25
1	Bobby Tolan	.90	.45	.25
2	Cookie Rojas	.90	.45	.25
3	Darrell Evans	1.50	.70	.45
4	Sal Bando	1.25	.60	.40
5	Joe Morgan	5.00	2.50	1.50
6	Mickey Lolich	2.00	1.00	.60
7	Don Sutton	3.00	1.50	.90
8	Bill Melton	.90	.45	.25
9	Tim Foli	.90	.45	.25
10	Joe Lahoud	.90	.45	.25
11	Bert Hooten (Burt Hooton)	1.25	.60	.40
12	Paul Blair	.90	.45	.25
13	Jim Barr	.90	.45	.25
14	Toby Harrah	.90	.45	.25
15	John Milner	.90	.45	.25
16	Ken Holtzman	.90	.45	.25
17	Cesar Cedeno	.90	.45	.25
18	Dwight Evans	2.00	1.00	.60
19	Willie McCovey	7.00	3.50	2.00
20	Tony Oliva	2.00	1.00	.60
21	Manny Sanguillen	.90	.45	.25
22	Mickey Rivers	.90	.45	.25
23	Lou Brock	6.50	3.25	2.00
24	Graig Nettles	3.00	1.50	.90
25	Jim Wynn	.90	.45	.25
26	George Scott	.90	.45	.25
27	Greg Luzinski	2.00	1.00	.60
28	Bert Campaneris	1.25	.60	.40
29	Pete Rose	20.00	10.00	6.00
30	Buddy Bell	1.25	.60	.40
31	Gary Matthews	1.25	.60	.40
32	Fred Patek	.90	.45	.25
33	Mike Lum	.90	.45	.25
34	Ellie Rodriguez	.90	.45	.25
35	Milt May (photo actually Lee May)	1.25	.60	.40
36	Willie Horton	.90	.45	.25
40	Joe Rudi	1.25	.60	.40
43	Garry Maddox	.90	.45	.25
46	Dave Chalk	.90	.45	.25
49	Steve Garvey	8.00	4.00	2.50
52	Rollie Fingers	4.00	2.00	1.25
58	Nolan Ryan	21.00	10.50	6.25
61	Ron Cey	1.50	.70	.45
64	Gene Tenace	.90	.45	.25
65	Jose Cardenal	.90	.45	.25
67	Dave Lopes	1.25	.60	.40
68	Wilbur Wood	.90	.45	.25
73	Chris Speier	.90	.45	.25
77	Don Kessinger	.90	.45	.25
79	Andy Messersmith	.90	.45	.25
80	Robin Yount	20.00	10.00	6.00
82	Bill Singer	.90	.45	.25
103	Glenn Beckert	.90	.45	.25
110	Jim Kaat	2.50	1.25	.70
112	Don Money	.90	.45	.25
113	Rick Monday	1.25	.60	.40
122	Jorge Orta	.90	.45	.25
125	Bill Madlock	2.25	1.25	.70
130	Hank Aaron	15.00	7.50	4.50
136	Ken Henderson	.90	.45	.25

1976 Hostess

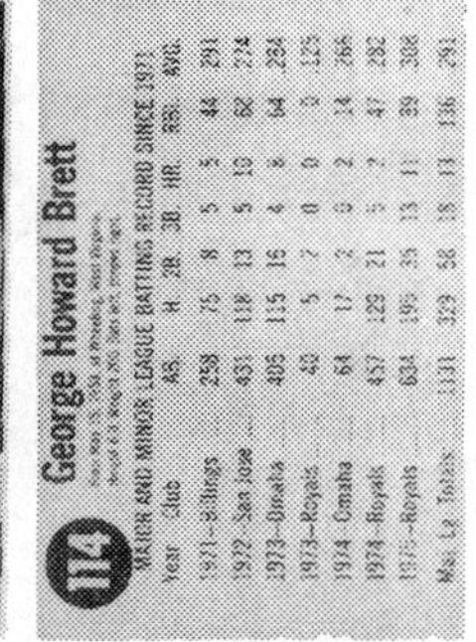

The second of five annual Hostess issues, the 1976 cards carried a "Bicentennial" color theme, with red, white and blue stripes at the bottom of the 2-1/4" by 3-1/4" cards. Like other Hostess issues, the cards were printed in panels of three as the bottom of family-size boxes of snack cake products. This leads to a degree of scarcity for some of the 150 cards in the set; those which were found on less-popular brands. A well-trimmed three-card panel measures 7-1/4" by 3-1/4" size. Some of the photos used in the 1976 Hostess set can also be found on Topps issues of the era.

		NR MT	EX	VG
Complete Panel Set:		435.00	217.00	130.00
Complete Singles Set:		225.00	112.00	67.00
Common Panel:		3.50	1.75	1.00
Common Single Player:		.40	.20	.12
	Panel 1	12.00	6.00	3.50
1	Fred Lynn	1.00	.50	.30
2	Joe Morgan	2.00	1.00	.60
3	Phil Niekro	2.00	1.00	.60
	Panel 2	6.00	3.00	1.75
4	Gaylord Perry	2.00	1.00	.60
5	Bob Watson	.40	.20	.12
6	Bill Freehan	.50	.25	.15
	Panel 3	8.00	4.00	2.50
7	Lou Brock	3.00	1.50	.90
8	Al Fitzmorris	.40	.20	.12
9	Rennie Stennett	.40	.20	.12
	Panel 4	15.00	7.50	4.50
10	Tony Oliva	.70	.35	.20
11	Robin Yount	10.00	5.00	3.00
12	Rick Manning	.40	.20	.12
	Panel 5	4.50	2.25	1.25
13	Bobby Grich	.50	.25	.15
14	Terry Forster	.40	.20	.12
15	Dave Kingman	.60	.30	.20
	Panel 6	9.00	4.50	2.75
16	Thurman Munson	2.50	1.25	.70
17	Rick Reuschel	.50	.25	.15
18	Bobby Bonds	.50	.25	.15
	Panel 7	10.00	5.00	3.00
19	Steve Garvey	3.00	1.50	.90
20	Vida Blue	.50	.25	.15
21	Dave Rader	.40	.20	.12
	Panel 8	9.00	4.50	2.75
22	Johnny Bench	4.00	2.00	1.25
23	Luis Tiant	.50	.25	.15
24	Darrell Evans	.60	.30	.20
	Panel 9	3.50	1.75	1.00
25	Larry Dierker	.40	.20	.12
26	Willie Horton	.50	.25	.15
27	John Ellis	.40	.20	.12
	Panel 10	4.00	2.00	1.25
28	Al Cowens	.40	.20	.12
29	Jerry Reuss	.50	.25	.15
30	Reggie Smith	.50	.25	.15
	Panel 11	13.00	6.50	4.00
31	Bobby Darwin	.40	.20	.12
32	Fritz Peterson	.40	.20	.12
33	Rod Carew	6.00	3.00	1.75
	Panel 12	21.00	10.50	6.25
34	Carlos May	.40	.20	.12
35	Tom Seaver	5.00	2.50	1.50
36	Brooks Robinson	5.00	2.50	1.50
	Panel 13	3.50	1.75	1.00
37	Jose Cardenal	.40	.20	.12
38	Ron Blomberg	.40	.20	.12
39	Lee Stanton	.40	.20	.12
	Panel 14	3.50	1.75	1.00
40	Dave Cash	.40	.20	.12
41	John Montefusco	.40	.20	.12
42	Bob Tolan	.40	.20	.12
	Panel 15	3.50	1.75	1.00
43	Carl Morton	.40	.20	.12
44	Rick Burleson	.40	.20	.12
45	Don Gullett	.40	.20	.12
	Panel 16	3.50	1.75	1.00
46	Vern Ruhle	.40	.20	.12
47	Cesar Cedeno	.50	.25	.15
48	Toby Harrah	.50	.25	.15
	Panel 17	7.00	3.50	2.00
49	Willie Stargell	3.00	1.50	.90
50	Al Hrabosky	.40	.20	.12
51	Amos Otis	.50	.25	.15
	Panel 18	3.50	1.75	1.00
52	Bud Harrelson	.50	.25	.15
53	Jim Hughes	.40	.20	.12
54	George Scott	.50	.25	.15
	Panel 19	11.00	5.50	3.25
55	Mike Vail	.40	.20	.12
56	Jim Palmer	3.00	1.50	.90
57	Jorge Orta	.40	.20	.12
	Panel 20	3.50	1.75	1.00
58	Chris Chambliss	.60	.30	.20
59	Dave Chalk	.40	.20	.12
60	Ray Burris	.40	.20	.12
	Panel 21	14.00	7.00	4.25
61	Bert Campaneris	.80	.40	.25
62	Gary Carter	5.00	2.50	1.50
63	Ron Cey	.65	.35	.20
	Panel 22	28.00	14.00	8.50
64	Carlton Fisk	2.00	1.00	.60
65	Marty Perez	.50	.25	.15
66	Pete Rose	10.00	5.00	3.00
	Panel 23	4.00	2.00	1.25
67	Roger Metzger	.40	.20	.12
68	Jim Sundberg	.60	.30	.20
69	Ron LeFlore	.60	.30	.20
	Panel 24	3.50	1.75	1.00
70	Ted Sizemore	.40	.20	.12
71	Steve Busby	.40	.20	.12
72	Manny Sanguillen	.40	.20	.12
	Panel 25	6.00	3.00	1.75
73	Larry Hisle	.50	.25	.15
74	Pete Broberg	.40	.20	.12
75	Boog Powell	1.25	.60	.40
	Panel 26	7.00	3.50	2.00
76	Ken Singleton	.60	.30	.20
77	Rich Gossage	2.00	1.00	.60
78	Jerry Grote	.50	.25	.15
	Panel 27	18.00	9.00	5.50
79	Nolan Ryan	12.00	6.00	3.50
80	Rick Monday	.70	.35	.20
81	Graig Nettles	.90	.45	.25
	Panel 28	19.00	9.50	5.75
82	Chris Speier	.40	.20	.12
83	Dave Winfield	4.00	2.00	1.25
84	Mike Schmidt	6.00	3.00	1.75
	Panel 29	5.00	2.50 1.25085	
Buzz Capra.40		.20	.12	
86	Tony Perez	1.00	.50	.30
87	Dwight Evans	.70	.35	.20
	Panel 30	3.50	1.75	1.00
88	Mike Hargrove	.40	.20	.12
89	Joe Coleman	.40	.20	.12
90	Greg Gross	.40	.20	.12
	Panel 31	3.50	1.75	1.00
91	John Mayberry	.40	.20	.12
92	John Candelaria	.50	.25	.15
93	Bake McBride	.40	.20	.12
	Panel 32	15.00	7.50	4.50
94	Hank Aaron	7.00	3.50	2.00
95	Buddy Bell	.50	.25	.15
96	Steve Braun	.40	.20	.12
	Panel 33	3.50	1.75	1.00
97	Jon Matlack	.40	.20	.12
98	Lee May	.40	.20	.12
99	Wilbur Wood	.50	.25	.15
	Panel 34	5.00	2.50	1.50
100	Bill Madlock	.90	.45	.25
101	Frank Tanana	.50	.25	.15
102	Mickey Rivers	.50	.25	.15
	Panel 35	5.00	2.50	1.50
103	Mike Ivie	.40	.20	.12
104	Rollie Fingers	1.25	.60	.40
105	Dave Lopes	.50	.25	.15
	Panel 36	4.50	2.25	1.25
106	George Foster	.65	.35	.20
107	Denny Doyle	.40	.20	.12
108	Earl Williams	.40	.20	.12
	Panel 37	3.50	1.75	1.00
109	Tom Veryzer	.40	.20	.12
110	J.R. Richard	.60	.30	.20
111	Jeff Burroughs	.40	.20	.12
	Panel 38	15.00	7.50	4.50
112	Al Oliver	.80	.40	.25
113	Ted Simmons	.60	.30	.20
114	George Brett	6.00	3.00	1.75
	Panel 39	4.00	1.50	.90
115	Frank Duffy	.40	.20	.12
116	Bert Blyleven	.80	.40	.25
117	Darrell Porter	.50	.25	.15
	Panel 40	4.00	2.00	1.25
118	Don Baylor	.70	.35	.20
119	Bucky Dent	.50	.25	.15
120	Felix Millan	.40	.20	.12
	Panel 41	4.00	2.00	1.25
121	Mike Cuellar	.50	.25	.15
122	Gene Tenace	.40	.20	.12
123	Bobby Murcer	.50	.25	.15
	Panel 42	8.50	4.25	2.50
124	Willie McCovey	3.00	1.50	.90
125	Greg Luzinski	.70	.35	.20
126	Larry Parrish	.50	.25	.15
	Panel 43	10.00	5.00	3.00
127	Jim Rice	2.00	1.00	.60
128	Dave Concepcion	.50	.25	.15
129	Jim Wynn	.50	.25	.15
	Panel 44	3.50	1.75	1.00
130	Tom Grieve	.40	.20	.12
131	Mike Cosgrove	.40	.20	.12
132	Dan Meyer	.40	.20	.12
	Panel 45	5.50	2.75	1.50
133	Dave Parker	1.50	.70	.45
134	Don Kessinger	.40	.20	.12
135	Hal McRae	.60	.30	.20
	Panel 46	8.00	4.00	2.50
136	Don Money	.50	.25	.15
137	Dennis Eckersley	4.00	2.00	1.25
138	Fergie Jenkins	1.50	.70	.45
	Panel 47	5.50	2.75	1.50
139	Mike Torrez	.40	.20	.12
140	Jerry Morales	.40	.20	.12
141	Catfish Hunter	1.50	.70	.45
	Panel 48	3.50	1.75	1.00
142	Gary Matthews	.50	.25	.15
143	Randy Jones	.40	.20	.12
144	Mike Jorgensen	.40	.20	.12
	Panel 49	14.00	7.00	4.25
145	Larry Bowa	.50	.25	.15
146	Reggie Jackson	5.00	2.50	1.50
147	Steve Yeager	.40	.20	.12
	Panel 50	16.00	8.00	4.75
148	Dave May	.40	.20	.12
149	Carl Yastrzemski	5.00	2.50	1.50
150	Cesar Geronimo	.40	.20	.12

1976 Hostess Twinkies

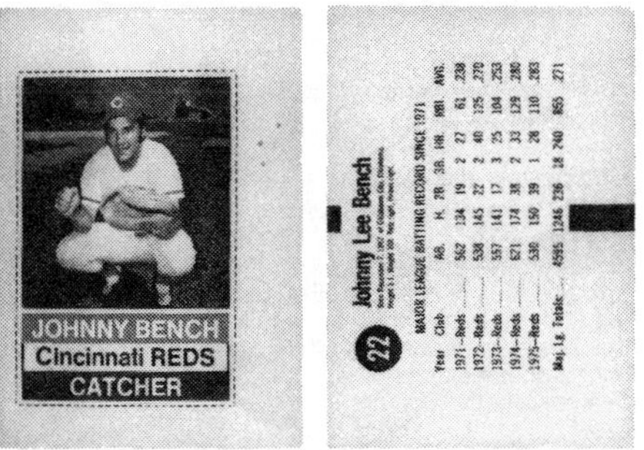

The 60 cards in this regionally-issued (West Coast only) set closely parallel the first 60 cards in the numerical sequence of the "regular" 1976 Hostess issue. The singular difference is the appearance on the back of a black band toward the center of the card at top and bottom. Also unlike the three-card panels of the regular Hostess issue, the 2-1/4" by 3-1/4" Twinkie cards were issued singly, as the cardboard stiffener for the cellophane-wrapped snack cakes. Values quoted are for complete bottom panels.

		NR MT	EX	VG
Complete Set (60):		125.00	62.00	37.00
Common Player:		.90	.45	.25
1	Fred Lynn	2.00	1.00	.60
2	Joe Morgan	5.00	2.50	1.50
3	Phil Niekro	3.00	1.50	.90
4	Gaylord Perry	5.00	2.50	1.50
5	Bob Watson	.90	.45	.25
6	Bill Freehan	1.25	.60	.40
7	Lou Brock	7.00	3.50	2.00
8	Al Fitzmorris	.90	.45	.25
9	Rennie Stennett	.90	.45	.25
10	Tony Oliva	2.00	1.00	.60
11	Robin Yount	12.00	6.00	3.50
12	Rick Manning	.90	.45	.25
13	Bobby Grich	1.25	.60	.40
14	Terry Forster	.90	.45	.25
15	Dave Kingman	1.25	.60	.40
16	Thurman Munson	6.50	3.25	2.00
17	Rick Reuschel	.90	.45	.25
18	Bobby Bonds	1.25	.60	.40
19	Steve Garvey	6.00	3.00	1.75
20	Vida Blue	1.75	.90	.50
21	Dave Rader	.90	.45	.25
22	Johnny Bench	8.00	4.00	2.50
23	Luis Tiant	1.50	.70	.45
24	Darrell Evans	1.25	.60	.40
25	Larry Dierker	.90	.45	.25
26	Willie Horton	.90	.45	.25
27	John Ellis	.90	.45	.25
28	Al Cowens	.90	.45	.25
29	Jerry Reuss	1.25	.60	.40
30	Reggie Smith	1.25	.60	.40
31	Bobby Darwin	.90	.45	.25
32	Fritz Peterson	.90	.45	.25
33	Rod Carew	8.00	4.00	2.50
34	Carlos May	.90	.45	.25
35	Tom Seaver	8.00	4.00	2.50
36	Brooks Robinson	9.00	4.50	2.75
37	Jose Cardenal	.90	.45	.25
38	Ron Blomberg	.90	.45	.25
39	Lee Stanton	.90	.45	.25
40	Dave Cash	.90	.45	.25
41	John Montefusco	.90	.45	.25
42	Bob Tolan	.90	.45	.25
43	Carl Morton	.90	.45	.25
44	Rick Burleson	.90	.45	.25
45	Don Gullett	.90	.45	.25
46	Vern Ruhle	.90	.45	.25
47	Cesar Cedeno	1.25	.60	.40
48	Toby Harrah	.90	.45	.25
49	Willie Stargell	6.00	3.00	1.75
50	Al Hrabosky	.90	.45	.25
51	Amos Otis	.90	.45	.25
52	Bud Harrelson	.90	.45	.25
53	Jim Hughes	.90	.45	.25
54	George Scott	.90	.45	.25
55	Mike Vail	.90	.45	.25
56	Jim Palmer	6.00	3.00	1.75
57	Jorge Orta	.90	.45	.25
58	Chris Chambliss	1.25	.60	.40
59	Dave Chalk	.90	.45	.25
60	Ray Burris	.90	.45	.25

1977 Hostess

The third of five consecutive annual issues, the 1977 Hostess cards retained the same card size 2-1/4" by 3-1/4", set size - 150 cards, and mode of issue - three cards on a 7-1/4" by 3-1/4" panel, as the previous two efforts. Because they were issued as the bottom panel of snack cake boxes, and because some brands of Hostess products were more popular than others, certain cards in the set are scarcer than others.

		NR MT	EX	VG
Complete Panel Set:		350.00	175.00	105.00
Complete Singles Set:		225.00	112.00	67.00
Common Panel:		4.00	2.00	1.25
Common Single Player:		.40	.20	.12
	Panel 1	22.50	11.25	6.75
1	Jim Palmer	3.00	1.50	.90
2	Joe Morgan	3.00	1.50	.90
3	Reggie Jackson	5.00	2.50	1.50
	Panel 2	23.00	11.50	7.00
4	Carl Yastrzemski	6.00	3.00	1.75
5	Thurman Munson	2.50	1.25	.70
6	Johnny Bench	4.00	2.00	1.25
	Panel 3	35.00	11.50	10.50
7	Tom Seaver	3.00	1.50	.90
8	Pete Rose	8.00	4.00	2.50
9	Rod Carew	4.00	2.00	1.25
	Panel 4	4.00	2.00	1.25
10	Luis Tiant	.60	.30	.20
11	Phil Garner	.40	.20	.12
12	Sixto Lezcano	.40	.20	.12
	Panel 5	4.00	2.00	1.25
13	Mike Torrez	.40	.20	.12
14	Dave Lopes	.50	.25	.15
15	Doug DeCinces	.40	.20	.12
	Panel 6	4.00	2.00	1.25
16	Jim Spencer	.40	.20	.12
17	Hal McRae	.50	.25	.15
18	Mike Hargrove	.40	.20	.12
	Panel 7	4.00	2.00	1.25
19	Willie Montanez	.50	.25	.15
20	Roger Metzger	.50	.25	.15
21	Dwight Evans	.70	.35	.20
	Panel 8	10.00	5.00	3.00
22	Steve Rogers	.40	.20	.12
23	Jim Rice	1.25	.60	.40
24	Pete Falcone	.40	.20	.12
	Panel 9	9.00	4.50	2.75
25	Greg Luzinski	.90	.45	.25
26	Randy Jones	.40	.20	.12
27	Willie Stargell	3.00	1.50	.90
	Panel 10	4.00	2.00	1.25
28	John Hiller	.40	.20	.12
29	Bobby Murcer	.60	.30	.20
30	Rick Monday	.60	.30	.20
	Panel 11	9.00	4.50	2.75
31	John Montefusco	.40	.20	.12
32	Lou Brock	4.00	2.00	1.25
33	Bill North	.40	.20	.12
	Panel 12	32.00	16.00	9.50
34	Robin Yount	6.00	3.00	1.75
35	Steve Garvey	2.00	1.00	.60
36	George Brett	6.00	3.00	1.75
	Panel 13	5.00	2.50	1.50
37	Toby Harrah	.50	.25	.15
38	Jerry Royster	.50	.25	.15
39	Bob Watson	.50	.25	.15
	Panel 14	8.00	4.00	2.50
40	George Foster	.60	.30	.20
41	Gary Carter	2.00	1.00	.60
42	John Denny	.40	.20	.12
	Panel 15	20.00	10.00	6.00
43	Mike Schmidt	7.00	3.50	2.00
44	Dave Winfield	4.00	2.00	1.25
45	Al Oliver	.90	.45	.25
	Panel 16	4.00	2.00	1.25
46	Mark Fidrych	.60	.30	.20
47	Larry Herndon	.40	.20	.12
48	Dave Goltz	.40	.20	.12
	Panel 17	4.00	2.00	1.25
49	Jerry Morales	.40	.20	.12
50	Ron LeFlore	.50	.25	.15
51	Fred Lynn	.90	.45	.25
	Panel 18	5.00	2.50	1.50
52	Vida Blue	.50	.25	.15
53	Rick Manning	.40	.20	.12
54	Bill Buckner	.70	.35	.20
	Panel 19	4.00	2.00	1.25
55	Lee May	.40	.20	.12
56	John Mayberry	.40	.20	.12
57	Darrel Chaney	.40	.20	.12
	Panel 20	5.00	2.50	1.50
58	Cesar Cedeno	.50	.25	.15
59	Ken Griffey	.50	.25	.15
60	Dave Kingman	.40	.20	.12
	Panel 21	5.00	2.50	1.50
61	Ted Simmons	.50	.25	.15
62	Larry Bowa	.50	.25	.15
63	Frank Tanana	.40	.20	.12
	Panel 22	4.00	2.00	1.25
64	Jason Thompson	.40	.20	.12
65	Ken Brett	.40	.20	.12
66	Roy Smalley	.40	.20	.12
	Panel 23	5.00	2.50	1.50
67	Ray Burris	.40	.20	.12
68	Rick Burleson	.40	.20	.12
69	Buddy Bell	.50	.25	.15
	Panel 24	6.00	3.00	1.75
70	Don Sutton	2.00	1.00	.60
71	Mark Belanger	.40	.20	.12
72	Dennis Leonard	.40	.20	.12
	Panel 25	5.00	2.50	1.50
73	Gaylord Perry	2.00	1.00	.60
74	Dick Ruthven	.40	.20	.12
75	Jose Cruz	.50	.25	.15
	Panel 26	6.00	3.00	1.75
76	Cesar Geronimo	.40	.20	.12
77	Jerry Koosman	.50	.25	.15
78	Garry Templeton	.50	.25	.15
	Panel 27	15.00	7.50	4.50
79	Catfish Hunter	2.00	1.00	.60
80	John Candelaria	.50	.25	.15
81	Nolan Ryan	10.00	5.00	3.00
	Panel 28	4.00	2.00	1.25
82	Rusty Staub	.50	.25	.15
83	Jim Barr	.40	.20	.12
84	Butch Wynegar	.40	.20	.12
	Panel 29	4.00	2.00	1.25
85	Jose Cardenal	.40	.20	.12
86	Claudell Washington	.40	.20	.12
87	Bill Travers	.40	.20	.12
	Panel 30	4.00	2.00	1.25
88	Rick Waits	.40	.20	.12
89	Ron Cey	.50	.25	.15
90	Al Bumbry	.40	.20	.12
	Panel 31	4.00	2.00	1.25
91	Bucky Dent	.50	.25	.15
92	Amos Otis	.50	.25	.15
93	Tom Grieve	.40	.20	.12
	Panel 32	4.00	2.00	1.25
94	Enos Cabell	.40	.20	.12
95	Dave Concepcion	.50	.25	.15
96	Felix Millan	.40	.20	.12
	Panel 33	4.00	2.00	1.25
97	Bake McBride	.40	.20	.12
98	Chris Chambliss	.40	.20	.12
99	Butch Metzger	.40	.20	.12
	Panel 34	4.00	2.00	1.25
100	Rennie Stennett	.40	.20	.12
101	Dave Roberts	.40	.20	.12
102	Lyman Bostock	.40	.20	.12
	Panel 35	4.50	2.25	1.25
103	Rick Reuschel	.50	.25	.15
104	Carlton Fisk	1.00	.50	.30
105	Jim Slaton	.40	.20	.12
	Panel 36	4.50	2.25	1.25
106	Dennis Eckersley	1.50	.70	.45
107	Ken Singleton	.40	.20	.12
108	Ralph Garr	.40	.20	.12
	Panel 37	8.00	4.00	2.50
109	Freddie Patek	.40	.20	.12
110	Jim Sundberg	.50	.25	.15
111	Phil Niekro	2.50	1.25	.70
	Panel 38	4.00	2.00	1.25
112	J.R. Richard	.50	.25	.15
113	Gary Nolan	.40	.20	.12
114	Jon Matlack	.40	.20	.12
	Panel 39	21.00	10.50	6.25
115	Keith Hernandez	.40	.20	.12
116	Graig Nettles	.70	.35	.20
117	Steve Carlton	5.00	2.50	1.50
	Panel 40	5.00	2.50	1.50
118	Bill Madlock	.80	.40	.25
119	Jerry Reuss	.50	.25	.15
120	Aurelio Rodriguez	.40	.20	.12
	Panel 41	4.00	2.00	1.25
121	Dan Ford	.40	.20	.12
122	Ray Fosse	.40	.20	.12
123	George Hendrick	.40	.20	.12
	Panel 42	4.00	2.00	1.25
124	Alan Ashby	.40	.20	.12
125	Joe Lis	.40	.20	.12
126	Sal Bando	.50	.25	.15
	Panel 43	6.00	3.00	1.75
127	Richie Zisk	.40	.20	.12
128	Rich Gossage	.90	.45	.25
129	Don Baylor	.70	.35	.20
	Panel 44	4.00	2.00	1.25
130	Dave McKay	.40	.20	.12
131	Bob Grich	.50	.25	.15
132	Dave Pagan	.40	.20	.12
	Panel 45	4.00	2.00	1.25
133	Dave Cash	.40	.20	.12
134	Steve Braun	.40	.20	.12
135	Dan Meyer	.40	.20	.12
	Panel 46	6.00	3.00	1.75
136	Bill Stein	.40	.20	.12
137	Rollie Fingers	2.00	1.00	.60
138	Brian Downing	.50	.25	.15
	Panel 47	4.00	2.00	1.25
139	Bill Singer	.40	.20	.12
140	Doyle Alexander	.40	.20	.12
141	Gene Tenace	.40	.20	.12
	Panel 48	4.00	2.00	1.25
142	Gary Matthews	.50	.25	.15
143	Don Gullett	.40	.20	.12
144	Wayne Garland	.40	.20	.12
	Panel 49	4.00	2.00	1.25
145	Pete Broberg	.40	.20	.12
146	Joe Rudi	.50	.25	.15
147	Glenn Abbott	.40	.20	.12
	Panel 50	4.00	2.00	1.25
148	George Scott	.50	.25	.15
149	Bert Campaneris	.50	.25	.15
150	Andy Messersmith	.40	.20	.12

1977 Hostess Twinkies

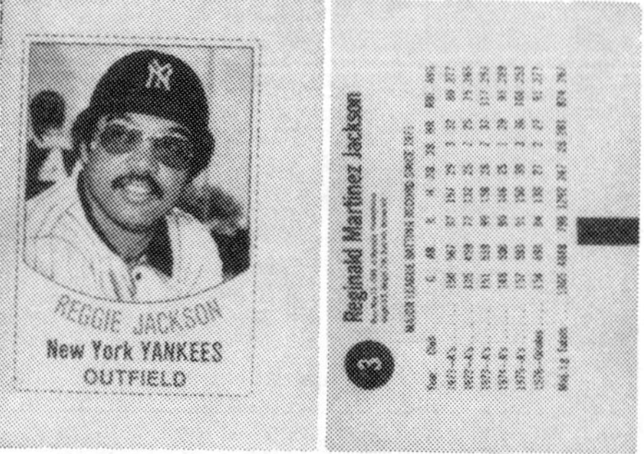

The 1977 Hostess Twinkie issue, at 150 different cards, is the largest of the single-panel Twinkie sets. It is also the most obscure. The cards, which measure 2-1/4" by 3-1/4", but are part of a larger panel, were found not only with Twinkies, but with Hostess Cupcakes as well. Card #'s 1-30 and 111-150 are Twinkies panels and #'s 31-135 are Cupcakes panels. Complete Cupcakes panels are approximately

2-1/4" by 4-1/2" in size, while complete Twinkies panels measure 3-1/8" by 4-1/4". The photos used in the set are identical to those in the 1977 Hostess three-card panel set. The main difference is the appearance of a black band at the center of the card back. The values quoted in the checklist that follows are for complete bottom panels.

		NR MT	EX	VG
Complete Set (150):		200.00	100.00	60.00
Common Player:		.80	.40	.25
1	Jim Palmer	4.00	2.00	1.25
2	Joe Morgan	4.00	2.00	1.25
3	Reggie Jackson	10.00	5.00	3.00
4	Carl Yastrzemski	10.00	5.00	3.00
5	Thurman Munson	5.00	2.50	1.50
6	Johnny Bench	8.00	4.00	2.50
7	Tom Seaver	7.00	3.50	2.00
8	Pete Rose	12.00	6.00	3.50
9	Rod Carew	7.00	3.50	2.00
10	Luis Tiant	1.00	.50	.30
11	Phil Garner	.80	.40	.25
12	Sixto Lezcano	.80	.40	.25
13	Mike Torrez	.80	.40	.25
14	Dave Lopes	1.00	.50	.30
15	Doug DeCinces	1.00	.50	.30
16	Jim Spencer	.80	.40	.25
17	Hal McRae	1.00	.50	.30
18	Mike Hargrove	.80	.40	.25
19	Willie Montanez	.80	.40	.25
20	Roger Metzger	.80	.40	.25
21	Dwight Evans	1.00	.50	.30
22	Steve Rogers	.80	.40	.25
23	Jim Rice	2.00	1.00	.60
24	Pete Falcone	.80	.40	.25
25	Greg Luzinski	2.00	1.00	.60
26	Randy Jones	.80	.40	.25
27	Willie Stargell	6.00	3.00	1.75
28	John Hiller	.80	.40	.25
29	Bobby Murcer	1.25	.60	.40
30	Rick Monday	1.00	.50	.30
31	John Montefusco	.80	.40	.25
32	Lou Brock	6.00	3.00	1.75
33	Bill North	.80	.40	.25
34	Robin Yount	8.00	4.00	2.50
35	Steve Garvey	5.00	2.50	1.50
36	George Brett	8.00	4.00	2.50
37	Toby Harrah	.80	.40	.25
38	Jerry Royster	.80	.40	.25
39	Bob Watson	1.00	.50	.30
40	George Foster	1.00	.50	.30
41	Gary Carter	4.00	2.00	1.25
42	John Denny	.80	.40	.25
43	Mike Schmidt	9.00	4.50	2.75
44	Dave Winfield	6.00	3.00	1.75
45	Al Oliver	1.75	.90	.50
46	Mark Fidrych	1.50	.70	.45
47	Larry Herndon	.80	.40	.25
48	Dave Goltz	.80	.40	.25
49	Jerry Morales	.80	.40	.25
50	Ron LeFlore	1.00	.50	.30
51	Fred Lynn	1.00	.50	.30
52	Vida Blue	1.00	.50	.30
53	Rick Manning	.80	.40	.25
54	Bill Buckner	1.00	.50	.30
55	Lee May	.80	.40	.25
56	John Mayberry	.80	.40	.25
57	Darrel Chaney	.80	.40	.25
58	Cesar Cedeno	1.00	.50	.30
59	Ken Griffey	1.00	.50	.30
60	Dave Kingman	1.00	.50	.30
61	Ted Simmons	1.00	.50	.30
62	Larry Bowa	1.00	.50	.30
63	Frank Tanana	.80	.40	.25
64	Jason Thompson	.80	.40	.25
65	Ken Brett	.80	.40	.25
66	Roy Smalley	.80	.40	.25
67	Ray Burris	.80	.40	.25
68	Rick Burleson	.80	.40	.25
69	Buddy Bell	1.25	.60	.40
70	Don Sutton	2.50	1.25	.70
71	Mark Belanger	.80	.40	.25
72	Dennis Leonard	.80	.40	.25
73	Gaylord Perry	4.00	2.00	1.25
74	Dick Ruthven	.80	.40	.25
75	Jose Cruz	1.25	.60	.40
76	Cesar Geronimo	.80	.40	.25
77	Jerry Koosman	1.25	.60	.40
78	Garry Templeton	1.50	.70	.45
79	Catfish Hunter	4.00	2.00	1.25
80	John Candelaria	1.00	.50	.30
81	Nolan Ryan	15.00	7.50	4.50
82	Rusty Staub	1.50	.70	.45
83	Jim Barr	.80	.40	.25
84	Butch Wynegar	.80	.40	.25
85	Jose Cardenal	.80	.40	.25
86	Claudell Washington	.80	.40	.25
87	Bill Travers	.80	.40	.25
88	Rick Waits	.80	.40	.25
89	Ron Cey	1.25	.60	.40
90	Al Bumbry	.80	.40	.25
91	Bucky Dent	1.00	.50	.30
92	Amos Otis	1.00	.50	.30
93	Tom Grieve	.80	.40	.25
94	Enos Cabell	.80	.40	.25
95	Dave Concepcion	1.25	.60	.40
96	Felix Millan	.80	.40	.25
97	Bake McBride	.80	.40	.25
98	Chris Chambliss	.80	.40	.25
99	Butch Metzger	.80	.40	.25
100	Rennie Stennett	.80	.40	.25
101	Dave Roberts	.80	.40	.25
102	Lyman Bostock	.80	.40	.25
103	Rick Reuschel	1.00	.50	.30
104	Carlton Fisk	2.25	1.25	.70
105	Jim Slaton	.80	.40	.25
106	Dennis Eckersley	2.00	1.00	.60
107	Ken Singleton	.80	.40	.25
108	Ralph Garr	.80	.40	.25
109	Freddie Patek	.80	.40	.25
110	Jim Sundberg	.80	.40	.25
111	Phil Niekro	2.00	1.00	.60
112	J. R. Richard	1.00	.50	.30
113	Gary Nolan	.80	.40	.25
114	Jon Matlack	.80	.40	.25
115	Keith Hernandez	1.00	.50	.30
116	Graig Nettles	1.00	.50	.30
117	Steve Carlton	6.00	3.00	1.75
118	Bill Madlock	1.00	.50	.30
119	Jerry Reuss	.80	.40	.25
120	Aurelio Rodriguez	.80	.40	.25
121	Dan Ford	.80	.40	.25
122	Ray Fosse	.80	.40	.25
123	George Hendrick	.80	.40	.25
124	Alan Ashby	.80	.40	.25
125	Joe Lis	.80	.40	.25
126	Sal Bando	.80	.40	.25
127	Richie Zisk	.80	.40	.25
128	Rich Gossage	1.50	.70	.45
129	Don Baylor	1.50	.70	.45
130	Dave McKay	.80	.40	.25
131	Bob Grich	1.00	.50	.30
132	Dave Pagan	.80	.40	.25
133	Dave Cash	.80	.40	.25
134	Steve Braun	.80	.40	.25
135	Dan Meyer	.80	.40	.25
136	Bill Stein	.80	.40	.25
137	Rollie Fingers	3.00	1.50	.90
138	Brian Downing	.80	.40	.25
139	Bill Singer	.80	.40	.25
140	Doyle Alexander	.80	.40	.25
141	Gene Tenace	.80	.40	.25
142	Gary Matthews	1.00	.50	.30
143	Don Gullett	.80	.40	.25
144	Wayne Garland	.80	.40	.25
145	Pete Broberg	.80	.40	.25
146	Joe Rudi	1.00	.50	.30
147	Glenn Abbott	.80	.40	.25
148	George Scott	1.00	.50	.30
149	Bert Campaneris	1.25	.60	.40
150	Andy Messersmith	.80	.40	.25

1978 Hostess

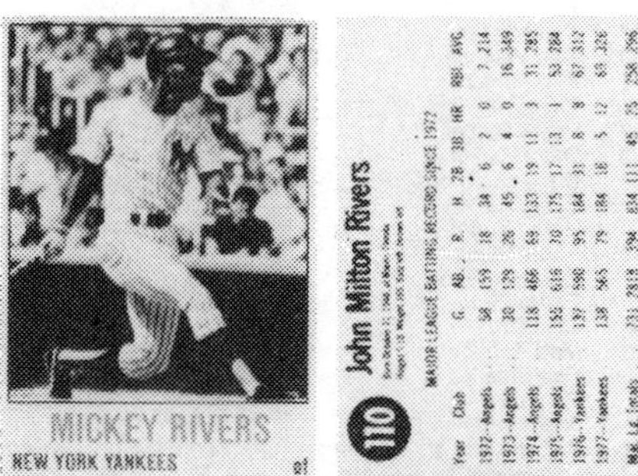

Other than the design on the front of the card, there was little different about the 1978 Hostess cards from the three years' issues which had preceded it, or the one which followed. The 2-1/4" by 3-1/4" cards were printed in panels of three (7-1/4" by 3-1/4") as the bottom of family-sized boxes of snake cakes. The 1978 set was again complete at 150 cards. Like other years of Hostess issues, there are scarcities within the 1978 set that are the result of those panels having been issued with less-popular brands of snack cakes.

		NR MT	EX	VG
Complete Panel Set:		325.00	162.00	97.00
Complete Singles Set:		225.00	112.00	67.00
Common Panel:		3.50	1.75	1.00
Common Single Player:		.40	.20	.12
	Panel 1	4.50	2.25	1.25
1	Butch Hobson	.40	.20	.12
2	George Foster	.60	.30	.20
3	Bob Forsch	.50	.25	.15
	Panel 2	7.50	3.75	2.25
4	Tony Perez	1.00	.50	.30
5	Bruce Sutter	.60	.30	.20
6	Hal McRae	.60	.30	.20
	Panel 3	6.00	3.00	1.75
7	Tommy John	1.50	.70	.45
8	Greg Luzinski	.80	.40	.25
9	Enos Cabell	.40	.20	.12
	Panel 4	7.50	3.75	2.25
10	Doug DeCinces	.50	.25	.15
11	Willie Stargell	3.00	1.50	.90
12	Ed Halicki	.40	.20	.12
	Panel 5	3.50	1.75	1.00
13	Larry Hisle	.40	.20	.12
14	Jim Slaton	.40	.20	.12
15	Buddy Bell	.50	.25	.15
	Panel 6	3.50	1.75	1.00
16	Earl Williams	.40	.20	.12
17	Glenn Abbott	.40	.20	.12
18	Dan Ford	.40	.20	.12
	Panel 7	3.50	1.75	1.00
19	Gary Mathews	.50	.25	.15
20	Eric Soderholm	.40	.20	.12
21	Bump Wills	.40	.20	.12
	Panel 8	3.50	1.75	1.00
22	Keith Hernandez	.50	.25	.15
23	Dave Cash	.40	.20	.12
24	George Scott	.50	.25	.15
	Panel 9	18.00	9.00	5.50
25	Ron Guidry	.90	.45	.25
26	Dave Kingman	.60	.30	.20
27	George Brett	7.00	3.50	2.00
	Panel 10	3.50	1.75	1.00
28	Bob Watson	.50	.25	.15
29	Bob Boone	.80	.40	.25
30	Reggie Smith	.60	.30	.20
	Panel 11	12.00	6.00	3.50
31	Eddie Murray	6.00	3.00	1.75
32	Gary Lavelle	.40	.20	.12
33	Rennie Stennett	.40	.20	.12
	Panel 12	3.50	1.75	1.00
34	Duane Kuiper	.40	.20	.12
35	Sixto Lezcano	.40	.20	.12
36	Dave Rozema	.40	.20	.12
	Panel 13	3.50	1.75	1.00
37	Butch Wynegar	.50	.25	.15
38	Mitchell Page	.40	.20	.12
39	Bill Stein	.40	.20	.12
	Panel 14	3.50	1.75	1.00
40	Elliott Maddox	.40	.20	.12
41	Mike Hargrove	.50	.25	.15
42	Bobby Bonds	.60	.30	.20
	Panel 15	16.00	7.50	4.50
43	Garry Templeton	.60	.30	.20
44	Johnny Bench	6.00	3.00	1.75
45	Jim Rice	1.00	.50	.30
	Panel 16	13.00	6.50	4.00
46	Bill Buckner	.60	.30	.20
47	Reggie Jackson	5.00	2.50	1.50
48	Freddie Patek	.40	.20	.12
	Panel 17	9.50	4.25	2.50
49	Steve Carlton	4.00	2.00	1.25
50	Cesar Cedeno	.40	.20	.12
51	Steve Yeager	.40	.20	.12
	Panel 18	3.50	1.75	1.00
52	Phil Garner	.50	.25	.15
53	Lee May	.50	.25	.15
54	Darrell Evans	.70	.35	.20
	Panel 19	4.00	2.00	1.25
55	Steve Kemp	.50	.25	.15
56	Dusty Baker	.70	.35	.20
57	Ray Fosse	.40	.20	.12
	Panel 20	3.50	1.75	1.00
58	Manny Sanguillen	.40	.20	.12
59	Tom Johnson	.40	.20	.12
60	Lee Stanton	.40	.20	.12
	Panel 21	12.00	6.00	3.50
61	Jeff Burroughs	.40	.20	.12
62	Bobby Grich	.50	.25	.15
63	Dave Winfield	4.00	2.00	1.25
	Panel 22	3.50	1.75	1.00
64	Dan Driessen	.40	.20	.12
65	Ted Simmons	.60	.30	.20
66	Jerry Remy	.40	.20	.12
	Panel 23	3.50	1.75	1.00
67	Al Cowens	.40	.20	.12
68	Sparky Lyle	.50	.25	.15
69	Manny Trillo	.50	.25	.15
	Panel 24	6.00	3.00	1.75
70	Don Sutton	1.50	.70	.45
71	Larry Bowa	.50	.25	.15
72	Jose Cruz	.50	.25	.15
	Panel 25	8.00	4.00	2.50
73	Willie McCovey	3.00	1.50	.90
74	Bert Blyleven	.70	.35	.20
75	Ken Singleton	.50	.25	.15
	Panel 26	4.00	2.00	1.25
76	Bill North	.40	.20	.12
77	Jason Thompson	.40	.20	.12
78	Dennis Eckersley	1.00	.50	.30
	Panel 27	3.50	1.75	1.00
79	Jim Sundberg	.50	.25	.15
80	Jerry Koosman	.50	.25	.15
81	Bruce Bochte	.40	.20	.12
	Panel 28	17.00	8.50	5.00
82	George Hendrick	.40	.20	.12
83	Nolan Ryan	10.00	5.00	3.00
84	Roy Howell	.40	.20	.12
	Panel 29	7.00	3.50	2.00
85	Butch Metzger	.40	.20	.12
86	George Medich	.40	.20	.12
87	Joe Morgan	3.00	1.50	.90
	Panel 30	3.50	1.75	1.00
88	Dennis Leonard	.40	.20	.12
89	Willie Randolph	.50	.25	.15
90	Bobby Murcer	.50	.25	.15
	Panel 31	3.50	1.75	.1.00
91	Rick Manning	.40	.20	.12
92	J.R. Richard	.50	.25	.15
93	Ron Cey	.60	.30	.20
	Panel 32	3.50	1.75	1.00
94	Sal Bando	.50	.25	.15
95	Ron LeFlore	.50	.25	.15
96	Dave Goltz	.40	.20	.12
	Panel 33	3.50	1.75	1.00
97	Dan Meyer	.40	.20	.12
98	Chris Chambliss	.50	.25	.15
99	Biff Pocoroba	.40	.20	.12
	Panel 34	3.50	1.75	1.00
100	Oscar Gamble	.40	.20	.12
101	Frank Tanana	.50	.25	.15
102	Lenny Randle	.40	.20	.12
	Panel 35	3.50	1.75	1.00
103	Tommy Hutton	.40	.20	.12
104	John Candelaria	.50	.25	.15
105	Jorge Orta	.40	.20	.12
	Panel 36	3.50	1.70	1.00
106	Ken Reitz	.40	.20	.12
107	Bill Campbell	.40	.20	.12
108	Dave Concepcion	.60	.30	.20

	Panel 37	3.50	1.75	1.00
109	Joe Ferguson	.40	.20	.12
110	Mickey Rivers	.50	.25	.15
111	Paul Splittorff	.40	.20	.12
	Panel 38	14.00	7.00	4.25
112	Davey Lopes	.50	.25	.15
113	Mike Schmidt	7.00	3.50	2.00
114	Joe Rudi	.50	.25	.15
	Panel 39	7.50	3.75	2.25
115	Milt May	.40	.20	.12
116	Jim Palmer	3.00	1.50	.90
117	Bill Madlock	.60	.30	.20
	Panel 40	3.50	1.75	1.00
118	Roy Smalley	.40	.20	.12
119	Cecil Cooper	.50	.25	.15
120	Rick Langford	.40	.20	.12
	Panel 41	5.75	2.75	1.75
121	Ruppert Jones	.40	.20	.12
122	Phil Niekro	2.25	1.25	.70
123	Toby Harrah	.50	.25	.15
	Panel 42	3.50	1.75	1.00
124	Chet Lemon	.50	.25	.15
125	Gene Tenace	.40	.20	.12
126	Steve Henderson	.40	.20	.12
	Panel 43	20.00	10.00	6.00
127	Mike Torrez	.40	.20	.12
128	Pete Rose	8.00	4.00	2.50
129	John Denny	.40	.20	.12
	Panel 44	4.00	2.00	1.25
130	Darrell Porter	.50	.25	.15
131	Rick Reuschel	.50	.25	.15
132	Graig Nettles	.90	.45	.25
	Panel 45	5.00	2.25	1.25
133	Garry Maddox	.50	.25	.15
134	Mike Flanagan	.50	.25	.15
135	Dave Parker	1.50	.70	.45
	Panel 46	13.50	6.75	4.00
136	Terry Whitfield	.40	.20	.12
137	Wayne Garland	.40	.20	.12
138	Robin Yount	6.00	3.00	1.75
	Panel 47	13.00	6.50	4.00
139	Gaylord Perry	2.50	1.25	.70
140	Rod Carew	6.00	3.00	1.75
141	Wayne Gross	.40	.20	.12
	Panel 48	5.00	2.50	1.50
142	Barry Bonnell	.40	.20	.12
143	Willie Montanez	.40	.20	.12
144	Rollie Fingers	2.00	1.00	.60
	Panel 49	13.50	6.75	4.00
145	Bob Bailor	.40	.20	.12
146	Tom Seaver	4.00	2.00	1.25
147	Thurman Munson	2.50	1.25	.70
	Panel 50	6.00	3.00	1.75
148	Lyman Bostock	.50	.25	.15
149	Gary Carter	2.00	1.00	.60
150	Ron Blomberg	.40	.20	.12

1979 Hostess

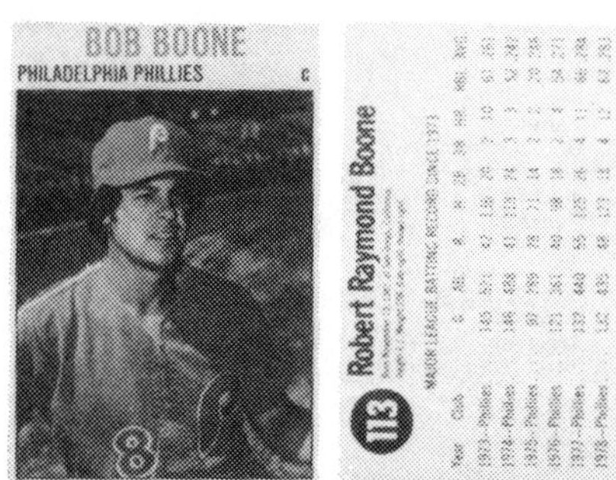

The last of five consecutive annual issues, the 1979 Hostess set retained the 150-card set size, 2-1/4" by 3-1/4" single-card size and 7-1/4" by 3-1/4" three-card panel format from the previous years. The cards were printed as the bottom panel on family-size boxes of Hostess snack cakes. Some panels, which were printed on less-popular brands, are somewhat scarcer today than the rest of the set. Like all Hostess issues, because the hobby was in a well-developed state at the time of issue, the 1979s survive today in complete panels and complete unused boxes, for collectors who like original packaging.

	NR MT	EX	VG
Complete Panel Set:	350.00	175.00	105.00
Complete Singles Set:	200.00	100.00	60.00
Common Panel:	3.50	1.75	1.00
Common Single Player:	.40	.20	.12

	Panel 1	7.00	3.50	2.00
1	John Denny	.40	.20	.12
2	Jim Rice	1.00	.50	.30
3	Doug Bair	.40	.20	.12
	Panel 2	3.50	1.75	1.00
4	Darrell Porter	.50	.25	.15
5	Ross Grimsley	.40	.20	.12
6	Bobby Murcer	.50	.25	.15
	Panel 3	18.00	9.00	5.50
7	Lee Mazzilli	.50	.25	.15
8	Steve Garvey	2.50	1.25	.70
9	Mike Schmidt	6.00	3.00	1.75
	Panel 4	7.00	3.50	2.00
10	Terry Whitfield	.40	.20	.12
11	Jim Palmer	3.00	1.50	.90
12	Omar Moreno	.40	.20	.12
	Panel 5	3.50	1.75	1.00
13	Duane Kuiper	.40	.20	.12
14	Mike Caldwell	.40	.20	.12
15	Steve Kemp	.50	.25	.15
	Panel 6	3.50	1.75	1.00
16	Dave Goltz	.40	.20	.12
17	Mitchell Page	.40	.20	.12
18	Bill Stein	.40	.20	.12
	Panel 7	3.50	1.75	1.00
19	Gene Tenace	.40	.20	.12
20	Jeff Burroughs	.40	.20	.12
21	Francisco Barrios	.40	.20	.12
	Panel 8	9.00	4.50	2.75
22	Mike Torrez	.40	.20	.12
23	Ken Reitz	.40	.20	.12
24	Gary Carter	2.00	1.00	.60
	Panel 9	10.00	5.00	3.00
25	Al Hrabosky	.50	.25	.15
26	Thurman Munson	2.50	1.25	.70
27	Bill Buckner	.60	.30	.20
	Panel 10	5.00	2.50	1.50
28	Ron Cey	.80	.40	.25
29	J.R. Richard	.60	.30	.20
30	Greg Luzinski	.80	.40	.25
	Panel 11	5.00	2.50	1.50
31	Ed Ott	.40	.20	.12
32	Denny Martinez	.60	.30	.20
33	Darrell Evans	.90	.45	.25
	Panel 12	3.50	1.75	1.00
34	Ron LeFlore	.50	.25	.15
35	Rick Waits	.40	.20	.12
36	Cecil Cooper	.50	.25	.15
	Panel 13	11.00	5.50	3.25
37	Leon Roberts	.40	.20	.12
38	Rod Carew	4.00	2.00	1.25
39	John Henry Johnson	.40	.20	.12
	Panel 14	3.50	1.75	1.00
40	Chet Lemon	.50	.25	.15
41	Craig Swan	.40	.20	.12
42	Gary Matthews	.50	.25	.15
	Panel 15	3.50	1.75	1.00
43	Lamar Johnson	.40	.20	.12
44	Ted Simmons	.80	.40	.25
45	Ken Griffey	.50	.25	.15
	Panel 16	4.00	2.00	1.25
46	Freddie Patek	.40	.20	.12
47	Frank Tanana	.50	.25	.15
48	Rich Gossage	1.25	.60	.40
	Panel 17	3.50	1.75	1.00
49	Burt Hooton	.40	.20	.12
50	Ellis Valentine	.40	.20	.12
51	Ken Forsch	.40	.20	.12
	Panel 18	5.00	2.50	1.50
52	Bob Knepper	.40	.20	.12
53	Dave Parker	2.00	1.00	.60
54	Doug DeCinces	.50	.25	.15
	Panel 19	12.50	6.25	3.75
55	Robin Yount	4.00	2.00	1.25
56	Rusty Staub	.80	.40	.25
57	Gary Alexander	.40	.20	.12
	Panel 20	3.50	1.75	1.00
58	Julio Cruz	.40	.20	.12
59	Matt Keough	.40	.20	.12
60	Roy Smalley	.40	.20	.12
	Panel 21	11.00	5.50	3.25
61	Joe Morgan	2.50	1.25	.70
62	Phil Niekro	2.00	1.00	.60
63	Don Baylor	.70	.35	.20
	Panel 22	10.00	5.00	3.00
64	Dwight Evans	.70	.35	.20
65	Tom Seaver	4.00	2.00	1.25
66	George Hendrick	.40	.20	.12
	Panel 23	15.00	7.50	4.50
67	Rick Reuschel	.40	.20	.12
68	George Brett	5.00	2.50	1.50
69	Lou Piniella	.80	.40	.25
	Panel 24	9.50	4.75	2.75
70	Enos Cabell	.40	.20	.12
71	Steve Carlton	3.50	1.75	1.00
72	Reggie Smith	.50	.25	.15
	Panel 25	5.00	2.50	1.50
73	Rick Dempsey	.50	.25	.15
74	Vida Blue	.80	.40	.25
75	Phil Garner	.70	.35	.20
	Panel 26	3.50	1.75	1.00
76	Rick Manning	.40	.20	.12
77	Mark Fidrych	.80	.40	.25
78	Mario Guerrero	.40	.20	.12
	Panel 27	5.00	2.50	1.50
79	Bob Stinson	.40	.20	.12
80	Al Oliver	1.25	.60	.40
81	Doug Flynn	.40	.20	.12
	Panel 28	6.00	3.00	1.75
82	John Mayberry	.40	.20	.12
83	Gaylord Perry	2.50	1.25	.70
84	Joe Rudi	.50	.25	.15
	Panel 29	4.50	2.75	1.25
85	Dave Concepcion	.70	.35	.20
86	John Candelaria	.50	.25	.15
87	Pete Vuckovich	.40	.20	.12
	Panel 30	5.00	2.50	1.50
88	Ivan DeJesus	.40	.20	.12
89	Ron Guidry	1.50	.70	.45
90	Hal McRae	.60	.30	.20
	Panel 31	7.00	3.50	2.00
91	Cesar Cedeno	.50	.25	.15
92	Don Sutton	2.00	1.00	.60
93	Andre Thornton	.50	.25	.15
	Panel 32	3.50	1.75	1.00
94	Roger Erickson	.40	.20	.12
95	Larry Hisle	.40	.20	.12
96	Jason Thompson	.40	.20	.12
	Panel 33	3.50	1.75	1.00
97	Jim Sundberg	.50	.25	.15
98	Bob Horner	.50	.25	.15
99	Ruppert Jones	.40	.20	.12
	Panel 34	20.00	10.00	6.00
100	Willie Montanez	.40	.20	.12
101	Nolan Ryan	8.00	4.00	2.50
102	Ozzie Smith	12.00	6.00	3.50
	Panel 35	7.50	3.75	2.25
103	Eric Soderholm	.40	.20	.12
104	Willie Stargell	3.00	1.50	.90
105	Bob Bailor	.40	.20	.12
	Panel 36	9.50	4.75	2.75
106	Carlton Fisk	2.00	1.00	.60
107	George Foster	.60	.30	.20
108	Keith Hernandez	.50	.25	.15
	Panel 37	4.00	2.00	1.25
109	Dennis Leonard	.40	.20	.12
110	Graig Nettles	.70	.35	.20
111	Jose Cruz	.50	.25	.15
	Panel 38	4.00	2.00	1.25
112	Bobby Grich	.50	.25	.15
113	Bob Boone	.70	.35	.20
114	Dave Lopes	.50	.25	.15
	Panel 39	12.00	6.00	3.50
115	Eddie Murray	3.00	1.50	.90
116	Jack Clark	.50	.25	.15
117	Lou Whitaker	1.00	.50	.30
	Panel 40	10.00	5.00	3.00
118	Miguel Dilone	.40	.20	.12
119	Sal Bando	.50	.25	.15
120	Reggie Jackson	5.00	2.50	1.50
	Panel 41	12.00	6.00	3.50
121	Dale Murphy	4.00	2.00	1.25
122	Jon Matlack	.40	.20	.12
123	Bruce Bochte	.40	.20	.12
	Panel 42	10.00	5.00	3.00
124	John Stearns	.40	.20	.12
125	Dave Winfield	4.00	2.00	1.25
126	Jorge Orta	.40	.20	.12
	Panel 43	9.00	4.50	2.75
127	Garry Templeton	.50	.25	.15
128	Johnny Bench	4.00	2.00	1.25
129	Butch Hobson	.40	.20	.12
	Panel 44	4.50	2.25	1.25
130	Bruce Sutter	1.25	.60	.40
131	Bucky Dent	.50	.25	.15
132	Amos Otis	.50	.25	.15
	Panel 45	4.50	2.25	1.25
133	Bert Blyleven	.70	.35	.20
134	Larry Bowa	.50	.25	.15
135	Ken Singleton	.50	.25	.15
	Panel 46	4.00	2.00	1.25
136	Sixto Lezcano	.40	.20	.12
137	Roy Howell	.40	.20	.12
138	Bill Madlock	.80	.40	.25
	Panel 47	3.50	1.25	.70
139	Dave Revering	.40	.20	.12
140	Richie Zisk	.40	.20	.12
141	Butch Wynegar	.40	.20	.12
	Panel 48	18.00	9.00	5.50
142	Alan Ashby	.40	.20	.12
143	Sparky Lyle	.50	.25	.15
144	Pete Rose	8.00	4.00	2.50
	Panel 49	4.50	2.25	1.25
145	Dennis Eckersley	1.50	.70	.45
146	Dave Kingman	.50	.25	.15
147	Buddy Bell	.50	.25	.15
	Panel 50	3.50	1.75	1.00
148	Mike Hargrove	.40	.20	.12
149	Jerry Koosman	.50	.25	.15
150	Toby Harrah	.50	.25	.15

1985 Hostess Braves

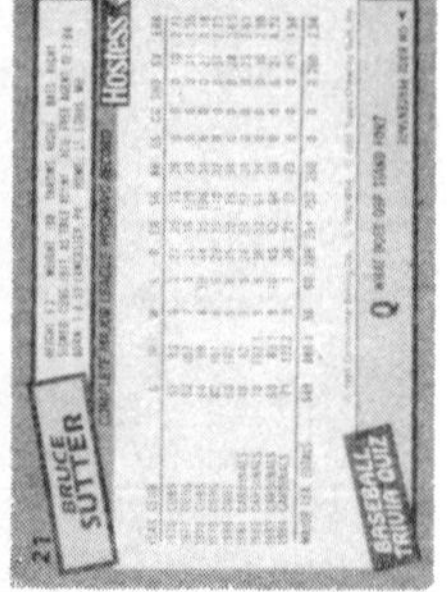

After a five-year hiatus, Hostess returned to the production of baseball cards in 1985 with an Atlanta Braves team set. The 22 cards in the set were printed by Topps and inserted into packages of snack cake products, three cello-wrapped player cards and a header card per box. The 2-1/2" by 3-1/2" cards share a common back design with the regular-issue Topps cards of 1985.

	MT	NR MT	EX
Complete Set (22):	7.00	5.25	2.75
Common Player:	.35	.25	.14

1	Eddie Haas	.35	.25	.14
2	Len Barker	.35	.25	.14
3	Steve Bedrosian	.50	.40	.20
4	Bruce Benedict	.35	.25	.14
5	Rick Camp	.35	.25	.14
6	Rick Cerone	.35	.25	.14
7	Chris Chambliss	.40	.30	.15
8	Terry Forster	.35	.25	.14

9	Gene Garber	.35	.25	.14
10	Albert Hall	.35	.25	.14
11	Bob Horner	.50	.40	.20
12	Glenn Hubbard	.35	.25	.14
13	Brad Komminsk	.35	.25	.14
14	Rick Mahler	.35	.25	.14
15	Craig McMurtry	.35	.25	.14
16	Dale Murphy	3.00	2.25	1.25
17	Ken Oberkfell	.40	.30	.15
18	Pascual Perez	.40	.30	.15
19	Gerald Perry	.50	.40	.20
20	Rafael Ramirez	.35	.25	.14
21	Bruce Sutter	.70	.50	.30
22	Claudell Washington	.40	.30	.15
----	Header Card	.10	.08	.04

1987 Hostess Stickers

Hostess of Canada issued a 30-card set of stickers in specially marked bags of potato chips. One sticker, measuring 1-3/4" by 1-3/8" in size, was found in each bag. The stickers have full-color fronts with the player's name appearing in black type in a white band. The Hostess logo and the sticker number are also included on the fronts. The backs are written in both English and French and contain the player's name, position and team.

		MT	NR MT	EX
Complete Set (30):		25.00	18.50	10.00
Common Player:		.15	.11	.06
1	Jesse Barfield	.25	.20	.10
2	Ernie Whitt	.15	.11	.06
3	George Bell	.50	.40	.20
4	Hubie Brooks	.15	.11	.06
5	Tim Wallach	.45	.35	.20
6	Floyd Youmans	.15	.11	.06
7	Dale Murphy	1.50	1.25	.60
8	Ryne Sandberg	2.00	1.50	.80
9	Eric Davis	.60	.45	.25
10	Mike Scott	.25	.20	.10
11	Fernando Valenzuela	.35	.25	.14
12	Gary Carter	1.00	.70	.40
13	Mike Schmidt	2.00	1.50	.80
14	Tony Pena	.15	.11	.06
15	Ozzie Smith	.60	.45	.25
16	Tony Gwynn	.60	.45	.25
17	Mike Krukow	.15	.11	.06
18	Eddie Murray	.80	.60	.30
19	Wade Boggs	1.75	1.25	.70
20	Wally Joyner	.60	.45	.25
21	Harold Baines	.25	.20	.10
22	Brook Jacoby	.25	.20	.10
23	Lou Whitaker	.50	.40	.20
24	George Brett	2.00	1.50	.80
25	Robin Yount	2.00	1.50	.80
26	Kirby Puckett	2.00	1.50	.80
27	Don Mattingly	1.75	1.25	.70
28	Jose Canseco	2.00	1.50	.80
29	Phil Bradley	.25	.20	.10
30	Pete O'Brien	.15	.11	.06

The values quoted are intended to reflect the market price.

1988 Hostess Potato Chips Expos

The Expos and Blue Jays are showcased in this set of 24 discs (1-1/2" diameter). Full-color head shots are framed in white, surrounded by red stars. A yellow-banner "1988 Collectors Edition" label is printed (English and French) beneath the photo, followed by the player's name in black. Numbered disc backs are bilingual, blue and white, and include player name and stats. This set was distributed inside Hostess potato chip packages sold in Canada.

		MT	NR MT	EX
Complete Panel Set:		15.00	11.00	6.00
Complete Singles Set:		9.00	6.75	3.50
Common Panel:		.75	.60	.30
Common Single Player:		.25	.20	.10
	Panel	.75	.60	.30
1	Mitch Webster	.25	.20	.10
20	Lloyd Moseby	.25	.20	.10
	Panel	.75	.60	.30
2	Tim Burke	.25	.20	.10
23	Tom Henke	.25	.20	.10
	Panel	.75	.60	.30
3	Tom Foley	.25	.20	.10
13	Jim Clancy	.25	.20	.10
	Panel	.75	.60	.30
4	Herm Winningham	.25	.20	.10
14	Rance Mulliniks	.25	.20	.10
	Panel	1.00	.75	.40
5	Hubie Brooks	.40	.30	.15
24	Jimmy Key	.40	.30	.15
	Panel	.90	.70	.35
6	Mike Fitzgerald	.25	.20	.10
17	Dave Stieb	.40	.30	.15
	Panel	4.00	3.00	1.50
7	Tim Wallach	.70	.50	.30
15	Fred McGriff	2.00	1.50	.80
	Panel	2.50	2.00	1.00
8	Andres Galarraga	1.50	1.25	.60
21	Tony Fernandez	.35	.25	.14
	Panel	.75	.60	.30
9	Floyd Youmans	.25	.20	.10
18	Mark Eichhorn	.25	.20	.10
	Panel	1.00	.75	.40
10	Neal Heaton	.25	.20	.10
19	Jesse Barfield	.40	.30	.15
	Panel	2.00	1.50	.80
11	Tim Raines	1.25	.90	.50
16	Ernie Whitt	.25	.20	.10
	Panel	2.00	1.30	.80
12	Casey Candaele	.25	.20	.10
22	George Bell	.75	.60	.30

1993 Hostess Twinkies

The Continental Baking Company, makers of Hostess Twinkies and cupcakes, returned to the baseball card market in 1993 with a 32-card set issued in two series. The promotion began around opening day with the first series; the second series was made available after the All-Star break. The cards were packaged in multi-packs with cupcakes that look like baseballs, with three cards in a box of eight cupcakes.

		MT	NR MT	EX
Complete Set (32):				
Common Player:				
1	Andy Van Slyke	.25	.20	.10
2	Ryne Sandberg	1.00	.70	.40
3	Bobby Bonilla	.35	.25	.14
4	John Kruk	.35	.25	.14
5	Ray Lankford	.25	.20	.10
6	Gary Sheffield	.35	.25	.14
7	Darryl Strawberry	.35	.25	.14
8	Barry Larkin	.35	.25	.14
9	Terry Pendleton	.25	.20	.10
10	Jose Canseco	.75	.60	.30
11	Dennis Eckersley	.25	.20	.10
12	Brian McRae	.25	.20	.10
13	Frank Thomas	1.50	1.25	.60
14	Roberto Alomar	.40	.30	.15
15	Cecil Fielder	.40	.30	.15
16	Carlos Baerga	.35	.25	.14
17	Will Clark	.75	.60	.30
18	Andres Galaraga	.35	.25	.14
19	Jeff Bagwell	.25	.20	.10
20	Brett Butler	.25	.20	.10
21	Benito Santiago	.25	.20	.10
22	Tom Glavine	.30	.25	.12
23	Rickey Henderson	.60	.45	.25
24	Wally Joyner	.40	.30	.15
25	Ken Griffey, Jr.	1.50	1.25	.60
26	Cal Ripken, Jr.	1.00	.70	.40
27	Roger Clemens	.60	.45	.25
28	Don Mattingly	.75	.60	.30
29	Kirby Puckett	.60	.45	.25
30	Larry Walker	.25	.20	.10
31	Jack McDowell	.25	.20	.10
32	Pat Listach	.25	.20	.10

1993 Humpty Dumpty

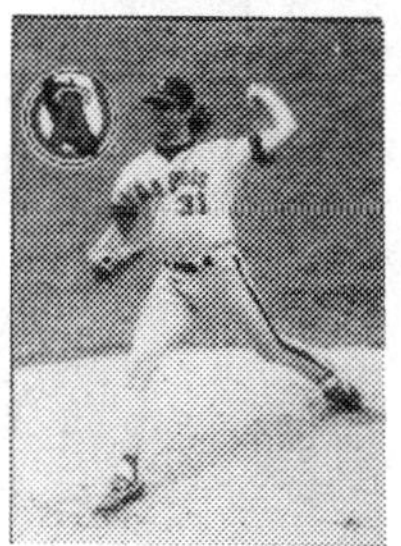

The Canadian potato chip company Humpty Dumpty issued a 50-card set of miniature cards in 1993. The UV coated cards measure 1-7/16" x 1-15/16", with a full-bleed color photo on the front along with the team logo. The backs have three-year statistics and biographical information about the player, along with appropriate product and baseball logos and a card number.

		MT	NR MT	EX
Complete Set (50):		25.00	18.50	10.00
Common Player:		.25	.20	.10
1	Cal Ripken, Jr.	2.00	1.50	.80
2	Mike Mussina	.25	.20	.10
3	Roger Clemens	.50	.40	.20
4	Chuck Finley	.25	.20	.10
5	Sandy Alomar	.25	.20	.10
6	Frank Thomas	3.00	2.25	1.25
7	Robin Ventura	.40	.30	.15
8	Cecil Fielder	.50	.40	.20
9	George Brett	1.50	1.25	.60
10	Cal Eldred	.25	.20	.10
11	Kirby Puckett	.60	.45	.25
12	Dave Winfield	.60	.45	.25
13	Jim Abbott	.45	.35	.20
14	Rickey Henderson	.60	.45	.25
15	Ken Griffey, Jr.	3.00	2.25	1.25
16	Nolan Ryan	3.00	2.25	1.25
17	Ivan Rodriguez	.45	.35	.20
18	Paul Molitor	.60	.45	.25
19	John Olerud	.45	.35	.20
20	Joe Carter	.35	.25	.14
21	Jack Morris	.25	.20	.10
22	Roberto Alomar	.50	.40	.20
23	Pat Borders	.25	.20	.10
24	Devon White	.25	.20	.10
25	Juan Guzman	.25	.20	.10
26	Steve Avery	.40	.30	.15
27	John Smoltz	.40	.30	.15
28	Mark Grace	.35	.25	.14
29	Jose Rijo	.25	.20	.10
30	Dave Nied	.35	.25	.14
31	Benito Santiago	.30	.25	.12
32	Jeff Bagwell	.40	.30	.15
33	Tim Wallach	.25	.20	.10
34	Eric Karros	.35	.25	.14
35	Delino DeShields	.35	.25	.14
36	Wilfredo Cordero	.35	.25	.14
37	Marquis Grissom	.30	.25	.12
38	Ken Hill	.25	.20	.10
39	Moises Alou	.25	.20	.10
40	Chris Nabholz	.25	.20	.10
41	Dennis Martinez	.25	.20	.10
42	Larry Walker	.35	.25	.14
43	Bobby Bonilla	.25	.20	.10
44	Lenny Dykstra	.35	.25	.14
45	Tim Wakefield	.25	.20	.10
46	Andy Van Slyke	.25	.20	.10
47	Tony Gwynn	.40	.30	.15
48	Fred McGriff	.45	.35	.20
49	Barry Bonds	.60	.45	.25
50	Ozzie Smith	.60	.45	.25
----	Checklist	2.00	1.50	.80

1953 Hunter Wieners Cardinals

From the great era of the regionally issued hot dog cards in the mid-1950s, the 1953 Hunter wieners set of St. Louis Cardinals is certainly among the rarest today. Originally issued in two-card panels, the cards are most often found as 2-1/4" by 3-1/4" singles today when they can be found at all. The

cards feature a light blue facsimile autograph printed over the stat box at the bottom. They are blank-backed.

		NR MT	EX	VG
Complete Set (26):		1900.	950.00	570.00
Common Player:		60.00	30.00	18.00
(1)	Steve Bilko	60.00	30.00	18.00
(2)	Alpha Brazle	60.00	30.00	18.00
(3)	Cloyd Boyer	60.00	30.00	18.00
(4)	Cliff Chambers	60.00	30.00	18.00
(5)	Michael Clark	60.00	30.00	18.00
(6)	Jack Crimian	60.00	30.00	18.00
(7)	Lester Fusselman	60.00	30.00	18.00
(8)	Harvey Haddix	65.00	32.00	19.50
(9)	Solly Hemus	60.00	30.00	18.00
(10)	Ray Jablonski	60.00	30.00	18.00
(11)	William Johnson	60.00	30.00	18.00
(12)	Harry Lowrey	60.00	30.00	18.00
(13)	Lawrence Miggins	60.00	30.00	18.00
(14)	Stuart Miller	60.00	30.00	18.00
(15)	Wilmer Mizell	60.00	30.00	18.00
(16)	Stanley Musial	600.00	300.00	180.00
(17)	Joseph Presko	60.00	30.00	18.00
(18)	Delbert Rice	60.00	30.00	18.00
(19)	Harold Rice	60.00	30.00	18.00
(20)	Willard Schmidt	60.00	30.00	18.00
(21)	Albert Schoendienst	150.00	75.00	45.00
(22)	Richard Sisler	60.00	30.00	18.00
(23)	Enos Slaughter	150.00	75.00	45.00
(24)	Gerald Staley	60.00	30.00	18.00
(25)	Edward Stanky	70.00	35.00	21.00
(26)	John Yuhas	60.00	30.00	18.00

1954 Hunter Wieners Cardinals

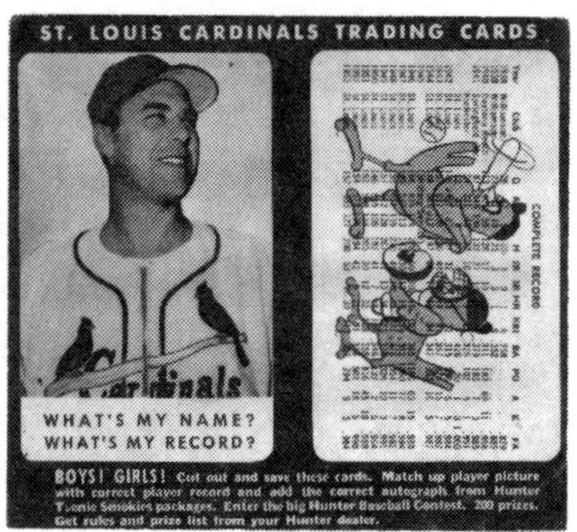

A nearly impossible set to complete today by virtue of the method of its issue, the 1954 Hunter hot dog set essentially features what would traditionally be the front and back of a normal baseball card on two different cards. The "front," containing a color photo of one of 30 St. Louis Cardinals has a box at bottom challenging the collector to name him and quote his stats. The "back" features cartoon Cardinals in action, and contains the answers. However, because both parts were printed on a single panel, and because most of the back (non-picture) panels were thrown away years ago, it is an impossible challenge to complete a '54 Hunter set today. There is no back printing on the 2-1/4" by 3-1/2" cards.

		NR MT	EX	VG
Complete Set (30):		2200.	1100.	660.00
Common Player:		60.00	30.00	18.00
(1)	Tom Alston	60.00	30.00	18.00
(2)	Steve Bilko	60.00	30.00	18.00
(3)	Al Brazle	60.00	30.00	18.00
(4)	Tom Burgess	60.00	30.00	18.00
(5)	Cot Deal	60.00	30.00	18.00
(6)	Alex Grammas	60.00	30.00	18.00
(7)	Harvey Haddix	65.00	32.00	19.50
(8)	Solly Hemus	60.00	30.00	18.00
(9)	Ray Jablonski	60.00	30.00	18.00
(10)	Royce Lint	60.00	30.00	18.00
(11)	Peanuts Lowrey	60.00	30.00	18.00
(12)	Memo Luna	60.00	30.00	18.00
(13)	Stu Miller	60.00	30.00	18.00
(14)	Stan Musial	600.00	300.00	180.00
(15)	Tom Poholsky	60.00	30.00	18.00
(16)	Bill Posedel	60.00	30.00	18.00
(17)	Joe Presko	60.00	30.00	18.00
(18)	Vic Raschi	60.00	30.00	18.00
(19)	Dick Rand	60.00	30.00	18.00
(20)	Rip Repulski	60.00	30.00	18.00
(21)	Del Rice	60.00	30.00	18.00
(22)	John Riddle	60.00	30.00	18.00
(23)	Mike Ryba	60.00	30.00	18.00
(24)	Red Schoendienst	150.00	75.00	45.00
(25)	Dick Schofield	100.00	50.00	30.00
(26)	Eddie Stanky	110.00	55.00	33.00
(27)	Enos Slaughter	150.00	75.00	45.00
(28)	Gerry Staley	60.00	30.00	18.00
(29)	Ed Yuhas	60.00	30.00	18.00
(30)	Sal Yvars	60.00	30.00	18.00

1955 Hunter Wieners Cardinals

The 1955 team set of St. Louis Cardinals, included with packages of Hunter hot dogs, features the third format change in three years of issue. For 1955, the cards were printed in a tall, narrow 2" by 4-3/4" format, two to a panel. The cards featured both a posed action photo and a portrait photo, along with a facsimile autograph and brief biographical data on the front. There is no back printing, as the cards were part of the wrapping for packages of hot dogs.

		NR MT	EX	VG
Complete Set (30):		3000.	1500.	900.00
Common Player:		75.00	37.00	22.00
(1)	Thomas Edison Alston	75.00	37.00	22.00
(2)	Kenton Lloyd Boyer	225.00	112.00	67.00
(3)	Harry Lewis Elliott	75.00	37.00	22.00
(4)	John Edward Faszholz	75.00	37.00	22.00
(5)	Joseph Filmore Frazier	75.00	37.00	22.00
(6)	Alexander Pete Grammas	75.00	37.00	22.00
(7)	Harvey Haddix	90.00	45.00	27.00
(8)	Solly Joseph Hemus	75.00	37.00	22.00
(9)	Lawrence Curtis Jackson	75.00	37.00	22.00
(10)	Tony R. Jacobs	75.00	37.00	22.00
(11)	Gordon Bassett Jones	75.00	37.00	22.00
(12)	Paul Edmore LaPalme	75.00	37.00	22.00
(13)	Brooks Ulysses Lawrence	75.00	37.00	22.00
(14)	Wallace Wade Moon	125.00	62.00	37.00
(15)	Stanley Frank Musial	1000.	500.00	300.00
(16)	Thomas George Poholsky	75.00	37.00	22.00
(17)	William John Posedel	75.00	37.00	22.00
(18)	Victor Angelo John Raschi	75.00	37.00	22.00
(19)	Eldon John Repulski	75.00	37.00	22.00
(20)	Delbert Rice	75.00	37.00	22.00
(21)	John Ludy Riddle	75.00	37.00	22.00
(22)	William F. Sarni	75.00	37.00	22.00
(23)	Albert Fred Schoendienst	175.00	87.00	52.00
(24)	Richard John Schofield (actually John Richard)	75.00	37.00	22.00
(25)	Frank Thomas Smith	75.00	37.00	22.00
(26)	Edward R. Stanky	90.00	45.00	27.00
(27)	Bobby Gene Tiefenauer	75.00	37.00	22.00
(28)	William Charles Virdon	175.00	87.00	52.00
(29)	Frederick E. Walker	75.00	37.00	22.00
(30)	Floyd Lewis Woolridge	75.00	37.00	22.00

1982 Hygrade Expos

This 24-card Montreal Expos team set was the object of intense collector speculation when it was first issued. Single cello-wrapped cards were included in packages of Hygrade luncheon meat in the province of Quebec only. Until a mail-in offer for the complete set appeared later in the season, the

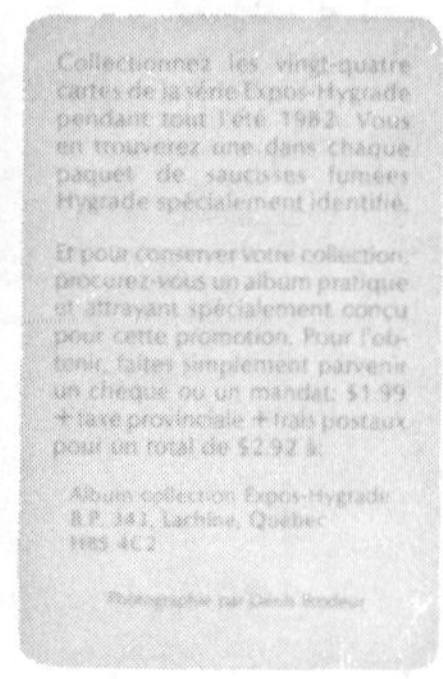

set was selling for as high as $50. It remains a relatively scarce issue today. The 2" by 3" cards are printed on heavy paper, with round corners. Backs are printed only in French, and contain an offer for an album to house the set.

		MT	NR MT	EX
Complete Set (24):		60.00	45.00	24.00
Common Player:		2.00	1.50	.80
Album:		12.00	9.00	4.75
0	Al Oliver	2.50	1.75	.90
4	Chris Speier	2.00	1.50	.80
5	John Milner	2.00	1.50	.80
6	Jim Fanning	2.00	1.50	.80
8	Gary Carter	7.00	5.25	2.75
10	Andre Dawson	7.00	5.25	2.75
11	Frank Tavaras (Taveras)	2.00	1.50	.80
16	Terry Francona	2.00	1.50	.80
17	Tim Blackwell	2.00	1.50	.80
18	Jerry White	2.00	1.50	.80
20	Bob James	2.00	1.50	.80
21	Scott Sanderson	2.50	2.00	1.00
24	Brad Mills	2.00	1.50	.80
29	Tim Wallach	4.00	3.00	1.50
30	Tim Raines	6.00	4.50	2.50
34	Bill Gullickson	2.50	2.00	1.00
35	Woodie Fryman	2.00	1.50	.80
38	Bryn Smith	2.00	1.50	.80
41	Jeff Reardon	3.00	2.25	1.25
44	Dan Norman	2.00	1.50	.80
45	Steve Rogers	2.00	1.50	.80
48	Ray Burris	2.00	1.50	.80
49	Warren Cromartie	2.00	1.50	.80
53	Charlie Lea	2.00	1.50	.80

The values quoted are intended to reflect the market price.

I

1976 Icee Drinks Reds

Issued in 1976 in the Cincinnati area by Icee Drinks, this 12-card set of circular cards features members of the Cincinnati Reds. The cards measure approximately 2" in diameter with the bottom of the disc squared off. The cards are unnumbered.

		NR MT	EX	VG
Complete Set (12):		25.00	12.50	7.50
Common Player:		.40	.20	.12
(1)	Johnny Bench	8.00	4.00	2.50
(2)	Dave Concepcion	.75	.40	.25
(3)	Rawley Eastwick	.40	.20	.12
(4)	George Foster	.75	.40	.25
(5)	Cesar Geronimo	.40	.20	.12
(6)	Ken Griffey	2.00	1.00	.60
(7)	Don Gullett	.50	.25	.15
(8)	Will McEnaney	.40	.20	.12
(9)	Joe Morgan	6.00	3.00	1.75
(10)	Gary Nolan	.40	.20	.12
(11)	Tony Perez	3.00	1.50	.90
(12)	Pete Rose	7.00	3.50	2.00

1963 I.D.L. Drug Store Pittsburgh Pirates

This set of 25 black-and-white cards was regionally distributed. The 4" x 5" semi-gloss cards are blank-backed and unnumbered. The checklist is arranged alphabetically.

		NR MT	EX	VG
Complete Set (25):		150.00	75.00	45.00
Common Player:		5.00	2.50	1.50
(1)	Bob Bailey	5.00	2.50	1.50
(2)	Forrest "Smokey" Burgess	5.00	2.50	1.50
(3)	Don Cardwell	5.00	2.50	1.50
(4)	Roberto Clemente	30.00	15.00	9.00
(5)	Donn Clendenon	7.50	3.75	2.25
(6)	Roy Face	5.00	2.50	1.50
(7)	Earl Francis	5.00	2.50	1.50
(8)	Bob Friend	5.00	2.50	1.50
(9)	Joe Gibbon	5.00	2.50	1.50
(10)	Julio Gotay	5.00	2.50	1.50
(11)	Harvey Haddix	7.50	3.75	2.25
(12)	Bill Mazeroski	10.00	5.00	3.00
(13)	Al McBean	5.00	2.50	1.50
(14)	Danny Murtaugh	5.00	2.50	1.50
(15)	Sam Narron	5.00	2.50	1.50
(16)	Ron Northey	5.00	2.50	1.50
(17)	Frank Oceak	5.00	2.50	1.50
(18)	Jim Pagliaroni	5.00	2.50	1.50
(19)	Ted Savage	5.00	2.50	1.50
(20)	Dick Schofield	5.00	2.50	1.50
(21)	Willie Stargell	20.00	10.00	6.00
(22)	Tom Sturdivant	5.00	2.50	1.50
(23)	Virgil "Fire" Trucks	5.00	2.50	1.50
(24)	Bob Veale	5.00	2.50	1.50
(25)	Bill Virdon	5.00	2.50	1.50

Regional interest may affect the value of a card.

1985 Indians Photo Cards

This set of blank-backed black-and-white cards was available by mail order or at the team's gift shop. Cards feature portrait photos of the manager, coaches and players on a 3-1/2" x 5-1/2" format with a semi-gloss front surface. The unnumbered cards are checklisted here alphabetically.

		MT	NR MT	EX
Complete Set (36):		8.00	6.00	3.25
Common Player:		.25	.20	.10
(1)	Chris Bando	.25	.20	.10
(2)	Rick Behenna	.25	.20	.10
(3)	Butch Benton	.25	.20	.10
(4)	Tony Bernazard	.25	.20	.10
(5)	Bert Blyleven	.75	.60	.30
(6)	Bobby Bonds	.50	.40	.20
(7)	Brett Butler	.50	.40	.20
(8)	Ernie Camacho	.25	.20	.10
(9)	Joe Carter	2.00	1.50	.80
(10)	Carmen Castillo	.25	.20	.10
(11)	Pat Corrales	.25	.20	.10
(12)	Jamie Easterly	.25	.20	.10
(13)	Mike Fischlin	.25	.20	.10
(14)	Julio Franco	.50	.40	.20
(15)	John Goryl	.25	.20	.10
(16)	Mel Hall	.25	.20	.10
(17)	Mike Hargrove	.35	.25	.14
(18)	Neal Heaton	.25	.20	.10
(19)	Brook Jacoby	.35	.25	.14
(20)	Mike Jeffcoat	.25	.20	.10
(21)	Don McMahon	.25	.20	.10
(22)	Ed Napoleon	.25	.20	.10
(23)	Otis Nixon	.60	.45	.25
(24)	Geno Petralli	.25	.20	.10
(25)	Ramon Romero	.25	.20	.10
(26)	Vern Ruhle	.25	.20	.10
(27)	Don Schulze	.25	.20	.10
(28)	Jim Siwy	.25	.20	.10
(29)	Roy Smith	.25	.20	.10
(30)	Dennis Sommers	.25	.20	.10
(31)	Pat Tabler	.25	.20	.10
(32)	Andre Thornton	.40	.30	.15
(33)	Dave Von Ohlen	.25	.20	.10
(34)	George Vukovich	.25	.20	.10
(35)	Tom Waddell	.25	.20	.10
(36)	Jerry Willard	.25	.20	.10

1923 Curtis Ireland Candy (E123)

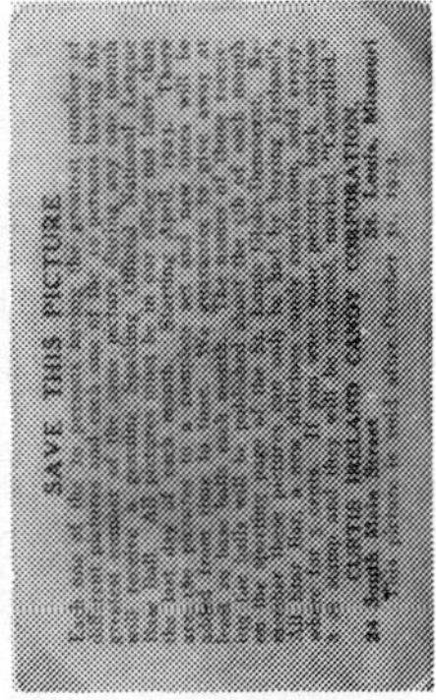

This set, identified in the ACC as E123, was issued in 1923 by the Curtis Ireland Candy Corporation of St. Louis and was distributed with Ireland's "All Star Bars." Except for the backs, the Ireland set is identical to the Willard Chocolate V100 set of the same year. Measuring 3-1/4" by 2-1/16", the cards feature sepia-toned photos with the player's name in script on the front. The backs advertise a contest which required the collector to mail in the cards in exchange for prizes, which probably explains their relative scarcity today.

		NR MT	EX	VG
Complete Set (180):		9500.	4750.	2850.
Common Player:		30.00	15.00	9.00
(1)	Chas. B Adams	30.00	15.00	9.00
(2)	Grover C. Alexander	175.00	87.00	52.00
(3)	J.P. Austin	30.00	15.00	9.00
(4)	J.C. Bagby	30.00	15.00	9.00
(5)	J. Franklin Baker	125.00	62.00	37.00
(6)	David J. Bancroft	125.00	62.00	37.00
(7)	Turner Barber	30.00	15.00	9.00
(8)	Jesse L. Barnes	30.00	15.00	9.00
(9)	J.C. Bassler	30.00	15.00	9.00
(10)	L.A. Blue	30.00	15.00	9.00
(11)	Norman D. Boeckel	30.00	15.00	9.00
(12)	F.L. Brazil (Brazill)	30.00	15.00	9.00
(13)	G.H. Burns	30.00	15.00	9.00
(14)	Geo. J. Burns	30.00	15.00	9.00
(15)	Leon Cadore	30.00	15.00	9.00
(16)	Max G. Carey	125.00	62.00	37.00
(17)	Harold G. Carlson	30.00	15.00	9.00
(18)	Lloyd R. Christenberry (Christenbury)	30.00	15.00	9.00
(19)	Vernon J. Clemons	30.00	15.00	9.00
(20)	T.R. Cobb	800.00	400.00	240.00
(21)	Bert Cole	30.00	15.00	9.00
(22)	John F. Collins	30.00	15.00	9.00
(23)	S. Coveleskie (Coveleski)	125.00	62.00	37.00
(24)	Walton E. Cruise	30.00	15.00	9.00
(25)	G.W. Cutshaw	30.00	15.00	9.00
(26)	Jacob E. Daubert	35.00	17.50	10.50
(27)	Geo. Dauss	30.00	15.00	9.00
(28)	F.T. Davis	30.00	15.00	9.00
(29)	Chas. A. Deal	30.00	15.00	9.00
(30)	William L. Doak	30.00	15.00	9.00
(31)	William E. Donovan	30.00	15.00	9.00
(32)	Hugh Duffy	125.00	62.00	37.00
(33)	J.A. Dugan	35.00	17.50	10.50
(34)	Louis B. Duncan	30.00	15.00	9.00
(35)	James Dykes	35.00	17.50	10.50
(36)	H.J. Ehmke	30.00	15.00	9.00
(37)	F.R. Ellerbe	30.00	15.00	9.00
(38)	E.G. Erickson	30.00	15.00	9.00
(39)	John J. Evers	125.00	62.00	37.00
(40)	U.C. Faber	125.00	62.00	37.00
(41)	B.A. Falk	30.00	15.00	9.00
(42)	Max Flack	30.00	15.00	9.00
(43)	Lee Fohl	30.00	15.00	9.00
(44)	Jacques F. Fournier	30.00	15.00	9.00
(45)	Frank F. Frisch	125.00	62.00	37.00
(46)	C.E. Galloway	30.00	15.00	9.00
(47)	W.C. Gardner	30.00	15.00	9.00
(48)	E.P. Gharrity	30.00	15.00	9.00
(49)	Geo. Gibson	30.00	15.00	9.00
(50)	Wm. Gleason	30.00	15.00	9.00
(51)	William Gleason	30.00	15.00	9.00
(52)	Henry M. Gowdy	30.00	15.00	9.00
(53)	I.M. Griffin	30.00	15.00	9.00
(54)	Clark Griffith	125.00	62.00	37.00
(55)	Burleigh A. Grimes	125.00	62.00	37.00
(56)	Charles J. Grimm	35.00	17.50	10.50
(57)	Jesse J. Haines	125.00	62.00	37.00
(58)	S.R. Harris	125.00	62.00	37.00
(59)	W.B. Harris	30.00	15.00	9.00
(60)	R.K. Hasty	30.00	15.00	9.00
(61)	H.E. Heilman (Heilmann)	125.00	62.00	37.00
(62)	Walter J. Henline	30.00	15.00	9.00
(63)	Walter L. Holke	30.00	15.00	9.00
(64)	Charles J. Hollocher	30.00	15.00	9.00
(65)	H.B. Hooper	125.00	62.00	37.00
(66)	Rogers Hornsby	175.00	87.00	52.00
(67)	W.C. Hoyt	125.00	62.00	37.00
(68)	Miller Huggins	125.00	62.00	37.00
(69)	W.C. Jacobsen (Jacobson)	30.00	15.00	9.00
(70)	C.D. Jamieson	30.00	15.00	9.00
(71)	Ernest Johnson	30.00	15.00	9.00
(72)	W.P. Johnson	400.00	200.00	120.00
(73)	James H. Johnston	30.00	15.00	9.00
(74)	R.W. Jones	30.00	15.00	9.00
(75)	Samuel Pond Jones	30.00	15.00	9.00
(76)	J.I. Judge	30.00	15.00	9.00
(77)	James W. Keenan	30.00	15.00	9.00
(78)	Geo. L. Kelly	125.00	62.00	37.00
(79)	Peter J. Kilduff	30.00	15.00	9.00
(80)	William Killefer	30.00	15.00	9.00
(81)	Lee King	30.00	15.00	9.00
(82)	Ray Kolp	30.00	15.00	9.00
(83)	John Lavan	30.00	15.00	9.00
(84)	H.L. Leibold	30.00	15.00	9.00
(85)	Connie Mack	250.00	125.00	75.00
(86)	J.W. Mails	30.00	15.00	9.00
(87)	Walter J. Maranville	125.00	62.00	37.00
(88)	Richard W. Marquard	125.00	62.00	37.00
(89)	C.W. Mays	35.00	17.50	10.50
(90)	Geo. F. McBride	30.00	15.00	9.00
(91)	H.M. McClellan	30.00	15.00	9.00
(92)	John J. McGraw	150.00	75.00	45.00
(93)	Austin B. McHenry	30.00	15.00	9.00
(94)	J. McInnis	30.00	15.00	9.00
(95)	Douglas McWeeney (McWeeny)	30.00	15.00	9.00
(96)	M. Menosky	30.00	15.00	9.00
(97)	Emil F. Meusel	30.00	15.00	9.00
(98)	R. Meusel	35.00	17.50	10.50
(99)	Henry W. Meyers	30.00	15.00	9.00
(100)	J.C. Milan	30.00	15.00	9.00
(101)	John K. Miljus	30.00	15.00	9.00
(102)	Edmund J. Miller	30.00	15.00	9.00
(103)	Elmer Miller	30.00	15.00	9.00
(104)	Otto L. Miller	30.00	15.00	9.00
(105)	Fred Mitchell	30.00	15.00	9.00
(106)	Geo. Mogridge	30.00	15.00	9.00
(107)	Patrick J. Moran	30.00	15.00	9.00
(108)	John D. Morrison	30.00	15.00	9.00
(109)	J.A. Mostil	30.00	15.00	9.00
(110)	Clarence F. Mueller	30.00	15.00	9.00
(111)	A. Earle Neale	35.00	17.50	10.50
(112)	Joseph Oeschger	30.00	15.00	9.00
(113)	Robert J. O'Farrell	30.00	15.00	9.00
(114)	J.C. Oldham	30.00	15.00	9.00
(115)	I.M. Olson	30.00	15.00	9.00
(116)	Geo. M. O'Neil	30.00	15.00	9.00
(117)	S.F. O'Neill	30.00	15.00	9.00
(118)	Frank J. Parkinson	30.00	15.00	9.00
(119)	Geo. H. Paskert	30.00	15.00	9.00
(120)	R.T. Peckinpaugh	30.00	15.00	9.00
(121)	H.J. Pennock	125.00	62.00	37.00
(122)	Ralph Perkins	30.00	15.00	9.00
(123)	Edw. J. Pfeffer	30.00	15.00	9.00
(124)	W.C. Pipp	125.00	62.00	37.00
(125)	Charles Elmer Ponder	30.00	15.00	9.00
(126)	Raymond R. Powell	30.00	15.00	9.00
(127)	D.B. Pratt	30.00	15.00	9.00
(128)	Joseph Rapp	30.00	15.00	9.00
(129)	John H. Rawlings	30.00	15.00	9.00
(130)	E.S. Rice (should be E.C.)	125.00	62.00	37.00
(131)	Branch Rickey	200.00	100.00	60.00
(132)	James J. Ring	30.00	15.00	9.00
(133)	Eppa J. Rixey	125.00	62.00	37.00
(134)	Davis A. Robertson	30.00	15.00	9.00
(135)	Edwin Rommel	30.00	15.00	9.00
(136)	Edd J. Roush	125.00	62.00	37.00
(137)	Harold Ruel (Herold)	30.00	15.00	9.00
(138)	Allen Russell	30.00	15.00	9.00
(139)	G.H. Ruth	1000.	500.00	300.00
(140)	Wilfred D. Ryan	30.00	15.00	9.00
(141)	Henry F. Sallee	30.00	15.00	9.00
(142)	W.H. Schang	30.00	15.00	9.00
(143)	Raymond H. Schmandt	30.00	15.00	9.00
(144)	Everett Scott	30.00	15.00	9.00
(145)	Henry Severeid	30.00	15.00	9.00
(146)	Jos. W. Sewell	125.00	62.00	37.00
(147)	Howard S. Shanks	30.00	15.00	9.00
(148)	E.H. Sheely	30.00	15.00	9.00
(149)	Ralph Shinners	30.00	15.00	9.00
(150)	U.J. Shocker	30.00	15.00	9.00
(151)	G.H. Sisler	125.00	62.00	37.00
(152)	Earl L. Smith	30.00	15.00	9.00
(153)	Earl S. Smith	30.00	15.00	9.00
(154)	Geo. A. Smith	30.00	15.00	9.00
(155)	J.W. Smith	30.00	15.00	9.00
(156)	Tris E. Speaker	200.00	100.00	60.00
(157)	Arnold Staatz	30.00	15.00	9.00
(158)	J.R. Stephenson	30.00	15.00	9.00
(159)	Milton J. Stock	30.00	15.00	9.00
(160)	John L. Sullivan	30.00	15.00	9.00
(161)	H.F. Tormahlen	30.00	15.00	9.00
(162)	Jas. A. Tierney	30.00	15.00	9.00
(163)	J.T. Tobin	30.00	15.00	9.00
(164)	Jas. L. Vaughn	30.00	15.00	9.00
(165)	R.H. Veach	30.00	15.00	9.00
(166)	C.W. Walker	30.00	15.00	9.00
(167)	A.L. Ward	30.00	15.00	9.00
(168)	Zack D. Wheat	125.00	62.00	37.00
(169)	George B. Whitted	30.00	15.00	9.00
(170)	Irvin K. Wilhelm	30.00	15.00	9.00
(171)	Roy H. Wilkinson	30.00	15.00	9.00
(172)	Fred C. Williams	35.00	17.50	10.50
(173)	K.R. Williams	30.00	15.00	9.00
(174)	Sam'l W. Wilson	30.00	15.00	9.00
(175)	Ivy B. Wingo	30.00	15.00	9.00
(176)	L.W. Witt	30.00	15.00	9.00
(177)	Joseph Wood	35.00	17.50	10.50
(178)	E. Yaryan	30.00	15.00	9.00
(179)	R.S. Young	30.00	15.00	9.00
(180)	Ross Young (Youngs)	125.00	62.00	37.00

A player's name in italic type indicates a rookie card. An (FC) indicates a player's first card for that particular card company.

J

1984 Jarvis Press Rangers

For its second annual "Baseball Card Day" game promotional set, the Rangers picked up a new sponsor, Jarvis Press of Dallas. The 30 cards in the set include 27 players, the manager, trainer and a group card of the coaches. Cards measure 2-3/8" by 3-1/2". Color game-action photos make up the card fronts. Backs, printed in black and white, include a portrait photo of the player. A source close to the promotion indicated 10,000 sets were produced.

		MT	NR MT	EX
Complete Set (30):		5.00	3.75	2.00
Common Player:		.12	.09	.05
1	Bill Stein	.12	.09	.05
2	Alan Bannister	.12	.09	.05
3	Wayne Tolleson	.12	.09	.05
5	Billy Sample	.12	.09	.05
6	Bobby Jones	.12	.09	.05
7	Ned Yost	.12	.09	.05
9	Pete O'Brien	.30	.25	.12
11	Doug Rader	.12	.09	.05
13	Tommy Dunbar	.12	.09	.05
14	Jim Anderson	.12	.09	.05
15	Larry Parrish	.20	.15	.08
16	Mike Mason	.12	.09	.05
17	Mickey Rivers	.20	.15	.08
19	Curtis Wilkerson	.12	.09	.05
20	Jeff Kunkel	.12	.09	.05
21	Odell Jones	.12	.09	.05
24	Dave Schmidt	.15	.11	.06
25	Buddy Bell	.35	.25	.14
26	George Wright	.12	.09	.05
28	Frank Tanana	.20	.15	.08
30	Marv Foley	.12	.09	.05
31	Dave Stewart	1.00	.70	.40
32	Gary Ward	.20	.15	.08
36	Dickie Noles	.12	.09	.05
43	Donnie Scott	.12	.09	.05
44	Danny Darwin	.25	.20	.10
49	Charlie Hough	.30	.25	.12
53	Joey McLaughlin	.12	.09	.05
----	Coaching Staff (Rich Donnelly, Glenn Ezell, Merv Rettenmund, Dick Such, Wayne Terwilliger)	.12	.09	.05
----	Trainer (Bill Zeigler)	.12	.09	.05

1958 Jay Publishing 5x7 Photos Type 1

The name "Picture Packs" has been used to describe this massive series of 5" x 7" black-and-white player photos issued by Jay Publishing's Big League Books division over the eight-year period from 1958-1965. The company also produced yearbooks for various major league teams during the same period, and many of the photos used in the yearbooks also appear in the Picture Packs sets. The Picture Packs were sold by teams, each set consisting of 12 player photos with his name and team at the bottom. The Picture Packs were available by mail, at the ballparks and in stores. They were sold in either plain brown or white envelopes, or in clear plastic. Most were printed on a glossy, slick paper stock, although the quality of the paper may vary from team to team and year to year. The photos were issued anonymously, with no indication of the producer or year of issue, making it nearly impossible to checklist the sets completely. It is known that two different types were issued, based on the typeface used in the captions. Type I photos, issued from 1958 through 1961, were printed with a sans-serif style typeface, while Type II photos, issued from 1962 through 1965, used a serif typeface. Attempts to thoroughly checklist the Picture Packs began only recently. To date nearly 1,500 different poses have been found, but more may exist.

		NR MT	EX	VG
Complete Set (681):		1500.	750.00	450.00
Common Player:		2.00	1.00	.60
(1)	Henry Aaron (Outfielder)	10.00	5.00	3.00
(2)	Henry Aaron (batting)	10.00	5.00	3.00
(3)	Hank Aaron (portrait, pose to neck)	10.00	5.00	3.00
(4)	Joe Adcock (portrait, pose to waist)	2.00	1.00	.60
(5)	Joe Adcock (batting, pose to chest)	2.00	1.00	.60
(6)	Joseph Adcock (Infielder, portrait, pose to neck)	2.00	1.00	.60
(7)	Bob Allison (portrait, pose to neck)	2.00	1.00	.60
(8)	Bob Allison (batting, pose to chest)	2.00	1.00	.60
(9)	Bob Allison (batting, pose to chest, scored background)	2.00	1.00	.60
(10)	Felipe Alou (kneeling, pose to waist, arms crossed)	2.00	1.00	.60
(11)	Walter Alston (portrait, pose to neck)	2.00	1.00	.60
(12)	George Altman (portrait, pose to chest)	2.00	1.00	.60
(13)	Ruben Amaro (batting, pose to chest, dark background)	2.00	1.00	.60
(14)	Ruben Amaro (batting, pose to chest, light background)	2.00	1.00	.60
(15)	Bob Anderson (portrait, pose to chest)	2.00	1.00	.60
(16)	Bob Anderson (pitching)	2.00	1.00	.60
(17)	Harry Anderson (Phillies, portrait, pose to neck)	2.00	1.00	.60
(18)	Harry Anderson (Philadelphia Phillies, portrait, pose to chest)	2.00	1.00	.60
(19)	John Antonelli (Giants, pitching)	2.00	1.00	.60
(20)	John Antonelli (portrait, pose to neck)	2.00	1.00	.60
(21)	John Antonelli (Indians, pitching)	2.00	1.00	.60
(22)	Luis Aparicio (portrait, pose to chest)	3.00	1.50	.90
(23)	Luis Aparicio (ready to throw)	3.00	1.50	.90
(24)	Luis Aparicio (portrait, pose to neck)	3.00	1.50	.90
(25)	Richie Ashburn (Phillies, portrait, pose to neck)	3.00	1.50	.90
(26)	Richie Ashburn (Philadelphia Phillies, portrait, pose to waist)	3.00	1.50	.90
(27)	Richie Asburn (Ashburn) (Cubs, portrait, pose to neck)	3.00	1.50	.90
(28)	Richie Ashburn (Cubs, portrait, pose to waist)	3.00	1.50	.90
(29)	Ken Aspromonte (portrait, pose to chest)	.75	.40	.25
(30)	Ed Bailey (portrait, pose to chest)	.75	.40	.25
(31)	Ed Bailey (batting, pose to waist)	.75	.40	.25
(32)	Ed Bailey (portrait, pose to neck, smile)	.75	.40	.25
(33)	Ed Bailey (portrait, pose to neck, no smile)	6.00	3.00	1.75
(34)	Ernie Banks (portrait, pose to neck)	6.00	3.00	1.75
(35)	Ernie Banks (portrait, pose to chest)	6.00	3.00	1.75
(36)	Curt Barclay (pitching, pitcher's follow through)	2.00	1.00	.60
(37)	Earl Battey (portrait, pose to neck)	2.00	1.00	.60
(38)	Earl Battey (catching, crouching)	2.00	1.00	.60
(39)	Hank Bauer (Yankees, portrait, pose to neck)	2.00	1.00	.60
(40)	Hank Bauer (Athletics, portrait, pose to neck)	2.00	1.00	.60
(41)	Hank Bauer (batting)	2.00	1.00	.60
(42)	Frank Baumann (portrait, pose to waist, glove)	2.00	1.00	.60
(43)	Jim Baumer (batting, pose to chest)	2.00	1.00	.60
(44)	Julio Becquer (portrait, pose to chest)	2.00	1.00	.60
(45)	Julio Becquer (kneeling, holding bat)	2.00	1.00	.60
(46)	Gus Bell (portrait, pose to neck)	2.00	1.00	.60
(47)	Gus Bell (hands on knees)	2.00	1.00	.60
(48)	Lou Berberet (portrait, pose to chest)	2.00	1.00	.60
(49)	Larry Berra (portrait, pose to neck)	7.00	3.50	2.00
(50)	Yogi Berra (batting, pose to waist)	7.00	3.50	2.00
(51)	Reno Bertoia (kneeling, holding bat)	2.00	1.00	.60
(52)	Reno Bertoia (fielding, Detroit uniform)	2.00	1.00	.60
(53)	Steve Bilko (portrait, pose to chest)	2.00	1.00	.60
(54)	Steve Bilko (portrait, pose to neck)	2.00	1.00	.60
(55)	Don Blasingame (bunting)	2.00	1.00	.60
(56)	Don Blasingame (fielding)	2.00	1.00	.60
(57)	Don Blasingame (portrait, pose to neck)	2.00	1.00	.60
(58)	Frank Bolling (Braves, portrait, pose to chest)	2.00	1.00	.60
(59)	Frank Bolling (Tigers, portrait, pose to chest)	2.00	1.00	.60
(60)	Steve Boros (portrait, pose to chest)	2.00	1.00	.60
(61)	Ed Bouchee (portrait, pose to waist, Philadelphia uniform)	2.00	1.00	.60
(62)	Ed Bouchee (portrait, pose to chest)	2.00	1.00	.60
(63)	Bob Bowman (portrait, pose to neck)	2.00	1.00	.60
(64)	Bob Boyd (portrait, pose to neck)	2.00	1.00	.60
(65)	Bob Boyd (Orioles, portrait, pose to chest)	2.00	1.00	.60
(66)	Bob Boyd (Athletics, portrait, pose to chest)	2.00	1.00	.60
(67)	Cletus Boyer (Cletis) (kneeling, holding bat)	2.00	1.00	.60
(68)	Ken Boyer (portrait, pose to neck)	2.00	1.00	.60
(69)	Ken Boyer (portrait, pose to chest)	2.00	1.00	.60
(70)	Jackie Brandt (Giants, portrait, pose to chest)	2.00	1.00	.60
(71)	Jackie Brandt (batting)	2.00	1.00	.60
(72)	Jackie Brandt (Orioles, portrait, pose to chest, dark background)	2.00	1.00	.60
(73)	Jackie Brandt (Orioles, portrait, pose to chest, light background)	2.00	1.00	.60
(74)	Marv Breeding (batting, pose to chest)	2.00	1.00	.60
(75)	Eddie Bressoud (fielding)	2.00	1.00	.60
(76)	Tom Brewer (portrait, pose to chest)	2.00	1.00	.60
(77)	Tom Brewer (portrait, pose to neck)	2.00	1.00	.60
(78)	Fritz Brickell (portrait, pose to chest)	2.00	1.00	.60
(79)	Rocky Bridges (portrait, pose to chest)	2.00	1.00	.60
(80)	Rocky Bridges (portrati, pose to neck)	2.00	1.00	.60
(81)	Harry Bright (portrait, pose to chest)	2.00	1.00	.60
(82)	Ernie Broglio (portrait, pose to chest)	2.00	1.00	.60
(83)	Jim Brosman (Brosnan) (portrait, pose to chest)	2.00	1.00	.60
(84)	Jim Brosnan (portrait, pose to neck)	2.00	1.00	.60
(85)	Dick Brown (catching, crouching)	2.00	1.00	.60
(86)	Bill Bruton (portrait, pose to chest)	2.00	1.00	.60
(87)	Billy Bruton (portrait, pose to waist)	2.00	1.00	.60
(88)	Billy Bruton (fielding, leaping)	2.00	1.00	.60
(89)	Don Buddin (portrait, pose to neck)	2.00	1.00	.60
(90)	Don Buddin (portrait, pose to chest)	2.00	1.00	.60
(91)	Don Buddin (fielding)	2.00	1.00	.60
(92)	Bob Buhl (portrait, pose to neck)	2.00	1.00	.60
(93)	Bob Buhl (pitching, pitcher's follow through)	2.00	1.00	.60
(94)	Jim Bunning (portrait, pose to chest)	2.00	1.00	.60
(95)	Lewis Burdette (Pitcher, portrait, pose to neck)	2.00	1.00	.60
(96)	Lou Burdette (portrait, pose to chest)	2.00	1.00	.60
(97)	Lou Burdette (pitching)	2.00	1.00	.60
(98)	"Smokey" Burgess (portrait, pose to neck)	2.00	1.00	.60
(99)	Forrest "Smokey" Burgess (portrait, pose to chest)	2.00	1.00	.60
(100)	Smokey Burgess (sitting, 3 bats)	2.00	1.00	.60
(101)	Smokey Burgess (portrait, pose to chest)	2.00	1.00	.60
(102)	Jim Busby (portrait, pose to neck)	2.00	1.00	.60
(103)	John Callison (White Sox, portrait, pose to neck)	2.00	1.00	.60
(104)	John Callison (batting, pose to neck)	2.00	1.00	.60
(105)	John Callison (Phillies, batting, pose to chest, 2 bats)	2.00	1.00	.60
(106)	Roy Campanella (Catcher, portrait, pose to neck)	7.00	3.50	2.00
(107)	Andy Carey (portrait, pose to neck)	2.00	1.00	.60
(108)	Andy Carey (portrait, pose to waist)	2.00	1.00	.60
(109)	Chico Carrasquel (portrait, pose to chest)	2.00	1.00	.60
(110)	Jerry Casale (portrait, pose to chest)	2.00	1.00	.60
(111)	Jerry Casale (pitching)	2.00	1.00	.60
(112)	Norm Cash (portrait, pose to chest)	2.50	1.25	.70
(113)	Orlando Cepeda (standing, 4 bats)	2.50	1.25	.70
(114)	Bob Cerv (portrait, pose to chest)	2.00	1.00	.60
(115)	Bob Cerv (portrait, pose to neck)	2.00	1.00	.60

(116) Bob Cerv (batting, pose to waist) 2.00 1.00 .60
(117) Harry Chiti (catching, crouching) 2.00 1.00 .60
(118) Gino Cimoli (outfielder, portrait, pose to neck) 2.00 1.00 .60
(119) Gino Cimoli (portrait, pose to chest) 2.00 1.00 .60
(120) Gino Cimoli (Cardinals, portrait, pose to neck) 2.00 1.00 .60
(121) Roberto Clemente (portrait, pose to neck) 9.00 4.50 2.75
(122) Roberto Clemente (batting, pose to chest) 9.00 4.50 2.75
(123) Roberto Clemente (portrait, pose to chest) 9.00 4.50 2.75
(124) Truman Clevenger (portrait, pose to chest) 2.00 1.00 .60
(125) Truman Clevenger (pitching, pitcher's follow through) 2.00 1.00 .60
(126) Jim Coker (catching, crouching) 2.00 1.00 .60
(127) Rocco "Rocky" Colavito (batting) 3.00 1.50 .90
(128) Rocky Colavito (portrait, pose to chest, glove) 3.00 1.50 .90
(129) Rocky Colavito (hands on knees) 3.00 1.50 .90
(130) Gordon Coleman (batting, pose to chest) 2.00 1.00 .60
(131) Billy Consolo (fielding) 2.00 1.00 .60
(132) Chuck Cottier (throwing) 2.00 1.00 .60
(133) Chuck Cottier (portrait, pose to chest, photo reversed) 2.00 1.00 .60
(134) Clint Courtney (portrait, pose to neck, dark background) 2.00 1.00 .60
(135) Clint Courtney (portrait, pose to neck, light background) 2.00 1.00 .60
(136) John Covington (Outfield, batting, pose to neck) 2.00 1.00 .60
(137) Wes Covington (batting) 2.00 1.00 .60
(138) Wes Covington (kneeling, holding bat) 2.00 1.00 .60
(139) Harry Craft (kneeling, pose to knees) 2.00 1.00 .60
(140) Harry Craft (portrait, pose to neck) 2.00 1.00 .60
(141) Roger Craig (portrait, pose to chest) 2.00 1.00 .60
(142) Del Crandall (batting, pose to waist) 2.00 1.00 .60
(143) Del Crandall (portrait, pose to neck) 2.00 1.00 .60
(144) Delmar Crandall (Catcher, portrait, pose to neck) 2.00 1.00 .60
(145) George Crowe (portrait, pose to neck) 2.00 1.00 .60
(146) Joe Cunningham (portrait, pose to neck) 2.00 1.00 .60
(147) Joe Cunningham (batting) 2.00 1.00 .60
(148) Bud Daley (portrait, pose to chest) 2.00 1.00 .60
(149) Bud Daley (pitching) 2.00 1.00 .60
(150) Pete Daley (kneeling, pose to knees) 2.00 1.00 .60
(151) Benny Daniels (portrait, pose to chest, hands over head) 2.00 1.00 .60
(152) Al Dark (batting, pose to chest) 2.00 1.00 .60
(153) Alvin Dark (Cardinals, portrait, pose to chest) 2.00 1.00 .60
(154) Alvin Dark (Manager-Giants, portrait, pose to chest) 2.00 1.00 .60
(155) Jim Davenport (throwing) 2.00 1.00 .60
(156) Jim Davenport (fielding, glove out) 2.00 1.00 .60
(157) Jim Davenport (fielding, low ball) 2.00 1.00 .60
(158) Ike Delock (portrait, pose to chest, light background) 2.00 1.00 .60
(159) Ivan Delock (portrait, pose to chest, dark background) 2.00 1.00 .60
(160) Bobby Del Greco (portrait, pose to chest) 2.00 1.00 .60
(161) Don Demeter (portrait, pose to waist) 2.00 1.00 .60
(162) Joe DeMaestri (batting, pose to waist) 2.00 1.00 .60
(163) Murray Dickson (Murry) (pitching, pitcher's follow through, pose to waist) 2.00 1.00 .60
(164) Art Ditmar (pitching, pitcher's follow through, pose to knees) 2.00 1.00 .60
(165) Dan Dobbek (portrait, pose to neck) 2.00 1.00 .60
(166) Dan Dobbek (kneeling, holding bat) 2.00 1.00 .60
(167) Dick Donovan (portrait, pose to neck) 2.00 1.00 .60
(168) Dick Donovan (portrait, pose to chest) 2.00 1.00 .60
(169) Dick Donovan (portrait, pose to chest, glove) 2.00 1.00 .60
(170) Dutch Dotterer (batting, pose to waist) 2.00 1.00 .60
(171) Moe Drabowski (Drabowsky) (portrait, pose to chest) 2.00 1.00 .60
(172) Charlie Dressen (portrait, pose to chest) 2.00 1.00 .60
(173) Don Drysdale (pitcher, portrait, pose to neck) 4.00 2.00 1.25
(174) Don Drysdale (portrait, pose to neck) 4.00 2.00 1.25
(175) Don Drysdale (portrait, pose to chest) 4.00 2.00 1.25
(176) Jimmy Dykes (portrait, pose to chest) 2.00 1.00 .60
(177) Bob Elliott (portrait, pose to neck) 2.00 1.00 .60
(178) Dick Ellsworth (portrait, pose to waist, arms crossed) 2.00 1.00 .60
(179) Don Elston (portrait, pose to neck) 2.00 1.00 .60
(180) Del Ennis (portrait, pose to neck) 2.00 1.00 .60
(181) Chuck Estrada (pitching, pose to knees) 2.00 1.00 .60
(182) Roy Face (portrait, pose to chest) 2.00 1.00 .60
(183) Roy Face (portrait, pose to neck) 2.00 1.00 .60
(184) Dick Farrell (Phillies, portrait, pose to neck) 2.00 1.00 .60
(185) Dick Farrell (Philadelphia Phillies, portrait, pose to neck, glove) 2.00 1.00 .60
(186) Dick Farrell (portrait, pose to chest) 2.00 1.00 .60
(187) Chico Fernandez (portrait, pose to neck) 2.00 1.00 .60
(188) Chico Fernandez (portrait, pose to chest) 2.00 1.00 .60
(189) Jack Fisher (portrait, pose to chest) 2.00 1.00 .60
(190) Jack Fisher (pitching, pitcher's follow through) 2.00 1.00 .60
(191) Ed FitzGerald (portrait, pose to neck) 2.00 1.00 .60
(192) Curt Flood (portrait, pose to neck) 2.00 1.00 .60
(193) Curt Flood (portrait, pose to waist) 2.00 1.00 .60
(194) Hank Foiles (portrait, pose to neck) 2.00 1.00 .60
(195) Hank Foiles (kneeling, holding bat) 2.00 1.00 .60
(196) Whitey Ford (portrait, pose to neck) 5.00 2.50 1.50
(197) Whitey Ford (portrait, pose to chest) 5.00 2.50 1.50
(198) Nellie Fox (ready to throw) 3.00 1.50 .90
(199) Nelson Fox (portrait, pose to neck) 3.00 1.50 .90
(200) Nelson Fox (portrait, pose to waist, "S" visible) 3.00 1.50 .90
(201) Nelson Fox (portrait, pose to chest, "Sox" visible) 2.00 1.00 .60
(202) Paul Foytack (portrait, pose to chest) 2.00 1.00 .60
(203) Tito Francona (batting, pose to chest) 2.00 1.00 .60
(204) Tito Francona (portrait, pose to neck) 2.00 1.00 .60
(205) Gene Freese (portrait, pose to neck) 2.00 1.00 .60
(206) Gene Freeze (portrait, pose to chest) 2.00 1.00 .60
(207) Bob Friend (portrait, pose to neck) 2.00 1.00 .60
(208) Bob Friend (pitching, pitcher's follow through) 2.00 1.00 .60
(209) Bob Friend (portrait, pose to chest, "P" on helmet) 2.00 1.00 .60
(210) Bob Friend (portrait, pose to neck, no "P" on cap) 2.00 1.00 .60
(211) Carl Furillo (Outfielder, portrait, pose to neck) 3.00 1.50 .90
(212) Carl Furillo (portrait, pose to neck) 3.00 1.50 .90
(213) Billy Gardner (portrait, pose to neck) 2.00 1.00 .60
(214) Billy Gardner (portrait, pose to chest) 2.00 1.00 .60
(215) William (Billy) Gardner (portrait, pose to neck) 2.00 1.00 .60
(216) Ned Garver (portrait, pose to chest) 2.00 1.00 .60
(217) Ned Garver (pitching, pitcher's follow through) 2.00 1.00 .60
(218) Ned Garver (pitching, hands over head) 2.00 1.00 .60
(219) Gary Geiger (portrait, pose to chest) 2.00 1.00 .60
(220) Jim Gentile (kneeling, holding bat) 2.00 1.00 .60
(221) Jim Gentile (portrait, pose to chest) 2.00 1.00 .60
(222) Dick Gernert (portrait, pose to neck) 2.00 1.00 .60
(223) Dick Gernert (portrait, pose to chest) 2.00 1.00 .60
(224) Paul Giel (portrait, pose to neck) 2.00 1.00 .60
(225) Bob Giggie (pitching, pitcher's follow through) 2.00 1.00 .60
(226) Junior Gilliam (portrait, pose to neck) 2.50 1.25 .70
(227) Junior Gilliam (portrait, pose to chest) 2.50 1.25 .70
(228) Reuben Gomez (portrait, pose to neck) 2.00 1.00 .60
(229) Ruben Gomez (portrait, pose to chest) 2.00 1.00 .60
(230) Bill Goodman (portrait, pose to neck) 2.00 1.00 .60
(231) Bill Goodman (portrait, pose to chest) 2.00 1.00 .60
(232) Joe Gordon (portrait, pose to chest) 2.00 1.00 .60
(233) Alex Grammas (portrait, pose to neck) 2.00 1.00 .60
(234) Jim Grant (pitching, pitcher's follow through, to knee) 2.00 1.00 .60
(235) Jim Grant (pitching, pitcher's follow through, left leg visible) 2.00 1.00 .60
(236) Dallas Green (portrait, pose to neck, hands over head) 2.00 1.00 .60
(237) Gene Green (portrait, pose to neck) 2.00 1.00 .60
(238) Jerry "Pumpsie" Green (portrait, pose to chest) 2.00 1.00 .60
(239) Lenny Green (portraint, pose to neck) 2.00 1.00 .60
(240) Lenny Green (portrait, pose to chest) 2.00 1.00 .60
(241) Bob Grim (pitching, pitcher's follow through) 2.00 1.00 .60
(242) Dick Groat (portrait, pose to neck) 2.00 1.00 .60
(243) Dick Groat (portrait, pose to chest, light background) 2.00 1.00 .60
(244) Dick Groat (portrait, pose to neck, dark background) 2.00 1.00 .60
(245) Dick Groat (kneeling, holding bat) 2.00 1.00 .60
(246) Harvey Haddix (portrait, pose to neck) 2.00 1.00 .60
(247) Harvey Haddix (portrait, pose to chest) 2.00 1.00 .60
(248) Granny Hammer (portrait, pose to neck) 2.00 1.00 .60
(249) Harry Hanebrink (portrait, pose to waist, MILW uniform) 2.00 1.00 .60
(250) Fred Haney (portrait, pose to neck) 2.00 1.00 .60
(251) Ron Hansen (portrait, pose to chest) 2.00 1.00 .60
(252) Ron Hansen (fielding) 2.00 1.00 .60
(253) Bill Harrell (portrait, pose to chest) 2.00 1.00 .60
(254) Jack Harshman (portrait, pose to chest) 2.00 1.00 .60
(255) Robert Hazel (Hazle) (outfielder, portrait, pose to neck) 2.00 1.00 .60
(256) Woody Held (batting, pose to waist) 2.00 1.00 .60
(257) Woody Held (portrait, pose to neck) 2.00 1.00 .60
(258) Solly Hemus (portrait, pose to chest) 2.00 1.00 .60
(259) Ray Herbert (pitching, pitcher's follow through) 2.00 1.00 .60
(260) Ray Herbert (portrait, pose to chest, "A" on cap) 2.00 1.00 .60
(261) Ray Herbert (portrait, pose to neck, no "A" on cap) 2.00 1.00 .60
(262) Frank Herrera (portrait, pose to neck, glove) 2.00 1.00 .60
(263) Pancho Herrera (portrait, pose to waist, glove) 2.00 1.00 .60
(264) Whitey Herzog (Orioles, portrait, pose to chest) 2.00 1.00 .60
(265) Whitey Herzog (Athletics, portrait, pose to chest) 2.00 1.00 .60
(266) Mike Higgins (portrait, pose to neck) 2.00 1.00 .60
(267) Mike Higgins (portrait, pose to chest, one ear showing) 2.00 1.00 .60
(268) Mike Higgins (portrait, pose to chest, two ears showing) 2.00 1.00 .60
(269) Don Hoak (portrait, pose to neck) 2.00 1.00 .60
(270) Don Hoak (portrait, pose to neck) 2.00 1.00 .60
(271) Don Hoak (portrait, pose to waist) 2.00 1.00 .60
(272) Glen Hobbie (portrait, pose to neck) 2.00 1.00 .60
(273) Gil Hodges (first base, portrait, pose to neck) 4.00 2.00 1.25
(274) Gil Hodges (portrait, pose to neck) 4.00 2.00 1.25
(275) Jay Hook (portrait, pose to neck) 2.00 1.00 .60
(276) Ralph Houk (portrait, pose to chest) 2.00 1.00 .60
(277) Frank House (portrait, pose to neck) 2.00 1.00 .60
(278) Elston Howard (portrait, pose to chest) 2.50 1.25 .70
(279) Elston Howard (batting, pose to chest) 2.50 1.25 .70
(280) Frank Howard (batting, pose to waist) 2.50 1.25 .70
(281) Fred Hutchinson (portrait, pose to neck) 2.00 1.00 .60
(282) Fred Hutchinson (portrait, pose to chest) 2.00 1.00 .60
(283) Dick Hyde (portrait, pose to chest) 2.00 1.00 .60
(284) Dick Hyde (pitching, pitcher's follow through to, pose to thighs) 2.00 1.00 .60
(285) Larry Jackson (portrait, pose to neck) 2.00 1.00 .60
(286) Larry Jackson (portrait, pose to chest) 2.00 1.00 .60
(287) Julian Javier (portrait, pose to chest) 2.00 1.00 .60
(288a) Joey Jay (portrait, pose to chest) 2.00 1.00 .60
(288b) Joey Jay (portrait, pose to neck) 2.00 1.00 .60
(289) Joey Jay (pitching) 2.00 1.00 .60
(291) Joey Jay (Reds, pitching, pitcher's follow through) 2.00 1.00 .60
(292) Hal Jeffcoat (portrait, portrait to neck) 2.00 1.00 .60
(293) Jack Jensen (portrait, pose to neck) 2.00 1.00 .60
(294) Jackie Jensen (portrait, pose to chest) 2.00 1.00 .60
(295) Jackie Jensen (sitting, pose to knees) 2.00 1.00 .60
(296) Bob Johnson (fielding) 2.00 1.00 .60
(297) Connie Johnson (portrait, pose to neck) 2.00 1.00 .60
(298) Sam Jones (portrait, pose to waist, trophy, St. Louis uniform) 2.00 1.00 .60
(299) Sam Jones (pitching) 2.00 1.00 .60
(300) Sam Jones (portrait, pose to neck) 2.00 1.00 .60
(301) Willie Jones (batting, pose to chest) 2.00 1.00 .60
(302) Bill Jurges (portrait, pose to waist) 2.00 1.00 .60
(303) Al Kaline (portrait, pose to chest) 7.00 3.50 2.00
(304) Al Kaline (kneeling, holding bat) 7.00 3.50 2.00

(305) Eddie Kasco (Kasko) (batting, pose to chest) 2.00 1.00 .60
(306) Eddie Kasko (portrait, pose to neck) 2.00 1.00 .60
(307) Marty Keough (portrait, pose to chest) 2.00 1.00 .60
(308) Harmon Killebrew (portrait, pose to chest) 5.00 2.50 1.50
(309) Harmon Killebrew (kneeling, holding bat) 5.00 2.50 1.50
(310) Harmon Killebrew (batting, pose to waist) 5.00 2.50 1.50
(311) Jerry Kindall (portrait, pose to chest) 2.00 1.00 .60
(312) Willie Kirkland (kneeling, five bats) 2.00 1.00 .60
(313) Willie Kirkland (portrait, pose to chest) 2.00 1.00 .60
(314) Willie Kirkland (batting) 2.00 1.00 .60
(315) Willie Kirkland (portrait, pose to chest) 2.00 1.00 .60
(316) Ronald Kline (portrait, pose to neck) 2.00 1.00 .60
(317) Ronnie Kline (Pirates, portrait, pose to chest) 2.00 1.00 .60
(318) Ronnie Kline (Cardinals, portrait, pose to chest) 2.00 1.00 .60
(319) Ted Kluszewksi (kneeling, holding bat) 3.00 1.50 .90
(320) Ted Kluszewski (batting, pose to chest) 3.00 1.50 .90
(321) Ted Kluzewski (Kluszewski) (portrait, pose to chest) 3.00 1.50 .90
(322) Steve Korcheck (batting, pose to chest) 2.00 1.00 .60
(323) Jack Kralick (portrait, pose to neck) 2.00 1.00 .60
(324) Tony Kubek (fielding) 2.50 1.25 .70
(325) Tony Kubek (portrait, pose to neck "NY" cap) 2.50 1.25 .70
(326) Tony Kubek (portrait, pose to neck, "NY" not visible on cap) 2.50 1.25 .70
(327) John Kucks (pitching) 2.00 1.00 .60
(328) Johnny Kucks (portrait, pose to neck) 2.00 1.00 .60
(329) Harvey Kuenn (Indians, portrait, pose to chest) 2.00 1.00 .60
(330) Harvey Kuenn (Giants, portrait, pose to chest) 2.00 1.00 .60
(331) Clem Labine (Pitcher, portrait, pose to neck) 2.00 1.00 .60
(332) Clem Labine (portrait, pose to neck) 2.00 1.00 .60
(333) Jim Landis (portrait, pose to chest) 2.00 1.00 .60
(334) Jim Landis (batting) 2.00 1.00 .60
(335) Hobie Landrith (catching, crouching) 2.00 1.00 .60
(336) Norm Larker (portrait, pose to chest) 2.00 1.00 .60
(337) Don Larsen (portrait, pose to neck) 2.00 1.00 .60
(338) Don Larsen (pitching, pitcher's follow through) 2.00 1.00 .60
(339) Frank Lary (portrait, pose to waist, arms crossed, one hand showing) 2.00 1.00 .60
(340) Frank Lary (portrait, pose to waist, arms crossed, both hands showing) 2.00 1.00 .60
(341) Barry Latman (portrait, pose to chest, W. SOX uniform) 2.00 1.00 .60
(342) Cookie Lavagetto (portrait, pose to chest) 2.00 1.00 .60
(343) Harry Lavagetto (portrait, pose to neck) 2.00 1.00 .60
(344) Harry Lavagetto (portrait, pose to chest) 2.00 1.00 .60
(345) Vern Law (portrait, pose to chest) 2.00 1.00 .60
(346) Brooks Lawrence (portrait, pose to neck) 2.00 1.00 .60
(347) Don Lee (portrait, pose to neck) 2.00 1.00 .60
(348) Jim Lemon (portrait, pose to neck) 2.00 1.00 .60
(349) Jim Lemon (kneeling, holding bat) 2.00 1.00 .60
(350) Jim Lemon (portrait, pose to chest) 2.00 1.00 .60
(351) Jim Lemon (batting, pose to chest) 2.00 1.00 .60
(352) Bobbie Locke (pitching, pitcher's follow through) 2.00 1.00 .60
(353) Carroll (Whitey) Lockman (portrait, pose to chest) 2.00 1.00 .60
(354) Whitey Lockman (fielding) 2.00 1.00 .60
(355) Billy Loes (portrait, pose to neck) 2.00 1.00 .60
(356) John Logan (Infielder, portrait, pose to chest) 2.00 1.00 .60
(357) Johnny Logan (batting, pose to waist) 2.00 1.00 .60
(358) Sherman Lollar (portrait, pose to neck) 2.00 1.00 .60
(359) Sherman Lollar (portrait, pose to chest) 2.00 1.00 .60
(360) Sherman Lollar (kneeling, two bats) 2.00 1.00 .60
(361) Dale Long (portrait, pose to neck) 2.00 1.00 .60
(362) Stan Lopata (batting in cage) 2.00 1.00 .60
(363) Stan Lopata (portrait, pose to chest) 2.00 1.00 .60
(364) Stan Lopata (batting) 2.00 1.00 .60
(365) Stan Lopata (portrait, pose to neck) 2.00 1.00 .60
(366) Al Lopez (portrait, pose to chest, jacket) 3.00 1.50 .90
(367) Al Lopez (portrait, pose to chest, no jacket) 3.00 1.50 .90
(368) Hector Lopez (Athletics, batting, pose to waist) 2.00 1.00 .60
(369) Hector Lopez (fielding) 2.00 1.00 .60
(370) Hector Lopez (Yankees, batting) 2.00 1.00 .60
(371) Jerry Lumpe (portrait, pose to neck) 2.00 1.00 .60
(372) Jerry Lumpe (portrait, pose to chest) 2.00 1.00 .60
(373) Jerry Lumpe (fielding) 2.00 1.00 .60
(374) Jerry Lynch (portrait, pose to chest, one ear showing) 2.00 1.00 .60
(375) Jerry Lynch (portrait, pose to chest, two ears showing) 2.00 1.00 .60
(376) Art Mahaffey (portrait, pose to chest, glove) 2.00 1.00 .60
(377) Bob Malkmus (portrait, pose to chest, glove) 2.00 1.00 .60
(378) Frank Malzone (portrait, pose to neck) 2.00 1.00 .60
(379) Frank Malzone (portrait, pose to chest, smile) 2.00 1.00 .60
(380) Frank Malzone (portrait, pose to chest, no smile) 2.00 1.00 .60
(381) Frank Malzone (batting, pose to thighs) 2.00 1.00 .60
(382) Felix Mantilla (portrait, pose to neck) 2.00 1.00 .60
(383) Felix Mantilla (fielding) 2.00 1.00 .60
(384) Mickey Mantle (portrait, pose to neck) 15.00 7.50 4.50
(385) Mickey Mantle (batting, pose to chest) 15.00 7.50 4.50
(386) Juan Marichal (pitching, pose to waist, hands over head) 3.00 1.50 .90
(387) Roger Maris (batting, pose to chest) 5.00 2.50 1.50
(388) Roger Maris (kneeling, holding bat) 5.00 2.50 1.50
(389) Roger Maris (portrait, pose to neck) 5.00 2.50 1.50
(390) Eddie Mathews (kneeling, holding bat, glove) 4.00 2.00 1.25
(391) Eddie Mathews (kneeling, holding bat, no glove) 4.00 2.00 1.25
(392) Edwin Mathews (Infielder, portrait, pose to chest) 4.00 2.00 1.25
(393) Gene Mauch (portrait, pose to chest) 2.00 1.00 .60
(394) Charlie Maxwell (portrait, pose to chest) 2.00 1.00 .60
(395) Charlie Maxwell (kneeling, holding bat) 2.00 1.00 .60
(396) Lee Maye (batting, pose to waist) 2.00 1.00 .60
(397) Willie Mays (leaping) 10.00 5.00 3.00
(398) Willie Mays (fielding) 10.00 5.00 3.00
(399) Willie Mays (batting, pose to waist) 10.00 5.00 3.00
(400) Willie Mays (batting) 10.00 5.00 3.00
(401) Bill Mazeroski (Pirates, portrait, pose to neck) 4.00 2.00 1.25
(402) Bill Mazeroski (Pittsburgh Pirates, portrait, pose to neck) 4.00 2.00 1.25
(403) Bill Mazeroski (portrait, pose to chest) 4.00 2.00 1.25
(404) Mike McCormick (pitching) 2.00 1.00 .60
(405) Mike McCormick (pitching, pose to waist) 2.00 1.00 .60
(406) Willie McCovey (kneeling, pose to waist, five bats) 4.00 2.00 1.25
(407) Lindy McDaniel (portrait, pose to neck) 2.00 1.00 .60
(408) Lindy McDaniel (portrait, pose to chest) 2.00 1.00 .60
(409) Von McDaniel (portrait, pose to chest) 2.00 1.00 .60
(410) Gil McDougald (portrait, pose to neck) 2.00 1.00 .60
(411) Don McMahon (portrait, pose to waist) 2.00 1.00 .60
(412) Don McMahon (pitching, pitcher's follow through) 2.00 1.00 .60
(413) Donald McMahon (pitcher, portrait, pose to neck) 2.00 1.00 .60
(414) Roy McMillan (portrait, pose to neck, glasses) 2.00 1.00 .60
(415) Roy McMillan (portrait, pose to neck, no glasses) 2.00 1.00 .60
(416) Roy McMillan (throwing, pose to knees) 2.00 1.00 .60
(417) Roman Mejias (portrait, pose to neck) 2.00 1.00 .60
(418) Stu Miller (portrait, pose to chest) 2.00 1.00 .60
(419) Stu Miller (pitching, pitcher's follow through) 2.00 1.00 .60
(420) Minnie Minoso (batting) 2.00 1.00 .60
(421) Orestes Minoso (portrait, pose to chest) 2.50 1.25 .70
(422) Willy Miranda (portrait, pose to neck) 2.00 1.00 .60
(423) Wilmer Mizell (portrait, pose to neck) 2.00 1.00 .60
(424) Bill Monbouquette (portrait, pose to chest) 2.00 1.00 .60
(425) Wally Moon (Cardinals, portrait, pose to neck) 2.00 1.00 .60
(426) Wally Moon (portrait, pose to waist) 2.00 1.00 .60
(427) Wally Moon (Dodgers, portrait, pose to neck) 2.00 1.00 .60
(428) Ray Moore (portrait, pose to neck) 2.00 1.00 .60
(429) Seth Morehead (standing, pose to knees) 2.00 1.00 .60
(430) Tom Morgan (portrait, pose to chest) 2.00 1.00 .60
(431) Walt Moryn (portrait, pose to chest) 2.00 1.00 .60
(432) Don Mossi (portrait, pose to chest) 2.00 1.00 .60
(433) Billy Muffett (portrait, pose to chest) 2.00 1.00 .60
(434) Danny Murtaugh (portrait, pose to neck) 2.00 1.00 .60
(435) Danny Murtaugh (portrait, pose to chest, one ear showing) 2.00 1.00 .60
(436) Danny Murtaugh (portrait, pose to chest, two ears showing) 2.00 1.00 .60
(437) Stan Musial (portrait, pose to neck) 10.00 5.00 3.00
(438) Stan Musial (portrait, pose to waist) 10.00 5.00 3.00
(439) Ray Narleski (portrait, pose to chest) 2.00 1.00 .60
(440) Charley Neal (Infielder, portrait, pose to neck) 2.00 1.00 .60
(441) Charlie Neal (portrait, pose to neck) 2.00 1.00 .60
(442) Charlie Neal (portrait, pose to chest) 2.00 1.00 .60
(443) Don Newcombe (Pitcher, portrait, pose to neck) 2.00 1.00 .60
(444) Don Newcombe (portrait, pose to neck) 2.00 1.00 .60
(445) Don Newcombe (pitching, hands over head) 2.00 1.00 .60
(446) Bob Nieman (Orioles, portrait, pose to neck) 2.00 1.00 .60
(447) Bob Nieman (portrait, pose to chest) 2.00 1.00 .60
(448) Bob Nieman (Cardinals, portrait, pose to neck) 2.00 1.00 .60
(449) Russ Nixon (portrait, pose to chest) 2.00 1.00 .60
(450) Russ Nixon (batting, pose to waist) 2.00 1.00 .60
(451) Don Nottebart (portrait, pose to chest) 2.00 1.00 .60
(452) Joe Nuxhall (pitching, pitcher's follow through) 2.00 1.00 .60
(453) Joe Nuxhall (portrait, pose to neck) 2.00 1.00 .60
(454) Danny O'Connell (portrait, pose to neck) 2.00 1.00 .60
(455) Bill Odell (O'Dell) (portrait, pose to neck) 2.00 1.00 .60
(456) Billy O'Dell (portrait, pose to chest) 2.00 1.00 .60
(457) Claude Osteen (portrait, pose to waist, glove) 2.00 1.00 .60
(458) Jim O'Toole (portrait, pose to neck) 2.00 1.00 .60
(459) Jim O'Toole (portrait, pose to chest) 2.00 1.00 .60
(460) Jim Owens (pitching, pitcher's follow through) 2.00 1.00 .60
(461) Andrew Pafko (outfielder, portrait, pose to neck) 2.00 1.00 .60
(462) Andy Pafko (batting, pose to waist) 2.00 1.00 .60
(463) Jim Pagliaroni (catching, crouching) 2.00 1.00 .60
(464) Milt Pappas (pitching, pitcher's follow through) 2.00 1.00 .60
(465) Milt Pappas (portrait, pose to chest, dark background) 2.00 1.00 .60
(466) Milt Pappas (portrait, pose to chest, light background) 2.00 1.00 .60
(467) Camilo Pascual (portrait, pose to neck, light background) 2.00 1.00 .60
(468) Camilo Pascual (pitching) 2.00 1.00 .60
(469) Camilo Pascual (portrait, pose to neck, dark background) 2.00 1.00 .60
(470) Camilo Pasqual (Pascual) (portrait, pose to neck) 2.00 1.00 .60
(471) Albie Pearson (portrait, pose to chest) 2.00 1.00 .60
(472) Albie Pearson (portrait, pose to neck, "W" on cap) 2.00 1.00 .60
(473) Albie Pearson (portrait, pose to neck, "W" not visible on cap) 2.00 1.00 .60
(474) Orlando Pena (batting, pose to waist) 2.00 1.00 .60
(475) Bubba Phillips (hands on knees) 2.00 1.00 .60
(476) Bubba Phillips (batting, pose to waist) 2.00 1.00 .60
(477) Bubba Phillips (portrait, pose to chest) 2.00 1.00 .60
(478) Bill Pierce (portrait, pose to neck) 2.00 1.00 .60
(479) Billy Pierce (portrait, pose to chest) 2.00 1.00 .60
(480) Billy Pierce (pitching, hands over head) 2.00 1.00 .60
(481) Jim Piersall (portrait, pose to neck) 2.00 1.00 .60
(482) Jim Piersall (batting, pose to chest) 2.00 1.00 .60
(483) Jimmy Piersall (batting, pose to chest) 2.00 1.00 .60
(484) Joe Pignatano (portrait, pose to chest) 2.00 1.00 .60
(485) Al Pilarcik (portrait, pose to neck) 2.00 1.00 .60
(486) Vada Pinson (portrait, pose to neck) 2.00 1.00 .60
(487) Vada Pinson (batting, pose to waist) 2.00 1.00 .60
(488) Juan Pizzarro (Pizarro) (pitching) 2.00 1.00 .60
(489) Herb Plews (batting, pose to waist) 2.00 1.00 .60
(490) Herb Plews (portrait, pose to neck) 2.00 1.00 .60
(491) Johnny Podres (Pitcher, portrait, pose to neck) 2.00 1.00 .60
(492) Johnny Podres (portrait, pose to neck) 2.00 1.00 .60

(493) Johnny Podres (portrait, pose to chest) 2.00 1.00 .60
(494) Arnie Portocarrero (portrait, pose to chest) 2.00 1.00 .60
(495) Wally Post (portrait, pose to waist) 2.00 1.00 .60
(496) Wally Post (batting, pose to waist) 2.00 1.00 .60
(497) Vic Power (batting, pose to waist) 2.00 1.00 .60
(498) Vic Power (batting, head shot) 2.00 1.00 .60
(499) Vic Power (fielding, pose to knees) 2.00 1.00 .60
(500) Bob Purkey (portrait, pose to neck) 2.00 1.00 .60
(501) Pedro Ramos (portrait, pose to chest, hands over head) 2.00 1.00 .60
(502) Pedro Ramos (Senators, portrait, pose to neck, dark background) 2.00 1.00 .60
(503) Pedro Ramos (portrait, pose to neck, light background) 2.00 1.00 .60
(504) Pedro Ramos (Twins, portrait, pose to neck) 2.00 1.00 .60
(505) Pee Wee Reese (Infielder, portrait, pose to neck) 5.00 2.50 1.50
(506) Rip Repulski (portrait, pose to neck) 2.00 1.00 .60
(507) Rip Repulski (portrait, pose to neck) 2.00 1.00 .60
(508) Paul Richards (portrait, pose to neck) 2.00 1.00 .60
(509) Paul Richards (portrait, pose to chest, Orioles uniform) 2.00 1.00 .60
(510) Paul Richards (portrait, pose to chest, Baltimore uniform) 2.00 1.00 .60
(511) Bobby Richardson (batting) 2.50 1.25 .70
(512) Bobby Richardson (fielding) 2.50 1.25 .70
(513) Bill Rigney (portrait, pose to chest) 2.00 1.00 .60
(514) Jim Rivera (portrait, pose to neck) 2.00 1.00 .60
(515) Mel Roach (throwing) 2.00 1.00 .60
(516) Robin Roberts (portrait, pose to neck) 3.00 1.50 .90
(517) Robin Roberts (pitching, hands on knees) 3.00 1.50 .90
(518) Robin Roberts (portrait, pose to chest) 3.00 1.50 .90
(519) Brooks Robinson (portrait, pose to chest) 6.00 3.00 1.75
(520) Brooks Robinson (fielding) 6.00 3.00 1.75
(521) Frank Robinson (portrait, pose to neck) 5.00 2.50 1.50
(522) Frank Robinson (portrait, pose to chest) 5.00 2.50 1.50
(523) Frank Robinson (batting, pose to waist) 5.00 2.50 1.50
(524) John Romano (portrait, pose to chest, W. Sox uniform) 2.00 1.00 .60
(525) John Romano (portrait, pose to chest, Indians uniform) 2.00 1.00 .60
(526) John Roseboro (portrait, pose to neck) 2.00 1.00 .60
(527) John Roseboro (portrait, pose to chest) 2.00 1.00 .60
(528) Pete Runnells (Runnels) (portrait, pose to neck) 2.00 1.00 .60
(529) Pete Runnels (portrait, pose to chest) 2.00 1.00 .60
(530) Pete Runnels (batting, pose to knees) 2.00 1.00 .60
(531) Bob Rush (pitching) 2.00 1.00 .60
(532) Ron Samford (kneeling, holding bat) 2.00 1.00 .60
(533) Jack Sandford (Sanford) (portrait, pose to neck) 2.00 1.00 .60
(534) Jack Sanford (pitching) 2.00 1.00 .60
(535) Jack Sanford (pitching, pitcher's follow through) 2.00 1.00 .60
(536) Ron Santo (portrait, pose to chest) 2.00 1.00 .60
(537) Hank Sauer (batting) 2.00 1.00 .60
(538) Hank Sauer (hands on knees) 2.00 1.00 .60
(539) Eddie Sawyer (portrait, pose to chest) 2.00 1.00 .60
(540) Bob Schmidt (catching, crouching) 2.00 1.00 .60
(541) Bob Schmidt (catching, throwing mask) 2.00 1.00 .60
(542) Bob Schmidt (portrait, pose to neck) 2.00 1.00 .60
(543) Albert Schoendienst (infielder, batting, pose to neck) 3.00 1.50 .90
(544) Red Schoendienst (portrait, pose to neck) 3.00 1.50 .90
(545) Red Schoendienst (throwing) 3.00 1.50 .90
(546) Don Schwall (pitching, pitcher's follow through) 2.00 1.00 .60
(547) Ray Semproch (portrait, pose to chest) 2.00 1.00 .60
(548) Bobby Shantz (portrait, pose to neck) 2.00 1.00 .60
(549) Bob Shaw (portrait, pose to neck) 2.00 1.00 .60
(550) Bob Sheffing (portrait, pose to chest) 2.00 1.00 .60
(551) Larry Sherry (portrait, pose to chest) 2.00 1.00 .60
(552) Chuck Shilling (portrait, pose to chest) 2.00 1.00 .60
(553) Norm Siebern (portrait, pose to chest) 2.00 1.00 .60
(554) Norm Siebern (throwing) 2.00 1.00 .60
(555) Roy Sievers (Senators, portrait, pose to neck) 2.00 1.00 .60
(556) Roy Sievers (batting, pose to waist) 2.00 1.00 .60
(557) Roy Sievers (White Sox, portrait, pose to neck) 2.00 1.00 .60
(558) Roy Sievers (batting, pose to chest) 2.00 1.00 .60
(559) Curt Simmons (portrait, pose to neck) 2.00 1.00 .60
(560) Curt Simmons (portrait, pose to chest) 2.00 1.00 .60
(561) Bob Skinner (Pirates, portrait, pose to neck) 2.00 1.00 .60
(562) Bob Skinner (Pittsburgh Pirates, portrait, pose to neck) 2.00 1.00 .60
(563) Bob Skinner (portrait, pose to thighs, five bats) 2.00 1.00 .60
(564) Bob Skinner (batting, pose to chest) 2.00 1.00 .60
(565) Bill Skowron (portrait, pose to neck) 2.50 1.25 .70
(566) Bill Skowron (batting, pose to waist) 2.50 1.25 .70
(567) Al Smith (portrait, pose to neck) 2.00 1.00 .60
(568) Al Smith (portrait, pose to chest) 2.00 1.00 .60
(569) Al Smith (kneeling, holding bat) 2.00 1.00 .60
(570) Hal Smith (portrait, pose to neck) 2.00 1.00 .60
(571) Hal Smith (catching, pose to waist) 2.00 1.00 .60
(572) Hal Smith (batting) 2.00 1.00 .60
(573) Hal Smith (batting, head shot) 2.00 1.00 .60
(574) Mayo Smith (portrait, pose to neck) 2.00 1.00 .60
(575) Duke Snider (Outfielder, portrait, pose to neck) 7.00 3.50 2.00
(576) Duke Snider (portrait, pose to neck) 7.00 3.50 2.00
(577) Duke Snider (portrait, pose to chest) 7.00 3.50 2.00
(578) Russ Snyder (portrait, pose to chest) 2.00 1.00 .60
(579) Warren Spahn (Pitcher, portrait, pose to neck) 4.00 2.00 1.25
(580) Warren Spahn (portrait, pose to neck) 4.00 2.00 1.25
(581) Warren Spahn (pitching) 4.00 2.00 1.25
(582) Daryl Spencer (fielding) 2.00 1.00 .60
(583) Daryl Spencer (throwing) 2.00 1.00 .60
(584) Daryl Spencer (portrait, pose to neck) 2.00 1.00 .60
(585) Daryl Spencer (portrait, pose to chest) 2.00 1.00 .60
(586) Gerry Staley (fielding) 2.00 1.00 .60
(587) Casey Stengel (portrait, pose to neck) 5.00 2.50 1.50
(588) Gene Stephens (batting, pose to chest) 2.00 1.00 .60
(589) Gene Stephens (portrait, pose to chest) 2.00 1.00 .60
(590) R.C. Stevens (portrait, pose to chest) 2.00 1.00 .60
(591) Chuck Stobbs (pitching, pitcher's follow through) 2.00 1.00 .60
(592) George Strickland (kneeling, holding bat) 2.00 1.00 .60
(593) Dick Stuart (portrait, pose to neck, no team designation) 2.00 1.00 .60
(594) Dick Stuart (batting, pose to chest) 2.00 1.00 .60
(595) Dick Stuart (kneeling, holding bat) 2.00 1.00 .60
(596) Dick Stuart (portrait, pose to neck, Pirates) 2.00 1.00 .60
(597) Tom Sturdivant (portrait, pose to neck) 2.00 1.00 .60
(598) Tom Sturdivant (portrait, pose to chest) 2.00 1.00 .60
(599) Frank Sullivan (portrait, pose to neck) 2.00 1.00 .60
(600) Frank Sullivan (portrait, pose to chest) 2.00 1.00 .60
(601) Haywood Sullivan (Red Sox, portrait, pose to chest) 2.00 1.00 .60
(602) Haywood Sullivan (Athletics, portrait, pose to chest) 2.00 1.00 .60
(603) Willie Tasby (batting, pose to chest) 2.00 1.00 .60
(604) Willie Tasby (Orioles, portrait, pose to chest) 2.00 1.00 .60
(605) Willie Tasby (Senators, portrait, pose to chest) 2.00 1.00 .60
(606) Sam Taylor (portrait, pose to neck) 2.00 1.00 .60
(607) Tony Taylor (portrait, pose to chest) 2.00 1.00 .60
(608) Tony Taylor (batting, pose to chest) 2.00 1.00 .60
(609) "Birdie" Tebbetts (portrait, pose to neck) 2.00 1.00 .60
(610) John Temple (kneeling, holding bat) 2.00 1.00 .60
(611) Johnny Temple (portrait, pose to neck) 2.00 1.00 .60
(612) Johnny Temple (kneeling, holding bat) 2.00 1.00 .60
(613) Ralph Terry (pitching, pitcher's follow through) 2.00 1.00 .60
(614) Ralph Terry (pitching, pitcher's follow through, pose to knees) 2.00 1.00 .60
(615) Moe Thacker (portrait, pose to chest) 2.00 1.00 .60
(616) Frank J. Thomas (batting, pose to waist) 2.00 1.00 .60
(617) Frank J. Thomas (batting, pose to chest) 2.00 1.00 .60
(618) Frank J. Thomas (portrait, pose to neck) 2.00 1.00 .60
(619) Bobby Thomson (batting, pose to waist, two bats) 2.00 1.00 .60
(620) Fay Throneberry (Faye) (batting, pose to chest) 2.00 1.00 .60
(621) Faye Throneberry (portrait, pose to chest) 2.00 1.00 .60
(622) Marv Throneberry (throwing) 2.00 1.00 .60
(623) Marv Throneberry (portrait, pose to chest) 2.00 1.00 .60
(624) Dick Tomanek (pitching, pitcher's follow through) 2.00 1.00 .60
(625) Frank Torre (portrait, pose to neck) 2.00 1.00 .60
(626) Frank Torre (fielding) 2.00 1.00 .60
(627) Gus Triandos (portrait, pose to neck) 2.00 1.00 .60
(628) Gus Triandos (portrait, pose to chest) 2.00 1.00 .60
(629) Gus Triandos (catching) 2.00 1.00 .60
(630) Bob Trowbridge (portrait, pose to waist) 2.00 1.00 .60
(631) Virgil Trucks (pitching, pitcher's follow through) 2.00 1.00 .60
(632) Bob Turley (pitching, pitcher's follow through) 2.00 1.00 .60
(633) Bob Turley (portrait, pose to neck, one ear showing) 2.00 1.00 .60
(634) Bob Turley (portrait, pose to neck, two ears showing) 2.00 1.00 .60
(635) Bill Tuttle (portrait, pose to neck, "A" on cap) 2.00 1.00 .60
(636) Bill Tuttle (portrait, pose to neck, no "A" on cap) 2.00 1.00 .60
(637) Bill Tuttle (batting, "KC" on cap) 2.00 1.00 .60
(638) Bill Tuttle (batting, "A" on cap) 2.00 1.00 .60
(639) Jack Urban (pitching, pitcher's follow through, pose to knees) 2.00 1.00 .60
(640) Coot Veal (batting, pose to thighs) 2.00 1.00 .60
(641) Mickey Vernon (portrait, pose to waist) 2.00 1.00 .60
(642) Zorro Versalles (portrait, pose to neck) 2.00 1.00 .60
(643) Bill Virdon (portrait, pose to neck) 2.00 1.00 .60
(644) Bill Virdon (kneeling, holding bat) 2.00 1.00 .60
(645) Bill Virdon (batting, pose to chest) 2.00 1.00 .60
(646) Jerry Walker (pitching, pitcher's follow through) 2.00 1.00 .60
(647) Jerry Walker (portrait, pose to chest, tower background) 2.00 1.00 .60
(648) Jerry Walker (portrait, pose to chest, no tower) 2.00 1.00 .60
(649) Lee Walls (portrait, pose to neck) 2.00 1.00 .60
(650) Ken Walters (portrait, pose to neck) 2.00 1.00 .60
(651) Vic Wertz (portrait, pose to chest) 2.00 1.00 .60
(652) Vic Wertz (batting, pose to chest) 2.00 1.00 .60
(653) Bill White (portrait, pose to neck) 2.00 1.00 .60
(654) Bill White (portrait, pose to chest) 2.00 1.00 .60
(655) Sam White (portrait, pose to neck) 2.00 1.00 .60
(656) Sammy White (portrait, pose to chest) 2.00 1.00 .60
(657) Hoyt Wilhelm (portrait, pose to chest) 3.00 1.50 .90
(658) James (Hoyt) Wilhelm (portrait, pose to chest) 3.00 1.50 .90
(659) Carl Willey (portrait, pose to neck) 2.00 1.00 .60
(660) Dick Williams (throwing) 2.00 1.00 .60
(661) Stan Williams (portrait, pose to chest) 2.00 1.00 .60
(662) Ted Williams (batting, pose to neck) 10.00 5.00 3.00
(663) Ted Williams (batting, pose to chest) 10.00 5.00 3.00
(664) Maury Wills (portrait, pose to waist) 2.50 1.25 .70
(665) Jim Wilson (portrait, pose to neck) 2.00 1.00 .60
(666) Gene Woodling (portrait, pose to chest) 2.00 1.00 .60
(667) Gene Woodling (portrait, pose to chest) 2.00 1.00 .60
(668) Al Worthington (portrait, pose to neck) 2.00 1.00 .60
(669) Early Wynn (portrait, pose to neck) 3.00 1.50 .90
(670) Early Wynn (portrait, pose to chest) 3.00 1.50 .90
(671) Early Wynn (fielding) 3.00 1.50 .90
(672) Carl Yastrzemski (portrait, pose to chest) 7.00 3.50 2.00
(673) Ed Yost (kneeling, pose to waist) 2.00 1.00 .60
(674) Ed Yost (portrait, pose to chest) 2.00 1.00 .60
(675) Eddie Yost (portrait, pose to neck) 2.00 1.00 .60
(676) Norm Zauchin (portrait, pose to neck) 2.00 1.00 .60
(677) Don Zimmer (portrait, pose to neck) 2.00 1.00 .60
(678) Don Zimmer (portrait, pose to chest) 2.00 1.00 .60
(679) Jerry Zimmerman (portrait, pose to chest) 2.00 1.00 .60
(680) George Zuverink (portrait, pose to neck) 2.00 1.00 .60
(681) Marion Zipfel (fielding) 2.00 1.00 .60

A player's name in italic type indicates a rookie card. An (FC) indicates a player's first card for that particular card company.

1962 Jay Publishing 5x7 Photos Type 2

	NR MT	EX	VG
Complete Set (811):	1200.	600.00	360.00
Common Player:	1.50	.70	.45

(1) Hank Aaron (batting, pose to chest) 10.00 5.00 3.00
(2) Hank Aaron (batting) 10.00 5.00 3.00
(3) Hank Aaron (kneeling, holding bat) 10.00 5.00 3.00
(4) Tommy Aaron (fielding) 1.50 .70 .45
(5) Jerry Adair (batting, pose to chest, "B" on cap) 1.50 .70 .45
(6) Jerry Adair (batting, pose to chest, bird on cap) 1.50 .70 .45
(7) Joe Adcock (Braves, portrait, pose to waist) 2.50 1.25 .70
(8) Joe Adcock (batting, pose to chest) 2.50 1.25 .70
(9) Joe Adcock (Indians, portrait, pose to waist) 2.50 1.25 .70
(10) Joe Adcock (batting, pose to neck) 2.50 1.25 .70
(11) Hank Aguirre (pitching) 1.50 .70 .45
(12) Hank Aguirre (portrait, pose to waist, glove) 1.50 .70 .45
(13) Bernie Allen (batting, pose to waist) 1.50 .70 .45
(14) Bernie Allen (fielding) 1.50 .70 .45
(15) Bob Allison (batting, pose to chest, plain uniform) 2.00 1.00 .60
(16) Bob Allison (batting, pose to chest, towers in background) 2.00 1.00 .60
(17) Bob Allison (batting, pose to chest, wire background) 2.00 1.00 .60
(18) Bob Allison (kneeling, holding bat) 2.00 1.00 .60
(19) Felipe Alou (portrait, pose to neck) 2.00 1.00 .60
(20) Felipe Alou (batting, pose to thighs) 2.00 1.00 .60
(21) Jesus Alou (kneeling, pose to waist) 1.50 .70 .45
(22) Matty Alou (portrait, pose to chest) 2.00 1.00 .60
(23) Walt Alston (portrait, pose to neck) 1.75 .90 .50
(24) Walt Alston (portrait, pose to chest, dark background) 1.75 .90 .50
(25) Walt Alston (portrait, pose to chest, light background) 1.75 .90 .50
(26) George Altman (portrait, pose to chest, dark background) 1.50 .70 .45
(27) George Altman (portrait, pose to chest, light background) 1.50 .70 .45
(28) Max Alvis (portrait, pose to chest) 1.50 .70 .45
(29) Max Alvis (batting, pose to chest) 1.50 .70 .45
(30) Joe Amalfitano (portrait, pose to chest) 1.50 .70 .45
(31) Ruben Amaro (batting, pose to chest) 1.50 .70 .45
(32) Bob Anderson (portrait, pose to chest) 1.50 .70 .45
(33) Luis Aparicio (fielding) 4.00 2.00 1.25
(34) Luis Aparicio (batting, pose to chest, "B" on cap) 4.00 2.00 1.25
(35) Luis Aparicio (batting, pose to chest, bird on cap) 4.00 2.00 1.25
(36) Luis Aparicio (kneeling, pose to waist) 4.00 2.00 1.25
(37) George Arrigo (Jerry) (portrait, pose to waist) 1.50 .70 .45
(38) Luis Arroyo (pitching, pitcher's follow through) 2.00 1.00 .60
(39) Bob Aspromonte (portrait, pose to chest) 1.50 .70 .45
(40) Bob Aspromonte (batting, pose to chest) 1.50 .70 .45
(41) Earl Averill (batting, pose to chest) 1.50 .70 .45
(42) Joe Azcue (batting, pose to chest) 1.50 .70 .45
(43) Jim Archer (pitching, pitcher's follow through) 1.50 .70 .45
(44) Bob Bailey (batting, pose to chest) 1.50 .70 .45
(45) Bob Bailey (kneeling, holding bat) 1.50 .70 .45
(46) Ed Bailey (catching, lifting mask) 1.50 .70 .45
(47) Jack Baldschun (portrait, pose to chest) 1.50 .70 .45
(48) Jack Baldschun (portrait, pose to chest, hands over head) 1.50 .70 .45
(49) Ernie Banks (fielding) 6.00 3.00 1.75
(50) Ernie Banks (portrait, pose to waist) 6.00 3.00 1.75
(51) Ernie Banks (batting, pose to chest) 6.00 3.00 1.75
(52) Steve Barber (pitching, pose to chest, hands over head) 1.50 .70 .45
(53) Steve Barber (portrait, pose to chest) 1.50 .70 .45
(54) Steve Barber (pitching, pitcher's follow through) 1.50 .70 .45
(55) Norm Bass (portrait, pose to chest) 1.50 .70 .45
(56) Norm Bass (portrait, pose to waist, glove) 1.50 .70 .45
(57) Earl Battey (batting, pose to chest) 1.50 .70 .45
(58) Earl Battey (catching, crouching) 1.50 .70 .45
(59) Hank Bauer (portrait, pose to chest) 1.50 .70 .45
(60) Frank Baumann (pitching, pitcher's follow through) 1.50 .70 .45
(61) Larry Bearnarth (pitching, pitcher's follow through) 1.50 .70 .45
(62) Bo Belinsky (portrait, pose to chest) 2.00 1.00 .60
(63) Gary Bell (portrait, pose to chest) 1.50 .70 .45
(64) Gary Bell (pitching) 1.50 .70 .45
(65) Gus Bell (portrait, pose to chest) 1.50 .70 .45
(66) Gus Bell (batting, pose to waist) 1.50 .70 .45
(67) Dennis Bennett (portrait, pose to chest) 1.50 .70 .45
(68) Yogi Berra (Manager, portrait, pose to chest) 7.00 3.50 2.00
(69) Yogi Berra (portrait, pose to chest) 7.00 3.50 2.00
(70) Yogi Berra (batting, pose to thighs) 7.00 3.50 2.00
(71) Dick Bertell (portrait, pose to waist, Cubs uniform) 1.50 .70 .45
(72) Dick Bertell (portrait, pose to chest, Chicago uniform) 1.50 .70 .45
(73) Steve Bilko (batting, pose to chest) 1.50 .70 .45
(74) John Blanchard (batting, pose to chest) 2.00 1.00 .60
(75) Don Blasingame (portrait, pose to chest) 1.50 .70 .45
(76) Don Blasingame (batting, pose to chest) 1.50 .70 .45
(77) Wade Blasingame (pitching, pitcher's follow through) 1.50 .70 .45
(78) Frank Bolling (batting, pose to chest) 1.50 .70 .45
(79) Frank Bolling (fielding, throwing) 1.50 .70 .45
(80) Frank Bolling (kneeling, holding bat) 1.50 .70 .45
(81) Steve Boros (kneeling, holding bat) 1.50 .70 .45
(82) Jim Bouton (pitching, pitcher's follow through) 2.50 1.25 .70
(83) Sam Bowens (batting, pose to chest) 1.50 .70 .45
(84) Clete Boyer (fielding) 2.00 1.00 .60
(85) Clete Boyer (batting, pose to chest, bat tilted) 2.00 1.00 .60
(86) Cletis Boyer (batting, pose to chest, bat vertical) 2.00 1.00 .60
(87) Ken Boyer (portrait, pose to chest) 3.00 1.50 .90
(88) Ken Boyer (fielding) 3.00 1.50 .90
(89) Ken Boyer (kneeling, holding bat) 3.00 1.50 .90
(90) Bobbie Bragan (portrait, pose to waist, looks left) 1.50 .70 .45
(91) Bobbie Bragan (portrait, pose to waist, looks right) 1.50 .70 .45
(92) Jackie Brandt (kneeling, holding bat) 1.50 .70 .45
(93) Jackie Brandt (batting, pose to waist) 1.50 .70 .45
(94) Jackie Brandt (hands on knees) 1.50 .70 .45
(95) Marv Breeding (kneeling, holding bat) 1.50 .70 .45
(96) Ed Bressoud (portrait, pose to chest) 1.50 .70 .45
(97) Ed Bressoud (batting, pose to thighs) 1.50 .70 .45
(98) Ed Bressoud (kneeling, pose to knees, arms crossed) 1.50 .70 .45
(99) Ed Brinkman (portrait, pose to chest) 1.50 .70 .45
(100) Lou Brock (portrait, pose to chest, dark background) 5.00 2.50 1.50
(101) Lou Brock (portrait, pose to waist, light background) 5.00 2.50 1.50
(102) Ernie Broglio (pitching, pitcher's follow through) 1.50 .70 .45
(103) Ernie Broglio (pitching, pose to waist, one ear showing) 1.50 .70 .45
(104) Ernie Broglio (pitching, pose to waist, two ears showing) 1.50 .70 .45
(105) Ernie Broglio (portrait, pose to chest) 1.50 .70 .45
(106) Jim Brosnan (portrait, pose to chest, hands over head) 1.50 .70 .45
(107) Jim Brosnan (pitching, pitcher's follow through) 1.50 .70 .45
(108) Dick Brown (portrait, pose to waist, glove) 1.50 .70 .45
(109) Hector (Skinny) Brown (portrait, pose to chest) 1.50 .70 .45
(110) Larry Brown (portrait, pose to chest) 1.50 .70 .45
(111) Bob Bruce (pitching, pose to chest, hands over head) 1.50 .70 .45
(112) Bob Bruce (portrait, pose to chest) 1.50 .70 .45
(113) Mike Brumley (portrait, pose to chest) 1.50 .70 .45
(114) Bill Bruton (kneeling, holding bat) 1.50 .70 .45
(115) Bill Bryan (batting, pose to chest) 1.50 .70 .45
(116) Don Buddin (portrait, pose to chest) 1.50 .70 .45
(117) Bob Buhl (pitching) 1.50 .70 .45
(118) Bob Buhl (portrait, pose to waist, cage background) 1.50 .70 .45
(119) Bob Buhl (portrait, pose to neck, hook background) 1.50 .70 .45
(120) Bob Buhl (portrait, pose to chest, bleacher background) 1.50 .70 .45
(121) Wally Bunker (pitching, pose to waist) 1.50 .70 .45
(122) Jim Bunning (portrait, pose to chest) 1.75 .90 .50
(123) Jim Bunning (pitching, pitcher's follow through) 1.75 .90 .50
(124) Jim Bunning (kneeling, pose to knees, arms crossed) 1.75 .90 .50
(125) Lew Burdette (pitching, photo reversed) 2.00 1.00 .60
(126) Lew Burdette (portrait, pose to thighs, glove) 2.00 1.00 .60
(127) Lou Burdette (pitching) 2.00 1.00 .60
(128) Lou Burdette (portrait, pose to chest) 2.00 1.00 .60
(129) Smokey Burgess (kneeling) 2.00 1.00 .60
(130) Pete Burnside (pitching) 1.50 .70 .45
(131) Larry Burright (portrait, pose to chest) 1.50 .70 .45
(132) Cecil Butler (pitching, pitcher's follow through) 1.50 .70 .45
(133) John Callison (batting, pose to chest) 2.00 1.00 .60
(134) John Callison (batting, pose to neck) 2.00 1.00 .60
(135) Chris Cannizzaro (batting, pose to chest) 1.50 .70 .45
(136) Leo Cardenas (fielding) 1.50 .70 .45
(137) Leo Cardenas (batting, pose to waist) 1.50 .70 .45
(138) Don Cardwell (portrait, pose to chest) 1.50 .70 .45
(139) Duke Carmel (portrait, pose to chest) 1.50 .70 .45
(140) Camilio Carreon (Camilo) (batting, pose to chest) 1.50 .70 .45
(141) Camilio Carreon (Camilo) (portrait, pose to chest) 1.50 .70 .45
(142) Norm Cash (batting, pose to chest) 2.00 1.00 .60
(143) Norm Cash (kneeling, holding bat) 2.00 1.00 .60
(144) Norm Cash (fielding) 2.00 1.00 .60
(145) Norm Cash (hands on knees) 2.00 1.00 .60
(146) Wayne Causey (kneeling, holding bat) 1.50 .70 .45
(147) Wayne Causey (portrait, pose to chest, stripe uniform) 1.50 .70 .45
(148) Wayne Causey (portrait, pose to chest, vest uniform) 1.50 .70 .45
(149) Orlando Cepeda (kneeling, pose to waist) 3.00 1.50 .90
(150) Orlando Cepeda (portrait, pose to chest, one ear showing) 3.00 1.50 .90
(151) Orlando Cepeda (portrait, pose to chest, two ears showing) 3.00 1.50 .90
(152) Orlando Cepeda (batting, pose to chest) 3.00 1.50 .90
(153) Elio Chacon (portrait, pose to waist) 1.50 .70 .45
(154) Dean Chance (pitching, pitcher's follow through, wrist over glove) 1.50 .70 .45
(155) Dean Chance (pitching, pitcher's follow through, hand over glove) 1.50 .70 .45
(156) Dean Chance (portrait, pose to chest) 1.50 .70 .45
(157) Ed Charles (batting, pose to chest, striped uniform) 1.50 .70 .45
(158) Ed Charles (batting, pose to chest, vest uniform) 1.50 .70 .45
(159) Tom Cheney (pitching, pitcher's follow through) 1.50 .70 .45
(160) Tom Cheney (portrait, pose to chest, hands over head, picture is Osteen) 1.50 .70 .45
(161) Frank Cipriani (batting, pose to waist) 1.50 .70 .45
(162) Galen Cisco (pitching, pose to knees) 1.50 .70 .45
(163) Roberto Clemente (batting, pose to chest, cap) 8.00 4.00 2.50
(164) Roberto Clemente (batting, pose to chest, helmet) 8.00 4.00 2.50
(165) Donn Clendenon (batting, pose to waist) 1.50 .70 .45
(166) Donn Clendenon (batting, pose to chest) 1.50 .70 .45
(167) Donn Clendenon (portrait, pose to chest) 1.50 .70 .45
(168) Lou Clinton (portrait, pose to chest) 1.50 .70 .45
(169) Lou Clinton (Red Sox, batting, pose to chest) 1.50 .70 .45
(170) Lou Clinton (Angels, batting, pose to chest) 1.50 .70 .45
(171) Tony Cloninger (pitching, hands over head) 1.50 .70 .45
(172) Tony Cloninger (portrait, pose to chest) 1.50 .70 .45
(173) Rocky Colavito (hands on knees) 4.00 2.00 1.20
(174) Rocky Colavito (batting, pose to chest) 4.00 2.00 1.20
(175) Choo Choo Coleman (portrait, pose to waist, glove) 1.50 .70 .45

(176) Gordy Coleman (batting, pose to chest) 1.50 .70 .45
(177) Gordy Coleman (fielding) 1.50 .70 .45
(178) Tony Conigliaro (portrait, pose to waist, glove) 2.00 1.00 .60
(179) Gene Conley (portrait, pose to chest) 1.50 .70 .45
(180) Jim Constable (pitching, pitcher's follow through) 1.50 .70 .45
(181) Chuck Cottier (kneeling, holding bat) 1.50 .70 .45
(182) Chuck Cottier (batting, pose to chest) 1.50 .70 .45
(183) Wes Covington (batting, pose to waist) 1.50 .70 .45
(184) Harry Craft (portrait, pose to chest, Colts uniform) 1.50 .70 .45
(185) Harry Craft (portrait, pose to chest, Houston uniform) 1.50 .70 .45
(186) Roger Craig (portrait, pose to waist) 2.00 1.00 .60
(187) Roger Craig (pitching, pitcher's follow through) 2.00 1.00 .60
(188) Del Crandall (portrait, pose to chest) 2.00 1.00 .60
(189) Del Crandall (kneeling, bats) 2.00 1.00 .60
(190) Del Crandall (catching, crouching) 2.00 1.00 .60
(191) Del Crandall (catching, crouching, throwing) 2.00 1.00 .60
(192) Del Crandall (kneeling, pose to waist) 2.00 1.00 .60
(193) Joe Cunningham (portrait, pose to chest) 1.50 .70 .45
(194) Joe Cunningham (batting, pose to chest) 1.50 .70 .45
(195) Jack Curtis (portrait, pose to chest) 1.50 .70 .45
(196) Bill Dailey (pitching, pose to chest, hands over head) 1.50 .70 .45
(197) Bud Daley (portrait, pose to chest, glove) 1.50 .70 .45
(198) Clay Dalrymple (batting, pose to chest) 1.50 .70 .45
(199) Clay Dalrymple (portrait, pose to chest) 1.50 .70 .45
(200) Bennie Daniels (pitching, pitcher's follow through) 1.50 .70 .45
(201) Bennie Daniels (portrait, pose to waist, glove) 1.50 .70 .45
(202) Alvin Dark (kneeling, pose to waist) 2.00 1.00 .60
(203) Alvin Dark (portriat, pose to chest) 2.00 1.00 .60
(204) Alvin Dark (sitting) 2.00 1.00 .60
(205) Jose Davalillo (Vic) (portrait, pose to waist) 1.50 .70 .45
(206) Jose Davalillo (Vic) (batting, pose to neck) 1.50 .70 .45
(207) Jose Davalillo (Vic) (batting, pose to chest) 1.50 .70 .45
(208) Jim Davenport (fielding) 1.50 .70 .45
(209) Jim Davenport (fielding, over bag) 1.50 .70 .45
(210) Jim Davenport (portrait, pose to chest, San Francisco uniform) 1.50 .70 .45
(211) Jim Davenport (portrait, pose to chest, Giants uniform) 1.50 .70 .45
(212) Tom Davis (batting, pose to waist) 2.00 1.00 .60
(213) Tom Davis (portrait, pose to chest) 2.00 1.00 .60
(214) Willie Davis (batting, pose to chest) 2.00 1.00 .60
(215) Willie Davis (hands on knees) 2.00 1.00 .60
(216) Mike de la Hoz (portriat, pose to waist, arms crossed) 1.50 .70 .45
(217) Charlie Dees (portrait, pose to chest) 1.50 .70 .45
(218) Ike Delock (sitting, pose to knees) 1.50 .70 .45
(219) Don Demeter (portrait, pose to chest) 1.50 .70 .45
(220) Don Demeter (batting, pose to chest) 1.50 .70 .45
(221) Dick Donovan (portrait, pose to chest) 1.50 .70 .45
(222) Dick Donovan (pitching, pitcher's follow through, pose to knees) 1.50 .70 .45
(223) Dick Donovan (crouching) 1.50 .70 .45
(224) Al Downing (portrait, pose to chest) 2.00 1.00 .60
(225) Al Downing (pitching, pitcher's follow through) 2.00 1.00 .60
(226) Moe Drabowski (Drabowsky) (portrait, pose to chest) 1.50 .70 .45
(227) Chuck Dressen (kneeling, pose to knees) 1.50 .70 .45
(228) Chuck Dressen (portrait, pose to chest) 1.50 .70 .45
(229) Don Drysdale (portrait, pose to chest, two ears showing) 2.50 1.25 .70
(230) Don Drysdale (portrait, pose to chest, one ear showing) 2.50 1.25 .70
(231) Ryne Duran (Duren) (pitching, pitcher's follow through) 2.00 1.00 .60
(232) Doc Edwards (kneeling, holding bat) 1.50 .70 .45
(233) Sammy Ellis (portrait, pose to chest) 1.50 .70 .45
(234) Dick Ellsworth (portrait, pose to chest, Cubs uniform) 1.50 .70 .45
(235) Dick Ellsworth (portrait, pose to waist, Chicago) 1.50 .70 .45
(236) Don Elston (portrait, pose to waist, arms crossed) 1.50 .70 .45
(237) Sam Esposito (portrait, pose to chest) 1.50 .70 .45
(238) Chuck Estrada (pitching, pitcher's follow through) 1.50 .70 .45
(239) Chuck Estrada (pitching, pose to knees) 1.50 .70 .45
(240) Roy Face (portrait, pose to chest, pole background) 2.00 1.00 .60
(241) Roy Face (portrait, pose to chest, no pole) 2.00 1.00 .60
(242) Ron Fairley (Fairly) (batting, pose to chest, tower in background) 1.50 .70 .45
(243) Ron Fairly (portrait, pose to chest, #6 visible) 1.50 .70 .45
(244) Ron Fairly (batting, pose to chest, no tower) 1.50 .70 .45
(245) Ron Fairly (portrait, pose to waist) 1.50 .70 .45
(246) Dick Farrell (portrait, pose to chest, Colts uniform) 1.50 .70 .45
(247) Dick Farrell (portrait, pose to chest, Houston uniform) 1.50 .70 .45
(248) Dick Farrell (portrait, pose to chest, glove) 1.50 .70 .45
(249) Bill Faul (portrait, pose to chest) 1.50 .70 .45
(250) Chico Fernandez (batting, pose to chest) 1.50 .70 .45
(251) Hank Fischer (pitching, pitcher's follow through) 1.50 .70 .45
(252) Bill Fisher (Fischer) (pitching, pitcher's follow through) 1.50 .70 .45
(253) Jack Fisher (kneeling, pose to waist, arms crossed) 1.50 .70 .45
(254) Curt Flood (portrait, pose to chest) 2.50 1.25 .70
(255) Curt Flood (hands on knees, background shows two men on left and one on right) 2.50 1.25 .70
(256) Curt Flood (hands on knees, background shows two men on left and none on right) 2.50 1.25 .70
(257) Curt Flood (hands on knees, background shows one man on left and none on right) 2.50 1.25 .70
(258) Whitey Ford (portrait, pose to chest) 5.00 2.50 1.50
(259) Whitey Ford (pitching, pose to knees) 5.00 2.50 1.50
(260) Whitey Ford (kneeling, pose to waist, arms crossed) 5.00 2.50 1.50
(261) Nellie Fox (portrait, pose to chest) 1.75 .90 .50
(262) Nellie Fox (portrait, pose to neck) 1.75 .90 .50
(263) Nellie Fox (fielding) 1.75 .90 .50
(264) Paul Foytack (pitching, hands over head) 1.50 .70 .45
(265) Tito Francona (batting, pose to waist) 1.50 .70 .45
(266) Tito Francona (hands on knees) 1.50 .70 .45
(267) Herman Franks (portrait, pose to chest) 1.50 .70 .45
(268) Bill Freehan (kneeling, holding bat) 2.00 1.00 .60
(269) Bill Freehan (portrait, pose to waist, arms crossed) 2.00 1.00 .60
(270) Jim Fregosi (portrait, pose to chest) 2.00 1.00 .60
(271) Jim Fregosi (batting, pose to chest) 2.00 1.00 .60
(272) Bob Friend (pitching, pitcher's follow through) 2.00 1.00 .60
(273) Bob Friend (portrait, pose to chest) 2.00 1.00 .60
(274) Frank Funk (pitching, pitcher's follow through) 1.50 .70 .45
(275) Gary Geiger (portrait, pose to chest) 1.50 .70 .45
(276) Gary Geiger (batting, pose to waist) 1.50 .70 .45
(277) Jim Gentile (kneeling, holding bat) 1.50 .70 .45
(278) Jim Gentile (batting, pose to chest) 1.50 .70 .45
(279) Jim Gentile (batting, pose to waist) 1.50 .70 .45
(280) Jim Gentile (kneeling, pose to waist, arms crossed) 1.50 .70 .45
(281) Bob Gibson (portrait, pose to chest) 2.50 1.25 .70
(282) Bob Gibson (pitching, pitcher's follow through) 2.50 1.25 .70
(283) Bob Gibson (pitching, pose to knees) 2.50 1.25 .70
(284) Jim Gilliam (portrait, pose to chest, clouds) 2.50 1.25 .70
(285) Jim Gilliam (portrait, pose to chest, no clouds) 2.50 1.25 .70
(286) Jim Gilliam (batting, pose to waist) 3.00 1.50 .90
(287) Jess Gonder (batting, pose to chest) 2.50 1.25 .70
(288) Jesse Gonder (portrait, pose to chest) 1.50 .70 .45
(289) Tony Gonzalez (hands on knees) 1.50 .70 .45
(290) Jim Grant (portrait, pose to thighs, glove) 1.50 .70 .45
(291) Jim Grant (pitching, pitcher's follow through, fuzzy background) 1.50 .70 .45
(292) Jim Grant (pitching, pitcher's follow through, stands in background) 1.50 .70 .45
(293) Eli Grba (pitching, pitcher's follow through) 1.50 .70 .45
(294) Dallas Green (pitching, pose to chest, hands over head) 1.50 .70 .45
(295) Dallas Green (pitching, pitcher's follow through) 1.50 .70 .45
(296) Dick Green (batting, pose to waist) 1.50 .70 .45
(297) Lenny Green (kneeling, holding bat) 1.50 .70 .45
(298) Dick Groat (kneeling, holding bat) 2.50 1.25 .70
(299) Dick Groat (kneeling, holding bat) 2.50 1.25 .70
(300) Dick Groat (batting, pose to waist) 2.50 1.25 .70
(301) Harvey Haddox (Haddix) (pitching, pitcher's follow through) 2.00 1.00 .60
(302) Jimmie Hall (portrait, pose to chest) 1.50 .70 .45
(303) Tom Haller (catching, crouching) 1.50 .70 .45
(304) Tom Haller (catching, throwing) 1.50 .70 .45
(305) Tom Haller (portrait, pose to chest, Giants uniform) 1.50 .70 .45
(306) Tom Haller (portrait, pose to chest, San Francisco uniform) 1.50 .70 .45
(307) Ken Hamlin (portrait, pose to chest) 1.50 .70 .45
(308) Ron Hansen (batting, pose to waist) 1.50 .70 .45
(309) Ron Hansen (fielding) 1.50 .70 .45
(310) Ron Hansen (kneeling, holding bat) 1.50 .70 .45
(311) Carroll Hardy (batting) 1.50 .70 .45
(312) Tim Harkness (fielding) 1.50 .70 .45
(313) Tommy Harper (hands on knees) 1.50 .70 .45
(314) Ken Harrelson (batting, pose to chest) 2.00 1.00 .60
(315) Ken Harrelson (portrait, pose to chest) 2.00 1.00 .60
(316) Woody Held (batting, pose to waist) 1.50 .70 .45
(317) Woody Held (portrait, pose to chest) 1.50 .70 .45
(318) Bob Hendley (portrait, pose to chest) 1.50 .70 .45
(319) Bob Hendley (pitching, pitcher's follow through) 1.50 .70 .45
(320) Ron Henry (batting, pose to chest) 1.50 .70 .45
(321) Ray Herbert (pitching, pitcher's follow through) 1.50 .70 .45
(322) Ron Herbert (pitching) 1.50 .70 .45
(323) Billy Herman (portrait, pose to chest) 3.00 1.50 .90
(324) Mike Hershberger (kneeling, holding bat) 1.50 .70 .45
(325) Mike Hershberger (portrait, pose to chest, arms crossed) 1.50 .70 .45
(326) Whitey Herzog (portrait, pose to chest) 2.50 1.25 .70
(327) Jim Hickman (batting, pose to chest) 1.50 .70 .45
(328) Jim Hickman (kneeling, pose to knees) 1.50 .70 .45
(329) Mike Higgins (portrait, pose to chest) 1.50 .70 .45
(330) Chuck Hiller (batting, pose to chest) 1.50 .70 .45
(331) Chuck Hiller (portrait, pose to chest, Giants uniform) 1.50 .70 .45
(332) Chuck Hiller (portrait, pose to chest, San Francisco uniform) 1.50 .70 .45
(333) Chuck Hinton (batting, pose to chest) 1.50 .70 .45
(334) Chuck Hinton (portrait, pose to chest) 1.50 .70 .45
(335) Chuck Hinton (portrait, pose to waist) 1.50 .70 .45
(336) Billy Hitchcock (portrait, pose to chest) 1.50 .70 .45
(337) Don Hoak (kneeling, holding bat) 1.50 .70 .45
(338) Don Hoak (batting, pose to chest) 1.50 .70 .45
(339) Glen Hobbie (portrait, pose to chest) 1.50 .70 .45
(340) Gil Hodges (portrait, pose to chest, dark background) 3.00 1.50 .90
(341) Gil Hodges (portrait, pose to chest, light background) 3.00 1.50 .90
(342) Gil Hodges (portrait, pose to waist) 2.75 1.50 .80
(343) Gil Hodges (batting, pose to chest) 2.75 1.50 .80
(344) Jay Hook (portrait, pose to waist) 1.50 .70 .45
(345) Jay Hook (pitching, pose to knees) 1.50 .70 .45
(346) Joel Horlen (pitching, pose to chest, hands over head) 1.50 .70 .45
(347) Ralph Houk (portrait, pose to chest, Mgr. on front) 2.00 1.00 .60
(348) Ralph Houk (portrait, pose to chest, Manager on front) 2.00 1.00 .60
(349) Elston Howard (batting, pose to waist) 3.00 1.50 .90
(350) Elston Howard (kneeling, holding bat, pose to knees) 3.00 1.50 .90
(351) Elston Howard (catching, crouching) 3.00 1.50 .90
(352) Frank Howard (batting, pose to thighs) 3.00 1.50 .90
(353) Frank Howard (kneeling, holding bat to thigh) 3.00 1.50 .90
(354) Frank Howard (kneeling, holding bat, tower background) 3.00 1.50 .90
(355) Frank Howard (portrait, pose to chest) 3.00 1.50 .90
(356) Dick Howser (portrait, pose to chest) 2.00 1.00 .60
(357) Ken Hubbs (portrait, pose to chest) 2.00 1.00 .60
(358) Ken Hunt (portrait, pose to chest) 1.50 .70 .45
(359) Ken Hunt (batting, pose to chest) 1.50 .70 .45
(360) Ron Hunt (batting, pose to waist) 1.50 .70 .45
(361) Ron Hunt (fielding) 1.50 .70 .45
(362) Fred Hutchinson (portrait, pose to chest) 1.50 .70 .45
(363) Al Jackson (portrait, pose to chest) 1.50 .70 .45
(364) Al Jackson (pitching, pitcher's follow through) 1.50 .70 .45

(365) Larry Jackson (portrait, pose to waist, tank in background) 1.50 .70 .45
(366) Larry Jackson (Cardinals, portrait, pose to chest, mouth closed) 1.50 .70 .45
(367) Larry Jackson (Cubs, portrait, pose to neck, mouth open) 1.50 .70 .45
(368) Larry Jackson (portrait, pose to neck) 1.50 .70 .45
(369) Charlie James (fielding) 1.50 .70 .45
(370) Julian Javier (batting, pose to waist) 1.50 .70 .45
(371) Julian Javier (portrait, pose to chest) 1.50 .70 .45
(372) Joey Jay (portrait, pose to chest) 1.50 .70 .45
(373) Joey Jay (pitching, pitcher's follow through) 1.50 .70 .45
(374) Manny Jiminez (Jimenez) (portrait, pose to chest) 1.50 .70 .45
(375) Manny Jiminez (Jimenez) (kneeling, holding bat) 1.50 .70 .45
(376) Manny Jiminez (Jimenez) (batting, pose to waist) 1.50 .70 .45
(377) Bob Johnson (batting, pose to waist) 1.50 .70 .45
(378) Ken Johnson (portrait, pose to chest) 1.50 .70 .45
(379) Mack Jones (batting) 1.50 .70 .45
(380) Mack Jones (batting, pose to chest) 1.50 .70 .45
(381) Jim Kaat (pitching, pitcher's follow through) 3.00 1.50 .90
(382) Jim Kaat (portrait, pose to waist, glove) 3.00 1.50 .90
(383) Al Kaline (portrait, pose to chest) 6.00 3.00 1.75
(384) Al Kaline (hands on knees) 6.00 3.00 1.75
(385) Al Kaline (batting, pose to chest) 6.00 3.00 1.75
(386) Rod Kanehl (batting, pose to chest, bat straight up) 1.50 .70 .45
(387) Rod Kanehl (batting, pose to chest, bat angled) 1.50 .70 .45
(388) Eddie Kasko (batting, pose to chest) 1.50 .70 .45
(389) John Keane (portrait, pose to waist) 1.50 .70 .45
(390) John Keane (standing) 1.50 .70 .45
(391) Johnny Keane (portrait, pose to waist) 1.50 .70 .45
(392) Russ Kemmerer (pitching, pose to knees) 1.50 .70 .45
(393) Bob Kennedy (portrait, pose to chest) 1.50 .70 .45
(394) Bob Kennedy (kneeling, holding bat) 1.50 .70 .45
(395) John Kennedy (batting, pose to waist) 1.50 .70 .45
(396) Marty Keough (batting, pose to chest) 1.50 .70 .45
(397) Marty Keough (hands on knees) 1.50 .70 .45
(398) Harmon Killebrew (batting, pose to chest) 3.25 1.75 1.00
(399) Harmon Killebrew (portrait, pose to chest) 3.25 1.75 1.00
(400) Jim King (batting, pose to chest) 1.50 .70 .45
(401) Jim King (portrait, pose to chest) 1.50 .70 .45
(402) Willie Kirkland (Indians, batting, pose to waist) 1.50 .70 .45
(403) Willie Kirkland (Orioles, batting, pose to waist) 1.50 .70 .45
(404) Ron Kline (pitching, pitcher's follow through) 1.50 .70 .45
(405) Ted Kluszewski (batting, pose to chest) 4.00 2.00 1.20
(406) Bob Knoop (portrait, pose to chest) 1.50 .70 .45
(407) Sandy Koufax (portrait, pose to waist, arms crossed) 7.00 3.50 2.00
(408) Sandy Koufax (portrait, pose to chest, smiling) 7.00 3.50 2.00
(409) Sandy Koufax (portrait, pose to chest, palm trees in background) 7.00 3.50 2.00
(410) Jack Kralick (pitching, pitcher's follow through) 1.50 .70 .45
(411) Jim Kralick (portrait, pose to chest) 1.50 .70 .45
(412) John Kralick (pitching, pitcher's follow through) 1.50 .70 .45
(413) Ed Kranepool (batting, pose to chest) 1.50 .70 .45
(414) Tony Kubek (fielding) 3.00 1.50 .90
(415) Tony Kubek (batting) 3.00 1.50 .90
(416) Harvey Kuenn (portrait, pose to chest, Giants uniform) 2.00 1.00 .60
(417) Harvey Kuenn (portrait, pose to chest, San Francisco uniform) 2.00 1.00 .60
(418) Marty Kutyna (pitching, pitcher's follow through) 1.50 .70 .45
(419) Jim Landis (batting) 1.50 .70 .45
(420) Jim Landis (kneeling, holding bat) 1.50 .70 .45
(421) Jim Landis (kneeling, pose to knees, arms crossed) 1.50 .70 .45
(422) Jim Landis (hands on knees) 1.50 .70 .45
(423) Hobie Landrith (batting) 1.50 .70 .45
(424) Don Landrum (fielding) 1.50 .70 .45
(425) Norm Larker (portrait, pose to chest) 1.50 .70 .45
(426) Norm Larker (fielding) 1.50 .70 .45
(427) Frank Lary (pitching, pitcher's follow through) 1.50 .70 .45
(428) Barry Latman (portrait) 1.50 .70 .45
(429) Barry Latman (pitching) 1.50 .70 .45
(430) Charlie Lau (batting) 1.50 .70 .45
(431) Vern Law (portrait) 2.00 1.00 .60
(432) Vernon Law (pitching) 2.00 1.00 .60
(433) Don Lee (pitching) 1.50 .70 .45
(434) Don Lee (portrait) 1.50 .70 .45
(435) Denny Lemaster (pitching, pitcher's follow through) 1.50 .70 .45
(436) Denny Lemaster (pitching, pose to knees) 1.50 .70 .45
(437) Jim Lemon (batting) 1.50 .70 .45
(438) Don Leppert (batting) 1.50 .70 .45
(439) Bob Lillis (batting) 1.50 .70 .45
(440) Don Lock (portrait, pose to chest, light background) 1.50 .70 .45
(441) Don Lock (portrait, pose to chest, dark background, Senators in block letters) 1.50 .70 .45
(442) Don Lock (portrait, pose to waist, dark background, Senators in script) 1.50 .70 .45
(443) Sherm Lollar (kneeling) 1.50 .70 .45
(444) Sherm Lollar (portrait) 1.50 .70 .45
(445) Ed Lopat (portrait) 2.00 1.00 .60
(446) Al Lopez (portrait) 3.00 1.50 .90
(447) Al Lopez (portrait, pose to chest, jacket has top of "S" visible) 3.00 1.50 .90
(448) Al Lopez (portrait, pose to chest, jacket has "S" and part of "O" visible) 3.00 1.50 .90
(449) Jerry Lumpe (batting, pose to waist) 1.50 .70 .45
(450) Jerry Lumpe (kneeling, pose to thighs) 1.50 .70 .45
(451) Jerry Lumpe (batting, pose to chest) 1.50 .70 .45
(452) Jerry Lynch (portrait, pose to chest) 1.50 .70 .45
(453) Art Mahaffey (portrait) 1.50 .70 .45
(454) Art Mahaffey (pitching) 1.50 .70 .45
(455) Roman Majias (portrait) 1.50 .70 .45
(456) Jim Maloney (pitching) 1.50 .70 .45
(457) Frank Malzone (batting, pose to chest, one ear showing) 1.50 .70 .45
(458) Frank Malzone (batting, pose to chest, two ears showing) 1.50 .70 .45
(459) Frank Malzone (portrait) 1.50 .70 .45
(460) Felix Mantilla (portrait, pose to neck, one ear showing) 1.50 .70 .45
(461) Felix Mantilla (portrait, pose to chest, two ears showing) 1.50 .70 .45
(462) Felix Mantilla (portrait, pose to waist) 1.50 .70 .45
(463) Mickey Mantle (portrait) 15.00 7.50 4.50
(464) Mickey Mantle (batting, pose to chest, one ear showing) 15.00 7.50 4.50
(465) Mickey Mantle (batting, pose to chest, two ears showing) 15.00 7.50 4.50
(466) Juan Marichal (portrait, pose to waist, hands over head) 2.50 1.25 .70
(467) Juan Marichal (pitching) 2.50 1.25 .70
(468) Juan Marichal (portrait, pose to chest) 2.50 1.25 .70
(469) Roger Maris (kneeling) 8.00 4.00 2.50
(470) Roger Maris (batting, pose to chest, one ear showing) 8.00 4.00 2.50
(471) Roger Maris (batting, pose to chest, two ears showing) 1.50 .70 .45
(472) J.C. Martin (batting, pose to waist) 1.50 .70 .45
(473) Joe Martin (batting, pose to waist) 1.50 .70 .45
(474) Eddie Mathews (batting) 3.25 1.75 1.00
(475) Eddie Mathews (batting, pose to waist) 3.25 1.75 1.00
(476) Eddie Mathews (kneeling) 3.25 1.75 1.00
(477) Gene Mauch (portrait, pose to knees, one ear showing) 2.00 1.00 .60
(478) Gene Mauch (portrait, pose to knees, two ears showing) 2.00 1.00 .60
(479) Gene Mauch (portrait, pose to chest) 2.00 1.00 .60
(480) Dal Maxvill (fielding) 1.50 .70 .45
(481) Charley Maxwell (batting) 1.50 .70 .45
(482) Lee Maye (portrait, pose to chest, holding bat) 1.50 .70 .45
(483) Lee Maye (portrait, pose to chest, no bat) 1.50 .70 .45
(484) Lee Maye (fielding) 1.50 .70 .45
(485) Willie Mays (portrait, pose to neck) 10.00 5.00 3.00
(486) Willie Mays (portrait, pose to chest) 10.00 5.00 3.00
(487) Willie Mays (kneeling) 10.00 5.00 3.00
(488) Willie Mays (hat, pose to waist) 10.00 5.00 3.00
(489) Bill Mazeroski (portrait) 2.50 1.25 .70
(490) Bill Mazeroski (batting) 2.50 1.25 .70
(491) Bill Mazeroski (fielding) 2.50 1.25 .70
(492) Ken McBride (portrait) 1.50 .70 .45
(493) Ken McBride (pitching) 1.50 .70 .45
(494) Tim McCarver (portrait) 2.50 1.25 .70
(495) Tim McCarver (catching) 2.50 1.25 .70
(496) Joe McClain (pitching) 1.50 .70 .45
(497) Mike McCormick (pitching) 1.50 .70 .45
(498) Willie McCovey (portrait) 3.25 1.75 1.00
(499) Willie McCovey (batting) 3.25 1.75 1.00
(500) Willie McCovey (kneeling) 3.25 1.75 1.00
(501) Tom McCraw (batting) 1.50 .70 .45
(502) Lindy McDaniel (portrait, pose to chest, Chicago uniform) 1.50 .70 .45
(503) Lindy McDaniel (portrait, pose to chest, Cubs uniform) 1.50 .70 .45
(504) Lindy McDaniel (Cardinals, portrait, pose to chest) 1.50 .70 .45
(505) Sam McDowell (portrait, pose to chest) 2.00 1.00 .60
(506) Mel McGaha (portrait, pose to waist, holding bat) 1.50 .70 .45
(507) Mel McGaha (portrait, pose to chest) 1.50 .70 .45
(508) Roy McMillan (fielding) 1.50 .70 .45
(509) Roy McMillan (batting) 1.50 .70 .45
(510) Roy McMillan (portrait) 1.50 .70 .45
(511) Ken McMullen (portrait) 1.50 .70 .45
(512) Sam Mele (portrait) 1.50 .70 .45
(513) Dennis Menke (Denis) (throwing) 1.50 .70 .45
(514) Dennis Menke (Denis) (portrait, pose to neck) 1.50 .70 .45
(515) Bob Miller (portrait) 1.50 .70 .45
(516) Stu Miller (pitching) 1.50 .70 .45
(517) Minnie Minoso (batting) 2.50 1.25 .70
(518) Bill Monbouquette (pitching, pitcher's follow through) 1.50 .70 .45
(519) Bill Monbouquette (kneeling, pose to knees) 1.50 .70 .45
(520) William Monbouquette (kneeling, pose to knees) 1.50 .70 .45
(521) Wally Moon (batting) 1.50 .70 .45
(522) Wally Moon (portrait) 1.50 .70 .45
(523) Billy Moran (batting) 1.50 .70 .45
(524) Tom Morgan (portrait) 1.50 .70 .45
(525) Don Mossi (portrait) 1.50 .70 .45
(526) Manny Mota (portrait) 2.00 1.00 .60
(527) Danny Murtaugh (portrait) 1.50 .70 .45
(528) Stan Musial (fielding) 10.00 5.00 3.00
(529) Stan Musial (kneeling) 10.00 5.00 3.00
(530) Don McMahon (pitching) 1.50 .70 .45
(531) Buster Narum (portrait) 1.50 .70 .45
(532) Charlie Neal (batting) 1.50 .70 .45
(533) Fred Newman (portrait) 1.50 .70 .45
(534) Dave Nicholson (kneeling, pose to waist, holding bat) 1.50 .70 .45
(535) Dave Nicholson (hands on knees) 1.50 .70 .45
(536) Phil Niekro (pitching) 2.25 1.25 .70
(537) Bob Nieman (hands on knees) 1.50 .70 .45
(538) Russ Nixon (batting) 1.50 .70 .45
(539) Joe Nuxhall (portrait) 2.00 1.00 .60
(540) Danny O'Connell (batting) 1.50 .70 .45
(541) Billy O'Dell (portrait) 1.50 .70 .45
(542) Billy O'Dell (Giants, pitching, pitcher's follow through) 1.50 .70 .45
(543) Billy O'Dell (pitching) 1.50 .70 .45
(544) Billy O'Dell (Braves, pitching, pitcher's follow through) 1.50 .70 .45
(545) Jim O'Toole (portrait) 1.50 .70 .45
(546) Jim O'Toole (pitching) 1.50 .70 .45
(547) Tony Oliva (batting) 4.00 2.00 1.25
(548) Gene Oliver (batting) 1.50 .70 .45
(549) Nate Oliver (batting) 1.50 .70 .45
(550) John Orsino (batting, pose to waist, one ear showing) 1.50 .70 .45
(551) John Orsino (batting, pose to waist, two ears showing) 1.50 .70 .45
(552) John Orsino (kneeling, pose to waist) 1.50 .70 .45
(553) Phil Ortega (portrait) 1.50 .70 .45
(554) Dan Osinski (portrait, pose to neck) 1.50 .70 .45
(555) Dan Osinski (portrait, pose to chest) 1.50 .70 .45
(556) Claude Osteen (portrait, pose to waist, glove) 1.50 .70 .45
(557) Claude Osteen (portrait, pose to chest) 1.50 .70 .45
(558) Claude Osteen (pitching, pose to knees) (photo actally Tom Cheney) 1.50 .70 .45
(559) Jose Pagan (portrait, pose to chest, Giants uniform) 1.50 .70 .45
(560) Jose Pagan (portrait, pose to chest, San Francisco uniform) 1.50 .70 .45
(561) Jose Pagan (portrait, pose to waist) 1.50 .70 .45
(562) Jose Pagan (fielding) 1.50 .70 .45
(563) James Pagliaroni (portrait, pose to chest) 1.50 .70 .45
(564) Jim Pagliaroni (portrait, pose to waist) 1.50 .70 .45
(565) Milt Pappas (pitching, pose to chest, hands over head) 2.00 1.00 .60
(566) Milt Pappas (pitching, pitcher's follow through, stands empty) 2.00 1.00 .60
(567) Milt Pappas (pitching, pitcher's follow through, people in stands) 2.00 1.00 .60
(568) Camilo Pascual (pitching, pitcher's follow through) 2.00 1.00 .60
(569) Camilo Pascual (pitching, pose to knees, glove at knee) 2.00 1.00 .60
(570) Camilo Pascual (pitching, pose to waist, glove in front) 2.00 1.00 .60
(571) Don Pavletich (batting) 1.50 .70 .45
(572) Albie Pearson (hands on knees) 1.50 .70 .45
(573) Albie Pearson (kneeling, holding bat) 1.50 .70 .45
(574) Jim Pendleton (batting) 1.50 .70 .45
(575) Joe Pepitone (portrait) 2.50 1.25 .70
(576) Joe Pepitone (batting) 2.50 1.25 .70
(577) Gaylord Perry (kneeling, pose to waist, holding bat) 2.25 1.25 .70
(578) Johnny Pesky (portrait, pose to chest) 1.50 .70 .45
(579) Johnny Pesky (portrait, pose to waist, arms crossed) 1.50 .70 .45
(580) Gary Peters (kneeling) 1.50 .70 .45
(581) Gary Peters (pitching) 1.50 .70 .45
(582) Bubba Phillips (kneeling) 1.50 .70 .45
(583) Bubba Phillips (hands on knees) 1.50 .70 .45
(584) Ron Piche (portrait) 1.50 .70 .45
(585) Billy Pierce (pitching) 2.00 1.00 .60
(586) Billy Pierce (portrait) 2.00 1.00 .60
(587) Jim Piersall (hands on knees) 2.50 1.25 .70
(588) Vada Pinson (batting, pose to waist, tower in background) 2.50 1.25 .70
(589) Vada Pinson (batting, pose to chest, stands in background) 1.50 .70 .45
(590) Juan Pizzaro (pitching, pose to waist) 1.50 .70 .45
(591) Juan Pizzaro (pitching, pitcher's follow through) 1.50 .70 .45
(592) John Podres (portrait) 2.50 1.25 .70
(593) John Podres (pitching) 2.50 1.25 .70
(594) Leo Posada (batting) 1.50 .70 .45
(595) Wally Post (batting) 1.50 .70 .45
(596) Boog Powell (portrait) 3.00 1.50 .90
(597) Boog Powell (batting) 3.00 1.50 .90
(598) Vic Power (batting, pose to chest) 1.50 .70 .45

(599) Vic Power (kneeling, holding bat)1.50 .70 .45

(600) Vic Power (batting, pose to waist) 1.50 .70 .45

(601) Bob Purkey (pitching) 1.50 .70 .45

(602) Bob Purkey (kneeling) 1.50 .70 .45

(603) Mel Queen (batting, pose to waist) 1.50 .70 .45

(604) Dick Radatz (portrait, pose to neck) 1.50 .70 .45

(605) Dick Radatz (portrait, pose to chest, two players in background) 1.50 .70 .45

(606) Dick Radatz (portrait, pose to chest, sky in background) 1.50 .70 .45

(607) Ed Rakow (portrait, pose to chest) 1.50 .70 .45

(608) Ed Rakow (kneeling, pose to knees, arms crossed) 1.50 .70 .45

(609) Ed Rakow (portrait, pose to chest) 1.50 .70 .45

(610) Pedro Ramos (standing) 1.50 .70 .45

(611) Merritt Ranew (batting) 1.50 .70 .45

(612) Claude Raymond (pitching) 1.50 .70 .45

(613) Phil Regan (portrait) 1.50 .70 .45

(614) Phil Regan (pitching) 1.50 .70 .45

(615) Ken Retzer (batting) 1.50 .70 .45

(616) Ken Retzer (kneeling) 1.50 .70 .45

(617) Paul Richards (portrait) 1.50 .70 .45

(618) Bobby Richardson (fielding) 3.00 1.50 .90

(619) Robby Richardson (portrait) 3.00 1.50 .90

(620) Pete Richert (portrait) 1.50 .70 .45

(621) Bill Rigney (portrait, pose to chest, one ear showing) 1.50 .70 .45

(622) Bill Rigney (portrait, pose to chest, two ears showing) 1.50 .70 .45

(623) Mike Roarke (catching) 1.50 .70 .45

(624) Robin Roberts (pitching) 2.50 1.25 .70

(625) Robin Roberts (kneeling) 2.50 1.25 .70

(626) Brooks Robinson (batting, pose to chest) 6.00 3.00 1.75

(627) Brooks Robinson (kneeling, pose to waist, "B" on cap) 6.00 3.00 1.75

(628) Brooks Robinson (kneeling, holding bat, bird on cap) 6.00 3.00 1.75

(629) Earl Robinson (hands on knees) 1.50 .70 .45

(630) Floyd Robinson (kneeling, holding bat) 1.50 .70 .45

(631) Floyd Robinson (batting, pose to chest, mouth open) 1.50 .70 .45

(632) Floyd Robinson (batting, pose to chest, mouth closed) 1.50 .70 .45

(633) Frank Robinson (batting, pose to thigh) 3.25 1.75 1.00

(634) Frank Robinson (kneeling, holding bat) 3.25 1.75 1.00

(635) Andre Rodgers (portrait, pose to chest, Chicago uniform) 1.50 .70 .45

(636) Andre Rodgers (portrait, pose to waist, Cubs uniform) 1.50 .70 .45

(637) Bob Rodgers (portrait) 2.00 1.00 .60

(638) Bob Rodgers (batting) 2.00 1.00 .60

(639) Ed Roebuck (pitching, pose to chest, hands over head) 1.50 .70 .45

(640) Rich Rollins (fielding) 1.50 .70 .45

(641) Rich Rollins (batting) 1.50 .70 .45

(642) John Romano (batting, pose to waist) 1.50 .70 .45

(643) John Romano (batting, pose to chest) 1.50 .70 .45

(644) Pete Rose (portrait) 10.00 5.00 3.00

(645) Pete Rose (kneeling) 10.00 5.00 3.00

(646) John Roseboro (portrait) 1.50 .70 .45

(647) John Roseboro (catching) 1.50 .70 .45

(648) Don Rudolph (pitching, pose to knees, glove on knee) 1.50 .70 .45

(649) Don Rudolph (pitching, pitcher's follow through, picture is Stenhouse) 1.50 .70 .45

(650) Pete Runnels (portrait, pose to chest) 1.50 .70 .45

(651) Pete Runnels (portrait, pose to chest) 1.50 .70 .45

(652) Pete Runnels (portrait, pose to neck) 1.50 .70 .45

(653) Ray Sadecki (pitching, pitcher's follow through, glasses) 1.50 .70 .45

(654) Ray Sadecki (pitching, pitcher's follow through, no glasses) 1.50 .70 .45

(655) Bob Sadowski (portrait, pose to neck) 1.50 .70 .45

(656) Amado Samuel (fielding, horizontal) 1.50 .70 .45

(657) Jack Sanford (pitching) 1.50 .70 .45

(658) Jack Sanford (pitching, pitcher's follow through) 1.50 .70 .45

(659) Jack Sanford (pitching, pose to chest) 1.50 .70 .45

(660) Ron Santo (portrait, pose to chest, teeth apart) 2.50 1.25 .70

(661) Ron Santo (portrait, pose to chest, teeth together) 2.50 1.25 .70

(662) Ron Santo (portrait, pose to waist, tank in background) 2.50 1.25 .70

(663) Ron Santo (kneeling, holding bat)1.50 .70 .45

(664) Bob Scheffing (portrait, pose to chest) 1.50 .70 .45

(665) Bob Sheffing (Scheffing) (portrait, pose to chest) 1.50 .70 .45

(666) Charles Schilling (portrait, pose to chest) 1.50 .70 .45

(667) Chuck Schilling (batting, pose to waist) 1.50 .70 .45

(668) Chuck Schilling (batting, pose to chest) 1.50 .70 .45

(669) Bob Schmidt (batting, pose to chest) 1.50 .70 .45

(670) Red Schoendienst (portrait, pose to knees) 1.75 .90 .50

(671) Dick Schofield (batting, stands in background) 1.50 .70 .45

(672) Dick Schofield (batting, screen in background) 1.50 .70 .45

(673) Barney Schultz (portrait, pose to waist, arms crossed) 1.50 .70 .45

(674) Don Schwall (portrait, pose to chest) 1.50 .70 .45

(675) Diego Segui (portrait, pose to chest) 1.50 .70 .45

(676) Mike Shannon (batting, pose to waist) 1.50 .70 .45

(677) Bob Shaw (portrait, pose to chest) 1.50 .70 .45

(678) Bob Shaw (pitching, pitcher's follow through) 1.50 .70 .45

(679) Larry Sherry (portrait, pose to chest) 1.50 .70 .45

(680) Chris Short (portrait, pose to chest) 1.50 .70 .45

(681) Chris Short (pitching, pitcher's follow through) 1.50 .70 .45

(682) Norm Siebern (batting, pose to waist) 1.50 .70 .45

(683) Norm Siebern (portrait, pose to chest) 1.50 .70 .45

(684) Norm Siebern (batting, pose to chest) 1.50 .70 .45

(685) Roy Sievers (kneeling, holding bat) 2.00 1.00 .60

(686) Roy Sievers (portrait, pose to chest) 2.00 1.00 .60

(687) Roy Sievers (batting, pose to chest) 2.00 1.00 .60

(688) Curt Simmons (portrait, pose to chest) 2.00 1.00 .60

(689) Curt Simmons (portrait, pose to chest, glove) 2.00 1.00 .60

(690) Dick Sisler (portrait, pose to chest) 1.50 .70 .45

(691) Bob Skinner (batting, pose to waist) 1.50 .70 .45

(692) Bill Skowron (Yankees, kneeling, holding bat) 3.00 1.50 .90

(693) Bill Skowron (White Sox, kneeling, holding bat) 1.50 .70 .45

(694) Ed Sadowski (batting, pose to waist) 1.50 .70 .45

(695) Al Smith (White Sox, kneeling, holding bat) 1.50 .70 .45

(696) Al Smith (Indians, kneeling, holding bat) 1.50 .70 .45

(697) Hal Smith (portrait, pose to chest) 1.50 .70 .45

(698) Hal Smith (batting, pose to chest)1.50 .70 .45

(699) Duke Snider (batting, pose to waist) 7.00 3.50 2.00

(700) Duke Snider (batting) 7.00 3.50 2.00

(701) Duke Snider (portrait, pose to chest) 7.00 3.50 2.00

(702) Russ Snyder (portrait, pose to chest) 1.50 .70 .45

(703) Warren Spahn (pitching) 3.00 1.50 .90

(704) Warren Spahn (pitching, pitcher's follow through) 3.00 1.50 .90

(705) Warren Spahn (kneeling, pose to knees, glove) 3.00 1.50 .90

(706) Al Spangler (portrait, pose to chest) 1.50 .70 .45

(707) Al Spangler (batting, pose to chest) 1.50 .70 .45

(708) Tracy Stallard (portrait, pose to waist, arms crossed) 1.50 .70 .45

(709) Willie Stargell (portrait, pose to waist) 3.00 1.50 .90

(710) Willie Stargell (hands on knees) 3.00 1.50 .90

(711) Casey Stengel (portrait, pose to chest) 5.00 2.50 1.50

(712) Dave Stenhouse (pitching, pitcher's follow through) (picture is actually Don Rudolph) 1.50 .70 .45

(713) Jim Stewart (batting, pose to waist) 1.50 .70 .45

(714) Dick Stigman (pitching, pitcher's follow through, arm down) 1.50 .70 .45

(715) Dick Stigman (pitching, pitcher's follow through, arm bent) 1.50 .70 .45

(716) Mel Stottlemeyer (Stottlemyre) (portrait, pose to waist) 2.50 1.25 .70

(717) Dick Stuart (portrait, pose to chest) 1.50 .70 .45

(718) Dick Stuart (batting, pose to neck) 1.50 .70 .45

(719) Dick Stuart (Pirates, batting, pose to chest) 1.50 .70 .45

(720) Dick Stuart (batting, pose to waist) 1.50 .70 .45

(721) Dick Stuart (Red Sox, batting, pose to chest) 1.50 .70 .45

(722) Frank Sullivan (portrait, pose to chest, glove) 1.50 .70 .45

(723) Hay Sullivan (portrait, pose to waist, arms crossed) 1.50 .70 .45

(724) Haywood Sullivan (batting, pose to chest) 1.50 .70 .45

(725) Rusty Staub (portrait, pose to chest) 2.50 1.25 .70

(726) Wes Stock (pitching, pitcher's follow through) 1.50 .70 .45

(727) Wes Stock (kneeling, pose to waist, arms crossed) 1.50 .70 .45

(728) Fred Talbot (portrait, pose to chest, arms crossed) 1.50 .70 .45

(729) Jose Tartabull (portrait, pose to waist, arms crossed) 1.50 .70 .45

(730) Jose Tartabull (batting, pose to chest) 1.50 .70 .45

(731) Willie Tasby (batting, pose to waist) 1.50 .70 .45

(732) Sam Taylor (portrait, pose to chest, stripe uniform) 1.50 .70 .45

(733) Sam Taylor (portrait, pose to chest, plain uniform) 1.50 .70 .45

(734) Tony Taylor (batting, pose to chest, 1 ear) 1.50 .70 .45

(735) Tony Taylor (batting, pose to chest, 2 ears) 1.50 .70 .45

(736) Birdie Tebbets (portrait, pose to neck) 1.50 .70 .45

(737) Birdie Tebbetts (arms crossed on knees) 1.50 .70 .45

(738) George "Birdie" Tebbetts (portrait, pose to chest) 1.50 .70 .45

(739) Johnny Temple (portrait, pose to chest) 1.50 .70 .45

(740) Ralph Terry (pitching, pitcher's follow through) 2.00 1.00 .60

(741) Ralph Terry (portrait, pose to neck) 1.50 .70 .45

(742) Frank J. Thomas (portrait, pose to chest) 1.50 .70 .45

(743) Frank J. Thomas (batting, pose to chest) 1.50 .70 .45

(744) George Thomas (portrait, pose to chest) 1.50 .70 .45

(745) Lee Thomas (portrait, pose to chest) 1.50 .70 .45

(746) Lee Thomas (batting, pose to chest, two ears) 1.50 .70 .45

(747) Lee Thomas (batting, pose to waist, one ear showing) 1.50 .70 .45

(748) Marv Throneberry (portrait, pose to chest) 2.00 1.00 .60

(749) Luis Tiant (portrait, pose to neck)3.00 1.50 .90

(750) Bob Tillman (batting, pose to chest, one ear showing) 1.50 .70 .45

(751) Bob Tillman (batting, pose to chest, two ears showing) 1.50 .70 .45

(752) Joe Torre (batting) 3.00 1.50 .90

(753) Joe Torre (portrait, pose to chest, no "M" seen on cap) 3.00 1.50 .90

(754) Joe Torre (portrait, pose to chest, sky in background) 3.00 1.50 .90

(755) Joe Torre (portrait, pose to chest, stands in background) 3.00 1.50 .90

(756) Dick Tracewksi (portrait, pose to chest) 1.50 .70 .45

(757) Tom Tresh (fielding) 2.00 1.00 .60

(758) Tom Tresh (portrait, pose to chest) 2.00 1.00 .60

(759) Tom Tresh (batting, pose to waist) 2.00 1.00 .60

(760) Gus Triandos (catching, crouching) 1.50 .70 .45

(761) Gus Triandos (batting, pose to waist) 1.50 .70 .45

(762) Gus Triandos (kneeling, holding bat) 1.50 .70 .45

(763) Bob Uecker (catching, crouching)3.00 1.50 .90

(764) Jose Valdivielso (batting, pose to waist) 1.50 .70 .45

(765) Bob Veale (portrait, pose to chest) 1.50 .70 .45

(766) Mickey Vernon (standing) 2.00 1.00 .60

(767) Zorro Versalles (batting, pose to chest) 1.50 .70 .45

(768) Zorro Versalles (fielding, left leg extended) 1.50 .70 .45

(769) Zorro Versalles (fielding, legs spaced evenly) 1.50 .70 .45

(770) Dave Vineyard (portrait, pose to chest) 1.50 .70 .45

(771) Bill Virdon (batting, pose to waist, screen in background) 2.00 1.00 .60

(772) Bill Virdon (batting, pose to chest, dark background) 2.00 1.00 .60

(773) Leon Wagner (hands on knees) 1.50 .70 .45

(774) Leon Wagner (portrait, pose to waist) 1.50 .70 .45

(775) Harry Walker (portrait, pose to chest, arms crossed) 1.50 .70 .45

(776) Jerry Walker (portrait, pose to waist, glove) 1.50 .70 .45

(777) Jerry Walker (pitching) 1.50 .70 .45

(778) Ken Walter (batting, pose to chest) 1.50 .70 .45

(779) Pete Ward (fielding) 1.50 .70 .45

(780) Pete Ward (kneeling, holding bat) 1.50 .70 .45

(781) Carl Warwick (batting, pose to chest) 1.50 .70 .45

(782) Carl Warwick (batting, pose to chest) 1.50 .70 .45

(783) Bill White (portrait, pose to chest)2.00 1.00 .60

(784) Bill White (batting, pose to chest)2.00 1.00 .60

(785) Carl Willey (pitching) 1.50 .70 .45

(786) Carlton Willey (pitching, pose to chest, hands over head) 1.50 .70 .45

(787) Billy Williams (portrait, pose to waist, fence background) 2.50 1.25 .70

(788) Billy Williams (portrait, pose to waist, arms crossed) 2.50 1.25 .70

(789) Billy Williams (portrait, pose to chest, dark background) 2.50 1.25 .70

(790) Hoyt Williams (Wilhelm) (pitching) 4.00 2.00 1.25

(791) Stan Williams (portrait, pose to chest) 1.50 .70 .45

(792) Maury Wills (portrait, pose to chest) 3.00 1.50 .90

(793) Maury Wills (batting, pose to waist) 3.00 1.50 .90

(794) Maury Wills (batting, pose to waist, photo reversed) 3.00 1.50 .90

(795) Earl Wilson (portrait, pose to waist) 1.50 .70 .45

(796) Bob Wine (fielding) 1.50 .70 .45

(797) Bob Wine (portrait, pose to chest) 1.50 .70 .45

(798) Jake Wood (batting, pose to chest) 1.50 .70 .45

(799)	Jake Wood (fielding)	1.50	.70	.45
(800)	Hal Woodeshick (portrait, pose to chest)	1.50	.70	.45
(801)	Gene Woodling (batting, pose to waist)	2.00	1.00	.60
(802)	Early Wynn (pitching)	2.50	1.25	.70
(803)	Jim Wynn (portrait, pose to chest)	1.50	.70	.45
(804)	Carl Yastrzemski (batting)	10.00	5.00	3.00
(805)	Carl Yastrzemski (portrait, pose to chest, Red Sox uniform)	10.00	5.00	3.00
(806)	Carl Yastrzemski (portrait, pose to chest, Boston uniform)	10.00	5.00	3.00
(807)	Carl Yastrzemski (batting, pose to waist, one ear showing)	10.00	5.00	3.00
(808)	Carl Yastrzemski (batting, pose to waist, two ears showing)	10.00	5.00	3.00
(809)	Eddie Yost (batting, pose to chest)	1.50	.70	.45
(810)	Don Zimmer (batting, pose to chest)	2.00	1.00	.60
(811)	Marion Zipfel (fielding)	1.50	.70	.45

1986 Jays Potato Chips

One of a handful of round baseball cards produced for inclusion in boxes of potato chips on a regional basis in 1986, the Jays set of 2-7/8" discs is believed to be the scarcest of the type. The 20 cards in the issue include the most popular Milwaukee Brewers and Chicago Cubs and White Sox players; the set having been distributed in the southern Wisconsin-northern Illinois area. Like many of the recent sets produced by Mike Schecter Associates, the '86 Jays cards feature player photos on which the team logos have been airbrushed off the caps.

		MT	NR MT	EX
Complete Set (20):		20.00	15.00	8.00
Common Player:		.60	.45	.25
(1)	Harold Baines	1.00	.70	.40
(2)	Cecil Cooper	.80	.60	.30
(3)	Jody Davis	.60	.45	.25
(4)	Bob Dernier	.60	.45	.25
(5)	Richard Dotson	.60	.45	.25
(6)	Shawon Dunston	1.00	.70	.40
(7)	Carlton Fisk	1.50	1.25	.60
(8)	Jim Gantner	.60	.45	.25
(9)	Ozzie Guillen	.80	.60	.30
(10)	Teddy Higuera	.75	.60	.30
(11)	Ron Kittle	.60	.45	.25
(12)	Paul Molitor	2.00	1.50	.80
(13)	Keith Moreland	.60	.45	.25
(14)	Ernie Riles	.60	.45	.25
(15)	Ryne Sandberg	3.00	2.25	1.25
(16)	Tom Seaver	2.00	1.50	.80
(17)	Lee Smith	.90	.70	.35
(18)	Rick Sutcliffe	.75	.60	.30
(19)	Greg Walker	.60	.45	.25
(20)	Robin Yount	2.50	2.00	1.00

1962 Jell-O

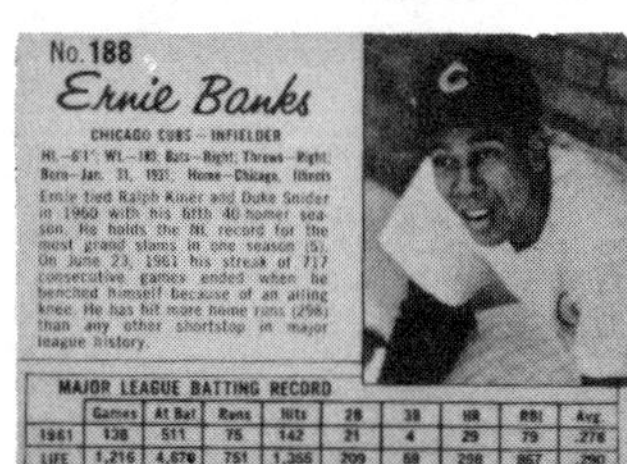

Virtually identical in content to the 1962 Post cereal cards, the '62 Jell-O set of 197 was only issued in the Midwest. Players and card numbers are identical in the two sets, except Brooks Robinson (#29), Ted Kluszewski (#82) and Smoky Burgess (#176) were not issued in the Jell-O version. The Jell-0 cards are easy to distinguish from the Post of that year by the absence of the red oval Post logo and red or blue border around the stat box. Cards which have been neatly trimmed from the box which they were printed will measure 3-1/2" by 2-1/2".

		NR MT	EX	VG
Complete Set (200):		4500.	2250.	1350.
Common Player:		5.00	2.50	1.50
1	Bill Skowron	20.00	10.00	6.00
2	Bobby Richardson	20.00	10.00	6.00
3	Cletis Boyer	10.00	5.00	3.00
4	Tony Kubek	15.00	7.50	4.50
5	Mickey Mantle	400.00	200.00	120.00
6	Roger Maris	125.00	62.00	37.00
7	Yogi Berra	60.00	30.00	18.00
8	Elston Howard	15.00	7.50	4.50
9	Whitey Ford	40.00	20.00	12.00
10	Ralph Terry	10.00	5.00	3.00
11	John Blanchard	6.00	3.00	1.75
12	Luis Arroyo	6.00	3.00	1.75
13	Bill Stafford	20.00	10.00	6.00
14	Norm Cash	10.00	5.00	3.00
15	Jake Wood	5.00	2.50	1.50
16	Steve Boros	5.00	2.50	1.50
17	Chico Fernandez	5.00	2.50	1.50
18	Billy Bruton	5.00	2.50	1.50
19	Ken Aspromonte	5.00	2.50	1.50
20	Al Kaline	40.00	20.00	12.00
21	Dick Brown	5.00	2.50	1.50
22	Frank Lary	6.00	3.00	1.75
23	Don Mossi	6.00	3.00	1.75
24	Phil Regan	5.00	2.50	1.50
25	Charley Maxwell	5.00	2.50	1.50
26	Jim Bunning	12.00	6.00	3.50
27	Jim Gentile	6.00	3.00	1.75
28	Marv Breeding	5.00	2.50	1.50
29	Not Issued			
30	Ron Hansen	5.00	2.50	1.50
31	Jackie Brandt	20.00	10.00	6.00
32	Dick Williams	6.00	3.00	1.75
33	Gus Triandos	6.00	3.00	1.75
34	Milt Pappas	6.00	3.00	1.75
35	Hoyt Wilhelm	20.00	10.00	6.00
36	Chuck Estrada	5.00	2.50	1.50
37	Vic Power	5.00	2.50	1.50
38	Johnny Temple	5.00	2.50	1.50
39	Bubba Phillips	20.00	10.00	6.00
40	Tito Francona	6.00	3.00	1.75
41	Willie Kirkland	5.00	2.50	1.50
42	John Romano	5.00	2.50	1.50
43	Jim Perry	10.00	5.00	3.00
44	Woodie Held	5.00	2.50	1.50
45	Chuck Essegian	5.00	2.50	1.50
46	Roy Sievers	6.00	3.00	1.75
47	Nellie Fox	15.00	7.50	4.50
48	Al Smith	5.00	2.50	1.50
49	Luis Aparicio	20.00	10.00	6.00
50	Jim Landis	5.00	2.50	1.50
51	Minnie Minoso	10.00	5.00	3.00
52	Andy Carey	20.00	10.00	6.00
53	Sherman Lollar	6.00	3.00	1.75
54	Bill Pierce	6.00	3.00	1.75
55	Early Wynn	20.00	10.00	6.00
56	Chuck Schilling	20.00	10.00	6.00
57	Pete Runnels	6.00	3.00	1.75
58	Frank Malzone	6.00	3.00	1.75
59	Don Buddin	10.00	5.00	3.00
60	Gary Geiger	5.00	2.50	1.50
61	Carl Yastrzemski	175.00	87.00	52.00
62	Jackie Jensen	20.00	10.00	6.00
63	Jim Pagliaroni	20.00	10.00	6.00
64	Don Schwall	5.00	2.50	1.50
65	Dale Long	6.00	3.00	1.75
66	Chuck Cottier	10.00	5.00	3.00
67	Billy Klaus	20.00	10.00	6.00
68	Coot Veal	5.00	2.50	1.50
69	Marty Keough	40.00	20.00	12.00
70	Willie Tasby	40.00	20.00	12.00
71	Gene Woodling	6.00	3.00	1.75
72	Gene Green	40.00	20.00	12.00
73	Dick Donovan	10.00	5.00	3.00
74	Steve Bilko	10.00	5.00	3.00
75	Rocky Bridges	20.00	10.00	6.00
76	Eddie Yost	10.00	5.00	3.00
77	Leon Wagner	10.00	5.00	3.00
78	Albie Pearson	10.00	5.00	3.00
79	Ken Hunt	10.00	5.00	3.00
80	Earl Averill	40.00	20.00	12.00
81	Ryne Duren	10.00	5.00	3.00
82	Not Issued			
83	Bob Allison	6.00	3.00	1.75
84	Billy Martin	15.00	7.50	4.50
85	Harmon Killebrew	40.00	20.00	12.00
86	Zorro Versalles	6.00	3.00	1.75
87	Lennie Green	20.00	10.00	6.00
88	Bill Tuttle	5.00	2.50	1.50
89	Jim Lemon	6.00	3.00	1.75
90	Earl Battey	20.00	10.00	6.00
91	Camilo Pascual	6.00	3.00	1.75
92	Norm Siebern	10.00	5.00	3.00
93	Jerry Lumpe	10.00	5.00	3.00
94	Dick Howser	10.00	5.00	3.00
95	Gene Stephens	40.00	20.00	12.00
96	Leo Posada	10.00	5.00	3.00
97	Joe Pignatano	10.00	5.00	3.00
98	Jim Archer	10.00	5.00	3.00
99	Haywood Sullivan	20.00	10.00	6.00
100	Art Ditmar	10.00	5.00	3.00
101	Gil Hodges	40.00	20.00	12.00
102	Charlie Neal	10.00	5.00	3.00
103	Daryl Spencer	10.00	5.00	3.00
104	Maury Wills	20.00	10.00	6.00
105	Tommy Davis	10.00	5.00	3.00
106	Willie Davis	10.00	5.00	3.00
107	John Roseboro	40.00	20.00	12.00
108	John Podres	12.00	6.00	3.50
109	Sandy Koufax	80.00	40.00	24.00
110	Don Drysdale	50.00	25.00	15.00
111	Larry Sherry	20.00	10.00	6.00
112	Jim Gilliam	20.00	10.00	6.00
113	Norm Larker	40.00	20.00	12.00
114	Duke Snider	70.00	35.00	21.00
115	Stan Williams	20.00	10.00	6.00
116	Gordon Coleman	70.00	35.00	21.00
117	Don Blasingame	20.00	10.00	6.00
118	Gene Freese	40.00	20.00	12.00
119	Ed Kasko	40.00	20.00	12.00
120	Gus Bell	20.00	10.00	6.00
121	Vada Pinson	10.00	5.00	3.00
122	Frank Robinson	40.00	20.00	12.00
123	Bob Purkey	10.00	5.00	3.00
124	Joey Jay	10.00	5.00	3.00
125	Jim Brosnan	10.00	5.00	3.00
126	Jim O'Toole	10.00	5.00	3.00
127	Jerry Lynch	10.00	5.00	3.00
128	Wally Post	10.00	5.00	3.00
129	Ken Hunt	10.00	5.00	3.00
130	Jerry Zimmerman	10.00	5.00	3.00
131	Willie McCovey	40.00	20.00	12.00
132	Jose Pagan	20.00	10.00	6.00
133	Felipe Alou	10.00	5.00	3.00
134	Jim Davenport	10.00	5.00	3.00
135	Harvey Kuenn	10.00	5.00	3.00
136	Orlando Cepeda	15.00	7.50	4.50
137	Ed Bailey	10.00	5.00	3.00
138	Sam Jones	10.00	5.00	3.00
139	Mike McCormick	10.00	5.00	3.00
140	Juan Marichal	40.00	20.00	12.00
141	Jack Sanford	10.00	5.00	3.00
142	Willie Mays	150.00	75.00	45.00
143	Stu Miller	70.00	35.00	21.00
144	Joe Amalfitano	10.00	5.00	3.00
145	Joe Adcock	10.00	5.00	3.00
146	Frank Bolling	5.00	2.50	1.50
147	Ed Mathews	40.00	20.00	12.00
148	Roy McMillan	6.00	3.00	1.75
149	Hank Aaron	150.00	75.00	45.00
150	Gino Cimoli	20.00	10.00	6.00
151	Frank J. Thomas	6.00	3.00	1.75
152	Joe Torre	10.00	5.00	3.00
153	Lou Burdette	6.00	3.00	1.75
154	Bob Buhl	6.00	3.00	1.75
155	Carlton Willey	5.00	2.50	1.50
156	Lee Maye	18.00	9.00	5.50
157	Al Spangler	40.00	20.00	12.00
158	Bill White	40.00	20.00	12.00
159	Ken Boyer	15.00	7.50	4.50
160	Joe Cunningham	10.00	5.00	3.00
161	Carl Warwick	10.00	5.00	3.00
162	Carl Sawatski	5.00	2.50	1.50
163	Lindy McDaniel	5.00	2.50	1.50
164	Ernie Broglio	10.00	5.00	3.00
165	Larry Jackson	5.00	2.50	1.50
166	Curt Flood	15.00	7.50	4.50
167	Curt Simmons	40.00	20.00	12.00
168	Alex Grammas	20.00	10.00	6.00
169	Dick Stuart	6.00	3.00	1.75
170	Bill Mazeroski	20.00	10.00	6.00
171	Don Hoak	10.00	5.00	3.00
172	Dick Groat	10.00	5.00	3.00
173	Roberto Clemente	150.00	75.00	45.00
174	Bob Skinner	20.00	10.00	6.00
175	Bill Virdon	40.00	20.00	12.00
176	Not Issued			
177	Elroy Face	10.00	5.00	3.00
178	Bob Friend	6.00	3.00	1.75
179	Vernon Law	20.00	10.00	6.00
180	Harvey Haddix	40.00	20.00	12.00
181	Hal Smith	20.00	10.00	6.00
182	Ed Bouchee	20.00	10.00	6.00
183	Don Zimmer	8.00	4.00	2.50
184	Ron Santo	10.00	5.00	3.00
185	Andre Rodgers	5.00	2.50	1.50
186	Richie Ashburn	15.00	7.50	4.50
187	George Altman	5.00	2.50	1.50
188	Ernie Banks	40.00	20.00	12.00
189	Sam Taylor	5.00	2.50	1.50
190	Don Elston	5.00	2.50	1.50
191	Jerry Kindall	20.00	10.00	6.00
192	Pancho Herrera	5.00	2.50	1.50
193	Tony Taylor	5.00	2.50	1.50
194	Ruben Amaro	20.00	10.00	6.00
195	Don Demeter	5.00	2.50	1.50
196	Bobby Gene Smith	5.00	2.50	1.50
197	Clay Dalrymple	5.00	2.50	1.50
198	Robin Roberts	25.00	12.50	7.50
199	Art Mahaffey	5.00	2.50	1.50
200	John Buzhardt	5.00	2.50	1.50

1963 Jell-O

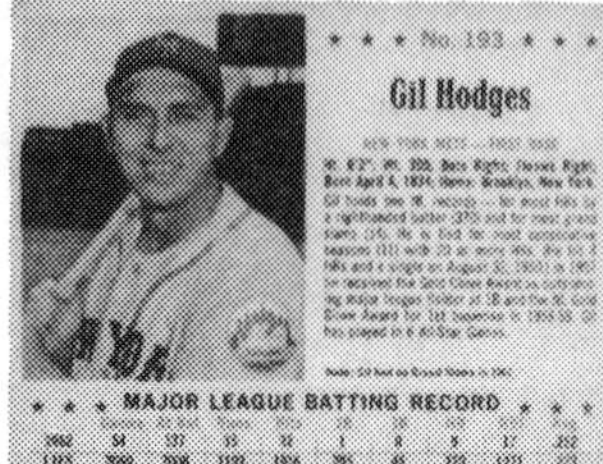

Like the other Post and Jell-O issues of the era, the '63 Jell-O set includes many scarce cards; primarily those which were printed as the backs of less popular brands and sizes of the gelatin dessert. Slightly smaller than the virtually identical Post cereal cards of the same year, the 200 cards in the Jell-O issue measure 3-3/8" by 2-1/2". The easiest way to distinguish 1963 Jell-O cards from Post cards is by the red line that separates the 1962 stats from the lifetime stats. On Post cards, the line extends almost all the way to the side borders, on the Jell-O cards, the line begins and ends much closer to the stats.

		NR MT	EX	VG
Complete Set (200):		3000.	1500.	900.00
Common Player:		3.00	1.50	.90
1	Vic Power	3.00	1.50	.90
2	Bernie Allen	20.00	10.00	6.00
3	Zoilo Versalles	20.00	10.00	6.00
4	Rich Rollins	3.00	1.50	.90
5	Harmon Killebrew	8.00	4.00	2.50
6	Lenny Green	20.00	10.00	6.00
7	Bob Allison	3.00	1.50	.90
8	Earl Battey	15.00	7.50	4.50
9	Camilo Pascual	3.00	1.50	.90
10	Jim Kaat	35.00	17.50	10.50
11	Jack Kralick	3.00	1.50	.90
12	Bill Skowron	20.00	10.00	6.00
13	Bobby Richardson	5.00	2.50	1.50
14	Cletis Boyer	3.00	1.50	.90
15	Mickey Mantle	250.00	125.00	75.00
16	Roger Maris	20.00	10.00	6.00
17	Yogi Berra	20.00	10.00	6.00
18	Elston Howard	20.00	10.00	6.00
19	Whitey Ford	10.00	5.00	3.00
20	Ralph Terry	3.00	1.50	.90
21	John Blanchard	15.00	7.50	4.50
22	Bill Stafford	20.00	10.00	6.00
23	Tom Tresh	3.00	1.50	.90
24	Steve Bilko	3.00	1.50	.90
25	Bill Moran	3.00	1.50	.90
26	Joe Koppe	3.00	1.50	.90
27	Felix Torres	3.00	1.50	.90
28	Leon Wagner	3.00	1.50	.90
29	Albie Pearson	3.00	1.50	.90
30	Lee Thomas	3.00	1.50	.90
31	Bob Rodgers	20.00	10.00	6.00
32	Dean Chance	3.00	1.50	.90
33	Ken McBride	20.00	10.00	6.00
34	George Thomas	20.00	10.00	6.00
35	Joe Cunningham	20.00	10.00	6.00
36	Nelson Fox	5.00	2.50	1.50
37	Luis Aparicio	6.00	3.00	1.75
38	Al Smith	3.00	1.50	.90
39	Floyd Robinson	3.00	1.50	.90
40	Jim Landis	3.00	1.50	.90
41	Charlie Maxwell	3.00	1.50	.90
42	Sherman Lollar	3.00	1.50	.90
43	Early Wynn	6.00	3.00	1.75
44	Juan Pizarro	20.00	10.00	6.00
45	Ray Herbert	20.00	10.00	6.00
46	Norm Cash	3.50	1.75	1.00
47	Steve Boros	20.00	10.00	6.00
48	Dick McAuliffe	3.00	1.50	.90
49	Bill Bruton	3.00	1.50	.90
50	Rocky Colavito	5.00	2.50	1.50
51	Al Kaline	12.00	6.00	3.50
52	Dick Brown	20.00	10.00	6.00
53	Jim Bunning	5.00	2.50	1.50
54	Hank Aguirre	3.00	1.50	.90
55	Frank Lary	20.00	10.00	6.00
56	Don Mossi	20.00	10.00	6.00
57	Jim Gentile	3.00	1.50	.90
58	Jackie Brandt	3.00	1.50	.90
59	Brooks Robinson	15.00	7.50	4.50
60	Ron Hansen	3.00	1.50	.90
61	Jerry Adair	55.00	27.00	16.50
62	John Powell	3.50	1.75	1.00
63	Russ Snyder	20.00	10.00	6.00
64	Steve Barber	3.00	1.50	.90
65	Milt Pappas	20.00	10.00	6.00
66	Robin Roberts	6.00	3.00	1.75
67	Tito Francona	3.00	1.50	.90
68	Jerry Kindall	20.00	10.00	6.00
69	Woodie Held	3.00	1.50	.90
70	Bubba Phillips	3.00	1.50	.90
71	Chuck Essegian	3.00	1.50	.90
72	Willie Kirkland	20.00	10.00	6.00
73	Al Luplow	3.00	1.50	.90
74	Ty Cline	20.00	10.00	6.00
75	Dick Donovan	3.00	1.50	.90
76	John Romano	3.00	1.50	.90
77	Pete Runnels	3.00	1.50	.90
78	Ed Bressoud	20.00	10.00	6.00
79	Frank Malzone	3.00	1.50	.90
80	Carl Yastrzemski	60.00	30.00	18.00
81	Gary Geiger	3.00	1.50	.90
82	Lou Clinton	20.00	10.00	6.00
83	Earl Wilson	3.00	1.50	.90
84	Bill Monbouquette	3.00	1.50	.90
85	Norm Siebern	3.00	1.50	.90
86	Jerry Lumpe	3.00	1.50	.90
87	Manny Jimenez	3.00	1.50	.90
88	Gino Cimoli	3.00	1.50	.90
89	Ed Charles	55.00	27.00	16.50
90	Ed Rakow	3.00	1.50	.90
91	Bob Del Greco	20.00	10.00	6.00
92	Haywood Sullivan	20.00	10.00	6.00
93	Chuck Hinton	3.00	1.50	.90
94	Ken Retzer	20.00	10.00	6.00
95	Harry Bright	20.00	10.00	6.00
96	Bob Johnson	3.00	1.50	.90
97	Dave Stenhouse	20.00	10.00	6.00
98	Chuck Cottier	3.00	1.50	.90
99	Tom Cheney	3.00	1.50	.90
100	Claude Osteen	20.00	10.00	6.00
101	Orlando Cepeda	5.00	2.50	1.50
102	Charley Hiller	20.00	10.00	6.00
103	Jose Pagan	20.00	10.00	6.00
104	Jim Davenport	3.00	1.50	.90
105	Harvey Kuenn	3.50	1.75	1.00
106	Willie Mays	75.00	37.00	22.00
107	Felipe Alou	3.00	1.50	.90
108	Tom Haller	3.00	1.50	.90
109	Juan Marichal	6.00	3.00	1.75
110	Jack Sanford	3.00	1.50	.90
111	Bill O'Dell	3.00	1.50	.90
112	Willie McCovey	90.00	45.00	27.00
113	Lee Walls	20.00	10.00	6.00
114	Jim Gilliam	20.00	10.00	6.00
115	Maury Wills	5.00	2.50	1.50
116	Ron Fairly	3.00	1.50	.90
117	Tommy Davis	3.00	1.50	.90
118	Duke Snider	9.00	4.50	2.75
119	Willie Davis	3.00	1.50	.90
120	John Roseboro	3.00	1.50	.90
121	Sandy Koufax	20.00	10.00	6.00
122	Stan Williams	20.00	10.00	6.00
123	Don Drysdale	9.00	4.50	2.75
124	Daryl Spencer	3.00	1.50	.90
125	Gordy Coleman	3.00	1.50	.90
126	Don Blasingame	20.00	10.00	6.00
127	Leo Cardenas	3.00	1.50	.90
128	Eddie Kasko	20.00	10.00	6.00
129	Jerry Lynch	3.00	1.50	.90
130	Vada Pinson	4.00	2.00	1.25
131	Frank Robinson	9.00	4.50	2.75
132	John Edwards	20.00	10.00	6.00
133	Joey Jay	3.00	1.50	.90
134	Bob Purkey	3.00	1.50	.90
135	Marty Keough	55.00	27.00	16.50
136	Jim O'Toole	20.00	10.00	6.00
137	Dick Stuart	3.00	1.50	.90
138	Bill Mazeroski	5.00	2.50	1.50
139	Dick Groat	3.00	1.50	.90
140	Don Hoak	3.00	1.50	.90
141	Bob Skinner	3.00	1.50	.90
142	Bill Virdon	3.00	1.50	.90
143	Roberto Clemente	75.00	37.00	22.00
144	Smoky Burgess	3.00	1.50	.90
145	Bob Friend	3.00	1.50	.90
146	Al McBean	20.00	10.00	6.00
147	ElRoy Face	3.00	1.50	.90
148	Joe Adcock	3.50	1.75	1.00
149	Frank Bolling	3.00	1.50	.90
150	Roy McMillan	3.00	1.50	.90
151	Eddie Mathews	8.00	4.00	2.50
152	Hank Aaron	75.00	37.00	22.00
153	Del Crandall	20.00	10.00	6.00
154	Bob Shaw	3.00	1.50	.90
155	Lew Burdette	3.50	1.75	1.00
156	Joe Torre	20.00	10.00	6.00
157	Tony Cloninger	35.00	17.50	10.50
158	Bill White	4.00	2.00	1.25
159	Julian Javier	20.00	10.00	6.00
160	Ken Boyer	4.00	2.00	1.25
161	Julio Gotay	20.00	10.00	6.00
162	Curt Flood	3.00	1.50	.90
163	Charlie James	35.00	17.50	10.50
164	Gene Oliver	20.00	10.00	6.00
165	Ernie Broglio	3.00	1.50	.90
166	Bob Gibson	75.00	37.00	22.00
167	Lindy McDaniel	20.00	10.00	6.00
168	Ray Washburn	3.00	1.50	.90
169	Ernie Banks	12.00	6.00	3.50
170	Ron Santo	4.00	2.00	1.25
171	George Altman	3.00	1.50	.90
172	Billy Williams	75.00	37.00	22.00
173	Andre Rodgers	20.00	10.00	6.00
174	Ken Hubbs	4.00	2.00	1.25
175	Don Landrum	20.00	10.00	6.00
176	Dick Bertell	20.00	10.00	6.00
177	Roy Sievers	3.00	1.50	.90
178	Tony Taylor	20.00	10.00	6.00
179	John Callison	3.00	1.50	.90
180	Don Demeter	3.00	1.50	.90
181	Tony Gonzalez	20.00	10.00	6.00
182	Wes Covington	20.00	10.00	6.00
183	Art Mahaffey	3.00	1.50	.90
184	Clay Dalrymple	3.00	1.50	.90
185	Al Spangler	3.00	1.50	.90
186	Roman Mejias	3.00	1.50	.90
187	Bob Aspromonte	50.00	25.00	15.00
188	Norm Larker	3.00	1.50	.90
189	Johnny Temple	3.00	1.50	.90
190	Carl Warwick	20.00	10.00	6.00
191	Bob Lillis	20.00	10.00	6.00
192	Dick Farrell	50.00	25.00	15.00
193	Gil Hodges	8.00	4.00	2.50
194	Marv Throneberry	3.00	1.50	.90
195	Charlie Neal	20.00	10.00	6.00
196	Frank J. Thomas	3.00	1.50	.90
197	Richie Ashburn	5.00	2.50	1.50
198	Felix Mantilla	20.00	10.00	6.00
199	Rod Kanehl	20.00	10.00	6.00
200	Roger Craig	20.00	10.00	6.00

Grading Guide

Mint (MT): A perfect card. Well-centered with all corners sharp and square. No creases, stains, edge nicks, surface marks, yellowing or fading.

Near Mint (NM): A nearly perfect card. At first glance, a NM card appears to be perfect. May be slightly off-center. No surface marks, creases or loss of gloss.

Excellent (EX): Corners are still fairly sharp with only moderate wear. Borders may be off-center. No creases or stains on fronts or backs, but may show slight loss of surface luster.

Very Good (VG): Shows obvious handling. May have rounded corners, minor creases, major gum or wax stains. No major creases, tape marks, writing, etc.

Good (G): A well-worn card, but exhibits no intentional damage. May have major or multiple creases. Corners may be rounded well beyond card border.

1973 Jewel Food Baseball Photos

Jewel Foods, a midwestern grocery chain, issued three team sets of large-format baseball player photos in 1973. The 5-7/8" x 9" blank-back photos are full color and feature a facsimile autograph and photos were sold in groups of four per week at five or ten cents per picture. There are 24 Milwaukee Brewers in the issue, and 16 each Chicago Cubs and Chicago White Sox. The unnumbered cards are alphabetized by team in the checklist below.

		NR MT	EX	VG
CHICAGO CUBS				
Complete Set (16):		45.00	22.50	13.50
Common Player:		2.00	1.00	.60
(1)	Jack Aker	2.00	1.00	.60
(2)	Glenn Beckert	3.00	1.50	.90
(3)	Jose Cardenal	2.00	1.00	.60
(4)	Carmen Fanzone	2.00	1.00	.60
(5)	Burt Hooton	2.00	1.00	.60
(6)	Fergie Jenkins	7.50	3.75	2.25
(7)	Don Kessinger	3.00	1.50	.90
(8)	Jim Hickman	2.00	1.00	.60
(9)	Randy Hundley	3.00	1.50	.90
(10)	Bob Locker	2.00	1.00	.60
(11)	Rick Monday	2.00	1.00	.60
(12)	Milt Pappas	2.00	1.00	.60
(13)	Rick Reuschel	3.00	1.50	.90
(14)	Ken Rudolph	2.00	1.00	.60
(15)	Ron Santo	5.00	2.50	1.50
(16)	Billy Williams	7.50	3.75	2.25
CHICAGO WHITE SOX				
Complete Set (16):		30.00	15.00	9.00
Common Player:		2.00	1.00	.60
(17)	Dick Allen	5.00	2.50	1.50
(18)	Mike Andrews	2.00	1.00	.60
(19)	Stan Bahnsen	2.00	1.00	.60
(20)	Eddie Fisher	2.00	1.00	.60
(21)	Terry Forster	2.00	1.00	.60
(22)	Ken Henderson	2.00	1.00	.60
(23)	Ed Hermann	2.00	1.00	.60
(24)	John Jeter	2.00	1.00	.60
(25)	Pat Kelly	2.00	1.00	.60
(26)	Eddie Leon	2.00	1.00	.60
(27)	Carlos May	2.00	1.00	.60
(28)	Bill Melton	2.00	1.00	.60
(29)	Tony Muser	2.00	1.00	.60
(30)	Jorge Orta	2.00	1.00	.60
(31)	Rick Reichardt	2.00	1.00	.60
(32)	Wilbur Wood	3.00	1.50	.90
MILWAUKEE BREWERS				
Complete Set (24):		45.00	22.50	13.50
Common Player:		2.00	1.00	.60
(33)	Jerry Bell	2.00	1.00	.60
(34)	John Briggs	2.00	1.00	.60
(35)	Ollie Brown	2.00	1.00	.60
(36)	Billy Champion	2.00	1.00	.60
(37)	Jim Colborn	2.00	1.00	.60
(38)	Bob Coluccio	2.00	1.00	.60
(39)	John Felske	2.00	1.00	.60
(40)	Pedro Garcia	2.00	1.00	.60
(41)	Rob Gardner	2.00	1.00	.60
(42)	Bob Heise	2.00	1.00	.60
(43)	Tim Johnson	2.00	1.00	.60
(44)	Joe Lahoud	2.00	1.00	.60
(45)	Frank Linzy	2.00	1.00	.60
(46)	Skip Lockwood	2.00	1.00	.60
(47)	Dave May	2.00	1.00	.60
(48)	Bob Mitchell	2.00	1.00	.60
(49)	Don Money	3.00	1.50	.90
(50)	Bill Parsons	2.00	1.00	.60
(51)	Darrell Porter	3.00	1.50	.90
(52)	Eduardo Rodriguez	2.00	1.00	.60
(53)	George Scott	4.00	2.00	1.20
(54)	Chris Short	2.00	1.00	.60
(55)	Jim Slaton	2.00	1.00	.60
(56)	John Vukovich	2.00	1.00	.60

A player's name in italic type indicates a rookie card. An (FC) indicates a player's first card for that particular card company.

1984 Jewel Food Chicago Cubs

Similar in format to previous issues by the Midwestern food company, this 16-piece set of 1984 National League East pennant winners is printed on 6" x 9" paper. Fronts feature a chest-to-cap color player photo with a black facsimile autograph. A logo and copyright notice by the players' association is at upper-left.

		MT	NR MT	EX
Complete Set (16):		23.00	17.00	9.25
Common Player:		.75	.60	.30
(1)	Larry Bowa	2.00	1.50	.80
(2)	Ron Cey	1.50	1.25	.60
(3)	Jody Davis	.75	.60	.30
(4)	Bob Dernier	.75	.60	.30
(5)	Leon Durham	.75	.60	.30
(6)	Dennis Eckersley	3.00	2.25	1.25
(7)	Richie Hebner	.75	.60	.30
(8)	Gary Matthews	1.50	1.25	.60
(9)	Keith Moreland	.75	.60	.30
(10)	Ryne Sandberg	8.00	6.00	3.25
(11)	Scott Sanderson	1.50	1.25	.60
(12)	Lee Smith	3.00	2.25	1.25
(13)	Tom Stoddard	.75	.60	.30
(14)	Rick Sutcliffe	2.00	1.50	.80
(15)	Steve Trout	.75	.60	.30
(16)	Gary Woods	.75	.60	.30

1986 Jiffy Pop/MSA Promos

This 20-card set was produced by Mike Schecter Associates in 1986 to provide attendees at a restaurant and food trade show with examples of his card promotions. The promos have the same fronts as the 1986 Jiffy Pop discs on a 2-7/8" diameter format. The backs have an advertisement for MSA's services. Like the regular issues, the uniform logos have been airbrushed from the discs due to lack of a license from Major League Baseball (the issue is licensed by the players' union). The unnumbered promo discs are checklisted here alphabetically.

		MT	NR MT	EX
Complete Set (20):		550.00	410.00	220.00
Common Player:		25.00	18.50	10.00
(1)	Wade Boggs	35.00	26.00	14.00
(2)	George Brett	40.00	30.00	16.00
(3)	Gary Carter	25.00	18.50	10.00
(4)	Steve Garvey	30.00	22.00	12.00
(5)	Dwight Gooden	25.00	18.50	10.00
(6)	Reggie Jackson	40.00	30.00	16.00
(7)	Don Mattingly	40.00	30.00	16.00
(8)	Willie McGee	25.00	18.50	10.00
(9)	Dale Murphy	30.00	22.00	12.00
(10)	Eddie Murray	35.00	26.00	14.00
(11)	Lance Parrish	25.00	18.50	10.00
(12)	Jim Rice	25.00	18.50	10.00
(13)	Cal Ripken, Jr.	40.00	30.00	16.00
(14)	Pete Rose	40.00	30.00	16.00
(15)	Nolan Ryan	45.00	34.00	18.00
(16)	Ryne Sandberg	40.00	30.00	16.00
(17)	Mike Schmidt	40.00	30.00	16.00
(18)	Fernando Valenzuela	25.00	18.50	10.00
(19)	Dave Winfield	35.00	26.00	14.00
(20)	Robin Yount	40.00	30.00	16.00

1986 Jiffy Pop

One of the scarcer of the 1986 "regionals," the 20-card Jiffy Pop issue was inserted in packages of heat-and-eat popcorn. A production of Mike Schecter Associates, the 2-7/8" round discs feature 20 popular stars, many in the same pictures found in other '86 regionals. Like other MSA issues, caps have had the team logos erased, allowing Jiffy Pop to avoid having to pay a licensing fee to the teams.

		MT	NR MT	EX
Complete Set (20):		30.00	22.00	12.00
Common Player:		1.00	.70	.40
1	Jim Rice	1.50	1.25	.60
2	Wade Boggs	2.00	1.50	.80
3	Lance Parrish	1.00	.70	.40
4	George Brett	2.50	2.00	1.00
5	Robin Yount	2.50	2.00	1.00
6	Don Mattingly	2.50	2.00	1.00
7	Dave Winfield	2.00	1.50	.80
8	Reggie Jackson	2.50	2.00	1.00
9	Cal Ripken	2.50	2.00	1.00
10	Eddie Murray	1.50	1.25	.60
11	Pete Rose	2.00	1.50	.80
12	Ryne Sandberg	2.50	2.00	1.00
13	Nolan Ryan	4.00	3.00	1.50
14	Fernando Valenzuela	1.00	.70	.40
15	Willie McGee	1.00	.70	.40
16	Dale Murphy	2.00	1.50	.80
17	Mike Schmidt	2.50	2.00	1.00
18	Steve Garvey	1.50	1.25	.60
19	Gary Carter	1.50	1.25	.60
20	Dwight Gooden	1.50	1.25	.60

1987 Jiffy Pop

For the second year in a row, Jiffy Pop inserted baseball discs in their packages of popcorn. The full-color discs measure 2-7/8" in diameter and were produced by Mike Schecter Associates of Cos Cob, Conn. Titled "2nd Annual Collectors' Edition," the card fronts feature player photos with all team insignias airbrushed away. Information on the backs of the discs are printed in bright red on white stock. Die-cut press sheets containing all 20 discs were available via a mail-in offer.

		MT	NR MT	EX
Complete Set (20):		25.00	18.50	10.00
Common Player:		1.00	.70	.40
1	Ryne Sandberg	2.50	2.00	1.00
2	Dale Murphy	1.50	1.25	.60
3	Jack Morris	1.00	.70	.40
4	Keith Hernandez	1.00	.70	.40
5	George Brett	2.50	2.00	1.00
6	Don Mattingly	2.50	2.00	1.00
7	Ozzie Smith	2.00	1.50	.80
8	Cal Ripken, Jr.	2.50	2.00	1.00
9	Dwight Gooden	1.50	1.25	.60
10	Pedro Guerrero	1.00	.70	.40
11	Lou Whitaker	1.00	.70	.40
12	Roger Clemens	1.50	1.25	.60
13	Lance Parrish	1.00	.70	.40
14	Rickey Henderson	1.50	1.25	.60
15	Fernando Valenzuela	1.00	.70	.40
16	Mike Schmidt	2.50	2.00	1.00
17	Darryl Strawberry	1.00	.70	.40
18	Mike Scott	1.00	.70	.40
19	Jim Rice	1.50	1.25	.60
20	Wade Boggs	2.50	2.00	1.00

1988 Jiffy Pop

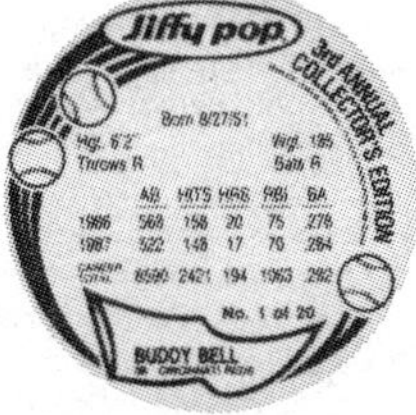

This 20-disc set is the third Jiffy Pop issue spotlighting leading players. Discs are 2-/12" in diameter, with a semi-gloss finish, and feature full-color close-ups on white stock. Team logos have been airbrushed off the player's caps. The Jiffy Pop logo appears in red at the top of the disc; a banner running across the bottom encloses a "1988" and player name, also in red. The circular border is blue, with two large baseballs streaking toward the top logo. A third baseball appears lower right under the curved label "3rd Annual Collector's Edition." Dsic backs are white, with dark blue lettering, and contain player information and disc number.

		MT	NR MT	EX
Complete Set (20):		18.00	13.50	7.25
Common Player:		.60	.45	.25
1	Buddy Bell	.60	.45	.25
2	Wade Boggs	2.00	1.50	.80
3	Gary Carter	.90	.70	.35
4	Jack Clark	.80	.60	.30
5	Will Clark	1.50	1.25	.60
6	Roger Clemens	1.00	.70	.40
7	Vince Coleman	.80	.60	.30
8	Andre Dawson	1.25	.90	.50
9	Keith Hernandez	.80	.60	.30
10	Kent Hrbek	.80	.60	.30
11	Wally Joyner	.80	.60	.30
12	Paul Molitor	1.50	1.25	.60
13	Eddie Murray	1.50	1.25	.60
14	Tim Raines	.90	.70	.35
15	Bret Saberhagen	.80	.60	.30
16	Alan Trammell	.80	.60	.30
17	Ozzie Virgil	.60	.45	.25
18	Tim Wallach	.60	.45	.25
19	Dave Winfield	1.50	1.25	.60
20	Robin Yount	1.50	1.25	.60

The values quoted are intended to reflect the market price.

1973 Johnny Pro Orioles

This regional set of large (4-1/2" by 7-1/4) die-cut cards was issued by Johnny Pro Enterprises Inc. of Baltimore and features only Orioles. The cards were designed to be punched out and folded to make baseball player figures that can stand up. The full-color die-cut figures appear against a green background. The card's are numbered according to the player's uniform number, which appears in a white box along with his name and position. The backs are blank. Three players (Robinson, Grich, and Palmer) appear in two poses each, and cards of Orlando Pena were not die-cut. Values listed are for complete cards not punched out.

		NR MT	EX	VG
Complete Set:		110.00	55.00	33.00
Common Player:		3.00	1.50	.90
1	Al Bumbry	3.00	1.50	.90
2	Rich Coggins	3.00	1.50	.90
3a	Bobby Grich (batting)	5.00	2.50	1.50
3b	Bobby Grich (fielding)	5.00	2.50	1.50
4	Earl Weaver	5.00	2.50	1.50
5a	Brooks Robinson (batting)	20.00	10.00	6.00
5b	Brooks Robinson (fielding)	20.00	10.00	6.00
6	Paul Blair	4.00	2.00	1.25
7	Mark Belanger	4.00	2.00	1.25
8	Andy Etchebarren	3.00	1.50	.90
10	Elrod Hendricks	3.00	1.50	.90
11	Terry Crowley	3.00	1.50	.90
12	Tommy Davis	4.00	2.00	1.25
13	Doyle Alexander	4.00	2.00	1.25
14	Merv Rettenmund	3.00	1.50	.90
15	Frank Baker	3.00	1.50	.90
19	Dave McNally	5.00	2.50	1.50
21	Larry Brown	3.00	1.50	.90
22a	Jim Palmer (follow-through)	20.00	10.00	6.00
22b	Jim Palmer (wind-up)	20.00	10.00	6.00
23	Grant Jackson	3.00	1.50	.90
25	Don Baylor	7.00	3.50	2.00
26	Boog Powell	7.00	3.50	2.00
27	Orlando Pena	8.00	4.00	2.50
32	Earl Williams	3.00	1.50	.90
34	Bob Reynolds	3.00	1.50	.90
35	Mike Cuellar	5.00	2.50	1.50
39	Eddie Watt	3.00	1.50	.90

1973 Johnny Pro Phillies

Although slightly smaller (3-1/4" by 7-1/8") and featuring members of the Phillies, this set is very similar to the Johnny Pro Orioles set of the same year. The full-color die-cut player figures are set against a white background. Again, the set is numbered according to the player's uniform number. The values listed are for complete cards.

		NR MT	EX	VG
Complete Set:		150.00	75.00	45.00
Common Player:		3.00	1.50	.90
8	Bob Boone	6.00	3.00	1.75
10	Larry Bowa	5.00	2.50	1.50
16	Dave Cash	3.00	1.50	.90
19	Greg Luzinski	6.00	3.00	1.75
20	Mike Schmidt	100.00	50.00	30.00
22	Mike Anderson	3.00	1.50	.90
24	Bill Robinson	3.00	1.50	.90
25	Del Unser	3.00	1.50	.90
27	Willie Montanez	3.00	1.50	.90
32	Steve Carlton	25.00	12.50	7.50
37	Ron Schueler	3.00	1.50	.90
41	Jim Lonborg	3.00	1.50	.90

1953 Johnston Cookies Braves

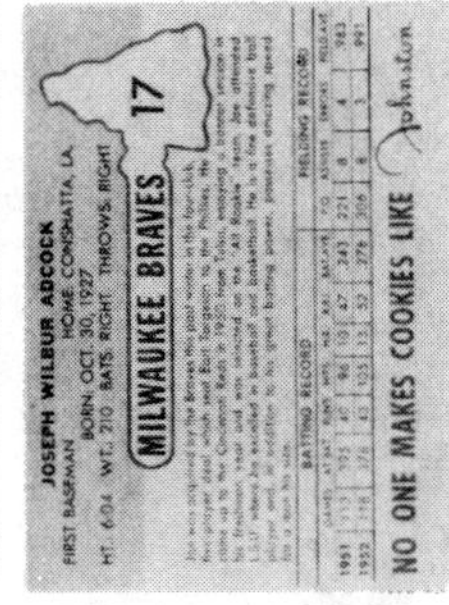

The first and most common of three annual issues, the '53 Johnston's were inserted into boxes of cookies on a regional basis. Complete sets were also available from the company, whose factory sits in the shadow of Milwaukee County Stadium. While at first glance appearing to be color photos, the pictures on the 25 cards in the set are actually well-done colorizations of black and white photos. Cards measure 2-9/16" by 3-5/8". Write-ups on the backs were "borrowed" from the Braves' 1953 yearbook.

		NR MT	EX	VG
Complete Set (25):		400.00	200.00	120.00
Common Player:		15.00	7.50	4.50
1	Charlie Grimm	15.00	7.50	4.50
2	John Antonelli	15.00	7.50	4.50
3	Vern Bickford	15.00	7.50	4.50
4	Bob Buhl	15.00	7.50	4.50
5	Lew Burdette	15.00	7.50	4.50
6	Dave Cole	15.00	7.50	4.50
7	Ernie Johnson	15.00	7.50	4.50
8	Dave Jolly	15.00	7.50	4.50
9	Don Liddle	15.00	7.50	4.50
10	Warren Spahn	60.00	30.00	18.00
11	Max Surkont	15.00	7.50	4.50
12	Jim Wilson	15.00	7.50	4.50
13	Sibby Sisti	15.00	7.50	4.50
14	Walker Cooper	15.00	7.50	4.50
15	Del Crandall	20.00	10.00	6.00
16	Ebba St. Claire	15.00	7.50	4.50
17	Joe Adcock	20.00	10.00	6.00
18	George Crowe	15.00	7.50	4.50
19	Jack Dittmer	15.00	7.50	4.50
20	Johnny Logan	15.00	7.50	4.50
21	Ed Mathews	60.00	30.00	18.00
22	Bill Bruton	15.00	7.50	4.50
23	Sid Gordon	15.00	7.50	4.50
24	Andy Pafko	15.00	7.50	4.50
25	Jim Pendleton	15.00	7.50	4.50

1954 Johnston Cookies Braves

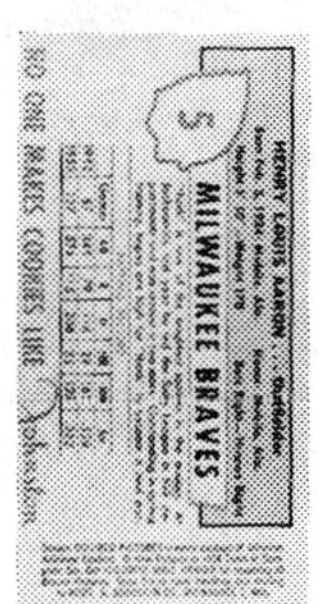

In its second of three annual issues, Johnston's increased the number of cards in its 1954 Braves issue to 35, and switched to an unusual size, a narrow format, 2" by 3-7/8". Besides the players and managers, the '54 set also includes unnumbered cards of the team trainer and equipment manager. Other cards are numbered by uniform number. After his early-season injury (which gave Hank Aaron a chance to play regularly), Bobby Thomson's card was withdrawn, accounting for its scarcity and high value. A cardboard wall-hanging display into which cards could be inserted was available as a premium offer.

		NR MT	EX	VG
Complete Set (35):		1350.	675.00	405.00
Common Player:		15.00	7.50	4.50
1	Del Crandall	20.00	10.00	6.00
3	Jim Pendleton	15.00	7.50	4.50
4	Danny O'Connell	15.00	7.50	4.50
5	Henry Aaron	500.00	250.00	150.00
6	Jack Dittmer	15.00	7.50	4.50
9	Joe Adcock	20.00	10.00	6.00
10	Robert Buhl	15.00	7.50	4.50
11	Phillip Paine (Phillips)	15.00	7.50	4.50
12	Ben Johnson	15.00	7.50	4.50
13	Sibby Sisti	15.00	7.50	4.50
15	Charles Gorin	15.00	7.50	4.50
16	Chet Nichols	15.00	7.50	4.50
17	Dave Jolly	15.00	7.50	4.50
19	Jim Wilson	15.00	7.50	4.50
20	Ray Crone	15.00	7.50	4.50
21	Warren Spahn	75.00	37.00	22.00
22	Gene Conley	15.00	7.50	4.50
23	Johnny Logan	15.00	7.50	4.50
24	Charlie White	15.00	7.50	4.50
27	George Metkovich	15.00	7.50	4.50
28	John Cooney	15.00	7.50	4.50
29	Paul Burris	15.00	7.50	4.50
31	Wm. Walters	15.00	7.50	4.50
32	Ernest T. Johnson	15.00	7.50	4.50
33	Lew Burdette	20.00	10.00	6.00
34	Bob Thomson	200.00	100.00	60.00
35	Robert Keely	15.00	7.50	4.50
38	Billy Bruton	15.00	7.50	4.50
40	Charles Grimm	15.00	7.50	4.50
41	Ed Mathews	75.00	37.00	22.00
42	Sam Calderone	15.00	7.50	4.50
47	Joey Jay	15.00	7.50	4.50
48	Andy Pafko	15.00	7.50	4.50
----	Dr. Charles Lacks (trainer), Joseph F. Taylor	15.00	5.00	3.00

1955 Johnston Cookies Braves

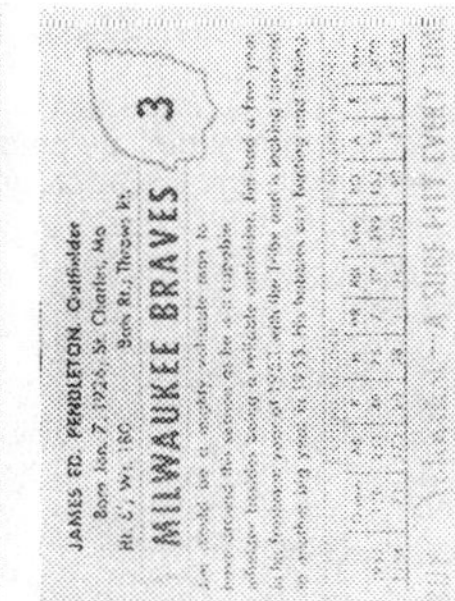

A third change in size and format was undertaken in the third and final year of Braves sets produced by Johnston's. The 35 cards in the 1955 set were issued in six fold-out panels of six cards each (Andy Pafko was double-printed). As in 1954, cards are numbered by uniform number, except those of the team equipment manager, trainer and road secretary (former Boston star Duffy Lewis). Single cards measure 2-7/8" by 4". Besides including panels in boxes of cookies, the '55 Johnston's could be ordered for 5¢ per panel by mail. The scarcest of the Johnston's issues, the 1955 set can be found today still in complete panels, or as single cards.

		NR MT	EX	VG
Complete Folder Set:		1500.	750.00	450.00
Complete Singles Set:		1000.	500.00	300.00
Common Player:		20.00	10.00	6.00
Common Folder:		125.00	62.00	37.00
1	Del Crandall	25.00	12.50	7.50
3	Jim Pendleton	20.00	10.00	6.00
4	Danny O'Connell	20.00	10.00	6.00
6	Jack Dittmer	20.00	10.00	6.00
9	Joe Adcock	25.00	12.50	7.50
10	Bob Buhl	20.00	10.00	6.00
11	Phil Paine	20.00	10.00	6.00
12	Ray Crone	20.00	10.00	6.00
15	Charlie Gorin	20.00	10.00	6.00
16	Dave Jolly	20.00	10.00	6.00
17	Chet Nichols	20.00	10.00	6.00
18	Chuck Tanner	25.00	12.50	7.50
19	Jim Wilson	20.00	10.00	6.00
20	Dave Koslo	20.00	10.00	6.00
21	Warren Spahn	80.00	40.00	24.00
22	Gene Conley	20.00	10.00	6.00
23	John Logan	20.00	10.00	6.00
24	Charlie White	20.00	10.00	6.00
28	Johnny Cooney	20.00	10.00	6.00
30	Roy Smalley	20.00	10.00	6.00
31	Bucky Walters	20.00	10.00	6.00
32	Ernie Johnson	20.00	10.00	6.00
33	Lew Burdette	25.00	12.50	7.50
34	Bobby Thomson	25.00	12.50	7.50
35	Bob Keely	20.00	10.00	6.00
38	Billy Bruton	20.00	10.00	6.00
39	George Crowe	20.00	10.00	6.00
40	Charlie Grimm	20.00	10.00	6.00
41	Eddie Mathews	80.00	40.00	24.00
44	Hank Aaron	400.00	200.00	120.00
47	Joe Jay	20.00	10.00	6.00
48	Andy Pakfo	20.00	10.00	6.00
----	Dr. Charles K. Lacks	20.00	10.00	6.00
----	Duffy Lewis	20.00	10.00	6.00
----	Joe Taylor	20.00	10.00	6.00
----	Series 1 Folder (Hank Aaron, Lew Burdette, Del Crandall, Charlie Gorin, Bob Keely, Danny O'Connell)	400.00	200.00	120.00
----	Series 2 Folder (Joe Adcock, Joe Jay, Dr. Charles K. Lacks, Chet Nichols, Andy Pafko, Charlie White)	125.00	62.00	37.00
----	Series 3 Folder (Gene Conley, George Crowe, Jim Pendleton, Roy Smalley, Warren Spahn, Joe Taylor)	175.00	87.00	52.00
----	Series 4 Folder (Billy Bruton, John Cooney, Dave Jolly, Dave Koslo, Johnny Logan, Andy Pafko)	125.00	62.00	37.00
----	Series 5 Folder (Ray Crone, Ernie Johnson, Duffy Lewis, Eddie Mathews, Phil Paine, Chuck Tanner)	200.00	100.00	60.00
----	Series 6 Folder (Bob Buhl, Jack Dittmer, Charlie Grimm, Bobby Thomson, Bucky Walters, Jim Wilson)	125.00	62.00	37.00

1910 Ju-Ju Drums (E286)

Issued in 1910 with Ju Ju Drum Candy, this extremely rare set of circular baseball cards is very similar in design to the more common Colgan's Chips cards. About the size of a silver dollar (1-7/16" in diameter) the cards display a player photo on the front with the player's name and team printed below in a semi-circle design. The backs carry advertising for Ju Ju Drums. The checklist contains 45 different players to datem but the issue - known as E286 in the American Card Catalog - is so rare that others are likely to exist.

		NR MT	EX	VG
Complete Set (45):		14000.	7000.	4200.
Common Player:		250.00	125.00	75.00
(1)	Eddie Ainsmith	250.00	125.00	75.00
(2)	Jimmy Austin	250.00	125.00	75.00
(3)	Chief Bender	500.00	250.00	150.00
(4)	Bob Bescher	250.00	125.00	75.00
(5)	Bruno Bloch (Block)	250.00	125.00	75.00
(6)	Frank Burke	250.00	125.00	75.00
(7)	Donie Bush	250.00	125.00	75.00

(8)	Frank Chance	500.00	250.00	150.00
(9)	Harry Cheek	250.00	125.00	75.00
(10)	Ed Cicotte	300.00	150.00	90.00
(11)	Ty Cobb	2500.	1250.	750.00
(12)	King Cole	250.00	125.00	75.00
(13)	Jack Coombs	250.00	125.00	75.00
(14)	Bill Dahlen	250.00	125.00	75.00
(15)	Bert Daniels	250.00	125.00	75.00
(16)	Harry Davis	250.00	125.00	75.00
(17)	Larry Doyle	250.00	125.00	75.00
(18)	Rube Ellis	250.00	125.00	75.00
(19)	Cecil Ferguson	250.00	125.00	75.00
(20)	Russ Ford	250.00	125.00	75.00
(21)	Bob Harnion (Harmon)	250.00	125.00	75.00
(22)	Ham Hyatt	250.00	125.00	75.00
(23)	Red Kellifer (Killifer)	250.00	125.00	75.00
(24)	Art Kruger (Krueger)	250.00	125.00	75.00
(25)	Tommy Leach	250.00	125.00	75.00
(26)	Harry Lumley	250.00	125.00	75.00
(27)	Christy Mathewson	800.00	400.00	240.00
(28)	John McGraw	500.00	250.00	150.00
(29)	Deacon McGuire	250.00	125.00	75.00
(30)	Chief Meyers	250.00	125.00	75.00
(31)	Otto Miller	250.00	125.00	75.00
(32)	Charlie Mullen	250.00	125.00	75.00
(33)	Tom Needham	250.00	125.00	75.00
(34)	Rube Oldring	250.00	125.00	75.00
(35)	Barney Pelty	250.00	125.00	75.00
(36)	Ed Reulbach	250.00	125.00	75.00
(37)	Jack Rowan	250.00	125.00	75.00
(38)	Dave Shean	250.00	125.00	75.00
(39)	Tris Speaker	750.00	375.00	225.00
(40)	Jeff Sweeney	250.00	125.00	75.00
(41)	Honus Wagner	1200.	600.00	360.00
(42)	Ed Walsh	500.00	250.00	150.00
(43)	Kirby White	250.00	125.00	75.00
(44)	Ralph Works	250.00	125.00	75.00
(45)	Elmer Zacher	250.00	125.00	75.00

1990 Jumbo Sunflower Seeds

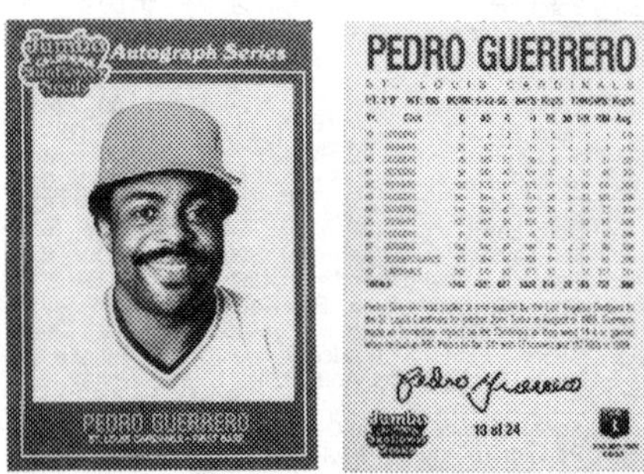

The 1990 Autograph Series of 24 cards came in packages of sunflower seeds and were produced by Mike Schecter Associates for Stagi & Scriven Farms Inc. The cards were found in specially-marked packages of Jumbo California Sunflower Seeds, three cards per package. Standard size with MLB logos airbrushed out, the cards are blue with a white frame. The numbered backs contain yearly statistics and biographical information along with a facsimile autograph.

		MT	NR MT	EX
Complete Set (24):		10.00	7.50	4.00
Common Player:		.25	.20	.10
(1)	Kevin Mitchell	.25	.20	.10
(2)	Ken Griffey, Jr.	2.00	1.50	.80
(3)	Howard Johnson	.25	.20	.10
(4)	Bo Jackson	.50	.40	.20
(5)	Kirby Puckett	.65	.50	.25
(6)	Robin Yount	.75	.60	.30
(7)	Dave Stieb	.25	.20	.10
(8)	Don Mattingly	.75	.60	.30
(9)	Barry Bonds	1.00	.70	.40
(10)	Pedro Guerrero	.25	.20	.10
(11)	Tony Gwynn	.25	.20	.10
(12)	Von Hayes	.25	.20	.10
(13)	Rickey Henderson	.45	.35	.20
(14)	Tim Raines	.25	.20	.10
(15)	Alan Trammell	.25	.20	.10
(16)	Dave Stewart	.25	.20	.10
(17)	Will Clark	.45	.35	.20
(18)	Roger Clemens	.35	.25	.14
(19)	Wally Joyner	.25	.20	.10
(20)	Ryne Sandberg	1.00	.70	.40
(21)	Eric Davis	.35	.25	.14
(22)	Mike Scott	.25	.20	.10
(23)	Cal Ripken, Jr.	1.00	.70	.40
(24)	Eddie Murray	.25	.20	.10

1991 Jumbo Sunflower Seeds

In its second year of baseball card production, Jumbo California Sunflower Seeds maintained the same basic format for its cards. Player photos, with uniform logos airbrushed away, in a white frame are surrounded by a red border with yellow pinstripe. At top left is the issuer's logo; above the photo in white is "Autograph Series II". A facsimile autograph is

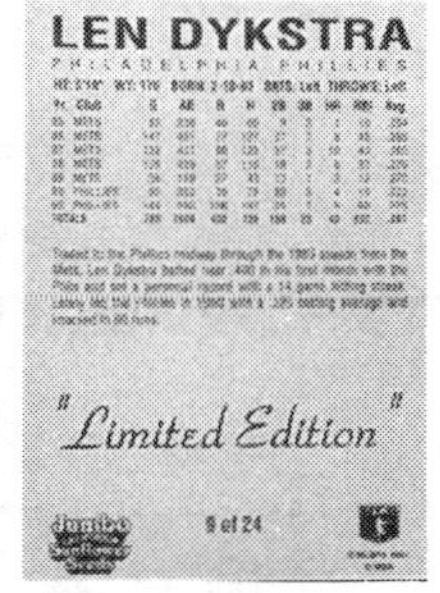

printed over the photo. Beneath the picture are the player's name, team and position. Backs are printed in red and include major league stats and a career summary.

		MT	NR MT	EX
Complete Set (24):		10.00	7.50	4.00
Common Player:		.25	.20	.10
1	Ozzie Smith	.45	.35	.20
2	Wade Boggs	.65	.50	.25
3	Bobby Bonilla	.25	.20	.10
4	George Brett	.75	.60	.30
5	Kal Daniels	.25	.20	.10
6	Glenn Davis	.25	.20	.10
7	Chuck Finley	.25	.20	.10
8	Cecil Fielder	.45	.35	.20
9	Len Dykstra	.35	.25	.14
10	Dwight Gooden	.35	.25	.14
11	Ken Griffey, Jr.	2.00	1.50	.80
12	Kelly Gruber	.25	.20	.10
13	Kent Hrbek	.35	.25	.14
14	Andre Dawson	.25	.20	.10
15	Dave Justice	.35	.25	.14
16	Barry Larkin	.25	.20	.10
17	Ben McDonald	.25	.20	.10
18	Mark McGwire	.35	.25	.14
19	Roberto Alomar	.35	.25	.14
20	Nolan Ryan	2.00	1.50	.80
21	Sandy Alomar, Jr.	.25	.20	.10
22	Bobby Thigpen	.25	.20	.10
23	Tim Wallach	.25	.20	.10
24	Mitch Williams	.25	.20	.10

1992 Jumbo Sunflower Seeds

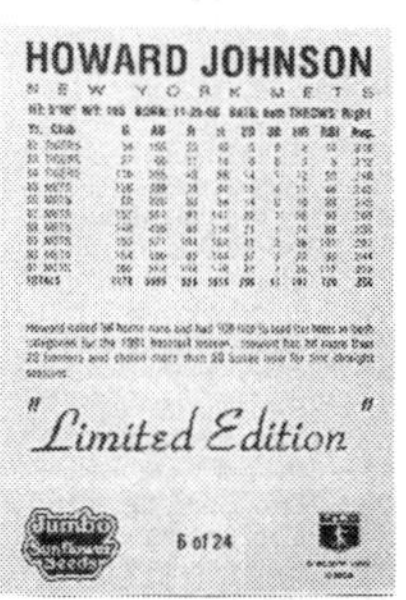

The basic format used in 1990-91 was returned for 1992 when Michael Schecter Associates produced another 24-card set for inclusion in packages of Jumbo Sunflower Seeds (the "California" identifier was dropped in 1992). Cards feature a player photo on which the uniform logos have been eliminated. Across the photo in black is a facsimile autograph. Around the photo are borders of, successively, white, blue, yellow and white. In the upper-left corner is the issuer's logo. "Autograph Series III appears in red at upper-right. Beneath the picture, the player's name is printed in red, with his team and position in white. Backs are printed in blue, with major league stats and a career summary, along with a few personal data and the appropriate logos.

		MT	NR MT	EX
Complete Set (24):		8.00	6.00	3.25
Common Player:		.25	.20	.10
1	Jeff Reardon	.25	.20	.10
2	Bill Gullickson	.25	.20	.10
3	Todd Zeile	.25	.20	.10
4	Terry Mulholland	.25	.20	.10
5	Kirby Puckett	.45	.35	.20
6	Howard Johnson	.25	.20	.10
7	Terry Pendleton	.25	.20	.10
8	Will Clark	.45	.35	.20
9	Cal Ripken, Jr.	1.00	.70	.40
10	Chris Sabo	.25	.20	.10
11	Jim Abbott	.35	.25	.14
12	Joe Carter	.25	.20	.10
13	Paul Molitor	.45	.35	.20
14	Ken Griffey, Jr.	2.00	1.50	.80
15	Randy Johnson	.25	.20	.10
16	Bobby Bonilla	.25	.20	.10
17	John Smiley	.25	.20	.10
18	Jose Canseco	.40	.30	.15
19	Tom Glavine	.25	.20	.10
20	Darryl Strawberry	.40	.30	.15
21	Brett Butler	.25	.20	.10
22	Devon White	.25	.20	.10
23	Scott Erickson	.25	.20	.10
24	Willie McGee	.25	.20	.10

1893 Just So Tobacco

This set, issued by the Just So tobacco brand in 1893, is so rare that only a dozen or so examples are known, although more undoubtedly exist. The set features only members of the Cleveland club, known then as the "Spiders". Measuring 2-1/2" by 3-7/8", these sepia-colored cards were printed on heavy paper. The player appears in a portrait photo with his name beneath and an ad for Just So Tobacco along the bottom. The existence of this set wasn't even established until the 1960s, and for 15 years only two subjects were known. In 1981 and 1989 several more cards were discovered. To date only one or two copies of the known cards have turned up in collectors' hands, making it among the rarest of all baseball card issues.

		NR MT	EX	VG
Common Player:		1200.	600.00	350.00
(1)	F.W. Boyd (Frank)	1200.	600.00	350.00
(2)	Burkette (Jesse Burkett)	2500.	12500.	750.00
(3)	C.L. Childs (Clarence "Cupid")	1200.	600.00	350.00
(4)	John Clarkson	3000.	1500.	900.00
(5)	J.O. Connor (John O'Connor)	1200.	600.00	350.00
(6)	G. Cuppy (George "Nig")	1200.	600.00	350.00
(7)	C.M. Hastings (Charlie)	1200.	600.00	350.00
(8)	E.J. McKean (Ed)	1200.	600.00	350.00
(9)	Capt. Tebeau ("Patsy")	1200.	600.00	350.00
(10)	J.K. Virtue (Jake)	1200.	600.00	350.00
(11)	T.C. Williams (Tom)	1200.	600.00	350.00
(12)	D.T. Young (Cy)	4000.	2000.	1250.
(13)	C.L. Zimmer (Charles "Chief")	1200.	600.00	350.00

K

1982 K-Mart

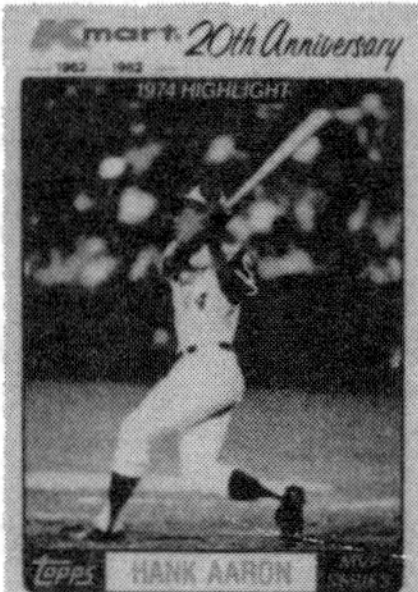

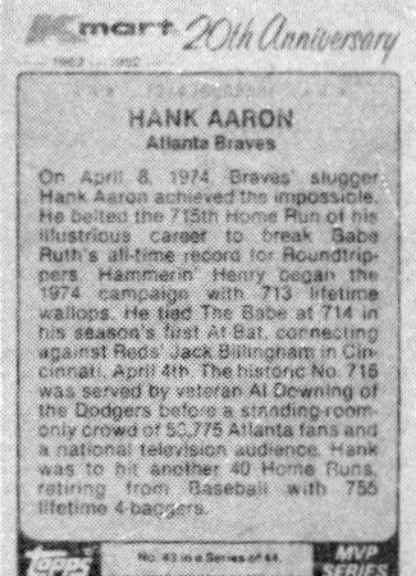

The first of what became dozens of boxed sets specially produced for retail chain stores by the major card producers, the 1982 K-Mart set has not enjoyed any collector popularity. The theme of the set is Most Valuable Players and selected record-breaking performances of the 1962-1981 seasons. The design used miniature reproductions of Topps cards of the era, except in a few cases where designs had to be created because original cards were never issued (1962 Maury Wills, 1975 Fred Lynn). Originally sold for about $2 per boxed set of 44, large quantities were bought up by speculators who got burned when over-production and lack of demand caused the set to drop as low as 10¢. The 2-1/2" by 3-1/2" cards were printed by Topps.

		MT	NR MT	EX
Complete Set (44):		2.00	1.50	.80
Common Player:		.03	.02	.01
1	Mickey Mantle	.25	.20	.10
2	Maury Wills	.05	.04	.02
3	Elston Howard	.03	.02	.01
4	Sandy Koufax	.10	.08	.04
5	Brooks Robinson	.05	.04	.02
6	Ken Boyer	.03	.02	.01
7	Zoilo Versalles	.03	.02	.01
8	Willie Mays	.10	.08	.04
9	Frank Robinson	.05	.04	.02
10	Bob Clemente	.10	.08	.04
11	Carl Yastrzemski	.10	.08	.04
12	Orlando Cepeda	.03	.02	.01
13	Denny McLain	.03	.02	.01
14	Bob Gibson	.05	.04	.02
15	Harmon Killebrew	.05	.04	.02
16	Willie McCovey	.05	.04	.02
17	Boog Powell	.03	.02	.01
18	Johnny Bench	.05	.04	.02
19	Vida Blue	.03	.02	.01
20	Joe Torre	.03	.02	.01
21	Rich Allen	.03	.02	.01
22	Johnny Bench	.05	.04	.02
23	Reggie Jackson	.07	.05	.03
24	Pete Rose	.07	.05	.03
25	Jeff Burroughs	.03	.02	.01
26	Steve Garvey	.07	.05	.03
27	Fred Lynn	.03	.02	.01
28	Joe Morgan	.05	.04	.02
29	Thurman Munson	.05	.04	.02
30	Joe Morgan	.05	.04	.02
31	Rod Carew	.07	.05	.03
32	George Foster	.03	.02	.01
33	Jim Rice	.03	.02	.01
34	Dave Parker	.05	.04	.02
35	Don Baylor	.03	.02	.01
36	Keith Hernandez	.03	.02	.01
37	Willie Stargell	.05	.04	.02
38	George Brett	.07	.05	.03
39	Mike Schmidt	.07	.05	.03
40	Rollie Fingers	.05	.04	.02
41	Mike Schmidt	.07	.05	.03
42	Don Drysdale	.05	.04	.02
43	Hank Aaron	.10	.08	.04
44	Pete Rose	.07	.05	.03

A card number in parentheses () indicates the set is unnumbered.

1987 K-Mart

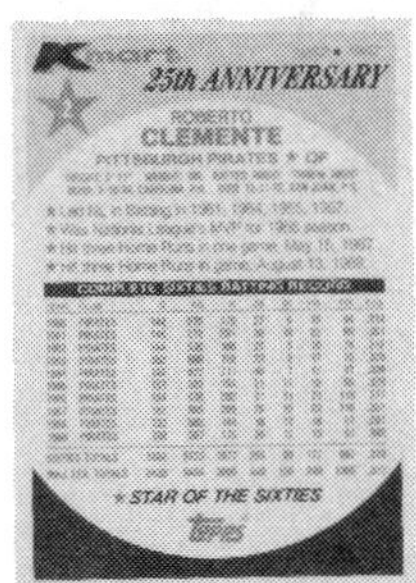

Produced by Topps for K Mart, the 1987 K Mart set was distributed by the department stores to celebrate their 25th anniversary. Entitled "Baseball's Stars of the Decades," the 33-card set was issued in a special cardboard box with one stick of bubblegum. The card fronts feature a full-color photo set diagonally against a red background. The backs contain career highlights plus pitching or batting statistics for the decade in which the player enjoyed his greatest success. Cards are the standard 2-1/2" by 3-1/2" size.

		MT	NR MT	EX
Complete Set (33):		4.00	3.00	1.50
Common Player:		.10	.08	.04
1	Hank Aaron	.50	.40	.20
2	Roberto Clemente	.50	.40	.20
3	Bob Gibson	.10	.08	.04
4	Harmon Killebrew	.10	.08	.04
5	Mickey Mantle	1.00	.70	.40
6	Juan Marichal	.10	.08	.04
7	Roger Maris	.30	.25	.12
8	Willie Mays	.50	.40	.20
9	Brooks Robinson	.30	.25	.12
10	Frank Robinson	.30	.25	.12
11	Carl Yastrzemski	.30	.25	.12
12	Johnny Bench	.30	.25	.12
13	Lou Brock	.20	.15	.08
14	Rod Carew	.30	.25	.12
15	Steve Carlton	.20	.15	.08
16	Reggie Jackson	.30	.25	.12
17	Jim Palmer	.20	.15	.08
18	Jim Rice	.10	.08	.04
19	Pete Rose	.30	.25	.12
20	Nolan Ryan	.40	.30	.15
21	Tom Seaver	.20	.15	.08
22	Willie Stargell	.10	.08	.04
23	Wade Boggs	.30	.25	.12
24	George Brett	.40	.30	.15
25	Gary Carter	.20	.15	.08
26	Dwight Gooden	.20	.15	.08
27	Rickey Henderson	.35	.25	.14
28	Don Mattingly	.50	.40	.20
29	Dale Murphy	.20	.15	.08
30	Eddie Murray	.20	.15	.08
31	Mike Schmidt	.40	.30	.15
32	Darryl Strawberry	.15	.11	.06
33	Fernando Valenzuela	.10	.08	.04

1988 K-Mart

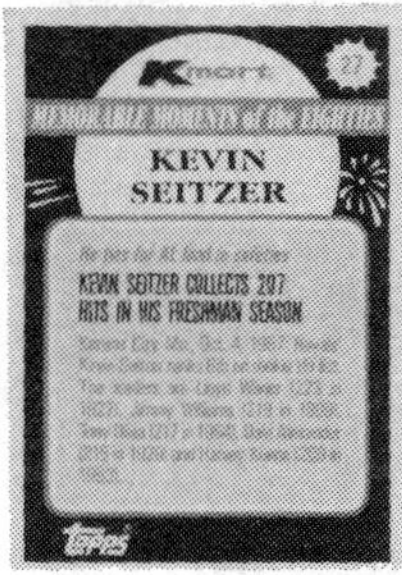

This 33-card boxed set, titled "Memorable Moments," was produced by Topps for distribution via K-Mart. Two previous Topps K-Mart sets were issued: a 44-card set in 1982 in honor of K-Mart's 20th anniversary and a 33-card set in 1987 for the company's 25th anniversary. The 1988 cards are standard-size with red, white and blue borders and a super glossy coating. Numbered card backs are printed in red and blue on white and highlight special events in the featured players' careers. The set was marketed in a bright yellow and green checklist box (gum included).

		MT	NR MT	EX
Complete Set (33):		3.00	2.25	1.25
Common Player:		.10	.08	.04
1	George Bell	.20	.15	.08
2	Wade Boggs	.50	.40	.20
3	George Brett	.50	.40	.20
4	Jose Canseco	.50	.40	.20
5	Jack Clark	.10	.08	.04
6	Will Clark	.40	.30	.15
7	Roger Clemens	.30	.25	.12
8	Vince Coleman	.15	.11	.06
9	Andre Dawson	.20	.15	.08
10	Dwight Gooden	.20	.15	.08
11	Pedro Guerrero	.10	.08	.04
12	Tony Gwynn	.25	.20	.10
13	Rickey Henderson	.35	.25	.14
14	Keith Hernandez	.10	.08	.04
15	Don Mattingly	.40	.30	.15
16	Mark McGwire	.30	.25	.12
17	Paul Molitor	.30	.25	.12
18	Dale Murphy	.20	.15	.08
19	Tim Raines	.20	.15	.08
20	Dave Righetti	.10	.08	.04
21	Cal Ripken, Jr.	.50	.40	.20
22	Pete Rose	.40	.30	.15
23	Nolan Ryan	.50	.40	.20
24	Benny Santiago	.15	.11	.06
25	Mike Schmidt	.30	.25	.12
26	Mike Scott	.10	.08	.04
27	Kevin Seitzer	.10	.08	.04
28	Ozzie Smith	.25	.20	.10
29	Darryl Strawberry	.15	.11	.06
30	Rick Sutcliffe	.10	.08	.04
31	Fernando Valenzuela	.10	.08	.04
32	Todd Worrell	.10	.08	.04
33	Robin Yount	.40	.30	.15

Values quoted in this guide reflect the retail price of a card – the price a collector can expect to pay when buying a card from a dealer. The wholesale price – that which a collector can expect to receive from a dealer when selling cards – will be significantly lower, depending on desirability and condition.

1989 K-Mart

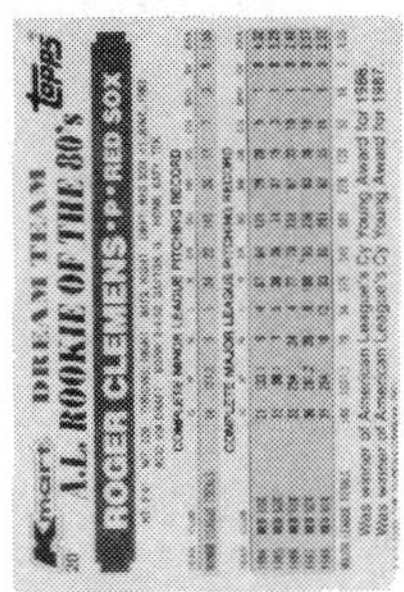

This 33-card, glossy set was produced by Topps for K-Mart, where it was sold in stores nationwide. The standard-size cards feature mostly action shots on the front, and include the Topps "Dream Team" logo at the top, with the K-Mart logo in the lower right corner. The first 11 cards in the set picture the top rookies of 1988, while next 11 picture the top A.L. rookies of the '80s, and the final 11 cards highlight the top N.L. rookies of the decade.

		MT	NR MT	EX
Complete Set (33):		4.00	3.00	1.50
Common Player:		.10	.08	.04
1	Mark Grace	.25	.20	.10
2	Ron Gant	.15	.11	.06
3	Chris Sabo	.15	.11	.06
4	Walt Weiss	.15	.11	.06
5	Jay Buhner	.15	.11	.06
6	Cecil Espy	.10	.08	.04
7	Dave Gallagher	.10	.08	.04
8	Damon Berryhill	.10	.08	.04
9	Tim Belcher	.10	.08	.04
10	Paul Gibson	.10	.08	.04
11	Gregg Jefferies	.25	.20	.10
12	Don Mattingly	.50	.40	.20
13	Harold Reynolds	.15	.11	.06
14	Wade Boggs	.40	.30	.15
15	Cal Ripken, Jr.	.60	.45	.25
16	Kirby Puckett	.40	.30	.15
17	George Bell	.15	.11	.06
18	Jose Canseco	.50	.40	.20
19	Terry Steinbach	.15	.11	.06
20	Roger Clemens	.25	.20	.10
21	Mark Langston	.20	.15	.08
22	Harold Baines	.15	.11	.06
23	Will Clark	.50	.40	.20
24	Ryne Sanberg	.60	.45	.25
25	Tim Wallach	.10	.08	.04
26	Shawon Dunston	.10	.08	.04
27	Tim Raines	.15	.11	.06
28	Darryl Strawberry	.15	.11	.06
29	Tony Gwynn	.35	.25	.14
30	Tony Pena	.10	.08	.04
31	Doc Gooden	.20	.15	.08
32	Fernando Valenzuela	.10	.08	.04
33	Pedro Guerrero	.10	.08	.04

1990 K-Mart

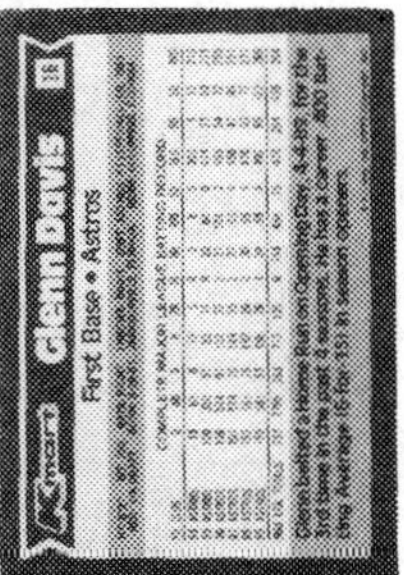

This 33-card, glossy set was produced by Topps for K-Mart, where it was available nationwide. The set is subtitled "Superstars" and features sixteen A.L. players, sixteen N.L. stars and a managers' card featuring both Tony LaRussa and Roger Craig. A special Superstars logo is featured on the card fronts. 1990 marks the fourth consecutive year that Topps has produced a set in cooperation with K-Mart.

		MT	NR MT	EX
Complete Set (33):		3.00	2.25	1.25
Common Player:		.08	.06	.03
1	Will Clark	.25	.20	.10
2	Ryne Sandberg	.40	.30	.15
3	Howard Johnson	.15	.11	.06
4	Ozzie Smith	.15	.11	.06

5	Tony Gwynn	.15	.11	.06
6	Kevin Mitchell	.10	.08	.04
7	Jerome Walton	.08	.06	.03
8	Craig Biggio	.08	.06	.03
9	Mike Scott	.08	.06	.03
10	Dwight Gooden	.20	.15	.08
11	Sid Fernandez	.08	.06	.03
12	Joe Magrane	.08	.06	.03
13	Jay Howell	.08	.06	.03
14	Mark Davis	.08	.06	.03
15	Pedro Guerrero	.08	.06	.03
16	Glenn Davis	.08	.06	.03
17	Don Mattingly	.25	.20	.10
18	Julio Franco	.10	.08	.04
19	Wade Boggs	.25	.20	.10
20	Cal Ripken, Jr.	.40	.30	.15
21	Jose Canseco	.40	.30	.15
22	Kirby Puckett	.20	.15	.08
23	Rickey Henderson	.25	.20	.10
24	Mickey Tettleton	.12	.09	.05
25	Nolan Ryan	.50	.40	.20
26	Bret Saberhagen	.10	.08	.04
27	Jeff Ballard	.08	.06	.03
28	Chuck Finley	.08	.06	.03
29	Dennis Eckersley	.15	.11	.06
30	Dan Plesac	.08	.06	.03
31	Fred McGriff	.15	.11	.06
32	Mark McGwire	.25	.20	.10
33	Managers (Tony LaRussa, Roger Craig)	.08	.06	.03

1955 Kahn's Wieners Reds

The first of what would become 15 successive years of baseball card issues by the Kahn's meat company of Cincinnati is also the rarest. The set consists of six Cincinnati Redlegs player cards, 3-1/4" by 4". Printed in black and white, with blank backs, the '55 Kahn's cards were distributed at a one-day promotional event at a Cincinnati amusement park, where the featured players were on hand to sign autographs. Like the other Kahn's issues through 1963, the '55 cards have a 1/2" white panel containing an advertising message below the player photo. These cards are sometimes found with this portion cut off, greatly reducing the value of the card.

		NR MT	EX	VG
Complete Set (6):		3100.	1550.	930.00
Common Player:		450.00	225.00	135.00
(1)	Gus Bell	750.00	375.00	225.00
(2)	Ted Kluszewski	800.00	400.00	240.00
(3)	Roy McMillan	450.00	225.00	135.00
(4)	Joe Nuxhall	450.00	225.00	135.00
(5)	Wally Post	450.00	225.00	135.00
(6)	Johnny Temple	450.00	225.00	135.00

Grading Guide

Mint (MT): A perfect card. Well-centered with all corners sharp and square. No creases, stains, edge nicks, surface marks, yellowing or fading.

Near Mint (NM): A nearly perfect card. At first glance, a NM card appears to be perfect. May be slightly off-center. No surface marks, creases or loss of gloss.

Excellent (EX): Corners are still fairly sharp with only moderate wear. Borders may be off-center. No creases or stains on fronts or backs, but may show slight loss of surface luster.

Very Good (VG): Shows obvious handling. May have rounded corners, minor creases, major gum or wax stains. No major creases, tape marks, writing, etc.

Good (G): A well-worn card, but exhibits no intentional damage. May have major or multiple creases. Corners may be rounded well beyond card border.

1956 Kahn's Wieners Reds

In 1956, Kahn's expanded its baseball card program to include 15 Redlegs players, and began issuing the cards one per pack in packages of hot dogs. Because the cards were packaged in direct contact with the meat, they are often found today in stained condition. In 3-1/4" by 4" format, black and white with blank backs, the '56 Kahn's cards can be distinguished from later issues by the presence of full stadium photographic backgrounds behind the player photos. Like all Kahn's issues, the 1956 set is unnumbered; the checklists are arranged alphabetically for convenience. The set features the first-ever baseball card of Hall of Famer Frank Robinson.

		NR MT	EX	VG
Complete set (15):		1600.	800.00	480.00
Common player:		75.00	37.00	22.00
(1)	Ed Bailey	75.00	37.00	22.00
(2)	Gus Bell	80.00	40.00	24.00
(3)	Joe Black	100.00	50.00	30.00
(4)	"Smokey" Burgess	100.00	50.00	30.00
(5)	Art Fowler	75.00	37.00	22.00
(6)	Hershell Freeman	75.00	37.00	22.00
(7)	Ray Jablonski	75.00	37.00	22.00
(8)	John Klippstein	75.00	37.00	22.00
(9)	Ted Kluszewski	175.00	87.00	52.00
(10)	Brooks Lawrence	75.00	37.00	22.00
(11)	Roy McMillan	75.00	37.00	22.00
(12)	Joe Nuxhall	75.00	37.00	22.00
(13)	Wally Post	75.00	37.00	22.00
(14)	Frank Robinson	350.00	175.00	105.00
(15)	Johnny Temple	75.00	37.00	22.00

1957 Kahn's Wieners

In its third season of baseball card issue, Kahn's kept the basic 3-1/4" by 4" format, with black and white photos and blank backs. The issue was expanded to 28 players, all Pirates or Reds. The last of the blank-backed Kahn's sets, the 1957 Reds players can be distinguished from the 1956 issue by the general lack of background photo detail, in favor of a neutral light gray background. The Dick Groat card appears with two name variations, a facsimile autograph, "Richard Groat," and a printed "Dick Groat." Both Groat varieties are included in the complete set price.

		NR MT	EX	VG
Complete Set (28):		2600.	1300.	780.00
Common Player:		60.00	30.00	18.00
(1)	Tom Acker	60.00	30.00	18.00
(2)	Ed Bailey	60.00	30.00	18.00
(3)	Gus Bell	80.00	40.00	24.00
(4)	Smokey Burgess	80.00	40.00	24.00
(5)	Roberto Clemente	650.00	325.00	195.00
(6)	George Crowe	60.00	30.00	18.00
(7)	Elroy Face	80.00	40.00	24.00
(8)	Hershell Freeman	60.00	30.00	18.00
(9)	Robert Friend	60.00	30.00	18.00
(10)	Don Gross	60.00	30.00	18.00
(11a)	Dick Groat	80.00	40.00	24.00
(11b)	Richard Groat	175.00	87.00	52.00
(12)	Warren Hacker	60.00	30.00	18.00
(13)	Don Hoak	80.00	40.00	24.00
(14)	Hal Jeffcoat	60.00	30.00	18.00
(15)	Ron Kline	60.00	30.00	18.00
(16)	John Klippstein	60.00	30.00	18.00
(17)	Ted Kluszewski	125.00	62.00	37.00
(18)	Brooks Lawrence	60.00	30.00	18.00
(19)	Dale Long	60.00	30.00	18.00
(20)	Bill Mazeroski	125.00	62.00	37.00
(21)	Roy McMillan	60.00	30.00	18.00
(22)	Joe Nuxhall	60.00	30.00	18.00
(23)	Wally Post	60.00	30.00	18.00
(24)	Frank Robinson	250.00	125.00	75.00
(25)	Johnny Temple	60.00	30.00	18.00
(26)	Frank J. Thomas	60.00	30.00	18.00
(27)	Bob Thurman	60.00	30.00	18.00
(28)	Lee Walls	60.00	30.00	18.00

The values quoted are intended to reflect the market price.

1958 Kahn's Wieners

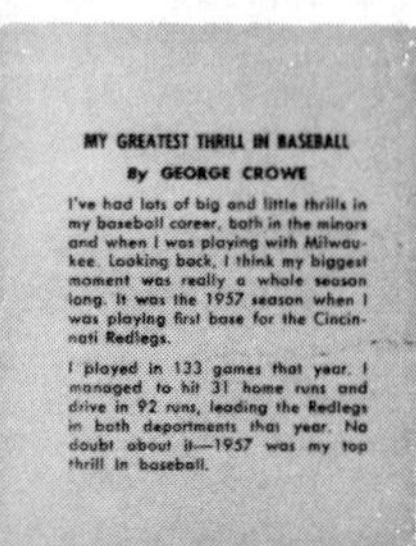

MY GREATEST THRILL IN BASEBALL

By GEORGE CROWE

I've had lots of big and little thrills in my baseball career, both in the minors and when I was playing with Milwaukee. Looking back, I think my biggest moment was really a whole season long. It was the 1957 season when I was playing first base for the Cincinnati Redlegs.

I played in 133 games that year. I managed to hit 31 home runs and drive in 92 runs, leading the Redlegs in both departments that year. No doubt about it—1957 was my top thrill in baseball.

Long-time Cincinnati favorite Wally Post became the only Philadelphia Phillies ballplayer to appear in the 15-year run of Kahn's issues when he was traded in 1958, but included as part of the otherwise exclusively Pirates-Reds set. Like previous years, the '58 Kahn's were 3-1/4" by 4", with black and white player photos. Unlike previous years, however, the cards had printing on the back, a story by the pictured player, titled "My Greatest Thrill in Baseball." Quite similar to the 1959 issue, the '58 Kahn's can be distinguished by the fact that the top line of the advertising panel at bottom has the word "Wieners" in 1958, but not in 1959.

		NR MT	EX	VG
Complete Set (29):		2600.	1300.	780.00
Common Player:		60.00	30.00	18.00
(1)	Ed Bailey	60.00	30.00	18.00
(2)	Gene Baker	60.00	30.00	18.00
(3)	Gus Bell	70.00	35.00	21.00
(4)	Smokey Burgess	70.00	35.00	21.00
(5)	Roberto Clemente	500.00	250.00	150.00
(6)	George Crowe	60.00	30.00	18.00
(7)	Elroy Face	70.00	35.00	21.00
(8)	Henry Foiles	60.00	30.00	18.00
(9)	Dee Fondy	60.00	30.00	18.00
(10)	Robert Friend	70.00	35.00	21.00
(11)	Richard Groat	80.00	40.00	24.00
(12)	Harvey Haddix	70.00	35.00	21.00
(13)	Don Hoak	70.00	35.00	21.00
(14)	Hal Jeffcoat	70.00	35.00	21.00
(15)	Ronald L. Kline	70.00	35.00	21.00
(16)	Ted Kluszewski	125.00	62.00	37.00
(17)	Vernon Law	70.00	35.00	21.00
(18)	Brooks Lawrence	60.00	30.00	18.00
(19)	Bill Mazeroski	125.00	62.00	37.00
(20)	Roy McMillan	60.00	30.00	18.00
(21)	Joe Nuxhall	70.00	35.00	21.00
(22)	Wally Post	275.00	137.00	82.00
(23)	John Powers	60.00	30.00	18.00
(24)	Robert T. Purkey	60.00	30.00	18.00
(25)	Charles Rabe	275.00	137.00	82.00
(26)	Frank Robinson	300.00	150.00	90.00
(27)	Robert Skinner	60.00	30.00	18.00
(28)	Johnny Temple	60.00	30.00	18.00
(29)	Frank J. Thomas	275.00	137.00	82.00

1959 Kahn's Wieners

THE MOST DIFFICULT PLAY I HAVE TO MAKE

by GARY BELL

"I think the most difficult play for me to make as a pitcher is a bunt down the third base line. It is difficult because you must charge off the mound toward the line, field the ball, turn completely around and throw the ball hard to first base to get the batter. I try to make this play by going over and fielding the ball with both feet planted firmly so I stay well balanced. That way, I don't have to throw off balance."

A third team was added to the Kahn's lineup in 1959, the Cleveland Indians joining the Pirates and Reds, bringing the number of cards in the set to 38. Again printed in black and white in the 3-1/4" by 4" size, the 1959 Kahn's cards can be differentiated from the previous issue by the lack of the word "Wieners" on the top line of the advertising panel at bottom. Backs again featured a story written by the pictured player, titled "The Toughest Play I Had to Make," "My Most Difficult Moment in Baseball," or "The Toughest Batters I Have to Face."

	NR MT	EX	VG
Complete Set (38):	4250.	2125.	1275.
Common Player:	45.00	22.00	13.50
(1) Ed Bailey	45.00	22.00	13.50
(2) Gary Bell	45.00	22.00	13.50
(3) Gus Bell	50.00	25.00	15.00
(4) Richard Brodowski	500.00	250.00	150.00
(5) Forrest Burgess	50.00	25.00	15.00
(6) Roberto Clemente	450.00	225.00	135.00
(7) Rocky Colavito	85.00	42.00	25.00
(8) ElRoy Face	50.00	25.00	15.00
(9) Robert Friend	50.00	25.00	15.00
(10) Joe Gordon	50.00	25.00	15.00
(11) Jim Grant	45.00	22.00	13.50
(12) Richard M. Groat	60.00	30.00	18.00
(13) Harvey Haddix	350.00	175.00	105.00
(14) Woodie Held	350.00	175.00	105.00
(15) Don Hoak	50.00	25.00	15.00
(16) Ronald Kline	45.00	22.00	13.50
(17) Ted Kluszewski	85.00	42.00	25.00
(18) Vernon Law	50.00	25.00	15.00
(19) Jerry Lynch	45.00	22.00	13.50
(20) Billy Martin	75.00	37.00	22.00
(21) Bill Mazeroski	80.00	40.00	24.00
(22) Cal McLish	350.00	175.00	105.00
(23) Roy McMillan	45.00	22.00	13.50
(24) Minnie Minoso	60.00	30.00	18.00
(25) Russell Nixon	45.00	22.00	13.50
(26) Joe Nuxhall	50.00	25.00	15.00
(27) Jim Perry	50.00	25.00	15.00
(28) Vada Pinson	60.00	30.00	18.00
(29) Vic Power	45.00	22.00	13.50
(30) Robert Purkey	45.00	22.00	13.50
(31) Frank Robinson	175.00	87.00	52.00
(32) Herb Score	50.00	25.00	15.00
(33) Robert Skinner	45.00	22.00	13.50
(34) George Strickland	45.00	22.00	13.50
(35) Richard L. Stuart	50.00	25.00	15.00
(36) John Temple	45.00	22.00	13.50
(37) Frank J. Thomas	50.00	25.00	15.00
(38) George A. Witt	45.00	22.00	13.50

Values quoted in this guide reflect the retail price of a card – the price a collector can expect to pay when buying a card from a dealer. The wholesale price – that which a collector can expect to receive from a dealer when selling cards – will be significantly lower, depending on desirability and condition.

1960 Kahn's Wieners

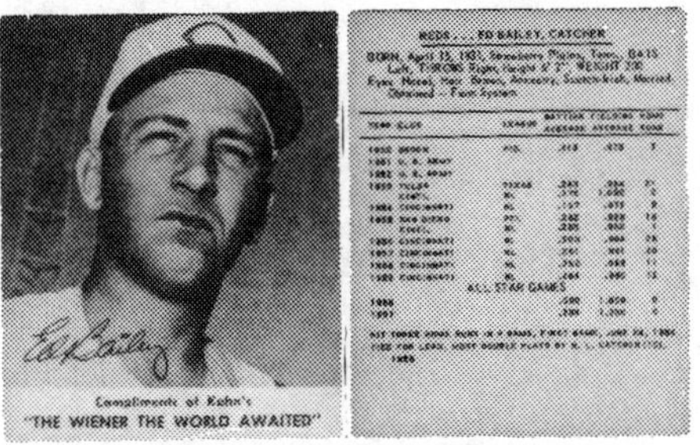

Three more teams joined the Kahn's roster in 1960, the Chicago Cubs, Chicago White Sox and St. Louis Cardinals. A total of 42 different players are represented in the set. Again 3-1/4" by 4" with black and white photos, the 1960 Kahn's cards featured for the first time player stats and personal data on the back, except Harvey Kuenn, which was issued with blank back, probably because of the lateness of his trade to the Indians.

	NR MT	EX	VG
Complete Set (42):	2000.	1000.	600.00
Common Player:	30.00	15.00	9.00
(1) Ed Bailey	30.00	15.00	9.00
(2) Gary Bell	30.00	15.00	9.00
(3) Gus Bell	35.00	17.50	10.50
(4) Forrest Burgess	35.00	17.50	10.50
(5) Gino N. Cimoli	30.00	15.00	9.00
(6) Roberto Clemente	300.00	150.00	90.00
(7) ElRoy Face	35.00	17.50	10.50
(8) Tito Francona	35.00	17.50	10.50
(9) Robert Friend	35.00	17.50	10.50
(10) Jim Grant	30.00	15.00	9.00
(11) Richard Groat	40.00	20.00	12.00
(12) Harvey Haddix	35.00	17.50	10.50
(13) Woodie Held	30.00	15.00	9.00
(14) Bill Henry	30.00	15.00	9.00
(15) Don Hoak	35.00	17.50	10.50
(16) Jay Hook	30.00	15.00	9.00
(17) Eddie Kasko	30.00	15.00	9.00
(18) Ronnie Kline	40.00	20.00	12.00
(19) Ted Kluszewski	60.00	30.00	18.00
(20) Harvey Kuenn	275.00	137.00	82.00
(21) Vernon S. Law	35.00	17.50	10.50
(22) Brooks Lawrence	30.00	15.00	9.00
(23) Jerry Lynch	30.00	15.00	9.00
(24) Billy Martin	60.00	30.00	18.00
(25) Bill Mazeroski	60.00	30.00	18.00
(26) Cal McLish	30.00	15.00	9.00
(27) Roy McMillan	30.00	15.00	9.00
(28) Don Newcombe	35.00	17.50	10.50
(29) Russ Nixon	30.00	15.00	9.00
(30) Joe Nuxhall	35.00	17.50	10.50
(31) James J. O'Toole	30.00	15.00	9.00
(32) Jim Perry	35.00	17.50	10.50
(33) Vada Pinson	40.00	20.00	12.00
(34) Vic Power	30.00	15.00	9.00
(35) Robert T. Purkey	30.00	15.00	9.00
(36) Frank Robinson	150.00	75.00	45.00
(37) Herb Score	35.00	17.50	10.50
(38) Robert R. Skinner	30.00	15.00	9.00
(39) Richard L. Stuart	35.00	17.50	10.50
(40) John Temple	30.00	15.00	9.00
(41) Frank J. Thomas	40.00	20.00	12.00
(42) Lee Walls	35.00	17.50	10.50

The values quoted are intended to reflect the market price.

1961 Kahn's Wieners

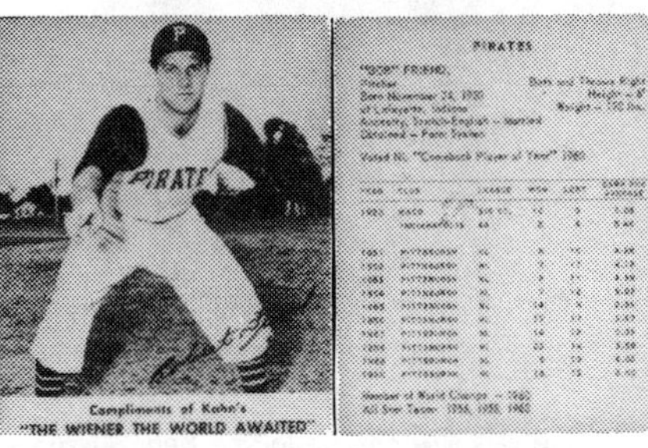

After a single season, the Chicago and St. Louis teams dropped out of the Kahn's program, but the 1961 set was larger than ever, at 43 cards. The same basic format - 3-1/4" by 4" size, black and white photos and statistical information on the back - was retained. For the first time in '61, the meat company made complete sets of the Kahn's cards available to collectors via a mail-in offer. This makes the 1961 and later Kahn's cards considerably easier to obtain than the earlier issues.

	NR MT	EX	VG
Complete Set (43):	1000.	500.00	300.00
Common Player:	18.00	9.00	5.50
(1) John A. Antonelli	20.00	10.00	6.00
(2) Ed Bailey	18.00	9.00	5.50
(3) Gary Bell	18.00	9.00	5.50
(4) Gus Bell	20.00	10.00	6.00
(5) James P. Brosnan	18.00	9.00	5.50
(6) Forrest Burgess	20.00	10.00	6.00
(7) Gino Cimoli	18.00	9.00	5.50
(8) Roberto Clemente	200.00	100.00	60.00
(9) Gordon Coleman	18.00	9.00	5.50
(10) Jimmie Dykes	18.00	9.00	5.50
(11) ElRoy Face	25.00	12.50	7.50
(12) Tito Francona	20.00	10.00	6.00
(13) Robert Friend	20.00	10.00	6.00
(14) Gene L. Freese	18.00	9.00	5.50
(15) Jim Grant	18.00	9.00	5.50
(16) Richard M. Groat	30.00	15.00	9.00
(17) Harvey Haddix	20.00	10.00	6.00
(18) Woodie Held	18.00	9.00	5.50
(19) Don Hoak	20.00	10.00	6.00
(20) Jay Hook	18.00	9.00	5.50
(21) Joe Jay	18.00	9.00	5.50
(22) Eddie Kasko	18.00	9.00	5.50
(23) Willie Kirkland	18.00	9.00	5.50
(24) Vernon S. Law	25.00	12.50	7.50
(25) Jerry Lynch	18.00	9.00	5.50
(26) Jim Maloney	25.00	12.50	7.50
(27) Bill Mazeroski	30.00	15.00	9.00
(28) Wilmer D. Mizell	20.00	10.00	6.00
(29) Glenn R. Nelson	18.00	9.00	5.50
(30) James J. O'Toole	18.00	9.00	5.50
(31) Jim Perry	20.00	10.00	6.00
(32) John M. Phillips	18.00	9.00	5.50
(33) Vada E. Pinson Jr.	30.00	15.00	9.00
(34) Wally Post	18.00	9.00	5.50
(35) Vic Power	18.00	9.00	5.50
(36) Robert T. Purkey	18.00	9.00	5.50
(37) Frank Robinson	125.00	62.00	37.00
(38) John A. Romano Jr.	18.00	9.00	5.50
(39) Dick Schofield	18.00	9.00	5.50
(40) Robert Skinner	18.00	9.00	5.50
(41) Hal Smith	18.00	9.00	5.50
(42) Richard Stuart	20.00	10.00	6.00
(43) John E. Temple	18.00	9.00	5.50

1962 Kahn's Wieners

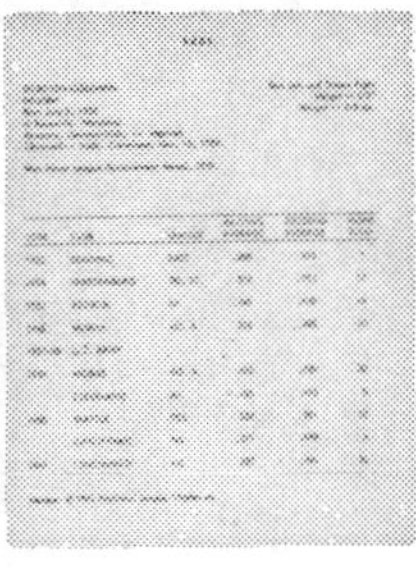

Besides the familiar Reds, Pirates and Indians players in the 1962 Kahn's set, a fourth team was added, the Minnesota Twins, though the overall size of the set was decreased from the previous year, to 38 players in 1962. The cards retained the 3-1/4" by 4" black and white format of previous years. The '62 Kahn's set is awash in variations. Besides the photo and front design variations on the Bell, Purkey and Power cards, each Cleveland player can be found with two back variations, listing the team either as "Cleveland" or "Cleveland Indians." The complete set values listed below include all variations.

	NR MT	EX	VG
Complete Set (38):	2000.	1000.	600.00
Common Player:	15.00	7.50	4.50
(1a) Gary Bell (fat man in background)	150.00	75.00	45.00
(1b) Gary Bell (no fat man)	40.00	20.00	12.00
(2) James P. Brosnan	15.00	7.50	4.50
(3) Forrest Burgess	20.00	10.00	6.00
(4) Leonardo Cardenas	15.00	7.50	4.50
(5) Roberto Clemente	175.00	87.00	52.00
(6a) Ty Cline (Cleveland Indians back)	75.00	37.00	22.00
(6b) Ty Cline (Cleveland back)	30.00	15.00	9.00
(7) Gordon Coleman	15.00	7.50	4.50
(8) Dick Donovan	30.00	15.00	9.00
(9) John Edwards	15.00	7.50	4.50
(10a) Tito Francona (Cleveland Indians back)	75.00	37.00	22.00
(10b) Tito Francona (Cleveland back)	30.00	15.00	9.00
(11) Gene Freese	15.00	7.50	4.50
(12) Robert B. Friend	20.00	10.00	6.00
(13) Joe Gibbon	90.00	45.00	27.00
(14a) Jim Grant (Cleveland Indians back)	75.00	37.00	22.00
(14b) Jim Grant (Cleveland back)	30.00	15.00	9.00
(15) Richard M. Groat	25.00	12.50	7.50
(16) Harvey Haddix	20.00	10.00	6.00
(17a) Woodie Held (Cleveland Indians back)	90.00	45.00	27.00
(17b) Woodie Held (Cleveland back)	30.00	15.00	9.00
(18) Bill Henry	15.00	7.50	4.50
(19) Don Hoak	20.00	10.00	6.00
(20) Ken Hunt	15.00	7.50	4.50
(21) Joseph R. Jay	15.00	7.50	4.50
(22) Eddie Kasko	15.00	7.50	4.50
(23a) Willie Kirkland (Cleveland Indians back)	75.00	37.00	22.00
(23b) Willie Kirkland (Cleveland back)	30.00	15.00	9.00
(24a) Barry Latman (Cleveland Indians back)	75.00	37.00	22.00
(24b) Barry Latman (Cleveland back)	30.00	15.00	9.00
(25) Jerry Lynch	15.00	7.50	4.50
(26) Jim Maloney	20.00	10.00	6.00
(27) Bill Mazeroski	30.00	15.00	9.00
(28) Jim O'Toole	15.00	7.50	4.50
(29a) Jim Perry (Cleveland Indians back)	90.00	45.00	27.00
(29b) Jim Perry (Cleveland back)	30.00	15.00	9.00
(30a) John M. Phillips (Cleveland Indians back)	75.00	37.00	22.00
(30b) John M. Phillips (Cleveland back)	30.00	15.00	9.00
(31) Vada E. Pinson	25.00	12.50	7.50
(32) Wally Post	15.00	7.50	4.50
(33a) Vic Power (Cleveland Indians back)	75.00	37.00	22.00
(33b) Vic Power (Cleveland back)	30.00	15.00	9.00
(33c) Vic Power (Minnesota Twins back)	150.00	75.00	45.00
(34a) Robert T. Purkey (no autograph)	150.00	75.00	45.00
(34b) Robert T. Purkey (with autograph)	40.00	20.00	12.00
(35) Frank Robinson	85.00	42.00	25.00
(36a) John Romano (Cleveland Indians back)	75.00	37.00	22.00
(36b) John Romano (Cleveland back)	30.00	15.00	9.00
(37) Dick Stuart	20.00	10.00	6.00
(38) Bill Virdon	20.00	10.00	6.00

Definitions for grading conditions are located in the Introduction of this price guide.

A player's name in italic type indicates a rookie card. An (FC) indicates a player's first card for that particular card company.

1963 Kahn's Wieners

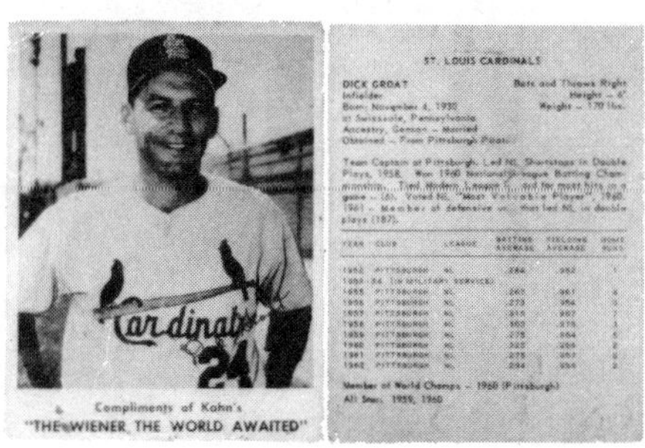

In 1963, for the first time since Kahn's began issuing baseball cards in 1955, the design underwent a significant change, white borders were added to the top and sides of player photo. Also, the card size was changed to 3-3/16" by 4-1/4". Statistical and personal data continued to be printed on the card backs. Joining traditional Reds, Pirates and Indians personnel in the 30-card 1963 set were a handful of New York Yankees and Dick Groat, in his new identity as a St. Louis Cardinal.

		NR MT	EX	VG
Complete Set (30):		800.00	400.00	240.00
Common Player:		15.00	7.50	4.50
(1)	Robert Bailey	15.00	7.50	4.50
(2)	Don Blasingame	15.00	7.50	4.50
(3)	Clete Boyer	25.00	12.50	7.50
(4)	Forrest Burgess	20.00	10.00	6.00
(5)	Leonardo Cardenas	15.00	7.50	4.50
(6)	Roberto Clemente	175.00	87.00	52.00
(7)	Don Clendennon (Donn Clendenon)	15.00	7.50	4.50
(8)	Gordon Coleman	15.00	7.50	4.50
(9)	John A. Edwards	15.00	7.50	4.50
(10)	Gene Freese	15.00	7.50	4.50
(11)	Robert B. Friend	20.00	10.00	6.00
(12)	Joe Gibbon	15.00	7.50	4.50
(13)	Dick Groat	25.00	12.50	7.50
(14)	Harvey Haddix	20.00	10.00	6.00
(15)	Elston Howard	30.00	15.00	9.00
(16)	Joey Jay	15.00	7.50	4.50
(17)	Eddie Kasko	15.00	7.50	4.50
(18)	Tony Kubek	30.00	15.00	9.00
(19)	Jerry Lynch	15.00	7.50	4.50
(20)	Jim Maloney	20.00	10.00	6.00
(21)	Bill Mazeroski	30.00	15.00	9.00
(22)	Joe Nuxhall	20.00	10.00	6.00
(23)	Jim O'Toole	15.00	7.50	4.50
(24)	Vada E. Pinson	25.00	12.50	7.50
(25)	Robert T. Purkey	15.00	7.50	4.50
(26)	Bob Richardson	30.00	15.00	9.00
(27)	Frank Robinson	75.00	37.00	22.00
(28)	Bill Stafford	20.00	10.00	6.00
(29)	Ralph W. Terry	25.00	12.50	7.50
(30)	Bill Virdon	20.00	10.00	6.00

1964 Kahn's Wieners

After nearly a decade of virtually identical card issues, the 1964 Kahn's issue was an abrupt change. In a new size, 3" by 3-1/2", the nearly square cards featured a borderless color photo. The only other design element on the front of the card was a facsimile autograph. The advertising slogan which had traditionally appeared on the front of the card was moved to the back, where it joined the player's stats and personal data. The teams in the 1964 issue once again reverted to the Reds, Pirates and Indians, for a total of 31 cards.

		NR MT	EX	VG
Complete Set (31):		900.00	450.00	270.00
Common Player:		10.00	5.00	3.00
(1)	Max Alvis	10.00	5.00	3.00
(2)	Bob Bailey	10.00	5.00	3.00
(3)	Leonardo Cardenas	10.00	5.00	3.00
(4)	Roberto Clemente	150.00	75.00	45.00
(5)	Donn A. Clendenon	10.00	5.00	3.00
(6)	Victor Davalillo	10.00	5.00	3.00
(7)	Dick Donovan	10.00	5.00	3.00
(8)	John A. Edwards	10.00	5.00	3.00
(9)	Robert Friend	12.00	6.00	3.50
(10)	Jim Grant	10.00	5.00	3.00
(11)	Tommy Harper	10.00	5.00	3.00
(12)	Woodie Held	10.00	5.00	3.00
(13)	Joey Jay	10.00	5.00	3.00
(14)	Jack Kralick	10.00	5.00	3.00
(15)	Jerry Lynch	10.00	5.00	3.00
(16)	Jim Maloney	14.00	7.00	4.25
(17)	Bill Mazeroski	25.00	12.50	7.50
(18)	Alvin McBean	10.00	5.00	3.00
(19)	Joe Nuxhall	14.00	7.00	4.25
(20)	Jim Pagliaroni	10.00	5.00	3.00
(21)	Vada E. Pinson Jr.	20.00	10.00	6.00
(22)	Robert T. Purkey	10.00	5.00	3.00
(23)	Pedro Ramos	10.00	5.00	3.00
(24)	Frank Robinson	75.00	37.00	22.00
(25)	John Romano	10.00	5.00	3.00
(26)	Pete Rose	350.00	175.00	105.00
(27)	John Tsitouris	10.00	5.00	3.00
(28)	Robert A. Veale Jr.	10.00	5.00	3.00
(29)	Bill Virdon	14.00	7.00	4.25
(30)	Leon Wagner	10.00	5.00	3.00
(31)	Fred Whitfield	10.00	5.00	3.00

The values quoted are intended to reflect the market price.

1965 Kahn's Wieners

There was little change for the Kahn's issue in 1965 beyond the addition of Milwaukee Braves players to the Reds, Pirates and Indians traditionally included in the set. At 45 players, the 1965 issue was the largest of the Kahn's sets. Once again in 3" by 3-1/2" size, the 1965s retained the borderless color photo design of the previous season. A look at the stats on the back will confirm the year of issue, however, since the last year of statistics is the year prior to the card's issue.

		NR MT	EX	VG
Complete Set (45):		1100.	550.00	330.00
Common Player:		12.00	6.00	3.50
(1)	Hank Aaron	150.00	75.00	45.00
(2)	Max Alvis	12.00	6.00	3.50
(3)	Jose Azcue	12.00	6.00	3.50
(4)	Bob Bailey	12.00	6.00	3.50
(5)	Frank Bolling	12.00	6.00	3.50
(6)	Leonardo Cardenas	12.00	6.00	3.50
(7)	Rico Ricardo Carty	15.00	7.50	4.50
(8)	Donn A. Clendenon	12.00	6.00	3.50
(9)	Tony Cloninger	12.00	6.00	3.50
(10)	Gordon Coleman	12.00	6.00	3.50
(11)	Victor Davalillo	12.00	6.00	3.50
(12)	John A. Edwards	12.00	6.00	3.50
(13)	Sam Ellis	12.00	6.00	3.50
(14)	Robert Friend	15.00	7.50	4.50
(15)	Tommy Harper	12.00	6.00	3.50
(16)	Chuck Hinton	12.00	6.00	3.50
(17)	Dick Howser	15.00	7.50	4.50
(18)	Joey Jay	12.00	6.00	3.50
(19)	Deron Johnson	12.00	6.00	3.50
(20)	Jack Kralick	12.00	6.00	3.50
(21)	Denny Lemaster	12.00	6.00	3.50
(22)	Jerry Lynch	12.00	6.00	3.50
(23)	Jim Maloney	15.00	7.50	4.50
(24)	Lee Maye	12.00	6.00	3.50
(25)	Bill Mazeroski	25.00	12.50	7.50
(26)	Alvin McBean	12.00	6.00	3.50
(27)	Bill McCool	12.00	6.00	3.50
(28)	Sam McDowell	15.00	7.50	4.50
(29)	Donald McMahon	12.00	6.00	3.50
(30)	Denis Menke	12.00	6.00	3.50
(31)	Joe Nuxhall	15.00	7.50	4.50
(32)	Gene Oliver	12.00	6.00	3.50
(33)	Jim O'Toole	12.00	6.00	3.50
(34)	Jim Pagliaroni	12.00	6.00	3.50
(35)	Vada E. Pinson Jr.	20.00	10.00	6.00
(36)	Frank Robinson	110.00	55.00	33.00
(37)	Pete Rose	250.00	125.00	75.00
(38)	Willie Stargell	110.00	55.00	33.00
(39)	Ralph W. Terry	12.00	6.00	3.50
(40)	Luis Tiant	20.00	10.00	6.00
(41)	Joe Torre	20.00	10.00	6.00
(42)	John Tsitouris	12.00	6.00	3.50
(43)	Robert A. Veale Jr.	12.00	6.00	3.50
(44)	Bill Virdon	15.00	7.50	4.50
(45)	Leon Wagner	12.00	6.00	3.50

1966 Kahn's Wieners

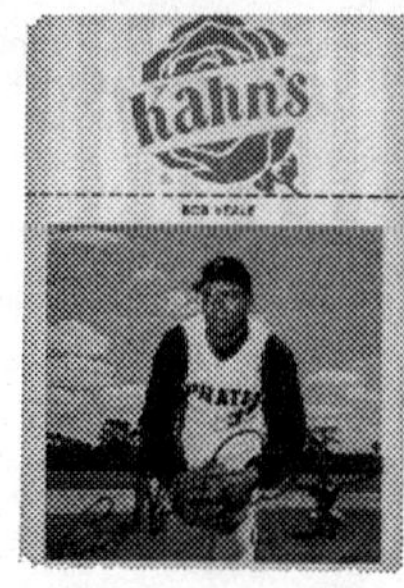

The fourth new format in five years greeted collector's with the introduction of Kahn's 1966 issue of 32 cards. The design consisted of a color photo bordered by white and yellow vertical stripes. The player's name was printed above the photo, and a facsimile autograph appeared across the photo. As printed, the cards were 2-13/16" by 4" in size. However, the top portion consisted of a 2-13/16" by 1-3/8" advertising panel with a red rose logo and the word "Kahn's," separated from the player portion of the card by a black dotted line. Naturally, many of the cards are found today with the top portion cut off. Values listed here are for cards with the top portion intact. Players from the Cincinnati Reds, Pittsburgh Pirates, Cleveland Indians and Atlanta Braves were included in the set. Since the cards are blank-backed, collectors must learn to differentiate player poses to determine year of issue for some cards.

		NR MT	EX	VG
Complete Set (32):		1000.	500.00	300.00
Common Player:		15.00	7.50	4.50
(1)	Henry Aaron	150.00	75.00	45.00
(2)	Felipe Alou	24.00	12.00	7.25
(3)	Max Alvis	15.00	7.50	4.50
(4)	Robert Bailey	15.00	7.50	4.50
(5)	Wade Blasingame	15.00	7.50	4.50
(6)	Frank Bolling	15.00	7.50	4.50
(7)	Leo Cardenas	15.00	7.50	4.50
(8)	Roberto Clemente	150.00	75.00	45.00
(9)	Tony Cloninger	15.00	7.50	4.50
(10)	Vic Davalillo	15.00	7.50	4.50
(11)	John Edwards	15.00	7.50	4.50
(12)	Sam Ellis	15.00	7.50	4.50
(13)	Pedro Gonzalez	15.00	7.50	4.50
(14)	Tommy Harper	15.00	7.50	4.50
(15)	Deron Johnson	15.00	7.50	4.50
(16)	Mack Jones	15.00	7.50	4.50
(17)	Denny Lemaster	15.00	7.50	4.50
(18)	Jim Maloney	18.00	9.00	5.50
(19)	Bill Mazeroski	28.00	14.00	8.50
(20)	Bill McCool	15.00	7.50	4.50
(21)	Sam McDowell	18.00	9.00	5.50
(22)	Denis Menke	15.00	7.50	4.50
(23)	Joe Nuxhall	18.00	9.00	5.50
(24)	Jim Pagliaroni	15.00	7.50	4.50
(25)	Milt Pappas	18.00	9.00	5.50
(26)	Vada Pinson	28.00	14.00	8.50
(27)	Pete Rose	200.00	100.00	60.00
(28)	Sonny Siebert	15.00	7.50	4.50
(29)	Willie Stargell	60.00	30.00	18.00
(30)	Joe Torre	18.00	9.00	5.50
(31)	Bob Veale	15.00	7.50	4.50
(32)	Fred Whitfield	15.00	7.50	4.50

1967 Kahn's Wieners

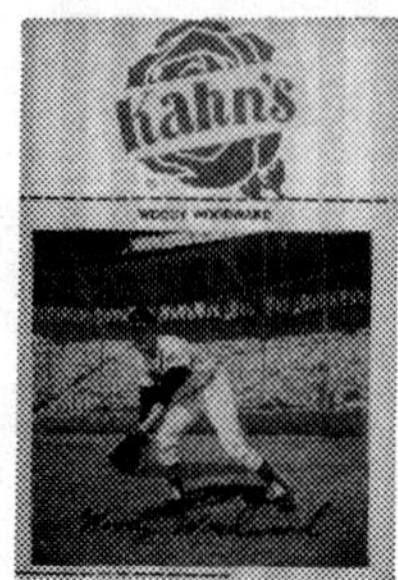

Retaining the basic format of the 1966 set (see listing for description), the '67 Kahn's set was expanded to 41 players through the addition of several New York Mets players to the previous season's lineup of Reds, Pirates, Indians and Braves. Making the 1967 set especially challenging for collectors is the fact that some cards are found in a smaller size and/or with different colored stripes bordering the color player photo. On the majority of cards, the size remained 2-13/16" by 4" (with ad at top; 2-13/16" by

2-5/8" without ad at top). However, because of packing in different products, the Ellis, Helms and Torre cards can be found in 2-13/16" by 3-1/4" size (with ad; 2-13/16" by 2-1/8" without ad). The handful of known border stripe variations are listed below. Values quoted are for cards with the top ad panel intact. All variation cards are included in the valuations given below for complete sets.

		NR MT	EX	VG
Complete Set (48):		1100.	550.00	330.00
Common Player:		15.00	7.50	4.50
(1)	Henry Aaron	150.00	75.00	45.00
(2)	Gene Alley	15.00	7.50	4.50
(3)	Felipe Alou	24.00	12.00	7.25
(4a)	Matty Alou (yellow & white striped border)	20.00	10.00	6.00
(4b)	Matty Alou (red & white striped border)	24.00	12.00	7.25
(5)	Max Alvis	15.00	7.50	4.50
(6a)	Ken Boyer (yellow & white striped border)	25.00	12.50	7.50
(6b)	Ken Boyer (red & white striped border)	30.00	15.00	9.00
(7)	Leo Cardenas	15.00	7.50	4.50
(8)	Rico Carty	18.00	9.00	5.50
(9)	Tony Cloninger	15.00	7.50	4.50
(10)	Tommy Davis	18.00	9.00	5.50
(11)	John Edwards	15.00	7.50	4.50
(12a)	Sam Ellis (large size)	15.00	7.50	4.50
(12b)	Sam Ellis (small size)	28.00	14.00	8.50
(13)	Jack Fisher	15.00	7.50	4.50
(14)	Steve Hargan	15.00	7.50	4.50
(15)	Tom Harper	15.00	7.50	4.50
(16a)	Tom Helms (large size)	15.00	7.50	4.50
(16b)	Tom Helms (small size)	28.00	14.00	8.50
(17)	Deron Johnson	15.00	7.50	4.50
(18)	Ken Johnson	15.00	7.50	4.50
(19)	Cleon Jones	15.00	7.50	4.50
(20a)	Ed Kranepool (yellow & white striped border)	15.00	7.50	4.50
(20b)	Ed Kranepool (red & white striped border)	25.00	12.50	7.50
(21a)	James Maloney (yellow & white striped border)	20.00	10.00	6.00
(21b)	James Maloney (red & white striped border)	24.00	12.00	7.25
(22)	Lee May	18.00	9.00	5.50
(23)	Wm. Mazeroski	28.00	14.00	8.50
(24)	Wm. McCool	15.00	7.50	4.50
(25)	Sam McDowell	18.00	9.00	5.50
(26)	Dennis Menke (Denis)	15.00	7.50	4.50
(27)	Jim Pagliaroni	15.00	7.50	4.50
(28)	Don Pavletich	15.00	7.50	4.50
(29)	Tony Perez	35.00	17.50	10.50
(30)	Vada Pinson	26.00	13.00	7.75
(31)	Dennis Ribant	15.00	7.50	4.50
(32)	Pete Rose	175.00	87.00	52.00
(33)	Art Shamsky	15.00	7.50	4.50
(34)	Bob Shaw	15.00	7.50	4.50
(35)	Sonny Siebert	15.00	7.50	4.50
(36)	Wm. Stargell (first name actually Wilver)	60.00	30.00	18.00
(37a)	Joe Torre (large size)	24.00	12.00	7.25
(37b)	Joe Torre (small size)	28.00	14.00	8.50
(38)	Bob Veale	15.00	7.50	4.50
(39)	Leon Wagner	15.00	7.50	4.50
(40)	Fred Whitfield	15.00	7.50	4.50
(41)	Woody Woodward	15.00	7.50	4.50

1968 Kahn's Wieners

The number of card size and stripe color variations increased with the 1968 Kahn's issue (see 1967 listing), though the basic card design was retained from the previous two seasons: 2-13/16" by 4" size (with ad panel at top; 2-13/16" by 2-5/8" with ad panel cut off), color photo bordered by yellow and white vertical stripes. In addition to the basic issue, a number of the cards appear in a smaller, 2-13/16" by 3-1/4", size, while some of them, and others, appear with variations in the color of border stripes. One card, Maloney, can be found with a top portion advertising Blue Mountain brand meats, as well as Kahn's. All in all, quite a challenge for the specialist. The 1968 set featured the largest number of teams represented in any Kahn's issue: Atlanta Braves, Chicago Cubs and White Sox, Cincinnati Reds, Cleveland Indians, Detroit Tigers, New York Mets and Pittsburgh Pirates. Values quoted below are for cards with the ad panel at top; complete set prices include all variations.

		NR MT	EX	VG
Complete Set (56):		1600.	800.00	480.00
Common Player:		15.00	7.50	4.50
(1a)	Hank Aaron (large size)	125.00	62.00	37.00
(1b)	Hank Aaron (small size)	150.00	75.00	45.00
(2)	Tommy Agee	15.00	7.50	4.50
(3a)	Gene Alley (large size)	15.00	7.50	4.50
(3b)	Gene Alley (small size)	24.00	12.00	7.25
(4)	Felipe Alou	18.00	9.00	5.50
(5a)	Matty Alou (yellow striped border)	20.00	10.00	6.00
(5b)	Matty Alou (red striped border)	24.00	12.00	7.25
(6a)	Max Alvis (large size)	15.00	7.50	4.50
(6b)	Max Alvis (small size)	24.00	12.00	7.25
(7)	Gerry Arrigo	15.00	7.50	4.50
(8)	John Bench	400.00	200.00	120.00
(9a)	Clete Boyer (large size)	15.00	7.50	4.50
(9b)	Clete Boyer (small size)	24.00	12.00	7.25
(10)	Larry Brown	15.00	7.50	4.50
(11a)	Leo Cardenas (large size)	15.00	7.50	4.50
(11b)	Leo Cardenas (small size)	24.00	12.00	7.25
(12a)	Bill Freehan (large size)	24.00	12.00	7.25
(12b)	Bill Freehan (small size)	28.00	14.00	8.50
(13)	Steve Hargan	15.00	7.50	4.50
(14)	Joel Horlen	15.00	7.50	4.50
(15)	Tony Horton	18.00	9.00	5.50
(16)	Willie Horton	18.00	9.00	5.50
(17)	Ferguson Jenkins	32.00	16.00	9.50
(18)	Deron Johnson	15.00	7.50	4.50
(19)	Mack Jones	15.00	7.50	4.50
(20)	Bob Lee	15.00	7.50	4.50
(21a)	Jim Maloney (large size, rose logo)	18.00	9.00	5.50
(21b)	Jim Maloney (large size, blue mountain logo)	32.00	16.00	9.50
(21c)	Jim Maloney (small size, yellow & white striped border)	24.00	12.00	7.25
(21d)	Jim Maloney (small size, yellow, white & green striped border)	24.00	12.00	7.25
(22a)	Lee May (large size)	20.00	10.00	6.00
(22b)	Lee May (small size)	24.00	12.00	7.25
(23a)	Wm. Mazeroski (large size)	28.00	14.00	8.50
(23b)	Wm. Mazeroski (small size)	32.00	16.00	9.50
(24)	Dick McAuliffe	15.00	7.50	4.50
(25)	Bill McCool	15.00	7.50	4.50
(26a)	Sam McDowell (yellow striped border)	20.00	10.00	6.00
(26b)	Sam McDowell (red striped border)	24.00	12.00	7.25
(27a)	Tony Perez (yellow striped border)	35.00	17.50	10.50
(27b)	Tony Perez (red striped border)	40.00	20.00	12.00
(28)	Gary Peters	15.00	7.50	4.50
(29a)	Vada Pinson (large size)	24.00	12.00	7.25
(29b)	Vada Pinson (small size)	28.00	14.00	8.50
(30)	Chico Ruiz	15.00	7.50	4.50
(31a)	Ron Santo (yellow striped border)	24.00	12.00	7.25
(31b)	Ron Santo (red striped border)	28.00	14.00	8.50
(32)	Art Shamsky	15.00	7.50	4.50
(33)	Luis Tiant	24.00	12.00	7.25
(34a)	Joe Torre (large size)	24.00	12.00	7.25
(34b)	Joe Torre (small size)	28.00	14.00	8.50
(35a)	Bob Veale (large size)	15.00	7.50	4.50
(35b)	Bob Veale (small size)	24.00	12.00	7.25
(36)	Leon Wagner	15.00	7.50	4.50
(37)	Billy Williams	50.00	25.00	15.00
(38)	Earl Wilson	15.00	7.50	4.50

A player's name in italic type indicates a rookie card. An (FC) indicates a player's first card for that particular card company.

1969 Kahn's Wieners

In its 15th consecutive year of baseball card issuing, Kahn's continued the basic format adopted in 1966. The basic card issue of 22 players was printed in 2-13/16" by 4" size (with ad panel at top; 2-13/16" by 2-5/8" without panel) and are blanked-backed. Teams represented in the set included the Braves, Cubs, White Sox, Reds, Cardinals, Indians and Pirates. The cards featured a color photo and facsimile autograph bordered by yellow and white vertical stripes. At top was an ad panel consisting of the Kahn's red rose logo. However, because some cards were produced for inclusion in packages other than the standard hot dogs, a number of variations in card size and stripe color were created, as noted in the listings below. The smaller size cards, 2-13/16" by 3-1/4" with ad, 2-13/16" by 2-1/8" without ad, were created by more closely cropping the player photo at top and bottom. Values quoted below are for cards with the top logo panel intact. Complete set values include all the variations.

		NR MT	EX	VG
Complete Set (29):		800.00	400.00	240.00
Common Player:		15.00	7.50	4.50
(1a)	Hank Aaron (large size)	125.00	62.00	37.00
(1b)	Hank Aaron (small size)	150.00	75.00	45.00
(2)	Matty Alou	18.00	9.00	5.50
(3)	Max Alvis	15.00	7.50	4.50
(4)	Gerry Arrigo	15.00	7.50	4.50
(5)	Steve Blass	15.00	7.50	4.50
(6)	Clay Carroll	15.00	7.50	4.50
(7)	Tony Cloninger	15.00	7.50	4.50
(8)	George Culver	15.00	7.50	4.50
(9)	Joel Horlen	15.00	7.50	4.50
(10)	Tony Horton	18.00	9.00	5.50
(11)	Alex Johnson	15.00	7.50	4.50
(12a)	Jim Maloney (large size)	20.00	10.00	6.00
(12b)	Jim Maloney (small size)	24.00	12.00	7.25
(13a)	Lee May (yellow striped border)	20.00	10.00	6.00
(13b)	Lee May (red striped border)	24.00	12.00	7.25
(14a)	Bill Mazeroski (yellow striped border)	28.00	14.00	8.50
(14b)	Bill Mazeroski (red striped border)	32.00	16.00	9.50
(15a)	Sam McDowell (yellow striped border)	20.00	10.00	6.00
(15b)	Sam McDowell (red striped border)	24.00	12.00	7.25
(16a)	Tony Perez (large size)	35.00	17.50	10.50
(16b)	Tony Perez (small size)	40.00	20.00	12.00
(17)	Gary Peters	15.00	7.50	4.50
(18a)	Ron Santo (yellow striped border)	24.00	12.00	7.25
(18b)	Ron Santo (red striped border)	28.00	14.00	8.50
(19)	Luis Tiant	24.00	12.00	7.25
(20)	Joe Torre	22.00	11.00	6.50
(21)	Bob Veale	15.00	7.50	4.50
(22)	Billy Williams	50.00	25.00	15.00

1987 Kahn's Reds

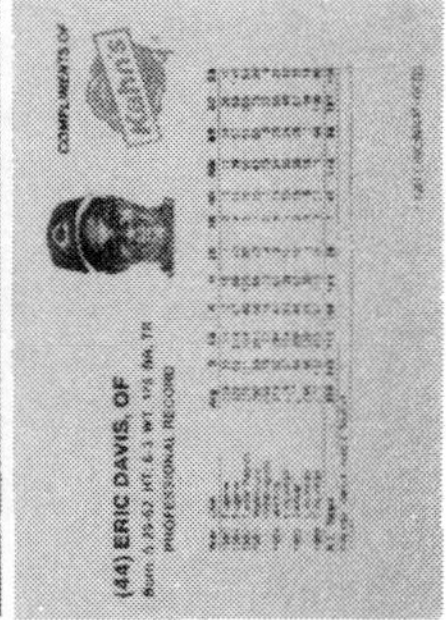

After a nearly 20-year layoff, Kahn's Wieners produced a baseball card set. Kahn's, who produced card sets between 1955 and 1968, sponsored a 28-card set that was distributed to fans attending the August 2nd game at Riverfront Stadium. The cards are the standard 2-1/2" by 3-1/2" size. The fronts offer a full-color player photo bordered in red and white. The backs carry the Kahn's logo and a head shot of the player.

		MT	NR MT	EX
Complete Set:		12.00	9.00	4.75
Common Player:		.25	.20	.10
6	Bo Diaz	.25	.20	.10
10	Terry Francona	.25	.20	.10
11	Kurt Stillwell	.30	.25	.12
12	Nick Esasky	.30	.25	.12
13	Dave Concepcion	.40	.30	.15
15	Barry Larkin	2.00	1.50	.80
16	Ron Oester	.25	.20	.10
21	Paul O'Neill	2.00	1.50	.80
23	Lloyd McClendon	.25	.20	.10
25	Buddy Bell	.35	.25	.14
28	Kal Daniels	.25	.20	.10
29	Tracy Jones	.25	.20	.10
30	Guy Hoffman	.25	.20	.10
31	John Franco	.80	.60	.30
32	Tom Browning	.60	.45	.25
33	Ron Robinson	.25	.20	.10
34	Bill Gullickson	.25	.20	.10
35	Pat Pacillo	.30	.25	.12
39	Dave Parker	1.25	.90	.50
43	Bill Landrum	.25	.20	.10
44	Eric Davis	1.50	1.25	.60
46	Rob Murphy	.40	.30	.15
47	Frank Williams	.25	.20	.10
48	Ted Power	.25	.20	.10

1988 Kahn's Mets

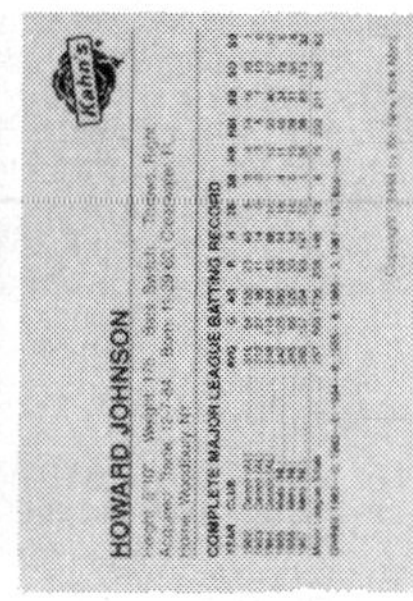

Approximately 50,000 Mets fans received this complimentary card set during a ballpark promotion sponsored by Kahn's Wieners. Twenty-five players are featured in the set, along with manager Davey Johnson, four coaches and a team photo. Card fronts have a dark blue border with an orange rectangle framing the full-color player photo. Card numbers reflecting the players' uniform numbers, are printed in white in the upper right corner of the card face, beside the team logo. The player name appears upper left and the player position is centered in the bottom margin. The card backs are black and white with red line accents. In addition to player acquisition date, birthday and residence, a paragraph-style career summary is included. The cards measure 2-1/2" by 3-1/2".

		MT	NR MT	EX
Complete Set:		11.00	8.25	4.50
Common Player:		.20	.15	.08
1	Mookie Wilson	.35	.25	.14
2	Mackey Sasser	.20	.15	.08
3	Bud Harrelson	.20	.15	.08
4	Lenny Dykstra	.50	.40	.20
5	Davey Johnson	.30	.25	.12
6	Wally Backman	.20	.15	.08
8	Gary Carter	.60	.45	.25
11	Tim Teufel	.20	.15	.08
12	Ron Darling	.40	.30	.15
13	Lee Mazzilli	.20	.15	.08
15	Rick Aguilera	.40	.30	.15
16	Dwight Gooden	1.00	.70	.40
17	Keith Hernandez	.60	.45	.25
18	Darryl Strawberry	.40	.30	.15
19	Bob Ojeda	.35	.25	.14
20	Howard Johnson	1.00	.70	.40
21	Kevin Elster	.30	.25	.12
22	Kevin McReynolds	.60	.45	.25
26	Terry Leach	.20	.15	.08
28	Bill Robinson	.20	.15	.08
29	Dave Magadan	.40	.30	.15
30	Mel Stottlemyre	.20	.15	.08
31	Gene Walter	.20	.15	.08
33	Barry Lyons	.20	.15	.08
34	Sam Perlozzo	.20	.15	.08
42	Roger McDowell	.30	.25	.12
44	David Cone	.70	.50	.30
48	Randy Myers	.50	.40	.20
50	Sid Fernandez	.35	.25	.14
52	Greg Pavlick	.20	.15	.08
----	Team Photo	.20	.15	.08

The values quoted are intended to reflect the market price.

1988 Kahn's Reds

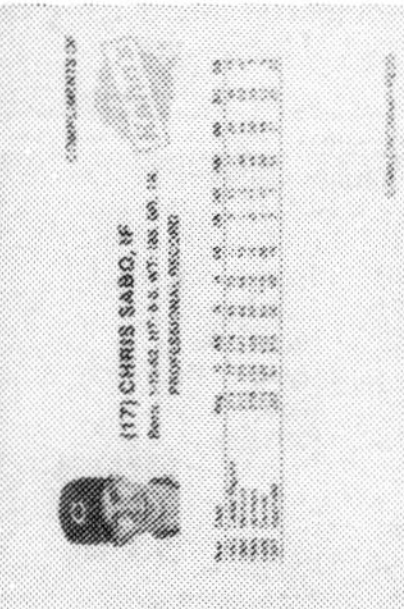

This 26-card set was a one-time giveaway during the August 14th, 1988 Cincinnati Reds game. The glossy cards (2-1/2" by 3-1/2") feature full-color action photos inside red and white borders. The Reds logo, player uniform number, name and position are printed below the photo. The backs are black and white, with small player close-ups and career stats. A promotional 25-cent coupon for Kahn's Wieners was included with each set.

		MT	NR MT	EX
Complete Set (26):		10.00	7.50	4.00
Common Player:		.25	.20	.10
6	Bo Diaz	.25	.20	.10
8	Terry McGriff	.25	.20	.10
9	Eddie Milner	.25	.20	.10
10	Leon Durham	.30	.25	.12
11	Barry Larkin	.70	.50	.30
12	Nick Esasky	.25	.20	.10
13	Dave Concepcion	.40	.30	.15
14	Pete Rose	1.25	.90	.50
15	Jeff Treadway	.35	.25	.14
17	Chris Sabo	.90	.70	.35
20	Danny Jackson	.60	.45	.25
21	Paul O'Neill	.40	.30	.15
22	Dave Collins	.25	.20	.10
27	Jose Rijo	.35	.25	.14
28	Kal Daniels	.35	.25	.14
29	Tracy Jones	.25	.20	.10
30	Lloyd McClendon	.25	.20	.10
31	John Franco	.50	.40	.20
32	Tom Browning	.30	.25	.12
33	Ron Robinson	.25	.20	.10
40	Jack Armstrong	.35	.25	.14
44	Eric Davis	1.00	.70	.40
46	Rob Murphy	.25	.20	.10
47	Frank Williams	.25	.20	.10
48	Tim Birtsas	.25	.20	.10
----	Coaches (Scott Breeden, Tommy Helms, Bruce Kimm, Jim Lett, Lee May, Tony Perez)	.25	.20	.10

1989 Kahn's Cooperstown Collection

This 11-player card set was available through a mail-in offer. One dollar and three proofs of purchase from Hillshire Farms were needed to obtain the set. The card fronts feature paintings of recent Hall of Fame inductees. A coupon card was also included with each set.

		MT	NR MT	EX
Complete Set (11):		6.00	4.50	2.50
Common Player:		.40	.30	.15
(1)	Cool Papa Bell	.40	.30	.15
(2)	Johnny Bench	.80	.60	.30
(3)	Lou Brock	.60	.45	.25
(4)	Whitey Ford	.80	.60	.30
(5)	Bob Gibson	.70	.50	.30
(6)	Billy Herman	.40	.30	.15
(7)	Harmon Killebrew	.80	.60	.30
(8)	Eddie Mathews	.80	.60	.30
(9)	Brooks Robinson	.80	.60	.30
(10)	Willie Stargell	.70	.50	.30
(11)	Carl Yastrzemski	.80	.60	.30

1989 Kahn's Mets

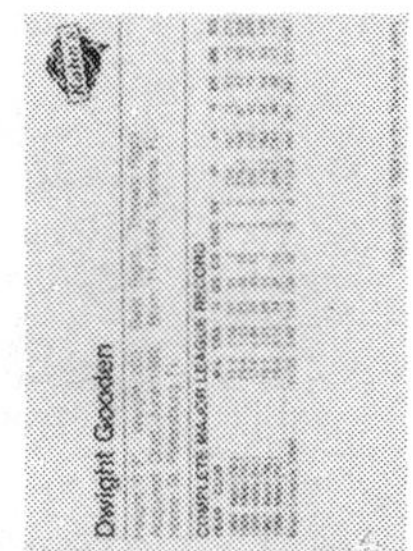

This 30-card New York Mets team set was sponsored by Kahn's Wieners and was given to fans attending the July 6, 1989 Mets game at Shea Stadium. The standard-size cards feature a full-color photo surrounded by a blue and orange border with the player's name and uniform number across the top. The backs include the Kahn's logo, along with player information and complete Major League stats. Four update cards were later added to the set.

		MT	NR MT	EX
Complete Set (30):		12.00	9.00	4.75
Common Player:		.20	.15	.08
1	Mookie Wilson	.30	.25	.12
2	Mackey Sasser	.20	.15	.08
3	Bud Harrelson	.20	.15	.08
5	Davey Johnson	.25	.20	.10
7	Juan Samuel	.30	.25	.12
8	Gary Carter	.50	.40	.20
9	Gregg Jefferies	1.00	.70	.40
12	Ron Darling	.30	.25	.12
13	Lee Mazzilli	.20	.15	.08
16	Dwight Gooden	1.00	.70	.40
17	Keith Hernandez	.30	.25	.12
18	Darryl Strawberry	.30	.25	.12
19	Bob Ojeda	.25	.20	.10
20	Howard Johnson	.70	.50	.30
21	Kevin Elster	.20	.15	.08
22	Kevin McReynolds	.50	.40	.20
28	Bill Robinson	.20	.15	.08
29	Dave Magadan	.40	.30	.15
30	Mel Stottlemyre	.20	.15	.08
32	Mark Carreon	.30	.25	.12
33	Barry Lyons	.20	.15	.08
34	Sam Perlozzo	.20	.15	.08
38	Rick Aguilera	.20	.15	.08
44	David Cone	.50	.40	.20
46	Dave West	.40	.30	.15
48	Randy Myers	.35	.25	.14
50	Sid Fernandez	.35	.25	.14
51	Don Aase	.20	.15	.08
52	Greg Pavlick	.20	.15	.08
----	Team Card	.20	.15	.08
----	Jeff Innis	.90	.70	.50
----	Keith Miller	.70	.50	.30
----	Jeff Musselman	.70	.50	.30
----	Frank Viola	1.00	.70	.40

1989 Kahn's Reds

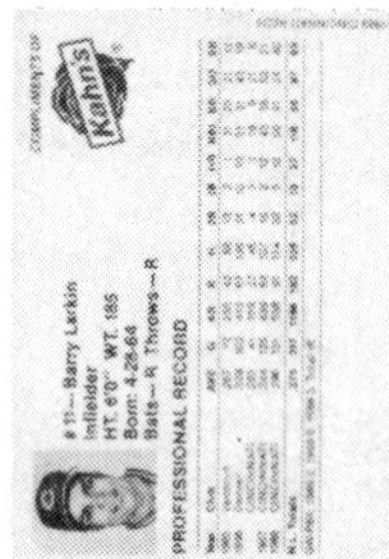

This 26-card Cincinnati Reds team set, sponsored by Kahn's Wieners, was distributed to fans attending the Aug. 6 Reds game at Riverfront Stadium. The standard-size, red-bordered cards feature action photos with the player's name in the upper left corner, his uniform number in the upper right and the Reds logo in the middle. The backs include a black-and-white head shot, player data and complete major and minor league stats. The Kahn's logo appears in the upper right corner of the back.

		MT	NR MT	EX
Complete Set:		8.00	6.00	3.25
Common Player:		.20	.15	.08
6	Bo Diaz	.20	.15	.08
7	Lenny Harris	.40	.30	.15
11	Barry Larkin	.75	.60	.30
12	Joel Youngblood	.20	.15	.08
14	Pete Rose	1.00	.70	.40
16	Ron Oester	.20	.15	.08
17	Chris Sabo	.40	.30	.15
20	Danny Jackson	.25	.20	.10
21	Paul O'Neill	.40	.30	.15
25	Todd Benzinger	.40	.30	.15
27	Jose Rijo	.25	.20	.10
28	Kal Daniels	.25	.20	.10
29	Herm Winningham	.20	.15	.08
30	Ken Griffey	.30	.25	.12
31	John Franco	.35	.25	.14
32	Tom Browning	.30	.25	.12
33	Ron Robinson	.20	.15	.08
34	Jeff Reed	.20	.15	.08
36	Rolando Roomes	.20	.15	.08
37	Norm Charlton	.50	.40	.20
42	Rick Mahler	.20	.15	.08
43	Kent Tekulve	.20	.15	.08
44	Eric Davis	1.00	.70	.40
48	Tim Birtsas	.20	.15	.08
49	Rob Dibble	.40	.30	.15
----	Coaches (Scott Breeden, Dave Bristol, Tommy Helms, Jim Leff, Lee May, Tony Perez)	.20	.15	.08

1990 Kahn's Mets

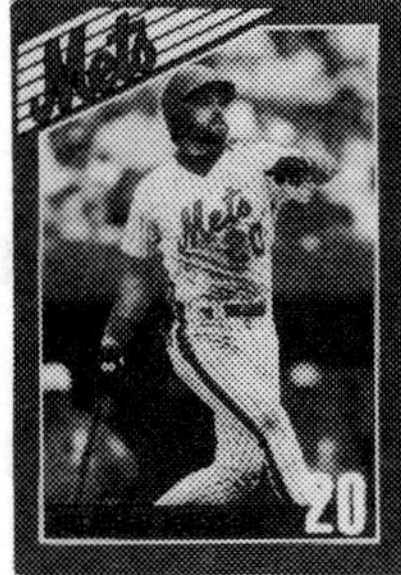

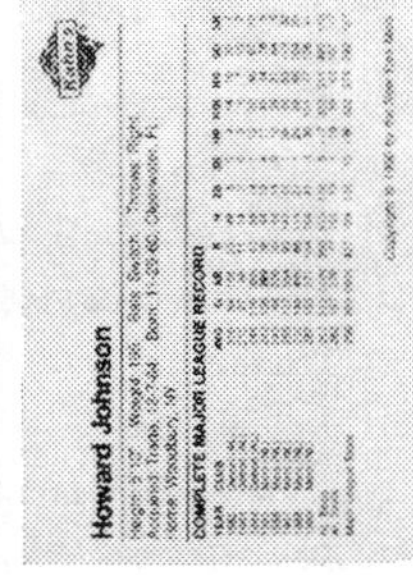

For the third consecutive year, Kahn's issued a set of baseball cards of members of the New York Mets. The sets were given out at Shea Stadium on May 3-prior to the Mets/Reds game. The cards feature blue and orange highlights like the team colors and are numbered according to uniform number. Two coupon cards were also included with each set.

		MT	NR MT	EX
Complete Set:		8.00	6.00	3.25
Common Player:		.20	.15	.08
1	Lou Thornton	.20	.15	.08
2	Mackey Sasser	.20	.15	.08
3	Bud Harrelson	.20	.15	.08
4	Mike Cubbage	.20	.15	.08
5	Davey Johnson	.20	.15	.08
6	Mike Marshall	.25	.20	.10
9	Gregg Jefferies	.80	.60	.30
10	Dave Magadan	.40	.30	.15
11	Tim Teufel	.20	.15	.08
13	Jeff Musselman	.20	.15	.08
15	Ron Darling	.30	.25	.12
16	Dwight Gooden	.80	.60	.30
18	Darryl Strawberry	.40	.30	.15
19	Bob Ojeda	.20	.15	.08
20	Howard Johnson	.50	.40	.20
21	Kevin Elster	.20	.15	.08
22	Kevin McReynolds	.40	.30	.15
25	Keith Miller	.25	.20	.10
26	Alejandro Pena	.20	.15	.08
27	Tom O'Malley	.20	.15	.08
29	Frank Viola	.60	.45	.25
30	Mel Stottlemyre	.20	.15	.08
31	John Franco	.40	.30	.15
32	Doc Edwards	.20	.15	.08
33	Barry Lyons	.20	.15	.08
35	Orlando Mercado	.20	.15	.08
40	Jeff Innis	.25	.20	.10
44	David Cone	.30	.25	.12
45	Mark Carreon	.30	.25	.12
47	Wally Whitehurst	.20	.15	.08
48	Julio Machado	.20	.15	.08
50	Sid Fernandez	.35	.25	.14
52	Greg Pavlick	.20	.15	.08
----	Team Card	.20	.15	.08

1990 Kahn's Reds

This 27-card set marks the fourth consecutive year in which Kahn's released a modern Reds issue. The cards feature full-color photos, red and white borders and the player's name, number, and postion on the card front. The flip sides feature biographical information, statistics, a posed photo and the Kahn's logo. The set is numbered by uniform.

		MT	NR MT	EX
Complete Set (27):		10.00	7.50	4.00
Common Player:		.25	.20	.10
7	Mariano Duncan	.40	.30	.15
9	Joe Oliver	.40	.30	.15
10	Luis Quinones	.25	.20	.10
11	Barry Larkin	.80	.60	.30
15	Glenn Braggs	.30	.25	.12
16	Ron Oester	.25	.20	.10
17	Chris Sabo	.70	.50	.30
20	Danny Jackson	.30	.25	.12
21	Paul O'Neill	.40	.30	.15
22	Billy Hatcher	.25	.20	.10
23	Hal Morris	.80	.60	.30
25	Todd Benzinger	.30	.25	.12
27	Jose Rijo	.50	.40	.20
28	Randy Myers	.35	.25	.14
29	Herm Winningham	.25	.20	.10
30	Ken Griffey	.40	.30	.15
32	Tom Browning	.40	.30	.15
34	Jeff Reed	.25	.20	.10
37	Norm Charlton	.40	.30	.15
40	Jack Armstrong	.40	.30	.15
41	Lou Pinella	.40	.30	.15
42	Rick Mahler	.25	.20	.10
43	Tim Layana	.30	.25	.12
44	Eric Davis	.60	.45	.25
48	Tim Birtsas	.25	.20	.10
49	Rob Dibble	.40	.30	.15
----	Coaches (Jackie Moore, Tony Perez, Sam Perlozzo, Larry Rothschild, Stan Williams)	.25	.20	.10

1991 Kahn's Mets

Kahn's kept its tradition in 1991 with the release of this 33-card set featuring members of the New York Mets. The cards measure 2 1/2" by 3 1/2" and the fronts feature a pinstripe design. The backs are printed horizontally and feature complete statistics. The cards are numbered according to uniform number. The complete set was distributed at a 1991 home game.

		MT	NR MT	EX
Complete Set (33):		8.00	6.00	3.25
Common Player:		.20	.15	.08
1	Vince Coleman	.50	.40	.20
2	Mackey Sasser	.20	.15	.08
3	Bud Harrelson	.20	.15	.08
4	Mike Cubbage	.20	.15	.08
5	Charlie O'Brien	.20	.15	.08
7	Hubie Brooks	.30	.25	.12
8	Daryl Boston	.20	.15	.08
9	Gregg Jefferies	.60	.45	.25
10	Dave Magadan	.30	.25	.12
11	Tim Teufel	.20	.15	.08
13	Rick Cerone	.20	.15	.08
15	Ron Darling	.25	.20	.10
16	Dwight Gooden	.60	.45	.25
17	David Cone	.50	.40	.20
20	Howard Johnson	.50	.40	.20
21	Kevin Elster	.20	.15	.08
22	Kevin McReynolds	.35	.25	.14
25	Keith Miller	.25	.20	.10
26	Alejandro Pena	.25	.20	.10
28	Tom Herr	.20	.15	.08
29	Frank Viola	.50	.40	.20
30	Mel Stottlemyre	.20	.15	.08
31	John Franco	.30	.25	.12
32	Doc Edwards	.20	.15	.08
40	Jeff Innis	.20	.15	.08
43	Doug Simons	.20	.15	.08
45	Mark Carreon	.20	.15	.08
47	Wally Whitehurst	.20	.15	.08
48	Pete Schourek	.20	.15	.08
50	Sid Fernandez	.30	.25	.12
51	Tom Spencer	.20	.15	.08
52	Greg Pavlick	.20	.15	.08
----	Team card	.20	.15	.08

1991 Kahn's Reds

The World Champion Cincinnati Reds are showcased in this 28-card set. The card fronts feature small full-color action photos on white stock. The backs feature statistics, biographical information and the Kahn's logo. A special card of Schottzie is included in this set.

		MT	NR MT	EX
Complete Set (28):		8.00	6.00	3.25
Common Player:		.25	.20	.10
7	Mariano Duncan	.30	.25	.12
9	Joe Oliver	.30	.25	.12
10	Luis Quinones	.25	.20	.10
11	Barry Larkin	.80	.60	.30
15	Glenn Braggs	.30	.25	.12
17	Chris Sabo	.60	.45	.25
19	Bill Doran	.35	.25	.14
21	Paul O'Neill	.40	.30	.15
22	Billy Hatcher	.25	.20	.10
23	Hal Morris	.80	.60	.30
25	Todd Benzinger	.30	.25	.12
27	Jose Rijo	.40	.30	.15
28	Randy Myers	.35	.25	.14
29	Herm Winningham	.25	.20	.10
32	Tom Browning	.35	.25	.14
34	Jeff Reed	.25	.20	.10
36	Don Carman	.25	.20	.10
37	Norm Charlton	.30	.25	.12
40	Jack Armstrong	.35	.25	.14
41	Lou Pinella	.35	.25	.14
44	Eric Davis	.60	.45	.25
45	Chris Hammond	.40	.30	.15
47	Scott Scudder	.30	.25	.12
48	Ted Power	.25	.20	.10
49	Rob Dibble	.40	.30	.15
57	Freddie Benavides	.40	.30	.15
----	Mascot (Schottzie)	.25	.20	.10

1992 Kahn's Mets

A Met's blue border surrounds the game-action photos in this 33-card set. Backs are horizontally formatted and present full major league stats and the '92 Mets team slogan, "Hardball is Back." A baseball on front carries the uniform number by which the set is checklisted here. Cents-offs coupons for Kahn's hot dogs and corn dogs were packaged with the set when it was distributed at a home game, but are not considered part of the set.

		MT	NR MT	EX
Complete Set (33):		8.00	6.00	3.25
Common Player:		.20	.15	.08
1	Vince Coleman	.25	.20	.10
2	Mackey Sasser	.20	.15	.08
3	Junior Noboa	.20	.15	.08
4	Mike Cubbage	.20	.15	.08
6	Daryl Boston	.25	.20	.10
8	Dave Gallagher	.20	.15	.08
9	Todd Hundley	.25	.20	.10
10	Jeff Torborg	.20	.15	.08
11	Dick Schofield	.20	.15	.08
12	Willie Randolph	.25	.20	.10
15	Kevin Elster	.20	.15	.08
16	Dwight Gooden	.60	.45	.25
17	David Cone	.35	.25	.14
18	Bret Saberhagen	.35	.25	.14
19	Anthony Young	.20	.15	.08
20	Howard Johnson	.40	.30	.15
22	Charlie O'Brien	.20	.15	.08
25	Bobby Bonilla	.45	.35	.20
26	Barry Foote	.20	.15	.08
27	Tom McCraw	.20	.15	.08
28	Dave LaRoche	.20	.15	.08
29	Dave Magadan	.35	.25	.14
30	Mel Stottlemyre	.25	.20	.10
31	John Franco	.35	.25	.14
32	Bill Pecota	.20	.15	.08
33	Eddie Murray	.40	.30	.15
40	Jeff Innis	.20	.15	.08
44	Tim Burke	.20	.15	.08
45	Paul Gibson	.20	.15	.08
47	Wally Whitehurst	.20	.15	.08
50	Sid Fernandez	.35	.25	.14
51	John Stephenson	.20	.15	.08
----	Mets Team	.20	.15	.08

1992 Kahn's Reds

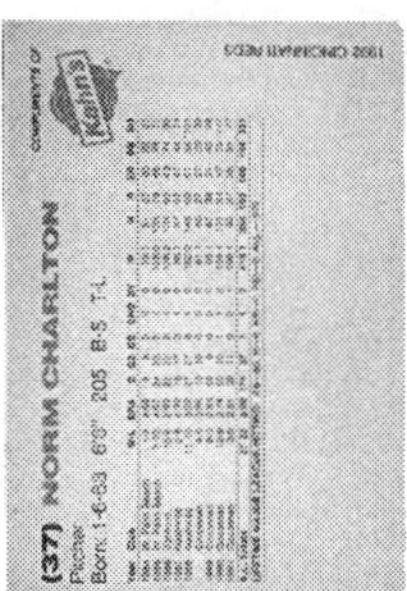

This 27-card set (two coupon cards distributed with the team set are not considered part of the set) was given to fans at a promotional home date. The 2-1/2" x 3-1/2" cards have a red border with the team name at top and player name at bottom in white. The player's uniform number and position in black flank his name. A team logo appears in the lower-left corner of the photo. Backs are printed in red and black and have complete pro stats, a few biographical details and the logo of the Riverfront Stadium hot dog concessionaire. The checklist presented here is in order of uniform number.

		MT	NR MT	EX
Complete Set (27):		8.00	6.00	3.25
Common Player:		.25	.20	.10
2	Mascot (Schottzie)	.35	.25	.14
9	Joe Oliver	.35	.25	.14
10	Bip Roberts	.30	.25	.12
11	Barry Larkin	.80	.60	.30
12	Freddie Benavides	.25	.20	.10
15	Glenn Braggs	.25	.20	.10
16	Reggie Sanders	.40	.30	.15
17	Chris Sabo	.35	.25	.14
19	Bill Doran	.25	.20	.10
21	Paul O'Neill	.35	.25	.14
23	Hal Morris	.40	.30	.15
25	Scott Bankhead	.25	.20	.10
26	Darnell Coles	.25	.20	.10
27	Jose Rijo	.35	.25	.14
28	Scott Ruskin	.25	.20	.10
29	Greg Swindell	.30	.25	.12
30	Dave Martinez	.25	.20	.10
31	Tim Belcher	.30	.25	.12
32	Tom Browning	.35	.25	.14
34	Jeff Reed	.25	.20	.10
37	Norm Charlton	.25	.20	.10

38	Troy Afenir	.25	.20	.10
41	Lou Piniella	.30	.25	.12
45	Chris Hammond	.25	.20	.10
48	Dwayne Henry	.25	.20	.10
49	Rob Dibble	.30	.25	.12
----	Coaches (Jackie Moore, John McLaren, Sam Perlozzo, Tony Perez, Larry Rothschild)	.30	.25	.12

1993 Kahn's Mets

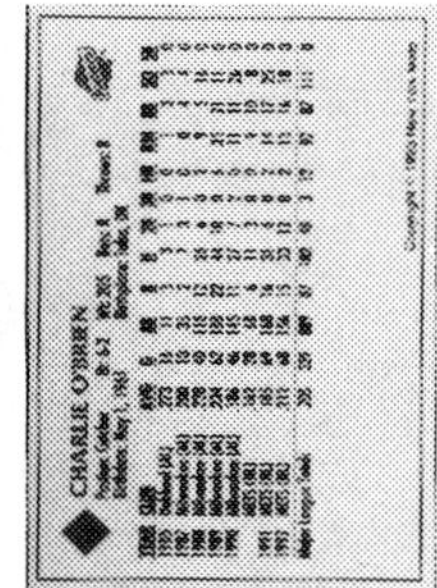

The New York Mets distributed the 1993 Kahn's card set to fans on May 23 at Shea Stadium. The 25-card set features color photos and the card fronts with a white border, the Mets logo at the bottom center and the player's name, position and uniform number at the top. The card backs include the player's career statistics and biography inside a red border. Also included in the set is a team photo card and a title card which features the New York skyline and the stadium.

		MT	NR MT	EX
Complete Set:		8.00	6.00	3.25
Common Player:		.25	.20	.10
(3)	Eddie Murray	.55	.40	.20
(4)	Bret Saberhagen	.40	.30	.15
(5)	Dwight Gooden	.60	.45	.25
(6)	Howard Johnson	.40	.30	.15
(7)	Tony Fernandez	.30	.25	.12
(8)	John Franco	.35	.25	.14
(9)	Bobby Bonilla	.40	.30	.15
(10)	Sid Fernandez	.30	.25	.12
(11)	Todd Hundley	.30	.25	.12
(12)	Vince Coleman	.30	.25	.12
(13)	Jeff Kent	.45	.35	.20
(14)	Chico Walker	.25	.20	.10
(15)	Pete Schourek	.25	.20	.10
(16)	Jeff Innis	.25	.20	.10
(17)	Charlie O'Brien	.25	.20	.10
(18)	Joe Orsulak	.30	.25	.12
(19)	Dave Gallagher	.25	.20	.10
(20)	Mike Maddux	.25	.20	.10
(21)	Ryan Thompson	.40	.30	.15
(22)	Tim Bogar	.35	.25	.14
(23)	Jeff McKnight	.25	.20	.10
(24)	Darren Reed	.25	.20	.10
(25)	Mike Draper	.25	.20	.10
----	Title card	.25	.20	.10
----	Team Photo Card	.25	.20	.10

1993 Kahn's Reds

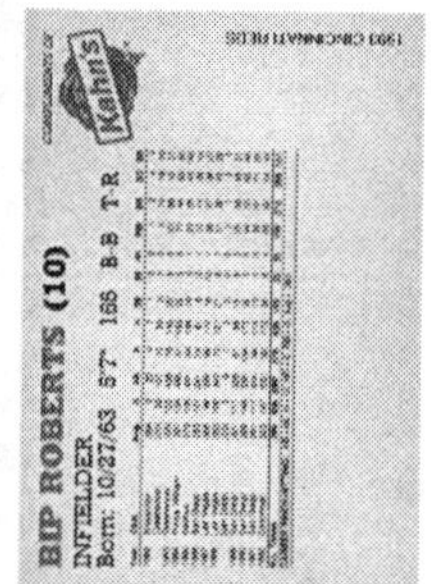

Kahn's produced a 28-card set of Cincinnati Reds that was given away to fans at Riverfront Stadium on August 1, 1993. The cards, organized by player's uniform number, show a photo of the player on the front with the player's name at the top and the Reds logo in the lower corner, surrounded by a pinstripe border. The backs of the cards have the player's lifetime statistics and biography. Card #2 in the set portrays team owner Marge Schott and her dog Schottzie II. Coupon cards good for discounts on packages of Kahn's hot dogs and corn dogs were packaged with the set but are not considered part of the set.

		MT	NR MT	EX
Complete Set (28):		8.00	6.00	3.25
Common Player:		.25	.20	.10
2	Schottzie, Marge Schott	.35	.25	.14
7	Kevin Mitchell	.60	.45	.25
8	Juan Samuel	.35	.25	.14
9	Joe Oliver	.50	.40	.20
10	Bip Roberts	.40	.30	.15
11	Barry Larkin	.80	.60	.30
15	Davey Johnson	.25	.20	.10
16	Reggie Sanders	.35	.25	.14
17	Chris Sabo	.50	.40	.20
19	Randy Milligan	.25	.20	.10
20	Jeff Branson	.25	.20	.10
23	Hal Morris	.50	.40	.20
25	Greg Cadaret	.25	.20	.10
27	Jose Rijo	.50	.40	.20
30	Bobby Kelly	.40	.30	.15
31	Tim Belcher	.30	.25	.12
32	Tom Browning	.30	.25	.12
40	Tim Pugh	.25	.20	.10
41	Jeff Reardon	.30	.25	.12
42	Gary Varsho	.25	.20	.10
43	Bill Landrum	.25	.20	.10
46	Jacob Brumfield	.25	.20	.10
49	Rob Dibble	.35	.25	.14
53	Kevin Wickander	.25	.20	.10
57	John Smiley	.25	.20	.10
59	Bobby Ayala	.25	.20	.10
----	Coaches (Jose Cardenal, Don Gullett, Ray Knight, Bobby Valentine, Dave Miley)	.25	.20	.10
----	Broadcasters (Marty Brennaman, Joe Nuxhall)	.25	.20	.10

1887 Kalamazoo Bats (N690)

This set, issued circa 1887 by Charles Gross & Co. of Philadelphia, is one of the most popular and most difficult of all 19th Century tobacco issues. The cards measure a rather large 2-1/4" by 4" and feature a sepia-toned photograph on heavy cardboard. The player's name and team appear inside a white rectangle at the bottom of the photo, while a small ad for Kalamazoo Bats cigarettes is included at the very bottom of the card. Some cards carry an 1887 copyright line, but there are indications that some of the cards date from 1886 or even 1888. The unnumbered set pictures players from four teams - two from New York (Giants and Mets) and two from Philadelphia (Athletics and Phillies). A few of the cards picture more than one player, and some cards have been found with an ad on the back offering various prizes in exchange for saving the cards. The set has been assigned the American Card Catalog number N690. Because of the rarity of Kalamazoo Bats, and the uncertainty as to completeness of this checklist, no complete set value is given.

		NR MT	EX	VG
Common Player:		600.00	300.00	180.00
(1)	Ed Andrews	600.00	300.00	180.00
(2)	Charles Bastian, Lyons	750.00	375.00	225.00
(3)	Louis Bierbauer	600.00	300.00	180.00
(4)	Louis Bierbauer, Gallagher	750.00	375.00	225.00
(5)	Buffington (Buffinton)	600.00	300.00	180.00
(6)	Daniel Casey	600.00	300.00	180.00
(7)	Jack Clements	600.00	300.00	180.00
(8)	Roger Connor	2800.	1400.	840.00
(9)	Larry Corcoran	1125.	562.00	337.00
(10)	Ed Cushman	1125.	562.00	337.00
(11)	Pat Deasley	1125.	562.00	337.00
(12)	Jim Devlin	600.00	300.00	180.00
(13)	Jim Donahue	1125.	562.00	337.00
(14)	Mike Dorgan	1125.	562.00	337.00
(15)	Dude Esterbrooke (Esterbrook)	1125.	562.00	337.00
(16)	Buck Ewing	2800.	1400.	840.00
(17)	Sid Farrar	600.00	300.00	180.00
(18)	Charlie Ferguson	600.00	300.00	180.00
(19)	Jim Fogarty	600.00	300.00	180.00
(20)	Fogarty, Deacon McGuire	750.00	375.00	225.00
(21)	Elmer Foster	1125.	562.00	337.00
(22)	Whitey Gibson	600.00	300.00	180.00
(23)	Pete Gillespie	600.00	300.00	180.00
(24)	Tom Gunning	600.00	300.00	180.00
(25)	Cutrate Irwin	600.00	300.00	180.00
(26)	Irwin, Smiling Al Maul	750.00	375.00	225.00
(27)	Tim Keefe	1700.	850.00	510.00
(28)	Ted Larkin	600.00	300.00	180.00
(29)	Ted Larkins (Larkin, Jocko Milligan)	750.00	375.00	225.00
(30)	Jack Lynch	1125.	562.00	337.00
(31)	Denny Lyons	600.00	300.00	180.00
(32)	Denny Lyons, Taylor	600.00	300.00	180.00
(33)	Fred Mann	600.00	300.00	180.00
(34)	Fred Mann, Uncle Robbie Robinson	1700.	850.00	510.00
(35)	Charlie Mason	600.00	300.00	180.00
(36)	Bobby Mathews	600.00	300.00	180.00
(37)	Smiling Al Maul	600.00	300.00	180.00
(38)	Al Mays	1125.	562.00	337.00
(39)	Jim McGan (McGarr)	600.00	300.00	180.00
(40)	Deacon McGuire (catching)	600.00	300.00	180.00
(41)	Deacon McGuire (throwing)	600.00	300.00	180.00
(42)	Jocko Milligan, Harry Stowe (Stovey)	750.00	375.00	225.00
(43)	Joseph Mulvey	600.00	300.00	180.00
(44)	Candy Nelson	1125.	562.00	337.00
(45)	Orator Jim O'Rourke	2800.	1400.	840.00
(46)	Dave Orr	1125.	562.00	337.00
(47)	Tom Poorman	600.00	300.00	180.00
(48)	Danny Richardson	1125.	562.00	337.00
(49)	Uncle Robbie Robinson	1900.	950.00	570.00
(50)	Chief Roseman	1125.	562.00	337.00
(51)	Harry Stowe (Stovey) (hands on hips)	700.00	350.00	210.00
(52)	Harry Stowe (Stovey) (hands outstretched)	700.00	350.00	210.00
(53)	Sleepy Townsend	600.00	300.00	180.00
(54)	Jocko Milligan, Sleepy Townsend	750.00	375.00	225.00
(55)	Monte Ward	2800.	1400.	840.00
(56)	Gus Weyhing	600.00	300.00	180.00
(57)	George "Dandy" Wood	600.00	300.00	180.00
(58)	Harry Wright	2500.	1250.	750.00

1887 Kalamazoo Bats Cabinets (N690)

Another extremely rare issue, this series of cabinet cards was issued either as a proof or a premium by Charles Gross & Co. of Philadelphia, makers of the Kalamazoo Bats brand of cigarettes. Two distinct types have been found, both measuring 4-1/4" by 6-1/2". One variety displays the photo on a black mount with the words "Smoke Kalamazoo Bats" embossed in gold to the left. The other contains no advertising, although there is an oval embossment on the card, along with the words "Chas. Gross & Co." and an 1887 copyright line. These cards also have a distinctive pink color on the back of the cardboard mount. Because of the rarity of Kalamazoo Bats cabinets, and uncertainty as to completeness of this checklist, no complete set value is quoted.

		NR MT	EX	VG
Common Player:		1200.	600.00	350.00
Common Team:		10000.	5000.	3000.
(1)	Ed Andrews	1200.	600.00	350.00
(2)	Charles Bastian, Daniel Casey, Taylor	1200.	600.00	350.00
(3)	Charles Bastian, Denny Lyons	1200.	600.00	350.00
(4)	Louis Bierbauer, Gallagher	1200.	600.00	350.00
(5)	Charles Buffington (Buffinton)	1200.	600.00	350.00
(6)	Daniel Casey	1200.	600.00	350.00
(7)	Jack Clements	1200.	600.00	350.00
(8)	Jim Devlin	1200.	600.00	350.00
(9)	Sid Farrar	1200.	600.00	350.00
(10)	Charlie Ferguson	1200.	600.00	350.00
(11)	Jim Fogarty	1200.	600.00	350.00
(12)	Whitey Gibson	1200.	600.00	350.00
(13)	Tom Gunning	1200.	600.00	350.00
(14)	Cutrate Irwin	1200.	600.00	350.00
(15)	Cutrate Irwin, Smiling Al Maul	1200.	600.00	350.00
(16)	Ted Larkins (Larkin), Jocko Milligan	1200.	600.00	350.00
(17)	Denny Lyons	1200.	600.00	350.00
(18)	Denny Lyons, Taylor	1200.	600.00	350.00
(19)	Fred Mann	1200.	600.00	350.00
(20)	Bobby Mathews	1200.	600.00	350.00
(21)	Smiling Al Maul	1200.	600.00	350.00
(22)	Chippy McCan (McGarr)	1200.	600.00	350.00
(23)	Deacon McGuire	1200.	600.00	350.00
(24)	Jocko Milligan, Harry Stowe (Stovey)	1200.	600.00	350.00
(25)	Joseph Mulvey	1200.	600.00	350.00
(26)	Tim Poorman	1200.	600.00	350.00
(27)	Ed Seward	1200.	600.00	350.00

(28)	Harry Stowe (Stovey)	1200.	600.00	350.00
(29)	Sleepy Townsend	1200.	600.00	350.00
(30)	George "Dandy" Wood	1200.	600.00	350.00
(31)	Athletic Club	10000.	5000.	3000.
(32)	Boston B.B.C.	20000.	10000.	6000.
(33)	Philadelphia B.B.C.	10000.	5000.	3000.
(34)	Pittsburg B.B.C.	10000.	5000.	3000.

1887 Kalamazoo Bats Team Cards (N690-1)

The six team photos in this set were issued by Charles Gross & Co. of Philadelphia as a promotion for its Kalamazoo Bats brand of cigarettes. The cards, which are similar in design to the related N690 series, are extremely rare. They feature a team photo with the caption in a white box at the bottom of the photo and an ad for Kalamazoo Bats to the left.

		NR MT	EX	VG
Complete Set (6):		13500.	6500.	4000.
Common Team:		2000.	1000.	600.00
(1)	Athletic Club	2000.	1000.	600.00
(2)	Baltimore B.B.C.	2000.	1000.	600.00
(3)	Boston B.B.C.	3500.	1750.	1050.
(4)	Detroit B.B.C.	2000.	1000.	600.00
(5)	Philadelphia B.B.C.	2000.	1000.	600.00
(6)	Pittsburg B.B.C.	2000.	1000.	600.00

The values quoted are intended to reflect the market price.

1986 Kas Potato Chips Cardinals

One of a handful of 2-7/8" round baseball card "discs" created by Mike Schecter Associates for inclusion in boxes of potato chips, the 20-card Kas set features players of the defending National League Champion St. Louis Cardinals. Fronts feature color photo on which the team logos have been removed from the caps by airbrushing the photos, indicating Kas did not license with the Cardinals for use of its uniform logos. Card backs have minimal personal data and 1985 stats.

		MT	NR MT	EX
Complete Set (20):		18.00	13.50	7.25
Common Player:		.70	.50	.30
1	Vince Coleman	1.00	.70	.40
2	Ken Dayley	.70	.50	.30
3	Tito Landrum	.70	.50	.30
4	Steve Braun	.70	.50	.30
5	Danny Cox	.90	.70	.35
6	Bob Forsch	.80	.60	.30
7	Ozzie Smith	3.00	2.25	1.25
8	Brian Harper	1.50	1.25	.60
9	Jack Clark	1.50	1.25	.60
10	Todd Worrell	.80	.60	.30
11	Joaquin Andujar	.70	.50	.30
12	Tom Nieto	.70	.50	.30
13	Kurt Kepshire	.70	.50	.30
14	Terry Pendleton	2.50	2.00	1.00
15	Tom Herr	.80	.60	.30
16	Darrell Porter	.70	.50	.30
17	John Tudor	.70	.50	.30
18	Jeff Lahti	.70	.50	.30
19	Andy Van Slyke	2.00	1.50	.80
20	Willie McGee	1.50	1.25	.60

1929 Kashin Publications (R316)

This set of 101 unnumbered cards was issued in 1929 and measures 3-1/2" by 4-1/2". The cards feature black-and-white photos with the player's name printed in script near the bottom of the photo. The backs of the cards are blank. Four of the cards (Hadley, Haines, Siebold and Todt) are considered to be scarcer than the rest of the set.

		NR MT	EX	VG
Complete Set:		2950.	1475.	885.00
Common Player:		20.00	10.00	6.00
(1)	Dale Alexander	20.00	10.00	6.00
(2)	Ethan N. Allen	20.00	10.00	6.00
(3)	Larry Benton	20.00	10.00	6.00
(4)	Moe Berg	30.00	15.00	9.00
(5)	Max Bishop	20.00	10.00	6.00
(6)	Del Bissonette	20.00	10.00	6.00
(7)	Lucerne A. Blue	20.00	10.00	6.00
(8)	James Bottomley	40.00	20.00	12.00
(9)	Guy T. Bush	20.00	10.00	6.00
(10)	Harold G. Carlson	20.00	10.00	6.00
(11)	Owen Carroll	20.00	10.00	6.00
(12)	Chalmers W. Cissell (Chalmer)	20.00	10.00	6.00
(13)	Earl Combs	40.00	20.00	12.00
(14)	Hugh M. Critz	20.00	10.00	6.00
(15)	H.J. DeBerry	20.00	10.00	6.00
(16)	Pete Donohue	20.00	10.00	6.00
(17)	Taylor Douthit	20.00	10.00	6.00
(18)	Chas. W. Dressen	20.00	10.00	6.00
(19)	Jimmy Dykes	20.00	10.00	6.00
(20)	Howard Ehmke	20.00	10.00	6.00
(21)	Elwood English	20.00	10.00	6.00
(22)	Urban Faber	40.00	20.00	12.00
(23)	Fred Fitzsimmons	20.00	10.00	6.00
(24)	Lewis A. Fonseca	20.00	10.00	6.00
(25)	Horace H. Ford	20.00	10.00	6.00
(26)	Jimmy Foxx	50.00	25.00	15.00
(27)	Frank Frisch	40.00	20.00	12.00
(28)	Lou Gehrig	225.00	112.00	67.00
(29)	Charles Gehringer	40.00	20.00	12.00
(30)	Leon Goslin	40.00	20.00	12.00
(31)	George Grantham	20.00	10.00	6.00
(32)	Burleigh Grimes	40.00	20.00	12.00
(33)	Robert Grove	40.00	20.00	12.00
(34)	Bump Hadley	100.00	50.00	30.00
(35)	Charlie Hafey	40.00	20.00	12.00
(36)	Jesse J. Haines	100.00	50.00	30.00
(37)	Harvey Hendrick	20.00	10.00	6.00
(38)	Floyd C. Herman	20.00	10.00	6.00
(39)	Andy High	20.00	10.00	6.00
(40)	Urban J. Hodapp	20.00	10.00	6.00
(41)	Frank Hogan	20.00	10.00	6.00
(42)	Rogers Hornsby	45.00	22.00	13.50
(43)	Waite Hoyt	40.00	20.00	12.00
(44)	Willis Hudlin	20.00	10.00	6.00
(45)	Frank O. Hurst	20.00	10.00	6.00
(46)	Charlie Jamieson	20.00	10.00	6.00
(47)	Roy C. Johnson	20.00	10.00	6.00
(48)	Percy Jones	20.00	10.00	6.00
(49)	Sam Jones	20.00	10.00	6.00
(50)	Joseph Judge	20.00	10.00	6.00
(51)	Willie Kamm	20.00	10.00	6.00
(52)	Charles Klein	40.00	20.00	12.00
(53)	Mark Koenig	20.00	10.00	6.00
(54)	Ralph Kress	20.00	10.00	6.00
(55)	Fred M. Leach	20.00	10.00	6.00
(56)	Fred Lindstrom	40.00	20.00	12.00
(57)	Ad Liska	20.00	10.00	6.00
(58)	Fred Lucas (Red)	20.00	10.00	6.00
(59)	Fred Maguire	20.00	10.00	6.00
(60)	Perce L. Malone	20.00	10.00	6.00
(61)	Harry Manush (Henry)	40.00	20.00	12.00
(62)	Walter Maranville	40.00	20.00	12.00
(63)	Douglas McWeeney (McWeeny)	20.00	10.00	6.00
(64)	Oscar Melillo	20.00	10.00	6.00
(65)	Ed "Bing" Miller	20.00	10.00	6.00
(66)	Frank O'Doul	25.00	12.50	7.50
(67)	Melvin Ott	40.00	20.00	12.00
(68)	Herbert Pennock	40.00	20.00	12.00
(69)	William W. Regan	20.00	10.00	6.00
(70)	Harry F. Rice	20.00	10.00	6.00
(71)	Sam Rice	40.00	20.00	12.00
(72)	Lance Richbourgh (Richbourg)	20.00	10.00	6.00
(73)	Eddie Rommel	20.00	10.00	6.00
(74)	Chas. H. Root	20.00	10.00	6.00
(75)	Ed Roush	40.00	20.00	12.00
(76)	Harold Ruel (Herold)	20.00	10.00	6.00
(77)	Charles Ruffing	40.00	20.00	12.00
(78)	Jack Russell	20.00	10.00	6.00
(79)	Babe Ruth	225.00	112.00	67.00
(80)	Fred Schulte	20.00	10.00	6.00
(81)	Harry Seibold	100.00	50.00	30.00
(82)	Joe Sewell	40.00	20.00	12.00
(83)	Luke Sewell	20.00	10.00	6.00
(84)	Art Shires	20.00	10.00	6.00
(85)	Al Simmons	40.00	20.00	12.00
(86)	Bob Smith	20.00	10.00	6.00
(87)	Riggs Stephenson	20.00	10.00	6.00
(88)	Wm. H. Terry	40.00	20.00	12.00
(89)	Alphonse Thomas	20.00	10.00	6.00
(90)	Lafayette F. Thompson	20.00	10.00	6.00
(91)	Phil Todt	100.00	50.00	30.00
(92)	Harold J. Traynor	40.00	20.00	12.00
(93)	Dazzy Vance	40.00	20.00	12.00
(94)	Lloyd Waner	40.00	20.00	12.00
(95)	Paul Waner	40.00	20.00	12.00
(96)	Jimmy Welsh	20.00	10.00	6.00
(97)	Earl Whitehill	20.00	10.00	6.00
(98)	A.C. Whitney	20.00	10.00	6.00
(99)	Claude Willoughby	20.00	10.00	6.00
(100)	Hack Wilson	40.00	20.00	12.00
(101)	Tom Zachary	20.00	10.00	6.00

1986 Kay Bee

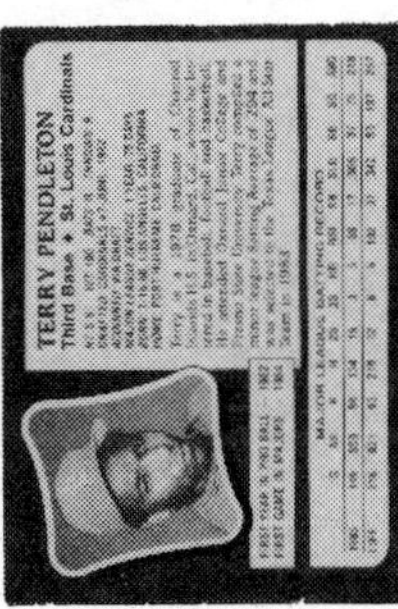

One of the most-widely distributed of the specialty boxed sets of 1986, the Kay Bee toy store chain sets of "Young Superstars of Baseball" was produced by Topps. The 2-1/2" by 3-1/2" cards are printed on white stock with a glossy surface finish. Backs, printed in red and black, are strongly reminiscent of the 1971 Topps cards. While the set concentrated on "young" stars of the game, few of the year's top rookies were included.

		MT	NR MT	EX
Complete Set:		4.00	3.00	1.50
Common Player:		.05	.04	.02
1	Rick Aguilera	.12	.09	.05
2	Chris Brown	.05	.04	.02
3	Tom Browning	.07	.05	.03
4	Tom Brunansky	.07	.05	.03
5	Vince Coleman	.15	.11	.06
6	Ron Darling	.10	.08	.04
7	Alvin Davis	.10	.08	.04
8	Mariano Duncan	.10	.08	.04
9	Shawon Dunston	.10	.08	.04
10	Sid Fernandez	.10	.08	.04
11	Tony Fernandez	.10	.08	.04
12	Brian Fisher	.07	.05	.03
13	John Franco	.07	.05	.03
14	Julio Franco	.10	.08	.04
15	Dwight Gooden	.50	.40	.20
16	Ozzie Guillen	.15	.11	.06
17	Tony Gwynn	.30	.25	.12
18	Jimmy Key	.10	.08	.04
19	Don Mattingly	.80	.60	.30
20	Oddibe McDowell	.07	.05	.03
21	Roger McDowell	.15	.11	.06
22	Dan Pasqua	.10	.08	.04
23	Terry Pendleton	.15	.11	.06
24	Jim Presley	.05	.04	.02
25	Kirby Puckett	.45	.35	.20
26	Earnie Riles	.07	.05	.03
27	Bret Saberhagen	.15	.11	.06
28	Mark Salas	.05	.04	.02
29	Juan Samuel	.12	.09	.05
30	Jeff Stone	.05	.04	.02
31	Darryl Strawberry	.20	.15	.08
32	Andy Van Slyke	.10	.08	.04
33	Frank Viola	.10	.08	.04

1987 Kay Bee

For a second straight year, Topps produced a 33-card set for the Kay Bee toy store chain. Called "Superstars of Baseball," the cards in the set measure the standard 2-1/2" by 3-1/2" size. The glossy-coated card fronts carry a full-color player photo plus the Kay Bee logo. The card backs, reminiscent of

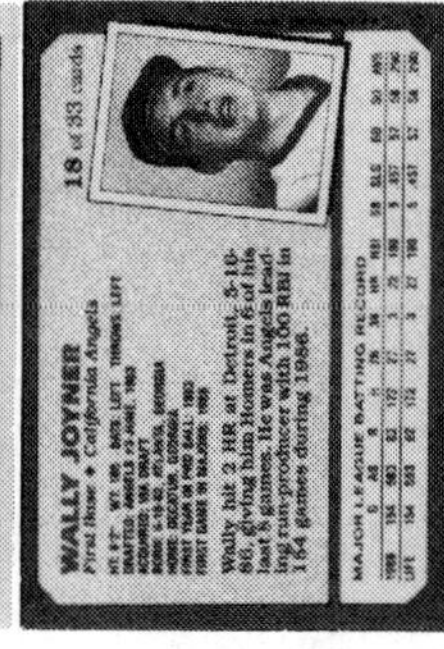

those found in the 1971 Topps set, offer a black and white head shot of the player along with his name, postion, personal information, playing record and a brief biography. The set was packaged in a specially designed box.

		MT	NR MT	EX
Complete Set:		4.00	3.00	1.50
Common Player:		.05	.04	.02
1	Harold Baines	.10	.08	.04
2	Jesse Barfield	.05	.04	.02
3	Don Baylor	.10	.08	.04
4	Wade Boggs	.80	.60	.30
5	George Brett	.60	.45	.25
6	Hubie Brooks	.07	.05	.03
7	Jose Canseco	.80	.60	.30
8	Gary Carter	.20	.15	.08
9	Joe Carter	.20	.15	.08
10	Roger Clemens	.40	.30	.15
11	Vince Coleman	.15	.11	.06
12	Glenn Davis	.07	.05	.03
13	Dwight Gooden	.40	.30	.15
14	Pedro Guerrero	.10	.08	.04
15	Tony Gwynn	.25	.20	.10
16	Rickey Henderson	.30	.25	.12
17	Keith Hernandez	.10	.08	.04
18	Wally Joyner	.20	.15	.08
19	Don Mattingly	.80	.60	.30
20	Jack Morris	.15	.11	.06
21	Dale Murphy	.30	.25	.12
22	Eddie Murray	.25	.20	.10
23	Dave Parker	.25	.20	.10
24	Kirby Puckett	.35	.25	.14
25	Tim Raines	.15	.11	.06
26	Jim Rice	.15	.11	.06
27	Dave Righetti	.12	.09	.05
28	Ryne Sandberg	.60	.45	.25
29	Mike Schmidt	.60	.45	.25
30	Mike Scott	.07	.05	.03
31	Darryl Strawberry	.20	.15	.08
32	Fernando Valenzuela	.10	.08	.04
33	Dave Winfield	.30	.25	.12

1988 Kay Bee Superstars of Baseball

This 33-card boxed set was produced by Topps for exclusive distribution via Kay Bee toy stores nationwide. Card fronts are super glossy and feature full-color player action photos below a bright red and yellow player name banner. Photos are framed in green above a large, cartoon-style Kay Bee logo. Card backs feature player closeups in a horizontal layout in blue ink on a green and white background. Card backs are numbered and carry a player name section that includes biographical information, career data and major league batting stats.

		MT	NR MT	EX
Complete Set:		4.00	3.00	1.50
Common Player:		.10	.08	.04
1	George Bell	.20	.15	.08
2	Wade Boggs	.60	.45	.25
3	Jose Canseco	.90	.70	.35
4	Joe Carter	.20	.15	.08
5	Jack Clark	.15	.11	.06
6	Alvin Davis	.10	.08	.04
7	Eric Davis	.40	.30	.15
8	Andre Dawson	.20	.15	.08
9	Darrell Evans	.10	.08	.04
10	Dwight Evans	.10	.08	.04
11	Gary Gaetti	.12	.09	.05
12	Pedro Guerrero	.10	.08	.04
13	Tony Gwynn	.25	.20	.10
14	Howard Johnson	.15	.11	.06
15	Wally Joyner	.20	.15	.08
16	Don Mattingly	.80	.60	.30
17	Willie McGee	.10	.08	.04
18	Mark McGwire	.40	.30	.15
19	Paul Molitor	.40	.30	.15
20	Dale Murphy	.30	.25	.12
21	Dave Parker	.25	.20	.10
22	Lance Parrish	.15	.11	.06
23	Kirby Puckett	.35	.25	.14
24	Tim Raines	.15	.11	.06
25	Cal Ripken, Jr.	.80	.60	.30
26	Juan Samuel	.12	.09	.05
27	Mike Schmidt	.50	.40	.20
28	Ruben Sierra	.20	.15	.08
29	Darryl Strawberry	.20	.15	.08
30	Danny Tartabull	.12	.09	.05
31	Alan Trammell	.15	.11	.06
32	Tim Wallach	.10	.08	.04
33	Dave Winfield	.30	.25	.12

1988 Kay Bee Team Leaders

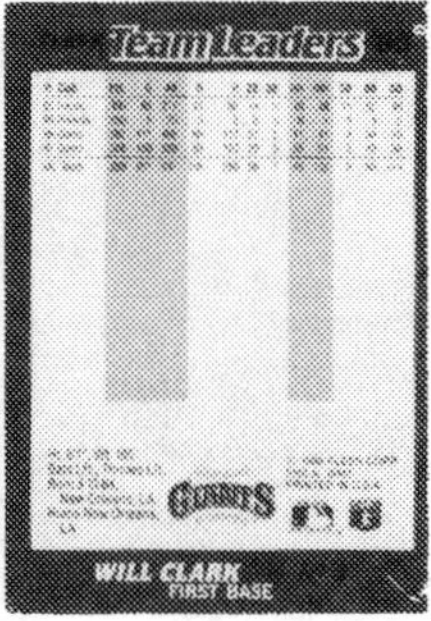

This first-year boxed edition of 44 player and 6 team logo cards was produced by Fleer for distribution by Kay Bee toy stores nationwide. Full-color player photos are framed in black against a bright red border. Lettering is blue, yellow and black. The "Fleer Team Leaders 1988" logo is printed vertically along the left side of the card front; the Kay Bee logo appears in the lower right corner of the photo; player's name, team and position are centered in the bottom margin. Card backs (red, white and pink) repeat the Team Leaders logo, followed by stats, personal data, team and major league baseball logos. The player's name, card number and position are listed on the lower border. The set includes six team logo sticker cards that feature black and white stadium photos on the backs.

		MT	NR MT	EX
Complete Set:		4.00	3.00	1.50
Common Player:		.05	.04	.02
1	George Bell	.10	.08	.04
2	Wade Boggs	.60	.45	.25
3	Jose Canseco	.90	.70	.35
4	Will Clark	.80	.60	.30
5	Roger Clemens	.40	.30	.15
6	Eric Davis	.40	.30	.15
7	Andre Dawson	.15	.11	.06
8	Julio Franco	.07	.05	.03
9	Andres Galarraga	.15	.11	.06
10	Dwight Gooden	.40	.30	.15
11	Tony Gwynn	.25	.20	.10
12	Tom Henke	.05	.04	.02
13	Orel Hershiser	.10	.08	.04
14	Kent Hrbek	.15	.11	.06
15	Ted Higuera	.10	.08	.04
16	Wally Joyner	.30	.25	.12
17	Jimmy Key	.07	.05	.03
18	Mark Langston	.10	.08	.04
19	Don Mattingly	.90	.70	.35
20	Willie McGee	.10	.08	.04
21	Mark McGwire	.40	.30	.15
22	Paul Molitor	.40	.30	.15
23	Jack Morris	.12	.09	.05
24	Dale Murphy	.30	.25	.12
25	Larry Parrish	.05	.04	.02
26	Kirby Puckett	.40	.30	.15
27	Tim Raines	.15	.11	.06
28	Jeff Reardon	.07	.05	.03
29	Dave Righetti	.10	.08	.04
30	Cal Ripken, Jr.	.90	.70	.35
31	Don Robinson	.05	.04	.02
32	Bret Saberhagen	.15	.11	.06
33	Juan Samuel	.12	.09	.05
34	Mike Schmidt	.60	.45	.25
35	Mike Scott	.07	.05	.03
36	Kevin Seitzer	.10	.08	.04
37	Dave Smith	.05	.04	.02
38	Ozzie Smith	.25	.20	.10
39	Zane Smith	.05	.04	.02
40	Darryl Strawberry	.20	.15	.08
41	Rick Sutcliffe	.10	.08	.04
42	Bobby Thigpen	.07	.05	.03
43	Alan Trammell	.15	.11	.06
44	Andy Van Slyke	.10	.08	.04

1989 Kay Bee Superstars

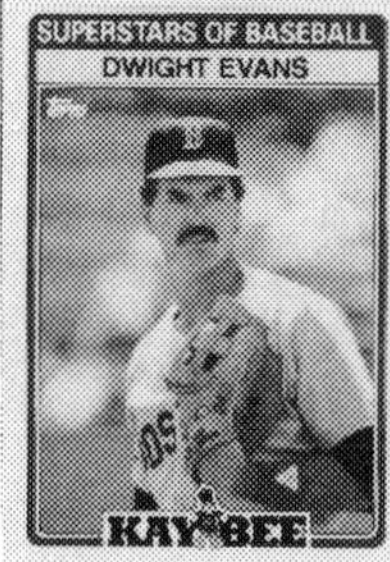

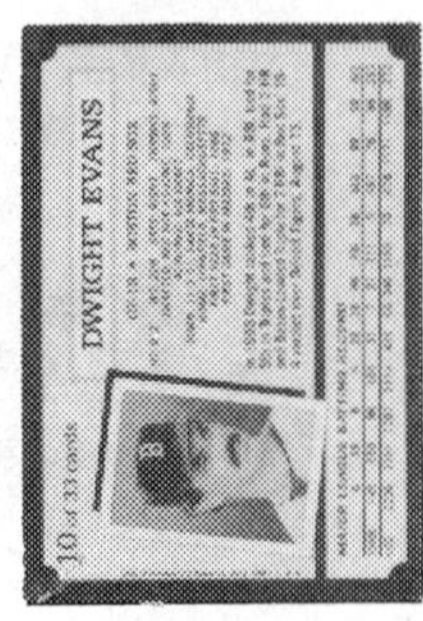

The top stars of baseball were featured in this 33-card boxed set produced by Topps for the Kay-Bee Toy store chain. The glossy, standard-size cards display the Kay-Bee logo below the player photo on the front. The top of the card is headlined "Superstars of Baseball," with the player's name underneath. The backs of the cards include a small black-and-white player photo and personal data.

		MT	NR MT	EX
Complete Set:		5.00	3.75	2.00
Common Player:		.10	.08	.04
1	Wade Boggs	.50	.40	.20
2	George Brett	.15	.11	.06
3	Jose Canseco	.90	.70	.35
4	Gary Carter	.20	.15	.08
5	Jack Clark	.10	.08	.04
6	Will Clark	.80	.60	.30
7	Roger Clemens	.35	.25	.14
8	Eric Davis	.25	.20	.10
9	Andre Dawson	.15	.11	.06
10	Dwight Evans	.10	.08	.04
11	Carlton Fisk	.15	.11	.06
12	Andres Galarraga	.15	.11	.06
13	Kirk Gibson	.10	.08	.04
14	Dwight Gooden	.30	.25	.12
15	Mike Greenwell	.30	.25	.12
16	Pedro Guerrero	.10	.08	.04
17	Tony Gwynn	.25	.20	.10
18	Rickey Henderson	.50	.40	.20
19	Orel Hershiser	.15	.11	.06
20	Don Mattingly	.80	.60	.30
21	Mark McGwire	.40	.30	.15
22	Dale Murphy	.20	.15	.08
23	Eddie Murray	.15	.11	.06
24	Kirby Puckett	.40	.30	.15
25	Tim Raines	.15	.11	.06
26	Ryne Sandberg	.80	.60	.30
27	Mike Schmidt	.50	.40	.20
28	Ozzie Smith	.25	.20	.10
29	Darryl Strawberry	.15	.11	.06
30	Alan Trammell	.12	.09	.05
31	Frank Viola	.12	.09	.05
32	Dave Winfield	.30	.25	.12
33	Robin Yount	.40	.30	.15

1990 Kay Bee Kings of Baseball

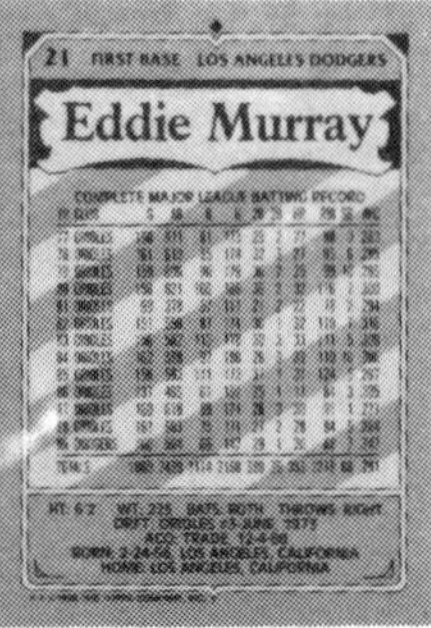

This 33-card set marked the fifth straight produced by Topps for the Kay Bee store chain. The standard sized cards feature full-color action photos on the card fronts and complete statistics on the flip sides. The cards were numbered alphabetically.

		MT	NR MT	EX
Complete Set:		5.00	3.75	2.00
Common Player:		.08	.06	.03
1	Doyle Alexander	.08	.06	.03
2	Bert Blyleven	.12	.09	.05

3	Wade Boggs	.40	.30	.15
4	George Brett	.40	.30	.15
5	John Candelaria	.08	.06	.03
6	Gary Carter	.20	.15	.08
7	Vince Coleman	.15	.11	.06
8	Andre Dawson	.20	.15	.08
9	Dennis Eckersley	.20	.15	.08
10	Darrell Evans	.08	.06	.03
11	Dwight Evans	.10	.08	.04
12	Carlton Fisk	.20	.15	.08
13	Ken Griffey	.15	.11	.06
14	Tony Gwynn	.25	.20	.10
15	Rickey Henderson	.40	.30	.15
16	Keith Hernandez	.10	.08	.04
17	Charlie Hough	.08	.06	.03
18	Don Mattingly	.40	.30	.15
19	Jack Morris	.15	.11	.06
20	Dale Murphy	.25	.20	.10
21	Eddie Murray	.20	.15	.08
22	Dave Parker	.15	.11	.06
23	Kirby Puckett	.40	.30	.15
24	Tim Raines	.15	.11	.06
25	Rick Reuschel	.08	.06	.03
26	Jerry Reuss	.08	.06	.03
27	Jim Rice	.12	.09	.05
28	Nolan Ryan	.90	.70	.35
29	Ozzie Smith	.25	.20	.10
30	Frank Tanana	.08	.06	.03
31	Willie Wilson	.08	.06	.03
32	Dave Winfield	.30	.25	.12
33	Robin Yount	.30	.25	.12

1968 KDKA Pittsburgh Pirates

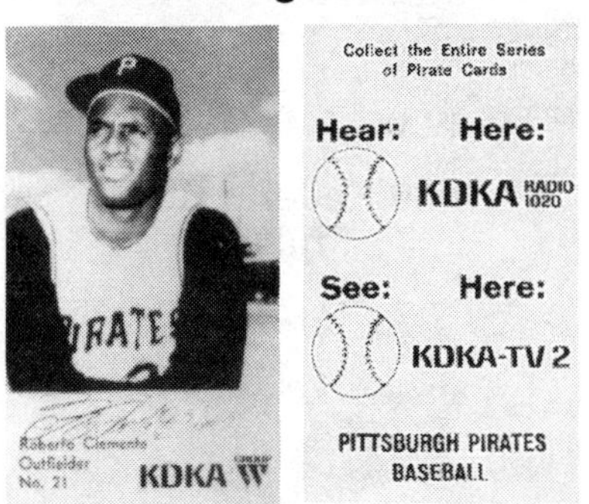

The most common of the many Pirates regional issues of the late 1960s, this 23-card set was sponsored by the Pirates' TV and radio flagship stations, KDKA in Pittsburgh. Cards measure 2-1/2" x 4" and feature at top front a color posed photo of the player, with no top or side borders. In the white panel beneath the photo are a facsimile autograph, the player's name, position and uniform number and the broadcasters' logo. Backs are printed in black on white and feature advertising for the radio and TV station. The checklist is presented here by uniform number.

		NR MT	EX	VG
Complete Set (23):		160.00	80.00	48.00
Common Player:		5.00	2.50	1.50
7	Larry Shepard	5.00	2.50	1.50
8	Willie Stargell	20.00	10.00	6.00
9	Bill Mazeroski	20.00	10.00	6.00
10	Gary Kolb	5.00	2.50	1.50
11	Jose Pagan	5.00	2.50	1.50
12	Gerry May	5.00	2.50	1.50
14	Jim Bunning	7.00	3.50	2.00
15	Manny Mota	6.00	3.00	1.75
17	Donn Clendenon	5.00	2.50	1.50
18	Matty Alou	5.00	2.50	1.50
21	Roberto Clemente	50.00	25.00	15.00
22	Gene Alley	5.00	2.50	1.50
25	Tommy Sisk	5.00	2.50	1.50
26	Roy Face	6.00	3.00	1.75
27	Ron Kline	5.00	2.50	1.50
28	Steve Blass	5.00	2.50	1.50
29	Juan Pizarro	5.00	2.50	1.50
30	Maury Wills	7.00	3.50	2.00
34	Al McBean	5.00	2.50	1.50
35	Manny Sanguillen	5.00	2.50	1.50
38	Bob Moose	5.00	2.50	1.50
39	Bob Veale	5.00	2.50	1.50
41	Dave Wickersham	5.00	2.50	1.50

1993 Keebler Texas Rangers

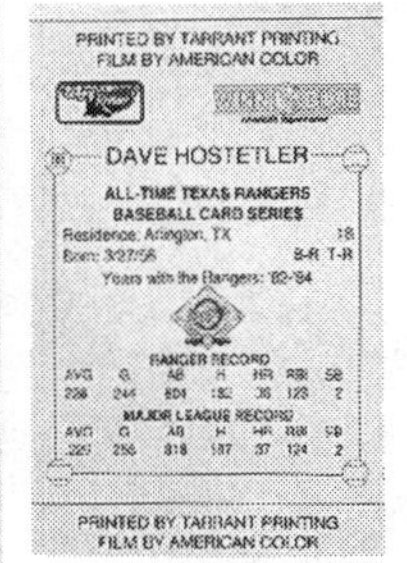

Over a series of eight home dates in Arlington Stadium's final season, the Keebler baking company along with a group of rotating co-sponsors produced and distributed a 446-card set featuring "all players, manager and coaches who have ever appeared in a Rangers game." Besides the player cards there were checklists, team photo cards, team-leader cards, logo cards and other specials. The cards were made up into 8-1/2" x 11" booklets, with the card perforated for removal. Series #2 and 3 booklets had 72 cards; the other series had 54 cards each. Single cards measure 2-1/2" x 3-1/2". Sepia-toned player portraits are featured with red borders. A blue banner at top has the team name. The player name is printed in black in the white bottom border. The Keebler logo is at the photo's lower-left, while the player's position is in a baseball diamond diagram at lower-right. Backs are printed in black, include a few biographical details and the player's Rangers' and major league career stats. The Keebler logo is repreated on the back, along with the logo of the co-sponsor of that particular series. A total of 42,000 of the first series booklets were distributed; 35,000 each of the other seven series were produced.

		MT	NR MT	EX
Complete Set:		35.00	26.00	14.00
Common Player:		.10	.08	.04
1	Ted Williams	3.00	2.25	1.25
2	Larry Biitner	.10	.08	.04
3	Rich Billings	.10	.08	.04
4	Dick Bosman	.10	.08	.04
5	Pete Broberg	.10	.08	.04
6	Jeff Burroughs	.10	.08	.04
7	Casey Cox	.10	.08	.04
8	Jim Drixcoll	.10	.08	.04
9	Jan Dukes	.10	.08	.04
10	Bill Fahey	.10	.08	.04
11	Ted Ford	.10	.08	.04
12	Bill Gogolewski	.10	.08	.04
13	Tom Grieve	.10	.08	.04
14	Rich Hand	.10	.08	.04
15	Toby Harrah	.15	.11	.06
16	Vic Harris	.10	.08	.04
17	Rich Hinton	.10	.08	.04
18	Frank Howard	.15	.11	.06
19	Gerry Janeski	.10	.08	.04
20	Dalton Jones	.10	.08	.04
21	Hal King	.10	.08	.04
22	Ted Kubiak	.10	.08	.04
23	Steve Lawson	.10	.08	.04
24	Paul Lindblad	.10	.08	.04
25	Joe Lovitto	.10	.08	.04
26	Elliott Maddox	.10	.08	.04
27	Marty Martinez	.10	.08	.04
28	Jim Mason	.10	.08	.04
29	Don Mincher	.10	.08	.04
30	Dave Nelson	.10	.08	.04
31	Jim Panther	.10	.08	.04
32	Mike Paul	.10	.08	.04
33	Horacio Pina	.10	.08	.04
34	Tom Ragland	.10	.08	.04
35	Lenny Randle	.10	.08	.04
36	Jim Roland	.10	.08	.04
37	Jim Shellenback	.10	.08	.04
38	Don Stanhouse	.10	.08	.04
39	Ken Suarez	.10	.08	.04
40	Joe Camacho	.10	.08	.04
41	Nellie Fox	.50	.40	.20
42	Sid Hudson	.10	.08	.04
43	George Susce	.10	.08	.04
44	Wayne Terwilliger	.10	.08	.04
45	Darrel Akerfelds	.10	.08	.04
46	Doyle Alexander	.10	.08	.04
47	Gerald Alexander	.10	.08	.04
48	Brian Allard	.10	.08	.04
49	Lloyd Allen	.10	.08	.04
50	Sandy Alomar	.10	.08	.04
51	Wilson Alvarez	.10	.08	.04
52	Jim Anderson	.10	.08	.04
53	Scott Anderson	.10	.08	.04
54	Brad Arnsberg	.10	.08	.04
55	Tucker Ashford	.10	.08	.04
56	Doug Ault	.10	.08	.04
57	Bob Babcock	.10	.08	.04
58	Mike Bacsik	.10	.08	.04
59	Harold Baines	.12	.09	.05
60	Alan Bannister	.10	.08	.04
61	Floyd Bannister	.10	.08	.04
62	John Barfield	.10	.08	.04
63	Len Barker	.10	.08	.04
64	Steve Barr	.10	.08	.04
65	Randy Bass	.10	.08	.04
66	Lew Beasley	.10	.08	.04
67	Kevin Belcher	.10	.08	.04
68	Buddy Bell	.12	.09	.05
69	Juan Beniquez	.10	.08	.04
70	Kurt Bevacqua	.10	.08	.04
71	Jim Bibby	.10	.08	.04
72	Joe Bitker	.10	.08	.04
73	Larvell Blanks	.10	.08	.04
74	Bert Blyleven	.20	.15	.08
75	Terry Bogener	.10	.08	.04
76	Tommy Boggs	.10	.08	.04
77	Dan Boitano	.10	.08	.04
78	Bobby Bonds	.25	.20	.10
79	Thad Bosley	.10	.08	.04
80	Dennis Boyd	.10	.08	.04
81	Nelson Briles	.10	.08	.04
82	Ed Brinkman	.10	.08	.04
83	Bob Brower	.10	.08	.04
84	Jackie Brown	.10	.08	.04
85	Larry Brown	.10	.08	.04
86	Jerry Browne	.10	.08	.04
87	Glenn Brummer	.10	.08	.04
88	Kevin Buckley	.10	.08	.04
89	Steve Buechele	.10	.08	.04
90	Ray Burris	.10	.08	.04
91	John Butcher	.10	.08	.04
92	Bert Campaneris	.12	.09	.05
93	Mike Campbell	.10	.08	.04
94	John Cangelosi	.10	.08	.04
95	Nick Capra	.10	.08	.04
96	Leo Cardenas	.10	.08	.04
97	Don Carman	.10	.08	.04
98	Rico Carty	.10	.08	.04
99	Don Castle	.10	.08	.04
100	Jose Cecena	.10	.08	.04
101	Dave Chalk	.10	.08	.04
102	Scott Chiamparino	.10	.08	.04
103	Ken Clay	.10	.08	.04
104	Reggie Cleveland	.10	.08	.04
105	Gene Clines	.10	.08	.04
106	David Clyde	.10	.08	.04
107	Cris Colon	.10	.08	.04
108	Merrill Combs	.10	.08	.04
109	Steve Comer	.10	.08	.04
110	Glen Cook	.10	.08	.04
111	Scott Coolbaugh	.10	.08	.04
112	Pat Corrales	.10	.08	.04
113	Edwin Correa	.10	.08	.04
114	Larry Cox	.10	.08	.04
115	Keith Creel	.10	.08	.04
116	Victor Cruz	.10	.08	.04
117	Mike Cubbage	.10	.08	.04
118	Bobby Cuellar	.10	.08	.04
119	Danny Darwin	.10	.08	.04
120	Jack Daugherty	.10	.08	.04
121	Doug Davis	.10	.08	.04
122	Odie Davis	.10	.08	.04
123	Willie Davis	.10	.08	.04
124	Bucky Dent	.12	.09	.05
125	Adrian Devine	.10	.08	.04
126	Mario Diaz	.10	.08	.04
127	Rich Donnelly	.10	.08	.04
128	Brian Downing	.12	.09	.05
129	Tommy Dunbar	.10	.08	.04
130	Steve Dunning	.10	.08	.04
131	Dan Duran	.10	.08	.04
132	Don Durham	.10	.08	.04
133	Dick Egan	.10	.08	.04
134	Dock Ellis	.10	.08	.04
135	John Ellis	.10	.08	.04
136	Mike Epstein	.10	.08	.04
137	Cecil Espy	.10	.08	.04
138	Chuck Estrada	.10	.08	.04
139	Glenn Ezell	.10	.08	.04
140	Hector Fajardo	.10	.08	.04
141	Monty Fariss	.10	.08	.04
142	Ed Farmer	.10	.08	.04
143	Jim Farr	.10	.08	.04
144	Joe Ferguson	.10	.08	.04
145	Ed Figueroa	.10	.08	.04
146	Steve Fireovid	.10	.08	.04
147	Scott Fletcher	.10	.08	.04
148	Doug Flynn	.10	.08	.04
149	Marv Foley	.10	.08	.04
150	Tim Foli	.10	.08	.04
151	Tony Fossas	.10	.08	.04
152	Steve Foucault	.10	.08	.04
153	Art Fowler	.10	.08	.04
154	Jim Fregosi	.10	.08	.04
155	Pepe Frias	.10	.08	.04
156	Oscar Gamble	.10	.08	.04
157	Barbaro Garbey	.10	.08	.04
158	Dick Gernert	.10	.08	.04
159	Jim Gideon	.10	.08	.04
160	Jerry Don Gleaton	.10	.08	.04
161	Orlando Gomez	.10	.08	.04
162	Rich Gossage	.15	.11	.06
163	Gary Gray	.10	.08	.04
164	Gary Green	.10	.08	.04
165	John Grubb	.10	.08	.04
166	Cecilio Guante	.10	.08	.04
167	Jose Guzman	.10	.08	.04
168	Drew Hall	.10	.08	.04
169	Bill Hands	.10	.08	.04
170	Steve Hargan	.10	.08	.04
171	Mike Hargrove	.12	.09	.05
172	Toby Harrah	.12	.09	.05
173	Bud Harrelson	.10	.08	.04
174	Donald Harris	.10	.08	.04
175	Greg Harris	.10	.08	.04
176	Mike Hart	.10	.08	.04
177	Bill Haselman	.10	.08	.04
178	Ray Hayward	.10	.08	.04
179	Tommy Helms	.10	.08	.04
180	Ken Henderson	.10	.08	.04
181	Rick Henninger	.10	.08	.04
182	Dwayne Henry	.10	.08	.04
183	Jose Hernandez	.10	.08	.04
184	Whitey Herzog	.12	.09	.05
185	Chuck Hiller	.10	.08	.04
186	Joe Hoerner	.10	.08	.04
187	Guy Hoffman	.10	.08	.04
188	Gary Holle	.10	.08	.04
189	Rick Honeycutt	.10	.08	.04
190	Burt Hooton	.10	.08	.04

191	John Hoover	.10	.08	.04
192	Willie Horton	.10	.08	.04
193	Dave Hostetler	.10	.08	.04
194	Charlie Hough	.12	.09	.05
195	Tom House	.10	.08	.04
196	Art Howe	.10	.08	.04
197	Steve Howe	.10	.08	.04
198	Roy Howell	.10	.08	.04
199	Charles Hudson	.10	.08	.04
200	Billy Hunter	.10	.08	.04
201	Pete Incaviglia	.12	.09	.05
202	Mike Jeffcoat	.10	.08	.04
203	Ferguson Jenkins	.50	.40	.20
204	Alex Johnson	.10	.08	.04
205	Bobby Johnson	.10	.08	.04
206	Cliff Johnson	.10	.08	.04
207	Darrell Johnson	.10	.08	.04
208	John Henry Johnson	.10	.08	.04
209	Lamar Johnson	.10	.08	.04
210	Bobby Jones	.10	.08	.04
211	Odell Jones	.10	.08	.04
212	Mike Jorgensen	.10	.08	.04
213	Don Kainer	.10	.08	.04
214	Mike Kekich	.10	.08	.04
215	Steve Kemp	.10	.08	.04
216	Jim Kern	.10	.08	.04
217	Paul Kilgus	.10	.08	.04
218	Ed Kirkpatrick	.10	.08	.04
219	Darold Knowles	.10	.08	.04
220	Fred Koenig	.10	.08	.04
221	Jim Kremmel	.10	.08	.04
222	Chad Kreuter	.10	.08	.04
223	Jeff Kunkel	.10	.08	.04
224	Bob Lacey	.10	.08	.04
225	Al Lachowicz	.10	.08	.04
226	Joe Lahoud	.10	.08	.04
227	Rick Leach	.10	.08	.04
228	Danny Leon	.10	.08	.04
229	Dennis Lewallyn	.10	.08	.04
230	Rick Lisi	.10	.08	.04
231	Davey Lopes	.12	.09	.05
232	John Lowenstein	.10	.08	.04
233	Mike Loynd	.10	.08	.04
234	Frank Lucceshi	.10	.08	.04
235	Sparky Lyle	.12	.09	.05
236	Pete Mackanin	.10	.08	.04
237	Bill Madlock	.12	.09	.05
238	Greg Mahlberg	.10	.08	.04
239	Mickey Mahler	.10	.08	.04
240	Bob Malloy	.10	.08	.04
241	Ramon Manon	.10	.08	.04
242	Fred Manrique	.10	.08	.04
243	Barry Manuel	.10	.08	.04
244	Mike Marshall	.10	.08	.04
245	Billy Martin	.20	.15	.08
246	Mike Mason	.10	.08	.04
247	Terry Mathews	.10	.08	.04
248	Jon Matlack	.10	.08	.04
249	Rob Maurer	.10	.08	.04
250	Dave May	.10	.08	.04
251	Scott May	.10	.08	.04
252	Lee Mazzilli	.10	.08	.04
253	Larry McCall	.10	.08	.04
254	Lance McCullers	.10	.08	.04
255	Oddibe McDowell	.10	.08	.04
256	Russ McGinnis	.10	.08	.04
257	Joey McLaughlin	.10	.08	.04
258	Craig McMurtry	.10	.08	.04
259	Doc Medich	.10	.08	.04
260	Dave Meier	.10	.08	.04
261	Mario Mendoza	.10	.08	.04
262	Orlando Mercado	.10	.08	.04
263	Mark Mercer	.10	.08	.04
264	Ron Meridith	.10	.08	.04
265	Jim Merritt	.10	.08	.04
266	Gary Mielke	.10	.08	.04
267	Eddie Miller	.10	.08	.04
268	Paul Mirabella	.10	.08	.04
269	Dave Moates	.10	.08	.04
270	Dale Mohorcic	.10	.08	.04
271	Willie Montanez	.10	.08	.04
272	Tommy Moore	.10	.08	.04
273	Roger Moret	.10	.08	.04
274	Jamie Moyer	.10	.08	.04
275	Dale Murray	.10	.08	.04
276	Al Newman	.10	.08	.04
277	Dickie Noles	.10	.08	.04
278	Eric Nolte	.10	.08	.04
279	Nelson Norman	.10	.08	.04
280	Jim Norris	.10	.08	.04
281	Edwin Nunez	.10	.08	.04
282	Pete O'Brien	.10	.08	.04
283	Al Oliver	.15	.11	.06
284	Tom O'Malley	.10	.08	.04
285	Tom Paciorek	.10	.08	.04
286	Ken Pape	.10	.08	.04
287	Mark Parent	.10	.08	.04
288	Larry Parrish	.10	.08	.04
289	Gaylord Perry	.50	.40	.20
290	Stan Perzanowski	.10	.08	.04
291	Fritz Peterson	.10	.08	.04
292	Mark Petkovsek	.10	.08	.04
293	Gary Pettis	.10	.08	.04
294	Jim Piersall	.20	.15	.08
295	John Poloni	.10	.08	.04
296	Jim Poole	.10	.08	.04
297	Tom Poquette	.10	.08	.04
298	Darrell Porter	.10	.08	.04
299	Ron Pruitt	.10	.08	.04
300	Greg Pryor	.10	.08	.04
301	Luis Pujols	.10	.08	.04
302	Pat Putnam	.10	.08	.04
303	Doug Rader	.10	.08	.04
304	Dave Rajsich	.10	.08	.04
305	Kevin Reimer	.10	.08	.04
306	Merv Rettenmund	.10	.08	.04
307	Mike Richardt	.10	.08	.04
308	Mickey Rivers	.10	.08	.04
309	Dave Roberts	.10	.08	.04
310	Leon Roberts	.10	.08	.04
311	Jeff Robinson	.10	.08	.04
312	Tom Robson	.10	.08	.04
313	Wayne Rosenthal	.10	.08	.04
314	Dave Rozema	.10	.08	.04
315	Jeff Russell	.10	.08	.04
316	Connie Ryan	.10	.08	.04
317	Billy Sample	.10	.08	.04
318	Jim Schaffer	.10	.08	.04
319	Calvin Schiraldi	.10	.08	.04
320	Dave Schmidt	.10	.08	.04
321	Donnie Scott	.10	.08	.04
322	Tony Scruggs	.10	.08	.04
323	Bob Sebra	.10	.08	.04
324	Larry See	.10	.08	.04
325	Sonny Siebert	.10	.08	.04
326	Ruben Sierra	.20	.15	.08
327	Charlie Silvera	.10	.08	.04
328	Duke Sims	.10	.08	.04
329	Bill Singer	.10	.08	.04
330	Craig Skok	.10	.08	.04
331	Don Slaught	.10	.08	.04
332	Roy Smalley	.10	.08	.04
333	Dan Smith	.10	.08	.04
334	Keith Smith	.10	.08	.04
335	Mike Smithson	.10	.08	.04
336	Eric Soderholm	.10	.08	.04
337	Sammy Sosa	.15	.11	.06
338	Jim Spencer	.10	.08	.04
339	Dick Such	.10	.08	.04
340	Eddie Stanky	.10	.08	.04
341	Mike Stanley	.10	.08	.04
342	Rusty Staub	.20	.15	.08
343	James Steels	.10	.08	.04
344	Bill Stein	.10	.08	.04
345	Rick Stelmaszek	.10	.08	.04
346	Ray Stephens	.10	.08	.04
347	Dave Stewart	.15	.11	.06
348	Jeff Stone	.10	.08	.04
349	Bill Sudakis	.10	.08	.04
350	Jim Sundberg	.12	.09	.05
351	Rich Surhoff	.10	.08	.04
352	Greg Tabor	.10	.08	.04
353	Frank Tanana	.10	.08	.04
354	Jeff Terpko	.10	.08	.04
355	Stan Thomas	.10	.08	.04
356	Bobby Thompson	.10	.08	.04
357	Danny Thompson	.10	.08	.04
358	Dickie Thon	.10	.08	.04
359	Dave Tobik	.10	.08	.04
360	Wayne Tolleson	.10	.08	.04
361	Cesar Tovar	.10	.08	.04
362	Jim Umbarger	.10	.08	.04
363	Bobby Valentine	.10	.08	.04
364	Ellis Valentine	.10	.08	.04
365	Ed Vande Berg	.10	.08	.04
366	Dewayne Vaughn	.10	.08	.04
367	Mark Wagner	.10	.08	.04
368	Rick Waits	.10	.08	.04
369	Duane Walker	.10	.08	.04
370	Mike Wallace	.10	.08	.04
371	Denny Walling	.10	.08	.04
372	Danny Walton	.10	.08	.04
373	Gary Ward	.10	.08	.04
374	Claudell Washington	.10	.08	.04
375	Larue Wasington	.10	.08	.04
376	Chris Welsh	.10	.08	.04
377	Don Werner	.10	.08	.04
378	Len Whitehouse	.10	.08	.04
379	Del Wilber	.10	.08	.04
380	Curtis Wilkerson	.10	.08	.04
381	Matt Williams	.10	.08	.04
382	Mitch Williams	.15	.11	.06
383	Bump Wills	.10	.08	.04
384	Paul Wilmet	.10	.08	.04
385	Steve Wilson	.10	.08	.04
386	Bobby Witt	.12	.09	.05
387	Clyde Wright	.10	.08	.04
388	George Wright	.10	.08	.04
389	Ricky Wright	.10	.08	.04
390	Ned Yost	.10	.08	.04
391	Don Zimmer	.12	.09	.05
392	Richie Zisk	.10	.08	.04
393	Kevin Kennedy	.10	.08	.04
394	Steve Balboni	.10	.08	.04
395	Brian Bohanon	.10	.08	.04
396	Jeff Bronkey	.10	.08	.04
397	Kevin Brown	.10	.08	.04
398	Todd Burns	.10	.08	.04
399	Jose Canseco	.35	.25	.14
400	Cris Carpenter	.10	.08	.04
401	Doug Dascenzo	.10	.08	.04
402	Butch Davis	.10	.08	.04
403	Steve Dreyer	.10	.08	.04
404	Rob Ducey	.10	.08	.04
405	Julio Franco	.12	.09	.05
406	Jeff Frye	.10	.08	.04
407	Benji Gil	.10	.08	.04
408	Juan Gonzalez	.50	.40	.20
409	Tom Henke	.10	.08	.04
410	David Hulse	.10	.08	.04
411	Jeff Huson	.10	.08	.04
412	Chris James	.10	.08	.04
413	Manuel Lee	.10	.08	.04
414	Craig Lefferts	.10	.08	.04
415	Charlie Leibrandt	.10	.08	.04
416	Gene Nelson	.10	.08	.04
417	Robb Nen	.10	.08	.04
418	Darren Oliver	.10	.08	.04
419	Rafael Palmeiro	.25	.20	.10
420	Dean Palmer	.20	.15	.08
421	Bob Patterson	.10	.08	.04
422	Roger Pavlik	.10	.08	.04
423	Dan Peltier	.10	.08	.04
424	Geno Petralli	.10	.08	.04
425	Gary Redus	.10	.08	.04
426	Rick Reed	.10	.08	.04
427	Bill Ripken	.10	.08	.04
428	Ivan Rodriguez	.25	.20	.10
429	Kenny Rogers	.10	.08	.04
430	John Russell	.10	.08	.04
431	Nolan Ryan	3.00	2.25	1.25
432	Mike Schooler	.10	.08	.04
433	Jon Shave	.10	.08	.04
434	Doug Strange	.10	.08	.04
435	Matt Whiteside	.10	.08	.04
436	Mickey Hatcher	.10	.08	.04
437	Perry Hill	.10	.08	.04
438	Jackie Moore	.10	.08	.04
439	Dave Oliver	.10	.08	.04
440	Claude Osteen	.10	.08	.04
441	Willie Upshaw	.10	.08	.04
442	Checklist 1-112	.10	.08	.04
443	Checklist 113-224	.10	.08	.04
444	Checklist 225-336	.10	.08	.04
445	Checklist 337-446	.10	.08	.04
446	Arlington Stadium	.10	.08	.04
1SP	1972 Texas Rangers	.10	.08	.04
2SP	1972-80 Team Records	.10	.08	.04
3SP	1981-83 Team Records	.10	.08	.04
4SP	1984-92 Team Records	.10	.08	.04
5SP	1993 Logo Card	.10	.08	.04
6SP	Homerun Leaders	.10	.08	.04
7SP	RBI Leaders	.10	.08	.04
8SP	Batting Leaders	.10	.08	.04
9SP	Win Leaders	.10	.08	.04
10SP	Save Leaders	.10	.08	.04
11SP	Hit Leaders	.10	.08	.04
12SP	Stolen Base Leaders	.10	.08	.04
13SP	Games Played Leaders	.10	.08	.04
14SP	Strikeout Leaders	.10	.08	.04
15SP	ERA Leaders	.10	.08	.04
16SP	Games Pitched Leaders	.10	.08	.04
17SP	Innings Pitched Leaders	.10	.08	.04
18SP	Attendance Records	.10	.08	.04
19SP	Top 20 Crowds	.10	.08	.04
20SP	Hitting Streaks	.10	.08	.04
21SP	All-Star Selections	.10	.08	.04
22SP	Top Draft Picks	.10	.08	.04

1986 Keller's Butter Phillies

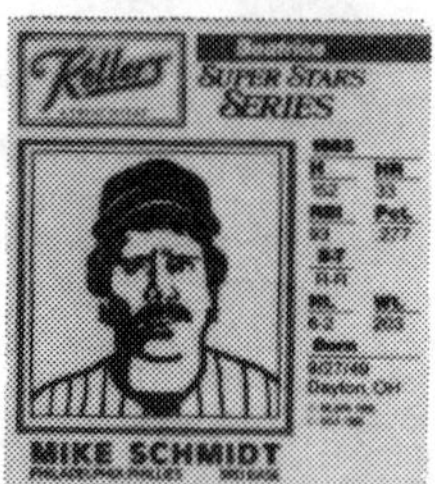

It's a good thing the Keller's Butter set of six Philadelphia Phillies players is downright unattractive or their value would be sky high. One card was printed on each one pound package of butter. The 2-1/2" by 2-3/4" cards feature crude drawings of the players, the backs are blank.

		MT	NR MT	EX
Complete Set (6):		18.00	13.50	7.25
Common Player:		1.00	.70	.40
(1)	Steve Carlton	4.00	3.00	1.50
(2)	Von Hayes	2.00	1.50	.80
(3)	Gary Redus	1.00	.70	.40
(4)	Juan Samuel	2.00	1.50	.80
(5)	Mike Schmidt	8.00	6.00	3.25
(6)	Glenn Wilson	1.00	.70	.40

1970 Kellogg's

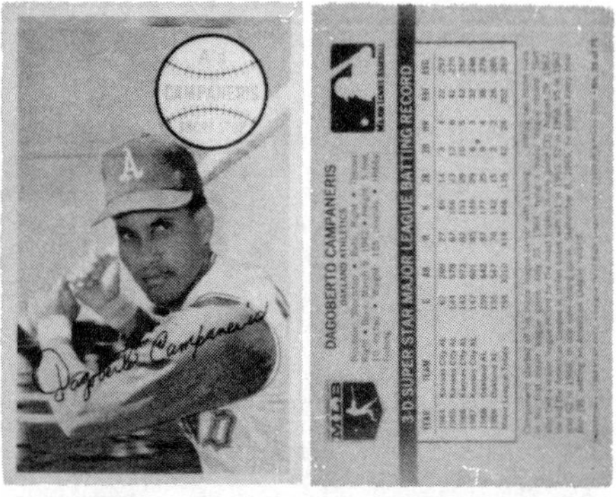

For 14 years in the 1970s and early 1980s, the Kellogg's cereal company provided Topps with virtually the only meaningful national competition in the baseball card market. Kellogg's kicked off its baseball card program in 1970 with a 75-player set of simulated 3-D cards. Single cards were available in selected brands of the company's cereal, while a mail-in program offered complete sets. The 3-D effect was achieved by the sandwiching of a clear color player photo between a purposely blurred stadium background scene and a layer of ribbed plastic. The relatively narrow dimension of the card, 2-1/4" by 3-1/2" and the nature of the plastic overlay seem to conspire to cause the cards to curl, often cracking the plastic layer, if not stored properly. Cards with major cracks in the plastic can be considered in Fair condition, at best.

		NR MT	EX	VG
Complete Set:		300.00	150.00	90.00
Common Player:		2.00	1.00	.60
1	Ed Kranepool	2.00	1.00	.60
2	Pete Rose	25.00	12.50	15.00
3	Cleon Jones	2.00	1.00	.60
4	Willie McCovey	8.00	4.00	2.50
5	Mel Stottlemyre	2.00	1.00	.60
6	Frank Howard	4.00	2.00	1.25
7	Tom Seaver	15.00	7.50	4.50
8	Don Sutton	4.00	2.00	1.25
9	Jim Wynn	2.00	1.00	.60
10	Jim Maloney	2.00	1.00	.60
11	Tommie Agee	2.00	1.00	.60
12	Willie Mays	20.00	10.00	6.00
13	Juan Marichal	8.00	4.00	2.50
14	Dave McNally	2.00	1.00	.60
15	Frank Robinson	12.00	6.00	3.50
16	Carlos May	2.00	1.00	.60
17	Bill Singer	2.00	1.00	.60
18	Rick Reichardt	2.00	1.00	.60
19	Boog Powell	4.00	2.00	1.25
20	Gaylord Perry	8.00	4.00	2.50
21	Brooks Robinson	12.00	6.00	3.50
22	Luis Aparicio	8.00	4.00	2.50
23	Joel Horlen	2.00	1.00	.60
24	Mike Epstein	2.00	1.00	.60
25	Tom Haller	2.00	1.00	.60
26	Willie Crawford	2.00	1.00	.60
27	Roberto Clemente	15.00	7.50	4.50
28	Matty Alou	2.00	1.00	.60
29	Willie Stargell	8.00	4.00	2.50
30	Tim Cullen	2.00	1.00	.60
31	Randy Hundley	2.00	1.00	.60
32	Reggie Jackson	15.00	7.50	4.50
33	Rich Allen	3.00	1.50	.90
34	Tim McCarver	3.00	1.50	.90
35	Ray Culp	2.00	1.00	.60
36	Jim Fregosi	3.00	1.50	.90
37	Billy Williams	8.00	4.00	2.50
38	Johnny Odom	2.00	1.00	.60
39	Bert Campaneris	3.00	1.50	.90
40	Ernie Banks	12.00	6.00	3.50
41	Chris Short	2.00	1.00	.60
42	Ron Santo	3.00	1.50	.90
43	Glenn Beckert	2.00	1.00	.60
44	Lou Brock	8.00	4.00	2.50
45	Larry Hisle	2.00	1.00	.60
46	Reggie Smith	2.00	1.00	.60
47	Rod Carew	8.00	4.00	2.50
48	Curt Flood	3.00	1.50	.90
49	Jim Lonborg	2.00	1.00	.60
50	Sam McDowell	2.00	1.00	.60
51	Sal Bando	2.00	1.00	.60
52	Al Kaline	12.00	6.00	3.50
53	Gary Nolan	2.00	1.00	.60
54	Rico Petrocelli	2.00	1.00	.60
55	Ollie Brown	2.00	1.00	.60
56	Luis Tiant	2.00	1.00	.60
57	Bill Freehan	2.00	1.00	.60
58	Johnny Bench	12.00	6.00	3.50
59	Joe Pepitone	2.00	1.00	.60
60	Bobby Murcer	2.00	1.00	.60
61	Harmon Killebrew	8.00	4.00	2.50
62	Don Wilson	2.00	1.00	.60
63	Tony Oliva	4.00	2.00	1.25
64	Jim Perry	2.00	1.00	.60
65	Mickey Lolich	3.00	1.50	.90
66	Coco Laboy	2.00	1.00	.60
67	Dean Chance	2.00	1.00	.60
68	Ken Harrelson	2.00	1.00	.60
69	Willie Horton	2.00	1.00	.60
70	Wally Bunker	2.00	1.00	.60
71a	Bob Gibson (1959 IP blank)	10.00	5.00	3.00
71b	Bob Gibson (1959 IP 76)	10.00	5.00	3.00
72	Joe Morgan	8.00	4.00	2.50
73	Denny McLain	3.00	1.50	.90
74	Tommy Harper	2.00	1.00	.60
75	Don Mincher	2.00	1.00	.60

Regional interest may affect the value of a card.

1971 Kellogg's

The scarcest and most valuable of the Kellogg's editions, the 75-card 1971 set was the only one not offered by the company on a mail-in basis; the only way to complete it was to buy ... and buy and buy ... boxes of cereal. Kellogg's again used the simulated 3-D effect in the cards' design, with the same result being many of the 2-1/4" by 3-1/2" cards are found today with cracks resulting from the cards' curling. A number of scarcer back variations are checklisted below. In addition, all 75 cards can be found with

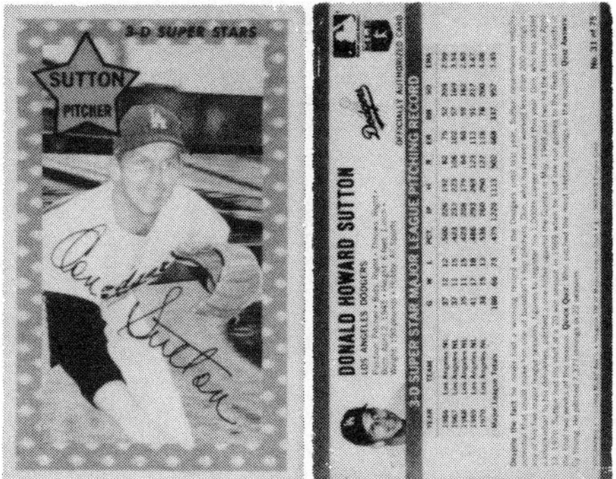

and without the 1970 date before the "Xograph" copyright line on the back; though there is no difference in value.

		NR MT	EX	VG
Complete Set:		950.00	475.00	285.00
Common Player:		12.00	6.00	3.50
1a	Wayne Simpson (SO 120)	12.00	6.00	3.50
1b	Wayne Simpson (SO 119)	15.00	7.50	4.50
2	Tom Seaver	35.00	17.50	10.50
3a	Jim Perry (IP 2238)	10.00	5.00	3.00
3b	Jim Perry (IP 2239)	15.00	7.50	4.50
4a	Bob Robertson (RBI 94)	12.00	6.00	3.50
4b	Bob Robertson (RBI 95)	12.00	6.00	3.50
5	Roberto Clemente	40.00	20.00	12.00
6a	Gaylord Perry (IP 2014)	20.00	10.00	6.00
6b	Gaylord Perry (IP 2015)	25.00	12.50	7.50
7a	Felipe Alou (1970 Oakland NL)	15.00	7.50	4.50
7b	Felipe Alou (1970 Oakland AL)	10.00	5.00	3.00
8	Denis Menke	12.00	6.00	3.50
9a	Don Kessinger (Hits 849)	10.00	5.00	3.00
9b	Don Kessinger (Hits 850)	15.00	7.50	4.50
10	Willie Mays	40.00	20.00	12.00
11	Jim Hickman	12.00	6.00	3.50
12	Tony Oliva	15.00	7.50	4.50
13	Manny Sanguillen	12.00	6.00	3.50
14a	Frank Howard (1968 Washington NL)	20.00	10.00	6.00
14b	Frank Howard (1968 Washington AL)	15.00	7.50	4.50
15	Frank Robinson	30.00	15.00	9.00
16	Willie Davis	10.00	5.00	3.00
17	Lou Brock	25.00	12.50	7.50
18	Cesar Tovar	12.00	6.00	3.50
19	Luis Aparicio	20.00	10.00	6.00
20	Boog Powell	15.00	7.50	4.50
21a	Dick Selma (SO 584)	12.00	6.00	3.50
21b	Dick Selma (SO 587)	12.00	6.00	3.50
22	Danny Walton	12.00	6.00	3.50
23	Carl Morton	12.00	6.00	3.50
24a	Sonny Siebert (SO 1054)	12.00	6.00	3.50
24b	Sonny Siebert (SO 1055)	12.00	6.00	3.50
25	Jim Merritt	12.00	6.00	3.50
26a	Jose Cardenal (Hits 828)	12.00	6.00	3.50
26b	Jose Cardenal (Hits 829)	12.00	6.00	3.50
27	Don Mincher	12.00	6.00	3.50
28a	Clyde Wright (California state logo)	12.00	6.00	3.50
28b	Clyde Wright (Angels crest logo)	12.00	6.00	3.50
29	Les Cain	12.00	6.00	3.50
30	Danny Cater	12.00	6.00	3.50
31	Don Sutton	15.00	7.50	4.50
32	Chuck Dobson	12.00	6.00	3.50
33	Willie McCovey	25.00	12.50	7.50
34	Mike Epstein	12.00	6.00	3.50
35a	Paul Blair (Runs 386)	12.00	6.00	3.50
35b	Paul Blair (Runs 385)	12.00	6.00	3.50
36a	Gary Nolan (SO 577)	12.00	6.00	3.50
36b	Gary Nolan (SO 581)	12.00	6.00	3.50
37	Sam McDowell	10.00	5.00	3.00
38	Amos Otis	10.00	5.00	3.00
39a	Ray Fosse (RBI 69)	12.00	6.00	3.50
39b	Ray Fosse (RBI 70)	12.00	6.00	3.50
40	Mel Stottlemyre	10.00	5.00	3.00
41	Cito Gaston	12.00	6.00	3.50
42	Dick Dietz	12.00	6.00	3.50
43	Roy White	10.00	5.00	3.00
44	Al Kaline	30.00	15.00	9.00
45	Carlos May	12.00	6.00	3.50
46a	Tommie Agee (RBI 313)	12.00	6.00	3.50
46b	Tommie Agee (RBI 314)	12.00	6.00	3.50
47	Tommy Harper	12.00	6.00	3.50
48	Larry Dierker	12.00	6.00	3.50
49	Mike Cuellar	10.00	5.00	3.00
50	Ernie Banks	30.00	15.00	9.00
51	Bob Gibson	25.00	12.50	7.50
52	Reggie Smith	10.00	5.00	3.00
53a	Matty Alou (RBI 273)	10.00	5.00	3.00
53b	Matty Alou (RBI 274)	15.00	7.50	4.50
54a	Alex Johnson (California state logo)	12.00	6.00	3.50
54b	Alex Johnson (Angels crest logo)	12.00	6.00	3.50
55	Harmon Killebrew	25.00	12.50	7.50
56	Billy Grabarkewitz	12.00	6.00	3.50
57	Rich Allen	15.00	7.50	4.50
58	Tony Perez	15.00	7.50	4.50
59a	Dave McNally (SO 1065)	10.00	5.00	3.00
59b	Dave McNally (SO 1067)	15.00	7.50	4.50
60a	Jim Palmer (SO 564)	20.00	10.00	6.00
60b	Jim Palmer (SO 567)	25.00	12.50	7.50
61	Billy Williams	20.00	10.00	6.00
62	Joe Torre	12.00	6.00	3.50
63a	Jim Northrup (AB 2773)	12.00	6.00	3.50
63b	Jim Northrup (AB 2772)	12.00	6.00	3.50
64a	Jim Fregosi (Calif. state logo - Hits 1326)	12.00	6.00	3.50
64b	Jim Fregosi (Calif. state logo - Hits 1327)	12.00	6.00	3.50
64c	Jim Fregosi (Angels crest logo)	12.00	6.00	3.50
65	Pete Rose	60.00	30.00	18.00
66a	Bud Harrelson (RBI 112)	12.00	6.00	3.50
66b	Bud Harrelson (RBI 113)	12.00	6.00	3.50
67	Tony Taylor	12.00	6.00	3.50
68	Willie Stargell	25.00	12.50	7.50
69	Tony Horton	8.50	4.25	2.50
70a	Claude Osteen (no number)	20.00	10.00	6.00
70b	Claude Osteen (#70 on back)	12.00	6.00	3.50
71	Glenn Beckert	10.00	5.00	3.00
72	Nate Colbert	12.00	6.00	3.50
73a	Rick Monday (AB 1705)	10.00	5.00	3.00
73b	Rick Monday (AB 1704)	15.00	7.50	4.50
74a	Tommy John (BB 444)	15.00	7.50	4.50
74b	Tommy John (BB 443)	20.00	10.00	6.00
75	Chris Short	12.00	6.00	3.50

1972 Kellogg's

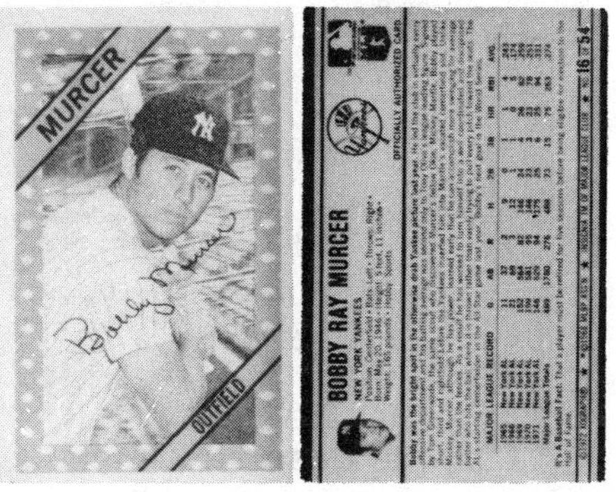

For 1972, Kellogg's reduced both the number of cards in its set and the dimensions of each card, moving to a 2-1/8" by 3-1/4" size and fixing the set at 54 cards. Once again, the cards were produced to simulate a 3-D effect (see description for 1970 Kellogg's). The set was available via a mail-in offer. The checklist includes variations which resulted from the correction of erroneous statistics on the backs of some cards. The complete set values quoted do not include the scarcer variations.

		NR MT	EX	VG
Complete Set:		75.00	37.00	22.00
Common Player:		.70	.35	.20
1a	Tom Seaver (1970 ERA 2.85)	9.00	4.50	2.75
1b	Tom Seaver (1970 ERA 2.81)	6.50	3.25	2.00
2	Amos Otis	.80	.40	.25
3a	Willie Davis (Runs 842)	1.25	.60	.40
3b	Willie Davis (Runs 841)	.80	.40	.25
4	Wilbur Wood	.80	.40	.25
5	Bill Parsons	.70	.35	.20
6	Pete Rose	20.00	10.00	6.00
7a	Willie McCovey (HR 360)	5.00	2.50	1.50
7b	Willie McCovey (HR 370)	3.50	1.75	1.00
8	Fergie Jenkins	3.00	1.50	.90
9a	Vida Blue (ERA 2.35)	1.50	.70	.45
9b	Vida Blue (ERA 2.31)	.90	.45	.25
10	Joe Torre	.90	.45	.25
11	Merv Rettenmund	.70	.35	.20
12	Bill Melton	.70	.35	.20
13a	Jim Palmer (Games 170)	4.75	2.50	1.50
13b	Jim Palmer (Games 168)	3.00	1.50	.90
14	Doug Rader	.70	.35	.20
15a	Dave Roberts (...Seaver, the NL leader...)	1.25	.60	.40
15b	Dave Roberts (...Seaver, the league leader...)	.70	.35	.20
16	Bobby Murcer	.80	.40	.25
17	Wes Parker	.70	.35	.20
18a	Joe Coleman (BB 394)	1.25	.60	.40
18b	Joe Coleman (BB 393)	.70	.35	.20
19	Manny Sanguillen	.70	.35	.20
20	Reggie Jackson	8.00	4.00	2.50
21	Ralph Garr	.70	.35	.20
22	Jim "Catfish" Hunter	3.00	1.50	.90
23	Rick Wise	.70	.35	.20
24	Glenn Beckert	.70	.35	.20
25	Tony Oliva	1.50	.70	.45
26a	Bob Gibson (SO 2577)	4.75	2.50	1.50
26b	Bob Gibson (SO 2578)	3.00	1.50	.90
27a	Mike Cuellar (1971 ERA 3.80)	1.25	.60	.40
27b	Mike Cuellar (1971 ERA 3.08)	.80	.40	.25
28	Chris Speier	.70	.35	.20
29a	Dave McNally (ERA 3.18)	1.25	.60	.40
29b	Dave McNally (ERA 3.15)	.80	.40	.25
30	Chico Cardenas	.70	.35	.20
31a	Bill Freehan (AVG. .263)	1.25	.60	.40
31b	Bill Freehan (AVG. .262)	.80	.40	.25
32a	Bud Harrelson (Hits 634)	1.25	.60	.40
32b	Bud Harrelson (Hits 624)	.70	.35	.20
33a	Sam McDowell (...less than 200 innings...)	1.25	.60	.40

33b	Sam McDowell (...less than 225 innings...)	.80	.40	.25
34a	Claude Osteen (1971 ERA 3.25)	1.25	.60	.40
34b	Claude Osteen (1971 ERA 3.51)	.70	.35	.20
35	Reggie Smith	.80	.40	.25
36	Sonny Siebert	.70	.35	.20
37	Lee May	.80	.40	.25
38	Mickey Lolich	.90	.45	.25
39a	Cookie Rojas (2B 149)	1.25	.60	.40
39b	Cookie Rojas (2B 150)	.70	.35	.20
40	Dick Drago	.70	.35	.20
41	Nate Colbert	.70	.35	.20
42	Andy Messersmith	.70	.35	.20
43a	Dave Johnson (AVG. .262)	1.50	.70	.45
43b	Dave Johnson (AVG. .264)	.90	.45	.25
44	Steve Blass	.70	.35	.20
45	Bob Robertson	.70	.35	.20
46a	Billy Williams (...missed only one last season...)	5.00	2.50	1.50
46b	Billy Williams (phrase omitted)	3.00	1.50	.90
47	Juan Marichal	3.00	1.50	.90
48	Lou Brock	3.50	1.75	1.00
49	Roberto Clemente	10.00	5.00	3.00
50	Mel Stottlemyre	.80	.40	.25
51	Don Wilson	.70	.35	.20
52a	Sal Bando (RBI 355)	1.25	.60	.40
52b	Sal Bando (RBI 356)	.80	.40	.25
53a	Willie Stargell (2B 197)	5.00	2.50	1.50
53b	Willie Stargell (2B 196)	3.00	1.50	.90
54a	Willie Mays (RBI 1855)	18.00	9.00	5.50
54b	Willie Mays (RBI 1856)	10.00	5.00	3.00

Values quoted in this guide reflect the retail price of a card – the price a collector can expect to pay when buying a card from a dealer. The wholesale price – that which a collector can expect to receive from a dealer when selling cards – will be significantly lower, depending on desirability and condition.

1972 Kellogg's All-Time Baseball Greats

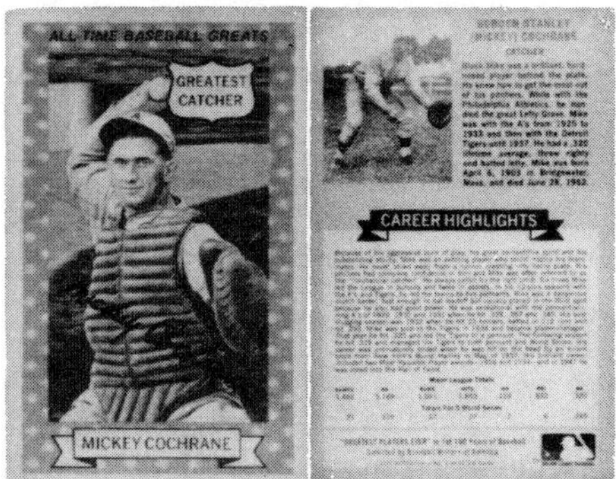

Kellogg's issued a second baseball card set in 1972, inserted into packages of breakfast rolls. The 2-1/4" by 3-1/2" cards also featured a simulated 3-D effect, but the 15 players in the set were "All-Time Baseball Greats", rather than current players. The set is virtually identical to a Rold Gold pretzel issue of 1970; the only difference being the 1972 copyright date on the back of the Kellog's cards, while the pretzel issue bears a 1970 date. The pretzel cards are considerably scarcer than the Kellogg's.

		NR MT	EX	VG
	Complete Set:	15.00	7.50	4.50
	Common Player:	.50	.25	.15
1	Walter Johnson	1.25	.60	.40
2	Rogers Hornsby	.80	.40	.25
3	John McGraw	.50	.25	.15
4	Mickey Cochrane	.50	.25	.15
5	George Sisler	.50	.25	.15
6	Babe Ruth	4.00	2.00	1.25
7	Robert "Lefty" Grove	.70	.35	.20
8	Harold "Pie" Traynor	.50	.25	.15
9	Honus Wagner	1.00	.50	.30
10	Eddie Collins	.50	.25	.15
11	Tris Speaker	.70	.35	.20
12	Cy Young	.80	.40	.25
13	Lou Gehrig	2.00	1.00	.60
14	Babe Ruth	4.00	2.00	1.25
15	Ty Cobb	2.00	1.00	.60

Values for recent cards and sets are listed in Mint (MT), Near Mint (NM), reflecting the fact that many cards from recent years have been preserved in top condition. Recent cards and sets in less than Excellent condition have little collector interest.

1973 Kellogg's

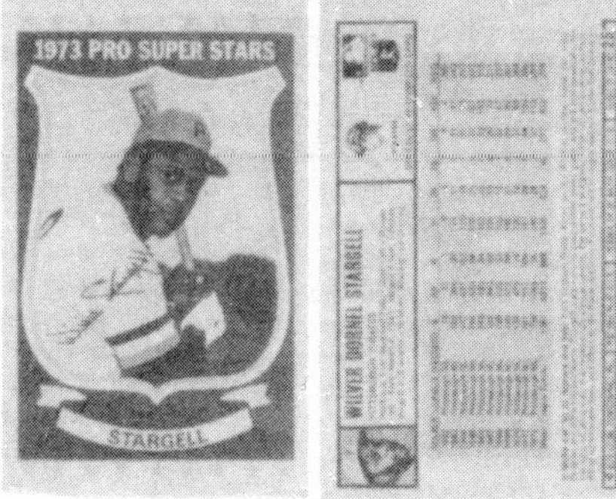

The lone exception to Kellogg's long run of simulated 3-D effect cards came in 1973, when the cereal company's 54-card set was produced by "normal" printing methods. In 2'1/4" by 3-1/2" size, the design was otherwise quite compatible with the issues which preceded and succeeded it. Because it was available via a mail-in offer, it is not as scarce as some other Kellogg's issues.

		NR MT	EX	VG
	Complete Set:	75.00	37.00	22.00
	Common Player:	.50	.25	.15
1	Amos Otis	.60	.30	.20
2	Ellie Rodriguez	.50	.25	.15
3	Mickey Lolich	.80	.40	.25
4	Tony Oliva	1.25	.60	.40
5	Don Sutton	1.25	.60	.40
6	Pete Rose	11.00	5.50	3.25
7	Steve Carlton	4.00	2.00	1.25
8	Bobby Bonds	.70	.35	.20
9	Wilbur Wood	.60	.30	.20
10	Billy Williams	2.50	1.25	.70
11	Steve Blass	.50	.25	.15
12	Jon Matlack	.50	.25	.15
13	Cesar Cedeno	.70	.35	.20
14	Bob Gibson	2.50	1.25	.70
15	Sparky Lyle	.60	.30	.20
16	Nolan Ryan	15.00	7.50	4.50
17	Jim Palmer	2.50	1.25	.70
18	Ray Fosse	.50	.25	.15
19	Bobby Murcer	.60	.30	.20
20	Jim "Catfish" Hunter	2.50	1.25	.70
21	Tug McGraw	.80	.40	.25
22	Reggie Jackson	7.00	3.50	2.00
23	Bill Stoneman	.50	.25	.15
24	Lou Piniella	.80	.40	.25
25	Willie Stargell	2.50	1.25	.70
26	Dick Allen	1.50	.70	.45
27	Carlton Fisk	1.25	.60	.40
28	Fergie Jenkins	2.50	1.25	.70
29	Phil Niekro	1.50	.70	.45
30	Gary Nolan	.50	.25	.15
31	Joe Torre	.80	.40	.25
32	Bobby Tolan	.50	.25	.15
33	Nate Colbert	.50	.25	.15
34	Joe Morgan	2.50	1.25	.70
35	Bert Blyleven	.90	.45	.25
36	Joe Rudi	.60	.30	.20
37	Ralph Garr	.50	.25	.15
38	Gaylord Perry	2.50	1.25	.70
39	Bobby Grich	.60	.30	.20
40	Lou Brock	2.50	1.25	.70
41	Pete Broberg	.50	.25	.15
42	Manny Sanguillen	.50	.25	.15
43	Willie Davis	.60	.30	.20
44	Dave Kingman	.60	.30	.20
45	Carlos May	.50	.25	.15
46	Tom Seaver	4.00	2.00	1.25
47	Mike Cuellar	.60	.30	.20
48	Joe Coleman	.50	.25	.15
49	Claude Osteen	.50	.25	.15
50	Steve Kline	.50	.25	.15
51	Rod Carew	4.00	2.00	1.25
52	Al Kaline	5.00	2.50	1.50
53	Larry Dierker	.50	.25	.15
54	Ron Santo	.70	.35	.20

Grading Guide

Mint (MT): A perfect card. Well-centered with all corners sharp and square. No creases, stains, edge nicks, surface marks, yellowing or fading.

Near Mint (NM): A nearly perfect card. At first glance, a NM card appears to be perfect. May be slightly off-center. No surface marks, creases or loss of gloss.

Excellent (EX): Corners are still fairly sharp with only moderate wear. Borders may be off-center. No creases or stains on fronts or backs, but may show slight loss of surface luster.

Very Good (VG): Shows obvious handling. May have rounded corners, minor creases, major gum or wax stains. No major creases, tape marks, writing, etc.

Good (G): A well-worn card, but exhibits no intentional damage. May have major or multiple creases. Corners may be rounded well beyond card border.

1974 Kellogg's

For 1974, Kellogg's returned to the use of simulated 3-D for its 54-player baseball card issue (see 1970 Kellogg's listing for description). In 2-1/8" by 3-1/4" size, the cards were available as a complete set via a mail-in offer.

		NR MT	EX	VG
	Complete Set:	65.00	32.00	19.50
	Common Player:	.50	.25	.15
1	Bob Gibson	5.00	2.50	1.50
2	Rick Monday	.70	.35	.20
3	Joe Coleman	.50	.25	.15
4	Bert Campaneris	.70	.35	.20
5	Carlton Fisk	1.25	.60	.40
6	Jim Palmer	2.50	1.25	.70
7a	Ron Santo (Chicago Cubs)	1.50	.70	.45
7b	Ron Santo (Chicago White Sox)	.80	.40	.25
8	Nolan Ryan	10.00	5.00	3.00
9	Greg Luzinski	.80	.40	.25
10a	Buddy Bell (Runs 134)	1.50	.70	.45
10b	Buddy Bell (Runs 135)	.80	.40	.25
11	Bob Watson	.50	.25	.15
12	Bill Singer	.50	.25	.15
13	Dave May	.50	.25	.15
14	Jim Brewer	.50	.25	.15
15	Manny Sanguillen	.50	.25	.15
16	Jeff Burroughs	.50	.25	.15
17	Amos Otis	.50	.25	.15
18	Ed Goodson	.50	.25	.15
19	Nate Colbert	.50	.25	.15
20	Reggie Jackson	4.00	2.00	1.25
21	Ted Simmons	.90	.45	.25
22	Bobby Murcer	.60	.30	.20
23	Willie Horton	.60	.30	.20
24	Orlando Cepeda	2.50	1.25	.70
25	Ron Hunt	.50	.25	.15
26	Wayne Twitchell	.50	.25	.15
27	Ron Fairly	.50	.25	.15
28	Johnny Bench	5.00	2.50	1.50
29	John Mayberry	.50	.25	.15
30	Rod Carew	4.00	2.00	1.25
31	Ken Holtzman	.50	.25	.15
32	Billy Williams	2.50	1.25	.70
33	Dick Allen	1.50	.70	.45
34a	Wilbur Wood (SO 959)	1.25	.60	.40
34b	Wilbur Wood (SO 960)	.70	.35	.20
35	Danny Thompson	.50	.25	.15
36	Joe Morgan	2.50	1.25	.70
37	Willie Stargell	3.00	1.50	.90
38	Pete Rose	12.00	6.00	3.50
39	Bobby Bonds	.70	.35	.20
40	Chris Speier	.50	.25	.15
41	Sparky Lyle	.60	.30	.20
42	Cookie Rojas	.50	.25	.15
43	Tommy Davis	.60	.30	.20
44	Jim "Catfish" Hunter	2.50	1.25	.70
45	Willie Davis	.60	.30	.20
46	Bert Blyleven	.90	.45	.25
47	Pat Kelly	.50	.25	.15
48	Ken Singleton	.60	.30	.20
49	Manny Mota	.60	.30	.20
50	Dave Johnson	.90	.45	.25
51	Sal Bando	.60	.30	.20
52	Tom Seaver	5.00	2.50	1.50
53	Felix Millan	.50	.25	.15
54	Ron Blomberg	.80	.40	.25

Definitions for grading conditions are located in the Introduction of this price guide.

1975 Kellogg's

While the card size remained the same at 2-1/8" by 3-1/4", the size of the 1975 Kellogg's "3-D" set was increased by three, to 57 cards. Despite the fact cards could be obtained by a mail-in offer, as well as in cereal boxes, the '75 Kellogg's are noticeably scarcer than the company's other issues, with the

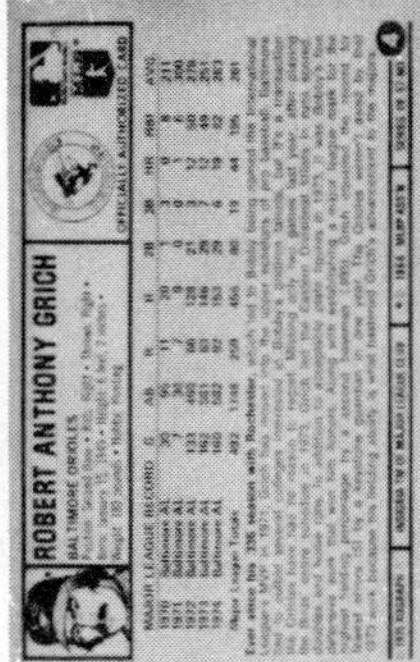

exception of the 1971 set. Also helping to raise the value of the cards is the presence of an unusually large number of current and future Hall of Famers.

		NR MT	EX	VG
Complete Set:		150.00	75.00	45.00
Common Player:		2.00	1.00	.60
1	Roy White	3.50	1.75	1.00
2	Ross Grimsley	2.00	1.00	.60
3	Reggie Smith	2.50	1.25	.70
4a	Bob Grich ("...1973 work..." in last line)	4.00	2.00	1.25
4b	Bob Grich (no "...1973 work...")	2.50	1.25	.70
5	Greg Gross	2.00	1.00	.60
6	Bob Watson	2.00	1.00	.60
7	Johnny Bench	12.00	6.00	3.50
8	Jeff Burroughs	2.00	1.00	.60
9	Elliott Maddox	2.00	1.00	.60
10	Jon Matlack	2.00	1.00	.60
11	Pete Rose	18.00	9.00	5.50
12	Leroy Stanton	2.00	1.00	.60
13	Bake McBride	2.00	1.00	.60
14	Jorge Orta	2.00	1.00	.60
15	Al Oliver	2.50	1.25	.70
16	John Briggs	2.00	1.00	.60
17	Steve Garvey	9.00	4.50	2.75
18	Brooks Robinson	12.00	6.00	3.50
19	John Hiller	2.00	1.00	.60
20	Lynn McGlothen	2.00	1.00	.60
21	Cleon Jones	2.00	1.00	.60
22	Fergie Jenkins	6.50	3.25	2.00
23	Bill North	2.00	1.00	.60
24	Steve Busby	2.00	1.00	.60
25	Richie Zisk	2.00	1.00	.60
26	Nolan Ryan	20.00	10.00	6.00
27	Joe Morgan	6.50	3.25	2.00
28	Joe Rudi	2.50	1.25	.70
29	Jose Cardenal	2.00	1.00	.60
30	Andy Messersmith	2.00	1.00	.60
31	Willie Montanez	2.00	1.00	.60
32	Bill Buckner	2.50	1.25	.70
33	Rod Carew	10.00	5.00	3.00
34	Lou Piniella	2.50	1.25	.70
35	Ralph Garr	2.00	1.00	.60
36	Mike Marshall	2.00	1.00	.60
37	Garry Maddox	2.00	1.00	.60
38	Dwight Evans	3.00	1.50	.90
39	Lou Brock	9.00	4.50	2.75
40	Ken Singleton	2.50	1.25	.70
41	Steve Braun	2.00	1.00	.60
42	Dick Allen	3.00	1.50	.90
43	Johnny Grubb	2.00	1.00	.60
44a	Jim Hunter (Oakland)	12.00	6.00	3.50
44b	Jim Hunter (New York)	8.00	4.00	2.50
45	Gaylord Perry	6.50	3.25	2.00
46	George Hendrick	2.00	1.00	.60
47	Sparky Lyle	2.50	1.25	.70
48	Dave Cash	2.00	1.00	.60
49	Luis Tiant	2.50	1.25	.70
50	Cesar Geronimo	2.00	1.00	.60
51	Carl Yastrzemski	16.00	8.00	4.75
52	Ken Brett	2.00	1.00	.60
53	Hal McRae	2.50	1.25	.70
54	Reggie Jackson	16.00	8.00	4.75
55	Rollie Fingers	6.00	3.00	1.75
56	Mike Schmidt	14.00	7.00	4.25
57	Richie Hebner	2.50	1.25	.70

Grading Guide

Mint (MT): A perfect card. Well-centered with all corners sharp and square. No creases, stains, edge nicks, surface marks, yellowing or fading.

Near Mint (NM): A nearly perfect card. At first glance, a NM card appears to be perfect. May be slightly off-center. No surface marks, creases or loss of gloss.

Excellent (EX): Corners are still fairly sharp with only moderate wear. Borders may be off-center. No creases or stains on fronts or backs, but may show slight loss of surface luster.

Very Good (VG): Shows obvious handling. May have rounded corners, minor creases, major gum or wax stains. No major creases, tape marks, writing, etc.

Good (G): A well-worn card, but exhibits no intentional damage. May have major or multiple creases. Corners may be rounded well beyond card border.

1976 Kellogg's

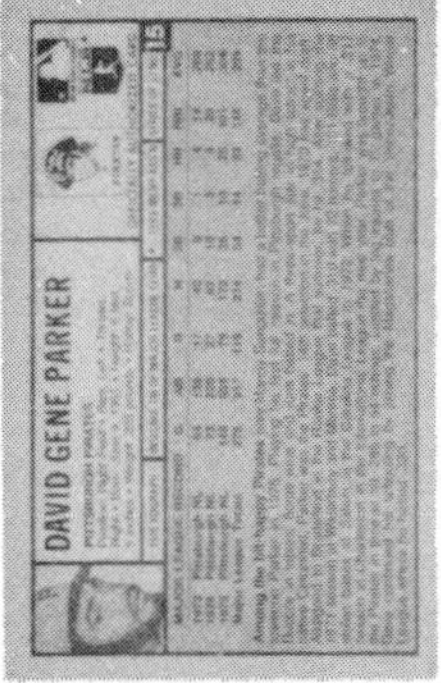

A sizeable list of corrected errors and other variation cards dots the checklist for the 57-card 1976 Kellogg's 3-D set. Again containing 57 cards, the first three cards in the set are found far less often than cards #4-57, indicating they were short-printed in relation to the rest of the set. The complete set values quoted below dot not include the scarcer variation cards. Card size remained at 2-1/8" by 3-1/4". Cards #1-3 were short-printed.

		NR MT	EX	VG
Complete Set:		80.00	40.00	24.00
Common Player:		1.25	.60	.40
1	Steve Hargan	8.00	4.00	2.50
2	Claudell Washington	8.00	4.00	2.50
3	Don Gullett	8.00	4.00	2.50
4	Randy Jones	1.25	.60	.40
5	Jim "Catfish" Hunter	6.50	3.25	2.00
6a	Clay Carroll (Cincinnati)	3.00	1.50	.90
6b	Clay Carroll (Chicago)	1.50	.70	.45
7	Joe Rudi	1.50	.70	.45
8	Reggie Jackson	10.00	5.00	3.00
9	Felix Millan	1.25	.60	.40
10	Jim Rice	5.00	2.50	1.50
11	Bert Blyleven	2.50	1.25	.70
12	Ken Singleton	1.50	.70	.45
13	Don Sutton	2.50	1.25	.70
14	Joe Morgan	6.00	3.00	1.75
15	Dave Parker	6.00	3.00	1.75
16	Dave Cash	1.25	.60	.40
17	Ron LeFlore	1.25	.60	.40
18	Greg Luzinski	2.00	1.00	.60
19	Dennis Eckersley	2.25	1.25	.70
20	Bill Madlock	2.25	1.25	.70
21	George Scott	1.25	.60	.40
22	Willie Stargell	6.50	3.25	2.00
23	Al Hrabosky	1.25	.60	.40
24	Carl Yastrzemski	13.00	6.50	4.00
25	Jim Kaat	2.50	1.25	.70
26	Marty Perez	1.25	.60	.40
27	Bob Watson	1.25	.60	.40
28	Eric Soderholm	1.25	.60	.40
29	Bill Lee	1.25	.60	.40
30a	Frank Tanana (1975 ERA 2.63)	2.50	1.25	.70
30b	Frank Tanana (1975 ERA 2.62)	1.50	.70	.45
31	Fred Lynn	3.50	1.75	1.00
32a	Tom Seaver (1967 PCT. 552)	10.00	5.00	3.00
32b	Tom Seaver (1967 Pct. .552)	8.00	4.00	2.50
33	Steve Busby	1.25	.60	.40
34	Gary Carter	10.00	5.00	3.00
35	Rick Wise	1.25	.60	.40
36	Johnny Bench	10.00	5.00	3.00
37	Jim Palmer	8.00	4.00	2.50
38	Bobby Murcer	2.00	1.00	.60
39	Von Joshua	1.25	.60	.40
40	Lou Brock	8.00	4.00	2.50
41a	Mickey Rivers (last line begins "In three...")	2.75	1.50	.80
41b	Mickey Rivers (last line begins "The Yankees...")	1.25	.60	.40
42	Manny Sanguillen	1.25	.60	.40
43	Jerry Reuss	1.50	.70	.45
44	Ken Griffey	1.50	.70	.45
45a	Jorge Orta (AB 1616)	2.25	1.25	.70
45b	Jorge Orta (AB 1615)	1.25	.60	.40
46	John Mayberry	1.25	.60	.40
47a	Vida Blue (2nd line reads "...pitched more innings...")	3.00	1.50	.90
47b	Vida Blue (2nd line reads "...struck out more...")	2.00	1.00	.60
48	Rod Carew	10.00	5.00	3.00
49a	Jon Matlack (1975 ER 87)	2.25	1.25	.70
49b	Jon Matlack (1975 ER 86)	1.25	.60	.40
50	Boog Powell	2.50	1.25	.70
51a	Mike Hargrove (AB 935)	2.25	1.25	.70
51b	Mike Hargrove (AB 934)	1.25	.60	.40
52a	Paul Lindblad (1975 ERA 2.72)	2.25	1.25	.70
52b	Paul Lindblad (1975 ERA 2.73)	1.25	.60	.40
53	Thurman Munson	6.50	3.25	2.00
54	Steve Garvey	6.00	3.00	1.75
55	Pete Rose	18.00	9.00	5.50
56a	Greg Gross (Games 302)	2.25	1.25	.70
56b	Greg Gross (Games 334)	1.25	.60	.40
57	Ted Simmons	2.50	1.25	.70

The values quoted are intended to reflect the market price.

1977 Kellogg's

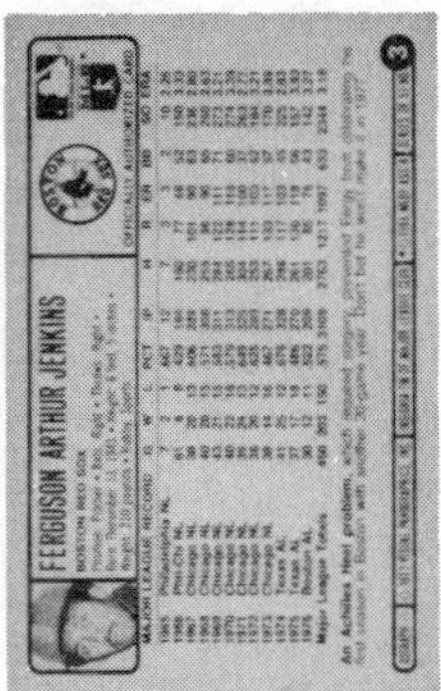

Other than another innovative card design to complement the simulated 3-D effect, there was little change in the 1977 Kellogg's issue. Set size remained at 57 cards, the set remained in the 2-1/8" by 3-1/4" format, and the cards were available either individually in boxes of cereal, or as a complete set via a mail-in box top offer. The 1977 set is the last in which Kellogg's used a player portrait photo on the back of the card.

		NR MT	EX	VG
Complete Set:		55.00	28.00	16.50
Common Player:		.40	.20	.12
1	George Foster	.90	.45	.25
2	Bert Campaneris	.60	.30	.20
3	Fergie Jenkins	2.00	1.00	.60
4	Dock Ellis	.40	.20	.12
5	John Montefusco	.40	.20	.12
6	George Brett	8.50	4.25	2.50
7	John Candelaria	.50	.25	.15
8	Fred Norman	.40	.20	.12
9	Bill Travers	.40	.20	.12
10	Hal McRae	.60	.30	.20
11	Doug Rau	.40	.20	.12
12	Greg Luzinski	.70	.35	.20
13	Ralph Garr	.40	.20	.12
14	Steve Garvey	4.50	2.25	1.25
15	Rick Manning	.40	.20	.12
16	Lyman Bostock	.50	.25	.15
17	Randy Jones	.40	.20	.12
18a	Ron Cey (58 homers in first sentence)	1.00	.50	.30
18b	Ron Cey (48 homers in first sentence)	.60	.30	.20
19	Dave Parker	1.25	.60	.40
20	Pete Rose	9.00	4.50	2.75
21a	Wayne Garland (last line begins "Prior to...")	.90	.45	.25
21b	Wayne Garland (last line begins "There he...")	.40	.20	.12
22	Bill North	.40	.20	.12
23	Thurman Munson	2.50	1.25	.70
24	Tom Poquette	.40	.20	.12
25	Ron LeFlore	.50	.25	.15
26	Mark Fidrych	.50	.25	.15
27	Sixto Lezcano	.40	.20	.12
28	Dave Winfield	4.00	2.00	1.25
29	Jerry Koosman	.50	.25	.15
30	Mike Hargrove	.40	.20	.12
31	Willie Montanez	.40	.20	.12
32	Don Stanhouse	.40	.20	.12
33	Jay Johnstone	.50	.25	.15
34	Bake McBride	.40	.20	.12
35	Dave Kingman	.70	.35	.20
36	Freddie Patek	.40	.20	.12
37	Garry Maddox	.50	.25	.15
38a	Ken Reitz (last line begins "The previous...")	.90	.45	.25
38b	Ken Reitz (last line begins "In late...")	.40	.20	.12
39	Bobby Grich	.60	.30	.20
40	Cesar Geronimo	.40	.20	.12
41	Jim Lonborg	.40	.20	.12
42	Ed Figueroa	.40	.20	.12
43	Bill Madlock	.80	.40	.25
44	Jerry Remy	.40	.20	.12
45	Frank Tanana	.50	.25	.15
46	Al Oliver	.90	.45	.25
47	Charlie Hough	.50	.25	.15
48	Lou Piniella	.70	.35	.20
49	Ken Griffey	.60	.30	.20
50	Jose Cruz	.60	.30	.20
51	Rollie Fingers	2.50	1.25	.70
52	Chris Chambliss	.50	.25	.15
53	Rod Carew	4.00	2.00	1.25
54	Andy Messersmith	.40	.20	.12
55	Mickey Rivers	.40	.20	.12
56	Butch Wynegar	.40	.20	.12
57	Steve Carlton	5.00	2.50	1.50

1978 Kellogg's

Besides the substitution of a Tony the Tiger drawing for a player portrait photo on the back of the card, the 1978 Kellogg's set offered no major changes from the previous few years issues. Cards

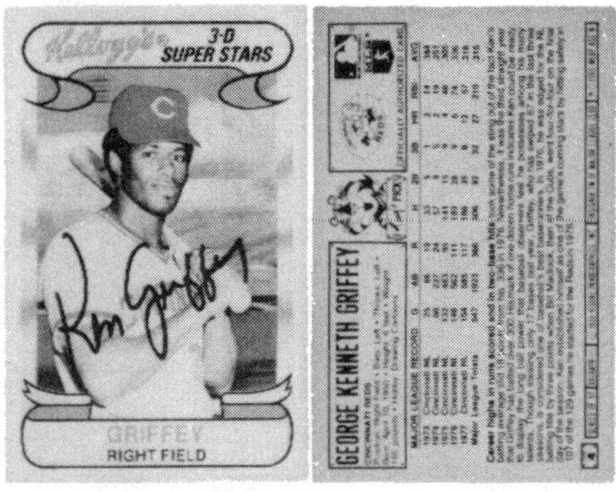

were once again in the 2-1/8" by 3-1/4" format, with 57 cards comprising a complete set. Single cards were available in selected brands of the company's cereal, while complete sets could be obtained by a mail-in offer.

		NR MT	EX	VG
Complete Set:		55.00	27.00	16.50
Common Player:		.40	.20	.12
1	Steve Carlton	4.00	2.00	1.25
2	Bucky Dent	.50	.25	.15
3	Mike Schmidt	4.00	2.00	1.25
4	Ken Griffey	.50	.25	.15
5	Al Cowens	.40	.20	.12
6	George Brett	5.00	2.50	1.50
7	Lou Brock	3.00	1.50	.90
8	Rich Gossage	.70	.35	.20
9	Tom Johnson	.40	.20	.12
10	George Foster	.70	.35	.20
11	Dave Winfield	3.50	1.75	1.00
12	Dan Meyer	.40	.20	.12
13	Chris Chambliss	.50	.25	.15
14	Paul Dade	.40	.20	.12
15	Jeff Burroughs	.40	.20	.12
16	Jose Cruz	.60	.30	.20
17	Mickey Rivers	.40	.20	.12
18	John Candelaria	.50	.25	.15
19	Ellis Valentine	.40	.20	.12
20	Hal McRae	.50	.25	.15
21	Dave Rozema	.40	.20	.12
22	Lenny Randle	.40	.20	.12
23	Willie McCovey	3.00	1.50	.90
24	Ron Cey	.70	.35	.20
25	Eddie Murray	9.00	4.50	2.75
26	Larry Bowa	.60	.30	.20
27	Tom Seaver	3.50	1.75	1.00
28	Garry Maddox	.50	.25	.15
29	Rod Carew	3.00	1.50	.90
30	Thurman Munson	2.50	1.25	.70
31	Garry Templeton	.60	.30	.20
32	Eric Soderholm	.40	.20	.12
33	Greg Luzinski	.70	.35	.20
34	Reggie Smith	.50	.25	.15
35	Dave Goltz	.40	.20	.12
36	Tommy John	.90	.45	.25
37	Ralph Garr	.40	.20	.12
38	Alan Bannister	.40	.20	.12
39	Bob Bailor	.40	.20	.12
40	Reggie Jackson	5.00	2.50	1.50
41	Cecil Cooper	.80	.40	.25
42	Burt Hooton	.40	.20	.12
43	Sparky Lyle	.50	.25	.15
44	Steve Ontiveros	.40	.20	.12
45	Rick Reuschel	.60	.30	.20
46	Lyman Bostock	.50	.25	.15
47	Mitchell Page	.40	.20	.12
48	Bruce Sutter	.70	.35	.20
49	Jim Rice	2.00	1.00	.60
50	Bob Forsch	.40	.20	.12
51	Nolan Ryan	8.00	4.00	2.50
52	Dave Parker	1.25	.60	.40
53	Bert Blyleven	.90	.45	.25
54	Frank Tanana	.50	.25	.15
55	Ken Singleton	.50	.25	.15
56	Mike Hargrove	.40	.20	.12
57	Don Sutton	1.25	.60	.40

1979 Kellogg's

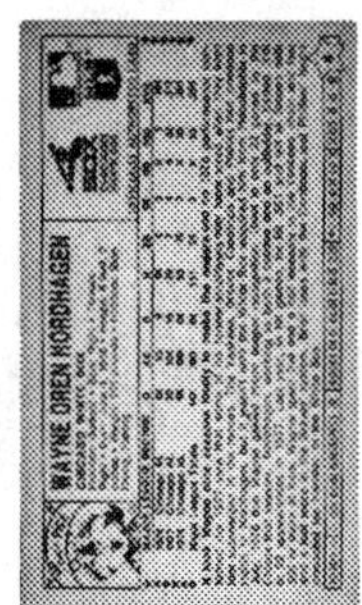

For its 1979 3-D issue, Kellogg's increased the size of the set to 60 cards, but reduced the width of the cards to 1-15/16". Depth stayed the same as in previous years, 3-1/4". The narrower card format seems to have compounded the problem of curling and subsequent cracking of the ribbed plastic surface which helps give the card a 3-D effect. Cards with major cracks can be graded no higher than VG. The complete set price in the checklist that follows does not include the scarcer variations. Numerous minor variations featuring copyright and trademark logos can be found in the set.

		NR MT	EX	VG
Complete Set:		35.00	17.50	10.50
Common Player:		.30	.15	.09
1	Bruce Sutter	.40	.20	.12
2	Ted Simmons	.40	.20	.12
3	Ross Grimsley	.30	.15	.09
4	Wayne Nordhagen	.30	.15	.09
5a	Jim Palmer (PCT. .649)	2.25	1.25	.70
5b	Jim Palmer (PCT. .650)	1.50	.70	.45
6	John Henry Johnson	.30	.15	.09
7	Jason Thompson	.30	.15	.09
8	Pat Zachry	.30	.15	.09
9	Dennis Eckersley	.75	.40	.25
10a	Paul Splittorff (IP 1665)	.60	.30	.20
10b	Paul Splittorff (IP 1666)	.30	.15	.09
11a	Ron Guidry (Hits 397)	1.00	.50	.30
11b	Ron Guidry (Hits 396)	.50	.25	.15
12	Jeff Burroughs	.30	.15	.09
13	Rod Carew	2.50	1.25	.70
14a	Buddy Bell (no trade line in bio)	1.25	.60	.40
14b	Buddy Bell (trade line in bio)	.30	.15	.09
15	Jim Rice	.60	.30	.20
16	Garry Maddox	.50	.25	.15
17	Willie McCovey	2.50	1.25	.70
18	Steve Carlton	2.50	1.25	.70
19a	J. R. Richard (stats begin with 1972)	.60	.30	.20
19b	J. R. Richard (stats begin with 1971)	.30	.15	.09
20	Paul Molitor	2.00	1.00	.60
21a	Dave Parker (AVG. .281)	2.00	1.00	.60
21b	Dave Parker (AVG. .318)	1.00	.50	.30
22a	Pete Rose (1978 3B 3)	6.00	6.00	3.50
22b	Pete Rose (1978 3B 33)	4.00	2.00	1.25
23a	Vida Blue (Runs 819)	.90	.45	.25
23b	Vida Blue (Runs 818)	.40	.20	.12
24	Richie Zisk	.30	.15	.09
25a	Darrell Porter (2B 101)	.80	.40	.25
25b	Darrell Porter (2B 111)	.40	.20	.12
26a	Dan Driessen (Games 642)	.80	.40	.25
26b	Dan Driessen (Games 742)	.40	.20	.12
27a	Geoff Zahn (1978 Minnessota)	.60	.30	.20
27b	Geoff Zahn (1978 Minnesota)	.30	.15	.09
28	Phil Niekro	1.25	.60	.40
29	Tom Seaver	2.50	1.25	.70
30	Fred Lynn	1.00	.50	.30
31	Bill Bonham	.30	.15	.09
32	George Foster	.40	.20	.12
33a	Terry Puhl (last line of bio begins "Terry...")	.60	.30	.20
33b	Terry Puhl (last line of bio begins "His...")	.30	.15	.09
34a	John Candelaria (age is 24)	.90	.45	.25
34b	John Candelaria (age is 25)	.50	.25	.15
35	Bob Knepper	.40	.20	.12
36	Freddie Patek	.30	.15	.09
37	Chris Chambliss	.40	.20	.12
38a	Bob Forsch (1977 Games 86)	.80	.40	.25
38b	Bob Forsch (1977 Games 35)	.40	.20	.12
39a	Ken Griffey (1978 AB 674)	.90	.45	.25
39b	Ken Griffey (1978 AB 614)	.50	.25	.15
40	Jack Clark	.40	.20	.12
41a	Dwight Evans (1978 Hits 13)	1.50	.70	.45
41b	Dwight Evans (1978 Hits 123)	.90	.45	.25
42	Lee Mazzilli	.30	.15	.09
43	Mario Guerrero	.30	.15	.09
44	Larry Bowa	.50	.25	.15
45a	Carl Yastrzemski (Games 9930)	6.00	3.00	1.75
45b	Carl Yastrzemski (Games 9929)	4.00	2.00	1.25
46a	Reggie Jackson (1978 Games 162)	5.00	2.50	1.50
46b	Reggie Jackson (1978 Games 139)	3.00	1.50	.90
47	Rick Reuschel	.60	.30	.20
48a	Mike Flanagan (1976 SO 57)	.90	.45	.25
48b	Mike Flanagan (1976 SO 56)	.50	.25	.15
49a	Gaylord Perry (1973 Hits 325)	2.00	1.00	.60
49b	Gaylord Perry (1973 Hits 315)	1.25	.60	.40
50	George Brett	3.50	1.75	1.00
51a	Craig Reynolds (last line of bio begins "He spent...")	.60	.30	.20
51b	Craig Reynolds (last line of bio begins "In those...")	.30	.15	.09
52	Davey Lopes	.40	.20	.12
53a	Bill Almon (2B 31)	.60	.30	.20
53b	Bill Almon (2B 41)	.30	.15	.09
54	Roy Howell	.30	.15	.09
55	Frank Tanana	.40	.20	.12
56a	Doug Rau (1978 PCT. .577)	.60	.30	.20
56b	Doug Rau (1978 PCT. .625)	.30	.15	.09
57a	Rick Monday (1976 Runs 197)	.90	.45	.25
57b	Rick Monday (1976 Runs 107)	.50	.25	.15
58	Jon Matlack	.30	.15	.09
59a	Ron Jackson (last line of bio begins "His best...")	.60	.30	.20
59b	Ron Jackson (last line of bio begins "The Twins...")	.30	.15	.09
60	Jim Sundberg	.50	.25	.15

Regional interest may affect the value of a card.

1980 Kellogg's

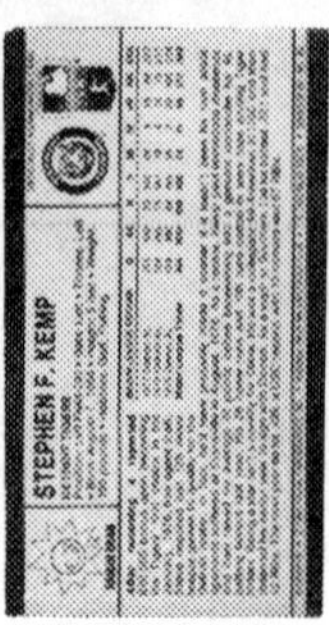

The 1980 cereal company issue featured the narrowest format of any Kellogg's card, 1-7/8" by 3-1/4". For the second straight year, set size remained at 60 cards, available either singly in boxes of cereal, or as complete sets by a mail-in offer.

		NR MT	EX	VG
Complete Set:		25.00	12.50	7.50
Common Player:		.30	.15	.09
1	Ross Grimsley	.30	.15	.09
2	Mike Schmidt	4.00	2.00	1.25
3	Mike Flanagan	.40	.20	.12
4	Ron Guidry	.40	.20	.12
5	Bert Blyleven	.80	.40	.25
6	Dave Kingman	.30	.15	.09
7	Jeff Newman	.30	.15	.09
8	Steve Rogers	.30	.15	.09
9	George Brett	4.00	2.00	1.25
10	Bruce Sutter	.60	.30	.20
11	Gorman Thomas	.30	.15	.09
12	Darrell Porter	.30	.15	.09
13	Roy Smalley	.30	.15	.09
14	Steve Carlton	1.50	.70	.45
15	Jim Palmer	1.50	.70	.45
16	Bob Bailor	.30	.15	.09
17	Jason Thompson	.30	.15	.09
18	Graig Nettles	.40	.20	.12
19	Ron Cey	.50	.25	.15
20	Nolan Ryan	5.00	2.50	1.50
21	Ellis Valentine	.30	.15	.09
22	Larry Hisle	.30	.15	.09
23	Dave Parker	.90	.45	.25
24	Eddie Murray	1.00	.50	.30
25	Willie Stargell	1.50	.70	.45
26	Reggie Jackson	2.50	1.25	.70
27	Carl Yastrzemski	3.50	1.75	1.00
28	Andre Thornton	.40	.20	.12
29	Davey Lopes	.40	.20	.12
30	Ken Singleton	.40	.20	.12
31	Steve Garvey	2.00	1.00	.60
32	Dave Winfield	2.50	1.25	.70
33	Steve Kemp	.40	.20	.12
34	Claudell Washington	.40	.20	.12
35	Pete Rose	5.00	2.50	1.50
36	Cesar Cedeno	.40	.20	.12
37	John Stearns	.30	.15	.09
38	Lee Mazzilli	.30	.15	.09
39	Larry Bowa	.40	.20	.12
40	Fred Lynn	.80	.40	.25
41	Carlton Fisk	.90	.45	.25
42	Vida Blue	.50	.25	.15
43	Keith Hernandez	.50	.25	.15
44	Jim Rice	.75	.40	.25
45	Ted Simmons	.50	.25	.15
46	Chet Lemon	.30	.15	.09
47	Fergie Jenkins	1.00	.50	.30
48	Gary Matthews	.40	.20	.12
49	Tom Seaver	2.50	1.25	.70
50	George Foster	.70	.35	.20
51	Phil Niekro	.75	.40	.25
52	Johnny Bench	2.50	1.25	.70
53	Buddy Bell	.50	.25	.15
54	Lance Parrish	.50	.25	.15
55	Joaquin Andujar	.30	.15	.09
56	Don Baylor	.50	.25	.15
57	Jack Clark	.40	.20	.12
58	J.R. Richard	.30	.15	.09
59	Bruce Bochte	.30	.15	.09
60	Rod Carew	2.50	1.25	.70

Grading Guide

Mint (MT): A perfect card. Well-centered with all corners sharp and square. No creases, stains, edge nicks, surface marks, yellowing or fading.

Near Mint (NM): A nearly perfect card. At first glance, a NM card appears to be perfect. May be slightly off-center. No surface marks, creases or loss of gloss.

Excellent (EX): Corners are still fairly sharp with only moderate wear. Borders may be off-center. No creases or stains on fronts or backs, but may show slight loss of surface luster.

Very Good (VG): Shows obvious handling. May have rounded corners, minor creases, major gum or wax stains. No major creases, tape marks, writing, etc.

Good (G): A well-worn card, but exhibits no intentional damage. May have major or multiple creases. Corners may be rounded well beyond card border.

1981 Kellogg's

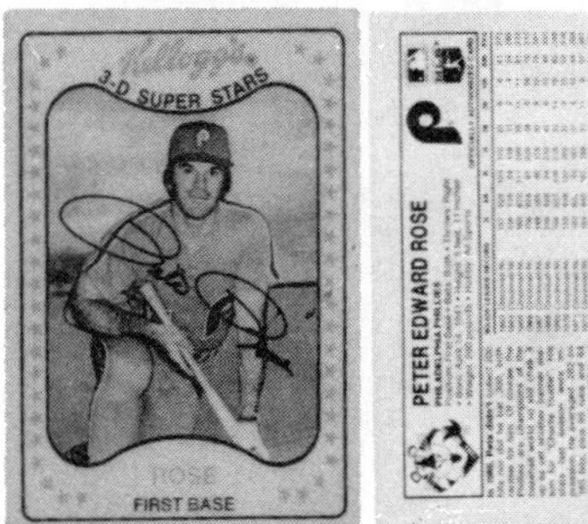

"Bigger" is the word to best describe Kellogg's 1981 card set. Not only were the cards themselves larger than ever before at 2-1/2" by 3-1/2", but the size of the set was increased to 66, the largest since the 75-card issues of 1970-71. The '81 Kellogg's set was available only as complete sets by mail. It is thought that the wider format of the 1981s may help prevent the problems of curling and cracking from which other years of Kellogg's issues suffer.

		MT	NR MT	EX
Complete Set:		12.00	9.00	4.75
Common Player:		.15	.11	.06
1	George Foster	.15	.11	.06
2	Jim Palmer	.60	.45	.25
3	Reggie Jackson	1.25	.90	.50
4	Al Oliver	.15	.11	.06
5	Mike Schmidt	1.25	.90	.50
6	Nolan Ryan	2.00	1.50	.80
7	Bucky Dent	.15	.11	.06
8	George Brett	1.25	.90	.50
9	Jim Rice	.35	.25	.14
10	Steve Garvey	.40	.30	.15
11	Willie Stargell	.60	.45	.25
12	Phil Niekro	.25	.20	.10
13	Dave Parker	.20	.15	.08
14	Cesar Cedeno	.15	.11	.06
15	Don Baylor	.15	.11	.06
16	J.R. Richard	.15	.11	.06
17	Tony Perez	.15	.11	.06
18	Eddie Murray	.60	.45	.25
19	Chet Lemon	.15	.11	.06
20	Ben Oglivie	.15	.11	.06
21	Dave Winfield	.60	.45	.25
22	Joe Morgan	.60	.45	.25
23	Vida Blue	.15	.11	.06
24	Willie Wilson	.15	.11	.06
25	Steve Henderson	.15	.11	.06
26	Rod Carew	1.00	.70	.40
27	Garry Templeton	.15	.11	.06
28	Dave Concepcion	.15	.11	.06
29	Davey Lopes	.15	.11	.06
30	Ken Landreaux	.15	.11	.06
31	Keith Hernandez	.20	.15	.08
32	Cecil Cooper	.15	.11	.06
33	Rickey Henderson	1.00	.70	.40
34	Frank White	.15	.11	.06
35	George Hendrick	.15	.11	.06
36	Reggie Smith	.15	.11	.06
37	Tug McGraw	.15	.11	.06
38	Tom Seaver	1.00	.70	.40
39	Ken Singleton	.15	.11	.06
40	Fred Lynn	.20	.15	.08
41	Rich "Goose" Gossage	.20	.15	.08
42	Terry Puhl	.15	.11	.06
43	Larry Bowa	.15	.11	.06
44	Phil Garner	.15	.11	.06
45	Ron Guidry	.20	.15	.08
46	Lee Mazzilli	.15	.11	.06
47	Dave Kingman	.15	.11	.06
48	Carl Yastrzemski	1.00	.70	.40
49	Rick Burleson	.15	.11	.06
50	Steve Carlton	.60	.45	.25
51	Alan Trammell	.30	.25	.12
52	Tommy John	.20	.15	.08
53	Paul Molitor	.50	.40	.20
54	Joe Charboneau	.15	.11	.06
55	Rick Langford	.15	.11	.06
56	Bruce Sutter	.15	.11	.06
57	Robin Yount	.60	.45	.25
58	Steve Stone	.15	.11	.06
59	Larry Gura	.15	.11	.06
60	Mike Flanagan	.15	.11	.06
61	Bob Horner	.15	.11	.06
62	Bruce Bochte	.15	.11	.06
63	Pete Rose	1.00	.70	.40
64	Buddy Bell	.15	.11	.06
65	Johnny Bench	1.00	.70	.40
66	Mike Hargrove	.15	.11	.06

Values for recent cards and sets are listed in Mint (MT), Near Mint (NM), reflecting the fact that many cards from recent years have been preserved in top condition. Recent cards and sets in less than Excellent condition have little collector interest.

1982 Kellogg's

For the second straight year in 1982, Kellogg's cards were not inserted into cereal boxes, but had to be obtained by sending cash and box tops to the company for complete sets. The '82 cards were downsized both in number of cards in the set - 64 - and in physical dimensions, 2-1/8" by 3-1/4".

		MT	NR MT	EX
Complete Set:		16.00	12.00	6.50
Common Player:		.12	.09	.05
1	Richie Zisk	.12	.09	.05
2	Bill Buckner	.12	.09	.05
3	George Brett	1.00	.70	.40
4	Rickey Henderson	.90	.70	.35
5	Jack Morris	.30	.25	.12
6	Ozzie Smith	.25	.20	.10
7	Rollie Fingers	.35	.25	.14
8	Tom Seaver	.50	.40	.20
9	Fernando Valenzuela	.20	.15	.08
10	Hubie Brooks	.12	.09	.05
11	Nolan Ryan	1.50	1.25	.60
12	Dave Winfield	.60	.45	.25
13	Bob Horner	.20	.15	.08
14	Reggie Jackson	1.00	.70	.40
15	Burt Hooton	.12	.09	.05
16	Mike Schmidt	1.00	.70	.40
17	Bruce Sutter	.20	.15	.08
18	Pete Rose	1.00	.70	.40
19	Dave Kingman	.12	.09	.05
20	Neil Allen	.12	.09	.05
21	Don Sutton	.25	.20	.10
22	Dave Concepcion	.20	.15	.08
23	Keith Hernandez	.12	.09	.05
24	Gary Carter	.30	.25	.12
25	Carlton Fisk	.30	.25	.12
26	Ron Guidry	.25	.20	.10
27	Steve Carlton	.75	.60	.30
28	Robin Yount	.60	.45	.25
29	John Castino	.12	.09	.05
30	Johnny Bench	1.00	.70	.40
31	Bob Knepper	.12	.09	.05
32	Rich "Goose" Gossage	.20	.15	.08
33	Buddy Bell	.20	.15	.08
34	Art Howe	.12	.09	.05
35	Tony Armas	.12	.09	.05
36	Phil Niekro	.30	.25	.12
37	Len Barker	.12	.09	.05
38	Bobby Grich	.20	.15	.08
39	Steve Kemp	.12	.09	.05
40	Kirk Gibson	.25	.20	.10
41	Carney Lansford	.12	.09	.05
42	Jim Palmer	.60	.45	.25
43	Carl Yastrzemski	.90	.70	.35
44	Rick Burleson	.12	.09	.05
45	Dwight Evans	.15	.11	.06
46	Ron Cey	.15	.11	.06
47	Steve Garvey	.40	.30	.15
48	Dave Parker	.30	.25	.12
49	Mike Easler	.12	.09	.05
50	Dusty Baker	.12	.09	.05
51	Rod Carew	.70	.50	.30
52	Chris Chambliss	.12	.09	.05
53	Tim Raines	.35	.25	.14
54	Chet Lemon	.12	.09	.05
55	Bill Madlock	.20	.15	.08
56	George Foster	.20	.15	.08
57	Dwayne Murphy	.12	.09	.05
58	Ken Singleton	.20	.15	.08
59	Mike Norris	.12	.09	.05
60	Cecil Cooper	.20	.15	.08
61	Al Oliver	.20	.15	.08
62	Willie Wilson	.25	.20	.10
63	Vida Blue	.20	.15	.08
64	Eddie Murray	.50	.40	.20

Definitions for grading conditions are located in the Introduction of this price guide.

1983 Kellogg's

In its 14th consecutive year of baseball card issue, Kellogg's returned to the policy of inserting single cards into cereal boxes, as well as offering complete sets by a mail-in box top redemption offer.

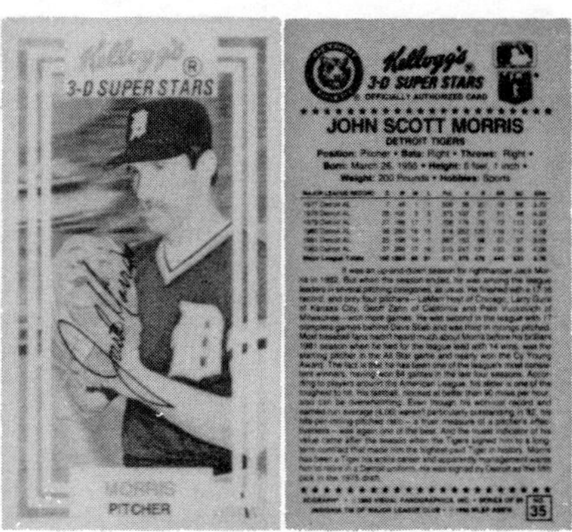

The 3-D cards themselves returned to a narrow 1-7/8" by 3-1/4" format, while the set size was reduced to 60 cards.

		MT	NR MT	EX
Complete Set:		15.00	11.00	6.00
Common Player:		.10	.08	.04
1	Rod Carew	.80	.60	.30
2	Rollie Fingers	.40	.30	.15
3	Reggie Jackson	.80	.60	.30
4	George Brett	.80	.60	.30
5	Hal McRae	.15	.11	.06
6	Pete Rose	.80	.60	.30
7	Fernando Valenzuela	.15	.11	.06
8	Rickey Henderson	.70	.50	.30
9	Carl Yastrzemski	.80	.60	.30
10	Rich "Goose" Gossage	.15	.11	.06
11	Eddie Murray	.50	.40	.20
12	Buddy Bell	.10	.08	.04
13	Jim Rice	.15	.11	.06
14	Robin Yount	.80	.60	.30
15	Dave Winfield	.80	.60	.30
16	Harold Baines	.20	.15	.08
17	Garry Templeton	.10	.08	.04
18	Bill Madlock	.10	.08	.04
19	Pete Vuckovich	.10	.08	.04
20	Pedro Guerrero	.10	.08	.04
21	Ozzie Smith	.25	.20	.10
22	George Foster	.10	.08	.04
23	Willie Wilson	.15	.11	.06
24	Johnny Ray	.10	.08	.04
25	George Hendrick	.10	.08	.04
26	Andre Thornton	.10	.08	.04
27	Leon Durham	.10	.08	.04
28	Cecil Cooper	.10	.08	.04
29	Don Baylor	.15	.11	.06
30	Lonnie Smith	.10	.08	.04
31	Nolan Ryan	1.25	.90	.50
32	Dan Quiesenberry (Quisenberry)	.10	.08	.04
33	Len Barker	.10	.08	.04
34	Neil Allen	.10	.08	.04
35	Jack Morris	.20	.15	.08
36	Dave Stieb	.15	.11	.06
37	Bruce Sutter	.15	.11	.06
38	Jim Sundberg	.10	.08	.04
39	Jim Palmer	.50	.40	.20
40	Lance Parrish	.20	.15	.08
41	Floyd Bannister	.10	.08	.04
42	Larry Gura	.10	.08	.04
43	Britt Burns	.10	.08	.04
44	Toby Harrah	.10	.08	.04
45	Steve Carlton	.50	.40	.20
46	Greg Minton	.10	.08	.04
47	Gorman Thomas	.10	.08	.04
48	Jack Clark	.15	.11	.06
49	Keith Hernandez	.15	.11	.06
50	Greg Luzinski	.15	.11	.06
51	Fred Lynn	.25	.20	.10
52	Dale Murphy	.70	.50	.30
53	Kent Hrbek	.20	.15	.08
54	Bob Horner	.10	.08	.04
55	Gary Carter	.30	.25	.12
56	Carlton Fisk	.30	.25	.12
57	Dave Concepcion	.15	.11	.06
58	Mike Schmidt	.80	.60	.30
59	Bill Buckner	.10	.08	.04
60	Bobby Grich	.10	.08	.04

A player's name in italic type indicates a rookie card. An (FC) indicates a player's first card for that particular card company.

1991 Kellogg's 3-D

In 1991, specially-marked packages of Kellogg's Corn Flakes included 3-D baseball cards, resuming a tradition that began in 1970 and continued without interruption until 1983. In the 1991 edition, there are 15 cards to collect, featuring many of the greatest living retired stars in the game. Most of the players are in the Hall of Fame. The card fronts show two pictures of the player, while the backs include career

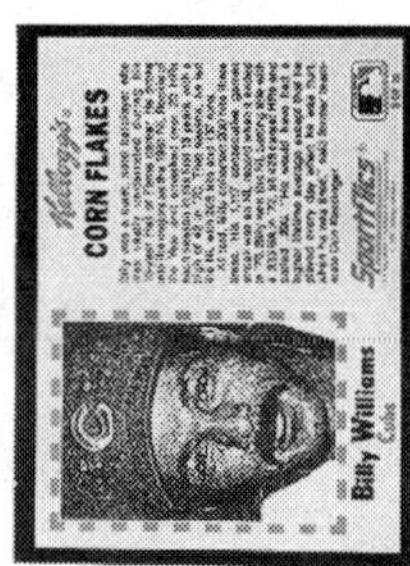

highlights and a portrait. The cards are 2-1/2" x 3-5/16", numbered and were made by Sportflics. A complete set was available via a mail-in offer for $4.95 plus proofs of purchase.

		MT	NR MT	EX
Complete Set:		6.00	4.50	2.50
Common Player:		.25	.20	.10
1	Gaylord Perry	.25	.20	.10
2	Hank Aaron	1.00	.70	.40
3	Willie Mays	1.00	.70	.40
4	Ernie Banks	.75	.60	.30
5	Bob Gibson	.50	.40	.20
6	Harmon Killebrew	.50	.40	.20
7	Rollie Fingers	.25	.20	.10
8	Steve Carlton	.25	.20	.10
9	Billy Williams	.25	.20	.10
10	Lou Brock	.25	.20	.10
11	Yogi Berra	.75	.60	.30
12	Warren Spahn	.50	.40	.20
13	Boog Powell	.25	.20	.10
14	Don Baylor	.25	.20	.10
15	Ralph Kiner	.25	.20	.10

1991 Kellogg's Baseball Greats

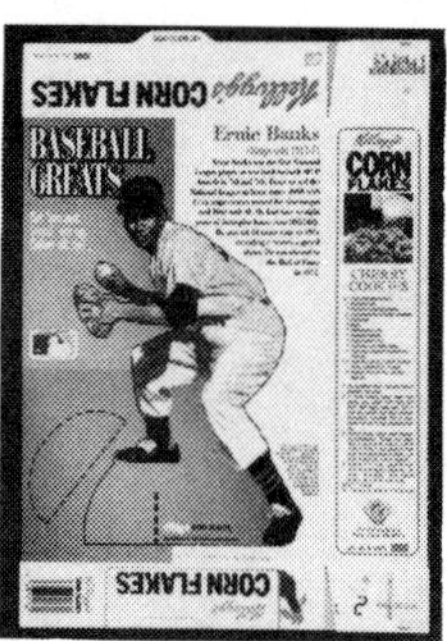

Six Hall of Famers are featured on the backs of 7- and 12-ounce Corn Flakes boxes. The photos are designed to be cut out and assembled as a stand-up figure. A career summary also appears on the box back.

		MT	NR MT	EX
Complete Set (6):		12.00	9.00	4.75
Common Player:		2.00	1.50	.80
(1)	Hank Aaron	3.00	2.25	1.25
(2)	Ernie Banks	2.50	2.00	1.00
(3)	Yogi Berra	2.50	2.00	1.00
(4)	Lou Brock	2.00	1.50	.80
(5)	Steve Carlton	2.00	1.50	.80
(6)	Bob Gibson	2.00	1.50	.80

1992 Kellogg's 3-D

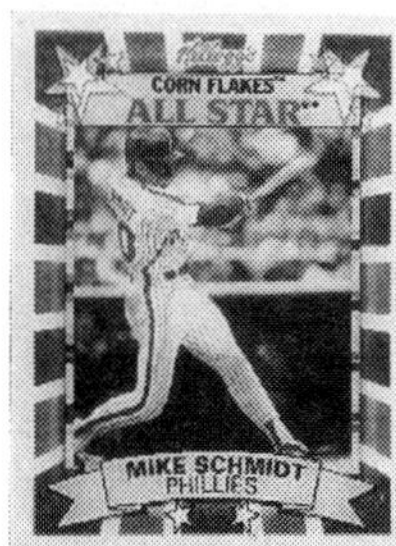

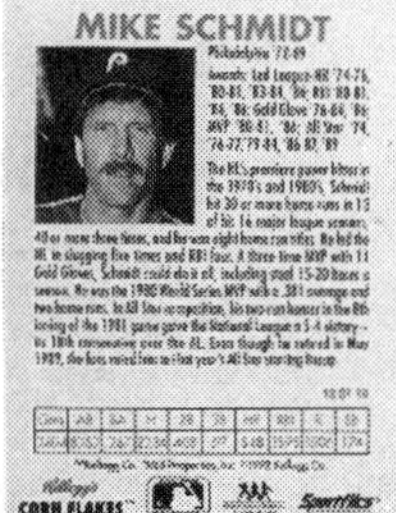

Kellogg's cereal company created a 10-card 1992 All Star set of retired stars, with one card inserted in specially-marked boxes of corn flakes, and complete sets available by mail. The cards, produced by Sportflics/Optigraphics feature two sequential action images on each front. Red, white and blue designs comprise the border, with yellow bands above and beneath the photo. On back is a black-and-white portrait photo, plus a career summary and a MLB, few stats, along with the logos for the cereal company, the Major League Baseball Players Alumni and Sportflics. As in the previous year, cards are slightly longer, at 2-1/2" x 5/16", than standard size.

		MT	NR MT	EX
Complete Set:		3.00	2.25	1.25
Common Player:		.25	.20	.10
1	Willie Stargell	.50	.40	.20
2	Tony Perez	.25	.20	.10
3	Jim Palmer	.50	.40	.20
4	Rod Carew	.50	.40	.20
5	Tom Seaver	.50	.40	.20
6	Phil Niekro	.25	.20	.10
7	Bill Madlock	.25	.20	.10
8	Jim Rice	.25	.20	.10
9	Dan Quisenberry	.25	.20	.10
10	Mike Schmidt	.50	.40	.20

1969 Kelly's Potato Chips Pins

Consisting of 20 pins, each measuring approximately 1-3/16" in diameter, this set was issued by Kelly's Potato Chips in 1969 and has a heavy emphasis on St. Louis Cardinals. The pin has a black and white player photo in the center surrounded by either a red border (for A.L. players) or a blue border (for N.L. players) that displays the player's team and name at the top and bottom. "Kelly's" appears to the left while the word "Zip!" is printed to the right. The pins are unnumbered.

		NR MT	EX	VG
Complete Set:		150.00	75.00	45.00
Common Player:		1.50	.70	.45
(1)	Luis Aparicio	7.00	3.50	2.00
(2)	Ernie Banks	15.00	7.50	4.50
(3)	Glenn Beckert	1.50	.70	.45
(4)	Lou Brock	10.00	5.00	3.00
(5)	Curt Flood	2.00	1.00	.60
(6)	Bob Gibson	10.00	5.00	3.00
(7)	Joel Horlen	1.50	.70	.45
(8)	Al Kaline	10.00	5.00	3.00
(9)	Don Kessinger	1.50	.70	.45
(10)	Mickey Lolich	2.50	1.25	.70
(11)	Juan Marichal	8.00	4.00	2.50
(12)	Willie Mays	22.00	11.00	6.50
(13)	Tim McCarver	2.50	1.25	.70
(14)	Denny McLain	2.50	1.25	.70
(15)	Pete Rose	20.00	10.00	6.00
(16)	Ron Santo	2.50	1.25	.70
(17)	Joe Torre	2.50	1.25	.70
(18)	Pete Ward	1.50	.70	.45
(19)	Billy Williams	7.00	3.50	2.00
(20)	Carl Yastrzemski	15.00	7.50	4.50

1988 Kenner Starting Lineup

This massive three-sport set was distributed in conjuntion with Kenner's Starting Lineup sports figurines, one card per statue. Cards were not sold separately. Baseball, football and basketball stars were included in the lineup of full-color figurines, with 123 figure/card combinations devoted to baseball. Individual major league team assortments include one to seven players per team. The figurines are mildly reminiscent of the 1950s Hartland Statues, but Kenner's version features smaller (4" to 6") figures and a more extensive catalog which includes athletes other than baseball players. The Starting Lineup cards feature action photos framed in red and white, with the "Starting Lineup" logo in the upper left corner and the player's name printed along the bottom border. Colorful team logos are superimposed in the lower right corner of the player photos. Card backs

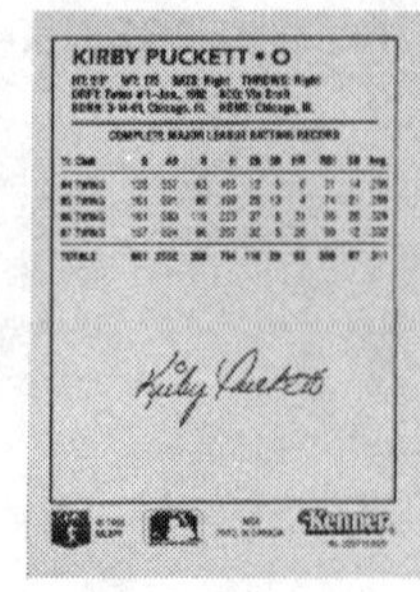

were printed in blue and contain major league stats, a few biographical details, a facsimile autograph and the major league and Kenner logos. The values in the checklist that follows include both the statue and card for the 123 baseball players in the set. Several players which were included in the checklist printed on the package were never produced.

		MT	NR MT	EX
Complete Set:		2200.	1650.	880.00
Common Player:		9.00	6.75	3.50
(1)	Alan Ashby	11.00	8.25	4.50
(2)	Harold Baines	11.00	8.25	4.50
(3)	Kevin Bass	10.00	7.50	4.00
(4)	Steve Bedrosian	9.00	6.75	3.50
(5)	Buddy Bell	9.00	6.75	3.50
(6)	George Bell	9.00	6.75	3.50
(7)	Mike Boddicker	11.00	8.25	4.50
(8)	Wade Boggs	21.00	15.50	8.50
(9)	Barry Bonds	50.00	37.00	20.00
(10)	Bobby Bonilla	15.00	11.00	6.00
(11)	Sid Bream	12.00	9.00	4.75
(12)	George Brett	42.00	31.00	17.00
(13)	Chris Brown	11.00	8.25	4.50
(14)	Tom Brunansky	9.00	6.75	3.50
(15)	Ellis Burks	17.50	13.00	7.00
(16)	Jose Canseco	28.00	21.00	11.00
(17)	Gary Carter	9.00	6.75	3.50
(18)	Joe Carter	24.00	18.00	9.50
(19)	Jack Clark	14.00	10.50	5.50
(20)	Will Clark	29.00	22.00	11.50
(21)	Roger Clemens	24.00	18.00	9.50
(22)	Vince Coleman	9.00	6.75	3.50
(23)	Kal Daniels	9.00	6.75	3.50
(24)	Alvin Davis	11.00	8.25	4.50
(25)	Eric Davis	9.00	6.75	3.50
(26)	Glenn Davis	11.00	8.25	4.50
(27)	Jody Davis	9.00	6.75	3.50
(28)	Andre Dawson	18.00	13.50	7.25
(29)	Rob Deer	11.00	8.25	4.50
(30)	Brian Downing	9.00	6.75	3.50
(31)	Mike Dunne	9.00	6.75	3.50
(32)	Shawon Dunston	15.00	11.00	6.00
(33)	Leon Durham	11.00	8.25	4.50
(34)	Len Dykstra	19.00	14.00	7.50
(35)	Dwight Evans	9.00	6.75	3.50
(36)	Carlton Fisk	49.00	37.00	19.50
(37)	John Franco	9.00	6.75	3.50
(38)	Julio Franco	9.00	6.75	3.50
(39)	Gary Gaetti	9.00	6.75	3.50
(40)	Dwight Gooden	11.00	8.25	4.50
(41)	Ken Griffey, Sr.	18.00	13.50	7.25
(42)	Pedro Guerrero	9.00	6.75	3.50
(43)	Ozzie Guillen	13.00	9.75	5.25
(44)	Tony Gwynn	26.00	19.50	10.50
(45)	Mel Hall	9.00	6.75	3.50
(46)	Billy Hatcher	9.00	6.75	3.50
(47)	Von Hayes	11.00	8.25	4.50
(48)	Rickey Henderson	22.00	16.50	8.75
(49)	Keith Hernandez	11.00	8.25	4.50
(50)	Willie Hernandez	11.00	8.25	4.50
(51)	Tom Herr	9.00	6.75	3.50
(52)	Ted Higuera	12.00	9.00	4.75
(53)	Charlie Hough	9.00	6.75	3.50
(54)	Kent Hrbek	9.00	6.75	3.50
(55)	Pete Incaviglia	9.00	6.75	3.50
(56)	Howard Johnson	15.00	11.00	6.00
(57)	Wally Joyner	9.00	6.75	3.50
(58)	Terry Kennedy	11.00	8.25	4.50
(59)	John Kruk	25.00	18.50	10.00
(60)	Mark Langston	25.00	18.50	10.00
(61)	Carney Lansford	18.00	13.50	7.25
(62)	Jeffrey Leonard	11.00	8.25	4.50
(63)	Fred Lynn	13.00	9.75	5.25
(64)	Candy Maldonado	12.00	9.00	4.75
(65)	Mike Marshall	15.00	11.00	6.00
(66)	Don Mattingly	23.00	17.00	9.25
(67)	Willie McGee	9.00	6.75	3.50
(68)	Mark McGwire	35.00	26.00	14.00
(69)	Kevin McReynolds	11.00	8.25	4.50
(70)	Paul Molitor	35.00	26.00	14.00
(71)	Donnie Moore	14.00	10.50	5.50
(72)	Jack Morris	15.00	11.00	6.00
(73)	Dale Murphy	11.00	8.25	4.50
(74)	Eddie Murray	20.00	15.00	8.00
(75)	Matt Nokes	9.00	6.75	3.50
(76)	Pete O'Brien	9.00	6.75	3.50
(77)	Ken Oberkfell	9.00	6.75	3.50
(78)	Dave Parker	22.00	16.50	8.75
(79)	Larry Parrish	9.00	6.75	3.50
(80)	Ken Phelps	15.00	11.00	6.00
(81)	Jim Presley	11.00	8.25	4.50

(82)	Kirby Puckett	32.00	24.00	13.00
(83)	Dan Quisenberry	9.00	6.75	3.50
(84)	Tim Raines	11.00	8.25	4.50
(85)	Willie Randolph	9.00	6.75	3.50
(86)	Shane Rawley	9.00	6.75	3.50
(87)	Jeff Reardon	15.00	11.00	6.00
(88)	Gary Redus	11.00	8.25	4.50
(89)	Rick Reuschel	9.00	6.75	3.50
(90)	Jim Rice	14.00	10.50	5.50
(91)	Dave Righetti	11.00	8.25	4.50
(92)	Cal Ripken, Jr.	100.00	75.00	40.00
(93)	Pete Rose	26.00	19.50	10.50
(94)	Nolan Ryan	265.00	199.00	106.00
(95)	Bret Saberhagen	9.00	6.75	3.50
(96)	Juan Samuel	9.00	6.75	3.50
(97)	Ryne Sandberg	50.00	37.00	20.00
(98)	Benito Santiago	11.00	8.25	4.50
(99)	Steve Sax	9.00	6.75	3.50
(100)	Mike Schmidt	41.00	31.00	16.50
(101)	Mike Scott	9.00	6.75	3.50
(102)	Kevin Seitzer	15.00	11.00	6.00
(103)	Ruben Sierra	24.00	18.00	9.50
(104)	Ozzie Smith	20.00	15.00	8.00
(105)	Zane Smith	9.00	6.75	3.50
(106)	Cory Snyder	9.00	6.75	3.50
(107)	Darryl Strawberry	9.00	6.75	3.50
(108)	Franklin Stubbs	15.00	11.00	6.00
(109)	B.J. Surhoff	9.00	6.75	3.50
(110)	Rick Sutcliffe	9.00	6.75	3.50
(111)	Pat Tabler	9.00	6.75	3.50
(112)	Danny Tartabull	15.00	11.00	6.00
(113)	Alan Trammell	13.00	9.75	5.25
(114)	Fernando Valenzuela	9.00	6.75	3.50
(115)	Andy Van Slyke	17.50	13.00	7.00
(116)	Frank Viola	12.00	9.00	4.75
(117)	Ozzie Virgil	9.00	6.75	3.50
(118)	Greg Walker	9.00	6.75	3.50
(119)	Lou Whitaker	19.00	14.00	7.50
(120)	Devon White	25.00	18.50	10.00
(121)	Dave Winfield	30.00	22.00	12.00
(122)	Mike Witt	9.00	6.75	3.50
(123)	Todd Worrell	11.00	8.25	4.50
(124)	Robin Yount	60.00	45.00	24.00

1989 Kenner Starting Lineup

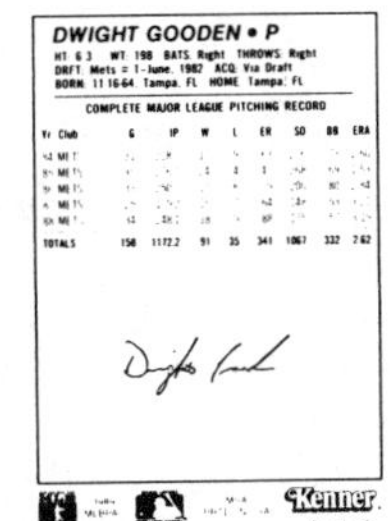

Kenner returned in 1989 with another set of sports figurines and accompanying trading cards. As in the previous year, the figurines were sold individually in a blister pack with one card packaged with each figure. No cards were sold separately. The 1989 cards have a green border with the "Starting Lineup" logo in the upper left, while the words "1989 Edition" and the player's name and uniform number appear at bottom. Backs are identical in format to the previous year. The values listed here are for complete, unopened packages of figure and card. Values are based on relative scarcity, resulting in some minor stars and common players being priced higher than superstars, whose cards and figures were produced in much greater numbers.

		MT	NR MT	EX
	Complete Set:	2550.	1912.	1020.
	Common Player:	8.00	6.00	3.25
(1)	Roberto Alomar	80.00	60.00	32.00
(2)	Brady Anderson	11.00	8.25	4.50
(3)	Harold Baines	12.00	9.00	4.75
(4)	Marty Barrett	9.00	6.75	3.50
(5)	Kevin Bass	9.00	6.75	3.50
(6)	Steve Bedrosian	9.00	6.75	3.50
(7)	George Bell	11.00	8.25	4.50
(8)	Damon Berryhill	9.00	6.75	3.50
(9)	Wade Boggs	14.00	10.50	5.50
(10)	Barry Bonds	50.00	37.00	20.00
(11)	Bobby Bonilla	12.00	9.00	4.75
(12)	Phil Bradley	9.00	6.75	3.50
(13)	Glenn Braggs	8.00	6.00	3.25
(14)	George Brett	40.00	30.00	16.00
(15)	Tom Brookens	9.00	6.75	3.50
(16)	Tom Brunansky	12.00	9.00	4.75
(17)	Steve Buechele	9.00	6.75	3.50
(18)	Ellis Burks	11.00	8.25	4.50
(19)	Brett Butler	11.00	8.25	4.50
(20)	Ivan Calderon	11.00	8.25	4.50
(21)	Jose Canseco	12.00	9.00	4.75
(22)	Gary Carter	8.00	6.00	3.25
(23)	Joe Carter	8.00	6.00	3.25
(24)	Will Clark	16.00	12.00	6.50
(25)	Roger Clemens	22.00	16.50	8.75
(26)	Vince Coleman	10.00	7.50	4.00
(27)	David Cone	11.00	8.25	4.50
(28)	Kal Daniels	8.00	6.00	3.25
(29)	Alvin Davis	8.00	6.00	3.25
(30)	Chili Davis	60.00	45.00	24.00
(31)	Eric Davis	9.00	6.75	3.50
(32)	Glenn Davis	8.00	6.00	3.25
(33)	Mark Davis	8.00	6.00	3.25
(34)	Andre Dawson	13.00	9.75	5.25
(35)	Rob Deer	9.00	6.75	3.50
(36)	Bo Diaz	9.00	6.75	3.50
(37)	Bill Doran	14.00	10.50	5.50
(38)	Doug Drabek	13.00	9.75	5.25
(39)	Shawon Dunston	12.00	9.00	4.75
(40)	Len Dykstra	13.00	9.75	5.25
(41)	Dennis Eckersley	40.00	30.00	16.00
(42)	Kevin Elster	8.00	6.00	3.25
(43)	Scott Fletcher	9.00	6.75	3.50
(44)	John Franco	8.00	6.00	3.25
(45)	Gary Gaetti	8.00	6.00	3.25
(46)	Ron Gant	70.00	52.00	28.00
(47)	Kirk Gibson	11.00	8.25	4.50
(48)	Dan Gladden	9.00	6.75	3.50
(49)	Dwight Gooden	11.00	8.25	4.50
(50)	Mark Grace	23.00	17.00	9.25
(51)	Mike Greenwell	9.00	6.75	3.50
(52)	Mark Gubicza	11.00	8.25	4.50
(53)	Pedro Guerrero	9.00	6.75	3.50
(54)	Ozzie Guillen	11.00	8.25	4.50
(55)	Tony Gwynn	35.00	26.00	14.00
(56)	Albert Hall	9.00	6.75	3.50
(57)	Mel Hall	9.00	6.75	3.50
(58)	Billy Hatcher	9.00	6.75	3.50
(59)	Von Hayes	9.00	6.75	3.50
(60)	Rickey Henderson	14.00	10.50	5.50
(61)	Mike Henneman	8.00	6.00	3.25
(62)	Keith Hernandez	8.00	6.00	3.25
(63)	Orel Hershiser	15.00	11.00	6.00
(64)	Ted Higuera	8.00	6.00	3.25
(65)	Jack Howell	50.00	37.00	20.00
(66)	Kent Hrbek	8.00	6.00	3.25
(67)	Pete Incaviglia	8.00	6.00	3.25
(68)	Bo Jackson	24.00	18.00	9.50
(69)	Danny Jackson	9.00	6.75	3.50
(70)	Brook Jacoby	8.00	6.00	3.25
(71)	Chris James	8.00	6.00	3.25
(72)	Dion James	8.00	6.00	3.25
(73)	Gregg Jefferies	24.00	18.00	9.50
(74)	Doug Jones	13.00	9.75	5.25
(75)	Wally Joyner	15.00	11.00	6.00
(76)	John Kruk	32.00	24.00	13.00
(77)	Mike LaValliere	9.00	6.75	3.50
(78)	Mark Langston	11.00	8.25	4.50
(79)	Carney Lansford	11.00	8.25	4.50
(80)	Barry Larkin	30.00	22.00	12.00
(81)	Tim Laudner	9.00	6.75	3.50
(82)	Al Leiter	9.00	6.75	3.50
(83)	Chet Lemon	9.00	6.75	3.50
(84)	Jose Lind	11.00	8.25	4.50
(85)	Greg Maddux	35.00	26.00	14.00
(86)	Candy Maldonado	11.00	8.25	4.50
(87)	Mike Marshall	9.00	6.75	3.50
(88)	Don Mattingly	14.00	10.50	5.50
(89)	Willie McGee	8.00	6.00	3.25
(90)	Mark McGwire	14.00	10.50	5.50
(91)	Kevin McReynolds	11.00	8.25	4.50
(92)	Kevin Mitchell	12.00	9.00	4.75
(93)	Paul Molitor	28.00	21.00	11.00
(94)	Jack Morris	11.00	8.25	4.50
(95)	Dale Murphy	11.00	8.25	4.50
(96)	Randy Myers	9.00	6.75	3.50
(97)	Matt Nokes	11.00	8.25	4.50
(98)	Mike Pagliarulo	9.00	6.75	3.50
(99)	Dave Parker	11.00	8.25	4.50
(100)	Dan Pasqua	9.00	6.75	3.50
(101)	Tony Pena	11.00	8.25	4.50
(102)	Terry Pendleton	20.00	15.00	8.00
(103)	Melido Perez	9.00	6.75	3.50
(104)	Gerald Perry	8.00	6.00	3.25
(105)	Dan Plesac	8.00	6.00	3.25
(106)	Kirby Puckett	24.00	18.00	9.50
(107)	Rey Quinones	9.00	6.75	3.50
(108)	Tim Raines	11.00	8.25	4.50
(109)	Johnny Ray	45.00	34.00	18.00
(110)	Jeff Reardon	13.00	9.75	5.25
(111)	Harold Reynolds	8.00	6.00	3.25
(112)	Jim Rice	9.00	6.75	3.50
(113)	Dave Righetti	11.00	8.25	4.50
(114)	Cal Ripken, Jr.	60.00	45.00	24.00
(115)	Jeff Russell	14.00	10.50	5.50
(116)	Bret Saberhagen	13.00	9.75	5.25
(117)	Chris Sabo	11.00	8.25	4.50
(118)	Luis Salazar	9.00	6.75	3.50
(119)	Juan Samuel	9.00	6.75	3.50
(120)	Ryne Sandberg	26.00	19.50	10.50
(121)	Benito Santiago	11.00	8.25	4.50
(122)	Mike Schmidt	36.00	27.00	14.50
(123)	Dick Schofield	50.00	37.00	20.00
(124)	Mike Scioscia	12.00	9.00	4.75
(125)	Mike Scott	9.00	6.75	3.50
(126)	Kevin Seitzer	14.00	10.50	5.50
(127)	Larry Sheets	9.00	6.75	3.50
(128)	John Shelby	9.00	6.75	3.50
(129)	Ruben Sierra	30.00	22.00	12.00
(130)	Don Slaught	9.00	6.75	3.50
(131)	Dave Smith	9.00	6.75	3.50
(132)	Lee Smith	23.00	17.00	9.25
(133)	Ozzie Smith	14.00	10.50	5.50
(134)	Zane Smith	9.00	6.75	3.50
(135)	Cory Snyder	8.00	6.00	3.25
(136)	Pete Stanicek	9.00	6.75	3.50
(137)	Terry Steinbach	11.00	8.25	4.50
(138)	Dave Stewart	16.00	12.00	6.50
(139)	Kurt Stillwell	8.00	6.00	3.25
(140)	Darryl Strawberry	9.00	6.75	3.50
(141)	B.J. Surhoff	8.00	6.00	3.25
(142)	Rick Sutcliffe	9.00	6.75	3.50
(143)	Bruce Sutter	12.00	9.00	4.75
(144)	Greg Swindell	9.00	6.75	3.50
(145)	Pat Tabler	10.00	7.50	4.00
(146)	Danny Tartabull	11.00	8.25	4.50
(147)	Bobby Thigpen	13.00	9.75	5.25
(148)	Milt Thompson	9.00	6.75	3.50
(149)	Robby Thompson	8.00	6.00	3.25
(150)	Alan Trammell	12.00	9.00	4.75
(151)	Jeff Treadway	22.00	16.50	8.75
(152)	Jose Uribe	9.00	6.75	3.50
(153)	Fernando Valenzuela	9.00	6.75	3.50
(154)	Andy Van Slyke	9.00	6.75	3.50
(155)	Frank Viola	11.00	8.25	4.50
(156)	Bob Walk	9.00	6.75	3.50
(157)	Greg Walker	13.00	9.75	5.25
(158)	Walt Weiss	13.00	9.75	5.25
(159)	Bob Welch	13.00	9.75	5.25
(160)	Lou Whitaker	11.00	8.25	4.50
(161)	Devon White	70.00	52.00	28.00
(162)	Dave Winfield	16.00	12.00	6.50
(163)	Mike Witt	35.00	26.00	14.00
(164)	Todd Worrell	10.00	7.50	4.00
(165)	Marvell Wynne	9.00	6.75	3.50
(166)	Gerald Young	9.00	6.75	3.50
(167)	Robin Yount	70.00	52.00	28.00

1989 Kenner Starting Lineup Baseball Greats

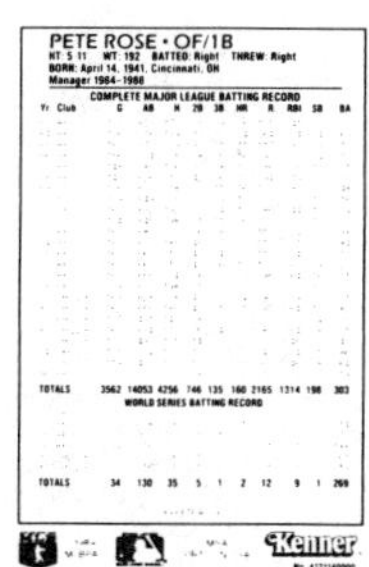

The "Baseball Greats" series of figurines and trading cards was an addition to the Kenner "Starting Lineup" series for 1989. The series features baseball greats of the past, and were packaged two figurines and two collector cards per package. The collector cards that accompany the figures feature an original action photo of the player done in a sepia-tone to enhance the historic nature of the set. The Starting Lineup logo and "Baseball Greats" heading appear at the top of the card. The player's name and a descriptive nickname, such as "Sultan of Swat" appear below the photo. The backs of the cards carry a blue-and-white color scheme and include career stats. The values listed below include both the figure and the card.

		MT	NR MT	EX
	Complete Set:	225.00	169.00	90.00
	Common Player:	20.00	15.00	8.00
(1)	Hank Aaron/Eddie Mathews	22.00	16.50	8.75
(2)	Ernie Banks/Billy Williams	20.00	15.00	8.00
(3)	Johnny Bench/Pete Rose	22.00	16.50	8.75
(4)	Roberto Clemente/Willie Stargell	20.00	15.00	8.00
(5)	Don Drysdale/Reggie Jackson	25.00	18.50	10.00
(6)	Mickey Mantle/Joe DiMaggio	40.00	30.00	16.00
(7)	Willie Mays/Willie McCovey	20.00	15.00	8.00
(8)	Stan Musial/Bob Gibson	22.00	16.50	8.75
(9)	Babe Ruth/Lou Gehrig	25.00	18.50	10.00
(10)	Carl Yastrzemski/Hank Aaron	26.00	19.50	10.50

1990 Kenner Starting Lineup

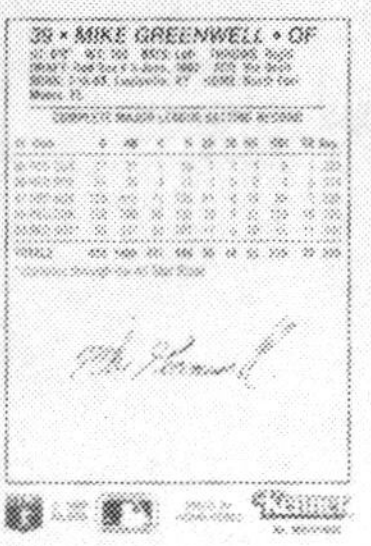

Kenner introduced special bonus rookie year cards with its regular card and statue in 1990. The cards follow designs much like the Kenner cards of 1988 and 1989. The values are based on relative scarcity. Esasky, Backman and Pettis Kenners were pulled when the players switched teams, thus making them rare. Five variations of figures are included in the 1990 set. Prices listed are for unopened package of statue and card.

	MT	NR MT	EX
Complete Set:	1250.	937.00	500.00
Common Player:	6.50	5.00	2.50
(1) Jim Abbott	24.00	18.00	9.50
(2) Sandy Alomar	11.00	8.25	4.50
(3) Allan Anderson	11.00	8.25	4.50
(4) Wally Backman	11.00	8.25	4.50
(5) Jeff Ballard	6.50	5.00	2.50
(6) Jesse Barfield	9.00	6.75	3.50
(7) Steve Bedrosian	6.50	5.00	2.50
(8) Todd Benzinger	11.00	8.25	4.50
(9) Damon Berryhill	8.00	6.00	3.25
(10) Wade Boggs	20.00	15.00	8.00
(11) Barry Bonds	30.00	22.00	12.00
(12) Bobby Bonilla	11.00	8.25	4.50
(13) Chris Bosio	10.00	7.50	4.00
(14) Ellis Burks	11.00	8.25	4.50
(15) Jose Canseco	13.00	9.75	5.25
(16) Joe Carter	22.00	16.50	8.75
(17a) Will Clark (bat held in one hand)	19.00	14.00	7.50
(17b) Will Clark (swinging)	19.00	14.00	7.50
(18) Roger Clemens	20.00	15.00	8.00
(19) Vince Coleman	6.50	5.00	2.50
(20) Ron Darling	6.50	5.00	2.50
(21) Eric Davis	6.50	5.00	2.50
(22) Andre Dawson	11.00	8.25	4.50
(23) Rob Dibble	11.00	8.25	4.50
(24) Len Dykstra	15.00	11.00	6.00
(25) Dennis Eckersley	30.00	22.00	12.00
(26) Nick Esasky	15.00	11.00	6.00
(27) Gary Gaetti	6.50	5.00	2.50
(28) Andres Galarraga	16.00	12.00	6.50
(29) Kirk Gibson	6.50	5.00	2.50
(30) Dwight Gooden	8.00	6.00	3.25
(31a) Mark Grace (standing at bat)	16.00	12.00	6.50
(31b) Mark Grace (swinging)	18.00	13.50	7.25
(32) Mike Greenwell	9.00	6.75	3.50
(33a) Ken Griffey, Jr. (sliding)	52.00	39.00	21.00
(33b) Ken Griffey,Jr. (fielding)	43.00	32.00	17.00
(34) Pedro Guerrero	6.50	5.00	2.50
(35) Von Hayes	6.50	5.00	2.50
(36) Dave Henderson	9.00	6.75	3.50
(37) Rickey Henderson	11.00	8.25	4.50
(38) Tom Herr	6.50	5.00	2.50
(39) Orel Hershiser	11.00	8.25	4.50
(40) Kent Hrbek	6.50	5.00	2.50
(41) Bo Jackson	11.00	8.25	4.50
(42) Gregg Jefferies	12.00	9.00	4.75
(43) Howard Johnson	9.00	6.75	3.50
(44) Ricky Jordan	10.00	7.50	4.00
(45) Roberto Kelly	11.00	8.25	4.50
(46) Barry Larkin	15.00	11.00	6.00
(47) Greg Maddux	15.00	11.00	6.00
(48) Joe Magrane	9.00	6.75	3.50
(49a) Don Mattingly (bat held in one hand)	15.00	11.00	6.00
(49b) Don Mattingly (swinging)	17.00	12.50	6.75
(50) Kevin Mitchell	7.50	5.75	3.00
(51) Ben McDonald	17.00	12.50	6.75
(52) Fred McGriff	20.00	15.00	8.00
(53) Mark McGwire	11.00	8.25	4.50
(54) Kevin McReynolds	6.50	5.00	2.50
(55) Paul Molitor	18.00	13.50	7.25
(56) Eddie Murray	20.00	15.00	8.00
(57) Matt Nokes	9.00	6.75	3.50
(58) Paul O'Neill	11.00	8.25	4.50
(59) Jose Oquendo	6.50	5.00	2.50
(60) Gary Pettis	15.00	11.00	6.00
(61) Kirby Puckett	20.00	15.00	8.00
(62) Willie Randolph	11.00	8.25	4.50
(63) Jody Reed	9.00	6.75	3.50
(64) Rick Reuschel	6.50	5.00	2.50
(65) Dave Righetti	7.50	5.75	3.00
(66) Cal Ripken, Jr.	47.00	35.00	19.00
(67) Nolan Ryan	32.00	24.00	13.00
(68) Chris Sabo	9.00	6.75	3.50
(69) Juan Samuel	9.00	6.75	3.50
(70) Ryne Sandberg	27.00	20.00	11.00
(71) Steve Sax	9.00	6.75	3.50
(72) Mike Scott	9.00	6.75	3.50
(73) Gary Sheffield	23.00	17.00	9.25
(74) John Smiley	6.50	5.00	2.50
(75) Ozzie Smith	14.00	10.50	5.50
(76) Dave Stewart	9.00	6.75	3.50
(77a) Darryl Strawberry (standing at bat)	9.00	6.75	3.50
(77b) Darryl Strawberry (fielding)	13.00	9.75	5.25
(78) Rick Sutcliffe	6.50	5.00	2.50
(79) Mickey Tettleton	11.00	8.25	4.50
(80) Alan Trammell	6.50	5.00	2.50
(81) Andy Van Slyke	13.00	9.75	5.25
(82) Frank Viola	9.00	6.75	3.50
(83) Jerome Walton	7.50	5.75	3.00
(84) Lou Whitaker	9.00	6.75	3.50
(85) Mitch Williams	10.00	7.50	4.00
(86) Dave Winfield	27.00	20.00	11.00
(87) Robin Yount	55.00	41.00	22.00

A card number in parentheses () indicates the set is unnumbered.

1991 Kenner Starting Lineup

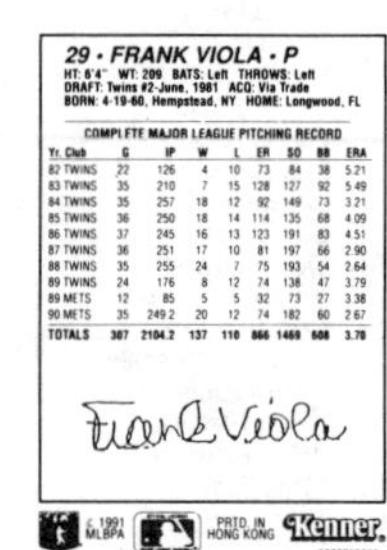

Kenner continued its Starting Lineup with 54 baseball figures for 1991. A bonus with the 1991 card and figure was an aluminum collector coin depicting the player. The 1991 cards featured a yellow border. The players are here alphabetically. Values are based on demand and relative scarcity for complete statue/card/coin unopened packages.

	MT	NR MT	EX
Complete Set:	600.00	450.00	240.00
Common Player:	6.50	5.00	2.50
(1) Jim Abbott	13.00	9.75	5.25
(2) Sandy Alomar, Jr.	9.00	6.75	3.50
(3) Jack Armstrong	9.00	6.75	3.50
(4) George Bell	7.50	5.75	3.00
(5) Barry Bonds	30.00	22.00	12.00
(6) Bobby Bonilla	10.00	7.50	4.00
(7) Tom Browning	6.50	5.00	2.50
(8) Jose Canseco	6.50	5.00	2.50
(9) Will Clark	13.00	9.75	5.25
(10) Vince Coleman	9.00	6.75	3.50
(11) Eric Davis	9.00	6.75	3.50
(12) Glenn Davis	7.50	5.75	3.00
(13) Andre Dawson	11.00	8.25	4.50
(14) Delino DeShields	11.00	8.25	4.50
(15) Doug Drabek	11.00	8.25	4.50
(16) Shawon Dunston	7.50	5.75	3.00
(17) Len Dykstra	9.00	6.75	3.50
(18) Cecil Fielder	10.00	7.50	4.00
(19) John Franco	9.00	6.75	3.50
(20) Dwight Gooden	6.50	5.00	2.50
(21) Mark Grace	9.00	6.75	3.50
(22a) Ken Griffey, Jr. (batting)	15.00	11.00	6.00
(22b) Ken Griffey, Jr.	15.00	11.00	6.00
(23) Ken Griffey, Sr.	16.00	12.00	6.50
(24) Kelly Gruber	7.50	5.75	3.00
(25) Ozzie Guillen	11.00	8.25	4.50
(26) Rickey Henderson	11.00	8.25	4.50
(27) Bo Jackson (White Sox)	16.00	12.00	6.50
(28) Bo Jackson (Royals)	9.00	6.75	3.50
(29) Gregg Jefferies	10.00	7.50	4.00
(30) Howard Johnson	9.00	6.75	3.50
(31) Dave Justice	26.00	19.50	10.50
(32) Roberto Kelly	10.00	7.50	4.00
(33) Barry Larkin	11.00	8.25	4.50
(34) Kevin Maas	8.00	6.00	3.25
(35) Dave Magadan	9.00	6.75	3.50
(36) Ramon Martinez	11.00	8.25	4.50
(37) Don Mattingly	11.00	8.25	4.50
(38) Ben McDonald	11.00	8.25	4.50
(39) Mark McGwire	9.00	6.75	3.50
(40) Kevin Mitchell	7.00	5.25	2.75
(41) Kirby Puckett	19.00	14.00	7.50
(42) Tim Raines	13.00	9.75	5.25
(43) Nolan Ryan	27.00	20.00	11.00
(44) Chris Sabo	7.50	5.75	3.00
(45) Ryne Sandberg	16.00	12.00	6.50
(46) Benito Santiago	9.00	6.75	3.50
(47) Steve Sax	10.00	7.50	4.00
(48) Dave Stewart	10.00	7.50	4.00
(49) Darryl Strawberry (Dodgers)	8.00	6.00	3.25
(50) Darryl Strawberry (Mets)	8.00	6.00	3.25
(51) Alan Trammell	9.00	6.75	3.50
(52) Frank Viola	9.00	6.75	3.50
(53) Matt Williams	22.00	16.50	8.75
(54) Todd Zeile	13.00	9.75	5.25

Grading Guide

Mint (MT): A perfect card. Well-centered with all corners sharp and square. No creases, stains, edge nicks, surface marks, yellowing or fading.

Near Mint (NM): A nearly perfect card. At first glance, a NM card appears to be perfect. May be slightly off-center. No surface marks, creases or loss of gloss.

Excellent (EX): Corners are still fairly sharp with only moderate wear. Borders may be off-center. No creases or stains on fronts or backs, but may show slight loss of surface luster.

Very Good (VG): Shows obvious handling. May have rounded corners, minor creases, major gum or wax stains. No major creases, tape marks, writing, etc.

Good (G): A well-worn card, but exhibits no intentional damage. May have major or multiple creases. Corners may be rounded well beyond card border.

1992 Kenner Starting Lineup

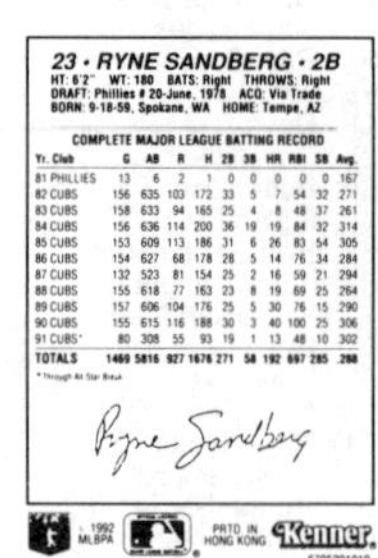

Kenner reduced its figurine/card set to 37 subjects in 1992. Unlike in past years, two cards were included with each figurine. A "rookie year" card and a regular card are featured. The players are listed here alphabetically. Values are based on demand and relative scarcity for complete unopened statue/card packages.

	MT	NR MT	EX
Complete Set:	525.00	394.00	210.00
Common Player:	6.00	4.50	2.50
(1) Roberto Alomar	15.00	11.00	6.00
(2) Steve Avery	19.00	14.00	7.50
(3) George Bell	6.00	4.50	2.50
(4) Albert Belle	12.00	9.00	4.75
(5) Craig Biggio	9.00	6.75	3.50
(6) Barry Bonds	19.00	14.00	7.50
(7) Bobby Bonilla	6.00	4.50	2.50
(8) Ivan Calderon	6.00	4.50	2.50
(9) Jose Canseco	6.00	4.50	2.50
(10) Will Clark	11.00	8.25	4.50
(11) Roger Clemens	14.00	10.50	5.50
(12) Eric Davis	6.00	4.50	2.50
(13) Rob Dibble	6.00	4.50	2.50
(14) Scott Erickson	8.00	6.00	3.25
(15) Cecil Fielder	9.00	6.75	3.50
(16) Chuck Finley	6.00	4.50	2.50
(17) Tom Glavine	20.00	15.00	8.00
(18) Juan Gonzalez	22.00	16.50	8.75
(19a) Ken Griffey, Jr. (gray)	12.00	9.00	4.75
(19b) Ken Griffey, Jr. (navy)	12.00	9.00	4.75
(20) Tony Gwynn	10.00	7.50	4.00
(21) Dave Henderson	6.00	4.50	2.50
(22) Rickey Henderson	9.00	6.75	3.50
(23 a) Bo Jackson (spring training)	11.00	8.25	4.50
(23 b) Bo Jackson (running)	10.00	7.50	4.00
(24) Howard Johnson	11.00	8.25	4.50
(25) Felix Jose	11.00	8.25	4.50
(26) Dave Justice	14.00	10.50	5.50
(27) Kevin Maas	6.00	4.50	2.50
(28) Ramon Martinez	6.00	4.50	2.50
(29) Fred McGriff	11.00	8.25	4.50
(30) Brian McRae	7.50	5.75	3.00
(31) Kirby Puckett	17.00	12.50	6.75
(32) Cal Ripken, Jr.	23.00	17.00	9.25
(33) Nolan Ryan	18.00	13.50	7.25
(34) Bret Saberhagen	6.00	4.50	2.50
(35) Chris Sabo	9.00	6.75	3.50
(36) Ryne Sandberg	12.00	9.00	4.75
(37) Tom Seaver	22.00	16.50	8.75
(38) Ruben Sierra	14.00	10.50	5.50
(39) Darryl Strawberry	7.50	5.75	3.00
(40) Danny Tartabull	6.00	4.50	2.50
(41a) Frank Thomas (batting)	29.00	22.00	11.50
(41b) Frank Thomas (fielding)	29.00	22.00	11.50
(42) Todd Van Poppel	13.00	9.75	5.25
(43) Matt Williams	11.00	8.25	4.50

1993 Kenner Starting Lineup

In its sixth year, the roster of these popular little figurines continued with 43 players in 45 collectible poses. As before, the moveable figures were blister-packed with two baseball cards. The "regular" card features a player portrait wiht a wide white border at left and bottom, highlighted by color stripes. At top-left is a color team logo. The player's name is in black at bottom. Back is the same format used since 1988. Each 1993 figure also includes a "Special Series" card on which the player action photo is bordered in color with white accent stripes. The theme of the "Special Series" is printed at bottom, above the player's name. On back, printed in blue is a short career summary of the player, along logos of the toy company and major league baseball. As in the past, values of complete, unopened statue/cards packages listed alphabetically here are based on relative scarcity as well as demand.

		MT	NR MT	EX
Complete Set:		425.00	319.00	170.00
Common Player:		6.00	4.50	2.50
(1)	Roberto Alomar	9.00	6.75	3.50
(2)	Carlos Baerga	16.00	12.00	6.50
(3)	Jeff Bagwell	18.00	13.50	7.25
(4a)	Barry Bonds (Pirates)	12.50	9.50	5.00
(4b)	Barry Bonds (Giants)	16.00	12.00	6.50
(5)	Kevin Brown	6.00	4.50	2.50
(6)	Jose Canseco	8.00	6.00	3.25
(7)	Will Clark	9.00	6.75	3.50
(8)	Roger Clemens	12.00	9.00	4.75
(9)	David Cone	6.00	4.50	2.50
(10)	Carlton Fisk	12.00	9.00	4.75
(11)	Travis Fryman	8.00	6.00	3.25
(12)	Tom Glavine	12.00	9.00	4.75
(13)	Juan Gonzalez	16.00	12.00	6.50
(14)	Ken Griffey, Jr.	12.00	9.00	4.75
(15)	Marquis Grissom	6.00	4.50	2.50
(16)	Juan Guzman	8.00	6.00	3.25
(17)	Bo Jackson	7.50	5.75	3.00
(18)	Eric Karros	9.00	6.75	3.50
(19)	Roberto Kelly	6.00	4.50	2.50
(20)	John Kruk	11.00	8.25	4.50
(21)	Ray Lankford	6.00	4.50	2.50
(22)	Barry Larkin	6.00	4.50	2.50
(23)	Greg Maddux	12.00	9.00	4.75
(24)	Shane Mack	8.00	6.00	3.25
(25)	Jack McDowell	9.00	6.75	3.50
(26)	Fred McGriff	8.00	6.00	3.25
(27)	Mark McGwire	6.00	4.50	2.50
(28)	Mike Mussina	13.00	9.75	5.25
(29)	David Neid	14.00	10.50	5.50
(30)	Dean Palmer	6.00	4.50	2.50
(31)	Terry Pendleton	8.00	6.00	3.25
(32)	Kirby Puckett	14.00	10.50	5.50
(33)	Cal Ripken, Jr.	12.00	9.00	4.75
(34)	Bip Roberts	6.00	4.50	2.50
(35)	Nolan Ryan	18.00	13.50	7.25
(36)	Nolan Ryan (Retirement)	40.00	30.00	16.00
(37)	Ryne Sandberg	9.00	6.75	3.50
(38)	Benito Santiago	9.00	6.75	3.50
(39)	Gary Sheffield	9.00	6.75	3.50
(40)	John Smoltz	14.00	10.50	5.50
(41)	Frank Thomas	15.00	11.00	6.00
(42)	Andy Van Slyke	6.00	4.50	2.50
(43)	Robin Ventura	9.00	6.75	3.50
(44)	Larry Walker	9.00	6.75	3.50

1994 Kenner Starting Lineup

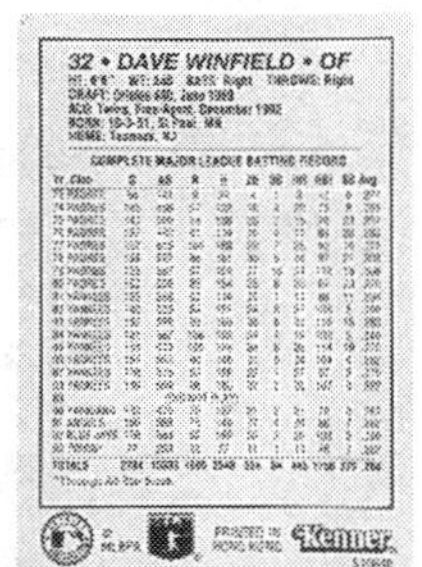

Many new players were added to Kenner's Starting Lineup for 1994, As in previous years, a blister pack containing a baseball card and a poseable plastic figure comprise the basic collectible unit. Cards have a player photo on a red background with white border. A team logo is in a purple stripe at top, while the player's name is in a yellow stripe at bottom. On back, personal data and complete career stats are printed in blue. Prices listed here are for complete, unopened statue/card packages. SLU values are determined by relative scarcity (not all figures are produced in similar quantities) as well as player popularity. Suggested retail price at issue was about $6.

		MT	NR MT	EX
Complete Set:		400.00	300.00	160.00
Common Player:		6.00	4.50	2.50
(1)	Kevin Appier	6.00	4.50	2.50
(2)	Steve Avery	6.00	4.50	2.50
(3)	Carlos Baerga	12.00	9.00	4.75
(4)	Jeff Bagwell	8.00	6.00	3.25
(5)	Albert Belle	7.00	5.25	2.75
(6)	Derek Bell	6.00	4.50	2.50
(7)	Jay Bell	6.00	4.50	2.50
(8)	Wade Boggs	10.00	7.50	4.00
(9)	Barry Bonds	10.00	7.50	4.00
(10)	John Burkett	6.00	4.50	2.50
(11)	Joe Carter	6.00	4.50	2.50
(12)	Roger Clemens	6.50	5.00	2.50
(13)	David Cone	6.00	4.50	2.50
(14)	Chad Curtis	7.00	5.25	2.75
(15)	Darren Daulton	14.00	10.50	5.50
(16)	Delino DeShields	6.00	4.50	2.50
(17)	Alex Fernandez	7.00	5.25	2.75
(18)	Cecil Fielder	6.00	4.50	2.50
(19)	Andres Galarraga	14.00	10.50	5.50
(20)	Juan Gonazlez	12.00	9.00	4.75
(21)	Mark Grace	6.00	4.50	2.50
(22)	Tommy Greene	12.00	9.00	4.75
(23)	Ken Griffey, Jr.	9.00	6.75	3.50
(24)	Brian Harper	6.00	4.50	2.50
(25)	Bryan Harvey	7.00	5.25	2.75
(26)	Charlie Hayes	6.00	4.50	2.50
(27)	Chris Hoiles	6.00	4.50	2.50
(28)	Dave Hollins	12.00	9.00	4.75
(29)	Gregg Jefferies	8.00	6.00	3.25
(30)	Randy Johnson	6.00	4.50	2.50
(31)	David Justice	10.00	7.50	4.00
(32)	Eric Karros	7.00	5.25	2.75
(33)	Jimmy Key	6.00	4.50	2.50
(34)	Darryl Kile	6.00	4.50	2.50
(35)	Chuck Knoblauch	6.00	4.50	2.50
(36)	Mark Langston	6.00	4.50	2.50
(37)	Kenny Lofton	6.00	4.50	2.50
(38)	Don Mattingly	10.00	7.50	4.00
(39)	Orlando Merced	6.00	4.50	2.50
(40)	Paul Molitor	12.00	9.00	4.75
(41)	Mike Mussina	12.00	9.00	4.75
(42)	John Olerud	15.00	11.00	6.00
(43)	Mike Piazza	32.00	24.00	13.00
(44)	Tony Phillips	6.00	4.50	2.50
(45)	Jose Rijo	6.00	4.50	2.50
(46)	Cal Ripken, Jr.	12.00	9.00	4.75
(47)	Ivan Rodriguez	8.00	6.00	3.25
(48)	Tim Salmon	21.00	15.50	8.50
(49)	Ryne Sandberg	7.00	5.25	2.75
(50)	Curt Schilling	14.00	10.50	5.50
(51)	Gary Sheffield	7.00	5.25	2.75
(52)	J.T. Snow	6.00	4.50	2.50
(53)	Frank Thomas	9.00	6.75	3.50
(54)	Robbie Thompson	6.00	4.50	2.50
(55)	Greg Vaughn	6.00	4.50	2.50
(56)	Mo Vaughn	10.00	7.50	4.00
(57)	Robin Ventura	7.00	5.25	2.75
(58)	Matt Williams	6.00	4.50	2.50
(59)	Dave Winfield	6.00	4.50	2.50

1994 Kenner Cooperstown Collection

		MT	NR MT	EX
Complete Set:		110.00	82.00	45.00
Common Player:		14.00	10.50	5.50
(1)	Ty Cobb	14.00	10.50	5.50
(2)	Lou Gehrig	14.00	10.50	5.50
(3)	Reggie Jackson	30.00	22.00	12.00
(4)	Willie Mays	15.00	11.00	6.00
(5)	Jackie Robinson	14.00	10.50	5.50
(6)	Babe Ruth	15.00	11.00	6.00
(7)	Honus Wagner	14.00	10.50	5.50
(8)	Cy Young	14.00	10.50	5.50

1887 W.S. Kimball Champions (N184)

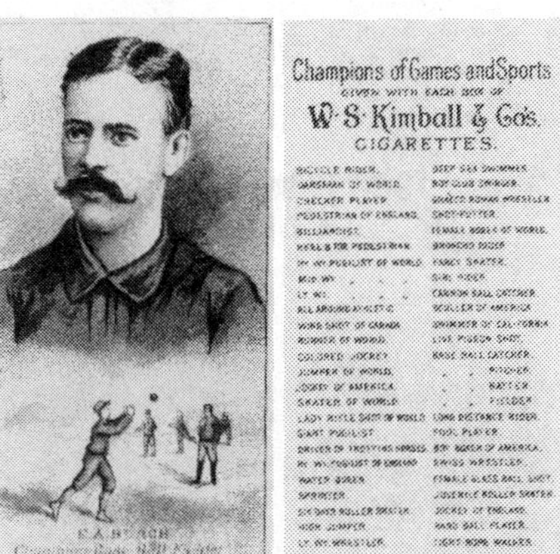

Similar to sets issued by Allen & Ginter and Goodwin, the Kimaball tobacco company of Rochester, N.Y., issued its own 50-card set of "Champions of Games and Sport" in 1888, and included four baseball players among the "billiardists, girl riders, tight-rope walkers" and other popular celebrities featured in the series. Measuring 1-1/2" by 2-3/4", the color lithographs were inserted in packages of Kimball Cigarettes. The artwork on the card features a posed portrait, which occupies the top three-fourths, and a drawing of the player in action at the bottom. The back of the card contains an ad for Kimball Cigarettes along with a list of the various sports and activities depicted in the set. James O'Neill, whose name is misspelled on the card, is the best known of the four baseball players. His .435 batting average in 1887 is the highest ever recorded. The Kimball promotion also included an album to house the card set.

		NR MT	EX	VG
Complete Set:		2500.	1250.	750.00
Common Player:		600.00	300.00	175.00
(1)	E.A. Burch	600.00	300.00	175.00
(2)	Dell Darling	600.00	300.00	175.00
(3)	Hardie Henderson	600.00	300.00	175.00
(4)	James O'Neil (O'Neill)	750.00	375.00	225.00

1988 King-B

Created by Mike Schechter Associates, the 1988 King-B set consists of 24 numbered discs that measure 2-3/4" in size. The cards were inserted in specially marked 7/16 ounce tubs of Jerky Stuff (shredded beef jerky). The card fronts feature full-color photos surrounded by a blue border. The King-B logo appears in the upper left portion of the disc. The disc backs are printed in blue on white stock and carry player personal and playing information. Team insignias have been airbrushed from the players' caps and jerseys.

		MT	NR MT	EX
Complete Set:		25.00	18.50	10.00
Common Player:		.75	.60	.30
1	Mike Schmidt	1.75	1.25	.70
2	Dale Murphy	1.00	.70	.40
3	Kirby Puckett	1.50	1.25	.60
4	Ozzie Smith	1.00	.70	.40
5	Tony Gwynn	1.00	.70	.40
6	Mark McGwire	1.50	1.25	.60
7	George Brett	1.75	1.25	.70
8	Darryl Strawberry	1.00	.70	.40
9	Wally Joyner	1.50	1.25	.60
10	Cory Snyder	1.00	.70	.40
11	Barry Bonds	1.75	1.25	.70
12	Darrell Evans	.75	.60	.30
13	Mike Scott	.75	.60	.30
14	Andre Dawson	1.25	.90	.50
15	Don Mattingly	1.75	1.25	.70
16	Candy Maldonado	.75	.60	.30
17	Alvin Davis	.75	.60	.30
18	Carlton Fisk	1.00	.70	.40
19	Fernando Valenzuela	.75	.60	.30
20	Roger Clemens	1.50	1.25	.60
21	Larry Parrish	.75	.60	.30
22	Eric Davis	1.00	.70	.40
23	Paul Molitor	1.25	.90	.50
24	Cal Ripken, Jr.	1.75	1.25	.70

1989 King-B

The second King-B baseball card set created by Mike Schechter Associates also consists of 24 circular baseball cards measuring 2-3/4" across. The cards were inserted into specially-marked tubs of "Jerky Stuff." The card fronts feature full-color photos bordered in red. The King-B logo appears in the upper left portion of the disc. Like the 1988 set, the team insignias have airbrushed from uniforms and caps. The backs are printed in red and display personal information and stats.

		MT	NR MT	EX
Complete Set:		25.00	18.50	10.00
Common Player:		.75	.60	.30
1	Kirk Gibson	.75	.60	.30
2	Eddie Murray	1.00	.70	.40
3	Wade Boggs	1.50	1.25	.60
4	Mark McGwire	1.00	.70	.40
5	Ryne Sandberg	1.75	1.25	.70
6	Ozzie Guillen	.75	.60	.30
7	Chris Sabo	.75	.60	.30
8	Joe Carter	1.00	.70	.40
9	Alan Trammell	1.00	.70	.40
10	Nolan Ryan	2.00	1.50	.80
11	Bo Jackson	1.50	1.25	.60
12	Orel Hershiser	.75	.60	.30
13	Robin Yount	1.50	1.25	.60
14	Frank Viola	.75	.60	.30
15	Darryl Strawberry	.75	.60	.30
16	Dave Winfield	1.00	.70	.40
17	Jose Canseco	1.75	1.25	.70
18	Von Hayes	.75	.60	.30
19	Andy Van Slyke	.75	.60	.30
20	Pedro Guerrero	.75	.60	.30
21	Tony Gwynn	1.25	.90	.50
22	Will Clark	1.75	1.25	.70
23	Danny Jackson	.75	.60	.30
24	Pete Incaviglia	.75	.60	.30

1990 King-B

King-B meat products offered baseball player discs inside specially-marked packages in 1990, the third year in a row the company inserted the discs with shredded beef jerky. Each disc measures 2-3/4" across and uses full-color pictures on the front. The backs have biographical information and statistics. Team insignias have been airbrushed from caps and uniforms. As in the first two years of the promotion, there are 24 cards in the set.

		MT	NR MT	EX
Complete Set:		16.50	12.50	6.50
Common Player:		.50	.40	.20
1	Mike Scott	.50	.40	.20
2	Kevin Mitchell	.60	.45	.25
3	Tony Gwynn	.90	.70	.35
4	Ozzie Smith	.90	.70	.35
5	Kirk Gibson	.50	.40	.20
6	Tim Raines	.60	.45	.25
7	Von Hayes	.50	.40	.20
8	Bobby Bonilla	.60	.45	.25
9	Wade Boggs	.90	.70	.35
10	Chris Sabo	.60	.45	.25
11	Dale Murphy	.90	.70	.35
12	Cory Snyder	.50	.40	.20
13	Fred McGriff	.80	.60	.30
14	Don Mattingly	.90	.70	.35
15	Jerome Walton	.50	.40	.20
16	Ken Griffey, Jr.	1.50	1.25	.60
17	Bo Jackson	.75	.60	.30
18	Robin Yount	.75	.60	.30
19	Rickey Henderson	.75	.60	.30
20	Jim Abbott	.60	.45	.25
21	Kirby Puckett	.75	.60	.30
22	Nolan Ryan	1.50	1.25	.60
23	Gregg Olson	.50	.40	.20
24	Lou Whitaker	.60	.45	.25

1993 King-B

The sixth annual edition of baseball player discs inserted into packages of King-B meat snacks followed the format of previous issues. Measuring 2-3/8" in diameter, the cards have a photo (with uniform logos airbrushed away) in a yellow baseball diamond design at center. The disc is bordered in black. Backs are printed in red and contain 1992 and career stats.

		MT	NR MT	EX
Complete Set (24):		6.00	4.50	2.50
Common Player:		.25	.20	.10
1	Barry Bonds	.50	.40	.20
2	Ken Griffey, Jr.	1.00	.70	.40
3	Cal Ripken, Jr.	.50	.40	.20
4	Frank Thomas	1.00	.70	.40
5	Steve Avery	.50	.40	.20
6	Benito Santiago	.25	.20	.10
7	Luis Polonia	.25	.20	.10
8	Jose Rijo	.25	.20	.10
9	George Brett	.50	.40	.20
10	Darren Daulton	.25	.20	.10
11	Cecil Fielder	.40	.30	.15
12	Ozzie Smith	.35	.25	.14
13	Joe Carter	.25	.20	.10
14	Dwight Gooden	.25	.20	.10
15	Tom Henke	.25	.20	.10
16	Brett Butler	.25	.20	.10
17	Nolan Ryan	1.00	.70	.40
18	Sandy Alomar, Jr.	.25	.20	.10
19	Tom Glavine	.25	.20	.10
20	Rafael Palmiero	.35	.25	.14
21	Roger Clemens	.40	.30	.15
22	Ryne Sandberg	.50	.40	.20
23	Doug Drabek	.25	.20	.10
24	Chuck Knoblauch	.25	.20	.10

Definitions for grading conditions are located in the Introduction of this price guide.

1994 King-B

King-B Beef Jerky included a disc featuring one of 24 major league stars with its products in 1994. The entire set with all 24 discs was also available in uncut sheet form which was found in each case. Discs measure 2-3/8 diameter and have a broad purple border with yellow and white typography surrounding the player photo at center. A black glove holds a King-B logo at bottom. Uniform logos have been airbrushed from the photos. Backs are printed in purple and include 1993 and career stats.

		MT	NR MT	EX
Complete Set (24):		6.00	4.50	2.50
Common Player:		.25	.20	.10
1	Fred McGriff	.50	.40	.20
2	Paul Molitor	.40	.30	.15
3	Jack McDowell	.25	.20	.10
4	Darren Daulton	.25	.20	.10
5	Wade Boggs	.60	.45	.25
6	Ken Griffey, Jr.	1.00	.70	.40
7	Tim Salmon	.60	.45	.25
8	Dennis Eckersley	.25	.20	.10
9	Albert Belle	.25	.20	.10
10	Travis Fryman	.25	.20	.10
11	Chris Hoiles	.25	.20	.10
12	Kirby Puckett	.40	.30	.15
13	John Olerud	.30	.25	.12
14	Frank Thomas	1.00	.70	.40
15	Lenny Dykstra	.30	.25	.12
16	Andres Galarraga	.25	.20	.10
17	Barry Larkin	.25	.20	.10
18	Greg Maddux	.25	.20	.10
19	Mike Piazza	.75	.60	.30
20	Roberto Alomar	.40	.30	.15
21	Robin Ventura	.30	.25	.12
22	Ryne Sandberg	.50	.40	.20
23	Andy Van Slyke	.25	.20	.10
24	Barry Bonds	.50	.40	.20

1986 Kitty Clover Potato Chips Royals

Twenty players of the 1985 World's Champion Kansas City Royals were featured in a round card set inserted into packages of potato chips in the K.C. area. The 2-7/8" discs were similar to a handful of snack issues produced by Mike Schecter Associates in that team logos have been airbrushed off the players' caps, and the photos of some of the players can be found on other regional issues of 1986.

		MT	NR MT	EX
Complete Set:		20.00	15.00	8.00
Common Player:		.70	.50	.30
1	Lonnie Smith	.70	.50	.30
2	Buddy Biancalana	.70	.50	.30
3	Bret Saberhagen	1.75	1.25	.70
4	Hal McRae	1.00	.70	.40
5	Onix Concepcion	.70	.50	.30
6	Jorge Orta	.70	.50	.30
7	Bud Black	.70	.50	.30
8	Dan Quisenberry	1.00	.70	.40
9	Dane Iorg	.70	.50	.30
10	Charlie Leibrandt	.80	.60	.30
11	Pat Sheridan	.70	.50	.30
12	John Wathan	.80	.60	.30
13	Frank White	1.00	.70	.40
14	Darryl Motley	.70	.50	.30
15	Willie Wilson	1.25	.90	.50
16	Danny Jackson	1.25	.90	.50
17	Steve Balboni	.70	.50	.30
18	Jim Sundberg	.70	.50	.30
19	Mark Gubicza	1.25	.90	.50
20	George Brett	4.00	3.00	1.50

1993 Kodak White Sox

Kodak produced a White Sox set of 30 cards in 1993 that was given away prior to the July 23 game between Chicago and Milwaukee. The full color cards are slightly oversized at 2-5/8" x 3-1/2" and are printed on a very heavy card stock. The photo on the front is full bleed, with the White Sox logo appearing in the upper corner and a metallic blue stripe at the card bottom displaying the player's uniform number, name and position. The backs are white with gray borders and a Kodak logo, with year and career statistics and biographical information. The cards are unnumbered.

		MT	NR MT	EX
Complete Set:		15.00	11.00	6.00
Common Player:		.25	.20	.10
1	Lance Johnson	.40	.30	.15
7	Steve Sax	.35	.25	.14
8	Bo Jackson	1.00	.70	.40
10	Mike LaValliere	.25	.20	.10
12	Mike Huff	.25	.20	.10
13	Ozzie Guillen	.35	.25	.14
14	Craig Grebeck	.25	.20	.10
20	Ron Karkovice	.35	.25	.14
21	George Bell	.30	.25	.12
22	Donn Pall	.25	.20	.10
23	Robin Ventura	.60	.45	.25
25	Kirk McCaskill	.35	.25	.14
26	Ellis Burks	.35	.25	.14
28	Joey Cora	.25	.20	.10
29	Jack McDowell	.50	.40	.20
30	Tim Raines	.60	.45	.25
31	Scott Radinsky	.35	.25	.14
32	Alex Fernandez	.35	.25	.14
33	Gene Lamont	.25	.20	.10
34	Terry Leach	.25	.20	.10
35	Frank Thomas	4.00	3.00	1.50
37	Bobby Thigpen	.25	.20	.10
39	Roberto Hernandez	.35	.25	.14
40	Wilson Alvarez	.50	.40	.20
42	Rod Bolton	.25	.20	.10
44	Dan Pasqua	.25	.20	.10
45	Chuck Cary	.25	.20	.10
49	Jeff Schwartz	.25	.20	.10
51	Jason Bere	.75	.60	.30
----	1993 Coaching Staff (Gene Lamont, Jackie Brown, Terry Bevington, Joe Nossek, Walt Hriniak, Doug Mansolino, Dewey Robinson, Jose Antigua)	.25	.20	.10

1987 Kraft

Kraft Foods, Inc. issued a 48-card set on specially marked packages of their Macaroni & Cheese Dinners. Titled "Home Plate Heroes," 24 two-card panels measuring 3-1/2" by 7-1/8" make up the set. Individual cards measure 2-1/4" by 3-1/2" and are numbered 1 through 48. The blank-backed cards feature fronts with full-color photos, although all team insignias have been erased. In conjunction with the card set, Kraft offered a contest to "Win A Day With A Major Leaguer." Mike Schecter Associates produced the set for Kraft. 120 different panel combinatons can be found.

		MT	NR MT	EX
Complete Set:		22.00	16.50	8.75
Common Player:		.20	.15	.08
1	Eddie Murray	.60	.45	.25
2	Dale Murphy	.60	.45	.25
3	Cal Ripken, Jr.	.75	.60	.30
4	Mike Scott	.35	.25	.14
5	Jim Rice	.40	.30	.15
6	Jody Davis	.20	.15	.08
7	Wade Boggs	.60	.45	.25
8	Ryne Sandberg	.75	.60	.30
9	Wally Joyner	.40	.30	.15
10	Eric Davis	.40	.30	.15
11	Ozzie Guillen	.20	.15	.08
12	Tony Pena	.20	.15	.08
13	Harold Baines	.35	.25	.14
14	Johnny Ray	.20	.15	.08
15	Joe Carter	.35	.25	.14
16	Ozzie Smith	.40	.30	.15
17	Cory Snyder	.20	.15	.08
18	Vince Coleman	.35	.25	.14
19	Kirk Gibson	.35	.25	.14
20	Steve Garvey	.50	.40	.20
21	George Brett	.90	.70	.35
22	John Tudor	.20	.15	.08
23	Robin Yount	.60	.45	.25
24	Von Hayes	.20	.15	.08
25	Kent Hrbek	.50	.40	.20
26	Darryl Strawberry	.30	.25	.12
27	Kirby Puckett	.80	.60	.30
28	Ron Darling	.35	.25	.14
29	Don Mattingly	.80	.60	.30
30	Mike Schmidt	.80	.60	.30
31	Rickey Henderson	.80	.60	.30
32	Fernando Valenzuela	.30	.25	.12
33	Dave Winfield	.60	.45	.25
34	Pete Rose	.80	.60	.30
35	Jose Canseco	.80	.60	.30
36	Glenn Davis	.20	.15	.08
37	Alvin Davis	.20	.15	.08
38	Steve Sax	.20	.15	.08
39	Pete Incaviglia	.30	.25	.12
40	Jeff Reardon	.35	.25	.14
41	Jesse Barfield	.20	.15	.08
42	Hubie Brooks	.20	.15	.08
43	George Bell	.30	.25	.12
44	Tony Gwynn	.60	.45	.25
45	Roger Clemens	.60	.45	.25
46	Chili Davis	.35	.25	.14
47	Mike Witt	.20	.15	.08
48	Nolan Ryan	1.00	.70	.40

1993 Kraft Pop-Up Action

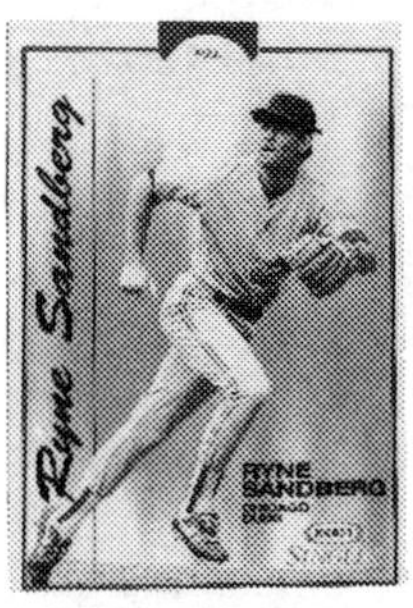

Kraft released a set of Pop-Up Action baseball cards in 1993 that was available in specially-marked packages of Kraft Singles. The cards are similar to the 1992 Canadian Post Cereal cards with a pop-up tab. The set is made up of 15 players each from the American and National leagues.

		MT	NR MT	EX
Complete Set (30):		18.00	13.50	7.25
Common Player:		.25	.20	.10
	American League			
(1)	Jim Abbott	.50	.40	.20
(2)	Roberto Alomar	.75	.60	.30
(3)	Sandy Alomar Jr.	.25	.20	.10
(4)	George Brett	1.00	.70	.40
(5)	Roger Clemens	.60	.45	.25
(6)	Dennis Eckersley	.35	.25	.14
(7)	Cecil Fielder	.50	.40	.20
(8)	Ken Griffey, Jr.	2.00	1.50	.80
(9)	Don Mattingly	.60	.45	.25
(10)	Mark McGwire	.60	.45	.25
(11)	Kirby Puckett	.60	.45	.25
(12)	Cal Ripken, Jr.	1.50	1.25	.60
(13)	Nolan Ryan	2.00	1.50	.80
(14)	Robin Ventura	.40	.30	.15
(15)	Robin Yount	1.00	.70	.40
	National League			
(1)	Bobby Bonilla	.25	.20	.10
(2)	Ken Caminiti	.25	.20	.10
(3)	Will Clark	.60	.45	.25
(4)	Darren Daulton	.25	.20	.10
(5)	Doug Drabek	.25	.20	.10
(6)	Delino DeShields	.30	.25	.12
(7)	Tom Glavine	.25	.20	.10
(8)	Tony Gwynn	.35	.25	.14
(9)	Orel Hershiser	.30	.25	.12
(10)	Barry Larkin	.25	.20	.10
(11)	Terry Pendleton	.25	.20	.10
(12)	Ryne Sandberg	1.50	1.25	.60
(13)	Gary Sheffield	.35	.25	.14
(14)	Lee Smith	.25	.20	.10
(15)	Andy Van Slyke	.25	.20	.10

1994 Kraft Pop-Ups

Kraft offered a 30-card set in 1994 that featured major stars and utilized a pop-up format. The cards show the players in action shots front and back, with the front picture "popping up." Kraft Singles consumers could find one card rectangular card (nearly regular size at 2 1/2 x 3 3/8) in each package of cheese, with 15 players from each league. The promotion ran from April through May, or as long as the supplies lasted. The cards were licensed by the Major League Baseball Players Association, but not by Major League Baseball, so the team logos were airbrushed from player's caps and uniforms. Through an on-pack and in-store mail-in offer, collectors could order complete sets of the cards for $1.95 per league (15 cards), plus the appropriate proofs of purchase. In a somewhat unusual move, officials of Kraft USA announced that the print run would be eight million cards, which works out to about 266,000 sets.

		MT	NR MT	EX
Complete Set:		12.00	9.00	4.75
Common Player:		.25	.20	.10
1	Carlos Baerga	.50	.40	.20
2	Dennis Eckersley	.35	.25	.14
3	Cecil Fielder	.50	.40	.20
4	Juan Gonzalez	.80	.60	.30
5	Ken Griffey Jr.	1.50	1.25	.60
6	Mark Langston	.25	.20	.10
7	Brian McRae	.25	.20	.10
8	Paul Molitor	.60	.45	.25
9	Kirby Puckett	.60	.45	.25
10	Cal Ripken Jr.	.90	.70	.35
11	Danny Tartabull	.25	.20	.10
12	Frank Thomas	1.50	1.25	.60
13	Greg Vaughn	.25	.20	.10
14	Mo Vaughn	.35	.25	.14
15	Dave Winfield	.45	.35	.20
16	Jeff Bagwell	.35	.25	.14
17	Barry Bonds	.75	.60	.30
18	Bobby Bonilla	.35	.25	.14
19	Delino DeShields	.35	.25	.14
20	Lenny Dykstra	.35	.25	.14
21	Andres Galarraga	.35	.25	.14
22	Tom Glavine	.25	.20	.10
23	Mark Grace	.35	.25	.14
24	Tony Gwynn	.35	.25	.14
25	David Justice	.45	.35	.20
26	Barry Larkin	.25	.20	.10
27	Mike Piazza	.45	.35	.20
28	Gary Sheffield	.25	.20	.10
29	Ozzie Smith	.35	.25	.14
30	Andy Van Slyke	.25	.20	.10

Grading Guide

Mint (MT): A perfect card. Well-centered with all corners sharp and square. No creases, stains, edge nicks, surface marks, yellowing or fading.

Near Mint (NM): A nearly perfect card. At first glance, a NM card appears to be perfect. May be slightly off-center. No surface marks, creases or loss of gloss.

Excellent (EX): Corners are still fairly sharp with only moderate wear. Borders may be off-center. No creases or stains on fronts or backs, but may show slight loss of surface luster.

Very Good (VG): Shows obvious handling. May have rounded corners, minor creases, major gum or wax stains. No major creases, tape marks, writing, etc.

Good (G): A well-worn card, but exhibits no intentional damage. May have major or multiple creases. Corners may be rounded well beyond card border.

L

1912 L1 Leathers

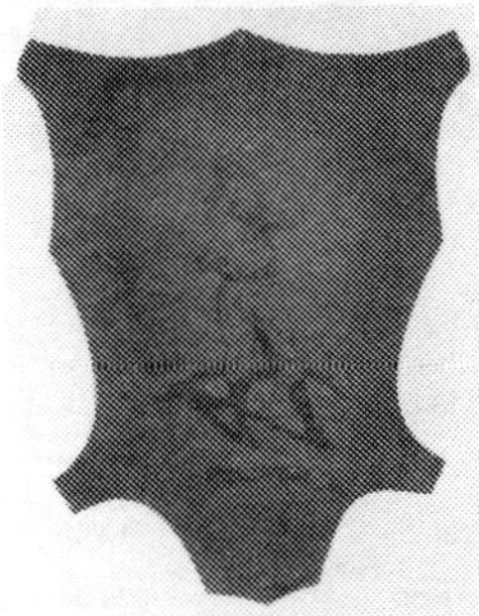

One of the more unusual baseball collectibles of the tobacco era, the L1 "Leathers" were issued by Helmar Tobacco Co. in 1912 as a premium with its "Turkish Trophies" brand of cigarettes. The set featured 25 of the top baseball players and shared a checklist with the closely-related S81 "Silks," which were another part of the same promotion. The "Leathers," advertised as being 10" by 12", featured drawings of baseball players on horsehide-shaped pieces of leather. The drawings were based on the pictures used for the popular T3 Turkey Red series issued a year earlier. Twenty of the 25 players in the "Leathers" set are from the T3 set. Five pitchers (Rube Marquard, Rube Benton, Marty O'Toole, Grover Alexander and Russ Ford) not pictured in T3 were added to the "Leathers" set, and the Frank Baker error was corrected. According to the promotion, each "Leather" was available in exchange for 50 Helmar coupons. In addition to the 25 baseball stars, the "Leathers" set also included more than 100 other subjects, including female athletes and bathing beauties, famous generals, Indian chiefs, actresses, national flags, college mascots and others.

		NR MT	EX	VG
Complete Set:		90000.	47500.	28500.
Common Player:		2250.	1125.	675.00
86	Rube Marquard	4500.	2250.	1350.
87	Marty O'Toole	2250.	1125.	675.00
88	Rube Benton	2250.	1125.	675.00
89	Grover Alexander	6000.	3000.	1800.
90	Russ Ford	2250.	1125.	675.00
91	John McGraw	4500.	2250.	1350.
92	Nap Rucker	2250.	1125.	675.00
93	Mike Mitchell	2250.	1125.	675.00
94	Chief Bender	4500.	2250.	1350.
95	Home Run Baker	4500.	2250.	1350.
96	Nap Lajoie	6000.	3000.	1800.
97	Joe Tinker	4500.	2250.	1350.
98	Sherry Magee	2250.	1125.	675.00
99	Howie Camnitz	2250.	1125.	675.00
100	Eddie Collins	4500.	2250.	1350.
101	Red Dooin	2250.	1125.	675.00
102	Ty Cobb	15000.	7500.	4500.
103	Hugh Jennings	4500.	2250.	1350.
104	Roger Bresnahan	4500.	2250.	1350.
105	Jake Stahl	2250.	1125.	675.00
106	Tris Speaker	5500.	2750.	1650.
107	Ed Walsh	4500.	2250.	1350.
108	Christy Mathewson	7500.	3750.	2250.
109	Johnny Evers	4500.	2250.	1350.
110	Walter Johnson	7500.	3750.	2250.

A player's name in italic type indicates a rookie card. An (FC) indicates a player's first card for that particular card company.

1960 Lake To Lake Dairy Braves

This 28-card set of unnumbered 2-1/2" by 3-1/4" cards offers a special challenge for the condition-conscious collector. Originally issued by being stapled to milk cartons, the cards were redeemable for prizes ranging from pen and pencil sets to Braves tickets. When sent in for redemption, the cards had a hole punched in the corner. Naturally, collectors most desire cards without the staple or punch holes. Cards are printed in blue ink on front, red ink on

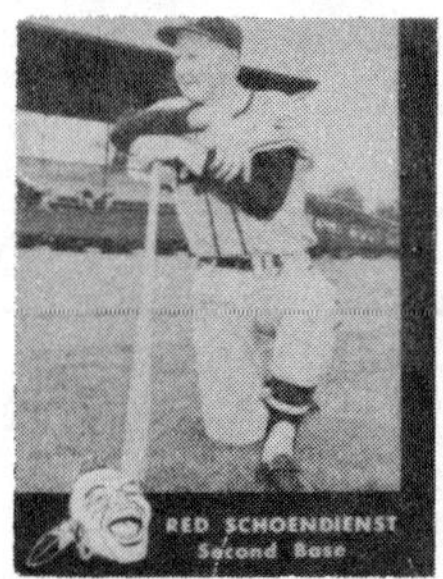

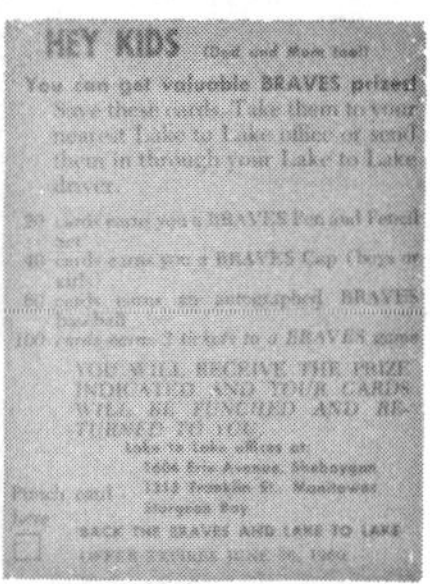

back. Because he was traded in May, and his card withdrawn, the Ray Boone card is scarce; the Billy Bruton card is unaccountably scarcer still.

		NR MT	EX	VG
Complete Set:		1200.	600.00	360.00
Common Player:		13.00	6.50	4.00
(1)	Henry Aaron	275.00	125.00	60.00
(2)	Joe Adcock	17.50	8.75	5.25
(3)	Ray Boone	125.00	62.00	37.00
(4)	Bill Bruton	275.00	137.00	82.00
(5)	Bob Buhl	17.50	8.75	5.25
(6)	Lou Burdette	17.50	8.75	5.25
(7)	Chuck Cottier	13.00	6.50	4.00
(8)	Wes Covington	15.00	7.50	4.50
(9)	Del Crandall	17.50	8.75	5.25
(10)	Charlie Dressen	15.00	7.50	4.50
(11)	Bob Giggie	13.00	6.50	4.00
(12)	Joey Jay	13.00	6.50	4.00
(13)	Johnny Logan	15.00	7.50	4.50
(14)	Felix Mantilla	13.00	6.50	4.00
(15)	Lee Maye	13.00	6.50	4.00
(16)	Don McMahon	13.00	6.50	4.00
(17)	George Myatt	13.00	6.50	4.00
(18)	Andy Pafko	15.00	7.50	4.50
(19)	Juan Pizarro	13.00	6.50	4.00
(20)	Mel Roach	13.00	6.50	4.00
(21)	Bob Rush	13.00	6.50	4.00
(22)	Bob Scheffing	13.00	6.50	4.00
(23)	Red Schoendienst	35.00	17.50	10.50
(24)	Warren Spahn	60.00	30.00	18.00
(25)	Al Spangler	13.00	6.50	4.00
(26)	Frank Torre	13.00	6.50	4.00
(27)	Carl Willey	13.00	6.50	4.00
(28)	Whitlow Wyatt	13.00	6.50	4.00

1967 Laughlin World Series

Apparently a prototype set for subsequent offerings by the sports artist R.G. Laughlin that were produced by Fleer, this set of 64 cards was printed in black and white with the cartoon line drawings for which Luaghlin was noted. The cards are an odd size, 2-3/4" x 3-1/2", like so many of the Laughlin/Fleer issues of the period. The texts on the back are printed in red and offer details of the World Series from that year.

		NR MT	EX	VG
Complete Set (64):		110.00	55.00	32.50
Common card:		1.00	.50	.30
1	1903 Red Sox/Pirates	1.00	.50	.30
2	1905 Giants/A's (Christy Mathewson)	3.00	1.50	.90
3	1906 White Sox/Cubs	1.00	.50	.30
4	1907 Cubs/Tigers	1.00	.50	.30
5	1908 Cubs/Tigers (Tinker/Evers/Chance)	4.00	2.00	1.25
6	1909 Pirates/Tigers (Wagner/Cobb)	5.00	2.50	1.50
7	1910 A's/Cubs	1.00	.50	.30
8	1911 A's/Giants (John McGraw)	3.00	1.50	.90
9	1912 Red Sox/Giants	1.00	.50	.30
10	1913 A's/Giants	1.00	.50	.30
11	1914 Braves/A's	1.00	.50	.30
12	1915 Red Sox/Phillies (Babe Ruth)	6.00	3.00	1.75
13	1916 White Sox/Dodgers (Babe Ruth)	6.00	3.00	1.75
14	1917 White Sox/Giants	1.00	.50	.30
15	1918 Red Sox/Cubs	1.00	.50	.30
16	1919 Reds/White Sox	4.00	2.00	1.25
17	1920 Indians/Dodgers	1.00	.50	.30
18	1921 Giants/Yankees (Waite Hoyt)	2.50	1.25	.70
19	1922 Giants/Yankees (Frisch/Groh)	2.50	1.25	.70
20	1923 Yankees/Giants (Babe Ruth)	6.00	3.00	1.75
21	1924 Senators/Giants	1.00	.50	.30
22	1925 Pirates/Senators (Walter Johnson)	4.00	2.00	1.25
23	1926 Cardinals/Yankees (Alexander/Lazzeri)	3.00	1.50	.90
24	1927 Yankees/Pirates	1.00	.50	.30
25	1928 Yankees/Cardinals (Ruth/Gehrig)	6.00	3.00	1.75
26	1929 A's/Cubs	1.00	.50	.30
27	1930 A's/Cardinals	1.00	.50	.30
28	1931 Cardinals/A's (Pepper Martin)	2.50	1.25	.70
29	1932 Yankees/Cubs (Babe Ruth)	6.00	3.00	1.75
30	1933 Giants/Seantors (Mel Ott)	3.00	1.50	.90
31	1934 Cardinals/Tigers (Dizzy/Paul Dean)	4.00	2.00	1.25
32	1935 Tigers/Cubs	1.00	.50	.30
33	1936 Yankees/Giants	1.00	.50	.30
34	1937 Yankees/Giants (Carl Hubbell)	3.00	1.50	.90
35	1938 Yankees/Cubs	1.00	.50	.30
36	1939 Yankees/Reds (Joe DiMaggio)	5.00	2.50	1.50
37	1940 Reds/Tigers	1.00	.50	.30
38	1941 Yankees/Dodgers (Mickey Owen)	2.50	1.25	.70
39	1942 Cardinals/Yankees	1.00	.50	.30
40	1943 Yankees/Cardinals (Joe McCarthy)	2.50	1.25	.70
41	1944 Cardinals/Browns	1.00	.50	.30
42	1945 Tigers/Cubs (Hank Greenberg)	3.00	1.50	.90
43	1946 Cardinals/Red Sox (Enos Slaughter)	3.00	1.50	.90
44	1947 Yankees/Dodgers (Al Gionfriddo)	1.00	.50	.30
45	1948 Indians/Braves (Bob Feller)	3.00	1.50	.90
46	1949 Yankees/Dodgers (Reynolds/Roe)	2.50	1.25	.70
47	1950 Yankees/Phillies	1.00	.50	.30
48	1951 Yankees/Giants	1.00	.50	.30
49	1952 Yankees/Dodgers (Mize/Snider)	3.00	1.50	.90
50	1953 Yankees/Dodgers (Casey Stengel)	3.00	1.50	.90
51	1954 Giants/Indians (Dusty Rhodes)	1.00	.50	.30
52	1955 Dodgers/Yankees (Johnny Podres)	2.50	1.25	.70
53	1956 Yankees/Dodgers (Don Larsen)	2.50	1.25	.70
54	1957 Braves/Yankees (Lew Burdette)	1.00	.50	.30
55	1958 Yankees/Braves (Hank Bauer)	1.00	.50	.30
56	1959 Dodgers/White Sox (Larry Sherry)	1.00	.50	.30
57	1960 Pirates/Yankees	2.50	1.25	.70
58	1961 Yankees/Reds (Whitey Ford)	3.00	1.50	.90
59	1962 Yankees/Giants	1.00	.50	.30
60	1963 Dodgers/Yankees (Sandy Koufax)	3.00	1.50	.90
61	1964 Cardinals/Yankees (Mickey Mantle)	6.00	3.00	1.75
62	1965 Dodgers/Twins	1.00	.50	.30
63	1966 Orioles/Dodgers	1.00	.50	.30
64	1967 Cardinals/Red Sox (Bob Gibson)	3.00	1.50	.90

1972 Laughlin Great Feats

Sports artist R.G. Laughlin created this set of 50 numbered cards and one unnumbered title card highlighting top performances by stars over the years. The cards depict the player in pen and ink, with one variation of the set adding flesh tones to the players. One variation of the set has red borders, the other (with the flesh tones) blue. The cards are blank backed and numbered on the front with a brief caption.

		NR MT	EX	VG
Complete Set (51):		30.00	15.00	9.00
Common Player:		.50	.25	.15
1	Joe DiMaggio	4.00	2.00	1.25
2	Walter Johnson	1.50	.70	.45
3	Rudy York	.50	.25	.15
4	Sandy Koufax	2.00	1.00	.60
5	George Sisler	.50	.25	.15
6	Iron Man McGinnity	.50	.25	.15
7	Johnny VanderMeer	.50	.25	.15
8	Lou Gehrig	3.00	1.50	.90
9	Max Carey	.50	.25	.15
10	Ed Delahanty	.50	.25	.15
11	Pinky Higgins	.50	.25	.15
12	Jack Chesbro	.50	.25	.15
13	Jim Bottomley	.50	.25	.15
14	Rube Marquard	.50	.25	.15
15	Rogers Hornsby	.75	.40	.25
16	Lefty Grove	.60	.30	.20
17	Johnny Mize	.60	.30	.20
18	Lefty Gomez	.60	.30	.20
19	Jimmie Fox	.75	.40	.25
20	Casey Stengel	.75	.40	.25
21	Dazzy Vance	.50	.25	.15
22	Jerry Lynch	.50	.25	.15
23	Hughie Jennings	.50	.25	.15
24	Stan Musial	2.00	1.00	.60
25	Christy Mathewson	1.50	.75	.40
26	Elroy Face	.50	.25	.15
27	Hack Wilson	.60	.30	.20
28	Smoky Burgess	.50	.25	.15
29	Cy Young	1.00	.50	.30
30	Wilbert Robinson	.50	.25	.15
31	Wee Willie Keeler	.50	.25	.15
32	Babe Ruth	5.00	2.50	1.50
33	Mickey Mantle	5.00	2.50	1.50
34	Hub Leonard	.50	.25	.15
35	Ty Cobb	2.00	1.00	.60
36	Carl Hubbell	.60	.30	.20
37	Joe Oeschger, Leon Cadore	.50	.25	.15
38	Don Drysdale	.75	.40	.25
39	Fred Toney, Hippo Vaughn	.50	.25	.15
40	Joe Sewell	.50	.25	.15
41	Grover Cleveland Alexander	.60	.30	.20
42	Joe Adcock	.50	.25	.15
43	Eddie Collins	.50	.25	.15
44	Bob Feller	.75	.40	.25
45	Don Larsen	.75	.40	.25
46	Dave Philley	.50	.25	.15
47	Bill Fischer	.50	.25	.15
48	Dale Long	.50	.25	.15
49	Bill Wambsganss	.50	.25	.15
50	Roger Maris	2.00	1.00	.60
----	Title Card	.50	.25	.15

1974 Laughlin All-Star Games

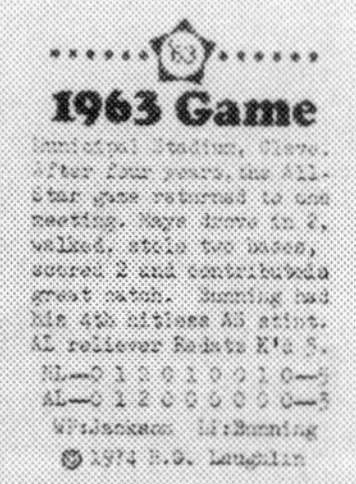

With pen and ink drawings by R.G. Laughlin on the fronts, this set (40 cards) features one card from each year of the game from 1933 to 1973. The 2-3/4" x 3-3/8" cards show a player in black ink in front of a light blue background with a glossy finish, with red printing for the title of the set and the year. The backs are printed in blue, with the year of the All-Star Game serving as the card number.

		NR MT	EX	VG
Complete set (40):		25.00	12.50	7.50
Common Player:		.50	.25	.15
33	Babe's Homer	5.00	2.50	1.50
34	Hubbell Fans Five	.75	.40	.25
35	Foxx Smashes Homer	.75	.40	.25
36	Ol' Diz Fogs 'Em	1.00	.50	.30
37	Four Hits for Ducky	.50	.25	.15
38	No-Hit Vandy	.50	.25	.15
39	DiMaggio Homers	3.00	1.50	.90
40	West's 3-Run Shot	.50	.25	.15
41	Vaughan Busts Two	.50	.25	.15
42	York's 2-Run Smash	.50	.25	.15
43	Doerr 3-Run Blast	.50	.25	.15
44	Cavarretta Reaches	.50	.25	.15
46	Field Day for Ted	2.00	1.00	.60
47	Big Cat Plants One	.50	.25	.15
48	Raschi Pitches	.50	.25	.15
49	Jackie Scores	2.00	1.00	.60
50	Schoendienst Breaks	.50	.25	.15
51	Kiner Homers	.50	.25	.15
52	Sauer's Shot	.50	.25	.15
53	Slaughter Hustles	.50	.25	.15
54	Rosen Hits	.50	.25	.15
55	Stan the Man's Homer	1.50	.75	.40
56	Ken Boyer Super	.50	.25	.15
57	Kaline Hits	1.00	.50	.30

58	Only Nellie Gets Two	.50	.25	.15
59	F. Robbie Perfect	.75	.40	.25
60	Willie 3-for-4	1.50	.70	.45
61	Bunning Hitless	.50	.25	.15
62	Roberto Perfect	2.50	1.25	.70
63	Monster Strikeouts	.50	.25	.15
64	Callison's Homer	.50	.25	.15
65	Stargell Big Day	.50	.25	.15
66	Brooks Hits	.75	.40	.25
67	Fergie Fans Six	.50	.25	.15
68	Tom Terrific	1.50	.70	.45
69	Stretch Belts Two	.75	.40	.25
70	Yaz Four Hits	1.00	.50	.30
71	Reggie Unloads	1.50	.70	.45
72	Henry Hammers	1.50	.70	.45
73	Bonds Perfect	.60	.30	.20

1974 Laughlin Old-Time Black Stars

31 BILL MONROE 2b

Bill Monroe started his career just after the turn of the century, and the N.Y. Giants' John McGraw said he would have starred in any league. Rube Foster called him the greatest ballplayer of them all. The second baseman began with the Philadelphia Giants in 1903, then played with the Quaker Giants and Brooklyn Royal Giants. Joining Foster's American Giants in 1912, he was a key figure on that club for three years, but died in 1915.

This set of slightly oversized cards (2-5/8" x 3-1/2") features 36 cards of drawings by R.G. Laughlin. The artwork is printed in brown and a light tan and the backs are printed in brown on white stock. The set features many of the greatest players from the old Negro leagues. The cards carry no dated copyright information and no mention of the prolific Laughlin, but the simple line drawings are obviously his work, and a subsequent issue four years later by Laughlin removes virtually any doubt.

		NR MT	EX	VG
Complete Set (36):		35.00	17.50	10.00
Common Player:		1.00	.50	.30
1	Smokey Joe Williams	3.00	1.50	.90
2	Rap Dixon	1.00	.50	.30
3	Oliver Marcelle	1.00	.50	.30
4	Bingo DeMoss	2.00	1.00	.60
5	Willie Foster	1.50	.70	.45
6	John Beckwith	1.00	.50	.30
7	Floyd (Jelly) Gardner	1.00	.50	.30
8	Josh Gibson	5.00	2.50	1.50
9	Jose Mendez	1.00	.50	.30
10	Pete Hill	1.00	.50	.30
11	Buck Leonard	3.00	1.50	.90
12	Jud Wilson	1.00	.50	.30
13	Willie Wells	2.00	1.00	.60
14	Jimmie Lyons	1.00	.50	.30
15	Satchel Paige	5.00	2.50	1.50
16	Louis Santop	1.00	.50	.30
17	Frank Grant	1.00	.50	.30
18	Christobel Torrienti	1.00	.50	.30
19	Bullet Rogan	1.50	.75	.45
20	Dave Malarcher	1.50	.70	.45
21	Spot Poles	1.00	.50	.30
22	Home Run Johnson	1.50	.70	.45
23	Charlie Grant	1.50	.75	.45
24	Cool Papa Bell	3.00	1.50	.90
25	Cannonball Dick Redding	1.00	.50	.30
26	Ray Dandridge	3.00	1.50	.90
27	Biz Mackey	2.00	1.00	.60
28	Fats Jenkins	1.00	.50	.30
29	Martin Dihigo	2.00	1.00	.60
30	Mule Suttles	1.00	.50	.30
31	Bill Monroe	1.00	.50	.30
32	Dan McClellan	1.00	.50	.30
33	John Henry Lloyd	1.50	.75	.45
34	Oscar Charleston	3.00	1.50	.90
35	Andrew (Rube) Foster	3.00	1.50	.90
36	William (Judy) Johnson	3.00	1.50	.90

1974 Laughlin Sportslang

Featuring the cartoon artwork of R.G. Laughlin, this 41-card set features 40 cards (plus one unnumbered title card) detailing the history and derivation of slang terms from several sports. The cards are 2-3/4" x 3-1/4", with red and blue printing on the front and red on the back. The cards are numbered on the back.

		NR MT	EX	VG
Complete set (41):		8.00	4.00	2.50
Common card:		.25	.13	.08
1	Bull Pen	.25	.13	.08
2	Charley Horse	.25	.13	.08
3	Derby	.25	.13	.08
4	Anchor Man	.25	.13	.08
5	Mascot	.25	.13	.08
6	Annie Oakley	.25	.13	.08
7	Taxi Squad	.25	.13	.08
8	Dukes	.25	.13	.08
9	Rookie	.25	.13	.08
10	Jinx	.25	.13	.08
11	Dark Horse	.25	.13	.08
12	Hat Trick	.25	.13	.08
13	Bell Wether	.25	.13	.08
14	Love	.25	.13	.08
15	Red Dog	.25	.13	.08
16	Barnstorm	.25	.13	.08
17	Bull's Eye	.25	.13	.08
18	Rabbit Punch	.25	.13	.08
19	The Upper Hand	.25	.13	.08
20	Handi Cap	.25	.13	.08
21	Marathon	.25	.13	.08
22	Southpaw	.25	.13	.08
23	Boner	.25	.13	.08
24	Gridiron	.25	.13	.08
25	Fan	.25	.13	.08
26	Moxie	.25	.13	.08
27	Birdie	.25	.13	.08
28	Sulky	.25	.13	.08
29	Dribble	.25	.13	.08
30	Donnybrook	.25	.13	.08
31	The Real McCoy	.25	.13	.08
32	Even Stephen	.25	.13	.08
33	Chinese Homer	.25	.13	.08
34	English	.25	.13	.08
35	Garrison Finish	.25	.13	.08
36	Foot in the Bucket	.25	.13	.08
37	Steeple Chase	.25	.13	.08
38	Long Shot	.25	.13	.08
39	Nip and Tuck	.25	.13	.08
40	Battery	.25	.13	.08
----	Header Card	.25	.13	.08

1975 Laughlin Batty Baseball

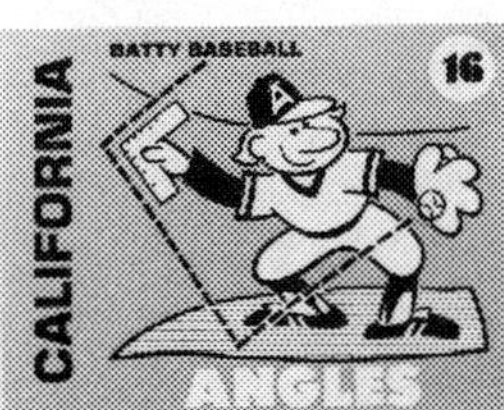

This 25-card set depicts one humorous nickname for each of 24 Major League teams, plus one unnumbered title card. The cards are approximately standard size at 2-1/2" x 3-1/2", with simple black and white cartoon drawings on the front with orange back- grounds. The backs are blank and the cards are numbered on front.

		NR MT	EX	VG
Complete set (25):		10.00	5.00	3.00
Common card:		.50	.25	.15
1	Oakland Daze	.50	.25	.15
2	Boston Wet Sox	.50	.25	.15
3	Cincinnati Dreads	.50	.25	.15
4	Chicago Wide Sox	.50	.25	.15
5	Milwaukee Boozers	.50	.25	.15
6	Philadelphia Fillies	.50	.25	.15
7	Cleveland Engines	.50	.25	.15
8	New York Mits	.50	.25	.15
9	Texas Ranchers	.50	.25	.15
10	San Francisco Gents	.50	.25	.15
11	Houston Disastros	.50	.25	.15
12	Chicago Clubs	.50	.25	.15
13	Minnesota Wins	.50	.25	.15
14	St. Louis Gardeners	.50	.25	.15
15	New York Yankers	.50	.25	.15
16	California Angles	.50	.25	.15
17	Pittsburgh Irates	.50	.25	.15
18	Los Angeles Smoggers	.50	.25	.15
19	Baltimore Oreos	.50	.25	.15
20	Montreal Expose	.50	.25	.15
21	San Diego Parties	.50	.25	.15
22	Detroit Taggers	.50	.25	.15
23	Kansas City Broils	.50	.25	.15
24	Atlanta Briefs	.50	.25	.15
----	Header Card	.50	.25	.15

A player's name in italic type indicates a rookie card. An (FC) indicates a player's first card for that particular card company.

1976 Laughlin Diamond Jubilee

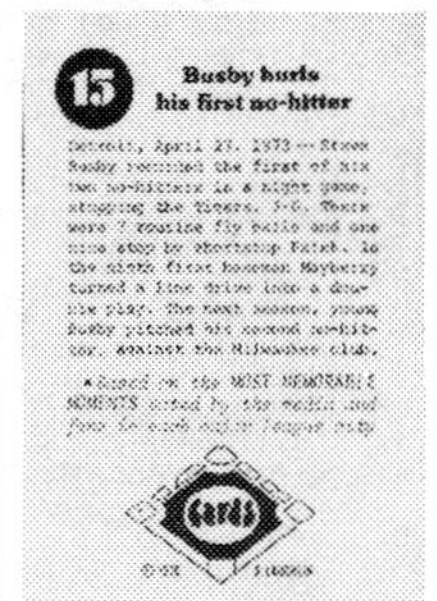

This set of 32 oversized cards (2-3/4" x 4") features Laughlin's drawings of baseball stars highlighting specific events or records. The fronts are printed in black and blue over a red background; the backs are numbered and printed in blue with information about the specific event.

		NR MT	EX	VG
Complete set (32):		35.00	17.50	10.50
Common player:		.50	.25	.15
1	Nolan Ryan	6.00	3.00	1.75
2	Ernie Banks	1.50	.70	.45
3	Mickey Lolich	.50	.25	.15
4	Sandy Koufax	2.50	1.25	.70
5	Frank Robinson	.75	.40	.25
6	Bill Mazeroski	.75	.40	.25
7	Catfish Hunter	.50	.25	.15
8	Hank Aaron	2.50	1.25	.70
9	Carl Yastrzemski	1.00	.50	.30
10	Jim Bunning	.50	.25	.15
11	Brooks Robinson	1.00	.50	.30
12	John VanderMeer	.50	.25	.15
13	Harmon Killebrew	1.25	.60	.40
14	Lou Brock	.75	.40	.25
15	Steve Busby	.50	.25	.15
16	Nate Colbert	.50	.25	.15
17	Don Larsen	.75	.40	.25
18	Willie Mays	2.50	1.25	.70
19	David Clyde	.50	.25	.15
20	Mack Jones	.50	.25	.15
21	Mike Hegan	.50	.25	.15
22	Jerry Koosman	.50	.25	.15
23	Early Wynn	.60	.30	.20
24	Nellie Fox	.75	.40	.25
25	Joe DiMaggio	4.00	2.00	1.20
26	Jackie Robinson	2.50	1.25	.70
27	Ted Williams	2.50	1.25	.70
28	Lou Gehrig	3.00	1.50	.90
29	Bobby Thomson	.50	.25	.15
30	Roger Maris	1.00	.50	.30
31	Harvey Haddix	.50	.25	.15
32	Babe Ruth	5.00	2.50	1.50

1976 Laughlin Indianapolis Clowns

Founder Syd Pollock

Syd Pollock organized the Miami Ethiopian Clowns in 1929. His concept was to create a black club that not only could play pro ball but add laughs and showmanship to the game. The Clowns preceded the Harlem Globetrotters by a year. The national semi-pro champions turned pro in 1942, becoming the Cincinnati Clowns and later the Indianapolis Clowns. as they won numerous Negro AL titles. Also a Braves scout, Pollock retired from traveling baseball in 1964, turning the team over to Ed Hamman. Syd passed away in 1968.

In a departure from the style of most Laughlin issues, this 42-card set does not use his artwork but rather black and white photos framed by a light blue border. The cards are oversized at 2-5/8" x 4-1/4", with red printing on front and back. The cards are numberd on the front.

		NR MT	EX	VG
Complete set (42):		30.00	15.00	9.00
Common player:		.50	.25	.15
1	Ed Hamman (Ed the Clown)	1.00	.50	.30
2	Dero Austin	.50	.25	.15
3	James Williams (Natureboy)	.50	.25	.15
4	Sam Brison (Birmingham)	.50	.25	.15
5	Richard King (King Tut)	.50	.25	.15

6	Syd Pollock (Founder)	.50	.25	.15
7	Nataniel (Lefty) Small	.50	.25	.15
8	Grant Greene (Double Duty)	.50	.25	.15
9	Nancy Miller (Lady Umpire)	1.00	.50	.30
10	Billy Vaughn	.50	.25	.15
11	Sam Brison (Putout for Sam)	.50	.25	.15
12	Ed Hamman	.50	.25	.15
13	Dero Austin (Home Delivery)	.50	.25	.15
14	Steve (Nub) Anderson	.50	.25	.15
15	Joe Cherry	.50	.25	.15
16	Reece (Goose) Tatum	3.00	1.50	.90
17	James Williams (Natureboy)	.50	.25	.15
18	Byron Purnell	.50	.25	.15
19	Bat Boy	.50	.25	.15
20	Spec BeBop	.50	.25	.15
21	Satchel Paige	5.00	2.50	1.50
22	Prince Jo Henry	.50	.25	.15
23	Ed Hamman, Syd Pollock	.50	.25	.15
24	Paul Casanova	.75	.40	.25
25	Steve (Nub) Anderson (Nub Singles)	.50	.25	.15
26	Comiskey Park	.50	.25	.15
27	Toni Stone (Second basewoman)	1.50	.75	.45
28	Dero Austin (Small target)	.50	.25	.15
29	Sam Brison, Natureboy Williams, Calling Dr. Kildare	.50	.25	.15
30	Oscar Charleston	2.00	1.00	.60
31	Richard King (King Tut)	.50	.25	.15
32	Ed Hamman, Joe Cherry, Hal King, Ed and prospects	.50	.25	.15
33	Team bus	.50	.25	.15
34	Hank Aaron	5.00	2.50	1.50
35	The Great Yogi	3.00	1.50	.90
36	W.H. (Chauff) Wilson	.50	.25	.15
37	Sam Brison, Sonny Jackson, Doin' their thing	.50	.25	.15
38	Billy Vaughn (The hard way)	.50	.25	.15
39	James Williams (18 the easy way)	.50	.25	.15
40	Ed Hamman, Casey Stengel, Casey & Ed	2.00	1.00	.60
----	Header Card	.50	.25	.15
----	Baseball Laff Book	.50	.25	.15

1978 Laughlin Long Ago Black Stars

2. LARRY BROWN C

In what appears very much like a second series save for slight title alteration, sports artist R.G. Laughlin produced this 36-card set in a format very similar to his 1974 issue highlighting Negro League stars. This set is printed in dark and light green on a non-glossy front, with printing on the back in black. Most of the more widely known Negro League stars appeared in the 1974 issue.

		NR MT	EX	VG
	Complete set (36):	20.00	10.00	6.00
	Common player:	.50	.25	.15
1	Ted Trent	.50	.25	.15
2	Larry Brown	.50	.25	.15
3	Newt Allen	1.00	.50	.30
4	Norman Stearns	.50	.25	.15
5	Leon Day	2.00	1.00	.60
6	Dick Lundy	.50	.25	.15
7	Bruce Petway	.50	.25	.15
8	Bill Drake	.50	.25	.15
9	Chaney White	.50	.25	.15
10	Webster McDonald	.75	.40	.25
11	Tommy Butts	.50	.25	.15
12	Ben Taylor	.50	.25	.15
13	James (Joe) Greene	.50	.25	.15
14	Dick Seay	.50	.25	.15
15	Sammy Hughes	.50	.25	.15
16	Ted Page	1.00	.50	.30
17	Willie Cornelius	.50	.25	.15
18	Pat Patterson	.50	.25	.15
19	Frank Wickware	.50	.25	.15
20	Albert Haywood	.50	.25	.15
21	Bill Holland	.50	.25	.15
22	Sol White	.75	.40	.25
23	Chet Brewer	1.00	.50	.30
24	Crush Holloway	.50	.25	.15
25	George Johnson	.50	.25	.15
26	George Scales	.50	.25	.15
27	Dave Brown	.50	.25	.15
28	John Donaldson	.50	.25	.15
29	William Johnson	1.00	.50	.30
30	Bill Yancey	1.00	.50	.30
31	Sam Bankhead	1.50	.75	.45
32	Leroy Matlock	.50	.25	.15
33	Quincy Troupe	.75	.40	.25
34	Hilton Smith	.50	.25	.15
35	Jim Crutchfield	1.00	.50	.30
36	Ted Radcliffe	1.25	.60	.40

1980 Laughlin 300/400/500

This unusual set features a combination of the line drawings of R.G. Laughlin and a photo head shot of the player depicted. The cards are actually square, 3-1/4" x 3-1/4", with a background in color depicting a baseball diamond. The set is based on 300 wins, batting .400 or better and 500 homers, with a total of 30 cards in the blank backed set. The cards are numbered on the front.

		NR MT	EX	VG
	Complete set (30):	16.00	8.00	4.75
	Common player:	.50	.25	.15
1	Header Card	.50	.25	.15
2	Babe Ruth	4.00	2.00	1.25
3	Walter Johnson	1.00	.50	.30
4	Ty Cobb	1.50	.70	.45
5	Christy Mathewson	1.00	.50	.30
6	Ted Williams	1.50	.70	.45
7	Bill Terry	.75	.40	.25
8	Grover C. Alexander	.75	.40	.25
9	Napoleon Lajoie	.75	.40	.25
10	Willie Mays	1.50	.70	.45
11	Cy Young	.75	.40	.25
12	Mel Ott	.50	.25	.15
13	Joe Jackson	3.00	1.50	.90
14	Harmon Killebrew	.75	.40	.25
15	Warren Spahn	.75	.40	.25
16	Hank Aaron	2.00	1.00	.60
17	Rogers Hornsby	.75	.40	.25
18	Mickey Mantle	4.00	2.00	1.25
19	Lefty Grove	.75	.40	.25
20	Ted Williams	2.00	1.00	.60
21	Jimmie Fox	.75	.40	.25
22	Eddie Plank	.50	.25	.15
23	Frank Robinson	.75	.40	.25
24	George Sisler	.50	.25	.15
25	Eddie Mathews	.75	.40	.25
26	Early Wynn	.50	.25	.15
27	Ernie Banks	1.00	.50	.30
28	Harry Heilmann	.50	.25	.15
29	Lou Gehrig	3.00	1.50	.90
30	Willie McCovey	.75	.40	.25

1980 Laughlin Famous Feats

A set of 40 cards, this Famous Feats set by sports artist R.G. Laughlin carries a subtitle as the Second Series, apparently a reference to a 1972 issue of the same name by Laughlin that was produced by Fleer. Unlike many of the odd sized Laughlin issues, this one is the standard 2-1/2" x 3-1/2", with full color used with the artist's pen and ink drawings on the front. The cards are numbered on the front and the backs are blank.

		NR MT	EX	VG
	Complete set (40):	8.00	4.00	2.50
	Common player:	.25	.13	.08
1	Honus Wagner	.75	.40	.25
2	Herb Pennock	.25	.13	.08
3	Al Simmons	.25	.13	.08
4	Hack Wilson	.25	.13	.08
5	Dizzy Dean	.50	.25	.15
6	Chuck Klein	.25	.13	.08
7	Nellie Fox	.25	.13	.08
8	Lefty Grove	.25	.13	.08
9	George Sisler	.25	.13	.08
10	Lou Gehrig	1.00	.50	.30
11	Rube Waddell	.25	.13	.08
12	Max Carey	.25	.13	.08
13	Thurman Munson	.50	.25	.15
14	Mel Ott	.25	.13	.08
15	Doc White	.25	.13	.08
16	Babe Ruth	2.00	1.00	.60
17	Schoolboy Rowe	.25	.13	.08
18	Jackie Robinson	.75	.40	.25
19	Joe Medwick	.25	.13	.08
20	Casey Stengel	.50	.25	.15
21	Roberto Clemente	2.00	1.00	.60
22	Christy Mathewson	.75	.40	.25
23	Jimmie Foxx	.35	.20	.11
24	Joe Jackson	2.00	1.00	.60
25	Walter Johnson	.75	.40	.25
26	Tony Lazzeri	.25	.13	.08
27	Hugh Casey	.25	.13	.08
28	Ty Cobb	1.00	.50	.30
29	Stuffy McInnis	.25	.13	.08
30	Cy Young	.50	.25	.15
31	Lefty O'Doul	.25	.13	.08
32	Eddie Collins	.25	.13	.08
33	Joe McCarty	.25	.13	.08
34	Ed Walsh	.25	.13	.08
35	George Burns	.25	.13	.08
36	Walt Dropo	.25	.13	.08
37	Connie Mack	.30	.15	.09
38	Babe Adams	.25	.13	.08
39	Rogers Hornsby	.35	.20	.11
40	Grover C. Alexander	.35	.20	.11

1948 Leaf

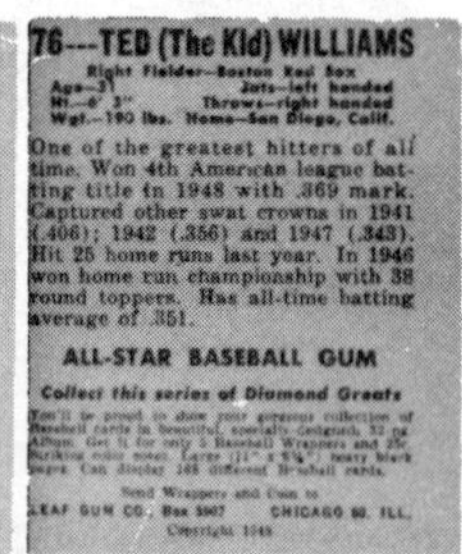
76---TED (The Kid) WILLIAMS

Right Fielder—Boston Red Sox

Age—31 Bats—left handed

Ht—6' 3" Throws—right handed

Wgt.—190 lbs. Home—San Diego, Calif.

One of the greatest hitters of all time. Won 4th American league batting title in 1948 with .369 mark. Captured other swat crowns in 1941 (.406); 1942 (.356) and 1947 (.343). Hit 25 home runs last year. In 1946 won home run championship with 38 round toppers. Has all-time batting average of .351.

ALL-STAR BASEBALL GUM

Collect this series of Diamond Greats

LEAF GUM CO., Box 5967 CHICAGO 80, ILL.

The first color baseball cards of the post-World War II era were the 98-card, 2-3/8" by 2-7/8", set produced by Chicago's Leaf Gum Company in 1948-1949. The color was crude, probably helping to make the set less popular than the Bowman issues of the same era. One of the toughest post-war sets to complete, exactly half of the Leaf issue - 49 of the cards - are significantly harder to find than the other 49. Probably intended to confound bubble gum buyers of the day, the set is skip-numbered between 1-168. Card backs contain offers of felt pennants, an album for the cards or 5-1/2" by 7-1/2" premium photos of Hall of Famers.

		NR MT	EX	VG
	Complete set (98):	30000.	15000.	9000.
	Common player:	25.00	12.50	7.50
	Common short-print:	300.00	150.00	90.00
1	Joe DiMaggio	2000.	750.00	475.00
3	Babe Ruth	2500.	1250.	750.00
4	*Stan Musial*	675.00	340.00	200.00
5	Virgil Trucks	400.00	200.00	120.00
8	*Satchel Paige*	2400.	1200.	720.00
10	Paul Trout	25.00	12.50	7.50
11	*Phil Rizzuto*	200.00	100.00	60.00
13	Casimer Michaels	300.00	150.00	90.00
14	Billy Johnson	30.00	15.00	9.00
17	Frank Overmire	25.00	12.50	7.50
19	John Wyrostek	300.00	150.00	90.00
20	*Hank Sauer*	400.00	200.00	120.00
22	Al Evans	25.00	12.50	7.50
26	Sam Chapman	25.00	12.50	7.50
27	Mickey Harris	25.00	12.50	7.50
28	*Jim Hegan*	30.00	15.00	9.00
29	*Elmer Valo*	30.00	15.00	9.00
30	*Bill Goodman*	300.00	150.00	90.00
31	Lou Brissie	25.00	12.50	7.50
32	*Warren Spahn*	300.00	150.00	90.00
33	Harry Lowrey	300.00	150.00	90.00
36	Al Zarilla	300.00	150.00	90.00
38	*Ted Kluszewski*	100.00	50.00	30.00
39	*Ewell Blackwell*	40.00	20.00	12.00
42	Kent Peterson	25.00	12.50	7.50
43	Eddie Stevens	300.00	150.00	90.00

45	Ken Keltner	300.00	150.00	90.00
46	Johnny Mize	90.00	45.00	27.00
47	George Vico	25.00	12.50	7.50
48	Johnny Schmitz	300.00	150.00	90.00
49	*Del Ennis*	40.00	20.00	12.00
50	Dick Wakefield	25.00	12.50	7.50
51	*Alvin Dark*	400.00	200.00	120.00
53	John Vandermeer	40.00	20.00	12.00
54	Bobby Adams	300.00	150.00	90.00
55	Tommy Henrich	400.00	200.00	120.00
56	*Larry Jensen*	30.00	15.00	9.00
57	Bob McCall	25.00	12.50	7.50
59	Luke Appling	80.00	40.00	24.00
61	Jake Early	25.00	12.50	7.50
62	Eddie Joost	300.00	150.00	90.00
63	Barney McCosky	300.00	150.00	90.00
65	Bob Elliot (Elliott)	25.00	12.50	7.50
66	Orval Grove	300.00	150.00	90.00
68	Ed Miller	300.00	150.00	90.00
70	Honus Wagner	250.00	125.00	75.00
72	Hank Edwards	25.00	12.50	7.50
73	Pat Seerey	25.00	12.50	7.50
75	Dom DiMaggio	550.00	270.00	165.00
76	Ted Williams	875.00	435.00	260.00
77	Roy Smalley	25.00	12.50	7.50
78	Walter Evers	300.00	150.00	90.00
79	*Jackie Robinson*	850.00	425.00	255.00
81	George Kurowski	300.00	150.00	90.00
82	Johnny Lindell	25.00	12.50	7.50
83	Bobby Doerr	95.00	47.00	28.00
84	Sid Hudson	25.00	12.50	7.50
85	*Dave Philley*	375.00	187.00	112.00
86	Ralph Weigel	25.00	12.50	7.50
88	Frank Gustine	300.00	150.00	90.00
91	*Ralph Kiner*	200.00	100.00	60.00
93	Bob Feller	1200.	600.00	360.00
95	George Stirnweiss	25.00	12.50	7.50
97	*Martin Marion*	50.00	25.00	15.00
98	*Hal Newhouser*	600.00	300.00	180.00
102a	Gene Hermansk (incorrect spelling)	300.00	150.00	90.00
102b	Gene Hermanski (correct spelling)	25.00	12.50	7.50
104	Edward Stewart	300.00	150.00	90.00
106	Lou Boudreau	100.00	50.00	30.00
108	Matthew Batts	300.00	150.00	90.00
111	Gerald Priddy	25.00	12.50	7.50
113	Emil Leonard	300.00	150.00	90.00
117	Joe Gordon	25.00	12.50	7.50
120	*George Kell*	550.00	275.00	165.00
121	*John Pesky*	400.00	200.00	120.00
123	Clifford Fannin	300.00	150.00	90.00
125	*Andy Pafko*	30.00	15.00	9.00
127	Enos Slaughter	725.00	362.00	217.00
128	Warren Rosar	25.00	12.50	7.50
129	Kirby Higbe	300.00	150.00	90.00
131	Sid Gordon	300.00	150.00	90.00
133	Tommy Holmes	400.00	200.00	120.00
136a	Cliff Aberson (full sleeve)	25.00	12.50	7.50
136b	Cliff Aberson (short sleeve)	175.00	87.00	52.00
137	Harry Walker	300.00	150.00	90.00
138	*Larry Doby*	500.00	250.00	150.00
139	Johnny Hopp	25.00	12.50	7.50
142	*Danny Murtaugh*	400.00	200.00	120.00
143	Dick Sisler	300.00	150.00	90.00
144	Bob Dillinger	300.00	150.00	90.00
146	Harold Reiser	400.00	200.00	120.00
149	Henry Majeski	300.00	150.00	90.00
153	Floyd Baker	300.00	150.00	90.00
158	*Harry Brecheen*	400.00	200.00	120.00
159	Mizell Platt	25.00	12.50	7.50
160	Bob Scheffing	400.00	200.00	120.00
161	*Vernon Stephens*	400.00	200.00	120.00
163	*Freddy Hutchinson*	400.00	200.00	120.00
165	*Dale Mitchell*	400.00	200.00	120.00
168	Phil Cavaretta	400.00	200.00	120.00

1960 Leaf

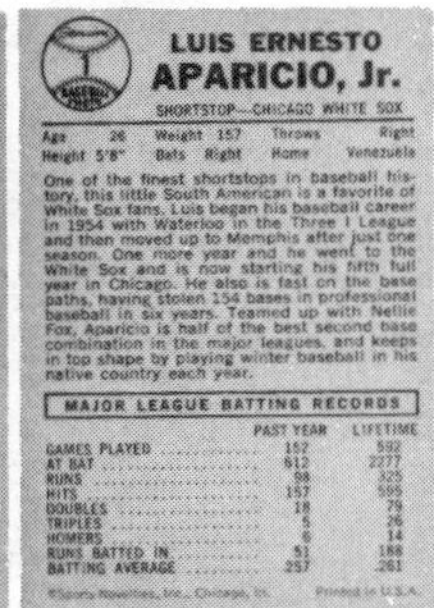

While known to the hobby as "Leaf" cards, this set of 144 cards carries the copyright of Sports Novelties Inc., Chicago. The 2-1/2" by 3-1/2" cards feature black and white player portrait photos, with background airbrushed away. Cards were sold in 5¢ wax packs with a marble, rather than a piece of bubble gum. The second half of the set, cards #73-144, are very scarce and make the set a real challenge for the collector. Card #25, Jim Grant, is found in two versions, with his own picture (black cap) and with a photo of Brooks Lawrence (white cap). Eight cards (#'s 1, 12, 17, 23, 35, 58, 61 and 72) exist with close-up photos that are much rarer than the normal cap to chest photos. It is believed the scarce "face only" cards are proof cards prepared by Leaf as only a handful are known to exist.

		NR MT	EX	VG
	Complete Set (145):	1400.	700.00	420.00
	Common Player (1-72):	4.00	2.00	1.25
	Common Player (73-145):	15.00	7.50	4.50
1	Luis Aparicio	25.00	12.50	7.50
2	Woody Held	4.00	2.00	1.25
3	Frank Lary	4.00	2.00	1.25
4	Camilo Pascual	4.00	2.00	1.25
5	Frank Herrera	4.00	2.00	1.25
6	Felipe Alou	9.00	4.50	2.75
7	Bennie Daniels	4.00	2.00	1.25
8	Roger Craig	7.00	3.50	2.00
9	Eddie Kasko	4.00	2.00	1.25
10	Bob Grim	4.00	2.00	1.25
11	Jim Busby	4.00	2.00	1.25
12	Ken Boyer	8.00	4.00	2.50
13	Bob Boyd	4.00	2.00	1.25
14	Sam Jones	4.00	2.00	1.25
15	Larry Jackson	4.00	2.00	1.25
16	Roy Face	6.00	3.00	1.75
17	Walt Moryn	4.00	2.00	1.25
18	Jim Gilliam	6.00	3.00	1.75
19	Don Newcombe	4.00	2.00	1.25
20	Glen Hobbie	4.00	2.00	1.25
21	Pedro Ramos	4.00	2.00	1.25
22	Ryne Duren	5.00	2.50	1.50
23	Joe Jay	4.00	2.00	1.25
24	Lou Berberet	4.00	2.00	1.25
25a	Jim Grant (white cap, photo actually Brooks Lawrence)	14.00	7.00	4.25
25b	Jim Grant (dark cap, correct photo)	20.00	10.00	6.00
26	Tom Borland	4.00	2.00	1.25
27	Brooks Robinson	40.00	20.00	12.00
28	Jerry Adair	4.00	2.00	1.25
29	Ron Jackson	4.00	2.00	1.25
30	George Strickland	4.00	2.00	1.25
31	Rocky Bridges	4.00	2.00	1.25
32	Bill Tuttle	4.00	2.00	1.25
33	Ken Hunt	4.00	2.00	1.25
34	Hal Griggs	4.00	2.00	1.25
35	Jim Coates	4.00	2.00	1.25
36	Brooks Lawrence	4.00	2.00	1.25
37	Duke Snider	50.00	25.00	15.00
38	Al Spangler	4.00	2.00	1.25
39	Jim Owens	4.00	2.00	1.25
40	Bill Virdon	4.00	2.00	1.25
41	Ernie Broglio	4.00	2.00	1.25
42	Andre Rodgers	4.00	2.00	1.25
43	Julio Becquer	4.00	2.00	1.25
44	Tony Taylor	4.00	2.00	1.25
45	Jerry Lynch	4.00	2.00	1.25
46	Clete Boyer	4.00	2.00	1.25
47	Jerry Lumpe	4.00	2.00	1.25
48	Charlie Maxwell	4.00	2.00	1.25
49	Jim Perry	4.00	2.00	1.25
50	Danny McDevitt	4.00	2.00	1.25
51	Juan Pizarro	4.00	2.00	1.25
52	*Dallas Green*	9.00	4.50	2.75
53	Bob Friend	4.00	2.00	1.25
54	Jack Sanford	4.00	2.00	1.25
55	Jim Rivera	4.00	2.00	1.25
56	Ted Wills	4.00	2.00	1.25
57	Milt Pappas	4.00	2.00	1.25
58a	Hal Smith (team & position on back)	4.00	2.00	1.25
58b	Hal Smith (team blackened out on back)	50.00	25.00	15.00
58c	Hal Smith (team missing on back)	50.00	25.00	15.00
59	Bob Avila	4.00	2.00	1.25
60	Clem Labine	4.00	2.00	1.25
61	Vic Rehm	4.00	2.00	1.25
62	John Gabler	4.00	2.00	1.25
63	John Tsitouris	4.00	2.00	1.25
64	Dave Sisler	4.00	2.00	1.25
65	Vic Power	4.00	2.00	1.25
66	Earl Battey	4.00	2.00	1.25
67	Bob Purkey	4.00	2.00	1.25
68	Moe Drabowsky	4.00	2.00	1.25
69	Hoyt Wilhelm	18.00	9.00	5.50
70	Humberto Robinson	4.00	2.00	1.25
71	Whitey Herzog	8.00	4.00	2.50
72	Dick Donovan	4.00	2.00	1.25
73	Gordon Jones	15.00	7.50	4.50
74	Joe Hicks	15.00	7.50	4.50
75	*Ray Culp*	18.00	9.00	5.50
76	Dick Drott	15.00	7.50	4.50
77	Bob Duliba	15.00	7.50	4.50
78	Art Ditmar	18.00	9.00	5.50
79	Steve Korcheck	15.00	7.50	4.50
80	Henry Mason	15.00	7.50	4.50
81	Harry Simpson	15.00	7.50	4.50
82	Gene Green	15.00	7.50	4.50
83	Bob Shaw	15.00	7.50	4.50
84	Howard Reed	15.00	7.50	4.50
85	Dick Stigman	15.00	7.50	4.50
86	Rip Repulski	15.00	7.50	4.50
87	Seth Morehead	15.00	7.50	4.50
88	Camilo Carreon	15.00	7.50	4.50
89	John Blanchard	18.00	9.00	5.50
90	Billy Hoeft	15.00	7.50	4.50
91	Fred Hopke	15.00	7.50	4.50
92	Joe Martin	15.00	7.50	4.50
93	Wally Shannon	15.00	7.50	4.50
94	Baseball's Two Hal Smiths (Hal Smith, Harold Wayne Smith)	20.00	10.00	6.00
95	Al Schroll	15.00	7.50	4.50
96	John Kucks	15.00	7.50	4.50
97	Tom Morgan	15.00	7.50	4.50
98	Willie Jones	15.00	7.50	4.50
99	Marshall Renfroe	18.00	9.00	5.50
100	Willie Tasby	15.00	7.50	4.50
101	Irv Noren	15.00	7.50	4.50
102	Russ Snyder	15.00	7.50	4.50
103	Bob Turley	20.00	10.00	6.00
104	Jim Woods	15.00	7.50	4.50
105	Ronnie Kline	15.00	7.50	4.50
106	Steve Bilko	15.00	7.50	4.50
107	Elmer Valo	15.00	7.50	4.50
108	Tom McAvoy	15.00	7.50	4.50
109	Stan Williams	15.00	7.50	4.50
110	Earl Averill	15.00	7.50	4.50
111	Lee Walls	15.00	7.50	4.50
112	Paul Richards	18.00	9.00	5.50
113	Ed Sadowski	15.00	7.50	4.50
114	Stover McIlwain	18.00	9.00	5.50
115	Chuck Tanner (photo actually Ken Kuhn)	20.00	10.00	6.00
116	Lou Klimchock	15.00	7.50	4.50
117	Neil Chrisley	15.00	7.50	4.50
118	John Callison	20.00	10.00	6.00
119	Hal Smith	15.00	7.50	4.50
120	Carl Sawatski	15.00	7.50	4.50
121	Frank Leja	15.00	7.50	4.50
122	Earl Torgeson	15.00	7.50	4.50
123	Art Schult	15.00	7.50	4.50
124	Jim Brosnan	18.00	9.00	5.50
125	Sparky Anderson	80.00	40.00	24.00
126	Joe Pignatano	15.00	7.50	4.50
127	Rocky Nelson	15.00	7.50	4.50
128	Orlando Cepeda	60.00	30.00	18.00
129	Daryl Spencer	15.00	7.50	4.50
130	Ralph Lumenti	15.00	7.50	4.50
131	Sam Taylor	15.00	7.50	4.50
132	Harry Brecheen	15.00	7.50	4.50
133	Johnny Groth	15.00	7.50	4.50
134	Wayne Terwilliger	15.00	7.50	4.50
135	Kent Hadley	15.00	7.50	4.50
136	Faye Throneberry	15.00	7.50	4.50
137	Jack Meyer	15.00	7.50	4.50
138	*Chuck Cottier*	15.00	7.50	4.50
139	Joe DeMaestri	15.00	7.50	4.50
140	Gene Freese	15.00	7.50	4.50
141	Curt Flood	35.00	17.50	10.50
142	Gino Cimoli	15.00	7.50	4.50
143	Clay Dalrymple	15.00	7.50	4.50
144	Jim Bunning	60.00	30.00	18.00

1985 Leaf-Donruss

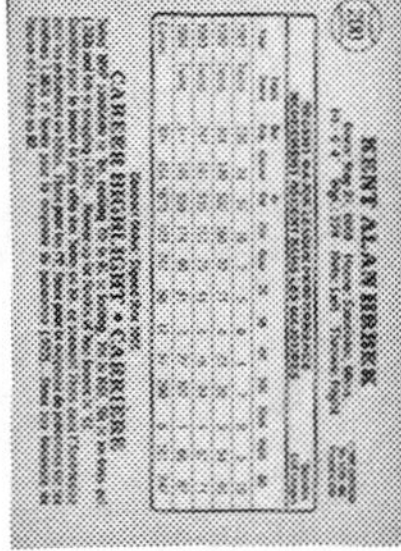

In an attempt to share in the Canadian baseball card market, Donruss, in 1985, issued a 264-card version of its regular set to be sold in Canada. Fronts of the 2-1/2" by 3-1/2" cards are virtually identical to the regular '85 Donruss cards of the same players, except that a green stylized leaf has been added to the logo in the upper-left. On back, player biographies have been re-written to accomodate both English and French versions, and new card numbers have been assigned. The 264 cards in this shortened set concentrate on star-caliber players, as well as those of Canada's two major league teams. A special two-card subset, "Canadian Greats," features paintings of Dave Stieb and Tim Raines. The Leaf-Donruss cards were widely distributed in the U.S. through hobby dealers.

		MT	NR MT	EX
	Complete Set (264):	82.00	61.00	33.00
	Common Player:	.08	.06	.03
1	Ryne Sandberg (DK)	3.00	2.25	1.25
2	Doug DeCinces (DK)	.08	.06	.03
3	Rich Dotson (DK)	.20	.15	.08
4	Bert Blyleven (DK)	.12	.09	.05
5	Lou Whitaker (DK)	.20	.15	.08
6	Dan Quisenberry (DK)	.20	.15	.08
7	Don Mattingly (DK)	2.75	2.00	1.00
8	Carney Lansford (DK)	.08	.06	.03
9	Frank Tanana (DK)	.08	.06	.03
10	Willie Upshaw (DK)	.08	.06	.03
11	Claudell Washington (DK)	.08	.06	.03
12	Mike Marshall (DK)	.15	.11	.06
13	Joaquin Andujar (DK)	.08	.06	.03
14	Cal Ripken, Jr. (DK)	4.25	3.25	1.75
15	Jim Rice (DK)	.30	.25	.12
16	Don Sutton (DK)	.20	.15	.08
17	Frank Viola (DK)	.20	.15	.08
18	Alvin Davis (DK)	.25	.20	.10
19	Mario Soto (DK)	.08	.06	.03
20	Jose Cruz (DK)	.08	.06	.03
21	Charlie Lea (DK)	.08	.06	.03
22	Jesse Orosco (DK)	.08	.06	.03

23	Juan Samuel (DK)	.25	.20	.10
24	Tony Pena (DK)	.08	.06	.03
25	Tony Gwynn (DK)	2.50	2.00	1.00
26	Bob Brenly (DK)	.08	.06	.03
27	Steve Kiefer (RR)	.08	.06	.03
28	Joe Morgan	.20	.15	.08
29	Luis Leal	.08	.06	.03
30	Dan Gladden	.15	.11	.06
31	Shane Rawley	.08	.06	.03
32	Mark Clear	.08	.06	.03
33	Terry Kennedy	.08	.06	.03
34	Hal McRae	.08	.06	.03
35	Mickey Rivers	.08	.06	.03
36	Tom Brunansky	.20	.15	.08
37	LaMarr Hoyt	.08	.06	.03
38	Orel Hershiser	2.50	2.00	1.00
39	Chris Bando	.08	.06	.03
40	Lee Lacy	.08	.06	.03
41	Lance Parrish	.25	.20	.10
42	George Foster	.12	.09	.05
43	Kevin McReynolds	.50	.40	.20
44	Robin Yount	3.50	2.75	1.50
45	Craig McMurtry	.08	.06	.03
46	Mike Witt	.20	.15	.08
47	Gary Redus	.08	.06	.03
48	Dennis Rasmussen	.20	.15	.08
49	Gary Woods	.08	.06	.03
50	Phil Bradley	.25	.20	.10
51	Steve Bedrosian	.20	.15	.08
52	Duane Walker	.08	.06	.03
53	Geoff Zahn	.08	.06	.03
54	Dave Stieb	.20	.15	.08
55	Pascual Perez	.08	.06	.03
56	Mark Langston	3.25	2.50	1.25
57	Bob Dernier	.08	.06	.03
58	Joe Cowley	.08	.06	.03
59	Dan Schatzeder	.08	.06	.03
60	Ozzie Smith	.15	.11	.06
61	Bob Knepper	.08	.06	.03
62	Keith Hernandez	.30	.25	.12
63	Rick Rhoden	.08	.06	.03
64	Alejandro Pena	.08	.06	.03
65	Damaso Garcia	.08	.06	.03
66	Chili Davis	.08	.06	.03
67	Al Oliver	.20	.15	.08
68	Alan Wiggins	.08	.06	.03
69	Darryl Motley	.08	.06	.03
70	Gary Ward	.08	.06	.03
71	John Butcher	.08	.06	.03
72	Scott McGregor	.08	.06	.03
73	Bruce Hurst	.20	.15	.08
74	Dwayne Murphy	.08	.06	.03
75	Greg Luzinski	.20	.15	.08
76	Pat Tabler	.08	.06	.03
77	Chet Lemon	.08	.06	.03
78	Jim Sundberg	.08	.06	.03
79	Wally Backman	.08	.06	.03
80	Terry Puhl	.08	.06	.03
81	Storm Davis	.08	.06	.03
82	Jim Wohlford	.08	.06	.03
83	Willie Randolph	.08	.06	.03
84	Ron Cey	.08	.06	.03
85	Jim Beattie	.08	.06	.03
86	Rafael Ramirez	.08	.06	.03
87	Cesar Cedeno	.08	.06	.03
88	Bobby Grich	.08	.06	.03
89	Jason Thompson	.08	.06	.03
90	Steve Sax	.15	.11	.06
91	Tony Fernandez	.15	.11	.06
92	Jeff Leonard	.08	.06	.03
93	Von Hayes	.08	.06	.03
94	Steve Garvey	.30	.25	.12
95	Steve Balboni	.08	.06	.03
96	Larry Parrish	.08	.06	.03
97	Tim Teufel	.08	.06	.03
98	Sammy Stewart	.08	.06	.03
99	Roger Clemens	32.50	24.00	13.00
100	Steve Kemp	.08	.06	.03
101	Tom Seaver	.80	.60	.30
102	Andre Thornton	.08	.06	.03
103	Kirk Gibson	.20	.15	.08
104	Ted Simmons	.20	.15	.08
105	David Palmer	.08	.06	.03
106	Roy Lee Jackson	.08	.06	.03
107	Kirby Puckett	42.50	32.00	17.00
108	Charlie Hough	.08	.06	.03
109	Mike Boddicker	.08	.06	.03
110	Willie Wilson	.20	.15	.08
111	Tim Lollar	.08	.06	.03
112	Tony Armas	.08	.06	.03
113	Steve Carlton	1.00	.70	.40
114	Gary Lavelle	.08	.06	.03
115	Cliff Johnson	.08	.06	.03
116	Ray Burris	.08	.06	.03
117	Rudy Law	.08	.06	.03
118	Mike Scioscia	.08	.06	.03
119	Kent Tekulve	.08	.06	.03
120	George Vukovich	.08	.06	.03
121	Barbaro Garbey	.08	.06	.03
122	Mookie Wilson	.08	.06	.03
123	Ben Oglivie	.08	.06	.03
124	Jerry Mumphrey	.08	.06	.03
125	Willie McGee	.15	.11	.06
126	Jeff Reardon	.20	.15	.08
127	Dave Winfield	3.25	2.50	1.25
128	Lee Smith	.08	.06	.03
129	Ken Phelps	.08	.06	.03
130	Rick Camp	.08	.06	.03
131	Dave Concepcion	.08	.06	.03
132	Rod Carew	.35	.25	.14
133	Andre Dawson	.25	.20	.10
134	Doyle Alexander	.08	.06	.03
135	Miguel Dilone	.08	.06	.03
136	Jim Gott	.08	.06	.03
137	Eric Show	.08	.06	.03
138	Phil Niekro	.20	.15	.08
139	Rick Sutcliffe	.20	.15	.08
140	Two For The Title (Don Mattingly, Dave Winfield)	3.25	2.50	1.25
141	Ken Oberkfell	.08	.06	.03
142	Jack Morris	.15	.11	.06
143	Lloyd Moseby	.20	.15	.08
144	Pete Rose	2.00	1.50	.80
145	Gary Gaetti	.20	.15	.08
146	Don Baylor	.20	.15	.08
147	Bobby Meacham	.08	.06	.03
148	Frank White	.08	.06	.03
149	Mark Thurmond	.08	.06	.03
150	Dwight Evans	.20	.15	.08
151	Al Holland	.08	.06	.03
152	Joel Youngblood	.08	.06	.03
153	Rance Mulliniks	.08	.06	.03
154	Bill Caudill	.08	.06	.03
155	Carlton Fisk	.15	.11	.06
156	Rick Honeycutt	.08	.06	.03
157	John Candelaria	.08	.06	.03
158	Alan Trammell	.25	.20	.10
159	Darryl Strawberry	2.25	1.75	.90
160	Aurelio Lopez	.08	.06	.03
161	Enos Cabell	.08	.06	.03
162	Dion James	.08	.06	.03
163	Bruce Sutter	.20	.15	.08
164	Razor Shines	.08	.06	.03
165	Butch Wynegar	.08	.06	.03
166	Rich Bordi	.08	.06	.03
167	Spike Owen	.08	.06	.03
168	Chris Chambliss	.08	.06	.03
169	Dave Parker	.20	.15	.08
170	Reggie Jackson	1.50	1.25	.60
171	Bryn Smith	.08	.06	.03
172	Dave Collins	.08	.06	.03
173	Dave Engle	.08	.06	.03
174	Buddy Bell	.08	.06	.03
175	Mike Flanagan	.08	.06	.03
176	George Brett	3.50	2.75	1.50
177	Graig Nettles	.20	.15	.08
178	Jerry Koosman	.08	.06	.03
179	Wade Boggs	4.50	3.50	1.75
180	Jody Davis	.08	.06	.03
181	Ernie Whitt	.08	.06	.03
182	Dave Kingman	.20	.15	.08
183	Vance Law	.08	.06	.03
184	Fernando Valenzuela	.20	.15	.08
185	Bill Madlock	.08	.06	.03
186	Brett Butler	.08	.06	.03
187	Doug Sisk	.08	.06	.03
188	Dan Petry	.08	.06	.03
189	Joe Niekro	.08	.06	.03
190	Rollie Fingers	.12	.09	.05
191	David Green	.08	.06	.03
192	Steve Rogers	.08	.06	.03
193	Ken Griffey	.08	.06	.03
194	Scott Sanderson	.08	.06	.03
195	Barry Bonnell	.08	.06	.03
196	Bruce Benedict	.08	.06	.03
197	Keith Moreland	.08	.06	.03
198	Fred Lynn	.20	.15	.08
199	Tim Wallach	.20	.15	.08
200	Kent Hrbek	.20	.15	.08
201	Pete O'Brien	.08	.06	.03
202	Bud Black	.08	.06	.03
203	Eddie Murray	1.75	1.25	.70
204	Goose Gossage	.15	.11	.06
205	Mike Schmidt	4.25	3.25	1.75
206	Mike Easler	.08	.06	.03
207	Jack Clark	.15	.11	.06
208	Rickey Henderson	3.00	2.25	1.25
209	Jesse Barfield	.12	.09	.05
210	Ron Kittle	.08	.06	.03
211	Pedro Guerrero	.15	.11	.06
212	Johnny Ray	.08	.06	.03
213	Julio Franco	.20	.15	.08
214	Hubie Brooks	.08	.06	.03
215	Darrell Evans	.20	.15	.08
216	Nolan Ryan	8.50	6.50	3.50
217	Jim Gantner	.08	.06	.03
218	Tim Raines	.35	.25	.14
219	Dave Righetti	.15	.11	.06
220	Gary Matthews	.08	.06	.03
221	Jack Perconte	.08	.06	.03
222	Dale Murphy	.40	.30	.15
223	Brian Downing	.08	.06	.03
224	Mickey Hatcher	.08	.06	.03
225	Lonnie Smith	.08	.06	.03
226	Jorge Orta	.08	.06	.03
227	Milt Wilcox	.08	.06	.03
228	John Denny	.08	.06	.03
229	Marty Barrett	.08	.06	.03
230	Alfredo Griffin	.08	.06	.03
231	Harold Baines	.12	.09	.05
232	Bill Russell	.08	.06	.03
233	Marvell Wynne	.08	.06	.03
234	Dwight Gooden	6.25	4.75	2.50
235	Willie Hernandez	.08	.06	.03
236	Bill Gullickson	.08	.06	.03
237	Ron Guidry	.15	.11	.06
238	Leon Durham	.08	.06	.03
239	Al Cowens	.08	.06	.03
240	Bob Horner	.20	.15	.08
241	Gary Carter	.30	.25	.12
242	Glenn Hubbard	.08	.06	.03
243	Steve Trout	.08	.06	.03
244	Jay Howell	.08	.06	.03
245	Terry Francona	.08	.06	.03
246	Cecil Cooper	.08	.06	.03
247	Larry McWilliams	.08	.06	.03
248	George Bell	.25	.20	.10
249	Larry Herndon	.08	.06	.03
250	Ozzie Virgil	.08	.06	.03
251	Dave Stieb (Canadian Great)	.50	.40	.20
252	Tim Raines (Canadian Great)	.80	.60	.30
253	Ricky Horton	.12	.09	.05
254	Bill Buckner	.20	.15	.08
255	Dan Driessen	.08	.06	.03
256	Ron Darling	.15	.11	.06
257	Doug Flynn	.08	.06	.03
258	Darrell Porter	.08	.06	.03
259	George Hendrick	.08	.06	.03
653	Lou Gehrig Puzzle Card	.08	.06	.03
----	Checklist 1-26 DK	.08	.05	.03
----	Checklist 27-102	.08	.05	.03
----	Checklist 103-178	.08	.05	.03
----	Checklist 179-259	.08	.05	.03

1986 Leaf

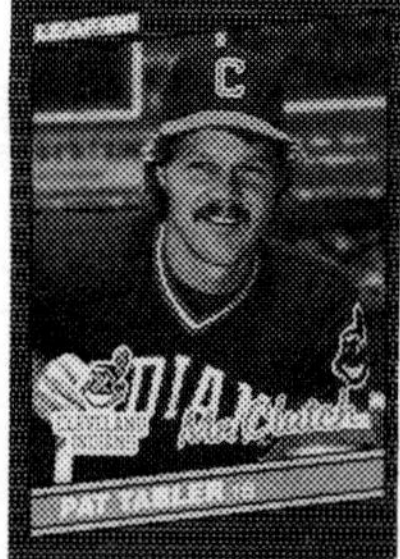

For its second Canadian card set, in 1986, the Donruss name was removed from the front of the company's 264-card issue, identifying the cards as "Leaf '86." Again concentrating on big-name stars and players from the Expos and Blue Jays, the 2-1/2" by 3-1/2" cards feature a design virtually identical to the 1986 Donruss cards. Backs were altered to allow the publication of career highlights in both English and French, and card numbers were changed. The "Canadian Greats" cards in the 1986 Leaf set, painted portraits rather than photos, were Jesse Barfield and Jeff Reardon. Besides being sold in its intended market in Canada, the set was widely distributed in the U.S. through hobby vendors.

		MT	NR MT	EX
	Complete Set (260):	46.00	45.00	25.00
	Common Player:	.08	.05	.03
1	Kirk Gibson (DK)	.20	.15	.08
2	Goose Gossage (DK)	.12	.09	.05
3	Willie McGee (DK)	.12	.09	.05
4	George Bell (DK)	.30	.25	.12
5	Tony Armas (DK)	.08	.06	.03
6	Chili Davis (DK)	.08	.06	.03
7	Cecil Cooper (DK)	.08	.06	.03
8	Mike Boddicker (DK)	.08	.06	.03
9	Davey Lopes (DK)	.08	.06	.03
10	Bill Doran (DK)	.08	.06	.03
11	Bret Saberhagen (DK)	.20	.15	.08
12	Brett Butler (DK)	.08	.06	.03
13	Harold Baines (DK)	.10	.08	.04
14	Mike Davis	.08	.06	.03
15	Tony Perez (DK)	.10	.08	.04
16	Willie Randolph (DK)	.08	.06	.03
17	Bob Boone (DK)	.08	.06	.03
18	Orel Hershiser (DK)	.60	.45	.25
19	Johnny Ray (DK)	.08	.06	.03
20	Gary Ward (DK)	.08	.06	.03
21	Rick Mahler (DK)	.08	.06	.03
22	Phil Bradley (DK)	.12	.09	.05
23	Jerry Koosman (DK)	.08	.06	.03
24	Tom Brunansky (DK)	.10	.08	.04
25	Andre Dawson (DK)	.25	.20	.10
26	Dwight Gooden (DK)	.80	.60	.30
27	Andres Galarraga (RR)	5.00	3.75	2.00
28	Fred McGriff (RR)	27.00	20.00	11.00
29	Dave Shipanoff (RR)	.08	.06	.03
30	Danny Jackson	.20	.15	.08
31	Robin Yount	1.75	1.25	.70
32	Mike Fitzgerald	.08	.06	.03
33	Lou Whitaker	.15	.11	.06
34	Alfredo Griffin	.08	.06	.03
35	"Oil Can" Boyd	.08	.06	.03
36	Ron Guidry	.15	.11	.06
37	Rickey Henderson	1.75	1.25	.70
38	Jack Morris	.50	.40	.20
39	Brian Downing	.08	.06	.03
40	Mike Marshall	.12	.09	.05
41	Tony Gwynn	2.50	2.00	1.00
42	George Brett	1.75	1.25	.70
43	Jim Gantner	.08	.06	.03
44	Hubie Brooks	.08	.06	.03
45	Tony Fernandez	.15	.11	.06
46	Oddibe McDowell	.20	.15	.08
47	Ozzie Smith	.15	.11	.06
48	Ken Griffey	.08	.06	.03
49	Jose Cruz	.08	.06	.03
50	Mariano Duncan	.08	.06	.03
51	Mike Schmidt	2.25	1.75	.90
52	Pat Tabler	.08	.06	.03
53	Pete Rose	1.00	.70	.40
54	Frank White	.08	.06	.03
55	Carney Lansford	.08	.06	.03
56	Steve Garvey	.30	.25	.12
57	Vance Law	.08	.06	.03
58	Tony Pena	.08	.06	.03
59	Wayne Tolleson	.08	.06	.03
60	Dale Murphy	.40	.30	.15
61	LaMarr Hoyt	.08	.06	.03
62	Ryne Sandberg	4.25	3.25	1.75
63	Gary Carter	1.00	.70	.40

64	Lee Smith	.08	.06	.03
65	Alvin Davis	.15	.11	.06
66	Edwin Nunez	.08	.06	.03
67	Kent Hrbek	.20	.15	.08
68	Dave Stieb	.10	.08	.04
69	Kirby Puckett	8.50	6.50	3.50
70	Paul Molitor	1.50	1.25	.60
71	Glenn Hubbard	.08	.06	.03
72	Lloyd Moseby	.08	.06	.03
73	Mike Smithson	.08	.06	.03
74	Jeff Leonard	.08	.06	.03
75	Danny Darwin	.08	.06	.03
76	Kevin McReynolds	.15	.11	.06
77	Bill Buckner	.08	.06	.03
78	Ron Oester	.08	.06	.03
79	Tommy Herr	.08	.06	.03
80	Mike Pagliarulo	.20	.15	.08
81	Ron Romanick	.08	.06	.03
82	Brook Jacoby	.10	.08	.04
83	Eddie Murray	.30	.25	.12
84	Gary Pettis	.08	.06	.03
85	Chet Lemon	.08	.06	.03
86	Toby Harrah	.08	.06	.03
87	Mike Scioscia	.08	.06	.03
88	Bert Blyleven	.12	.09	.05
89	Dave Righetti	.15	.11	.06
90	Bob Knepper	.08	.06	.03
91	Fernando Valenzuela	.20	.15	.08
92	Dave Dravecky	.08	.06	.03
93	Julio Franco	.10	.08	.04
94	Keith Moreland	.08	.06	.03
95	Darryl Motley	.08	.06	.03
96	Jack Clark	.15	.11	.06
97	Tim Wallach	.12	.09	.05
98	Steve Balboni	.08	.06	.03
99	Storm Davis	.08	.06	.03
100	Jay Howell	.08	.06	.03
101	Alan Trammell	.25	.20	.10
102	Willie Hernandez	.08	.06	.03
103	Don Mattingly	2.50	2.00	1.00
104	Lee Lacy	.08	.06	.03
105	Pedro Guerrero	.15	.11	.06
106	Willie Wilson	.10	.08	.04
107	Craig Reynolds	.08	.06	.03
108	Tim Raines	1.00	.70	.40
109	Shane Rawley	.08	.06	.03
110	Larry Parrish	.08	.06	.03
111	Eric Show	.08	.06	.03
112	Mike Witt	.08	.06	.03
113	Dennis Eckersley	.10	.08	.04
114	Mike Moore	.08	.06	.03
115	Vince Coleman	.50	.40	.20
116	Damaso Garcia	.08	.06	.03
117	Steve Carlton	.30	.25	.12
118	Floyd Bannister	.08	.06	.03
119	Mario Soto	.08	.06	.03
120	Fred Lynn	.10	.08	.04
121	Bob Horner	.10	.08	.04
122	Rick Sutcliffe	.10	.08	.04
123	Walt Terrell	.08	.06	.03
124	Keith Hernandez	.25	.20	.10
125	Dave Winfield	1.00	.70	.40
126	Frank Viola	.20	.15	.08
127	Dwight Evans	.10	.08	.04
128	Willie Upshaw	.08	.06	.03
129	Andre Thornton	.08	.06	.03
130	Donnie Moore	.08	.06	.03
131	Darryl Strawberry	.85	.60	.35
132	Nolan Ryan	5.00	3.75	2.00
133	Garry Templeton	.08	.06	.03
134	John Tudor	.08	.06	.03
135	Dave Parker	.15	.11	.06
136	Larry McWilliams	.08	.06	.03
137	Terry Pendleton	1.25	.90	.50
138	Terry Puhl	.08	.06	.03
139	Bob Dernier	.08	.06	.03
140	Ozzie Guillen	.20	.15	.08
141	Jim Clancy	.08	.06	.03
142	Cal Ripken, Jr.	4.25	3.25	1.75
143	Mickey Hatcher	.08	.06	.03
144	Dan Petry	.08	.06	.03
145	Rich Gedman	.08	.06	.03
146	Jim Rice	.30	.25	.12
147	Butch Wynegar	.08	.06	.03
148	Donnie Hill	.08	.06	.03
149	Jim Sundberg	.08	.06	.03
150	Joe Hesketh	.08	.06	.03
151	Chris Codiroli	.08	.06	.03
152	Charlie Hough	.08	.06	.03
153	Herman Winningham	.08	.06	.03
154	Dave Rozema	.08	.06	.03
155	Don Slaught	.08	.06	.03
156	Juan Beniquez	.08	.06	.03
157	Ted Higuera	.60	.45	.25
158	Andy Hawkins	.08	.06	.03
159	Don Robinson	.08	.06	.03
160	Glenn Wilson	.08	.06	.03
161	Earnest Riles	.08	.06	.03
162	Nick Esasky	.08	.06	.03
163	Carlton Fisk	1.00	.70	.40
164	Claudell Washington	.08	.06	.03
165	Scott McGregor	.08	.06	.03
166	Nate Snell	.08	.06	.03
167	Ted Simmons	.10	.08	.04
168	Wade Boggs	2.50	2.00	1.00
169	Marty Barrett	.08	.06	.03
170	Bud Black	.08	.06	.03
171	Charlie Leibrandt	.08	.06	.03
172	Charlie Lea	.08	.06	.03
173	Reggie Jackson	1.00	.70	.40
174	Bryn Smith	.08	.06	.03
175	Glenn Davis	.40	.30	.15
176	Von Hayes	.08	.06	.03
177	Danny Cox	.08	.06	.03
178	Sam Khalifa	.08	.06	.03
179	Tom Browning	.12	.09	.05
180	Scott Garrelts	.08	.06	.03
181	Shawon Dunston	.10	.08	.04
182	Doyle Alexander	.08	.06	.03
183	Jim Presley	.10	.08	.04
184	Al Cowens	.08	.06	.03
185	Mark Salas	.08	.06	.03
186	Tom Niedenfuer	.08	.06	.03
187	Dave Henderson	.08	.06	.03
188	Lonnie Smith	.08	.06	.03
189	Bruce Bochte	.08	.06	.03
190	Leon Durham	.08	.06	.03
191	Terry Francona	.08	.06	.03
192	Bruce Sutter	.10	.08	.04
193	Steve Crawford	.08	.06	.03
194	Bob Brenly	.08	.06	.03
195	Dan Pasqua	.10	.08	.04
196	Juan Samuel	.12	.09	.05
197	Floyd Rayford	.08	.06	.03
198	Tim Burke	.12	.09	.05
199	Ben Oglivie	.08	.06	.03
200	Don Carman	.12	.09	.05
201	Lance Parrish	.20	.15	.08
202	Terry Forster	.08	.06	.03
203	Neal Heaton	.08	.06	.03
204	Ivan Calderon	.25	.20	.10
205	Jorge Orta	.08	.06	.03
206	Tom Henke	.10	.08	.04
207	Rick Reuschel	.10	.08	.04
208	Dan Quisenberry	.10	.08	.04
209	Ty-Breaking Hit (Pete Rose)	.30	.25	.12
210	Floyd Youmans	.15	.11	.06
211	Tom Filer	.08	.06	.03
212	R.J. Reynolds	.08	.06	.03
213	Gorman Thomas	.08	.06	.03
214	Canadian Great (Jeff Reardon)	1.00	.70	.40
215	Chris Brown	.25	.20	.10
216	Rick Aguilera	1.50	1.25	.60
217	Ernie Whitt	.08	.06	.03
218	Joe Orsulak	.08	.06	.03
219	Jimmy Key	.10	.08	.04
220	Atlee Hammaker	.08	.06	.03
221	Ron Darling	.12	.09	.05
222	Zane Smith	.08	.06	.03
223	Bob Welch	.08	.06	.03
224	Reid Nichols	.08	.06	.03
225	Fleet Feet (Vince Coleman, Willie McGee)	.15	.11	.06
226	Mark Gubicza	.12	.09	.05
227	Tim Birtsas	.08	.06	.03
228	Mike Hargrove	.08	.06	.03
229	Randy St. Claire	.08	.06	.03
230	Larry Herndon	.08	.06	.03
231	Dusty Baker	.08	.06	.03
232	Mookie Wilson	.08	.06	.03
233	Jeff Lahti	.08	.06	.03
234	Tom Seaver	1.00	.70	.40
235	Mike Scott	.15	.11	.06
236	Don Sutton	.20	.15	.08
237	Roy Smalley	.08	.06	.03
238	Bill Madlock	.08	.06	.03
239	Charles Hudson	.08	.06	.03
240	John Franco	.10	.08	.04
241	Frank Tanana	.08	.06	.03
242	Sid Fernandez	.10	.08	.04
243	Knuckle Brothers (Joe Niekro, Phil Niekro)	.10	.08	.04
244	Dennis Lamp	.08	.06	.03
245	Gene Nelson	.08	.06	.03
246	Terry Harper	.08	.06	.03
247	Vida Blue	.08	.06	.03
248	Roger McDowell	.20	.15	.08
249	Tony Bernazard	.08	.06	.03
250	Cliff Johnson	.08	.06	.03
251	Hal McRae	.08	.06	.03
252	Garth Iorg	.08	.06	.03
253	Mitch Webster	.20	.15	.08
254	Jesse Barfield (Canadian Great)	.60	.45	.25
255	Dan Driessen	.08	.06	.03
256	Mike Brown	.08	.06	.03
257	Ron Kittle	.08	.06	.03
258	Bo Diaz	.08	.06	.03
259	Hank Aaron Puzzle Card	.08	.06	.03
260	Pete Rose (King of Kings)	1.00	.70	.40
----	Checklist 1-26 DK	.08	.05	.03
----	Checklist 27-106	.08	.05	.03
----	Checklist 107-186	.08	.05	.03
----	Checklist 187-260	.08	.05	.03

1987 Leaf

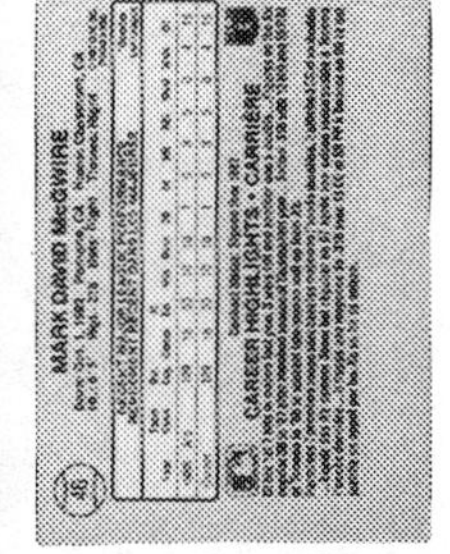

For the third consecutive season, Leaf-Donruss issued a Canadian baseball card set. The Canadian cards are nearly identical to the American set except for the name "Leaf" which appears on the front in place of "Donruss." The set contains 264 cards, each measuring the standard 2-1/2" by 3-1/2", with a special emphasis being placed on players from the Montreal and Toronto teams. The card backs feature career highlights written in both English and French. As in the previous years, two "Canadian Greats" cards appear in the set. These painted portraits feature Mark Eichhorn and Floyd Youmans.

		MT	NR MT	EX
	Complete Set (264):	46.00	30.00	15.00
	Common Player:	.08	.05	.02
1	Wally Joyner (DK)	.80	.60	.30
2	Roger Clemens (DK)	.50	.40	.20
3	Dale Murphy (DK)	.30	.25	.12
4	Darryl Strawberry (DK)	.30	.25	.12
5	Ozzie Smith (DK)	.30	.25	.12
6	Jose Canseco (DK)	.50	.40	.20
7	Charlie Hough (DK)	.08	.06	.03
8	Brook Jacoby (DK)	.08	.06	.03
9	Fred Lynn (DK)	.10	.08	.04
10	Rick Rhoden (DK)	.08	.06	.03
11	Chris Brown (DK)	.08	.06	.03
12	Von Hayes (DK)	.08	.06	.03
13	Jack Morris (DK)	.30	.25	.12
14	Kevin McReynolds (DK)	.12	.09	.05
15	George Brett (DK)	.30	.25	.12
16	Ted Higuera (DK)	.12	.09	.05
17	Hubie Brooks (DK)	.08	.06	.03
18	Mike Scott (DK)	.10	.08	.04
19	Kirby Puckett (DK)	.80	.60	.30
20	Dave Winfield (DK)	.80	.60	.30
21	Lloyd Moseby (DK)	.08	.06	.03
22	Eric Davis (DK)	.50	.40	.20
23	Jim Presley (DK)	.08	.06	.03
24	Keith Moreland (DK)	.08	.06	.03
25	Greg Walker (DK)	.08	.06	.03
26	Steve Sax (DK)	.10	.08	.04
27	Checklist 1-27	.08	.06	.03
28	B.J. Surhoff (RR)	.35	.25	.14
29	Randy Myers (RR)	.20	.15	.08
30	Ken Gerhart (RR)	.12	.09	.05
31	Benito Santiago (RR)	.70	.50	.30
32	Greg Swindell (RR)	.50	.40	.20
33	Mike Birkbeck (RR)	.10	.08	.04
34	Terry Steinbach (RR)	.25	.20	.10
35	Bo Jackson (RR)	1.00	.70	.40
36	Greg Maddux (RR)	5.75	4.25	2.25
37	Jim Lindeman (RR)	.10	.08	.04
38	Devon White (RR)	1.75	1.25	.70
39	Eric Bell (RR)	.08	.06	.03
40	Will Fraser (RR)	.10	.08	.04
41	Jerry Browne (RR)	.10	.08	.04
42	Chris James (RR)	.35	.25	.14
43	Rafael Palmeiro (RR)	4.50	3.50	1.75
44	Pat Dodson (RR)	.08	.06	.03
45	Duane Ward (RR)	1.25	.90	.50
46	Mark McGwire (RR)	3.50	2.75	1.50
47	Bruce Fields (RR) (photo actually Darnell Coles)	.08	.06	.03
48	Jody Davis	.08	.06	.03
49	Roger McDowell	.10	.08	.04
50	Jose Guzman	.08	.06	.03
51	Oddibe McDowell	.08	.06	.03
52	Harold Baines	.10	.08	.04
53	Dave Righetti	.12	.09	.05
54	Moose Haas	.08	.06	.03
55	Mark Langston	.10	.08	.04
56	Kirby Puckett	1.75	1.25	.70
57	Dwight Evans	.08	.06	.03
58	Willie Randolph	.08	.06	.03
59	Wally Backman	.08	.06	.03
60	Bryn Smith	.08	.06	.03
61	Tim Wallach	.10	.08	.04
62	Joe Hesketh	.08	.06	.03
63	Garry Templeton	.08	.06	.03
64	Rob Thompson	.10	.08	.04
65	Canadian Greats (Floyd Youmans)	.75	.60	.30
66	Ernest Riles	.08	.06	.03
67	Robin Yount	.60	.45	.25
68	Darryl Strawberry	1.00	.70	.40
69	Ernie Whitt	.08	.06	.03
70	Dave Winfield	1.00	.70	.40
71	Paul Molitor	.40	.30	.15
72	Dave Stieb	.10	.08	.04
73	Tom Henke	.08	.06	.03
74	Frank Viola	.15	.11	.06
75	Scott Garrelts	.08	.06	.03
76	Mike Boddicker	.08	.06	.03
77	Keith Moreland	.08	.06	.03
78	Lou Whitaker	.15	.11	.06
79	Dave Parker	.15	.11	.06
80	Lee Smith	.08	.06	.03
81	Tom Candiotti	.08	.06	.03
82	Greg Harris	.08	.06	.03
83	Fred Lynn	.10	.08	.04
84	Dwight Gooden	.70	.50	.30
85	Ron Darling	.10	.08	.04
86	Mike Krukow	.08	.06	.03
87	Spike Owen	.08	.06	.03
88	Len Dykstra	.10	.08	.04
89	Rick Aguilera	.08	.06	.03
90	Jim Clancy	.08	.06	.03
91	Joe Johnson	.08	.06	.03
92	Damaso Garcia	.08	.06	.03
93	Sid Fernandez	.08	.06	.03
94	Bob Ojeda	.08	.06	.03
95	Ted Higuera	.10	.08	.04
96	George Brett	.60	.45	.25
97	Willie Wilson	.08	.06	.03
98	Cal Ripken	1.25	.90	.50
99	Kent Hrbek	.15	.11	.06
100	Bert Blyleven	.10	.08	.04
101	Ron Guidry	.12	.09	.05
102	Andy Allanson	.08	.06	.03

103	Dave Henderson	.08	.06	.03
104	Kirk Gibson	.20	.15	.08
105	Lloyd Moseby	.08	.06	.03
106	Tony Fernandez	.10	.08	.04
107	Lance Parrish	.15	.11	.06
108	Ozzie Smith	.15	.11	.06
109	Gary Carter	.60	.45	.25
110	Eddie Murray	.40	.30	.15
111	Mike Witt	.08	.06	.03
112	Bobby Witt	.15	.11	.06
113	Willie McGee	.10	.08	.04
114	Steve Garvey	.20	.15	.08
115	Glenn Davis	.15	.11	.06
116	Jose Cruz	.08	.06	.03
117	Ozzie Guillen	.08	.06	.03
118	Alvin Davis	.10	.08	.04
119	Jose Rijo	.08	.06	.03
120	Bill Madlock	.08	.06	.03
121	Tommy Herr	.08	.06	.03
122	Mike Schmidt	.85	.60	.35
123	Mike Scioscia	.08	.06	.03
124	Terry Pendleton	.25	.20	.10
125	Leon Durham	.08	.06	.03
126	Alan Trammell	.20	.15	.08
127	Jesse Barfield	.10	.08	.04
128	Shawon Dunston	.08	.06	.03
129	Pete Rose	.50	.40	.20
130	Von Hayes	.08	.06	.03
131	Julio Franco	.25	.20	.10
132	Juan Samuel	.12	.09	.05
133	Joe Carter	1.00	.70	.40
134	Brook Jacoby	.08	.06	.03
135	Jack Morris	.25	.20	.10
136	Bob Horner	.08	.06	.03
137	Calvin Schiraldi	.08	.06	.03
138	Tom Browning	.08	.06	.03
139	Shane Rawley	.08	.06	.03
140	Mario Soto	.08	.06	.03
141	Dale Murphy	.30	.25	.12
142	Hubie Brooks	.08	.06	.03
143	Jeff Reardon	.25	.20	.10
144	Will Clark	6.25	4.75	2.50
145	Ed Correa	.08	.06	.03
146	Glenn Wilson	.08	.06	.03
147	Johnny Ray	.08	.06	.03
148	Fernando Valenzuela	.15	.11	.06
149	Tim Raines	.50	.40	.20
150	Don Mattingly	.85	.60	.35
151	Jose Canseco	2.25	1.75	.90
152	Gary Pettis	.08	.06	.03
153	Don Sutton	.15	.11	.06
154	Jim Presley	.08	.06	.03
155	Checklist 28-105	.08	.06	.03
156	Dale Sveum	.10	.08	.04
157	Cory Snyder	.50	.40	.20
158	Jeff Sellers	.08	.06	.03
159	Denny Walling	.08	.06	.03
160	Danny Cox	.08	.06	.03
161	Bob Forsch	.08	.06	.03
162	Joaquin Andujar	.08	.06	.03
163	Roberto Clemente Puzzle Card	.08	.06	.03
164	Paul Assenmacher	.08	.06	.03
165	Marty Barrett	.08	.06	.03
166	Ray Knight	.08	.06	.03
167	Rafael Santana	.08	.06	.03
168	Bruce Ruffin	.10	.08	.04
169	Buddy Bell	.08	.06	.03
170	Kevin Mitchell	1.00	.70	.40
171	Ken Oberkfell	.08	.06	.03
172	Gene Garber	.08	.06	.03
173	Canadian Greats (Mark Eichhorn)	.25	.20	.10
174	Don Carman	.08	.06	.03
175	Jesse Orosco	.08	.06	.03
176	Mookie Wilson	.08	.06	.03
177	Gary Ward	.08	.06	.03
178	John Franco	.08	.06	.03
179	Eric Davis	.80	.60	.30
180	Walt Terrell	.08	.06	.03
181	Phil Niekro	.15	.11	.06
182	Pat Tabler	.08	.06	.03
183	Brett Butler	.08	.06	.03
184	George Bell	.20	.15	.08
185	Pete Incaviglia	.30	.25	.12
186	Pete O'Brien	.08	.06	.03
187	Jimmy Key	.08	.06	.03
188	Frank White	.08	.06	.03
189	Mike Pagliarulo	.08	.06	.03
190	Roger Clemens	1.75	1.25	.70
191	Rickey Henderson	.75	.60	.30
192	Mike Easler	.08	.06	.03
193	Wade Boggs	.80	.60	.30
194	Vince Coleman	.15	.11	.06
195	Charlie Kerfeld	.08	.06	.03
196	Dickie Thon	.08	.06	.03
197	Bill Doran	.08	.06	.03
198	Alfredo Griffin	.08	.06	.03
199	Carlton Fisk	.60	.45	.25
200	Phil Bradley	.08	.06	.03
201	Reggie Jackson	.60	.45	.25
202	Bob Boone	.08	.06	.03
203	Steve Sax	.10	.08	.04
204	Tom Niedenfuer	.08	.06	.03
205	Tim Burke	.08	.06	.03
206	Floyd Youmans	.08	.06	.03
207	Jay Tibbs	.08	.06	.03
208	Chili Davis	.08	.06	.03
209	Larry Parrish	.08	.06	.03
210	John Cerutti	.10	.08	.04
211	Kevin Bass	.08	.06	.03
212	Andre Dawson	.50	.40	.20
213	Bob Sebra	.08	.06	.03
214	Kevin McReynolds	.12	.09	.05
215	Jim Morrison	.08	.06	.03
216	Candy Maldonado	.08	.06	.03
217	John Kruk	2.50	2.00	1.00
218	Todd Worrell	.10	.08	.04
219	Barry Bonds	10.25	7.75	4.00
220	Andy McGaffigan	.08	.06	.03
221	Andres Galarraga	.12	.09	.05
222	Mike Fitzgerald	.08	.06	.03
223	Kirk McCaskill	.08	.06	.03
224	Dave Smith	.08	.06	.03
225	Ruben Sierra	3.25	2.50	1.25
226	Scott Fletcher	.08	.06	.03
227	Chet Lemon	.08	.06	.03
228	Dan Petry	.08	.06	.03
229	Mark Eichhorn	.10	.08	.04
230	Cecil Cooper	.08	.06	.03
231	Willie Upshaw	.08	.06	.03
232	Don Baylor	.08	.06	.03
233	Keith Hernandez	.20	.15	.08
234	Ryne Sandberg	1.25	.90	.50
235	Tony Gwynn	.75	.60	.30
236	Chris Brown	.08	.06	.03
237	Pedro Guerrero	.12	.09	.05
238	Mark Gubicza	.08	.06	.03
239	Sid Bream	.08	.06	.03
240	Joe Cowley	.08	.06	.03
241	Bill Buckner	.08	.06	.03
242	John Candelaria	.08	.06	.03
243	Scott McGregor	.08	.06	.03
244	Tom Brunansky	.10	.08	.04
245	Gary Gaetti	.12	.09	.05
246	Orel Hershiser	.20	.15	.08
247	Jim Rice	.20	.15	.08
248	Oil Can Boyd	.08	.06	.03
249	Bob Knepper	.08	.06	.03
250	Danny Tartabull	.20	.15	.08
251	John Cangelosi	.08	.06	.03
252	Wally Joyner	1.00	.70	.40
253	Bruce Hurst	.08	.06	.03
254	Rich Gedman	.08	.06	.03
255	Jim Deshaies	.10	.08	.04
256	Tony Pena	.08	.06	.03
257	Nolan Ryan	2.25	1.75	.90
258	Mike Scott	.10	.08	.04
259	Checklist 106-183	.08	.06	.03
260	Dennis Rasmussen	.08	.06	.03
261	Bret Saberhagen	.15	.11	.06
262	Steve Balboni	.08	.06	.03
263	Tom Seaver	1.00	.70	.40
264	Checklist 184-264	.08	.06	.03

1987 Leaf Candy City Team

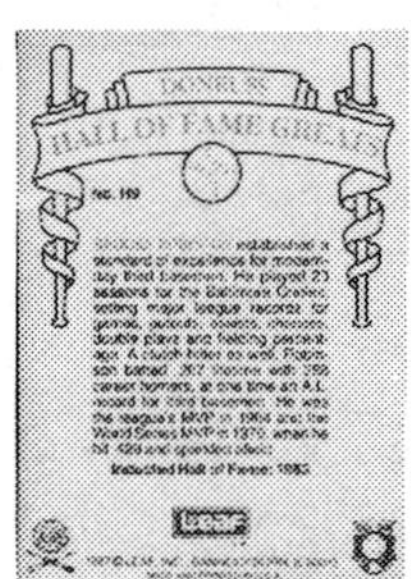

As part of their endorsement for the Seventh International Special Olympics Summer Games, Leaf produced an 18-card set of trading cards. Twelve of the 18 cards feature Baseball Hall of Fame greats. These cards measure 2-1/2" by 3-1/2" and are numbered H1 through H12. The remaining six cards in the set are numbered S1-S6 and feature unnamed Special Olympics champions. All cards feature the artwork of Dick Perez. The cards were available through a mail-in offer advertised at special store displays. Only the baseball-related subjects are listed in the checklist that follows.

		MT	NR MT	EX
	Complete Set:	4.00	3.00	1.50
	Common Player:	.15	.11	.06
1	Mickey Mantle	1.00	.70	.40
2	Yogi Berra	.40	.30	.15
3	Roy Campanella	.40	.30	.15
4	Stan Musial	.50	.40	.20
5	Ted Williams	.50	.40	.20
6	Duke Snider	.40	.30	.15
7	Hank Aaron	.50	.40	.20
8	Pee Wee Reese	.30	.25	.12
9	Brooks Robinson	.30	.25	.12
10	Al Kaline	.30	.25	.12
11	Willie McCovey	.25	.20	.10
12	Cool Papa Bell	.15	.11	.06

1988 Leaf

This 264-card set features full-color player photos from the 1988 Donruss 660-card standard issue, with emphasis on players from Montreal and Toronto. A graphic arts style border of red, blue and black stripes duplicates the design of the Donruss set, with the exception of a "Leaf '88" logo in the upper left corner that replaces the Donruss logo. Two special Canadian Greats cards are included in this set: Perez-Steele portraits of Tim Wallach and George Bell. The set also includes the portrait-style

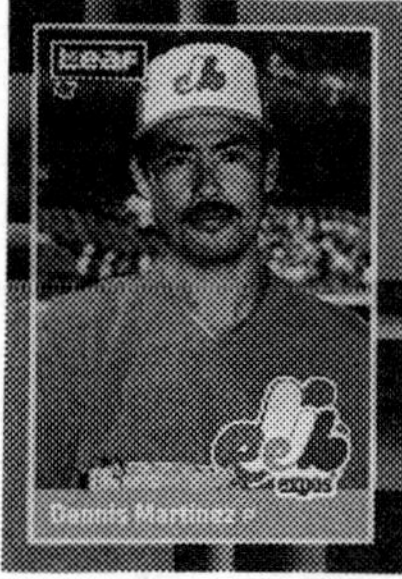

Diamond Kings cards (the set's first 26 cards, one for each individual team). The DK's carry the Donruss logo above the gold DK banner. All card backs in the 1988 Leaf set are bilingual (French/English), numbered, and printed in black on white stock with a light blue border. Regular player card backs have a horizontal format containing personal data, stats and career summary. This set was sold in 10-card wax packs with one triple-piece puzzle card per pack and was distributed via larger hobby and retail shops in the U.S. and Canada.

		MT	NR MT	EX
	Complete Set (264):	14.50	22.00	12.50
	Common Player:	.08	.05	.02
1	Mark McGwire (DK)	.30	.25	.12
2	Tim Raines (DK)	.20	.15	.08
3	Benito Santiago (DK)	.15	.11	.06
4	Alan Trammell (DK)	.20	.15	.08
5	Danny Tartabull (DK)	.15	.11	.06
6	Ron Darling (DK)	.10	.08	.04
7	Paul Molitor (DK)	.10	.08	.04
8	Devon White (DK)	.15	.11	.06
9	Andre Dawson (DK)	.15	.11	.06
10	Julio Franco (DK)	.08	.06	.03
11	Scott Fletcher (DK)	.08	.06	.03
12	Tony Fernandez (DK)	.10	.08	.04
13	Shane Rawley (DK)	.08	.06	.03
14	Kal Daniels (DK)	.15	.11	.06
15	Jack Clark (DK)	.12	.09	.05
16	Dwight Evans (DK)	.08	.06	.03
17	Tommy John (DK)	.08	.06	.03
18	Andy Van Slyke (DK)	.10	.08	.04
19	Gary Gaetti (DK)	.10	.08	.04
20	Mark Langston (DK)	.08	.06	.03
21	Will Clark (DK)	.40	.30	.15
22	Glenn Hubbard (DK)	.08	.06	.03
23	Billy Hatcher (DK)	.08	.06	.03
24	Bob Welch (DK)	.08	.06	.03
25	Ivan Calderon (DK)	.08	.06	.03
26	Cal Ripken, Jr. (DK)	1.00	.70	.40
27	Checklist 1-27	.08	.06	.03
28	Mackey Sasser (RR)	.12	.09	.05
29	Jeff Treadway (RR)	.25	.20	.10
30	Mike Campbell (RR)	.12	.09	.05
31	Lance Johnson (RR)	.10	.08	.04
32	Nelson Liriano (RR)	.10	.08	.04
33	Shawn Abner (RR)	.15	.11	.06
34	Roberto Alomar (RR)	3.25	2.50	1.25
35	Shawn Hillegas (RR)	.15	.11	.06
36	Joey Meyer (RR)	.10	.08	.04
37	Kevin Elster (RR)	.15	.11	.06
38	Jose Lind (RR)	.20	.15	.08
39	Kirt Manwaring (RR)	.20	.15	.08
40	Mark Grace (RR)	1.25	.90	.50
41	Jody Reed (RR)	.30	.25	.12
42	John Farrell (RR)	.20	.15	.08
43	Al Leiter (RR)	.70	.50	.30
44	Gary Thurman (RR)	.25	.20	.10
45	Vincente Palacios (RR)	.10	.08	.04
46	Eddie Williams (RR)	.10	.08	.04
47	Jack McDowell (RR)	1.50	1.25	.60
48	Dwight Gooden	.40	.30	.15
49	Mike Witt	.08	.06	.03
50	Wally Joyner	.60	.45	.25
51	Brook Jacoby	.08	.06	.03
52	Bert Blyleven	.10	.08	.04
53	Ted Higuera	.10	.08	.04
54	Mike Scott	.10	.08	.04
55	Jose Guzman	.08	.06	.03
56	Roger Clemens	.30	.25	.12
57	Dave Righetti	.12	.09	.05
58	Benito Santiago	.20	.15	.08
59	Ozzie Guillen	.08	.06	.03
60	Matt Nokes	.35	.25	.14
61	Fernando Valenzuela	.15	.11	.06
62	Orel Hershiser	.20	.15	.08
63	Sid Fernandez	.08	.06	.03
64	Ozzie Virgil	.08	.06	.03
65	Wade Boggs	.70	.50	.30
66	Floyd Youmans	.08	.06	.03
67	Jimmy Key	.08	.06	.03
68	Bret Saberhagen	.15	.11	.06
69	Jody Davis	.08	.06	.03
70	Shawon Dunston	.08	.06	.03
71	Julio Franco	.20	.15	.08
72	Danny Cox	.08	.06	.03
73	Jim Clancy	.08	.06	.03
74	Mark Eichhorn	.08	.06	.03
75	Scott Bradley	.08	.06	.03
76	Charlie Liebrandt	.08	.06	.03
77	Nolan Ryan	.75	.60	.30

78	Ron Darling	.10	.08	.04
79	John Franco	.08	.06	.03
80	Dave Stieb	.08	.06	.03
81	Mike Fitzgerald	.08	.06	.03
82	Steve Bedrosian	.08	.06	.03
83	Dale Murphy	.30	.25	.12
84	Tim Burke	.08	.06	.03
85	Jack Morris	.20	.15	.08
86	Greg Walker	.08	.06	.03
87	Kevin Mitchell	.08	.06	.03
88	Doug Drabek	.08	.06	.03
89	Charlie Hough	.08	.06	.03
90	Tony Gwynn	.30	.25	.12
91	Rick Sutcliffe	.10	.08	.04
92	Shane Rawley	.08	.06	.03
93	George Brett	.50	.40	.20
94	Frank Viola	.12	.09	.05
95	Tony Pena	.08	.06	.03
96	Jim Deshaies	.08	.06	.03
97	Mike Scioscia	.08	.06	.03
98	Rick Rhoden	.08	.06	.03
99	Terry Kennedy	.08	.06	.03
100	Cal Ripken	.40	.30	.15
101	Pedro Guerrero	.12	.09	.05
102	Andy Van Slyke	.10	.08	.04
103	Willie McGee	.08	.06	.03
104	Mike Kingery	.08	.06	.03
105	Kevin Seitzer	.60	.45	.25
106	Robin Yount	.20	.15	.08
107	Tracy Jones	.08	.06	.03
108	Dave Magadan	.08	.06	.03
109	Mel Hall	.08	.06	.03
110	Billy Hatcher	.08	.06	.03
111	Todd Benzinger	.25	.20	.10
112	Mike LaValliere	.08	.06	.03
113	Barry Bonds	.60	.45	.25
114	Tim Raines	.20	.15	.08
115	Ozzie Smith	.12	.09	.05
116	Dave Winfield	.25	.20	.10
117	Keith Hernandez	.15	.11	.06
118	Jeffrey Leonard	.08	.06	.03
119	Larry Parrish	.08	.06	.03
120	Rob Thompson	.08	.06	.03
121	Andres Galarraga	.15	.11	.06
122	Mickey Hatcher	.08	.06	.03
123	Mark Langston	.10	.08	.04
124	Mike Schmidt	.50	.40	.20
125	Cory Snyder	.12	.09	.05
126	Andre Dawson	.15	.11	.06
127	Devon White	.10	.08	.04
128	Vince Coleman	.12	.09	.05
129	Bryn Smith	.08	.06	.03
130	Lance Parrish	.12	.09	.05
131	Willie Upshaw	.08	.06	.03
132	Pete O'Brien	.08	.06	.03
133	Tony Fernandez	.10	.08	.04
134	Billy Ripken	.12	.09	.05
135	Len Dykstra	.08	.06	.03
136	Kirk Gibson	.20	.15	.08
137	Kevin Bass	.08	.06	.03
138	Jose Canseco	.30	.25	.12
139	Kent Hrbek	.15	.11	.06
140	Lloyd Moseby	.08	.06	.03
141	Marty Barrett	.08	.06	.03
142	Carmelo Martinez	.08	.06	.03
143	Tom Foley	.08	.06	.03
144	Kirby Puckett	.40	.30	.15
145	Rickey Henderson	.30	.25	.12
146	Juan Samuel	.10	.08	.04
147	Pete Incaviglia	.10	.08	.04
148	Greg Brock	.08	.06	.03
149	Eric Davis	.50	.40	.20
150	Kal Daniels	.12	.09	.05
151	Bob Boone	.08	.06	.03
152	John Cerutti	.08	.06	.03
153	Mike Greenwell	1.00	.70	.40
154	Oddibe McDowell	.08	.06	.03
155	Scott Fletcher	.08	.06	.03
156	Gary Carter	.40	.30	.15
157	Harold Baines	.12	.09	.05
158	Greg Swindell	.15	.11	.06
159	Mark McLemore	.08	.06	.03
160	Keith Moreland	.08	.06	.03
161	Jim Gantner	.08	.06	.03
162	Willie Randolph	.08	.06	.03
163	Fred Lynn	.10	.08	.04
164	B.J. Surhoff	.08	.06	.03
165	Ken Griffey	.08	.06	.03
166	Chet Lemon	.08	.06	.03
167	Alan Trammell	.15	.11	.06
168	Paul Molitor	.12	.09	.05
169	Lou Whitaker	.12	.09	.05
170	Will Clark	.40	.30	.15
171	Dwight Evans	.10	.08	.04
172	Eddie Murray	.25	.20	.10
173	Darrell Evans	.08	.06	.03
174	Ellis Burks	.30	.25	.12
175	Ivan Calderon	.08	.06	.03
176	John Kruk	.25	.20	.10
177	Don Mattingly	.30	.25	.12
178	Dick Schofield	.08	.06	.03
179	Bruce Hurst	.08	.06	.03
180	Ron Guidry	.10	.08	.04
181	Jack Clark	.12	.09	.05
182	Franklin Stubbs	.08	.06	.03
183	Bill Doran	.08	.06	.03
184	Joe Carter	.10	.08	.04
185	Steve Sax	.12	.09	.05
186	Glenn Davis	.12	.09	.05
187	Bo Jackson	.30	.25	.12
188	Bobby Bonilla	.35	.25	.14
189	Willie Wilson	.08	.06	.03
190	Danny Tartabull	.10	.08	.04
191	Bo Diaz	.08	.06	.03
192	Buddy Bell	.08	.06	.03
193	Tim Wallach	.10	.08	.04
194	Mark McGwire	.30	.25	.12
195	Carney Lansford	.08	.06	.03
196	Alvin Davis	.10	.08	.04
197	Von Hayes	.08	.06	.03
198	Mitch Webster	.08	.06	.03
199	Casey Candaele	.08	.06	.03
200	Gary Gaetti	.10	.08	.04
201	Tommy Herr	.08	.06	.03
202	Wally Backman	.08	.06	.03
203	Brian Downing	.08	.06	.03
204	Rance Mulliniks	.08	.06	.03
205	Craig Reynolds	.08	.06	.03
206	Ruben Sierra	.30	.25	.12
207	Ryne Sandberg	.40	.30	.15
208	Carlton Fisk	.12	.09	.05
209	Checklist 28-107	.08	.06	.03
210	Gerald Young	.20	.15	.08
211	MVP (Tim Raines)	.50	.40	.20
212	John Tudor	.08	.06	.03
213	Canadian Greats (George Bell)	.70	.50	.30
214	MVP (George Bell)	.40	.30	.15
215	Jim Rice	.20	.15	.08
216	Gerald Perry	.08	.06	.03
217	Dave Stewart	.08	.06	.03
218	Jose Uribe	.08	.06	.03
219	Rick Rueschel	.08	.06	.03
220	Darryl Strawberry	.30	.25	.12
221	Chris Brown	.08	.06	.03
223	Lee Mazzilli	.08	.06	.03
224	Denny Walling	.08	.06	.03
225	Jesse Barfield	.10	.08	.04
226	Barry Larkin	.30	.25	.12
227	Harold Reynolds	.08	.06	.03
228	Kevin McReynolds	.08	.06	.03
229	Todd Worrell	.08	.06	.03
230	Tommy John	.08	.06	.03
231	Rick Aguilera	.08	.06	.03
232	Bill Madlock	.08	.06	.03
233	Roy Smalley	.08	.06	.03
234	Jeff Musselman	.08	.06	.03
235	Mike Dunne	.08	.06	.03
236	Jerry Browne	.08	.06	.03
237	Sam Horn	.20	.15	.08
238	Howard Johnson	.08	.06	.03
239	Candy Maldonado	.08	.06	.03
240	Nick Esasky	.08	.06	.03
241	Geno Petralli	.08	.06	.03
242	Herm Winningham	.08	.06	.03
243	Roger McDowell	.08	.06	.03
244	Brian Fisher	.08	.06	.03
245	John Marzano	.12	.09	.05
246	Terry Pendleton	.15	.11	.06
247	Rick Leach	.08	.06	.03
248	Pascual Perez	.08	.06	.03
249	Mookie Wilson	.08	.06	.03
250	Ernie Whitt	.08	.06	.03
251	Ron Kittle	.08	.06	.03
252	Oil Can Boyd	.08	.06	.03
253	Jim Gott	.08	.06	.03
254	George Bell	.20	.15	.08
255	Canadian Greats (Tim Wallach)	.60	.45	.25
256	Luis Polonia	.10	.08	.04
257	Hubie Brooks	.08	.06	.03
258	Mickey Brantley	.08	.06	.03
259	Gregg Jefferies	2.50	2.00	1.00
260	Johnny Ray	.08	.06	.03
261	Checklist 108-187	.08	.06	.03
262	Dennis Martinez	.20	.15	.08
263	Stan Musial Puzzle Card	.08	.06	.03
264	Checklist 188-264	.08	.06	.03

1990 Leaf Previews

This 12-card set was produced for dealer distribution to introduce Leaf as Donruss' preium-quality brand in mid-1990. Cards have the same format as the regular-issue versions with metallic silver ink highlights on front and back. The preview cards have a white undertype on back over the stats and career highlights. It reads "Special Preview Card".

		MT	NR MT	EX
Complete Set (12):		600.00	450.00	240.00
Common Player:		25.00	18.50	10.00
1	Steve Sax	25.00	18.50	10.00
2	Joe Carter	50.00	37.00	20.00
3	Dennis Eckersley	35.00	26.00	14.00
4	Ken Griffey, Jr.	250.00	185.00	100.00
5	Barry Larkin	35.00	26.00	14.00
6	Mark Langston	25.00	18.50	10.00
7	Eric Anthony	25.00	18.50	10.00
8	Robin Ventura	60.00	45.00	24.00
9	Greg Vaughn	25.00	18.50	10.00
10	Bobby Bonilla	35.00	26.00	14.00
11	Gary Gaetti	25.00	18.50	10.00
12	Ozzie Smith	45.00	34.00	18.00

1990 Leaf

This 528-card set was issued in two 264-card series. The cards were printed on heavy quality stock and both the card fronts and backs have full color player photos. Cards also have an ultra-glossy finish on both the fronts and the backs. A high-tech foil Hall of Fame puzzle features former Yankee great Yogi Berra.

		MT	NR MT	EX
Complete Set (528):		275.00	200.00	125.00
Common Player:		.25	.20	.10
1	Introductory Card	.25	.20	.10
2	Mike Henneman	.25	.20	.10
3	Steve Bedrosian	.25	.20	.10
4	Mike Scott	.25	.20	.10
5	Allan Anderson	.25	.20	.10
6	Rick Sutcliffe	.35	.25	.14
7	Gregg Olson	.75	.60	.30
8	Kevin Elster	.25	.20	.10
9	Pete O'Brien	.30	.25	.12
10	Carlton Fisk	.75	.60	.30
11	Joe Magrane	.25	.20	.10
12	Roger Clemens	4.00	3.00	1.50
13	Tom Glavine	7.50	5.00	2.75
14	Tom Gordon	.25	.20	.10
15	Todd Benzinger	.25	.20	.10
16	Hubie Brooks	.25	.20	.10
17	Roberto Kelly	.50	.40	.20
18	Barry Larkin	.75	.60	.30
19	Mike Boddicker	.25	.20	.10
20	Roger McDowell	.25	.20	.10
21	Nolan Ryan	7.00	5.25	2.75
22	John Farrell	.25	.20	.10
23	Bruce Hurst	.25	.20	.10
24	Wally Joyner	.40	.30	.15
25	Greg Maddux	6.00	4.50	2.50
26	Chris Bosio	.30	.25	.12
27	John Cerutti	.25	.20	.10
28	Tim Burke	.25	.20	.10
29	Dennis Eckersley	.50	.40	.20
30	Glenn Davis	.25	.20	.10
31	Jim Abbott	4.00	3.00	1.50
32	Mike LaValliere	.25	.20	.10
33	Andres Thomas	.25	.20	.10
34	Lou Whitaker	.35	.25	.14
35	Alvin Davis	.25	.20	.10
36	Melido Perez	.25	.20	.10
37	Craig Biggio	.80	.60	.30
38	Rick Aguilera	.35	.25	.14
39	Pete Harnisch	.75	.60	.30
40	David Cone	.60	.45	.25
41	Scott Garrelts	.25	.20	.10
42	Jay Howell	.25	.20	.10
43	Eric King	.25	.20	.10
44	Pedro Guerrero	.35	.25	.14
45	Mike Bielecki	.25	.20	.10
46	Bob Boone	.35	.25	.14
47	Kevin Brown	.50	.40	.20
48	Jerry Browne	.25	.20	.10
49	Mike Scioscia	.25	.20	.10
50	Chuck Cary	.25	.20	.10
51	Wade Boggs	2.00	1.50	.80
52	Von Hayes	.25	.20	.10
53	Tony Fernandez	.35	.25	.14
54	Dennis Martinez	.35	.25	.14
55	Tom Candiotti	.30	.25	.12
56	Andy Benes	2.50	2.00	1.00
57	Rob Dibble	.35	.25	.14
58	Chuck Crim	.30	.25	.12
59	John Smoltz	4.00	3.00	1.50
60	Mike Heath	.25	.20	.10
61	Kevin Gross	.25	.20	.10
62	Mark McGwire	1.75	1.25	.70
63	Bert Blyleven	.35	.25	.14
64	Bob Walk	.30	.25	.12
65	Mickey Tettleton	.50	.40	.20
66	Sid Fernandez	.35	.25	.14
67	Terry Kennedy	.25	.20	.10
68	Fernando Valenzuela	.40	.30	.15
69	Don Mattingly	3.00	2.25	1.25
70	Paul O'Neill	.35	.25	.14
71	Robin Yount	2.00	1.50	.80
72	Bret Saberhagen	.30	.25	.12
73	Geno Petralli	.25	.20	.10
74	Brook Jacoby	.25	.20	.10
75	Roberto Alomar	7.00	5.25	2.75
76	Devon White	.35	.25	.14

77	Jose Lind	.30	.25	.12
78	Pat Combs	.25	.20	.10
79	Dave Steib	.35	.25	.14
80	Tim Wallach	.35	.25	.14
81	Dave Stewart	.35	.25	.14
82	*Eric Anthony*	2.50	2.00	1.00
83	Randy Bush	.25	.20	.10
84	Checklist	.25	.20	.10
85	Jaime Navarro	.40	.30	.15
86	Tommy Gregg	.30	.25	.12
87	Frank Tanana	.25	.20	.10
88	Omar Vizquel	.30	.25	.12
89	Ivan Calderon	.30	.25	.12
90	Vince Coleman	.35	.25	.14
91	Barry Bonds	6.00	4.50	2.50
92	Randy Milligan	.35	.25	.14
93	Frank Viola	.35	.25	.14
94	Matt Williams	2.50	2.00	1.00
95	Alfredo Griffin	.30	.25	.12
96	Steve Sax	.35	.25	.14
97	Gary Gaetti	.35	.25	.14
98	Ryne Sandberg	4.00	3.00	1.50
99	Danny Tartabull	.35	.25	.14
100	Rafael Palmeiro	2.50	2.00	1.00
101	Jesse Orosco	.25	.20	.10
102	Garry Templeton	.25	.20	.10
103	Frank DiPino	.25	.20	.10
104	Tony Pena	.25	.20	.10
105	Dickie Thon	.25	.20	.10
106	Kelly Gruber	.30	.25	.12
107	*Marquis Grissom*	6.00	4.50	2.50
108	Jose Canseco	2.00	1.50	.80
109	Mike Blowers	.30	.25	.12
110	Tom Browning	.25	.20	.10
111	Greg Vaughn	2.00	1.50	.80
112	Oddibe McDowell	.25	.20	.10
113	Gary Ward	.25	.20	.10
114	Jay Buhner	1.00	.70	.40
115	Eric Show	.30	.25	.12
116	Bryan Harvey	1.00	.70	.40
117	Andy Van Slyke	.35	.25	.14
118	Jeff Ballard	.25	.20	.10
119	Barry Lyons	.25	.20	.10
120	Kevin Mitchell	.50	.40	.20
121	Mike Gallego	.30	.25	.12
122	Dave Smith	.25	.20	.10
123	Kirby Puckett	4.00	3.00	1.50
124	Jerome Walton	.25	.20	.10
125	Bo Jackson	3.00	2.25	1.25
126	Harold Baines	.35	.25	.14
127	Scott Bankhead	.25	.20	.10
128	Ozzie Guillen	.35	.25	.14
129	Jose Oquendo	.30	.25	.12
130	John Dopson	.30	.25	.12
131	Charlie Hayes	1.00	.70	.40
132	Fred McGriff	3.75	2.75	1.50
133	Chet Lemon	.25	.20	.10
134	Gary Carter	.35	.25	.14
135	Rafael Ramirez	.25	.20	.10
136	Shane Mack	.50	.40	.20
137	Mark Grace	.80	.60	.30
138	Phil Bradley	.25	.20	.10
139	Dwight Gooden	.40	.30	.15
140	Harold Reynolds	.35	.25	.14
141	Scott Fletcher	.30	.25	.12
142	Ozzie Smith	1.00	.75	.40
143	Mike Greenwell	.40	.30	.15
144	Pete Smith	.30	.25	.12
145	Mark Gubicza	.30	.25	.12
146	Chris Sabo	.30	.25	.12
147	Ramon Martinez	.35	.25	.14
148	Tim Leary	.25	.20	.10
149	Randy Myers	.35	.25	.14
150	Jody Reed	.25	.20	.10
151	Bruce Ruffin	.25	.20	.10
152	Jeff Russell	.35	.25	.14
153	Doug Jones	.25	.20	.10
154	Tony Gwynn	2.00	1.50	.80
155	Mark Langston	.35	.25	.14
156	Mitch Williams	.35	.25	.14
157	Gary Sheffield	6.00	4.50	2.50
158	Tom Henke	.25	.20	.10
159	Oil Can Boyd	.25	.20	.10
160	Rickey Henderson	1.75	1.25	.70
161	Bill Doran	.25	.20	.10
162	Chuck Finley	.40	.30	.15
163	Jeff King	.35	.25	.14
164	Nick Esasky	.25	.20	.10
165	Cecil Fielder	2.00	1.50	.80
166	Dave Valle	.30	.25	.12
167	Robin Ventura	6.00	4.50	2.50
168	Jim Deshaies	.25	.20	.10
169	Juan Berenguer	.25	.20	.10
170	Craig Worthington	.25	.20	.10
171	Gregg Jefferies	4.50	3.50	1.75
172	Will Clark	3.00	2.25	1.25
173	Kirk Gibson	.35	.25	.14
174	Checklist	.25	.20	.10
175	Bobby Thigpen	.25	.20	.10
176	John Tudor	.25	.20	.10
177	Andre Dawson	.75	.60	.30
178	George Brett	2.50	2.00	1.00
179	Steve Buechele	.30	.25	.12
180	Albert Belle	15.00	11.00	6.00
181	Eddie Murray	.80	.60	.30
182	Bob Geren	.25	.20	.10
183	Rob Murphy	.30	.25	.12
184	Tom Herr	.25	.20	.10
185	George Bell	.50	.40	.20
186	Spike Owen	.25	.20	.10
187	Cory Snyder	.25	.20	.10
188	Fred Lynn	.40	.30	.15
189	Eric Davis	.60	.45	.25
190	Dave Parker	.50	.40	.20
191	Jeff Blauser	.35	.25	.14
192	Matt Nokes	.30	.25	.12
193	*Delino DeShields*	5.00	3.75	2.00
194	Scott Sanderson	.25	.20	.10
195	Lance Parrish	.25	.20	.10
196	Bobby Bonilla	.60	.45	.25
197	Cal Ripken, Jr.	4.50	3.50	1.75
198	Kevin McReynolds	.35	.25	.14
199	Robby Thompson	.40	.30	.15
200	Tim Belcher	.25	.20	.10
201	Jesse Barfield	.25	.20	.10
202	Mariano Duncan	.25	.20	.10
203	Bill Spiers	.25	.20	.10
204	Frank White	.25	.20	.10
205	Julio Franco	.35	.25	.14
206	Greg Swindell	.25	.20	.10
207	Benito Santiago	.30	.25	.12
208	Johnny Ray	.25	.20	.10
209	Gary Redus	.30	.25	.12
210	Jeff Parrett	.30	.25	.12
211	Jimmy Key	.30	.25	.12
212	Tim Raines	.35	.25	.14
213	Carney Lansford	.25	.20	.10
214	Gerald Young	.25	.20	.10
215	Gene Larkin	.25	.20	.10
216	Dan Plesac	.25	.20	.10
217	Lonnie Smith	.25	.20	.10
218	Alan Trammell	.40	.30	.15
219	Jeffrey Leonard	.25	.20	.10
220	*Sammy Sosa*	5.00	3.75	2.00
221	Todd Zeile	1.75	1.25	.70
222	Bill Landrum	.25	.20	.10
223	Mike Devereaux	.60	.45	.25
224	Mike Marshall	.25	.20	.10
225	Jose Uribe	.25	.20	.10
226	Juan Samuel	.25	.20	.10
227	Mel Hall	.25	.20	.10
228	Kent Hrbek	.40	.30	.15
229	Shawon Dunston	.30	.25	.12
230	Kevin Seitzer	.25	.20	.10
231	Pete Incaviglia	.35	.25	.14
232	Sandy Alomar	.50	.40	.20
233	Bip Roberts	.30	.25	.12
234	Scott Terry	.25	.20	.10
235	Dwight Evans	.35	.25	.14
236	Ricky Jordan	.25	.20	.10
237	John Olerud	17.50	13.00	7.00
238	Zane Smith	.25	.20	.10
239	Walt Weiss	.30	.25	.12
240	Alvaro Espinoza	.25	.20	.10
241	Billy Hatcher	.30	.25	.12
242	Paul Molitor	2.50	2.00	1.00
243	Dale Murphy	.35	.25	.14
244	Dave Bergman	.30	.25	.12
245	Ken Griffey, Jr.	30.00	22.00	12.00
246	Ed Whitson	.25	.20	.10
247	Kirk McCaskill	.25	.20	.10
248	Jay Bell	.50	.40	.20
249	Ben McDonald	3.50	2.75	1.50
250	Darryl Strawberry	.50	.40	.20
251	Brett Butler	.30	.25	.12
252	Terry Steinbach	.30	.25	.12
253	Ken Caminiti	.30	.25	.12
254	Dan Gladden	.25	.20	.10
255	Dwight Smith	.25	.20	.10
256	Kurt Stillwell	.25	.20	.10
257	Ruben Sierra	1.25	.90	.50
258	Mike Schooler	.25	.20	.10
259	Lance Johnson	.35	.25	.14
260	Terry Pendleton	.50	.40	.20
261	Ellis Burks	.40	.30	.15
262	Len Dykstra	1.00	.75	.40
263	Mookie Wilson	.25	.20	.10
264	Checklist (Nolan Ryan)	.50	.40	.20
265	Nolan Ryan (No-Hit King)	6.00	4.50	2.50
266	Brian DuBois	.35	.25	.14
267	Don Robinson	.30	.25	.12
268	Glenn Wilson	.25	.20	.10
269	*Kevin Tapani*	1.25	.90	.50
270	Marvell Wynne	.25	.20	.10
271	Billy Ripken	.25	.20	.10
272	Howard Johnson	.50	.40	.20
273	Brian Holman	.35	.25	.14
274	Dan Pasqua	.30	.25	.12
275	Ken Dayley	.25	.20	.10
276	Jeff Reardon	.30	.25	.12
277	Jim Presley	.25	.20	.10
278	Jim Eisenreich	.30	.25	.12
279	Danny Jackson	.25	.20	.10
280	Orel Hershiser	.35	.25	.14
281	Andy Hawkins	.25	.20	.10
282	Jose Rijo	.40	.30	.15
283	Luis Rivera	.25	.20	.10
284	John Kruk	.75	.60	.30
285	Jeff Huson	.25	.20	.10
286	Joel Skinner	.25	.20	.10
287	Jack Clark	.35	.25	.14
288	Chili Davis	.35	.25	.14
289	Joe Girardi	.30	.25	.12
290	B.J. Surhoff	.25	.20	.10
291	Luis Sojo	.25	.20	.10
292	Tom Foley	.25	.20	.10
293	Mike Moore	.25	.20	.10
294	Ken Oberkfell	.25	.20	.10
295	Luis Polonia	.30	.25	.12
296	Doug Drabek	.35	.25	.14
297	*Dave Justice*	15.00	11.00	6.00
298	Paul Gibson	.25	.20	.10
299	Edgar Martinez	.60	.45	.25
300	Frank Thomas	62.00	46.00	25.00
301	Eric Yelding	.25	.20	.10
302	Greg Gagne	.30	.25	.12
303	Brad Komminsk	.25	.20	.10
304	Ron Darling	.25	.20	.10
305	Kevin Bass	.25	.20	.10
306	Jeff Hamilton	.25	.20	.10
307	Ron Karkovice	.25	.20	.10
308	Milt Thompson	.25	.20	.10
309	Mike Harkey	.25	.20	.10
310	Mel Stottlemyre	.25	.20	.10
311	Kenny Rogers	.35	.25	.14
312	Mitch Webster	.30	.25	.12
313	Kal Daniels	.25	.20	.10
314	Matt Nokes	.25	.20	.10
315	Dennis Lamp	.25	.20	.10
316	Ken Howell	.30	.25	.12
317	Glenallen Hill	.25	.20	.10
318	Dave Martinez	.30	.25	.12
319	Chris James	.25	.20	.10
320	Mike Pagliarulo	.30	.25	.12
321	Hal Morris	.40	.30	.15
322	Rob Deer	.25	.20	.10
323	Greg Olson	.30	.25	.12
324	Tony Phillips	.30	.25	.12
325	*Larry Walker*	7.50	5.50	3.00
326	Ron Hassey	.30	.25	.12
327	Jack Howell	.30	.25	.12
328	John Smiley	.25	.20	.10
329	Steve Finley	.50	.40	.20
330	Dave Magadan	.35	.25	.14
331	Greg Litton	.25	.20	.10
332	Mickey Hatcher	.30	.25	.12
333	Lee Guetterman	.25	.20	.10
334	Norm Charlton	.35	.25	.14
335	Edgar Diaz	.25	.20	.10
336	Willie Wilson	.30	.25	.12
337	Bobby Witt	.35	.25	.14
338	Candy Maldonado	.25	.20	.10
339	Craig Lefferts	.25	.20	.10
340	Dante Bichette	1.75	1.25	.70
341	Wally Backman	.25	.20	.10
342	Dennis Cook	.25	.20	.10
343	Pat Borders	.40	.30	.15
344	Wallace Johnson	.25	.20	.10
345	Willie Randolph	.25	.20	.10
346	Danny Darwin	.25	.20	.10
347	Al Newman	.25	.20	.10
348	Mark Knudson	.25	.20	.10
349	Joe Boever	.25	.20	.10
350	Larry Sheets	.25	.20	.10
351	Mike Jackson	.25	.20	.10
352	Wayne Edwards	.25	.20	.10
353	*Bernard Gilkey*	3.00	2.25	1.25
354	Don Slaught	.30	.25	.12
355	Joe Orsulak	.30	.25	.12
356	John Franco	.35	.25	.14
357	Jeff Brantley	.25	.20	.10
358	Mike Morgan	.30	.25	.12
359	Deion Sanders	6.00	4.50	2.50
360	Terry Leach	.25	.20	.10
361	Les Lancaster	.25	.20	.10
362	Storm Davis	.25	.20	.10
363	Scott Coolbaugh	.25	.20	.10
364	Checklist	.25	.20	.10
365	Cecilio Guante	.25	.20	.10
366	Joey Cora	.25	.20	.10
367	Willie McGee	.35	.25	.14
368	Jerry Reed	.25	.20	.10
369	Darren Daulton	1.50	1.25	.60
370	Manny Lee	.25	.20	.10
371	Mark Gardner	.25	.20	.10
372	Rick Honeycutt	.25	.20	.10
373	Steve Balboni	.25	.20	.10
374	Jack Armstrong	.30	.25	.12
375	Charlie O'Brien	.25	.20	.10
376	Ron Gant	2.00	1.50	.80
377	Lloyd Moseby	.25	.20	.10
378	Gene Harris	.30	.25	.12
379	Joe Carter	2.50	2.00	1.00
380	Scott Bailes	.25	.20	.10
381	R.J. Reynolds	.25	.20	.10
382	Bob Melvin	.25	.20	.10
383	Tim Teufel	.30	.25	.12
384	John Burkett	2.00	1.50	.80
385	Felix Jose	.75	.60	.30
386	Larry Andersen	.30	.25	.12
387	David West	.30	.25	.12
388	Luis Salazar	.20	.15	.08
389	Mike Macfarlane	.35	.25	.14
390	Charlie Hough	.30	.25	.12
391	Greg Briley	.35	.25	.14
392	Donn Pall	.30	.25	.12
393	Bryn Smith	.25	.20	.10
394	Carlos Quintana	.25	.20	.10
395	Steve Lake	.25	.20	.10
396	*Mark Whiten*	2.50	2.00	1.00
397	Edwin Nunez	.25	.20	.10
398	Rick Parker	.25	.20	.10
399	Mark Portugal	.25	.20	.10
400	Roy Smith	.25	.20	.10
401	Hector Villanueva	.25	.20	.10
402	Bob Milacki	.25	.20	.10
403	Alejandro Pena	.25	.20	.10
404	Scott Bradley	.25	.20	.10
405	Ron Kittle	.25	.20	.10
406	Bob Tewksbury	.30	.25	.12
407	Wes Gardner	.30	.25	.12
408	Ernie Whitt	.25	.20	.10
409	Terry Shumpert	.30	.25	.12
410	Tim Layana	.25	.20	.10
411	Chris Gwynn	.25	.20	.10
412	Jeff Robinson	.30	.25	.12
413	Scott Scudder	.25	.20	.10
414	Kevin Romine	.25	.20	.10
415	Jose DeJesus	.25	.20	.10
416	Mike Jeffcoat	.25	.20	.10
417	Rudy Seanez	.25	.20	.10
418	Mike Dunne	.25	.20	.10
419	Dick Schofield	.25	.20	.10
420	Steve Wilson	.35	.25	.14
421	Bill Krueger	.25	.20	.10
422	Junior Felix	.35	.25	.14
423	Drew Hall	.25	.20	.10
424	Curt Young	.25	.20	.10
425	Franklin Stubbs	.25	.20	.10
426	Dave Winfield	1.50	1.25	.60
427	Rick Reed	.25	.20	.10
428	Charlie Leibrandt	.25	.20	.10
429	Jeff Robinson	.30	.25	.12
430	Erik Hanson	.75	.60	.30

431	Barry Jones	.25	.20	.10
432	Alex Trevino	.25	.20	.10
433	John Moses	.25	.20	.10
434	Dave Johnson	.25	.20	.10
435	Mackey Sasser	.25	.20	.10
436	Rick Leach	.25	.20	.10
437	Lenny Harris	.25	.20	.10
438	Carlos Martinez	.25	.20	.10
439	Rex Hudler	.25	.20	.10
440	Domingo Ramos	.25	.20	.10
441	Gerald Perry	.25	.20	.10
442	John Russell	.25	.20	.10
443	*Carlos Baerga*	16.00	12.00	6.50
444	Checklist	.25	.20	.10
445	Stan Javier	.25	.20	.10
446	*Kevin Maas*	.35	.25	.14
447	Tom Brunansky	.25	.20	.10
448	Carmelo Martinez	.25	.20	.10
449	*Willie Blair*	.25	.20	.10
450	Andres Galarraga	1.50	1.25	.60
451	Bud Black	.30	.25	.12
452	Greg Harris	.30	.25	.12
453	Joe Oliver	.40	.30	.15
454	Greg Brock	.25	.20	.10
455	Jeff Treadway	.25	.20	.10
456	Lance McCullers	.25	.20	.10
457	Dave Schmidt	.25	.20	.10
458	Todd Burns	.25	.20	.10
459	Max Venable	.25	.20	.10
460	Neal Heaton	.25	.20	.10
461	Mark Williamson	.25	.20	.10
462	Keith Miller	.25	.20	.10
463	Mike LaCoss	.25	.20	.10
464	*Jose Offerman*	.50	.40	.20
465	*Jim Leyritz*	.50	.40	.20
466	Glenn Braggs	.25	.20	.10
467	Ron Robinson	.25	.20	.10
468	Mark Davis	.25	.20	.10
469	Gary Pettis	.25	.20	.10
470	Keith Hernandez	.25	.20	.10
471	Dennis Rasmussen	.25	.20	.10
472	Mark Eichhorn	.25	.20	.10
473	Ted Power	.25	.20	.10
474	Terry Mulholland	.30	.25	.12
475	Todd Stottlemyre	.40	.30	.15
476	Jerry Goff	.25	.20	.10
477	Gene Nelson	.25	.20	.10
478	Rich Gedman	.25	.20	.10
479	Brian Harper	.25	.20	.10
480	Mike Felder	.25	.20	.10
481	Steve Avery	11.00	8.25	4.50
482	Jack Morris	.35	.25	.14
483	Randy Johnson	3.50	2.75	1.50
484	Scott Radinsky	.30	.25	.12
485	Jose DeLeon	.30	.25	.12
486	*Stan Belinda*	.40	.30	.15
487	Brain Holton	.30	.25	.12
488	Mark Carreon	.25	.20	.10
489	Trevor Wilson	.30	.25	.12
490	Mike Sharperson	.25	.20	.10
491	*Alan Mills*	.35	.25	.14
492	John Candelaria	.25	.20	.10
493	Paul Assenmacher	.25	.20	.10
494	Steve Crawford	.25	.20	.10
495	Brad Arnsberg	.25	.20	.10
496	Sergio Valdez	.25	.20	.10
497	Mark Parent	.25	.20	.10
498	Tom Pagnozzi	.25	.20	.10
499	Greg Harris	.30	.25	.12
500	Randy Ready	.25	.20	.10
501	Duane Ward	.30	.25	.12
502	Nelson Santovenia	.25	.20	.10
503	Joe Klink	.25	.20	.10
504	Eric Plunk	.25	.20	.10
505	Jeff Reed	.25	.20	.10
506	Ted Higuera	.25	.20	.10
507	Joe Hesketh	.25	.20	.10
508	Dan Petry	.25	.20	.10
509	Matt Young	.25	.20	.10
510	Jerald Clark	.40	.30	.15
511	*John Orton*	.40	.30	.15
512	Scott Ruskin	.30	.25	.12
513	Chris Hoiles	4.00	3.00	1.50
514	Daryl Boston	.25	.20	.10
515	Francisco Oliveras	.25	.20	.10
516	Ozzie Canseco	.30	.25	.12
517	*Xavier Hernandez*	.40	.30	.15
518	Fred Manrique	.25	.20	.10
519	Shawn Boskie	.30	.25	.12
520	Jeff Montgomery	.75	.60	.30
521	Jack Daugherty	.25	.20	.10
522	Keith Comstock	.25	.20	.10
523	*Greg Hibbard*	.30	.25	.12
524	Lee Smith	.40	.30	.15
525	Dana Kiecker	.25	.20	.10
526	Darrel Akerfelds	.25	.20	.10
527	Greg Myers	.25	.20	.10
528	Checklist	.25	.20	.10

Values for recent cards and sets are listed in Mint (MT), Near Mint (NM), reflecting the fact that many cards from recent years have been preserved in top condition. Recent cards and sets in less than Excellent condition have little collector interest.

Values quoted in this guide reflect the retail price of a card – the price a collector can expect to pay when buying a card from a dealer. The wholesale price – that which a collector can expect to receive from a dealer when selling cards – will be significantly lower, depending on desirability and condition.

1991 Leaf Previews

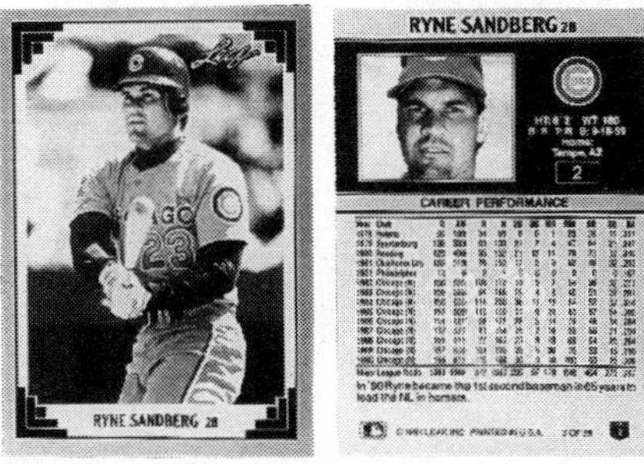

Cello packs of four cards previewing the 1991 Leaf set were included in each 1991 Donruss hobby factory set. The cards are identical in format to the regular 1991 Leafs, except there is a white notation, "1991 PREVIEW CARD" in white print beneath the statistics and career information on the back.

		MT	NR MT	EX
Complete Set (26):		45.00	34.00	18.00
Common Player:		.75	.60	.30
1	Dave Justice	1.50	1.25	.60
2	Ryne Sandberg	4.50	3.50	1.75
3	Barry Larkin	1.00	.70	.40
4	Craig Biggio	.75	.60	.30
5	Ramon Martinez	.75	.60	.30
6	Tim Wallach	.75	.60	.30
7	Dwight Gooden	1.00	.70	.40
8	Len Dykstra	1.00	.70	.40
9	Barry Bonds	3.00	2.25	1.25
10	Ray Lankford	.90	.70	.35
11	Tony Gwynn	2.25	1.75	.90
12	Will Clark	3.00	2.25	1.25
13	Leo Gomez	.75	.60	.30
14	Wade Boggs	2.25	1.75	.90
15	Chuck Finley	.75	.60	.30
16	Carlton Fisk	1.00	.70	.40
17	Sandy Alomar, Jr.	.75	.60	.30
18	Cecil Fielder	3.00	2.25	1.25
19	Bo Jackson	3.00	2.25	1.25
20	Paul Molitor	2.25	1.75	.90
21	Kirby Puckett	3.00	2.25	1.25
22	Don Mattingly	3.00	2.25	1.25
23	Rickey Henderson	3.00	2.25	1.25
24	Tino Martinez	.75	.60	.30
25	Nolan Ryan	7.50	5.75	3.00
26	Dave Steib	.75	.60	.30

1991 Leaf

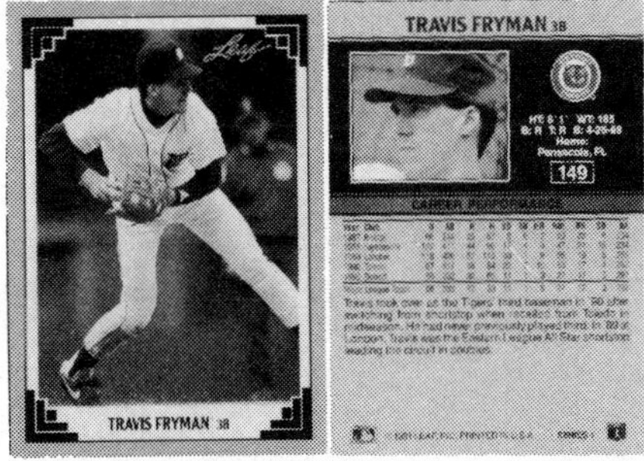

Silver borders and black insets surround the full-color action photos on the 1991 Leaf cards. The set was once again released in two series. Series I consists of cards 1-264. Card backs feature an additional player photo, biographical information, statistics and career highlights. The 1991 issue is not considered as scarce as the 1990 release.

		MT	NR MT	EX
Complete Set (528):		32.00	20.00	10.00
Common Player:		.08	.06	.03
1	The Leaf Card	.08	.06	.03
2	Kurt Stillwell	.08	.06	.03
3	Bobby Witt	.08	.06	.03
4	Tony Phillips	.08	.06	.03
5	Scott Garrelts	.08	.06	.03
6	Greg Swindell	.10	.08	.04
7	Billy Ripken	.08	.06	.03
8	Dave Martinez	.08	.06	.03
9	Kelly Gruber	.10	.08	.04
10	Juan Samuel	.10	.08	.04
11	Brian Holman	.08	.06	.03
12	Craig Biggio	.12	.09	.05
13	Lonnie Smith	.08	.06	.03
14	Ron Robinson	.08	.06	.03
15	Mike LaValliere	.08	.06	.03
16	Mark Davis	.08	.06	.03
17	Jack Daugherty	.08	.06	.03
18	Mike Henneman	.08	.06	.03
19	Mike Greenwell	.20	.15	.08
20	Dave Magadan	.12	.09	.05
21	Mark Williamson	.08	.06	.03
22	Marquis Grissom	.50	.40	.20
23	Pat Borders	.08	.06	.03
24	Mike Scioscia	.08	.06	.03
25	Shawon Dunston	.15	.11	.06
26	Randy Bush	.08	.06	.03
27	John Smoltz	.30	.25	.12
28	Chuck Crim	.08	.06	.03
29	Don Slaught	.08	.06	.03
30	Mike Macfarlane	.08	.06	.03
31	Wally Joyner	.20	.15	.08
32	Pat Combs	.10	.08	.04
33	Tony Pena	.10	.08	.04
34	Howard Johnson	.25	.20	.10
35	Leo Gomez	.12	.09	.05
36	Spike Owen	.08	.06	.03
37	Eric Davis	.15	.11	.06
38	Roberto Kelly	.15	.11	.06
39	Jerome Walton	.10	.07	.04
40	Shane Mack	.15	.11	.06
41	Kent Mercker	.10	.08	.04
42	B.J. Surhoff	.08	.06	.03
43	Jerry Browne	.08	.06	.03
44	Lee Smith	.10	.08	.04
45	Chuck Finley	.20	.15	.08
46	Terry Mulholland	.10	.08	.04
47	Tom Bolton	.08	.06	.03
48	Tom Herr	.08	.06	.03
49	Jim Deshaies	.08	.06	.03
50	Walt Weiss	.10	.08	.04
51	Hal Morris	.15	.11	.06
52	Lee Guetterman	.08	.06	.03
53	Paul Assenmacher	.08	.06	.03
54	Brian Harper	.10	.08	.04
55	Paul Gibson	.08	.06	.03
56	John Burkett	.08	.06	.03
57	Doug Jones	.08	.06	.03
58	Jose Oquendo	.08	.06	.03
59	Dick Schofield	.08	.06	.03
60	Dickie Thon	.08	.06	.03
61	Ramon Martinez	.12	.09	.05
62	Jay Buhner	.15	.11	.06
63	Mark Portugal	.08	.06	.03
64	Bob Welch	.10	.08	.04
65	Chris Sabo	.20	.15	.08
66	Chuck Cary	.08	.06	.03
67	Mark Langston	.15	.11	.06
68	Joe Boever	.08	.06	.03
69	Jody Reed	.10	.08	.04
70	Alejandro Pena	.08	.06	.03
71	Jeff King	.10	.08	.04
72	Tom Pagnozzi	.08	.06	.03
73	Joe Oliver	.08	.06	.03
74	Mike Witt	.08	.06	.03
75	Hector Villanueva	.15	.11	.06
76	Dan Gladden	.08	.06	.03
77	Dave Justice	1.25	.90	.50
78	Mike Gallego	.08	.06	.03
79	Tom Candiotti	.08	.06	.03
80	Ozzie Smith	.25	.20	.10
81	Luis Polonia	.08	.06	.03
82	Randy Ready	.08	.06	.03
83	Greg Harris	.08	.06	.03
84	Checklist (David Justice)	.25	.20	.10
85	Kevin Mitchell	.30	.25	.12
86	Mark McLemore	.08	.06	.03
87	Terry Steinbach	.08	.06	.03
88	Tom Browning	.10	.08	.04
89	Matt Nokes	.10	.08	.04
90	Mike Harkey	.12	.09	.05
91	Omar Vizquel	.08	.06	.03
92	Dave Bergman	.08	.06	.03
93	Matt Williams	.30	.25	.12
94	Steve Olin	.08	.06	.03
95	Craig Wilson	.20	.15	.08
96	Dave Stieb	.10	.08	.04
97	Ruben Sierra	.20	.15	.08
98	Jay Howell	.08	.06	.03
99	Scott Bradley	.08	.06	.03
100	Eric Yelding	.08	.06	.03
101	Rickey Henderson	.30	.25	.12
102	Jeff Reed	.08	.06	.03
103	Jimmy Key	.10	.08	.04
104	Terry Shumpert	.08	.06	.03
105	Kenny Rogers	.08	.06	.03
106	Cecil Fielder	.40	.30	.15
107	Robby Thompson	.08	.06	.03
108	Alex Cole	.10	.08	.04
109	Randy Milligan	.10	.08	.04
110	Andres Galarraga	.10	.08	.04
111	Bill Spiers	.08	.06	.03
112	Kal Daniels	.15	.11	.06
113	Henry Cotto	.08	.06	.03
114	Casy Candaele	.08	.06	.03
115	Jeff Blauser	.08	.06	.03
116	Robin Yount	.40	.30	.15
117	Ben McDonald	.25	.20	.10
118	Bret Saberhagen	.15	.11	.06
119	Juan Gonzalez	5.00	3.75	2.00
120	Lou Whitaker	.10	.08	.04
121	Ellis Burks	.20	.15	.08
122	Charlie O'Brien	.08	.06	.03
123	John Smiley	.10	.08	.04
124	Tim Burke	.08	.06	.03
125	John Olerud	1.25	.90	.50
126	Eddie Murray	.30	.25	.12
127	Greg Maddux	.30	.25	.12
128	Kevin Tapani	.12	.09	.05
129	Ron Gant	.25	.20	.10
130	Jay Bell	.10	.08	.04
131	Chris Hoiles	.20	.15	.08
132	Tom Gordon	.10	.08	.04
133	Kevin Seitzer	.08	.06	.03
134	Jeff Huson	.10	.08	.04
135	Jerry Don Gleaton	.08	.06	.03

136	Jeff Brantley	.08	.06	.03
137	Felix Fermin	.08	.06	.03
138	Mike Devereaux	.10	.08	.04
139	Delino DeShields	.20	.15	.08
140	David Wells	.08	.06	.03
141	Tim Crews	.08	.06	.03
142	Erik Hanson	.15	.11	.06
143	Mark Davidson	.08	.06	.03
144	Tommy Gregg	.08	.06	.03
145	Jim Gantner	.08	.06	.03
146	Jose Lind	.08	.06	.03
147	Danny Tartabull	.15	.11	.06
148	Geno Petralli	.08	.06	.03
149	Travis Fryman	2.50	2.00	1.00
150	Tim Naehring	.15	.11	.06
151	Kevin McReynolds	.12	.09	.05
152	Joe Orsulak	.08	.06	.03
153	Steve Frey	.15	.11	.06
154	Duane Ward	.08	.06	.03
155	Stan Javier	.08	.06	.03
156	Damon Berryhill	.08	.06	.03
157	Gene Larkin	.08	.06	.03
158	Greg Olson	.10	.08	.04
159	Mark Knudson	.08	.06	.03
160	Carmelo Martinez	.08	.06	.03
161	Storm Davis	.08	.06	.03
162	Jim Abbott	.20	.15	.08
163	Len Dykstra	.15	.11	.06
164	Tom Brunansky	.08	.06	.03
165	Dwight Gooden	.10	.08	.04
166	Jose Mesa	.08	.06	.03
167	Oil Can Boyd	.08	.06	.03
168	Barry Larkin	.15	.11	.06
169	Scott Sanderson	.08	.06	.03
170	Mark Grace	.20	.15	.08
171	Mark Guthrie	.08	.06	.03
172	Tom Glavine	.60	.45	.25
173	Gary Sheffield	.75	.60	.30
174	Checklist (Roger Clemens)	.08	.06	.03
175	Chris James	.08	.06	.03
176	Milt Thompson	.08	.06	.03
177	Donnie Hill	.08	.06	.03
178	Wes Chamberlain	.15	.11	.06
179	John Marzano	.08	.06	.03
180	Frank Viola	.15	.11	.06
181	Eric Anthony	.15	.11	.06
182	Jose Canseco	.40	.30	.15
183	Scott Scudder	.10	.08	.04
184	Dave Eiland	.08	.06	.03
185	Luis Salazar	.08	.06	.03
186	Pedro Munoz	.20	.15	.08
187	Steve Searcy	.08	.06	.03
188	Don Robinson	.08	.06	.03
189	Sandy Alomar	.15	.11	.06
190	Jose DeLeon	.08	.06	.03
191	John Orton	.08	.06	.03
192	Darren Daulton	.08	.06	.03
193	Mike Morgan	.08	.06	.03
194	Greg Briley	.08	.06	.03
195	Karl Rhodes	.15	.11	.06
196	Harold Baines	.10	.08	.04
197	Bill Doran	.10	.08	.04
198	Alvaro Espinoza	.08	.06	.03
199	Kirk McCaskill	.10	.08	.04
200	Jose DeJesus	.10	.08	.04
201	Jack Clark	.10	.08	.04
202	Daryl Boston	.08	.06	.03
203	Randy Tomlin	.15	.11	.06
204	Pedro Guerrero	.15	.11	.06
205	Billy Hatcher	.08	.06	.03
206	Tim Leary	.08	.06	.03
207	Ryne Sandberg	.80	.60	.30
208	Kirby Puckett	.50	.40	.20
209	Charlie Leibrandt	.08	.06	.03
210	Rick Honeycutt	.08	.06	.03
211	Joel Skinner	.08	.06	.03
212	Rex Hudler	.08	.06	.03
213	Bryan Harvey	.10	.08	.04
214	Charlie Hayes	.10	.08	.04
215	Matt Young	.08	.06	.03
216	Terry Kennedy	.08	.06	.03
217	Carl Nichols	.08	.06	.03
218	Mike Moore	.08	.06	.03
219	Paul O'Neill	.10	.08	.04
220	Steve Sax	.10	.08	.04
221	Shawn Boskie	.10	.08	.04
222	Rich DeLucia	.30	.25	.12
223	Lloyd Moseby	.08	.06	.03
224	Mike Kingery	.08	.06	.03
225	Carlos Baerga	1.25	.90	.50
226	Bryn Smith	.08	.06	.03
227	Todd Stottlemyre	.10	.08	.04
228	Julio Franco	.10	.08	.04
229	Jim Gott	.08	.06	.03
230	Mike Schooler	.10	.08	.04
231	Steve Finley	.10	.08	.04
232	Dave Henderson	.10	.08	.04
233	Luis Quinones	.08	.06	.03
234	Mark Whiten	.25	.20	.10
235	Brian McRae	.50	.40	.20
236	Rich Gossage	.10	.08	.04
237	Rob Deer	.08	.06	.03
238	Will Clark	.50	.40	.20
239	Albert Belle	1.00	.70	.40
240	Bob Melvin	.08	.06	.03
241	Larry Walker	.50	.40	.20
242	Dante Bichette	.08	.06	.03
243	Orel Hershiser	.15	.11	.06
244	Pete O'Brien	.08	.06	.03
245	Pete Harnisch	.10	.08	.04
246	Jeff Treadway	.08	.06	.03
247	Julio Machado	.08	.06	.03
248	Dave Johnson	.08	.06	.03
249	Kirk Gibson	.12	.09	.05
250	Kevin Brown	.08	.06	.03
251	Milt Cuyler	.15	.11	.06
252	Jeff Reardon	.10	.08	.04
253	David Cone	.15	.11	.06
254	Gary Redus	.08	.06	.03
255	Junior Noboa	.08	.06	.03
256	Greg Myers	.08	.06	.03
257	Dennis Cook	.08	.06	.03
258	Joe Girardi	.08	.06	.03
259	Allan Anderson	.08	.06	.03
260	Paul Marak	.20	.15	.08
261	Barry Bonds	.75	.60	.30
262	Juan Bell	.10	.08	.04
263	Russ Morman	.08	.06	.03
264	Checklist (George Brett)	.20	.15	.08
265	Jerald Clark	.10	.08	.04
266	Dwight Evans	.10	.08	.04
267	Roberto Alomar	1.00	.70	.40
268	Danny Jackson	.08	.06	.03
269	Brian Downing	.08	.06	.03
270	John Cerutti	.08	.06	.03
271	Robin Ventura	.75	.60	.30
273	Wade Boggs	.20	.15	.08
274	Dennis Martinez	.15	.11	.06
275	Andy Benes	.20	.15	.08
276	Tony Fossas	.08	.06	.03
277	Franklin Stubbs	.08	.06	.03
278	John Kruk	.20	.15	.08
279	Kevin Gross	.10	.08	.04
280	Von Hayes	.10	.08	.04
281	Frank Thomas	5.00	3.75	2.00
282	Rob Dibble	.15	.11	.06
283	Mel Hall	.10	.08	.04
284	Rick Mahler	.08	.06	.03
285	Dennis Eckersley	.20	.15	.08
286	Bernard Gilkey	.25	.20	.10
287	Dan Plesac	.08	.06	.03
288	Jason Grimsley	.10	.08	.04
289	Mark Lewis	.15	.11	.06
290	Tony Gwynn	.40	.30	.15
291	Jeff Russell	.10	.08	.04
292	Curt Schilling	.10	.08	.04
293	Pascual Perez	.08	.06	.03
294	Jack Morris	.15	.11	.06
295	Hubie Brooks	.10	.08	.04
296	Alex Fernandez	1.00	.70	.40
297	Harold Reynolds	.10	.08	.04
298	Craig Worthington	.08	.06	.03
299	Willie Wilson	.08	.06	.03
300	Mike Maddux	.08	.06	.03
301	Dave Righetti	.10	.08	.04
302	Paul Molitor	.40	.30	.15
303	Gary Gaetti	.10	.08	.04
304	Terry Pendleton	.20	.15	.08
305	Kevin Elster	.08	.06	.03
306	Scott Fletcher	.08	.06	.03
307	Jeff Robinson	.08	.06	.03
308	Jesse Barfield	.10	.08	.04
309	Mike LaCoss	.08	.06	.03
310	Andy Van Slyke	.15	.11	.06
311	Glenallen Hill	.15	.11	.06
312	Bud Black	.08	.06	.03
313	Kent Hrbek	.15	.11	.06
314	Tim Teufel	.08	.06	.03
315	Tony Fernandez	.15	.11	.06
316	Beau Allred	.08	.06	.03
317	Curtis Wilkerson	.08	.06	.03
318	Bill Sampen	.08	.06	.03
319	Randy Johnson	.15	.11	.06
320	Mike Heath	.08	.06	.03
321	Sammy Sosa	.50	.40	.20
322	Mickey Tettleton	.15	.11	.06
323	Jose Vizcaino	.08	.06	.03
324	John Candelaria	.08	.06	.03
325	David Howard	.15	.11	.06
326	Jose Rijo	.10	.08	.04
327	Todd Zeile	.25	.20	.10
328	Gene Nelson	.08	.06	.03
329	Dwayne Henry	.08	.06	.03
330	Mike Boddicker	.08	.06	.03
331	Ozzie Guillen	.10	.08	.04
332	Sam Horn	.08	.06	.03
333	Wally Whitehurst	.08	.06	.03
334	Dave Parker	.10	.08	.04
335	George Brett	.25	.20	.10
336	Bobby Thigpen	.10	.08	.04
337	Ed Whitson	.08	.06	.03
338	Ivan Calderon	.10	.08	.04
339	Mike Pagliarulo	.08	.06	.03
340	Jack McDowell	.15	.11	.06
341	Dana Kiecker	.08	.06	.03
342	Fred McGriff	.40	.30	.15
343	Mark Lee	.08	.06	.03
344	Alfredo Griffin	.08	.06	.03
345	Scott Bankhead	.08	.06	.03
346	Darrin Jackson	.10	.08	.04
347	Rafael Palmeiro	.25	.20	.10
348	Steve Farr	.08	.06	.03
349	Hensley Meulens	.10	.08	.04
350	Danny Cox	.08	.06	.03
351	Alan Trammell	.15	.11	.06
352	Edwin Nunez	.08	.06	.03
353	Joe Carter	.25	.20	.10
354	Eric Show	.08	.06	.03
355	Vance Law	.08	.06	.03
356	Jeff Gray	.08	.06	.03
357	Bobby Bonilla	.20	.15	.08
358	Ernest Riles	.08	.06	.03
359	Ron Hassey	.08	.06	.03
360	Willie McGee	.12	.09	.05
361	Mackey Sasser	.08	.06	.03
362	Glenn Braggs	.08	.06	.03
363	Mario Diaz	.08	.06	.03
364	Checklist Barry Bonds	.08	.06	.03
365	Kevin Bass	.08	.06	.03
366	Pete Incaviglia	.10	.08	.04
367	Luis Sojo	.10	.08	.04
368	Lance Parrish	.10	.08	.04
369	Mark Leonard	.15	.11	.06
370	Heathcliff Slocumb	.10	.08	.04
371	Jimmy Jones	.08	.06	.03
372	Ken Griffey, Jr.	3.00	2.25	1.25
373	Chris Hammond	.20	.15	.08
374	Chili Davis	.10	.08	.04
375	Joey Cora	.08	.06	.03
376	Ken Hill	.15	.11	.06
377	Darryl Strawberry	.20	.15	.08
378	Ron Darling	.08	.06	.03
379	Sid Bream	.08	.06	.03
380	Bill Swift	.10	.08	.04
381	Shawn Abner	.08	.06	.03
382	Eric King	.08	.06	.03
383	Mickey Morandini	.15	.11	.06
384	Carlton Fisk	.20	.15	.08
385	Steve Lake	.08	.06	.03
386	Mike Jeffcoat	.08	.06	.03
387	Darren Holmes	.08	.06	.03
388	Tim Wallach	.10	.08	.04
389	George Bell	.12	.09	.05
390	Craig Lefferts	.08	.06	.03
391	Ernie Whitt	.08	.06	.03
392	Felix Jose	.15	.11	.06
393	Kevin Maas	.10	.08	.04
394	Devon White	.12	.09	.05
395	Otis Nixon	.10	.08	.04
396	Chuck Knoblauch	.50	.40	.20
397	Scott Coolbaugh	.08	.06	.03
398	Glenn Davis	.12	.09	.05
399	Manny Lee	.08	.06	.03
400	Andre Dawson	.20	.15	.08
401	Scott Chiamparino	.10	.08	.04
402	Bill Gullickson	.10	.08	.04
403	Lance Johnson	.08	.06	.03
404	Juan Agosto	.08	.06	.03
405	Danny Darwin	.08	.06	.03
406	Barry Jones	.08	.06	.03
407	Larry Andersen	.08	.06	.03
408	Luis Rivera	.08	.06	.03
409	Jaime Navarro	.12	.09	.05
410	Roger McDowell	.08	.06	.03
411	Brett Butler	.10	.08	.04
412	Dale Murphy	.15	.11	.06
413	Tim Raines	.15	.11	.06
414	Norm Charlton	.10	.08	.04
415	Greg Cadaret	.08	.06	.03
416	Chris Nabholz	.15	.11	.06
417	Dave Stewart	.10	.08	.04
418	Rich Gedman	.08	.06	.03
419	Willie Randolph	.10	.08	.04
420	Mitch Williams	.10	.08	.04
421	Brook Jacoby	.08	.06	.03
422	Greg Harris	.08	.06	.03
423	Nolan Ryan	2.00	1.50	.80
424	Dave Rohde	.10	.08	.04
425	Don Mattingly	.50	.40	.20
426	Greg Gagne	.08	.06	.03
427	Vince Coleman	.10	.08	.04
428	Dan Pasqua	.08	.06	.03
429	Alvin Davis	.08	.06	.03
430	Cal Ripken, Jr.	.75	.60	.30
431	Jamie Quirk	.08	.06	.03
432	Benito Santiago	.15	.11	.06
433	Jose Uribe	.08	.06	.03
434	Candy Maldonado	.08	.06	.03
435	Junior Felix	.10	.08	.04
436	Deion Sanders	.75	.60	.30
437	John Franco	.10	.08	.04
438	Greg Hibbard	.08	.06	.03
439	Floyd Bannister	.08	.06	.03
440	Steve Howe	.08	.06	.03
441	Steve Decker	.25	.20	.10
442	Vicente Palacios	.08	.06	.03
443	Pat Tabler	.08	.06	.03
444	Checklist (Darryl Strawberry)	.08	.06	.03
445	Mike Felder	.08	.06	.03
446	Al Newman	.08	.06	.03
447	Chris Donnels	.25	.20	.10
448	Rich Rodriguez	.10	.08	.04
449	Turner Ward	.15	.11	.06
450	Bob Walk	.08	.06	.03
451	Gilberto Reyes	.08	.06	.03
452	Mike Jackson	.08	.06	.03
453	Rafael Belliard	.08	.06	.03
454	Wayne Edwards	.08	.06	.03
455	Andy Allanson	.08	.06	.03
456	Dave Smith	.08	.06	.03
457	Gary Carter	.15	.11	.06
458	Warren Cromartie	.08	.06	.03
459	Jack Armstrong	.08	.06	.03
460	Bob Tewksbury	.10	.08	.04
461	Joe Klink	.08	.06	.03
462	Xavier Hernandez	.08	.06	.03
463	Scott Radinsky	.08	.06	.03
464	Jeff Robinson	.08	.06	.03
465	Gregg Jefferies	.40	.30	.15
466	Denny Neagle	.20	.15	.08
467	Carmelo Martinez	.08	.06	.03
468	Donn Pall	.08	.06	.03
469	Bruce Hurst	.10	.08	.04
470	Eric Bullock	.08	.06	.03
471	Rick Aguilera	.10	.08	.04
472	Charlie Hough	.08	.06	.03
473	Carlos Quintana	.08	.06	.03
474	Marty Barrett	.08	.06	.03
475	Kevin Brown	.10	.08	.04
476	Bobby Ojeda	.08	.06	.03
477	Edgar Martinez	.15	.11	.06
478	Bip Roberts	.08	.06	.03
479	Mike Flanagan	.08	.06	.03
480	John Habyan	.08	.06	.03
481	Larry Casian	.10	.08	.04
482	Wally Backman	.08	.06	.03
483	Doug Dascenzo	.08	.06	.03
484	Rick Dempsey	.08	.06	.03
485	Ed Sprague	.10	.08	.04
486	Steve Chitren	.10	.08	.04
487	Mark McGwire	.30	.25	.12
488	Roger Clemens	.50	.40	.20
489	Orlando Merced	.25	.20	.10
490	Rene Gonzales	.08	.06	.03

491	Mike Stanton	.08	.06	.03
492	Al Osuna	.15	.11	.06
493	Rick Cerone	.08	.06	.03
494	Mariano Duncan	.08	.06	.03
495	Zane Smith	.08	.06	.03
496	John Morris	.08	.06	.03
497	Frank Tanana	.08	.06	.03
498	Junior Ortiz	.08	.06	.03
499	Dave Winfield	.40	.30	.15
500	Gary Varsho	.08	.06	.03
501	Chico Walker	.08	.06	.03
502	Ken Caminiti	.08	.06	.03
503	Ken Griffey, Sr.	.10	.08	.04
504	Randy Myers	.10	.08	.04
505	Steve Bedrosian	.08	.06	.03
506	Cory Snyder	.10	.08	.04
507	Cris Carpenter	.08	.06	.03
508	Tim Belcher	.10	.08	.04
509	Jeff Hamilton	.08	.06	.03
510	Steve Avery	1.00	.70	.40
511	Dave Valle	.08	.06	.03
512	Tom Lampkin	.08	.06	.03
513	Shawn Hillegas	.08	.06	.03
514	Reggie Jefferson	.35	.25	.14
515	Ron Karkovice	.08	.06	.03
516	Doug Drabek	.10	.08	.04
517	Tom Henke	.10	.08	.04
518	Chris Bosio	.08	.06	.03
519	Gregg Olson	.12	.09	.05
520	Bob Scanlan	.10	.08	.04
521	Alonzo Powell	.10	.08	.04
522	Jeff Ballard	.08	.06	.03
523	Ray Lankford	.75	.60	.30
524	Tommy Greene	.15	.11	.06
525	Mike Timlin	.15	.11	.06
526	Juan Berenguer	.08	.06	.03
527	Scott Erickson	.12	.09	.05
528	Checklist (Sandy Alomar, Jr.)	.08	.06	.03

1991 Leaf Gold Rookies

Special gold rookie and gold bonus cards were randomly inserted in 1991 Leaf packs. The card backs are designed in the same style as the regular Leaf cards with the exception of a gold back instead of silver. The card fronts feature a partial top inset with a banner on the bottom featuring the player's name and position. Variations of Series I cards exist. They can be found numbered 265-276 as an extension of the first series. The more common cards are numbered with a "BC" designation, BC1-BC12.

		MT	NR MT	EX
	Complete Set (26):	60.00	45.00	24.00
	Common Player:	1.00	.70	.40
1	Scott Leius	1.00	.70	.40
265	Scott Leius	8.00	6.00	3.25
2	Luis Gonzalez	3.00	2.25	1.25
266	Luis Gonzalez	25.00	18.50	10.00
3	Wil Cordero	3.00	2.25	1.25
267	Wil Cordero	25.00	18.50	10.00
4	Gary Scott	1.00	.70	.40
268	Gary Scott	8.00	6.00	3.25
5	Willie Banks	1.00	.70	.40
269	Willie Banks	8.00	6.00	3.25
6	Arthur Rhodes	2.00	1.50	.80
270	Arthur Rhodes	15.00	11.00	6.00
7	Mo Vaughn	6.00	4.50	2.50
271	Mo Vaughn	45.00	34.00	18.00
8	Henry Rodriguez	3.00	2.25	1.25
272	Henry Rodriguez	25.00	18.50	10.00
9	Todd Van Poppel	2.50	2.00	1.00
273	Todd Van Poppel	20.00	15.00	8.00
10	Reggie Sanders	2.50	2.00	1.00
274	Reggie Sanders	20.00	15.00	8.00
11	Rico Brogna	1.00	.70	.40
275	Rico Brogna	8.00	6.00	3.25
12	Mike Mussina	8.00	6.00	3.25
276	Mike Mussina	55.00	41.00	22.00
13	Kirk Dressendorfer	1.00	.70	.40
14	Jeff Bagwell	7.00	5.25	2.75
15	Pete Schourek	2.00	1.50	.80
16	Wade Taylor	1.00	.70	.40
17	Pat Kelly	2.00	1.50	.80
18	Tim Costo	2.00	1.50	.80
19	Roger Salkeld	2.00	1.50	.80
20	Andujar Cedeno	2.50	2.00	1.00
21	Ryan Klesko	6.00	4.50	2.50
22	Mike Huff	1.00	.70	.40
23	Anthony Young	1.00	.70	.40
24	Eddie Zosky	2.00	1.50	.80
25	Nolan Ryan	3.00	2.25	1.25
26	Rickey Henderson (Record Steal)	1.50	1.25	.60

1992 Leaf Previews

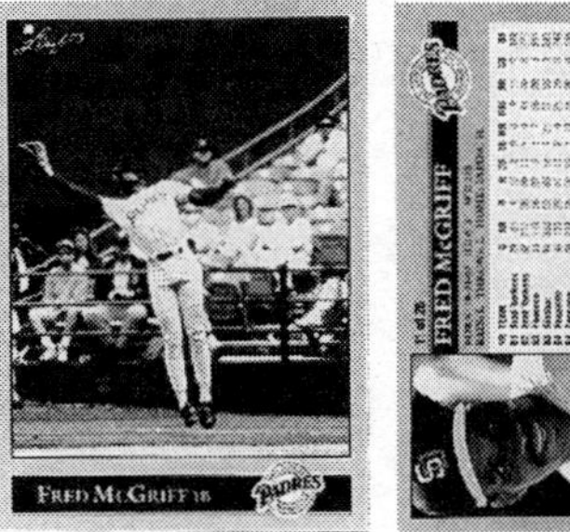

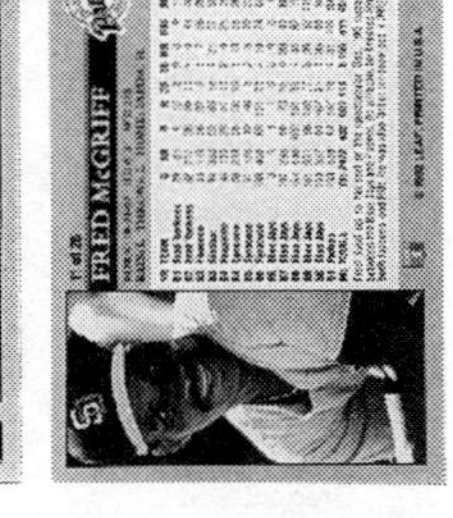

In a format identical to the regular-issue 1992 Leaf cards, this 26-card preview set was issued as a bonus in packs of four cards in each 1992 Donruss hobby factory set.

		MT	NR MT	EX
	Complete Set (26):	80.00	60.00	32.00
	Common Player:	1.00	.70	.40
1	Steve Avery	2.00	1.50	.80
2	Ryne Sandberg	5.00	3.75	2.00
3	Chris Sabo	1.50	1.25	.60
4	Jeff Bagwell	2.00	1.50	.80
5	Darryl Strawberry	2.00	1.50	.80
6	Bret Barberie	1.50	1.25	.60
7	Howard Johnson	1.50	1.25	.60
8	John Kruk	2.50	2.00	1.00
9	Andy Van Slyke	1.25	.90	.50
10	Felix Jose	1.50	1.25	.60
11	Fred McGriff	3.00	2.25	1.25
12	Will Clark	4.00	3.00	1.50
13	Cal Ripken, Jr.	5.00	3.75	2.00
14	Phil Plantier	2.00	1.50	.80
15	Lee Stevens	1.00	.70	.40
16	Frank Thomas	9.00	6.75	3.50
17	Mark Whiten	1.50	1.25	.60
18	Cecil Fielder	2.00	1.50	.80
19	George Brett	5.00	3.75	2.00
20	Robin Yount	4.00	3.00	1.50
21	Scott Erickson	1.00	.70	.40
22	Don Mattingly	4.00	3.00	1.50
23	Jose Canseco	3.00	2.25	1.25
24	Ken Griffey, Jr.	9.00	6.75	3.50
25	Nolan Ryan	9.00	6.75	3.50
26	Joe Carter	2.50	2.00	1.00

1992 Leaf

Two 264-card series comprise this 528-card set. The cards feature action photos on both the front and the back. Silver borders surround the photo on the card front. Each leaf card was also produced in a gold foil version. One gold card was issued per pack and a complete Leaf Gold Edition set can be assembled. Traded players and free agents are shown in uniform with their new teams.

		MT	NR MT	EX
	Complete Set (528):	28.00	21.00	11.00
	Common Player:	.05	.04	.02
1	Jim Abbott	.15	.10	.05
2	Cal Eldred	.40	.30	.15
3	Bud Black	.05	.04	.02
4	Dave Howard	.05	.04	.02
5	Luis Sojo	.05	.04	.02
6	Gary Scott	.12	.09	.05
7	Joe Oliver	.10	.08	.04
8	Chris Gardner	.08	.06	.03
9	Sandy Alomar	.10	.08	.04
10	Greg Harris	.10	.08	.04
11	Doug Drabek	.05	.04	.02
12	Darryl Hamilton	.15	.11	.06
13	Mike Mussina	.60	.45	.25
14	Kevin Tapani	.15	.11	.06
15	Ron Gant	.15	.11	.06
16	Mark McGwire	.25	.15	.08
17	Robin Ventura	.25	.15	.08
18	Pedro Guerrero	.15	.11	.06
19	Roger Clemens	.35	.25	.14
20	Steve Farr	.05	.04	.02
21	Frank Tanana	.05	.04	.02
22	Joe Hesketh	.05	.04	.02
23	Erik Hanson	.12	.09	.05
24	Greg Cadaret	.05	.04	.02
25	Rex Hudler	.05	.04	.02
26	Mark Grace	.15	.11	.06
27	Kelly Gruber	.10	.08	.04
28	Jeff Bagwell	.50	.40	.20
29	Darryl Strawberry	.10	.07	.04
30	Dave Smith	.05	.04	.02
31	Kevin Appier	.15	.11	.06
32	Steve Chitren	.05	.04	.02
33	Kevin Gross	.05	.04	.02
34	Rick Aguilera	.10	.08	.04
35	Juan Guzman	.25	.20	.10
36	Joe Orsulak	.05	.04	.02
37	Tim Raines	.15	.11	.06
38	Harold Reynolds	.10	.08	.04
39	Charlie Hough	.05	.04	.02
40	Tony Phillips	.10	.08	.04
41	Nolan Ryan	1.25	.90	.50
42	Vince Coleman	.10	.08	.04
43	Andy Van Slyke	.15	.11	.06
44	Tim Burke	.05	.04	.02
45	Luis Polonia	.05	.04	.02
46	Tom Browning	.10	.08	.04
47	Willie McGee	.10	.08	.04
48	Gary DiSarcina	.10	.08	.04
49	Mark Lewis	.10	.08	.04
50	Phil Plantier	.25	.15	.08
51	Doug Dascenzo	.05	.04	.02
52	Cal Ripken, Jr.	.50	.30	.15
53	Pedro Munoz	.10	.08	.04
54	Carlos Hernandez	.15	.11	.06
55	Jerald Clark	.10	.08	.04
56	Jeff Brantley	.05	.04	.02
57	Don Mattingly	.25	.15	.08
58	Roger McDowell	.05	.04	.02
59	Steve Avery	.40	.30	.15
60	John Olerud	.75	.50	.25
61	Bill Gullickson	.05	.04	.02
62	Juan Gonzalez	2.00	1.50	.75
63	Felix Jose	.10	.08	.04
64	Robin Yount	.25	.20	.10
65	Greg Briley	.05	.04	.02
66	Steve Finley	.12	.09	.05
67	Checklist	.05	.04	.02
68	Tom Gordon	.05	.04	.02
69	Rob Dibble	.15	.11	.06
70	Glenallen Hill	.05	.04	.02
71	Calvin Jones	.05	.04	.02
72	Joe Girardi	.05	.04	.02
73	Barry Larkin	.15	.10	.05
74	Andy Benes	.10	.07	.04
75	Milt Cyler	.05	.04	.02
76	Kevin Bass	.05	.04	.02
77	Pete Harnisch	.10	.08	.04
78	Wilson Alvarez	.10	.08	.04
79	Mike Devereaux	.15	.11	.06
80	Doug Henry	.10	.08	.04
81	Orel Hershiser	.15	.11	.06
82	Shane Mack	.10	.08	.04
83	Mike Macfarlane	.10	.08	.04
84	Thomas Howard	.10	.08	.04
85	Alex Fernandez	.20	.15	.08
86	Reggie Jefferson	.20	.15	.08
87	Leo Gomez	.20	.15	.08
88	Mel Hall	.10	.08	.04
89	Mike Greenwell	.15	.11	.06
90	Jeff Russell	.10	.08	.04
91	Steve Buechele	.10	.08	.04
92	David Cone	.15	.11	.06
93	Kevin Reimer	.10	.08	.04
94	Mark Lemke	.10	.08	.04
95	Bob Tewksbury	.10	.08	.04
96	Zane Smith	.10	.08	.04
97	Mark Eichhorn	.05	.04	.02
98	Kirby Puckett	.50	.30	.15
99	Paul O'Neill	.12	.09	.05
100	Dennis Eckersley	.10	.07	.04
101	Duane Ward	.10	.08	.04
102	Matt Nokes	.10	.08	.04
103	Mo Vaughn	.30	.25	.12
104	Pat Kelly	.10	.08	.04
105	Ron Karkovice	.05	.04	.02
106	Bill Spiers	.05	.04	.02
107	Gary Gaetti	.10	.08	.04
108	Mackey Sasser	.05	.04	.02
109	Robby Thompson	.10	.08	.04
110	Marvin Freeman	.05	.04	.02
111	Jimmy Key	.10	.08	.04
112	Dwight Gooden	.12	.09	.05
113	Charlie Leibrandt	.05	.04	.02
114	Devon White	.10	.08	.04
115	Charles Nagy	.10	.08	.04
116	Rickey Henderson	.25	.15	.08
117	Paul Assenmacher	.05	.04	.02
118	Junior Felix	.10	.08	.04
119	Julio Franco	.20	.15	.08
120	Norm Charlton	.10	.08	.04
121	Scott Servais	.10	.08	.04
122	Gerald Perry	.05	.04	.02
123	Brian McRae	.10	.07	.04
124	Don Slaught	.05	.04	.02
125	Juan Samuel	.05	.04	.02
126	Harold Baines	.15	.11	.06
127	Scott Livingstone	.15	.11	.06
128	Jay Buhner	.10	.08	.04
129	Darrin Jackson	.10	.08	.04
130	Luis Mercedes	.08	.06	.03
131	Brian Harper	.10	.08	.04
132	Howard Johnson	.05	.04	.02
133	Checklist	.05	.04	.02
134	Dante Bichette	.05	.04	.02
135	Dave Righetti	.10	.08	.04
136	Jeff Montgomery	.10	.08	.04

137	Joe Grahe	.10	.08	.04
138	Delino DeShields	.20	.15	.08
139	Jose Rijo	.12	.09	.05
140	Ken Caminiti	.10	.08	.04
141	Steve Olin	.10	.08	.04
142	Kurt Stillwell	.10	.08	.04
143	Jay Bell	.12	.09	.05
144	Jaime Navarro	.12	.09	.05
145	Ben McDonald	.30	.25	.12
146	Greg Gagne	.05	.04	.02
147	Jeff Blauser	.10	.08	.04
148	Carney Lansford	.10	.08	.04
149	Ozzie Guillen	.10	.08	.04
150	Milt Thompson	.05	.04	.02
151	Jeff Reardon	.15	.11	.06
152	Scott Sanderson	.05	.04	.02
153	Cecil Fielder	.25	.15	.08
154	Greg Harris	.05	.04	.02
155	Rich DeLucia	.05	.04	.02
156	Roberto Kelly	.10	.08	.04
157	Bryn Smith	.05	.04	.02
158	Chuck McElroy	.05	.04	.02
159	Tom Henke	.12	.09	.05
160	Luis Gonzalez	.05	.04	.02
161	Steve Wilson	.05	.04	.02
162	Shawn Boskie	.05	.04	.02
163	Mark Davis	.05	.04	.02
164	Mike Moore	.10	.08	.04
165	Mike Scioscia	.10	.08	.04
166	Scott Erickson	.10	.08	.04
167	Todd Stottlemyre	.10	.08	.04
168	Alvin Davis	.10	.08	.04
169	Greg Hibbard	.10	.08	.04
170	David Valle	.05	.04	.02
171	Dave Winfield	.25	.15	.08
172	Alan Trammell	.12	.09	.05
173	Kenny Rogers	.05	.04	.02
174	John Franco	.10	.08	.04
175	Jose Lind	.05	.04	.02
176	Pete Schourek	.10	.08	.04
177	Von Hayes	.05	.04	.02
178	Chris Hammond	.10	.08	.04
179	John Burkett	.05	.04	.02
180	Dickie Thon	.05	.04	.02
181	Joel Skinner	.05	.04	.02
182	Scott Cooper	.12	.09	.05
183	Andre Dawson	.15	.10	.05
184	Billy Ripken	.05	.04	.02
185	Kevin Mitchell	.10	.08	.04
186	Brett Butler	.10	.08	.04
187	Tony Fernandez	.10	.08	.04
188	Cory Snyder	.10	.08	.04
189	John Habyan	.05	.04	.02
190	Dennis Martinez	.12	.09	.05
191	John Smoltz	.10	.07	.04
192	Greg Myers	.05	.04	.02
193	Rob Deer	.10	.08	.04
194	Ivan Rodriguez	.40	.30	.15
195	Ray Lankford	.25	.15	.08
196	Bill Wegman	.10	.08	.04
197	Edgar Martinez	.15	.11	.06
198	Darryl Kile	.10	.08	.04
199	Checklist	.05	.04	.02
200	Brent Mayne	.05	.04	.02
201	Larry Walker	.20	.15	.08
202	Carlos Baerga	.40	.30	.15
203	Russ Swan	.05	.04	.02
204	Mike Morgan	.10	.08	.04
205	Hal Morris	.10	.08	.04
206	Tony Gwynn	.20	.15	.08
207	Mark Leiter	.05	.04	.02
208	Kirt Manwaring	.05	.04	.02
209	Al Osuna	.05	.04	.02
210	Bobby Thigpen	.05	.04	.02
211	Chris Hoiles	.15	.10	.05
212	B.J. Surhoff	.10	.08	.04
213	Lenny Harris	.05	.04	.02
214	Scott Leius	.10	.08	.04
215	Gregg Jefferies	.25	.20	.10
216	Bruce Hurst	.10	.08	.04
217	Steve Sax	.12	.09	.05
218	Dave Otto	.05	.04	.02
219	Sam Horn	.05	.04	.02
220	Charlie Hayes	.10	.08	.04
221	Frank Viola	.10	.08	.04
222	Jose Guzman	.10	.08	.04
223	Gary Redus	.05	.04	.02
224	Dave Gallagher	.05	.04	.02
225	Dean Palmer	.25	.20	.10
226	Greg Olson	.10	.08	.04
227	Jose DeLeon	.05	.04	.02
228	Mike LaValliere	.05	.04	.02
229	Mark Langston	.15	.11	.06
230	Chuck Knoblauch	.20	.15	.08
231	Bill Doran	.10	.08	.04
232	Dave Henderson	.10	.08	.04
233	Roberto Alomar	.40	.30	.15
234	Scott Fletcher	.05	.04	.02
235	Tim Naehring	.05	.04	.02
236	Mike Gallego	.05	.04	.02
237	Lance Johnson	.10	.08	.04
238	Paul Molitor	.25	.15	.08
239	Dan Gladden	.05	.04	.02
240	Willie Randolph	.10	.08	.04
241	Will Clark	.30	.20	.10
242	Sid Bream	.05	.04	.02
243	Derek Bell	.40	.30	.15
244	Bill Pecota	.05	.04	.02
245	Terry Pendleton	.10	.07	.04
246	Randy Ready	.05	.04	.02
247	Jack Armstrong	.05	.04	.02
248	Todd Van Poppel	.20	.15	.08
249	Shawon Dunston	.10	.08	.04
250	Bobby Rose	.05	.04	.02
251	Jeff Huson	.05	.04	.02
252	Bip Roberts	.12	.09	.05
253	Doug Jones	.10	.08	.04
254	Lee Smith	.15	.11	.06
255	George Brett	.40	.30	.15
256	Randy Tomlin	.10	.08	.04
257	Todd Benzinger	.05	.04	.02
258	Dave Stewart	.15	.11	.06
259	Mark Carreon	.05	.04	.02
260	Pete O'Brien	.05	.04	.02
261	Tim Teufel	.05	.04	.02
262	Bob Milacki	.05	.04	.02
263	Mark Guthrie	.05	.04	.02
264	Darrin Fletcher	.05	.04	.02
265	Omar Vizquel	.05	.04	.02
266	Chris Bosio	.10	.08	.04
267	Jose Canseco	.25	.15	.08
268	Mike Boddicker	.05	.04	.02
269	Lance Parrish	.10	.08	.04
270	Jose Vizcaino	.05	.04	.02
271	Chris Sabo	.15	.11	.06
272	Royce Clayton	.20	.15	.08
273	Marquis Grissom	.20	.15	.08
274	Fred McGriff	.25	.20	.10
275	Barry Bonds	.60	.45	.25
276	Greg Vaughn	.15	.11	.06
277	Gregg Olson	.12	.09	.05
278	Dave Hollins	.20	.15	.08
279	Tom Glavine	.20	.15	.08
280	Bryan Hickerson	.15	.11	.06
281	Scott Radinsky	.05	.04	.02
282	Omar Olivares	.10	.08	.04
283	Ivan Calderon	.12	.09	.05
284	Kevin Maas	.15	.11	.06
285	Mickey Tettleton	.15	.11	.06
286	Wade Boggs	.15	.11	.06
287	Stan Belinda	.05	.04	.02
288	Bret Barberie	.10	.08	.04
289	Jose Oquendo	.05	.04	.02
290	Frank Castillo	.12	.09	.05
291	Dave Stieb	.10	.08	.04
292	Tommy Greene	.12	.09	.05
293	Eric Karros	.30	.25	.12
294	Greg Maddux	.20	.15	.08
295	Jim Eisenreich	.05	.04	.02
296	Rafael Palmeiro	.15	.11	.06
297	Ramon Martinez	.10	.07	.04
298	Tim Wallach	.10	.08	.04
299	Jim Thome	.60	.45	.25
300	Chito Martinez	.10	.08	.04
301	Mitch Williams	.12	.09	.05
302	Randy Johnson	.10	.08	.04
303	Carlton Fisk	.10	.07	.04
304	Travis Fryman	.50	.40	.20
305	Bobby Witt	.10	.08	.04
306	Dave Magadan	.10	.08	.04
307	Alex Cole	.05	.04	.02
308	Bobby Bonilla	.15	.10	.05
309	Bryan Harvey	.12	.09	.05
310	Rafael Belliard	.05	.04	.02
311	Mariano Duncan	.05	.04	.02
312	Chuck Crim	.05	.04	.02
313	John Kruk	.15	.11	.06
314	Ellis Burks	.15	.11	.06
315	Craig Biggio	.15	.11	.06
316	Glenn Davis	.10	.08	.04
317	Ryne Sandberg	.50	.30	.15
318	Mike Sharperson	.05	.04	.02
319	Rich Rodriguez	.05	.04	.02
320	Lee Guetterman	.05	.04	.02
321	Benito Santiago	.15	.11	.06
322	Jose Offerman	.12	.09	.05
323	Tony Pena	.10	.08	.04
324	Pat Borders	.10	.08	.04
325	Mike Henneman	.10	.08	.04
326	Kevin Brown	.15	.11	.06
327	Chris Nabholz	.10	.08	.04
328	Franklin Stubbs	.05	.04	.02
329	Tino Martinez	.15	.11	.06
330	Mickey Morandini	.15	.11	.06
331	Checklist	.05	.04	.02
332	Mark Gubicza	.10	.08	.04
333	Bill Landrum	.05	.04	.02
334	Mark Whiten	.08	.06	.03
335	Darren Daulton	.15	.11	.06
336	Rick Wilkins	.12	.09	.05
337	*Brian Jordan*	.50	.40	.20
338	Kevin Ward	.12	.09	.05
339	Ruben Amaro	.12	.09	.05
340	Trevor Wilson	.10	.08	.04
341	Andujar Cedeno	.15	.11	.06
342	Michael Huff	.05	.04	.02
343	Brady Anderson	.15	.11	.06
344	Craig Grebeck	.05	.04	.02
345	Bobby Ojeda	.05	.04	.02
346	Mike Pagliarulo	.05	.04	.02
347	Terry Shumpert	.05	.04	.02
348	Dann Bilardello	.05	.04	.02
349	Frank Thomas	3.50	2.25	1.25
350	Albert Belle	.50	.40	.20
351	Jose Mesa	.05	.04	.02
352	Rich Monteleone	.05	.04	.02
353	Bob Walk	.05	.04	.02
354	Monty Fariss	.10	.08	.04
355	Luis Rivera	.05	.04	.02
356	Anthony Young	.12	.09	.05
357	Geno Petralli	.05	.04	.02
358	Otis Nixon	.10	.08	.04
359	Tom Pagnozzi	.10	.08	.04
360	Reggie Sanders	.50	.40	.20
361	Lee Stevens	.05	.04	.02
362	Kent Hrbek	.15	.11	.06
363	Orlando Merced	.10	.08	.04
364	Mike Bordick	.20	.15	.08
365	Dion James	.05	.04	.02
366	Jack Clark	.10	.08	.04
367	Mike Stanley	.05	.04	.02
368	Randy Velarde	.05	.04	.02
369	Dan Pasqua	.05	.04	.02
370	Pat Listach	.25	.20	.10
371	Mike Fitzgerald	.05	.04	.02
372	Tom Foley	.05	.04	.02
373	Matt Williams	.20	.15	.06
374	Brian Hunter	.15	.11	.06
375	Joe Carter	.25	.20	.10
376	Bret Saberhagen	.15	.11	.06
377	Mike Stanton	.05	.04	.02
378	Hubie Brooks	.05	.04	.02
379	Eric Bell	.12	.09	.05
380	Walt Weiss	.10	.08	.04
381	Danny Jackson	.05	.04	.02
382	Manuel Lee	.05	.04	.02
383	Ruben Sierra	.15	.10	.05
384	Greg Swindell	.15	.11	.06
385	Ryan Bowen	.12	.09	.05
386	Kevin Ritz	.10	.08	.04
387	Curtis Wilkerson	.05	.04	.02
388	Gary Varsho	.05	.04	.02
389	Dave Hansen	.05	.04	.02
390	Bob Welch	.10	.08	.04
391	Lou Whitaker	.12	.09	.05
392	Ken Griffey, Jr.	2.00	1.25	.60
393	Mike Maddux	.05	.04	.02
394	Arthur Rhodes	.15	.11	.06
395	Chili Davis	.10	.08	.04
396	Eddie Murray	.15	.11	.06
397	Checklist	.05	.04	.02
398	Dave Cochrane	.05	.04	.02
399	Kevin Seitzer	.10	.08	.04
400	Ozzie Smith	.20	.15	.08
401	Paul Sorrento	.10	.08	.04
402	Les Lancaster	.05	.04	.02
403	Junior Noboa	.05	.04	.02
404	Dave Justice	.60	.40	.20
405	Andy Ashby	.12	.09	.05
406	Danny Tartabull	.15	.11	.06
407	Bill Swift	.10	.08	.04
408	Craig Lefferts	.10	.08	.04
409	Tom Candiotti	.10	.08	.04
410	Lance Blankenship	.05	.04	.02
411	Jeff Tackett	.15	.11	.06
412	Sammy Sosa	.25	.15	.08
413	Jody Reed	.10	.08	.04
414	Bruce Ruffin	.05	.04	.02
415	Gene Larkin	.05	.04	.02
416	John Vanderwal	.10	.08	.04
417	Tim Belcher	.10	.08	.04
418	Steve Frey	.05	.04	.02
419	Dick Schofield	.05	.04	.02
420	Jeff King	.10	.08	.04
421	Kim Batiste	.12	.09	.05
422	Jack McDowell	.15	.11	.06
423	Damon Berryhill	.05	.04	.02
424	Gary Wayne	.05	.04	.02
425	Jack Morris	.08	.06	.03
426	Moises Alou	.15	.11	.06
427	Mark McLemore	.05	.04	.02
428	Juan Guerrero	.08	.06	.03
429	Scott Scudder	.05	.04	.02
430	Eric Davis	.20	.15	.08
431	Joe Slusarski	.10	.08	.04
432	Todd Zeile	.15	.11	.06
433	Dwayne Henry	.05	.04	.02
434	Cliff Brantley	.15	.11	.06
435	Butch Henry	.15	.11	.06
436	Todd Worrell	.10	.08	.04
437	Bob Scanlan	.05	.04	.02
438	Wally Joyner	.15	.11	.06
439	John Flaherty	.12	.09	.05
440	Brian Downing	.05	.04	.02
441	Darren Lewis	.12	.09	.05
442	Gary Carter	.10	.07	.04
443	Wally Ritchie	.05	.04	.02
444	Chris Jones	.10	.08	.04
445	Jeff Kent	.15	.11	.06
446	Gary Sheffield	.25	.20	.10
447	Ron Darling	.10	.08	.04
448	Deion Sanders	.30	.25	.12
449	Andres Galarraga	.10	.08	.04
450	Chuck Finley	.10	.08	.04
451	Derek Lilliquist	.05	.04	.02
452	Carl Willis	.05	.04	.02
453	Wes Chamberlain	.10	.08	.04
454	Roger Mason	.05	.04	.02
455	Spike Owen	.05	.04	.02
456	Thomas Howard	.05	.04	.02
457	Dave Martinez	.05	.04	.02
458	Pete Incaviglia	.10	.08	.04
459	Keith Miller	.10	.08	.04
460	Mike Fetters	.05	.04	.02
461	Paul Gibson	.05	.04	.02
462	George Bell	.10	.08	.04
463	Checklist	.05	.04	.02
464	Terry Mulholland	.10	.08	.04
465	Storm Davis	.05	.04	.02
466	Gary Pettis	.05	.04	.02
467	Randy Bush	.05	.04	.02
468	Ken Hill	.12	.09	.05
469	Rheal Cormier	.12	.09	.05
470	Andy Stankiewicz	.08	.06	.03
471	Dave Burba	.05	.04	.02
472	Henry Cotto	.05	.04	.02
473	Dale Sveum	.05	.04	.02
474	Rich Gossage	.10	.08	.04
475	William Suero	.05	.04	.02
476	Doug Strange	.05	.04	.02
477	Bill Krueger	.10	.08	.04
478	John Wetteland	.15	.11	.06
479	Melido Perez	.10	.08	.04
480	Lonnie Smith	.10	.08	.04
481	Mike Jackson	.05	.04	.02
482	Mike Gardiner	.05	.04	.02
483	David Wells	.05	.04	.02
484	Barry Jones	.05	.04	.02
485	Scott Bankhead	.05	.04	.02
486	Terry Leach	.05	.04	.02
487	Vince Horseman	.08	.06	.03
488	Dave Eiland	.05	.04	.02
489	Alejandro Pena	.05	.04	.02
490	Julio Valera	.15	.11	.06

491	Joe Boever	.05	.04	.02
492	Paul Miller	.08	.06	.03
493	*Arci Cianfrocco*	.20	.15	.08
494	Dave Fleming	.25	.20	.10
495	Kyle Abbott	.12	.09	.05
496	Chad Kreuter	.05	.04	.02
497	Chris James	.05	.04	.02
498	Donnie Hill	.05	.04	.02
499	Jacob Brumfield	.15	.11	.06
500	Ricky Bones	.10	.08	.04
501	Terry Steinbach	.10	.08	.04
502	Bernard Gilkey	.10	.08	.04
503	Dennis Cook	.05	.04	.02
504	Len Dykstra	.15	.11	.06
505	Mike Bielecki	.05	.04	.02
506	Bob Kipper	.05	.04	.02
507	Jose Melendez	.15	.11	.06
508	Rick Sutcliffe	.12	.09	.05
509	Ken Patterson	.05	.04	.02
510	Andy Allanson	.05	.04	.02
511	Al Newman	.05	.04	.02
512	Mark Gardner	.05	.04	.02
513	Jeff Schaefer	.05	.04	.02
514	Jim McNamara	.15	.11	.06
515	Peter Hoy	.12	.09	.05
516	Curt Schilling	.12	.09	.05
517	Kirk McCaskill	.10	.08	.04
518	Chris Gwynn	.05	.04	.02
519	Sid Fernandez	.12	.09	.05
520	Jeff Parrett	.05	.04	.02
521	Scott Ruskin	.05	.04	.02
522	Kevin McReynolds	.12	.09	.05
523	Rick Cerone	.05	.04	.02
524	Jesse Orosco	.05	.04	.02
525	Troy Afenir	.05	.04	.02
526	John Smiley	.12	.09	.05
527	Dale Murphy	.12	.09	.05
528	Leaf Set Card	.05	.04	.02

The values quoted are intended to reflect the market price.

1992 Leaf Gold Previews

In the same format as the chase cards which would be included in the regular 1992 Leaf packs, this preview set was produced for distribution to the Donruss dealer network. Cards feature the same black borders and gold highlights as the regular-issue Leaf Gold cards, but are numbered "X of 33" on the back.

		MT	NR MT	EX
Complete Set (33):		125.00	94.00	50.00
Common Player:		2.00	1.50	.80
1	Steve Avery	3.00	2.25	1.25
2	Ryne Sandberg	8.00	6.00	3.25
3	Chris Sabo	2.00	1.50	.80
4	Jeff Bagwell	2.50	2.00	1.00
5	Darryl Strawberry	3.00	2.25	1.25
6	Bret Barbarie	2.00	1.50	.80
7	Howard Johnson	2.50	2.00	1.00
8	John Kruk	3.00	2.25	1.25
9	Andy Van Slyke	2.00	1.50	.80
10	Felix Jose	2.00	1.50	.80
11	Fred McGriff	6.00	4.50	2.50
12	Will Clark	6.00	4.50	2.50
13	Cal Ripken, Jr.	8.00	6.00	3.25
14	Phil Plantier	4.00	3.00	1.50
15	Lee Stevens	2.00	1.50	.80
16	Frank Thomas	12.00	9.00	4.75
17	Mark Whiten	2.50	2.00	1.00
18	Cecil Fielder	5.00	3.75	2.00
19	George Brett	8.00	6.00	3.25
20	Robin Yount	6.00	4.50	2.50
21	Scott Erickson	2.00	1.50	.80
22	Don Mattingly	5.00	3.75	2.00
23	Jose Canseco	6.00	4.50	2.50
24	Ken Griffey, Jr.	12.00	9.00	4.75
25	Nolan Ryan	12.00	9.00	4.75
26	Joe Carter	4.00	3.00	1.50
27	Deion Sanders	3.50	2.75	1.50
28	Dean Palmer	2.00	1.50	.80
29	Andy Benes	2.50	2.00	1.00
30	Gary DiCarcina	2.00	1.50	.80
31	Chris Hoiles	2.00	1.50	.80
32	Mark McGwire	3.50	2.75	1.50
33	Reggie Sanders	2.50	2.00	1.00

1992 Leaf Gold Edition

This set is a gold foil version of Leaf's regular 1992 set. The cards do not use the traditional silver like the regular cards do; a gold metallic ink and gold foil are used instead. A Gold Edition card was inserted in each 15-card 1992 Leaf foil pack.

	MT	NR MT	EX
Complete Set (528):	300.00	225.00	120.00
Common Player:	.50	.40	.20
Gold stars: 5X to 7X			

1992 Leaf Gold Rookies

Two dozen of the major league's most promising players are featured in this insert set. Cards 1-12 were randomly included in Series I foil packs, while cards 13-24 were in Series II packs. Cards, numbered with a BC prefix, are standard size and enhanced with gold foil.

		MT	NR MT	EX
Complete Set (24):		34.00	25.00	13.50
Common Player:		.60	.45	.25
1	Chad Curtis	3.50	2.75	1.50
2	Brent Gates	3.00	2.25	1.25
3	Pedro Martinez	2.00	1.50	.80
4	Kenny Lofton	4.50	3.50	1.75
5	Turk Wendell	.90	.70	.35
6	Mark Hutton	.75	.60	.30
7	Todd Hundley	.60	.45	.25
8	Matt Stairs	.75	.60	.30
9	Ed Taubensee	.60	.45	.25
10	David Nied	2.50	2.00	1.00
11	Salomon Torres	3.00	2.25	1.25
12	Bret Boone	1.50	1.25	.60
13	John Ruffin	1.25	.90	.50
14	Ed Martel	.75	.60	.30
15	Rick Trlicek	.75	.60	.30
16	Raul Mondesi	2.00	1.50	.80
17	Pat Mahomes	1.25	.90	.50
18	Dan Wilson	.60	.45	.25
19	Donovan Osborne	1.25	.90	.50
20	Dave Silvestri	1.00	.70	.40
21	Gary DiSarcina	.60	.45	.25
22	Denny Neagle	.60	.45	.25
23	Steve Hosey	2.00	1.50	.80
24	John Doherty	1.50	1.25	.60

1993 Leaf

Leaf issued this set in three series: two 220-card series and a 110-card update set. Card fronts have full-bleed action photos and players' names stamped in gold foil. Color-coded slate corners are used to differentiate teams. Backs have player photos against cityscapes or landmarks from the team's home city, a holographic embossed team logo and 1992 and career statistics. Cards are UV coated on both sides and are printed on premium stock. Insert sets are titled Fasttrack, Gold All-Stars, Gold Rookies, Heading for the Hall, and Frank Thomas. Players from the National League's expansion teams, the Colorado Rockies and Florida Marlins, along with the Cincinnati Reds, California Angels and Seattle Mariners were featured in Series II packs so they could be pictured in their new uniforms. The Update series included a specially numbered "DW" insert card honoring Dave Winfield's 3,000-hit landmark, plus 3,500 special Frank Thomas autographed cards.

		MT	NR MT	EX
Complete Set (550):		70.00	50.00	25.00
Common Player:		.10	.08	.04
1	Ben McDonald	.10	.08	.04
2	Sid Fernandez	.10	.08	.04
3	Juan Guzman	.15	.11	.06
4	Curt Schilling	.10	.08	.04
5	Ivan Rodriguez	.40	.30	.15
6	Don Slaught	.10	.08	.04
7	Terry Steinbach	.10	.08	.04
8	Todd Zeile	.10	.08	.04
9	Andy Stankiewicz	.10	.08	.04
10	Tim Teufel	.10	.08	.04
11	Marvin Freeman	.10	.08	.04
12	Jim Austin	.10	.08	.04
13	Bob Scanlan	.10	.08	.04
14	Rusty Meacham	.10	.08	.04
15	Casey Candaele	.10	.08	.04
16	Travis Fryman	.75	.60	.30
17	Jose Offerman	.10	.08	.04
18	Albert Belle	.75	.60	.30
19	John Vander Wahl	.10	.08	.04
20	Dan Pasqua	.10	.08	.04
21	Frank Viola	.10	.08	.04
22	Terry Mulholland	.10	.08	.04
23	Gregg Olson	.10	.08	.04
24	Randy Tomlin	.10	.08	.04
25	Todd Stottlemyre	.10	.08	.04
26	Jose Oquendo	.10	.08	.04
27	Julio Franco	.10	.08	.04
28	Tony Gwynn	.30	.25	.12
29	Ruben Sierra	.15	.11	.06
30	Bobby Thigpen	.10	.08	.04
31	Jim Bullinger	.10	.08	.04
32	Rick Aguilera	.10	.08	.04
33	Scott Servais	.10	.08	.04
34	Cal Eldred	.20	.15	.08
35	Mike Piazza	5.00	3.75	2.00
36	Brent Mayne	.10	.08	.04
37	Wil Cordero	.30	.25	.12
38	Milt Cuyler	.10	.08	.04
39	Howard Johnson	.10	.08	.04
40	Kenny Lofton	.50	.40	.20
41	Alex Fernandez	.15	.11	.06
42	Denny Neagle	.10	.08	.04
43	Tony Pena	.10	.08	.04
44	Bob Tewksbury	.10	.08	.04
45	Glenn Davis	.10	.08	.04
46	Fred McGriff	.50	.40	.20
47	John Olerud	1.00	.70	.40
48	Steve Hosey	.15	.11	.06
49	Rafael Palmeiro	.20	.15	.08
50	Dave Justice	.75	.60	.30
51	Pete Harnisch	.10	.08	.04
52	Sam Militello	.10	.08	.04
53	Orel Hershiser	.10	.08	.04
54	Pat Mahomes	.10	.08	.04
55	Greg Colbrunn	.10	.08	.04
56	Greg Vaughn	.10	.08	.04
57	Vince Coleman	.10	.08	.04
58	Brian McRae	.10	.08	.04
59	Len Dykstra	.25	.20	.10
60	Dan Gladden	.10	.08	.04
61	Ted Power	.10	.08	.04
62	Donovan Osborne	.15	.11	.06
63	Ron Karkovice	.10	.08	.04
64	Frank Seminara	.10	.08	.04
65	Bob Zupcic	.10	.08	.04
66	Kirt Manwaring	.10	.08	.04
67	Mike Devereaux	.10	.08	.04
68	Mark Lemke	.10	.08	.04
69	Devon White	.10	.08	.04
70	Sammy Sosa	.12	.09	.05
71	Pedro Astacio	.15	.11	.06
72	Dennis Eckersley	.10	.08	.04
73	Chris Nabholz	.10	.08	.04
74	Melido Perez	.10	.08	.04
75	Todd Hundley	.10	.08	.04
76	Kent Hrbek	.10	.08	.04
77	Mickey Morandini	.10	.08	.04
78	Tim McIntosh	.10	.08	.04
79	Andy Van Slyke	.10	.08	.04
80	Kevin McReynolds	.10	.08	.04
81	Mike Henneman	.10	.08	.04
82	Greg Harris	.10	.08	.04
83	Sandy Alomar Jr.	.10	.08	.04
84	Mike Jackson	.10	.08	.04
85	Ozzie Guillen	.10	.08	.04
86	Jeff Blauser	.10	.08	.04
87	John Valentin	.20	.15	.08
88	Rey Sanchez	.10	.08	.04
89	Rick Sutcliffe	.10	.08	.04
90	Luis Gonzalez	.10	.08	.04
91	Jeff Fassero	.10	.08	.04
92	Kenny Rogers	.10	.08	.04
93	Bret Saberhagen	.10	.08	.04
94	Bob Welch	.10	.08	.04
95	Darren Daulton	.15	.11	.06
96	Mike Gallego	.10	.08	.04
97	Orlando Merced	.10	.08	.04
98	Chuck Knoblauch	.15	.11	.06
99	Bernard Gilkey	.10	.08	.04
100	Billy Ashley	.50	.40	.20
101	Kevin Appier	.10	.08	.04
102	Jeff Brantley	.10	.08	.04
103	Bill Gullickson	.10	.08	.04
104	John Smoltz	.10	.08	.04
105	Paul Sorrento	.10	.08	.04
106	Steve Buechele	.10	.08	.04

107	Steve Sax	.10	.08	.04
108	Andujar Cedeno	.10	.08	.04
109	Billy Hatcher	.10	.08	.04
110	Checklist	.10	.08	.04
111	Alan Mills	.10	.08	.04
112	John Franco	.10	.08	.04
113	Jack Morris	.10	.08	.04
114	Mitch Williams	.10	.08	.04
115	Nolan Ryan	2.00	1.50	.80
116	Jay Bell	.10	.08	.04
117	Mike Bordick	.10	.08	.04
118	Geronimo Pena	.10	.08	.04
119	Danny Tartabull	.10	.08	.04
120	Checklist	.10	.08	.04
121	Steve Avery	.40	.30	.15
122	Ricky Bones	.10	.08	.04
123	Mike Morgan	.10	.08	.04
124	Jeff Montgomery	.10	.08	.04
125	Jeff Bagwell	.50	.40	.20
126	Tony Phillips	.10	.08	.04
127	Lenny Harris	.10	.08	.04
128	Glenallen Hill	.10	.08	.04
129	Marquis Grissom	.25	.20	.10
130	Bernie Williams	.10	.08	.04
131	Greg Harris	.10	.08	.04
132	Tommy Greene	.10	.08	.04
133	Chris Hoiles	.10	.08	.04
134	Bob Walk	.10	.08	.04
135	Duane Ward	.10	.08	.04
136	Tom Pagnozzi	.10	.08	.04
137	Jeff Huson	.10	.08	.04
138	Kurt Stillwell	.10	.08	.04
139	Dave Henderson	.10	.08	.04
140	Darrin Jackson	.10	.08	.04
141	Frank Castillo	.10	.08	.04
142	Scott Erickson	.10	.08	.04
143	Darryl Kile	.10	.08	.04
144	Bill Wegman	.10	.08	.04
145	Steve Wilson	.10	.08	.04
146	George Brett	.50	.40	.20
147	Moises Alou	.20	.15	.08
148	Lou Whitaker	.10	.08	.04
149	Chico Walker	.10	.08	.04
150	Jerry Browne	.10	.08	.04
151	Kirk McCaskill	.10	.08	.04
152	Zane Smith	.10	.08	.04
153	Matt Young	.10	.08	.04
154	Lee Smith	.10	.08	.04
155	Leo Gomez	.10	.08	.04
156	Dan Walters	.10	.08	.04
157	Pat Borders	.10	.08	.04
158	Matt Williams	.20	.15	.08
159	Dean Palmer	.40	.30	.15
160	John Patterson	.10	.08	.04
161	Doug Jones	.10	.08	.04
162	John Habyan	.10	.08	.04
163	Pedro Martinez	.25	.20	.10
164	Carl Willis	.10	.08	.04
165	Darrin Fletcher	.10	.08	.04
166	B.J. Surhoff	.10	.08	.04
167	Eddie Murray	.20	.15	.08
168	Keith Miller	.10	.08	.04
169	Ricky Jordan	.10	.08	.04
170	Juan Gonzalez	3.25	2.50	1.25
171	Charles Nagy	.10	.08	.04
172	Mark Clark	.10	.08	.04
173	Bobby Thigpen	.10	.08	.04
174	Tim Scott	.10	.08	.04
175	Scott Cooper	.10	.08	.04
176	Royce Clayton	.10	.08	.04
177	Brady Anderson	.10	.08	.04
178	Sid Bream	.10	.08	.04
179	Derek Bell	.20	.15	.08
180	Otis Nixon	.10	.08	.04
181	Kevin Gross	.10	.08	.04
182	Ron Darling	.10	.08	.04
183	John Wetteland	.10	.08	.04
184	Mike Stanley	.10	.08	.04
185	Jeff Kent	.10	.08	.04
186	Brian Harper	.10	.08	.04
187	Mariano Duncan	.10	.08	.04
188	Robin Yount	.50	.40	.20
189	Al Martin	.70	.50	.30
190	Eddie Zosky	.10	.08	.04
191	Mike Munoz	.10	.08	.04
192	Andy Benes	.10	.08	.04
193	Dennis Cook	.10	.08	.04
194	Bill Swift	.10	.08	.04
195	Frank Thomas	4.00	3.00	1.50
196	Damon Berryhill	.10	.08	.04
197	Mike Greenwell	.10	.08	.04
198	Mark Grace	.20	.15	.08
199	Darryl Hamilton	.10	.08	.04
200	Derrick May	.10	.08	.04
201	Ken Hill	.10	.08	.04
202	Kevin Brown	.10	.08	.04
203	Dwight Gooden	.10	.08	.04
204	Bobby Witt	.10	.08	.04
205	Juan Bell	.10	.08	.04
206	Kevin Maas	.10	.08	.04
207	Jeff King	.10	.08	.04
208	Scott Leius	.10	.08	.04
209	Rheal Cormier	.10	.08	.04
210	Darryl Strawberry	.10	.08	.04
211	Tom Gordon	.10	.08	.04
212	Bud Black	.10	.08	.04
213	Mickey Tettleton	.10	.08	.04
214	Pete Smith	.10	.08	.04
215	Felix Fermin	.10	.08	.04
216	Rick Wilkins	.10	.08	.04
217	George Bell	.10	.08	.04
218	Eric Anthony	.10	.08	.04
219	Pedro Munoz	.10	.08	.04
220	Checklist	.10	.08	.04
221	Lance Blankenship	.10	.08	.04
222	Deion Sanders	.25	.20	.10
223	Craig Biggio	.10	.08	.04
224	Ryne Sandberg	.75	.60	.30
225	Ron Gant	.15	.11	.06
226	Tom Brunansky	.10	.08	.04
227	Chad Curtis	.30	.25	.12
228	Joe Carter	.35	.25	.14
229	Brian Jordan	.10	.08	.04
230	Brett Butler	.10	.08	.04
231	Frank Bolick	.10	.08	.04
232	Rod Beck	.10	.08	.04
233	Carlos Baerga	.80	.60	.30
234	Eric Karros	.30	.25	.12
235	Jack Armstrong	.10	.08	.04
236	Bobby Bonilla	.10	.08	.04
237	Don Mattingly	.30	.25	.12
238	Jeff Gardner	.10	.08	.04
239	Dave Hollins	.30	.25	.12
240	Steve Cooke	.20	.15	.08
241	Jose Canseco	.25	.20	.10
242	Ivan Calderon	.10	.08	.04
243	Tim Belcher	.10	.08	.04
244	Freddie Benavides	.10	.08	.04
245	Roberto Alomar	.80	.60	.30
246	Rob Deer	.10	.08	.04
247	Will Clark	.40	.30	.15
248	Mike Felder	.10	.08	.04
249	Harold Baines	.10	.08	.04
250	David Cone	.10	.08	.04
251	Mark Guthrie	.10	.08	.04
252	Ellis Burks	.10	.08	.04
253	Jim Abbott	.20	.15	.08
254	Chili Davis	.10	.08	.04
255	Chris Bosio	.10	.08	.04
256	Bret Barberie	.10	.08	.04
257	Hal Morris	.10	.08	.04
258	Dante Bichette	.10	.08	.04
259	Storm Davis	.10	.08	.04
260	Gary DiSarcina	.10	.08	.04
261	Ken Caminiti	.10	.08	.04
262	Paul Molitor	.25	.20	.10
263	Joe Oliver	.10	.08	.04
264	Pat Listach	.15	.11	.06
265	Gregg Jefferies	.15	.11	.06
266	Jose Guzman	.10	.08	.04
267	Eric Davis	.10	.08	.04
268	Delino DeShields	.15	.11	.06
269	Barry Bonds	1.00	.70	.40
270	Mike Bielecki	.10	.08	.04
271	Jay Buhner	.10	.08	.04
272	*Scott Pose*	.40	.30	.15
273	Tony Fernandez	.10	.08	.04
274	Chito Martinez	.10	.08	.04
275	Phil Plantier	.25	.20	.10
276	Pete Incaviglia	.10	.08	.04
277	Carlos Garcia	.25	.20	.10
278	Tom Henke	.10	.08	.04
279	Roger Clemens	.60	.45	.25
280	Rob Dibble	.10	.08	.04
281	Daryl Boston	.10	.08	.04
282	Greg Gagne	.10	.08	.04
283	Cecil Fielder	.40	.30	.15
284	Carlton Fisk	.10	.08	.04
285	Wade Boggs	.20	.15	.08
286	Damion Easley	.25	.20	.10
287	Norm Charlton	.10	.08	.04
288	Jeff Conine	.10	.08	.04
289	Roberto Kelly	.10	.08	.04
290	Jerald Clark	.10	.08	.04
291	Rickey Henderson	.25	.20	.10
292	Chuck Finley	.10	.08	.04
293	Doug Drabek	.10	.08	.04
294	Dave Stewart	.10	.08	.04
295	Tom Glavine	.50	.40	.20
296	Jaime Navarro	.10	.08	.04
297	Ray Lankford	.10	.08	.04
298	Greg Hibbard	.10	.08	.04
299	Jody Reed	.10	.08	.04
300	Dennis Martinez	.10	.08	.04
301	Dave Martinez	.10	.08	.04
302	Reggie Jefferson	.10	.08	.04
303	*John Cummings*	.30	.25	.12
304	Orestes Destrade	.10	.08	.04
305	Mike Maddux	.10	.08	.04
306	David Segui	.10	.08	.04
307	Gary Sheffield	.30	.25	.12
308	Danny Jackson	.10	.08	.04
309	Criag Lefferts	.10	.08	.04
310	Andre Dawson	.15	.11	.06
311	Barry Larkin	.10	.08	.04
312	Alex Cole	.10	.08	.04
313	Mark Gardner	.10	.08	.04
314	Kirk Gibson	.10	.08	.04
315	Shane Mack	.10	.08	.04
316	Bo Jackson	.25	.20	.10
317	Jimmy Key	.10	.08	.04
318	Greg Myers	.10	.08	.04
319	Ken Griffey, Jr.	3.25	2.50	1.25
320	Monty Fariss	.10	.08	.04
321	Kevin Mitchell	.10	.08	.04
322	Andres Galarraga	.15	.11	.06
323	Mark McGwire	.25	.20	.10
324	Mark Langston	.10	.08	.04
325	Steve Finley	.10	.08	.04
326	Greg Maddux	.30	.25	.12
327	Dave Nilsson	.10	.08	.04
328	Ozzie Smith	.20	.15	.08
329	Candy Maldonado	.10	.08	.04
330	Checklist	.10	.08	.04
331	*Tim Pugh*	.40	.30	.15
332	Joe Girardi	.10	.08	.04
333	Junior Feliz	.10	.08	.04
334	Greg Swindell	.10	.08	.04
335	Ramon Martinez	.10	.08	.04
336	Sean Berry	.10	.08	.04
337	Joe Orsulak	.10	.08	.04
338	Wes Chamberlain	.10	.08	.04
339	Stan Belinda	.10	.08	.04
340	Checklist	.10	.08	.04
341	Bruce Hurst	.10	.08	.04
342	John Burkett	.10	.08	.04
343	Mike Mussina	.60	.45	.25
344	Scott Fletcher	.10	.08	.04
345	Rene Gonzales	.10	.08	.04
346	Roberto Hernandez	.10	.08	.04
347	Carlos Martinez	.10	.08	.04
348	Bill Krueger	.10	.08	.04
349	Felix Jose	.10	.08	.04
350	John Jaha	.25	.20	.10
351	Willie Banks	.10	.08	.04
352	Matt Nokes	.10	.08	.04
353	Kevin Seitzer	.10	.08	.04
354	Erik Hanson	.10	.08	.04
355	*David Hulse*	.30	.25	.12
356	*Domingo Martinez*	.30	.25	.12
357	Greg Olson	.10	.08	.04
358	Randy Myers	.10	.08	.04
359	Tom Browning	.10	.08	.04
360	Charlie Hayes	.10	.08	.04
361	Bryan Harvey	.10	.08	.04
362	Eddie Taubensee	.10	.08	.04
363	Tim Wallach	.10	.08	.04
364	Mel Rojas	.10	.08	.04
365	Frank Tanana	.10	.08	.04
366	John Kruk	.15	.11	.06
367	*Tim Laker*	.30	.25	.12
368	Rich Rodriguez	.10	.08	.04
369	Darren Lewis	.10	.08	.04
370	Harold Reynolds	.10	.08	.04
371	Jose Melendez	.10	.08	.04
372	Joe Grahe	.10	.08	.04
373	Lance Johnson	.10	.08	.04
374	Jose Mesa	.10	.08	.04
375	Scott Livingstone	.10	.08	.04
376	Wally Joyner	.10	.08	.04
377	Kevin Reimer	.10	.08	.04
378	Kirby Puckett	.60	.45	.25
379	Paul O'Neill	.10	.08	.04
380	Randy Johnson	.15	.11	.06
381	Manuel Lee	.10	.08	.04
382	Dick Schofield	.10	.08	.04
383	Darren Holmes	.10	.08	.04
384	Charlie Hough	.10	.08	.04
385	John Orton	.10	.08	.04
386	Edgar Martinez	.10	.08	.04
387	Terry Pendleton	.10	.08	.04
388	Dan Plesac	.10	.08	.04
389	Jeff Reardon	.10	.08	.04
390	David Nied	.60	.45	.25
391	Dave Magadan	.10	.08	.04
392	Larry Walker	.25	.20	.10
393	Ben Rivera	.10	.08	.04
394	Lonnie Smith	.10	.08	.04
395	Craig Shipley	.10	.08	.04
396	Willie McGee	.10	.08	.04
397	Arthur Rhodes	.10	.08	.04
398	Mike Stanton	.10	.08	.04
399	Luis Polonia	.10	.08	.04
400	Jack McDowell	.25	.20	.10
401	Mike Moore	.10	.08	.04
402	Jose Lind	.10	.08	.04
403	Bill Spiers	.10	.08	.04
404	Kevin Tapani	.10	.08	.04
405	Spike Owen	.10	.08	.04
406	Tino Martinez	.10	.08	.04
407	Charlie Leibrandt	.10	.08	.04
408	Ed Sprague	.10	.08	.04
409	Bryn Smith	.10	.08	.04
410	Benito Santiago	.10	.08	.04
411	Jose Rijo	.10	.08	.04
412	Pete O'Brien	.10	.08	.04
413	Willie Wilson	.10	.08	.04
414	Bip Roberts	.10	.08	.04
415	Eric Young	.40	.30	.15
416	Walt Weiss	.10	.08	.04
417	Milt Thompson	.10	.08	.04
418	Chris Sabo	.10	.08	.04
419	Scott Sanderson	.10	.08	.04
420	Tim Raines	.10	.08	.04
421	Alan Trammell	.10	.08	.04
422	Mike Macfarlane	.10	.08	.04
423	Dave Winfield	.40	.30	.15
424	Bob Wickman	.30	.25	.12
425	David Valle	.10	.08	.04
426	Gary Redus	.10	.08	.04
427	Turner Ward	.10	.08	.04
428	Reggie Sanders	.25	.20	.10
429	Todd Worrell	.10	.08	.04
430	Julio Valera	.10	.08	.04
431	Cal Ripken, Jr.	.80	.60	.30
432	Mo Vaughn	.40	.30	.15
433	John Smiley	.10	.08	.04
434	Omar Vizquel	.10	.08	.04
435	Billy Ripken	.10	.08	.04
436	Cory Snyder	.10	.08	.04
437	Carlos Quintana	.10	.08	.04
438	Omar Olivares	.10	.08	.04
439	Robin Ventura	.50	.40	.20
440	Checklist	.10	.08	.04
441	Kevin Higgins	.10	.08	.04
442	Carlos Hernandez	.10	.08	.04
443	Dan Peltier	.15	.11	.06
444	Derek Lilliquist	.10	.08	.04
445	Tim Salmon	4.00	3.00	1.50
446	*Sherman Obando*	.25	.20	.10
447	Pat Kelly	.15	.11	.06
448	Todd Van Poppel	.25	.20	.10
449	Mark Whiten	.10	.08	.04
450	Checklist	.10	.08	.04
451	Pat Meares	.25	.20	.10
452	*Tony Tarasco*	.75	.60	.30
453	Chris Gwynn	.10	.08	.04
454	Armando Reynoso	.15	.11	.06
455	Danny Darwin	.10	.08	.04
456	Willie Greene	.25	.20	.10
457	Mike Blowers	.10	.08	.04
458	*Kevin Roberson*	.60	.45	.25
459	*Graeme Lloyd*	.25	.20	.10
460	David West	.10	.08	.04

461	Joey Cora	.10	.08	.04
462	Alex Arias	.10	.08	.04
463	Chad Kreuter	.10	.08	.04
464	Mike Lansing	.50	.40	.20
465	Mike Timlin	.10	.08	.04
466	Paul Wagner	.10	.08	.04
467	Mark Portugal	.10	.08	.04
468	Jim Leyritz	.10	.08	.04
469	Ryan Klesko	.60	.45	.25
470	Mario Diaz	.10	.08	.04
471	Guillermo Velasquez	.15	.11	.06
472	Fernando Valenzuela	.15	.11	.06
473	Raul Mondesi	.60	.45	.25
474	Mike Pagliarulo	.10	.08	.04
475	Chris Hammond	.10	.08	.04
476	Torey Lovullo	.10	.08	.04
477	Trevor Wilson	.10	.08	.04
478	*Marcos Armas*	.40	.30	.15
479	Dave Gallagher	.10	.08	.04
480	Jeff Treadway	.10	.08	.04
481	Jeff Branson	.10	.08	.04
482	Dickie Thon	.10	.08	.04
483	Eduardo Perez	1.00	.75	.40
484	David Wells	.10	.08	.04
485	Brian Williams	.10	.08	.04
486	Domingo Cedeno	.20	.15	.08
487	Tom Candiotti	.10	.08	.04
488	Steve Frey	.10	.08	.04
489	Greg McMichael	.25	.20	.10
490	Marc Newfield	.20	.15	.08
491	Larry Andersen	.10	.08	.04
492	Damon Buford	.15	.11	.06
493	Ricky Gutierrez	.10	.08	.04
494	Jeff Russell	.10	.08	.04
495	Vinny Castilla	.10	.08	.04
496	Wilson Alvarez	.15	.11	.06
497	Scott Bullett	.10	.08	.04
498	Larry Casian	.15	.11	.06
499	Jose Vizcaino	.10	.08	.04
500	J.T. Snow	.75	.60	.30
501	Bryan Hickerson	.10	.08	.04
502	Jeremy Hernandez	.20	.15	.08
503	Jeromy Burnitz	.25	.20	.10
504	Steve Farr	.10	.08	.04
505	J. Owens	.35	.25	.14
506	Craig Paquette	.10	.08	.04
507	Jim Eisenreich	.10	.08	.04
508	Matt Whiteside	.15	.11	.06
509	Luis Aquino	.10	.08	.04
510	Mike LaValliere	.10	.08	.04
511	Jim Gott	.10	.08	.04
512	Mark McLemore	.10	.08	.04
513	Randy Milligan	.10	.08	.04
514	Gary Gaetti	.15	.11	.06
515	Lou Frazier	.20	.15	.08
516	Rich Amaral	.10	.08	.04
517	Gene Harris	.10	.08	.04
518	Aaron Sele	2.00	1.50	.80
519	Mark Wohlers	.10	.08	.04
520	Scott Kamieniecki	.15	.11	.06
521	Kent Mercker	.10	.08	.04
522	Jim Deshaies	.10	.08	.04
523	Kevin Stocker	1.00	.70	.40
524	Jason Bere	1.50	1.25	.60
525	Tim Bogar	.15	.11	.06
526	Brad Pennington	.15	.11	.06
527	Curt Leskanic	.15	.11	.06
528	Wayne Kirby	.10	.08	.04
529	Tim Costo	.10	.08	.04
530	Doug Henry	.10	.08	.04
531	Trevor Hoffman	.20	.15	.08
532	Kelly Gruber	.10	.08	.04
533	Mike Harkey	.10	.08	.04
534	John Doherty	.10	.08	.04
535	Erik Pappas	.15	.11	.06
536	Brent Gates	.15	.11	.06
537	Roger McDowell	.10	.08	.04
538	Chris Haney	.10	.08	.04
539	Blas Minor	.10	.08	.04
540	Pat Hentgen	.20	.15	.08
541	Chuck Carr	.20	.15	.08
542	Doug Strange	.10	.08	.04
543	Xavier Hernandez	.10	.08	.04
544	Paul Quantrill	.10	.08	.04
545	Anthony Young	.15	.11	.06
546	Bret Boone	.15	.11	.06
547	Dwight Smith	.10	.08	.04
548	Bobby Munoz	.20	.15	.08
549	Russ Springer	.10	.08	.04
550	Roger Pavlik	.10	.08	.04
----	Dave Winfield (3000 Major League Career Hits)	3.00	2.25	1.25
----	Autographed Frank Thomas	300.00	225.00	125.00

1993 Leaf Fasttrack

This 20-card insert set was released in two series; cards 1-10 were randomly included in Leaf Series I retail packs, while 11-20 were in Series II packs. Card fronts and backs are similar with a player photo and a diagonal white strip with "on the Fasttrack" printed in black and red. Fronts have the gold embossed Leaf logo, backs have the silver holographic team logo.

		MT	NR MT	EX
	Complete Set (20):	80.00	60.00	32.00
	Common Player:	2.00	1.50	.80
1	Frank Thomas	20.00	15.00	8.00
2	Tim Wakefield	2.00	1.50	.80
3	Kenny Lofton	5.00	3.75	2.00
4	Mike Mussina	6.00	4.50	2.50
5	Juan Gonzalez	18.00	13.50	7.25
6	Chuck Knoblauch	2.00	1.50	.80
7	Eric Karros	6.00	4.50	2.50
8	Ray Lankford	3.00	2.25	1.25
9	Juan Guzman	3.00	2.25	1.25
10	Pat Listach	2.00	1.50	.80
11	Carlos Baerga	7.00	5.25	2.75
12	Felix Jose	2.00	1.50	.80
13	Steve Avery	3.00	2.25	1.25
14	Robin Ventura	3.00	2.25	1.25
15	Ivan Rodriguez	4.00	3.00	1.50
16	Cal Eldred	3.00	2.25	1.25
17	Jeff Bagwell	4.00	3.00	1.50
18	David Justice	5.00	3.75	2.00
19	Travis Fryman	5.00	3.75	2.00
20	Marquis Grissom	3.00	2.25	1.25

1993 Leaf Gold All-Stars

Cards 1-10 in this insert set were randomly inserted one per Leaf Series I jumbo packs, while cards 11-20 were in Series II jumbo packs. Cards feature two players per card, one on each side. Only one side is numbered, but both sides have gold foil.

		MT	NR MT	EX
	Complete Set (20):	35.00	26.00	14.00
	Common Player:	1.00	.70	.40
1	Ivan Rodriquez, Darren Daulton	1.50	1.25	.60
2	Don Mattingly, Fred McGriff	3.00	2.25	1.25
3	Cecil Fielder, Jeff Bagwell	2.50	2.00	1.00
4	Carlos Baerga, Ryne Sandberg	4.00	3.00	1.50
5	Chuck Knoblauch, Delino DeShields	1.25	.90	.50
6	Robin Ventura, Terry Pendleton	1.50	1.25	.60
7	Ken Griffey Jr., Andy Van Slyke	6.00	4.50	2.50
8	Joe Carter, Dave Justice	3.00	2.25	1.25
9	Jose Canseco, Tony Gwynn	1.25	.90	.50
10	Dennis Eckersley, Rob Dibble	1.00	.70	.40
11	Mark McGwire, Will Clark	2.00	1.50	.80
12	Frank Thomas, Mark Grace	7.50	5.75	3.00
13	Roberto Alomar, Craig Biggio	2.50	2.00	1.00
14	Barry Larkin, Cal Ripken Jr.	3.00	2.25	1.25
15	Gary Sheffield, Edgar Martinez	1.25	.90	.50
16	Juan Gonzalez, Barry Bonds	8.00	6.00	3.25
17	Kirby Puckett, Marquis Grissom	3.00	2.25	1.25
18	Jim Abbott, Tom Glavine	1.50	1.25	.60
19	Nolan Ryan, Greg Maddux	5.00	3.75	2.00
20	Roger Clemens, Doug Drabek	2.00	1.50	.80

1993 Leaf Gold Rookies

These cards, numbered 1 of 20 etc., feature 20 1993 rookies. Cards were randomly inserted into hobby foil packs, 10 different cards per series. Card fronts feature action photos, while the backs show a player photo against a landmark from his team's city.

		MT	NR MT	EX
	Complete Set (20):	60.00	45.00	24.00
	Common Player:	1.25	.90	.50
1	Kevin Young	3.00	2.25	1.25
2	Wil Cordero	2.00	1.50	.80
3	Mark Kiefer	1.25	.90	.50
4	Gerald Williams	1.25	.90	.50
5	Brandon Wilson	1.25	.90	.50
6	Greg Gohr	1.25	.90	.50
7	Ryan Thompson	2.00	1.50	.80
8	Tim Wakefield	1.50	1.25	.60
9	Troy Neel	2.50	2.00	1.00
10	Tim Salmon	18.00	13.50	7.25
11	Kevin Rogers	1.50	1.25	.60
12	Rod Bolton	1.25	.90	.50
13	Ken Ryan	1.25	.90	.50
14	Phil Hiatt	2.50	2.00	1.00
15	Rene Arocha	2.50	2.00	1.00
16	Nigel Wilson	6.00	4.50	2.50
17	J.T. Snow	5.00	3.75	2.00
18	Benji Gil	2.50	2.00	1.00
19	Chipper Jones	7.50	5.75	3.00
20	Darrell Sherman	1.25	.90	.50

1993 Leaf Heading for the Hall

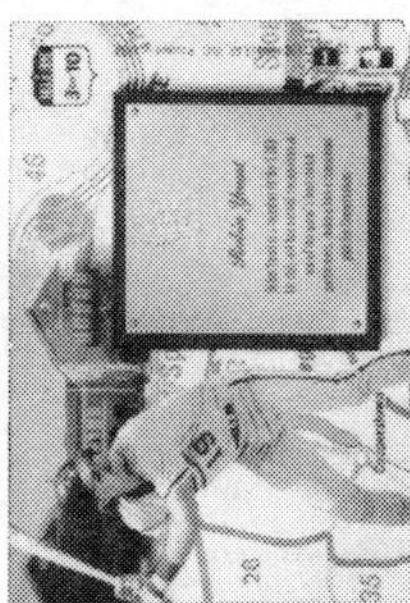

Ten players on the way to the Baseball Hall of Fame are featured in this insert set. Series I Leaf packs had cards 1-5 randomly included; Series II packs had cards 6-10. The front of the card states the player is Heading for the Hall.

		MT	NR MT	EX
	Complete Set (10):	45.00	34.00	18.00
	Common Player:	2.50	2.00	1.00
1	Nolan Ryan	15.00	11.00	6.00
2	Tony Gwynn	2.50	2.00	1.00
3	Robin Yount	4.00	3.00	1.50
4	Eddie Murray	2.50	2.00	1.00
5	Cal Ripken, Jr.	6.00	4.50	2.50
6	Roger Clemens	4.00	3.00	1.50
7	George Brett	5.00	3.75	2.00
8	Ryne Sandberg	6.00	4.50	2.50
9	Kirby Puckett	5.00	3.75	2.00
10	Ozzie Smith	2.50	2.00	1.00

1993 Leaf Frank Thomas

Leaf signed Frank Thomas as its spokesman for 1993, and honored him with a 10-card insert set. Cards 1-5 were randomly included in Series I packs; cards 6-10 were in Series II packs. A custom designed "Frank" logo in a holographic foil stamp is featured on each card front which includes a one-word character trait. On back is a color portrait photo of Thomas superimposed on a Chicago skyline. A paragraph on back describes how the charater trait on front applies to Thomas.

		MT	NR MT	EX
Complete Set (10):		50.00	35.00	20.00
Common Thomas:		5.00	3.00	1.50
Autographed Thomas:		300.00	225.00	125.00
1	Aggressive	5.00	3.75	2.00
2	Serious	5.00	3.75	2.00
3	Intense	5.00	3.75	2.00
4	Confident	5.00	3.75	2.00
5	Assertive	5.00	3.75	2.00
6	Power	5.00	3.75	2.00
7	Control	5.00	3.75	2.00
8	Strength	5.00	3.75	2.00
9	Concentration	5.00	3.75	2.00
10	Preparation	5.00	3.75	2.00

1993 Leaf Update Gold All-Stars

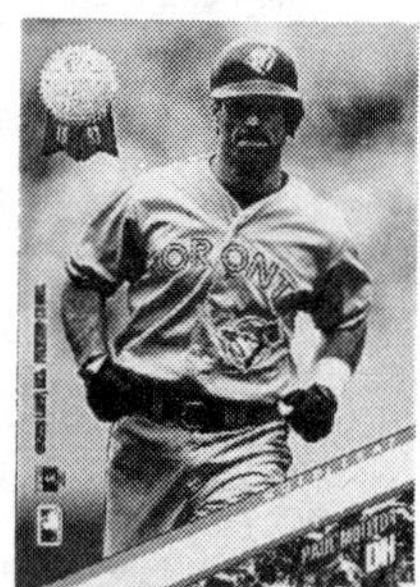

These 10 cards, featuring 20 all-stars, were randomly inserted in Leaf Update packs. Each card features two players, one on each side. Cards are distinguished from the regular Gold All-Stars by indicating on the front the card is number X of 10, with a tiny white "Update" in the red stripe above the card number.

		MT	NR MT	EX
Complete Set (10):		20.00	15.00	8.00
Common Player:		.75	.60	.30
1	Mark Langston/Terry Mulholland	.75	.60	.30
2	Ivan Rodriguez/Darren Daulton	1.50	1.25	.60
3	John Olerud/John Kruk	3.00	2.25	1.25
4	Roberto Alomar/Ryne Sandberg	4.00	3.00	1.50
5	Wade Boggs/Gary Sheffield	1.25	.90	.50
6	Cal Ripken, Jr./Barry Larkin	3.00	2.25	1.25
7	Kirby Puckett/Barry Bonds	7.50	5.75	3.00
8	Ken Griffey, Jr./Marquis Grissom	5.00	3.75	2.00
9	Joe Carter/Dave Justice	3.00	2.25	1.25
10	Paul Molitor/Mark Grace	3.00	2.25	1.25

1993 Leaf Update Gold Rookies

These five cards were randomly inserted in Leaf Update packs. Cards are similiar in design to the regular Gold Rookies cards, except the logo on the back indicates they are from the Update series.

		MT	NR MT	EX
Complete Set (5):		35.00	26.00	14.00
Common Player:		3.00	2.25	1.25
1	Allen Watson	5.00	3.75	2.00
2	Jeffrey Hammonds	7.50	5.75	3.00
3	David McCarty	4.00	3.00	1.50
4	Mike Piazza	25.00	18.50	10.00
5	Roberto Meija	3.00	2.25	1.25

1993 Leaf Update Frank Thomas Super

This 10-card insert set features Leaf's 1993 spokesman, Frank Thomas. Cards, which measure 5" by 7", were included one per every Leaf Update

foil box and are identical to the inserts found in Series I and II except in size. Cards are individually numbered. Thomas autographed 3,500 cards.

		MT	NR MT	EX
Complete Set (10):		90.00	67.00	36.00
Common Thomas:		10.00	7.50	4.00
1	Aggressive	10.00	7.50	4.00
2	Serious	10.00	7.50	4.00
3	Intense	10.00	7.50	4.00
4	Confident	10.00	7.50	4.00
5	Assertive	10.00	7.50	4.00
6	Power	10.00	7.50	4.00
7	Control	10.00	7.50	4.00
8	Strength	10.00	7.50	4.00
9	Concentration	10.00	7.50	4.00
10	Preparation	10.00	7.50	4.00

1994 Leaf Promos

Identical in format to the regular issue, this nine-card set was produced as a preview for the 1994 Leaf cards. The only differences on the promo cards are a large, black "Promotional Sample" notice over-printed diagonally on both the front and back of the cards. Instead of the regular card numbers, the promos are numbered "X of 9" at top to the left of the team logo hologram.

		MT	NR MT	EX
Complete Set (9):		35.00	26.00	14.00
Common Player:		3.00	2.25	1.25
1	Roberto Alomar	4.00	3.00	1.50
2	Darren Daulton	3.00	2.25	1.25
3	Ken Griffey, Jr.	7.00	5.25	2.75
4	David Justice	4.00	3.00	1.50
5	Don Mattingly	4.00	3.00	1.50
6	Mike Piazza	4.00	3.00	1.50
7	Cal Ripken, Jr.	6.00	4.50	2.50
8	Ryne Sandberg	6.00	4.50	2.50
9	Frank Thomas	7.00	5.25	2.75

1994 Leaf

Donruss returned its premium-brand Leaf set in 1994 with an announced 25% production cut from the previous season, to fewer than 20,000 20-box cases of each 220-card series. Game-action photos dominate the fronts of the '94 Leaf cards, borderless at the top and sides. At bottom are team color-coded faux-marble borders with the player's name (last name in gold foil) and team. An embossed gold-foil Leaf logo is at lower-left. Backs have a background of the player's home stadium with another action photo superimposed. In a ticket-stub device at upper-left is a portrait photo and a few personal numbers. Previous season and career stats are in white stripes at bottom. The team logo is presented in holographic foil at upper-right. To feature 1994's new stadiums and uniforms, cards featuring Indians, Rangers, Brewers and Astros were included only in the second series. Seven different types of insert cards were produced and distributed among the various types of Leaf packaging.

		MT	NR MT	EX
Complete Set (220):		18.00	13.50	7.25
Common Player:		.10	.08	.04
1	Cal Ripken, Jr.	.50	.40	.20
2	Tony Tarasco	.35	.25	.14
3	Joe Girardi	.10	.08	.04
4	Bernie Williams	.10	.08	.04
5	Chad Kreuter	.10	.08	.04
6	Troy Neel	.15	.11	.06
7	Tom Pagnozzi	.10	.08	.04
8	Kirk Rueter	.40	.30	.15
9	Chris Bosio	.10	.08	.04
10	Dwight Gooden	.12	.09	.05
11	Mariano Duncan	.10	.08	.04
12	Jay Bell	.10	.08	.04
13	Lance Johnson	.10	.08	.04
14	Richie Lewis	.10	.08	.04
15	Dave Martinez	.10	.08	.04
16	Orel Hershiser	.10	.08	.04
17	Rob Butler	.20	.15	.08
18	Glenallen Hill	.10	.08	.04
19	Chad Curtis	.12	.09	.05
20	Mike Stanton	.10	.08	.04
21	Tim Wallach	.10	.08	.04
22	Milt Thompson	.10	.08	.04
23	Kevin Young	.10	.08	.04
24	John Smiley	.10	.08	.04
25	Jeff Montgomery	.10	.08	.04
26	Robin Ventura	.20	.15	.08
27	Scott Lydy	.10	.08	.04
28	Todd Stottlemyre	.10	.08	.04
29	Mark Whiten	.10	.08	.04
30	Robby Thompson	.10	.08	.04
31	Bobby Bonilla	.12	.09	.05
32	Andy Ashby	.10	.08	.04
33	Greg Myers	.10	.08	.04
34	Billy Hatcher	.10	.08	.04
35	Brad Holman	.10	.08	.04
36	Mark McLemore	.10	.08	.04
37	Scott Sanders	.10	.08	.04
38	Jim Abbott	.12	.09	.05
39	David Wells	.10	.08	.04
40	Roberto Kelly	.10	.08	.04
41	Jeff Conine	.10	.08	.04
42	Sean Berry	.10	.08	.04
43	Mark Grace	.12	.09	.05
44	Eric Young	.10	.08	.04
45	Rick Aguilera	.10	.08	.04
46	Chipper Jones	.30	.25	.12
47	Mel Rojas	.10	.08	.04
48	Ryan Thompson	.10	.08	.04
49	Al Martin	.10	.08	.04
50	Cecil Fielder	.20	.15	.08
51	Pat Kelly	.10	.08	.04
52	Kevin Tapani	.10	.08	.04
53	Tim Costo	.10	.08	.04
54	Dave Hollins	.10	.08	.04
55	Kirt Manwaring	.10	.08	.04
56	Gregg Jefferies	.10	.08	.04
57	Ron Darling	.10	.08	.04
58	Bill Haselman	.10	.08	.04
59	Phil Plantier	.12	.09	.05
60	Frank Viola	.10	.08	.04
61	Todd Zeile	.10	.08	.04
62	Bret Barberie	.10	.08	.04
63	Roberto Mejia	.10	.08	.04
64	Chuck Knoblach	.12	.09	.05
65	Jose Lind	.10	.08	.04
66	Brady Anderson	.10	.08	.04
67	Ruben Sierra	.12	.09	.05
68	Jose Vizcaino	.10	.08	.04
69	Joe Grahe	.10	.08	.04
70	Kevin Appier	.10	.08	.04
71	Wilson Alvarez	.12	.09	.05
72	Tom Candiotti	.10	.08	.04
73	John Burkett	.10	.08	.04
74	Anthony Young	.10	.08	.04
75	Scott Cooper	.10	.08	.04
76	Nigel Wilson	.15	.11	.06
77	John Valentin	.10	.08	.04
78	Dave McCarty	.15	.11	.06
79	Archi Cianfrocco	.10	.08	.04
80	Lou Whitaker	.10	.08	.04
81	Dante Bichette	.10	.08	.04
82	Mark Dewey	.10	.08	.04
83	Danny Jackson	.10	.08	.04
84	Harold Baines	.10	.08	.04
85	Todd Benzinger	.10	.08	.04
86	Damion Easley	.12	.09	.05
87	Danny Cox	.10	.08	.04
88	Jose Bautista	.10	.08	.04
89	Mike Lansing	.15	.11	.06

90	Phil Hiatt	.20	.15	.08
91	Tim Pugh	.10	.08	.04
92	Tino Martinez	.10	.08	.04
93	Raul Mondesi	.50	.40	.20
94	Greg Maddux	.25	.20	.10
95	Al Leiter	.10	.08	.04
96	Benito Santiago	.10	.08	.04
97	Len Dykstra	.15	.11	.06
98	Sammy Sosa	.12	.09	.05
99	Tim Bogar	.10	.08	.04
100	Checklist	.10	.08	.04
101	Deion Sanders	.25	.20	.10
102	Bobby Witt	.10	.08	.04
103	Wil Cordero	.15	.11	.06
104	Rich Amaral	.10	.08	.04
105	Mike Mussina	.30	.25	.12
106	Reggie Sanders	.12	.09	.05
107	Ozzie Guillen	.10	.08	.04
108	Paul O'Neill	.10	.08	.04
109	Tim Salmon	1.50	1.25	.60
110	Rheal Cormier	.10	.08	.04
111	Billy Ashley	.25	.20	.10
112	Jeff Kent	.10	.08	.04
113	Derek Bell	.10	.08	.04
114	Danny Darwin	.10	.08	.04
115	Chip Hale	.10	.08	.04
116	Tim Raines	.10	.08	.04
117	Ed Sprague	.10	.08	.04
118	Darrin Fletcher	.10	.08	.04
119	Darren Holmes	.10	.08	.04
120	Alan Trammell	.10	.08	.04
121	Don Mattingly	.25	.20	.10
122	Greg Gagne	.10	.08	.04
123	Jose Offerman	.10	.08	.04
124	Joe Orsulak	.10	.08	.04
125	Jack McDowell	.12	.09	.05
126	Barry Larkin	.10	.08	.04
127	Ben McDonald	.15	.11	.06
128	Mike Bordick	.10	.08	.04
129	Devon White	.12	.09	.05
130	Mike Perez	.10	.08	.04
131	Jay Buhner	.10	.08	.04
132	Phil Leftwich	.10	.08	.04
133	Tommy Greene	.10	.08	.04
134	Charlie Hayes	.10	.08	.04
135	Don Slaught	.10	.08	.04
136	Mike Gallego	.10	.08	.04
137	Dave Winfield	.20	.15	.08
138	Steve Avery	.20	.15	.08
139	Derrick May	.10	.08	.04
140	Bryan Harvey	.10	.08	.04
141	Wally Joyner	.10	.08	.04
142	Andre Dawson	.12	.09	.05
143	Andy Benes	.10	.08	.04
144	John Franco	.10	.08	.04
145	Jeff King	.10	.08	.04
146	Joe Oliver	.10	.08	.04
147	Bill Gullickson	.10	.08	.04
148	Armando Reynoso	.10	.08	.04
149	Dave Fleming	.10	.08	.04
150	Checklist	.10	.08	.04
151	Todd Van Poppel	.12	.09	.05
152	Bernard Gilkey	.10	.08	.04
153	Kevin Gross	.10	.08	.04
154	Mike Devereaux	.10	.08	.04
155	Tim Wakefield	.10	.08	.04
156	Andres Galarraga	.10	.08	.04
157	Pat Meares	.10	.08	.04
158	Jim Leyritz	.10	.08	.04
159	Mike Macfarlane	.10	.08	.04
160	Tony Phillips	.10	.08	.04
161	Brent Gates	.15	.11	.06
162	Mark Langston	.10	.08	.04
163	Allen Watson	.40	.30	.15
164	Randy Johnson	.10	.08	.04
165	Doug Brocail	.10	.08	.04
166	Rob Dibble	.10	.08	.04
167	Roberto Hernandez	.10	.08	.04
168	Felix Jose	.10	.08	.04
169	Steve Cooke	.10	.08	.04
170	Darren Daulton	.12	.09	.05
171	Eric Karros	.12	.09	.05
172	Geronimo Pena	.10	.08	.04
173	Gary DiSarcina	.10	.08	.04
174	Marquis Grissom	.12	.09	.05
175	Joey Cora	.10	.08	.04
176	Jim Eisenreich	.10	.08	.04
177	Brad Pennington	.10	.08	.04
178	Terry Steinbach	.10	.08	.04
179	Pat Borders	.10	.08	.04
180	Steve Buechele	.10	.08	.04
181	Jeff Fassero	.10	.08	.04
182	Mike Greenwell	.10	.08	.04
183	Mike Henneman	.10	.08	.04
184	Ron Karkovice	.10	.08	.04
185	Pat Hentgen	.12	.09	.05
186	Jose Guzman	.10	.08	.04
187	Brett Butler	.10	.08	.04
188	Charlie Hough	.10	.08	.04
189	Terry Pendleton	.10	.08	.04
190	Melido Perez	.10	.08	.04
191	Orestes Destrade	.10	.08	.04
192	Mike Morgan	.10	.08	.04
193	Joe Carter	.25	.20	.10
194	Jeff Blauser	.10	.08	.04
195	Chris Hoiles	.10	.08	.04
196	Ricky Gutierrez	.10	.08	.04
197	Mike Moore	.10	.08	.04
198	Carl Willis	.10	.08	.04
199	Aaron Sele	.50	.40	.20
200	Checklist	.10	.08	.04
201	Tim Naehring	.10	.08	.04
202	Scott Livingstone	.10	.08	.04
203	Luis Alicea	.15	.11	.06
204	*Torey Lovullo*	.25	.20	.10
205	Jim Gott	.15	.11	.06
206	Bob Wickman	.10	.08	.04
207	Greg McMichael	.15	.11	.06
208	Scott Brosius	.10	.08	.04
209	Chris Gwynn	.10	.08	.04
210	Steve Sax	.10	.08	.04
211	Dick Schofield	.10	.08	.04
212	Robb Nen	.15	.11	.06
213	Ben Rivera	.10	.08	.04
214	Vinny Castilla	.10	.08	.04
215	Jamie Moyer	.15	.11	.06
216	Wally Whitehurst	.10	.08	.04
217	Frank Castillo	.10	.08	.04
218	Mike Blowers	.10	.08	.04
219	Tim Scott	.15	.11	.06
220	Paul Wagner	.15	.11	.06

1994 Leaf Clean-Up Crew

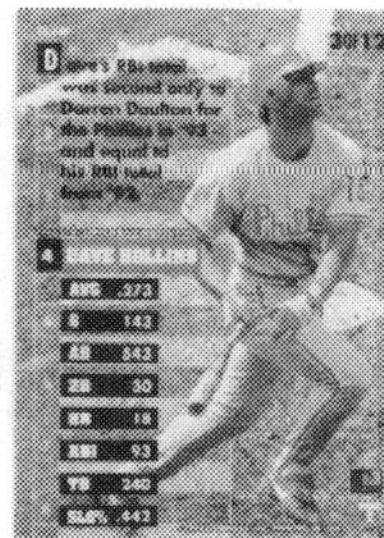

The number four spot in the line-up is featured on this 12-card insert set (six per series) found only in magazine distributor packaging.

		MT	NR MT	EX
Complete Set (6):		10.00	7.50	4.00
Common Player:		1.50	1.25	.60
1	Larry Walker	2.00	1.50	.80
2	Andres Galarraga	2.00	1.50	.80
3	Dave Hollins	1.50	1.25	.60
4	Bobby Bonilla	1.75	1.25	.70
5	Cecil Fielder	2.50	2.00	1.00
6	Danny Tartabull	1.50	1.25	.60

1994 Leaf 5th Anniversary

The card which insured the success of the Leaf brand name when it was re-introduced in 1990, the Frank Thomas rookie card, was re-issued in a 5th anniversary commemorative form as an insert in the 1994 set. On the chase card, silver foil rays emanate from the White Sox logo at lower-left, while a silver-foil 5th anniversary logo at upper-right replaces the Leaf script on the 1990 version. The card back carries a 1994 copyright. The Thomas anniversary card is found on average of once every 36 Series I hobby packs.

		MT	NR MT	EX
Complete Set:		5.00	3.75	2.00
300	Frank Thomas	5.00	3.75	2.00

1994 Leaf Gamers

Leaf jumbo packs are the exclusive venue for the six cards of this insert set which were issued in each series.

		MT	NR MT	EX
Complete Set (6):		25.00	18.00	10.00
Common Player:		1.50	1.25	.60
1	Ken Griffey, Jr.	12.00	9.00	4.75
2	Len Dykstra	3.50	2.75	1.50
3	Juan Gonzalez	8.00	6.00	3.25
4	Don Mattingly	6.00	4.50	2.50
5	Dave Justice	4.00	3.00	1.50
6	Mark Grace	1.50	1.25	.60

1994 Gold Leaf Rookies

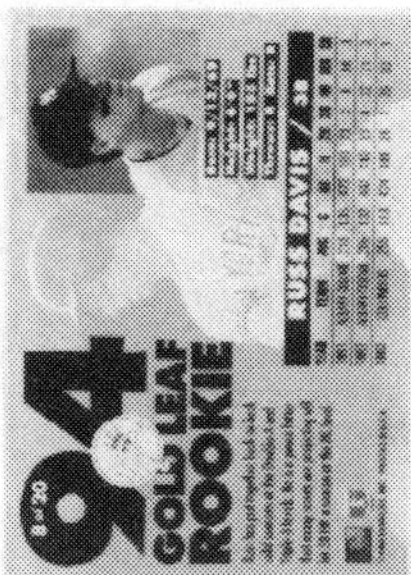

A gold-foil rendered stadium background and huge black "94 Gold Leaf Rookie" serve as a backdrop for a player photo on these insert cards found at the rate of about one per 18 foil packs. The player's name and team are in silver at bottom and there is a gold-foil Leaf seal at upper-right. Horizontal backs have a ghosted action photo of the player in the background. A portrait photo is in the upper-right corner, above some personal data and stats. Cards are numbered "X of 20".

		MT	NR MT	EX
Complete Set (10):		40.00	30.00	15.00
Common Player:		2.00	1.50	.80
1	Javier Lopez	8.00	6.00	3.25
2	Rondell White	3.50	2.75	1.50
3	Butch Huskey	2.00	1.50	.80
4	Midre Cummings	2.00	1.50	.80
5	Scott Ruffcorn	3.00	2.25	1.25
6	Manny Ramirez	8.00	6.00	3.25
7	Danny Bautista	2.00	1.50	.80
8	Russ Davis	2.00	1.50	.80
9	Steve Karsay	3.00	2.25	1.25
10	Carlos Delgado	10.00	7.50	4.00

1994 Leaf Gold Stars

The "Cadillac" of 1994 Leaf inserts, this 15-card series (#1-8 in Series I; 9-15 in Series II) is found on average only one card per 90 packs. The edition of 10,000 of each player's card is serially numbered. Fronts feature a rather small photo in a diamond-shaped frame against a green marble-look background. The border, facsimile autograph and several other graphic elements are presented in prismatic foil. The back repeats the basic front design with a few sentences about the player and a serial number strip at bottom.

		MT	NR MT	EX
Complete Set (8):		250.00	185.00	100.00
Common Player:		20.00	15.00	8.00
1	Roberto Alomar	35.00	26.00	14.00
2	Barry Bonds	55.00	41.00	22.00
3	David Justice	40.00	30.00	15.00
4	Ken Griffey, Jr.	100.00	75.00	40.00
5	Len Dykstra	25.00	18.00	10.00
6	Don Mattingly	40.00	30.00	15.00
7	Andres Galarraga	20.00	15.00	8.00
8	Greg Maddux	35.00	26.00	14.00

1994 Leaf Slide Show

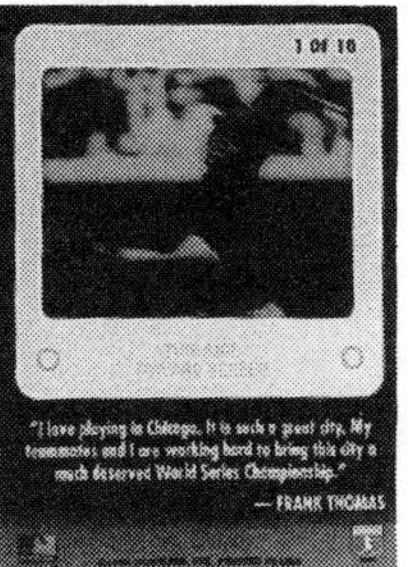

A new level of high-tech insert card production values was reached with the creation of Leaf's "Slide Show" chase cards. The cards feature a printed acetate center sandwiched between cardboard front and back. The see-through acetate portion of the card is bordered in white to give it the appearance of a slide. The player's name, location and date of the photo are printed on the front of the "slide," with the card number on back. The pseudo-slide is bordered in black, with a blue "Slide Show" logo at bottom and a silver-foil Leaf logo. Backs of the Slide Show inserts have a few sentences about the featured player from Frank Thomas, Leaf's official spokesman again in 1994. The first five cards were released in Series I; cards 6-10 in Series II. Stated odds of finding a Slide Show insert are one per 54 packs.

		MT	NR MT	EX
Complete Set (5):		35.00	26.00	14.00
Common Player:		3.00	2.25	1.25
1	Frank Thomas	14.00	10.50	5.50
2	Mike Piazza	10.00	7.50	4.00
3	Darren Daulton	3.00	2.25	1.25
4	Ryne Sandberg	6.00	4.50	2.50
5	Roberto Alomar	6.00	4.50	2.50

1994 Leaf Statistical Standouts

Significant statistical acheivements from the 1993 season are marked in this insert set found in both retail and hobby packs at a rate of about once every 12 packs. Fronts feature player action photos set against a foil background of silver at right and a team color at left. A gold embossed Leaf seal is at upper-left. Backs are bordered in the complementary team color at right, silver at left and have a vertical player photo along with the statistical achievement. Cards are numbered "x-10".

		MT	NR MT	EX
Complete Set (10):		40.00	30.00	15.00
Common Player:		1.50	1.25	.60
1	Frank Thomas	10.00	7.50	4.00
2	Barry Bonds	5.00	3.75	2.00
3	Juan Gonzalez	6.00	4.50	2.50
4	Mike Piazza	8.00	6.00	3.25
5	Greg Maddux	1.50	1.25	.60
6	Ken Griffey, Jr.	10.00	7.50	4.00
7	Joe Carter	2.00	1.50	.80
8	Dave Winfield	2.00	1.50	.80
9	Tony Gwynn	1.50	1.25	.60
10	Cal Ripken, Jr.	5.00	3.75	2.00

1991 Lewis Negro League

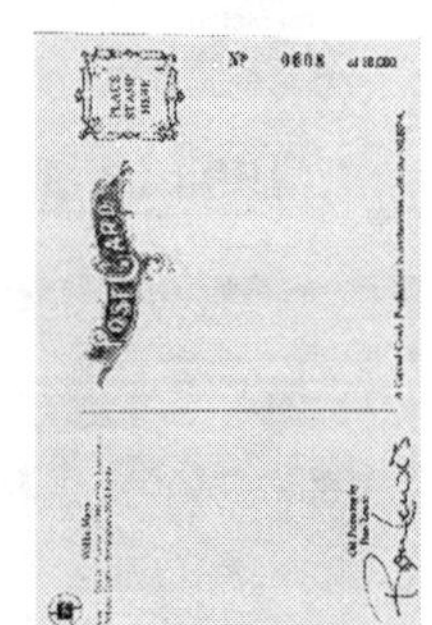

The 1991 Negro League Living Legends Postcard Set features paintings by artist Ron Lewis. Cards measure 3-1/2" x 5-1/2" and are stamped with a number within the 10,000 sets produced. In between each player's image and the player's name at the bottom of the card, is ample space for an autograph. There are 30 cards in the set which was created as a fund raiser for the Negro League Baseball Players Association.

		MT	NR MT	EX
Complete Set:		25.00	18.50	10.00
Common Player:		.50	.40	.20
1	George Giles	.50	.40	.20
2	Bill Cash	.50	.40	.20
3	Bob Harvey	.50	.40	.20
4	Lyman Bostock Sr.	.75	.60	.30
5	Ray Dandridge	2.00	1.50	.80
6	Leon Day	.75	.60	.30
7	Verdell "Lefty" Mathis	.50	.40	.20
8	Jimmie Crutchfield	.75	.60	.30
9	Clyde McNeal	.50	.40	.20
10	Bill Wright	.50	.40	.20
11	Mahlon Duckett	.50	.40	.20
12	William "Bobby" Robinson	.50	.40	.20
13	Max Manning	.50	.40	.20
14	Armando Vazquez	.50	.40	.20
15	Jehosie Heard	.75	.60	.30
16	Quincy Trouppe	.75	.60	.30
17	Wilmer Fields	.50	.40	.20
18	Lonnie Blair	.50	.40	.20
19	Garnett Blair	.75	.60	.30
20	Monte Irvin	2.00	1.50	.80
21	Willie Mays	6.00	4.50	2.50
22	Buck Leonard	4.00	3.00	1.50
23	Frank Evans	.50	.40	.20
24	Josh Gibson Jr.	4.00	3.00	1.50
25	Ted "Double Duty" Radcliffe	1.00	.70	.40
26	Josh Johnson	.50	.40	.20
27	Gene Benson	.75	.60	.30
28	Lester Lockett	.50	.40	.20
29	Cowan "Bubba" Hyde	.50	.40	.20
30	Rufus Lewis	.50	.40	.20

1993 Line Up Venezuelan Baseball

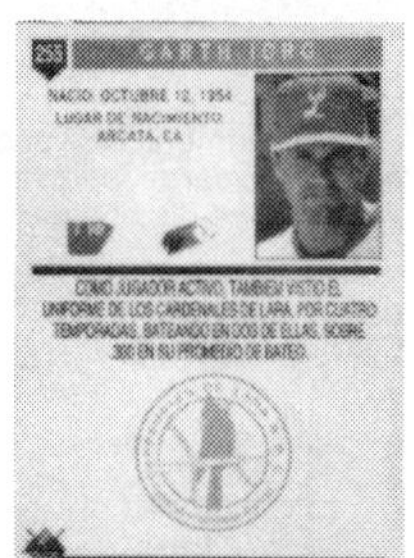

With names like Aparicio, Valenzuela, Armas, Galarraga and Cedeno, the 1993-94 LineUp Venezuelan Baseball Spanish language set has a certain major league flavor, and the cards could also boast a quality that rivals the myriad sets produced each year in North America. The set contains 350 cards, full color front and back and UV coating, all in a card design reminiscent of Upper Deck issues. The backs of the cards are in Spanish, with a portrait of the player, biographical information, statistics and a large team logo at the bottom of the card. There are two subsets within the regular issue; seven cards honoring former major leaguer and home run champion Tony Armas and 27 cards picturing the Caribbean Series. There are also autographed cards that are randomly inserted in the foil packs (14 cards).

		MT	NR MT	EX
Complete Set (350):		15.00	11.00	6.00
Common Player:		.05	.04	.02
1	Luis Salazar	.05	.04	.02
2	Antonio Castillo	.05	.04	.02
3	Pedro J. Chavez	.05	.04	.02
4	Erick Ojeda, Felix Leon	.05	.04	.02
5	Ivan Arteaga	.05	.04	.02
6	Wilson Alvarez	.35	.25	.14
7	Ismael Rodriguez	.05	.04	.02
8	Urbano Lugo	.05	.04	.02
9	Todd Pratt	.05	.04	.02
10	Jose Cardona	.05	.04	.02
11	Luis Aparicio	.90	.70	.35
12	Frank Campos	.05	.04	.02
13	Pedro P. Belmonte	.05	.04	.02
14	Alejandro Alvarez	.05	.04	.02
15	Juan F. Castillo	.05	.04	.02
16	Jay Baller	.05	.04	.02
17	Jose L. Zambrano	.05	.04	.02
18	Argenis Conde	.05	.04	.02
19	Yonni Naveda	.05	.04	.02
20	Damaso Betancourt	.05	.04	.02
21	Giovanni Carrara	.05	.04	.02
22	Julio Franco	.35	.25	.14
23	Omar Vizquel	.25	.20	.10
24	Jose Marchan	.05	.04	.02
25	Edgar Naveda	.05	.04	.02
26	Pedro Castellano	.05	.04	.02
27	Jalro Ramos	.05	.04	.02
28	Dave Burba	.05	.04	.02
29	Pat Hentgen	.15	.11	.06
30	Ramon Garcia	.05	.04	.02
31	Robinson Garces	.05	.04	.02
32	Remigio Hermoso	.05	.04	.02
33	Malvin Matos	.05	.04	.02
34	Miguel A. Garcia	.05	.04	.02
35	Brad Holman	.05	.04	.02
36	Johnny Malaver	.05	.04	.02
37	Omar Daal	.15	.11	.06
38	Edwin Hurtado	.05	.04	.02
39	Ifrain Linares	.05	.04	.02
40	Richard Delgado	.05	.04	.02
41	Quinn Mack	.05	.04	.02
42	Luis Lunar	.05	.04	.02
43	Luis Gonzalez	.25	.20	.10
44	Gilberto Cllsanchez	.05	.04	.02
45	Dave Masters	.05	.04	.02
46	Jesus Hernandez	.05	.04	.02
47	Johanne Manaure	.05	.04	.02
48	Dean Hartgraves	.05	.04	.02
49	Henrique A. Gomez	.05	.04	.02
50	Oscar Azocar	.05	.04	.02
51	Edgar Herrera	.05	.04	.02
52	Luis Dorante	.05	.04	.02
53	Carlos Landines	.05	.04	.02
54	Marcos Manrique	.05	.04	.02
55	Dave Pavias	.05	.04	.02
56	Jose Garcia	.05	.04	.02
57	Mark Ohims	.05	.04	.02
58	Todd Jones	.05	.04	.02
59	Julio Machado	.05	.04	.02
60	Jose G. Urdaneta	.05	.04	.02
61	Antonio Lopez	.05	.04	.02
62	Alfredo Ortiz	.05	.04	.02
63	Scott Cepicky	.05	.04	.02
64	Gustavo Pinto	.05	.04	.02
65	Tom McGraw	.15	.11	.06
66	Oswald Peraza	.15	.11	.06
67	Benito Malave	.05	.04	.02
68	Esmily Guerra	.05	.04	.02
69	Todd Trafton	.05	.04	.02
70	Jesus Mendez	.05	.04	.02
71	Amallo Carreno	.05	.04	.02
72	Graciano Ravelo	.05	.04	.02
73	Jose L. Ramos	.05	.04	.02
74	Paul Marak	.05	.04	.02
75	Oscar Sarmiento	.05	.04	.02
76	Alfonzo Osuna	.05	.04	.02
77	Felix Perez	.05	.04	.02
78	Marlon Nava	.05	.04	.02
79	Melvin Mora	.05	.04	.02
80	Steve Wapnick	.05	.04	.02
81	Ricky Rojas	.05	.04	.02
82	Flores Bolivar	.05	.04	.02
83	Donald Strange	.05	.04	.02
84	Mike Soper	.05	.04	.02
85	Juan C. Pulido	.05	.04	.02
86	Daniel Rambo	.05	.04	.02
87	Jorge Velandia	.05	.04	.02
88	Silverio Navas	.05	.04	.02
89	Trent Hubbard	.05	.04	.02
90	Cliff Young	.05	.04	.02
91	Julio C. Strauss	.05	.04	.02
92	Cesar Tovar	.05	.04	.02
93	Dilson Torres	.05	.04	.02
94	Jose Villa	.05	.04	.02
95	Jose Solarte	.05	.04	.02
96	Francisco Munoz	.05	.04	.02
97	Jesus Garces	.05	.04	.02
98	Luis M. Sanchez	.05	.04	.02
99	Jose Monzon	.05	.04	.02
100	Luis Sojo	.05	.04	.02
101	Ugueth Urbina	.05	.04	.02
102	Williams Ereu	.05	.04	.02
103	Mike Maksudian	.05	.04	.02
104	Clemente Alvarez	.20	.15	.08
105	Luis Portillo	.05	.04	.02
106	Dan Urbina	.05	.04	.02
107	Lester Straker	.05	.04	.02
108	Jose Guarache	.05	.04	.02
109	Miguel Soto	.05	.04	.02
110	Henry Contreras	.05	.04	.02
111	Jose Moreno	.05	.04	.02
112	Luis Leal	.05	.04	.02
113	Jesus Laya	.05	.04	.02
114	Heberto Andrade	.05	.04	.02
115	Angel Escovar	.05	.04	.02
116	Jim Bruske	.05	.04	.02
117	Edgar Marquez	.05	.04	.02
118	Miguel Castellanos	.05	.04	.02
119	Howard Battle	.05	.04	.02
120	Amador Arias	.05	.04	.02
121	Alexander Delgado	.05	.04	.02
122	Omar Malave	.05	.04	.02
123	Lipso Nava	.05	.04	.02
124	Omar Bencomo	.05	.04	.02
125	Oswaldo Olivares	.05	.04	.02
126	Mahaly Carrera	.05	.04	.02
127	Jesus Gonzalez	.05	.04	.02
128	Doug Jennings	.05	.04	.02
129	Egardo Alfonzo	.05	.04	.02
130	Rob Natal	.05	.04	.02
131	Joel Cartaya	.05	.04	.02
132	Antonio Torres	.05	.04	.02
133	Jose Betancourt	.05	.04	.02
134	Carlos Lopez	.05	.04	.02
135	Mario Gonzalez	.05	.04	.02
136	Jose Stella	.05	.04	.02
137	Oscar Ecobar	.05	.04	.02
138	Eddy Diaz	.05	.04	.02
139	Mario Labastidas	.05	.04	.02
140	Rafael DeLima	.05	.04	.02
141	Edgar Toval	.05	.04	.02
142	Gregorio Machado	.05	.04	.02
143	Harry Guanchez	.05	.04	.02
144	Jesus Alfaro	.05	.04	.02
145	Asdrubal Estrada	.05	.04	.02
146	Henry Centeno	.05	.04	.02
147	Pedro Blanco	.05	.04	.02
148	Kevin Noriega	.05	.04	.02
149	Julio Armas	.05	.04	.02
150	Cristobal Colon	.15	.11	.06
151	Edgar Alfonzo	.05	.04	.02
152	Pablo Torrealba	.05	.04	.02
153	Alexis Infante	.15	.11	.06
154	Andres Espinoza	.05	.04	.02
155	Jeff Grotewold	.05	.04	.02
156	Robert Machado	.05	.04	.02

157	Sherman Obando	.05	.04	.02
158	Willfredo Polldor	.05	.04	.02
159	Henry Blanco	.05	.04	.02
160	Jeff Kent	.35	.25	.14
161	Alexander Sutherland	.05	.04	.02
162	Noe Maduro	.05	.04	.02
163	Jose G. Hil	.05	.04	.02
164	Fernando Soto	.05	.04	.02
165	Jose Leiva	.05	.04	.02
166	Carlos Subero	.05	.04	.02
167	Edgar Caceres	.05	.04	.02
168	Rodolfo Hernandez	.05	.04	.02
169	William Mota	.05	.04	.02
170	Jesus Acevedo	.05	.04	.02
171	Jose Leon	.05	.04	.02
172	Cesar Gutierrez	.05	.04	.02
173	Blas Cedric	.05	.04	.02
174	Fernando Ramsey	.05	.04	.02
175	Marcos Armas	.05	.04	.02
176	Roberto Castillo	.05	.04	.02
177	Felipe Lira	.05	.04	.02
178	Joe Hall	.05	.04	.02
179	Freddy Torres	.05	.04	.02
180	Juan Querecuto	.05	.04	.02
181	Rouglas Odor	.05	.04	.02
182	Ruben Amaro	.15	.11	.06
183	Matt Maysey	.05	.04	.02
184	Eduardo Perez	.05	.04	.02
185	Freddy Gonzalez	.05	.04	.02
186	Donald Harris	.15	.11	.06
187	Ernesto Gomez	.05	.04	.02
188	William Canate	.05	.04	.02
189	Hector Rincines	.05	.04	.02
190	Johnny Paredes	.05	.04	.02
191	Roberto Espinoza	.05	.04	.02
192	Jesus M. Trillo	.05	.04	.02
193	Jaime Torres	.05	.04	.02
194	Bob K. Abreu	.05	.04	.02
195	Jeff Frye	.05	.04	.02
196	Shawn Jeter	.15	.11	.06
197	Jesus Marquez	.05	.04	.02
198	Scott Bryant	.05	.04	.02
199	Robert Taylor	.05	.04	.02
200	Carlos Garcia	.05	.04	.02
201	Temis Liendo	.05	.04	.02
202	Mauro Mendez	.05	.04	.02
203	Jerry Kutzler	.05	.04	.02
204	Troy O'Leary	.05	.04	.02
205	Phil Regan	.05	.04	.02
206	Lino Conell	.05	.04	.02
207	Luis R. Salazar	.05	.04	.02
208	Len Picota	.05	.04	.02
209	William Magallanes	.05	.04	.02
210	Luis Gonzalez	.15	.11	.06
211	Carlos Burgillos	.05	.04	.02
212	Justo Massaro	.05	.04	.02
213	Carlos T. Trillo	.05	.04	.02
214	Richard Garces	.05	.04	.02
215	Rick Sweet	.05	.04	.02
216	Jim Newlin	.05	.04	.02
217	Hector Ortega	.05	.04	.02
218	Roger Cedeño	.05	.04	.02
219	Eric Anthony	.25	.20	.10
220	Jason Grimsley	.05	.04	.02
221	Juan C. Abreu	.05	.04	.02
222	Leonel Carrion	.05	.04	.02
223	Alejandro Rodriguez	.05	.04	.02
224	Jeff Pierce	.05	.04	.02
225	Gustavo Polidor	.05	.04	.02
226	Steve Pegues	.05	.04	.02
227	William Pennyfeather	.05	.04	.02
228	Eminson Soto	.05	.04	.02
229	Karl Rhodes	.05	.04	.02
230	Barry Manuel	.05	.04	.02
231	Simon Pinango	.05	.04	.02
232	Elias Lugo	.05	.04	.02
233	Raul P. Tovar	.05	.04	.02
234	Roberto Petaguine	.05	.04	.02
235	Oswaldo Virgil	.10	.08	.04
236	Gregory O'Halloran	.05	.04	.02
237	Adrian Jordan	.05	.04	.02
238	Orangel Lopez	.05	.04	.02
239	Roberto Zambrano	.05	.04	.02
240	Mauricio Ruiz	.05	.04	.02
241	Igor Ovledo	.05	.04	.02
242	Angel Leon	.05	.04	.02
243	Wilfredo Romero	.05	.04	.02
244	Richard Romeo	.05	.04	.02
245	Pompeyo Davaillio	.10	.08	.04
246	Jack Voight	.05	.04	.02
247	Danilo Leon	.05	.04	.02
248	Mike Draper	.05	.04	.02
249	Dan Urbina	.05	.04	.02
250	Carlos Hernandez	.05	.04	.02
251	Carlos Martinez	.05	.04	.02
252	Brian Keyser	.05	.04	.02
253	Jorge Uribe	.05	.04	.02
254	Jesus Delgado	.05	.04	.02
255	Garth Iorg	.05	.04	.02
256	Jose Centeno	.05	.04	.02
257	Douglas Moreno	.05	.04	.02
258	Jose F. Malave	.05	.04	.02
259	Oscar Henriquez	.05	.04	.02
260	Eduardo Zembrano	.05	.04	.02
261	Doug Linton	.05	.04	.02
262	Robert Perez	.05	.04	.02
263	Raul Chavez	.05	.04	.02
264	Darrin Chapin	.05	.04	.02
265	Mike Hart	.05	.04	.02
266	Ender Perozo	.05	.04	.02
267	Rick Polak	.05	.04	.02
268	Orlando Munoz	.05	.04	.02
269	Carlos Quintana	.15	.11	.06
270	Oswaldo Guillen	.25	.20	.10
271	Todd Stephen	.05	.04	.02
272	Manuel Gonzalez	.05	.04	.02
273	Terry Francona	.05	.04	.02
274	Jorge Mitchell	.05	.04	.02
275	Alfredo Pedrique	.05	.04	.02
276	Gallarraga/Tovar	.10	.08	.04
277	Cedeno/Abreu	.05	.04	.02
278	Novato Del Ano 92-93	.05	.04	.02
279	Jugador Mas Valioso 92-93	.05	.04	.02
280	Andres Gallarraga	.35	.25	.14
281	Antonio Armas	.05	.04	.02
282	El Slugger de Venezuela	.05	.04	.02
283	El Slugger de Venezuela	.05	.04	.02
284	El Slugger de Venezuela	.05	.04	.02
285	El Slugger de Venezuela	.05	.04	.02
286	El Slugger de Venezuela	.05	.04	.02
287	El Slugger de Venezuela	.05	.04	.02
288	Pratt-Natal-O'Halloran	.05	.04	.02
289	Agullas del Zulla BBC	.05	.04	.02
290	Cangrejeros de Santurce BBC	.05	.04	.02
291	Agullas Cibaenas BBC	.05	.04	.02
292	Venados de Mazatian BBC	.05	.04	.02
293	Refuerzos Pitchers	.05	.04	.02
294	Refuerzos Jugadores	.05	.04	.02
295	Las Maximas Autoridades	.05	.04	.02
296	Bryant-Grotewold	.05	.04	.02
297	Villanueva	.10	.08	.04
298	Pena	.10	.08	.04
299	Munoz	.10	.08	.04
300	Cedeno	.10	.08	.04
301	Colon	.05	.04	.02
302	Alicea	.05	.04	.02
303	Alou	.25	.20	.10
304	Carrillo	.05	.04	.02
305	Thon	.05	.04	.02
306	Moreno	.05	.04	.02
307	Cook	.05	.04	.02
308	Polonia	.15	.11	.06
309	Fermin	.05	.04	.02
310	Ortiz	.05	.04	.02
311	Arias	.05	.04	.02
312	Valenzuela	.05	.04	.02
313	Paredes-Alou	.05	.04	.02
314	Bryant-Villanueva	.05	.04	.02
315	Wilson-Simmons	.05	.04	.02
316	Olivarez-Davaillio-Montaya-Dilone	.05	.04	.02
317	Villanueva-Delgado-Pena	.05	.04	.02
318	Suero-Naveda-Velazquez	.05	.04	.02
319	Colon-Lopex Jr.-Cedeno	.05	.04	.02
320	Polonia-Escalera-Perez	.05	.04	.02
321	Alou-Canate-Fox	.05	.04	.02
322	Lugo-Valenzuela	.05	.04	.02
323	Liga Venezolana de Beisbol Profesional	.05	.04	.02
324	Asociacion de Peloteros	.05	.04	.02
325	Info: Zulla	.05	.04	.02
326	Info: Magallanes	.05	.04	.02
327	Info: Caracas	.05	.04	.02
328	Info: Lara	.05	.04	.02
329	Info: La Guaira	.05	.04	.02
330	Info: Aragua	.05	.04	.02
331	Info: Caribes	.05	.04	.02
332	Info: Cabimas	.05	.04	.02
333	Checklist: Zulla	.05	.04	.02
334	Checklist: Magallanes	.05	.04	.02
335	Checklist: Caracas	.05	.04	.02
336	Checklist: Lara	.05	.04	.02
337	Checklist: La Guaira	.05	.04	.02
338	Checklist: Aragua	.05	.04	.02
339	Checklist: Caribes	.05	.04	.02
340	Checklist: Cabimas	.05	.04	.02
341	Omar Vizquel	.05	.04	.02
342	William Canate	.05	.04	.02
343	Musiu	.05	.04	.02
344	Andres Gallarraga	.35	.25	.14
345	Luis Salazar	.05	.04	.02
346	Wilson Alzarez	.35	.25	.14
347	La Gran Serie Checklsit	.05	.04	.02
348	Checklist 1-122	.05	.04	.02
349	Checklist 123-246	.05	.04	.02
350	Checklist 247-350	.05	.04	.02

1976 Linnett Superstars

This frequently encountered set of 36 cards has enjoyed little collector interest since its issue in 1976. Officially known as "Pee-Wee Superstars," the cards measure 4" x 5-5/8". Player portraits by artist Charles Linnett are rendered in black-and-white pencil and set against a pale yellow background. Players are shown without caps or uniforms (most appear to be wearing white T-shirts). According to the logos at top the set was fully licensed by both the players' association and Major League Baseball, and team logos do appear in the lower-left corner. A facsimile autograph in red or purple appears on each card. Front borders are bright purple, red, green, dark brown or white. Card backs feature either a photo of an antique auto or a drawing of an historic sailing ship. Each of the 12 different back designs appears on one card from each team set. The Linnetts were sold in panels of six perforated cards. An offer on the back of each card makes 8x10" premium portraits of each player available for 95 cents. The premium pictures have about the same value as the cards. Inexplicably, the cards are numbered from 90-125. Only the World's Champion Cincinnati Reds, A.L. Champion Boston Red Sox and N.L. runner-up Dodgers are represented in the issue.

		NR MT	EX	VG
Complete Panel Set (6):		15.00	7.50	4.50
Complete Singles Set (36):		12.00	6.00	3.50
Common Player:		.50	.25	.15
	Panel 1	7.00	3.50	2.00
90	Don Gullett	.50	.25	.15
91	Johnny Bench	2.00	1.00	.60
92	Tony Perez	1.00	.50	.30
93	Mike Lum	.50	.25	.15
94	Ken Griffey	.60	.30	.20
95	George Foster	.60	.30	.20
	Panel 2	8.00	4.00	2.25
96	Joe Morgan	1.50	.75	.45
97	Pete Rose	3.00	1.50	.90
98	Dave Concepcion	.60	.30	.20
99	Cesar Geronimo	.50	.25	.15
100	Dan Driessen	.50	.25	.15
101	Pedro Borbon	.50	.25	.15
	Panel 3	7.50	3.75	2.25
102	Carl Yastrzemski	2.00	1.00	.60
103	Fred Lynn	1.00	.50	.30
104	Dwight Evans	.60	.30	.20
105	Ferguson Jenkins	1.00	.50	.30
106	Rico Petrocelli	.50	.25	.15
107	Denny Doyle	.50	.25	.15
	Panel 4	5.00	2.50	1.50
108	Luis Tiant	.60	.30	.20
109	Carlton Fisk	1.00	.50	.30
110	Rick Burleson	.50	.25	.15
111	Bill Lee	.50	.25	.15
112	Rick Wise	.50	.25	.15
113	Jim Rice	.75	.35	.25
	Panel 5	5.00	2.50	1.50
114	Davey Lopes	.60	.30	.20
115	Steve Garvey	1.00	.50	.30
116	Bill Russell	.60	.30	.20
117	Ron Cey	.60	.30	.20
118	Steve Yaeger	.50	.25	.15
119	Doug Rau	.50	.25	.15
	Panel 6	4.75	2.25	1.40
120	Don Sutton	1.00	.50	.30
121	Joe Ferguson	.50	.25	.15
122	Mike Marshall	.50	.25	.15
123	Bill Buckner	.60	.30	.20
124	Rick Rhoden	.50	.25	.15
125	Ted Sizemore	.50	.25	.15

1985 Lion Photo Chicago Cubs

Sponsored by a Chicago photography store chain, this set features the players, coaches and manager on large-format (3-1/2" x 5") cards. Fronts have a color portrait photo of the players surrounded by a white border. The player's name appears in blue at the bottom. Backs are printed in dark blue and have an ad for Lion Photo and its product lines. The unnumbered cards are checklisted here alphabetically.

		MT	NR MT	EX
Complete Set (27):		11.00	8.25	4.50
Common Player:		.25	.20	.10
(1)	Thad Bosley	.25	.20	.10
(2)	Larry Bowa	.35	.25	.14
(3)	Warren Brusstar	.25	.20	.10
(4)	Ron Cey	.35	.25	.14
(5)	Jody Davis	.25	.20	.10
(6)	Brian Dayett	.25	.20	.10
(7)	Bob Dernier	.25	.20	.10
(8)	Shawn Dunston	.50	.40	.20
(9)	Leon Durham	.25	.20	.10
(10)	Dennis Eckersley	1.25	.90	.50
(11)	Ray Fontenot	.25	.20	.10
(12)	George Frazier	.25	.20	.10

(13)	Jim Frey	.25	.20	.10
(14)	Steve Lake	.25	.20	.10
(15)	Davy Lopes	.25	.20	.10
(16)	Gary Matthews	.25	.20	.10
(17)	Keith Moreland	.25	.20	.10
(18)	Dick Ruthven	.25	.20	.10
(19)	Ryne Sandberg	4.00	3.00	1.50
(20)	Scott Sanderson	.35	.25	.14
(21)	Lee Smith	.60	.45	.25
(22)	Lary Sorenson	.25	.20	.10
(23)	Chris Speir	.25	.20	.10
(24)	Rick Sutcliffe	.25	.20	.10
(25)	Steve Trout	.25	.20	.10
(26)	Gary Woods	.25	.20	.10
(27)	Don Zimmer	.35	.25	.14

1986 Lite Beer Astros

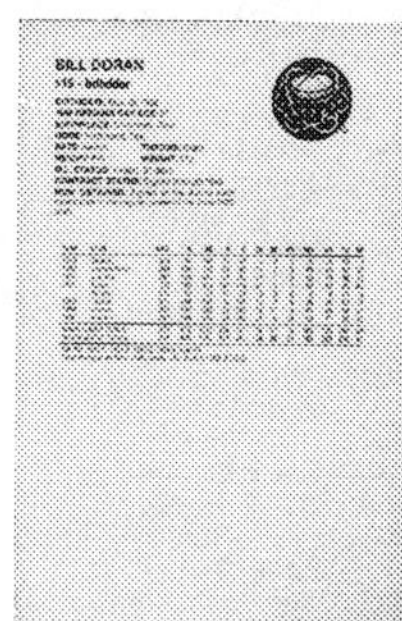

This 22-card regional set of the Houston Astros was sponsored by Lite Beer and given away in a special stadium promotion. The large (4-1/2" by 6-3/4") cards featured full-color photos surrounded by a wide, white border. Diagonal color bands of yellow, orange, red and purple extend throught the upper right and lower left corners of the card, which also displays the Astros' 25th Anniversary logo and the Lite Beer logo in opposite corners. The backs include player information and statistics.

		MT	NR MT	EX
Complete Set:		55.00	41.00	22.00
Common Player:		1.50	1.25	.60
3	Phil Garner	2.00	1.50	.80
6	Mark Bailey	1.50	1.25	.60
10	Dickie Thon	2.00	1.50	.80
11	Frank DiPino	1.50	1.25	.60
12	Craig Reynolds	1.50	1.25	.60
14	Alan Ashby	1.50	1.25	.60
17	Kevin Bass	3.00	2.25	1.25
19	Bill Doran	3.00	2.25	1.25
20	Jim Pankovits	1.50	1.25	.60
21	Terry Puhl	1.50	1.25	.60
22	Hal Lanier	1.50	1.25	.60
25	Jose Cruz	3.00	2.25	1.25
27	Glenn Davis	3.00	2.25	1.25
28	Billy Hatcher	3.00	2.25	1.25
29	Denny Walling	1.50	1.25	.60
33	Mike Scott	3.00	2.25	1.25
34	Nolan Ryan	15.00	11.00	6.00
37	Charlie Kerfeld	1.50	1.25	.60
39	Bob Knepper	2.00	1.50	.80
43	Jim Deshaies	3.00	2.25	1.25
45	Dave Smith	1.50	1.25	.60
53	Mike Madden	1.50	1.25	.60

1986 Lite Beer Rangers

This postcard-size (approximately 4" by 6") regional set of 28 Texas Rangers cards was sponsored by Lite Beer and was available by mail directly from the Rangers. The fronts featured full-color photos surrounded by a wide, white border with the player's name, uniform number and postion appearing below. The Rangers logo is displayed in the lower left corner, while the Lite Beer logo is in the lower right.

		MT	NR MT	EX
Complete Set:		50.00	37.00	20.00
Common Player:		1.50	1.25	.60
0	Oddibe McDowell	2.00	2.25	1.25
1	Scott Fletcher	3.00	2.25	1.25
2	Bobby Valentine	2.00	1.50	.80
4	Don Slaught	2.00	1.50	.80
5	Pete Incaviglia	3.00	2.25	1.25
9	Pete O'Brien	3.00	2.25	1.25
10	Art Howe	2.00	1.50	.80
11	Toby Harrah	2.00	1.50	.80
12	Geno Petralli	1.50	1.25	.60
13	Joe Ferguson	1.50	1.25	.60
14	Tim Foli	1.50	1.25	.60
15	Larry Parrish	2.00	1.50	.80
16	Mike Mason	1.50	1.25	.60
17	Darrell Porter	2.00	1.50	.80
18	Ed Correa	1.50	1.25	.60
19	Curtis Wilkerson	1.50	1.25	.60
22	Steve Buechele	4.00	3.00	1.50
23	Jose Guzman	1.50	1.25	.60
24	Ricky Wright	1.50	1.25	.60
27	Greg Harris	1.50	1.25	.60
31	Tom Robson	1.50	1.25	.60
32	Gary Ward	2.00	1.50	.80
35	Tom House	1.50	1.25	.60
44	Tom Paciorek	1.50	1.25	.60
45	Dwayne Henry	1.50	1.25	.60
48	Bobby Witt	3.00	2.25	1.25
49	Charlie Hough	3.00	2.25	1.25
----	Arlington Stadium	1.50	1.25	.60

Values quoted in this guide reflect the retail price of a card – the price a collector can expect to pay when buying a card from a dealer. The wholesale price – that which a collector can expect to receive from a dealer when selling cards – will be significantly lower, depending on desirability and condition.

1886 Lone Jack St. Louis Browns (N370)

The 1886 Lone Jack set is among the rarest of all 19th Century tobacco issues. Issued by the Lone Jack Cigarette Co. of Lynchburg, Va., the set consists of 13 subjects, all members of the champion St. Louis Browns. Photos for the set are enlarged versions of those used in the more popular N172 Old Judge series. Cards in the set measure 2-1/2" by 1-1/2" and carry an ad for Lond Jack Cigarettes along the bottom of the front. The set features the Browns' starting lineup for 1886 along with their two top pitchers, backup catcher and owner, Chris Von Der Ahe.

		NR MT	EX	VG
Complete Set:		12000.	6000.	3300.
Common Player:		750.00	375.00	225.00
(1)	Doc Bushong	750.00	375.00	225.00
(2)	Parisian Bob Caruthers	750.00	375.00	225.00
(3)	Commy Commiskey (Comiskey)	2500.	1250.	750.00
(4)	Dave Foutz	750.00	375.00	225.00
(5)	Will Gleason	750.00	375.00	225.00
(6)	Nat Hudson	750.00	375.00	225.00
(7)	Rudy Kimler (Kemmler)	750.00	375.00	225.00
(8)	Arlie Latham	750.00	375.00	225.00
(9)	Little Nick Nicol	750.00	375.00	225.00
(10)	Tip O'Neil (O'Neill)	750.00	375.00	225.00
(11)	Yank Robinson	750.00	375.00	225.00
(12)	Chris Von Der Ahe	1250.	625.00	400.00
(13)	Curt Welsh (Welch)	750.00	375.00	225.00

Values for recent cards and sets are listed in Mint (MT), Near Mint (NM), reflecting the fact that many cards from recent years have been preserved in top condition. Recent cards and sets in less than Excellent condition have little collector interest.

1886 Lorillard Team Card

Issued in 1886 by Lorillard Tobacco Co., these 4" by 5-1/2" cards were issued for the Chicago, Detroit and New York baseball clubs. Each card carries the team's schedule (starting with June) on one side and features 11 player portraits enclosed in circles on the other. Both sides have advertising for Lorillard's Climax Plug tobacco.

		NR MT	EX	VG
Complete Set:		25000.	12500.	7500.
Common Team:		5000.	2500.	1500.
(1)	Chicago League Base Ball Club	6500.	3250.	2000.
(2)	Detroit League Base Ball Club	5500.	2750.	1650.
(3)	New York League Base Ball Club	9000.	4500.	2750.
(4)	Philadelphia League Base Ball Club	5000.	2500.	1500.

A player's name in italic type indicates a rookie card. An (FC) indicates a player's first card for that particular card company.

1988 Louisville Slugger

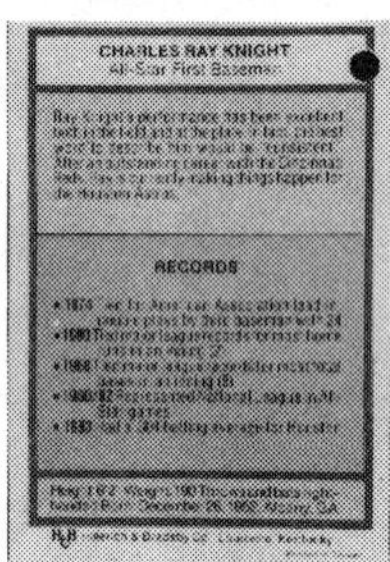

Two more cards were added to the Hillerich & Bradsby hangtag collection in 1988. Hillerich & Bradsby, makers of Louisville Slugger bats and gloves, produced the cards to be attached to the company's baseball gloves. The 1988 Eric Davis and Mike Pagliarulo cards bring the total number of Hillerich & Bradsby hangtags issued since the first ones in 1981 (Graig Nettles and Steve Garvey) to 13. A small round hole is punched in the upper left corner of each standard-size card to enable them to be attached to the gloves, making it hard to find undamaged cards. The 1988 cards are numbered and follow the same basic design as previous issues - bright blue and green borders, player name and position above the full-color photo (with autograph overprint), yellow Louisville Slugger logo across the bottom border. Beneath the logo are the words "Member Louisville Slugger Bat & Glove Advisory Staff." The card backs are blue and green and include the player name, short biography and a list of personal records and information.

		MT	NR MT	EX
Complete Set:		120.00	90.00	48.00
Common Player:		5.00	3.75	2.00
(1)	Eric Davis (1988)	8.00	6.00	3.25
(2)	Steve Garvey (Dodgers-1981)	25.00	18.50	10.00
(3)	Steve Garvey (Padres - 1985)	10.00	7.50	4.00
(4)	Pedro Guerrero (1982)	8.00	6.00	3.25
(5)	Orel Hershiser (1986)	15.00	11.00	6.00
(6)	Ray Knight (Astros - 1984)	10.00	7.50	4.00
(7)	Ray Knight (Mets - 1984)	8.00	6.00	3.25
(8)	Fred Lynn (1982)	5.00	3.75	2.00
(9)	Gary Matthews (1985)	10.00	7.50	4.00
(10)	Graig Nettles (Yankees-1981)	12.00	9.00	4.75
(11)	Graig Nettles (Padres - 1984)	10.00	7.50	4.00
(12)	Mike Pagliarulo (1988)	5.00	3.75	2.00
(13)	Rick Rhoden (1985)	8.00	6.00	3.25

1949 Lummis Peanut Butter Phillies

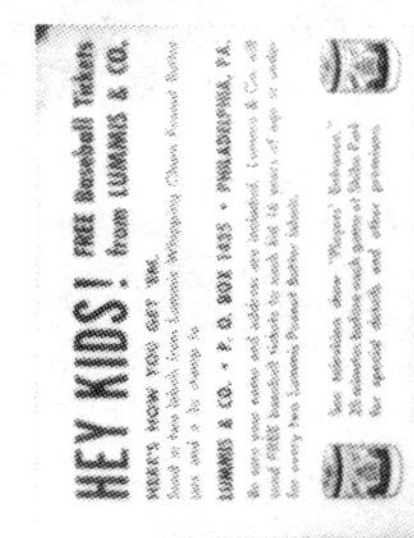

This 12-card regional set featuring the Phillies was issued in the Philadelphia area by Lummis Peanut Butter in 1949. The cards measure 3-1/4" by 4-1/4" and are unnumbered. The fronts feature an action photo with a facsimile autograph, while the backs advertise a game ticket promotion by Lummis Peanut Butter. The same photos and checklist were also used for a regional sticker card set issued by Sealtest Dairy the same year.

	NR MT	EX	VG
Complete Set:	850.00	425.00	255.00
Common Player:	60.00	30.00	18.00

(1)	Rich Ashburn	150.00	75.00	45.00
(2)	Hank Borowy	60.00	30.00	18.00
(3)	Del Ennis	80.00	40.00	24.00
(4)	Granny Hamner	60.00	30.00	18.00
(5)	Puddinhead Jones	60.00	30.00	18.00
(6)	Russ Meyer	60.00	30.00	18.00
(7)	Bill Nicholson	60.00	30.00	18.00
(8)	Robin Roberts	200.00	100.00	60.00
(9)	"Schoolboy" Rowe	60.00	30.00	18.00
(10)	Andy Seminick	60.00	30.00	18.00
(11)	Curt Simmons	80.00	40.00	24.00
(12)	Eddie Waitkus	60.00	30.00	18.00

1992 Lyke's Braves Team Photo Set

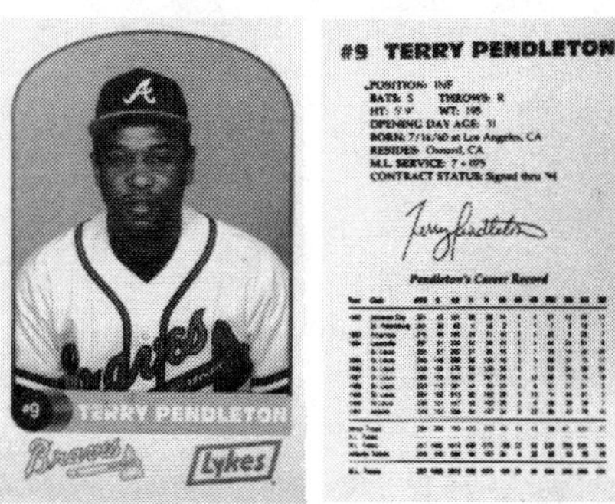

When Lykes Meats was awarded the Braves hot dog contract for 1992 they continued the previous years' baseball card promotions, including this early-May team photo/player card panel. Three 9-1/2" x 10-1/2" panels feature a team photo and 30 player cards. The cards have player portraits against a blue background in a tombstone shape. A blue ball at lower-left has the player's uniform number, while his name is in white in a red strip beneath the photo. Red logos of the team and hot dog vendor are at bottom. Backs are printed in red and dark blue and feature full stats, player data and a facsimile autograph. These cards are much more common than the Lykes singles distributed later in the season. The checklist here is alphabetized.

	MT	NR MT	EX
Complete Set:	8.00	6.00	3.25
Common Player:	.25	.20	.10

(1)	Steve Avery	.75	.60	.30
(2)	Rafael Belliard	.35	.25	.14
(3)	Juan Berenguer	.25	.20	.10
(4)	Damon Berryhill	.25	.20	.10
(5)	Mike Bielecki	.25	.20	.10
(6)	Jeff Blauser	.50	.40	.20
(7)	Sid Bream	.50	.40	.20
(8)	Francisco Cabrera	.25	.20	.10
(9)	Bobby Cox	.25	.20	.10
(10)	Nick Esasky	.25	.20	.10
(11)	Marvin Freeman	.25	.20	.10
(12)	Ron Gant	1.00	.70	.40
(13)	Tom Glavine	.75	.60	.30
(14)	Tommy Gregg	.25	.20	.10
(15)	Brian Hunter	.25	.20	.10
(16)	David Justice	1.00	.70	.40
(17)	Charlie Leibrandt	.25	.20	.10
(18)	Mark Lemke	.35	.25	.14
(19)	Kent Mercker	.25	.20	.10
(20)	Otis Nixon	.35	.25	.14
(21)	Greg Olson	.25	.20	.10
(22)	Alejandro Pena	.25	.20	.10
(23)	Terry Pendleton	.65	.50	.25
(24)	Deion Sanders	1.00	.70	.40
(25)	Lonnie Smith	.25	.20	.10
(26)	John Smoltz	.50	.40	.20
(27)	Mike Stanton	.25	.20	.10
(28)	Jeff Treadway	.25	.20	.10
(29)	Jerry Willard	.25	.20	.10
(30)	Mark Wohlers	.25	.20	.10

1992 Lyke's Braves

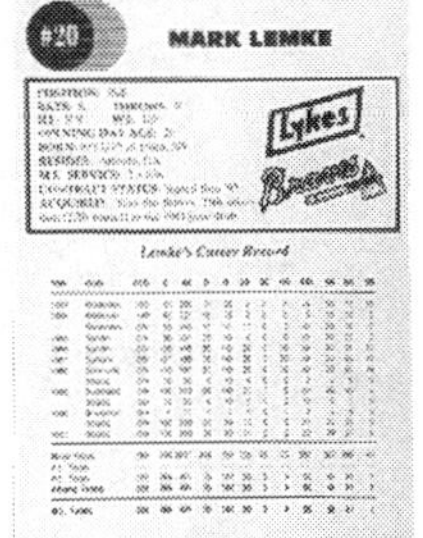

Though Braves players no longer appeared at an autograph booth on card giveaway days in 1992, the team's hot dog vendor, Lyke's, continued to offer small groups of cards to kids attending Tuesday home games. This distribution makes assembling complete sets very challenging. In standard 2-1/2" x 3-1/2" size, the cards have a player photo border in, successively, white, dark blue, red and white. A red-and-blue Lyke's logo is at lower-right. Above is a blue ball with the year of issue, and the team and player name printed in white. Backs are in black with the player's uniform number, full minor and major league stats, and biographical vitae.

	MT	NR MT	EX
Complete Set:	24.00	18.00	9.50
Common Player:	.50	.40	.20

(1)	Steve Avery	2.00	1.50	.80
(2)	Jim Beauchamp	.50	.40	.20
(3)	Rafael Belliard	.60	.45	.25
(4)	Juan Berenguer	.50	.40	.20
(5)	Damon Berryhill	.50	.40	.20
(6)	Mike Bielecki	.50	.40	.20
(7)	Jeff Blauser	.90	.70	.35
(8)	Sid Bream	.75	.60	.30
(9)	Francisco Cabrera	.50	.40	.20
(10)	Pat Corrales	.50	.40	.20
(11)	Bobby Cox	.50	.40	.20
(12)	Marvin Freeman	.50	.40	.20
(13)	Ron Gant	2.00	1.50	.80
(14)	Tom Glavine	2.00	1.50	.80
(15)	Tommy Gregg	.50	.40	.20
(16)	Brian Hunter	.50	.40	.20
(17)	Clarence Jones	.50	.40	.20
(18)	David Justice	2.00	1.50	.80
(19)	Charlie Leibrandt	.50	.40	.20
(20)	Mark Lemke	.60	.45	.25
(21)	Leo Mazzone	.50	.40	.20
(22)	Kent Mercker	.50	.40	.20
(23)	Otis Nixon	.60	.45	.25
(24)	Greg Olson	.50	.40	.20
(25)	Alejandro Pena	.50	.40	.20
(26)	Terry Pendleton	1.00	.70	.40
(27)	Deion Sanders	2.00	1.50	.80
(28)	Lonnie Smith	.50	.40	.20
(29)	John Smoltz	.75	.60	.30
(30)	Mike Stanton	.50	.40	.20
(31)	Jeff Treadway	.50	.40	.20
(32)	Jerry Willard	.50	.40	.20
(33)	Jimy Williams	.50	.40	.20
(34)	Mark Wohlers	.50	.40	.20
(35)	Ned Yost	.50	.40	.20
(36)	Homer the Brave (mascot)	.50	.40	.20
(37)	Rally (mascot)	.50	.40	.20

1993 Lyke's Braves Team Photo Set

The Atlanta Braves offered a perforated, uncut sheet team set in 1992 that was handed out in an early season game. The set, sponsored by Lykes, includes 30 cards and a team photo and carries the player's name and uniform number on the front of the card along with the Braves and Lykes logos. The backs contain the player's biography, career statistics and a facsimile autograph. The first card of Fred McGriff as a Brave appears in this promotional set issued later in the season than in previous years. The 30 individual player cards also include Ryan Klesko, who was not in the single-card season-long giveaways. Three 9-1/2" x 10-1/2" panels comprise this issue, with each of the player cards perforated at the edges. Also for the first time in 1992, the same photos were used for the team sheet and single card promotions. Single cards measure 2-1/4" x 3-1/2" and are checklisted alphabetically here.

	MT	NR MT	EX
Complete Set:	8.00	6.00	3.25
Common Player:	.25	.20	.10

(1)	Steve Avery	1.00	.70	.40
(2)	Steve Bedrosian	.25	.20	.10
(3)	Rafael Belliard	.35	.25	.14
(4)	Damon Berryhill	.25	.20	.10
(5)	Jeff Blauser	.50	.40	.20
(6)	Sid Bream	.50	.40	.20
(7)	Francisco Cabrera	.25	.20	.10
(8)	Bobby Cox	.25	.20	.10
(9)	Marvin Freeman	.25	.20	.10
(10)	Ron Gant	1.00	.70	.40
(11)	Tom Glavine	1.00	.70	.40
(12)	Jay Howell	.25	.20	.10
(13)	Brian Hunter	.25	.20	.10
(14)	David Justice	1.00	.70	.40
(15)	Ryan Klesko	.75	.60	.30
(16)	Mark Lemke	.35	.25	.14
(17)	Greg Maddux	1.00	.70	.40
(18)	Fred McGriff	.75	.60	.30
(19)	Greg McMichael	.60	.45	.25
(20)	Kent Mercker	.25	.20	.10
(21)	Otis Nixon	.35	.25	.14
(22)	Greg Olson	.25	.20	.10
(23)	Bill Pecota	.25	.20	.10
(24)	Terry Pendleton	.65	.50	.25
(25)	Deion Sanders	1.00	.70	.40
(26)	Pete Smith	.25	.20	.10
(27)	John Smoltz	.50	.40	.20
(28)	Mike Stanton	.25	.20	.10
(29)	Tony Tarasco	.65	.50	.25
(30)	Mark Wohlers	.25	.20	.10

1993 Lyke's Braves

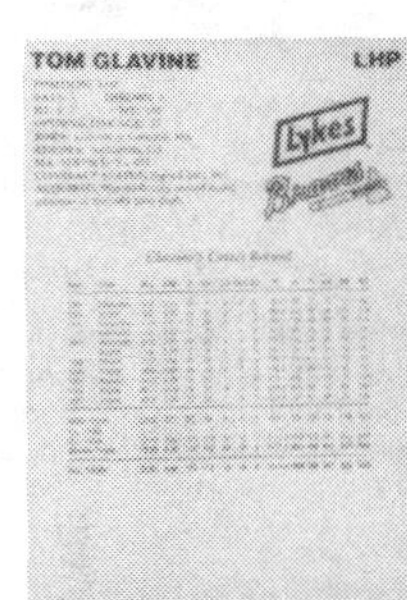

Each home Tuesday during the 1993 season, three player cards were distributed to youngsters, sponsored by the team's hot dog vendor, Lyke's. This style of distribution makes collecting a complete 38-card set very challenging. Standard 2-1/2" x 3-1/2" size cards have a player portrait photo against a blue background. The card's front border is a darker blue separated from the photo by a yellow stripe. Red-white-and-blue team and vendor logos appear at the corners and the player's name and position are in white at lower-left. Backs are printed in black with complete career stats, biographical data and sponsors' logos. The unnumbered cards are checklisted here alphabetically. The final Tuesday's handouts, Javier, McGriff and Tarasco have slightly different back printing and are somewhat scarcer than other cards.

	MT	NR MT	EX
Complete Set:	75.00	56.00	30.00
Common Player:	1.00	.70	.40

(1)	Steve Avery	3.00	2.25	1.25
(2)	Jim Beauchamp	1.00	.70	.40
(3)	Steve Bedrosian	1.00	.70	.40
(4)	Rafael Belliard	1.00	.70	.40
(5)	Damon Berryhill	1.00	.70	.40
(6)	Jeff Blauser	1.50	1.25	.60
(7)	Sid Bream	1.50	1.25	.60
(8)	Francisco Cabrera	1.00	.70	.40
(9)	Pat Corrales	1.00	.70	.40
(10)	Bobby Cox	1.00	.70	.40
(11)	Marvin Freeman	1.00	.70	.40
(12)	Ron Gant	3.00	2.25	1.25
(13)	Tom Glavine	3.00	2.25	1.25
(14)	Jay Howell	1.00	.70	.40
(15)	Brian Hunter	1.00	.70	.40
(16)	Clarence Jones	1.00	.70	.40
(17)	David Justice	5.00	3.75	2.00
(18)	Mark Lemke	1.25	.90	.50
(19)	Javier Lopez	5.00	3.75	2.00
(20)	Greg Maddux	3.00	2.25	1.25
(21)	Leo Mazzone	1.00	.70	.40
(22)	Fred McGriff	7.00	5.25	2.75
(23)	Greg McMichael	1.50	1.25	.60
(24)	Kent Mercker	1.00	.70	.40

(25)	Otis Nixon	1.50	1.25	.60
(26)	Greg Olson	1.00	.70	.40
(27)	Bill Pecota	1.00	.70	.40
(28)	Terry Pendleton	2.00	1.50	.80
(29)	Deion Sanders	5.00	3.75	2.00
(30)	Pete Smith	1.00	.70	.40
(31)	John Smoltz	2.00	1.50	.80
(32)	Mike Stanton	1.00	.70	.40
(33)	Tony Tarasco	5.00	3.75	2.00
(34)	Jimy Williams	1.00	.70	.40
(35)	Mark Wohlers	1.00	.70	.40
(36)	Ned Yost	1.00	.70	.40
(37)	Homer the Brave (mascot)	1.00	.70	.40
(38)	Rally (mascot)	1.00	.70	.40

M

1987 M & M's

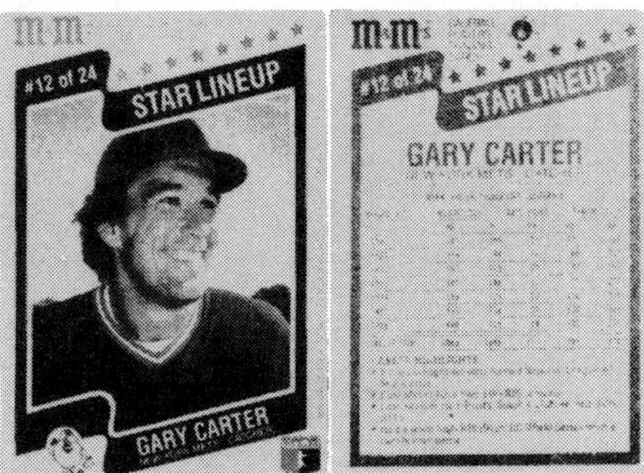

The M&M's "Star Lineup" set consists of 12 two card panels inserted in specially marked packages of large M&M's candy. The two-card panels measure 5" by 3-1/2" with individual cards measuring 2-1/2" by 3-1/2" in size. The full-color photos are enclosed by a wavy blue frame and a white border. Card backs are printed in red ink on white stock and carry the player's career statistics and highlights. All team insignias have been airbrushed away. The set was designed and produced by Mike Schechter and Associates.

		MT	NR MT	EX
Complete Panel Set:		15.00	11.00	6.00
Complete Singles Set:		6.00	4.50	2.50
Common Panel:		1.00	.70	.40
Common Single Player:		.10	.08	.04
	Panel	1.25	.90	.50
1	Wally Joyner	.25	.20	.10
2	Tony Pena	.10	.08	.04
	Panel	1.50	1.25	.60
3	Mike Schmidt	.40	.30	.15
4	Ryne Sandberg	.40	.30	.15
	Panel	1.25	.90	.50
5	Wade Boggs	.40	.30	.15
6	Jack Morris	.10	.08	.04
	Panel	1.25	.90	.50
7	Roger Clemens	.40	.30	.15
8	Harold Baines	.15	.11	.06
	Panel	1.50	1.25	.60
9	Dale Murphy	.30	.25	.12
10	Jose Canseco	.40	.30	.15
	Panel	1.75	1.25	.70
11	Don Mattingly	.40	.30	.15
12	Gary Carter	.20	.15	.08
	Panel	2.50	2.00	1.00
13	Cal Ripken, Jr.	.40	.30	.15
14	George Brett	.40	.30	.15
	Panel	1.25	.90	.50
15	Kirby Puckett	.30	.25	.12
16	Joe Carter	.20	.15	.08
	Panel	1.00	.70	.40
17	Mike Witt	.10	.08	.04
18	Mike Scott	.10	.08	.04
	Panel	1.00	.70	.40
19	Fernando Valenzuela	.10	.08	.04
20	Steve Garvey	.20	.15	.08
	Panel	2.00	1.50	.80
21	Steve Sax	.15	.11	.06
22	Nolan Ryan	.70	.50	.30
	Panel	1.50	1.25	.60
23	Tony Gwynn	.25	.20	.10
24	Ozzie Smith	.25	.20	.10

1960 MacGregor

The MacGregor Sporting Goods Company was one of the pioneers in celebrity marketing, creating an advisory staff in 1960 to promote its products. The 25-card set features black-and-white photography of several stars and lesser lights, and even a couple of managers. The cards are 3-3/4" x 5" with a thin white border and the words "MacGregor Baseball Advisory Staff of Champions" on the bottom panel. The cards are not numbered and are blank-backed, and include a facsimile autograph in white on the front photo. The checklist is arranged here alphabetically.

		NR MT	EX	VG
Complete Set (25):		550.00	275.00	165.00
Common Player:		10.00	5.00	3.00
1	Hank Aaron	125.00	62.00	37.00
2	Richie Ashburn	30.00	15.00	9.00
3	Gus Bell	10.00	5.00	3.00
4	Lou Berberet	10.00	5.00	3.00
5	Jerry Casale	10.00	5.00	3.00
6	Del Crandall	10.00	5.00	3.00
7	Art Ditmar	10.00	5.00	3.00
8	Gene Freese	10.00	5.00	3.00
9	James Gilliam	15.00	7.50	4.50
10	Ted Kluszewski	24.00	12.00	7.25
11	Jim Landis	10.00	5.00	3.00
12	Al Lopez	15.00	7.50	4.50
13	Willie Mays	125.00	62.00	37.00
14	Bill Mazeroski	24.00	12.00	7.25
15	Mike McCormick	10.00	5.00	3.00
16	Gil McDougald	15.00	7.50	4.50
17	Russ Nixon	10.00	5.00	3.00
18	Bill Rigney	10.00	5.00	3.00
19	Robin Roberts	25.00	12.50	7.50
20	Frank Robinson	45.00	22.00	13.50
21	John Roseboro	12.50	6.25	3.75
22	Red Schoendienst	20.00	10.00	6.00
23	Bill Skowron	15.00	7.50	4.50
24	Daryl Spencer	10.00	5.00	3.00
25	Johnny Temple	10.00	5.00	3.00

1965 MacGregor

The 1965 MacGregor set is similar to earlier issues, with only a slight change in dimension to 3-1/2" x 5" and reduced in size to only 10 players. The cards are blank-backed and unnumbered and have a glossy finish. They are checklisted here alphabetically.

		NR MT	EX	VG
Complete Set (10):		275.00	137.00	82.00
Common Player:		8.00	4.00	2.50
1	Roberto Clemente	125.00	62.00	37.00
2	Al Downing	8.00	4.00	2.50
3	Johnny Edwards	8.00	4.00	2.50
4	Ron Hansen	8.00	4.00	2.50
5	Deron Johnson	8.00	4.00	2.50
6	Willie Mays	125.00	62.00	37.00
7	Tony Oliva	15.00	7.50	4.50
8	Claude Osteen	8.00	4.00	2.50
9	Bobby Richardson	12.00	6.00	3.50
10	Zoilo Versalles	8.00	4.00	2.50

1923 Walter Mails Card Game

This set of playing cards features 56 subjects. Card backs are printed in a dark blue design featuring player and umpire figures in each corner. At center is the picture of a picture with the name of the game's creator beneath. Walter Mails was a major league pitcher between 1915-26. Fronts feature a black-and-white player photo with a facsimile autograph. Printed beneath are the player's name, position and team. At bottom is the designation of a play used in the card game. Both major and minor league players are included in the set. Cards are round-cornered and measure 2-5/16" x 3-1/2". The unnumbered cards are checklisted here alphabetically.

		NR MT	EX	VG
Complete Set:		3000.	1500.	900.00
Common Player:		30.00	15.00	9.00
(1)	Russell "Buzz" Arlett	30.00	15.00	9.00
(2)	J.C. "Jim" Bagby	30.00	15.00	9.00
(3)	Dave "Beauty" Bancroft	125.00	62.00	37.00
(4)	Johnny Basseler (Bassler)	60.00	30.00	18.00
(5)	Jack Bentley	60.00	30.00	18.00
(6)	J.C. "Rube" Benton	60.00	30.00	18.00
(7)	Geo. Burns	60.00	30.00	18.00
(8)	"Bullet Joe" Bush	75.00	37.00	22.00
(9)	Harold P. Chavezo	30.00	15.00	9.00
(10)	Hugh Critz	40.00	20.00	12.00
(11)	"Jake" E. Daubert	60.00	30.00	18.00
(12)	Wheezer Dell	30.00	15.00	9.00
(13)	Joe Dugan	60.00	30.00	18.00
(14)	Pat Duncan	60.00	30.00	18.00
(15)	Howard J. Ehmke	60.00	30.00	18.00
(16)	Lewis Fonseca	60.00	30.00	18.00
(17)	Ray French	60.00	30.00	18.00
(18)	Ed Gharity	60.00	30.00	18.00
(19)	Heinie Groh	60.00	30.00	18.00
(20)	George N. Groves	30.00	15.00	9.00
(21)	E.F. "Red" Hargrave	60.00	30.00	18.00
(22)	Elmer Jacobs	60.00	30.00	18.00
(23)	Walter Johnson	500.00	250.00	150.00
(24)	WM. "Duke" Kenworthy	30.00	15.00	9.00
(25)	Harry Krause	30.00	15.00	9.00
(26)	Ray Kremer	60.00	30.00	18.00
(27)	Walter Mails	50.00	25.00	15.00
(28)	Walter "Rabbitt" Maranville	150.00	75.00	45.00
(29)	John "Stuffy" McInnis	60.00	30.00	18.00
(30)	Marty McManus	60.00	30.00	18.00
(31)	Bob Meusel	75.00	37.00	22.00
(32)	Hack Miller	60.00	30.00	18.00
(33)	Pat J. Moran	60.00	30.00	18.00
(34)	Guy Morton	60.00	30.00	18.00
(35)	Johnny Mostil	60.00	30.00	18.00
(36)	Rod Murphy	30.00	15.00	9.00
(37)	Jimmy O'Connell	60.00	30.00	18.00
(38)	Steve O'Neil	60.00	30.00	18.00
(39)	Joe Oeschger	60.00	30.00	18.00
(40)	Roger Peckinpaugh	75.00	37.00	22.00
(41)	Ralph "Babe" Pinelli	60.00	30.00	18.00
(42)	Wally Pipp	75.00	37.00	22.00
(43)	Elmer Ponder	30.00	15.00	9.00
(44)	Sam Rice	125.00	62.00	37.00
(45)	Edwin Rommell	75.00	37.00	22.00
(46)	Walter Schmidt	60.00	30.00	18.00
(47)	Wilford Shupes	30.00	15.00	9.00
(48)	Joe Sewell	125.00	62.00	37.00
(49)	Pat Shea	30.00	15.00	9.00
(50)	W. "Paddy" Siglin	30.00	15.00	9.00
(51)	Geo. H. Sisler	175.00	87.00	52.00
(52)	William "Bill" Skiff	30.00	15.00	9.00
(53)	J. Smith	60.00	30.00	18.00
(54)	Harry "Suds" Sutherland	30.00	15.00	9.00
(55)	James A. Tierney	60.00	30.00	18.00
(56)	Geo. Uhle	60.00	30.00	18.00

1969 Major League Baseball Photostamps

This set of 216 player stamps, sponsored by Major League Baseball, was issued in professional baseball's centennial year of 1969 and was sold in 18 different uncut sheets, with 12 stamps on each sheet. Each individual stamp measured 2" by 3-1/4". There were nine sheets picturing National League players and nine picturing American Leaguers. The full-color stamps displayed facsimilie autographs on

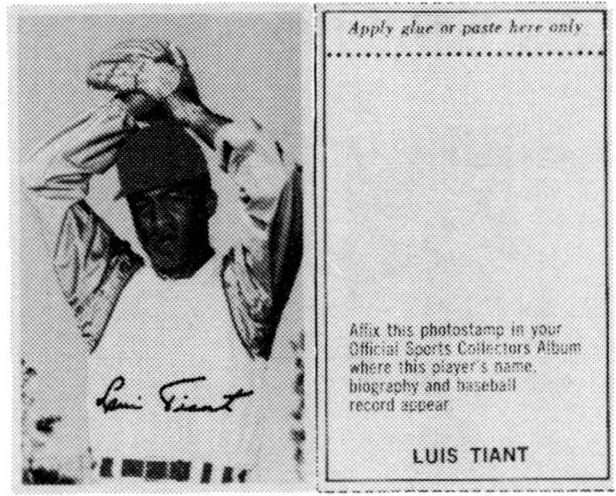

the fronts. The backs carried instructions to moisten the stamps and place them in a special album that was also available. Many sheets of these stamps were uncovered by a dealer in the early 1980's and they were available at inexpensive prices.

	NR MT	EX	VG
Complete Sheet Set:	24.00	12.00	7.25
Complete Singles Set:	18.00	9.00	5.50
Common Sheet:	.75	.40	.25
Common Player:	.10	.05	.03

No.	Player	NR MT	EX	VG
	Sheet A.L. 1	1.50	.75	.45
(1)	Don Buford	.10	.05	.03
(2)	Mike Andrews	.10	.05	.03
(3)	Max Alvis	.10	.05	.03
(4)	Bill Freehan	.20	.10	.06
(5)	Horace Clarke	.10	.05	.03
(6)	Bernie Allen	.10	.05	.03
(7)	Jim Fregosi	.10	.05	.03
(8)	Joe Horlen	.10	.05	.03
(9)	Jerry Adair	.10	.05	.03
(10)	Harmon Killebrew	.50	.25	.15
(11)	Johnny Odom	.10	.05	.03
(12)	Steve Barber	.10	.05	.03
	Sheet A.L. 2	1.00	.50	.30
(13)	Tom Harper	.10	.05	.03
(14)	Boog Powell	.20	.10	.06
(15)	Jose Santiago	.10	.05	.03
(16)	Sonny Siebert	.10	.05	.03
(17)	Mickey Lolich	.20	.10	.06
(18)	Tom Tresh	.15	.08	.05
(19)	Camilo Pascual	.10	.05	.03
(20)	Bob Rodgers	.10	.05	.03
(21)	Pete Ward	.10	.05	.03
(22)	Dave Morehead	.10	.05	.03
(23)	John Roseboro	.10	.05	.03
(24)	Bert Campaneris	.15	.08	.05
	Sheet A.L. 3	1.50	.75	.45
(25)	Danny Cater	.10	.05	.03
(26)	Rich Rollins	.10	.05	.03
(27)	Brooks Robinson	.60	.30	.20
(28)	Rico Petrocelli	.10	.05	.03
(29)	Larry Brown	.10	.05	.03
(30)	Norm Cash	.20	.10	.06
(31)	Jake Gibbs	.10	.05	.03
(32)	Mike Epstein	.10	.05	.03
(33)	George Brunet	.10	.05	.03
(34)	Tom McCraw	.10	.05	.03
(35)	Steve Whitaker	.10	.05	.03
(36)	Bob Allison	.10	.05	.03
	Sheet A.L. 4	1.00	.50	.30
(37)	Jim Kaat	.20	.10	.06
(38)	Sal Bando	.10	.05	.03
(39)	Ray Oyler	.10	.05	.03
(40)	Dave McNally	.10	.05	.03
(41)	George Scott	.10	.05	.03
(42)	Joe Azcue	.10	.05	.03
(43)	Jim Northrup	.10	.05	.03
(44)	Fritz Peterson	.10	.05	.03
(45)	Paul Casanova	.10	.05	.03
(46)	Roger Repoz	.10	.05	.03
(47)	Tommy John	.20	.10	.06
(48)	Moe Drabowsky	.10	.05	.03
	Sheet A.L. 5	1.00	.50	.30
(49)	Ed Kirkpatrick	.10	.05	.03
(50)	Dean Chance	.10	.05	.03
(51)	Mike Hershberger	.10	.05	.03
(52)	Jack Aker	.10	.05	.03
(53)	Andy Etchebarren	.10	.05	.03
(54)	Ray Culp	.10	.05	.03
(55)	Luis Tiant	.15	.08	.05
(56)	Willie Horton	.10	.05	.03
(57)	Roy White	.10	.05	.03
(58)	Ken McMullen	.10	.05	.03
(59)	Rick Reichardt	.10	.05	.03
(60)	Luis Aparicio	.35	.20	.11
	Sheet A.L. 6	1.00	.50	.30
(61)	Ken Berry	.10	.05	.03
(62)	Wally Bunker	.10	.05	.03
(63)	Tony Oliva	.20	.10	.06
(64)	Rick Monday	.10	.05	.03
(65)	Chico Salmon	.10	.05	.03
(66)	Paul Blair	.10	.05	.03
(67)	Jim Lonborg	.10	.05	.03
(68)	Zoilo Versalles	.10	.05	.03
(69)	Denny McLain	.20	.10	.06
(70)	Mel Stottlemyre	.10	.05	.03
(71)	Joe Coleman	.10	.05	.03
(72)	Bob Knoop	.10	.05	.03
	Sheet A.L. 7	1.00	.50	.30
(73)	Chuck Hinton	.10	.05	.03
(74)	Duane Josephson	.10	.05	.03
(75)	Roger Nelson	.10	.05	.03
(76)	Ted Uhlaender	.10	.05	.03
(77)	John Donaldson	.10	.05	.03
(78)	Tommy Davis	.10	.05	.03
(79)	Frank Robinson	.60	.30	.20
(80)	Dick Ellsworth	.10	.05	.03
(81)	Sam McDowell	.10	.05	.03
(82)	Dick McAuliffe	.10	.05	.03
(83)	Bill Robinson	.10	.05	.03
(84)	Frank Howard	.20	.10	.06
	Sheet A.L. 8	2.00	1.00	.60
(85)	Ed Brinkman	.10	.05	.03
(86)	Vic Davalillo	.10	.05	.03
(87)	Gary Peters	.10	.05	.03
(88)	Joe Foy	.10	.05	.03
(89)	Rod Carew	.50	.25	.15
(90)	Jim "Catfish" Hunter	.35	.20	.11
(91)	Gary Bell	.10	.05	.03
(92)	Dave Johnson	.10	.05	.03
(93)	Ken Harrelson	.10	.05	.03
(94)	Tony Horton	.10	.05	.03
(95)	Al Kaline	.50	.25	.15
(96)	Steve Hamilton	.10	.05	.03
	Sheet A.L. 9	1.00	.50	.30
(97)	Joseph Pepitone	.15	.08	.05
(98)	Ed Stroud	.10	.05	.03
(99)	Jim McGlothlin	.10	.05	.03
(100)	Wilbur Wood	.10	.05	.03
(101)	Paul Schaal	.10	.05	.03
(102)	Cesar Tovar	.10	.05	.03
(103)	Jim Nash	.10	.05	.03
(104)	Don Mincher	.10	.05	.03
(105)	Thomas Phoebus	.10	.05	.03
(106)	Reggie Smith	.10	.05	.03
(107)	Jose Cardenal	.10	.05	.03
(108)	Mickey Stanley	.10	.05	.03
	Sheet N.L. 1	2.00	1.00	.60
(109)	Billy Williams	.35	.20	.11
(110)	Mack Jones	.10	.05	.03
(111)	Tom Seaver	.50	.25	.15
(112)	Rich Allen	.20	.10	.06
(113)	Bob Veale	.10	.05	.03
(114)	Curt Flood	.15	.08	.05
(115)	Pat Jarvis	.10	.05	.03
(116)	Jim Merritt	.10	.05	.03
(117)	Joe Morgan	.35	.20	.11
(118)	Tom Haller	.10	.05	.03
(119)	Larry Stahl	.10	.05	.03
(120)	Willie McCovey	.50	.25	.15
	Sheet N.L. 2	2.50	1.25	.70
(121)	Ron Hunt	.10	.05	.03
(122)	Ernie Banks	.75	.40	.25
(123)	Jim Fairey	.10	.05	.03
(124)	Tommy Agee	.10	.05	.03
(125)	Cookie Rojas	.10	.05	.03
(126)	Mateo Alou	.10	.05	.03
(127)	Mike Shannon	.10	.05	.03
(128)	Milt Pappas	.10	.05	.03
(129)	Johnny Bench	.50	.25	.15
(130)	Larry Dierker	.10	.05	.03
(131)	Willie Davis	.15	.08	.05
(132)	Tony Gonzalez	.10	.05	.03
	Sheet N.L. 3	1.50	.75	.45
(133)	Dick Selma	.10	.05	.03
(134)	Jim Ray Hart	.10	.05	.03
(135)	Phil Regan	.10	.05	.03
(136)	Manny Mota	.10	.05	.03
(137)	Cleon Jones	.10	.05	.03
(138)	Rick Wise	.10	.05	.03
(139)	Willie Stargell	.50	.25	.15
(140)	Bobert Gibson	.35	.20	.11
(141)	Rico Carty	.10	.05	.03
(142)	Gary Nolan	.10	.05	.03
(143)	Doug Rader	.10	.05	.03
(144)	Wes Parker	.10	.05	.03
	Sheet N.L. 4	1.00	.50	.30
(145)	Bill Singer	.10	.05	.03
(146)	Bill McCool	.10	.05	.03
(147)	Juan Marichal	.35	.20	.11
(148)	Randy Hundley	.10	.05	.03
(149)	"Mudcat" Grant	.15	.08	.05
(150)	Ed Kranepool	.10	.05	.03
(151)	Tony Taylor	.10	.05	.03
(152)	Gene Alley	.10	.05	.03
(153)	Dal Maxvill	.10	.05	.03
(154)	Felipe Alou	.15	.08	.05
(155)	Jim Maloney	.10	.05	.03
(156)	Jesus Alou	.10	.05	.03
	Sheet N.L. 5	3.00	1.50	.90
(157)	Curt Blefary	.10	.05	.03
(158)	Ron Fairly	.10	.05	.03
(159)	Dick Kelley	.10	.05	.03
(160)	Frank Linzy	.10	.05	.03
(161)	Fergie Jenkins	.35	.20	.11
(162)	Maury Wills	.15	.08	.05
(163)	Jerry Grote	.10	.05	.03
(164)	Chris Short	.10	.05	.03
(165)	Jim Bunning	.15	.08	.05
(166)	Nelson Briles	.10	.05	.03
(167)	Orlando Cepeda	.20	.10	.06
(168)	Pete Rose	.75	.40	.25
	Sheet N.L. 6	1.25	.60	.40
(169)	Tony Cloninger	.10	.05	.03
(170)	Jim Wynn	.10	.05	.03
(171)	Jim Lefebvre	.10	.05	.03
(172)	Ron Davis	.10	.05	.03
(173)	Mike McCormick	.10	.05	.03
(174)	Ron Santo	.15	.08	.05
(175)	Ty Cline	.10	.05	.03
(176)	Jerry Koosman	.10	.05	.03
(177)	Mike Ryan	.10	.05	.03
(178)	Jerry May	.10	.05	.03
(179)	Tim McCarver	.15	.08	.05
(180)	Phil Niekro	.20	.10	.06
	Sheet N.L. 7	5.00	2.50	1.50
(181)	Hank Aaron	.90	.45	.25
(182)	Tommy Helms	.10	.05	.03
(183)	Denis Menke	.10	.05	.03
(184)	Don Sutton	.20	.10	.06
(185)	Al Ferrera	.10	.05	.03
(186)	Willie Mays	.90	.45	.25
(187)	Bill Hands	.10	.05	.03
(188)	Rusty Staub	.20	.10	.06
(189)	Bud Harrelson	.10	.05	.03
(190)	Johnny Callison	.10	.05	.03
(191)	Roberto Clemente	.90	.45	.25
(192)	Julian Javier	.10	.05	.03
	Sheet N.L. 8	1.00	.50	.30
(193)	Joe Torre	.20	.10	.06
(194)	Bob Aspromonte	.10	.05	.03
(195)	Lee May	.10	.05	.03
(196)	Don Wilson	.10	.05	.03
(197)	Claude Osteen	.10	.05	.03
(198)	Ed Spiezio	.10	.05	.03
(199)	Hal Lanier	.10	.05	.03
(200)	Glenn Beckert	.10	.05	.03
(201)	Bob Bailey	.10	.05	.03
(202)	Ron Swoboda	.10	.05	.03
(203)	John Briggs	.10	.05	.03
(204)	Bill Mazeroski	.25	.13	.08
	Sheet N.L. 9	1.50	.75	.45
(205)	Tommie Sisk	.10	.05	.03
(206)	Lou Brock	.45	.25	.14
(207)	Felix Millan	.10	.05	.03
(208)	Tony Perez	.20	.10	.06
(209)	John Edwards	.10	.05	.03
(210)	Len Gabrielson	.10	.05	.03
(211)	Ollie Brown	.10	.05	.03
(212)	Gaylord Perry	.35	.20	.11
(213)	Don Kessinger	.15	.08	.05
(214)	John Bateman	.10	.05	.03
(215)	Ed Charles	.10	.05	.03
(216)	Woodie Fryman	.10	.05	.03

1969 MLBPA Pins

Issued by the Major League Baseball Players Association in 1969, this unnumbered set consists of 60 pins - 30 players from the N.L. and 30 from the A.L. Each pin measures approximately 7/8" in diameter and features a black-and-white player photo. A.L. players are surrounded by a red border, while N.L. players are framed in blue. The player's name and team appear at the top and bottom. Also along the bottom is a line reading "1969 MLBPA MFG. R.R. Winona, MINN."

	NR MT	EX	VG
Complete Set:	175.00	87.00	52.00
Common Player:	.75	.40	.25

No.	Player	NR MT	EX	VG
(1)	Hank Aaron	15.00	7.50	4.50
(2)	Richie Allen	3.00	1.50	.90
(3)	Felipe Alou	1.50	.70	.45
(4)	Max Alvis	.75	.40	.25
(5)	Luis Aparicio	4.00	2.00	1.25
(6)	Ernie Banks	8.00	4.00	2.50
(7)	Johnny Bench	8.00	4.00	2.50
(8)	Lou Brock	4.00	2.00	1.25
(9)	George Brunet	.75	.40	.25
(10)	Johnny Callison	1.00	.50	.30
(11)	Rod Carew	7.00	3.50	2.00
(12)	Orlando Cepeda	3.00	1.50	.90
(13)	Dean Chance	.75	.40	.25
(14)	Roberto Clemente	15.00	7.50	4.50
(15)	Willie Davis	1.00	.50	.30
(16)	Don Drysdale	7.00	3.50	2.00
(17)	Ron Fairly	1.00	.50	.30
(18)	Curt Flood	2.50	1.25	.70
(19)	Bill Freehan	1.00	.50	.30
(20)	Jim Fregosi	1.00	.50	.30
(21)	Bob Gibson	7.00	3.50	2.00
(22)	Ken Harrelson	.75	.40	.25
(23)	Bud Harrelson	.75	.40	.25
(24)	Jim Ray Hart	.75	.40	.25
(25)	Tommy Helms	.75	.40	.25
(26)	Joe Horlen	.75	.40	.25
(27)	Willie Horton	1.00	.50	.30
(28)	Frank Howard	2.50	1.25	.70
(29)	Tony Horton	1.00	.50	.30
(30)	Al Kaline	8.00	4.00	2.50
(31)	Don Kessinger	1.00	.50	.30
(32)	Harmon Killebrew	8.00	4.00	2.50
(33)	Jerry Koosman	1.00	.50	.30
(34)	Mickey Lolich	2.00	1.00	.60
(35)	Jim Lonborg	1.00	.50	.30
(36)	Jim Maloney	.75	.40	.25
(37)	Juan Marichal	7.00	3.50	2.00
(38)	Willie Mays	15.00	7.50	4.50
(39)	Tim McCarver	2.00	1.00	.60
(40)	Willie McCovey	7.00	3.50	2.00
(41)	Sam McDowell	1.00	.50	.30
(42)	Denny McLain	2.00	1.00	.60
(43)	Rick Monday	1.00	.50	.30
(44)	Tony Oliva	2.00	1.00	.60

(45)	Joe Pepitone	1.00	.50	.30
(46)	Boog Powell	2.50	1.25	.70
(47)	Rick Reichardt	.75	.40	.25
(48)	Pete Richert	.75	.40	.25
(49)	Brooks Robinson	8.00	4.00	2.50
(50)	Frank Robinson	8.00	4.00	2.50
(51)	Pete Rose	15.00	7.50	4.50
(52)	Ron Santo	2.00	1.00	.60
(53)	Mel Stottlemyre	1.00	.50	.30
(54)	Ron Swoboda	.75	.40	.25
(55)	Luis Tiant	1.00	.50	.30
(56)	Joe Torre	1.50	.70	.45
(57)	Pete Ward	.75	.40	.25
(58)	Billy Williams	5.00	2.50	1.50
(59)	Jim Wynn	1.00	.50	.30
(60)	Carl Yastrzemski	15.00	7.50	4.50

1923 Maple Crispette

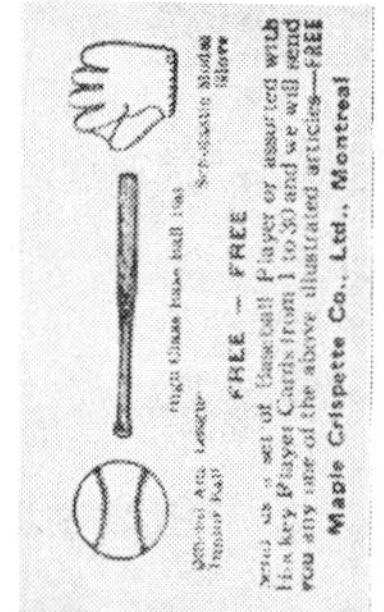

Issued by a Montreal candy company, these small (1-3/8x2-1/4") black-and-white cards were redeemable for baseball equipment, accounting for their scarcity today. Card #15, Stengel, was only discovered in late 1992 and was obviously short-printed by the issuer to avoid giving away many bats, balls and gloves.

		NR MT	EX	VG
Complete Set:		11000.	5500.	3300.
Common Player:		90.00	45.00	27.00
1	Jesse Barnes	90.00	45.00	27.00
2	Harold Traynor	300.00	150.00	90.00
3	Ray Schalk	300.00	150.00	90.00
4	Eddie Collins	300.00	150.00	90.00
5	Lee Fohl	90.00	45.00	27.00
6	Howard Summa	90.00	45.00	27.00
7	Waite Hoyt	300.00	150.00	90.00
8	Babe Ruth	3600.	1800.	1000.
9	Cozy Dolan	90.00	45.00	27.00
10	Johnny Bassler	90.00	45.00	27.00
11	George Dauss	90.00	45.00	27.00
12	Joe Sewell	300.00	150.00	90.00
13	Syl Johnson	90.00	45.00	27.00
14	Ivy Wingo	90.00	45.00	27.00
15	Casey Stengel	1200.	600.00	360.00
16	Arnold Statz	90.00	45.00	27.00
17	Emil Meusel	90.00	45.00	27.00
18	Bill Jacobson	90.00	45.00	27.00
19	Jim Bottomley	300.00	150.00	90.00
20	Sam Bohne	90.00	45.00	27.00
21	Bucky Harris	300.00	150.00	90.00
22	Ty Cobb	2100.	1000.	600.00
23	Roger Peckinpaugh	90.00	45.00	27.00
24	Muddy Ruel	90.00	45.00	27.00
25	Bill McKechnie	300.00	150.00	90.00
26	Riggs Stephenson	90.00	45.00	27.00
27	Herb Pennock	300.00	150.00	90.00
28	Edd Roush	300.00	150.00	90.00
29	Bill Wambsganss	90.00	45.00	27.00
30	Walter Johnson	1400.	700.00	420.00

1989 Marathon Cubs

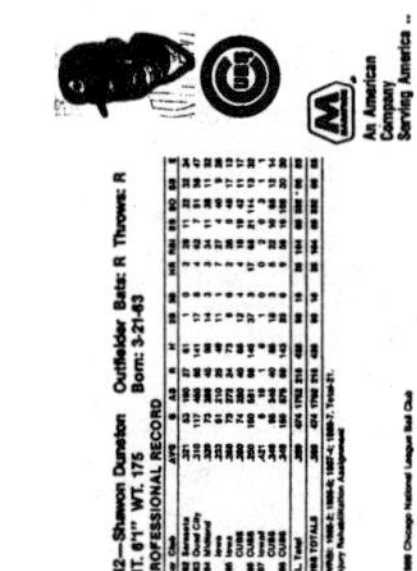

This colorful 25-card Cubs team set was sponsored by Marathon and was distributed as a stadium promotion to fans attending the August 10, 1989, game at Chicago's Wrigley Field. The oversize (2-3/4" by 4-1/4") feature an action photo inside a diagonal box on the card front, with the Chicago Cubs logo at the top and the player's uniform number, name and position along the bottom. The backs include a small black-and-white photo, player data and the Cubs and Marathon logos.

		MT	NR MT	EX
Complete Set:		8.00	6.00	3.25
Common Player:		.10	.08	.04
2	Vance Law	.10	.08	.04
4	Don Zimmer	.15	.11	.06
7	Joe Girardi	.50	.40	.20
8	Andre Dawson	.70	.50	.30
9	Damon Berryhill	.10	.08	.04
10	Lloyd McClendon	.10	.08	.04
12	Shawon Dunston	.50	.40	.20
15	Domingo Ramos	.10	.08	.04
17	Mark Grace	.75	.60	.30
18	Dwight Smith	.20	.15	.08
19	Curt Wilkerson	.10	.08	.04
20	Jerome Walton	.20	.15	.08
21	Scott Sanderson	.20	.15	.08
23	Ryne Sandberg	3.00	2.25	1.25
28	Mitch Williams	.40	.30	.15
31	Greg Maddux	.90	.70	.35
32	Calvin Schiraldi	.10	.08	.04
33	Mitch Webster	.10	.08	.04
36	Mike Bielecki	.10	.08	.04
39	Paul Kilgus	.10	.08	.04
40	Rick Sutcliffe	.40	.30	.15
41	Jeff Pico	.10	.08	.04
44	Steve Wilson	.10	.08	.04
50	Les Lancaster	.15	.11	.06
----	Coaches (Joe Altobelli, Chuck Cottier, Larry Cox, Jose Martinez, Dick Pole)	.10	.08	.04

The values quoted are intended to reflect the market price.

1989 Marathon Tigers

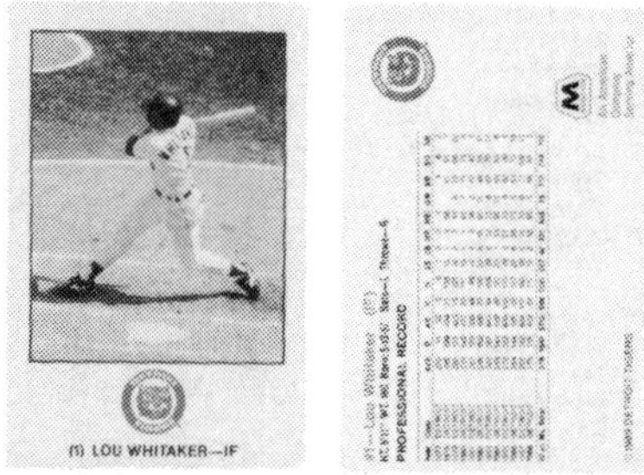

Marathon sponsored this give-away set for a 1989 Tigers home game. The oversized cards feature thin white stock and full-color player photos. The cards are numbered according to uniform number.

		MT	NR MT	EX
Complete Set:		7.00	5.25	2.75
Common Player:		.10	.08	.04
1	Lou Whitaker	.50	.40	.20
3	Alan Trammell	.60	.45	.25
8	Mike Heath	.10	.08	.04
9	Fred Lynn	.30	.25	.12
10	Keith Moreland	.10	.08	.04
11	Sparky Anderson	.40	.30	.15
12	Mike Brumley	.10	.08	.04
14	Dave Bergman	.10	.08	.04
15	Pat Sheridan	.10	.08	.04
17	Al Pedrique	.10	.08	.04
18	Ramon Pena	.10	.08	.04
19	Doyle Alexander	.10	.08	.04
21	Guillermo Hernandez	.20	.15	.08
23	Torey Lovullo	.30	.25	.12
24	Gary Pettis	.20	.15	.08
25	Ken Williams	.10	.08	.04
26	Frank Tanana	.20	.15	.08
27	Charles Hudson	.10	.08	.04
32	Gary Ward	.10	.08	.04
33	Matt Nokes	.40	.30	.15
34	Chet Lemon	.25	.20	.10
35	Rick Schu	.10	.08	.04
36	Frank Williams	.10	.08	.04
39	Mike Henneman	.30	.25	.12
44	Jeff Robinson	.20	.15	.08
47	Jack Morris	.40	.30	.15
48	Paul Gibson	.10	.08	.04
----	Coaches (Billy Consolo, Alex Grammas, Billy Muffett, Vada Pinson, Dick Tracewski)	.10	.08	.04

Values for recent cards and sets are listed in Mint (MT), Near Mint (NM), reflecting the fact that many cards from recent years have been preserved in top condition. Recent cards and sets in less than Excellent condition have little collector interest.

1990 Marathon Cubs

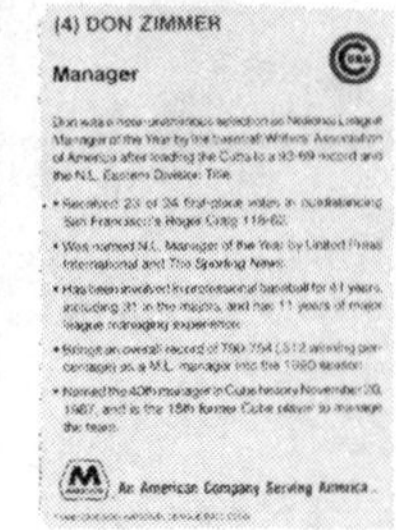

Marathon sponsored its second consecutive Chicago Cubs team set. The oversized cards feature thin white stock and full-color photos. The cards are numbered according to uniform number, and were distributed at a Cubs home game.

		MT	NR MT	EX
Complete Set:		8.00	6.00	3.25
Common Player:		.10	.08	.04
4	Don Zimmer	.15	.11	.06
7	Joe Girardi	.20	.15	.08
8	Andre Dawson	.60	.45	.25
10	Lloyd McClendon	.10	.08	.04
11	Luis Salazar	.10	.08	.04
12	Shawon Dunston	.50	.40	.20
15	Domingo Ramos	.10	.08	.04
17	Mark Grace	.75	.60	.30
18	Dwight Smith	.20	.15	.08
19	Curtis Wilkerson	.10	.08	.04
20	Jerome Walton	.10	.08	.04
22	Mike Harkey	.40	.30	.15
23	Ryne Sandberg	3.00	2.25	1.25
25	Marvell Wynne	.10	.08	.04
28	Mitch Williams	.30	.25	.12
29	Doug Dascenzo	.20	.15	.08
30	Dave Clark	.10	.08	.04
31	Greg Maddux	.75	.60	.30
32	Hector Villanueva	.40	.30	.15
36	Mike Bielecki	.20	.15	.08
37	Bill Long	.10	.08	.04
40	Rick Sutcliffe	.30	.25	.12
41	Jeff Pico	.10	.08	.04
44	Steve Wilson	.10	.08	.04
45	Paul Assenmacher	.10	.08	.04
47	Shawn Boskie	.30	.25	.12
50	Les Lancaster	.10	.08	.04
----	Coaches (Joe Altobelli, Chuck Cottier, Jose Martinez, Dick Pole, Phil Roof)	.10	.08	.04

A player's name in italic type indicates a rookie card. An (FC) indicates a player's first card for that particular card company.

1991 Marathon Cubs

Marathon Oil once again sponsored a set featuring the Chicago Cubs. This 28-card release features oversized cards measuring 2-7/8" by 4-1/4". The card fronts feature full-color action photos. The flip sides feature complete statistics. The cards are numbered according to uniform number. This number appears on both the front and back of the card.

		MT	NR MT	EX
Complete Set:		7.00	5.25	2.75
Common Player:		.20	.15	.08
7	Joe Girardi	.25	.20	.10
8	Andre Dawson	.80	.60	.30
9	Damon Berryhill	.20	.15	.08
10	Luis Salazar	.20	.15	.08
11	George Bell	.35	.25	.14
12	Shawon Dunston	.35	.25	.14
16	Jose Vizcaino	.45	.35	.20
17	Mark Grace	.70	.50	.30
18	Dwight Smith	.20	.15	.08
19	Hector Villanueva	.20	.15	.08
20	Jerome Walton	.20	.15	.08
22	Mike Harkey	.30	.25	.12
23	Ryne Sandberg	2.00	1.50	.80
24	Chico Walker	.20	.15	.08
29	Doug Dascenzo	.20	.15	.08
30	Bob Scanlan	.20	.15	.08
31	Greg Maddux	.60	.45	.25
32	Danny Jackson	.25	.20	.10
35	Chuck McElroy	.20	.15	.08
36	Mike Bielecki	.20	.15	.08
40	Rick Sutcliffe	.35	.25	.14
41	Jim Essian	.20	.15	.08
42	Dave Smith	.20	.15	.08
45	Paul Assenmacher	.20	.15	.08
47	Shawn Boskie	.30	.25	.12
50	Les Lancaster	.20	.15	.08
51	Heathcliff Slocumb	.20	.15	.08
----	(Joe Altobelli, Billy Connors, Chuck Cottier, Jose Martinez, Phil Roof, Richie Zisk)	.20	.15	.08

1992 Marathon Cubs

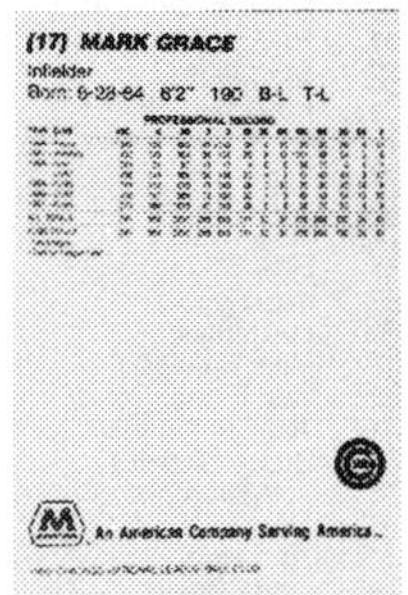

The fourth consecutive year of a Cubs team set sponsored by Marathon Oil consists of 28 cards, including manager Jim Lefebvre and his coaching staff. The set was originally given away at the July 10, 1993 game at Wrigley Field. Cards are checklisted here by uniform number.

		MT	NR MT	EX
Complete Set (28):		9.00	6.75	3.50
Common Player:		.25	.20	.10
1	Doug Strange	.35	.25	.14
2	Frank Castillo	.25	.20	.10
5	Jim Lefebvre	.25	.20	.10
6	Rey Sanchez	.25	.20	.10
7	Joe Girardi	.35	.25	.14
8	Andre Dawson	.60	.45	.25
10	Luis Salazar	.25	.20	.10
12	Shawon Dunston	.60	.45	.25
16	Jose Vazcaino	.35	.25	.14
17	Mark Grace	.75	.60	.30
18	Dwight Smith	.25	.20	.10
19	Hector Villanueva	.25	.20	.10
20	Jerome Walton	.25	.20	.10
21	Sammy Sosa	.60	.45	.25
23	Ryne Sandberg	3.00	2.25	1.25
27	Derrick May	.60	.45	.25
29	Doug Dascenzo	.25	.20	.10
30	Bob Scanlan	.25	.20	.10
31	Greg Maddux	.75	.60	.30
32	Danny Jackson	.25	.20	.10
34	Ken Patterson	.25	.20	.10
35	Chuck McElroy	.25	.20	.10
36	Mike Morgan	.25	.20	.10
38	Jeff Robinson	.25	.20	.10
42	Dave Smith	.25	.20	.10
45	Paul Assenmacher	.25	.20	.10
47	Shawn Boskie	.25	.20	.10
----	Coaches (Tom Trebelhorn, Jose Martinez, Billy Williams, Sammy Ellis, Chuck Cottier, Billy Connors)	.10	.08	.04

1993 Marathon Cubs

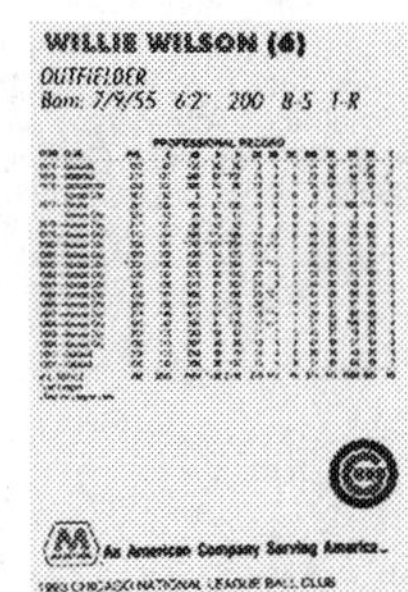

The Cubs distributed the 1993 Marathon Oil set on July 28 in a game against the Padres. The cards, measuring an oversized 4-1/4" x 2-7/8", are unnumbered, with uniform numbers appearing on the back. The cards have a vertical blue stripe down the right side with the player's last name in large, white letters. Backs carry complete major and minor league statistics. There are 27 cards in the set. The checklist is presented here by uniform number.

		MT	NR MT	EX
Complete Set (27):		8.00	6.00	3.25
Common Player:		.25	.20	.10
2	Rick Wilkins	.40	.30	.15
5	Jim Lefebvre	.25	.20	.10
6	Willie Wilson	.30	.25	.12
10	Steve Lake	.25	.20	.10
11	Rey Sanchez	.25	.20	.10
16	Jose Vizcaino	.25	.20	.10
17	Mark Grace	.60	.45	.25
18	Dwight Smith	.25	.20	.10
20	Eric Yelding	.25	.20	.10
21	Sammy Sosa	.40	.30	.15
22	Mike Harkey	.25	.20	.10
23	Ryne Sandberg	2.00	1.50	.80
24	Steve Buechele	.35	.25	.14
25	Candy Maldonado	.25	.20	.10
27	Derrick May	.35	.25	.14
28	Randy Myers	.30	.25	.12
29	Jose Guzman	.25	.20	.10
30	Bob Scanlan	.25	.20	.10
32	Dan Plesac	.25	.20	.10
36	Mike Morgan	.25	.20	.10
37	Greg Hibbard	.25	.20	.10
38	Jose Bautista	.25	.20	.10
45	Paul Assenmacher	.25	.20	.10
49	Frank Castillo	.25	.20	.10
53	Doug Jennings	.25	.20	.10
----	Coaches (Billy Williams, Jose Martinez, Billy Connors, Tony Muser)	.25	.20	.10
----	Coaches (Dan Simonds, Tom Treblehorn, Chuck Cottier)	.25	.20	.10

1988 Master Bread Twins

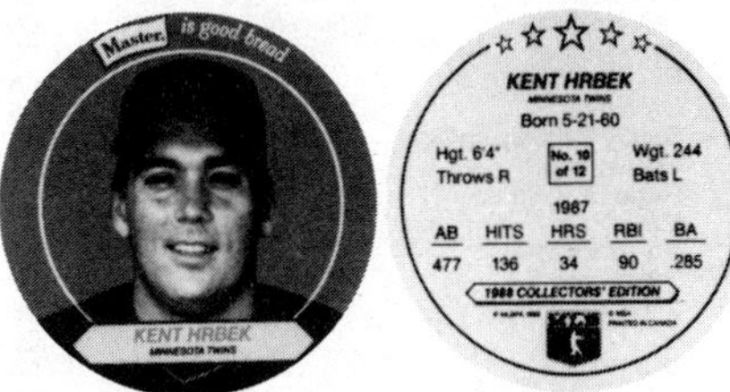

This set of 12 cardboard discs (2-3/4" diameter) features full-color photos of Minnesota Twins team members. Disc fronts have a bright blue background with red, yellow and black printing. A thin white line frames the player photo which is centered beneath a "Master Is Good Bread" headliner and a vivid yellow player/team name banner. Disc backs are black and white with five stars printed above the player's name, team, personal data, disc number, stats and "1988 Collector's Edition" banner. The discs were printed in Canada and marketed exclusively in Minnesota in packages of Master Bread, one disc per loaf.

		MT	NR MT	EX
Complete Set:		12.00	9.00	4.75
Common Player:		.50	.40	.20
1	Bert Blyleven	1.00	.70	.40
2	Frank Viola	1.50	1.25	.60
3	Juan Berenguer	.50	.40	.20
4	Jeff Reardon	.80	.60	.30
5	Tim Laudner	.50	.40	.20
6	Steve Lombardozzi	.50	.40	.20
7	Randy Bush	.50	.40	.20
8	Kirby Puckett	4.00	3.00	1.50
9	Gary Gaetti	1.75	1.25	.70
10	Kent Hrbek	1.75	1.25	.70
11	Greg Gagne	.70	.50	.30
12	Tom Brunansky	.50	.40	.20

1895 Mayo's Cut Plug (N300)

These 1-5/8" by 2-7/8" cards were issued by the Mayo Tobacco Works of Richmond, Virginia. There are 48 cards in the set, with 40 different players pictured. Twenty-eight of the players are pictured in uniform and 12 are shown in street clothes. Eight players appear both ways. Eight of the uniformed players also appear in two variations, creating the 48-card total. Card fronts are black and white or sepia portraits on black cardboard, with a Mayo's Cut Pug ad at the bottom of each card. Cards are unnumbered.

		NR MT	EX	VG
Complete Set:		23500.	11750.	7000.
Common Player:		350.00	175.00	105.00
(1)	Charlie Abbey	350.00	175.00	105.00
(2)	Cap Anson	2400.	1200.	720.00
(3)	Jimmy Bannon	350.00	175.00	105.00
(4a)	Dan Brouthers (Baltimore on shirt)	900.00	450.00	270.00
(4b)	Dan Brouthers (Louisville on shirt)	1000.	500.00	300.00
(5)	Ed Cartwright	350.00	175.00	105.00
(6)	John Clarkson	900.00	450.00	270.00
(7)	Tommy Corcoran	350.00	175.00	105.00
(8)	Lave Cross	350.00	175.00	105.00
(9)	Bill Dahlen	350.00	175.00	105.00
(10)	Tom Daly	350.00	175.00	105.00
(11)	Ed Delehanty (Delahanty)	1000.	500.00	300.00
(12)	Hugh Duffy	900.00	450.00	270.00
(13a)	Buck Ewing (Cleveland on shirt)	900.00	450.00	270.00
(13b)	Buck Ewing (Cincinnati on shirt)	1000.	500.00	300.00
(14)	Dave Foutz	350.00	175.00	105.00
(15)	Charlie Ganzel	350.00	175.00	105.00
(16a)	Jack Glasscock (Pittsburg on shirt)	350.00	175.00	105.00
(16b)	Jack Glasscock (Louisville on shirt)	400.00	200.00	120.00
(17)	Mike Griffin	350.00	175.00	105.00
(18a)	George Haddock (no team on shirt)	400.00	200.00	120.00
(18b)	George Haddock (Philadelphia on shirt)	350.00	175.00	105.00
(19)	Bill Hallman	350.00	175.00	105.00
(20)	Billy Hamilton	900.00	450.00	270.00
(21)	Bill Joyce	350.00	175.00	105.00
(22)	Brickyard Kennedy	350.00	175.00	105.00
(23a)	Tom Kinslow (no team on shirt)	400.00	200.00	120.00
(23b)	Tom Kinslow (Pittsburg on shirt)	350.00	175.00	105.00
(24)	Arlie Latham	350.00	175.00	105.00
(25)	Herman Long	350.00	175.00	105.00
(26)	Tom Lovett	350.00	175.00	105.00
(27)	Bobby Lowe	400.00	200.00	120.00
(28)	Tommy McCarthy	775.00	387.00	232.00
(29)	Yale Murphy	350.00	175.00	105.00
(30)	Billy Nash	350.00	175.00	105.00
(31)	Kid Nichols	950.00	475.00	285.00
(32a)	Fred Pfeffer (2nd Base)	350.00	175.00	105.00
(32b)	Fred Pfeffer (Retired)	400.00	200.00	120.00
(33)	Wilbert Robinson	975.00	487.00	292.00
(34a)	Amos Russie (incorrect spelling)	975.00	487.00	292.00
(34b)	Amos Rusie (correct spell)	900.00	450.00	270.00
(35)	Jimmy Ryan	350.00	175.00	105.00
(36)	Bill Shindle	350.00	175.00	105.00
(37)	Germany Smith	350.00	175.00	105.00
(38)	Otis Stocksdale (Stockdale)	350.00	175.00	105.00
(39)	Tommy Tucker	350.00	175.00	105.00
(40a)	Monte Ward (2nd Base)	900.00	450.00	270.00
(40b)	Monte Ward (Retired)	1000.	500.00	300.00

1896 Mayo's Die-Cut Game Cards (N301)

Mayo Tobacco Works of Richmond, Va., issued an innovative, if not very popular, series of die-cut baseball player figures in 1896. These tiny (1-1/2" long by just 3/16" wide) cardboard figures were inserted in packages of Mayo's Cut Plug Tobacco and were designed to be used as part of a baseball board game. A "grandstand, base and teetotum" were available free by mail to complete the game pieces. Twenty-eight different die-cut figures were available, representing 26 unspecified New York and Boston players along with two umpires. The players are shown in various action poses--either running, batting, pitching or fielding. The backs carry an ad for Mayo's Tobacco. The players shown do not relate to any actual members of the New York or Boston clubs, diminishing the popularity of this issue, which has an American Card Catalog designation of N301.

		NR MT	EX	VG
Complete Set:		900.00	450.00	270.00
Common Player:		35.00	17.50	10.50
(1a)	Pitcher (Boston)	35.00	17.50	10.50
(1b)	Pitcher (New York)	35.00	17.50	10.50
(2a)	1st Baseman (Boston)	35.00	17.50	10.50
(2b)	1st Baseman (New York)	35.00	17.50	10.50
(3a)	2nd Baseman (Boston)	35.00	17.50	10.50
(3b)	2nd Baseman (New York)	35.00	17.50	10.50
(4a)	3rd Baseman (Boston)	35.00	17.50	10.50
(4b)	3rd Baseman (New York)	35.00	17.50	10.50
(5a)	Right Fielder (Boston)	35.00	17.50	10.50
(5b)	Right Fielder (New York)	35.00	17.50	10.50
(6a)	Center Fielder (Boston)	35.00	17.50	10.50
(6b)	Center Fielder (New York)	35.00	17.50	10.50
(7a)	Left Fielder (Boston)	35.00	17.50	10.50
(7b)	Left Fielder (New York)	35.00	17.50	10.50
(8a)	Short Stop (Boston)	35.00	17.50	10.50
(8b)	Short Stop (New York)	35.00	17.50	10.50
(9a)	Catcher (Boston)	35.00	17.50	10.50
(9b)	Catcher (New York)	35.00	17.50	10.50
(10a)	Batman (Boston)	35.00	17.50	10.50
(10b)	Batman (New York)	35.00	17.50	10.50
(11a)	Runner (Boston, standing upright)	35.00	17.50	10.50

(11b)	Runner (New York, standing upright)	35.00	17.50	10.50
(12a)	Runner (Boston, bent slightly forward)	35.00	17.50	10.50
(12b)	Runner (New York, bent slightly forward)	35.00	17.50	10.50
(13a)	Runner (Boston, bent well forward)	35.00	17.50	10.50
(13b)	Runner (New York, bent well forward)	35.00	17.50	10.50
(14)	Umpire (facing front)	35.00	17.50	10.50
(15)	Field Umpire (rear view)	35.00	17.50	10.50

1900 Mayo's Baseball Comics (T203)

As their name implies, the T203 Baseball Comics feature cartoon-like drawings that illustrate various baseball phrases and terminology. Issued with Winner Cut Plug and Mayo Cut Plug tobacco products, the complete set consists of 25 different comics, each measuring approximately 2-1/16" by 3-1/8". Because they do not picture individual players, these cards have never attracted much of a following among serious baseball card collectors. They do, however, hold some interest as a novelty item of the period.

		NR MT	EX	VG
Complete Set:		600.00	300.00	180.00
Common Player:		25.00	12.50	7.50
(1)	"A Crack Outfielder"	25.00	12.50	7.50
(2)	"A Fancy Twirler"	25.00	12.50	7.50
(3)	"A Fine Slide"	25.00	12.50	7.50
(4)	"A Fowl Bawl"	25.00	12.50	7.50
(5)	"A Great Game"	25.00	12.50	7.50
(6)	"A Home Run"	25.00	12.50	7.50
(7)	"An All Star Battery"	25.00	12.50	7.50
(8)	"A Short Stop"	25.00	12.50	7.50
(9)	"A Star Catcher"	25.00	12.50	7.50
(10)	"A White Wash"	25.00	12.50	7.50
(11)	"A Tie Game"	25.00	12.50	7.50
(12)	"A Two Bagger"	25.00	12.50	7.50
(13)	"A Wild Pitch"	25.00	12.50	7.50
(14)	"Caught Napping"	25.00	12.50	7.50
(15)	"On To The Curves"	25.00	12.50	7.50
(16)	"Out"	25.00	12.50	7.50
(17)	"Put Out On 1st"	25.00	12.50	7.50
(18)	"Right Over The Plate"	25.00	12.50	7.50
(19)	"Rooting For The Home Team"	25.00	12.50	7.50
(20)	"Stealing A Base"	25.00	12.50	7.50
(21)	"Stealing Home"	25.00	12.50	7.50
(22)	"Strike One"	25.00	12.50	7.50
(23)	"The Bleacher"	25.00	12.50	7.50
(24)	"The Naps"	25.00	12.50	7.50
(25)	"The Red Sox"	25.00	12.50	7.50

1970 McDonald's Brewers

Milwaukee in 1970 by issuing a set of six baseball card panels. Five of the panels picture five players and a team logo, while the sixth panel contains six players, resulting in 31 different players. The panels measure 9" by 9-1/2" and feature full-color paintings of the players. Each sheet displays the heading, "The original Milwaukee Brewers, 1970". The cards are unnumbered and the backs are blank. Although distributed by McDonald's, their name does not appear on the cards.

		NR MT	EX	VG
Complete Sheet:		8.00	4.00	2.50
Complete Singles Set:		5.00	2.50	1.50
Common Player:		.20	.10	.06
1	Ted Kubiak	.20	.10	.06
2	Ted Savage	.20	.10	.06
4	Dave Bristol	.20	.10	.06
5	Phil Roof	.20	.10	.06
6	Mike Hershberger	.20	.10	.06
7	Russ Snyder	.20	.10	.06
8	Mike Hegan	.20	.10	.06
9	Rich Rollins	.20	.10	.06
10	Max Alvis	.20	.10	.06
11	John Kennedy	.20	.10	.06
12	Dan Walton	.20	.10	.06
15	Jerry McNertney	.20	.10	.06
18	Wes Stock	.20	.10	.06
20	Wayne Comer	.20	.10	.06
21	Tommy Harper	.30	.15	.09
23	Bob Locker	.20	.10	.06
24	Lew Krausse	.20	.10	.06
25	John Gelnar	.20	.10	.06
26	Roy McMillan	.20	.10	.06
27	Cal Ermer	.20	.10	.06
28	Sandy Valdespino	.20	.10	.06
30	Jackie Moore	.20	.10	.06
32	Gene Brabender	.20	.10	.06
33	Marty Pattin	.20	.10	.06
34	Greg Goossen	.20	.10	.06
35	John Morris	.20	.10	.06
36	Steve Hovley	.20	.10	.06
38	Bob Meyer	.20	.10	.06
39	Bob Bolin	.20	.10	.06
43	John O'Donoghue	.20	.10	.06
49	George Lauzerique	.20	.10	.06
----	Logo Card	.20	.10	.06

A card number in parentheses () indicates the set is unnumbered.

1992 McDonald's Cardinals

Pacific Trading Cards and McDonald's combined in 1992 to produce this 55-card (plus checklist) team set for the benefit of Ronald McDonald Children's Charities on the occasion of the St. Louis Cardinals' 100th anniversary. Sets were sold initially for $1.49. Cards are standard 2-1/2" x 3-1/2" size and UV coated on each side. There is a sepia-toned or color photo on both front and back; generally an action photo on front and a portrait on back. Player selection is largely weighted to the last half of the 20th Century, with only a few cards of players predating the Gashouse Gang era. The front design is completed with a Cardinals anniversary logo in the upper-left corner, a McDonalds logo at lower-right and gold stripes top and bottom. The player's name and position appear in red at the bottom of the photo. Besides the portrait photo, backs have a career summary stats for the player's Cardinals year and major league career and all appropriate logos.

		MT	NR MT	EX
Complete Set (55):		18.00	13.50	7.25
Common Player:		.25	.20	.10
1	Jim Bottomley	.50	.40	.20
2	Rip Collins	.25	.20	.10
3	Johnny Mize	.50	.40	.20
4	Rogers Hornsby	.75	.60	.30
5	Miller Huggins	.30	.25	.12
6	Marty Marion	.30	.25	.12
7	Frank Frisch	.35	.25	.14
8	Whitey Kurowski	.25	.20	.10
9	Joe Medwick	.25	.20	.10
10	Terry Moore	.25	.20	.10
11	Chick Hafey	.25	.20	.10
12	Pepper Martin	.35	.25	.14
13	Bob O'Farrell	.25	.20	.10
14	Walker Cooper	.25	.20	.10
15	Dizzy Dean	1.50	1.25	.60
16	Grover Cleveland Alexander	.75	.60	.30
17	Jesse Haines	.25	.20	.10
18	Bill Hallahan	.25	.20	.10
19	Mort Cooper	.25	.20	.10
20	Burleigh Grimes	.25	.20	.10
21	Red Schoendienst	.35	.25	.14
22	Stan Musial	2.00	1.50	.80
23	Enos Slaughter	.35	.25	.14
24	Keith Hernandez	.30	.25	.12
25	Bill White	.25	.20	.10
26	Orlando Cepeda	.30	.25	.12
27	Julian Javier	.25	.20	.10
28	Dick Groat	.25	.20	.10
29	Ken Boyer	.30	.25	.12
30	Lou Brock	.35	.25	.14
31	Mike Shannon	.25	.20	.10
32	Curt Flood	.30	.25	.12
33	Joe Cunningham	.25	.20	.10
34	Reggie Smith	.25	.20	.10
35	Ted Simmons	.25	.20	.10
36	Tim McCarver	.35	.25	.14
37	Tom Herr	.25	.20	.10
38	Ozzie Smith	.50	.40	.20
39	Joe Torre	.25	.20	.10
40	Terry Pendleton	.30	.25	.12
41	Ken Reitz	.25	.20	.10
42	Vince Coleman	.30	.25	.12
43	Willie McGee	.30	.25	.12
44	Bake McBride	.25	.20	.10
45	George Hendrick	.25	.20	.10
46	Bob Gibson	1.00	.70	.40
47	Whitey Herzog	.30	.25	.12
48	Harry Brecheen	.25	.20	.10
49	Howard Pollet	.25	.20	.10
50	John Tudor	.25	.20	.10
51	Bob Forsch	.25	.20	.10
52	Bruce Sutter	.25	.20	.10
53	Lee Smith	.30	.25	.12
54	Todd Worrell	.25	.20	.10
55	Al Hrabosky	.25	.20	.10
----	Checklist	.25	.20	.10

1974 McDonalds Padres Discs

Envisioned as the first in a line of sports promotional sets, this concept died following the test with San Diego area McDonalds. At the July 30, 1974, game, Padres fans were given a hinged plastic baseball containing five Padres player photo discs plus a dsic with the team's schedule and a Ronald McDonald disc which listed the dates on which the remaining eight player cards would be distributed at area McDonalds. Only 60,000 of the "starter set" discs were made, while 180,000 of each of the other player discs were printed. The 2-3/8" diameter discs feature a color photo on front and player stats on back. The promotion was the work of Photo Sports, Inc., of Los Angeles.

		NR MT	EX	VG
Complete Set (15):		125.00	90.00	50.00
Common Player:		3.00	1.50	.90
(1)	Matty Alou	3.00	1.50	.90
(2)	Glenn Beckert	9.00	4.50	2.50
(3)	Nate Colbert	3.00	1.50	.90
(4)	Bill Grief	3.00	1.50	.90
(5)	John Grubb	3.00	1.50	.90
(6)	Enzo Hernandez	9.00	4.50	2.50
(7)	Randy Jones	9.00	4.50	2.50
(8)	Fred Kendall	9.00	4.50	2.50
(9)	Willie McCovey	15.00	7.50	4.50
(10)	John McNamara	9.00	4.50	2.50
(11)	Dave Roberts	3.00	1.50	.90
(12)	Bobby Tolan	3.00	1.50	.90
(13)	Dave Winfield	45.00	34.00	18.00
(14)	Padres home game schedule	6.00	3.00	1.75
(15)	Ronald McDonald	9.00	4.50	2.50

1991 McDonald's Cleveland Indians

Distributed only at northern Ohio area McDonalds, this 30-card set features the players, coaches and manager of the Indians on an oversize (2-7/8" x 4-1/4") format. Color photos on front are framed in white and red with a white border all around. In the upper-left corner is a "Tribe Kids Fan Club" logo, while the McDonald's logo appears at

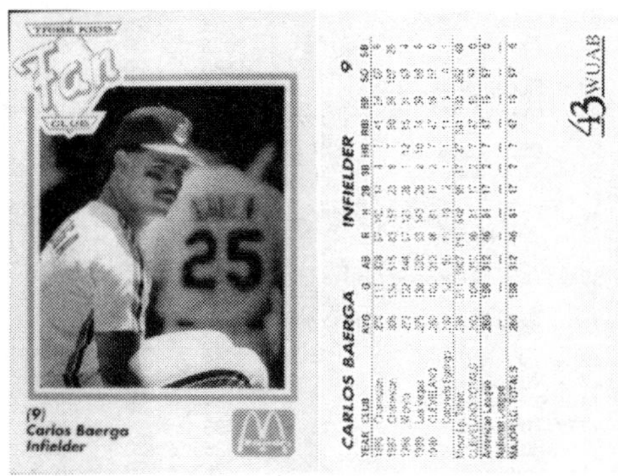

lower-right. The player's uniform number, name and position are in black at lower-left. Backs are printed in black and have complete major and minor league statistics.

		MT	NR MT	EX
Complete Set (30):		6.00	4.50	2.50
Common Player:		.10	.08	.04
1	John McNamara	.10	.08	.04
2	Alex Cole	.10	.08	.04
4	Joel Skinner	.10	.08	.04
6	Jose Escobar	.10	.08	.04
7	Chris James	.10	.08	.04
8	Albert Belle	1.50	1.25	.60
9	Carlos Baerga	1.50	1.25	.60
11	Doug Jones	.10	.08	.04
14	Jerry Browne	.10	.08	.04
15	Sandy Alomar	.25	.20	.10
16	Felix Fermin	.10	.08	.04
20	Turner Ward	.25	.20	.10
21	Greg Swindell	.50	.40	.20
23	Mitch Webster	.10	.08	.04
26	Brook Jacoby	.10	.08	.04
27	Dave Otto	.10	.08	.04
31	Steve Olin	.10	.08	.04
37	Beau Allred	.10	.08	.04
38	Shawn Hillegas	.10	.08	.04
40	Eric King	.10	.08	.04
41	Charles Nagy	.50	.40	.20
44	Mike Huff	.10	.08	.04
45	Jeff Manto	.10	.08	.04
46	Bruce Egloff	.10	.08	.04
47	Jesse Orosco	.10	.08	.04
48	Mike Walker	.10	.08	.04
49	Tom Candiotti	.10	.08	.04
52	John Farrell	.10	.08	.04
54	Rod Nichols	.10	.08	.04
----	Cleveland Indians Coaches (Billy Williams, Jose Morales, Rich Dauer, Mike Hargrove, Luis Isaac, Mark Wiley)	.10	.08	.04

1992 McDonald's Baseball's Best

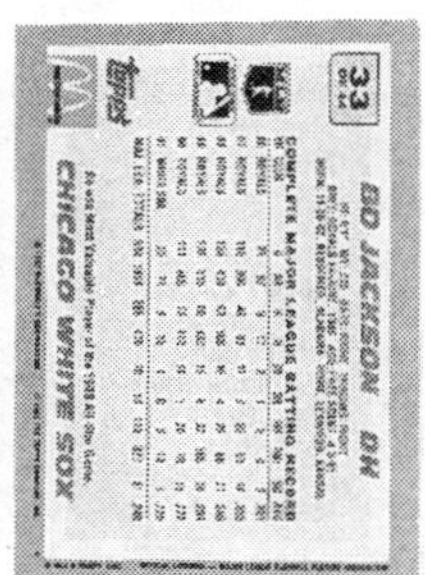

Sold in five-card cello packs with a food purchase at McDonald's stores in New York, New Jersey and Connecticut, this 44-card set was produced by Topps and carries the Topps logo, along with the Golden Arches, on front and back. Player photos on front are framed in yellow, surrounded by a black border. A red and blue "Baseball's Best" logo appears at top-right of the photo. Above that is a gold-foil stripe announcing "Limited Edition". At lower-right is another gold-foil stripe with the McDonald's logo and the player's name embossed thereon. On cards #34-44, which were distributed one per pack, there is an additional gold embossed "Rookie" shield at upper-left. Backs have a red border with a yellow stat box at center framed in white.

		MT	NR MT	EX
Complete Set (44):		25.00	18.50	10.00
Common Player:		.15	.11	.06
1	Cecil Fielder	.90	.70	.35
2	Benito Santiago	.25	.20	.10
3	Rickey Henderson	.90	.70	.35
4	Roberto Alomar	.90	.70	.35
5	Ryne Sandberg	1.50	1.25	.60
6	George Brett	1.50	1.25	.60
7	Terry Pendleton	.15	.11	.06
8	Ken Griffey, Jr.	2.50	2.00	1.00
9	Bobby Bonilla	.25	.20	.10
10	Roger Clemens	.35	.25	.14
11	Ozzie Smith	.60	.45	.25
12	Barry Bonds	1.25	.90	.50
13	Cal Ripken, Jr.	1.50	1.25	.60
14	Ron Gant	.25	.20	.10
15	Carlton Fisk	.25	.20	.10
16	Steve Avery	.25	.20	.10
17	Robin Yount	1.50	1.25	.60
18	Will Clark	.90	.70	.35
19	Kirby Puckett	1.00	.70	.40
20	Jim Abbott	.25	.20	.10
21	Barry Larkin	.25	.20	.10
22	Jose Canseco	.90	.70	.35
23	Howard Johnson	.25	.20	.10
24	Nolan Ryan	2.50	2.00	1.00
25	Frank Thomas	2.50	2.00	1.00
26	Danny Tartabull	.15	.11	.06
27	Julio Franco	.15	.11	.06
28	David Justice	.45	.35	.20
29	Joe Carter	.25	.20	.10
30	Dale Murphy	.35	.25	.14
31	Andre Dawson	.35	.25	.14
32	Dwight Gooden	.25	.20	.10
33	Bo Jackson	.60	.45	.25
34	Jeff Bagwell	.35	.25	.14
35	Chuck Knoblauch	.35	.25	.14
36	Derek Bell	.15	.11	.06
37	Jim Thome	.35	.25	.14
38	Royce Clayton	.35	.25	.14
39	Ryan Klesko	.45	.35	.20
40	Chito Martinez	.25	.20	.10
41	Ivan Rodriguez	.35	.25	.14
42	Todd Hundley	.15	.11	.06
43	Eric Karros	.35	.25	.14
44	Todd Van Poppel	.35	.25	.14

The values quoted are intended to reflect the market price.

1993 MCI Ambassadors

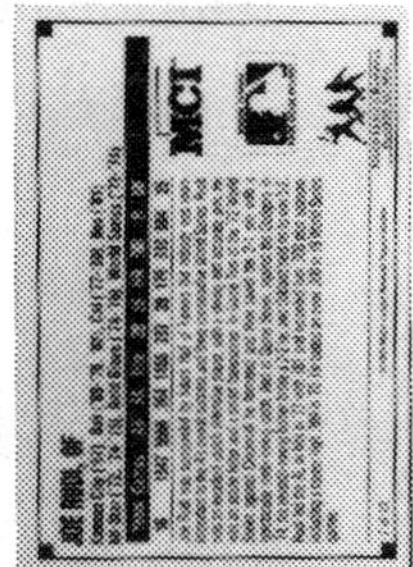

The Major League Baseball Players Alumni Association produced a set of 13 former players who were featured in 1993's MCI Ambassadors of Baseball World Tour. The card set was available free to military personnel who completed an MCI application. The tour of military bases worldwide included appearances by the players at base exchanges, clinics for dependent children and a softball game against base all-stars. The cards feature a photo of the player on the front with logos from the Ambassador tour and MCI in opposite corners.

		MT	NR MT	EX
Complete Set (14):		18.00	13.50	7.25
Common Player:		1.00	.70	.40
1	Vida Blue	1.00	.70	.40
2	Paul Blair	1.00	.70	.40
3	Mudcat Grant	1.00	.70	.40
4	Phil Niekro	1.50	1.25	.60
5	Bob Feller	4.00	3.00	1.50
6	Joe Charboneau	1.50	1.25	.60
7	Joe Rudi	1.00	.70	.40
8	Catfish Hunter	2.50	2.00	1.00
9	Manny Sanguillen	1.00	.70	.40
10	Harmon Killebrew	4.00	3.00	1.50
11	Al Oliver	1.50	1.25	.60
12	Bob Dernier	1.00	.70	.40
13	Graig Nettles, Sparky Lyle	1.50	1.25	.60
----	Header card	.25	.20	.10

Values for recent cards and sets are listed in Mint (MT), Near Mint (NM), reflecting the fact that many cards from recent years have been preserved in top condition. Recent cards and sets in less than Excellent condition have little collector interest.

1986 Meadow Gold Blank Backs

This was the second set to be distributed by Meadow Gold Dairy (Beatrice Foods) in 1986. It was issued on Double Play ice cream cartons, one card per package. Full-color player photos have team logos and insignias airbrushed away. This 16-card set is very similar to the Meadow Gold popsicle set, but the photos are different in some instances. The cards measure 2-3/8" by 3-1/2". The Willie McGee card is reportedly tougher to find than other cards in the set.

		MT	NR MT	EX
Complete Set:		100.00	75.00	40.00
Common Player:		4.00	3.00	1.50
(1)	George Brett	7.00	5.25	2.75
(2)	Wade Boggs	7.00	5.25	2.75
(3)	Carlton Fisk	6.00	4.50	2.50
(4)	Steve Garvey	6.00	4.50	2.50
(5)	Dwight Gooden	6.00	4.50	2.50
(6)	Pedro Guerrero	4.00	3.00	1.50
(7)	Reggie Jackson	8.00	6.00	3.25
(8)	Don Mattingly	8.00	6.00	3.25
(9)	Willie McGee	4.00	3.00	1.50
(10)	Dale Murphy	6.00	4.50	2.50
(11)	Cal Ripken, Jr.	8.00	6.00	3.25
(12)	Pete Rose	8.00	6.00	3.25
(13)	Ryne Sandberg	8.00	6.00	3.25
(14)	Mike Schmidt	8.00	6.00	3.25
(15)	Fernando Valenzuela	4.00	3.00	1.50
(16)	Dave Winfield	7.00	5.25	2.75

1986 Meadow Gold Statistic Backs

Beatrice Foods produced this set of 20 cards on specially marked boxes of Meadow Gold Double Play popsicles, fudgesicles and bubble gum coolers. They came in two-card panels and have full-color player pictures with player name, team and position printed below the photo. Card backs are printed in red ink and feature player career highlights. The cards measure 2-3/8" by 3-1/2" and were distributed in the West and Midwest. It is considered one of the toughest 1986 regional sets to complete.

		MT	NR MT	EX
Complete Panel Set:		40.00	30.00	16.00
Complete Singles Set:		20.00	15.00	8.00
Common Panel:		2.00	1.50	.80
Common Single Player:		.30	.25	.12
	Panel 1	5.00	3.75	2.00
1	George Brett	2.00	1.50	.80
2	Fernando Valenzuela	.40	.30	.15
	Panel 2	5.00	3.75	2.00
3	Dwight Gooden	1.00	.70	.40
4	Dale Murphy	1.50	1.25	.60
	Panel 3	7.00	5.25	2.75
5	Don Mattingly	1.50	1.25	.60
6	Reggie Jackson	2.00	1.50	.80
	Panel 4	6.00	4.50	2.50
7	Dave Winfield	1.00	.70	.40
8	Pete Rose	2.00	1.50	.80
	Panel 5	4.00	3.00	1.50

9	Wade Boggs	1.50	1.25	.60
10	Willie McGee	.50	.40	.20
	Panel 6	8.00	6.00	3.25
11	Cal Ripkin (Ripken)	2.00	1.50	.80
12	Ryne Sandberg	2.00	1.50	.80
	Panel 7	2.50	2.00	1.00
13	Carlton Fisk	.80	.60	.30
14	Jim Rice	.40	.30	.15
	Panel 8	5.50	4.00	2.25
15	Steve Garvey	.75	.60	.30
16	Mike Schmidt	2.00	1.50	.80
	Panel 9	2.00	1.50	.80
17	Bruce Sutter	.60	.45	.25
18	Pedro Guerrero	.30	.25	.12
	Panel 10	2.00	1.50	.80
19	Rick Sutcliff (Sutcliffe)	.50	.40	.20
20	Rich Gossage	.50	.40	.20

1986 Meadow Gold Milk

The third set from Meadow Gold from 1986 came on milk cartons; on pint, quart and half-gallon size containers. The cards measure 2-1/2" by 3-1/2" and feature drawings instead of photographs. Different dairies distributed the cards in various colors of ink. The cards can be found printed in red, brown or black ink. The crude drawings have prevented this rare set from being higher in price. It was believed that Don Mattingly and Fernando Valenzuela were part of the original set, but it has since been proven they were not.

		MT	NR MT	EX
Complete Set:		50.00	37.00	20.00
Common Player:		2.00	1.50	.80
(1)	Wade Boggs	5.00	3.75	2.00
(2)	George Brett	6.00	4.50	2.50
(3)	Steve Carlton	4.00	3.00	1.50
(4)	Dwight Gooden	3.00	2.25	1.25
(5)	Willie McGee	2.00	1.50	.80
(6)	Dale Murphy	4.00	3.00	1.50
(7)	Cal Ripken, Jr.	6.00	4.50	2.50
(8)	Pete Rose	8.00	6.00	3.25
(9)	Ryne Sandberg	6.00	4.50	2.50
(10)	Mike Schmidt	6.00	4.50	2.50

1991 Medford Phillies

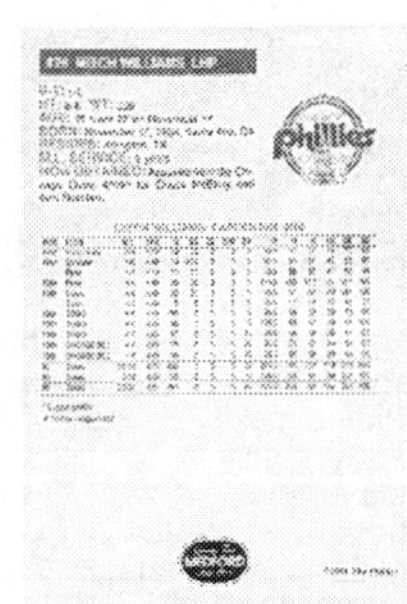

In 1991 Medford Foods took over sponsorship of the Phillies' traditional large-format (4-1/8" x 6") baseball card series. The main body of 35 cards of players and coaches was issued early in the season. Later, a three-card set highlighting career milestones was issued. The three-card update set differs from the regular issue in that the cards feature a white border on front with the player's name in white on a red strip at top-center. Still later another eight cards, including the manager and mascot, were produced, following the basic format of borderless color photos with the player's name in white on a red strip somewhere on the front of the card. Backs are printed in red and black and include biographical details, full major and minor league stats and the Phillies and Medford logos. While the cards feature a uniform number on back, the checklist is presented here alphabetically.

		MT	NR MT	EX
Complete Set:		13.50	10.00	5.50
Common Player:		.25	.20	.10
(1)	Darrel Akerfelds	.25	.20	.10
(2)	Andy Ashby	.25	.20	.10
(3)	Wally Backman	.25	.20	.10
(4)	Joe Boever	.25	.20	.10
(5)	Rod Booker	.25	.20	.10
(6)	Larry Bowa	.30	.25	.12
(7)	Sil Campusano	.25	.20	.10
(8)	Wes Chamberlain	.30	.25	.12
(9)	Pat Combs	.25	.20	.10
(10)	Danny Cox	.25	.20	.10
(11)	Darren Daulton	.75	.60	.30
(12)	Jose DeJesus	.25	.20	.10
(13)	Len Dykstra	1.25	.90	.50
(14)	Darrin Fletcher	.25	.20	.10
(15)	Jim Fregosi	.35	.25	.14
(16a)	Tommy Greene	.35	.25	.14
16b	Tommy Greene (5-23-91 no-hitter)	.45	.35	.20
(17)	Jason Grimsley	.25	.20	.10
(18)	Charlie Hayes	.35	.25	.14
(19)	Von Hayes	.25	.20	.10
(20)	Dave Hollins	.45	.35	.20
(21)	Ken Howell	.25	.20	.10
(22)	Ron Jones	.25	.20	.10
(23)	Ricky Jordan	.25	.20	.10
(24)	John Kruk	1.25	.90	.50
(25)	Steve Lake	.25	.20	.10
(26)	Hal Lanier	.25	.20	.10
(27)	Jim Lindeman	.25	.20	.10
(28)	Tim Mauser	.25	.20	.10
(29)	Roger McDowell	.25	.20	.10
(30)	Denis Menke	.25	.20	.10
(31)	Mickey Morandini	.30	.25	.12
(32)	John Morris	.25	.20	.10
(33a)	Terry Mulholland	.35	.25	.14
(33b)	Terry Mulholland (8-15-90 no-hitter)	.50	.40	.20
(34a)	Dale Murphy	1.00	.70	.40
(34b)	Dale Murphy (5-29-91 2,000 hit)	1.50	1.25	.60
(35)	Johnny Podres	.35	.25	.14
(36)	Randy Ready	.25	.20	.10
(37)	Wally Ritchie	.25	.20	.10
(38)	Bruce Ruffin	.25	.20	.10
(39)	Steve Searcy	.25	.20	.10
(40)	Dickie Thon	.25	.20	.10
(41)	John Vukovich	.25	.20	.10
(42)	Mitch Williams	.40	.30	.15
(43)	Phillie Phanatic (mascot)	.25	.20	.10

1992 Medford Phillies

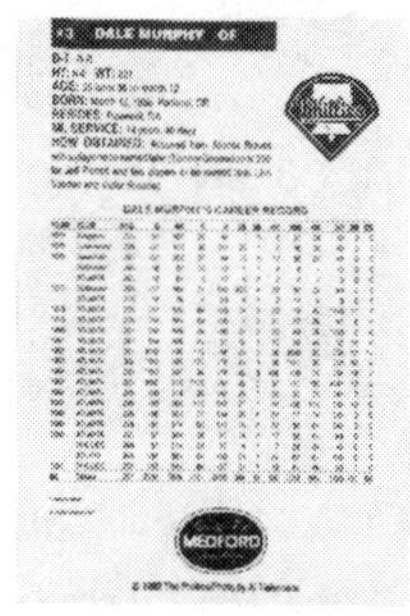

Issued in two series, a 36-card release early in the season and a 10-card update (Terry Mulholland appears in each), these cards continue the Phillies' tradition of large-format presenations. Measuring 4-1/8" x 6" they feature full-bleed color studio portrait photos on front. The player's name appears in white letters on a red strip somewhere on the card front. Backs are printed in red and black and include full major and minor league stats and some biographical data, along with the logos of the Phillies and the sponsoring Medford food company. The cards are checklisted here by uniform numbers on back.

		MT	NR MT	EX
Complete Set (46):		12.00	9.00	4.75
Common Player:		.25	.20	.10
2	Larry Bowa	.30	.25	.12
3	Dale Murphy	.90	.70	.35
4	Len Dykstra	1.25	.90	.50
5	Kim Batiste	.30	.25	.12
6	Wally Backman	.25	.20	.10
7	Mariano Duncan	.35	.25	.14
8	Dale Sveum	.25	.20	.10
9	Tom Marsh	.25	.20	.10
10	Darren Daulton	.75	.60	.30
11	Jim Fregosi	.40	.30	.15
12	Mickey Morandini	.35	.25	.14
14	Denis Menke	.25	.20	.10
15	Dave Hollins	.40	.30	.15
17	Ricky Jordan	.25	.20	.10
18	John Vukovich	.25	.20	.10
19	Jim Lindeman	.25	.20	.10
21	Pat Combs	.25	.20	.10
23	Brad Brink	.25	.20	.10
24	Steve Searcy	.25	.20	.10
25	Mike Ryan	.25	.20	.10
26	Mel Roberts	.25	.20	.10
28	Mitch Williams	.35	.25	.14
29	John Kruk	1.25	.90	.50
30	Steve Lake	.25	.20	.10
33	Ruben Amaro	.25	.20	.10
34a	Danny Cox	.25	.20	.10
34b	Ben Rivera	.25	.20	.10
35	Don Robinson	.25	.20	.10
38	Curt Schilling	.25	.20	.10
39	Wally Ritchie	.25	.20	.10
40	Andy Ashby	.25	.20	.10
42	Mike Hartley	.25	.20	.10
44	Wes Chamberlain	.35	.25	.14
45a	Terry Mulholland (cap-to-chest photo)	.35	.25	.14
45b	Terry Mulholland (cap-to-waist photo)	.35	.25	.14
46	Johnny Podres	.35	.25	.14
47	Kyle Abbott	.35	.25	.14
48	Jeff Grotewold	.25	.20	.10
49	Tommy Greene	.35	.25	.14
50	Barry Jones	.25	.20	.10
51	Cliff Brantley	.25	.20	.10
55	Bob Ayrault	.25	.20	.10
----	Phillie Phanatic (mascot)	.25	.20	.10
----	1992 Philadelphia Phillies (team photo)	.25	.20	.10
----	Uniforms Through The Years	.25	.20	.10
----	Veterans Stadium	.25	.20	.10

1993 Medford Phillies

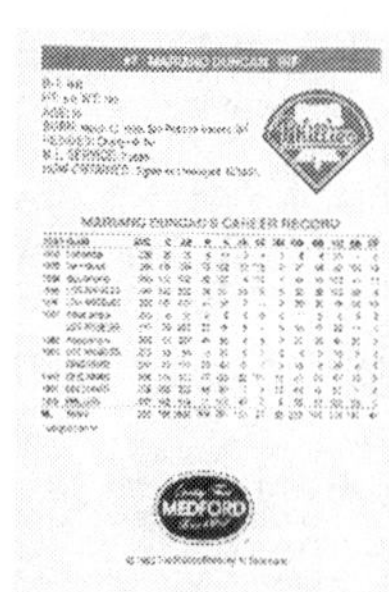

The third in an annual series of large-format (4-1/8" x 6") cards issued by Medford Foods, this set retains the same basic format as previous issues. Cards feature a borderless color photo on front with the player's name in white on a red strip. Several of the cards in the 1993 issue feature players in turn-back-the-clock uniforms and there are a few horizontal-format photos included. Backs are printed in red and black and feature the Phillies and sponsor's logos, biographical data and major and minor league stats. Cards are checklisted here by the player number which appears at top on the back.

		MT	NR MT	EX
Complete Set:		9.00	6.75	3.50
Common Player:		.25	.20	.10
2	Larry Bowa	.30	.25	.12
4	Lenny Dykstra	1.00	.70	.40
5	Kim Batiste	.25	.20	.10
7	Mariano Duncan	.30	.25	.12
9	Mike Ryan	.25	.20	.10
10	Darren Daulton	.60	.45	.25
11	Jim Fregosi	.35	.25	.14
12	Mickey Morandini	.25	.20	.10
14	Denis Menke	.25	.20	.10
15	Dave Hollins	.40	.30	.15
17	Ricky Jordan	.25	.20	.10
18	John Vukovich	.25	.20	.10
22	Pete Incaviglia	.35	.25	.14
23	Todd Pratt	.25	.20	.10
24	Juan Bell	.25	.20	.10
25	Milt Thompson	.25	.20	.10
26	Mel Roberts	.25	.20	.10
27	Danny Jackson	.25	.20	.10
28	Tyler Green	.30	.25	.12
29	John Kruk	1.00	.70	.40
33	Ruben Amaro	.25	.20	.10
34	Ben Rivera	.25	.20	.10
37	Kyle Abbott	.25	.20	.10
38	Curt Schilling	.25	.20	.10
40	David West	.25	.20	.10
44	Wes Chamberlain	.35	.25	.14
45	Terry Mulholland	.30	.25	.12
46	Johnny Podres	.35	.25	.14
47	Larry Andersen	.25	.20	.10
50	Jose DeLeon	.25	.20	.10
53	Bob Ayrault	.25	.20	.10
99	Mitch Williams	.40	.30	.15
----	Phillie Phanatic (mascot)	.25	.20	.10

Values quoted in this guide reflect the retail price of a card – the price a collector can expect to pay when buying a card from a dealer. The wholesale price – that which a collector can expect to receive from a dealer when selling cards – will be significantly lower, depending on desirability and condition.

1992 Megacards Babe Ruth

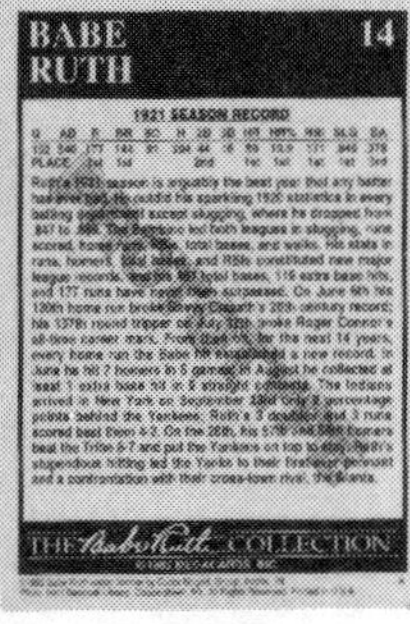

This 165-card set chronicles the life and times of Babe Ruth. The set was produced by Megacards and is officially entitled "The Babe Ruth Collection". The cards feature classic black and white photos with black borders and captions below the photo. The card backs feature coordinating statistics and information.

		MT	NR MT	EX
Complete Set:		15.00	11.00	6.00
Common Player:		.10	.08	.04
1	Career Pitching	.10	.08	.04
2	Career Batting	.10	.08	.04
3	Series Pitching	.10	.08	.04
4	Series Batting	.10	.08	.04
5	Year 1914, Minors	.10	.08	.04
6	Year 1914, Majors	.10	.08	.04
7	Year In Review 1915	.10	.08	.04
8	Year In Review 1916	.10	.08	.04
9	Year In Review 1917	.10	.08	.04
10	Year In Review 1918	.10	.08	.04
11	Year In Review 1919	.10	.08	.04
12	Year In Review 1920	.10	.08	.04
13	Year In Review 1921	.10	.08	.04
14	Year In Review 1922	.10	.08	.04
15	Year In Review 1923	.10	.08	.04
16	Year In Review 1924	.10	.08	.04
17	Year In Review 1925	.10	.08	.04
18	Year In Review 1926	.10	.08	.04
19	Year In Review 1927	.20	.15	.08
20	Year In Review 1928	.10	.08	.04
21	Year In Review 1929	.10	.08	.04
22	Year In Review 1930	.10	.08	.04
23	Year In Review 1931	.10	.08	.04
24	Year In Review 1932	.10	.08	.04
25	Year In Review 1933	.10	.08	.04
26	Year In Review 1934	.10	.08	.04
27	Year In Review 1935	.10	.08	.04
28	Year In Review 1938	.10	.08	.04
29	Babe In Retirement	.10	.08	.04
30	Series Year, 1915	.10	.08	.04
31	Series Year, 1916	.10	.08	.04
32	Series Year, 1918	.10	.08	.04
33	Series Year, 1921	.10	.08	.04
34	Series Year, 1922	.10	.08	.04
35	Series Year, 1923	.10	.08	.04
36	Series Year, 1926	.15	.11	.06
37	Series Year, 1927	.15	.11	.06
38	Series Year, 1928	.10	.08	.04
39	Series Year, 1932	.15	.11	.06
40	PIH-CR-WALKS	.10	.08	.04
41	PIH-CR-STRIKEOUTS	.10	.08	.04
42	PIH-CR-MOST RUNS	.15	.11	.06
43	PIH-CR-TOTAL BASES	.15	.11	.06
44	PIH-CR-XTRA BASE HT	.10	.08	.04
45	PIH-CR-HOME RUNS	.10	.08	.04
46	PIH-CR-GRAND SLAMS	.10	.08	.04
47	PIH-CR-HOME RUN "	.15	.11	.06
48	PIH-CR-2 HRs/Game	.10	.08	.04
49	PIH-CR-40 Home Runs	.10	.08	.04
50	PIH-CR-RBIs	.15	.11	.06
51	PIH-CR-Batting AVG.	.15	.11	.06
52	PIH-CR-SLG AVG.	.15	.11	.06
53	PIH-SSN-Shutouts	.10	.08	.04
54	PIH-SSN-Walks	.10	.08	.04
55	PIH-SSN-Most Runs	.20	.15	.08
56	PIH-SSN-On Base "	.10	.08	.04
57	PIH-SSN-Total Bases	.15	.11	.06
58	Xtra Base H	.15	.11	.06
59	Xtra Base H RBI's	.15	.11	.06
60	Xtra Base H Home Runs	.10	.08	.04
61	Xtra Base H Home Run "	.10	.08	.04
62	Xtra Base H SLG AVG.	.15	.11	.06
63	PIH-SRS-Winning "	.10	.08	.04
64	PIH-SRS-ERA	.10	.08	.04
65	PIH-SRS-Most Walks	.10	.08	.04
66	PIH-SRS-Most Runs	.10	.08	.04
67	PIH-SRS-Total Bases	.10	.08	.04
68	PIH-SRS-Home Runs	.10	.08	.04
69	PIH-SRS-RBI's	.10	.08	.04
70	PIH-SRS-SLG AVG.	.20	.15	.08
71	CH: ML Victory	.10	.08	.04
72	CH: 1st ML Home Run	.10	.08	.04
73	CH: Walter J Duel	.10	.08	.04
74	CH: Led AL Fielding	.10	.08	.04
75	CH: 1st HR Record	.10	.08	.04
76	CH: Sold To NY	.10	.08	.04
77	CH: 1st Yankee HR	.10	.08	.04
78	CH: AL MVP	.10	.08	.04
79	CH: League Leader	.15	.11	.06
80	CH: 3 HRs in 1 Series	.10	.08	.04
81	CH: Babe & Lou's 107	.20	.15	.08
82	CH: 60th Home Run	.20	.15	.08
83	CH: 3 HRs/WS Again	.10	.08	.04
84	CH: Called Shot-1	.10	.08	.04
85	CH: Called Shot-2	.10	.08	.04
86	CH: Called Shot-3	.10	.08	.04
87	CH: Called Shot-4	.10	.08	.04
88	CH: Called Shot-5	.10	.08	.04
89	CH: All-Star Games	.15	.11	.06
90	CH: Pitch Last Game	.10	.08	.04
91	CH: 700th Home Run	.10	.08	.04
92	CH: Japan	.10	.08	.04
93	CH: Hits Last 3 HRs	.10	.08	.04
94	CH: Hall of Fame	.10	.08	.04
95	CH: 1942 Exhibition	.10	.08	.04
96	CH: Babe Ruth Day	.10	.08	.04
97	CH: Babe's Farewell	.25	.20	.10
98	CH: Perfect Game	.10	.08	.04
99	TRIV: Leads in Steals	.10	.08	.04
100	TRIV: Hub Pruett	.10	.08	.04
101	TRIV: Out in WS	.10	.08	.04
102	TRIV: No Triple CRWN	.10	.08	.04
103	TRIV: 54-ounce bat	.10	.08	.04
104	TRIV: Right-Handed	.10	.08	.04
105	SULTN: Greatness	.10	.08	.04
106	SULTN: Babe's Best	.10	.08	.04
107	SULTN: Beats Teams	.10	.08	.04
108	SULTN: Hack Wilson	.10	.08	.04
109	SULTN: Pitkin	.10	.08	.04
110	SULTN: Ball In Orbit	.10	.08	.04
111	SULTN: Afraid To Kill	.10	.08	.04
112	SULTN: Wonder YRS	.10	.08	.04
113	SULTN: Opening Day	.10	.08	.04
114	SULTN: Hit/Miss Big	.10	.08	.04
115	SULTN: No Equal	.10	.08	.04
116	MAN: Childhood	.10	.08	.04
117	MAN: ST. MARY'S	.10	.08	.04
118	MAN: BR. Mathias	.10	.08	.04
119	MAN: Nicknames	.10	.08	.04
120	MAN: Wife Helen	.10	.08	.04
121	MAN: Wife Claire	.10	.08	.04
122	MAN: With Gehrig	.20	.15	.08
123	MAN: With Pennock	.10	.08	.04
124	MAN: With Huggins	.10	.08	.04
125	MAN: With Ty Cobb	.15	.11	.06
126	MAN: With Walter J	.15	.11	.06
127	MAN: Drawing Card	.10	.08	.04
128	MAN: Brainstorming	.10	.08	.04
129	MAN: Fines	.10	.08	.04
130	MAN: Injuries	.10	.08	.04
131	MAN: Highest Paid	.10	.08	.04
132	MAN: To Be A MGR	.10	.08	.04
133	MAN: Golf	.10	.08	.04
134	MAN: Babe In Movies	.10	.08	.04
135	MAN: War Efforts	.10	.08	.04
136	MAN: Negotiator	.10	.08	.04
137	MAN: Everyone Loved	.10	.08	.04
138	MAN: Children	.10	.08	.04
139	MAN: Time For Kids	.10	.08	.04
140	MAN: J Sylvester	.10	.08	.04
141	MAN: With the Great	.10	.08	.04
142	MAN: And America	.10	.08	.04
143	REMEM: Bill James-1	.10	.08	.04
144	REMEM: Bill James-2	.10	.08	.04
145	REMEM: Bill James-3	.10	.08	.04
146	REMEM: Mel Allen-1	.10	.08	.04
147	REMEM: Mel Allen-2	.10	.08	.04
148	REMEM: Wes Ferrell	.10	.08	.04
149	REMEM: George Bush	.50	.40	.20
150	REMEM: Ethan Allen	.20	.15	.08
151	REMEM: Dorothy	.10	.08	.04
152	REMEM: Julia-1	.10	.08	.04
153	REMEM: Julia-2	.10	.08	.04
154	REMEM: Mark Koenig	.10	.08	.04
155	REMEM: D Honig	.10	.08	.04
156	REMEM: Waner/Hoyt	.10	.08	.04
157	REMEM: Waite Hoyt	.10	.08	.04
158	REMEM: Bill Dickey	.10	.08	.04
159	REMEM: Bob Meusel	.10	.08	.04
160	REMEM: Jim Chapman	.10	.08	.04
161	REMEM: C Walsh	.10	.08	.04
162	REMEM: Passes Away	.10	.08	.04
163	REMEM: G Rice	.10	.08	.04
164	Checklist	.10	.08	.04
165	Checklist	.10	.08	.04

1910 Mello-Mint (E105)

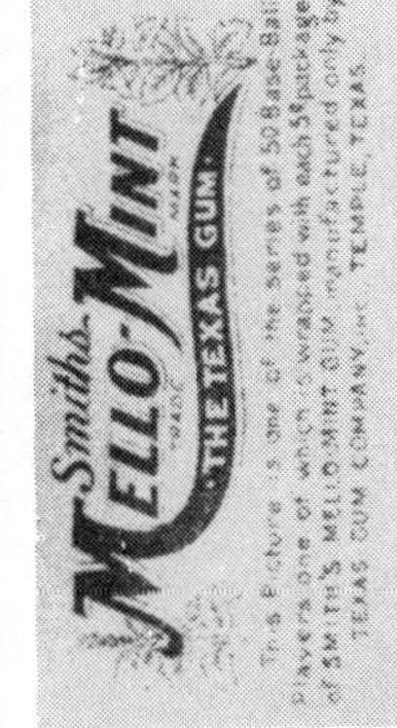

Issued circa 1910 by Smith's Mello-Mint, "The Texas Gum", this set of 50 cards shares the same checklist and artwork as the better known E101 set. The Mello-Mint cards, however, are slightly smaller, measuring approximately 2-5/8" by 1-3/8", and were printed on thin paper, making them difficult to find in top condition. The backs contain an advertisement for Mello-Mint Gum. The set carries an ACC designation of E105.

		NR MT	EX	VG
Complete Set:		7500.	9000.	5400.
Common Player:		150.00	75.00	45.00
(1)	Jack Barry	150.00	75.00	45.00
(2)	Harry Bemis	150.00	75.00	45.00
(3)	Chief Bender (white hat)	300.00	150.00	90.00
(4)	Chief Bender (striped hat)	300.00	150.00	90.00
(5)	Bill Bergen	150.00	75.00	45.00
(6)	Bob Bescher	150.00	75.00	45.00
(7)	Al Bridwell	150.00	75.00	45.00
(8)	Doc Casey	150.00	75.00	45.00
(9)	Frank Chance	400.00	200.00	120.00
(10)	Hal Chase	250.00	125.00	75.00
(11)	Ty Cobb	2000.	1000.	600.00
(12)	Eddie Collins	300.00	150.00	90.00
(13)	Sam Crawford	300.00	150.00	90.00
(14)	Harry Davis	150.00	75.00	45.00
(15)	Art Devlin	150.00	75.00	45.00
(16)	Wild Bill Donovan	150.00	75.00	45.00
(17)	Red Dooin	150.00	75.00	45.00
(18)	Mickey Doolan	150.00	75.00	45.00
(19)	Patsy Dougherty	150.00	75.00	45.00
(20)	Larry Doyle (with bat)	150.00	75.00	45.00
(21)	Larry Doyle (throwing)	150.00	75.00	45.00
(22)	Johnny Evers	300.00	150.00	90.00
(23)	George Gibson	150.00	75.00	45.00
(24)	Topsy Hartsel	150.00	75.00	45.00
(25)	Fred Jacklitsch	150.00	75.00	45.00
(26)	Hugh Jennings	300.00	150.00	90.00
(27)	Red Kleinow	150.00	75.00	45.00
(28)	Otto Knabe	150.00	75.00	45.00
(29)	Jack Knight	150.00	75.00	45.00
(30)	Nap Lajoie	500.00	250.00	150.00
(31)	Hans Lobert	150.00	75.00	45.00
(32)	Sherry Magee	150.00	75.00	45.00
(33)	Christy Matthewson (Mathewson)	900.00	450.00	270.00
(34)	John McGraw	300.00	150.00	90.00
(35)	Larry McLean	150.00	75.00	45.00
(36)	Dots Miller (batting)	150.00	75.00	45.00
(37)	Dots Miller (fielding)	150.00	75.00	45.00
(38)	Danny Murphy	150.00	75.00	45.00
(39)	Bill O'Hara	150.00	75.00	45.00
(40)	Germany Schaefer	150.00	75.00	45.00
(41)	Admiral Schlei	150.00	75.00	45.00
(42)	Boss Schmidt	150.00	75.00	45.00
(43)	Johnny Seigle	150.00	75.00	45.00
(44)	Dave Shean	150.00	75.00	45.00
(45)	Boss Smith (Schmidt)	150.00	75.00	45.00
(46)	Joe Tinker	300.00	150.00	90.00
(47)	Honus Wagner (batting)	1000.	500.00	300.00
(48)	Honus Wagner (throwing)	1000.	500.00	300.00
(49)	Cy Young	600.00	300.00	180.00
(50)	Heinie Zimmerman	150.00	75.00	45.00

1993 Metallic Images Cooperstown Collection

A company known as Metallic Images Inc. created the Cooperstown Collection in 1993, a unique, 20-card set of retired players produced of durable, embossed metal with rolled edges. The set, limited to 49,900 came packaged in a collector's tin with a numbered certificate of authenticity. The cards feature full-color photos on the front and back and statistics on the reverse. Half of the players in the set are members of the Hall of Fame.

		MT	NR MT	EX
Complete Set (20):		25.00	18.50	10.00
Common Player:		.50	.40	.20
(1)	Yogi Berra	2.00	1.50	.80
(2)	Willie Mays	7.50	5.50	3.00
(3)	Johnny Mize	1.00	.75	.40
(4)	Hank Aaron	7.50	5.50	3.00
(5)	Willie Stargell	1.00	.75	.40
(6)	Lou Brock	1.00	.75	.40
(7)	Rod Carew	1.00	.75	.40
(8)	Bob Gibson	1.00	.75	.40

(9)	Gaylord Perry	1.00	.75	.40
(10)	Warren Spahn	1.50	1.25	.60
(11)	Vida Blue	.50	.40	.20
(12)	Bobby Bonds	.50	.40	.20
(13)	Lew Burdette	.50	.40	.20
(14)	Rocky Colavito	.75	.60	.30
(15)	George Foster	.50	.40	.20
(16)	Mickey Lolich	.50	.40	.20
(17)	Don Newcombe	.50	.40	.20
(18)	Boog Powell	.50	.40	.20
(19)	Bill Skowron	.50	.40	.20
(20)	Luis Tiant	.50	.40	.20

1931 Metropolitan Studio St. Louis Cardinals

Members of the St. Louis Cardinals are featured in this 30-card set. The cards were printed on heavy paper and feature sepia-toned photos. The player's name appears along the bottom white border below the photo. The cards measure 6-1/4" by 9-1/2" and are not numbered.

		NR MT	EX	VG
Complete Set:		600.00	325.00	200.00
Common Player:		15.00	7.50	4.50
(1)	Earl "Spanky" Adams	15.00	7.50	4.50
(2)	Ray Blades	15.00	7.50	4.50
(3)	James Bottomley	35.00	17.50	10.50
(4)	Sam Breadon	25.00	12.50	7.50
(5)	James "Rip" Collins	20.00	10.00	6.00
(6)	Dizzy Dean	60.00	30.00	18.00
(7)	Paul Derringer	20.00	10.00	6.00
(8)	Jake Flowers	15.00	7.50	4.50
(9)	Frank Frisch	35.00	17.50	10.50
(10)	Charles Gelbert	15.00	7.50	4.50
(11)	Miguel Gonzales	15.00	7.50	4.50
(12)	Burleigh Grimes	35.00	17.50	10.50
(13)	Charles "Chick" Hafey	35.00	17.50	10.50
(14)	William Hallahan	15.00	7.50	4.50
(15)	Jesse Haines	35.00	17.50	10.50
(16)	Andrew High	15.00	7.50	4.50
(17)	Sylvester Johnson	15.00	7.50	4.50
(18)	Tony Kaufmann	15.00	7.50	4.50
(19)	James Lindsey	15.00	7.50	4.50
(20)	Gus Mancuso	15.00	7.50	4.50
(21)	John Leonard "Pepper" Martin	25.00	12.50	7.50
(22)	Ernest Orsatti	15.00	7.50	4.50
(23)	Charles Flint Rhem	15.00	7.50	4.50
(24)	Branch Rickey	40.00	20.00	12.00
(25)	Walter Roettger	15.00	7.50	4.50
(26)	Allyn Stout	15.00	7.50	4.50
(27)	"Gabby" Street	15.00	7.50	4.50
(28)	Coach Clyde Wares	15.00	7.50	4.50
(29)	George Watkins	15.00	7.50	4.50
(30)	James Wilson	15.00	7.50	4.50

1993 Metz Bakeries

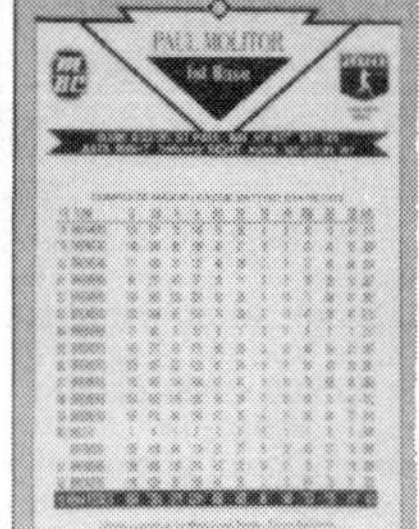

Metz Baking Company of Sioux City, Iowa produced a 40-card set utilizing drawings of players rather than photos. The company also made available uncut sheets of the sets by writing directly. Cards have either a yellow background with blue pinstripes or a blue background with yellow pinstripes. Players are shown in a red, white and black porthole at center, flanked by a pair of bats. The player's name and team are in yellow and red in a black banner beneath the picture, with his position in a baseball at bottom. Backs are printed in black-and-white with complete major and minor league stats. Because the cards are licensed only by the players' union and not Major League Baseball, the player paintings omit uniform logos. The unnumbered cards are checklisted here in alphabetical order.

		MT	NR MT	EX
Complete Set (40):		16.00	12.00	6.50
Common Player:		.25	.20	.10
(1)	Dante Bichette	.25	.20	.10
(2)	Wade Boggs	.50	.40	.20
(3)	Barry Bonds	.60	.45	.25
(4)	Bobby Bonilla	.30	.25	.12
(5)	Jose Canseco	.45	.35	.20
(6)	Joe Carter	.35	.25	.14
(7)	Will Clark	.50	.40	.20
(8)	Roger Clemens	.35	.25	.14
(9)	Doug Drabek	.25	.20	.10
(10)	Shawon Dunston	.25	.20	.10
(11)	Dennis Eckersley	.25	.20	.10
(12)	Cecil Fielder	.40	.30	.15
(13)	Carlton Fisk	.35	.25	.14
(14)	Andres Galarraga	.35	.25	.14
(15)	Kirk Gibson	.25	.20	.10
(16)	Dwight Gooden	.30	.25	.12
(17)	Mark Grace	.30	.25	.12
(18)	Ken Griffey, Jr.	2.00	1.50	.80
(19)	Tony Gwynn	.35	.25	.14
(20)	Rickey Henderson	.40	.30	.15
(21)	Kent Hrbek	.25	.20	.10
(22)	Howard Johnson	.25	.20	.10
(23)	Wally Joyner	.35	.25	.14
(24)	Dave Justice	.35	.25	.14
(25)	Barry Larkin	.25	.20	.10
(26)	Don Mattingly	.50	.40	.20
(27)	Jack McDowell	.25	.20	.10
(28)	Paul Molitor	.40	.30	.15
(29)	Terry Pendleton	.25	.20	.10
(30)	Kirby Puckett	.40	.30	.15
(31)	Cal Ripken, Jr.	.75	.60	.30
(32)	Nolan Ryan	2.00	1.50	.80
(33)	Ryne Sandberg	.75	.60	.30
(34)	Ozzie Smith	.40	.30	.15
(35)	Darryl Strawberry	.25	.20	.10
(36)	Danny Tartabull	.25	.20	.10
(37)	Mickey Tettleton	.25	.20	.10
(38)	Alan Trammell	.35	.25	.14
(39)	Andy Van Slyke	.25	.20	.10
(40)	Dave Winfield	.50	.40	.20

1993 Milk Bone Super Stars

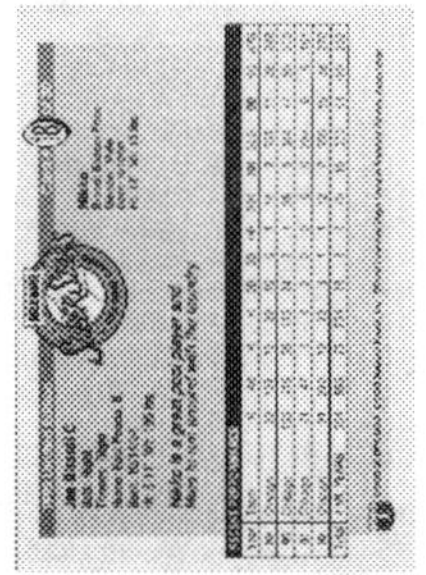

Milk Bone Flavor Snacks and Dog Treats issued a 20-card Super Stars set in 1993 in a format comparable to the NFL Pro Line cards. The cards show the player at home with his dog, with the player shown in an action photo in the lower left corner of the card. The card backs have the player's stats and biography, along with information about the pet and a quote from the player about his dog. The cards were available, two at a time, in specially-marked packages of the company's products. The set also could be obtained through the mail by following instructions on the boxes.

		MT	NR MT	EX
Complete Set (20):		16.00	12.00	6.50
Common Player:		.50	.40	.20
(1)	Brady Anderson	.50	.40	.20
(2)	Craig Biggio	.50	.40	.20
(3)	Brett Butler	.50	.40	.20
(4)	Ken Caminiti	.50	.40	.20
(5)	Will Clark	2.00	1.50	.80
(6)	Rob Dibble	.50	.40	.20
(7)	Tom Foley	.50	.40	.20
(8)	Joe Girardi	.50	.40	.20
(9)	Tom Glavine	1.00	.70	.40
(10)	Wally Joyner	.75	.60	.30
(11)	Barry Larkin	.75	.60	.30
(12)	Ben McDonald	.60	.45	.25
(13)	Mark McGwire	2.00	1.50	.80
(14)	Paul Molitor	2.50	2.00	1.00
(15)	Rafael Palmeiro	1.50	1.25	.60
(16)	Cal Ripken, Jr.	4.00	3.00	1.50
(17)	Bill Swift	.50	.40	.20
(18)	Larry Walker	.50	.40	.20
(19)	Matt Young	.50	.40	.20
(20)	Todd Zeile	.50	.40	.20

1971 Milk Duds

These cards were issued on the backs of five-cent packages of Milk Duds candy. Most collectors prefer to collect complete boxes, rather than cut-out cards, which measure approximately 1-13/16" by 2-5/8" when trimmed tightly. Values quoted below are for complete boxes. The set includes 37 National League and 32 American League players. Card numbers appear on the box flap, with each number from 1 through 24 being shared by three different players. A suffix (a, b and c) has been added for the collector's convenience. Harmon Killebrew, Brooks Robinson and Pete Rose were double-printed.

		NR MT	EX	VG
Complete Set (72):		1800.	900.00	540.00
Common Player:		9.00	4.50	2.75
1a	Frank Howard	12.00	6.00	3.50
1b	Fritz Peterson	9.00	4.50	2.75
1c	Pete Rose	85.00	42.00	25.00
2a	Johnny Bench	37.50	18.50	11.00
2b	Rico Carty	9.00	4.50	2.75
2c	Pete Rose	85.00	42.00	25.00
3a	Ken Holtzman	9.00	4.50	2.75
3b	Willie Mays	65.00	32.00	19.50
3c	Cesar Tovar	9.00	4.50	2.75
4a	Willie Davis	11.00	5.50	3.25
4b	Harmon Killebrew	22.00	11.00	6.50
4c	Felix Millan	9.00	4.50	2.75
5a	Billy Grabarkewitz	9.00	4.50	2.75
5b	Andy Messersmith	9.00	4.50	2.75
5c	Thurman Munson	22.00	11.00	6.50
6a	Luis Aparicio	22.00	11.00	6.50
6b	Lou Brock	22.00	11.00	6.50
6c	Bill Melton	9.00	4.50	2.75
7a	Ray Culp	9.00	4.50	2.75
7b	Willie McCovey	30.00	15.00	9.00
7c	Luke Walker	9.00	4.50	2.75
8a	Roberto Clemente	55.00	27.00	16.50
8b	Jim Merritt	9.00	4.50	2.75
8c	Claud Osteen (Claude)	9.00	4.50	2.75
9a	Stan Bahnsen	9.00	4.50	2.75
9b	Sam McDowell	11.00	5.50	3.25
9c	Billy Williams	22.00	11.00	6.50
10a	Jim Hickman	9.00	4.50	2.75
10b	Dave McNally	11.00	5.50	3.25
10c	Tony Perez	16.00	8.00	4.75
11a	Hank Aaron	65.00	32.00	19.50
11b	Glen Beckert (Glenn)	9.00	4.50	2.75
11c	Ray Fosse	9.00	4.50	2.75
12a	Alex Johnson	9.00	4.50	2.75
12b	Gaylord Perry	22.00	11.00	6.50
12c	Wayne Simpson	9.00	4.50	2.75
13a	Dave Johnson	9.00	4.50	2.75
13b	George Scott	9.00	4.50	2.75
13c	Tom Seaver	40.00	20.00	12.00
14a	Bill Freehan	11.00	5.50	3.25
14b	Bud Harrelson	9.00	4.50	2.75
14c	Manny Sanguillen	9.00	4.50	2.75
15a	Bob Gibson	25.00	12.50	7.50
15b	Rusty Staub	12.00	6.00	3.50
15c	Roy White	9.00	4.50	2.75
16a	Jim Fregosi	9.00	4.50	2.75
16b	Catfish Hunter	22.00	11.00	6.50
16c	Mel Stottlemyer (Stottlemyre)	9.00	4.50	2.75
17a	Tommy Harper	9.00	4.50	2.75
17b	Frank Robinson	30.00	15.00	9.00
17c	Reggie Smith	9.00	4.50	2.75
18a	Orlando Cepeda	12.00	6.00	3.50
18b	Rico Petrocelli	9.00	4.50	2.75
18c	Brooks Robinson	30.00	15.00	9.00
19a	Tony Oliva	12.00	6.00	3.50
19b	Milt Pappas	9.00	4.50	2.75
19c	Bobby Tolan	9.00	4.50	2.75
20a	Ernie Banks	35.00	17.50	10.50
20b	Don Kessinger	9.00	4.50	2.75
20c	Joe Torre	11.00	5.50	3.25
21a	Fergie Jenkins	22.00	11.00	6.50
21b	Jim Palmer	24.00	12.00	7.25
21c	Ron Santo	15.00	7.50	4.50
22a	Randy Hundley	9.00	4.50	2.75
22b	Dennis Menke (Denis)	9.00	4.50	2.75
22c	Boog Powell	12.00	6.00	3.50
23a	Dick Dietz	9.00	4.50	2.75

23b	Tommy John	13.00	6.50	4.00
23c	Brooks Robinson	30.00	15.00	9.00
24a	Danny Cater	9.00	4.50	2.75
24b	Harmon Killebrew	22.00	11.00	6.50
24c	Jim Perry	9.00	4.50	2.75

1933 George C. Miller

The George C. Miller & Co. of Boston, Mass. issued a 32-card set in 1933. The set, which received limited distribution, consists of 16 National League and 16 American League players. The cards are color art reproductions of actual photographs and measure 2-3/8" by 2-7/8" in size. Two distinct variations can be found for each card in the set. Two different typefaces were used, one being much smaller than the other. The most substantial difference is "R" and "L" being used for the "Bats/Throws" information on one version, while the other spells out "Right" and "Left." Collectors were advised on the card backs to collect all 32 cards and return them for prizes. The cards, with a cancellation at the bottom, were returned to the collector with the prize. Two forms of cancellation were used; one involved the complete trimming of the bottom one-quarter of the card, the other a series of diamond-shaped punch holes. Cancelled cards have a significantly decreased value.

		NR MT	EX	VG
	Complete Set (32):	14000.	7000.	4200.
	Common Player:	290.00	145.00	87.00
(1)	Dale Alexander	290.00	145.00	87.00
(2)	"Ivy" Paul Andrews	2000.	1000.	600.00
(3)	Earl Averill	450.00	225.00	135.00
(4)	Dick Bartell	290.00	145.00	87.00
(5)	Walter Berger	290.00	145.00	87.00
(6)	Jim Bottomley	450.00	225.00	135.00
(7)	Joe Cronin	575.00	287.00	172.00
(8)	Jerome "Dizzy" Dean	900.00	450.00	270.00
(9)	William Dickey	675.00	337.00	202.00
(10)	Jimmy Dykes	290.00	145.00	87.00
(11)	Wesley Ferrell	290.00	145.00	87.00
(12)	Jimmy Foxx	675.00	337.00	202.00
(13)	Frank Frisch	500.00	250.00	150.00
(14)	Charlie Gehringer	500.00	250.00	150.00
(15)	Leon "Goose" Goslin	450.00	225.00	135.00
(16)	Charlie Grimm	290.00	145.00	87.00
(17)	Bob "Lefty" Grove	575.00	287.00	172.00
(18)	Charles "Chick" Hafey	450.00	225.00	135.00
(19)	Ray Hayworth	290.00	145.00	87.00
(20)	Charles "Chuck" Klein	450.00	225.00	135.00
(21)	Walter "Rabbit" Maranville	450.00	225.00	135.00
(22)	Oscar Melillo	290.00	145.00	87.00
(23)	Frank "Lefty" O'Doul	290.00	145.00	87.00
(24)	Melvin Ott	575.00	287.00	172.00
(25)	Carl Reynolds	290.00	145.00	87.00
(26)	Charles Ruffing	450.00	225.00	135.00
(27)	Al Simmons	450.00	225.00	135.00
(28)	Joe Stripp	290.00	145.00	87.00
(29)	Bill Terry	500.00	250.00	150.00
(30)	Lloyd Waner	450.00	225.00	135.00
(31)	Paul Waner	450.00	225.00	135.00
(32)	Lonnie Warneke	290.00	145.00	87.00

1990 Miller Beer Milwaukee Brewers

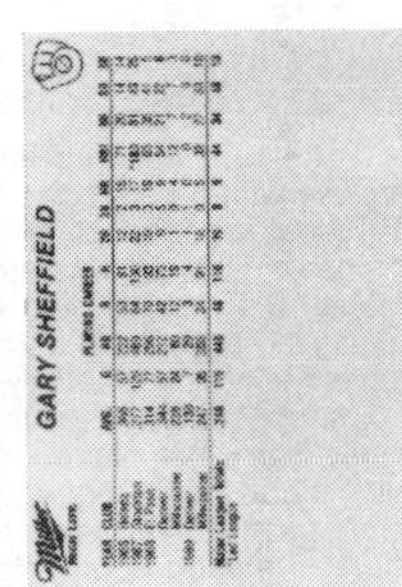

This 32-card set was given away with an album to adults attending an August Brewers game. Cards are standard 2-1/2' x 3-1/2" and feature borderless color photos above gold and black bottom stripes. The beer company's logo is featured in the upper-right corner, with the team logo at lower-left. Black-and-white backs feature player stats. The set has been checklisted below in alphabetical order. Cards are not numbered.

		MT	NR MT	EX
	Complete Set w/Album:	20.00	15.00	8.00
	Common Player:	.25	.20	.10
(1)	Chris Bosio	.35	.25	.14
(2)	Greg Brock	.25	.20	.10
(3)	Chuck Crim	.25	.20	.10
(4)	Rob Deer	.25	.20	.10
(5)	Edgar Diaz	.25	.20	.10
(6)	Tom Edens	.25	.20	.10
(7)	Mike Felder	.25	.20	.10
(8)	Tom Filer	.25	.20	.10
(9)	Jim Gantner	.25	.20	.10
(10)	Darryl Hamilton	.40	.30	.15
(11)	Teddy Higuera	.35	.25	.14
(12)	Mark Knudson	.25	.20	.10
(13)	Bill Krueger	.25	.20	.10
(14)	Paul Mirabella	.25	.20	.10
(15)	Paul Molitor	3.00	2.25	1.25
(16)	Jaime Navarro	.25	.20	.10
(17)	Charlie O'Brien	.25	.20	.10
(18)	Dave Parker	1.50	1.25	.60
(19)	Dan Plesac	.25	.20	.10
(20)	Dennis Powell	.25	.20	.10
(21)	Ron Robinson	.25	.20	.10
(22)	Bob Sebra	.25	.20	.10
(23)	Gary Sheffield	2.00	1.50	.80
(24)	Bill Spiers	.35	.25	.14
(25)	B.J. Surhoff	.35	.25	.14
(26)	Dale Sveum	.25	.20	.10
(27)	Tom Trebelhorn	.25	.20	.10
(28)	Greg Vaughn	.50	.40	.20
(29)	Randy Veres	.25	.20	.10
(30)	Bill Wegman	.35	.25	.14
(31)	Robin Yount	4.00	3.00	1.50
(32)	Coaches (Don Baylor, Ray Burris, Duffy Dyer, Andy Etchebarren, Larry Haney)	.25	.20	.10

1991 Miller High Life Brewers

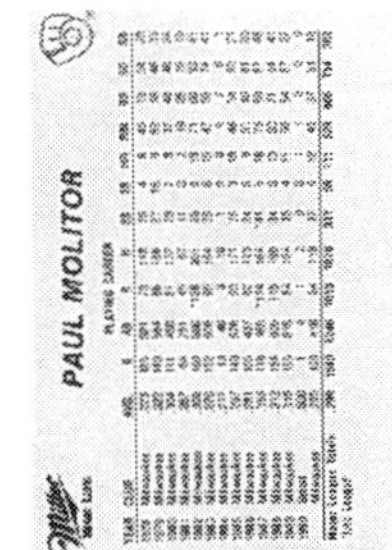

The Miller High Life Brewing Company, in conjunction with the Milwaukee Brewers, sponsored a 32-card limited edition baseball card set in 1991. The set, which features 30 cards of Brewer players plus additional cards of manager Tom Trebelhorn and his coaching staff, employs a home plate window for the front photo, with the player's name and words "Miller High Life" along the bottom of the card. Complete major and minor league stats are printed on the black-and-white backs, which also include sponsors' logos.

		MT	NR MT	EX
	Complete Set w/Album:	20.00	15.00	8.00
	Common Player:	.25	.20	.10
(1)	Don August	.25	.20	.10
(2)	James Austin	.25	.20	.10
(3)	Dante Bichette	.40	.30	.15
(4)	Chris Bosio	.25	.20	.10
(5)	Kevin Brown	.25	.20	.10
(6)	Chuck Crim	.25	.20	.10
(7)	Rick Dempsey	.25	.20	.10
(8)	Jim Gantner	.25	.20	.10
(9)	Darryl Hamilton	.40	.30	.15
(10)	Teddy Higuera	.35	.25	.14
(11)	Darren Holmes	.25	.20	.10
(12)	Jim Hunter	.25	.20	.10
(13)	Mark Knudson	.25	.20	.10
(14)	Mark Lee	.35	.25	.14
(15)	Julio Machado	.25	.20	.10
(16)	Candy Maldonado	.25	.20	.10
(17)	Paul Molitor	3.00	2.25	1.25
(18)	Jaime Navarro	.35	.25	.14
(19)	Edwin Nunez	.25	.20	.10
(20)	Dan Plesac	.25	.20	.10
(21)	Willie Randolph	.35	.25	.14
(22)	Ron Robinson	.25	.20	.10
(23)	Gary Sheffield	1.50	1.25	.60
(24)	Bill Spiers	.35	.25	.14
(25)	Franklin Stubbs	.25	.20	.10
(26)	B.J. Surhoff	.35	.25	.14
(27)	Dale Sveum	.25	.20	.10
(28)	Tom Treblehorn	.25	.20	.10
(29)	Greg Vaughn	.50	.40	.20
(30)	Bill Wegman	.35	.25	.14
(31)	Robin Yount	4.00	3.00	1.50
----	Coaches (Don Baylor, Ray Burris, Duffy Dyer, Andy Etchebarren, Larry Haney, Fred Stanley)			

1969 Milton Bradley

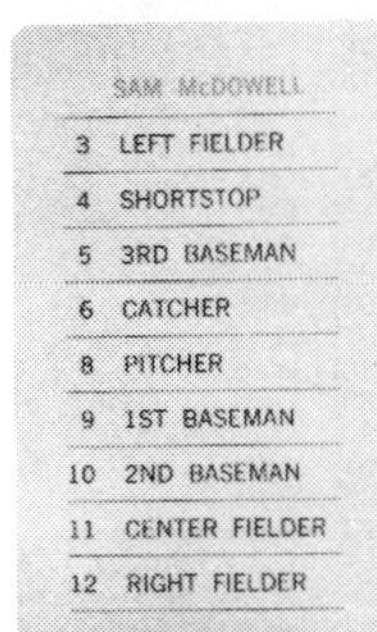

The first of three sets issued by Milton Bradley over a four-year period, the 1969 set contains 296 cards that were part of a baseball board game. The unnumbered cards measure 2" by 3" and have a white border surrounding the black-and-white player photo. The player's name appears above the photo in upper case letters. There are no team designations and the photos are airbrushed to eliminate all team insignias. The back of the card displays the player's name, position, birthdate, height and batting and throwing preferences along the top followed by a list of various game situations used in playing the board game. The cards have square corners.

		NR MT	EX	VG
	Complete Set:	400.00	200.00	120.00
	Common Player:	.50	.25	.15
(1)	Hank Aaron	30.00	15.00	9.00
(2)	Ted Abernathy	.50	.25	.15
(3)	Jerry Adair	.50	.25	.15
(4)	Tommy Agee	.50	.25	.15
(5)	Bernie Allen	.50	.25	.15
(6)	Hank Allen	.50	.25	.15
(7)	Richie Allen	2.00	1.00	.60
(8)	Gene Alley	.50	.25	.15
(9)	Bob Allison	.70	.35	.20
(10)	Felipe Alou	2.00	1.00	.60
(11)	Jesus Alou	.50	.25	.15
(12)	Matty Alou	.50	.25	.15
(13)	Max Alvis	.50	.25	.15
(14)	Mike Andrews	.50	.25	.15
(15)	Luis Aparicio	6.00	3.00	1.75
(16)	Jose Arcia	.50	.25	.15
(17)	Bob Aspromonte	.50	.25	.15
(18)	Joe Azcue	.50	.25	.15
(19)	Ernie Banks	20.00	10.00	6.00
(20)	Steve Barber	.50	.25	.15
(21)	John Bateman	.50	.25	.15
(22)	Glen Beckert (Glenn)	.70	.35	.20
(23)	Gary Bell	.50	.25	.15
(24)	John Bench	20.00	10.00	6.00
(25)	Ken Berry	.50	.25	.15
(26)	Frank Bertaina	.50	.25	.15
(27)	Paul Blair	.50	.25	.15
(28)	Wade Blasingame	.50	.25	.15
(29)	Curt Blefary	.50	.25	.15
(30)	John Boccabella	.50	.25	.15
(31)	Bobby Lee Bonds	2.00	1.00	.60
(32)	Sam Bowens	.50	.25	.15
(33)	Ken Boyer	1.50	.70	.45
(34)	Charles Bradford	.50	.25	.15
(35)	Darrell Brandon	.50	.25	.15
(36)	Jim Brewer	.50	.25	.15
(37)	John Briggs	.50	.25	.15
(38)	Nelson Briles	.50	.25	.15
(39)	Ed Brinkman	.50	.25	.15
(40)	Lou Brock	12.50	6.25	3.75
(41)	Gates Brown	.50	.25	.15
(42)	Larry Brown	.50	.25	.15
(43)	George Brunet	.50	.25	.15
(44)	Jerry Buchek	.50	.25	.15
(45)	Don Buford	.50	.25	.15
(46)	Jim Bunning	2.75	1.50	.80
(47)	Johnny Callison	.80	.40	.25
(48)	Campy Campaneris	.80	.40	.25
(49)	Jose Cardenal	.50	.25	.15
(50)	Leo Cardenas	.50	.25	.15
(51)	Don Cardwell	.50	.25	.15
(52)	Rod Carew	12.50	6.25	3.75
(53)	Paul Casanova	.50	.25	.15
(54)	Norm Cash	1.50	.70	.45
(55)	Danny Cater	.50	.25	.15
(56)	Orlando Cepeda	3.00	1.50	.90
(57)	Dean Chance	.70	.35	.20
(58)	Ed Charles	.70	.35	.20
(59)	Horace Clarke	.50	.25	.15
(60)	Roberto Clemente	30.00	15.00	9.00

(61)	Donn Clendenon	.70	.35	.20
(62)	Ty Cline	.50	.25	.15
(63)	Nate Colbert	.50	.25	.15
(64)	Joe Coleman	.50	.25	.15
(65)	Bob Cox	.50	.25	.15
(66)	Mike Cuellar	.70	.35	.20
(67)	Ray Culp	.50	.25	.15
(68)	Clay Dalrymple	.50	.25	.15
(69)	Vic Davalillo	.50	.25	.15
(70)	Jim Davenport	.50	.25	.15
(71)	Ron Davis	.50	.25	.15
(72)	Tommy Davis	.80	.40	.25
(73)	Willie Davis	.80	.40	.25
(74)	Chuck Dobson	.50	.25	.15
(75)	John Donaldson	.50	.25	.15
(76)	Al Downing	.50	.25	.15
(77)	Moe Drabowsky	.50	.25	.15
(78)	Dick Ellsworth	.50	.25	.15
(79)	Mike Epstein	.50	.25	.15
(80)	Andy Etchebarren	.50	.25	.15
(81)	Ron Fairly	.70	.35	.20
(82)	Dick Farrell	.50	.25	.15
(83)	Curt Flood	1.50	.70	.45
(84)	Joe Foy	.50	.25	.15
(85)	Tito Francona	.50	.25	.15
(86)	Bill Freehan	.70	.35	.20
(87)	Jim Fregosi	.80	.40	.25
(88)	Woodie Fryman	.50	.25	.15
(89)	Len Gabrielson	.50	.25	.15
(90)	Cito Gaston	.80	.40	.25
(91)	Jake Gibbs	.50	.25	.15
(92)	Russ Gibson	.50	.25	.15
(93)	Dave Giusti	.50	.25	.15
(94)	Tony Gonzalez	.50	.25	.15
(95)	Jim Gosger	.50	.25	.15
(96)	Julio Gotay	.50	.25	.15
(97)	Dick Green	.50	.25	.15
(98)	Jerry Grote	.50	.25	.15
(99)	Jimmie Hall	.50	.25	.15
(100)	Tom Haller	.50	.25	.15
(101)	Steve Hamilton	.50	.25	.15
(102)	Ron Hansen	.50	.25	.15
(103)	Jim Hardin	.50	.25	.15
(104)	Tommy Harper	.70	.35	.20
(105)	Bud Harrelson	.50	.25	.15
(106)	Ken Harrelson	.70	.35	.20
(107)	Jim Hart	.50	.25	.15
(108)	Woodie Held	.50	.25	.15
(109)	Tommy Helms	.50	.25	.15
(110)	Elrod Hendricks	.50	.25	.15
(111)	Mike Hershberger	.50	.25	.15
(112)	Jack Hiatt	.50	.25	.15
(113)	Jim Hickman	.50	.25	.15
(114)	John Hiller	.50	.25	.15
(115)	Chuck Hinton	.50	.25	.15
(116)	Ken Holtzman	.70	.35	.20
(117)	Joel Horlen	.50	.25	.15
(118)	Tony Horton	.50	.25	.15
(119)	Willie Horton	.50	.25	.15
(120)	Frank Howard	1.00	.50	.30
(121)	Dick Howser	.70	.35	.20
(122)	Randy Hundley	.50	.25	.15
(123)	Ron Hunt	.50	.25	.15
(124)	Catfish Hunter	6.00	3.00	1.75
(125)	Al Jackson	.50	.25	.15
(126)	Larry Jackson	.50	.25	.15
(127)	Reggie Jackson	50.00	25.00	15.00
(128)	Sonny Jackson	.50	.25	.15
(129)	Pat Jarvis	.50	.25	.15
(130)	Julian Javier	.50	.25	.15
(131)	Ferguson Jenkins	6.00	3.00	1.75
(132)	Manny Jimenez	.50	.25	.15
(133)	Tommy John	4.00	2.00	1.25
(134)	Bob Johnson	.50	.25	.15
(135)	Dave Johnson	.80	.40	.25
(136)	Deron Johnson	.50	.25	.15
(137)	Lou Johnson	.50	.25	.15
(138)	Jay Johnstone	.70	.35	.20
(139)	Cleon Jones	.50	.25	.15
(140)	Dalton Jones	.50	.25	.15
(141)	Duane Josephson	.50	.25	.15
(142)	Jim Kaat	2.75	1.50	.80
(143)	Al Kaline	15.00	7.50	4.50
(144)	Don Kessinger	.70	.35	.20
(145)	Harmon Killebrew	12.50	6.25	3.75
(146)	Harold King	.50	.25	.15
(147)	Ed Kirkpatrick	.50	.25	.15
(148)	Fred Klages	.50	.25	.15
(149)	Ron Kline	.50	.25	.15
(150)	Bobby Knoop	.50	.25	.15
(151)	Gary Kolb	.50	.25	.15
(152)	Andy Kosco	.50	.25	.15
(153)	Ed Kranepool	.70	.35	.20
(154)	Lew Krausse	.50	.25	.15
(155)	Harold Lanier	.50	.25	.15
(156)	Jim Lefebvre	.70	.35	.20
(157)	Denny Lemaster	.50	.25	.15
(158)	Dave Leonhard	.50	.25	.15
(159)	Don Lock	.50	.25	.15
(160)	Mickey Lolich	1.50	.70	.45
(161)	Jim Lonborg	.70	.35	.20
(162)	Mike Lum	.50	.25	.15
(163)	Al Lyle	.70	.35	.20
(164)	Jim Maloney	.50	.25	.15
(165)	Juan Marichal	8.00	4.00	2.50
(166)	J.C. Martin	.50	.25	.15
(167)	Marty Martinez	.50	.25	.15
(168)	Tom Matchick	.50	.25	.15
(169)	Ed Mathews	12.50	6.25	3.75
(170)	Dal Maxvill	.50	.25	.15
(171)	Jerry May	.50	.25	.15
(172)	Lee May	.50	.25	.15
(173)	Lee Maye	.50	.25	.15
(174)	Willie Mays	30.00	15.00	9.00
(175)	Bill Mazeroski	4.00	2.00	1.25
(176)	Richard McAuliffe	.50	.25	.15
(177)	Al McBean	.50	.25	.15
(178)	Tim McCarver	1.00	.50	.30
(179)	Bill McCool	.50	.25	.15
(180)	Mike McCormick	.50	.25	.15
(181)	Willie McCovey	15.00	7.50	4.50
(182)	Tom McCraw	.50	.25	.15
(183)	Lindy McDaniel	.50	.25	.15
(184)	Sam McDowell	.80	.40	.25
(185)	Orlando McFarlane	.50	.25	.15
(186)	Jim McGlothlin	.50	.25	.15
(187)	Denny McLain	1.25	.60	.40
(188)	Ken McMullen	.50	.25	.15
(189)	Dave McNally	.50	.25	.15
(190)	Gerry McNertney	.50	.25	.15
(191)	Dennis Menke (Denis)	.50	.25	.15
(192)	Felix Millan	.50	.25	.15
(193)	Don Mincher	.50	.25	.15
(194)	Rick Monday	.50	.25	.15
(195)	Joe Morgan	8.00	4.00	2.50
(196)	Bubba Morton	.50	.25	.15
(197)	Manny Mota	.70	.35	.20
(198)	Jim Nash	.50	.25	.15
(199)	Dave Nelson	.50	.25	.15
(200)	Dick Nen	.50	.25	.15
(201)	Phil Niekro	4.50	2.25	1.25
(202)	Jim Northrup	.50	.25	.15
(203)	Richard Nye	.50	.25	.15
(204)	Johnny Odom	.80	.40	.25
(205)	Tony Oliva	2.00	1.00	.60
(206)	Gene Oliver	.50	.25	.15
(207)	Phil Ortega	.50	.25	.15
(208)	Claude Osteen	.50	.25	.15
(209)	Ray Oyler	.50	.25	.15
(210)	Jose Pagan	.50	.25	.15
(211)	Jim Pagliaroni	.50	.25	.15
(212)	Milt Pappas	.70	.35	.20
(213)	Wes Parker	.50	.25	.15
(214)	Camilo Pascual	.70	.35	.20
(215)	Don Pavletich	.50	.25	.15
(216)	Joe Pepitone	.80	.40	.25
(217)	Tony Perez	3.00	1.50	.90
(218)	Gaylord Perry	6.00	3.00	1.75
(219)	Jim Perry	.70	.35	.20
(220)	Gary Peters	.50	.25	.15
(221)	Rico Petrocelli	.70	.35	.20
(222)	Adolfo Phillips	.50	.25	.15
(223)	Tom Phoebus	.50	.25	.15
(224)	Vada Pinson	2.00	1.00	.60
(225)	Boog Powell	2.25	1.25	.70
(226)	Frank Quilici	.50	.25	.15
(227)	Doug Rader	.50	.25	.15
(228)	Rich Reese	.50	.25	.15
(229)	Phil Regan	.50	.25	.15
(230)	Rick Reichardt	.50	.25	.15
(231)	Rick Renick	.50	.25	.15
(232)	Roger Repoz	.50	.25	.15
(233)	Dave Ricketts	.50	.25	.15
(234)	Bill Robinson	.50	.25	.15
(235)	Brooks Robinson	15.00	7.50	4.50
(236)	Frank Robinson	15.00	7.50	4.50
(237)	Bob Rodgers	.50	.25	.15
(238)	Cookie Rojas	.50	.25	.15
(239)	Rich Rollins	.50	.25	.15
(240)	Phil Roof	.50	.25	.15
(241)	Pete Rose	30.00	15.00	9.00
(242)	John Roseboro	.70	.35	.20
(243)	Chico Ruiz	.50	.25	.15
(244)	Ray Sadecki	.50	.25	.15
(245)	Chico Salmon	.50	.25	.15
(246)	Jose Santiago	.50	.25	.15
(247)	Ron Santo	2.25	1.25	.70
(248)	Tom Satriano	.50	.25	.15
(249)	Paul Schaal	.50	.25	.15
(250)	Tom Seaver	12.00	6.00	3.50
(251)	Art Shamsky	.50	.25	.15
(252)	Mike Shannon	.50	.25	.15
(253)	Chris Short	.50	.25	.15
(254)	Dick Simpson	.50	.25	.15
(255)	Duke Sims	.50	.25	.15
(256)	Reggie Smith	.70	.35	.20
(257)	Willie Smith	.50	.25	.15
(258)	Russ Snyder	.50	.25	.15
(259)	Al Spangler	.50	.25	.15
(260)	Larry Stahl	.50	.25	.15
(261)	Lee Stange	.50	.25	.15
(262)	Mickey Stanley	.50	.25	.15
(263)	Willie Stargell	12.50	6.25	3.75
(264)	Rusty Staub	2.00	1.00	.60
(265)	Mel Stottlemyre	.60	.30	.20
(266)	Ed Stroud	.50	.25	.15
(267)	Don Sutton	2.50	1.25	.70
(268)	Ron Swoboda	.50	.25	.15
(269)	Jose Tartabull	.50	.25	.15
(270)	Tony Taylor	.50	.25	.15
(271)	Luis Tiant	2.50	1.25	.70
(272)	Bob Tillman	.50	.25	.15
(273)	Bobby Tolan	.50	.25	.15
(274)	Jeff Torborg	.70	.35	.20
(275)	Joe Torre	.80	.40	.25
(276)	Cesar Tovar	.50	.25	.15
(277)	Dick Tracewski	.50	.25	.15
(278)	Tom Tresh	.70	.35	.20
(279)	Ted Uhlaender	.50	.25	.15
(280)	Del Unser	.50	.25	.15
(281)	Hilario Valdespino	.50	.25	.15
(282)	Fred Valentine	.50	.25	.15
(283)	Bob Veale	.50	.25	.15
(284)	Zoilo Versalles	.50	.25	.15
(285)	Pete Ward	.50	.25	.15
(286)	Al Weis	.50	.25	.15
(287)	Don Wert	.50	.25	.15
(288)	Bill White	.80	.40	.25
(289)	Roy White	.50	.25	.15
(290)	Fred Whitfield	.50	.25	.15
(291)	Hoyt Wilhelm	6.00	3.00	1.75
(292)	Billy Williams	12.50	6.25	3.75
(293)	Maury Wills	.90	.45	.25
(294)	Earl Wilson	.50	.25	.15
(295)	Wilbur Wood	.70	.35	.20
(296)	Jerry Zimmerman	.50	.25	.15

1970 Milton Bradley

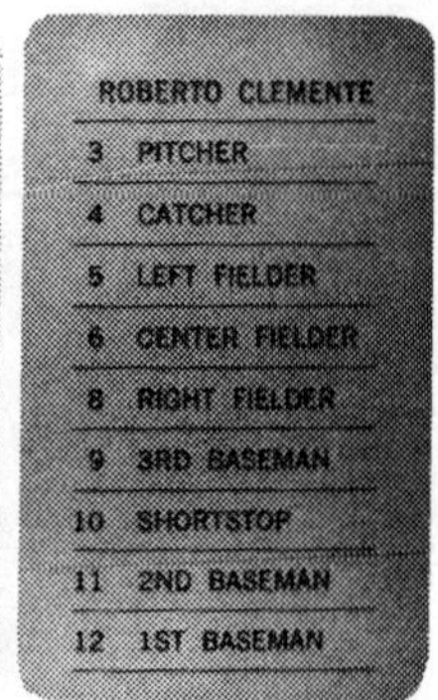

Except for the slightly larger (2-3/8" by 3-1/2") size, the format of the 1970 Milton Bradley set is similar to the 1969 Milton Bradley issue. Again designed for use with a baseball board game, the unnumbered black and white cards have rounded corners and wide white borders. The player's name appears in capital letters beneath the photo with his position, birthdate, height and batting and throwing preference on a line below. The back of the card shows the player's name along the top followed by a list of possible game situations used in playing the board game. There are no team designations on the cards and all team insignias have been airbrushed from the photos.

		NR MT	EX	VG
	Complete Set:	275.00	135.00	82.50
	Common Player:	2.00	1.00	.60
(1)	Hank Aaron	30.00	15.00	9.00
(2)	Ernie Banks	20.00	10.00	6.00
(3)	Lou Brock	15.00	7.50	4.50
(4)	Rod Carew	15.00	7.50	4.50
(5)	Roberto Clemente	30.00	15.00	9.00
(6)	Tommy Davis	2.00	1.00	.60
(7)	Bill Freehan	2.00	1.00	.60
(8)	Jim Fregosi	2.00	1.00	.60
(9)	Tom Haller	2.00	1.00	.60
(10)	Frank Howard	2.00	1.00	.60
(11)	Reggie Jackson	25.00	12.50	7.50
(12)	Harmon Killebrew	15.00	7.50	4.50
(13)	Mickey S. Lolich	3.50	1.75	1.00
(14)	Juan Marichal	10.00	5.00	3.00
(15)	Willie Mays	30.00	15.00	9.00
(16)	Willie McCovey	15.00	7.50	4.50
(17)	Sam McDowell	2.00	1.00	.60
(18)	Dennis Menke (Denis)	2.00	1.00	.60
(19)	Don Mincher	2.00	1.00	.60
(20)	Phil Niekro	10.00	5.00	3.00
(21)	Rico Petrocelli	2.00	1.00	.60
(22)	Boog Powell	3.50	1.75	1.00
(23)	Frank Robinson	15.00	7.50	4.50
(24)	Pete Rose	30.00	15.00	9.00
(25)	Ron Santo	3.50	1.75	1.00
(26)	Tom Seaver	15.00	7.50	4.50
(27)	Mel Stottlemyre	2.00	1.00	.60
(28)	Tony Taylor	2.00	1.00	.60

1972 Milton Bradley

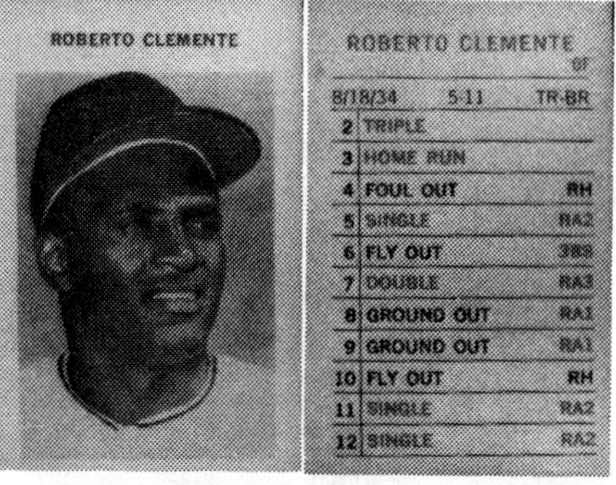

The 1972 Milton Bradley set was again designed for use with a baseball table game. The cards in the 1972 set are identical to the 1969 issue with square corners. The unnumbered black and white cards measure 2" by 3" and display the player's name along the top of the card. Again, all team insignias have been eliminated by airbrushing, and there are no team designations indicated. The back of the cards carry the player's name along with his position, birthdate, height and batting and throwing preferences followed by a list of possible game situations used in playing the baseball board game.

The same cards are not found in every set and it is possible cards other than those checklisted here may exist.

		NR MT	EX	VG
Complete Set:		650.00	325.00	195.00
Common Player:		.50	.25	.15
(1)	Hank Aaron	30.00	15.00	9.00
(2)	Tommie Aaron	.75	.40	.25
(3)	Ted Abernathy	.50	.25	.15
(4)	Jerry Adair	.50	.25	.15
(5)	Tommy Agee	.50	.25	.15
(6)	Bernie Allen	.50	.25	.15
(7)	Hank Allen	.50	.25	.15
(8)	Richie Allen	1.00	.50	.30
(9)	Gene Alley	.50	.25	.15
(10)	Bob Allison	.70	.35	.20
(11)	Sandy Alomar	.70	.35	.20
(12)	Felipe Alou	1.00	.50	.30
(13)	Jesus Alou	.50	.25	.15
(14)	Matty Alou	.50	.25	.15
(15)	Max Alvis	.50	.25	.15
(16)	Brant Alyea	.50	.25	.15
(17)	Mike Andrews	.50	.25	.15
(18)	Luis Aparicio	6.00	3.00	1.75
(19)	Jose Arcia	.50	.25	.15
(20)	Gerald Arrigo	.50	.25	.15
(21)	Bob Aspromonte	.50	.25	.15
(22)	Joe Azcue	.50	.25	.15
(23)	Robert Bailey	.50	.25	.15
(24)	Sal Bando	.70	.35	.20
(25)	Ernie Banks	20.00	10.00	6.00
(26)	Steve Barber	.50	.25	.15
(27)	Robert Barton	.50	.25	.15
(28)	John Bateman	.50	.25	.15
(29)	Glen Beckert (Glenn)	.70	.35	.20
(30)	John Bench	20.00	10.00	6.00
(31)	Ken Berry	.50	.25	.15
(32)	Frank Bertaina	.50	.25	.15
(33)	Paul Blair	.50	.25	.15
(34)	Stephen Blass	.50	.25	.15
(35)	Curt Blefary	.50	.25	.15
(36)	Bobby Bolin	.50	.25	.15
(37)	Bobby Lee Bonds	1.50	.70	.45
(38)	Donald Bosch	.50	.25	.15
(39)	Richard Bosman	.50	.25	.15
(40)	Dave Boswell	.50	.25	.15
(41)	Kenneth Boswell	.50	.25	.15
(42)	Cletis Boyer	.80	.40	.25
(43)	Ken Boyer	1.50	.70	.45
(44)	Charles Bradford	.50	.25	.15
(45)	Ronald Brand	.50	.25	.15
(46)	Ken Brett	.50	.25	.15
(47)	Jim Brewer	.50	.25	.15
(48)	John Briggs	.50	.25	.15
(49)	Nelson Briles	.50	.25	.15
(50)	Ed Brinkman	.50	.25	.15
(51)	James Britton	.50	.25	.15
(52)	Lou Brock	12.50	6.25	3.75
(53)	Gates Brown	.50	.25	.15
(54)	Larry Brown	.50	.25	.15
(55)	Ollie Brown	.50	.25	.15
(56)	George Brunet	.50	.25	.15
(57)	Don Buford	.50	.25	.15
(58)	Wallace Bunker	.50	.25	.15
(59)	Jim Bunning	2.75	1.50	.80
(60)	William Butler	.50	.25	.15
(61)	Johnny Callison	.80	.40	.25
(62)	Campy Campaneris	.80	.40	.25
(63)	Jose Cardenal	.50	.25	.15
(64)	Leo Cardenas	.50	.25	.15
(65)	Don Cardwell	.50	.25	.15
(66)	Rod Carew	12.50	6.25	3.75
(67)	Cisco Carlos	.50	.25	.15
(68)	Steve Carlton	15.00	7.50	4.50
(69)	Clay Carroll	.50	.25	.15
(70)	Paul Casanova	.50	.25	.15
(71)	Norm Cash	1.50	.70	.45
(72)	Danny Cater	.50	.25	.15
(73)	Orlando Cepeda	2.75	1.50	.80
(74)	Dean Chance	.70	.35	.20
(75)	Horace Clarke	.50	.25	.15
(76)	Roberto Clemente	30.00	15.00	9.00
(77)	Donn Clendenon	.70	.35	.20
(78)	Ty Cline	.50	.25	.15
(79)	Nate Colbert	.50	.25	.15
(80)	Joe Coleman	.50	.25	.15
(81)	William Conigliaro	.80	.40	.25
(82)	Casey Cox	.50	.25	.15
(83)	Mike Cuellar	.70	.35	.20
(84)	Ray Culp	.50	.25	.15
(85)	George Culver	.50	.25	.15
(86)	Vic Davalillo	.50	.25	.15
(87)	Jim Davenport	.50	.25	.15
(88)	Tommy Davis	.80	.40	.25
(89)	Willie Davis	.80	.40	.25
(90)	Larry Dierker	.50	.25	.15
(91)	Richard Dietz	.50	.25	.15
(92)	Chuck Dobson	.50	.25	.15
(93)	Pat Dobson	.50	.25	.15
(94)	John Donaldson	.50	.25	.15
(95)	Al Downing	.50	.25	.15
(96)	Moe Drabowsky	.50	.25	.15
(97)	John Edwards	.50	.25	.15
(98)	Thomas Egan	.50	.25	.15
(99)	Dick Ellsworth	.50	.25	.15
(100)	Mike Epstein	.50	.25	.15
(101)	Andy Etchebarren	.50	.25	.15
(102)	Ron Fairly	.70	.35	.20
(103)	Frank Fernandez	.50	.25	.15
(104)	Alfred Ferrara	.50	.25	.15
(105)	Michael Fiore	.50	.25	.15
(106)	Curt Flood	1.50	.70	.45
(107)	Vern Fuller	.50	.25	.15
(108)	Joe Foy	.50	.25	.15
(109)	Tito Francona	.50	.25	.15
(110)	Bill Freehan	.70	.35	.20
(111)	Jim Fregosi	.80	.40	.25
(112)	Woodie Fryman	.50	.25	.15
(113)	Len Gabrielson	.50	.25	.15
(114)	Philip Gagliano	.50	.25	.15
(115)	Cito Gaston	.80	.40	.25
(116)	Jake Gibbs	.50	.25	.15
(117)	Russ Gibson	.50	.25	.15
(118)	Dave Giusti	.50	.25	.15
(119)	Fred Gladding	.50	.25	.15
(120)	Tony Gonzalez	.50	.25	.15
(121)	Jim Gosger	.50	.25	.15
(122)	James Grant	.80	.40	.25
(123)	Thomas Griffin	.50	.25	.15
(124)	Dick Green	.50	.25	.15
(125)	Jerry Grote	.50	.25	.15
(126)	Tom Hall	.50	.25	.15
(127)	Tom Haller	.50	.25	.15
(128)	Steve Hamilton	.50	.25	.15
(129)	William Hands	.50	.25	.15
(130)	James Hannan	.50	.25	.15
(131)	Ron Hansen	.50	.25	.15
(132)	Jim Hardin	.50	.25	.15
(133)	Steve Hargan	.50	.25	.15
(134)	Tommy Harper	.70	.35	.20
(135)	Bud Harrelson	.70	.35	.20
(136)	Ken Harrelson	.80	.40	.25
(137)	Jim Hart	.50	.25	.15
(138)	Rich Hebner	.70	.35	.20
(139)	Michael Hedlund	.50	.25	.15
(140)	Tommy Helms	.50	.25	.15
(141)	Elrod Hendricks	.50	.25	.15
(142)	Ronald Herbel	.50	.25	.15
(143)	Jack Hernandez	.50	.25	.15
(144)	Mike Hershberger	.50	.25	.15
(145)	Jack Hiatt	.50	.25	.15
(146)	Jim Hickman	.50	.25	.15
(147)	Dennis Higgins	.50	.25	.15
(148)	John Hiller	.50	.25	.15
(149)	Chuck Hinton	.50	.25	.15
(150)	Larry Hisle	.70	.35	.20
(151)	Ken Holtzman	.70	.35	.20
(152)	Joel Horlen	.50	.25	.15
(153)	Tony Horton	.50	.25	.15
(154)	Willie Horton	.50	.25	.15
(155)	Frank Howard	1.00	.50	.30
(156)	Robert Humphreys	.50	.25	.15
(157)	Randy Hundley	.50	.25	.15
(158)	Ron Hunt	.50	.25	.15
(159)	Catfish Hunter	6.00	3.00	1.75
(160)	Grant Jackson	.50	.25	.15
(161)	Reggie Jackson	20.00	10.00	6.00
(162)	Sonny Jackson	.50	.25	.15
(163)	Pat Jarvis	.50	.25	.15
(164)	Larry Jaster	.50	.25	.15
(165)	Julian Javier	.50	.25	.15
(166)	Ferguson Jenkins	6.00	3.00	1.75
(167)	Tommy John	4.00	2.00	1.25
(168)	Alexander Johnson	.50	.25	.15
(169)	Bob Johnson	.50	.25	.15
(170)	Dave Johnson	.80	.40	.25
(171)	Deron Johnson	.50	.25	.15
(172)	Jay Johnstone	.70	.35	.20
(173)	Cleon Jones	.50	.25	.15
(174)	Dalton Jones	.50	.25	.15
(175)	Mack Jones	.50	.25	.15
(176)	Richard Joseph	.50	.25	.15
(177)	Duane Josephson	.50	.25	.15
(178)	Jim Kaat	2.75	1.50	.80
(179)	Al Kaline	15.00	7.50	4.50
(180)	Richard Kelley	.50	.25	.15
(181)	Harold Kelly	.50	.25	.15
(182)	Gerald Kenney	.50	.25	.15
(183)	Don Kessinger	.70	.35	.20
(184)	Harmon Killebrew	12.50	6.25	3.75
(185)	Ed Kirkpatrick	.50	.25	.15
(186)	Bobby Knoop	.50	.25	.15
(187)	Calvin Koonce	.50	.25	.15
(188)	Jerry Koosman	.80	.40	.25
(189)	Andy Kosco	.50	.25	.15
(190)	Ed Kranepool	.70	.35	.20
(191)	Ted Kubiak	.50	.25	.15
(192)	Jose Laboy	.50	.25	.15
(193)	Joseph Lahoud	.50	.25	.15
(194)	William Landis	.50	.25	.15
(195)	Harold Lanier	.70	.35	.20
(196)	Fred Lasher	.50	.25	.15
(197)	John Lazar	.50	.25	.15
(198)	Jim Lefebvre	.80	.40	.25
(199)	Denny Lemaster	.50	.25	.15
(200)	Dave Leonhard	.50	.25	.15
(201)	Frank Linzy	.50	.25	.15
(202)	Mickey Lolich	1.50	.70	.45
(203)	Jim Lonborg	.70	.35	.20
(204)	Mike Lum	.50	.25	.15
(205)	Al Lyle	.70	.35	.20
(206)	Jim Maloney	.50	.25	.15
(207)	Juan Marichal	8.00	4.00	2.50
(208)	David Marshall	.50	.25	.15
(209)	J.C. Martin	.50	.25	.15
(210)	Marty Martinez	.50	.25	.15
(211)	Tom Matchick	.50	.25	.15
(212)	Dal Maxvill	.50	.25	.15
(213)	Carlos May	.50	.25	.15
(214)	Jerry May	.50	.25	.15
(215)	Lee May	.50	.25	.15
(216)	Lee Maye	.50	.25	.15
(217)	Willie Mays	30.00	15.00	9.00
(218)	Bill Mazeroski	4.00	2.00	1.25
(219)	Richard McAuliffe	.50	.25	.15
(220)	Al McBean	.50	.25	.15
(221)	Tim McCarver	1.00	.50	.30
(222)	Bill McCool	.50	.25	.15
(223)	Mike McCormick	.50	.25	.15
(224)	Willie McCovey	15.00	7.50	4.50
(225)	Tom McCraw	.50	.25	.15
(226)	Lindy McDaniel	.50	.25	.15
(227)	Sam McDowell	.80	.40	.25
(228)	Leon McFadden	.50	.25	.15
(229)	Daniel McGinn	.50	.25	.15
(230)	Jim McGlothlin	.50	.25	.15
(231)	Fred McGraw	.50	.25	.15
(232)	Denny McLain	1.25	.60	.40
(233)	Ken McMullen	.50	.25	.15
(234)	Dave McNally	.70	.35	.20
(235)	Gerry McNertney	.50	.25	.15
(236)	William Melton	.50	.25	.15
(237)	Dennis Menke (Denis)	.50	.25	.15
(238)	John Messersmith	.50	.25	.15
(239)	Felix Millan	.50	.25	.15
(240)	Norman Miller	.50	.25	.15
(241)	Don Mincher	.50	.25	.15
(242)	Rick Monday	.50	.25	.15
(243)	Donald Money	.50	.25	.15
(244)	Barry Moore	.50	.25	.15
(245)	Bob Moose	.50	.25	.15
(246)	David Morehead	.50	.25	.15
(247)	Joe Morgan	12.50	6.25	3.75
(248)	Curt Motton	.50	.25	.15
(249)	Manny Mota	.70	.35	.20
(250)	Bob Murcer	1.25	.60	.40
(251)	Thomas Murphy	.50	.25	.15
(252)	Ivan Murrell	.50	.25	.15
(253)	Jim Nash	.50	.25	.15
(254)	Joe Niekro	2.00	1.00	.60
(255)	Phil Niekro	4.00	2.00	1.25
(256)	Gary Nolan	.50	.25	.15
(257)	Jim Northrup	.50	.25	.15
(258)	Richard Nye	.50	.25	.15
(259)	Johnny Odom	.80	.40	.25
(260)	John O'Donaghue	.50	.25	.15
(261)	Tony Oliva	2.50	1.25	.70
(262)	Al Oliver	2.00	1.00	.60
(263)	Robert Oliver	.50	.25	.15
(264)	Claude Osteen	.50	.25	.15
(265)	Ray Oyler	.50	.25	.15
(266)	Jose Pagan	.50	.25	.15
(267)	Jim Palmer	8.00	4.00	2.50
(268)	Milt Pappas	.70	.35	.20
(269)	Wes Parker	.50	.25	.15
(270)	Fred Patek	.50	.25	.15
(271)	Mike Paul	.50	.25	.15
(272)	Joe Pepitone	1.00	.50	.30
(273)	Tony Perez	4.00	2.00	1.25
(274)	Gaylord Perry	6.00	3.00	1.75
(275)	Jim Perry	.70	.35	.20
(276)	Gary Peters	.50	.25	.15
(277)	Rico Petrocelli	.70	.35	.20
(278)	Tom Phoebus	.50	.25	.15
(279)	Lou Piniella	2.50	1.25	.70
(280)	Vada Pinson	2.50	1.25	.70
(281)	Boog Powell	2.50	1.25	.70
(282)	Jim Price	.50	.25	.15
(283)	Frank Quilici	.50	.25	.15
(284)	Doug Rader	.70	.35	.20
(285)	Ron Reed	.50	.25	.15
(286)	Rich Reese	.50	.25	.15
(287)	Phil Regan	.50	.25	.15
(288)	Rick Reichardt	.50	.25	.15
(289)	Rick Renick	.50	.25	.15
(290)	Roger Repoz	.50	.25	.15
(291)	Mervin Rettenmund	.50	.25	.15
(292)	Dave Ricketts	.50	.25	.15
(293)	Juan Rios	.50	.25	.15
(294)	Bill Robinson	.70	.35	.20
(295)	Brooks Robinson	15.00	7.50	4.50
(296)	Frank Robinson	15.00	7.50	4.50
(297)	Aurelio Rodriguez	.50	.25	.15
(298)	Ellie Rodriguez	.50	.25	.15
(299)	Cookie Rojas	.50	.25	.15
(300)	Rich Rollins	.50	.25	.15
(301)	Vicente Romo	.50	.25	.15
(302)	Phil Roof	.50	.25	.15
(303)	Pete Rose	30.00	15.00	9.00
(304)	John Roseboro	.70	.35	.20
(305)	Chico Ruiz	.50	.25	.15
(306)	Mike Ryan	.50	.25	.15
(307)	Ray Sadecki	.50	.25	.15
(308)	Chico Salmon	.50	.25	.15
(309)	Manuel Sanguillen	.80	.40	.25
(310)	Ron Santo	2.25	1.25	.70
(311)	Tom Satriano	.50	.25	.15
(312)	Theodore Savage	.50	.25	.15
(313)	Paul Schaal	.50	.25	.15
(314)	Dick Schofield	.70	.35	.20
(315)	George Scott	.80	.40	.25
(316)	Tom Seaver	15.00	7.50	4.50
(317)	Art Shamsky	.50	.25	.15
(318)	Mike Shannon	.50	.25	.15
(319)	Chris Short	.50	.25	.15
(320)	Sonny Siebert	.50	.25	.15
(321)	Duke Sims	.50	.25	.15
(322)	William Singer	.50	.25	.15
(323)	Reggie Smith	.70	.35	.20
(324)	Willie Smith	.50	.25	.15
(325)	Russ Snyder	.50	.25	.15
(326)	Al Spangler	.50	.25	.15
(327)	James Spencer	.50	.25	.15
(328)	Ed Spiezio	.50	.25	.15
(329)	Larry Stahl	.50	.25	.15
(330)	Lee Stange	.50	.25	.15
(331)	Mickey Stanley	.50	.25	.15
(332)	Willie Stargell	12.50	6.25	3.75
(333)	Rusty Staub	2.50	1.25	.70
(334)	James Stewart	.50	.25	.15
(335)	George Stone	.50	.25	.15
(336)	William Stoneman	.50	.25	.15
(337)	Mel Stottlemyre	.80	.40	.25
(338)	Ed Stroud	.50	.25	.15
(339)	Ken Suarez	.50	.25	.15
(340)	Gary Sutherland	.50	.25	.15
(341)	Don Sutton	4.00	2.00	1.25
(342)	Ron Swoboda	.50	.25	.15
(343)	Fred Talbot	.50	.25	.15
(344)	Jose Tartabull	.50	.25	.15
(345)	Kenneth Tatum	.50	.25	.15

(346)	Tony Taylor	.50	.25	.15
(347)	Luis Tiant	2.00	1.00	.60
(348)	Bob Tillman	.50	.25	.15
(349)	Bobby Tolan	.50	.25	.15
(350)	Jeff Torborg	.70	.35	.20
(351)	Joe Torre	2.00	1.00	.60
(352)	Cesar Tovar	.50	.25	.15
(353)	Tom Tresh	.70	.35	.20
(354)	Ted Uhlaender	.50	.25	.15
(355)	Del Unser	.50	.25	.15
(356)	Bob Veale	.50	.25	.15
(357)	Zoilo Versalles	.50	.25	.15
(358)	Luke Walker	.50	.25	.15
(359)	Pete Ward	.50	.25	.15
(360)	Eddie Watt	.50	.25	.15
(361)	Ramon Webster	.50	.25	.15
(362)	Al Weis	.50	.25	.15
(363)	Don Wert	.50	.25	.15
(364)	Bill White	1.00	.50	.30
(365)	Roy White	.70	.35	.20
(366)	Hoyt Wilhelm	6.00	3.00	1.75
(367)	Billy Williams	12.50	6.25	3.75
(368)	Walter Williams	.50	.25	.15
(369)	Maury Wills	1.50	.70	.45
(370)	Don Wilson	.50	.25	.15
(371)	Earl Wilson	.50	.25	.15
(372)	Robert Wine	.50	.25	.15
(373)	Richard Wise	.50	.25	.15
(374)	Wilbur Wood	.70	.35	.20
(375)	William Woodward	.50	.25	.15
(376)	Clyde Wright	.50	.25	.15
(377)	James Wynn	.80	.40	.25
(378)	Jerry Zimmerman	.50	.25	.15

1984 Milton Bradley

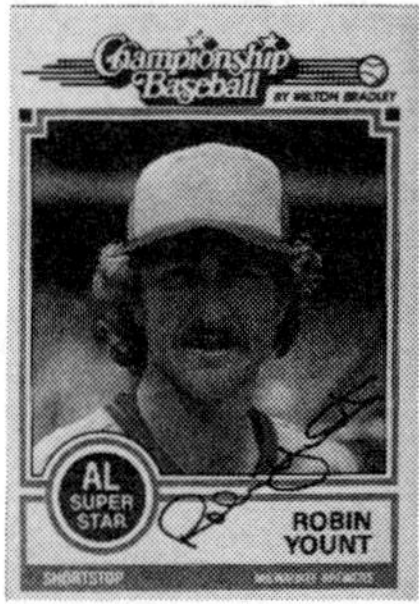

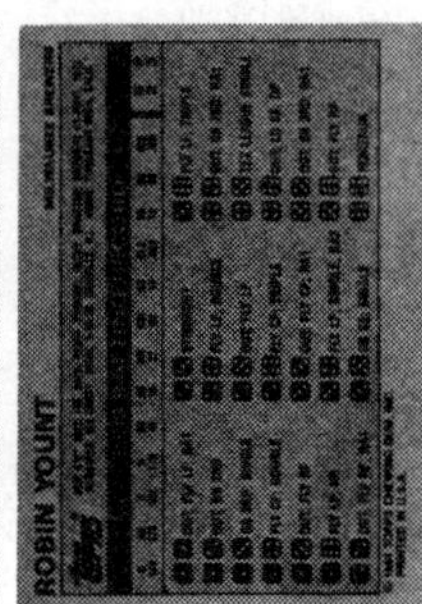

In 1984 Milton Bradley printed their baseball game cards in full-color and adopted the standard baseball card size of 2-1/2" by 3-1/2". A total of 30 cards were in the set. The card fronts show the player photos with the team insignias and logos air-brushed away. The game is called Championship Baseball. Card backs varied in style; some had player statistics plus game information, and others only game information.

		MT	NR MT	EX
Complete Set:		11.00	8.25	4.50
Common Player:		.25	.20	.10
(1)	Wade Boggs	.80	.60	.30
(2)	George Brett	1.00	.70	.40
(3)	Rod Carew	.50	.40	.20
(4)	Steve Carlton	.40	.30	.15
(5)	Gary Carter	.30	.25	.12
(6)	Dave Concepcion	.25	.20	.10
(7)	Cecil Cooper	.25	.20	.10
(8)	Andre Dawson	.50	.40	.20
(9)	Carlton Fisk	.40	.30	.15
(10)	Steve Garvey	.50	.40	.20
(11)	Pedro Guerrero	.25	.20	.10
(12)	Ron Guidry	.25	.20	.10
(13)	Rickey Henderson	.80	.60	.30
(14)	Reggie Jackson	.80	.60	.30
(15)	Ron Kittle	.25	.20	.10
(16)	Bill Madlock	.25	.20	.10
(17)	Dale Murphy	.80	.60	.30
(18)	Al Oliver	.25	.20	.10
(19)	Darrell Porter	.25	.20	.10
(20)	Cal Ripken, Jr.	1.00	.70	.40
(21)	Pete Rose	1.00	.70	.40
(22)	Steve Sax	.25	.20	.10
(23)	Mike Schmidt	1.00	.70	.40
(24)	Ted Simmons	.25	.20	.10
(25)	Ozzie Smith	.40	.30	.15
(26)	Dave Stieb	.25	.20	.10
(27)	Fernando Valenzuela	.25	.20	.10
(28)	Lou Whitaker	.35	.25	.14
(29)	Dave Winfield	.80	.60	.30
(30)	Robin Yount	.80	.60	.30

1933 Minneapolis Star Worch Tobacco

This set of unnumbered postcard-size cards, apparently produced by the Minneapolis Star newspaper, was used as a promotion by Worch Cigar Co. of St. Paul, Minn. Although there is no advertising for Worch Cigars on the cards themselves, the cards were mailed in envelopes bearing the Worch name. The borderless cards featured action photos with the player's name and team appearing in hand-lettered type near the bottom.

		NR MT	EX	VG
Complete Set:		7500.	3750.	2250.
Common Player:		18.00	9.00	5.50
(1)	Sparky Adams	18.00	9.00	5.50
(2)	Dale Alexander	18.00	9.00	5.50
(3)	Ivy Paul Andrews	18.00	9.00	5.50
(4a)	Earl Averill (Cleveland)	40.00	20.00	12.00
(4b)	Earl Averill (no team designation)	40.00	20.00	12.00
(5)	Richard Bartell	18.00	9.00	5.50
(6)	Herman Bell	18.00	9.00	5.50
(7)	Walter Berger	18.00	9.00	5.50
(8)	Huck Betts	18.00	9.00	5.50
(9)	Max Bishop	18.00	9.00	5.50
(10)	Jim Bottomley	40.00	20.00	12.00
(11a)	Tom Bridges (name and team in box)	18.00	9.00	5.50
(11b)	Tom Bridges (no box)	18.00	9.00	5.50
(12)	Clint Brown	18.00	9.00	5.50
(13)	Max Carey	40.00	20.00	12.00
(14)	Tex Carlton	18.00	9.00	5.50
(15)	Chalmer Cissell	18.00	9.00	5.50
(16)	Mickey Cochrane	40.00	20.00	12.00
(17)	Ripper Collins	18.00	9.00	5.50
(18)	Earle Combs	40.00	20.00	12.00
(19)	Adam Comorosky	18.00	9.00	5.50
(20)	Estel Crabtree	18.00	9.00	5.50
(21)	Rodger Cramer (Roger)	18.00	9.00	5.50
(22)	Pat Crawford	18.00	9.00	5.50
(23)	Hugh Critz	18.00	9.00	5.50
(24)	Frank Crosetti	25.00	12.50	7.50
(25a)	Joe Cronin (name and team in box)	40.00	20.00	12.00
(25b)	Joe Cronin (no box)	40.00	20.00	12.00
(26)	Alvin Crowder	18.00	9.00	5.50
(27)	Tony Cuccinello	18.00	9.00	5.50
(28)	KiKi Cuyler	40.00	20.00	12.00
(29)	Geo. Davis	18.00	9.00	5.50
(30)	Dizzy Dean	100.00	50.00	30.00
(31)	Wm. Dickey	100.00	50.00	30.00
(32)	Leo Durocher	60.00	30.00	18.00
(33)	James Dykes	25.00	12.50	7.50
(34)	George Earnshaw	18.00	9.00	5.50
(35)	Woody English	18.00	9.00	5.50
(36a)	Richard Ferrell (name and team in box)	40.00	20.00	12.00
(36b)	Richard Ferrell (no box)	40.00	20.00	12.00
(37a)	Wesley Ferrell (name and team in box)	18.00	9.00	5.50
(37b)	Wesley Ferrell (no box)	18.00	9.00	5.50
(38)	Fred Fitzsimmons	18.00	9.00	5.50
(39)	Lew Fonseca	25.00	12.50	7.50
(40)	James Foxx	100.00	50.00	30.00
(41)	Fred Frankhouse	18.00	9.00	5.50
(42)	Frank Frisch	40.00	20.00	12.00
(43a)	Leon Gaslin (name incorrect)	40.00	20.00	12.00
(43b)	Leon Goslin (name correct)	40.00	20.00	12.00
(44)	Lou Gehrig	350.00	175.00	105.00
(45)	Charles Gehringer	40.00	20.00	12.00
(46)	Vernon Gomez	40.00	20.00	12.00
(47)	George Grantham	18.00	9.00	5.50
(48)	Grimes The Lord Of Burleigh (Burleigh Grimes)	40.00	20.00	12.00
(49)	Charlie Grimm	25.00	12.50	7.50
(50)	Robert Grove	60.00	30.00	18.00
(51)	Chic Hafey (Chick)	40.00	20.00	12.00
(52)	Jess Haines	40.00	20.00	12.00
(53)	Bill Hallahan	18.00	9.00	5.50
(54)	Mel Harder	18.00	9.00	5.50
(55)	Dave Harris	18.00	9.00	5.50
(56)	Gabby Hartnett	40.00	20.00	12.00
(57)	George Hass	18.00	9.00	5.50
(58)	Ray Hayworth	18.00	9.00	5.50
(59)	Harvey Hendrick	18.00	9.00	5.50
(60)	Dutch Henry	18.00	9.00	5.50
(61)	"Babe" Herman	25.00	12.50	7.50
(62)	Bill Herman	40.00	20.00	12.00
(63)	Frank Higgins	18.00	9.00	5.50
(64)	Oral Hildebrand	18.00	9.00	5.50
(65)	Roger Hornsby (Rogers)	150.00	75.00	45.00
(66)	Carl Hubbell	55.00	27.00	16.50
(67)	Travis Jackson	40.00	20.00	12.00
(68)	Smead Jolley	18.00	9.00	5.50
(69)	Wm. Kamm	18.00	9.00	5.50
(70)	Charles Klein	40.00	20.00	12.00
(71)	Jos. Kuhel	18.00	9.00	5.50
(72)	Tony Lazzeri	40.00	20.00	12.00
(73)	Sam Leslie	18.00	9.00	5.50
(74)	Al Lopez	40.00	20.00	12.00
(75)	Red Lucas	18.00	9.00	5.50
(76)	Adolfo Luque	18.00	9.00	5.50
(77)	Connie Mack	100.00	50.00	30.00
(78)	Gus Mancuso	18.00	9.00	5.50
(79)	Henry Manush	40.00	20.00	12.00
(80)	Fred Marberry	18.00	9.00	5.50
(81)	Pepper Martin	25.00	12.50	7.50
(82)	Wm. McKechnie	40.00	20.00	12.00
(83)	Joe Medwick	40.00	20.00	12.00
(84)	Jim Mooney	18.00	9.00	5.50
(85)	Joe Moore	18.00	9.00	5.50
(86)	Joe Mowry	18.00	9.00	5.50
(87)	Van Mungo	18.00	9.00	5.50
(88)	Buddy Myer	18.00	9.00	5.50
(89)	"Lefty" O'Doul	25.00	12.50	7.50
(90)	Bob O'Farrell	18.00	9.00	5.50
(91)	Ernie Orsatti	18.00	9.00	5.50
(92)	Melvin Ott	65.00	32.00	19.50
(93)	Roy Parmelee	18.00	9.00	5.50
(94)	Homer Peel	18.00	9.00	5.50
(95)	George Pipgras	18.00	9.00	5.50
(96)	Harry Rice	18.00	9.00	5.50
(97)	Paul Richards	25.00	12.50	7.50
(98)	Eppa Rixey	40.00	20.00	12.00
(99)	Charles Ruffing	40.00	20.00	12.00
(100)	Jack Russell	18.00	9.00	5.50
(101)	Babe Ruth	900.00	450.00	270.00
(102)	"Blondy" Ryan	18.00	9.00	5.50
(103)	Wilfred Ryan	18.00	9.00	5.50
(104)	Fred Schulte	18.00	9.00	5.50
(105)	Hal Schumacher	18.00	9.00	5.50
(106)	Luke Sewel (Sewell)	18.00	9.00	5.50
(107)	Al Simmons	40.00	20.00	12.00
(108)	Ray Spencer	18.00	9.00	5.50
(109)	Casey Stengel	300.00	150.00	90.00
(110)	Riggs Stephenson	25.00	12.50	7.50
(111)	Walter Stewart	18.00	9.00	5.50
(112)	John T. Stone	18.00	9.00	5.50
(113)	Gus Suhr	18.00	9.00	5.50
(114)	Dan Taylor	18.00	9.00	5.50
(115)	Bill Terry	65.00	32.00	19.50
(116)	Pie Traynor	40.00	20.00	12.00
(117)	William Urbanski	18.00	9.00	5.50
(118)	Lloyd Vaughan	40.00	20.00	12.00
(119)	Johnny Vergez	18.00	9.00	5.50
(120)	George Walberg	18.00	9.00	5.50
(121)	Bill Walker	18.00	9.00	5.50
(122)	Gerald Walker	18.00	9.00	5.50
(123a)	Lloyd Waner (background blanked out)	40.00	20.00	12.00
(123b)	Lloyd Waner (with background)	40.00	20.00	12.00
(124a)	Paul Waner (background blanked out)	40.00	20.00	12.00
(124b)	Paul Waner (with background)	40.00	20.00	12.00
(125)	Lon Warneke	18.00	9.00	5.50
(126)	George Watkins	18.00	9.00	5.50
(127)	Monte Weaver	18.00	9.00	5.50
(128)	Sam West	18.00	9.00	5.50
(129)	Earl Whitehill	18.00	9.00	5.50
(130)	Hack Wilson	40.00	20.00	12.00
(131)	Jimmy Wilson	18.00	9.00	5.50

1983 Minnesota Twins Team Issue

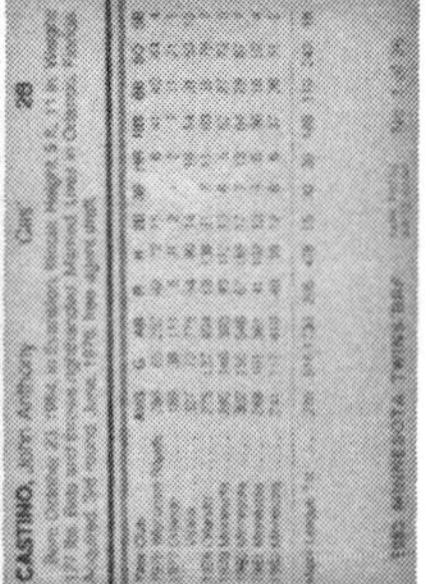

The Minnesota Twins produced a 36-card set in 1983 to be sold at concession stands and through the mail. The full-color borderless cards measure 2-1/2" by 3-1/2" and displayed the player's uniform number on a white Twins jersey at the bottom of the card. The backs contain full career statistics.

		MT	NR MT	EX
Complete Set:		9.00	6.75	3.50
Common Player:		.10	.08	.04
1	John Anthony Castino	.10	.08	.04
2	James Michael Eisenreich	.20	.15	.08
3	Raymond Edward Smith	.10	.08	.04
4	Scott Matthew Ullger	.10	.08	.04
5	Gary Joseph Gaetti	.50	.40	.20
6	Michael Vaughn Hatcher	.10	.08	.04
7	Robert Van Mitchell	.10	.08	.04
8	Leonardo Lago Faedo, Jr.	.10	.08	.04
9	Kent Alan Hrbek	.75	.60	.30
10	Timothy Jon Laudner	.15	.11	.06
11	Frank John Viola, Jr.	.75	.60	.30
12	Bryan Alois Oelkers	.10	.08	.04
13	Richard Eugene Lysander	.10	.08	.04
14	Ralph David Engle	.10	.08	.04
15	Leonard Joseph Whitehouse, Jr.	.10	.08	.04
16	William Peter Filson	.10	.08	.04

17	Thomas Andrew Brunansky	.20	.15	.08
18	Robert Randall Bush	.10	.08	.04
19	Bradley David Havens	.10	.08	.04
20	Albert Hamilton Williams	.10	.08	.04
21	Gary Lamell Ward	.10	.08	.04
22	Jack William O'Connor	.10	.08	.04
23	Robert Ernie Castillo, Jr.	.10	.08	.04
24	Ronald Washington	.10	.08	.04
25	Ronald Gene Davis	.10	.08	.04
26	Jay Thomas Kelly	.15	.11	.06
27	William Frederick Gardner	.10	.08	.04
28	Richard Francis Stelmaszek	.10	.08	.04
29	James Robert Lemon	.20	.15	.08
30	John Joseph Podres	.20	.15	.08
31	Minnesota's Native Sons (Jim Eisenreich, Kent Hrbek, Tim Laudner)	.25	.20	.10
32	Twins' Catchers (Dave Engle, Tim Laudner)	.10	.08	.04
33	The Lumber Company (Tom Brunansky, Gary Gaetti, Kent Hrbek, Gary Ward)	.35	.25	.14
34	Twins' Coaches (Billy Gardner, Tom Kelly, Jim Lemon, Johnny Podres, Rick Stelmaszek)	.10	.08	.04
35	Team Photo	.10	.08	.04
36	Metrodome/Checklist	.10	.08	.04

1984 Minnesota Twins Team Issue

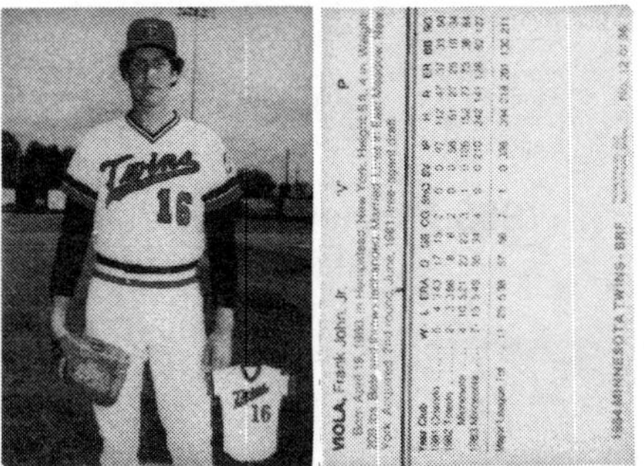

This team-issued set from the Minnesota Twins consists of 36 full-color, borderless cards, each measuring 2-1/2" by 3-1/2". As in the previous year, the player's uniform number appears on a white Twins jersey at the bottom of the card. The backs are printed in red and blue on white stock and include career stats. The set feaqtures several special cards, including one of Harmon Killebrew.

		MT	NR MT	EX
	Complete Set:	7.00	5.25	2.75
	Common Player:	.10	.08	.04
1	John Anthony Castino	.10	.08	.04
2	James Michael Eisenreich	.10	.08	.04
3	Alfonso Jimenez	.10	.08	.04
4	David Keith Meier	.10	.08	.04
5	Gary Joseph Gaetti	.35	.25	.14
6	Michael Vaughn Hatcher	.10	.08	.04
7	Jeffrey Scott Reed	.10	.08	.04
8	Timothy Shawn Teufel	.10	.08	.04
9	Leonardo Lago Faedo, Jr.	.10	.08	.04
10	Kent Alan Hrbek	.50	.40	.20
11	Timothy Jon Laudner	.15	.11	.06
12	Frank John Viola, Jr.	.50	.40	.20
13	Kenneth Marvin Schrom	.10	.08	.04
14	Larry John Pashnick	.10	.08	.04
15	Ralph David Engle	.10	.08	.04
16	Keith Martin Comstock	.10	.08	.04
17	William Peter Filson	.10	.08	.04
18	Thomas Andrew Brunansky	.20	.15	.08
19	Robert Randall Bush	.10	.08	.04
20	Darrell Wayne Brown	.10	.08	.04
21	Albert Hamilton Williams	.10	.08	.04
22	Michael Charles Walters	.10	.08	.04
23	John David Butcher	.10	.08	.04
24	Robert Ernie Castillo, Jr.	.10	.08	.04
25	Ronald Washington	.10	.08	.04
26	Ronald Gene Davis	.10	.08	.04
27	Jay Thomas Kelly	.15	.11	.06
28	William Frederick Gardner	.10	.08	.04
29	Richard Francis Stelmaszek	.10	.08	.04
30	James Robert Lemon	.20	.15	.08
31	John Joseph Podres	.20	.15	.08
32	Billy Mike Smithson	.10	.08	.04
33	Harmon Killebrew	1.00	.70	.40
34	Team Photo	.10	.08	.04
35	Logo Card	.10	.08	.04
36	Metrodome/Checklist	.10	.08	.04

1985 Minnesota Twins Team Issue

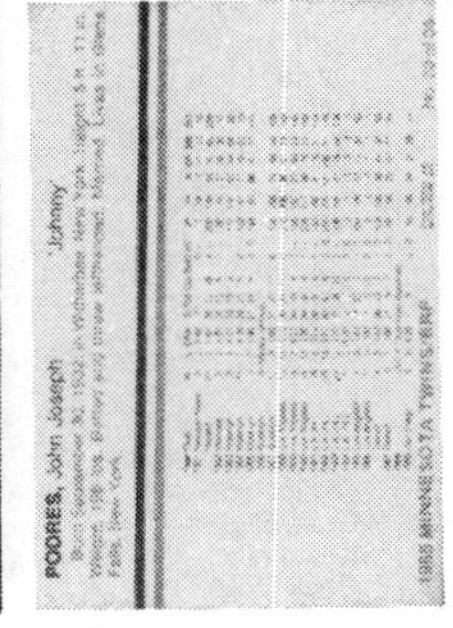

Similar in format to the previous two years, this 36-card team-issued set features full-color, borderless cards. The player's uniform number is again displayed on a white Twins jersey in the lower right corner, and the 1985 All-Star Game logo is shown in the lower left. The All-Star Game logo also appears on a special card in the set that lists on the back all Twins who have been selected for previous All-Star Games. The set was sold at ballpark concession stands and through the mail.

		MT	NR MT	EX
	Complete Set:	8.00	4.50	2.50
	Common Player:	.08	.06	.03
1	Alvaro Alberto Espinoza	.10	.08	.04
2	Roy Frederick Smalley, III	.10	.08	.04
3	Pedro Oliva, Jr.	.10	.08	.04
4	David Keith Meier	.10	.08	.04
5	Gary Joseph Gaetti	.35	.25	.14
6	Michael Vaughn Hatcher	.10	.08	.04
7	Jeffrey Scott Reed	.10	.08	.04
8	Timothy Shawn Teufel	.25	.20	.10
9	Mark Bruce Salas	.10	.08	.04
10	Kent Alan Hrbek	.50	.40	.20
11	Timothy Jon Laudner	.15	.11	.06
12	Frank John Viola, Jr.	.50	.40	.20
13	Kenneth Marvin Schrom	.10	.08	.04
14	Richard Eugene Lysander	.10	.08	.04
15	Ralph David Engle	.10	.08	.04
16	Andre Anter David	.10	.08	.04
17	Leonard Joseph Whitehouse, Jr.	.10	.08	.04
18	William Peter Filson	.10	.08	.04
19	Thomas Andrew Brunansky	.20	.15	.08
20	Robert Randall Bush	.10	.08	.04
21	Gregory Carpenter Gagne	.35	.25	.14
22	John Daniel Butcher	.10	.08	.04
23	Michael Steven Stenhouse	.10	.08	.04
24	Kirby Puckett	2.00	1.50	.80
25	Thomas Carl Klawitter	.10	.08	.04
26	Curtis Ray Wardle	.10	.08	.04
27	Richard Martin Yett	.10	.08	.04
28	Ronald Washington	.10	.08	.04
29	Ronald Gene Davis	.10	.08	.04
30	Jay Thomas Kelly	.15	.11	.06
31	William Frederick Gardner	.10	.08	.04
32	Richard Francis Stelmaszek	.10	.08	.04
33	John Joseph Podres	.20	.15	.08
34	Billy Mike Smithson	.10	.08	.04
35	1985 All-Star Game Logo Card	.10	.08	.04
36	Twins Logo/Checklist	.10	.08	.04

1986 Minnesota Twins Team Issue

This team-issued set contains 36 2-9/16" by 3-1/2" full-color cards. Fronts feature the Twins 25th anniversary logo and a jersey at the bottom of each card with the player's uniform number. All cards, except an action shot of Bert Blyleven, are posed photos, with a facsimile autograph on each. The set also includes a checklist and a team photo.

		MT	NR MT	EX
	Complete Set:	7.00	5.25	2.75
	Common Player:	.10	.08	.04
1	Christopher Francis Pittaro	.10	.08	.04
2	Stephen Paul Lombardozzi	.10	.08	.04
3	Roy Frederick Smalley, III	.10	.08	.04
4	Pedro Oliva, Jr.	.10	.08	.04
5	Gary Joseph Gaetti	.50	.40	.20
6	Michael Vaughn Hatcher	.10	.08	.04
7	Jeffrey Scott Reed	.10	.08	.04
8	Mark Bruce Salas	.10	.08	.04
9	Kent Alan Hrbek	.60	.45	.25
10	Timothy Jon Laudner	.15	.11	.06
11	Frank John Viola, Jr.	.50	.40	.20
12	Dennis Allen Burtt	.10	.08	.04
13	Alejandro Sanchez	.10	.08	.04
14	LeRoy Purdy Smith, III	.10	.08	.04
15	William Lamar Beane, III	.10	.08	.04
16	William Peter Filson	.10	.08	.04
17	Thomas Andrew Brunansky	.20	.15	.08
18	Robert Randall Bush	.10	.08	.04
19	Frank Anthony Eufemia, III	.10	.08	.04
20	John Mark Davidson	.10	.08	.04
21	Rik Aalbert Blyleven	.25	.20	.10
22	Gregory Carpenter Gagne	.15	.11	.06
23	John Daniel Butcher	.10	.08	.04
24	Kirby Puckett	1.00	.70	.40
25	William Carol Latham, Jr.	.10	.08	.04
26	Ronald Washington	.10	.08	.04
27	Ronald Gene Davis	.10	.08	.04
28	Jay Thomas Kelly	.15	.11	.06
29	Richard Stanley Such	.10	.08	.04
30	Richard Francis Stelmaszek	.10	.08	.04
31	Raymond Robert Miller	.10	.08	.04
32	Willard Wayne Terwilliger	.10	.08	.04
33	Billy Mike Smithson	.10	.08	.04
34	Alvis Woods	.10	.08	.04
35	Team Photo	.10	.08	.04
36	Twins Logo/Checklist	.10	.08	.04

1987 Minnesota Twins Team Issue

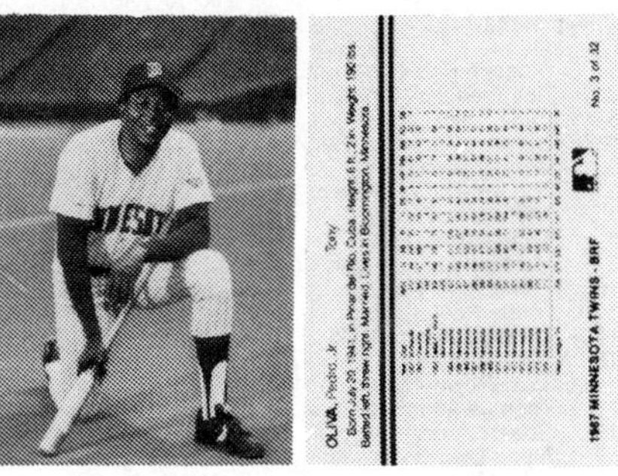

The Minnesota Twins produced a 32-card set of 2-1/2" by 3-1/2" full-color baseball cards to be sold at the ballpark and through their souvenir catalog. The card fronts are borderless, containing only the player photo. The backs are printed in blue and red on white card stock and carry the player's personal data and career record. The Twins also produced a post card set which was similar in design to the standard-size card set, but utilized different photos.

		MT	NR MT	EX
	Complete Set:	7.00	4.50	2.50
	Common Player:	.10	.06	.03
1	Stephen Paul Lombardozzi	.10	.08	.04
2	Roy Frederick Smalley III	.10	.08	.04
3	Pedro Oliva, Jr.	.10	.08	.04
4	Gregory Carpenter Gagne	.15	.11	.06
5	Gary Joseph Gaetti	.50	.40	.20
6	Jay Thomas Kelly	.15	.11	.06
7	Thomas Andrew Nieto	.10	.08	.04
8	Mark Bruce Salas	.10	.08	.04
9	Kent Alan Hrbek	.40	.30	.15
10	Timothy Jon Laudner	.15	.11	.06
11	Frank John Viola, Jr.	.50	.40	.20
12	Lester Paul Straker	.10	.08	.04
13	George Allen Frazier	.10	.08	.04
14	Keith Rowe Atherton	.10	.08	.04
15	Thomas Andrew Brunansky	.20	.15	.08
16	Robert Randall Bush	.10	.08	.04
17	Albert Dwayne Newman	.10	.08	.04
18	John Mark Davidson	.10	.08	.04
19	Rik Aalbert Blyleven	.25	.20	.10
20	Clinton Daniel Gladden III	.15	.11	.06
21	Kirby Puckett	1.00	.70	.40
22	Mark Steven Portugal	.10	.08	.04
23	Juan Bautista Berenguer	.10	.08	.04
24	Jeffrey James Reardon	.30	.25	.12
25	Richard Stanley Such	.10	.08	.04
26	Richard Francis Stelmaszek	.10	.08	.04
27	Warren Richard Renick	.10	.08	.04
28	Willard Wayne Terwilliger	.10	.08	.04
29	Joseph Charles Klink	.10	.08	.04
30	Billy Mike Smithson	.10	.08	.04
31	Team Photo	.10	.08	.04
32	Twins Logo/Checklist	.10	.08	.04

1988 Minnesota Twins Team Issue

The Twins issued this 33-card set (including checklist) to commemorate the team's 1987 Series victory. The slightly oversized cards (2-5/8" x 3-7/16") feature deluxe player photos printed on heavy stock with a gold-embossed "1987 World Champions" logo in the lower left corner. Many photos are

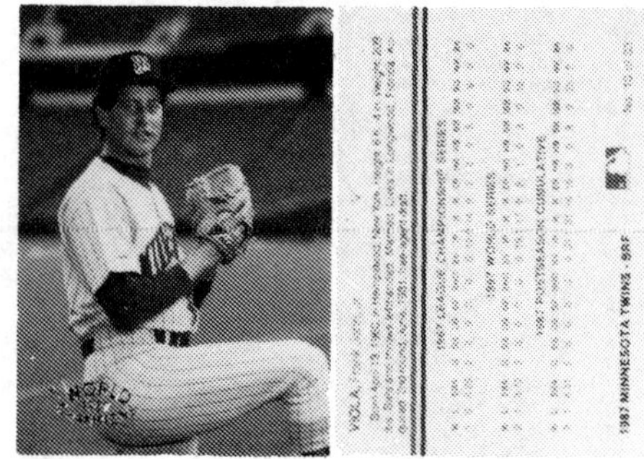

duplicates of the regular season set but several new photos, including a group team shot, are included. Numbered card backs are red, white and blue and contain a player name, personal info and stats. A limited edition of 5000 sets were printed but only a few hundred were sold before the cards were taken off the market due to Major League Baseball licensing restrictions.

		MT	NR MT	EX
Complete Set:		100.00	75.00	40.00
Common Player:		1.25	.90	.50
1	Stephen Paul Lombardozzi	1.25	.90	.50
2	Roy Frederick Smalley, III	1.25	.90	.50
3	Pedro Oliva, Jr.	1.25	.90	.50
4	Gregory Carpenter Gagne	3.00	2.25	1.25
5	Gary Joseph Gaetti	6.00	4.50	2.50
6	Eugene Thomas Larkin	1.25	.90	.50
7	Jay Thomas Kelly	2.00	1.50	.80
8	Kent Alan Hrbek	12.00	9.00	4.75
9	Timothy Jon Laudner	2.00	1.50	.80
10	Frank John Viola, Jr.	8.00	6.00	3.25
11	Lester Paul Straker	1.25	.90	.50
12	Donald Edward Baylor	3.00	2.25	1.25
13	George Allen Frazier	1.25	.90	.50
14	Keith Rowe Atherton	1.25	.90	.50
15	Thomas Andrew Brunansky	3.00	2.25	1.25
16	Robert Randall Bush	2.00	1.50	.80
17	Albert Dwayne Newman	1.25	.90	.50
18	John Mark Davidson	1.25	.90	.50
19	Rik Aalbert Blyleven	8.00	6.00	3.25
20	Daniel Ernest Schatzeder	1.25	.90	.50
21	Clinton Daniel Gladden III	3.00	2.25	1.25
22	Salvatore Philip Butera	1.25	.90	.50
23	Kirby Puckett	25.00	18.50	10.00
24	Joseph Franklin Niekro	2.00	1.50	.80
25	Juan Bautista Berenguer	1.25	.90	.50
26	Jeffrey James Reardon	4.00	3.00	1.50
27	Richard Stanley Such	1.25	.90	.50
28	Richard Francis Stelmaszek	1.25	.90	.50
29	Warren Richard Renick	1.25	.90	.50
30	Willard Wayne Terwilliger	1.25	.90	.50
31	Team Photo	1.25	.90	.50
32	World Champions Team Logo Card	1.25	.90	.50
33	Team Logo Card/Checklist	1.25	.90	.50

1991 Mootown Snackers

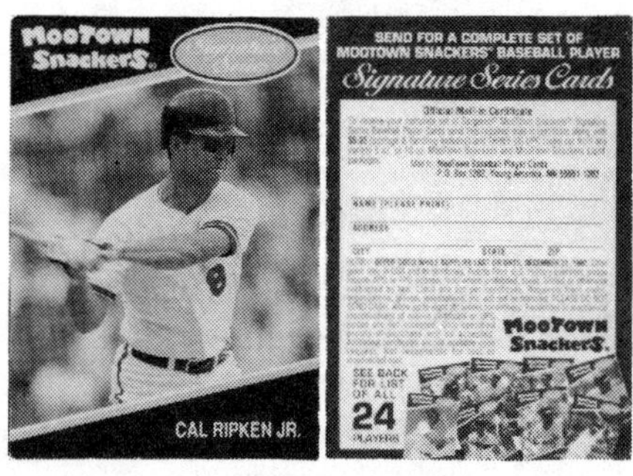

Produced by the Sargento Cheese Co., this 24-card set features the superstars of baseball. Cards were available in Mootown Snacker packages or by sending in a special set redemption coupon from a package to obtain the entire set for $5.95 and three UPC codes. The card fronts feature full-color action photos, but uniform insignias are airbrushed. The backs feature statistics and a facsimile autograph. Sargento is located in Plymouth, Wis.

		MT	NR MT	EX
Complete Set:		8.00	6.00	3.25
Common Player:		.25	.20	.10
1	Jose Canseco	.60	.45	.25
2	Kirby Puckett	.35	.25	.14
3	Barry Bonds	.35	.25	.14
4	Ken Griffey, Jr.	1.25	.90	.50
5	Ryne Sandberg	.50	.40	.20
6	Tony Gwynn	.35	.25	.14
7	Kal Daniels	.25	.20	.10
8	Ozzie Smith	.35	.25	.14
9	Dave Justice	.60	.45	.25
10	Sandy Alomar, Jr.	.25	.20	.10
11	Wade Boggs	.35	.25	.14
12	Ozzie Guillen	.25	.20	.10
13	Dave Magadan	.25	.20	.10
14	Cal Ripken, Jr.	.50	.40	.20
15	Don Mattingly	.50	.40	.20
16	Ruben Sierra	.35	.25	.14
17	Robin Yount	.35	.25	.14
18	Len Dykstra	.25	.20	.10
19	George Brett	.35	.25	.14
20	Lance Parrish	.25	.20	.10
21	Chris Sabo	.25	.20	.10
22	Craig Biggio	.25	.20	.10
23	Kevin Mitchell	.30	.25	.12
24	Cecil Fielder	.50	.40	.20

1959 Morrell Meats Dodgers

This popular set of Los Angeles Dodgers player cards was the first issue of a three-year run for the Southern California meat company. The 12 cards in this 2-1/2" by 3-1/2" set are unnumbered and feature fullframe, unbordered color photos. Card backs feature a company ad and list only the player's name, birthdate and birthplace. Two interesting errors exist in the set, as the cards for Clem Labine and Norm Larker show photos of Stan Williams and Joe Pignatano, respectively. Dodger greats Sandy Koufax and Duke Snider are key cards in the set.

		NR MT	EX	VG
Complete Set (12):		1200.	600.00	360.00
Common Player:		50.00	25.00	15.00
(1)	Don Drysdale	150.00	75.00	45.00
(2)	Carl Furillo	75.00	37.00	22.00
(3)	Jim Gilliam	65.00	32.00	19.50
(4)	Gil Hodges	125.00	62.00	37.00
(5)	Sandy Koufax	250.00	125.00	75.00
(6)	Clem Labine (photo actually Stan Williams)	50.00	25.00	15.00
(7)	Norm Larker (photo actually Joe Pignatano)	50.00	25.00	15.00
(8)	Charlie Neal	50.00	25.00	15.00
(9)	Johnny Podres	60.00	30.00	18.00
(10)	John Roseboro	50.00	25.00	15.00
(11)	Duke Snider	225.00	112.00	67.00
(12)	Don Zimmer	75.00	37.00	22.00

1960 Morrell Meats Dodgers

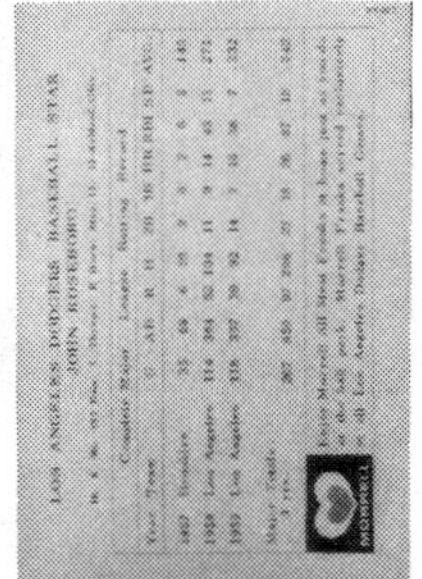

This 12-card set is the same 2-1/2" by 3-1/2" size as the 1959 set, and again features unbordered color card fronts. Five of the players included are new to the Morrell's sets. Card backs in 1960 list player statistics and brief personal data on each player. Cards for Gil Hodges, Carl Furillo and Duke Snider are apparently more scarce than others in the set. The 1960 set is again unnumbered.

		NR MT	EX	VG
Complete Set:		900.00	450.00	270.00
Common Player:		20.00	10.00	6.00
(1)	Walt Alston	30.00	15.00	9.00
(2)	Roger Craig	25.00	12.50	7.50
(3)	Don Drysdale	60.00	30.00	18.00
(4)	Carl Furillo	120.00	60.00	36.00
(5)	Gil Hodges	175.00	87.00	52.00
(6)	Sandy Koufax	150.00	75.00	45.00
(7)	Wally Moon	20.00	10.00	6.00
(8)	Charlie Neal	20.00	10.00	6.00
(9)	Johnny Podres	25.00	12.50	7.50
(10)	John Roseboro	20.00	10.00	6.00
(11)	Larry Sherry	20.00	10.00	6.00
(12)	Duke Snider	250.00	125.00	75.00

1961 Morrell Meats Dodgers

The Morrell set shrunk to just six cards in 1961, with a format almost identical to the 1960 cards. Card fronts are again full-color, unbordered photos, with player statistics on the backs. The unnumbered cards measure a slightly smaller 2-1/4" by 3-1/4", and comparison of statistical information can also distinguish the cards from the 1960 version. Top cards in the set are Don Drysdale and Sandy Koufax, who are also the only two players to appear in all three years of the Morrell Meats sets.

		NR MT	EX	VG
Complete Set:		275.00	137.00	82.00
Common Player:		20.00	10.00	6.00
(1)	Tommy Davis	25.00	12.50	7.50
(2)	Don Drysdale	80.00	40.00	24.00
(3)	Frank Howard	30.00	15.00	9.00
(4)	Sandy Koufax	100.00	50.00	30.00
(5)	Norm Larker	20.00	10.00	6.00
(6)	Maury Wills	30.00	15.00	9.00

1983 Mother's Cookies Giants

After putting out Pacific Coast League sets in 1952 and 1953 Mother's Cookies distributed this full-color set of 20 San Francisco Giants cards three decades later. The 2-1/2" by 3-1/2" cards were produced by Barry Colla and included the Giants logo and player's name on the attractive card fronts. Card backs are numbered and contain biographical information, the Mother's Cookies logo, and a space for the player's autograph. Fifteen cards were given to every fan at the August 7, 1983 Giants game, with each fan also receiving a coupon good for five additional cards.

		MT	NR MT	EX
Complete Set:		16.00	12.00	6.50
Common Player:		.50	.40	.20
1	Frank Robinson	2.50	2.00	1.00
2	Jack Clark	.75	.60	.30
3	Chili Davis	2.00	1.50	.80
4	Johnnie LeMaster	.50	.40	.20
5	Greg Minton	.50	.40	.20
6	Bob Brenly	.50	.40	.20
7	Fred Breining	.50	.40	.20
8	Jeff Leonard	.60	.45	.25
9	Darrell Evans	.75	.60	.30
10	Tom O'Malley	.50	.40	.20
11	Duane Kuiper	.50	.40	.20
12	Mike Krukow	.50	.40	.20
13	Atlee Hammaker	.50	.40	.20
14	Gary Lavelle	.50	.40	.20
15	Bill Laskey	.50	.40	.20
16	Max Venable	.50	.40	.20
17	Joel Youngblood	.50	.40	.20
18	Dave Bergman	.50	.40	.20
19	Mike Vail	.50	.40	.20
20	Andy McGaffigan	.50	.40	.20

1984 Mother's Cookies Astros

Mother's Cookies also issued a full-color team set for the Houston Astros in 1984. The Astros set measures 2-1/2" by 3-1/2", and card fronts feature unbordered color photos with rounded corners. Card backs are quite similar in format to the 1983

Mother's Cookies Giants, with brief biographical information, card numbers, Mother's Cookies logo and space for player autograph. There are 28 cards in the Astros set, with 20 of the cards distributed during a stadium promotion. Fans also received a coupon redeemable for eight additional cards. Since these additional cards do not necessarily complete collectors' sets, Mother's Cookies cards became very popular among card traders. The Astros set includes one card for the coaches and a checklist.

		MT	NR MT	EX
	Complete Set:	22.00	16.50	8.75
	Common Player:	.50	.40	.20
1	Nolan Ryan	8.00	6.00	3.25
2	Joe Niekro	.60	.45	.25
3	Alan Ashby	.50	.40	.20
4	Bill Doran	.60	.45	.25
5	Phil Garner	.60	.45	.25
6	Ray Knight	.60	.45	.25
7	Dickie Thon	.60	.45	.25
8	Jose Cruz	.70	.50	.30
9	Jerry Mumphrey	.50	.40	.20
10	Terry Puhl	.50	.40	.20
11	Enos Cabell	.50	.40	.20
12	Harry Spilman	.50	.40	.20
13	Dave Smith	.50	.40	.20
14	Mike Scott	.60	.45	.25
15	Bob Lillis	.50	.40	.20
16	Bob Knepper	.50	.40	.20
17	Frank DiPino	.50	.40	.20
18	Tom Wieghaus	.50	.40	.20
19	Denny Walling	.50	.40	.20
20	Tony Scott	.50	.40	.20
21	Alan Bannister	.50	.40	.20
22	Bill Dawley	.50	.40	.20
23	Vern Ruhle	.50	.40	.20
24	Mike LaCoss	.50	.40	.20
25	Mike Madden	.50	.40	.20
26	Craig Reynolds	.50	.40	.20
27	Astros Coaches (Cot Deal, Don Leppert, Denis Menke, Les Moss, Jerry Walker)	.50	.40	.20
28	Astros Logo/Checklist	.50	.40	.20

1984 Mother's Cookies Athletics

Following the success of their one set in 1983, Mother's Cookies issued five more team sets of cards in 1984. The A's set measures 2-1/2" by 3-1/2", and card fronts feature unbordered color photos with rounded corners. Card backs are quite similar in format to the 1983 Mother's Cookies Giants, with brief biographical information, card numbers, Mother's Cookies logo and space for player autograph. There are 28 cards in the A's set, with 20 of the cards distributed during a stadium promotion. Fans also received a coupon redeemable for eight additional cards. Since these additional cards do not necessarily complete collectors' sets, Mother's Cookies cards become very popular among card traders. The A's set includes cards for the manager, coaches and a checklist.

		MT	NR MT	EX
	Complete Set:	18.00	13.50	7.25
	Common Player:	.50	.40	.20
1	Steve Boros	.50	.40	.20
2	Rickey Henderson	4.00	3.00	1.50
3	Joe Morgan	1.50	1.25	.60
4	Dwayne Murphy	.50	.40	.20
5	Mike Davis	.50	.40	.20
6	Bruce Bochte	.50	.40	.20
7	Carney Lansford	.60	.45	.25
8	Steve McCatty	.50	.40	.20
9	Mike Heath	.50	.40	.20
10	Chris Codiroli	.50	.40	.20
11	Bill Almon	.50	.40	.20
12	Bill Caudill	.50	.40	.20
13	Donnie Hill	.50	.40	.20
14	Lary Sorenson	.50	.40	.20
15	Dave Kingman	.80	.60	.30
16	Garry Hancock	.50	.40	.20
17	Jeff Burroughs	.60	.45	.25
18	Tom Burgmeier	.50	.40	.20
19	Jim Essian	.50	.40	.20
20	Mike Warren	.50	.40	.20
21	Davey Lopes	.60	.45	.25
22	Ray Burris	.50	.40	.20
23	Tony Phillips	.50	.40	.20
24	Tim Conroy	.50	.40	.20
25	Jeff Bettendorf	.50	.40	.20
26	Keith Atherton	.50	.40	.20
27	A's Coaches (Clete Boyer, Bob Didier, Jackie Moore, Ron Schueler, Billy Williams)	.50	.40	.20
28	Oakland Coliseum/Checklist	.50	.40	.20

1984 Mother's Cookies Giants

Mother's Cookies issued a second annual full-color card set for the San Francisco Giants in 1984. The Giants set measures 2-1/2" by 3-1/2", and the round-cornered cards feature drawings of former Giant All-Star team selections. Card backs are quite similar in format to the 1983 Mother's Cookies Giants, with brief biographical information, card numbers and Mother's Cookies logo. No autograph space is included. There are 28 cards in the Giants set, with 20 of the cards distributed during a stadium promotion. Fans also received a coupon redeemable for eight additional cards. Since these additional cards do not necessarily complete collectors' sets, Mother's Cookies cards became very popular among card traders. Card number 28 is a checklist chart.

		MT	NR MT	EX
	Complete Set:	18.00	13.50	7.25
	Common Player:	.50	.40	.20
1	Willie Mays	3.50	2.75	1.50
2	Willie McCovey	2.00	1.50	.80
3	Juan Marichal	1.50	1.25	.60
4	Gaylord Perry	1.50	1.25	.60
5	Tom Haller	.50	.40	.20
6	Jim Davenport	.50	.40	.20
7	Jack Clark	.75	.60	.30
8	Greg Minton	.50	.40	.20
9	Atlee Hammaker	.50	.40	.20
10	Gary Lavelle	.50	.40	.20
11	Orlando Cepeda	1.00	.70	.40
12	Bobby Bonds	.80	.60	.30
13	John Antonelli	.60	.45	.25
14	Bob Schmidt (photo actually Wes Westrum)	.50	.40	.20
15	Sam Jones	.50	.40	.20
16	Mike McCormick	.60	.45	.25
17	Ed Bailey	.50	.40	.20
18	Stu Miller	.50	.40	.20
19	Felipe Alou	.70	.50	.30
20	Jim Hart	.60	.45	.25
21	Dick Dietz	.50	.40	.20
22	Chris Speier	.50	.40	.20
23	Bobby Murcer	.70	.50	.30
24	John Montefusco	.50	.40	.20
25	Vida Blue	.70	.50	.30
26	Ed Whitson	.50	.40	.20
27	Darrell Evans	.70	.50	.30
28	All-Star Game Logo/Checklist	.50	.40	.20

The values quoted are intended to reflect the market price.

1984 Mother's Cookies Mariners

Mother's Cookies also issued a full-color set for the Seattle Mariners in 1984. The Mariners set measures 2-1/2" by 3-1/2", and card fronts feature unbordered color photos with rounded corners. Card backs are quite similar in format to the 1983 Mother's Cookies Giants, with brief biographical information, card numbers, Mother's Cookies logo and space for player autograph. There are 28 cards in the Mariners set, with 20 of the cards distributed during a stadium promotion. Fans also received a coupon redeemable for eight additional cards. Since these additional cards do not necessarily complete collectors' sets, Mother's Cookies cards became very popular among card traders. The Mariners set includes one card each for the manager, coaches and a checklist.

		MT	NR MT	EX
	Complete Set:	16.00	12.00	6.50
	Common Player:	.50	.40	.20
1	Del Crandall	.60	.45	.25
2	Barry Bonnell	.50	.40	.20
3	Dave Henderson	.70	.50	.30
4	Bob Kearney	.50	.40	.20
5	Mike Moore	.50	.40	.20
6	Spike Owen	.70	.50	.30
7	Gorman Thomas	.50	.40	.20
8	Ed Vande Berg	.50	.40	.20
9	Matt Young	.50	.40	.20
10	Larry Milbourne	.50	.40	.20
11	Dave Beard	.50	.40	.20
12	Jim Beattie	.50	.40	.20
13	Mark Langston	2.00	1.50	.80
14	Orlando Mercado	.50	.40	.20
15	Jack Perconte	.50	.40	.20
16	Pat Putnam	.50	.40	.20
17	Paul Mirabella	.50	.40	.20
18	Domingo Ramos	.50	.40	.20
19	Al Cowens	.50	.40	.20
20	Mike Stanton	.50	.40	.20
21	Steve Henderson	.50	.40	.20
22	Bob Stoddard	.50	.40	.20
23	Alvin Davis	.75	.60	.30
24	Phil Bradley	.60	.45	.25
25	Roy Thomas	.50	.40	.20
26	Darnell Coles	.50	.40	.20
27	Mariners Coaches (Chuck Cottier, Frank Funk, Ben Hines, Phil Roof, Rick Sweet)	.50	.40	.20
28	Seattle Kingdome/Checklist	.50	.40	.20

1984 Mother's Cookies Padres

Mother's Cookies also issued a full-color set for the San Diego Padres in 1984. The Padres set measures 2-1/2" by 3-1/2", and card fronts feature unbordered color photos with rounded corners. Card backs are quite similar in format to the 1983 Mother's Cookies Giants, with brief biographical information, card numbers, Mother's Cookies logo and space for player autograph. There are 28 cards in the Padres set, with 20 of the cards distributed during a stadium promotion. Fans also received a coupon redeemable for eight additional cards. Since these additional cards do not necessarily complete collector's sets, Mother's Cookies cards became very popular among card traders. The Padres set includes one card each for the manager, coaches and a checklist.

		MT	NR MT	EX
	Complete Set:	20.00	15.00	8.00
	Common Player:	.50	.40	.20
1	Dick Williams	.50	.40	.20
2	Rich Gossage	.60	.45	.25
3	Tim Lollar	.50	.40	.20
4	Eric Show	.60	.45	.25
5	Terry Kennedy	.60	.45	.25
6	Kurt Bevacqua	.50	.40	.20
7	Steve Garvey	2.00	1.50	.80
8	Garry Templeton	.60	.45	.25
9	Tony Gwynn	3.50	2.75	1.50
10	Alan Wiggins	.50	.40	.20
11	Dave Dravecky	.60	.45	.25
12	Tim Flannery	.50	.40	.20
13	Kevin McReynolds	2.25	1.75	.90
14	Bobby Brown	.50	.40	.20
15	Ed Whitson	.50	.40	.20
16	Doug Gwosdz	.50	.40	.20
17	Luis DeLeon	.50	.40	.20
18	Andy Hawkins	.50	.40	.20
19	Craig Lefferts	.50	.40	.20
20	Carmelo Martinez	.50	.40	.20
21	Sid Monge	.50	.40	.20
22	Graig Nettles	.80	.60	.30
23	Mario Ramirez	.50	.40	.20
24	Luis Salazar	.50	.40	.20
25	Champ Summers	.50	.40	.20
26	Mark Thurmond	.50	.40	.20
27	Padres Coaches (Harry Dunlop, Deacon Jones, Jack Krol, Norm Sherry, Ozzie Virgil)	.50	.40	.20
28	Jack Murphy Stadium/Checklist	.50	.40	.20

1985 Mother's Cookies Astros

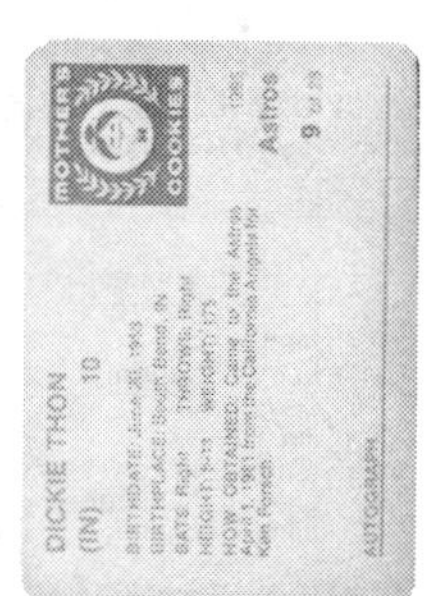

Mother's Cookies issued a second annual full-color set for the Houston Astros in 1985. The Astros set measures 2-1/2" by 3-1/2", and card fronts feature unbordered color photos with rounded corners. Card backs are quite similar in format to the 1984 Mother's Cookies Astros, with brief biographical information, card number, Mother's Cookies logo and space for player autograph. Card backs are dated 1985. There are 28 cards in the Astros set, which was distributed in its entirety during a stadium promotion. The Astros set includes one card each for the manager, coaches and a checklist.

		MT	NR MT	EX
	Complete Set:	16.00	12.00	6.50
	Complete Player:	.40	.30	.15
1	Bob Lillis	.40	.30	.15
2	Nolan Ryan	6.00	4.50	2.50
3	Phil Garner	.50	.40	.20
4	Jose Cruz	.60	.45	.25
5	Denny Walling	.40	.30	.15
6	Joe Niekro	.60	.45	.25
7	Terry Puhl	.40	.30	.15
8	Bill Doran	.60	.45	.25
9	Dickie Thon	.40	.30	.15
10	Enos Cabell	.40	.30	.15
11	Frank Dipino (DiPino)	.40	.30	.15
12	Julio Solano	.40	.30	.15
13	Alan Ashby	.40	.30	.15
14	Craig Reynolds	.40	.30	.15
15	Jerry Mumphrey	.40	.30	.15
16	Bill Dawley	.40	.30	.15
17	Mark Bailey	.40	.30	.15
18	Mike Scott	.50	.40	.20
19	Harry Spilman	.40	.30	.15
20	Bob Knepper	.50	.40	.20
21	Dave Smith	.50	.40	.20
22	Kevin Bass	.60	.45	.25
23	Tim Tolman	.40	.30	.15
24	Jeff Calhoun	.40	.30	.15
25	Jim Pankovits	.40	.30	.15
26	Ron Mathis	.40	.30	.15
27	Astros Coaches (Cot Deal, Matt Galante, Don Leppert, Denis Menke, Jerry Walker)	.40	.30	.15
28	Astros Logo/Checklist	.40	.30	.15

1985 Mother's Cookies Athletics

Mother's Cookies again issued five full-color sets for major league teams in 1985. The A's set measures 2-1/2" by 3-1/2", and card fronts feature unbordered color photos with rounded corners. Card backs are quite similar in format to the 1984 Mother's Cookies A's, with brief biographical information card numbers, Mother's Cookies logo and space for player autograph. Card backs are dated 1985. There are 28 cards in the A's set, which was distributed in its entirety during a stadium promotion. The A's set includes one card each for the manager, coaches and a checklist.

		MT	NR MT	EX
	Complete Set:	16.00	12.00	6.50
	Common Player:	.40	.30	.15
1	Jackie Moore	.40	.30	.15
2	Dave Kingman	.70	.50	.30
3	Don Sutton	1.00	.70	.40
4	Mike Heath	.40	.30	.15
5	Alfredo Griffin	.40	.30	.15
6	Dwayne Murphy	.40	.30	.15
7	Mike Davis	.40	.30	.15
8	Carney Lansford	.50	.40	.20
9	Chris Codiroli	.40	.30	.15
10	Bruce Bochte	.40	.30	.15
11	Mickey Tettleton	2.00	1.50	.80
12	Donnie Hill	.40	.30	.15
13	Rob Picciolo	.40	.30	.15
14	Dave Collins	.40	.30	.15
15	Dusty Baker	.70	.50	.30
16	Tim Conroy	.40	.30	.15
17	Keith Atherton	.40	.30	.15
18	Jay Howell	.60	.45	.25
19	Mike Warren	.40	.30	.15
20	Steve McCatty	.40	.30	.15
21	Bill Krueger	.40	.30	.15
22	Curt Young	.40	.30	.15
23	Dan Meyer	.40	.30	.15
24	Mike Gallego	.50	.40	.20
25	Jeff Kaiser	.40	.30	.15
26	Steve Henderson	.40	.30	.15
27	A's Coaches (Clete Boyer, Bob Didier, Dave McKay, Wes Stock, Billy Williams)	.40	.30	.15
28	Oakland Coliseum/Checklist	.40	.30	.15

1985 Mother's Cookies Giants

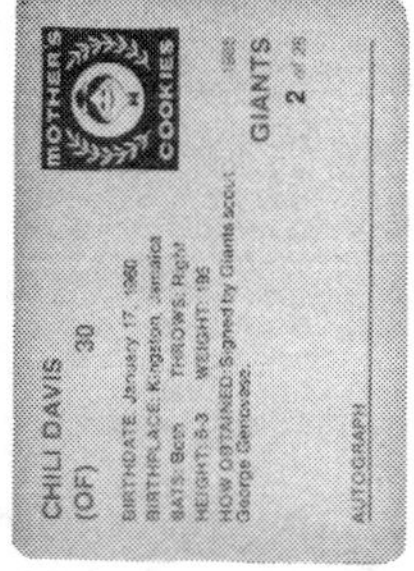

Mother's Cookies issued a third annual full-color set for the San Francisco Giants in 1985. The Giants set measures 2-1/2" by 3-1/2", and card fronts feature unbordered color photos of current players with rounded corners. Card backs are quite similar in format to the 1983 Mother's Cookies Giants, with brief biographical information, card numbers, Mother's Cookies logo and space for player autograph. Card backs are dated 1985. There are 28 cards in the Giants set, which was distributed in its entirety during a stadium promotion. The Giants set includes one card each for the manager, coaches and a checklist.

		MT	NR MT	EX
	Complete Set:	12.00	9.00	4.75
	Common Player:	.40	.30	.15
1	Jim Davenport	.40	.30	.15
2	Chili Davis	.70	.50	.30
3	Dan Gladden	.60	.45	.25
4	Jeff Leonard	.50	.40	.20
5	Manny Trillo	.50	.40	.20
6	Atlee Hammaker	.40	.30	.15
7	Bob Brenly	.40	.30	.15
8	Greg Minton	.40	.30	.15
9	Bill Laskey	.40	.30	.15
10	Vida Blue	.60	.45	.25
11	Mike Krukow	.40	.30	.15
12	Frank Williams	.40	.30	.15
13	Jose Uribe	.40	.30	.15
14	Johnnie LeMaster	.40	.30	.15
15	Scot Thompson	.40	.30	.15
16	Dave LaPoint	.40	.30	.15
17	David Green	.40	.30	.15
18	Chris Brown	.50	.40	.20
19	Joel Youngblood	.40	.30	.15
20	Mark Davis	.40	.30	.15
21	Jim Gott	.40	.30	.15
22	Doug Gwosdz	.40	.30	.15
23	Scott Garrelts	.40	.30	.15
24	Gary Rajsich	.40	.30	.15
25	Rob Deer	.50	.40	.20
26	Brad Wellman	.40	.30	.15
27	Coaches (Rocky Bridges, Chuck Hiller, Tom McCraw, Bob Miller, Jack Mull)	.40	.30	.15
28	Candlestick Park/Checklist	.40	.30	.15

1985 Mother's Cookies Mariners

Mother's Cookies issued a second annual full-color set for the Seattle Mariners in 1985. The Mariners set measures 2-1/2" by 3-1/2", and card fronts feature unbordered color photos with rounded corners. Card backs are quite similar in format to the 1984 Mother's Cookies Mariners, with brief biographical information, card numbers, Mother's Cookies logo and space for player autograph. Card backs are dated 1985. There are 28 cards in the Mariners set, which was distributed in its entirety during a stadium promotion. The Mariners set includes one card each for the coaches and a checklist.

		MT	NR MT	EX
	Complete Set:	13.00	9.75	5.25
	Common Player:	.40	.30	.15
1	Chuck Cottier	.40	.30	.15
2	Alvin Davis	.50	.40	.20
3	Mark Langston	1.00	.70	.40
4	Dave Henderson	.50	.40	.20
5	Ed Vande Berg	.40	.30	.15
6	Al Cowens	.40	.30	.15
7	Spike Owen	.50	.40	.20
8	Mike Moore	.40	.30	.15
9	Gorman Thomas	.40	.30	.15
10	Barry Bonnell	.40	.30	.15
11	Jack Perconte	.40	.30	.15
12	Domingo Ramos	.40	.30	.15
13	Bob Kearney	.40	.30	.15
14	Matt Young	.40	.30	.15
15	Jim Beattie	.40	.30	.15
16	Mike Stanton	.40	.30	.15
17	David Valle	.50	.40	.20
18	Ken Phelps	.50	.40	.20
19	Salome Barojas	.40	.30	.15
20	Jim Presley	.50	.40	.20
21	Phil Bradley	.50	.40	.20
22	Dave Geisel	.40	.30	.15
23	Harold Reynolds	.80	.60	.30
24	Edwin Nunez	.40	.30	.15
25	Mike Morgan	.50	.40	.20
26	Ivan Calderon	.80	.60	.30
27	Mariners Coaches (Deron Johnson, Jim Mahoney, Marty Martinez, Phil Regan, Phil Roof)	.40	.30	.15
28	Seattle Kingdome/Checklist	.40	.30	.15

Definitions for grading conditions are located in the Introduction of this price guide.

1985 Mother's Cookies Padres

Mother's Cookies issued a second annual full-color set for the San Diego Padres in 1985. The Padres set measures 2-1/2" by 3-1/2", and card fronts feature unbordered color photos with rounded corners. Card backs are quite similar in format to the 1984 Mother's Cookies Padres, with brief biographical information, card numbers, Mother's Cookies logo and space for player autograph. Card backs are dated 1985. There are 28 cards in the Padres set, which was distributed in its entirety during a stadium promotion. The Padres set includes one card each for the manager, coaches and a checklist.

		MT	NR MT	EX
Complete Set:		14.00	10.50	5.50
Common Player:		.40	.30	.15
1	Dick Williams	.40	.30	.15
2	Tony Gwynn	3.00	2.25	1.25
3	Kevin McReynolds	.80	.60	.30
4	Graig Nettles	.70	.50	.30
5	Rich Gossage	.75	.60	.30
6	Steve Garvey	1.50	1.25	.60
7	Garry Templeton	.50	.40	.20
8	Dave Dravecky	.50	.40	.20
9	Eric Show	.40	.30	.15
10	Terry Kennedy	.50	.40	.20
11	Luis DeLeon	.40	.30	.15
12	Bruce Bochy	.40	.30	.15
13	Andy Hawkins	.40	.30	.15
14	Kurt Bevacqua	.40	.30	.15
15	Craig Lefferts	.40	.30	.15
16	Mario Ramirez	.40	.30	.15
17	LaMarr Hoyt	.40	.30	.15
18	Jerry Royster	.40	.30	.15
19	Tim Stoddard	.40	.30	.15
20	Tim Flannery	.40	.30	.15
21	Mark Thurmond	.40	.30	.15
22	Greg Booker	.40	.30	.15
23	Bobby Brown	.40	.30	.15
24	Carmelo Martinez	.40	.30	.15
25	Al Bumbry	.40	.30	.15
26	Jerry Davis	.40	.30	.15
27	Padres Coaches (Galen Cisco, Harry Dunlop, Deacon Jones, Jack Krol, Ozzie Virgil)	.40	.30	.15
28	Jack Murphy Stadium/Checklist	.40	.30	.15

1986 Mother's Cookies Astros

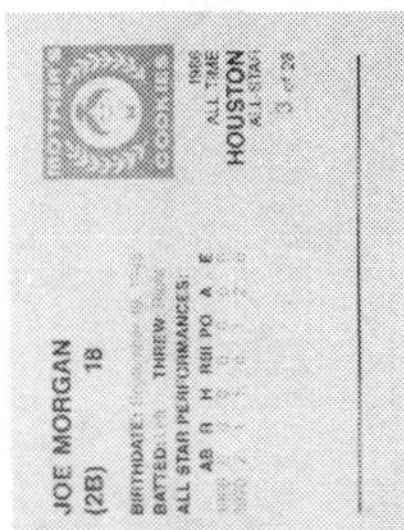

Mother's Cookies produced a third annual set for the Houston Astros in 1985. The set measure 2-1/2" by 3-1/2", and card fronts feature unbordered color paintings of Houston's past All-Star Game performers. The round-cornered cards have backs quite similar in format to previous years, with brief biographical information, card numbers and the Mother's Cookies logo. Card backs are dated 1986. There are 28 cards in the Astros set, with 20 of the cards distributed during a stadium promotion. Each fan also received a coupon redeemable for eight additional cards. The Astros set also includes a checklist card.

		MT	NR MT	EX
Complete Set:		13.00	9.75	5.25
Common Player:		.30	.25	.12
1	Dick Farrell	.30	.25	.12
2	Hal Woodeschick (Woodeshick)	.30	.25	.12
3	Joe Morgan	1.00	.70	.40
4	Claude Raymond	.30	.25	.12
5	Mike Cuellar	.40	.30	.15
6	Rusty Staub	.60	.45	.25
7	Jimmy Wynn	.40	.30	.15
8	Larry Dierker	.40	.30	.15
9	Denis Menke	.30	.25	.12
10	Don Wilson	.30	.25	.12
11	Cesar Cedeno	.50	.40	.20
12	Lee May	.40	.30	.15
13	Bob Watson	.40	.30	.15
14	Ken Forsch	.30	.25	.12
15	Joaquin Andujar	.40	.30	.15
16	Terry Puhl	.30	.25	.12
17	Joe Niekro	.40	.30	.15
18	Craig Reynolds	.30	.25	.12
19	Joe Sambito	.30	.25	.12
20	Jose Cruz	.60	.45	.25
21	J.R. Richard	.40	.30	.15
22	Bob Knepper	.30	.25	.12
23	Nolan Ryan	3.00	2.25	1.25
24	Ray Knight	.40	.30	.15
25	Bill Dawley	.30	.25	.12
26	Dickie Thon	.40	.30	.15
27	Jerry Mumphrey	.30	.25	.12
28	Astros Logo/Checklist	.30	.25	.12

1986 Mother's Cookies Athletics

Mother's Cookies produced four more full-color team card sets in 1986, with only the San Diego Padres not repeating from the 1985 group. The third annual set for the Oakland A's measures 2-1/2" by 3-1/2", and card fronts feature unbordered color photos with rounded corners. Card backs are quite similar in format to previous years, with brief biographical information, card numbers and the Mother's Cookies logo. Card backs are dated 1986. There are 28 cards in the A's set, with 20 of the cards distributed during a stadium promotion. Each fan also received a coupon redeemable for eight additional cards. The A's set includes one card each for the manager, coaches and a checklist.

		MT	NR MT	EX
Complete Set:		19.00	14.00	7.50
Common Player:		.30	.25	.12
1	Jackie Moore	.30	.25	.12
2	Dave Kingman	.60	.45	.25
3	Dusty Baker	.40	.30	.15
4	Joaquin Andujar	.40	.30	.15
5	Alfredo Griffin	.30	.25	.12
6	Dwayne Murphy	.30	.25	.12
7	Mike Davis	.30	.25	.12
8	Carney Lansford	.40	.30	.15
9	Jose Canseco	10.00	7.50	4.00
10	Bruce Bochte	.30	.25	.12
11	Mickey Tettleton	.90	.70	.35
12	Donnie Hill	.30	.25	.12
13	Jose Rijo	.60	.45	.25
14	Rick Langford	.30	.25	.12
15	Chris Codiroli	.30	.25	.12
16	Moose Haas	.30	.25	.12
17	Keith Atherton	.30	.25	.12
18	Jay Howell	.40	.30	.15
19	Tony Phillips	.50	.40	.20
20	Steve Henderson	.30	.25	.12
21	Bill Krueger	.30	.25	.12
22	Steve Ontiveros	.30	.25	.12
23	Bill Bathe	.30	.25	.12
24	Rickey Peters	.30	.25	.12
25	Tim Birtsas	.30	.25	.12
26	Trainers Card (Frank Ciensczyk, Larry Davis, Steve Vucinich, Barry Weinberg)	.30	.25	.12
27	Coaches Card (Bob Didier, Dave McKay, Jeff Newman, Ron Plaza, Wes Stock, Bob Watson)	.30	.25	.12
28	Oakland Coliseum/Checklist	.30	.25	.12

The values quoted are intended to reflect the market price.

1986 Mother's Cookies Giants

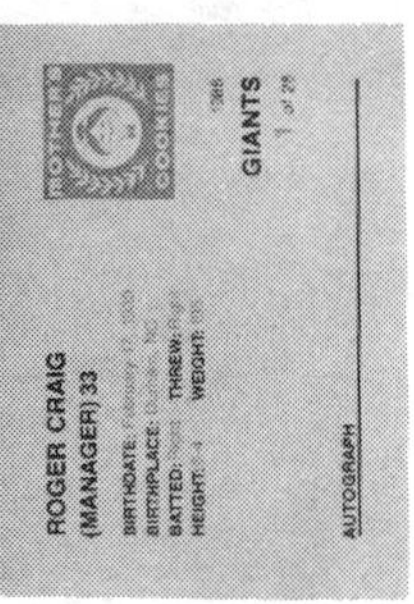

Mother's Cookies produced a fourth annual set for the San Francisco Giants in 1985. Cards in the set measure 2-1/2" by 3-1/2", and the fronts feature unbordered color photos with rounded corners. Card backs are quite similar in format to previous years, with brief biographical information, card numbers, and the Mother's Cookies logo. Card backs are dated 1986. There are 28 cards in the Giants set, with 20 of the cards distributed during a stadium promotion. Each fan also received a coupon redeemable for eight additional cards. The Giants set also includes a card for the manager and a checklist.

		MT	NR MT	EX
Complete Set:		18.00	13.50	7.25
Common Player:		.30	.25	.12
1	Roger Craig	.40	.30	.15
2	Chili Davis	.60	.45	.25
3	Dan Gladden	.40	.30	.15
4	Jeff Leonard	.40	.30	.15
5	Bob Brenly	.30	.25	.12
6	Atlee Hammaker	.30	.25	.12
7	Will Clark	10.00	7.50	4.00
8	Greg Minton	.30	.25	.12
9	Candy Maldonado	.30	.25	.12
10	Vida Blue	.50	.40	.20
11	Mike Krukow	.30	.25	.12
12	Bob Melvin	.30	.25	.12
13	Jose Uribe	.30	.25	.12
14	Dan Driessen	.30	.25	.12
15	Jeff Robinson	.40	.30	.15
16	Rob Thompson	.80	.60	.30
17	Mike LaCoss	.30	.25	.12
18	Chris Brown	.30	.25	.12
19	Scott Garrelts	.30	.25	.12
20	Mark Davis	.30	.25	.12
21	Jim Gott	.30	.25	.12
22	Brad Wellman	.30	.25	.12
23	Roger Mason	.30	.25	.12
24	Bill Laskey	.30	.25	.12
25	Brad Gulden	.30	.25	.12
26	Joel Youngblood	.30	.25	.12
27	Juan Berenguer	.30	.25	.12
28	Coaches/Checklist (Bill Fahey, Bob Lillis, Gordy MacKenzie, Jose Morales, Norm Sherry)	.30	.25	.12

1986 Mother's Cookies Mariners

Mother's Cookies produced a third annual set for the Seattle Mariners in 1985. The set measures 2-1/2" by 3-1/2", and card fronts feature unbordered color photos with rounded corners. Card backs are quite similar in format to previous years, with brief biographical information, card numbers and the Mother's Cookies logo. Card backs are dated 1986. There are 28 cards in the Mariners set, with 20 of the cards distributed during a stadium promotion. Each fan also received a coupon redeemable for eight additional cards. The Mariners set also includes a card for the manager and a checklist.

		MT	NR MT	EX
Complete Set:		11.00	8.25	4.50
Common Player:		.30	.25	.12
1	Dick Williams	.30	.25	.12
2	Alvin Davis	.40	.30	.15
3	Mark Langston	.80	.60	.30
4	Dave Henderson	.50	.40	.20
5	Steve Yeager	.30	.25	.12
6	Al Cowens	.30	.25	.12
7	Jim Presley	.30	.25	.12
8	Phil Bradley	.40	.30	.15
9	Gorman Thomas	.30	.25	.12
10	Barry Bonnell	.30	.25	.12
11	Milt Wilcox	.30	.25	.12
12	Domingo Ramos	.30	.25	.12
13	Paul Mirabella	.30	.25	.12
14	Matt Young	.30	.25	.12
15	Ivan Calderon	.40	.30	.15
16	Bill Swift	.75	.60	.30
17	Pete Ladd	.30	.25	.12
18	Ken Phelps	.40	.30	.15
19	Karl Best	.30	.25	.12
20	Spike Owen	.40	.30	.15
21	Mike Moore	.30	.25	.12
22	Danny Tartabull	1.75	1.25	.70
23	Bob Kearney	.30	.25	.12
24	Edwin Nunez	.30	.25	.12
25	Mike Morgan	.30	.25	.12
26	Roy Thomas	.30	.25	.12
27	Jim Beattie	.30	.25	.12
28	Coaches/Checklist (Deron Johnson, Marty Martinez, Phil Regan, Phil Roof, Ozzie Virgil)	.30	.25	.12

1987 Mother's Cookies Astros

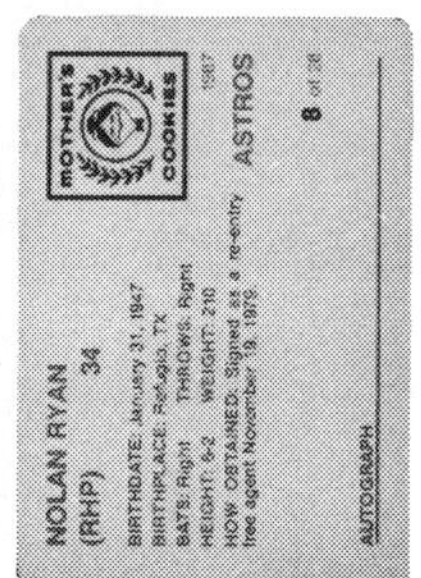

Twenty of 28 cards featuring Astros players were given out to the first 25,000 fans attending the July 17th game at the Astrodome. An additional eight cards (though not necessarily the exact eight needed to complete a set) were available from the card producer, Mother's Cookies, by redeeming a mail-in certificate. The cards have rounded corners and measure the standard 2-1/2" by 3-1/2". The backs are printed in purple and orange and contain personal player information, the Mother's Cookies logo, the card number and a spot for the player's autograph.

		MT	NR MT	EX
Complete Set:		14.00	10.50	5.50
Common Player:		.30	.25	.12
1	Hal Lanier	.30	.25	.12
2	Mike Scott	.40	.30	.15
3	Jose Cruz	.50	.40	.20
4	Bill Doran	.40	.30	.15
5	Bob Knepper	.30	.25	.12
6	Phil Garner	.40	.30	.15
7	Terry Puhl	.30	.25	.12
8	Nolan Ryan	6.00	4.50	2.50
9	Kevin Bass	.50	.40	.20
10	Glenn Davis	.40	.30	.15
11	Alan Ashby	.30	.25	.12
12	Charlie Kerfeld	.30	.25	.12
13	Denny Walling	.30	.25	.12
14	Danny Darwin	.30	.25	.12
15	Mark Bailey	.30	.25	.12
16	Davey Lopes	.40	.30	.15
17	Dave Meads	.30	.25	.12
18	Aurelio Lopez	.30	.25	.12
19	Craig Reynolds	.30	.25	.12
20	Dave Smith	.30	.25	.12
21	Larry Anderson (Andersen)	.30	.25	.12
22	Jim Pankovits	.30	.25	.12
23	Jim Deshaies	.50	.40	.20
24	Bert Pena	.30	.25	.12
25	Dickie Thon	.30	.25	.12
26	Billy Hatcher	.50	.40	.20
27	Astros Coaches (Yogi Berra, Matt Galante, Denis Menke, Les Moss, Gene Tenace)	.30	.25	.12
28	Houston Astrodome/Checklist	.30	.25	.12

Regional interest may affect the value of a card.

The values quoted are intended to reflect the market price.

1987 Mother's Cookies Athletics

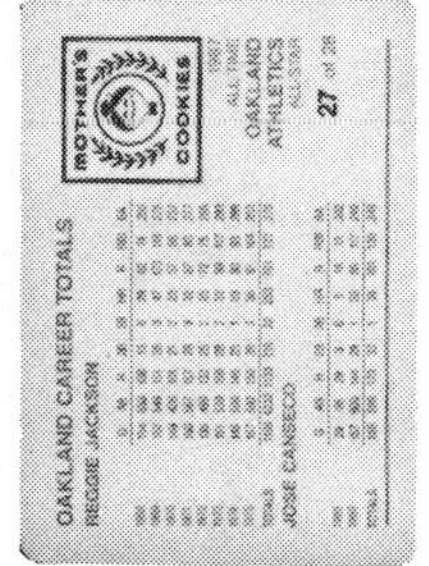

Continuing with a tradition of producing beautiful baseball cards, Mother's Cookies of Oakland, Calif. issued a 28-card set featuring every Oakland A's player to have been elected to the All-Star Game since 1968. The full-color photos came from the private collection of nationally known photographer Doug McWilliams. Twenty of the 28 cards were given out to fans attending the A's game of July 5th. An additional eight cards were available by redeeming a mail-in certificate. The cards, which measure 2-1/2" by 3-1/2", feature rounded corners. The card backs carry the player's All-Star Game statistics.

		MT	NR MT	EX
Complete Set:		18.00	13.50	7.25
Common Player:		.30	.25	.12
1	Bert Campaneris	.40	.30	.15
2	Rick Monday	.40	.30	.15
3	John Odom	.40	.30	.15
4	Sal Bando	.40	.30	.15
5	Reggie Jackson	3.00	2.25	1.25
6	Catfish Hunter	1.00	.70	.40
7	Vida Blue	.50	.40	.20
8	Dave Duncan	.30	.25	.12
9	Joe Rudi	.40	.30	.15
10	Rollie Fingers	.70	.50	.30
11	Ken Holtzman	.40	.30	.15
12	Dick Williams	.40	.30	.15
13	Alvin Dark	.30	.25	.12
14	Gene Tenace	.40	.30	.15
15	Claudell Washington	.30	.25	.12
16	Phil Garner	.40	.30	.15
17	Wayne Gross	.30	.25	.12
18	Matt Keough	.30	.25	.12
19	Jeff Newman	.30	.25	.12
20	Rickey Henderson	3.00	2.25	1.25
21	Tony Armas	.40	.30	.15
22	Mike Norris	.30	.25	.12
23	Billy Martin	.50	.40	.20
24	Bill Caudill	.30	.25	.12
25	Jay Howell	.40	.30	.15
26	Jose Canseco	4.00	3.00	1.50
27	Jose and Reggie (Jose Canseco, Reggie Jackson)	2.00	1.50	.80
28	A's Logo/Checklist	.30	.25	.12

1987 Mother's Cookies Dodgers

Mother's Cookies produced for the first time in 1987 a baseball card set featuring the Los Angeles Dodgers. Twenty of the 28 cards in the set were given out to youngsters 14 and under at Dodger Stadium on August 9th. An additional eight cards were available from Mother's Cookies via a mail-in coupon card. The borderless, full-color cards measure 2-1/2" by 3-1/2" and have rounded corners. A special album designed to house the set was available for $3.95 through a mail-in offer.

		MT	NR MT	EX
Complete Set:		10.00	7.50	4.00
Common Player:		.30	.25	.12
1	Tom Lasorda	.50	.40	.20
2	Pedro Guerrero	.40	.30	.15
3	Steve Sax	.40	.30	.15
4	Fernando Valenzuela	.50	.40	.20
5	Mike Marshall	.40	.30	.15
6	Orel Hershiser	.80	.60	.30
7	Mariano Duncan	.40	.30	.15
8	Bill Madlock	.40	.30	.15
9	Bob Welch	.60	.45	.25
10	Mike Scioscia	.40	.30	.15
11	Mike Ramsey	.30	.25	.12
12	Matt Young	.30	.25	.12
13	Franklin Stubbs	.30	.25	.12
14	Tom Niedenfuer	.30	.25	.12
15	Reggie Williams	.30	.25	.12
16	Rick Honeycutt	.30	.25	.12
17	Dave Anderson	.30	.25	.12
18	Alejandro Pena	.40	.30	.15
19	Ken Howell	.30	.25	.12
20	Len Matuszek	.30	.25	.12
21	Tim Leary	.40	.30	.15
22	Tracy Woodson	.30	.25	.12
23	Alex Trevino	.30	.25	.12
24	Ken Landreaux	.30	.25	.12
25	Mickey Hatcher	.30	.25	.12
26	Brian Holton	.40	.30	.15
27	Dodgers' Coaches (Joey Amalfitano, Mark Cresse, Don McMahon, Manny Mota, Ron Perranoski, Bill Russell)	.30	.25	.12
28	Dodger Stadium/Checklist	.30	.25	.12

1987 Mother's Cookies Giants

Distribution of the 1987 Mother's Cookies Giants, cards took place at Candlestick Park for the Giants' June 27th game. Twenty of the 28 cards in the set were given to the first 25,000 fans entering the park. The starter packet of 20 cards contained a mail-in coupon card which was good for an additional eight cards. The cards, which measure 2-1/2" by 3-1/2" in size have rounded corners. The card backs are printed in red and purple and contain personal and statistical information along with the Mother's Cookies logo.

		MT	NR MT	EX
Complete Set:		12.00	9.00	4.75
Common Player:		.30	.25	.12
1	Roger Craig	.40	.30	.15
2	Will Clark	3.00	2.25	1.25
3	Chili Davis	.50	.40	.20
4	Bob Brenly	.30	.25	.12
5	Chris Brown	.30	.25	.12
6	Mike Krukow	.30	.25	.12
7	Candy Maldonado	.30	.25	.12
8	Jeffrey Leonard	.30	.25	.12
9	Greg Minton	.30	.25	.12
10	Robby Thompson	.50	.40	.20
11	Scott Garrelts	.30	.25	.12
12	Bob Melvin	.30	.25	.12
13	Jose Uribe	.30	.25	.12
14	Mark Davis	.30	.25	.12
15	Eddie Milner	.30	.25	.12
16	Harry Spilman	.30	.25	.12
17	Kelly Downs	.40	.30	.15
18	Chris Speier	.30	.25	.12
19	Jim Gott	.30	.25	.12
20	Joel Youngblood	.30	.25	.12
21	Mike LaCoss	.30	.25	.12
22	Matt Williams	2.00	1.50	.80
23	Roger Mason	.30	.25	.12
24	Mike Aldrete	.30	.25	.12
25	Jeff Robinson	.40	.30	.15
26	Mark Grant	.30	.25	.12
27	Coaches (Bill Fahey, Bob Lillis, Gordon MacKenzie, Jose Morales, Norm Sherry, Don Zimmer)	.30	.25	.12
28	Candlestick Park/Checklist	.30	.25	.12

Values quoted in this guide reflect the retail price of a card – the price a collector can expect to pay when buying a card from a dealer. The wholesale price – that which a collector can expect to receive from a dealer when selling cards – will be significantly lower, depending on desirability and condition.

1987 Mother's Cookies Mariners

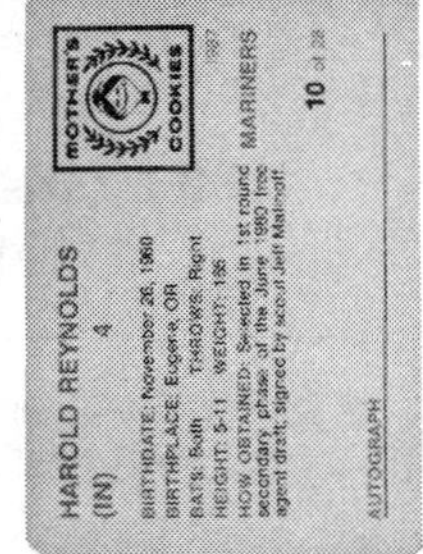

For the fourth consecutive year, Mother's Cookies issued a baseball card set featuring the Seattle Mariners. Twenty of the 28 cards in the set were distributed to the first 20,000 fans entering the Kingdome on August 9th. An additional eight cards (though not necessarily the eight cards needed to complete the set) were available by redeeming a mail-in certificate. Collectors were encouraged to trade to complete a set. The 2-1/2" by 3-1/2" full-color cards feature glossy finishes and rounded corners. A specially designed album to house the set was available.

		MT	NR MT	EX
Complete Set:		9.00	6.75	3.50
Common Player:		.30	.25	.12
1	Dick Williams	.30	.25	.12
2	Alvin Davis	.40	.30	.15
3	Mike Moore	.30	.25	.12
4	Jim Presley	.30	.25	.12
5	Mark Langston	.70	.50	.30
6	Phil Bradley	.40	.30	.15
7	Ken Phelps	.40	.30	.15
8	Mike Morgan	.30	.25	.12
9	David Valle	.40	.30	.15
10	Harold Reynolds	.60	.45	.25
11	Edwin Nunez	.30	.25	.12
12	Bob Kearney	.30	.25	.12
13	Scott Bankhead	.40	.30	.15
14	Scott Bradley	.30	.25	.12
15	Mickey Brantley	.30	.25	.12
16	Mark Huismann	.30	.25	.12
17	Mike Kingery	.30	.25	.12
18	John Moses	.30	.25	.12
19	Donell Nixon	.30	.25	.12
20	Rey Quinones	.30	.25	.12
21	Domingo Ramos	.30	.25	.12
22	Jerry Reed	.30	.25	.12
23	Rich Renteria	.30	.25	.12
24	Rich Monteleone	.30	.25	.12
25	Mike Trujillo	.30	.25	.12
26	Bill Wilkinson	.30	.25	.12
27	John Christensen	.30	.25	.12
28	Coaches/Checklist (Billy Connors, Frank Howard, Phil Roof, Bobby Tolan, Ozzie Virgil)	.30	.25	.12

1987 Mother's Cookies Rangers

While Mother's Cookies of Oakland, Calif., had been producing high-quality baseball card sets of various teams, the Texas Rangers were highlighted for the first time in 1987. Twenty cards from the 28-card set were handed out to the first 25,000 fans entering Arlington Stadium on July 17th. An additional eight cards (though not necessarily the eight needed to complete a set) were available by redeeming a mail-in certificate. The cards, which measure 2-1/2" by 3-1/2", have rounded corners and glossy finishes like all Mother's Cookies issued in 1987.

		MT	NR MT	EX
Complete Set:		10.00	7.50	4.00
Common Player:		.30	.25	.12
1	Bobby Valentine	.40	.30	.15
2	Pete Incaviglia	.60	.45	.25
3	Charlie Hough	.40	.30	.15
4	Oddibe McDowell	.40	.30	.15
5	Larry Parrish	.35	.25	.14
6	Scott Fletcher	.45	.35	.20
7	Steve Buechele	.45	.35	.20
8	Tom Paciorek	.30	.25	.12
9	Pete O'Brien	.40	.30	.15
10	Darrell Porter	.30	.25	.12
11	Greg Harris	.30	.25	.12
12	Don Slaught	.30	.25	.12
13	Ruben Sierra	1.75	1.25	.70
14	Curtis Wilkerson	.30	.25	.12
15	Dale Mohorcic	.30	.25	.12
16	Ron Meredith	.30	.25	.12
17	Mitch Williams	.50	.40	.20
18	Bob Brower	.40	.30	.15
19	Edwin Correa	.30	.25	.12
20	Geno Petralli	.30	.25	.12
21	Mike Loynd	.30	.25	.12
22	Jerry Browne	.40	.30	.15
23	Jose Guzman	.30	.25	.12
24	Jeff Kunkel	.30	.25	.12
25	Bobby Witt	.40	.30	.15
26	Jeff Russell	.30	.25	.12
27	Trainers (Danny Wheat, Bill Zeigler)	.30	.25	.12
28	Rangers' Coaches/Checklist (Joe Ferguson, Tim Foli, Tom House, Art Howe, Dave Oliver, Tom Robson)	.30	.25	.12

1987 Mother's Cookies Mark McGwire

A four-card set featuring outstanding rookie Mark McGwire of the Oakland Athletics was produced by Mother's Cookies of Oakland, Calif. Cards are 2-1/2" by 3-1/2" and have rounded corners and glossy finishes like other Mother's issues. The four-card set was obtainable by two methods. A complete set could be received by sending in eight proof-of-purchase seals. Also, sets could be secured at the National Sports Collectors Convention held July 9-12 in San Francisco. Convention goers received one card as a bonus for each Mother's Cookies baseball card album purchased.

		MT	NR MT	EX
Complete Set:		12.00	9.00	4.75
Common Player:		3.00	2.25	1.25
1	Mark McGwire (portrait)	3.00	2.25	1.25
2	Mark McGwire (leaning on bat rack)	3.00	2.25	1.25
3	Mark McGwire (beginning batting swing)	3.00	2.25	1.25
4	Mark McGwire (batting follow-through)	3.00	2.25	1.25

1988 Mother's Cookies Astros

One of six team sets issued by Mother's Cookies in 1988, the 28-card Houston Astros set is similar in design to other Mother's Cookies sets. The cards are the standard 2-1/2" by 3-1/2" size with rounded corners and feature full-color, borderless photos on the fronts with the player's name in an upper or lower corner. The backs feature red and purple printing on white and include brief biographical information, the Mother's logo and card number. Twenty of the cards were distributed in a stadium promotion, along with a redemption card that could be exchanged for an additional eight cards (but not necessarily the eight needed to complete the set). An album was also available to house the set.

		MT	NR MT	EX
Complete Set:		12.00	9.00	4.75
Common Player:		.30	.25	.12
1	Hal Lanier	.30	.25	.12
2	Mike Scott	.40	.30	.15
3	Gerald Young	.40	.30	.15
4	Bill Doran	.50	.40	.20
5	Bob Knepper	.30	.25	.12
6	Billy Hatcher	.50	.40	.20
7	Terry Puhl	.30	.25	.12
8	Nolan Ryan	4.00	3.00	1.50
9	Kevin Bass	.50	.40	.20
10	Glenn Davis	.50	.40	.20
11	Alan Ashby	.30	.25	.12
12	Steve Henderson	.30	.25	.12
13	Denny Walling	.30	.25	.12
14	Danny Darwin	.30	.25	.12
15	Mark Bailey	.30	.25	.12
16	Ernie Camacho	.30	.25	.12
17	Rafael Ramirez	.30	.25	.12
18	Jeff Heathcock	.30	.25	.12
19	Craig Reynolds	.30	.25	.12
20	Dave Smith	.30	.25	.12
21	Larry Andersen	.30	.25	.12
22	Jim Pankovits	.30	.25	.12
23	Jim Deshaies	.40	.30	.15
24	Juan Agosto	.30	.25	.12
25	Chuck Jackson	.40	.30	.15
26	Joaquin Andujar	.40	.30	.15
27	Astros Coaches (Yogi Berra, Gene Clines, Matt Galante, Marc Hill, Denis Menke, Les Moss)	.30	.25	.12
28	Trainers Card/Checklist (Doc Ewell, Dave Labossiere, Dennis Liborio)	.30	.25	.12

1988 Mother's Cookies Athletics

Complete at 28 cards (including checklist), the 1988 Mother's Cookies A's set features full-color, borderless cards with rounded corners in the standard 2-1/2" by 3-1/2" size. The backs are printed in red and purple on white and include biographical information, the Mother's Cookies logo and card number. Starter sets of 20 cards were distributed at the stadium along with a promotional card redeemable for another eights cards (not necessarily those needed to complete the set). An album to house the cards was also available.

		MT	NR MT	EX
Complete Set:		16.00	12.00	6.50
Common Player:		.30	.25	.12
1	Tony LaRussa	.40	.30	.15
2	Mark McGwire	3.00	2.25	1.25
3	Dave Stewart	.50	.40	.20
4	Mickey Tettleton	.50	.40	.20
5	Dave Parker	.70	.50	.30
6	Carney Lansford	.40	.30	.15
7	Jose Canseco	4.00	3.00	1.50
8	Don Baylor	.50	.40	.20
9	Bob Welch	.40	.30	.15
10	Dennis Eckersley	.50	.40	.20
11	Walt Weiss	.80	.60	.30
12	Tony Phillips	.40	.30	.15
13	Steve Ontiveros	.30	.25	.12
14	Dave Henderson	.40	.30	.15
15	Stan Javier	.30	.25	.12
16	Ron Hassey	.30	.25	.12
17	Curt Young	.30	.25	.12
18	Glenn Hubbard	.30	.25	.12
19	Storm Davis	.30	.25	.12
20	Eric Plunk	.30	.25	.12

21	Matt Young	.30	.25	.12
22	Mike Gallego	.30	.25	.12
23	Rick Honeycutt	.30	.25	.12
24	Doug Jennings	.50	.40	.20
25	Gene Nelson	.30	.25	.12
26	Greg Cadaret	.30	.25	.12
27	A's Coaches (Dave Duncan, Rene Lachemann, Jim Lefebvre, Dave McKay, Mike Paul, Bob Watson)	.30	.25	.12
28	Jose Canseco, Mark McGwire	2.00	1.50	.80

1988 Mother's Cookies Dodgers

Similar in design to other Mother's Cookies sets, the 1988 Dodgers issue featured full-color, borderless photos with backs printed in red and purple. The 28 cards in the set measure the standard 2-1/2" by 3-1/2" with rounded corners. Starter packs of 20 cards were distributed at a ballpark promotion along with a coupon card that could be exchanged for an additional eight cards at a local card show or through the mail. The backs of the cards include brief player information, the Mother's Cookies logo and card number. The promotion also included a special album to house the set.

		MT	NR MT	EX
Complete Set:		11.00	8.25	4.50
Common Player:		.30	.25	.12
1	Tom Lasorda	.40	.30	.15
2	Pedro Guerrero	.40	.30	.15
3	Steve Sax	.40	.30	.15
4	Fernando Valenzuela	.40	.30	.15
5	Mike Marshall	.40	.30	.15
6	Orel Hershiser	.60	.45	.25
7	Alfredo Griffin	.30	.25	.12
8	Kirk Gibson	.60	.45	.25
9	Don Sutton	.50	.40	.20
10	Mike Scioscia	.60	.45	.25
11	Franklin Stubbs	.30	.25	.12
12	Mike Davis	.30	.25	.12
13	Jesse Orosco	.30	.25	.12
14	John Shelby	.30	.25	.12
15	Rick Dempsey	.40	.30	.15
16	Jay Howell	.40	.30	.15
17	Dave Anderson	.30	.25	.12
18	Alejandro Pena	.40	.30	.15
19	Jeff Hamilton	.40	.30	.15
20	Danny Heep	.30	.25	.12
21	Tim Leary	.30	.25	.12
22	Brad Havens	.30	.25	.12
23	Tim Belcher	.60	.45	.25
24	Ken Howell	.30	.25	.12
25	Mickey Hatcher	.30	.25	.12
26	Brian Holton	.30	.25	.12
27	Mike Devereaux	.80	.60	.30
28	Dodgers Coaches/Checklist (Joe Amalfitano, Mark Cresse, Joe Ferguson, Ben Hines, Manny Mota, Ron Perranoski, Bill Russell)	.30	.25	.12

1988 Mother's Cookies Giants

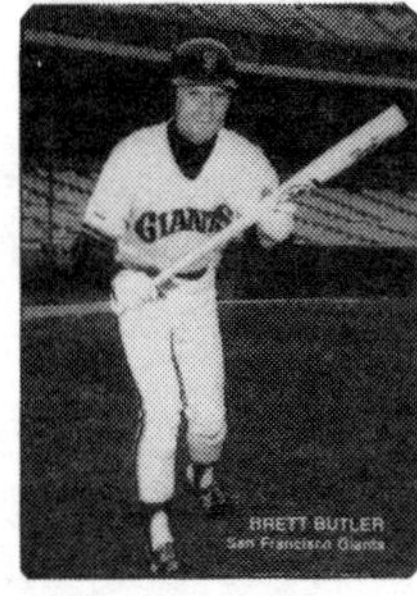

One of six team sets issued in 1988 by Mother's Cookies, this 28-card Giants set featured full-color borderless photos on a standard-size card with rounded corners. The backs, printed in red and purple, include brief player information, the Mother's Cookies logo and card number. Twenty different cards were distributed as a starter set at a stadium promotion along with a coupon card that could be redeemed for an additional eight cards (not necessarily those needed to complete the set). The redemption cards could be exchanged through the mail or redeemed at a local card show.

		MT	NR MT	EX
Complete Set:		12.00	9.00	4.75
Common Player:		.30	.25	.12
1	Roger Craig	.40	.30	.15
2	Will Clark	3.00	2.25	1.25
3	Kevin Mitchell	1.50	1.25	.60
4	Bob Brenly	.30	.25	.12
5	Mike Aldrete	.30	.25	.12
6	Mike Krukow	.30	.25	.12
7	Candy Maldonado	.30	.25	.12
8	Jeffrey Leonard	.30	.25	.12
9	Dave Dravecky	.40	.30	.15
10	Robby Thompson	.60	.45	.25
11	Scott Garrelts	.30	.25	.12
12	Bob Melvin	.30	.25	.12
13	Jose Uribe	.30	.25	.12
14	Brett Butler	.40	.30	.15
15	Rick Reuschel	.50	.40	.20
16	Harry Spilman	.40	.30	.15
17	Kelly Downs	.50	.40	.20
18	Chris Speier	.30	.25	.12
19	Atlee Hammaker	.30	.25	.12
20	Joel Youngblood	.30	.25	.12
21	Mike LaCoss	.30	.25	.12
22	Don Robinson	.30	.25	.12
23	Mark Wasinger	.30	.25	.12
24	Craig Lefferts	.30	.25	.12
25	Phil Garner	.40	.30	.15
26	Joe Price	.30	.25	.12
27	Giants Coaches (Dusty Baker, Bill Fahey, Bob Lillis, Gordie MacKenzie, Jose Morales, Norm Sherry)	.30	.25	.12
28	Logo Card/Checklist	.30	.25	.12

1988 Mother's Cookies Mariners

Similar in design to other Mother's Cookies sets, the 28-card Mariners issue featured full-color, borderless photos on a standard-size card with rounded corners. The backs, printed in red and purple, included brief biographical information, the Mother's Cookies logo and card number. Twenty-card starter packs were distributed at a stadium promotion, where fans also received a coupon card that could be exchanged for an additional eight cards (not necessarily those needed to complete the set). The coupon card could be redeemed through the mail or exchanged at a local baseball card show. As with the rest of the 1988 Mother's Cookies sets, an album was also available to house the cards.

		MT	NR MT	EX
Complete Set:		9.00	6.75	3.50
Common Player:		.30	.25	.12
1	Dick Williams	.30	.25	.12
2	Alvin Davis	.40	.30	.15
3	Mike Moore	.30	.25	.12
4	Jim Presley	.30	.25	.12
5	Mark Langston	.60	.45	.25
6	Henry Cotto	.30	.25	.12
7	Ken Phelps	.30	.25	.12
8	Steve Trout	.30	.25	.12
9	David Valle	.40	.30	.15
10	Harold Reynolds	.40	.30	.15
11	Edwin Nunez	.30	.25	.12
12	Glenn Wilson	.30	.25	.12
13	Scott Bankhead	.30	.25	.12
14	Scott Bradley	.30	.25	.12
15	Mickey Brantley	.30	.25	.12
16	Bruce Fields	.30	.25	.12
17	Mike Kingery	.30	.25	.12
18	Mike Campbell	.30	.25	.12
19	Mike Jackson	.30	.25	.12
20	Rey Quinones	.30	.25	.12
21	Mario Diaz	.30	.25	.12
22	Jerry Reed	.30	.25	.12
23	Rich Renteria	.30	.25	.12
24	Julio Solano	.30	.25	.12
25	Bill Swift	.50	.40	.20
26	Bill Wilkinson	.30	.25	.12
27	Mariners Coaches (Billy Connors, Frank Howard, Phil Roof, Jim Snyder, Ozzie Virgil)	.30	.25	.12
28	Trainers Card/Checklist (Henry Genzale, Rick Griffin)	.30	.25	.12

1988 Mother's Cookies Rangers

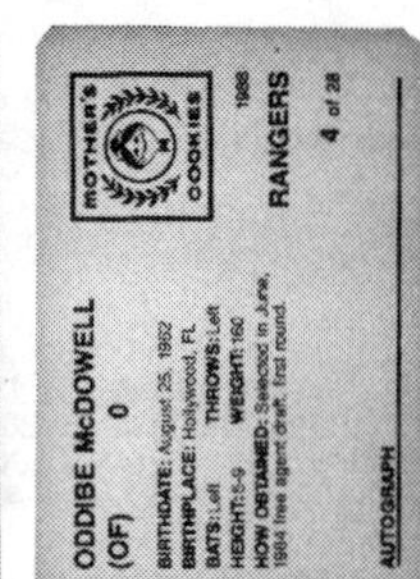

This 28-card set featuring the Texas Rangers was one of six team sets issued in 1988 by Mother's Cookies. Similar to other Mother's Cookies sets, the Rangers issue features full-color, borderless cards printed in the standard 2-1/2" by 3-1/2" format with rounded corners. The backs were printed in red and purple on white and included player information, the Mother's Cookies logo and card number. Twenty-card starter packs were distributed at a stadium promotion that included a redemption card good for another eight cards (not necessarily those needed to complete the set) either through the mail or at a local card show.

		MT	NR MT	EX
Complete Set:		10.00	7.50	4.00
Common Player:		.30	.25	.12
1	Bobby Valentine	.40	.30	.15
2	Pete Incaviglia	.50	.40	.20
3	Charlie Hough	.40	.30	.15
4	Oddibe McDowell	.40	.30	.15
5	Larry Parrish	.30	.25	.12
6	Scott Fletcher	.40	.30	.15
7	Steve Buechele	.40	.30	.15
8	Steve Kemp	.40	.30	.15
9	Pete O'Brien	.40	.30	.15
10	Ruben Sierra	.90	.70	.35
11	Mike Stanley	.50	.40	.20
12	Jose Cecena	.30	.25	.12
13	Cecil Espy	.40	.30	.15
14	Curtis Wilkerson	.30	.25	.12
15	Dale Mohorcic	.30	.25	.12
16	Ray Hayward	.30	.25	.12
17	Mitch Williams	.40	.30	.15
18	Bob Brower	.30	.25	.12
19	Paul Kilgus	.30	.25	.12
20	Geno Petralli	.30	.25	.12
21	James Steels	.30	.25	.12
22	Jerry Browne	.40	.30	.15
23	Jose Guzman	.30	.25	.12
24	DeWayne Vaughn	.30	.25	.12
25	Bobby Witt	.40	.30	.15
26	Jeff Russell	.30	.25	.12
27	Rangers Coaches (Richard Egan, Tom House, Art Howe, Davey Lopes, David Oliver, Tom Robson)	.30	.25	.12
28	Trainers Card/Checklist (Danny Wheat, Bill Zeigler)	.30	.25	.12

Regional interest may affect the value of a card.

1988 Mother's Cookies Will Clark

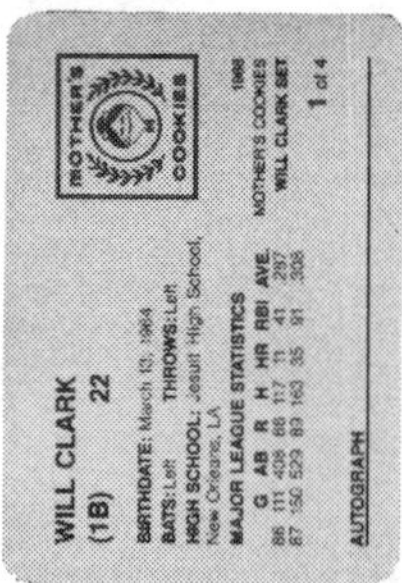

In a baseball spring training-related promotion, Mother's Cookies of Oakland, Calif. produced a full-color four-card set featuring San Francisco Giants first baseman Will Clark. The cards, which have glossy finishes and rounded corners, came cellophane-wrapped in specially marked 18-ounce packages of Mother's Cookies products. The cards are identical in style to the regular Mother's Cookies issues.

		MT	NR MT	EX
Complete Set:		8.00	6.00	3.25
Common Player:		2.00	1.50	.80
1	Will Clark (bat on shoulder)	2.00	1.50	.80
2	Will Clark (kneeling)	2.00	1.50	.80
3	Will Clark (batting follow-thru)	2.00	1.50	.80
4	Will Clark (heading for first base)	2.00	1.50	.80

1988 Mother's Cookies Mark McGwire

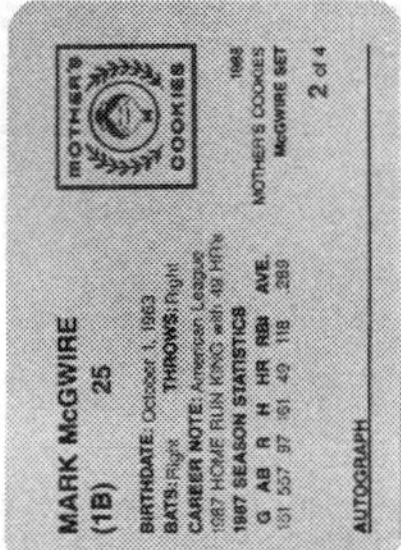

For the second consecutive year, Mother's Cookies devoted a four-card set to Oakland A's slugger Mark McGwire. The full-color cards have rounded corners and measure 2-1/2" by 3-1/2" in size. The cards were issued in specially marked 18-ounce packages of Mother's Cookies products in the northern California area. The cards are identical in design to the regular team issues produced by Mother's.

		MT	NR MT	EX
Complete Set:		8.00	6.00	3.25
Common Player:		2.00	1.50	.80
1	Mark McGwire (holding oversized bat)	2.00	1.50	.80
2	Mark McGwire (fielding)	2.00	1.50	.80
3	Mark McGwire (kneeling)	2.00	1.50	.80
4	Mark McGwire (bat in air)	2.00	1.50	.80

1989 Mother's Cookies Astros

The 1989 Houston Astros team set issued by Mother's Cookies consisted of 28 cards designed in the traditional style of borderless photos and rounded corners. Partial sets were distributed to fans attending the July 22 Astros game at the Houston Astrodome. The cards feature the photography of Barry Colla and display the Mother's Cookies logo on the back.

		MT	NR MT	EX
Complete Set:		10.00	7.50	4.00
Common Player:		.30	.25	.12
1	Art Howe	.30	.25	.12
2	Mike Scott	.30	.25	.12
3	Gerald Young	.50	.40	.20
4	Bill Doran	.40	.30	.15
5	Billy Hatcher	.50	.40	.20
6	Terry Puhl	.30	.25	.12
7	Bob Knepper	.30	.25	.12
8	Kevin Bass	.40	.30	.15
9	Glenn Davis	.40	.30	.15
10	Alann Ashby	.30	.25	.12
11	Bob Forsch	.30	.25	.12
12	Greg Gross	.30	.25	.12
13	Danny Darwin	.30	.25	.12
14	Craig Biggio	2.00	1.50	.80
15	Jim Clancy	.30	.25	.12
16	Rafael Ramirez	.30	.25	.12
17	Alex Trevino	.30	.25	.12
18	Craig Reynolds	.30	.25	.12
19	Dave Smith	.30	.25	.12
20	Larry Andersen	.30	.25	.12
21	Eric Yelding	.60	.45	.25
22	Jim Deshaies	.40	.30	.15
23	Juan Agosto	.30	.25	.12
24	Rick Rhoden	.30	.25	.12
25	Ken Caminiti	.40	.30	.15
26	Dave Meads	.30	.25	.12
27	Astro Coaches (Yogi Berra, Matt Galante, Phil Garner, Les Moss, Ed Napoleon, Ed Ott)	.30	.25	.12
28	Trainers Card/Checklist (Dave Labossiere, Doc Ewell Equip. Mgr.-Dennis Liborio)	.30	.25	.12

1989 Mother's Cookies Athletics

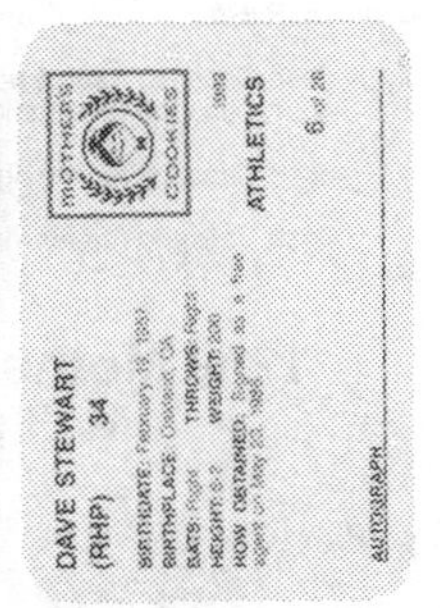

The 1989 Mother's Cookies A's set consists of 28 cards designed in the traditional style: a glossy card with a borderless photo and rounded corners. A starter set of the cards was used as a stadium promotion and distributed to fans attending the July 30 Oakland game.

		MT	NR MT	EX
Complete Set:		15.00	11.00	6.00
Common Player:		.30	.25	.12
1	Tony LaRussa	.30	.25	.12
2	Mark McGwire	2.00	1.50	.80
3	Terry Steinbach	.60	.45	.25
4	Dave Parker	.80	.60	.30
5	Carney Lansford	.30	.25	.12
6	Dave Stewart	.60	.45	.25
7	Jose Canseco	4.00	3.00	1.50
8	Walt Weiss	.50	.40	.20
9	Bob Welch	.40	.30	.15
10	Dennis Eckersley	.60	.45	.25
11	Tony Phillips	.50	.40	.20
12	Mike Moore	.35	.25	.14
13	Dave Henderson	.40	.30	.15
14	Curt Young	.30	.25	.12
15	Ron Hassey	.30	.25	.12
16	Eric Plunk	.30	.25	.12
17	Luis Polonia	.50	.40	.20
18	Storm Davis	.30	.25	.12
19	Glenn Hubbard	.30	.25	.12
20	Greg Cadaret	.30	.25	.12
21	Stan Javier	.30	.25	.12
22	Felix Jose	.40	.30	.15
23	Mike Gallego	.30	.25	.12
24	Todd Burns	.30	.25	.12
25	Rick Honeycutt	.30	.25	.12
26	Gene Nelson	.30	.25	.12
27	A's Coaches (Dave Duncan, Rene Lachemann, Art Kusnyer, Tommie Reynolds, Merv Rettenmund)	.30	.25	.12
28	Walt Wiess, Mark McGwire & Jose Canseco	.60	.45	.25

1989 Mother's Cookies Dodgers

This 28-card set features the players and coaching staff of the Los Angeles Dodgers. The cards follow the traditional Mother's Cookies style featuring rounded corners, borderless color photos, horizontal backs and are 2-1/2" by 3-1/2" in size. Initially twenty cards were given away as starter sets at Dodger Stadium.

		MT	NR MT	EX
Complete Set:		10.00	7.50	4.00
Common Player:		.30	.25	.12
1	Tom Lasorda	.40	.30	.15
2	Eddie Murray	.70	.50	.30
3	Mike Scioscia	.40	.30	.15
4	Fernando Valenzuela	.40	.30	.15
5	Mike Marshall	.50	.40	.20
6	Orel Hershiser	.80	.60	.30
7	Alfredo Griffin	.35	.25	.14
8	Kirk Gibson	.40	.30	.15
9	John Tudor	.30	.25	.12
10	Willie Randolph	.40	.30	.15
11	Franklin Stubbs	.30	.25	.12
12	Mike Davis	.30	.25	.12
13	Mike Morgan	.30	.25	.12
14	John Shelby	.30	.25	.12
15	Rick Dempsey	.30	.25	.12
16	Jay Howell	.40	.30	.15
17	Dave Anderson	.30	.25	.12
18	Alejandro Pena	.35	.25	.14
19	Jeff Hamilton	.35	.25	.14
20	Ricky Horton	.30	.25	.12
21	Tim Leary	.30	.25	.12
22	Ray Searage	.30	.25	.12
23	Tim Belcher	.50	.40	.20
24	Tim Crews	.30	.25	.12
25	Mickey Hatcher	.30	.25	.12
26	Mariano Duncan	.40	.30	.15
27	Dodgers Coaches (Joe Amalfitano, Mark Cresse, Joe Ferguson, Ben Hines, Manny Mota, Ron Perranoski, Bill Russell)	.30	.25	.12
28	Checklist	.30	.25	.12

1989 Mother's Cookies Giants

The 1989 Mother's Cookies Giants set consists of 28 cards, all featuring borderless, color photos with rounded corners. Starter sets of the cards were distributed as a stadium promotion to fans attending the Aug. 6, 1989, Giants game at Candlestick Park.

		MT	NR MT	EX
Complete Set:		11.00	8.25	4.50
Common Player:		.30	.25	.12
1	Roger Craig	.40	.30	.15
2	Will Clark	1.25	.90	.50
3	Kevin Mitchell	.75	.60	.30
4	Kelly Downs	.30	.25	.12
5	Brett Butler	.40	.30	.15
6	Mike Krukow	.30	.25	.12
7	Candy Maldonado	.30	.25	.12
8	Terry Kennedy	.30	.25	.12
9	Dave Dravecky	.40	.30	.15
10	Robby Thompson	.50	.40	.20
11	Scott Garrelts	.30	.25	.12
12	Matt Williams	.70	.50	.30
13	Jose Uribe	.30	.25	.12
14	Tracy Jones	.30	.25	.12
15	Rick Reuschel	.30	.25	.12
16	Ernest Riles	.30	.25	.12
17	Jeff Brantley	.30	.25	.12
18	Chris Speier	.30	.25	.12
19	Atlee Hammaker	.30	.25	.12
20	Ed Jurak	.30	.25	.12
21	Mike LaCoss	.30	.25	.12
22	Don Robinson	.30	.25	.12
23	Kirt Manwaring	.50	.40	.20
24	Craig Lefferts	.30	.25	.12
25	Donnell Nixon	.30	.25	.12
26	Joe Price	.30	.25	.12
27	Rich Gossage	.40	.30	.15
28	Coaches/Checklist (Bill Fahey, Dusty Baker, Bob Lillis, Wendell Kim, Norm Sherry)	.30	.25	.12

1989 Mother's Cookies Mariners

For the sixth straight season Mother's Cookies released a set of the Seattle Mariners. The 1989 issue features 28 cards. Starter sets featuring 20 cards were distribted at a Mariner home game. The cards are 2-1/2" by 3-1/2" in size and feature borderless full color photos. The card backs are printed horizontally. Rookie sensation Ken Griffey Jr. was included in the 1989 issue.

		MT	NR MT	EX
Complete Set:		19.00	14.00	7.50
Common Player:		.30	.25	.12
1	Jim Lefebvre	.30	.25	.12
2	Alvin Davis	.30	.25	.12
3	Ken Griffey, Jr.	10.00	7.50	4.00

No.	Player	MT	NR MT	EX
4	Jim Presley	.30	.25	.12
5	Mark Langston	.70	.50	.30
6	Henry Cotto	.30	.25	.12
7	Mickey Brantley	.30	.25	.12
8	Jeffrey Leonard	.30	.25	.12
9	Dave Valle	.35	.25	.14
10	Harold Reynolds	.70	.50	.30
11	Edgar Martinez	.50	.40	.20
12	Tom Niedenfuer	.30	.25	.12
13	Scott Bankhead	.40	.30	.15
14	Scott Bradley	.35	.25	.14
15	Omar Vizquel	.60	.45	.25
16	Erik Hanson	.60	.45	.25
17	Bill Swift	.40	.30	.15
18	Mike Campbell	.30	.25	.12
19	Mike Jackson	.30	.25	.12
20	Rich Renteria	.30	.25	.12
21	Mario Diaz	.30	.25	.12
22	Jerry Reed	.30	.25	.12
23	Darnell Coles	.30	.25	.12
24	Steve Trout	.30	.25	.12
25	Mike Schooler	.30	.25	.12
26	Julio Solano	.30	.25	.12
27	Mariners Coaches (Gene Clines, Bob Didier, Rusty Kuntz, Mike Paul, Bill Plummer)	.30	.25	.12
28	Checklist / Trainers (Henry Genzale, Rick Griffin)	.30	.25	.12

A player's name in italic type indicates a rookie card. An (FC) indicates a player's first card for that particular card company.

1989 Mother's Cookies Rangers

The 1989 Mother's Cookies Rangers team set featured the traditional borderless photos and rounded corners. The standard-size set consisted of 28 cards featuring the photography of Barry Colla. Partial sets were distributed to fans attending the July 30, 1989 game at Arlington Stadium.

		MT	NR MT	EX
	Complete Set:	13.00	9.75	5.25
	Common Player:	.30	.25	.12
1	Bobby Valentine	.40	.30	.15
2	Nolan Ryan	3.00	2.25	1.25
3	Julio Franco	.60	.45	.25
4	Charlie Hough	.40	.30	.15
5	Rafael Palmeiro	.80	.60	.30
6	Jeff Russell	.50	.40	.20
7	Ruben Sierra	.90	.70	.35
8	Steve Buechele	.40	.30	.15
9	Buddy Bell	.40	.30	.15
10	Pete Incaviglia	.40	.30	.15
11	Geno Petralli	.30	.25	.12
12	Cecil Espy	.30	.25	.12
13	Scott Fletcher	.40	.30	.15
14	Bobby Witt	.30	.25	.12
15	Brad Arnsberg	.30	.25	.12
16	Rick Leach	.30	.25	.12
17	Jamie Moyer	.30	.25	.12
18	Kevin Brown	.50	.40	.20
19	Jeff Kunkel	.30	.25	.12
20	Craig McMurtry	.30	.25	.12
21	Kenny Rogers	.40	.30	.15
22	Mike Stanley	.40	.30	.15
23	Cecilio Guante	.30	.25	.12
24	Jim Sundberg	.40	.30	.15
25	Jose Guzman	.30	.25	.12
26	Jeff Stone	.30	.25	.12
27	Rangers Coaches (Dick Egan, Tom Robson, Toby Harrah, Dave Oliver, Tom House, Dave Lopes)	.30	.25	.12
28	Trainers Card/Checklist (Bill Ziegler, Danny Wheat)	.30	.25	.12

1989 Mother's Cookies Jose Canseco

This special insert 4-card glossy set features Canseco in two posed (one standing, one kneeling) and two action (one batting, one running) shots. Full-color card fronts have rounded corners. Flip sides are numbered, printed in red and purple, and carry

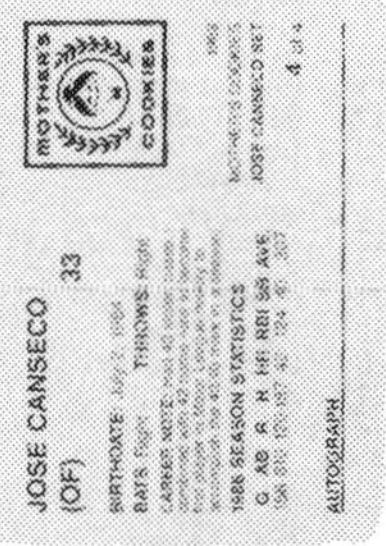

1988 stats and career notes. Cards are individually cello-wrapped and inserted in Mother's Fudge 'N Chips, Oatmeal Raisin and Cocadas cookie bags.

		MT	NR MT	EX
	Complete Set:	12.00	9.00	4.75
	Common Player:	3.00	2.25	1.25
1	Jose Canseco (ball in hand)	3.00	2.25	1.25
2	Jose Canseco (on one knee grasping bat)	3.00	2.25	1.25
3	Jose Canseco (swinging-in action)	3.00	2.25	1.25
4	Jose Canseco (baserunning)	3.00	2.25	1.25

1989 Mother's Cookies Will Clark

Will Clark is featured on a special-edition glossy 4-card set inserted in Mother's big bag chocolate chip cookies. The standard-size (2-1/2" by 3-1/2") cards feature Clark in two posed (batting and catching) and two action (batting and running) shots. Purple and red backs (numbered) list 1986-88 stats.

		MT	NR MT	EX
	Complete Set:	8.00	6.00	3.25
	Common Player:	2.00	1.50	.80
1	Will Clark (displaying ball in glove)	2.00	1.50	.80
2	Will Clark (batting stance)	2.00	1.50	.80
3	Will Clark (in action-after swing)	2.00	1.50	.80
4	Will Clark (heading towards first)	2.00	1.50	.80

1989 Mother's Cookies Ken Griffey, Jr.

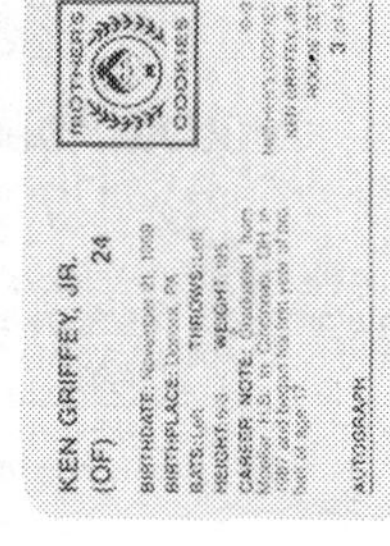

This four-card set featuring Ken Griffey, Jr. was issued by Mother's Cookies and was available only in cookie packages in the states of Washington and Oregon. The cards were also available at a Seattle Mariners Kingdome Baseball Card Show on Aug. 20, 1989, where the set was introduced. The cards were then packed inside specially-marked bags of cookies, one card per bag. The cards display the traditional Mother's Cookie's design: glossy, borderless cards with rounded corners.

		MT	NR MT	EX
	Complete Set:	14.00	10.50	5.50
	Common Player:	3.50	2.75	1.50
1	Ken Griffey, Jr. (arms folded)	3.50	2.75	1.50
2	Ken Griffey, Jr. (ball in hand)	3.50	2.75	1.50
3	Ken Griffey, Jr. (bat over left shoulder)	3.50	2.75	1.50
4	Ken Griffey, Jr. (back of jersey showing)	3.50	2.75	1.50

1989 Mother's Cookies Mark McGwire

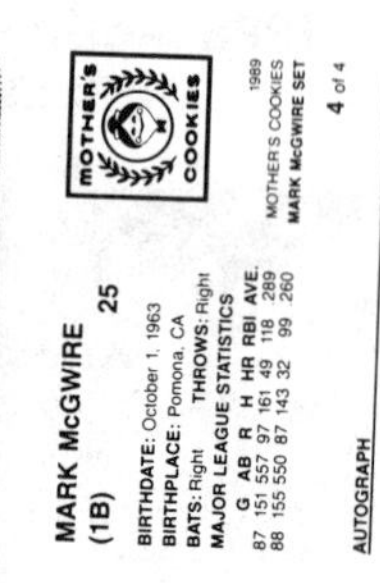

This special edition 4-card set features full-color glossy player photos by Barry Colla on standard-size (2-1/2" by 3-1/2") cards with rounded corners. Photos feature four different batting poses. Numbered flip sides, printed in purple and red, carry 1987 and 1988 statistics. Cards are individually cello-wrapped and inserted in Mother's Cookie Parade variety cookie bags.

		MT	NR MT	EX
	Complete Set:	8.00	6.00	3.25
	Common Player:	2.00	1.50	.80
1	Mark McGwire (bat on shoulder)	2.00	1.50	.80
2	Mark McGwire (batting stance)	2.00	1.50	.80
3	Mark McGwire (bat in front)	2.00	1.50	.80
4	Mark McGwire (batting follow through)	2.00	1.50	.80

1989 Mother's Cookies Rookies of the Year

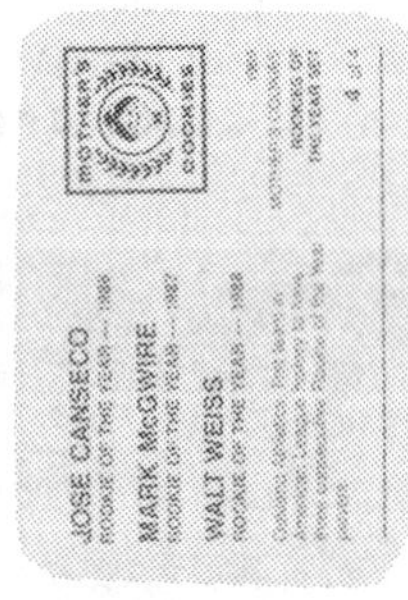

This four-card set features the American League Rookies of the Year for 1986, 1987 and 1988, all members of the Oakland A's. The 2-1/2" by 3-1/2" cards feature full color photos in the traditional Mother's Cookies style. One card was devoted to each player along with a special card showcasing all three players, Weiss, McGwire and Canseco, together. The cards were distributed one per box in Mother's Cookies.

		MT	NR MT	EX
	Complete Set:	7.50	5.75	3.00
	Common Player:	1.00	.70	.40
1	Jose Canseco	2.50	2.00	1.00
2	Mark McGwire	2.00	1.50	.80
3	Walt Weiss	1.00	.70	.40
4	Walt Weiss, Mark McGwire, & Jose Canseco	2.00	1.50	.80

The values quoted are intended to reflect the market price.

1990 Mother's Cookies Astros

This 28-card set features cards styled like past Mother's Cookies releases. The cards were distributed in 20 card packs at an Astro home game. The cards were never distributed in complete set form.

		MT	NR MT	EX
	Complete Set:	8.00	6.00	3.25
	Common Player:	.25	.20	.10
1	Art Howe	.30	.25	.12
2	Glenn Davis	.30	.25	.12
3	Eric Anthony	.60	.45	.25
4	Mike Scott	.35	.25	.14
5	Craig Biggio	.75	.60	.30
6	Ken Caminiti	.40	.30	.15
7	Bill Doran	.30	.25	.12
8	Gerald Young	.25	.20	.10
9	Terry Puhl	.25	.20	.10
10	Mark Portugal	.25	.20	.10
11	Mark Davidson	.25	.20	.10
12	Jim Deshaies	.25	.20	.10
13	Bill Gullickson	.30	.25	.12
14	Franklin Stubbs	.25	.20	.10
15	Danny Darwin	.25	.20	.10
16	Ken Oberkfell	.25	.20	.10
17	Dave Smith	.25	.20	.10
18	Dan Schatzeder	.25	.20	.10
19	Rafael Ramirez	.25	.20	.10
20	Larry Andersen	.25	.20	.10
21	Alex Trevino	.25	.20	.10
22	Glenn Wilson	.25	.20	.10
23	Jim Clancy	.25	.20	.10
24	Eric Yelding	.35	.25	.14
25	Casey Candaele	.25	.20	.10
26	Juan Agosto	.25	.20	.10
27	Coaches (Billy Bowman, Bob Cluck, Phil Garner, Matt Galante, Rudy Jaramillo, Ed Napoleon)	.25	.20	.10
28	Checklist/Trainers (Doc Ewell, Dave Labossiere, Dennis Liborio)	.25	.20	.10

1990 Mother's Cookies Athletics

This 28-card set features cards distributed at an Oakland A's home game. The cards measure 2 1/2" by 3 1/2" and feature rounded corners. The card backs include biographical information and autograph space. Oakland players Mark McGwire and Jose Canseco are also featured in single player sets from Mother's Cookies.

		MT	NR MT	EX
	Complete Set:	11.00	7.50	4.00
	Common Player:	.25	.20	.10
1	Tony LaRussa	.35	.25	.14
2	Mark McGwire	.80	.60	.30
3	Terry Steinbach	.40	.30	.15
4	Rickey Henderson	2.00	1.50	.80
5	Dave Stewart	.60	.45	.25
6	Jose Canseco	3.00	2.25	1.25
7	Dennis Eckersley	.60	.45	.25
8	Carney Lansford	.35	.25	.14
9	Mike Moore	.30	.25	.12
10	Walt Weiss	.35	.25	.14
11	Scott Sanderson	.35	.25	.14
12	Ron Hassey	.25	.20	.10
13	Rick Honeycutt	.25	.20	.10
14	Ken Phelps	.25	.20	.10
15	Jamie Quirk	.25	.20	.10
16	Bob Welch	.40	.30	.15
17	Felix Jose	.60	.45	.25
18	Dave Henderson	.40	.30	.15
19	Mike Norris	.25	.20	.10
20	Todd Burns	.25	.20	.10
21	Lance Blankenship	.25	.20	.10
22	Gene Nelson	.25	.20	.10
23	Stan Javier	.25	.20	.10
24	Curt Young	.25	.20	.10
25	Mike Gallego	.30	.25	.12
26	Joe Klink	.25	.20	.10
27	Coaches (Dave Duncan, Art Kusnyer, Rene Lachemann, Dave McKay, Merv Rettenmund, Tommie Reynolds)	.25	.20	.10
28	Checklist/Trainers (Frank Cienscyk, Larry Davis, Steve Vuchinich, Barry Weinberg)	.25	.20	.10

1990 Mother's Cookies Dodgers

Distributed as a promotional item, these cards are styled like past Mother's Cookies releases. Fans fourteen and under received a 20-card pack at a Dodger home game. Cards were also available at a Labor Day card show at the Anaheim Convention Center. The cards were not distributed in complete set form.

		MT	NR MT	EX
	Complete Set:	8.00	6.00	3.25
	Common Player:	.25	.20	.10
1	Tom Lasorda	.40	.30	.15
2	Fernando Valenzuela	.30	.25	.12
3	Kal Daniels	.25	.20	.10
4	Mike Scioscia	.30	.25	.12
5	Eddie Murray	.70	.50	.30
6	Mickey Hatcher	.25	.20	.10
7	Juan Samuel	.30	.25	.12
8	Alfredo Griffin	.30	.25	.12
9	Tim Belcher	.40	.30	.15
10	Hubie Brooks	.30	.25	.12
11	Jose Gonzalez	.25	.20	.10
12	Orel Hershiser	.60	.45	.25
13	Kirk Gibson	.40	.30	.15
14	Chris Gwynn	.35	.25	.14
15	Jay Howell	.35	.25	.14
16	Rick Dempsey	.25	.20	.10
17	Ramon Martinez	.80	.60	.30
18	Lenny Harris	.30	.25	.12
19	John Wetteland	.60	.45	.25
20	Mike Sharperson	.25	.20	.10
21	Mike Morgan	.35	.25	.14
22	Ray Searage	.25	.20	.10
23	Jeff Hamilton	.25	.20	.10
24	Jim Gott	.25	.20	.10
25	John Shelby	.25	.20	.10
26	Tim Crews	.25	.20	.10
27	Don Aase	.25	.20	.10
28	Coaches (Joe Amalfitano, Mark Cresse, Joe Ferguson, Ben Hines, Manny Mota, Ron Perranoski, Bill Russell)	.25	.20	.10

1990 Mother's Cookies Giants

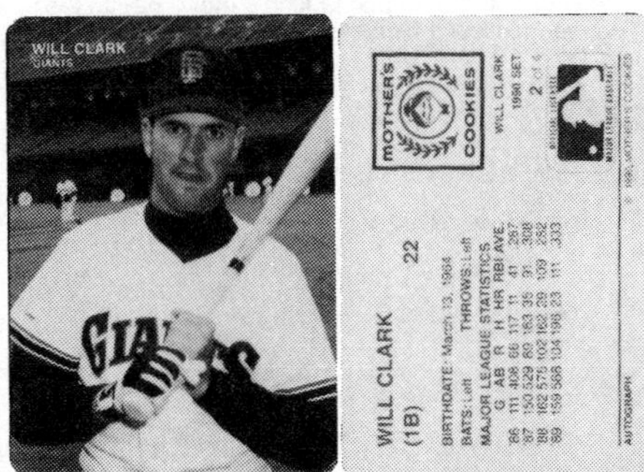

Like the other Mother's Cookies issues of 1990, Giants cards were distributed as a promotional item. Fans fourteen and under were given a 20-card pack at a home game. Cards could also be redeemed at the Labor Day card show in San Francisco. The cards were not released in complete set form.

		MT	NR MT	EX
	Complete Set:	8.00	6.00	3.25
	Common Player:	.25	.20	.10
1	Roger Craig	.35	.25	.14
2	Will Clark	2.00	1.50	.80
3	Gary Carter	.50	.40	.20
4	Kelly Downs	.25	.20	.10
5	Kevin Mitchell	.50	.40	.20
6	Steve Bedrosian	.30	.25	.12
7	Brett Butler	.40	.30	.15
8	Rick Reuschel	.25	.20	.10
9	Matt Williams	1.25	.90	.50
10	Robby Thompson	.60	.45	.25
11	Mike LaCoss	.25	.20	.10
12	Terry Kennedy	.25	.20	.10
13	Atlee Hammaker	.25	.20	.10
14	Rick Leach	.25	.20	.10
15	Ernest Riles	.25	.20	.10
16	Scott Garrelts	.25	.20	.10
17	Jose Uribe	.25	.20	.10
18	Greg Litton	.25	.20	.10
19	Dave Anderson	.25	.20	.10
20	Don Robinson	.25	.20	.10
21	Coaches (Dusty Baker, Bill Fahey, Wendell Kim, Bob Lillis, Norm Sherry)	.25	.20	.10
22	Bill Bathe	.25	.20	.10
23	Randy O'Neal	.25	.20	.10
24	Kevin Bass	.35	.25	.14
25	Jeff Brantley	.25	.20	.10
26	John Burkett	.60	.45	.25
27	Ernie Camacho	.25	.20	.10
28	Checklist	.25	.20	.10

1990 Mother's Cookies Mariners

This 28-card set features the traditional Mother's Cookies style with borderless full-color photos with rounded corners. The card backs feature biographical information and autograph space. The cards were released as a promotion at a Mariners home game and at a Kingdome card show.

		MT	NR MT	EX
	Complete Set:	12.00	7.50	4.00
	Common Player:	.25	.20	.10
1	Jim Lefebvre	.25	.20	.10
2	Alvin Davis	.35	.25	.14
3	Ken Griffey, Jr.	6.00	4.50	2.50
4	Jeffrey Leonard	.25	.20	.10
5	David Valle	.30	.25	.12
6	Harold Reynolds	.40	.30	.15
7	Jay Buhner	.50	.40	.20
8	Erik Hanson	.40	.30	.15
9	Henry Cotto	.25	.20	.10
10	Edgar Martinez	.60	.45	.25
11	Bill Swift	.60	.45	.25
12	Omar Vizquel	.45	.35	.20
13	Randy Johnson	.60	.45	.25
14	Greg Briley	.25	.20	.10
15	Gene Harris	.25	.20	.10
16	Matt Young	.25	.20	.10
17	Pete O'Brien	.30	.25	.12
18	Brent Knackert	.25	.20	.10
19	Mike Jackson	.25	.20	.10
20	Brian Holman	.25	.20	.10
21	Mike Schooler	.25	.20	.10
22	Darnell Coles	.25	.20	.10
23	Keith Comstock	.25	.20	.10
24	Scott Bankhead	.25	.20	.10
25	Scott Bradley	.25	.20	.10
26	Mike Brumley	.25	.20	.10
27	Coaches (Gene Cline, Bob Didier, Rusty Kuntz, Mike Paul, Bill Plummer)	.25	.20	.10
28	Checklist/Trainers (Henry Genzale, Rick Griffin, Tom Newberg)	.25	.20	.10

1990 Mother's Cookies Rangers

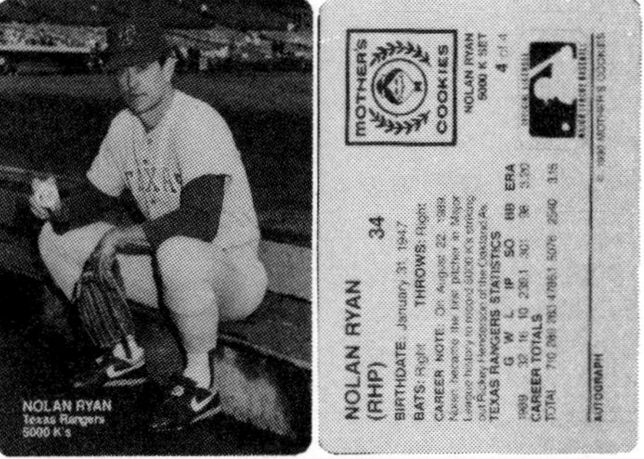

Putting together a complete set of these cards was not an easy task. The cards were distributed in 20-card packs at a Ranger home game and also could be redeemed at the Dallas Card Convention. The cards were not released in complete set form. The cards feature the traditional Mother's Cookies style.

		MT	NR MT	EX
	Complete Set:	12.00	9.00	4.75
	Common Player:	.25	.20	.10
1	Bobby Valentine	.30	.25	.12
2	Nolan Ryan	6.00	4.50	2.50
3	Ruben Sierra	.90	.70	.35
4	Pete Incaviglia	.30	.25	.12
5	Charlie Hough	.35	.25	.14
6	Harold Baines	.40	.30	.15
7	Gino Petralli	.25	.20	.10
8	Jeff Russell	.35	.25	.14

9	Rafael Palmeiro	.75	.60	.30
10	Julio Franco	.50	.40	.20
11	Jack Daugherty	.25	.20	.10
12	Gary Pettis	.25	.20	.10
13	Brian Bohanon	.25	.20	.10
14	Steve Buechele	.35	.25	.14
15	Bobby Witt	.25	.20	.10
16	Thad Bosley	.25	.20	.10
17	Gary Mielke	.25	.20	.10
18	Jeff Kunkel	.25	.20	.10
19	Mike Jeffcoat	.25	.20	.10
20	Mike Stanley	.25	.20	.10
21	Kevin Brown	.50	.40	.20
22	Kenny Rogers	.25	.20	.10
23	Jeff Huson	.35	.25	.14
24	Jamie Moyer	.25	.20	.10
25	Cecil Espy	.25	.20	.10
26	John Russell	.25	.20	.10
27	Coaches (Toby Harrah, Tom House, Davey Lopes, Dave Oliver, Tom Robson)	.25	.20	.10
28	Checklist/Trainers (Joe Macko, Marty Stajduhar, Danny Wheat, Bill Zeigler)	.25	.20	.10

A player's name in italic type indicates a rookie card. An (FC) indicates a player's first card for that particular card company.

1990 Mother's Cookies Jose Canseco

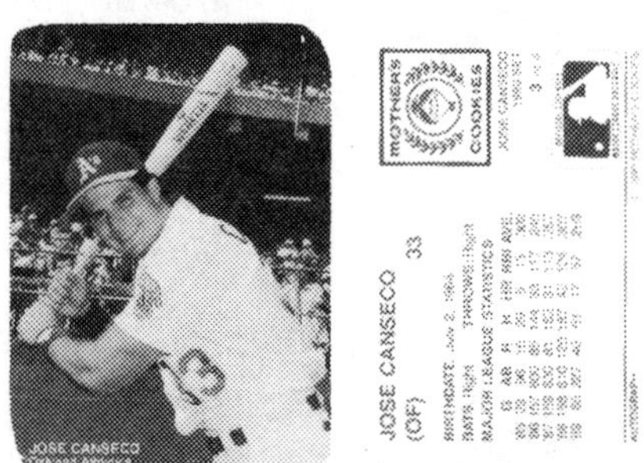

This special insert 4-card glossy set features Canseco in four posed shots. Full-color card fronts have rounded corners. Flip sides are numbered, printed in red and purple and feature the Mother's Cookies logo. The cards are individually cello-wrapped and inserted one per Mother's Cookies bag.

		MT	NR MT	EX
	Complete Set:	12.00	15.00	8.00
	Common Card:	3.00	3.00	1.50
1	Jose Canseco (sitting, bat on shoulder)	3.00	2.25	1.25
2	Jose Canseco (bat behind neck)	3.00	2.25	1.25
3	Jose Canseco (batting stance)	3.00	2.25	1.25
4	Jose Canseco (on dugout step)	3.00	2.25	1.25

1990 Mother's Cookies Will Clark

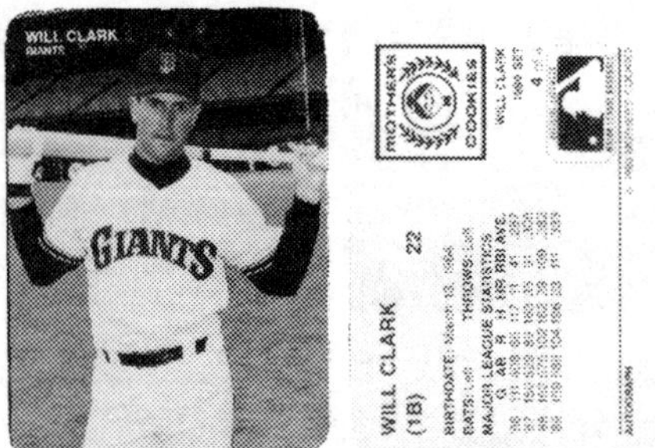

1990 marks the third consecutive year that Mother's Cookies devoted a set to Giant slugger Will Clark. This 4-card set features four posed full-color shots. The cards follow the same design as all recent Mother's Cookies cards.

		MT	NR MT	EX
	Complete Set:	10.00	7.50	4.00
	Common Card:	2.50	2.00	1.00
1	Will Clark (bat on shoulder)	2.50	2.00	1.00
2	Will Clark (closeup in stance)	2.50	2.00	1.00
3	Will Clark (open in stance)	2.50	2.00	1.00
4	Will Clark (bat behind neck)	2.50	2.00	1.00

1990 Mother's Cookies Mark McGwire

1990 marks the fourth year that A's slugger Mark McGwire has been featured on a special 4-card Mother's Cookies set. The photos for the cards were once again by Barry Colla. Four different posed shots of McGwire are showcased.

		MT	NR MT	EX
	Complete Set:	8.00	6.00	3.25
	Common Card:	2.00	1.50	.80
1	Mark McGwire (bat on shoulder)	2.00	1.50	.80
2	Mark McGwire (leaning against bat rack)	2.00	1.50	.80
3	Mark McGwire (glove in hand)	2.00	1.50	.80
4	Mark McGwire (on dugout step)	2.00	1.50	.80

1990 Mother's Cookies Nolan Ryan

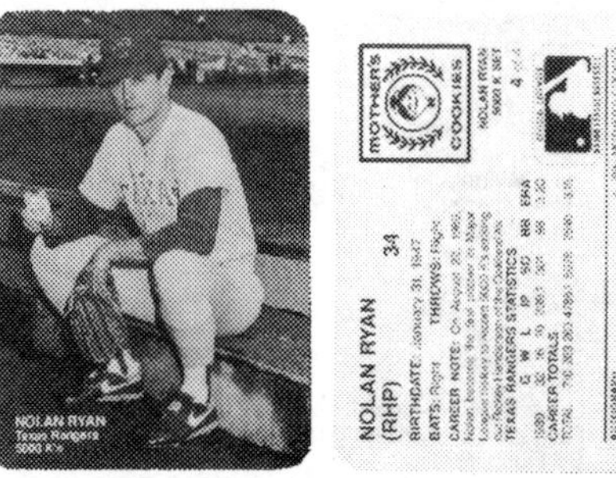

Unlike other special Mother's Cookies player sets, the Nolan Ryan cards feature 5000 K's along with his name and team on the card fronts. This 4-card set honors the strikout king's monumental feat. The cards follow the classic Mother's Cookies style.

		MT	NR MT	EX
	Complete Set:	16.00	12.00	6.50
	Common Card:	4.00	3.00	1.50
1	Nolan Ryan (facing with ball in hand)	4.00	3.00	1.50
2	Nolan Ryan (standing in dugout)	4.00	3.00	1.50
3	Nolan Ryan (gripping ball behind back)	4.00	3.00	1.50
4	Nolan Ryan (sitting on dugout step)	4.00	3.00	1.50

1990 Mother's Cookies Matt Williams

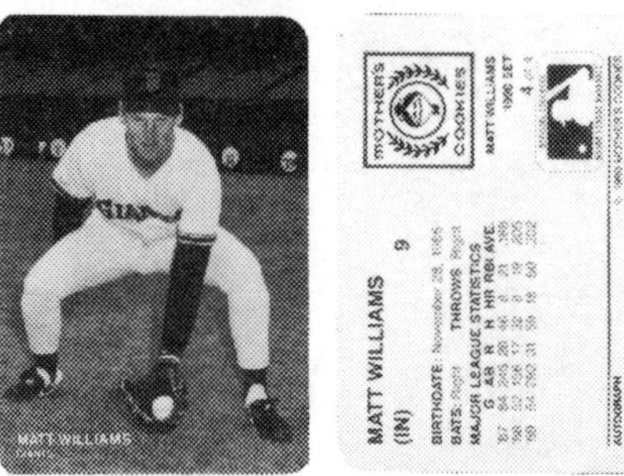

Matt Williams made his Mother's Cookies single player card set debut in 1990. Four posed shots of the Giant third baseman are showcased. Williams is featured twice in batting related poses and also twice as a fielder.

		MT	NR MT	EX
	Complete Set:	6.00	4.50	2.50
	Common Player:	1.50	2.75	1.50
1	Matt Williams (bat on shoulder)	1.50	1.25	.60
2	Matt Williams (in batting stance)	1.50	1.25	.60
3	Matt Williams (glove in hand)	1.50	1.25	.60
4	Matt Williams (fielding)	1.50	1.25	.60

1991 Mother's Cookies Astros

This 28-card set was produced in the now-familiar Mother's Cookies card format. Glossy fronts feature rounded corners and full-bleed posed color photos (apparently taken at San Francisco's Candlestick Park, home base of photographer Barry Colla) with the player's name and team in white in an upper corner. Backs are printed in red and purple and include a few biographical details, along with cookie company and MLB logos, uniform and card numbers and a line for autographing.

		MT	NR MT	EX
	Complete Set (28):	9.00	6.75	3.50
	Common Player:	.25	.20	.10
1	Art Howe	.25	.20	.10
2	Steve Finley	.35	.25	.14
3	Pete Harnisch	.35	.25	.14
4	Mike Scott	.25	.20	.10
5	Craig Biggio	.75	.60	.30
6	Ken Caminiti	.45	.35	.20
7	Eric Yelding	.35	.25	.14
8	Jeff Bagwell	.75	.60	.30
9	Jim Deshaises	.25	.20	.10
10	Mark Portugal	.25	.20	.10
11	Mark Davidson	.25	.20	.10
12	Jimmy Jones	.25	.20	.10
13	Luis Gonzalez	.35	.25	.14
14	Karl Rhodes	.35	.25	.14
15	Curt Schilling	.35	.25	.14
16	Ken Oberkfell	.25	.20	.10
17	Mark McLemore	.25	.20	.10
18	David Rohde	.25	.20	.10
19	Rafael Ramirez	.25	.20	.10
20	Al Osuna	.25	.20	.10
21	Jim Corsi	.25	.20	.10
22	Carl Nichols	.25	.20	.10
23	Jim Clancy	.25	.20	.10
24	Dwayne Henry	.25	.20	.10
25	Casey Candaele	.25	.20	.10
26	Xavier Hernandez	.35	.25	.14
27	Darryl Kile	.45	.35	.20
28	Coaches / Checklist (Matt Galante, Rudy Jaramillo, Phil Garner, Bob Cluck, Ed Ott)	.25	.20	.10

1991 Mother's Cookies Athletics

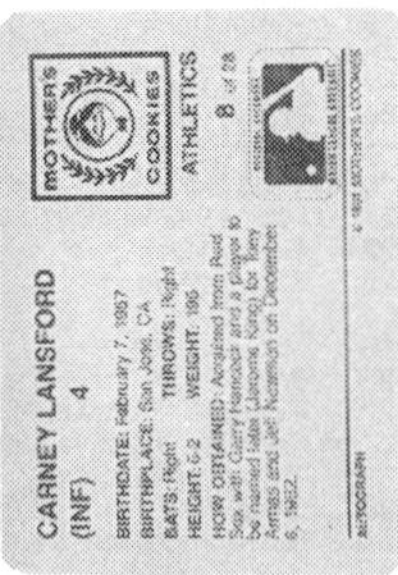

The incomparable photography of Barry Colla captures the Oakland A's in their home-field environs for the 28 cards in this set. Glossy fronts feature borderless posed photos. The player's name and team appear in white in an upper corner. Backs have minimal biographical data, player position, uniform and card numbers and appropriate logos.

		MT	NR MT	EX
Complete Set (28):		10.00	7.50	4.00
Common Player:		.25	.20	.10
1	Tony LaRussa	.25	.20	.10
2	Mark McGwire	.75	.60	.30
3	Terry Steinbach	.35	.25	.14
4	Rickey Henderson	.90	.70	.35
5	Dave Stewart	.40	.30	.15
6	Jose Canseco	1.50	1.25	.60
7	Dennis Eckersley	.50	.40	.20
8	Carney Lansford	.35	.25	.14
9	Bob Welch	.35	.25	.14
10	Walt Weiss	.35	.25	.14
11	Mike Moore	.35	.25	.14
12	Vance Law	.25	.20	.10
13	Rick Honeycutt	.25	.20	.10
14	Harold Baines	.40	.30	.15
15	Jamie Quirk	.25	.20	.10
16	Ernest Riles	.25	.20	.10
17	Willie Wilson	.35	.25	.14
18	Dave Henderson	.35	.25	.14
19	Kirk Dressendorfer	.40	.30	.15
20	Todd Burns	.25	.20	.10
21	Lance Blankenship	.25	.20	.10
22	Gene Nelson	.25	.20	.10
23	Eric Show	.25	.20	.10
24	Curt Young	.25	.20	.10
25	Mike Gallego	.25	.20	.10
26	Joe Klink	.25	.20	.10
27	Steve Chitren	.25	.20	.10
28	Coaches / Checklist (Rene Lachemann, Dave Duncan, Dave McKay, Tommie Reynolds, Art Kusnyer, Reggie Jackson, Rich Burlson)	.35	.25	.14

1991 Mother's Cookies Dodgers

Dodger Stadium is the background for Barry Colla's portraits of the Los Angeles manager, coaches and players appearing in this 28-card set. Standard-size cards with rounded corners feature borderless UV-coated fronts on which the only printing is the player's name and team in white in an upper corner. Backs are in red and purple and include a few biographical details, position, uniform and card numbers, a space for an autograph and the logos of the cookie company and MLB.

		MT	NR MT	EX
Complete Set (28):		8.00	6.00	3.25
Common Player:		.25	.20	.10
1	Tom Lasorda	.35	.25	.14
2	Darryl Strawberry	.35	.25	.14
3	Kal Daniels	.25	.20	.10
4	Mike Scioscia	.25	.20	.10
5	Eddie Murray	.45	.35	.20
6	Brett Butler	.35	.25	.14
7	Juan Samuel	.25	.20	.10
8	Alfredo Griffin	.25	.20	.10
9	Tim Belcher	.25	.20	.10
10	Ramon Martinez	.35	.25	.14
11	Jose Gonzalez	.25	.20	.10
12	Orel Hershiser	.45	.35	.20
13	Bob Ojeda	.35	.25	.14
14	Chris Gwynn	.25	.20	.10
15	Jay Howell	.35	.25	.14
16	Gary Carter	.40	.30	.15
17	Kevin Gross	.25	.20	.10
18	Lenny Harris	.25	.20	.10
19	Mike Hartley	.25	.20	.10
20	Mike Sharperson	.25	.20	.10
21	Mike Morgan	.25	.20	.10
22	John Candelaria	.25	.20	.10
23	Jeff Hamilton	.25	.20	.10
24	Jim Gott	.25	.20	.10
25	Barry Lyons	.25	.20	.10
26	Tim Crews	.25	.20	.10
27	Stan Javier	.25	.20	.10
28	Coaches / Checklist (Ron Perranoski, Bill Russell, Manny Mota, Joe Ferguson, Ben Hines, Joe Amalfitano, Mark Cresse)	.25	.20	.10

1991 Mother's Cookies Giants

For the ninth consecutive year Mother's Cookies sponsored a promotional card set for the Giants. As in the beginning, the cards highlight the work of photographer Barry Colla with posed portraits of the personnel in Candlestick Park. Fronts of the round-cornered borderless cards are UV-coated and have the player's name and team printed in white in an upper corner. Backs are in red and purple and include cookie company and Major League Baseball logos along with a few biographical details and both uniform and card numbers. The unusual venue of the players' locker room provides the backdrop for photos for this 28-card set sponsored by Mother's Cookies. Besides a look at the player's wardrobe, the full-bleed glossy front photos feature the player's name and position vertically along the left side. Backs have logos, uniform and card numbers, some biographical data and logos of the cookie company and Major League Baseball.

		MT	NR MT	EX
Complete Set:		9.00	6.75	3.50
Common Player:		.25	.20	.10
1	Roger Craig	.30	.25	.12
2	Will Clark	1.25	.90	.50
3	Steve Decker	.25	.20	.10
4	Kelly Downs	.25	.20	.10
5	Kevin Mitchell	.60	.45	.25
6	Willie McGee	.40	.30	.15
7	Buddy Black	.35	.25	.14
8	Dave Righetti	.25	.20	.10
9	Matt Williams	.50	.40	.20
10	Robby Thompson	.40	.30	.15
11	Mike LaCoss	.25	.20	.10
12	Terry Kennedy	.25	.20	.10
13	Mark Leonard	.25	.20	.10
14	Rick Reuschel	.25	.20	.10
15	Mike Felder	.25	.20	.10
16	Scott Garrelts	.25	.20	.10
17	Jose Uribe	.25	.20	.10
18	Greg Litton	.25	.20	.10
19	Dave Anderson	.25	.20	.10
20	Don Robinson	.25	.20	.10
21	Mike Kingery	.25	.20	.10
22	Trevor Wilson	.25	.20	.10
23	Kirt Manwaring	.25	.20	.10
24	Kevin Bass	.25	.20	.10
25	Jeff Brantley	.25	.20	.10
26	John Burkett	.40	.30	.15
27	Cocahes (Norm Sherry, Wendell Kim, Bob Lillis, Dusty Baker, Bill Fahey)	.25	.20	.10
28	Trainers / Checklist (Mark Letendre, Greg Lynn)	.25	.20	.10

1991 Mother's Cookies Rangers

		MT	NR MT	EX
Complete Set (28):		12.00	9.00	4.75
Common Player:		.25	.20	.10
1	Bobby Valentine	.25	.20	.10
2	Nolan Ryan	4.00	3.00	1.50
3	Ruben Sierra	.60	.45	.25
4	Juan Gonzalez	2.50	2.00	1.00
5	Steve Buechele	.35	.25	.14
6	Bobby Witt	.25	.20	.10
7	Geno Petralli	.25	.20	.10
8	Jeff Russell	.35	.25	.14
9	Rafael Palmeiro	.80	.60	.30
10	Julio Franco	.40	.30	.15
11	Jack Daugherty	.25	.20	.10
12	Gary Pettis	.25	.20	.10
13	John Barfield	.25	.20	.10
14	Scott Chiamparino	.25	.20	.10
15	Kevin Reimer	.25	.20	.10
16	Rich Gossage	.35	.25	.14
17	Brian Downing	.25	.20	.10
18	Denny Walling	.25	.20	.10
19	Mike Jeffcoat	.25	.20	.10
20	Mike Stanley	.25	.20	.10
21	Kevin Brown	.25	.20	.10
22	Kenny Rogers	.25	.20	.10
23	Jeff Huson	.25	.20	.10
24	Mario Diaz	.25	.20	.10
25	Brad Arnsberg	.25	.20	.10
26	John Russell	.25	.20	.10
27	Gerald Alexander	.25	.20	.10
28	Coaches / Checklist (Dave Oliver, Tom House, Davey Lopes, Toby Harrah, Tom Robson, Orlando Gomez)	.25	.20	.10

1991 Mother's Cookies Griffeys

This four-card set was packaged with Mother's Cookies sold in the Pacific Northwest. Each card features a borderless glossy posed photo on front. The traditional rounded corners of Mother's cards are found on the issue. Backs have a few stats and career notes.

		MT	NR MT	EX
Complete Set (4):		7.50	5.75	3.00
Common Card:		.50	.40	.20
1	Ken Griffey, Jr.	3.00	2.25	1.25
2	Ken Griffey, Sr.	.50	.40	.20
3	Ken Griffey, Jr. (holding gloves, Ken Griffey, Sr.)	2.00	1.50	.80
4	Ken Griffey, Jr. (holding bats, Ken Griffey, Sr.)	2.00	1.50	.80

1991 Mother's Cookies Nolan Ryan 300 Wins

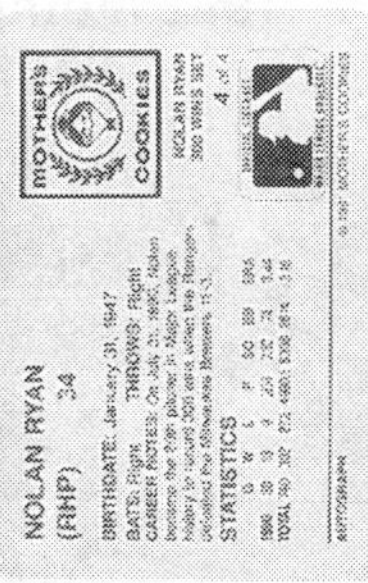

Mother's Cookies in 1991 created a four-card Nolan Ryan set honoring baseball's most recent 300-game winner. One card was included in specially-marked packages of cookies. Card fronts have the traditional Mother's Cookies look; Barry Colla photography on full-bleed cards with rounded corners. Backs have a few statistics and career notes.

		MT	NR MT	EX
Complete Set (4):		8.00	6.00	3.25
Common Card:		2.00	1.50	.80
1	Nolan Ryan (standing, front view)	2.00	1.50	.80
2	Nolan Ryan (kneeling)	2.00	1.50	.80
3	Nolan Ryan (standing, side view)	2.00	1.50	.80
4	Nolan Ryan (gripping "300" ball)	2.00	1.50	.80

1992 Mother's Cookies Astros

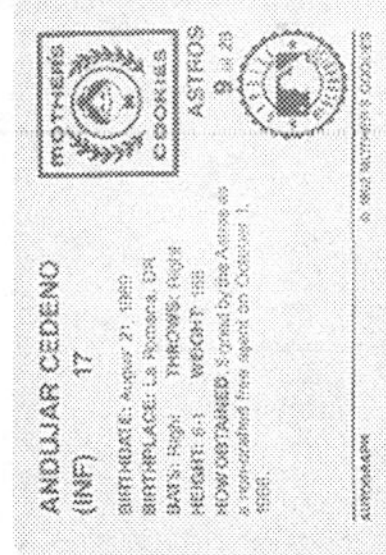

The Astrodome provides the backdrop for Barry Colla's photos of Astros personnel seen on this 28-card set sponsored by Mother's Cookies. Cards are in standard 2-1/2" x 3-1/2" but feature rounded corners. Glossy fronts are borderless and feature no graphics except the player's name and team in an upper corner. Backs are printed in red and purple and have a few biographical details along with uniform and card numbers, the player's position, an autograph line and the logos of the cookie company and MLB.

		MT	NR MT	EX
Complete Set (28):		10.00	7.50	4.00
Common Player:		.25	.20	.10
1	Art Howe	.25	.20	.10
2	Steve Finley	.45	.35	.20
3	Pete Harnisch	.35	.25	.14
4	Pete Incaviglia	.35	.25	.14
5	Craig Biggio	.50	.40	.20
6	Ken Caminiti	.35	.25	.14
7	Eric Anthony	.35	.25	.14
8	Jeff Bagwell	.75	.60	.30
9	Andujar Cedeno	.35	.25	.14
10	Mark Portugal	.35	.25	.14
11	Eddie Taubensee	.25	.20	.10
12	Jimmy Jones	.25	.20	.10
13	Joe Boever	.25	.20	.10
14	Benny Distefano	.25	.20	.10
15	Juan Guerrero	.25	.20	.10
16	Doug Jones	.30	.25	.12
17	Scott Servais	.25	.20	.10
18	Butch Henry	.25	.20	.10
19	Rafael Ramirez	.25	.20	.10
20	Al Osuna	.25	.20	.10
21	Rob Murphy	.25	.20	.10
22	Chris Jones	.25	.20	.10
23	Rob Mallicoat	.25	.20	.10
24	Darryl Kile	.35	.25	.14
25	Casey Candaele	.25	.20	.10
26	Xavier Hernandez	.25	.20	.10
27	Coaches (Bob Cluck, Tom Spencer, Rudy Jaramillo, Ed Ott, Matt Galante)	.25	.20	.10
28	Trainers / Checklist (Dave Labossiere, Dennis Liborio, Doc Ewell)	.25	.20	.10

1992 Mother's Cookies Athletics

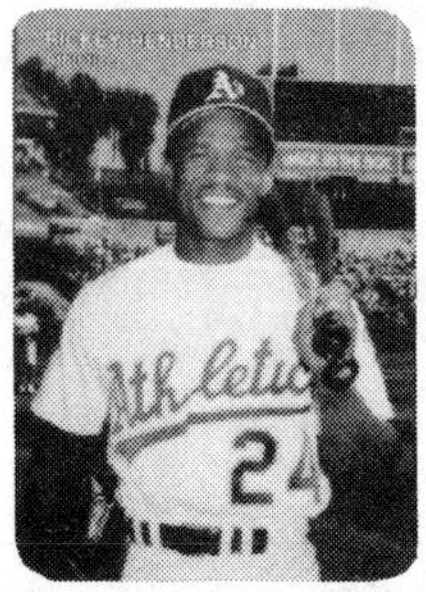

The commemorative patch marking the Oakland A's 25th season on the West Coast is visible on several of Barry Colla's photos used in this 28-card issue. The traditional Mother's Cookies card format of standard-sized, round-cornered cards with UV-coated borderless front photos is followed in this set. The player's name and team are in white in an upper corner. Backs have cookie company and Major League Baseball logos, along with the player's position, uniform and card numbers, space for an autograph and minimal biographical data. Back printing is in red and purple on white.

		MT	NR MT	EX
Complete Set (28):		11.00	8.25	4.50
Common Card:		.25	.20	.10
1	Tony LaRussa	.25	.20	.10
2	Mark McGwire	.60	.45	.25
3	Terry Steinbach	.35	.25	.14
4	Rickey Henderson	.90	.70	.35
5	Dave Stewart	.40	.30	.15
6	Jose Canseco	1.50	1.25	.60
7	Dennis Eckersley	.45	.35	.20
8	Carney Lansford	.25	.20	.10
9	Bob Welch	.25	.20	.10
10	Walt Weiss	.35	.25	.14
11	Mike Moore	.25	.20	.10
12	Goose Gossage	.35	.25	.14
13	Rick Honeycutt	.25	.20	.10
14	Harold Baines	.35	.25	.14
15	Jamie Quirk	.25	.20	.10
16	Jeff Parrett	.25	.20	.10
17	Willie Wilson	.35	.25	.14
18	Dave Henderson	.35	.25	.14
19	Joe Slusarski	.25	.20	.10
20	Mike Bordick	.35	.25	.14
21	Lance Blankenship	.25	.20	.10
22	Gene Nelson	.25	.20	.10
23	Vince Horsman	.25	.20	.10
24	Ron Darling	.25	.20	.10
25	Randy Ready	.25	.20	.10
26	Scott Hemond	.25	.20	.10
27	Scott Brosius	.35	.25	.14
28	Coaches / Checklist (Tommie Reynolds, Dave Duncan, Doug Rader, Rene Lachemann, Art Kusnyer, Dave McKay)	.25	.20	.10

1992 Mother's Cookies Dodgers

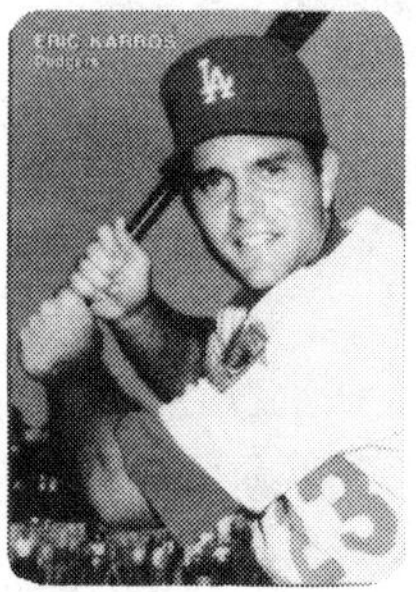

Another commemorative patch, marking Dodger Stadium's 30th anniversary, is featured on some of the Barry Colla photos seen on this 28-card set. Cards have the now-traditional round-corner, glossy-front borderless format with player name and team in white in an upper corner. Printed in red and purple on white, the backs have a few biographical details along with uniform and card numbers and appropriate logos.

		MT	NR MT	EX
Complete Set (28):		9.00	6.75	3.50
Common Player:		.25	.20	.10
1	Tom Lasorda	.35	.25	.14
2	Brett Butler	.35	.25	.14
3	Tom Candiotti	.25	.20	.10
4	Eric Davis	.40	.30	.15
5	Lenny Harris	.25	.20	.10
6	Orel Hershiser	.40	.30	.15
7	Ramon Martinez	.50	.40	.20
8	Jose Offerman	.35	.25	.14
9	Mike Scioscia	.25	.20	.10
10	Darryl Strawberry	.40	.30	.15
11	Todd Benzinger	.45	.35	.20
12	John Candelaria	.25	.20	.10
13	Tim Crews	.25	.20	.10
14	Kal Daniels	.25	.20	.10
15	Jim Gott	.25	.20	.10
16	Kevin Gross	.25	.20	.10
17	Dave Hansen	.25	.20	.10
18	Carlos Hernandez	.75	.60	.30
19	Jay Howell	.25	.20	.10
20	Stan Javier	.25	.20	.10
21	Eric Karros	.90	.70	.35
22	Roger McDowell	.25	.20	.10
23	Bob Ojeda	.25	.20	.10
24	Juan Samuel	.25	.20	.10
25	Mike Sharperson	.25	.20	.10
26	Mitch Webster	.25	.20	.10
27	Steve Wilson	.25	.20	.10
28	Coaches / Checklist (Ben Hines, Manny Mota, Joe Amalfitano, Mark Cresse, Ron Perranoski, Joe Ferguson, Ron Roenicke)	.25	.20	.10

1992 Mother's Cookies Giants

In 1983 Mother's Cookies re-entered the baseball card world with a set of S.F. Giants cards. In 1992, the company sponsored its 10th consecutive

Giants team issue. As in the '83 set, the cards feature the photography of Barry Colla. In 2-1/2" x 3-1/2" size, with rounded corners and UV-coating on the borderless fronts, the cards continue the format used since 1984. Backs are also in the familiar style, with a bit of biographical data and appropriate logos.

		MT	NR MT	EX
Complete Set (28):		9.00	6.75	3.50
Common Player:		.25	.20	.10
1	Roger Craig	.30	.25	.12
2	Will Clark	.90	.70	.35
3	Bill Swift	.30	.25	.12
4	Royce Clayton	.35	.25	.14
5	John Burkett	.45	.35	.20
6	Willie McGee	.35	.25	.14
7	Buddy Black	.25	.20	.10
8	Dave Righetti	.25	.20	.10
9	Matt Williams	.50	.40	.20
10	Robby Thompson	.45	.35	.20
11	Darren Lewis	.35	.25	.14
12	Mike Jackson	.25	.20	.10
13	Mark Leonard	.25	.20	.10
14	Rod Beck	.40	.30	.15
15	Mike Felder	.25	.20	.10
16	Bryan Hickerson	.25	.20	.10
17	Jose Uribe	.25	.20	.10
18	Greg Litton	.25	.20	.10
19	Cory Snyder	.25	.20	.10
20	Jim McNamara	.25	.20	.10
21	Kelly Downs	.25	.20	.10
22	Trevor Wilson	.25	.20	.10
23	Kirt Manwaring	.25	.20	.10
24	Kevin Bass	.25	.20	.10
25	Jeff Brantley	.25	.20	.10
26	Dave Burba	.25	.20	.10
27	Chris James	.25	.20	.10
28	Coaches / Checklist (Carlos Alfonso, Wendell Kim, Bob Lillis, Dusty Baker, Bob Brenly)	.25	.20	.10

1992 Mother's Cookies Mariners

After a one-year absence from the Mother's Cookies lineup, the M's returned in 1992 with a set. Standard-size cards have rounded corners and UV-coated fronts. The only graphics appearing on the borderless photos are the player and team name in white in an upper corner. Backs are printed in red and purple on white and have basic biographical data, uniform and cards numbers, space for an autograph and appropriate sponsor and licensor logos.

		MT	NR MT	EX
Complete Set (28):		9.00	6.75	3.50
Common Player:		.25	.20	.10
1	Bill Plummer	.25	.20	.10
2	Ken Griffey, Jr.	3.00	2.25	1.25
3	Harold Reynolds	.35	.25	.14
4	Kevin Mitchell	.35	.25	.14
5	David Valle	.25	.20	.10
6	Jay Buhner	.35	.25	.14
7	Erik Hanson	.25	.20	.10
8	Pete O'Brien	.25	.20	.10
9	Henry Cotto	.25	.20	.10
10	Mike Schooler	.25	.20	.10

		MT	NR MT	EX
11	Tino Martinez	.35	.25	.14
12	Dennis Powell	.25	.20	.10
13	Randy Johnson	.35	.25	.14
14	Dave Cochrane	.25	.20	.10
15	Greg Briley	.25	.20	.10
16	Omar Vizquel	.25	.20	.10
17	Dave Fleming	.25	.20	.10
18	Matt Sinatro	.25	.20	.10
19	Jeff Nelson	.25	.20	.10
20	Edgar Martinez	.35	.25	.14
21	Calvin Jones	.25	.20	.10
22	Russ Swan	.25	.20	.10
23	Jim Acker	.25	.20	.10
24	Jeff Schaffer	.25	.20	.10
25	Clay Parker	.25	.20	.10
26	Brian Holman	.25	.20	.10
27	Coaches (Marty Martinez, Gene Clines, Roger Hansen, Dan Warthen, Russ Nixon, Rusty Kuntz)	.25	.20	.10
28	Mascot / Checklist	.25	.20	.10

1992 Mother's Cookies Padres

The Padres ended a six-year hiatus when they re-appeared in the Mother's Cookies lineup for 1992. The 28-card set follows the traditional Mother's format: standard-size cards with rounded corners, glossy borderless front photos and the player and team name in white in an upper corner. Backs have appropriate logos, uniform and card numbers, player data and room for an autograph, all printed in red and purple.

		MT	NR MT	EX
Complete Set (28):		10.00	7.50	4.00
Common Player:		.25	.20	.10
1	Greg Riddoch	.25	.20	.10
2	Greg Harris	.60	.45	.25
3	Gary Sheffield	.75	.60	.30
4	Fred McGriff	.45	.35	.20
5	Kurt Stillwell	.45	.35	.20
6	Benito Santiago	.75	.60	.30
7	Tony Gwynn	.45	.35	.20
8	Tony Fernandez	.35	.25	.14
9	Jerald Clark	.35	.25	.14
10	Dave Eiland	.25	.20	.10
11	Randy Myers	.30	.25	.12
12	Oscar Azocar	.25	.20	.10
13	Dann Bilardello	.25	.20	.10
14	Jose Melendez	.25	.20	.10
15	Darrin Jackson	.35	.25	.14
16	Andy Benes	.40	.30	.15
17	Tim Teufel	.25	.20	.10
18	Jeremy Hernandez	.25	.20	.10
19	Kevin Ward	.25	.20	.10
20	Bruce Hurst	.25	.20	.10
21	Larry Andersen	.25	.20	.10
22	Rich Rodriguez	.25	.20	.10
23	Pat Clements	.25	.20	.10
24	Craig Lefferts	.25	.20	.10
25	Craig Shipley	.25	.20	.10
26	Mike Maddux	.25	.20	.10
27	Coaches (Merv Rettenmund, Bruce Kimm, Jim Snyder, Mike Roarke, Rob Picciolo)	.25	.20	.10
28	Team logo / checklist	.25	.20	.10

1992 Mother's Cookies Rangers

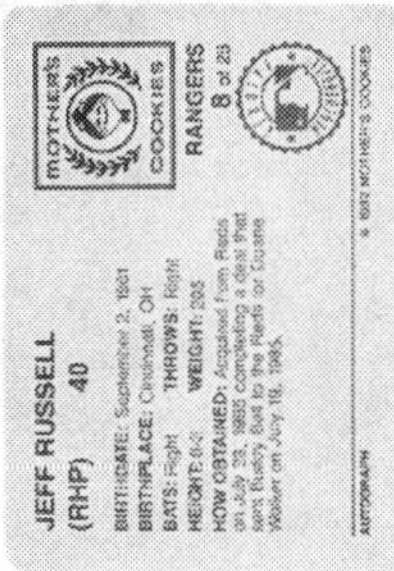

The clubhouse wall provides the universal backdrop for the posed photos in this 28-card set. Standard-size cards have a high-gloss borderless front photo with rounded corners and the player and team name in white in an upper corner. Backs are in red and purple and have a few player biographical details along with uniform and card numbers, space for an autograph and the logos of the sponsor and licensor.

		MT	NR MT	EX
Complete Set (28):		12.00	9.00	4.75
Common Player:		.25	.20	.10
1	Bobby Valentine	.25	.20	.10
2	Nolan Ryan	3.00	2.25	1.25
3	Ruben Sierra	.60	.45	.25
4	Juan Gonzalez	1.75	1.25	.70
5	Ivan Rodriguez	.40	.30	.15
6	Bobby Witt	.25	.20	.10
7	Geno Petralli	.25	.20	.10
8	Jeff Russell	.35	.25	.14
9	Rafael Palmeiro	.60	.45	.25
10	Julio Franco	.75	.60	.30
11	Jack Daugherty	.25	.20	.10
12	Dickie Thon	.25	.20	.10
13	Floyd Bannister	.25	.20	.10
14	Scott Chiamparino	.25	.20	.10
15	Kevin Reimer	.25	.20	.10
16	Jeff Robinson	.25	.20	.10
17	Brian Downing	.25	.20	.10
18	Brian Bohanon	.25	.20	.10
19	Jose Guzman	.25	.20	.10
20	Terry Mathews	.25	.20	.10
21	Kevin Brown	.25	.20	.10
22	Kenny Rogers	.25	.20	.10
23	Jeff Huson	.25	.20	.10
24	Monty Fariss	.35	.25	.14
25	Al Newman	.25	.20	.10
26	Dean Palmer	.35	.25	.14
27	John Cangelosi	.25	.20	.10
28	Coaches / Checklist (Dave Oliver, Tom House, Orlando Gomez, Tom Robson, Ray Burris, Toby Harrah)	.25	.20	.10

1992 Mother's Cookies Jeff Bagwell

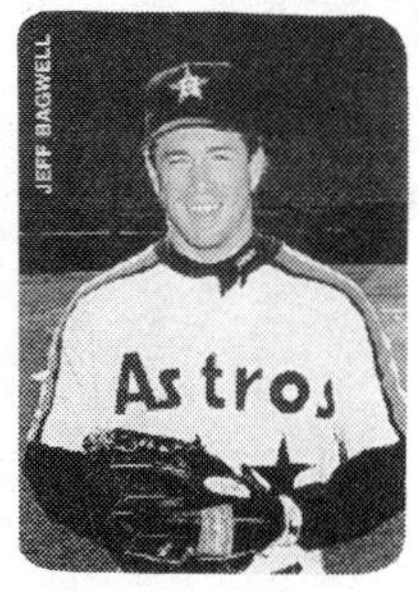

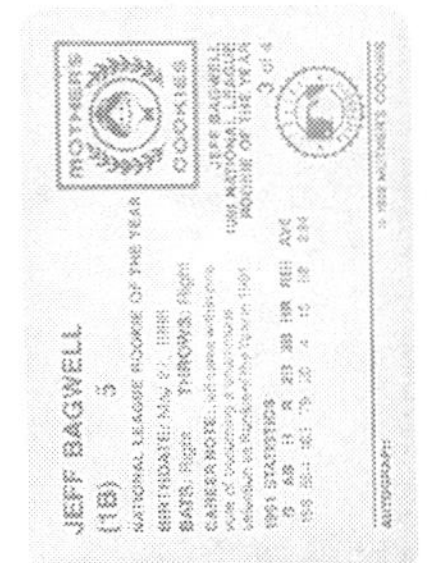

The set consists of four, standard size cards, with a full-bleed color photo on the fronts of the cards with rounded corners. Bagwell's name appears horizontally in white on the front of the card and the backs are printed in purple and red on white stock. Along with the Major League merchandise logo on the bottom of the card there is an area for the player's autograph.

		MT	NR MT	EX
Complete Set (4):		8.00	6.00	3.25
Common Card:		2.00	1.50	.80
1	Jeff Bagwell (Head and shoulders)	2.00	1.50	.80
2	Jeff Bagwell (Bat on shoulder)	2.00	1.50	.80
3	Jeff Bagwell (Waist up)	2.00	1.50	.80
4	Jeff Bagwell (Ball in glove)	2.00	1.50	.80

Grading Guide

Mint (MT): A perfect card. Well-centered with all corners sharp and square. No creases, stains, edge nicks, surface marks, yellowing or fading.

Near Mint (NM): A nearly perfect card. At first glance, a NM card appears to be perfect. May be slightly off-center. No surface marks, creases or loss of gloss.

Excellent (EX): Corners are still fairly sharp with only moderate wear. Borders may be off-center. No creases or stains on fronts or backs, but may show slight loss of surface luster.

Very Good (VG): Shows obvious handling. May have rounded corners, minor creases, major gum or wax stains. No major creases, tape marks, writing, etc.

Good (G): A well-worn card, but exhibits no intentional damage. May have major or multiple creases. Corners may be rounded well beyond card border.

1992 Mother's Cookies Chuck Knoblauch

American League 1991 Rookie of the Year Chuck Knoblauch is featured in this four-card set. Similar in format to other Mother's cards, the glossy fronts have rounded corners and feature full-bleed color photos. The red and purple backs have statistical and biographical data along with appropriate logos.

		MT	NR MT	EX
Complete Set (4):		6.00	4.50	2.50
Common Card:		1.50	1.25	.60
1	Chuck Knoblauch (bat on shoulder)	1.50	1.25	.60
2	Chuck Knoblauch (head and shoulders close-up)	1.50	1.25	.60
3	Chuck Knoblauch (waist-up)	1.50	1.25	.60
4	Chuck Knoblauch (fielding)	1.50	1.25	.60

1992 Mother's Cookies Nolan Ryan 7 No-Hitters

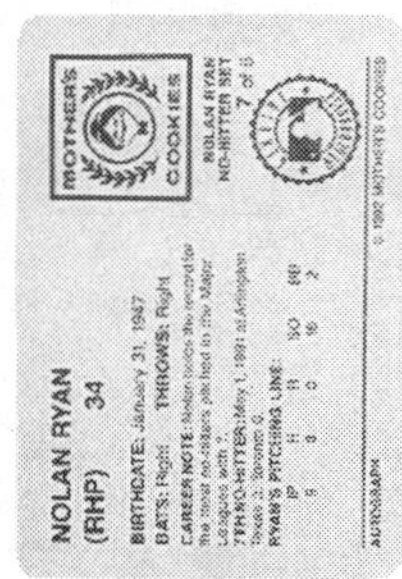

Mother's Cookie Company produced an eight-card set in 1992 commemorating Nolan Ryan's seven no-hitters. Cards were found in specially-marked packages of Mother's Cookies products. The company also made available uncut sheets of the eight cards through the mail. Card fronts feature photos contemporary with Ryan's no-hitters in a borderless, round-cornered format with glossy surface. "Nolan Ryan/7 No-Hitters" appears in white vertically in the upper-left corner. Backs are printed in red and purple on white and include a bit of biographical data along with details of each no-hitter. The eighth card in the set offers room to write in information about a future no-hitter which never materialized prior to Ryan's retirement following the 1993 season.

		MT	NR MT	EX
Complete Set (8):		12.00	9.00	4.75
Common Card:		1.50	1.25	.60
1	Nolan Ryan (Angels, portrait)	1.50	1.25	.60
2	Nolan Ryan (Angels, pitching)	1.50	1.25	.60
3	Nolan Ryan (Angels, waving)	1.50	1.25	.60
4	Nolan Ryan (Angels, holding four "0" balls)	1.50	1.25	.60
5	Nolan Ryan (Astros)	1.50	1.25	.60
6	Nolan Ryan (Rangers, pitching)	1.50	1.25	.60
7	Nolan Ryan (Rangers, pointing)	1.50	1.25	.60
8	Nolan Ryan (Rangers, palms up)	1.50	1.25	.60

1993 Mother's Cookies Angels

In its 11th year of renewed baseball card production, Mother's Cookies sponsored trading card promotions with seven major league teams, including, for the first time, the California Angels. At special promotional games, youngsters entering the

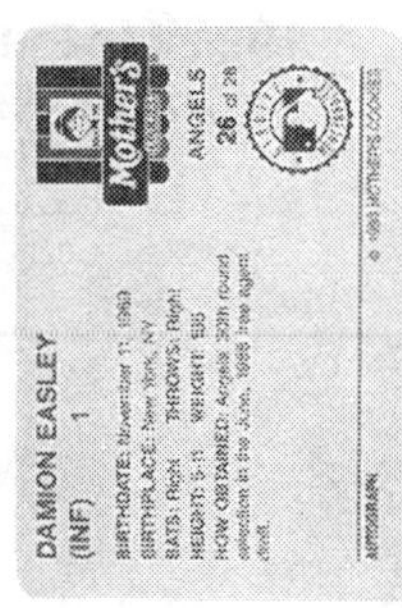

ballpark were given packs of 28 cards. Each of the paper envelopes contained 20 different player cards and eight cards of another player. Instructions on the envelope encouraged trading to complete a set of 28. All of the team sets were identical in format. Cards measure the standard 2-1/2" x 3-1/2" with rounded corners. Fronts feature borderless posed photos, the work of photographer Barry Colla. The only graphic elements on the front are the player's name and team in white, generally in an upper corner. In 1993 the Mother's cards featured a somewhat less glossy front finish than in previous years. Backs are printed in red and purple on white. Data includes the player's position, uniform and card numbers, a few biographical bits, a "How Obtained" statement and a space for an autograph, along with the logos of the cookie company and Major League Baseball.

		MT	NR MT	EX
Complete Set (28):		10.00	7.50	4.00
Common Player:		.25	.20	.10
1	Buck Rodgers	.25	.20	.10
2	Gary DiSarcina	.35	.25	.14
3	Chuck Finley	.25	.20	.10
4	J.T. Snow	.50	.40	.20
5	Gary Gaetti	.45	.35	.20
6	Chili Davis	.50	.40	.20
7	Tim Salmon	2.00	1.50	.80
8	Mark Langston	.35	.25	.14
9	Scott Sanderson	.25	.20	.10
10	John Orton	.25	.20	.10
11	Julio Valera	.25	.20	.10
12	Chad Curtis	.45	.35	.20
13	Kelly Gruber	.25	.20	.10
14	Rene Gonzalez	.25	.20	.10
15	Luis Polonia	.35	.25	.14
16	Greg Myers	.25	.20	.10
17	Gene Nelson	.25	.20	.10
18	Torey Lovullo	.35	.25	.14
19	Scott Lewis	.25	.20	.10
20	Chuck Crim	.25	.20	.10
21	John Farrell	.25	.20	.10
22	Steve Frey	.25	.20	.10
23	Stan Javier	.25	.20	.10
24	Ken Patterson	.25	.20	.10
25	Ron Tingley	.25	.20	.10
26	Damion Easley	.45	.35	.20
27	Joe Grahe	.25	.20	.10
28	Coaches / Checklist (Jimmie Reese, Rod Carew, Bobby Knoop, Chuck Hernandez, Ken Macha, John Wathan, Rick Turner)	.25	.20	.10

1993 Mother's Cookies Astros

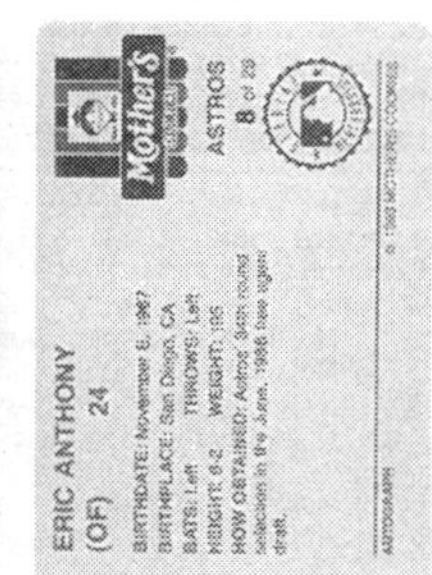

		MT	NR MT	EX
Complete Set (28):		10.00	7.50	4.00
Common Player:		.25	.20	.10
1	Art Howe	.25	.20	.10
2	Steve Finley	.35	.25	.14
3	Pete Harnisch	.35	.25	.14
4	Craig Biggio	.35	.25	.14
5	Doug Drabek	.35	.25	.14
6	Scott Servais	.25	.20	.10
7	Jeff Bagwell	.60	.45	.25
8	Eric Anthony	.35	.25	.14
9	Ken Caminiti	.35	.25	.14
10	Andujar Cedeno	.35	.25	.14
11	Mark Portugal	.25	.20	.10
12	Jose Uribe	.25	.20	.10
13	Rick Parker	.25	.20	.10
14	Doug Jones	.25	.20	.10
15	Luis Gonzalez	.35	.25	.14
16	Kevin Bass	.25	.20	.10
17	Greg Swindell	.35	.25	.14
18	Eddie Taubensee	.25	.20	.10
19	Darryl Kile	.35	.25	.14
20	Brian Williams	.25	.20	.10
21	Chris James	.25	.20	.10
22	Chris Donnels	.25	.20	.10
23	Xavier Hernandez	.40	.30	.15
24	Casey Candaele	.25	.20	.10
25	Eric Bell	.25	.20	.10
26	Mark Grant	.25	.20	.10
27	Tom Edens	.25	.20	.10
28	Coaches / Checklist (Bob Cluck, Billy Joe Bowman, Tom Spencer, Ed Ott, Matt Galante, Rudy Jaramillo)	.25	.20	.10

1993 Mother's Cookies Athletics

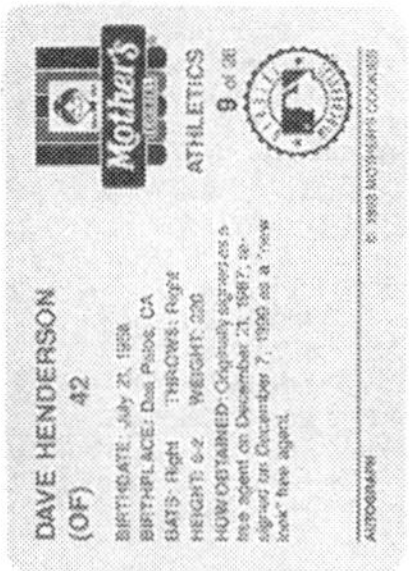

		MT	NR MT	EX
Complete Set (28):		8.00	6.00	3.25
Common Player:		.25	.20	.10
1	Tony LaRussa	.35	.25	.14
2	Mark McGwire	.50	.40	.20
3	Terry Steinbach	.35	.25	.14
4	Dennis Eckersley	.35	.25	.14
5	Ruben Sierra	.50	.40	.20
6	Rickey Henderson	.75	.60	.30
7	Mike Bordick	.35	.25	.14
8	Rick Honeycutt	.25	.20	.10
9	Dave Henderson	.35	.25	.14
10	Bob Welch	.35	.25	.14
11	Dale Sveum	.25	.20	.10
12	Ron Darling	.25	.20	.10
13	Jerry Browne	.25	.20	.10
14	Bobby Witt	.25	.20	.10
15	Troy Neel	.35	.25	.14
16	Goose Gossage	.35	.25	.14
17	Brent Gates	.35	.25	.14
18	Storm Davis	.25	.20	.10
19	Scott Hemond	.25	.20	.10
20	Kelly Downs	.25	.20	.10
21	Kevin Seitzer	.25	.20	.10
22	Lance Blankenship	.25	.20	.10
23	Mike Mohler	.25	.20	.10
24	Edwin Nunez	.25	.20	.10
25	Joe Boever	.25	.20	.10
26	Shawn Hillegas	.25	.20	.10
27	Coaches (Dave Duncan, Art Kusnyer, Dave McKay, Tommie Reynolds, Greg Luzinski)	.25	.20	.10
28	Checklist (Frank Ciensczyk, equipment manager)	.25	.20	.10

1993 Mother's Cookies Dodgers

		MT	NR MT	EX
Complete Set (28):		10.00	7.50	4.00
Common Player:		.25	.20	.10
1	Tommy Lasorda	.35	.25	.14
2	Eric Karros	.50	.40	.20
3	Brett Butler	.25	.20	.10
4	Mike Piazza	2.50	2.00	1.00
5	Jose Offerman	.35	.25	.14
6	Tim Wallach	.35	.25	.14
7	Eric Davis	.35	.25	.14
8	Darryl Strawberry	.35	.25	.14
9	Jody Reed	.25	.20	.10
10	Orel Hershiser	.40	.30	.15
11	Tom Candiotti	.25	.20	.10
12	Ramon Martinez	.35	.25	.14
13	Lenny Harris	.25	.20	.10
14	Mike Sharperson	.25	.20	.10
15	Omar Daal	.25	.20	.10
16	Pedro Martinez	.35	.25	.14
17	Jim Gott	.25	.20	.10
18	Carlos Hernandez	.35	.25	.14
19	Kevin Gross	.25	.20	.10
20	Cory Snyder	.25	.20	.10
21	Todd Worrell	.25	.20	.10
22	Mitch Webster	.25	.20	.10
23	Steve Wilson	.25	.20	.10
24	Dave Hansen	.25	.20	.10
25	Roger McDowell	.25	.20	.10
26	Pedro Astacio	.35	.25	.14
27	Rick Trlicek	.25	.20	.10
28	Coaches / Checklist (Joe Ferguson, Mark Cresse, Joe Amalfitano, Ben Hines, Manny Mota, Ron Perranoski, Ron Roenicke)	.25	.20	.10

1993 Mother's Cookies Giants

		MT	NR MT	EX
Complete Set (28):		11.00	8.25	4.50
Common Player:		.25	.20	.10
1	Dusty Baker	.35	.25	.14
2	Will Clark	.90	.70	.35
3	Matt Williams	.60	.45	.25
4	Barry Bonds	2.00	1.50	.80
5	Bill Swift	.35	.25	.14
6	Royce Clayton	.35	.25	.14
7	John Burkett	.35	.25	.14
8	Willie McGee	.35	.25	.14
9	Kirt Manwaring	.25	.20	.10
10	Dave Righetti	.25	.20	.10
11	Todd Benzinger	.35	.25	.14
12	Rod Beck	.35	.25	.14
13	Darren Lewis	.35	.25	.14
14	Robby Thompson	.45	.35	.20
15	Mark Carreon	.25	.20	.10
16	Dave Martinez	.25	.20	.10
17	Jeff Brantley	.25	.20	.10
18	Dave Burba	.25	.20	.10
19	Mike Benjamin	.25	.20	.10
20	Mike Jackson	.25	.20	.10
21	Craig Colbert	.25	.20	.10
22	Bud Black	.35	.25	.14
23	Trevor Wilson	.25	.20	.10
24	Kevin Rogers	.25	.20	.10
25	Jeff Reed	.25	.20	.10
26	Bryan Hickerson	.25	.20	.10
27	Gino Minutelli	.25	.20	.10
28	Coaches / Checklist (Wendell Kim, Bob Lillis, Bob Brenly, Dick Pole, Bobby Bonds, Denny Sommers)	.25	.20	.10

1993 Mother's Cookies Mariners

		MT	NR MT	EX
Complete Set (28):		10.00	7.50	4.00
Common Player:		.25	.20	.10

1	Lou Piniella	.30	.25	.12
2	Dave Fleming	.25	.20	.10
3	Pete O'Brien	.25	.20	.10
4	Ken Griffey, Jr.	3.00	2.25	1.25
5	Henry Cotto	.25	.20	.10
6	Jay Buhner	.45	.35	.20
7	David Valle	.35	.25	.14
8	Dwayne Henry	.25	.20	.10
9	Mike Felder	.25	.20	.10
10	Norm Charlton	.35	.25	.14
11	Edgar Martinez	.35	.25	.14
12	Erik Hanson	.35	.25	.14
13	Mike Blowers	.35	.25	.14
14	Omar Vizquel	.35	.25	.14
15	Randy Johnson	.50	.40	.20
16	Russ Swan	.25	.20	.10
17	Tino Martinez	.45	.35	.20
18	Rich DeLucia	.25	.20	.10
19	Jeff Nelson	.25	.20	.10
20	Chris Bosio	.25	.20	.10
21	Tim Leary	.25	.20	.10
22	Mackey Sasser	.25	.20	.10
23	Dennis Powell	.25	.20	.10
24	Mike Hampton	.25	.20	.10
25	Fernando Vina	.25	.20	.10
26	John Cummings	.25	.20	.10
27	Rich Amaral	.25	.20	.10
28	Coaches / Checklist (Sammy Ellis, John McLaren, Ken Griffey, Sr., Sam Perlozzo, Sam Mejias, Lee Elia)	.25	.20	.10

Definitions for grading conditions are located in the Introduction of this price guide.

1993 Mother's Cookies Padres

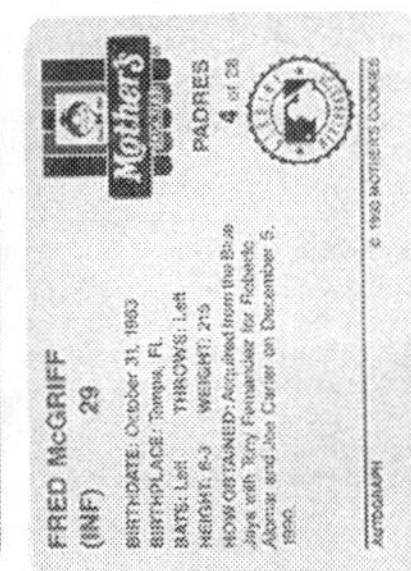

		MT	NR MT	EX
Complete Set (28):		9.00	6.75	3.50
Common Player:		.25	.20	.10
1	Jim Riggleman	.25	.20	.10
2	Gary Sheffield	.50	.40	.20
3	Tony Gwynn	.75	.60	.30
4	Fred McGriff	.65	.50	.25
5	Greg Harris	.25	.20	.10
6	Tim Teufel	.25	.20	.10
7	Dave Eiland	.25	.20	.10
8	Phil Plantier	.50	.40	.20
9	Bruce Hurst	.25	.20	.10
10	Ricky Gutierrez	.50	.40	.20
11	Rich Rodriguez	.35	.25	.14
12	Derek Bell	.35	.25	.14
13	Bob Geren	.25	.20	.10
14	Andy Benes	.45	.35	.20
15	Darrell Sherman	.25	.20	.10
16	Frank Seminara	.25	.20	.10
17	Guillermo Velasquez	.25	.20	.10
18	Gene Harris	.25	.20	.10
19	Dan Walters	.25	.20	.10
20	Craig Shipley	.25	.20	.10
21	Phil Clark	.25	.20	.10
22	Jeff Gardner	.25	.20	.10
23	Mike Scioscia	.25	.20	.10
24	Wally Whitehurst	.25	.20	.10
25	Roger Mason	.25	.20	.10
26	Kerry Taylor	.25	.20	.10
27	Tim Scott	.25	.20	.10
28	Coaches / Checklist (Dave Bialas, Rob Picciolo, Merv Rettenmund, Bruce Bochy, Dan Radison, Mike Roarke)	.25	.20	.10

1993 Mother's Cookies Nolan Ryan Farewell

Nolan Ryan's final 10 major league seasons with the Astros and Rangers are captured in this set. Cards are in standard Mother's Cookies format: 2-1/2" x 3-1/2" with rounded corners, borderless front photos and UV-coated. Each card has a "Nolan Ryan Farewell Set" diamond logo in an upper corner. Backs are printed in red and purple and have a few biographical details along with the year the picture on front was created. Each card has stats for one year from 1984-1992 or cumulative All-Star

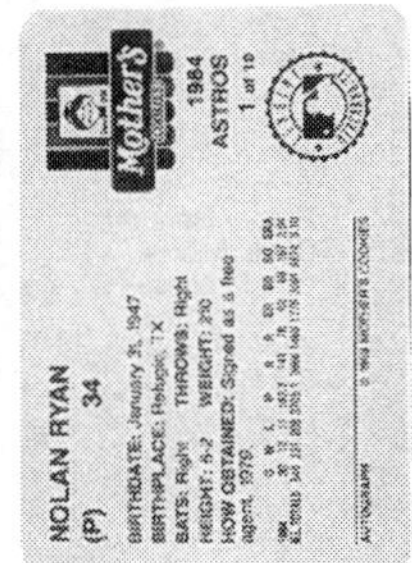

stats along with Major League totals. Cards were available either cello-wrapped singly in cookie packages or as a complete set via a mail-in offer.

		MT	NR MT	EX
Complete Set (10):		18.00	13.50	7.25
Common Card:		2.00	1.50	.80
1	Nolan Ryan (1984 Astros)	2.00	1.50	.80
2	Nolan Ryan (1985 Astros)	2.00	1.50	.80
3	Nolan Ryan (1986 Astros)	2.00	1.50	.80
4	Nolan Ryan (1987 Astros)	2.00	1.50	.80
5	Nolan Ryan (1988 Astros)	2.00	1.50	.80
6	Nolan Ryan (1989 Rangers)	2.00	1.50	.80
7	Nolan Ryan (1990 Rangers)	2.00	1.50	.80
8	Nolan Ryan (1991 Rangers)	2.00	1.50	.80
9	Nolan Ryan (1992 Rangers)	2.00	1.50	.80

1994 Mother's Cookies Rookies of the Year

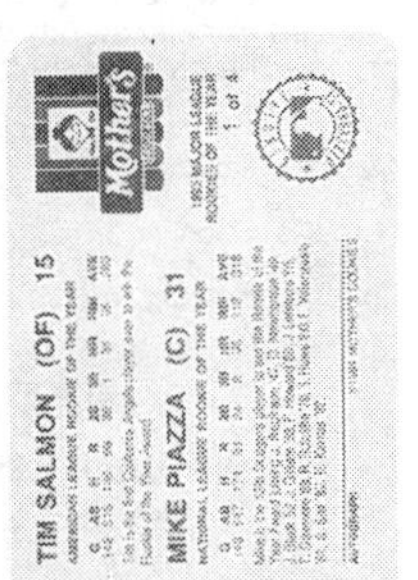

In 1994 Mother's Cookies issued three different four-card sets of the 1993 Rookies of the Year. That means a four-card set of Mike Piazza of the Dodgers and another of Tim Salmon of California available, one per package, in each of six varieties of Mother's Big Cookies. There was also a four-card set featuring both players on each of the four cards. These cards were packaged one per bag of Mother's Major League Double Headers. The specially-marked packages with the trading cards inside also carried details about Mother's Commemorative Uncut Strips of each of the three different sets in a mail-in offer. In addition, the company created two chase cards designed to put the real cookie fans to the test. The "One in a Thousand - Rookies of the Year" - foil trading cards were inserted one in every 1,000 packages, with either blue or red foil, and fewer than 10,000 of the foil cards produced.

		MT	NR MT	EX
Complete Set (12):		20.00	15.00	8.00
Common Card:		.50	.40	.20
1	Tim Salmon (bat on shoulder)	1.50	1.25	.60
2	Tim Salmon (batting stance)	1.50	1.25	.60
3	Tim Salmon (dugout pose)	1.50	1.25	.60
4	Tim Salmon (fielding pose)	1.50	1.25	.60
1	Mike Piazza (bat on shoulder)	2.00	1.50	.80
2	Mike Piazza (batting stance)	2.00	1.50	.80
3	Mike Piazza (dugout pose)	2.00	1.50	.80
4	Mike Piazza (catching pose)	2.00	1.50	.80
1	Tim Salmon, Mike Piazza (bats on shoulder)	2.00	1.50	.80
2	Tim Salmon, Mike Piazza (arm around shoulders)	2.00	1.50	.80
3	Tim Salmon, Mike Piazza (shaking hands)	2.00	1.50	.80
4	Tim Salmon, Mike Piazza (back to back)	2.00	1.50	.80
1	Tim Salmon, Mike Piazza (shaking hands) (1 in 1,000 blue foil)	15.00	11.00	6.00
1	Tim Salmon, Mike Piazza (kneeling) (1 in 1,000 red foil)	15.00	11.00	6.00

1994 Mother's Cookies Nolan Ryan Farewell

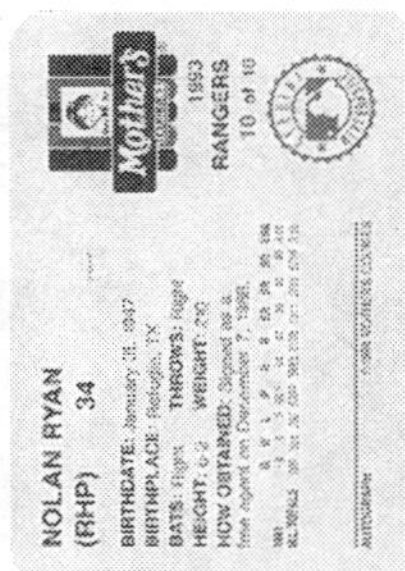

A virtual reprint of the 1993 Farewell Set, the 1994 version uses the same photos and, except for card #10, presents the same information on the card backs. Card #10 in the 1994 set offers 1993 season and final Major League stats instead of the All-Star stats on the 1993 version. Some minor differences in photo cropping between the two sets will be noticed, as well as the fact that many of the back elements which had been printed in red on the 1993 cards are in purple on the 1994 cards, and vice versa. Cards can be distinguished by the presence of a 1993 or 1994 copyright line on the back.

		MT	NR MT	EX
Complete Set (10):		20.00	15.00	8.00
Common Card:		2.00	1.50	.80
1	Nolan Ryan (1984 Astros)	2.00	1.50	.80
2	Nolan Ryan (1985 Astros)	2.00	1.50	.80
3	Nolan Ryan (1986 Astros)	2.00	1.50	.80
4	Nolan Ryan (1987 Astros)	2.00	1.50	.80
5	Nolan Ryan (1988 Astros)	2.00	1.50	.80
6	Nolan Ryan (1989 Rangers)	2.00	1.50	.80
7	Nolan Ryan (1990 Rangers)	2.00	1.50	.80
8	Nolan Ryan (1991 Rangers)	2.00	1.50	.80
9	Nolan Ryan (1992 Rangers)	2.00	1.50	.80
10	Nolan Ryan (1993 Rangers)	2.00	1.50	.80

1943 M.P. & Co. (R302-1)

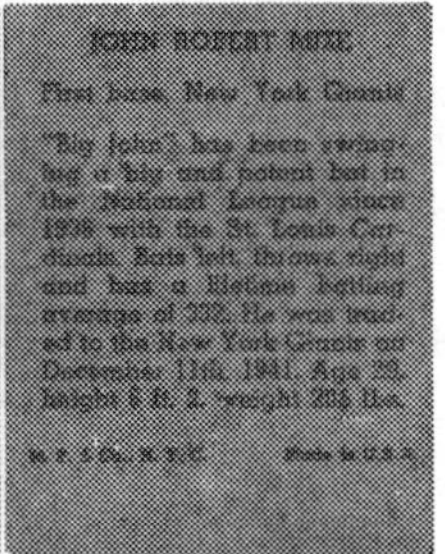

One of the few baseball card sets issued during the war years, this set of unnumbered cards, each measuring approximately 2-11/16" by 2-1/4", feature rather crude drawings that have little resemblance to the player named. The cards were originally produced in strips and sold inexpensively in candy stores. The backs contain brief player write-ups.

		NR MT	EX	VG
Complete Set:		400.00	200.00	120.00
Common Player:		8.00	4.00	2.50
(1)	Ernie Bonham	8.00	4.00	2.50
(2)	Lou Boudreau	12.00	6.00	3.50
(3)	Dolph Camilli	8.00	4.00	2.50
(4)	Mort Cooper	8.00	4.00	2.50
(5)	Walker Cooper	8.00	4.00	2.50
(6)	Joe Cronin	12.00	6.00	3.50
(7)	Hank Danning	8.00	4.00	2.50
(8)	Bill Dickey	18.00	9.00	5.50
(9)	Joe DiMaggio	90.00	45.00	27.00
(10)	Bobby Feller	18.00	9.00	5.50
(11)	Jimmy Foxx	25.00	12.50	7.50
(12)	Hank Greenberg	18.00	9.00	5.50
(13)	Stan Hack	8.00	4.00	2.50
(14)	Tom Henrich	8.00	4.00	2.50
(15)	Carl Hubbell	12.00	6.00	3.50
(16)	Joe Medwick	12.00	6.00	3.50
(17)	John Mize	12.00	6.00	3.50
(18)	Lou Novikoff	8.00	4.00	2.50
(19)	Mel Ott	12.00	6.00	3.50
(20)	Pee Wee Reese	25.00	12.50	7.50
(21)	Pete Reiser	8.00	4.00	2.50
(22)	Charlie Ruffing	12.00	6.00	3.50
(23)	Johnny Vander Meer	9.00	4.50	2.75
(24)	Ted Williams	60.00	30.00	18.00

1949 M.P. & Co. (R302-2)

This set appears to be a re-issue of M.P. & Company's 1943 card set with different players and numbers added to the back. The cards, which measure 2-11/16" by 2-1/4", feature crude drawings of generic baseball players which have little resemblance to the player named. The backs include the card number and player information. The numbering sequence begins with card 100, and numbers 104, 118, and 120 are unknown, while two of the cards (Henrich and Kozar) are unnumbered. The set is assigned the American Card Catalog number R302-2.

		NR MT	EX	VG
Complete Set:		350.00	175.00	105.00
Common Player:		8.00	4.00	2.50
100	Lou Boudreau	12.00	6.00	3.50
101	Ted Williams	60.00	30.00	18.00
102	Buddy Kerr	8.00	4.00	2.50
103	Bobby Feller	18.00	9.00	5.50
104	Unknown			
105	Joe DiMaggio	90.00	45.00	27.00
106	Pee Wee Reese	25.00	12.50	7.50
107	Ferris Fain	8.00	4.00	2.50
108	Andy Pafko	8.00	4.00	2.50
109	Del Ennis	8.00	4.00	2.50
110	Ralph Kiner	12.00	6.00	3.50
111	Nippy Jones	8.00	4.00	2.50
112	Del Rice	8.00	4.00	2.50
113	Hank Sauer	8.00	4.00	2.50
114	Gil Coan	8.00	4.00	2.50
115	Eddie Joost	8.00	4.00	2.50
116	Alvin Dark	8.00	4.00	2.50
117	Larry Berra	25.00	12.50	7.50
118	Unknown			
119	Bob Lemon	12.00	6.00	3.50
120	Unknown			
121	Johnny Pesky	8.00	4.00	2.50
122	Johnny Sain	9.00	4.50	2.75
123	Hoot Evers	8.00	4.00	2.50
124	Larry Doby	8.00	4.00	2.50
----	Tom Henrich	9.00	4.50	2.75
----	Al Kozar	8.00	4.00	2.50

1992 Mr. Turkey

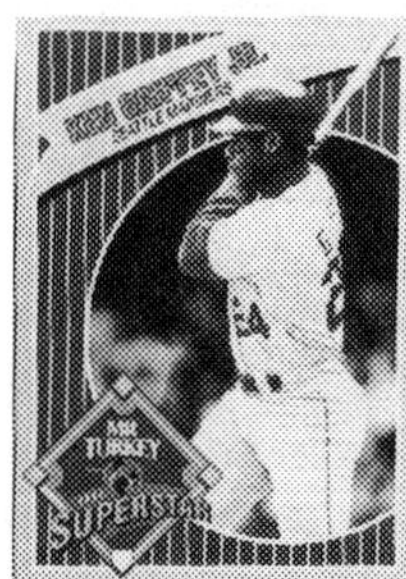

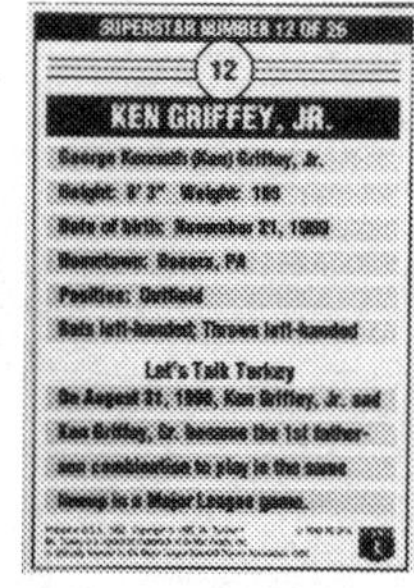

Mr. Turkey, a division of Sara Lee, offered a set of Major League Superstar cards during the 1992 season. A total of 26 cards, one player representing each team, were included in various Mr. Turkey meat packages. The cardboard packaging allows for the printing directly on the carton instead of inserting the cards inside the package. Collectors were able to collect the cards individually or as an uncut sheet, available by sending to the company.

		MT	NR MT	EX
Complete Set (26):		18.00	13.50	7.25
Common Player:		.25	.20	.10
1	Jim Abbott	.50	.40	.20
2	Roberto Alomar	.75	.60	.30
3	Sandy Alomar, Jr.	.25	.20	.10
4	Craig Biggio	.25	.20	.10
5	George Brett	1.00	.70	.40
6	Will Clark	.75	.60	.30
7	Roger Clemens	.50	.40	.20
8	Cecil Fielder	.60	.45	.25
9	Carlton Fisk	.50	.40	.20
10	Andres Galarraga	.40	.30	.15
11	Dwight Gooden	.45	.35	.20
12	Ken Griffey, Jr.	3.00	2.25	1.25
13	Tony Gwynn	.45	.35	.20
14	Rickey Henderson	.60	.45	.25
15	Dave Justice	.50	.40	.20
16	Don Mattingly	.75	.60	.30
17	Dale Murphy	.50	.40	.20
18	Kirby Puckett	.60	.45	.25
19	Cal Ripken, Jr.	2.00	1.50	.80
20	Nolan Ryan	3.00	2.25	1.25
21	Chris Sabo	.25	.20	.10
22	Ryne Sandberg	2.00	1.50	.80
23	Ozzie Smith	.60	.45	.25
24	Darryl Strawberry	.35	.25	.14
25	Andy Van Slyke	.25	.20	.10
26	Robin Yount	.75	.60	.30

1983 Mr. Z's Milwaukee Brewers

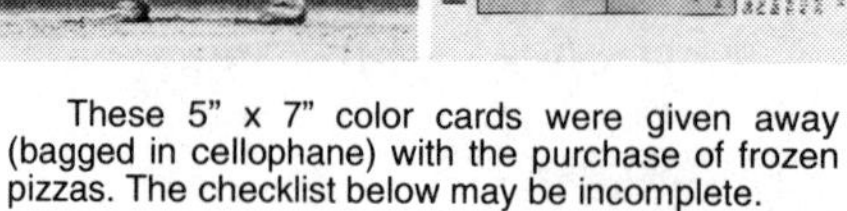

These 5" x 7" color cards were given away (bagged in cellophane) with the purchase of frozen pizzas. The checklist below may be incomplete.

		MT	NR MT	EX
Common Player:		2.00	1.50	.80
(1)	Cecil Cooper	2.00	1.50	.80
(2)	Paul Molitor	5.00	3.75	2.00
(3)	Robin Yount	8.00	6.00	3.25

1984 Mr. Z's Milwaukee Brewers

These 5x7" color cards were given away with the purchase of frozen pizza and other Brewer-logo food products. The checklist below may be incomplete.

		MT	NR MT	EX
Common player:		2.00	1.50	.80
(1)	Rollie Fingers	5.00	3.75	2.00
(2)	Jim Gantner	2.00	1.50	.80

Grading Guide

Mint (MT): A perfect card. Well-centered with all corners sharp and square. No creases, stains, edge nicks, surface marks, yellowing or fading.

Near Mint (NM): A nearly perfect card. At first glance, a NM card appears to be perfect. May be slightly off-center. No surface marks, creases or loss of gloss.

Excellent (EX): Corners are still fairly sharp with only moderate wear. Borders may be off-center. No creases or stains on fronts or backs, but may show slight loss of surface luster.

Very Good (VG): Shows obvious handling. May have rounded corners, minor creases, major gum or wax stains. No major creases, tape marks, writing, etc.

Good (G): A well-worn card, but exhibits no intentional damage. May have major or multiple creases. Corners may be rounded well beyond card border.

N

1969 Nabisco Team Flakes

This set of cards is seen in two different sizes: 1-15/16" by 3" and 1-3/4" by 2-15/16". This is explained by the varying widths of the card borders on the backs of Nabisco cereal packages. Cards are action color photos bordered in yellow. Twenty-four of the top players in the game are included in the set, which was issued in three series of eight cards each. No team insignias are visible on any of the cards. Packages described the cards as "Mini Posters."

		NR MT	EX	VG
Complete Set:		500.00	250.00	150.00
Common Player:		4.00	2.00	1.25
(1)	Hank Aaron	55.00	27.00	16.50
(2)	Richie Allen	7.00	3.50	2.00
(3)	Lou Brock	40.00	20.00	12.00
(4)	Paul Casanova	4.00	2.00	1.25
(5)	Roberto Clemente	70.00	35.00	21.00
(6)	Al Ferrara	4.00	2.00	1.25
(7)	Bill Freehan	5.00	2.50	1.50
(8)	Jim Fregosi	5.00	2.50	1.50
(9)	Bob Gibson	25.00	12.50	7.50
(10)	Tony Horton	5.00	2.50	1.50
(11)	Tommy John	10.00	5.00	3.00
(12)	Al Kaline	40.00	20.00	12.00
(13)	Jim Lonborg	4.00	2.00	1.25
(14)	Juan Marichal	25.00	12.50	7.50
(15)	Willie Mays	60.00	30.00	18.00
(16)	Rick Monday	5.00	2.50	1.50
(17)	Tony Oliva	8.00	4.00	2.50
(18)	Brooks Robinson	45.00	22.00	13.50
(19)	Frank Robinson	40.00	20.00	12.00
(20)	Pete Rose	65.00	32.00	19.50
(21)	Ron Santo	6.00	3.00	1.75
(22)	Tom Seaver	50.00	25.00	15.00
(23)	Rusty Staub	8.00	4.00	2.50
(24)	Mel Stottlemyre	5.00	2.50	1.50

1992 Nabisco Canadian Tradition

Nabisco released a 36-card set of former Toronto Blue Jays and Montreal Expos inside several of its products in 1992. Three cards were included per box, and the company also made available a collectors album for the cards which are artist renderings of the various players, similar in style to the famous sports drawings that appeared on the pages of the Sporting News over the years. Text on the drawings is in both English and French.

		MT	NR MT	EX
Complete Set (36):		18.00	13.50	7.25
Common Player:		.50	.40	.20
1	Bill Lee	.60	.45	.25
2	Cliff Johnson	.50	.40	.20
3	Ken Singleton	.60	.45	.25
4	Al Woods	.50	.40	.20
5	Ron Hunt	.50	.40	.20
6	Barry Bonnell	.50	.40	.20
7	Tony Perez	.90	.70	.35
8	Willie Upshaw	.50	.40	.20
9	Coco Laboy	.50	.40	.20
10	Famous Moments (Blue Jays Win A.L. East - 1985)	.50	.40	.20
11	Bob Bailey	.50	.40	.20
12	Dave McKay	.50	.40	.20
13	Rodney Scott	.50	.40	.20
14	Jerry Garvin	.50	.40	.20
15	Famous Moments (Expos Win N.L. East - 1981)	.50	.40	.20
16	Rick Bosetti	.50	.40	.20
17	Larry Parrish	.50	.40	.20
18	Bill Singer	.50	.40	.20
19	Ron Fairly	.50	.40	.20
20	Damaso Garcia	.60	.45	.25
21	Al Oliver	.75	.60	.30
22	Famous Moments (Blue Jays Win Eastern Division - 1989)	.50	.40	.20
23	Claude Raymond	.50	.40	.20
24	Buck Martinez	.50	.40	.20
25	Rusty Staub	.75	.60	.30
26	Otto Velez	.50	.40	.20
27	Mack Jones	.50	.40	.20
28	Garth Iorg	.50	.40	.20
29	Bill Stoneman	.50	.40	.20
30	Doug Ault	.50	.40	.20
31	Famous Moments (Expos Host All-Star Game 1982)	.50	.40	.20
32	Jesse Jefferson	.50	.40	.20
33	Steve Rogers	.60	.45	.25
34	Ernie Whitt	.50	.40	.20
35	John Boccabella	.50	.40	.20
36	Bob Bailor	.60	.45	.25

1993 Nabisco All-Star Autographs

In a promotion with the Major League Baseball Players Alumni, Nabisco produced this six-card set of former stars. For $5 and proofs of purchase, collectors could receive an authentically autographed card. The 2-1/2" x 3-1/2" cards featured color photos on front on which the team logos have been airbrushed away, since Major League Baseball did not license the issue. Backs gave biographical and career information along with a black-and-white childhood photo of the player. The unnumbered cards are checklisted here in alphabetical order. Don Drysdale's death on July 3 in the midst of the promotion curtailed availability of cards with his autograph.

		MT	NR MT	EX
Complete Set (6):		70.00	52.00	28.00
Common Player:		6.00	4.50	2.50
(1)	Ernie Banks	10.00	7.50	4.00
(2)	Don Drysdale	35.00	26.00	14.00
(3)	Catfish Hunter	6.00	4.50	2.50
(4)	Phil Niekro	6.00	4.50	2.50
(5)	Brooks Robinson	10.00	7.50	4.00
(6)	Willie Stargell	6.00	4.50	2.50

1994 Nabisco All-Star Legends

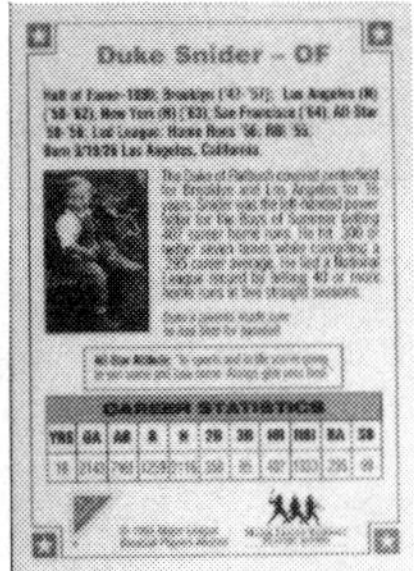

For a second year in 1994 Nabisco continued its program of offering autographed cards of former stars for $5 and proofs of purchase from its snack products. Cards retained the same basic format of using airbrushed color photos on front and black-and-white childhood photos on back. Fronts have a "Nabisco All-Star Legends" logo in the upper-left. Backs have career and biographical data and the logos of the sponsor and the Major League Baseball Players Alumni. The unnumbered cards are checklisted here alphabetically. Each card came with a certificate of authenticity.

		MT	NR MT	EX
Complete Set (4):		25.00	18.50	10.00
Common Player:		6.00	4.5C	2.50
(1)	Bob Gibson	6.00	4.50	2.50
(2)	Jim Palmer	6.00	4.50	2.50
(3)	Frank Robinson	8.00	6.00	3.25
(4)	Duke Snider	8.00	6.00	3.25

1909 Nadja Caramels (E92)

One of several 1909-1910 issues produced for Nadja Caramels, this set can be distinguished by the players in the checklist (alphabetized here) and the type beneath the color player lithograph. In this set, the player's last name is in upper and lower case letters, and his position is given, along with the team. Backs of these 1-1/2" x 2-3/4" cards are identical to later Nadja issues and feature an ad for the candy brand. Cataloged (along with the cards of Croft's Candy/Cocoa and Dockman Gum) as E92 in the old "American Card Catalog," the Nadja set checklist differs from those issues in that it it is larger and contains a group of St. Louis players not found in the other sets. Discoveries of additions to the 1909 Nadja checklist continue to this day. Gaps are left in this checklist to accommodate possible future finds of the other "original" E92 cards with Nadja backs.

		NR MT	EX	VG
Complete Set:		7350.	3675.	2200.
Common Player:		125.00	62.00	37.00
(1)	Bill Bailey	125.00	62.00	37.00
(3)	Harry Bemis	125.00	62.00	37.00
(4)	Chief Bender (striped cap)	400.00	200.00	120.00
(5)	Chief Bender (white cap)	400.00	200.00	120.00
(6)	Bill Bergen	125.00	62.00	37.00
(7)	Bob Bescher	125.00	62.00	37.00
(8)	Roger Bresnahan	400.00	200.00	120.00
(9)	Al Bridwell	125.00	62.00	37.00
(10)	Doc Casey	125.00	62.00	37.00
(11)	Frank Chance	400.00	200.00	120.00
(12)	Hal Chase	175.00	85.00	50.00
(15)	Sam Crawford	400.00	200.00	120.00
(16)	Harry Davis	125.00	62.00	37.00
(17)	Art Devlin	125.00	62.00	37.00
(21)	Patsy Dougherty	125.00	62.00	37.00
(22)	Larry Doyle (throwing)	125.00	62.00	37.00
(23)	Larry Doyle (with bat)	125.00	62.00	37.00
(24)	Rube Ellis	125.00	62.00	37.00
(26)	George Gibson	125.00	62.00	37.00
(27)	Topsy Hartsel	125.00	62.00	37.00
(28)	Roy Hartzell (batting)	125.00	62.00	37.00
(29)	Roy Hartzell (fielding)	125.00	62.00	37.00
(30)	Harry Howell (ready to pitch)	125.00	62.00	37.00
(31)	Harry Howell (follow-through)	125.00	62.00	37.00
(32)	Fred Jacklitsch	125.00	62.00	37.00
(33)	Hugh Jennings	400.00	200.00	120.00
(34)	Red Kleinow	125.00	62.00	37.00
(36)	Jack Knight	125.00	62.00	37.00
(37)	Nap Lajoie	400.00	200.00	120.00
(38)	Hans Lobert	125.00	62.00	37.00
(39)	Sherry Magee	125.00	62.00	37.00
(40)	Christy Matthewson (Mathewson)	600.00	300.00	180.00
(41)	John McGraw	400.00	200.00	120.00
(42)	Larry McLean	125.00	62.00	37.00
(43)	Dots Miller (batting)	125.00	62.00	37.00
(44)	Dots Miller (fielding)	125.00	62.00	37.00
(45)	Danny Murphy	125.00	62.00	37.00
(46)	Rebel Oakes	125.00	62.00	37.00
(47)	Bill O'Hara	125.00	62.00	37.00
(48)	Eddie Phelps	125.00	62.00	37.00
(49)	Germany Schaefer	125.00	62.00	37.00
(50)	Admiral Schlei	125.00	62.00	37.00
(51)	Boss Schmidt	125.00	62.00	37.00
(52)	Johnny Seigle (Siegle)	125.00	62.00	37.00
(53)	Dave Shean	125.00	62.00	37.00
(54)	Boss Smith (Schmidt)	125.00	62.00	37.00
(55)	George Stone (blue background)	125.00	62.00	37.00
(56)	George Stone (green background)	125.00	62.00	37.00
(57)	Joe Tinker	400.00	200.00	120.00
(58)	Honus Wagner (batting)	600.00	300.00	180.00
(60)	Bobby Wallace	400.00	200.00	120.00

1910 Nadja Philadelphia Athletics (E104-I)

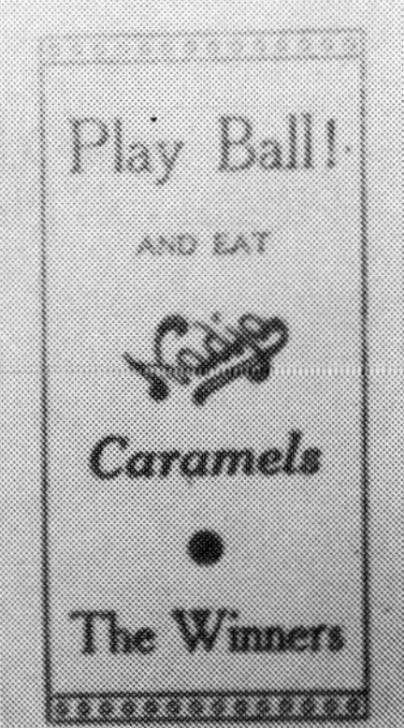

While there are 18 Philadelphia Athletics players in this set, it should be assumed that each can be found in three different variations. Each of the 1-1/2" x 2-3/4" cards can be found with a plain portrait lithograph on front, with either a blank back or a back containing a Nadja ad. Each player can also be found with a black overprint on front, comprised of a white elephant figure on the uniform and the notation "World's Champions 1910" above. The overprinted cards are known only with blank backs, and are somewhat scarcer than the plain cards of either type. Nadja-back cards should be value about the same as the overprinted type.

		NR MT	EX	VG
Complete Set (18):		2750.	1375.	825.00
Common Player:		125.00	62.00	37.00
(1a)	Home Run Baker (no "World's Champions" at top)	250.00	125.00	75.00
(1b)	Home Run Baker ("World's Champions" at top)	300.00	150.00	90.00
(2a)	Jack Barry (no "World's Champions" at top)	125.00	62.00	37.00
(2b)	Jack Barry ("World's Champions" at top)	150.00	75.00	45.00
(3a)	Chief Bender (no "World's Champions" at top)	250.00	125.00	75.00
(3b)	Chief Bender ("World's Champions" at top)	300.00	150.00	90.00
(4a)	Eddie Collins (no "World's Champions" at top)	250.00	125.00	75.00
(4b)	Eddie Collins ("World's Champions" at top)	300.00	150.00	90.00
(5a)	Harry Davis (no "World's Champions" at top)	125.00	62.00	37.00
(5b)	Harry Davis ("World's Champions" at top)	150.00	75.00	45.00
(6a)	Jimmy Dygert (no "World's Champions" at top)	125.00	62.00	37.00
(6b)	Jimmy Dygert ("World's Champions" at top)	150.00	75.00	45.00
(7a)	Topsy Hartsel (no "World's Champions" at top)	125.00	62.00	37.00
(7b)	Topsy Hartel ("World's Champions" at top)	150.00	75.00	45.00
(8a)	Harry Krause (no "World's Champions" at top)	125.00	62.00	37.00
(8b)	Harry Krause ("World's Champions" at top)	150.00	75.00	45.00
(9a)	Jack Lapp (no "World's Champions" at top)	125.00	62.00	37.00
(9b)	Jack Lapp ("World's Champions" at top)	150.00	75.00	45.00
(10a)	Paddy Livingstone (Livingston) (no "World's Champions" at top)	125.00	62.00	37.00
(10b)	Paddy Livingstone (Livingston) ("World's Champions" at top)	150.00	75.00	45.00
(11a)	Bris Lord (no "World's Champions" at top)	125.00	62.00	37.00
(11b)	Bris Lord ("World's Champions" at top)	150.00	75.00	45.00
(12a)	Connie Mack (no "World's Champions" at top)	275.00	137.00	82.00
(12b)	Connie Mack ("World's Champions" at top)	350.00	175.00	105.00
(13a)	Cy Morgan (no "World's Champions" at top)	125.00	62.00	37.00
(13b)	Cy Morgan ("World's Champions" at top)	150.00	75.00	45.00
(14a)	Danny Murphy (no "World's Champions" at top)	125.00	62.00	37.00
(14b)	Danny Murphy ("World's Champions" at top)	150.00	75.00	45.00
(15a)	Rube Oldring (no "World's Champions" at top)	125.00	62.00	37.00

		NR MT	EX	VG
(15b)	Rube Oldring ("World's Champions" at top)	150.00	75.00	45.00
(16a)	Eddie Plank (no "World's Champions" at top)	250.00	125.00	75.00
(16b)	Eddie Plank ("World's Champions" at top)	300.00	150.00	90.00
(17a)	Amos Strunk (no "World's Champions" at top)	125.00	62.00	37.00
(17b)	Amos Strunk ("World's Champions" at top)	150.00	75.00	45.00
(18a)	Ira Thomas (no "World's Champions" at top)	125.00	62.00	37.00
(18b)	Ira Thomas ("World's Champions" at top)	150.00	75.00	45.00

1910 Nadja Pittsburgh Pirates (E104-II)

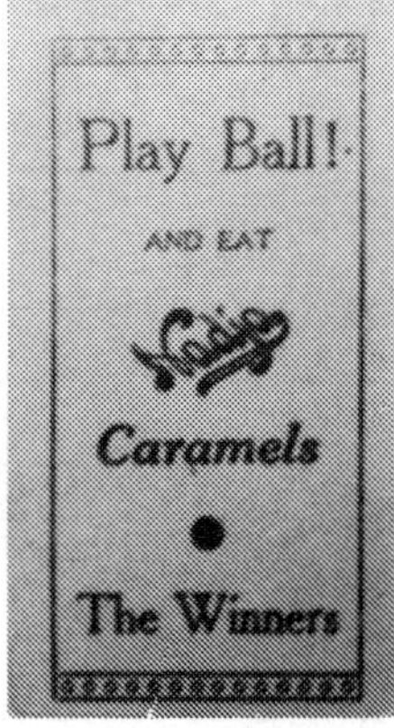

Similar to the contemporary American Caramel issue, this set of 1-1/2" x 2-3/4" cards features portrait color lithographs of the 1909 World's champion Pittsburgh (spelled "Pittsburg" on the cards) Pirates. Each card can be presumed to have been issued with both blank back and with a back bearing a Nadja ad. The Nadja-backed cards are scarcer but command little or no premium.

		NR MT	EX	VG
Complete Set (11):		2225.	1112.	667.00
Common Player:		125.00	62.00	37.00
(1)	Babe Adams	125.00	62.00	37.00
(2)	Fred Clarke	300.00	150.00	90.00
(3)	George Gibson	125.00	62.00	37.00
(4)	Ham Hyatt	125.00	62.00	37.00
(5)	Tommy Leach	125.00	62.00	37.00
(6)	Sam Leever	125.00	62.00	37.00
(7)	Nick Maddox	125.00	62.00	37.00
(8)	Dots Miller	125.00	62.00	37.00
(9)	Deacon Phillippe	125.00	62.00	37.00
(10)	Honus Wagner	800.00	400.00	240.00
(11)	Owen Wilson	125.00	62.00	37.00

1910 Nadja Carmels (E104-III)

It should be assumed that the 30 cards in this issue can each be found with or without a Nadja ad on back; the latter being somewhat scarcer and carrying a premium of 10 to 20 percent over the values quoted. These 1-1/2" x 2-3/4" cards can be distinguished from the 1909 issue by the line of type beneath the player portrait. On the 1910 cards, the player's last name is in all blue capital letters and there is no position designation given.

		NR MT	EX	VG
Complete Set:		5750.	2875.	1725.
Common Player:		175.00	87.00	52.00
(1)	Bill Abstein	175.00	87.00	52.00
(2)	Red Ames	175.00	87.00	52.00
(3)	Johnny Bates	175.00	87.00	52.00
(4)	Kitty Bransfield	175.00	87.00	52.00
(5)	Al Bridwell	175.00	87.00	52.00
(6)	Doc Crandall	175.00	87.00	52.00
(7)	Sam Crawford	400.00	200.00	120.00
(8)	Jim Delehanty (Delahanty)	175.00	87.00	52.00
(9)	Larry Doyle	175.00	87.00	52.00
(10)	Eddie Grant	175.00	87.00	52.00
(11)	Fred Jacklitsch	175.00	87.00	52.00
(12)	Hugh Jennings	400.00	200.00	120.00
(13)	Davy Jones	175.00	87.00	52.00
(14)	Tom Jones	175.00	87.00	52.00
(15)	Otto Knabe	175.00	87.00	52.00
(16)	John McGraw	450.00	225.00	135.00
(17)	Matty McIntyre	175.00	87.00	52.00
(18)	Earl Moore	175.00	87.00	52.00
(19)	Pat Moren (Moran)	175.00	87.00	52.00
(20)	George Moriarity	175.00	87.00	52.00
(21)	George Mullin	175.00	87.00	52.00
(22)	Red Murray	175.00	87.00	52.00
(23)	Simon Nicholls	175.00	87.00	52.00
(24)	Charley O'Leary	175.00	87.00	52.00
(25)	Admiral Schlei	175.00	87.00	52.00
(26)	Cy Seymore (Seymour)	175.00	87.00	52.00
(27)	Tully Sparks	175.00	87.00	52.00
(28)	Ed Summers	175.00	87.00	52.00
(29)	Ed Willetts (Willetts)	175.00	87.00	52.00
(30)	Vic Willis	175.00	87.00	52.00

1983 Nalley Potato Chips Mariners

These large (8-11/16" by 10-11/16") photo cards were issued only in the area of Washington state by Nalley Potato Chips. The six Seattle Mariners are pictured in full color on the entire back panel of each box. On the side panels, detailed player stats and biographies are listed on one side, with a Mariners schedule and ticket discount offer on the other side.

		MT	NR MT	EX
Complete Set:		20.00	15.00	8.00
Common Player:		2.50	2.00	1.00
8	Rick Sweet	2.50	2.00	1.00
16	Al Cowens	2.50	2.00	1.00
21	Todd Cruz	2.50	2.00	1.00
22	Richie Zisk	3.50	2.75	1.50
36	Gaylord Perry	10.00	7.50	4.00
37	Bill Caudill	2.50	2.00	1.00

1921 - 23 National Caramel (E220)

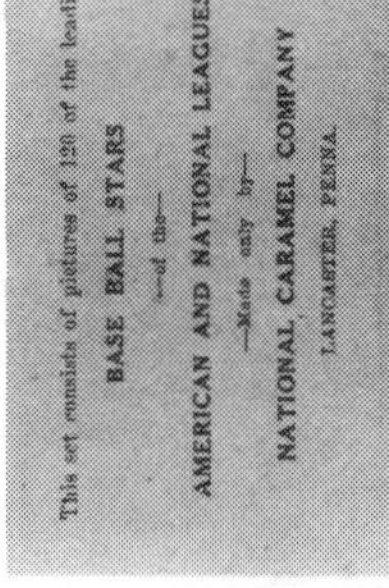

Issued circa 1921 to 1923, this 120-card set is sometimes confused with the E121 or E122 sets, but is easy to identify because of the words "Made only by National Caramel Company" on the back. It is the only baseball card set issued by National Caramel of Lancaster, Pa. The cards measure 2" by 3-1/4" and feature black and white photos with the player's name, position and team at the bottom. In addition to the line indicating the manufacturer, the backs read "This set consists of pictures of 120 of the leading Base Ball Stars of the American and National Leagues". There are 115 different players included in the set, with five players shown on two cards each. About half of the photos in the set are identical to those used in either the E120 or E121 sets, leading to some confusion regarding the three sets.

		NR MT	EX	VG
Complete Set:		11000.	5500.	3300.
Common Player:		45.00	22.00	13.50
(1)	Charles "Babe" Adams	45.00	22.00	13.50
(2)	G.C. Alexander	150.00	75.00	45.00
(3)	James Austin	45.00	22.00	13.50
(4)	Jim Bagbyk (Bagby)	45.00	22.00	13.50
(5)	Franklin "Home Run Baker"	150.00	75.00	45.00
(6)	Dave Bancroft	150.00	75.00	45.00
(7)	Turner Barber	45.00	22.00	13.50
(8)	George Burns (Cincinnati)	45.00	22.00	13.50
(9)	George Burns (Cleveland)	45.00	22.00	13.50
(10)	Joe Bush	50.00	25.00	15.00
(11)	Leon Cadore	45.00	22.00	13.50
(12)	Max Carey	150.00	75.00	45.00
(13)	Ty Cobb	800.00	400.00	240.00
(14)	Eddie Collins	150.00	75.00	45.00
(15)	John Collins	45.00	22.00	13.50
(16)	Wilbur Cooper	45.00	22.00	13.50
(17)	S. Coveleskie (Coveleski)	150.00	75.00	45.00
(18)	Walton Cruise	45.00	22.00	13.50
(19)	Wm. Cunningham	45.00	22.00	13.50
(20)	George Cutshaw	45.00	22.00	13.50
(21)	Jake Daubert	50.00	25.00	15.00
(22)	Chas. A. Deal	45.00	22.00	13.50
(23)	Bill Doak	45.00	22.00	13.50
(24)	Joe Dugan	60.00	30.00	18.00
(25)	Jimmy Dykes (batting)	50.00	25.00	15.00
(26)	Jimmy Dykes (fielding)	50.00	25.00	15.00
(27)	"Red" Faber	150.00	75.00	45.00
(28)	"Chick" Fewster	45.00	22.00	13.50
(29)	Wilson Fewster	45.00	22.00	13.50
(30)	Ira Flagstead	45.00	22.00	13.50
(31)	Arthur Fletcher	45.00	22.00	13.50
(32)	Frank Frisch	150.00	75.00	45.00
(33)	Larry Gardner	45.00	22.00	13.50
(34)	Walter Gerber	45.00	22.00	13.50
(35)	Charles Glazner	45.00	22.00	13.50
(36)	Hank Gowdy	45.00	22.00	13.50
(37)	J.C. Graney (should be J.G.)	45.00	22.00	13.50
(38)	Tommy Griffith	45.00	22.00	13.50
(39)	Charles Grimm	50.00	25.00	15.00
(40)	Heinie Groh	45.00	22.00	13.50
(41)	Byron Harris	45.00	22.00	13.50
(42)	Sam Harris (Stanley or Bucky)	150.00	75.00	45.00
(43)	Harry Heilman (Heilmann)	150.00	75.00	45.00
(44)	Claude Hendrix	45.00	22.00	13.50
(45)	Walter Henline	45.00	22.00	13.50
(46)	Chas. Hollocher	45.00	22.00	13.50
(47)	Harry Hooper	150.00	75.00	45.00
(48)	Rogers Hornsby	200.00	100.00	60.00
(49)	Waite Hoyt	150.00	75.00	45.00
(50)	Wilbert Hubbell	45.00	22.00	13.50
(51)	Wm. Jacobson	45.00	22.00	13.50
(52)	Walter Johnson	400.00	200.00	120.00
(53)	Jimmy Johnston	45.00	22.00	13.50
(54)	Joe Judge	45.00	22.00	13.50
(55)	Geo. "Bingo" Kelly	150.00	75.00	45.00
(56)	Dick Kerr	45.00	22.00	13.50
(57)	Pete Kilduff (bending)	45.00	22.00	13.50
(58)	Pete Kilduff (leaping)	45.00	22.00	13.50
(59)	Larry Kopf	45.00	22.00	13.50
(60)	H.B. Leonard	45.00	22.00	13.50
(61)	Harry Liebold (Leibold)	45.00	22.00	13.50
(62)	Walter "Buster" Mails ("Duster")	45.00	22.00	13.50
(63)	Walter "Rabbit" Maranville	150.00	75.00	45.00
(64)	Carl Mays	50.00	25.00	15.00
(65)	Lee Meadows	45.00	22.00	13.50
(66)	Bob Meusel	60.00	30.00	18.00
(67)	Emil Meusel	45.00	22.00	13.50
(68)	J.C. Milan	45.00	22.00	13.50
(69)	Earl Neale	60.00	30.00	18.00
(70)	Albert Nehf (Arthur)	45.00	22.00	13.50
(71)	Robert Nehf (Arthur)	45.00	22.00	13.50
(72)	Bernie Neis	45.00	22.00	13.50
(73)	Joe Oeschger	45.00	22.00	13.50
(74)	Robert O'Farrell	45.00	22.00	13.50
(75)	Ivan Olson	45.00	22.00	13.50
(76)	Steve O'Neill	45.00	22.00	13.50
(77)	Geo. Paskert	45.00	22.00	13.50
(78)	Roger Peckinpaugh	50.00	25.00	15.00
(79)	Herb Pennock	150.00	75.00	45.00
(80)	Ralph "Cy" Perkins	45.00	22.00	13.50
(81)	Scott Perry (photo actually Ed Rommel)	45.00	22.00	13.50
(82)	Jeff Pfeffer	45.00	22.00	13.50
(83)	V.J. Picinich	45.00	22.00	13.50
(84)	Walter Pipp	75.00	37.00	22.00
(85)	Derrill Pratt	45.00	22.00	13.50
(86)	Goldie Rapp	45.00	22.00	13.50
(87)	Edgar Rice	150.00	75.00	45.00
(88)	Jimmy Ring	45.00	22.00	13.50
(89)	Eddie Rousch (Roush)	150.00	75.00	45.00
(90)	Babe Ruth	2500.	1250.	750.00
(91)	Raymond Schmandt	45.00	22.00	13.50
(92)	Everett Scott	50.00	25.00	15.00

		NR MT	EX	VG
(93)	Joe Sewell	150.00	75.00	45.00
(94)	Wally Shang (Schang)	45.00	22.00	13.50
(95)	Maurice Shannon	45.00	22.00	13.50
(96)	Bob Shawkey	50.00	25.00	15.00
(97)	Urban Shocker	45.00	22.00	13.50
(98)	George Sisler	150.00	75.00	45.00
(99)	Earl Smith	45.00	22.00	13.50
(100)	John Smith	45.00	22.00	13.50
(101)	Sherrod Smith	45.00	22.00	13.50
(102)	Frank Snyder (crouching)	45.00	22.00	13.50
(103)	Frank Snyder (standing)	45.00	22.00	13.50
(104)	Tris Speaker	150.00	75.00	45.00
(105)	Vernon Spencer	45.00	22.00	13.50
(106)	Chas. "Casey" Stengle (Stengel)	275.00	137.00	82.00
(107)	Milton Stock (batting)	45.00	22.00	13.50
(108)	Milton Stock (fielding)	45.00	22.00	13.50
(109)	James Vaughn	45.00	22.00	13.50
(110)	Robert Veach	45.00	22.00	13.50
(111)	Wm. Wambsgauss (Wambsganss)	50.00	25.00	15.00
(112)	Aaron Ward	45.00	22.00	13.50
(113)	Zach Wheat	150.00	75.00	45.00
(114)	George Whitted (batting)	45.00	22.00	13.50
(115)	George Whitted (fielding)	45.00	22.00	13.50
(116)	Fred C. Williams	50.00	25.00	15.00
(117)	Arthur Wilson	45.00	22.00	13.50
(118)	Ivy Wingo	45.00	22.00	13.50
(119)	Lawton Witt	45.00	22.00	13.50
(120)	"Pep" Young (photo actually Ralph Young)	45.00	22.00	13.50
(121)	Ross Young (Youngs)	150.00	75.00	45.00

1936 National Chicle Co. "Fine Pens" (R313)

Issued in 1936 by the National Chicle Company, this set consists of 120 cards, each measuring 3-1/4" by 5-3/8". The black and white cards are blank-backed and unnumbered. Although issued by National Chicle, the name of the company does not appear on the cards. The set includes individual player portraits with facsimilie autographs, multi-player cards and action photos. The cards, known in the hobby as "Fine Pen" because of the thin style of writing used for the facsimilie autographs, were originally available as an in-store premium.

		NR MT	EX	VG
	Complete Set:	3500.	1750.	1000.
	Common Player:	20.00	10.00	6.00
(1)	Melo Almada	20.00	10.00	6.00
(2)	Nick Altrock, Al Schacht	20.00	10.00	6.00
(3)	Paul Andrews	20.00	10.00	6.00
(4)	Elden Auker (Eldon)	20.00	10.00	6.00
(5)	Earl Averill	40.00	20.00	12.00
(6)	John Babich, James Bucher	20.00	10.00	6.00
(7)	Jim Becher (Bucher)	20.00	10.00	6.00
(8)	Moe Berg	32.00	16.00	9.50
(9)	Walter Berger	20.00	10.00	6.00
(10)	Charles Berry	20.00	10.00	6.00
(11)	Ralph Birkhofer (Birkofer)	20.00	10.00	6.00
(12)	"Cy" Blanton	20.00	10.00	6.00
(13)	O. Bluege	20.00	10.00	6.00
(14)	Cliff Bolton	20.00	10.00	6.00
(15)	Zeke Bonura	20.00	10.00	6.00
(16)	Stan Bordagaray, George Earnshaw	20.00	10.00	6.00
(17)	Jim Bottomley, Charley Gelbert	28.00	14.00	8.50
(18)	Thos. Bridges	20.00	10.00	6.00
(19)	Sam Byrd	20.00	10.00	6.00
(20)	Dolph Camilli	20.00	10.00	6.00
(21)	Dolph Camilli, Billy Jurges	20.00	10.00	6.00
(22)	Bruce Campbell	20.00	10.00	6.00
(23)	Walter "Kit" Carson	20.00	10.00	6.00
(24)	Ben Chapman	20.00	10.00	6.00
(25)	Harlond Clift, Luke Sewell	20.00	10.00	6.00
(26)	Mickey Cochrane, Jimmy Fox (Foxx), Al Simmons	50.00	25.00	15.00
(27)	"Rip" Collins	20.00	10.00	6.00
(28)	Joe Cronin	40.00	20.00	12.00
(29)	Frank Crossetti (Crosetti)	24.00	12.00	7.25
(30)	Frank Crosetti, Jimmy Dykes	24.00	12.00	7.25
(31)	Kiki Cuyler, Gabby Hartnett	40.00	20.00	12.00
(32)	Paul Derringer	20.00	10.00	6.00
(33)	Bill Dickey, Hank Greenberg	50.00	25.00	15.00
(34)	Bill Dietrich	20.00	10.00	6.00
(35)	Joe DiMaggio, Hank Erickson	295.00	145.00	85.00
(36)	Carl Doyle	20.00	10.00	6.00
(37)	Charles Dressen, Bill Myers	20.00	10.00	6.00
(38)	Jimmie Dykes	24.00	12.00	7.25
(39)	Rick Ferrell, Wess Ferrell (Wes)	40.00	20.00	12.00
(40)	Pete Fox	20.00	10.00	6.00
(41)	Frankie Frisch	40.00	20.00	12.00
(42)	Milton Galatzer	20.00	10.00	6.00
(43)	Chas. Gehringer	40.00	20.00	12.00
(44)	Charley Gelbert	20.00	10.00	6.00
(45)	Joe Glenn	20.00	10.00	6.00
(46)	Jose Gomez	20.00	10.00	6.00
(47)	Lefty Gomez, Red Ruffing	40.00	20.00	12.00
(48)	Vernon Gomez	40.00	20.00	12.00
(49)	Leon Goslin	40.00	20.00	12.00
(50)	Hank Gowdy	20.00	10.00	6.00
(51)	"Hank" Greenberg	40.00	20.00	12.00
(52)	"Lefty" Grove	40.00	20.00	12.00
(53)	Stan Hack	20.00	10.00	6.00
(54)	Odell Hale	20.00	10.00	6.00
(55)	Wild Bill Hallahan	20.00	10.00	6.00
(56)	Mel Harder	20.00	10.00	6.00
(57)	Stanley Bucky Harriss (Harris)	40.00	20.00	12.00
(58)	Gabby Hartnett, Rip Radcliff	28.00	14.00	8.50
(59)	Gabby Hartnett, L. Waner	28.00	14.00	8.50
(60)	Gabby Hartnett, Lon Warnecke (Warneke)	24.00	12.00	7.25
(61)	Buddy Hassett	20.00	10.00	6.00
(62)	Babe Herman	24.00	12.00	7.25
(63)	Frank Higgins	20.00	10.00	6.00
(64)	Oral C. Hildebrand	20.00	10.00	6.00
(65)	Myril Hoag	20.00	10.00	6.00
(66)	Rogers Hornsby	60.00	30.00	18.00
(67)	Waite Hoyt	40.00	20.00	12.00
(68)	Willis G. Hudlin	20.00	10.00	6.00
(69)	"Woody" Jensen	20.00	10.00	6.00
(70)	Woody Jenson (Jensen)	20.00	10.00	6.00
(71)	William Knickerbocker	20.00	10.00	6.00
(72)	Joseph Kuhel	20.00	10.00	6.00
(73)	Cookie Lavagetto	24.00	12.00	7.25
(74)	Thornton Lee	20.00	10.00	6.00
(75)	Ernie Lombardi	40.00	20.00	12.00
(76)	Red Lucas	20.00	10.00	6.00
(77)	Connie Mack, John McGraw	60.00	30.00	18.00
(78)	Pepper Martin	24.00	12.00	7.25
(79)	George McQuinn	20.00	10.00	6.00
(80)	George McQuinn, Lee Stine	20.00	10.00	6.00
(81)	Joe Medwick	40.00	20.00	12.00
(82)	Oscar Melillo	20.00	10.00	6.00
(83)	"Buddy" Meyer	20.00	10.00	6.00
(84)	Randy Moore	20.00	10.00	6.00
(85)	T. Moore, Jimmie Wilson	20.00	10.00	6.00
(86)	Wallace Moses	20.00	10.00	6.00
(87)	V. Mungo	20.00	10.00	6.00
(88)	Lamar Newsom	20.00	10.00	6.00
(89)	Lewis "Buck" Newsom (Louis)	20.00	10.00	6.00
(90)	Steve O'Neill	20.00	10.00	6.00
(91)	Tommie Padden	20.00	10.00	6.00
(92)	E. Babe Philips (Phelps)	20.00	10.00	6.00
(93)	Bill Rogel (Rogell)	20.00	10.00	6.00
(94)	Lynn "Schoolboy" Rowe	20.00	10.00	6.00
(95)	Luke Sewell	20.00	10.00	6.00
(96)	Al Simmons	40.00	20.00	12.00
(97)	Casey Stengel	80.00	40.00	24.00
(98)	Bill Swift	20.00	10.00	6.00
(99)	Cecil Travis	20.00	10.00	6.00
(100)	"Pie" Traynor	40.00	20.00	12.00
(101)	William Urbansky (Urbanski)	20.00	10.00	6.00
(102)	Arky Vaughn (Vaughan)	40.00	20.00	12.00
(103)	Joe Vosmik	20.00	10.00	6.00
(104)	Honus Wagner	80.00	40.00	24.00
(105)	Rube Walberg	20.00	10.00	6.00
(106)	Bill Walker	20.00	10.00	6.00
(107)	Gerald Walker	20.00	10.00	6.00
(108)	L. Waner, P. Waner, Big Jim Weaver	40.00	20.00	12.00
(109)	George Washington	20.00	10.00	6.00
(110)	Bill Werber	20.00	10.00	6.00
(111)	Sam West	20.00	10.00	6.00
(112)	Pinkey Whitney	20.00	10.00	6.00
(113)	Vernon Wiltshere (Wilshere)	20.00	10.00	6.00
(114)	"Pep" Young	20.00	10.00	6.00
(115)	Chicago White Sox 1936	20.00	10.00	6.00
(116)	Fence Busters	20.00	10.00	6.00
(117)	Talking It Over (Leo Durocher)	24.00	12.00	7.25
(118)	There She Goes! Chicago City Series	20.00	10.00	6.00
(119)	Ump Says No - Cleveland vs. Detroit	20.00	10.00	6.00
(120)	World Series 1935 (Phil Cavarretta, Goose Goslin, Lon Warneke)	24.00	12.00	7.25

1936 National Chicle (R344)

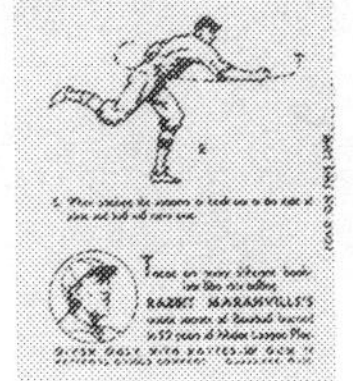

Issued by National Chicle in 1936, this 20-card set was a paper issue distributed with Batter-Up Gum. Unfolded, each paper measured 3-5/8" by 6". The numbered set featured a series of baseball tips from Rabbit Maranville and are illustrated with line drawings.

		NR MT	EX	VG
	Complete Set:	400.00	200.00	120.00
	Common Card:	22.00	11.00	6.50
1	How to Pitch the Out Shoot	22.00	11.00	6.50
2	How to Throw the In Shoot	22.00	11.00	6.50
3	How to Pitch the Drop	22.00	11.00	6.50
4	How to Pitch the Floater	22.00	11.00	6.50
5	How to Run Bases	22.00	11.00	6.50
6	How to Slide	22.00	11.00	6.50
7	How to Catch Flies	22.00	11.00	6.50
8	How to Field Grounders	22.00	11.00	6.50
9	How to Tag A Man Out	22.00	11.00	6.50
10	How to Cover A Base	22.00	11.00	6.50
11	How to Bat	22.00	11.00	6.50
12	How to Steal Bases	22.00	11.00	6.50
13	How to Bunt	22.00	11.00	6.50
14	How to Coach Base Runner	22.00	11.00	6.50
15	How to Catch Behind the Bat	22.00	11.00	6.50
16	How to Throw to Bases	22.00	11.00	6.50
17	How to Signal	22.00	11.00	6.50
18	How to Umpire Balls and Strikes	22.00	11.00	6.50
19	How to Umpire Bases	22.00	11.00	6.50
20	How to Lay Out a Ball Field	22.00	11.00	6.50

1913 The National Game

The patent date on the ornate red-and-white backs identify this as a 1913 issue. Fronts of the 2-1/2" x 3-1/2" cards have a black-and-white photo and a pair of baseball play scenarios used to play the card game. Corners are rounded. The set contains 45 identified player cards, a group of nine action photos in which the players are not identified and two header cards. The unnumbered cards are checklisted here in alphabetical order.

		NR MT	EX	VG
	Complete Set:	4250.	2125.	1275.
	Common Player:	45.00	22.00	13.50
	Action Photo Card:	20.00	10.00	6.00
(1)	Grover Alexander	90.00	45.00	27.00
(2)	Frank Baker	90.00	45.00	27.00
(3)	Chief Bender	90.00	45.00	27.00
(4)	Bob Bescher	45.00	22.00	13.50
(5)	Joe Birmingham	45.00	22.00	13.50
(6)	Roger Bresnahan	90.00	45.00	27.00
(7)	Nixey Callahan	45.00	22.00	13.50
(8)	Frank Chance	90.00	45.00	27.00
(9)	Hal Chase	55.00	27.00	16.50
(10)	Fred Clarke	90.00	45.00	27.00
(11)	Ty Cobb	800.00	400.00	240.00
(12)	Sam Crawford	90.00	45.00	27.00
(13)	Bill Dahlen	45.00	22.00	13.50
(14)	Jake Daubert	45.00	22.00	13.50
(15)	Red Dooin	45.00	22.00	13.50
(16)	Johnny Evers	90.00	45.00	27.00
(17)	Vean Gregg	45.00	22.00	13.50
(18)	Clark Griffith	90.00	45.00	27.00
(19)	Dick Hoblitzel	45.00	22.00	13.50
(20)	Miller Huggins	90.00	45.00	27.00
(21)	Joe Jackson	1000.	500.00	300.00
(22)	Hughie Jennings	90.00	45.00	27.00
(23)	Walter Johnson	150.00	75.00	45.00
(24)	Ed Konetchy	45.00	22.00	13.50
(25)	Nap Lajoie	125.00	62.00	37.00
(26)	Connie Mack	125.00	62.00	37.00
(27)	Rube Marquard	90.00	45.00	27.00
(28)	Christy Mathewson	150.00	75.00	45.00
(29)	John McGraw	90.00	45.00	27.00
(30)	Larry McLean	45.00	22.00	13.50
(31)	Chief Meyers	45.00	22.00	13.50
(32)	Clyde Milan	45.00	22.00	13.50
(33)	Marty O'Toole	45.00	22.00	13.50
(34)	Nap Rucker	45.00	22.00	13.50
(35)	Tris Speaker	125.00	62.50	37.50
(36)	Jake Stahl	45.00	22.00	13.50
(37)	George Stallings	45.00	22.00	13.50
(38)	George Stovall	45.00	22.00	13.50
(39)	Bill Sweeney	45.00	22.00	13.50
(40)	Joe Tinker	90.00	45.00	27.00
(41)	Honus Wagner	150.00	75.00	45.00
(42)	El Walsh	90.00	45.00	27.00
(43)	Zach Wheat	90.00	45.00	27.00
(44)	Joe Wood	45.00	22.00	13.50
(45)	Cy Young	90.00	45.00	27.00
(46)	Rules card	60.00	30.00	18.00
(47)	Score card	60.00	30.00	18.00

(1A)	Batter swinging, looking forward	20.00	10.00	6.00
(2A)	Batter swinging, looking back	20.00	10.00	6.00
(3A)	Runner sliding, fielder at bag	20.00	10.00	6.00
(4A)	Runner sliding, umpire behind	20.00	10.00	6.00
(5A)	Runner sliding, hugging base	20.00	10.00	6.00
(6A)	Sliding play at plate, umpire at left	20.00	10.00	6.00
(7A)	Sliding play at plate, umpire at right	20.00	10.00	6.00
(8A)	Play at plate, runner standing	20.00	10.00	6.00
(9A)	Runner looking backwards	20.00	10.00	6.00

1986 National Photo Royals

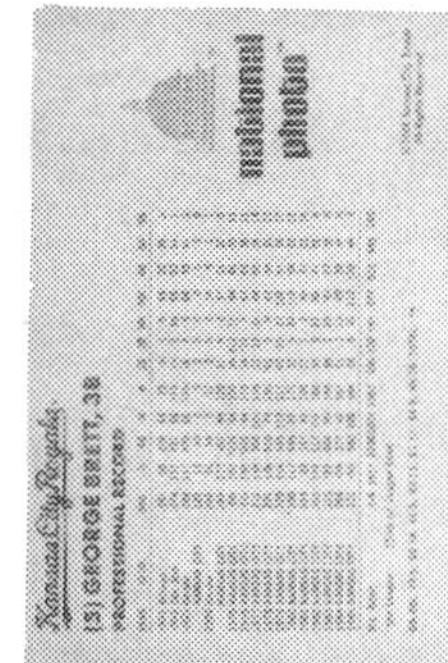

These 2-7/8" by 4-1/4" cards were a team issue produced in conjunction with National Photo. The 24-card set includes 21 players, manager Dick Howser, a card commemorating the Royals' 1985 World Championship and a discount offer card from National Photo. Card fronts feature full-color action photos with a blue "Kansas City Royals" at the top of each card. Each player's name, number and position are also included. Card backs list complete professional career statistics, along with the National Photo logo.

		MT	NR MT	EX
Complete Set:		12.00	9.00	4.75
Common Player:		.25	.20	.10
1	Buddy Biancalana	.25	.20	.10
3	Jorge Orta	.25	.20	.10
4	Greg Pryor	.25	.20	.10
5	George Brett	3.00	2.25	1.25
6	Willie Wilson	.70	.50	.30
8	Jim Sundberg	.25	.20	.10
10	Dick Howser	.35	.25	.14
11	Hal McRae	.70	.50	.30
20	Frank White	.50	.40	.20
21	Lonnie Smith	.40	.30	.15
22	Dennis Leonard	.35	.25	.14
23	Mark Gubicza	.70	.50	.30
24	Darryl Motley	.25	.20	.10
25	Danny Jackson	.70	.50	.30
26	Steve Farr	.25	.20	.10
29	Dan Quisenberry	.50	.40	.20
31	Bret Saberhagen	.70	.50	.30
35	Lynn Jones	.25	.20	.10
37	Charlie Leibrandt	.25	.20	.10
38	Mark Huismann	.25	.20	.10
40	Buddy Black	.45	.35	.20
45	Steve Balboni	.25	.20	.10
----	Header Card	.25	.20	.10

1952 National Tea Labels

Another set of bread end-labels, this checklist now comprises 44 players, although there is speculation that others remain to be cataloged. The unnumbered labels measure approximately 2-3/4" x 2-11/16" and are sometimes referred to as "Red Borders" because of their wide, red borders. The player's name and team are printed alongside his photo, and the slogan "Eat More Bread for Health" also appears.

		NR MT	EX	VG
Complete Set:		2250.	1125.	675.00
Common Player:		110.00	55.00	33.00
(1)	Gene Bearden	110.00	55.00	33.00
(2)	Yogi Berra	300.00	150.00	90.00
(3)	Lou Brissie	110.00	55.00	33.00
(4)	Sam Chapman	110.00	55.00	33.00
(5)	Chuck Diering	110.00	55.00	33.00
(6)	Dom DiMaggio	125.00	62.00	37.00
(7)	Bruce Edwards	110.00	55.00	33.00
(8)	Del Ennis	110.00	55.00	33.00
(9)	Ferris Fain	110.00	55.00	33.00
(10)	Bob Feller	200.00	100.00	60.00
(11)	Howie Fox	110.00	55.00	33.00
(12)	Sid Gordon	110.00	55.00	33.00
(13)	John Groth	110.00	55.00	33.00
(14)	Granny Hamner	110.00	55.00	33.00
(15)	Jim Hegan	110.00	55.00	33.00
(16)	Sheldon Jones	110.00	55.00	33.00
(17)	Howie Judson	110.00	55.00	33.00
(18)	Sherman Lollar	110.00	55.00	33.00
(19)	Clarence Marshall	110.00	55.00	33.00
(20)	Don Mueller	110.00	55.00	33.00
(21)	Danny Murtaugh	110.00	55.00	33.00
(22)	Dave Philley	110.00	55.00	33.00
(23)	Jerry Priddy	110.00	55.00	33.00
(24)	Bill Rigney	110.00	55.00	33.00
(25)	Robin Roberts	175.00	87.00	52.00
(26)	Eddie Robinson	110.00	55.00	33.00
(27)	Preacher Roe	125.00	62.00	37.00
(28)	Stan Rojek	110.00	55.00	33.00
(29)	Al Rosen	125.00	62.00	37.00
(30)	Bob Rush	110.00	55.00	33.00
(31)	Hank Sauer	110.00	55.00	33.00
(32)	Johnny Schmitz	110.00	55.00	33.00
(33)	Enos Slaughter	175.00	87.00	52.00
(34)	Duke Snider	300.00	150.00	90.00
(35)	Warren Spahn	200.00	100.00	60.00
(36)	Gerry Staley	110.00	55.00	33.00
(37)	Virgil Stallcup	110.00	55.00	33.00
(38)	George Stirnweiss	110.00	55.00	33.00
(39)	Earl Torgeson	110.00	55.00	33.00
(40)	Dizzy Trout	110.00	55.00	33.00
(41)	Mickey Vernon	110.00	55.00	33.00
(42)	Wally Westlake	110.00	55.00	33.00
(43)	Johnny Wyrostek	110.00	55.00	33.00
(44)	Eddie Yost	110.00	55.00	33.00

1992 Nationwide Insurance Pirates

Nationwide Insurance sponsored a 12-card Pittsburgh Pirates set. Released in June of 1993, the set includes a card of by-then departed MVP Barry Bonds. Each of the 12 cards in the set includes a fire safety tip on the reverse.

		MT	NR MT	EX
Complete Set (12):		8.00	6.00	3.25
Common Player:		.50	.25	.15
(1)	Andy Van Slyke	.75	.40	.25
(2)	Orlando Merced	.50	.40	.20
(3)	Jose Lind	.60	.45	.25
(4)	Mike LaValliere	.50	.40	.20
(5)	Steve Buechele	.60	.45	.25
(6)	Zane Smith	.50	.40	.20
(7)	Jim Leyland	.50	.40	.20
(8)	Barry Bonds	3.00	2.25	1.25
(9)	Jeff King	.60	.45	.25
(10)	Jay Bell	.75	.60	.30
(11)	Randy Tomlin	.50	.40	.20
(12)	Doug Drabek	.60	.45	.25

1921 Neilson's Chocolate (V61)

Another set closely related to the popular 1922 American Caramel set (E120), this 120-card set was issued by Neilson's Chocolate Bars and carries the American Card Catalog designation V61. The front of the black and white cards is very similar to the E120 set, while the backs contain an ad for Neilson's Chocolates. Backs exist with the Neilson's name printed in Old English type or in regular printing. Two types of cards exist, one is printed on heavy paper and has a card number to the left of the player's name. The second type is printed on cardboard and is unnumbered. The unnumbered cardboard version carries a 50 percent premium over the values shown here.

		NR MT	EX	VG
Complete Set:		12500.	6250.	3750.
Common Player:		70.00	35.00	21.00
1	George Burns	70.00	35.00	21.00
2	John Tobin	70.00	35.00	21.00
3	J.T. Zachary	70.00	35.00	21.00
4	"Bullet" Joe Bush	75.00	37.00	22.00
5	Lu Blue	70.00	35.00	21.00
6	Clarence (Tillie) Walker	70.00	35.00	21.00
7	Carl Mays	75.00	37.00	22.00
8	Leon Goslin	140.00	70.00	42.00
9	Ed Rommel	70.00	35.00	21.00
10	Charles Robertson	70.00	35.00	21.00
11	Ralph (Cy) Perkins	70.00	35.00	21.00
12	Joe Sewell	140.00	70.00	42.00
13	Harry Hooper	140.00	70.00	42.00
14	Urban (Red) Faber	140.00	70.00	42.00
15	Bib Falk (Bibb)	70.00	35.00	21.00
16	George Uhle	70.00	35.00	21.00
17	Emory Rigney	70.00	35.00	21.00
18	George Dauss	70.00	35.00	21.00
19	Herman Pillette	70.00	35.00	21.00
20	Wallie Schang	70.00	35.00	21.00
21	Lawrence Woodall	70.00	35.00	21.00
22	Steve O'Neill	70.00	35.00	21.00
23	Edmund (Bing) Miller	70.00	35.00	21.00
24	Sylvester Johnson	70.00	35.00	21.00
25	Henry Severeid	70.00	35.00	21.00
26	Dave Danforth	70.00	35.00	21.00
27	Harry Heilmann	140.00	70.00	42.00
28	Bert Cole	70.00	35.00	21.00
29	Eddie Collins	140.00	70.00	42.00
30	Ty Cob (Cobb)	1750.	875.00	525.00
31	Bill Wambsganss	75.00	37.00	22.00
32	George Sisler	140.00	70.00	42.00
33	Bob Veach	70.00	35.00	21.00
34	Earl Sheely	70.00	35.00	21.00
35	T.P. (Pat) Collins	70.00	35.00	21.00
36	Frank (Dixie) Davis	70.00	35.00	21.00
37	Babe Ruth	2200.	1100.	660.00
38	Bryan Harris	70.00	35.00	21.00
39	Bob Shawkey	75.00	37.00	22.00
40	Urban Shocker	70.00	35.00	21.00
41	Martin McManus	70.00	35.00	21.00
42	Clark Pittenger	70.00	35.00	21.00
43	"Deacon" Sam Jones	70.00	35.00	21.00
44	Waite Hoyt	140.00	70.00	42.00
45	Johnny Mostil	70.00	35.00	21.00
46	Mike Menosky	70.00	35.00	21.00
47	Walter Johnson	750.00	375.00	225.00
48	Wallie Pipp	80.00	40.00	24.00
49	Walter Gerber	70.00	35.00	21.00
50	Ed Gharrity	70.00	35.00	21.00
51	Frank Ellerbe	70.00	35.00	21.00
52	Kenneth Williams	70.00	35.00	21.00
53	Joe Hauser	70.00	35.00	21.00
54	Carson Bigbee	70.00	35.00	21.00
55	Emil (Irish) Meusel	70.00	35.00	21.00
56	Milton Stock	70.00	35.00	21.00
57	Wilbur Cooper	70.00	35.00	21.00
58	Tom Griffith	70.00	35.00	21.00
59	Clarence (Shovel) Hodge	70.00	35.00	21.00
60	Gene (Bubbles) Hargrave	70.00	35.00	21.00
61	Russell Wrightstone	70.00	35.00	21.00
62	Frank Frisch	140.00	70.00	42.00
63	Jack Peters	70.00	35.00	21.00
64	Walter (Dutch) Reuther	70.00	35.00	21.00
65	Bill Doak	70.00	35.00	21.00
66	Marty Callaghan	70.00	35.00	21.00
67	Sammy Bohne	70.00	35.00	21.00
68	Earl Hamilton	70.00	35.00	21.00
69	Grover C. Alexander	200.00	100.00	60.00
70	George Burns	70.00	35.00	21.00
71	Max Carey	140.00	70.00	42.00
72	Adolfo Luque	70.00	35.00	21.00
73	Walt Barbare	70.00	35.00	21.00
74	Vic Aldridge	70.00	35.00	21.00
75	Jack Smith	70.00	35.00	21.00
76	Bob O'Farrell	70.00	35.00	21.00
77	Pete Donohue	70.00	35.00	21.00
78	Ralph Pinelli	75.00	37.00	22.00
79	Eddie Roush	140.00	70.00	42.00
80	Norman Boeckel	70.00	35.00	21.00
81	Rogers Hornsby	400.00	200.00	120.00
82	George Toporcer	70.00	35.00	21.00
83	Ivy Wingo	70.00	35.00	21.00
84	Virgil Cheeves	70.00	35.00	21.00
85	Vern Clemons	70.00	35.00	21.00
86	Lawrence (Hack) Miller	70.00	35.00	21.00
87	Johnny Kelleher	70.00	35.00	21.00
88	Heinie Groh	70.00	35.00	21.00
89	Burleigh Grimes	140.00	70.00	42.00
90	"Rabbit" Maranville	140.00	70.00	42.00
91	Charles (Babe) Adams	70.00	35.00	21.00
92	Lee King	70.00	35.00	21.00
93	Art Nehf	70.00	35.00	21.00
94	Frank Snyder	70.00	35.00	21.00
95	Raymond Powell	70.00	35.00	21.00
96	Wilbur Hubbell	70.00	35.00	21.00
97	Leon Cadore	70.00	35.00	21.00
98	Joe Oeschger	70.00	35.00	21.00
99	Jake Daubert	75.00	37.00	22.00
100	Will Sherdel	70.00	35.00	21.00

101	Hank DeBerry	70.00	35.00	21.00
102	Johnny Lavan	70.00	35.00	21.00
103	Jesse Haines	140.00	70.00	42.00
104	Joe (Goldie) Rapp	70.00	35.00	21.00
105	Oscar Ray Grimes	70.00	35.00	21.00
106	Ross Young (Youngs)	140.00	70.00	42.00
107	Art Fletcher	70.00	35.00	21.00
108	Clyde Barnhart	70.00	35.00	21.00
109	Louis (Pat) Duncan	70.00	35.00	21.00
110	Charlie Hollocher	70.00	35.00	21.00
111	Horace Ford	70.00	35.00	21.00
112	Bill Cunningham	70.00	35.00	21.00
113	Walter Schmidt	70.00	35.00	21.00
114	Joe Schultz	70.00	35.00	21.00
115	John Morrison	70.00	35.00	21.00
116	Jimmy Caveney	70.00	35.00	21.00
117	Zach Wheat	140.00	70.00	42.00
118	Fred (Cy) Williams	75.00	37.00	22.00
119	George Kelly	140.00	70.00	42.00
120	Jimmy Ring	70.00	35.00	21.00

1984 Nestle

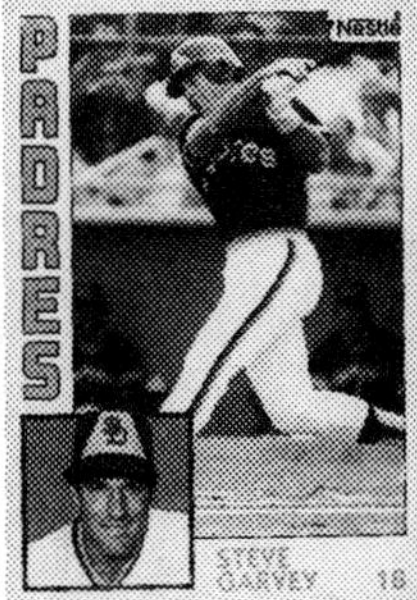

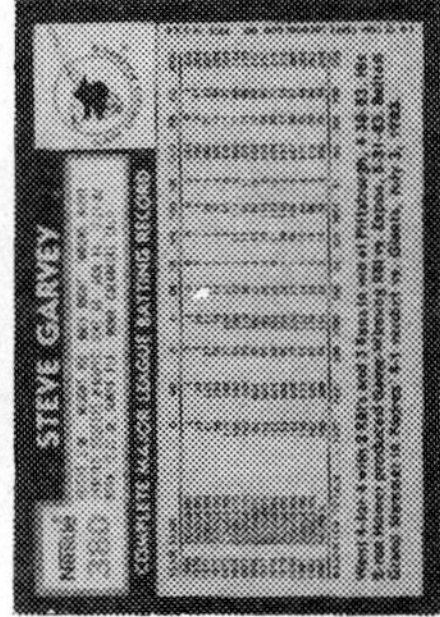

The 792 cards in the 1984 Nestle set are identical to those in the 1984 Topps regular issue set except for the Nestle logo which replaces the Topps logo in the upper right corner of the card front. The set was issued by Nestle as six sheets (24" by 48" each) of 132 cards. A few enterprising dealers bought up the major portion of the 5,000 sheet sets that were supposedly issued and had them professionally cut into individual cards. Due to the ease in handling single cards, sets of individual cards have a greater value than complete sheet sets.

	MT	NR MT	EX
Complete Singles Set:	450.00	337.00	180.00
Common Single Player:	.20	.15	.08
Complete Sheet Set:	300.00	225.00	120.00
Sheet A:	200.00	150.00	80.00
Sheet B:	20.00	15.00	8.00
Sheet C:	20.00	15.00	8.00
Sheet D:	20.00	15.00	8.00
Sheet E:	20.00	15.00	8.00
Sheet F:	20.00	15.00	8.00

1	1983 Highlight (Steve Carlton)	1.75	1.25	.70
2	1983 Highlight (Rickey Henderson)	1.75	1.25	.70
3	1983 Highlight (Dan Quisenberry)	.30	.25	.12
4	1983 Highlight (Steve Carlton, Gaylord Perry, Nolan Ryan)	2.00	1.50	.80
5	1983 Highlight (Bob Forsch, Dave Righetti, Mike Warren)	.35	.25	.14
6	1983 Highlight (Johnny Bench, Gaylord Perry, Carl Yastrzemski)	2.00	1.50	.80
7	Gary Lucas	.20	.15	.08
8	Don Mattingly	225.00	169.00	90.00
9	Jim Gott	.20	.15	.08
10	Robin Yount	15.00	11.00	6.00
11	Twins Batting & Pitching Leaders (Kent Hrbek, Ken Schrom)	.70	.50	.30
12	Billy Sample	.20	.15	.08
13	Scott Holman	.20	.15	.08
14	Tom Brookens	.20	.15	.08
15	Burt Hooton	.30	.25	.12
16	Omar Moreno	.20	.15	.08
17	John Denny	.20	.15	.08
18	Dale Berra	.20	.15	.08
19	Ray Fontenot	.30	.25	.12
20	Greg Luzinski	.60	.45	.25
21	Joe Altobelli	.20	.15	.08
22	Bryan Clark	.20	.15	.08
23	Keith Moreland	.30	.25	.12
24	John Martin	.20	.15	.08
25	Glenn Hubbard	.30	.25	.12
26	Bud Black	.30	.25	.12
27	Daryl Sconiers	.20	.15	.08
28	Frank Viola	5.00	3.75	2.00
29	Danny Heep	.20	.15	.08
30	Wade Boggs	40.00	30.00	16.00
31	Andy McGaffigan	.20	.15	.08
32	Bobby Ramos	.20	.15	.08
33	Tom Burgmeier	.20	.15	.08
34	Eddie Milner	.20	.15	.08
35	Don Sutton	2.00	1.50	.80
36	Denny Walling	.20	.15	.08
37	Rangers Batting & Pitching Leaders (Buddy Bell, Rick Honeycutt)	.40	.30	.15
38	Luis DeLeon	.20	.15	.08
39	Garth Iorg	.20	.15	.08
40	Dusty Baker	.40	.30	.15
41	Tony Bernazard	.20	.15	.08
42	Johnny Grubb	.20	.15	.08
43	Ron Reed	.20	.15	.08
44	Jim Morrison	.20	.15	.08
45	Jerry Mumphrey	.20	.15	.08
46	Ray Smith	.20	.15	.08
47	Rudy Law	.20	.15	.08
48	Julio Franco	1.50	1.25	.60
49	John Stuper	.20	.15	.08
50	Chris Chambliss	.30	.25	.12
51	Jim Frey	.20	.15	.08
52	Paul Splittorff	.30	.25	.12
53	Juan Beniquez	.20	.15	.08
54	Jesse Orosco	.30	.25	.12
55	Dave Concepcion	.50	.40	.20
56	Gary Allenson	.20	.15	.08
57	Dan Schatzeder	.20	.15	.08
58	Max Venable	.20	.15	.08
59	Sammy Stewart	.20	.15	.08
60	Paul Molitor	6.00	4.50	2.50
61	Chris Codiroli	.30	.25	.12
62	Dave Hostetler	.20	.15	.08
63	Ed Vande Berg	.20	.15	.08
64	Mike Scioscia	.30	.25	.12
65	Kirk Gibson	3.00	2.25	1.25
66	Astros Batting & Pitching Leaders (Jose Cruz, Nolan Ryan)	1.00	.70	.40
67	Gary Ward	.30	.25	.12
68	Luis Salazar	.20	.15	.08
69	Rod Scurry	.20	.15	.08
70	Gary Matthews	.30	.25	.12
71	Leo Hernandez	.20	.15	.08
72	Mike Squires	.20	.15	.08
73	Jody Davis	.30	.25	.12
74	Jerry Martin	.20	.15	.08
75	Bob Forsch	.30	.25	.12
76	Alfredo Griffin	.30	.25	.12
77	Brett Butler	.30	.25	.12
78	Mike Torrez	.30	.25	.12
79	Rob Wilfong	.20	.15	.08
80	Steve Rogers	.30	.25	.12
81	Billy Martin	.50	.40	.20
82	Doug Bird	.20	.15	.08
83	Richie Zisk	.30	.25	.12
84	Lenny Faedo	.20	.15	.08
85	Atlee Hammaker	.20	.15	.08
86	John Shelby	.20	.15	.08
87	Frank Pastore	.20	.15	.08
88	Rob Picciolo	.20	.15	.08
89	Mike Smithson	.20	.15	.08
90	Pedro Guerrero	2.00	1.50	.80
91	Dan Spillner	.20	.15	.08
92	Lloyd Moseby	.40	.30	.15
93	Bob Knepper	.30	.25	.12
94	Mario Ramirez	.20	.15	.08
95	Aurelio Lopez	.20	.15	.08
96	Royals Batting & Pitching Leaders (Larry Gura, Hal McRae)	.40	.30	.15
97	LaMarr Hoyt	.20	.15	.08
98	Steve Nicosia	.20	.15	.08
99	Craig Lefferts	.70	.50	.30
100	Reggie Jackson	10.00	7.50	4.00
101	Porfirio Altamirano	.20	.15	.08
102	Ken Oberkfell	.20	.15	.08
103	Dwayne Murphy	.30	.25	.12
104	Ken Dayley	.30	.25	.12
105	Tony Armas	.30	.25	.12
106	Tim Stoddard	.20	.15	.08
107	Ned Yost	.20	.15	.08
108	Randy Moffitt	.20	.15	.08
109	Brad Wellman	.20	.15	.08
110	Ron Guidry	2.75	2.00	1.00
111	Bill Virdon	.30	.25	.12
112	Tom Niedenfuer	.30	.25	.12
113	Kelly Paris	.20	.15	.08
114	Checklist 1-132	.20	.15	.08
115	Andre Thornton	.30	.25	.12
116	George Bjorkman	.20	.15	.08
117	Tom Veryzer	.20	.15	.08
118	Charlie Hough	.30	.25	.12
119	Johnny Wockenfuss	.20	.15	.08
120	Keith Hernandez	3.00	2.25	1.25
121	Pat Sheridan	.30	.25	.12
122	Cecilio Guante	.30	.25	.12
123	Butch Wynegar	.30	.25	.12
124	Damaso Garcia	.20	.15	.08
125	Britt Burns	.20	.15	.08
126	Braves Batting & Pitching Leaders (Craig McMurtry, Dale Murphy)	1.25	.90	.50
127	Mike Madden	.20	.15	.08
128	Rick Manning	.20	.15	.08
129	Bill Laskey	.20	.15	.08
130	Ozzie Smith	6.00	4.50	2.50
131	Batting Leaders (Wade Boggs, Bill Madlock)	2.50	2.00	1.00
132	Home Run Leaders (Jim Rice, Mike Schmidt)	2.00	1.50	.80
133	Runs Batted in Leaders (Cecil Cooper, Dale Murphy, Jim Rice)	2.00	1.50	.80
134	Stolen Base Leaders (Rickey Henderson, Tim Raines)	1.75	1.25	.70
135	Victory Leaders (John Denny, LaMarr Hoyt)	.30	.25	.12
136	Strikeout Leaders (Steve Carlton, Jack Morris)	1.00	.70	.40
137	Earned Run Average Leaders (Atlee Hammaker, Rick Honeycutt)	.30	.25	.12
138	Leading Firemen (Al Holland, Dan Quisenberry)	.30	.25	.12
139	Bert Campaneris	.40	.30	.15
140	Storm Davis	.20	.15	.08
141	Pat Corrales	.20	.15	.08
142	Rich Gale	.20	.15	.08
143	Jose Morales	.20	.15	.08
144	Brian Harper	.20	.15	.08
145	Gary Lavelle	.20	.15	.08
146	Ed Romero	.20	.15	.08
147	Dan Petry	.30	.25	.12
148	Joe Lefebvre	.20	.15	.08
149	Jon Matlack	.30	.25	.12
150	Dale Murphy	15.00	11.00	6.00
151	Steve Trout	.20	.15	.08
152	Glenn Brummer	.20	.15	.08
153	Dick Tidrow	.20	.15	.08
154	Dave Henderson	.40	.30	.15
155	Frank White	.40	.30	.15
156	Athletics Batting & Pitching Leaders (Tim Conroy, Rickey Henderson)	1.00	.70	.40
157	Gary Gaetti	2.50	2.00	1.00
158	John Curtis	.20	.15	.08
159	Darryl Cias	.20	.15	.08
160	Mario Soto	.30	.25	.12
161	Junior Ortiz	.20	.15	.08
162	Bob Ojeda	.40	.30	.15
163	Lorenzo Gray	.20	.15	.08
164	Scott Sanderson	.20	.15	.08
165	Ken Singleton	.40	.30	.15
166	Jamie Nelson	.20	.15	.08
167	Marshall Edwards	.20	.15	.08
168	Juan Bonilla	.20	.15	.08
169	Larry Parrish	.40	.30	.15
170	Jerry Reuss	.30	.25	.12
171	Frank Robinson	.40	.30	.15
172	Frank DiPino	.20	.15	.08
173	Marvell Wynne	.30	.25	.12
174	Juan Berenguer	.20	.15	.08
175	Graig Nettles	.80	.60	.30
176	Lee Smith	.60	.45	.25
177	Jerry Hairston	.20	.15	.08
178	Bill Krueger	.20	.15	.08
179	Buck Martinez	.20	.15	.08
180	Manny Trillo	.30	.25	.12
181	Roy Thomas	.20	.15	.08
182	Darryl Strawberry	20.00	15.00	8.00
183	Al Williams	.20	.15	.08
184	Mike O'Berry	.20	.15	.08
185	Sixto Lezcano	.20	.15	.08
186	Cardinals Batting & Pitching Leaders (Lonnie Smith, John Stuper)	.20	.15	.08
187	Luis Aponte	.20	.15	.08
188	Bryan Little	.20	.15	.08
189	Tim Conroy	.30	.25	.12
190	Ben Oglivie	.30	.25	.12
191	Mike Boddicker	.30	.25	.12
192	Nick Esasky	.40	.30	.15
193	Darrell Brown	.20	.15	.08
194	Domingo Ramos	.20	.15	.08
195	Jack Morris	3.50	2.75	1.50
196	Don Slaught	.40	.30	.15
197	Gary Hancock	.20	.15	.08
198	Bill Doran	1.50	1.25	.60
199	Willie Hernandez	.30	.25	.12
200	Andre Dawson	4.50	3.50	1.75
201	Bruce Kison	.20	.15	.08
202	Bobby Cox	.20	.15	.08
203	Matt Keough	.20	.15	.08
204	Bobby Meacham	.40	.30	.15
205	Greg Minton	.20	.15	.08
206	Andy Van Slyke	5.00	3.75	2.00
207	Donnie Moore	.20	.15	.08
208	Jose Oquendo	.20	.15	.08
209	Manny Sarmiento	.20	.15	.08
210	Joe Morgan	3.00	2.25	1.25
211	Rick Sweet	.20	.15	.08
212	Broderick Perkins	.20	.15	.08
213	Bruce Hurst	.60	.45	.25
214	Paul Householder	.20	.15	.08
215	Tippy Martinez	.20	.15	.08
216	White Sox Batting & Pitching Leaders (Richard Dotson, Carlton Fisk)	.40	.30	.15
217	Alan Ashby	.20	.15	.08
218	Rick Waits	.20	.15	.08
219	Joe Simpson	.20	.15	.08
220	Fernando Valenzuela	2.00	1.50	.80
221	Cliff Johnson	.20	.15	.08
222	Rick Honeycutt	.20	.15	.08
223	Wayne Krenchicki	.20	.15	.08
224	Sid Monge	.20	.15	.08
225	Lee Mazzilli	.30	.25	.12
226	Juan Eichelberger	.20	.15	.08
227	Steve Braun	.20	.15	.08
228	John Rabb	.20	.15	.08
229	Paul Owens	.20	.15	.08
230	Rickey Henderson	15.00	11.00	6.00
231	Gary Woods	.20	.15	.08
232	Tim Wallach	.70	.50	.30
233	Checklist 133-264	.20	.15	.08
234	Rafael Ramirez	.20	.15	.08
235	Matt Young	.40	.30	.15
236	Ellis Valentine	.20	.15	.08
237	John Castino	.20	.15	.08
238	Reid Nichols	.20	.15	.08
239	Jay Howell	.30	.25	.12
240	Eddie Murray	8.00	6.00	3.25
241	Billy Almon	.20	.15	.08
242	Alex Trevino	.20	.15	.08
243	Pete Ladd	.20	.15	.08
244	Candy Maldonado	.30	.25	.12
245	Rick Sutcliffe	.30	.25	.12
246	Mets Batting & Pitching Leaders (Tom Seaver, Mookie Wilson)	.70	.50	.30
247	Onix Concepcion	.20	.15	.08
248	Bill Dawley	.20	.15	.08
249	Jay Johnstone	.30	.25	.12
250	Bill Madlock	.60	.45	.25
251	Tony Gwynn	12.00	9.00	4.75
252	Larry Christenson	.20	.15	.08
253	Jim Wohlford	.20	.15	.08
254	Shane Rawley	.30	.25	.12
255	Bruce Benedict	.20	.15	.08
256	Dave Geisel	.20	.15	.08
257	Julio Cruz	.20	.15	.08
258	Luis Sanchez	.20	.15	.08
259	Sparky Anderson	.30	.25	.12
260	Scott McGregor	.30	.25	.12
261	Bobby Brown	.20	.15	.08
262	Tom Candiotti	.30	.25	.12

263 Jack Fimple .20 .15 .08
264 Doug Frobel .20 .15 .08
265 Donnie Hill .20 .15 .08
266 Steve Lubratich .20 .15 .08
267 Carmelo Martinez .20 .15 .08
268 Jack O'Connor .20 .15 .08
269 Aurelio Rodriguez .30 .25 .12
270 Jeff Russell .40 .30 .15
271 Moose Haas .20 .15 .08
272 Rick Dempsey .30 .25 .12
273 Charlie Puleo .20 .15 .08
274 Rick Monday .30 .25 .12
275 Len Matuszek .20 .15 .08
276 Angels Batting & Pitching Leaders (Rod Carew, Geoff Zahn) .70 .50 .30
277 Eddie Whitson .20 .15 .08
278 Jorge Bell 6.00 4.50 2.50
279 Ivan DeJesus .20 .15 .08
280 Floyd Bannister .30 .25 .12
281 Larry Milbourne .20 .15 .08
282 Jim Barr .20 .15 .08
283 Larry Biittner .20 .15 .08
284 Howard Bailey .20 .15 .08
285 Darrell Porter .30 .25 .12
286 Lary Sorensen .20 .15 .08
287 Warren Cromartie .20 .15 .08
288 Jim Beattie .20 .15 .08
289 Randy Johnson .20 .15 .08
290 Dave Dravecky .30 .25 .12
291 Chuck Tanner .30 .25 .12
292 Tony Scott .20 .15 .08
293 Ed Lynch .20 .15 .08
294 U.L. Washington .20 .15 .08
295 Mike Flanagan .30 .25 .12
296 Jeff Newman .20 .15 .08
297 Bruce Berenyi .20 .15 .08
298 Jim Gantner .30 .25 .12
299 John Butcher .20 .15 .08
300 Pete Rose 25.00 18.50 10.00
301 Frank LaCorte .20 .15 .08
302 Barry Bonnell .20 .15 .08
303 Marty Castillo .20 .15 .08
304 Warren Brusstar .20 .15 .08
305 Roy Smalley .20 .15 .08
306 Dodgers Batting & Pitching Leaders (Pedro Guerrero, Bob Welch) .60 .45 .25
307 Bobby Mitchell .20 .15 .08
308 Ron Hassey .20 .15 .08
309 Tony Phillips .30 .25 .12
310 Willie McGee 3.00 2.25 1.25
311 Jerry Koosman .40 .30 .15
312 Jorge Orta .20 .15 .08
313 Mike Jorgensen .20 .15 .08
314 Orlando Mercado .20 .15 .08
315 Bob Grich .30 .25 .12
316 Mark Bradley .20 .15 .08
317 Greg Pryor .20 .15 .08
318 Bill Gullickson .20 .15 .08
319 Al Bumbry .20 .15 .08
320 Bob Stanley .20 .15 .08
321 Harvey Kuenn .20 .15 .08
322 Ken Schrom .20 .15 .08
323 Alan Knicely .20 .15 .08
324 Alejandro Pena .30 .25 .12
325 Darrell Evans .40 .30 .15
326 Bob Kearney .20 .15 .08
327 Ruppert Jones .20 .15 .08
328 Vern Ruhle .20 .15 .08
329 Pat Tabler .20 .15 .08
330 John Candelaria .40 .30 .15
331 Bucky Dent .30 .25 .12
332 Kevin Gross .30 .25 .12
333 Larry Herndon .20 .15 .08
334 Chuck Rainey .20 .15 .08
335 Don Baylor .50 .40 .20
336 Mariners Batting & Pitching Leaders (Pat Putnam, Matt Young) .20 .15 .08
337 Kevin Hagen .20 .15 .08
338 Mike Warren .20 .15 .08
339 Roy Lee Jackson .20 .15 .08
340 Hal McRae .40 .30 .15
341 Dave Tobik .20 .15 .08
342 Tim Foli .20 .15 .08
343 Mark Davis .20 .15 .08
344 Rick Miller .20 .15 .08
345 Kent Hrbek 4.00 3.00 1.50
346 Kurt Bevacqua .20 .15 .08
347 Allan Ramirez .20 .15 .08
348 Toby Harrah .30 .25 .12
349 Bob Gibson .20 .15 .08
350 George Foster .40 .30 .15
351 Russ Nixon .20 .15 .08
352 Dave Stewart .60 .45 .25
353 Jim Anderson .20 .15 .08
354 Jeff Burroughs .20 .15 .08
355 Jason Thompson .20 .15 .08
356 Glenn Abbott .20 .15 .08
357 Ron Cey .40 .30 .15
358 Bob Dernier .20 .15 .08
359 Jim Acker .30 .25 .12
360 Willie Randolph .50 .40 .20
361 Dave Smith .30 .25 .12
362 David Green .20 .15 .08
363 Tim Laudner .20 .15 .08
364 Scott Fletcher .40 .30 .15
365 Steve Bedrosian .40 .30 .15
366 Padres Batting & Pitching Leaders (Dave Dravecky, Terry Kennedy) .20 .15 .08
367 Jamie Easterly .20 .15 .08
368 Hubie Brooks .30 .25 .12
369 Steve McCatty .20 .15 .08
370 Tim Raines 5.00 3.75 2.00
371 Dave Gumpert .20 .15 .08
372 Gary Roenicke .20 .15 .08
373 Bill Scherrer .20 .15 .08
374 Don Money .20 .15 .08
375 Dennis Leonard .30 .25 .12
376 Dave Anderson .30 .25 .12
377 Danny Darwin .30 .25 .12
378 Bob Brenly .20 .15 .08
379 Checklist 265-396 .20 .15 .08
380 Steve Garvey 8.00 6.00 3.25
381 Ralph Houk .20 .15 .08
382 Chris Nyman .20 .15 .08
383 Terry Puhl .20 .15 .08
384 Lee Tunnell .20 .15 .08
385 Tony Perez 1.00 .70 .40
386 George Hendrick AS .30 .25 .12
387 Johnny Ray AS .30 .25 .12
388 Mike Schmidt AS 3.00 2.25 1.25
389 Ozzie Smith AS 2.50 2.00 1.00
390 Tim Raines AS 2.00 1.50 .80
391 Dale Murphy AS 3.00 2.25 1.25
392 Andre Dawson AS 1.75 1.25 .70
393 Gary Carter AS 2.00 1.50 .80
394 Steve Rogers AS .30 .25 .12
395 Steve Carlton AS 2.00 1.50 .80
396 Jesse Orosco AS .30 .25 .12
397 Eddie Murray AS 2.50 2.00 1.00
398 Lou Whitaker AS 1.25 .90 .50
399 George Brett AS 4.00 3.00 1.50
400 Cal Ripken AS 3.50 2.75 1.50
401 Jim Rice AS 1.75 1.25 .70
402 Dave Winfield AS 2.50 2.00 1.00
403 Lloyd Moseby AS .30 .25 .12
404 Ted Simmons AS .40 .30 .15
405 LaMarr Hoyt AS .30 .25 .12
406 Ron Guidry AS 1.25 .90 .50
407 Dan Quisenberry AS .30 .25 .12
408 Lou Piniella .80 .60 .30
409 Juan Agosto .40 .30 .15
410 Claudell Washington .30 .25 .12
411 Houston Jimenez .20 .15 .08
412 Doug Rader .20 .15 .08
413 Spike Owen .30 .25 .12
414 Mitchell Page .20 .15 .08
415 Tommy John 1.25 .90 .50
416 Dane Iorg .20 .15 .08
417 Mike Armstrong .20 .15 .08
418 Ron Hodges .20 .15 .08
419 John Henry Johnson .20 .15 .08
420 Cecil Cooper .30 .25 .12
421 Charlie Lea .20 .15 .08
422 Jose Cruz .30 .25 .12
423 Mike Morgan .20 .15 .08
424 Dann Bilardello .20 .15 .08
425 Steve Howe .30 .25 .12
426 Orioles Batting & Pitching Leaders (Mike Boddicker, Cal Ripken) .90 .70 .35
427 Rick Leach .20 .15 .08
428 Fred Breining .20 .15 .08
429 Randy Bush .20 .15 .08
430 Rusty Staub .50 .40 .20
431 Chris Bando .20 .15 .08
432 Charlie Hudson .30 .25 .12
433 Rich Hebner .20 .15 .08
434 Harold Baines 1.75 1.25 .70
435 Neil Allen .20 .15 .08
436 Rick Peters .20 .15 .08
437 Mike Proly .20 .15 .08
438 Biff Pocoroba .20 .15 .08
439 Bob Stoddard .20 .15 .08
440 Steve Kemp .30 .25 .12
441 Bob Lillis .20 .15 .08
442 Byron McLaughlin .20 .15 .08
443 Benny Ayala .20 .15 .08
444 Steve Renko .20 .15 .08
445 Jerry Remy .20 .15 .08
446 Luis Pujols .20 .15 .08
447 Tom Brunansky .40 .30 .15
448 Ben Hayes .20 .15 .08
449 Joe Pettini .20 .15 .08
450 Gary Carter 6.00 4.50 2.50
451 Bob Jones .20 .15 .08
452 Chuck Porter .20 .15 .08
453 Willie Upshaw .30 .25 .12
454 Joe Beckwith .20 .15 .08
455 Terry Kennedy .30 .25 .12
456 Cubs Batting & Pitching Leaders (Keith Moreland, Fergie Jenkins) .50 .40 .20
457 Dave Rozema .20 .15 .08
458 Kiko Garcia .20 .15 .08
459 Kevin Hickey .20 .15 .08
460 Dave Winfield 9.00 6.75 3.50
461 Jim Maler .20 .15 .08
462 Lee Lacy .20 .15 .08
463 Dave Engle .20 .15 .08
464 Jeff Jones .20 .15 .08
465 Mookie Wilson .30 .25 .12
466 Gene Garber .20 .15 .08
467 Mike Ramsey .20 .15 .08
468 Geoff Zahn .20 .15 .08
469 Tom O'Malley .20 .15 .08
470 Nolan Ryan 20.00 15.00 8.00
471 Dick Howser .30 .25 .12
472 Mike Brown .20 .15 .08
473 Jim Dwyer .20 .15 .08
474 Greg Bargar .20 .15 .08
475 Gary Redus .40 .30 .15
476 Tom Tellmann .20 .15 .08
477 Rafael Landestoy .20 .15 .08
478 Alan Bannister .20 .15 .08
479 Frank Tanana .30 .25 .12
480 Ron Kittle .80 .60 .30
481 Mark Thurmond .30 .25 .12
482 Enos Cabell .20 .15 .08
483 Fergie Jenkins 3.00 2.25 1.25
484 Ozzie Virgil .20 .15 .08
485 Rick Rhoden .40 .30 .15
486 Yankees Batting & Pitching Leaders (Don Baylor, Ron Guidry) .60 .45 .25
487 Ricky Adams .20 .15 .08
488 Jesse Barfield .40 .30 .15
489 Dave Von Ohlen .20 .15 .08
490 Cal Ripken 16.00 12.00 6.50
491 Bobby Castillo .20 .15 .08
492 Tucker Ashford .20 .15 .08
493 Mike Norris .20 .15 .08
494 Chili Davis .30 .25 .12
495 Rollie Fingers 3.00 2.25 1.25
496 Terry Francona .20 .15 .08
497 Bud Anderson .20 .15 .08
498 Rich Gedman .30 .25 .12
499 Mike Witt .70 .50 .30
500 George Brett 15.00 11.00 6.00
501 Steve Henderson .20 .15 .08
502 Joe Torre .30 .25 .12
503 Elias Sosa .20 .15 .08
504 Mickey Rivers .20 .15 .08
505 Pete Vuckovich .20 .15 .08
506 Ernie Whitt .20 .15 .08
507 Mike LaCoss .20 .15 .08
508 Mel Hall .30 .25 .12
509 Brad Havens .20 .15 .08
510 Alan Trammell 5.00 3.75 2.00
511 Marty Bystrom .20 .15 .08
512 Oscar Gamble .20 .15 .08
513 Dave Beard .20 .15 .08
514 Floyd Rayford .20 .15 .08
515 Gorman Thomas .30 .25 .12
516 Expos Batting & Pitching Leaders (Charlie Lea, Al Oliver) .20 .15 .08
517 John Moses .20 .15 .08
518 Greg Walker .30 .25 .12
519 Ron Davis .20 .15 .08
520 Bob Boone .30 .25 .12
521 Pete Falcone .20 .15 .08
522 Dave Bergman .20 .15 .08
523 Glenn Hoffman .20 .15 .08
524 Carlos Diaz .20 .15 .08
525 Willie Wilson .60 .45 .25
526 Ron Oester .20 .15 .08
527 Checklist 397-528 .20 .15 .08
528 Mark Brouhard .20 .15 .08
529 Keith Atherton .60 .45 .25
530 Dan Ford .20 .15 .08
531 Steve Boros .20 .15 .08
532 Eric Show .40 .30 .15
533 Ken Landreaux .20 .15 .08
534 Pete O'Brien .50 .40 .20
535 Bo Diaz .30 .25 .12
536 Doug Bair .20 .15 .08
537 Johnny Ray .40 .30 .15
538 Kevin Bass .40 .30 .15
539 George Frazier .20 .15 .08
540 George Hendrick .30 .25 .12
541 Dennis Lamp .20 .15 .08
542 Duane Kuiper .20 .15 .08
543 Craig McMurtry .40 .30 .15
544 Cesar Geronimo .20 .15 .08
545 Bill Buckner .30 .25 .12
546 Indians Batting & Pitching Leaders (Mike Hargrove, Lary Sorensen) .20 .15 .08
547 Mike Moore .20 .15 .08
548 Ron Jackson .20 .15 .08
549 Walt Terrell .40 .30 .15
550 Jim Rice 3.00 2.25 1.25
551 Scott Ullger .20 .15 .08
552 Ray Burris .20 .15 .08
553 Joe Nolan .20 .15 .08
554 Ted Power .30 .25 .12
555 Greg Brock .20 .15 .08
556 Joey McLaughlin .20 .15 .08
557 Wayne Tolleson .20 .15 .08
558 Mike Davis .30 .25 .12
559 Mike Scott .40 .30 .15
560 Carlton Fisk 6.00 4.50 2.50
561 Whitey Herzog .30 .25 .12
562 Manny Castillo .20 .15 .08
563 Glenn Wilson .30 .25 .12
564 Al Holland .20 .15 .08
565 Leon Durham .30 .25 .12
566 Jim Bibby .20 .15 .08
567 Mike Heath .20 .15 .08
568 Pete Filson .20 .15 .08
569 Bake McBride .20 .15 .08
570 Dan Quisenberry .40 .30 .15
571 Bruce Bochy .20 .15 .08
572 Jerry Royster .20 .15 .08
573 Dave Kingman .40 .30 .15
574 Brian Downing .30 .25 .12
575 Jim Clancy .30 .25 .12
576 Giants Batting & Pitching Leaders (Atlee Hammaker, Jeff Leonard) .20 .15 .08
577 Mark Clear .20 .15 .08
578 Lenn Sakata .20 .15 .08
579 Bob James .20 .15 .08
580 Lonnie Smith .30 .25 .12
581 Jose DeLeon .40 .30 .15
582 Bob McClure .20 .15 .08
583 Derrel Thomas .20 .15 .08
584 Dave Schmidt .20 .15 .08
585 Dan Driessen .30 .25 .12
586 Joe Niekro .40 .30 .15
587 Von Hayes .40 .30 .15
588 Milt Wilcox .20 .15 .08
589 Mike Easler .30 .25 .12
590 Dave Stieb .50 .40 .20
591 Tony LaRussa .30 .25 .12
592 Andre Robertson .20 .15 .08
593 Jeff Lahti .20 .15 .08
594 Gene Richards .20 .15 .08
595 Jeff Reardon .50 .40 .20
596 Ryne Sandberg 18.00 13.50 7.25
597 Rick Camp .20 .15 .08
598 Rusty Kuntz .20 .15 .08
599 Doug Sisk .20 .15 .08
600 Rod Carew 7.00 5.25 2.75
601 John Tudor .30 .25 .12
602 John Wathan .30 .25 .12
603 Renie Martin .20 .15 .08
604 John Lowenstein .20 .15 .08
605 Mike Caldwell .20 .15 .08
606 Blue Jays Batting & Pitching Leaders (Lloyd

Moseby, Dave Stieb) .40 .30 .15
607 Tom Hume .20 .15 .08
608 Bobby Johnson .20 .15 .08
609 Dan Meyer .20 .15 .08
610 Steve Sax .40 .30 .15
611 Chet Lemon .30 .25 .12
612 Harry Spilman .20 .15 .08
613 Greg Gross .20 .15 .08
614 Len Barker .20 .15 .08
615 Garry Templeton .30 .25 .12
616 Don Robinson .20 .15 .08
617 Rick Cerone .20 .15 .08
618 Dickie Noles .20 .15 .08
619 Jerry Dybzinski .20 .15 .08
620 Al Oliver .70 .50 .30
621 Frank Howard .30 .25 .12
622 Al Cowens .20 .15 .08
623 Ron Washington .20 .15 .08
624 Terry Harper .20 .15 .08
625 Larry Gura .20 .15 .08
626 Bob Clark .20 .15 .08
627 Dave LaPoint .40 .30 .15
628 Ed Jurak .20 .15 .08
629 Rick Langford .20 .15 .08
630 Ted Simmons .40 .30 .15
631 Denny Martinez .30 .25 .12
632 Tom Foley .20 .15 .08
633 Mike Krukow .30 .25 .12
634 Mike Marshall .50 .40 .20
635 Dave Righetti 2.00 1.50 .80
636 Pat Putnam .20 .15 .08
637 Phillies Batting & Pitching Leaders (John Denny, Gary Matthews) .20 .15 .08
638 George Vukovich .20 .15 .08
639 Rick Lysander .20 .15 .08
640 Lance Parrish 1.50 1.25 .60
641 Mike Richardt .20 .15 .08
642 Tom Underwood .20 .15 .08
643 Mike Brown .20 .15 .08
644 Tim Lollar .20 .15 .08
645 Tony Pena .40 .30 .15
646 Checklist 529-660 .20 .15 .08
647 Ron Roenicke .20 .15 .08
648 Len Whitehouse .20 .15 .08
649 Tom Herr .40 .30 .15
650 Phil Niekro 3.00 2.25 1.25
651 John McNamara .20 .15 .08
652 Rudy May .20 .15 .08
653 Dave Stapleton .20 .15 .08
654 Bob Bailor .20 .15 .08
655 Amos Otis .30 .25 .12
656 Bryn Smith .20 .15 .08
657 Thad Bosley .20 .15 .08
658 Jerry Augustine .20 .15 .08
659 Duane Walker .20 .15 .08
660 Ray Knight .30 .25 .12
661 Steve Yeager .20 .15 .08
662 Tom Brennan .20 .15 .08
663 Johnnie LeMaster .20 .15 .08
664 Dave Stegman .20 .15 .08
665 Buddy Bell .40 .30 .15
666 Tigers Batting & Pitching Leaders (Jack Morris, Lou Whitaker) .70 .50 .30
667 Vance Law .30 .25 .12
668 Larry McWilliams .20 .15 .08
669 Dave Lopes .20 .15 .08
670 Rich Gossage 2.00 1.50 .80
671 Jamie Quirk .20 .15 .08
672 Ricky Nelson .20 .15 .08
673 Mike Walters .20 .15 .08
674 Tim Flannery .20 .15 .08
675 Pascual Perez .30 .25 .12
676 Brian Giles .20 .15 .08
677 Doyle Alexander .30 .25 .12
678 Chris Speier .20 .15 .08
679 Art Howe .20 .15 .08
680 Fred Lynn 3.00 2.25 1.25
681 Tom Lasorda .40 .30 .15
682 Dan Morogiello .20 .15 .08
683 Marty Barrett .60 .45 .25
684 Bob Shirley .20 .15 .08
685 Willie Aikens .20 .15 .08
686 Joe Price .20 .15 .08
687 Roy Howell .20 .15 .08
688 George Wright .20 .15 .08
689 Mike Fischlin .20 .15 .08
690 Jack Clark .80 .60 .30
691 Steve Lake .20 .15 .08
692 Dickie Thon .30 .25 .12
693 Alan Wiggins .20 .15 .08
694 Mike Stanton .20 .15 .08
695 Lou Whitaker 3.00 2.25 1.25
696 Pirates Batting & Pitching Leaders (Bill Madlock, Rick Rhoden) .50 .40 .20
697 Dale Murray .20 .15 .08
698 Marc Hill .20 .15 .08
699 Dave Rucker .20 .15 .08
700 Mike Schmidt 18.00 13.50 7.25
701 NL Active Career Batting Leaders (Bill Madlock, Dave Parker, Pete Rose) 2.00 1.50 .80
702 NL Active Career Hit Leaders (Tony Perez, Pete Rose, Rusty Staub) 2.00 1.50 .80
703 NL Active Career Home Run Leaders (Dave Kingman, Tony Perez, Mike Schmidt) 2.00 1.50 .80
704 NL Active Career RBI Leaders (Al Oliver, Tony Perez, Rusty Staub) .60 .45 .25
705 NL Active Career Stolen Bases Leaders (Larry Bowa, Cesar Cedeno, Joe Morgan) .70 .50 .30
706 NL Active Career Victory Leaders (Steve Carlton, Fergie Jenkins, Tom Seaver) 1.75 1.25 .70
707 NL Active Career Strikeout Leaders (Steve Carlton, Nolan Ryan, Tom Seaver) 2.00 1.50 .80
708 NL Active Career ERA Leaders (Steve Carlton, Steve Rogers, Tom Seaver) 1.75 1.25 .70
709 NL Active Career Save Leaders (Gene Garber, Tug McGraw, Bruce Sutter) .50 .40 .20
710 AL Active Career Batting Leaders (George Brett, Rod Carew, Cecil Cooper) 2.00 1.50 .80
711 AL Active Career Hit Leaders (Bert Campaneris, Rod Carew, Reggie Jackson) 1.75 1.25 .70
712 AL Active Career Home Run Leaders (Reggie Jackson, Greg Luzinski, Graig Nettles) 1.50 1.25 .60
713 AL Active Career RBI Leaders (Reggie Jackson, Graig Nettles, Ted Simmons) 1.50 1.25 .60
714 AL Active Career Stolen Bases Leaders (Bert Campaneris, Dave Lopes, Omar Moreno) .40 .30 .15
715 AL Active Career Victory Leaders (Tommy John, Jim Palmer, Don Sutton) 1.25 .90 .50
716 AL Active Strikeout Leaders (Bert Blyleven, Jerry Koosman, Don Sutton) .70 .50 .30
717 AL Active Career ERA Leaders (Rollie Fingers, Ron Guidry, Jim Palmer) 1.25 .90 .50
718 AL Active Career Save Leaders (Rollie Fingers, Rich Gossage, Dan Quisenberry) .90 .70 .35
719 Andy Hassler .20 .15 .08
720 Dwight Evans .80 .60 .30
721 Del Crandall .20 .15 .08
722 Bob Welch .40 .30 .15
723 Rich Dauer .20 .15 .08
724 Eric Rasmussen .20 .15 .08
725 Cesar Cedeno .30 .25 .12
726 Brewers Batting & Pitching Leaders (Moose Haas, Ted Simmons) .30 .25 .12
727 Joel Youngblood .20 .15 .08
728 Tug McGraw .30 .25 .12
729 Gene Tenace .30 .25 .12
730 Bruce Sutter .90 .70 .35
731 Lynn Jones .20 .15 .08
732 Terry Crowley .20 .15 .08
733 Dave Collins .30 .25 .12
734 Odell Jones .20 .15 .08
735 Rick Burleson .30 .25 .12
736 Dick Ruthven .20 .15 .08
737 Jim Essian .20 .15 .08
738 Bill Schroeder .60 .45 .25
739 Bob Watson .30 .25 .12
740 Tom Seaver 9.00 6.75 3.50
741 Wayne Gross .20 .15 .08
742 Dick Williams .20 .15 .08
743 Don Hood .20 .15 .08
744 Jamie Allen .20 .15 .08
745 Dennis Eckersley 4.00 3.00 1.50
746 Mickey Hatcher .20 .15 .08
747 Pat Zachry .20 .15 .08
748 Jeff Leonard .30 25 .12
749 Doug Flynn .20 .15 .08
750 Jim Palmer 6.00 4.50 2.50
751 Charlie Moore .20 .15 .08
752 Phil Garner .30 .25 .12
753 Doug Gwosdz .20 .15 .08
754 Kent Tekulve .30 .25 .12
755 Garry Maddox .30 .25 .12
756 Reds Batting & Pitching Leaders (Ron Oester, Mario Soto) .20 .15 .08
757 Larry Bowa .40 .30 .15
758 Bill Stein .20 .15 .08
759 Richard Dotson .40 .30 .15
760 Bob Horner .40 .30 .15
761 John Montefusco .20 .15 .08
762 Rance Mulliniks .20 .15 .08
763 Craig Swan .20 .15 .08
764 Mike Hargrove .20 .15 .08
765 Ken Forsch .20 .15 .08
766 Mike Vail .20 .15 .08
767 Carney Lansford .40 .30 .15
768 Champ Summers .20 .15 .08
769 Bill Caudill .20 .15 .08
770 Ken Griffey .30 .25 .12
771 Billy Gardner .20 .15 .08
772 Jim Slaton .20 .15 .08
773 Todd Cruz .20 .15 .08
774 Tom Gorman .20 .15 .08
775 Dave Parker 3.00 2.25 1.25
776 Craig Reynolds .20 .15 .08
777 Tom Paciorek .20 .15 .08
778 Andy Hawkins .80 .60 .30
779 Jim Sundberg .20 .15 .08
780 Steve Carlton 9.00 6.75 3.50
781 Checklist 661-792 .20 .15 .08
782 Steve Balboni .30 .25 .12
783 Luis Leal .20 .15 .08
784 Leon Roberts .20 .15 .08
785 Joaquin Andujar .30 .25 .12
786 Red Sox Batting & Pitching Leaders (Wade Boggs, Bob Ojeda) 1.25 .90 .50
787 Bill Campbell .20 .15 .08
788 Milt May .20 .15 .08
789 Bert Blyleven 1.25 .90 .50
790 Doug DeCinces .30 .25 .12
791 Terry Forster .30 .25 .12
792 Bill Russell .30 .25 .12

Values quoted in this guide reflect the retail price of a card – the price a collector can expect to pay when buying a card from a dealer. The wholesale price – that which a collector can expect to receive from a dealer when selling cards – will be significantly lower, depending on desirability and condition.

Values for recent cards and sets are listed in Mint (MT), Near Mint (NM), reflecting the fact that many cards from recent years have been preserved in top condition. Recent cards and sets in less than Excellent condition have little collector interest.

1984 Nestle Dream Team

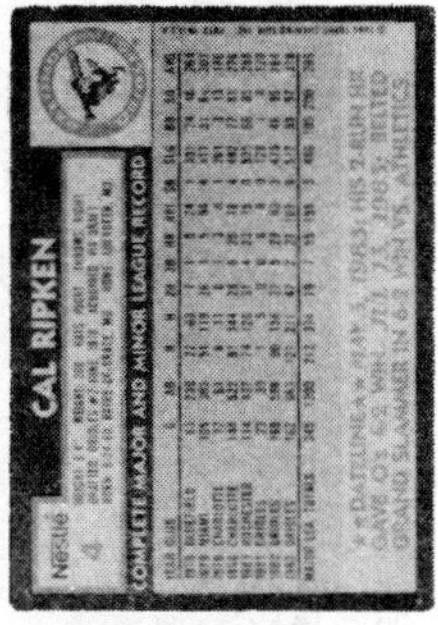

This set was issued by the Nestle candy company in conjunction with Topps. Cards are in standard 2-1/2" by 3-1/2" size and feature the top 22 players of 1984, 11 from each league. This full-color "Dream Team" includes one player at each position, plus right- and left-handed starting pitchers and one reliever. Card fronts have a Nestle logo in the upper-right corner and card backs have the candy company logo in the upper left. An unnumbered checklist was included with the set.

		MT	NR MT	EX
Complete Set (23):		21.00	15.50	8.50
Common Player:		.60	.45	.25
1	Eddie Murray	1.75	1.25	.70
2	Lou Whitaker	1.00	.70	.40
3	George Brett	3.00	2.25	1.25
4	Cal Ripken	3.00	2.25	1.25
5	Jim Rice	1.25	.90	.50
6	Dave Winfield	2.50	2.00	1.00
7	Lloyd Moseby	.60	.45	.25
8	Lance Parrish	.75	.60	.30
9	LaMarr Hoyt	.60	.45	.25
10	Ron Guidry	.75	.60	.30
11	Dan Quisenberry	.60	.45	.25
12	Steve Garvey	1.50	1.25	.60
13	Johnny Ray	.60	.45	.25
14	Mike Schmidt	3.00	2.25	1.25
15	Ozzie Smith	1.50	1.25	.60
16	Andre Dawson	1.00	.70	.40
17	Tim Raines	1.00	.70	.40
18	Dale Murphy	2.25	1.75	.90
19	Tony Pena	.60	.45	.25
20	John Denny	.60	.45	.25
21	Steve Carlton	2.00	1.50	.80
22	Al Holland	.60	.45	.25
----	Checklist	.30	.25	.12

1987 Nestle

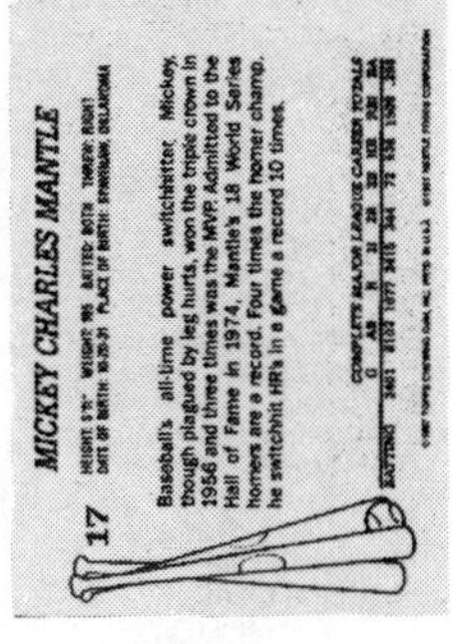

Nestle, in conjunction with Topps, issued a 33-card set in 1987. Card #'s 1-11 feature black and white photos of players from the "Golden Era." Card #'s 12-33 feature full-color photos of American (12-22) and National League (23-33) players from the "Modern Era" of baseball. Interestingly, the Feller card is not a photo but rather a color rendering of his 1953 Topps card. The cards measure 2-1/2" by 3-1/2" and have all team emblems airbrushed away. Three cards were inserted in specially marked six-packs of various Nestle candy bars. Two complete sets were available through a mail-in offer for $1.50 and three proof of purchase seals.

		MT	NR MT	EX
Complete Set:		9.00	6.75	3.50
Common Player:		.12	.09	.05
1	Lou Gehrig	.50	.40	.20
2	Rogers Hornsby	.25	.20	.10
3	Pie Traynor	.12	.09	.05
4	Honus Wagner	.30	.25	.12
5	Babe Ruth	1.00	.70	.40
6	Tris Speaker	.20	.15	.08
7	Ty Cobb	.60	.45	.25
8	Mickey Cochrane	.12	.09	.05
9	Walter Johnson	.30	.25	.12

10	Carl Hubbell	.12	.09	.05
11	Jimmie Foxx	.25	.20	.10
12	Rod Carew	.30	.25	.12
13	Nellie Fox	.12	.09	.05
14	Brooks Robinson	.30	.25	.12
15	Luis Aparicio	.12	.09	.05
16	Frank Robinson	.20	.15	.08
17	Mickey Mantle	1.00	.70	.40
18	Ted Williams	.50	.40	.20
19	Yogi Berra	.30	.25	.12
20	Bob Feller	.25	.20	.10
21	Whitey Ford	.25	.20	.10
22	Harmon Killebrew	.20	.15	.08
23	Stan Musial	.50	.40	.20
24	Jackie Robinson	.40	.30	.15
25	Eddie Mathews	.20	.15	.08
26	Ernie Banks	.20	.15	.08
27	Roberto Clemente	.40	.30	.15
28	Willie Mays	.50	.40	.20
29	Hank Aaron	.50	.40	.20
30	Johnny Bench	.30	.25	.12
31	Bob Gibson	.20	.15	.08
32	Warren Spahn	.20	.15	.08
33	Duke Snider	.25	.20	.10

1988 Nestle

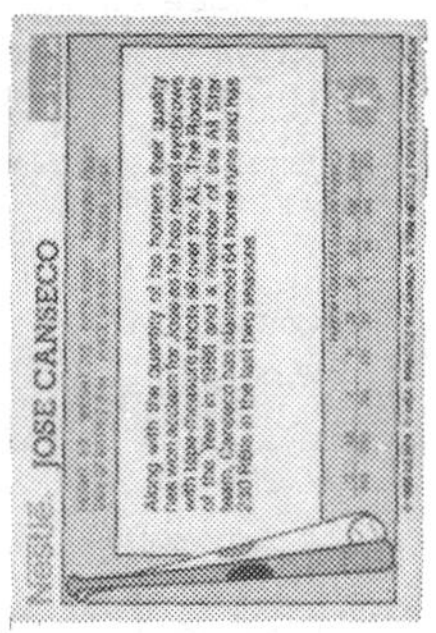

This 44-card set was produced by Mike Schechter Associates for Nestle. "Dream Team" packets of 3 player cards and one checklist card were inserted in 6-packs of Nestle's chocolate candy bars. The 1988 issue, similar to the 33-card Nestle set produced by Topps, features current players divided into four Dream Teams (East and West teams for each league). The "1988 Nestle" header appears at the top of the red and yellow-bordered cards. Below the player closeup (in a plain air-brushed cap) is a blue oval player name banner. Card backs are red, white and blue with card numbers printed upper right above personal stats, career highlights and major league totals. The bright red, blue and yellow checklist card outlines two special offers; one for an uncut sheet of all 44 player cards and one for a 1988 replica autographed baseball.

		MT	NR MT	EX
Complete Set:		20.00	15.00	8.00
Common Player:		.25	.20	.10
1	Roger Clemens	.90	.70	.35
2	Dale Murphy	.60	.45	.25
3	Eric Davis	.40	.30	.15
4	Gary Gaetti	.30	.25	.12
5	Ozzie Smith	.45	.35	.20
6	Mike Schmidt	1.00	.70	.40
7	Ozzie Guillen	.25	.20	.10
8	John Franco	.25	.20	.10
9	Andre Dawson	.50	.40	.20
10	Mark McGwire	.50	.40	.20
11	Bret Saberhagen	.35	.25	.14
12	Benny Santiago	.35	.25	.14
13	Jose Uribe	.25	.20	.10
14	Will Clark	1.75	1.25	.70
15	Don Mattingly	1.25	.90	.50
16	Juan Samuel	.30	.25	.12
17	Jack Clark	.30	.25	.12
18	Darryl Strawberry	.40	.30	.15
19	Bill Doran	.25	.20	.10
20	Pete Incaviglia	.30	.25	.12
21	Dwight Gooden	.75	.60	.30
22	Willie Randolph	.25	.20	.10
23	Tim Wallach	.35	.25	.14
24	Pedro Guerrero	.30	.25	.12
25	Steve Bedrosian	.25	.20	.10
26	Gary Carter	.50	.40	.20
27	Jeff Reardon	.25	.20	.10
28	Dave Righetti	.35	.25	.14
29	Frank White	.25	.20	.10
30	Buddy Bell	.25	.20	.10
31	Tim Raines	.50	.40	.20
32	Wade Boggs	1.00	.70	.40
33	Dave Winfield	.75	.60	.30
34	George Bell	.40	.30	.15
35	Alan Trammell	.40	.30	.15
36	Joe Carter	.35	.25	.14
37	Jose Canseco	1.00	.70	.40
38	Carlton Fisk	.60	.45	.25
39	Kirby Puckett	.90	.70	.35
40	Tony Gwynn	.50	.40	.20
41	Matt Nokes	.40	.30	.15
42	Keith Hernandez	.40	.30	.15
43	Nolan Ryan	2.00	1.50	.80
44	Wally Joyner	.50	.40	.20

1895 Newsboy Cabinets (N566)

Issued in the 1890s by the National Tobacco Works, this massive cabinet card set was distributed as a premium with the Newsboy tobacco brand. Although the set contained over 500 popular actresses, athletes, politicians and other celebrities of the day, only a dozen cards of baseball players have been found. The cards measure 4-1/4" by 6-1/2" and feature sepia-toned photographs mounted on a backing that has "Newsboy" written in script in the lower left corner. Each photograph is numbered. The baseball players uncluded in the set are all members of the 1894 New York Giants, except Dave Foutz, who was Brooklyn's playing manager. There are two known poses of John Ward.

		NR MT	EX	VG
Complete Set:		11000.	5500.	3300.
Common Player:		600.00	300.00	180.00
174	W.H. Murphy	600.00	300.00	180.00
175	Amos Rusie	2350.	1175.	705.00
176	Michael Tiernan	600.00	300.00	180.00
177	E.D. Burke	600.00	300.00	180.00
178	J.J. Doyle	600.00	300.00	180.00
179	W.B. Fuller	600.00	300.00	180.00
180	Geo. Van Haltren	600.00	300.00	180.00
181	Dave Foutz	600.00	300.00	180.00
182	Jouett Meekin	600.00	300.00	180.00
201	W.H. Clark (Clarke)	600.00	300.00	180.00
202	Parke Wilson	600.00	300.00	180.00
586	John M. Ward (portrait, arms folded)	1650.	825.00	495.00
587	John M. Ward (standing, with bat)	1200.	600.00	360.00

1969 N.Y. Boy Scouts

Cards featuring N.Y. Mets and Yankees players were used as a recruitment incentive in 1969. Cards are 2-1/2" x 3-1/2" and printed in black-and-white on thin cardboard. It is unknown, but likely, that players other than those checklisted here were also issued.

		NR MT	EX	VG
Common Player:		12.50	6.25	3.75
(1)	Tommy Agee	12.50	6.25	3.75
(2)	Bud Harrelson	12.50	6.25	3.75
(3)	Cleon Jones	12.50	6.25	3.75
(4)	Bobby Murcer	12.50	6.25	3.75
(5)	Art Shamsky	12.50	6.25	3.75
(6)	Tom Seaver	200.00	100.00	60.00
(7)	Mel Stottlemyre	12.50	6.25	3.75
(8)	Ron Swoboda	12.50	6.25	3.75

Values quoted in this guide reflect the retail price of a card – the price a collector can expect to pay when buying a card from a dealer. The wholesale price – that which a collector can expect to receive from a dealer when selling cards – will be significantly lower, depending on desirability and condition.

1954 N.Y. Journal-American

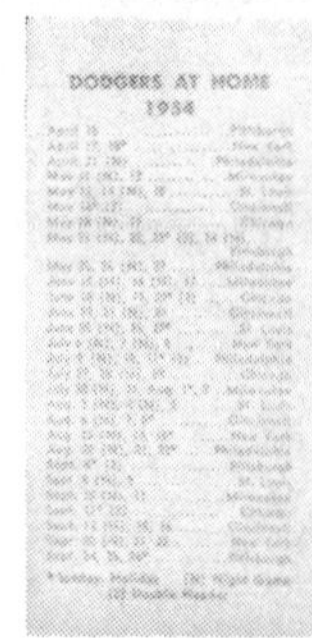

Issued during the Golden Age of baseball in New York City, this 59-card set features only players from the three New York teams of the day - the Giants, Yankees and Dodgers. The 2" by 4" cards were issued at newsstands with the purchase of the now-extinct newspaper. Card fronts have promotional copy and a contest serial number in addition to the player's name and photo. Cards are black and white and unnumbered. Many of the game's top stars are included, such as Mickey Mantle, Willie Mays, Gil Hodges, Duke Snider, Jackie Robinson and Yogi Berra. Card backs featured team schedules. It has been theorized that a 60th Dodgers card should exist. Don Hoak and Bob Milliken have been suggested as the missing card, but the existence of either card has never been confirmed.

		NR MT	EX	VG
Complete Set (59):		2000.	1000.	600.00
Common Player:		13.00	6.50	4.00
(1)	Johnny Antonelli	13.00	6.50	4.00
(2)	Hank Bauer	25.00	12.50	7.50
(3)	Yogi Berra	125.00	62.00	37.00
(4)	Joe Black	15.00	7.50	4.50
(5)	Harry Byrd	13.00	6.50	4.00
(6)	Roy Campanella	125.00	62.00	37.00
(7)	Andy Carey	13.00	6.50	4.00
(8)	Jerry Coleman	13.00	6.50	4.00
(9)	Joe Collins	13.00	6.50	4.00
(10)	Billy Cox	13.00	6.50	4.00
(11)	Al Dark	15.00	7.50	4.50
(12)	Carl Erskine	25.00	12.50	7.50
(13)	Whitey Ford	45.00	22.00	13.50
(14)	Carl Furillo	27.50	13.50	8.25
(15)	Junior Gilliam	25.00	12.50	7.50
(16)	Ruben Gomez	13.00	6.50	4.00
(17)	Marv Grissom	13.00	6.50	4.00
(18)	Jim Hearn	13.00	6.50	4.00
(19)	Gil Hodges	45.00	22.00	13.50
(20)	Bobby Hofman	13.00	6.50	4.00
(21)	Jim Hughes	13.00	6.50	4.00
(22)	Monte Irvin	32.50	16.00	9.75
(23)	Larry Jansen	13.00	6.50	4.00
(24)	Ray Katt	13.00	6.50	4.00
(25)	Steve Kraly	13.00	6.50	4.00
(26)	Bob Kuzava	13.00	6.50	4.00
(27)	Clem Labine	15.00	7.50	4.50
(28)	Frank Leja	13.00	6.50	4.00
(29)	Don Liddle	13.00	6.50	4.00
(30)	Whitey Lockman	13.00	6.50	4.00
(31)	Billy Loes	13.00	6.50	4.00
(32)	Eddie Lopat	25.00	12.50	7.50
(33)	Gil McDougald	27.50	13.50	8.25
(34)	Sal Maglie	15.00	7.50	4.50
(35)	Mickey Mantle	550.00	275.00	165.00
(36)	Willie Mays	275.00	137.00	82.00
(37)	Russ Meyer	13.00	6.50	4.00
(38)	Bill Miller	13.00	6.50	4.00
(39)	Tom Morgan	13.00	6.50	4.00
(40)	Don Mueller	13.00	6.50	4.00
(41)	Don Newcombe	25.00	12.50	7.50
(42)	Irv Noren	13.00	6.50	4.00
(43)	Erv Palica	13.00	6.50	4.00
(44)	Pee Wee Reese	75.00	37.00	22.00
(45)	Allie Reynolds	27.50	13.50	8.25
(46)	Dusty Rhodes	13.00	6.50	4.00
(47)	Phil Rizzuto	70.00	35.00	21.00
(48)	Ed Robinson	13.00	6.50	4.00
(49)	Jackie Robinson	275.00	137.00	82.00
(50)	Preacher Roe	25.00	12.50	7.50
(51)	George Shuba	13.00	6.50	4.00
(52)	Duke Snider	195.00	97.00	58.00
(53)	Hank Thompson	13.00	6.50	4.00
(54)	Wes Westrum	13.00	6.50	4.00
(55)	Hoyt Wilhelm	32.50	16.00	9.75
(56)	Davey Williams	13.00	6.50	4.00
(57)	Dick Williams	15.00	7.50	4.50
(58)	Gene Woodling	15.00	7.50	4.50
(59)	Al Worthington	13.00	6.50	4.00

1984 N.Y. Mets M.V.P. Club

This nine-card, uncut panel was issued - along with other souvenir items - as a promotion by the New York Mets M.V.P. (Most Valuable Person)

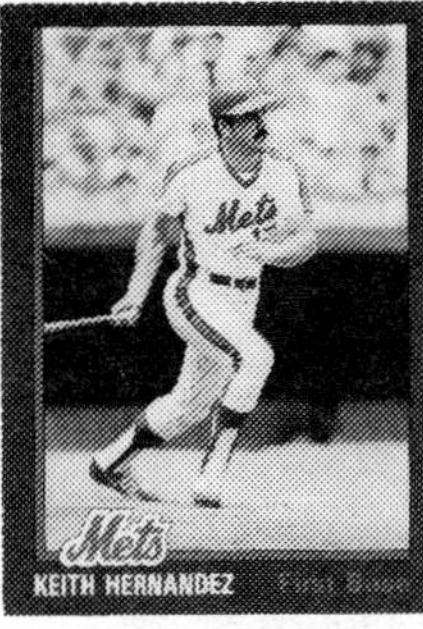

Club. Available from the club by mail, the perforated panel features eight full-color player cards, plus a special promotional card in the center. The full panel measures 7-1/2" by 10-1/2", with individual cards measuring the standard 2-1/2" by 3-1/2". Card backs are numbered in the upper right corner and include player stats and career highlights.

		MT	NR MT	EX
Complete Panel Set:		9.00	6.75	3.50
Complete Singles Set:		3.00	2.25	1.25
Common Single Player:		.15	.11	.06
	Panel	12.00	9.00	4.75
1	Dave Johnson	.30	.25	.12
2	Ron Darling	.40	.30	.15
3	George Foster	.40	.30	.15
4	Keith Hernandez	.40	.30	.15
5	Jesse Orosco	.15	.11	.06
6	Rusty Staub	.30	.25	.12
7	Darryl Strawberry	1.00	.70	.40
8	Mookie Wilson	.30	.25	.12
----	Membership Card	.05	.04	.02

A player's name in italic type indicates a rookie card. An (FC) indicates a player's first card for that particular card company.

1985 N.Y. Mets Super Fan Club

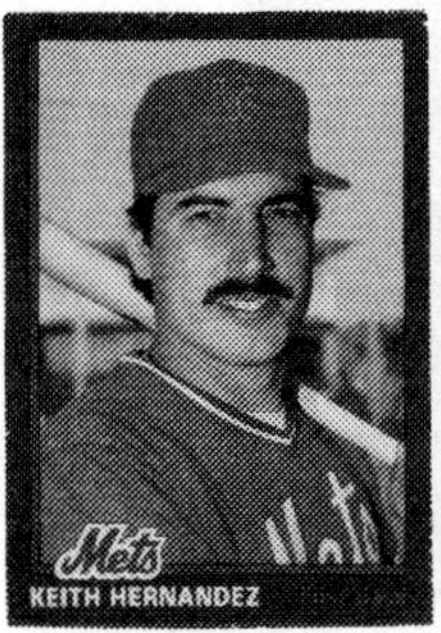

This specially-produced nine-card panel was issued as part of a souvenir package by the New York Mets Super Fan Club. The full-color, perforated panel measures 7-1/2" by 10-1/2" and features eight standard-size player cards, plus a special promotional card in the center. The uncut sheet was available by mail directly from the club. The backs are numbered in the upper right corner and include player statistics and career highlights.

		MT	NR MT	EX
Complete Panel Set:		12.00	9.00	4.75
Complete Singles Set:		4.00	3.00	1.50
Common Single Player:		.15	.11	.06
	Panel	12.00	11.00	6.00
1	Wally Backman	.15	.11	.06
2	Bruce Berenyi	.15	.11	.06
3	Gary Carter	.60	.45	.25
4	George Foster	.40	.30	.15
5	Dwight Gooden	1.50	1.25	.60
6	Keith Hernandez	.40	.30	.15
7	Doug Sisk	.15	.11	.06
8	Darryl Strawberry	.90	.70	.35
----	Membership Card	.05	.04	.02

Values for recent cards and sets are listed in Mint (MT), Near Mint (NM), reflecting the fact that many cards from recent years have been preserved in top condition. Recent cards and sets in less than Excellent condition have little collector interest.

1986 N.Y. Mets Super Fan Club

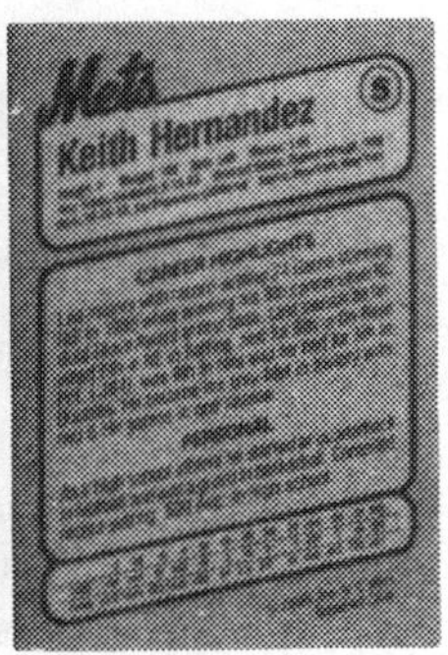

This special nine-card panel was issued by the fan club of the 1986 World Champion New York Mets, along with other souvenir items gained with membership in the club. Included in the full-color set are eight top Mets players, with a promotional card in the center of the panel. Individual cards measure 2-1/2" by 3-1/2", and are perforated at the edges to facilitate separation. The full panel measures 70-1/2" by 10-1/2". Card fronts feature posed photos of each player, along with name, position and team logo. Backs feature career and personal data, and are printed in the team's blue and orange colors.

		MT	NR MT	EX
Complete Panel Set:		8.00	6.00	3.25
Complete Singles Set:		4.00	3.00	1.50
Common Single Player:		.15	.11	.06
	Panel	8.00	7.50	4.00
1	Wally Backman	.15	.11	.06
2	Gary Carter	.70	.50	.30
3	Ron Darling	.40	.30	.15
4	Dwight Gooden	.90	.70	.35
5	Keith Hernandez	.40	.30	.15
6	Howard Johnson	.70	.50	.30
7	Roger McDowell	.40	.30	.15
8	Darryl Strawberry	1.25	.90	.50
----	Membership Card	.05	.04	.02

1886 New York Baseball Club (H812)

This extremely rare 19th Century baseball card issue can be classified under the general category of "trade" cards, a popular advertising vehicle of the period. The cards measure 3" by 4-3/4" and feature blue line drawings of members of the "New York Base Ball Club," which is printed along the top. As was common with this type of trade card, the bottom was left blank to accomodate various messages. The known examples of this set carry ads for local tobacco merchants, and the player potraits are all based on the photographs used in the N167 Goodwin set. The cards, which have been assigned an ACC designation of H812, are printed on thin paper rather than cardboard.

		NR MT	EX	VG
Complete Set:		27000.	13500.	8100.
Common Player:		3000.	1500.	900.00
(1)	T. Dealsey	3000.	1500.	900.00
(2)	M. Dorgan	3000.	1500.	900.00
(3)	T. Esterbrook	3000.	1500.	900.00
(4)	W. Ewing	5000.	2500.	1500.
(5)	J. Gerhardt	3000.	1500.	900.00
(6)	J. O'Rourke	5000.	2500.	1500.
(7)	D. Richardson	3000.	1500.	900.00
(8)	M. Welch	5000.	2500.	1500.

Regional interest may affect the value of a card.

1985 Nike

Nike, the athletic shoe company, has produced posters and counter display cards of its posters for several years, but in 1985 issued a five-card set. The cards are borderless, color miniature versions (3-1/16" by 5-1/16") of the Nike posters. Backs feature personal data and career highlights, along with the warning, "Promotional Use Only/Not For Resale." The five-card set includes two baseball players.

		MT	NR MT	EX
Complete Set:		40.00	30.00	16.00
Common Player:		2.00	1.50	.80
(1)	Dwight Gooden (baseball)	4.00	3.00	1.50
(2)	Michael Jordan (basketball)	30.00	22.00	12.00
(3)	James Lofton (football)	3.00	2.25	1.25
(4)	John McEnroe (tennis)	10.00	7.50	4.00
(5)	Lance Parrish (baseball)	2.00	1.50	.80

1953 Northland Bread Labels

This bread end-label set consists of 32 players - two from each major league team. The unnumbered black and white labels measure approximately 2-11/16" square and include the slogan "Bread for Energy" along the top. An album to house the labels was also part of the promotion.

		NR MT	EX	VG
Complete Set:		1800.	900.00	540.00
Common Player:		50.00	25.00	15.00
(1)	Cal Abrams	50.00	25.00	15.00
(2)	Richie Ashburn	75.00	37.00	22.00
(3)	Gus Bell	50.00	25.00	15.00
(4)	Jim Busby	50.00	25.00	15.00
(5)	Clint Courtney	50.00	25.00	15.00
(6)	Billy Cox	50.00	25.00	15.00
(7)	Jim Dyck	50.00	25.00	15.00
(8)	Nellie Fox	65.00	32.00	19.50
(9)	Sid Gordon	50.00	25.00	15.00
(10)	Warren Hacker	50.00	25.00	15.00
(11)	Jim Hearn	50.00	25.00	15.00
(12)	Fred Hutchinson	55.00	27.00	16.50
(13)	Monte Irvin	80.00	40.00	24.00
(14)	Jackie Jensen	65.00	32.00	19.50
(15)	Ted Kluszewski	80.00	40.00	24.00
(16)	Bob Lemon	80.00	40.00	24.00
(17)	Maury McDermott	50.00	25.00	15.00
(18)	Minny Minoso	65.00	32.00	19.50
(19)	Johnny Mize	80.00	40.00	24.00
(20)	Mel Parnell	50.00	25.00	15.00
(21)	Howie Pollet	50.00	25.00	15.00
(22)	Jerry Priddy	50.00	25.00	15.00
(23)	Allie Reynolds	60.00	30.00	18.00
(24)	Preacher Roe	60.00	30.00	18.00
(25)	Al Rosen	60.00	30.00	18.00
(26)	Connie Ryan	50.00	25.00	15.00
(27)	Hank Sauer	50.00	25.00	15.00
(28)	Red Schoendienst	80.00	40.00	24.00
(29)	Bobby Shantz	55.00	27.00	16.50
(30)	Enos Slaughter	80.00	40.00	24.00
(31)	Warren Spahn	100.00	50.00	30.00
(32)	Gus Zernial	50.00	25.00	15.00

1960 Nu-Card

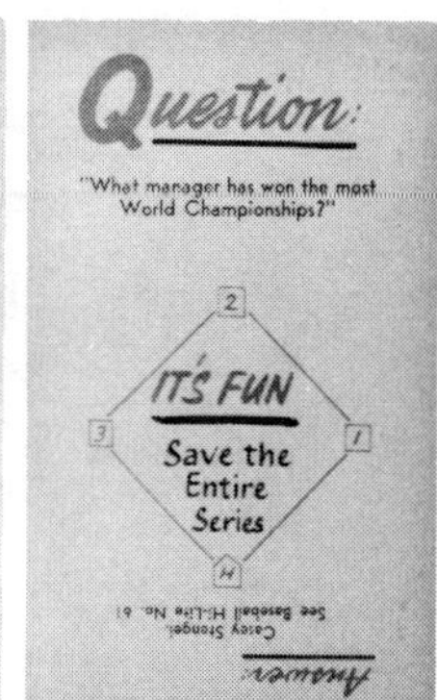

These large, 3-1/4" by 5-3/8" cards are printed in a mock newspaper format, with a headline, picture and story describing one of baseball's greatest events. There are 72 events featured in the set, which is printed in red and black. Each card is numbered in the upper left corner. The card backs offer a quiz question and answer. Certain cards in the set can be found with the fronts printed entirely in black. These cards may command a slight premium.

		NR MT	EX	VG
	Complete Set (72):	225.00	112.00	67.00
	Common Player:	3.00	1.50	.90
1	Babe Hits 3 Homers In A Series Game	15.00	7.50	4.50
2	Podres Pitching Wins Series	3.00	1.50	.90
3	Bevans Pitches No Hitter, Almost	3.00	1.50	.90
4	Box Score Devised By Reporter	3.00	1.50	.90
5	VanderMeer Pitches 2 No Hitters	3.00	1.50	.90
6	Indians Take Bums	3.00	1.50	.90
7	DiMag Comes Thru	12.00	6.00	3.50
8	Mathewson Pitches 3 W.S. Shutouts	3.00	1.50	.90
9	Haddix Pitches 12 Perfect Innings	3.00	1.50	.90
10	Thomson's Homer Sinks Dodgers	3.00	1.50	.90
11	Hubbell Strikes Out 5 A.L. Stars	3.00	1.50	.90
12	Pickoff Ends Series (Marty Marion)	3.00	1.50	.90
13	Cards Take Series From Yanks (Grover Cleveland Alexander)	3.00	1.50	.90
14	Dizzy And Daffy Win Series	3.00	1.50	.90
15	Owen Drops 3rd Strike	3.00	1.50	.90
16	Ruth Calls His Shot	12.00	6.00	3.50
17	Merkle Pulls Boner	3.00	1.50	.90
18	Larsen Hurls Perfect World Series Game	3.00	1.50	.90
19	Bean Ball Ends Career of Mickey Cochrane	3.00	1.50	.90
20	Banks Belts 47 Homers, Earns MVP Honors	3.00	1.50	.90
21	Stan Musial Hits 5 Homers In 1 Day	3.00	1.50	.90
22	Mickey Mantle Hits Longest Homer	18.00	9.00	5.50
23	Sievers Captures Home Run Title	3.00	1.50	.90
24	Gehrig Consecutive Game Record Ends	15.00	7.50	4.50
25	Red Schoendienst Key Player In Victory	3.00	1.50	.90
26	Midget Pinch-Hits For St. Louis Browns (Eddie Gaedel)	3.00	1.50	.90
27	Willie Mays Makes Greatest Catch	8.00	4.00	2.50
28	Homer By Berra Puts Yanks In 1st Place	3.00	1.50	.90
29	Campy National League's MVP	3.00	1.50	.90
30	Bob Turley Hurls Yanks To Championship	3.00	1.50	.90
31	Dodgers Take Series From Sox In Six	3.00	1.50	.90
32	Furillo Hero As Dodgers Beat Chicago	3.00	1.50	.90
33	Adcock Gets Four Homers And A Double	3.00	1.50	.90
34	Dickey Chosen All Star Catcher	3.00	1.50	.90
35	Burdette Beats Yanks In 3 Series Games	3.00	1.50	.90
36	Umpires Clear White Sox Bench	3.00	1.50	.90
37	Reese Honored As Greatest Dodger S.S.	3.00	1.50	.90
38	Joe DiMaggio Hits In 56 Straight Games	12.00	6.00	3.50
39	Ted Williams Hits .406 For Season	7.50	3.75	2.25
40	Johnson Pitches 56 Scoreless Innings	3.00	1.50	.90
41	Hodges Hits 4 Home Runs In Nite Game	3.00	1.50	.90
42	Greenberg Returns To Tigers From Army	3.00	1.50	.90
43	Ty Cobb Named Best Player Of All Time	10.00	5.00	3.00
44	Robin Roberts Wins 28 Games	3.00	1.50	.90
45	Rizzuto's 2 Runs Save 1st Place	3.00	1.50	.90
46	Tigers Beat Out Senators For Pennant (Hal Newhouser)	3.00	1.50	.90
47	Babe Ruth Hits 60th Home Run	12.00	6.00	3.50
48	Cy Young Honored	3.00	1.50	.90
49	Killebrew Starts Spring Training	3.00	1.50	.90
50	Mantle Hits Longest Homer At Stadium	15.00	7.50	4.50
51	Braves Take Pennant (Hank Aaron)	3.00	1.50	.90
52	Ted Williams Hero Of All Star Game	7.50	3.75	2.25
53	Robinson Saves Dodgers For Playoffs (Jackie Robinson)	3.00	1.50	.90
54	Snodgrass Muffs A Fly Ball	3.00	1.50	.90
55	Snider Belts 2 Homers	3.00	1.50	.90
56	New York Giants Win 26 Straight Games (Christy Mathewson)	3.00	1.50	.90
57	Ted Kluszewski Stars In 1st Game Win	3.00	1.50	.90
58	Ott Walks 5 Times In A Single Game (Mel Ott)	3.00	1.50	.90
59	Harvey Kuenn Takes Batting Title	3.00	1.50	.90
60	Bob Feller Hurls 3rd No-Hitter Of Career	3.00	1.50	.90
61	Yanks Champs Again! (Casey Stengel)	3.00	1.50	.90
62	Aaron's Bat Beats Yankees In Series	8.00	4.00	2.50
63	Warren Spahn Beats Yanks in World Series	3.00	1.50	.90
64	Ump's Wrong Call Helps Dodgers	3.00	1.50	.90
65	Kaline Hits 3 Homers, 2 In Same Inning	3.00	1.50	.90
66	Bob Allison Named A.L. Rookie of Year	3.00	1.50	.90
67	McCovey Blasts Way Into Giant Lineup	3.00	1.50	.90
68	Colavito Hits Four Homers In One Game	3.00	1.50	.90
69	Erskine Sets Strike Out Record In W.S.	3.00	1.50	.90
70	Sal Maglie Pitches No-Hit Game	3.00	1.50	.90
71	Early Wynn Victory Crushes Yanks	3.00	1.50	.90
72	Nellie Fox American League's M.V.P.	3.00	1.50	.90

1961 Nu-Card

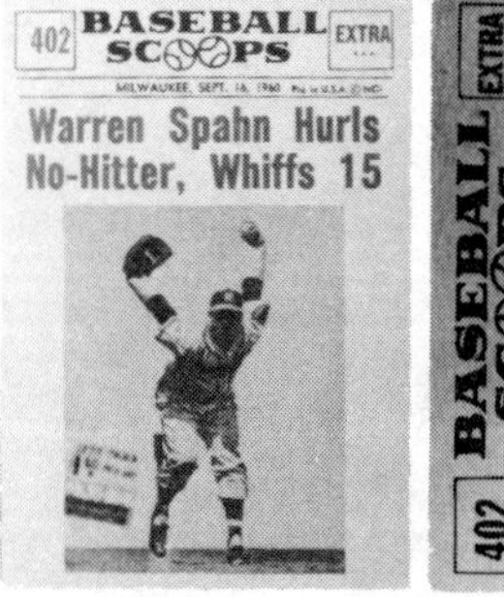

Very similar in style to their set of the year before, the Nu-Card Baseball Scoops were issued in a smaller 2-1/2" by 3-1/2" size, but still featured the mock newspaper card front. This 80-card set is numbered from 401 to 480, with numbers shown on both the card front and back. These cards, which commemorate great moments in individual players' careers, included only the headline and black and white photo on the fronts, with the descriptive story on the card backs. Cards are again printed in red and black. It appears the set may have been counterfeited, though when is not known. These cards can be determined by examining the card photo for unusual blurring and fuzziness.

		NR MT	EX	VG
	Complete Set (80):	230.00	115.00	69.00
	Common Player:	2.00	1.00	.60
401	Gentile Powers Birds Into 1st	2.00	1.00	.60
402	Warren Spahn Hurls No-Hitter, Whiffs 15	4.00	2.00	1.25
403	Mazeroski's Homer Wins Series For Bucs	8.00	4.00	2.50
404	Willie Mays' 3 Triples Paces Giants	10.00	5.00	3.00
405	Woodie Held Slugs 2 Homers, 6 RBIs	2.00	1.00	.60
406	Vern Law Winner Of Cy Young Award	2.00	1.00	.60
407	Runnels Makes 9 Hits in Twin-Bill	2.00	1.00	.60
408	Braves' Lew Burdette Wins No-Hitter, 1-0	2.00	1.00	.60
409	Dick Stuart Hits 3 Homers, Single	2.00	1.00	.60
410	Don Cardwell Of Cubs Pitches No-Hit Game	2.00	1.00	.60
411	Camilo Pascual Strikes Out 15 Bosox	2.00	1.00	.60
412	Eddie Mathews Blasts 300th Big League HR	2.00	1.00	.60
413	Groat, NL Bat King, Named Loop's MVP	2.00	1.00	.60
414	AL Votes To Expand To 10 Teams (Gene Autry)	2.00	1.00	.60
415	Bobby Richardson Sets Series Mark	2.00	1.00	.60
416	Maris Nips Mantle For AL MVP Award	3.50	1.75	1.00
417	Merkle Pulls Boner	2.00	1.00	.60
418	Larsen Hurls Perefect World Series Game	2.00	1.00	.60
419	Bean Ball Ends Career Of Mickey Cochrane	2.00	1.00	.60
420	Banks Belts 47 Homers, Earns MVP Award	2.00	1.00	.60
421	Stan Musial Hits 5 Homers In 1 Day	4.00	2.00	1.25
422	Mickey Mantle Hits Longest Homer	15.00	7.50	4.50
423	Sievers Captures Home Run Title	2.00	1.00	.60
424	Gehrig Consecutive Game Record Ends	10.00	5.00	3.00
425	Red Schoendienst Key Player In Victory	2.00	1.00	.60
426	Midget Pinch-Hits For St. Louis Browns (Eddie Gaedel)	2.00	1.00	.60
427	Willie Mays Makes Greatest Catch	10.00	5.00	3.00
428	Robinson Saves Dodgers For Playoffs	5.00	2.50	1.50
429	Campy Most Valuable Player	2.50	1.25	.70
430	Turley Hurls Yanks To Championship	2.00	1.00	.60
431	Dodgers Take Series From Sox In Six (Larry Sherry)	2.00	1.00	.60
432	Furillo Hero In 3rd World Series Game	2.00	1.00	.60
433	Adcock Gets Four Homers, Double	2.00	1.00	.60
434	Dickey Chosen All Star Catcher	2.00	1.00	.60
435	Burdette Beats Yanks In 3 Series Games	2.00	1.00	.60
436	Umpires Clear White Sox Bench	2.00	1.00	.60
437	Reese Honored As Greatest Dodgers S.S.	2.00	1.00	.60
438	Joe DiMaggio Hits In 56 Straight Games	12.00	6.00	3.50
439	Ted Williams Hits .406 For Season	7.50	3.75	2.25
440	Johnson Pitches 56 Scoreless Innings	2.00	1.00	.60
441	Hodges Hits 4 Home Runs In Nite Game	2.00	1.00	.60
442	Greenberg Returns To Tigers From Army	2.00	1.00	.60
443	Ty Cobb Named Best Player Of All Time	9.00	4.50	2.75
444	Robin Roberts Wins 28 Games	2.00	1.00	.60
445	Rizzuto's 2 Runs Save 1st Place	2.00	1.00	.60
446	Tigers Beat Out Senators For Pennant (Hal Newhouser)	2.00	1.00	.60
447	Babe Ruth Hits 60th Home Run	12.00	6.00	3.50
448	Cy Young Honored	2.00	1.00	.60
449	Killebrew Starts Spring Training	2.00	1.00	.60
450	Mantle Hits Longest Homer At Stadium	15.00	7.50	4.50
451	Braves Take Pennant	2.00	1.00	.60
452	Ted Williams Hero Of All Star Game	7.50	3.75	2.25
453	Homer By Berra Puts Yanks In 1st Place	2.00	1.00	.60
454	Snodgrass Muffs A Fly Ball	2.00	1.00	.60
455	Babe Hits 3 Homers In A Series Game	12.00	6.00	3.50
456	New York Wins 26 Straight Games	2.00	1.00	.60
457	Ted Kluszewski Stars In 1st Series Win	2.00	1.00	.60
458	Ott Walks 5 Times In A Single Game	2.00	1.00	.60
459	Harvey Kuenn Takes Batting Title	2.00	1.00	.60
460	Bob Feller Hurls 3rd No-Hitter Of Career	2.00	1.00	.60
461	Yanks Champs Again! (Casey Stengel)	2.00	1.00	.60
462	Aaron's Bat Beats Yankees In Series	7.50	3.75	2.25
463	Warren Spahn Beats Yanks In World Series	2.00	1.00	.60
464	Ump's Wrong Call Helps Dodgers	2.00	1.00	.60
465	Kaline Hits 3 Homers, 2 In Same Inning	2.00	1.00	.60
466	Bob Allison Named A.L. Rookie Of Year	2.00	1.00	.60
467	DiMag Comes Thru	12.00	6.00	3.50
468	Colavito Hits Four Homers In One Game	2.00	1.00	.60
469	Erskine Sets Strike Out Record In W.S.	2.00	1.00	.60
470	Sal Maglie Pitches No-Hit Game	2.00	1.00	.60
471	Early Wynn Victory Crushes Yanks	2.00	1.00	.60

472	Nellie Fox American League's MVP	2.00	1.00	.60
473	Pickoff Ends Series (Marty Marion)	2.00	1.00	.60
474	Podres Pitching Wins Series	2.00	1.00	.60
475	Owen Drops 3rd Strike	2.00	1.00	.60
476	Dizzy And Daffy Win Series	4.00	2.00	1.25
477	Mathewson Pitches 3 W.S. Shutouts	2.00	1.00	.60
478	Haddix Pitches 12 Perfect Innings	2.00	1.00	.60
479	Hubbell Strike Out 5 A.L. Stars	2.00	1.00	.60
480	Homer Sinks Dodgers (Bobby Thomson)	4.00	2.00	1.25

1889 Number 7/Diamond S Cigars (N526)

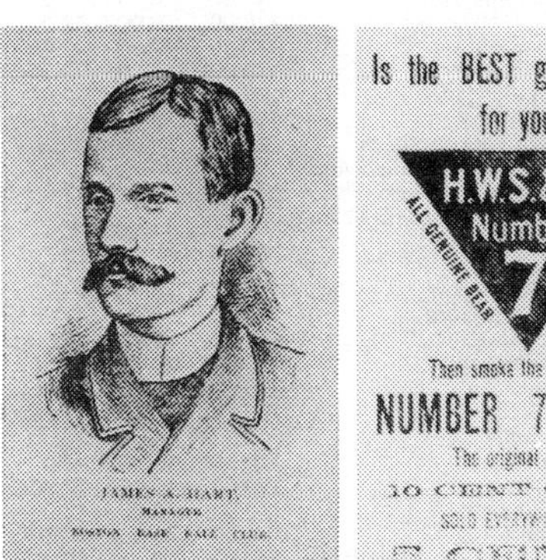

Two versions of this set picturing Boston players were issued in 1889 by Number 7 Cigars and Diamond S Cigars. The cards measure approximately 3-1/8" by 4-1/2" and feature black and white line portrait drawings of the players with their name printed below in capital letters along with the team name ("Boston Base Ball Club"). The backs carry an ad for either Number 7 Cigars, a product of H.W.S. & Co., or Diamond S Cigars, advertised as the "Best 10 cent Cigar in America." Except for the backs, the two sets are identical.

		NR MT	EX	VG
Complete Set:		7750.	3875.	2325.
Common Player:		400.00	200.00	120.00
(1)	C.W. Bennett	400.00	200.00	120.00
(2)	Dennis Brothers	800.00	400.00	240.00
(3)	T.T. Brown	400.00	200.00	120.00
(4)	John G. Clarkson	800.00	400.00	240.00
(5)	C.W. Ganzel	400.00	200.00	120.00
(6)	James A. Hart	400.00	200.00	120.00
(7)	R.F. Johnston	400.00	200.00	120.00
(8)	M.J. Kelly	1000.	500.00	300.00
(9)	M.J. Madden	400.00	200.00	120.00
(10)	Wm. Nash	400.00	200.00	120.00
(11)	Jos. Quinn	400.00	200.00	120.00
(12)	Chas. Radbourn	800.00	400.00	240.00
(13)	J.B. Ray (should be I.B.)	400.00	200.00	120.00
(14)	Hardie Richardson	400.00	200.00	120.00
(15)	Wm. Sowders	400.00	200.00	120.00

1950 Num Num Cleveland Indians

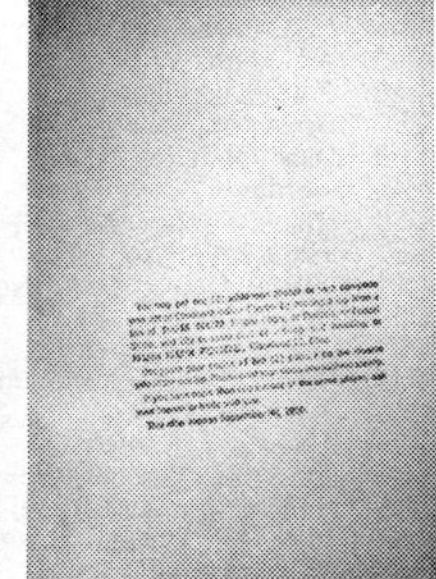

The 6-1/2" x 9" photopack pictures sold at Municipal Stadium did double duty in 1950 when they were also used as a premium for Num Num snack foods. A rubber-stamped notice on the back of the black-and-white photos offered two pictures for 10 cents and a box top, while encouraging trading. The pictures generally feature posed action shots with a facsimile autograph and white border. Backs are blank except for the rubber stamping. The unnumbered cards are checklisted here alphabetically.

		NR MT	EX	VG
Complete Set:		1350.	650.00	400.00
Common Player:		30.00	15.00	9.00
(1)	Bob Avila	40.00	20.00	12.00
(2)	Gene Bearden	30.00	15.00	9.00
(3)	Al Benton	30.00	15.00	9.00
(4)	John Berardino	50.00	25.00	15.00
(5)	Ray Boone	30.00	15.00	9.00
(6)	Lou Boudreau	65.00	32.00	19.50
(7)	Allie Clark	30.00	15.00	9.00
(8)	Larry Doby	45.00	22.00	13.50
(9)	Luke Easter	35.00	17.50	10.50
(10)	Bob Feller	125.00	62.00	37.00
(11)	Jess Flores	30.00	15.00	9.00
(12)	Mike Garcia	35.00	17.50	10.50
(13)	Joe Gordon	30.00	15.00	9.00
(14)	Hank Greenberg	90.00	45.00	27.00
(15)	Steve Gromek	30.00	15.00	9.00
(16)	Jim Hegan	30.00	15.00	9.00
(17)	Ken Keltner	35.00	17.50	10.50
(18)	Bob Kennedy	150.00	75.00	45.00
(19)	Bob Lemon	65.00	32.00	19.50
(20)	Dale Mitchell	30.00	15.00	9.00
(21)	Ray Murray	30.00	15.00	9.00
(22)	Satchell Paige	200.00	100.00	60.00
(23)	Frank Papish	30.00	15.00	9.00
(24)	Hal Peck	30.00	15.00	9.00
(25)	Chick Pieretti	30.00	15.00	9.00
(26)	Al Rosen	35.00	17.50	10.50
(27)	Dick Rozek	30.00	15.00	9.00
(28)	Mike Tresh	30.00	15.00	9.00
(29)	Thurman Tucker	30.00	15.00	9.00
(30)	Bill Veeck	75.00	37.00	22.00
(31)	Mickey Vernon	30.00	15.00	9.00
(32)	Early Wynn	65.00	32.00	19.50
(33)	Sam Zoldak	30.00	15.00	9.00
(34)	Coaches (George Susce, Herold Ruel, Bill McKechnie, Steve O'Neill, Mel Harder)	30.00	15.00	9.00

1952 Num Num Cleveland Indians

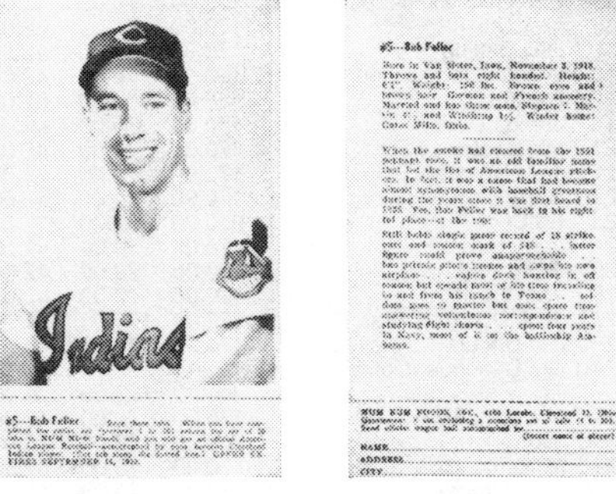

Distributed with packages of Num Num potato chips, pretzels and other snack foods, this black-and-white set, like the 1950 issue, was also issued in a slightly different format directly by the team. The Num Num cards have a 1" tab at the bottom which could be redeemed, when a complete set was collected, for an autographed baseball. The team-issued version of the cards was printed without the tabs. Also like the 1950 Num Nums, Bob Kennedy's card is unaccountably scarce in the 1952 set. The '52 cards measure 3-1/2" x 5-1/2" including the tab, which has the card number on front, along with redemption details. Backs, also printed in black-and-white, repeat the card number in the upper-left corner. There is significant player biographical information and some 1951 season highlights. Cards with no tabs are worth about 1/3 less than the values quoted.

		NR MT	EX	VG
Complete Set:		1100.	550.00	325.00
Common Player:		35.00	17.50	10.50
1	Lou Brissie	35.00	17.50	10.50
2	Jim Hegan	35.00	17.50	10.50
3	Bridie Tebbetts	35.00	17.50	10.50
4	Bob Lemon	75.00	37.00	22.00
5	Bob Feller	150.00	75.00	45.00
6	Early Wynn	75.00	37.00	22.00
7	Mike Garcia	45.00	22.00	13.50
8	Steve Gromek	35.00	17.50	10.50
9	Bob Chakales	35.00	17.50	10.50
10	Al Rosen	45.00	22.00	13.50
11	Dick Rozek	35.00	17.50	10.50
12	Luke Easter	40.00	20.00	12.00
13	Ray Boone	35.00	17.50	10.50
14	Bobby Avila	40.00	20.00	12.00
15	Dale Mitchell	35.00	17.50	10.50
16	Bob Kennedy	250.00	125.00	75.00
17	Harry Simpson	35.00	17.50	10.50
18	Larry Doby	45.00	22.00	13.50
19	Sam Jones	35.00	17.50	10.50
20	Al Lopez	75.00	37.00	22.00

1886 Old Judge New York Giants (N167)

Produced in 1886, the rare N167 Old Judge tobacco cards were the first to be issued by New York's Goodwin & Co., the parent firm of Old Judge Cigarettes. The 1-1/2" by 2-1/2" sepia-toned cards were printed on thin paper and featured only members of the New York National League club. Twelve subjects are known to exist, five of whom are Hall of Famers. The front of each card lists the player's name, position and team and has the words "Old Judge" at the top. The backs contain another ad for the Old Judge brand and also include a line noting that the player poses were "copied from by J. Wood, 208, N.Y."

		NR MT	EX	VG
Complete Set:		24000.	12000.	7000.
Common Player:		1500.	750.00	450.00
(1)	Roger Connor	2500.	1250.	750.00
(2)	Larry Corcoran	1500.	750.00	450.00
(3)	Mike Dorgan	1500.	750.00	450.00
(4)	Dude Esterbrook	1500.	750.00	450.00
(5)	Buck Ewing	2500.	1250.	750.00
(6)	Joe Gerhardt	1500.	750.00	450.00
(7)	Pete Gillespie	1500.	750.00	450.00
(8)	Tim Keefe	2500.	1250.	750.00
(9)	Orator Jim O'Rourke	2500.	1250.	750.00
(10)	Danny Richardson	1500.	750.00	450.00
(11)	Monte Ward	2500.	1250.	750.00
(12)	Mickey Welsh (Welch)	2500.	1250.	750.00

1887 Old Judge (N172)

This is one of the most fascinating of all card sets, as the number of cards issued will probably never be finally determined. These cards were issued by the Goodwin & Co. tobacco firm in their Old Judge and, to a lesser extent, Gypsy Queen cigarettes. Players from more than 40 major and minor league teams are pictured on the approximately 1-1/

2" by 2-1/2" cards, with some 518 different players known to exist. Up to 17 different pose and team variations exist for some players, and the cards were issued both with and without dates on the card fronts, numbered and unnumbered, and with both handwritten and machine-printed names. Known variations number in the thousands. The cards themselves are sepia-toned photographs pasted onto thick cardboard. They are blank-backed. The N172 listings are based on the recordings in The Cartophilic Society's (of Great Britian) World Index, Part IV, compiled by E.C. Wharton-Tigar with the help of many collectors, especially Donald J. McPherson of California and Lew Lipset of New York. Because of the vastness of the N172 issue, no complete set price is given.

		NR MT	EX	VG
	Common Player:	170.00	70.00	42.00
	Brown's Champions:	275.00	113.00	69.00
	Dotted Ties:	300.00	123.00	75.00
1	Gus Albert (Alberts)	170.00	70.00	42.00
2	Alcott	170.00	70.00	42.00
3	Alexander	170.00	70.00	42.00
4	Myron Allen (Kansas City - fielding, 32)	170.00	70.00	42.00
5	Bob Allen (Pittsburgh, Philadelphia)	170.00	70.00	42.00
6	Uncle Bill Alvord	170.00	70.00	42.00
7	Varney Anderson	170.00	70.00	42.00
8	Wally Andrews (Omaha)	170.00	70.00	42.00
9	Ed Andrews (Philadelphia)	170.00	70.00	42.00
9-6	Ed Andrews, Buster Hoover	250.00	102.00	62.00
10	Bill Annis	170.00	70.00	42.00
11	Cap Anson	2400.	984.00	600.00
12	Old Hoss Ardner	170.00	70.00	42.00
13	Tug Arundel	170.00	70.00	42.00
14	Jersey Bakley (Bakely)	170.00	70.00	42.00
15	Fido Baldwin (Chicago, Columbus)	170.00	70.00	42.00
16	Kid Baldwin (Cincinnati)	170.00	70.00	42.00
17	Lady Baldwin (Detroit, Cincinnati)	170.00	70.00	42.00
18	James Banning	170.00	70.00	42.00
19	Samuel Barkley	170.00	70.00	42.00
20	John Barnes	170.00	70.00	42.00
21	Bald Billy Barnie	170.00	70.00	42.00
22	Charles Bassett	170.00	70.00	42.00
23	Charles Bastian	170.00	70.00	42.00
23-6	Charles Bastian, Schriver	250.00	102.00	62.00
24	Ed Beatin	170.00	70.00	42.00
25	Jake Beckley	950.00	389.00	237.00
26	Stephen Behel (dotted tie)	350.00	143.00	87.00
27	Charles Bennett	170.00	70.00	42.00
28	Louis Bierbauer	170.00	70.00	42.00
28-5	Louis Bierbauer, Gamble	250.00	102.00	62.00
29	Bill Bishop	170.00	70.00	42.00
30	Bill Blair	170.00	70.00	42.00
31	Ned Bligh	170.00	70.00	42.00
32	Bogart	170.00	70.00	42.00
33	Boyce	170.00	70.00	42.00
34	Boyd	170.00	70.00	42.00
35	Honest John Boyle (St. Louis, Chicago)	170.00	70.00	42.00
36	Handsome Boyle (Indianapolis, New York)	170.00	70.00	42.00
37	Nick Bradley (Kansas City, Worcester)	170.00	70.00	42.00
38	Grin Bradley (Sioux City)	170.00	70.00	42.00
39	Stephen Brady (dotted tie)	350.00	143.00	87.00
40	Breckenridge	300.00	123.00	75.00
41	Timothy Brosnam	170.00	70.00	42.00
42	Cal Broughton	170.00	70.00	42.00
43	Dan Brouthers	850.00	348.00	212.00
44	Thomas Brown (Pittsburgh, Boston)	170.00	70.00	42.00
45	California Brown (New York)	170.00	70.00	42.00
46	Pete Browning	250.00	102.00	62.00
47	Charles Brynan	170.00	70.00	42.00
48	Al Buckenberger	250.00	102.00	62.00
49	Dick Buckley	170.00	70.00	42.00
50	Charles Buffinton	170.00	70.00	42.00
51	Ernest Burch	170.00	70.00	42.00
52	Bill Burdick	170.00	70.00	42.00
53	Black Jack Burdock	170.00	70.00	42.00
54	Robert Burks (Burk)	170.00	70.00	42.00
55	Watch Burnham	250.00	102.00	62.00
56	James Burns (Kansas City, Omaha)	170.00	70.00	42.00
57	No World Index listing			
58	Oyster Burns (Baltimore, Brooklyn)	170.00	70.00	42.00
59	Thomas Burns (Chicago)	170.00	70.00	42.00
60	Doc Bushong (Brooklyn)	170.00	70.00	42.00
60-1	Doc Bushong (Brown's Champions)	275.00	113.00	69.00
61	Patsy Cahill	170.00	70.00	42.00
62	Count Campau	170.00	70.00	42.00
63	Jimmy Canavan	170.00	70.00	42.00
64	Bart Cantz	170.00	70.00	42.00
65	Handsome Jack Carney	170.00	70.00	42.00
66	Hick Carpenter	170.00	70.00	42.00
67	Cliff Carroll (Washington)	170.00	70.00	42.00
68	Scrappy Carroll (St. Paul, Chicago)	170.00	70.00	42.00
69	Fred Carroll (Pittsburgh)	170.00	70.00	42.00
70	Jumbo Cartwright	170.00	70.00	42.00
71	Parisian Bob Caruthers (Brooklyn)	200.00	82.00	50.00
71-1	Parisian Bob Caruthers (Brown's Champions)	225.00	92.00	56.00
72	Dan Casey	170.00	70.00	42.00
73	Icebox Chamberlain	170.00	70.00	42.00
74	Cupid Childs	170.00	70.00	42.00
75	Spider Clark (Washington)	170.00	70.00	42.00
76	Bob Clark (Brooklyn)	170.00	70.00	42.00
76-6	Bob Clark, Mickey Hughes	250.00	102.00	62.00
77	Dad Clarke	170.00	70.00	42.00
78	John Clarkson	850.00	348.00	212.00
79	Jack Clements	170.00	70.00	42.00
80	Elmer Cleveland	170.00	70.00	42.00
81	Monk Cline	170.00	70.00	42.00
82	Cody	170.00	70.00	42.00
83	John Coleman	170.00	70.00	42.00
84	Bill Collins (NY, Newark)	170.00	70.00	42.00
85	Hub Collins (Louisville, Brooklyn)	170.00	70.00	42.00
86	Commy Comiskey (St. Louis, Chicago)	950.00	389.00	237.00
86-1	Commy Comiskey (Brown's Champions)	1100.	451.00	275.00
87	Pete Connell	170.00	70.00	42.00
88	Roger Connor	800.00	328.00	200.00
89	Dick Conway (Boston, Worcester)	170.00	70.00	42.00
90	Pete Conway (Detroit, Pittsburgh, Indianapolis)	170.00	70.00	42.00
91	Jim Conway (Kansas City)	170.00	70.00	42.00
92	Paul Cook	170.00	70.00	42.00
93	Jimmy Cooney	170.00	70.00	42.00
94	Larry Corcoran	170.00	70.00	42.00
95	Pop Corkhill	170.00	70.00	42.00
96	Cannonball Crane (NY)	170.00	70.00	42.00
97	Samuel Crane (Washington)	170.00	70.00	42.00
98	Jack Crogan (Croghan)	170.00	70.00	42.00
99	John Crooks	170.00	70.00	42.00
100	Lave Cross	170.00	70.00	42.00
101	N.C. Crossley	170.00	70.00	42.00
102	Joe Crotty (Sioux City)	170.00	70.00	42.00
102-1	Joe Crotty (dotted tie)	300.00	123.00	75.00
103	Billy Crowell	170.00	70.00	42.00
104	Jim Cudworth	170.00	70.00	42.00
105	Bert Cunningham	170.00	70.00	42.00
106	Tacks Curtis	170.00	70.00	42.00
107	Ed Cushman (dotted tie)	350.00	143.00	87.00
107-2	Ed Cushman (Toledo)	250.00	102.00	62.00
108	Tony Cusick	170.00	70.00	42.00
109	Dailey (Oakland)	325.00	133.00	81.00
110	Edward Dailey (Daily) (Philadelphia, Washington, Columbus)	170.00	70.00	42.00
111	Bill Daley (Boston)	170.00	70.00	42.00
112	Con Daley (Daily) (Boston, Indianapolis)	170.00	70.00	42.00
113	Abner Dalrymple	170.00	70.00	42.00
114	Tido Daly (Chicago, Washington)	170.00	70.00	42.00
115	Sun Daly (Minneapolis)	170.00	70.00	42.00
116	Law Daniels	170.00	70.00	42.00
117	Dell Darling	170.00	70.00	42.00
118	William Darnbrough	170.00	70.00	42.00
118-1	Davin	325.00	133.00	81.00
119	Jumbo Davis	170.00	70.00	42.00
120	Pat Dealey	170.00	70.00	42.00
121	Tom Deasley	170.00	70.00	42.00
122	Harry Decker	170.00	70.00	42.00
123	Ed Delahanty	950.00	389.00	237.00
124	Jerry Denny	170.00	70.00	42.00
125	Jim Devlin	170.00	70.00	42.00
126	Tom Dolan	170.00	70.00	42.00
127	Jack Donahue (San Fran)	325.00	133.00	81.00
128	Jim Donahue (Kansas City)	170.00	70.00	42.00
128-1	Jim Donohue (Donahue) (dotted tie)	300.00	123.00	75.00
129	Jim Donnelly	170.00	70.00	42.00
130	Dooley	300.00	123.00	75.00
131	Doran	170.00	70.00	42.00
132	Mike Dorgan	170.00	70.00	42.00
133	Doyle	300.00	123.00	75.00
134	Home Run Duffe (Duffee)	170.00	70.00	42.00
135	Hugh Duffy	850.00	348.00	212.00
136	Dan Dugdale	170.00	70.00	42.00
137	Duck Duke	170.00	70.00	42.00
138	Sure Shot Dunlap	170.00	70.00	42.00
139	Dunn	170.00	70.00	42.00
140	Jesse Duryea	170.00	70.00	42.00
141	Frank Dwyer	170.00	70.00	42.00
142	Billy Earle	170.00	70.00	42.00
143	Buck Ebright	170.00	70.00	42.00
144	Red Ehret	170.00	70.00	42.00
145	R. Emmerke	170.00	70.00	42.00
146	Dude Esterbrook	170.00	70.00	42.00
147	Henry Esterday	170.00	70.00	42.00
148	Long John Ewing (Louisville)	170.00	70.00	42.00
149	Buck Ewing (New York)	800.00	328.00	200.00
149-11	Willie Breslin - mascot, Buck Ewing	750.00	307.00	187.00
150	Jay Faatz	170.00	70.00	42.00
151	Bill Fagan	170.00	70.00	42.00
152	Bill Farmer	170.00	70.00	42.00
153	Sid Farrar	170.00	70.00	42.00
154	Jack Farrell (Washington, Baltimore)	170.00	70.00	42.00
155	Duke Farrell (Chicago)	170.00	70.00	42.00
156	Frank Fennelly	170.00	70.00	42.00
157	Charlie Ferguson	170.00	70.00	42.00
158	Alex Ferson	170.00	70.00	42.00
159	Wallace Fessenden (umpire)	275.00	113.00	69.00
160	Jocko Fields	170.00	70.00	42.00
161	Fischer	170.00	70.00	42.00
162	Thomas Flanigan (Flanagan)	170.00	70.00	42.00
163	Silver Flint	170.00	70.00	42.00
164	Thomas Flood	170.00	70.00	42.00
164-1	Jocko Flynn	315.00	129.00	79.00
165	Jim Fogarty	170.00	70.00	42.00
166	Frank Foreman	170.00	70.00	42.00
167	Tom Forster (Hartford)	250.00	102.00	62.00
167-2	Tom Forster (dotted tie, incorrect name (F.W. Foster) on front)	350.00	143.00	87.00
168	Elmer Foster (New York, Minneapolis)	170.00	70.00	42.00
168-1	Elmer Foster (dotted tie)	300.00	123.00	75.00
169	No World Index listing			
170	Dave Foutz (Brooklyn)	170.00	70.00	42.00
170-1	Dave Foutz (Brown's Champions)	275.00	113.00	69.00
171	Julie Freeman	170.00	70.00	42.00
172	Will Fry	170.00	70.00	42.00
172-1	Fudger	325.00	133.00	81.00
173	William Fuller (Milwaukee)	170.00	70.00	42.00
174	Shorty Fuller (St. Louis)	170.00	70.00	42.00
175	Chris Fulmer	170.00	70.00	42.00
175-6	Chris Fulmer, Foghorn Tucker	250.00	102.00	62.00
176	Honest John Gaffney	170.00	70.00	42.00
177	Pud Galvin	800.00	328.00	200.00
178	Bob Gamble	170.00	70.00	42.00
179	Charlie Ganzel	170.00	70.00	42.00
180	Gid Gardner	170.00	70.00	42.00
180-5	Gid Gardner, Miah Murray	200.00	82.00	50.00
181	Hank Gastreich	170.00	70.00	42.00
182	Emil Geiss	170.00	70.00	42.00
183	Frenchy Genins	170.00	70.00	42.00
184	Bill George	170.00	70.00	42.00
185	Joe Gerhardt	170.00	70.00	42.00
186	Charlie Getzein	170.00	70.00	42.00
187	Bobby Gilks	170.00	70.00	42.00
188	Pete Gillespie	170.00	70.00	42.00
189	Barney Gilligan	170.00	70.00	42.00
190	Frank Gilmore	170.00	70.00	42.00
191	Pebbly Jack Glasscock	200.00	82.00	50.00
192	Kid Gleason (Philadelphia)	110.00	45.00	27.00
193	Will Gleason (Athletics)	170.00	70.00	42.00
193-1	Will Gleason (Brown's Champions)	275.00	113.00	69.00
194	Mouse Glenn	170.00	70.00	42.00
195	Mike Goodfellow	170.00	70.00	42.00
196	Piano Legs Gore	170.00	70.00	42.00
197	Frank Graves	170.00	70.00	42.00
198	Bill Greenwood	170.00	70.00	42.00
199	Ed Greer	170.00	70.00	42.00
200	Mike Griffin	170.00	70.00	42.00
201	Clark Griffith	950.00	389.00	237.00
202	Henry Gruber	170.00	70.00	42.00
203	Ad Gumbert	170.00	70.00	42.00
204	Tom Gunning	170.00	70.00	42.00
205	Joe Gunson	170.00	70.00	42.00
206	Gentleman George Haddock	170.00	70.00	42.00
207	Bill Hafner (Hoffner)	170.00	70.00	42.00
208	Willie Hahm (mascot)	200.00	82.00	50.00
209	Bill Hallman	170.00	70.00	42.00
210	Sliding Billy Hamilton	850.00	348.00	212.00
211	Frank Hankinson (dotted tie)	275.00	113.00	69.00
212	Ned Hanlon	110.00	45.00	27.00
213	William Hanrahan	170.00	70.00	42.00
2131	Hapeman	300.00	123.00	75.00
214	Pa Harkins	170.00	70.00	42.00
215	Bill Hart	170.00	70.00	42.00
216	Bill Hasamdear	170.00	70.00	42.00
217	Gill Hatfield	170.00	70.00	42.00
218	Egyptian Healey (Healy)	170.00	70.00	42.00
219	Healy	170.00	70.00	42.00
220	Guy Hecker	170.00	70.00	42.00
221	Tony Hellman	170.00	70.00	42.00
222	Hardie Henderson	170.00	70.00	42.00
222-10	Ed Greer, Henderson	250.00	102.00	62.00
223	Moxie Hengle	170.00	70.00	42.00
224	John Henry	170.00	70.00	42.00
225	Ed Herr	170.00	70.00	42.00
226	Hunkey Hines (St. Louis Whites)	170.00	70.00	42.00
227	Paul Hines (Washington, Indianapolis)	170.00	70.00	42.00
228	Texas Wonder Hoffman	170.00	70.00	42.00
229	Eddie Hogan	170.00	70.00	42.00
230	Bill Holbert	170.00	70.00	42.00
230-1	Bill Holbert (dotted tie)	300.00	123.00	75.00
231	Bug Holliday	170.00	70.00	42.00
232	Charles Hoover (Chicago, Kansas City)	170.00	70.00	42.00
233	Buster Hoover (Philadelphia)	170.00	70.00	42.00
234	Jack Horner	170.00	70.00	42.00
234-3	Jack Horner, E.H. Warner	250.00	102.00	62.00
235	Joe Hornung	170.00	70.00	42.00
236	Pete Hotaling	170.00	70.00	42.00
237	Bill Howes (Hawes)	170.00	70.00	42.00
238	Dummy Hoy	300.00	123.00	75.00
239	Nat Hudson (St. Louis)	170.00	70.00	42.00
239-1	Nat Hudson (Brown's Champions)	275.00	113.00	69.00
240	Mickey Hughes	170.00	70.00	42.00
241	Hungler	170.00	70.00	42.00
242	Wild Bill Hutchinson	170.00	70.00	42.00
243	John Irwin (Washington)	170.00	70.00	42.00
244	Cutrate Irwin (Philadelphia)	170.00	70.00	42.00
245	A.C. Jantzen	170.00	70.00	42.00
246	Frederick Jevne	170.00	70.00	42.00
247	Spud Johnson	170.00	70.00	42.00
248	Dick Johnston	170.00	70.00	42.00
249	Jordan	170.00	70.00	42.00
250	Heinie Kappell (Kappel)	170.00	70.00	42.00
251	Tim Keefe (New York)	800.00	328.00	200.00
251-8	Keefe, Danny Richardson	800.00	328.00	200.00
252	George Keefe	800.00	328.00	200.00
251-8	Danny Richardson	800.00	328.00	200.00
252	George Keefe (Washington)	170.00	70.00	42.00
253	Jim Keenan	170.00	70.00	42.00
254	King Kelly (Boston)	950.00	389.00	237.00
255	John Kelly (Louisville)	170.00	70.00	42.00
255-3	Honest John Kelly (umpire)	200.00	82.00	50.00
255-4	Kelly, Jim Powell	200.00	82.00	50.00
256	No World Index listing			
257	Charles Kelly (Philadelphia)	170.00	70.00	42.00
258	Rudy Kemmler (St. Paul)	170.00	70.00	42.00
258-1	Rudy Kemler (Kemmler) (Brown's Champions)	275.00	113.00	69.00
259	Theodore Kennedy	170.00	70.00	42.00
260	J.J. Kenyon	170.00	70.00	42.00
261	John Kerins	170.00	70.00	42.00
262	Matt Kilroy	170.00	70.00	42.00
263	Silver King	170.00	70.00	42.00

264 August Kloff (Klopf) 170.00 70.00 42.00
265 William Klusman 170.00 70.00 42.00
266 Philip Knell 170.00 70.00 42.00
267 Fred Knouff 170.00 70.00 42.00
268 Charles Kremmeyer (Krehmeyer)
300.00 123.00 75.00
269 Bill Krieg 170.00 70.00 42.00
269-10August Kloff, Bill Krieg 250.00 102.00 62.00
270 Gus Krock 170.00 70.00 42.00
271 Willie Kuehne 170.00 70.00 42.00
272 Fred Lange 170.00 70.00 42.00
273 Ted Larkin 170.00 70.00 42.00
274 Arlie Latham (St. Louis) 200.00 82.00 50.00
274-1 Arlie Latham (Brown's Champions)
250.00 102.00 62.00
275 Chuck Lauer (Laver) 170.00 70.00 42.00
276 John Leighton 170.00 70.00 42.00
276-5 Levy 325.00 133.00 81.00
277 Tom Loftus 250.00 102.00 62.00
278 Germany Long (Kansas City, Chicago Maroons)
170.00 70.00 42.00
279 Danny Long (Oakland) 325.00 133.00 81.00
280 Tom Lovett 170.00 70.00 42.00
281 Bobby Lowe 250.00 102.00 62.00
282 Jack Lynch 170.00 70.00 42.00
282-1 Jack Lynch (dotted tie) 350.00 143.00 87.00
283 Denny Lyons (Athletics) 170.00 70.00 42.00
284 Harry Lyons (St. Louis) 170.00 70.00 42.00
285 Connie Mack (Washington) 1750. 717.00 437.00
286 Reddie Mack (Louisville, Baltimore)
170.00 70.00 42.00
287 Little Mac Macullar 170.00 70.00 42.00
288 Kid Madden 170.00 70.00 42.00
289 Danny Mahoney 170.00 70.00 42.00
290 Grasshopper Maines (Mains) 170.00 70.00 42.00
291 Fred Mann 170.00 70.00 42.00
292 Jimmy Manning 170.00 70.00 42.00
293 Lefty Marr 170.00 70.00 42.00
294 Willie Breslin (mascot) 250.00 102.00 62.00
295 Leech Maskrey 170.00 70.00 42.00
296 Bobby Mathews 170.00 70.00 42.00
297 Mike Mattimore 170.00 70.00 42.00
298 Smiling Al Maul 170.00 70.00 42.00
299 Al Mays (Columbus) 170.00 70.00 42.00
299-1 Al Mays (dotted tie) 300.00 123.00 75.00
300 Jimmy McAleer 170.00 70.00 42.00
301 Tommy McCarthy (Philadelphia, St. Louis)
800.00 328.00 200.00
302 John McCarthy (McCarty) (Kansas City)
170.00 70.00 42.00
303 Jim McCauley 170.00 70.00 42.00
304 Bill McClellan 170.00 70.00 42.00
305 Jerry McCormack (McCormick)
170.00 70.00 42.00
306 Jim McCormick 170.00 70.00 42.00
307 McCreachery (photo actually Deacon White)
170.00 70.00 42.00
308 McCullum (McCallum) 170.00 70.00 42.00
308-1 McDonald 300.00 123.00 75.00
309 Chippy McGarr 170.00 70.00 42.00
310 Jack McGeachy 170.00 70.00 42.00
311 John McGlone 170.00 70.00 42.00
312 Deacon McGuire 170.00 70.00 42.00
313 Bill McGunnigle 250.00 102.00 62.00
314 Ed McKean 170.00 70.00 42.00
315 Alex McKinnon 170.00 70.00 42.00
316 Tom McLaughlin (dotted tie) 300.00 123.00 75.00
317 Bid McPhee 170.00 70.00 42.00
318 James McQuaid (Denver) 170.00 70.00 42.00
319 John McQuaid (umpire) 250.00 102.00 62.00
320 Jim McTamany 170.00 70.00 42.00
321 George McVey 170.00 70.00 42.00
321-1 Steady Pete Meegan 300.00 123.00 75.00
322 John Messitt 170.00 70.00 42.00
323 Doggie Miller (Pittsburgh) 170.00 70.00 42.00
324 Joseph Miller (Omaha, Minneapolis)
170.00 70.00 42.00
325 Jocko Milligan 170.00 70.00 42.00
326 E.L. Mills 170.00 70.00 42.00
327 Daniel Minnehan (Minahan) 170.00 70.00 42.00
328 Sam Moffet 170.00 70.00 42.00
329 Honest John Morrill 170.00 70.00 42.00
330 Ed Morris 170.00 70.00 42.00
331 Count Mullane 190.00 78.00 47.00
332 Joseph Mulvey 170.00 70.00 42.00
333 P.L. Murphy (St. Paul) 170.00 70.00 42.00
334 Pat Murphy (New York) 170.00 70.00 42.00
335 Miah Murray 170.00 70.00 42.00
336 Truthful Jim Mutrie 200.00 82.00 50.00
337 George Myers (Indianapolis) 170.00 70.00 42.00
338 Al Myers (Washington, Philadelphia)
170.00 70.00 42.00
339 Tom Nagle 170.00 70.00 42.00
340 Billy Nash 170.00 70.00 42.00
341 Candy Nelson (dotted tie) 300.00 123.00 75.00
342 Kid Nichols (Omaha) 900.00 369.00 225.00
343 Samuel Nichols (Nichol) (Pittsburgh)
170.00 70.00 42.00
344 J.W. Nicholson (Chicago Maroons)
170.00 70.00 42.00
345 Parson Nicholson (St. Louis, Cleveland)
170.00 70.00 42.00
346 Little Nick Nicol (Cincinnati) 170.00 70.00 42.00
346-1 Little Nick Nicoll (Nicol) (Brown's Champions)
275.00 113.00 69.00
346-8 Little Nick Nicol, Big John Reilly
250.00 102.00 62.00
347 Frederick Nyce 170.00 70.00 42.00
348 Doc Oberlander 170.00 70.00 42.00
349 Jack O'Brien (Brooklyn, Baltimore)
170.00 70.00 42.00
350 Billy O'Brien (Washington) 170.00 70.00 42.00
351 Darby O'Brien (Brooklyn) 170.00 70.00 42.00
352 John O'Brien (Cleveland) 170.00 70.00 42.00
353 P.J. O'Connell 170.00 70.00 42.00
354 Rowdy Jack O'Connor 170.00 70.00 42.00
355 Hank O'Day 170.00 70.00 42.00
356 Tip O'Neil (O'Neill) (St. Louis) 170.00 70.00 42.00
356-6 Tip O'Neil (O'Neill) (Brown's Champions)
275.00 113.00 69.00
357 Tip O'Neill (photo actually Deacon White, St. Louis)
170.00 70.00 42.00
357-1 O'Neill (Oakland) 325.00 133.00 81.00
358 Orator Jim O'Rourke (New York)
800.00 328.00 200.00
359 Tom O'Rourke (Boston) 170.00 70.00 42.00
360 Dave Orr 170.00 70.00 42.00
360-1 Dave Orr (dotted tie) 300.00 123.00 75.00
361 Charles Parsons 170.00 70.00 42.00
362 Owen Patton 170.00 70.00 42.00
363 Jimmy Peeples (Peoples) 170.00 70.00 42.00
363-3 Hardie Henderson, Jimmy Peeples
250.00 102.00 62.00
364 Hip Perrier 300.00 123.00 75.00
365 Patrick Pettee 170.00 70.00 42.00
365-5 Bobby Lowe, Patrick Pettee 250.00 102.00 62.00
366 Fred Pfeffer 170.00 70.00 42.00
367 Dick Phelan 170.00 70.00 42.00
368 Bill Phillips 170.00 70.00 42.00
369 Jack Pickett 170.00 70.00 42.00
370 George Pinkney 170.00 70.00 42.00
371 Tom Poorman 170.00 70.00 42.00
372 Henry Porter 170.00 70.00 42.00
373 Jim Powell 170.00 70.00 42.00
373-1 Thomas Powers 300.00 123.00 75.00
374 Blondie Purcell 170.00 70.00 42.00
375 Tom Quinn (Baltimore) 170.00 70.00 42.00
376 Joe Quinn (Boston, Des Moines)
170.00 70.00 42.00
377 Old Hoss Radbourn 800.00 328.00 200.00
378 Shorty Radford 170.00 70.00 42.00
379 Toad Ramsey 170.00 70.00 42.00
380 Rehse 170.00 70.00 42.00
381 Long John Reilly (Cincinnati) 170.00 70.00 42.00
382 Princeton Charlie Reilly (St. Paul)
170.00 70.00 42.00
383 Charlie Reynolds 170.00 70.00 42.00
384 Hardy Richardson (Detroit, Boston)
170.00 70.00 42.00
385 Danny Richardson (NY) 170.00 70.00 42.00
386 Charles Ripslager (dotted tie) 300.00 123.00 75.00
387 John Roach 170.00 70.00 42.00
388 Uncle Robbie Robinson (Athletics)
850.00 348.00 212.00
389 M.C. Robinson (Minneapolis) 170.00 70.00 42.00
390 Yank Robinson (St. Louis) 170.00 70.00 42.00
390-6 Yank Robinson (Brown's Champions)
275.00 113.00 69.00
391 George Rooks 170.00 70.00 42.00
392 Chief Roseman (dotted tie) 300.00 123.00 75.00
393 Dave Rowe (Kansas City) 170.00 70.00 42.00
394 Jack Rowe (Detroit) 170.00 70.00 42.00
395 Amos Rusie 900.00 369.00 225.00
396 Jimmy Ryan 170.00 70.00 42.00
397 Doc Sage 170.00 70.00 42.00
397-4 Doc Sage, Bill Van Dyke 200.00 82.00 50.00
398 Ben Sanders 170.00 70.00 42.00
399 Frank Scheibeck 170.00 70.00 42.00
400 Al Schellhase (Schellhasse) 170.00 70.00 42.00
401 William Schenkel 170.00 70.00 42.00
402 Schildknecht 170.00 70.00 42.00
403 Gus Schmelz 170.00 70.00 42.00
404 Jumbo Schoeneck 170.00 70.00 42.00
405 Pop Schriver 170.00 70.00 42.00
406 Emmett Seery 170.00 70.00 42.00
407 Billy Serad 170.00 70.00 42.00
408 Ed Seward 170.00 70.00 42.00
409 Orator Shafer (Shaffer) (Des Moines)
170.00 70.00 42.00
410 Taylor Shafer (Shaffer) (St. Paul)
170.00 70.00 42.00
411 Daniel Shannon 170.00 70.00 42.00
412 William Sharsig 170.00 70.00 42.00
413 Samuel Shaw (Baltimore, Newark)
170.00 70.00 42.00
414 John Shaw (Minneapolis) 170.00 70.00 42.00
415 Bill Shindle 170.00 70.00 42.00
416 George Shoch 170.00 70.00 42.00
417 Otto Shomberg (Schomberg) 170.00 70.00 42.00
418 Lev Shreve 170.00 70.00 42.00
419 Ed Silch 170.00 70.00 42.00
420 Mike Slattery 170.00 70.00 42.00
421 Skyrocket Smith (Louisville) 170.00 70.00 42.00
422 Phenomenal Smith (Baltimore, Athletics)
300.00 123.00 75.00
423 Mike Smith (Cincinnati) 170.00 70.00 42.00
424 Sam Smith (Des Moines) 170.00 70.00 42.00
425 Germany Smith (Brooklyn) 170.00 70.00 42.00
426 Pap Smith (Pittsburgh, Boston)
170.00 70.00 42.00
427 Nick Smith (St. Joseph) 170.00 70.00 42.00
428 P.T. Somers 170.00 70.00 42.00
429 Joe Sommer 170.00 70.00 42.00
430 Pete Sommers 170.00 70.00 42.00
431 Little Bill Sowders (Boston) 170.00 70.00 42.00
432 John Sowders (St. Paul, Kansas City)
170.00 70.00 42.00
433 Charlie Sprague 170.00 70.00 42.00
434 Ed Sproat 170.00 70.00 42.00
435 Harry Staley 170.00 70.00 42.00
436 Dan Stearns 170.00 70.00 42.00
437 Cannonball Stemmyer (Stemmeyer)
170.00 70.00 42.00
438 B.F. Stephens 170.00 70.00 42.00
439 John Sterling 170.00 70.00 42.00
439-1 Stockwell 300.00 123.00 75.00
440 Harry Stovey 250.00 102.00 62.00
441 Scott Stratton 170.00 70.00 42.00
442 Joe Straus (Strauss) 170.00 70.00 42.00
443 Cub Stricker 170.00 70.00 42.00
444 Marty Sullivan (Chicago, Indianapolis)
170.00 70.00 42.00
445 Mike Sullivan (Athletics) 170.00 70.00 42.00
446 Billy Sunday 800.00 328.00 200.00
447 Sy Sutcliffe 170.00 70.00 42.00
448 Ezra Sutton 170.00 70.00 42.00
449 Ed Swartwood 170.00 70.00 42.00
450 Park Swartzel 170.00 70.00 42.00
451 Pete Sweeney 170.00 70.00 42.00
451-1 Louis Sylvester 300.00 123.00 75.00
452 Pop Tate 170.00 70.00 42.00
453 Patsy Tebeau 170.00 70.00 42.00
454 John Tener 200.00 82.00 50.00
455 Adonis Terry 170.00 70.00 42.00
456 Big Sam Thompson 500.00 205.00 125.00
457 Silent Mike Tiernan 170.00 70.00 42.00
458 Cannonball Titcomb 170.00 70.00 42.00
459 Buster Tomney 170.00 70.00 42.00
460 Stephen Toole 170.00 70.00 42.00
461 Sleepy Townsend 170.00 70.00 42.00
462 Bill Traffley 170.00 70.00 42.00
463 George Treadway 170.00 70.00 42.00
464 Sam Trott 170.00 70.00 42.00
464-6 Oyster Burns, Sam Trott 250.00 102.00 62.00
465 Foghorn Tucker 170.00 70.00 42.00
466 A.M. Tuckerman 170.00 70.00 42.00
467 George Turner 170.00 70.00 42.00
468 Larry Twitchell 170.00 70.00 42.00
469 Jim Tyng 170.00 70.00 42.00
470 Bill Van Dyke 170.00 70.00 42.00
471 Rip Van Haltren 170.00 70.00 42.00
472 Farmer Vaughn 170.00 70.00 42.00
472-1 Veach 300.00 123.00 75.00
473 Lee Viau 170.00 70.00 42.00
474 Bill Vinton 170.00 70.00 42.00
475 Joe Visner 170.00 70.00 42.00
476 Christian Von Der Ahe (Brown's Champions)
300.00 123.00 75.00
477 Reddy Walsh 170.00 70.00 42.00
478 Monte Ward 800.00 328.00 200.00
479 E.H. Warner 170.00 70.00 42.00
480 Bill Watkins 170.00 70.00 42.00
481 Farmer Weaver 170.00 70.00 42.00
482 Count Weber 170.00 70.00 42.00
483 Stump Weidman 170.00 70.00 42.00
484 Wild Bill Weidner (Widner) 170.00 70.00 42.00
485 Curt Welch (Athletics) 170.00 70.00 42.00
485-1 Curt Welch (Brown's Champions)
275.00 113.00 69.00
485-7 Will Gleason, Curt Welch 250.00 102.00 62.00
486 Smiling Mickey Welch (New York)
800.00 328.00 200.00
487 Jake Wells (Kansas City) 170.00 70.00 42.00
488 Frank Wells (Milwaukee) 170.00 70.00 42.00
489 Joe Werrick 170.00 70.00 42.00
490 Buck West 170.00 70.00 42.00
491 A.C. "Cannonball" Weyhing 170.00 70.00 42.00
492 John Weyhing 170.00 70.00 42.00
493 Bobby Wheelock 170.00 70.00 42.00
494 Pat Whitacre (Whitaker) 170.00 70.00 42.00
495 Pat Whitaker 170.00 70.00 42.00
496 Deacon White (Detroit, Pittsburgh)
170.00 70.00 42.00
497 Bill White (Louisville) 170.00 70.00 42.00
498 Grasshopper Whitney (Washington, Indianapolis)
170.00 70.00 42.00
499 Art Whitney (Pittsburgh, New York)
170.00 70.00 42.00
500 G. Whitney (St. Joseph) 170.00 70.00 42.00
501 James Williams 170.00 70.00 42.00
502 Ned Williamson 170.00 70.00 42.00
502-7 Willie Hahm - mascot, Ned Williamson
160.00 66.00 40.00
503 C.H. Willis 170.00 70.00 42.00
504 Watt Wilmot 170.00 70.00 42.00
505 George Winkleman (Winkelman)
170.00 70.00 42.00
506 Medoc Wise 170.00 70.00 42.00
507 Chicken Wolf 170.00 70.00 42.00
508 George "Dandy" Wood (L.F.) 170.00 70.00 42.00
509 Pete Wood (P.) 170.00 70.00 42.00
510 Harry Wright 1450. 594.00 362.00
511 Chief Zimmer 170.00 70.00 42.00
512 Frank Zinn 170.00 70.00 42.00

1887 Old Judge (N172)

Known photo variations

1 1a Gus Albert (bat at 45 degrees, Clevelands)
1 1b Gus Albert (bat at 45 degrees, Milwaukees)
1 2a Gus Albert (bat over shoulder, Clevelands)
1 2b Gus Albert (bat over shoulder, Milwaukees)
1 3 Gus Albert (fielding grounder)
1 4a Gus Albert (throwing, Cleveland's)
1 4b Gus Albert (throwing, Milwaukees)
2 1a Alcott (hands on hips, St. Louis Whites)
2 1b Alcott (hands on hips, Mansfields)
2 2 Alcott (ball in hand above head)
2 3a Alcott (bat at ready position, left arm across belt, 3d B., St. Louis Whites)
2 3b Alcott (bat at ready position, left arm across belt, 3rd B., St. Louis Whites)
2 3c Alcott (bat at ready position, left arm across belt, Mansfields)

2 4 Alcott (bat at ready position, left arm clear of belt)
2 5 Alcott (fielding grounder)
3 1 Alexander (ball in hands at chest)
3 2a Alexander (ball in hand above head, Des Moines)
3 2b Alexander (ball in hand above head, Des Moine)
3 3 Alexander (ball in hand head-high)
3 4 Alexander (batting)
4 1 Myron Allen (fielding high ball, well clear of glove, Kansas City)
4 2 Myron Allen (fielding high ball, touching glove, Kansas City)
4 3 Myron Allen (stooping, feet apart, looking at ball, Kansas City)
4 4 Myron Allen (stooping, right foot behind left leg, Kansas City)
4 5 Myron Allen (ball in hand head-high, Kansas City)
4 6 Myron Allen (batting, Kansas City)
5 1 Bob Allen (batting, Pittsburghs)
5 2 Bob Allen (hands on thighs, Philadelphia N.L.)
5 3 Bob Allen (hands clasped at waist, Pittsburghs)
5 4a Bob Allen (fielding, hands at waist, Pittsburghs)
5 4b Bob Allen (fielding, hands at waist, Philadelphia N.L.)
5 5 Bob Allen (fielding grounder, Pittsburghs)
6 1 Uncle Bill Alvord (fielding grounder)
6 2 Uncle Bill Alvord (batting)
6 3 Uncle Bill Alvord (sliding)
7 1 Varney Anderson (pitching, right hand head-high)
7 2 Varney Anderson (batting)
7 3 Varney Anderson (pitching, hands chest-high)
8 1 Wally Andrews (fielding, stretching to right, Omaha)
8 2 Wally Andrews (fielding, hands by right shoulder, Omaha)
8 3 Wally Andrews (batting, Omaha)
9 1a Ed Andrews (bat in hand at side, Phila)
9 1b Ed Andrews (bat in hand at side, Phila's)
9 2a Ed Andrews (striking ball, bat nearly horizontal, Phila)
9 2b Ed Andrews (striking ball, bat nearly horizontal, Philadelphias)
9 3 Ed Andrews (bat at ready position, no ball visible, Phila's)
9 4 Ed Andrews (right hand above head, left hand behind at side, Phila)
9 5a Ed Andrews (fielding, hands shoulder-high, Phila's)
9 5b Ed Andrews (fielding, hands shoulder-high, Philadelphias)
9 6a Ed Andrews (Andrews being tagged by Hoover, Phila)
9 6a Buster Hoover (Andrews being tagged by Hoover, Phila)
9 6b Ed Andrews (Andrews being tagged by Hoover, Phila's)
9 6b Buster Hoover (Andrews being tagged by Hoover, Phila's)
10 1a Bill Annis (bat in hand at side, Worcesters)
10 1b Bill Annis (bat in hand at side, Omaha)
10 2 Bill Annis (striking ball, bat nearly horizontal)
10 3 Bill Annis (lying on ground by base)
11 1a Cap Anson (portrait, no arms visible, Chicagoes)
11 1b Cap Anson (portrait, no arms visible, Chicagos)
11 1c Cap Anson (portrait, no arms visible, Chicagos N.L.)
11 2 Cap Anson (portrait, arms folded)
12 1 Old Hoss Ardner (throwing)
12 2 Old Hoss Ardner (hands on hips)
12 3 Old Hoss Ardner (batting)
13 1 Tug Arundel (fielding, hands head-high)
13 2 Tug Arundel (ball in hands thigh-high)
13 3 Tug Arundel (bat in hand at side)
13 4 Tug Arundel (bat at ready position)
13 5 Tug Arundel (throwing)
14 1a Jersey Bakley (Bakely) (pitching, hands at chest, Clevelands)
14 1b Jersey Bakley (Bakely) (pitching, hands at chest, Cleveland's)
14 2a Jersey Bakley (Bakely) (pitching, left arm half concealing face, Cleveland's)
14 2b Jersey Bakley (Bakely) (pitching, left arm half concealing face, Clevelands)
14 3a Jersey Bakley (Bakely) (pitching, right hand head-high, Cleveland's)
14 3b Jersey Bakley (Bakely) (pitching, right hand head-high, Clevelands)
14 4 Jersey Bakley (Bakely) (batting, feet together)
14 5 Jersey Bakley (Bakely) (batting, feet apart)
15 1a Fido Baldwin (portrait, P. Chicago)
15 1b Fido Baldwin (portrait, P., Chicago)
15 1c Fido Baldwin (portrait, P. (PL))
15 2a Fido Baldwin (pitching, right hand in back waist-high, Chicago)
15 2b Fido Baldwin (pitching, right hand in back waist-high, Columbus)
15 3a Fido Baldwin (pitching, hands neck-high, Chicago)
15 3b Fido Baldwin (pitching, hands neck-high, Columbus)
15 4 Fido Baldwin (pitching, right hand above head, Chicago)
15 5 Fido Baldwin (batting, heels together, Chicago)
15 6 Fido Baldwin (batting, right foot behind left foot)
15 7a Fido Baldwin (bat in hand at side, Chicago)
15 7b Fido Baldwin (bat in hand at side, Chicagos)
16 1a Kid Baldwin (ball in hands head-high, Cincinnati)
16 1b Kid Baldwin (ball in hands head-high, Cincinnatti)
16 2a Kid Baldwin (ball in right hand head-high, Cincinnati)
16 2b Kid Baldwin (ball in right hand head-high, Cincinnatis)
16 2c Kid Baldwin (ball in right hand head-high, Cincinnatti)
16 3a Kid Baldwin (batting, Cincinnati)
16 3b Kid Baldwin (batting, Cincinnatis)
16 4 Kid Baldwin (fielding ball by right foot, Cincinnati)
16 5a Kid Baldwin (ball falling in hands above head, Cincinnati)
16 5b Kid Baldwin (ball falling in hands above head, Cincinnatti)
17 1 Lady Baldwin (batting, Detroits)
17 2 Lady Baldwin (pitching, hands neck-high, Detroits)
17 3a Lady Baldwin (pitching, left hand thigh-high, Detroits)
17 3b Lady Baldwin (pitching, left hand thigh-high, Cincinnati)
17 4 Lady Baldwin (pitching, left hand head-high, Detroits)
18 1 James Banning (hands on knees)
18 2 James Banning (fielding, hands above head)
18 3 James Banning (throwing)
18 4 James Banning (batting)
18 5 James Banning (stooping, hands by left foot)
19 1a Sam Barkley (portrait, 2d B.)
19 1b Sam Barkley (portrait, 2d Base)
19 2a Sam Barkley (fielding, right hand above head, 2d B., Pittsburg)
19 2b Sam Barkley (fielding, right hand above head, 2d Base, Pittsburg)
19 2c Sam Barkley (fielding, right hand above head, Kansas City)
19 2d Sam Barkley (fielding, right hand above head, 2nd B., Pittsburgh)
19 3a Sam Barkley (throwing, 2d B.)
19 3b Sam Barkley (throwing, 2d Base)
19 3c Sam Barkley (throwing, 2nd B.)
19 4a Sam Barkley (tagging player on ground, 2d B. Pittsburg)
19 4b Sam Barkley (tagging player on ground, 2d Base, Pittsburg)
19 4c Sam Barkley (tagging player on ground, 2d B., Kansas City)
19 4d Sam Barkley (tagging player on ground, 2nd B.. Pittsburg)
19 5a Sam Barkley (fielding grounder, 2d B.)
19 5b Sam Barkley (fielding grounder, 2d Base)
19 5c Sam Barkley (fielding grounder, 2nd B.)
19 6a Sam Barkley (batting, 2d B.)
19 6b Sam Barkley (batting, 2d Base)
20 1a John Barnes (portrait, bare head, St. Pauls)
20 1b John Barnes (portrait, bare head, St. Paul)
20 2a John Barnes (portrait, top hat, St. Pauls)
20 2b John Barns (Barnes) (portrait, top hat, St. Paul)
21 1 Bald Billy Barnie (portrait)
22 1a Charles Bassett (bat at ready position, Indianapolis)
22 1b Charles Bassett (bat at ready position, New Yorks (N.L.))
22 2a Charles Bassett (bat in hand at side, 2d B.)
22 2b Charles Bassett (bat in hand at side, 2nd B.)
23 1 Charles Bastian (batting, looking at camera)
23 2 Charles Bastian (batting, looking at ball)
23 3a Charles Bastian (bat over shoulder, Phila)
23 3b Charles Bastian (bat over shoulder, Chicagos)
23 3c Charles Bastian (bat over shoulder, Chicagos (PL))
23 4 Charles Bastian (fielding, hands chest-high)
23 5 Charles Bastian (stooping for low ball)
23 6 Charles Bastian (Schriver tagging Bastian)
23 6 Pop Schriver (Schriver tagging Bastian)
24 1a Ed Beatin (pitching, hands at chest, name correct)
24 1b Ed Beattin (Beatin) (pitching, hands at chest, name incorrect)
24 2 Ed Beatin (pitching, chin concealed behind left arm)
24 4 Ed Beatin (batting)
25 1a Jake Beckley (batting, "O" just visible on shirt, St. Louis Whites)
25 1b Jake Beckley (batting, "O" just visible on shirt, Pittsburghs)
25 1c Jake Beckley (batting, "O" just visible on shirt, Pittsburgs)
25 2 Jake Beckley (batting, "TLO" visible on shirt)
25 3a Jake Beckley (fielding, hands neck-high, St. Louis Whites)
25 3b Jake Beckley (fielding, hands neck-high, Pittsburghs)
25 3c Jake Beckley (fielding, hands neck-high, Pittsburgs)
25 3d Jake Beckley (fielding, hands neck-high, Pittsburgh)
25 4a Jake Beckley (fielding, ball knee-high, St. Louis Whites)
25 4b Jake Beckley (fielding, ball knee-high, Pittsburgs)
26 1 Stephen Behel (dotted tie)
27 1 Charles Bennett (batting)
28 1 Louis Bierbauer (fielding grounder)
28 2a Louis Bierbauer (fielding, hands chest-high, name correct)
28 2b Louis Bierbaur (Bierbauer) (fielding, hands chest-high, name incorrect)
28 3a Louis Bierbauer (batting, name correct)
28 3b Louis Bierbaur (Bierbauer) (batting, name incorrect)
28 4 Louis Bierbauer (running, cap in hand)
28 5 Louis Bierbaur (Bierbauer) (tagging Gamble)
28 5 Bob Gamble (tagging Gamble)
29 1a Bill Bishop (fielding, hands above waist, P.)
29 1b Bill Bishop (fielding, hands above waist, Pitcher)
29 2a Bill Bishop (batting, P.)
29 2b Bill Bishop (batting, Pitcher)
29 3a Bill Bishop (ball in right hand head-high, Pittsburg)
29 3b Bill Bishop (ball in right hand head-high, Syracuse)
30 1a Bill Blair (throwing, looking front, Athletics)
30 1b Bill Blair (throwing, looking front, Hamiltons)
30 2a Bill Blair (throwing, looking to left, Athletics)
30 2b Bill Blair (throwing, looking to left, Hamiltons)
30 3a Bill Blair (pitching, hands shoulder-high, Athletics)
30 3b Bill Blair (pitching, hands shoulder-high, Hamiltons)
30 4 Bill Blair (batting)
30 5 Bill Blair (fielding)
31 1 Ned Bligh (hands on knees)
31 2 Ned Bligh (fielding, hands head-high)
31 3 Ned Bligh (fielding, hands chest-high)
31 4 Ned Bligh (throwing)
31 5 Ned Bligh (bat at ready position at 45 degrees)
31 6 Ned Bligh (bat at ready position over shoulder)
32 1 Bogart (fielding grounder)
32 2 Bogart (throwing)
32 3 Bogart (batting)
32 4 Bogart (fielding, hands chest-high)
32 5 Bogart (fielding, hands thigh-high)
33 1 Boyce (batting)
33 2 Boyce (throwing)
33 3 Boyce (fielding, ball above head)
33 4 Boyce (fielding, ball in hands)
34 1 Boyd (fielding)
34 2 Boyd (throwing)
35 1a Honest John Boyle (fielding, hands thigh-high, Boyle on front, St. Louis Browns)
35 1b Honest John Boyle (fielding, hands thigh-high, J. Boyle on front, St. Louis Browns)
35 2a Honest John Boyle (fielding grounder, St. Louis Browns)
35 2b Honest John Boyle (fielding grounder, St., Louis)
35 3a Honest John Boyle (bat in hand at side, St. Louis Browns)
35 3b Honest John Boyle (bat in hand at side, St. Louis)
35 3c Honest John Boyle (bat in hand at side, Chicagos)
35 4a Honest John Boyle (hands thigh-high, J. Boyle on front, St. Louis Browns)
35 4b Honest John Boyle (hands thigh-high, Boyle on front, St. Louis)
35 4c Honest John Boyle (hands thigh-high, Boyle on front, St. Louis Browns)
35 5a Honest John Boyle (bat at ready position, 45 degrees, St. Louis Browns)
35 5b Honest John Boyle (bat at ready position, 45 degrees, St. Louis)
36 1 Handsome Boyle (pitching, hands above waist, Indianapolis)
36 2a Handsome Boyle (pitching, right hand neck-high, P., Indianapolis)
36 2b Handsome Boyle (pitching, right hand neck-high, Pitcher, Indianapolis)
36 2c Handsome Boyle (pitching, right hand neck-high, New Yorks N.L.)
36 3a Handsome Boyle (end of pitch, right arm extended, P. Indianapolis)
36 3b Handsome Boyle (end of pitch, right arm extended, Pitcher, Indianapolis)
36 3c Handsome Boyle (end of pitch, right arm extended, New Yorks (NL))
36 4a Handsome Boyle (batting, no comma after P., Indianapolis)
36 4b Handsome Boyle (batting, Pitcher, Indianapolis)
36 4c Handsome Boyle (batting, comma after P., Indianapolis)
37 1 Nick Bradley (leaning to left, arms at sides, Kansas City)
37 2 Nick Bradley (bat over shoulder, Worcesters)
37 3 Nick Bradley (bat in hand at side, Worcesters)
37 4 Nick Bradley (fielding, Kansas City)
38 1 Grin Bradley (batting, looking at camera, Sioux City)
38 2 Grin Bradley (batting, looking at ball, Soiux City)
38 3a Grin Bradley (throwing, ball in right hand waist-high, Sioux Citys)
38 3b Grin Bradley (throwing, ball in right hand waist-high, Sioux City)
38 4 Grin Bradley (fielding, looking up at ball, Sioux City)
38 5 Grin Bradley (fielding, looking down at ball, Sioux City)
39 1 Stephen Brady (dotted tie)
40 1 Breckenridge (bat over shoulder)
41 1a Timothy Brosnam (fielding low ball, Minneapolis)
41 1b Timothy Brosnam (fielding low ball, Sioux Citys)
41 2a Timothy Brosnam (stooping to right to tag base, Minneapolis)
41 2b Timothy Brosnam (stooping to right to tag base, Sioux Citys)
41 3a Timothy Brosnam (fielding, hands neck-high, Minneapolis)
41 3b Timothy Brosnam (fielding, hands neck-high, Sioux Citys)
41 4 Timothy Brosnam (bat at ready position)
41 5 Timothy Brosnam (leaning on bat at back)
42 1a Cal Broughton (batting, looking at camera, St. Pauls)
42 1b Cal Broughton (batting, looking at camera, St. Paul)
42 2a Cal Broughton (batting, looking at ball, St. Pauls)
42 2b Cal Broughton (batting, looking at ball, St. Paul)
42 3 Cal Broughton (fielding, hands chest-high)
42 4 Cal Broughton (fielding, hands head-high)
42 5a Cal Broughton (fielding, hands by right thigh, St. Pauls)
42 5b Cal Broughton (fielding, hands by right thigh, St. Paul)
43 1a Dan Brouthers (fielding, Brouthers on front, Detroits)
43 1b Dan Brouthers (fielding, D. Brouthers on front, Detroits)
43 1d Dan Brouthers (fielding, Brouthers on front, Bostons)
43 2a Dan Brouthers (bat at ready position, looking to right, Detroits)
43 2b Dan Brouthers (bat at ready position, looking to right, Bostons)
43 3 Dan Brouthers (bat at ready position, looking down at ball)
44 1a Thomas Brown (fielding, hands above head, C.F., Pittsburg)
44 1b Thomas Brown (fielding, hands above head, Centre Field, Pittsburg)
44 1c Thomas Brown (fielding, hands above head, Boston)
44 2a Thomas Brown (bat in hand at side, C.F., Pittsburg)
44 2b Thomas Brown (bat in hand at side, Centre Field, Pittsburg)
44 2c Thomas Brown (bat in hand at side, Boston (PL))
44 3a Thomas Brown (fielding, hands chest-high, C.F., Pittsburg)
44 3b Thomas Brown (fielding, hands chest-high, Centre Field, Pittsburg)
44 3d Thomas Brown (fielding, hands chest-high, Boston (PL))
44 4a Thomas Brown (batting, C.F., Pittsburg)
44 4b Thomas Brown (batting, Centre Field, Pittsburg)
45 1a California Brown (batting, no comma after C., N.Y's)
45 1b California Brown (batting, C., New Yorks)
45 1c California Brown (batting, comma after C., N.Y's)
45 2a California Brown (fielding, hands chest-high, N.Y's)
45 2b California Brown (fielding, hands chest-high, New York)

45 3a California Brown (throwing, no comma after C., N.Y's)
45 3b California Brown (throwing, comma after C., N.Y's)
45 3c California Brown (throwing, New Yorks)
45 4a California Brown (bat in hand at side, no comma after C., N.Y's)
45 4b California Brown (bat in hand at side, comma after C., N.Y's)
45 4c California Brown (bat in hand at side, New Yorks)
45 4d California Brown (bat in hand at side, New York (PL))
45 5a California Brown (in mask, hands on knees, no comma after C., N.Y's)
45 5b California Brown (in mask, hands on knees, comma after C., N.Y's)
46 1a Pete Browning (fielding, stooping, hands head-high, Pete Browning on front)
46 1b Pete Browning (fielding, stooping, hands head-high, Browning on front)
46 2 Pete Browning (fielding grounder)
46 3 Pete Browning (batting, feet together)
46 4 Pete Browning (batting, feet apart)
46 5 Pete Browning (throwing)
47 1 Charles Brynan (pitching, hands chest-high)
47 2 Charles Brynan (pitching, hands below chest)
47 3a Charles Brynan (pitching, right hand neck-high, Brynan on front)
47 3c Charles Brynan (pitching, right hand neck-high, C. Brynan on front)
47 4a Charles Brynan (pitching, right arm stretched forward, Chicago)
47 4b Charles Brynan (pitching, right arm stretched forward, Des Moines)
47 5 Charles Brynan (bat at ready position over right shoulder)
48 1 Al Buckenberger (portrait, looking to left)
48 2 Al Buckenberger (portrait, looking to right)
49 1a Dick Buckley (fielding ball ankle-high, no comma after C.)
49 1b Dick Buckley (fielding ball ankle-high, comma after C.)
49 2a Dick Buckley (stooping, hands on knees, Indianapolis)
49 2b Dick Buckley (stooping, hands on knees, New Yorks N.L.)
49 3a Dick Buckley (fielding, hands chest-high, no comma after C.)
49 3b Dick Buckley (fielding, hands chest-high, comma after C.)
49 4a Dick Buckley (bat at ready position, nearly vertical, comma after C., Indianapolis)
49 4b Dick Buckley (bat at ready position, nearly vertical, no comma after C., Indinapolis)
49 4c Dick Buckley (bat at ready position, nearly vertical, New Yorks (N.L.))
49 5 Dick Buckley (about to hit low ball)
50 1a Charles Buffinton (pitching, hands chest-high, Phila)
50 1b Charles Buffinton (pitching, hands chest-high, Philadelphia)
50 1d Charles Buffington (Buffinton) (pitching, hands chest-high, Philadelphias)
50 1e Charles Buffinton (pitching, hands chest-high, Philadelphias (PL))
50 2a Charles Buffington (Buffinton) (bat at ready position, name incorrect)
50 2b Charles Buffinton (bat at ready position, name correct)
50 3 Charles Buffinton (pitching, right hand above head)
51 1 Ernest Burch (dark uniform, leaning to left, tagging base)
51 2 Ernest Burch (dark uniform, both hands stretching up to left)
51 3 Ernest Burch (dark uniform, fielding, right hand stretching up to left)
51 4 Ernest Burch (dark uniform, throwing, right hand head-high)
51 5 Ernest Burch (dark uniform, bat by left shoulder)
51 6 Ernest Burch (white uniform, bat on left shoulder)
51 7 Ernest Burch (white uniform, leaning left to field)
51 8 Ernest Burch (white uniform, fielding, hands above head on left)
52 1 Bill Burdick (ball in hand above head)
52 2 Bill Burdick (fielding)
52 3a Bill Burdick (bat in hand at side, C.)
52 3b Bill Burdick (bat in hand at side, P.)
53 1a Black Jack Burdock (portrait, 2d B.)
53 1b Black Jack Burdock (portrait, Second Base)
53 2a Black Jack Burdock (throwing, 2d B.)
53 2b Black Jack Burdock (throwing, 2d Base)
53 3a Black Jack Burdock (batting, 2d B.)
53 3b Black Jack Burdock (batting, 2d Base)
53 4a Black Jack Burdock (fielding grounder, 2d B.)
53 4b Black Jack Burdock (fielding grounder, 2d Base)
53 5a Black Jack Burdock (bat in hand at side, 2d B.)
53 5b Black Jack Burdock (bat in hand at side, 2d Base)
54 1 Robert Burks (Burk) (fielding, hands at chest)
54 2 Robert Burks (Burk) (fielding, hands head-high)
54 3 Robert Burks (Burk) (batting)
55 1a Watch Burnham (portrait, Man'gr)
55 1b Watch Burnham (portrait, Manager)
56 1 James Burns (fielding grounder by right foot, Kansas Citys)
56 2 James Burns (fielding, hands just above waist, Kansas Citys)
56 3 James Burns (fielding, hands shoulder-high, Kansas Citys)
56 4 James Burns (bat at ready position over shoulder, Kansas Citys)
56 5 James Burns (bat at 70 degrees, ball nearby, Kansas Citys)
56 6 James Burns (sliding, Kansas Citys)
56 7 James Burns (bat in hand at side, Omaha)
56 8 James Burns (ball in hands above head, Omaha)
58 1a Oyster Burns (bat at ready position vertically, Baltimores)
58 1b Oyster Burns (bat at ready position vertically, Brooklyns)
58 2a Oyster Burns (swinging bat, Brooklyns)
58 2b Oyster Burns (swinging bat, Baltimores)
58 3a Oyster Burns (fielding, Baltimores)
58 3b Oyster Burns (fielding, Brooklyns)
58 4a Oyster Burns (throwing, right hand head-high, Brooklyns)
58 4b Oyster Burns (throwing, right hand head-high, Baltimores)
58 5 Oyster Burns (throwing, left hand out of picture)
59 1a Thomas Burns (tagging player, Chicago's)
59 1b Thomas Burns (tagging player, Chicagos (NL))
59 1c Thomas Burns (tagging player, Chicagos)
59 2a Thomas Burns (bat in hand at side, Chicago's)
59 2c Thomas Burns (bat in hand at side, Chicago)
59 3a Thomas Burns (fielding, Chicago's)
59 3c Thomas Burns (fielding, Chicagos)
59 3d Thomas E. Burns (fielding, Chicagos (NL))
59 4 Thomas E. Burns (batting)
60 1 Doc Bushong (Brown's Champions)
60 2a Doc Bushong (in mask, hands on knees, no comma after C.)
60 2b Doc Bushong (in mask, hands on knees, comma after C.)
60 3a Doc Bushong (stooping, hands waist-high, no comma after C.)
60 3c Doc Bushong (stooping, hands waist-high, comma after C.)
60 4 Doc Bushong (standing, ball in hands chest-high)
60 5 Doc Bushong (throwing)
60 6a Doc Bushong (batting, no comma after C.)
60 6b Doc Bushong (batting, comma after C.)
61 1a Patsy Cahill (fielding, R.F.)
61 1b Patsy Cahill (fielding, Right Field)
61 2a Patsy Cahill (batting, R.F.)
61 2b Patsy Cahill (batting, Right Field)
62 1 Count Campau (throwing)
62 2 Count Campau (fielding, hands head-high)
62 3a Count Campau (fielding, bending to left, Detroits)
62 3b Count Campau (fielding, bending to left, Kansas City)
62 4a Count Campau (fielding, bending to right, Detroits)
62 4b Count Campau (fielding, bending to right, Kansas City)
62 5 Count Campau (bat in hand at side)
63 1 Jimmy Canavan (batting, looking at camera)
63 2a Jimmy Canavan (batting, looking down at ball, Omahas)
63 2b Jimmy Canavan (batting, looking down at ball, Omaha)
63 3 Jimmy Canavan (fielding)
64 1a Bart Cantz (hands on knees, St. Louis Whites)
64 1b Bart Cantz (hands on knees, Baltimores)
64 2 Bart Cantz (fielding, in mask)
64 3a Bart Cantz (fielding, no mask, St. Louis Whites)
64 3b Bart Cantz (fielding, no mask, Baltimores)
64 4a Bart Cantz (batting, St. Louis Whites)
64 4b Bart Cantz (batting, Baltimores)
64 5 Bart Cantz (throwing)
65 1a Handsome Jack Carney (fielding, hands head-high, Washingtons)
65 1b Handsome Jack Carney (fielding, hands head-high, Washington)
65 2a Handsome Jack Carney (throwing, Washingtons)
65 2b Handsome Jack Carney (throwing, Washington)
65 3a Handsome Jack Carney (bat in hand at side, Washingtons)
65 3b Handsome Jack Carney (bat in hand at side, Washington)
65 4 Handsome Jack Carney (batting)
65 5 Handsome Jack Carney (fielding, bending to left)
66 1a Hick Carpenter (tagging player, Cincinnati)
66 1b Hick Carpenter (tagging player, Cincinnatis)
66 2a Hick Carpenter (fielding grounder, Cincinnati)
66 2b Hick Carpenter (fielding grounder, Cin.)
66 3a Hick Carpenter (fielding, ball knee-high, Cincinnati)
66 3b Hick Carpenter (fielding, ball knee-high, Cincinnatis)
66 3c Hick Carpenter (fielding, ball knee-high, Cin)
66 4a Hick Carpenter (batting, Cincinnati)
66 4b Hick Carpenter (batting, Cin'ati)
66 4c Hick Carpenter (batting, Cin., N.L.)
66 5a Hick Carpenter (fielding, hands neck-high, Cincinnati)
66 5b Hick Carpenter (fielding, hands neck-high, Cin.)
67 1 Cliff Carroll (batting, Washington)
67 2a Cliff Carroll (fielding, L.F., Washington)
67 2b Cliff Carroll (fielding, Left Field, Washington)
68 1a Scrappy Carroll (batting, looking at camera, St. Pauls)
68 1b Scrappy Carroll (batting, looking at camera, St. Paul)
68 2a Scrappy Carroll (batting, looking at ball, St. Pauls)
68 2b Scrappy Carroll (batting, looking at ball, Chicagos (NL))
68 3a Scrappy Carroll (fielding, hands waist-high, ball visible, St. Pauls)
68 3b Scrappy Carroll (fielding, hands waist-high, no ball visible, St. Paul)
68 4a Scrappy Carroll (fielding, hands chin-high, St. Pauls)
68 4b Scrappy Carroll (fielding, hands chin-high, St. Paul)
68 5a Scrappy Carroll (fielding, hands chest-high, St. Pauls)
68 5b Scrappy Carroll (fielding, hands chest-high, St. Paul)
68 5c Scrappy Carroll (fielding, hands chest-high, Chicagos (NL))
69 1a Fred Carroll (throwing, C., Pittsburg)
69 1b Fred Carroll (throwing, Catcher, Pittsburg)
69 2a Fred Carroll (batting, C., Pittsburg)
69 2b Fred Carroll (batting, Catcher, Pittsburg)
69 3a Fred Carroll (bat in hand at side, C., Pittsburg)
69 3b Fred Carroll (bat in hand at side, Catcher, Pittsburg)
70 1 Jumbo Cartwright (arms folded, St. Josep)
70 1a Jumbo Cartwright (arms folded, St. Joes)
70 1c Jumbo Cartwright (arms folded, Kansas City)
70 2 Jumbo Cartwright (batting)
70 4 Jumbo Cartwright (bat in hand at side)
70 5 Jumbo Cartwright (throwing)
71 1 Parisian Bob Caruthers (Brown's Champions)
71 2 Parisian Bob Caruthers (holding up ball in left hand)
71 3a Parisian Bob Caruthers (ready to pitch, no comma after P.)
71 3b Parisian Bob Caruthers (ready to pitch, comma after P.)
71 4a Parisian Bob Caruthers (end of pitch, no comma after P.)
71 4b Parisian Bob Caruthers (end of pitch, comma after P.)
71 5a Parisian Bob Caruthers (fielding, no comma after P.)
71 5b Parisian Bob Caruthers (fielding, comma after P.)
71 6 Parisian Bob Caruthers (batting, feet together)
71 7a Parisian Bob Caruthers (batting, feet apart, no comma after P.)
71 7b Parisian Bob Caruthers (batting, feet apart, comma after P.)
72 1a Dan Casey (ball in hand at side, P., Phila)
72 1b Dan Casey (ball in hand at side, Pitcher, Philadelphia)
72 1c Dan Casey (ball in hand at side, Casey on front, P., Philadelphias)
72 1d Dan Casey (ball in hand at side, D.M. Casey on front, P., Philadelphias)
72 2a Dan Casey (ready to pitch, Phila)
72 2b Dan Casey (ready to pitch, Philadelphis)
72 3a Dan Casey (start of pitch, Phila)
72 3b Dan Casey (start of pitch, Philadelphia)
72 3c Dan Casey (start of pitch, Philadelphias)
73 1a Icebox Chamberlain (pitching, hands at chest, P.)
73 1c Icebox Chamberlain (pitching, hands at chest, S.)
73 2 Icebox Chamberlain (pitching, hands neck-high)
73 3 Icebox Chamberlain (pitching, right hand head-high)
73 4 Icebox Chamberlain (pitching, right hand chest-high)
73 5a Icebox Chamberlain (batting, looking at camera, P., St. Louis)
73 5b Icebox Chamberlain (batting, looking at camera, P., St. Loui)
73 5d Icebox Chamberlain (batting, looking at camera, S.)
73 6 Icebox Chamberlain (batting, looking at ball)
74 1 Cupid Childs (batting, heels together)
74 2 Cupid Childs (batting, heels well apart)
74 3 Cupid Childs (fielding)
74 4a Cupid Childs (throwing, Phila)
74 4b Cupid Childs (throwing, Syracuse)
75 1a Spider Clark (fielding, facing to left, Washingtons)
75 1b Spider Clark (fielding, facing to left, Washington)
75 2a Spider Clark (fielding, facing front, Washingtons)
75 2b Spider Clark (fielding, facing front, Washington)
75 3 Spider Clark (batting)
75 4 Spider Clark (throwing)
76 1 Bob Clark (hands on hips, Brooklyns)
76 2 Bob Clark (stooping, hands on knees, Brooklyns)
76 3 Bob Clark (fielding, hands above waist, Brooklyns)
76 4 Bob Clark (fielding, hands shoulder-high, Brooklyns)
76 5 Bob Clark (throwing, Brooklyns)
76 6 Bob Clark (Clark tagging Hughes)
76 6 Mickey Hughes (Clark tagging Hughes)
77 1 Dad Clark (Clarke) (with cap, hands at chest, Omahas)
77 2 Dad Clark (Clarke) (with cap, bat in hand at side, Omahas)
77 3 Dad Clark (Clarke) (with cap, ball in right hand head-high, Omahas)
77 4 Dad Clark (Clarke) (with cap, ball in right hand by right knee, Omahas)
77 5a Dad Clark (Clarke) (no cap, about to hit low ball, name incorrect, Omahas, W.A.) 65.00 32.00 19.50
77 5b Dad Clarke (no cap, about to hit low ball, name correct, Chicago)
77 6 Dad Clark (Clarke) (no cap, bat at ready position, Chicago)
77 7 Dad Clark (Clarke) (no cap, facing left, hands chest high, Chicago)
77 8 Dad Clarke (no cap, facing front, hands at chest)
77 9a Dad Clark (Clarke) (no cap, right arm extended forward, Omahas)
77 9b Dad Clark (Clarke) (no cap, right arm extended forward, Chicago)
78 1 John Clarkson (throwing, right arm extended horizontally, looking front, left hand on thigh)
78 2a John Clarkson (throwing, right arm extrended horizontally, right profile, left hand clear of thigh, Chicago)
78 2b John Clarkson (throwing, right arm extrended horizontally, right profile, left hand clear of thigh, Bostons)
78 3a John Clarkson (throwing, right hand hip-high, right profile, Chicago)
78 3b John Clarkson (throwing, right hand hip-high, right profile, Bostons)
78 4 John Clarkson (ready to pitch, hands at chest)
78 5a John Clarkson (end of pitch, right arm extended forward, left hand on thigh, Chicago)
78 5b John Clarkson (end of pitch, right arm extended forward, left hand on thigh, Boston)
78 5c John Clarkson (end of pitch, right arm extended forward, left hand on thigh, Bostons)
78 6 John Clarkson (fielding)
78 7a John Clarkson (batting, Chicago)
78 7b John Clarkson (batting, Bostons)
79 1a Jack Clements (hands on knees, Phila)
79 1b Jack Clements (hands on knees, Philadelphia)
79 1c Jack Clements (hands on knees, Philadelphias)
79 1d Jack Clements (hands on knees, Phila (N.L.))
79 2a Jack Clements (fielding, Phila)
79 2b Jack Clements (fielding, Philadelphia)
79 2c Jack Clements (fielding, Philadelphias)
79 3a Jack Clements (batting, Phila)
79 3b Jack Clements (batting, Philadelphia)
79 3c Jack Clements (batting, Philadelphias)
79 3d Jack Clements (batting, Phil)
80 1 Elmer Cleveland (sliding)
80 2 Elmer Cleveland (bending forward, hands at back)

80 3 Elmer Cleveland (fielding)
80 4 Elmer Cleveland (bat at ready, over shoulder)
80 5 Elmer Cleveland (bat held nearly horizontal)
80 6 Elmer Cleveland (throwing)
81 1 Monk Cline (fielding, hands at waist looking upwards)
81 2 Monk Cline (fielding, hands by right shoulder, looking front, ball above head)
81 3a Monk Cline (fielding, hands by right shoulder, looking at ball just above hands, Sioux Citys)
81 3b Monk Cline (fielding, hands by right shoulder, looking at ball just above hands, Sioux City)
81 4a Monk Cline (about to hit, bat held vertically, Sioux Citys)
81 4b Monk Cline (about to hit, bat held vertically, Sioux City)
81 5 Monk Cline (bat at 45 degrees)
82 1 Cody (fielding)
82 2 Cody (throwing)
82 3 Cody (bat at ready, looking at camera)
82 4 Cody (about to hit, looking at ball)
83 1 John Coleman (fielding, hands chest-high)
83 2a John Coleman (ball in hands at waist, R.F.)
83 2b John Coleman (ball in hands at waist, Right Field)
83 3 John Coleman (throwing)
83 4a John Coleman (bat in hands below waist, R.F., Pittsburg)
83 4b John Coleman (bat in hands below waist, Right Field)
83 4c John Coleman (bat in hand at side, R.F., Pittsburgs)
83 5a John Coleman (bat in hand at side, R.F.)
83 5b John Coleman (bat in hand at side, Right Field)
84 1a Bill Collins (throwing, right hand head-high, in mask, N.Y's)
84 1b Bill Collins (throwing, right hand head-high, in mask, Newarks)
84 2a Bill Collins (sliding, N.Y's)
84 2b Bill Collins (sliding, Newarks)
84 3 Bill Collins (batting)
84 4a Bill Collins (bat in hand at side, N.Y's)
84 4b Bill Collins (bat in hand at side, Newarks)
84 5 Bill Collins (fielding ball waist-high, in mask, N.Y's)
84 6a Bill Collins (hands on knees, in mask, N.Y's)
84 6b Bill Collins (hands on knees, in mask, Newarks)
84 7 Bill Collins (fielding, hands above head, full length photo, N.Y's)
84 8 Bill Collins (fielding, hands above head, 3/4-length photo, Newarks)
85 1 Hub Collins (fielding grounder, Louisville)
85 2 Hub Collins (batting, Louisville)
85 3a Hub Collins (fielding, Louisville)
85 3b Hub Collins (fielding, Brooklyns)
85 4 Hub Collins (throwing, Louisville)
85 5 Hub Collins (sliding, Louisville)
86 1 Commy Comiskey (Brown's Champions)
86 2a Commy Comiskey (sliding, Chas. Comiskey on front)
86 2b Commy Comiskey (sliding, Comiskey on front)
86 3a Commy Comiskey (fielding, hands shoulder-high, looking to left, name correct)
86 3b Commy Commiskey (Comiskey) (fielding, hands shoulder-high, looking to left, name incorrect)
86 4 Commy Comiskey (fielding, hands chin-high, looking up at ball)
86 5 Commy Comiskey (batting)
86 6a Commy Comiskey (arms folded, St. Louis Browns)
86 6c Commy Comiskey (arms folded, Chicagos)
87 1 Pete Connell (fielding, dark uniform)
87 2 Pete Connell (fielding, light uniform)
88 1a Roger Connor (hands on knees, name in script)
88 1b Roger Connor (hands on knees, New Yorks)
88 1c Roger Connor (hands on knees, N.Y's)
88 1d Roger Connor (hands on knees, New York)
88 2 Roger Connor (fielding)
88 4a Roger Connor (bat held up nearly vertical, name in script)
88 4b Roger Connor (bat held up nearly vertical, N.Y's)
89 1a Dick Conway (ball in right hand head-high, head level, P., Boston)
89 1b Dick Conway (ball in right hand head-high, head level, P., Bostons)
89 1c Dick Conway (ball in right hand head-high, head level, P., Worcesters)
89 2a Dick Conway (ball in right hand chin-high, head tilted to left, P., Boston)
89 2b Dick Conway (ball in right hand chin-high, head tilted to left, Pitcher, Boston)
89 3a Dick Conway (batting, P., Boston)
89 3b Dick Conway (batting, Pitcher, Boston)
89 4a Dick Conway (ready to pitch, P., Boston)
89 4b Dick Conway (ready to pitch, Pitcher, Boston)
89 5a Dick Conway (bat in hand at side, P., Boston)
89 5b Dick Conway (bat in hand at side, Pitcher, Boston)
90 1a Pete Conway (batting, Detroits)
90 1b Pete Conway (batting, Pittsburgs)
90 2 Pete Conway (pitching, feet on ground, Detroits)
90 3a Pete Conway (pitching, hands chest-high, left foot off ground, Detroits)
90 3b Pete Conway (pitching, hands chest-high, left foot off ground, Pittsburgs)
90 3c Pete Conway (pitching, hands chest-high, left foot off ground, Pittsburghs)
90 4a Pete Conway (pitching, right hand by head, heels on ground, Detroits)
90 4b Pete Conway (pitching, right hand by head, heels on ground, Pittsburgs)
90 4c Pete Conway (pitching, right hand by head, heels on ground, Pittsburghs)
90 5a Pete Conway (pitching, right hand stretched forward, right heel off ground, Detroits)
90 5c Pete Conway (pitching, right hand stretched forward, right heel off ground, Indianapolis)
91 1 Jim Conway (batting, Kansas City)
91 2 Jim Conway (bat in hand at side, Kansas Citys)
65.00 32.00 19.50
91 3 Jim Conway (ready to pitch, hands chest-high, Kansas City)
91 4 Jim Conway (pitching, left ear not visible, Kansas City)
91 5 Jim Conway (pitching, left ear cleary visible, Kansas City)
92 1 Paul Cook (tagging player)
92 2 Paul Cook (fielding grounder)
92 3a Paul Cook (throwing, Louisville)
92 3b Paul Cook (throwing, Louisvilles)
92 4a Paul Cook (in mask, Louisville)
92 4b Paul Cook (in mask, Louisvilles)
93 1 Jimmy Cooney (throwing)
93 2a Jimmy Cooney (batting, Omahas)
93 2b Jimmy Cooney (batting, Chicago)
94 1a Larry Corcoran (pitching, hands above waist, P., Indianapolis)
94 1b Larry Corcoran (pitching, hands above waist, Pitcher)
94 1c Larry Corcoran (pitching, hands above waist, P., London, Ont.)
94 2a Larry Corcoran (pitching, hands near left shoulder, P., Indianapolis)
94 2b Larry Corcoran (Pitching, hands near left shoulder, Pitcher)
94 2c Larry Corcoran (pitching, hands near left shoulder, P., London, Ont.)
95 1 Pop Corkhill (sliding)
95 2a Pop Corkhill (fielding, hands neck-high, Cincinnati)
95 2b Pop Corkhill (fielding, hands neck-high, Brooklyns)
95 3 Pop Corkhill (fielding, hands above head)
95 4a Pop Corkhill (stooping, hands knee-high, Cincinnati)
95 4b Pop Corkhill (stooping, hands knee-high, Brooklyns)
95 5 Pop Corkhill (batting)
96 1a Cannonball Crane (bat at 60 degrees, N.Y.)
96 1b Cannonball Crane (bat at 60 degrees, New Yorks)
96 2a Cannonball Crane (bat nearly horizontal, N.Y.)
96 2b Cannonball Crane (bat nearly horizontal, New Yorks)
96 3a Cannonball Crane (bat in hand at side, N.Y.)
96 3b Cannonball Crane (bat in hand at side, New Yorks)
96 4a Cannonball Crane (ready to pitch, hands above waist, N.Y.)
96 4b Cannonball Crane (ready to pitch, hands above wais, New Yorks)
96 4c Cannonball Crane (ready to pitch, hands above waist, New Yorks (P.L.))
96 5a Cannonball Crane (pitching, hands below waist, N.Y.)
96 5b Cannonball Crane (pitching, hands below waist, New Yorks)
96 6a Cannonball Crane (pitching, right hand head-high, N.Y.)
96 6b Cannonball Crane (pitching, right hand head-high, New Yorks)
97 1a Sam Crane (batting, 2d B., Washington)
97 1b Sam Crane (batting, Second Base, Washington)
97 2a Sam Crane (fielding grounder, 2d B., Washington)
97 2b Sam Crane (fielding grounder, Second Base, Washington)
97 3a Sam Crane (bat in hand at side, 2d B., Washington)
97 3b Sam Crane (bat in hand at side, Second Base, Washington)
98 1 Jack Crogan (Croghan) (fielding grounder)
98 2 Jack Crogan (Croghan) (leaning to right, hands thigh-high)
98 3 Jack Crogan (Croghan) (bat in hand at side)
98 4 Jack Crogan (Croghan) (fielding, hands chest-high)
98 5 Jack Crogan (Croghan) (batting)
99 1a John Crooks (sliding, St. Louis Whites)
99 1b John Crooks (sliding, Omahas)
99 2 John Crooks (bat at ready position behind head)
99 3 John Crooks (bat nearly horizontal)
99 4a John Crooks (ball in hands waist-high, St. Louis Whites)
99 4b John Crooks (ball in hands waist-high, C. Crooks on front, Omahas)
99 4c John Crooks (ball in hands waist-high, Crooks on front, Omahas)
99 5 John Crooks (fielding, hands head-high)
100 1 Lave Cross (batting)
100 2aLave Cross (hands on thighs, Louisville)
100 2bLave Cross (hands on thighs, Philadelphias (PL))
100 3 Lave Cross (fielding low throw)
100 4aLave Cross (throwing, Louisville)
100 4bLave Cross (throwing, Philadelphias (PL))
101 1aN.C. Crossley (fielding, hands by right knee, Milwaukee)
101 1bN.C. Crossley (fielding, hands by right knee, Milwaukees)
101 2 N.C. Crossley (fielding, hands waist-high)
101 3aN.C. Crossley (fielding, hands neck-high, Milwaukee)
101 3bN.C. Crossley (fielding, hands neck-high, Milwaukees)
101 4 N.C. Crossley (batting, looking at camera)
101 5 N.C. Crossley (batting, looking at bat)
102 1 Joe Crotty (dotted tie)
102 2aJoe Crotty (fielding ball waist-high, Sioux Citys)
102 2bJoe Crotty (fielding ball waist-high, Sioux City)
102 3aJoe Crotty (fielding, hands shoulder-high, Sioux Citys)
102 3bJoe Crotty (fielding, hands shoulder-high, Sioux City)
102 4 Joe Crotty (batting, looking at camera)
102 5aJoe Crotty (batting, looking at ball, Sioux Citys)
102 5bJoe Crotty (batting, looking at ball, Sioux City)
103 1aBilly Crowell (pitching, facing front, hands above waist, Cleveland's)
103 1bBilly Crowell (pitching, facing front, hands above waist, St. Joes)
103 2 Billy Crowell (pitching, facing half way to left, hands waist-high)
103 3aBilly Crowell (pitching, facing left, hands behind body, Cleveland's)
103 3bBilly Crowell (pitching, facing left, hands behind body, St. Joes)
103 4aBilly Crowell (pitching, right arm extended, Clevelands)
103 4bBilly Crowell (pitching, right arm extended, St. Joes)
103 5aBilly Crowell (batting, Clevelands)
103 5bBilly Crowell (batting, St. Joes)
104 1 Jim Cubworth (fielding low ball)
104 2 Jim Cubworth (fielding, hands head-high)
104 3 Jim Cubworth (throwing)
104 4 Jim Cubworth (batting)
105 1 Bert Cunningham (fielding)
105 2aBert Cunningham (pitching, hands chest-high, Baltimores)
105 2bBert Cunningham (pitching, hands chest-high, Philadelphias)
105 3 Bert Cunningham (pitching, ball in right hand waist-high)
105 4 Bert Cunningham (bat at ready position, held vertically)
105 5 Bert Cunningham (bat at ready position at about 20 degrees)
106 1 Tacks Curtis (fielding, hands ankle-high, feet together)
106 2 Tacks Curtis (fielding, hands ankle-high, feet apart)
106 3 Tacks Curtis (bat at ready position by ground)
106 4 Tacks Curtis (bat at ready position by head)
106 5 Tacks Curtis (fielding, hands head-high)
107 1 Ed Cushman (dotted tie)
107 2 Ed Cushman (pitching, left hand forward, head high)
108 1 Tony Cusick (batting)
108 2 Tony Cusick (throwing)
109 1 Dailey (mask in hand at side, Oakland)
110 1aEdward Dailey (Daily) (pitching, right hand head-high, Phila)
110 1bEdward Daley (Daily) (pitching, right hand head-high, Philadelphia)
110 1cEdward Dailey (Daily) (pitching, right hand head-high, Washington)
110 2aEdward Dailey (Daily) (pitching, hands neck-high, Phila)
110 2bEdward Daley (Daily) (pitching, hands neck-high, Philadelphia)
110 2cEdward Dailey (Daily) (pitching, hands neck-high, Washington)
110 3aEdward Dailey (Daily) (bat at ready position at 30 degrees, Phila)
110 3bEdward Daley (Daily) (bat at ready position at 30 degrees, Philadelphia)
110 3cEdward Dailey (Daily) (bat at ready position at 30 degrees, Washington)
110 3dEdward Daley (Daily) (bat at ready position at 30 degrees, Columbus)
111 1aBill Daley (pitching, hands above waist, Bostons)
111 1bBill Daley (pitching, hands above waist, Bostons (PL))
112 1aCon Daley (Daily) (hands on knees, C., Boston)
112 1bCon Daley (Daily) (hands on knees, Catcher, Boston)
112 1cCon Daley (Daily) (hands on knees, no comma after C., Indianapolis)
112 1dCon Daley (Daily) (hands on knees, comma after C., Indianapolis)
112 2aCon Daley (Daily) (right hand on hip, left arm at side, C., Boston)
112 2bCon Daley (Daily) (right hand on hip, left arm at side, Indianapolis)
112 2cCon Daley (Daily) (right hand on hip, left arm at side, Catcher, Boston)
112 3aCon Daley (Daily) (throwing, right hand head-high, Boston)
112 3bCon Daley (Daily) (throwing, right hand head-high, no comma after C., Indianapolis)
112 3cCon Daley (Daily) (throwing, right hand head-high, comma after C., Indianapolis)
112 4aCon Daley (Daily) (batting, bat over left shoulder, C., Boston)
112 4bCon Daley (Daily) (batting, bat over left shoulder, Catcher, Boston)
112 4cCon Daley (Daily) (batting, bat over left shoulder, Indianapolis)
112 5aCon Daley (Daily) (ready to hit, bat vertical, Catcher)
112 5bBobby Wheelock (photo actually Con Daily - caption error) (ready to hit, bat vertical, R.F.)
113 1aAbner Dalrymple (hands on hips, feet apart, L.F., Pittsburg)
113 1bAbner Dalrymple (hands on hips, feet apart, Left Field)
113 1cAbner Dalrymple (hands on hips, feet apart, L.F., Denvers)
113 2aAbner Dalrymple (hands on hips, left foot behind right foot, L.F., Pittsburg)
113 2bAbner Dalrymple (hands on hips, left foot behind right foot, Left Field)
113 2cAbner Dalrymple (hands on hips, left foot behing right foot, L.F., Denvers)
113 4aAbner Dalrymple (throwing, L.F., Pittsburg)
113 4bAbner Dalrymple (throwing, Left Field)
113 4cAbner Dalrymple (throwing, L.F., Denvers)
113 5aAbner Dalrymple (batting, L.F.)
113 5bAbner Dalrymple (batting, Left Field)
114 1aTom Daly (portrait, Chicagos)
114 1bTom Daly (portrait, Chicago)
114 2 Tom Daly (fielding, with cap, Chicagos)
114 3 Tom Daly (fielding, no cap, Washington)
114 4aTom Daly (bat in hand at side, Chicagos)
114 4bTom Daly (bat in hand at side, Chicago)
114 4cTom Daly (bat in hand at side, Clevelands)
114 5aTom Daly (batting, with or without ball visible, Chicagos)
114 5bTom Daly (batting, with or without ball visible, Chicago)
114 5cTom Daly (batting, with or without ball visible, Chicago's)
114 6aTom Daly (hands on knees, Chicagos)
114 6bTom Daly (hands on knees, Chicago's)
115 1 Sun Daly (batting, looking at camera, Minneapolis)
115 2 Sun Daly (batting, looking at ball, Minneapolis)
115 3 Sun Daly (fielding, hands by right thigh, Minneapolis)
115 4 Sun Daly (fielding, hands chest-high, Minneapolis)
115 5 Sun Daly (fielding, hands neck-high, Minneapolis)
116 1 Law Daniels (batting)

116 2 Law Daniels (fielding, head-high)
116 3 Law Daniels (fielding, hands by right thigh)
116 4 Law Daniels (throwing)
117 1 Dell Darling (portrait)
117 2aDell Darling (arms folded, Del. Darling on front, Chicago)
117 2bDell Darling (arms folded, Dell Darling on front, Chicago)
117 2cDell Darling (arms folded, Chicagos)
117 3aDell Darling (fielding, hands chin-high, Del. Darling on front, Chicago)
117 3bDell Darling (fielding, hands chin-high, Dell Darling on front, Chicago)
117 3cDell Darling (fielding, hands chin-high, Chicagos)
117 4aDell Darling (fielding, hands waist-high, Chicago)
117 4bDell Darling (fielding, hands waist-high, Chicagos)
117 4cDell Darling (fielding, hands waist-high, Chicago's)
117 5 Dell Darling (batting)
118 1aWilliam Darnbrough (batting, Denver)
118 1bWilliam Darnbrough (batting, Denvers)
118 2 William Darnbrough (pitching)
118 51 Davin (bat in hand at side)
119 1aJumbo Davis (sliding, 3d B.)
119 1bJumbo Davis (sliding, 3d B.)
119 2 Jumbo Davis (fielding grounder)
119 3aJumbo Davis (fielding, hands shoulder-high, Kansas City)
119 3bJumbo Davis (fielding, hands shoulder-high, Kansas Citys)
119 4 Jumbo Davis (throwing)
119 5aJumbo Davis (bat in hand at side, no comma after 3d B.)
119 5bJumbo Davis (bat in hand at side, comma after 3d B.)
120 1aPat Dealey (fielding, hands waist-high, standing upright, name correct)
120 1bPat Dealy (Dealey) (fielding, hands waist-high, standing upright, name incorrect)
120 2aPat Dealey (fielding, hands waist-high, leaning to left, name correct)
120 2bPat Dealy (Dealey) (fielding, hands waist-high, leaning to left, name incorrect)
120 3aPat Dealey (bat in hand at side, name correct)
120 3bPat Dealy (Dealey) (bat in hand at side, name incorrect)
120 4aPat Dealey (hands on thighs, name correct)
120 4bPat Dealy (Dealey) (hands on thighs, name incorrect)
120 5aPat Dealey (bat on right shoulder, name correct)
120 5bPat Dealy (Dealey) (bat on right shoulder, name incorrect)
120 6aPat Dealey (throwing, name correct)
120 6bPat Dealy (Dealey) (throwing, name incorrect)
121 1 Tom Deasley (fielding, hands level with cap)
121 2aTom Deasley (sliding, N.Y's)
121 2bTom Deasley (sliding, Washington)
121 3 Tom Deasley (leaning left, hands touching above waist)
121 4aTom Deasley (leaning left, hands clasped neck-high, N.Y.'s)
121 4bTom Deasley (leaning left, hands clasped neck-high, Washington)
121 5aTom Deasley (bat in hand at side, N.Y's)
121 5bTom Deasley (bat in hand at side, Washington)
121 6 Tom Deasley (leaning left, ball in hands by chin)
121 7aTom Deasley (fielding, hands chest-high, N.Y's)
121 7bTom Deasley (fielding, hands chest-high, Washington)
121 8 Tom Deasley (fielding, hands in front of face)
121 9 Tom Deasley (bat at ready position at about 80 degrees)
121 10Tom Deasley (right hand hip-high, left hand by left knee)
121 11Tom Deasley (throwing, hands to left, chest-high)
121 12aTom Deasley (throwing, right hand neck-high, N.Y's)
121 12bTom Deasley (throwing, right hand neck-high, Washington)
121 13aTom Deasley (bat at ready position, bat end behind head, N.Y's)
121 13bTom Deasley (bat at ready position, bat end behind head, Washington)
121 14Tom Deasley (fielding grounder)
122 1 Harry Decker (bat at ready position, almost horizontal)
122 2aHarry Decker (bat at ready position, over shoulder, Philadelphias)
122 2bHarry Decker (bat at ready position, over shoulder, Philadelphia (NL))
122 3 Harry Decker (fielding, hands thigh-high)
122 4aHarry Decker (fielding, hands chest-high, Philadelphias)
122 4bHarry Decker (fielding, hands chest-high, Philadelphia)
122 5aHarry Decker (throwing, Philadelphias)
122 5bHarry Decker (throwing, Philadelphia)
122 5cHarry Decker (throwing, Philadelphia (NL))
123 1aEd Delahanty (bat at ready position by shoulder, Phila)
123 1bEd Delahanty (bat at ready position by shoulder, Phila's)
123 2 Ed Delahanty (bat at ready position, nearly horizontal)
123 3aEd Delahanty (fielding, hands at waist, Phila)
123 3bEd Delahanty (fielding, hands at waist, Phila's)
123 4aEd Delahanty (throwing, Phila)
123 4bEd Delahanty (throwing, Phila's)
123 5 Ed Delahanty (fielding grounder)
124 1aJerry Denny (batting, 3d B. Indianapolis)
124 1bJerry Denny (batting, 3d Base, Indianapolis)
124 1cJerry Denny (batting, 3d B., Indianapolis)
124 2aJerry Denny (in jacket, arms at sides, 3d B. Indianapolis)
124 2bJerry Denny (in jacket, arms at sides, 3d Base, Indianapolis)
124 2cJerry Denny (in jacket, arms at sides, 3d B., Indianapolis)
124 2dJerry Denny (in jacket, arms at sides, 3rd B., Indianapolis)
124 2eJerry Denny (in jacket, arms at sides, 3d B., New Yorks (NL))
124 3aJerry Denny (fielding, 3d B.)
124 3bJerry Denny (fielding, 3d Base)
125 1 Jim Devlin (sliding)
125 2aJim Devlin (pitching, left hand at back, shoulder-high, name correct, St. Louis)
125 2bJim Delvin (Devlin) (pitching, left hand at back, shoulder-high, name incorrect, St. Louis)
125 2cJim Devlin (pitching, left hand at back, shoulder-high, Devlin on front, St. Louis Browns)
125 2dJim Devlin (pitching, left hand at back, shoulder-high, J. Devlin on front, St. Louis Browns)
125 3 Jim Devlin (pitching, hands held out, shoulder-high)
125 4aJim Devlin (end of pitch, left hand waist-high, St. Louis Browns)
125 4bJim Devlin (end of pitch, left hand waist-high, St. Louis)
125 5 Jim Devlin (batting)
126 1aTom Dolan (sliding, Thos. Dolan on front)
126 1bTom Dolan (sliding, Dolan on front)
126 2aTom Dolan (batting, Thos. Dolan on front)
126 2bTom Dolan (batting, Dolan on front)
126 3 Tom Dolan (bat in hand at side)
126 4 Tom Dolan (fielding, hands above waist)
126 5 Tom Dolan (fielding, hands by right knee)
127 1 Jack Donahue (fielding, San Francisco)
128 1 Jim Donohue (Donahue) (dotted tie)
128 2aJim Donahue (throwing, name correct, Kansas City)
128 2bJim Donohue (Donahue) (throwing, name incorrect, Kansas City)
128 3aJim Donohue (Donahue) (batting, no comma after C., Kansas City)
128 3bJim Donohue (Donahue) (batting, no comma after C., Kansas City)
128 4aJim Donahue (fielding grounder by left foot, Kansas City)
128 4bJim Donohue (Donahue) (fielding grounder by left foot, Kansas Citys)
128 5 Jim Donohue (Donahue) (fielding ball knee-high, Kansas City)
128 6 Jim Donahue (ball in hands, head-high, Kansas City)
129 1aJim Donnelly (Donely) (fielding, hands shoulder-high, 3d B.)
129 1bJim Donnelly (Donely) (fielding, hands shoulder-high, Third Base)
129 2aJim Donnelly (Donely) (batting, 3d B.)
129 2bJim Donnelly (Donely) (batting, Third Base)
129 3aJim Donnelly (Donely) (fielding grounder, 3d B.)
129 3bJim Donnelly (Donely) (fielding grounder, Third Base)
130 1 Coley (fielding)
131 1 J. Doran (batting)
131 2 J. Doran (fielding)
132 1 Mike Dorgan (sliding, left hand raised)
132 2 Mike Dorgan (sliding, left hand on ground)
132 3 Mike Dorgan (throwing, right hand eye-high, looking front)
132 4 Mike Dorgan (throwing, right hand cap-high, looking left)
132 5aMike Dorgan (throwing, right hand chest-high, N.Y's)
132 5bMike Dorgan (throwing, right hand chest-high, New Yorks)
132 6 Mike Dorgan (fielding, right hand upstretched to left)
132 7aMike Dorgan (fielding, hands above head, N.Y's)
132 7bMike Dorgan (fielding, hands above head, New Yorks)
132 8 Mike Dorgan (fielding, hands chin-high)
132 9aMike Dorgan (fielding, hands ankle-high, N.Y's)
132 9bMike Dorgan (fielding, hands ankle-high, New Yorks)
132 10Mike Dorgan (fielding grounder with both hands)
132 11aMike Dorgan (fielding grounder with right hand by right foot, N.Y's)
132 11bMike Dorgan (fielding grounder with right hand by right foot, New Yorks)
132 12aMike Dorgan (hands on knees, N.Y's)
132 12bMike Dorgan (hands on knees, New Yorks)
132 13Mike Dorgan (arms folded)
132 14aMike Dorgan (running to left, N.Y's)
132 14bMike Dorgan (running to left, New Yorks)
132 15aMike Dorgan (bat in hand at side, N.Y's)
132 15bMike Dorgan (bat in hand at side, New Yorks)
132 16Mike Dorgan (bat at ready position over shoulder)
132 17aMike Dorgan (bat at ready position nearly vertical, N.Y's)
132 17bMike Dorgan (bat at ready position nearly vertical, New Yorks)
133 1 Doyle (throwing)
134 1 Home Run Duffe (Duffee) (batting)
134 2 Home Run Duffe (Duffee) (fielding grounder)
134 3 Home Run Duffe (Duffee) (fielding, bending to left, hands waist-high)
134 4 Home Run Duffe (Duffee) (fielding, standing upright, hands above waist)
134 5 Home Run Duffe (Duffee) (fielding, leaning forward, hands shoulder-high)
135 1aHugh Duffy (batting, Chicago)
135 1bHugh Duffy (batting, Chicago's)
135 1cHugh Duffy (batting, Chicagos)
135 2aHugh Duffy (fielding grounder, Chicagos)
135 2bHugh Duffy (fielding grounder, Chicago)
135 3aHugh Duffy (throwing, Chicago)
135 3bHugh Duffy (throwing, Chicagos)
135 4 Hugh Duffy (fielding, hands neck-high, feet apart)
135 5aHugh Duffy (fielding, hands chin-high, right heel behind left leg, Chicago)
135 5bHugh Duffy (fielding, hands chin-high, right heel behind left leg, Chicago's)
135 5cHugh Duffy (fielding, hands chin-high, right heel behind left leg, Chicagos)
136 1 Dan Dugdale (hands on knees, looking at camera)
136 2 Dan Dugdale (hands on knees, left profile)
136 3aDan Dugdale (bat in hand at side, Chicago Maroons)
136 3bDan Dugdale (bat in hand at side, Minpls)
136 4 Dan Dugdale (ball in right hand, head-high)
137 1 Duck Duke (batting)
137 2 Duck Duke (pitching, right hand by chin, left arm on thigh)
137 3 Duck Duke (pitching, hands waist-high)
137 4 Duck Duke (pitching, hands chest-high)
137 5 Duck Duke (pitching, right arm extended head-high)
138 1aSure Shot Dunlap (sliding, Pittsburgs)
138 1bSure Shot Dunlap (sliding, Pittsburghs)
138 2aSure Shot Dunlap (hands on thighs, Pittsburg)
138 2bSure Shot Dunlap (hands on thighs, Pittsburgs)
138 3 Sure Shot Dunlap (bat in hand at side)
138 4 Sure Shot Dunlap (batting)
138 5aSure Shot Dunlap (fielding, hands above waist, Pittsburg)
138 5bSure Shot Dunlap (fielding, hands above waist, Pittsburgs)
138 6aSure Shot Dunlap (fielding, hands shoulder-high, Pittsburg)
138 6bSure Shot Dunlap (fielding, hands shoulder-high, Pittsburgs)
138 7aSure Shot Dunlap (throwing, right hand waist-high, Pittsburg)
138 7bSure Shot Dunlap (throwing, right hand waist-high, Pittsburgs)
138 8 Sure Shot Dunlap (throwing, right hand above head)
139 1 Dunn (batting)
139 2 Dunn (pitching, hands chest-high)
139 3 Dunn (ball in right hand head-high, facing front)
139 4 Dunn (ball in right hand chin-high, looking to right)
139 5 Dunn (fielding, hands chest-high)
140 2 Jesse Duryea (bat under left arm, hands together)
140 3aJesse Duryea (throwing, right hand head-high, Cincinatti)
140 3bJesse Duryea (throwing, right hand head-high, Cincinnatis)
140 3cJesse Duryea (throwing, right hand head-high, Cincinnatti)
140 4aJesse Duryea (throwing, right hand chest-high, Cincinnati)
140 4bJesse Duryea (throwing, right hand chest-high, Cincinnati (NL))
140 5 Jesse Duryea (ready to pitch, hands chest-high)
141 1aFrank Dwyer (fielding, hands chest-high, Chicagos)
141 1bFrank Dwyer (fielding, hands chest-high, Chicago Maroons)
141 2aFrank Dwyer (throwing, Chicago's)
141 2bFrank Dwyer (throwing, Chicago Maroons)
141 3aFrank Dwyer (bat in hand at side, Chicago's)
141 3bFrank Dwyer (bat in hand at side, Chicagos)
142 1 Billy Earle (fielding, hands above head)
142 2 Billy Earle (fielding, hands thigh-high)
142 3aBilly Earle (bat in hand at side, name correct, Cincinnati)
142 3bBilly Earl (Earle) (bat in hand at side, name incorrect, St. Paul)
143 1aBuck Ebright (hands on knees, Washingtons)
143 1bBuck Ebright (hands on knees, Washington)
143 2 Buck Ebright (throwing)
144 1 Red Ehret (throwing)
144 2 Red Ehret (pitching, hands by left shoulder)
144 3 Red Ehret (pitching, hands head-high)
144 4 Red Ehret (batting)
145 1 R. Emmerke (batting, looking at camera)
145 2 R. Emmerke (batting, looking at ball)
145 3 R. Emmerke (pitching, hands at chest)
145 4 R. Emmerke (pitching, right hand head-high)
145 5 R. Emmerke (pitching, left foot off ground)
146 1 Dude Esterbrook (standing upright, right hand on hip)
146 2 Dude Esterbrook (bending, facing to left, hands on knees)
146 3aDude Esterbrook (bending, facing front, hands on knees, Indianapolis)
146 3bDude Esterbrook (bending, facing front, hands on knees, N. Ys (NL))
146 4 Dude Esterbrook (kneeling to field grounder)
146 5aDude Esterbrook (batting, Indianapolis)
146 5bDude Esterbrook (batting, Louisvilles)
146 6 Dude Esterbrook (fielding)
146 7aDude Esterbrook (right hand over ball in left hand waist-high, Lo'villes)
146 7bDude Esterbrook (right hand over ball in left hand waist-high, N. Ys (NL))
147 1 Henry Esterday (fielding grounder by left foot)
147 2aHenry Esterday (fielding grounder, hands ankle-high, Kansas City)
147 2bHenry Esterday (fielding grounder, hands ankle-high, Columbus)
147 3aHenry Esterday (fielding, hands above head, Kansas City)
147 3bHenry Esterday (fielding, hands above head, Columbus)
147 4 Henry Esterday (throwing)
148 1 Long John Ewing (bat over right shoulder, Louisville)
148 2 Long John Ewing (bat almost vertical, Louisville)
148 3 Long John Ewing (pitching, hands at cap, Louisville)
148 4 Long John Ewing (pitching, hands neck-high, Louisville)
149 1aBuck Ewing (sliding, Capt., New York)
149 1bBuck Ewing (sliding, C., New York)
149 2aBuck Ewing (hands on knees, Capt. N.Y's)
149 2bBuck Ewing (hands on knees, Captain, New Yorks)
149 2dBuck Ewing (hands on knees, C. New Yorks)
149 2eBuck Ewing (hands on knees, C. New York (PL))
149 3 Buck Ewing (throwing, right hand waist-high at side, New Yorks)
149 4aBuck Ewing (throwing, right arm extended forward, Capt., New Yorks)
149 4bBuck Ewing (throwing, right arm extended forward, C., New Yorks)
149 5aBuck Ewing (fielding, hands head-high, New Yorks)
149 5bBuck Ewing (fielding, hands head-high, N. Y's)
149 6aBuck Ewing (walking to left, hands thigh-high, Captain, New Yorks)
149 6bBuck Ewing (walking to left, hands thigh-high, C., New Yorks)

149 7 Buck Ewing (fielding grounder, New Yorks)
149 8 Buck Ewing (bat in hand at side, New Yorks)
149 9aBuck Ewing (bat at 45 degrees, looking to front, New Yorks)
149 9bBuck Ewing (bat at 45 degrees, looking to front, N.Y's)
149 10aBuck Ewing (bat nearly horizontal, looking down at ball, Captian, New Yorks)
149 10bBuck Ewing (bat nearly horizontal, looking down at ball, Capt., New Yorks)
149 11aWillie Breslin - mascot (New Yorks)
149 11aBuck Ewing (New Yorks)
149 11bWillie Breslin - mascot (N.Y's)
149 11bBuck Ewing (N.Y's)
150 1aJay Faatz (fielding grounder, Clevelands)
150 1bJay Faatz (fielding grounder, Cleveland's)
150 2aJay Faatz (batting, Capt.)
150 2bJay Faatz (batting, Captain)
150 3aJay Faatz (throwing, Capt.)
150 3bJay Faatz (throwing, Captain)
151 1aBill Fagan (pitching, left hand chin-high, Kansas City)
151 1bBill Fagan (pitching, left hand chin-high, Denvers)
151 2 Bill Fagan (pitching, hands neck-high) 65.00 32.00 19.50
151 3 Bill Fagan (left profile, left hand forward waist-high) 65.00 32.00 19.50
151 4 Bill Fagan (batting) 65.00 32.00 19.50
152 1 Bill Farmer (tagging player on ground) 65.00 32.00 19.50
152 2aBill Farmer (hands on knees, Pittsburgh) 65.00 32.00 19.50
152 2bBill Farmer (hands on knees, Pittsburgh's) 65.00 32.00 19.50
152 2dBill Farmer (hands on knees, St. Pauls) 65.00 32.00 19.50
152 3aBill Farmer (fielding, hands thigh-high, Pittsburgh's) 65.00 32.00 19.50
152 3bBill Farmer (fielding, hands thigh-high, St. Pauls) 65.00 32.00 19.50
152 3cBill Farmer (fielding, hands thigh-high, St. Paul) 65.00 32.00 19.50
152 4aBill Farmer (throwing, Pittsburgh) 65.00 32.00 19.50
152 4bBill Farmer (throwing, St. Pauls) 65.00 32.00 19.50
152 5 Bill Farmer (batting) 65.00 32.00 19.50
153 1aSid Farrar (fielding, hands head-high, Phila) 65.00 32.00 19.50
153 1bSid Farrar (fielding, hands head-high, Philadelphia) 65.00 32.00 19.50
153 1cSid Farrar (fielding, hands head-high, Philadelphias) 65.00 32.00 19.50
153 2aSid Farrar (fielding grounder, Phila) 65.00 32.00 19.50
153 2bSid Farrar (fielding grounder, Philadelphia) 65.00 32.00 19.50
153 2cSid Farrar (fielding grounder, name correct, Philadelphias) 65.00 32.00 19.50
153 2eSid Faraer (Farrar) (fielding grounder, name incorrect, Philadelphias) 65.00 32.00 19.50
153 3aSid Farrar (right hand at belt, left arm at side, with cap, Phila) 65.00 32.00 19.50
153 3bSid Farrar (right hand at belt, left arm at side, with cap, Philadelphia) 65.00 32.00 19.50
153 3cSid Farrar (right hand at belt, left arm at side, with cap, Phil) 65.00 32.00 19.50
153 3dSid Farrar (right hand at belt, left arm at side, with cap, name correct, Philadelphias) 65.00 32.00 19.50
153 3eSid Farrer (Farrar) (right hand at belt, left arm at side, with cap, name incorrect, Philadelphias) 65.00 32.00 19.50
153 4aSid Farrar (fielding, hands chin-high, Phila) 65.00 32.00 19.50
153 4bSid Farrar (fielding, hands chin-high, Philadelphia) 65.00 32.00 19.50
153 5aSid Farrar (fielding, hands ankle-high, Phila) 65.00 32.00 19.50
153 5bSid Farrar (fielding, hands ankle-high, Philadelphia) 65.00 32.00 19.50
153 5cSid Farrar (fielding, hands ankle-high, Philadelphias) 65.00 32.00 19.50
153 6aSid Farrar (arms folded, no cap, Phila) 65.00 32.00 19.50
153 6bSid Farrar (arms folded, no cap, Philadelphia) 65.00 32.00 19.50
153 6cSid Farrar (arms folded, no cap, Philadelphias) 65.00 32.00 19.50
153 7 Sid Farrar (hands on thighs, looking at ball head-high) 65.00 32.00 19.50
154 1 Jack Farrell (bat in hand at side, looking at camera, Washington) 65.00 32.00 19.50
154 2aJack Farrell (batting, looking at ball head-high, 2d B., Washington) 65.00 32.00 19.50
154 2bJack Farrell (batting, looking at ball head-high, Second Base, Washington) 65.00 32.00 19.50
154 3aJack Farrell (Farrell tagging Hines, 2d B.) 65.00 32.00 19.50
154 3aPaul Hines (Farrell tagging Hines, 2d B.) 65.00 32.00 19.50
154 3bJack Farrell (Farrell tagging Hines, Second Base) 65.00 32.00 19.50
154 3bPaul Hines (Farrell tagging Hines, Second Base) 65.00 32.00 19.50
154 4aJack Farrell (fielding grounder, 2d B., Washington) 65.00 32.00 19.50
154 4bJack Farrell (fielding grounder, Second Base, Washington) 65.00 32.00 19.50
154 5aJack Farrell (hands on thighs, 2d B., Washington) 65.00 32.00 19.50
154 5bJack Farrell (hands on thighs, Second Base, Washington) 65.00 32.00 19.50
154 6aJack Farrell (bat at ready, looking at camera, wall background, 2d B., Washington) 65.00 32.00 19.50
154 6bJack Farrell (bat at ready, looking at camera, wall background, Second Base, Washington) 65.00 32.00 19.50
154 7aJack Farrell (fielding, hands head-high, 2d B., Washington) 65.00 32.00 19.50
154 7bJack Farrell (fielding, hands head-high, Second Base, Washington) 65.00 32.00 19.50
154 8aJack Farrell (hands on hips, 2nd B., Baltimores) 65.00 32.00 19.50
154 8bJack Farrell (hands on hips, S.S., Baltimores) 65.00 32.00 19.50
154 9aJack Farrell (bat at ready position, looking at camera, field background, 2nd B., Baltimores) 65.00 32.00 19.50
154 9bJack Farrell (bat at ready position, looking at camera, field background, 2d B., Baltimores) 65.00 32.00 19.50
154 10Jack Farrell (fielding, hands above head, Baltimores) 65.00 32.00 19.50
154 11aJack Farrell (throwing, 2nd B., Baltimores) 65.00 32.00 19.50
154 11bJack Farrell (throwing, no comma after 2d B., Baltimores) 65.00 32.00 19.50
154 11cJack Farrell (throwing, comma after 2d B., Baltimores) 65.00 32.00 19.50
154 12Jack Farrell (bat in hand at side, looking to right, Baltimores) 65.00 32.00 19.50
155 1aDuke Farrell (batting, name correct, Chicago) 65.00 32.00 19.50
155 1bDuke Farrel (Farrell) (batting, name incorrect, Chicago's) 65.00 32.00 19.50
155 2aDuke Farrell (fielding, hands above head, name correct, Chicago) 65.00 32.00 19.50
155 2bDuke Farrel (Farrell) (fielding, hands above head, name incorrect, Chicago) 65.00 32.00 19.50
155 3aDuke Farrell (hands on knees, name correct, Chicago's) 65.00 32.00 19.50
155 3bDuke Farrel (Farrell) (hands on knees, name incorrect, Chicago) 65.00 32.00 19.50
155 3cDuke Farrell (hands on knees, name incorrect, Chicago's) 65.00 32.00 19.50
155 4aDuke Farrell (fielding grounder by right foot, name correct, Chicago) 65.00 32.00 19.50
155 4bDuke Farrel (Farrell) (fielding grounder by right foot, name incorrect, Chicagos) 65.00 32.00 19.50
155 5aDuke Farrel (Farrell) (fielding low ball, hands by left ankle, name incorrect, Chicago) 65.00 32.00 19.50
155 5bDuke Farrell (fielding low ball, hands by left ankle, name correct, Chicagos) 65.00 32.00 19.50
156 1 Frank Fennelly (fielding grounder by right foot) 65.00 32.00 19.50
156 2 Frank Fennelly (batting) 65.00 32.00 19.50
156 3aFrank Fennelly (fielding, hands thigh-high, Cincinnati) 65.00 32.00 19.50
156 3bFrank Fennelly (fielding, hands thigh-high, Athletics) 65.00 32.00 19.50
156 4aFrank Fennelly (fielding, hands head-high, Cincinnati) 65.00 32.00 19.50
156 4bFrank Fennelly (fielding, hands head-high, Athletics) 65.00 32.00 19.50
156 5aFrank Fennelly (throwing, Cincinnati) 65.00 32.00 19.50
156 5bFrank Fennelly (throwing, Athletics) 65.00 32.00 19.50
157 1aCharlie Ferguson (batting, Phila) 65.00 32.00 19.50
157 1bCharlie Ferguson (batting, Philadelphia) 65.00 32.00 19.50
157 1cCharlie Ferguson (batting, Philadelphias) 65.00 32.00 19.50
157 2aCharlie Ferguson (pitching, Phila) 65.00 32.00 19.50
157 2bCharlie Ferguson (pitching, Philadelphia) 65.00 32.00 19.50
157 3aCharlie Ferguson (throwing, Phila) 65.00 32.00 19.50
157 3bCharlie Ferguson (throwing, Philadelphia) 65.00 32.00 19.50
157 4aCharlie Ferguson (tagging player, Phila) 65.00 32.00 19.50
157 4bCharlie Ferguson (tagging player, Philadelphia) 65.00 32.00 19.50
158 1 Alex Ferson (pitching, hands chest-high, looking to right) 65.00 32.00 19.50
158 2 Alex Ferson (pitching, hands neck-high, looking to front) 65.00 32.00 19.50
158 3aAlex Ferson (ball in right hand neck-high, looking at camera, Washington) 65.00 32.00 19.50
158 3bAlex Ferson (ball in right hand neck-high, looking at camera, Washingtons) 65.00 32.00 19.50
158 4 Alex Ferson (looking at ball in right hand cap-high) 65.00 32.00 19.50
158 5aAlex Ferson (batting, Washington) 65.00 32.00 19.50
158 5bAlex Ferson (batting, Washingtons) 65.00 32.00 19.50
159 1 Wallace Fessenden (umpire) (hands at back) 120.00 60.00 36.00
159 2 Wallace Fessenden (umpire) (arms at sides) 120.00 60.00 36.00
159 3 Wallace Fessenden (umpire) (left hand on left thigh) 120.00 60.00 36.00
159 4 Wallace Fessenden (umpire) (arms folded) 120.00 60.00 36.00
160 1aSam Barkley (Fields fielding with Barkley looking on, C.) 65.00 32.00 19.50
160 1aJocko Fields (Fields fielding with Barkley looking on, C.) 65.00 32.00 19.50
160 1bSam Barkley (Fields fielding with Barkley looking on, Catcher) 65.00 32.00 19.50
160 1bJocko Fields (Fields fielding with Barkley looking on, Catcher) 65.00 32.00 19.50
160 2aJocko Fields (batting, C.) 65.00 32.00 19.50
160 2bJocko Fields (batting, Catcher) 65.00 32.00 19.50
160 3aJocko Fields (fielding, hands neck-high, C.) 65.00 32.00 19.50
160 3bJocko Fields (fielding, hands neck-high, Catcher) 65.00 32.00 19.50
160 4aSam Barkley (Fields tagging Barkley, C.) 65.00 32.00 19.50
160 4aJocko Fields (Fields tagging Barkley, C.) 65.00 32.00 19.50
160 4bSam Barkley (Fields tagging Barkley, Catcher) 65.00 32.00 19.50
160 4bJocko Fields (Fields tagging Barkley, Catcher) 65.00 32.00 19.50
160 5aJocko Fields (throwing, name correct, C.) 65.00 32.00 19.50
160 5bJocko Fields (throwing, Catcher) 65.00 32.00 19.50
160 5cJocko Field (Fields) (throwing, name incorrect, C.) 65.00 32.00 19.50
160 6aJocko Fields (hands on thighs, C.) 65.00 32.00 19.50
160 6bJocko Fields (hands on thighs, Catcher) 65.00 32.00 19.50
161 1 Fischer (batting) 100.00 50.00 30.00
161 2 Fischer (fielding) 100.00 50.00 30.00
161 3 Fischer (throwing) 100.00 50.00 30.00
162 1 Thomas Flanigan (Flanagan) (batting) 65.00 32.00 19.50
162 2 Thomas Flanigan (Flanagan) (pitching, hands at neck) 65.00 32.00 19.50
162 3aThomas Flanigan (Flanagan) (pitching, right hand head-high, Clevelands) 65.00 32.00 19.50
162 3bThomas Flanigan (Flanagan) (pitching, right hand head-high, Sioux City) 65.00 32.00 19.50
162 4 Thomas Flanigan (Flanagan) (pitching, right arm chin-high) 65.00 32.00 19.50
163 1aSilver Flint (portrait, Chicago) 65.00 32.00 19.50
163 1bSilver Flint (portrait, Chicagos) 65.00 32.00 19.50
163 2 Silver Flint (fielding, hands chest-high) 65.00 32.00 19.50
163 3aSilver Flint (hands on hips, Chicago) 65.00 32.00 19.50
163 3bSilver Flint (hands on hips, Chicago's) 65.00 32.00 19.50
163 4aSilver Flint (batting, Flint on front, Chicago) 65.00 32.00 19.50
163 4bSilver Flint (batting, Silver Flint on front, Chicago) 65.00 32.00 19.50
163 4dSilver Flint (batting, Silver Flint on front, Chicagos) 65.00 32.00 19.50
163 4eSilver Flint (batting, Flint on front, Chicago's) 65.00 32.00 19.50
163 5aSilver Flint (stooping hands waist-high, with mask, Chicago) 65.00 32.00 19.50
163 5bSilver Flint (stooping hands waist-high, with mask, Chicago's) 65.00 32.00 19.50
164 1 Thomas Flood (batting) 65.00 32.00 19.50
164 2aThomas Flood (pitching, hands at chest, St. Josephs) 65.00 32.00 19.50
164 2bThomas Flood (pitching, hands at chest, St. Joe) 65.00 32.00 19.50
164 4aThomas Flood (pitching, right hand held out chest-high, St. Josephs) 65.00 32.00 19.50
164 4bThomas Flood (pitching, right hand held out chest-high, St. Joe) 65.00 32.00 19.50
164 5 Thomas Flood (ball in left hand, chin-high) 65.00 32.00 19.50
164 51Jocko Flynn (pitching) 160.00 80.00 48.00
165 1aJim Fogarty (fielding on run to left, hands head-high, R.F.)
165 1bJim Fogarty (fielding on run to left, hands head-high, Right Field)
165 2aJim Fogarty (fielding, hands neck-high, R.F.)
165 2bJim Fogarty (fielding, hands neck-high, Right Field)
165 3aJim Fogarty (fielding grounder, R.F.)
165 3bJim Fogarty (fielding grounder, Right Field)
165 4aJim Fogarty (batting, name correct, R.F.)
165 4bJim Fogarty (batting, Right Field)
165 4cJim Fogerty (Fogarty) (batting, name incorrect, R.F., Phila)
165 4dJim Fogerty (Fogarty) (batting, name incorrect, R.F., Philadelphias)
165 5aJim Fogarty (sliding, R.F.)
165 5bJim Fogarty (sliding, Right Field)
166 1 Frank Foreman (batting)
166 2aFrank Foreman (ball in left hand head-high, Baltimores)
166 2bFrank Foreman (ball in left hand head-high, Cincinnati (NL))
166 3 Frank Foreman (ball in right hand head-high)
166 4 Frank Foreman (ready to pitch, hands by right thigh)
166 5 Frank Foreman (end of pitch, left hand by left knee)
167 1aTom Forster (throwing, Hartfords)
167 1bTom Forster (throwing, Milwaukee)
167 2 F.W. Foster (photo actually Tom Forster) (dotted tie)
168 1 Elmer Foster (dotted tie)
168 2 Elmer Foster (sliding)
168 3aElmer Foster (bat at ready position by head, N.Y.)
168 3bElmer Foster (bat at ready position by head, New Yorks)
168 4 Elmer Foster (bat at ready position at about 50 degrees)
168 5 Elmer Foster (bat in hand at side)
168 6aElmer Foster (fielding, N.Y.)
168 6cElmer Foster (fielding, New Yorks)
168 7aElmer Foster (throwing, N.Y.)
168 7bElmer Foster (throwing, New Yorks)
169 No World Index Listing
170 1 Dave Foutz (Brown's Champions)
170 3 Dave Foutz (bat at ready position over shoulder)
170 4 Dave Foutz (bat at ready position at 30 degrees)
170 5 Dave Foutz (ready to pitch, hands above waist)
170 6aDave Foutz (throwing, no comma after P.)
170 6bDave Foutz (throwing, comma after P.)
171 1 Julie Freeman (batting)
171 2 Julie Freeman (pitching, hands neck-high)
171 3 Julie Freeman (pitching, hands thigh-high)
171 4 Julie Freeman (pitching, right hand neck-high at back)
171 5 Julie Freeman (pitching, right hand extended

forward)
172 1 Will Fry (batting, looking at camera)
172 2 Will Fry (batting, looking at ball)
172 3 Will Fry (fielding, hands above waist)
172 4 Will Fry (fielding grounder)
172 51 Fudger (standing)
173 1 William Fuller (bat at ready position by left shoulder, Milwaukees)
173 2aWilliam Fuller (bat in hand at side, Milwaukee)
173 2bWilliam Fuller (bat in hand at side, Milwaukees)
173 3aWilliam Fuller (throwing, Milwaukees)
173 3bWilliam Fuller (throwing, Milwaukees, W. Ass'n)
173 4 William Fuller (fielding, ball approaching, Milwaukees)
173 5 William Fuller (fielding, ball in hands, Milwaukees)
174 1 Shorty Fuller (bat at ready position, elbows above belt, St. Louis)
174 2 Shorty Fuller (batting, right elbow level with belt, St. Louis)
174 3 Shorty Fuller (hands on knees, St. Louis)
174 4 Shorty Fuller (fielding, hands at knees, St. Louis)
174 5 Shorty Fuller (fielding, hands shoulder-high, St. Louis)
175 1aChris Fulmer (bat at ready position at 80 degrees, name correct)
175 1bChris Fullmer (Fulmer) (bat at ready position at 80 degrees, name incorrect)
175 2 Chris Fullmer (Fulmer) (bat at 40 degrees, looking at camera)
175 3 Chris Fullmer (Fulmer) (batting at 40 degrees, looking at ball)
175 4 Chris Fullmer (Fulmer) (fielding, hands by chin)
175 5 Chris Fullmer (Fulmer) (hands on knees)
175 6aChris Fulmer (Fulmer tagging Tucker, Baltimore)
175 6aFoghorn Tucker (Fulmer tagging Tucker, Baltimore)
175 6bChris Fulmer (Fulmer tagging Tucker, Baltimores)
175 6bFoghorn Tucker (Fulmer tagging Tucker, Baltimores)
176 1aHonest John Gaffney (leaning to right, Manager, Washington)
176 1bHonest John Gaffney (leaning right, Manager of Washington Club)
177 1aPud Galvin (bat at ready position, P.)
177 1bPud Galvin (bat at ready position, Pitcher)
177 2aPud Galvin (in jacket, arms at sides, P., Pittsburg)
177 2bPud Galvin (in jacket, arms at sides, Pitcher)
177 2cPud Galvin (in Jacket, arms at sides, P., Pittsburgs)
177 3aPud Galvin (ready to pitch, hands above waist, P.)
177 3bPud Galvin (ready to pitch, hands above waist, Pitcher)
177 4aPud Galvin (in jacket, bat in hand at side, Galvin on front, P. Pittsburg)
177 4bPud Galvin (in jacket, bat in hand at side, Pitcher)
177 4cPud Galvin (in jacket, bat in hand at side, Galvin on front, P., Pittsburgs)
177 4dPud Galvin (in jacket, bat in hand at side, J. Galvin on front)
177 4ePud Galvin (in jacket, bat in hand at side, Jim Galvin on front)
178 1 Bob Gamble (batting)
178 2 Bob Gamble (pitching, right hand thigh-high)
178 3 Bob Gamble (pitching, right hand chin-high)
179 1aCharlie Ganzel (fielding, hands thigh-high, Detroits)
179 1bCharlie Ganzel (fielding, hands thigh-high, Bostons)
179 2aCharlie Ganzel (fielding, hands shoulder-high, Detroits)
179 2cCharlie Ganzel (fielding, hands shoulder-high, Bostons)
179 3aCharlie Ganzel (batting, name correct)
179 3bCharlie Gauzel (Ganzel) (batting, name incorrect)
180 1 Gid Gardner (fielding low ball)
180 2 Gid Gardner (batting)
180 3 Gid Gardner (throwing)
180 4 Gid Gardner (fielding, hands above head)
180 5 Gid Gardner (Gardner tagging Murray)
180 5 Miah Murray (Gardner tagging Murray)
181 1 Hank Gastreich (Gastright) (bat at ready position well clear of cap)
181 2 Hank Gastreich (Gastright) (bat at ready position partly behind cap)
181 3 Hank Gastreich (Gastright) (ready to pitch, hands at neck)
181 4 Hank Gastreich (Gastright) (pitching, left hand off picture)
181 5 Hank Gastreich (Gastright) (pitching, left hand by left thigh)
182 1 Emil Geiss (bat in hand at side)
182 2 Emil Geiss (ready to pitch, hands above waist)
182 3 Emil Geiss (batting)
182 4 Emil Geiss (pitching, right hand shoulder high)
182 5 Emil Geiss (pitching, right hand chin-high)
182 6 Emil Geiss (portrait)
183 1aFrenchy Genins (fielding, hands cupped neck-high, name correct)
183 1bFrenchy Genius (Genins) (fielding, hands cupped neck-high, name incorrect)
183 2aFrenchy Genins (fielding, hands with fingers touching neck-high, name correct)
183 2bFrenchy Genius (Genins) (fielding, hands with fingers touching neck-high, name incorrect)
183 3 Frenchy Genius (Genins) (fielding, hands with fingers touching on chest)
183 4 Frenchy Genins (batting, looking at camera)
183 5 Frenchy Genius (Genins) (batting, looking at ball near bat)
184 1aBill George (pitching, left hand forward, head-high, N.Y's)
184 1bBill George (pitching, left hand forward, head-high, New Yorks)
184 2aBill George (batting, N.Y's)
184 2bBill George (batting, New Yorks)
184 3aBill George (sliding, N.Y's)
184 3bBill George (sliding, New Yorks)
184 4aBill George (pitching, left hand head-high, N.Y's)
184 4bBill George (pitching, left hand head-high, New Yorks)
184 5aBill George (pitching, hands chest-high, N.Y's)
184 5bBill George (pitching, hands chest-high, New Yorks)
184 6 Bill George (bat in hand at side)
185 1 Joe Gerhardt (hands on thighs)
185 2aJoe Gerhardt (throwing, no position)
185 2bJoe Gerhardt (throwing, 1st B.)
185 3 Joe Gerhardt (fielding)
185 4aJoe Gerhardt (tagging player, 2nd B.)
185 4bJoe Gerhardt (tagging player, 1st B.)
186 1aCharlie Getzein (batting, Indianapolis)
186 1bCharlie Getzein (batting, Detroits)
186 2 Charlie Getzein (pitching, hands above waist)
186 3aCharlie Getzein (pitching, right hand chin-high at side, comma after P., Indianapolis)
186 3bCharlie Getzein (pitching, right hand chin-high at side, no comma after P., Indianapolis)
186 3cCharlie Getzein (pitching, right hand chin-high at side, Detroits)
186 4aCharlie Getzein (end of pitch, right hand forward neck-high, Detroit)
186 4bCharlie Getzein (end of pitch, right hand forward neck-high, Indianapolis)
187 1 Bobby Gilks (bat at ready position, nearly vertical)
187 2 Bobby Gilks (bat at ready position, nearly horizontal)
187 3 Bobby Gilks (bat at ready position, at about 45 degrees)
187 4aBobby Gilks (pitching, hands at neck, Cleveland's)
187 4bBobby Gilks (pitching, hands at neck, Clevelands)
187 5aBobby Gilks (pitching, right hand at back waist-high, Cleveland's)
187 5bBobby Gilks (pitching, right hand at back waist-high, Clevelands)
187 6 Bobby Gilks (pitching, right hand forward chest-high)
188 1 Pete Gillespie (right hand on hip, left arm at side)
188 2 Pete Gillespie (batting)
188 3 Pete Gillespie (fielding)
188 4 Pete Gillespie (throwing)
188 5 Pete Gillespie (moving to left)
189 1aBarney Gilligan (fielding ball thigh-high, C.)
189 1bBarney Gilligan (fielding ball thigh-high, Catcher)
189 2aBarney Gilligan (hands on thighs, C., Washington)
189 2bBarney Gilligan (hands on thighs, Catcher)
189 2cBarney Gilligan (hands on thighs, C., Detroit)
190 1 Frank Gilmore (batting, feet apart)
190 2 Frank Gilmore (batting, right foot behind left foot)
190 3 Frank Gilmore (ball in hands above head)
190 4 Frank Gilmore (ball touching right hand above head)
190 5 Frank Gilmore (pitching)
191 1aPebbly Jack Glasscock (throwing, S.S., Indianapolis)
191 1bPebbly Jack Glasscock (Glasscock) (throwing)
191 1cPebbly Jack Glasscock (throwing, s.s.)
191 1dPebbly Jack Glasscock (throwing, S.S., Indpls)
191 1ePebbly Jack Glasscock (throwing, S.S., New York (NL))
191 2aPebbly Jack Glasscock (hands on knees, S.S., Indianapolis)
191 2bPebbly Jack Glasscock (Glasscock) (hands on knees)
191 2cPebbly Jack Glasscock (hands on knees, S.S., Indpls)
191 3aPebbly Jack Glasscock (batting)
191 3bPebbly Jack Glasscock (Glasscock) (batting)
191 3cPebbly Jack Glass Cock (Glasscock) (batting)
191 4aPebbly Jack Glasscock (bat in hand at side, s.s.)
191 4bPebbly Jack Glasscock (bat in hand at side, S.S., Indpls)
191 4cPebbly Jack Glasscock (Glasscock) (bat in hand at side, name correct, S.S., Indianapolis)
191 4dPebbly Jack Glasscock (Glasscock) (bat in hand at side, S.S. Indianapoli)
191 4ePebbly Jack Glasscock (bat in hand at side, name correct, S.S., Indianapolis)
192 1aKid Gleason (fielding grounder, Phila)
192 1bKid Gleason (fielding grounder, Philadelphias)
192 2aKid Gleason (bat at ready position over shoulder, Phila)
192 2bKid Gleason (bat at ready position over shoulder, Philadelphias)
192 3aKid Gleason (bat horizontal, Phila)
192 3bKid Gleason (bat horizontal, Philadelphias)
192 3cKid Gleason (bat horizontal, Phil'a (NL))
192 4 Kid Gleason (pitching, hands at neck, Philadelphias)
192 5 Kid Gleason (pitching, right hand forward head-high, Phila)
193 1 Will Gleason (Brown's Champions)
193 2aWill Gleason (batting, no comma after S.S., Athletics)
193 2bWill Gleason (batting, comma after S.S., Athletics)
193 3aWill Gleason (hands on knees, no comma after S.S., Athletics)
193 3bWill Gleason (hands on knees, comma after S.S., Athletics)
193 4aWill Gleason (leaning to right, hands thigh-high, no comma after S.S., Athletics)
193 4bWill Gleason (leaning to right, hands thigh-high, comma after S.S., Athletics)
193 5 Will Gleason (stooping, hands clasped hip-high, Louisvilles)
194 1 Mouse Glenn (batting, looking at camera)
194 2 Mouse Glenn (batting, looking at ball)
194 3 Mouse Glenn (fielding, hands neck-high, comma after L.F.)
194 4 Mouse Glenn (fielding, hands thigh-high)
194 5 Mouse Glenn (fielding, hands chin-high)
195 1aMike Goodfellow (bat at ready position by head, Cleveland's)
195 1bMike Goodfellow (bat at ready position by head, Detroits)
195 2 Mike Goodfellow (bat at ready position, nearly horizontal)
195 3aMike Goodfellow (fielding, hands chest-high, Cleveland's)
195 3bMike Goodfellow (fielding, hands chest-high, Detroits)
195 4aMike Goodfellow (fielding, hands waist high, Clevelands)
195 4bMike Goodfellow (fielding, hands waist-high, Detroits)
195 5aMike Goodfellow (throwing, Cleveland's)
195 5bMike Goodfellow (throwing, Detroits)
196 1aPiano Legs Gore (fielding grounder, facing to right, N.Y's)
196 1bGeorge Gore (fielding grounder, facing to right, New York)
196 1cGeorge Gore (fielding grounder, facing to right, New York's)
196 2 George Gore (throwing, right hand head-high)
196 3aGeorge Gore (sliding, N.Y's)
196 3bGeorge Gore (sliding, New Yorks)
196 4aGeorge Gore (bat in hand at side, N.Y's)
196 4bGeorge Gore (bat in hand at side, New Yorks)
196 4cGeorge Gore (bat in hand at side, New York)
196 5aGeorge Gore (bat nearly horizontal, N.Y's)
196 5bGeorge Gore (bat nearly horizontal, New Yorks)
196 6 George Gore (fielding, hands above head)
196 7 George Gore (bat at ready position over shoulder)
196 8 George Gore (fielding low ball, facing front)
196 9 George Gore (throwing, right hand forward, left hand on hip)
197 1 Frank Graves (in mask, hands on knees)
197 2 Frank Graves (in mask, fielding, hands by right shoulder)
197 3 Frank Graves (fielding grounder)
197 4 Frank Graves (batting)
197 5 Frank Graves (throwing, hands waist high)
197 6 Frank Graves (fielding, hands cap-high)
198 1 Bill Greenwood (sliding)
198 2aBill Greenwood (batting, looking at camera, Baltimores)
198 2bBill Greenwood (batting, looking at camera, Columbus)
198 3aBill Greenwood (batting, looking at ball, Baltimores)
198 3bBill Greenwood (batting, looking at ball, Columbus)
198 4aBill Greenwood (throwing, Baltimores)
198 4bBill Greenwood (throwing, Columbus)
198 5 Bill Greenwood (hands on knees)
199 1 Ed Greer (bat at ready position by head)
199 2 Ed Greer (throwing)
199 3 Ed Greer (bat at ready position, nearly horizontal)
199 4 Ed Greer (Greer catching and Henderson batting) (same card as 222-10)
199 4 Hardie Henderson (Greer catching and Henderson batting) (same card as 222-10)
200 1 Mike Griffin (sliding)
200 2 Mike Griffin (batting)
200 3 Mike Griffin (fielding)
200 4aMike Griffin (throwing, Baltimores)
200 4bMike Griffin (throwing, Philadelphias (PL))
200 5 Mike Griffin (arms folded)
201 1aClark Griffith (batting, looking at camera, Milwaukees)
201 1bClark Griffith (batting, looking at camera, Milwaukee)
201 2 Clark Griffith (batting, looking at ball)
201 3 Clark Griffith (pitching, hands at chest)
201 4 Clark Griffith (pitching, hands at neck)
201 5 Clark Griffith (pitching, right hand head-high)
202 1 Henry Gruber (batting)
202 2aHenry Gruber (pitching, hands at chest, Cleveland)
202 2bHenry Gruber (pitching, hands at chest, Clevelands)
202 3aHenry Gruber (pitching, right hand chin-high, left hand just clear of left thigh, Clevelands)
202 3bHenry Gruber (pitching, right hand chin-high, left hand just clear of left thigh, Cleveland)
202 4aHenry Gruber (pitching, right hand cap-high, left hand on left thigh, Clevelands)
202 4bHenry Gruber (pitching, right hand cap-high, left hand on left thigh, Cleveland)
202 5 Henry Gruber (bat in hand at side)
203 1 Ad Gumbert (batting)
203 2 Ad Gumbert (pitching, right hand level with eyes)
203 3 Ad Gumbert (pitching, right hand waist-high)
203 4 Ad Gumbert (pitching, right hand level with chin)
204 1aTom Gunning (fielding low ball on left, Phila)
204 1bTom Gunning (fielding low ball on left, Philadelphia)
204 1cTom Gunning (fielding low ball on left, Athletics)
204 2aTom Gunning (bending forward, hands by right knee, Phila)
204 2bTom Gunning (bending forward, hands by right knee, Philadelphia)
204 2cTom Gunning (bending forward, hands by right knee, Athletics)
205 1 Joe Gunson (bat in hand at side)
205 2 Joe Gunson (fielding, hands by left shoulder)
205 3 Joe Gunson (throwing, right hand head high, no cap)
205 4 Joe Gunson (in jacket, gloves in right hand at side)
206 1aGentleman George Haddock (pitching, hands at chest, Washington)
206 1bGentleman George Haddock (pitching, hands at chest, Washingtons)
206 2 Gentleman George Haddock (pitching, hands neck-high)
206 3 Gentleman George Haddock (pitching, hands waist-high)
206 4 Gentleman George Haddock (end of pitch, right hand chin-high)
206 5 Gentleman George Haddock (batting)
207 1 Bill Hafner (Hoffner) (batting)
207 2 Bill Hafner (Hoffner) (pitching, hands by chin)
207 3 Bill Hafner (Hoffner) (pitching, hands above head)
207 4 Bill Hafner (Hoffner) (pitching, right hand neck-high)
207 5 Bill Hafner (Hoffner) (end of pitch, right hand shoulder-high)
208 1 Willie Hahm - mascot (card same as 502-7)
208 1 Ned Williamson (card same as 502-7)
209 1 Bill Hallman (bat on shoulder)
209 2aBill Hallman (throwing, right hand head-high, Philadelphia)
209 2bBill Hallman (throwing, right hand head-high, Philadelphias)
209 3aBill Hallman (fielding, hands chest-high, Philadelphia)
209 3bBill Hallman (fielding, hands chest-high, Philadelphias)
209 4 Bill Hallman (leaning to left, about to catch ball chest-high)

209 5aBill Hallman (bat horizontal, Philadelphias PL)
209 5bBill Hallman (bat horizontal, Phila)
210 1 Sliding Billy Hamilton (batting, looking at camera)
210 2aSliding Billy Hamilton (batting, looking up at ball, Kansas Citys)
210 2cSliding Billy Hamilton (batting, looking up at ball, K.Cs)
210 3 Sliding Billy Hamilton (fielding grounder)
210 4aSliding Billy Hamilton (fielding, hands above waist, Kansas Citys)
210 4bSliding Billy Hamilton (fielding, hands above waist, Philadelphia N.L.)
210 5aSliding Billy Hamilton (fielding, hands neck-high, Kansas Citys)
210 5bSliding Billy Hamilton (fielding, hands neck-high, Philadelphia N.L.)
211 1 Frank Hankinson (dotted tie)
212 1aNed Hanlon (bat in hand at side, Detroits)
212 1bNed Hanlon (bat in hand at side, Bostons)
212 2aNed Hanlon (batting, Detroits)
212 2bNed Hanlon (batting, Pittsburgs)
212 3aNed Hanlon (fielding, Detroits)
212 3bNed Hanlon (fielding, Pittsburghs)
213 1 William Hanrahan (squatting on bat)
213 2 William Hanrahan (fielding grounder)
213 3aWilliam Hanrahan (hands on knees, Chicago Maroons)
213 3bWilliam Hanrahan (hands on knees, Minneap'l's)
213 4aWilliam Hanrahan (bat in hand at side, Chicago Maroons)
213 4bWilliam Hanrahan (bat in hand at side, Minneap'l's)
213 5aWilliam Hanrahan (fielding, hands head-high, Chicago Maroons)
213 5bWilliam Hanrahan (fielding, hands head-high, Minneapolis)
213 5cWilliam Hanrahan (fielding, hands head-high, Minneap'l's)
213 6 William Hanrahan (leaning left, right hand thigh-high, left arm at back)
21351 Hapeman (ball in right hand above waist)
214 1 Pa Harkins (light uniform, bat at ready position)
214 2aPa Harkins (light uniform, fielding, hands above waist, Brooklyn)
214 2bPa Harkens (Harkins) (light uniform, fielding, hands above waist, name incorrect, Baltimore)
214 2cPa Harkins (light uniform, fielding, hands above waist, name correct, Baltimore)
214 3 Pa Harkins (light uniform, throwing, right hand head-high)
214 4 Pa Harkins (dark uniform, bat on shoulder)
214 5 Pa Harkins (dark uniform, bat at ready position at 60 degrees)
214 6 Pa Harkins (dark uniform, hands at chest)
214 7 Pa Harkins (dark uniform, ball in right hand at back)
214 8 Pa Harkins (dark uniform, ball in right hand extended forward chin-high)
215 1 Bill Hart (pitching, hands at chest)
215 2 Bill Hart (pitching, hands above head, feet on ground)
215 3aBill Hart (pitching, hands above head, left foot off ground, Cincinnati)
215 3bBill Hart (pitching, hands above head, left foot off ground, Des Moines)
215 4 Bill Hart (ready to pitch, right hand by head, left arm at side)
216 1 Bill Hasamdear (Hassamaer) (fielding, hands head-high)
216 2 Bill Hasamdear (Hassamaer) (fielding, hands thigh-high)
216 3 Bill Hasamdear (Hassamaer) (throwing)
217 1aGill Hatfield (bat over right shoulder behind head, New Yorks)
217 1bGill Hatfield (bat over right shoulder behind head, N.Y.)
217 2 Gill Hatfield (bat at ready position, nearly vertical)
217 4aGill Hatfield (fielding, hands chest-high, looking at ball neck-high, New Yorks)
217 4bGill Hatfield (fielding, hands chest-high, looking at ball neck-high, N.Y.)
217 5aGill Hatfield (fielding, hands cupped chest-high, looking upwards, New Yorks)
217 5bGill Hatfield (fielding, hands cupped chest-high, looking upwards, N.Y.)
217 6aGill Hatfield (fielding, hands by right knee, New Yorks)
217 6bGill Hatfield (fielding, hands by right knee, N.Y.)
217 6cGill Hatfield (fielding, hands by right knee, New York (P.L.))
218 1aEgyptian Healey (Healy) (dark cap, pitching, P., Indianapolis)
218 1bEgyptian Healey (Healy) (dark cap, pitching, Pitcher, Indianapolis)
218 1cEgyptian Healey (Healy) (dark cap, pitching, P., Washingtons)
218 2aEgyptian Healey (Healy) (dark cap, batting, P., Indianapolis)
218 2bEgyptian Healey (Healy) (dark cap, batting, Pitcher, Indianapolis)
218 2cEgyptian Healey (Healy) (dark cap, batting, P., Washingtons)
219 1a Healey (Healy) (ringed cap, pitching, hands above head, Omaha)
219 1b Healy (ringed cap, pitching, hands above head, name correct, Washingtons)
219 1c Healy (ringed cap, pitching, hands above head, name correct, Denvers)
219 2a Healey (Healy) (ringed cap, pitching, right hand head-high, name incorrect, Omaha)
219 2b Healy (ringed cap, pitching, right hand head-high, name correct, Washingtons)
219 3 Healy (plain white cap, moustache, pitching, hands neck high, Washingtons)
219 4 Healy (portrait, looking to left, no cap, Washingtons)
220 1aGuy Hecker (batting, Louisvilles)
220 1bGuy Hecker (batting, Louisville)
220 2aGuy Hecker (ball in hands on chest, feet wide apart, Louisvilles)
220 2bGuy Hecker (ball in hands on chest, feet wide apart, Louisville)
220 3 Guy Hecker (right hand extended at side chest-high)
220 4aGuy Hecker (right hand extended forward, Louisvilles)
220 4bGuy Hecker (right hand extended forward, Louisville)
220 5 Guy Hecker (ball in hands on chest, right foot behind left foot)
221 1 Tony Hellman (batting, looking at camera)
221 2 Tony Hellman (batting, looking at ball)
221 3 Tony Hellman (fielding, hands thigh-high, ball by face)
221 4 Tony Hellman (fielding, hands thigh-high, ball by right wrist)
221 5 Tony Hellman (fielding, hands chin-high)
222 1 Hardie Henderson (white cap, bat over shoulder)
222 2 Hardie Henderson (white cap, throwing, right hand head-high)
222 3aHardie Henderson (white cap, hands at chest, Brooklyn)
222 3bHardie Henderson (white cap, hands at chest, Pitts)
222 4 Hardie Henderson (white cap, pitching, right hand raised)
222 5 Hardie Henderson (dark cap, bat at ready position at 30 degrees)
222 6 Hardie Henderson (no cap, batting, ball by bat)
222 7 Hardie Henderson (dark cap, throwing, right hand head-high)
222 8 Hardie Henderson (dark cap, hands at waist)
222 9 Hardie Henderson (dark cap, pitching, left arm across neck)
222 10Ed Greer (Greer catching and Henderson batting) (card same as 199-4)
222 10Hardie Henderson (Greer catching and Henderson batting) (card same as 199-4)
223 1aMoxie Hengle (sliding, Minneapolis)
223 1bMoxie Hengle (sliding, Chicago Maroons)
223 2aMoxie Hengle (batting, Minneapolis)
223 2bMoxie Hengle (batting, Chicago Maroons)
223 3aMoxie Hengle (hands on knees, Minneapolis)
223 3bMoxie Hengle (hands on knees, Chicago Maroons)
223 4 Moxie Hengle (fielding)
223 5aMoxie Hengle (bat in hand at side, Minneapolis)
223 5bMoxie Hengle (bat in hand at side, Chicago Maroons)
223 6 Moxie Hengle (leaning right, right hand pointing at camera, ball in left hand)
224 1 John Henry (bat over shoulder)
224 2 John Henry (batting)
224 3 John Henry (fielding)
224 4 John Henry (throwing)
224 5 John Henry (pitching)
225 1aEd Herr (bat over shoulder, St. Louis White)
225 1bEd Herr (bat over shoulder, looking front, J. Herr on front, Milwaukees)
225 1cEd Herr (bat over shoulder, looking front, Herr on front, Milwaukees)
225 2 Ed Herr (batting, looking at ball chin-high)
225 3 Ed Herr (fielding grounder)
225 4aEd Herr (bat in hand at side, St. Louis Whites)
225 4bEd Herr (bat in hand at side, Milwaukees)
225 5 Ed Herr (ball in hands by neck)
226 1 Hunkey Hines (fielding, hands knee-high, St. Louis Whites)
226 2 Hunkey Hines (bat on shoulder, St. Louis Whites)
226 3 Hunkey Hines (fielding, hands head-high, St. Louis Whites)
226 4 Hunkey Hines (bat in hand at side, St. Louis Whites)
227 1aPaul Hines (batting, C.F., Washington)
227 1bPaul Hines (batting, Centre Field, Washington)
227 1cPaul Hines (batting, C.F., Indianapolis)
227 2aPaul Hines (arms at sides, C.F., Washington)
227 2bPaul Hines (arms at sides, Centre Field, Washington)
227 3aPaul Hines (arms folded, C.F., Washington)
227 3bPaul Hines (arms folded, Centre Field, Washington)
227 3cPaul Hines (arms folded, L.F., Indianapolis)
227 4aPaul Hines (fielding, C.F., Washington)
227 4bPaul Hines (fielding, Centre Field, Washington)
227 4cPaul Hines (fielding, C.F., Indianapolis)
228 1 Texas Wonder Hoffman (pitching, hands chest-high on left)
228 2 Texas Wonder Hoffman (pitching, hands head-high)
228 3 Texas Wonder Hoffman (pitching, right hand head-high)
228 4 Texas Wonder Hoffman (end of pitch, right hand forward head-high)
229 1 Eddie Hogan (batting, looking at camera)
229 2 Eddie Hogan (batting, looking right)
229 3 Eddie Hogan (fielding grounder)
229 4 Eddie Hogan (fielding, hands head-high)
229 5 Eddie Hogan (throwing)
230 1 Bill Holbert (dotted tie)
230 2aBill Holbert (batting, Brooklyns)
230 2bBill Holbert (batting, Mets)
230 3 Bill Holbert (throwing)
230 4 Bill Holbert (fielding, ball by left shoulder)
230 5aBill Holbert (fielding, hands cupped chin-high, Brooklyns)
230 5bBill Holbert (fielding, hands cupped chin-high, Mets)
230 6aBill Holbert (in mask, no comma after C., Brooklyns)
230 6bBill Holbert (in mask, comma after C., Brooklyns)
230 6cBill Holbert (in mask, Mets)
230 6dBill Holbert (in mask, Jersey Citys)
231 1 Bug Holliday (Halliday) (hands at back)
231 2aBug Holliday (Halliday) (arms at sides, Des Moines)
231 2bBug Holliday (Halliday) (arms at sides, Cincinnatis)
231 2cBug Holliday (arms at sides, Holliday on front)
231 2dBug Holliday (arms at sides, W. Holliday on front)
231 3aBug Holliday (hands crossed below waist on bat, name correct)
231 3bBug Halliday (Holliday) (hands crossed below waist on bat, name incorrect)
231 4aBug Halliday (Holliday) (batting, name incorrect)
231 4bBug Holliday (batting, name correct)
231 5 Bug Halliday (Holliday) (ball in hands by left shoulder)
231 6 Bug Halliday (Holliday) (fielding, hands at waist)
232 1aCharles Hoover (hands on thighs, Chicago)
232 1bCharles Hoover (hands on thighs, Kansas City)
232 2aCharles Hoover (kneeling to field low ball, Hoover on front, Chicago)
232 2bCharles Hoover (kneeling to field low ball, C.E. Hoover on front, Chicago)
232 2dCharles Hoover (kneeling to field low ball, C.E. Hoover on front, Kansas Citys)
232 3 Charles Hoover (batting, Chicago)
232 4 Charles Hoover (throwing, Chicago)
232 5 Charles Hoover (ball in hands chin-high, Chicago)
233 1 Buster Hoover (batting, Philadelphia)
233 2 Buster Hoover (fielding, hands head-high, Philadelphia)
233 3 Buster Hoover (fielding, hands thigh-high, Philadelphia)
233 4 Buster Hoover (throwing, Philadelphia)
234 1aJack Horner (ball in hand, name correct)
234 1bJack Hodner (Horner) (ball in hand, name incorrect)
234 2aJack Horner (fielding, hands neck-high, Milwaukee)
234 2bJack Horner (fielding, hands neck-high, New Havens)
234 3 Jack Horner
234 3 E.H. Warner
234 4 Jack Horner (bat in hand at side)
235 1aJoe Horning (Hornung) (bat at ready position, nearly horizontal, Horning on front, L.F.)
235 1bJoe Horning (Hornung) (bat at ready position, nearly horizontal, Horning on front, Left Field)
235 1cJoe Horning (Hornung) (bat at ready position, nearly horizontal, Joe Horning on front, L.F.)
235 1dJoe Hornung (bat at ready position, nearly horizontal, Joe Hornung on front, L.F.)
235 2aJoe Horning (Hornung) (throwing, Horning on front, L.F.)
235 2bJoe Horning (Hornung) (throwing, Horning on front, Left Field)
235 2cJoe Horning (Hornung) (throwing, Joe Horning on front, L.F.)
235 2dJoe Hornung (throwing, Hornung on front, L.F.)
235 3aJoe Horning (Hornung) (ball in hands neck-high, L.F.)
235 3bJoe Horning (Hornung) (ball in hands neck-high, Left Field)
235 4aJoe Horning (Hornung) (bat in hand at side, Horning on front, L.F.)
235 4bJoe Horning (Hornung) (bat in hand at side, Horning on front, Left Field)
235 4cJoe Horning (Hornung) (bat in hand at side, Joe Horning on front, L.F.)
235 5aJoe Horning (Hornung) (bat at ready position at 60 degrees, Horning on front, L.F.)
235 5bJoe Horning (Hornung) (bat at ready position at 60 degrees, Horning on front, Left Field)
235 5dJoe Hornung (bat at ready position at 60 degrees, Hornung on front, L.F.)
235 6aJoe Horning (Hornung) (leaning to left, hands thigh-high, Horning on front, L.F.)
235 6bJoe Horning (Hornung) (leaning to left, hands thigh-high, Horning on front, Left Field)
235 6cJoe Horning (Hornung) (leaning to left, hands thigh-high, Joe Horning on front, L.F.)
235 6dJoe Hornung (leaning to left, hands thigh-high, Joe Hornung on front, L.F.)
235 6eJoe Hornung (leaning to left, hands thigh-high, Hornung on front, L.F.)
236 1 Pete Hotaling (batting)
236 2 Pete Hotaling (right hand across waist, left hand at back)
236 3 Pete Hotoling (Hotaling) (stooping to left, hands thigh-high)
236 4 Pete Hotoling (Hotaling) (throwing)
237 1aBill Howes (Hawes) (fielding, hands neck-high, looking up, Minneapolis)
237 1bBill Hawes (fielding, hands neck-high, looking up, St. Pauls)
237 2 Bill Howes (Hawes) (fielding, hands neck-high, looking at approaching ball)
237 3 Bill Howes (Hawes) (fielding ball by right foot)
237 4 Bill Howes (Hawes) (ball in hands, thigh-high on left)
237 5 Bill Howes (Hawes) (ball near hands by right knee)
237 6 Bill Howes (Hawes) (batting)
238 1aDummy Hoy (bat in hand at side, Washington)
238 1bDummy Hoy (bat in hand at side, Washingtons)
238 2aDummy Hoy (batting, no comma after C.F., Washington)
238 2bDummy Hoy (batting, comma after C.F., Washington)
238 2cDummy Hoy (batting, C.F., Washingtons)
238 3 Dummy Hoy (fielding grounder)
238 4aDummy Hoy (throwing, Washington)
238 4bDummy Hoy (throwing, Washingtons)
238 5 Dummy Hoy (fielding, hands neck-high)
239 1 Nat Hudson (Brown's Champions)
239 2aNat Hudson (batting, St. Louis)
239 2bNat Hudson (batting, St. Louis Browns)
239 3 Nat Hudson (pitching, hands at waist)
239 4aNat Hudson (pitching, hands chest-high, St. Louis)
239 4bNat Hudson (pitching, hands chest-high, St. Louis Browns)
239 5aNat Hudson (pitching, right hand waist-high, N. Hudson on front, St. Louis Browns)
239 5cNat Hudson (pitching, right hand waist-high, Hudson on front, St. Louis Browns)
239 5dNat Hudson (pitching, right hand waist-high, St. Louis)
239 6aNat Hudson (pitching, right hand head-high, no comma after P., St. Louis Browns)
239 6bNat Hudson (pitching, right hand head-high, comma after P., St. Louis Browns)
239 6cNat Hudson (pitching, right hand head-high, St. Louis)
240 2 Mickey Hughes (bat at ready position over shoulder)
240 3 Mickey Hughes (bat at ready position at about 30

degrees)
240 4 Mickey Hughes (fielding, hands chest-high)
240 5 Mickey Hughes (pitching, hands shoulder-high)
240 6 Mickey Hughes (pitching, ball in right hand chest-high)
240 7 Mickey Hughes (pitching, ball in right hand at side)
240 8 Mickey Hughes (pitching, right hand forward head-high)
241 1a Hungler (batting, Sioux City)
241 1b Hungler (batting, Sioux Citys)
241 2 Hungler (pitching, hands chin-high close to body)
241 3 Hungler (pitching, hands chest-high well away from body)
241 4 Hungler (pitching, right hand forward chin-high)
242 1 Wild Bill Hutchinson (ball in right hand above head, right heel visible behind left leg)
242 2 Wild Bill Hutchinson (ball in right hand above head, right heel concealed behind left leg)
242 3aWild Bill Hutchinson (batting, Chic.)
242 3cWild Bill Hutchinson (batting, Chicago's)
242 4 Wild Bill Hutchinson (pitching)
243 1 John Irwin (hands on knees, Washington)
243 2 John Irwin (batting, Washington)
243 3 John Irwin (throwing, Washington)
243 4 John Irwin (fielding, Washington)
244 1 Cutrate Irwin (portrait, looking to left, Philadelphias)
244 2 Cutrate Irwin (portrait, looking to right, Philadelphias)
244 3aCutrate Irwin (fielding, hands cupped chest-high, Phila)
244 3bCutrate Irwin (fielding, hands cupped chest-high, Philadelphia)
244 3cCutrate Irwin (fielding, hands cupped chest-high, Philadelphias)
244 4aCutrate Irwin (batting, Phila)
244 4bCutrate Irwin (batting, Philadelphia)
244 4cCutrate Irwin (batting, Philadelphias)
244 4dCutrate Irwin (batting, Washingtons)
244 5aCutrate Irwin (throwing, Phila)
244 5bCutrate Irwin (throwing, Philadelphia)
244 5cCutrate Irwin (throwing, Philadelphias)
244 6aCutrate Irwin (fielding grounder, hands between knees, Phila)
244 6bCutrate Irwin (fielding grounder, hands between knees, Philadelphia)
244 6cCutrate Irwin (fielding grounder, hands between knees, Philadelphias)
244 7 Cutrate Irwin (stooping right to field ball by left foot)
244 8 Cutrate Irwin (bat on left shoulder, heels together)
244 9 Cutrate Irwin (bat horizontal, ball not visible)
244 10aCutrate Irwin (fielding, hands above head, Philadelphias)
244 10bCutrate Irwin (fielding, hands above head, Bostons (P.L.))
244 11Cutrate Irwin (doffing cap)
245 1 A.C. Jantzen (batting, looking at camera)
245 2 A.C. Jantzen (batting, looking at ball)
245 3 A.C. Jantzen (fielding, hands at right knee)
245 4 A.C. Jantzen (fielding, hands chest-high)
245 5 A.C. Jantzen (fielding, hands head-high)
246 1 Frederick Jevne (sliding)
246 2 Frederick Jevne (bat in hand at side)
246 3 Frederick Jevne (fielding, hands above head)
246 4 Frederick Jevne (fielding low ball)
246 5 Frederick Jevne (batting)
247 1 Spud Johnson (hands inside tunic above waist)
247 2aSpud Johnson (fielding, hands head-high, Columbus)
247 2bSpud Johnson (fielding, hands head-high, Kansas City)
247 4 Spud Johnson (throwing)
247 5 Spud Johnson (fielding, hands waist-high)
248 1aDick Johnston (fielding, hands by right thigh, Johnston on front, C.F.)
248 1bDick Johnston (fielding, hands by right thigh, Johnston on front, Centre Field)
248 1cDick Johnston (fielding, hands by right thigh, R.F. Johnston on front, C.F.)
248 2aDick Johnston (batting, looking at ball, Johnston on front, C.F.)
248 2bDick Johnston (batting, looking at ball, Johnston on front, Centre Field)
248 2cDick Johnston (batting, looking at ball, R.F. Johnston on front, C.F.)
248 3aDick Johnston (batting, looking at camera, C.F., Boston)
248 3bDick Johnston (batting, looking at camera, Centre Field)
248 3cDick Johnston (batting, looking at camera, C.F., Bostons)
248 4aDick Johnston (hands on hips, C.F., Boston)
248 4bDick Johnston (hands on hips, Centre Field, Boston)
248 4cDick Johnston (hands on hips, C.F., Bostons)
248 4dDick Johnston (hands on hips, C.F., Bostons (PL))
248 5aDick Johnston (throwing, C.F.)
248 5bDick Johnston (throwing, Centre Field)
248 5cDick Johnston (throwing, C.F.)
248 6aDick Johnston (fielding, hands neck-high, C.F.)
248 6bDick Johnston (fielding, hands neck-high, Centre Field)
249 1 Jordan (bat over shoulder, ball in hand)
249 2 Jordan (throwing)
249 3 Jordan (fielding, in mask)
249 4 Jordan (fielding, no mask)
249 5 Jordan (batting)
250 1aHeinie Kappell (Kappel) (fielding grounder, Columbus)
250 1bHeinie Kappell (Kappel) (fielding grounder, Cincinnati)
250 2aHeinie Kappell (Kappel) (fielding, hands knee-high, Columbus)
250 2bHeinie Kappell (Kappel) (fielding, hands knee-high, Cincinnati)
250 3aHeinie Kappell (Kappel) (fielding, hands above head, Columbus)
250 3bHeinie Kappell (Kappel) (fielding, hands above head, Cincinnati)
250 4 Heinie Kappell (Kappel) (throwing)
250 5 Heinie Kappell (Kappel) (batting)
251 1aTim Keefe (pitching, hands at chest, N.Y's)
251 1bJim Keefe (Tim) (pitching, hands at chest, name incorrect, New Yorks)
251 1cTim Keefe (pitching, hands at chest, name correct, New Yorks)
251 2aTim Keefe (pitching, right hand at back waist-high, N.Y's)
251 2bJim Keefe (Tim) (pitching, right hand at back waist-high, Jim Keefe on front, New Yorks)
251 2cTim Keefe (pitching, right hand at back waist-high, Keefe on front, New Yorks)
251 2dTim Keef (Keefe) (pitching, right hand at back waist-high, Keef on front, New Yorks)
251 3aTim Keefe (pitching, right hand forward head-high, N.Y's)
251 3bTim Keefep (Keefe) (pitching, right hand forward head-high, New Yorks)
251 4aTim Keefe (bat nearly horizontal, N.Y's)
251 4bTim Keefe (bat nearly horizontal, name correct, New Yorks)
251 4cTim Keef (Keefe) (bat nearly horizontal, name incorrect, New Yorks)
251 5aTim Keefe (pitching, right hand held out waist-high, N.Y's)
251 5bTim Keefe (pitching, right hand held out waist-high, New Yorks)
251 6 Tim Keefe (bat at ready position, nearly vertical, N.Y's)
251 7aTim Keefe (pitching, hands above waist, N.Y's)
251 7bTim Keefe (pitching, hands above waist, New Yorks)
251 8aTim Keefe (Keefe tagging Richardson, caption reads "Keefe")
251 8aDanny Richardson (Keefe tagging Richardson, caption reads "Keefe")
251 8bTim Keefe (Keefe tagging Richardson, caption reads "Keefe and Richardson Stealing 2d")
251 8bDanny Richardson (Keefe tagging Richardson, caption reads "Keefe and Richardson Stealing 2d")
251 8cTim Keefe (Keefe tagging Richardson, caption reads "Keefe & Richardson")
251 8cDanny Richardson (Keefe tagging Richardson, caption reads "Keefe & Richardson")
251 9 Tim Keefe (Keefe fielding ball, Richardson sliding to base)
251 9 Danny Richardson (Keefe fielding ball, Richardson sliding to base)
252 1 George Keefe (batting, Washington)
252 2aGeorge Keefe (pitching, hands at chest, looking to front, Washington)
252 2bGeorge Keefe (pitching, hands at chest, looking to front, Washingtons)
252 3 George Keefe (pitching, hands at chest, right profile,Washingtons)
252 4 George Keefe (pitching, hands above head, Washington)
252 5aGeorge Keefe (pitching, left hand forward head-high, Washington)
252 5bGeorge Keefe (pitching, left hand forward head-high, Washingtons)
253 1aJim Keenan (hands on knees, Cincinnatis)
253 1bJim Keenan (hands on knees, Cincinnati)
253 2aJim Keenan (fielding grounder, Cinncinnatti)
253 2bJim Keenan (fielding grounder, Cincinnati)
253 3aJim Keenan (batting, Cincinnatti)
253 3bJim Keenan (batting, Cincinnati)
253 4 Jim Keenan (fielding, hands chest-high)
253 5aJim Keenan (fielding, hands above head, Keenan on front)
253 5bJim Keenan (fielding, hands above head, J.M. Keenan on front)
254 1 King Kelly (portrait, in cap, "Chicago" on shirt)
254 2 King Kelly (portrait, bare head, "Chicago" on shirt)
254 3 King Kelly (portrait, bare head, "Boston" on shirt)
254 4 King Kelly (bat at ready position at 45 degrees, left-handed, $10,000 Kelly on front)
254 5aKing Kelly (bat at ready position at 45 degrees, right-handed, $10,000 Kelly on front)
254 5bKing Kelly (bat at ready position at 45 degrees, right-handed, Boston)
254 5cKing Kelly (bat at ready position at 45 degrees, right-handed, Bostons)
254 5dKing Kelly (bat at ready position at 45 degrees, right-handed, no position on front, Boston)
254 5eKing Kelly (bat at ready position at 45 degrees, right-handed, no position on front, Boston (PL))
254 6 King Kelly (bat at ready position, horizontal, right-handed, $10,000 Kelly on front)
254 7 King Kelly (bat in left hand at side, $10,000 Kelly on front)
254 8 King Kelly (bat on right shoulder, $10,000 Kelly on front)
254 9 King Kelly (fielding, hands chest-high, $10,000 Kelly on front)
254 10King Kelly (fielding, hands head-high, $10,000 Kelly on front)
255 1 Honest John Kelly (portrait, looking to left, Louisville)
255 2 Honest John Kelly (full length, coat over left arm. Louisville)
255 3aHonest John Kelly (umpire) (looking at approaching ball, Western Ass')
255 3bHonest John Kelly (umpire) (looking at approaching ball, Western Ass'n)
255 4 Honest John Kelly (umpire)
255 4 Jim Powell (manager)
256 No World Index Listing
257 1 Charles Kelly (batting, hands close to body, Philadelphia)
257 2 Charles Kelly (batting, hands clear of body, Philadelphia)
257 3 Charles Kelly (fielding, hands head-high, Philadelphia)
257 4 Charles Kelly (fielding, hands thigh-high, Philadelphia)
257 5 Charles Kelly (throwing, Philadelphia)
258 1 Rudy Kemler (Kemmler) (portrait in striped cap)
258 2 Rudy Kemmler (batting)
259 1 Theodore Kennedy (batting)
259 2aTheodore Kennedy (bat in hand at side, Des Moines)
259 2bTheodore Kennedy (bat in hand at side, Omaha's)
259 3aTheodore Kennedy (fielding, Des Moines)
259 3bTheodore Kennedy (fielding, Omahas)
259 4aTheodore Kennedy (pitching, hands chest-high, Des Moines)
259 4bTheodore Kennedy (pitching, hands chest-high, Omahas)
259 5aTheodore Kennedy (pitching, right arm extended at side, Des Moines)
259 5bTheodore Kennedy (pitching, right arm extended at side, Omahas)
260 1aJ.J. Kenyon (batting, Des Moines)
260 1bJ.J. Kenyon (batting, St. Louis Whites)
260 2 J.J. Kenyon (bat in hand at side)
260 3aJ.J. Kenyon (fielding, hands chest-high, Des Moines)
260 3bJ.J. Kenyon (fielding, hands chest-high, St. Louis Whites)
260 4 J.J. Kenyon (in mask, hands on knees)
260 5 J.J. Kenyon (right hand in glove head-high)
261 1aJohn Kerins (batting, Louisville)
261 1bJohn Kerins (batting, Louisvilles)
261 2aJohn Kerins (hands on thighs, Louisville)
261 2bJohn Kerins (hands on thighs, Louisvilles)
261 3 John Kerins (in mask, stooping, hands thigh-high)
261 4 John Kerins (fielding, kneeling, hands by left knee)
261 5aJohn Kerins (fielding, hands chest-high, Louisville)
261 5bJohn Kerins (fielding, hands chest-high, Louisvilles)
262 1aMatt Kilroy (batting, Bostons (PL))
262 1bMatt Kilroy (batting, Baltimores)
262 2aMatt Kilroy (pitching, hand chest-high, Bostons)
262 2bMatt Kilroy (pitching, hand chest-high, Bostons (PL))
262 2cMatt Kilroy (pitching, hand chest-high, Baltimores)
262 3 Matt Kilroy (fielding, hands head-high)
262 4 Matt Kilroy (pitching, hands to left waist-high)
262 5 Matt Kilroy (pitching, left hand head-high)
263 1 Silver King (pitching, hands chin-high)
263 2aSilver King (pitching, hands chest-high, no comma after P., St. Louis Browns)
263 2bSilver King (pitching, hands chest-high, comma after P., St. Louis Browns)
263 2cSilver King (pitching, hands chest-high, St. Louis)
263 2dSilver King (pitching, hands chest-high, Chicagos (PL))
264 1 August Kloff (Klopf) (pitching, right hand above head, arm bent)
264 2 August Kloff (Klopf) (pitching, ball leaving hand head-high)
264 3 August Kloff (Klopf) (hands at neck)
264 4aAugust Kloff (Klopf) (fielding, leaning to right, hands waist high, Minneapolis)
264 4bAugust Kloff (Klopf) (fielding, leaning to right, hands waist high, St. Joes)
264 5 August Kloff (Klopf) (batting)
264 6 August Kloff (Klopf) (pitching, right hand vertically above head, arm almost straight)
265 1 William Klusman (fielding, hands by right foot)
265 2aWilliam Klusman (batting, looking at camera, Denvers)
265 2bWilliam Klusman (batting, looking at camera, Milwaukee)
265 3aWilliam Klusman (batting, looking at ball, Denvers)
265 3bWilliam Klusman (batting, looking at ball, Milwaukee)
265 4aWilliam Klusman (fielding, hands head-high, Denvers)
265 4bWilliam Klusman (fielding, hands head-high, Milwaukee)
265 5 William Klusman (fielding, hands waist-high)
266 1aPhilip Knell (pitching, hands at chest, St. Josephs)
266 1bPhilip Knell (pitching, hands at chest, St. Joes)
266 2 Philip Knell (pitching, left hand by head, looking at camera)
266 3aPhilip Knell (pitching, nearly back view, left hand head-high, St. Joes)
266 3bPhilip Knell (pitching, nearly back view, left hand head-high, St. Josephs)
266 4 Philip Knell (pitching, left hand forward head-high)
266 5 Philip Knell (batting)
267 1 Fred Knouff (sliding)
267 2 Fred Knouff (batting)
267 3 Fred Knouff (pitching)
267 4 Fred Knouff (ball in right hand waist-high)
267 5 Fred Knouff (ball in right hand head-high)
268 1 Charles Kremmeyer (Krehmeyer) (fielding)
269 1aBill Krieg (ringed cap, fielding, hands chest-high, 1st B., Washington)
269 1bBill Krieg (Kreig) (ringed cap, fielding, hands chest-high, First Base, Washington)
269 1cBill Krieg (ringed cap, fielding, hands chest-high, St. Joes)
269 2aBill Krieg (ringed cap, fielding, hands thigh-high, 1st B., Washington)
269 2bBill Kreig (Krieg) (ringed cap, fielding, hands thigh-high, First Base, Washington)
269 2cBill Krieg (ringed cap, fielding, hands thigh-high, Minne)
269 2dBill Krieg (ringed cap, fielding, hands thigh-high, C., St. Joes)
269 2eBill Krieg (ringed cap, fielding hands thigh-high, 1st B., St. Joe)
269 3aBill Krieg (ringed cap, batting, 1st B.)
269 3bBill Kreig (Krieg) (ringed cap, batting, First Base)
269 4 Bill Krieg (dark cap, tagging player)
269 5aBill Krieg (dark cap, batting, C.)
269 5bBill Krieg (dark cap, batting, 1st B.)
269 6aBill Krieg (dark cap, throwing, Minneapolis)
269 6bBill Kreig (Krieg) (dark cap, throwing, St. Joes)
269 7 Bill Krieg (dark cap, fielding, stretching up to left)
269 8 Bill Krieg (dark cap, fielding, hands by left shoulder)
269 9 Bill Krieg (in mask, hands on knees)
269 10August Kloff (Klopf)
269 10Bill Krieg
270 1aGus Krock (batting, Chicago)

270 1bGus Krock (batting, Chicagos)
270 1cGus Krock (batting, Chicago's)
270 2aGus Krock (pitching, hands above waist, Chicagos)
270 2bGus Krock (pitching, hands above waist, Chicago)
270 3aGus Krock (pitching, right hand thigh-high, Chicago)
270 3bGus Krock (pitching, right hand thigh-high, Chicagos)
270 4aGus Krock (pitching, right hand head-high, Chicago)
270 4bGus Krock (pitching, right hand head-high, Chicagos)
270 5aGus Krock (pitching, right hand chin-high, Chicago)
270 5bGus Krock (pitching, right hand chin-high, Chicagos)
270 5cGus Krock (pitching, right hand chin-high, Chicago's)
271 1 Willie Kuehne (bunting)
271 2aWillie Kuehne (fielding grounder, Pittsburgh's)
271 2bWillie Kuehne (fielding grounder, Pittsburgs)
271 2cWillie Kuehne (fielding grounder, Pittsburghs)
271 3aWillie Kuehne (walking to left, Pittsburgh's)
271 3bWillie Kuehne (walking to left, Pittsburgs)
271 4aWillie Kuehne (throwing, Pittsburgs)
271 4bWillie Kuchne (Kuehne) (throwing, Pittsburgh)
271 5aWillie Kuehne (fielding, hands thigh-high, Pittsburgs)
271 5bWillie Kuehne (fielding, hands thigh-high, Pittsburghs)
271 5cWillie Kuehne (fielding, hands thigh-high, Pittsburgh's)
272 1 Fred Lange (batting)
272 2 Fred Lange (bending left, hands ankle-high)
272 3 Fred Lange (bending to right, hand on ground ball)
272 4 Fred Lange (fielding, hands chest-high)
272 5 Fred Lange (throwing)
273 1 Ted Larkin (batting)
273 2aTed Larkin (fielding, hands thigh-high, Capt. Larkin on front)
273 2bTed Larkin (fielding, hands thigh-high, Larkin, Captain on front)
273 3 Ted Larkin (throwing)
273 4 Ted Larkin (fielding, left hand above head)
274 1 Arlie Latham (Brown's Champions)
274 2aArlie Latham (sliding, St. Louis Browns)
274 2bArlie Latham (sliding, St. Louis)
274 3 Arlie Latham (batting, standing upright)
274 4aArlie Latham (batting, bending to left, Latham on front, St. Louis Browns)
274 4bArlie Latham (batting, bending to left, W. Latham on front, St. Louis Browns)
274 4cArlie Latham (batting, bending to left, Chicagos (PL))
274 5 Arlie Latham (fielding)
274 6aArlie Latham (throwing, St. Louis)
274 6bArlie Latham (throwing, St. Louis Browns)
275 1 Chuck Lauer (Laver) (fielding, hands chest-high)
275 2 Chuck Lauer (Laver) (throwing, right hand head-high)
275 3 Chuck Lauer (Laver) (batting, looking at camera)
65.00 32.00 19.50
275 4 Chuck Lauer (Laver) (batting, looking at ball)
276 1 John Leighton (batting)
276 2 John Leighton (fielding, hands by left ankle)
276 3 John Leighton (fielding, hands neck-high)
276 4 John Leighton (fielding, hands above head)
276 5 John Leighton (fielding, left hand head-high)
276 51 Levy (bat in hand at side)
277 1aTom Loftus (bowler hat in hand, F.J. Loftus on front)
277 1bTom Loftus (bowler hat in hand, J. Loftus on front)
277 1cTom Loftus (bowler hat in hand, Loftus on front)
277 2 Tom Loftus (bowler hat on head)
278 1aGermany Long (batting, Kansas City)
278 1bGermany Long (batting, Chicago Maroons)
278 2 Germany Long (bat in hand at side, Chicago Maroons)
278 3 Germany Long (fielding, hands thigh-high, Kansas City)
278 4aGermany Long (fielding, hands chest-high, Kansas Citys)
278 4bGermany Long (fielding, hands chest-high, Kansas City)
278 4dGermany Long (fielding, hands chest-high, Chicago Maroons)
278 5 Germany Long (throwing, Kansas City)
279 1 Danny Long (batting, Oakland)
280 1aTom Lovett (batting, Brooklyns)
280 1bTom Lovett (batting, Omaha)
280 2 Tom Lovett (pitching, hands chest-high)
280 3 Tom Lovett (pitching, hands above head)
280 4 Tom Lovett (fielding)
280 6 Tom Lovett (bat in hand at side)
281 1aBobby Lowe (bat in hand at side, Milwaukee)
281 1bBobby Lowe (bat in hand at side, Milw. W.A.)
281 1cBobby Lowe (bat in hand at side, Milwaukees)
281 2 Bobby Lowe (sliding)
281 3 Bobby Lowe (batting)
281 4 Bobby Lowe (fielding grounder)
281 5 Bobby Lowe (fielding, hands shoulder-high)
282 1 Jack Lynch (dotted tie)
282 2 Jack Lynch (batting)
282 3 Jack Lynch (throwing, hands chest-high, right leg clear of left leg)
282 4 Jack Lynch (throwing, right hand neck-high)
282 5 Jack Lynch (throwing, hands chest-high, right foot behind left leg)
283 1 Denny Lyons (hands on knees, Athletics)
283 2 Denny Lyons (bat over shoulder, Athletics)
283 3aDenny Lyons (bat at ready position nearly horizontal, no comma after 3d B.)
283 3bDenny Lyons (bat at ready position nearly horizontal, comma after 3d B.)
283 4 Denny Lyons (fielding, left hand above head)
284 1 Harry Lyons (sliding, St. Louis)
284 2 Harry Lyons (batting, St. Louis)
284 3 Harry Lyons (bending to left, hands thigh-high, St. Louis)
284 4 Harry Lyons (fielding, hands at knees, St. Louis)
284 5 Harry Lyons (throwing, St. Louis)
285 1aConnie Mack (throwing, C., Washington)
285 1bConnie Mack (throwing, Catcher, Mack on front, Washington)
285 1cConnie Mack (throwing, Catcher, C. Mack on front, Washington)
285 2aConnie Mack (stooping, hands on knees, C., Washington)
285 2bConnie Mack (stooping, hands on knees, Catcher, Washington)
285 3aConnie Mack (batting, C., Washington)
285 3bConnie Mack (batting, Catcher, Washington)
286 1 Reddie Mack (sliding, Louisville)
286 2 Reddie Mack (batting, Louisville)
286 3 Reddie Mack (fielding, hands chin-high, Louisville)
286 4aReddie Mack (bending to right, left hand thigh-high, Louisville)
286 4bReddie Mack (bending to right, left hand thigh-high, 2d B., Baltimores)
286 4cReddie Mack (bending to right, left hand thigh-high, 2nd B., Baltimores)
286 5 Reddie Mack (fielding grounder, Louisville)
287 1 Little Mac Macullar (hands on knees)
287 2 Little Mac Macullar (fielding, hands head-high)
287 3 Little Mac Macullar (bat in hand at side)
287 4 Little Mac Macullar (fielding grounder)
287 5 Little Mac Macullar (throwing)
287 6aLeech Maskrey (Little Mac Macullar) (arms at sides, R.F., Des Moines)
287 6bLittle Mac Macollar (arms at sides, S.S. Des Moins)
288 1aKid Madden (portrait, Boston's)
288 1bKid Madden (portrait, Boston)
288 1cKid Madden (portrait, Bostons)
288 2aKid Madden (bat in hand at side, P., Boston)
288 2bKid Madden (bat in hand at side, Pitcher)
288 2cKid Madden (bat in hand at side, Bostons (PL))
288 3aKid Madden (ball in hands at neck, P., Boston)
288 3bKid Madden (ball in hands at neck, Pitcher)
288 3cKid Madden (ball in hands at neck, Bostons (P.L.))
288 4aKid Madden (batting, P., Boston)
288 4bKid Madden (batting, Pitcher)
288 4cKid Madden (batting, Bostons (P.L.))
288 5 Kid Madden (ball in left hand just above head)
288 6 Kid Madden (arms folded, bat against rock)
289 1 Danny Mahoney (hands on thighs)
290 1 Grasshopper Maines (Mains) (batting, looking at camera)
290 2aGrasshopper Maines (Mains) (batting, looking down at ball, St. Pauls)
290 2bGrasshopper Maines (Mains) (batting, looking down at ball, St. Paul)
290 3 Grasshopper Maines (Mains) (pitching, hands by neck)
290 4aGrasshopper Maines (Mains) (ball in bent right hand head-high, St. Pauls)
290 4bGrasshopper Maines (Mains) (ball in bent right hand head-high, St. Paul)
290 5 Grasshopper Maines (Mains) (ball in extended right hand head-high)
291 1aFred Mann (fielding, hands head-high, St. Louis Browns)
291 1bFred Mann (fielding, hands head-high, St. Louis Brown)
291 1cFred Mann (fielding, hands head-high, Hartfords)
291 2 Fred Mann (batting)
291 3 Fred Mann (sliding)
291 4aFred Mann (fielding grounder, St. Louis Brown)
291 4bFred Mann (fielding grounder, St. Louis Browns)
292 1 Jimmy Manning (fielding grounder)
292 2 Jimmy Manning (batting)
292 3aJimmy Manning (throwing, right hand above head, Kansas City)
292 3bJimmy Manning (throwing, right hand above head, Kansas Citys)
292 4 Jimmy Manning (fielding, hands neck-high)
292 5aJimmy Manning (bat in hand at side, no comma after S.S.)
292 5bJimmy Manning (bat in hand at side, comma after S.S.)
292 6 Jimmy Manning (hands on thighs)
293 1 Lefty Marr (fielding grounder)
293 2 Lefty Marr (bat over left shoulder)
293 3aLefty Marr (bat at 45 degree angle, Cincinnati (NL))
293 3bLefty Marr (bat at 45 degree angle, Columbus)
293 4 Lefty Marr (throwing)
293 5aLefty Marr (fielding, hands neck-high, Columbus)
293 5bLefty Marr (fielding, hands neck-high, Cincinnati (NL))
294 1aWillie Breslin - mascot (caption reads "Mascot, New York")
294 1bWillie Breslin Mascot (caption reads "New York Mascot")
295 1aLeech Maskrey (fielding, hands chest-high, R.F.)
295 1bLittle Mac Macullar (Leech Maskrey) (fielding, hands chest-high, S.S.)
295 2 Leech Maskrey (ball in hands chin-high)
295 3aLeech Maskrey (throwing, Des Moines)
295 3bLeech Maskrey (throwing, Milwaukee)
296 1 Bobby Mathews (pitching)
296 2 Bobby Mathews (throwing)
296 3 Bobby Mathews (fielding)
297 1aMike Mattimore (pitching, hands shoulder-high on left, N.Y's)
297 1bMike Mattimore (pitching, hands shoulder-high on left, Athletics)
297 11Mike Mattimore (throwing)
297 2 Mike Mattimore (pitching, hands above head)
297 3aMike Mattimore (batting, standing upright, N.Y's)
297 3bMike Mattimore (batting, standing upright, Athletics)
297 4aMike Mattimore (pitching, hands at neck, N.Y's)
297 4bMike Mattimore (pitching, hands at neck, Athletics)
297 5aMike Mattimore (batting, left knee bent, N.Y's)
297 5bMike Mattimore (batting, left knee bent, Athletics)
297 6aMike Mattimore (pitching, hands waist-high on left, N.Y's)
297 6bMike Mattimore (pitching, hands waist-high on left, Athletics)
297 7 Mike Mattimore (sliding)
297 8aMike Mattimore (fielding grounder, N.Y's)
297 8bMike Mattimore (fielding grounder, name correct, Athletics)
297 8cMike Mattemore (Mattimore) (fielding grounder, name incorrect, Athletics)
297 9aMike Mattimore (sliding, left hand raised, N.Y's)
297 9bMike Mattimore (sliding, left hand raised, Athletics)
297 10aMike Mattimore (bat in hand at side, N.Y's)
297 10bMike Mattimore (bat in hand at side, Athletics)
298 1aSmiling Al Maul (batting, left foot pointing at camera, Pittsburghs)
298 1bSmiling Al Maul (batting, left foot pointing at camera, Pittsburgs)
298 1cSmiling Al Maul (batting, left foot pointing at camera, Pittsburgh)
298 2 Smiling Al Maul (batting, left foot pointing diagonally left)
298 3aSmiling Al Maul (pitching, hands at chest, Pittsburghs)
298 3bSmiling Al Maul (pitching, hands at chest, Pittsburgh)
298 4 Smiling Al Maul (ball in right hand above head, both heels on ground)
298 5 Smiling Al Maul (ball in right hand above head, right heel off ground)
298 6aSmiling Al Maul (fielding, hands head-high, Pittsburgh's)
298 6bSmiling Al Maul (fielding, hands head-high, Pittsburgs)
298 7aSmiling Al Maul (fielding, hands thigh-high, Pittsburgh's)
298 7bSmiling Al Maul (fielding, hands thigh-high, Pittsburgs)
299 1 Al Mays (portrait, dotted tie)
299 2 Al Mays (pitching, hands waist-high)
299 3 Al Mays (pitching, hands chest-high)
299 4 Al Mays (pitching, right hand head-high)
299 5 Al Mays (batting)
300 1 Jimmy McAleer (batting, looking at camera)
300 3 Jimmy McAleer (fielding low ball)
300 4 Jimmy McAleer (fielding, hands above head)
300 5 Jimmy McAleer (fielding, hands above waist)
301 1aTommy McCarthy (sliding, indoor background, Phila)
301 1bTommy McCarthy (sliding, indoor background, Philadelphia)
301 1cTommy McCarthy (sliding, indoor background, 2d B., St. Louis)
301 1dTommy McCarthy (sliding, indoor background, C.F., St. Louis)
301 2aTommy McCarthy (throwing, indoor background, Phila)
301 2bTommy McCarthy (throwing, indoor background, Philadelphia)
301 2cTommy McCarthy (throwing, indoor background, St. Louis)
301 3aTommy McCarthy (tagging player, Phila)
301 3bTommy McCarthy (tagging player, Philadelphia)
301 3cTommy McCarthy (tagging player, C.F., St. Louis)
301 3dTommy McCarthy (tagging player, 2d B., St. Louis)
301 4aTommy McCarthy (batting, indoor background, Phila)
301 4bTommy McCarthy (batting, indoor background, Philadelphia)
301 4cTommy McCarthy (batting, indoor background, St. Louis)
301 5aTommy McCarthy (fielding, hands chest-high, Phila)
301 5bTommy McCarthy (fielding, hands chest-high, Philadelphia)
301 5cTommy McCarthy (fielding, hands chest-high, 2d B. St. Louis)
301 5dTommy McCarthy (fielding, hands chest-high, C.F., St. Louis)
301 6aTommy McCarthy (sliding, outdoor background, St. Louis Browns)
301 6bTommy McCarthy (sliding, outdoor background, St. Louis)
301 7aTommy McCarthy (batting, outdoor background, St. Louis Browns)
301 7bTommy McCarthy (batting, outdoor background, St. Louis)
301 8aTommy McCarthy (throwing, outdoor background, T. McCarthy on front, St. Louis Browns)
301 8bTommy McCarthy (throwing, outdoor background, St. Louis)
301 8cTommy McCarthy (throwing, outdoor background, McCarthy on front, St. Louis Browns)
301 9aTommy McCarthy (fielding, hands head-high, St. Louis Browns)
301 9bTommy McCarthy (fielding, hands head-high, name correct, St. Louis Brown)
301 9cTommy Carthy (McCarthy) (fielding, hands head-high, name incorrect, St. Louis Brown)
302 1 John McCarthy (McCarty) (pitching, hands head-high, Kansas Citys)
302 2 John McCarthy (McCarty) (pitching, hands below chin, Kansas City)
302 3 John McCarthy (McCarty) (fielding, Kansas City)
303 1 Jim McCauley (batting)
303 2 Jim McCauley (fielding)
303 3 Jim McCauley (throwing)
304 1aBill McClellan (stooping, hands knee-high, name correct)
304 1bBill McClennan (McClellan)) (stooping, hands knee-high, name incorrect))
304 2 Bill McClellan (fielding, hands head-high)
304 3aBill McClellan (batting, name correct)
304 3bBill McClennan (McClellan) (batting, name incorrect)
305 1 Jerry McCormack (McCormick) (batting)
305 2 Jerry McCormack (McCormick) (fielding, hands shoulder-high)
305 3 Jerry McCormack (McCormick) (fielding grounder)
305 4 Jerry McCormack (McCormick) (throwing)
306 1 Jim McCormick (portrait, bare head)
306 2 Jim McCormick (portrait, peaked cap)
306 3 Jim McCormick (portrait, bowler hat)
306 4 Jim McCormick (standing, arms folded)
306 5aJim McCormick (pitching, hands at chest, looking at

camera, P.)
306 5bJim McCormick (pitching, hands at chest, looking at camera, Pitcher)
306 6 Jim McCormick (batting, left-handed)
306 7aJim McCormick (fielding, Pitcher)
306 7bJim McCormick (fielding, P.)
306 8 Jim McCormick (standing, arms at sides)
306 9aJim McCormick (batting, right-handed, Pitcher)
306 9bJim McCormick (batting, right-handed, P.)
306 10aJim McCormick (pitching, hands at chest, right profile, Pitcher)
30610bJim McCormick (pitching, hands at chest, right profile, P.)
307 1 McCreachery (photo actually Deacon White) (portrait)
308 1 Thomas McCullum (McCallum) (batting)
308 2 Thomas McCullum (McCallum) (fielding)
308 3 Thomas McCullum (McCallum) (throwing)
308 4 Thomas McCullum (McCallum) (bat in hand at side)
308 51 McDonald (standing, ball in hand)
309 1 Chippy McGarr (stooping, hands thigh-high)
309 2 Chippy McGarr (fielding, hands head-high)
309 3 Chippy McGarr (batting, looking at camera)
309 4aChippy McGarr (batting, umpire behind, St. Louis Browns)
309 4bChippy McGarr (batting, umpire behind, K.C.)
309 4cChippy McGarr (batting, umpire behind, Kansas City)
310 1aJack McGeachy (bat in hand at side, Indianapolis)
310 1bJack McGeachy (bat in hand at side, Indianap's)
310 2 Jack McGeachy (batting)
310 3aJack McGeachy (fielding, McGeachy on front, no comma after C.F., Indianapolis)
310 3bJack McGeachy (fielding, McGeachy on front, comma after C.F., Indianapolis)
310 3cJack McGeachy (fielding, Indianap's)
310 3dJack McGeachy (fielding, C. McGeachy on front)
310 4 Jack McGeachy (throwing)
311 1aJohn McGlone (tagging player, Cleveland's)
311 1bJohn McGlone (tagging player, Detroits)
311 2 John McGlone (fielding, hands neck-high)
311 3 John McGlone (throwing)
311 4 John McGlone (fielding grounder)
311 5 John McGlone (batting)
312 1aDeacon McGuire (hands on knees, Phila)
312 1bDeacon McGuire (hands on knees, Philadelphia)
312 2aDeacon McGuire (right hand on hip, left arm at side, Phila)
312 2bDeacon McGuire (right hand on hip, left arm at side, Philadelphia)
312 2cDeacon McGuire (right hand on hip, left arm at side, Phil)
312 3aDeacon McGuire (fielding, hands shoulder-high, Phila)
312 3bDeacon McGuire (fielding, hands shoulder-high, Philadelphia)
312 3dDeacon McGuire (fielding, hands shoulder-high, Torontos)
312 4aDeacon McGuire (batting, Phila)
312 4bDeacon McGuire (batting, Philadelphia)
313 1aBill McGunnigle (three-quarter length, looking to right, Brooklyns)
313 1bBill McGunnigle (three-quarter length, looking to right, Brookly)
314 1 Ed McKean (batting, looking at camera)
314 2 Ed McKean (batting, looking at ball)
314 3 Ed McKean (fielding, hands thigh-high)
314 4 Ed McKean (fielding, hands chest-high)
314 5 Ed McKean (fielding, hands above head)
315 1aAlex McKinnon (fielding grounder, 1st B.)
315 1bAlex McKinnon (fielding grounder, First Base)
315 2aAlex McKinnon (fielding, hands waist-high, 1st B.)
315 2bAlex McKinnon (fielding, hands waist-high, 1st Base)
315 3aAlex McKinnon (batting, 1st B.)
315 3bAlex McKinnon (batting, 1st Base)
315 4aAlex McKinnon (bat in hand at side, 1st B.)
315 4bAlex McKinnon (bat in hand at side, 1st Base)
316 1 Tom McLaughlin (portrait, dotted tie)
317 1aBid McPhee (batting, looking at camera, Cincinnati)
317 1bBid McPhee (batting, looking at camera, Cincinnati (NL))
317 1cBid McPhee (batting, looking at camera, Cincinnati)
317 2aBid McPhee (batting, looking at ball, McPhee on front)
317 2bBid McPhee (batting, looking at ball, John McPhee on front)
317 3aBid McPhee (fielding, hands ankle-high, Cincinnatis)
317 3bBid McPhee (fielding, hands ankle-high, Cincinnati)
317 3cBid McPhee (fielding, hands ankle-high, Cincinnatis)
317 4aBid McPhee (fielding, hands head-high, McPhee on front, Cincinnati)
317 4bBid McPhee (fielding, hands head-high, Cincinnatis)
317 4cBid McPhee (fielding, hands head-high, Cincinnatti)
317 4dBid McPhee (fielding, hands head-high, John McPhee on front, Cincinnati)
317 5aBid McPhee (throwing, Cincinnati)
317 5bBid McPhee (throwing, Cincinnatti)
318 1 James McQuaid (batting, Denver)
318 2 James McQuaid (fielding, hands near chin, Denver)
318 3 James McQuaid (fielding, hands head-high, Denver)
319 1aJohn McQuaid (umpire) (McQuaid on front)
319 1bJohn McQuaid (umpire) (Jack McQuaid on front)
320 1 Jim McTamany (fielding, hands head-high)
320 2aJim McTamany (fielding, right hand above head, Brooklyn)
320 2bJim McTammany (McTamany) (fielding, right hand above head, Columbus)
320 2cJim McTammany (McTamany) (fielding, right hand above head, Kansas City)
320 3aJim McTamany (batting, name correct)
320 3bJim McTammany (McTamany) (batting, name incorrect)
320 4 Jim McTammany (McTamany) (right hand extended head-high on left)
321 1aGeorge McVey (bending to left, hands knee-high, left foot forward, Denvers)
321 1bGeorge McVey (bending to left, hands knee-high, left foot forward, St. Joe)
321 2aGeorge McVey (bending to left , hands nearly waist-high, feet level, Denvers)
321 2bGeorge McVey (bending to left, hands nearly waist-high, feet level, Milwaukees)
321 3aGeorge McVey (standing upright, hands outstretched shoulder-high, St. Joe)
321 4aGeorge McVey (batting, looking at camera, Denvers)
321 4bGeorge McVey (batting, looking at camera, St. Joe)
321 5aGeorge McVey (batting, looking down at bat, Denvers)
321 51Steady Pete Meegan (standing, hands together at waist)
322 1 John Messitt (leaning left, arms at sides)
322 2aJohn Massitt (Messitt) (throwing)
322 2bJohn Wassitt (Messitt) (throwing)
322 3 John Messitt (bat in hand at side)
323 1aDoggie Miller (batting, C., Pittsburg)
323 1bDoggie Miller (batting, Catcher, Pittsburg)
323 1cDoggie Miller (batting, Miller on front, Pittsburgh)
323 1dDoggie Miller (batting, Geo. F. Miller on front, Pittsburgh)
323 1eDoggie Miller (batting, Pittsburghs)
323 2aDoggie Miller (bat in hand at side, C., Pittsburg)
323 2bDoggie Miller (bat in hand at side, Catcher, Pittsburg)
323 3aDoggie Miller (fielding, hands chest-high, C., Pittsburg)
323 3bDoggie Miller (fielding, hands chest-high, Catcher, Pittsburg)
323 4aDoggie Miller (ball in hands at waist, C., Pittsburg)
323 4bDoggie Miller (ball in hands at waist, Catcher, Pittsburg)
323 5 Doggie Miller (hands on thighs, Pittsburghs)
324 1 Joseph Miller (batting, Omaha)
324 2 Joseph Miller (fielding, hands at ankles, Minneapolis)
324 3 Joseph Miller (bat in hand at side, Omaha)
325 1aJocko Milligan (batting, looking at camera, St. Louis)
325 1bJocko Milligan (batting, looking at camera, no comma after C., St. Louis Browns)
325 1cJocko Milligan (batting, looking at camera, comma after C., St. Louis Browns)
325 1dJocko Milligan (batting, looking at camera, Philadelphias (PL))
325 2aJocko Milligan (bat in hand at side, Milligan on front)
325 2bJocko Milligan (bat in hand at side, J. Milligan on front)
325 3aJocko Milligan (throwing, St. Louis)
325 3bJocko Milligan (throwing, Philadelphias)
325 3cJocko Milligan (throwing, Philadelphias (PL))
325 4 Jocko Milligan (fielding)
326 1 E.L. Mills (batting)
326 2 E.L. Mills (bat in hand at side)
326 3aE.L. Mills (fielding, hands shoulder-high, Milwaukees)
326 3bE.L. Mills (fielding, hands shoulder-high, Milwaukees, W. Ass'n)
326 4 E.L. Mills (ball in left hand above head)
326 5 E.L. Mills (throwing, ball in right hand head-high)
327 1 Daniel Minnehan (Minahan) (batting, looking at camera)
327 2 Daniel Minnehan (Minahan) (batting, looking at ball)
327 3 Daniel Minnehan (Minahan) (fielding, hands chin-high)
327 4 Daniel Minnehan (Minahan) (fielding, hands chest-high)
328 1 Sam Moffet (batting)
328 2 Sam Moffet (pitching)
328 3 Sam Moffet (throwing)
329 1aHonest John Morrell (Morrill) (portrait, no position)
329 1bHonest John Morrill (portrait, First Base, Manager)
329 1cJohn Morrell (Morrill) (portrait, 1st B.)
329 1dJohn Morrell (Morrill) (portrait, 1st Base and Manager)
329 2aJohn Morrell (Morrill) (hands on hips, name incorrect)
329 2bJohn Morrill (hands on hips, name correct)
329 3 John Morrill (bat in hand at side)
329 4 John Morrill (batting)
330 1aEd Morris (bat at ready position, clear of head, Pittsburgh)
330 1bEd Morris (bat at ready position, clear of head, Pittsburgs)
330 2aEd Morris (bat at ready position, partly behind cap, Pittsburgh)
330 2bEd Morris (bat at ready position, partly behind cap, Pittsburgh's)
330 3aEd Morris (ball in left hand head-high, right hand over right thigh, Pittsburgh)
330 3bEd Morris (ball in left hand head-high, right hand over right thigh, Pittsburgs)
330 4aEd Morris (ball in left hand head-high, right hand clear of right thigh, Pittsburgh)
330 4bEd Morris (ball in left hand head-high, right hand clear of right thigh, Pittsburghs)
330 5 Ed Morris (hands at chest, feet together, no space between ankles)
330 6aEd Morris (hands at chest, feet just apart with background visible between ankles, Pittsburgh)
330 6bEd Morris (hands at chest, feet just apart with background visible between ankles, Pittsburgh's)
331 1aCount Mullane (bat at ready position, looking at camera, Tony Mullane on front)
331 1bCount Mullane (bat at ready position, looking at camera, Mullane on front)
331 2aCount Mullane (pitching, hands above head, Tony Mullane on front)
331 2bCount Mullane (pitching, hands above head, Mullane on front)
331 3aCount Mullane (pitching, hands above waist clear of belt, Cincinnati)
331 3bCount Mullane (pitching, hands above waist clear of belt, Cincinnatti)
331 3cCount Mullane (pitching, hands above waist clear of belt, Cincinnatis)
331 4 Count Mullane (pitching, hands at waist left arm across belt)
331 5aCount Mullane (pitching, hands held out on left clear of belt, Cincinnati)
331 5bCount Mullane (pitching, hands held out on left clear of belt, Cincinnatti)
331 5cCount Mullane (pitching, hands held out on left clear of belt, Cincinnatis)
331 6aCount Mullane (pitching, right hand hip-high at back, Tony Mullane on front, Cincinnati)
331 6bCount Mullane (pitching, right hand hip-high at back, Cincinnatti)
331 6cCount Mullane (pitching, right hand hip-high at back, Mullane on front, Cincinnati)
331 6dCount Mullane (pitching, right hand hip-high at back, Cincinnatis)
331 7aCount Mullane (pitching, right hand extended forward thigh-high, Cincinnati)
331 7bCount Mullane (pitching, right hand extended forward thigh-high, Cincinnatti)
332 1aJoseph Mulvey (hands on thighs, ball head-high, 3d B.)
332 1bJoseph Mulvey (hands on thighs, ball head-high, Third Base)
332 2aJoseph Mulvey (batting, 3d B.)
332 2bJoseph Mulvey (batting, Third Base)
332 3aJoseph Mulvey (fielding, hands above waist, 3d B., Phila)
332 3bJoseph Mulvey (fielding, hands above waist, Third Base)
332 3dJoseph Mulvey (fielding, hand above waist, 3d B., Philadelphia)
332 3eJoseph Mulvey (fielding, hands above waist, Philadelphia (PL))
333 1 P.L. Murphy (bat in hand at side, St. Pauls)
333 2 P.L. Murphy (batting, St. Pauls)
333 3 P.L. Murphy (standing, hands on thighs, St. Pauls)
333 4aP.L. Murphy (throwing, St. Pauls)
333 4bP.L. Murphy (throwing, St. Paul)
333 5 P.L. Murphy (fielding, St. Paul)
334 1aPat Murphy (bat in hand at side, New Yorks)
334 1bPat Murphy (bat in hand at side, N.Y's)
334 2aPat Murphy (fielding, hands chin-high, New Yorks)
334 2cPat Murphy (fielding, hands chin-high, N.Y's)
334 2dPat Murphy (fielding, hands chin-high, New Yorks (N.L.))
334 3 Pat Murphy (ball almost in right hand, neck-high, New Yorks)
335 1 Miah Murray (on right knee, hands by left shoulder)
335 2 Miah Murray (bat over right shoulder)
335 3 Miah Murray (bat held horizontally)
335 4 Miah Murray (fielding, stretching to high right)
335 5 Miah Murray (throwing)
336 1aTruthful Jim Mutrie (portrait, bare head, N.Y.)
336 1bTruthful Jim Mutrie (portrait, bare head, New Yorks)
336 2aTruthful Jim Mutrie (seated, bowler hat in right hand, N.Y.)
336 2bTruthful Jim Mutrie (seated, bowler hat in right hand, New Yorks)
336 3aTruthful Jim Mutrie (standing, bowler hat on head, N.Y.)
336 3bTruthful Jim Mutrie (standing, bowler hat on head, New Yorks)
337 1aGeorge Myers (batting, no comma after C., Indianapolis)
337 1bGeorge Myers (batting, Catcher, Indianpolis)
337 1cGeorge Myers (batting, comma after C., Indianapolis)
337 2aGeorge Myers (stooping, hands waist-high, C., Indianapolis)
337 2bGeorge Myers (stooping, hands waist-high, Catcher, Indianapolis)
337 3 George Myers (tagging player, Indianapolis)
338 1aAl Myers (portrait, no comma after S.S., Washingtons)
338 1bAl Myers (portrait, Short Stop, Washington)
338 1cAl Myers (portrait, comma after S.S., Washingtons)
338 2aAl Myers (batting, no comma after S.S., Washingtons)
338 2bAl Myers (batting, Short Stop, Washington)
338 2cAl Myers (batting, comma after S.S., Washingtons)
338 2eAl Myers (batting, 2 B, Philadelphia (N.L.))
338 3aAl Myers (hands on knees, no comma after S.S., Washingtons)
338 3bAl Myers (hands on knees, Short Stop, Washington)
338 3cAl Myers (hands on knees, comma after S.S., Washingtons)
338 4 Al Myers (fielding, Washingtons)
338 5 Al Myers (right hand at side, left hand at back, Washington's)
339 1aTom Nagle (batting, looking at camera, Omahas)
339 1bTom Nagle (batting, looking at camera, Chicagos (NL))
339 2 Tom Nagle (batting, looking at ball)
339 3 Tom Nagle (stooping, hands by right foot)
339 4 Tom Nagle (hands on knees)
339 5aTom Nagle (fielding, hands chest-high, Omahas)
339 5bTom Nagle (fielding, hands chest-high, Chicagos (NL))
340 1aBilly Nash (tagging falling player, 3d B., Boston)
340 1bBilly Nash (tagging falling player, Third Base)
340 1cBilly Nash (tagging falling player, 3d B., Bostons)
340 1dBilly Nash (tagging falling player, 3rd.)
340 2aBilly Nash (portrait, 3d B.)
340 2bBilly Nash (portrait, Third Base)
340 3aBilly Nash (hands on knees, 3d B.)
340 3bBilly Nash (hands on knees, Third Base)
340 4aBilly Nash (hands on bat between knees, Nash on front)
340 4bBilly Nash (hands on bat between knees, Billie Nash on front)
340 4cBilly Nash (hands on bat between knees, B. Nash on front)
340 5aBilly Nash (batting, 3d B.)
340 5bBilly Nash (batting, Third Base)
340 6aBilly Nash (throwing, Nash on front)
340 6bBilly Nash (throwing, B. Nash on front)
340 6cBilly Nash (throwing, Billie Nash on front)

341 1 Candy Nelson (dotted tie)
342 1aKid Nichols (batting, looking at camera, Omahas)
342 1bKid Nichols (batting, looking at camera, Omaha)
342 2 Kid Nichols (batting, looking at ball, Omaha)
342 3 Kid Nichols (pitching, hands at chest, Omaha)
342 4 Kid Nichols (pitching, right hand behind back, Omaha)
342 5aKid Nichols (pitching, right hand forward, Omahas)
342 5bKid Nichols (pitching, right hand forward, Omaha)
343 1 Samuel Nichols (Nichol) (bat in hand at side, Pittsburghs)
343 2 Samuel Nichols (Nichol) (fielding, hands above waist, Pittsburghs)
343 3 Samuel Nichols (Nichol) (fielding, hands by neck, Pittsburghs)
343 4 Samuel Nichols (Nichol) (batting, Pittsburghs)
344 1 J.W. Nicholson (leaning to left, hands on knees, Chicago Maroons)
344 2 J.W. Nicholson (bat in hand at side, Chicago Maroons)
344 3 J.W. Nicholson (pitching, hands at chest, Chicago Maroons)
344 4 J.W. Nicholson (pitching, right hand head-high, Chicago Maroons)
344 5 J.W. Nicholson (pitching, right hand head-high close to cap, Chicago Maroons)
345 1aParson Nicholson (bat in hand at side, St. Louis Whites)
345 1bParson Nicholson (bat in hand at side, Cleveland)
345 2aParson Nicholson (fielding, ball in hands by right knee, St. Louis Whites)
345 2bParson Nicholson (fielding, ball in hands by right knee, Clevelan)
345 2cParson Nicholson (fielding, ball in hands by right knee, C. Nicholson, Cleveland)
345 2dParson Nicholson (fielding, ball in hands by right knee, Nicholson on front, Cleveland)
345 3 Parson Micholson (Nicholson) (fielding, hands by right knee, no ball, St. Louis Whites)
345 4aParson Micholson (Nicholson) (tagging player, name incorrect, St. Louis Whites)
345 4bParson Nicholson (tagging player, name correct, St. Louis Whites)
345 5 Parson Nicholson (batting, St. Louis Whites)
346 1 Little Nick Nicoll (Nicol) (Brown's Champions)
346 2aLittle Nick Nicol (batting, Nicol on front)
346 2bLittle Nick Nicol (batting, H. Nicol on front)
346 3aLittle Nick Nicol (sliding, Nicol on front)
346 3bLittle Nick Nicol (sliding, Little Nick on front)
346 4aLittle Nick Nicol (fielding, stretching up to left, Cincinnatis)
346 4bLittle Nick Nicol (fielding, stretching up to left, Cincinnatti)
346 4cLittle Nick Nicol (fielding, stretching up to left, Cincinnati)
346 4dLittle Nick Nicol (fielding, stretching up to left, Cincinnati (N.L.))
346 5aLittle Nick Nicol (leaning forward, hands outstretched for catch, Hugh Nicol on front, Cincinnatis)
346 5bLittle Nick Nicol (leaning forward, hands outstretched for catch, Nicol on front, Cincinnatis)
346 5cLittle Nick Nicol (leaning forward, hands outstretched for catch, Cincinnatti)
346 5dLittle Nick Nicol (leaning forward, hands outstretched for catch, Cincinnati)
346 6 Little Nick Nicol (leaning forward, right hand at hip, left hand by knee)
346 7aLittle Nick Nicol (Nicol and Reilly side by side, Cincinnatti)
346 7aBig John Reilly (Nicol and Reilly side by side, Cincinnatti)
346 7bLittle Nick Nicol (Nicol and Reilly side by side, caption reads "(Long & Short)")
346 7bBig John Reilly (Nicol and Reilly side by side, caption reads "(Long & Short)")
346 7cLittle Nick Nicol (Nicol and Reilly side by side, caption reads "(Long & Short) Cin")
346 7cBig John Reilly (Nicol and Reilly side by side, caption reads "(Long & Short) Cin")
346 8 Little Nick Nicol (Nicol and Reilly facing each other)
346 8 Big John Reilly (Nicol and Reilly facing each other)
347 1 Frederick Nyce (batting)
347 2aFrederick Nyce (ball in right hand neck-high, St. Louis Whites)
347 2bFrederick Nyce (ball in right hand neck-high, Burlingtons (Fc))
347 3 Frederick Nyce (ball in right hand thigh-high)
347 4 Frederick Nyce (ball in hands at chest)
348 1aDoc Oberlander (batting, Cleveland's)
348 1bDoc Oberlander (batting, Syracuse)
348 2 Doc Oberlander (pitching, hands above waist)
348 3aDoc Oberlander (pitching, left hand cap-high, looking to left, Cleveland's)
348 3bDoc Oberlander (pitching, left hand cap-high, looking to left, Syracuse)
348 4aDoc Oberlander (pitching, left hand cap-high, looking at camera, hand at back, Clevelands)
348 4bDoc Oberlander (pitching, left hand cap-high, looking at camera, hand at back, Syracuse)
348 5 Doc Oberlander (pitching, left hand cap-high, looking at camera, hand well forward)
349 1 Jack O'Brien (in mask, hands on knees, Brooklyn)
349 2 Jack O'Brien (mask in left hand, Brooklyn)
349 3 Jack O'Brien (bat over right shoulder, Brooklyn)
349 4 Jack O'Brien (ball in right hand head-high, Brooklyn)
349 5 Jack O'Brien (throwing, right hand neck-high, Baltimores)
349 6 Jack O'Brien (fielding, hands at chest, Baltimores)
349 7 Jack O'Brien (batting, feet well apart, Baltimores)
349 8 Jack O'Brien (batting, heels together, Baltimores)
350 1aBilly O'Brien (batting, feet close together, Washington)
350 1bBilly O'Brien (batting, feet close together, Washingtons)
350 2 Billy O'Brien (batting, feet wide apart, Washingtons)
350 3aBilly O'Brien (hands on knees, Washington)
350 3bBilly O'Brien (hands on knees, Washingtons)
350 4aBilly O'Brien (fielding, hands waist-high, Washington)
350 4bBilly O'Brien (fielding, hands waist-high, Washingtons)
350 5 Billy O'Brien (fielding grounder, Washington)
351 1aDarby O'Brien (batting, looking at camera, Brooklyns)
351 1bDarby O'Brien (batting, looking at camera, Bk'ns)
351 2aDarby O'Brien (batting, looking at ball, Brooklyns)
351 2bDarby O'Brien (batting, looking at ball, Bk'ns)
351 3 Darby O'Brien (fielding, right hand high to left, Brooklyns)
351 4 Darby O'Brien (fielding, hands head-high on left, Brooklyns)
351 5aDarby O'Brien (throwing, Brooklyns)
351 5bDarby O'Brien (throwing, Bk'ns)
352 1 John O'Brien (batting, Clevelands)
352 2 John O'Brien (pitching, ball in right hand at chest, Clevelands)
352 3 John O'Brien (pitching, hands shoulder-high, feet on ground, Clevelands)
352 4 John O'Brien (pitching, hands shoulder-high, left foot off ground, Clevelands)
353 1aP.J. O'Connell (batting, Des Moines)
353 1bP.J. O'Connell (batting, Omaha)
353 2 P.J. O'Connell (fielding grounder)
353 3aP.J. O'Connell (tagging player, Des Moines)
353 3bP.J. O'Connell (tagging player, Omaha)
353 4 P.J. O'Connell (bat in hand at side)
354 1aRowdy Jack O'Connor (batting, Cincinnati)
354 1bRowdy Jack O'Connor (batting, Columbus)
354 2aRowdy Jack O'Connor (fielding grounder, Cincinnati)
354 2bRowdy Jack O'Connor (fielding grounder, Columbus)
354 3aRowdy Jack O'Connor (fielding, hands above waist, Cincinnati)
354 3bRowdy Jack O'Connor (fielding, hands above waist, Columbus)
354 4aJack O'Connor (throwing, Cincinnati)
354 4bJack O'Connor (throwing, Columbus)
355 1aHank O'Day (batting, P.)
355 1bHank O'Day (batting, Pitcher)
355 2aHank O'Day (ball in right hand head-high, P. Washington)
355 2bHank O'Day (ball in right hand head-high, Pitcher, Washington)
355 2cHank O'Day (ball in right hand head-high, Washingtons)
355 3aHank O'Day (pitching, hands at chest, O'Day on front, P., Washington)
355 3bHank O'Day (pitching, hands at chest, Pitcher, Washington)
355 3cHank O'Day (pitching, hands at chest, Washingtons)
355 3dHank O'Day (pitching, hands at chest, H. O'Day on front, P. Washington)
356 1 Tip O'Neil (O'Neill) (bat over right shoulder, St. Louis)
356 2 Tip O'Neil (O'Neill) (bat at ready, St. Louis)
356 3 Tip O'Neil (O'Neill) (fielding grounder, St. Louis)
356 4 Tip O'Neil (O'Neill) (fielding, hands head-high, St. Louis)
356 5 Tip O'Neil (O'Neill) (throwing, St. Louis)
356 6 Tip O'Neil (O'Neill) (Brown's Champions)
357 1 O'Neill (photo actually Bill White) (batting, St. Louis Browns)
357 2a O'Neill (photo actually Bill White) (fielding grounder, name correct, St. Louis Browns)
357 2b O'Neil (O'Neill) (photo actually Bill White) (fielding grounder, name incorrect, St. Louis Bro.)
357 3 O'Neill (photo actually Bill White) (throwing, St. Louis Browns)
357 4 O'Neill (photo actually Bill White) (fielding, hands above head, St. Louis Browns)
357 51 O'Neill (bat in hand at side, Oaklands)
358 1 Orator Jim O'Rourke (fielding, N.Y's)
358 2aOrator Jim O'Rourke (bat in hand at side, 3d B., N.Y's)
358 2bOrator Jim O'Rourke (bat in hand at side, C., New Yorks)
358 2cOrator Jim O'Rourke (bat in hand at side, 3d B., New Yorks)
358 3 Orator Jim O'Rourke (throwing, 3d B., N.Y's)
358 4aOrator Jim O'Rourke (batting, 3d B., N.Y's)
358 4bOrator Jim O'Rourke (batting, 3d B., New Yorks)
359 1aTom O'Rourke (fielding, hands head-high, C., Boston)
359 1bTom Rourke (O'Rourke) (known in proof form only) (fielding, hands head-high, Catcher, Boston)
359 2aTom O'Rourke (fielding, hands thigh-high, Boston)
359 2bTom Rourke (O'Rourke) (known in proof form only) (fielding, hands thigh-high, Catcher, Boston)
359 2dTom O'Rourke (fielding, hands thigh-high, Jersey Citys)
359 3aTom O'Rourke (throwing, right hand head-high, Boston)
359 3bTom Rourke (O'Rourke) (throwing, right hand head-high, Boston)
359 4aTom O'Rourke (batting, Boston)
359 4bTom Rourke (O'Rourke) (known in proof form only) (batting, Boston)
359 5aTom O'Rourke (bat in hand at side, Boston)
359 5bTom Rourke (O'Rourke) (known in proof form only) (bat in hand at side, Boston)
359 5cTom O'Rourke (bat in hand at side, Jersey Citys)
359 6aTom O'Rourke (fielding, hands at neck, C., Boston)
359 6bTom Rourke (O'Rourke) (fielding, hands at neck, Boston)
359 6cTom O'Rourke (fielding, hands at neck, Catcher, Boston)
360 1 Dave Orr (portrait, dotted tie)
360 2aDave Orr (fielding, hands by right knee, no team designation)
360 2bDave Orr (fielding, hands by right knee, Columbus)
360 3 Dave Orr (fielding, hands head-high on left)
360 4aDave Orr (fielding, hands head-high on right, Brooklyns)
360 4bDave Orr (fielding, hands head-high on right, Columbus)
360 5aDave Orr (bat at ready position, nearly vertical, Brooklyns)
360 5bDave Orr (bat at ready position, nearly vertical, Columbus)
360 6aDave Orr (bat at ready position at about 45 degrees, Brooklyns)
360 6bDave Orr (bat at ready position at about 45 degrees, Columbus)
361 1 Charles Parsons (moving forward, hands waist-high)
361 2 Charles Parsons (bat in hand at side)
361 3 Charles Parsons (pitching, hands chest-high)
361 4 Charles Parsons (batting)
362 1 Owen Patton (batting)
362 2 Owen Patton (fielding ball by right foot)
362 3aOwen Patton (fielding, ball in hands by neck, Minneapolis)
362 3bOwen Patton (fielding, ball in hands by neck, Des Moines)
362 4 Owen Patton (fielding, right hand above head)
362 5aOwen Patton (fielding, hands chin-high, Minneapolis)
362 5bOwen Patton (fielding, hands chin-high, Des Moines)
362 6 Owen Patton (throwing)
363 1aJimmy Peeples (Peoples) (in mask, hands waist-high, Brooklyn)
363 1bJimmy Peeples (Peoples) (in mask, hands waist-high, Columbus)
363 2aJimmy Peeples (Peoples) (batting, Brooklyn)
363 2bJimmy Peeples (Peoples) (batting, Columbus)
363 3aHardie Henderson (Henderson tagging Peoples, Columbus)
363 3aJimmy Peeples (Peoples) (Henderson tagging Peoples, Columbus)
363 3bHardie Henderson (Henderson tagging Peoples, Brooklyn)
363 3bJimmy Peeples (Peoples) (Henderson tagging Peoples, Brooklyn)
364 1 Hip Perrier (batting)
365 1 Patrick Pettee (batting)
365 3 Patrick Pettee (throwing)
365 4 Patrick Pettee (sliding)
365 5 Bobby Lowe (Pettee about to tag Lowe)
365 5 Patrick Pettee (Pettee about to tag Lowe)
366 1 Fred Pfeffer (fielding)
366 2aFred Pfeffer (throwing, right hand neck-high, Pfeffer on front, Chicago)
366 2bFred Pfeffer (throwing, right hand neck-high, Pfeffer on front, Chicago's)
366 2cFred Pfeffer (throwing, right hand neck-high, W.T. Pfeffer on front, Chicago)
366 2dFred Pfeffer (throwing, right hand neck-high, W.T. Pfeffer on front, Chicagos)
366 3 Fred Pfeffer (batting, looking at ball by bat)
366 4aFred Pfeffer (bat on right shoulder, Pfeffer on front, Chicago)
366 4bFred Pfeffer (bat on right shoulder, Pfeffer on front, Chicago's)
366 4cFred Pfeffer (bat on right shoulder, W.T. Pfeffer on front)
366 4dFred Pfeffer (bat on right shoulder, N.F. Pfeffer on front)
366 5aFred Pfeffer (tagging player, Pfeffer on front)
366 5bFred Pfeffer (tagging player, N.T. Pfeffer on front)
366 5cFred Pfeffer (tagging player, N.F. Pfeffer on front)
367 1 Dick Phelan (batting, looking at camera)
367 2 Dick Phelan (batting, looking at ball)
367 3 Dick Phelan (fielding, hands waist-high)
367 4aDick Phelan (fielding, hands chest-high, Des Moines)
367 4bDick Phelan (fielding, hands chest-high, Des Moine)
367 5 Dick Phelan (fielding, hands chin-high)
368 1aBill Phillips (hands on knees, Brooklyn)
368 1bBill Phillips (hands on knees, Kansas City)
368 2aBill Phillips (fielding, hands head-high, Brooklyn)
368 2bBill Phillips (fielding, hands head-high, Kansas City)
368 3 Bill Phillips (stooping to left)
368 4aBill Phillips (batting, Brooklyn)
368 4bBill Phillips (batting, Kansas City)
369 1aJack Pickett (bat over right shoulder, Kansas Citys)
369 1bJack Pickett (bat over right shoulder, St. Pauls)
369 1dJack Pickett (bat over right shoulder, Philadelphias)
369 2 Jack Pickett (bat in hand at side)
369 3aJack Pickett (fielding, bending to left, hands neck-high, Kansas City)
369 3bJack Pickett (fielding, bending to left, hands neck-high, St. Pauls)
369 4 Jack Pickett (fielding, bending to left, hands thigh-high)
369 5 Jack Pickett (ball in right hand on ground by left foot)
369 6 Jack Pickett (fielding grounder by feet)
369 7bJack Pickett (throwing, St. Pauls)
369 7cJack Pickett (throwing, Philadelphias)
369 8 Jack Pickett (bending to left, side view)
370 1 George Pinkney (fielding, hands chest-high)
370 2 George Pinkney (hands on knees)
370 3aGeorge Pinkney (bat at ready position, nearly vertical, Brooklyn)
370 3bGeorge Pinkney (bat at ready position, nearly vertical, Brooklyns)
370 4 George Pinkney (fielding, hands ankle-high)
370 5 George Pinkney (bat over right shoulder)
371 1 Tom Poorman (sliding)
371 2aTom Poorman (fielding, ankle-high, Athletics)
371 2bTom Poorman (fielding, ankle-high, Milwaukees)
371 3aTom Poorman (throwing, Athletics)
371 3bTom Poorman (throwing, Milwaukees)
371 4aTom Poorman (fielding, hands chest-high, Athletics)
371 4bTom Porrman (Poorman) (fielding, hands chest-high, Milwaukees)
372 1 Henry Porter (tagging player)
372 2 Henry Porter (pitching, hands chest-high)
372 3 Henry Porter (batting)
372 4aHenry Porter (throwing, right hand neck-high,

Brooklyn)
372 4bHenry Porter (throwing, right hand neck-high, Kansas City)
372 5 Henry Porter (throwing, right hand cap-high)
372 6 Henry Porter (fielding, hands head-high)
373 1aJim Powell (bat at ready position, looking at camera, Mgr.)
373 1bJim Powell (bat at ready position, looking at camera, 1st B.)
373 2aJim Powell (swinging bat, looking at camera, Mgr.)
373 2bJim Powell (swinging bat, looking at camera, 1st B.)
373 3 Jim Powell (fielding, hands on knees, ball approaching)
373 4 Jim Powell (fielding, looking at ball head-high)
373 5aJim Powell (fielding, looking at ball above head, Mgr.)
373 5bJim Powell (fielding, looking at ball above head, 1st B.)
373 51Thomas Powers (Power) (batting)
374 1aBlondie Purcell (sliding, Baltimores)
374 1bBlondie Purcell (sliding, Athletics)
374 2aBlondie Purcell (fielding, stretching up to left, Baltimores)
374 2bBlondie Purcell (fielding, stretching up to left, Athletics)
374 3 Blondie Purcell (fielding, stretching up to right)
374 4 Blondie Purcell (throwing)
374 5 Blondie Purcell (batting)
375 1 Tom Quinn (hands on knees, Baltimore)
375 2 Tom Quinn (batting, Baltimore)
375 3 Tom Quinn (arms at sides, Baltimore)
375 4 Tom Quinn (throwing, Baltimore)
375 5 Tom Quinn (fielding, hands at waist, Baltimore)
376 1 Joe Quinn (sliding, Bostons)
376 2aJoe Quinn (ball in hands by chin, Boston)
376 2bJoe Quinn (ball in hands by chin, Bostons)
376 4 Joe Quinn (right hand extended forward head-high, Des Moines)
377 1aOld Hoss Radbourn (hands on hips, bat on left, P., Boston)
377 1bOld Hoss Radbourn (hands on hips, bat on left, Pitcher, Boston)
377 1cOld Hoss Radbourn (hands on hips, bat on left, Boston (PL))
377 2aOld Hoss Radbourn (tagging player, P.)
377 2bOld Hoss Radbourn (tagging player, Pitcher)
377 3aOld Hoss Radbourn (batting, P., Boston)
377 3bOld Hoss Radbourn (batting, Pitcher, Boston)
377 3cOld Hoss Radbourn (batting, Bostons)
377 4aOld Hoss Radbourn (hands clasped at waist, no space visible between hands and belt, P.)
377 4bOld Hoss Radbourn (hands clasped at waist, no space visible between hands and belt, Pitcher)
377 5aOld Hoss Radbourn (hands clasped at waist, white uniform visible between hands and belt, P.)
377 5bOld Hoss Radbourn (hands clasped at waist, white uniform visible between hands and belt, Pitcher)
377 6aOld Hoss Radbourn (portrait, P.)
377 6bOld Hoss Radbourn (portrait, Pitcher)
378 1 Shorty Radford (batting, looking at camera)
378 2aShorty Radford (batting, looking at ball, Brooklyns)
378 2bShorty Radford (batting, looking at ball, Clevelands)
378 3aShorty Radford (leaning to left, ball in right hand by right knee, Brooklyns)
378 3bShorty Radford (leaning to left, ball in right hand by right knee, Clevelands)
378 4 Shorty Radford (throwing)
378 5aShorty Radford (fielding, hands above head, Brooklyns)
378 5bShorty Radford (fielding, hands above head, Clevelands)
379 1aToad Ramsey (bat over right shoulder, Louisville)
379 1bToad Ramsey (bat over right shoulder, Louisvills)
379 2aToad Ramsey (bat nearly vertical, Ramsey on front)
379 2bToad Ramsey (bat nearly vertical, Thomas Rmasey on front)
379 3aToad Ramsey (pitching, Louisvills)
379 3bToad Ramsey (pitching, Louisville)
380 1 Rehse (batting)
380 2 Rehse (bat in hand at side)
380 3 Rehse (fielding, hands head-high)
380 4 Rehse (fielding, hands thigh-high)
380 5 Rehse (pitching)
381 1 Big John Reilly (batting, Cincinnati)
381 2aBig John Reilly (fielding, 1st B., Cincinnati)
381 2bBig John Reilly (fielding, 1 B., Cincinnati)
381 2cBig John Reilly (fielding, Cincinnatti)
381 2dBig John Reilly (fielding, Cincinnatis)
381 3aBig John Reilly (throwing, Cincinnati)
381 3bBig John Reilly (throwing, Cincinnatti)
381 3cBig John Reilly (throwing, Cincinnatis)
382 1aPrinceton Charlie Reilly (hands on thighs, St. Pauls)
382 1bPrinceton Charlie Riley (Reilly) (hands on thighs, St. Paul)
382 2 Princeton Charlie Reilly (fielding, hands waist-high, St. Pauls)
382 3 Princeton Charlie Reilly (throwing, St. Pauls)
382 4 Princeton Charlie Reilly (batting, St. Pauls)
383 Charlie Reynolds (throwing)
383 1 Charlie Reynolds (hands on thighs)
383 2 Charlie Reynolds (arms at sides)
383 3 Charlie Reynolds (bat in hand at side)
384 1aHardy Richardson (fielding, hands head-high, Detroits)
384 1cHardy Richardson (fielding, hands head-high, Bostons)
384 2aHardy Richardson (bat over right shoulder, Detroits)
384 2bHardy Richardson (bat over right shoulder, Bostons)
384 3 Hardy Richardson (bat nearly horizontal, Detroits)
385 1aDanny Richardson (bat over right shoulder, Danny Richardson on front, N.Y's)
385 1bDanny Richardson (bat over right shoulder, New Yorks)
385 1cDanny Richardson (bat over right shoulder, Richardson on front, N.Y's)
385 2aDanny Richardson (moving to left, arms at sides, Danny Richardson on front, N.Y's)
385 2bDanny Richardson (moving to left, arms at sides, New Yorks)
385 2dDanny Richardson (moving to left, arms at sides, Richardson on front, N.Y's)
385 3aDanny Richardson (bat at ready position at 45 degrees, N.Y's)
385 3bDanny Richardson (bat at ready position at 45 degrees, New Yorks)
385 4aDanny Richardson (throwing, N.Y's)
385 4bDanny Richardson (throwing, New Yorks)
385 5aDanny Richardson (fielding grounder, N.Y's)
385 5bDanny Richardson (fielding grounder, New Yorks)
386 1 Charles Ripslager (Reipschlager) (dotted tie)
387 1 John Roach (pitching, hands by chin)
387 2 John Roach (bat at ready position, standing upright)
387 3 John Roach (bat in hand at side)
387 4 John Roach (leaning to left, hands on thighs)
387 5 John Roach (pitching, left hand chest-high at back)
387 6 John Roach (bat at ready position, leaning forward)
388 1 Uncle Robbie Robinson (batting, Athletics)
388 2aUncle Robbie Robinson (fielding, hands above head, no comma after C., Athletics)
388 2bUncle Robbie Robinson (fielding, hands above head, comma after C., Athletics)
388 3 Uncle Robbie Robinson (fielding, hands neck-high, Athletics)
388 4 Uncle Robbie Robinson (fielding, hands thigh-high, Athletics)
388 5 Uncle Robbie Robinson (throwing, Athletics)
389 1 M.C. Robinson (batting, Minneapolis)
389 2 M.C. Robinson (tagging player, Minneapolis)
389 3 M.C. Robinson (fielding grounder, Minneapolis)
389 4 M.C. Robinson (throwing, right hand head-high, Minneapolis)
389 5 M.C. Robinson (fielding, hands chest-high, Minneapolis)
389 6 M.C. Robinson (ball in hands waist-high, Minneapolis)
390 1aYank Robinson (batting, St. Louis Browns)
390 1bYank Robinson (batting, St. Louis)
390 2aYank Robinson (fielding grounder, St. Louis Browns)
390 2bYank Robinson (fielding grounder, St. L. Brow)
390 3 Yank Robinson (throwing, right hand neck-high, St. Louis)
390 4 Yank Robinson (sliding, St. Louis)
390 5 Yank Robinson (fielding, hands shoulder-high, St. Louis)
390 6 Yank Robinson (Brown's Champions)
391 1aGeorge Rooks (bat in hand at side, Chicago Maroons)
391 1bGeorge Rooks (bat in hand at side, Detroits)
391 2 George Rooks (bat over left shoulder)
391 3 George Rooks (fielding, hands chin-high)
391 4 George Rooks (fielding, hands head-high)
391 5 George Rooks (throwing)
392 1 Chief Roseman (dotted tie)
393 1 Dave Rowe (portrait, Kansas City)
393 2aDave Rowe (throwing, Kansas City)
393 2bDave Rowe (throwing, Mgr. & C.F., Denvers)
393 2cDave Rowe (throwing, Mg'r., Denvers)
393 3 Dave Rowe (fielding, hands shoulder-high, Kansas City)
393 4 Dave Rowe (fielding, hands thigh-high, Kansas City)
393 5 Dave Rowe (fielding grounder, Kansas City)
393 6 Dave Rowe (batting, Kansas City)
394 1aJack Rowe (batting, looking at camera, no comma after S.S., Detroits)
394 1cJack Rowe (batting, looking at camera, comma after S.S., Detroits)
394 2 Jack Rowe (bat in hand at side, Detroits)
394 3 Jack Rowe (batting, looking at approaching ball, Detroits)
395 1aAmos Rusie (pitching, hands at neck, Indianapolis)
395 1bAmos Rusie (pitching, hands at neck, New Yorks (N.L.))
395 2 Amos Rusie (pitching, right hand thigh-high)
395 3aAmos Rusie (pitching, right hand head-high at side, name correct)
395 3bAmos Russie (Rusie) (pitching, right hand head-high at side, name incorrect)
395 4aAmos Rusie (pitching, right hand forward chin-high, Indianapolis)
395 4bAmos Rusie (pitching, right hand forward chin-high, New Yorks (N.L.))
395 5 Amos Rusie (batting)
396 1aJimmy Ryan (stooping for catch knee-high, Chicago)
396 1bJimmy Ryan (stooping for catch knee-high, Chicago's)
396 1cJimmy Ryan (stooping for catch knee-high, Chicago (PL))
396 2aJimmy Ryan (ball in hands at neck, Ryan on front)
396 2bJimmy Ryan (ball in hands at neck, J. Ryan on front)
396 3 Jimmy Ryan (throwing, left hand head-high)
396 4aJimmy Ryan (bat in hand at side, Chicago)
396 4bJimmy Ryan (bat in hand at side, Chicagos (PL))
396 5aJimmy Ryan (fielding, hands head-high, Ryan on front)
396 5bJimmy Ryan (fielding, hands head-high, J. Ryan on front)
3966 Jimmy Ryan (batting)
397 1 Doc Sage (stooping for low ball)
397 2 Doc Sage (bat on right shoulder, looking at camera)
397 3 Doc Sage (batting, looking at approaching ball)
397 4aDoc Sage (Toledos)
397 4aBill Van Dyke (Toledos)
397 4bDoc Sage (Des Moines)
397 4bBill Van Dyke (Des Moines)
398 1 Ben Sanders (pitching)
398 2aBen Sanders (throwing, Phila)
398 2bBen Sanders (throwing, Philadelphias)
398 3aBen Sanders (fielding, Phila)
398 3bBen Sanders (fielding, Philadelphias)
398 3dBen Sanders (fielding, Philadelphias (PL))
398 4 Ben Sanders (batting)
399 1 Frank Scheibeck (fielding, hands waist-high)
399 2 Frank Scheibeck (fielding, hands above head)
399 3 Frank Scheibeck (fielding ball at feet)
399 4 Frank Scheibeck (batting)
400 1 Al Schellhase (Schellhasse) (fielding, hands above head)
400 2 Al Schellhase (Schellhasse) (fielding, ball by hands chest-high)
400 3 Al Schellhase (Schellhasse) (fielding, hands thigh-high, left leg straight)
400 4 Al Schellhase (Schellhasse) (fielding, hands thigh-high, left leg bent)
400 5 Al Schellhase (Schellhasse) (batting)
401 1 William Schenkel (batting)
401 2 William Schenkel (ball in hands chest-high)
401 3aWilliam Schenkel (fielding, hands cupped chest-high, name correct)
401 3bWilliam Schenkle (Schenkel) (fielding, hands cupped chest-high, name incorrect)
401 4 William Schenkle (Schenkel) (left hand chin-high, right arm at side)
402 1a Schildknecht (batting, Milwa'k's)
402 1b Schildknecht (batting, Milwaukee)
402 1c Schildknecht (batting, Milwaukees)
402 1d Schildknecht (batting, Des Moines)
402 2 Schildknecht (fielding, hands thigh-high)
402 3 Schildknecht (fielding, ball in hands chest-high)
403 1 Gus Schmelz (head and shoulder portrait)
403 2aGus Schmelz (full length, street clothes, G.H. Schmelz on front)
403 2bGus Schmelz (full length, street clothes, H. Schmelz on front)
403 2cGus Schmelz (full length, street clothes, Schmelz on front)
403 2dGus Schmelz (full length, street clothes, Cincinnatis)
404 1aJumbo Schoeneck (batting, Chicago Maroons)
404 1bJumbo Schoeneck (batting, Indianapoli)
404 1cJumbo Schoeneck (batting, Indianapolis)
404 1dJumbo Schoeneck (batting, Indianap's)
404 2 Jumbo Schoeneck (hands on knees)
404 3aJumbo Schoeneck (fielding grounder, Chicago Maroons)
404 3bJumbo Schoeneck (fielding grounder, Indianapoli)
404 3cJumbo Schoeneck (fielding grounder, Indianapolis)
404 3dJumbo Schoeneck (fielding grounder, Indianap's)
404 4 Jumbo Schoeneck (fielding, hands chin-high)
404 5aJumbo Schoeneck (ball in left hand head-high, Chicago Maroons)
404 5bJumbo Schoeneck (ball in left hand head-high, Indianapolis)
404 5cJumbo Schoeneck (ball in left hand head-high, Indianap's)
405 1aPop Schriver (bat over right shoulder, Phila)
405 1bPop Schriver (bat over right shoulder, Philadelphias)
405 2 Pop Schriver (bat held horizontally)
405 3 Pop Schriver (fielding, hands ankle-high)
405 4aPop Schriver (fielding, hands chest-high, Phila)
405 4bPop Schriver (fielding, hands chest-high, Philadelphias)
405 5aPop Schriver (throwing, Phila)
405 5bPop Schriver (throwing, Philadelphias)
405 5cPop Schriver (throwing, Phila (N.L.))
406 1aEmmett Seery (fielding, hands above head, L.F.)
406 1bEmmett Seery (fielding, hands above head, Left Field)
406 2aEmmett Seery (ball in hands at neck, no comma after L.F.)
406 2bEmmett Seery (ball in hands at neck, Left Field)
406 2cEmmett Seery (ball in hands at neck, comma after L.F.)
406 3aEmmett Seery (arms folded, no comma after L.F.)
406 3bEmmett Seery (arms folded, Left Field)
406 3cEmmett Seery (arms folded, comma after L.F.)
406 4aEmmett Seery (batting, no comma after L.F.)
406 4bEmmett Seery (batting, comma after L.F.)
407 1aBilly Serad (batting, Cincinnati)
407 1bBilly Serad (batting, Toronto)
407 2 Billy Serad (ball in hands chin-high)
407 3aBilly Serad (ball in right hand neck-high, Cincinnati)
407 3bBilly Serad (ball in right hand neck-high, Toronto)
408 1aEd Seward (ball in hands neck-high, no comma after P.)
408 1cEd Seward (ball in hands neck-high, comma after P.)
408 2aEd Seward (pitching, right hand head-high at back, no comma after P.)
408 2bEd Seward (pitching, right hand head-high at back, comma after P.)
408 3aEd Seward (pitching, right hand forward head-high, no comma after P.)
408 3bEd Seward (pitching, right hand forward head-high, comma after P.)
409 1 Orator Shafer (Shaffer) (arms folded, Des Moines)
409 2 Orator Shafer (Shaffer) (throwing, right hand head-high, Des Moines)
409 3 Orator Shafer (Shaffer) (bat in left hand at side, Des Moines)
409 4 Orator Shafer (Shaffer) (bat at ready position, looking at camera, Des Moines)
410 1 Taylor Shafer (Shaffer) (bending to right, hands over base, St. Louis)
410 2 Taylor Shafer (Shaffer) (throwing, St. Paul)
410 3 Taylor Shafer (Shaffer) (ball in hands by left shoulder, St. Paul)
411 1aDaniel Shannon (batting, name correct)
411 1bDaniel Hannon (Shannon) (batting, name incorrect)
411 2aDaniel Shannon (ball in hands at chest, leaning towards player sliding, Philadelphias (PL))
411 2bDaniel Shannon (ball in hands at chest, leaning towards player sliding, Louisvilles)
411 3 Daniel Shannon (fielding, hands at chest)
411 4 Daniel Shannon (sliding)
411 5 Daniel Shannon (bat in hand at side)
412 1aWilliam Sharsig (full length, in bowler hat, Mg'r.)
412 1bWilliam Sharsig (full length, in bowler hat, Manager)
413 1aSamuel Shaw (pitching, hands above waist, Baltimores)

413 1bSamuel Shaw (pitching, hands above waist, Newarks)
413 2aSamuel Shaw (pitching, right arm extended forward, Baltimores)
413 2bSamuel Shaw (pitching, right arm extended forward, Newarks)
413 3 Samuel Shaw (batting, Baltimores)
414 1 John Shaw (batting, Minneapolis)
414 2 John Shaw (stooping to left, Minneapolis)
414 3 John Shaw (sliding, Minneapolis)
414 4 John Shaw (fielding hands neck-high, Minneapolis)
414 5 John Shaw (throwing, Minneapolis)
415 1 Bill Shindle (fielding grounder)
415 2 Bill Shindle (fielding, hands above head)
415 3aBill Shindle (batting, name correct)
415 3bBill Shindel (batting, name incorrect)
415 4aBill Shindle (hands on knees, name correct, Baltimores)
415 4bBill Shindel (Shindle) (hands on knees, name incorrect, Baltimores)
415 4cBill Shindle (hands on knees, Philadelphias)
415 5aBill Shindle (throwing, 3rd B.)
415 5bBill Shindle (throwing, 3d B., Baltimores)
415 5cBill Shindle (throwing, 3d B., Philadelphias)
416 1aGeorge Schoch (Shoch) (fielding grounder, R.F., Washington)
416 1bGeorge Shoch (fielding grounder, Right Field)
416 1dGeorge Shoch (fielding grounder, R.F., Washingtons)
416 2aGeorge Shoch (fielding, hands head-high, Right Field)
416 2bGeorge Schoch (Shoch) (fielding, hands head-high, G. Schoch on front)
416 2cGeorge Shoch (fielding, hands head-high, Washingtons)
416 2dGeorge Schoch (Shoch) (fielding, hands head-high, Schoch on front)
416 3aGeorge Schoch (Shoch) (batting, Schoch on front)
416 3bGeorge Shoch (batting, Right Field)
416 3cGeorge Shoch (batting, G. Schoch on front)
416 4 Honest John Gaffney (Shoch batting and Gaffney behind him)
416 4 George Shoch (Shoch batting with Gaffney behind him)
417 1aOtto Shomberg (Schomberg) (fielding, hands head-high, 1st B.)
417 1bOtto Shomberg (Schomberg) (fielding, hands head-high, 1st Base)
417 2aOtto Shomberg (Schomberg) (throwing, 1st B.)
417 2bOtto Shomberg (Schomberg) (throwing, 1st Base)
417 3aOtto Shomberg (Schomberg) (fielding, hands waist-high, 1st B.)
417 3bOtto Shomberg (Schomberg) (fielding, hands waist-high, 1st Base)
418 1aLev Shreve (batting, name correct)
418 1bLev Chreve (Shreve) (batting, name incorrect)
418 2aLev Shreve (pitching, ball in hands at chest, comma after P.)
418 2bLev Shreve (pitching, ball in hands at chest, no comma after P.)
418 3aLev Shreve (pitching, right hand above head, facing front, name correct)
418 3bLev Chreve (Shreve) (pitching, right hand above head, facing front, name incorrect)
418 4aLev Shreve (pitching, right hand level with cap, looking at camera, name correct)
418 4bLev Shreve (pitching, right hand level with cap, looking at camera, name incorrect)
418 5aLev Shreve (pitching, right hand level with eyes, looking at camera, comma after P.)
418 5bLev Shreve (pitching, right hand level with eyes, looking at camera, no comma after P.)
418 6aLev Shreve (pitching, right hand level with chin, looking to left, comma after P., Indianapolis)
418 6bLev Shreve (pitching, right hand level with chin, looking to left, no comma after P., Indianapolis)
418 6cLev Shreve (pitching, right hand level with chin, looking to left, Ind'p'l's)
418 7aLev Shreve (pitching, right hand at rear level with cap, right profile, name correct)
418 7bLev Shreve (pitching, right hand at rear level with cap, right profile, name incorrect)
419 1 Ed Silch (batting, looking at camera)
419 2 Ed Silch (batting, looking at ball)
419 3aEd Silch (fielding, hands head-high, Denvers)
419 3bEd Silch (fielding, hands head-high, Brooklyns)
419 4aEd Silch (ball in hands above head, Brooklyns)
419 4bEd Silch (ball in hands above head, Denvers)
419 5aEd Silch (throwing, Brooklyns)
419 5bEd Silch (throwing, Denvers)
420 1aMike Slattery (batting, N.Y.)
420 1bMike Slattery (batting, New Yorks)
420 2aMike Slattery (fielding, hands chest-high, N.Y.)
420 2bMike Slattery (fielding, hands chest-high, New York)
420 3 Mike Slattery (fielding, left hand extended head-high)
420 4aMike Slattery (ready to pitch, N.Y.)
420 4bMike Slattery (ready to pitch, New Yorks)
420 4cMike Slattery (ready to pitch, New York PL)
420 5aMike Slattery (right hand across body by left thigh, N.Y.)
420 5bMike Slattery (right hand across body by left thigh, New Yorks)
421 1 Skyrocket Smith (batting, ball about thigh-high, Louisville)
421 2 Skyrocket Smith (ball in hands head-high on left, Louisville)
421 3 Skyrocket Smith (catching, stooping, hands by right knee, Louisville)
421 4 Skyrocket Smith (stooping to field grounder by right foot, Louisville)
422 1 Phenomenal Smith (portrait, no team designation)
422 2aPhenomenal Smith (pitching, hands above waist, Baltimores)
422 2bPhenomenal Smith (pitching, hands above waist, Athletics)
422 3aPhenomenal Smith (pitching, hands by right shoulder, Baltimores)
422 3bPhenomenal Smith (pitching, hands by right shoulder, Athletics)
422 4aPhenomenal Smith (batting, Baltimores)
422 4bPhenomenal Smith (batting, Athleticss)
422 5aPhenomenal Smith (pitching, left hand neck-high, both ears visible, Baltimores)
422 5bPhenomenal Smith (pitching, left hand neck-high, both ears visible, Athletics)
422 6 Phenomenal Smith (pitching, left hand shoulder-high, left ear only visible, Baltimores)
423 1 Mike Smith (batting, looking at approaching ball, Cincinnati)
423 2aMike Smith (pitching, hands at chest, E. Smith on front, Cincinnati)
423 2bMike Smith (pitching, hands at chest, Smith on front, Cincinnati)
423 2cMike Smith (pitching, hands at chest, Cincinnatti)
423 3aMike Smith (pitching, left hand chest-high at rear, looking to left, Cincinnatis)
423 3bMike Smith (pitching, left hand chest-high at rear, looking to left, Cincinnati)
423 3cMike Smith (pitching, left hand chest-high at rear, looking to left, Cincinnatti)
423 4aMike Smith (pitching, left hand head-high, looking at camera, right hand by right thigh, Cincinnatis)
423 4bMike Smith (pitching, left hand head-high, looking at camera, right hand by right thigh, Cincinnati)
423 5 Mike Smith (pitching, left hand head-high, glancing to left, right arm across waist, Cincinnati)
424 1 Sam Smith (pitching, hands at throat, ball visible between palms, Des Moines)
424 2 Sam Smith (pitching, ball in right hand by face, Des Moines)
424 3aSam Smith (fielding grounder, no comma after P., Des Moines)
424 3bSam Smith (fielding grounder, comma after P., Des Moines)
424 4 Sam Smith (pitching, hands at throat, ball not visible, Des Moines)
425 1aGermany Smith (hands on knees, Brooklyn)
425 1cGermany Smith (hands on knees, Brooklyn's)
425 2aGermany Smith (batting, looking at camera, Smith on front, Brooklyns)
425 2bGermany Smith (batting, looking at camera, G. Smith on front, Brooklyns)
425 2cGermany Smith (batting, looking at camera, Geo. Smith on front, Brooklyns)
425 3aGermany Smith (batting, looking at ball, comma after S.S., Brooklyns)
425 3bGermany Smith (batting, looking at ball, no comma after S.S., Brooklyns)
425 4aGermany Smith (fielding grounder, Smith on front, Brooklyn's)
425 4bGermany Smith (fielding grounder, Geo. Smith on front, Brooklyns)
425 5aGermany Smith (throwing, Smith on front, Brooklyns)
425 5bGermany Smith (throwing, G. Smith on front, Brooklyns)
426 1aPap Smith (fielding grounder with right hand, S.S., Pittsburg)
426 1bPap Smith (fielding grounder with right hand, Short Stop, Pittsburg)
426 1cPap Smith (fielding grounder with right hand, Pittsburgs)
426 1dPap Smith (fielding grounder with right hand, Bostons)
426 2aPap Smith (batting, S.S., Pittsburg)
426 2bPap Smith (batting, Short Stop, Pittsburg)
426 2cPap Smith (batting, S.S., Pittsburgs)
426 3aPap Smith (hands on knees, S.S., Pittsburg)
426 3bPap Smith (hands on knees, Short Stop, Pittsburg)
426 3cPap Smith (hands on knees, Pittsburgh)
426 3dPap Smith (hands on knees, Pittsburgs)
426 4aPap Smith (fielding grounder with both hands, S.S., Pittsburg)
426 4bPap Smith (fielding grounder with both hands, Short Stop, Pittsburg)
426 4cPap Smith (fielding grounder with both hands, Pittsburgh)
427 1aNick Smith (fielding, hands head-high, feet together, St. Josephs)
427 1bNick Smith (fielding, hands head-high, feet together, St. Joe)
427 2aNick Smith (fielding, hands head-high, feet apart, St. Josephs)
427 2bNick Smith (fielding, hands head-high, feet apart, St. Joe)
427 3 Nick Smith (batting, looking at camera, St. Josephs)
427 4aNick Smith (batting, looking down at bat, St. Josephs)
427 4bNick Smith (batting, looking down at bat, St. Joe)
427 5 Nick Smith (fielding, hands at right knee, St. Josephs)
428 1 P.T. Somers (batting)
428 2 P.T. Somers (arms folded)
428 3 P.T. Somers (pitching, looking to left)
428 4 P.T. Somers (pitching, looking to right)
429 1aJoe Sommer (sliding, name correct)
429 1bJoe Sommers (Sommer) (sliding, name incorrect, Baltimores)
429 2aJoe Sommer (fielding grounder, name correct)
429 2bJoe Sommers (Sommer) (fielding grounder, name incorrect, Baltimores)
429 3 Joe Sommers (Sommer) (throwing, Baltimores)
429 4 Joe Sommers (Sommer) (fielding, hands above head, Baltimores)
429 5aJoe Sommer (batting, name correct)
429 5bJoe Sommers (Sommer) (batting, incorrect, Baltimores)
430 1 Pete Sommers (batting, Chicago's)
430 2aPete Sommers (fielding, ball by hands chest-high, Chicago's)
430 2bPete Sommers (fielding, ball by hands chest-high, New Yorks (NL))
430 3 Pete Sommers (fielding, hands head-high, Chicago's)
430 4 Pete Sommers (fielding, right hand above head, Chicagos)
430 5 Pete Sommers (fielding, arms extended left at waist, Chicago's)
430 6 Pete Sommers (portrait, Chicagos)
431 1aLittle Bill Sowders (in light uniform, pitching, hands at throat, Sowders on front, Boston)
431 1bLittle Bill Sowders (in light uniform, pitching, hands at throat, Bostons)
431 1cLittle Bill Sowders (in light uniform, pitching, hands at throat, W. Sowders on front, Boston)
431 2aLittle Bill Sowders (in light uniform, pitching, ball in right hand chin-high, left elbow held up shoulder-high, Bostons)
431 2bLittle Bill Sowders (in light uniform, pitching, ball in right hand chin-high, left elbow held up shoulder-high, Boston)
431 3aLittle Bill Sowders (in light uniform, pitching, ball in right hand cap-high, left hand waist-high, Bostons)
431 3bLittle Bill Sowders (in light uniform, pitching, ball in right hand cap-high, left hand waist-high, Boston)
431 4aLittle Bill Sowders (in light uniform, pitching, right hand forward head-high, ball just released, Sowders on front, Boston)
431 4bLittle Bill Souders (Sowders) (in light uniform, pitching, right hand forward head-high, ball just released, Bostons)
431 4cLittle Bill Sowders (in light uniform, pitching, right hand forward head-high, ball just released, W. Sowders on front, Bostons)
431 5aLittle Bill Sowders (in light uniform, hands at sides, ball at top right, Bostons)
431 5bLittle Bill Sowders (in light uniform, hands at sides, ball at top right, Boston)
431 6aLittle Bill Sowders (in light uniform, bat at ready by head, Bostons)
431 6bLittle Bill Sowders (in light uniform, bat at ready position by head, Boston)
431 7aLittle Bill Sowders (in light uniform, batting, ball cap-high, Bostons)
431 7bLittle Bill Sowders (in light uniform, batting, ball cap-high, Boston)
432 1 John Sowders (in dark uniform, pitching, hands at chest, St. Pauls)
432 2aJohn Sowders (in dark uniform, fielding, ball in right hand thigh-high, St. Paul)
432 2bJohn Sowders (in dark uniform, fielding, ball in right hand thigh-high, St. Pauls)
432 3 John Sowders (in dark uniform, pitching, ball in left hand chin-high, Kansas Citys)
432 4aJohn Sowders (in dark uniform, batting, Kansas City)
432 4bJohn Sowders (in dark uniform, batting, Kansas Citys)
433 1 Charlie Sprague (batting, light cap)
433 2 Charlie Sprague (batting, dark cap)
433 3 Charlie Sprague (bat at side in hand)
433 4 Charlie Sprague (pitching, hands at waist, light cap)
433 5 Charlie Sprague (pitching, hands at waist, dark cap)
433 6 Charlie Sprague (pitching, left hand head-high, light cap)
433 7aCharlie Sprague (pitching, left hand head-high, no cap, Sprague on front, Chicago)
433 7bCharlie Sprague (pitching, left hand head-high, no cap, C.W. Sprague on front, Chicago)
433 7cCharlie Sprague (pitching, left hand head-high, no cap, Sprague on front, Clevelands)
433 7dCharlie Sprague (pitching, left hand head-high, no cap, C.W.Sprague on front, Clevelands)
433 8 Charlie Sprague (pitching, left hand extended forward, no cap)
434 1 Ed Sproat (bat at ready position on shoulder)
434 2 Ed Sproat (batting, ball thigh-high)
434 3 Ed Sproat (pitching, hands at chin)
434 4 Ed Sproat (pitching, right hand head-high)
434 5 Ed Sproat (pitching, right hand waist-high)
435 1aHarry Staley (pitching, hands at chest, St. Louis Whites)
435 1bHarry Staley (pitching, hands at chest, Pittsburgs)
435 1cHarry Staley (pitching, hands at chest, Pittsburghs)
435 2aHarry Staley (pitching, right hand neck-high, right heel off ground, St. Louis Whites)
435 2bHarry Staley (pitching, right hand neck-high, right heel off ground, Pittsburgs)
435 2cHarry Staley (pitching, right hand neck-high, right heel off ground, St. Louis Whites)
435 3 Harry Staley (pitching, right hand chest-high, both heels on ground)
435 4aHarry Staley (bat at ready, looking at camera, name correct)
435 4bHarry Stoley (Staley) (bat at ready, looking at camera, name incorrect)
435 5 Harry Staley (batting, ball by horizontal bat)
436 1aDan Stearns (fielding, hands neck-high, Kansas City)
436 1bDan Stearns (fielding, hands neck-high, Kansas Citys)
436 2aDan Stearns (fielding, hands thigh-high, name correct)
436 2bDan Tearns (Stearns) (fielding, hands thigh-high, name incorrect)
436 3 Dan Stearns (throwing, right hand thigh-high)
436 4 Dan Stearns (batting)
437 1aCannonball Stemmeyer (pitching, hands at chest, name correct)
437 1bCannonball Stemmyer (Stemmeyer) (pitching, hands at chest, name incorrect)
437 2aCannonball Stemmeyer (batting, white uniform, name correct)
437 2bCannonball Stemmyer (Stemmeyer) (batting, white uniform, name incorrect)
437 3aCannonball Stemmeyer (pitching, right hand head-high, white uniform, name correct)
437 3bCannonball Stemmyer (Stemmeyer) (pitching, right hand head-high, white uniform, name incorrect)
437 4aCannonball Stemmeyer (ball in right hand waist high, name correct)
437 4bCannonball Stemmyer (Stemmeyer) (ball in right

hand waist high, name incorrect)
437 5 Cannonball Stemmyer (Stemmeyer) (batting, dark uniform)
437 6 Cannonball Stemmeyer (right hand vertically above head)
438 1 B.F. Stephens (batting)
438 2 B.F. Stephens (catching)
438 3 B.F. Stephens (ready to pitch)
439 1 John Sterling (bat in right hand, looking at camera)
439 2 John Sterling (batting, looking down at ball)
439 3 John Sterling (pitching, hands at chest)
439 4 John Sterling (pitching, right hand thigh-high)
439 51 Stockwell (batting)
440 1aHarry Stovey (hands on knees, no comma after L.F.)
440 1bHarry Stovey (hands on knees, comma after L.F.)
440 2 Harry Stovey (bat in hand at side)
440 3aHarry Stovey (bat at ready position by head, no comma after L.F.)
440 3cHarry Stovey (bat at ready position by head, comma after L.F.)
440 4 Harry Stovey (bat at ready position, horizontal)
440 5aHarry Stovey (fielding, hands above head, no comma after L.F., Athletics)
440 5bHarry Stovey (fielding, hands above head, comma after L.F., Athletics)
440 5cHarry Stovey (fielding, hands above head, Bostons (PL))
440 6 Harry Stovey (fielding, hands at chest)
440 7 Harry Stovey (fielding, right hand above head)
440 8 Harry Stovey (throwing)
441 1 Scott Stratton (batting)
441 2aScott Stratton (pitching, hands at chest, Louisville)
441 2bScott Stratton (pitching, hands at chest, Louisvilles)
441 3aScott Stratton (pitching, right hand at side head-high, Louisville)
441 3bScott Stratton (pitching, right hand at side head-high, Louisvilles)
441 4aScott Stratton (pitching, right hand forward head-high, Louisville)
441 4bScott Stratton (pitching, right hand forward head-high, Louisvilles)
441 5aScott Stratton (underhand throw, right hand waist-high, Louisville)
441 5bScott Stratton (underhand throw, right hand waist-high, Louisvilles)
442 1aJoe Straus (Strauss) (kneeling looking left, Omahas)
442 1bJoe Struck (Strauss) (kneeling looking left, Milwaukee)
442 2 Joe Straus (Strauss) (kneeling, looking to right)
442 3 Joe Straus (Strauss) (throwing)
442 4aJoe Straus (Strauss) (fielding, stooping, hands waist-high, Omahas)
442 4bJoe Strauss (fielding, stooping, hands waist-high, Omahas, W.A.)
442 4cJoe Straus (Strauss) (fielding, stooping, hands waist-high, Milwaukee)
442 5 Joe Straus (Strauss) (fielding, stooping, hands by right ankle)
442 6 Joe Straus (Strauss) (batting)
443 1 Cub Stricker (batting)
443 2 Cub Stricker (fielding ball by left foot)
443 3 Cub Stricker (fielding, hands above head)
444 1aMarty Sullivan (dark uniform, throwing, right hand head-high, Chicago's)
444 1bMarty Sullivan (dark uniform, throwing, right hand head-high, Chicago)
444 2aMarty Sullivan (dark uniform, fielding, hands chest-high, Chicago's)
444 2bMarty Sullivan (dark uniform, fielding, hands chest-high, Chicago)
444 2cMarty Sullivan (dark uniform, fielding, hands chest-high, Indianapolis)
444 3 Marty Sullivan (dark uniform, batting, looking at camera, Chicago's)
444 4 Marty Sullivan (dark uniform, bat in hand at side, Chicago's)
444 5aMarty Sullivan (dark uniform, batting, looking at approaching ball, Chicago's)
444 5cMarty Sullivan (dark uniform, batting, looking at approaching ball, Indianapolis)
445 1 Mike Sullivan (light shirt, bat at ready position on base, Athletics)
445 2 Mike Sullivan (light shirt, hands on knees, Athletics)
445 3 Mike Sullivan (light shirt, sliding, Athletics)
446 1aBilly Sunday (fielding, hands thigh-high, Chicago)
446 1bBilly Sunday (fielding, hands thigh-high, Pittsburgs)
446 2aBilly Sunday (batting, Chicago)
446 2bBilly Sunday (batting, Pittsburghs)
446 3aBilly Sunday (throwing, Chicago)
446 3bBilly Sunday (throwing, Pittsburgs)
446 4aBilly Sunday (fielding, hands chin-high, Chicago)
446 4bBilly Sunday (fielding, hands chin-high, Pittsburgs)
446 5aBilly Sunday (bat in hand at side, Chicago)
446 5bBilly Sunday (bat in hand at side, Pittsburghs)
447 1 Sy Sutcliffe (fielding grounder)
447 2 Sy Sutcliffe (fielding, hands neck-high)
447 3 Sy Sutcliffe (fielding, hands above waist)
447 4 Sy Sutcliffe (batting, looking at camera)
447 5 Sy Sutcliffe (batting, looking at ball)
448 1aEzra Sutton (fielding, hands shoulder-high, 3d B.)
448 1bEzra Sutton (fielding, hands shoulder-high, Third Base)
448 2aEzra Sutton (throwing, hands chest-high, 3d B.)
448 2bEzra Sutton (throwing, hands chest-high, Third Base)
448 3aEzra Sutton (fielding grounder, 3d B.)
448 3bEzra Sutton (fielding grounder, Third Base)
448 3cEzra Sutton (fielding grounder, 2d B.)
448 4aEzra Sutton (batting, ball above bat, 3d B.)
448 4bEzra Sutton (batting, ball above bat, Third Base)
448 5aEzra Sutton (bat in hand at side, 3d B.)
448 5bEzra Sutton (bat in hand at side, Third Base)
448 5cEzra Sutton (bat in hand at side, 2nd B.)
448 6aEzra Sutton (throwing, right hand just releasing ball, 3d B.)
448 6bEzra Sutton (throwing, right hand just releasing ball, Third Base)
448 7aEzra Sutton (batting, looking down at ball, 3d B., Boston)
448 7bEzra Sutton (batting, looking down at ball, Third Base)
448 7cEzra Sutton (batting, looking down at ball, 3d B., Milwaukees)
448 7dEzra Sutton (batting, looking down at ball, 3d B. Milwaukee)
449 1aEd Swartwood (fielding, hands above head, Brooklyn)
449 1bEd Schwartwood (Swartwood) (fielding, hands above head, Des Moines)
449 2aEd Swartwood (fielding, kneeling, hands ankle-high, Brooklyn)
449 2bEd Schwartwood (Swartwood) (fielding, kneeling, hands ankle-high, Des Moines)
449 3aEd Schwartwood (Swartwood) (on ground, right hand on base)
449 4aEd Schwartwood (Swartwood) (tagging player, Des Moines)
449 4bEd Schwartwood (Swartwood) (tagging player, Hamlts)
450 1aPark Swartzel (batting, no comma after P.)
450 1bPark Swartzel (batting, comma after P.)
450 2aPark Swartzel (fielding, stooping, hands cupped, Kansas City)
450 2bPark Swartzel (fielding, stooping, hands cupped, Kansas Citys)
450 3 Park Swartzel (pitching, hands by left shoulder)
450 4 Park Swartzel (pitching, ball in right hand thigh-high)
450 5 Park Swartzel (pitching, right hand by head)
450 6 Park Swartzel (in jacket, arms at sides)
451 1aPete Sweeney (hands on knees, name correct)
451 1bPete Sweeny (Sweeney) (hands on knees, name incorrect, Washington)
451 1cPete Sweeny (Sweeney) (hands on knees, name incorrect, Washingtons)
451 2aPete Sweeny (Sweeney) (batting, Washington)
451 2bPete Sweeny (Sweeney) (batting, Washingtons)
451 3aPete Sweeny (Sweeney) (fielding, hands head-high, Washington)
451 3bPete Sweeny (Sweeney) (fielding, hands head-high, Washingtons)
451 4 Pete Sweeny (Sweeney) (throwing)
451 51Louis Sylvester (batting)
452 1aPop Tate (hands on knees, C.)
452 1bPop Tate (hands on knees, Catcher)
452 2aPop Tate (batting, C., Boston)
452 2bPop Tate (batting, Catcher)
452 2cPop Tate (batting, C., Baltimores)
452 3aPop Tate (fielding, hands chest-high, Catcher)
452 3bPop Tate (fielding, hands chest-high, E.C. Tate on front, C., Boston)
452 3cPop Tate (fielding, hands chest-high, Baltimores)
452 3ePop Tate (fielding, hands chest-high, Tate on front, C., Boston)
453 1aPatsy Tebeau (bat by head, looking at camera, Chicago)
453 1bPatsy Tebeau (bat by head, looking at camera, Clevelands)
453 2aPatsy Tebeau (batting, ball thigh-high, Chicago)
453 2bPatsy Tebeau (batting, ball thigh-high, Clevelands)
453 3aPatsy Tebeau (fielding, hands by right ankle, Tebeau on front)
453 3bPatsy Tebeau (fielding, hands by right ankle, Oliver Tebeau on front)
453 4aPatsy Tebeau (ball in right hand chest-high, Chicago)
453 4bPatsy Tebeau (ball in right hand chest-high, Clevelands)
453 5 Patsy Tebeau (ball in left hand knee-high)
454 1 John Tener (ball in right hand cap-high, arm bent)
454 2 John Tener (ball in right hand chin-high, arm straight)
454 3 John Tener (ball in right hand thigh-high)
454 4 John Tener (ball in hands by right shoulder)
454 5 John Tener (batting)
455 1aAdonis Terry (throwing, pivoting on right foot)
455 2aAdonis Terry (pitching, hands chest-high, P., Brooklyn)
455 2bAdonis Terry (pitching, hands chest-high, Brooklyns)
455 2cAdonis Terry (pitching, hands chest-high, Pitcher, Brooklyn)
455 3aAdonis Terry (batting, P.)
455 3cAdonis Terry (batting, Pitcher)
455 4 Adonis Terry (throwing, arms extended horizontally)
455 5 Adonis Terry (fielding, hands chest-high)
456 1 Big Sam Thompson (batting, ball chest-high)
456 2 Big Sam Thompson (bat at ready position at 45 degrees)
456 3aBig Sam Thompson (arms folded, Detroits)
456 3bBig Sam Thompson (arms folded, Phil'a (NL))
456 4aBig Sam Thompson (bat in hand at side, Detroits)
456 4bBig Sam Thompson (bat in hand at side, Phila's)
456 4cBig Sam Thompson (bat in hand at side, Philadelphia)
456 4dBig Sam Thompson (bat in hand at side, Philadelphias)
456 5 Big Sam Thompson (batting, ball above head)
457 1aSilent Mike Tiernan (ball in hands above waist, R.F.)
457 1bSilent Mike Tiernan (ball in hands above waist, C.F.)
457 2 Silent Mike Tiernan (fielding, hands chest-high)
457 3 Silent Mike Tiernan (fielding grounder)
457 4aSilent Mike Tiernan (throwing, left hand chin-high, R.F.)
457 4bSilent Mike Tiernan (throwing, left hand chin-high, C.F.)
457 5aSilent Mike Tiernan (sliding, R.F.)
457 5bSilent Mike Tiernan (sliding, C.F.)
457 6aSilent Mike Tiernan (batting, N.Y's)
457 6bSilent Mike Tiernan (batting, New Yorks)
458 1 Cannonball Titcomb (batting)
458 2aCannonball Titcomb (bat in hand at side, N.Y.)
458 2bCannonball Titcomb (bat in hand at side, New Yorks)
458 3 Cannonball Titcomb (pitching, looking front)
458 4 Cannonball Titcomb (pitching, right profile)
458 5 Cannonball Titcomb (pitching, right arm across body, hand at thigh)
459 1 Buster Tomney (batting)
459 2 Buster Tomney (fielding, hands by right foot)
459 3 Buster Tomney (fielding, hands above waist)
459 4 Buster Tomney (fielding, hands above head)
460 1 Stephen Toole (pitching, left hand extended chin-high)
460 2 Stephen Toole (pitching, hands shoulder-high)
460 3aStephen Toole (pitching, ball in left hand above head, Brooklyn)
460 3bStephen Toole (pitching, ball in left hand above head, Rochesters)
460 4aStephen Toole (batting, Brooklyn)
460 4bStephen Toole (batting, Rochesters)
460 5 Stephen Toole (pitching, hands at chest)
461 1 Sleepy Townsend (bat at ready position behind head)
461 2aSleepy Townsend (bat at ready position, nearly horizontal, no comma after C.)
461 2bSleepy Townsend (bat at ready position, nearly horizontal, comma after C.)
461 3aSleepy Townsend (fielding, hands chest-high, no comma after C.)
461 3bSleepy Townsend (fielding, hands chest-high, comma after C.)
462 1 Bill Traffley (fielding, hands above head)
462 2 Bill Traffley (fielding, hands chest-high)
462 3 Bill Traffley (hands on thighs)
462 4 Bill Traffley (throwing)
463 1aGeorge Treadway (batting, looking at ball, Denver)
463 1bGeorge Tredway (Treadway) (batting, looking at ball, St. Pauls)
463 2aGeorge Treadway (fielding, hands thigh-high, St. Paul)
463 2bGeorge Tredway (Treadway) (fielding, hands thigh-high, St. Pauls)
463 3 George Tredway (Treadway) (fielding, hands chin-high)
463 4 George Tredway (Treadway) (fielding, hands chest-high)
463 5 George Tredway (Treadway) (batting, facing front)
464 1 Sam Trott (fielding, hands neck-high)
464 2aSam Trott (throwing, left hand head-high, Baltimores)
464 2bSam Trott (throwing, left hand head-high, Newarks)
464 3aSam Trott (fielding, hands knee-high, Baltimores)
464 3bSam Trott (fielding, hands knee-high, Newarks)
464 4aSam Trott (hand on thighs, Baltimores)
464 4bSam Trott (hands on thighs, Newarks)
464 5aSam Trott (batting, Baltimores)
464 5bSam Trott (batting, Newarks)
464 6 Oyster Burns (Trott tagging Burns)
464 6 Sam Trott (Trott tagging Burns)
465 1 Tom Tucker (fielding, hands ankle-high)
465 2 Tom Tucker (fielding, hands chin-high)
465 3 Tom Tucker (throwing)
465 4 Tom Tucker (ball in hands at chest)
465 5 Tom Tucker (batting)
466 1aA.M. Tuckerman (batting, looking at camera, St. Paul)
466 1bA.M. Tuckerman (batting, looking at camera, St. Pauls)
466 2aA.M. Tuckerman (batting, looking down at bat, St. Paul)
466 2bA.M. Tuckerman (batting, looking down at bat, St. Pauls)
466 3 A.M. Tuckerman (pitching, hands at chest)
466 4aA.M. Tuckerman (pitching, right hand head-high, St. Paul)
466 4bA.M. Tuckerman (pitching, right hand head-high, St. Pauls)
466 5 A.M. Tuckerman (pitching, right hand above head)
467 1 George Turner (batting, looking at camera)
467 2 George Turner (batting, looking down at ball)
467 3 George Turner (fielding, hands waist-high)
467 4 George Turner (fielding, hands head-high)
467 5 George Turner (stooping to catch ball by left knee)
468 1aLarry Twitchell (batting, Detroits)
468 1bLarry Twitchell (batting, Clevelands)
468 2aLarry Twitchell (pitching, hands by chest, Detroits)
468 2cLarry Twitchell (pitching, hands by chest, Clevelands)
468 3aLarry Twitchell (pitching, right hand head-high, Twitchell on front, Detroits)
468 3bLarry Twitchell (pitching, right hand head-high, L.G. Twitchell on front, Detroits)
468 3cLarry Twitchell (pitching, right hand head-high, Clevelands)
469 1 Jim Tyng (batting, looking at camera)
469 2 Jim Tyng (bat in hand at side)
469 3 Jim Tyng (pitching, hands at chest)
470 1aBill Van Dyke (fielding, Toledos)
470 1bBill Van Dyke (fielding, Des Moines)
470 2 Bill Van Dyke (sliding)
471 1aRip Van Haltren (batting, Chicago)
471 1bRip Van Haltren (batting, Chicagos)
471 1cRip Van Haltren (batting, Chicago's)
471 2 Rip Van Haltren (pitching, right hand at right thigh)
471 3aRip Van Haltren (pitching, hands above center of belt, Chicago)
471 3bRip Van Haltren (pitching, hands above center of belt, Chicagos)
471 3cRip Van Haltren (pitching, hands above center of belt, Chicago's)
471 4 Rip Van Haltren (fielding, hands chest-high)
472 1 Farmer Vaughn (batting, looking at camera)
472 2 Farmer Vaughn (batting, looking down at ball)
472 3 Farmer Vaughn (fielding, stooping, hands knee-high)
472 4 Farmer Vaughn (fielding, stooping, hands by right shoulder)
472 5 Farmer Vaughn (fielding, hands by left shoulder)
472 6 Harry Vaughn (ball in right hand, head-high)
472 51 Veach (kneeling, ball in right hand head-high)
472 52 Veach (fielding, side view, hands stretched forward)
472 53 Veach (fielding, front view, hands just above head)

473 1aLee Viau (batting, Cincinnati)
473 1bLee Viau (batting, Cincinnati (N.L.))
473 2 Lee Viau (pitching, right hand head-high)
473 3aLee Viau (pitching, right hand at chest, looking at camera, no comma after P., Cincinnati)
473 3bLee Viau (pitching, right hand at chest, looking at camera, comma after P., Cincinnati)
473 3cLee Viau (pitching, right hand at chest, looking at camera, Cincinnatis)
473 4aLee Viau (pitching, right hand out waist-high, right profile, no comma after P., Cincinnati)
473 4bLee Viau (pitching, right hand out waist-high, right profile, comma after P., Cincinnati)
473 4cLee Viau (pitching, right hand out waist-high, right profile, Cincinnatti)
473 4dLee Viau (pitching, right hand out waist-high, right profile, Cincinnatis)
473 5aLee Viau (pitching, right hand out thigh-high, looking at camera, Cincinnati)
473 5bLee Viau (pitching, right hand out thigh-high, looking at camera, Cincinnatti)
474 1 Bill Vinton (batting, looking at camera)
474 2 Bill Vinton (batting, looking at ball)
474 3 Bill Vinton (pitching, hands at chest)
474 4 Bill Vinton (pitching, right hand head-high)
475 1 Joe Visner (batting)
475 2 Joe Visner (standing, arms at sides)
475 3 Joe Visner (throwing)
475 4 Joe Visner (fielding, hands chest-high)
475 5 Joe Visner (bending forward, hands on thighs)
476 1 Chris Von Der Ahe (Brown's Champions)
477 1 Reddy Walsh (striped shirt, bat at ready position by head, looking at camera)
477 2 Reddy Walsh (striped shirt, bat at ready position, left profile)
477 3 Reddy Walsh (fielding, hands waist-high)
477 4 Reddy Walsh (fielding, hands neck-high)
477 5 Reddy Walsh (plain uniform, bat at ready position)
478 1aMonte Ward (portrait, looking to left, Capt. John Ward on front)
478 1bMonte Ward (portrait, looking to left, J. Ward on front)
478 1cMonte Ward (portrait, looking to left, J.M. Ward on front)
478 2aMonte Ward (sliding, right hand raised, N.Y's)
478 2bMonte Ward (sliding, right hand raised, New Yorks)
478 3aMonte Ward (cap in right hand at side, left hand on hip, Capt. John Ward on front)
478 3bMonte Ward (cap in right hand at side, left hand on hip, John Ward on front)
478 3cMonte Ward (cap in right hand at side, left hand on hip, J. Ward on front)
478 4aMonte Ward (hands on hips, N.Y's)
478 4bMonte Ward (hands on hips, New Yorks)
478 5aMonte Ward (throwing, right profile, Capt. John Ward on front)
478 5bMonte Ward (throwing, right profile, John Ward on front)
478 6aMonte Ward (batting, N.Y's)
478 6bMonte Ward (batting, New Yorks)
478 7aMonte Ward (hands behind back, N.Y's)
478 7bMonte Ward (hands behind back, New Yorks)
478 8aMonte Ward (sliding, left hand raised, Capt. John Ward on front)
478 8bMonte Ward (sliding, left hand raised, J.M. Ward on front)
478 8cMonte Ward (sliding, left hand raised, Ward on front)
478 9aMonte Ward (throwing, left profile, N.Y's)
478 9bMonte Ward (throwing, left profile, New Yorks)
479 1 E.H. Warner (fielding)
479 2 E.H. Warner (bat in hand at side)
480 1aBill Watkins (portrait, Detroits)
480 1cBill Watkins (portrait, Kansas Citys)
481 1 Farmer Weaver (batting)
481 2 Farmer Weaver (fielding, left hand above head)
481 3 Farmer Weaver (fielding, hands head-high)
481 4 Farmer Weaver (fielding, hands waist-high)
482 1 Count Weber (batting, looking at camera)
482 2aCount Weber (batting, looking down at ball, Sioux City)
482 2bCount Weber (batting, looking down at ball, Sioux Citys)
482 3 Count Weber (pitching, hands at chest)
482 4 Count Weber (pitching, hands waist-high)
482 5aCount Weber (pitching, right hand chin-high, Sioux City)
482 5bCount Weber (pitching, right hand chin-high, Sioux Citys)
483 1 Stump Weidman (pitching, right hand forward, ball released)
483 2 Stump Weidman (batting)
483 3 Stump Weidman (pitching, hands chest-high)
483 4 Stump Weidman (bat in hand at side)
484 1 Bill Weidner (Widner) (batting)
484 2 Bill Weidner (Widner) (fielding grounder)
484 3 Bill Weidner (Widner) (pitching, hands at chest)
484 4 Bill Weidner (Widner) (pitching, right hand neck-high)
484 5aBill Weidner (Widner) (pitching, right hand chest-high, Weidner on front)
484 5bBill Eidner (Widner) (pitching, right hand chest-high, Eidner on front)
485 1 Curt Welsh (Welch) (Brown's Champions)
485 2 Curt Welch (batting, looking at camera, Athletics)
485 3 Curt Welch (batting, looking at ball by bat, Athletics)
485 4aCurt Welch (fielding grounder, name correct, Athletics)
485 4bCurt Welch (fielding grounder, Athletic's)
485 4cCurt Welsh (Welch) (fielding grounder, name incorrect, Athletics)
485 5 Curt Welsh (Welch) (fielding, Athletics)
485 6aCurt Welsh (Welch) (throwing, C.F., Athletics)
485 6bCurt Welsh (Welch) (throwing, L.F., Athletics)
485 7aWill Gleason
485 7aCurt Welsh (Welch)
485 7bWill Gleason
485 7bCurt Welch
486 1aSmiling Mickey Welch (pitching, right hand head-high, name correct, New York)
486 1bSmiling Mickey Welsh (Welch) (pitching, right hand head-high, name incorrect, New York)
486 2aSmiling Mickey Welch (pitching, right hand at right thigh, name correct, New Yorks)
486 2bSmiling Mickey Welsh (Welch) (pitching, right hand at right thigh, name incorrect, New Yorks)
486 2cSmiling Mickey Welch (pitching, right hand at right thigh, New Yorks (N.L.))
486 3aSmiling Mickey Welch (pitching, hands above waist, Welsh on front, New York)
486 3bSmiling Mickey Welch (pitching, hands above waist, Smiling Mickey on front)
486 4aSmiling Mickey Welch (pitching, right arm extended forward, Smiling Mickey on front)
487 1 Jake Wells (holding bat, Kansas City)
487 2 Jake Wells (fielding, Kansas City)
488 1 Frank Wells (fielding, Milwaukee)
489 1 Joe Werrick (tagging)
489 2 Joe Werrick (throwing)
489 3aJoe Werrick (fielding, Louisville)
489 3bJoe Werrick (fielding, St. Pau.)
489 4 Joe Werrick (batting)
490 1 Buck West (batting, looking at camera)
490 2 Buck West (striking, looking down at ball by bat)
490 3 Buck West (fielding, hands by right thigh)
490 4 Buck West (fielding, hands shoulder-high)
490 5 Buck West (fielding low ball)
491 1 Cannonball Weyhing (pitching, hands at throat, Athletics)
491 2aCannonball Weyhing (pitching, right hand chest-high, A.C. Weyhing on front, Athletics)
491 2cCannonball Weyhing (pitching, right hand chest-high, Weyhing on front, Athletics)
491 3aCannonball Weyhing (pitching, right hand cap-high, A.C. Weyhing on front, Athletics)
491 3bCannonball Weyhing (pitching, right hand cap-high, Weyhing on front, Athletics)
492 1aJohn Weyhing (pitching, hands at neck, Athletics)
492 1bJohn Weyhing (pitching, hands at neck, Columbus)
492 2aJohn Weyhing (pitching, left hand out chest-high, Athletics)
493 1aBobby Wheelock (fielding, R.F., Boston)
493 1bBobby Wheelock (fielding, Right Field)
493 1cBobby Wheelock (fielding, R.F., Detroits)
493 2aBobby Wheelock (batting, looking at camera, R.F.)
493 2bBobby Wheelock (batting, looking at camera, Right Field)
493 3aBobby Wheelock (throwing, Right Field)
493 3bBobby Wheelock (throwing, R.F.)
493 4aBobby Wheelock (batting, looking down at ball, R.F.)
493 4bBobby Wheelock (batting, looking down at ball, Right Field)
493 5aBobby Wheelock (hands on hips, R.F.)
493 5bBobby Wheelock (hands on hips, Right Field)
493 6 Bobby Wheelock (bat in hand at side)
493 7 Bobby Wheelock (bat at ready position at 60 degrees, looking at camera)
494 1 Pat Whitacre (Whitaker) (batting)
494 2 Pat Whitacre (Whitaker) (pitching, hands out head-high)
494 3 Pat Whitacre (Whitaker) (pitching, right hand back head-high)
495 1 Pat Whitaker (pitching, hands behind right thigh)
495 2 Pat Whitaker (pitching, hands out above waist)
495 3 Pat Whitaker (pitching, hands neck-high)
495 4 Pat Whitaker (pitching, right hand forward neck-high)
496 1 Deacon White (batting, looking at camera, Detroits)
496 2 Deacon White (batting, looking down at ball, Detroits)
496 3 Deacon White (fielding, hands waist-high, Detroits)
496 4 Deacon White (fielding, hands neck-high, Detroits)
496 5aDeacon White (fielding, hands above head, Detroits)
496 5bDeacon White (fielding, hands above head, Pittsburghs)
496 6aDeacon White (throwing, Detroits)
496 6bDeacon White (throwing, Pittsburghs)
496 7 Deacon White (fielding grounder, hands together by left foot, Detroits)
496 8 Deacon White (fielding grounder with right hand, Detroits)
497 1 Bill White (batting, Louisville)
497 2 Bill White (stooping, ball in left hand on grass, Louisville)
497 3 Bill White (fielding ground ball, Louisville)
497 4 Bill White (throwing, Louisville)
497 5 Bill White (fielding, hands neck-high, Louisville)
498 1aGrasshopper Whitney (batting, looking at camera, P., Washington)
498 1bGrasshopper Whitney (batting, looking at camera, Pitcher, Washington)
498 2aGrasshopper Whitney (pitching, hands at chest, no comma after P., Washington)
498 2bGrasshopper Whitney (pitching, hands at chest, Pitcher, Washington)
498 2cGrasshopper Whitney (pitching, hands at chest, comma after P., Washington)
498 3aGrasshopper Whitney (pitching, right hand waist-high, P., Washington)
498 3bGrasshopper Whitney (pitching, right hand waist-high, Pitcher, Washington)
498 3cGrasshopper Whitney (pitching, right hand waist-high, Indianapolis)
499 1aArt Whitney (white uniform, stooping, dog with paw on his knee, 3d B., Pittsburg)
499 1bArt Whitney (white uniform, stooping, dog with paw on his knee, 3d Base, Pittsburg)
499 1cArt Whitney (white uniform, stooping, dog with paw on his knee, Whitney on front, New Yorks)
499 1dArt Whitney (white uniform, stooping, dog with paw on his knee, A. Whitney on front, New Yorks)
499 2aArt Whitney (white uniform, bending to left, hands thigh-high, 3d B. Pittsburg)
499 2bArt Whitney (white uniform, bending to left, hands thigh-high, 3d Base, Pittsburg)
499 2cArt Whitney (white uniform, bending to left, hands thigh-high, Whitney on front, New Yorks)
499 2dArt Whitney (white uniform, bending to left, hands thigh-high, A. Whitney on front, New Yorks)
499 2eArt Whitney (white uniform, bending to left, hands thigh-high, New York (PL))
499 3aArt Whitney (white uniform, batting, 3d B., Pittsburg)
499 3bArt Whitney (white uniform, batting, 3d Base, Pittsburg)
499 3cArt Whitney (white uniform, batting, New Yorks)
500 1 G. Whitney (dark uniform, batting, looking at camera, St. Joes)
500 2 G. Whitney (dark uniform, batting, looking down at ball, St. Joes)
500 3 G. Whitney (dark uniform, fielding grounder, St. Joes)
500 4 G. Whitney (dark uniform, throwing, St. Joes)
500 5 G. Whitney (dark uniform, fielding, hands at waist, St. Joes)
501 1 James Williams (hat in right hand)
501 2 James Williams (hat on head)
502 1 Ned Williamson (in top hat, looking to right)
502 2 Ned Williamson (fielding, hands neck-high)
502 3aNed Williamson (throwing, Chicago's)
502 3bNed Williamson (throwing, Chicago)
502 3cNed Williamson (throwing, W. Williamson on front, Chicagos)
502 3dNed Williamson (throwing, Chicag.)
502 3eNed Williamson (throwing, C.W. Williamson on front, Chicagos)
502 4aNed Williamson (fielding, hands above head, Chicago's)
502 4bNed Williamson (fielding, hands above head, E. Williamson on front, Chicago)
502 4cNed Williamson (fielding, hands above head, Chica.)
502 4dNed Williamson (fielding, hands above head, C.W. Williamson on front, Chicago)
502 4eNed Williamson (fielding, hands above head, Chicagos)
502 4fNed Williamson (fielding, hands above head, W. Williamson on front, Chicago)
502 5aNed Williamson (arms folded, no comma after S.S., Chicago's)
502 5bNed Williamson (arms folded, comma after S.S., Chicago's)
502 5cNed Williamson (arms folded, Chicago)
502 6aNed Williamson (batting, looking down at ball, Chicago's)
502 6cNed Williamson (batting, looking down at ball, E. Williamson on front, Chicago)
502 6dNed Williamson (batting, looking down at ball, Chicagos)
502 6eNed Williamson (batting, looking down at ball, W. Williamson on front, Chicago)
502 7 Willie Hahm - mascot
502 7 Ned Williamson
503 1 C.H. Willis (pitching, hands in front of cap)
503 2 C.H. Willis (pitching, hands at waist)
503 3 C.H. Willis (pitching, hands out to left chin-high)
503 4 C.H. Willis (pitching, right hand forward head-high)
503 5 C.H. Willis (batting)
504 1aWatt Wilmot (batting, looking down at ball, Washington)
504 1bWatt Wilmot (batting, looking down at ball, Chicagos (N L))
504 2aWatt Wilmot (bat in hand at side, Washingtons)
504 2bWatt Wilmot (bat in hand at side, Chicagos (N L))
504 3aWatt Wilmot (catching, hands thigh-high, Washingtons)
504 3bWatt Wilmot (catching, hands thigh-high, Washington)
504 4aWatt Wilmot (catching, hands at chest, Washingtons)
504 4bWatt Wilmot (catching, hands at chest, Washington)
504 4cWatt Wilmot (catching, hands at chest, Chicagos (N.L.))
504 5aWatt Wilmot (throwing, Washingtons)
504 5bWatt Wilmot (throwing, Washington)
505 1 George Winkleman (Winkelman) (throwing, hands out to right shoulder-high)
505 2 George Winkleman (Winkelman) (pitching, hands chest-high)
505 3 George Winkleman (Winkelman) (pitching, right hand above waist, left hand by left hip)
505 4 George Winkleman (Winkelman) (fielding)
506 1aMedoc Wise (stooping, hands on knees, S.S., Boston)
506 1bMedoc Wise (stooping, hands on knees, Short Stop)
506 1cMedoc Wise (stooping, hands on knees, S.S., Washingtons)
506 2aMedoc Wise (batting, Wise on front, S.S.)
506 2bMedoc Wise (batting, Short Stop)
506 2cMedoc Wise (batting, Sam W. Wise on front, S.S.)
506 3aMedoc Wise (bat in hand at side, S.S.)
506 3bMedoc Wise (bat in hand at side, Short Stop)
506 4aMedoc Wise (portrait, Wise on front, S.S.)
506 4bMedoc Wise (portrait, Short Stop)
506 4cMedoc Wise (portrait, Sam W. Wise on front, S.S.)
507 1 Chicken Wolf (batting, "Louisville" visible on shirt)
507 2aChicken Wolf (batting, team name not visible, Louisville)
507 2bChicken Wolf (batting, team name not visible, Louisvilles)
507 3aChicken Wolf (lying on grass, feet on base, Louisville)
507 3bChicken Wolf (lying on grass, feet on base, Louisvilles)
507 4aChicken Wolf (fielding, hands chin-high, Louisville)
507 4bChicken Wolf (fielding, hands chin-high, Louisvilles)
507 5aChicken Wolf (fielding, hands by right ankle, Louisville)
507 5bChicken Wolf (fielding, hands by right ankle, Louisvilles)
508 1aGeorge "Dandy" Wood (batting, L.F., Phila)
508 1bGeorge "Dandy" Wood (batting, Left Field, Philadelphia)
508 1cGeorge "Dandy" Wood (batting, L.F., Philadelphias)
508 2aGeorge "Dandy" Wood (fielding, hands neck-high,

L.F., Phila)
508 2bGeorge "Dandy" Wood (fielding, hands neck-high, Left Field, Philadelphia)
508 2cGeorge "Dandy" Wood (fielding, hands neck-high, L.F., Philadelphias)
508 3aGeorge "Dandy" Wood (fielding grounder, L.F., Phila)
508 3bGeorge "Dandy" Wood (fielding grounder, Left Field, Philadelphia)
508 3cGeorge "Dandy" Wood (fielding grounder, L.F., Philadelphias)
508 4aGeorge "Dandy" Wood (throwing, L.F., Phila)
508 4bGeorge "Dandy" Wood (throwing, Left Field, Philadelphia)
508 4cGeorge "Dandy" Wood (throwing, L.F., Philadelphias)
509 1 Pete Wood (bat on shoulder, P., Philadelphias)
509 2 Pete Wood (bat at ready position, nearly horizontal, P., Philadelphias)
509 3 Pete Wood (pitching, hands at neck, P., Philadelphia)
509 4 Pete Wood (pitching, right hand forward neck-high, P., Philadelphias)
509 5 Pete Wood (pitching, right hand extended at side head-high, P., Philadelphias)
510 1aHarry Wright (portrait, looking to right, Phila)
510 1bHarry Wright (portrait, looking to right, Phila's)
510 1dHarry Wright (portrait, looking to right, Phila (N L))
510 2 Harry Wright (portrait, looking to left, beard clear of right side of collar)
510 3 Harry Wright (portrait, looking to left, beard just over right side of collar)
511 1 Chief Zimmer (batting)
511 2 Chief Zimmer (fielding, hands chest-high, feet together)
511 3 Chief Zimmer (fielding, hands chest-high, feet well apart)
511 4aChief Zimmer (throwing, Cleveland's)
511 4bChief Zimmer (throwing, Clevelands)
512 1 Frank Zinn (fielding grounder)
512 2 Frank Zinn (fielding, hands thigh-high)
512 3 Frank Zinn (fielding, hands head-high)

1888 Old Judge Cabinets (N173)

These large cabinet cards were issued by Goodwin & Co. in 1888 and 1889. They were a popular premium available by exchanging coupons found in Old Judge or Dogs Head brand cigarettes. The cabinet cards consist of 3-3/4" by 5-3/4" photographs affixed to a cardboard backing that measures approximately 4-1/4" by 6-1/2". The mounting is usually a yellow color, but backins have also been found in pink, blue or black. An ad for Olf Judge Cigarettes appears along the bottom of the cabinet. (Cabinets obtained by exchanging coupons from Dogs Head cigarettes include an ad for both Old Judge and Dogs Head, and are considered scarcer.) According to an advertising sheet, cabinets were available of "every prominent player in the National League, Western League and American Association." There are additions to the following checklist that will be included in subsequent editions of this catalog. The poses used for the cabinet photos are enlarged versions of the popular N172 Old Judge cards.

	NR MT	EX	VG
Common Player:	300.00	150.00	90.00
(1) Bob Allen	300.00	150.00	90.00
(2) Ed Andrews (both hands at shoulder level)	300.00	150.00	90.00
(3) Ed Andrews (one hand above head)	300.00	150.00	90.00
(4) Ed Andrews, Buster Hoover	600.00	300.00	180.00
(5) Cap Anson (Dogs Head)	4500.	2250.	1350.
(6) Fido Baldwin (Chicago, pitching)	300.00	150.00	90.00
(7) Fido Baldwin (Chicago, with bat)	300.00	150.00	90.00
(8) Kid Baldwin (Detroit)	300.00	150.00	90.00
(9) John Barnes	300.00	150.00	90.00
(10) Bald Billy Barnie	300.00	150.00	90.00
(11) Charles Bassett	300.00	150.00	90.00
(12) Charles Bastian (Chicago)	300.00	150.00	90.00
(13) Charles Bastian (Philly)	300.00	150.00	90.00
(14) Bastian, Pop Schriver	600.00	300.00	180.00
(15) Ed Beatin	300.00	150.00	90.00
(16) Charles Bennett (Dogs H)	300.00	150.00	90.00
(17) Louis Bierbauer	300.00	150.00	90.00
(18) Ned Bligh	300.00	150.00	90.00
(19) Bogart	300.00	150.00	90.00
(20) Handsome Boyle (Indy)	300.00	150.00	90.00
(21) Honest John Boyle (St. Louis, bat at side)	300.00	150.00	90.00
(22) Honest John Boyle (St. Louis, bat in air)	300.00	150.00	90.00
(23) Grin Bradley	300.00	150.00	90.00
(24) Dan Brouthers (catching)	1375.	687.00	412.00
(25) Dan Brouthers (with bat, Dogs Head)	1300.	650.00	390.00
(26) California Brown (Boston, catching)	300.00	150.00	90.00
(27) California Brown (Boston, with bat)	300.00	150.00	90.00
(28) Thomas Brown (New York, throwing)	300.00	150.00	90.00
(29) Thomas Brown (New York, with bat)	300.00	150.00	90.00
(30) Charles Brynan (Chicago)	300.00	150.00	90.00
(31) Charles Brynan (Des Moines)	300.00	150.00	90.00
(32) Al Buckenberger	300.00	150.00	90.00
(33) Dick Buckley	300.00	150.00	90.00
(34) Charles Buffinton (hands chest high)	300.00	150.00	90.00
(35) Charles Buffinton (right hand above head, Dogs Head)	300.00	150.00	90.00
(36) Black Jack Burdock	300.00	150.00	90.00
(37) James Burns (Kansas City)	300.00	150.00	90.00
(38) Oyster Burns (Brooklyn)	300.00	150.00	90.00
(39) Thomas Burns (Chicago, bat at side)	300.00	150.00	90.00
(40) Thomas Burns (Chicago, bat in air)	300.00	150.00	90.00
(41) Thomas Burns (catching)	300.00	150.00	90.00
(42) Doc Bushong	300.00	150.00	90.00
(43) Hick Carpenter	300.00	150.00	90.00
(44) Jumbo Cartwright	300.00	150.00	90.00
(45) Parisian Bob Caruthers (holding ball)	300.00	150.00	90.00
(46) Parisian Bob Caruthers (with bat)	300.00	150.00	90.00
(47) Daniel Casey	300.00	150.00	90.00
(48) Icebox Chamberlain (boths hands at chest level)	300.00	150.00	90.00
(49) Icebox Chamberlain (right hand extended)	300.00	150.00	90.00
(50) Chamberlain (with bat)	300.00	150.00	90.00
(51) Cupid Childs	300.00	150.00	90.00
(52) Clark (Brooklyn, catching)	300.00	150.00	90.00
(53) Bob Clark (Brooklyn, right hand shoulder high)	300.00	150.00	90.00
(54) Bob Clark (Dogs Head, Mickey Hughes)	300.00	150.00	90.00
(55) Dad Clark (Clarke) (Chicago)	300.00	150.00	90.00
(56) John Clarkson (Dogs Head)	1950.	975.00	585.00
(57) John Clarkson (right arm extended)	1375.	687.00	412.00
(58) John Clarkson (with bat)	1375.	687.00	412.00
(59) Jack Clements (hands on knees)	300.00	150.00	90.00
(60) Jack Clements (hands outstretched at neck level)	300.00	150.00	90.00
(61) Jack Clements (with bat)	300.00	150.00	90.00
(62) Monk Cline	300.00	150.00	90.00
(63) John Coleman (holding ball)	300.00	150.00	90.00
(64) John Coleman (with bat)	300.00	150.00	90.00
(65) Hub Collins	300.00	150.00	90.00
(66) Commy Comiskey (arms folded)	1375.	687.00	412.00
(67) Commy Comiskey (Dogs Head)	1300.	650.00	390.00
(68) Roger Connor (catching)	1375.	687.00	412.00
(69) Roger Connor (hands on knees)	1375.	687.00	412.00
(70) Roger Connor (with bat)	1375.	687.00	412.00
(71) Jim Conway (Kansas City)	300.00	150.00	90.00
(72) Pete Conway (Detroit)	300.00	150.00	90.00
(73) Paul Cook (fielding)	300.00	150.00	90.00
(74) Paul Cook (wearing mask)	300.00	150.00	90.00
(75) Pop Corkhill	300.00	150.00	90.00
(76) Samuel Crane	300.00	150.00	90.00
(77) Lave Cross	300.00	150.00	90.00
(78) Edward Daily	300.00	150.00	90.00
(79) Bill Daley (Boston)	300.00	150.00	90.00
(80) Con Daley (Daily) (Indianapolis)	300.00	150.00	90.00
(81) Abner Dalrymple	300.00	150.00	90.00
(82) Sun Daly (Minneapolis)	300.00	150.00	90.00
(83) Tido Daly (Washington)	300.00	150.00	90.00
(84) Tido Daly (Chicago)	300.00	150.00	90.00
(85) Dell Darling	300.00	150.00	90.00
(86) William Darnbrough	300.00	150.00	90.00
(87) Big Ed Delehanty (bat held at right shoulder)	1600.	800.00	480.00
(88) Big Ed Delehanty (bat held at horizontal level)	1600.	800.00	480.00
(89) Jerry Denny	300.00	150.00	90.00
(90) Jim Devlin (pitching)	300.00	150.00	90.00
(91) Jim Devlin (sliding)	300.00	150.00	90.00
(92) Jim Donnelly	300.00	150.00	90.00
(93) Home Run Duffe (Duffee) (bending)	300.00	150.00	90.00
(94) Home Run Duffe (Duffee) (catching, standing upright)	300.00	150.00	90.00
(95) Home Run Duffe (Duffee) (with bat)	300.00	150.00	90.00
(96) Hugh Duffy (catching)	1375.	687.00	412.00
(97) Hugh Duffy (fielding)	1375.	687.00	412.00
(98) Hugh Duffy (with bat)	1375.	687.00	412.00
(99) Duck Duke	300.00	150.00	90.00
(100) Sure Shot Dunlap (arms at side)	300.00	150.00	90.00
(101) Sure Shot Dunlap (Dogs H)	300.00	150.00	90.00
(102) Jesse Duryea	300.00	150.00	90.00
(103) Frank Dwyer (bat at side)	300.00	150.00	90.00
(104) Frank Dwyer (bat in air)	300.00	150.00	90.00
(105) Frank Dwyer (ball in hands)	300.00	150.00	90.00
(106) Frank Dwyer (hands cupped at chest)	300.00	150.00	90.00
(107) Billy Earle	300.00	150.00	90.00
(108) Red Ehret	300.00	150.00	90.00
(109) Dude Esterbrook	300.00	150.00	90.00
(110) Buck Ewing (New York, bat at side)	1375.	687.00	412.00
(111) Buck Ewing (New York, bat in air)	1375.	687.00	412.00
(112) Buck Ewing (New York, hands at head level)	1375.	687.00	412.00
(113) Buck Ewing (New York, hands on knees)	1375.	687.00	412.00
(114) Willie Breslin-mascot, Buck Ewing	1300.	650.00	390.00
(115) Long John Ewing (Louisville)	300.00	150.00	90.00
(116) Jay Faatz	300.00	150.00	90.00
(117) Bill Farmer	300.00	150.00	90.00
(118) Sid Farrar (hands outstretched at head level)	300.00	150.00	90.00
(119) Sid Farrar (stooping)	300.00	150.00	90.00
(120) Duke Farrell (fielding)	300.00	150.00	90.00
(121) Duke Farrell (hands on knees)	300.00	150.00	90.00
(122) Frank Fennelly	300.00	150.00	90.00
(123) Charlie Ferguson	300.00	150.00	90.00
(124) Alex Ferson	300.00	150.00	90.00
(125) Jocko Fields	300.00	150.00	90.00
(126) Silver Flint (with bat)	300.00	150.00	90.00
(127) Silver Flint (with mask)	300.00	150.00	90.00
(128) Jim Fogarty (catching, hands at neck level)	300.00	150.00	90.00
(129) Jim Fogarty (running to left, hands at head level)	300.00	150.00	90.00
(130) Jim Fogarty (sliding)	300.00	150.00	90.00
(131) Jim Fogarty (with bat)	300.00	150.00	90.00
(132) Elmer Foster (Minneapolis)	300.00	150.00	90.00
(133) Elmer Foster (New York)	300.00	150.00	90.00
(134) Dave Foutz	300.00	150.00	90.00
(135) Shorty Fuller (catching)	300.00	150.00	90.00
(136) Shorty Fuller (hands on knees)	300.00	150.00	90.00
(137) Shorty Fuller (swinging bat)	300.00	150.00	90.00
(138) Chris Fulmer (Dogs Head, Foghorn Tucker)	875.00	437.00	262.00
(139) Pud Galvin	300.00	150.00	90.00
(140) Charlie Ganzel (catching, hands at shoulder level)	300.00	150.00	90.00
(141) Charlie Ganzel (catching, hands at thigh level)	300.00	150.00	90.00
(142) Charlie Ganzel (with bat)	300.00	150.00	90.00
(143) Gid Gardner	300.00	150.00	90.00
(144) Hank Gastreich	300.00	150.00	90.00
(145) Frenchy Genins (bat in air, looking at camera)	300.00	150.00	90.00
(146) Frenchy Genins (swinging at ball)	300.00	150.00	90.00
(147) Bill George	300.00	150.00	90.00
(148) Charlie Getzein	300.00	150.00	90.00
(149) Bobby Gilks	300.00	150.00	90.00
(150) Barney Gilligan	300.00	150.00	90.00
(151) Frank Gilmore	300.00	150.00	90.00
(152) Pebbly Jack Glasscock (Dogs Head)	300.00	150.00	90.00
(153) Pebbly Jack Glasscock (hands on knees)	300.00	150.00	90.00
(154) Pebbly Jack Glasscock (throwing)	300.00	150.00	90.00
(155) Kid Gleason (Philadelphia, fielding)	300.00	150.00	90.00
(156) Kid Gleason (Philadelphia, pitching)	300.00	150.00	90.00
(157) Will Gleason (Louisville)	300.00	150.00	90.00
(158) Mouse Glenn	300.00	150.00	90.00
(159) Piano Legs Gore (fielding)	300.00	150.00	90.00
(160) Piano Legs Gore (with bat)	300.00	150.00	90.00
(161) Henry Gruber	300.00	150.00	90.00
(162) Ad Gumbert (right hand at eye level)	300.00	150.00	90.00
(163) Ad Gumbert (right hand at waist level)	300.00	150.00	90.00
(164) Tom Gunning	300.00	150.00	90.00
(165) Joe Gunson	300.00	150.00	90.00
(166) Bill Hallman	300.00	150.00	90.00
(167) Billy Hamilton (fielding)	1375.	687.00	412.00
(168) Billy Hamilton (with bat)	1375.	687.00	412.00
(169) Ned Hanlon	300.00	150.00	90.00
(170) William Hanrahan	300.00	150.00	90.00
(171) Gill Hatfield (bat at waist)	300.00	150.00	90.00
(172) Hatfield (bat over shoulder)	300.00	150.00	90.00
(173) Gill Hatfield (catching)	300.00	150.00	90.00
(174) Egyptian Healey	300.00	150.00	90.00
(175) Hardie Henderson	300.00	150.00	90.00
(176) Moxie Hengle	300.00	150.00	90.00
(177) John Henry	300.00	150.00	90.00
(178) Paul Hines	300.00	150.00	90.00
(179) Texas Wonder Hoffman	300.00	150.00	90.00
(180) Bug Holliday	300.00	150.00	90.00
(181) Buster Hoover (Philadelphia)	300.00	150.00	90.00
(182) Charles Hoover (Chicago or Kansas City)	300.00	150.00	90.00
(183) Joe Hornung	300.00	150.00	90.00
(184) Dummy Hoy	300.00	150.00	90.00
(185) Nat Hudson	300.00	150.00	90.00
(186) Mickey Hughes (holding ball at chest)	300.00	150.00	90.00
(187) Mickey Hughes (holding ball at side)	300.00	150.00	90.00
(188) Mickey Hughes (right hand extended)	300.00	150.00	90.00
(189) Wild Bill Hutchinson (ball in hand, right heel hidden)	300.00	150.00	90.00
(190) Wild Bill Hutchinson (ball in hand, right heel visible)	300.00	150.00	90.00
(191) Bill Hutchinson (with bat)	300.00	150.00	90.00
(192) Cutrate Irwin (Philadelphia, catching)	300.00	150.00	90.00

(193)	Cutrate Irwin (Philadelphia, throwing)	300.00	150.00	90.00
(194)	John Irwin (Washington)	300.00	150.00	90.00
(195)	A.C. Jantzen	300.00	150.00	90.00
(196)	Spud Johnson	300.00	150.00	90.00
(197)	Johnston (hands on hip)	300.00	150.00	90.00
(198)	Dick Johnston (with bat)	300.00	150.00	90.00
(199)	Tim Keefe (Dogs Head)	1700.	850.00	510.00
(200)	Tim Keefe (hands at chest)	1375.	687.00	412.00
(201)	Tim Keefe (pitching, right hand at head level)	1375.	687.00	412.00
(202)	Tim Keefe (pitching, right hand at waist level)	1375.	687.00	412.00
(203)	Charles Kelly (Philadelphia)	300.00	150.00	90.00
(204)	King Kelly (Boston, Dogs H)	1500.	750.00	450.00
(205)	John Kerins	300.00	150.00	90.00
(206)	Silver King (hands at chest level)	300.00	150.00	90.00
(207)	Silver King (hands at chin)	300.00	150.00	90.00
(208)	William Klusman	300.00	150.00	90.00
(209)	Gus Krock (right hand extended)	300.00	150.00	90.00
(210)	Gus Krock (with bat)	300.00	150.00	90.00
(211)	Willie Kuehne	300.00	150.00	90.00
(212)	Ted Larkin	300.00	150.00	90.00
(213)	Arlie Latham (throwing)	300.00	150.00	90.00
(214)	Arlie Latham (with bat)	300.00	150.00	90.00
(215)	Germany Long	300.00	150.00	90.00
(216)	Tom Lovett (right hand extended)	300.00	150.00	90.00
(217)	Tom Lovett (with bat)	300.00	150.00	90.00
(218)	Denny Lyons (left hand above head)	300.00	150.00	90.00
(219)	Denny Lyons (with bat)	300.00	150.00	90.00
(220)	Connie Mack	4500.	2250.	1350.
(221)	Little Mac Macullar	300.00	150.00	90.00
(222)	Kid Madden (ball in left hand at eye level)	300.00	150.00	90.00
(223)	Kid Madden (ball in hand above head)	300.00	150.00	90.00
(224)	Kid Madden (ball in hands at neck level)	300.00	150.00	90.00
(225)	Jimmy Manning (fielding)	300.00	150.00	90.00
(226)	Jimmy Manning (with bat)	300.00	150.00	90.00
(227)	Lefty Marr	300.00	150.00	90.00
(228)	Leech Maskrey	300.00	150.00	90.00
(229)	Mike Mattimore	300.00	150.00	90.00
(230)	Smiling Al Maul	300.00	150.00	90.00
(231)	Al Mays	300.00	150.00	90.00
(232)	Jimmy McAleer	300.00	150.00	90.00
(233)	Tommy McCarthy (right hand at head level)	1300.	650.00	390.00
(234)	Tommy McCarthy (with bat)	1300.	650.00	390.00
(235)	Deacon McGuire	300.00	150.00	90.00
(236)	Bill McGunnigle	300.00	150.00	90.00
(237)	Ed McKean (hands above head)	300.00	150.00	90.00
(238)	Ed McKean (with bat)	300.00	150.00	90.00
(239)	James McQuaid	300.00	150.00	90.00
(240)	Doggie Miller (Pittsburgh, ball in hands)	300.00	150.00	90.00
(241)	Doggie Miller (Pittsburgh, Dogs Head)	300.00	150.00	90.00
(242)	Joseph Miller (Minneapolis, hands outstretched)	300.00	150.00	90.00
(243)	Joseph Miller (Minneapolis, with bat)	300.00	150.00	90.00
(244)	Jocko Milligan (bat at side)	300.00	150.00	90.00
(245)	Jocko Milligan (bat in air)	300.00	150.00	90.00
(246)	Jocko Milligan (stooping)	300.00	150.00	90.00
(247)	Daniel Minnehan (Minahan)	300.00	150.00	90.00
(248)	Sam Moffet	300.00	150.00	90.00
(249)	Honest John Morrill	300.00	150.00	90.00
(250)	Joseph Mulvey (catching)	300.00	150.00	90.00
(251)	Joseph Mulvey (with bat)	300.00	150.00	90.00
(252)	Pat Murphy	300.00	150.00	90.00
(253)	Miah Murray	300.00	150.00	90.00
(254)	Truthful Jim Mutrie	300.00	150.00	90.00
(255)	Al Myers (Washington)	300.00	150.00	90.00
(256)	George Myers (Indianapolis)	300.00	150.00	90.00
(257)	Tom Nagle	300.00	150.00	90.00
(258)	Billy Nash (hands on knees)	300.00	150.00	90.00
(259)	Billy Nash (throwing)	300.00	150.00	90.00
(260)	Kid Nichols	1800.	900.00	550.00
(261)	Little Nick Nicol, Big John Reilly	600.00	300.00	180.00
(262)	Darby O'Brien (Brooklyn)	300.00	150.00	90.00
(263)	John O'Brien (Cleveland)	300.00	150.00	90.00
(264)	Rowdy Jack O'Connor	300.00	150.00	90.00
(265)	Hank O'Day	300.00	150.00	90.00
(266)	Tip O'Neill (bat held horizontally)	300.00	150.00	90.00
(267)	O'Neill (bat over shoulder)	300.00	150.00	90.00
(268)	Tip O'Neill (fielding)	300.00	150.00	90.00
(269)	Tip O'Neill (throwing)	300.00	150.00	90.00
(270)	Orator Jim O'Rourke (New York, right hand in air)	1375.	687.00	412.00
(271)	Orator Jim O'Rourke (New York, with bat)	1375.	687.00	412.00
(272)	Tom O'Rourke (Boston)	300.00	150.00	90.00
(273)	Dave Orr	300.00	150.00	90.00
(274)	Fred Pfeffer (right hand at neck level)	300.00	150.00	90.00
(275)	Fred Pfeffer (with bat)	300.00	150.00	90.00
(276)	Dick Phelan	300.00	150.00	90.00
(277)	Jack Pickett (right hand at head level)	300.00	150.00	90.00
(278)	Jack Pickett (stooping)	300.00	150.00	90.00
(279)	Jack Pickett (with bat)	300.00	150.00	90.00
(280)	George Pinkney (bat in air, nearly vertical)	300.00	150.00	90.00
(281)	George Pinkney (bat over right shoulder)	300.00	150.00	90.00
(282)	Jim Powell	300.00	150.00	90.00
(283)	Blondie Purcell	300.00	150.00	90.00
(284)	Joe Quinn (ball in hands)	300.00	150.00	90.00
(285)	Joe Quinn (ready to run)	300.00	150.00	90.00
(286)	Old Hoss Radbourn (Dogs Head)	1700.	850.00	510.00
(287)	Old Hoss Radbourn (hands on hips with bat)	1375.	687.00	412.00
(288)	Toad Ramsey	300.00	150.00	90.00
(289)	Princeton Charlie Reilly (St. Paul)	300.00	150.00	90.00
(290)	Long John Reilly (Cincinnati)	300.00	150.00	90.00
(291)	Danny Richardson (New York, arms at side)	300.00	150.00	90.00
(292)	Danny Richardson (New York, right hand at head level)	300.00	150.00	90.00
(293)	Hardy Richardson (Boston, hands at head level)	300.00	150.00	90.00
(294)	Hardy Richardson (Boston or Detroit, with bat)	300.00	150.00	90.00
(295)	Uncle Robbie Robinson (Athletics, catching)	1450.	725.00	435.00
(296)	Uncle Robbie Robinson (Athletics, with bat)	1450.	725.00	435.00
(297)	Yank Robinson (St. Louis, fielding)	300.00	150.00	90.00
(298)	Yank Robinson (St. Louis, with bat)	300.00	150.00	90.00
(299)	Dave Rowe (Kansas City, Dogs Head)	300.00	150.00	90.00
(300)	Jack Rowe (Detroit)	300.00	150.00	90.00
(301)	Jimmy Ryan (fielding)	300.00	150.00	90.00
(302)	Jimmy Ryan (with bat)	300.00	150.00	90.00
(303)	Ben Sanders (hands at neck level)	300.00	150.00	90.00
(304)	Ben Sanders (right hand at head level)	300.00	150.00	90.00
(305)	Frank Scheibeck	300.00	150.00	90.00
(306)	Gus Schmelz	300.00	150.00	90.00
(307)	Jumbo Schoeneck	300.00	150.00	90.00
(308)	Pop Schriver (hands at ankle level)	300.00	150.00	90.00
(309)	Pop Schriver (hands cupped at chest level)	300.00	150.00	90.00
(310)	Emmett Seery	300.00	150.00	90.00
(311)	Ed Seward	300.00	150.00	90.00
(312)	Daniel Shannon	300.00	150.00	90.00
(313)	William Sharsig	300.00	150.00	90.00
(314)	George Shoch	300.00	150.00	90.00
(315)	Otto Shomberg (Schomberg)	300.00	150.00	90.00
(316)	Lev Shreve	300.00	150.00	90.00
(317)	Mike Slattery	300.00	150.00	90.00
(318)	Germany Smith (Brooklyn, hands on knees)	300.00	150.00	90.00
(319)	Germany Smith (Brooklyn, right hand at head level)	300.00	150.00	90.00
(320)	Germany Smith (Brooklyn, with bat)	300.00	150.00	90.00
(321)	Pap Smith (Pittsburg, hands on knees)	300.00	150.00	90.00
(322)	Pap Smith (Pittsburg or Boston, with bat)	300.00	150.00	90.00
(323)	Little Bill Sowders	300.00	150.00	90.00
(324)	Charlie Sprague	300.00	150.00	90.00
(325)	Harry Staley	300.00	150.00	90.00
(326)	Dan Stearns	300.00	150.00	90.00
(327)	Stovey (hands on knees)	300.00	150.00	90.00
(328)	Harry Stovey (with bat)	300.00	150.00	90.00
(329)	Joe Straus (Strauss)	300.00	150.00	90.00
(330)	Cub Stricker	300.00	150.00	90.00
(331)	Marty Sullivan (Indianapolis)	300.00	150.00	90.00
(332)	Marty Sullivan (Chicago)	300.00	150.00	90.00
(333)	Billy Sunday (bending to left)	875.00	437.00	262.00
(334)	Billy Sunday (with bat)	875.00	437.00	262.00
(335)	Ezra Sutton (hands at shoulder level)	300.00	150.00	90.00
(336)	Ezra Sutton (with bat)	300.00	150.00	90.00
(337)	Park Swartzel	300.00	150.00	90.00
(338)	Pop Tate	300.00	150.00	90.00
(339)	Patsy Tebeau	300.00	150.00	90.00
(340)	John Tener	300.00	150.00	90.00
(341)	Adonis Terry (arms extended)	300.00	150.00	90.00
(342)	Adonis Terry (with bat)	300.00	150.00	90.00
(343)	Big Sam Thompson (Detroit)	1375.	687.00	412.00
(344)	Big Sam Thompson (Philadelphia)	1375.	687.00	412.00
(345)	Silent Mike Tiernan	300.00	150.00	90.00
(346)	Cannonball Titcomb	300.00	150.00	90.00
(347)	Buster Tomney	300.00	150.00	90.00
(348)	Sleepy Townsend (hands at head level)	300.00	150.00	90.00
(349)	Sleepy Townsend (with bat)	300.00	150.00	90.00
(350)	Bill Traffley	300.00	150.00	90.00
(351)	Foghorn Tucker	300.00	150.00	90.00
(352)	George Turner	300.00	150.00	90.00
(353)	Larry Twitchell	300.00	150.00	90.00
(354)	Jim Tyng	300.00	150.00	90.00
(355)	Rip Van Haltren (hands above waist)	300.00	150.00	90.00
(356)	Rip Van Haltren (right hand at right thigh)	300.00	150.00	90.00
(357)	Rip Van Haltren (with bat)	300.00	150.00	90.00
(358)	Farmer Vaughn	300.00	150.00	90.00
(359)	Joe Visner (arms at side)	300.00	150.00	90.00
(360)	Joe Visner (with bat)	300.00	150.00	90.00
(361)	Monte Ward (Dogs Head)	1700.	850.00	510.00
(362)	Monte Ward (hands on hips)	1375.	687.00	412.00
(363)	Monte Ward (throwing)	1375.	687.00	412.00
(364)	Bill Watkins	300.00	150.00	90.00
(365)	Farmer Weaver	300.00	150.00	90.00
(366)	Stump Weidman	300.00	150.00	90.00
(367)	Wild Bill Weidner	300.00	150.00	90.00
(368)	Curt Welch (Athletics)	300.00	150.00	90.00
(369)	Will Gleason, Curt Welch	875.00	437.00	262.00
(370)	Mickey Welch (New York)	300.00	150.00	90.00
(371)	A.C. "Cannonball" Weyhing	300.00	150.00	90.00
(372)	John Weyhing	300.00	150.00	90.00
(373)	Deacon White (hands above head)	300.00	150.00	90.00
(374)	Deacon White (looking down at ball)	300.00	150.00	90.00
(375)	Art Whitney (Pittsburg)	300.00	150.00	90.00
(376)	Grasshopper Whitney (Washington)	300.00	150.00	90.00
(377)	Ned Williamson (arm folded)	300.00	150.00	90.00
(378)	Ned Williamson (with bat)	300.00	150.00	90.00
(379)	Watt Wilmot	300.00	150.00	90.00
(380)	Medoc Wise	300.00	150.00	90.00
(381)	Chicken Wolf	300.00	150.00	90.00
(382)	George "Dandy" Wood (L.F., both hands at neck level)	300.00	150.00	90.00
(383)	George "Dandy" Wood (L.F., right hand at head level)	300.00	150.00	90.00
(384)	Pete Wood (P., with bat)	300.00	150.00	90.00
(385)	Harry Wright	3500.	1750.	1050

1937 O-Pee-Chee

Kind of a combination of 1934 Goudeys and 1934-36 Batter Ups, the '37 OPC "Baseball Stars" set features black-and-white action photos against a stylized ballpark. About halfway up the 2-5/8" x 2-15/16" cards, the background was die-cut to allow it to be folded back to create a stand-up card. Backs are printed in English and French. The 40 cards in "Series A" are all American Leaguers, leading to speculation that a Series B of National League players was to have been issued at a later date. The set carries the American Card Catalog designation of V300.

		NR MT	EX	VG
Complete Set (40):		10000.	5000.	3000.
Common Player:		100.00	50.00	30.00
101	John Lewis	100.00	50.00	30.00
102	"Jack" Hayes	100.00	50.00	30.00
103	Earl Averill	250.00	125.00	75.00
104	Harland Clift (Harlond)	100.00	50.00	30.00
105	"Beau" Bell	100.00	50.00	30.00
106	Jimmy Foxx (Jimmie)	800.00	400.00	240.00
107	Hank Greenberg	750.00	375.00	225.00
108	George Selkirk	100.00	50.00	30.00
109	Wally Moses	100.00	50.00	30.00
110	"Gerry" Walker	100.00	50.00	30.00
111	"Goose" Goslin	250.00	125.00	75.00
112	Charlie Gehringer	400.00	200.00	120.00
113	Hal Trosky	100.00	50.00	30.00
114	"Buddy" Myer	100.00	50.00	30.00
115	Luke Appling	250.00	125.00	75.00
116	"Zeke" Bonura	100.00	50.00	30.00
117	Tony Lazzeri	250.00	125.00	75.00
118	Joe DiMaggio	5000.	2500.	1500.
119	Bill Dickey	600.00	300.00	180.00
120	Bob Feller	900.00	450.00	270.00
121	Harry Kelley	100.00	50.00	30.00
122	Johnny Allen	100.00	50.00	30.00
123	Bob Johnson	125.00	62.00	37.00
124	Joe Cronin	250.00	125.00	75.00
125	"Rip" Radcliff	100.00	50.00	30.00
126	Cecil Travis	100.00	50.00	30.00
127	Joe Kuhel	100.00	50.00	30.00
128	Odell Hale	100.00	50.00	30.00
129	Sam West	100.00	50.00	30.00
130	Ben Chapman	100.00	50.00	30.00
131	Monte Pearson	100.00	50.00	30.00
132	"Rick" Ferrell	250.00	125.00	75.00
133	Tommy Bridges	100.00	50.00	30.00
134	"Schoolboy" Rowe	125.00	62.00	37.00
135	Vernon Kennedy	100.00	50.00	30.00
136	"Red" Ruffing	250.00	125.00	75.00
137	"Lefty" Grove	300.00	150.00	90.00
138	Wes Farrell	100.00	50.00	30.00
139	"Buck" Newsom	100.00	50.00	30.00
140	Rogers Hornsby	800.00	400.00	240.00

A card number in parentheses () indicates the set is unnumbered.

Values for recent cards and sets are listed in Mint (MT), Near Mint (NM), reflecting the fact that many cards from recent years have been preserved in top condition. Recent cards and sets in less than Excellent condition have little collector interest.

1965 O-Pee-Chee

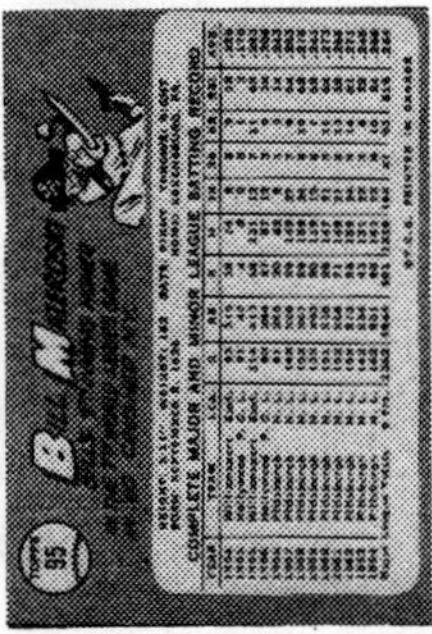

Identical in design to the 1965 Topps set, the Canadian-issued 1965 O-Pee-Chee set was printed on gray stock and consists of 283 cards, each measuring the standard 2-1/2" by 3-1/2". The words "Printed in Canada" appear along the bottom of the back of the cards.

	NR MT	EX	VG
Complete Set (283):	2400.	1200.	725.00
Common Player (1-196):	2.75	1.75	1.00
Common Player (197-283):	6.25	3.25	2.00

#	Card	NR MT	EX	VG
1	A.L. Batting Leaders (Elston Howard, Tony Oliva, Brooks Robinson)	21.00	10.50	6.25
2	N.L. Batting Leaders (Hank Aaron, Rico Carty, Bob Clemente)	17.00	8.50	5.00
3	A.L. Home Run Leaders (Harmon Killebrew, Mickey Mantle, Boog Powell)	30.00	15.00	9.00
4	N.L. Home Run Leaders (Johnny Callison, Jim Ray Hart, Willie Mays, Billy Williams)	12.75	6.50	3.75
5	A.L. RBI Leaders (Harmon Killebrew, Mickey Mantle, Brooks Robinson, Dick Stuart)	30.00	15.00	9.00
6	N.L. RBI Leaders (Ken Boyer, Willie Mays, Ron Santo)	3.50	1.75	1.00
7	A.L. ERA Leaders (Dean Chance, Joel Horlen)	2.75	1.50	.80
8	N.L. ERA Leaders (Don Drysdale, Sandy Koufax)	17.00	8.50	5.00
9	A.L. Pitching Leaders (Wally Bunker, Dean Chance, Gary Peters, Juan Pizarro, Dave Wickersham)	2.75	1.50	.80
10	N.L. Pitching Leaders (Larry Jackson, Juan Marichal, Ray Sadecki)	2.75	1.50	.80
11	A.L. Strikeout Leaders (Dean Chance, Al Downing, Camilo Pascual)	2.75	1.50	.80
12	N.L. Strikeout Leaders (Don Drysdale, Bob Gibson, Bob Veale)	2.75	1.50	.80
13	Pedro Ramos	2.75	1.50	.80
14	Len Gabrielson	2.75	1.50	.80
15	Robin Roberts	10.25	5.25	3.00
16	Astros Rookies (Sonny Jackson, Joe Morgan)	135.00	67.00	40.00
17	Johnny Romano	2.75	1.50	.80
18	Bill McCool	2.75	1.50	.80
19	Gates Brown	2.75	1.50	.80
20	Jim Bunning	3.00	1.50	.90
21	Don Blasingame	2.75	1.50	.80
22	Charlie Smith	2.75	1.50	.80
23	Bob Tiefenauer	2.75	1.50	.80
24	Twins Team	3.00	1.50	.90
25	Al McBean	2.75	1.50	.80
26	Bobby Knoop	2.75	1.50	.80
27	Dick Bertell	2.75	1.50	.80
28	Barney Schultz	2.75	1.50	.80
29	Felix Mantilla	2.75	1.50	.80
30	Jim Bouton	2.75	1.50	.80
31	Mike White	2.75	1.50	.80
32	Herman Franks	2.75	1.50	.80
33	Jackie Brandt	2.75	1.50	.80
34	Cal Koonce	2.75	1.50	.80
35	Ed Charles	2.75	1.50	.80
36	Bobby Wine	2.75	1.50	.80
37	Fred Gladding	2.75	1.50	.80
38	Jim King	2.75	1.50	.80
39	Gerry Arrigo	2.75	1.50	.80
40	Frank Howard	2.75	1.50	.80
41	White Sox Rookies (Bruce Howard, Marv Staehle)	2.75	1.50	.80
42	Earl Wilson	2.75	1.50	.80
43	Mike Shannon	2.75	1.50	.80
44	Wade Blasingame	2.75	1.50	.80
45	Roy McMillan	2.75	1.50	.80
46	Bob Lee	2.75	1.50	.80
47	Tommy Harper	2.75	1.50	.80
48	Claude Raymond	2.75	1.50	.80
49	Orioles Rookies (Curt Blefary, John Miller)	2.75	1.50	.80
50	Juan Marichal	12.75	6.50	3.75
51	Billy Bryan	2.75	1.50	.80
52	Ed Roebuck	2.75	1.50	.80
53	Dick McAuliffe	2.75	1.50	.80
54	Joe Gibbon	2.75	1.50	.80
55	Tony Conigliaro	12.75	6.50	3.75
56	Ron Kline	2.75	1.50	.80
57	Cards Team	2.75	1.50	.80
58	Fred Talbot	2.75	1.50	.80
59	Nate Oliver	2.75	1.50	.80
60	Jim O'Toole	2.75	1.50	.80
61	Chris Cannizzaro	2.75	1.50	.80
62	Jim Katt (Kaat)	3.00	1.50	.90
63	Ty Cline	2.75	1.50	.80
64	Lou Burdette	2.75	1.50	.80
65	Tony Kubek	3.00	1.50	.90
66	N.L. Home Run Leaders (Orlando Cepeda, Bill Rigney)	3.50	1.75	1.00
67	Harvey Haddix	2.75	1.50	.80
68	Del Crandall	2.75	1.50	.80
69	Bill Virdon	2.75	1.50	.80
70	Bill Skowron	2.75	1.50	.80
71	John O'Donoghue	2.75	1.50	.80
72	Tony Gonzalez	2.75	1.50	.80
73	Dennis Ribant	2.75	1.50	.80
74	Red Sox Rookies (Rico Petrocelli, Jerry Stephenson)	2.75	1.50	.80
75	Deron Johnson	2.75	1.50	.80
76	Sam McDowell	2.75	1.50	.80
77	Doug Camilli	2.75	1.50	.80
78	Dal Maxvill	2.75	1.50	.80
79	Checklist 1	15.00	7.50	4.50
80	Turk Farrell	2.75	1.50	.80
81	Don Buford	2.75	1.50	.80
82	Brave Rookies (Santos Alomar, John Braun)	2.75	1.50	.80
83	George Thomas	2.75	1.50	.80
84	Ron Herbel	2.75	1.50	.80
85	Willie Smith	2.75	1.50	.80
86	Les Narum	2.75	1.50	.80
87	Nelson Mathews	2.75	1.50	.80
88	Jack Lamabe	2.75	1.50	.80
89	Mike Hershberger	2.75	1.50	.80
90	Rich Rollins	2.75	1.50	.80
91	Cubs Team	2.75	1.50	.80
92	Dick Howser	2.75	1.50	.80
93	Jack Fisher	2.75	1.50	.80
94	Charlie Lau	2.75	1.50	.80
95	Bill Mazeroski	2.75	1.50	.80
96	Sonny Siebert	2.75	1.50	.80
97	Pedro Gonzalez	2.75	1.50	.80
98	Bob Miller	2.75	1.50	.80
99	Gil Hodges	4.00	2.00	1.25
100	Ken Boyer	2.75	1.50	.80
101	Fred Newman	2.75	1.50	.80
102	Steve Boros	2.75	1.50	.80
103	Harvey Kuenn	2.75	1.50	.80
104	Checklist 2	15.00	7.50	4.50
105	Chico Salmon	2.75	1.50	.80
106	Gene Oliver	2.75	1.50	.80
107	Phillies Rookies (Pat Corrales, Costen Shockley)	2.75	1.50	.80
108	Don Mincher	2.75	1.50	.80
109	Walt Bond	2.75	1.50	.80
110	Ron Santo	2.75	1.50	.80
111	Lee Thomas	2.75	1.50	.80
112	Derrell Griffith	2.75	1.50	.80
113	Steve Barber	2.75	1.50	.80
114	Jim Hickman	2.75	1.50	.80
115	Bobby Richardson	2.75	1.50	.80
116	Cardinals Rookies (Dave Dowling, Bob Tolan)	2.75	1.50	.80
117	Wes Stock	2.75	1.50	.80
118	Hal Lanier	2.75	1.50	.80
119	John Kennedy	2.75	1.50	.80
120	Frank Robinson	32.50	16.00	9.75
121	Gene Alley	2.75	1.50	.80
122	Bill Pleis	2.75	1.50	.80
123	Frank Thomas	2.75	1.50	.80
124	Tom Satriano	2.75	1.50	.80
125	Juan Pizarro	2.75	1.50	.80
126	Dodgers Team	3.00	1.50	.90
127	Frank Lary	2.75	1.50	.80
128	Vic Davalillo	2.75	1.50	.80
129	Bennie Daniels	2.75	1.50	.80
130	Al Kaline	30.00	15.00	9.00
131	Johnny Keane	2.75	1.50	.80
132	World Series Game 1 (Cards Take Opener)	2.75	1.50	.80
133	World Series Game 2 (Stottlemyre Wins)	2.75	1.50	.80
134	World Series Game 3 (Mantle's Clutch HR)	60.00	30.00	18.00
135	World Series Game 4 (Boyer's Grand Slam)	2.75	1.50	.80
136	World Series Game 5 (10th Inning Triumph)	2.75	1.50	.80
137	World Series Game 6 (Bouton Wins Again)	2.75	1.50	.80
138	World Series Game 7 (Gibson Wins Finale)	12.75	6.50	3.75
139	World Series Summary (The Cards Celebrate)	2.75	1.50	.80
140	Dean Chance	2.75	1.50	.80
141	Charlie James	2.75	1.50	.80
142	Bill Monbouquette	2.75	1.50	.80
143	Pirates Rookies (John Gelnar, Jerry May)	2.75	1.50	.80
144	Ed Kranepool	2.75	1.50	.80
145	Luis Tiant	21.00	10.50	6.25
146	Ron Hansen	2.75	1.50	.80
147	Dennis Bennett	2.75	1.50	.80
148	Willie Kirkland	2.75	1.50	.80
149	Wayne Schurr	2.75	1.50	.80
150	Brooks Robinson	32.50	16.00	9.75
151	Athletics Team	2.75	1.50	.80
152	Phil Ortega	2.75	1.50	.80
153	Norm Cash	2.75	1.50	.80
154	Bob Humphreys	2.75	1.50	.80
155	Roger Maris	72.00	36.00	22.00
156	Bob Sadowski	2.75	1.50	.80
157	Zolio Versalles	2.75	1.50	.80
158	Dick Sisler	2.75	1.50	.80
159	Jim Duffalo	2.75	1.50	.80
160	Bob Clemente	85.00	42.00	25.00
161	Frank Baumann	2.75	1.50	.80
162	Russ Nixon	2.75	1.50	.80
163	John Briggs	2.75	1.50	.80
164	Al Spangler	2.75	1.50	.80
165	Dick Ellsworth	2.75	1.50	.80
166	Indians Rookies (Tommie Agee, George Culver)	2.75	1.50	.80
167	Bill Wakefield	2.75	1.50	.80
168	Dick Green	2.75	1.50	.80
169	Dave Vineyard	2.75	1.50	.80
170	Hank Aaron	105.00	52.00	31.00
171	Jim Roland	2.75	1.50	.80
172	Jim Piersall	2.75	1.50	.80
173	Tigers Team	2.75	1.50	.80
174	Joe Jay	2.75	1.50	.80
175	Bob Aspromonte	2.75	1.50	.80
176	Willie McCovey	23.00	11.50	7.00
177	Pete Mikkelsen	2.75	1.50	.80
178	Dalton Jones	2.75	1.50	.80
179	Hal Woodeshick	2.75	1.50	.80
180	Bob Allison	2.75	1.50	.80
181	Senators Rookies (Don Loun, Joe McCabe)	2.75	1.50	.80
182	Mike de la Hoz	2.75	1.50	.80
183	Dave Nicholson	2.75	1.50	.80
184	John Boozer	2.75	1.50	.80
185	Max Alvis	2.75	1.50	.80
186	Billy Cowan	2.75	1.50	.80
187	Casey Stengel	17.00	8.50	5.00
188	Sam Bowens	2.75	1.50	.80
189	Checklist 3	15.00	7.50	4.50
190	Bill White	2.75	1.50	.80
191	Phil Regan	2.75	1.50	.80
192	Jim Coker	2.75	1.50	.80
193	Gaylord Perry	25.00	12.50	7.50
194	Rookie Stars (Bill Kelso, Rick Reichardt)	2.75	1.50	.80
195	Bob Veale	2.75	1.50	.80
196	Ron Fairly	2.75	1.50	.80
197	Diego Segui	6.25	3.25	2.00
198	Smoky Burgess	6.25	3.25	2.00
199	Bob Heffner	6.25	3.25	2.00
200	Joe Torre	6.25	3.25	2.00
201	Twins Rookies (Cesar Tovar, Sandy Valdespino)	6.25	3.25	2.00
202	Leo Burke	6.25	3.25	2.00
203	Dallas Green	6.25	3.25	2.00
204	Russ Snyder	6.25	3.25	2.00
205	Warren Spahn	38.00	19.00	11.50
206	Willie Horton	6.25	3.25	2.00
207	Pete Rose	235.00	117.00	70.00
208	Tommy John	21.00	10.50	6.25
209	Pirates Team	6.25	3.25	2.00
210	Jim Fregosi	6.25	3.25	2.00
211	Steve Ridzik	6.25	3.25	2.00
212	Ron Brand	6.25	3.25	2.00
213	Jim Davenport	6.25	3.25	2.00
214	Bob Purkey	6.25	3.25	2.00
215	Pete Ward	6.25	3.25	2.00
216	Al Worthington	6.25	3.25	2.00
217	Walt Alston	6.25	3.25	2.00
218	Dick Schofield	6.25	3.25	2.00
219	Bob Meyer	6.25	3.25	2.00
220	Bill Williams	21.00	10.50	6.25
221	John Tsitouris	6.25	3.25	2.00
222	Bob Tillman	6.25	3.25	2.00
223	Dan Osinski	6.25	3.25	2.00
224	Bob Chance	6.25	3.25	2.00
225	Bo Belinsky	6.25	3.25	2.00
226	Yankees Rookies (Jake Gibbs, Elvio Jimenez)	6.25	3.25	2.00
227	Bobby Klaus	6.25	3.25	2.00
228	Jack Sanford	6.25	3.25	2.00
229	Lou Clinton	6.25	3.25	2.00
230	Ray Sadecki	6.25	3.25	2.00
231	Jerry Adair	6.25	3.25	2.00
232	Steve Blass	6.25	3.25	2.00
233	Don Zimmer	6.25	3.25	2.00
234	White Sox Team	6.25	3.25	2.00
235	Chuck Hinton	6.25	3.25	2.00
236	Dennis McLain	32.50	16.00	9.75
237	Bernie Allen	6.25	3.25	2.00
238	Joe Moeller	6.25	3.25	2.00
239	Doc Edwards	6.25	3.25	2.00
240	Bob Bruce	6.25	3.25	2.00
241	Mack Jones	6.25	3.25	2.00
242	George Brunet	6.25	3.25	2.00
243	Reds Rookies (Ted Davidson, Tommy Helms)	6.25	3.25	2.00
244	Lindy McDaniel	6.25	3.25	2.00
245	Joe Pepitone	6.25	3.25	2.00
246	Tom Butters	6.25	3.25	2.00
247	Wally Moon	6.25	3.25	2.00
248	Gus Triandos	6.25	3.25	2.00
249	Dave McNally	6.25	3.25	2.00
250	Willie Mays	150.00	75.00	45.00
251	Billy Herman	6.25	3.25	2.00
252	Pete Richert	6.25	3.25	2.00
253	Danny Cater	6.25	3.25	2.00
254	Roland Sheldon	6.25	3.25	2.00
255	Camilo Pascual	6.25	3.25	2.00
256	Tito Francona	6.25	3.25	2.00
257	Jim Wynn	6.25	3.25	2.00
258	Larry Bearnarth	6.25	3.25	2.00
259	Tigers Rookies (Jim Northrup, Ray Oyler)	6.25	3.25	2.00
260	Don Drysdale	30.00	15.00	9.00
261	Duke Carmel	6.25	3.25	2.00
262	Bud Daley	6.25	3.25	2.00
263	Marty Keough	6.25	3.25	2.00
264	Bob Buhl	6.25	3.25	2.00
265	Jim Pagliaroni	6.25	3.25	2.00
266	Bert Campaneris	11.00	5.50	3.25
267	Senators Team	6.25	3.25	2.00
268	Ken McBride	6.25	3.25	2.00
269	Frank Bolling	6.25	3.25	2.00
270	Milt Pappas	6.25	3.25	2.00
271	Don Wert	6.25	3.25	2.00
272	Chuck Schilling	6.25	3.25	2.00
273	Checklist 4	17.00	8.50	5.00
274	Lum Harris	6.25	3.25	2.00
275	Dick Groat	6.25	3.25	2.00
276	Hoyt Wilhelm	11.00	5.50	3.25
277	Johnny Lewis	6.25	3.25	2.00
278	Ken Retzer	6.25	3.25	2.00

#	Player	NR MT	EX	VG
279	Dick Tracewski	6.25	3.25	2.00
280	Dick Stuart	6.25	3.25	2.00
281	Bill Stafford	6.25	3.25	2.00
282	Giants Rookies (Dick Estelle, Masanori Murakami)	12.75	6.50	3.75
283	Fred Whitfield	6.25	3.25	2.00

1966 O-Pee-Chee

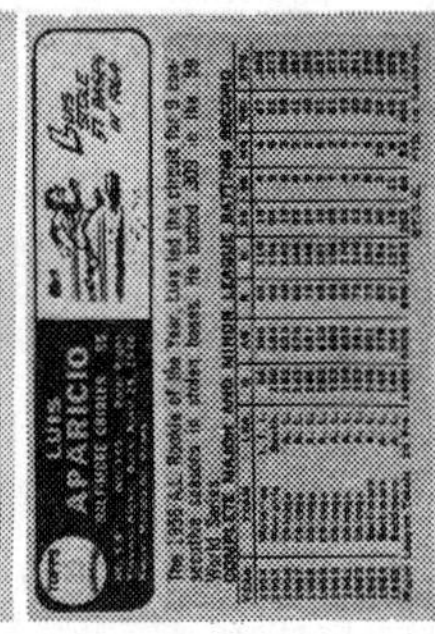

Utilizing the same design as the 1966 Topps set, the 1966 O-Pee-Chee set consists of 196 cards, measuring 2-1/2" by 3-1/2". The words "Ptd. in Canada" appear along the bottom on the back of the cards.

	NR MT	EX	VG
Complete Set (196):	1600.	800.00	475.00
Common Player (1-109):	2.25	1.00	.60
Common Player (110-196):	2.50	1.25	.70

#	Player	NR MT	EX	VG
1	Willie Mays	210.00	105.00	63.00
2	Ted Abernathy	2.25	1.25	.70
3	Sam Mele	2.25	1.25	.70
4	Ray Culp	2.25	1.25	.70
5	Jim Fregosi	2.25	1.25	.70
6	Chuck Schilling	2.25	1.25	.70
7	Tracy Stallard	2.25	1.25	.70
8	Floyd Robinson	2.25	1.25	.70
9	Clete Boyer	2.25	1.25	.70
10	Tony Cloninger	2.25	1.25	.70
11	Senators Rookies (Brant Alyea, Pete Craig)	2.25	1.25	.70
12	John Tsitouris	2.25	1.25	.70
13	Lou Johnson	2.25	1.25	.70
14	Norm Siebern	2.25	1.25	.70
15	Vern Law	2.25	1.25	.70
16	Larry Brown	2.25	1.25	.70
17	Johnny Stephenson	2.25	1.25	.70
18	Roland Sheldon	2.25	1.25	.70
19	Giants Team	2.25	1.25	.70
20	Willie Horton	2.25	1.25	.70
21	Don Nottebart	2.25	1.25	.70
22	Joe Nossek	2.25	1.25	.70
23	Jack Sanford	2.25	1.25	.70
24	Don Kessinger	2.25	1.25	.70
25	Pete Ward	2.25	1.25	.70
26	Ray Sadecki	2.25	1.25	.70
27	Orioles Rookies (Andy Etchebarren, Darold Knowles)	2.25	1.25	.70
28	Phil Niekro	21.00	10.50	6.25
29	Mike Brumley	2.25	1.25	.70
30	Pete Rose	55.00	27.00	16.50
31	Jack Cullen	2.25	1.25	.70
32	Adolfo Phillips	2.25	1.25	.70
33	Jim Pagliaroni	2.25	1.25	.70
34	Checklist 1	12.00	6.00	3.50
35	Ron Swoboda	2.25	1.25	.70
36	Jim Hunter	32.50	16.00	9.75
37	Billy Herman	2.25	1.25	.70
38	Ron Nischwitz	2.25	1.25	.70
39	Ken Henderson	2.25	1.25	.70
40	Jim Grant	2.25	1.25	.70
41	Don LeJohn	2.25	1.25	.70
42	Aubrey Gatewood	2.25	1.25	.70
43	Don Landrum	2.25	1.25	.70
44	Indians Rookies (Bill Davis, Tom Kelley)	2.25	1.25	.70
45	Jim Gentile	2.25	1.25	.70
46	Howie Koplitz	2.25	1.25	.70
47	J.C. Martin	2.25	1.25	.70
48	Paul Blair	2.25	1.25	.70
49	Woody Woodward	2.25	1.25	.70
50	Mickey Mantle	275.00	137.00	82.00
51	Gordon Richardson	2.25	1.25	.70
52	Power Plus (Johnny Callison, Wes Covington)	2.25	1.25	.70
53	Bob Duliba	2.25	1.25	.70
54	Jose Pagan	2.25	1.25	.70
55	Ken Harrelson	2.25	1.25	.70
56	Sandy Valdespino	2.25	1.25	.70
57	Jim Lefebvre	2.25	1.25	.70
58	Dave Wickersham	2.25	1.25	.70
59	Reds Team	2.25	1.25	.70
60	Curt Flood	2.25	1.25	.70
61	Bob Bolin	2.25	1.25	.70
62	Merritt Ranew	2.25	1.25	.70
63	Jim Stewart	2.25	1.25	.70
64	Bob Bruce	2.25	1.25	.70
65	Leon Wagner	2.25	1.25	.70
66	Al Weis	2.25	1.25	.70
67	Mets Rookies (Cleon Jones, Dick Selma)	2.25	1.25	.70
68	Hal Reniff	2.25	1.25	.70
69	Ken Hamlin	2.25	1.25	.70
70	Carl Yastrzemski	50.00	25.00	15.00
71	Frank Carpin	2.25	1.25	.70
72	Tony Perez	38.00	19.00	11.50
73	Jerry Zimmerman	2.25	1.25	.70
74	Don Mossi	2.25	1.25	.70
75	Tommy Davis	2.25	1.25	.70
76	Red Schoendienst	2.25	1.25	.70
77	Johnny Orsino	2.25	1.25	.70
78	Frank Linzy	2.25	1.25	.70
79	Joe Pepitone	2.25	1.25	.70
80	Richie Allen	6.25	3.25	2.00
81	Ray Oyler	2.25	1.25	.70
82	Bob Hendley	2.25	1.25	.70
83	Albie Pearson	2.25	1.25	.70
84	Braves Rookies (Jim Beauchamp, Dick Kelley)	2.25	1.25	.70
85	Eddie Fisher	2.25	1.25	.70
86	John Bateman	2.25	1.25	.70
87	Dan Napoleon	2.25	1.25	.70
88	Fred Whitfield	2.25	1.25	.70
89	Ted Davidson	2.25	1.25	.70
90	Luis Aparicio	10.25	5.25	3.00
91	Bob Uecker	18.00	9.00	5.50
92	Yankees Team	3.00	1.50	.90
93	Jim Lonborg	2.25	1.25	.70
94	Matty Alou	2.25	1.25	.70
95	Pete Richert	2.25	1.25	.70
96	Felipe Alou	2.25	1.25	.70
97	Jim Merritt	2.25	1.25	.70
98	Don Demeter	2.25	1.25	.70
99	Buc Belters (Donn Clendenon, Willie Stargell)	2.25	1.25	.70
100	Sandy Koufax	120.00	60.00	36.00
101	Checklist 2	12.00	6.00	3.50
102	Ed Kirkpatrick	2.25	1.25	.70
103	Dick Groat	2.25	1.25	.70
104	Alex Johnson	2.25	1.25	.70
105	Milt Pappas	2.25	1.25	.70
106	Rusty Staub	2.25	1.25	.70
107	Athletics Rookies (Larry Stahl, Ron Tompkins)	2.25	1.25	.70
108	Bobby Klaus	2.25	1.25	.70
109	Ralph Terry	2.25	1.25	.70
110	Ernie Banks	30.00	15.00	9.00
111	Gary Peters	2.50	1.25	.70
112	Manny Mota	2.50	1.25	.70
113	Hank Aguirre	2.50	1.25	.70
114	Jim Gosger	2.50	1.25	.70
115	Bill Henry	2.50	1.25	.70
116	Walt Alston	2.50	1.25	.70
117	Jake Gibbs	2.50	1.25	.70
118	Mike McCormick	2.50	1.25	.70
119	Art Shamsky	2.50	1.25	.70
120	Harmon Killebrew	25.00	12.50	7.50
121	Ray Herbert	2.50	1.25	.70
122	Joe Gaines	2.50	1.25	.70
123	Pirates Rookies (Frank Bork, Jerry May)	2.50	1.25	.70
124	Tug McGraw	2.50	1.25	.70
125	Lou Brock	30.00	15.00	9.00
126	Jim Palmer	240.00	120.00	72.00
127	Ken Berry	2.50	1.25	.70
128	Jim Landis	2.50	1.25	.70
129	Jack Kralick	2.50	1.25	.70
130	Joe Torre	2.50	1.25	.70
131	Angels Team	2.50	1.25	.70
132	Orlando Cepeda	6.25	3.25	2.00
133	Don McMahon	2.50	1.25	.70
134	Wes Parker	2.50	1.25	.70
135	Dave Morehead	2.50	1.25	.70
136	Woody Held	2.50	1.25	.70
137	Pat Corrales	2.50	1.25	.70
138	Roger Repoz	2.50	1.25	.70
139	Cubs Rookies (Byron Browne, Don Young)	2.50	1.25	.70
140	Jim Maloney	2.50	1.25	.70
141	Tom McCraw	2.50	1.25	.70
142	Don Dennis	2.50	1.25	.70
143	Jose Tartabull	2.50	1.25	.70
144	Don Schwall	2.50	1.25	.70
145	Bill Freehan	2.50	1.25	.70
146	George Altman	2.50	1.25	.70
147	Lum Harris	2.50	1.25	.70
148	Bob Johnson	2.50	1.25	.70
149	Dick Nen	2.50	1.25	.70
150	Rocky Colavito	7.50	3.75	2.25
151	Gary Wagner	2.50	1.25	.70
152	Frank Malzone	2.50	1.25	.70
153	Rico Carty	2.50	1.25	.70
154	Chuck Hiller	2.50	1.25	.70
155	Marcelino Lopez	2.50	1.25	.70
156	Double Play Combo (Hal Lanier, Dick Schofield)	2.50	1.25	.70
157	Rene Lachemann	2.50	1.25	.70
158	Jim Brewer	2.50	1.25	.70
159	Chico Ruiz	2.50	1.25	.70
160	Whitey Ford	30.00	15.00	9.00
161	Jerry Lumpe	2.50	1.25	.70
162	Lee Maye	2.50	1.25	.70
163	Tito Francona	2.50	1.25	.70
164	White Sox Rookies (Tommie Agee, Marv Staehle)	2.50	1.25	.70
165	Don Lock	2.50	1.25	.70
166	Chris Krug	2.50	1.25	.70
167	Boog Powell	2.50	1.25	.70
168	Dan Osinski	2.50	1.25	.70
169	Duke Sims	2.50	1.25	.70
170	Cookie Rojas	2.50	1.25	.70
171	Nick Willhite	2.50	1.25	.70
172	Mets Team	2.50	1.25	.70
173	Al Spangler	2.50	1.25	.70
174	Ron Taylor	2.50	1.25	.70
175	Bert Campaneris	2.50	1.25	.70
176	Jim Davenport	2.50	1.25	.70
177	Hector Lopez	2.50	1.25	.70
178	Bob Tillman	2.50	1.25	.70
179	Cards Rookies (Dennis Aust, Bob Tolan)	2.50	1.25	.70
180	Vada Pinson	2.50	1.25	.70
181	Al Worthington	2.50	1.25	.70
182	Jerry Lynch	2.50	1.25	.70
183	Checklist 3	12.75	6.50	3.75
184	Denis Menke	2.50	1.25	.70
185	Bob Buhl	2.50	1.25	.70
186	Ruben Amaro	2.50	1.25	.70
187	Chuck Dressen	2.50	1.25	.70
188	Al Luplow	2.50	1.25	.70
189	John Roseboro	2.50	1.25	.70
190	Jimmie Hall	2.50	1.25	.70
191	Darrell Sutherland	2.50	1.25	.70
192	Vic Power	2.50	1.25	.70
193	Dave McNally	2.50	1.25	.70
194	Senators Team	2.50	1.25	.70
195	Joe Morgan	38.00	19.00	11.50
196	Don Pavletich	2.50	1.25	.70

1967 O-Pee-Chee

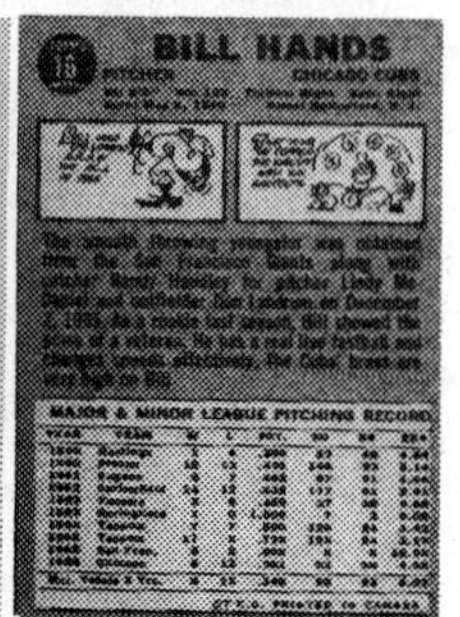

Cards in the 196-card Canadian set are nearly identical in design to the 1967 Topps set, except the words "Printed in Canada" are found on the back in the lower right corner. Cards measure 2-1/2" by 3-1/2".

	NR MT	EX	VG
Complete Set (196):	1400.	700.00	400.00
Common Player (1-109):	2.25	1.00	.60
Common Player (110-196):	3.00	1.50	.90

#	Player	NR MT	EX	VG
1	The Champs (Hank Bauer, Brooks Robinson, Frank Robinson)	25.00	12.50	7.50
2	Jack Hamilton	2.25	1.25	.70
3	Duke Sims	2.25	1.25	.70
4	Hal Lanier	2.25	1.25	.70
5	Whitey Ford	25.00	12.50	7.50
6	Dick Simpson	2.25	1.25	.70
7	Don McMahon	2.25	1.25	.70
8	Chuck Harrison	2.25	1.25	.70
9	Ron Hansen	2.25	1.25	.70
10	Matty Alou	2.25	1.25	.70
11	Barry Moore	2.25	1.25	.70
12	Dodgers Rookies (Jim Campanis, Bill Singer)	2.25	1.25	.70
13	Joe Sparma	2.25	1.25	.70
14	Phil Linz	2.25	1.25	.70
15	Earl Battey	2.25	1.25	.70
16	Bill Hands	2.25	1.25	.70
17	Jim Gosger	2.25	1.25	.70
18	Gene Oliver	2.25	1.25	.70
19	Jim McGlothlin	2.25	1.25	.70
20	Orlando Cepeda	8.50	4.25	2.50
21	Dave Bristol	2.25	1.25	.70
22	Gene Brabender	2.25	1.25	.70
23	Larry Elliot	2.25	1.25	.70
24	Bob Allen	2.25	1.25	.70
25	Elston Howard	2.25	1.25	.70
26	Bob Priddy	2.25	1.25	.70
27	Bob Saverine	2.25	1.25	.70
28	Barry Latman	2.25	1.25	.70
29	Tom McCraw	2.25	1.25	.70
30	Al Kaline	21.00	10.50	6.25
31	Jim Brewer	2.25	1.25	.70
32	Bob Bailey	2.25	1.25	.70
33	Athletic Rookies (Sal Bando, Randy Schwartz)	2.25	1.25	.70
34	Pete Cimino	2.25	1.25	.70
35	Rico Carty	2.25	1.25	.70
36	Bob Tillman	2.25	1.25	.70
37	Rick Wise	2.25	1.25	.70
38	Bob Johnson	2.25	1.25	.70
39	Curt Simmons	2.25	1.25	.70
40	Rick Reichardt	2.25	1.25	.70
41	Joe Hoerner	2.25	1.25	.70
42	Mets Team	8.50	4.25	2.50
43	Chico Salmon	2.25	1.25	.70
44	Joe Nuxhall	2.25	1.25	.70
45	Roger Maris	55.00	27.00	16.50
46	Lindy McDaniel	2.25	1.25	.70
47	Ken McMullen	2.25	1.25	.70
48	Bill Freehan	2.25	1.25	.70
49	Roy Face	2.25	1.25	.70
50	Tony Oliva	2.25	1.25	.70
51	Astros Rookies (Dave Adlesh, Wes Bales)	2.25	1.25	.70
52	Dennis Higgins	2.25	1.25	.70
53	Clay Dalrymple	2.25	1.25	.70
54	Dick Green	2.25	1.25	.70
55	Don Drysdale	21.00	10.50	6.25
56	Jose Tartabull	2.25	1.25	.70
57	Pat Jarvis	2.25	1.25	.70
58	Paul Schaal	2.25	1.25	.70
59	Ralph Terry	2.25	1.25	.70

60	Luis Aparicio	8.50	4.25	2.50
61	Gordy Coleman	2.25	1.25	.70
62	Checklist 1 (Frank Robinson)	11.00	5.50	3.25
63	Cards' Clubbers (Lou Brock, Curt Flood)	10.25	5.25	3.00
64	Fred Valentine	2.25	1.25	.70
65	Tom Haller	2.25	1.25	.70
66	Manny Mota	2.25	1.25	.70
67	Ken Berry	2.25	1.25	.70
68	Bob Buhl	2.25	1.25	.70
69	Vic Davalillo	2.25	1.25	.70
70	Ron Santo	2.25	1.25	.70
71	Camilo Pascual	2.25	1.25	.70
72	Tigers Rookies (George Korince, John Matchick)	2.25	1.25	.70
73	Rusty Staub	2.25	1.25	.70
74	Wes Stock	2.25	1.25	.70
75	George Scott	2.25	1.25	.70
76	Jim Barbieri	2.25	1.25	.70
77	Dooley Womack	2.25	1.25	.70
78	Pat Corrales	2.25	1.25	.70
79	Bubba Morton	2.25	1.25	.70
80	Jim Maloney	2.25	1.25	.70
81	Eddie Stanky	2.25	1.25	.70
82	Steve Barber	2.25	1.25	.70
83	Ollie Brown	2.25	1.25	.70
84	Tommie Sisk	2.25	1.25	.70
85	Johnny Callison	2.25	1.25	.70
86	Mike McCormick	2.25	1.25	.70
87	George Altman	2.25	1.25	.70
88	Mickey Lolich	2.25	1.25	.70
89	Felix Millan	2.25	1.25	.70
90	Jim Nash	2.25	1.25	.70
91	Johnny Lewis	2.25	1.25	.70
92	Ray Washburn	2.25	1.25	.70
93	Yankees Rookies (Stan Bahnsen, Bobby Murcer)	2.25	1.25	.70
94	Ron Fairly	2.25	1.25	.70
95	Sonny Siebert	2.25	1.25	.70
96	Art Shamsky	2.25	1.25	.70
97	Mike Cuellar	2.25	1.25	.70
98	Rich Rollins	2.25	1.25	.70
99	Lee Stange	2.25	1.25	.70
100	Frank Robinson	21.00	10.50	6.25
101	Ken Johnson	2.25	1.25	.70
102	Phillies Team	2.25	1.25	.70
103	Checklist 2 (Mickey Mantle)	13.50	6.75	4.00
104	Minnie Rojas	2.25	1.25	.70
105	Ken Boyer	2.25	1.25	.70
106	Randy Hundley	2.25	1.25	.70
107	Joel Horlen	2.25	1.25	.70
108	Alex Johnson	2.25	1.25	.70
109	Tribe Thumpers (Rocky Colavito, Leon Wagner)	2.25	1.25	.70
110	Jack Aker	3.00	1.50	.90
111	John Kennedy	3.00	1.50	.90
112	Dave Wickersham	3.00	1.50	.90
113	Dave Nicholson	3.00	1.50	.90
114	Jack Balschun	3.00	1.50	.90
115	Paul Casanova	3.00	1.50	.90
116	Herman Franks	3.00	1.50	.90
117	Darrell Brandon	3.00	1.50	.90
118	Bernie Allen	3.00	1.50	.90
119	Wade Blasingame	3.00	1.50	.90
120	Floyd Robinson	3.00	1.50	.90
121	Ed Bressoud	3.00	1.50	.90
122	George Brunet	3.00	1.50	.90
123	Pirates Rookies (Jim Price, Luke Walker)	3.00	1.50	.90
124	Jim Stewart	3.00	1.50	.90
125	Moe Drabowsky	3.00	1.50	.90
126	Tony Taylor	3.00	1.50	.90
127	John O'Donoghue	3.00	1.50	.90
128	Ed Spiezio	3.00	1.50	.90
129	Phil Roof	3.00	1.50	.90
130	Phil Regan	3.00	1.50	.90
131	Yankees Team	8.50	4.25	2.50
132	Ozzie Virgil	3.00	1.50	.90
133	Ron Kline	3.00	1.50	.90
134	Gates Brown	3.00	1.50	.90
135	Deron Johnson	3.00	1.50	.90
136	Carroll Sembera	3.00	1.50	.90
137	Twins Rookies (Ron Clark, Jim Ollum)	3.00	1.50	.90
138	Dick Kelley	3.00	1.50	.90
139	Dalton Jones	3.00	1.50	.90
140	Willie Stargell	25.00	12.50	7.50
141	John Miller	3.00	1.50	.90
142	Jackie Brandt	3.00	1.50	.90
143	Sox Sockers (Don Buford, Pete Ward)	3.00	1.50	.90
144	Bill Hepler	3.00	1.50	.90
145	Larry Brown	3.00	1.50	.90
146	Steve Carlton	150.00	75.00	45.00
147	Tom Egan	3.00	1.50	.90
148	Adolfo Phillips	3.00	1.50	.90
149	Joe Moeller	3.00	1.50	.90
150	Mickey Mantle	320.00	160.00	96.00
151	World Series Game 1 (Moe Mows Down 11)	3.00	1.50	.90
152	World Series Game 2 (Palmer Blanks Dodgers)	8.50	4.25	2.50
153	World Series Game 3 (Blair's Homer Defeats L.A.)	3.00	1.50	.90
154	World Series Game 4 (Orioles Win 4th Straight)	3.00	1.50	.90
155	World Series Summary (The Winners Celebrate)	3.00	1.50	.90
156	Ron Herbel	3.00	1.50	.90
157	Danny Cater	3.00	1.50	.90
158	Jimmy Coker	3.00	1.50	.90
159	Bruce Howard	3.00	1.50	.90
160	Willie Davis	3.00	1.50	.90
161	Dick Williams	3.00	1.50	.90
162	Billy O'Dell	3.00	1.50	.90
163	Vic Roznovsky	3.00	1.50	.90
164	Dwight Siebler	3.00	1.50	.90
165	Cleon Jones	3.00	1.50	.90
166	Ed Matthews	17.00	8.50	5.00
167	Senators Rookies (Joe Coleman, Tim Cullen)	3.00	1.50	.90
168	Ray Culp	3.00	1.50	.90
169	Horace Clarke	3.00	1.50	.90
170	Dick McAuliffe	3.00	1.50	.90
171	Calvin Koonce	3.00	1.50	.90
172	Bill Heath	3.00	1.50	.90
173	Cards Team	3.00	1.50	.90
174	Dick Radatz	3.00	1.50	.90
175	Bobby Knoop	3.00	1.50	.90
176	Sammy Ellis	3.00	1.50	.90
177	Tito Fuentes	3.00	1.50	.90
178	John Buzhardt	3.00	1.50	.90
179	1967 Braves Rookies (Cecil Upshaw, Charles Vaughan)	3.00	1.50	.90
180	Curt Blefary	3.00	1.50	.90
181	Terry Fox	3.00	1.50	.90
182	Ed Charles	3.00	1.50	.90
183	Jim Pagliaroni	3.00	1.50	.90
184	George Thomas	3.00	1.50	.90
185	Ken Holtzman	3.00	1.50	.90
186	Mets Maulers (Ed Kranepool, Ron Swoboda)	3.00	1.50	.90
187	Pedro Ramos	3.00	1.50	.90
188	Ken Harrelson	3.00	1.50	.90
189	Chuck Hinton	3.00	1.50	.90
190	Turk Farrell	3.00	1.50	.90
191	Checklist 3 (Willie Mays)	12.75	6.50	3.75
192	Fred Gladding	3.00	1.50	.90
193	Jose Cardenal	3.00	1.50	.90
194	Bob Allison	3.00	1.50	.90
195	Al Jackson	3.00	1.50	.90
196	Johnny Romano	3.00	1.50	.90

1968 O-Pee-Chee

The O-Pee-Chee set for 1968 again consisted of 196 cards, each measuring the standard 2-1/2" by 3-1/2". The card design is identical to the 1968 Topps set, except the color of the backs is slightly different and the words "Ptd. in Canada" appear in the lower right corner of the back.

		NR MT	EX	VG
	Complete Set (196):	2425.	1500.	900.00
	Common Player:	2.25	1.25	.70
1	N.L. Batting Leaders (Matty Alou, Bob Clemente, Tony Gonzales)	25.00	12.50	7.50
2	A.L. Batting Leaders (Al Kaline, Frank Robinson, Carl Yastrzemski)	12.75	6.50	3.75
3	N.L. RBI Leaders (Hank Aaron, Orlando Cepeda, Bob Clemente)	13.50	6.75	4.00
4	A.L. RBI Leaders (Harmon Killebrew, Frank Robinson, Carl Yastrzemski)	13.50	6.75	4.00
5	N.L. Home Run Leaders (Hank Aaron, Willie McCovey, Ron Santo, Jim Wynn)	10.25	5.25	3.00
6	N.L. Home Run Leaders (Frank Howard, Harmon Killebrew, Carl Yastrzemski)	10.25	5.25	3.00
7	N.L. ERA Leaders (Jim Bunning, Phil Niekro, Chris Short)	2.25	1.25	.70
8	A.L. ERA Leaders (Joe Horlen, Gary Peters, Sonny Siebert)	2.25	1.25	.70
9	N.L. Pitching Leaders (Jim Bunning, Ferguson Jenkins, Mike McCormick, Claude Osteen)	2.25	1.25	.70
10	A.L. Pitching Leaders (Dean Chance, Jim Lonborg, Earl Wilson)	2.25	1.25	.70
11	N.L. Strikeout Leaders (Jim Bunning, Ferguson Jenkins, Gaylord Perry)	2.25	1.25	.70
12	A.L. Strikeout Leaders (Dean Chance, Jim Lonborg, Sam McDowell)	2.25	1.25	.70
13	Chuck Hartenstein	2.25	1.25	.70
14	Jerry McNertney	2.25	1.25	.70
15	Ron Hunt	2.25	1.25	.70
16	Indians Rookies (Lou Piniella, Richie Scheinblum)	2.25	1.25	.70
17	Dick Hall	2.25	1.25	.70
18	Mike Hershberger	2.25	1.25	.70
19	Juan Pizarro	2.25	1.25	.70
20	Brooks Robinson	30.00	15.00	9.00
21	Ron Davis	2.25	1.25	.70
22	Pat Dobson	2.25	1.25	.70
23	Chico Cardenas	2.25	1.25	.70
24	Bobby Locke	2.25	1.25	.70
25	Julian Javier	2.25	1.25	.70
26	Darrell Brandon	2.25	1.25	.70
27	Gil Hodges	8.50	4.25	2.50
28	Ted Uhlaender	2.25	1.25	.70
29	Joe Verbanic	2.25	1.25	.70
30	Joe Torre	2.25	1.25	.70
31	Ed Stroud	2.25	1.25	.70
32	Joe Gibbon	2.25	1.25	.70
33	Pete Ward	2.25	1.25	.70
34	Al Ferrara	2.25	1.25	.70
35	Steve Hargan	2.25	1.25	.70
36	Pirates Rookies (Bob Moose, Bob Robertson)	2.25	1.25	.70
37	Billy Williams	12.75	6.50	3.75
38	Tony Pierce	2.25	1.25	.70
39	Cookie Rojas	2.25	1.25	.70
40	Denny McLain	15.00	7.50	4.50
41	Julio Gotay	2.25	1.25	.70
42	Larry Haney	2.25	1.25	.70
43	Gary Bell	2.25	1.25	.70
44	Frank Kostro	2.25	1.25	.70
45	Tom Seaver	235.00	117.00	70.00
46	Dave Ricketts	2.25	1.25	.70
47	Ralph Houk	2.25	1.25	.70
48	Ted Davidson	2.25	1.25	.70
49	Ed Brinkman	2.25	1.25	.70
50	Willie Mays	95.00	47.00	28.00
51	Bob Locker	2.25	1.25	.70
52	Hawk Taylor	2.25	1.25	.70
53	Gene Alley	2.25	1.25	.70
54	Stan Williams	2.25	1.25	.70
55	Felipe Alou	2.25	1.25	.70
56	Orioles Rookies (Dave Leonhard, Dave May)	2.25	1.25	.70
57	Dan Schneider	2.25	1.25	.70
58	Ed Mathews	17.00	8.50	5.00
59	Don Lock	2.25	1.25	.70
60	Ken Holtzman	2.25	1.25	.70
61	Reggie Smith	2.25	1.25	.70
62	Chuck Dobson	2.25	1.25	.70
63	Dick Kenworthy	2.25	1.25	.70
64	Jim Merritt	2.25	1.25	.70
65	John Roseboro	2.25	1.25	.70
66	Casey Cox	2.25	1.25	.70
67	Checklist 1 (Jim Kaat)	2.25	1.25	.70
68	Ron Willis	2.25	1.25	.70
69	Tom Tresh	2.25	1.25	.70
70	Bob Veale	2.25	1.25	.70
71	Vern Fuller	2.25	1.25	.70
72	Tommy John	2.25	1.25	.70
73	Jim Hart	2.25	1.25	.70
74	Milt Pappas	2.25	1.25	.70
75	Don Mincher	2.25	1.25	.70
76	Braves Rookies (Jim Britton, Ron Reed)	2.25	1.25	.70
77	Don Wilson	2.25	1.25	.70
78	Jim Northrup	2.25	1.25	.70
79	Ted Kubiak	2.25	1.25	.70
80	Rod Carew	135.00	67.00	40.00
81	Larry Jackson	2.25	1.25	.70
82	Sam Bowens	2.25	1.25	.70
83	John Stephenson	2.25	1.25	.70
84	Bob Tolan	2.25	1.25	.70
85	Gaylord Perry	13.50	6.75	4.00
86	Willie Stargell	17.00	8.50	5.00
87	Dick Williams	2.25	1.25	.70
88	Phil Regan	2.25	1.25	.70
89	Jake Gibbs	2.25	1.25	.70
90	Vada Pinson	2.25	1.25	.70
91	Jim Ollom	2.25	1.25	.70
92	Ed Kranepool	2.25	1.25	.70
93	Tony Cloninger	2.25	1.25	.70
94	Lee Maye	2.25	1.25	.70
95	Bob Aspromonte	2.25	1.25	.70
96	Senators Rookies (Frank Coggins, Dick Nold)	2.25	1.25	.70
97	Tom Phoebus	2.25	1.25	.70
98	Gary Sutherland	2.25	1.25	.70
99	Rocky Colavito	2.25	1.25	.70
100	Bob Gibson	30.00	15.00	9.00
101	Glenn Beckert	2.25	1.25	.70
102	Jose Cardenal	2.25	1.25	.70
103	Don Sutton	17.00	8.50	5.00
104	Dick Dietz	2.25	1.25	.70
105	Al Downing	2.25	1.25	.70
106	Dalton Jones	2.25	1.25	.70
107	Checklist 2 (Juan Marichal)	2.50	1.25	.70
108	Don Pavletich	2.25	1.25	.70
109	Bert Campaneris	2.25	1.25	.70
110	Hank Aaron	85.00	42.00	25.00
111	Rich Reese	2.25	1.25	.70
112	Woody Fryman	2.25	1.25	.70
113	Tigers Rookies (Tom Matchick, Daryl Patterson)	2.25	1.25	.70
114	Ron Swoboda	2.25	1.25	.70
115	Sam McDowell	2.25	1.25	.70
116	Ken McMullen	2.25	1.25	.70
117	Larry Jaster	2.25	1.25	.70
118	Mark Belanger	2.25	1.25	.70
119	Ted Savage	2.25	1.25	.70
120	Mel Stottlemyre	2.25	1.25	.70
121	Jimmie Hall	2.25	1.25	.70
122	Gene Mauch	2.25	1.25	.70
123	Jose Santiago	2.25	1.25	.70
124	Nate Oliver	2.25	1.25	.70
125	Joe Horlen	2.25	1.25	.70
126	Bob Etheridge	2.25	1.25	.70
127	Paul Lindblad	2.25	1.25	.70
128	Astros Rookies (Tom Dukes, Alonzo Harris)	2.25	1.25	.70
129	Mickey Stanley	2.25	1.25	.70
130	Tony Perez	17.00	8.50	5.00
131	Frank Bertaina	2.25	1.25	.70
132	Bud Harrelson	2.25	1.25	.70
133	Fred Whitfield	2.25	1.25	.70
134	Pat Jarvis	2.25	1.25	.70
135	Paul Blair	2.25	1.25	.70
136	Randy Hundley	2.25	1.25	.70
137	Twins Team	2.25	1.25	.70
138	Ruben Amaro	2.25	1.25	.70
139	Chris Short	2.25	1.25	.70
140	Tony Conigliaro	2.25	1.25	.70
141	Dal Maxvill	2.25	1.25	.70
142	White Sox Rookies (Buddy Bradford, Bill Voss)	2.25	1.25	.70

No.	Player			
143	Pete Cimino	2.25	1.25	.70
144	Joe Morgan	21.00	10.50	6.25
145	Don Drysdale	15.00	7.50	4.50
146	Sal Bando	2.25	1.25	.70
147	Frank Linzy	2.25	1.25	.70
148	Dave Bristol	2.25	1.25	.70
149	Bob Saverine	2.25	1.25	.70
150	Bob Clemente	65.00	32.00	19.50
151	World Series Game 1 (Brock Socks 4-Hits)	10.25	5.25	3.00
152	World Series Game 2 (Yaz Smashes Two Homers)	11.00	5.50	3.25
153	World Series Game 3 (Briles Cools Off Boston)	2.25	1.25	.70
154	World Series Game 4 (Gibson Hurls Shutout)	10.25	5.25	3.00
155	World Series Game 5 (Lonborg Wins Again)	2.25	1.25	.70
156	World Series Game 6 (Petrocelli Socks Two Homers)	1.75	.90	.50
157	World Series Game 7 (St. Louis Wins It)	2.25	1.25	.70
158	World Series Summary (The Cardinals Celebrate)	2.25	1.25	.70
159	Don Kessinger	2.25	1.25	.70
160	Earl Wilson	2.25	1.25	.70
161	Norm Miller	2.25	1.25	.70
162	Cards Rookies (Hal Gilson, Mike Torrez)	2.25	1.25	.70
163	Gene Brabender	2.25	1.25	.70
164	Ramon Webster	2.25	1.25	.70
165	Tony Oliva	2.25	1.25	.70
166	Claude Raymond	2.25	1.25	.70
167	Elston Howard	2.25	1.25	.70
168	Dodgers Team	2.25	1.25	.70
169	Bob Bolin	2.25	1.25	.70
170	Jim Fregosi	2.25	1.25	.70
171	Don Nottebart	2.25	1.25	.70
172	Walt Williams	2.25	1.25	.70
173	John Boozer	2.25	1.25	.70
174	Bob Tillman	2.25	1.25	.70
175	Maury Wills	2.50	1.25	.70
176	Bob Allen	2.25	1.25	.70
177	Mets Rookies (Jerry Koosman, Nolan Ryan)	2000.	1000.	600.00
178	Don Wert	2.25	1.25	.70
179	Bill Stoneman	2.25	1.25	.70
180	Curt Flood	2.25	1.25	.70
181	Jerry Zimmerman	2.25	1.25	.70
182	Dave Gusti	2.25	1.25	.70
183	Bob Kennedy	2.25	1.25	.70
184	Lou Johnson	2.25	1.25	.70
185	Tom Haller	2.25	1.25	.70
186	Eddie Watt	2.25	1.25	.70
187	Sonny Jackson	2.25	1.25	.70
188	Cap Peterson	2.25	1.25	.70
189	Bill Landis	2.25	1.25	.70
190	Bill White	2.25	1.25	.70
191	Dan Frisella	2.25	1.25	.70
192	Checklist 3 (Carl Yastrzemski)	3.50	1.75	1.00
193	Jack Hamilton	2.25	1.25	.70
194	Don Buford	2.25	1.25	.70
195	Joe Pepitone	2.25	1.25	.70
196	Gary Nolan	2.25	1.25	.70

1969 O-Pee-Chee

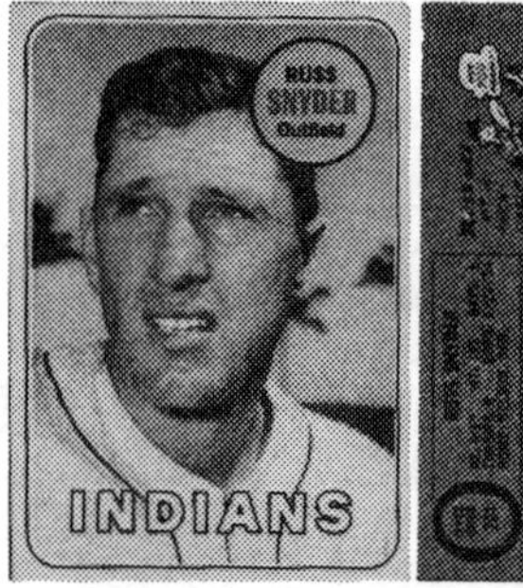

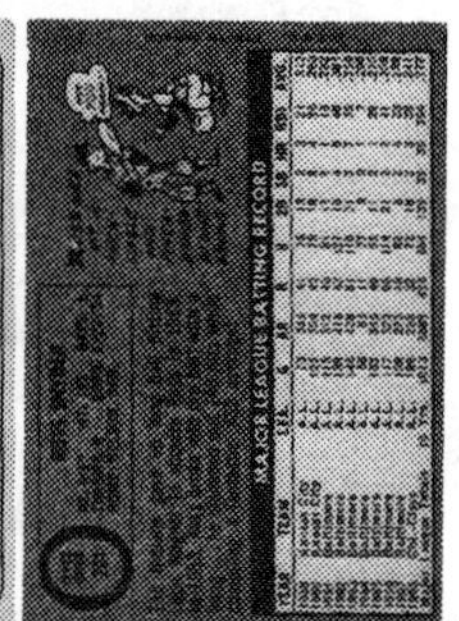

O-Pee-Chee increased the number of cards in its 1969 O-Pee-Chee set to 218, maintaining the standard 2-1/2" by 3-1/2" size. The card design is identical to the 1969 Topps set, except for a slightly different color on the back of the cards and the words "Ptd. in Canada," which appear along the bottom.

	NR MT	EX	VG
Complete Set (218):	850.00	425.00	250.00
Common Player:	2.25	1.25	.70

No.	Player	NR MT	EX	VG
1	A.L. Batting Leaders (Danny Cater, Tony Oliva, Carl Yastrzemski)	17.00	8.50	5.00
2	N.L. Batting Leaders (Felipe Alou, Matty Alou, Pete Rose)	8.50	4.25	2.50
3	A.L. RBI Leaders (Ken Harrelson, Frank Howard, Jim Northrup)	2.25	1.25	.70
4	N.L. RBI Leaders (Willie McCovey, Ron Santo, Billy Williams)	8.50	4.25	2.50
5	A.L. Home Run Leaders (Ken Harrelson, Willie Horton, Frank Howard)	2.25	1.25	.70
6	N.L. Home Run Leaders (Richie Allen, Ernie Banks, Willie McCovey)	8.50	4.25	2.50
7	A.L. ERA Leaders (Sam McDowell, Dave McNally, Luis Tiant)	2.25	1.25	.70
8	N.L. ERA Leaders (Bobby Bolin, Bob Gibson, Bob Veale)	2.25	1.25	.70
9	A.L. Pitching Leaders (Denny McLain, Dave McNally, Mel Stottlemyre, Luis Tiant)	2.25	1.25	.70
10	N.L. Pitching Leaders (Bob Gibson, Fergie Jenkins, Juan Marichal)	8.50	4.25	2.50
11	A.L. Strikeout Leaders (Sam McDowell, Denny McLain, Luis Tiant)	2.25	1.25	.70
12	N.L. Strikeout Leaders (Bob Gibson, Fergie Jenkins, Bill Singer)	2.25	1.25	.70
13	Mickey Stanley	2.25	1.25	.70
14	Al McBean	2.25	1.25	.70
15	Boog Powell	2.25	1.25	.70
16	Giants Rookies (Cesar Gutierrez, Rich Robertson)	2.25	1.25	.70
17	Mike Marshall	2.25	1.25	.70
18	Dick Schofield	2.25	1.25	.70
19	Ken Suarez	2.25	1.25	.70
20	Ernie Banks	23.00	11.50	7.00
21	Jose Santiago	2.25	1.25	.70
22	Jesus Alou	2.25	1.25	.70
23	Lew Krausse	2.25	1.25	.70
24	Walt Alston	2.25	1.25	.70
25	Roy White	2.25	1.25	.70
26	Clay Carroll	2.25	1.25	.70
27	Bernie Allen	2.25	1.25	.70
28	Mike Ryan	2.25	1.25	.70
29	Dave Morehead	2.25	1.25	.70
30	Bob Allison	2.25	1.25	.70
31	Mets Rookies (Gary Gentry, Amos Otis)	2.25	1.25	.70
32	Sammy Ellis	2.25	1.25	.70
33	Wayne Causey	2.25	1.25	.70
34	Gary Peters	2.25	1.25	.70
35	Joe Morgan	17.00	8.50	5.00
36	Luke Walker	2.25	1.25	.70
37	Curt Motton	2.25	1.25	.70
38	Zoilo Versalles	2.25	1.25	.70
39	Dick Hughes	2.25	1.25	.70
40	Mayo Smith	2.25	1.25	.70
41	Bob Barton	2.25	1.25	.70
42	Tommy Harper	2.25	1.25	.70
43	Joe Niekro	2.25	1.25	.70
44	Danny Cater	2.25	1.25	.70
45	Maury Wills	2.25	1.25	.70
46	Fritz Peterson	2.25	1.25	.70
47	Paul Popovich	2.25	1.25	.70
48	Brant Alyea	2.25	1.25	.70
49	Royals Rookies (Steve Jones, Eliseo Rodriguez)	2.25	1.25	.70
50	Bob Clemente	60.00	30.00	18.00
51	Woody Fryman	2.25	1.25	.70
52	Mike Andrews	2.25	1.25	.70
53	Sonny Jackson	2.25	1.25	.70
54	Cisco Carlos	2.25	1.25	.70
55	Jerry Grote	2.25	1.25	.70
56	Rich Reese	2.25	1.25	.70
57	Checklist 1 (Denny McLain)	2.25	1.25	.70
58	Fred Gladding	2.25	1.25	.70
59	Jay Johnstone	2.25	1.25	.70
60	Nelson Briles	2.25	1.25	.70
61	Jimmie Hall	2.25	1.25	.70
62	Chico Salmon	2.25	1.25	.70
63	Jim Hickman	2.25	1.25	.70
64	Bill Monbouquette	2.25	1.25	.70
65	Willie Davis	2.25	1.25	.70
66	Orioles Rookies (Mike Adamson, Merv Rettenmund)	2.25	1.25	.70
67	Bill Stoneman	2.25	1.25	.70
68	Dave Duncan	2.25	1.25	.70
69	Steve Hamilton	2.25	1.25	.70
70	Tommy Helms	2.25	1.25	.70
71	Steve Whitaker	2.25	1.25	.70
72	Ron Taylor	2.25	1.25	.70
73	Johnny Briggs	2.25	1.25	.70
74	Preston Gomez	2.25	1.25	.70
75	Luis Aparicio	2.25	1.25	.70
76	Norm Miller	2.25	1.25	.70
77	Ron Perranoski	2.25	1.25	.70
78	Tom Satriano	2.25	1.25	.70
79	Milt Pappas	2.25	1.25	.70
80	Norm Cash	2.25	1.25	.70
81	Mel Queen	2.25	1.25	.70
82	Pirates Rookies (Rich Hebner, Al Oliver)	17.00	8.50	5.00
83	Mike Ferraro	2.25	1.25	.70
84	Bob Humphreys	2.25	1.25	.70
85	Lou Brock	30.00	15.00	9.00
86	Pete Richert	2.25	1.25	.70
87	Horace Clarke	2.25	1.25	.70
88	Rich Nye	2.25	1.25	.70
89	Russ Gibson	2.25	1.25	.70
90	Jerry Koosman	8.50	4.25	2.50
91	Al Dark	2.25	1.25	.70
92	Jack Billingham	2.25	1.25	.70
93	Joe Foy	2.25	1.25	.70
94	Hank Aguirre	2.25	1.25	.70
95	Johnny Bench	135.00	67.00	40.00
96	Denver Lemaster	2.25	1.25	.70
97	Buddy Bradford	2.25	1.25	.70
98	Dave Giusti	2.25	1.25	.70
99	Twins Rookies (Danny Morris, Graig Nettles)	30.00	15.00	9.00
100	Hank Aaron	65.00	32.00	19.50
101	Daryl Patterson	2.25	1.25	.70
102	Jim Davenport	2.25	1.25	.70
103	Roger Repoz	2.25	1.25	.70
104	Steve Blass	2.25	1.25	.70
105	Rick Monday	2.25	1.25	.70
106	Jim Hannan	2.25	1.25	.70
107	Checklist 2 (Bob Gibson)	2.25	1.25	.70
108	Tony Taylor	2.25	1.25	.70
109	Jim Lonborg	2.25	1.25	.70
110	Mike Shannon	2.25	1.25	.70
111	Johnny Morris	2.25	1.25	.70
112	J.C. Martin	2.25	1.25	.70
113	Dave May	2.25	1.25	.70
114	Yankees Rookies (Alan Closter, John Cumberland)	2.25	1.25	.70
115	Bill Hands	2.25	1.25	.70
116	Chuck Harrison	2.25	1.25	.70
117	Jim Fairey	2.25	1.25	.70
118	Stan Williams	2.25	1.25	.70
119	Doug Rader	2.25	1.25	.70
120	Pete Rose	42.50	21.00	12.50
121	Joe Grzenda	2.25	1.25	.70
122	Ron Fairly	2.25	1.25	.70
123	Wilbur Wood	2.25	1.25	.70
124	Hank Bauer	2.25	1.25	.70
125	Ray Sadecki	2.25	1.25	.70
126	Dick Tracewski	2.25	1.25	.70
127	Kevin Collins	2.25	1.25	.70
128	Tommie Aaron	2.25	1.25	.70
129	Bill McCool	2.25	1.25	.70
130	Carl Yastrzemski	32.00	16.00	9.50
131	Chris Cannizzaro	2.25	1.25	.70
132	Dave Baldwin	2.25	1.25	.70
133	Johnny Callison	2.25	1.25	.70
134	Jim Weaver	2.25	1.25	.70
135	Tommy Davis	2.25	1.25	.70
136	Cards Rookies (Steve Huntz, Mike Torrez)	2.25	1.25	.70
137	Wally Bunker	2.25	1.25	.70
138	John Bateman	2.25	1.25	.70
139	Andy Kosco	2.25	1.25	.70
140	Jim Lefebvre	2.25	1.25	.70
141	Bill Dillman	2.25	1.25	.70
142	Woody Woodward	2.25	1.25	.70
143	Joe Nossek	2.25	1.25	.70
144	Bob Hendley	2.25	1.25	.70
145	Max Alvis	2.25	1.25	.70
146	Jim Perry	2.25	1.25	.70
147	Leo Durocher	2.25	1.25	.70
148	Lee Stange	2.25	1.25	.70
149	Ollie Brown	2.25	1.25	.70
150	Denny McLain	2.25	1.25	.70
151	Clay Dalrymple	2.25	1.25	.70
152	Tommie Sisk	2.25	1.25	.70
153	Ed Brinkman	2.25	1.25	.70
154	Jim Britton	2.25	1.25	.70
155	Pete Ward	2.25	1.25	.70
156	Astros Rookies (Hal Gilson, Leon McFadden)	2.25	1.25	.70
157	Bob Rodgers	2.25	1.25	.70
158	Joe Gibbon	2.25	1.25	.70
159	Jerry Adair	2.25	1.25	.70
160	Vada Pinson	2.25	1.25	.70
161	John Purdin	2.25	1.25	.70
162	World Series Game 1 (Gibson Fans 17; Sets New Record)	8.50	4.25	2.50
163	World Series Game 2 (Tiger Homers Deck The Cards)	2.25	1.25	.70
164	World Series Game 3 (McCarver's Homer Puts St. Louis Ahead)	8.50	4.25	2.50
165	World Series Game 4 (Brock's Lead-Off Homer Starts Cards' Romp)	8.50	4.25	2.50
166	World Series Game 5 (Kaline's Key Hit Sparks Tiger Rally)	11.00	5.50	3.25
167	World Series Game 6 (Tiger 10-Run Inning Ties Mark)	2.25	1.25	.70
168	World Series Game 7 (Lolich Series Hero, Outduels Gibson)	8.50	4.25	2.50
169	World Series Summary (Tigers Celebrate Their Victory)	2.25	1.25	.70
170	Frank Howard	2.25	1.25	.70
171	Glenn Beckert	2.25	1.25	.70
172	Jerry Stephenson	2.25	1.25	.70
173	White Sox Rookies (Bob Christian, Gerry Nyman)	2.25	1.25	.70
174	Grant Jackson	2.25	1.25	.70
175	Jim Bunning	2.50	1.25	.70
176	Joe Azcue	2.25	1.25	.70
177	Ron Reed	2.25	1.25	.70
178	Ray Oyler	2.25	1.25	.70
179	Don Pavletich	2.25	1.25	.70
180	Willie Horton	2.25	1.25	.70
181	Mel Nelson	2.25	1.25	.70
182	Bill Rigney	2.25	1.25	.70
183	Don Shaw	2.25	1.25	.70
184	Roberto Pena	2.25	1.25	.70
185	Tom Phoebus	2.25	1.25	.70
186	John Edwards	1.00	.50	.30
187	Leon Wagner	2.25	1.25	.70
188	Rick Wise	2.25	1.25	.70
189	Red Sox Rookies (Joe Lahoud, John Thibdeau)	2.25	1.25	.70
190	Willie Mays	75.00	37.00	22.00
191	Lindy McDaniel	2.25	1.25	.70
192	Jose Pagan	2.25	1.25	.70
193	Don Cardwell	2.25	1.25	.70
194	Ted Uhlaender	2.25	1.25	.70
195	John Odom	2.25	1.25	.70
196	Lum Harris	2.25	1.25	.70
197	Dick Selma	2.25	1.25	.70
198	Willie Smith	2.25	1.25	.70
199	Jim French	2.25	1.25	.70
200	Bob Gibson	21.00	10.50	6.25
201	Russ Snyder	2.25	1.25	.70
202	Don Wilson	2.25	1.25	.70
203	Dave Johnson	2.25	1.25	.70
204	Jack Hiatt	2.25	1.25	.70
205	Rick Reichardt	2.25	1.25	.70
206	Phillies Rookies (Larry Hisle, Barry Lersch)	2.25	1.25	.70
207	Roy Face	2.25	1.25	.70
208	Donn Clendenon	2.25	1.25	.70
209	Larry Haney	2.25	1.25	.70
210	Felix Millan	2.25	1.25	.70
211	Galen Cisco	2.25	1.25	.70
212	Tom Tresh	2.25	1.25	.70
213	Gerry Arrigo	2.25	1.25	.70
214	Checklist 3	2.25	1.25	.70
215	Rico Petrocelli	2.25	1.25	.70
216	Don Sutton	10.25	5.25	3.00
217	John Donaldson	2.25	1.25	.70
218	John Roseboro	2.25	1.25	.70

1969 O-Pee-Chee Deckle

Very similar in design to the Topps Deckle Edge set of the same year, the 1969 O-Pee-Chee Deckle-Edge set consists of 24 unnumbered black and white cards. The Canadian-issued O-Pee-Chee cards, measuring 2-1/8" by 3-1/8", are slightly smaller than the corresponding Topps set, but feature the same "deckle cut" borders. The O-Pee-Chee set is blank-backed and has the facsimile autographs in black ink, rather than blue.

		NR MT	EX	VG
Complete Set:		250.00	125.00	75.00
Common Player:		1.50	1.00	.60
(1)	Rich Allen	3.00	1.50	.90
(2)	Luis Aparicio	6.00	3.00	1.75
(3)	Rodney Carew	12.00	6.00	3.50
(4)	Roberto Clemente	50.00	25.00	15.00
(5)	Curt Flood	2.00	1.00	.60
(6)	Bill Freehan	2.00	1.00	.60
(7)	Robert Gibson	10.00	5.00	3.00
(8)	Ken Harrelson	1.50	.70	.45
(9)	Tommy Helms	1.50	.70	.45
(10)	Tom Haller	1.75	.90	.50
(11)	Willie Horton	1.50	.70	.45
(12)	Frank Howard	2.50	1.25	.70
(13)	Willie McCovey	12.00	6.00	3.50
(14)	Denny McLain	4.00	2.00	1.25
(15)	Juan Marichal	10.00	5.00	3.00
(16)	Willie Mays	50.00	25.00	15.00
(17)	John "Boog" Powell	4.00	2.00	1.25
(18)	Brooks Robinson	20.00	10.00	6.00
(19)	Ronald Santo	2.25	1.25	.70
(20)	Rusty Staub	2.00	1.00	.60
(21)	Mel Stottlemyre	1.50	.70	.45
(22)	Luis Tiant	1.50	.70	.45
(23)	Maurie Wills	2.25	1.25	.70
(24)	Carl Yastrzemski	20.00	10.00	6.00

1970 O-Pee-Chee

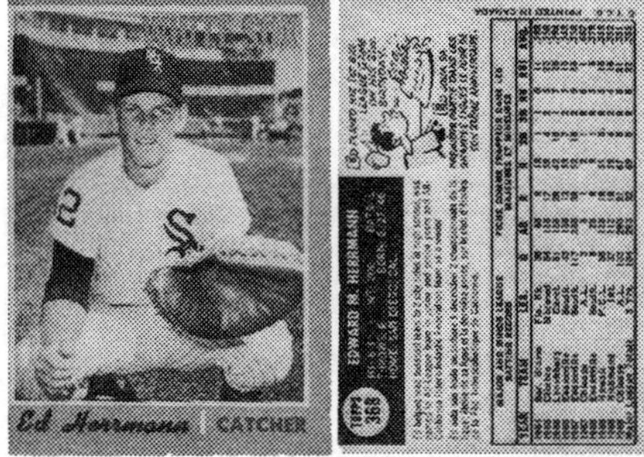

The 1970 O-Pee-Chee set, identical in design to the 1970 Topps set, expanded to 546 cards, measuring 2-1/2" by 3-1/2". The Canadian-issued O-Pee-Chee set is easy to distinguish because the backs are printed in both French and English and include the words "Printed in Canada."

		NR MT	EX	VG
Complete Set (546):		1700.	850.00	500.00
Common Player (1-263):		1.00	.50	.30
Common Player (264-459):		1.75	.90	.50
Common Player (460-546):		2.25	1.25	.70
1	World Champions (Mets Team)	17.00	8.50	5.00
2	Diego Segui	1.00	.50	.30
3	Darrel Chaney	1.00	.50	.30
4	Tom Egan	1.00	.50	.30
5	Wes Parker	1.00	.50	.30
6	Grant Jackson	1.00	.50	.30
7	Indians Rookies (Gary Boyd, Russ Nagelson)	1.00	.50	.30
8	Jose Martinez	1.00	.50	.30
9	Checklist 1	1.50	.70	.45
10	Carl Yastrzemski	25.00	12.50	7.50
11	Nate Colbert	1.00	.50	.30
12	John Hiller	1.00	.50	.30
13	Jack Hiatt	1.00	.50	.30
14	Hank Allen	1.00	.50	.30
15	Larry Dierker	1.00	.50	.30
16	Charlie Metro	1.00	.50	.30
17	Hoyt Wilhelm	2.50	1.25	.70
18	Carlos May	1.00	.50	.30
19	John Boccabella	1.00	.50	.30
20	Dave McNally	1.00	.50	.30
21	Athletics Rookies (Vida Blue, Gene Tenace)	1.00	.50	.30
22	Ray Washburn	1.00	.50	.30
23	Bill Robinson	1.00	.50	.30
24	Dick Selma	1.00	.50	.30
25	Cesar Tovar	1.00	.50	.30
26	Tug McGraw	1.25	.60	.40
27	Chuck Hinton	1.00	.50	.30
28	Billy Wilson	1.00	.50	.30
29	Sandy Alomar	1.00	.50	.30
30	Matty Alou	1.00	.50	.30
31	Marty Pattin	1.00	.50	.30
32	Harry Walker	1.00	.50	.30
33	Don Wert	1.00	.50	.30
34	Willie Crawford	1.00	.50	.30
35	Joe Horlen	1.00	.50	.30
36	Red Rookies (Danny Breeden, Bernie Carbo)	1.00	.50	.30
37	Dick Drago	1.00	.50	.30
38	Mack Jones	1.00	.50	.30
39	Mike Nagy	1.00	.50	.30
40	Rich Allen	1.50	.70	.45
41	George Lauzerique	1.00	.50	.30
42	Tito Fuentes	1.00	.50	.30
43	Jack Aker	1.00	.50	.30
44	Roberto Pena	1.00	.50	.30
45	Dave Johnson	1.25	.60	.40
46	Ken Rudolph	1.00	.50	.30
47	Bob Miller	1.00	.50	.30
48	Gil Garrido	1.00	.50	.30
49	Tim Cullen	1.00	.50	.30
50	Tommie Agee	1.00	.50	.30
51	Bob Christian	1.00	.50	.30
52	Bruce Dal Canton	1.00	.50	.30
53	John Kennedy	1.00	.50	.30
54	Jeff Torborg	1.00	.50	.30
55	John Odom	1.00	.50	.30
56	Phillies Rookies (Joe Lis, Scott Reid)	1.00	.50	.30
57	Pat Kelly	1.00	.50	.30
58	Dave Marshall	1.00	.50	.30
59	Dick Ellsworth	1.00	.50	.30
60	Jim Wynn	1.00	.50	.30
61	N.L. Batting Leaders (Bob Clemente, Cleon Jones, Pete Rose)	8.50	4.25	2.50
62	A.L. Batting Leaders (Rod Carew, Tony Oliva, Reggie Smith)	1.75	.90	.50
63	N.L. RBI Leaders (Willie McCovey, Tony Perez, Ron Santo)	1.75	.90	.50
64	A.L. RBI Leaders (Reggie Jackson, Harmon Killebrew, Boog Powell)	2.00	1.00	.60
65	N.L. Home Run Leaders (Hank Aaron, Lee May, Willie McCovey)	2.25	1.25	.70
66	A.L. Home Run Leaders (Frank Howard, Reggie Jackson, Harmon Killebrew)	2.00	1.00	.60
67	N.L. ERA Leaders (Steve Carlton, Bob Gibson, Juan Marichal)	7.50	3.75	2.25
68	A.L. ERA Leaders (Dick Bosman, Mike Cuellar, Jim Palmer)	1.50	.70	.45
69	N.L. Pitching Leaders (Fergie Jenkins, Juan Marichal, Phil Niekro, Tom Seaver)	7.50	3.75	2.25
70	A.L. Pitching Leaders (Dave Boswell, Mike Cuellar, Dennis McLain, Dave McNally, Jim Perry, Mel Stottlemyre)	1.25	.60	.40
71	N.L. Strikeout Leaders (Bob Gibson, Fergie Jenkins, Bill Singer)	1.75	.90	.50
72	A.L. Strikeout Leaders (Mickey Lolich, Sam McDowell, Andy Messersmith)	1.25	.60	.40
73	Wayne Granger	1.00	.50	.30
74	Angels Rookies (Greg Washburn, Wally Wolf)	1.00	.50	.30
75	Jim Kaat	1.50	.70	.45
76	Carl Taylor	1.00	.50	.30
77	Frank Linzy	1.00	.50	.30
78	Joe Lahoud	1.00	.50	.30
79	Clay Kirby	1.00	.50	.30
80	Don Kessinger	1.00	.50	.30
81	Dave May	1.00	.50	.30
82	Frank Fernandez	1.00	.50	.30
83	Don Cardwell	1.00	.50	.30
84	Paul Casanova	1.00	.50	.30
85	Max Alvis	1.00	.50	.30
86	Lum Harris	1.00	.50	.30
87	Steve Renko	1.00	.50	.30
88	Pilots Rookies (Dick Baney, Miguel Fuentes)	1.00	.50	.30
89	Juan Rios	1.00	.50	.30
90	Tim McCarver	1.25	.60	.40
91	Rich Morales	1.00	.50	.30
92	George Culver	1.00	.50	.30
93	Rick Renick	1.00	.50	.30
94	Fred Patek	1.00	.50	.30
95	Earl Wilson	1.00	.50	.30
96	Cards Rookies (Leron Lee, Jerry Reuss)	1.50	.70	.45
97	Joe Moeller	1.00	.50	.30
98	Gates Brown	1.00	.50	.30
99	Bobby Pfeil	1.00	.50	.30
100	Mel Stottlemyre	1.00	.50	.30
101	Bobby Floyd	1.00	.50	.30
102	Joe Rudi	1.00	.50	.30
103	Frank Reberger	1.00	.50	.30
104	Gerry Moses	1.00	.50	.30
105	Tony Gonzalez	1.00	.50	.30
106	Darold Knowles	1.00	.50	.30
107	Bobby Etheridge	1.00	.50	.30
108	Tom Burgmeier	1.00	.50	.30
109	Expos Rookies (Garry Jestadt, Carl Morton)	1.00	.50	.30
110	Bob Moose	1.00	.50	.30
111	Mike Hegan	1.00	.50	.30
112	Dave Nelson	1.00	.50	.30
113	Jim Ray	1.00	.50	.30
114	Gene Michael	1.00	.50	.30
115	Alex Johnson	1.00	.50	.30
116	Sparky Lyle	1.25	.60	.40
117	Don Young	1.00	.50	.30
118	George Mitterwald	1.00	.50	.30
119	Chuck Taylor	1.00	.50	.30
120	Sal Bando	1.00	.50	.30
121	Orioles Rookies (Fred Beene, Terry Crowley)	1.00	.50	.30
122	George Stone	1.00	.50	.30
123	Don Gutteridge	1.00	.50	.30
124	Larry Jaster	1.00	.50	.30
125	Deron Johnson	1.00	.50	.30
126	Marty Martinez	1.00	.50	.30
127	Joe Coleman	1.00	.50	.30
128	Checklist 2	1.50	.70	.45
129	Jimmie Price	1.00	.50	.30
130	Ollie Brown	1.00	.50	.30
131	Dodgers Rookies (Ray Lamb, Bob Stinson)	1.00	.50	.30
132	Jim McGlothlin	1.00	.50	.30
133	Clay Carroll	1.00	.50	.30
134	Danny Walton	1.00	.50	.30
135	Dick Dietz	1.00	.50	.30
136	Steve Hargan	1.00	.50	.30
137	Art Shamsky	1.00	.50	.30
138	Joe Foy	1.00	.50	.30
139	Rich Nye	1.00	.50	.30
140	Reggie Jackson	175.00	87.00	52.00
141	Pirates Rookies (Dave Cash, Johnny Jeter)	1.00	.50	.30
142	Fritz Peterson	1.00	.50	.30
143	Phil Gagliano	1.00	.50	.30
144	Ray Culp	1.00	.50	.30
145	Rico Carty	1.00	.50	.30
146	Danny Murphy	1.00	.50	.30
147	Angel Hermoso	1.00	.50	.30
148	Earl Weaver	1.25	.60	.40
149	Billy Champion	1.00	.50	.30
150	Harmon Killebrew	10.25	5.25	3.00
151	Dave Roberts	1.00	.50	.30
152	Ike Brown	1.00	.50	.30
153	Gary Gentry	1.00	.50	.30
154	Senators Rookies (Jan Dukes, Jim Miles)	1.00	.50	.30
155	Denis Menke	1.00	.50	.30
156	Eddie Fisher	1.00	.50	.30
157	Manny Mota	1.00	.50	.30
158	Jerry McNertney	1.00	.50	.30
159	Tommy Helms	1.00	.50	.30
160	Phil Niekro	2.50	1.25	.70
161	Richie Scheinblum	1.00	.50	.30
162	Jerry Johnson	1.00	.50	.30
163	Syd O'Brien	1.00	.50	.30
164	Ty Cline	1.00	.50	.30
165	Ed kirkpatrick	1.00	.50	.30
166	Al Oliver	2.50	1.25	.70
167	Bill Burbach	1.00	.50	.30
168	Dave Watkins	1.00	.50	.30
169	Tom Hall	1.00	.50	.30
170	Billy Williams	8.50	4.25	2.50
171	Jim Nash	1.00	.50	.30
172	Braves Rookies (Ralph Garr, Garry Hill)	1.00	.50	.30
173	Jim Hicks	1.00	.50	.30
174	Ted Sizemore	1.00	.50	.30
175	Dick Bosman	1.00	.50	.30
176	Jim Hart	1.00	.50	.30
177	Jim Northrup	1.00	.50	.30
178	Denny Lemaster	1.00	.50	.30
179	Ivan Murrell	1.00	.50	.30
180	Tommy John	1.75	.90	.50
181	Sparky Anderson	1.25	.60	.40
182	Dick Hall	1.00	.50	.30
183	Jerry Grote	1.00	.50	.30
184	Ray Fosse	1.00	.50	.30
185	Don Mincher	1.00	.50	.30
186	Rick Joseph	1.00	.50	.30
187	Mike Hedlund	1.00	.50	.30
188	Manny Sanguillen	1.00	.50	.30
189	Yankees Rookies (Dave McDonald, Thurman Munson)	105.00	52.00	31.00
190	Joe Torre	1.25	.60	.40
191	Vicente Romo	1.00	.50	.30
192	Jim Qualls	1.00	.50	.30
193	Mike Wegener	1.00	.50	.30
194	Chuck Manuel	1.00	.50	.30
195	N.L. Playoff Game 1 (Seaver Wins Opener!)	18.00	9.00	5.50
196	N.L. Playoff Game 2 (Mets Show Muscle!)	1.00	.50	.30
197	N.L. Playoff Game 3 (Ryan Saves The Day!)	34.00	17.00	10.00
198	N.L. Playoff Summary (We're Number One!)	12.75	6.50	3.75
199	A.L. Playoff Game 1 (Orioles Win A Squeaker!)	1.00	.50	.30
200	A.L. Playoff Game 2 (Powell Scores Winning Run!)	1.25	.60	.40
201	A.L. Playoff Game 3 (Birds Wrap It Up!)	1.00	.50	.30
202	A.L. Playoffs Summary (Sweep Twins In Three!)	1.00	.50	.30
203	Rudy May	1.00	.50	.30
204	Len Gabrielson	1.00	.50	.30
205	Bert Campaneris	1.00	.50	.30
206	Clete Boyer	1.00	.50	.30
207	Tigers Rookies (Norman McRae, Bob Reed)	1.00	.50	.30
208	Fred Gladding	1.00	.50	.30
209	Ken Suarez	1.00	.50	.30
210	Juan Marichal	7.50	3.75	2.25
211	Ted Williams	12.00	6.00	3.50
212	Al Santorini	1.00	.50	.30

213 Andy Etchebarren 1.00 .50 .30
214 Ken Boswell 1.00 .50 .30
215 Reggie Smith 1.00 .50 .30
216 Chuck Hartenstein 1.00 .50 .30
217 Ron Hansen 1.00 .50 .30
218 Ron Stone 1.00 .50 .30
219 Jerry Kenney 1.00 .50 .30
220 Steve Carlton 42.50 21.00 12.50
221 Ron Brand 1.00 .50 .30
222 Jim Rooker 1.00 .50 .30
223 Nate Oliver 1.00 .50 .30
224 Steve Barber 1.00 .50 .30
225 Lee May 1.00 .50 .30
226 Ron Perranoski 1.00 .50 .30
227 Astros Rookies (John Mayberry, Bob Watkins) 1.00 .50 .30
228 Aurelio Rodriguez 1.00 .50 .30
229 Rich Robertson 1.00 .50 .30
230 Brooks Robinson 15.00 7.50 4.50
231 Luis Tiant 1.00 .50 .30
232 Bob Didier 1.00 .50 .30
233 Lew Krausse 1.00 .50 .30
234 Tommy Dean 1.00 .50 .30
235 Mike Epstein 1.00 .50 .30
236 Bob Veale 1.00 .50 .30
237 Russ Gibson 1.00 .50 .30
238 Jose Laboy 1.00 .50 .30
239 Ken Berry 1.00 .50 .30
240 Fergie Jenkins 12.75 6.50 3.75
241 Royals Rookies (Al Fitzmorris, Scott Northey) 1.00 .50 .30
242 Walter Alston 1.25 .60 .40
243 Joe Sparma 1.00 .50 .30
244 Checklist 3 1.50 .70 .45
245 Leo Cardenas 1.00 .50 .30
246 Jim McAndrew 1.00 .50 .30
247 Lou Klimchock 1.00 .50 .30
248 Jesus Alou 1.00 .50 .30
249 Bob Locker 1.00 .50 .30
250 Willie McCovey 12.75 6.50 3.75
251 Dick Schofield 1.00 .50 .30
252 Lowell Palmer 1.00 .50 .30
253 Ron Woods 1.00 .50 .30
254 Camilo Pascual 1.00 .50 .30
255 Jim Spencer 1.00 .50 .30
256 Vic Davalillo 1.00 .50 .30
257 Dennis Higgins 1.00 .50 .30
258 Paul Popovich 1.00 .50 .30
259 Tommie Reynolds 1.00 .50 .30
260 Claude Osteen 1.00 .50 .30
261 Curt Motton 1.00 .50 .30
262 Padres Rookies (Jerry Morales, Jim Williams) 1.00 .50 .30
263 Duane Josephson 1.00 .50 .30
264 Rich Hebner 1.75 .90 .50
265 Randy Hundley 1.75 .90 .50
266 Wally Bunker 1.75 .90 .50
267 Twins Rookies (Herman Hill, Paul Ratliff) 1.75 .90 .50
268 Claude Raymond 1.75 .90 .50
269 Cesar Gutierrez 1.75 .90 .50
270 Chris Short 1.75 .90 .50
271 Greg Goossen 1.75 .90 .50
272 Hector Torres 1.75 .90 .50
273 Ralph Houk 1.75 .90 .50
274 Gerry Arrigo 1.75 .90 .50
275 Duke Sims 1.75 .90 .50
276 Ron Hunt 1.75 .90 .50
277 Paul Doyle 1.75 .90 .50
278 Tommie Aaron 1.75 .90 .50
279 Bill Lee 1.75 .90 .50
280 Donn Clendenon 1.75 .90 .50
281 Casey Cox 1.75 .90 .50
282 Steve Huntz 1.75 .90 .50
283 Angel Bravo 1.75 .90 .50
284 Jack Baldschun 1.75 .90 .50
285 Paul Blair 1.75 .90 .50
286 Dodgers Rookies (Bill Buckner, Jack Jenkins) 10.25 5.25 3.00
287 Fred Talbot 1.75 .90 .50
288 Larry Hisle 1.75 .90 .50
289 Gene Brabender 1.75 .90 .50
290 Rod Carew 46.00 23.00 14.00
291 Leo Durocher 1.75 .90 .50
292 Eddie Leon 1.75 .90 .50
293 Bob Bailey 1.75 .90 .50
294 Jose Azcue 1.75 .90 .50
295 Cecil Upshaw 1.75 .90 .50
296 Woody Woodward 1.75 .90 .50
297 Curt Blefary 1.75 .90 .50
298 Ken Henderson 1.75 .90 .50
299 Buddy Bradford 1.75 .90 .50
300 Tom Seaver 85.00 42.00 25.00
301 Chico Salmon 1.75 .90 .50
302 Jeff James 1.75 .90 .50
303 Brant Alyea 1.75 .90 .50
304 Bill Russell 1.75 .90 .50
305 World Series Game 1 (Buford Belts Leadoff Homer!) 1.75 .90 .50
306 World Series Game 2 (Clendenon's Homer Breaks Ice!) 1.75 .90 .50
307 World Series Game 3 (Agee's Catch Saves The Day!) 1.75 .90 .50
308 World Series Game 4 (Martin's Bunt Ends Deadlock!) 1.75 .90 .50
309 World Series Game 5 (Koosman Shuts The Door!) 1.75 .90 .50
310 World Series Summary (Mets Whoop It Up!) 1.75 .90 .50
311 Dick Green 1.75 .90 .50
312 Mike Torrez 1.75 .90 .50
313 Mayo Smith 1.75 .90 .50
314 Bill McCool 1.75 .90 .50
315 Luis Aparicio 3.50 1.75 1.00
316 Skip Guinn 1.75 .90 .50
317 Red Sox Rookies (Luis Alvarado, Billy Conigliaro) 1.75 .90 .50
318 Willie Smith 1.75 .90 .50
319 Clayton Dalrymple 1.75 .90 .50
320 Jim Maloney 1.75 .90 .50
321 Lou Piniella 1.75 .90 .50
322 Luke Walker 1.75 .90 .50
323 Wayne Comer 1.75 .90 .50
324 Tony Taylor 1.75 .90 .50
325 Dave Boswell 1.75 .90 .50
326 Bill Voss 1.75 .90 .50
327 Hal King 1.75 .90 .50
328 George Brunet 1.75 .90 .50
329 Chris Cannizzaro 1.75 .90 .50
330 Lou Brock 12.75 6.50 3.75
331 Chuck Dobson 1.75 .90 .50
332 Bobby Wine 1.75 .90 .50
333 Bobby Murcer 1.75 .90 .50
334 Phil Regan 1.75 .90 .50
335 Bill Freehan 1.75 .90 .50
336 Del Unser 1.75 .90 .50
337 Mike McCormick 1.75 .90 .50
338 Paul Schaal 1.75 .90 .50
339 Johnny Edwards 1.75 .90 .50
340 Tony Conigliaro 1.75 .90 .50
341 Bill Sudakis 1.75 .90 .50
342 Wilbur Wood 1.75 .90 .50
343 Checklist 4 2.00 1.00 .60
344 Marcelino Lopez 1.75 .90 .50
345 Al Ferrara 1.75 .90 .50
346 Red Schoendienst 1.75 .90 .50
347 Russ Snyder 1.75 .90 .50
348 Mets Rookies (Jesse Hudson, Mike Jorgensen) 1.75 .90 .50
349 Steve Hamilton 1.75 .90 .50
350 Roberto Clemente 63.00 31.00 19.00
351 Tom Murphy 1.75 .90 .50
352 Bob Barton 1.75 .90 .50
353 Stan Williams 1.75 .90 .50
354 Amos Otis 1.75 .90 .50
355 Doug Rader 1.75 .90 .50
356 Fred Lasher 1.75 .90 .50
357 Bob Burda 1.75 .90 .50
358 Pedro Borbon 1.75 .90 .50
359 Phil Roof 1.75 .90 .50
360 Curt Flood 1.75 .90 .50
361 Ray Jarvis 1.75 .90 .50
362 Joe Hague 1.75 .90 .50
363 Tom Shopay 1.75 .90 .50
364 Dan McGinn 1.75 .90 .50
365 Zoilo Versalles 1.75 .90 .50
366 Barry Moore 1.75 .90 .50
367 Mike Lum 1.75 .90 .50
368 Ed Herrmann 1.75 .90 .50
369 Alan Foster 1.75 .90 .50
370 Tommy Harper 1.75 .90 .50
371 Rod Gaspar 1.75 .90 .50
372 Dave Giusti 1.75 .90 .50
373 Roy White 1.75 .90 .50
374 Tommie Sisk 1.75 .90 .50
375 Johnny Callison 1.75 .90 .50
376 Lefty Phillips 1.75 .90 .50
377 Bill Butler 1.75 .90 .50
378 Jim Davenport 1.75 .90 .50
379 Tom Tischinski 1.75 .90 .50
380 Tony Perez 11.00 5.50 3.25
381 Athletics Rookies (Bobby Brooks, Mike Olivo) 1.75 .90 .50
382 Jack DiLauro 1.75 .90 .50
383 Mickey Stanley 1.75 .90 .50
384 Gary Neibauer 1.75 .90 .50
385 George Scott 1.75 .90 .50
386 Bill Dillman 1.75 .90 .50
387 Orioles Team 1.75 .90 .50
388 Byron Browne 1.75 .90 .50
389 Jim Shellenback 1.75 .90 .50
390 Willie Davis 1.75 .90 .50
391 Larry Brown 1.75 .90 .50
392 Walt Hriniak 1.75 .90 .50
393 John Gelnar 1.75 .90 .50
394 Gil Hodges 2.50 1.25 .70
395 Walt Williams 1.75 .90 .50
396 Steve Blass 1.75 .90 .50
397 Roger Repoz 1.75 .90 .50
398 Bill Stoneman 1.75 .90 .50
399 Yankees Team 2.00 1.00 .60
400 Denny McLain 1.75 .90 .50
401 Giants Rookies (John Harrell, Bernie Williams) 1.75 .90 .50
402 Ellie Rodriguez 1.75 .90 .50
403 Jim Bunning 2.00 1.00 .60
404 Rich Reese 1.75 .90 .50
405 Bill Hands 1.75 .90 .50
406 Mike Andrews 1.75 .90 .50
407 Bob Watson 1.75 .90 .50
408 Paul Lindblad 1.75 .90 .50
409 Bob Tolan 1.75 .90 .50
410 Boog Powell 1.75 .90 .50
411 Dodgers Team 1.75 .90 .50
412 Larry Burchart 1.75 .90 .50
413 Sonny Jackson 1.75 .90 .50
414 Paul Edmondson 1.75 .90 .50
415 Julian Javier 1.75 .90 .50
416 Joe Verbanic 1.75 .90 .50
417 John Bateman 1.75 .90 .50
418 John Donaldson 1.75 .90 .50
419 Ron Taylor 1.75 .90 .50
420 Ken McMullen 1.75 .90 .50
421 Pat Dobson 1.75 .90 .50
422 Royals Team 1.75 .90 .50
423 Jerry May 1.75 .90 .50
424 Mike Kilkenny 1.75 .90 .50
425 Bobby Bonds 12.00 6.00 3.50
426 Bill Rigney 1.75 .90 .50
427 Fred Norman 1.75 .90 .50
428 Don Buford 1.75 .90 .50
429 Cubs Rookies (Randy Bobb, Jim Cosman) 1.75 .90 .50
430 Andy Messersmith 1.75 .90 .50
431 Ron Swoboda 1.75 .90 .50
432 Checklist 5 1.75 .90 .50
433 Ron Bryant 1.75 .90 .50
434 Felipe Alou 1.75 .90 .50
435 Nelson Briles 1.75 .90 .50
436 Phillies Team 1.75 .90 .50
437 Danny Cater 1.75 .90 .50
438 Pat Jarvis 1.75 .90 .50
439 Lee Maye 1.75 .90 .50
440 Bill Mazeroski 1.75 .90 .50
441 John O'Donoghue 1.75 .90 .50
442 Gene Mauch 1.75 .90 .50
443 Al Jackson 1.75 .90 .50
444 White Sox Rookies (Billy Farmer, John Matias) 1.75 .90 .50
445 Vada Pinson 1.75 .90 .50
446 Billy Grabarkewitz 1.75 .90 .50
447 Lee Stange 1.75 .90 .50
448 Astros Team 1.75 .90 .50
449 Jim Palmer 25.00 12.50 7.50
450 Willie McCovey AS 2.50 1.25 .70
451 Boog Powell AS 1.75 .90 .50
452 Felix Millan AS 1.75 .90 .50
453 Rod Carew AS 10.25 5.25 3.00
454 Ron Santo AS 1.75 .90 .50
455 Brooks Robinson AS 2.50 1.25 .70
456 Don Kessinger AS 1.75 .90 .50
457 Rico Petrocelli AS 1.75 .90 .50
458 Pete Rose AS 15.00 7.50 4.50
459 Reggie Jackson AS 30.00 15.00 9.00
460 Matty Alou AS 2.25 1.25 .70
461 Carl Yastrzemski AS 12.75 6.50 3.75
462 Hank Aaron As 20.00 10.00 6.00
463 Frank Robinson AS 8.50 4.25 2.50
464 Johnny Bench AS 15.00 7.50 4.50
465 Bill Freehan AS 2.25 1.25 .70
466 Juan Marichal AS 3.00 1.50 .90
467 Denny McLain AS 3.00 1.50 .90
468 Jerry Koosman AS 2.25 1.25 .70
469 Sam McDowell AS 2.25 1.25 .70
470 Willie Stargell 12.75 6.50 3.75
471 Chris Zachary 2.25 1.25 .70
472 Braves Team 2.25 1.25 .70
473 Don Bryant 2.25 1.25 .70
474 Dick Kelley 2.25 1.25 .70
475 Dick McAuliffe 2.25 1.25 .70
476 Don Shaw 2.25 1.25 .70
477 Orioles Rookies (Roger Freed, Al Severinsen) 2.25 1.25 .70
478 Bob Heise 2.25 1.25 .70
479 Dick Woodson 2.25 1.25 .70
480 Glenn Beckert 2.25 1.25 .70
481 Jose Tartabull 2.25 1.25 .70
482 Tom Hilgendorf 2.25 1.25 .70
483 Gail Hopkins 2.25 1.25 .70
484 Gary Nolan 2.25 1.25 .70
485 Jay Johnstone 2.25 1.25 .70
486 Terry Harmon 2.25 1.25 .70
487 Cisco Carlos 2.25 1.25 .70
488 J.C. Martin 2.25 1.25 .70
489 Eddie Kasko 2.25 1.25 .70
490 Bill Singer 2.25 1.25 .70
491 Graig Nettles 7.50 3.75 2.25
492 Astros Rookies (Keith Lampard, Scipio Spinks) 2.25 1.25 .70
493 Lindy McDaniel 2.25 1.25 .70
494 Larry Stahl 2.25 1.25 .70
495 Dave Morehead 2.25 1.25 .70
496 Steve Whitaker 2.25 1.25 .70
497 Eddie Watt 2.25 1.25 .70
498 Al Weis 2.25 1.25 .70
499 Skip Lockwood 2.25 1.25 .70
500 Hank Aaron 75.00 37.00 22.00
501 White Sox Team 2.25 1.25 .70
502 Rollie Fingers 34.00 17.00 10.00
503 Dal Maxvill 2.25 1.25 .70
504 Don Pavletich 2.25 1.25 .70
505 Ken Holtzman 2.25 1.25 .70
506 Ed Stroud 2.25 1.25 .70
507 Pat Corrales 2.25 1.25 .70
508 Joe Niekro 2.25 1.25 .70
509 Expos Team 2.25 1.25 .70
510 Tony Oliva 2.25 1.25 .70
511 Joe Hoerner 2.25 1.25 .70
512 Billy Harris 2.25 1.25 .70
513 Preston Gomez 2.25 1.25 .70
514 Steve Hovley 2.25 1.25 .70
515 Don Wilson 2.25 1.25 .70
516 Yankees Rookies (John Ellis, Jim Lyttle) 2.25 1.25 .70
517 Joe Gibbon 2.25 1.25 .70
518 Bill Melton 2.25 1.25 .70
519 Don McMahon 2.25 1.25 .70
520 Willie Horton 2.25 1.25 .70
521 Cal Koonce 2.25 1.25 .70
522 Angels Team 2.25 1.25 .70
523 Jose Pena 2.25 1.25 .70
524 Alvin Dark 2.25 1.25 .70
525 Jerry Adair 2.25 1.25 .70
526 Ron Herbel 2.25 1.25 .70
527 Don Bosch 2.25 1.25 .70
528 Elrod Hendricks 2.25 1.25 .70
529 Bob Aspromonte 2.25 1.25 .70
530 Bob Gibson 17.00 8.50 5.00
531 Ron Clark 2.25 1.25 .70
532 Danny Murtaugh 2.25 1.25 .70
533 Buzz Stephen 2.25 1.25 .70
534 Twins Team 2.25 1.25 .70
535 Andy Kosco 2.25 1.25 .70
536 Mike Kekich 2.25 1.25 .70
537 Joe Morgan 3.00 1.50 .90
538 Bob Humphreys 2.25 1.25 .70
539 Phillies Rookies (Larry Bowa, Dennis Doyle) 7.50 3.75 2.25
540 Gary Peters 2.25 1.25 .70
541 Bill Heath 2.25 1.25 .70
542 Checklist 6 2.25 1.25 .70
543 Clyde Wright 2.25 1.25 .70
544 Reds Team 2.25 1.25 .70
545 Ken Harrelson 2.25 1.25 .70
546 Ron Reed 2.25 1.25 .70

1971 O-Pee-Chee

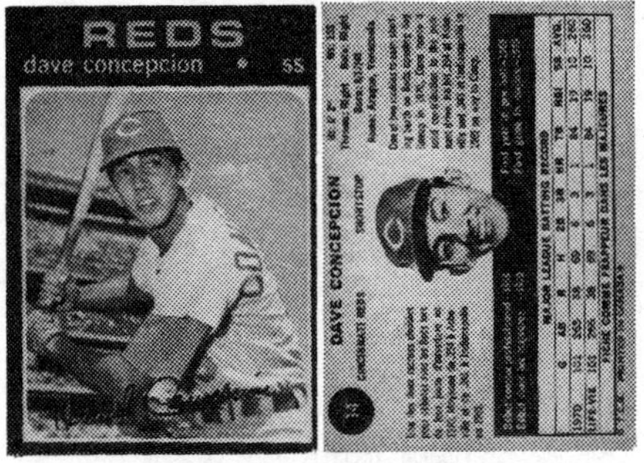

For 1971 O-Pee-Chee increased the number of cards in its set to 752, the same as the 1971 Topps set, which shares the same black-bordered design. The backs of the Canadian-issued O-Pee-Chee cards are yellow, rather than green, and the backs (except card numbers 524-752) are printed in both French and English. The words "Printed in Canada" appear on the back. Fourteen of the O-Pee-Chee cards have different photos from their corresponding Topps' cards or list the player with a different team. The cards measure the standard 2-1/2" by 3-1/2".

	NR MT	EX	VG
Complete Set (752):	2550.	1275.	750.00
Common Player (1-393):	1.50	.70	.45
Common Player (394-523):	2.50	1.25	.70
Common Player (524-643):	5.00	2.50	1.50
Common Player (644-752):	6.75	3.50	2.00

#	Player	NR MT	EX	VG
1	World Champions (Orioles Team)	15.00	7.50	4.50
2	Dock Ellis	1.50	.70	.45
3	Dick McAuliffe	1.50	.70	.45
4	Vic Davalillo	1.50	.70	.45
5	Thurman Munson	50.00	25.00	15.00
6	Ed Spiezio	1.50	.70	.45
7	Jim Holt	1.50	.70	.45
8	Mike McQueen	1.50	.70	.45
9	George Scott	1.50	.70	.45
10	Claude Osteen	1.50	.70	.45
11	Elliott Maddox	1.50	.70	.45
12	Johnny Callison	1.50	.70	.45
13	White Sox Rookies (Charlie Brinkman, Dick Moloney)	1.50	.70	.45
14	Dave Concepcion	30.00	15.00	9.00
15	Andy Messersmith	1.50	.70	.45
16	Ken Singleton	1.50	.70	.45
17	Billy Sorrell	1.50	.70	.45
18	Norm Miller	1.50	.70	.45
19	Skip Pitlock	1.50	.70	.45
20	Reggie Jackson	127.50	64.00	38.00
21	Dan McGinn	1.50	.70	.45
22	Phil Roof	1.50	.70	.45
23	Oscar Gamble	1.50	.70	.45
24	Rich Hand	1.50	.70	.45
25	Clarence Gaston	1.50	.70	.45
26	Bert Blyleven	46.00	23.00	14.00
27	Pirates Rookies (Fred Cambria, Gene Clines)	1.50	.70	.45
28	Ron Klimkowski	1.50	.70	.45
29	Don Buford	1.50	.70	.45
30	Phil Niekro	2.25	1.25	.70
31	John Bateman	1.50	.70	.45
32	Jerry DaVanon	1.50	.70	.45
33	Del Unser	1.50	.70	.45
34	Sandy Vance	1.50	.70	.45
35	Lou Piniella	1.50	.70	.45
36	Dean Chance	1.50	.70	.45
37	Rich McKinney	1.50	.70	.45
38	Jim Colborn	1.50	.70	.45
39	Tigers Rookies (Gene Lamont, Lerrin LaGrow)	1.50	.70	.45
40	Lee May	1.50	.70	.45
41	Rick Austin	1.50	.70	.45
42	Boots Day	1.50	.70	.45
43	Steve Kealey	1.50	.70	.45
44	Johnny Edwards	1.50	.70	.45
45	Jim Hunter	10.25	5.25	3.00
46	Dave Campbell	1.50	.70	.45
47	Johnny Jeter	1.50	.70	.45
48	Dave Baldwin	1.50	.70	.45
49	Don Money	1.50	.70	.45
50	Willie McCovey	12.75	6.50	3.75
51	Steve Kline	1.50	.70	.45
52	Braves Rookies (Oscar Brown, Earl Williams)	1.50	.70	.45
53	Paul Blair	1.50	.70	.45
54	Checklist 1	1.50	.70	.45
55	Steve Carlton	32.00	16.00	9.50
56	Duane Josephson	1.50	.70	.45
57	Von Joshua	1.50	.70	.45
58	Bill Lee	1.50	.70	.45
59	Gene Mauch	1.50	.70	.45
60	Dick Bosman	1.50	.70	.45
61	A.L. Batting Leaders (Alex Johnson, Tony Oliva, Carl Yastrzemski)	1.50	.70	.45
62	N.L. Batting Leaders (Rico Carty, Manny Sanguillen, Joe Torre)	1.50	.70	.45
63	A.L. RBI Leaders (Tony Conigliaro, Frank Howard, Boog Powell)	1.50	.70	.45
64	N.L. RBI Leaders (Johnny Bench, Tony Perez, Billy Williams)	1.50	.70	.45
65	A.L. HR Leaders (Frank Howard, Harmon Killebrew, Carl Yastrzemski)	1.50	.70	.45
66	N.L. HR Leaders (Johnny Bench, Tony Perez, Billy Williams)	1.50	.70	.45
67	A.L. ERA Leaders (Jim Palmer, Diego Segui, Clyde Wright)	1.50	.70	.45
68	N.L. ERA Leader (Tom Seaver, Wayne Simpson, Luke Walker)	1.50	.70	.45
69	A.L. Pitching Leaders (Mike Cuellar, Dave McNally, Jim Perry)	1.50	.70	.45
70	N.L. Pitching Leaders (Bob Gibson, Fergie Jenkins, Gaylord Perry)	1.50	.70	.45
71	A.L. Strikeout Leaders (Bob Johnson, Mickey Lolich, Sam McDowell)	1.50	.70	.45
72	N.L. Strikeout Leaders (Bob Gibson, Fergie Jenkins, Tom Seaver)	7.50	3.75	2.25
73	George Brunet	1.50	.70	.45
74	Twins Rookies (Pete Hamm, Jim Nettles)	1.50	.70	.45
75	Gary Nolan	1.50	.70	.45
76	Ted Savage	1.50	.70	.45
77	Mike Compton	1.50	.70	.45
78	Jim Spencer	1.50	.70	.45
79	Wade Blasingame	1.50	.70	.45
80	Bill Melton	1.50	.70	.45
81	Felix Millan	1.50	.70	.45
82	Casey Cox	1.50	.70	.45
83	Met Rookies (Randy Bobb, Tim Foli)	1.50	.70	.45
84	Marcel Lachemann	1.50	.70	.45
85	Billy Grabarkewitz	1.50	.70	.45
86	Mike Kilkenny	1.50	.70	.45
87	Jack Heidemann	1.50	.70	.45
88	Hal King	1.50	.70	.45
89	Ken Brett	1.50	.70	.45
90	Joe Pepitone	1.50	.70	.45
91	Bob Lemon	1.50	.70	.45
92	Fred Wenz	1.50	.70	.45
93	Senators Rookies (Norm McRae, Denny Riddleberger)	1.50	.70	.45
94	Don Hahn	1.50	.70	.45
95	Luis Tiant	1.50	.70	.45
96	Joe Hague	1.50	.70	.45
97	Floyd Wicker	1.50	.70	.45
98	Joe Decker	1.50	.70	.45
99	Mark Belanger	1.50	.70	.45
100	Pete Rose	50.00	25.00	15.00
101	Les Cain	1.50	.70	.45
102	Astros Rookies (Ken Forsch, Larry Howard)	1.50	.70	.45
103	Rich Severson	1.50	.70	.45
104	Dan Frisella	1.50	.70	.45
105	Tony Conigliaro	1.50	.70	.45
106	Tom Dukes	1.50	.70	.45
107	Roy Foster	1.50	.70	.45
108	John Cumberland	1.50	.70	.45
109	Steve Hovley	1.50	.70	.45
110	Bill Mazeroski	1.50	.70	.45
111	Yankees Rookies (Loyd Colson, Bobby Mitchell)	1.50	.70	.45
112	Manny Mota	1.50	.70	.45
113	Jerry Crider	1.50	.70	.45
114	Billy Conigliaro	1.50	.70	.45
115	Donn Clendenon	1.50	.70	.45
116	Ken Sanders	1.50	.70	.45
117	Ted Simmons	25.00	12.50	7.50
118	Cookie Rojas	1.50	.70	.45
119	Frank Lucchesi	1.50	.70	.45
120	Willie Horton	1.50	.70	.45
121	Cubs Rookies (Jim Dunegan, Roe Skidmore)	1.50	.70	.45
122	Eddie Watt	1.50	.70	.45
123	Checklist 2	1.50	.70	.45
124	Don Gullett	1.50	.70	.45
125	Ray Fosse	1.50	.70	.45
126	Danny Coombs	1.50	.70	.45
127	Danny Thompson	1.50	.70	.45
128	Frank Johnson	1.50	.70	.45
129	Aurelio Monteagudo	1.50	.70	.45
130	Denis Menke	1.50	.70	.45
131	Curt Blefary	1.50	.70	.45
132	Jose Laboy	1.50	.70	.45
133	Mickey Lolich	1.50	.70	.45
134	Jose Arcia	1.50	.70	.45
135	Rick Monday	1.50	.70	.45
136	Duffy Dyer	1.50	.70	.45
137	Marcelino Lopez	1.50	.70	.45
138	Phillies Rookies (Joe Lis, Willie Montanez)	1.50	.70	.45
139	Paul Casanova	1.50	.70	.45
140	Gaylord Perry	10.25	5.25	3.00
141	Frank Quilici	1.50	.70	.45
142	Mack Jones	1.50	.70	.45
143	Steve Blass	1.50	.70	.45
144	Jackie Hernandez	1.50	.70	.45
145	Bill Singer	1.50	.70	.45
146	Ralph Houk	1.50	.70	.45
147	Bob Priddy	1.50	.70	.45
148	John Mayberry	1.50	.70	.45
149	Mike Hershberger	1.50	.70	.45
150	Sam McDowell	1.50	.70	.45
151	Tommy Davis	1.50	.70	.45
152	Angels Rookies (Lloyd Allen, Winston Llenas)	1.50	.70	.45
153	Gary Ross	1.50	.70	.45
154	Cesar Gutierrez	1.50	.70	.45
155	Ken Henderson	1.50	.70	.45
156	Bart Johnson	1.50	.70	.45
157	Bob Bailey	1.50	.70	.45
158	Jerry Reuss	1.50	.70	.45
159	Jarvis Tatum	1.50	.70	.45
160	Tom Seaver	63.00	31.00	19.00
161	Ron Hunt	1.50	.70	.45
162	Jack Billingham	1.50	.70	.45
163	Buck Martinez	1.50	.70	.45
164	Reds Rookies (Frank Duffy, Milt Wilcox)	1.50	.70	.45
165	Cesar Tovar	1.50	.70	.45
166	Joe Hoerner	1.50	.70	.45
167	Tom Grieve	1.50	.70	.45
168	Bruce Dal Canton	1.50	.70	.45
169	Ed Herrmann	1.50	.70	.45
170	Mike Cuellar	1.50	.70	.45
171	Bobby Wine	1.50	.70	.45
172	Duke Sims	1.50	.70	.45
173	Gil Garrido	1.50	.70	.45
174	Dave LaRoche	1.50	.70	.45
175	Jim Hickman	1.50	.70	.45
176	Red Sox Rookies (Doug Griffin, Bob Montgomery)	1.50	.70	.45
177	Hal McRae	1.50	.70	.45
178	Dave Duncan	1.50	.70	.45
179	Mike Corkins	1.50	.70	.45
180	Al Kaline	25.00	12.50	7.50
181	Hal Lanier	1.50	.70	.45
182	Al Downing	1.50	.70	.45
183	Gil Hodges	2.50	1.25	.70
184	Stan Bahnsen	1.50	.70	.45
185	Julian Javier	1.50	.70	.45
186	Bob Spence	1.50	.70	.45
187	Ted Abernathy	1.50	.70	.45
188	Dodgers Rookies (Mike Strahler, Bob Valentine)	1.50	.70	.45
189	George Mitterwald	1.50	.70	.45
190	Bob Tolan	1.50	.70	.45
191	Mike Andrews	1.50	.70	.45
192	Billy Wilson	1.50	.70	.45
193	Bob Grich	1.50	.70	.45
194	Mike Lum	1.50	.70	.45
195	A.L. Playoff Game 1 (Powell Muscles Twins!)	1.50	.70	.45
196	A.L. Playoff Game 2 (McNally Makes It Two Straight!)	1.50	.70	.45
197	A.L. Playoff Game 3 (Palmer Mows 'Em Down!)	1.50	.70	.45
198	A.L. Playoffs Summary (A Team Effort!)	1.50	.70	.45
199	N.L. Playoff Game 1 (Cline Pinch-Triple Decides It!)	1.50	.70	.45
200	N.L. Playoff Game 2 (Tolan Scores For Third Time!)	1.50	.70	.45
201	N.L. Playoff Game 3 (Cline Scores Winning Run!)	1.50	.70	.45
202	Claude Raymond	1.50	.70	.45
203	Larry Gura	1.50	.70	.45
204	Brewers Rookies (George Kopacz, Bernie Smith)	1.50	.70	.45
205	Gerry Moses	1.50	.70	.45
206	Checklist 3	1.50	.70	.45
207	Alan Foster	1.50	.70	.45
208	Billy Martin	1.50	.70	.45
209	Steve Renko	1.50	.70	.45
210	Rod Carew	46.00	23.00	14.00
211	Phil Hennigan	1.50	.70	.45
212	Rich Hebner	1.50	.70	.45
213	Frank Baker	1.50	.70	.45
214	Al Ferrara	1.50	.70	.45
215	Diego Segui	1.50	.70	.45
216	Cardinals Rookies (Reggie Cleveland, Luis Melendez)	1.50	.70	.45
217	Ed Stroud	1.50	.70	.45
218	Tony Cloninger	1.50	.70	.45
219	Elrod Hendricks	1.50	.70	.45
220	Ron Santo	1.50	.70	.45
221	Dave Morehead	1.50	.70	.45
222	Bob Watson	1.50	.70	.45
223	Cecil Upshaw	1.50	.70	.45
224	Alan Gallagher	1.50	.70	.45
225	Gary Peters	1.50	.70	.45
226	Bill Russell	1.50	.70	.45
227	Floyd Weaver	1.50	.70	.45
228	Wayne Garrett	1.50	.70	.45
229	Jim Hannan	1.50	.70	.45
230	Willie Stargell	12.75	6.50	3.75
231	Indians Rookies (Vince Colbert, John Lowenstein)	1.50	.70	.45
232	John Strohmayer	1.50	.70	.45
233	Larry Bowa	1.50	.70	.45
234	Jim Lyttle	1.50	.70	.45
235	Nate Colbert	1.50	.70	.45
236	Bob Humphreys	1.50	.70	.45
237	Cesar Cedeno	1.50	.70	.45
238	Chuck Dobson	1.50	.70	.45
239	Red Schoendienst	1.50	.70	.45
240	Clyde Wright	1.50	.70	.45
241	Dave Nelson	1.50	.70	.45
242	Jim Ray	1.50	.70	.45
243	Carlos May	1.50	.70	.45
244	Bob Tillman	1.50	.70	.45
245	Jim Kaat	1.50	.70	.45
246	Tony Taylor	1.50	.70	.45
247	Royals Rookies (Jerry Cram, Paul Splittorff)	1.50	.70	.45
248	Hoyt Wilhelm	3.50	1.75	1.00
249	Chico Salmon	1.50	.70	.45
250	Johnny Bench	46.00	23.00	14.00
251	Frank Reberger	1.50	.70	.45
252	Eddie Leon	1.50	.70	.45
253	Bill Sudakis	1.50	.70	.45
254	Cal Koonce	1.50	.70	.45
255	Bob Robertson	1.50	.70	.45
256	Tony Gonzalez	1.50	.70	.45
257	Nelson Briles	1.50	.70	.45
258	Dick Green	1.50	.70	.45
259	Dave Marshall	1.50	.70	.45
260	Tommy Harper	1.50	.70	.45
261	Darold Knowles	1.50	.70	.45
262	Padres Rookies (Dave Robinson, Jim Williams)	1.50	.70	.45
263	John Ellis	1.50	.70	.45
264	Joe Morgan	12.75	6.50	3.75
265	Jim Northrup	1.50	.70	.45
266	Bill Stoneman	1.50	.70	.45
267	Rich Morales	1.50	.70	.45
268	Phillies Team	1.50	.70	.45
269	Gail Hopkins	1.50	.70	.45

270	Rico Carty	1.50	.70	.45
271	Bill Zepp	1.50	.70	.45
272	Tommy Helms	1.50	.70	.45
273	Pete Richert	1.50	.70	.45
274	Ron Slocum	1.50	.70	.45
275	Vada Pinson	1.50	.70	.45
276	Giants Rookies (Mike Davison, George Foster)	10.25	5.25	3.00
277	Gary Waslewski	1.50	.70	.45
278	Jerry Grote	1.50	.70	.45
279	Lefty Phillips	1.50	.70	.45
280	Fergie Jenkins	14.50	7.25	4.25
281	Danny Walton	1.50	.70	.45
282	Jose Pagan	1.50	.70	.45
283	Dick Such	1.50	.70	.45
284	Jim Gosger	1.50	.70	.45
285	Sal Bando	1.50	.70	.45
286	Jerry McNertney	1.50	.70	.45
287	Mike Fiore	1.50	.70	.45
288	Joe Moeller	1.50	.70	.45
290	Tony Oliva	1.50	.70	.45
291	George Culver	1.50	.70	.45
292	Jay Johnstone	1.50	.70	.45
293	Pat Corrales	1.50	.70	.45
294	Steve Dunning	1.50	.70	.45
295	Bobby Bonds	1.50	.70	.45
296	Tom Timmermann	1.50	.70	.45
297	Johnny Briggs	1.50	.70	.45
298	Jim Nelson	1.50	.70	.45
299	Ed Kirkpatrick	1.50	.70	.45
300	1.50 Robinson	25.00	12.50	7.50
301	Earl Wilson	1.50	.70	.45
302	Phil Gagliano	1.50	.70	.45
303	Lindy McDaniel	1.50	.70	.45
304	Ron Brand	1.50	.70	.45
305	Reggie Smith	1.50	.70	.45
306	Jim Nash	1.50	.70	.45
307	Don Wert	1.50	.70	.45
308	Cards Team	1.50	.70	.45
309	Dick Ellsworth	1.50	.70	.45
310	Tommie Agee	1.50	.70	.45
311	Lee Stange	1.50	.70	.45
312	Harry Walker	1.50	.70	.45
313	Tom Hall	1.50	.70	.45
314	Jeff Torborg	1.50	.70	.45
315	Ron Fairly	1.50	.70	.45
316	Fred Scherman	1.50	.70	.45
317	Athletics Rookies (Jim Driscoll, Angel Mangual)	1.50	.70	.45
318	Rudy May	1.50	.70	.45
319	Ty Cline	1.50	.70	.45
320	Dave McNally	1.50	.70	.45
321	Tom Matchick	1.50	.70	.45
322	Jim Beauchamp	1.50	.70	.45
323	Billy Champion	1.50	.70	.45
324	Graig Nettles	1.75	.90	.50
325	Juan Marichal	5.00	2.50	1.50
326	Richie Scheinblum	1.50	.70	.45
327	World Series Game 1 (Powell Homers To Opposite Field!)	1.50	.70	.45
328	World Series Game 2 (Buford Goes 2-For 4!)	1.50	.70	.45
329	World Series Game 3 (F. Robinson Shows Muscle!)	1.50	.70	.45
330	World Series Game 4 (Reds Stay Alive!)	1.50	.70	.45
331	World Series Game 5 (B. Robinson Commits Robbery!)	1.50	.70	.45
332	World Series Summary (Clinching Performance!)	1.50	.70	.45
333	Clay Kirby	1.50	.70	.45
334	Roberto Pena	1.50	.70	.45
335	Jerry Koosman	1.50	.70	.45
336	Tigers Team	1.50	.70	.45
337	Jesus Alou	1.50	.70	.45
338	Gene Tenace	1.50	.70	.45
339	Wayne Simpson	1.50	.70	.45
340	Rico Petrocelli	1.50	.70	.45
341	Steve Garvey	75.00	37.00	22.00
342	Frank Tepedino	1.50	.70	.45
343	Pirates Rookies (Ed Acosta, Milt May)	1.50	.70	.45
344	Ellie Rodriguez	1.50	.70	.45
345	Joe Horlen	1.50	.70	.45
346	Lum Harris	1.50	.70	.45
347	Ted Uhlaender	1.50	.70	.45
348	Fred Norman	1.50	.70	.45
349	Rich Reese	1.50	.70	.45
350	Billy Williams	3.00	1.50	.90
351	Jim Shellenback	1.50	.70	.45
352	Denny Doyle	1.50	.70	.45
353	Carl Taylor	1.50	.70	.45
354	Don McMahon	1.50	.70	.45
355	Bud Harrelson	1.50	.70	.45
356	Bob Locker	1.50	.70	.45
357	Reds Team	1.50	.70	.45
358	Danny Cater	1.50	.70	.45
359	Ron Reed	1.50	.70	.45
360	Jim Fregosi	1.50	.70	.45
361	Don Sutton	10.25	5.25	3.00
362	Orioles Rookies (Mike Adamson, Roger Freed)	1.50	.70	.45
363	Mike Nagy	1.50	.70	.45
364	Tommy Dean	1.50	.70	.45
365	Bob Johnson	1.50	.70	.45
366	Ron Stone	1.50	.70	.45
367	Dalton Jones	1.50	.70	.45
368	Bob Veale	1.50	.70	.45
369	Checklist 4	1.50	.70	.45
370	Joe Torre	1.50	.70	.45
371	Jack Hiatt	1.50	.70	.45
372	Lew Krausse	1.50	.70	.45
373	Tom McCraw	1.50	.70	.45
374	Clete Boyer	1.50	.70	.45
375	Steve Hargan	1.50	.70	.45
376	Expos Rookies (Clyde Mashore, Ernie McAnally)	1.50	.70	.45
377	Greg Garrett	1.50	.70	.45
378	Tito Fuentes	1.50	.70	.45
379	Wayne Granger	1.50	.70	.45
380	Ted Williams	10.25	5.25	3.00
381	Fred Gladding	1.50	.70	.45
382	Jake Gibbs	1.50	.70	.45
383	Rod Gaspar	1.50	.70	.45
384	Rollie Fingers	13.50	6.75	4.00
385	Maury Wills	1.50	.70	.45
386	Red Sox Team	1.50	.70	.45
387	Ron Herbel	1.50	.70	.45
388	Al Oliver	1.50	.70	.45
389	Ed Brinkman	1.50	.70	.45
390	Glenn Beckert	1.50	.70	.45
391	Twins Rookies (Steve Brye, Cotton Nash)	1.50	.70	.45
392	Grant Jackson	1.50	.70	.45
393	Merv Rettenmund	1.50	.70	.45
394	Clay Carroll	2.50	1.25	.70
395	Roy White	2.50	1.25	.70
396	Dick Schofield	2.50	1.25	.70
397	Alvin Dark	2.50	1.25	.70
398	Howie Reed	2.50	1.25	.70
399	Jim French	2.50	1.25	.70
400	Hank Aaron	65.00	32.00	19.50
401	Tom Murphy	2.50	1.25	.70
402	Dodgers Team	2.50	1.25	.70
403	Joe Coleman	2.50	1.25	.70
404	Astros Rookies (Buddy Harris, Roger Metzger)	2.50	1.25	.70
405	Leo Cardenas	2.50	1.25	.70
406	Ray Sadecki	2.50	1.25	.70
407	Joe Rudi	2.50	1.25	.70
408	Rafael Robles	2.50	1.25	.70
409	Don Pavletich	2.50	1.25	.70
410	Ken Holtzman	2.50	1.25	.70
411	George Spriggs	2.50	1.25	.70
412	Jerry Johnson	2.50	1.25	.70
413	Pat Kelly	2.50	1.25	.70
414	Travis Fryman	2.50	1.25	.70
415	Mike Hegan	2.50	1.25	.70
416	Gene Alley	2.50	1.25	.70
417	Dick Hall	2.50	1.25	.70
418	Adolfo Phillips	2.50	1.25	.70
419	Ron Hansen	2.50	1.25	.70
420	Jim Merritt	2.50	1.25	.70
421	John Stephenson	2.50	1.25	.70
422	Frank Bertaina	2.50	1.25	.70
423	Tigers Rookies (Tim Marting, Dennis Saunders)	2.50	1.25	.70
424	Roberto Rodriguez	2.50	1.25	.70
425	Doug Rader	2.50	1.25	.70
426	Chris Cannizzaro	2.50	1.25	.70
427	Bernie Allen	2.50	1.25	.70
428	Jim McAndrew	2.50	1.25	.70
429	Chuck Hinton	2.50	1.25	.70
430	Wes Parker	2.50	1.25	.70
431	Tom Burgmeier	2.50	1.25	.70
432	Bob Didier	2.50	1.25	.70
433	Skip Lockwood	2.50	1.25	.70
434	Gary Sutherland	2.50	1.25	.70
435	Jose Cardenal	2.50	1.25	.70
436	Wilbur Wood	2.50	1.25	.70
437	Danny Murtaugh	2.50	1.25	.70
438	Mike McCormick	2.50	1.25	.70
439	Phillie Rookies (Greg Luzinski, Scott Reid)	2.50	1.25	.70
440	Bert Campaneris	2.50	1.25	.70
441	Milt Pappas	2.50	1.25	.70
442	Angels Team	2.50	1.25	.70
443	Rich Robertson	2.50	1.25	.70
444	Jimmie Price	2.50	1.25	.70
445	Art Shamsky	2.50	1.25	.70
446	Bobby Bolin	2.50	1.25	.70
447	Cesar Geronimo	2.50	1.25	.70
448	Dave Roberts	2.50	1.25	.70
449	Brant Alyea	2.50	1.25	.70
450	Bob Gibson	18.00	9.00	5.50
451	Joe Keough	2.50	1.25	.70
452	John Boccabella	2.50	1.25	.70
453	Terry Crowley	2.50	1.25	.70
454	Mike Paul	2.50	1.25	.70
455	Don Kessinger	2.50	1.25	.70
456	Bob Meyer	2.50	1.25	.70
457	Willie Smith	2.50	1.25	.70
458	White Sox Rookies (Dave Lemonds, Ron Lolich)	2.50	1.25	.70
459	Jim LeFebvre	2.50	1.25	.70
460	Fritz Peterson	2.50	1.25	.70
461	Jim Hart	2.50	1.25	.70
462	Senators Team	2.50	1.25	.70
463	Tom Kelley	2.50	1.25	.70
464	Aurelio Rodriguez	2.50	1.25	.70
465	Tim McCarver	2.50	1.25	.70
466	Ken Berry	2.50	1.25	.70
467	Al Santorini	2.50	1.25	.70
468	Frank Fernandez	2.50	1.25	.70
469	Bob Aspromonte	2.50	1.25	.70
470	Bob Oliver	2.50	1.25	.70
471	Tom Griffin	2.50	1.25	.70
472	Ken Rudolph	2.50	1.25	.70
473	Gary Wagner	2.50	1.25	.70
474	Jim Fairey	2.50	1.25	.70
475	Ron Perranoski	2.50	1.25	.70
476	Dal Maxvill	2.50	1.25	.70
477	Earl Weaver	2.50	1.25	.70
478	Bernie Carbo	2.50	1.25	.70
479	Dennis Higgins	2.50	1.25	.70
480	Manny Sanguillen	2.50	1.25	.70
481	Daryl Patterson	2.50	1.25	.70
482	Padres Team	2.50	1.25	.70
483	Gene Michael	2.50	1.25	.70
484	Don Wilson	2.50	1.25	.70
485	Ken McMullen	2.50	1.25	.70
486	Steve Huntz	2.50	1.25	.70
487	Paul Schaal	2.50	1.25	.70
488	Jerry Stephenson	2.50	1.25	.70
489	Luis Alvarado	2.50	1.25	.70
490	Deron Johnson	2.50	1.25	.70
491	Jim Hardin	2.50	1.25	.70
492	Ken Boswell	2.50	1.25	.70
493	Dave May	2.50	1.25	.70
494	Braves Rookies (Ralph Garr, Rick Kester)	2.50	1.25	.70
495	Felipe Alou	2.50	1.25	.70
496	Woody Woodward	2.50	1.25	.70
497	Horacio Pina	2.50	1.25	.70
498	John Kennedy	2.50	1.25	.70
499	Checklist 5	2.50	1.25	.70
500	Jim Perry	2.50	1.25	.70
501	Andy Etchebarren	2.50	1.25	.70
502	Cubs Team	2.50	1.25	.70
503	Gates Brown	2.50	1.25	.70
504	Ken Wright	2.50	1.25	.70
505	Ollie Brown	2.50	1.25	.70
506	Bobby Knoop	2.50	1.25	.70
507	George Stone	2.50	1.25	.70
508	Roger Repoz	2.50	1.25	.70
509	Jim Grant	2.50	1.25	.70
510	Ken Harrelson	2.50	1.25	.70
511	Chris Short	2.50	1.25	.70
512	Red Sox Rookies (Mike Garman, Dick Mills)	2.50	1.25	.70
513	Nolan Ryan	315.00	157.00	94.00
514	Ron Woods	2.50	1.25	.70
515	Carl Morton	2.50	1.25	.70
516	Ted Kubiak	2.50	1.25	.70
517	Charlie Fox	2.50	1.25	.70
518	Joe Grzenda	2.50	1.25	.70
519	Willie Crawford	2.50	1.25	.70
520	Tommy John	2.50	1.25	.70
521	Leron Lee	2.50	1.25	.70
522	Twins Team	2.50	1.25	.70
523	John Odom	2.50	1.25	.70
524	Mickey Stanley	5.00	2.50	1.50
525	Ernie Banks	50.00	25.00	15.00
526	Ray Jarvis	5.00	2.50	1.50
527	Cleon Jones	5.00	2.50	1.50
528	Wally Bunker	5.00	2.50	1.50
529	N.L. Rookies (Bill Buckner, Enzo Hernandez, Marty Perez)	5.00	2.50	1.50
530	Carl Yastrzemski	50.00	25.00	15.00
531	Mike Torrez	5.00	2.50	1.50
532	Bill Rigney	5.00	2.50	1.50
533	Mike Ryan	5.00	2.50	1.50
534	Luke Walker	5.00	2.50	1.50
535	Curt Flood	5.00	2.50	1.50
536	Claude Raymond	5.00	2.50	1.50
537	Tom Egan	5.00	2.50	1.50
538	Angel Bravo	5.00	2.50	1.50
539	Larry Brown	5.00	2.50	1.50
540	Larry Dierker	5.00	2.50	1.50
541	Bob Burda	5.00	2.50	1.50
542	Bob Miller	5.00	2.50	1.50
543	Yankees Team	5.00	2.50	1.50
544	Vida Blue	5.00	2.50	1.50
545	Dick Dietz	5.00	2.50	1.50
546	John Matias	5.00	2.50	1.50
547	Pat Dobson	5.00	2.50	1.50
548	Don Mason	5.00	2.50	1.50
549	Jim Brewer	5.00	2.50	1.50
550	Harmon Killebrew	30.00	15.00	9.00
551	Frank Linzy	5.00	2.50	1.50
552	Buddy Bradford	5.00	2.50	1.50
553	Kevin Collins	5.00	2.50	1.50
554	Lowell Palmer	5.00	2.50	1.50
555	Walt Williams	5.00	2.50	1.50
556	Jim McGlothlin	5.00	2.50	1.50
557	Tom Satriano	5.00	2.50	1.50
558	Hector Torres	5.00	2.50	1.50
559	A.L. Rookies (Terry Cox, Bill Gogolewski, Gary Jones)	5.00	2.50	1.50
560	Rusty Staub	5.00	2.50	1.50
561	Syd O'Brien	5.00	2.50	1.50
562	Dave Giusti	5.00	2.50	1.50
563	Giants Team	5.00	2.50	1.50
564	Al Fitzmorris	5.00	2.50	1.50
565	Jim Wynn	5.00	2.50	1.50
566	Tim Cullen	5.00	2.50	1.50
567	Walt Alston	5.00	2.50	1.50
568	Sal Campisi	5.00	2.50	1.50
569	Ivan Murrell	5.00	2.50	1.50
570	Jim Palmer	42.50	21.00	12.50
571	Ted Sizemore	5.00	2.50	1.50
572	Jerry Kenney	5.00	2.50	1.50
573	Ed Kranepool	5.00	2.50	1.50
574	Jim Bunning	5.00	2.50	1.50
575	Bill Freehan	5.00	2.50	1.50
576	Cubs Rookies (Brock Davis, Adrian Garrett, Garry Jestadt)	5.00	2.50	1.50
577	Jim Lonborg	5.00	2.50	1.50
578	Eddie Kasko	5.00	2.50	1.50
579	Marty Pattin	5.00	2.50	1.50
580	Tony Perez	17.00	8.50	5.00
581	Roger Nelson	5.00	2.50	1.50
582	Dave Cash	5.00	2.50	1.50
583	Ron Cook	5.00	2.50	1.50
584	Indians Team	5.00	2.50	1.50
585	Willie Davis	5.00	2.50	1.50
586	Dick Woodson	5.00	2.50	1.50
587	Sonny Jackson	5.00	2.50	1.50
588	Tom Bradley	5.00	2.50	1.50
589	Bob Barton	5.00	2.50	1.50
590	Alex Johnson	5.00	2.50	1.50
591	Jackie Brown	5.00	2.50	1.50
592	Randy Hundley	5.00	2.50	1.50
593	Jack Aker	5.00	2.50	1.50
594	Cards Rookies (Bob Chlupsa, Al Hrabosky, Bob Stinson)	5.00	2.50	1.50
595	Dave Johnson	5.00	2.50	1.50
596	Mike Jorgensen	5.00	2.50	1.50
597	Ken Suarez	5.00	2.50	1.50
598	Rick Wise	5.00	2.50	1.50
599	Norm Cash	5.00	2.50	1.50
600	Willie Mays	127.50	64.00	38.00
601	Ken Tatum	5.00	2.50	1.50
602	Marty Martinez	5.00	2.50	1.50

603	Pirates Team	5.00	2.50	1.50
604	John Gelnar	5.00	2.50	1.50
605	Orlando Cepeda	5.00	2.50	1.50
606	Chuck Taylor	5.00	2.50	1.50
607	Paul Ratliff	5.00	2.50	1.50
608	Mike Wegener	5.00	2.50	1.50
609	Leo Durocher	5.00	2.50	1.50
610	Amos Otis	5.00	2.50	1.50
611	Tom Phoebus	5.00	2.50	1.50
612	Indians Rookies (Lou Camilli, Ted Ford, Steve Mingori)	.75	.40	.25
613	Pedro Borbon	5.00	2.50	1.50
614	Billy Cowan	5.00	2.50	1.50
615	Mel Stottlemyre	5.00	2.50	1.50
616	Larry Hisle	5.00	2.50	1.50
617	Clay Dalrymple	5.00	2.50	1.50
618	Tug McGraw	5.00	2.50	1.50
619	Checklist 6	5.00	2.50	1.50
620	Frank Howard	5.00	2.50	1.50
621	Ron Bryant	5.00	2.50	1.50
622	Joe LaHoud	5.00	2.50	1.50
623	Pat Jarvis	5.00	2.50	1.50
624	Athletics Team	5.00	2.50	1.50
625	Lou Brock	34.00	17.00	10.00
626	Freddie Patek	5.00	2.50	1.50
627	Steve Hamilton	5.00	2.50	1.50
628	John Bateman	5.00	2.50	1.50
629	John Hiller	5.00	2.50	1.50
630	Roberto Clemente	80.00	40.00	24.00
631	Eddie Fisher	5.00	2.50	1.50
632	Darrel Chaney	5.00	2.50	1.50
633	A.L. Rookies (Bobby Brooks, Pete Koegel, Scott Northey)	5.00	2.50	1.50
634	Phil Regan	5.00	2.50	1.50
635	Bob Murcer	5.00	2.50	1.50
636	Denny Lemaster	5.00	2.50	1.50
637	Dave Bristol	5.00	2.50	1.50
638	Stan Williams	5.00	2.50	1.50
639	Tom Haller	5.00	2.50	1.50
640	Frank Robinson	50.00	25.00	15.00
641	Mets Team	13.50	6.75	4.00
642	Jim Roland	5.00	2.50	1.50
643	Rick Reichardt	5.00	2.50	1.50
644	Jim Stewart (SP)	12.00	6.00	3.50
645	Jim Maloney (SP)	12.00	6.00	3.50
646	Bobby Floyd (SP)	12.00	6.00	3.50
647	Juan Pizarro	6.75	3.50	2.00
648	Mets Rookies (Rich Folkers, Ted Martinez, Jon Matlack), (SP)	12.00	6.00	3.50
649	Sparky Lyle (SP)	12.00	6.00	3.50
650	Rich Allen	30.00	15.00	9.00
651	Jerry Robertson (SP)	12.00	6.00	3.50
652	Braves Team	7.00	3.50	2.00
653	Russ Snyder (SP)	12.00	6.00	3.50
654	Don Shaw (SP)	12.00	6.00	3.50
655	Mike Epstein (SP)	12.00	6.00	3.50
656	Gerry Nyman (SP)	12.00	6.00	3.50
657	Jose Azcue	6.75	3.50	2.00
658	Paul Lindblad (SP)	12.00	6.00	3.50
659	Byron Browne (SP)	12.00	6.00	3.50
660	Ray Culp	6.75	3.50	2.00
661	Chuck Tanner (SP)	12.00	6.00	3.50
662	Mike Hedlund (SP)	12.00	6.00	3.50
663	Marv Staehle	6.75	3.50	2.00
664	Major League Rookies (Archie Reynolds, Bob Reynolds, Ken Reynolds), (SP)	12.00	6.00	3.50
665	Ron Swoboda (SP)	12.00	6.00	3.50
666	Gene Brabender (SP)	12.00	6.00	3.50
667	Pete Ward	6.75	3.50	2.00
668	Gary Neibauer	6.75	3.50	2.00
669	Ike Brown (SP)	12.00	6.00	3.50
670	Bill Hands	6.75	3.50	2.00
671	Bill Voss (SP)	12.00	6.00	3.50
672	Ed Crosby (SP)	12.00	6.00	3.50
673	Gerry Janeski (SP)	12.00	6.00	3.50
674	Expos Team	6.75	3.50	2.00
675	Dave Boswell	6.75	3.50	2.00
676	Tommie Reynolds	6.75	3.50	2.00
677	Jack DiLauro (SP)	12.00	6.00	3.50
678	George Thomas	6.75	3.50	2.00
679	Don O'Riley	6.75	3.50	2.00
680	Don Mincher (SP)	12.00	6.00	3.50
681	Bill Butler	6.75	3.50	2.00
682	Terry Harmon	6.75	3.50	2.00
683	Bill Burbach (SP)	12.00	6.00	3.50
684	Curt Motton	6.75	3.50	2.00
685	Moe Drabowsky	6.75	3.50	2.00
686	Chico Ruiz (SP)	12.00	6.00	3.50
687	Ron Taylor (SP)	12.00	6.00	3.50
688	Sparky Anderson	34.00	17.00	10.00
689	Frank Baker	6.75	3.50	2.00
690	Bob Moose	6.75	3.50	2.00
691	Bob Heise	6.75	3.50	2.00
692	A.L. Rookies (Hal Haydel, Rogelio Moret, Wayne Twitchell), (SP)	12.00	6.00	3.50
693	Jose Pena (SP)	12.00	6.00	3.50
694	Rick Renick (SP)	12.00	6.00	3.50
695	Joe Niekro	6.75	3.50	2.00
696	Jerry Morales	6.75	3.50	2.00
697	Rickey Clark (SP)	12.00	6.00	3.50
698	Brewers Team	21.00	10.50	6.25
699	Jim Britton	6.75	3.50	2.00
700	Boog Powell	23.00	11.50	7.00
701	Bob Garibaldi	6.75	3.50	2.00
702	Milt Ramirez	6.75	3.50	2.00
703	Mike Kekich	6.75	3.50	2.00
704	J.C. Martin (SP)	12.00	6.00	3.50
705	Dick Selma (SP)	12.00	6.00	3.50
706	Joe Foy (SP)	12.00	6.00	3.50
707	Fred Lasher	6.75	3.50	2.00
708	Russ Nagelson (SP)	12.00	6.00	3.50
709	Major League Rookies (Dusty Baker, Don Baylor, Tom Paciorek)	115.00	57.00	34.00
710	Sonny Siebert	6.75	3.50	2.00
711	Larry Stahl (SP)	12.00	6.00	3.50
712	Jose Martinez	6.75	3.50	2.00
713	Mike Marshall (SP)	12.00	6.00	3.50
714	Dick Williams (SP)	12.00	6.00	3.50
715	Horace Clarke (SP)	12.00	6.00	3.50
716	Dave Leonhard	6.75	3.50	2.00
717	Tommie Aaron (SP)	12.00	6.00	3.50
718	Billy Wynne	6.75	3.50	2.00
719	Jerry May (SP)	12.00	6.00	3.50
720	Matty Alou	6.75	3.50	2.00
721	John Morris	6.75	3.50	2.00
722	Astros Team	18.00	9.00	5.50
723	Vicente Romo (SP)	12.00	6.00	3.50
724	Tom Tischinski (SP)	12.00	6.00	3.50
725	Gary Gentry (SP)	12.00	6.00	3.50
726	Paul Popovich	6.75	3.50	2.00
727	Ray Lamb (SP)	12.00	6.00	3.50
728	N.L. Rookies (Keith Lampard, Wayne Redmond, Bernie Williams)	6.75	3.50	2.00
729	Dick Billings	6.75	3.50	2.00
730	Jim Rooker	6.75	3.50	2.00
731	Jim Qualls (SP)	12.00	6.00	3.50
732	Bob Reed	6.75	3.50	2.00
733	Lee Maye (SP)	12.00	6.00	3.50
734	Rob Gardner (SP)	12.00	6.00	3.50
735	Mike Shannon (SP)	12.00	6.00	3.50
736	Mel Queen (SP)	12.00	6.00	3.50
737	Preston Gomez (SP)	12.00	6.00	3.50
738	Russ Gibson (SP)	12.00	6.00	3.50
739	Barry Lersch (SP)	12.00	6.00	3.50
740	Luis Aparicio	30.00	15.00	9.00
741	Skip Guinn	6.75	3.50	2.00
742	Royals Team	6.75	3.50	2.00
743	John O'Donoghue (SP)	12.00	6.00	3.50
744	Chuck Manuel (SP)	12.00	6.00	3.50
745	Sandy Alomar (SP)	12.00	6.00	3.50
746	Andy Kosco	6.75	3.50	2.00
747	N.L. Rookies (Balor Moore, Al Severinsen, Scipio Spinks)	6.75	3.50	2.00
748	John Purdin (SP)	12.00	6.00	3.50
749	Ken Szotkiewicz	6.75	3.50	2.00
750	Denny McLain (SP)	12.00	6.00	3.50
751	Al Weis (SP)	12.00	6.00	3.50
752	Dick Drago	6.75	3.50	2.00

1972 O-Pee-Chee

Identical in design to the Topps cards of the same year, the Canadian-issued 1972 O-Pee-Chee set numbers 525 cards, measuring 2-1/2" by 3-1/2". The backs state "Printed in Canada" and are written in both French and English. Unlike the 1972 Topps set, the O-Pee-Chee card of Gil Hodges notes the Mets' manager's death.

		NR MT	EX	VG
	Complete Set (525):	1360.	675.00	400.00
	Common Player (1-263):	.75	.40	.25
	Common Player (264-394):	1.25	.60	.40
	Common Player (395-525):	1.75	.90	.50
1	World Champions (Pirates Team)	9.25	4.75	2.75
2	Ray Culp	.75	.40	.25
3	Bob Tolan	.75	.40	.25
4	Checklist 1	1.25	.60	.40
5	John Bateman	.75	.40	.25
6	Fred Scherman	.75	.40	.25
7	Enzo Hernandez	.75	.40	.25
8	Ron Swoboda	.75	.40	.25
9	Stan Williams	.75	.40	.25
10	Amos Otis	.75	.40	.25
11	Bobby Valentine	.75	.40	.25
12	Jose Cardenal	.75	.40	.25
13	Joe Grzenda	.75	.40	.25
14	Phillies Rookies (Mike Anderson, Pete Koegel, Wayne Twitchell)	.75	.40	.25
15	Walt Williams	.75	.40	.25
16	Mike Jorgensen	.75	.40	.25
17	Dave Duncan	.75	.40	.25
18	Juan Pizarro	.75	.40	.25
19	Billy Cowan	.75	.40	.25
20	Don Wilson	.75	.40	.25
21	Braves Team	.75	.40	.25
22	Rob Gardner	.75	.40	.25
23	Ted Kubiak	.75	.40	.25
24	Ted Ford	.75	.40	.25
25	Bill Singer	.75	.40	.25
26	Andy Etchebarren	.75	.40	.25
27	Bob Johnson	.75	.40	.25
28	Twins Rookies (Steve Brye, Bob Gebhard, Hal Haydel)	.75	.40	.25
29	Bill Bonham	.75	.40	.25
30	Rico Petrocelli	.75	.40	.25
31	Cleon Jones	.75	.40	.25
32	Cleon Jones IA	.75	.40	.25
33	Billy Martin	1.25	.60	.40
34	Billy Martin IA	.75	.40	.25
35	Jerry Johnson	.75	.40	.25
36	Jerry Johnson IA	.75	.40	.25
37	Carl Yastrzemski	15.00	7.50	4.50
38	Carl Yastrzemski IA	7.50	3.75	2.25
39	Bob Barton	.75	.40	.25
40	Bob Barton IA	.75	.40	.25
41	Tommy Davis	.75	.40	.25
42	Tommy Davis IA	.75	.40	.25
43	Rick Wise	.75	.40	.25
44	Rick Wise IA	.75	.40	.25
45	Glenn Beckert	.75	.40	.25
46	Glenn Beckert IA	.75	.40	.25
47	John Ellis	.75	.40	.25
48	John Ellis IA	.75	.40	.25
49	Willie Mays	32.00	16.00	9.50
50	Willie Mays IA	15.00	7.50	4.50
51	Harmon Killebrew	7.50	3.75	2.25
52	Harmon Killebrew IA	1.50	.70	.45
53	Bud Harrelson	.75	.40	.25
54	Bud Harrelson IA	.75	.40	.25
55	Clyde Wright	.75	.40	.25
56	Rich Chiles	.75	.40	.25
57	Bob Oliver	.75	.40	.25
58	Ernie McAnally	.75	.40	.25
59	Fred Stanley	.75	.40	.25
60	Manny Sanguillen	.75	.40	.25
61	Cubs Rookies (Gene Hiser, Burt Hooton, Earl Stephenson)	.75	.40	.25
62	Angel Mangual	.75	.40	.25
63	Duke Sims	.75	.40	.25
64	Pete Broberg	.75	.40	.25
65	Cesar Cedeno	.75	.40	.25
66	Ray Corbin	.75	.40	.25
67	Red Schoendienst	.75	.40	.25
68	Jim York	.75	.40	.25
69	Roger Freed	.75	.40	.25
70	Mike Cuellar	.75	.40	.25
71	Angels Team	.75	.40	.25
72	Bruce Kison	.75	.40	.25
73	Steve Huntz	.75	.40	.25
74	Cecil Upshaw	.75	.40	.25
75	Bert Campaneris	.75	.40	.25
76	Don Carrithers	.75	.40	.25
77	Ron Theobald	.75	.40	.25
78	Steve Arlin	.75	.40	.25
79	Red Sox Rookies (Cecil Cooper, Carlton Fisk, Mike Garman)	120.00	60.00	36.00
80	Tony Perez	6.00	3.00	1.75
81	Mike Hedlund	.75	.40	.25
82	Ron Woods	.75	.40	.25
83	Dalton Jones	.75	.40	.25
84	Vince Colbert	.75	.40	.25
85	N.L. Batting Leaders (Glenn Beckert, Ralph Garr, Joe Torre)	.75	.40	.25
86	A.L. Batting Leaders (Bobby Murcer, Tony Oliva, Merv Rettenmund)	.75	.40	.25
87	N.L. RBI Leaders (Hank Aaron, Willie Stargell, Joe Torre)	1.25	.60	.40
88	A.L. RBI Leaders (Harmon Killebrew, Frank Robinson, Reggie Smith)	1.25	.60	.40
89	N.L. Home Run Leaders (Hank Aaron, Lee May, Willie Stargell)	1.25	.60	.40
90	A.L. Home Run Leaders (Norm Cash, Reggie Jackson, Bill Melton)	1.00	.50	.30
91	N.L. ERA Leaders (Dave Roberts) ((photo actually Danny Coombs), Tom Seaver, Don Wilson)	1.00	.50	.30
92	A.L ERA Leaders (Vida Blue, Jim Palmer, Wilbur Wood)	1.00	.50	.30
93	N.L. Pitching Leaders (Steve Carlton, Al Downing, Fergie Jenkins, Tom Seaver)	5.00	2.50	1.50
94	A.L. Pitching Leaders (Vida Blue, Mickey Lolich, Wilbur Wood)	.75	.40	.25
95	N.L. Strikeout Leaders (Fergie Jenkins, Tom Seaver, Bill Stoneman)	1.00	.50	.30
96	A.L. Strikeout Leaders (Vida Blue, Joe Coleman, Mickey Lolich)	.75	.40	.25
97	Tom Kelley	.75	.40	.25
98	Chuck Tanner	.75	.40	.25
99	Ross Grimsley	.75	.40	.25
100	Frank Robinson	6.75	3.50	2.00
101	Astros Rookies (Ray Busse, Bill Greif, J.R. Richard)	.75	.40	.25
102	Lloyd Allen	.75	.40	.25
103	Checklist 2	1.25	.60	.40
104	Toby Harrah	.75	.40	.25
105	Gary Gentry	.75	.40	.25
106	Brewers Team	.75	.40	.25
107	Jose Cruz	1.25	.60	.40
108	Gary Waslewski	.75	.40	.25
109	Jerry May	.75	.40	.25
110	Ron Hunt	.75	.40	.25
111	Jim Grant	.75	.40	.25
112	Greg Luzinski	.75	.40	.25
113	Rogelio Moret	.75	.40	.25
114	Bill Buckner	.75	.40	.25
115	Jim Fregosi	.75	.40	.25
116	Ed Farmer	.75	.40	.25
117	Cleo James	.75	.40	.25
118	Skip Lockwood	.75	.40	.25
119	Marty Perez	.75	.40	.25
120	Bill Freehan	.75	.40	.25
121	Ed Sprague	.75	.40	.25
122	Larry Biittner	.75	.40	.25
123	Ed Acosta	.75	.40	.25
124	Yankees Rookies (Alan Closter, Roger Hambright, Rusty Torres)	.75	.40	.25
125	Dave Cash	.75	.40	.25
126	Bart Johnson	.75	.40	.25
127	Duffy Dyer	.75	.40	.25
128	Eddie Watt	.75	.40	.25
129	Charlie Fox	.75	.40	.25
130	Bob Gibson	7.50	3.75	2.25
131	Jim Nettles	.75	.40	.25
132	Joe Morgan	6.25	3.25	2.00
133	Joe Keough	.75	.40	.25
134	Carl Morton	.75	.40	.25

135	Vada Pinson	.75	.40	.25
136	Darrel Chaney	.75	.40	.25
137	Dick Williams	.75	.40	.25
138	Mike Kekich	.75	.40	.25
139	Tim McCarver	.75	.40	.25
140	Pat Dobson	.75	.40	.25
141	Mets Rookies (Buzz Capra, Jon Matlack, Leroy Stanton)	.75	.40	.25
142	Chris Chambliss	1.00	.50	.30
143	Garry Jestadt	.75	.40	.25
144	Marty Pattin	.75	.40	.25
145	Don Kessinger	.75	.40	.25
146	Steve Kealey	.75	.40	.25
147	Dave Kingman	7.25	3.75	2.25
148	Dick Billings	.75	.40	.25
149	Gary Neibauer	.75	.40	.25
150	Norm Cash	.75	.40	.25
151	Jim Brewer	.75	.40	.25
152	Gene Clines	.75	.40	.25
153	Rick Auerbach	.75	.40	.25
154	Ted Simmons	1.25	.60	.40
155	Larry Dierker	.75	.40	.25
156	Twins Team	.75	.40	.25
157	Don Gullett	.75	.40	.25
158	Jerry Kenney	.75	.40	.25
159	John Boccabella	.75	.40	.25
160	Andy Messersmith	.75	.40	.25
161	Brock Davis	.75	.40	.25
162	Brewers Rookies (Jerry Bell, Darrell Porter, Bob Reynolds)	.75	.40	.25
163	Tug McGraw	1.00	.50	.30
164	Tug McGraw IA	.75	.40	.25
165	Chris Speier	.75	.40	.25
166	Chris Speier IA	.75	.40	.25
167	Deron Johnson	.75	.40	.25
168	Deron Johnson IA	.75	.40	.25
169	Vida Blue	1.00	.50	.30
170	Vida Blue IA	.75	.40	.25
171	Darrell Evans	1.00	.50	.30
172	Darrell Evans IA	.75	.40	.25
173	Clay Kirby	.75	.40	.25
174	clay Kirby IA	.75	.40	.25
175	Tom Haller	.75	.40	.25
176	Tom Haller IA	.75	.40	.25
177	Paul Schaal	.75	.40	.25
178	Paul Schaal IA	.75	.40	.25
179	Dock Ellis	.75	.40	.25
180	Dock Ellis IA	.75	.40	.25
181	Ed Kranepool	.75	.40	.25
182	Ed Kranepool IA	.75	.40	.25
183	Bill Melton	.75	.40	.25
184	Bill Melton IA	.75	.40	.25
185	Ron Bryant	.75	.40	.25
186	Ron Bryant IA	.75	.40	.25
187	Gates Brown	.75	.40	.25
188	Frank Lucchesi	.75	.40	.25
189	Gene Tenace	.75	.40	.25
190	Dave Giusti	.75	.40	.25
191	Jeff Burroughs	.75	.40	.25
192	Cubs Team	.75	.40	.25
193	Kurt Bevacqua	.75	.40	.25
194	Fred Norman	.75	.40	.25
195	Orlando Cepeda	1.25	.60	.40
196	Mel Queen	.75	.40	.25
197	Johnny Briggs	.75	.40	.25
198	Dodgers Rookies (Charlie Hough, Bob O'Brien, Mike Strahler)	8.00	4.00	2.50
199	Mike Fiore	.75	.40	.25
200	Lou Brock	7.50	3.75	2.25
201	Phil Roof	.75	.40	.25
202	Scipio Spinks	.75	.40	.25
203	Ron Blomberg	.75	.40	.25
204	Tommy Helms	.75	.40	.25
205	Dick Drago	.75	.40	.25
206	Dal Maxvill	.75	.40	.25
207	Tom Egan	.75	.40	.25
208	Milt Pappas	.75	.40	.25
209	Joe Rudi	.75	.40	.25
210	Denny McLain	1.00	.50	.30
211	Gary Sutherland	.75	.40	.25
212	Grant Jackson	.75	.40	.25
213	Angels Rookies (Art Kusnyer, Billy Parker, Tom Silverio)	.75	.40	.25
214	Mike McQueen	.75	.40	.25
215	Alex Johnson	.75	.40	.25
216	Joe Niekro	.75	.40	.25
217	Roger Metzger	.75	.40	.25
218	Eddie Kasko	.75	.40	.25
219	Rennie Stennett	.75	.40	.25
220	Jim Perry	.75	.40	.25
221	N.L. Playoffs	.75	.40	.25
222	A.L. Playoffs	.75	.40	.25
223	World Series Game 1	.75	.40	.25
224	World Series Game 2	.75	.40	.25
225	World Series Game 3	.75	.40	.25
226	World Series Game 4	5.00	2.50	1.50
227	World Series Game 5	.75	.40	.25
228	World Series Game 6	.75	.40	.25
229	World Series Game 7	.75	.40	.25
230	World Series Summary	.75	.40	.25
231	Casey Cox	.75	.40	.25
232	Giants Rookies (Chris Arnold, Jim Barr, Dave Rader)	.75	.40	.25
233	Jay Johnstone	.75	.40	.25
234	Ron Taylor	.75	.40	.25
235	Merv Rettenmund	.75	.40	.25
236	Jim McGlothlin	.75	.40	.25
237	Yankees Team	1.00	.50	.30
238	Leron Lee	.75	.40	.25
239	Tom Timmermann	.75	.40	.25
240	Rich Allen	1.25	.60	.40
241	Rollie Fingers	8.50	4.25	2.50
242	Don Mincher	.75	.40	.25
243	Frank Linzy	.75	.40	.25
244	Steve Braun	.75	.40	.25
245	Tommie Agee	.75	.40	.25
246	Tom Burgmeier	.75	.40	.25
247	Milt May	.75	.40	.25
248	Tom Bradley	.75	.40	.25
249	Harry Walker	.75	.40	.25
250	Boog Powell	1.00	.50	.30
251	Checklist 3	1.25	.60	.40
252	Ken Reynolds	.75	.40	.25
253	Sandy Alomar	.75	.40	.25
254	Boots Day	.75	.40	.25
255	Jim Lonborg	.75	.40	.25
256	George Foster	1.25	.60	.40
257	Tigers Rookies (Jim Foor, Tim Hosley, Paul Jata)	.75	.40	.25
258	Randy Hundley	.75	.40	.25
259	Sparky Lyle	.75	.40	.25
260	Ralph Garr	.75	.40	.25
261	Steve Mingori	.75	.40	.25
262	Padres Team	.75	.40	.25
263	Felipe Alou	.75	.40	.25
264	Tommy John	1.50	.70	.45
265	Wes Parker	1.25	.60	.40
266	Bobby Bolin	1.25	.60	.40
267	Dave Concepcion	1.50	.70	.45
268	A's Rookies (Dwain Anderson, Chris Floethe)	1.25	.60	.40
269	Don Hahn	1.25	.60	.40
270	Jim Palmer	17.00	8.50	5.00
271	Ken Rudolph	1.25	.60	.40
272	Mickey Rivers	1.25	.60	.40
273	Bobby Floyd	1.25	.60	.40
274	Al Severinsen	1.25	.60	.40
275	Cesar Tovar	1.25	.60	.40
276	Gene Mauch	1.25	.60	.40
277	Elliot Maddox	1.25	.60	.40
278	Dennis Higgins	1.25	.60	.40
279	Larry Brown	1.25	.60	.40
280	Willie McCovey	8.00	4.00	2.50
281	Bill Parsons	1.25	.60	.40
282	Astros Team	1.25	.60	.40
283	Darrell Brandon	1.25	.60	.40
284	Ike Brown	1.25	.60	.40
285	Gaylord Perry	9.25	4.75	2.75
286	Gene Alley	1.25	.60	.40
287	Jim Hardin	1.25	.60	.40
288	Johnny Jeter	1.25	.60	.40
289	Syd O'Brien	1.25	.60	.40
290	Sonny Siebert	1.25	.60	.40
291	Hal McRae	1.25	.60	.40
292	Hal McRae IA	1.25	.60	.40
293	Danny Frisella	1.25	.60	.40
294	Dan Frisella IA	1.25	.60	.40
295	Dick Dietz	1.25	.60	.40
296	Dick Dietz IA	1.25	.60	.40
297	Claude Osteen	1.25	.60	.40
298	Claude Osteen IA	1.25	.60	.40
299	Hank Aaron	38.00	19.00	11.50
300	Hank Aaron IA	18.00	9.00	5.50
301	George Mitterwald	1.25	.60	.40
302	George Mitterwald IA	1.25	.60	.40
303	Joe Pepitone	1.25	.60	.40
304	Joe Pepitone IA	1.25	.60	.40
305	Ken Boswell	1.25	.60	.40
306	Ken Boswell IA	1.25	.60	.40
307	Steve Renko	1.25	.60	.40
308	Steve Renko IA	1.25	.60	.40
309	Roberto Clemente	42.50	21.00	12.50
310	Roberto Clemente IA	21.00	10.50	6.25
311	Clay Carroll	1.25	.60	.40
312	Clay Carroll IA	1.25	.60	.40
313	Luis Aparicio	2.00	1.00	.60
314	Luis Aparicio IA	1.25	.60	.40
315	Paul Splittorff	1.25	.60	.40
316	Cardinals Rookies (Jim Bibby, Santiago Guzman, Jorge Roque)	1.25	.60	.40
317	Rich Hand	1.25	.60	.40
318	Sonny Jackson	1.25	.60	.40
319	Aurelio Rodriguez	1.25	.60	.40
320	Steve Blass	1.25	.60	.40
321	Joe Lahoud	1.25	.60	.40
322	Jose Pena	1.25	.60	.40
323	Earl Weaver	1.25	.60	.40
324	Mike Ryan	1.25	.60	.40
325	Mel Stottlemyre	1.25	.60	.40
326	Pat Kelly	1.25	.60	.40
327	Steve Stone	1.25	.60	.40
328	Red Sox Team	1.25	.60	.40
329	Roy Foster	1.25	.60	.40
330	Jim Hunter	6.00	3.00	1.75
331	Stan Swanson	1.25	.60	.40
332	Buck Martinez	1.25	.60	.40
333	Steve Barber	1.25	.60	.40
334	Rangers Rookies (Bill Fahey, Jim Mason, Tom Ragland)	1.25	.60	.40
335	Bill Hands	1.25	.60	.40
336	Marty Martinez	1.25	.60	.40
337	Mike Kilkenny	1.25	.60	.40
338	Bob Grich	1.25	.60	.40
339	Ron Cook	1.25	.60	.40
340	Roy White	1.25	.60	.40
341	Boyhood Photo (Joe Torre)	1.25	.60	.40
342	Boyhood Photo (Wilbur Wood)	1.25	.60	.40
343	Boyhood Photo (Willie Stargell)	1.25	.60	.40
344	Boyhood Photo (Dave McNally)	1.25	.60	.40
345	Boyhood Photo (Rick Wise)	1.25	.60	.40
346	Boyhood Photo (Jim Fregosi)	1.25	.60	.40
347	Boyhood Photo (Tom Seaver)	5.00	2.50	1.50
348	Boyhood Photo (Sal Bando)	1.25	.60	.40
349	Al Fitzmorris	1.25	.60	.40
350	Frank Howard	1.25	.60	.40
351	Braves Rookies (Jimmy Britton, Tom House, Rick Kester)	1.25	.60	.40
352	Dave LaRoche	1.25	.60	.40
353	Art Shamsky	1.25	.60	.40
354	Tom Murphy	1.25	.60	.40
355	Bob Watson	1.25	.60	.40
356	Gerry Moses	1.25	.60	.40
357	Woodie Fryman	1.25	.60	.40
358	Sparky Anderson	1.25	.60	.40
359	Don Pavletich	1.25	.60	.40
360	Dave Roberts	1.25	.60	.40
361	Mike Andrews	1.25	.60	.40
362	Mets Team	1.25	.60	.40
363	Ron Klimkowski	1.25	.60	.40
364	Johnny Callison	1.25	.60	.40
365	Dick Bosman	1.25	.60	.40
366	Jimmy Rosario	1.25	.60	.40
367	Ron Perranoski	1.25	.60	.40
368	Danny Thompson	1.25	.60	.40
369	Jim LeFebvre	1.25	.60	.40
370	Don Buford	1.25	.60	.40
371	Denny LeMaster	1.25	.60	.40
372	Royals Rookies (Lance Clemons, Monty Montgomery)	1.25	.60	.40
373	John Mayberry	1.25	.60	.40
374	Jack Heidemann	1.25	.60	.40
375	Reggie Cleveland	1.25	.60	.40
376	Andy Kosco	1.25	.60	.40
377	Terry Harmon	1.25	.60	.40
378	Checklist 4	1.50	.70	.45
379	Ken Berry	1.25	.60	.40
380	Earl Williams	1.25	.60	.40
381	White Sox Team	1.25	.60	.40
382	Joe Gibbon	1.25	.60	.40
383	Brant Alyea	1.25	.60	.40
384	Dave Campbell	1.25	.60	.40
385	Mickey Stanley	1.25	.60	.40
386	Jim Colborn	1.25	.60	.40
387	Horace Clarke	1.25	.60	.40
388	Charlie Williams	1.25	.60	.40
389	Bill Rigney	1.25	.60	.40
390	Willie Davis	1.25	.60	.40
391	Ken Sanders	1.25	.60	.40
392	Pirates Rookies (Fred Cambria, Richie Zisk)	.75	.40	.25
393	Curt Motton	1.25	.60	.40
394	Ken Forsch	1.25	.60	.40
395	Matty Alou	1.75	.90	.50
396	Paul Lindblad	1.75	.90	.50
397	Phillies Team	1.75	.90	.50
398	Larry Hisle	1.75	.90	.50
399	Milt Wilcox	1.75	.90	.50
400	Tony Oliva	1.75	.90	.50
401	Jim Nash	1.75	.90	.50
402	Bobby Heise	1.75	.90	.50
403	John Cumberland	1.75	.90	.50
404	Jeff Torborg	1.75	.90	.50
405	Ron Fairly	1.75	.90	.50
406	George Hendrick	1.75	.90	.50
407	Chuck Taylor	1.75	.90	.50
408	Jim Northrup	1.75	.90	.50
409	Frank Baker	1.75	.90	.50
410	Fergie Jenkins	9.25	4.75	2.75
411	Bob Montgomery	1.75	.90	.50
412	Dick Kelley	1.75	.90	.50
413	White Sox Rookies (Don Eddy, Dave Lemonds)	1.75	.90	.50
414	Bob Miller	1.75	.90	.50
415	Cookie Rojas	1.75	.90	.50
416	Johnny Edwards	1.75	.90	.50
417	Tom Hall	1.75	.90	.50
418	Tom Shopay	1.75	.90	.50
419	Jim Spencer	1.75	.90	.50
420	Steve Carlton	30.00	15.00	9.00
421	Ellie Rodriguez	1.75	.90	.50
422	Ray Lamb	1.75	.90	.50
423	Oscar Gamble	1.75	.90	.50
424	Bill Gogolewski	1.75	.90	.50
425	Ken Singleton	1.75	.90	.50
426	Ken Singleton IA	1.75	.90	.50
427	Tito Fuentes	1.75	.90	.50
428	Tito Fuentes IA	1.75	.90	.50
429	Bob Robertson	1.75	.90	.50
430	Bob Robertson IA	1.75	.90	.50
431	Clarence Gaston	1.75	.90	.50
432	Clarence Gaston IA	1.75	.90	.50
433	Johnny Bench	42.50	21.00	12.50
434	Johnny Bench IA	21.00	10.50	6.25
435	Reggie Jackson	60.00	30.00	18.00
436	Reggie Jackson IA	30.00	15.00	9.00
437	Maury Wills	1.75	.90	.50
438	Maury Wills IA	1.75	.90	.50
439	Billy Williams	1.75	.90	.50
440	Billy Williams IA	1.75	.90	.50
441	Thurman Munson	25.00	12.50	7.50
442	Thurman Munson IA	12.75	6.50	3.75
443	Ken Henderson	1.75	.90	.50
444	Ken Henderson IA	1.75	.90	.50
445	Tom Seaver	42.50	21.00	12.50
446	Tom Seaver IA	21.00	10.50	6.25
447	Willie Stargell	8.50	4.25	2.50
448	Willie Stargell IA	1.75	.90	.50
449	Bob Lemon	1.75	.90	.50
450	Mickey Lolich	1.75	.90	.50
451	Tony LaRussa	1.75	.90	.50
452	Ed Herrmann	1.75	.90	.50
453	Barry Lersch	1.75	.90	.50
454	A's Team	1.75	.90	.50
455	Tommy Harper	1.75	.90	.50
456	Mark Belanger	1.75	.90	.50
457	Padres Rookies (Darcy Fast, Mike Ivie, Derrel Thomas)	1.75	.90	.50
458	Aurelio Monteagudo	1.75	.90	.50
459	Rick Renick	1.75	.90	.50
460	Al Downing	1.75	.90	.50
461	Tim Cullen	1.75	.90	.50
462	Rickey Clark	1.75	.90	.50
463	Bernie Carbo	1.75	.90	.50
464	Jim Roland	1.75	.90	.50
465	Gil Hodges	2.50	1.25	.70
466	Norm Miller	1.75	.90	.50
467	Steve Kline	1.75	.90	.50
468	Richie Scheinblum	1.75	.90	.50
469	Ron Herbel	1.75	.90	.50
470	Ray Fosse	1.75	.90	.50
471	Luke Walker	1.75	.90	.50
472	Phil Gagliano	1.75	.90	.50
473	Dan McGinn	1.75	.90	.50
474	Orioles Rookies (Don Baylor, Roric Harrison, Johnny Oates)	15.00	7.50	4.50

475 Gary Nolan 1.75 .90 .50
476 Lee Richard 1.75 .90 .50
477 Tom Phoebus 1.75 .90 .50
478 Checklist 5 1.75 .90 .50
479 Don Shaw 1.75 .90 .50
480 Lee May 1.75 .90 .50
481 Billy Conigliaro 1.75 .90 .50
482 Joe Hoerner 1.75 .90 .50
483 Ken Suarez 1.75 .90 .50
484 Lum Harris 1.75 .90 .50
485 Phil Regan 1.75 .90 .50
486 John Lowenstein 1.75 .90 .50
487 Tigers Team 1.75 .90 .50
488 Mike Nagy 1.75 .90 .50
489 Expos Rookies (Terry Humphrey, Keith Lampard) 1.75 .90 .50
490 Dave McNally 1.75 .90 .50
491 Boyhood Photos (Lou Piniella) 1.75 .90 .50
492 Boyhood Photos (Mel Stottlemyre) 1.75 .90 .50
493 Boyhood Photos (Bob Bailey) 1.75 .90 .50
494 Boyhood Photos (Willie Horton) 1.75 .90 .50
495 Boyhood Photos (Bill Melton) 1.75 .90 .50
496 Boyhood Photos (Bud Harrelson) 1.75 .90 .50
497 Boyhood Photos (Jim Perry) 1.75 .90 .50
498 Boyhood Photos (Brooks Robinson) 1.75 .90 .50
499 Vicente Romo 1.75 .90 .50
500 Joe Torre 1.75 .90 .50
501 Pete Hamm 1.75 .90 .50
502 Jackie Hernandez 1.75 .90 .50
503 Gary Peters 1.75 .90 .50
504 Ed Spiezio 1.75 .90 .50
505 Mike Marshall 1.75 .90 .50
506 Indians Rookies (Terry Ley, Jim Moyer, Dick Tidrow) 1.75 .90 .50
507 Fred Gladding 1.75 .90 .50
508 Ellie Hendricks 1.75 .90 .50
509 Don McMahon 1.75 .90 .50
510 Ted Williams 10.25 5.25 3.00
511 Tony Taylor 1.75 .90 .50
512 Paul Popovich 1.75 .90 .50
513 Lindy McDaniel 1.75 .90 .50
514 Ted Sizemore 1.75 .90 .50
515 Bert Blyleven 11.00 5.50 3.25
516 Oscar Brown 1.75 .90 .50
517 Ken Brett 1.75 .90 .50
518 Wayne Garrett 1.75 .90 .50
519 Ted Abernathy 1.75 .90 .50
520 Larry Bowa 1.75 .90 .50
521 Alan Foster 1.75 .90 .50
522 Dodgers Team 1.75 .90 .50
523 Chuck Dobson 1.75 .90 .50
524 Reds Rookies (Ed Armbrister, Mel Behney) 1.75 .90 .50
525 Carlos May 1.75 .90 .50

1973 O-Pee-Chee

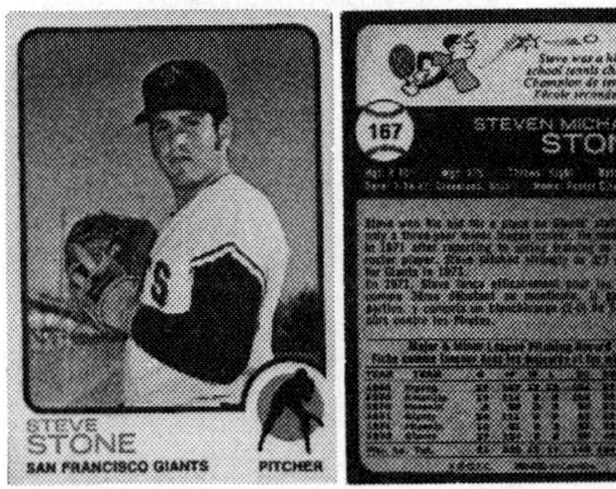

The 1973 Canadian-issued O-Pee-Chee set numbered 660 cards and is identical in design to the 1973 Topps set. The backs of the O-Pee-Chee cards are written in both French and English and contain the line "Printed in Canada" along the bottom. The cards measure 2-1/2" by 3-1/2".

	NR MT	EX	VG
Complete Set (660):	1275.	625.00	375.00
Common Player (1-396):	.75	.40	.25
Common Player (397-528):	1.25	.60	.40
Common Player (529-660):	3.50	1.75	1.00

1 All Time Home Run Leaders (Hank Aaron, Willie Mays, Babe Ruth) 38.00 19.00 11.50
2 Rich Hebner .75 .40 .25
3 Jim Lonborg .75 .40 .25
4 John Milner .75 .40 .25
5 Ed Brinkman .75 .40 .25
6 Mac Scarce .75 .40 .25
7 Rangers Team .75 .40 .25
8 Tom Hall .75 .40 .25
9 Johnny Oates .75 .40 .25
10 Don Sutton 1.20 .60 .35
11 Chris Chambliss .75 .40 .25
12 Padres Mgr./Coaches (Dave Garcia, Johnny Podres, Bob Skinner, Whitey Wietelmann, Don Zimmer) .75 .40 .25
13 George Hendrick .75 .40 .25
14 Sonny Siebert .75 .40 .25
15 Ralph Garr .75 .40 .25
16 Steve Braun .75 .40 .25
17 Fred Gladding .75 .40 .25
18 Leroy Stanton .75 .40 .25
19 Tim Foli .75 .40 .25
20 Stan Bahnsen .75 .40 .25
21 Randy Hundley .75 .40 .25
22 Ted Abernathy .75 .40 .25
23 Dave Kingman 1.00 .50 .30
24 Al Santorini .75 .40 .25
25 Roy White .75 .40 .25
26 Pirates Team .75 .40 .25
27 Bill Gogolewski .75 .40 .25
28 Hal McRae .75 .40 .25
29 Tony Taylor .75 .40 .25
30 Tug McGraw .75 .40 .25
31 Buddy Bell 2.50 1.25 .70
32 Fred Norman .75 .40 .25
33 Jim Breazeale .75 .40 .25
34 Pat Dobson .75 .40 .25
35 Willie Davis .75 .40 .25
36 Steve Barber .75 .40 .25
37 Bill Robinson .75 .40 .25
38 Mike Epstein .75 .40 .25
39 Dave Roberts .75 .40 .25
40 Reggie Smith .75 .40 .25
41 Tom Walker .75 .40 .25
42 Mike Andrews .75 .40 .25
43 Randy Moffitt .75 .40 .25
44 Rick Monday .75 .40 .25
45 Ellie Rodriguez .75 .40 .25
46 Lindy McDaniel .75 .40 .25
47 Luis Melendez .75 .40 .25
48 Paul Splittorff .75 .40 .25
49 Twins Mgr./Coaches (Vern Morgan, Frank Quilici, Bob Rodgers, Ralph Rowe, Al Worthington) .75 .40 .25
50 Roberto Clemente 38.00 19.00 11.50
51 Chuck Seelbach .75 .40 .25
52 Denis Menke .75 .40 .25
53 Steve Dunning .75 .40 .25
54 Checklist 1 1.00 .50 .30
55 Jon Matlack .75 .40 .25
56 Merv Rettenmund .75 .40 .25
57 Derrel Thomas .75 .40 .25
58 Mike Paul .75 .40 .25
59 Steve Yeager .75 .40 .25
60 Ken Holtzman .75 .40 .25
61 Batting Leaders (Rod Carew, Billy Williams) 1.25 .60 .40
62 Home Run Leaders (Dick Allen, Johnny Bench) 1.00 .50 .30
63 Runs Batted In Leaders (Dick Allen, Johnny Bench) 1.00 .50 .30
64 Stolen Base Leaders (Lou Brock, Bert Campaneris) .75 .40 .25
65 Earned Run Average Leaders (Steve Carlton, Luis Tiant) .75 .40 .25
66 Victory Leaders (Steve Carlton, Gaylord Perry, Wilbur Wood) 1.00 .50 .30
67 Strikeout Leaders (Steve Carlton, Nolan Ryan) 23.00 11.50 7.00
68 Leading Firemen (Clay Carroll, Sparky Lyle) .75 .40 .25
69 Phil Gagliano .75 .40 .25
70 Milt Pappas .75 .40 .25
71 Johnny Briggs .75 .40 .25
72 Ron Reed .75 .40 .25
73 Ed Herrmann .75 .40 .25
74 Billy Champion .75 .40 .25
75 Vada Pinson .75 .40 .25
76 Doug Rader .75 .40 .25
77 Mike Torrez .75 .40 .25
78 Richie Scheinblum .75 .40 .25
79 Jim Willoughby .75 .40 .25
80 Tony Oliva 1.00 .50 .30
81 Cubs Mgr./Coaches (Hank Aguirre, Ernie Banks, Larry Jansen, Whitey Lockman, Pete Reiser) .75 .40 .25
82 Fritz Peterson .75 .40 .25
83 Leron Lee .75 .40 .25
84 Rollie Fingers 7.25 3.75 2.25
85 Ted Simmons 1.00 .50 .30
86 Tom McCraw .75 .40 .25
87 Ken Boswell .75 .40 .25
88 Mickey Stanley .75 .40 .25
89 Jack Billingham .75 .40 .25
90 Brooks Robinson 7.50 3.75 2.25
91 Dodgers Team 1.00 .50 .30
92 Jerry Bell .75 .40 .25
93 Jesus Alou .75 .40 .25
94 Dick Billings .75 .40 .25
95 Steve Blass .75 .40 .25
96 Doug Griffin .75 .40 .25
97 Willie Montanez .75 .40 .25
98 Dick Woodson .75 .40 .25
99 Carl Taylor .75 .40 .25
100 Hank Aaron 30.00 15.00 9.00
101 Ken Henderson .75 .40 .25
102 Rudy May .75 .40 .25
103 Celerino Sanchez .75 .40 .25
104 Reggie Cleveland .75 .40 .25
105 Carlos May .75 .40 .25
106 Terry Humphrey .75 .40 .25
107 Phil Hennigan .75 .40 .25
108 Bill Russell .75 .40 .25
109 Doyle Alexander .75 .40 .25
110 Bob Watson .75 .40 .25
111 Dave Nelson .75 .40 .25
112 Gary Ross .75 .40 .25
113 Jerry Grote .75 .40 .25
114 Lynn McGlothen .75 .40 .25
115 Ron Santo .75 .40 .25
116 Yankees Mgr./Coaches (Jim Hegan, Ralph Houk, Elston Howard, Dick Howser, Jim Turner) .75 .40 .25
117 Ramon Hernandez .75 .40 .25
118 John Mayberry .75 .40 .25
119 Larry Bowa .75 .40 .25
120 Joe Coleman .75 .40 .25
121 Dave Rader .75 .40 .25
122 Jim Strickland .75 .40 .25
123 Sandy Alomar .75 .40 .25
124 Jim Hardin .75 .40 .25
125 Ron Fairly .75 .40 .25
126 Jim Brewer .75 .40 .25
127 Brewers Team .75 .40 .25
128 Ted Sizemore .75 .40 .25
129 Terry Forster .75 .40 .25
130 Pete Rose 18.00 9.00 5.50
131 Red Sox Mgr./Coaches (Doug Camilli, Eddie Kasko, Don Lenhardt, Eddie Popowski, Lee Stange) .75 .40 .25
132 Matty Alou .75 .40 .25
133 Dave Roberts .75 .40 .25
134 Milt Wilcox .75 .40 .25
135 Lee May .75 .40 .25
136 Orioles Mgr./Coaches (George Bamberger, Jim Frey, Billy Hunter, George Staller, Earl Weaver) .75 .40 .25
137 Jim Beauchamp .75 .40 .25
138 Horacio Pina .75 .40 .25
139 Carmen Fanzone .75 .40 .25
140 Lou Piniella .75 .40 .25
141 Bruce Kison .75 .40 .25
142 Thurman Munson 12.75 6.50 3.75
143 John Curtis .75 .40 .25
144 Marty Perez .75 .40 .25
145 Bobby Bonds .75 .40 .25
146 Woodie Fryman .75 .40 .25
147 Mike Anderson .75 .40 .25
148 Dave Goltz .75 .40 .25
149 Ron Hunt .75 .40 .25
150 Wilbur Wood .75 .40 .25
151 Wes Parker .75 .40 .25
152 Dave May .75 .40 .25
153 Al Hrabosky .75 .40 .25
154 Jeff Torborg .75 .40 .25
155 Sal Bando .75 .40 .25
156 Cesar Geronimo .75 .40 .25
157 Denny Riddleberger .75 .40 .25
158 Astros Team .75 .40 .25
159 Clarence Gaston .75 .40 .25
160 Jim Palmer 13.50 6.75 4.00
161 Ted Martinez .75 .40 .25
162 Pete Broberg .75 .40 .25
163 Vic Davalillo .75 .40 .25
164 Monty Montgomery .75 .40 .25
165 Luis Aparicio 1.75 .90 .50
166 Terry Harmon .75 .40 .25
167 Steve Stone .75 .40 .25
168 Jim Northrup .75 .40 .25
169 Ron Schueler .75 .40 .25
170 Harmon Killebrew 6.00 3.00 1.75
171 Bernie Carbo .75 .40 .25
172 Steve Kline .75 .40 .25
173 Hal Breeden .75 .40 .25
174 Rich Gossage 21.00 10.50 6.25
175 Frank Robinson 6.75 3.50 2.00
176 Chuck Taylor .75 .40 .25
177 Bill Plummer .75 .40 .25
178 Don Rose .75 .40 .25
179 A's Mgr./Coaches (Jerry Adair, Vern Hoscheit, Irv Noren, Wes Stock, Dick Williams) .75 .40 .25
180 Fergie Jenkins 6.00 3.00 1.75
181 Jack Brohamer .75 .40 .25
182 Mike Caldwell .75 .40 .25
183 Don Buford .75 .40 .25
184 Jerry Koosman .75 .40 .25
185 Jim Wynn .75 .40 .25
186 Bill Fahey .75 .40 .25
187 Luke Walker .75 .40 .25
188 Cookie Rojas .75 .40 .25
189 Grg Luzinski .75 .40 .25
190 Bob Gibson 6.75 3.50 2.00
191 Tigers Team 1.00 .50 .30
192 Pat Jarvis .75 .40 .25
193 Carlton Fisk 46.00 23.00 14.00
194 Jorge Orta .75 .40 .25
195 Clay Carroll .75 .40 .25
196 Ken McMullen .75 .40 .25
197 Ed Goodson .75 .40 .25
198 Horace Clarke .75 .40 .25
199 Bert Blyleven 6.00 3.00 1.75
200 Billy Williams 1.75 .90 .50
201 A.L. Playoffs (Hendrick Scores Winning Run) .75 .40 .25
202 N.L. Playoffs (Foster's Run Decides It) .75 .40 .25
203 World Series Game 1 (Tenace The Menace) .75 .40 .25
204 World Series Game 2 (A's Make It Two Straight) .75 .40 .25
205 World Series Game 3 (Reds Win Squeeker) .75 .40 .25
206 World Series Game 4 (Tenace Singles In Ninth) .75 .40 .25
207 World Series Game 5 (Odom Out At Plate) .75 .40 .25
208 World Series Game 6 (Reds' Slugging Ties Series) .75 .40 .25
209 World Series Game 7 (Campy Starts Winning Rally) .75 .40 .25
210 World Series Summary (World Champions) .75 .40 .25
211 Balor Moore .75 .40 .25
212 Joe Lahoud .75 .40 .25
213 Steve Garvey 12.75 6.50 3.75
214 Dave Hamilton .75 .40 .25
215 Dusty Baker .75 .40 .25
216 Toby Harrah .75 .40 .25
217 Don Wilson .75 .40 .25
218 Aurelio Rodriguez .75 .40 .25
219 Cardinals Team .75 .40 .25
220 Nolan Ryan 105.00 52.00 31.00
221 Fred Kendall .75 .40 .25
222 Rob Gardner .75 .40 .25
223 Bud Harrelson .75 .40 .25
224 Bill Lee .75 .40 .25
225 Al Oliver 1.00 .50 .30

226 Ray Fosse .75 .40 .25
227 Wayne Twitchell .75 .40 .25
228 Bobby Darwin .75 .40 .25
229 Roric Harrison .75 .40 .25
230 Joe Morgan 6.75 3.50 2.00
231 Bill Parsons .75 .40 .25
232 Ken Singleton .75 .40 .25
233 Ed Kirkpatrick .75 .40 .25
234 Bill North .75 .40 .25
235 Jim Hunter 5.00 2.50 1.50
236 Tito Fuentes .75 .40 .25
237 Braves Mgr./Coaches (Lew Burdette, Jim Busby, Roy Hartsfield, Eddie Mathews, Ken Silvestri) 1.00 .50 .30
238 Tony Muser .75 .40 .25
239 Pete Richert .75 .40 .25
240 Bobby Murcer .75 .40 .25
241 Dwain Anderson .75 .40 .25
242 George Culver .75 .40 .25
243 Angels Team .75 .40 .25
244 Ed Acosta .75 .40 .25
245 Carl Yastrzemski 17.00 8.50 5.00
246 Ken Sanders .75 .40 .25
247 Del Unser .75 .40 .25
248 Jerry Johnson .75 .40 .25
249 Larry Biittner .75 .40 .25
250 Manny Sanguillen .75 .40 .25
251 Roger Nelson .75 .40 .25
252 Giants Mgr./Coaches (Joe Amalfitano, Charlie Fox, Andy Gilbert, Don McMahon, John McNamara) .75 .40 .25
253 Mark Belanger .75 .40 .25
254 Bill Stoneman .75 .40 .25
255 Reggie Jackson 38.00 19.00 11.50
256 Chris Zachary .75 .40 .25
257 Mets Mgr./Coaches (Yogi Berra, Roy McMillan, Joe Pignatano, Rube Walker, Eddie Yost) 1.00 .50 .30
258 Tommy John 1.25 .60 .40
259 Jim Holt .75 .40 .25
260 Gary Nolan .75 .40 .25
261 Pat Kelly .75 .40 .25
262 Jack Aker .75 .40 .25
263 George Scott .75 .40 .25
264 Checklist 2 1.00 .50 .30
265 Gene Michael .75 .40 .25
266 Mike Lum .75 .40 .25
267 Lloyd Allen .75 .40 .25
268 Jerry Morales .75 .40 .25
269 Tim McCarver .75 .40 .25
270 Luis Tiant .75 .40 .25
271 Tom Hutton .75 .40 .25
272 Ed Farmer .75 .40 .25
273 Chris Speier .75 .40 .25
274 Darold Knowles .75 .40 .25
275 Tony Perez 1.25 .60 .40
276 Joe Lovitto .75 .40 .25
277 Bob Miller .75 .40 .25
278 Orioles Team .75 .40 .25
279 Mike Strahler .75 .40 .25
280 Al Kaline 7.50 3.75 2.25
281 Mike Jorgensen .75 .40 .25
282 Steve Hovley .75 .40 .25
283 Ray Sadecki .75 .40 .25
284 Glenn Borgmann .75 .40 .25
285 Don Kessinger .75 .40 .25
286 Frank Linzy .75 .40 .25
287 Eddie Leon .75 .40 .25
288 Gary Gentry .75 .40 .25
289 Bob Oliver .75 .40 .25
290 Cesar Cedeno .75 .40 .25
291 Rogelio Moret .75 .40 .25
292 Jose Cruz .75 .40 .25
293 Bernie Allen .75 .40 .25
294 Steve Arlin .75 .40 .25
295 Bert Campaneris .75 .40 .25
296 Reds Mgr./Coaches (Sparky Anderson, Alex Grammas, Ted Kluszewski, George Scherger, Larry Shepard) .75 .40 .25
297 Walt Williams .75 .40 .25
298 Ron Bryant .75 .40 .25
299 Ted Ford .75 .40 .25
300 Steve Carlton 17.00 8.50 5.00
301 Billy Grabarkewitz .75 .40 .25
302 Terry Crowley .75 .40 .25
303 Nelson Briles .75 .40 .25
304 Duke Sims .75 .40 .25
305 Willie Mays 42.50 21.00 12.50
306 Tom Burgmeier .75 .40 .25
307 Boots Day .75 .40 .25
308 Skip Lockwood .75 .40 .25
309 Paul Popovich .75 .40 .25
310 Dick Allen .75 .40 .25
311 Joe Decker .75 .40 .25
312 Oscar Brown .75 .40 .25
313 Jim Ray .75 .40 .25
314 Ron Swoboda .75 .40 .25
315 John Odom .75 .40 .25
316 Padres Team .75 .40 .25
317 Danny Cater .75 .40 .25
318 Jim McGlothlin .75 .40 .25
319 Jim Spencer .75 .40 .25
320 Lou Brock 7.50 3.75 2.25
321 Rich Hinton .75 .40 .25
322 Garry Maddox .75 .40 .25
323 Tigers Mgr./Coaches (Art Fowler, Billy Martin, Charlie Silvera, Dick Tracewski) 1.00 .50 .30
324 Al Downing .75 .40 .25
325 Boog Powell .75 .40 .25
326 Darrell Brandon .75 .40 .25
327 John Lowenstein .75 .40 .25
328 Bill Bonham .75 .40 .25
329 Ed Kranepool .75 .40 .25
330 Rod Carew 12.75 6.50 3.75
331 Carl Morton .75 .40 .25
332 John Felske .75 .40 .25
333 Gene Clines .75 .40 .25
334 Freddie Patek .75 .40 .25
335 Bob Tolan .75 .40 .25
336 Tom Bradley .75 .40 .25
337 Dave Duncan .75 .40 .25
338 Checklist 3 1.00 .50 .30
339 Dick Tidrow .75 .40 .25
340 Nate Colbert .75 .40 .25
341 Boyhood Photo (Jim Palmer) 1.00 .50 .30
342 Boyhood Photo (Sam McDowell) .75 .40 .25
343 Boyhood Photo (Bobby Murcer) .75 .40 .25
344 Boyhood Photo (Jim Hunter) 1.00 .50 .30
345 Boyhood Photo (Chris Speier) .75 .40 .25
346 Boyhood Photo (Gaylord Perry) 1.00 .50 .30
347 Royals Team .75 .40 .25
348 Rennie Stennett .75 .40 .25
349 Dick McAuliffe .75 .40 .25
350 Tom Seaver 25.00 12.50 7.50
351 Jimmy Stewart .75 .40 .25
352 Don Stanhouse .75 .40 .25
353 Steve Brye .75 .40 .25
354 Billy Parker .75 .40 .25
355 Mike Marshall .75 .40 .25
356 White Sox Mgr./Coaches (Joe Lonnett, Jim Mahoney, Al Monchak, Johnny Sain, Chuck Tanner) .75 .40 .25
357 Ross Grimsley .75 .40 .25
358 Jim Nettles .75 .40 .25
359 Cecil Upshaw .75 .40 .25
360 Joe Rudi (photo actually Gene Tenace) .75 .40 .25
361 Fran Healy .75 .40 .25
362 Eddie Watt .75 .40 .25
363 Jackie Hernandez .75 .40 .25
364 Rick Wise .75 .40 .25
365 Rico Petrocelli .75 .40 .25
366 Brock Davis .75 .40 .25
367 Burt Hooton .75 .40 .25
368 Bill Buckner .75 .40 .25
369 Lerrin laGrow .75 .40 .25
370 Willie Stargell 6.00 3.00 1.75
371 Mike Kekich .75 .40 .25
372 Oscar Gamble .75 .40 .25
373 Clyde Wright .75 .40 .25
374 Darrell Evans .75 .40 .25
375 Larry Dierker .75 .40 .25
376 Frank Duffy .75 .40 .25
377 Expos Mgr./Coaches (Dave Bristol, Larry Doby, Gene Mauch, Cal McLish, Jerry Zimmerman) .75 .40 .25
378 Lenny Randle .75 .40 .25
379 Cy Acosta .75 .40 .25
380 Johnny Bench 22.00 11.00 6.50
381 Vicente Romo .75 .40 .25
382 Mike Hegan .75 .40 .25
383 Diego Segui .75 .40 .25
384 Don Baylor 1.00 .50 .30
385 Jim Perry .75 .40 .25
386 Don Money .75 .40 .25
387 Jim Barr .75 .40 .25
388 Ben Oglivie .75 .40 .25
389 Mets Team 1.00 .50 .30
390 Mickey Lolich .75 .40 .25
391 Lee Lacy .75 .40 .25
392 Dick Drago .75 .40 .25
393 Jose Cardenal .75 .40 .25
394 Sparky Lyle .75 .40 .25
395 Roger Metzger .75 .40 .25
396 Grant Jackson .75 .40 .25
397 Dave Cash 1.25 .60 .40
398 Rich Hand 1.25 .60 .40
399 George Foster 1.25 .60 .40
400 Gaylord Perry 6.00 3.00 1.75
401 Clyde Mashore 1.25 .60 .40
402 Jack Hiatt 1.25 .60 .40
403 Sonny Jackson 1.25 .60 .40
404 Chuck Brinkman 1.25 .60 .40
405 Cesar Tovar 1.25 .60 .40
406 Paul Lindblad 1.25 .60 .40
407 Felix Millan 1.25 .60 .40
408 Jim Colborn 1.25 .60 .40
409 Ivan Murrell 1.25 .60 .40
410 Willie McCovey 6.75 3.50 2.00
411 Ray Corbin 1.25 .60 .40
412 Manny Mota 1.25 .60 .40
413 Tom Timmermann 1.25 .60 .40
414 Ken Rudolph 1.25 .60 .40
415 Marty Pattin 1.25 .60 .40
416 Paul Schaal 1.25 .60 .40
417 Scipio Spinks 1.25 .60 .40
418 Bobby Grich 1.25 .60 .40
419 Casey Cox 1.25 .60 .40
420 Tommie Agee 1.25 .60 .40
421 Angels Mgr./Coaches (Tom Morgan, Salty Parker, Jimmie Reese, John Roseboro, Bobby Winkles) 1.25 .60 .40
422 Bob Robertson 1.25 .60 .40
423 Johnny Jeter 1.25 .60 .40
424 Denny Doyle 1.25 .60 .40
425 Alex Johnson 1.25 .60 .40
426 Dave Laroche 1.25 .60 .40
427 Rick Auerbach 1.25 .60 .40
428 Wayne Simpson 1.25 .60 .40
429 Jim Fairey 1.25 .60 .40
430 Vida Blue 1.25 .60 .40
431 Gerry Moses 1.25 .60 .40
432 Dan Frisella 1.25 .60 .40
433 Willie Horton 1.25 .60 .40
434 Giants Team 1.25 .60 .40
435 Rico Carty 1.25 .60 .40
436 Jim McAndrew 1.25 .60 .40
437 John Kennedy 1.25 .60 .40
438 Enzo Hernandez 1.25 .60 .40
439 Eddie Fisher 1.25 .60 .40
440 Glenn Beckert 1.25 .60 .40
441 Gail Hopkins 1.25 .60 .40
442 Dick Dietz 1.25 .60 .40
443 Danny Thompson 1.25 .60 .40
444 Ken Brett 1.25 .60 .40
445 Ken Berry 1.25 .60 .40
446 Jerry Reuss 1.25 .60 .40
447 Joe Hague 1.25 .60 .40
448 John Hiller 1.25 .60 .40
449 Indians Mgr./Coaches (Ken Aspromonte, Rocky Colavito, Joe Lutz, Warren Spahn) 1.25 .60 .40
450 Joe Torre 1.25 .60 .40
451 John Vukovich 1.25 .60 .40
452 Paul Casanova 1.25 .60 .40
453 Checklist 4 1.25 .60 .40
454 Tom Haller 1.25 .60 .40
455 Bill Melton 1.25 .60 .40
456 Dick Green 1.25 .60 .40
457 John Strohmayer 1.25 .60 .40
458 Jim Mason 1.25 .60 .40
459 Jimmy Howarth 1.25 .60 .40
460 Bill Freehan 1.25 .60 .40
461 Mike Corkins 1.25 .60 .40
462 Ron Blomberg 1.25 .60 .40
463 Ken Tatum 1.25 .60 .40
464 Cubs Team 1.25 .60 .40
465 Dave Giusti 1.25 .60 .40
466 Jose Arcia 1.25 .60 .40
467 Mike Ryan 1.25 .60 .40
468 Tom Griffin 1.25 .60 .40
469 Dan Monzon 1.25 .60 .40
470 Mike Cuellar 1.25 .60 .40
471 Hit Leader (Ty Cobb) 6.75 3.50 2.00
472 Grand Slam Leader (Lou Gehrig) 6.75 3.50 2.00
473 Total Bases Leader (Hank Aaron) 6.75 3.50 2.00
474 R.B.I. Leader (Babe Ruth) 13.50 6.75 4.00
475 Batting Leader (Ty Cobb) 6.75 3.50 2.00
476 Shutout Leader (Walter Johnson) 1.25 .60 .40
477 Victory Leader (Cy Young) 1.25 .60 .40
478 Strikeout Leader (Walter Johnson) 1.25 .60 .40
479 Hal Lanier 1.25 .60 .40
480 Juan Marichal 2.50 1.25 .70
481 White Sox Team 1.25 .60 .40
482 Rick Reuschel 4.00 2.00 1.25
483 Dal Maxvill 1.25 .60 .40
484 Ernie McAnally 1.25 .60 .40
485 Norm Cash 1.25 .60 .40
486 Phillies Mgr./Coaches (Carroll Beringer, Billy DeMars, Danny Ozark, Ray Rippelmeyer, Bobby Wine) 1.25 .60 .40
487 Bruce Dal Canton 1.25 .60 .40
488 Dave Campbell 1.25 .60 .40
489 Jeff Burroughs 1.25 .60 .40
490 Claude Osteen 1.25 .60 .40
491 Bob Montgomery 1.25 .60 .40
492 Pedro Borbon 1.25 .60 .40
493 Duffy Dyer 1.25 .60 .40
494 Rich Morales 1.25 .60 .40
495 Tommy Helms 1.25 .60 .40
496 Ray Lamb 1.25 .60 .40
497 Cardinals Mgr./Coaches (Vern Benson, George Kissell, Red Schoendienst, Barney Schultz) 1.25 .60 .40
498 Graig Nettles 1.50 .70 .45
499 Bob Moose 1.25 .60 .40
500 A's Team 1.25 .60 .40
501 Larry Gura 1.25 .60 .40
502 Bobby Valentine 1.25 .60 .40
503 Phil Niekro 5.00 2.50 1.50
504 Earl Williams 1.25 .60 .40
505 Bob Bailey 1.25 .60 .40
506 Bart Johnson 1.25 .60 .40
507 Darrel Chaney 1.25 .60 .40
508 Gates Brown 1.25 .60 .40
509 Jim Nash 1.25 .60 .40
510 Amos Otis 1.25 .60 .40
511 Sam McDowell 1.25 .60 .40
512 Dalton Jones 1.25 .60 .40
513 Dave Marshall 1.25 .60 .40
514 Jerry Kenney 1.25 .60 .40
515 Andy Messersmith 1.25 .60 .40
516 Danny Walton 1.25 .60 .40
517 Pirates Mgr./Coaches (Don Leppert, Bill Mazeroski, Dave Ricketts, Bill Virdon, Mel Wright) 1.25 .60 .40
518 Bob Veale 1.25 .60 .40
519 John Edwards 1.25 .60 .40
520 Mel Stottlemyre 1.25 .60 .40
521 Braves Team 1.25 .60 .40
522 Leo Cardenas 1.25 .60 .40
523 Wayne Granger 1.25 .60 .40
524 Gene Tenace 1.25 .60 .40
525 Jim Fregosi 1.25 .60 .40
526 Ollie Brown 1.25 .60 .40
527 Dan McGinn 1.25 .60 .40
528 Paul Blair 1.25 .60 .40
529 Milt May 3.50 1.75 1.00
530 Jim Kaat 3.50 1.75 1.00
531 Ron Woods 3.50 1.75 1.00
532 Steve Mingori 3.50 1.75 1.00
533 Larry Stahl 3.50 1.75 1.00
534 Dave Lemonds 3.50 1.75 1.00
535 John Callison 3.50 1.75 1.00
536 Phillies Team 3.50 1.75 1.00
537 Bill Slayback 3.50 1.75 1.00
538 Jim Hart 3.50 1.75 1.00
539 Tom Murphy 3.50 1.75 1.00
540 Cleon Jones 3.50 1.75 1.00
541 Bob Bolin 3.50 1.75 1.00
542 Pat Corrales 3.50 1.75 1.00
543 Alan Foster 3.50 1.75 1.00
544 Von Joshua 3.50 1.75 1.00
545 Orlando Cepeda 3.50 1.75 1.00
546 Jim York 3.50 1.75 1.00
547 Bobby Heise 3.50 1.75 1.00
548 Don Durham 3.50 1.75 1.00
549 Rangers Mgr./Coaches (Chuck Estrada, Whitey Herzog, Chuck Hiller, Jackie Moore) 3.50 1.75 1.00

550	Dave Johnson	3.50	1.75	1.00
551	Mike Kilkenny	3.50	1.75	1.00
552	J.C. Martin	3.50	1.75	1.00
553	Mickey Scott	3.50	1.75	1.00
554	Dave Concepcion	3.50	1.75	1.00
555	Bill Hands	3.50	1.75	1.00
556	Yankees Team	3.50	1.75	1.00
557	Bernie Williams	3.50	1.75	1.00
558	Jerry May	3.50	1.75	1.00
559	Barry Lersch	3.50	1.75	1.00
560	Frank Howard	3.50	1.75	1.00
561	Jim Geddes	3.50	1.75	1.00
562	Wayne Garrett	3.50	1.75	1.00
563	Larry Haney	3.50	1.75	1.00
564	Mike Thompson	3.50	1.75	1.00
565	Jim Hickman	3.50	1.75	1.00
566	Lew Krausse	3.50	1.75	1.00
567	Bob Fenwick	3.50	1.75	1.00
568	Ray Newman	3.50	1.75	1.00
569	Dodgers Mgr./Coaches (Red Adams, Walt Alston, Monty Basgall, Jim Gilliam, Tom Lasorda)	3.50	1.75	1.00
570	Bill Singer	3.50	1.75	1.00
571	Rusty Torres	3.50	1.75	1.00
572	Gary Sutherland	3.50	1.75	1.00
573	Fred Beene	3.50	1.75	1.00
574	Bob Didier	3.50	1.75	1.00
575	Dock Ellis	3.50	1.75	1.00
576	Expos Team	3.50	1.75	1.00
577	Eric Soderholm	3.50	1.75	1.00
578	Ken Wright	3.50	1.75	1.00
579	Tom Grieve	3.50	1.75	1.00
580	Joe Pepitone	3.50	1.75	1.00
581	Steve Kealey	3.50	1.75	1.00
582	Darrell Porter	3.50	1.75	1.00
583	Bill Grief	3.50	1.75	1.00
584	Chris Arnold	3.50	1.75	1.00
585	Joe Niekro	3.50	1.75	1.00
586	Bill Sudakis	3.50	1.75	1.00
587	Rich McKinney	3.50	1.75	1.00
588	Checklist 5	30.00	15.00	9.00
589	Ken Forsch	3.50	1.75	1.00
590	Deron Johnson	3.50	1.75	1.00
591	Mike Hedlund	3.50	1.75	1.00
592	John Boccabella	3.50	1.75	1.00
593	Royals Mgr./Coaches (Galen Cisco, Harry Dunlop, Charlie Lau, Jack McKeon)	3.50	1.75	1.00
594	Vic Harris	3.50	1.75	1.00
595	Don Gullett	3.50	1.75	1.00
596	Red Sox Team	3.50	1.75	1.00
597	Mickey Rivers	3.50	1.75	1.00
598	Phil Roof	3.50	1.75	1.00
599	Ed Crosby	3.50	1.75	1.00
600	Dave McNally	3.50	1.75	1.00
601	Rookie Catchers (George Pena, Sergio Robles, Rick Stelmaszek)	3.50	1.75	1.00
602	Rookie Pitchers (Mel Behney, Ralph Garcia, Doug Rau)	3.50	1.75	1.00
603	Rookie Third Basemen (Terry Hughes, Bill McNulty, Ken Reitz)	3.50	1.75	1.00
604	Rookie Pitchers (Jesse Jefferson, Dennis O'Toole, Bob Strampe)	3.50	1.75	1.00
605	Rookie First Basemen (Pat Bourque, Enos Cabell, Gonzalo Marquez)	3.50	1.75	1.00
606	Rookie Outfielders (Gary Matthews, Tom Paciorek, Jorge Roque)	3.50	1.75	1.00
607	Rookie Shortstops (Ray Busse, Pepe Frias, Mario Guerrero)	3.50	1.75	1.00
608	Rookie Pitchers (Steve Busby, Dick Colpaert, George Medich)	3.50	1.75	1.00
609	Rookie Second Basemen (Larvell Blanks, Pedro Garcia, Dave Lopes)	3.50	1.75	1.00
610	Rookie Pitchers (Jimmy Freeman, Charlie Hough, Hank Webb)	3.50	1.75	1.00
611	Rookie Outfielders (Rich Coggins, Jim Wohlford, Richie Zisk)	3.50	1.75	1.00
612	Rookie Pitchers (Steve Lawson, Bob Reynolds, Brent Strom)	3.50	1.75	1.00
613	Rookie Catchers (Bob Boone, Mike Ivie, Skip Jutze)	42.50	21.00	12.50
614	Rookie Outfielders (Alonza Bumbry, Dwight Evans, Charlie Spikes)	42.50	21.00	12.50
615	Rookie Third Basemen (Ron Cey, John Hilton, Mike Schmidt)	535.00	267.00	160.00
616	Rookie Pitchers (Norm Angelini, Steve Blateric, Mike Garman)	3.50	1.75	1.00
617	Rich Chiles	3.50	1.75	1.00
618	Andy Etchebarren	3.50	1.75	1.00
619	Billy Wilson	3.50	1.75	1.00
620	Tommy Harper	3.50	1.75	1.00
621	Joe Ferguson	3.50	1.75	1.00
622	Larry Hisle	3.50	1.75	1.00
623	Steve Renko	3.50	1.75	1.00
624	Astros Mgr./Coaches (Leo Durocher, Preston Gomez, Grady Hatton, Hub Kittle, Jim Owens)	3.50	1.75	1.00
625	Angel Mangual	3.50	1.75	1.00
626	Bob Barton	3.50	1.75	1.00
627	Luis Alvarado	3.50	1.75	1.00
628	Jim Slaton	3.50	1.75	1.00
629	Indians Team	3.50	1.75	1.00
630	Denny McLain	3.50	1.75	1.00
631	Tom Matchick	3.50	1.75	1.00
632	Dick Selma	3.50	1.75	1.00
633	Ike Brown	3.50	1.75	1.00
634	Alan Closter	3.50	1.75	1.00
635	Gene Alley	3.50	1.75	1.00
636	Rick Clark	3.50	1.75	1.00
637	Norm Miller	3.50	1.75	1.00
638	Ken Reynolds	3.50	1.75	1.00
639	Willie Crawford	3.50	1.75	1.00
640	Dick Bosman	3.50	1.75	1.00
641	Reds Team	3.50	1.75	1.00
642	Jose LaBoy	3.50	1.75	1.00
643	Al Fitzmorris	3.50	1.75	1.00
644	Jack Heidemann	3.50	1.75	1.00
645	Bob Locker	3.50	1.75	1.00
646	Brewers Mgr./Coaches (Del Crandall, Harvey Kuenn, Joe Nossek, Bob Shaw, Jim Walton)	3.50	1.75	1.00
647	George Stone	3.50	1.75	1.00
648	Tom Egan	3.50	1.75	1.00
649	Rich Folkers	3.50	1.75	1.00
650	Felipe Alou	3.50	1.75	1.00
651	Don Carrithers	3.50	1.75	1.00
652	Ted Kubiak	3.50	1.75	1.00
653	Joe Hoerner	3.50	1.75	1.00
654	Twins Team	3.50	1.75	1.00
655	Clay Kirby	3.50	1.75	1.00
656	John Ellis	3.50	1.75	1.00
657	Bob Johnson	3.50	1.75	1.00
658	Elliott Maddox	3.50	1.75	1.00
659	Jose Pagan	3.50	1.75	1.00
660	Fred Scherman	3.50	1.75	1.00

1973 O-Pee-Chee Team Checklists

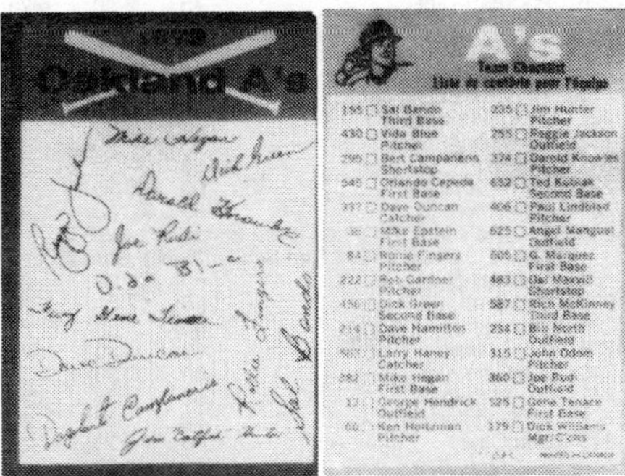

Similar to the 1973 Topps Team Checklists cards, this set was produced in Canada. The set consists of 24 unnumbered cards (2-1/2" x 3-1/2") with blue borders. The card fronts contain facsimile autographs of players from the same team. The backs contain team checklists of players found in the 1973 O-Pee-Chee regular issue set. The card backs contain the French translation for Team Checklist plus a copyright line "O.P.C. Printed in Canada."

		NR MT	EX	VG
Complete Set:		40.00	20.00	12.00
Common Card:		2.00	1.00	.60
(1)	Atlanta Braves	2.00	1.00	.60
(2)	Baltimore Orioles	2.00	1.00	.60
(3)	Boston Red Sox	2.00	1.00	.60
(4)	California Angels	2.00	1.00	.60
(5)	Chicago Cubs	2.00	1.00	.60
(6)	Chicago White Sox	2.00	1.00	.60
(7)	Cincinnati Reds	2.00	1.00	.60
(8)	Cleveland Indians	2.00	1.00	.60
(9)	Detroit Tigers	3.50	1.75	1.00
(10)	Houston Astros	2.00	1.00	.60
(11)	Kansas City Royals	2.00	1.00	.60
(12)	Los Angeles Dodgers	2.00	1.00	.60
(13)	Milwaukee Brewers	2.00	1.00	.60
(14)	Minnesota Twins	2.00	1.00	.60
(15)	Montreal Expos	2.00	1.00	.60
(16)	New York Mets	3.50	1.75	1.00
(17)	New York Yankees	2.00	1.00	.60
(18)	Oakland A's	3.50	1.75	1.00
(19)	Philadelphia Phillies	2.00	1.00	.60
(20)	Pittsburgh Pirates	2.00	1.00	.60
(21)	St. Louis Cardinals	2.00	1.00	.60
(22)	San Diego Padres	2.00	1.00	.60
(23)	San Francisco Giants	2.00	1.00	.60
(24)	Texas Rangers	2.00	1.00	.60

1974 O-Pee-Chee

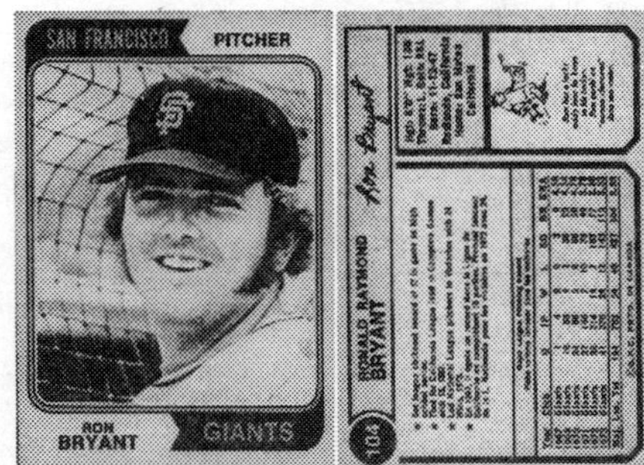

Again numbering 660 cards, the 1974 O-Pee-Chee set borrows its design from the Topps set of the same year. The cards measure the standard 2-1/2" by 3-1/2" and the backs are printed in both French and English and state "Printed in Canada." Ten of the cards in the O-Pee-Chee set have fronts that differ from their corresponding Topps cards, including most of the Hank Aaron "specials" that lead off the set. And, because the O-Pee-Chee cards were printed later than the corresponding Topps cards, there are no "Washington, Nat'l. League" variations in the O-Pee-Chee set.

		NR MT	EX	VG
Complete Set (660):		745.00	375.00	225.00
Common Player:		.60	.30	.20
1	Hank Aaron	38.00	19.00	11.50
2	Aaron Special 1954-57	8.50	4.25	2.50
3	Aaron Special 1958-59	8.50	4.25	2.50
4	Aaron Special 1960-61	8.50	4.25	2.50
5	Aaron Special 1962-63	8.50	4.25	2.50
6	Aaron Special 1964-65	8.50	4.25	2.50
7	Aaron Special 1966-67	8.50	4.25	2.50
8	Aaron Special 1968-69	8.50	4.25	2.50
9	Aaron Special 1970-73	8.50	4.25	2.50
10	Johnny Bench	18.00	9.00	5.50
11	Jim Bibby	.60	.30	.20
12	Dave May	.60	.30	.20
13	Tom Hilgendorf	.60	.30	.20
14	Paul Popovich	.60	.30	.20
15	Joe Torre	.75	.40	.25
16	Orioles Team	.75	.40	.25
17	Doug Bird	.60	.30	.20
18	Gary Thomasson	.60	.30	.20
19	Gerry Moses	.60	.30	.20
20	Nolan Ryan	90.00	45.00	27.00
21	Bob Gallagher	.60	.30	.20
22	Cy Acosta	.60	.30	.20
23	Craig Robinson	.60	.30	.20
24	John Hiller	.60	.30	.20
25	Ken Singleton	.60	.30	.20
26	Bill Campbell	.60	.30	.20
27	George Scott	.60	.30	.20
28	Manny Sanguillen	.60	.30	.20
29	Phil Niekro	1.50	.70	.45
30	Bobby Bonds	.60	.30	.20
31	Astros Mgr./Coaches (Roger Craig, Preston Gomez, Grady Hatton, Hub Kittle, Bob Lillis)	.60	.30	.20
32	John Grubb	.60	.30	.20
33	Don Newhauser	.60	.30	.20
34	Andy Kosco	.60	.30	.20
35	Gaylord Perry	5.00	2.50	1.50
36	Cardinals Team	.75	.40	.25
37	Dave Sells	.60	.30	.20
38	Don Kessinger	.60	.30	.20
39	Ken Suarez	.60	.30	.20
40	Jim Palmer	12.75	6.50	3.75
41	Bobby Floyd	.60	.30	.20
42	Claude Osteen	.60	.30	.20
43	Jim Wynn	.60	.30	.20
44	Mel Stottlemyre	.60	.30	.20
45	Dave Johnson	.60	.30	.20
46	Pat Kelly	.60	.30	.20
47	Dick Ruthven	.60	.30	.20
48	Dick Sharon	.60	.30	.20
49	Steve Renko	.60	.30	.20
50	Rod Carew	12.00	6.00	3.50
51	Bob Heise	.60	.30	.20
52	Al Oliver	1.00	.50	.30
53	Fred Kendall	.60	.30	.20
54	Elias Sosa	.60	.30	.20
55	Frank Robinson	6.75	3.50	2.00
56	Mets Team	1.00	.50	.30
57	Darold Knowles	.60	.30	.20
58	Charlie Spikes	.60	.30	.20
59	Ross Grimsley	.60	.30	.20
60	Lou Brock	6.75	3.50	2.00
61	Luis Aparicio	1.75	.90	.50
62	Bob Locker	.60	.30	.20
63	Bill Sudakis	.60	.30	.20
64	Doug Rau	.60	.30	.20
65	Amos Otis	.60	.30	.20
66	Sparky Lyle	.60	.30	.20
67	Tommy Helms	.60	.30	.20
68	Grant Jackson	.60	.30	.20
69	Del Unser	.60	.30	.20
70	Dick Allen	.75	.40	.25
71	Danny Frisella	.60	.30	.20
72	Aurelio Rodriguez	.60	.30	.20
73	Mike Marshall	.60	.30	.20
74	Twins Team	.75	.40	.25
75	Jim Colborn	.60	.30	.20
76	Mickey Rivers	.60	.30	.20
77	Rich Troedson	.60	.30	.20
78	Giants Mgr./Coaches (Joe Amalfitano, Charlie Fox, Andy Gilbert, Don McMahon, John McNamara)	.60	.30	.20
79	Gene Tenace	.60	.30	.20
80	Tom Seaver	20.00	10.00	6.00
81	Frank Duffy	.60	.30	.20
82	Dave Giusti	.60	.30	.20
83	Orlando Cepeda	1.00	.50	.30
84	Rick Wise	.60	.30	.20
85	Joe Morgan	7.25	3.75	2.25
86	Joe Ferguson	.60	.30	.20
87	Fergie Jenkins	5.00	2.50	1.50
88	Freddie Patek	.60	.30	.20
89	Jackie Brown	.60	.30	.20
90	Bobby Murcer	.60	.30	.20
91	Ken Forsch	.60	.30	.20
92	Paul Blair	.60	.30	.20
93	Rod Gilbreath	.60	.30	.20
94	Tigers Team	.60	.30	.20
95	Steve Carlton	12.75	6.50	3.75
96	Jerry Hairston	.60	.30	.20
97	Bob Bailey	.60	.30	.20
98	Bert Blyleven	1.00	.50	.30
99	George Theodore	1.00	.50	.30
100	Willie Stargell	5.50	2.75	1.75

101 Bobby Valentine .60 .30 .20
102 Bill Greif .60 .30 .20
103 Sal Bando .60 .30 .20
104 Ron Bryant .60 .30 .20
105 Carlton Fisk 23.00 11.50 7.00
106 Harry Parker .60 .30 .20
107 Alex Johnson .60 .30 .20
108 Al Hrabosky .60 .30 .20
109 Bob Grich .60 .30 .20
110 Billy Williams 1.75 .90 .50
111 Clay Carroll .60 .30 .20
112 Dave Lopes .60 .30 .20
113 Dick Drago .60 .30 .20
114 Angels Team .75 .40 .25
115 Willie Horton .60 .30 .20
116 Jerry Reuss .60 .30 .20
117 Ron Blomberg .60 .30 .20
118 Bill Lee .60 .30 .20
119 Phillies Mgr./Coaches (Carroll Beringer, Billy DeMars, Danny Ozark, Ray Ripplemeyer, Bobby Wine) .60 .30 .20
120 Wilbur Wood .60 .30 .20
121 Larry Lintz .60 .30 .20
122 Jim Holt .60 .30 .20
123 Nelson Briles .60 .30 .20
124 Bob Coluccio .60 .30 .20
125 Nate Colbert .60 .30 .20
126 Checklist 1 1.00 .50 .30
127 Tom Paciorek .60 .30 .20
128 John Ellis .60 .30 .20
129 Chris Speier .60 .30 .20
130 Reggie Jackson 38.00 19.00 11.50
131 Bob Boone .60 .30 .20
132 Felix Millan .60 .30 .20
133 David Clyde .60 .30 .20
134 Denis Menke .60 .30 .20
135 Roy White .60 .30 .20
136 Rick Reuschel .75 .40 .25
137 Al Bumbry .60 .30 .20
138 Ed Brinkman .60 .30 .20
139 Aurelio Monteagudo .60 .30 .20
140 Darrell Evans .60 .30 .20
141 Pat Bourque .60 .30 .20
142 Pedro Garcia .60 .30 .20
143 Dick Woodson .60 .30 .20
144 Dodgers Mgr./Coaches (Red Adams, Walter Alston, Monty Basgall, Jim Gilliam, Tom Lasorda) 1.25 .60 .40
145 Dock Ellis .60 .30 .20
146 Ron Fairly .60 .30 .20
147 Bart Johnson .60 .30 .20
148 Dave Hilton .60 .30 .20
149 Mac Scarce .60 .30 .20
150 John Mayberry .60 .30 .20
151 Diego Segui .60 .30 .20
152 Oscar Gamble .60 .30 .20
153 Jon Matlack .60 .30 .20
154 Astros Team .75 .40 .25
155 Bert Campaneris .60 .30 .20
156 Randy Moffitt .60 .30 .20
157 Vic Harris .60 .30 .20
158 Jack Billingham .60 .30 .20
159 Jim Ray Hart .60 .30 .20
160 Brooks Robinson 7.25 3.75 2.25
161 Ray Burris .60 .30 .20
162 Bill Freehan .60 .30 .20
163 Ken Berry .60 .30 .20
164 Tom House .60 .30 .20
165 Willie Davis .60 .30 .20
166 Mickey Lolich 1.50 .70 .45
167 Luis Tiant .60 .30 .20
168 Danny Thompson .60 .30 .20
169 Steve Rogers .60 .30 .20
170 Bill Melton .60 .30 .20
171 Eduardo Rodriguez .60 .30 .20
172 Gene Clines .60 .30 .20
173 Randy Jones .60 .30 .20
174 Bill Robinson .60 .30 .20
175 Reggie Cleveland .60 .30 .20
176 John Lowenstein .60 .30 .20
177 Dave Roberts .60 .30 .20
178 Garry Maddox .60 .30 .20
179 Mets Mgr./Coaches (Yogi Berra, Roy McMillan, Joe Pignatano, Rube Walker, Eddie Yost) 1.00 .50 .30
180 Ken Holtzman .60 .30 .20
181 Cesar Geronimo .60 .30 .20
182 Lindy McDaniel .60 .30 .20
183 Johnny Oates .60 .30 .20
184 Rangers Team .75 .40 .25
185 Jose Cardenal .60 .30 .20
186 Fred Scherman .60 .30 .20
187 Don Baylor .75 .40 .25
188 Rudy Meoli .60 .30 .20
189 Jim Brewer .60 .30 .20
190 Tony Oliva .75 .40 .25
191 Al Fitzmorris .60 .30 .20
192 Mario Guerrero .60 .30 .20
193 Tom Walker .60 .30 .20
194 Darrell Porter .60 .30 .20
195 Carlos May .60 .30 .20
196 Jim Hunter 6.25 3.25 2.00
197 Vicente Romo .60 .30 .20
198 Dave Cash .60 .30 .20
199 Mike Kekich .60 .30 .20
200 Cesar Cedeno .60 .30 .20
201 Batting Leaders (Rod Carew, Pete Rose) 6.75 3.50 2.00
202 1963 - MVPs (Ken Boyer, Reggie Jackson, Willie Stargell) 6.25 3.25 2.00
203 Runs Batted In (Reggie Jackson, Willie Stargell) 6.25 3.25 2.00
204 Stolen Base Leaders (Lou Brock, Tommy Harper) 1.00 .50 .30
205 Victory Leaders (Ron Bryant, Wilbur Wood) .60 .30 .20
206 Earned Run Average Leaders (Jim Palmer, Tom Seaver) 6.25 3.25 2.00
207 Strikeout Leaders (Nolan Ryan, Tom Seaver) 22.00 11.00 6.50
208 Leading Firemen (John Hiller, Mike Marshall) .60 .30 .20
209 Ted Sizemore .60 .30 .20
210 Bill Singer .60 .30 .20
211 Cubs Team .75 .40 .25
212 Rollie Fingers 6.00 3.00 1.75
213 Dave Rader .60 .30 .20
214 Billy Grabarkewitz .60 .30 .20
215 Al Kaline 7.25 3.75 2.25
216 Ray Sadecki .60 .30 .20
217 Tim Foli .60 .30 .20
218 Johnny Briggs .60 .30 .20
219 Doug Griffin .60 .30 .20
220 Don Sutton 1.25 .60 .40
221 White Sox Mgr./Coaches (Joe Lonnett, Jim Mahoney, Alex Monchak, Johnny Sain, Chuck Tanner) .60 .30 .20
222 Ramon Hernandez .60 .30 .20
223 Jeff Burroughs .60 .30 .20
224 Roger Metzger .60 .30 .20
225 Paul Splittorff .60 .30 .20
226 Padres Team .75 .40 .25
227 Mike Lum .60 .30 .20
228 Ted Kubiak .60 .30 .20
229 Fritz Peterson .60 .30 .20
230 Tony Perez 1.00 .50 .30
231 Dick Tidrow .60 .30 .20
232 Steve Brye .60 .30 .20
233 Jim Barr .60 .30 .20
234 John Milner .60 .30 .20
235 Dave McNally .60 .30 .20
236 Cardinals Mgr./Coaches (Vern Benson, George Kissell, Johnny Lewis, Red Schoendienst, Barney Schultz) .60 .30 .20
237 Ken Brett .60 .30 .20
238 Fran Healy .60 .30 .20
239 Bill Russell .60 .30 .20
240 Joe Coleman .60 .30 .20
241 Glenn Beckert .60 .30 .20
242 Bill Gogolewski .60 .30 .20
243 Bob Oliver .60 .30 .20
244 Carl Morton .60 .30 .20
245 Cleon Jones .60 .30 .20
246 A's Team 1.00 .50 .30
247 Rick Miller .60 .30 .20
248 Tom Hall .60 .30 .20
249 George Mitterwald .60 .30 .20
250 Willie McCovey 6.75 3.50 2.00
251 Graig Nettles 1.25 .60 .40
252 Dave Parker 25.00 12.50 7.50
253 John Boccabella .60 .30 .20
254 Stan Bahnsen .60 .30 .20
255 Larry Bowa .60 .30 .20
256 Tom Griffin .60 .30 .20
257 Buddy Bell .75 .40 .25
258 Jerry Morales .60 .30 .20
259 Bob Reynolds .60 .30 .20
260 Ted Simmons .75 .40 .25
261 Jerry Bell .60 .30 .20
262 Ed Kirkpatrick .60 .30 .20
263 Checklist 2 1.00 .50 .30
264 Joe Rudi .60 .30 .20
265 Tug McGraw .60 .30 .20
266 Jim Northrup .60 .30 .20
267 Andy Messersmith .60 .30 .20
268 Tom Grieve .60 .30 .20
269 Bob Johnson .60 .30 .20
270 Ron Santo .60 .30 .20
271 Bill Hands .60 .30 .20
272 Paul Casanova .60 .30 .20
273 Checklist 3 1.00 .50 .30
274 Fred Beene .60 .30 .20
275 Ron Hunt .60 .30 .20
276 Angels Mgr./Coaches (Tom Morgan, Salty Parker, Jimmie Reese, John Roseboro, Bobby Winkles) .60 .30 .20
277 Gary Nolan .60 .30 .20
278 Cookie Rojas .60 .30 .20
279 Jim Crawford .60 .30 .20
280 Carl Yastrzemski 12.75 6.50 3.75
281 Giants Team .75 .40 .25
282 Doyle Alexander .60 .30 .20
283 Mike Schmidt 105.00 52.00 31.00
284 Dave Duncan .60 .30 .20
285 Reggie Smith .60 .30 .20
286 Tony Muser .60 .30 .20
287 Clay Kirby .60 .30 .20
288 Gorman Thomas 1.00 .50 .30
289 Rick Auerbach .60 .30 .20
290 Vida Blue .60 .30 .20
291 Don Hahn .60 .30 .20
292 Chuck Seelbach .60 .30 .20
293 Milt May .60 .30 .20
294 Steve Foucault .60 .30 .20
295 Rick Monday .60 .30 .20
296 Ray Corbin .60 .30 .20
297 Hal Breeden .60 .30 .20
298 Roric Harrison .60 .30 .20
299 Gene Michael .60 .30 .20
300 Pete Rose 15.00 7.50 4.50
301 Bob Montgomery .60 .30 .20
302 Rudy May .60 .30 .20
303 George Hendrick .60 .30 .20
304 Don Wilson .60 .30 .20
305 Tito Fuentes .60 .30 .20
306 Orioles Mgr./Coaches (George Bamberger, Jim Frey, Billy Hunter, George Staller, Earl Weaver) .60 .30 .20
307 Luis Melendez .60 .30 .20
308 Bruce Dal Canton .60 .30 .20
309 Dave Roberts .60 .30 .20
310 Terry Forster .60 .30 .20
311 Jerry Grote .60 .30 .20
312 Deron Johnson .60 .30 .20
313 Barry Lersch .60 .30 .20
314 Brewers Team .75 .40 .25
315 Ron Cey .60 .30 .20
316 Jim Perry .60 .30 .20
317 Richie Zisk .60 .30 .20
318 Jim Merritt .60 .30 .20
319 Randy Hundley .60 .30 .20
320 Dusty Baker .60 .30 .20
321 Steve Braun .60 .30 .20
322 Ernie McAnally .60 .30 .20
323 Richie Scheinblum .60 .30 .20
324 Steve Kline .60 .30 .20
325 Tommy Harper .60 .30 .20
326 Reds Mgr./Coaches (Sparky Anderson, Alex Grammas, Ted Kluszewski, George Scherger, Larry Shepard) .60 .30 .20
327 Tom Timmermann .60 .30 .20
328 Skip Jutze .60 .30 .20
329 Mark Belanger .60 .30 .20
330 Juan Marichal 1.75 .90 .50
331 All-Star Catchers (Johnny Bench, Carlton Fisk) 6.75 3.50 2.00
332 All-Star First Basemen (Hank Aaron, Dick Allen) 1.50 .70 .45
333 All-Star Second Basemen (Rod Carew, Joe Morgan) 1.50 .70 .45
334 All-Star Third Baseman (Brooks Robinson, Ron Santo) 1.00 .50 .30
335 All-Star Shortstops (Bert Campaneris, Chris Speier) .60 .30 .20
336 All-Star Left Fielders (Bobby Murcer, Pete Rose) 2.00 1.00 .60
337 All-Star Center Fielders (Cesar Cedeno, Amos Otis) .60 .30 .20
338 All-Star Right Fielders (Reggie Jackson, Billy Williams) 6.00 3.00 1.75
339 All-Star Pitchers (Jim Hunter, Rick Wise) .60 .30 .20
340 Thurman Munson 12.00 6.00 3.50
341 Dan Driessen .60 .30 .20
342 Jim Lonborg .60 .30 .20
343 Royals Team .75 .40 .25
344 Mike Caldwell .60 .30 .20
345 Bill North .60 .30 .20
346 Ron Reed .60 .30 .20
347 Sandy Alomar .60 .30 .20
348 Pete Richert .60 .30 .20
349 John Vukovich .60 .30 .20
350 Bob Gibson 6.75 3.50 2.00
351 Dwight Evans 6.75 3.50 2.00
352 Bill Stoneman .60 .30 .20
353 Rich Coggins .60 .30 .20
354 Cubs Mgr./Coaches (Hank Aguirre, Whitey Lockman, Jim Marshall, J.C. Martin, Al Spangler) .60 .30 .20
355 Dave Nelson .60 .30 .20
356 Jerry Koosman .60 .30 .20
357 Buddy Bradford .60 .30 .20
358 Dal Maxvill .60 .30 .20
359 Brent Strom .60 .30 .20
360 Greg Luzinski .75 .40 .25
361 Don Carrithers .60 .30 .20
362 Hal King .60 .30 .20
363 Yankees Team 1.00 .50 .30
364 Clarence Gaston .60 .30 .20
365 Steve Busby .60 .30 .20
366 Larry Hisle .60 .30 .20
367 Norm Cash .60 .30 .20
368 Manny Mota .60 .30 .20
369 Paul Lindblad .60 .30 .20
370 Bob Watson .60 .30 .20
371 Jim Slaton .60 .30 .20
372 Ken Reitz .60 .30 .20
373 John Curtis .60 .30 .20
374 Marty Perez .60 .30 .20
375 Earl Williams .60 .30 .20
376 Jorge Orta .60 .30 .20
377 Ron Woods .60 .30 .20
378 Burt Hooton .60 .30 .20
379 Rangers Mgr./Coaches (Art Fowler, Frank Lucchesi, Billy Martin, Jackie Moore, Charlie Silvera) .75 .40 .25
380 Bud Harrelson .60 .30 .20
381 Charlie Sands .60 .30 .20
382 Bob Moose .60 .30 .20
383 Phillies Team .75 .40 .25
384 Chris Chambliss .60 .30 .20
385 Don Gullett .60 .30 .20
386 Gary Matthews .60 .30 .20
387 Rich Morales .60 .30 .20
388 Phil Roof .60 .30 .20
389 Gates Brown .60 .30 .20
390 Lou Piniella .60 .30 .20
391 Billy Champion .60 .30 .20
392 Dick Green .60 .30 .20
393 Orlando Pena .60 .30 .20
394 Ken Henderson .60 .30 .20
395 Doug Rader .60 .30 .20
396 Tommy Davis .60 .30 .20
397 George Stone .60 .30 .20
398 Duke Sims .60 .30 .20
399 Mike Paul .60 .30 .20
400 Harmon Killebrew 6.00 3.00 1.75
401 Elliot Maddox .60 .30 .20
402 Jim Rooker .60 .30 .20
403 Red Sox Mgr./Coaches (Don Bryant, Darrell Johnson, Eddie Popowski, Lee Stange, Don Zimmer) .60 .30 .20
404 Jim Howarth .60 .30 .20
405 Ellie Rodriguez .60 .30 .20
406 Steve Arlin .60 .30 .20
407 Jim Wohlford .60 .30 .20
408 Charlie Hough .60 .30 .20
409 Ike Brown .60 .30 .20
410 Pedro Borbon .60 .30 .20
411 Frank Baker .60 .30 .20
412 Chuck Taylor .60 .30 .20
413 Don Money .60 .30 .20
414 Checklist 4 1.00 .50 .30
415 Gary Gentry .60 .30 .20

416 White Sox Team .75 .40 .25
417 Rich Folkers .60 .30 .20
418 Walt Williams .60 .30 .20
419 Wayne Twitchell .60 .30 .20
420 Ray Fosse .60 .30 .20
421 Dan Fife .60 .30 .20
422 Gonzalo Marquez .60 .30 .20
423 Fred Stanley .60 .30 .20
424 Jim Beauchamp .60 .30 .20
425 Pete Broberg .60 .30 .20
426 Rennie Stennett .60 .30 .20
427 Bobby Bolin .60 .30 .20
428 Gary Sutherland .60 .30 .20
429 Dick Lange .60 .30 .20
430 Matty Alou .60 .30 .20
431 Gene Garber .60 .30 .20
432 Chris Arnold .60 .30 .20
433 Lerrin LaGrow .60 .30 .20
434 Ken McMullen .60 .30 .20
435 Dave Concepcion .60 .30 .20
436 Don Hood .60 .30 .20
437 Jim Lyttle .60 .30 .20
438 Ed Herrmann .60 .30 .20
439 Norm Miller .60 .30 .20
440 Jim Kaat 1.00 .50 .30
441 Tom Ragland .60 .30 .20
442 Alan Foster .60 .30 .20
443 Tom Hutton .60 .30 .20
444 Vic Davalillo .60 .30 .20
445 George Medich .60 .30 .20
446 Len Randle .60 .30 .20
447 Twins Mgr./Coaches (Vern Morgan, Frank Quilici, Bob Rodgers, Ralph Rowe) .60 .30 .20
448 Ron Hodges .60 .30 .20
449 Tom McCraw .60 .30 .20
450 Rich Hebner .60 .30 .20
451 Tommy John 1.25 .60 .40
452 Gene Hiser .60 .30 .20
453 Balor Moore .60 .30 .20
454 Kurt Bevacqua .60 .30 .20
455 Tom Bradley .60 .30 .20
456 Dave Winfield 250.00 125.00 75.00
457 Chuck Goggin .60 .30 .20
458 Jim Ray .60 .30 .20
459 Reds Team .75 .40 .25
460 Boog Powell .75 .40 .25
461 John Odom .60 .30 .20
462 Luis Alvarado .60 .30 .20
463 Pat Dobson .60 .30 .20
464 Jose Cruz .60 .30 .20
465 Dick Bosman .60 .30 .20
466 Dick Billings .60 .30 .20
467 Winston Llenas .60 .30 .20
468 Pepe Frias .60 .30 .20
469 Joe Decker .60 .30 .20
470 A.L. Playoffs 8.50 4.25 2.50
471 N.L. Playoffs .75 .40 .25
472 World Series Game 1 .75 .40 .25
473 World Series Game 2 6.75 3.50 2.00
474 World Series Game 3 .75 .40 .25
475 World Series Game 4 .75 .40 .25
476 World Series Game 5 .75 .40 .25
477 World Series Game 6 8.50 4.25 2.50
478 World Series Game 7 .75 .40 .25
479 World Series Summary .75 .40 .25
480 Willie Crawford .60 .30 .20
481 Jerry Terrell .60 .30 .20
482 Bob Didier .60 .30 .20
483 Braves Team .75 .40 .25
484 Carmen Fanzone .60 .30 .20
485 Felipe Alou .60 .30 .20
486 Steve Stone .60 .30 .20
487 Ted Martinez .60 .30 .20
488 Andy Etchebarren .60 .30 .20
489 Pirates Mgr./Coaches (Don Leppert, Bill Mazeroski, Danny Murtaugh, Don Osborn, Bob Skinner) .60 .30 .20
490 Vada Pinson .60 .30 .20
491 Roger Nelson .60 .30 .20
492 Mike Rogodzinski .60 .30 .20
493 Joe Hoerner .60 .30 .20
494 Ed Goodson .60 .30 .20
495 Dick McAuliffe .60 .30 .20
496 Tom Murphy .60 .30 .20
497 Bobby Mitchell .60 .30 .20
498 Pat Corrales .60 .30 .20
499 Rusty Torres .60 .30 .20
500 Lee May .60 .30 .20
501 Eddie Leon .60 .30 .20
502 Dave LaRoche .60 .30 .20
503 Eric Soderholm .60 .30 .20
504 Joe Niekro .60 .30 .20
505 Bill Buckner .60 .30 .20
506 Ed Farmer .60 .30 .20
507 Larry Stahl .60 .30 .20
508 Expos Team .75 .40 .25
509 Jesse Jefferson .60 .30 .20
510 Wayne Garrett .60 .30 .20
511 Toby Harrah .60 .30 .20
512 Joe Lahoud .60 .30 .20
513 Jim Campanis .60 .30 .20
514 Paul Schaal .60 .30 .20
515 Willie Montanez .60 .30 .20
516 Horacio Pina .60 .30 .20
517 Mike Hegan .60 .30 .20
518 Derrel Thomas .60 .30 .20
519 Bill Sharp .60 .30 .20
520 Tim McCarver .60 .30 .20
521 Indians Mgr./Coaches (Ken Aspromonte, Clay Bryant, Tony Pacheco) .60 .30 .20
522 J.R. Richard .60 .30 .20
523 Cecil Cooper 1.25 .60 .40
524 Bill Plummer .60 .30 .20
525 Clyde Wright .60 .30 .20
526 Frank Tepedino .60 .30 .20
527 Bobby Darwin .60 .30 .20
528 Bill Bonham .60 .30 .20
529 Horace Clarke .60 .30 .20
530 Mickey Stanley .60 .30 .20
531 Expos Mgr./Coaches (Dave Bristol, Larry Doby, Gene Mauch, Cal McLish, Jerry Zimmerman) .60 .30 .20
532 Skip Lockwood .60 .30 .20
533 Mike Phillips .60 .30 .20
534 Eddie Watt .60 .30 .20
535 Bob Tolan .60 .30 .20
536 Duffy Dyer .60 .30 .20
537 Steve Mingori .60 .30 .20
538 Cesar Tovar .60 .30 .20
539 Lloyd Allen .60 .30 .20
540 Bob Robertson .60 .30 .20
541 Indians Team .75 .40 .25
542 Rich Gossage 4.50 2.25 1.25
543 Danny Cater .60 .30 .20
544 Ron Schueler .60 .30 .20
545 Billy Conigliaro .60 .30 .20
546 Mike Corkins .60 .30 .20
547 Glenn Borgmann .60 .30 .20
548 Sonny Siebert .60 .30 .20
549 Mike Jorgensen .60 .30 .20
550 Sam McDowell .60 .30 .20
551 Von Joshua .60 .30 .20
552 Denny Doyle .60 .30 .20
553 Jim Willoughby .60 .30 .20
554 Tim Johnson .60 .30 .20
555 Woodie Fryman .60 .30 .20
556 Dave Campbell .60 .30 .20
557 Jim McGlothlin .60 .30 .20
558 Bill Fahey .60 .30 .20
559 Darrel Chaney .60 .30 .20
560 Mike Cuellar .60 .30 .20
561 Ed Kranepool .60 .30 .20
562 Jack Aker .60 .30 .20
563 Hal McRae .60 .30 .20
564 Mike Ryan .60 .30 .20
565 Milt Wilcox .60 .30 .20
566 Jackie Hernandez .60 .30 .20
567 Red Sox Team .75 .40 .25
568 Mike Torrez .60 .30 .20
569 Rick Dempsey .60 .30 .20
570 Ralph Garr .60 .30 .20
571 Rich Hand .60 .30 .20
572 Enzo Hernandez .60 .30 .20
573 Mike Adams .60 .30 .20
574 Bill Parsons .60 .30 .20
575 Steve Garvey 9.25 4.75 2.75
576 Scipio Spinks .60 .30 .20
577 Mike Sadek .60 .30 .20
578 Ralph Houk .60 .30 .20
579 Cecil Upshaw .60 .30 .20
580 Jim Spencer .60 .30 .20
581 Fred Norman .60 .30 .20
582 Bucky Dent .75 .40 .25
583 Marty Pattin .60 .30 .20
584 Ken Rudolph .60 .30 .20
585 Merv Rettenmund .60 .30 .20
586 Jack Brohamer .60 .30 .20
587 Larry Christenson .60 .30 .20
588 Hal Lanier .60 .30 .20
589 Boots Day .60 .30 .20
590 Rogelio Moret .60 .30 .20
591 Sonny Jackson .60 .30 .20
592 Ed Bane .60 .30 .20
593 Steve Yeager .60 .30 .20
594 Lee Stanton .60 .30 .20
595 Steve Blass .60 .30 .20
596 Rookie Pitchers (Wayne Garland, Fred Holdsworth, Mark Littell, Dick Pole) .60 .30 .20
597 Rookie Shortstops (Dave Chalk, John Gamble, Pete MacKanin, Manny Trillo) .75 .40 .25
598 Rookie Outfielders (Dave Augustine, Ken Griffey, Steve Ontiveros, Jim Tyrone) 21.00 10.50 6.25
599 Rookie Pitchers (Ron Diorio, Dave Freisleben, Frank Riccelli, Greg Shanahan) .60 .30 .20
600 Rookie Infielders (Ron Cash, Jim Cox, Bill Madlock, Reggie Sanders) 6.00 3.00 1.75
601 Rookie Outfielders (Ed Armbrister, Rich Bladt, Brian Downing, Bake McBride) 5.50 2.75 1.75
602 Rookie Pitchers (Glenn Abbott, Rick Henninger, Craig Swan, Dan Vossler) .60 .30 .20
603 Rookie Catchers (Barry Foote, Tom Lundstedt, Charlie Moore, Sergio Robles) .60 .30 .20
604 Rookie Infielders (Terry Hughes, John Knox, Andy Thornton, Frank White) 5.50 2.75 1.75
605 Rookie Pitchers (Vic Albury, Ken Frailing, Kevin Kobel, Frank Tanana) 7.25 3.75 2.25
606 Rookie Outfielders (Jim Fuller, Wilbur Howard, Tommy Smith, Otto Velez) .60 .30 .20
607 Rookie Shortstops (Leo Foster, Tom Heintzelman, Dave Rosello, Frank Taveras) .60 .30 .20
608 Rookie Pitchers (Bob Apodaco, Dick Baney, John D'Acquisto, Mike Wallace) .60 .30 .20
609 Rico Petrocelli .60 .30 .20
610 Dave Kingman .75 .40 .25
611 Rick Stelmaszek .60 .30 .20
612 Luke Walker .60 .30 .20
613 Dan Monzon .60 .30 .20
614 Adrian Devine .60 .30 .20
615 Rookie Pitchers (Johnny Jeter, Tom Underwood) .60 .30 .20
616 Larry Gura .60 .30 .20
617 Ted Ford .60 .30 .20
618 Jim Mason .60 .30 .20
619 Mike Anderson .60 .30 .20
620 Al Downing .60 .30 .20
621 Bernie Carbo .60 .30 .20
622 Phil Gagliano .60 .30 .20
623 Celerino Sanchez .60 .30 .20
624 Bob Miller .60 .30 .20
625 Ollie Brown .60 .30 .20
626 Pirates Team .75 .40 .25
627 Carl Taylor .60 .30 .20
628 Ivan Murrell .60 .30 .20
629 Rusty Staub .60 .30 .20
630 Tommie Agee .60 .30 .20
631 Steve Barber .60 .30 .20
632 George Culver .60 .30 .20
633 Dave Hamilton .60 .30 .20
634 Braves Mgr./Coaches (Jim Busby, Eddie Mathews, Connie Ryan, Ken Silvestri, Herm Starrette) .75 .40 .25
635 John Edwards .60 .30 .20
636 Dave Goltz .60 .30 .20
637 Checklist 5 1.00 .50 .30
638 Ken Sanders .60 .30 .20
639 Joe Lovitto .60 .30 .20
640 Milt Pappas .60 .30 .20
641 Chuck Brinkman .60 .30 .20
642 Terry Harmon .60 .30 .20
643 Dodgers Team .75 .40 .25
644 Wayne Granger .60 .30 .20
645 Ken Boswell .60 .30 .20
646 George Foster 1.25 .60 .40
647 Juan Beniquez .60 .30 .20
648 Terry Crowley .60 .30 .20
649 Fernando Gonzalez .60 .30 .20
650 Mike Epstein .60 .30 .20
651 Leron Lee .60 .30 .20
652 Gail Hopkins .60 .30 .20
653 Bob Stinson .60 .30 .20
654 Jesus Alou .60 .30 .20
655 Mike Tyson .60 .30 .20
656 Adrian Garrett .60 .30 .20
657 Jim Shellenback .60 .30 .20
658 Lee Lacy .60 .30 .20
659 Joe Lis .60 .30 .20
660 Larry Dierker .60 .30 .20

1974 O-Pee-Chee Team Checklists

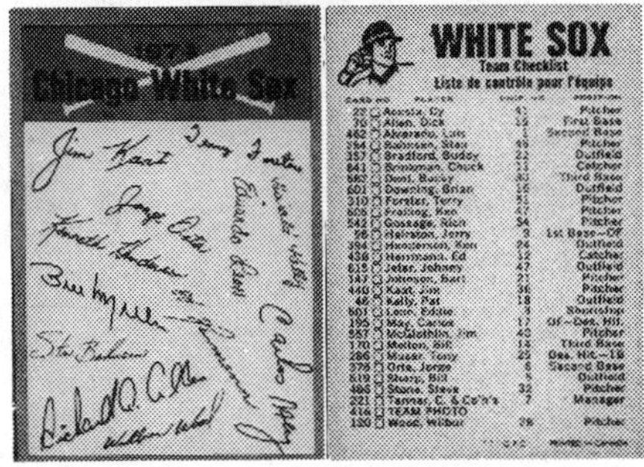

The 1974 O-Pee-Chee Team Checklists set is nearly identical to its Topps counterpart of the same year. Twenty-four unnumbered cards that measure 2-1/2" by 3-1/2" make up the set. The card fronts contain facsimile autographs while the backs carry a team checklist of players found in the regular issue O-Pee-Chee set of 1974. The cards have red borders and can be differentiated from the U.S. version by the "O.P.C. Printed in Canada" line on the back.

	NR MT	EX	VG
Complete Set:	30.00	15.00	9.00
Common Checklist:	1.50	.70	.40
(1) Atlanta Braves	1.50	.70	.45
(2) Baltimore Orioles	1.50	.70	.45
(3) Boston Red Sox	1.50	.70	.45
(4) California Angels	1.50	.70	.45
(5) Chicago Cubs	1.50	.70	.45
(6) Chicago White Sox	1.50	.70	.45
(7) Cincinnati Reds	1.50	.70	.45
(8) Cleveland Indians	1.50	.70	.45
(9) Detroit Tigers	1.50	.70	.45
(10) Houston Astros	1.50	.70	.45
(11) Kansas City Royals	1.50	.70	.45
(12) Los Anglees Dodgers	1.50	.70	.45
(13) Milwaukee Brewers	1.50	.70	.45
(14) Minnesota Twins	1.50	.70	.45
(15) Montreal Expos	1.50	.70	.45
(16) New York Mets	1.50	.70	.45
(17) New York Yankees	1.50	.70	.45
(18) Oakland A's	1.50	.70	.45
(19) Philadelphia Phillies	1.50	.70	.45
(20) Pittsburgh Pirates	1.50	.70	.45
(21) St. Louis Cardinals	1.50	.70	.45
(22) San Diego Padres	1.50	.70	.45
(23) San Francisco Giants	1.50	.70	.45
(24) Texas Rangers	1.50	.70	.45

Regional interest may affect the value of a card.

The values quoted are intended to reflect the market price.

1975 O-Pee-Chee

The 1975 O-Pee-Chee set was again complete at 660 cards, each measuring 2-1/2" by 3-1/2", and using the same design as the 1975 Topps set. The

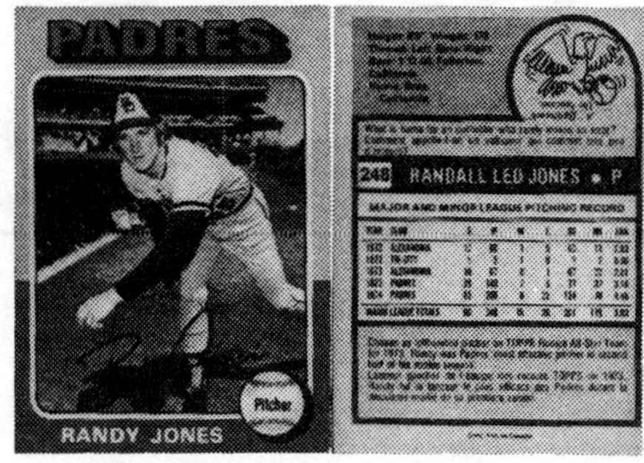

backs of the O-Pee-Chee cards are written in both French and English and state that the cards were printed in Canada.

	NR MT	EX	VG
Complete Set (660):	1020.	500.00	300.00
Common Player:	.55	.30	.15

No.	Player	NR MT	EX	VG
1	'74 Highlights (Hank Aaron)	34.00	17.00	10.00
2	'74 Highlights (Lou Brock)	1.25	.60	.40
3	'74 Highlights (Bob Gibson)	1.25	.60	.40
4	'74 Highlights (Al Kaline)	4.50	2.25	1.25
5	'74 Highlights (Nolan Ryan)	30.00	15.00	9.00
6	'74 Highlights (Mike Marshall)	.55	.30	.15
7	'74 Highlights (Dick Bosman, Steve Busby, Nolan Ryan)	8.50	4.25	2.50
8	Rogelio Moret	.55	.30	.15
9	Frank Tepedino	.55	.30	.15
10	Willie Davis	.55	.30	.15
11	Bill Melton	.55	.30	.15
12	David Clyde	.55	.30	.15
13	Gene Locklear	.55	.30	.15
14	Milt Wilcox	.55	.30	.15
15	Jose Cardenal	.55	.30	.15
16	Frank Tanana	.55	.30	.15
17	Dave Concepcion	.55	.30	.15
18	Tigers Team (Ralph Houk)	.75	.40	.25
19	Jerry Koosman	.55	.30	.15
20	Thurman Munson	10.25	5.25	3.00
21	Rollie Fingers	5.00	2.50	1.50
22	Dave Cash	.55	.30	.15
23	Bill Russell	.55	.30	.15
24	Al Fitzmorris	.55	.30	.15
25	Lee May	.55	.30	.15
26	Dave McNally	.55	.30	.15
27	Ken Reitz	.55	.30	.15
28	Tom Murphy	.55	.30	.15
29	Dave Parker	6.00	3.00	1.75
30	Bert Blyleven	.75	.40	.25
31	Dave Rader	.55	.30	.15
32	Reggie Cleveland	.55	.30	.15
33	Dusty Baker	.55	.30	.15
34	Steve Renko	.55	.30	.15
35	Ron Santo	.55	.30	.15
36	Joe Lovitto	.55	.30	.15
37	Dave Freisleben	.55	.30	.15
38	Buddy Bell	.75	.40	.25
39	Andy Thornton	.60	.30	.20
40	Bill Singer	.55	.30	.15
41	Cesar Geronimo	.55	.30	.15
42	Joe Coleman	.55	.30	.15
43	Cleon Jones	.55	.30	.15
44	Pat Dobson	.55	.30	.15
45	Joe Rudi	.55	.30	.15
46	Phillies Team (Danny Ozark)	.60	.30	.20
47	Tommy John	1.00	.50	.30
48	Freddie Patek	.55	.30	.15
49	Larry Dierker	.55	.30	.15
50	Brooks Robinson	6.25	3.25	2.00
51	Bob Forsch	.75	.40	.25
52	Darrell Porter	.55	.30	.15
53	Dave Giusti	.55	.30	.15
54	Eric Soderholm	.55	.30	.15
55	Bobby Bonds	.55	.30	.15
56	Rick Wise	.55	.30	.15
57	Dave Johnson	.55	.30	.15
58	Chuck Taylor	.55	.30	.15
59	Ken Henderson	.55	.30	.15
60	Fergie Jenkins	4.25	2.25	1.25
61	Dave Winfield	75.00	37.00	22.00
62	Fritz Peterson	.55	.30	.15
63	Steve Swisher	.55	.30	.15
64	Dave Chalk	.55	.30	.15
65	Don Gullett	.55	.30	.15
66	Willie Horton	.55	.30	.15
67	Tug McGraw	.55	.30	.15
68	Ron Blomberg	.55	.30	.15
69	John Odom	.55	.30	.15
70	Mike Schmidt	65.00	32.00	19.50
71	Charlie Hough	.55	.30	.15
72	Royals Team (Jack McKeon)	.60	.30	.20
73	J.R. Richard	.55	.30	.15
74	Mark Belanger	.55	.30	.15
75	Ted Simmons	.60	.30	.20
76	Ed Sprague	.55	.30	.15
77	Richie Zisk	.55	.30	.15
78	Ray Corbin	.55	.30	.15
79	Gary Matthews	.55	.30	.15
80	Carlton Fisk	20.00	10.00	6.00
81	Ron Reed	.55	.30	.15
82	Pat Kelly	.55	.30	.15
83	Jim Merritt	.55	.30	.15
84	Enzo Hernandez	.55	.30	.15
85	Bill Bonham	.55	.30	.15
86	Joe Lis	.55	.30	.15
87	George Foster	1.00	.50	.30
88	Tom Egan	.55	.30	.15
89	Jim Ray	.55	.30	.15
90	Rusty Staub	.55	.30	.15
91	Dick Green	.55	.30	.15
92	Cecil Upshaw	.55	.30	.15
93	Dave Lopes	.55	.30	.15
94	Jim Lonborg	.55	.30	.15
95	John Mayberry	.55	.30	.15
96	Mike Cosgrove	.55	.30	.15
97	Earl Williams	.55	.30	.15
98	Rich Folkers	.55	.30	.15
99	Mike Hegan	.55	.30	.15
100	Willie Stargell	2.00	1.00	.60
101	Expos Team (Gene Mauch)	.60	.30	.20
102	Joe Decker	.55	.30	.15
103	Rick Miller	.55	.30	.15
104	Bill Madlock	1.25	.60	.40
105	Buzz Capra	.55	.30	.15
106	Mike Hargrove	.55	.30	.15
107	Jim Barr	.55	.30	.15
108	Tom Hall	.55	.30	.15
109	George Hendrick	.55	.30	.15
110	Wilbur Wood	.55	.30	.15
111	Wayne Garrett	.55	.30	.15
112	Larry Hardy	.55	.30	.15
113	Elliott Maddox	.55	.30	.15
114	Dick Lange	.55	.30	.15
115	Joe Ferguson	.55	.30	.15
116	Lerrin LaGrow	.55	.30	.15
117	Orioles Team (Earl Weaver)	.75	.40	.25
118	Mike Anderson	.55	.30	.15
119	Tommy Helms	.55	.30	.15
120	Steve Busby (photo actually Fran Healy)	.55	.30	.15
121	Bill North	.55	.30	.15
122	Al Hrabosky	.55	.30	.15
123	Johnny Briggs	.55	.30	.15
124	Jerry Reuss	.55	.30	.15
125	Ken Singleton	.55	.30	.15
126	Checklist 1-132	1.00	.50	.30
127	Glenn Borgmann	.55	.30	.15
128	Bill Lee	.55	.30	.15
129	Rick Monday	.55	.30	.15
130	Phil Niekro	1.50	.70	.45
131	Toby Harrah	.55	.30	.15
132	Randy Moffitt	.55	.30	.15
133	Dan Driessen	.55	.30	.15
134	Ron Hodges	.55	.30	.15
135	Charlie Spikes	.55	.30	.15
136	Jim Mason	.55	.30	.15
137	Terry Forster	.55	.30	.15
138	Del Unser	.55	.30	.15
139	Horacio Pina	.55	.30	.15
140	Steve Garvey	6.75	3.50	2.00
141	Mickey Stanley	.55	.30	.15
142	Bob Reynolds	.55	.30	.15
143	Cliff Johnson	.55	.30	.15
144	Jim Wohlford	.55	.30	.15
145	Ken Holtzman	.55	.30	.15
146	Padres Team (John McNamara)	.60	.30	.20
147	Pedro Garcia	.55	.30	.15
148	Jim Rooker	.55	.30	.15
149	Tim Foli	.55	.30	.15
150	Bob Gibson	6.25	3.25	2.00
151	Steve Brye	.55	.30	.15
152	Mario Guerrero	.55	.30	.15
153	Rick Reuschel	.55	.30	.15
154	Mike Lum	.55	.30	.15
155	Jim Bibby	.55	.30	.15
156	Dave Kingman	1.00	.50	.30
157	Pedro Borbon	.55	.30	.15
158	Jerry Grote	.55	.30	.15
159	Steve Arlin	.55	.30	.15
160	Graig Nettles	1.25	.60	.40
161	Stan Bahnsen	.55	.30	.15
162	Willie Montanez	.55	.30	.15
163	Jim Brewer	.55	.30	.15
164	Mickey Rivers	.55	.30	.15
165	Doug Rader	.55	.30	.15
166	Woodie Fryman	.55	.30	.15
167	Rich Coggins	.55	.30	.15
168	Bill Greif	.55	.30	.15
169	Cookie Rojas	.55	.30	.15
170	Bert Campaneris	.55	.30	.15
171	Ed Kirkpatrick	.55	.30	.15
172	Red Sox Team (Darrell Johnson)	1.00	.50	.30
173	Steve Rogers	.55	.30	.15
174	Bake McBride	.55	.30	.15
175	Don Money	.55	.30	.15
176	Burt Hooton	.55	.30	.15
177	Vic Correll	.55	.30	.15
178	Cesar Tovar	.55	.30	.15
179	Tom Bradley	.55	.30	.15
180	Joe Morgan	7.50	3.75	2.25
181	Fred Beene	.55	.30	.15
182	Don Hahn	.55	.30	.15
183	Mel Stottlemyre	.55	.30	.15
184	Jorge Orta	.55	.30	.15
185	Steve Carlton	10.25	5.25	3.00
186	Willie Crawford	.55	.30	.15
187	Denny Doyle	.55	.30	.15
188	Tom Griffin	.55	.30	.15
189	1951 - MVPs (Larry (Yogi) Berra, Roy Campanella)	3.00	1.50	.90
190	1952 - MVPs (Hank Sauer, Bobby Shantz)	.55	.30	.15
191	1953 - MVPs (Roy Campanella, Al Rosen)	.75	.40	.25
192	1954 - MVPs (Yogi Berra, Willie Mays)	5.00	2.50	1.50
193	1955 - MVPs (Yogi Berra, Roy Campanella)	3.00	1.50	.90
194	1956 - MVPs (Mickey Mantle, Don Newcombe)	6.75	3.50	2.00
195	1957 - MVPs (Hank Aaron, Mickey Mantle)	12.75	6.50	3.75
196	1958 - MVPs (Ernie Banks, Jackie Jensen)	3.00	1.50	.90
197	1959 - MVPs (Ernie Banks, Nellie Fox)	3.00	1.50	.90
198	1960 - MVPs (Dick Groat, Roger Maris)	3.00	1.50	.90
199	1961 - MVPs (Roger Maris, Frank Robinson)	3.00	1.50	.90
200	1962- MVPs (Mickey Mantle, Maury Wills)	6.75	3.50	2.00
201	1963 - MVPs (Elston Howard, Sandy Koufax)	3.00	1.50	.90
202	1964 - MVPs (Ken Boyer, Brooks Robinson)	2.00	1.00	.60
203	1965 - MVPs (Willie Mays, Zoilo Versalles)	5.00	2.50	1.50
204	1966 - MVPs (Bob Clemente, Frank Robinson)	4.00	2.00	1.25
205	1967 - MVPs (Orlando Cepeda, Carl Yastrzemski)	3.00	1.50	.90
206	1968 - MVPs (Bob Gibson, Denny McLain)	2.00	1.00	.60
207	1969 - MVPs (Harmon Killebrew, Willie McCovey)	2.00	1.00	.60
208	1970 - MVPs (Johnny Bench, Boog Powell)	3.00	1.50	.90
209	1971 - MVPs (Vida Blue, Joe Torre)	.55	.30	.15
210	1972 - MVPs (Rich Allen, Johnny Bench)	3.00	1.50	.90
211	1973 - MVPs (Reggie Jackson, Pete Rose)	6.00	3.00	1.75
212	1974 - MVPs (Jeff Burroughs, Steve Garvey)	.75	.40	.25
213	Oscar Gamble	.55	.30	.15
214	Harry Parker	.55	.30	.15
215	Bobby Valentine	.55	.30	.15
216	Giants Team (Wes Westrum)	.60	.30	.20
217	Lou Piniella	.55	.30	.15
218	Jerry Johnson	.55	.30	.15
219	Ed Herrmann	.55	.30	.15
220	Don Sutton	2.00	1.00	.60
221	Aurelio Rodriquez (Rodriguez)	.55	.30	.15
222	Dan Spillner	.55	.30	.15
223	Robin Yount	205.00	102.00	61.00
224	Ramon Hernandez	.55	.30	.15
225	Bob Grich	.55	.30	.15
226	Bill Campbell	.55	.30	.15
227	Bob Watson	.55	.30	.15
228	George Brett	245.00	122.00	73.00
229	Barry Foote	.55	.30	.15
230	Jim Hunter	1.50	.70	.45
231	Mike Tyson	.55	.30	.15
232	Diego Segui	.55	.30	.15
233	Billy Grabarkewitz	.55	.30	.15
234	Tom Grieve	.55	.30	.15
235	Jack Billingham	.55	.30	.15
236	Angels Team (Dick Williams)	.60	.30	.20
237	Carl Morton	.55	.30	.15
238	Dave Duncan	.55	.30	.15
239	George Stone	.55	.30	.15
240	Garry Maddox	.55	.30	.15
241	Dick Tidrow	.55	.30	.15
242	Jay Johnstone	.55	.30	.15
243	Jim Kaat	1.00	.50	.30
244	Bill Buckner	.55	.30	.15
245	Mickey Lolich	.55	.30	.15
246	Cardinals Team (Red Schoendienst)	.60	.30	.20
247	Enos Cabell	.55	.30	.15
248	Randy Jones	.55	.30	.15
249	Danny Thompson	.55	.30	.15
250	Ken Brett	.55	.30	.15
251	Fran Healy	.55	.30	.15
252	Fred Scherman	.55	.30	.15
253	Jesus Alou	.55	.30	.15
254	Mike Torrez	.55	.30	.15
255	Dwight Evans	6.00	3.00	1.75
256	Billy Champion	.55	.30	.15
257	Checklist 133-264	1.00	.50	.30
258	Dave LaRoche	.55	.30	.15
259	Len Randle	.55	.30	.15
260	Johnny Bench	15.00	7.50	4.50
261	Andy Hassler	.55	.30	.15
262	Rowland Office	.55	.30	.15
263	Jim Perry	.55	.30	.15
264	John Milner	.55	.30	.15
265	Ron Bryant	.55	.30	.15
266	Sandy Alomar	.55	.30	.15
267	Dick Ruthven	.55	.30	.15
268	Hal McRae	.55	.30	.15
269	Doug Rau	.55	.30	.15
270	Ron Fairly	.55	.30	.15
271	Jerry Moses	.55	.30	.15
272	Lynn McGlothen	.55	.30	.15
273	Steve Braun	.55	.30	.15
274	Vicente Romo	.55	.30	.15
275	Paul Blair	.55	.30	.15
276	White Sox Team (Chuck Tanner)	.60	.30	.20
277	Frank Taveras	.55	.30	.15
278	Paul Lindblad	.55	.30	.15
279	Milt May	.55	.30	.15
280	Carl Yastrzemski	10.25	5.25	3.00
281	Jim Slaton	.55	.30	.15
282	Jerry Morales	.55	.30	.15
283	Steve Foucault	.55	.30	.15
284	Ken Griffey	4.25	2.25	1.25
285	Ellie Rodriguez	.55	.30	.15
286	Mike Jorgensen	.55	.30	.15
287	Roric Harrison	.55	.30	.15
288	Bruce Ellingsen	.55	.30	.15
289	Ken Rudolph	.55	.30	.15
290	Jon Matlack	.55	.30	.15
291	Bill Sudakis	.55	.30	.15
292	Ron Schueler	.55	.30	.15
293	Dick Sharon	.55	.30	.15
294	Geoff Zahn	.55	.30	.15

295	Vada Pinson	.55	.30	.15
296	Alan Foster	.55	.30	.15
297	Craig Kusick	.55	.30	.15
298	Johnny Grubb	.55	.30	.15
299	Bucky Dent	.55	.30	.15
300	Reggie Jackson	30.00	15.00	9.00
301	Dave Roberts	.55	.30	.15
302	Rick Burleson	.55	.30	.15
303	Grant Jackson	.55	.30	.15
304	Pirates Team (Danny Murtaugh)	.60	.30	.20
305	Jim Colborn	.55	.30	.15
306	Batting Leaders (Rod Carew, Ralph Garr)	.75	.40	.25
307	Home Run Leaders (Dick Allen, Mike Schmidt)	4.00	2.00	1.25
308	Runs Batted In (Johnny Bench, Jeff Burroughs)	2.00	1.00	.60
309	Stolen Base Leaders (Lou Brock, Bill North)	.75	.40	.25
310	Victory Leaders (Jim Hunter, Fergie Jenkins, Andy Messersmith, Phil Niekro)	.75	.40	.25
311	Earned Run Average Leaders (Buzz Capra, Jim Hunter)	.55	.30	.15
312	Strikeout Leaders (Steve Carlton, Nolan Ryan)	18.00	9.00	5.50
313	Leading Firemen (Terry Forster, Mike Marshall)	.55	.30	.15
314	Buck Martinez	.55	.30	.15
315	Don Kessinger	.55	.30	.15
316	Jackie Brown	.55	.30	.15
317	Joe Lahoud	.55	.30	.15
318	Ernie McAnally	.55	.30	.15
319	Johnny Oates	.55	.30	.15
320	Pete Rose	17.00	8.50	5.00
321	Rudy May	.55	.30	.15
322	Ed Goodson	.55	.30	.15
323	Fred Holdsworth	.55	.30	.15
324	Ed Kranepool	.55	.30	.15
325	Tony Oliva	.75	.40	.25
326	Wayne Twitchell	.55	.30	.15
327	Jerry Hairston	.55	.30	.15
328	Sonny Siebert	.55	.30	.15
329	Ted Kubiak	.55	.30	.15
330	Mike Marshall	.55	.30	.15
331	Indians Team (Frank Robinson)	.60	.30	.20
332	Fred Kendall	.55	.30	.15
333	Dick Drago	.55	.30	.15
334	Greg Gross	.55	.30	.15
335	Jim Palmer	10.25	5.25	3.00
336	Rennie Stennett	.55	.30	.15
337	Kevin Kobel	.55	.30	.15
338	Rick Stelmaszek	.55	.30	.15
339	Jim Fregosi	.55	.30	.15
340	Paul Splittorff	.55	.30	.15
341	Hal Breeden	.55	.30	.15
342	Leroy Stanton	.55	.30	.15
343	Danny Frisella	.55	.30	.15
344	Ben Oglivie	.55	.30	.15
345	Clay Carroll	.55	.30	.15
346	Bobby Darwin	.55	.30	.15
347	Mike Caldwell	.55	.30	.15
348	Tony Muser	.55	.30	.15
349	Ray Sadecki	.55	.30	.15
350	Bobby Murcer	.55	.30	.15
351	Bob Boone	.55	.30	.15
352	Darold Knowles	.55	.30	.15
353	Luis Melendez	.55	.30	.15
354	Dick Bosman	.55	.30	.15
355	Chris Cannizzaro	.55	.30	.15
356	Rico Petrocelli	.55	.30	.15
357	Ken Forsch	.55	.30	.15
358	Al Bumbry	.55	.30	.15
359	Paul Popovich	.55	.30	.15
360	George Scott	.55	.30	.15
361	Dodgers Team (Walter Alston)	.75	.40	.25
362	Steve Hargan	.55	.30	.15
363	Carmen Fanzone	.55	.30	.15
364	Doug Bird	.55	.30	.15
365	Bob Bailey	.55	.30	.15
366	Ken Sanders	.55	.30	.15
367	Craig Robinson	.55	.30	.15
368	Vic Albury	.55	.30	.15
369	Merv Rettenmund	.55	.30	.15
370	Tom Seaver	18.00	9.00	5.50
371	Gates Brown	.55	.30	.15
372	John D'Acquisto	.55	.30	.15
373	Bill Sharp	.55	.30	.15
374	Eddie Watt	.55	.30	.15
375	Roy White	.55	.30	.15
376	Steve Yeager	.55	.30	.15
377	Tom Hilgendorf	.55	.30	.15
378	Derrel Thomas	.55	.30	.15
379	Bernie Carbo	.55	.30	.15
380	Sal Bando	.55	.30	.15
381	John Curtis	.55	.30	.15
382	Don Baylor	.75	.40	.25
383	Jim York	.55	.30	.15
384	Brewers Team (Del Crandall)	.60	.30	.20
385	Dock Ellis	.55	.30	.15
386	Checklist 265-396	1.00	.50	.30
387	Jim Spencer	.55	.30	.15
388	Steve Stone	.55	.30	.15
389	Tony Solaita	.55	.30	.15
390	Ron Cey	.55	.30	.15
391	Don DeMola	.55	.30	.15
392	Bruce Bochte	.55	.30	.15
393	Gary Gentry	.55	.30	.15
394	Larvell Blanks	.55	.30	.15
395	Bud Harrelson	.55	.30	.15
396	Fred Norman	.55	.30	.15
397	Bill Freehan	.55	.30	.15
398	Elias Sosa	.55	.30	.15
399	Terry Harmon	.55	.30	.15
400	Dick Allen	.75	.40	.25
401	Mike Wallace	.55	.30	.15
402	Bob Tolan	.55	.30	.15
403	Tom Buskey	.55	.30	.15
404	Ted Sizemore	.55	.30	.15
405	John Montague	.55	.30	.15
406	Bob Gallagher	.55	.30	.15
407	Herb Washington	.55	.30	.15
408	Clyde Wright	.55	.30	.15
409	Bob Robertson	.55	.30	.15
410	Mike Cueller (Cuellar)	.55	.30	.15
411	George Mitterwald	.55	.30	.15
412	Bill Hands	.55	.30	.15
413	Marty Pattin	.55	.30	.15
414	Manny Mota	.55	.30	.15
415	John Hiller	.55	.30	.15
416	Larry Lintz	.55	.30	.15
417	Skip Lockwood	.55	.30	.15
418	Leo Foster	.55	.30	.15
419	Dave Goltz	.55	.30	.15
420	Larry Bowa	.55	.30	.15
421	Mets Team (Yogi Berra)	.75	.40	.25
422	Brian Downing	.55	.30	.15
423	Clay Kirby	.55	.30	.15
424	John Lowenstein	.55	.30	.15
425	Tito Fuentes	.55	.30	.15
426	George Medich	.55	.30	.15
427	Clarence Gaston	.55	.30	.15
428	Dave Hamilton	.55	.30	.15
429	Jim Dwyer	.55	.30	.15
430	Luis Tiant	.55	.30	.15
431	Rod Gilbreath	.55	.30	.15
432	Ken Berry	.55	.30	.15
433	Larry Demery	.55	.30	.15
434	Bob Locker	.55	.30	.15
435	Dave Nelson	.55	.30	.15
436	Ken Frailing	.55	.30	.15
437	Al Cowens	.55	.30	.15
438	Don Carrithers	.55	.30	.15
439	Ed Brinkman	.55	.30	.15
440	Andy Messersmith	.55	.30	.15
441	Bobby Heise	.55	.30	.15
442	Maximino Leon	.55	.30	.15
443	Twins Team (Frank Quillici)	.60	.30	.20
444	Gene Garber	.55	.30	.15
445	Felix Millan	.55	.30	.15
446	Bart Johnson	.55	.30	.15
447	Terry Crowley	.55	.30	.15
448	Frank Duffy	.55	.30	.15
449	Charlie Williams	.55	.30	.15
450	Willie McCovey	5.50	2.75	1.75
451	Rick Dempsey	.55	.30	.15
452	Angel Mangual	.55	.30	.15
453	Claude Osteen	.55	.30	.15
454	Doug Griffin	.55	.30	.15
455	Don Wilson	.55	.30	.15
456	Bob Coluccio	.55	.30	.15
457	Mario Mendoza	.55	.30	.15
458	Ross Grimsley	.55	.30	.15
459	A.L. Championships	.75	.40	.25
460	N.L. Championships	.75	.40	.25
461	World Series Game 1	4.25	2.25	1.25
462	World Series Game 2	.75	.40	.25
463	World Series Game 3	1.00	.50	.30
464	World Series Game 4	.75	.40	.25
465	World Series Game 5	.75	.40	.25
466	World Series Summary	.75	.40	.25
467	Ed Halicki	.55	.30	.15
468	Bobby Mitchell	.55	.30	.15
469	Tom Dettore	.55	.30	.15
470	Jeff Burroughs	.55	.30	.15
471	Bob Stinson	.55	.30	.15
472	Bruce Dal Canton	.55	.30	.15
473	Ken McMullen	.55	.30	.15
474	Luke Walker	.55	.30	.15
475	Darrell Evans	.55	.30	.15
476	Ed Figueroa	.55	.30	.15
477	Tom Hutton	.55	.30	.15
478	Tom Burgmeier	.55	.30	.15
479	Ken Boswell	.55	.30	.15
480	Carlos May	.55	.30	.15
481	Will McEnaney	.55	.30	.15
482	Tom McCraw	.55	.30	.15
483	Steve Ontiveros	.55	.30	.15
484	Glenn Beckert	.55	.30	.15
485	Sparky Lyle	.55	.30	.15
486	Ray Fosse	.55	.30	.15
487	Astros Team (Preston Gomez)	.60	.30	.20
488	Bill Travers	.55	.30	.15
489	Cecil Cooper	.75	.40	.25
490	Reggie Smith	.55	.30	.15
491	Doyle Alexander	.55	.30	.15
492	Rich Hebner	.55	.30	.15
493	Don Stanhouse	.55	.30	.15
494	Pete LaCock	.55	.30	.15
495	Nelson Briles	.55	.30	.15
496	Pepe Frias	.55	.30	.15
497	Jim Nettles	.55	.30	.15
498	Al Downing	.55	.30	.15
499	Marty Perez	.55	.30	.15
500	Nolan Ryan	90.00	45.00	27.00
501	Bill Robinson	.55	.30	.15
502	Pat Bourque	.55	.30	.15
503	Fred Stanley	.55	.30	.15
504	Buddy Bradford	.55	.30	.15
505	Chris Speier	.55	.30	.15
506	Leron Lee	.55	.30	.15
507	Tom Carroll	.55	.30	.15
508	Bob Hansen	.55	.30	.15
509	Dave Hilton	.55	.30	.15
510	Vida Blue	.55	.30	.15
511	Rangers Team (Billy Martin)	.60	.30	.20
512	Larry Milbourne	.55	.30	.15
513	Dick Pole	.55	.30	.15
514	Jose Cruz	.55	.30	.15
515	Manny Sanguillen	.55	.30	.15
516	Don Hood	.55	.30	.15
517	Checklist 397-528	1.00	.50	.30
518	Leo Cardenas	.55	.30	.15
519	Jim Todd	.55	.30	.15
520	Amos Otis	.55	.30	.15
521	Dennis Blair	.55	.30	.15
522	Gary Sutherland	.55	.30	.15
523	Tom Paciorek	.55	.30	.15
524	John Doherty	.55	.30	.15
525	Tom House	.55	.30	.15
526	Larry Hisle	.55	.30	.15
527	Mac Scarce	.55	.30	.15
528	Eddie Leon	.55	.30	.15
529	Gary Thomasson	.55	.30	.15
530	Gaylord Perry	2.00	1.00	.60
531	Reds Team (Sparky Anderson)	.75	.40	.25
532	Gorman Thomas	.55	.30	.15
533	Rudy Meoli	.55	.30	.15
534	Alex Johnson	.55	.30	.15
535	Gene Tenace	.55	.30	.15
536	Bob Moose	.55	.30	.15
537	Tommy Harper	.55	.30	.15
538	Duffy Dyer	.55	.30	.15
539	Jesse Jefferson	.55	.30	.15
540	Lou Brock	5.50	2.75	1.75
541	Roger Metzger	.55	.30	.15
542	Pete Broberg	.55	.30	.15
543	Larry Biittner	.55	.30	.15
544	Steve Mingori	.55	.30	.15
545	Billy Williams	2.00	1.00	.60
546	John Knox	.55	.30	.15
547	Von Joshua	.55	.30	.15
548	Charlie Sands	.55	.30	.15
549	Bill Butler	.55	.30	.15
550	Ralph Garr	.55	.30	.15
551	Larry Christenson	.55	.30	.15
552	Jack Brohamer	.55	.30	.15
553	John Boccabella	.55	.30	.15
554	Rich Gossage	1.00	.50	.30
555	Al Oliver	.75	.40	.25
556	Tim Johnson	.55	.30	.15
557	Larry Gura	.55	.30	.15
558	Dave Roberts	.55	.30	.15
559	Bob Montgomery	.55	.30	.15
560	Tony Perez	.75	.40	.25
561	A's Team (Alvin Dark)	.75	.40	.25
562	Gary Nolan	.55	.30	.15
563	Wilbur Howard	.55	.30	.15
564	Tommy Davis	.55	.30	.15
565	Joe Torre	.55	.30	.15
566	Ray Burris	.55	.30	.15
567	Jim Sundberg	.60	.30	.20
568	Dale Murray	.55	.30	.15
569	Frank White	.55	.30	.15
570	Jim Wynn	.55	.30	.15
571	Dave Lemanczyk	.55	.30	.15
572	Roger Nelson	.55	.30	.15
573	Orlando Pena	.55	.30	.15
574	Tony Taylor	.55	.30	.15
575	Gene Clines	.55	.30	.15
576	Phil Roof	.55	.30	.15
577	John Morris	.55	.30	.15
578	Dave Tomlin	.55	.30	.15
579	Skip Pitlock	.55	.30	.15
580	Frank Robinson	5.00	2.50	1.50
581	Darrel Chaney	.55	.30	.15
582	Eduardo Rodriguez	.55	.30	.15
583	Andy Etchebarren	.55	.30	.15
584	Mike Garman	.55	.30	.15
585	Chris Chambliss	.55	.30	.15
586	Tim McCarver	.55	.30	.15
587	Chris Ward	.55	.30	.15
588	Rick Auerbach	.55	.30	.15
589	Braves Team (Clyde King)	.60	.30	.20
590	Cesar Cedeno	.55	.30	.15
591	Glenn Abbott	.55	.30	.15
592	Balor Moore	.55	.30	.15
593	Gene Lamont	.55	.30	.15
594	Jim Fuller	.55	.30	.15
595	Joe Niekro	.55	.30	.15
596	Ollie Brown	.55	.30	.15
597	Winston Llenas	.55	.30	.15
598	Bruce Kison	.55	.30	.15
599	Nate Colbert	.55	.30	.15
600	Rod Carew	10.25	5.25	3.00
601	Juan Beniquez	.55	.30	.15
602	John Vukovich	.55	.30	.15
603	Lew Kruasse	.55	.30	.15
604	Oscar Zamora	.55	.30	.15
605	John Ellis	.55	.30	.15
606	Bruce Miller	.55	.30	.15
607	Jim Holt	.55	.30	.15
608	Gene Michael	.55	.30	.15
609	Ellie Hendricks	.55	.30	.15
610	Ron Hunt	.55	.30	.15
611	Yankees Team (Bill Virdon)	1.00	.50	.30
612	Terry Hughes	.55	.30	.15
613	Bill Parsons	.55	.30	.15
614	Rookie Pitchers (Jack Kecek, Dyar Miller, Vern Ruhle, Paul Siebert)	.55	.30	.15
615	Rookie Pitchers (Pat Darcy, Dennis Leonard, Tom Underwood, Hank Webb)	.55	.30	.15
616	Rookie Outfielders (Dave Augustine, Pepe Mangual, Jim Rice, John Scott)	18.00	9.00	5.50
617	Rookie Infielders (Mike Cubbage, Doug DeCinces, Reggie Sanders, Manny Trillo)	1.00	.50	.30
618	Rookie Pitchers (Jamie Easterly, Tom Johnson, Scott McGregor, Rick Rhoden)	2.50	1.25	.70
619	Rookie Outfielders (Benny Ayala, Nyls Nyman, Tommy Smith, Jerry Turner)	.55	.30	.15
620	Catchers-Outfielders (Gary Carter, Marc Hill, Danny Meyer, Leon Roberts)	46.00	23.00	14.00
621	Rookie Pitchers (John Denny, Rawly Eastwick, Jim Kern, Juan Veintidos)	.55	.30	.15
622	Rookie Outfielders (Ed Armbrister, Fred Lynn, Tom Poquette, Terry Whitfield)	12.00	6.00	3.50
623	Rookie Infielders (Phil Garner, Keith Hernandez, Bob Sheldon, Tom Veryzer)	17.00	8.50	5.00
624	Rookie Pitchers (Doug Knoieczny, Gary Lavelle, Jim Otten, Eddie Solomon)	.55	.30	.15
625	Boog Powell	.60	.30	.20
626	Larry Haney	.55	.30	.15
627	Tom Walker	.55	.30	.15
628	Ron LeFlore	.60	.30	.20

629	Joe Hoerner	.55	.30	.15
630	Greg Luzinski	.55	.30	.15
631	Lee Lacy	.55	.30	.15
632	Morris Nettles	.55	.30	.15
633	Paul Casanova	.55	.30	.15
634	Cy Acosta	.55	.30	.15
635	Chuck Dobson	.55	.30	.15
636	Charlie Moore	.55	.30	.15
637	Ted Martinez	.55	.30	.15
638	Cubs Team (Jim Marshall)	.60	.30	.20
639	Steve Kline	.55	.30	.15
640	Harmon Killebrew	5.50	2.75	1.75
641	Jim Northrup	.55	.30	.15
642	Mike Phillips	.55	.30	.15
643	Brent Strom	.55	.30	.15
644	Bill Fahey	.55	.30	.15
645	Danny Cater	.55	.30	.15
646	Checklist 529-660	1.00	.50	.30
647	Claudell Washington	1.00	.50	.30
648	Dave Pagan	.55	.30	.15
649	Jack Heidemann	.55	.30	.15
650	Dave May	.55	.30	.15
651	John Morlan	.55	.30	.15
652	Lindy McDaniel	.55	.30	.15
653	Lee Richards	.55	.30	.15
654	Jerry Terrell	.55	.30	.15
655	Rico Carty	.55	.30	.15
656	Bill Plummer	.55	.30	.15
657	Bob Oliver	.55	.30	.15
658	Vic Harris	.55	.30	.15
659	Bob Apodaca	.55	.30	.15
660	Hank Aaron	34.00	17.00	10.00

1976 O-Pee-Chee

Identical in design to the 1976 Topps set, the Canadian-issued 1976 O-Pee-Chee set again contained 660 cards, each measuring 2-1/2" by 3 1/2". The backs are printed in both French and English and state "Ptd. in Canada."

	NR MT	EX	VG
Complete Set (660):	485.00	240.00	150.00
Common Player:	.35	.20	.11

1	'75 Record Breaker (Hank Aaron)	21.00	10.50	6.25
2	'75 Record Breaker (Bobby Bonds)	.40	.20	.12
3	'75 Record Breaker (Mickey Lolich)	.35	.20	.11
4	'75 Record Breaker (Dave Lopes)	.35	.20	.11
5	'75 Record Breaker (Tom Seaver)	5.00	2.50	1.50
6	'75 Record Breaker (Rennie Stennett)	.35	.20	.11
7	Jim Umbarger	.35	.20	.11
8	Tito Fuentes	.35	.20	.11
9	Paul Lindblad	.35	.20	.11
10	Lou Brock	5.00	2.50	1.50
11	Jim Hughes	.35	.20	.11
12	Richie Zisk	.35	.20	.11
13	Johnny Wockenfuss	.35	.20	.11
14	Gene Garber	.35	.20	.11
15	George Scott	.35	.20	.11
16	Bob Apodaca	.35	.20	.11
17	Yankees Team (Billy Martin)	1.00	.50	.30
18	Dale Murray	.35	.20	.11
19	George Brett	65.00	32.00	19.50
20	Bob Watson	.35	.20	.11
21	Dave LaRoche	.35	.20	.11
22	Bill Russell	.35	.20	.11
23	Brian Downing	.35	.20	.11
24	Cesar Geronimo	.35	.20	.11
25	Mike Torrez	.35	.20	.11
26	Andy Thornton	.35	.20	.11
27	Ed Figueroa	.35	.20	.11
28	Dusty Baker	.35	.20	.11
29	Rick Burleson	.35	.20	.11
30	John Montefusco	.35	.20	.11
31	Len Randle	.35	.20	.11
32	Danny Frisella	.35	.20	.11
33	Bill North	.35	.20	.11
34	Mike Garman	.35	.20	.11
35	Tony Oliva	.50	.25	.15
36	Frank Taveras	.35	.20	.11
37	John Hiller	.35	.20	.11
38	Garry Maddox	.35	.20	.11
39	Pete Broberg	.35	.20	.11
40	Dave Kingman	.75	.40	.25
41	Tippy Martinez	.40	.20	.12
42	Barry Foote	.35	.20	.11
43	Paul Splittorff	.35	.20	.11
44	Doug Rader	.35	.20	.11
45	Boog Powell	.40	.20	.12
46	Dodgers Team (Walter Alston)	1.00	.50	.30
47	Jesse Jefferson	.35	.20	.11
48	Dave Concepcion	.40	.20	.12
49	Dave Duncan	.35	.20	.11
50	Fred Lynn	1.75	.90	.50
51	Ray Burris	.35	.20	.11
52	Dave Chalk	.35	.20	.11
53	Mike Beard	.35	.20	.11
54	Dave Rader	.35	.20	.11
55	Gaylord Perry	3.00	1.50	.90
56	Bob Tolan	.35	.20	.11
57	Phil Garner	.35	.20	.11
58	Ron Reed	.35	.20	.11
59	Larry Hisle	.35	.20	.11
60	Jerry Reuss	.35	.20	.11
61	Ron LeFlore	.35	.20	.11
62	Johnny Oates	.35	.20	.11
63	Bobby Darwin	.35	.20	.11
64	Jerry Koosman	.35	.20	.11
65	Chris Chambliss	.35	.20	.11
66	Father and Son (Buddy Bell, Gus Bell)	.40	.20	.12
67	Father and Son (Bob Boone, Ray Boone)	.35	.20	.11
68	Father and Son (Joe Coleman, Joe Coleman, Jr.)	.35	.20	.11
69	Father and Son (Jim Hegan, Mike Hegan)	.35	.20	.11
70	Father and Son (Roy Smalley, Roy Smalley, Jr.)	.35	.20	.11
71	Steve Rogers	.35	.20	.11
72	Hal McRae	.35	.20	.11
73	Orioles Team (Earl Weaver)	.75	.40	.25
74	Oscar Gamble	.35	.20	.11
75	Larry Dierker	.35	.20	.11
76	Willie Crawford	.35	.20	.11
77	Pedro Bobon	.35	.20	.11
78	Cecil Cooper	.75	.40	.25
79	Jerry Morales	.35	.20	.11
80	Jim Kaat	.75	.40	.25
81	Darrell Evans	.40	.20	.12
82	Von Joshua	.35	.20	.11
83	Jim Spencer	.35	.20	.11
84	Brent Strom	.35	.20	.11
85	Mickey Rivers	.35	.20	.11
86	Mike Tyson	.35	.20	.11
87	Tom Burgmeier	.35	.20	.11
88	Duffy Dyer	.35	.20	.11
89	Vern Ruhle	.35	.20	.11
90	Sal Bando	.35	.20	.11
91	Tom Hutton	.35	.20	.11
92	Eduardo Rodriguez	.35	.20	.11
93	Mike Phillips	.35	.20	.11
94	Jim Dwyer	.35	.20	.11
95	Brooks Robinson	6.00	3.00	1.75
96	Doug Bird	.35	.20	.11
97	Wilbur Howard	.35	.20	.11
98	Dennis Eckersley	63.00	31.00	19.00
99	Lee Lacy	.35	.20	.11
100	Jim Hunter	3.00	1.50	.90
101	Pete LaCock	.35	.20	.11
102	Jim Willoughby	.35	.20	.11
103	Biff Pocoroba	.35	.20	.11
104	Reds Team (Sparky Anderson)	.75	.40	.25
105	Gary Lavelle	.35	.20	.11
106	Tom Grieve	.35	.20	.11
107	Dave Roberts	.35	.20	.11
108	Don Kirkwood	.35	.20	.11
109	Larry Lintz	.35	.20	.11
110	Carlos May	.35	.20	.11
111	Danny Thompson	.35	.20	.11
112	Kent Tekulve	.75	.40	.25
113	Gary Sutherland	.35	.20	.11
114	Jay Johnstone	.35	.20	.11
115	Ken Holtzman	.35	.20	.11
116	Charlie Moore	.35	.20	.11
117	Mike Jorgensen	.35	.20	.11
118	Red Sox Team (Darrell Johnson)	.75	.40	.25
119	Checklist 1-132	1.00	.50	.30
120	Rusty Staub	.40	.20	.12
121	Tony Solaita	.35	.20	.11
122	Mike Cosgrove	.35	.20	.11
123	Walt Williams	.35	.20	.11
124	Doug Rau	.35	.20	.11
125	Don Baylor	.50	.25	.15
126	Tom Dettore	.35	.20	.11
127	Larvell Blanks	.35	.20	.11
128	Ken Griffey	.35	.20	.11
129	Andy Etchebarren	.35	.20	.11
130	Luis Tiant	.40	.20	.12
131	Bill Stein	.35	.20	.11
132	Don Hood	.35	.20	.11
133	Gary Matthews	.35	.20	.11
134	Mike Ivie	.35	.20	.11
135	Bake McBride	.35	.20	.11
136	Dave Goltz	.35	.20	.11
137	Bill Robinson	.35	.20	.11
138	Lerrin LaGrow	.35	.20	.11
139	Gorman Thomas	.35	.20	.11
140	Vida Blue	.40	.20	.12
141	Larry Parrish	1.50	.70	.45
142	Dick Drago	.35	.20	.11
143	Jerry Grote	.35	.20	.11
144	Al Fitzmorris	.35	.20	.11
145	Larry Bowa	.35	.20	.11
146	George Medich	.35	.20	.11
147	Astros Team (Bill Virdon)	.60	.30	.20
148	Stan Thomas	.35	.20	.11
149	Tommy Davis	.35	.20	.11
150	Steve Garvey	4.50	2.25	1.25
151	Bill Bonham	.35	.20	.11
152	Leroy Stanton	.35	.20	.11
153	Buzz Capra	.35	.20	.11
154	Bucky Dent	.35	.20	.11
155	Jack Billingham	.35	.20	.11
156	Rico Carty	.35	.20	.11
157	Mike Caldwell	.35	.20	.11
158	Ken Reitz	.35	.20	.11
159	Jerry Terrell	.35	.20	.11
160	Dave Winfield	42.50	21.00	12.50
161	Bruce Kison	.35	.20	.11
162	Jack Pierce	.35	.20	.11
163	Jim Slaton	.35	.20	.11
164	Pepe Mangual	.35	.20	.11
165	Gene Tenace	.35	.20	.11
166	Skip Lockwood	.35	.20	.11
167	Freddie Patek	.35	.20	.11
168	Tom Hilgendorf	.35	.20	.11
169	Graig Nettles	1.00	.50	.30
170	Rick Wise	.35	.20	.11
171	Greg Gross	.35	.20	.11
172	Rangers Team (Frank Lucchesi)	.60	.30	.20
173	Steve Swisher	.35	.20	.11
174	Charlie Hough	.35	.20	.11
175	Ken Singleton	.35	.20	.11
176	Dick Lange	.35	.20	.11
177	Marty Perez	.35	.20	.11
178	Tom Buskey	.35	.20	.11
179	George Foster	.75	.40	.25
180	Rich Gossage	1.00	.50	.30
181	Willie Montanez	.35	.20	.11
182	Harry Rasmussen	.35	.20	.11
183	Steve Braun	.35	.20	.11
184	Bill Greif	.35	.20	.11
185	Dave Parker	7.00	3.50	2.00
186	Tom Walker	.35	.20	.11
187	Pedro Garcia	.35	.20	.11
188	Fred Scherman	.35	.20	.11
189	Claudell Washington	.40	.20	.12
190	Jon Matlack	.35	.20	.11
191	N.L. Batting Leaders (Bill Madlock, Manny Sanguillen, Ted Simmons)	.50	.25	.15
192	A.L. Batting Leaders (Rod Carew, Fred Lynn, Thurman Munson)	2.00	1.00	.60
193	N.L. Home Run Leaders (Dave Kingman, Greg Luzinski, Mike Schmidt)	2.00	1.00	.60
194	A.L. Home Run Leaders (Reggie Jackson, John Mayberry, George Scott)	2.00	1.00	.60
195	N.L. Runs Batted In Ldrs. (Johnny Bench, Greg Luzinski, Tony Perez)	2.00	1.00	.60
196	A.L. Runs Batted In Ldrs. (Fred Lynn, John Mayberry, George Scott)	.50	.25	.15
197	N.L. Stolen Base Leaders (Lou Brock, Dave Lopes, Joe Morgan)	2.00	1.00	.60
198	A.L. Stolen Base Leaders (Amos Otis, Mickey Rivers, Claudell Washington)	.40	.20	.12
199	N.L. Victory Leaders (Randy Jones, Andy Messersmith, Tom Seaver)	2.00	1.00	.60
200	A.L. Victory Leaders (Vida Blue, Jim Hunter, Jim Palmer)	2.00	1.00	.60
201	N.L. Earned Run Average Ldrs. (Randy Jones, Andy Messersmith, Tom Seaver)	2.00	1.00	.60
202	A.L. Earned Run Average Ldrs. (Dennis Eckersley, Jim Hunter, Jim Palmer, Jim Palmer)	5.00	2.50	1.50
203	N.L. Strikeout Leaders (Andy Messersmith, John Montefusco, Tom Seaver)	2.00	1.00	.60
204	A.L. Strikeout Leaders (Bert Blyleven, Gaylord Perry, Frank Tanana)	.50	.25	.15
205	Major League Leading Firemen (Rich Gossage, Al Hrabosky)	.40	.20	.12
206	Manny Trillo	.35	.20	.11
207	Andy Hassler	.35	.20	.11
208	Mike Lum	.35	.20	.11
209	Alan Ashby	.35	.20	.11
210	Lee May	.35	.20	.11
211	Clay Carroll	.35	.20	.11
212	Pat Kelly	.35	.20	.11
213	Dave Heaverlo	.35	.20	.11
214	Eric Soderholm	.35	.20	.11
215	Reggie Smith	.35	.20	.11
216	Expos Team (Karl Kuehl)	.60	.30	.20
217	Dave Freisleben	.35	.20	.11
218	John Knox	.35	.20	.11
219	Tom Murphy	.35	.20	.11
220	Manny Sanguillen	.35	.20	.11
221	Jim Todd	.35	.20	.11
222	Wayne Garrett	.35	.20	.11
223	Ollie Brown	.35	.20	.11
224	Jim York	.35	.20	.11
225	Roy White	.35	.20	.11
226	Jim Sundberg	.35	.20	.11
227	Oscar Zamora	.35	.20	.11
228	John Hale	.35	.20	.11
229	Jerry Remy	.35	.20	.11
230	Carl Yastrzemski	8.50	4.25	2.50
231	Tom House	.35	.20	.11
232	Frank Duffy	.35	.20	.11
233	Grant Jackson	.35	.20	.11
234	Mike Sadek	.35	.20	.11
235	Bert Blyleven	1.00	.50	.30
236	Royals Team (Whitey Herzog)	.60	.30	.20
237	Dave Hamilton	.35	.20	.11
238	Larry Biittner	.35	.20	.11
239	John Curtis	.35	.20	.11
240	Pete Rose	12.75	6.50	3.75
241	Hector Torres	.35	.20	.11
242	Dan Meyer	.35	.20	.11
243	Jim Rooker	.35	.20	.11
244	Bill Sharp	.35	.20	.11
245	Felix Millan	.35	.20	.11
246	Cesar Tovar	.35	.20	.11
247	Terry Harmon	.35	.20	.11
248	Dick Tidrow	.35	.20	.11
249	Cliff Johnson	.35	.20	.11
250	Fergie Jenkins	4.25	2.25	1.25
251	Rick Monday	.35	.20	.11
252	Tim Nordbrook	.35	.20	.11
253	Bill Buckner	.40	.20	.12
254	Rudy Meoli	.35	.20	.11
255	Fritz Peterson	.35	.20	.11
256	Rowland Office	.35	.20	.11
257	Ross Grimsley	.35	.20	.11
258	Nyls Nyman	.35	.20	.11

259	Darrel Chaney	.35	.20	.11
260	Steve Busby	.35	.20	.11
261	Gary Thomasson	.35	.20	.11
262	Checklist 133-264	1.00	.50	.30
263	Lyman Bostock	.75	.40	.25
264	Steve Renko	.35	.20	.11
265	Willie Davis	.35	.20	.11
266	Alan Foster	.35	.20	.11
267	Aurelio Rodriguez	.35	.20	.11
268	Del Unser	.35	.20	.11
269	Rick Austin	.35	.20	.11
270	Willie Stargell	2.25	1.25	.70
271	Jim Lonborg	.35	.20	.11
272	Rick Dempsey	.35	.20	.11
273	Joe Niekro	.35	.20	.11
274	Tommy Harper	.35	.20	.11
275	Rick Manning	.35	.20	.11
276	Mickey Scott	.35	.20	.11
277	Cubs Team (Jim Marshall)	.60	.30	.20
278	Bernie Carbo	.35	.20	.11
279	Roy Howell	.35	.20	.11
280	Burt Hooton	.35	.20	.11
281	Dave May	.35	.20	.11
282	Dan Osborn	.35	.20	.11
283	Merv Rettenmund	.35	.20	.11
284	Steve Ontiveros	.35	.20	.11
285	Mike Cuellar	.35	.20	.11
286	Jim Wohlford	.35	.20	.11
287	Pete Mackanin	.35	.20	.11
288	Bill Campbell	.35	.20	.11
289	Enzo Hernandez	.35	.20	.11
290	Ted Simmons	.60	.30	.20
291	Ken Sanders	.35	.20	.11
292	Leon Roberts	.35	.20	.11
293	Bill Castro	.35	.20	.11
294	Ed Kirkpatrick	.35	.20	.11
295	Dave Cash	.35	.20	.11
296	Pat Dobson	.35	.20	.11
297	Roger Metzger	.35	.20	.11
298	Dick Bosman	.35	.20	.11
299	Champ Summers	.35	.20	.11
300	Johnny Bench	12.75	6.50	3.75
301	Jackie Brown	.35	.20	.11
302	Rick Miller	.35	.20	.11
303	Steve Foucault	.35	.20	.11
304	Angels Team (Dick Williams)	.60	.30	.20
305	Andy Messersmith	.35	.20	.11
306	Rod Gilbreath	.35	.20	.11
307	Al Bumbry	.35	.20	.11
308	Jim Barr	.35	.20	.11
309	Bill Melton	.35	.20	.11
310	Randy Jones	.35	.20	.11
311	Cookie Rojas	.35	.20	.11
312	Don Carrithers	.35	.20	.11
313	Dan Ford	.35	.20	.11
314	Ed Kranepool	.35	.20	.11
315	Al Hrabosky	.35	.20	.11
316	Robin Yount	55.00	27.00	16.50
317	John Candelaria	1.75	.90	.50
318	Bob Boone	.35	.20	.11
319	Larry Gura	.35	.20	.11
320	Willie Horton	.35	.20	.11
321	Jose Cruz	.35	.20	.11
322	Glenn Abbott	.35	.20	.11
323	Rob Sperring	.35	.20	.11
324	Jim Bibby	.35	.20	.11
325	Tony Perez	.60	.30	.20
326	Dick Pole	.35	.20	.11
327	Dave Moates	.35	.20	.11
328	Carl Morton	.35	.20	.11
329	Joe Ferguson	.35	.20	.11
330	Nolan Ryan	75.00	37.00	22.00
331	Padres Team (John McNamara)	.60	.30	.20
332	Charlie Williams	.35	.20	.11
333	Bob Coluccio	.35	.20	.11
334	Dennis Leonard	.35	.20	.11
335	Bob Grich	.35	.20	.11
336	Vic Albury	.35	.20	.11
337	Bud Harrelson	.35	.20	.11
338	Bob Bailey	.35	.20	.11
339	John Denny	.50	.25	.15
340	Jim Rice	4.50	2.25	1.25
341	All Time All-Stars (Lou {Gehrig)	7.25	3.75	2.25
342	All Time All-Stars (Rogers Hornsby)	2.00	1.00	.60
343	All Time All-Stars (Pie Traynor)	1.50	.70	.45
344	All Time All-Stars (Honus Wagner)	4.25	2.25	1.25
345	All Time All-Stars (Babe Ruth)	12.75	6.50	3.75
346	All Time All-Stars (Ty Cobb)	8.00	4.00	2.50
347	All Time All-Stars (Ted Williams)	10.25	5.25	3.00
348	All Time All-Stars (Mickey Cochrane)	.75	.40	.25
349	All Time All-Stars (Walter Johnson)	2.00	1.00	.60
350	All Time All-Stars (Lefty Grove)	1.50	.70	.45
351	Randy Hundley	.35	.20	.11
352	Dave Giusti	.35	.20	.11
353	Sixto Lezcano	.35	.20	.11
354	Ron Blomberg	.35	.20	.11
355	Steve Carlton	8.50	4.25	2.50
356	Ted Martinez	.35	.20	.11
357	Ken Forsch	.35	.20	.11
358	Buddy Bell	.40	.20	.12
359	Rick Reuschel	.35	.20	.11
360	Jeff Burroughs	.35	.20	.11
361	Tigers Team (Ralph Houk)	.75	.40	.25
362	Will McEnaney	.35	.20	.11
363	Dave Collins	.60	.30	.20
364	Elias Sosa	.35	.20	.11
365	Carlton Fisk	10.25	5.25	3.00
366	Bobby Valentine	.35	.20	.11
367	Bruce Miller	.35	.20	.11
368	Wilbur Wood	.35	.20	.11
369	Frank White	.35	.20	.11
370	Ron Cey	.35	.20	.11
371	Ellie Hendricks	.35	.20	.11
372	Rick Baldwin	.35	.20	.11
373	Johnny Briggs	.35	.20	.11
374	Dan Warthen	.35	.20	.11
375	Ron Fairly	.35	.20	.11
376	Rich Hebner	.35	.20	.11
377	Mike Hegan	.35	.20	.11
378	Steve Stone	.35	.20	.11
379	Ken Boswell	.35	.20	.11
380	Bobby Bonds	.35	.20	.11
381	Denny Doyle	.35	.20	.11
382	Matt Alexander	.35	.20	.11
383	John Ellis	.35	.20	.11
384	Phillies Team (Danny Ozark)	.60	.30	.20
385	Mickey Lolich	.40	.20	.12
386	Ed Goodson	.35	.20	.11
387	Mike Miley	.35	.20	.11
388	Stan Perzanowski	.35	.20	.11
389	Glenn Adams	.35	.20	.11
390	Don Gullett	.35	.20	.11
391	Jerry Hairston	.35	.20	.11
392	Checklist 265-396	1.00	.50	.30
393	Paul Mitchell	.35	.20	.11
394	Fran Healy	.35	.20	.11
395	Jim Wynn	.35	.20	.11
396	Bill Lee	.35	.20	.11
397	Tim Foli	.35	.20	.11
398	Dave Tomlin	.35	.20	.11
399	Luis Melendez	.35	.20	.11
400	Rod Carew	8.50	4.25	2.50
401	Ken Brett	.35	.20	.11
402	Don Money	.35	.20	.11
403	Geoff Zahn	.35	.20	.11
404	Enos Cabell	.35	.20	.11
405	Rollie Fingers	4.25	2.25	1.25
406	Ed Herrmann	.35	.20	.11
407	Tom Underwood	.35	.20	.11
408	Charlie Spikes	.35	.20	.11
409	Dave Lemanczyk	.35	.20	.11
410	Ralph Garr	.35	.20	.11
411	Bill Singer	.35	.20	.11
412	Toby Harrah	.35	.20	.11
413	Pete Varney	.35	.20	.11
414	Wayne Garland	.35	.20	.11
415	Vada Pinson	.40	.20	.12
416	Tommy John	1.00	.50	.30
417	Gene Clines	.35	.20	.11
418	Jose Morales	.35	.20	.11
419	Reggie Cleveland	.35	.20	.11
420	Joe Morgan	6.75	3.50	2.00
421	A's Team	.60	.30	.20
422	Johnny Grubb	.35	.20	.11
423	Ed Halicki	.35	.20	.11
424	Phil Roof	.35	.20	.11
425	Rennie Stennett	.35	.20	.11
426	Bob Forsch	.35	.20	.11
427	Kurt Bevacqua	.35	.20	.11
428	Jim Crawford	.35	.20	.11
429	Fred Stanley	.35	.20	.11
430	Jose Cardenal	.35	.20	.11
431	Dick Ruthven	.35	.20	.11
432	Tom Veryzer	.35	.20	.11
433	Rick Waits	.35	.20	.11
434	Morris Nettles	.35	.20	.11
435	Phil Niekro	1.75	.90	.50
436	Bill Fahey	.35	.20	.11
437	Terry Forster	.35	.20	.11
438	Doug DeCinces	.40	.20	.12
439	Rick Rhoden	.50	.25	.15
440	John Mayberry	.35	.20	.11
441	Gary Carter	10.25	5.25	3.00
442	Hank Webb	.35	.20	.11
443	Giants Team	.60	.30	.20
444	Gary Nolan	.35	.20	.11
445	Rico Petrocelli	.35	.20	.11
446	Larry Haney	.35	.20	.11
447	Gene Locklear	.35	.20	.11
448	Tom Johnson	.35	.20	.11
449	Bob Robertson	.35	.20	.11
450	Jim Palmer	8.00	4.00	2.50
451	Buddy Bradford	.35	.20	.11
452	Tom Hausman	.35	.20	.11
453	Lou Piniella	.50	.25	.15
454	Tom Griffin	.35	.20	.11
455	Dick Allen	.50	.25	.15
456	Joe Coleman	.35	.20	.11
457	Ed Crosby	.35	.20	.11
458	Earl Williams	.35	.20	.11
459	Jim Brewer	.35	.20	.11
460	Cesar Cedeno	.35	.20	.11
461	NL and AL Championships	.75	.40	.25
462	1975 World Series	.75	.40	.25
463	Steve Hargan	.35	.20	.11
464	Ken Henderson	.35	.20	.11
465	Mike Marshall	.35	.20	.11
466	Bob Stinson	.35	.20	.11
467	Woodie Fryman	.35	.20	.11
468	Jesus Alou	.35	.20	.11
469	Rawly Eastwick	.35	.20	.11
470	Bobby Murcer	.40	.20	.12
471	Jim Burton	.35	.20	.11
472	Bob Davis	.35	.20	.11
473	Paul Blair	.35	.20	.11
474	Ray Corbin	.35	.20	.11
475	Joe Rudi	.35	.20	.11
476	Bob Moose	.35	.20	.11
477	Indians Team (Frank Robinson)	.60	.30	.20
478	Lynn McGlothen	.35	.20	.11
479	Bobby Mitchell	.35	.20	.11
480	Mike Schmidt	34.00	17.00	10.00
481	Rudy May	.35	.20	.11
482	Tim Hosley	.35	.20	.11
483	Mickey Stanley	.35	.20	.11
484	Eric Raich	.35	.20	.11
485	Mike Hargrove	.35	.20	.11
486	Bruce Dal Canton	.35	.20	.11
487	Leron Lee	.35	.20	.11
488	Claude Osteen	.35	.20	.11
489	Skip Jutze	.35	.20	.11
490	Frank Tanana	.35	.20	.11
491	Terry Crowley	.35	.20	.11
492	Marty Pattin	.35	.20	.11
493	Derrel Thomas	.35	.20	.11
494	Craig Swan	.35	.20	.11
495	Nate Colbert	.35	.20	.11
496	Juan Beniquez	.35	.20	.11
497	Joe McIntosh	.35	.20	.11
498	Glenn Borgmann	.35	.20	.11
499	Mario Guerrero	.35	.20	.11
500	Reggie Jackson	23.00	11.50	7.00
501	Billy Champion	.35	.20	.11
502	Tim McCarver	.40	.20	.12
503	Elliott Maddox	.35	.20	.11
504	Pirates Team (Danny Murtaugh)	.60	.30	.20
505	Mark Belanger	.35	.20	.11
506	George Mitterwald	.35	.20	.11
507	Ray Bare	.35	.20	.11
508	Duane Kuiper	.35	.20	.11
509	Bill Hands	.35	.20	.11
510	Amos Otis	.35	.20	.11
511	Jamie Easterley	.35	.20	.11
512	Ellie Rodriguez	.35	.20	.11
513	Bart Johnson	.35	.20	.11
514	Dan Driessen	.35	.20	.11
515	Steve Yeager	.35	.20	.11
516	Wayne Granger	.35	.20	.11
517	John Milner	.35	.20	.11
518	Doug Flynn	.35	.20	.11
519	Steve Brye	.35	.20	.11
520	Willie McCovey	4.25	2.25	1.25
521	Jim Colborn	.35	.20	.11
522	Ted Sizemore	.35	.20	.11
523	Bob Montgomery	.35	.20	.11
524	Pete Falcone	.35	.20	.11
525	Billy Williams	1.75	.90	.50
526	Checklist 397-528	1.00	.50	.30
527	Mike Anderson	.35	.20	.11
528	Dock Ellis	.35	.20	.11
529	Deron Johnson	.35	.20	.11
530	Don Sutton	1.25	.60	.40
531	Mets Team (Joe Frazier)	.75	.40	.25
532	Milt May	.35	.20	.11
533	Lee Richard	.35	.20	.11
534	Stan Bahnsen	.35	.20	.11
535	Dave Nelson	.35	.20	.11
536	Mike Thompson	.35	.20	.11
537	Tony Muser	.35	.20	.11
538	Pat Darcy	.35	.20	.11
539	John Balaz	.35	.20	.11
540	Bill Freehan	.35	.20	.11
541	Steve Mingori	.35	.20	.11
542	Keith Hernandez	5.00	2.50	1.50
543	Wayne Twitchell	.35	.20	.11
544	Pepe Frias	.35	.20	.11
545	Sparky Lyle	.35	.20	.11
546	Dave Rosello	.35	.20	.11
547	Roric Harrison	.35	.20	.11
548	Manny Mota	.35	.20	.11
549	Randy Tate	.35	.20	.11
550	Hank Aaron	30.00	15.00	9.00
551	Jerry DaVanon	.35	.20	.11
552	Terry Humphrey	.35	.20	.11
553	Randy Moffitt	.35	.20	.11
554	Ray Fosse	.35	.20	.11
555	Dyar Miller	.35	.20	.11
556	Twins Team (Gene Mauch)	.60	.30	.20
557	Dan Spillner	.35	.20	.11
558	Clarence Gaston	.35	.20	.11
559	Clyde Wright	.35	.20	.11
560	Jorge Orta	.35	.20	.11
561	Tom Carroll	.35	.20	.11
562	Adrian Garrett	.35	.20	.11
563	Larry Demery	.35	.20	.11
564	Bubble Gum Blowing Champ (Kurt Bevacqua)	.35	.20	.11
565	Tug McGraw	.35	.20	.11
566	Ken McMullen	.35	.20	.11
567	George Stone	.35	.20	.11
568	Rob Andrews	.35	.20	.11
569	Nelson Briles	.35	.20	.11
570	George Hendrick	.35	.20	.11
571	Don DeMola	.35	.20	.11
572	Rich Coggins	.35	.20	.11
573	Bill Travers	.35	.20	.11
574	Don Kessinger	.35	.20	.11
575	Dwight Evans	3.00	1.50	.90
576	Maximino Leon	.35	.20	.11
577	Marc Hill	.35	.20	.11
578	Ted Kubiak	.35	.20	.11
579	Clay Kirby	.35	.20	.11
580	Bert Campaneris	.35	.20	.11
581	Cardinals Team (Red Schoendienst)	.60	.30	.20
582	Mike Kekich	.35	.20	.11
583	Tommy Helms	.35	.20	.11
584	Stan Wall	.35	.20	.11
585	Joe Torre	.40	.20	.12
586	Ron Schueler	.35	.20	.11
587	Leo Cardenas	.35	.20	.11
588	Kevin Kobel	.35	.20	.11
589	Rookie Pitchers (Santo Alcala, Mike Flanagan, Joe Pactwa, Pablo Torrealba)	1.25	.60	.40
590	Rookie Outfielders (Henry Cruz, Chet Lemon, Ellis Valentine, Terry Whitfield)	.75	.40	.25
591	Rookie Pitchers (Steve Grilli, Craig Mitchell, Jose Sosa, George Throop)	.35	.20	.11
592	Rookie Infielders (Dave McKay, Willie Randolph, Jerry Royster, Roy Staiger)	8.50	4.25	2.50
593	Rookie Pitchers (Larry Anderson, Ken Crosby, Mark Littell, Butch Metzger)	.35	.20	.11
594	Rookie Catchers & Outfielders (Andy Merchant, Ed Ott, Royle Stillman, Jerry White)	.35	.20	.11
595	Rookie Pitchers (Steve Barr, Art DeFilippis, Randy Lerch, Sid Monge)	.35	.20	.11
596	Rookie Infielders (Lamar Johnson, Johnnie LeMaster, Jerry Manuel, Craig Reynolds)	.35	.20	.11

597	Rookie Pitchers (Don Aase, Jack Kucek, Frank LaCorte, Mike Pazik)	.40	.20	.12
598	Rookie Outfielders (Hector Cruz, Jamie Quirk, Jerry Turner, Joe Wallis)	.35	.20	.11
599	Rookie Pitchers (Rob Dressler, Ron Guidry, Bob McClure, Pat Zachry)	8.50	4.25	2.50
600	Tom Seaver	17.00	8.50	5.00
601	Ken Rudolph	.35	.20	.11
602	Doug Konieczny	.35	.20	.11
603	Jim Holt	.35	.20	.11
604	Joe Lovitto	.35	.20	.11
605	Al Downing	.35	.20	.11
606	Brewers Team (Alex Grammas)	.60	.30	.20
607	Rich Hinton	.35	.20	.11
608	Vic Correll	.35	.20	.11
609	Fred Norman	.35	.20	.11
610	Greg Luzinski	.40	.20	.12
611	Rich Folkers	.35	.20	.11
612	Joe Lahoud	.35	.20	.11
613	Tim Johnson	.35	.20	.11
614	Fernando Arroyo	.35	.20	.11
615	Mike Cubbage	.35	.20	.11
616	Buck Martinez	.35	.20	.11
617	Darold Knowles	.35	.20	.11
618	Jack Brohamer	.35	.20	.11
619	Bill Butler	.35	.20	.11
620	Al Oliver	.60	.30	.20
621	Tom Hall	.35	.20	.11
622	Rick Auerbach	.35	.20	.11
623	Bob Allietta	.35	.20	.11
624	Tony Taylor	.35	.20	.11
625	J.R. Richard	.35	.20	.11
626	Bob Sheldon	.35	.20	.11
627	Bill Plummer	.35	.20	.11
628	John D'Acquisto	.35	.20	.11
629	Sandy Alomar	.35	.20	.11
630	Chris Speier	.35	.20	.11
631	Braves Team (Dave Bristol)	.60	.30	.20
632	Rogelio Moret	.35	.20	.11
633	John Stearns	.35	.20	.11
634	Larry Christenson	.35	.20	.11
635	Jim Fregosi	.35	.20	.11
636	Joe Decker	.35	.20	.11
637	Bruce Bochte	.35	.20	.11
638	Doyle Alexander	.35	.20	.11
639	Fred Kendall	.35	.20	.11
640	Bill Madlock	.75	.40	.25
641	Tom Paciorek	.35	.20	.11
642	Dennis Blair	.35	.20	.11
643	Checklist 529-660	1.00	.50	.30
644	Tom Bradley	.35	.20	.11
645	Darrell Porter	.35	.20	.11
646	John Lowenstein	.35	.20	.11
647	Ramon Hernandez	.35	.20	.11
648	Al Cowens	.35	.20	.11
649	Dave Roberts	.35	.20	.11
650	Thurman Munson	8.50	4.25	2.50
651	John Odom	.35	.20	.11
652	Ed Armbrister	.35	.20	.11
653	Mike Norris	.35	.20	.11
654	Doug Griffin	.35	.20	.11
655	Mike Vail	.35	.20	.11
656	White Sox Team (Chuck Tanner)	.60	.30	.20
657	Roy Smalley	.35	.20	.11
658	Jerry Johnson	.35	.20	.11
659	Ben Oglivie	.35	.20	.11
660	Dave Lopes	.35	.20	.11

1977 O-Pee-Chee

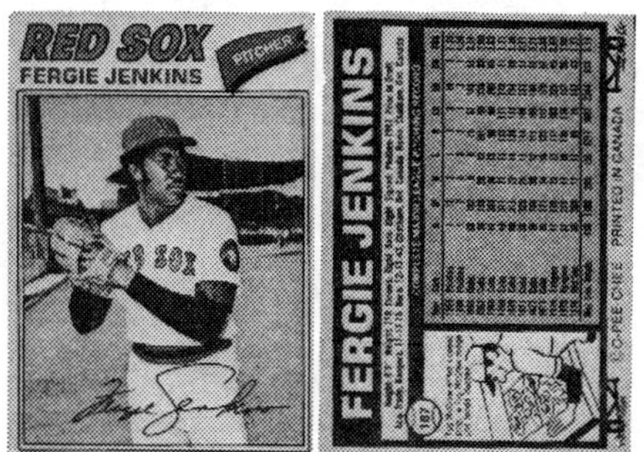

The 1977 O-Pee-Chee set represents a change in philosphy for the Canadian company. The design of the set is still identical to the Topps set of the same year, but the number of cards was reduced to 264 with more emphasis on players from the two Canadian teams. The backs are printed in English only but state "O-Pee-Chee Printed in Canada." Some of the photos in the O-Pee-Chee set differ from the 1977 Topps set. The cards measure the standard 2-1/2" by 3-1/2".

	NR MT	EX	VG
Complete Set (264):	245.00	125.00	75.00
Common Player:	.30	.15	.09

1	Batting Leaders (George Brett, Bill Madlock)	6.00	3.00	1.75
2	Home Run Leaders (Graig Nettles, Mike Schmidt)	3.00	1.50	.90
3	Runs Batted In Leaders (George Foster, Lee May)	.40	.20	.12
4	Stolen Base Leaders (Dave Lopes, Bill North)	.30	.15	.09
5	Victory Leaders (Randy Jones, Jim Palmer)	2.00	1.00	.60
6	Strikeout Leaders (Nolan Ryan, Tom Seaver)	15.00	7.50	4.50
7	Earned Run Avg. Leaders (John Denny, Mark Fidrych)	.30	.15	.09
8	Leading Firemen (Bill Campbell, Rawly Eastwick)	.30	.15	.09
9	Mike Jorgensen	.30	.15	.09
10	Jim Hunter	1.50	.70	.45
11	Ken Griffey	.30	.15	.09
12	Bill Campbell	.30	.15	.09
13	Otto Velez	.30	.15	.09
14	Milt May	.30	.15	.09
15	Dennis Eckersley	12.75	6.50	3.75
16	John Mayberry	.30	.15	.09
17	Larry Bowa	.30	.15	.09
18	Don Carrithers	.30	.15	.09
19	Ken Singleton	.30	.15	.09
20	Bill Stein	.30	.15	.09
21	Ken Brett	.30	.15	.09
22	Gary Woods	.30	.15	.09
23	Steve Swisher	.30	.15	.09
24	Don Sutton	1.25	.60	.40
25	Willie Stargell	2.25	1.25	.70
26	Jerry Koosman	.30	.15	.09
27	Del Unser	.30	.15	.09
28	Bob Grich	.30	.15	.09
29	Jim Slaton	.30	.15	.09
30	Thurman Munson	6.00	3.00	1.75
31	Dan Driessen	.30	.15	.09
32	Tom Bruno	.30	.15	.09
33	Larry Hisle	.30	.15	.09
34	Phil Garner	.30	.15	.09
35	Mike Hargrove	.30	.15	.09
36	Jackie Brown	.30	.15	.09
37	Carl Yastrzemski	6.25	3.25	2.00
38	Dave Roberts	.30	.15	.09
39	Ray Fosse	.30	.15	.09
40	Dave McKay	.30	.15	.09
41	Paul Splittorff	.30	.15	.09
42	Garry Maddox	.30	.15	.09
43	Phil Niekro	1.25	.60	.40
44	Roger Metzger	.30	.15	.09
45	Gary Carter	6.75	3.50	2.00
46	Jim Spencer	.30	.15	.09
47	Ross Grimsley	.30	.15	.09
48	Bob Bailor	.30	.15	.09
49	Chris Chambliss	.30	.15	.09
50	Will McEnaney	.30	.15	.09
51	Lou Brock	4.25	2.25	1.25
52	Rollie Fingers	3.75	2.00	1.25
53	Chris Speier	.30	.15	.09
54	Bombo Rivera	.30	.15	.09
55	Pete Broberg	.30	.15	.09
56	Bill Madlock	.50	.25	.15
57	Rick Rhoden	.30	.15	.09
58	Blue Jay Coaches (Don Leppert, Bob Miller, Jackie Moore, Harry Warner)	.50	.25	.15
59	John Candelaria	.40	.20	.12
60	Ed Kranepool	.30	.15	.09
61	Dave LaRoche	.30	.15	.09
62	Jim Rice	4.25	2.25	1.25
63	Don Stanhouse	.30	.15	.09
64	Jason Thompson	.50	.25	.15
65	Nolan Ryan	55.00	27.00	16.50
66	Tom Poquette	.30	.15	.09
67	Leon Hooten	.30	.15	.09
68	Bob Boone	.30	.15	.09
69	Mickey Rivers	.30	.15	.09
70	Gary Nolan	.30	.15	.09
71	Sixto Lezcano	.30	.15	.09
72	Larry Parrish	.30	.15	.09
73	Dave Goltz	.30	.15	.09
74	Bert Campaneris	.30	.15	.09
75	Vida Blue	.30	.15	.09
76	Rick Cerone	.30	.15	.09
77	Ralph Garr	.30	.15	.09
78	Ken Forsch	.30	.15	.09
79	Willie Montanez	.30	.15	.09
80	Jim Palmer	7.25	3.75	2.25
81	Jerry White	.30	.15	.09
82	Gene Tenace	.30	.15	.09
83	Bobby Murcer	.30	.15	.09
84	Garry Templeton	.75	.40	.25
85	Bill Singer	.30	.15	.09
86	Buddy Bell	.30	.15	.09
87	Luis Tiant	.40	.20	.12
88	Rusty Staub	.30	.15	.09
89	Sparky Lyle	.30	.15	.09
90	Jose Morales	.30	.15	.09
91	Dennis Leonard	.30	.15	.09
92	Tommy Smith	.30	.15	.09
93	Steve Carlton	7.50	3.75	2.25
94	John Scott	.30	.15	.09
95	Bill Bonham	.30	.15	.09
96	Dave Lopes	.30	.15	.09
97	Jerry Reuss	.30	.15	.09
98	Dave Kingman	.50	.25	.15
99	Dan Warthen	.30	.15	.09
100	Johnny Bench	10.25	5.25	3.00
101	Bert Blyleven	.50	.25	.15
102	Cecil Cooper	.50	.25	.15
103	Mike Willis	.30	.15	.09
104	Dan Ford	.30	.15	.09
105	Frank Tanana	.30	.15	.09
106	Bill North	.30	.15	.09
107	Joe Ferguson	.30	.15	.09
108	Dick Williams	.30	.15	.09
109	John Denny	.30	.15	.09
110	Willie Randolph	.40	.20	.12
111	Reggie Cleveland	.30	.15	.09
112	Doug Howard	.30	.15	.09
113	Randy Jones	.30	.15	.09
114	Rico Carty	.30	.15	.09
115	Mark Fidrych	.40	.20	.12
116	Darrell Porter	.30	.15	.09
117	Wayne Garrett	.30	.15	.09
118	Greg Luzinski	.40	.20	.12
119	Jim Barr	.30	.15	.09
120	George Foster	.75	.40	.25
121	Phil Roof	.30	.15	.09
122	Bucky Dent	.30	.15	.09
123	Steve Braun	.30	.15	.09
124	Checklist 1-132	1.00	.50	.30
125	Lee May	.30	.15	.09
126	Woodie Fryman	.30	.15	.09
127	Jose Cardenal	.30	.15	.09
128	Doug Rau	.30	.15	.09
129	Rennie Stennett	.30	.15	.09
130	Pete Vuckovich	.40	.20	.12
131	Cesar Cedeno	.30	.15	.09
132	Jon Matlack	.30	.15	.09
133	Don Baylor	.50	.25	.15
134	Darrel Chaney	.30	.15	.09
135	Tony Perez	.75	.40	.25
136	Aurelio Rodriguez	.30	.15	.09
137	Carlton Fisk	9.25	4.75	2.75
138	Wayne Garland	.30	.15	.09
139	Dave Hilton	.30	.15	.09
140	Rawly Eastwick	.30	.15	.09
141	Amos Otis	.30	.15	.09
142	Tug McGraw	.30	.15	.09
143	Rod Carew	7.50	3.75	2.25
144	Mike Torrez	.30	.15	.09
145	Sal Bando	.30	.15	.09
146	Dock Ellis	.30	.15	.09
147	Jose Cruz	.30	.15	.09
148	Alan Ashby	.30	.15	.09
149	Gaylord Perry	1.50	.70	.45
150	Keith Hernandez	2.50	1.25	.70
151	Dave Pagan	.30	.15	.09
152	Richie Zisk	.30	.15	.09
153	Steve Rogers	.30	.15	.09
154	Mark Belanger	.30	.15	.09
155	Andy Messersmith	.30	.15	.09
156	Dave Winfield	30.00	15.00	9.00
157	Chuck Hartenstein	.30	.15	.09
158	Manny Trillo	.30	.15	.09
159	Steve Yeager	.30	.15	.09
160	Cesar Geronimo	.30	.15	.09
161	Jim Rooker	.30	.15	.09
162	Tim Foli	.30	.15	.09
163	Fred Lynn	1.25	.60	.40
164	Ed Figueroa	.30	.15	.09
165	Johnny Grubb	.30	.15	.09
166	Pedro Garcia	.30	.15	.09
167	Ron LeFlore	.30	.15	.09
168	Rich Hebner	.30	.15	.09
169	Larry Herndon	.30	.15	.09
170	George Brett	38.00	19.00	11.50
171	Joe Kerrigan	.30	.15	.09
172	Bud Harrelson	.30	.15	.09
173	Bobby Bonds	.30	.15	.09
174	Bill Travers	.30	.15	.09
175	John Lowenstein	.30	.15	.09
176	Butch Wynegar	.40	.20	.12
177	Pete Falcone	.30	.15	.09
178	Claudell Washington	.30	.15	.09
179	Checklist 133-264	1.00	.50	.30
180	Dave Cash	.30	.15	.09
181	Fred Norman	.30	.15	.09
182	Roy White	.30	.15	.09
183	Marty Perez	.30	.15	.09
184	Jesse Jefferson	.30	.15	.09
185	Jim Sundberg	.30	.15	.09
186	Dan Meyer	.30	.15	.09
187	Fergie Jenkins	.75	.40	.25
188	Tom Veryzer	.30	.15	.09
189	Dennis Blair	.30	.15	.09
190	Rick Manning	.30	.15	.09
191	Doug Bird	.30	.15	.09
192	Al Bumbry	.30	.15	.09
193	Dave Roberts	.30	.15	.09
194	Larry Christenson	.30	.15	.09
195	Chet Lemon	.30	.15	.09
196	Ted Simmons	.50	.25	.15
197	Ray Burris	.30	.15	.09
198	Expos Coaches (Jim Brewer, Billy Gardner, Mickey Vernon, Ozzie Virgil)	.30	.15	.09
199	Ron Cey	.30	.15	.09
200	Reggie Jackson	17.00	8.50	5.00
201	Pat Zachry	.30	.15	.09
202	Doug Ault	.30	.15	.09
203	Al Oliver	.60	.30	.20
204	Robin Yount	32.00	16.00	9.50
205	Tom Seaver	10.25	5.25	3.00
206	Joe Rudi	.30	.15	.09
207	Barry Foote	.30	.15	.09
208	Toby Harrah	.30	.15	.09
209	Jeff Burroughs	.30	.15	.09
210	George Scott	.30	.15	.09
211	Jim Mason	.30	.15	.09
212	Vern Ruhle	.30	.15	.09
213	Fred Kendall	.30	.15	.09
214	Rick Reuschel	.30	.15	.09
215	Hal McRae	.30	.15	.09
216	Chip Lang	.30	.15	.09
217	Graig Nettles	.75	.40	.25
218	George Hendrick	.30	.15	.09
219	Glenn Abbott	.30	.15	.09
220	Joe Morgan	5.00	2.50	1.50
221	Sam Ewing	.30	.15	.09
222	George Medich	.30	.15	.09
223	Reggie Smith	.30	.15	.09
224	Dave Hamilton	.30	.15	.09
225	Pepe Frias	.30	.15	.09
226	Jay Johnstone	.30	.15	.09
227	J.R. Richard	.30	.15	.09
228	Doug DeCinces	.35	.20	.11
229	Dave Lemanczyk	.30	.15	.09
230	Rick Monday	.30	.15	.09
231	Manny Sanguillen	.30	.15	.09
232	John Montefusco	.30	.15	.09
233	Duane Kuiper	.30	.15	.09
234	Ellis Valentine	.30	.15	.09

235	Dick Tidrow	.30	.15	.09
236	Ben Oglivie	.30	.15	.09
237	Rick Burleson	.30	.15	.09
238	Roy Hartsfield	.30	.15	.09
239	Lyman Bostock	.30	.15	.09
240	Pete Rose	8.50	4.25	2.50
241	Mike Ivie	.30	.15	.09
242	Dave Parker	3.00	1.50	.90
243	Bill Greif	.30	.15	.09
244	Freddie Patek	.30	.15	.09
245	Mike Schmidt	20.50	10.00	6.25
246	Brian Downing	.30	.15	.09
247	Steve Hargan	.30	.15	.09
248	Dave Collins	.30	.15	.09
249	Felix Millan	.30	.15	.09
250	Don Gullett	.30	.15	.09
251	Jerry Royster	.30	.15	.09
252	Earl Williams	.30	.15	.09
253	Frank Duffy	.30	.15	.09
254	Tippy Martinez	.30	.15	.09
255	Steve Garvey	4.00	2.00	1.25
256	Alvis Woods	.30	.15	.09
257	John Hiller	.30	.15	.09
258	Dave Concepcion	.30	.15	.09
259	Dwight Evans	.75	.40	.25
260	Pete MacKanin	.30	.15	.09
261	Record Breaker (George Brett)	11.00	5.50	3.25
262	Record Breaker (Minnie Minoso)	.30	.15	.09
263	Record Breaker (Jose Morales)	.30	.15	.09
264	Record Breaker (Nolan Ryan)	18.00	9.00	5.50

1978 O-Pee-Chee

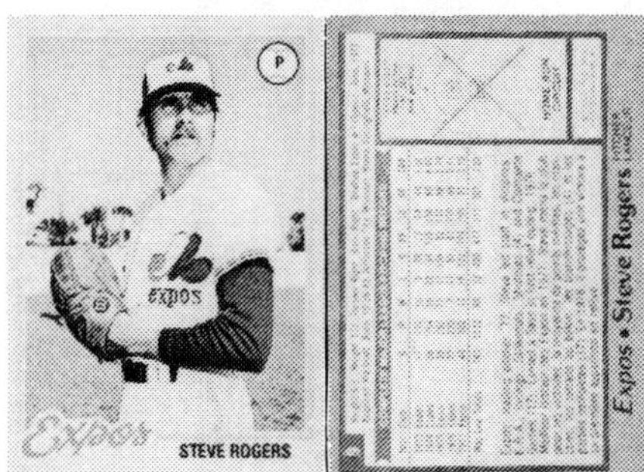

The 1978 O-Pee-Chee set was further reduced to 242 cards and again had heavy representation from the two Canadian teams. The cards measure the standard 2-1/2" by 3-1/2" and the backs are printed in both French and English. The cards use the same design as the 1978 Topps set. Some of the cards contain an extra line on the front indicating a team change.

		NR MT	EX	VG
	Complete Set:	170.00	85.00	50.00
	Common Player:	.25	.13	.08
1	Batting Leaders (Rod Carew, Dave Parker)	.75	.40	.25
2	Home Run Leaders (George Foster, Jim Rice)	.25	.13	.08
3	Runs Batted In Ldrs. (George Foster, Larry Hisle)	.25	.13	.08
4	Stolen Base Leaders (Freddie Patek, Frank Taveras)	.25	.13	.08
5	Victory Leaders (Steve Carlton, Dave Goltz, Dennis Leonard, Jim Palmer)	.50	.25	.15
6	Strikeout Leaders (Phil Niekro, Nolan Ryan)	3.75	2.00	1.25
7	Earned Run Avg. Ldrs. (John Candelaria, Frank Tanana)	.25	.13	.08
8	Leading Firemen (Bill Campbell, Rollie Fingers)	1.00	.50	.30
9	Steve Rogers	.25	.13	.08
10	Graig Nettles	.25	.13	.08
11	Doug Capilla	.25	.13	.08
12	George Scott	.25	.13	.08
13	Gary Woods	.25	.13	.08
14	Tom Veryzer	.25	.13	.08
15	Wayne Garland	.25	.13	.08
16	Amos Otis	.25	.13	.08
17	Larry Christenson	.25	.13	.08
18	Dave Cash	.25	.13	.08
19	Jim Barr	.25	.13	.08
20	Ruppert Jones	.25	.13	.08
21	Eric Soderholm	.25	.13	.08
22	Jesse Jefferson	.25	.13	.08
23	Jerry Morales	.25	.13	.08
24	Doug Rau	.25	.13	.08
25	Rennie Stennett	.25	.13	.08
26	Lee Mazzilli	.25	.13	.08
27	Dick Williams	.25	.13	.08
28	Joe Rudi	.25	.13	.08
29	Robin Yount	18.00	9.00	5.50
30	Don Gullett	.25	.13	.08
31	Roy Howell	.25	.13	.08
32	Cesar Geronimo	.25	.13	.08
33	Rick Langford	.25	.13	.08
34	Dan Ford	.25	.13	.08
35	Gene Tenace	.25	.13	.08
36	Santo Alcala	.25	.13	.08
37	Rick Burleson	.25	.13	.08
38	Dave Rozema	.25	.13	.08
39	Duane Kuiper	.25	.13	.08
40	Ron Fairly	.25	.13	.08
41	Dennis Leonard	.25	.13	.08
42	Greg Luzinski	.30	.15	.09
43	Willie Montanez	.25	.13	.08
44	Enos Cabell	.25	.13	.08
45	Ellis Valentine	.25	.13	.08
46	Steve Stone	.25	.13	.08
47	Lee May	.25	.13	.08
48	Roy White	.25	.13	.08
49	Jerry Garvin	.25	.13	.08
50	Johnny Bench	5.00	2.50	1.50
51	Garry Templeton	.25	.13	.08
52	Doyle Alexander	.25	.13	.08
53	Steve Henderson	.25	.13	.08
54	Stan Bahnsen	.25	.13	.08
55	Dan Meyer	.25	.13	.08
56	Rick Reuschel	.25	.13	.08
57	Reggie Smith	.25	.13	.08
58	Blue Jays Team	.25	.13	.08
59	John Montefusco	.25	.13	.08
60	Dave Parker	1.75	.90	.50
61	Jim Bibby	.25	.13	.08
62	Fred Lynn	.75	.40	.25
63	Jose Morales	.25	.13	.08
64	Aurelio Rodriguez	.25	.13	.08
65	Frank Tanana	.25	.13	.08
66	Darrell Porter	.25	.13	.08
67	Otto Velez	.25	.13	.08
68	Larry Bowa	.25	.13	.08
69	Jim Hunter	1.50	.70	.45
70	George Foster	.60	.30	.20
71	Cecil Cooper	.25	.13	.08
72	Gary Alexander	.25	.13	.08
73	Paul Thormodsgard	.25	.13	.08
74	Toby Harrah	.25	.13	.08
75	Mitchell Page	.25	.13	.08
76	Alan Ashby	.25	.13	.08
77	Jorge Orta	.25	.13	.08
78	Dave Winfield	25.00	12.50	7.50
79	Andy Messersmith	.25	.13	.08
80	Ken Singleton	.25	.13	.08
81	Will McEnaney	.25	.13	.08
82	Lou Piniella	.30	.15	.09
83	Bob Forsch	.25	.13	.08
84	Dan Driessen	.25	.13	.08
85	Dave Lemanczyk	.25	.13	.08
86	Paul Dade	.25	.13	.08
87	Bill Campbell	.25	.13	.08
88	Ron LeFlore	.25	.13	.08
89	Bill Madlock	.40	.20	.12
90	Tony Perez	.25	.13	.08
91	Freddie Patek	.25	.13	.08
92	Glenn Abbott	.25	.13	.08
93	Garry Maddox	.25	.13	.08
94	Steve Staggs	.25	.13	.08
95	Bobby Murcer	.25	.13	.08
96	Don Sutton	1.00	.50	.30
97	Al Oliver	.75	.40	.25
98	Jon Matlack	.25	.13	.08
99	Sam Mejias	.25	.13	.08
100	Pete Rose	4.50	2.25	1.25
101	Randy Jones	.25	.13	.08
102	Sixto Lezcano	.25	.13	.08
103	Jim Clancy	.25	.13	.08
104	Butch Wynegar	.25	.13	.08
105	Nolan Ryan	42.50	21.00	12.50
106	Wayne Gross	.25	.13	.08
107	Bob Watson	.25	.13	.08
108	Joe Kerrigan	.25	.13	.08
109	Keith Hernandez	3.00	1.50	.90
110	Reggie Jackson	14.50	7.25	4.25
111	Denny Doyle	.25	.13	.08
112	Sam Ewing	.25	.13	.08
113	Bert Blyleven	.75	.40	.25
114	Andre Thornton	.25	.13	.08
115	Milt May	.25	.13	.08
116	Jim Colborn	.25	.13	.08
117	Warren Cromartie	.25	.13	.08
118	Ted Sizemore	.25	.13	.08
119	Checklist 1-121	.75	.40	.25
120	Tom Seaver	6.75	3.50	2.00
121	Luis Gomez	.25	.13	.08
122	Jim Spencer	.25	.13	.08
123	Leroy Stanton	.25	.13	.08
124	Luis Tiant	.25	.13	.08
125	Mark Belanger	.25	.13	.08
126	Jackie Brown	.25	.13	.08
127	Bill Buckner	.25	.13	.08
128	Bill Robinson	.25	.13	.08
129	Rick Cerone	.25	.13	.08
130	Ron Cey	.25	.13	.08
131	Jose Cruz	.25	.13	.08
132	Len Randle	.25	.13	.08
133	Bob Grich	.25	.13	.08
134	Jeff Burroughs	.25	.13	.08
135	Gary Carter	5.00	2.50	1.50
136	Milt Wilcox	.25	.13	.08
137	Carl Yastrzemski	4.25	2.25	1.25
138	Dennis Eckersley	8.50	4.25	2.50
139	Tim Nordbrook	.25	.13	.08
140	Ken Griffey	.25	.13	.08
141	Bob Boone	.25	.13	.08
142	Dave Goltz	.25	.13	.08
143	Al Cowens	.25	.13	.08
144	Bill Atkinson	.25	.13	.08
145	Chris Chambliss	.25	.13	.08
146	Jim Slaton	.25	.13	.08
147	Bill Stein	.25	.13	.08
148	Bob Bailor	.25	.13	.08
149	J.R. Richard	.25	.13	.08
150	Ted Simmons	.40	.20	.12
151	Rick Manning	.25	.13	.08
152	Lerrin LaGrow	.25	.13	.08
153	Larry Parrish	.25	.13	.08
154	Eddie Murray	75.00	37.00	22.00
155	Phil Niekro	1.00	.50	.30
156	Bake McBride	.25	.13	.08
157	Pete Vuckovich	.25	.13	.08
158	Ivan DeJesus	.25	.13	.08
159	Rick Rhoden	.25	.13	.08
160	Joe Morgan	3.50	1.75	1.00
161	Ed Ott	.25	.13	.08
162	Don Stanhouse	.25	.13	.08
163	Jim Rice	5.00	2.50	1.50
164	Bucky Dent	.25	.13	.08
165	Jim Kern	.25	.13	.08
166	Doug Rader	.25	.13	.08
167	Steve Kemp	.25	.13	.08
168	John Mayberry	.25	.13	.08
169	Tim Foli	.25	.13	.08
170	Steve Carlton	6.00	3.00	1.75
171	Pepe Frias	.25	.13	.08
172	Pat Zachry	.25	.13	.08
173	Don Baylor	.40	.20	.12
174	Sal Bando	.25	.13	.08
175	Alvis Woods	.25	.13	.08
176	Mike Hargrove	.25	.13	.08
177	Vida Blue	.25	.13	.08
178	George Hendrick	.25	.13	.08
179	Jim Palmer	5.00	2.50	1.50
180	Andre Dawson	23.00	11.50	7.00
181	Paul Moskau	.25	.13	.08
182	Mickey Rivers	.25	.13	.08
183	Checklist 122-242	.75	.40	.25
184	Jerry Johnson	.25	.13	.08
185	Willie McCovey	1.75	.90	.50
186	Enrique Romo	.25	.13	.08
187	Butch Hobson	.25	.13	.08
188	Rusty Staub	.30	.15	.09
189	Wayne Twitchell	.25	.13	.08
190	Steve Garvey	3.50	1.75	1.00
191	Rick Waits	.25	.13	.08
192	Doug DeCinces	.25	.13	.08
193	Tom Murphy	.25	.13	.08
194	Rich Hebner	.25	.13	.08
195	Ralph Garr	.25	.13	.08
196	Bruce Sutter	.60	.30	.20
197	Tom Poquette	.25	.13	.08
198	Wayne Garrett	.25	.13	.08
199	Pedro Borbon	.25	.13	.08
200	Thurman Munson	5.00	2.50	1.50
201	Rollie Fingers	3.00	1.50	.90
202	Doug Ault	.25	.13	.08
203	Phil Garner	.25	.13	.08
204	Lou Brock	3.50	1.75	1.00
205	Ed Kranepool	.25	.13	.08
206	Bobby Bonds	.30	.15	.09
207	Expos Team	.25	.13	.08
208	Bump Wills	.25	.13	.08
209	Gary Matthews	.25	.13	.08
210	Carlton Fisk	6.75	3.50	2.00
211	Jeff Byrd	.25	.13	.08
212	Jason Thompson	.25	.13	.08
213	Larvell Blanks	.25	.13	.08
214	Sparky Lyle	.25	.13	.08
215	George Brett	25.00	12.50	7.50
216	Del Unser	.25	.13	.08
217	Manny Trillo	.25	.13	.08
218	Roy Hartsfield	.25	.13	.08
219	Carlos Lopez	.25	.13	.08
220	Dave Concepcion	.25	.13	.08
221	John Candelaria	.25	.13	.08
222	Dave Lopes	.25	.13	.08
223	Tim Blackwell	.25	.13	.08
224	Chet Lemon	.25	.13	.08
225	Mike Schmidt	17.00	8.50	5.00
226	Cesar Cedeno	.25	.13	.08
227	Mike Willis	.25	.13	.08
228	Willie Randolph	.25	.13	.08
229	Doug Bair	.25	.13	.08
230	Rod Carew	6.00	3.00	1.75
231	Mike Flanagan	.25	.13	.08
232	Chris Speier	.25	.13	.08
233	Don Aase	.25	.13	.08
234	Buddy Bell	.25	.13	.08
235	Mark Fidrych	.25	.13	.08
236	Record Breaker (Lou Brock)	3.00	1.50	.90
237	Record Breaker (Sparky Lyle)	.25	.13	.08
238	Record Breaker (Willie McCovey)	.60	.30	.20
239	Record Breaker (Brooks Robinson)	1.00	.50	.30
240	Record Breaker (Pete Rose)	3.25	1.75	1.00
241	Record Breaker (Nolan Ryan)	15.00	7.50	4.50
242	Record Breaker (Reggie Jackson)	6.25	3.25	2.00

1979 O-Pee-Chee

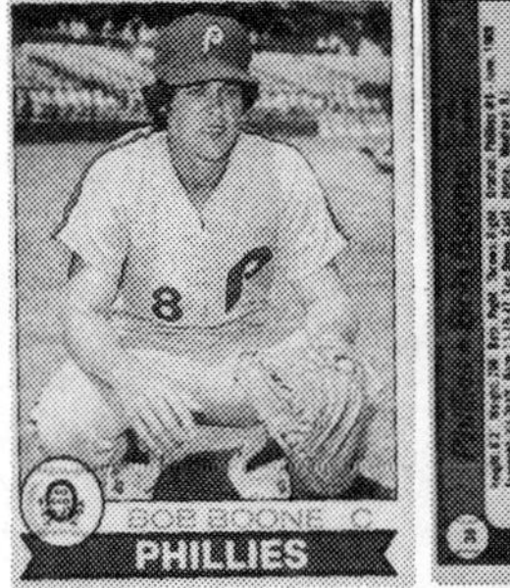

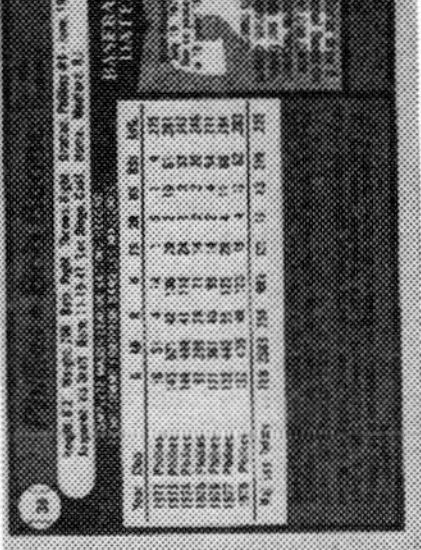

The 1979 O-Pee-Chee cards are nearly identical in design to the Topps set of the same year, but display the O-Pee-Chee logo inside the baseball in the lower left corner of the front. The number of cards in the set was increased to 374, each measuring 2-1/2" by 3-1/2".

		NR MT	EX	VG
Complete Set (374):		140.00	70.00	45.00
Common Player:		.25	.13	.08
1	Lee May	.30	.15	.09
2	Dick Drago	.25	.13	.08
3	Paul Dade	.25	.13	.08
4	Ross Grimsley	.25	.13	.08
5	Joe Morgan	3.00	1.50	.90
6	Kevin Kobel	.25	.13	.08
7	Terry Forster	.25	.13	.08
8	Paul Molitor	34.00	17.00	10.00
9	Steve Carlton	4.25	2.25	1.25
10	Dave Goltz	.25	.13	.08
11	Dave Winfield	17.00	8.50	5.00
12	Dave Rozema	.25	.13	.08
13	Ed Figueroa	.25	.13	.08
14	Alan Ashby	.25	.13	.08
15	Dale Murphy	5.50	2.75	1.75
16	Dennis Eckersley	6.00	3.00	1.75
17	Ron Blomberg	.25	.13	.08
18	Wayne Twitchell	.25	.13	.08
19	Al Hrabosky	.25	.13	.08
20	Fred Norman	.25	.13	.08
21	Steve Garvey	1.75	.90	.50
22	Willie Stargell	1.75	.90	.50
23	John Hale	.25	.13	.08
24	Mickey Rivers	.25	.13	.08
25	Jack Brohamer	.25	.13	.08
26	Tom Underwood	.25	.13	.08
27	Mark Belanger	.25	.13	.08
28	Elliott Maddox	.25	.13	.08
29	John Candelaria	.25	.13	.08
30	Shane Rawley	.25	.13	.08
31	Steve Yeager	.25	.13	.08
32	Warren Cromartie	.25	.13	.08
33	Jason Thompson	.25	.13	.08
34	Roger Erickson	.25	.13	.08
35	Gary Matthews	.25	.13	.08
36	Pete Falcone	.25	.13	.08
37	Dick Tidrow	.25	.13	.08
38	Bob Boone	.25	.13	.08
39	Jim Bibby	.25	.13	.08
40	Len Barker	.25	.13	.08
41	Robin Yount	12.75	6.50	3.75
42	Sam Mejias	.25	.13	.08
43	Ray Burris	.25	.13	.08
44	Tom Seaver	3.25	1.75	1.00
45	Roy Howell	.25	.13	.08
46	Jim Todd	.25	.13	.08
47	Frank Duffy	.25	.13	.08
48	Joel Youngblood	.25	.13	.08
49	Vida Blue	.25	.13	.08
50	Cliff Johnson	.25	.13	.08
51	Nolan Ryan	32.00	16.00	9.50
52	Ozzie Smith	85.00	42.00	25.00
53	Jim Sundberg	.25	.13	.08
54	Mike Paxton	.25	.13	.08
55	Lou Whitaker	10.25	5.25	3.00
56	Dan Schatzeder	.25	.13	.08
57	Rick Burleson	.25	.13	.08
58	Doug Bair	.25	.13	.08
59	Ted Martinez	.25	.13	.08
60	Bob Watson	.25	.13	.08
61	Jim Clancy	.25	.13	.08
62	Rowland Office	.25	.13	.08
63	Bobby Murcer	.25	.13	.08
64	Don Gullett	.25	.13	.08
65	Tom Paciorek	.25	.13	.08
66	Rick Rhoden	.25	.13	.08
67	Duane Kuiper	.25	.13	.08
68	Bruce Boisclair	.25	.13	.08
69	Manny Sarmiento	.25	.13	.08
70	Wayne Cage	.25	.13	.08
71	John Hiller	.25	.13	.08
72	Rick Cerone	.25	.13	.08
73	Dwight Evans	.40	.20	.12
74	Buddy Solomon	.25	.13	.08
75	Roy White	.25	.13	.08
76	Mike Flanagan	.25	.13	.08
77	Tom Johnson	.25	.13	.08
78	Glenn Burke	.25	.13	.08
79	Frank Taveras	.25	.13	.08
80	Don Sutton	1.75	.90	.50
81	Leon Roberts	.25	.13	.08
82	George Hendrick	.25	.13	.08
83	Aurelio Rodriguez	.25	.13	.08
84	Ron Reed	.25	.13	.08
85	Alvis Woods	.25	.13	.08
86	Jim Beattie	.25	.13	.08
87	Larry Hisle	.25	.13	.08
88	Mike Garman	.25	.13	.08
89	Tim Johnson	.25	.13	.08
90	Paul Splittorff	.25	.13	.08
91	Darrel Chaney	.25	.13	.08
92	Mike Torrez	.25	.13	.08
93	Eric Soderholm	.25	.13	.08
94	Ron Cey	.25	.13	.08
95	Randy Jones	.25	.13	.08
96	Bill Madlock	.30	.15	.09
97	Steve Kemp	.25	.13	.08
98	Bob Apodaca	.25	.13	.08
99	Johnny Grubb	.25	.13	.08
100	Larry Milbourne	.25	.13	.08
101	Johnny Bench	3.00	1.50	.90
102	Dave Lemanczyk	.25	.13	.08
103	Reggie Cleveland	.25	.13	.08
104	Larry Bowa	.25	.13	.08
105	Denny Martinez	3.00	1.50	.90
106	Bill Travers	.25	.13	.08
107	Willie McCovey	1.25	.60	.40
108	Wilbur Wood	.25	.13	.08
109	Dennis Leonard	.25	.13	.08
110	Roy Smalley	.25	.13	.08
111	Cesar Geronimo	.25	.13	.08
112	Jesse Jefferson	.25	.13	.08
113	Dave Revering	.25	.13	.08
114	Rich Gossage	.60	.30	.20
115	Steve Stone	.25	.13	.08
116	Doug Flynn	.25	.13	.08
117	Bob Forsch	.25	.13	.08
118	Paul Mitchell	.25	.13	.08
119	Toby Harrah	.25	.13	.08
120	Steve Rogers	.25	.13	.08
121	Checklist 1-125	.25	.13	.08
122	Balor Moore	.25	.13	.08
123	Rick Reuschel	.25	.13	.08
124	Jeff Burroughs	.25	.13	.08
125	Willie Randolph	.25	.13	.08
126	Bob Stinson	.25	.13	.08
127	Rick Wise	.25	.13	.08
128	Luis Gomez	.25	.13	.08
129	Tommy John	.25	.13	.08
130	Richie Zisk	.25	.13	.08
131	Mario Guerrero	.25	.13	.08
132	Oscar Gamble	.25	.13	.08
133	Don Money	.25	.13	.08
134	Joe Rudi	.25	.13	.08
135	Woodie Fryman	.25	.13	.08
136	Butch Hobson	.25	.13	.08
137	Jim Colborn	.25	.13	.08
138	Tom Grieve	.25	.13	.08
139	Andy Messersmith	.25	.13	.08
140	Andre Thornton	.25	.13	.08
141	Kevin Kravec	.25	.13	.08
142	Bobby Bonds	.25	.13	.08
143	Jose Cruz	.25	.13	.08
144	Dave Lopes	.25	.13	.08
145	Jerry Garvin	.25	.13	.08
146	Pepe Frias	.25	.13	.08
147	Mitchell Page	.25	.13	.08
148	Ted Sizemore	.25	.13	.08
149	Rich Gale	.25	.13	.08
150	Steve Ontiveros	.25	.13	.08
151	Rod Carew	4.25	2.25	1.25
152	Lary Sorensen	.25	.13	.08
153	Willie Montanez	.25	.13	.08
154	Floyd Bannister	.25	.13	.08
155	Bert Blyleven	.30	.15	.09
156	Ralph Garr	.25	.13	.08
157	Thurman Munson	3.50	1.75	1.00
158	Bob Robertson	.25	.13	.08
159	Jon Matlack	.25	.13	.08
160	Carl Yastrzemski	3.75	2.00	1.25
161	Gaylord Perry	1.25	.60	.40
162	Mike Tyson	.25	.13	.08
163	Cecil Cooper	.30	.15	.09
164	Pedro Borbon	.25	.13	.08
165	Art Howe	.25	.13	.08
166	Joe Coleman	.25	.13	.08
167	George Brett	21.00	10.50	6.25
168	Gary Alexander	.25	.13	.08
169	Chet Lemon	.25	.13	.08
170	Craig Swan	.25	.13	.08
171	Chris Chambliss	.25	.13	.08
172	John Montague	.25	.13	.08
173	Ron Jackson	.25	.13	.08
174	Jim Palmer	4.00	2.00	1.25
175	Willie Upshaw	.75	.40	.25
176	Tug McGraw	.25	.13	.08
177	Bill Buckner	.25	.13	.08
178	Doug Rau	.25	.13	.08
179	Andre Dawson	13.50	6.75	4.00
180	Jim Wright	.25	.13	.08
181	Garry Templeton	.25	.13	.08
182	Bill Bonham	.25	.13	.08
183	Lee Mazzilli	.25	.13	.08
184	Alan Trammell	15.00	7.50	4.50
185	Amos Otis	.25	.13	.08
186	Tom Dixon	.25	.13	.08
187	Mike Cubbage	.25	.13	.08
188	Sparky Lyle	.25	.13	.08
189	Juan Bernhardt	.25	.13	.08
190	Bump Wills	.25	.13	.08
191	Dave Kingman	.30	.15	.09
192	Lamar Johnson	.25	.13	.08
193	Lance Rautzhan	.25	.13	.08
194	Ed Herrmann	.25	.13	.08
195	Bill Campbell	.25	.13	.08
196	Gorman Thomas	.25	.13	.08
197	Paul Moskau	.25	.13	.08
198	Dale Murray	.25	.13	.08
199	John Mayberry	.25	.13	.08
200	Phil Garner	.25	.13	.08
201	Dan Ford	.25	.13	.08
202	Gary Thomasson	.25	.13	.08
203	Rollie Fingers	2.00	1.00	.60
204	Al Oliver	.25	.13	.08
205	Doug Ault	.25	.13	.08
206	Scott McGregor	.25	.13	.08
207	Dave Cash	.25	.13	.08
208	Bill Plummer	.25	.13	.08
209	Ivan DeJesus	.25	.13	.08
210	Jim Rice	3.50	1.75	1.00
211	Ray Knight	.25	.13	.08
212	Paul Hartzell	.25	.13	.08
213	Tim Foli	.25	.13	.08
214	Butch Wynegar	.25	.13	.08
215	Darrell Evans	.25	.13	.08
216	Ken Griffey	.25	.13	.08
217	Doug DeCinces	.25	.13	.08
218	Ruppert Jones	.25	.13	.08
219	Bob Montgomery	.25	.13	.08
220	Rick Manning	.25	.13	.08
221	Chris Speier	.25	.13	.08
222	Bobby Valentine	.25	.13	.08
223	Dave Parker	1.75	.90	.50
224	Larry Biittner	.25	.13	.08
225	Ken Clay	.25	.13	.08
226	Gene Tenace	.25	.13	.08
227	Frank White	.25	.13	.08
228	Rusty Staub	.25	.13	.08
229	Lee Lacy	.25	.13	.08
230	Doyle Alexander	.25	.13	.08
231	Bruce Bochte	.25	.13	.08
232	Steve Henderson	.25	.13	.08
233	Jim Lonborg	.25	.13	.08
234	Dave Concepcion	.25	.13	.08
235	Jerry Morales	.25	.13	.08
236	Len Randle	.25	.13	.08
237	Bill Lee	.25	.13	.08
238	Bruce Sutter	.60	.30	.20
239	Jim Essian	.25	.13	.08
240	Graig Nettles	.40	.20	.12
241	Otto Velez	.25	.13	.08
242	Checklist 126-250	.25	.13	.08
243	Reggie Smith	.25	.13	.08
244	Stan Bahnsen	.25	.13	.08
245	Garry Maddox	.25	.13	.08
246	Joaquin Andujar	.25	.13	.08
247	Dan Driessen	.25	.13	.08
248	Bob Grich	.25	.13	.08
249	Fred Lynn	.60	.30	.20
250	Skip Lockwood	.25	.13	.08
251	Craig Reynolds	.25	.13	.08
252	Willie Horton	.25	.13	.08
253	Rick Waits	.25	.13	.08
254	Bucky Dent	.25	.13	.08
255	Bob Knepper	.25	.13	.08
256	Miguel Dilone	.25	.13	.08
257	Bob Owchinko	.25	.13	.08
258	Al Cowens	.25	.13	.08
259	Bob Bailor	.25	.13	.08
260	Larry Christenson	.25	.13	.08
261	Tony Perez	.50	.25	.15
262	Blue Jays Team	.25	.13	.08
263	Glenn Abbott	.25	.13	.08
264	Ron Guidry	.75	.40	.25
265	Ed Kranepool	.25	.13	.08
266	Charlie Hough	.25	.13	.08
267	Ted Simmons	.30	.15	.09
268	Jack Clark	3.00	1.50	.90
269	Enos Cabell	.25	.13	.08
270	Gary Carter	3.75	2.00	1.25
271	Sam Ewing	.25	.13	.08
272	Tom Burgmeier	.25	.13	.08
273	Freddie Patek	.25	.13	.08
274	Frank Tanana	.25	.13	.08
275	Leroy Stanton	.25	.13	.08
276	Ken Forsch	.25	.13	.08
277	Ellis Valentine	.25	.13	.08
278	Greg Luzinski	.30	.15	.09
279	Rick Bosetti	.25	.13	.08
280	John Stearns	.25	.13	.08
281	Enrique Romo	.25	.13	.08
282	Bob Bailey	.25	.13	.08
283	Sal Bando	.25	.13	.08
284	Matt Keough	.25	.13	.08
285	Biff Pocoroba	.25	.13	.08
286	Mike Lum	.25	.13	.08
287	Jay Johnstone	.25	.13	.08
288	John Montefusco	.25	.13	.08
289	Ed Ott	.25	.13	.08
290	Dusty Baker	.25	.13	.08
291	Rico Carty	.25	.13	.08
292	Nino Espinosa	.25	.13	.08
293	Rich Hebner	.25	.13	.08
294	Cesar Cedeno	.25	.13	.08
295	Darrell Porter	.25	.13	.08
296	Rod Gilbreath	.25	.13	.08
297	Jim Kern	.25	.13	.08
298	Claudell Washington	.25	.13	.08
299	Luis Tiant	.30	.15	.09
300	Mike Parrott	.25	.13	.08
301	Pete Broberg	.25	.13	.08
302	Greg Gross	.25	.13	.08
303	Darold Knowles	.25	.13	.08
304	Paul Blair	.25	.13	.08
305	Julio Cruz	.25	.13	.08
306	Hal McRae	.25	.13	.08
307	Ken Reitz	.25	.13	.08
308	Tom Murphy	.25	.13	.08
309	Terry Whitfield	.25	.13	.08
310	J.R. Richard	.25	.13	.08
311	Mike Hargrove	.25	.13	.08
312	Rick Dempsey	.25	.13	.08
313	Phil Niekro	1.75	.90	.50
314	Bob Stanley	.25	.13	.08
315	Jim Spencer	.25	.13	.08
316	George Foster	.50	.25	.15
317	Dave LaRoche	.25	.13	.08
318	Rudy May	.25	.13	.08
319	Jeff Newman	.25	.13	.08
320	Rick Monday	.25	.13	.08
321	Omar Moreno	.25	.13	.08
322	Dave McKay	.25	.13	.08
323	Mike Schmidt	8.50	4.25	2.50
324	Ken Singleton	.25	.13	.08
325	Jerry Remy	.25	.13	.08
326	Bert Campaneris	.25	.13	.08
327	Pat Zachry	.25	.13	.08
328	Larry Herndon	.25	.13	.08
329	Mark Fidrych	.25	.13	.08
330	Del Unser	.25	.13	.08
331	Gene Garber	.25	.13	.08
332	Bake McBride	.25	.13	.08
333	Jorge Orta	.25	.13	.08
334	Don Kirkwood	.25	.13	.08
335	Don Baylor	.40	.20	.12
336	Bill Robinson	.25	.13	.08
337	Manny Trillo	.25	.13	.08
338	Eddie Murray	25.00	12.50	7.50
339	Tom Hausman	.25	.13	.08
340	George Scott	.25	.13	.08
341	Rick Sweet	.25	.13	.08
342	Lou Piniella	.25	.13	.08

343	Pete Rose	5.00	2.50	1.50
344	Stan Papi	.25	.13	.08
345	Jerry Koosman	.25	.13	.08
346	Hosken Powell	.25	.13	.08
347	George Medich	.25	.13	.08
348	Ron LeFlore	.25	.13	.08
349	Expos Team	.25	.13	.08
350	Lou Brock	3.00	1.50	.90
351	Bill North	.25	.13	.08
352	Jim Hunter	.60	.30	.20
353	Checklist 251-374	.25	.13	.08
354	Ed Halicki	.25	.13	.08
355	Tom Hutton	.25	.13	.08
356	Mike Caldwell	.25	.13	.08
357	Larry Parrish	.25	.13	.08
358	Geoff Zahn	.25	.13	.08
359	Derrel Thomas	.25	.13	.08
360	Carlton Fisk	5.00	2.50	1.50
361	John Henry Johnson	.25	.13	.08
362	Dave Chalk	.25	.13	.08
363	Dan Meyer	.25	.13	.08
364	Sixto Lezcano	.25	.13	.08
365	Rennie Stennett	.25	.13	.08
366	Mike Willis	.25	.13	.08
367	Buddy Bell	.25	.13	.08
368	Mickey Stanley	.25	.13	.08
369	Dave Rader	.25	.13	.08
370	Burt Hooton	.25	.13	.08
371	Keith Hernandez	1.50	.70	.45
372	Bill Stein	.25	.13	.08
373	Hal Dues	.25	.13	.08
374	Reggie Jackson	3.25	1.75	1.00

1980 O-Pee-Chee

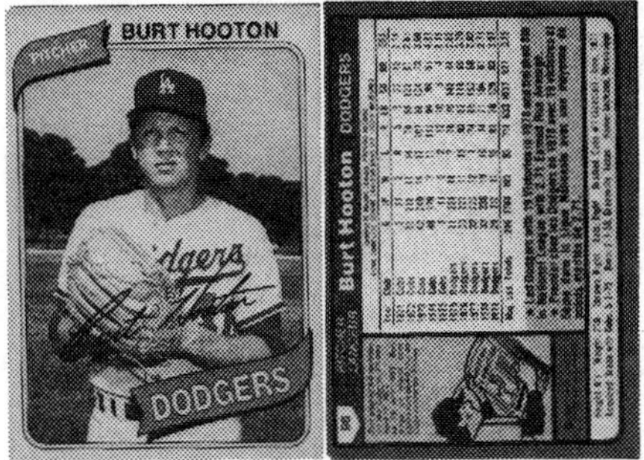

The 1980 Canadian-issued O-Pee-Chee set was again complete at 374 cards, which measure 2-1/2" by 3-1/2" and share the same design as the 1980 Topps set. The O-Pee-Chee cards are printed on a white stock, rather than the traditional gray stock used by Topps, and the backs of the Canadian-issued cards are written in both French and English. Some of the cards include an extra line on the front indicating a new team designation.

		NR MT	EX	VG
Complete Set (374):		110.00	55.00	33.00
Common Player:		.15	.08	.05
1	Craig Swan	.15	.08	.05
2	Denny Martinez	.15	.08	.05
3	Dave Cash	.15	.08	.05
4	Bruce Sutter	.50	.25	.15
5	Ron Jackson	.15	.08	.05
6	Balor Moore	.15	.08	.05
7	Dan Ford	.15	.08	.05
8	Pat Putnam	.15	.08	.05
9	Derrel Thomas	.15	.08	.05
10	Jim Slaton	.15	.08	.05
11	Lee Mazzilli	.15	.08	.05
12	Del Unser	.15	.08	.05
13	Mark Wagner	.15	.08	.05
14	Vida Blue	.20	.10	.06
15	Jay Johnstone	.15	.08	.05
16	Julio Cruz	.15	.08	.05
17	Tony Scott	.15	.08	.05
18	Jeff Newman	.15	.08	.05
19	Luis Tiant	.25	.13	.08
20	Carlton Fisk	4.50	2.25	1.25
21	Dave Palmer	.30	.15	.09
22	Bombo Rivera	.15	.08	.05
23	Bill Fahey	.15	.08	.05
24	Frank White	.20	.10	.06
25	Rico Carty	.15	.08	.05
26	Bill Bonham	.15	.08	.05
27	Rick Miller	.15	.08	.05
28	J.R. Richard	.15	.08	.05
29	Joe Ferguson	.15	.08	.05
30	Bill Madlock	.30	.15	.09
31	Pete Vuckovich	.15	.08	.05
32	Doug Flynn	.15	.08	.05
33	Bucky Dent	.20	.10	.06
34	Mike Ivie	.15	.08	.05
35	Bob Stanley	.15	.08	.05
36	Al Bumbry	.15	.08	.05
37	Gary Carter	2.75	1.50	.80
38	John Milner	.15	.08	.05
39	Sid Monge	.15	.08	.05
40	Bill Russell	.15	.08	.05
41	John Stearns	.15	.08	.05
42	Dave Stieb	2.50	1.25	.70
43	Ruppert Jones	.15	.08	.05
44	Bob Owchinko	.15	.08	.05
45	Ron LeFlore	.20	.10	.06
46	Ted Sizemore	.15	.08	.05
47	Ted Simmons	.30	.15	.09
48	Pepe Frias	.15	.08	.05
49	Ken Landreaux	.15	.08	.05
50	Manny Trillo	.15	.08	.05
51	Rick Dempsey	.15	.08	.05
52	Cecil Cooper	.30	.15	.09
53	Bill Lee	.15	.08	.05
54	Victor Cruz	.15	.08	.05
55	Johnny Bench	4.25	2.25	1.25
56	Rich Dauer	.15	.08	.05
57	Frank Tanana	.15	.08	.05
58	Francisco Barrios	.15	.08	.05
59	Bob Horner	.90	.45	.25
60	Fred Lynn	.30	.15	.09
61	Bob Knepper	.15	.08	.05
62	Sparky Lyle	.15	.08	.05
63	Larry Cox	.15	.08	.05
64	Dock Ellis	.15	.08	.05
65	Phil Garner	.15	.08	.05
66	Greg Luzinski	.30	.15	.09
67	Checklist 1-125	.40	.20	.12
68	Dave Lemanczyk	.15	.08	.05
69	Tony Perez	.50	.25	.15
70	Gary Thomasson	.15	.08	.05
71	Craig Reynolds	.15	.08	.05
72	Amos Otis	.15	.08	.05
73	Biff Pocoroba	.15	.08	.05
74	Matt Keough	.15	.08	.05
75	Bill Buckner	.25	.13	.08
76	John Castino	.15	.08	.05
77	Rich Gossage	.50	.25	.15
78	Gary Alexander	.15	.08	.05
79	Phil Huffman	.15	.08	.05
80	Bruce Bochte	.15	.08	.05
81	Darrell Evans	.25	.13	.08
82	Terry Puhl	.15	.08	.05
83	Jason Thompson	.15	.08	.05
84	Lary Sorenson	.15	.08	.05
85	Jerry Remy	.15	.08	.05
86	Tony Brizzolara	.15	.08	.05
87	Willie Wilson	.25	.13	.08
88	Eddie Murray	12.75	6.50	3.75
89	Larry Christenson	.15	.08	.05
90	Bob Randall	.15	.08	.05
91	Greg Pryor	.15	.08	.05
92	Glenn Abbott	.15	.08	.05
93	Jack Clark	1.00	.50	.30
94	Rick Waits	.15	.08	.05
95	Luis Gomez	.15	.08	.05
96	Burt Hooton	.15	.08	.05
97	John Henry Johnson	.15	.08	.05
98	Ray Knight	.15	.08	.05
99	Rick Reuschel	.20	.10	.06
100	Champ Summers	.15	.08	.05
101	Ron Davis	.20	.10	.06
102	Warren Cromartie	.15	.08	.05
103	Ken Reitz	.15	.08	.05
104	Hal McRae	.20	.10	.06
105	Alan Ashby	.15	.08	.05
106	Kevin Kobel	.15	.08	.05
107	Buddy Bell	.25	.13	.08
108	Dave Goltz	.20	.10	.06
109	John Montefusco	.15	.08	.05
110	Lance Parrish	1.25	.60	.40
111	Mike LaCoss	.15	.08	.05
112	Jim Rice	2.00	1.00	.60
113	Steve Carlton	4.25	2.25	1.25
114	Sixto Lezcano	.15	.08	.05
115	Ed Halicki	.15	.08	.05
116	Jose Morales	.15	.08	.05
117	Dave Concepcion	.25	.13	.08
118	Joe Cannon	.15	.08	.05
119	Willie Montanez	.15	.08	.05
120	Lou Piniella	.25	.13	.08
121	Bill Stein	.15	.08	.05
122	Dave Winfield	12.00	6.00	3.50
123	Alan Trammell	6.25	3.25	2.00
124	Andre Dawson	9.25	4.75	2.75
125	Marc Hill	.15	.08	.05
126	Don Aase	.15	.08	.05
127	Dave Kingman	.40	.20	.12
128	Checklist 126-250	.40	.20	.12
129	Dennis Lamp	.15	.08	.05
130	Phil Niekro	.75	.40	.25
131	Tim Foli	.15	.08	.05
132	Jim Clancy	.15	.08	.05
133	Bill Atkinson	.15	.08	.05
134	Paul Dade	.15	.08	.05
135	Dusty Baker	.20	.10	.06
136	Al Oliver	.30	.15	.09
137	Dave Chalk	.15	.08	.05
138	Bill Robinson	.15	.08	.05
139	Robin Yount	11.00	5.50	3.25
140	Dan Schatzeder	.15	.08	.05
141	Mike Schmidt	4.25	2.25	1.25
142	Ralph Garr	.15	.08	.05
143	Dale Murphy	3.50	1.75	1.00
144	Jerry Koosman	.20	.10	.06
145	Tom Veryzer	.15	.08	.05
146	Rick Bosetti	.15	.08	.05
147	Jim Spencer	.15	.08	.05
148	Gaylord Perry	.75	.40	.25
149	Paul Blair	.15	.08	.05
150	Don Baylor	.30	.15	.09
151	Dave Rozema	.15	.08	.05
152	Steve Garvey	1.75	.90	.50
153	Elias Sosa	.15	.08	.05
154	Larry Gura	.15	.08	.05
155	Tim Johnson	.15	.08	.05
156	Steve Henderson	.15	.08	.05
157	Ron Guidry	.75	.40	.25
158	Mike Edwards	.15	.08	.05
159	Butch Wynegar	.15	.08	.05
160	Randy Jones	.15	.08	.05
161	Denny Walling	.15	.08	.05
162	Mike Hargrove	.15	.08	.05
163	Dave Parker	.75	.40	.25
164	Roger Metzger	.15	.08	.05
165	Johnny Grubb	.15	.08	.05
166	Steve Kemp	.15	.08	.05
167	Bob Lacey	.15	.08	.05
168	Chris Speier	.15	.08	.05
169	Dennis Eckersley	2.75	1.50	.80
170	Keith Hernandez	1.25	.60	.40
171	Claudell Washington	.15	.08	.05
172	Tom Underwood	.15	.08	.05
173	Dan Driessen	.15	.08	.05
174	Al Cowens	.15	.08	.05
175	Rich Hebner	.15	.08	.05
176	Willie McCovey	1.25	.60	.40
177	Carney Lansford	2.00	1.00	.60
178	Ken Singleton	.20	.10	.06
179	Jim Essian	.15	.08	.05
180	Mike Vail	.15	.08	.05
181	Randy Lerch	.15	.08	.05
182	Larry Parrish	.20	.10	.06
183	Checklist 251-374	.40	.20	.12
184	George Hendrick	.15	.08	.05
185	Bob Davis	.15	.08	.05
186	Gary Matthews	.15	.08	.05
187	Lou Whitaker	5.00	2.50	1.50
188	Darrell Porter	.15	.08	.05
189	Wayne Gross	.15	.08	.05
190	Bobby Murcer	.20	.10	.06
191	Willie Aikens	.15	.08	.05
192	Jim Kern	.15	.08	.05
193	Cesar Cedeno	.20	.10	.06
194	Joel Youngblood	.15	.08	.05
195	Ross Grimsley	.15	.08	.05
196	Jerry Mumphrey	.20	.10	.06
197	Kevin Bell	.15	.08	.05
198	Garry Maddox	.15	.08	.05
199	Dave Freisleben	.15	.08	.05
200	Ed Ott	.15	.08	.05
201	Enos Cabell	.15	.08	.05
202	Pete LaCock	.15	.08	.05
203	Fergie Jenkins	.40	.20	.12
204	Milt Wilcox	.15	.08	.05
205	Ozzie Smith	21.00	10.50	6.25
206	Ellis Valentine	.15	.08	.05
207	Dan Meyer	.15	.08	.05
208	Barry Foote	.15	.08	.05
209	George Foster	.40	.20	.12
210	Dwight Evans	.50	.25	.15
211	Paul Molitor	15.00	7.50	4.50
212	Tony Solaita	.15	.08	.05
213	Bill North	.15	.08	.05
214	Paul Splittorff	.15	.08	.05
215	Bobby Bonds	.25	.13	.08
216	Butch Hobson	.15	.08	.05
217	Mark Belanger	.15	.08	.05
218	Grant Jackson	.15	.08	.05
219	Tom Hutton	.15	.08	.05
220	Pat Zachry	.15	.08	.05
221	Duane Kuiper	.15	.08	.05
222	Larry Hisle	.15	.08	.05
223	Mike Krukow	.15	.08	.05
224	Johnnie LeMaster	.15	.08	.05
225	Billy Almon	.15	.08	.05
226	Joe Niekro	.15	.08	.05
227	Dave Revering	.15	.08	.05
228	Don Sutton	.75	.40	.25
229	John Hiller	.15	.08	.05
230	Alvis Woods	.15	.08	.05
231	Mark Fidrych	.15	.08	.05
232	Duffy Dyer	.15	.08	.05
233	Nino Espinosa	.15	.08	.05
234	Doug Bair	.15	.08	.05
235	George Brett	15.00	7.50	4.50
236	Mike Torrez	.15	.08	.05
237	Frank Taveras	.15	.08	.05
238	Bert Blyleven	.30	.15	.09
239	Willie Randolph	.15	.08	.05
240	Mike Sadek	.15	.08	.05
241	Jerry Royster	.15	.08	.05
242	John Denny	.15	.08	.05
243	Rick Monday	.15	.08	.05
244	Jesse Jefferson	.15	.08	.05
245	Aurelio Rodriguez	.15	.08	.05
246	Bob Boone	.15	.08	.05
247	Cesar Geronimo	.15	.08	.05
248	Bob Shirley	.15	.08	.05
249	Expos Team	.20	.10	.06
250	Bob Watson	.15	.08	.05
251	Mickey Rivers	.15	.08	.05
252	Mke Tyson	.15	.08	.05
253	Wayne Nordhagen	.15	.08	.05
254	Roy Howell	.15	.08	.05
255	Lee May	.15	.08	.05
256	Jerry Martin	.15	.08	.05
257	Bake McBride	.15	.08	.05
258	Silvio Martinez	.15	.08	.05
259	Jim Mason	.15	.08	.05
260	Tom Seaver	4.25	2.25	1.25
261	Rick Wortham	.15	.08	.05
262	Mike Cubbage	.15	.08	.05
263	Gene Garber	.15	.08	.05
264	Bert Campaneris	.15	.08	.05
265	Tom Buskey	.15	.08	.05
266	Leon Roberts	.15	.08	.05
267	Ron Cey	.20	.10	.06
268	Steve Ontiveros	.15	.08	.05
269	Mike Caldwell	.15	.08	.05
270	Nelson Norman	.15	.08	.05
271	Steve Rogers	.15	.08	.05
272	Jim Morrison	.15	.08	.05
273	Clint Hurdle	.15	.08	.05
274	Dale Murray	.15	.08	.05
275	Jim Barr	.15	.08	.05
276	Jim Sundberg	.15	.08	.05
277	Willie Horton	.15	.08	.05
278	Andre Thornton	.20	.10	.06
279	Bob Forsch	.15	.08	.05
280	Joe Strain	.15	.08	.05

281	Rudy May	.15	.08	.05
282	Pete Rose	4.25	2.25	1.25
283	Jeff Burroughs	.15	.08	.05
284	Rick Langford	.15	.08	.05
285	Ken Griffey	.20	.10	.06
286	Bill Nahorodny	.15	.08	.05
287	Art Howe	.15	.08	.05
288	Ed Figueroa	.15	.08	.05
289	Joe Rudi	.15	.08	.05
290	Alfredo Griffin	.15	.08	.05
291	Dave Lopes	.15	.08	.05
292	Rick Manning	.15	.08	.05
293	Dennis Leonard	.15	.08	.05
294	Bud Harrelson	.15	.08	.05
295	Skip Lockwood	.15	.08	.05
296	Roy Smalley	.15	.08	.05
297	Kent Tekulve	.15	.08	.05
298	Scot Thompson	.15	.08	.05
299	Ken Kravec	.15	.08	.05
300	Blue Jays Team	.20	.10	.06
301	Scott Sanderson	.15	.08	.05
302	Charlie Moore	.15	.08	.05
303	Nolan Ryan	21.00	10.50	6.25
304	Bob Bailor	.15	.08	.05
305	Bob Stinson	.15	.08	.05
306	Al Hrabosky	.15	.08	.05
307	Mitchell Page	.15	.08	.05
308	Garry Templeton	.15	.08	.05
309	Chet Lemon	.15	.08	.05
310	Jim Palmer	3.25	1.75	1.00
311	Rick Cerone	.15	.08	.05
312	Jon Matlack	.15	.08	.05
313	Don Money	.15	.08	.05
314	Reggie Jackson	8.50	4.25	2.50
315	Brian Downing	.15	.08	.05
316	Woodie Fryman	.15	.08	.05
317	Alan Bannister	.15	.08	.05
318	Ron Reed	.15	.08	.05
319	Willie Stargell	1.25	.60	.40
320	Jerry Garvin	.15	.08	.05
321	Cliff Johnson	.15	.08	.05
322	Doug DeCinces	.20	.10	.06
323	Gene Richards	.15	.08	.05
324	Joaquin Andujar	.15	.08	.05
325	Richie Zisk	.15	.08	.05
326	Bob Grich	.20	.10	.06
327	Gorman Thomas	.15	.08	.05
328	Chris Chambliss	.15	.08	.05
329	Blue Jays Future Stars (Butch Edge, Pat Kelly, Ted Wilborn)	.15	.08	.05
330	Larry Bowa	.20	.10	.06
331	Barry Bonnell	.15	.08	.05
332	John Candelaria	.15	.08	.05
333	Toby Harrah	.15	.08	.05
334	Larry Biittner	.15	.08	.05
335	Mike Flanagan	.15	.08	.05
336	Ed Kranepool	.15	.08	.05
337	Ken Forsch	.15	.08	.05
338	John Mayberry	.15	.08	.05
339	Rick Burleson	.15	.08	.05
340	Milt May	.15	.08	.05
341	Roy White	.15	.08	.05
342	Joe Morgan	3.00	1.50	.90
343	Rollie Fingers	.40	.20	.12
344	Mario Mendoza	.15	.08	.05
345	Stan Bahnsen	.15	.08	.05
346	Tug McGraw	.20	.10	.06
347	Rusty Staub	.25	.13	.08
348	Tommy John	.50	.25	.15
349	Ivan DeJesus	.15	.08	.05
350	Reggie Smith	.20	.10	.06
351	Expos Future Stars (Tony Bernazard, Randy Miller, John Tamargo)	.25	.13	.08
352	Floyd Bannister	.15	.08	.05
353	Rod Carew	2.00	1.00	.60
354	Otto Velez	.15	.08	.05
355	Gene Tenace	.15	.08	.05
356	Freddie Patek	.15	.08	.05
357	Elliott Maddox	.15	.08	.05
358	Pat Underwood	.15	.08	.05
359	Graig Nettles	.30	.15	.09
360	Rodney Scott	.15	.08	.05
361	Terry Whitfield	.15	.08	.05
362	Fred Norman	.15	.08	.05
363	Sal Bando	.15	.08	.05
364	Greg Gross	.60	.30	.20
365	Carl Yastrzemski	1.00	.50	.30
366	Paul Hartzell	.15	.08	.05
367	Jose Cruz	.20	.10	.06
368	Shane Rawley	.15	.08	.05
369	Jerry White	.15	.08	.05
370	Rick Wise	.15	.08	.05
371	Steve Yeager	.15	.08	.05
372	Omar Moreno	.15	.08	.05
373	Bump Wills	.15	.08	.05
374	Craig Kusick	.15	.08	.05

Values for recent cards and sets are listed in Mint (MT), Near Mint (NM), reflecting the fact that many cards from recent years have been preserved in top condition. Recent cards and sets in less than Excellent condition have little collector interest.

1981 O-Pee-Chee

The Canadian version of the 1981 Topps set consists of 374 cards. This O-Pee-Chee set features many cards which note a player team change. These notations could be accomplished as the O-Pee-Chee cards were printed after the Topps. The

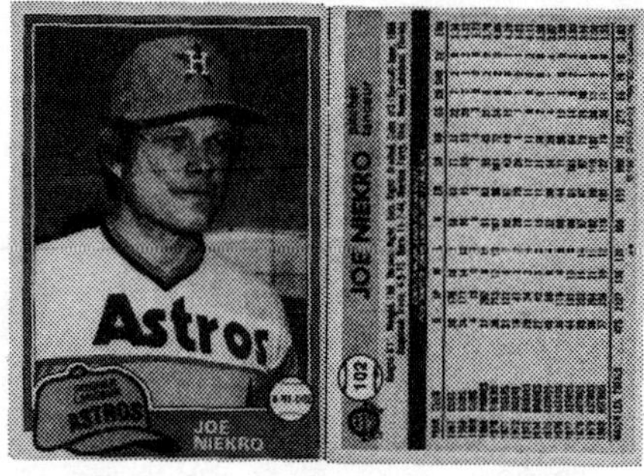

cards measure 2-1/2" by 3-1/2" and have texts that are written in both English and French. The cards were printed on both white and grey stock. Cards with grey stock are valued three times greater than those with white stock.

		MT	NR MT	EX
	Complete Set (374):	63.00	45.00	22.50
	Common Player:	.12	.09	.05
1	Frank Pastore	.12	.09	.05
2	Phil Huffman	.12	.09	.05
3	Len Barker	.12	.09	.05
4	Robin Yount	3.75	2.75	1.50
5	Dave Stieb	.40	.30	.15
6	Gary Carter	1.00	.70	.40
7	Butch Hobson	.12	.09	.05
8	Lance Parrish	.60	.45	.25
9	Bruce Sutter	.25	.20	.10
10	Mike Flanagan	.12	.09	.05
11	Paul Mirabella	.12	.09	.05
12	Craig Reynolds	.12	.09	.05
13	Joe Charboneau	.12	.09	.05
14	Dan Driessen	.12	.09	.05
15	Larry Parrish	.12	.09	.05
16	Ron Davis	.12	.09	.05
17	Cliff Johnson	.12	.09	.05
18	Bruce Bochte	.12	.09	.05
19	Jim Clancy	.12	.09	.05
20	Bill Russell	.12	.09	.05
21	Ron Oester	.12	.09	.05
22	Danny Darwin	.12	.09	.05
23	Willie Aikens	.12	.09	.05
24	Don Stanhouse	.12	.09	.05
25	Sixto Lezcano	.12	.09	.05
26	U.L. Washington	.12	.09	.05
27	Champ Summers	.12	.09	.05
28	Enrique Romo	.12	.09	.05
29	Gene Tenace	.12	.09	.05
30	Jack Clark	.40	.30	.15
31	Checklist 1-125	.12	.09	.05
32	Ken Oberkfell	.12	.09	.05
33	Rick Honeycutt	.12	.09	.05
34	Al Bumbry	.12	.09	.05
35	John Tamargo	.12	.09	.05
36	Ed Farmer	.12	.09	.05
37	Gary Roenicke	.12	.09	.05
38	Tim Foli	.12	.09	.05
39	Eddie Murray	4.00	3.00	1.50
40	Roy Howell	.12	.09	.05
41	Bill Gullickson	.25	.20	.10
42	Jerry White	.12	.09	.05
43	Tim Blackwell	.12	.09	.05
44	Steve Henderson	.12	.09	.05
45	Enos Cabell	.12	.09	.05
46	Rick Bossetti	.12	.09	.05
47	Bill North	.12	.09	.05
48	Rich Gossage	.30	.25	.12
49	Bob Shirley	.12	.09	.05
50	Dave Lopes	.12	.09	.05
51	Shane Rawley	.12	.09	.05
52	Lloyd Moseby	1.50	1.25	.60
53	Burt Hooton	.12	.09	.05
54	Ivan DeJesus	.12	.09	.05
55	Mike Norris	.12	.09	.05
56	Del Unser	.12	.09	.05
57	Dave Revering	.12	.09	.05
58	Joel Youngblood	.12	.09	.05
59	Steve McCatty	.12	.09	.05
60	Willie Randolph	.12	.09	.05
61	Butch Wynegar	.12	.09	.05
62	Gary Lavelle	.12	.09	.05
63	Willie Montanez	.12	.09	.05
64	Terry Puhl	.12	.09	.05
65	Scott McGregor	.12	.09	.05
66	Buddy Bell	.15	.11	.06
67	Toby Harrah	.12	.09	.05
68	Jim Rice	.75	.60	.30
69	Darrell Evans	.15	.11	.06
70	Al Oliver	.12	.09	.05
71	Hal Dues	.12	.09	.05
72	Barry Evans	.12	.09	.05
73	Doug Bair	.12	.09	.05
74	Mike Hargrove	.12	.09	.05
75	Reggie Smith	.12	.09	.05
76	Mario Mendoza	.12	.09	.05
77	Mike Barlow	.12	.09	.05
78	Garth Iorg	.12	.09	.05
79	Jeff Reardon	4.50	3.50	1.75
80	Roger Erickson	.12	.09	.05
81	Dave Stapleton	.12	.09	.05
82	Barry Bonnell	.12	.09	.05
83	Dave Concepcion	.15	.11	.06
84	Johnnie LeMaster	.12	.09	.05
85	Mike Caldwell	.12	.09	.05
86	Wayne Gross	.12	.09	.05
87	Rick Camp	.12	.09	.05
88	Joe Lefebvre	.12	.09	.05
89	Darrell Jackson	.12	.09	.05
90	Bake McBride	.12	.09	.05
91	Tim Stoddard	.12	.09	.05
92	Mike Easler	.12	.09	.05
93	Jim Bibby	.12	.09	.05
94	Kent Tekulve	.12	.09	.05
95	Jim Sundberg	.12	.09	.05
96	Tommy John	.40	.30	.15
97	Chris Speier	.12	.09	.05
98	Clint Hurdle	.12	.09	.05
99	Phil Garner	.12	.09	.05
100	Rod Carew	2.50	2.00	1.00
101	Steve Stone	.12	.09	.05
102	Joe Niekro	.12	.09	.05
103	Jerry Martin	.12	.09	.05
104	Ron LeFlore	.12	.09	.05
105	Jose Cruz	.12	.09	.05
106	Don Money	.12	.09	.05
107	Bobby Brown	.12	.09	.05
108	Larry Herndon	.12	.09	.05
109	Dennis Eckersley	1.75	1.25	.70
110	Carl Yastrzemski	2.50	2.00	1.00
111	Greg Minton	.12	.09	.05
112	Dan Schatzeder	.12	.09	.05
113	George Brett	5.50	4.25	2.25
114	Tom Underwood	.12	.09	.05
115	Roy Smalley	.12	.09	.05
116	Carlton Fisk	2.50	2.00	1.00
117	Pete Falcone	.12	.09	.05
118	Dale Murphy	2.25	1.75	.90
119	Tippy Martinez	.12	.09	.05
120	Larry Bowa	.12	.09	.05
121	Julio Cruz	.12	.09	.05
122	Jim Gantner	.12	.09	.05
123	Al Cowens	.12	.09	.05
124	Jerry Garvin	.12	.09	.05
125	Andre Dawson	3.00	2.25	1.25
126	Charlie Leibrandt	.40	.30	.15
127	Willie Stargell	.75	.60	.30
128	Andre Thornton	.12	.09	.05
129	Art Howe	.12	.09	.05
130	Larry Gura	.12	.09	.05
131	Jerry Remy	.12	.09	.05
132	Rick Dempsey	.12	.09	.05
133	Alan Trammell	1.50	1.25	.60
134	Mike LaCoss	.12	.09	.05
135	Gorman Thomas	.12	.09	.05
136	Expos Future Stars (Bobby Pate, Tim Raines, Roberto Ramos)	7.25	5.50	3.00
137	Bill Madlock	.20	.15	.08
138	Rich Dotson	.15	.11	.06
139	Oscar Gamble	.12	.09	.05
140	Bob Forsch	.12	.09	.05
141	Miguel Dilone	.12	.09	.05
142	Jackson Todd	.12	.09	.05
143	Dan Meyer	.12	.09	.05
144	Garry Templeton	.12	.09	.05
145	Mickey Rivers	.12	.09	.05
146	Alan Ashby	.12	.09	.05
147	Dale Berra	.12	.09	.05
148	Randy Jones	.12	.09	.05
149	Joe Nolan	.12	.09	.05
150	Mark Fidrych	.12	.09	.05
151	Tony Armas	.12	.09	.05
152	Steve Kemp	.12	.09	.05
153	Jerry Reuss	.12	.09	.05
154	Rick Langford	.12	.09	.05
155	Chris Chambliss	.12	.09	.05
156	Bob McClure	.12	.09	.05
157	John Wathan	.12	.09	.05
158	John Curtis	.12	.09	.05
159	Steve Howe	.15	.11	.06
160	Garry Maddox	.12	.09	.05
161	Dan Graham	.12	.09	.05
162	Doug Corbett	.12	.09	.05
163	Rob Dressler	.12	.09	.05
164	Bucky Dent	.12	.09	.05
165	Alvis Woods	.12	.09	.05
166	Floyd Bannister	.12	.09	.05
167	Lee Mazzilli	.12	.09	.05
168	Don Robinson	.12	.09	.05
169	John Mayberry	.12	.09	.05
170	Woodie Fryman	.12	.09	.05
171	Gene Richards	.12	.09	.05
172	Rick Burleson	.12	.09	.05
173	Bump Wills	.12	.09	.05
174	Glenn Abbott	.12	.09	.05
175	Dave Collins	.12	.09	.05
176	Mike Krukow	.12	.09	.05
177	Rick Monday	.12	.09	.05
178	Dave Parker	.50	.40	.20
179	Rudy May	.12	.09	.05
180	Pete Rose	3.00	2.25	1.25
181	Elias Sosa	.12	.09	.05
182	Bob Grich	.12	.09	.05
183	Fred Norman	.12	.09	.05
184	Jim Dwyer	.12	.09	.05
185	Dennis Leonard	.12	.09	.05
186	Gary Matthews	.12	.09	.05
187	Ron Hassey	.12	.09	.05
188	Doug DeCinces	.12	.09	.05
189	Craig Swan	.12	.09	.05
190	Cesar Cedeno	.12	.09	.05
191	Rick Sutcliffe	.40	.30	.15
192	Kiko Garcia	.12	.09	.05
193	Pete Vuckovich	.12	.09	.05
194	Tony Bernazard	.12	.09	.05
195	Keith Hernandez	.60	.45	.25
196	Jerry Mumphrey	.12	.09	.05
197	Jim Kern	.12	.09	.05
198	Jerry Dybzinski	.12	.09	.05
199	John Lowenstein	.12	.09	.05
200	George Foster	.12	.09	.05
201	Phil Niekro	.12	.09	.05

202	Bill Buckner	.60	.45	.25
203	Steve Carlton	2.50	2.00	1.00
204	John D'Acquisto	.12	.09	.05
205	Rick Reuschel	.12	.09	.05
206	Dan Quisenberry	.20	.15	.08
207	Mike Schmidt	2.50	2.00	1.00
208	Bob Watson	.12	.09	.05
209	Jim Spencer	.12	.09	.05
210	Jim Palmer	2.25	1.75	.90
211	Derrel Thomas	.12	.09	.05
212	Steve Nicosia	.12	.09	.05
213	Omar Moreno	.12	.09	.05
214	Richie Zisk	.12	.09	.05
215	Larry Hisle	.12	.09	.05
216	Mike Torrez	.12	.09	.05
217	Rich Hebner	.12	.09	.05
218	Britt Burns	.15	.11	.06
219	Ken Landreaux	.12	.09	.05
220	Tom Seaver	2.50	2.00	1.00
221	Bob Davis	.12	.09	.05
222	Jorge Orta	.12	.09	.05
223	Bobby Bonds	.12	.09	.05
224	Pat Zachry	.12	.09	.05
225	Ruppert Jones	.12	.09	.05
226	Duane Kuiper	.12	.09	.05
227	Rodney Scott	.12	.09	.05
228	Tom Paciorek	.12	.09	.05
229	Rollie Fingers	.50	.40	.20
230	George Hendrick	.12	.09	.05
231	Tony Perez	.25	.20	.10
232	Grant Jackson	.12	.09	.05
233	Damaso Garcia	.15	.11	.06
234	Lou Whitaker	.40	.30	.15
235	Scott Sanderson	.12	.09	.05
236	Mike Ivie	.12	.09	.05
237	Charlie Moore	.12	.09	.05
238	Blue Jays Future Stars (Luis Leal, Brian Milner, Ken Schrom)	.15	.11	.06
239	Rick Miller	.12	.09	.05
240	Nolan Ryan	11.00	8.25	4.50
241	Checklist 126-250	.12	.09	.05
242	Chet Lemon	.12	.09	.05
243	Dave Palmer	.12	.09	.05
244	Ellis Valentine	.12	.09	.05
245	Carney Lansford	.15	.11	.06
246	Ed Ott	.12	.09	.05
247	Glenn Hubbard	.12	.09	.05
248	Joey McLaughlin	.12	.09	.05
249	Jerry Narron	.12	.09	.05
250	Ron Guidry	.40	.30	.15
251	Steve Garvey	1.00	.70	.40
252	Victor Cruz	.12	.09	.05
253	Bobby Murcer	.12	.09	.05
254	Ozzie Smith	4.25	3.25	1.75
255	John Stearns	.12	.09	.05
256	Bill Campbell	.12	.09	.05
257	Rennie Stennett	.12	.09	.05
258	Rick Waits	.12	.09	.05
259	Gary Lucas	.12	.09	.05
260	Ron Cey	.15	.11	.06
261	Rickey Henderson	11.00	8.25	4.50
262	Sammy Stewart	.12	.09	.05
263	Brian Downing	.12	.09	.05
264	Mark Bomback	.12	.09	.05
265	John Candelaria	.12	.09	.05
266	Renie Martin	.12	.09	.05
267	Stan Bahnsen	.12	.09	.05
268	Expos Team	.12	.09	.05
269	Ken Forsch	.12	.09	.05
270	Greg Luzinski	.20	.15	.08
271	Ron Jackson	.12	.09	.05
272	Wayne Garland	.12	.09	.05
273	Milt May	.12	.09	.05
274	Rick Wise	.12	.09	.05
275	Dwight Evans	.25	.20	.10
276	Sal Bando	.12	.09	.05
277	Alfredo Griffin	.12	.09	.05
278	Rick Sofield	.12	.09	.05
279	Bob Knepper	.12	.09	.05
280	Ken Griffey	.12	.09	.05
281	Ken Singleton	.12	.09	.05
282	Ernie Whitt	.12	.09	.05
283	Billy Sample	.12	.09	.05
284	Jack Morris	.50	.40	.20
285	Dick Ruthven	.12	.09	.05
286	Johnny Bench	2.50	2.00	1.00
287	Dave Smith	.30	.25	.12
288	Amos Otis	.12	.09	.05
289	Dave Goltz	.12	.09	.05
290	Bob Boone	.12	.09	.05
291	Aurelio Lopez	.12	.09	.05
292	Tom Hume	.12	.09	.05
293	Charlie Lea	.15	.11	.06
294	Bert Blyleven	.20	.15	.08
295	Hal McRae	.12	.09	.05
296	Bob Stanley	.12	.09	.05
297	Bob Bailor	.12	.09	.05
298	Jerry Koosman	.12	.09	.05
299	Eliott Maddox	.12	.09	.05
300	Paul Molitor	5.50	4.25	2.25
301	Matt Keough	.12	.09	.05
302	Pat Putnam	.12	.09	.05
303	Dan Ford	.12	.09	.05
304	John Castino	.12	.09	.05
305	Barry Foote	.12	.09	.05
306	Lou Piniella	.12	.09	.05
307	Gene Garber	.12	.09	.05
308	Rick Manning	.12	.09	.05
309	Don Baylor	.15	.11	.06
310	Vida Blue	.12	.09	.05
311	Doug Flynn	.08	.06	.03
312	Rick Rhoden	.12	.09	.05
313	Fred Lynn	.25	.20	.10
314	Rich Dauer	.12	.09	.05
315	Kirk Gibson	4.50	3.50	1.75
316	Ken Reitz	.12	.09	.05
317	Lonnie Smith	.12	.09	.05
318	Steve Yeager	.12	.09	.05
319	Rowland Office	.12	.09	.05
320	Tom Burgmeier	.12	.09	.05
321	Leon Durham	.60	.45	.25
322	Neil Allen	.12	.09	.05
323	Ray Burris	.12	.09	.05
324	Mike Willis	.12	.09	.05
325	Ray Knight	.12	.09	.05
326	Rafael Landestoy	.12	.09	.05
327	Moose Haas	.12	.09	.05
328	Ross Baumgarten	.12	.09	.05
329	Joaquin Andujar	.12	.09	.05
330	Frank White	.12	.09	.05
331	Blue Jays Team	.12	.09	.05
332	Dick Drago	.12	.09	.05
333	Sid Monge	.12	.09	.05
334	Joe Sambito	.12	.09	.05
335	Rick Cerone	.12	.09	.05
336	Eddie Whitson	.12	.09	.05
337	Sparky Lyle	.12	.09	.05
338	Checklist 251-374	.12	.09	.05
339	Jon Matlack	.12	.09	.05
340	Ben Oglivie	.12	.09	.05
341	Dwayne Murphy	.12	.09	.05
342	Terry Crowley	.12	.09	.05
343	Frank Taveras	.12	.09	.05
344	Steve Rogers	.12	.09	.05
345	Warren Cromartie	.12	.09	.05
346	Bill Caudill	.12	.09	.05
347	Harold Baines	4.50	3.50	1.75
348	Frank LaCorte	.12	.09	.05
349	Glenn Hoffman	.12	.09	.05
350	J.R. Richard	.12	.09	.05
351	Otto Velez	.12	.09	.05
352	Ted Simmons	.20	.15	.08
353	Terry Kennedy	.12	.09	.05
354	Al Hrabosky	.12	.09	.05
355	Bob Horner	.30	.25	.12
356	Cecil Cooper	.15	.11	.06
357	Bob Welch	.15	.11	.06
358	Paul Moskau	.12	.09	.05
359	Dave Rader	.12	.09	.05
360	Willie Wilson	.15	.11	.06
361	Dave Kingman	.12	.09	.05
362	Joe Rudi	.12	.09	.05
363	Rich Gale	.12	.09	.05
364	Steve Trout	.12	.09	.05
365	Graig Nettles	.12	.09	.05
366	Lamar Johnson	.12	.09	.05
367	Denny Martinez	.12	.09	.05
368	Manny Trillo	.12	.09	.05
369	Frank Tanana	.12	.09	.05
370	Reggie Jackson	3.25	2.50	1.25
371	Bill Lee	.12	.09	.05
372	Jay Johnstone	.12	.09	.05
373	Jason Thompson	.12	.09	.05
374	Tom Hutton	.12	.09	.05

1981 O-Pee-Chee Posters

Inserted inside the regular 1981 O-Pee-Chee wax packs, these full-color posters measure approximately 4-7/8" by 6-7/8". The set is complete at 24 posters and includes 12 players from the Blue Jays and 12 from the Expos. The blank-backed posters are numbered in the border below the photo where the caption is written in both French and English. The photos are surrounded by a blue border for Blue Jays players or a red border for Expos. Because they were inserted in wax packs, the posters generally contain folds.

		MT	NR MT	EX
	Complete Set:	5.00	3.75	2.00
	Common Player:	.25	.20	.10
1	Willie Montanez	.25	.20	.10
2	Rodney Scott	.25	.20	.10
3	Chris Speier	.25	.20	.10
4	Larry Parrish	.25	.20	.10
5	Warren Cromartie	.25	.20	.10
6	Andre Dawson	2.50	2.00	1.00
7	Ellis Valentine	.25	.20	.10
8	Gary Carter	2.00	1.50	.80
9	Steve Rogers	.25	.20	.10
10	Woodie Fryman	.25	.20	.10
11	Jerry White	.25	.20	.10
12	Scott Sanderson	.25	.20	.10
13	John Mayberry	.25	.20	.10
14	Damasa Garcia (Damaso)	.25	.20	.10
15	Alfredo Griffin	.25	.20	.10
16	Garth Iorg	.25	.20	.10
17	Alvis Woods	.25	.20	.10
18	Rick Bosetti	.25	.20	.10
19	Barry Bonnell	.25	.20	.10
20	Ernie Whitt	.25	.20	.10
21	Jim Clancy	.25	.20	.10
22	Dave Stieb	.75	.60	.30
23	Otto Velez	.25	.20	.10
24	Lloyd Moseby	.30	.25	.12

1982 O-Pee-Chee

The 1982 O-Pee-Chee set, complete at 396 cards, is nearly identical in design to the 1982 Topps set, except the Canadian-issued cards display the O-Pee-Chee logo on the front of the card and list the player's position in both French and English. The backs of the cards, which measure the standard 2-1/2" by 3-1/2", are also bilingual. Some of the cards carry an extra line on the front indicating an off-season trade.

		MT	NR MT	EX
	Complete Set (396):	55.00	41.00	22.00
	Common Player:	.12	.09	.05
1	Dan Spillner	.12	.09	.05
2	Ken Singleton AS	.12	.09	.05
3	John Candelaria	.12	.09	.05
4	Frank Tanana	.12	.09	.05
5	Reggie Smith	.12	.09	.05
6	Rick Monday	.12	.09	.05
7	Scott Sanderson	.12	.09	.05
8	Rich Dauer	.12	.09	.05
9	Ron Guidry	.30	.25	.12
10	Ron Guidry IA	.15	.11	.06
11	Tom Brookens	.12	.09	.05
12	Moose Haas	.12	.09	.05
13	Chet Lemon	.12	.09	.05
14	Steve Howe	.12	.09	.05
15	Ellis Valentine	.12	.09	.05
16	Toby Harrah	.12	.09	.05
17	Darrell Evans	.12	.09	.05
18	Johnny Bench	1.50	1.25	.60
19	Ernie Whitt	.12	.09	.05
20	Garry Maddox	.12	.09	.05
21	Graig Nettles IA	.12	.09	.05
22	Al Oliver IA	.12	.09	.05
23	Bob Boone	.12	.09	.05
24	Pete Rose IA	1.00	.70	.40
25	Jerry Remy	.12	.09	.05
26	Jorge Orta	.12	.09	.05
27	Bobby Bonds	.12	.09	.05
28	Jim Clancy	.12	.09	.05
29	Dwayne Murphy	.12	.09	.05
30	Tom Seaver	2.00	1.50	.80
31	Tom Seaver IA	1.00	.70	.40
32	Claudell Washington	.12	.09	.05
33	Bob Shirley	.12	.09	.05
34	Bob Forsch	.12	.09	.05
35	Willie Aikens	.12	.09	.05
36	Rod Carew AS	.30	.25	.12
37	Willie Randolph	.12	.09	.05
38	Charlie Lea	.12	.09	.05
39	Lou Whitaker	.25	.20	.10
40	Dave Parker	.25	.20	.10
41	Dave Parker IA	.12	.09	.05
42	Mark Belanger	.12	.09	.05
43	Rick Langford	.12	.09	.05
44	Rollie Fingers IA	.12	.09	.05
45	Rick Cerone	.12	.09	.05
46	Johnny Wockenfuss	.12	.09	.05
47	Jack Morris AS	.20	.15	.08
48	Cesar Cedeno	.12	.09	.05
49	Alvis Woods	.12	.09	.05
50	Buddy Bell	.12	.09	.05
51	Mickey Rivers IA	.12	.09	.05
52	Steve Rogers	.12	.09	.05
53	Blue Jays Team	.12	.09	.05
54	Ron Hassey	.12	.09	.05
55	Rick Burleson	.12	.09	.05
56	Harold Baines	.60	.45	.25
57	Craig Reynolds	.12	.09	.05
58	Carlton Fisk AS	.12	.09	.05
59	Jim Kern	.12	.09	.05
60	Tony Armas	.12	.09	.05
61	Warren Cromartie	.12	.09	.05
62	Graig Nettles	.15	.11	.06
63	Jerry Koosman	.12	.09	.05
64	Pat Zachry	.12	.09	.05
65	Terry Kennedy	.12	.09	.05
66	Richie Zisk	.12	.09	.05
67	Rich Gale	.12	.09	.05
68	Steve Carlton	.75	.60	.30

69	Greg Luzinski IA	.12	.09	.05
70	Tim Raines	2.50	2.00	1.00
71	Roy Lee Jackson	.12	.09	.05
72	Carl Yastrzemski	1.50	1.25	.60
73	John Castino	.12	.09	.05
74	Joe Niekro	.12	.09	.05
75	Tommy John	.20	.15	.08
76	Dave Winfield AS	.20	.15	.08
77	Miguel Dilone	.12	.09	.05
78	Gary Gray	.12	.09	.05
79	Tom Hume	.12	.09	.05
80	Jim Palmer	1.25	.90	.50
81	Jim Palmer IA	.25	.20	.10
82	Vida Blue IA	.12	.09	.05
83	Garth Iorg	.12	.09	.05
84	Rennie Stennett	.12	.09	.05
85	Dave Lopes IA	.12	.09	.05
86	Dave Concepcion	.15	.11	.06
87	Matt Keough	.12	.09	.05
88	Jim Spencer	.12	.09	.05
89	Steve Henderson	.12	.09	.05
90	Nolan Ryan	12.00	9.00	4.75
91	Carney Lansford	.12	.09	.05
92	Bake McBride	.12	.09	.05
93	Dave Stapleton	.12	.09	.05
94	Expos Team	.12	.09	.05
95	Ozzie Smith	2.75	2.00	1.00
96	Rich Hebner	.12	.09	.05
97	Tim Foli	.12	.09	.05
98	Darrell Porter	.12	.09	.05
99	Barry Bonnell	.12	.09	.05
100	Mike Schmidt	3.00	2.25	1.25
101	Mike Schmidt IA	1.50	1.25	.60
102	Dan Briggs	.12	.09	.05
103	Al Cowens	.12	.09	.05
104	Grant Jackson	.12	.09	.05
105	Kirk Gibson	.60	.45	.25
106	Dan Schatzeder	.12	.09	.05
107	Juan Berenguer	.12	.09	.05
108	Jack Morris	2.25	1.75	.90
109	Dave Revering	.12	.09	.05
110	Carlton Fisk	2.00	1.50	.80
111	Carlton Fisk IA	1.00	.70	.40
112	Billy Sample	.12	.09	.05
113	Steve McCatty	.12	.09	.05
114	Ken Landreaux	.12	.09	.05
115	Gaylord Perry	.30	.25	.12
116	Elias Sosa	.12	.09	.05
117	Rich Gossage IA	.12	.09	.05
118	Expos Future Stars (Terry Francona, Brad Mills, Bryn Smith)	.25	.20	.10
119	Billy Almon	.12	.09	.05
120	Gary Lucas	.08	.06	.03
121	Ken Oberkfell	.08	.06	.03
122	Steve Carlton IA	.30	.25	.12
123	Jeff Reardon	1.75	1.25	.70
124	Bill Buckner	.15	.11	.06
125	Danny Ainge	2.25	1.75	.90
126	Paul Splittorff	.12	.09	.05
127	Lonnie Smith	.12	.09	.05
128	Rudy May	.12	.09	.05
129	Checklist 1-132	.12	.09	.05
130	Julio Cruz	.12	.09	.05
131	Stan Bahnsen	.12	.09	.05
132	Pete Vuckovich	.12	.09	.05
133	Luis Salazar	.12	.09	.05
134	Dan Ford	.12	.09	.05
135	Denny Martinez	.12	.09	.05
136	Lary Sorensen	.12	.09	.05
137	Fergie Jenkins	.20	.15	.08
138	Rick Camp	.12	.09	.05
139	Wayne Nordhagen	.12	.09	.05
140	Ron LeFlore	.12	.09	.05
141	Rick Sutcliffe	.20	.15	.08
142	Rick Waits	.12	.09	.05
143	Mookie Wilson	.12	.09	.05
144	Greg Minton	.12	.09	.05
145	Bob Horner	.30	.25	.12
146	Joe Morgan IA	.15	.11	.06
147	Larry Gura	.12	.09	.05
148	Alfredo Griffin	.12	.09	.05
149	Pat Putnam	.12	.09	.05
150	Ted Simmons	.20	.15	.08
151	Gary Matthews	.12	.09	.05
152	Greg Luzinski	.15	.11	.06
153	Mike Flanagan	.12	.09	.05
154	Jim Morrison	.12	.09	.05
155	Otto Velez	.12	.09	.05
156	Frank White	.12	.09	.05
157	Doug Corbett	.12	.09	.05
158	Brian Downing	.12	.09	.05
159	Willie Randolph IA	.12	.09	.05
160	Luis Tiant	.15	.11	.06
161	Andre Thornton	.12	.09	.05
162	Amos Otis	.12	.09	.05
163	Paul Mirabella	.12	.09	.05
164	Bert Blyleven	.20	.15	.08
165	Rowland Office	.12	.09	.05
166	Gene Tenace	.12	.09	.05
167	Cecil Cooper	.15	.11	.06
168	Bruce Benedict	.12	.09	.05
169	Mark Clear	.12	.09	.05
170	Jim Bibby	.12	.09	.05
171	Ken Griffey IA	.12	.09	.05
172	Bill Gullickson	.12	.09	.05
173	Mike Scioscia	.12	.09	.05
174	Doug DeCinces	.12	.09	.05
175	Jerry Mumphrey	.12	.09	.05
176	Rollie Fingers	.20	.15	.08
177	George Foster IA	.12	.09	.05
178	Mitchell Page	.12	.09	.05
179	Steve Garvey	.75	.60	.30
180	Steve Garvey IA	.30	.25	.12
181	Woodie Fryman	.12	.09	.05
182	Larry Herndon	.12	.09	.05
183	Frank White IA	.12	.09	.05
184	Alan Ashby	.12	.09	.05
185	Phil Niekro	.40	.30	.15
186	Leon Roberts	.12	.09	.05
187	Rod Carew	2.00	1.50	.80
188	Willie Stargell IA	.30	.25	.12
189	Joel Youngblood	.12	.09	.05
190	J.R. Richard	.12	.09	.05
191	Tim Wallach	1.75	1.25	.70
192	Broderick Perkins	.12	.09	.05
193	Johnny Grubb	.12	.09	.05
194	Larry Bowa	.12	.09	.05
195	Paul Molitor	5.00	3.75	2.00
196	Willie Upshaw	.12	.09	.05
197	Roy Smalley	.12	.09	.05
198	Chris Speier	.12	.09	.05
199	Don Aase	.12	.09	.05
200	George Brett	3.75	2.75	1.50
201	George Brett IA	2.00	1.50	.80
202	Rick Manning	.12	.09	.05
203	Blue Jays Future Stars (Jesse Barfield, Brian Milner, Boomer Wells)	3.00	2.25	1.25
204	Rick Reuschel	.12	.09	.05
205	Neil Allen	.12	.09	.05
206	Leon Durham	.12	.09	.05
207	Jim Gantner	.12	.09	.05
208	Joe Morgan	.30	.25	.12
209	Gary Lavelle	.12	.09	.05
210	Keith Hernandez	.50	.40	.20
211	Joe Charboneau	.12	.09	.05
212	Mario Mendoza	.12	.09	.05
213	Willie Randolph AS	.12	.09	.05
214	Lance Parrish	.40	.30	.15
215	Mike Krukow	.12	.09	.05
216	Ron Cey	.12	.09	.05
217	Ruppert Jones	.12	.09	.05
218	Dave Lopes	.12	.09	.05
219	Steve Yeager	.12	.09	.05
220	Manny Trillo	.12	.09	.05
221	Dave Concepcion IA	.12	.09	.05
222	Butch Wynegar	.12	.09	.05
223	Lloyd Moseby	.20	.15	.08
224	Bruce Bochte	.12	.09	.05
225	Ed Ott	.12	.09	.05
226	Checklist 133-264	.12	.09	.05
227	Ray Burris	.12	.09	.05
228	Reggie Smith IA	.12	.09	.05
229	Oscar Gamble	.12	.09	.05
230	Willie Wilson	.15	.11	.06
231	Brian Kingman	.12	.09	.05
232	John Stearns	.12	.09	.05
233	Duane Kuiper	.12	.09	.05
234	Don Baylor	.15	.11	.06
235	Mike Easler	.12	.09	.05
236	Lou Piniella	.12	.09	.05
237	Robin Yount	3.00	2.25	1.25
238	Kevin Saucier	.12	.09	.05
239	Jon Matlack	.12	.09	.05
240	Bucky Dent	.12	.09	.05
241	Bucky Dent IA	.12	.09	.05
242	Milt May	.12	.09	.05
243	Lee Mazzilli	.12	.09	.05
244	Gary Carter	.75	.60	.30
245	Ken Reitz	.12	.09	.05
246	Scott McGregor AS	.12	.09	.05
247	Pedro Guerrero	.60	.45	.25
248	Art Howe	.12	.09	.05
249	Dick Tidrow	.12	.09	.05
250	Tug McGraw	.12	.09	.05
251	Fred Lynn	.25	.20	.10
252	Fred Lynn IA	.12	.09	.05
253	Gene Richards	.12	.09	.05
254	Jorge Bell	4.25	3.25	1.75
255	Tony Perez	.25	.20	.10
256	Tony Perez IA	.12	.09	.05
257	Rich Dotson	.12	.09	.05
258	Bo Diaz	.12	.09	.05
259	Rodney Scott	.12	.09	.05
260	Bruce Sutter	.15	.11	.06
261	George Brett AS	.60	.45	.25
262	Rick Dempsey	.12	.09	.05
263	Mike Phillips	.12	.09	.05
264	Jerry Garvin	.12	.09	.05
265	Al Bumbry	.12	.09	.05
266	Hubie Brooks	.15	.11	.06
267	Vida Blue	.12	.09	.05
268	Rickey Henderson	6.00	4.50	2.50
269	Rick Peters	.12	.09	.05
270	Rusty Staub	.15	.11	.06
271	Sixto Lezcano	.12	.09	.05
272	Bump Wills	.12	.09	.05
273	Gary Allenson	.12	.09	.05
274	Randy Jones	.12	.09	.05
275	Bob Watson	.12	.09	.05
276	Dave Kingman	.15	.11	.06
277	Terry Puhl	.12	.09	.05
278	Jerry Reuss	.12	.09	.05
279	Sammy Stewart	.12	.09	.05
280	Ben Oglivie	.12	.09	.05
281	Kent Tekulve	.12	.09	.05
282	Ken Macha	.12	.09	.05
283	Ron Davis	.12	.09	.05
284	Bob Grich	.12	.09	.05
285	Sparky Lyle	.12	.09	.05
286	Rich Gossage AS	.12	.09	.05
287	Dennis Eckersley	1.50	1.25	.60
288	Garry Templeton	.12	.09	.05
289	Bob Stanley	.12	.09	.05
290	Ken Singleton	.12	.09	.05
291	Mickey Hatcher	.12	.09	.05
292	Dave Palmer	.12	.09	.05
293	Damaso Garcia	.12	.09	.05
294	Don Money	.12	.09	.05
295	George Hendrick	.12	.09	.05
296	Steve Kemp	.12	.09	.05
297	Dave Smith	.12	.09	.05
298	Bucky Dent AS	.12	.09	.05
299	Steve Trout	.12	.09	.05
300	Reggie Jackson	2.75	2.00	1.00
301	Reggie Jackson IA	1.00	.70	.40
302	Doug Flynn	.12	.09	.05
303	Wayne Gross	.12	.09	.05
304	Johnny Bench IA	.40	.30	.15
305	Don Sutton	.40	.30	.15
306	Don Sutton IA	.20	.15	.08
307	Mark Bomback	.12	.09	.05
308	Charlie Moore	.12	.09	.05
309	Jeff Burroughs	.12	.09	.05
310	Mike Hargrove	.12	.09	.05
311	Enos Cabell	.12	.09	.05
312	Lenny Randle	.12	.09	.05
313	Ivan DeJesus	.12	.09	.05
314	Buck Martinez	.12	.09	.05
315	Burt Hooton	.12	.09	.05
316	Scott McGregor	.12	.09	.05
317	Dick Ruthven	.12	.09	.05
318	Mike Heath	.12	.09	.05
319	Ray Knight	.12	.09	.05
320	Chris Chambliss	.12	.09	.05
321	Chris Chambliss IA	.12	.09	.05
322	Ross Baumgarten	.12	.09	.05
323	Bill Lee	.12	.09	.05
324	Gorman Thomas	.12	.09	.05
325	Jose Cruz	.12	.09	.05
326	Al Oliver	.15	.11	.06
327	Jackson Todd	.12	.09	.05
328	Ed Farmer	.12	.09	.05
329	U.L. Washington	.12	.09	.05
330	Ken Griffey	.15	.11	.06
331	John Milner	.12	.09	.05
332	Don Robinson	.12	.09	.05
333	Cliff Johnson	.12	.09	.05
334	Fernando Valenzuela	1.25	.90	.50
335	Jim Sundberg	.12	.09	.05
336	George Foster	.15	.11	.06
337	Pete Rose AS	.75	.60	.30
338	Dave Lopes AS	.12	.09	.05
339	Mike Schmidt AS	.40	.30	.15
340	Dave Concepcion AS	.12	.09	.05
341	Andre Dawson AS	.20	.15	.08
342	George Foster AS	.12	.09	.05
343	Dave Parker AS	.15	.11	.06
344	Gary Carter AS	.30	.25	.12
345	Fernando Valenzuela AS	.30	.25	.12
346	Tom Seaver AS	.30	.25	.12
347	Bruce Sutter AS	.12	.09	.05
348	Darrell Porter IA	.12	.09	.05
349	Dave Collins	.12	.09	.05
350	Amos Otis IA	.12	.09	.05
351	Frank Taveras	.12	.09	.05
352	Dave Winfield	3.75	2.75	1.50
353	Larry Parrish	.12	.09	.05
354	Roberto Ramos	.12	.09	.05
355	Dwight Evans	.20	.15	.08
356	Mickey Rivers	.12	.09	.05
357	Butch Hobson	.12	.09	.05
358	Carl Yastrzemski IA	.30	.25	.12
359	Ron Jackson	.12	.09	.05
360	Len Barker	.12	.09	.05
361	Pete Rose	2.25	1.75	.90
362	Kevin Hickey	.12	.09	.05
363	Rod Carew IA	.30	.25	.12
364	Hector Cruz	.12	.09	.05
365	Bill Madlock	.15	.11	.06
366	Jim Rice	.75	.60	.30
367	Ron Cey IA	.12	.09	.05
368	Luis Leal	.12	.09	.05
369	Dennis Leonard	.12	.09	.05
370	Mike Norris	.12	.09	.05
371	Tom Paciorek	.12	.09	.05
372	Willie Stargell	.60	.45	.25
373	Dan Driessen	.12	.09	.05
374	Larry Bowa IA	.12	.09	.05
375	Dusty Baker	.12	.09	.05
376	Joey McLaughlin	.12	.09	.05
377	Reggie Jackson AS	.40	.30	.15
378	Mike Caldwell	.12	.09	.05
379	Andre Dawson	2.75	2.00	1.00
380	Dave Stieb	.15	.11	.06
381	Alan Trammell	.12	.09	.05
382	John Mayberry	.12	.09	.05
383	John Wathan	.12	.09	.05
384	Hal McRae	.12	.09	.05
385	Ken Forsch	.12	.09	.05
386	Jerry White	.12	.09	.05
387	Tom Veryzer	.12	.09	.05
388	Joe Rudi	.12	.09	.05
389	Bob Knepper	.12	.09	.05
390	Eddie Murray	2.75	2.00	1.00
391	Dale Murphy	1.75	1.25	.70
392	Bob Boone IA	.12	.09	.05
393	Al Hrabosky	.12	.09	.05
394	Checklist 265-396	.12	.09	.05
395	Omar Moreno	.12	.09	.05
396	Rich Gossage	.25	.20	.10

A player's name in italic type indicates a rookie card. An (FC) indicates a player's first card for that particular card company.

1982 O-Pee-Chee Posters

The 24 posters in this Canadian set, which features 12 players from the Expos and 12 from the Blue Jays, were inserted in regular 1982 O-Pee-Chee wax packs. The posters measure approximately 4-7/8" by 6-7/8" and are usually found with fold marks. The blank-backed posters are numbered in the bottom border where the captions appear in

both French and English. Red borders surround the photos of Blue Jays players, while blue borders are used for the Expos.

		MT	NR MT	EX
Complete Set:		7.00	5.25	2.75
Common Player:		.25	.20	.10
1	John Mayberry	.25	.20	.10
2	Damaso Garcia	.25	.20	.10
3	Ernie Whitt	.25	.20	.10
4	Lloyd Moseby	.30	.25	.12
5	Alvis Woods	.25	.20	.10
6	Dave Stieb	.40	.30	.15
7	Roy Lee Jackson	.25	.20	.10
8	Joey McLaughlin	.25	.20	.10
9	Luis Leal	.25	.20	.10
10	Aurelio Rodriguez	.25	.20	.10
11	Otto Velez	.25	.20	.10
12	Juan Berenger (Berenguer)	.25	.20	.10
13	Warren Cromartie	.25	.20	.10
14	Rodney Scott	.25	.20	.10
15	Larry Parrish	.25	.20	.10
16	Gary Carter	1.50	1.25	.60
17	Tim Raines	1.50	1.25	.60
18	Andre Dawson	1.50	1.25	.60
19	Terry Francona	.25	.20	.10
20	Steve Rogers	.25	.20	.10
21	Bill Gullickson	.25	.20	.10
22	Scott Sanderson	.25	.20	.10
23	Jeff Reardon	.75	.60	.30
24	Jerry White	.25	.20	.10

1983 O-Pee-Chee

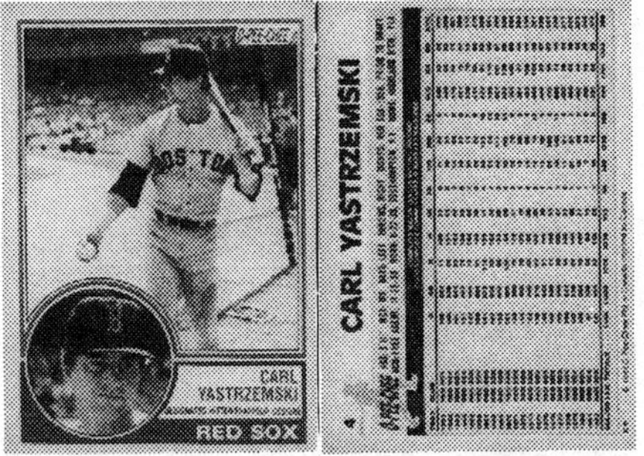

Again complete at 396 cards, the 1983 O-Pee-Chee set borrows its design from the 1983 Topps set, except the Canadian-issued cards display the O-Pee-Chee logo on the front of the card and show the player's position in both French and English. The backs of the cards are also printed in both languages. The cards measure the standard 2-1/2" by 3-1/2". Some cards carry the extra line on the front indicating an off-season trade.

		MT	NR MT	EX
Complete Set (396):		90.00	67.00	36.00
Common Player:		.12	.09	.05
1	Rusty Staub	.15	.11	.06
2	Larry Parrish	.12	.09	.05
3	George Brett	3.00	2.25	1.25
4	Carl Yastrzemski	.75	.60	.30
5	Al Oliver (Super Veteran)	.12	.09	.05
6	Bill Virdon	.12	.09	.05
7	Gene Richards	.12	.09	.05
8	Steve Balboni	.12	.09	.05
9	Joey McLaughlin	.12	.09	.05
10	Gorman Thomas	.12	.09	.05
11	Chris Chambliss	.12	.09	.05
12	Ray Burris	.12	.09	.05
13	Larry Herndon	.12	.09	.05
14	Ozzie Smith	2.25	1.75	.90
15	Ron Cey	.12	.09	.05
16	Willie Wilson	.15	.11	.06
17	Kent Tekulve	.12	.09	.05
18	Kent Tekulve (Super Veteran)	.12	.09	.05
19	Oscar Gamble	.12	.09	.05
20	Carlton Fisk	2.00	1.50	.80
21	Dale Murphy AS	.60	.45	.25
22	Randy Lerch	.12	.09	.05
23	Dale Murphy	1.25	.90	.50
24	Steve Mura	.12	.09	.05
25	Hal McRae	.12	.09	.05
26	Dennis Lamp	.12	.09	.05
27	Ron Washington	.12	.09	.05
28	Bruce Bochte	.12	.09	.05
29	Randy Jones	.12	.09	.05
30	Jim Rice	.60	.45	.25
31	Bill Gullickson	.12	.09	.05
32	Dave Concepcion AS	.12	.09	.05
33	Ted Simmons (Super Veteran)	.12	.09	.05
34	Bobby Cox	.12	.09	.05
35	Rollie Fingers	.25	.20	.10
36	Rollie Fingers (Super Veteran)	.15	.11	.06
37	Mike Hargrove	.12	.09	.05
38	Roy Smalley	.12	.09	.05
39	Terry Puhl	.12	.09	.05
40	Fernando Valenzuela	.25	.20	.10
41	Garry Maddox	.12	.09	.05
42	Dale Murray	.12	.09	.05
43	Bob Dernier	.12	.09	.05
44	Don Robinson	.12	.09	.05
45	John Mayberry	.12	.09	.05
46	Richard Dotson	.12	.09	.05
47	Wayne Nordhagen	.12	.09	.05
48	Lary Sorenson	.12	.09	.05
49	Willie McGee	3.75	2.75	1.50
50	Bob Horner	.20	.15	.08
51	Rusty Staub (Super Veteran)	.12	.09	.05
52	Tom Seaver	1.75	1.25	.70
53	Chet Lemon	.12	.09	.05
54	Scott Sanderson	.12	.09	.05
55	Mookie Wilson	.12	.09	.05
56	Reggie Jackson	2.00	1.50	.80
57	Tim Blackwell	.12	.09	.05
58	Keith Moreland	.12	.09	.05
59	Alvis Woods	.12	.09	.05
60	Johnny Bench	1.50	1.25	.60
61	Johnny Bench (Super Veteran)	.75	.60	.30
62	Jim Gott	.12	.09	.05
63	Rick Monday	.12	.09	.05
64	Gary Matthews	.12	.09	.05
65	Jack Morris	1.50	1.25	.60
66	Lou Whitaker	.30	.25	.12
67	U.L. Washington	.12	.09	.05
68	Eric Show	.20	.15	.08
69	Lee Lacy	.12	.09	.05
70	Steve Carlton	.50	.40	.20
71	Steve Carlton (Super Veteran)	.25	.20	.10
72	Tom Paciorek	.12	.09	.05
73	Manny Trillo	.12	.09	.05
74	Tony Perez (Super Veteran)	.12	.09	.05
75	Amos Otis	.12	.09	.05
76	Rick Mahler	.12	.09	.05
77	Hosken Powell	.12	.09	.05
78	Bill Caudill	.12	.09	.05
79	Dan Petry	.12	.09	.05
80	George Foster	.15	.11	.06
81	Joe Morgan	.30	.25	.12
82	Burt Hooton	.12	.09	.05
83	Ryne Sandberg	42.50	32.00	17.00
84	Alan Ashby	.12	.09	.05
85	Ken Singleton	.12	.09	.05
86	Tom Hume	.12	.09	.05
87	Dennis Leonard	.12	.09	.05
88	Jim Gantner	.12	.09	.05
89	Leon Roberts	.12	.09	.05
90	Jerry Reuss	.12	.09	.05
91	Ben Oglivie	.12	.09	.05
92	Sparky Lyle (Super Veteran)	.12	.09	.05
93	John Castino	.12	.09	.05
94	Phil Niekro	.30	.25	.12
95	Alan Trammell	.40	.30	.15
96	Gaylord Perry	.30	.25	.12
97	Tom Herr	.12	.09	.05
98	Vance Law	.12	.09	.05
99	Dickie Noles	.12	.09	.05
100	Pete Rose	2.00	1.50	.80
101	Pete Rose (Super Veteran)	.70	.50	.30
102	Dave Concepcion	.12	.09	.05
103	Darrell Porter	.12	.09	.05
104	Ron Guidry	.25	.20	.10
105	Don Baylor	.15	.11	.06
106	Steve Rogers AS	.12	.09	.05
107	Greg Minton	.12	.09	.05
108	Glenn Hoffman	.12	.09	.05
109	Luis Leal	.12	.09	.05
110	Ken Griffey	.12	.09	.05
111	Expos Team	.12	.09	.05
112	Luis Pujols	.12	.09	.05
113	Julio Cruz	.12	.09	.05
114	Jim Slaton	.12	.09	.05
115	Chili Davis	.15	.11	.06
116	Pedro Guerrero	.30	.25	.12
117	Mike Ivie	.12	.09	.05
118	Chris Welsh	.12	.09	.05
119	Frank Pastore	.12	.09	.05
120	Len Barker	.12	.09	.05
121	Chris Speier	.12	.09	.05
122	Bobby Murcer	.12	.09	.05
123	Bill Russell	.12	.09	.05
124	Lloyd Moseby	.12	.09	.05
125	Leon Durham	.12	.09	.05
126	Carl Yastrzemski (Super Veteran)	.30	.25	.12
127	John Candelaria	.12	.09	.05
128	Phil Garner	.12	.09	.05
129	Checklist 1-132	.12	.09	.05
130	Dave Stieb	.15	.11	.06
131	Geoff Zahn	.12	.09	.05
132	Todd Cruz	.12	.09	.05
133	Tony Pena	.12	.09	.05
134	Hubie Brooks	.12	.09	.05
135	Dwight Evans	.15	.11	.06
136	Willie Aikens	.12	.09	.05
137	Woodie Fryman	.12	.09	.05
138	Rick Dempsey	.12	.09	.05
139	Bruce Berenyi	.12	.09	.05
140	Willie Randolph	.12	.09	.05
141	Eddie Murray	2.25	1.75	.90
142	Mike Caldwell	.12	.09	.05
143	Tony Gwynn	30.00	22.00	12.00
144	Tommy John (Super Veteran)	.12	.09	.05
145	Don Sutton	.30	.25	.12
146	Don Sutton (Super Veteran)	.15	.11	.06
147	Rick Manning	.12	.09	.05
148	George Hendrick	.12	.09	.05
149	Johnny Ray	.15	.11	.06
150	Bruce Sutter	.15	.11	.06
151	Bruce Sutter (Super Veteran)	.12	.09	.05
152	Jay Johnstone	.12	.09	.05
153	Jerry Koosman	.12	.09	.05
154	Johnnie LeMaster	.12	.09	.05
155	Dan Quisenberry	.15	.11	.06
156	Luis Salazar	.12	.09	.05
157	Steve Bedrosian	.15	.11	.06
158	Jim Sundberg	.12	.09	.05
159	Gaylord Perry (Super Veteran)	.15	.11	.06
160	Dave Kingman	.15	.11	.06
161	Dave Kingman (Super Veteran)	.12	.09	.05
162	Mark Clear	.12	.09	.05
163	Cal Ripken	18.00	13.50	7.25
164	Dave Palmer	.12	.09	.05
165	Dan Driessen	.12	.09	.05
166	Tug McGraw	.12	.09	.05
167	Denny Martinez	.12	.09	.05
168	Juan Eichelberger	.12	.09	.05
169	Doug Flynn	.12	.09	.05
170	Steve Howe	.12	.09	.05
171	Frank White	.12	.09	.05
172	Mike Flanagan	.12	.09	.05
173	Andre Dawson AS	.15	.11	.06
174	Manny Trillo AS	.12	.09	.05
175	Bo Diaz	.12	.09	.05
176	Dave Righetti	.30	.25	.12
177	Harold Baines	.25	.20	.10
178	Vida Blue	.12	.09	.05
179	Luis Tiant (Super Veteran)	.12	.09	.05
180	Rickey Henderson	4.25	3.25	1.75
181	Rick Rhoden	.12	.09	.05
182	Fred Lynn	.20	.15	.08
183	Ed Vande Berg	.12	.09	.05
184	Dwayne Murphy	.12	.09	.05
185	Tim Lollar	.12	.09	.05
186	Dave Tobik	.12	.09	.05
187	Tug McGraw (Super Veteran)	.12	.09	.05
188	Rick Miller	.12	.09	.05
189	Dan Schatzeder	.12	.09	.05
190	Cecil Cooper	.12	.09	.05
191	Jim Beattie	.12	.09	.05
192	Rich Dauer	.12	.09	.05
193	Al Cowens	.12	.09	.05
194	Roy Lee Jackson	.12	.09	.05
195	Mike Gates	.12	.09	.05
196	Tommy John	.20	.15	.08
197	Bob Forsch	.12	.09	.05
198	Steve Garvey	.60	.45	.25
199	Brad Mills	.12	.09	.05
200	Rod Carew	1.50	1.25	.60
201	Rod Carew (Super Veteran)	.30	.25	.12
202	Blue Jays Team	.12	.09	.05
203	Floyd Bannister	.12	.09	.05
204	Bruce Benedict	.12	.09	.05
205	Dave Parker	.30	.25	.12
206	Ken Oberkfell	.12	.09	.05
207	Graig Nettles (Super Veteran)	.12	.09	.05
208	Sparky Lyle	.12	.09	.05
209	Jason Thompson	.12	.09	.05
210	Jack Clark	.20	.15	.08
211	Jim Kaat	.15	.11	.06
212	John Stearns	.12	.09	.05
213	Tom Burgmeier	.12	.09	.05
214	Jerry White	.12	.09	.05
215	Mario Soto	.12	.09	.05
216	Scott McGregor	.12	.09	.05
217	Tim Stoddard	.12	.09	.05
218	Bill Laskey	.12	.09	.05
219	Reggie Jackson (Super Veteran)	.30	.25	.12
220	Dusty Baker	.12	.09	.05
221	Joe Niekro	.12	.09	.05
222	Damaso Garcia	.12	.09	.05
223	John Montefusco	.12	.09	.05
224	Mickey Rivers	.12	.09	.05
225	Enos Cabell	.12	.09	.05
226	LaMarr Hoyt	.12	.09	.05
227	Tim Raines	.40	.30	.15
228	Joaquin Andujar	.12	.09	.05
229	Tim Wallach	.25	.20	.10
230	Fergie Jenkins	.15	.11	.06
231	Fergie Jenkins (Super Veteran)	.12	.09	.05
232	Tom Brunansky	.25	.20	.10
233	Ivan DeJesus	.12	.09	.05
234	Bryn Smith	.12	.09	.05
235	Claudell Washington	.12	.09	.05
236	Steve Renko	.12	.09	.05
237	Dan Norman	.12	.09	.05
238	Cesar Cedeno	.12	.09	.05
239	Dave Stapleton	.12	.09	.05
240	Rich Gossage	.25	.20	.10
241	Rich Gossage (Super Veteran)	.12	.09	.05
242	Bob Stanley	.12	.09	.05
243	Rich Gale	.12	.09	.05
244	Sixto Lezcano	.12	.09	.05
245	Steve Sax	.25	.20	.10
246	Jerry Mumphrey	.12	.09	.05
247	Dave Smith	.12	.09	.05
248	Bake McBride	.12	.09	.05
249	Checklist 133-264	.12	.09	.05
250	Bill Buckner	.15	.11	.06
251	Kent Hrbek	.50	.40	.20
252	Gene Tenace	.12	.09	.05
253	Charlie Lea	.12	.09	.05
254	Rick Cerone	.12	.09	.05
255	Gene Garber	.12	.09	.05
256	Gene Garber (Super Veteran)	.12	.09	.05
257	Jesse Barfield	.75	.60	.30

258	Dave Winfield	3.25	2.50	1.25
259	Don Money	.12	.09	.05
260	Steve Kemp	.12	.09	.05
261	Steve Yeager	.12	.09	.05
262	Keith Hernandez	.40	.30	.15
263	Tippy Martinez	.12	.09	.05
264	Joe Morgan (Super Veteran)	.12	.09	.05
265	Joel Youngblood	.12	.09	.05
266	Bruce Sutter AS	.12	.09	.05
267	Terry Francona	.12	.09	.05
268	Neil Allen	.12	.09	.05
269	Ron Oester	.12	.09	.05
270	Dennis Eckersley	.12	.09	.05
271	Dale Berra	.12	.09	.05
272	Al Bumbry	.12	.09	.05
273	Lonnie Smith	.12	.09	.05
274	Terry Kennedy	.12	.09	.05
275	Ray Knight	.12	.09	.05
276	Mike Norris	.12	.09	.05
277	Rance Mulliniks	.12	.09	.05
278	Dan Spillner	.12	.09	.05
279	Bucky Dent	.12	.09	.05
280	Bert Blyleven	.15	.11	.06
281	Barry Bonnell	.12	.09	.05
282	Reggie Smith	.12	.09	.05
283	Reggie Smith (Super Veteran)	.12	.09	.05
284	Ted Simmons	.15	.11	.06
285	Lance Parrish	.30	.25	.12
286	Larry Christenson	.12	.09	.05
287	Ruppert Jones	.12	.09	.05
288	Bob Welch	.12	.09	.05
289	John Wathan	.12	.09	.05
290	Jeff Reardon	.12	.09	.05
291	Dave Revering	.12	.09	.05
292	Craig Swan	.12	.09	.05
293	Graig Nettles	.15	.11	.06
294	Alfredo Griffin	.12	.09	.05
295	Jerry Remy	.12	.09	.05
296	Joe Sambito	.12	.09	.05
297	Ron LeFlore	.12	.09	.05
298	Brian Downing	.12	.09	.05
299	Jim Palmer	1.50	1.25	.60
300	Mike Schmidt	2.50	2.00	1.00
301	Mike Schmidt (Super Veteran)	1.50	1.25	.60
302	Ernie Whitt	.12	.09	.05
303	Andre Dawson	2.25	1.75	.90
304	Bobby Murcer (Super Veteran)	.12	.09	.05
305	Larry Bowa	.12	.09	.05
306	Lee Mazzilli	.12	.09	.05
307	Lou Piniella	.12	.09	.05
308	Buck Martinez	.12	.09	.05
309	Jerry Martin	.12	.09	.05
310	Greg Luzinski	.15	.11	.06
311	Al Oliver	.15	.11	.06
312	Mike Torrez	.12	.09	.05
313	Dick Ruthven	.12	.09	.05
314	Gary Carter AS	.30	.25	.12
315	Rick Burleson	.12	.09	.05
316	Phil Niekro (Super Veteran)	.15	.11	.06
317	Moose Haas	.12	.09	.05
318	Carney Lansford	.12	.09	.05
319	Tim Foli	.12	.09	.05
320	Steve Rogers	.12	.09	.05
321	Kirk Gibson	.30	.25	.12
322	Glenn Hubbard	.12	.09	.05
323	Luis DeLeon	.12	.09	.05
324	Mike Marshall	.20	.15	.08
325	Von Hayes	.20	.15	.08
326	Garth Iorg	.12	.09	.05
327	Jose Cruz	.12	.09	.05
328	Jim Palmer (Super Veteran)	.15	.11	.06
329	Darrell Evans	.12	.09	.05
330	Buddy Bell	.12	.09	.05
331	Mike Krukow	.12	.09	.05
332	Omar Moreno	.12	.09	.05
333	Dave LaRoche	.12	.09	.05
334	Dave LaRoche (Super Veteran)	.12	.09	.05
335	Bill Madlock	.15	.11	.06
336	Garry Templeton	.12	.09	.05
337	John Lowenstein	.12	.09	.05
338	Willie Upshaw	.12	.09	.05
339	Dave Hostetler	.12	.09	.05
340	Larry Gura	.12	.09	.05
341	Doug DeCinces	.12	.09	.05
342	Mike Schmidt AS	.40	.30	.15
343	Charlie Hough	.12	.09	.05
344	Andre Thornton	.12	.09	.05
345	Jim Clancy	.12	.09	.05
346	Ken Forsch	.12	.09	.05
347	Sammy Stewart	.12	.09	.05
348	Alan Bannister	.12	.09	.05
349	Checklist 265-396	.12	.09	.05
350	Robin Yount	2.50	2.00	1.00
351	Warren Cromartie	.12	.09	.05
352	Tim Raines AS	.30	.25	.12
353	Tony Armas	.12	.09	.05
354	Tom Seaver (Super Veteran)	1.00	.70	.40
355	Tony Perez	.20	.15	.08
356	Toby Harrah	.12	.09	.05
357	Dan Ford	.12	.09	.05
358	Charlie Puleo	.12	.09	.05
359	Dave Collins	.12	.09	.05
360	Nolan Ryan	10.25	7.75	4.00
361	Nolan Ryan (Super Veteran)	5.00	3.75	2.00
362	Bill Almon	.12	.09	.05
363	Eddie Milner	.12	.09	.05
364	Gary Lucas	.12	.09	.05
365	Dave Lopes	.12	.09	.05
366	Bob Boone	.12	.09	.05
367	Biff Pocoroba	.12	.09	.05
368	Richie Zisk	.12	.09	.05
369	Tony Bernazard	.12	.09	.05
370	Gary Carter	.50	.40	.20
371	Paul Molitor	3.00	2.25	1.25
372	Art Howe	.12	.09	.05
373	Pete Rose AS	.60	.45	.25
374	Glenn Adams	.12	.09	.05
375	Pete Vukovich	.12	.09	.05
376	Gary Lavelle	.12	.09	.05
377	Lee May	.12	.09	.05
378	Lee May (Super Veteran)	.12	.09	.05
379	Butch Wynegar	.12	.09	.05
380	Ron Davis	.12	.09	.05
381	Bob Grich	.12	.09	.05
382	Gary Roenicke	.12	.09	.05
383	Jim Kaat	.15	.11	.06
384	Steve Carlton AS	.30	.25	.12
385	Mike Easler	.12	.09	.05
386	Rod Carew AS	.30	.25	.12
387	Bobby Grich AS	.12	.09	.05
388	George Brett AS	.40	.30	.15
389	Robin Yount AS	.20	.15	.08
390	Reggie Jackson AS	.30	.25	.12
391	Rickey Henderson AS	1.50	1.25	.60
392	Fred Lynn AS	.12	.09	.05
393	Carlton Fisk AS	.12	.09	.05
394	Pete Vukovich AS	.12	.09	.05
395	Larry Gura AS	.12	.09	.05
396	Dan Quisenberry AS	.12	.09	.05

1984 O-Pee-Chee

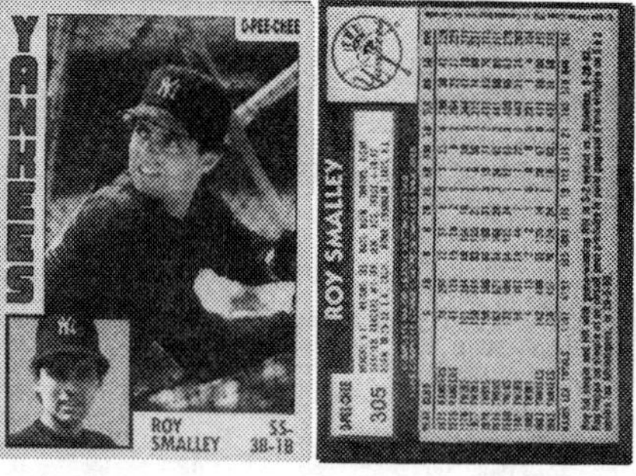

Almost identical in design to the 1984 Topps set, the 1984 O-Pee-Chee set contains 396 cards. The O-Pee-Chee cards display the Canadian company's logo in the upper right corner and the backs of the cards are printed in both English and French. The cards measure 2-1/2" by 3-1/2", and some include the extra line on the front of the card to indicate a trade.

		MT	NR MT	EX
Complete Set (396):		42.50	32.00	17.00
Common Player:		.12	.09	.05
1	Pascual Perez	.20	.15	.08
2	Cal Ripken	5.50	4.25	2.25
3	Lloyd Moseby	.20	.15	.08
4	Mel Hall	.25	.20	.10
5	Willie Wilson	.30	.25	.12
6	Mike Morgan	.12	.09	.05
7	Gary Lucas	.12	.09	.05
8	Don Mattingly	13.50	10.00	5.50
9	Jim Gott	.12	.09	.05
10	Robin Yount	1.50	1.25	.60
11	Joey McLaughlin	.12	.09	.05
12	Billy Sample	.12	.09	.05
13	Oscar Gamble	.12	.09	.05
14	Bill Russell	.20	.15	.08
15	Burt Hooton	.20	.15	.08
16	Omar Moreno	.12	.09	.05
17	Dave Lopes	.20	.15	.08
18	Dale Berra	.12	.09	.05
19	Rance Mulliniks	.12	.09	.05
20	Greg Luzinski	.20	.15	.08
21	Doug Sisk	.20	.15	.08
22	Don Robinson	.12	.09	.05
23	Keith Moreland	.20	.15	.08
24	Richard Dotson	.20	.15	.08
25	Glenn Hubbard	.12	.09	.05
26	Rod Carew	1.00	.70	.40
27	Alan Wiggins	.12	.09	.05
28	Frank Viola	.50	.40	.20
29	Phil Niekro	.50	.40	.20
30	Wade Boggs	3.75	2.75	1.50
31	Dave Parker	.50	.40	.20
32	Bobby Ramos	.12	.09	.05
33	Tom Burgmeier	.12	.09	.05
34	Eddie Milner	.12	.09	.05
35	Don Sutton	.50	.40	.20
36	Glenn Wilson	.25	.20	.10
37	Mike Krukow	.20	.15	.08
38	Dave Collins	.12	.09	.05
39	Garth Iorg	.12	.09	.05
40	Dusty Baker	.20	.15	.08
41	Tony Bernazard	.12	.09	.05
42	Claudell Washington	.20	.15	.08
43	Cecil Cooper	.25	.20	.10
44	Dan Driessen	.20	.15	.08
45	Jerry Mumphrey	.12	.09	.05
46	Rick Rhoden	.20	.15	.08
47	Rudy Law	.12	.09	.05
48	Julio Franco	.85	.60	.35
49	Mike Norris	.12	.09	.05
50	Chris Chambliss	.20	.15	.08
51	Pete Falcone	.12	.09	.05
52	Mike Marshall	.30	.25	.12
53	Amos Otis	.20	.15	.08
54	Jesse Orosco	.20	.15	.08
55	Dave Concepcion	.25	.20	.10
56	Gary Allenson	.12	.09	.05
57	Dan Schatzeder	.12	.09	.05
58	Jerry Remy	.12	.09	.05
59	Carney Lansford	.25	.20	.10
60	Paul Molitor	1.75	1.25	.70
61	Chris Codiroli	.12	.09	.05
62	Dave Hostetler	.12	.09	.05
63	Ed Vande Berg	.12	.09	.05
64	Ryne Sandberg	6.25	4.75	2.50
65	Kirk Gibson	.60	.45	.25
66	Nolan Ryan	6.00	4.50	2.50
67	Gary Ward	.12	.09	.05
68	Luis Salazar	.12	.09	.05
69	Dan Quisenberry	.30	.25	.12
70	Gary Matthews	.20	.15	.08
71	Pete O'Brien	1.25	.90	.50
72	John Wathan	.20	.15	.08
73	Jody Davis	.25	.20	.10
74	Kent Tekulve	.20	.15	.08
75	Bob Forsch	.20	.15	.08
76	Alfredo Griffin	.20	.15	.08
77	Bryn Smith	.20	.15	.08
78	Mike Torrez	.20	.15	.08
79	Mike Hargrove	.20	.15	.08
80	Steve Rogers	.20	.15	.08
81	Bake McBride	.12	.09	.05
82	Doug DeCinces	.25	.20	.10
83	Richie Zisk	.20	.15	.08
84	Randy Bush	.12	.09	.05
85	Atlee Hammaker	.20	.15	.08
86	Chet Lemon	.20	.15	.08
87	Frank Pastore	.12	.09	.05
88	Alan Trammell	.60	.45	.25
89	Terry Francona	.12	.09	.05
90	Pedro Guerrero	.60	.45	.25
91	Dan Spillner	.12	.09	.05
92	Lloyd Moseby	.20	.15	.08
93	Bob Knepper	.20	.15	.08
94	Ted Simmons	.30	.25	.12
95	Aurelio Lopez	.12	.09	.05
96	Bill Buckner	.30	.25	.12
97	LaMarr Hoyt	.12	.09	.05
98	Tom Brunansky	.30	.25	.12
99	Ron Oester	.12	.09	.05
100	Reggie Jackson	1.00	.70	.40
101	Ron Davis	.12	.09	.05
102	Ken Oberkfell	.12	.09	.05
103	Dwayne Murphy	.20	.15	.08
104	Jim Slaton	.12	.09	.05
105	Tony Armas	.20	.15	.08
106	Ernie Whitt	.12	.09	.05
107	Johnnie LeMaster	.12	.09	.05
108	Randy Moffitt	.12	.09	.05
109	Terry Forster	.20	.15	.08
110	Ron Guidry	.50	.40	.20
111	Bill Virdon	.12	.09	.05
112	Doyle Alexander	.25	.20	.10
113	Lonnie Smith	.20	.15	.08
114	Checklist	.12	.09	.05
115	Andre Thornton	.20	.15	.08
116	Jeff Reardon	.30	.25	.12
117	Tom Herr	.25	.20	.10
118	Charlie Hough	.20	.15	.08
119	Phil Garner	.20	.15	.08
120	Keith Hernandez	.60	.45	.25
121	Rich Gossage	.40	.30	.15
122	Ted Simmons	.30	.25	.12
123	Butch Wynegar	.20	.15	.08
124	Damaso Garcia	.20	.15	.08
125	Britt Burns	.12	.09	.05
126	Bert Blyleven	.30	.25	.12
127	Carlton Fisk	.40	.30	.15
128	Rick Manning	.12	.09	.05
129	Bill Laskey	.12	.09	.05
130	Ozzie Smith	1.00	.70	.40
131	Bo Diaz	.12	.09	.05
132	Tom Paciorek	.12	.09	.05
133	Dave Rozema	.12	.09	.05
134	Dave Stieb	.30	.25	.12
135	Brian Downing	.20	.15	.08
136	Rick Camp	.12	.09	.05
137	Willie Aikens	.12	.09	.05
138	Charlie Moore	.12	.09	.05
139	George Frazier	.12	.09	.05
140	Storm Davis	.20	.15	.08
141	Glenn Hoffman	.12	.09	.05
142	Charlie Lea	.12	.09	.05
143	Mike Vail	.12	.09	.05
144	Steve Sax	.30	.25	.12
145	Gary Lavelle	.12	.09	.05
146	Gorman Thomas	.20	.15	.08
147	Dan Petry	.20	.15	.08
148	Mark Clear	.12	.09	.05
149	Dave Beard	.12	.09	.05
150	Dale Murphy	1.25	.90	.50
151	Steve Trout	.12	.09	.05
152	Tony Pena	.20	.15	.08
153	Geoff Zahn	.12	.09	.05
154	Dave Henderson	.20	.15	.08
155	Frank White	.25	.20	.10
156	Dick Ruthven	.12	.09	.05
157	Gary Gaetti	.70	.50	.30
158	Lance Parrish	.60	.45	.25
159	Joe Price	.12	.09	.05
160	Mario Soto	.20	.15	.08
161	Tug McGraw	.25	.20	.10
162	Bob Ojeda	.20	.15	.08
163	George Hendrick	.20	.15	.08
164	Scott Sanderson	.12	.09	.05
165	Ken Singleton	.20	.15	.08
166	Terry Kennedy	.20	.15	.08
167	Gene Garber	.12	.09	.05
168	Juan Bonilla	.12	.09	.05
169	Larry Parrish	.20	.15	.08
170	Jerry Reuss	.20	.15	.08
171	John Tudor	.25	.20	.10
172	Dave Kingman	.30	.25	.12
173	Garry Templeton	.20	.15	.08
174	Bob Boone	.20	.15	.08

175	Graig Nettles	.25	.20	.10
176	Lee Smith	.20	.15	.08
177	LaMarr Hoyt	.12	.09	.05
178	Bill Krueger	.12	.09	.05
179	Buck Martinez	.12	.09	.05
180	Manny Trillo	.20	.15	.08
181	Lou Whitaker	.50	.40	.20
182	Darryl Strawberry	4.50	3.50	1.75
183	Neil Allen	.12	.09	.05
184	Jim Rice	.60	.45	.25
185	Sixto Lezcano	.12	.09	.05
186	Tom Hume	.12	.09	.05
187	Garry Maddox	.20	.15	.08
188	Bryan Little	.12	.09	.05
189	Jose Cruz	.25	.20	.10
190	Ben Oglivie	.20	.15	.08
191	Cesar Cedeno	.25	.20	.10
192	Nick Esasky	.60	.45	.25
193	Ken Forsch	.12	.09	.05
194	Jim Palmer	1.00	.70	.40
195	Jack Morris	1.00	.70	.40
196	Steve Howe	.20	.15	.08
197	Harold Baines	.30	.25	.12
198	Bill Doran	1.00	.70	.40
199	Willie Hernandez	.25	.20	.10
200	Andre Dawson	1.00	.70	.40
201	Bruce Kison	.12	.09	.05
202	Bobby Cox	.12	.09	.05
203	Matt Keough	.12	.09	.05
204	Ron Guidry	.50	.40	.20
205	Greg Minton	.12	.09	.05
206	Al Holland	.12	.09	.05
207	Luis Leal	.12	.09	.05
208	Jose Oquendo	.12	.09	.05
209	Leon Durham	.25	.20	.10
210	Joe Morgan	.50	.40	.20
211	Lou Whitaker AS	.25	.20	.10
212	George Brett AS	.40	.30	.15
213	Bruce Hurst	.20	.15	.08
214	Steve Carlton	.70	.50	.30
215	Tippy Martinez	.12	.09	.05
216	Ken Landreaux	.12	.09	.05
217	Alan Ashby	.12	.09	.05
218	Dennis Eckersley	.85	.60	.35
219	Craig McMurtry	.12	.09	.05
220	Fernando Valenzuela	.60	.45	.25
221	Cliff Johnson	.12	.09	.05
222	Rick Honeycutt	.12	.09	.05
223	George Brett	1.75	1.25	.70
224	Rusty Staub	.25	.20	.10
225	Lee Mazzilli	.20	.15	.08
226	Pat Putnam	.12	.09	.05
227	Bob Welch	.20	.15	.08
228	Rick Cerone	.12	.09	.05
229	Lee Lacy	.12	.09	.05
230	Rickey Henderson	3.00	2.25	1.25
231	Gary Redus	.50	.40	.20
232	Tim Wallach	.30	.25	.12
233	Checklist	.12	.09	.05
234	Rafael Ramirez	.12	.09	.05
235	Matt Young	.25	.20	.10
236	Ellis Valentine	.12	.09	.05
237	John Castino	.12	.09	.05
238	Eric Show	.20	.15	.08
239	Bob Horner	.30	.25	.12
240	Eddie Murray	1.25	.90	.50
241	Billy Almon	.12	.09	.05
242	Greg Brock	.20	.15	.08
243	Bruce Sutter	.30	.25	.12
244	Dwight Evans	.30	.25	.12
245	Rick Sutcliffe	.25	.20	.10
246	Terry Crowley	.12	.09	.05
247	Fred Lynn	.40	.30	.15
248	Bill Dawley	.12	.09	.05
249	Dave Stapleton	.12	.09	.05
250	Bill Madlock	.30	.25	.12
251	Jim Sundberg	.20	.15	.08
252	Steve Yeager	.12	.09	.05
253	Jim Wohlford	.12	.09	.05
254	Shane Rawley	.20	.15	.08
255	Bruce Benedict	.12	.09	.05
256	Dave Geisel	.12	.09	.05
257	Julio Cruz	.12	.09	.05
258	Luis Sanchez	.12	.09	.05
259	Von Hayes	.25	.20	.10
260	Scott McGregor	.20	.15	.08
261	Tom Seaver	1.25	.90	.50
262	Doug Flynn	.12	.09	.05
263	Wayne Gross	.12	.09	.05
264	Larry Gura	.12	.09	.05
265	John Montefusco	.12	.09	.05
266	Dave Winfield	1.75	1.25	.70
267	Tim Lollar	.12	.09	.05
268	Ron Washington	.12	.09	.05
269	Mickey Rivers	.20	.15	.08
270	Mookie Wilson	.20	.15	.08
271	Moose Haas	.12	.09	.05
272	Rick Dempsey	.20	.15	.08
273	Dan Quisenberry	.30	.25	.12
274	Steve Henderson	.12	.09	.05
275	Len Matuszek	.12	.09	.05
276	Frank Tanana	.20	.15	.08
277	Dave Righetti	.40	.30	.15
278	Jorge Bell	.40	.30	.15
279	Ivan DeJesus	.12	.09	.05
280	Floyd Bannister	.20	.15	.08
281	Dale Murray	.12	.09	.05
282	Andre Robertson	.12	.09	.05
283	Rollie Fingers	.40	.30	.15
284	Tommy John	.40	.30	.15
285	Darrell Porter	.20	.15	.08
286	Lary Sorensen	.12	.09	.05
287	Warren Cromartie	.12	.09	.05
288	Jim Beattie	.12	.09	.05
289	Blue Jays Team	.25	.20	.10
290	Dave Dravecky	.20	.15	.08
291	Eddie Murray AS	.50	.40	.20
292	Greg Bargar	.12	.09	.05
293	Tom Underwood	.12	.09	.05
294	U.L. Washington	.12	.09	.05
295	Mike Flanagan	.20	.15	.08
296	Rich Gedman	.20	.15	.08
297	Bruce Berenyi	.12	.09	.05
298	Jim Gantner	.12	.09	.05
299	Bill Caudill	.12	.09	.05
300	Pete Rose	1.00	.70	.40
301	Steve Kemp	.20	.15	.08
302	Barry Bonnell	.12	.09	.05
303	Joel Youngblood	.12	.09	.05
304	Rick Langford	.12	.09	.05
305	Roy Smalley	.12	.09	.05
306	Ken Griffey	.25	.20	.10
307	Al Oliver	.25	.20	.10
308	Ron Hassey	.12	.09	.05
309	Len Barker	.12	.09	.05
310	Willie McGee	.60	.45	.25
311	Jerry Koosman	.20	.15	.08
312	Jorge Orta	.12	.09	.05
313	Pete Vuckovich	.20	.15	.08
314	George Wright	.12	.09	.05
315	Bob Grich	.25	.20	.10
316	Jesse Barfield	.50	.40	.20
317	Willie Upshaw	.20	.15	.08
318	Bill Gullickson	.20	.15	.08
319	Ray Burris	.12	.09	.05
320	Bob Stanley	.20	.15	.08
321	Ray Knight	.20	.15	.08
322	Ken Schrom	.12	.09	.05
323	Johnny Ray	.20	.15	.08
324	Brian Giles	.12	.09	.05
325	Darrell Evans	.25	.20	.10
326	Mike Caldwell	.12	.09	.05
327	Ruppert Jones	.12	.09	.05
328	Chris Speier	.12	.09	.05
329	Bobby Castillo	.12	.09	.05
330	John Candelaria	.20	.15	.08
331	Bucky Dent	.20	.15	.08
332	Expos Team	.25	.20	.10
333	Larry Herndon	.12	.09	.05
334	Chuck Rainey	.12	.09	.05
335	Don Baylor	.30	.25	.12
336	Bob James	.25	.20	.10
337	Jim Clancy	.20	.15	.08
338	Duane Kuiper	.12	.09	.05
339	Roy Lee Jackson	.12	.09	.05
340	Hal McRae	.25	.20	.10
341	Larry McWilliams	.12	.09	.05
342	Tim Foli	.12	.09	.05
343	Fergie Jenkins	.30	.25	.12
344	Dickie Thon	.20	.15	.08
345	Kent Hrbek	.60	.45	.25
346	Larry Bowa	.25	.20	.10
347	Buddy Bell	.25	.20	.10
348	Toby Harrah	.20	.15	.08
349	Dan Ford	.12	.09	.05
350	George Foster	.30	.25	.12
351	Lou Piniella	.25	.20	.10
352	Dave Stewart	.25	.20	.10
353	Mike Easler	.20	.15	.08
354	Jeff Burroughs	.20	.15	.08
355	Jason Thompson	.12	.09	.05
356	Glenn Abbott	.12	.09	.05
357	Ron Cey	.25	.20	.10
358	Bob Dernier	.12	.09	.05
359	Jim Acker	.12	.09	.05
360	Willie Randolph	.20	.15	.08
361	Mike Schmidt	2.25	1.75	.90
362	David Green	.12	.09	.05
363	Cal Ripken AS	1.75	1.25	.70
364	Jim Rice AS	.50	.40	.20
365	Steve Bedrosian	.20	.15	.08
366	Gary Carter	.70	.50	.30
367	Chili Davis	.25	.20	.10
368	Hubie Brooks	.25	.20	.10
369	Steve McCatty	.12	.09	.05
370	Tim Raines	.60	.45	.25
371	Joaquin Andujar	.20	.15	.08
372	Gary Roenicke	.12	.09	.05
373	Ron Kittle	.25	.20	.10
374	Rich Dauer	.12	.09	.05
375	Dennis Leonard	.20	.15	.08
376	Rick Burleson	.20	.15	.08
377	Eric Rasmussen	.12	.09	.05
378	Dave Winfield	.60	.45	.25
379	Checklist	.12	.09	.05
380	Steve Garvey	.70	.50	.30
381	Jack Clark	.40	.30	.15
382	Odell Jones	.12	.09	.05
383	Terry Puhl	.12	.09	.05
384	Joe Niekro	.20	.15	.08
385	Tony Perez	.30	.25	.12
386	George Hendrick AS	.20	.15	.08
387	Johnny Ray AS	.20	.15	.08
388	Mike Schmidt AS	.60	.45	.25
389	Ozzie Smith AS	.20	.15	.08
390	Tim Raines AS	.40	.30	.15
391	Dale Murphy AS	.60	.45	.25
392	Andre Dawson AS	.30	.25	.12
393	Gary Carter AS	.40	.30	.15
394	Steve Rogers AS	.20	.15	.08
395	Steve Carlton AS	.40	.30	.15
396	Jesse Orosco AS	.20	.15	.08

1985 O-Pee-Chee

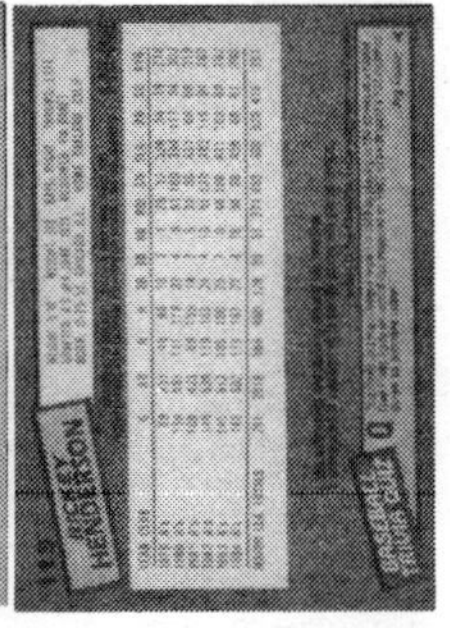

This 396-card set is almost identical in design to the 1985 Topps set. Measuring 2-1/2" by 3-1/2", the fronts of the Canadian-issued cards display the O-Pee-Chee logo in the upper left corner, and the backs of the cards are printed in both French and English. A "traded" line appears on the front of some of the cards to indicate a change in teams.

		MT	NR MT	EX
Complete Set (396):		35.00	26.00	14.00
Common Player:		.08	.06	.03
1	Tom Seaver	.25	.20	.10
2	Gary Lavelle	.08	.06	.03
3	Tim Wallach	.12	.09	.05
4	Jim Wohlford	.08	.06	.03
5	Jeff Robinson	.10	.08	.04
6	Willie Wilson	.15	.11	.06
7	Cliff Johnson	.08	.06	.03
8	Willie Randolph	.08	.06	.03
9	Larry Herndon	.08	.06	.03
10	Kirby Puckett	17.00	12.50	6.75
11	Mookie Wilson	.08	.06	.03
12	Dave Lopes	.08	.06	.03
13	Tim Lollar	.08	.06	.03
14	Chris Bando	.08	.06	.03
15	Jerry Koosman	.08	.06	.03
16	Bobby Meacham	.08	.06	.03
17	Mike Scott	.15	.11	.06
18	Rich Gedman	.08	.06	.03
19	George Frazier	.08	.06	.03
20	Chet Lemon	.08	.06	.03
21	Dave Concepcion	.10	.08	.04
22	Jason Thompson	.08	.06	.03
23	Bret Saberhagen	1.00	.70	.40
24	Jesse Barfield	.15	.11	.06
25	Steve Bedrosian	.10	.08	.04
26	Roy Smalley	.08	.06	.03
27	Bruce Berenyi	.08	.06	.03
28	Butch Wynegar	.08	.06	.03
29	Alan Ashby	.08	.06	.03
30	Cal Ripken	3.25	2.50	1.25
31	Luis Leal	.08	.06	.03
32	Dave Dravecky	.08	.06	.03
33	Tito Landrum	.08	.06	.03
34	Pedro Guerrero	.20	.15	.08
35	Graig Nettles	.12	.09	.05
36	Fred Breining	.08	.06	.03
37	Roy Lee Jackson	.08	.06	.03
38	Steve Henderson	.08	.06	.03
39	Gary Pettis	.10	.08	.04
40	Phil Niekro	.20	.15	.08
41	Dwight Gooden	3.00	2.25	1.25
42	Luis Sanchez	.08	.06	.03
43	Lee Smith	.10	.08	.04
44	Dickie Thon	.10	.08	.04
45	Greg Minton	.08	.06	.03
46	Mike Flanagan	.10	.08	.04
47	Bud Black	.10	.08	.04
48	Tony Fernandez	.75	.60	.30
49	Carlton Fisk	.15	.11	.06
50	John Candelaria	.08	.06	.03
51	Bob Watson	.08	.06	.03
52	Rick Leach	.08	.06	.03
53	Rick Rhoden	.08	.06	.03
54	Cesar Cedeno	.10	.08	.04
55	Frank Tanana	.08	.06	.03
56	Larry Bowa	.10	.08	.04
57	Willie McGee	.20	.15	.08
58	Rich Dauer	.08	.06	.03
59	Jorge Bell	.50	.40	.20
60	George Hendrick	.08	.06	.03
61	Donnie Moore	.08	.06	.03
62	Mike Ramsey	.08	.06	.03
63	Nolan Ryan	4.00	3.00	1.50
64	Mark Bailey	.08	.06	.03
65	Bill Buckner	.10	.08	.04
66	Jerry Reuss	.08	.06	.03
67	Mike Schmidt	1.25	.90	.50
68	Von Hayes	.12	.09	.05
69	Phil Bradley	.70	.50	.30
70	Don Baylor	.12	.09	.05
71	Julio Cruz	.08	.06	.03
72	Rick Sutcliffe	.10	.08	.04
73	Storm Davis	.08	.06	.03
74	Mike Krukow	.08	.06	.03
75	Willie Upshaw	.08	.06	.03
76	Craig Lefferts	.08	.06	.03
77	Lloyd Moseby	.10	.08	.04
78	Ron Davis	.08	.06	.03
79	Rick Mahler	.08	.06	.03
80	Keith Hernandez	.25	.20	.10
81	Vance Law	.08	.06	.03
82	Joe Price	.08	.06	.03
83	Dennis Lamp	.08	.06	.03
84	Gary Ward	.08	.06	.03
85	Mike Marshall	.12	.09	.05
86	Marvell Wynne	.08	.06	.03

87	David Green	.08	.06	.03
88	Bryn Smith	.08	.06	.03
89	Sixto Lezcano	.08	.06	.03
90	Rich Gossage	.15	.11	.06
91	Jeff Burroughs	.08	.06	.03
92	Bobby Brown	.08	.06	.03
93	Oscar Gamble	.08	.06	.03
94	Rick Dempsey	.08	.06	.03
95	Jose Cruz	.10	.08	.04
96	Johnny Ray	.10	.08	.04
97	Joel Youngblood	.08	.06	.03
98	Eddie Whitson	.08	.06	.03
99	Milt Wilcox	.08	.06	.03
100	George Brett	1.00	.70	.40
101	Jim Acker	.08	.06	.03
102	Jim Sundberg	.08	.06	.03
103	Ozzie Virgil	.08	.06	.03
104	Mike Fitzgerald	.08	.06	.03
105	Ron Kittle	.10	.08	.04
106	Pascual Perez	.08	.06	.03
107	Barry Bonnell	.08	.06	.03
108	Lou Whitaker	.20	.15	.08
109	Gary Roenicke	.08	.06	.03
110	Alejandro Pena	.08	.06	.03
111	Doug DeCinces	.10	.08	.04
112	Doug Flynn	.08	.06	.03
113	Tom Herr	.10	.08	.04
114	Bob James	.08	.06	.03
115	Rickey Henderson	.85	.60	.35
116	Pete Rose	.75	.60	.30
117	Greg Gross	.08	.06	.03
118	Eric Show	.08	.06	.03
119	Buck Martinez	.08	.06	.03
120	Steve Kemp	.08	.06	.03
121	Checklist 1-132	.08	.06	.03
122	Tom Brunansky	.12	.09	.05
123	Dave Kingman	.12	.09	.05
124	Garry Templeton	.08	.06	.03
125	Kent Tekulve	.08	.06	.03
126	Darryl Strawberry	.85	.60	.35
127	Mark Gubicza	.25	.20	.10
128	Ernie Whitt	.08	.06	.03
129	Don Robinson	.08	.06	.03
130	Al Oliver	.10	.08	.04
131	Mario Soto	.08	.06	.03
132	Jeff Leonard	.08	.06	.03
133	Andre Dawson	.25	.20	.10
134	Bruce Hurst	.08	.06	.03
135	Bobby Cox	.08	.06	.03
136	Matt Young	.08	.06	.03
137	Bob Forsch	.08	.06	.03
138	Ron Darling	.70	.50	.30
139	Steve Trout	.08	.06	.03
140	Geoff Zahn	.08	.06	.03
141	Ken Forsch	.08	.06	.03
142	Jerry Willard	.08	.06	.03
143	Bill Gullickson	.08	.06	.03
144	Mike Mason	.08	.06	.03
145	Alvin Davis	1.25	.90	.50
146	Gary Redus	.08	.06	.03
147	Willie Aikens	.08	.06	.03
148	Steve Yeager	.08	.06	.03
149	Dickie Noles	.08	.06	.03
150	Jim Rice	.30	.25	.12
151	Moose Haas	.08	.06	.03
152	Steve Balboni	.08	.06	.03
153	Frank LaCorte	.08	.06	.03
154	Argenis Salazar	.08	.06	.03
155	Bob Grich	.10	.08	.04
156	Craig Reynolds	.08	.06	.03
157	Bill Madlock	.10	.08	.04
158	Pat Tabler	.10	.08	.04
159	Don Slaught	.08	.06	.03
160	Lance Parrish	.20	.15	.08
161	Ken Schrom	.08	.06	.03
162	Wally Backman	.08	.06	.03
163	Dennis Eckersley	.10	.08	.04
164	Dave Collins	.08	.06	.03
165	Dusty Baker	.08	.06	.03
166	Claudell Washington	.08	.06	.03
167	Rick Camp	.08	.06	.03
168	Garth Iorg	.08	.06	.03
169	Shane Rawley	.08	.06	.03
170	George Foster	.12	.09	.05
171	Tony Bernazard	.08	.06	.03
172	Don Sutton	.20	.15	.08
173	Jerry Remy	.08	.06	.03
174	Rick Honeycutt	.08	.06	.03
175	Dave Parker	.20	.15	.08
176	Buddy Bell	.10	.08	.04
177	Steve Garvey	.30	.25	.12
178	Miguel Dilone	.08	.06	.03
179	Tommy John	.15	.11	.06
180	Dave Winfield	1.25	.90	.50
181	Alan Trammell	.30	.25	.12
182	Rollie Fingers	.15	.11	.06
183	Larry McWilliams	.08	.06	.03
184	Carmen Castillo	.08	.06	.03
185	Al Holland	.08	.06	.03
186	Jerry Mumphrey	.08	.06	.03
187	Chris Chambliss	.08	.06	.03
188	Jim Clancy	.08	.06	.03
189	Glenn Wilson	.10	.08	.04
190	Rusty Staub	.10	.08	.04
191	Ozzie Smith	1.00	.70	.40
192	Howard Johnson	3.00	2.25	1.25
193	Jimmy Key	1.75	1.25	.70
194	Terry Kennedy	.08	.06	.03
195	Glenn Hubbard	.08	.06	.03
196	Pete O'Brien	.10	.08	.04
197	Keith Moreland	.08	.06	.03
198	Eddie Milner	.08	.06	.03
199	Dave Engle	.08	.06	.03
200	Reggie Jackson	.85	.60	.35
201	Burt Hooton	.08	.06	.03
202	Gorman Thomas	.08	.06	.03
203	Larry Parrish	.08	.06	.03
204	Bob Stanley	.08	.06	.03
205	Steve Rogers	.08	.06	.03
206	Phil Garner	.08	.06	.03
207	Ed Vande Berg	.08	.06	.03
208	Jack Clark	.15	.11	.06
209	Bill Campbell	.08	.06	.03
210	Gary Matthews	.08	.06	.03
211	Dave Palmer	.08	.06	.03
212	Tony Perez	.15	.11	.06
213	Sammy Stewart	.08	.06	.03
214	John Tudor	.10	.08	.04
215	Bob Brenly	.08	.06	.03
216	Jim Gantner	.08	.06	.03
217	Bryan Clark	.08	.06	.03
218	Doyle Alexander	.10	.08	.04
219	Bo Diaz	.08	.06	.03
220	Fred Lynn	.15	.11	.06
221	Eddie Murray	.40	.30	.15
222	Hubie Brooks	.10	.08	.04
223	Tom Hume	.08	.06	.03
224	Al Cowens	.08	.06	.03
225	Mike Boddicker	.10	.08	.04
226	Len Matuszek	.08	.06	.03
227	Danny Darwin	.08	.06	.03
228	Scott McGregor	.08	.06	.03
229	Dave LaPoint	.08	.06	.03
230	Gary Carter	.30	.25	.12
231	Joaquin Andujar	.08	.06	.03
232	Rafael Ramirez	.08	.06	.03
233	Wayne Gross	.08	.06	.03
234	Neil Allen	.08	.06	.03
235	Gary Maddox	.08	.06	.03
236	Mark Thurmond	.08	.06	.03
237	Julio Franco	1.00	.70	.40
238	Ray Burris	.08	.06	.03
239	Tim Teufel	.08	.06	.03
240	Dave Stieb	.12	.09	.05
241	Brett Butler	.08	.06	.03
242	Greg Brock	.08	.06	.03
243	Barbaro Garbey	.08	.06	.03
244	Greg Walker	.10	.08	.04
245	Chili Davis	.10	.08	.04
246	Darrell Porter	.08	.06	.03
247	Tippy Martinez	.08	.06	.03
248	Terry Forster	.08	.06	.03
249	Harold Baines	.15	.11	.06
250	Jesse Orosco	.08	.06	.03
251	Brad Gulden	.08	.06	.03
252	Mike Hargrove	.08	.06	.03
253	Nick Esasky	.08	.06	.03
254	Frank Williams	.08	.06	.03
255	Lonnie Smith	.08	.06	.03
256	Daryl Sconiers	.08	.06	.03
257	Bryan Little	.08	.06	.03
258	Terry Francona	.08	.06	.03
259	Mark Langston	1.75	1.25	.70
260	Dave Righetti	.15	.11	.06
261	Checklist 133-264	.08	.06	.03
262	Bob Horner	.15	.11	.06
263	Mel Hall	.08	.06	.03
264	John Shelby	.08	.06	.03
265	Juan Samuel	.15	.11	.06
266	Frank Viola	.12	.09	.05
267	Jim Fanning	.08	.06	.03
268	Dick Ruthven	.08	.06	.03
269	Bobby Ramos	.08	.06	.03
270	Dan Quisenberry	.12	.09	.05
271	Dwight Evans	.15	.11	.06
272	Andre Thornton	.08	.06	.03
273	Orel Hershiser	1.00	.70	.40
274	Ray Knight	.08	.06	.03
275	Bill Caudill	.08	.06	.03
276	Charlie Hough	.08	.06	.03
277	Tim Raines	.30	.25	.12
278	Mike Squires	.08	.06	.03
279	Alex Trevino	.08	.06	.03
280	Ron Romanick	.15	.11	.06
281	Tom Niedenfuer	.08	.06	.03
282	Mike Stenhouse	.08	.06	.03
283	Terry Puhl	.08	.06	.03
284	Hal McRae	.10	.08	.04
285	Dan Driessen	.08	.06	.03
286	Rudy Law	.08	.06	.03
287	Walt Terrell	.08	.06	.03
288	Jeff Kunkel	.08	.06	.03
289	Bob Knepper	.08	.06	.03
290	Cecil Cooper	.12	.09	.05
291	Bob Welch	.10	.08	.04
292	Frank Pastore	.08	.06	.03
293	Dan Schatzeder	.08	.06	.03
294	Tom Nieto	.08	.06	.03
295	Joe Niekro	.10	.08	.04
296	Ryne Sandberg	3.25	2.50	1.25
297	Gary Lucas	.08	.06	.03
298	John Castino	.08	.06	.03
299	Bill Doran	.08	.06	.03
300	Rod Carew	.30	.25	.12
301	John Montefusco	.08	.06	.03
302	Johnnie LeMaster	.08	.06	.03
303	Jim Beattie	.08	.06	.03
304	Gary Gaetti	.12	.09	.05
305	Dale Berra	.08	.06	.03
306	Rick Reuschel	.10	.08	.04
307	Ken Oberkfell	.08	.06	.03
308	Kent Hrbek	.20	.15	.08
309	Mike Witt	.10	.08	.04
310	Manny Trillo	.08	.06	.03
311	Jim Gott	.08	.06	.03
312	LaMarr Hoyt	.08	.06	.03
313	Dave Schmidt	.08	.06	.03
314	Ron Oester	.08	.06	.03
315	Doug Sisk	.08	.06	.03
316	John Lowenstein	.08	.06	.03
317	Derrel Thomas	.08	.06	.03
318	Ted Simmons	.12	.09	.05
319	Darrell Evans	.10	.08	.04
320	Dale Murphy	.50	.40	.20
321	Ricky Horton	.20	.15	.08
322	Ken Phelps	.08	.06	.03
323	Lee Mazzilli	.08	.06	.03
324	Don Mattingly	3.00	2.25	1.25
325	John Denny	.08	.06	.03
326	Ken Singleton	.08	.06	.03
327	Brook Jacoby	.15	.11	.06
328	Greg Luzinski	.12	.09	.05
329	Bob Ojeda	.08	.06	.03
330	Leon Durham	.08	.06	.03
331	Bill Laskey	.08	.06	.03
332	Ben Oglivie	.08	.06	.03
333	Willie Hernandez	.08	.06	.03
334	Bob Dernier	.08	.06	.03
335	Bruce Benedict	.08	.06	.03
336	Rance Mulliniks	.08	.06	.03
337	Rick Cerone	.08	.06	.03
338	Britt Burns	.08	.06	.03
339	Danny Heep	.08	.06	.03
340	Robin Yount	1.00	.70	.40
341	Andy Van Slyke	.10	.08	.04
342	Curt Wilkerson	.08	.06	.03
343	Bill Russell	.08	.06	.03
344	Dave Henderson	.08	.06	.03
345	Charlie Lea	.08	.06	.03
346	Terry Pendleton	3.00	2.25	1.25
347	Carney Lansford	.10	.08	.04
348	Bob Boone	.08	.06	.03
349	Mike Easler	.08	.06	.03
350	Wade Boggs	1.50	1.25	.60
351	Atlee Hammaker	.08	.06	.03
352	Joe Morgan	.15	.11	.06
353	Damaso Garcia	.08	.06	.03
354	Floyd Bannister	.08	.06	.03
355	Bert Blyleven	.15	.11	.06
356	John Butcher	.08	.06	.03
357	Fernando Valenzuela	.30	.25	.12
358	Tony Pena	.08	.06	.03
359	Mike Smithson	.08	.06	.03
360	Steve Carlton	.30	.25	.12
361	Alfredo Griffin	.08	.06	.03
362	Craig McMurtry	.08	.06	.03
363	Bill Dawley	.08	.06	.03
364	Richard Dotson	.08	.06	.03
365	Carmelo Martinez	.08	.06	.03
366	Ron Cey	.10	.08	.04
367	Tony Scott	.08	.06	.03
368	Dave Bergman	.08	.06	.03
369	Steve Sax	.15	.11	.06
370	Bruce Sutter	.12	.09	.05
371	Mickey Rivers	.08	.06	.03
372	Kirk Gibson	.25	.20	.10
373	Scott Sanderson	.08	.06	.03
374	Brian Downing	.08	.06	.03
375	Jeff Reardon	.12	.09	.05
376	Frank DiPino	.08	.06	.03
377	Checklist 265-396	.08	.06	.03
378	Alan Wiggins	.08	.06	.03
379	Charles Hudson	.08	.06	.03
380	Ken Griffey	.10	.08	.04
381	Tom Paciorek	.08	.06	.03
382	Jack Morris	.20	.15	.08
383	Tony Gwynn	2.00	1.50	.80
384	Jody Davis	.08	.06	.03
385	Jose DeLeon	.08	.06	.03
386	Bob Kearney	.08	.06	.03
387	George Wright	.08	.06	.03
388	Ron Guidry	.20	.15	.08
389	Rick Manning	.08	.06	.03
390	Sid Fernandez	.75	.60	.30
391	Bruce Bochte	.08	.06	.03
392	Dan Petry	.08	.06	.03
393	Tim Stoddard	.08	.06	.03
394	Tony Armas	.08	.06	.03
395	Paul Molitor	1.25	.90	.50
396	Mike Heath	.08	.06	.03

1985 O-Pee-Chee Posters

The 1985 O-Pee-Chee Poster set consists of 24 players, 12 from the Expos and 12 from the Blue Jays. The blank-backed posters measure approximately 4-7/8" by 6-7/8" and generally have fold marks because they were inserted in the regular 1985 O-Pee-Chee wax packs. The card number, written inboth French and English, appears in the bottom border. The full-color player photos are surrounded by a red border for Expos and a blue border for Blue Jays.

		MT	NR MT	EX
Complete Set:		6.00	4.50	2.50
Common Player:		.25	.20	.10
1	Mike Fitzgerald	.25	.20	.10
2	Dan Driessen	.25	.20	.10
3	Dave Palmer	.25	.20	.10
4	U.L. Washington	.25	.20	.10
5	Hubie Brooks	.25	.20	.10
6	Tim Wallach	.40	.30	.15
7	Tim Raines	1.00	.70	.40
8	Herm Winningham	.25	.20	.10
9	Andre Dawson	1.50	1.25	.60
10	Charlie Lea	.25	.20	.10
11	Steve Rogers	.25	.20	.10

12	Jeff Reardon	.75	.60	.30
13	Buck Martinez	.25	.20	.10
14	Willie Upshaw	.25	.20	.10
15	Damaso Garcia	.25	.20	.10
16	Tony Fernandez	.50	.40	.20
17	Rance Mulliniks	.25	.20	.10
18	George Bell	.75	.60	.30
19	Lloyd Moseby	.25	.20	.10
20	Jesse Barfield	.30	.25	.12
21	Doyle Alexander	.25	.20	.10
22	Dave Stieb	.40	.30	.15
23	Bill Caudill	.25	.20	.10
24	Gary Lavelle	.25	.20	.10

1986 O-Pee-Chee

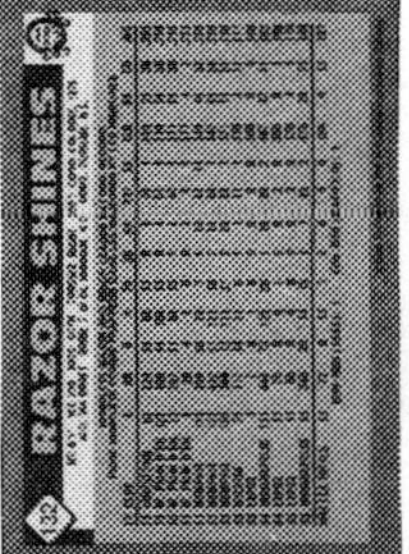

As usual, the 1986 O-Pee-Chee set was issued in close simulation of the Topps cards for the same year. The 396 cards in the set are 2-1/2" by 3-1/2" and use almost all of the same pictures as the Topps set. The O-Pee-Chee cards, being a Canadian issue, list player information in both English and French. There is an abundance of players from the two Canadian teams - Toronto and Montreal. As the O-Pee-Chee set was issued later in the year than the Topps regular issue, players who changed teams after the printing date are noted with a traded line at the bottom of the player photo. O-Pee-Chee's logo appears in the upper right of each card front.

		MT	NR MT	EX
Complete Set (396):		22.00	16.50	8.75
Common Player:		.08	.06	.03
1	Pete Rose	1.00	.70	.40
2	Ken Landreaux	.08	.06	.03
3	Rob Picciolo	.08	.06	.03
4	Steve Garvey	.25	.20	.10
5	Andy Hawkins	.08	.06	.03
6	Rudy Law	.08	.06	.03
7	Lonnie Smith	.08	.06	.03
8	Dwayne Murphy	.08	.06	.03
9	Moose Haas	.08	.06	.03
10	Tony Gwynn	1.00	.70	.40
11	Bob Ojeda	.08	.06	.03
12	Jose Uribe	.12	.09	.05
13	Bob Kearney	.08	.06	.03
14	Julio Cruz	.08	.06	.03
15	Eddie Whitson	.08	.06	.03
16	Rick Schu	.08	.06	.03
17	Mike Stenhouse	.08	.06	.03
18	Lou Thornton	.08	.06	.03
19	Ryne Sandberg	1.75	1.25	.70
20	Lou Whitaker	.15	.11	.06
21	Mark Brouhard	.08	.06	.03
22	Gary Lavelle	.08	.06	.03
23	Manny Lee	.10	.08	.04
24	Don Slaught	.08	.06	.03
25	Willie Wilson	.10	.08	.04
26	Mike Marshall	.10	.08	.04
27	Ray Knight	.08	.06	.03
28	Mario Soto	.08	.06	.03
29	Dave Anderson	.08	.06	.03
30	Eddie Murray	.35	.25	.14
31	Dusty Baker	.08	.06	.03
32	Steve Yeager	.08	.06	.03
33	Andy Van Slyke	.12	.09	.05
34	Dave Righetti	.15	.11	.06
35	Jeff Reardon	.10	.08	.04
36	Burt Hooton	.08	.06	.03
37	Johnny Ray	.08	.06	.03
38	Glenn Hoffman	.08	.06	.03
39	Rick Mahler	.08	.06	.03
40	Ken Griffey	.08	.06	.03
41	Brad Wellman	.08	.06	.03
42	Joe Hesketh	.08	.06	.03
43	Mark Salas	.08	.06	.03
44	Jorge Orta	.08	.06	.03
45	Damaso Garcia	.08	.06	.03
46	Jim Acker	.08	.06	.03
47	Bill Madlock	.10	.08	.04
48	Bill Almon	.08	.06	.03
49	Rick Manning	.08	.06	.03
50	Dan Quisenberry	.08	.06	.03
51	Jim Gantner	.08	.06	.03
52	Kevin Bass	.08	.06	.03
53	Len Dykstra	2.50	2.00	1.00
54	John Franco	.10	.08	.04
55	Fred Lynn	.12	.09	.05
56	Jim Morrison	.08	.06	.03
57	Bill Doran	.08	.06	.03
58	Leon Durham	.08	.06	.03
59	Andre Thornton	.08	.06	.03
60	Dwight Evans	.10	.08	.04
61	Larry Herndon	.08	.06	.03
62	Bob Boone	.08	.06	.03
63	Kent Hrbek	.15	.11	.06
64	Floyd Bannister	.08	.06	.03
65	Harold Baines	.10	.08	.04
66	Pat Tabler	.08	.06	.03
67	Carmelo Martinez	.08	.06	.03
68	Ed Lynch	.08	.06	.03
69	George Foster	.10	.08	.04
70	Dave Winfield	.50	.40	.20
71	Ken Schrom	.08	.06	.03
72	Toby Harrah	.08	.06	.03
73	Jackie Gutierrez	.08	.06	.03
74	Rance Mulliniks	.08	.06	.03
75	Jose DeLeon	.08	.06	.03
76	Ron Romanick	.08	.06	.03
77	Charlie Leibrandt	.08	.06	.03
78	Bruce Benedict	.08	.06	.03
79	Dave Schmidt	.08	.06	.03
80	Darryl Strawberry	.40	.30	.15
81	Wayne Krenchicki	.08	.06	.03
82	Tippy Martinez	.08	.06	.03
83	Phil Garner	.08	.06	.03
84	Darrell Porter	.08	.06	.03
85	Tony Perez	.10	.08	.04
86	Tom Waddell	.08	.06	.03
87	Tim Hulett	.08	.06	.03
88	Barbaro Garbey	.08	.06	.03
89	Randy St. Claire	.08	.06	.03
90	Garry Templeton	.08	.06	.03
91	Tim Teufel	.08	.06	.03
92	Al Cowens	.08	.06	.03
93	Scot Thompson	.08	.06	.03
94	Tom Herr	.08	.06	.03
95	Ozzie Virgil	.08	.06	.03
96	Jose Cruz	.08	.06	.03
97	Gary Gaetti	.12	.09	.05
98	Roger Clemens	3.25	2.50	1.25
99	Vance Law	.08	.06	.03
100	Nolan Ryan	2.50	2.00	1.00
101	Mike Smithson	.08	.06	.03
102	Rafael Santana	.08	.06	.03
103	Darrell Evans	.10	.08	.04
104	Rich Gossage	.12	.09	.05
105	Gary Ward	.08	.06	.03
106	Jim Gott	.08	.06	.03
107	Rafael Ramirez	.08	.06	.03
108	Ted Power	.08	.06	.03
109	Ron Guidry	.15	.11	.06
110	Scott McGregor	.08	.06	.03
111	Mike Scioscia	.08	.06	.03
112	Glenn Hubbard	.08	.06	.03
113	U.L. Washington	.08	.06	.03
114	Al Oliver	.10	.08	.04
115	Jay Howell	.08	.06	.03
116	Brook Jacoby	.10	.08	.04
117	Willie McGee	.12	.09	.05
118	Jerry Royster	.08	.06	.03
119	Barry Bonnell	.08	.06	.03
120	Steve Carlton	.25	.20	.10
121	Alfredo Griffin	.08	.06	.03
122	David Green	.08	.06	.03
123	Greg Walker	.08	.06	.03
124	Frank Tanana	.08	.06	.03
125	Dave Lopes	.08	.06	.03
126	Mike Krukow	.08	.06	.03
127	Jack Howell	.20	.15	.08
128	Greg Harris	.08	.06	.03
129	Herm Winningham	.10	.08	.04
130	Alan Trammell	.25	.20	.10
131	Checklist 1-132	.08	.06	.03
132	Razor Shines	.08	.06	.03
133	Bruce Sutter	.10	.08	.04
134	Carney Lansford	.08	.06	.03
135	Joe Niekro	.08	.06	.03
136	Ernie Whitt	.08	.06	.03
137	Charlie Moore	.08	.06	.03
138	Mel Hall	.08	.06	.03
139	Roger McDowell	.30	.25	.12
140	John Candelaria	.08	.06	.03
141	Bob Rodgers	.08	.06	.03
142	Manny Trillo	.08	.06	.03
143	Dave Palmer	.08	.06	.03
144	Robin Yount	.75	.60	.30
145	Pedro Guerrero	.15	.11	.06
146	Von Hayes	.08	.06	.03
147	Lance Parrish	.15	.11	.06
148	Mike Heath	.08	.06	.03
149	Brett Butler	.08	.06	.03
150	Joaquin Andujar	.08	.06	.03
151	Graig Nettles	.10	.08	.04
152	Pete Vuckovich	.08	.06	.03
153	Jason Thompson	.08	.06	.03
154	Bert Roberge	.08	.06	.03
155	Bob Grich	.08	.06	.03
156	Roy Smalley	.08	.06	.03
157	Ron Hassey	.08	.06	.03
158	Bob Stanley	.08	.06	.03
159	Orel Hershiser	.70	.50	.30
160	Chet Lemon	.08	.06	.03
161	Terry Puhl	.08	.06	.03
162	Dave LaPoint	.08	.06	.03
163	Onix Concepcion	.08	.06	.03
164	Steve Balboni	.08	.06	.03
165	Mike Davis	.08	.06	.03
166	Dickie Thon	.08	.06	.03
167	Zane Smith	.08	.06	.03
168	Jeff Burroughs	.08	.06	.03
169	Alex Trevino	.08	.06	.03
170	Gary Carter	.25	.20	.10
171	Tito Landrum	.08	.06	.03
172	Sammy Stewart	.08	.06	.03
173	Wayne Gross	.08	.06	.03
174	Britt Burns	.08	.06	.03
175	Steve Sax	.12	.09	.05
176	Jody Davis	.08	.06	.03
177	Joel Youngblood	.08	.06	.03
178	Fernando Valenzuela	.20	.15	.08
179	Storm Davis	.08	.06	.03
180	Don Mattingly	.85	.60	.35
181	Steve Bedrosian	.10	.08	.04
182	Jesse Orosco	.08	.06	.03
183	Gary Roenicke	.08	.06	.03
184	Don Baylor	.10	.08	.04
185	Rollie Fingers	.15	.11	.06
186	Ruppert Jones	.08	.06	.03
187	Scott Fletcher	.08	.06	.03
188	Bob Dernier	.08	.06	.03
189	Mike Mason	.08	.06	.03
190	George Hendrick	.08	.06	.03
191	Wally Backman	.08	.06	.03
192	Oddibe McDowell	.20	.15	.08
193	Bruce Hurst	.10	.08	.04
194	Ron Cey	.08	.06	.03
195	Dave Concepcion	.08	.06	.03
196	Doyle Alexander	.08	.06	.03
197	Dale Murray	.08	.06	.03
198	Mark Langston	.12	.09	.05
199	Dennis Eckersley	.10	.08	.04
200	Mike Schmidt	.85	.60	.35
201	Nick Esasky	.08	.06	.03
202	Ken Dayley	.08	.06	.03
203	Rick Cerone	.08	.06	.03
204	Larry McWilliams	.08	.06	.03
205	Brian Downing	.08	.06	.03
206	Danny Darwin	.08	.06	.03
207	Bill Caudill	.08	.06	.03
208	Dave Rozema	.08	.06	.03
209	Eric Show	.08	.06	.03
210	Brad Komminsk	.08	.06	.03
211	Chris Bando	.08	.06	.03
212	Chris Speier	.08	.06	.03
213	Jim Clancy	.08	.06	.03
214	Randy Bush	.08	.06	.03
215	Frank White	.08	.06	.03
216	Dan Petry	.08	.06	.03
217	Tim Wallach	.10	.08	.04
218	Mitch Webster	.20	.15	.08
219	Dennis Lamp	.08	.06	.03
220	Bob Horner	.10	.08	.04
221	Dave Henderson	.08	.06	.03
222	Dave Smith	.08	.06	.03
223	Willie Upshaw	.08	.06	.03
224	Cesar Cedeno	.08	.06	.03
225	Ron Darling	.12	.09	.05
226	Lee Lacy	.08	.06	.03
227	John Tudor	.08	.06	.03
228	Jim Presley	.12	.09	.05
229	Bill Gullickson	.08	.06	.03
230	Terry Kennedy	.08	.06	.03
231	Bob Knepper	.08	.06	.03
232	Rick Rhoden	.08	.06	.03
233	Richard Dotson	.08	.06	.03
234	Jesse Barfield	.12	.09	.05
235	Butch Wynegar	.08	.06	.03
236	Jerry Reuss	.08	.06	.03
237	Juan Samuel	.12	.09	.05
238	Larry Parrish	.08	.06	.03
239	Bill Buckner	.08	.06	.03
240	Pat Sheridan	.08	.06	.03
241	Tony Fernandez	.10	.08	.04
242	Rich Thompson	.08	.06	.03
243	Rickey Henderson	.75	.60	.30
244	Craig Lefferts	.08	.06	.03
245	Jim Sundberg	.08	.06	.03
246	Phil Niekro	.20	.15	.08
247	Terry Harper	.08	.06	.03
248	Spike Owen	.08	.06	.03
249	Bret Saberhagen	.25	.20	.10
250	Dwight Gooden	.40	.30	.15
251	Rich Dauer	.08	.06	.03
252	Keith Hernandez	.25	.20	.10
253	Bo Diaz	.08	.06	.03
254	Ozzie Guillen	.25	.20	.10
255	Tony Armas	.08	.06	.03
256	Andre Dawson	.15	.11	.06
257	Doug DeCinces	.08	.06	.03
258	Tim Burke	.15	.11	.06
259	Dennis Boyd	.08	.06	.03
260	Tony Pena	.08	.06	.03
261	Sal Butera	.08	.06	.03
262	Wade Boggs	1.00	.70	.40
263	Checklist 133-254	.08	.06	.03
264	Ron Oester	.08	.06	.03
265	Ron Davis	.08	.06	.03
266	Keith Moreland	.08	.06	.03
267	Paul Molitor	.60	.45	.25
268	John Denny	.08	.06	.03
269	Frank Viola	.12	.09	.05
270	Jack Morris	.15	.11	.06
271	Dave Collins	.08	.06	.03
272	Bert Blyleven	.10	.08	.04
273	Jerry Willard	.08	.06	.03
274	Matt Young	.08	.06	.03
275	Charlie Hough	.08	.06	.03
276	Dave Dravecky	.08	.06	.03
277	Garth Iorg	.08	.06	.03
278	Hal McRae	.08	.06	.03
279	Curt Wilkerson	.08	.06	.03
280	Tim Raines	.25	.20	.10
281	Bill Laskey	.08	.06	.03
282	Jerry Mumphrey	.08	.06	.03
283	Pat Clements	.08	.06	.03
284	Bob James	.08	.06	.03
285	Buddy Bell	.08	.06	.03
286	Tom Brookens	.08	.06	.03
287	Dave Parker	.12	.09	.05
288	Ron Kittle	.08	.06	.03
289	Johnnie LeMaster	.08	.06	.03
290	Carlton Fisk	.15	.11	.06
291	Jimmy Key	.10	.08	.04
292	Gary Matthews	.08	.06	.03
293	Marvell Wynne	.08	.06	.03
294	Danny Cox	.08	.06	.03
295	Kirk Gibson	.20	.15	.08
296	Mariano Duncan	.08	.06	.03
297	Ozzie Smith	.12	.09	.05
298	Craig Reynolds	.08	.06	.03
299	Bryn Smith	.08	.06	.03
300	George Brett	.75	.60	.30
301	Walt Terrell	.08	.06	.03
302	Greg Gross	.08	.06	.03
303	Claudell Washington	.08	.06	.03
304	Howard Johnson	.40	.30	.15

305	Phil Bradley	.10	.08	.04
306	R.J. Reynolds	.08	.06	.03
307	Bob Brenly	.08	.06	.03
308	Hubie Brooks	.08	.06	.03
309	Alvin Davis	.12	.09	.05
310	Donnie Hill	.08	.06	.03
311	Dick Schofield	.08	.06	.03
312	Tom Filer	.08	.06	.03
313	Mike Fitzgerald	.08	.06	.03
314	Marty Barrett	.08	.06	.03
315	Mookie Wilson	.08	.06	.03
316	Alan Knicely	.08	.06	.03
317	Ed Romero	.08	.06	.03
318	Glenn Wilson	.08	.06	.03
319	Bud Black	.08	.06	.03
320	Jim Rice	.25	.20	.10
321	Terry Pendleton	.50	.40	.20
322	Dave Kingman	.10	.08	.04
323	Gary Pettis	.08	.06	.03
324	Dan Schatzeder	.08	.06	.03
325	Juan Beniquez	.08	.06	.03
326	Kent Tekulve	.08	.06	.03
327	Mike Pagliarulo	.10	.08	.04
328	Pete O'Brien	.08	.06	.03
329	Kirby Puckett	3.25	2.50	1.25
330	Rick Sutcliffe	.10	.08	.04
331	Alan Ashby	.08	.06	.03
332	Willie Randolph	.08	.06	.03
333	Tom Henke	.08	.06	.03
334	Ken Oberkfell	.08	.06	.03
335	Don Sutton	.20	.15	.08
336	Dan Gladden	.08	.06	.03
337	George Vuckovich	.08	.06	.03
338	Jorge Bell	.25	.20	.10
339	Jim Dwyer	.08	.06	.03
340	Cal Ripken	2.00	1.50	.80
341	Willie Hernandez	.08	.06	.03
342	Gary Redus	.08	.06	.03
343	Jerry Koosman	.08	.06	.03
344	Jim Wohlford	.08	.06	.03
345	Donnie Moore	.08	.06	.03
346	Floyd Youmans	.20	.15	.08
347	Gorman Thomas	.08	.06	.03
348	Cliff Johnson	.08	.06	.03
349	Ken Howell	.08	.06	.03
350	Jack Clark	.12	.09	.05
351	Gary Lucas	.08	.06	.03
352	Bob Clark	.08	.06	.03
353	Dave Stieb	.10	.08	.04
354	Tony Bernazard	.08	.06	.03
355	Lee Smith	.08	.06	.03
356	Mickey Hatcher	.08	.06	.03
357	Ed Vande Berg	.08	.06	.03
358	Rick Dempsey	.08	.06	.03
359	Bobby Cox	.08	.06	.03
360	Lloyd Moseby	.08	.06	.03
361	Shane Rawley	.08	.06	.03
362	Garry Maddox	.08	.06	.03
363	Buck Martinez	.08	.06	.03
364	Ed Nunez	.08	.06	.03
365	Luis Leal	.08	.06	.03
366	Dale Berra	.08	.06	.03
367	Mike Boddicker	.08	.06	.03
368	Greg Brock	.08	.06	.03
369	Al Holland	.08	.06	.03
370	Vince Coleman	.30	.25	.12
371	Rod Carew	.25	.20	.10
372	Ben Oglivie	.08	.06	.03
373	Lee Mazzilli	.08	.06	.03
374	Terry Francona	.08	.06	.03
375	Rich Gedman	.08	.06	.03
376	Charlie Lea	.08	.06	.03
377	Joe Carter	1.25	.90	.50
378	Bruce Bochte	.08	.06	.03
379	Bobby Meacham	.08	.06	.03
380	LaMarr Hoyt	.08	.06	.03
381	Jeff Leonard	.08	.06	.03
382	Ivan Calderon	.30	.25	.12
383	Chris Brown	.20	.15	.08
384	Steve Trout	.08	.06	.03
385	Cecil Cooper	.08	.06	.03
386	Cecil Fielder	5.50	4.25	2.25
387	Tim Flannery	.08	.06	.03
388	Chris Codiroli	.08	.06	.03
389	Glenn Davis	.40	.30	.15
390	Tom Seaver	.25	.20	.10
391	Julio Franco	.10	.08	.04
392	Tom Brunansky	.10	.08	.04
393	Rob Wilfong	.08	.06	.03
394	Reggie Jackson	.40	.30	.15
395	Scott Garrelts	.08	.06	.03
396	Checklist 255-396	.08	.06	.03

1986 O-Pee-Chee Box Panels

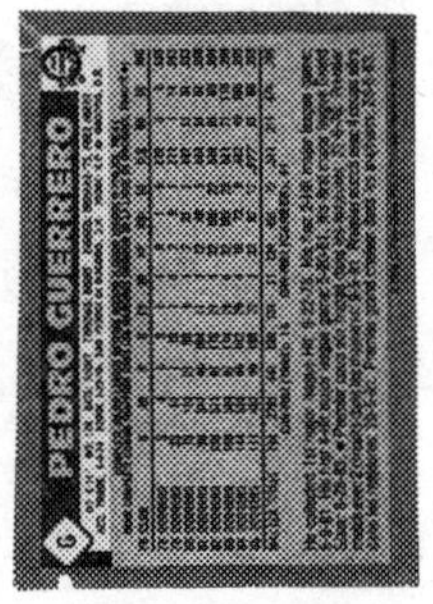

The Canadian card company licensed by Topps to distribute cards in Canada is O-Pee-Chee. In 1986, O-Pee-Chee issued wax pack boxes with baseball cards printed on the box bottoms. Four cards appear on four different boxes making a complete set of 16. The cards are identical to the 1986 Topps wax box issue with the exception of the O-Pee-Chee logo replacing Topps and the addition of French on the card backs. These bilingual cards were issued in Canada but are readily available in the USA. The cards are the standard 2-1/2" by 3-1/2" size, printed in full-color with black and red card backs. The panel cards are not numbered but instead are lettered from A through P.

		MT	NR MT	EX
Complete Set:		12.00	9.00	4.75
Complete Singles Set:		7.00	5.25	2.75
Common Panel:		3.00	2.25	1.25
Common Single Player:		.15	.11	.06
	Panel	3.50	2.75	1.50
A	Jorge Bell	.30	.25	.12
B	Wade Boggs	.70	.50	.30
C	George Brett	.50	.40	.20
D	Vince Coleman	.30	.40	.20
	Panel	3.00	2.25	1.25
E	Carlton Fisk	.40	.15	.08
F	Dwight Gooden	.60	.50	.30
G	Pedro Guerrero	.20	.15	.08
H	Ron Guidry	.20	.15	.08
	Panel	3.75	2.75	1.50
I	Reggie Jackson	.60	.30	.15
J	Don Mattingly	.90	.70	.35
K	Oddibe McDowell	.15	.11	.06
L	Willie McGee	.20	.15	.08
	Panel	3.50	2.75	1.50
M	Dale Murphy	.60	.40	.20
N	Pete Rose	.70	.50	.30
O	Bret Saberhagen	.20	.15	.08
P	Fernando Valenzuela	.15	.20	.10

1987 O-Pee-Chee

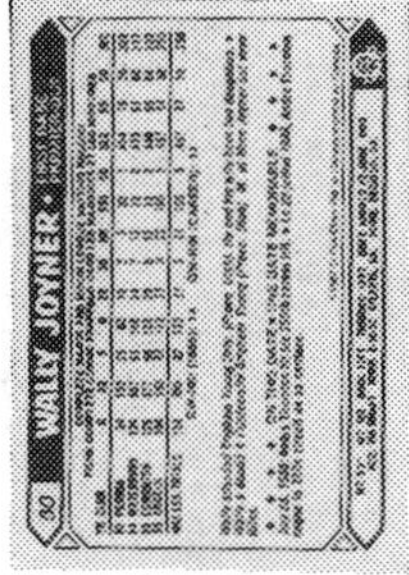

O-Pee-Chee of London, Ont., under license from the Topps Chewing Gum Co., continued a practice started in 1965 by issuing a baseball card set for 1987. The 396-card set is identical in design to the regular Topps set, save the name "O-Pee-Chee" replacing "Topps" in the lower right corner. Because the set is issued after its American counterpart, several cards appear with trade notations and corrected logos on the fronts. The cards, which are printed on white stock and are the standard 2-1/2" by 3-1/2", feature backs written in both English and French.

		MT	NR MT	EX
Complete Set (396):		17.50	13.00	6.50
Common Player:		.08	.06	.03
1	Ken Oberkfell	.08	.06	.03
2	Jack Howell	.08	.06	.03
3	Hubie Brooks	.08	.06	.03
4	Bob Grich	.08	.06	.03
5	Rick Leach	.08	.06	.03
6	Phil Niekro	.15	.11	.06
7	Rickey Henderson	.30	.25	.12
8	Terry Pendleton	.08	.06	.03
9	Jay Tibbs	.08	.06	.03
10	Cecil Cooper	.10	.08	.04
11	Mario Soto	.08	.06	.03
12	George Bell	.20	.15	.08
13	Nick Esasky	.08	.06	.03
14	Larry McWilliams	.08	.06	.03
15	Dan Quisenberry	.08	.06	.03
16	Ed Lynch	.08	.06	.03
17	Pete O'Brien	.08	.06	.03
18	Luis Aguayo	.08	.06	.03
19	Matt Young	.08	.06	.03
20	Gary Carter	.20	.15	.08
21	Tom Paciorek	.08	.06	.03
22	Doug DeCinces	.08	.06	.03
23	Lee Smith	.08	.06	.03
24	Jesse Barfield	.10	.08	.04
25	Bert Blyleven	.10	.08	.04
26	Greg Brock	.08	.06	.03
27	Dan Petry	.08	.06	.03
28	Rick Dempsey	.08	.06	.03
29	Jimmy Key	.10	.08	.04
30	Tim Raines	.20	.15	.08
31	Bruce Hurst	.08	.06	.03
32	Manny Trillo	.08	.06	.03
33	Andy Van Slyke	.10	.08	.04
34	Ed Vande Berg	.08	.06	.03
35	Sid Bream	.08	.06	.03
36	Dave Winfield	.20	.15	.08
37	Scott Garrelts	.08	.06	.03
38	Dennis Leonard	.08	.06	.03
39	Marty Barrett	.08	.06	.03
40	Dave Righetti	.12	.09	.05
41	Bo Diaz	.08	.06	.03
42	Gary Redus	.08	.06	.03
43	Tom Niedenfuer	.08	.06	.03
44	Greg Harris	.08	.06	.03
45	Jim Presley	.08	.06	.03
46	Danny Gladden	.08	.06	.03
47	Ron Smalley	.08	.06	.03
48	Wally Backman	.08	.06	.03
49	Tom Seaver	.20	.15	.08
50	Dave Smith	.08	.06	.03
51	Mel Hall	.08	.06	.03
52	Tim Flannery	.08	.06	.03
53	Julio Cruz	.08	.06	.03
54	Dick Schofield	.08	.06	.03
55	Tim Wallach	.10	.08	.04
56	Glenn Davis	.12	.09	.05
57	Darren Daulton	.08	.06	.03
58	Chico Walker	.08	.06	.03
59	Garth Iorg	.08	.06	.03
60	Tony Pena	.08	.06	.03
61	Ron Hassey	.08	.06	.03
62	Dave Dravecky	.08	.06	.03
63	Jorge Orta	.08	.06	.03
64	Al Nipper	.08	.06	.03
65	Tom Browning	.10	.08	.04
66	Marc Sullivan	.08	.06	.03
67	Todd Worrell	.15	.11	.06
68	Glenn Hubbard	.08	.06	.03
69	Carney Lansford	.08	.06	.03
70	Charlie Hough	.08	.06	.03
71	Lance McCullers	.08	.06	.03
72	Walt Terrell	.08	.06	.03
73	Bob Kearney	.08	.06	.03
74	Dan Pasqua	.08	.06	.03
75	Ron Darling	.10	.08	.04
76	Robin Yount	.30	.25	.12
77	Pat Tabler	.08	.06	.03
78	Tom Foley	.08	.06	.03
79	Juan Nieves	.10	.08	.04
80	Wally Joyner	.40	.30	.15
81	Wayne Krenchicki	.08	.06	.03
82	Kirby Puckett	1.00	.70	.40
83	Bob Ojeda	.08	.06	.03
84	Mookie Wilson	.08	.06	.03
85	Kevin Bass	.08	.06	.03
86	Kent Tekulve	.08	.06	.03
87	Mark Salas	.08	.06	.03
88	Brian Downing	.08	.06	.03
89	Ozzie Guillen	.08	.06	.03
90	Dave Stieb	.10	.08	.04
91	Rance Mulliniks	.08	.06	.03
92	Mike Witt	.08	.06	.03
93	Charlie Moore	.08	.06	.03
94	Jose Uribe	.08	.06	.03
95	Oddibe McDowell	.08	.06	.03
96	Ray Soff	.08	.06	.03
97	Glenn Wilson	.08	.06	.03
98	Brook Jacoby	.08	.06	.03
99	Darryl Motley	.08	.06	.03
100	Steve Garvey	.20	.15	.08
101	Frank White	.08	.06	.03
102	Mike Moore	.08	.06	.03
103	Rick Aguilera	.08	.06	.03
104	Buddy Bell	.08	.06	.03
105	Floyd Youmans	.08	.06	.03
106	Lou Whitaker	.15	.11	.06
107	Ozzie Smith	.12	.09	.05
108	Jim Gantner	.08	.06	.03
109	R.J. Reynolds	.08	.06	.03
110	John Tudor	.08	.06	.03
111	Alfredo Griffin	.08	.06	.03
112	Mike Flanagan	.08	.06	.03
113	Neil Allen	.08	.06	.03
114	Ken Griffey	.08	.06	.03
115	Donnie Moore	.08	.06	.03
116	Bob Horner	.10	.08	.04
117	Ron Shepherd	.08	.06	.03
118	Cliff Johnson	.08	.06	.03
119	Vince Coleman	.15	.11	.06
120	Eddie Murray	.25	.20	.10
121	Dwayne Murphy	.08	.06	.03
122	Jim Clancy	.08	.06	.03
123	Ken Landreaux	.08	.06	.03
124	Tom Nieto	.08	.06	.03
125	Bob Brenly	.08	.06	.03
126	George Brett	.30	.25	.12
127	Vance Law	.08	.06	.03
128	Checklist 1-132	.08	.06	.03
129	Bob Knepper	.08	.06	.03
130	Dwight Gooden	.50	.40	.20
131	Juan Bonilla	.08	.06	.03
132	Tim Burke	.08	.06	.03
133	Bob McClure	.08	.06	.03
134	Scott Bailes	.10	.08	.04
135	Mike Easler	.08	.06	.03
136	Ron Romanick	.08	.06	.03
137	Rich Gedman	.08	.06	.03
138	Bob Dernier	.08	.06	.03
139	John Denny	.08	.06	.03
140	Bret Saberhagen	.15	.11	.06
141	Herm Winningham	.08	.06	.03
142	Rick Sutcliffe	.10	.08	.04
143	Ryne Sandberg	.85	.60	.35
144	Mike Scioscia	.08	.06	.03
145	Charlie Kerfeld	.08	.06	.03
146	Jim Rice	.20	.15	.08
147	Steve Trout	.08	.06	.03
148	Jesse Orosco	.08	.06	.03

149	Mike Boddicker	.08	.06	.03
150	Wade Boggs	.40	.30	.15
151	Dane Iorg	.08	.06	.03
152	Rick Burleson	.08	.06	.03
153	Duane Ward	.60	.45	.25
154	Rick Reuschel	.08	.06	.03
155	Nolan Ryan	1.00	.70	.40
156	Bill Caudill	.08	.06	.03
157	Danny Darwin	.08	.06	.03
158	Ed Romero	.08	.06	.03
159	Bill Almon	.08	.06	.03
160	Julio Franco	.10	.08	.04
161	Kent Hrbek	.15	.11	.06
162	Chili Davis	.08	.06	.03
163	Kevin Gross	.08	.06	.03
164	Carlton Fisk	.12	.09	.05
165	Jeff Reardon	.10	.08	.04
166	Bob Boone	.08	.06	.03
167	Rick Honeycutt	.08	.06	.03
168	Dan Schatzeder	.08	.06	.03
169	Jim Wohlford	.08	.06	.03
170	Phil Bradley	.10	.08	.04
171	Ken Schrom	.08	.06	.03
172	Ron Oester	.08	.06	.03
173	Juan Beniquez	.08	.06	.03
174	Tony Armas	.08	.06	.03
175	Bob Stanley	.08	.06	.03
176	Steve Buechele	.08	.06	.03
177	Keith Moreland	.08	.06	.03
178	Cecil Fielder	.85	.60	.35
179	Gary Gaetti	.12	.09	.05
180	Chris Brown	.08	.06	.03
181	Tom Herr	.08	.06	.03
182	Lee Lacy	.08	.06	.03
183	Ozzie Virgil	.08	.06	.03
184	Paul Molitor	.10	.08	.04
185	Roger McDowell	.08	.06	.03
186	Mike Marshall	.10	.08	.04
187	Ken Howell	.08	.06	.03
188	Rob Deer	.08	.06	.03
189	Joe Hesketh	.08	.06	.03
190	Jim Sundberg	.08	.06	.03
191	Kelly Gruber	.30	.25	.12
192	Cory Snyder	.40	.30	.15
193	Dave Concepcion	.08	.06	.03
194	Kirk McCaskill	.08	.06	.03
195	Mike Pagliarulo	.08	.06	.03
196	Rick Manning	.08	.06	.03
197	Brett Butler	.08	.06	.03
198	Tony Gwynn	.40	.30	.15
199	Mariano Duncan	.08	.06	.03
200	Pete Rose	.50	.40	.20
201	John Cangelosi	.08	.06	.03
202	Danny Cox	.08	.06	.03
203	Butch Wynegar	.08	.06	.03
204	Chris Chambliss	.08	.06	.03
205	Graig Nettles	.08	.06	.03
206	Chet Lemon	.08	.06	.03
207	Don Aase	.08	.06	.03
208	Mike Mason	.08	.06	.03
209	Alan Trammell	.20	.15	.08
210	Lloyd Moseby	.08	.06	.03
211	Richard Dotson	.08	.06	.03
212	Mike Fitzgerald	.08	.06	.03
213	Darrell Porter	.08	.06	.03
214	Checklist 133-264	.08	.06	.03
215	Mark Langston	.10	.08	.04
216	Steve Farr	.08	.06	.03
217	Dann Bilardello	.08	.06	.03
218	Gary Ward	.08	.06	.03
219	Cecilio Guante	.08	.06	.03
220	Joe Carter	.60	.45	.25
221	Ernie Whitt	.08	.06	.03
222	Denny Walling	.08	.06	.03
223	Charlie Leibrandt	.08	.06	.03
224	Wayne Tolleson	.08	.06	.03
225	Mike Smithson	.08	.06	.03
226	Zane Smith	.08	.06	.03
227	Terry Puhl	.08	.06	.03
228	Eric Davis	.80	.60	.30
229	Don Mattingly	.40	.30	.15
230	Don Baylor	.08	.06	.03
231	Frank Tanana	.08	.06	.03
232	Tom Brookens	.08	.06	.03
233	Steve Bedrosian	.10	.08	.04
234	Wallace Johnson	.08	.06	.03
235	Alvin Davis	.10	.08	.04
236	Tommy John	.12	.09	.05
237	Jim Morrison	.08	.06	.03
238	Ricky Horton	.08	.06	.03
239	Shane Rawley	.08	.06	.03
240	Steve Balboni	.08	.06	.03
241	Mike Krukow	.08	.06	.03
242	Rick Mahler	.08	.06	.03
243	Bill Doran	.08	.06	.03
244	Mark Clear	.08	.06	.03
245	Willie Upshaw	.08	.06	.03
246	Hal McRae	.08	.06	.03
247	Jose Canseco	.85	.60	.35
248	George Hendrick	.08	.06	.03
249	Doyle Alexander	.08	.06	.03
250	Teddy Higuera	.10	.08	.04
251	Tom Hume	.08	.06	.03
252	Denny Martinez	.08	.06	.03
253	Eddie Milner	.08	.06	.03
254	Steve Sax	.12	.09	.05
255	Juan Samuel	.10	.08	.04
256	Dave Bergman	.08	.06	.03
257	Bob Forsch	.08	.06	.03
258	Steve Yeager	.08	.06	.03
259	Don Sutton	.12	.09	.05
260	Vida Blue	.08	.06	.03
261	Tom Brunansky	.10	.08	.04
262	Joe Sambito	.08	.06	.03
263	Mitch Webster	.08	.06	.03
264	Checklist 265-396	.08	.06	.03
265	Darrell Evans	.10	.08	.04
266	Dave Kingman	.12	.09	.05
267	Howard Johnson	.08	.06	.03
268	Greg Pryor	.08	.06	.03
269	Tippy Martinez	.08	.06	.03
270	Jody Davis	.08	.06	.03
271	Steve Carlton	.20	.15	.08
272	Andres Galarraga	.20	.15	.08
273	Fernando Valenzuela	.20	.15	.08
274	Jeff Hearron	.08	.06	.03
275	Ray Knight	.08	.06	.03
276	Bill Madlock	.08	.06	.03
277	Tom Henke	.08	.06	.03
278	Gary Pettis	.08	.06	.03
279	Jimy Williams	.08	.06	.03
280	Jeffrey Leonard	.08	.06	.03
281	Bryn Smith	.08	.06	.03
282	John Cerutti	.10	.08	.04
283	Gary Roenicke	.08	.06	.03
284	Joaquin Andujar	.08	.06	.03
285	Dennis Boyd	.08	.06	.03
286	Tim Hulett	.08	.06	.03
287	Craig Lefferts	.08	.06	.03
288	Tito Landrum	.08	.06	.03
289	Manny Lee	.08	.06	.03
290	Leon Durham	.08	.06	.03
291	Johnny Ray	.08	.06	.03
292	Franklin Stubbs	.08	.06	.03
293	Bob Rodgers	.08	.06	.03
294	Terry Francona	.08	.06	.03
295	Len Dykstra	.10	.08	.04
296	Tom Candiotti	.08	.06	.03
297	Frank DiPino	.08	.06	.03
298	Craig Reynolds	.08	.06	.03
299	Jerry Hairston	.08	.06	.03
300	Reggie Jackson	.25	.20	.10
301	Luis Aquino	.08	.06	.03
302	Greg Walker	.08	.06	.03
303	Terry Kennedy	.08	.06	.03
304	Phil Garner	.08	.06	.03
305	John Franco	.10	.08	.04
306	Bill Buckner	.08	.06	.03
307	Kevin Mitchell	.50	.40	.20
308	Don Slaught	.08	.06	.03
309	Harold Baines	.10	.08	.04
310	Frank Viola	.12	.09	.05
311	Dave Lopes	.08	.06	.03
312	Cal Ripken	.75	.60	.30
313	John Candelaria	.08	.06	.03
314	Bob Sebra	.08	.06	.03
315	Bud Black	.08	.06	.03
316	Brian Fisher	.08	.06	.03
317	Clint Hurdle	.08	.06	.03
318	Ernie Riles	.08	.06	.03
319	Dave LaPoint	.08	.06	.03
320	Barry Bonds	3.00	2.25	1.25
321	Tim Stoddard	.08	.06	.03
322	Ron Cey	.08	.06	.03
323	Al Newman	.08	.06	.03
324	Jerry Royster	.08	.06	.03
325	Garry Templeton	.08	.06	.03
326	Mark Gubicza	.10	.08	.04
327	Andre Thornton	.08	.06	.03
328	Bob Welch	.08	.06	.03
329	Tony Fernandez	.10	.08	.04
330	Mike Scott	.10	.08	.04
331	Jack Clark	.12	.09	.05
332	Danny Tartabull	.60	.45	.25
333	Greg Minton	.08	.06	.03
334	Ed Correa	.08	.06	.03
335	Candy Maldonado	.08	.06	.03
336	Dennis Lamp	.08	.06	.03
337	Sid Fernandez	.08	.06	.03
338	Greg Gross	.08	.06	.03
339	Willie Hernandez	.08	.06	.03
340	Roger Clemens	.85	.60	.35
341	Mickey Hatcher	.08	.06	.03
342	Bob James	.08	.06	.03
343	Jose Cruz	.08	.06	.03
344	Bruce Sutter	.10	.08	.04
345	Andre Dawson	.15	.11	.06
346	Shawon Dunston	.08	.06	.03
347	Scott McGregor	.08	.06	.03
348	Carmelo Martinez	.08	.06	.03
349	Storm Davis	.08	.06	.03
350	Keith Hernandez	.20	.15	.08
351	Andy McGaffigan	.08	.06	.03
352	Dave Parker	.12	.09	.05
353	Ernie Camacho	.08	.06	.03
354	Eric Show	.08	.06	.03
355	Don Carman	.15	.11	.06
356	Floyd Bannister	.08	.06	.03
357	Willie McGee	.10	.08	.04
358	Atlee Hammaker	.08	.06	.03
359	Dale Murphy	.35	.25	.14
360	Pedro Guerrero	.12	.09	.05
361	Will Clark	1.75	1.25	.70
362	Bill Campbell	.08	.06	.03
363	Alejandro Pena	.08	.06	.03
364	Dennis Rasmussen	.08	.06	.03
365	Rick Rhoden	.08	.06	.03
366	Randy St. Claire	.08	.06	.03
367	Willie Wilson	.10	.08	.04
368	Dwight Evans	.10	.08	.04
369	Moose Haas	.08	.06	.03
370	Fred Lynn	.10	.08	.04
371	Mark Eichhorn	.08	.06	.03
372	Dave Schmidt	.08	.06	.03
373	Jerry Reuss	.08	.06	.03
374	Lance Parrish	.15	.11	.06
375	Ron Guidry	.12	.09	.05
376	Jack Morris	.15	.11	.06
377	Willie Randolph	.08	.06	.03
378	Joel Youngblood	.08	.06	.03
379	Darryl Strawberry	.40	.30	.15
380	Rich Gossage	.10	.08	.04
381	Dennis Eckersley	.10	.08	.04
382	Gary Lucas	.08	.06	.03
383	Ron Davis	.08	.06	.03
384	Pete Incaviglia	.35	.25	.14
385	Orel Hershiser	.20	.15	.08
386	Kirk Gibson	.20	.15	.08
387	Don Robinson	.08	.06	.03
388	Darnell Coles	.08	.06	.03
389	Von Hayes	.08	.06	.03
390	Gary Matthews	.08	.06	.03
391	Jay Howell	.08	.06	.03
392	Tim Laudner	.08	.06	.03
393	Rod Scurry	.08	.06	.03
394	Tony Bernazard	.08	.06	.03
395	Damasco Garcia	.08	.06	.03
396	Mike Schmidt	.50	.40	.20

1987 O-Pee-Chee Box Panels

For the second consecutive year, O-Pee-Chee placed baseball cards on the bottoms of their retail wax pack boxes. The 2-1/8" by 3" cards were issued in panels of four and are slightly smaller in size than the regular issue O-Pee-Chee cards. The card fronts are identical in design to the regular issue, while the backs contain a newspaper-type commentary written in both French and English. Collectors may note the 1987 Topps wax box cards were issued on side panels as opposed to box bottoms. Because the O-Pee-Chee wax boxes are smaller in size than their U.S. counterparts, printing cards on side panels could not be accomplished.

		MT	NR MT	EX
	Complete Panel Set:	8.00	6.00	3.25
	Complete Singles Set:	2.50	2.00	1.00
	Common Single Player:	.15	.11	.06
	Panel	4.00	3.00	1.50
A	Don Baylor	.15	.11	.06
B	Steve Carlton	.30	.25	.12
C	Ron Cey	.15	.11	.06
D	Cecil Cooper	.15	.11	.06
	Panel	4.00	3.00	1.50
E	Rickey Henderson	.40	.30	.15
F	Jim Rice	.20	.25	.12
G	Don Sutton	.20	.15	.08
H	Dave Winfield	.40	.25	.14

1988 O-Pee-Chee

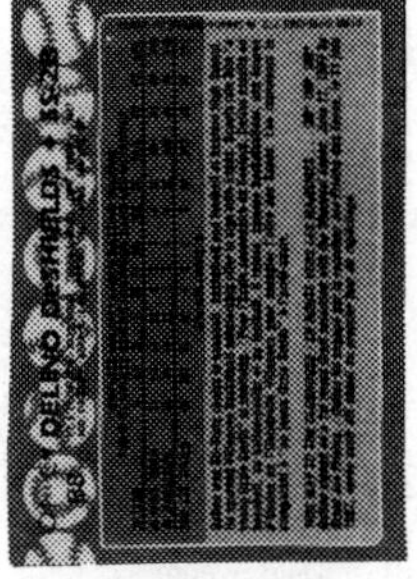

Under license from Topps, O-Pee-Chee uses the same player photos as the Toppps issue, but the Canadian edition includes only 396 cards (one-half the number in the Topps set). The OPC set was printed after the U.S. press run, so several cards carry overprints on the fronts, indicating changes in players' teams. New teams are named in the overprints; card headers bear the former team names. This set follows the same basic design as the 1988 Topps cards. The team name appears in large bright letters above the player photo and the player name is printed on a colorful diagonal strip across the lower right corner. The O-Pee-Chee logo appears in place of the Topps logo, both front and back. A four-card subset consists of #1 and #2 draft choices for the Expos (Nathan Minchey and Delino DeShields) and Blue Jays (Alex Sanchez and Derek Bell). Top draft subset cards are distinguished by a yellow or orange triangle in the lower right corner bearing the player's name above the words "Choisi au repechage." Card backs are bilingual (English-French)

and printed in black on orange. This series was marketed primarily in Canada in four separate display boxes, with four cards printed one each box bottom. Individual card packs contain seven cards and one stick of gum.

		MT	NR MT	EX
Complete Set (396):		20.00	15.00	8.00
Common Player:		.08	.06	.03
1	Chris James	.08	.06	.03
2	Steve Buechele	.08	.06	.03
3	Mike Henneman	.12	.09	.05
4	Eddie Murray	.20	.15	.08
5	Bret Saberhagen	.12	.09	.05
6	Nathan Minchey	.20	.15	.08
7	Harold Reynolds	.08	.06	.03
8	Bo Jackson	.30	.25	.12
9	Mike Easler	.08	.06	.03
10	Ryne Sandberg	.40	.30	.15
11	Mike Young	.08	.06	.03
12	Tony Phillips	.08	.06	.03
13	Andres Thomas	.08	.06	.03
14	Tim Burke	.08	.06	.03
15	Chili Davis	.08	.06	.03
16	Jim Lindeman	.08	.06	.03
17	Ron Oester	.08	.06	.03
18	Craig Reynolds	.08	.06	.03
19	Juan Samuel	.09	.07	.04
20	Kevin Gross	.08	.06	.03
21	Cecil Fielder	.30	.25	.12
22	Greg Swindell	.09	.07	.04
23	Jose DeLeon	.08	.06	.03
24	Jim Deshaies	.08	.06	.03
25	Andres Galarraga	.10	.08	.04
26	Mitch Williams	.08	.06	.03
27	R.J. Reynolds	.08	.06	.03
28	Jose Nunez	.12	.09	.05
29	Angel Salazar	.08	.06	.03
30	Sid Fernandez	.08	.06	.03
31	Keith Moreland	.08	.06	.03
32	John Kruk	.09	.07	.04
33	Rob Deer	.08	.06	.03
34	Ricky Horton	.08	.06	.03
35	Harold Baines	.09	.07	.04
36	Jamie Moyer	.08	.06	.03
37	Kevin McReynolds	.08	.06	.03
38	Ozzie Smith	.09	.07	.04
39	Ron Darling	.09	.07	.04
40	Orel Hershiser	.15	.11	.06
41	Bob Melvin	.08	.06	.03
42	Alfredo Griffin	.08	.06	.03
43	Dick Schofield	.08	.06	.03
44	Terry Steinbach	.09	.07	.04
45	Kent Hrbek	.12	.09	.05
46	Darnell Coles	.08	.06	.03
47	Jimmy Key	.08	.06	.03
48	Alan Ashby	.08	.06	.03
49	Julio Franco	.08	.06	.03
50	Hubie Brooks	.08	.06	.03
51	Chris Bando	.08	.06	.03
52	Fernando Valenzuela	.12	.09	.05
53	Kal Daniels	.12	.09	.05
54	Jim Clancy	.08	.06	.03
55	Phil Bradley	.08	.06	.03
56	Andy McGaffigan	.08	.06	.03
57	Mike LaVaillere	.08	.06	.03
58	Dave Magadan	.08	.06	.03
59	Danny Cox	.08	.06	.03
60	Rickey Henderson	.30	.25	.12
61	Jim Rice	.15	.11	.06
62	Calvin Schiraldi	.08	.06	.03
63	Jerry Mumphrey	.08	.06	.03
64	Ken Caminiti	.09	.07	.04
65	Leon Durham	.08	.06	.03
66	Shane Rawley	.08	.06	.03
67	Ken Oberkfell	.08	.06	.03
68	Keith Hernandez	.12	.09	.05
69	Bob Brenly	.08	.06	.03
70	Roger Clemens	.30	.25	.12
71	Gary Pettis	.08	.06	.03
72	Dennis Eckersley	.08	.06	.03
73	Dave Smith	.08	.06	.03
74	Cal Ripken	.50	.40	.20
75	Joe Carter	.09	.07	.04
76	Denny Martinez	.08	.06	.03
77	Juan Beniquez	.08	.06	.03
78	Tim Laudner	.08	.06	.03
79	Ernie Whitt	.08	.06	.03
80	Mark Langston	.09	.07	.04
81	Dale Sveum	.08	.06	.03
82	Dion James	.08	.06	.03
83	Dave Valle	.08	.06	.03
84	Bill Wegman	.08	.06	.03
85	Howard Johnson	.08	.06	.03
86	Benito Santiago	.35	.25	.14
87	Casey Candaele	.08	.06	.03
88	Delino DeShields	6.25	4.75	2.50
89	Dave Winfield	.15	.11	.06
90	Dale Murphy	.25	.20	.10
91	Jay Howell	.08	.06	.03
92	Ken Williams	.12	.09	.05
93	Bob Sebra	.08	.06	.03
94	Tim Wallach	.08	.06	.03
95	Lance Parrish	.09	.07	.04
96	Todd Benzinger	.20	.15	.08
97	Scott Garrelts	.08	.06	.03
98	Jose Guzman	.08	.06	.03
99	Jeff Reardon	.08	.06	.03
100	Jack Clark	.09	.07	.04
101	Tracy Jones	.09	.07	.04
102	Barry Larkin	.09	.07	.04
103	Curt Young	.08	.06	.03
104	Juan Nieves	.08	.06	.03
105	Terry Pendleton	.08	.06	.03
106	Rod Ducey	.09	.07	.04
107	Scott Bailes	.08	.06	.03
108	Eric King	.08	.06	.03
109	Mike Pagliarulo	.08	.06	.03
110	Teddy Higuera	.08	.06	.03
111	Pedro Guerrero	.09	.07	.04
112	Chris Brown	.08	.06	.03
113	Kelly Gruber	.08	.06	.03
114	Jack Howell	.08	.06	.03
115	Johnny Ray	.08	.06	.03
116	Mark Eichhorn	.08	.06	.03
117	Tony Pena	.08	.06	.03
118	Bob Welch	.08	.06	.03
119	Mike Kingery	.08	.06	.03
120	Kirby Puckett	.40	.30	.15
121	Charlie Hough	.08	.06	.03
122	Tony Bernazard	.08	.06	.03
123	Tom Candiotti	.08	.06	.03
124	Ray Knight	.08	.06	.03
125	Bruce Hurst	.08	.06	.03
126	Steve Jeltz	.08	.06	.03
127	Ron Guidry	.09	.07	.04
128	Duane Ward	.08	.06	.03
129	Greg Minton	.08	.06	.03
130	Buddy Bell	.08	.06	.03
131	Denny Walling	.08	.06	.03
132	Donnie Hill	.08	.06	.03
133	Wayne Tolleson	.08	.06	.03
134	Bob Rodgers	.08	.06	.03
135	Todd Worrell	.08	.06	.03
136	Brian Dayett	.08	.06	.03
137	Chris Bosio	.08	.06	.03
138	Mitch Webster	.08	.06	.03
139	Jerry Browne	.08	.06	.03
140	Jesse Barfield	.09	.07	.04
141	Doug DeCinces	.08	.06	.03
142	Andy Van Slyke	.08	.06	.03
143	Doug Drabek	.08	.06	.03
144	Jeff Parrett	.12	.09	.05
145	Bill Madlock	.08	.06	.03
146	Larry Herndon	.08	.06	.03
147	Bill Buckner	.08	.06	.03
148	Carmelo Martinez	.08	.06	.03
149	Ken Howell	.08	.06	.03
150	Eric Davis	.40	.30	.15
151	Randy Ready	.08	.06	.03
152	Jeffrey Leonard	.08	.06	.03
153	Dave Steib	.08	.06	.03
154	Jeff Stone	.08	.06	.03
155	Dave Righetti	.09	.07	.04
156	Gary Matthews	.08	.06	.03
157	Gary Carter	.15	.11	.06
158	Bob Boone	.08	.06	.03
159	Glenn Davis	.09	.07	.04
160	Willie McGee	.08	.06	.03
161	Bryn Smith	.08	.06	.03
162	Mark McLemore	.08	.06	.03
163	Dale Mohorcic	.08	.06	.03
164	Mike Flanagan	.08	.06	.03
165	Robin Yount	.15	.11	.06
166	Bill Doran	.08	.06	.03
167	Rance Mulliniks	.08	.06	.03
168	Wally Joyner	.40	.30	.15
169	Cory Snyder	.12	.09	.05
170	Rich Gossage	.08	.06	.03
171	Rick Mahler	.08	.06	.03
172	Henry Cotto	.08	.06	.03
173	George Bell	.15	.11	.06
174	B.J. Surhoff	.09	.07	.04
175	Kevin Bass	.08	.06	.03
176	Jeff Reed	.08	.06	.03
177	Frank Tanana	.08	.06	.03
178	Darryl Strawberry	.30	.25	.12
179	Lou Whitaker	.09	.07	.04
180	Terry Kennedy	.08	.06	.03
181	Mariano Duncan	.08	.06	.03
182	Ken Phelps	.08	.06	.03
183	Bob Dernier	.08	.06	.03
184	Ivan Calderon	.08	.06	.03
185	Rick Rhoden	.08	.06	.03
186	Rafael Palmeiro	.40	.30	.15
187	Kelly Downs	.08	.06	.03
188	Spike Owen	.08	.06	.03
189	Bobby Bonilla	.09	.07	.04
190	Candy Maldonado	.08	.06	.03
191	John Cerutti	.08	.06	.03
192	Devon White	.12	.09	.05
193	Brian Fisher	.08	.06	.03
194	Alex Sanchez	.20	.15	.08
195	Dan Quisenberry	.08	.06	.03
196	Dave Engle	.08	.06	.03
197	Lance McCullers	.08	.06	.03
198	Franklin Stubbs	.08	.06	.03
199	Scott Bradley	.08	.06	.03
200	Wade Boggs	.70	.50	.30
201	Kirk Gibson	.12	.09	.05
202	Brett Butler	.08	.06	.03
203	Dave Anderson	.08	.06	.03
204	Donnie Moore	.08	.06	.03
205	Nelson Liriano	.09	.07	.04
206	Danny Gladden	.08	.06	.03
207	Dan Pasqua	.08	.06	.03
208	Robbie Thompson	.08	.06	.03
209	Richard Dotson	.08	.06	.03
210	Willie Randolph	.08	.06	.03
211	Danny Tartabull	.12	.09	.05
212	Greg Brock	.08	.06	.03
213	Albert Hall	.08	.06	.03
214	Dave Schmidt	.08	.06	.03
215	Von Hayes	.08	.06	.03
216	Herm Winningham	.08	.06	.03
217	Mike Davis	.08	.06	.03
218	Charlie Leibrandt	.08	.06	.03
219	Mike Stanley	.08	.06	.03
220	Tom Henke	.08	.06	.03
221	Dwight Evans	.08	.06	.03
222	Willie Wilson	.08	.06	.03
223	Stan Jefferson	.08	.06	.03
224	Mike Dunne	.09	.07	.04
225	Mike Scioscia	.08	.06	.03
226	Larry Parrish	.08	.06	.03
227	Mike Scott	.09	.07	.04
228	Wallace Johnson	.08	.06	.03
229	Jeff Musselman	.08	.06	.03
230	Pat Tabler	.08	.06	.03
231	Paul Molitor	.09	.07	.04
232	Bob James	.08	.06	.03
233	Joe Niekro	.08	.06	.03
234	Oddibe McDowell	.08	.06	.03
235	Gary Ward	.08	.06	.03
236	Ted Power	.08	.06	.03
237	Pascual Perez	.08	.06	.03
238	Luis Polonia	.09	.07	.04
239	Mike Diaz	.08	.06	.03
240	Lee Smith	.08	.06	.03
241	Willie Upshaw	.08	.06	.03
242	Tim Neidenfuer	.08	.06	.03
243	Tim Raines	.20	.15	.08
244	Jeff Robinson	.12	.09	.05
245	Rich Gedman	.08	.06	.03
246	Scott Bankhead	.08	.06	.03
247	Andre Dawson	.12	.09	.05
248	Brook Jacoby	.08	.06	.03
249	Mike Marshall	.08	.06	.03
250	Nolan Ryan	.75	.60	.30
251	Tom Foley	.08	.06	.03
252	Bob Brower	.08	.06	.03
254	Scott McGregor	.08	.06	.03
255	Ken Griffey	.08	.06	.03
256	Ken Schrom	.08	.06	.03
257	Gary Gaetti	.09	.07	.04
258	Ed Nunez	.08	.06	.03
259	Frank Viola	.09	.07	.04
260	Vince Coleman	.09	.07	.04
261	Reid Nichols	.08	.06	.03
262	Tim Flannery	.08	.06	.03
263	Glenn Braggs	.08	.06	.03
264	Garry Templeton	.08	.06	.03
265	Bo Diaz	.08	.06	.03
266	Matt Nokes	.30	.25	.12
267	Barry Bonds	.60	.45	.25
268	Bruce Ruffin	.08	.06	.03
269	Ellis Burks	.30	.25	.12
270	Mike Witt	.08	.06	.03
271	Ken Gerhart	.08	.06	.03
272	Lloyd Moseby	.08	.06	.03
273	Garth Iorg	.08	.06	.03
274	Mike Greenwell	.80	.60	.30
275	Kevin Seitzer	.60	.45	.25
276	Luis Salazar	.08	.06	.03
277	Shawon Dunston	.08	.06	.03
278	Rick Reuschel	.08	.06	.03
279	Randy St. Claire	.08	.06	.03
280	Pete Incaviglia	.08	.06	.03
281	Mike Boddicker	.08	.06	.03
282	Jay Tibbs	.08	.06	.03
283	Shane Mack	.30	.25	.12
284	Walt Terrell	.08	.06	.03
285	Jim Presley	.08	.06	.03
286	Greg Walker	.08	.06	.03
287	Dwight Gooden	.30	.25	.12
288	Jim Morrison	.08	.06	.03
289	Gene Garber	.08	.06	.03
290	Tony Fernandez	.08	.06	.03
291	Ozzie Virgil	.08	.06	.03
292	Carney Lansford	.08	.06	.03
293	Jim Acker	.08	.06	.03
294	Tommy Hinzo	.08	.06	.03
295	Bert Blyleven	.09	.07	.04
296	Ozzie Guillen	.08	.06	.03
297	Zane Smith	.08	.06	.03
298	Milt Thompson	.08	.06	.03
299	Len Dykstra	.08	.06	.03
300	Don Mattingly	.30	.25	.12
301	Bud Black	.08	.06	.03
302	Jose Uribe	.08	.06	.03
303	Manny Lee	.08	.06	.03
304	Sid Bream	.08	.06	.03
305	Steve Sax	.09	.07	.04
306	Billy Hatcher	.08	.06	.03
307	John Shelby	.08	.06	.03
308	Lee Mazzilli	.08	.06	.03
309	Bill Long	.09	.07	.04
310	Tom Herr	.08	.06	.03
311	Derek Bell	4.50	3.50	1.75
312	George Brett	.25	.20	.10
313	Bob McClure	.08	.06	.03
314	Jimy Williams	.08	.06	.03
315	Dave Parker	.09	.07	.04
316	Doyle Alexander	.08	.06	.03
317	Dan Plesac	.08	.06	.03
318	Mel Hall	.08	.06	.03
319	Ruben Sierra	.30	.25	.12
320	Alan Trammell	.12	.09	.05
321	Mike Schmidt	.30	.25	.12
322	Wally Ritchie	.08	.06	.03
324	Danny Jackson	.08	.06	.03
325	Glenn Hubbard	.08	.06	.03
326	Frank White	.08	.06	.03
327	Larry Sheets	.08	.06	.03
328	John Cangelosi	.08	.06	.03
329	Bill Gullickson	.08	.06	.03
330	Eddie Whitson	.08	.06	.03
331	Brian Downing	.08	.06	.03
332	Gary Redus	.08	.06	.03
333	Wally Backman	.08	.06	.03
334	Dwayne Murphy	.08	.06	.03
335	Claudell Washington	.08	.06	.03
336	Dave Concepcion	.08	.06	.03
337	Jim Gantner	.08	.06	.03
338	Marty Barrett	.08	.06	.03
339	Mickey Hatcher	.08	.06	.03
340	Jack Morris	.12	.09	.05
341	John Franco	.08	.06	.03
342	Ron Robinson	.08	.06	.03
343	Greg Gagne	.08	.06	.03
344	Steve Bedrosian	.08	.06	.03
345	Scott Fletcher	.08	.06	.03

346	Vance Law	.08	.06	.03
347	Joe Johnson	.08	.06	.03
348	Jim Eisenreich	.08	.06	.03
349	Alvin Davis	.09	.07	.04
350	Will Clark	.40	.30	.15
351	Mike Aldrete	.08	.06	.03
352	Billy Ripken	.12	.09	.05
353	Dave Stewart	.08	.06	.03
354	Neal Heaton	.08	.06	.03
355	Roger McDowell	.08	.06	.03
356	John Tudor	.08	.06	.03
357	Floyd Bannister	.08	.06	.03
358	Rey Quinones	.08	.06	.03
359	Glenn Wilson	.08	.06	.03
360	Tony Gwynn	.30	.25	.12
361	Greg Maddux	.60	.45	.25
362	Juan Castillo	.08	.06	.03
363	Willie Fraser	.08	.06	.03
364	Nick Esasky	.08	.06	.03
365	Floyd Youmans	.08	.06	.03
366	Chet Lemon	.08	.06	.03
367	Matt Young	.08	.06	.03
368	Gerald Young	.20	.15	.08
369	Bob Stanley	.08	.06	.03
370	Jose Canseco	.35	.25	.14
371	Joe Hesketh	.08	.06	.03
372	Rick Sutcliffe	.08	.06	.03
375	Tom Brunansky	.08	.06	.03
376	Jody Davis	.08	.06	.03
377	Sam Horn	.15	.11	.06
378	Mark Gubicza	.08	.06	.03
379	Rafael Ramirez	.08	.06	.03
380	Joe Magrane	.15	.11	.06
381	Pete O'Brien	.08	.06	.03
382	Lee Guetterman	.08	.06	.03
383	Eric Bell	.08	.06	.03
384	Gene Larkin	.12	.09	.05
385	Carlton Fisk	.09	.07	.04
386	Mike Fitzgerald	.08	.06	.03
387	Kevin Mitchell	.08	.06	.03
388	Jim Winn	.08	.06	.03
389	Mike Smithson	.08	.06	.03
390	Darrell Evans	.08	.06	.03
391	Terry Leach	.08	.06	.03
392	Charlie Kerfeld	.08	.06	.03
393	Mike Krukow	.08	.06	.03
394	Mark McGwire	.30	.25	.12
395	Fred McGriff	.50	.40	.20
396	DeWayne Buice	.08	.06	.03

1988 O-Pee-Chee Box Panels

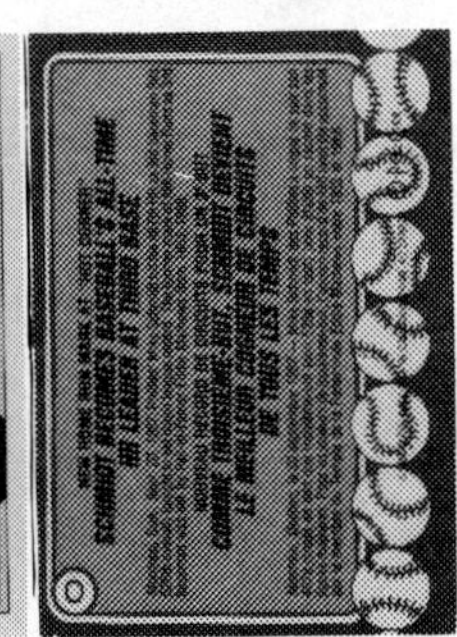

A Topps licensee, O-Pee-Chee of Canada issued this 16-card set on retail display box bottoms. Cards feature popular current players and are identified by alphabet (A-P) rather than numbers. Player photos are the same ones used on the 1988 Topps U.S. issue and cards follow the same design as Topps' regular issue set - team name in large, brightly colored letters at the top of the player photo, player name in a diagonal strip across the lower right corner of the card. The O-Pee-Chee logo replaces the Topps logo on both front and back. O-Pee-Chee horizontal orange and black card backs are bilingual (French/English) and include complete major and minor league career stats.

		MT	NR MT	EX
Complete Panel Set:		8.00	6.00	3.25
Complete Singles Set:		3.50	2.75	1.50
Common Single Player:		.08	.06	.03
	Panel	1.00	.70	.40
A	Don Baylor	.15	.11	.06
B	Steve Bedrosian	.15	.11	.06
C	Juan Beniquez	.08	.06	.03
D	Bob Boone	.08	.06	.03
	Panel	2.00	1.50	.80
E	Darrell Evans	.10	.08	.04
F	Tony Gwynn	.40	.30	.15
G	John Kruk	.20	.15	.08
H	Marvell Wynne	.08	.06	.03
	Panel	2.00	1.50	.80
I	Joe Carter	.25	.11	.06
J	Eric Davis	.30	.30	.15
K	Howard Johnson	.10	.08	.04
L	Darryl Strawberry	.20	.30	.15
	Panel	3.50	2.75	1.50
M	Rickey Henderson	.40	.30	.15
N	Nolan Ryan	.90	.25	.12
O	Mike Schmidt	.60	.30	.15
P	Kent Tekulve	.08	.06	.03

1990 O-Pee-Chee

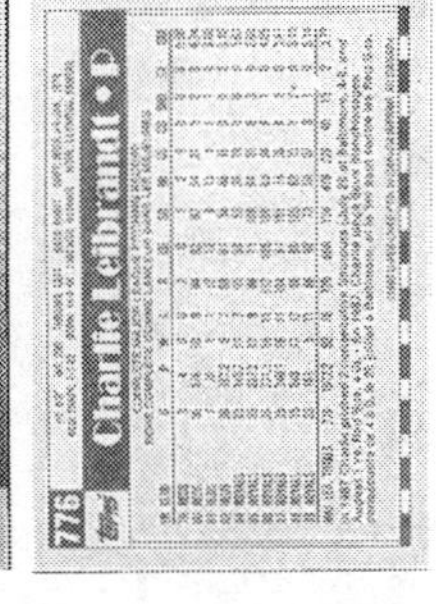

Virtually identical to the contemporary 1990 Topps set, the 1990 OPC issue features the same 792 cards. On most cards the fronts are indistinguishable, even to the use of a Topps logo on the Canadian product. A number of the OPC cards differ from their Topps counterparts in that there is a notice of team change printed in black on the front. Backs of the OPC cards feature a few lines of French in areas such as the stat headings, the career summary and monthly scoreboard. The OPC cards omit the Topps copyright line and feature an OPC copyright line. The 1990 Topps set again included 792 cards, and sported a newly-designed front that featured six different color schemes. The set led off with a special four-card salute to Nolan Ryan, and featured various other specials, including All-Stars, Number 1 Draft Picks, Record Breakers, manager cards, rookies, and "Turn Back the Clock" cards. The set also includes a special card commemorating A. Bartlett Giamatti, the late Baseball Commissioner. The backs are printed in black on a chartreuse background with the card number in the upper left corner. The set features 725 different individual player cards, the most ever, including 138 players making their first appearance in a regular Topps set.

		MT	NR MT	EX
Complete Set (792):		25.00	18.50	10.00
Common Player:		.03	.02	.01
1	Nolan Ryan	.35	.25	.14
2	Nolan Ryan (Mets)	.20	.15	.08
3	Nolan Ryan (Angels)	.20	.15	.08
4	Nolan Ryan (Astros)	.20	.15	.08
5	Nolan Ryan (Rangers)	.20	.15	.08
6	Vince Coleman (Record Breaker)	.10	.08	.04
7	Rickey Henderson (Record Breaker)	.20	.15	.08
8	Cal Ripken, Jr. (Record Breaker)	.15	.11	.06
9	Eric Plunk	.03	.02	.01
10	Barry Larkin	.15	.11	.06
11	Paul Gibson	.04	.03	.02
12	Joe Girardi (FC)	.15	.11	.06
13	Mark Williamson	.03	.02	.01
14	*Mike Fetters* (FC)	.20	.15	.08
15	Teddy Higuera	.06	.05	.02
16	*Kent Anderson*	.10	.08	.04
17	Kelly Downs	.05	.04	.02
18	Carlos Quintana	.09	.07	.04
19	Al Newman	.03	.02	.01
20	Mark Gubicza	.12	.09	.05
21	Jeff Torborg	.03	.02	.01
22	Bruce Ruffin	.03	.02	.01
23	Randy Velarde	.07	.05	.03
24	Joe Hesketh	.03	.02	.01
25	Willie Randolph	.08	.06	.03
26	Don Slaught	.03	.02	.01
27	Rick Leach	.03	.02	.01
28	Duane Ward	.04	.03	.02
29	John Cangelosi	.03	.02	.01
30	David Cone	.10	.08	.04
31	Henry Cotto	.03	.02	.01
32	John Farrell	.05	.04	.02
33	Greg Walker	.05	.04	.02
34	*Tony Fossas* (FC)	.07	.05	.03
35	Benito Santiago	.12	.09	.05
36	John Costello	.04	.03	.02
37	Domingo Ramos	.03	.02	.01
38	Wes Gardner	.04	.03	.02
39	Curt Ford	.04	.03	.02
40	Jay Howell	.06	.05	.02
41	Matt Williams	.15	.11	.06
42	Jeff Robinson	.05	.04	.02
43	Dante Bichette	.07	.05	.03
44	*Roger Salkeld* (#1 Draft Pick)	.25	.20	.10
45	Dave Parker	.09	.07	.04
46	Rob Dibble	.07	.05	.03
47	Brian Harper	.04	.03	.02
48	Zane Smith	.03	.02	.01
49	Tom Lawless	.03	.02	.01
50	Glenn Davis	.08	.06	.03
51	Doug Rader	.03	.02	.01
52	*Jack Daugherty* (FC)	.20	.15	.08
53	Mike LaCoss	.04	.03	.02
54	Joel Skinner	.04	.03	.02
55	Darrell Evans	.05	.04	.02
56	Franklin Stubbs	.04	.03	.02
57	*Greg Vaughn* (FC)	.60	.45	.25
58	Keith Miller	.10	.08	.04
59	Ted Power	.03	.02	.01
60	George Brett	.20	.15	.08
61	*Deion Sanders*	.35	.25	.14
62	Ramon Martinez	.25	.20	.10
63	Mike Pagliarulo	.04	.03	.02
64	Danny Darwin	.03	.02	.01
65	Devon White	.07	.05	.03
66	*Greg Litton*	.15	.11	.06
67	Scott Sanderson	.04	.03	.02
68	Dave Henderson	.06	.05	.02
69	Todd Frohwirth	.03	.02	.01
70	Mike Greenwell	.30	.25	.12
71	Allan Anderson	.05	.04	.02
72	*Jeff Huson*	.20	.15	.08
73	Bob Milacki	.05	.04	.02
74	*Jeff Jackson* (#1 Draft Pick)	.20	.15	.08
75	Doug Jones	.05	.04	.02
76	Dave Valle	.03	.02	.01
77	Dave Bergman	.03	.02	.01
78	Mike Flanagan	.04	.03	.02
79	Ron Kittle	.05	.04	.02
80	Jeff Russell	.05	.04	.02
81	Bob Rodgers	.03	.02	.01
82	Scott Terry	.04	.03	.02
83	Hensley Meulens	.30	.25	.12
84	Ray Searage	.03	.02	.01
85	Juan Samuel	.05	.04	.02
86	Paul Kilgus	.03	.02	.01
87	*Rick Luecken* (FC)	.15	.11	.06
88	Glenn Braggs	.05	.04	.02
89	*Clint Zavaras* (FC)	.15	.11	.06
90	Jack Clark	.06	.05	.02
91	*Steve Frey* (FC)	.20	.15	.08
92	Mike Stanley	.03	.02	.01
93	Shawn Hillegas	.03	.02	.01
94	Herm Winningham	.03	.02	.01
95	Todd Worrell	.05	.04	.02
96	Jody Reed	.04	.03	.02
97	Curt Schilling (FC)	.25	.20	.10
98	Jose Gonzalez (FC)	.10	.08	.04
99	*Rich Monteleone* (FC)	.15	.11	.06
100	Will Clark	.50	.40	.20
101	Shane Rawley	.04	.03	.02
102	Stan Javier	.04	.03	.02
103	Marvin Freeman	.09	.07	.04
104	Bob Knepper	.03	.02	.01
105	Randy Myers	.05	.04	.02
106	Charlie O'Brien	.03	.02	.01
107	Fred Lynn	.05	.04	.02
108	Rod Nichols	.04	.03	.02
109	Roberto Kelly	.08	.06	.03
110	Tommy Helms	.03	.02	.01
111	Ed Whited	.20	.15	.08
112	Glenn Wilson	.03	.02	.01
113	Manny Lee	.03	.02	.01
114	Mike Bielecki	.05	.04	.02
115	Tony Pena	.06	.05	.02
116	Floyd Bannister	.04	.03	.02
117	Mike Sharperson (FC)	.09	.07	.04
118	Erik Hanson	.10	.08	.04
119	Billy Hatcher	.04	.03	.02
120	John Franco	.05	.04	.02
121	Robin Ventura	.60	.45	.25
122	Shawn Abner	.03	.02	.01
123	Rich Gedman	.04	.03	.02
124	Dave Dravecky	.04	.03	.02
125	Kent Hrbek	.07	.05	.03
126	Randy Kramer	.03	.02	.01
127	Mike Devereaux	.06	.05	.02
128	Checklist 1-132	.03	.02	.01
129	Ron Jones	.10	.08	.04
130	Bert Blyleven	.05	.04	.02
131	Matt Nokes	.06	.05	.02
132	Lance Blankenship (FC)	.10	.08	.04
133	Ricky Horton	.03	.02	.01
134	*Earl Cunningham* (#1 Draft Pick)	.15	.11	.06
135	Dave Magadan	.05	.04	.02
136	Kevin Brown	.06	.05	.02
137	*Marty Pevey* (FC)	.15	.11	.06
138	Al Leiter	.04	.03	.02
139	Greg Brock	.04	.03	.02
140	Andre Dawson	.12	.09	.05
141	John Hart	.05	.04	.02
142	*Jeff Wetherby* (FC)	.15	.11	.06
143	Rafael Belliard	.03	.02	.01
144	Bud Black	.03	.02	.01
145	Terry Steinbach	.07	.05	.03
146	*Rob Richie* (FC)	.15	.11	.06
147	Chuck Finley	.04	.03	.02
148	Edgar Martinez (FC)	.09	.07	.04
149	Steve Farr	.04	.03	.02
150	Kirk Gibson	.09	.07	.04
151	Rick Mahler	.03	.02	.01
152	Lonnie Smith	.05	.04	.02
153	Randy Milligan	.05	.04	.02
154	Mike Maddux	.05	.04	.02
155	Ellis Burks	.25	.20	.10
156	Ken Patterson	.04	.03	.02
157	Craig Biggio	.15	.11	.06
158	Craig Lefferts	.04	.03	.02
159	Mike Felder	.03	.02	.01
160	Dave Righetti	.06	.05	.02
161	Harold Reynolds	.06	.05	.02
162	*Todd Zeile* (FC)	.60	.45	.25
163	Phil Bradley	.05	.04	.02
164	*Jeff Juden* (FC) (#1 Draft Pick)	.30	.25	.12
165	Walt Weiss	.08	.06	.03
166	Bobby Witt	.04	.03	.02
167	*Kevin Appier* (FC)	.35	.25	.14
168	Jose Lind	.04	.03	.02
169	Richard Dotson	.03	.02	.01
170	George Bell	.12	.09	.05
171	Russ Nixon	.03	.02	.01
172	Tom Lampkin (FC)	.10	.08	.04
173	Tim Belcher	.12	.09	.05

No.	Player			
174	Jeff Kunkel	.03	.02	.01
175	Mike Moore	.07	.05	.02
176	Luis Quinones	.03	.02	.01
177	Mike Henneman	.05	.04	.02
178	Chris James	.06	.05	.02
179	Brian Holton	.04	.03	.02
180	Rock Raines	.10	.08	.04
181	Juan Agosto	.03	.02	.01
182	Mookie Wilson	.05	.04	.02
183	Steve Lake	.03	.02	.01
184	Danny Cox	.04	.03	.02
185	Ruben Sierra	.20	.15	.08
186	Dave LaPoint	.03	.02	.01
187	*Rick Wrona* (FC)	.12	.09	.05
188	Mike Smithson	.03	.02	.01
189	Dick Schofield	.04	.03	.02
190	Rick Reuschel	.06	.05	.02
191	Pat Borders	.08	.06	.03
192	Don August	.04	.03	.02
193	Andy Benes	.25	.20	.10
194	Glenallen Hill (FC)	.25	.20	.10
195	Tim Burke	.05	.04	.02
196	Gerald Young	.04	.03	.02
197	Doug Drabek	.07	.05	.03
198	Mike Marshall	.06	.05	.02
199	*Sergio Valdez* (FC)	.20	.15	.08
200	Don Mattingly	.40	.30	.15
201	Cito Gaston	.03	.02	.01
202	Mike Macfarlane	.03	.02	.01
203	*Mike Roesler* (FC)	.15	.11	.06
204	Bob Dernier	.03	.02	.01
205	Mark Davis	.09	.07	.04
206	Nick Esasky	.07	.05	.02
207	Bob Ojeda	.04	.03	.02
208	Brook Jacoby	.04	.03	.02
209	Greg Mathews	.04	.03	.02
210	Ryne Sandberg	.30	.25	.12
211	John Cerutti	.04	.03	.02
212	Joe Orsulak	.03	.02	.01
213	Scott Bankhead	.05	.04	.02
214	Terry Francona	.03	.02	.01
215	Kirk McCaskill	.04	.03	.02
216	Ricky Jordan	.20	.15	.08
217	Don Robinson	.04	.03	.02
218	Wally Backman	.04	.03	.02
219	Donn Pall	.03	.02	.01
220	Barry Bonds	.10	.08	.04
221	*Gary Mielke* (FC)	.15	.11	.06
222	Kurt Stillwell	.05	.04	.02
223	Tommy Gregg	.06	.05	.02
224	*Delino DeShields* (FC)	.60	.45	.25
225	Jim Deshaies	.05	.04	.02
226	Mickey Hatcher	.03	.02	.01
227	*Kevin Tapani* (FC)	.30	.25	.12
228	Dave Martinez	.03	.02	.01
229	David Wells	.03	.02	.01
230	Keith Hernandez	.07	.05	.03
231	Jack McKeon	.03	.02	.01
232	Darnell Coles	.04	.03	.02
233	Ken Hill	.10	.08	.06
234	Mariano Duncan	.05	.04	.02
235	Jeff Reardon	.04	.03	.02
236	Hal Morris (FC)	.50	.40	.20
237	*Kevin Ritz* (FC)	.15	.11	.06
238	Felix Jose (FC)	.10	.08	.04
239	Eric Show	.04	.03	.02
240	Mark Grace	.40	.30	.15
241	Mike Krukow	.04	.03	.02
242	Fred Manrique	.03	.02	.01
243	Barry Jones	.03	.02	.01
244	Bill Schroeder	.03	.02	.01
245	Roger Clemens	.25	.20	.10
246	Jim Eisenreich	.03	.02	.01
247	Jerry Reed	.03	.02	.01
248	Dave Anderson	.03	.02	.01
249	*Mike Smith* (FC)	.12	.09	.05
250	Jose Canseco	.70	.50	.30
251	Jeff Blauser	.05	.04	.02
252	Otis Nixon	.03	.02	.01
253	Mark Portugal	.03	.02	.01
254	Francisco Cabrera	.25	.20	.10
255	Bobby Thigpen	.07	.05	.03
256	Marvell Wynne	.03	.02	.01
257	Jose DeLeon	.07	.05	.03
258	Barry Lyons	.03	.02	.01
259	Lance McCullers	.05	.04	.02
260	Eric Davis	.30	.25	.12
261	Whitey Herzog	.03	.02	.01
262	Checklist 133-264	.03	.02	.01
263	*Mel Stottlemyre, Jr.* (FC)	.12	.09	.05
264	Bryan Clutterbuck	.03	.02	.01
265	Pete O'Brien	.06	.05	.02
266	German Gonzalez	.04	.03	.02
267	Mark Davidson	.03	.02	.01
268	Rob Murphy	.03	.02	.01
269	Dickie Thon	.03	.02	.01
270	Dave Stewart	.08	.06	.03
271	Chet Lemon	.05	.04	.02
272	Bryan Harvey	.04	.03	.02
273	Bobby Bonilla	.15	.11	.06
274	*Goose Gozzo* (FC)	.15	.11	.06
275	Mickey Tettleton	.07	.05	.03
276	Gary Thurman	.03	.02	.01
277	Lenny Harris (FC)	.12	.09	.05
278	Pascual Perez	.04	.03	.02
279	Steve Buechele	.04	.03	.02
280	Lou Whitaker	.07	.05	.03
281	Kevin Bass	.05	.04	.02
282	Derek Lilliquist	.10	.08	.04
283	*Albert Belle*	1.00	.75	.40
284	*Mark Gardner* (FC)	.30	.25	.12
285	Willie McGee	.06	.05	.02
286	Lee Guetterman	.03	.02	.01
287	Vance Law	.03	.02	.01
288	Greg Briley	.15	.11	.06
289	Norm Charlton	.10	.08	.04
290	Robin Yount	.25	.20	.10
291	Dave Johnson	.03	.02	.01
292	Jim Gott	.04	.03	.02
293	Mike Gallego	.04	.03	.02
294	Craig McMurtry	.03	.02	.01
295	Fred McGriff	.25	.20	.10
296	Jeff Ballard	.07	.05	.03
297	Tom Herr	.06	.05	.02
298	Danny Gladden	.05	.04	.02
299	Adam Peterson (FC)	.09	.07	.04
300	Bo Jackson	.60	.45	.25
301	Don Aase	.03	.02	.01
302	*Marcus Lawton* (FC)	.08	.06	.03
303	Rick Cerone	.03	.02	.01
304	Marty Clary (FC)	.08	.06	.03
305	Eddie Murray	.15	.11	.06
306	Tom Niedenfuer	.03	.02	.01
307	Bip Roberts	.08	.06	.03
308	Jose Guzman	.05	.04	.02
309	*Eric Yelding* (FC)	.20	.15	.08
310	Steve Bedrosian	.05	.04	.02
311	Dwight Smith	.25	.20	.10
312	Dan Quisenberry	.05	.04	.02
313	Gus Polidor	.03	.02	.01
314	*Donald Harris* (#1 Draft Pick)	.20	.15	.08
315	Bruce Hurst	.06	.05	.02
316	Carney Lansford	.06	.05	.02
317	*Mark Guthrie* (FC)	.20	.15	.08
318	Wallace Johnson	.03	.02	.01
319	Dion James	.04	.03	.02
320	Dave Steib	.07	.05	.03
321	Joe M. Morgan	.03	.02	.01
322	Junior Ortiz	.03	.02	.01
323	Willie Wilson	.04	.03	.02
324	Pete Harnisch (FC)	.10	.08	.04
325	Robby Thompson	.06	.05	.02
326	*Tom McCarthy*	.10	.08	.04
327	Ken Williams	.03	.02	.01
328	Curt Young	.03	.02	.01
329	Oddibe McDowell	.06	.05	.02
330	Ron Darling	.09	.07	.04
331	*Juan Gonzalez* (FC)	1.50	1.25	.60
332	Paul O'Neill	.07	.05	.03
333	Bill Wegman	.03	.02	.01
334	Johnny Ray	.05	.04	.02
335	Andy Hawkins	.05	.04	.02
336	Ken Griffey, Jr.	1.25	.90	.50
337	Lloyd McClendon	.06	.05	.02
338	Dennis Lamp	.03	.02	.01
339	Dave Clark	.04	.03	.02
340	Fernando Valenzuela	.06	.05	.02
341	Tom Foley	.03	.02	.01
342	Alex Trevino	.03	.02	.01
343	Frank Tanana	.04	.03	.02
344	*George Canale* (FC)	.15	.11	.06
345	Harold Baines	.09	.07	.04
346	Jim Presley	.04	.03	.02
347	*Junior Felix*	.20	.15	.08
348	*Gary Wayne* (FC)	.12	.09	.05
349	*Steve Finley* (FC)	.30	.25	.12
350	Bret Saberhagen	.10	.08	.04
351	Roger Craig	.03	.02	.01
352	Bryn Smith	.05	.04	.02
353	Sandy Alomar	.25	.20	.10
354	*Stan Belinda* (FC)	.20	.15	.08
355	Marty Barrett	.05	.04	.02
356	Randy Ready	.03	.02	.01
357	Dave West	.20	.15	.08
358	Andres Thomas	.04	.03	.02
359	Jimmy Jones	.03	.02	.01
360	Paul Molitor	.09	.07	.04
361	*Randy McCament* (FC)	.15	.11	.06
362	Damon Berryhill	.06	.05	.02
363	Dan Petry	.03	.02	.01
364	Rolando Roomes (FC)	.15	.11	.06
365	Ozzie Guillen	.05	.04	.02
366	Mike Heath	.03	.02	.01
367	Mike Morgan	.03	.02	.01
368	Bill Doran	.06	.05	.02
369	Todd Burns	.04	.03	.02
370	Tim Wallach	.07	.05	.03
371	Jimmy Key	.08	.06	.03
372	Terry Kennedy	.03	.02	.01
373	Alvin Davis	.08	.06	.03
374	*Steve Cummings* (FC)	.15	.11	.06
375	Dwight Evans	.08	.06	.03
376	Checklist 265-396	.03	.02	.01
377	*Mickey Weston* (FC)	.15	.11	.06
378	Luis Salazar	.03	.02	.01
379	Steve Rosenberg	.03	.02	.01
380	Dave Winfield	.15	.11	.06
381	Frank Robinson	.03	.02	.01
382	Jeff Musselman	.03	.02	.01
383	John Morris	.04	.03	.02
384	*Pat Combs*	.20	.15	.08
385	Fred McGriff (All-Star)	.20	.15	.08
386	Julio Franco (All-Star)	.10	.08	.04
387	Wade Boggs (All-Star)	.20	.15	.08
388	Cal Ripken, Jr. (All-Star)	.15	.11	.06
389	Robin Yount (All-Star)	.25	.20	.10
390	Ruben Sierra (All-Star)	.15	.11	.06
391	Kirby Puckett (All-Star)	.20	.15	.08
392	Carlton Fisk (All-Star)	.08	.06	.03
393	Bret Saberhagen (All-Star)	.10	.08	.04
394	Jeff Ballard (All-Star)	.08	.06	.03
395	Jeff Russell (All-Star)	.08	.06	.03
396	A. Bartlett Giamatti	.30	.25	.12
397	Will Clark (All-Star)	.25	.20	.10
398	Ryne Sandberg (All-Star)	.20	.15	.08
399	Howard Johnson (All-Star)	.08	.06	.03
400	Ozzie Smith (All-Star)	.15	.11	.06
401	Kevin Mitchell (All-Star)	.10	.08	.04
402	Eric Davis (All-Star)	.10	.08	.04
403	Tony Gwynn (All-Star)	.15	.11	.06
404	Craig Biggio (All-Star)	.10	.07	.04
405	Mike Scott (All-Star)	.08	.06	.03
406	Joe Magrane (All-Star)	.08	.06	.03
407	Mark Davis (All-Star)	.08	.06	.03
408	Trevor Wilson	.06	.05	.02
409	Tom Brunansky	.09	.07	.04
410	Joe Boever	.06	.05	.02
411	Ken Phelps	.03	.02	.01
412	Jamie Moyer	.04	.03	.02
413	*Brian DuBois*	.15	.11	.06
414	*Frank Thomas* (#1 Draft Pick)	3.00	2.25	1.25
415	Shawon Dunston	.06	.05	.02
416	*Dave Johnson* (FC)	.12	.09	.05
417	Jim Gantner	.06	.05	.02
418	Tom Browning	.08	.06	.03
419	*Beau Allred*	.20	.15	.08
420	Carlton Fisk	.08	.06	.03
421	Greg Minton	.03	.02	.01
422	Pat Sheridan	.03	.02	.01
423	Fred Toliver	.03	.02	.01
424	Jerry Reuss	.05	.04	.02
425	Bill Landrum	.05	.04	.02
426	Jeff Hamilton	.05	.04	.02
427	Carmem Castillo	.03	.02	.01
428	*Steve Davis* (FC)	.12	.09	.05
429	Tom Kelly	.03	.02	.01
430	Pete Incaviglia	.06	.05	.02
431	Randy Johnson	.10	.08	.04
432	Damaso Garcia	.03	.02	.01
433	*Steve Olin* (FC)	.12	.08	.04
434	Mark Carreon (FC)	.09	.07	.04
435	Kevin Seitzer	.09	.07	.04
436	Mel Hall	.05	.04	.02
437	Les Lancaster	.05	.04	.02
438	Greg Myers (FC)	.10	.08	.04
439	Jeff Parrett	.06	.05	.02
440	Alan Trammell	.09	.07	.04
441	Bob Kipper	.03	.02	.01
442	Jerry Browne	.07	.05	.02
443	Cris Carpenter	.09	.07	.04
444	*Kyle Abbott* (FDP)	.20	.15	.08
445	Danny Jackson	.05	.04	.02
446	Dan Pasqua	.05	.04	.02
447	Atlee Hammaker	.03	.02	.01
448	Greg Gagne	.04	.03	.02
449	Dennis Rasmussen	.04	.03	.02
450	Rickey Henderson	.25	.20	.10
451	Mark Lemke (FC)	.10	.08	.04
452	Luis de los Santos (FC)	.10	.08	.04
453	Jody Davis	.03	.02	.01
454	Jeff King (FC)	.15	.11	.06
455	Jeffrey Leonard	.06	.05	.02
456	Chris Gwynn (FC)	.09	.07	.03
457	Gregg Jefferies	.30	.25	.12
458	Bob McClure	.03	.02	.01
459	Jim Lefebvre	.03	.02	.01
460	Mike Scott	.09	.07	.03
461	*Carlos Martinez* (FC)	.15	.11	.06
462	Denny Walling	.03	.02	.01
463	Drew Hall	.03	.02	.01
464	*Jerome Walton*	.25	.20	.10
465	Kevin Gross	.06	.05	.02
466	Rance Mulliniks	.03	.02	.01
467	Juan Nieves	.04	.03	.02
468	Billy Ripken	.04	.03	.02
469	John Kruk	.07	.05	.02
470	Frank Viola	.09	.07	.04
471	Mike Brumley	.03	.02	.01
472	Jose Uribe	.04	.03	.02
473	Joe Price	.03	.02	.01
474	Rich Thompson	.04	.03	.02
475	Bob Welch	.06	.05	.02
476	Brad Komminsk	.03	.02	.02
477	Willie Fraser	.03	.02	.02
478	Mike LaValliere	.04	.03	.02
479	Frank White	.06	.05	.02
480	Sid Fernandez	.09	.07	.04
481	Garry Templeton	.05	.04	.02
482	*Steve Carter* (FC)	.15	.11	.06
483	Alejandro Pena	.04	.03	.02
484	Mike Fitzgerald	.03	.02	.01
485	John Candelaria	.05	.04	.02
486	Jeff Treadway	.05	.04	.02
487	Steve Searcy	.05	.04	.02
488	Ken Oberkfell	.03	.02	.01
489	Nick Leyva	.03	.02	.01
490	Dan Plesac	.07	.05	.03
491	*Dave Cochrane* (FC)	.15	.11	.06
492	Ron Oester	.04	.03	.02
493	*Jason Grimsley* (FC)	.25	.20	.10
494	Terry Puhl	.03	.02	.01
495	Lee Smith	.06	.05	.02
496	Cecil Espy	.06	.05	.02
497	Dave Schmidt	.03	.02	.01
498	Rick Schu	.03	.02	.01
499	Bill Long	.04	.03	.02
500	Kevin Mitchell	.35	.25	.14
501	Matt Young	.03	.02	.01
502	Mitch Webster	.04	.03	.02
503	Randy St. Claire	.03	.02	.01
504	Tom O'Malley	.03	.02	.01
505	Kelly Gruber	.08	.06	.03
506	Tom Glavine	.20	.15	.08
507	Gary Redus	.04	.03	.02
508	Terry Leach	.03	.02	.01
509	Tom Pagnozzi	.03	.02	.01
510	Doc Gooden	.25	.20	.10
511	Clay Parker	.07	.05	.03
512	Gary Pettis	.03	.02	.01
513	Mark Eichhorn	.03	.02	.01
514	Andy Allanson	.03	.02	.01
515	Len Dykstra	.06	.05	.02
516	Tim Leary	.05	.04	.02
517	Roberto Alomar	.15	.11	.06
518	Bill Krueger	.03	.02	.01
519	Bucky Dent	.03	.02	.01
520	Mitch Williams	.09	.07	.03
521	Craig Worthington	.15	.11	.06
522	Mike Dunne	.04	.03	.02
523	Jay Bell	.03	.02	.01
524	Daryl Boston	.03	.02	.01
525	Wally Joyner	.20	.15	.08
526	Checklist 397-528	.03	.02	.01
527	Ron Hassey	.03	.02	.01

528	*Kevin Wickander* (FC)	.20	.15	.08
529	Greg Harris	.03	.02	.01
530	Mark Langston	.10	.08	.04
531	Ken Caminiti	.06	.05	.02
532	Cecilio Guante	.03	.02	.01
533	Tim Jones (FC)	.07	.05	.03
534	Louie Meadows	.07	.05	.03
535	John Smoltz	.15	.11	.06
536	*Bob Geren*	.15	.11	.06
537	Mark Grant	.03	.02	.01
538	*Billy Spiers*	.20	.15	.08
539	Neal Heaton	.03	.02	.01
540	Danny Tartabull	.09	.07	.03
541	Pat Perry	.03	.02	.01
542	Darren Daulton	.03	.02	.01
543	Nelson Liriano	.03	.02	.01
544	Dennis Boyd	.05	.04	.02
545	Kevin McReynolds	.09	.07	.04
546	Kevin Hickey	.05	.04	.02
547	Jack Howell	.05	.04	.02
548	Pat Clements	.03	.02	.01
549	Don Zimmer	.03	.02	.01
550	Julio Franco	.09	.07	.04
551	Tim Crews	.03	.02	.01
552	*Mike Smith* (FC)	.12	.09	.05
553	*Scott Scudder* (FC)	.20	.15	.11
554	Jay Buhner	.08	.06	.03
555	Jack Morris	.07	.05	.03
556	Gene Larkin	.03	.02	.01
557	*Jeff Innis*	.15	.11	.08
558	Rafael Ramirez	.04	.03	.02
559	Andy McGaffigan	.04	.03	.02
560	Steve Sax	.08	.06	.03
561	Ken Dayley	.03	.02	.01
562	Chad Kreuter	.10	.08	.04
563	Alex Sanchez	.10	.08	.04
564	*Tyler Houston* (#1 Draft Pick)	.20	.15	.08
565	Scott Fletcher	.05	.04	.02
566	Mark Knudson	.06	.05	.02
567	Ron Gant	.10	.08	.04
568	John Smiley	.07	.05	.03
569	Ivan Calderon	.05	.04	.02
570	Cal Ripken, Jr.	.35	.25	.14
571	Brett Butler	.06	.05	.02
572	Greg Harris	.09	.07	.04
573	Danny Heep	.03	.02	.01
574	Bill Swift	.04	.03	.02
575	Lance Parrish	.07	.05	.03
576	*Mike Dyer* (FC)	.20	.15	.08
577	Charlie Hayes (FC)	.10	.08	.04
578	Joe Magrane	.09	.07	.04
579	Art Howe	.03	.02	.01
580	Joe Carter	.15	.11	.06
581	Ken Griffey	.05	.04	.02
582	Rick Honeycutt	.03	.02	.01
583	Bruce Benedict	.03	.02	.01
584	*Phil Stephenson* (FC)	.09	.07	.04
585	Kal Daniels	.10	.08	.04
586	Ed Nunez	.03	.02	.01
587	Lance Johnson	.08	.06	.03
588	Rick Rhoden	.03	.02	.01
589	Mike Aldrete	.03	.02	.01
590	Ozzie Smith	.10	.08	.04
591	Todd Stottlemyre	.08	.06	.03
592	R.J. Reynolds	.03	.02	.01
593	Scott Bradley	.03	.02	.01
594	*Luis Sojo* (FC)	.20	.15	.08
595	Greg Swindell	.10	.08	.04
596	Jose DeJesus (FC)	.10	.08	.04
597	Chris Bosio	.07	.05	.03
598	Brady Anderson	.05	.04	.02
599	Frank Williams	.03	.02	.01
600	Darryl Strawberry	.15	.11	.06
601	Luis Rivera	.04	.03	.02
602	Scott Garrelts	.07	.05	.03
603	Tony Armas	.03	.02	.01
604	Ron Robinson	.03	.02	.01
605	Mike Scioscia	.07	.05	.03
606	Storm Davis	.07	.05	.03
607	Steve Jeltz	.03	.02	.01
608	*Eric Anthony* (FC)	.30	.25	.12
609	Sparky Anderson	.03	.02	.01
610	Pedro Guererro	.12	.09	.05
611	Walt Terrell	.05	.04	.02
612	Dave Gallagher	.07	.05	.02
613	Jeff Pico	.04	.03	.02
614	Nelson Santovenia	.09	.07	.04
615	Rob Deer	.07	.05	.03
616	Brian Holman	.10	.08	.04
617	Geronimo Berroa	.08	.06	.03
618	Eddie Whitson	.05	.04	.02
619	Rob Ducey	.08	.06	.03
620	*Tony Castillo* (FC)	.20	.15	.08
621	Melido Perez	.07	.05	.03
622	Sid Bream	.05	.04	.02
623	Jim Corsi	.05	.04	.02
624	Darrin Jackson	.04	.03	.02
625	Roger McDowell	.07	.05	.03
626	Bob Melvin	.03	.02	.01
627	Jose Rijo	.07	.05	.03
628	Candy Maldonado	.04	.03	.02
629	Eric Hetzel (FC)	.10	.08	.04
630	Gary Gaetti	.10	.08	.04
631	*John Wetteland* (FC)	.25	.20	.10
632	Scott Lusader	.06	.05	.02
633	Dennis Cook (FC)	.25	.20	.10
634	Luis Polonia	.06	.05	.02
635	Brian Downing	.06	.05	.02
636	Jesse Orosco	.03	.02	.01
637	Craig Reynolds	.03	.02	.01
638	Jeff Montgomery	.07	.05	.03
639	Tony LaRussa	.03	.02	.01
640	Rick Sutcliffe	.06	.05	.02
641	*Doug Strange* (FC)	.15	.11	.06
642	Jack Armstrong	.04	.03	.02
643	Alfredo Griffin	.04	.03	.02
644	Paul Assenmacher	.04	.03	.02
645	Jose Oquendo	.06	.05	.02
646	Checklist 529-660	.03	.02	.01
647	Rex Hudler	.03	.02	.01
648	Jim Clancy	.03	.02	.01
649	*Dan Murphy* (FC)	.15	.11	.06
650	Mike Witt	.06	.05	.02
651	Rafael Santana	.06	.05	.02
652	Mike Boddicker	.06	.05	.02
653	John Moses	.03	.02	.01
654	*Paul Coleman* (#1 Draft Pick)	.20	.15	.08
655	Gregg Olson	.30	.25	.12
656	Mackey Sasser	.05	.04	.02
657	Terry Mulholland	.06	.05	.02
658	Donell Nixon	.03	.02	.01
659	Greg Cadaret	.03	.02	.01
660	Vince Coleman	.10	.08	.04
661	Turn Back The Clock - 1985 (Dick Howser)	.07	.05	.03
662	Turn Back The Clock - 1980 (Mike Schmidt)	.07	.05	.03
663	Turn Back The Clock - 1975 (Fred Lynn)	.07	.05	.03
664	Turn Back The Clock - 1970 (Johnny Bench)	.07	.05	.03
665	Turn Back The Clock - 1965 (Sandy Koufax)	.07	.05	.03
666	Brian Fisher	.05	.04	.02
667	Curt Wilkerson	.03	.02	.01
668	*Joe Oliver* (FC)	.30	.25	.12
669	Tom Lasorda	.03	.02	.01
670	Dennis Eckersley	.09	.07	.04
671	Bob Boone	.09	.07	.04
672	Roy Smith	.03	.02	.01
673	Joey Meyer	.03	.02	.01
674	Spike Owen	.05	.04	.02
675	Jim Abbott	.35	.25	.12
676	Randy Kutcher (FC)	.07	.05	.03
677	Jay Tibbs	.03	.02	.01
678	Kirt Manwaring	.10	.08	.04
679	Gary Ward	.04	.03	.02
680	Howard Johnson	.15	.11	.06
681	Mike Schooler	.07	.05	.03
682	Dann Bilardello	.03	.02	.01
683	*Kenny Rogers*	.10	.08	.04
684	*Julio Machado* (FC)	.20	.15	.08
685	Tony Fernandez	.09	.07	.04
686	Carmelo Martinez	.06	.05	.02
687	Tim Birtsas	.03	.02	.01
688	Milt Thompson	.06	.05	.02
689	Rich Yett	.03	.02	.01
690	Mark McGwire	.30	.25	.12
691	Chuck Cary	.03	.02	.01
692	Sammy Sosa	.50	.40	.20
693	Calvin Schiraldi	.03	.02	.01
694	*Mike Stanton* (FC)	.30	.25	.12
695	Tom Henke	.06	.05	.02
696	B.J. Surhoff	.07	.05	.03
697	Mike Davis	.03	.02	.01
698	*Omar Vizquel*	.10	.08	.04
699	Jim Leyland	.03	.02	.01
700	Kirby Puckett	.25	.20	.10
701	*Bernie Williams* (FC)	.30	.25	.12
702	Tony Phillips	.04	.03	.02
703	*Jeff Brantley*	.12	.09	.05
704	*Chip Hale* (FC)	.15	.11	.06
705	Claudell Washington	.07	.05	.03
706	Geno Petralli	.03	.02	.01
707	Luis Aquino	.03	.02	.01
708	Larry Sheets	.03	.02	.01
709	Juan Berneguer	.03	.02	.01
710	Von Hayes	.09	.07	.04
711	Rick Aguilera	.05	.04	.02
712	Todd Benzinger	.09	.07	.04
713	*Tim Drummond* (FC)	.15	.11	.06
714	*Marquis Grissom* (FC)	.50	.40	.20
715	Greg Maddux	.15	.11	.06
716	Steve Balboni	.03	.02	.01
717	Ron Kakovice	.03	.02	.01
718	Gary Sheffield	.25	.20	.10
719	*Wally Whitehurst*	.15	.11	.06
720	Andres Galarraga	.25	.20	.10
721	Lee Mazzilli	.03	.02	.01
722	Felix Fermin	.03	.02	.01
723	Jeff Robinson	.05	.04	.02
724	Juan Bell (FC)	.10	.08	.04
725	Terry Pendleton	.06	.05	.02
726	Gene Nelson	.03	.02	.01
727	Pat Tabler	.05	.04	.02
728	Jim Acker	.03	.02	.01
729	Bobby Valentine	.03	.02	.01
730	Tony Gwynn	.20	.15	.08
731	Don Carman	.05	.04	.02
732	Ernie Riles	.03	.02	.01
733	John Dopson	.09	.07	.04
734	Kevin Elster	.06	.05	.02
735	Charlie Hough	.06	.05	.02
736	Rick Dempsey	.03	.02	.01
737	Chris Sabo	.15	.11	.06
738	*Gene Harris*	.10	.08	.04
739	Dale Sveum	.04	.03	.02
740	Jesse Barfield	.08	.06	.03
741	Steve Wilson	.10	.08	.04
742	Ernie Whitt	.05	.04	.02
743	Tom Candiotti	.05	.04	.02
744	*Kelly Mann*	.20	.15	.08
745	Hubie Brooks	.06	.05	.02
746	Dave Smith	.06	.05	.02
747	Randy Bush	.03	.02	.01
748	Doyle Alexander	.06	.05	.02
749	Mark Parent	.04	.03	.02
750	Dale Murphy	.10	.08	.04
751	Steve Lyons	.04	.03	.02
752	Tom Gordon	.15	.11	.06
753	Chris Speier	.03	.02	.01
754	Bob Walk	.05	.04	.02
755	Rafael Palmeiro	.10	.07	.04
756	Ken Howell	.03	.02	.01
757	*Larry Walker*	.40	.30	.15
758	Mark Thurmond	.03	.02	.01
759	Tom Trebelhorn	.03	.02	.01
760	Wade Boggs	.30	.25	.12
761	Mike Jackson	.05	.04	.02
762	Doug Dascenzo	.07	.05	.03
763	Denny Martinez	.07	.05	.03
764	Tim Teufel	.05	.04	.02
765	Chili Davis	.07	.05	.03
766	Brian Meyer (FC)	.10	.08	.04
767	Tracy Jones	.06	.05	.02
768	Chuck Crim	.04	.03	.02
769	*Greg Hibbard* (FC)	.30	.25	.12
770	Cory Snyder	.09	.07	.04
771	Pete Smith	.06	.05	.02
772	Jeff Reed	.03	.02	.01
773	Dave Leiper	.03	.02	.01
774	*Ben McDonald*	.40	.30	.15
775	Andy Van Slyke	.08	.06	.03
776	Charlie Leibrandt	.04	.03	.02
777	Tim Laudner	.03	.02	.01
778	Mike Jeffcoat	.03	.02	.01
779	Lloyd Moseby	.06	.05	.02
780	Orel Hershiser	.15	.11	.06
781	Mario Diaz	.03	.02	.01
782	Jose Alvarez	.03	.02	.01
783	Checklist 661-792	.03	.02	.01
784	Scott Bailes	.03	.02	.01
785	Jim Rice	.07	.05	.03
786	Eric King	.04	.03	.02
787	Rene Gonzales	.03	.02	.01
788	Frank DiPino	.03	.02	.01
789	John Wathan	.03	.02	.01
790	Gary Carter	.06	.05	.02
791	Alvaro Espinoza	.15	.11	.06
792	Gerald Perry	.06	.05	.02

1991 O-Pee-Chee Premier

The O-Pee-Chee Co. of London, Ontario, Canada produced this 132-card set. The card fronts feature action photos, while the flip sides display a posed photo and career statistics. The cards were packaged seven cards per pack in a tamper-proof foil wrap. Several Expo and Blue Jay players are featured. Two special cards are included in this set. Card #62 honors Rickey Henderson's stolen base record, while card #102 commemorates Nolan Ryan's seventh no-hitter. Traded players and free agents are featured with their new teams.

		MT	NR MT	EX
Complete Set (132):		25.00	18.00	10.00
Common Player:		.10	.08	.04
1	Roberto Alomar	.70	.50	.30
2	Sandy Alomar	.20	.15	.08
3	Moises Alou	.12	.09	.05
4	Brian Barnes	.25	.20	.10
5	Steve Bedrosian	.10	.08	.04
6	George Bell	.20	.15	.08
7	Juan Bell	.12	.09	.05
8	Albert Belle	.70	.50	.30
9	Bud Black	.10	.08	.04
10	Mike Boddicker	.10	.08	.04
11	Wade Boggs	.60	.45	.25
12	Barry Bonds	.60	.45	.25
13	Denis Boucher	.25	.20	.10
14	George Brett	.40	.30	.15
15	Hubie Brooks	.10	.08	.04
16	Brett Butler	.12	.09	.05
17	Ivan Calderon	.15	.11	.06
18	Jose Canseco	1.50	1.25	.60
19	Gary Carter	.20	.15	.08
20	Joe Carter	.25	.20	.10
21	Jack Clark	.15	.11	.06
22	Will Clark	1.50	1.25	.60
23	Roger Clemens	1.50	1.25	.60
24	Alex Cole	.15	.11	.06
25	Vince Coleman	.15	.11	.06
26	Jeff Conine	.20	.15	.08
27	Milt Cuyler	.60	.45	.25
28	Danny Darwin	.10	.08	.04
29	Eric Davis	.30	.25	.12
30	Glenn Davis	.15	.11	.06
31	Andre Dawson	.30	.25	.12
32	Ken Dayley	.10	.08	.04
33	Steve Decker	.50	.40	.20
34	Delino DeShields	.30	.25	.12
35	Lance Dickson	.50	.40	.20
36	Kirk Dressendorfer	.80	.60	.30
37	Shawon Dunston	.15	.11	.06
38	Dennis Eckersley	.15	.11	.06
39	Dwight Evans	.12	.09	.05
40	Howard Farmer	.20	.15	.08

41	Junior Felix	.15	.11	.06
42	Alex Fernandez	.50	.40	.20
43	Tony Fernandez	.12	.09	.05
44	Cecil Fielder	1.00	.70	.40
45	Carlton Fisk	.50	.40	.20
46	Willie Fraser	.10	.08	.04
47	Gary Gaetti	.12	.09	.05
48	Andres Galarraga	.10	.08	.04
49	Ron Gant	.80	.60	.30
50	Kirk Gibson	.15	.11	.06
51	Bernard Gilkey	.30	.25	.12
52	Leo Gomez	.50	.40	.20
53	Rene Gonzalez	.10	.08	.04
54	Juan Gonzalez	3.00	2.25	1.25
55	Doc Gooden	.40	.30	.15
56	Ken Griffey,Jr.	3.00	2.25	1.25
57	Kelly Gruber	.20	.15	.08
58	Pedro Guerrero	.15	.11	.06
59	Tony Gwynn	.60	.45	.25
60	Chris Hammond	.20	.15	.08
61	Ron Hassey	.10	.08	.04
62	Rickey Henderson	1.00	.70	.40
63	Tom Henke	.12	.09	.05
64	Orel Hershiser	.20	.15	.08
65	Chris Hoiles	.20	.15	.08
66	Todd Hundley	.30	.25	.12
67	Pete Incaviglia	.10	.08	.04
68	Danny Jackson	.10	.08	.04
69	Barry Jones	.10	.08	.04
70	David Justice	3.00	2.25	1.25
71	Jimmy Key	.12	.09	.05
72	Ray Lankford	1.00	.70	.40
73	Darren Lewis	.80	.60	.30
74	Kevin Maas	.60	.45	.25
75	Denny Martinez	.12	.09	.05
76	Tino Martinez	.50	.40	.20
77	Don Mattingly	1.00	.70	.40
78	Willie McGee	.15	.11	.06
79	Fred McGriff	.30	.25	.12
80	Hensley Meulens	.20	.15	.08
81	Kevin Mitchell	.30	.25	.12
82	Paul Molitor	.25	.20	.10
83	Mickey Morandini	.25	.20	.10
84	Jack Morris	.25	.20	.10
85	Dale Murphy	.25	.20	.10
86	Eddie Murray	.30	.25	.12
87	Chris Nabholz	.15	.11	.06
88	Tim Naehring	.20	.15	.08
89	Otis Nixon	.12	.09	.05
90	Jose Offerman	.20	.15	.08
91	Bob Ojeda	.10	.08	.04
92	John Olerud	.50	.40	.20
93	Gregg Olson	.15	.11	.06
94	Dave Parker	.15	.11	.06
95	Terry Pendleton	.20	.15	.08
96	Kirby Puckett	1.00	.70	.40
97	Rock Raines	.15	.11	.06
98	Jeff Reardon	.12	.09	.05
99	Dave Righetti	.12	.09	.05
100	Cal Ripken	3.00	2.25	1.25
101	Mel Rojas	.15	.11	.06
102	Nolan Ryan	4.00	3.00	1.50
103	Ryne Sandberg	2.00	1.50	.80
104	Scott Sanderson	.10	.08	.04
105	Benito Santiago	.15	.11	.06
106	Pete Schourek	.25	.20	.10
107	Gary Scott	.25	.20	.10
108	Terry Shumpert	.10	.08	.04
109	Ruben Sierra	.80	.60	.30
110	Doug Simons	.20	.15	.08
111	Dave Smith	.10	.08	.04
112	Ozzie Smith	.35	.25	.14
113	Cory Snyder	.10	.08	.04
114	Luis Sojo	.10	.08	.04
115	Dave Stewart	.15	.11	.06
116	Dave Stieb	.12	.09	.05
117	Darryl Strawberry	1.25	.90	.50
118	Pat Tabler	.10	.08	.04
119	Wade Taylor	.30	.25	.12
120	Bobby Thigpen	.15	.11	.06
121	Frank Thomas	6.00	4.50	2.50
122	Mike Timlin	.30	.25	.12
123	Alan Trammell	.20	.15	.08
124	Mo Vaughn	2.00	1.50	.80
125	Tim Wallach	.12	.09	.05
126	Devon White	.12	.09	.05
127	Mark Whiten	.60	.45	.25
128	Bernie Williams	1.25	.90	.50
129	Willie Wilson	.10	.08	.04
130	Dave Winfield	.30	.25	.12
131	Robin Yount	.60	.45	.25
132	Checklist	.10	.08	.04

1992 O-Pee-Chee

Once again closely following the format of the 1992 Topps set, and for the most part corresponding to its 792-card checklist, the 1992 OPCs differ on the front only in the substitution of an O-Pee-Chee logo for the Topps logo, and in the inclusion of team-change information for many of the players who moved after the Topps cards were printed. On backs, the light blue "Topps" logo printed behind the stats has been removed, and the logo beneath the card number changed from "Topps" to "O-Pee-Chee". The addition of a few lines of French above the stats and in the career summary can be seen on the OPC cards, as well as the substitution of an OPC copyright line for that of Topps. Where the 1992 Topps set features All-Star cards in the number range 386-407, the OPC set has a group of player cards who are not represented in the Topps set, including four "Tribute" cards honoring Gary Carter. Card #45 in the OPC set is also a Carter Trbitue card, whereas in the Topps set it is a regular card. This 792-card set features white stock much like the 1991 issue. The card fronts feature full-color action and posed photos with a gray inner frame and the player name and position on the bottom. The backs feature biographical information, statistics and stadium photos on player cards where space is available. All-Star cards and #1 Draft Pick cards are once again included. Topps brought back four-player rookie cards in 1992. Nine Top Prospect cards of this nature can be found within the set. Several cards can once again be found with horizontal fronts.

		MT	NR MT	EX
	Complete Set (792):	24.00	18.00	9.50
	Common Player:	.03	.02	.01
1	Nolan Ryan	.50	.40	.20
2	Record Breaker (Rickey Henderson)	.10	.08	.04
3	Record Breaker (Jeff Reardon)	.05	.04	.02
4	Record Breaker (Nolan Ryan)	.10	.08	.04
5	Record Breaker (Dave Winfield)	.06	.05	.02
6	*Brien Taylor* (Draft Pick)	1.50	1.25	.60
7	*Jim Olander* (FC)	.10	.08	.04
8	*Bryan Hickerson* (FC)	.10	.08	.04
9	John Farrell (Draft Pick)	.03	.02	.01
10	Wade Boggs	.15	.11	.06
11	Jack McDowell	.08	.06	.03
12	Luis Gonzalez	.08	.06	.03
13	Mike Scioscia	.04	.03	.02
14	Wes Chamberlain	.08	.06	.03
15	Denny Martinez	.04	.03	.02
16	Jeff Montgomery	.04	.03	.02
17	Randy Milligan	.06	.05	.02
18	Greg Cadaret	.03	.02	.01
19	Jamie Quirk	.03	.02	.01
20	Bip Roberts	.05	.04	.02
21	Buck Rodgers	.03	.02	.01
22	Bill Wegman	.04	.03	.02
23	Chuck Knoblauch	.10	.08	.04
24	Randy Myers	.05	.04	.02
25	Ron Gant	.15	.11	.06
26	Mike Bielecki	.03	.02	.01
27	Juan Gonzalez	.60	.45	.25
28	Mike Schooler	.04	.03	.02
29	Mickey Tettleton	.05	.04	.02
30	John Kruk	.06	.05	.02
31	Bryn Smith	.03	.02	.01
32	Chris Nabholz	.06	.05	.02
33	Carlos Baerga	.20	.15	.08
34	Jeff Juden	.15	.11	.06
35	Dave Righetti	.06	.05	.02
36	*Scott Ruffcorn* (Draft Pick)	.30	.25	.12
37	Luis Polonia	.04	.03	.02
38	Tom Candiotti	.04	.03	.02
39	Greg Olson	.04	.03	.02
40	Cal Ripken, Jr.	.20	.15	.08
41	Craig Lefferts	.04	.03	.02
42	Mike Macfarlane	.04	.03	.02
43	Jose Lind	.04	.03	.02
44	Rick Aguilera	.05	.04	.02
45	Gary Carter	.08	.06	.03
46	Steve Farr	.04	.03	.02
47	Rex Hudler	.04	.03	.02
48	Scott Scudder	.05	.04	.02
49	Damon Berryhill	.04	.03	.02
50	Ken Griffey, Jr.	.60	.45	.25
51	Tom Runnells	.03	.02	.01
52	Juan Bell	.05	.04	.02
53	Tommy Gregg	.03	.02	.01
54	David Wells	.04	.03	.02
55	Rafael Palmeiro	.10	.08	.04
56	Charlie O'Brien	.03	.02	.01
57	Donn Pall	.03	.02	.01
58	Top Prospects-Catchers (*Brad Ausmus* (FC), Jim Campanis, Dave Nilsson, Doug Robbins)	.20	.15	.08
59	Mo Vaughn	.25	.20	.10
60	Tony Fernandez	.05	.04	.02
61	Paul O'Neill	.06	.05	.02
62	Gene Nelson	.03	.02	.01
63	Randy Ready	.03	.02	.01
64	Bob Kipper	.03	.02	.01
65	Willie McGee	.08	.06	.03
66	*Scott Stahoviak* (Draft Pick)	.30	.25	.12
67	Luis Salazar	.03	.02	.01
68	Marvin Freeman	.03	.02	.01
69	Kenny Lofton	.40	.30	.15
70	Gary Gaetti	.06	.05	.02
71	Erik Hanson	.08	.06	.03
72	Eddie Zosky (FC)	.10	.08	.04
73	Brian Barnes	.10	.08	.04
74	Scott Leius	.10	.08	.04
75	Bret Saberhagen	.08	.06	.03
76	Mike Gallego	.03	.02	.01
77	Jack Armstrong	.05	.04	.02
78	*Ivan Rodriguez*	.30	.25	.12
79	Jesse Orosco	.03	.02	.01
80	David Justice	.30	.25	.12
81	*Ced Landrum* (FC)	.15	.11	.06
82	*Doug Simons*	.10	.08	.04
83	Tommy Greene	.06	.05	.02
84	Leo Gomez	.15	.11	.06
85	Jose DeLeon	.04	.03	.02
86	Steve Finley	.06	.05	.02
87	*Bob MacDonald* (FC)	.15	.11	.06
88	Darrin Jackson	.04	.03	.02
89	Neal Heaton	.03	.02	.01
90	Robin Yount	.12	.09	.05
91	Jeff Reed	.03	.02	.01
92	Lenny Harris	.04	.03	.02
93	Reggie Jefferson	.15	.11	.06
94	Sammy Sosa	.08	.06	.03
95	Scott Bailes	.03	.02	.01
96	*Tom McKinnon* (Draft Pick)	.15	.11	.06
97	Luis Rivera	.03	.02	.01
98	Mike Harkey	.06	.05	.02
99	Jeff Treadway	.04	.03	.02
100	Jose Canseco	.10	.08	.04
101	Omar Vizquel	.03	.02	.01
102	*Scott Kamieniecki*	.12	.09	.05
103	Ricky Jordan	.06	.05	.02
104	Jeff Ballard	.04	.03	.02
105	Felix Jose	.10	.08	.04
106	Mike Boddicker	.05	.04	.02
107	Dan Pasqua	.04	.03	.02
108	*Mike Timlin*	.12	.09	.05
109	Roger Craig	.04	.03	.02
110	Ryne Sandberg	.20	.15	.08
111	Mark Carreon	.03	.02	.01
112	Oscar Azocar	.04	.03	.02
113	Mike Greenwell	.10	.08	.04
114	Mark Portugal	.03	.02	.01
115	Terry Pendleton	.08	.06	.03
116	Willie Randolph	.05	.04	.02
117	Scott Terry	.03	.02	.01
118	Chili Davis	.08	.06	.03
119	Mark Gardner	.05	.04	.02
120	Alan Trammell	.10	.08	.04
121	Derek Bell	.15	.11	.06
122	Gary Varsho	.03	.02	.01
123	Bob Ojeda	.04	.03	.02
124	*Shawn Livsey* (Draft Pick)	.15	.11	.06
125	Chris Hoiles	.08	.06	.03
126	Top Prospects-1st Baseman (Rico Brogna (FC), John Jaha, Ryan Klesko, Dave Staton)	.80	.60	.30
127	Carlos Quintana	.06	.05	.02
128	Kurt Stillwell	.04	.03	.02
129	Melido Perez	.04	.03	.02
130	Alvin Davis	.06	.05	.02
131	Checklist 1	.03	.02	.01
132	Eric Show	.03	.02	.01
133	Rance Mulliniks	.03	.02	.01
134	Darryl Kile	.08	.06	.03
135	Von Hayes	.05	.04	.02
136	Bill Doran	.05	.04	.02
137	Jeff Robinson	.03	.02	.01
138	Monty Fariss	.08	.06	.03
139	Jeff Innis	.05	.04	.02
140	Mark Grace	.12	.09	.05
141	Jim Leyland	.03	.02	.01
142	Todd Van Poppel (FC)	.30	.25	.12
143	Paul Gibson	.03	.02	.01
144	Bill Swift	.04	.03	.02
145	Danny Tartabull	.08	.06	.03
146	Al Newman	.03	.02	.01
147	Cris Carpenter	.04	.03	.02
148	*Anthony Young* (FC)	.25	.20	.10
149	*Brian Bohanon* (FC)	.15	.11	.06
150	Roger Clemens	.15	.11	.06
151	Jeff Hamilton	.03	.02	.01
152	Charlie Leibrandt	.04	.03	.02
153	Ron Karkovice	.04	.03	.02
154	Hensley Meulens	.08	.06	.03
155	Scott Bankhead	.04	.03	.02
156	*Manny Ramirez* (Draft Pick)	1.00	.70	.40
157	Keith Miller	.03	.02	.01
158	Todd Frohwirth	.03	.02	.01
159	Darrin Fletcher	.05	.04	.02
160	Bobby Bonilla	.12	.09	.05
161	Casey Candaele	.03	.02	.01
162	Paul Faries (FC)	.10	.08	.04
163	Dana Kiecker	.03	.02	.01
164	Shane Mack	.08	.06	.03
165	Mark Langston	.10	.08	.04
166	Geronimo Pena	.06	.05	.02
167	Andy Allanson	.03	.02	.01
168	Dwight Smith	.04	.03	.02
169	Chuck Crim	.03	.02	.01
170	Alex Cole	.05	.04	.02
171	Bill Plummer	.03	.02	.01
172	Juan Berenguer	.03	.02	.01
173	Brian Downing	.04	.03	.02
174	Steve Frey	.03	.02	.01
175	Orel Hershiser	.08	.06	.03
176	*Ramon Garcia* (FC)	.15	.11	.06
177	Danny Gladden	.04	.03	.02
178	Jim Acker	.03	.02	.01
179	Top Prospects-2nd Baseman (*Cesar Bernhardt*, Bobby DeJardin, Armando Moreno, Andy Stankiewicz)	.25	.20	.10
180	Kevin Mitchell	.10	.08	.04
181	Hector Villanueva	.06	.05	.02
182	Jeff Reardon	.06	.05	.02
183	Brent Mayne	.06	.05	.02
184	Jimmy Jones	.03	.02	.01
185	Benny Santiago	.08	.06	.03

No.	Player			
186	*Cliff Floyd* (Draft Pick)	1.50	1.25	.60
187	Ernie Riles	.03	.02	.01
188	Jose Guzman	.05	.04	.02
189	Junior Felix	.06	.05	.02
190	Glenn Davis	.08	.06	.03
191	Charlie Hough	.04	.03	.02
192	*Dave Fleming* (FC)	.20	.15	.08
193	Omar Oliveras (FC)	.08	.06	.03
194	Eric Karros (FC)	.30	.25	.12
195	David Cone	.08	.06	.03
196	*Frank Castillo* (FC)	.12	.09	.05
197	Glenn Braggs	.04	.03	.02
198	Scott Aldred	.06	.05	.02
199	Jeff Blauser	.04	.03	.02
200	Len Dykstra	.08	.06	.03
201	Buck Showalter	.03	.02	.01
202	Rick Honeycutt	.03	.02	.01
203	Greg Myers	.03	.02	.01
204	Trevor Wilson	.05	.04	.02
205	Jay Howell	.04	.03	.02
206	Luis Sojo	.05	.04	.02
207	Jack Clark	.08	.06	.03
208	Julio Machado	.03	.02	.01
209	Lloyd McClendon	.03	.02	.01
210	Ozzie Guillen	.06	.05	.02
211	*Jeremy Hernandez* (FC)	.15	.11	.06
212	Randy Velarde	.03	.02	.01
213	Les Lancaster	.03	.02	.01
214	*Andy Mota* (FC)	.15	.11	.06
215	Rich Gossage	.05	.04	.02
216	*Brent Gates* (Draft Pick)	.40	.30	.15
217	Brian Harper	.05	.04	.02
218	Mike Flanagan	.03	.02	.01
219	Jerry Browne	.04	.03	.02
220	Jose Rijo	.08	.06	.03
221	Skeeter Barnes	.04	.03	.02
222	Jaime Navarro	.04	.03	.02
223	Mel Hall	.04	.03	.02
224	*Brett Barberie*	.20	.15	.08
225	Roberto Alomar	.15	.11	.06
226	Pete Smith	.03	.02	.01
227	Daryl Boston	.03	.02	.01
228	Eddie Whitson	.04	.03	.02
229	Shawn Boskie	.04	.03	.02
230	Dick Schofield	.03	.02	.01
231	*Brian Drahman* (FC)	.10	.08	.04
232	John Smiley	.05	.04	.02
233	Mitch Webster	.04	.03	.02
234	Terry Steinbach	.05	.04	.02
235	Jack Morris	.08	.06	.03
236	Bill Pecota	.04	.03	.02
237	*Jose Hernandez* (FC)	.10	.08	.04
238	Greg Litton	.03	.02	.01
239	Brian Holman	.05	.04	.02
240	Andres Galarraga	.06	.05	.02
241	Gerald Young	.03	.02	.01
242	Mike Mussina (FC)	.50	.40	.20
243	Alvaro Espinoza	.03	.02	.01
244	Darren Daulton	.04	.03	.02
245	John Smoltz	.08	.06	.03
246	*Jason Pruitt* (Draft Pick)	.15	.11	.06
247	Chuck Finley	.08	.06	.03
248	Jim Gantner	.04	.03	.02
249	Tony Fossas	.03	.02	.01
250	Ken Griffey	.05	.04	.02
251	Kevin Elster	.04	.03	.02
252	Dennis Rasmussen	.03	.02	.01
253	Terry Kennedy	.03	.02	.01
254	*Ryan Bowen* (FC)	.15	.11	.06
255	Robin Ventura	.15	.11	.06
256	Mike Aldrete	.03	.02	.01
257	Jeff Russell	.04	.03	.02
258	Jim Lindeman	.03	.02	.01
259	Ron Darling	.05	.04	.02
260	Devon White	.06	.05	.02
261	Tom Lasorda	.04	.03	.02
262	Terry Lee (FC)	.10	.08	.04
263	Bob Patterson	.03	.02	.01
264	Checklist 2	.03	.02	.01
265	Teddy Higuera	.05	.04	.02
266	Roberto Kelly	.08	.06	.03
267	Steve Bedrosian	.04	.03	.02
268	Brady Anderson	.03	.02	.01
269	*Ruben Amaro* (FC)	.15	.11	.06
270	Tony Gwynn	.12	.09	.05
271	Tracy Jones	.03	.02	.01
272	Jerry Don Gleaton	.03	.02	.01
273	Craig Grebeck	.04	.03	.02
274	*Bob Scanlan*	.10	.08	.04
275	Todd Zeile	.10	.08	.04
276	*Shawn Green* (Draft Pick)	.25	.20	.10
277	Scott Chiamparino	.04	.03	.02
278	Darryl Hamilton	.04	.03	.02
279	Jim Clancy	.03	.02	.01
280	Carlos Martinez	.04	.03	.02
281	Kevin Appier	.05	.04	.02
282	*John Wehner* (FC)	.15	.11	.06
283	Reggie Sanders	.20	.15	.08
284	Gene Larkin	.04	.03	.02
285	Bob Welch	.06	.05	.02
286	Gilberto Reyes (FC)	.05	.04	.02
287	*Pete Schourek*	.15	.11	.06
288	Andujar Cedeno	.15	.11	.06
289	Mike Morgan	.04	.03	.02
290	Bo Jackson	.20	.15	.08
291	Phil Garner	.03	.02	.01
292	Ray Lankford	.15	.11	.06
293	Mike Henneman	.05	.04	.02
294	Dave Valle	.03	.02	.01
295	Alonzo Powell (FC)	.08	.06	.03
296	Tom Brunansky	.05	.04	.02
297	Kevin Brown	.05	.04	.02
298	Kelly Gruber	.08	.06	.03
299	Charles Nagy	.06	.05	.02
300	Don Mattingly	.15	.11	.06
301	Kirk McCaskill	.04	.03	.02
302	Joey Cora	.04	.03	.02
303	Dan Plesac	.04	.03	.02
304	Joe Oliver	.04	.03	.02
305	Tom Glavine	.08	.06	.03
306	*Al Shirley* (Draft Pick)	.15	.11	.06
307	Bruce Ruffin	.03	.02	.01
308	*Craig Shipley* (FC)	.08	.06	.03
309	Dave Martinez	.04	.03	.02
310	Jose Mesa	.03	.02	.01
311	Henry Cotto	.03	.02	.01
312	Mike LaValliere	.04	.03	.02
313	Kevin Tapani	.08	.06	.03
314	Jeff Huson	.04	.03	.02
315	Juan Samuel	.06	.05	.02
316	Curt Schilling	.06	.05	.02
317	Mike Bordick (FC)	.06	.05	.02
318	Steve Howe	.04	.03	.02
319	Tony Phillips	.04	.03	.02
320	George Bell	.10	.08	.04
321	Lou Pinella	.03	.02	.01
322	Tim Burke	.04	.03	.02
323	Milt Thompson	.04	.03	.02
324	Danny Darwin	.04	.03	.02
325	Joe Orsulak	.03	.02	.01
326	Eric King	.04	.03	.02
327	Jay Buhner	.05	.04	.02
328	*Joel Johnston* (FC)	.15	.11	.06
329	Franklin Stubbs	.03	.02	.01
330	Will Clark	.20	.15	.08
331	Steve Lake	.03	.02	.01
332	*Chris Jones*	.10	.08	.04
333	Pat Tabler	.03	.02	.01
334	Kevin Gross	.03	.02	.01
335	Dave Henderson	.08	.06	.03
336	*Greg Anthony* (Draft Pick)	.15	.11	.06
337	Alejandro Pena	.04	.03	.02
338	Shawn Abner	.03	.02	.01
339	Tom Browning	.06	.05	.02
340	Otis Nixon	.04	.03	.02
341	Bob Geren	.03	.02	.01
342	*Tim Spehr* (FC)	.10	.08	.04
343	*Jon Vander Wal* (FC)	.20	.15	.08
344	Jack Daugherty	.03	.02	.01
345	Zane Smith	.04	.03	.02
346	*Rheal Cormier* (FC)	.15	.11	.06
347	Kent Hrbek	.06	.05	.02
348	*Rick Wilkins* (FC)	.15	.11	.06
349	Steve Lyons	.03	.02	.01
350	Gregg Olson	.08	.06	.03
351	Greg Riddoch	.03	.02	.01
352	Ed Nunez	.03	.02	.01
353	*Braulio Castillo* (FC)	.08	.06	.03
354	Dave Bergman	.03	.02	.01
355	*Warren Newson* (FC)	.15	.11	.06
356	Luis Quinones	.03	.02	.01
357	Mike Witt	.04	.03	.02
358	*Ted Wood*	.15	.11	.06
359	Mike Moore	.04	.03	.02
360	Lance Parrish	.06	.05	.02
361	Barry Jones	.03	.02	.01
362	*Javier Ortiz* (FC)	.10	.08	.04
363	John Candelaria	.04	.03	.02
364	Glenallen Hill	.06	.05	.02
365	Duane Ward	.04	.03	.02
366	Checklist 3	.03	.02	.01
367	Rafael Belliard	.03	.02	.01
368	Bill Krueger	.03	.02	.01
369	*Steve Whitaker* (Draft Pick)	.20	.15	.08
370	Shawon Dunston	.06	.05	.02
371	Dante Bichette	.04	.03	.02
372	*Kip Gross* (FC)	.10	.08	.04
373	Don Robinson	.03	.02	.01
374	Bernie Williams	.03	.02	.01
375	Bert Blyleven	.05	.04	.02
376	*Chris Donnels* (FC)	.15	.11	.06
377	*Bob Zupcic* (FC)	.30	.25	.12
378	Joel Skinner	.03	.02	.01
379	Steve Chitren	.06	.05	.02
380	Barry Bonds	.40	.30	.15
381	Sparky Anderson	.03	.02	.01
382	Sid Fernandez	.05	.04	.02
383	Dave Hollins	.06	.05	.02
384	Mark Lee	.03	.02	.01
385	Tim Wallach	.05	.04	.02
386	Lance Blankenship	.10	.08	.04
387	Gary Carter (Tribute)	.10	.08	.04
388	Ron Tingley	.05	.04	.02
389	Gary Carter (Tribute)	.10	.08	.04
390	Gene Harris	.05	.04	.02
391	Jeff Schaefer	.08	.06	.03
392	Mark Grant	.08	.06	.03
393	Carl Willis	.05	.04	.02
394	Al Leiter	.04	.03	.02
395	Ron Robinson	.05	.04	.02
396	Tim Hulett	.08	.06	.03
397	Craig Worthington	.10	.08	.04
398	John Orton	.08	.06	.03
399	Gary Carter (Tribute)	.10	.08	.04
400	John Dopson	.08	.06	.03
401	Moises Alou	.15	.11	.06
402	Gary Carter (Tribute)	.10	.08	.04
403	Matt Young	.05	.04	.02
404	Wayne Edwards	.04	.03	.02
405	Nick Esasky	.05	.04	.02
406	Dave Eiland	.08	.06	.03
407	Mike Brumley	.05	.04	.02
408	Bob Milacki	.03	.02	.01
409	Geno Petralli	.03	.02	.01
410	Dave Stewart	.08	.06	.03
411	Mike Jackson	.03	.02	.01
412	Luis Aquino	.03	.02	.01
413	Tim Teufel	.03	.02	.01
414	*Jeff Ware* (Draft Pick)	.15	.11	.06
415	Jim Deshaies	.04	.03	.02
416	Ellis Burks	.10	.08	.04
417	Allan Anderson	.03	.02	.01
418	Alfredo Griffin	.03	.02	.01
419	Wally Whitehurst	.05	.04	.02
420	Sandy Alomar	.08	.06	.03
421	Juan Agosto	.03	.02	.01
422	Sam Horn	.03	.02	.01
423	*Jeff Fassero*	.10	.08	.04
424	*Paul McClellan* (FC)	.10	.08	.04
425	Cecil Fielder	.15	.11	.06
426	Tim Raines	.10	.08	.04
427	*Eddie Taubensee* (FC)	.20	.15	.08
428	Dennis Boyd	.05	.04	.02
429	Tony LaRussa	.03	.02	.01
430	Steve Sax	.06	.05	.02
431	Tom Gordon	.08	.06	.03
432	Billy Hatcher	.04	.03	.02
433	Cal Eldred (FC)	.25	.20	.10
434	Wally Backman	.03	.02	.01
435	Mark Eichhorn	.03	.02	.01
436	Mookie Wilson	.03	.02	.01
437	*Scott Servais*	.10	.08	.04
438	Mike Maddux	.03	.02	.01
439	*Chico Walker* (FC)	.10	.08	.04
440	Doug Drabek	.08	.06	.03
441	Rob Deer	.04	.03	.02
442	Dave West	.04	.03	.02
443	Spike Owen	.03	.02	.01
444	*Tyrone Hill* (Draft Pick)	.25	.20	.10
445	Matt Williams	.12	.09	.05
446	Mark Lewis	.12	.09	.05
447	David Segui	.08	.06	.03
448	Tom Pagnozzi	.04	.03	.02
449	*Jeff Johnson*	.12	.09	.05
450	Mark McGwire	.12	.09	.05
451	Tom Henke	.05	.04	.02
452	Wilson Alvarez	.08	.06	.03
453	Gary Redus	.03	.02	.01
454	Darren Holmes	.03	.02	.01
455	Pete O'Brien	.03	.02	.01
456	Pat Combs	.04	.03	.02
457	Hubie Brooks	.04	.03	.02
458	Frank Tanana	.03	.02	.01
459	Tom Kelly	.03	.02	.01
460	Andre Dawson	.12	.09	.05
461	Doug Jones	.04	.03	.02
462	Rich Rodriguez	.04	.03	.02
463	*Mike Simms*	.10	.08	.04
464	Mike Jeffcoat	.03	.02	.01
465	Barry Larkin	.12	.09	.05
466	Stan Belinda	.04	.03	.02
467	Lonnie Smith	.04	.03	.02
468	Greg Harris	.03	.02	.01
469	Jim Eisenreich	.03	.02	.01
470	Pedro Guerrero	.08	.06	.03
471	Jose DeJesus	.04	.03	.02
472	*Rich Rowland* (FC)	.15	.11	.06
473	Top Prospects-3rd Baseman (*Frank Bolick* (FC), Craig Paquette, Tom Redington, Paul Russo)	.35	.25	.14
474	*Mike Rossiter* (Draft Pick)	.25	.20	.10
475	Robby Thompson	.04	.03	.02
476	Randy Bush	.03	.02	.01
477	Greg Hibbard	.04	.03	.02
478	Dale Sveum	.03	.02	.01
479	*Chito Martinez* (FC)	.10	.08	.04
480	Scott Sanderson	.04	.03	.02
481	Tino Martinez	.10	.08	.04
482	Jimmy Key	.05	.04	.02
483	Terry Shumpert	.03	.02	.01
484	Mike Hartley	.03	.02	.01
485	Chris Sabo	.08	.06	.03
486	Bob Walk	.03	.02	.01
487	John Cerutti	.03	.02	.01
488	Scott Cooper (FC)	.10	.08	.04
489	Bobby Cox	.03	.02	.01
490	Julio Franco	.10	.08	.04
491	Jeff Brantley	.04	.03	.02
492	Mike Devereaux	.04	.03	.02
493	Jose Offerman	.10	.08	.04
494	Gary Thurman	.03	.02	.01
495	Carney Lansford	.06	.05	.02
496	Joe Grahe	.04	.03	.02
497	*Andy Ashby* (FC)	.08	.06	.03
498	Gerald Perry	.03	.02	.01
499	Dave Otto	.03	.02	.01
500	Vince Coleman	.08	.06	.03
501	*Rob Mallicoat* (FC)	.06	.05	.02
502	Greg Briley	.03	.02	.01
503	Pascual Perez	.03	.02	.01
504	*Aaron Sele* (Draft Pick)	.90	.70	.35
505	Bobby Thigpen	.08	.06	.03
506	Todd Benzinger	.04	.03	.02
507	Candy Maldonado	.04	.03	.02
508	Bill Gullickson	.05	.04	.02
509	Doug Dascenzo	.03	.02	.01
510	Frank Viola	.08	.06	.03
511	Kenny Rogers	.04	.03	.02
512	Mike Heath	.03	.02	.01
513	Kevin Bass	.04	.03	.02
514	*Kim Batiste* (FC)	.10	.08	.04
515	Delino DeShields	.08	.06	.03
516	*Ed Sprague*	.10	.08	.04
517	Jim Gott	.03	.02	.01
518	*Jose Melendez* (FC)	.10	.08	.04
519	Hal McRae	.03	.02	.01
520	*Jeff Bagwell*	.30	.25	.12
521	Joe Hesketh	.03	.02	.01
522	Milt Cuyler	.12	.09	.05
523	Shawn Hillegas	.03	.02	.01
524	Don Slaught	.03	.02	.01
525	Randy Johnson	.06	.05	.02
526	*Doug Piatt*	.10	.08	.04
527	Checklist 4	.03	.02	.01
528	*Steve Foster* (FC)	.15	.11	.06
529	Joe Girardi	.04	.03	.02
530	Jim Abbott	.10	.08	.04
531	Larry Walker	.08	.06	.03
532	Mike Huff	.04	.03	.02
533	Mackey Sasser	.03	.02	.01
534	*Benji Gil* (Draft Pick)	.35	.25	.14
535	Dave Stieb	.06	.05	.02
536	Willie Wilson	.04	.03	.02
537	*Mark Leiter* (FC)	.10	.08	.04

538	Jose Uribe	.03	.02	.01
539	Thomas Howard	.03	.02	.01
540	Ben McDonald	.12	.09	.05
541	*Jose Tolentino* (FC)	.15	.11	.06
542	*Keith Mitchell* (FC)	.10	.08	.04
543	Jerome Walton	.08	.06	.03
544	*Cliff Brantley* (FC)	.15	.11	.06
545	Andy Van Slyke	.08	.06	.03
546	Paul Sorrento	.04	.03	.02
547	Herm Winningham	.03	.02	.01
548	Mark Guthrie	.04	.03	.02
549	Joe Torre	.03	.02	.01
550	Darryl Strawberry	.12	.09	.05
551	Top Prospects-Shortstops (*Manny Alexander*, Alex Arias, Wil Cordero, Chipper Jones)	.60	.45	.25
552	Dave Gallagher	.04	.03	.02
553	Edgar Martinez	.06	.05	.02
554	Donald Harris	.15	.11	.06
555	Frank Thomas	.90	.70	.35
556	Storm Davis	.04	.03	.02
557	Dickie Thon	.03	.02	.01
558	Scott Garrelts	.03	.02	.01
559	Steve Olin	.03	.02	.01
560	Rickey Henderson	.15	.11	.06
561	Jose Vizcaino	.04	.03	.02
562	*Wade Taylor*	.10	.08	.04
563	Pat Borders	.04	.03	.02
564	*Jimmy Gonzalez* (Draft Pick)	.20	.15	.08
565	Lee Smith	.05	.04	.02
566	Bill Sampen	.05	.04	.02
567	Dean Palmer	.12	.09	.05
568	Bryan Harvey	.05	.04	.02
569	Tony Pena	.05	.04	.02
570	Lou Whitaker	.06	.05	.02
571	Randy Tomlin	.06	.05	.02
572	Greg Vaughn	.12	.09	.05
573	Kelly Downs	.03	.02	.01
574	Steve Avery	.20	.15	.08
575	Kirby Puckett	.15	.11	.06
576	*Heathcliff Slocumb* (FC)	.10	.08	.04
577	Kevin Seitzer	.04	.03	.02
578	Lee Guetterman	.03	.02	.01
579	Johnny Oates	.03	.02	.01
580	Greg Maddux	.05	.04	.02
581	Stan Javier	.03	.02	.01
582	Vicente Palacios	.03	.02	.01
583	Mel Rojas	.03	.02	.01
584	*Wayne Rosenthal* (FC)	.10	.08	.04
585	Lenny Webster (FC)	.10	.08	.04
586	Rod Nichols	.03	.02	.01
587	Mickey Morandini	.08	.06	.03
588	Russ Swan	.03	.02	.01
589	Mariano Duncan	.04	.03	.02
590	Howard Johnson	.10	.08	.04
591	Top Prospects-Outfielders (*Jacob Brumfield*, Jeremy Burnitz, Alan Cockrell, D.J. Dozier)	.50	.40	.20
592	*Denny Neagle* (FC)	.15	.11	.06
593	Steve Decker	.10	.08	.04
594	*Brian Barber* (Draft Pick)	.15	.11	.06
595	Bruce Hurst	.04	.03	.02
596	Kent Mercker	.04	.03	.02
597	*Mike Magnante*	.10	.08	.04
598	Jody Reed	.04	.03	.02
599	Steve Searcy	.03	.02	.01
600	Paul Molitor	.10	.08	.04
601	Dave Smith	.05	.04	.02
602	Mike Fetters	.04	.03	.02
603	*Luis Mercedes* (FC)	.10	.08	.04
604	Chris Gwynn	.03	.02	.01
605	Scott Erickson	.10	.08	.04
606	Brook Jacoby	.04	.03	.02
607	Todd Stottlemyre	.05	.04	.02
608	Scott Bradley	.03	.02	.01
609	Mike Hargrove	.03	.02	.01
610	Eric Davis	.12	.09	.05
611	*Brian Hunter* (FC)	.10	.08	.04
612	Pat Kelly	.10	.08	.04
613	Pedro Munoz (FC)	.15	.11	.06
614	Al Osuna	.04	.03	.02
615	Matt Merullo	.03	.02	.01
616	Larry Andersen	.03	.02	.01
617	Junior Ortiz	.03	.02	.01
618	Top Prospects-Outfielders (*Cesar Hernandez*, Steve Hosey, Dan Peltier, Jeff McNeely)	.50	.40	.20
619	Danny Jackson	.04	.03	.02
620	George Brett	.12	.09	.05
621	*Dan Gakeler* (FC)	.10	.08	.04
622	Steve Buechele	.04	.03	.02
623	Bob Tewksbury	.03	.02	.01
624	*Shawn Estes* (Draft Pick)	.15	.11	.06
625	Kevin McReynolds	.08	.06	.03
626	*Chris Haney* (FC)	.08	.06	.03
627	Mike Sharperson	.03	.02	.01
628	Mark Williamson	.03	.02	.01
629	Wally Joyner	.10	.08	.04
630	Carlton Fisk	.12	.09	.05
631	*Armando Reynoso* (FC)	.10	.08	.04
632	Felix Fermin	.03	.02	.01
633	Mitch Williams	.05	.04	.02
634	Manuel Lee	.04	.03	.02
635	Harold Baines	.08	.06	.03
636	Greg Harris	.05	.04	.02
637	Orlando Merced	.12	.09	.05
638	Chris Bosio	.04	.03	.02
639	*Wayne Housie* (FC)	.10	.08	.04
640	Xavier Hernandez	.04	.03	.02
641	*David Howard* (FC)	.10	.08	.04
642	Tim Crews	.03	.02	.01
643	Rick Cerone	.03	.02	.01
644	Terry Leach	.03	.02	.01
645	Deion Sanders	.12	.09	.05
646	Craig Wilson	.04	.03	.02
647	Marquis Grissom	.12	.09	.05
648	Scott Fletcher	.03	.02	.01
649	Norm Charlton	.04	.03	.02

650	Jesse Barfield	.06	.05	.02
651	*Joe Slusarski*	.10	.08	.04
652	Bobby Rose	.04	.03	.02
653	Dennis Lamp	.03	.02	.01
654	*Allen Watson* (Draft Pick)	.50	.40	.20
655	Brett Butler	.06	.05	.02
656	Top Prospects-Outfielders (*Rudy Pemberton* (FC), Henry Rodriguez, Lee Tinsley, Gerald Williams)	.50	.40	.20
657	Dave Johnson	.03	.02	.01
658	Checklist 5	.03	.02	.01
659	Brian McRae	.10	.08	.04
660	Fred McGriff	.10	.08	.04
661	Bill Landrum	.03	.02	.01
662	*Juan Guzman* (FC)	.50	.40	.20
663	Greg Gagne	.03	.02	.01
664	Ken Hill	.04	.03	.02
665	*Dave Haas* (FC)	.10	.08	.04
666	Tom Foley	.03	.02	.01
667	*Roberto Hernandez* (FC)	.10	.08	.04
668	Dwayne Henry	.03	.02	.01
669	Jim Fregosi	.03	.02	.01
670	Harold Reynolds	.05	.04	.02
671	Mark Whiten	.10	.08	.04
672	Eric Plunk	.03	.02	.01
673	Todd Hundley	.10	.08	.04
674	*Mo Sanford* (FC)	.10	.08	.04
675	Bobby Witt	.04	.03	.02
676	Top Prospects-Pitchers (*Pat Mahomes* (FC), Sam Militello, Roger Salkeld, Turk Wendell)	.30	.25	.12
677	John Marzano	.03	.02	.01
678	Joe Klink	.03	.02	.01
679	Pete Incaviglia	.04	.03	.02
680	Dale Murphy	.08	.06	.03
681	Rene Gonzales	.03	.02	.01
682	Andy Benes	.08	.06	.03
683	Jim Poole (FC)	.08	.06	.03
684	*Trever Miller* (Draft Pick)	.15	.11	.06
685	*Scott Livingstone* (FC)	.12	.09	.05
686	Rich DeLucia	.04	.03	.02
687	*Harvey Pulliam* (FC)	.10	.08	.04
688	Tim Belcher	.04	.03	.02
689	Mark Lemke	.05	.04	.02
690	John Franco	.06	.05	.02
691	Walt Weiss	.06	.05	.02
692	Scott Ruskin	.04	.03	.02
693	Jeff King	.04	.03	.02
694	Mike Gardiner (FC)	.06	.05	.02
695	Gary Sheffield	.12	.09	.05
696	Joe Boever	.03	.02	.01
697	Mike Felder	.03	.02	.01
698	John Habyan	.03	.02	.01
699	Cito Gaston	.03	.02	.01
700	Ruben Sierra	.15	.11	.06
701	Scott Radinsky	.03	.02	.01
702	Lee Stevens	.06	.05	.02
703	*Mark Wohlers* (FC)	.10	.08	.04
704	Curt Young	.03	.02	.01
705	Dwight Evans	.06	.05	.02
706	Rob Murphy	.03	.02	.01
707	Gregg Jefferies	.10	.08	.04
708	Tom Bolton	.03	.02	.01
709	Chris James	.03	.02	.01
710	Kevin Maas	.12	.09	.05
711	*Ricky Bones* (FC)	.10	.08	.04
712	Curt Wilkerson	.03	.02	.01
713	Roger McDowell	.04	.03	.02
714	*Calvin Reese* (Draft Pick)	.20	.15	.08
715	Craig Biggio	.08	.06	.03
716	*Kirk Dressendorfer*	.10	.08	.04
717	Ken Dayley	.03	.02	.01
718	B.J. Surhoff	.05	.04	.02
719	Terry Mulholland	.05	.04	.02
720	Kirk Gibson	.06	.05	.02
721	Mike Pagliarulo	.04	.03	.02
722	Walt Terrell	.03	.02	.01
723	Jose Oquendo	.03	.02	.01
724	Kevin Morton (FC)	.08	.06	.03
725	Dwight Gooden	.12	.09	.05
726	Kirt Manwaring	.04	.03	.02
727	Chuck McElroy	.03	.02	.01
728	Dave Burba (FC)	.06	.05	.02
729	Art Howe	.03	.02	.01
730	Ramon Martinez	.10	.08	.04
731	Donnie Hill	.03	.02	.01
732	Nelson Santovenia	.03	.02	.01
733	Bob Melvin	.03	.02	.01
734	*Scott Hatteberg* (Draft Pick)	.15	.11	.06
735	Greg Swindell	.05	.04	.02
736	Lance Johnson	.03	.02	.01
737	Kevin Reimer	.05	.04	.02
738	Dennis Eckersley	.08	.06	.03
739	Rob Ducey	.03	.02	.01
740	Ken Caminiti	.04	.03	.02
741	Mark Gubicza	.04	.03	.02
742	Billy Spiers	.04	.03	.02
743	Darren Lewis	.08	.06	.03
744	Chris Hammond	.05	.04	.02
745	Dave Magadan	.05	.04	.02
746	Bernard Gilkey	.10	.08	.04
747	Willie Banks (FC)	.10	.08	.04
748	Matt Nokes	.04	.03	.02
749	Jerald Clark	.04	.03	.02
750	Travis Fryman	.15	.11	.06
751	Steve Wilson	.03	.02	.01
752	Billy Ripken	.03	.02	.01
753	Paul Assenmacher	.03	.02	.01
754	Charlie Hayes	.04	.03	.02
755	Alex Fernandez	.15	.11	.06
756	Gary Pettis	.03	.02	.01
757	Rob Dibble	.08	.06	.03
758	Tim Naehring	.08	.06	.03
759	Jeff Torborg	.03	.02	.01
760	Ozzie Smith	.10	.08	.04
761	Mike Fitzgerald	.03	.02	.01
762	John Burkett	.04	.03	.02
763	Kyle Abbott	.06	.05	.02

764	*Tyler Green* (Draft Pick)	.30	.25	.12
765	Pete Harnisch	.06	.05	.02
766	Mark Davis	.03	.02	.01
767	Kal Daniels	.06	.05	.02
768	*Jim Thome* (FC)	.20	.15	.08
769	Jack Howell	.03	.02	.01
770	Sid Bream	.05	.04	.02
771	*Arthur Rhodes* (FC)	.20	.15	.08
772	Garry Templeton	.04	.03	.02
773	Hal Morris	.12	.09	.05
774	Bud Black	.04	.03	.02
775	Ivan Calderon	.06	.05	.02
776	*Doug Henry* (FC)	.15	.11	.06
777	John Olerud	.12	.09	.05
778	Tim Leary	.04	.03	.02
779	Jay Bell	.05	.04	.02
780	Eddie Murray	.10	.08	.04
781	Paul Abbott (FC)	.08	.06	.03
782	Phil Plantier	.20	.15	.08
783	Joe Magrane	.05	.04	.02
784	Ken Patterson	.03	.02	.01
785	Albert Belle	.15	.11	.06
786	Royce Clayton (FC)	.25	.20	.10
787	Checklist 6	.03	.02	.01
788	Mike Stanton	.04	.03	.02
789	Bobby Valentine	.03	.02	.01
790	Joe Carter	.10	.08	.04
791	Danny Cox	.03	.02	.01
792	Dave Winfield	.12	.09	.05

1992 O-Pee-Chee Premier

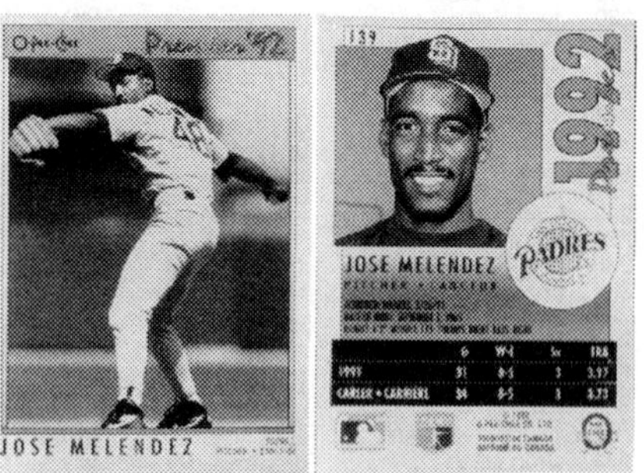

O-Pee-Chee increased the number of cards in its premier set to 198 for 1992. The cards feature white borders surrounding full-color player photos. The O-Pee-Chee banner appears at the top of the card and the player's name and position appear at the bottom. The backs feature an additional player photo, statistics and player information. Traded players and free agents are featured with their new teams.

		MT	NR MT	EX
	Complete Set (198):	25.00	18.00	10.00
	Common Player:	.08	.06	.03
1	Wade Boggs	.40	.30	.15
2	John Smiley	.10	.08	.04
3	Checklist	.08	.06	.03
4	Ron Gant	.20	.15	.08
5	Mike Bordick	.20	.15	.08
6	Charlie Hayes	.08	.06	.03
7	Kevin Morton	.08	.06	.03
8	Checklist	.08	.06	.03
9	Chris Gwynn	.08	.06	.03
10	Scott Bankhead	.08	.06	.03
11	Danny Gladden	.08	.06	.03
12	Brian McRae	.20	.15	.08
13	Denny Martinez	.10	.08	.04
14	Bob Scanlan	.15	.11	.06
15	Julio Franco	.10	.08	.04
16	Ruben Amaro	.15	.11	.06
17	Mo Sanford	.15	.11	.06
18	Melido Perez	.08	.06	.03
19	Dickie Thon	.08	.06	.03
20	Chris James	.08	.06	.03
21	Mike Huff	.08	.06	.03
22	Orlando Merced	.10	.08	.04
23	Chris Sabo	.15	.11	.06
24	Jose Canseco	.50	.40	.20
25	Reggie Sanders	.50	.40	.20
26	Chris Nabholz	.10	.08	.04
27	Kevin Seitzer	.08	.06	.03
28	Ryan Bowen	.15	.11	.06
29	Gary Carter	.15	.11	.06
30	Wayne Rosenthal	.08	.06	.03
31	Alan Trammell	.20	.15	.08
32	Doug Drabek	.20	.15	.08
33	Craig Shipley	.10	.08	.04
34	Ryne Sandberg	.30	.25	.12
35	Chuck Knoblauch	.25	.20	.10
36	Bret Barberie	.20	.15	.08
37	Tim Naehring	.12	.09	.05
38	Omar Olivares	.12	.09	.05
39	Royce Clayton	.25	.20	.10
40	Brent Mayne	.12	.09	.05
41	Darrin Fletcher	.08	.06	.03
42	Howard Johnson	.15	.11	.06
43	Steve Sax	.12	.09	.05
44	Greg Swindell	.20	.15	.08
45	Andre Dawson	.20	.15	.08
46	Kent Hrbek	.15	.11	.06
47	Doc Gooden	.35	.25	.14

48	Mark Leiter	.08	.06	.03
49	Tom Glavine	.20	.15	.08
50	Mo Vaughn	.20	.15	.08
51	Doug Jones	.08	.06	.03
52	Brian Barnes	.12	.09	.05
53	Rob Dibble	.15	.11	.06
54	Kevin McReynolds	.12	.09	.05
55	Ivan Rodriguez	.40	.30	.15
56	Scott Livingstone	.20	.15	.08
57	Mike Magnante	.12	.09	.05
58	Pete Schourek	.10	.08	.04
59	Frank Thomas	1.50	1.25	.60
60	Kirk McCaskill	.12	.09	.05
61	Wally Joyner	.15	.11	.06
62	Rick Aguilera	.15	.11	.06
63	Eric Karros	2.00	1.50	.80
64	Tino Martinez	.20	.15	.08
65	Bryan Hickerson	.20	.15	.08
66	Ruben Sierra	.30	.25	.12
67	Willie Randolph	.10	.08	.04
68	Bill Landrum	.08	.06	.03
69	Bip Roberts	.15	.11	.06
70	Cecil Fielder	.40	.30	.15
71	Pat Kelly	.15	.11	.06
72	Kenny Lofton	.50	.40	.20
73	John Franco	.10	.08	.04
74	Phil Plantier	.20	.15	.08
75	Dave Martinez	.08	.06	.03
76	Warren Newson	.08	.06	.03
77	Chito Martinez	.15	.11	.06
78	Brian Hunter	.15	.11	.06
79	Jack Morris	.20	.15	.08
80	Eric King	.08	.06	.03
81	Nolan Ryan	.60	.45	.25
82	Bret Saberhagen	.15	.11	.06
83	Roberto Kelly	.15	.11	.06
84	Ozzie Smith	.20	.15	.08
85	Chuck McElroy	.08	.06	.03
86	Carlton Fisk	.25	.20	.10
87	Mike Mussina	1.00	.70	.40
88	Mark Carreon	.08	.06	.03
89	Ken Hill	.15	.11	.06
90	Rick Cerone	.08	.06	.03
91	Deion Sanders	.40	.30	.15
92	Don Mattingly	.40	.30	.15
93	Danny Tartabull	.15	.11	.06
94	Keith Miller	.12	.09	.05
95	Gregg Jefferies	.15	.11	.06
96	Barry Larkin	.20	.15	.08
97	Kevin Mitchell	.15	.11	.06
98	Rick Sutcliffe	.15	.11	.06
99	Mark McGwire	.30	.25	.12
100	Albert Belle	.30	.25	.12
101	Gregg Olson	.15	.11	.06
102	Kirby Puckett	.50	.40	.20
103	Luis Gonzalez	.20	.15	.08
104	Randy Myers	.10	.08	.04
105	Roger Clmens	.50	.40	.20
106	Tony Gwynn	.40	.30	.15
107	Jeff Bagwell	.50	.40	.20
108	John Wetteland	.15	.11	.06
109	Bernie Williams	.15	.11	.06
110	Scott Kamieniecki	.15	.11	.06
111	Robin Yount	.25	.20	.10
112	Dean Palmer	.15	.11	.06
113	Tim Belcher	.10	.08	.04
114	George Brett	.25	.20	.10
115	Frank Viola	.20	.15	.08
116	Kelly Gruber	.10	.08	.04
117	David Justice	.25	.20	.10
118	Scott Leuis	.10	.08	.04
119	Jeff Fassero	.10	.08	.04
120	Sammy Sosa	.12	.09	.05
121	Al Osuna	.08	.06	.03
122	Wilson Alvarez	.10	.08	.04
123	Jose Offerman	.15	.11	.06
124	Mel Rojas	.10	.08	.04
125	Shawon Dunston	.10	.08	.04
126	Pete Incaviglia	.10	.08	.04
127	Von Hayes	.08	.06	.03
128	Dave Gallagher	.08	.06	.03
129	Eric Davis	.15	.11	.06
130	Roberto Alomar	.50	.40	.20
131	Mike Gallego	.08	.06	.03
132	Robin Ventura	.40	.30	.15
133	Bill Swift	.10	.08	.04
134	John Kruk	.15	.11	.06
135	Craig Biggio	.15	.11	.06
136	Eddie Taubensee	.25	.20	.10
137	Cal Ripken, Jr.	.75	.60	.30
138	Charles Nagy	.15	.11	.06
139	Jose Melendez	.20	.15	.08
140	Jim Abbott	.20	.15	.08
141	Paul Molitor	.20	.15	.08
142	Tom Candiotti	.08	.06	.03
143	Bobby Bonilla	.40	.30	.15
144	Matt Williams	.15	.11	.06
145	Brett Butler	.12	.09	.05
146	Will Clark	.50	.40	.20
147	Rickey Henderson	.30	.25	.12
148	Ray Lankford	.30	.25	.12
149	Bill Pecota	.08	.06	.03
150	Dave Winfield	.20	.15	.08
151	Darren Lewis	.10	.08	.04
152	Bob MacDonald	.10	.08	.04
153	David Segui	.10	.08	.04
154	Benny Santiago	.20	.15	.08
155	Chuck Finley	.12	.09	.05
156	Andujar Cedeno	.25	.20	.10
157	Barry Bonds	.50	.40	.20
158	Joe Grahe	.08	.06	.03
159	Frank Castillo	.15	.11	.06
160	Dave Burba	.08	.06	.03
161	Leo Gomez	.15	.11	.06
162	Orel Hershiser	.15	.11	.06
163	Delino DeShields	.20	.15	.08
164	Sandy Alomar	.30	.25	.12
165	Denny Neagle	.20	.15	.08
166	Fred McGriff	.25	.20	.10
167	Ken Griffey, Jr.	.80	.60	.30
168	Juan Guzman	.50	.40	.20
169	Bobby Rose	.08	.06	.03
170	Steve Avery	.15	.11	.06
171	Rich DeLucia	.10	.08	.04
172	Mike Timlin	.15	.11	.06
173	Randy Johnson	.10	.08	.04
174	Paul Gibson	.08	.06	.03
175	David Cone	.15	.11	.06
176	Marquis Grissom	.20	.15	.08
177	Kurt Stillwell	.08	.06	.03
178	Mark Whiten	.15	.11	.06
179	Darryl Strawberry	.25	.20	.10
180	Mike Morgan	.08	.06	.03
181	Scott Scudder	.08	.06	.03
182	George Bell	.15	.11	.06
183	Alvin Davis	.08	.06	.03
184	Len Dykstra	.15	.11	.06
185	Kyle Abbott	.15	.11	.06
186	Chris Haney	.15	.11	.06
187	Junior Noboa	.08	.06	.03
188	Dennis Eckersley	.20	.15	.08
189	Derek Bell	.35	.25	.14
190	Lee Smith	.12	.09	.05
191	Andres Galarraga	.10	.08	.04
192	Jack Armstrong	.08	.06	.03
193	Eddie Murray	.15	.11	.06
194	Joe Carter	.20	.15	.08
195	Terry Pendleton	.20	.15	.08
196	Darryl Kile	.15	.11	.06
197	Rod Beck	.15	.11	.06
198	Hubie Brooks	.08	.06	.03

1993 O-Pee-Chee

For the first time in history, the 1993 O-Pee-Chee set differed significantly from the Topps set; photographs and designs are entirely different. Team names are scripted across the top, but a yellow triangle with a new team name appears on the front for players who have been traded. Two insert sets honoring the 1992 World Champion Toronto Blue Jays were also produced.

		MT	NR MT	EX
	Complete Set (396):	80.00	60.00	32.00
	Common Player:	.15	.11	.06
1	Jim Abbott	.30	.25	.12
2	Eric Anthony	.15	.11	.06
3	Harold Baines	.15	.11	.06
4	Roberto Alomar	1.75	1.25	.70
5	Steve Avery	1.00	.70	.40
6	James Austin	.15	.11	.06
7	Mark Wohlers	.15	.11	.06
8	Steve Buechele	.15	.11	.06
9	Pedro Astacio	1.00	.70	.40
10	Moises Alou	.30	.25	.12
11	Rod Beck	.25	.20	.10
12	Sandy Alomar	.15	.11	.06
13	Brett Boone	.40	.30	.15
14	Bryan Harvey	.15	.11	.06
15	Bobby Bonilla	.20	.15	.08
16	Brady Anderson	.15	.11	.06
17	Andy Benes	.20	.15	.08
18	Ruben Amaro	.15	.11	.06
19	Jay Bell	.15	.11	.06
20	Kevin Brown	.15	.11	.06
21	Scott Bankhead	.15	.11	.06
22	Denis Boucher	.15	.11	.06
23	Kevin Appier	.20	.15	.08
24	Pat Kelly	.15	.11	.06
25	Rick Aguilera	.15	.11	.06
26	George Bell	.15	.11	.06
27	Steve Farr	.15	.11	.06
28	Chad Curtis	1.00	.70	.40
29	Jeff Bagwell	1.25	.90	.50
30	Lance Blankenship	.10	.08	.04
31	Derek Bell	.40	.30	.15
32	Damon Berryhill	.10	.08	.04
33	Ricky Bones	.15	.11	.06
34	Rheal Cormier	.15	.11	.06
35	Andre Dawson	.25	.20	.10
36	Brett Butler	.15	.11	.06
37	Sean Berry	.15	.11	.06
38	Bud Black	.15	.11	.06
39	Carlos Baerga	2.00	1.50	.80
40	Jay Buhner	.15	.11	.06
41	Charlie Hough	.15	.11	.06
42	Sid Fernandez	.15	.11	.06
43	Luis Mercedes	.15	.11	.06
44	Jerald Clark	.15	.11	.06
45	Wes Chamberlain	.15	.11	.06
46	Barry Bonds	2.50	2.00	1.00
47	Jose Canseco	.40	.30	.15
48	Tim Belcher	.15	.11	.06
49	David Nied	2.50	2.00	1.00
50	George Brett	1.00	.70	.40
51	Cecil Fielder	.80	.60	.30
52	Chili Davis	.15	.11	.06
53	Alex Fernandez	.50	.40	.20
54	Charlie Hayes	.15	.11	.06
55	Rob Ducey	.15	.11	.06
56	Craig Biggio	.15	.11	.06
57	Mike Bordick	.15	.11	.06
58	Pat Borders	.15	.11	.06
59	Jeff Blauser	.15	.11	.06
60	Chris Bosio	.15	.11	.06
61	Bernard Gilkey	.15	.11	.06
62	Shawon Dunston	.15	.11	.06
63	Tom Candiotti	.15	.11	.06
64	Darrin Fletcher	.15	.11	.06
65	Jeff Brantley	.15	.11	.06
66	Albert Belle	2.00	1.50	.80
67	Dave Fleming	.40	.30	.15
68	John Franco	.15	.11	.06
69	Glenn Davis	.15	.11	.06
70	Tony Fernandez	.15	.11	.06
71	Darren Daulton	.30	.25	.12
72	Doug Drabek	.15	.11	.06
73	Julio Franco	.15	.11	.06
74	Tom Browning	.15	.11	.06
75	Tom Gordon	.15	.11	.06
76	Travis Fryman	2.00	1.50	.80
77	Scott Erickson	.15	.11	.06
78	Carlton Fisk	.15	.11	.06
79	Roberto Kelly	.15	.11	.06
80	Gary DiSarcina	.15	.11	.06
81	Ken Caminiti	.15	.11	.06
82	Ron Darling	.15	.11	.06
83	Joe Carter	.90	.70	.35
84	Sid Bream	.15	.11	.06
85	Cal Eldred	.40	.30	.15
86	Mark Grace	.40	.30	.15
87	Eric Davis	.15	.11	.06
88	Ivan Calderon	.15	.11	.06
89	John Burkett	.15	.11	.06
90	Felix Fermin	.15	.11	.06
91	Ken Griffey Jr.	7.50	5.75	3.00
92	Doc Gooden	.15	.11	.06
93	Mike Devereaux	.15	.11	.06
94	Tony Gwynn	.50	.40	.20
95	Mariano Duncan	.15	.11	.06
96	Jeff King	.15	.11	.06
97	Juan Gonzalez	7.50	5.75	3.00
98	Norm Charlton	.15	.11	.06
99	Mark Gubicza	.15	.11	.06
100	Danny Gladden	.15	.11	.06
101	Greg Gagne	.15	.11	.06
102	Ozzie Guillen	.15	.11	.06
103	Don Mattingly	1.00	.70	.40
104	Damion Easley	.60	.45	.25
105	Casey Candaele	.15	.11	.06
106	Dennis Eckersley	.15	.11	.06
107	David Cone	.15	.11	.06
108	Ron Gant	.60	.45	.25
109	Mike Fetters	.15	.11	.06
110	Mike Harkey	.15	.11	.06
111	Kevin Gross	.15	.11	.06
112	Archi Cianfrocco	.15	.11	.06
113	Will Clark	1.00	.70	.40
114	Glenallen Hill	.15	.11	.06
115	Erik Hanson	.15	.11	.06
116	Todd Hundley	.15	.11	.06
117	Leo Gomez	.15	.11	.06
118	Bruce Hurst	.15	.11	.06
119	Len Dykstra	.40	.30	.15
120	Jose Lind	.15	.11	.06
121	Jose Guzman	.15	.11	.06
122	Rob Dibble	.15	.11	.06
123	Gregg Jefferies	.20	.15	.08
124	Bill Gulickson	.15	.11	.06
125	Brian Harper	.15	.11	.06
126	Roberto Hernandez	.15	.11	.06
127	Sam Millitello	.40	.30	.15
128	Junior Felix	.15	.11	.06
129	Andujar Cedeno	.15	.11	.06
130	Rickey Henderson	.40	.30	.15
131	Bob MacDonald	.15	.11	.06
132	Tom Glavine	1.00	.70	.40
133	Scott Fletcher	.15	.11	.06
134	Brian Jordan	.50	.40	.20
135	Greg Maddux	.60	.45	.25
136	Orel Hershiser	.15	.11	.06
137	Greg Colbrunn	.15	.11	.06
138	Royce Clayton	.15	.11	.06
139	Thomas Howard	.15	.11	.06
140	Randy Johnson	.30	.25	.12
141	Jeff Innis	.15	.11	.06
142	Chris Hoiles	.15	.11	.06
143	Darrin Jackson	.15	.11	.06
144	Tommy Greene	.15	.11	.06
145	Mike LaValliere	.15	.11	.06
146	*David Hulse*	1.25	.90	.50
147	Barry Larkin	.20	.15	.08
148	Wally Joyner	.15	.11	.06
149	Mike Henneman	.15	.11	.06
150	Kent Hrbek	.15	.11	.06
151	Bo Jackson	.50	.40	.20
152	Rich Monteleone	.15	.11	.06
153	Chuck Finley	.15	.11	.06
154	Steve Finley	.15	.11	.06
155	Dave Henderson	.15	.11	.06
156	Kelly Gruber	.15	.11	.06
157	Brian Hunter	.15	.11	.06
158	Darryl Hamilton	.15	.11	.06
159	Derrick May	.30	.25	.12
160	Jay Howell	.15	.11	.06
161	Wil Cordero	.50	.40	.20
162	Bryan Hickerson	.15	.11	.06

163	Reggie Jefferson	.15	.11	.06
164	Edgar Martinez	.15	.11	.06
165	Nigel Wilson	3.50	2.75	1.50
166	Howard Johnson	.15	.11	.06
167	Tim Hulett	.15	.11	.06
168	Mike Maddux	.15	.11	.06
169	Dave Hollins	.60	.45	.25
170	Zane Smith	.15	.11	.06
171	Rafael Palmeiro	.25	.20	.10
172	Dave Martinez	.15	.11	.06
173	Rusty Meacham	.15	.11	.06
174	Mark Leiter	.15	.11	.06
175	Chuck Knoblauch	.30	.25	.12
176	Lance Johnson	.15	.11	.06
177	Matt Nokes	.15	.11	.06
178	Luis Gonzalez	.15	.11	.06
179	Jack Morris	.15	.11	.06
180	David Justice	1.75	1.25	.70
181	Doug Henry	.15	.11	.06
182	Felix Jose	.15	.11	.06
183	Delino DeShields	.40	.30	.15
184	Rene Gonzales	.15	.11	.06
185	Pete Harnisch	.15	.11	.06
186	Mike Moore	.15	.11	.06
187	Juan Guzman	1.00	.70	.40
188	John Olerud	2.00	1.50	.80
189	Ryan Klesko	2.00	1.50	.80
190	John Jaha	.40	.30	.15
191	Ray Lankford	.50	.40	.20
192	Jeff Fassero	.15	.11	.06
193	Darren Lewis	.15	.11	.06
194	Mark Lewis	.15	.11	.06
195	Alan Mills	.15	.11	.06
196	Wade Boggs	.40	.30	.15
197	Hal Morris	.15	.11	.06
198	Ron Karkovice	.15	.11	.06
199	John Grahe	.15	.11	.06
200	Butch henry	.15	.11	.06
201	Mark McGwire	.60	.45	.25
202	Tom Henke	.15	.11	.06
203	Ed Sprague	.15	.11	.06
204	Charlie Leibrandt	.15	.11	.06
205	Pat Listach	.50	.40	.20
206	Omar Olivares	.15	.11	.06
207	Mike Morgan	.15	.11	.06
208	Eric Karros	1.00	.70	.40
209	Marquis Grissom	.75	.60	.30
210	Willie McGee	.15	.11	.06
211	Derek Lilliquist	.15	.11	.06
212	Tino Martinez	.15	.11	.06
213	Jeff Kent	.15	.11	.06
214	Mike Mussina	1.75	1.25	.70
215	Randy Myers	.15	.11	.06
216	John Kruk	.25	.20	.10
217	Tom Brunansky	.15	.11	.06
218	Paul O'Neill	.15	.11	.06
219	Scott Livingstone	.15	.11	.06
220	John Valentin	.60	.45	.25
221	Eddie Zosky	.15	.11	.06
222	Pete Smith	.15	.11	.06
223	Bill Wegman	.15	.11	.06
224	Todd Zeile	.30	.25	.12
225	Tim Wallach	.15	.11	.06
226	Mitch Williams	.15	.11	.06
227	Tim Wakefield	.30	.25	.12
228	Frank Viola	.15	.11	.06
229	Nolan Ryan	5.00	3.75	2.00
230	Kirk McCaskill	.15	.11	.06
231	Melido Perez	.15	.11	.06
232	Mark Langston	.15	.11	.06
233	Xavier Hernandez	.15	.11	.06
234	Jerry Browne	.15	.11	.06
235	Dave Stieb	.15	.11	.06
236	Mark Lemke	.15	.11	.06
237	Paul Molitor	.50	.40	.20
238	Geronimo Pena	.15	.11	.06
239	Ken Hill	.15	.11	.06
240	Jack Clark	.15	.11	.06
241	Greg Myers	.15	.11	.06
242	Pete Incaviglia	.15	.11	.06
243	Ruben Sierra	.40	.30	.15
244	Todd Stottlemyre	.15	.11	.06
245	Pat Hentgen	2.00	1.50	.80
246	Melvin Nieves	1.50	1.25	.60
247	Jaime Navarro	.15	.11	.06
248	Donovan Osborne	.40	.30	.15
249	Brian Barnes	.15	.11	.06
250	Cory Snyder	.15	.11	.06
251	Kenny Lofton	1.50	1.25	.60
252	Kevin Mitchell	.15	.11	.06
253	Dave Magadan	.15	.11	.06
254	Ben McDonald	.40	.30	.15
255	Fred McGriff	.80	.60	.30
256	Mickey Morandini	.15	.11	.06
257	Randy Tomlin	.15	.11	.06
258	Dean Palmer	.75	.60	.30
259	Roger Clemens	1.50	1.25	.60
260	Joe Oliver	.15	.11	.06
261	Jeff Montgomery	.15	.11	.06
262	Tony Phillips	.15	.11	.06
263	Shane Mack	.15	.11	.06
264	Jack McDowell	.75	.60	.30
265	Mike Macfarlane	.15	.11	.06
266	Luis Polonia	.15	.11	.06
267	Doug Jones	.15	.11	.06
268	Terry Steinbach	.15	.11	.06
269	Jimmy Key	.15	.11	.06
270	Pat Taber	.15	.11	.06
271	Otis Nixon	.15	.11	.06
272	Dave Nilsson	.30	.25	.12
273	Tom Pagnozzi	.15	.11	.06
274	Ryne Sandberg	2.00	1.50	.80
275	Ramon Martinez	.20	.15	.08
276	*Tim Laker*	.60	.45	.25
277	Bill Swift	.15	.11	.06
278	Charles Nagy	.15	.11	.06
279	Harold Reynolds	.15	.11	.06
280	Eddie Murray	.40	.30	.15
281	Gregg Olson	.15	.11	.06
282	Frank Seminara	.15	.11	.06
283	Terry Mulholland	.15	.11	.06
284	Kevin Palmer	.40	.30	.15
285	Mike Greenwell	.20	.15	.08
286	Jose Rijo	.15	.11	.06
287	Brian McRae	.15	.11	.06
288	Frank Tanana	.15	.11	.06
289	Pedro Munoz	.15	.11	.06
290	Tim Raines	.15	.11	.06
291	Andy Stankiewicz	.15	.11	.06
292	Tim Salmon	14.00	10.50	5.50
293	Jimmy Jones	.15	.11	.06
294	Dave Stewart	.15	.11	.06
295	Mike Timlin	.15	.11	.06
296	Greg Olson	.15	.11	.06
297	Dan Plesac	.15	.11	.06
298	Mike Perez	.15	.11	.06
299	Jose Offerman	.15	.11	.06
300	Denny Martinez	.15	.11	.06
301	Robby Thompson	.15	.11	.06
302	Bret Saberhagen	.15	.11	.06
303	Joe Orsulak	.15	.11	.06
304	Tim Naehring	.15	.11	.06
305	Bip Roberts	.15	.11	.06
306	Kirby Puckett	2.00	1.50	.80
307	Steve Sax	.15	.11	.06
308	Danny Tartabull	.15	.11	.06
309	Jeff Juden	.15	.11	.06
310	Duane Ward	.15	.11	.06
311	Alejandro Pena	.15	.11	.06
312	Kevin Seitzer	.15	.11	.06
313	Ozzie Smith	.90	.70	.35
314	Mike Piazza	22.00	16.50	8.75
315	Chris Nabholz	.15	.11	.06
316	Tony Pena	.15	.11	.06
317	Gary Sheffield	.75	.60	.30
318	Mark Portugal	.15	.11	.06
319	Walt Weiss	.15	.11	.06
320	Manuel Lee	.15	.11	.06
321	David Wells	.15	.11	.06
322	Terry Pendleton	.15	.11	.06
323	Billy Spiers	.15	.11	.06
324	Lee Smith	.15	.11	.06
325	Bob Scanlan	.15	.11	.06
326	Mike Scioscia	.15	.11	.06
327	Spike Owen	.15	.11	.06
328	Mackey Sasser	.15	.11	.06
329	Arthur Rhodes	.40	.30	.15
330	Ben Rivera	.15	.11	.06
331	Ivan Rodriguez	1.75	1.25	.70
332	Phil Plantier	.60	.45	.25
333	Chris Sabo	.15	.11	.06
334	Mickey Tettleton	.15	.11	.06
335	John Smiley	.15	.11	.06
336	Bobby Thigpen	.15	.11	.06
337	Randy Velarde	.15	.11	.06
338	Luis Sojo	.15	.11	.06
339	Scott Servais	.15	.11	.06
340	Bob Welch	.15	.11	.06
341	Devon White	.30	.25	.12
342	Jeff Reardon	.15	.11	.06
343	B.J. Surhoff	.15	.11	.06
344	Bob Tewksbury	.15	.11	.06
345	Jose Vizcaino	.15	.11	.06
346	Mike Sharperson	.15	.11	.06
347	Mel Rojas	.15	.11	.06
348	Matt Williams	.60	.45	.25
349	Steve Olin	.15	.11	.06
350	Mike Schooler	.15	.11	.06
351	Ryan Thompson	.75	.60	.30
352	Cal Ripken	2.00	1.50	.80
353	Benny Santiago	.15	.11	.06
354	Curt Schilling	.15	.11	.06
355	Andy Van Slyke	.30	.25	.12
356	Kenny Rogers	.15	.11	.06
357	Jody Reed	.15	.11	.06
358	Reggie Sanders	.90	.70	.35
359	Kevin McReynolds	.15	.11	.06
360	Alan Trammell	.15	.11	.06
361	Kevin Tapani	.15	.11	.06
362	Frank Thomas	9.00	6.75	3.50
363	Bernie Williams	.30	.25	.12
364	John Smoltz	.40	.30	.15
365	Robin Yount	.90	.70	.35
366	John Wetteland	.15	.11	.06
367	Bob Zupcic	.15	.11	.06
368	Julio Valera	.15	.11	.06
369	Brian Williams	.15	.11	.06
370	Willie Wilson	.15	.11	.06
371	Dave Winfield	1.00	.70	.40
372	Deion Sanders	.75	.60	.30
373	Greg Vaughn	.40	.30	.15
374	Todd Worrell	.15	.11	.06
375	Darryl Strawberry	.15	.11	.06
376	John Vander Wal	.15	.11	.06
377	Mike Benjamin	.15	.11	.06
378	Mark Whiten	.15	.11	.06
379	Omar Vizquel	.15	.11	.06
380	Anthony Young	.15	.11	.06
381	Rick Sutcliffe	.15	.11	.06
382	Candy Maldonado	.15	.11	.06
383	Francisco Cabrera	.15	.11	.06
384	Larry Walker	.75	.60	.30
385	Scott Cooper	.30	.25	.12
386	Gerald Williams	.15	.11	.06
387	Robin Ventura	1.00	.70	.40
388	Carl Willis	.15	.11	.06
389	Lou Whitaker	.15	.11	.06
390	Hipolito Pichardo	.15	.11	.06
391	Rudy Seanez	.15	.11	.06
392	Greg Swindell	.15	.11	.06
393	Mo Vaughn	1.25	.90	.50
394	Checklist (1 of 3)	.15	.11	.06
395	Checklist (2 of 3)	.15	.11	.06
396	Checklist (3 of 3)	.15	.11	.06

1993 O-Pee-Chee World Champs

This 18-card insert set commemorates the Toronto Blue Jays' 1992 World Series victory; seventeen players and Manager Cito Gaston are featured. Cards were randomly inserted, one World Champs or World Series Heroes card per every 69-cent, eight-card pack.

		MT	NR MT	EX
Complete Set (18):		11.00	8.25	4.50
Common Player:		.25	.20	.10
1	Roberto Alomar	2.50	2.00	1.00
2	Pat Borders	.30	.25	.12
3	Joe Carter	2.00	1.50	.80
4	David Cone	.35	.25	.14
5	Kelly Gruber	.25	.20	.10
6	Juan Guzman	1.25	.90	.50
7	Tom Henke	.25	.20	.10
8	Jimmy Key	.60	.45	.25
9	Manuel Lee	.25	.20	.10
10	Candy Maldonado	.25	.20	.10
11	Jack Morris	.40	.30	.15
12	John Olerud	3.00	2.25	1.25
13	Ed Sprague	.30	.25	.12
14	Todd Stottlemyre	.25	.20	.10
15	Duane Ward	.35	.25	.14
16	Devon White	.75	.60	.30
17	Dave Winfield	1.25	.90	.50
18	Cito Gaston	.50	.40	.20

1993 O-Pee-Chee World Series Heroes

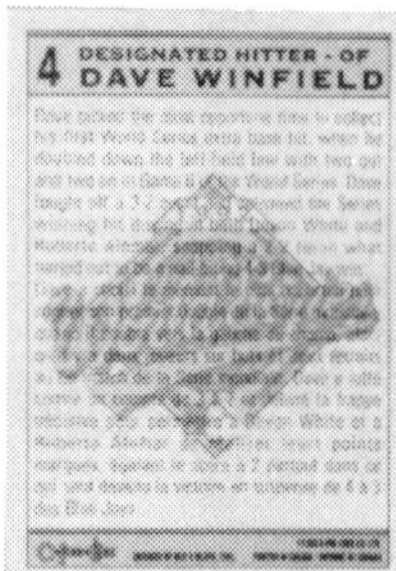

This insert set honors four of the Toronto Blue Jays' World Series stars. Cards were randomly inserted in every 69-cent, eight-card pack, one World Champs or World Series Heroes card per pack.

		MT	NR MT	EX
Complete Set (4):		2.00	1.50	.80
Common Player:		.50	.40	.20
1	Pat Borders	.50	.40	.20
2	Jimmy Key	.50	.40	.20
3	Ed Sprague	.50	.40	.20
4	Dave Winfield	1.00	.70	.40

1993 O-Pee-Chee Premier

For the third consecutive year, O-Pee-Chee produced a set under its Premier brand name. The regular set, issued in three series, has 132 cards and 48 insert cards. The insert sets are titled Star Performers (gold borders), Foil Star Performers (full-bleed photos and gold stamping), and Top Draft Picks (four cards, two each featuring the Toronto Blue Jays and Montreal Expos top picks). O-Pee-Chee announced it produced only 4,000 cases for this set.

		MT	NR MT	EX
Complete Set (132):		15.00	11.00	6.00
Common Player:		.10	.08	.04
1	Barry Bonds	1.00	.70	.40
2	Chad Curtis	.30	.25	.12
3	Chris Bosio	.10	.08	.04
4	Cal Eldred	.20	.15	.08
5	Dan Walter	.10	.08	.04
6	*Rene Arocha*	.70	.50	.30
7	Delino DeShields	.15	.11	.06
8	Spike Owen	.10	.08	.04
9	Jeff Russell	.10	.08	.04
10	Phil Plantier	.20	.15	.08
11	Mike Christopher	.10	.08	.04
12	Darren Daulton	.20	.15	.08
13	Scott Cooper	.10	.08	.04
14	Paul O'Neill	.10	.08	.04
15	Jimmy Key	.10	.08	.04
16	Dickie Thon	.10	.08	.04
17	Greg Gohr	.10	.08	.04
18	Andre Dawson	.15	.11	.06
19	Steve Cooke	.50	.40	.20
20	Tony Fernandez	.10	.08	.04
21	Mark Gardner	.10	.08	.04
22	Dave Martinez	.10	.08	.04
23	Jose Guzman	.10	.08	.04
24	Chili Davis	.10	.08	.04
25	Randy Knorr	.10	.08	.04
26	Mike Piazza	5.00	3.75	2.00
27	Benji Gil	.75	.60	.30
28	Dave Winfield	.30	.25	.12
29	Wil Cordero	.15	.11	.06
30	Butch Henry	.10	.08	.04
31	Eric Young	.50	.40	.20
32	Orestes Destrade	.10	.08	.04
33	Randy Myers	.10	.08	.04
34	Tom Brunansky	.10	.08	.04
35	Dan Wilson	.10	.08	.04
36	Juan Guzman	.40	.30	.15
37	Tim Salmon	3.50	2.75	1.50
38	Bill Krueger	.10	.08	.04
39	Larry Walker	.30	.25	.12
40	*David Hulse*	.50	.40	.20
41	*Ken Ryan*	.25	.20	.10
42	Jose Lind	.10	.08	.04
43	Benny Santiago	.10	.08	.04
44	Ray Lankford	.20	.15	.08
45	Dave Stewart	.10	.08	.04
46	Don Mattingly	.40	.30	.15
47	Fernando Valenzuela	.10	.08	.04
48	Scott Fletcher	.10	.08	.04
49	Wade Boggs	.20	.15	.08
50	Norm Charlton	.10	.08	.04
51	Carlos Baerga	.80	.60	.30
52	John Olerud	1.00	.70	.40
53	Willie Wilson	.10	.08	.04
54	Dennis Moeller	.10	.08	.04
55	Joe Orsulak	.10	.08	.04
56	John Smiley	.10	.08	.04
57	Al Martin	.60	.45	.25
58	Andres Galarraga	.10	.08	.04
59	Billy Ripken	.10	.08	.04
60	Dave Stieb	.10	.08	.04
61	Dave Magadan	.10	.08	.04
62	Todd Worrell	.10	.08	.04
63	*Sherman Obando*	.30	.25	.12
64	Kent Bottenfield	.10	.08	.04
65	Vinny Castilla	.10	.08	.04
66	Charlie Hayes	.10	.08	.04
67	Mike Hartley	.10	.08	.04
68	Harold Baines	.10	.08	.04
69	*John Cummings*	.25	.20	.10
70	*J.T. Snow*	1.75	1.25	.70
71	*Graeme Lloyd*	.40	.30	.15
72	Frank Bolick	.10	.08	.04
73	Doug Drabek	.10	.08	.04
74	Milt Thompson	.10	.08	.04
75	*Tim Pugh*	.50	.40	.20
76	John Kruk	.15	.11	.06
77	Tom Henke	.10	.08	.04
78	Kevin Young	.75	.60	.30
79	Ryan Thompson	.25	.20	.10
80	Mike Hampton	.10	.08	.04
81	Jose Canseco	.20	.15	.08
82	*Mike Lansing*	.60	.45	.25
83	Candy Maldonado	.10	.08	.04
84	Alex Arias	.10	.08	.04
85	Troy Neel	.50	.40	.20
86	Greg Swindell	.10	.08	.04
87	Tim Wallach	.10	.08	.04
88	Andy Van Slyke	.15	.11	.06
89	Harold Baines	.10	.08	.04
90	Bryan Harvey	.10	.08	.04
91	Jerald Clark	.10	.08	.04
92	David Cone	.10	.08	.04
93	Ellis Burks	.10	.08	.04
94	Scott Bankhead	.10	.08	.04
95	Pete Incaviglia	.10	.08	.04
96	Cecil Fielder	.35	.25	.14
97	Sean Berry	.10	.08	.04
98	Gregg Jefferies	.15	.11	.06
99	*Billy Brewer*	.40	.30	.15
100	Scott Sanderson	.10	.08	.04
101	Walt Weiss	.10	.08	.04
102	Travis Fryman	.80	.60	.30
103	Barry Larkin	.15	.11	.06
104	Darren Holmes	.10	.08	.04
105	Ivan Calderon	.10	.08	.04
106	Terry Jorgensen	.10	.08	.04
107	David Nied	1.25	.90	.50
108	*Tim Bogar*	.40	.30	.15
109	Roberto Kelly	.10	.08	.04
110	Mike Moore	.10	.08	.04
111	Carlos Garcia	.20	.15	.08
112	Mike Bielecki	.10	.08	.04
113	Trevor Hoffman	.10	.08	.04
114	Rich Amaral	.10	.08	.04
115	Jody Reed	.10	.08	.04
116	Charlie Leibrandt	.10	.08	.04
117	Greg Gagne	.10	.08	.04
118	*Darrell Sherman*	.80	.60	.30
119	Jeff Conine	.15	.11	.06
120	*Tim Laker*	.30	.25	.12
121	Kevin Seitzer	.10	.08	.04
122	Jeff Mutis	.10	.08	.04
123	Rico Rossy	.10	.08	.04
124	Paul Molitor	.20	.15	.08
125	Cal Ripken	.70	.50	.30
126	Greg Maddux	.25	.20	.10
127	*Greg McMichael*	.30	.25	.12
128	Felix Jose	.10	.08	.04
129	Dick Schofield	.10	.08	.04
130	Jim Abbott	.20	.15	.08
131	Kevin Reimer	.10	.08	.04
132	Checklist	.10	.08	.04

1993 O-Pee-Chee Premier Star Performers

O-Pee-Chee released a 22-card insert set in two forms: Star Performers (featuring a gold border design) and Foil Star Performers (featuring full-bleed photos and gold stamping). The players are identical in both sets, but foil cards are generally worth more. There are 34 Star Performers per 36-card wax box and one Foil Star Performer card per box.

		MT	NR MT	EX
Complete Set (22):		15.00	11.00	6.00
Common Player:		.15	.11	.06
1	Frank Thomas	3.00	2.25	1.25
2	Fred McGriff	.35	.25	.14
3	Roberto Alomar	.60	.45	.25
4	Ryne Sandberg	.60	.45	.25
6	Gary Sheffield	.30	.25	.12
7	Juan Gonzalez	2.00	1.50	.80
8	Eric Karros	.30	.25	.12
9	Ken Griffey Jr.	2.00	1.50	.80
10	Deion Sanders	.20	.15	.08
11	Kirby Puckett	.60	.45	.25
12	Will Clark	.35	.25	.14
13	Joe Carter	.40	.30	.15
14	Barry Bonds	1.00	.70	.40
15	Pat Listach	.15	.11	.06
16	Mark McGwire	.25	.20	.10
17	Kenny Lofton	.40	.30	.15
18	Roger Clemens	.50	.40	.20
19	Greg Maddux	.25	.20	.10
20	Nolan Ryan	2.00	1.50	.80
21	Tom Glavine	.25	.20	.10

1993 O-Pee-Chee Premier Top Draft Picks

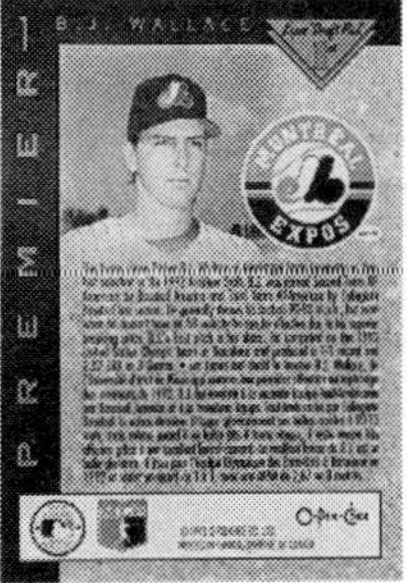

These randomly inserted cards feature four prospects; two each for Montreal and Toronto. Card fronts are foil-stamped and have a vertical banner with the player's name. The OPC Premier logo is in the corner. On back is another player photo, a team logo and a bi-lingual rationale for the player's draft status.

		MT	NR MT	EX
Complete Set (4):		14.00	10.50	5.50
Common Player:		3.50	2.75	1.50
1	B.J. Wallace	6.00	4.50	2.50
2	Shannon Stewart	3.50	2.75	1.50
3	Rod Henderson	5.00	3.75	2.00
4	Todd Steverson	4.50	3.50	1.75

1986 Oh Henry Indians

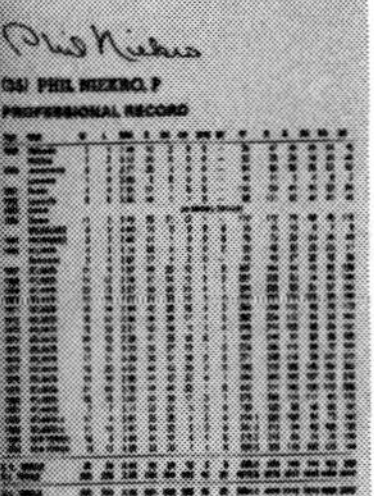

This 30-card set of Cleveland Indians players was distributed by the team at a special Photo/Baseball Card Day at Municipal Stadium. The cards were printed within a special three-panel, perforated fold-out piece which featured four action shots of the Indians on the cover. Unfolded, there are two panels containing the baseball cards and a third which contains a team photo. Cards measure 2-1/4" by 3-1/8" and are full-color studio portraits. Photos are framed in blue with a white border and list player name, number and position. Card fronts also include a picture of the sponsoring candy bar. Card backs include facsimile autograph and professional records. Each card is perforated for separation.

		MT	NR MT	EX
Complete Set:		8.00	6.00	3.25
Common Player:		.15	.11	.06
2	Brett Butler	.30	.25	.12
4	Tony Bernazard	.15	.11	.06
6	Andy Allanson	.15	.11	.06
7	Pat Corrales	.15	.11	.06
8	Carmen Castillo	.15	.11	.06
10	Pat Tabler	.20	.15	.08
13	Ernie Camacho	.15	.11	.06
14	Julio Franco	.80	.60	.30
15	Dan Rohn	.15	.11	.06
18	Ken Schrom	.15	.11	.06
20	Otis Nixon	.20	.15	.08
22	Fran Mullins	.15	.11	.06
23	Chris Bando	.15	.11	.06
24	Ed Williams	.15	.11	.06
26	Brook Jacoby	.60	.45	.25
27	Mel Hall	.30	.25	.12
29	Andre Thornton	.30	.25	.12
30	Joe Carter	2.00	1.50	.80
35	Phil Niekro	.80	.60	.30
36	Jamie Easterly	.15	.11	.06
37	Don Schulze	.15	.11	.06
42	Rich Yett	.15	.11	.06
43	Scott Bailes	.15	.11	.06
44	Neal Heaton	.15	.11	.06
46	Jim Kern	.15	.11	.06
48	Dickie Noles	.15	.11	.06
49	Tom Candiotti	.15	.11	.06
53	Reggie Ritter	.15	.11	.06
54	Tom Waddell	.15	.11	.06
----	Coaching Staff (Jack Aker, Bobby Bonds, Doc Edwards, Johnny Goryl)	.15	.11	.06

1965 Old London Coins

These 1-1/2" diameter metal coins were included in Old London snack food packages. The 40 coins in this set feature two players from each of the major leagues' 20 teams, except St. Louis (3)

and the New York Mets (1). Coin fronts have color photos and player names, while the silver-colored coin backs give brief biographies of each player. An Old London logo is also displayed on each coin back. Space Magic Ltd. produced the coins. This is the same company which produced similar sets for Topps in 1964 and 1971.

		NR MT	EX	VG
Complete Set (40):		700.00	350.00	210.00
Common Player:		5.00	2.50	1.50
(1)	Henry Aaron	75.00	37.00	22.00
(2)	Richie Allen	8.00	4.00	2.50
(3)	Bob Allison	6.50	3.25	2.00
(4)	Ernie Banks	35.00	17.50	10.50
(5)	Ken Boyer	8.00	4.00	2.50
(6)	Jim Bunning	11.00	5.50	3.25
(7)	Orlando Cepeda	9.00	4.50	2.75
(8)	Dean Chance	5.00	2.50	1.50
(9)	Rocky Colavito	11.00	5.50	3.25
(10)	Vic Davalillo	5.00	2.50	1.50
(11)	Tommy Davis	8.00	4.00	2.50
(12)	Ron Fairly	6.50	3.25	2.00
(13)	Dick Farrell	5.00	2.50	1.50
(14)	Jim Fregosi	6.50	3.25	2.00
(15)	Bob Friend	6.50	3.25	2.00
(16)	Dick Groat	8.00	4.00	2.50
(17)	Ron Hunt	5.00	2.50	1.50
(18)	Chuck Hinton	5.00	2.50	1.50
(19)	Ken Johnson	5.00	2.50	1.50
(20)	Al Kaline	35.00	17.50	10.50
(21)	Harmon Killebrew	27.50	13.50	8.25
(22)	Don Lock	5.00	2.50	1.50
(23)	Mickey Mantle	175.00	87.00	52.00
(24)	Roger Maris	35.00	17.50	10.50
(25)	Willie Mays	75.00	37.00	22.00
(26)	Bill Mazeroski	11.00	5.50	3.25
(27)	Gary Peters	5.00	2.50	1.50
(28)	Vada Pinson	8.00	4.00	2.50
(29)	Boog Powell	8.00	4.00	2.50
(30)	Dick Radatz	5.00	2.50	1.50
(31)	Brooks Robinson	35.00	17.50	10.50
(32)	Frank Robinson	35.00	17.50	10.50
(33)	Tracy Stallard	5.00	2.50	1.50
(34)	Joe Torre	8.00	4.00	2.50
(35)	Leon Wagner	5.00	2.50	1.50
(36)	Pete Ward	5.00	2.50	1.50
(37)	Dave Wickersham	5.00	2.50	1.50
(38)	Billy Williams	25.00	12.50	7.50
(39)	John Wyatt	5.00	2.50	1.50
(40)	Carl Yastrzemski	75.00	37.00	22.00

1910 Orange Borders

Known in the hobby as "Orange Borders", these 1-1/2" by 2-7/16" cards were issued in 1910 and were printed on candy boxes that displayed the words "American Sports and Candy and Jewelry." The end flaps indicate the producers as the "Geo. Davis Co., Inc." and the "P.R. Warren Co., Warrenville Lowell, Mass." According to the box, the complete set includes "144 leading ballplayers," but to date fewer than three dozen different subjects are known. When found today, these black and white photos are often surrounded by orange borders which, in reality, were part of the candy box.

		NR MT	EX	VG
Common Player:		100.00	50.00	30.00
(1)	Bill Bergen	100.00	50.00	30.00
(2)	Al Bridwell	100.00	50.00	30.00
(3)	Bill Carrigan	100.00	50.00	30.00
(4)	Hal Chase	120.00	60.00	35.00
(5)	Fred Clark (Clarke)	150.00	75.00	45.00
(6)	Ty Cobb	600.00	300.00	180.00
(7)	Sam Crawford	150.00	75.00	45.00
(8)	Lou Criger	100.00	50.00	30.00
(9)	Harry Davis	100.00	50.00	30.00
(10)	Jim Delahanty	100.00	50.00	30.00
(11)	Art Devlin	100.00	50.00	30.00
(12)	Mickey Doolan	100.00	50.00	30.00
(13)	George Gibson	100.00	50.00	30.00
(14)	Walter Johnson	350.00	175.00	100.00
(15)	Nap Lajoie	200.00	100.00	60.00
(16)	Frank LaPorte	100.00	50.00	30.00
(17)	Harry Lord	100.00	50.00	30.00
(18)	Christy Mathewson	300.00	150.00	90.00
(19)	John McGraw	150.00	75.00	45.00
(20)	Dots Miller	100.00	50.00	30.00
(21)	George Mullin	100.00	50.00	30.00
(22)	Tom Needham	100.00	50.00	30.00
(23)	Eddie Plank	150.00	75.00	45.00
(24)	Jimmy Sheckard	100.00	50.00	30.00
(25)	Tris Speaker	200.00	100.00	60.00
(26)	Jake Stahl	100.00	50.00	30.00
(27)	Honus Wagner (batting)	375.00	187.00	112.00
(28)	Honus Wagner (portrait)	375.00	187.00	112.00
(29)	Ed Walsh	150.00	75.00	40.00
(30)	Jack Warhop	100.00	50.00	30.00
(31)	American League Champions, 1909	100.00	50.00	30.00
(32)	National League Champions, 1909	100.00	50.00	30.00

1994 Oscar Mayer Superstar Pop-Ups

Oscar Mayer Bologna packages in 1994 included one pop-up card in each, but unlike the similar Kraft cards, in this case it was 30 round cards (2-1/2 inches in diameter), with the Oscar Mayer logo on the front and trivia questions on the backs. The promotion ran from April through May, or as long as the supplies lasted. The cards were licensed by the Major League Baseball Players Association, but not by Major League Baseball, so the team logos were airbrushed from player's caps and uniforms. Through an on-pack and in-store mail-in offer, collectors could order complete sets of cards for $1.95 per league (15 cards), plus the appropriate proofs of purchase. Officials of Kraft USA, parent company of Oscar Mayer, announced that they printed 266,000 sets.

		MT	NR MT	EX
Complete Set (30):		25.00	18.50	10.00
Common Player:		.50	.40	.20
1	Jim Abbott	.75	.60	.30
2	Kevin Appier	.50	.40	.20
3	Roger Clemens	.80	.60	.30
4	Cecil Fielder	.80	.60	.30
5	Juan Gonzalez	2.00	1.50	.80
6	Ken Griffey Jr.	5.00	3.75	2.00
7	Kenny Lofton	.75	.60	.30
8	Jack McDowell	.60	.45	.25
9	Paul Molitor	1.25	.90	.50
10	Kirby Puckett	1.25	.90	.50
11	Cal Ripken Jr.	4.00	3.00	1.50
12	Tim Salmon	1.25	.90	.50
13	Ruben Sierra	.60	.45	.25
14	Frank Thomas	5.00	3.75	2.00
15	Greg Vaughn	.50	.40	.20
16	Jeff Bagwell	.80	.60	.30
17	Barry Bonds	2.50	2.00	1.00
18	Bobby Bonilla	.60	.45	.25
19	Jeff Conine	.60	.45	.25
20	Lenny Dykstra	.60	.45	.25
21	Andres Galarraga	.80	.60	.30
22	Marquis Grissom	.50	.40	.20
23	Tony Gwynn	.75	.60	.30
24	Gregg Jefferies	.60	.45	.25
25	John Kruk	.60	.45	.25
26	Greg Maddux	.60	.45	.25
27	Mike Piazza	3.00	2.25	1.25
28	Jose Rijo	.60	.45	.25
29	Ryne Sandberg	4.00	3.00	1.50
30	Andy Van Slyke	.50	.40	.20

A player's name in italic type indicates a rookie card. An (FC) indicates a player's first card for that particular card company.

1921 Oxford Confectionery (E253)

Issued in 1921 by Oxford Confectionary of Oxford, Pa., this 2-card set was printed on thin paper and distributed with caramels. Each card measures 1-5/8" by 2-3/4" and features a black and white player photo with the player's name and team printed in a white band along the bottom. The back

THE following star baseball players of both major leagues make up the complete set of lithographed cards, one of which is wrapped with each piece of caramel. These cards are reproduced solely for the OXFORD CONFECTIONERY CO., OXFORD, PA.

EDDIE COLLINS.	White Sox
WALTER JOHNSON,	Washington
ROUSCH.	Cincinnati
ALEXANDER.	Chicago Nat.
SPEAKER.	Cleveland
BANCROFT.	Giants
"BILL" HOLKE.	Boston Nat.
SISLER.	St. Louis Amer.
PRATT.	Boston Amer.
COBB.	Detroit
"BABE" RUTH.	Yankees
WITT.	Athletics
FRISCH.	Giants
LEE MEADOWS.	Phillies
CY WILLIAMS.	Phillies
CAREY.	Pittsburgh
RAY SCHALK.	White Sox
GRIMES.	Brooklyn
CY PERKINS.	Athletics
HORNSBY.	St. Louis Nat.

carries the Oxford Confectionary name and a checklist of the 20 major leaguers in the set, 14 of whom are now in the Hall of Fame. The set is designated as E253 in the ACC.

		NR MT	EX	VG
Complete Set (20):		6000.	3000.	1800.
Common Player:		75.00	37.00	22.00
(1)	Grover Alexander	200.00	100.00	60.00
(2)	Dave Bancroft	150.00	75.00	45.00
(3)	Max Carey	150.00	75.00	45.00
(4)	Ty Cobb	1500.	750.00	450.00
(5)	Eddie Collins	150.00	75.00	45.00
(6)	Frankie Frisch	150.00	75.00	45.00
(7)	Burleigh Grimes	150.00	75.00	45.00
(8)	"Bill" Holke (Walter)	75.00	37.00	22.00
(9)	Rogers Hornsby	300.00	150.00	90.00
(10)	Walter Johnson	500.00	250.00	150.00
(11)	Lee Meadows	75.00	37.00	22.00
(12)	Cy Perkins	75.00	37.00	22.00
(13)	Derrill Pratt	75.00	37.00	22.00
(14)	Ed Rousch (Roush)	150.00	75.00	45.00
(15)	"Babe" Ruth	2000.	1000.	600.00
(16)	Ray Schalk	150.00	75.00	45.00
(17)	George Sisler	150.00	75.00	45.00
(18)	Tris Speaker	200.00	100.00	60.00
(19)	Cy Williams	75.00	37.00	22.00
(20)	Whitey Witt	75.00	37.00	22.00

P

1910 P2 Sweet Caporal Pins

Expanding its premiums to include more than just trading cards, the American Tobacco Co. issued a series of baseball pins between 1910 and 1912. The sepia-colored pins, each measuring 7/8" in diameter, were distributed under the Sweet Caporal brand name. The set includes 152 different major league players, but because of numerous "large letter" variations, collectors generally consider the set complete at 204 different pins. Fifty of the players are pictured on a second pin that usually displays the same photo but has the player's name and team designation printed in larger letters. Two players (Roger Bresnahan and Bobby Wallace) have three pins each. It is now generally accepted that there are 153 pins with "small letters" and another 51 "large letter" variations in a complete set. Research among advanced collectors has shown that 19 of the pins, including six of the "large letter" variations, are considered more difficult to find. The back of each pin has either a black or a red paper insert advertising Sweet Caporal Cigarettes. The red backings, issued only with the "large letter" pins, are generally less common. The Sweet Caporal pins are closely related to the popular T205 Gold Border tobacco cards, also issued by the American Tobacco Co.

about the same time. All but nine of the players featured in the pin set were also pictured on T205 cards, and in nearly all cases the photos are identical. The Sweet Caporal pins are designated as P2 in the American Card Catalog. The complete set price includes all variations.

		NR MT	EX	VG
Complete Set:		5250.	2625.	1575.
Common Player:		15.00	7.50	4.50
(1)	Ed Abbaticchio	15.00	7.50	4.50
(2)	Red Ames	15.00	7.50	4.50
(3a)	Jimmy Archer (small letters)	15.00	7.50	4.50
(3b)	Jimmy Archer (large letters)	20.00	10.00	6.00
(4a)	Jimmy Austin (small letters)	15.00	7.50	4.50
(4b)	Jimmy Austin (large letters)	20.00	10.00	6.00
(5)	Home Run Baker	30.00	15.00	9.00
(6)	Neal Ball	15.00	7.50	4.50
(7)	Cy Barger	15.00	7.50	4.50
(8)	Jack Barry	15.00	7.50	4.50
(9)	Johnny Bates	15.00	7.50	4.50
(10)	Beals Becker	15.00	7.50	4.50
(11)	Fred Beebe	15.00	7.50	4.50
(12a)	George Bell (small letters)	15.00	7.50	4.50
(12b)	George Bell (large letters)	20.00	10.00	6.00
(13a)	Chief Bender (small letters)	30.00	15.00	9.00
(13b)	Chief Bender (large letters)	50.00	25.00	15.00
(14)	Bill Bergen	15.00	7.50	4.50
(15)	Bob Bescher	15.00	7.50	4.50
(16)	Joe Birmingham	15.00	7.50	4.50
(17)	Kitty Bransfield	35.00	17.50	10.50
(18a)	Roger Bresnahan (mouth closed, small letters)	30.00	15.00	9.00
(18b)	Roger Bresnahan (mouth closed, large letters)	90.00	45.00	27.00
(19)	Roger Bresnahan (mouth open)	30.00	15.00	9.00
(20)	Al Bridwell	15.00	7.50	4.50
(21a)	Mordecai Brown (small letters)	30.00	15.00	9.00
(21b)	Mordecai Brown (large letters)	50.00	25.00	15.00
(22)	Bobby Byrne	15.00	7.50	4.50
(23)	Nixey Callahan	15.00	7.50	4.50
(24a)	Howie Camnitz (small letters)	15.00	7.50	4.50
(24b)	Howie Camnitz (large letters)	20.00	10.00	6.00
(25a)	Bill Carrigan (small letters)	15.00	7.50	4.50
(25b)	Bill Carrigan (large letters)	20.00	10.00	6.00
(26a)	Frank Chance (small letters)	35.00	17.50	10.50
(26b)	Frank Chance (large letters)	50.00	25.00	15.00
(27)	Hal Chase (different photo, small letters)	15.00	7.50	4.50
(28)	Hal Chase (different photo, large letters)	25.00	12.50	7.50
(29)	Ed Cicotte	15.00	7.50	4.50
(30a)	Fred Clarke (small letters)	30.00	15.00	9.00
(30b)	Fred Clarke (large letters)	50.00	25.00	15.00
(31a)	Ty Cobb (small letters)	250.00	125.00	75.00
(31b)	Ty Cobb (large letters)	375.00	187.00	112.00
(32a)	Eddie Collins (small letters)	30.00	15.00	9.00
(32b)	Eddie Collins (large letters)	70.00	35.00	21.00
(33)	Doc Crandall	15.00	7.50	4.50
(34)	Birdie Cree	35.00	17.50	10.50
(35)	Bill Dahlen	15.00	7.50	4.50
(36)	Jim Delahanty	15.00	7.50	4.50
(37)	Art Devlin	15.00	7.50	4.50
(38)	Josh Devore	15.00	7.50	4.50
(39)	Wild Bill Donovan	35.00	17.50	10.50
(40a)	Red Dooin (small letters)	15.00	7.50	4.50
(40b)	Red Dooin (large letters)	20.00	10.00	6.00
(41a)	Mickey Doolan (small letters)	15.00	7.50	4.50
(41b)	Mickey Doolan (large letters)	20.00	10.00	6.00
(42)	Patsy Dougherty	15.00	7.50	4.50
(43a)	Tom Downey (small letters)	15.00	7.50	4.50
(43b)	Tom Downey (large letters)	20.00	10.00	6.00
(44a)	Larry Doyle (small letters)	15.00	7.50	4.50
(44b)	Larry Doyle (large letters)	20.00	10.00	6.00
(45)	Louis Drucke	15.00	7.50	4.50
(46a)	Hugh Duffy (small letters)	30.00	15.00	9.00
(46b)	Hugh Duffy (large letters)	50.00	25.00	15.00
(47)	Jimmy Dygert	15.00	7.50	4.50
(48a)	Kid Elberfeld (small letters)	15.00	7.50	4.50
(48b)	Kid Elberfeld (large letters)	20.00	10.00	6.00
(49a)	Clyde Engle (small letters)	15.00	7.50	4.50
(49b)	Clyde Engle (large letters)	20.00	10.00	6.00
(50)	Tex Erwin	15.00	7.50	4.50
(51)	Steve Evans	15.00	7.50	4.50
(52)	Johnny Evers	30.00	15.00	9.00
(53)	Cecil Ferguson	15.00	7.50	4.50
(54)	John Flynn	15.00	7.50	4.50
(55a)	Russ Ford (small letters)	15.00	7.50	4.50
(55b)	Russ Ford (large letters)	20.00	10.00	6.00
(56)	Art Fromme	15.00	7.50	4.50
(57)	Harry Gaspar	15.00	7.50	4.50
(58a)	George Gibson (small letters)	15.00	7.50	4.50
(58b)	George Gibson (large letters)	20.00	10.00	6.00
(59)	Eddie Grant	35.00	17.50	10.50
(60)	Dolly Gray	15.00	7.50	4.50
(61a)	Clark Griffith (small letters)	30.00	15.00	9.00
(61b)	Clark Griffith (large letters)	50.00	25.00	15.00
(62)	Bob Groom	15.00	7.50	4.50
(63)	Bob Harmon	15.00	7.50	4.50
(64)	Topsy Hartsel	15.00	7.50	4.50
(65)	Arnold Hauser	35.00	17.50	10.50
(66)	Ira Hemphill	15.00	7.50	4.50
(67a)	Buck Herzog (small letters)	15.00	7.50	4.50
(67b)	Buck Herzog (large letters)	20.00	10.00	6.00
(68)	Dick Hoblitzell	15.00	7.50	4.50
(69)	Danny Hoffman	15.00	7.50	4.50
(70)	Harry Hooper	15.00	7.50	4.50
(71a)	Miller Huggins (small letters)	30.00	15.00	9.00
(71b)	Miller Huggins (large letters)	50.00	25.00	15.00
(72)	John Hummel	15.00	7.50	4.50
(73)	Hugh Jennings (different photo, small letters)	30.00	15.00	9.00
(74)	Hugh Jennings (different photo, large letters)	50.00	25.00	15.00
(75a)	Walter Johnson (small letters)	90.00	45.00	27.00
(75b)	Walter Johnson (large letters)	125.00	62.00	37.00
(76)	Tom Jones	35.00	17.50	10.50
(77)	Ed Karger	15.00	7.50	4.50
(78)	Ed Killian	35.00	17.50	10.50
(79a)	Jack Knight (small letters)	15.00	7.50	4.50
(79b)	Jack Knight (large letters)	20.00	10.00	6.00
(80)	Ed Konetchy	15.00	7.50	4.50
(81)	Harry Krause	15.00	7.50	4.50
(82)	Rube Kroh	15.00	7.50	4.50
(83)	Nap Lajoie	60.00	30.00	18.00
(84a)	Frank LaPorte (small letters)	15.00	7.50	4.50
(84b)	Frank LaPorte (large letters)	20.00	10.00	6.00
(85)	Arlie Latham	15.00	7.50	4.50
(86a)	Tommy Leach (small letters)	15.00	7.50	4.50
(86b)	Tommy Leach (large letters)	20.00	10.00	6.00
(87)	Sam Leever	15.00	7.50	4.50
(88)	Lefty Leifield	15.00	7.50	4.50
(89)	Hans Lobert	15.00	7.50	4.50
(90a)	Harry Lord (small letters)	15.00	7.50	4.50
(90b)	Harry Lord (large letters)	20.00	10.00	6.00
(91)	Paddy Livingston	15.00	7.50	4.50
(92)	Nick Maddox	15.00	7.50	4.50
(93)	Sherry Magee	15.00	7.50	4.50
(94)	Rube Marquard	30.00	15.00	9.00
(95a)	Christy Mathewson (small letters)	90.00	45.00	27.00
(95b)	Christy Mathewson (large letters)	110.00	55.00	33.00
(96a)	Al Mattern (small letters)	15.00	7.50	4.50
(96b)	Al Mattern (large letters)	20.00	10.00	6.00
(97)	George McBride	15.00	7.50	4.50
(98a)	John McGraw (small letters)	40.00	20.00	12.00
(98b)	John McGraw (large letters)	60.00	30.00	18.00
(99a)	Larry McLean (small letters)	15.00	7.50	4.50
(99b)	Larry McLean (large letters)	20.00	10.00	6.00
(100)	Harry McIntyre (Cubs)	15.00	7.50	4.50
(101a)	Matty McIntyre (White Sox, small letters)	15.00	7.50	4.50
(101b)	Matty McIntyre (White Sox, large letters)	20.00	10.00	6.00
(102)	Fred Merkle	15.00	7.50	4.50
(103)	Chief Meyers	15.00	7.50	4.50
(104)	Clyde Milan	15.00	7.50	4.50
(105)	Dots Miller	15.00	7.50	4.50
(106)	Mike Mitchell	15.00	7.50	4.50
(107)	Pat Moran	15.00	7.50	4.50
(108a)	George Mullen (Mullin) (small letters)	15.00	7.50	4.50
(108b)	George Mullen (Mullin) (large letters)	20.00	10.00	6.00
(109)	Danny Murphy	15.00	7.50	4.50
(110a)	Red Murray (small letters)	20.00	10.00	6.00
(110b)	Red Murray (large letters)	15.00	7.50	4.50
(111)	Tom Needham	35.00	17.50	10.50
(112a)	Rebel Oakes (small letters)	15.00	7.50	4.50
(112b)	Rebel Oakes (large letters)	20.00	10.00	6.00
(113)	Rube Oldring	15.00	7.50	4.50
(114)	Charley O'Leary	15.00	7.50	4.50
(115)	Orval Overall	35.00	17.50	10.50
(116)	Fred Parent	15.00	7.50	4.50
(117a)	Dode Paskert (small letters)	15.00	7.50	4.50
(117b)	Dode Paskert (large letters)	20.00	10.00	6.00
(118)	Barney Pelty	15.00	7.50	4.50
(119)	Jake Pfeister	15.00	7.50	4.50
(120)	Eddie Phelps	15.00	7.50	4.50
(121)	Deacon Phillippe	15.00	7.50	4.50
(122)	Jack Quinn	15.00	7.50	4.50
(123)	Ed Reulbach	15.00	7.50	4.50
124	Lew Richie	15.00	7.50	4.50
(125)	Jack Rowan	15.00	7.50	4.50
(126a)	Nap Rucker (small letters)	15.00	7.50	4.50
(126b)	Nap Rucker (large letters)	20.00	10.00	6.00
(127)	Doc Scanlon (Scanlan)	35.00	17.50	10.50
(128)	Germany Schaefer	15.00	7.50	4.50
(129)	Jimmy Scheckard (Sheckard)	15.00	7.50	4.50
(130a)	Boss Schmidt (small letters)	15.00	7.50	4.50
(130b)	Boss Schmidt (large letters)	20.00	10.00	6.00
(131)	Wildfire Schulte	15.00	7.50	4.50
(132)	Hap Smith	15.00	7.50	4.50
(133a)	Tris Speaker (small letters)	50.00	25.00	15.00
(133b)	Tris Speaker (large letters)	70.00	35.00	21.00
(134)	Oscar Stanage	15.00	7.50	4.50
(135)	Harry Steinfeldt	15.00	7.50	4.50
(136)	George Stone	15.00	7.50	4.50
(137a)	George Stoval (Stovall) (small letters)	15.00	7.50	4.50
(137b)	George Stoval (Stovall) (large letters)	20.00	10.00	6.00
(138a)	Gabby Street (small letters)	15.00	7.50	4.50
(138b)	Gabby Street (large letters)	20.00	10.00	6.00
(139)	George Suggs	15.00	7.50	4.50
(140a)	Ira Thomas (small letters)	15.00	7.50	4.50
(140b)	Ira Thomas (large letters)	20.00	10.00	6.00
(141a)	Joe Tinker (small letters)	30.00	15.00	9.00
(141b)	Joe Tinker (large letters)	50.00	25.00	15.00
(142a)	John Titus (small letters)	15.00	7.50	4.50
(142b)	John Titus (large letters)	20.00	10.00	6.00
(143)	Terry Turner	20.00	10.00	6.00
(144)	Heinie Wagner	15.00	7.50	4.50
(145a)	Bobby Wallace (with cap, small letters)	30.00	15.00	9.00
(145b)	Bobby Wallace (with cap, large letters)	50.00	25.00	15.00
(146)	Bobby Wallace (without cap)	30.00	15.00	9.00
(147)	Ed Walsh	30.00	15.00	9.00
(148)	Jack Warhop	35.00	17.50	10.50
(149a)	Zach Wheat (small letters)	30.00	15.00	9.00
(149b)	Zach Wheat (large letters)	50.00	25.00	15.00
(150)	Doc White	15.00	7.50	4.50
(151)	Art Wilson (Giants)	35.00	17.50	10.50
(152)	Owen Wilson (Pirates)	15.00	7.50	4.50
(153)	Hooks Wiltse	15.00	7.50	4.50
(154)	Harry Wolter	15.00	7.50	4.50
(155a)	Cy Young (small letters)	55.00	27.00	16.50
(155b)	Cy Young (large letters)	75.00	37.00	22.00

1930 PM8 Our National Game Pins

This unnumbered 30-pin set issued in the 1930s carries the American Card Catalog designation of PM8 and is known as "Our National Game." The pins, which measure 7/8" in diameter, have a "tab" rather than a pin back. The black-and-white player photo is tinted blue, and the player's name and team are printed in a band near the bottom.

		NR MT	EX	VG
Complete Set (30):		525.00	262.00	157.00
Common Player:		6.00	3.00	1.75
(1)	Wally Berger	6.00	3.00	1.75
(2)	Lou Chiozza	6.00	3.00	1.75
(3)	Joe Cronin	15.00	7.50	4.50
(4)	Frank Crosetti	8.00	4.00	2.50
(5)	Jerome (Dizzy) Dean	25.00	12.50	7.50
(6)	Frank DeMaree	6.00	3.00	1.75
(7)	Joe DiMaggio	90.00	45.00	27.00
(8)	Bob Feller	20.00	10.00	6.00
(9)	Jimmy Foxx	20.00	10.00	6.00
(10)	Charles Gehringer	15.00	7.50	4.50
(11)	Lou Gehrig	90.00	45.00	27.00
(12)	Lefty Gomez	15.00	7.50	4.50
(13)	Hank Greenberg	15.00	7.50	4.50
(14)	Irving (Bump) Hadley	6.00	3.00	1.75
(15)	Leo Hartnett	15.00	7.50	4.50
(16)	Carl Hubbell	15.00	7.50	4.50
(17)	John (Buddy) Lewis	6.00	3.00	1.75
(18)	Gus Mancuso	6.00	3.00	1.75
(19)	Joe McCarthy	15.00	7.50	4.50
(20)	Joe Medwick	15.00	7.50	4.50
(21)	Joe Moore	6.00	3.00	1.75
(22)	Mel Ott	15.00	7.50	4.50
(23)	Jake Powell	6.00	3.00	1.75
(24)	Jimmy Ripple	6.00	3.00	1.75
(25)	Red Ruffing	15.00	7.50	4.50
(26)	Hal Schumacher	6.00	3.00	1.75
(27)	George Selkirk	6.00	3.00	1.75
(28)	"Al" Simmons	15.00	7.50	4.50
(29)	Bill Terry	15.00	7.50	4.50
(30)	Harold Trosky	6.00	3.00	1.75

1956 PM15 Yellow Basepath Pins

These pins were issued circa 1956; the sponsor of this 32-pin set is not indicated. The set, which has been assigned the American Card Catalog designation PM15, is commonly called "Yellow Basepaths" because of the design of the pin, which features a black-and-white player photo set inside a green infield with yellow basepaths. The unnumbered pins measure 7/8" in diameter. The names of Kluszewski and Mathews are misspelled.

		NR MT	EX	VG
Complete Set (32):		2200.	1100.	660.00
Common Player:		25.00	12.50	7.50
(1)	Hank Aaron	175.00	87.00	52.00
(2)	Joe Adcock	40.00	20.00	12.00
(3)	Luis Aparicio	60.00	30.00	18.00
(4)	Richie Ashburn	60.00	30.00	18.00
(5)	Gene Baker	25.00	12.50	7.50
(6)	Ernie Banks	90.00	45.00	27.00
(7)	Yogi Berra	90.00	45.00	27.00
(8)	Bill Bruton	25.00	12.50	7.50
(9)	Larry Doby	35.00	17.50	10.50
(10)	Bob Friend	25.00	12.50	7.50
(11)	Nellie Fox	45.00	22.00	13.50
(12)	Jim Greengrass	25.00	12.50	7.50
(13)	Steve Gromek	25.00	12.50	7.50

(14)	Johnny Groth	25.00	12.50	7.50
(15)	Gil Hodges	75.00	37.00	22.00
(16)	Al Kaline	90.00	45.00	27.00
(17)	Ted Kluzewski (Kluszewski)	50.00	25.00	15.00
(18)	Johnny Logan	25.00	12.50	7.50
(19)	Dale Long	25.00	12.50	7.50
(20)	Mickey Mantle	450.00	225.00	135.00
(21)	Ed Mathews	80.00	40.00	24.00
(22)	Minnie Minoso	35.00	17.50	10.50
(23)	Stan Musial	175.00	87.00	52.00
(24)	Don Newcombe	40.00	20.00	12.00
(25)	Bob Porterfield	25.00	12.50	7.50
(26)	Pee Wee Reese	75.00	37.00	22.00
(27)	Robin Roberts	50.00	25.00	15.00
(28)	Red Schoendienst	40.00	20.00	12.00
(29)	Duke Snider	100.00	50.00	30.00
(30)	Vern Stephens	25.00	12.50	7.50
(31)	Gene Woodling	25.00	12.50	7.50
(32)	Gus Zernial	25.00	12.50	7.50

1932 PR2 Orbit Gum Pins Numbered

Issued circa 1932, this skip-numbered set of small (13/16" in diameter) pins was produced by Orbit Gum and carries the Amerian Card Catalog designation of PR2. A player lithograph is set against a green background with the player's name and team printed on a strip of yellow below. The pin number is at the very bottom.

		NR MT	EX	VG
Complete Set:		1200.	500.00	300.00
Common Player:		15.00	7.50	4.50
1	Ivy Andrews	15.00	7.50	4.50
2	Carl Reynolds	15.00	7.50	4.50
3	Riggs Stephenson	18.00	9.00	5.50
4	Lon Warneke	15.00	7.50	4.50
5	Frank Grube	15.00	7.50	4.50
6	Kiki Cuyler	30.00	15.00	9.00
7	Marty McManus	15.00	7.50	4.50
8	Lefty Clark	15.00	7.50	4.50
9	George Blaeholder	15.00	7.50	4.50
10	Willie Kamm	15.00	7.50	4.50
11	Jimmy Dykes	18.00	9.00	5.50
12	Earl Averill	30.00	15.00	9.00
13	Pat Malone	15.00	7.50	4.50
14	Dizzy Dean	95.00	47.00	28.00
15	Dick Bartell	15.00	7.50	4.50
16	Guy Bush	15.00	7.50	4.50
17	Bud Tinning	15.00	7.50	4.50
18	Jimmy Foxx	50.00	25.00	15.00
19	Mule Haas	15.00	7.50	4.50
20	Lew Fonseca	15.00	7.50	4.50
21	Pepper Martin	25.00	12.50	7.50
22	Phil Collins	15.00	7.50	4.50
23	Bill Cissell	15.00	7.50	4.50
24	Bump Hadley	15.00	7.50	4.50
25	Smead Jolley	15.00	7.50	4.50
26	Burleigh Grimes	30.00	15.00	9.00
27	Dale Alexander	15.00	7.50	4.50
28	Mickey Cochrane	35.00	17.50	10.50
29	Mel Harder	15.00	7.50	4.50
30	Mark Koenig	15.00	7.50	4.50
31a	Lefty O'Doul (Dodgers)	45.00	22.00	13.50
31b	Lefty O'Doul (Giants)	25.00	12.50	7.50
32a	Woody English (with bat)	15.00	7.50	4.50
32b	Woody English (without bat)	45.00	22.00	13.50
33a	Billy Jurges (with bat)	15.00	7.50	4.50
33b	Billy Jurges (without bat)	45.00	22.00	13.50
34	Bruce Campbell	15.00	7.50	4.50
35	Joe Vosmik	15.00	7.50	4.50
36	Dick Porter	15.00	7.50	4.50
37	Charlie Grimm	18.00	9.00	5.50
38	George Earnshaw	15.00	7.50	4.50
39	Al Simmons	30.00	15.00	9.00
40	Red Lucas	15.00	7.50	4.50
51	Wally Berger	15.00	7.50	4.50
52	Jim Levey	15.00	7.50	4.50
58	Ernie Lombardi	30.00	15.00	9.00
64	Jack Burns	15.00	7.50	4.50
67	Billy Herman	30.00	15.00	9.00
72	Bill Hallahan	15.00	7.50	4.50
92	Don Brennan	15.00	7.50	4.50
96	Sam Byrd	15.00	7.50	4.50
99	Ben Chapman	15.00	7.50	4.50
103	John Allen	15.00	7.50	4.50
107	Tony Lazzeri	30.00	15.00	9.00
111	Earl Combs (Earle)	30.00	15.00	9.00
116	Joe Sewell	30.00	15.00	9.00
120	Vernon Gomez	35.00	17.50	10.50

1932 PR3 Orbit Gum Pins Unnumbered

This set, issued by Orbit Gum circa 1932, has the American Card Catalog designation PR3. The pins are identical to the PR2 set, except they are unnumbered.

		NR MT	EX	VG
Complete Set (60):		2400.	900.00	540.00
Common Player:		30.00	15.00	9.00
(1)	Dale Alexander	30.00	15.00	9.00
(2)	Ivy Andrews	30.00	15.00	9.00
(3)	Earl Averill	60.00	30.00	18.00
(4)	Dick Bartell	30.00	15.00	9.00
(5)	Wally Berger	30.00	15.00	9.00
(6)	George Blaeholder	30.00	15.00	9.00
(7)	Jack Burns	30.00	15.00	9.00
(8)	Guy Bush	30.00	15.00	9.00
(9)	Bruce Campbell	30.00	15.00	9.00
(10)	Bill Cissell	30.00	15.00	9.00
(11)	Lefty Clark	30.00	15.00	9.00
(12)	Mickey Cochrane	75.00	37.00	22.00
(13)	Phil Collins	30.00	15.00	9.00
(14)	Kiki Cuyler	60.00	30.00	18.00
(15)	Dizzy Dean	150.00	75.00	45.00
(16)	Jimmy Dykes	40.00	20.00	12.00
(17)	George Earnshaw	30.00	15.00	9.00
(18)	Woody English	30.00	15.00	9.00
(19)	Lew Fonseca	30.00	15.00	9.00
(20)	Jimmy Foxx	90.00	45.00	27.00
(21)	Burleigh Grimes	60.00	30.00	18.00
(22)	Charlie Grimm	40.00	20.00	12.00
(23)	Lefty Grove	90.00	45.00	27.00
(24)	Frank Grube	30.00	15.00	9.00
(25)	Mule Haas	30.00	15.00	9.00
(26)	Bump Hadley	30.00	15.00	9.00
(27)	Chick Hafey	60.00	30.00	18.00
(28)	Jesse Haines	60.00	30.00	18.00
(29)	Bill Hallahan	30.00	15.00	9.00
(30)	Mel Harder	30.00	15.00	9.00
(31)	Gabby Hartnett	60.00	30.00	18.00
(32)	Babe Herman	40.00	20.00	12.00
(33)	Billy Herman	60.00	30.00	18.00
(34)	Rogers Hornsby	100.00	50.00	30.00
(35)	Roy Johnson	30.00	15.00	9.00
(36)	Smead Jolley	30.00	15.00	9.00
(37)	Billy Jurges	30.00	15.00	9.00
(38)	Willie Kamm	30.00	15.00	9.00
(39)	Mark Koenig	30.00	15.00	9.00
(40)	Jim Levey	30.00	15.00	9.00
(41)	Ernie Lombardi	60.00	30.00	18.00
(42)	Red Lucas	30.00	15.00	9.00
(43)	Ted Lyons	60.00	30.00	18.00
(44)	Connie Mack	80.00	40.00	24.00
(45)	Pat Malone	30.00	15.00	9.00
(46)	Pepper Martin	40.00	20.00	12.00
(47)	Marty McManus	30.00	15.00	9.00
(48)	Lefty O'Doul	40.00	20.00	12.00
(49)	Dick Porter	30.00	15.00	9.00
(50)	Carl Reynolds	30.00	15.00	9.00
(51)	Charlie Root	30.00	15.00	9.00
(52)	Bob Seeds	30.00	15.00	9.00
(53)	Al Simmons	60.00	30.00	18.00
(54)	Riggs Stephenson	35.00	17.50	10.50
(55)	Bud Tinning	30.00	15.00	9.00
(56)	Joe Vosmik	30.00	15.00	9.00
(57)	Rube Walberg	30.00	15.00	9.00
(58)	Paul Waner	60.00	30.00	18.00
(59)	Lon Warneke	30.00	15.00	9.00
(60)	Pinky Whitney	30.00	15.00	9.00

1930 PR4 Cracker Jack Pins

Although no manufacturer is indicated on the pins themselves, this 25-player set was apparently issued by Cracker Jack in the early 1930s. Each pin measures 13/16" in diameter and features a line drawing of a player portrait. The unnumbered pins are printed in blue and gray with a background of yellow. The player's name appears below.

		NR MT	EX	VG
Complete Set (25):		700.00	350.00	210.00
Common Player:		15.00	7.50	4.50
(1)	Charles Berry	15.00	7.50	4.50
(2)	Bill Cissell	15.00	7.50	4.50
(3)	KiKi Cuyler	25.00	12.50	7.50
(4)	Dizzy Dean	40.00	20.00	12.00
(5)	Wesley Ferrell	15.00	7.50	4.50
(6)	Frank Frisch	25.00	12.50	7.50
(7)	Lou Gehrig	100.00	50.00	30.00
(8)	Vernon Gomez	25.00	12.50	7.50
(9)	Goose Goslin	25.00	12.50	7.50
(10)	George Grantham	15.00	7.50	4.50
(11)	Charley Grimm	15.00	7.50	4.50
(12)	Lefty Grove	30.00	15.00	9.00
(13)	Gabby Hartnett	25.00	12.50	7.50
(14)	Travis Jackson	25.00	12.50	7.50
(15)	Tony Lazzeri	25.00	12.50	7.50
(16)	Ted Lyons	25.00	12.50	7.50
(17)	Rabbit Maranville	25.00	12.50	7.50
(18)	Carl Reynolds	15.00	7.50	4.50
(19)	Charles Ruffing	25.00	12.50	7.50
(20)	Al Simmons	25.00	12.50	7.50
(21)	Gus Suhr	15.00	7.50	4.50
(22)	Bill Terry	25.00	12.50	7.50
(23)	Dazzy Vance	25.00	12.50	7.50
(24)	Paul Waner	25.00	12.50	7.50
(25)	Lon Warneke	15.00	7.50	4.50

1933 PX3 Double Header Pins

Issued by Gum Inc. circa 1933, this unnumbered set consists of 43 metal discs approximately 1-1/4" in diameter. The front of the pin lists the player's name and team beneath his picture. The numbers "1" or "2" also appear inside a small circle at the bottom of the disc, and the wrapper advised collectors to "put 1 and 2 together and make a double header." The set is designated as PX3 in the American Card Catalog.

		NR MT	EX	VG
Complete Set (43):		900.00	450.00	270.00
Common Player:		25.00	12.50	7.50
(1)	Sparky Adams	25.00	12.50	7.50
(2)	Dale Alexander	25.00	12.50	7.50
(3)	Earl Averill	45.00	22.00	13.50
(4)	Dick Bartell	25.00	12.50	7.50
(5)	Walter Berger	25.00	12.50	7.50
(6)	Jim Bottomley	45.00	22.00	13.50
(7)	Lefty Brandt	25.00	12.50	7.50
(8)	Owen Carroll	25.00	12.50	7.50
(9)	Lefty Clark	25.00	12.50	7.50
(10)	Mickey Cochrane	50.00	25.00	15.00
(11)	Joe Cronin	45.00	22.00	13.50
(12)	Jimmy Dykes	25.00	12.50	7.50
(13)	George Earnshaw	25.00	12.50	7.50
(14)	Wes Ferrell	25.00	12.50	7.50
(15)	Neal Finn	25.00	12.50	7.50
(16)	Lew Fonseca	25.00	12.50	7.50
(17)	Jimmy Foxx	90.00	45.00	27.00
(18)	Frankie Frisch	50.00	25.00	15.00
(19)	Chick Fullis	25.00	12.50	7.50
(20)	Charley Gehringer	45.00	22.00	13.50
(21)	Goose Goslin	45.00	22.00	13.50
(22)	Johnny Hodapp	25.00	12.50	7.50
(23)	Frank Hogan	25.00	12.50	7.50
(24)	Si Johnson	25.00	12.50	7.50
(25)	Joe Judge	25.00	12.50	7.50
(26)	Chuck Klein	45.00	22.00	13.50
(27)	Al Lopez	45.00	22.00	13.50
(28)	Ray Lucas	25.00	12.50	7.50
(29)	Red Lucas	25.00	12.50	7.50
(30)	Ted Lyons	45.00	22.00	13.50
(31)	Firpo Marberry	25.00	12.50	7.50
(32)	Oscar Melillo	25.00	12.50	7.50
(33)	Lefty O'Doul	30.00	15.00	9.00
(34)	George Pipgras	25.00	12.50	7.50
(35)	Flint Rhem	25.00	12.50	7.50
(36)	Sam Rice	45.00	22.00	13.50
(37)	Muddy Ruel	25.00	12.50	7.50
(38)	Harry Seibold	25.00	12.50	7.50
(39)	Al Simmons	45.00	22.00	13.50
(40)	Joe Vosmik	25.00	12.50	7.50
(41)	Gerald Walker	25.00	12.50	7.50
(42)	Pinky Whitney	25.00	12.50	7.50
(43)	Hack Wilson	45.00	22.00	13.50

1909 PX7 Domino Discs

Domino Discs, distributed by Sweet Caporal Cigarettes from 1909 to 1912, are among the more obscure 20th-century tobacco issues. Although the disc set contains many of the same players - some even pictured in the same poses - as the Sweet Caporal P2 pin set, the discs have always lagged behind the pins in collector appeal. The Domino Discs, so called because each disc has a large, white domino printed on the back, measure approximately 1-1/8" in diameter and are made of thin card cardboard surrounded by a metal rim. The fronts of the discs contain a player portrait set against a background of either red, green or blue. The words "Sweet Caporal Cigarettes" appear on the front along with the player's last name and team. There are 135 different major leaguers featured in the set, each pictured in two different poses for a total of 270 different subjects. Also known to exist as part of the set is a "game disc" which pictures a "generic" player and contains the words "Home Team" against a red background on one side and "Visiting Team" with a green background on the reverse. Because each of the 135 players in the set can theoretically be found with three different background colors and with varying numbers of dots on the dominoes, there is almost an impossible number of variations available. Collectors, however, generally collect the discs without regard to background color or domino arrangement. The Domino Disc set was assigned the designation PX7 in the American Card Catalog.

		NR MT	EX	VG
Complete Set:		5500.	2700.	1650.
Common Player:		25.00	12.50	7.50
(1)	Red Ames	25.00	12.50	7.50
(2)	Jimmy Archer	25.00	12.50	7.50
(3)	Jimmy Austin	25.00	12.50	7.50
(4)	Home Run Baker	60.00	30.00	18.00
(5)	Neal Ball	25.00	12.50	7.50
(6)	Cy Barger	25.00	12.50	7.50
(7)	Jack Barry	25.00	12.50	7.50
(8)	Johnny Bates	25.00	12.50	7.50
(9)	Beals Becker	25.00	12.50	7.50
(10)	George Bell	25.00	12.50	7.50
(11)	Chief Bender	60.00	30.00	18.00
(12)	Bill Bergen	25.00	12.50	7.50
(13)	Bob Bescher	25.00	12.50	7.50
(14)	Joe Birmingham	25.00	12.50	7.50
(15)	Roger Bresnahan	60.00	30.00	18.00
(16)	Al Bridwell	25.00	12.50	7.50
(17)	Mordecai Brown	60.00	30.00	18.00
(18)	Bobby Byrne	25.00	12.50	7.50
(19)	Nixey Callahan	25.00	12.50	7.50
(20)	Howie Camnitz	25.00	12.50	7.50
(21)	Bill Carrigan	25.00	12.50	7.50
(22)	Frank Chance	60.00	30.00	18.00
(23)	Hal Chase	40.00	20.00	12.00
(24)	Ed Cicotte	40.00	20.00	12.00
(25)	Fred Clarke	60.00	30.00	18.00
(26a)	Ty Cobb ("D" on cap)	600.00	300.00	180.00
(26b)	Ty Cobb (no "D" on cap)	600.00	300.00	180.00
(27)	Eddie Collins	60.00	30.00	18.00
(28)	Doc Crandall	25.00	12.50	7.50
(29)	Birdie Cree	25.00	12.50	7.50
(30)	Bill Dahlen	25.00	12.50	7.50
(31)	Jim Delahanty	25.00	12.50	7.50
(32)	Art Devlin	25.00	12.50	7.50
(33)	Josh Devore	25.00	12.50	7.50
(34)	Red Dooin	25.00	12.50	7.50
(35)	Mickey Doolan	25.00	12.50	7.50
(36)	Patsy Dougherty	25.00	12.50	7.50
(37)	Tom Downey	25.00	12.50	7.50
(38)	Larry Doyle	25.00	12.50	7.50
(39)	Louis Drucke	25.00	12.50	7.50
(40)	Clyde Engle	25.00	12.50	7.50
(41)	Tex Erwin	25.00	12.50	7.50
(42)	Steve Evans	25.00	12.50	7.50
(43)	Johnny Evers	60.00	30.00	18.00
(44)	Cecil Ferguson	25.00	12.50	7.50
(45)	Russ Ford	25.00	12.50	7.50
(46)	Art Fromme	25.00	12.50	7.50
(47)	Harry Gaspar	25.00	12.50	7.50
(48)	George Gibson	25.00	12.50	7.50
(49)	Eddie Grant	35.00	17.50	10.50
(50)	Clark Griffith	60.00	30.00	18.00
(51)	Bob Groom	25.00	12.50	7.50
(52)	Bob Harmon	25.00	12.50	7.50
(53)	Topsy Hartsel	25.00	12.50	7.50
(54)	Arnold Hauser	25.00	12.50	7.50
(55)	Dick Hoblitzell	25.00	12.50	7.50
(56)	Danny Hoffman	25.00	12.50	7.50
(57)	Miller Huggins	60.00	30.00	18.00
(58)	John Hummel	25.00	12.50	7.50
(59)	Hugh Jennings	60.00	30.00	18.00
(60)	Walter Johnson	300.00	150.00	90.00
(61)	Ed Karger	25.00	12.50	7.50
(62a)	Jack Knight (Yankees)	25.00	12.50	7.50
(62b)	Jack Knight (Senators)	25.00	12.50	7.50
(63)	Ed Konetchy	25.00	12.50	7.50
(64)	Harry Krause	25.00	12.50	7.50
(65)	Frank LaPorte	25.00	12.50	7.50
(66)	Nap Lajoie	150.00	75.00	45.00
(67)	Tommy Leach	25.00	12.50	7.50
(68)	Sam Leever	25.00	12.50	7.50
(69)	Lefty Leifield	25.00	12.50	7.50
(70)	Paddy Livingston	25.00	12.50	7.50
(71)	Hans Lobert	25.00	12.50	7.50
(72)	Harry Lord	25.00	12.50	7.50
(73)	Nick Maddox	25.00	12.50	7.50
(74)	Sherry Magee	25.00	12.50	7.50
(75)	Rube Marquard	60.00	30.00	18.00
(76)	Christy Mathewson	300.00	150.00	90.00
(77)	Al Mattern	25.00	12.50	7.50
(78)	George McBride	25.00	12.50	7.50
(79)	John McGraw	60.00	30.00	18.00
(80)	Harry McIntire (McIntyre)	25.00	12.50	7.50
(81)	Matty McIntyre	25.00	12.50	7.50
(82)	Larry McLean	25.00	12.50	7.50
(83)	Fred Merkle	25.00	12.50	7.50
(84)	Chief Meyers	25.00	12.50	7.50
(85)	Clyde Milan	25.00	12.50	7.50
(86)	Dots Miller	25.00	12.50	7.50
(87)	Mike Mitchell	25.00	12.50	7.50
(88a)	Pat Moran (Cubs)	25.00	12.50	7.50
(88b)	Pat Moran (Phillies)	25.00	12.50	7.50
(89)	George Mullen (Mullin)	25.00	12.50	7.50
(90)	Danny Murphy	25.00	12.50	7.50
(91)	Red Murray	25.00	12.50	7.50
(92)	Tom Needham	25.00	12.50	7.50
(93)	Rebel Oakes	25.00	12.50	7.50
(94)	Rube Oldring	25.00	12.50	7.50
(95)	Fred Parent	25.00	12.50	7.50
(96)	Dode Paskert	25.00	12.50	7.50
(97)	Barney Pelty	25.00	12.50	7.50
(98)	Eddie Phelps	25.00	12.50	7.50
(99)	Deacon Phillippe	25.00	12.50	7.50
(100)	Jack Quinn	25.00	12.50	7.50
(101)	Ed Reulbach	25.00	12.50	7.50
(102)	Lew Richie	25.00	12.50	7.50
(103)	Jack Rowan	25.00	12.50	7.50
(104)	Nap Rucker	25.00	12.50	7.50
(105a)	Doc Scanlon (Scanlan) (Superbas)	25.00	12.50	7.50
(105b)	Doc Scanlon (Scanlan) (Phillies)	25.00	12.50	7.50
(106)	Germany Schaefer	25.00	12.50	7.50
(107)	Boss Schmidt	25.00	12.50	7.50
(108)	Wildfire Schulte	25.00	12.50	7.50
(109)	Jimmy Sheckard	25.00	12.50	7.50
(110)	Hap Smith	25.00	12.50	7.50
(111)	Tris Speaker	100.00	50.00	30.00
(112)	Harry Stovall	25.00	12.50	7.50
(113a)	Gabby Street (Senators)	25.00	12.50	7.50
(113b)	Gabby Street (Yankees)	25.00	12.50	7.50
(114)	George Suggs	25.00	12.50	7.50
(115)	Ira Thomas	25.00	12.50	7.50
(116)	Joe Tinker	60.00	30.00	18.00
(117)	John Titus	25.00	12.50	7.50
(118)	Terry Turner	25.00	12.50	7.50
(119)	Heinie Wagner	25.00	12.50	7.50
(120)	Bobby Wallace	60.00	30.00	18.00
(121)	Ed Walsh	60.00	30.00	18.00
(122)	Jack Warhop	25.00	12.50	7.50
(123)	Zach Wheat	60.00	30.00	18.00
(124)	Doc White	25.00	12.50	7.50
(125a)	Art Wilson (dark cap, Pirates)	25.00	12.50	7.50
(125b)	Art Wilson (dark cap, Giants)	25.00	12.50	7.50
(126a)	Owen Wilson (white cap, Giants)	25.00	12.50	7.50
(126b)	Owen Wilson (white cap, Pirates)	25.00	12.50	7.50
(127)	Hooks Wiltse	25.00	12.50	7.50
(128)	Harry Wolter	25.00	12.50	7.50
(129)	Cy Young	250.00	125.00	75.00

1992 Paccar/Alrak Ken Griffey Jr.

Ken Griffey Jr. was the subject of a 1992, five-card set of plastic trading cards issued by ALRAK Enterprises and PACCAR Automotive Inc. The cards were available at PACCAR retail outlets in the West. Each purchaser was limited to three cards purchased per store visit.

		MT	NR MT	EX
Complete Set (5):		10.00	7.50	4.00
(1)	Ken Griffey Jr. (Golden Moments)	2.00	1.50	.80
(2)	Ken Griffey Jr. (Golden Moments)	2.00	1.50	.80
(3)	Ken Griffey Jr. (Golden Moments)	2.00	1.50	.80
(4)	Ken Griffey Jr. (Golden Moments)	2.00	1.50	.80
(5)	Ken Griffey Jr. (Golden Moments)	2.00	1.50	.80

1988 Pacific Trading Cards Baseball Legends

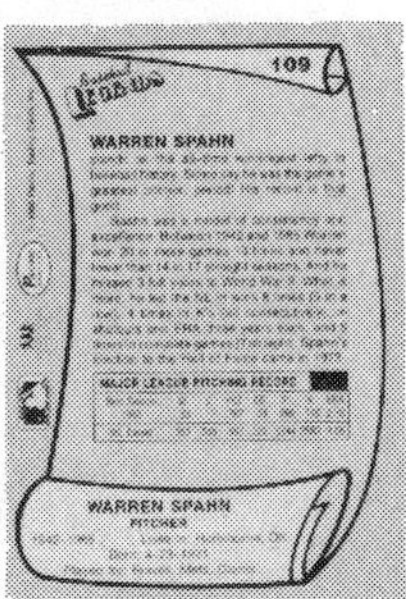

Pacific Trading Cards rounded up 110 photos of the greatest baseball players from the past 40 years for its 1988 "Baseball Legends" set. All players featured in the set are (or were) members of the Major League Baseball Alumni Association. Card fronts feature silver outer borders and large, clear full-color player photos outlined in black against colorful banner-style inner borders of red, blue, green, orange or gold. The player's name and position are printed in white letters on the lower portion of the banner. Card backs are numbered and carry the Baseball Legends logo, player biography, major league career stats, and personal information. The cards were sold in boxed sets via candy wholesalers, with emphasis on Midwest and New England states. Complete collector sets in clear plastic boxes were made available via dealers or directly from Pacific Trading Cards. Pacific

		MT	NR MT	EX
Complete Set (110):		12.00	9.00	4.75
Common Player:		.06	.05	.02
1	Hank Aaron	.50	.40	.20
2	Red Shoendienst (Schoendienst)	.10	.08	.04
3	Brooks Robinson	.30	.25	.12
4	Luke Appling	.15	.11	.06
5	Gene Woodling	.06	.05	.02
6	Stan Musial	.50	.40	.20
7	Mickey Mantle	1.00	.70	.40
8	Richie Ashburn	.10	.08	.04
9	Ralph Kiner	.20	.15	.08
10	Phil Rizzuto	.20	.15	.08
11	Harvey Haddix	.06	.05	.02
12	Ken Boyer	.10	.08	.04
13	Clete Boyer	.06	.05	.02
14	Ken Harrelson	.06	.05	.02
15	Robin Roberts	.20	.15	.08
16	Catfish Hunter	.20	.15	.08
17	Frank Howard	.10	.08	.04
18	Jim Perry	.06	.05	.02
19	Elston Howard	.10	.08	.04
20	Jim Bouton	.10	.08	.04
21	Pee Wee Reese	.25	.20	.10
22	Mel Stottlemyer (Stottlemyre)	.10	.08	.04
23	Hank Sauer	.06	.05	.02
24	Willie Mays	.50	.40	.20
25	Tom Tresh	.06	.05	.02
26	Roy Sievers	.06	.05	.02
27	Leo Durocher	.15	.11	.06
28	Al Dark	.10	.08	.04
29	Tony Kubek	.15	.11	.06
30	Johnny Vander Meer	.10	.08	.04
31	Joe Adcock	.10	.08	.04
32	Bob Lemon	.20	.15	.08
33	Don Newcombe	.15	.11	.06
34	Thurman Munson	.20	.15	.08
35	Earl Battey	.06	.05	.02
36	Ernie Banks	.30	.25	.12
37	Matty Alou	.06	.05	.02
38	Dave McNally	.06	.05	.02
39	Mickey Lolich	.10	.08	.04
40	Jackie Robinson	.50	.40	.20
41	Allie Reynolds	.15	.11	.06
42	Don Larson (Larsen)	.10	.08	.04
43	Fergie Jenkins	.15	.11	.06
44	Jim Gilliam	.10	.08	.04
45	Bobby Thomson	.10	.08	.04
46	Sparky Anderson	.10	.08	.04
47	Roy Campanella	.30	.25	.12
48	Marv Throneberry	.10	.08	.04
49	Bill Virdon	.06	.05	.02
50	Ted Williams	.50	.40	.20
51	Minnie Minoso	.10	.08	.04
52	Bob Turley	.10	.08	.04
53	Yogi Berra	.30	.25	.12
54	Juan Marichal	.20	.15	.08
55	Duke Snider	.30	.25	.12
56	Harvey Kuenn	.10	.08	.04
57	Nellie Fox	.15	.11	.06
58	Felipe Alou	.06	.05	.02
59	Tony Oliva	.10	.08	.04
60	Bill Mazeroski	.10	.08	.04
61	Bobby Shantz	.10	.08	.04
62	Mark Fidrych	.06	.05	.02
63	Johnny Mize	.15	.11	.06
64	Ralph Terry	.06	.05	.02
65	Gus Bell	.06	.05	.02
66	Jerry Koosman	.10	.08	.04

67	Mike McCormick	.06	.05	.02
68	Lou Burdette	.10	.08	.04
69	George Kell	.15	.11	.06
70	Vic Raschi	.10	.08	.04
71	Chuck Connors	.20	.15	.08
72	Ted Kluszewski	.10	.08	.04
73	Bobby Doerr	.15	.11	.06
74	Bobby Richardson	.15	.11	.06
75	Carl Erskine	.15	.11	.06
76	Hoyt Wilhelm	.20	.15	.08
77	Bob Purkey	.06	.05	.02
78	Bob Friend	.06	.05	.02
79	Monte Irvin	.15	.11	.06
80	Jim Longborg (Lonborg)	.06	.05	.02
81	Wally Moon	.06	.05	.02
82	Moose Skowron	.10	.08	.04
83	Tommy Davis	.10	.08	.04
84	Enos Slaughter	.20	.15	.08
85	Sal Maglie	.10	.08	.04
86	Harmon Killebrew	.25	.20	.10
87	Gil Hodges	.25	.20	.10
88	Jim Kaat	.10	.08	.04
89	Roger Maris	.30	.25	.12
90	Billy Williams	.20	.15	.08
91	Luis Aparicio	.15	.11	.06
92	Jim Bunning	.15	.11	.06
93	Bill Freehan	.06	.05	.02
94	Orlando Cepeda	.10	.08	.04
95	Early Wynn	.20	.15	.08
96	Tug McGraw	.10	.08	.04
97	Ron Santo	.10	.08	.04
98	Del Crandall	.06	.05	.02
99	Sal Bando	.06	.05	.02
100	Joe DiMaggio	.70	.50	.30
101	Bob Feller	.30	.25	.12
102	Larry Doby	.15	.11	.06
103	Rollie Fingers	.15	.11	.06
104	Al Kaline	.30	.25	.12
105	Johnny Podres	.10	.08	.04
106	Lou Boudreau	.15	.11	.06
107	Zoilo Versalles	.06	.05	.02
108	Dick Groat	.06	.05	.02
109	Warren Spahn	.25	.20	.10
110	Johnny Bench	.40	.30	.15

1988 Pacific Trading Cards "Eight Men Out"

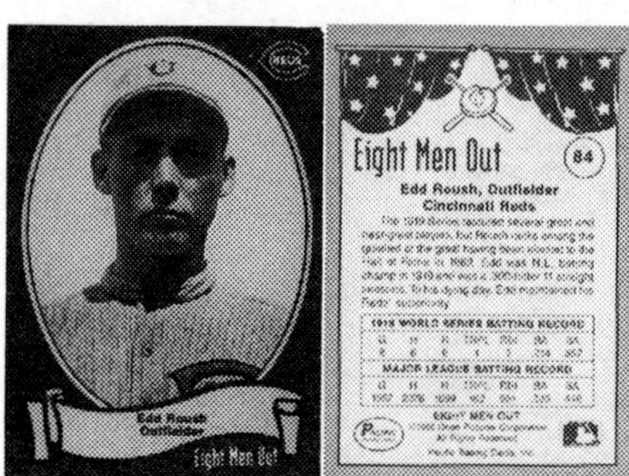

Trading Cards produced this 110-card set featuring actual players from the 1919 World Series (#78-110) and actors from Orion's movie (#1-77) "Eight Men Out." Card fronts feature a burgundy outer border and thin silver inner border framing the player photos (actor photos are full-color, vintage photos are sepia-toned). A silver banner beneath the photo, outlined in black, bears a brief photo caption. The Eight Men Out logo appears lower right. The card backs are printed in burgundy and black on white, with a gray border, and include the actor/player's name and a paragraph-style biography or description of the action. Pacific Trading Cards' "Eight Men Out" set was distributed by hobby stores nationwide in 10-card wax packs and in complete boxed sets.

		MT	NR MT	EX
Complete Set (110):		9.00	6.75	3.50
Common Player:		.03	.02	.01
1	We're going to see the Sox!	.03	.02	.01
2	White Sox Win the Pennant!	.03	.02	.01
3	The Series	.03	.02	.01
4	1919 Chicago White Sox	.03	.02	.01
5	The Black Sox Scandal	.03	.02	.01
6	Eddie Cicotte - 29-7 in 1919	.03	.02	.01
7	"Buck's there faverit"	.03	.02	.01
8	Eddie Collins	.03	.02	.01
9	Michael Rooker as Arnold "Chick" Gandil	.03	.02	.01
10	Charlie Sheen as Oscar "Happy" Felsch	.03	.02	.01
11	James Read as Claude "Lefty" Williams	.03	.02	.01
12	John Cusack as George Buck Weaver	.03	.02	.01
13	D.B. Sweeney as "Shoeless" Joe Jackson	.03	.02	.01
14	David Strathairn as Eddie Cicotte	.03	.02	.01
15	Perry Lang as Fred McMullin	.03	.02	.01
16	Don Harvey as Charles "Swede" Risberg	.03	.02	.01
17	The Gamblers - Burns and Maharg	.03	.02	.01
18	Sleepy Bill Burns	.03	.02	.01
19	The Key is Cicotte	.03	.02	.01
20	C'moan, Betsy	.03	.02	.01
21	The Fix	.03	.02	.01
22	Chick approaches Cicotte	.03	.02	.01
23	"Kid" Gleason	.03	.02	.01
24	Charles Comiskey - Owner	.03	.02	.01
25	Arnold "Chick" Gandil - First Baseman	.03	.02	.01
26	Charles "Swede" Risberg	.03	.02	.01
27	Sport Sullivan	.03	.02	.01
28	Abe Attell/Arnold Rothstein	.03	.02	.01
29	Hugh Fullerton - Sports Writer	.03	.02	.01
30	Ring Lardner - Sports Writer	.03	.02	.01
31	"Shoeless" Joe's batting eye	.03	.02	.01
32	"Shoeless" Joe	.03	.02	.01
33	Buck can't sleep	.03	.02	.01
34	George "Buck" Weaver	.03	.02	.01
35	Hugh and Ring confront Kid	.03	.02	.01
36	Joe doesn't want to play.	.03	.02	.01
37	"Shoeless" Joe Jackson	.03	.02	.01
38	"Sore Arm, Cicotte", "Old Man Cicotte"	.03	.02	.01
39	The fix is on.	.03	.02	.01
40	Buck's playing to win.	.03	.02	.01
41	Hap makes a great catch.	.03	.02	.01
42	Hugh and Ring suspect!	.03	.02	.01
43	Ray gets things going.	.03	.02	.01
44	Lefty loses Game Two	.03	.02	.01
45	Lefty crosses up Ray Schalk's signals.	.03	.02	.01
46	Chick's RBI wins Game Three	.03	.02	.01
47	Dickie Kerr Wins Game Three	.03	.02	.01
48	Chick leaves Buck stranded at third.	.03	.02	.01
49	Williams loses Game Five	.03	.02	.01
50	Ray Schalk	.03	.02	.01
51	Schalk blocks the plate.	.03	.02	.01
52	Schalk is thrown out.	.03	.02	.01
53	Chicago stick ball game.	.03	.02	.01
54	I'm forever blowing ballgames.	.03	.02	.01
55	Felsch Scores Jackson	.03	.02	.01
56	Kerr wins Game Six.	.03	.02	.01
57	Where's the money?	.03	.02	.01
58	Cicotte wins Game Seven.	.03	.02	.01
59	Kid watches Eddie.	.03	.02	.01
60	Lefty is threatened	.03	.02	.01
61	James! Get your arm ready! Fast!	.03	.02	.01
62	"Shoeless" Joe's Home Run	.03	.02	.01
63	Buck played his best	.03	.02	.01
64	Hugh exposes the fix.	.03	.02	.01
65	Sign the petition	.03	.02	.01
66	Baseball owners hire a commissioner	.03	.02	.01
67	Judge Kenesaw Mountain Landis	.03	.02	.01
68	Grand jury summoned	.03	.02	.01
69	Say it ain't so, Joe!	.03	.02	.01
70	"The Swede's a Hard Guy"	.03	.02	.01
71	Buck loves the game.	.03	.02	.01
72	The trial.	.03	.02	.01
73	Kid Gleason take the stand.	.03	.02	.01
74	The Verdict	.03	.02	.01
75	Eight Men Out	.03	.02	.01
76	Oscar "Happy" Felsch	.03	.02	.01
77	Who's Joe Jackson?	.03	.02	.01
78	Ban Johnson - President	.03	.02	.01
79	Judge Landis - Commissioner of Baseball	.03	.02	.01
80	Charles A. Comiskey - Owner	.03	.02	.01
81	Heinie Groh - Third Baseman	.03	.02	.01
82	Slim Sallee - Pitcher	.03	.02	.01
83	Dutch Ruether - Pitcher	.03	.02	.01
84	Edd Roush - Outfielder	.03	.02	.01
85	Morrie Rath - Second Baseman	.03	.02	.01
86	Bill Rariden - Catcher	.03	.02	.01
87	Jimmy Ring - Pitcher	.03	.02	.01
88	Greasy Neale - Outfielder	.03	.02	.01
89	Pat Moran - Manager	.03	.02	.01
90	Adolfo Luque - Pitcher	.03	.02	.01
91	Larry Kopf - Shortstop	.03	.02	.01
92	Ray Fisher - Pitcher	.03	.02	.01
93	Hod Eller - Pitcher	.03	.02	.01
94	Pat Duncan - Outfielder	.03	.02	.01
95	Jake Daubert - First Baseman	.03	.02	.01
96	Red Faber - Pitcher	.03	.02	.01
97	Dickie Kerr - Pitcher	.03	.02	.01
98	Shano Collins - Outfielder	.03	.02	.01
99	Eddie Collins - Second Baseman	.03	.02	.01
100	Ray Schalk - Catcher	.03	.02	.01
101	Nemo Liebold - Outfielder	.03	.02	.01
102	Kid Gleason - Manager	.03	.02	.01
103	Swede Risberg - Shortstop	.03	.02	.01
104	Eddie Cicotte - Pitcher	.03	.02	.01
105	Fred McMullin - Infielder	.03	.02	.01
106	Chick Gandil - First Baseman	.03	.02	.01
107	Buck Weaver - Third Baseman	.03	.02	.01
108	Lefty Williams - Pitcher	.03	.02	.01
109	Happy Felsch - Outfielder	.03	.02	.01
110	Shoeless Joe Jackson - Outfielder	.03	.02	.01

1989 Pacific Trading Cards Legends II

Pacific Trading Cards issued its Baseball Legends II set as a carry over of its initial set. The photos are printed on silver background and have colorful inner borders of red, blue, orange or gold. Players' names and positions are printed in white letters below the photos. The card backs once again

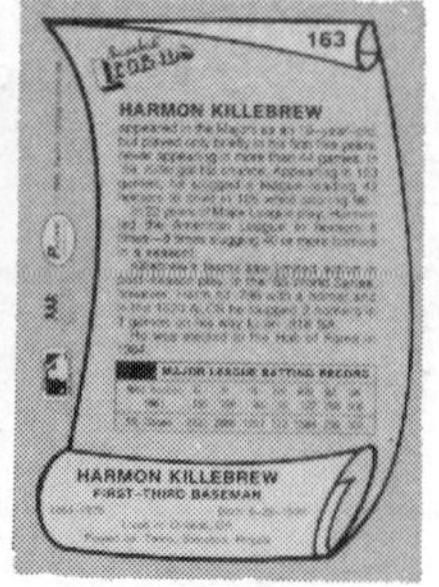

present the "Baseball Legends" logo, player biography, major league career statistics, and personal information. The Baseball Legends II are numbered 110-220 and were available in wax packs at a limited number of retail chains. The complete set was also made available via dealers or could be ordered directly from Pacific Trading Cards.

		MT	NR MT	EX
Complete Set (110):		10.00	7.50	4.00
Common Player:		.06	.05	.02
111	Reggie Jackson	.30	.25	.12
112	Rich Reese	.06	.05	.02
113	Frankie Frisch	.15	.11	.06
114	Ed Kranepool	.06	.05	.02
115	Al Hrabosky	.06	.05	.02
116	Eddie Mathews	.25	.20	.10
117	Ty Cobb	.50	.40	.20
118	Jim Davenport	.06	.05	.02
119	Buddy Lewis	.06	.05	.02
120	Virgil Trucks	.10	.08	.04
121	Del Ennis	.06	.05	.02
122	Dick Radatz	.06	.05	.02
123	Andy Pafko	.12	.09	.05
124	Wilbur Wood	.10	.08	.04
125	Joe Sewell	.15	.11	.06
126	Herb Score	.06	.05	.02
127	Paul Waner	.06	.05	.02
128	Lloyd Waner	.06	.05	.02
129	Brooks Robinson	.30	.25	.12
130	Bo Belinsky	.10	.08	.04
131	Phil Cavaretta	.06	.05	.02
132	Claude Osteen	.06	.05	.02
133	Tito Francona	.06	.05	.02
134	Billy Pierce	.06	.05	.02
135	Roberto Clemente	.50	.40	.20
136	Spud Chandler	.06	.05	.02
137	Enos Slaughter	.25	.20	.10
138	Ken Holtzman	.06	.05	.02
139	John Hopp	.06	.05	.02
140	Tony LaRussa	.06	.05	.02
141	Ryne Duren	.06	.05	.02
142	Glenn Beckert	.06	.05	.02
143	Ken Keltner	.06	.05	.02
144	Hank Bauer	.15	.11	.06
145	Roger Craig	.10	.08	.04
146	Frank Baker	.10	.08	.04
147	Jim O'Toole	.06	.05	.02
148	Rogers Hornsby	.30	.25	.12
149	Jose Cardenal	.06	.05	.02
150	Bobby Doerr	.10	.08	.04
151	Mickey Cochrane	.10	.08	.04
152	Gaylord Perry	.10	.08	.04
153	Frank Thomas	.06	.05	.02
154	Ted Williams	.40	.30	.15
155	Sam McDowell	.10	.08	.04
156	Bob Feller	.20	.15	.08
157	Bert Campaneris	.06	.05	.02
158	Thornton Lee	.06	.05	.02
159	Gary Peters	.06	.05	.02
160	Joe Medwick	.10	.08	.04
161	Joe Nuxhall	.10	.08	.04
162	Joe Schultz	.06	.05	.02
163	Harmon Killebrew	.25	.20	.10
164	Bucky Walters	.06	.05	.02
165	Bobby Allison	.10	.08	.04
166	Lou Boudreau	.15	.11	.08
167	Joe Cronin	.10	.08	.04
168	Mike Torrez	.10	.08	.04
169	Rich Rollins	.06	.05	.02
170	Tony Cuccinello	.06	.05	.02
171	Hoyt Wilhelm	.20	.15	.08
172	Ernie Harwell	.10	.08	.04
173	George Foster	.06	.05	.02
174	Lou Gehrig	.80	.60	.30
175	Dave Kingman	.06	.05	.02
176	Babe Ruth	1.00	.70	.40
177	Joe Black	.10	.08	.04
178	Roy Face	.10	.08	.04
179	Earl Weaver	.06	.05	.02
180	Johnny Mize	.15	.11	.06
181	Roger Cramer	.06	.05	.02
182	Jim Piersall	.06	.05	.02
183	Ned Garver	.06	.05	.02
184	Billy Williams	.25	.20	.10
185	Lefty Grove	.15	.11	.06
186	Jim Grant	.06	.05	.02
187	Elmer Valo	.06	.05	.02
188	Ewell Blackwell	.10	.08	.04
189	Mel Ott	.20	.15	.08
190	Harry Walker	.06	.05	.02
191	Bill Campbell	.06	.05	.02

192	Walter Johnson	.30	.25	.12
193	Jim "Catfish" Hunter	.10	.08	.04
194	Charlie Keller	.10	.08	.04
195	Hank Greenberg	.15	.11	.06
196	Bobby Murcer	.06	.05	.02
197	Al Lopez	.06	.05	.02
198	Vida Blue	.10	.08	.04
199	Shag Crawford	.06	.05	.02
200	Arky Vaughan	.10	.08	.04
201	Smoky Burgess	.25	.20	.10
202	Rip Sewell	.06	.05	.02
203	Earl Averill	.10	.08	.04
204	Milt Pappas	.06	.05	.02
205	Mel Harder	.06	.05	.02
206	Sam Jethroe	.06	.05	.02
207	Randy Hundley	.06	.05	.02
208	Jessie Haines	.10	.08	.04
209	Jack Brickhouse	.10	.08	.04
210	Whitey Ford	.20	.15	.08
211	Honus Wagner	1.00	.70	.40
212	Phil Niekro	.10	.08	.04
213	Gary Bell	.06	.05	.02
214	Jon Matlack	.06	.05	.02
215	Moe Drabowsky	.06	.05	.02
216	Edd Roush	.10	.08	.04
217	Joel Horlen	.06	.05	.02
218	Casey Stengel	.30	.25	.12
219	Burt Hooton	.06	.05	.02
220	Joe Jackson	.80	.60	.30

1990 Pacific Senior League

An early supporter of the short-lived "old-timers" league, Pacific Trading Cards issued a 220-card set depicting the players of the Senior Professional Baseball Association. Sold in wax packs as well as complete boxed sets, the cards have silver borders on front with yellow stars above and to the right of the player photo. Color team logos are at bottom-left, with the player's name and position at lower-right in a white band beneath the photo. Red, white and blue backs have appropriate logos, card number, a few biographical details and a short career summary in a horizontal format. The cards were issued with a set of 15 team logo stickers with a puzzle back. Shades of the 1989 Fleer Billy Ripken card, the card of Jim Nettles contains a photo which shows a vulgarity written on the knob of his bat. A cleaned-up version was issued later, and is much scarcer.

		MT	NR MT	EX
	Complete Set (220):	8.00	6.00	3.25
	Common Player:	.05	.04	.02
1	Bobby Tolan	.05	.04	.02
2	Sergio Ferrer	.05	.04	.02
3	David Rajsich	.05	.04	.02
4	Ron LeFlore	.10	.08	.04
5	Steve Henderson	.05	.04	.02
6	Jerry Martin	.05	.04	.02
7	Gary Rajsich	.05	.04	.02
8	Elias Sosa	.05	.04	.02
9	Jon Matlack	.05	.04	.02
10	Steve Kemp	.05	.04	.02
11	Lenny Randle	.05	.04	.02
12	Roy Howell	.05	.04	.02
13	Milt Wilcox	.05	.04	.02
14	Alan Bannister	.05	.04	.02
15	Dock Ellis	.05	.04	.02
16	Mike Williams	.05	.04	.02
17	Luis Gomez	.05	.04	.02
18	Joe Sambito	.05	.04	.02
19	Bake McBride	.05	.04	.02
20	Pat Zachry (photo actually Dick Bosman)	.05	.04	.02
21	Dwight Lowry	.05	.04	.02
22	Ozzie Virgil Sr.	.05	.04	.02
23	Randy Lerch	.05	.04	.02
24	Butch Benton	.05	.04	.02
25	Tom Zimmer	.05	.04	.02
26	Al Holland (photo actually Nardi Contreras)	.05	.04	.02
27	Sammy Stewart	.05	.04	.02
28	Bill Lee	.05	.04	.02
29	Ferguson Jenkins	.50	.40	.20
30	Leon Roberts	.05	.04	.02
31	Rick Wise	.05	.04	.02
32	Butch Hobson	.10	.08	.04
33	Pete LaCock	.05	.04	.02
34	Bill Campbell	.05	.04	.02
35	Doug Simunic	.05	.04	.02
36	Mario Guerrero	.05	.04	.02
37	Jim Willoughby	.05	.04	.02
38	Joe Pittman	.05	.04	.02
39	Mark Bomback	.05	.04	.02
40	Tommy McMillian	.05	.04	.02
41	Gary Allanson	.05	.04	.02
42	Cecil Cooper	.10	.08	.04
43	John LaRosa	.05	.04	.02
44	Darrell Brandon	.05	.04	.02
45	Bernie Carbo	.05	.04	.02
46	Mike Cuellar	.10	.08	.04
47	Al Bumbry	.05	.04	.02
48	Gene Richards	.05	.04	.02
49	Pedro Borbon	.05	.04	.02
50	Julio Solo	.05	.04	.02
51	Ed Nottle	.05	.04	.02
52	Jim Bibby	.05	.04	.02
53	Doug Griffin	.05	.04	.02
54	Ed Clements	.05	.04	.02
55	Dalton Jones	.05	.04	.02
56	Earl Weaver	.25	.20	.10
57	Jesus DeLaRosa	.05	.04	.02
58	Paul Casanova	.05	.04	.02
59	Frank Riccelli	.05	.04	.02
60	Rafael Landestoy	.05	.04	.02
61	George Hendrick	.05	.04	.02
62	Cesar Cedeno	.10	.08	.04
63	Bert Campaneris	.10	.08	.04
64	Derrel Thomas	.05	.04	.02
65	Bobby Ramos	.05	.04	.02
66	Grant Jackson	.05	.04	.02
67	Steve Whitaker	.05	.04	.02
68	Pedro Ramos	.05	.04	.02
69	Joe Hicks	.05	.04	.02
70	Taylor Duncan	.05	.04	.02
71	Tom Shopay	.05	.04	.02
72	Ken Clay	.05	.04	.02
73	Mike Kekich	.05	.04	.02
74	Ed Halicki	.05	.04	.02
75	Ed Figueroa	.05	.04	.02
76	Paul Blair	.05	.04	.02
77	Luis Tiant	.10	.08	.04
78	Stan Bahnsen	.05	.04	.02
79	Rennie Stennett	.05	.04	.02
80	Bobby Molinaro	.05	.04	.02
81	Jim Gideon	.05	.04	.02
82	Orlando Gonzalez	.05	.04	.02
83	Amos Otis	.05	.04	.02
84	Dennis Leonard	.05	.04	.02
85	Pat Putman	.05	.04	.02
86	Rick Manning	.05	.04	.02
87	Pat Dobson	.05	.04	.02
88	Marty Castillo	.05	.04	.02
89	Steve McCatty	.05	.04	.02
90	Doug Bird	.05	.04	.02
91	Rick Waits	.05	.04	.02
92	Ron Jackson	.05	.04	.02
93	Tim Hosley	.05	.04	.02
94	Steve Luebber	.05	.04	.02
95	Rich Gale	.05	.04	.02
96	Champ Summers	.05	.04	.02
97	Dave LaRoche	.05	.04	.02
98	Bobby Jones	.05	.04	.02
99	Kim Allen	.05	.04	.02
100	Wayne Garland	.05	.04	.02
101	Tom Spencer	.05	.04	.02
102	Dan Driessen	.05	.04	.02
103	Ron Pruitt	.05	.04	.02
104	Tim Ireland	.05	.04	.02
105	Dan Driessen	.05	.04	.02
106	Pepe Frias	.05	.04	.02
107	Eric Rasmussen	.05	.04	.02
108	Don Hood	.05	.04	.02
109	Joe Coleman (photo actually Tony Torchia)	.05	.04	.02
110	Jim Slaton	.05	.04	.02
111	Clint Hurdle	.05	.04	.02
112	Larry Milbourne	.05	.04	.02
113	Al Holland	.05	.04	.02
114	George Foster	.10	.08	.04
115	Graig Nettles	.10	.08	.04
116	Oscar Gamble	.05	.04	.02
117	Ross Grimsley	.05	.04	.02
118	Bill Travers	.05	.04	.02
119	Jose Beniquez	.05	.04	.02
120	Jerry Grote	.05	.04	.02
121	John D'Acquisto	.05	.04	.02
122	Tom Murphy	.05	.04	.02
123	Walt Williams	.05	.04	.02
124	Roy Thomas	.05	.04	.02
125	Jerry Grote	.05	.04	.02
126A	Jim Nettles (vulgarity on bat knob)	.50	.40	.20
126B	Jim Nettles (no vulgarity)	3.00	2.25	1.25
127	Randy Niemann	.05	.04	.02
128	Bobby Bonds	.10	.08	.04
129	Ed Glynn	.05	.04	.02
130	Ed Hicks	.05	.04	.02
131	Ivan Murrell	.05	.04	.02
132	Graig Nettles	.10	.08	.04
133	Hal McRae	.20	.15	.08
134	Pat Kelly	.05	.04	.02
135	Sammy Stewart	.05	.04	.02
136	Bruce Kison	.05	.04	.02
137	Jim Morrison	.05	.04	.02
138	Omar Moreno	.05	.04	.02
139	Tom Brown	.05	.04	.02
140	Steve Dillard	.05	.04	.02
141	Gary Alexander	.05	.04	.02
142	Al Oliver	.15	.11	.06
143	Rick Lysander	.05	.04	.02
144	Tippy Martinez	.05	.04	.02
145	Al Cowens	.05	.04	.02
146	Gene Clines	.05	.04	.02
147	Willie Aikens	.05	.04	.02
148	Tommy Moore	.05	.04	.02
149	Clete Boyer	.05	.04	.02
150	Stan Cliburn	.05	.04	.02
151	Ken Kravec	.05	.04	.02
152	Garth Iorg	.05	.04	.02
153	Rick Peterson	.05	.04	.02
154	Wayne Nordhagen	.05	.04	.02
155	Danny Meyer	.05	.04	.02
156	Wayne Garrett	.05	.04	.02
157	Wayne Krenchicki	.05	.04	.02
158	Graig Nettles	.10	.08	.04
159	Earl Stephenson	.05	.04	.02
160	Carl Taylor	.05	.04	.02
161	Rollie Fingers	.50	.40	.20
162	Toby Harrah	.10	.08	.04
163	Mickey Rivers	.05	.04	.02
164	Dave Kingman	.10	.08	.04
165	Paul Mirabella	.05	.04	.02
166	Dick Williams	.10	.08	.04
167	Luis Pujols	.05	.04	.02
168	Tito Landrum	.05	.04	.02
169	Tom Underwood	.05	.04	.02
170	Mark Wagner	.05	.04	.02
171	Odell Jones	.05	.04	.02
172	Doug Capilla	.05	.04	.02
173	Alfie Rondon	.05	.04	.02
174	Lowell Palmer	.05	.04	.02
175	Juan Eichelberger	.05	.04	.02
176	Wes Clements	.05	.04	.02
177	Rodney Scott	.05	.04	.02
178	Ron Washington	.05	.04	.02
179	Al Hrabosky	.05	.04	.02
180	Sid Monge	.05	.04	.02
181	Randy Johnson	.05	.04	.02
182	Tim Stoddard	.05	.04	.02
183	Dick Williams	.10	.08	.04
184	Lee Lacy	.05	.04	.02
185	Jerry White	.05	.04	.02
186	Dave Kingman	.10	.08	.04
187	Checklistt 1-110	.05	.04	.02
188	Jose Cruz	.10	.08	.04
189	Jamie Easterly	.05	.04	.02
190	Ike Blessit	.05	.04	.02
191	Johnny Grubb	.05	.04	.02
192	Dave Cash	.05	.04	.02
193	Doug Corbett	.05	.04	.02
194	Bruce Bochy	.05	.04	.02
195	Mark Corey	.05	.04	.02
196	Gil Rondon	.05	.04	.02
197	Jerry Martin	.05	.04	.02
198	Gerry Pirtle	.05	.04	.02
199	Gates Brown	.05	.04	.02
200	Bob Galasso	.05	.04	.02
201	Bake McBride	.05	.04	.02
202	Wayne Granger	.05	.04	.02
203	Larry Milbourne	.05	.04	.02
204	Tom Paciorek	.05	.04	.02
205	U.L. Washington	.05	.04	.02
206	Larvell Blanks	.05	.04	.02
207	Bob Shirley	.05	.04	.02
208	Pete Falcone	.05	.04	.02
209	Sal Butera	.05	.04	.02
210	Roy Branch	.05	.04	.02
211	Dyar Miller	.05	.04	.02
212	Paul Siebert	.05	.04	.02
213	Ken Reitz	.05	.04	.02
214	Bill Madlock	.10	.08	.04
215	Vida Blue	.15	.11	.06
216	Dave Hilton	.05	.04	.02
217	Pedro Ramos, Charlie Bree	.05	.04	.02
218	Checklist 111-220	.05	.04	.02
219	Pat Dobson, Earl Weaver	.05	.04	.02
220	Curt Flood	.15	.11	.06

Values for recent cards and sets are listed in Mint (MT), Near Mint (NM), reflecting the fact that many cards from recent years have been preserved in top condition. Recent cards and sets in less than Excellent condition have little collector interest.

1990 Pacific Legends

The cards in this 110-card set feature the same style as the previous Pacific Legends releases. The cards were available in wax packs as well as in complete set form. Several players found in the first two legends releases are also found in this issue along with new players.

		MT	NR MT	EX
	Complete Set (110):	10.00	7.50	4.00
	Common Player:	.05	.04	.02
1	Hank Aaron	.50	.40	.20
2	Tommie Agee	.05	.04	.02
3	Luke Appling	.15	.11	.06
4	Sal Bando	.05	.04	.02
5	Ernie Banks	.40	.30	.15
6	Don Baylor	.05	.04	.02
7	Yogi Berra	.40	.30	.15
8	Vida Blue	.05	.04	.02
9	Lou Boudreau	.10	.08	.04
10	Clete Boyer	.05	.04	.02
11	George Bamberger	.05	.04	.02

12	Lou Brock	.30	.25	.12
13	Ralph Branca	.05	.04	.02
14	Carl Erskine	.05	.04	.02
15	Bert Campaneris	.05	.04	.02
16	Steve Carlton	.30	.25	.12
17	Rod Carew	.50	.40	.20
18	Rocky Colovito	.15	.11	.06
19	Frank Crosetti	.10	.08	.04
20	Larry Doby	.05	.04	.02
21	Bobby Doerr	.10	.08	.04
22	Walt Dropo	.05	.04	.02
23	Rick Ferrell	.05	.04	.02
24	Joe Garagiola	.25	.20	.10
25	Ralph Garr	.05	.04	.02
26	Dick Groat	.10	.08	.04
27	Steve Garvey	.20	.15	.08
28	Bob Gibson	.25	.20	.10
29	Don Drysdale	.15	.11	.06
30	Billy Herman	.10	.08	.04
31	Bobby Grich	.05	.04	.02
32	Monte Irvin	.15	.11	.06
33	Dave Johnson	.05	.04	.02
34	Don Kessinger	.05	.04	.02
35	Harmon Killebrew	.25	.20	.10
36	Ralph Kiner	.15	.11	.06
37	Vern Law	.05	.04	.02
38	Ed Lopat	.05	.04	.02
39	Bill Mazeroski	.15	.11	.06
40	Rick Monday	.05	.04	.02
41	Manny Mota	.05	.04	.02
42	Don Newcombe	.10	.08	.04
43	Gaylord Perry	.20	.15	.08
44	Jim Piersall	.10	.08	.04
45	Johnny Podres	.05	.04	.02
46	Boog Powell	.10	.08	.04
47	Robin Roberts	.15	.11	.06
48	Ron Santo	.15	.11	.06
49	Herb Score	.10	.08	.04
50	Enos Slaughter	.20	.15	.08
51	Warren Spahn	.35	.25	.14
52	Rusty Staub	.05	.04	.02
53	Frank Torre	.05	.04	.02
54	Bob Horner	.05	.04	.02
55	Lee May	.05	.04	.02
56	Bill White	.10	.08	.04
57	Hoyt Wilhelm	.20	.15	.08
58	Billy Williams	.20	.15	.08
59	Ted Williams	.50	.40	.20
60	Tom Seaver	.35	.25	.14
61	Carl Yaztrzemski	.50	.40	.20
62	Marv Throneberry	.10	.08	.04
63	Steve Stone	.05	.04	.02
64	Rico Petrocelli	.05	.04	.02
65	Orlando Cepeda	.10	.08	.04
66	Eddie Mathews	.25	.20	.10
67	Joe Sewell	.10	.08	.04
68	Jim "Catfish" Hunter	.15	.11	.06
69	Alvin Dark	.05	.04	.02
70	Richie Ashburn	.10	.08	.04
71	Dusty Baker	.05	.04	.02
72	George Foster	.05	.04	.02
73	Eddie Yost	.05	.04	.02
74	Buddy Bell	.05	.04	.02
75	Manny Sanguillen	.05	.04	.02
76	Jim Bunning	.10	.08	.04
77	Smokey Burgess	.10	.08	.04
78	Al Rosen	.10	.08	.04
79	Gene Conley	.05	.04	.02
80	Dave Dravecky	.05	.04	.02
81	Charlie Gehringer	.15	.11	.06
82	Billy Pierce	.05	.04	.02
83	Willie Horton	.05	.04	.02
84	Ron Hunt	.05	.04	.02
85	Bob Feller	.20	.15	.08
86	George Kell	.10	.08	.04
87	Dave Kingman	.10	.08	.04
88	Jerry Koosman	.05	.04	.02
89	Clem Labine	.05	.04	.02
90	Tony LaRussa	.05	.04	.02
91	Dennis Leonard	.05	.04	.02
92	Dale Long	.05	.04	.02
93	Sparky Lyle	.05	.04	.02
94	Gil McDougald	.05	.04	.02
95	Don Mossi	.05	.04	.02
96	Phil Niekro	.15	.11	.06
97	Tom Paciorek	.05	.04	.02
98	Mel Parnell	.05	.04	.02
99	Lou Pinella	.05	.04	.02
100	Bobby Richardson	.10	.08	.04
101	Phil Rizzuto	.20	.15	.08
102	Brooks Robinson	.20	.15	.08
103	Pete Runnels	.05	.04	.02
104	Diego Segui	.05	.04	.02
105	Bobby Shantz	.05	.04	.02
106	Bobby Thomson	.10	.08	.04
107	Joe Torre	.10	.08	.04
108	Earl Weaver	.05	.04	.02
109	Willie Wilson	.05	.04	.02
110	Jesse Barfield	.05	.04	.02

1991 Pacific Senior League

In 1991 Pacific Trading Cards produced its second set of cards of Senior Professional Baseball Association players. The cards feature color photos on the front, with the player's name and position along the bottom and team nickname and logo on a banner vertically on the left side. There are 160 cards in the glossy set, with some multi-player and

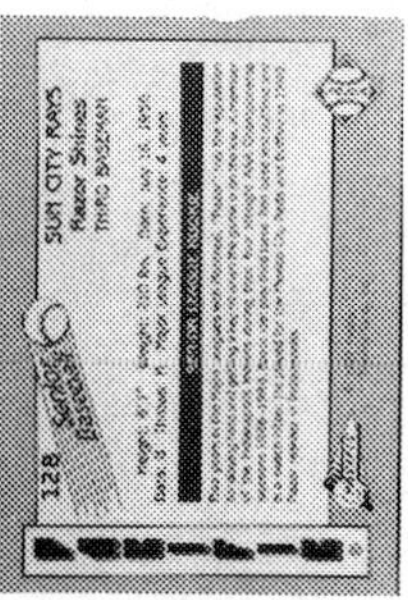

in-action cards included. For reasons unknown, some of the cards (including those of Rice, Fingers, Blue, Dave Cash, Dan Norman, Ron LeFlore, Cesar Cedeno, Rafael Landestoy and Dan Driessen) were apparently printed in two versions.

		MT	NR MT	EX
	Complete Set (160):	8.00	6.00	3.25
	Common Player:	.05	.04	.02
1	Dan Driessen	.05	.04	.02
2	Marty Castillo	.05	.04	.02
3	Jerry White	.05	.04	.02
4	Bud Anderson	.05	.04	.02
5	Ron Jackson	.05	.04	.02
6	Fred Stanley	.05	.04	.02
7	Steve Luebber	.05	.04	.02
8	Jery Terrell	.05	.04	.02
9	Pat Dobson	.05	.04	.02
10	Ken Kravec	.05	.04	.02
11	Gil Rondon	.05	.04	.02
12	Dyar Miller	.05	.04	.02
13	Bobby Molinaro	.05	.04	.02
14	Jerry Martin	.05	.04	.02
15	Rick Waits	.05	.04	.02
16	Steve McCatty	.05	.04	.02
17	Roger Slagle	.05	.04	.02
18	Mike Ramsey	.05	.04	.02
19	Rich Gale	.05	.04	.02
20	Larry Harlow	.05	.04	.02
21	Dan Rohn	.05	.04	.02
22	Don Cooper	.05	.04	.02
23	Marv Foley	.05	.04	.02
24	Rafael Landestoy	.05	.04	.02
25	Eddie Milner	.05	.04	.02
26	Amos Otis	.05	.04	.02
27	Odell Jones	.05	.04	.02
28	Tippy Martinez	.05	.04	.02
29	Stu Cliburn	.05	.04	.02
30	Stan Cliburn	.05	.04	.02
31	Tony Cloninger	.05	.04	.02
32	Jeff Jones	.05	.04	.02
33	Ken Reitz	.05	.04	.02
34	Dave Sax	.05	.04	.02
35	Orlando Gonzalez	.05	.04	.02
36	Jose Cruz	.10	.08	.04
37	Mickey Mahler	.05	.04	.02
38	Derek Botelho	.05	.04	.02
39	Rick Lysander	.05	.04	.02
40	Cesar Cedeno	.10	.08	.04
41	Garth Iorg	.05	.04	.02
42	Wayne Krenchicki	.05	.04	.02
43	Clete Boyer	.05	.04	.02
44	Dan Boone	.05	.04	.02
45	George Vukovich	.05	.04	.02
46	Omar Moreno	.05	.04	.02
47	Ron Washington	.05	.04	.02
48	Ron Washington (MVP)	.05	.04	.02
49	Rick Peterson	.05	.04	.02
50	Tack Wilson	.05	.04	.02
51	Stan & Stu Cliburn	.05	.04	.02
52	Rick Lysander (POY)	.05	.04	.02
53	Cesar Cedeno, Pete LaCock	.05	.04	.02
54	Jim Marshall, Clete Boyer	.05	.04	.02
55	Doug Simunic	.05	.04	.02
56	Pat Kelly	.05	.04	.02
57	Roy Branch	.05	.04	.02
58	Dave Cash	.05	.04	.02
59	Bobby Jones	.05	.04	.02
60	Hector Cruz	.05	.04	.02
61	Reggie Cleveland	.05	.04	.02
62	Gary Lance	.05	.04	.02
63	Ron LeFlore	.05	.04	.02
64	Dan Norman	.05	.04	.02
65	Renie Martin	.05	.04	.02
66	Pete Mackanin	.05	.04	.02
67	Frank Riccelli	.05	.04	.02
68	Alfie Rondon	.05	.04	.02
69	Rodney Scott	.05	.04	.02
70	Jim Tracy	.05	.04	.02
71	Ed Dennis	.05	.04	.02
72	Rick Lindell	.05	.04	.02
73	Stu Pepper	.05	.04	.02
74	Jeff Youngbauer	.05	.04	.02
75	Russ Foster	.05	.04	.02
76	Jeff Capriati	.05	.04	.02
77	Art DeFreites	.05	.04	.02
78	Alfie Rondon (Action)	.05	.04	.02
79	Reggie Cleveland (Action)	.05	.04	.02
80	Dave Cash (Action)	.05	.04	.02
81	Vida Blue	.15	.11	.06
82	Ed Glynn	.05	.04	.02
83	Bob Owchinko	.05	.04	.02
84	Bill Fleming	.05	.04	.02
85	Ron & Gary Roenicke	.05	.04	.02
86	Tom Thompson	.05	.04	.02
87	Derrell Thomas	.05	.04	.02
88	Jim Willoughby	.05	.04	.02
89	Jim Pankovits	.05	.04	.02
90	Jack Cooley	.05	.04	.02
91	Lenn Sakata	.05	.04	.02
92	Mike Brocki	.05	.04	.02
93	Chuck Fick	.05	.04	.02
94	Tom Benedict	.05	.04	.02
95	Anthony Davis	.05	.04	.02
96	Cardell Camper	.05	.04	.02
97	Leon Roberts	.05	.04	.02
98	Roger Erickson	.05	.04	.02
99	Kim Allen	.05	.04	.02
100	Dave Skaggs	.05	.04	.02
101	Joe Decker	.05	.04	.02
102	U.L. Washington	.05	.04	.02
103	Don Fletcher	.05	.04	.02
104	Gary Roenicke	.05	.04	.02
105	Rich Dauer	.05	.04	.02
106	Ron Roenicke	.05	.04	.02
107	Mike Norris	.05	.04	.02
108	Ferguson Jenkins	.50	.40	.20
109	Ronn Reynolds	.05	.04	.02
110	Pete Falcone	.05	.04	.02
111	Gary Allenson	.05	.04	.02
112	Mark Wagner	.05	.04	.02
113	Jack Lazorko	.05	.04	.02
114	Bob Galasso	.05	.04	.02
115	Ron Davis	.05	.04	.02
116	Lenny Randle	.05	.04	.02
117	Ricky Peters	.05	.04	.02
118	Jim Dwyer	.05	.04	.02
119	Juan Eichelberger	.05	.04	.02
120	Pete LaCock	.05	.04	.02
121	Tony Scott	.05	.04	.02
122	Rick Lancelloti	.05	.04	.02
123	Barry Bonnell	.05	.04	.02
124	Dave Hilton	.05	.04	.02
125	Bill Campbell	.05	.04	.02
126	Rollie Fingers	.50	.40	.20
127	Jim Marshall	.05	.04	.02
128	Razor Shines	.05	.04	.02
129	Guy Sularz	.05	.04	.02
130	Roy Thomas	.05	.04	.02
131	Joel Youngblood	.05	.04	.02
132	Ernie Camacho	.05	.04	.02
133	Dave Hilton, Jim Marshall, Fred Stanley	.05	.04	.02
134	Ken Landreaux	.05	.04	.02
135	Dave Rozema	.05	.04	.02
136	Tom Zimmer	.05	.04	.02
137	Elias Sosa	.05	.04	.02
138	Ozzie Virgil Sr.	.05	.04	.02
139	Al Holland	.05	.04	.02
140	Milt Wilcox	.05	.04	.02
141	Jerry Reed	.05	.04	.02
142	Chris Welch	.05	.04	.02
143	Luis Gomez	.05	.04	.02
144	Steve Henderson	.05	.04	.02
145	Butch Benton	.05	.04	.02
146	Bill Lee	.05	.04	.02
147	Todd Cruz	.05	.04	.02
148	Jim Rice	.20	.15	.08
149	Tito Landrum	.05	.04	.02
150	Ozzie Virgil Jr.	.05	.04	.02
151	Joe Pittman	.05	.04	.02
152	Bobby Tolan	.05	.04	.02
153	Len Barker	.05	.04	.02
154	Dave Rajsich	.05	.04	.02
155	Glenn Gulliver	.05	.04	.02
156	Gary Rajsich	.05	.04	.02
157	Joe Sambito	.05	.04	.02
158	Frank Vito	.05	.04	.02
159	Ozzie Virgil Jr. & Sr.	.05	.04	.02
160	Dave & Gary Rajsich	.05	.04	.02

1991 Pacific Nolan Ryan

The career and family life of Nolan Ryan (to 1991) were the subject matter of this 110-card set by Pacific Trading Card Co. Sold in both foil packs and factory sets, the cards have a UV-coated front featuring a photo flanked on the left by "Nolan Ryan" printed vertically in a color accent stripe. At lower left is a flaming baseball "Texas Express" logo. A photo caption appears beneath the photo. On back the blazing ball motif is repeated, with a photo or career highlights in its center.

		MT	NR MT	EX
Complete Set (110):		10.00	7.50	4.00
Common Card:		.10	.08	.04
1	Future Hall of Famer	.10	.08	.04
2	From Little League to the Major Leagues	.10	.08	.04
3	A Dream Come True	.10	.08	.04
4	Signed by the Mets	.10	.08	.04
5	Fireball Pitcher	.10	.08	.04
6	Mets Rookie Pitcher	.10	.08	.04
7	First Major League Win	.10	.08	.04
8	Early in 1969	.10	.08	.04
9	Tensions of a Pennant Race	.10	.08	.04
10	Mets Clinch NL East	.10	.08	.04
11	Keep the Ball Down	.10	.08	.04
12	Playoff Victory	.10	.08	.04
13	World Series Victory	.10	.08	.04
14	The Amazin' Mets	.10	.08	.04
15	Met Strikeout Record	.10	.08	.04
16	One of the Worst Trades in Baseball	.10	.08	.04
17	Slow Start with Mets	.10	.08	.04
18	Pitcher New York Mets	.10	.08	.04
19	Traded to the Angels	.10	.08	.04
20	Meeting New Friends	.10	.08	.04
21	Throwing Fast Balls	.10	.08	.04
22	Move the Ball Around	.10	.08	.04
23	Nolan Heat	.10	.08	.04
24	No-Hitter Number 1	.10	.08	.04
25	Looking Back on Number 1	.10	.08	.04
26	No-Hitter Number 2	.10	.08	.04
27	Single Season Strikeout Record	.10	.08	.04
28	21 Wins in 1973	.10	.08	.04
29	Fastest Pitch Ever Thrown at 100.9 MPH	.10	.08	.04
30	No-Hitter Number 3	.10	.08	.04
31	No-Hitter Number 4	.10	.08	.04
32	Ryan and Tanana	.10	.08	.04
33	Learning Change-Up	.10	.08	.04
34	Pitcher California Angels	.10	.08	.04
35	Nolan Joins Astros	.10	.08	.04
36	Starting Pitcher Nolan Ryan	.10	.08	.04
37	Taking Batting Practice	.10	.08	.04
38	The Game's Greatest Power Pitcher	.10	.08	.04
39	3000 Career Strikeouts	.10	.08	.04
40	A Ryan Home Run	.10	.08	.04
41	The Fast Ball Grip	.10	.08	.04
42	Record 5th No-Hitter	.10	.08	.04
43	No-Hitter Number 5	.10	.08	.04
44	A Dream Fulfilled	.10	.08	.04
45	Nolan Passes Walter Johnson	.10	.08	.04
46	Strikeout 4000	.10	.08	.04
47	Astros Win Western Division Title	.10	.08	.04
48	Pitcher Houston Astros	.10	.08	.04
49	Milestone Strikeouts	.10	.08	.04
50	Post Season Participant	.10	.08	.04
51	Hurling for Houston	.10	.08	.04
52	135 N.L. Wins	.10	.08	.04
53	Through with Chew	.10	.08	.04
54	Signed by Rangers 1989	.10	.08	.04
55	Pleasant Change for Nolan	.10	.08	.04
56	Real Special Moment	.10	.08	.04
57	1989 All-Star Game	.10	.08	.04
58	Pitching in 1989 All-Star Game	.10	.08	.04
59	5000 Strikeouts; A Standing Ovation	.10	.08	.04
60	Great Moments in 1989	.10	.08	.04
61	Nolan with Dan Smith, Rangers First Pick	.10	.08	.04
62	Ranger Club Record 16 Strikeouts	.10	.08	.04
63	Last Pitch No-Hitter Number 6	.10	.08	.04
64	Sweet Number 6	.10	.08	.04
65	Oldest to Throw No-Hitter	.10	.08	.04
66	Another Ryan Win	.10	.08	.04
67	20th Pitcher to Win 300	.10	.08	.04
68	300 Win Battery	.10	.08	.04
69	300 Game Winner	.10	.08	.04
70	Perfect Mechanics	.10	.08	.04
71	22 Seasons with 100 or more Strikeouts	.10	.08	.04
72	11th Strikeout Title	.10	.08	.04
73	232 Strikeouts, 1990	.10	.08	.04
74	The 1990 Season	.10	.08	.04
75	Pitcher Texas Rangers	.10	.08	.04
76	1991, Nolan's 25th Season	.10	.08	.04
77	Throwing Spirals	.10	.08	.04
78	Running the Steps	.10	.08	.04
79	Hard Work and Conditioning	.10	.08	.04
80	The Rigid Workout	.10	.08	.04
81	Ryan's Routine	.10	.08	.04
82	Ryan's Routine Between Starts	.10	.08	.04
83	Running in Outfield	.10	.08	.04
84	B.P. in Texas	.10	.08	.04
85	18 Career Low-Hitters	.10	.08	.04
86	My Job is to Give My Team/Chance to Win	.10	.08	.04
87	The Spring Workout	.10	.08	.04
88	Power versus Power	.10	.08	.04
89	Awesome Power	.10	.08	.04
90	Blazing Speed	.10	.08	.04
91	The Pick Off	.10	.08	.04
92	Real Gamer	.10	.08	.04
93	Ranger Battery Mates	.10	.08	.04
94	The Glare	.10	.08	.04
95	The High Leg Kick	.10	.08	.04
96	Day Off	.10	.08	.04
97	A New Ball	.10	.08	.04
98	Going to Rosin Bag	.10	.08	.04
99	Time for Relief	.10	.08	.04
100	Lone Star Legend	.10	.08	.04
101	Fans' Favorite	.10	.08	.04
102	Watching Nolan Pitch	.10	.08	.04
103	Our Family of Five	.10	.08	.04
104	Texas Beefmaster	.10	.08	.04
105	Gentleman Rancher	.10	.08	.04
106	Texas Cowboy Life	.10	.08	.04
107	The Ryan Family	.10	.08	.04
108	Participating in Cutting Horse Contest	.10	.08	.04
109	Nolan Interviews	.10	.08	.04
110	Lynn Nolan Ryan	.10	.08	.04

1991 Pacific Nolan Ryan Milestones

Issued as inserts in the 1991 Nolan Ryan foil packs was this set of eight career highlight cards. The format is basically the same as the regular-issue cards, except that the inserts are bordered in either silver (edition of 10,000) or gold (edition of 1,000). The unnumbered cards are checklisted here in chronolgical order. The inserts were found only in foil and wax packs.

		MT	NR MT	EX
Complete Set, Silver (8):		80.00	60.00	32.00
Complete Set, Gold (8):		300.00	225.00	115.00
Common Ryan, Silver:		15.00	11.00	6.00
Common Ryan, Gold:		50.00	37.00	20.00
(1a)	Rookie Pitcher (silver)	15.00	11.00	6.00
(1b)	Rookie Pitcher (gold)	50.00	37.00	20.00
(2a)	No-Hitter 1 (silver)	15.00	11.00	6.00
(2b)	No-Hitter 1 (gold)	50.00	37.00	20.00
(3a)	No-Hitter 2 (silver)	15.00	11.00	6.00
(3b)	No-Hitter 2 (gold)	50.00	37.00	20.00
(4a)	No-Hitter 3 (silver)	15.00	11.00	6.00
(4b)	No-Hitter 3 (gold)	50.00	37.00	20.00
(5a)	No-Hitter 4 (silver)	15.00	11.00	6.00
(5b)	No-Hitter 4 (gold)	50.00	37.00	20.00
(6a)	No-Hitter 5 (silver)	15.00	11.00	6.00
(6b)	No-Hitter 5 (gold)	50.00	37.00	20.00
(7a)	Sweet 6 (silver)	15.00	11.00	6.00
(7b)	Sweet 6 (gold)	50.00	37.00	20.00
(8a)	25th Season (silver)	15.00	11.00	6.00
(8b)	25th Season (gold)	50.00	37.00	20.00

Definitions for grading conditions are located in the Introduction of this price guide.

1991 Pacific Nolan Ryan 7th No-Hitter

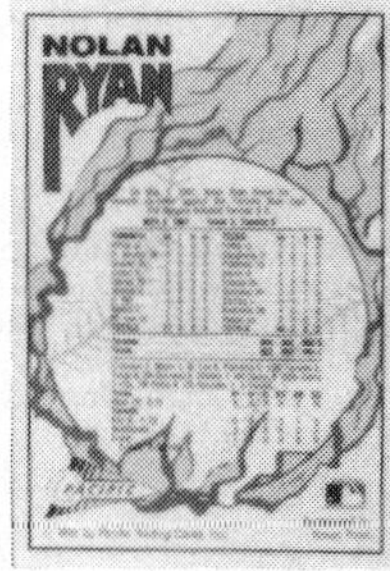

On May 1, 1991, before the home crowd at Arlington, Nolan Ryan posted his seventh career no-hitter, blanking the Blue Jays. In commemoration of the event, Pacific produced a seven-card insert set for random inclusion in its Nolan Ryan "Texas Express" foil packs. Each card was produced in an edition of 10,000 silver-foil bordered cards and 1,000 with gold-foil borders. The design follows the basic format of the regular Ryan issue, with the flaming baseball series logo at lower-left on the front, the card's title in a colored stripe beneath the photo, and Ryan's name printed vertically in a colored stripe at left. Backs repeat the flaming ball design at center, containing information about the no-hitter.

		MT	NR MT	EX
Complete Set, Silver (7):		80.00	60.00	32.00
Complete Set, Gold (7):		300.00	225.00	115.00
Common Card, Silver:		15.00	11.00	6.00
Common Card, Gold:		50.00	37.00	20.00
1a	Last Pitch (silver)	15.00	11.00	6.00
1b	Last Pitch (gold)	50.00	37.00	20.00
2a	No-Hitter #7 (silver)	15.00	11.00	6.00
2b	No-Hitter #7 (gold)	50.00	37.00	20.00
3a	The Best (silver)	15.00	11.00	6.00
3b	The Best (gold)	50.00	37.00	20.00
4a	Time to Celebrate (silver)	15.00	11.00	6.00
4b	Time to Celebrate (gold)	50.00	37.00	20.00
5a	Congratulations from Rangers Fans (silver)	15.00	11.00	6.00
5b	Congratulationd from Rangers Fans (gold)	50.00	37.00	20.00
6a	Catcher Mike Stanley (silver)	15.00	11.00	6.00
6b	Catcher Mike Stanley (gold)	50.00	37.00	20.00
7a	All in a Day's Work (silver)	15.00	11.00	6.00
7b	All in a Day's Work (gold)	50.00	37.00	20.00

Values quoted in this guide reflect the retail price of a card – the price a collector can expect to pay when buying a card from a dealer. The wholesale price – that which a collector can expect to receive from a dealer when selling cards – will be significantly lower, depending on desirability and condition.

1991 Pacific Ryan 7th No-Hitter Hologram

Even more elusive and exclusive than the gold- and silver-foil bordered "7th No-Hitter" inserts found in wax and foil packs was this edition produced with gold and silver holographic borders (1,000 each in gold and silver. The hologram 7th No-Hitter inserts were found only in 99-cent cello packs.

		MT	NR MT	EX
Complete Set, Silver (7):		300.00	225.00	125.00
Complete Set, Gold (7):		300.00	225.00	125.00
Common Card, Silver:		50.00	37.00	20.00
Common Card, Gold:		50.00	37.00	20.00
1a	Last Pitch (silver)	50.00	37.00	20.00
1b	Last Pitch (gold)	50.00	37.00	20.00
2a	No-Hitter #7 (silver)	50.00	37.00	20.00
2b	No-Hitter #7 (gold)	50.00	37.00	20.00
3a	The Best (silver)	50.00	37.00	20.00
3b	The Best (gold)	50.00	37.00	20.00
4a	Time to Celebrate (silver)	50.00	37.00	20.00
4b	Time to Celebrate (gold)	50.00	37.00	20.00
5a	Congratulations from Rangers Fans (silver)	50.00	37.00	20.00
5b	Congratulations from Rangers Fans (gold)	50.00	37.00	20.00
6a	Catcher Mike Stanley (silver)	50.00	37.00	20.00
6b	Catcher Mike Stanley (gold)	50.00	37.00	20.00
7a	All in a Day's Work (silver)	50.00	37.00	20.00
7b	All in a Day's Work (gold)	50.00	37.00	20.00

A player's name in italic type indicates a rookie card. An (FC) indicates a player's first card for that particular card company.

1992 Pacific Nolan Ryan

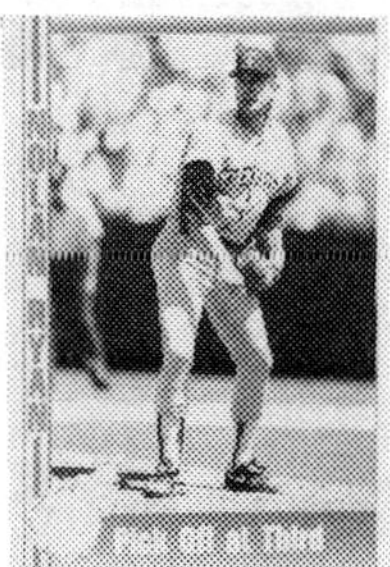

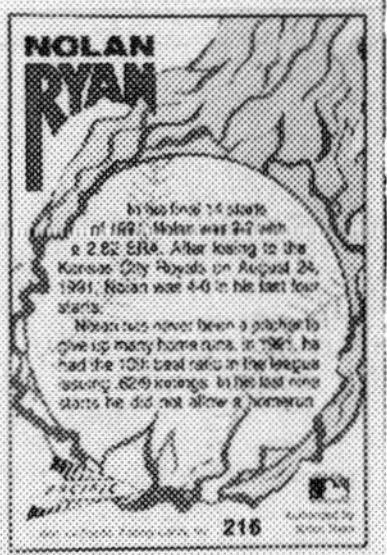

The 1992 Nolan Ryan "Texas Express" Series II is numbered 111 to 220, featuring the same design as the original 110-card issue of 1991. The set includes photos of Ryan from boyhood to his seventh no-hitter, and two bonus subsets were also randomly inserted in the foil packs.

		MT	NR MT	EX
Complete Set (110):		9.00	6.75	3.50
Common Card:		.10	.08	.04
111	The Golden Arm	.10	.08	.04
112	Little League All-Star	.10	.08	.04
113	All-State Pitcher	.10	.08	.04
114	Nolan Ryan Field	.10	.08	.04
115	Nolan at Age 20	.10	.08	.04
116	Nolan Ryan Jacksonville Suns	.10	.08	.04
117	Surrounded By Friends	.10	.08	.04
118	Nolan the Cowboy	.10	.08	.04
119	The Simple Life	.10	.08	.04
120	Nolan Loves Animals	.10	.08	.04
121	Growing Up in New York	.10	.08	.04
122	New York Strikeout Record	.10	.08	.04
123	Traded	.10	.08	.04
124	Hall of Fame Victims	.10	.08	.04
125	Number 500	.10	.08	.04
126	California Victory	.10	.08	.04
127	20 Win Season	.10	.08	.04
128	Throwing Heat	.10	.08	.04
129	Strikeout Record	.10	.08	.04
130	Number One	.10	.08	.04
131	1,000th Strikeout	.10	.08	.04
132	Number Two	.10	.08	.04
133	2,000th Strikeout	.10	.08	.04
134	Number Three	.10	.08	.04
135	Pure Speed	.10	.08	.04
136	Independence Day Fireworks	.10	.08	.04
137	Fast Ball Pitcher	.10	.08	.04
138	Number Four	.10	.08	.04
139	Free Agent	.10	.08	.04
140	Houston Bound	.10	.08	.04
141	Big Dollars	.10	.08	.04
142	Strong Houston Staff	.10	.08	.04
143	Number Five	.10	.08	.04
144	Astro MVp	.10	.08	.04
145	Western Divison Game	.10	.08	.04
146	National League All-Star	.10	.08	.04
147	Major League Record	.10	.08	.04
148	Nolan Breaks Johnson's Record	.10	.08	.04
149	Reese and Nolan	.10	.08	.04
150	100th National League Win	.10	.08	.04
151	4,000th Strikeout	.10	.08	.04
152	League Leader	.10	.08	.04
153	250th Career Win	.10	.08	.04
154	The Seldom of Swat	.10	.08	.04
155	4,500th Strikeout	.10	.08	.04
156	Like Father Like Son	.10	.08	.04
157	Spoiled in the Ninth	.10	.08	.04
158	Leaving Houston	.10	.08	.04
159	Houston Star	.10	.08	.04
160	Ryan Test Free Agency	.10	.08	.04
161	Awesome Heat	.10	.08	.04
162	Brotherly Love	.10	.08	.04
163	Astros Return	.10	.08	.04
164	Texas Size Decision	.10	.08	.04
165	Texas Legend	.10	.08	.04
166	Drawing a Crowd	.10	.08	.04
167	Great Start	.10	.08	.04
168	5,000th Strikeout	.10	.08	.04
169	Texas All-Star	.10	.08	.04
170	Number Six	.10	.08	.04
171	300th Win	.10	.08	.04
172	1990 League Leader	.10	.08	.04
173	Man of the Year	.10	.08	.04
174	Spring Training 1991	.10	.08	.04
175	Fast Ball Grip	.10	.08	.04
176	Strong Arm	.10	.08	.04
177	Stanley's Delight	.10	.08	.04
178	After Nolan's 7th No-Hitter	.10	.08	.04
179	Stretching Before the Game	.10	.08	.04
180	The Rangers Sign Nolan for 1992 and 1993	.10	.08	.04
181	Heading to the Bullpen	.10	.08	.04
182	Nolan Ryan - Banker	.10	.08	.04
183	Time with Fans	.10	.08	.04
184	Solid 1992 Season	.10	.08	.04
185	Ranger Team Leader	.10	.08	.04
186	More Records	.10	.08	.04
187	Number Seven	.10	.08	.04
188	Nolan Passes Niekro	.10	.08	.04
189	Ryan Trails Sutton	.10	.08	.04
190	Ranger Strikeout Mark	.10	.08	.04
191	Consectutive K's	.10	.08	.04
192	5,500th Strikeout	.10	.08	.04
193	Twenty-Five First Timers	.10	.08	.04
194	No-Hitters Ended in the Ninth	.10	.08	.04
195	Constant Work-Outs	.10	.08	.04
196	Nolan in Motion	.10	.08	.04
197	Pitching in Fenway Park	.10	.08	.04
198	Goose and Nolan	.10	.08	.04
199	Talking Over Strategy	.10	.08	.04
200	Don't Mess With Texas	.10	.08	.04
201	314-278 Thru 1991	.10	.08	.04
202	All-Time Leader	.10	.08	.04
203	High Praise	.10	.08	.04
204	Manager's Delight	.10	.08	.04
205	733 Major League Starts	.10	.08	.04
206	Ryan the Quarterback	.10	.08	.04
207	Hard Work Pays Off	.10	.08	.04
208	Passing Along Wisdom	.10	.08	.04
209	Still Dominant	.10	.08	.04
210	Nolan's Fast Ball	.10	.08	.04
211	Seven No-Hitters	.10	.08	.04
212	Training for Perfection	.10	.08	.04
213	Nolan's Edge - Speed	.10	.08	.04
214	This One was for Them	.10	.08	.04
215	Another Day's Work	.10	.08	.04
216	Pick Off at Third	.10	.08	.04
217	Ready to Pitch	.10	.08	.04
218	Spring Training 1992	.10	.08	.04
219	Nolan Receives The Victor Award	.10	.08	.04
220	Nolan's 26th Season	.10	.08	.04

Regional interest may affect the value of a card.

1992 Pacific Nolan Ryan Gold Inserts

Pacific produced this insert set for the 1992 Nolan Ryan "Texas Express" sequel. There are eight different gold-foil bordered cards, one for each of Ryan's no-hitters, plus an additional card combining all seven. Design is similar to the 1991-92 Ryan cards from Pacific. Backs feature box scores of the no-hitters. The cards are unnumbered. According to the manufacturer, 10,000 of each insert were produced.

		MT	NR MT	EX
Complete Set (8):		80.00	60.00	32.00
Common Ryan:		15.00	11.00	6.00
(1)	Number One	15.00	11.00	6.00
(2)	Number Two	15.00	11.00	6.00
(3)	Number Three	15.00	11.00	6.00
(4)	Number Four	15.00	11.00	6.00
(5)	Number Five	15.00	11.00	6.00
(6)	Number Six	15.00	11.00	6.00
(7)	Number Seven	15.00	11.00	6.00
(8)	Seven No-Hitters	15.00	11.00	6.00

1992 Pacific Nolan Ryan Limited

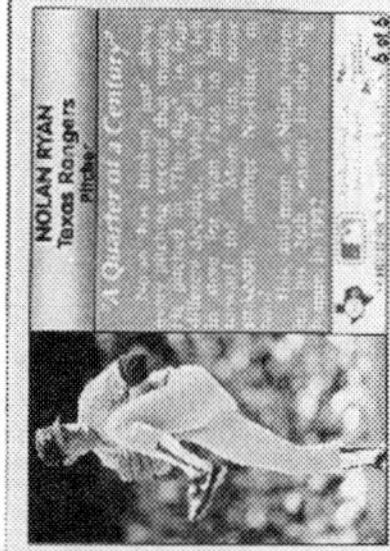

One of two insert sets included in both regular and jumbo foil packs of 1992 Pacific Nolan Ryan cards was this six-card presentation. Cards have the basic format of the regular issue except the "Texas Express" logo on front has been replaced by a Rangers team logo. Vertically formatted backs have a color photo at left and a few paragraphs of career summary at center. Each card was printed in an edition of 3,000, and Ryan personally autographed 1,000 of card #1. A second version of these cards, without the words "Limited Edition" on back beneath the Rangers and MLB logos, was produced for inclusion in the July, 1992, issue of "Trading Cards" magazine. The magazine versions of these cards are worth about 10" of the inserts.

		MT	NR MT	EX
Complete Set (6):		90.00	67.00	36.00
Common Ryan:		20.00	15.00	8.00
1	Nolan Ryan	20.00	15.00	8.00
2	Nolan Ryan	20.00	15.00	8.00
3	The Texas Express	20.00	15.00	8.00
4	Seventh No-Hitter	20.00	15.00	8.00
5	Texas Legacy	20.00	15.00	8.00
6	Quarter Century	20.00	15.00	8.00

1992 Pacific Tom Seaver

In a style similar to its popular Nolan Ryan sets, Pacific produced a Tom Seaver set of 110 cards in 1992. The company also produced two limited edition subsets as part of the "Tom Terrific" card series. Cards were sold in both foil packs and factory sets.

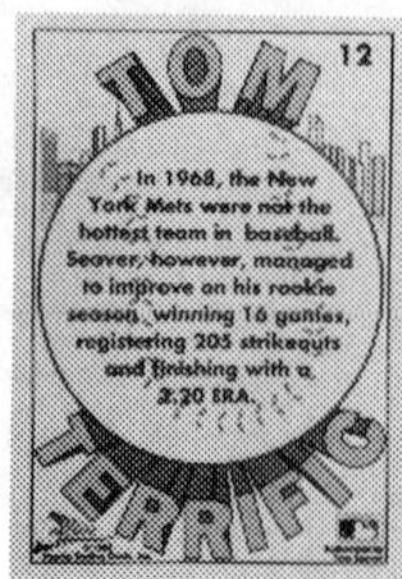

UV-coated fronts have white borders with silver, violet or magenta highlight stripes. A baseball symbol at lower-left has "Tom" above and "Terrific" beneath. This image is duplicated on back, with the ball containing either a photo or career highlights.

		MT	NR MT	EX
Complete Set (110):		8.00	6.00	3.25
Common Card:		.10	.08	.04
1	Stand-out High School Basketball Player	.10	.08	.04
2	Pro Ball Player	.10	.08	.04
3	Destined to be a Met	.10	.08	.04
4	Brave or Met	.10	.08	.04
5	Mets Luck of the Draw	.10	.08	.04
6	Sent to Jacksonville	.10	.08	.04
7	First Major League Win	.10	.08	.04
8	1967 Rookie of the Year	.10	.08	.04
9	Humble Beginnings	.10	.08	.04
10	Predicting the Future	.10	.08	.04
11	Rookie All-Star	.10	.08	.04
12	16 Wins in 1968	.10	.08	.04
13	1968 N.L. All-Star	.10	.08	.04
14	The Amazing Mets	.10	.08	.04
15	1969 Cy Young Winner	.10	.08	.04
16	Pitcher of the Year	.10	.08	.04
17	Strikeout Leader	.10	.08	.04
18	Ties Major League Record	.10	.08	.04
19	Mr. Consistency	.10	.08	.04
20	Finishing in Style	.10	.08	.04
21	Twenty-Game Winner	.10	.08	.04
22	Second Cy Young Award	.10	.08	.04
23	Batting Star	.10	.08	.04
24	At Bat in the World Series	.10	.08	.04
25	Championship Series Record	.10	.08	.04
26	Injury Plagued Season	.10	.08	.04
27	Comeback	.10	.08	.04
28	Super September	.10	.08	.04
29	Sporting News All-Star	.10	.08	.04
30	Strikeout Record	.10	.08	.04
31	USC Alumni Star	.10	.08	.04
32	Winning Smile	.10	.08	.04
33	One-Hitter	.10	.08	.04
34	Traded to the Reds	.10	.08	.04
35	New York Mets Pitcher	.10	.08	.04
36	Winning with the Reds	.10	.08	.04
37	No-Hitter	.10	.08	.04
38	N.L. Leader	.10	.08	.04
39	Smooth Swing	.10	.08	.04
40	No Decision in the Championship Series	.10	.08	.04
41	Injury Shortened Season	.10	.08	.04
42	Bouncing Back	.10	.08	.04
43	Eighth All-Star Appearance	.10	.08	.04
44	Spring Training 1982	.10	.08	.04
45	Back to New York	.10	.08	.04
46	Cincinnati Reds Pitcher	.10	.08	.04
47	Back in the Big Apple	.10	.08	.04
48	Opening Day Star	.10	.08	.04
49	Not Much Run Support	.10	.08	.04
50	Pair of Shutouts	.10	.08	.04
51	4,000 Inning Mark	.10	.08	.04
52	One Season in New York	.10	.08	.04
53	Chicago Bound	.10	.08	.04
54	Chicago White Sox Pitcher	.10	.08	.04
55	Win 300	.10	.08	.04
56	16 Wins in 1985	.10	.08	.04
57	Blast From the Past	.10	.08	.04
58	Moving Up in the Record Book	.10	.08	.04
59	Cy Young Winners	.10	.08	.04
60	Two Legends of the Game	.10	.08	.04
61	Singing Praise	.10	.08	.04
62	300th Win Tribute	.10	.08	.04
63	The Seaver Family	.10	.08	.04
64	20th Major League Season	.10	.08	.04
65	Traded to the Red Sox	.10	.08	.04
66	Chicago White Sox Career Record	.10	.08	.04
67	Red Sox Man	.10	.08	.04
68	Boston Red Sox Pitcher	.10	.08	.04
69	One Last Try	.10	.08	.04
70	Major League Records	.10	.08	.04
71	Lowest N.L. Career ERA	.10	.08	.04
72	Pitching in Comsikey Park	.10	.08	.04
73	273 N.L. Wins	.10	.08	.04
74	300 Win Honors	.10	.08	.04
75	311 Major League Wins	.10	.08	.04
76	41 Retired	.10	.08	.04
77	Championship Series 2.84 ERA	.10	.08	.04
78	June 1976 Age 32	.10	.08	.04
79	8-Time N.L. All-Star	.10	.08	.04
80	Broadcasting Career	.10	.08	.04
81	300th Win Celebration	.10	.08	.04

		MT	NR MT	EX
82	Tom and Nolan	.10	.08	.04
83	4th Best ERA All-Time	.10	.08	.04
84	15th All-Time in Victories	.10	.08	.04
85	300 Win Club	.10	.08	.04
86	Hall of Fame	.10	.08	.04
87	Pitching in Wrigley Field	.10	.08	.04
88	Power Pitching	.10	.08	.04
89	Spring Training 1980	.10	.08	.04
90	Pitching in Riverfront Stadium 1980	.10	.08	.04
91	Tom Terrific	.10	.08	.04
92	Super Seaver	.10	.08	.04
93	Top 10 All-Time	.10	.08	.04
94	16 Opening Day Starts	.10	.08	.04
95	3,272 Strikeouts	.10	.08	.04
96	Six Opening Day Wins	.10	.08	.04
97	239 Innings Pitched in 1985	.10	.08	.04
98	A Day Off	.10	.08	.04
99	Concentration (You Can't Let Up)	.10	.08	.04
100	Velocity, Movement, and Location	.10	.08	.04
101	Strikeout King	.10	.08	.04
102	The Most Important Pitch	.10	.08	.04
103	Cincinnati Reds Number 41	.10	.08	.04
104	George Thomas Seaver	.10	.08	.04
105	Dazzling Dean of the Reds' Staff	.10	.08	.04
106	Tom Receives the Judge Emil Fuchs Award	.10	.08	.04
107	Boston Mound Ace	.10	.08	.04
108	Fly Ball to Center	.10	.08	.04
109	August 4, 1985 Yankee Stadium	.10	.08	.04
110	Breaking Walter Johnson's Record	.10	.08	.04

Regional interest may affect the value of a card.

1992 Pacific Tom Seaver Milestones

Inserted into foil packs of its 1992 Seaver set, Pacific produced a gold-foil bordered set limited to 10,000 each of six different cards featuring career milestones. A white-bordered version of 3,000 cards each was also produced. One thousand of the "Rookie Phenomenon" cards were personally autographed by Seaver among the inserts. On each card, an action photo of Seaver is flanked at left with his name vertically printed in a fading color stripe. The "Tom Terrific" baseball logo carried is carried over from the regular set at lower-left. Backs have a second photo at left, and a summary of the career highlight.

		MT	NR MT	EX
Complete Set (6):		50.00	37.00	20.00
Complete Set, Gold (6):		60.00	45.00	24.00
Common Seaver:		10.00	7.50	4.00
Common Seaver, Gold:		12.50	9.50	5.00
1a	Rookie Phenomenon	10.00	7.50	4.00
1b	Rookie Phenomenon (gold)	12.50	9.50	5.00
2a	Miracle Mets	10.00	7.50	4.00
2b	Miracle Mets (gold)	12.50	9.50	5.00
3a	Strikeout Record	10.00	7.50	4.00
3b	Strikeout Record (gold)	12.50	9.50	5.00
4a	No-Hitter	10.00	7.50	4.00
4b	No-Hitter (gold)	12.50	9.50	5.00
5a	300th Win	10.00	7.50	4.00
5b	300th Win (gold)	12.50	9.50	5.00
6a	Hall of Fame	10.00	7.50	4.00
6b	Hall of Fame (gold)	12.50	9.50	5.00

1993 Pacific Nolan Ryan 27th Season

The Pacific Trading Card Company marked the record-breaking 27th season of Nolan Ryan's career by re-issuing all 220 cards in its popular Nolan Ryan set with a special logo. The first series of the set (110 cards) had been issued in 1991 and the second series was issued in 1992 and numbered 111-220. In 1993 the company released a 30-card update for the pitcher's final season, complete with the special logo. Later the company decided to reissue cards 1-

220 with the same logo because of the demand for the cards. Refer to 1991 and 1992 sets for card 1-220 checklists.

		MT	NR MT	EX
Complete Set (250):		22.00	16.50	8.75
Common Card:		.10	.08	.04
221	Rangers' Opening Night	.10	.08	.04
222	Slow Start in 1992	.10	.08	.04
223	Still Productive	.10	.08	.04
224	Getting Hot	.10	.08	.04
225	Closing Strong	.10	.08	.04
226	No Decision	.10	.08	.04
227	No Run Support	.10	.08	.04
228	Two Complete Games	.10	.08	.04
229	8-2/3 Inning Shutout	.10	.08	.04
230	Multiple Stikeout Games	.10	.08	.04
231	Ejected!	.10	.08	.04
232	319 and Counting	.10	.08	.04
233	Strikeout	.10	.08	.04
234	24 of 26 Seasons	.10	.08	.04
235	Smile, Nolan!	.10	.08	.04
236	Texas Ranger Marks	.10	.08	.04
237	Ranger Ace	.10	.08	.04
238	Another Record	.10	.08	.04
239	6th Place All-Time Innings Pitched	.10	.08	.04
240	27 Games Started in 1992	.10	.08	.04
241	Seaver & Ryan	.10	.08	.04
242	Angels' Number 30 Retired	.10	.08	.04
243	Angels' Nolan Ryan Night	.10	.08	.04
244	Angels' Hall of Fame	.10	.08	.04
245	Great Friends	.10	.08	.04
246	Cowboys	.10	.08	.04
247	Spring Training	.10	.08	.04
248	Smokin' Fastball	.10	.08	.04
249	The Texas Express	.10	.08	.04
250	Pacific Pride	.10	.08	.04

1993 Pacific Nolan Ryan Prism

An insert set unique to the 1993 Pacific Nolan Ryan 27th Season set was this issue of 20 prism cards. Fronts feature an action photo of Ryan against a prismatic background. Backs have another photo and a few brief biographical notes on a marbled background. Each prism card was produced in an edition of 10,000.

		MT	NR MT	EX
Complete Set (20):		225.00	170.00	90.00
Common Card:		15.00	11.00	6.00
1	Nolan Ryan	15.00	11.00	6.00
2	Nolan Ryan	15.00	11.00	6.00
3	Nolan Ryan	15.00	11.00	6.00
4	Nolan Ryan	15.00	11.00	6.00
5	Nolan Ryan	15.00	11.00	6.00
6	Nolan Ryan	15.00	11.00	6.00
7	Nolan Ryan	15.00	11.00	6.00
8	Nolan Ryan	15.00	11.00	6.00
9	Nolan Ryan	15.00	11.00	6.00
10	Nolan Ryan	15.00	11.00	6.00
11	Nolan Ryan	15.00	11.00	6.00
12	Nolan Ryan	15.00	11.00	6.00
13	Nolan Ryan	15.00	11.00	6.00
14	Nolan Ryan	15.00	11.00	6.00
15	Nolan Ryan	15.00	11.00	6.00
16	Nolan Ryan	15.00	11.00	6.00
17	Nolan Ryan	15.00	11.00	6.00
18	Nolan Ryan	15.00	11.00	6.00
19	Nolan Ryan	15.00	11.00	6.00
20	Nolan Ryan	15.00	11.00	6.00

1993 Pacific Nolan Ryan 27th Season Limited

Continuing with its "Limited Edition" insert set from the 1992 Nolan Ryan issue, this insert set picks up with numbers 7-12, featuring 1992 highlights in Ryan's career.

		MT	NR MT	EX
Complete Set (6):		65.00	49.00	26.00
Common Card:		15.00	11.00	6.00
7	Nolan Ryan	15.00	11.00	6.00
8	Nolan Ryan	15.00	11.00	6.00
9	Nolan Ryan	15.00	11.00	6.00
10	Nolan Ryan	15.00	11.00	6.00
11	Nolan Ryan	15.00	11.00	6.00
12	Nolan Ryan	15.00	11.00	6.00

1993 Pacific Nolan Ryan 27th Season Gold Ltd.

A gold-foil bordered version of the six 1993 Nolan Ryan "Limited Edition" insert cards was created as a card show give-away and random pack insert. Gold versions of cards #7-9 were given out at a Bellevue, Wash., show, while gold cards of #10-12 were found in foil packs. Just 3,000 of each foil-pack insert was produced.

		MT	NR MT	EX
Complete Set (6):		65.00	49.00	26.00
Common Card:		15.00	11.00	6.00
7	Nolan Ryan	15.00	11.00	6.00
8	Nolan Ryan	15.00	11.00	6.00
9	Nolan Ryan	15.00	11.00	6.00
10	Nolan Ryan	15.00	11.00	6.00
11	Nolan Ryan	15.00	11.00	6.00
12	Nolan Ryan	15.00	11.00	6.00

1993 Pacific Spanish

This set marks the first time a major league set was designed entirely for the Spanish-speaking market. Distribution areas included retail markets in the United States, Mexico, South America and the Caribbean. The cards are glossy and are written in Spanish on both sides. Cards are numbered in alphabetical order by team, beginning with Atlanta. Insert sets are titled Prism (20 cards featuring Spanish players and their accomplishments), Beisbol De Estralla (Stars of Baseball), Hot Players and Amigos (a 30-card set which features two players per card).

		MT	NR MT	EX
Complete Set (660):		20.00	15.00	8.00
Complete Series 1 (330):		12.00	9.00	4.75
Complete Series 2 (330):		8.00	6.00	3.25
Common Player:		.05	.04	.02
1	Rafael Belliard	.05	.04	.02
2	Sid Bream	.05	.04	.02
3	Francisco Cabrera	.05	.04	.02
4	Marvin Freeman	.05	.04	.02
5	Ron Gant	.15	.11	.06
6	Tom Glavine	.15	.11	.06
7	Brian Hunter	.05	.04	.02
8	Dave Justice	.20	.15	.08
9	Ryan Klesko	.50	.40	.20
10	Melvin Nieves	.20	.15	.08
11	Deion Sanders	.20	.15	.08
12	John Smoltz	.15	.11	.06
13	Mark Wohlers	.05	.04	.02
14	Brady Anderson	.15	.11	.06
15	Glenn Davis	.05	.04	.02
16	Mike Devereaux	.05	.04	.02
17	Leo Gomez	.05	.04	.02

18	Chris Hoiles	.15	.11	.06
19	Chito Martinez	.05	.04	.02
20	Ben McDonald	.15	.11	.06
21	Mike Mussina	.40	.30	.15
22	Gregg Olson	.05	.04	.02
23	Joe Orsulak	.05	.04	.02
24	Cal Ripken,Jr.	.50	.40	.20
25	David Segui	.05	.04	.02
26	Rick Sutcliffe	.05	.04	.02
27	Wade Boggs	.20	.15	.08
28	Tom Brunansky	.05	.04	.02
29	Ellis Burks	.05	.04	.02
30	Roger Clemens	.50	.40	.20
31	John Dopson	.05	.04	.02
32	John Flaherty	.05	.04	.02
33	Mike Greenwell	.05	.04	.02
34	Tony Pena	.05	.04	.02
35	Carlos Quintana	.05	.04	.02
36	Luis Rivera	.05	.04	.02
37	Mo Vaughn	.05	.04	.02
38	Frank Viola	.05	.04	.02
39	Matt Young	.05	.04	.02
40	Scott Bailes	.05	.04	.02
41	Bert Blyleven	.05	.04	.02
42	Chad Curtis	.50	.40	.20
43	Gary DiSarcina	.05	.04	.02
44	Chuck Finley	.05	.04	.02
45	Mike Fitzgerald	.05	.04	.02
46	Gary Gaetti	.05	.04	.02
47	Rene Gonzales	.05	.04	.02
48	Mark Langston	.05	.04	.02
49	Scott Lewis	.05	.04	.02
50	Luis Polonia	.05	.04	.02
51	Tim Salmon	.50	.40	.20
52	Lee Stevens	.05	.04	.02
53	Steve Buechele	.05	.04	.02
54	Frank Castillo	.05	.04	.02
55	Doug Dascenzo	.05	.04	.02
56	Andre Dawson	.20	.15	.08
57	Shawon Dunston	.05	.04	.02
58	Mark Grace	.20	.15	.08
59	Mike Morgan	.05	.04	.02
60	Luis Salazar	.05	.04	.02
61	Rey Sanchez	.05	.04	.02
62	Ryne Sandberg	.50	.40	.20
63	Dwight Smith	.05	.04	.02
64	Jerome Walton	.05	.04	.02
65	Rick Wilkins	.05	.04	.02
66	Wilson Alvarez	.05	.04	.02
67	George Bell	.05	.04	.02
68	Joey Cora	.05	.04	.02
69	Alex Fernandez	.05	.04	.02
70	Carlton Fisk	.05	.04	.02
71	Craig Grebeck	.05	.04	.02
72	Ozzie Guillen	.05	.04	.02
73	Jack McDowell	.20	.15	.08
74	Scott Radinsky	.05	.04	.02
75	Tim Raines	.05	.04	.02
76	Bobby Thigpen	.05	.04	.02
77	Frank Thomas	2.00	1.50	.80
78	Robin Ventura	.30	.25	.12
79	Tom Browning	.05	.04	.02
80	Jacob Brumfield	.05	.04	.02
81	Rob Dibble	.05	.04	.02
82	Bill Doran	.05	.04	.02
83	Billy Hatcher	.05	.04	.02
84	Barry Larkin	.20	.15	.08
85	Hal Morris	.05	.04	.02
86	Joe Oliver	.05	.04	.02
87	Jeff Reed	.05	.04	.02
88	Jose Rijo	.05	.04	.02
89	Bip Roberts	.05	.04	.02
90	Chris Sabo	.05	.04	.02
91	Sandy Alomar, Jr.	.20	.15	.08
92	Brad Arnsberg	.05	.04	.02
93	Carlos Baerga	.30	.25	.12
94	Albert Belle	.30	.25	.12
95	Felix Fermin	.05	.04	.02
96	Mark Lewis	.05	.04	.02
97	Kenny Lofton	.50	.40	.20
98	Carlos Martinez	.05	.04	.02
99	Rod Nicholos	.05	.04	.02
100	Dave Rohde	.05	.04	.02
101	Scott Scudder	.05	.04	.02
102	Paul Sorrento	.05	.04	.02
103	Mark Whiten	.05	.04	.02
104	Mark Carreon	.05	.04	.02
105	Milt Cuyler	.05	.04	.02
106	Rob Deer	.05	.04	.02
107	Cecil Fielder	.25	.20	.10
108	Travis Fryman	.40	.30	.15
109	Dan Gladden	.05	.04	.02
110	Bill Gullickson	.05	.04	.02
111	Les Lancaster	.05	.04	.02
112	Mark Leiter	.05	.04	.02
113	Tony Phillips	.05	.04	.02
114	Mickey Tettleton	.05	.04	.02
115	Alan Trammell	.05	.04	.02
116	Lou Whitaker	.05	.04	.02
117	Jeff Bagwell	.30	.25	.12
118	Craig Biggio	.05	.04	.02
119	Joe Boever	.05	.04	.02
120	Casey Candaele	.05	.04	.02
121	Andujar Cedeno	.05	.04	.02
122	Steve Finley	.05	.04	.02
123	Luis Gonzalez	.05	.04	.02
124	Pete Harnisch	.05	.04	.02
125	Jimmy Jones	.05	.04	.02
126	Mark Portugal	.05	.04	.02
127	Rafael Ramirez	.05	.04	.02
128	Mike Simms	.05	.04	.02
129	Eric Yelding	.05	.04	.02
130	Luis Aquino	.05	.04	.02
131	Kevin Appier	.05	.04	.02
132	Mike Boddicker	.05	.04	.02
133	George Brett	.30	.25	.12
134	Tom Gordon	.05	.04	.02
135	Mark Gubicza	.05	.04	.02
136	David Howard	.05	.04	.02
137	Gregg Jefferies	.20	.15	.08
138	Wally Joyner	.20	.15	.08
139	Brian McRae	.05	.04	.02
140	Jeff Montgomery	.05	.04	.02
141	Terry Shumpert	.05	.04	.02
142	Curtis Wilkerson	.05	.04	.02
143	Brett Butler	.05	.04	.02
144	Eric Davis	.20	.15	.08
145	Kevin Gross	.05	.04	.02
146	Dave Hansen	.05	.04	.02
147	Lenny Harris	.05	.04	.02
148	Carlos Hernandez	.05	.04	.02
149	Orel Hershiser	.05	.04	.02
150	Jay Howell	.05	.04	.02
151	Eric Karros	.50	.40	.20
152	Ramon Martinez	.20	.15	.08
153	Jose Offerman	.05	.04	.02
154	Mike Sharperson	.05	.04	.02
155	Darryl Strawberry	.30	.25	.12
156	Jim Gantner	.05	.04	.02
157	Darryl Hamilton	.05	.04	.02
158	Doug Henry	.05	.04	.02
159	John Jaha	.20	.15	.08
160	Pat Listach	.50	.40	.20
161	Jaime Navarro	.05	.04	.02
162	Dave Nilsson	.25	.20	.10
163	Jesse Orosco	.05	.04	.02
164	Kevin Seitzer	.05	.04	.02
165	B.J. Surhoff	.05	.04	.02
166	Greg Vaughn	.05	.04	.02
167	Robin Yount	.30	.25	.12
168	Rick Aguilera	.05	.04	.02
169	Scott Erickson	.05	.04	.02
170	Mark Guthrie	.05	.04	.02
171	Kent Hrbek	.05	.04	.02
172	Chuck Knoblauch	.30	.25	.12
173	Gene Larkin	.05	.04	.02
174	Shane Mack	.15	.11	.06
175	Pedro Munoz	.05	.04	.02
176	Mike Pagliarulo	.05	.04	.02
177	Kirby Puckett	.50	.40	.20
178	Kevin Tapani	.05	.04	.02
179	Gary Wayne	.05	.04	.02
180	Moises Alou	.20	.15	.08
181	Brian Barnes	.05	.04	.02
182	Archie Cianfrocco	.05	.04	.02
183	Delino DeShields	.20	.15	.08
184	Darrin Fletcher	.05	.04	.02
185	Marquis Grissom	.30	.25	.12
186	Ken Hill	.05	.04	.02
187	Dennis Martinez	.05	.04	.02
188	Bill Sampen	.05	.04	.02
189	John VanderWal	.05	.04	.02
190	Larry Walker	.30	.25	.12
191	Tim Wallach	.05	.04	.02
192	Bobby Bonilla	.25	.20	.10
193	Daryl Boston	.05	.04	.02
194	Vince Coleman	.05	.04	.02
195	Kevin Elster	.05	.04	.02
196	Sid Fernandez	.05	.04	.02
197	John Franco	.05	.04	.02
198	Dwight Gooden	.25	.20	.10
199	Howard Johnson	.05	.04	.02
200	Willie Randolph	.05	.04	.02
201	Bret Saberhagen	.05	.04	.02
202	Dick Schofield	.05	.04	.02
203	Pete Schourek	.05	.04	.02
204	Greg Cadaret	.05	.04	.02
205	John Habyan	.05	.04	.02
206	Pat Kelly	.05	.04	.02
207	Kevin Maas	.05	.04	.02
208	Don Mattingly	.30	.25	.12
209	Matt Nokes	.05	.04	.02
210	Melido Perez	.05	.04	.02
211	Scott Sanderson	.05	.04	.02
212	Andy Stankiewicz	.05	.04	.02
213	Danny Tartabull	.05	.04	.02
215	Bernie Williams	.05	.04	.02
216	Harold Baines	.05	.04	.02
217	Mike Bordick	.05	.04	.02
218	Scott Brosius	.05	.04	.02
219	Jerry Browne	.05	.04	.02
220	Ron Darling	.05	.04	.02
221	Dennis Eckersley	.25	.20	.10
222	Rickey Henderson	.30	.25	.12
223	Rick Honeycutt	.05	.04	.02
224	Mark McGwire	.30	.25	.12
225	Ruben Sierra	.15	.11	.06
226	Terry Steinbach	.05	.04	.02
227	Bob Welch	.05	.04	.02
228	Willie Wilson	.05	.04	.02
229	Ruben Amaro	.05	.04	.02
230	Kim Batiste	.05	.04	.02
231	Juan Bell	.05	.04	.02
232	Wes Chamberlain	.05	.04	.02
233	Darren Daulton	.15	.11	.06
234	Mariano Duncan	.05	.04	.02
235	Len Dykstra	.10	.07	.04
236	Dave Hollins	.15	.11	.06
237	Stan Javier	.05	.04	.02
238	John Kruk	.05	.04	.02
239	Mickey Morandini	.05	.04	.02
240	Terry Mulholland	.05	.04	.02
241	Mitch Williams	.05	.04	.02
242	Stan Belinda	.05	.04	.02
243	Jay Bell	.05	.04	.02
244	Carlos Garcia	.30	.25	.12
245	Jeff King	.05	.04	.02
246	Mike LaValliere	.05	.04	.02
247	Lloyd McClendon	.05	.04	.02
248	Orlando Merced	.05	.04	.02
249	Paul Miller	.05	.04	.02
250	Gary Redus	.05	.04	.02
251	Don Slaught	.05	.04	.02
252	Zane Smith	.05	.04	.02
253	Andy Van Slyke	.15	.11	.06
254	Tim Wakefield	.60	.45	.25
255	Andy Benes	.05	.04	.02
256	Dann Bilardello	.05	.04	.02
257	Tony Gwynn	.25	.20	.10
258	Greg Harris	.05	.04	.02
259	Darrin Jackson	.05	.04	.02
260	Mike Maddux	.05	.04	.02
261	Fred McGriff	.25	.20	.10
262	Rich Rodriguez	.05	.04	.02
263	Benito Santiago	.05	.04	.02
264	Gary Sheffield	.50	.40	.20
265	Kurt Stillwell	.05	.04	.02
266	Tim Teufel	.05	.04	.02
267	Bud Black	.05	.04	.02
268	John Burkett	.05	.04	.02
269	Will Clark	.40	.30	.15
270	Royce Calyton	.15	.11	.06
271	Bryan Hickerson	.05	.04	.02
272	Chris James	.05	.04	.02
273	Darren Lewis	.05	.04	.02
274	Willie McGee	.05	.04	.02
275	Jim McNamara	.05	.04	.02
276	Francisco Oliveras	.05	.04	.02
277	Robby Thompson	.05	.04	.02
278	Matt Williams	.15	.11	.06
279	Trevor Wilson	.05	.04	.02
280	Bret Boone	.25	.20	.10
281	Greg Briley	.05	.04	.02
282	Jay Buhner	.05	.04	.02
283	Henry Cotto	.05	.04	.02
284	Rich DeLucia	.05	.04	.02
285	Dave Fleming	.25	.20	.10
286	Ken Griffey, Jr.	1.00	.70	.40
287	Erik Hanson	.05	.04	.02
288	Randy Johnson	.05	.04	.02
289	Tino Martinez	.05	.04	.02
290	Edgar Martinez	.20	.15	.08
291	Dave Valle	.05	.04	.02
292	Omar Vizquel	.05	.04	.02
293	Luis Alicea	.05	.04	.02
294	Bernard Gilkey	.05	.04	.02
295	Felix Jose	.05	.04	.02
296	Ray Lankford	.30	.25	.12
297	Omar Olivares	.05	.04	.02
298	Jose Oquendo	.05	.04	.02
299	Tom Pagnozzi	.05	.04	.02
300	Geronimo Pena	.05	.04	.02
301	Gerald Perry	.05	.04	.02
302	Ozzie Smith	.30	.25	.12
303	Lee Smith	.05	.04	.02
304	Bob Tewksbury	.05	.04	.02
305	Todd Zeile	.15	.11	.06
306	Kevin Brown	.05	.04	.02
307	Todd Burns	.05	.04	.02
308	Jose Canseco	.50	.40	.20
309	Hector Fajardo	.05	.04	.02
310	Julio Franco	.05	.04	.02
311	Juan Gonzalez	.50	.40	.20
312	Jeff Huson	.05	.04	.02
313	Rob Maurer	.05	.04	.02
314	Rafael Palmeiro	.20	.15	.08
315	Dean Palmer	.20	.15	.08
316	Ivan Rodriguez	.30	.25	.12
317	Nolan Ryan	.60	.45	.25
318	Dickie Thon	.05	.04	.02
319	Roberto Alomar	.50	.40	.20
320	Derek Bell	.05	.04	.02
321	Pat Borders	.05	.04	.02
322	Joe Carter	.30	.25	.12
323	Kelly Gruber	.05	.04	.02
324	Juan Guzman	.25	.20	.10
325	Manny Lee	.05	.04	.02
326	Jack Morris	.05	.04	.02
327	John Olerud	.05	.04	.02
328	Ed Sprague	.05	.04	.02
329	Todd Stottlemyre	.05	.04	.02
330	Duane Ward	.05	.04	.02
331	Steve Avery	.20	.15	.08
332	Damon Berryhill	.05	.04	.02
333	Jeff Blauser	.05	.04	.02
334	Mark Lemke	.05	.04	.02
335	Greg Maddux	.20	.15	.08
336	Kent Mercker	.05	.04	.02
337	Otis Nixon	.07	.05	.03
338	Greg Olson	.05	.04	.02
339	Bill Pecota	.05	.04	.02
340	Terry Pendleton	.08	.06	.03
341	Mike Stanton	.05	.04	.02
342	Todd Frohwirth	.05	.04	.02
343	Tim Hulett	.05	.04	.02
344	Mark McLemore	.05	.04	.02
345	*Luis Mercedes*	.08	.06	.03
346	Alan Mills	.05	.04	.02
347	*Sherman Obando*	.10	.07	.04
348	Jim Poole	.05	.04	.02
349	Harold Reynolds	.05	.04	.02
350	Arthur Rhodes	.05	.04	.02
351	Jeff Tackett	.05	.04	.02
352	Fernando Valenzuela	.05	.04	.02
353	Scott Bankhead	.05	.04	.02
354	Ivan Calderon	.05	.04	.02
355	Scott Cooper	.08	.06	.03
356	Danny Darwin	.05	.04	.02
357	Scott Fletcher	.05	.04	.02
358	Tony Fossas	.05	.04	.02
359	Greg Harris	.05	.04	.02
360	Joe Hasketh	.05	.04	.02
361	Jose Melendez	.05	.04	.02
362	Paul Quantrill	.08	.06	.03
363	John Valentin	.07	.05	.03
364	*Mike Butcher*	.08	.06	.03
365	Chuck Crim	.05	.04	.02
366	Chili Davis	.05	.04	.02
367	Damion Easley	.10	.07	.04
368	Steve Frey	.05	.04	.02
369	Joe Grahe	.05	.04	.02
370	Greg Myers	.05	.04	.02
371	John Orton	.05	.04	.02
372	*J.T. Snow*	.60	.45	.25

373	Ron Tingley	.05	.04	.02
374	Julio Valera	.05	.04	.02
375	Paul Assenmacher	.05	.04	.02
376	Jose Bautista	.05	.04	.02
377	Jose Guzman	.05	.04	.02
378	Greg Hibbard	.05	.04	.02
379	Candy Maldonado	.05	.04	.02
380	Derrick May	.08	.06	.03
381	Dan Plesac	.05	.04	.02
382	*Tommy Shields*	.08	.06	.03
383	Sammy Sosa	.10	.07	.04
384	Jose Vizcaino	.05	.04	.02
385	*Greg Walbeck*	.08	.06	.03
386	Ellis Burks	.05	.04	.02
387	Roberto Hernandez	.05	.04	.02
388	Mike Huff	.08	.06	.03
389	Bo Jackson	.15	.11	.06
390	Lance Johnson	.05	.04	.02
391	Ron Karkovice	.05	.04	.02
392	Kirk McCaskill	.05	.04	.02
393	Donn Pall	.05	.04	.02
394	Dan Pasqua	.05	.04	.02
395	Steve Sax	.05	.04	.02
396	Dave Stieb	.05	.04	.02
397	*Bobby Ayala*	.07	.05	.03
398	Tim Belcher	.05	.04	.02
399	*Jeff Branson*	.08	.06	.03
400	Cesar Hernandez	.07	.05	.03
401	Roberto Kelly	.08	.06	.03
402	Randy Milligan	.05	.04	.02
403	Kevin Mitchell	.05	.04	.02
404	Juan Samuel	.05	.04	.02
405	Reggie Sanders	.10	.07	.04
406	John Smiley	.05	.04	.02
407	*Dan Wilson*	.15	.11	.06
408	Mike Christopher	.05	.04	.02
409	Dennis Cook	.05	.04	.02
410	Alvaro Espinoza	.05	.04	.02
411	Glenallen Hill	.05	.04	.02
412	Reggie Jefferson	.08	.06	.03
413	Derek Lilliquist	.05	.04	.02
414	Jose Mesa	.05	.04	.02
415	Charles Nagy	.05	.04	.02
416	Junior Ortiz	.05	.04	.02
417	Eric Plunk	.05	.04	.02
418	Ted Power	.05	.04	.02
419	Scott Aldred	.05	.04	.02
420	Andy Ashby	.05	.04	.02
421	Freddie Benavides	.05	.04	.02
422	Dante Bichette	.05	.04	.02
423	Willie Blair	.05	.04	.02
424	Vinny Castilla	.05	.04	.02
425	Jerald Clark	.05	.04	.02
426	Alex Cole	.05	.04	.02
427	Andres Galarraga	.08	.06	.03
428	Joe Girardi	.05	.04	.02
429	Charlie Hayes	.07	.05	.03
430	Butch Henry	.05	.04	.02
431	Darren Holmes	.05	.04	.02
432	Dale Murphy	.08	.06	.03
433	*David Nied*	.20	.15	.08
434	Jeff Parrett	.05	.04	.02
435	Steve Reed	.05	.04	.02
436	Armando Reynoso	.05	.04	.02
437	Bruce Ruffin	.05	.04	.02
438	Bryn Smith	.05	.04	.02
439	*Jim Tatum*	.10	.07	.04
440	Eric Young	.10	.07	.04
441	Skeeter Barnes	.05	.04	.02
442	Tom Bolton	.05	.04	.02
443	Kirk Gibson	.05	.04	.02
444	Chad Krueter	.05	.04	.02
445	Bill Krueger	.05	.04	.02
446	Scott Livingstone	.05	.04	.02
447	Bob MacDonald	.05	.04	.02
448	Mike Moore	.05	.04	.02
449	Mike Munoz	.05	.04	.02
450	Gary Thurman	.05	.04	.02
451	David Wells	.05	.04	.02
452	Alex Arias	.07	.05	.03
453	Jack Armstrong	.05	.04	.02
454	Bret Barberie	.05	.04	.02
455	Ryan Bowen	.08	.06	.03
456	Cris Carpenter	.05	.04	.02
457	Chuck Carr	.08	.06	.03
458	Jeff Conine	.08	.06	.03
459	Steve Decker	.08	.06	.03
460	Orestes Destrade	.07	.05	.03
461	Monty Fariss	.07	.05	.03
462	Junior Felix	.05	.04	.02
463	Bryan Harvey	.07	.05	.03
464	*Trevor Hoffman*	.08	.06	.03
465	Charlie Hough	.05	.04	.02
466	Dave Magadan	.05	.04	.02
467	Bob McClure	.05	.04	.02
468	*Rob Natal*	.07	.05	.03
469	*Scott Pose*	.07	.05	.03
470	Rich Renteria	.05	.04	.02
471	Benito Santiago	.05	.04	.02
472	*Matt Turner*	.08	.06	.03
473	Walt Weiss	.05	.04	.02
474	Eric Anthony	.08	.06	.03
475	Chris Donnels	.05	.04	.02
476	Doug Drabek	.05	.04	.02
477	Xavier Hernandez	.05	.04	.02
478	Doug Jones	.05	.04	.02
479	Darryl Kile	.05	.04	.02
480	Scott Servais	.05	.04	.02
481	Greg Swindell	.05	.04	.02
482	Eddie Taubensee	.05	.04	.02
483	Jose Uribe	.05	.04	.02
484	Brian Williams	.07	.05	.03
485	*Billy Brewer*	.08	.06	.03
486	David Cone	.05	.04	.02
487	Greg Gagne	.05	.04	.02
488	*Phil Hiatt*	.25	.20	.10
489	Jose Lind	.05	.04	.02
490	Brent Mayne	.05	.04	.02
491	Kevin Mcreynolds	.05	.04	.02
492	Keith Miller	.05	.04	.02
493	*Hipolito Pichardo*	.07	.05	.03
494	Harvey Pulliam	.05	.04	.02
495	Rico Rossay	.05	.04	.02
496	*Pedro Astacio*	.15	.11	.06
497	Tom Candiotti	.05	.04	.02
498	Tom Goodwin	.05	.04	.02
499	Jim Gott	.05	.04	.02
500	*Pedro Martinez*	.10	.07	.04
501	Roger McDowell	.05	.04	.02
502	*Mike Piazza*	2.00	1.50	.80
503	Jody Reed	.05	.04	.02
504	Rick Trlicek	.08	.06	.03
505	Mitch Weber	.08	.06	.03
506	Steve Wilson	.05	.04	.02
507	James Austin	.05	.04	.02
508	Ricky Bones	.05	.04	.02
509	*Alex Diaz*	.08	.06	.03
510	Mike Fetters	.05	.04	.02
511	Teddy Higuera	.05	.04	.02
512	*Graeme Lloyd*	.10	.07	.04
513	Carlos Maldonado	.05	.04	.02
514	*Josias Manzanillo*	.08	.06	.03
515	Kevin Reimer	.05	.04	.02
516	Bill Spiers	.05	.04	.02
517	Bill Wegman	.05	.04	.02
518	Willie Banks	.05	.04	.02
519	*J.T. Bruett*	.08	.06	.03
520	Brian Harper	.05	.04	.02
521	Terry Jorgensen	.05	.04	.02
522	Scott Leius	.05	.04	.02
523	Pat Mahomes	.08	.06	.03
524	Dave McCarty	.15	.11	.06
525	Jeff Reboulet	.08	.06	.03
526	Mike Trombley	.05	.04	.02
527	Carl Willis	.05	.04	.02
528	Dave Winfield	.10	.07	.04
529	Sean Berry	.05	.04	.02
530	Frank Bolick	.08	.06	.03
531	Kent Bottenfield	.05	.04	.02
532	Wil Cordero	.10	.07	.04
533	Jeff Fassero	.08	.06	.03
534	*Tim Laker*	.10	.07	.04
535	*Mike Lansing*	.20	.15	.08
536	Chris Nabholz	.05	.04	.02
537	Mel Rojas	.05	.04	.02
538	John Wetteland	.05	.04	.02
539	Ted Wood	.05	.04	.02
540	Mike Draper	.05	.04	.02
541	Tony Fernandez	.05	.04	.02
542	Todd Hundley	.05	.04	.02
543	Jeff Innis	.05	.04	.02
544	Jeff McKnight	.05	.04	.02
545	Eddie Murray	.10	.07	.04
546	Charlie O'Brien	.05	.04	.02
547	Frank Tanana	.05	.04	.02
548	*Ryan Thompson*	.08	.06	.03
549	*Chico Walker*	.10	.07	.04
550	Anthony Young	.05	.04	.02
551	Jim Abbott	.10	.07	.04
552	Wade Boggs	.10	.07	.04
553	Steve Farr	.05	.04	.02
554	Neal Heaton	.05	.04	.02
555	Steve Howe	.05	.04	.02
556	Dion James	.05	.04	.02
557	Scott Kamieniecki	.05	.04	.02
558	Jimmy Key	.05	.04	.02
559	Jim Leyritz	.05	.04	.02
560	Paul O'Neill	.07	.05	.03
561	Spike Owen	.05	.04	.02
562	Lance Blankenship	.05	.04	.02
563	Joe Boever	.05	.04	.02
564	Storm Davis	.05	.04	.02
565	Kelly Downs	.05	.04	.02
566	*Eric Fox*	.10	.07	.04
567	Rich Gossage	.05	.04	.02
568	Dave Henderson	.05	.04	.02
569	Shawn Hillegas	.05	.04	.02
570	Mike Mohler	.08	.06	.03
571	*Troy Neel*	.15	.11	.06
572	Dale Sveum	.05	.04	.02
573	Larry Anderson	.05	.04	.02
574	Bob Ayrault	.05	.04	.02
575	Jose DeLeon	.05	.04	.02
576	Jim Eisenreich	.05	.04	.02
577	Pete Incaviglia	.05	.04	.02
578	Danny Jackson	.05	.04	.02
579	Ricky Jordan	.05	.04	.02
580	Ben Rivera	.05	.04	.02
581	Curt Schilling	.05	.04	.02
582	Milt Thompson	.05	.04	.02
583	David West	.05	.04	.02
584	John Candelaria	.05	.04	.02
585	Steve Cooke	.05	.04	.02
586	Tom Foley	.05	.04	.02
587	*Al Martin*	.10	.07	.04
588	*Blas Minor*	.10	.07	.04
589	Dennis Moeller	.07	.05	.03
590	Denny Neagle	.05	.04	.02
591	Tom Prince	.05	.04	.02
592	Randy Tomlin	.05	.04	.02
593	Bob Walk	.05	.04	.02
594	*Kevin Young*	.10	.07	.04
595	Pat Gomez	.05	.04	.02
596	Ricky Gutierrez	.05	.04	.02
597	Gene Harris	.05	.04	.02
598	Jeremy Hernandez	.05	.04	.02
599	Phil Plantier	.10	.07	.04
600	Tim Scott	.07	.05	.03
601	Frank Seminara	.07	.05	.03
602	*Darrell Sherman*	.07	.05	.03
603	Craig Shipley	.05	.04	.02
604	Guillermo Velasquez	.05	.04	.02
605	Dan Walters	.08	.06	.03
606	Mike Benjamin	.05	.04	.02
607	Barry Bonds	.20	.15	.08
608	Jeff Brantley	.05	.04	.02
609	Dave Burba	.05	.04	.02
610	*Craig Colbert*	.08	.06	.03
611	Mike Jackson	.05	.04	.02
612	Kirt Manwaring	.05	.04	.02
613	Dave Martinez	.05	.04	.02
614	Dave Righetti	.05	.04	.02
615	Kevin Rogers	.05	.04	.02
616	Bill Swift	.05	.04	.02
617	Rich Amaral	.05	.04	.02
618	Mike Blowers	.05	.04	.02
619	Chris Bosio	.05	.04	.02
620	Norm Charlton	.05	.04	.02
621	*John Cummings*	.10	.07	.04
622	Mike Felder	.05	.04	.02
623	Bill Haselman	.05	.04	.02
624	Tim Leary	.05	.04	.02
625	Pete O'Brien	.05	.04	.02
626	Russ Swan	.05	.04	.02
627	*Fernando Vina*	.08	.06	.03
628	*Rene Arocha*	.10	.07	.04
629	Rod Brewer	.05	.04	.02
630	Ozzie Canseco	.05	.04	.02
631	Rheal Cormier	.08	.06	.03
632	Brian Jordan	.08	.06	.03
633	Joe Magrane	.05	.04	.02
634	Donovan Osborne	.05	.04	.02
635	Mike Perez	.05	.04	.02
636	Stan Royer	.05	.04	.02
637	Hector Villanueva	.05	.04	.02
638	Tracy Woodson	.05	.04	.02
639	*Benji Gil*	.35	.25	.14
640	Tom Henke	.05	.04	.02
641	*David Hulse*	.15	.11	.06
642	Charlie Leibrandt	.05	.04	.02
643	*Robb Nen*	.08	.06	.03
644	*Dan Peltier*	.10	.07	.04
645	Billy Ripken	.05	.04	.02
646	Kenny Rogers	.05	.04	.02
647	John Russell	.05	.04	.02
648	*Dan Smith*	.08	.06	.03
649	Matt Whiteside	.08	.06	.03
650	*William Canate*	.10	.07	.04
651	Darnell Coles	.05	.04	.02
652	Al Leiter	.05	.04	.02
653	*Dominigo Martinez*	.08	.06	.03
654	Paul Molitor	.10	.07	.04
655	Luis Sojo	.05	.04	.02
656	Dave Stewart	.05	.04	.02
657	Mike Timlin	.05	.04	.02
658	Turner Ward	.05	.04	.02
659	Devon White	.08	.06	.03
660	Eddie Zosky	.08	.06	.03

1993 Pacific Spanish Gold Foil Stars

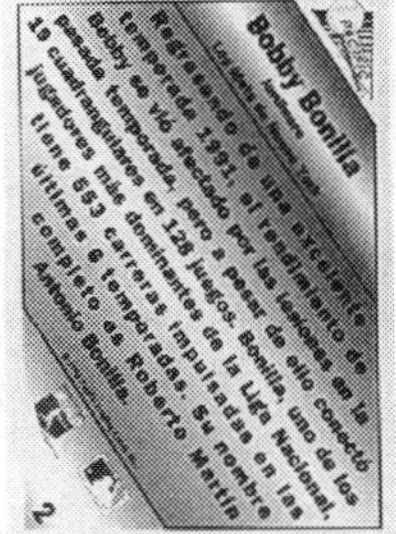

Pacific produced a Gold Foil Stars of Baseball set of 20 that was randomly inserted as part of the company's first-ever Spanish Language Major League set in 1993. Each card features a color action photo on the front surrounded by a gold-foil border. Both the Stars of Baseball and the Pacific Prism sets were limited to 10,000 of each.

		MT	NR MT	EX
Complete Set (20):		300.00	225.00	125.00
Common Player:		12.00	9.00	4.75
1	Moises Alou	18.00	13.50	7.25
2	Bobby Bonilla	15.00	11.00	6.00
3	Tony Fernandez	12.00	9.00	4.75
4	Felix Jose	12.00	9.00	4.75
5	Dennis Martinez	12.00	9.00	4.75
6	Orlando Merced	12.00	9.00	4.75
7	Jose Oquendo	12.00	9.00	4.75
8	Geronimo Pena	12.00	9.00	4.75
9	Jose Rijo	12.00	9.00	4.75
10	Benito Santiago	15.00	11.00	6.00
11	Sandy Alomar Jr.	15.00	11.00	6.00
12	Carlos Baerga	35.00	26.00	14.00
13	Jose Canseco	20.00	15.00	8.00
14	Juan "Igor" Gonzalez	45.00	34.00	18.00
15	Juan Guzman	18.00	13.50	7.25
16	Edgar Martinez	12.00	9.00	4.75
17	Rafael Palmerio	18.00	13.50	7.25
18	Ruben Sierra	18.00	13.50	7.25
19	Danny Tartabull	17.00	12.50	6.75
20	Omar Vizquel	12.00	9.00	4.75

1993 Pacific Prism Insert

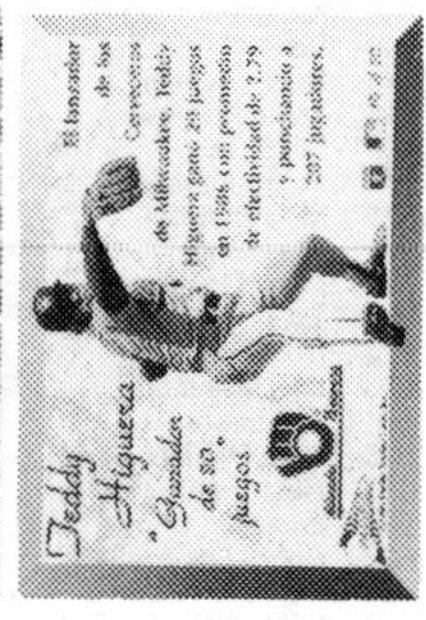

Pacific also produced a Prism card that was randomly inserted in the Spanish Language Major League set in 1993. Each card in the 20-card set has a color photo of the player on the front superimposed over a prismatic background. The card backs contain a color action photo and a brief player biography on a marbelized background.

		MT	NR MT	EX
Complete Set (20):		300.00	225.00	125.00
Common Player:		12.00	9.00	4.75
1	Francisco Cabrera	12.00	9.00	4.75
2	Jose Lind	12.00	9.00	4.75
3	Dennis Martinez	12.00	9.00	4.75
4	Ramon Martinez	14.00	10.50	5.50
5	Jose Rijo	12.00	9.00	4.75
6	Benito Santiago	12.00	9.00	4.75
7	Roberto Alomar	35.00	26.00	14.00
8	Sandy Alomar Jr.	12.00	9.00	4.75
9	Carlos Baerga	35.00	26.00	14.00
10	George Bell	14.00	10.50	5.50
11	Jose Canseco	20.00	15.00	8.00
12	Alex Fernandez	20.00	15.00	8.00
13	Julio Franco	15.00	11.00	6.00
14	Igor (Juan) Gonzalez	45.00	34.00	18.00
15	Ozzie Guillen	12.00	9.00	4.75
16	Teddy Higuera	12.00	9.00	4.75
17	Edgar Martinez	12.00	9.00	4.75
18	Hipolito Pichardo	12.00	9.00	4.75
19	Luis Polonia	12.00	9.00	4.75
20	Ivan Rodriguez	20.00	15.00	8.00

1994 Pacific Crown Promos

Virtually identical in format to the regular 1994 Pacific Crown issue, the eight cards in the promo set have a "P-" prefix to the card number. Each side has a large "For Promotional Use Only" printed diagonally in black. The cards were sent to dealers as a preview to Pacific's 1994 bilingual issue.

		MT	NR MT	EX
Complete Set (8):		27.50	21.00	11.00
Common Player:		3.00	2.25	1.25
1	Carlos Baerga	3.00	2.25	1.25
2	Joe Carter	3.00	2.25	1.25
3	Juan Gonzalez	6.00	4.50	2.50
4	Ken Griffey, Jr.	6.00	4.50	2.50
5	Greg Maddux	3.00	2.25	1.25
6	Mike Piazza	4.50	3.50	1.75
7	Tim Salmon	4.00	3.00	1.50
8	Frank Thomas	7.50	5.75	3.00

1994 Pacific Crown

Following its 1993 Spanish-language set, Pacific's 1994 "Crown Collection" offering is bi-lingual, featuring both English and Spanish for most of the back printing. Fronts have an action photo which is borderless at the top and sides. A gold-foil line separates the bottom of the photo from a marbled strip that is color-coded by team. The player's name appears in two lines at the left of the strip, a gold-foil

crown logo is at left. A Pacific logo appears in one of the upper corners of the photo. Backs have a photo, again borderless at top and sides, with a Pacific logo in one upper corner and the card number and MLB logos in the lower corners. At bottom is a gray marble strip with a few biographical details, 1993 and career stats and a ghost-image color team logo. The 660 cards in the set were issued in a single series.

		MT	NR MT	EX
Complete Set (660):		42.00	32.00	17.00
Common Player:		.08	.06	.03
1	Steve Avery	.15	.11	.06
2	Steve Bedrosian	.08	.06	.03
3	Damon Beryhill	.08	.06	.03
4	Jeff Blauser	.08	.06	.03
5	Sid Bream	.08	.06	.03
6	Francisco Cabrera	.08	.06	.03
7	*Ramon Caraballo*	.15	.11	.06
8	Ron Gant	.12	.09	.05
9	Tom Glavine	.20	.15	.08
10	Chipper Jones	.40	.30	.15
11	Dave Justice	.25	.20	.10
12	Ryan Klesko	.15	.11	.06
13	Mark Lemke	.08	.06	.03
14	Javier Lopez	.50	.40	.20
15	Greg Maddux	.20	.15	.08
16	Fred McGriff	.50	.40	.20
17	Greg McMichael	.10	.08	.04
18	Kent Merker	.08	.06	.03
19	Otis Nixon	.08	.06	.03
20	Terry Pendleton	.10	.08	.04
21	Deion Sanders	.15	.11	.06
22	John Smoltz	.10	.08	.04
23	Tony Tarasco	.35	.25	.14
24	Manny Alexander	.15	.11	.06
25	Brady Anderson	.08	.06	.03
26	Harold Baines	.08	.06	.03
27	Damion Buford	.15	.11	.06
28	Paul Carey	.15	.11	.06
29	Mike Devereaux	.08	.06	.03
30	Todd Frohwirth	.08	.06	.03
31	Leo Gomez	.08	.06	.03
32	Jeffrey Hammonds	.60	.45	.25
33	Chris Hoiles	.08	.06	.03
34	Tim Hullett	.08	.06	.03
35	Ben McDonald	.10	.08	.04
36	Mark McLemore	.08	.06	.03
37	Alan Mills	.10	.08	.04
38	Mike Mussina	.20	.15	.08
39	Sherman Obando	.10	.08	.04
40	Gregg Olson	.08	.06	.03
41	Mike Pagliarulo	.08	.06	.03
42	Jim Poole	.10	.08	.04
43	Harold Reynolds	.08	.06	.03
44	Cal Ripken	.50	.40	.20
45	David Segui	.08	.06	.03
46	Fernando Valenzuela	.08	.06	.03
47	Jack Voight	.08	.06	.03
48	Scott Bankhead	.08	.06	.03
49	Roger Clemens	.20	.15	.08
50	Scott Cooper	.08	.06	.03
51	Danny Darwin	.08	.06	.03
52	Andre Dawson	.10	.08	.04
53	John Dopson	.08	.06	.03
54	Scott Fletcher	.08	.06	.03
55	Tony Fossas	.08	.06	.03
56	Mike Greenwell	.08	.06	.03
57	Billy Hatcher	.08	.06	.03
58	Jeff McNeely	.15	.11	.06
59	Jose Melendez	.08	.06	.03
60	Tim Neahring	.08	.06	.03
61	Tony Pena	.08	.06	.03
62	Carlos Quintana	.08	.06	.03
63	Paul Quantrill	.08	.06	.03
64	Luis Rivera	.08	.06	.03
65	Jeff Russell	.08	.06	.03
66	Aaron Sele	.60	.45	.25
67	John Valentin	.10	.08	.04
68	Mo Vaughn	.12	.09	.05
69	Frank Viola	.08	.06	.03
70	Bob Zupcic	.08	.06	.03
71	Mike Butcher	.08	.06	.03
72	Ron Correia	.08	.06	.03
73	Chad Curtis	.15	.11	.06
74	Chili Davis	.08	.06	.03
75	Gary DiSarcia	.08	.06	.03
76	Damion Easley	.15	.11	.06
77	John Farrell	.08	.06	.03
78	Chuck Finley	.08	.06	.03
79	Joe Grahe	.08	.06	.03
80	Stan Javier	.08	.06	.03
81	Mark Langston	.08	.06	.03
82	*Phil Leftwich*	.20	.15	.08
83	Torey Lovullo	.08	.06	.03
84	Joe Magrane	.08	.06	.03
85	Greg Myers	.08	.06	.03
86	Eduardo Perez	.30	.25	.12
87	Luis Polonia	.08	.06	.03
88	Tim Salmon	1.25	.90	.50
89	J.T. Snow	.40	.30	.15
90	Kurt Stillwell	.08	.06	.03
91	Ron Tingley	.08	.06	.03
92	Chris Turner	.15	.11	.06
93	Julio Valera	.08	.06	.03
94	Jose Bautista	.08	.06	.03
95	Shawn Boskie	.08	.06	.03
96	Steve Buechele	.08	.06	.03
97	Frank Castillo	.08	.06	.03
98	Mark Grace	.10	.08	.04
99	Jose Guzman	.08	.06	.03
100	Mike Harkey	.08	.06	.03
101	Greg Hibbard	.08	.06	.03
102	Doug Jennings	.10	.08	.04
103	Derrick May	.08	.06	.03
104	Mike Morgan	.08	.06	.03
105	Randy Myers	.08	.06	.03
106	Karl Rhodes	.15	.11	.06
107	Kevin Robinson	.15	.11	.06
108	Rey Sanchez	.08	.06	.03
109	Ryne Sandberg	.35	.25	.14
110	*Tommy Shields*	.20	.15	.08
111	Dwight Smith	.08	.06	.03
112	Sammy Sosa	.15	.11	.06
113	Jose Vizcaino	.08	.06	.03
114	Turk Wendell	.10	.08	.04
115	Rick Wilkins	.08	.06	.03
116	Willie Wilson	.08	.06	.03
117	*Eddie Zambrano*	.20	.15	.08
118	Wilson Alvarez	.08	.06	.03
119	Tim Belcher	.08	.06	.03
120	Jason Bere	1.00	.70	.40
121	Rodney Bolton	.08	.06	.03
122	Ellis Burks	.08	.06	.03
123	Joey Cora	.08	.06	.03
124	Alex Fernandez	.10	.08	.04
125	Ozzie Guillen	.08	.06	.03
126	Craig Grebeck	.08	.06	.03
127	Roberto Hernandez	.08	.06	.03
128	Bo Jackson	.15	.11	.06
129	Lance Johnson	.08	.06	.03
130	Ron Karkovice	.08	.06	.03
131	Mike Lavalliere	.08	.06	.03
132	Norberto Martin	.08	.06	.03
133	Kirk McCaskill	.08	.06	.03
134	Jack McDowell	.15	.11	.06
135	Scott Radinsky	.08	.06	.03
136	Tim Raines	.08	.06	.03
137	Steve Sax	.08	.06	.03
138	Frank Thomas	2.50	2.00	1.00
139	Dan Pasqua	.08	.06	.03
140	Robin Ventura	.20	.15	.08
141	Jeff Branson	.08	.06	.03
142	Tom Browning	.08	.06	.03
143	Jacob Brumfield	.15	.11	.06
144	Tim Costo	.10	.08	.04
145	Rob Dibble	.08	.06	.03
146	Brian Dorsett	.15	.11	.06
147	Steve Foster	.08	.06	.03
148	Cesar Hernandez	.08	.06	.03
149	Roberto Kelly	.08	.06	.03
150	Barry Larkin	.10	.08	.04
151	*Larry Luebbers*	.15	.11	.06
152	Kevin Mitchell	.08	.06	.03
153	Joe Oliver	.08	.06	.03
154	Tim Pugh	.08	.06	.03
155	Jeff Reardon	.08	.06	.03
156	Jose Rijo	.08	.06	.03
157	Bip Roberts	.08	.06	.03
158	Chris Sabo	.08	.06	.03
159	Juan Samuel	.08	.06	.03
160	Reggie Sanders	.10	.08	.04
161	John Smiley	.08	.06	.03
162	*Jerry Spradlin*	.15	.11	.06
163	Gary Varsho	.08	.06	.03
164	Sandy Alomar Jr.	.08	.06	.03
165	Carlos Baerga	.25	.20	.10
166	Albert Belle	.25	.20	.10
167	Mark Clark	.08	.06	.03
168	Alvaro Espinoza	.08	.06	.03
169	Felix Fermin	.08	.06	.03
170	Reggie Jefferson	.10	.08	.04
171	Wayne Kirby	.08	.06	.03
172	Tom Kramer	.08	.06	.03
173	Jesse Levis	.08	.06	.03
174	Kenny Lofton	.15	.11	.06
175	Candy Maldonado	.08	.06	.03
176	Carlos Martinez	.08	.06	.03
177	Jose Mesa	.08	.06	.03
178	Jeff Mutis	.10	.08	.04
179	Charles Nagy	.08	.06	.03
180	Bob Ojeda	.08	.06	.03
181	Junior Ortiz	.08	.06	.03
182	Eric Plunk	.08	.06	.03
183	Manny Ramirez	.75	.60	.30
184	Paul Sorrento	.08	.06	.03
185	Jeff Treadway	.08	.06	.03
186	Bill Wertz	.08	.06	.03
187	Freddie Benavides	.08	.06	.03
188	Dante Bichette	.10	.07	.04
189	Willie Blair	.08	.06	.03
190	Daryl Boston	.08	.06	.03
191	Pedro Castellano	.10	.08	.04
192	Vinny Castilla	.08	.06	.03
193	Jerald Clark	.08	.06	.03
194	Alex Cole	.08	.06	.03
195	Andre Galarraga	.10	.08	.04
196	Joe Girardi	.08	.06	.03
197	Charlie Hayes	.08	.06	.03
198	Darren Holmes	.08	.06	.03

199	Chris Jones	.10	.08	.04
200	Curt Leskanic	.10	.08	.04
201	Roberto Mejia	.20	.15	.08
202	David Nied	.25	.20	.10
203	*J. Owens*	.15	.11	.06
204	Steve Reed	.10	.08	.04
205	Armando Reynoso	.08	.06	.03
206	Bruce Ruffin	.08	.06	.03
207	Keith Shepherd	.08	.06	.03
208	Jim Tatum	.10	.08	.04
209	Eric Young	.15	.11	.06
210	Skeeter Barnes	.08	.06	.03
211	Danny Bautista	.08	.06	.03
212	Tom Bolton	.08	.06	.03
213	Eric Davis	.08	.06	.03
214	Storm Davis	.08	.06	.03
215	John Doherty	.08	.06	.03
216	Cecil Fielder	.20	.15	.08
217	Travis Fryman	.25	.20	.10
218	Kirk Gibson	.08	.06	.03
219	Dan Gladden	.08	.06	.03
220	Chris Gomez	.08	.06	.03
221	David Haas	.08	.06	.03
222	Bill Krueger	.08	.06	.03
223	Chad Kreuter	.08	.06	.03
224	Mark Leiter	.08	.06	.03
225	Bob MacDonald	.08	.06	.03
226	Mike Moore	.08	.06	.03
227	Tony Phillips	.08	.06	.03
228	Rich Rowland	.10	.08	.04
229	Mickey Tettleton	.08	.06	.03
230	Alan Trammell	.08	.06	.03
231	David Wells	.08	.06	.03
232	Lou Whitaker	.08	.06	.03
233	Luis Aquino	.08	.06	.03
234	Alex Arias	.10	.08	.04
235	Jack Armstrong	.08	.06	.03
236	Ryan Bowen	.10	.08	.04
237	Chuck Carr	.08	.06	.03
238	*Matias Carrillo*	.15	.11	.06
239	Jeff Conine	.08	.06	.03
240	Henry Cotto	.08	.06	.03
241	Orestes Destrade	.08	.06	.03
242	Chris Hammond	.08	.06	.03
243	Bryan Harvey	.08	.06	.03
244	Charlie Hough	.08	.06	.03
245	Richie Lewis	.10	.08	.04
246	Mitch Lyden	.10	.08	.04
247	Dave Magadan	.08	.06	.03
248	Bob Natal	.08	.06	.03
249	Benito Santiago	.08	.06	.03
250	Gary Sheffield	.15	.11	.06
251	Matt Turner	.08	.06	.03
252	Walt Weiss	.08	.06	.03
253	David Weathers	.10	.08	.04
254	Darrell Whitmore	.15	.11	.06
255	Nigel Wilson	.20	.15	.08
256	Eric Anthony	.10	.08	.04
257	Jeff Bagwell	.20	.15	.08
258	Kevin Bass	.08	.06	.03
259	Craig Biggio	.08	.06	.03
260	Ken Caminiti	.08	.06	.03
261	Andujar Cedeno	.10	.08	.04
262	Chris Donnels	.08	.06	.03
263	Doug Drabek	.08	.06	.03
264	Tom Edens	.08	.06	.03
265	Steve Finley	.08	.06	.03
266	Luis Gonzalez	.08	.06	.03
267	Pete Harnisch	.08	.06	.03
268	Xavier Hernandez	.08	.06	.03
269	Todd Jones	.08	.06	.03
270	Darryl Kile	.08	.06	.03
271	Al Osuna	.08	.06	.03
272	Rick Parker	.10	.08	.04
273	Mark Portugal	.08	.06	.03
274	Scott Servais	.08	.06	.03
275	Greg Swindell	.08	.06	.03
276	Eddie Taubensee	.08	.06	.03
277	Jose Uribe	.08	.06	.03
278	Brian Williams	.08	.06	.03
279	Kevin Appier	.08	.06	.03
280	Billy Brewer	.10	.08	.04
281	David Cone	.08	.06	.03
282	Greg Gagne	.08	.06	.03
283	Tom Gordon	.08	.06	.03
284	Chris Gwynn	.08	.06	.03
285	John Habyan	.08	.06	.03
286	Chris Haney	.08	.06	.03
287	Phil Hiatt	.12	.09	.05
288	David Howard	.08	.06	.03
289	Felix Jose	.08	.06	.03
290	Wally Joyner	.08	.06	.03
291	Kevin Koslofski	.10	.08	.04
292	Jose Lind	.08	.06	.03
293	Brent Mayne	.08	.06	.03
294	Mike Mcfarlane	.08	.06	.03
295	Brian McRae	.08	.06	.03
296	Kevin McReynolds	.08	.06	.03
297	Keith Miller	.08	.06	.03
298	Jeff Montgomery	.08	.06	.03
299	Hipolito Pichardo	.08	.06	.03
300	Rico Rossy	.08	.06	.03
301	Curtis Wilkerson	.08	.06	.03
302	Pedro Astacio	.15	.11	.06
303	Rafael Bournigal	.08	.06	.03
304	Brett Butler	.08	.06	.03
305	Tom Candiotti	.08	.06	.03
306	Omar Daal	.10	.08	.04
307	Jim Gott	.08	.06	.03
308	Kevin Gross	.08	.06	.03
309	Dave Hansen	.08	.06	.03
310	Carlos Hernandez	.08	.06	.03
311	Orel Hershiser	.08	.06	.03
312	Eric Karros	.12	.09	.05
313	Pedro Martinez	.15	.11	.06
314	Ramon Martinez	.10	.08	.04
315	Roger McDowell	.08	.06	.03
316	Raul Mondesi	1.00	.75	.40
317	Jose Offerman	.08	.06	.03
318	Mike Piazza	2.00	1.50	.80
319	Jody Reed	.08	.06	.03
320	Henry Rodriguez	.08	.06	.03
321	Cory Snyder	.08	.06	.03
322	Darryl Strawberry	.10	.07	.04
323	Tim Wallach	.08	.06	.03
324	Steve Wilson	.08	.06	.03
325	Juan Bell	.08	.06	.03
326	Ricky Bones	.08	.06	.03
327	*Alex Diaz*	.15	.11	.06
328	Cal Eldred	.15	.11	.06
329	Darryl Hamilton	.08	.06	.03
330	Doug Henry	.08	.06	.03
331	John Jaha	.15	.11	.06
332	Pat Listach	.10	.08	.04
333	Graeme Lloyd	.10	.08	.04
334	Carlos Maldonado	.08	.06	.03
335	Angel Miranda	.10	.08	.04
336	Jaime Navarro	.08	.06	.03
337	Dave Nilsson	.08	.06	.03
338	Rafael Novoa	.08	.06	.03
339	*Troy O'Leary*	.15	.11	.06
340	Jesse Orosco	.08	.06	.03
341	Kevin Seitzer	.08	.06	.03
342	Bill Spiers	.08	.06	.03
343	William Suero	.08	.06	.03
344	B.J. Surhoff	.08	.06	.03
345	Dickie Thon	.08	.06	.03
346	Jose Valentin	.08	.06	.03
347	Greg Vaughn	.10	.08	.04
348	Robin Yount	.20	.15	.08
349	Willie Banks	.08	.06	.03
350	Bernardo Brito	.10	.08	.04
351	Scott Erickson	.08	.06	.03
352	Mark Guthrie	.08	.06	.03
353	Chip Hale	.08	.06	.03
354	Brian Harper	.08	.06	.03
355	Kent Hrbek	.08	.06	.03
356	Terry Jorgenson	.08	.06	.03
357	Chuck Knoblauch	.10	.08	.04
358	Gene Larkin	.08	.06	.03
359	Scott Leius	.08	.06	.03
360	Shane Mack	.08	.06	.03
361	David McCarty	.15	.11	.06
362	Pat Meares	.10	.08	.04
363	Pedro Munoz	.08	.06	.03
364	Derek Parks	.10	.08	.04
365	Kirby Puckett	.35	.25	.14
366	Jeff Reboulet	.10	.08	.04
367	Kevin Tapani	.08	.06	.03
368	Mike Trombley	.08	.06	.03
369	George Tsamis	.10	.08	.04
370	Carl Willis	.08	.06	.03
371	Dave Winfield	.25	.20	.10
372	Moises Alou	.15	.11	.06
373	Brian Barnes	.08	.06	.03
374	Sean Berry	.08	.06	.03
375	Frank Bolick	.08	.06	.03
376	Wil Cordero	.15	.11	.06
377	Delino DeShields	.10	.08	.04
378	Jeff Fassero	.08	.06	.03
379	Darren Fletcher	.08	.06	.03
380	Cliff Floyd	1.25	.90	.50
381	Lou Frazier	.10	.08	.04
382	Marquis Grissom	.15	.11	.06
383	Gil Heredia	.10	.08	.04
384	Mike Lansing	.15	.11	.06
385	*Oreste Marrero*	.15	.11	.06
386	Dennis Martinez	.08	.06	.03
387	*Curtis Pride*	.60	.45	.25
388	Mel Rojas	.08	.06	.03
389	*Kirk Rueter*	1.00	.75	.40
390	Joe Siddall	.10	.08	.04
391	John Vander Wal	.08	.06	.03
392	Larry Walker	.15	.11	.06
393	John Wetteland	.08	.06	.03
394	Rondell White	.40	.30	.15
395	Tom Bogar	.08	.06	.03
396	Bobby Bonilla	.10	.08	.04
397	Jeromy Burnitz	.10	.08	.04
398	Mike Draper	.08	.06	.03
399	Sid Fernandez	.08	.06	.03
400	John Franco	.08	.06	.03
401	Dave Gallagher	.08	.06	.03
402	Dwight Gooden	.08	.06	.03
403	Eric Hillman	.08	.06	.03
404	Todd Hundley	.08	.06	.03
405	Butch Huskey	.08	.06	.03
406	Jeff Innis	.08	.06	.03
407	Howard Johnson	.08	.06	.03
408	Jeff Kent	.08	.06	.03
409	Ced Landrum	.08	.06	.03
410	Mike Maddux	.08	.06	.03
411	Jeff McKnight	.08	.06	.03
412	Josias Manzanillo	.08	.06	.03
413	Eddie Murray	.10	.08	.04
414	Tito Navarro	.10	.08	.04
415	Joe Orlusak	.08	.06	.03
416	Bret Saberhagen	.08	.06	.03
417	Dave Telgheder	.08	.06	.03
418	Ryan Thompson	.15	.11	.06
419	Chico Walker	.15	.11	.06
420	Jim Abbott	.10	.08	.04
421	Wade Boggs	.15	.11	.06
422	Mike Gallego	.08	.06	.03
423	Mark Hutton	.08	.06	.03
424	Dion James	.08	.06	.03
425	Domingo Jean	.10	.08	.04
426	Pat Kelly	.08	.06	.03
427	Jimmy Key	.08	.06	.03
428	Jim Leyritz	.08	.06	.03
429	Kevin Maas	.08	.06	.03
430	Don Mattingly	.25	.20	.10
431	Bobby Munoz	.08	.06	.03
432	Matt Nokes	.08	.06	.03
433	Paul O'Neill	.08	.06	.03
434	Spike Owen	.08	.06	.03
435	Melido Perez	.08	.06	.03
436	Lee Smith	.08	.06	.03
437	Andy Stankiewicz	.08	.06	.03
438	Mike Stanley	.08	.06	.03
439	Danny Tartabull	.10	.08	.04
440	Randy Velarde	.08	.06	.03
441	Bernie Williams	.10	.08	.04
442	Gerald Williams	.10	.08	.04
443	Mike Witt	.08	.06	.03
444	Marcos Armas	.10	.08	.04
445	Lance Blankenship	.08	.06	.03
446	Mike Bordick	.08	.06	.03
447	Ron Darling	.08	.06	.03
448	Dennis Eckersley	.10	.08	.04
449	Brent Gates	.20	.15	.08
450	Goose Gossage	.08	.06	.03
451	Scott Hemond	.10	.08	.04
452	Dave Henderson	.08	.06	.03
453	Shawn Hillegas	.08	.06	.03
454	Rick Honeycutt	.08	.06	.03
455	Scott Lydy	.10	.08	.04
456	Mark McGwire	.15	.11	.06
457	Henry Mercedes	.10	.08	.04
458	Mike Mohler	.08	.06	.03
459	Troy Neel	.15	.11	.06
460	Edwin Nunez	.08	.06	.03
461	Craig Paquette	.08	.06	.03
462	Ruben Sierra	.15	.11	.06
463	Terry Steinbach	.08	.06	.03
464	Todd Van Poppel	.15	.11	.06
465	Bob Welch	.08	.06	.03
466	Bobby Witt	.08	.06	.03
467	Ruben Amaro	.10	.08	.04
468	Larry Anderson	.08	.06	.03
469	Kim Batiste	.08	.06	.03
470	Wes Chamberlain	.08	.06	.03
471	Darren Daulton	.10	.08	.04
472	Mariano Duncan	.08	.06	.03
473	Len Dykstra	.12	.09	.05
474	Jim Eisenreich	.08	.06	.03
475	Tommy Greene	.08	.06	.03
476	Dave Hollins	.10	.08	.04
477	Pete Incaviglia	.08	.06	.03
478	Danny Jackson	.08	.06	.03
479	John Kruk	.10	.08	.04
480	Tony Longmire	.10	.08	.04
481	Jeff Manto	.08	.06	.03
482	Mike Morandini	.08	.06	.03
483	Terry Mulholland	.08	.06	.03
484	Todd Pratt	.08	.06	.03
485	Ben Rivera	.08	.06	.03
486	Curt Shilling	.08	.06	.03
487	*Kevin Stocker*	.60	.45	.25
488	Milt Thompson	.08	.06	.03
489	David West	.08	.06	.03
490	Mitch Williams	.08	.06	.03
491	Jeff Ballard	.08	.06	.03
492	Jay Bell	.08	.06	.03
493	Scott Bullett	.08	.06	.03
494	Dave Clark	.08	.06	.03
495	Steve Cooke	.10	.08	.04
496	Midre Cummings	.25	.20	.10
497	Mark Dewey	.10	.08	.04
498	Carlos Garcia	.15	.11	.06
499	Jeff King	.08	.06	.03
500	Al Martin	.10	.08	.04
501	Lloyd McClendon	.08	.06	.03
502	Orlando Merced	.08	.06	.03
503	Blas Minor	.10	.08	.04
504	Denny Neagle	.08	.06	.03
505	Tom Prince	.08	.06	.03
506	Don Slaught	.08	.06	.03
507	Zane Smith	.08	.06	.03
508	Randy Tomlin	.08	.06	.03
509	Andy Van Slyke	.10	.08	.04
510	Paul Wagner	.08	.06	.03
511	Tim Wakefield	.10	.08	.04
512	Bob Walk	.08	.06	.03
513	John Wehner	.08	.06	.03
514	Kevin Young	.10	.08	.04
515	Billy Bean	.08	.06	.03
516	Andy Benes	.10	.08	.04
517	Derek Bell	.08	.06	.03
518	Doug Brocail	.08	.06	.03
519	Jarvis Brown	.10	.08	.04
520	Phil Clark	.08	.06	.03
521	Mark Davis	.08	.06	.03
522	Jeff Gardner	.08	.06	.03
523	Pat Gomez	.08	.06	.03
524	Ricky Gutierrez	.08	.06	.03
525	Tony Gwynn	.15	.11	.06
526	Gene Harris	.08	.06	.03
527	Kevin Higgins	.08	.06	.03
528	Trevor Hoffman	.08	.06	.03
529	Luis Lopez	.08	.06	.03
530	Pedro A. Martinez	.10	.08	.04
531	Melvin Nieves	.15	.11	.06
532	Phil Plantier	.15	.11	.06
533	Frank Seminara	.08	.06	.03
534	Craig Shipley	.08	.06	.03
535	Tim Tuefel	.08	.06	.03
536	Guillermo Velasquez	.08	.06	.03
537	Wally Whitehurst	.08	.06	.03
538	Rod Beck	.08	.06	.03
539	Todd Benzinger	.08	.06	.03
540	Barry Bonds	.50	.40	.20
541	Jeff Brantley	.08	.06	.03
542	Dave Burba	.08	.06	.03
543	John Burkett	.08	.06	.03
544	Will Clark	.20	.15	.08
545	Royce Clayton	.10	.08	.04
546	Brian Hickerson	.10	.08	.04
547	Mike Jackson	.08	.06	.03
548	Darren Lewis	.10	.08	.04
549	Kirt Manwaring	.08	.06	.03
550	Dave Martinez	.08	.06	.03
551	Willie McGee	.08	.06	.03
552	Jeff Reed	.08	.06	.03

553	Dave Righetti	.08	.06	.03
554	Kevin Rogers	.08	.06	.03
555	Steve Scarsone	.08	.06	.03
556	Bill Swift	.08	.06	.03
557	Robby Thompson	.08	.06	.03
558	Solomon Torres	.15	.11	.06
559	Matt Williams	.10	.08	.04
560	Trevor Wilson	.08	.06	.03
561	Rich Amaral	.10	.08	.04
562	Mike Blowers	.08	.06	.03
563	Chris Bosio	.08	.06	.03
564	Jay Buhner	.08	.06	.03
565	Norm Charlton	.08	.06	.03
566	Jim Converse	.08	.06	.03
567	Rich DeLucia	.08	.06	.03
568	Mike Felder	.08	.06	.03
569	Dave Fleming	.08	.06	.03
570	Ken Griffey, Jr.	2.00	1.50	.80
571	Bill Haselman	.08	.06	.03
572	Dwayne Henry	.08	.06	.03
573	Brad Holman	.08	.06	.03
574	Randy Johnson	.10	.08	.04
575	Greg Litton	.08	.06	.03
576	Edgar Martinez	.08	.06	.03
577	Tino Martinez	.08	.06	.03
578	Jeff Nelson	.08	.06	.03
579	Mark Newfield	.20	.15	.08
580	Roger Salkeld	.15	.11	.06
581	Mackey Sasser	.08	.06	.03
582	*Brian Turang*	.15	.11	.06
583	Omar Vizquel	.08	.06	.03
584	Dave Valle	.08	.06	.03
585	Luis Alicea	.08	.06	.03
586	Rene Arocha	.10	.08	.04
587	Rheal Cormier	.08	.06	.03
588	Tripp Cromer	.10	.08	.04
589	Bernard Gilkey	.08	.06	.03
590	Lee Guetterman	.08	.06	.03
591	Gregg Jefferies	.10	.08	.04
592	Tim Jones	.08	.06	.03
593	Paul Kilgus	.08	.06	.03
594	Les Lancaster	.08	.06	.03
595	Omar Olivares	.08	.06	.03
596	Jose Oquendo	.08	.06	.03
597	Donovan Osborne	.08	.06	.03
598	Tom Pagnozzi	.08	.06	.03
599	Erik Pappas	.08	.06	.03
600	Geronimo Pena	.08	.06	.03
601	Mike Perez	.08	.06	.03
602	Gerald Perry	.08	.06	.03
603	Stan Royer	.08	.06	.03
604	Ozzie Smith	.15	.11	.06
605	Bob Tewksbury	.08	.06	.03
606	Allen Watson	.30	.25	.12
607	Mark Whiten	.10	.08	.04
608	Todd Zeile	.08	.06	.03
609	Jeff Bronkey	.08	.06	.03
610	Kevin Brown	.08	.06	.03
611	Jose Canseco	.15	.11	.06
612	Doug Dascenzo	.08	.06	.03
613	Butch Davis	.10	.08	.04
614	Mario Diaz	.08	.06	.03
615	Julio Franco	.08	.06	.03
616	Benji Gil	.20	.15	.08
617	Juan Gonzalez	1.75	1.25	.70
618	Tom Henke	.08	.06	.03
619	Jeff Huson	.10	.08	.04
620	David Hulse	.15	.11	.06
621	Craig Lefferts	.08	.06	.03
622	Rafael Palmeiro	.10	.08	.04
623	Dean Palmer	.10	.08	.04
624	Bob Patterson	.08	.06	.03
625	Roger Pavlik	.10	.08	.04
626	Gary Redus	.08	.06	.03
627	Ivan Rodriguez	.15	.11	.06
628	Kenny Rogers	.08	.06	.03
629	Jon Shave	.08	.06	.03
630	Doug Strange	.08	.06	.03
631	Matt Whiteside	.08	.06	.03
632	Roberto Alomar	.35	.25	.14
633	Pat Borders	.08	.06	.03
634	Scott Brow	.15	.11	.06
635	*Rob Butler*	.20	.15	.08
636	Joe Carter	.25	.20	.10
637	Tony Castillo	.08	.06	.03
638	Mark Eichhorn	.08	.06	.03
639	Tony Fernandez	.08	.06	.03
640	*Huck Flener*	.15	.11	.06
641	Alfredo Griffin	.08	.06	.03
642	Juan Guzman	.15	.11	.06
643	Rickey Henderson	.15	.11	.06
644	Pat Hentgen	.20	.15	.08
645	Randy Knorr	.08	.06	.03
646	Al Leiter	.08	.06	.03
647	Dominigo Martinez	.08	.06	.03
648	Paul Molitor	.15	.11	.06
649	Jack Morris	.08	.06	.03
650	John Olerud	.25	.20	.10
651	Ed Sprague	.08	.06	.03
652	Dave Stewart	.08	.06	.03
653	Devon White	.10	.08	.04
654	Woody Williams	.15	.11	.06
655	Barry Bonds (MVP)	.40	.30	.15
656	Greg Maddux (CY)	.20	.15	.08
657	Jack McDowell (CY)	.10	.08	.04
658	Mike Piazza (ROY)	1.00	.75	.40
659	Tim Salmon (ROY)	.60	.45	.25
660	Frank Thomas (MVP)	1.50	1.25	.60

A player's name in italic type indicates a rookie card. An (FC) indicates a player's first card for that particular card company.

1994 Pacific Crown Jewels of the Crown

One of three inserts into 1994 Pacific Spanish foil packs. The design features a player action photo set against a silver prismatic background. On back is another color player photo against a background of colored silk and a large jewel. Season highlight stats and awards won are presented in both English and Spanish. The announced production run of these inserts was 8,000 sets.

		MT	NR MT	EX
Complete Set (36):		350.00	260.00	140.00
Common Player:		8.00	6.00	3.25
1	Robin Yount	14.00	10.50	5.50
2	Juan Gonzalez	25.00	18.50	10.00
3	Rafael Palmeiro	10.00	7.50	4.00
4	Paul Molitor	12.00	9.00	4.75
5	Roberto Alomar	15.00	11.00	6.00
6	John Olerud	12.00	9.00	4.75
7	Randy Johnson	8.00	6.00	3.25
8	Ken Griffey Jr.	25.00	18.50	10.00
9	Wade Boggs	9.00	6.75	3.50
10	Don Mattingly	14.00	10.50	5.50
11	Kirby Puckett	15.00	11.00	6.00
12	Tim Salmon	18.00	13.50	7.25
13	Frank Thomas	30.00	22.00	12.00
14	Fernando Valenzuela (Comeback Player)	8.00	6.00	3.25
15	Cal Ripken, Jr.	15.00	11.00	6.00
16	Carlos Baerga	12.00	9.00	4.75
17	Kenny Lofton	9.00	6.75	3.50
18	Cecil Fielder	12.00	9.00	4.75
19	John Burkett	8.00	6.00	3.25
20	Andres Galarraga (Comeback Player)	8.00	6.00	3.25
21	Charlie Hayes	8.00	6.00	3.25
22	Orestes Destrade	8.00	6.00	3.25
23	Jeff Conine	8.00	6.00	3.25
24	Jeff Bagwell	10.00	7.50	4.00
25	Mark Grace	10.00	7.50	4.00
26	Ryne Sandberg	14.00	10.50	5.50
27	Gregg Jefferies	8.00	6.00	3.25
28	Barry Bonds	25.00	18.50	10.00
29	Mike Piazza	25.00	18.50	10.00
30	Greg Maddux	10.00	7.50	4.00
31	Darren Dalton	9.00	6.75	3.50
32	John Kruk	9.00	6.75	3.50
33	Len Dykstra, Robby Thompson	10.00	7.50	4.00
34	Orlando Merced	8.00	6.00	3.25
35	Tony Gwynn	12.00	9.00	4.75

The values quoted are intended to reflect the market price.

1994 Pacific Crown Homerun Leaders

A gold prismatic background behind a color action player photo is the featured design on this Pacific insert set. Backs have another player photo against a ballfield backdrop. A huge baseball is overprinted with the player's name and number of 1993 homers. A league designation is among the logos featured on back. A total of 8,000 of these inserts sets was the announced production.

		MT	NR MT	EX
Complete Set (20):		200.00	150.00	80.00
Common Player:		8.00	6.00	3.25
1	Juan "Igor" Gonzalez	25.00	18.50	10.00
2	Ken Griffey Jr.	25.00	18.50	10.00
3	Frank Thomas	30.00	22.00	12.00
4	Albert Belle	14.00	10.50	5.50
5	Rafael Palmeiro	10.00	7.50	4.00
6	Joe Carter	12.00	9.00	4.75
7	Dean Palmer	8.00	6.00	3.25
8	Mickey Tettleton	8.00	6.00	3.25
9	Tim Salmon	20.00	15.00	8.00
10	Danny Tartabull	8.00	6.00	3.25
11	Barry Bonds	25.00	18.50	10.00
12	Dave Justice	16.00	12.00	6.50
13	Matt Williams	9.00	6.75	3.50
14	Fred McGriff	12.00	9.00	4.75
15	Ron Gant	9.00	6.75	3.50
16	Mike Piazza	25.00	18.50	10.00
17	Bobby Bonilla	8.00	6.00	3.25
18	Phil Plantier	8.00	6.00	3.25
19	Sammy Sosa	8.00	6.00	3.25
20	Rick Wilkins	8.00	6.00	3.25

1994 Pacific Crown All Latino All-Star Team

Latino All-Stars is the theme of the third insert set found randomly packed in Pacific Spanish for 1994. Cards feature a player action photo on front, with a gold foil pinstripe around the sides and top. The player's name appears in gold script at bottom and there is a baseball logo in the corner. On backs a portrait photo of the player is set against a background of his native flag. Season highlights of 1993 are presented in English and Spanish. Eight thousand sets were produced.

		MT	NR MT	EX
Complete Set (20):		55.00	41.00	22.00
Common Player:		2.50	2.00	1.00
1	Ivan Rodriguez	4.00	3.00	1.50
2	Alex Fernandez	3.50	2.75	1.50
3	Rafael Palmeiro	5.00	3.75	2.00
4	Roberto Alomar	8.00	6.00	3.25
5	Omar Vizquel	2.50	2.00	1.00
6	Eduardo Perez	3.00	2.25	1.25
7	Juan "Igor" Gonzalez	18.00	13.50	7.25
8	Jose Canseco	7.50	5.00	3.00
9	Ruben Sierra	5.00	3.75	2.00
10	Danny Tartabull	4.00	3.00	1.50
11	Benito Santiago	2.50	2.00	1.00
12	Dennis Martinez	2.50	2.00	1.00
13	Andres Galarraga	2.50	2.00	1.00
14	Mariano Duncan	2.50	2.00	1.00
15	Jose Offerman	2.50	2.00	1.00
16	Dave Magadan	2.50	2.00	1.00
17	Luis Gonzalez	2.50	2.00	1.00
18	Bobby Bonilla	4.00	3.00	1.50
19	Orlando Merced	2.50	2.00	1.00
20	Jose Rijo	2.50	2.00	1.00

1958 Packard-Bell

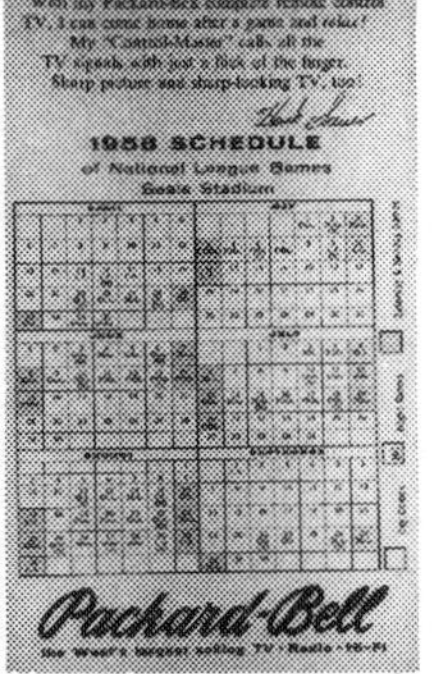

Issued in 1958 by Packard-Bell, the "world's largest seller of TVs, radios and hi-fis", this seven-card set was distributed in California and features members of the Los Angeles Dodgers and San Francisco Giants. The large (3-1/2" by 5-1/2") cards are unnumbered and carry an American Card Catalog designation of H801-5.

		NR MT	EX	VG
Complete Set (7):		260.00	130.00	78.00
Common Player:		12.00	6.00	3.50
(1)	Walter Alston	30.00	15.00	9.00
(2)	John A. Antonelli	12.00	6.00	3.50
(3)	Jim Gilliam	25.00	12.50	7.50
(4)	Gil Hodges	55.00	27.00	16.50
(5)	Willie Mays	125.00	62.00	37.00
(6)	Bill Rigney	12.00	6.00	3.50
(7)	Hank Sauer	12.00	6.00	3.50

1988 Panini Stickers

This set of 480 stickers features 312 major league players, both rookies and superstar veterans. The full-color stickers measure 2-11/16" by 1-7/8" (team emblem and uniform stickers are slightly larger). Individual players, duos and group action shots are included in the set which also contains 14 stickers that depict 1987 season highlights such as Paul Molitor's 39-game hitting streak. Panini produced a 64-page album with two pages devoted to each team and a space marked for each sticker in the set. Individual sticker packets contained a total of six stickers; four players, one team logo, one uniform sticker. Panini offered a collectors' sticker exchange service in which up to 30 stickers could be traded or specific stickers purchased for 10 cents each. The 26 team logo/pennant stickers (numbered A-1 through Z-1) are checklisted as #'s 455 through 480 in the following checklist.

		MT	NR MT	EX
Complete Set (480):		24.00	18.00	9.50
Common Player:		.04	.03	.02
Sticker Album:		.90	.70	.35
1	World Series Trophy	.04	.03	.02
2	Orioles Logo	.04	.03	.02
3	Orioles Uniform	.04	.03	.02
4	Eric Bell	.04	.03	.02
5	Mike Boddicker	.04	.03	.02
6	Dave Schmidt	.04	.03	.02
7	Terry Kennedy	.04	.03	.02
8	Eddie Murray	.20	.15	.08
9	Bill Ripken	.04	.03	.02
10	Orioles Action (Tony Armas, Cal Ripken Jr.)	.10	.08	.04
11	Orioles Action (Tony Armas, Cal Ripken Jr.)	.10	.08	.04
12	Ray Knight	.04	.03	.02
13	Cal Ripken, Jr.	.50	.40	.20
14	Ken Gerhart	.04	.03	.02
15	Fred Lynn	.06	.05	.02
16	Larry Sheets	.04	.03	.02
17	Mike Young	.04	.03	.02
18	Red Sox Logo	.04	.03	.02
19	Red Sox Uniform	.04	.03	.02
20	Oil Can Boyd	.04	.03	.02
21	Roger Clemens	.30	.25	.12
22	Bruce Hurst	.06	.05	.02
23	Bob Stanley	.04	.03	.02
24	Rich Gedman	.04	.03	.02
25	Dwight Evans	.06	.05	.02
26	Red Sox Action (Marty Barrett, Tim Laudner)	.04	.03	.02
27	Red Sox Action (Marty Barrett, Tim Laudner)	.04	.03	.02
28	Marty Barrett	.04	.03	.02
29	Wade Boggs	.50	.40	.20
30	Spike Owen	.04	.03	.02
31	Ellis Burks	.20	.15	.08
32	Mike Greenwell	.25	.20	.10
33	Jim Rice	.15	.11	.06
34	Angels Logo	.04	.03	.02
35	Angels Uniform	.04	.03	.02
36	Kirk McCaskill	.04	.03	.02
37	Don Sutton	.10	.08	.04
38	Mike Witt	.04	.03	.02
39	Bob Boone	.04	.03	.02
40	Wally Joyner	.20	.15	.08
41	Mark McLemore	.04	.03	.02
42	Angels Action (Juan Bonilla, Devon White)	.06	.05	.02
43	Angels Action (Juan Bonilla, Devon White)	.06	.05	.02
44	Jack Howell	.04	.03	.02
45	Dick Schofield	.04	.03	.02
46	Brian Downing	.04	.03	.02
47	Ruppert Jones	.04	.03	.02
48	Gary Pettis	.04	.03	.02
49	Devon White	.15	.11	.06
50	White Sox Logo	.04	.03	.02
51	White Sox Uniform	.04	.03	.02
52	Floyd Bannister	.04	.03	.02
53	Richard Dotson	.04	.03	.02
54	Bob James	.04	.03	.02
55	Carlton Fisk	.20	.15	.08
56	Greg Walker	.04	.03	.02
57	Fred Manrique	.04	.03	.02
58	White Sox Action (Ozzie Guillen, Donnie Hill, Pat Sheridan)	.04	.03	.02
59	White Sox Action (Ozzie Guillen, Donnie Hill, Pat Sheridan)	.04	.03	.02
60	Steve Lyons	.04	.03	.02
61	Ozzie Guillen	.04	.03	.02
62	Harold Baines	.08	.06	.03
63	Ivan Calderon	.04	.03	.02
64	Gary Redus	.04	.03	.02
65	Ken Williams	.06	.05	.02
66	Indians Logo	.04	.03	.02
67	Indians Uniform	.04	.03	.02
68	Scott Bailes	.04	.03	.02
69	Tom Candiotti	.04	.03	.02
70	Greg Swindell	.08	.06	.03
71	Chris Bando	.04	.03	.02
72	Joe Carter	.25	.20	.10
73	Tommy Hinzo	.04	.03	.02
74	Indians Action (Juan Bonilla, Joe Carter)	.06	.05	.02
75	Indians Action (Juan Bonilla, Joe Carter)	.06	.05	.02
76	Brook Jacoby	.06	.05	.02
77	Julio Franco	.08	.06	.03
78	Brett Butler	.04	.03	.02
79	Mel Hall	.04	.03	.02
80	Cory Snyder	.04	.03	.02
81	Pat Tabler	.04	.03	.02
82	Tigers Logo	.04	.03	.02
83	Tigers Uniform	.04	.03	.02
84	Willie Hernandez	.04	.03	.02
85	Jack Morris	.10	.08	.04
86	Frank Tanana	.04	.03	.02
87	Walt Terrell	.04	.03	.02
88	Matt Nokes	.12	.09	.05
89	Darrell Evans	.06	.05	.02
90	Tigers Action (Darrell Evans, Carlton Fisk)	.06	.05	.02
91	Tigers Action (Darrell Evans, Carlton Fisk)	.06	.05	.02
92	Lou Whitaker	.12	.09	.05
93	Tom Brookens	.04	.03	.02
94	Alan Trammell	.20	.15	.08
95	Kirk Gibson	.08	.06	.03
96	Chet Lemon	.04	.03	.02
97	Pat Sheridan	.04	.03	.02
98	Royals Logo	.04	.03	.02
99	Royals Uniform	.04	.03	.02
100	Charlie Leibrandt	.04	.03	.02
101	Dan Quisenberry	.04	.03	.02
102	Bret Saberhagen	.12	.09	.05
103	Jamie Quirk	.04	.03	.02
104	George Brett	.50	.40	.20
105	Frank White	.04	.03	.02
106	Royals Action (Bret Saberhagen)	.08	.06	.03
107	Royals Action (Bret Saberhagen)	.08	.06	.03
108	Kevin Seitzer	.08	.06	.03
109	Angel Salazar	.04	.03	.02
110	Bo Jackson	.20	.15	.08
111	Lonnie Smith	.04	.03	.02
112	Danny Tartabull	.15	.11	.06
113	Willie Wilson	.06	.05	.02
114	Brewers Logo	.04	.03	.02
115	Brewers Uniform	.04	.03	.02
116	Ted Higuera	.06	.05	.02
117	Juan Nieves	.04	.03	.02
118	Dan Plesac	.06	.05	.02
119	Bill Wegman	.04	.03	.02
120	B.J. Surhoff	.06	.05	.02
121	Greg Brock	.04	.03	.02
122	Brewers Action (Jim Gantner, Lou Whitaker)	.04	.03	.02
123	Brewers Action (Jim Gantner, Lou Whitaker)	.04	.03	.02
124	Jim Gantner	.04	.03	.02
125	Paul Molitor	.08	.06	.03
126	Dale Sveum	.04	.03	.02
127	Glenn Braggs	.04	.03	.02
128	Rob Deer	.04	.03	.02
129	Robin Yount	.50	.40	.20
130	Twins Logo	.04	.03	.02
131	Twins Uniform	.04	.03	.02
132	Bert Blyleven	.08	.06	.03
133	Jeff Reardon	.06	.05	.02
134	Frank Viola	.10	.08	.04
135	Tim Laudner	.04	.03	.02
136	Kent Hrbek	.12	.09	.05
137	Steve Lombardozzi	.04	.03	.02
138	Twins Action (Steve Lombardozzi, Frank White)	.04	.03	.02
139	Twins Action (Steve Lombardozzi, Frank White)	.04	.03	.02
140	Gary Gaetti	.10	.08	.04
141	Greg Gagne	.04	.03	.02
142	Tom Brunansky	.08	.06	.03
143	Dan Gladden	.04	.03	.02
144	Kirby Puckett	.40	.30	.15
145	Gene Larkin	.06	.05	.02
146	Yankees Logo	.04	.03	.02
147	Yankees Uniform	.04	.03	.02
148	Tommy John	.10	.08	.04
149	Rick Rhoden	.04	.03	.02
150	Dave Righetti	.10	.08	.04
151	Rick Cerone	.04	.03	.02
152	Don Mattingly	.50	.40	.20
153	Willie Randolph	.04	.03	.02
154	Yankees Action (Scott Fletcher, Don Mattingly)	.40	.30	.15
155	Yankees Action (Scott Fletcher, Don Mattingly)	.40	.30	.15
156	Mike Pagliarulo	.06	.05	.02
157	Wayne Tolleson	.04	.03	.02
158	Rickey Henderson	.40	.30	.15
159	Dan Pasqua	.04	.03	.02
160	Gary Ward	.04	.03	.02
161	Dave Winfield	.40	.30	.15
162	Athletics Logo	.04	.03	.02
163	Athletics Uniform	.04	.03	.02
164	Dave Stewart	.15	.11	.06
165	Curt Young	.04	.03	.02
166	Terry Steinbach	.06	.05	.02
167	Mark McGwire	.40	.30	.15
168	Tony Phillips	.04	.03	.02
169	Carney Lansford	.04	.03	.02
170	Athletics Action (Mike Gallego, Tony Phillips)	.04	.03	.02
171	Athletics Action (Mike Gallego, Tony Phillips)	.04	.03	.02
172	Alfredo Griffin	.04	.03	.02
173	Jose Canseco	.45	.35	.20
174	Mike Davis	.04	.03	.02
175	Reggie Jackson	.35	.25	.14
176	Dwayne Murphy	.04	.03	.02
177	Luis Polonia	.06	.05	.02
178	Mariners Logo	.04	.03	.02
179	Mariners Uniform	.04	.03	.02
180	Scott Bankhead	.04	.03	.02
181	Mark Langston	.08	.06	.03
182	Edwin Nunez	.04	.03	.02
183	Scott Bradley	.04	.03	.02
184	Dave Valle	.04	.03	.02
185	Alvin Davis	.08	.06	.03
186	Mariners Action (Jack Howell, Rey Quinones)	.04	.03	.02
187	Mariners Action (Jack Howell, Rey Quinones)	.04	.03	.02
188	Harold Reynolds	.04	.03	.02
189	Jim Presley	.06	.05	.02
190	Rey Quinones	.04	.03	.02
191	Phil Bradley	.06	.05	.02
192	Mickey Brantley	.04	.03	.02
193	Mike Kingery	.04	.03	.02
194	Rangers Logo	.04	.03	.02
195	Rangers Uniform	.04	.03	.02
196	Edwin Correa	.04	.03	.02
197	Charlie Hough	.04	.03	.02
198	Bobby Witt	.06	.05	.02
199	Mike Stanley	.04	.03	.02
200	Pete O'Brien	.04	.03	.02
201	Jerry Browne	.04	.03	.02
202	Rangers Action (Steve Buechele, Eddie Murray)	.08	.06	.03
203	Rangers Action (Steve Buechele, Eddie Murray)	.08	.06	.03
204	Steve Buechele	.04	.03	.02
205	Larry Parrish	.04	.03	.02
206	Scott Fletcher	.04	.03	.02
207	Pete Incaviglia	.08	.06	.03
208	Oddibe McDowell	.04	.03	.02
209	Ruben Sierra	.20	.15	.08
210	Blue Jays Logo	.04	.03	.02
211	Blue Jays Uniform	.04	.03	.02
212	Mark Eichhorn	.04	.03	.02
213	Tom Henke	.04	.03	.02
214	Jimmy Key	.06	.05	.02
215	Dave Stieb	.06	.05	.02
216	Ernie Whitt	.04	.03	.02
217	Willie Upshaw	.04	.03	.02
218	Blue Jays Action (Harold Reynolds, Willie Upshaw)	.04	.03	.02
219	Blue Jays Action (Harold Reynolds, Willie Upshaw)	.04	.03	.02
220	Garth Iorg	.04	.03	.02
221	Kelly Gruber	.04	.03	.02
222	Tony Fernandez	.06	.05	.02
223	Jesse Barfield	.08	.06	.03
224	George Bell	.08	.06	.03
225	Lloyd Moseby	.04	.03	.02
226	American League Logo, National League Logo	.04	.03	.02
227	Terry Kennedy, Don Mattingly	.30	.25	.12
228	Wade Boggs, Willie Randolph	.30	.25	.12
229	Bret Saberhagen	.12	.09	.05
230	George Bell, Cal Ripken Jr.	.25	.20	.10
231	Rickey Henderson, Dave Winfield	.35	.25	.14
232	Gary Carter, Jack Clark	.12	.09	.05
233	Mike Scott	.08	.06	.03
234	Ryne Sandberg, Mike Schmidt	.35	.25	.14
235	Eric Davis, Ozzie Smith	.15	.11	.06
236	Andre Dawson, Darryl Strawberry	.20	.15	.08
237	Braves Logo	.04	.03	.02
238	Braves Uniform	.04	.03	.02
239	Rick Mahler	.04	.03	.02
240	Zane Smith	.04	.03	.02
241	Ozzie Virgil	.04	.03	.02
242	Gerald Perry	.06	.05	.02
243	Glenn Hubbard	.04	.03	.02
244	Ken Oberkfell	.04	.03	.02
245	Braves Action (Glenn Hubbard, Jeffrey Leonard)	.04	.03	.02
246	Braves Action (Glenn Hubbard, Jeffrey Leonard)	.04	.03	.02
247	Rafael Ramirez	.04	.03	.02
248	Ken Griffey	.04	.03	.02

249 Albert Hall .04 .03 .02
250 Dion James .04 .03 .02
251 Dale Murphy .25 .20 .10
252 Gary Roenicke .04 .03 .02
253 Cubs Logo .04 .03 .02
254 Cubs Uniform .04 .03 .02
255 Jamie Moyer .04 .03 .02
256 Lee Smith .06 .05 .02
257 Rick Sutcliffe .08 .06 .03
258 Jody Davis .04 .03 .02
259 Leon Durham .04 .03 .02
260 Ryne Sandberg .45 .35 .20
261 Cubs Action (Jody Davis) .04 .03 .02
262 Cubs Action (Jody Davis) .04 .03 .02
263 Keith Moreland .04 .03 .02
264 Shawon Dunston .06 .05 .02
265 Andre Dawson .20 .15 .08
266 Dave Martinez .04 .03 .02
267 Jerry Mumphrey .04 .03 .02
268 Rafael Palmeiro .25 .20 .10
269 Reds Logo .04 .03 .02
270 Reds Uniform .04 .03 .02
271 John Franco .06 .05 .02
272 Ted Power .04 .03 .02
273 Bo Diaz .04 .03 .02
274 Nick Esasky .04 .03 .02
275 Dave Concepcion .04 .03 .02
276 Kurt Stillwell .06 .05 .02
277 Reds Action (Bob Melvin, Dave Parker) .04 .03 .02
278 Reds Action (Bob Melvin, Dave Parker) .04 .03 .02
279 Buddy Bell .06 .05 .02
280 Barry Larkin .15 .11 .06
281 Kal Daniels .08 .06 .03
282 Eric Davis .15 .11 .06
283 Tracy Jones .06 .05 .02
284 Dave Parker .15 .11 .06
285 Astros Logo .04 .03 .02
286 Astros Uniform .04 .03 .02
287 Jim Deshaies .04 .03 .02
288 Nolan Ryan .90 .70 .35
289 Mike Scott .08 .06 .03
290 Dave Smith .04 .03 .02
291 Alan Ashby .04 .03 .02
292 Glenn Davis .10 .08 .04
293 Astros Action (Alan Ashby, Gary Carter) .06 .05 .02
294 Astros Action (Alan Ashby, Gary Carter) .06 .05 .02
295 Bill Doran .04 .03 .02
296 Denny Walling .04 .03 .02
297 Craig Reynolds .04 .03 .02
298 Kevin Bass .04 .03 .02
299 Jose Cruz .04 .03 .02
300 Billy Hatcher .04 .03 .02
301 Dodgers Logo .04 .03 .02
302 Dodgers Uniform .04 .03 .02
303 Orel Hershiser .15 .11 .06
304 Fernando Valenzuela .08 .06 .03
305 Bob Welch .06 .05 .02
306 Matt Young .04 .03 .02
307 Mike Scioscia .04 .03 .02
308 Franklin Stubbs .04 .03 .02
309 Dodgers Action (Mariano Duncan, Junior Ortiz) .04 .03 .02
310 Dodgers Action (Mariano Duncan, Junior Ortiz) .04 .03 .02
311 Steve Sax .10 .08 .04
312 Jeff Hamilton .04 .03 .02
313 Dave Anderson .04 .03 .02
314 Pedro Guerrero .10 .08 .04
315 Mike Marshall .08 .06 .03
316 John Shelby .04 .03 .02
317 Expos Logo .04 .03 .02
318 Expos Uniform .04 .03 .02
319 Neal Heaton .04 .03 .02
320 Bryn Smith .04 .03 .02
321 Floyd Youmans .04 .03 .02
322 Mike Fitzgerald .04 .03 .02
323 Andres Galarraga .20 .15 .08
324 Vance Law .04 .03 .02
325 Expos Action (John Kruk, Tim Raines) .06 .05 .02
326 Expos Action (John Kruk, Tim Raines) .06 .05 .02
327 Tim Wallach .08 .06 .03
328 Hubie Brooks .04 .03 .02
329 Casey Candaele .04 .03 .02
330 Tim Raines .15 .11 .06
331 Mitch Webster .04 .03 .02
332 Herm Winningham .04 .03 .02
333 Mets Logo .04 .03 .02
334 Mets Uniform .04 .03 .02
335 Ron Darling .08 .06 .03
336 Sid Fernandez .06 .05 .02
337 Dwight Gooden .30 .25 .12
338 Gary Carter .15 .11 .06
339 Keith Hernandez .08 .06 .03
340 Wally Backman .04 .03 .02
341 Mets Action (Mike Diaz, Darryl Strawberry, Tim Teufel, Mookie Wilson) .10 .08 .04
342 Mets Action (Mike Diaz, Darryl Strawberry, Tim Teufel, Mookie Wilson) .10 .08 .04
343 Howard Johnson .06 .05 .02
344 Rafael Santana .04 .03 .02
345 Lenny Dykstra .06 .05 .02
346 Kevin McReynolds .10 .08 .04
347 Darryl Strawberry .15 .11 .06
348 Mookie Wilson .04 .03 .02
349 Phillies Logo .04 .03 .02
350 Phillies Uniform .04 .03 .02
351 Steve Bedrosian .06 .05 .02
352 Shane Rawley .04 .03 .02
353 Bruce Ruffin .04 .03 .02
354 Kent Tekulve .04 .03 .02
355 Lance Parrish .12 .09 .05
356 Von Hayes .04 .03 .02
357 Phillies Action (Tony Pena, Glenn Wilson) .04 .03 .02
358 Phillies Action (Tony Pena, Glenn Wilson) .04 .03 .02
359 Juan Samuel .10 .08 .04
360 Mike Schmidt .45 .35 .20
361 Steve Jeltz .04 .03 .02
362 Chris James .06 .05 .02
363 Milt Thompson .04 .03 .02
364 Glenn Wilson .04 .03 .02
365 Pirates Logo .04 .03 .02
366 Pirates Uniform .04 .03 .02
367 Mike Dunne .06 .05 .02
368 Brian Fisher .04 .03 .02
369 Mike LaValliere .04 .03 .02
370 Sid Bream .04 .03 .02
371 Jose Lind .08 .06 .03
372 Bobby Bonilla .15 .11 .06
373 Pirates Action (Bobby Bonilla) .06 .05 .02
374 Pirates Action (Bobby Bonilla) .06 .05 .02
375 Al Pedrique .04 .03 .02
376 Barry Bonds .50 .40 .20
377 John Cangelosi .04 .03 .02
378 Mike Diaz .04 .03 .02
379 R.J. Reynolds .04 .03 .02
380 Andy Van Slyke .15 .11 .06
381 Cardinals Logo .04 .03 .02
382 Cardinals Uniform .04 .03 .02
383 Danny Cox .04 .03 .02
384 Bob Forsch .04 .03 .02
385 Joe Magrane .06 .05 .02
386 Todd Worrell .08 .06 .03
387 Tony Pena .04 .03 .02
388 Jack Clark .10 .08 .04
389 Cardinals Action (Jody Davis, Tom Herr) .04 .03 .02
390 Cardinals Action (Jody Davis, Tom Herr) .04 .03 .02
391 Tom Herr .04 .03 .02
392 Terry Pendleton .15 .11 .06
393 Ozzie Smith .25 .20 .10
394 Vince Coleman .12 .09 .05
395 Curt Ford .04 .03 .02
396 Willie McGee .08 .06 .03
397 Padres Logo .04 .03 .02
398 Padres Uniform .04 .03 .02
399 Lance McCullers .04 .03 .02
400 Eric Show .04 .03 .02
401 Ed Whitson .04 .03 .02
402 Benito Santiago .12 .09 .05
403 John Kruk .15 .11 .06
404 Tim Flannery .04 .03 .02
405 Padres Action (Randy Ready, Benito Santiago) .06 .05 .02
406 Padres Action (Randy Ready, Benito Santiago) .06 .05 .02
407 Randy Ready .04 .03 .02
408 Chris Brown .04 .03 .02
409 Gary Templeton .04 .03 .02
410 Tony Gwynn .25 .20 .10
411 Stan Jefferson .04 .03 .02
412 Carmelo Martinez .04 .03 .02
413 Giants Logo .04 .03 .02
414 Giants Uniform .04 .03 .02
415 Kelly Downs .04 .03 .02
416 Scott Garrelts .04 .03 .02
417 Mike Krukow .04 .03 .02
418 Mike LaCoss .04 .03 .02
419 Bob Brenly .04 .03 .02
420 Will Clark .45 .35 .20
421 Giants Action (Will Clark, Mike Fitzgerald) .15 .11 .06
422 Giants Action (Will Clark, Mike Fitzgerald) .15 .11 .06
423 Robby Thompson .20 .15 .08
424 Kevin Mitchell .15 .11 .06
425 Jose Uribe .04 .03 .02
426 Mike Aldrete .04 .03 .02
427 Jeffrey Leonard .04 .03 .02
428 Candy Maldonado .04 .03 .02
429 Mike Schmidt .40 .30 .15
430 Don Mattingly .50 .40 .20
431 Juan Nieves .04 .03 .02
432 Paul Molitor .25 .20 .10
433 Benito Santiago .12 .09 .05
434 Rickey Henderson .35 .25 .14
435 Nolan Ryan .90 .70 .35
436 Kevin Seitzer .25 .20 .10
437 Tony Gwynn .25 .20 .10
438 Mark McGwire .40 .30 .15
439 Howard Johnson .15 .11 .06
440 Steve Bedrosian .06 .05 .02
441 Darrell Evans .06 .05 .02
442 Eddie Murray .20 .15 .08
443 1987 American League Championship Series (Kirby Puckett, Alan Trammell, Lou Whitaker) .08 .06 .03
444 1987 American League Championship Series (Kirby Puckett, Alan Trammell, Lou Whitaker) .08 .06 .03
445 American League Championship Series MVP (Gary Gaetti) .08 .06 .03
446 National League Championship Series MVP (Jeffrey Leonard) .04 .03 .02
447 1987 National League Championship Series (Kevin Mitchell, Tony Pena) .04 .03 .02
448 1987 National League Championship Series (Kevin Mitchell, Tony Pena) .04 .03 .02
449 1987 World Series (Tom Brunansky, Tony Pena) .04 .03 .02
450 1987 World Series (Tom Brunansky, Tony Pena) .04 .03 .02
451 World Series Celebration .04 .03 .02
452 World Series Celebration .04 .03 .02
453 World Series Celebration .04 .03 .02
454 World Series Celebration .04 .03 .02
(455) Orioles Logo/Pennant .04 .03 .02
(456) Red Sox Logo/Pennant .04 .03 .02
(457) Angels Logo/Pennant .04 .03 .02
(458) White Sox Logo/Pennant .04 .03 .02
(459) Indians Logo/Pennant .04 .03 .02
(460) Tigers Logo/Pennant .04 .03 .02
(461) Royals Logo/Pennant .04 .03 .02
(462) Brewers Logo/Pennant .04 .03 .02
(463) Twins Logo/Pennant .04 .03 .02
(464) Yankees Logo/Pennant .04 .03 .02
(465) Athletics Logo/Pennant .04 .03 .02
(466) Mariners Logo/Pennant .04 .03 .02
(467) Rangers Logo/Pennant .04 .03 .02
(468) Blue Jays Logo/Pennant .04 .03 .02
(469) Braves Logo/Pennant .04 .03 .02
(470) Cubs Logo/Pennant .04 .03 .02
(471) Reds Logo/Pennant .04 .03 .02
(472) Astros Logo/Pennant .04 .03 .02
(473) Dodgers Logo/Pennant .04 .03 .02
(474) Expos Logo/Pennant .04 .03 .02
(475) Mets Logo/Pennant .04 .03 .02
(476) Phillies Logo/Pennant .04 .03 .02
(477) Pirates Logo/Pennant .04 .03 .02
(478) Cardinals Logo/Pennant .04 .03 .02
(479) Padres Logo/Pennant .04 .03 .02
(480) Giants Logo/Pennant .04 .03 .02

1968 - 69 Partridge Meats Reds

The extent of the checklist for this scarce regional issue is unknown. Cards have been seen for seven players and coach Jimmy Bragan. Players' service with the Reds indicates this set was issued over a period of at least two years. Similar cards are known for other Cincinnati pro sports teams. The cards measure 4" x 5" and feature a black-and-white player photo set against a borderless white background. The player's name and team and the word "Likes" are printed in black, the ad for the issuing meat company at bottom is printed in red. Cards have a blank back. The unnumbered cards are checklisted here in alphabetical order.

	NR MT	EX	VG
Common Player:	30.00	15.00	9.00
(1) Johnny Bench	90.00	45.00	27.00
(2) Jimmy Bragan	30.00	15.00	9.00
(3) Tommy Helms	30.00	15.00	9.00
(4) Gary Nolan	30.00	15.00	9.00
(5) Don Pavletich	30.00	15.00	9.00
(6) Mel Queen	30.00	15.00	9.00
(7) Pete Rose	125.00	60.00	40.00
(8) Jim Stewart	30.00	15.00	9.00

1970 - 72 Partridge Meats Reds

Similar in format to the meat company's 1968-69 issue, these later cards are in a slightly different size -- 3-3/4" x 5-1/2". The extent of the issue is as yet unknown. All known players are listed below.

	NR MT	EX	VG
Common Player:	25.00	12.50	7.50
(1) Denis Menke	25.00	12.50	7.50
(2) Jim Merritt	25.00	12.50	7.50
(3) Gary Nolan	25.00	12.50	7.50
(4) Tony Perez	60.00	30.00	18.00
(5) Bob Tolan	25.00	12.50	7.50

1963 Pepsi-Cola Colt .45's

This 16-card set was distributed regionally in Texas in bottled six-packs of Pepsi. The cards were issued on panels 2-3/8" by 9-1/8", which were fit in between the bottles in each carton. Values quoted in the checklist below are for complete panels. A standard 2-3/8" by 3-3/4" card was printed on each panel, which also included promos for Pepsi and the Colt .45's, as well as a team schedule. Card fronts were black and white posed action photos with blue and red trim. Player name and position and Pepsi

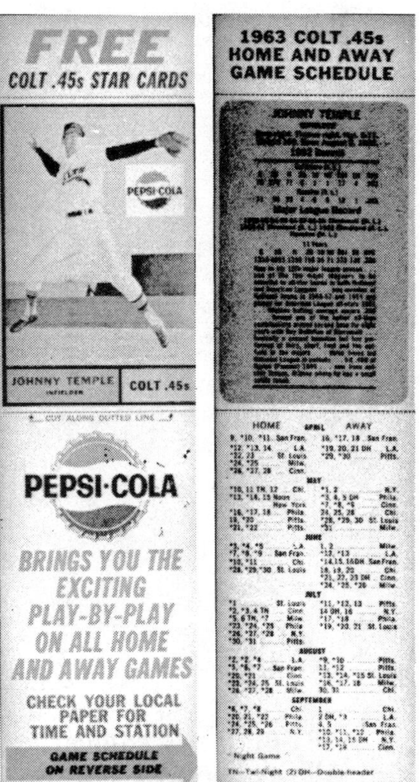

logo are also included. Card backs offer player statistics and career highlights. The John Bateman card, which was apparently never distributed publicly, is among the rarest collectible baseball cards of the 1960s. The complete set price does not include the Bateman card.

		NR MT	EX	VG
Complete Set (16):		210.00	105.00	63.00
Common Player:		7.00	3.50	2.00
1	Bob Aspromonte	7.00	3.50	2.00
2	John Bateman	500.00	250.00	150.00
3	Bob Bruce	7.00	3.50	2.00
4	Jim Campbell	7.00	3.50	2.00
5	Dick Farrell	7.00	3.50	2.00
6	Ernie Fazio	7.00	3.50	2.00
7	Carroll Hardy	7.00	3.50	2.00
8	J.C. Hartman	7.00	3.50	2.00
9	Ken Johnson	7.00	3.50	2.00
10	Bob Lillis	7.00	3.50	2.00
11	Don McMahon	7.00	3.50	2.00
12	Pete Runnels	15.00	7.50	4.50
13	Al Spangler	7.00	3.50	2.00
14	Rusty Staub	30.00	15.00	9.00
15	Johnny Temple	7.00	3.50	2.00
16	Carl Warwick	60.00	30.00	18.00

1977 Pepsi-Cola Baseball Stars

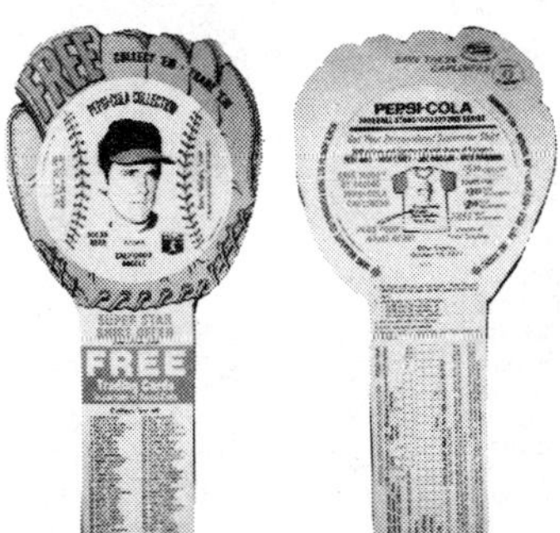

An Ohio regional promotion (the checklist is extra heavy with Indians and Reds players), large numbers of these cards found their way into hobby dealers' hands with the result that they are fairly common even today. Designed to be inserted into cartons of soda, the cards have 3-3/8" diameter central disc attached with perforations to a baseball glove design. A tab beneath the glove contains the checklist (the card discs themselves are unnumbered) and a coupon on back for ordering a player t-shirt, the offer for which is made on the back of the player. The players' association logo appears on front, but the producer, Mike Schecter Associates, did not seek licensing by Major League Baseball, with the result that uniform logos have been removed from the black-and-white player photos. Prices shown are for complete glove/disc/tab cards. Values for unattached player discs would be no more than one-half of those shown.

		NR MT	EX	VG
Complete Set (72):		24.00	12.00	7.25
Common Player:		.25	.13	.08
1	Robin Yount	3.00	1.50	.90
2	Rod Carew	1.50	.70	.45
3	Butch Wynegar	.25	.13	.08
4	Manny Sanguillen	.25	.13	.08
5	Mike Hargrove	.25	.13	.08
6	Larvel (Larvell) Blanks	.25	.13	.08
7	Jim Kern	.25	.13	.08
8	Pat Dobson	.25	.13	.08
9	Rico Carty	.35	.20	.11
10	John Grubb	.25	.13	.08
11	Buddy Bell	.35	.20	.11
12	Rick Manning	.25	.13	.08
13	Dennis Eckersley	.90	.45	.25
14	Wayne Garland	.25	.13	.08
15	Dave LaRoche	.25	.13	.08
16	Rick Waits	.25	.13	.08
17	Ray Fosse	.25	.13	.08
18	Frank Duffy	.25	.13	.08
19	Duane Kuiper	.25	.13	.08
20	Jim Palmer	1.50	.70	.45
21	Fred Lynn	.75	.40	.25
22	Carlton Fisk	.75	.40	.25
23	Carl Yastrzemski	2.00	1.00	.60
24	Nolan Ryan	5.00	2.50	1.50
25	Bobby Grich	.50	.25	.15
26	Ralph Garr	.25	.13	.08
27	Richie Zisk	.25	.13	.08
28	Ron LeFlore	.25	.13	.08
29	Rusty Staub	.50	.25	.15
30	Mark Fidrych	.35	.20	.11
31	Willie Horton	.25	.13	.08
32	George Brett	3.00	1.50	.90
33	Amos Otis	.25	.13	.08
34	Reggie Jackson	3.00	1.50	.90
35	Don Gullett	.25	.13	.08
36	Thurman Munson	.90	.45	.25
37	Al Hrabosky	.25	.13	.08
38	Mike Tyson	.25	.13	.08
39	Gene Tenace	.25	.13	.08
40	George Hendrick	.25	.13	.08
41	Chris Speier	.25	.13	.08
42	John Montefusco	.25	.13	.08
43	Pete Rose	3.00	1.50	.90
44	Johnny Bench	3.00	1.50	.90
45	Dan Driessen	.25	.13	.08
46	Joe Morgan	1.50	.70	.45
47	Dave Concepcion	.35	.20	.11
48	George Foster	.35	.20	.11
49	Cesar Geronimo	.25	.13	.08
50	Ken Griffey	.35	.20	.11
51	Gary Nolan	.25	.13	.08
52	Santo Alcala	.25	.13	.08
53	Jack Billingham	.25	.13	.08
54	Pedro Borbon	.25	.13	.08
55	Rawly Eastwick	.25	.13	.08
56	Fred Norman	.25	.13	.08
57	Pat Zachary	.25	.13	.08
58	Jeff Burroughs	.25	.13	.08
59	Manny Trillo	.25	.13	.08
60	Bob Watson	.25	.13	.08
61	Steve Garvey	.50	.25	.15
62	Don Sutton	.35	.20	.11
63	John Candalaria	.25	.13	.08
64	Willie Stargell	1.50	.70	.45
65	Jerry Reuss	.25	.13	.08
66	Dave Cash	.25	.13	.08
67	Tom Seaver	1.50	.70	.45
68	Jon Matlock	.25	.13	.08
69	Dave Kingman	.35	.20	.11
70	Mike Schmidt	3.00	1.50	.90
71	Jay Johnstone	.25	.13	.08
72	Greg Luzinski	.35	.20	.11

1978 Pepsi-Cola Superstars

		NR MT	EX	VG
Complete Set (40):		20.00	15.00	8.00
Common Player:		.25	.13	.08
(1)	Sparky Anderson	.50	.25	.15
(2)	Rick Auerbach	.25	.13	.08
(3)	Doug Bair	.25	.13	.08
(4)	Buddy Bell	.25	.13	.08
(5)	Johnny Bench	2.00	1.00	.60
(6)	Bill Bonham	.25	.13	.08
(7)	Pedro Borbon	.25	.13	.08
(8)	Larry Bowa	.35	.25	.14
(9)	George Brett	2.00	1.00	.60
(10)	Jeff Burroughs	.25	.13	.08
(11)	Rod Carew	1.00	.50	.30
(12)	Dave Collins	.25	.13	.08
(13)	Dave Concepcion	.35	.20	.11
(14)	Dan Driessen	.25	.13	.08
(15)	George Foster	.35	.20	.11
(16)	Steve Garvey	.40	.20	.12
(17)	Cesar Geronimo	.25	.13	.08
(18)	Ken Griffey	.35	.20	.11
(19)	Ken Henderson	.25	.13	.08
(20)	Tom Hume	.25	.13	.08
(21)	Reggie Jackson	2.00	1.00	.60
(22)	Junior Kennedy	.25	.13	.08
(23)	Dave Kingman	.25	.13	.08
(24)	Ray Knight	.25	.13	.08
(25)	Jerry Koosman	.25	.13	.08
(26)	Mike Lum	.25	.13	.08
(27)	Bill Madlock	.30	.15	.09
(28)	Joe Morgan	1.00	.50	.30
(29)	Paul Moskau	.25	.13	.08
(30)	Fred Norman	.25	.13	.08
(31)	Jim Palmer	1.00	.50	.30
(32)	Pete Rose	1.50	.70	.45
(33)	Nolan Ryan	3.00	1.50	.90
(34)	Manny Sarmiento	.25	.13	.08
(35)	Tom Seaver	1.50	.70	.45
(36)	Ted Simmons	.25	.13	.08
(37)	Dave Tomlin	.25	.13	.08
(38)	Don Werner	.25	.13	.08
(39)	Carl Yastrzemski	2.00	1.00	.60
(40)	Richie Zisk	.25	.13	.08

1988 Pepsi-Cola/Kroger Tigers

Approximately 38,000 sets of cards were given to fans at Tiger Stadium on July 30th, 1988. The set, sponsored by Pepsi-Cola and Kroger, includes 25 oversized (2-7/8" by 4-1/4") cards printed on glossy white stock with blue and orange borders. The card backs include small black and white close-up photos, the players' professional records and sponsor logos. The numbers in the following checklist refer to the players' uniform.

		MT	NR MT	EX
Complete Set (25):		8.00	6.00	3.25
Common Player:		.20	.15	.08
1	Lou Whitaker	.70	.50	.30
2	Alan Trammell	.90	.70	.35
8	Mike Heath	.20	.15	.08
11	Sparky Anderson	.40	.30	.15
12	Luis Salazar	.20	.15	.08
14	Dave Bergman	.20	.15	.08
15	Pat Sheridan	.20	.15	.08
16	Tom Brookens	.20	.15	.08
19	Doyle Alexander	.25	.20	.10
21	Guillermo Hernandez	.25	.20	.10
22	Ray Knight	.25	.20	.10
24	Gary Pettis	.20	.15	.08
25	Eric King	.20	.15	.08
26	Frank Tanana	.30	.25	.12
31	Larry Herndon	.20	.15	.08
32	Jim Walewander	.20	.15	.08
33	Matt Nokes	.40	.30	.15
34	Chet Lemon	.25	.20	.10
35	Walt Terrell	.25	.20	.10
39	Mike Henneman	.40	.30	.15
41	Darrell Evans	.40	.30	.15
44	Jeff Robinson	.25	.20	.10
47	Jack Morris	.70	.50	.30
48	Paul Gibson	.25	.20	.10
----	Coaches (Billy Consolo, Alex Grammas, Billy Muffett, Vada Pinson, Dick Tracewski)	.20	.15	.08

1990 Pepsi-Cola Red Sox

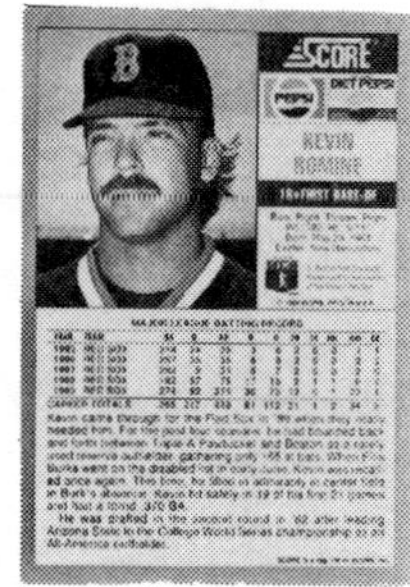

Pepsi combined with Score to produce this special 20-card Boston Red Sox team set. Cards were inserted regionally in 12-packs of Pepsi and Diet Pepsi. The card fronts feature full-color action photos with the team name across the top border and the player's name along the bottom border. The Pepsi and Diet Pepsi logos also appear on the bottom border. The card backs represent standard Score card backs, but are not numbered and also once again feature the Pepsi and Diet Pepsi logos.

		MT	NR MT	EX
Complete Set (20):		8.00	6.00	3.25
Common Player:		.25	.20	.10
(1)	Marty Barrett	.25	.20	.10
(2)	Mike Boddicker	.35	.25	.14
(3)	Wade Boggs	1.50	1.25	.60
(4)	Bill Buckner	.25	.20	.10
(5)	Ellis Burks	.80	.60	.30
(6)	Roger Clemens	1.50	1.25	.60
(7)	John Dopson	.25	.20	.10
(8)	Dwight Evans	.35	.25	.14
(9)	Wes Gardner	.25	.20	.10
(10)	Rich Gedman	.25	.20	.10
(11)	Mike Greenwell	.60	.45	.25
(12)	Dennis Lamp	.25	.20	.10
(13)	Rob Murphy	.35	.25	.14
(14)	Tony Pena	.35	.25	.14
(15)	Carlos Quintana	.35	.25	.14
(16)	Jeff Reardon	.40	.30	.15
(17)	Jody Reed	.40	.30	.15
(18)	Luis Rivera	.25	.20	.10
(19)	Kevin Romine	.25	.20	.10
(20)	Lee Smith	.50	.40	.20

1991 Pepsi-Cola Red Sox

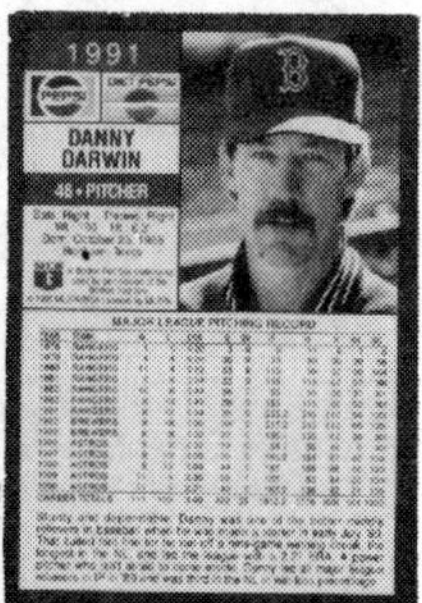

For the second consecutive year, Pepsi/Diet Pepsi sponsored Boston Red Sox trading cards. The cards were inserted in specially marked packs of Pepsi and Diet Pepsi and were made available from July 1 through August 10. A consumer sweepstakes was also included with this promotion. Player jersey numbers are featured on the backs of the cards. Danny Darwin's jersey is incorrectly listed as #46. He actually wears #44 for the BoSox. Wade Boggs is not featured on a 1991 Pepsi-Cola Red Sox card.

		MT	NR MT	EX
Complete Set:		8.00	6.00	3.25
Common Player:		.25	.20	.10
2	Luis Rivera	.25	.20	.10
3	Jody Reed	.40	.30	.15
6	Tony Pena	.40	.30	.15
11	Tim Naehring	.50	.40	.20
12	Ellis Burks	.60	.45	.25
15	Dennis Lamp	.25	.20	.10
18	Carlos Quintana	.30	.25	.12
19	Dana Kiecker	.25	.20	.10
20	John Marzano	.25	.20	.10
21	Roger Clemens	1.00	.70	.40
23	Tom Brunansky	.25	.20	.10
25	Jack Clark	.30	.25	.12
27	Greg Harris	.30	.25	.12
29	Phil Plantier	1.25	.90	.50
30	Matt Young	.25	.20	.10
38	Jeff Gray	.30	.25	.12
39	Mike Greenwell	.60	.45	.25
41	Jeff Reardon	.40	.30	.15
46	Danny Darwin	.25	.20	.10
50	Tom Bolton	.25	.20	.10

1985 Performance Printing Rangers

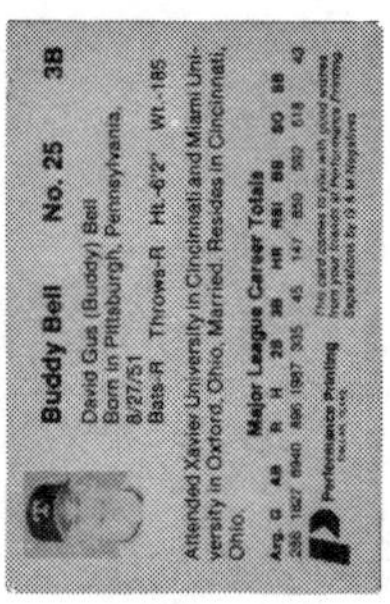

A local printing company sponsored this 28-card set of the Texas Rangers. The 2-3/8" by 3-1/2" cards are in full color and are numbered on the back by uniform number. Card fronts feature full-color, game-action photos. The 25 players on the Rangers' active roster at press time are included, along with manager Bobby Valentine and unnumbered coaches and trainer cards. The black and white card backs have a smaller portrait photo of each player, as well as biographical information and career statistics.

		MT	NR MT	EX
Complete Set (28):		7.00	5.25	2.75
Common Player:		.25	.20	.10
0	Oddibe McDowell	.30	.25	.12
1	Bill Stein	.25	.20	.10
2	Bobby Valentine	.25	.20	.10
3	Wayne Tolleson	.25	.20	.10
4	Don Slaught	.25	.20	.10
5	Alan Bannister	.25	.20	.10
6	Bobby Jones	.25	.20	.10
7	Glenn Brummer	.25	.20	.10
8	Luis Pujols	.25	.20	.10
9	Pete O'Brien	.30	.25	.12
11	Toby Harrah	.25	.20	.10
13	Tommy Dunbar	.25	.20	.10
15	Larry Parrish	.30	.25	.12
16	Mike Mason	.25	.20	.10
19	Curtis Wilkerson	.25	.20	.10
24	Dave Schmidt	.25	.20	.10
25	Buddy Bell	.30	.25	.12
27	Greg Harris	.25	.20	.10
30	Dave Rozema	.25	.20	.10
32	Gary Ward	.25	.20	.10
36	Dickie Noles	.25	.20	.10
41	Chris Welsh	.25	.20	.10
44	Cliff Johnson	.25	.20	.10
46	Burt Hooton	.25	.20	.10
48	Dave Stewart	.50	.40	.20
49	Charlie Hough	.30	.25	.12
----	Trainers (Danny Wheat, Bill Ziegler)	.25	.09	.05
----	Rangers Coaches (Rich Donnelly, Glenn Ezell, Tom House, Art Howe, Wayne Terwilliger)	.25	.09	.05

1986 Performance Printing Rangers

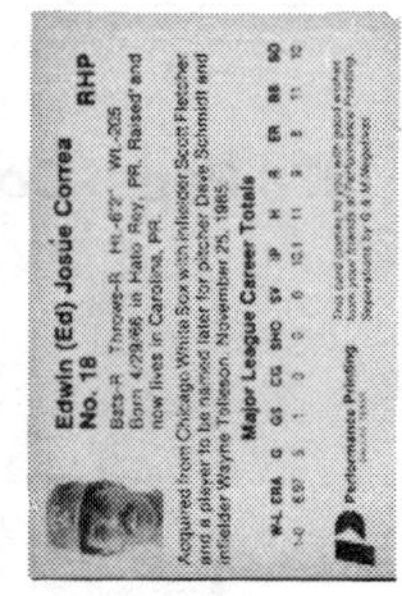

For the second time, the Texas Rangers issued a full-color card set in conjunction with this local printing company. Fronts of the 28-card set include player name, position and team logo beneath the color photo. Backs of the 2-3/8" by 3-1/2" cards are in black and white, with a small portrait photo of each player along with personal and professional statistics. Cards were distributed at the August 23 Rangers home game, and the set includes all of the Rangers' fine rookies such as Bobby Witt, Pete Incaviglia, Edwin Correa and Ruben Sierra.

		MT	NR MT	EX
Complete Set (28):		10.00	7.50	4.00
Common Player:		.25	.20	.10
0	Oddibe McDowell	.25	.15	.08
1	Scott Fletcher	.25	.20	.10
2	Bobby Valentine	.25	.20	.10
3	Ruben Sierra	3.00	2.25	1.25
4	Don Slaught	.25	.20	.10
9	Pete O'Brien	.25	.20	.10
11	Toby Harrah	.25	.20	.10
12	Geno Petralli	.25	.20	.10
15	Larry Parrish	.25	.20	.10
16	Mike Mason	.25	.20	.10
17	Darrell Porter	.25	.20	.10
18	Edwin Correa	.25	.20	.10
19	Curtis Wilkerson	.25	.20	.10
22	Steve Buechele	.40	.30	.15
23	Jose Guzman	.25	.20	.10
24	Ricky Wright	.25	.20	.10
27	Greg Harris	.25	.20	.10
28	Mitch Williams	.30	.25	.12
29	Pete Incaviglia	.40	.30	.15
32	Gary Ward	.25	.20	.10
34	Dale Mohorcic	.25	.20	.10
40	Jeff Russell	.25	.20	.10
44	Tom Paciorek	.25	.20	.10
46	Mike Loynd	.25	.20	.10
48	Bobby Witt	.40	.30	.15
49	Charlie Hough	.25	.20	.10
----	Coaching Staff (Joe Ferguson, Tim Foli, Tom House, Art Howe, Tom Robson)	.25	.08	.04
----	Trainers (Danny Wheat, Bill Zeigler)	.25	.08	.04

1981 Perma-Graphics All-Star Credit Cards

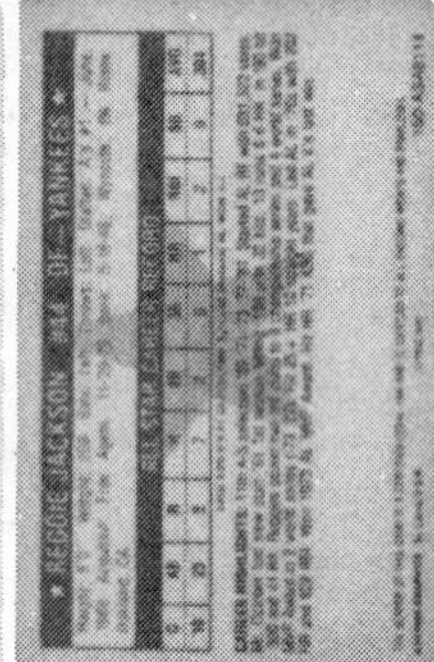

Using the same "credit card" style of its previous 1981 issue, Perma-Graphics issued an 18-card set in the fall of 1981 featuring the starting players from the 1981 All-Star Game. The front of the card contains a full-color photo, plus the player's name, position and team. The back includes personal data, career records, highlights and an "autograph panel."

		MT	NR MT	EX
Complete Set (18):		30.00	22.00	12.00
Common Player:		1.00	.70	.40
1	Gary Carter	1.25	.90	.50
2	Dave Concepcion	1.00	.70	.40
3	Andre Dawson	1.25	.90	.50
4	George Foster	1.00	.70	.40
5	Davey Lopes	1.00	.70	.40
6	Dave Parker	1.25	.90	.50
7	Pete Rose	4.00	3.00	1.50
8	Mike Schmidt	4.00	3.00	1.50
9	Fernando Valenzuela	1.00	.70	.40
10	George Brett	4.00	3.00	1.50
11	Rod Carew	3.00	2.25	1.25
12	Bucky Dent	1.00	.70	.40
13	Carlton Fisk	1.25	.90	.50
14	Reggie Jackson	2.50	2.00	1.00
15	Jack Morris	1.00	.70	.40
16	Willie Randolph	1.00	.70	.40
17	Ken Singleton	1.00	.70	.40
18	Dave Winfield	3.00	2.25	1.25

1981 Perma-Graphics Super Star Credit Cards

Issued in 1981 by Perma-Graphics of Maryland Heights, Mo., this innovative 32-card set was printed on high-impact, permanently laminated vinyl to give the appearance of a real credit card. The front of the

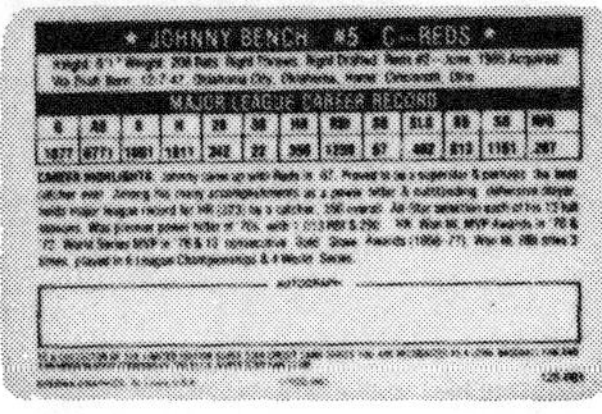

wallet-sized cards includes career statistics and highlights, along with an "autograph panel" for obtaining the player's signature.

		MT	NR MT	EX
Complete Set (32):		40.00	30.00	16.00
Common Player:		1.00	.70	.40
1	Johnny Bench	3.00	2.25	1.25
2	Mike Schmidt	4.00	3.00	1.50
3	George Brett	4.00	3.00	1.50
4	Carl Yastrzemski	3.00	2.25	1.25
5	Pete Rose	4.00	3.00	1.50
6	Bob Horner	1.00	.70	.40
7	Reggie Jackson	2.50	2.00	1.00
8	Keith Hernandez	1.00	.70	.40
9	George Foster	1.00	.70	.40
10	Garry Templeton	1.00	.70	.40
11	Tom Seaver	3.00	2.25	1.25
12	Steve Garvey	1.25	.90	.50
13	Dave Parker	1.00	.70	.40
14	Willie Stargell	2.00	1.50	.80
15	Cecil Cooper	1.00	.70	.40
16	Steve Carlton	3.00	2.25	1.25
17	Ted Simmons	1.00	.70	.40
18	Dave Kingman	1.00	.70	.40
19	Rickey Henderson	3.00	2.25	1.25
20	Fred Lynn	1.00	.70	.40
21	Dave Winfield	3.00	2.25	1.25
22	Rod Carew	3.00	2.25	1.25
23	Jim Rice	1.00	.70	.40
24	Bruce Sutter	1.00	.70	.40
25	Cesar Cedeno	1.00	.70	.40
26	Nolan Ryan	8.00	6.00	3.25
27	Dusty Baker	1.00	.70	.40
28	Jim Palmer	4.00	3.00	1.50
29	Gorman Thomas	1.00	.70	.40
30	Ben Oglivie	1.00	.70	.40
31	Willie Wilson	1.00	.70	.40
32	Gary Carter	1.25	.90	.50

1982 Perma-Graphics Super Star Credit Cards

Perma-Graphics reduced its "Superstar Credit Card Set" to 24 players in 1982, maintaining the same basic credit card appearance. The player photos on the front of the cards are surrounded by a wood-tone border and the backs include the usual personal data, career statistics, highlights and autograph panel. The set was also issued in a limited-edition "gold" version. The special "gold" cards are generally worth two to three times the value of a regular-edition card.

		MT	NR MT	EX
Complete Set (24):		35.00	26.00	14.00
Common Player:		1.00	.70	.40
1	Johnny Bench	2.00	1.50	.80
2	Tom Seaver	2.00	1.50	.80
3	Mike Schmidt	3.00	2.25	1.25
4	Gary Carter	1.25	.90	.50
5	Willie Stargell	2.00	1.50	.80
6	Tim Raines	1.00	.70	.40
7	Bill Madlock	1.00	.70	.40
8	Keith Hernandez	1.00	.70	.40
9	Pete Rose	3.00	2.25	1.25
10	Steve Carlton	2.00	1.50	.80
11	Steve Garvey	1.25	.90	.50
12	Fernando Valenzuela	1.00	.70	.40
13	Carl Yastrzemski	2.00	1.50	.80
14	Dave Winfield	2.00	1.50	.80
15	Carney Lansford	1.00	.70	.40
16	Rollie Fingers	1.50	1.25	.60
17	Tony Armas	1.00	.70	.40
18	Cecil Cooper	1.00	.70	.40
19	George Brett	3.00	2.25	1.25
20	Reggie Jackson	2.00	1.50	.80
21	Rod Carew	2.00	1.50	.80
22	Eddie Murray	1.25	.90	.50
23	Rickey Henderson	2.00	1.50	.80
24	Kirk Gibson	1.00	.70	.40

1982 Perma-Graphics All-Star Credit Cards

Perma-Graphics issued its second "All-Star Credit Card" set in the fall of 1982. Consisting of 18 cards, the set pictured the starters from both leagues in the 1982 All-Star Game. It was also available in a limited-edition "gold" version, which is generally two to three times the value of the regular edition.

		MT	NR MT	EX
Complete Set (18):		25.00	18.50	10.00
Common Player:		1.00	.70	.40
1	Dennis Eckersley	1.50	1.25	.60
2	Cecil Cooper	1.00	.70	.40
3	Carlton Fisk	1.50	1.25	.60
4	Robin Yount	3.00	2.25	1.25
5	Bobby Grich	1.00	.70	.40
6	Rickey Henderson	3.00	2.25	1.25
7	Reggie Jackson	2.00	1.50	.80
8	Fred Lynn	1.00	.70	.40
9	George Brett	3.00	2.25	1.25
10	Gary Carter	1.25	.90	.50
11	Dave Concepcion	1.00	.70	.40
12	Andre Dawson	1.25	.90	.50
13	Tim Raines	1.00	.70	.40
14	Dale Murphy	1.50	1.25	.60
15	Steve Rogers	1.00	.70	.40
16	Pete Rose	3.00	2.25	1.25
17	Mike Schmidt	3.00	2.25	1.25
18	Manny Trillo	1.00	.70	.40

1983 Perma-Graphics Super Star Credit Cards

Similar in design to its previous sets, Perma-Graphics increased the number of cards in its 1983 "Superstar" set to 36, including 18 players from each league. The front of the vinyl card has a full-color photo with the player's name, team, league and position below. The backs contain career records, highlights and autograph panel. The cards were also issued in a special "gold" edition, which are valued at two to three times a regular edition card.

		MT	NR MT	EX
Complete Set (36):		40.00	30.00	16.00
Common Player:		.80	.60	.30
1	Bill Buckner	1.00	.70	.40
2	Steve Carlton	3.00	2.25	1.25
3	Gary Carter	1.75	1.25	.70
4	Andre Dawson	2.00	1.50	.80
5	Pedro Guerrero	1.00	.70	.40
6	George Hendrick	1.00	.70	.40
7	Keith Hernandez	1.00	.70	.40
8	Bill Madlock	1.00	.70	.40
9	Dale Murphy	2.00	1.50	.80
10	Al Oliver	1.00	.70	.40
11	Dave Parker	1.25	.90	.50
12	Darrell Porter	1.00	.70	.40
13	Pete Rose	3.00	2.25	1.25
14	Mike Schmidt	4.00	3.00	1.50
15	Lonnie Smith	1.00	.70	.40
16	Ozzie Smith	1.50	1.25	.60
17	Bruce Sutter	1.00	.70	.40
18	Fernando Valenzuela	1.00	.70	.40
19	George Brett	4.00	3.00	1.50
20	Rod Carew	3.00	2.25	1.25
21	Cecil Cooper	1.00	.70	.40
22	Doug DeCinces	1.00	.70	.40
23	Rollie Fingers	1.50	1.25	.60
24	Damaso Garcia	1.00	.70	.40
25	Toby Harrah	1.00	.70	.40
26	Rickey Henderson	3.00	2.25	1.25
27	Reggie Jackson	3.00	2.25	1.25
28	Hal McRae	1.00	.70	.40
29	Eddie Murray	1.75	1.25	.70
30	Lance Parrish	1.00	.70	.40
31	Jim Rice	1.00	.70	.40
32	Gorman Thomas	1.00	.70	.40
33	Willie Wilson	1.00	.70	.40
34	Dave Winfield	3.00	2.25	1.25
35	Carl Yastrzemski	3.00	2.25	1.25
36	Robin Yount	3.00	2.25	1.25

1983 Perma-Graphics All-Star Credit Cards

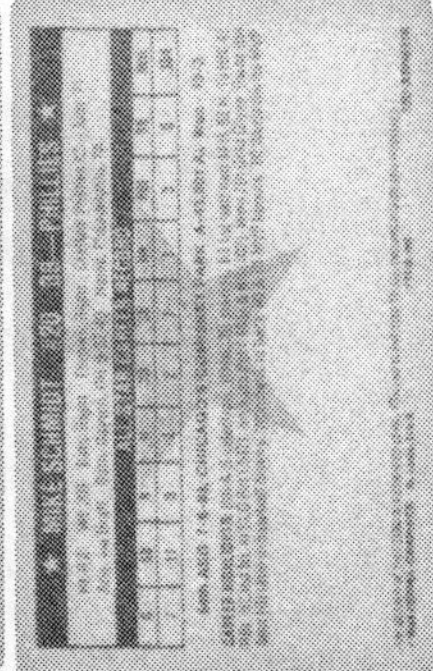

The final issue from Perma-Graphics, this 18-card set was produced in the fall of 1983 and features the 18 starting players from the 1983 All-Star Game. Similar to other Perma-Graphics sets, the cards were printed on wallet-size vinyl to give the appearance of a real credit card. The set was also available in a limited-edition "gold" version, which carries a value two to three times a regular set or card.

		MT	NR MT	EX
Complete Set (18):		25.00	18.50	10.00
Common Player:		1.00	.70	.40
1	George Brett	2.00	1.50	.80
2	Rod Carew	1.50	1.25	.60
3	Fred Lynn	1.00	.70	.40
4	Jim Rice	1.00	.70	.40
5	Ted Simmons	1.00	.70	.40
6	Dave Stieb	1.00	.70	.40
7	Manny Trillo	1.00	.70	.40
8	Dave Winfield	2.00	1.50	.80
9	Robin Yount	2.00	1.50	.80
10	Gary Carter	1.25	.90	.50
11	Andre Dawson	1.50	1.25	.60
12	Dale Murphy	1.50	1.25	.60
13	Al Oliver	1.00	.70	.40
14	Tim Raines	1.00	.70	.40
15	Steve Sax	1.00	.70	.40
16	Mike Schmidt	2.00	1.50	.80
17	Ozzie Smith	1.25	.90	.50
18	Mario Soto	1.00	.70	.40

1961 Peters Meats Twins

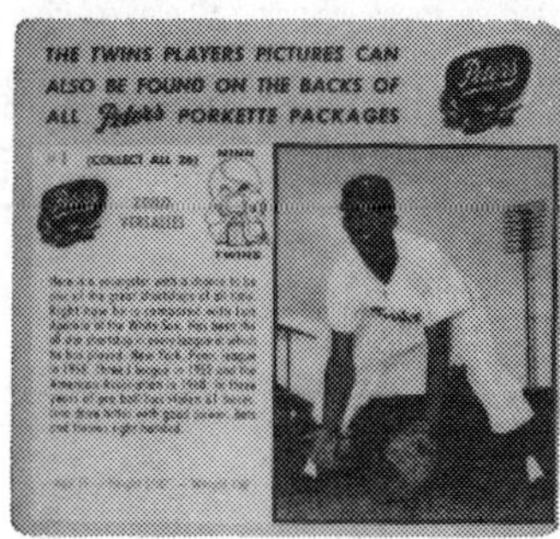

This set, featuring the first-year 1961 Minnesota Twins, is in a large, 4-5/8" by 3-1/2", format. Cards are on thick cardboard and heavily waxed, as they were used as partial packaging for the company's meat products. Card fronts feature full-color photos, team and Peters logos, and biographical information. The cards are blank-backed.

		NR MT	EX	VG
Complete Set (26):		675.00	337.00	202.00
Common Player:		17.50	8.75	5.25
1	Zoilo Versalles	24.00	12.00	7.25
2	Eddie Lopat	24.00	12.00	7.25
3	Pedro Ramos	17.50	8.75	5.25
4	Charles "Chuck" Stobbs	17.50	8.75	5.25
5	Don Mincher	24.00	12.00	7.25
6	Jack Kralick	17.50	8.75	5.25
7	Jim Kaat	55.00	27.00	16.50
8	Hal Naragon	17.50	8.75	5.25
9	Don Lee	17.50	8.75	5.25
10	Harry "Cookie" Lavagetto	17.50	8.75	5.25
11	Tom "Pete" Whisenant	17.50	8.75	5.25
12	Elmer Valo	17.50	8.75	5.25
13	Ray Moore	17.50	8.75	5.25
14	Billy Gardner	17.50	8.75	5.25
15	Lenny Green	17.50	8.75	5.25
16	Sam Mele	17.50	8.75	5.25
17	Jim Lemon	17.50	8.75	5.25
18	Harmon "Killer" Killebrew	175.00	87.00	52.00
19	Paul Giel	17.50	8.75	5.25
20	Reno Bertoia	17.50	8.75	5.25
21	Clyde McCullough	17.50	8.75	5.25
22	Earl Battey	24.00	12.00	7.25
23	Camilo Pascual	24.00	12.00	7.25
24	Dan Dobbek	17.50	8.75	5.25
25	Joe "Valvy" Valdivielso	17.50	8.75	5.25
26	Billy Consolo	17.50	8.75	5.25

1991 Petro Canada All-Star Fanfest Standups

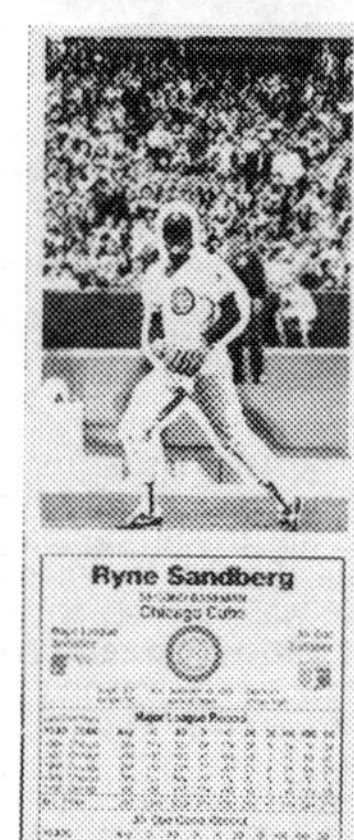

1991 Petro-Canada Standups are vaguely reminiscent of the 1964 Topps Standups. The set was distributed at Fanfest in Toronto in conjunction with the All-Star Game. There are 26 players in the set, with the folded card measuring 2-7/8" x 3-7/8". Unfolded, the card shows a cutout figure of the player superimposed in front of a photo of stadium surroundings. The base which the player stands on has major league and All-Star Game statistics, with career highlights on the back and a player quiz.

		MT	NR MT	EX
Complete Set (26):		20.00	15.00	8.00
Common Player:		.25	.20	.10
1	Cal Ripken, Jr.	2.00	1.50	.80
2	Greg Olson	.25	.20	.10
3	Roger Clemens	.60	.45	.25
4	Ryne Sandberg	2.00	1.50	.80
5	Dave Winfield	.75	.60	.30
6	Eric Davis	.35	.25	.14
7	Carlton Fisk	.60	.45	.25
8	Mike Scott	.25	.20	.10
9	Sandy Alomar, Jr.	.25	.20	.10
10	Tim Wallach	.35	.25	.14
11	Cecil Fielder	.60	.45	.25
12	Dwight Gooden	.60	.45	.25
13	George Brett	2.00	1.50	.80
14	Dale Murphy	.60	.45	.25
15	Paul Molitor	.75	.60	.30
16	Barry Bonds	.75	.60	.30
17	Kirby Puckett	.75	.60	.30
18	Ozzie Smith	.75	.60	.30
19	Don Mattingly	.75	.60	.30
20	Will Clark	.75	.60	.30
21	Rickey Henderson	.75	.60	.30
22	Orel Hershiser	.35	.25	.14
23	Ken Griffey, Jr.	4.00	3.00	1.50
24	Tony Gwynn	.45	.35	.20
25	Nolan Ryan	4.00	3.00	1.50
26	Kelly Gruber	.25	.20	.10

1909 Philadelphia Carmel (E95)

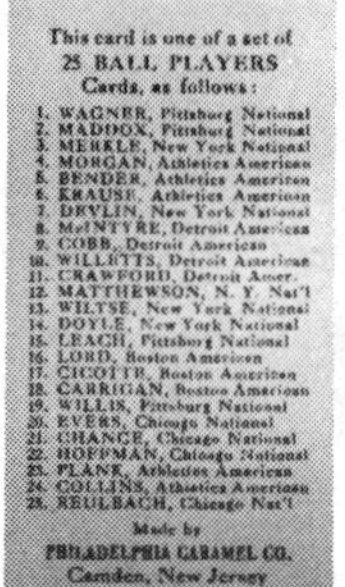

Similar in style to the many other early candy and caramel cards, the set designated as E95 by the American Card Catalog is a 25-card issue produced by the Philadelphia Caramel Co. (actually of Camden, N.J.) in 1909. The cards measure approximately 2-5/8" by 1-1/2" and contain a full-color player drawing. The back, which differentiates the set from other similar issues, checklists the 25 players in black ink and displays the Philadelphia Caramel Co. name at the bottom.

		NR MT	EX	VG
Complete Set (25):		9800.	4750.	2750.
Common Player:		110.00	55.00	33.00
(1)	Chief Bender	400.00	200.00	120.00
(2)	Bill Carrigan	110.00	55.00	33.00
(3)	Frank Chance	400.00	200.00	120.00
(4)	Ed Cicotte	175.00	85.00	50.00
(5)	Ty Cobb	3900.	1850.	1100.
(6)	Eddie Collins	400.00	200.00	120.00
(7)	Sam Crawford	400.00	200.00	120.00
(8)	Art Devlin	110.00	55.00	33.00
(9)	Larry Doyle	110.00	55.00	33.00
(10)	Johnny Evers	400.00	200.00	120.00
(11)	Solly Hoffman (Hofman)	110.00	55.00	33.00
(12)	Harry Krause	110.00	55.00	33.00
(13)	Tommy Leach	110.00	55.00	33.00
(14)	Harry Lord	110.00	55.00	33.00
(15)	Nick Maddox	110.00	55.00	33.00
(16)	Christy Matthewson (Mathewson)	1200.	600.00	350.00
(17)	Matty McIntyre	110.00	55.00	33.00
(18)	Fred Merkle	150.00	75.00	45.00
(19)	Cy Morgan	110.00	55.00	33.00
(20)	Eddie Plank	500.00	250.00	150.00
(21)	Ed Reulbach	110.00	55.00	33.00
(22)	Honus Wagner	1400.	700.00	425.00
(23)	Ed Willetts (Willett)	110.00	55.00	33.00
(24)	Vic Willis	110.00	55.00	33.00
(25)	Hooks Wiltse	110.00	55.00	33.00

1910 Philadelphia Carmel (E96)

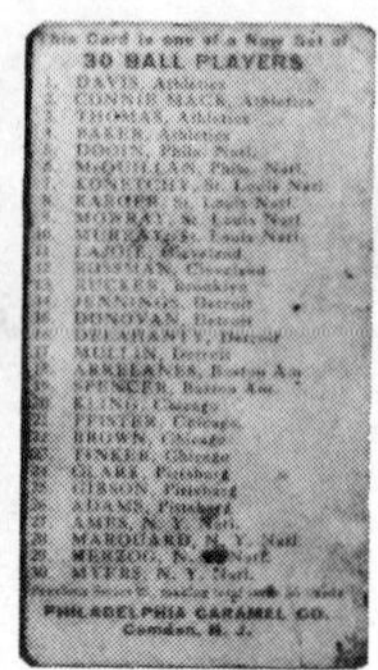

This set of 30 subjects, known by the ACC designation E96, was issued in 1910 by the Philadelphia Caramel Co. as a continuation of the E95 set of the previous year. The front design remained the same, but the two issues can be identified by the backs. The backs of the E96 cards are printed in red and carry a checklist of 30 players. There is also a line at the bottom advising "Previous series 25, making total issue 55 cards." Just below that appears "Philadelphia Caramel Co./Camden, N.J."

		NR MT	EX	VG
Complete Set (30):		5750.	2700.	1650.
Common Player:		120.00	60.00	36.00
(1)	Babe Adams	120.00	60.00	36.00
(2)	Red Ames	120.00	60.00	36.00
(3)	Frank Arrelanes (Arellanes)	120.00	60.00	36.00
(4)	Home Run Baker	400.00	200.00	120.00
(5)	Mordecai Brown	400.00	200.00	120.00
(6)	Fred Clark (Clarke)	400.00	200.00	120.00
(7)	Harry Davis	120.00	60.00	36.00
(8)	Wild Bill Donovan	120.00	60.00	36.00
(9)	Jim Delehanty	120.00	60.00	36.00
(10)	Red Dooin	120.00	60.00	36.00
(11)	George Gibson	120.00	60.00	36.00
(12)	Buck Herzog	120.00	60.00	36.00
(13)	Hugh Jennings	400.00	200.00	120.00
(14)	Ed Karger	120.00	60.00	36.00
(15)	Johnny Kling	120.00	60.00	36.00
(16)	Ed Konetchy	120.00	60.00	36.00
(17)	Nap Lajoie	600.00	300.00	180.00
(18)	Connie Mack	700.00	350.00	210.00
(19)	Rube Marquard	400.00	200.00	120.00
(20)	George McQuillan	120.00	60.00	36.00
(21)	Chief Meyers	120.00	60.00	36.00
(22)	Mike Mowrey	120.00	60.00	36.00
(23)	George Mullin	120.00	60.00	36.00
(24)	Red Murray	120.00	60.00	36.00
(25)	Jack Pfeister (Pfiester)	120.00	60.00	36.00
(26)	Nap Rucker	120.00	60.00	36.00
(27)	Claude Rossman	120.00	60.00	36.00
(28)	Tubby Spencer	120.00	60.00	36.00
(29)	Ira Thomas	120.00	60.00	36.00
(30)	Joe Tinker	400.00	200.00	120.00

1994 Phillies Photocards

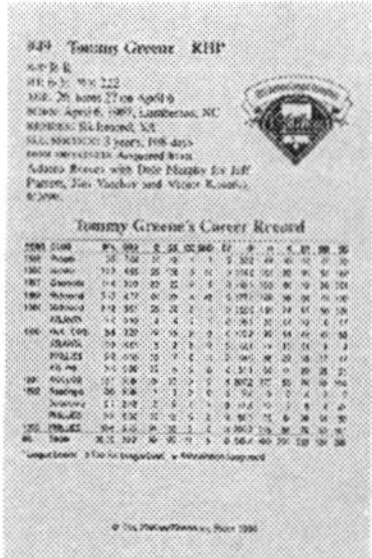

For 1994 the team took over full sponsorship for its traditional large-format photocard issue. The 4" x 6" cards are in the same style as previous years, with a borderless color photto on front and the player's name in white on a red strip. Red and black backs feature the Phillies' 1993 N.L. Championship logo, biographical data and full major and minor league stats. The cards are numbered according to the player's uniform number at upper-left.

		MT	NR MT	EX
Complete Set (36):		9.00	6.75	3.50
Common Player:		.25	.20	.10
2	Larry Bowa	.35	.25	.14
4	Lenny Dykstra	.75	.60	.30
5	Kim Batiste	.25	.20	.10
6	Todd Pratt	.25	.20	.10
7	Mariano Duncan	.35	.25	.14
8	Jim Eisenreich	.25	.20	.10
9	Mike Ryan	.25	.20	.10
10	Darren Daulton	.45	.35	.20
11	Jim Fregosi	.35	.25	.14
12	Mickey Morandini	.35	.25	.14

14	Denis Menke	.25	.20	.10
15	Dave Hollins	.45	.35	.20
16	Tony Longmire	.25	.20	.10
17	Ricky Jordan	.25	.20	.10
18	John Vukovich	.25	.20	.10
19	Kevin Stocker	.35	.25	.14
22	Pete Incaviglia	.35	.25	.14
23	Doug Jones	.25	.20	.10
25	Milt Thompson	.25	.20	.10
26	Mel Roberts	.25	.20	.10
27	Danny Jackson	.25	.20	.10
28	Tyler Green	.25	.20	.10
29	John Kruk	.75	.60	.30
34	Ben Rivera	.25	.20	.10
35	Bobby Munoz	.45	.35	.20
37	Norm Charlton	.25	.20	.10
38	Curt Schilling	.30	.25	.12
40	David West	.25	.20	.10
41	Mike Williams	.25	.20	.10
43	Jeff Juden	.35	.25	.14
44	Wes Chamberlain	.35	.25	.14
46	Johnny Podres	.35	.25	.14
47	Larry Andersen	.25	.20	.10
48	Roger Mason	.25	.20	.10
49	Tommy Greene	.30	.25	.12
51	Heathcliff Slocumb	.25	.20	.10

1993 Photo File 500 HR Supercards

Photo File produced a set of 8" x 10" cards of members of the 500 Home Run Club. The Supercards feature all 14 current members of the club, plus a header card with the 14 players in one. The card fronts feature a photo of the player plus statistics and biographical information.

		MT	NR MT	EX
Complete Set (15):		40.00	30.00	16.00
Common Player:		3.00	2.25	1.25
1	Hank Aaron	5.00	3.75	2.00
2	Willie Mays	5.00	3.75	2.00
3	Mickey Mantle	8.00	6.00	3.25
4	Reggie Jackson	4.00	3.00	1.50
5	Ted Williams	5.00	3.75	2.00
6	Mel Ott	3.00	2.25	1.25
7	Babe Ruth	8.00	6.00	3.25
8	Frank Robinson	3.00	2.25	1.25
9	Harmon Killebrew	3.00	2.25	1.25
10	Ed Mathews	3.00	2.25	1.25
11	Jimmie Foxx	3.00	2.25	1.25
12	Ernie Banks	4.00	3.00	1.50
13	Mike Schmidt	4.00	3.00	1.50
14	Willie McCovey	3.00	2.25	1.25
----	Header card	3.00	2.25	1.25

1951 - 59 Photo-Film Fotos Pirates Postcards

This series of black-and-white postcards was issued over a period which seems to have spanned virtually the entire decade of the 1950s. In standard 3-1/2" x 5-1/2" size, the cards have minor variations in the size and styles of type used for the player name in the bottom border on front and for the typography on the backs. Some cards are seen with pre-printed autographs on front. Most of the cards have printing on the back which includes versions of "Genuine Photo-Film Fotos, Inc., New York, N.Y., U.S.A." and "Souvenir of Forbes Field Home of the Pittsburgh Pirates. The checklist here, arranged alphabetically, indicates by the use of "a, b, c" and "d" suffixes different known poses for that particular player. Future additions to the checklist are likely, therefore no complete set price is given.

		NR MT	EX	VG
Common Player:		15.00	7.50	4.50
(1)	Gair Allie	15.00	7.50	4.50
(2)	Toby Atwell	15.00	7.50	4.50
(3)	Tony Bartirome	15.00	7.50	4.50
(4)	Ron Blackburn	15.00	7.50	4.50
(5)	Don Carlsen	15.00	7.50	4.50
(6a)	Pete Castiglione	15.00	7.50	4.50
(6b)	Pete Castiglione	15.00	7.50	4.50
(7)	Cliff Chambers	15.00	7.50	4.50
(8)	Dick Cole	15.00	7.50	4.50
(9)	Dale Coogan	15.00	7.50	4.50
(10)	Bobby Del Greco	15.00	7.50	4.50
(11 a)	Roy Face	20.00	10.00	6.00
(11b)	Roy Face	20.00	10.00	6.00
(11c)	Roy Face	20.00	10.00	6.00
(12)	Hank Foiles	15.00	7.50	4.50
(13)	Gene Freese	15.00	7.50	4.50
(14 a)	Bob Friend	17.00	8.50	5.00
(14 b)	Bob Friend	17.00	8.50	5.00
(14 c)	Bob Friend	17.00	8.50	5.00
(15)	Dick Groat	20.00	10.00	6.00
(16)	Fred Haney	15.00	7.50	4.50
(17)	Ralph Kiner	50.00	25.00	15.00
(18 a)	Ron Kline	15.00	7.50	4.50
(18 b)	Ron Kline	15.00	7.50	4.50
(19)	Clem Koshorek	15.00	7.50	4.50
(20a)	Vern Law	17.00	8.50	5.00
(20b)	Vern Law	17.00	8.50	5.00
(20c)	Vern Law	17.00	8.50	5.00
(20d)	Vern Law	17.00	8.50	5.00
(21a)	Dale Long	15.00	7.50	4.50
(21b)	Dale Long	15.00	7.50	4.50
(22a)	Jerry Lynch	15.00	7.50	4.50
(22b)	Jerry Lynch	15.00	7.50	4.50
(23)	Bill MacDonald	15.00	7.50	4.50
(24a)	Bill Mazeroski	30.00	15.00	9.00
(24b)	Bill Mazeroski	30.00	15.00	9.00
(25)	Danny Murtaugh	15.00	7.50	4.50
(26)	Johnny O'Brien	15.00	7.50	4.50
(27)	Bob Oldis	15.00	7.50	4.50
(28)	Laurin Pepper	15.00	7.50	4.50
(29)	Hardy Peterson	15.00	7.50	4.50
(30)	Jack Phillips	15.00	7.50	4.50
(31)	Buddy Pritchard	15.00	7.50	4.50
(32)	Bob Purkey	15.00	7.50	4.50
(33)	Dino Restelli	15.00	7.50	4.50
(34)	Bob Smith	15.00	7.50	4.50
(35)	Red Swanson	15.00	7.50	4.50
(36a)	Frank J. Thomas	17.00	8.50	5.00
(36b)	Frank J. Thomas	17.00	8.50	5.00
(36c)	Frank J. Thomas	17.00	8.50	5.00
(37)	Bill Virdon	17.00	8.50	5.00
(38a)	Lee Walls	15.00	7.50	4.50
(38b)	Lee Walls	15.00	7.50	4.50
(39)	Junior Walsh	15.00	7.50	4.50
(40)	Pete Ward	15.00	7.50	4.50
(41)	Fred Waters	15.00	7.50	4.50
(42)	Bill Werle	15.00	7.50	4.50

1970 Pictures of Champions Orioles

Issued in 1970 in the Baltimore area, this 16-card regional set pictures members of the Baltimore Orioles. The cards measure 2-1/8" by 2-3/4" and feature black and white player photos on orange card stock. Little is known about the method of distribution.

		NR MT	EX	VG
Complete Set:		30.00	15.00	9.00
Common Player:		.50	.25	.15
4	Earl Weaver	2.00	1.00	.60
5	Brooks Robinson	10.00	5.00	3.00
7	Mark Belanger	.75	.40	.25
8	Andy Etchebarren	.50	.25	.15
9	Don Buford	.50	.25	.15
10	Ellie Hendricks	.50	.25	.15
12	Dave May	.50	.25	.15
15	Dave Johnson	2.00	1.00	.60
16	Dave McNally	.75	.40	.25
20	Frank Robinson	8.00	4.00	2.50
22	Jim Palmer	7.00	3.50	2.00
24	Pete Richert	.50	.25	.15
29	Dick Hall	.50	.25	.15
35	Mike Cuellar	.75	.40	.25
39	Eddie Watt	.50	.25	.15
40	Dave Leonhard	.50	.25	.15

1914 Piedmont Art Stamps (T330-2)

The 1914 series of "Piedmont Art Stamps" look like a fragile "stamp" version of the more popular T205 Gold Border tobacco cards. Issued by employed the same basic design as the T205 set produced three years earlier. The stamps in the Piedmont series measure 1-1/2" by 2-5/8". Even though the backs of the stamps advertise "100 designs," at leat 102 different players are known. And, because four of the players (Hal Chase, Eddie Collins, Russ Ford and Bobby Wallace) are pictured in two separate poses, there are actually 106 different stamps in a complete set. All but three of the subjects in the Piedmont series were taken from the T205 set, with the exceptions being Joe Wood, Walt Blair and Bill Killifer. Because of their fragile composition, and since they are "stamps" that were frequently stuck to album pages, examples of Piedmont Art Stamps in Mint or Near Mint condition are very scarce. The back of the stamps offered a "handsome" album in exchange for 25 Piedmont coupons. The set has an American Card Catalog designation of T330-2.

		NR MT	EX	VG
Complete Set (106):		12500.	6250.	3750.
Common Player:		125.00	62.00	37.00
(1)	Jimmy Archer	125.00	62.00	37.00
(2)	Jimmy Austin	125.00	62.00	37.00
(3)	Home Run Baker	225.00	112.00	67.00
(4)	Cy Barger	125.00	62.00	37.00
(5)	Jack Barry	125.00	62.00	37.00
(6)	Johnny Bates	125.00	62.00	37.00
(7)	Beals Becker	125.00	62.00	37.00
(8)	Chief Bender	225.00	112.00	67.00
(9)	Bob Bescher	125.00	62.00	37.00
(10)	Joe Birmingham	125.00	62.00	37.00
(11)	Walt Blair	125.00	62.00	37.00
(12)	Roger Bresnahan	225.00	112.00	67.00
(13)	Al Bridwell	125.00	62.00	37.00
(14)	Mordecai Brown	225.00	112.00	67.00
(15)	Bobby Byrne	125.00	62.00	37.00
(16)	Howie Camnitz	125.00	62.00	37.00
(17)	Bill Carrigan	125.00	62.00	37.00
(18)	Frank Chance	225.00	112.00	67.00
(19)	Hal Chase ("Chase" on front)	150.00	75.00	45.00
(20)	Hal Chase ("Hal Chase" on front)	150.00	75.00	45.00
(21)	Ed Cicotte	150.00	75.00	45.00
(22)	Fred Clarke	225.00	112.00	67.00
(23)	Ty Cobb	1850.	925.00	500.00
(24)	Eddie Collins (mouth closed)	225.00	112.00	67.00
(25)	Eddie Collins (mouth open)	225.00	112.00	67.00
(26)	Otis "Doc" Crandall	125.00	62.00	37.00
(27)	Bill Dahlen	125.00	62.00	37.00
(28)	Jake Daubert	125.00	62.00	37.00
(29)	Jim Delanhanty	125.00	62.00	37.00
(30)	Josh Devore	125.00	62.00	37.00
(31)	Red Dooin	125.00	62.00	37.00
(32)	Mickey Doolan	125.00	62.00	37.00
(33)	Tom Downey	125.00	62.00	37.00
(34)	Larry Doyle	125.00	62.00	37.00
(35)	Dick Egan	125.00	62.00	37.00
(36)	Kid Elberfield (Elberfeld)	125.00	62.00	37.00
(37)	Clyde Engle	125.00	62.00	37.00
(38)	Johnny Evers	225.00	112.00	67.00
(39)	Art Fletcher	125.00	62.00	37.00
(40)	Russ Ford (dark cap)	125.00	62.00	37.00
(41)	Russ Ford (white cap)	125.00	62.00	37.00
(42)	Art Fromme	125.00	62.00	37.00
(43)	George Gibson	125.00	62.00	37.00
(44)	William Goode (Wilbur Good)	125.00	62.00	37.00
(45)	Clark Griifith	225.00	112.00	67.00
(46)	Bob Groom	125.00	62.00	37.00
(47)	Bob Harmon	125.00	62.00	37.00
(48)	Arnold Hauser	125.00	62.00	37.00
(49)	Buck Herzog	125.00	62.00	37.00

(50)	Dick Hoblitzell	125.00	62.00	37.00
(51)	Miller Huggins	225.00	112.00	67.00
(52)	John Hummel	125.00	62.00	37.00
(53)	Hughie Jennings	225.00	112.00	67.00
(54)	Walter Johnson	700.00	350.00	210.00
(55)	Davy Jones	125.00	62.00	37.00
(56)	Bill Killifer (Killefer)	125.00	62.00	37.00
(57)	Ed Konetchy	125.00	62.00	37.00
(58)	Frank LaPorte	125.00	62.00	37.00
(59)	Hans Lobert	125.00	62.00	37.00
(60)	Harry Lord	125.00	62.00	37.00
(61)	Sherry Magee	125.00	62.00	37.00
(62)	Rube Marquard	225.00	112.00	67.00
(63)	Christy Mathewson	700.00	350.00	210.00
(64)	George McBride	125.00	62.00	37.00
(65)	Larry McLean	125.00	62.00	37.00
(66)	Fred Merkle	125.00	62.00	37.00
(67)	Chief Meyers	125.00	62.00	37.00
(68)	Clyde Milan	125.00	62.00	37.00
(69)	Dots Miller	125.00	62.00	37.00
(70)	Mike Mitchell	125.00	62.00	37.00
(71)	Pat Moran	125.00	62.00	37.00
(72)	George Moriarity (Moriarty)	125.00	62.00	37.00
(73)	George Mullin	125.00	62.00	37.00
(74)	Danny Murphy	125.00	62.00	37.00
(75)	Jack "Red" Murray	125.00	62.00	37.00
(76)	Tom Needham	125.00	62.00	37.00
(77)	Rebel Oakes	125.00	62.00	37.00
(78)	Rube Oldring	125.00	62.00	37.00
(79)	Fred Parent	125.00	62.00	37.00
(80)	Dode Paskert	125.00	62.00	37.00
(81)	Jack Quinn	125.00	62.00	37.00
(82)	Ed Reulbach	125.00	62.00	37.00
(83)	Lewis Ritchie	125.00	62.00	37.00
(84)	Jack Rowan	125.00	62.00	37.00
(85)	Nap Rucker	125.00	62.00	37.00
(86)	Germany Schaefer	125.00	62.00	37.00
(87)	Wildfire Schulte	125.00	62.00	37.00
(88)	Jim Scott	125.00	62.00	37.00
(89)	Fred Snodgrass	125.00	62.00	37.00
(90)	Tris Speaker	500.00	250.00	150.00
(91)	Oscar Stamage (Stanage)	125.00	62.00	37.00
(92)	Jeff Sweeney	125.00	62.00	37.00
(93)	Ira Thomas	125.00	62.00	37.00
(94)	Joe Tinker	225.00	112.00	67.00
(95)	Terry Turner	125.00	62.00	37.00
(96)	Hippo Vaughn	125.00	62.00	37.00
(97)	Heinie Wagner	125.00	62.00	37.00
(98)	Bobby Wallace (no cap)	225.00	112.00	67.00
(99)	Bobby Wallace (with cap)	225.00	112.00	67.00
(100)	Ed Walsh	225.00	112.00	67.00
(101)	Zach Wheat	225.00	112.00	67.00
(102)	Irwin "Kaiser" Wilhelm	125.00	62.00	37.00
(103)	Ed Willett	125.00	62.00	37.00
(104)	Owen Wilson	125.00	62.00	37.00
(105)	Hooks Wiltse	125.00	62.00	37.00
(106)	Joe Wood	150.00	75.00	45.00

1992 Pinnacle

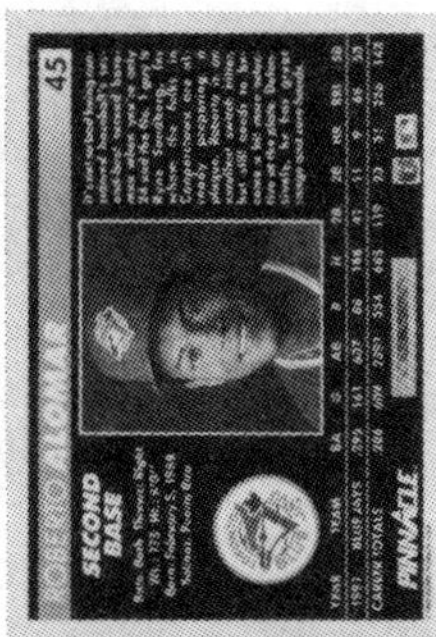

Score entered the high-end card market with the release of this 620-card set. The cards feature black borders surrounding a white frame with a full-color action photo inside. The player extends beyond the natural background. The backs are horizontal and feature a closeup photo, statistics, team logo, biographical information and player information. Several subsets can be found within the set including "Idols, Sidelines, Grips, Shades" and "Technicians". Score produced Pinnacle lines in football and hockey as well as in baseball.

		MT	NR MT	EX
Complete Set (620):		50.00	37.00	20.00
Common Player:		.10	.08	.04
1	Frank Thomas	4.00	3.00	1.50
2	Benito Santiago	.15	.11	.06
3	Carlos Baerga	.75	.60	.30
4	Cecil Fielder	.40	.30	.15
5	Barry Larkin	.15	.11	.06
6	Ozzie Smith	.30	.25	.12
7	Willie McGee	.12	.09	.05
8	Paul Moltior	.30	.25	.12
9	Andy Van Slyke	.12	.09	.05
10	Ryne Sandberg	.75	.60	.30
11	Kevin Seitzer	.10	.08	.04
12	Len Dykstra	.25	.20	.10
13	Edgar Martinez	.15	.11	.06
14	Ruben Sierra	.15	.11	.06
15	Howard Johnson	.20	.15	.08
16	Dave Henderson	.10	.08	.04
17	Devon White	.10	.08	.04
18	Terry Pendleton	.15	.11	.06
19	Steve Finley	.10	.08	.04
20	Kirby Puckett	.60	.45	.25
21	Orel Hershiser	.10	.08	.04
22	Hal Morris	.10	.08	.04
23	Don Mattingly	.40	.30	.15
24	Delino DeShields	.15	.11	.06
25	Dennis Eckersley	.15	.11	.06
26	Ellis Burks	.10	.08	.04
27	Jay Buhner	.10	.08	.04
28	Matt Williams	.20	.15	.08
29	Lou Whitaker	.10	.08	.04
30	Alex Fernandez	.12	.09	.05
31	Albert Belle	.60	.45	.25
32	Todd Zeile	.12	.09	.05
33	Tony Pena	.10	.08	.04
34	Jay Bell	.10	.08	.04
35	Rafael Palmeiro	.25	.20	.10
36	Wes Chamberlain	.10	.08	.04
37	George Bell	.12	.09	.05
38	Robin Yount	.60	.45	.25
39	Vince Coleman	.10	.08	.04
40	Bruce Hurst	.10	.08	.04
41	Harold Baines	.12	.09	.05
42	Chuck Finley	.12	.09	.05
43	Ken Caminiti	.10	.08	.04
44	Ben McDonald	.25	.20	.10
45	Roberto Alomar	.75	.60	.30
46	Chili Davis	.10	.08	.04
47	Bill Doran	.10	.08	.04
48	Jerald Clark	.10	.08	.04
49	Jose Lind	.10	.08	.04
50	Nolan Ryan	2.00	1.50	.80
51	Phil Plantier	.60	.45	.25
52	Gary DiSarcina	.10	.08	.04
53	Kevin Bass	.10	.08	.04
54	Pat Kelly	.10	.08	.04
55	Mark Wohlers	.10	.08	.04
56	Walt Weiss	.10	.08	.04
57	Lenny Harris	.10	.08	.04
58	Ivan Calderon	.10	.08	.04
59	Harold Reynolds	.10	.08	.04
60	George Brett	.75	.60	.30
61	Gregg Olson	.12	.09	.05
62	Orlando Merced	.10	.08	.04
63	Steve Decker	.10	.08	.04
64	John Franco	.10	.08	.04
65	Greg Maddux	.35	.25	.14
66	Alex Cole	.10	.08	.04
67	Dave Holins	.15	.11	.06
68	Kent Hrbek	.10	.08	.04
69	Tom Pagnozzi	.10	.08	.04
70	Jeff Bagwell	.60	.45	.25
71	Jim Gantner	.10	.08	.04
72	Matt Nokes	.10	.08	.04
73	Brian Harper	.10	.08	.04
74	Andy Benes	.15	.11	.06
75	Tom Glavine	.30	.25	.12
76	Terry Steinbach	.10	.08	.04
77	Dennis Martinez	.10	.08	.04
78	John Olerud	1.00	.70	.40
79	Ozzie Guillen	.10	.08	.04
80	Darryl Strawberry	.10	.07	.04
81	Gary Gaetti	.10	.08	.04
82	Dave Righetti	.10	.08	.04
83	Chris Hoiles	.15	.11	.06
84	Andujar Cedeno	.20	.15	.08
85	Jack Clark	.15	.08	.04
86	David Howard	.10	.08	.04
87	Bill Gullickson	.10	.08	.04
88	Bernard Gilkey	.15	.11	.06
89	Kevin Elster	.10	.08	.04
90	Kevin Maas	.15	.11	.06
91	Mark Lewis	.15	.11	.06
92	Greg Vaughn	.15	.11	.06
93	Bret Barberie	.15	.11	.06
94	Dave Smith	.10	.08	.04
95	Roger Clemens	.50	.40	.20
96	Doug Drabek	.15	.11	.06
97	Omar Vizquel	.10	.08	.04
98	Jose Guzman	.10	.08	.04
99	Juan Samuel	.10	.08	.04
100	Dave Justice	.75	.60	.30
101	Tom Browning	.10	.08	.04
102	Mark Gubicza	.10	.08	.04
103	Mickey Morandini	.10	.08	.04
104	Ed Whitson	.10	.08	.04
105	Lance Parrish	.10	.08	.04
106	Scott Erickson	.10	.08	.04
107	Jack McDowell	.30	.25	.12
108	Dave Stieb	.10	.08	.04
109	Mike Moore	.10	.08	.04
110	Travis Fryman	.60	.45	.25
111	Dwight Gooden	.10	.07	.04
112	Fred McGriff	.35	.25	.14
113	Alan Trammell	.12	.09	.05
114	Roberto Kelly	.15	.11	.06
115	Andre Dawson	.15	.11	.06
116	Bill Landrum	.10	.08	.04
117	Brian McRae	.10	.08	.04
119	Chuck Knoblauch	.15	.11	.06
120	Steve Olin	.12	.09	.05
121	Robin Ventura	.40	.30	.15
122	Will Clark	.50	.40	.20
123	Tino Martinez	.15	.11	.06
124	Dale Murphy	.15	.11	.06
125	Pete O'Brien	.10	.08	.04
126	Ray Lankford	.15	.11	.06
127	Juan Gonzalez	3.00	2.25	1.25
128	Ron Gant	.15	.11	.06
129	Marquis Grissom	.20	.15	.08
130	Jose Canseco	.40	.30	.15
131	Mike Greenwell	.15	.11	.06
132	Mark Langston	.12	.09	.05
133	Brett Butler	.12	.09	.05
134	Kelly Gruber	.10	.08	.04
135	Chris Sabo	.15	.11	.06
136	Mark Grace	.20	.15	.08
137	Tony Fernandez	.12	.09	.05
138	Glenn Davis	.12	.09	.05
139	Pedro Munoz	.15	.11	.06
140	Craig Biggio	.12	.09	.05
141	Pete Schourek	.10	.08	.04
142	Mike Boddicker	.10	.08	.04
143	Robby Thompson	.10	.08	.04
144	Mel Hall	.12	.09	.05
145	Bryan Harvey	.12	.09	.05
146	Mike LaValliere	.10	.08	.04
147	John Kruk	.12	.09	.05
148	Joe Carter	.30	.25	.12
149	Greg Olson	.10	.08	.04
150	Julio Franco	.12	.09	.05
151	Darryl Hamilton	.12	.09	.05
152	Felix Fermin	.10	.08	.04
153	Jose Offerman	.12	.09	.05
154	Paul O'Neill	.12	.09	.05
155	Tommy Greene	.12	.09	.05
156	Ivan Rodriguez	.35	.25	.14
157	Dave Stewart	.12	.09	.05
158	Jeff Reardon	.12	.09	.05
159	Felix Jose	.15	.11	.06
160	Doug Dascenzo	.10	.08	.04
161	Tim Wallach	.10	.08	.04
162	Dan Plesac	.10	.08	.04
163	Luis Gonzalez	.12	.09	.05
164	Mike Henneman	.12	.09	.05
165	Mike Devereaux	.12	.09	.05
166	Luis Polonia	.10	.08	.04
167	Mike Sharperson	.10	.08	.04
168	Chris Donnels	.10	.08	.04
169	Greg Harris	.10	.08	.04
170	Deion Sanders	.60	.45	.25
171	Mike Schooler	.10	.08	.04
172	Jose DeJesus	.10	.08	.04
173	Jeff Montgomery	.10	.08	.04
174	Milt Cuyler	.10	.08	.04
175	Wade Boggs	.20	.15	.08
176	Kevin Tapani	.15	.11	.06
177	Bill Spiers	.10	.08	.04
178	Tim Raines	.15	.11	.06
179	Randy Milligan	.10	.08	.04
180	Rob Dibble	.15	.11	.06
181	Kirt Manwaring	.10	.08	.04
182	Pascual Perez	.10	.08	.04
183	Juan Guzman	.50	.40	.20
184	John Smiley	.12	.09	.05
185	David Segui	.10	.08	.04
186	Omar Olivares	.10	.08	.04
187	Joe Slusarski	.10	.08	.04
188	Erik Hanson	.10	.08	.04
189	Mark Portugal	.10	.08	.04
190	Walt Terrell	.10	.08	.04
191	John Smoltz	.15	.11	.06
192	Wilson Alvarez	.15	.11	.06
193	Jimmy Key	.12	.09	.05
194	Larry Walker	.20	.15	.08
195	Lee Smith	.12	.09	.05
196	Pete Harnisch	.12	.09	.05
197	Mike Harkey	.10	.08	.04
198	Frank Tanana	.10	.08	.04
199	Terry Mulholland	.10	.08	.04
200	Cal Ripken, Jr.	1.00	.70	.40
201	Dave Magadan	.10	.08	.04
202	Bud Black	.10	.08	.04
203	Terry Shumpert	.10	.08	.04
204	Mike Mussina	.75	.60	.30
205	Mo Vaughn	.75	.60	.30
206	Steve Farr	.10	.08	.04
207	Darrin Jackson	.10	.08	.04
208	Jerry Browne	.10	.08	.04
209	Jeff Russell	.10	.08	.04
210	Mike Scioscia	.10	.08	.04
211	Rick Aguilera	.12	.09	.05
212	Jaime Navarro	.12	.09	.05
213	Randy Tomlin	.12	.09	.05
214	Bobby Thigpen	.10	.08	.04
215	Mark Gardner	.10	.08	.04
216	Norm Charlton	.12	.09	.05
217	Mark McGwire	.30	.25	.12
219	Bob Tewksbury	.12	.09	.05
220	Junior Felix	.10	.08	.04
221	Sam Horn	.10	.08	.04
222	Jody Reed	.10	.08	.04
223	Luis Sojo	.10	.08	.04
224	Jerome Walton	.10	.08	.04
225	Darryl Kile	.12	.09	.05
226	Mickey Tettleton	.15	.11	.06
227	Dan Pasqua	.10	.08	.04
228	Jim Gott	.10	.08	.04
229	Bernie Williams	.12	.09	.05
230	Shane Mack	.12	.09	.05
231	Steve Avery	.50	.40	.20
232	Dave Valle	.10	.08	.04
233	Mark Leonard	.10	.08	.04
234	Spike Owen	.10	.08	.04
235	Gary Sheffield	.30	.25	.12
236	Steve Chitren	.10	.08	.04
237	Zane Smith	.10	.08	.04
238	Tom Gordon	.10	.08	.04
239	Jose Oquendo	.10	.08	.04
240	Todd Stottlemyre	.10	.08	.04
241	Darren Daulton	.15	.11	.06
242	Tim Naehring	.12	.09	.05
243	Tony Phillips	.12	.09	.05
244	Shawon Dunston	.12	.09	.05
245	Manuel Lee	.10	.08	.04
246	Mike Pagliarulo	.10	.08	.04
247	Jim Thome	1.00	.75	.40
248	Luis Mercedes (Rookie Prospect)	.15	.11	.06
249	Cal Eldred	.30	.25	.12
250	Derek Bell (Rookie Prospect)	.20	.15	.08
251	Arthur Rhodes (Rookie Prospect)	.15	.11	.06
252	Scott Cooper	.25	.20	.10
253	Roberto Hernandez (Rookie Prospect)	.15	.11	.06
254	Mo Sanford (Rookie Prospect)	.15	.11	.06

255 Scott Servais (Rookie Prospect) .10 .08 .04
256 Eric Karros .40 .30 .15
259 Joel Johnston (Rookie Prospect) .12 .09 .05
260 John Wehner (Rookie Prospect) .12 .09 .05
261 Gino Minutelli (Rookie Prospect) .12 .09 .05
262 Greg Gagne .10 .08 .04
263 Stan Royer (Rookie Prospect) .15 .11 .06
264 Carlos Garcia .20 .15 .08
265 Andy Ashby (Rookie Prospect) .12 .09 .05
266 Kim Batiste (Rookie Prospect) .10 .08 .04
267 Julio Valera (Rookie Prospect) .12 .09 .05
268 Royce Clayton .40 .30 .15
269 Gary Scott (Rookie Prospect) .10 .08 .04
270 Kirk Dressendorfer (Rookie Prospect) .10 .08 .04
271 Sean Berry (Rookie Prospect) .12 .09 .05
272 Lance Dickson (Rookie Prospect) .12 .09 .05
273 Rob Maurer (Rookie Prospect) .15 .11 .06
274 Scott Brosius (Rookie Prospect) .20 .15 .08
275 Dave Fleming .30 .25 .12
276 Lenny Webster (Rookie Prospect) .12 .09 .05
278 Freddie Benavides (Rookie Prospect) .12 .09 .05
279 Harvey Pulliam (Rookie Prospect) .12 .09 .05
280 Jeff Carter (Rookie Prospect) .12 .09 .05
281 Jim Abbott/Nolan Ryan (Idols) .15 .11 .06
282 Wade Boggs/George Brett (Idols) .15 .11 .06
283 Ken Griffey, Jr./Rickey Henderson (Idols) .75 .60 .30
284 Wally Joyner/Dale Murphy (Idols) .15 .11 .06
285 Chuck Knoblauch/Ozzie Smith (Idols) .15 .11 .06
286 Robin Ventura/Lou Gehrig (Idols) .25 .20 .10
287 Robin Yount (Sidelines - Motocross) .35 .25 .14
288 Bob Tewksbury (Sidelines - Cartoonist) .12 .09 .05
289 Kirby Puckett (Sidelines - Pool Player) .40 .30 .15
290 Kenny Lofton (Sidelines - Basketball Player) .40 .30 .15
291 Jack McDowell (Sidelines - Cuitarist) .20 .15 .08
292 John Burkett (Sidelines - Bowler) .12 .09 .05
293 Dwight Smith (Sidelines - Singer) .12 .09 .05
294 Nolan Ryan (Sidelines - Cattle Rancher) 1.00 .70 .40
295 *Manny Ramirez* 3.50 2.75 1.50
296 *Cliff Floyd* 4.00 3.00 1.50
297 *Al Shirley* .20 .15 .08
298 *Brian Barber* .40 .30 .15
299 *Jon Farrell* .30 .25 .12
300 *Scott Ruffcorn* 1.00 .75 .40
301 *Tyrone Hill* .35 .25 .14
302 *Benji Gil* .80 .60 .30
303 *Tyler Green* .30 .25 .12
304 Allen Watson (Shades) .15 .11 .06
305 Jay Buhner (Shades) .12 .09 .05
306 Roberto Alomar (Shades) .30 .25 .12
307 Chuck Knoblauch (Shades) .10 .07 .04
308 Darryl Strawberry (Shades) .10 .08 .04
309 Danny Tartabull (Shades) .12 .09 .05
310 Bobby Bonilla (Shades) .10 .08 .04
311 Mike Felder .10 .08 .04
312 Storm Davis .10 .08 .04
313 Tim Teufel .10 .08 .04
314 Tom Brunansky .10 .08 .04
315 Rex Hudler .10 .08 .04
316 Dave Otto .10 .08 .04
317 Jeff King .10 .08 .04
318 Dan Gladden .10 .08 .04
319 Bill Pecota .10 .08 .04
320 Franklin Stubbs .10 .08 .04
321 Gary Carter .15 .11 .06
322 Melido Perez .10 .08 .04
323 Eric Davis .15 .11 .06
324 Greg Myers .10 .08 .04
325 Pete Incaviglia .10 .08 .04
326 Von Hayes .10 .08 .04
327 Greg Swindell .15 .11 .06
328 Steve Sax .10 .08 .04
329 Chuck McElroy .10 .08 .04
330 Gregg Jefferies .20 .15 .08
331 Joe Oliver .10 .08 .04
332 Paul Faries .10 .08 .04
333 David West .10 .08 .04
334 Craig Grebeck .10 .08 .04
335 Chris Hammond .10 .08 .04
336 Billy Ripken .10 .08 .04
337 Scott Sanderson .10 .08 .04
338 Dick Schofield .10 .08 .04
339 Bob Milacki .10 .08 .04
340 Kevin Reimer .10 .08 .04
341 Jose DeLeon .10 .08 .04
342 Henry Cotto .10 .08 .04
343 Daryl Boston .10 .08 .04
344 Kevin Gross .10 .08 .04
345 Milt Thompson .10 .08 .04
346 Luis Rivera .10 .08 .04
347 Al Osuna .10 .08 .04
348 Rob Deer .10 .08 .04
349 Tim Leary .10 .08 .04
350 Mike Stanton .10 .08 .04
351 Dean Palmer .15 .11 .06
352 Trevor Wilson .10 .08 .04
353 Mark Eichhorn .10 .08 .04
354 Scott Aldred .12 .09 .05
355 Mark Whiten .15 .11 .06
356 Leo Gomez .12 .09 .05
357 Rafael Belliard .10 .08 .04
358 Carlos Quintana .10 .08 .04
359 Mark Davis .10 .08 .04
360 Chris Nabholz .10 .08 .04
361 Carlton Fisk .15 .11 .06
362 Joe Orsulak .10 .08 .04
363 Eric Anthony .12 .09 .05
364 Greg Hibbard .12 .09 .05
365 Scott Leius .12 .09 .05
366 Hensley Meulens .12 .09 .05
367 Chris Bosio .12 .09 .05
368 Brian Downing .10 .08 .04
369 Sammy Sosa .12 .09 .05
370 Stan Belinda .10 .08 .04
371 Joe Grahe .10 .08 .04
372 Luis Salazar .10 .08 .04
373 Lance Johnson .10 .08 .04
374 Kal Daniels .10 .08 .04
375 Dave Winfield .35 .25 .14
376 Brook Jacoby .10 .08 .04
377 Mariano Duncan .10 .08 .04
378 Ron Darling .12 .09 .05
379 Randy Johnson .12 .09 .05
380 Chito Martinez .12 .09 .05
381 Andres Galarraga .12 .09 .05
382 Willie Randolph .12 .09 .05
383 Charles Nagy .15 .11 .06
384 Tim Belcher .12 .09 .05
385 Duane Ward .10 .08 .04
386 Vicente Palacios .10 .08 .04
387 Mike Gallego .10 .08 .04
388 Rich DeLucia .10 .08 .04
389 Scott Radinsky .10 .08 .04
390 Damon Berryhill .10 .08 .04
391 Kirk McCaskill .10 .08 .04
392 Pedro Guerrero .12 .09 .05
393 Kevin Mitchell .10 .08 .04
394 Dickie Thon .10 .08 .04
395 Bobby Bonilla .20 .15 .08
396 Bill Wegman .10 .08 .04
397 Dave Martinez .10 .08 .04
398 Rick Sutcliffe .12 .09 .05
399 Larry Andersen .10 .08 .04
400 Tony Gwynn .30 .25 .12
401 Rickey Henderson .40 .30 .15
402 Greg Cadaret .10 .08 .04
403 Keith Miller .10 .08 .04
404 Bip Roberts .12 .09 .05
405 Kevin Brown .12 .09 .05
406 Mitch Williams .10 .08 .04
407 Frank Viola .10 .08 .04
408 Darren Lewis .10 .08 .04
409 Bob Walk .12 .09 .05
410 Bob Walk .10 .08 .04
411 Todd Frohwirth .10 .08 .04
412 Brian Hunter .15 .11 .06
413 Ron Karkovice .10 .08 .04
414 Mike Morgan .10 .08 .04
415 Joe Hesketh .10 .08 .04
416 Don Slaught .10 .08 .04
417 Tom Henke .12 .09 .05
418 Kurt Stillwell .10 .08 .04
419 Hector Villanueva .10 .08 .04
420 Glenallen Hill .10 .08 .04
421 Pat Borders .10 .08 .04
422 Charlie Hough .10 .08 .04
423 Charlie Leibrandt .10 .08 .04
424 Eddie Murray .20 .15 .08
425 Jesse Barfield .10 .08 .04
426 Mark Lemke .10 .08 .04
427 Kevin McReynolds .12 .09 .05
428 Gilberto Reyes .10 .08 .04
429 Ramon Martinez .10 .08 .04
430 Steve Buechele .10 .08 .04
431 David Wells .10 .08 .04
432 Kyle Abbott (Rookie Prospect) .15 .11 .06
433 John Habyan .10 .08 .04
434 Kevin Appier .15 .11 .06
435 Gene Larkin .10 .08 .04
436 Sandy Alomar, Jr. .10 .08 .04
437 Mike Jackson .10 .08 .04
438 Todd Benzinger .10 .08 .04
439 Teddy Higuera .10 .08 .04
440 Reggie Sanders .40 .30 .15
441 Mark Carreon .10 .08 .04
442 Bret Saberhagen .10 .08 .04
443 Gene Nelson .10 .08 .04
444 Jay Howell .10 .08 .04
445 Roger McDowell .10 .08 .04
446 Sid Bream .10 .08 .04
447 Mackey Sasser .10 .08 .04
448 Bill Swift .10 .08 .04
449 Hubie Brooks .10 .08 .04
450 David Cone .10 .08 .04
451 Bobby Witt .12 .09 .05
452 Brady Anderson .10 .08 .04
453 Lee Stevens .10 .08 .04
454 Luis Aquino .10 .08 .04
455 Carney Lansford .12 .09 .05
456 Carlos Hernandez (Rookie Prospect) .15 .11 .06
457 Danny Jackson .10 .08 .04
458 Gerald Young .10 .08 .04
459 Tom Candiotti .10 .08 .04
460 Billy Hatcher .10 .08 .04
461 John Wetteland .15 .11 .06
462 Mike Bordick .15 .11 .06
463 Don Robinson .10 .08 .04
464 Jeff Johnson .12 .09 .05
465 Lonnie Smith .10 .08 .04
466 Paul Assenmacher .10 .08 .04
467 Alvin Davis .10 .08 .04
468 Jim Eisenreich .10 .08 .04
469 Brent Mayne .10 .08 .04
470 Jeff Brantley .10 .08 .04
471 Tim Burke .10 .08 .04
472 *Pat Mahomes* .40 .30 .15
473 Ryan Bowen .20 .15 .08
474 Bryn Smith .10 .08 .04
475 Mike Flanagan .10 .08 .04
476 Reggie Jefferson (Rookie Prospect) .15 .11 .06
477 Jeff Blauser .10 .08 .04
478 Craig Lefferts .10 .08 .04
479 Todd Worrell .10 .08 .04
480 Scott Scudder .10 .08 .04
481 Kirk Gibson .10 .08 .04
482 Kenny Rogers .10 .08 .04
483 Jack Morris .12 .09 .05
484 Russ Swan .10 .08 .04
485 Mike Huff .10 .08 .04
486 Ken Hill .15 .11 .06
487 Geronimo Pena .12 .09 .05
488 Charlie O'Brien .10 .08 .04
489 Mike Maddux .10 .08 .04
490 Scott Livingstone (Rookie Prospect) .12 .09 .05
491 Carl Willis .10 .08 .04
492 Kelly Downs .10 .08 .04
493 Dennis Cook .10 .08 .04
494 Joe Magrane .10 .08 .04
495 Bob Kipper .10 .08 .04
496 Jose Mesa .10 .08 .04
497 Charlie Hayes .10 .08 .04
498 Joe Girardi .10 .08 .04
499 Doug Jones .10 .08 .04
500 Barry Bonds 1.00 .70 .40
501 Bill Krueger .10 .08 .04
502 Glenn Braggs .10 .08 .04
503 Eric King .10 .08 .04
504 Frank Castillo .10 .08 .04
505 Mike Gardiner .10 .08 .04
506 Cory Snyder .10 .08 .04
507 Steve Howe .10 .08 .04
508 Jose Rijo .12 .09 .05
509 Sid Fernandez .12 .09 .05
510 *Archi Cianfrocco* .20 .15 .08
511 Mark Guthrie .10 .08 .04
512 Bob Ojeda .10 .08 .04
513 John Doherty (Rookie Prospect) .15 .11 .06
514 Dante Bichette .10 .08 .04
515 Juan Berenguer .10 .08 .04
516 Jeff Robinson .10 .08 .04
517 Mike MacFarlane .10 .08 .04
518 Matt Young .10 .08 .04
519 Otis Nixon .12 .09 .05
520 Brian Holman .10 .08 .04
521 Chris Haney .20 .15 .08
522 *Jeff Kent* .60 .45 .25
523 *Chad Curtis* 1.00 .75 .40
524 Vince Horsman .12 .09 .05
525 Rod Nichols .10 .08 .04
526 *Peter Hoy* (Rookie Prospect) .15 .11 .06
527 Shawn Boskie .12 .09 .05
528 Alejandro Pena .10 .08 .04
529 Dave Burba (Rookie Prospect) .10 .08 .04
530 Ricky Jordan .15 .11 .06
531 David Silvestri (Rookie Prospect) .20 .15 .08
532 John Patterson (Rookie Prospect) .20 .15 .08
533 Jeff Branson (Rookie Prospect) .12 .09 .05
534 Derrick May (Rookie Prospect) .15 .11 .06
535 Esteban Beltre (Rookie Prospect) .20 .15 .08
536 Jose Melendez .15 .11 .06
537 Wally Joyner .12 .09 .05
538 Eddie Taubensee (Rookie Prospect) .12 .09 .05
539 Jim Abbott .20 .15 .08
540 *Brian Williams* (Rookie Prospect) .15 .11 .06
541 Donovan Osborne .25 .20 .10
542 Patrick Lennon (Rookie Prospect) .20 .15 .08
543 *Mike Groppuso* (Rookie Prospect) .12 .09 .05
544 *Jarvis Brown* (Rookie Prospect) .12 .09 .05
545 *Shawn Livesy* .20 .15 .08
546 Jeff Ware (1st Round Draft Pick) .15 .11 .06
547 Danny Tartabull .12 .09 .05
548 *Bobby Jones* 1.00 .75 .40
549 Ken Griffey, Jr. 4.00 3.00 1.50
550 *Rey Sanchez* .25 .20 .10
551 *Pedro Astacio* .25 .20 .10
552 *Juan Guerrero* (Rookie Prospect) .12 .09 .05
553 *Jacob Brumfield* (Rookie Prospect) .12 .09 .05
554 *Ben Rivera* (Rookie Prospect) .12 .09 .05
555 *Brian Jordan* .40 .30 .15
556 Denny Neagle (Rookie Prospect) .12 .09 .05
557 Cliff Brantley (Rookie Prospect) .12 .09 .05
558 Anthony Young (Rookie Prospect) .10 .08 .04
559 *John VanderWal* (Rookie Prospect) .15 .11 .06
560 *Monty Fariss* (Rookie Prospect) .15 .11 .06
561 *Russ Springer* .20 .15 .08
562 *Pat Listach* .30 .25 .12
563 Pat Hentgen .70 .50 .30
564 Andy Stankiewicz (Rookie Prospect) .12 .09 .05
565 Mike Perez (Rookie Prospect) .15 .11 .06
566 Mike Bielecki .10 .08 .04
567 Butch Henry (Rookie Prospect) .12 .09 .05
568 *Dave Nilsson* .20 .15 .08
569 *Scott Hatteberg* .20 .15 .08
570 Ruben Amaro, Jr. (Rookie Prospect) .12 .09 .05
571 Todd Hundley (Rookie Prospect) .15 .11 .06
572 *Moises Alou* .50 .40 .20
573 Hector Fajardo (Rookie Prospect) .15 .11 .06
574 Todd Van Poppel .25 .20 .10
575 Willie Banks (Rookie Prospect) .15 .11 .06
576 Bob Zupcic (Rookie Prospect) .15 .11 .06
577 *J.J. Johnson* .25 .20 .10
578 John Burkett .10 .08 .04
579 Trever Miller .25 .20 .10
580 Scott Bankhead .10 .08 .04
581 Rich Amaral (Rookie Prospect) .10 .08 .04
582 Kenny Lofton .80 .60 .30
583 Matt Stairs (Rookie Prospect) .20 .15 .08
584 Don Mattingly/Rod Carew (Idols) .20 .15 .08
585 Steve Avery/Jack Morris (Idols) .20 .15 .08
586 Roberto Alomar/Sandy Alomar (Idols) .25 .20 .10
587 Scott Sanderson/Catfish Hunter (Idols) .10 .08 .04
588 Dave Justice/Willie Stargell (Idols) .30 .25 .12
589 Rex Hudler/Roger Staubach (Idols) .10 .08 .04

590	David Cone/Jackie Gleason (Idols)	.12	.09	.05
591	Tony Gwynn/Willie Davis (Idols)	.15	.11	.06
592	Orel Hershiser (Sidelines - Golfer)	.15	.11	.06
593	John Wetteland (Sidelines - Musician)	.15	.11	.06
594	Tom Glavine (Sidelines - Hockey Player)	.15	.11	.06
595	Randy Johnson (Sidelines - Photographer)	.15	.11	.06
596	Jim Gott (Sidelines - Black Belt)	.10	.08	.04
597	Donald Harris	.10	.08	.04
598	*Shawn Hare*	.15	.11	.06
599	Chris Gardner	.15	.11	.06
600	Rusty Meacham	.10	.08	.04
601	Benito Santiago (Shades)	.10	.08	.04
602	Eric Davis (Shades)	.15	.11	.06
603	Jose Lind (Shades)	.10	.08	.04
604	Dave Justice (Shades)	.30	.25	.12
605	Tim Raines (Shades)	.15	.11	.06
606	Randy Tomlin (Grips -Vulcan Change)	.15	.11	.06
607	Jack McDowell	.20	.15	.08
608	Greg Maddux	.20	.15	.08
609	Charles Nagy (Grips - Slider)	.12	.09	.05
610	Tom Candiotti (Grips - Knuckleball)	.10	.08	.04
611	David Cone (Grips - Curveball)	.10	.08	.04
612	Steve Avery	.25	.20	.10
613	*Rod Beck*	.50	.40	.20
614	Rickey Henderson	.25	.20	.10
615	Benito Santiago (Technician - Catching)	.10	.08	.04
616	Ruben Sierra (Technician - Outfield)	.15	.11	.06
617	Ryne Sandberg	.40	.30	.15
618	Nolan Ryan	.75	.60	.30
619	Brett Butler (Technician - Bunting)	.10	.08	.04
620	Dave Justice	.30	.25	.12

1992 Pinnacle Rookies

Styled after the regular 1992 Score Pinnacle cards, this 30-card boxed set features the top rookies of 1992. The cards have a player action photo which is borderless on the top and sides. Beneath the photo a team color-coded strip carries the player's name in gold foil, with a round gold-bordered team logo at left. A black strip at bottom has the notation "1992 Rookie". Horizontal-format backs follow a similar design and include a bit of player information, Pinnacle's anti-counterfeiting strip and some gold-foil enhancements.

		MT	NR MT	EX
Complete Set (30):		10.00	7.50	4.00
Common Player:		.20	.15	.08
1	Luis Mercedes	.25	.20	.10
2	Scott Cooper	.25	.20	.10
3	Kenny Lofton	1.50	1.25	.60
4	John Doherty	.25	.20	.10
5	Pat Listach	.50	.40	.20
6	Andy Stankiewicz	.30	.25	.12
7	Derek Bell	.30	.25	.12
8	Gary DiSarcina	.20	.15	.08
9	Roberto Hernandez	.30	.25	.12
10	Joel Johnston	.25	.20	.10
11	Pat Mahomes	.50	.40	.20
12	Todd Van Poppel	.50	.40	.20
13	Dave Fleming	.50	.40	.20
14	Monty Fariss	.25	.20	.10
15	Gary Scott	.25	.20	.10
16	Moises Alou	.35	.25	.14
17	Todd Hundley	.25	.20	.10
18	Kim Batiste	.20	.15	.08
19	Denny Neagle	.25	.20	.10
20	Donovan Osborne	.35	.25	.14
21	Mark Wohlers	.20	.15	.08
22	Reggie Sanders	.75	.60	.30
23	Brian Williams	.20	.15	.08
24	Eric Karros	1.00	.75	.40
25	Frank Seminara	.25	.20	.10
26	Royce Clayton	.30	.25	.12
27	Dave Nilsson	.35	.25	.14
28	Matt Stairs	.20	.15	.08
29	Chad Curtis	.35	.25	.14
30	Carlos Hernandez	.25	.20	.10

Regional interest may affect the value of a card.

Values for recent cards and sets are listed in Mint (MT), Near Mint (NM), reflecting the fact that many cards from recent years have been preserved in top condition. Recent cards and sets in less than Excellent condition have little collector interest.

1992 Pinnacle Team 2000

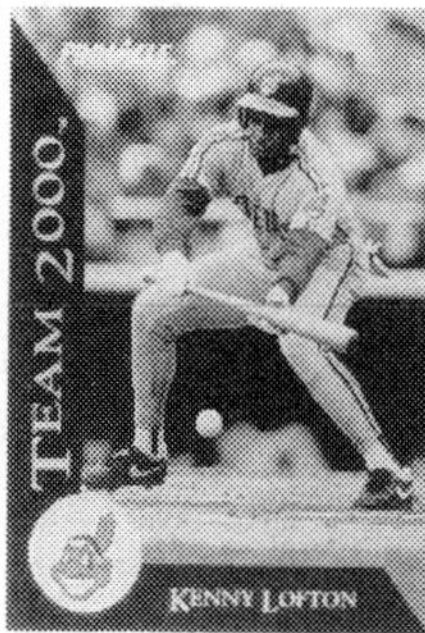

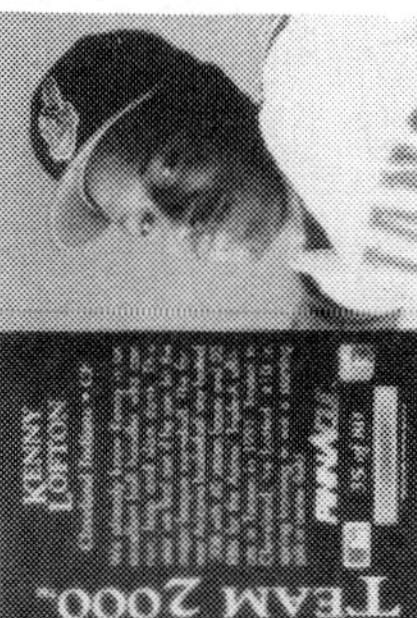

Young stars who were projected to be the game's superstars in the year 2000 were chosen for this 80-card insert set found three at a time in jumbo packs. Cards #1-40 were included in Series I packaging, while cards 41-80 were inserted with Series II Pinnacle. Cards feature gold foil stamping on both front and back.

		MT	NR MT	EX
Complete Set (80):		32.00	24.00	13.00
Common Player:		.10	.08	.04
1	Mike Mussina	1.00	.75	.40
2	Phil Plantier	.60	.45	.25
3	Frank Thomas	6.00	4.50	2.25
4	Travis Fryman	1.00	.75	.40
5	Kevin Appier	.10	.08	.04
6	Chuck Knoblauch	.30	.25	.12
7	Pat Kelly	.10	.08	.04
8	Ivan Rodriguez	.60	.45	.25
9	Dave Justice	1.50	1.25	.60
10	Jeff Bagwell	1.25	.90	.50
11	Marquis Grissom	.40	.30	.15
12	Andy Benes	.10	.08	.04
13	Gregg Olson	.10	.08	.04
14	Kevin Morton	.10	.08	.04
15	Tim Naehring	.10	.08	.04
16	Dave Hollins	.40	.30	.15
17	Sandy Alomar Jr.	.10	.08	.04
18	Albert Belle	1.25	.90	.50
19	Charles Nagy	.10	.08	.04
20	Brian McRae	.10	.08	.04
21	Larry Walker	.50	.40	.20
22	Delino DeShields	.25	.15	.10
23	Jeff Johnson	.10	.08	.04
24	Bernie Williams	.15	.11	.06
25	Jose Offerman	.10	.08	.04
26	Juan Gonzalez	4.00	3.00	1.50
27	Juan Guzman	.40	.30	.15
28	Eric Anthony	.10	.08	.04
29	Brian Hunter	.10	.08	.04
30	John Smoltz	.30	.25	.12
31	Deion Sanders	.75	.60	.30
32	Greg Maddux	.25	.20	.10
33	Andujar Cedeno	.20	.15	.08
34	Royce Clayton	.50	.40	.20
35	Kenny Lofton	1.25	.90	.50
36	Cal Eldred	.50	.40	.20
37	Jim Thome	.75	.60	.30
38	Gary DiSarcina	.10	.08	.04
39	Brian Jordan	.30	.25	.12
40	Chad Curtis	.50	.40	.20
41	Ben McDonald	.15	.11	.06
42	Jim Abbott	.20	.15	.08
43	Robin Ventura	.50	.40	.20
44	Milt Cuyler	.10	.08	.04
45	Gregg Jefferies	.40	.30	.15
46	Scott Radinsky	.10	.08	.04
47	Ken Griffey, Jr.	5.00	3.75	2.00
48	Roberto Alomar	1.00	.75	.40
49	Ramon Martinez	.10	.08	.04
50	Bret Barberie	.10	.08	.04
51	Ray Lankford	.20	.15	.08
52	Leo Gomez	.10	.08	.04
53	Tommy Greene	.20	.15	.08
54	Mo Vaughn	.75	.60	.30
55	Sammy Sosa	.75	.60	.30
56	Carlo baerga	.10	.08	.04
57	Mark Lewis	.10	.08	.04
58	Carlos Baerga	1.00	.75	.40
59	Gary Sheffield	.50	.40	.20
60	Scott Erickson	.10	.08	.04
61	Pedro Munoz	.10	.08	.04
62	Tino Martinez	.10	.08	.04
63	Darren Lewis	.10	.08	.04
64	Dean Palmer	.35	.25	.14
65	John Olerud	.75	.60	.30
66	Steve Avery	.80	.60	.30
67	Pete Harnisch	.10	.08	.04
68	Luis Gonzalez	.10	.08	.04
69	Kim Batiste	.10	.08	.04
70	Reggie Sanders	.60	.45	.25
71	Luis Mercedes	.10	.08	.04
72	Todd Van Poppel	.25	.20	.10
73	Gary Scott	.10	.08	.04
74	Monty Fariss	.10	.08	.04
75	Kyle Abbott	.10	.08	.04
76	Eric Karros	.25	.20	.10
77	Mo Sanford	.10	.08	.04
78	Todd Hundley	.10	.08	.04
79	Reggie Jefferson	.20	.15	.08
80	Pat Mahomes	.30	.25	.12

1992 Pinnacle Slugfest

Each specially marked Slugfest jumbo pack of '92 Pinnacle contained one of these horizontal-format cards of the game's top hitters. The player's name is printed in gold foil at the bottom of the card, along with a red and white Slugfest logo. Backs, which are vertical in orientation have a color player photo, a career summary and a few lifetime stats.

		MT	NR MT	EX
Complete Set (15):		30.00	22.00	12.00
Common Player:		1.00	.70	.40
1	Cecil Fielder	1.50	1.25	.60
2	Mark McGwire	2.00	1.50	.80
3	Jose Canseco	2.00	1.50	.80
4	Barry Bonds	3.00	2.25	1.25
5	Dave Justice	2.00	1.50	.80
6	Bobby Bonilla	1.00	.70	.40
7	Ken Griffey, Jr.	6.00	4.50	2.50
8	Ron Gant	1.00	.70	.40
9	Ryne Sandberg	5.00	3.75	2.00
10	Ruben Sierra	1.50	1.25	.60
11	Frank Thomas	9.00	6.75	3.50
12	Will Clark	3.00	2.25	1.25
13	Kirby Puckett	4.00	3.00	1.50
14	Cal Ripken, Jr.	5.00	3.75	2.00
15	Jeff Bagwell	2.00	1.50	.80

1992 Pinnacle Team Pinnacle

The most sought-after and valuable of the 1992 Pinnacle insert cards is this 12-piece set of "two-headed" cards. An American and a National League superstar at each position are featured on each card, with two cards each for starting and relief pitchers. The ultra-realistic artwork of Chris Greco is featured on the cards, which were inserted into Series I foil packs.

		MT	NR MT	EX
Complete Set (12):		200.00	150.00	80.00
Common Player:		6.00	4.50	2.50
1	Roger Clemens/Ramon Martinez	15.00	11.00	6.00
2	Jim Abbott/Steve Avery	15.00	11.00	6.00
3	Ivan Rodriguez/Benito Santiago	10.00	7.50	4.00
4	Frank Thomas/Will Clark	45.00	35.00	18.00
5	Roberto Alomar/Ryne Sandberg	40.00	30.00	16.00
6	Robin Ventura/Matt Williams	15.00	11.00	6.00
7	Cal Ripken, Jr./Barry Larkin	35.00	26.00	14.00
8	Danny Tartabull/Barry Bonds	25.00	18.50	10.00
9	Ken Griffey, Jr./Brett Butler	40.00	30.00	15.00
10	Ruben Sierra/Dave Justice	20.00	15.00	8.00
11	Dennis Eckersley/Rob Dibble	6.00	4.50	2.50
12	Scott Radinsky/John Franco	6.00	4.50	2.50

1992 Pinnacle Rookie Idols

Carrying on with the Idols subset theme in the regular issue, these Series II foil-pack inserts feature 18 of the year's rookie prospects sharing cards with

their baseball heroes. Both front and back are horizontal in format and include photos of both the rookie and his idol.

		MT	NR MT	EX
	Complete Set (18):	125.00	90.00	50.00
	Common Player:	5.00	3.75	2.00
1	Reggie Sanders/Eric Davis	5.00	3.75	2.00
2	Hector Fajardo/Jim Abbott	5.00	3.75	2.00
3	Gary Cooper/George Brett	10.00	7.50	4.00
4	Mark Wohlers/Roger Clemens	8.00	6.00	3.25
5	Luis Mercedes/Julio Franco	5.00	3.75	2.00
6	Willie Banks/Dwight Gooden	5.00	3.75	2.00
7	Kenny Lofton/Rickey Henderson	16.00	12.00	6.50
8	Keith Mitchell/Dave Henderson	5.00	3.75	2.00
9	Kim Batiste/Barry Larkin	5.00	3.75	2.00
10	Todd Hundley/Thurman Munson	7.50	5.50	3.00
11	Eddie Zosky/Cal Ripken, Jr.	20.00	15.00	8.00
12	Todd Van Poppel/Nolan Ryan	25.00	19.00	10.00
13	Jim Thome/Ryne Sandberg	20.00	15.00	8.00
14	Dave Fleming/Bobby Murcer	5.00	3.75	2.00
15	Royce Clayton/Ozzie Smith	8.00	6.00	3.25
16	Don Harris/Darryl Strawberry	5.00	3.75	2.00
17	Chad Curtis/Alan Trammell	6.00	4.50	2.50
18	Derek Bell/Dave Winfield	8.00	6.00	3.25

1993 Pinnacle

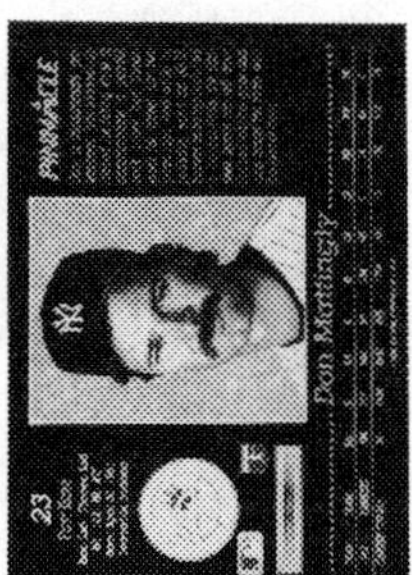

This 620-card set offers many of the same features which made the first Pinnacle set so popular in 1992. Subsets are titled Rookies, Now & Then (which shows the player as he looks now and as a rookie), Idols (active players and their heroes on the same card), Hometown Heroes (players who are playing with their hometown team), Draft Picks and Rookies. More than 100 rookies and 10 draft picks are featured. All regular cards have an action photo, a black border and the Pinnacle name stamped on in gold. Series I cards feature portraits of players on the two new expansion teams; Series II cards feature action shots of them. Team Pinnacle insert cards return, while Rookie Team Pinnacle cards make their debut. Other insert sets are titled Team 2001, Slugfest and Tribute, which features five cards each of Nolan Ryan and George Brett.

		MT	NR MT	EX
	Complete Set (620):	55.00	41.00	22.00
	Common Player:	.06	.05	.02
1	Gary Sheffield	.35	.25	.14
2	Cal Eldred	.20	.15	.08
3	Larry Walker	.20	.15	.08
4	Deion Sanders	.25	.20	.10
5	Dave Fleming	.12	.09	.05
6	Carlos Baerga	.50	.40	.20
7	Bernie Williams	.12	.09	.05
8	John Kruk	.08	.06	.03
9	Jimmy Key	.06	.05	.02
10	Jeff Bagwell	.30	.25	.12
11	Jim Abbott	.06	.05	.02
12	Terry Steinbach	.06	.05	.02
13	Bob Tewksbury	.06	.05	.02
14	Eric Karros	.25	.20	.10
15	Ryne Sandberg	.60	.45	.25
16	Will Clark	.25	.20	.10
17	Edgar Martinez	.06	.05	.02
18	Eddie Murray	.15	.11	.06
19	Andy Van Slyke	.06	.05	.02
20	Cal Ripken, Jr.	.60	.45	.25
21	Ivan Rodriguez	.25	.20	.10
22	Barry Larkin	.12	.09	.05
23	Don Mattingly	.40	.30	.15
24	Gregg Jefferies	.06	.05	.02
25	Roger Clemens	.50	.40	.20
26	Cecil Fielder	.20	.15	.08
27	Kent Hrbek	.06	.05	.02
28	Robin Ventura	.20	.15	.08
29	Rickey Henderson	.20	.15	.08
30	Roberto Alomar	.50	.40	.20
31	Luis Polonia	.06	.05	.02
32	Andujar Cedeno	.06	.05	.02
33	Pat Listach	.15	.11	.06
34	Mark Grace	.06	.05	.02
35	Otis Nixon	.06	.05	.02
36	Felix Jose	.06	.05	.02
37	Mike Sharperson	.06	.05	.02
38	Dennis Martinez	.06	.05	.02
39	Willie McGee	.06	.05	.02
40	Kenny Lofton	.40	.30	.15
41	Randy Johnson	.06	.05	.02
42	Andy Benes	.06	.05	.02
43	Bobby Bonilla	.06	.05	.02
44	Mike Mussina	.60	.45	.25
45	Len Dykstra	.20	.15	.08
46	Ellis Burks	.06	.05	.02
47	Chris Sabo	.06	.05	.02
48	Jay Bell	.06	.05	.02
49	Jose Canseco	.25	.20	.10
50	Craig Biggio	.06	.05	.02
51	Wally Joyner	.06	.05	.02
52	Mickey Tettleton	.06	.05	.02
53	Tim Raines	.06	.05	.02
54	Brian Harper	.06	.05	.02
55	Rene Gonzales	.06	.05	.02
56	Mark Langston	.06	.05	.02
57	Jack Morris	.06	.05	.02
58	Mark McGwire	.25	.20	.10
59	Ken Caminiti	.06	.05	.02
60	Terry Pendleton	.06	.05	.02
61	Dave Nilsson	.06	.05	.02
62	Tom Pagnozzi	.06	.05	.02
63	Mike Morgan	.06	.05	.02
64	Darryl Strawberry	.10	.08	.04
65	Charles Nagy	.06	.05	.02
66	Ken Hill	.06	.05	.02
67	Matt Williams	.06	.05	.02
68	Jay Buhner	.06	.05	.02
69	Vince Coleman	.06	.05	.02
70	Brady Anderson	.06	.05	.02
71	Fred McGriff	.25	.20	.10
72	Ben McDonald	.06	.05	.02
73	Terry Mulholland	.06	.05	.02
74	Randy Tomlin	.06	.05	.02
75	Nolan Ryan	2.00	1.50	.80
76	Frank Viola	.06	.05	.02
77	Jose Rijo	.06	.05	.02
78	Shane Mack	.06	.05	.02
79	Travis Fryman	.50	.40	.20
80	Jack McDowell	.06	.05	.02
81	Mark Gubicza	.06	.05	.02
82	Matt Nokes	.06	.05	.02
83	Bert Blyleven	.06	.05	.02
84	Eric Anthony	.06	.05	.02
85	Mike Bordick	.06	.05	.02
86	John Olerud	.50	.40	.20
87	B.J. Surhoff	.06	.05	.02
88	Bernard Gilkey	.06	.05	.02
89	Shawon Dunston	.06	.05	.02
90	Tom Glavine	.25	.20	.10
91	Brett Butler	.06	.05	.02
92	Moises Alou	.06	.05	.02
93	Albert Belle	.60	.45	.25
94	Darren Lewis	.06	.05	.02
95	Omar Vizquel	.06	.05	.02
96	Dwight Gooden	.06	.05	.02
97	Gregg Olson	.06	.05	.02
98	Tony Gwynn	.25	.20	.10
99	Darren Daulton	.06	.05	.02
100	Dennis Eckersley	.06	.05	.02
101	Rob Dibble	.06	.05	.02
102	Mike Greenwell	.06	.05	.02
103	Jose Lind	.06	.05	.02
104	Julio Franco	.06	.05	.02
105	Tom Gordon	.06	.05	.02
106	Scott Livingstone	.06	.05	.02
107	Chuck Knoblauch	.12	.09	.05
108	Frank Thomas	3.50	2.75	1.50
109	Melido Perez	.06	.05	.02
110	Ken Griffey, Jr.	3.00	2.25	1.25
111	Harold Baines	.06	.05	.02
112	Gary Gaetti	.06	.05	.02
113	Pete Harnisch	.06	.05	.02
114	David Wells	.06	.05	.02
115	Charlie Leibrandt	.06	.05	.02
116	Ray Lankford	.35	.25	.14
117	Kevin Seitzer	.06	.05	.02
118	Robin Yount	.40	.30	.15
119	Lenny Harris	.06	.05	.02
120	Chris James	.06	.05	.02
121	Delino DeShields	.06	.05	.02
122	Kirt Manwaring	.06	.05	.02
123	Glenallen Hill	.06	.05	.02
124	Hensley Meulens	.06	.05	.02
125	Darrin Jackson	.06	.05	.02
126	Todd Hundley	.06	.05	.02
127	Dave Hollins	.15	.11	.06
128	Sam Horn	.06	.05	.02
129	Roberto Hernandez	.06	.05	.02
130	Vicente Palacios	.06	.05	.02
131	George Brett	.50	.40	.20
132	Dave Martinez	.06	.05	.02
133	Kevin Appier	.06	.05	.02
134	Pat Kelly	.06	.05	.02
135	Pedro Munoz	.06	.05	.02
136	Mark Carreon	.06	.05	.02
137	Lance Johnson	.06	.05	.02
138	Devon White	.06	.05	.02
139	Julio Valera	.06	.05	.02
140	Eddie Taubensee	.06	.05	.02
141	Willie Wilson	.06	.05	.02
142	Stan Belinda	.06	.05	.02
143	John Smoltz	.06	.05	.02
144	Darryl Hamilton	.06	.05	.02
145	Sammy Sosa	.06	.05	.02
146	Carlos Hernandez	.06	.05	.02
147	Tom Candiotti	.06	.05	.02
148	Mike Felder	.06	.05	.02
149	Rusty Meacham	.06	.05	.02
150	Ivan Calderon	.06	.05	.02
151	Pete O'Brien	.06	.05	.02
152	Erik Hanson	.06	.05	.02
153	Billy Ripken	.06	.05	.02
154	Kurt Stillwell	.06	.05	.02
155	Jeff Kent	.06	.05	.02
156	Mickey Morandini	.06	.05	.02
157	Randy Milligan	.06	.05	.02
158	Reggie Sanders	.20	.15	.08
159	Luis Rivera	.06	.05	.02
160	Orlando Merced	.06	.05	.02
161	Dean Palmer	.06	.05	.02
162	Mike Perez	.06	.05	.02
163	Scott Erikson	.06	.05	.02
164	Kevin McReynolds	.06	.05	.02
165	Kevin Maas	.06	.05	.02
166	Ozzie Guillen	.06	.05	.02
167	Rob Deer	.06	.05	.02
168	Danny Tartabull	.06	.05	.02
169	Lee Stevens	.06	.05	.02
170	Dave Henderson	.06	.05	.02
171	Derek Bell	.06	.05	.02
172	Steve Finley	.06	.05	.02
173	Greg Olson	.06	.05	.02
174	Geronimo Pena	.06	.05	.02
175	Paul Quantrill	.06	.05	.02
176	Steve Buechele	.06	.05	.02
177	Kevin Gross	.06	.05	.02
178	Tim Wallach	.06	.05	.02
179	Dave Valle	.06	.05	.02
180	Dave Silvestri	.06	.05	.02
181	Bud Black	.06	.05	.02
182	Henry Rodriguez	.06	.05	.02
183	Tim Teufel	.06	.05	.02
184	Mark McLemore	.06	.05	.02
185	Bret Saberhagen	.06	.05	.02
186	Chris Hoiles	.06	.05	.02
187	Ricky Jordan	.06	.05	.02
188	Don Slaught	.06	.05	.02
189	Mo Vaughn	.06	.05	.02
190	Joe Oliver	.06	.05	.02
191	Juan Gonzalez	2.50	2.00	1.00
192	Scott Leius	.06	.05	.02
193	Milt Cuyler	.06	.05	.02
194	Chris Haney	.06	.05	.02
195	Ron Karkovice	.06	.05	.02
196	Steve Farr	.06	.05	.02
197	John Orton	.06	.05	.02
198	Kelly Gruber	.06	.05	.02
199	Ron Darling	.06	.05	.02
200	Ruben Sierra	.20	.15	.08
201	Chuck Finley	.06	.05	.02
202	Mike Moore	.06	.05	.02
203	Pat Borders	.06	.05	.02
204	Sid Bream	.06	.05	.02
205	Todd Zeile	.06	.05	.02
206	Rick Wilkins	.06	.05	.02
207	Jim Gantner	.06	.05	.02
208	Frank Castillo	.06	.05	.02
209	Dave Hansen	.06	.05	.02
210	Trevor Wilson	.06	.05	.02
211	Sandy Alomar, Jr.	.06	.05	.02
212	Sean Berry	.06	.05	.02
213	Tino Martinez	.06	.05	.02
214	Chito Martinez	.06	.05	.02
215	Dan Walters	.06	.05	.02
216	John Franco	.06	.05	.02
217	Glenn Davis	.06	.05	.02
218	Mariano Duncan	.06	.05	.02
219	Mike LaValliere	.06	.05	.02
220	Rafael Palmeiro	.06	.05	.02
221	Jack Clark	.06	.05	.02
222	Hal Morris	.06	.05	.02
223	Ed Sprague	.06	.05	.02
224	John Valentin	.06	.05	.02
225	Sam Militello	.15	.11	.06
226	Bob Wickman	.20	.15	.08
227	Damion Easley	.15	.11	.06
228	John Jaha	.15	.11	.06
229	Bob Ayrault	.06	.05	.02
230	Mo Sanford (Expansion Draft)	.06	.05	.02
231	Walt Weiss (Expansion Draft)	.06	.05	.02
232	Dante Bichette (Expansion Draft)	.06	.05	.02
233	Steve Decker (Expansion Draft)	.06	.05	.02
234	Jerald Clark (Expansion Draft)	.06	.05	.02
235	Bryan Harvey (Expansion Draft)	.06	.05	.02
236	Joe Girardi (Expansion Draft)	.06	.05	.02
237	Dave Magadan (Expansion Draft)	.06	.05	.02
238	David Nied	.60	.45	.25
239	*Eric Wedge*	.30	.25	.12
240	Rico Brogna (Rookie Prospect)	.06	.05	.02
241	J.T. Bruett (Rookie Prospect)	.06	.05	.02
242	Jonathan Hurst (Rookie Prospect)	.06	.05	.02
243	Bret Boone (Rookie Prospect)	.15	.11	.06
244	Manny Alexander (Rookie Prospect)	.15	.11	.06
245	Scooter Tucker (Rookie Prospect)	.06	.05	.02
246	Troy Neel	.30	.25	.12
247	Eddie Zosky (Rookie Prospect)	06	.05	.02
248	Melvin Nieves	.30	.25	.12
249	Ryan Thompson (Rookie Prospect)	.12	.09	.05
250	Shawn Barton (Rookie Prospect)	.15	.11	.06

251	Ryan Klesko	.75	.60	.30
252	Mike Piazza	6.50	5.00	2.75
253	Steve Hosey (Rookie Prospect)	.15	.11	.06
254	Shane Reynolds (Rookie Prospect)	.06	.05	.02
255	Dan Wilson (Rookie Prospect)	.06	.05	.02
256	Tom Marsh (Rookie Prospect)	.06	.05	.02
257	Barry Manuel (Rookie Prospect)	.06	.05	.02
258	Paul Miller (Rookie Prospect)	.06	.05	.02
259	Pedro Martinez	.20	.15	.08
260	Steve Cooke	.30	.25	.12
261	Johnny Guzman (Rookie Prospect)	.06	.05	.02
262	Mike Butcher (Rookie Prospect)	.08	.06	.03
263	Bien Figueroa (Rookie Prospect)	.08	.06	.03
264	Rich Rowland (Rookie Prospect)	.08	.06	.03
265	Shawn Jeter (Rookie Prospect)	.10	.07	.04
266	Gerald Williams (Rookie Prospect)	.08	.06	.03
267	Derek Parks (Rookie Prospect)	.06	.05	.02
268	Henry Mercedes (Rookie Prospect)	.08	.06	.03
269	David Hulse	.25	.20	.10
270	Tim Pugh	.30	.25	.12
271	William Suero (Rookie Prospect)	.06	.05	.02
272	Ozzie Canseco (Rookie Prospect)	.06	.05	.02
273	Fernando Ramsey (Rookie Prospect)	.12	.09	.05
274	Bernardo Brito (Rookie Prospect)	.06	.05	.02
275	Dave Mlicki (Rookie Prospect)	.08	.06	.03
276	Tim Salmon	3.00	2.25	1.25
277	Mike Raczka (Rookie Prospect)	.06	.05	.02
278	Ken Ryan	.25	.20	.10
279	Rafael Boumigal	.20	.15	.08
280	Wil Cordero (Rookie Prospect)	.15	.11	.06
281	Billy Ashley	.35	.25	.14
282	Paul Wagner (Rookie Prospect)	.10	.07	.04
283	Blas Minor (Rookie Prospect)	.10	.07	.04
284	Rick Trlicek (Rookie Prospect)	.08	.06	.03
285	Willie Greene	.20	.15	.08
286	Ted Wood (Rookie Prospect)	.06	.05	.02
287	Phil Clark (Rookie Prospect)	.08	.06	.03
288	Jesse Levis (Rookie Prospect)	.08	.06	.03
289	Tony Gwynn (Now & Then)	.20	.15	.08
290	Nolan Ryan (Now & Then)	.75	.60	.30
291	Dennis Martinez (Now & Then)	.06	.05	.02
292	Eddie Murray (Now & Then)	.06	.05	.02
293	Robin Yount (Now & Then)	.30	.25	.12
294	George Brett (Now & Then)	.35	.25	.14
295	Dave Winfield (Now & Then)	.25	.20	.10
296	Bert Blyleven (Now & Then)	.06	.05	.02
297	Jeff Bagwell (Idols - Carl Yastrzemski)	.12	.09	.05
298	John Smoltz (Idols - Jack Morris)	.06	.05	.02
299	Larry Walker (Idols - Mike Bossy)	.06	.05	.02
300	Gary Sheffield (Idols - Barry Larkin)	.08	.06	.03
301	Ivan Rodriguez (Idols - Carlton Fisk)	.06	.05	.02
302	Delino DeShields (Idols - Malcolm X)	.06	.05	.02
303	Tim Salmon (Idols - Dwight Evans)	.60	.45	.25
304	Bernard Gilkey (Hometown Heroes)	.06	.05	.02
305	Cal Ripken, Jr. (Hometown Heroes)	.25	.20	.10
306	Barry Larkin (Hometown Heroes)	.06	.05	.02
307	Kent Hrbek (Hometown Heroes)	.06	.05	.02
308	Rickey Henderson (Hometown Heroes)	.06	.05	.02
309	Darryl Strawberry (Hometown Heroes)	.06	.05	.02
310	John Franco (Hometown Heroes)	.06	.05	.02
311	Todd Stottlemyre	.06	.05	.02
312	Luis Gonzalez	.06	.05	.02
313	Tommy Greene	.12	.09	.05
314	Randy Velarde	.06	.05	.02
315	Steve Avery	.25	.20	.10
316	Jose Oquendo	.06	.05	.02
317	Rey Sanchez	.06	.05	.02
318	Greg Vaughn	.15	.11	.06
319	Orel Hershiser	.06	.05	.02
320	Paul Sorrento	.06	.05	.02
321	Royce Clayton	.15	.11	.06
322	John Vander Wal	.06	.05	.02
323	Henry Cotto	.06	.05	.02
324	Pete Schourek	.06	.05	.02
325	David Segui	.06	.05	.02
326	Arthur Rhodes	.06	.05	.02
327	Bruce Hurst	.06	.05	.02
328	Wes Chamberlain	.06	.05	.02
329	Ozzie Smith	.25	.20	.10
330	Scott Cooper	.15	.11	.06
331	Felix Fermin	.06	.05	.02
332	Mike Macfarlane	.06	.05	.02
333	Dan Gladden	.06	.05	.02
334	Kevin Tapani	.06	.05	.02
335	Steve Sax	.06	.05	.02
336	Jeff Montgomery	.06	.05	.02
337	Gary DiSarcina	.06	.05	.02
338	Lance Blankenship	.06	.05	.02
339	Brian Williams	.06	.05	.02
340	Duane Ward	.06	.05	.02
341	Chuck McElroy	.06	.05	.02
342	Joe Magrane	.06	.05	.02
343	Jaime Navarro	.06	.05	.02
344	Dave Justice	.60	.45	.25
345	Jose Offerman	.06	.05	.02
346	Marquis Grissom	.20	.15	.08
347	Bill Swift	.06	.05	.02
348	Jim Thome	.06	.05	.02
349	Archi Cianfrocco	.06	.05	.02
350	Anthony Young	.06	.05	.02
351	Leo Gomez	.06	.05	.02
352	Bill Gullickson	.06	.05	.02
353	Alan Trammell	.06	.05	.02
354	Dan Pasqua	.06	.05	.02
355	Jeff King	.06	.05	.02
356	Kevin Brown	.06	.05	.02
357	Tim Belcher	.06	.05	.02
358	Bip Roberts	.06	.05	.02
359	Brent Mayne	.06	.05	.02
360	Rheal Cormier	.06	.05	.02
361	Mark Guthrie	.06	.05	.02
362	Craig Grebeck	.06	.05	.02
363	Andy Stankiewicz	.06	.05	.02
364	Juan Guzman	.20	.15	.08
365	Bobby Witt	.06	.05	.02
366	Mark Portugal	.06	.05	.02
367	Brian McRae	.06	.05	.02
368	Mark Lemke	.06	.05	.02
369	Bill Wegman	.06	.05	.02
370	Donovan Osborne	.15	.11	.06
371	Derrick May	.15	.11	.06
372	Carl Willis	.06	.05	.02
373	Chris Nabholz	.06	.05	.02
374	Mark Lewis	.06	.05	.02
375	John Burkett	.06	.05	.02
376	Luis Mercedes	.06	.05	.02
377	Ramon Martinez	.20	.15	.08
378	Kyle Abbott	.06	.05	.02
379	Mark Wohlers	.06	.05	.02
380	Bob Walk	.06	.05	.02
381	Kenny Rogers	.06	.05	.02
382	Tim Naehring	.06	.05	.02
383	Alex Fernandez	.06	.05	.02
384	Keith Miller	.06	.05	.02
385	Mike Henneman	.06	.05	.02
386	Rick Aguilera	.06	.05	.02
387	George Bell	.06	.05	.02
388	Mike Gallego	.06	.05	.02
389	Howard Johnson	.06	.05	.02
390	Kim Batiste	.06	.05	.02
391	Jerry Browne	.06	.05	.02
392	Damon Berryhill	.06	.05	.02
393	Ricky Bones	.06	.05	.02
394	Omar Olivares	.06	.05	.02
395	Mike Harkey	.06	.05	.02
396	Pedro Astacio	.15	.11	.06
397	John Wetteland	.06	.05	.02
398	Rod Beck	.15	.11	.06
399	Thomas Howard	.06	.05	.02
400	Mike Devereaux	.06	.05	.02
401	Tim Wakefield	.10	.07	.04
402	Curt Schilling	.12	.09	.05
403	Zane Smith	.06	.05	.02
404	Bob Zupcic	.06	.05	.02
405	Tom Browning	.06	.05	.02
406	Tony Phillips	.06	.05	.02
407	John Doherty	.06	.05	.02
408	Pat Mahomes	.06	.05	.02
409	John Habyan	.06	.05	.02
410	Steve Olin	.06	.05	.02
411	Chad Curtis	.15	.11	.06
412	Joe Grahe	.06	.05	.02
413	John Patterson	.06	.05	.02
414	Brian Hunter	.06	.05	.02
415	Doug Henry	.06	.05	.02
416	Lee Smith	.06	.05	.02
417	Bob Scanlan	.06	.05	.02
418	Kent Mercker	.06	.05	.02
419	Mel Rojas	.06	.05	.02
420	Mark Whiten	.06	.05	.02
421	Carlton Fisk	.12	.09	.05
422	Candy Maldonado	.06	.05	.02
423	Doug Drabek	.06	.05	.02
424	Wade Boggs	.20	.15	.08
425	Mark Davis	.06	.05	.02
426	Kirby Puckett	.50	.40	.20
427	Joe Carter	.40	.30	.15
428	Paul Molitor	.35	.25	.14
429	Eric Davis	.12	.09	.05
430	Darryl Kile	.06	.05	.02
431	Jeff Parrett (Expansion Draft)	.06	.05	.02
432	Jeff Blauser	.06	.05	.02
433	Dan Plesac	.06	.05	.02
434	Andres Galarraga (Expansion Draft)	.12	.09	.05
435	Jim Gott	.06	.05	.02
436	Jose Mesa	.06	.05	.02
437	Ben Rivera	.06	.05	.02
438	Dave Winfield	.25	.20	.10
439	Norm Charlton	.06	.05	.02
440	Chris Bosio	.06	.05	.02
441	Wilson Alvarez	.06	.05	.02
442	Dave Stewart	.06	.05	.02
443	Doug Jones	.06	.05	.02
444	Jeff Russell	.06	.05	.02
445	Ron Gant	.12	.09	.05
446	Paul O'Neill	.06	.05	.02
447	Charlie Hayes (Expansion Draft)	.06	.05	.02
448	Joe Hesketh	.06	.05	.02
449	Chris Hammond	.06	.05	.02
450	Hipolito Pichardo	.06	.05	.02
451	Scott Radinsky	.06	.05	.02
452	Bobby Thigpen	.06	.05	.02
453	Xavier Hernandez	.08	.06	.03
454	Lonnie Smith	.06	.05	.02
455	Jamie Arnold	.40	.30	.15
456	B.J. Wallace	.50	.40	.20
457	*Derek Jeter*	1.25	.90	.50
458	*Jason Kendall*	.40	.30	.15
459	Rick Helling	.60	.45	.25
460	*Derek Wallace*	.40	.30	.15
461	*Sean Lowe*	.50	.40	.20
462	*Shannon Stewart*	.50	.40	.20
463	*Benji Grigsby*	.40	.30	.15
464	*Todd Steverson*	.50	.40	.20
465	*Dan Serafini*	.40	.30	.15
466	Michael Tucker	.75	.60	.30
467	Chris Roberts	.50	.40	.20
468	*Pete Janicki* (1st Draft Pick)	.15	.11	.06
469	*Jeff Schmidt* (1st Draft Pick)	.15	.11	.06
470	Don Mattingly (Now & Then)	.30	.25	.12
471	Cal Ripken, Jr. (Now & Then)	.35	.25	.14
472	Jack Morris (Now & Then)	.06	.05	.02
473	Terry Pendleton (Now & Then)	.06	.05	.02
474	Dennis Eckersley (Now & Then)	.10	.07	.04
475	Carlton Fisk (Now & Then)	.12	.09	.05
476	Wade Boggs (Now & Then)	.15	.11	.06
477	Len Dykstra (Idols - Ken Stabler)	.12	.09	.05
478	Danny Tartabull (Idols - Jose Tartabull)	.10	.08	.04
479	Jeff Conine (Idols - Dale Murphy)	.10	.08	.04
480	Gregg Jefferies (Idols - Ron Cey)	.15	.11	.06
481	Paul Molitor (Idols - Harmon Killebrew)	.20	.15	.08
482	John Valentin (Idols - Dave Concepcion)	.10	.08	.04
483	Alex Arias (Idols - Dave Winfield)	.10	.08	.04
484	Barry Bonds (Hometown Heroes)	.50	.40	.20
485	Doug Drabek (Hometown Heroes)	.08	.06	.03
486	Dave Winfield (Hometown Heroes)	.12	.09	.05
487	Brett Butler (Hometown Heroes)	.10	.08	.04
488	Harold Baines (Hometown Heroes)	.10	.08	.04
489	David Cone (Hometown Heroes)	.10	.08	.04
490	Willie McGee (Hometown Heroes)	.10	.08	.04
491	Robby Thompson	.08	.06	.04
492	Pete Incaviglia	.06	.05	.02
493	Manuel Lee	.06	.05	.02
494	Rafael Belliard	.06	.05	.02
495	Scott Fletcher	.06	.05	.02
496	Jeff Frye	.06	.05	.02
497	Andre Dawson	.15	.11	.06
498	Mike Scioscia	.06	.05	.02
499	Spike Owen	.06	.05	.02
500	Sid Fernandez	.06	.05	.02
501	Joe Orsulak	.06	.05	.02
502	Benito Santiago (Expansion Draft)	.06	.05	.02
503	Dale Murphy	.06	.05	.02
504	Barry Bonds	.75	.60	.30
505	Jose Guzman	.06	.05	.02
506	Tony Pena	.06	.05	.02
507	Greg Swindell	.06	.05	.02
508	Mike Pagliarulo	.06	.05	.02
509	Lou Whitaker	.06	.05	.02
510	Greg Gagne	.06	.05	.02
511	Butch Henry (Expansion Draft)	.06	.05	.02
512	Jeff Brantley	.06	.05	.02
513	Jack Armstrong (Expansion Draft)	.06	.05	.02
514	Danny Jackson	.06	.05	.02
515	Junior Felix (Expansion Draft)	.06	.05	.02
516	Milt Thompson	.06	.05	.02
517	Greg Maddux	.25	.20	.10
518	Eric Young (Expansion Draft)	.06	.05	.02
519	Jody Reed	.06	.05	.02
520	Roberto Kelly	.06	.05	.02
521	Darren Holmes (Expansion Draft)	.06	.05	.02
522	Craig Lefferts	.06	.05	.02
523	Charlie Hough (Expansion Draft)	.06	.05	.02
524	Bo Jackson	.25	.20	.10
525	Bill Spiers	.06	.05	.02
526	Orestes Destrade (Expansion Draft)	.12	.09	.05
527	Greg Hibbard	.06	.05	.02
528	Roger McDowell	.06	.05	.02
529	Cory Snyder	.06	.05	.02
530	Harold Reynolds	.06	.05	.02
531	Kevin Reimer	.06	.05	.02
532	Rick Sutcliffe	.06	.05	.02
533	Tony Fernandez	.06	.05	.02
534	Tom Brunansky	.06	.05	.02
535	Jeff Reardon	.06	.05	.02
536	Chili Davis	.06	.05	.02
537	Bob Ojeda	.06	.05	.02
538	Greg Colbrunn	.06	.05	.02
539	Phil Plantier	.30	.25	.12
540	Brian Jordan	.12	.09	.05
541	Pete Smith	.06	.05	.02
542	Frank Tanana	.06	.05	.02
543	John Smiley	.06	.05	.02
544	David Cone	.06	.05	.02
545	Daryl Boston (Expansion Draft)	.06	.05	.02
546	Tom Henke	.06	.05	.02
547	Bill Krueger	.06	.05	.02
548	Freddie Benavides (Expansion Draft)	.06	.05	.02
549	Randy Myers	.06	.05	.02
550	Reggie Jefferson	.06	.05	.02
551	Kevin Mitchell	.06	.05	.02
552	Dave Stieb	.06	.05	.02
553	Bret Barberie (Expansion Draft)	.06	.05	.02
554	Tim Crews	.06	.05	.02
555	Doug Dascenzo	.06	.05	.02
556	Alex Cole (Expansion Draft)	.06	.05	.02
557	Jeff Innis	.06	.05	.02
558	Carlos Garcia	.15	.11	.06
559	Steve Howe	.06	.05	.02
560	Kirk McCaskill	.06	.05	.02
561	Frank Seminara	.06	.05	.02
562	Cris Carpenter (Expansion Draft)	.06	.05	.02
563	Mike Stanley	.06	.05	.02
564	Carlos Quintana	.06	.05	.02
565	Mitch Williams	.06	.05	.02
566	Juan Bell	.06	.05	.02
567	Eric Fox	.06	.05	.02
568	Al Leiter	.06	.05	.02
569	Mike Stanton	.06	.05	.02
570	Scott Kamieniecki	.06	.05	.02
571	Ryan Bowen (Expansion Draft)	.06	.05	.02
572	Andy Ashby (Expansion Draft)	.06	.05	.02
573	Bob Welch	.06	.05	.02
574	Scott Sanderson	.06	.05	.02
575	Joe Kmak (Rookie Prospect)	.20	.15	.08
576	Scott Pose (Rookie Prospect/Expansion Draft)	.15	.11	.06
577	Ricky Gutierrez (Rookie Prospect)	.15	.11	.06
578	Mike Trombley (Rookie Prospect)	.12	.09	.05
579	*Sterling Hitchcock*	.25	.20	.10
580	Rodney Bolton (Rookie Prospect)	.12	.09	.05

581	Tyler Green (Rookie Prospect)	.15	.11	.06
582	Tim Costo (Rookie Prospect)	.12	.09	.05
583	*Tim Laker* (Rookie Prospect)	.15	.11	.06
584	*Steve Reed* (Rookie Prospect/Expansion Draft)	.12	.09	.05
585	*Tom Kramer*	.25	.20	.10
586	Robb Nen (Rookie Prospect)	.15	.11	.06
587	*Jim Tatum*	.20	.15	.08
588	Frank Bolick (Rookie Prospect)	.15	.11	.06
589	Kevin Young	.50	.40	.20
590	*Matt Whiteside* (Rookie Prospect)	.15	.11	.06
591	Cesar Hernandez (Rookie Prospect)	.15	.11	.06
592	Mike Mohler (Rookie Prospect)	.15	.11	.06
593	Alan Embree (Rookie Prospect)	.15	.11	.06
594	Terry Jorgensen (Rookie Prospect)	.12	.09	.05
595	*John Cummings*	.25	.20	.10
596	Domingo Martinez (Rookie Prospect)	.12	.09	.05
597	Benji Gil	.50	.40	.20
598	*Todd Pratt*	.35	.25	.14
599	*Rene Arocha*	.40	.30	.15
600	Dennis Moeller (Rookie Prospect)	.20	.15	.08
601	Jeff Conine (Rookie Prospect/Expansion Draft)	.40	.30	.15
602	Trevor Hoffman (Rookie Prospect/Expansion Draft)	.15	.11	.06
603	Daniel Smith (Rookie Prospect)	.12	.09	.05
604	Lee Tinsley (Rookie Prospect)	.12	.09	.05
605	Dan Peltier (Rookie Prospect)	.12	.09	.05
606	Billy Brewer (Rookie Prospect)	.15	.11	.06
607	*Matt Walbeck*	.30	.25	.12
608	Richie Lewis (Rookie Prospect/Expansion Draft)	.12	.09	.05
609	J.T. Snow (Rookie Prospect	.50	.40	.20
610	*Pat Gomez* (Rookie Prospect)	.12	.09	.05
611	Phil Hiatt	.25	.20	.10
612	Alex Arias (Rookie Prospect/Expansion Draft)	.12	.09	.05
613	Kevin Rogers (Rookie Prospect)	.15	.11	.06
614	Al Martin	.50	.40	.20
615	Greg Gohr (Rookie Prospect)	.12	.09	.05
616	*Grame Lloyd*	.20	.15	.08
617	Kent Bottenfield (Rookie Prospect)	.15	.11	.06
618	Chuck Carr (Rookie Prospect/Expansion Draft)	.15	.11	.06
619	*Darrell Sherman* (Rookie Prospect)	.25	.20	.10
620	*Mike Lansing* (Rookie Prospect)	.50	.40	.20

Values quoted in this guide reflect the retail price of a card – the price a collector can expect to pay when buying a card from a dealer. The wholesale price – that which a collector can expect to receive from a dealer when selling cards – will be significantly lower, depending on desirability and condition.

1993 Pinnacle Expansion Opening Day

This nine-card set features 18 players for the two new expansion teams: the Florida Marlins and Colorado Rockies; each card side shows a projected Opening Day starter for each team. Cards were available one per every Series II hobby box. Complete sets were available through a special mail-in offer.

		MT	NR MT	EX
Complete Set (9):		10.00	7.50	4.00
Common Player:		.75	.60	.30
1	Charlie Hough/David Nied	2.00	1.50	.80
2	Benito Santiago/Joe Girardi	.90	.70	.35
3	Orestes Destrade/Andres Galarraga	3.00	2.25	1.20
4	Bret Barberie/Eric Young	.75	.60	.30
5	Dave Magadan/Charlie Hayes	1.50	1.00	.80
6	Walt Weiss/Freddie Benevides	.75	.60	.30
7	Jeff Conine/Jerald Clark	1.00	.75	.40
8	Scott Pose/Alex Cole	.75	.60	.30
9	Junior Felix/Dante Bichette	1.50	1.00	.80

1993 Pinnacle Rookie Team Pinnacle

These 10 cards were randomly inserted into Score Pinnacle Series II packs. Rookie Team Pinnacle is written in gold foil on both sides of the card. Cards are numbered 1 of 10, etc., and use the special Dufex process. Each card shows two players painted by artist Christopher Greco. Stated odds of finding a Rookie Team Pinnacle insert were given as one in 90 packs.

		MT	NR MT	EX
Complete Set (10):		250.00	185.00	100.00
Common Player:		12.00	8.00	5.00
1	Pedro Martinez, Mike Trombley	12.00	8.00	4.00
2	Kevin Rogers, Sterling Hitchcock	12.00	8.00	4.00
3	Mike Piazza, Jesse Levis	100.00	75.00	40.00
4	Ryan Klesko, J.T. Snow	45.00	30.00	20.00
5	John Patterson, Bret Boone	15.00	11.00	6.00
6	Domingo Martinez, Kevin Young	20.00	12.00	8.00
7	Wil Cordero, Manny Alexander	16.00	12.00	6.50
8	Steve Hosey, Tim Salmon	70.00	52.00	28.00
9	Ryan Thompson, Gerald Williams	12.00	8.00	5.00
10	Melvin Nieves, David Hulse	20.00	15.00	8.00

Regional interest may affect the value of a card.

1993 Pinnacle Slugfest

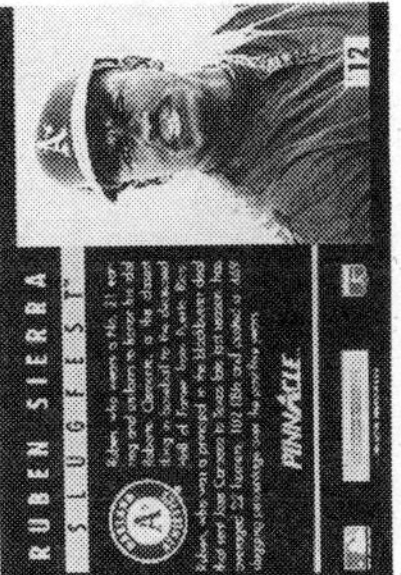

Baseball's top sluggers are featured in this 30-card insert set. Cards were available one per Series II jumbo packs. Slugfest is written in gold foil on the card front.

		MT	NR MT	EX
Complete Set (30):		40.00	30.00	16.00
Common Player:		.50	.40	.20
1	Juan Gonzalez	5.00	3.75	2.00
2	Mark McGwire	1.00	.70	.40
3	Cecil Fielder	1.25	.90	.50
4	Joe Carter	2.00	1.50	.80
5	Fred McGriff	2.00	1.50	.80
6	Barry Bonds	3.50	2.75	1.50
7	Gary Sheffield	1.25	.90	.50
8	Dave Hollins	1.50	1.25	.60
9	Frank Thomas	7.50	5.75	3.00
11	Albert Belle	2.00	1.50	.80
12	Ruben Sierra	.75	.60	.30
13	Larry Walker	.90	.70	.35
14	Jeff Bagwell	1.50	1.25	.60
15	Dave Justice	2.50	2.00	1.00
16	Kirby Puckett	2.50	2.00	1.00
20	Will Clark	1.25	.90	.50
23	Don Mattingly	2.00	1.50	.80
24	Jose Canseco	1.00	.70	.40
26	Andre Dawson	.75	.60	.30
27	Ryne Sandberg	2.75	2.00	1.00
28	Ken Griffey, Jr.	6.00	4.50	2.50
29	Carlos Baerga	2.50	2.00	1.00
30	Travis Fryman	2.50	2.00	1.00

1993 Pinnacle Team Pinnacle

These cards were randomly inserted in Pinnacle Series I packs; cards were included one in about every 24 packs. Each card features two players painted by artist Christopher Greco. An eleventh card, featuring relief pitchers, was available only via a mail-in offer.

		MT	NR MT	EX
Complete Set (11):		150.00	110.00	60.00
Common Player:		10.00	7.50	4.00
1	Greg Maddux, Mike Mussina	15.00	11.25	6.00
2	Tom Glavine, John Smiley	10.00	7.50	4.00
3	Darren Daulton, Ivan Rodriguez	12.50	9.00	5.00
4	Fred McGriff, Frank Thomas	45.00	32.50	18.00
5	Delino DeShields, Carlos Baerga	12.00	9.00	4.75
6	Gary Sheffield, Edagar Martinez	10.00	7.50	4.00
7	Ozzie Smith, Pat Listach	12.00	9.00	4.75
8	Barry Bonds, Juan Gonzalez	45.00	34.00	18.00
9	Kirby Puckett, Andy Van Slyke	15.00	11.00	6.00
10	Larry Walker, Joe Carter	10.00	7.50	4.00
11	Rick Aguilera, Rob Dibble	10.00	7.50	4.00

1993 Pinnacle Team 2001

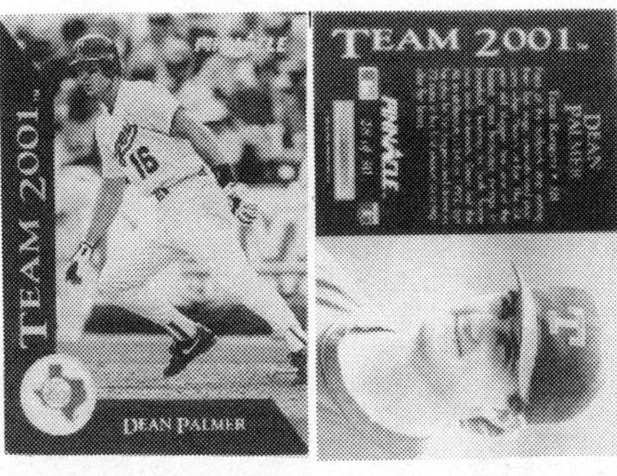

This insert set features 30 players who are expected to be stars in the year 2001. Cards were randomly inserted into 27-card jumbo packs from Series I.

		MT	NR MT	EX
Complete Set (30):		32.00	24.00	13.00
Common Player:		.50	.40	.20
1	Wil Cordero	.60	.45	.25
2	Cal Eldred	.75	.60	.30
3	Mike Mussina	2.00	1.50	.80
4	Chuck Knoblauch	.50	.40	.20
5	Melvin Nieves	1.50	1.25	.60
6	Tim Wakefield	.50	.40	.20
7	Carlos Baerga	2.50	2.00	1.00
8	Bret Boone	.75	.60	.30
9	Jeff Bagwell	1.75	1.25	.70
10	Travis Fryman	2.00	1.50	.80
11	Royce Clayton	.75	.60	.30
12	Delino DeSheilds	.50	.40	.20
13	Juan Gonzalez	5.00	3.75	2.00
14	Pedro Martinez	.75	.60	.30
15	Bernie Williams	.50	.40	.20
16	Billy Ashley	1.50	1.25	.60
17	Marquis Grissom	.90	.70	.35
18	Kenny Lofton	1.50	1.25	.60
19	Ray Lankford	.50	.40	.20
20	Tim Salmon	7.50	5.75	3.00
21	Steve Hosey	.75	.60	.30
22	Charles Nagy	.50	.40	.20
23	Dave Fleming	.50	.40	.20
24	Reggie Sanders	.75	.60	.30
25	Sam Millitello	.50	.40	.20
26	Eric Karros	1.00	.70	.40
27	Ryan Klesko	2.00	1.50	.80
28	Dean Palmer	.50	.40	.20
29	Ivan Rodriguez	1.00	.75	.40
30	Sterling Hitchcock	1.00	.75	.40

1993 Pinnacle Tribute

These two future Hall of Famers each have five-card sets devoted to their career achievements. Each card commemorates a milestone reached by George Brett or Nolan Ryan. Cards were random inserts in 1993 Score Pinnacle Series II packs, about one per every 24 packs. Fronts have a gold-foil stamped "Tribute" vertically at right.

		MT	NR MT	EX
Complete Set (10):		60.00	45.00	25.00
George Brett Card (1-5):		5.00	3.75	2.00
Nolan Ryan Card (6-10):		10.00	7.50	4.00
1	Kansas City Royalty (George Brett)	6.00	4.50	2.50
2	The Chase for .400 (George Brett)	6.00	4.50	2.50
3	Pine Tar Pandemonium ("The bat")	6.00	4.50	2.50
4	MVP and a World Series, Too (George Brett)	6.00	4.50	2.50
5	3,000 or Bust (George Brett)	6.00	4.50	2.50
6	The Rookie (Nolan Ryan)	10.00	7.50	4.00
7	Angel of No Mercy (Nolan Ryan)	10.00	7.50	4.00
8	Astronomical Success (Nolan Ryan)	10.00	7.50	4.00
9	5,000 Ks (Nolan Ryan)	10.00	7.50	4.00
10	No-Hitter No. 7 (Nolan Ryan)	10.00	7.50	4.00

1993 Pinnacle Cooperstown

This 30-card boxed set features "today's superstar players bound to become Cooperstown inductees." In standard 2-1/2" x 3-1/2" format, the cards feature on both front and back an action photo which is borderless at the top and sides. At bottom-center of each photo is a half-moon green and gold-foil "Cooperstown Card" logo. The Pinnacle logo appears in black or white in one of the upper corners of each side. On front, the player's name is gold-foil stamped in a black bar at bottom. On back is a black box, again with the player's name in gold-foil, plus a few stats justifying the player's Hall of Fame potential. Pinnacle's trademark optical-variable anti-counterfeiting device is at the bottom, flanked by the card number in red and the licensors' logos. Cards are UV coated on both sides.

		MT	NR MT	EX
Complete Set (30):		9.00	6.75	3.50
Common Player:		.25	.20	.10
1	Nolan Ryan	1.00	.75	.40
2	George Brett	.50	.40	.20
3	Robin Yount	.50	.40	.20
4	Carlton Fisk	.30	.25	.12
5	Dale Murphy	.30	.25	.12
6	Dennis Eckserley	.25	.20	.10
7	Rickey Henderson	.30	.25	.12
8	Ryne Sandberg	.50	.40	.20
9	Ozzie Smith	.30	.25	.12
10	Dave Winfield	.35	.25	.14
11	Andre Dawson	.25	.20	.10
12	Kirby Puckett	.35	.25	.14
13	Wade Boggs	.35	.25	.14
14	Don Mattingly	.45	.35	.20
15	Barry Bonds	.35	.25	.14
16	Will Clark	.35	.25	.14
17	Cal Ripken, Jr.	.50	.40	.20
18	Roger Clemens	.30	.25	.12
19	Dwight Gooden	.25	.20	.10
20	Tony Gwynn	.30	.25	.12
21	Joe Carter	.25	.20	.10
22	Ken Griffey, Jr.	.75	.60	.30
23	Paul Molitor	.30	.25	.12
24	Frank Thomas	1.00	.75	.40
25	Juan Gonzalez	.50	.40	.20
26	Barry Larkin	.25	.20	.10
27	Eddie Murray	.25	.20	.10
28	Cecil Fielder	.30	.25	.12
29	Roberto Alomar	.30	.25	.12
30	Mark McGwire	.35	.25	.14

1993 Pinnacle Home Run Club

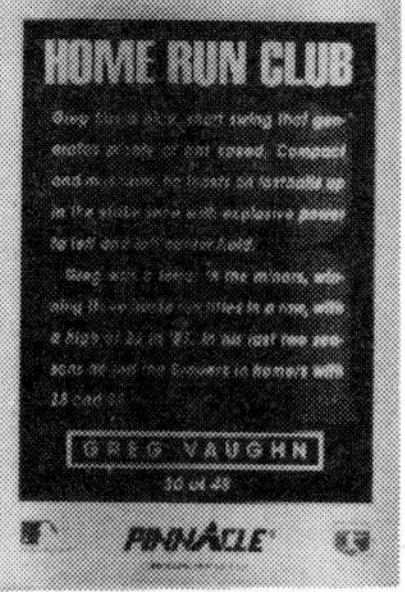

Pinnacle Brands Inc. released a 48-card boxed set in 1993 done in a special printing process called "Dufex," which gives the cards a 3-D metallic appearance. Limited to 200,000 numbered sets, the cards are UV coated and gold-foil stamped. The checklist includes 28 American League and 20 National League sluggers.

		MT	NR MT	EX
Complete Set (30):		25.00	19.00	10.00
Common Player:		.25	.20	.10
1	Juan Gonzalez	2.00	1.50	.80
2	Fred McGriff	.50	.40	.20
3	Cecil Fielder	.75	.60	.30
4	Barry Bonds	2.00	1.50	.80
5	Albert Belle	1.00	.70	.40
6	Gary Sheffield	.50	.40	.20
7	Joe Carter	.50	.40	.20
8	Mark McGwire	.75	.60	.30
9	Darren Daulton	.35	.25	.14
10	Jose Canseco	1.00	.70	.40
11	Dave Hollins	.35	.25	.14
12	Ryne Sandberg	3.00	2.25	1.25
13	Ken Griffey Jr.	3.00	2.25	1.25
14	Larry Walker	.25	.20	.10
15	Rob Deer	.25	.20	.10
16	Andre Dawson	.35	.25	.14
17	Frank Thomas	3.00	2.25	1.25
18	Mickey Tettleton	.25	.20	.10
19	Charlie Hayes	.25	.20	.10
20	Ron Gant	.35	.25	.14
21	Rickey Henderson	.50	.40	.20
22	Matt Williams	.35	.25	.14
23	Kevin Mitchell	.25	.20	.10
24	Robin Ventura	.35	.25	.14
25	Dean Palmer	.25	.20	.10
26	Mike Piazza	2.00	1.50	.80
27	J.T. Snow	.75	.60	.30
28	Jeff Bagwell	.50	.40	.20
29	John Olerud	.50	.40	.20
30	Greg Vaughn	.25	.20	.10
31	Dave Justice	.60	.45	.25
32	Dave Winfield	.75	.60	.30
33	Danny Tartabull	.25	.20	.10
34	Eric Anthony	.25	.20	.10
35	Eddie Murray	.50	.40	.20
36	Jay Buhner	.25	.20	.10
37	Derek Bell	.25	.20	.10
38	Will Clark	.75	.60	.30
39	Carlos Baerga	.50	.40	.20
40	Mo Vaughn	.50	.40	.20
41	Bobby Bonilla	.35	.25	.14
42	Tim Salmon	2.00	1.50	.80
43	Bo Jackson	.75	.60	.30
44	Howard Johnson	.35	.25	.14
45	Kent Hrbek	.25	.20	.10
46	Ruben Sierra	.35	.25	.14
47	Cal Ripken, Jr.	3.00	2.25	1.25
48	Travis Fryman	.35	.25	.14

1993 Pinnacle Joe DiMaggio

Sold in a special tin box in a limited edition of 200,000 sets, this 30-card issue highlights the career of "The Yankee Clipper." Fronts feature black-and-white or colorized photos with a black border and gold-foil highlights. Backs feature a woodgrain center panel with a portion of DiMaggio's career recounted. As on the front, there is a black border and gold highlights. The Pinnacle anti-counterfeiting device is printed at bottom center. The boxed set includes an "Authenticator" lens through which the name "DiMaggio" can be seen when placed over the optical-variable printing on back.

		MT	NR MT	EX
Complete Set:		20.00	15.00	8.00
Common Card:		.75	.60	.30
1	An American Hero	2.00	1.50	.80
2	San Francisco Seals	.75	.60	.30
3	Seals Farewell	.75	.60	.30
4	First Game	.75	.60	.30
5	The Rookie	.75	.60	.30
6	Rookie All-Star (with Dizzy Dean)	1.50	1.25	.60
7	Fan Favorite	.75	.60	.30
8	Teammates' Awe	.75	.60	.30
9	Classic Swing	.75	.60	.30
10	Joltin' Power	.75	.60	.30
11	Rapid Robert vs. Joltin' Joe (with Bob Feller)	1.00	.70	.40
12	The Complete Hitter	.75	.60	.30
13	Makin' It Look Easy	.75	.60	.30
14	Extra Swings	.75	.60	.30
15	The Run Producer	.75	.60	.30
16	Quiet Confidence	.76	.60	.30
17	Sticks 'N' Bones	.75	.60	.30
18	A Link to the Past (with Lou Gehrig)	2.00	1.50	.80
19	The Center of Attention	.75	.60	.30
20	The DiMaggio Mystique	.75	.60	.30
21	Joe McCarthy (with Joe McCarthy)	.75	.60	.30
22	World War II	.75	.60	.30
23	Fearless Baserunner	.75	.60	.30
24	The Summer of '41	.75	.60	.30
25	Career Statistics	2.00	1.50	.80
26	No. 45	.75	.60	.30
27	Chasing Ruth	.75	.60	.30
28	The Final Season	.75	.60	.30
29	Retirement	.75	.60	.30
30	Baseball's Greatest Living Player	2.00	1.50	.80

1994 Pinnacle

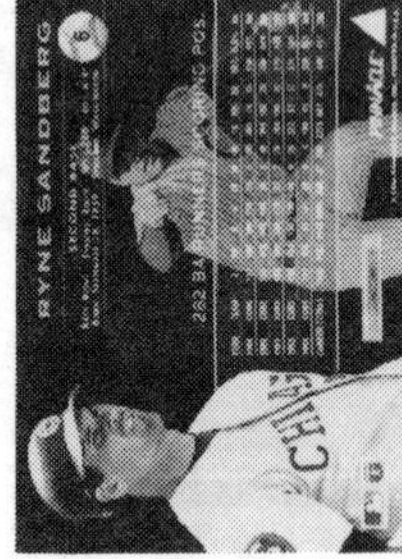

Typical of each card company's 1994 mid-priced brand, Pinnacle features full bleed photos, gold-foil stamping and UV coating. On front, player and team names appear in a shield-and-bar motif in the lower-left corner. The Pinnacle logo appears in gold foil and the brand name in white in an upper corner. On horizontally oriented backs, the front photo is reproduced as a subdued background photo, over which are printed recent stats and a few biographical details. A different player photo is featured at left. The card number appears in a baseball at upper-right. Pinnacle's trademarks appear at lower-right, while the brand's optical-variable anti-counterfeiting device is at bottom center. Subsets include major award winners, Rookie Prospects and Draft Picks which are appropriately noted with gold-foil lettering on front. The issue was produced in two series of 270 cards each.

		MT	NR MT	EX
Complete Set (270):		28.00	21.00	11.00
Common Player:		.10	.08	.04
1	Frank Thomas	3.50	2.75	1.50
2	Carlos Baerga	.50	.40	.20
3	Sammy Sosa	.15	.11	.06
4	Tony Gwynn	.30	.25	.12
5	John Olerud	.40	.30	.15
6	Ryne Sandberg	.50	.40	.20
7	Moises Alou	.20	.15	.08
8	Steve Avery	.25	.20	.10
9	Tim Salmon	1.50	1.25	.60
10	Cecil Fielder	.20	.15	.08
11	Greg Maddux	.40	.30	.15
12	Barry Larkin	.15	.11	.06
13	Mike Devereaux	.10	.08	.04
14	Charlie Hayes	.10	.08	.04
15	Albert Belle	.50	.40	.20
16	Andy Van Slyke	.10	.08	.04
17	Mo Vaughn	.15	.11	.06
18	Brian McRae	.10	.08	.04
19	Cal Eldred	.10	.08	.04
20	Craig Biggio	.10	.08	.04
21	Kirby Puckett	.60	.45	.25
22	Derek Bell	.10	.08	.04
23	Don Mattingly	.50	.40	.20
24	John Burkett	.10	.08	.04
25	Roger Clemens	.50	.40	.20
26	Barry Bonds	.75	.60	.30
27	Paul Molitor	.25	.20	.10
28	Mike Piazza	2.50	2.00	1.00
29	Robin Ventura	.20	.15	.08
30	Jeff Conine	.10	.08	.04
31	Wade Boggs	.15	.11	.06
32	Dennis Eckersley	.10	.08	.04
33	Bobby Bonilla	.15	.11	.06
34	Len Dykstra	.15	.11	.06
35	Manny Alexander	.10	.08	.04
36	Ray Lankford	.10	.08	.04
37	Greg Vaughn	.12	.09	.05
38	Chuck Finley	.10	.08	.04
39	Todd Benzinger	.10	.08	.04
40	Dave Justice	.35	.25	.14
41	Rob Dibble	.10	.08	.04
42	Tom Henke	.10	.08	.04
43	David Nied	.30	.25	.12
44	Sandy Alomar Jr.	.10	.08	.04
45	Pete Harnisch	.10	.08	.04
46	Jeff Russell	.10	.08	.04
47	Terry Mulholland	.10	.08	.04
48	Kevin Appier	.10	.08	.04
49	Randy Tomlin	.10	.08	.04
50	Cal Ripken, Jr.	.50	.40	.20
51	Andy Benes	.15	.11	.06
52	Jimmy Key	.10	.08	.04
53	Kirt Manwaring	.10	.08	.04
54	Kevin Tapani	.10	.08	.04
55	Jose Guzman	.10	.08	.04
56	Todd Stottlemyre	.10	.08	.04
57	Jack McDowell	.15	.11	.06
58	Orel Hershiser	.10	.08	.04
59	Chris Hammond	.10	.08	.04
60	Chris Nabholz	.10	.08	.04
61	Ruben Sierra	.15	.11	.06
62	Dwight Gooden	.10	.08	.04
63	John Kruk	.10	.08	.04
64	Omar Vizquel	.10	.08	.04
65	Tim Naehring	.10	.08	.04
66	Dwight Smith	.10	.08	.04
67	Mickey Tettleton	.10	.08	.04
68	J.T. Snow	.25	.20	.10
69	Greg McMichael	.10	.08	.04
70	Kevin Mitchell	.10	.08	.04
71	Kevin Brown	.10	.08	.04
72	Scott Cooper	.10	.08	.04
73	Jim Thome	.30	.25	.12
74	Joe Girardi	.10	.08	.04
75	Eric Anthony	.10	.08	.04
76	Orlando Merced	.10	.08	.04
77	Felix Jose	.10	.08	.04
78	Tommy Greene	.10	.08	.04
79	Bernard Gilkey	.10	.08	.04
80	Phil Plantier	.15	.11	.06
81	Danny Tartabull	.10	.08	.04
82	Trevor Wilson	.10	.08	.04
83	Chuck Knoblauch	.10	.08	.04
84	Rick Wilkins	.10	.08	.04
85	Devon White	.10	.08	.04
86	Lance Johnson	.10	.08	.04
87	Eric Karros	.15	.11	.06
88	Gary Sheffield	.20	.15	.08
89	Wil Cordero	.10	.08	.04
90	Ron Darling	.10	.08	.04
91	Darren Daulton	.10	.08	.04
92	Joe Orsulak	.10	.08	.04
93	Steve Cooke	.10	.08	.04
94	Darryl Hamilton	.10	.08	.04
95	Aaron Sele	.75	.60	.30
96	John Doherty	.10	.08	.04
97	Gary DiSarcina	.10	.08	.04
98	Jeff Blauser	.10	.08	.04
99	John Smiley	.10	.08	.04
100	Ken Griffey, Jr.	3.00	2.25	1.25
101	Dean Palmer	.15	.11	.06
102	Felix Fermin	.10	.08	.04
103	Jerald Clark	.10	.08	.04
104	Doug Drabek	.10	.08	.04
105	Curt Schilling	.10	.08	.04
106	Jeff Montgomery	.10	.08	.04
107	Rene Arocha	.15	.11	.06
108	Carlos Garcia	.15	.11	.06
109	Wally Whitehurst	.10	.08	.04
110	Jim Abbott	.15	.11	.06
111	Royce Clayton	.15	.11	.06
112	Chris Hoiles	.10	.08	.04
113	Mike Morgan	.10	.08	.04
114	Joe Magrane	.10	.08	.04
115	Tom Candiotti	.10	.08	.04
116	Ron Karkovice	.10	.08	.04
117	Ryan Bowen	.10	.08	.04
118	Rod Beck	.10	.08	.04
119	John Wetteland	.10	.08	.04
120	Terry Steinbach	.10	.08	.04
121	Dave Hollins	.15	.11	.06
122	Jeff Kent	.10	.08	.04
123	Ricky Bones	.10	.08	.04
124	Brian Jordan	.10	.08	.04
125	Chad Kreuter	.10	.08	.04
126	John Valentin	.10	.08	.04
127	Billy Hathaway	.10	.08	.04
128	Wilson Alvarez	.10	.08	.04
129	Tino Martinez	.10	.08	.04
130	Rodney Bolton	.10	.08	.04
131	David Segui	.10	.08	.04
132	Wayne Kirby	.10	.08	.04
133	Eric Young	.10	.08	.04
134	Scott Servais	.10	.08	.04
135	Scott Radinsky	.10	.08	.04
136	Bret Barberie	.10	.08	.04
137	John Roper	.10	.08	.04
138	Ricky Gutierrez	.10	.08	.04
139	Bernie Williams	.10	.08	.04
140	Bud Black	.10	.08	.04
141	Jose Vizcaino	.10	.08	.04
142	Gerald Williams	.10	.08	.04
143	Duane Ward	.10	.08	.04
144	Danny Jackson	.10	.08	.04
145	Allen Watson	.15	.11	.06
146	Scott Fletcher	.10	.08	.04
147	Delino DeShields	.15	.11	.06
148	Shane Mack	.10	.08	.04
149	Jim Eisenreich	.10	.08	.04
150	Troy Neel	.15	.11	.06
151	Jay Bell	.10	.08	.04
152	B.J. Surhoff	.10	.08	.04
153	Mark Whiten	.10	.08	.04
154	Mike Henneman	.10	.08	.04
155	Todd Hundley	.10	.08	.04
156	Greg Myers	.10	.08	.04
157	Ryan Klesko	.75	.60	.30
158	Dave Fleming	.10	.08	.04
159	Mickey Morandini	.10	.08	.04
160	Blas Minor	.10	.08	.04
161	Reggie Jefferson	.10	.08	.04
162	David Hulse	.10	.08	.04
163	Greg Swindell	.10	.08	.04
164	Roberto Hernandez	.10	.08	.04
165	Brady Anderson	.10	.08	.04
166	Jack Armstrong	.10	.08	.04
167	Phil Clark	.10	.08	.04
168	Melido Perez	.10	.08	.04
169	Darren Lewis	.10	.08	.04
170	Sam Horn	.10	.08	.04
171	Mike Harkey	.10	.08	.04
172	Juan Guzman	.15	.11	.06
173	Bob Natal	.10	.08	.04
174	Deion Sanders	.25	.20	.10
175	Carlos Quintana	.10	.08	.04
176	Mel Rojas	.10	.08	.04
177	Willie Banks	.10	.08	.04
178	Ben Rivera	.10	.08	.04
179	Kenny Lofton	.20	.15	.08
180	Leo Gomez	.10	.08	.04
181	Roberto Mejia	.25	.20	.10
182	Mike Perez	.10	.08	.04
183	Travis Fryman	.25	.20	.10
184	Ben McDonald	.10	.08	.04
185	Steve Frey	.10	.08	.04
186	Kevin Young	.10	.08	.04
187	Dave Magadan	.10	.08	.04
188	Bobby Munoz	.10	.08	.04
189	Pat Rapp	.10	.08	.04
190	Jose Offerman	.10	.08	.04
191	Vinny Castilla	.10	.08	.04
192	Ivan Calderon	.10	.08	.04
193	Ken Caminiti	.10	.08	.04
194	Benji Gil	.15	.11	.06
195	Chuck Carr	.10	.08	.04
196	Derrick May	.10	.08	.04
197	Pat Kelly	.10	.08	.04
198	Jeff Brantley	.10	.08	.04
199	Jose Lind	.10	.08	.04
200	Steve Buechele	.10	.08	.04
201	Wes Chamberlain	.10	.08	.04
202	Eduardo Perez	.60	.45	.25
203	Bret Saberhagen	.10	.08	.04
204	Gregg Jefferies	.15	.11	.06
205	Darrin Fletcher	.10	.08	.04
206	Kent Hrbek	.10	.08	.04
207	Kim Batiste	.10	.08	.04
208	Jeff King	.10	.08	.04
209	Donovan Osborne	.10	.08	.04
210	Dave Nilsson	.10	.08	.04
211	Al Martin	.10	.08	.04
212	Mike Moore	.10	.08	.04
213	Sterling Hitchcock	.15	.11	.06
214	Geronimo Pena	.10	.08	.04
215	Kevin Higgins	.10	.08	.04
216	Norm Charlton	.10	.08	.04
217	Don Slaught	.10	.08	.04
218	Mitch Williams	.10	.08	.04
219	Derek Lilliquist	.10	.08	.04
220	Armando Reynoso	.10	.08	.04
221	Kenny Rogers	.10	.08	.04
222	Doug Jones	.10	.08	.04
223	Luis Aquino	.10	.08	.04
224	Mike Oquist	.10	.08	.04
225	Darryl Scott	.10	.08	.04
226	Kurt Abbott	.10	.08	.04
227	Andy Tomberlin	.10	.08	.04
228	Norberto Martin	.10	.08	.04
229	Pedro Castellano	.10	.08	.04
230	*Curtis Pride*	.60	.45	.25
231	Jeff McNeely	.15	.11	.06
232	Scott Lydy	.10	.08	.04
233	Darren Oliver	.10	.08	.04
234	Danny Bautista	.10	.08	.04
235	Butch Huskey	.10	.08	.04
236	Chipper Jones	.35	.25	.14
237	Eddie Zambrano	.10	.08	.04
238	Jean Domingo	.10	.08	.04
239	Javier Lopez	1.00	.75	.40
240	Nigel Wilson	.20	.15	.08
241	*Drew Denson*	.20	.15	.08
242	Raul Mondesi	1.25	.90	.50
243	Luis Ortiz	.10	.08	.04
244	Manny Ramirez	2.00	1.50	.80
245	Greg Blosser	.10	.08	.04
246	Rondell White	.75	.60	.30
247	Steve Karsay	.10	.08	.04
248	Scott Stahoviak	.10	.08	.04
249	Jose Valentin	.10	.08	.04
250	Marc Newfield	.25	.20	.10
251	Keith Kessinger	.10	.08	.04
252	Carl Everett	.15	.11	.06
253	John O'Donoghue	.10	.08	.04
254	Turk Wendell	.10	.08	.04
255	Scott Ruffcorn	.50	.40	.20
256	Tony Tarasco	.50	.40	.20
257	Andy Cook	.10	.08	.04
258	Matt Mieske	.10	.08	.04
259	Luis Lopez	.10	.08	.04
260	Ramon Caraballo	.10	.08	.04
261	Salomon Torres	.20	.15	.08
262	*Brooks Kieschnick*	1.50	1.25	.60
263	*Daron Kirkreit*	.25	.20	.10
264	*Bill Wagner*	.20	.15	.08
265	Matt Drews	.10	.08	.04
266	Scott Christman	.10	.08	.04
267	*Torii Hunter*	.20	.15	.08
268	*Jamey Wright*	.20	.15	.08
269	Jeff Granger	.10	.08	.04
270	*Trot Nixon*	2.50	2.00	1.00

1994 Pinnacle Artist's Proof

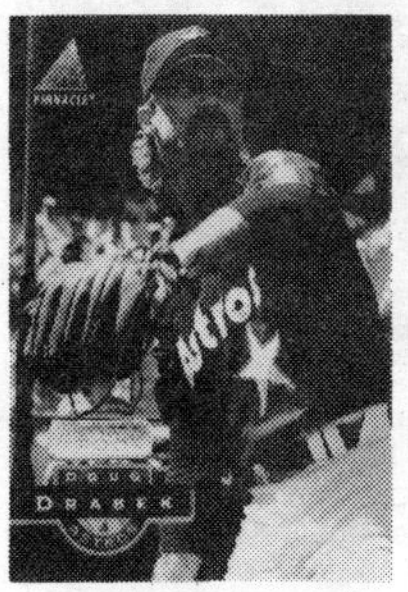

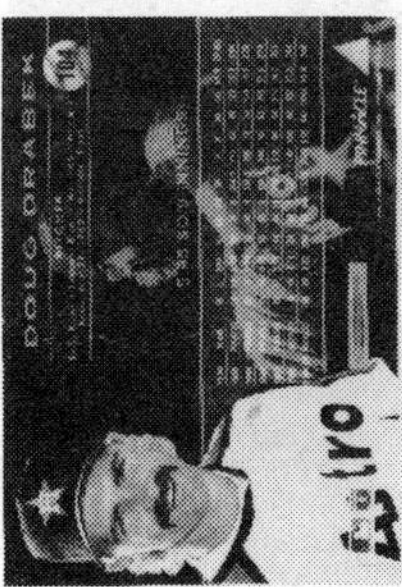

A specially designated version of the regular Pinnacle set, described as the first day's production of the first 1,000 of each card, was issued as a random insert. The cards feature a small gold-foil "Artist's Proof" rectangle embossed above the player/team name shield on front. In all other respects the cards are identical to the regular-issue versions.

		MT	NR MT	EX
Complete Set (270):		4500.	3400.	1800.
Common Player:		7.50	5.50	3.00
Minor Stars 50X-80X:				
1	Frank Thomas	250.00	185.00	100.00
6	Ryne Sandberg	35.00	26.00	14.00
9	Tim Salmon	110.00	82.50	45.00
26	Barry Bonds	55.00	41.00	22.00
28	Mike Piazza	210.00	155.00	85.00
50	Cal Ripken, Jr.	35.00	26.00	14.00
100	Ken Griffey, Jr.	210.00	155.00	85.00
239	Javier Lopez	45.00	34.00	18.00
244	Manny Ramirez	60.00	45.00	24.00
246	Rondell White	60.00	45.00	24.00
270	Trot Nixon	140.00	105.00	55.00

1994 Pinnacle Museum Collection

One of the most popular of 1994's chase cards is the "Museum Collection" version of Pinnacle's regular-issue cards. Each '94 Pinnacle card can be found printed with the company's "Dufex" foil-printing technology on front. Another special effect is rays emanating from the Pinnacle logo in an upper corner. Card backs are virtually identical to the regular cards, except for the substitution of a "1994 Museum Collection" logo for the optical-variable anti-counterfeiting bar at bottom center. Museum Collection cards were randomly packaged, appearing on average once every four packs.

		MT	NR MT	EX
Complete Set (270):		1500.	1100.	600.00
Common Player:		2.50	2.00	1.00
Minor Stars 20X to 25X:				
1	Frank Thomas	85.00	64.00	34.00
6	Ryne Sandberg	12.00	9.00	4.75
9	Tim Salmon	40.00	30.00	15.00
26	Barry Bonds	18.00	13.50	7.25
28	Mike Piazza	75.00	56.00	30.00
50	Cal Ripken, Jr.	12.00	9.00	4.75
100	Ken Griffey, Jr.	75.00	56.00	30.00
239	Javier Lopez	15.00	11.00	6.00
244	Manny Ramirez	20.00	15.00	8.00
246	Rondell White	20.00	15.00	8.00
270	Trot Nixon	50.00	37.00	20.00

1994 Pinnacle New Generation

Twenty-five of baseball hottest rookies and second-year players are featured in this boxed set. Cards are typical Pinnacle quality with full-bleed action photos, UV coating and gold-foil stamping on front and back. A total of 100,000 sets was produced, with a suggested retail price of $9.95.

		MT	NR MT	EX
Complete Set (25):		8.00	6.00	3.25
Common Player:		.25	.20	.10
1	Tim Salmon	.50	.40	.20
2	Mike Piazza	.50	.40	.20
3	Jason Bere	.35	.25	.14
4	Jeffrey Hammonds	.50	.40	.20
5	Aaron Sele	.35	.25	.14
6	Salomon Torres	.25	.20	.10
7	Wil Cordero	.25	.20	.10
8	Allen Watson	.25	.20	.10
9	J.T. Snow	.25	.20	.10
10	Cliff Floyd	.75	.60	.30
10a	Cliff Floyd (overprinted "SAMPLE" card)	3.00	2.25	1.25
11	Jeff McNeely	.25	.20	.10
12	Butch Huskey	.25	.20	.10
13	J.R. Phillips	.25	.20	.10
14	Bobby Jones	.25	.20	.10
15	Javier Lopez	.50	.40	.20
16	Scott Ruffcorn	.25	.20	.10
17	Manny Ramirez	.50	.40	.20
18	Carlos Delgado	.50	.40	.20
19	Rondell White	.50	.40	.20
20	Chipper Jones	.35	.25	.14
21	Billy Ashley	.25	.20	.10
22	Nigel Wilson	.35	.25	.14
23	Jeromy Burnitz	.25	.20	.10
24	Danny Bautista	.25	.20	.10
25	Darrell Whitmore	.25	.20	.10

Regional interest may affect the value of a card.

1994 Pinnacle Rookie Team Pinnacle

The very popular Rookie Team Pinnacle insert card tradition continued in 1994 with a series of nine "two-headed" cards featuring the top prospect from each league at each position. The cards again feature the ultra-realistic artwork of Chris Greco. Each side is enhanced with gold-foil presentations of the player's name, the Pinnacle logo and the Rookie

Team Pinnacle logo. These highly-valued inserts were packaged, on average, one per 90 packs of hobby foil only.

		MT	NR MT	EX
Complete Set (9):		275.00	210.00	110.00
Common Player:		20.00	15.00	8.00
1	Carlos Delgado, Javier Lopez	45.00	34.00	18.00
2	Bob Hamelin, J.R. Phillips	30.00	22.00	12.00
3	Jon Shave, Keith Kessinger	20.00	15.00	8.00
4	Butch Huskey, Luis Ortiz	25.00	18.50	10.00
5	Chipper Jones, Kurt Abbott	35.00	26.00	14.00
6	Rondell White, Manny Ramirez	50.00	37.00	20.00
7	Cliff Floyd, Jeffrey Hammonds	75.00	56.00	30.00
8	Marc Newfield, Nigel Wilson	25.00	18.50	10.00
9	Salomon Torres, Mark Hutton	20.00	15.00	8.00

Definitions for grading conditions are located in the Introduction of this price guide.

1994 Pinnacle Run Creators

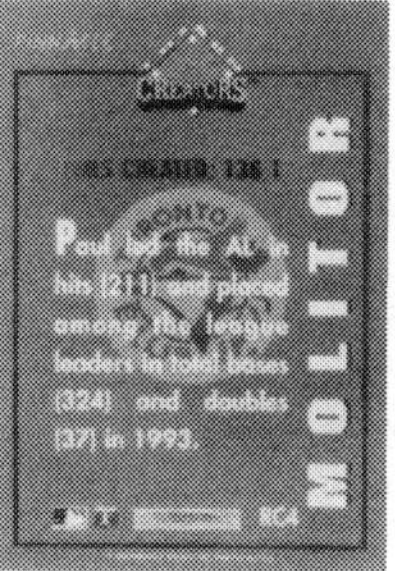

This insert set, exclusive to Pinnacle jumbo packaging, features the top 22 performers of the previous season in the arcane statistic of "runs created." Fronts have an action player photo on which the stadium background has been muted in soft-focus red or blue. The player's last name appears at right in gold foil the logo, "The Run Creators" is in one of the lower corners. Backs are printed in teal with a color team logo at center, beneath the stats that earned the player's inclusion in the series. The player's runs created are in gold foil above the write-up. Cards are numbered with an RC prefix.

		MT	NR MT	EX
Complete Set:		50.00	37.00	20.00
Common Player:		1.00	.70	.40
1	John Olerud	2.00	1.50	.80
2	Frank Thomas	8.00	6.00	3.25
3	Ken Griffey, Jr	8.00	6.00	3.25
4	Paul Molitor	2.00	1.50	.80
5	Rafael Palmeiro	2.00	1.50	.80
6	Roberto Alomar	2.00	1.50	.80
7	Juan Gonzalez	4.50	3.50	1.75
8	Albert Belle	2.00	1.50	.80
9	Travis Fryman	2.00	1.50	.80
10	Rickey Henderson	3.50	2.75	1.50
11	Tony Phillips	1.00	.70	.40
12	Mo Vaughn	1.50	1.25	.60
13	Tim Salmon	3.00	2.25	1.25
14	Kenny Lofton	2.00	1.50	.80
15	Carlos Baerga	2.50	2.00	1.00
16	Greg Vaughn	1.50	1.25	.60
17	Jay Buhner	1.00	.70	.40
18	Chris Hoiles	1.00	.70	.40
19	Mickey Tettleton	1.50	1.25	.60
20	Kirby Puckett	4.00	3.00	1.50
21	Danny Tartabull	1.50	1.25	.60
22	Devon White	1.50	1.25	.60

1994 Pinnacle Power Surge

Twenty-five of the major leagues' heaviest hitters are featured in this boxed set. Cards are typical Pinnacle quality with gold-foil stamping (player's last name at top and Pinnacle logo at bottom) on front, UV coating on both sides and high-tech graphics. Fronts feature game-action photos while backs have smaller portrait and action photos on a marbled background, along with 1993 and career stats and a description of the player's power potential. Cards are numbered with a PS prefix in the upper-right on back. A total of 100,000 set was produced.

		MT	NR MT	EX
Complete Set (25):		10.00	7.50	4.00
Common Player:		.25	.20	.10
1	Dave Justice	.50	.40	.20
2	Chris Hoiles	.35	.25	.14
3	Mo Vaughn	.40	.30	.15
4	Tim Salmon	.50	.40	.20
5	J.T. Snow	.25	.20	.10
6	Frank Thomas	1.50	1.25	.60
7	Sammy Sosa	.25	.20	.10
8	Rick Wilkins	.25	.20	.10
9	Robin Ventura	.35	.25	.14
10	Reggie Sanders	.35	.25	.14
11	Albert Belle	.40	.30	.15
12	Carlos Baerga	.40	.30	.15
12a	Carlos Baerga (overprinted "SAMPLE" card)	3.00	2.25	1.25
13	Manny Ramirez	.50	.40	.20
14	Travis Fryman	.30	.25	.12
15	Gary Sheffield	.30	.25	.12
16	Jeff Bagwell	.30	.25	.12
17	Mike Piazza	.75	.60	.30
18	Eric Karros	.30	.25	.12
19	Cliff Floyd	.50	.40	.20
20	Mark Whiten	.30	.25	.12
21	Phil Plantier	.25	.20	.10
22	Derek Bell	.25	.20	.10
23	Ken Griffey Jr.	1.50	1.25	.60
24	Juan Gonzalez	.60	.45	.25
25	Dean Palmer	.25	.20	.10

1994 Pinnacle Tribute

A hobby-only insert set, found approximately one per 18 foil packs, this nine-card series honors players who reached significant season or career milestones or otherwise had special achievements in 1993. Fronts feature full-bleed action photos. At left is a black strip with "TRIBUTE" in gold foil. A colored strip at bottom has the player name in gold foil and a short description of why he is being feted beneath. The Pinnacle logo is in gold foil at top. The same gold-foil enhancements are found on back, along with a portrait photo. In a black box at bottom are details of the tribute. The Pinnacle optical-variable anti-counterfeiting device is at bottom center. Card numbers are prefixed with "TR".

		MT	NR MT	EX
Complete Set:		32.00	24.00	13.00
Common Player:		2.00	1.50	.80
1	Paul Molitor	6.00	4.50	2.50
2	Jim Abbott	4.00	3.00	1.50

3	Dave Winfield	6.00	4.50	2.50
4	Bo Jackson	6.00	4.50	2.50
5	Dave Justice	5.00	3.75	2.00
6	Len Dykstra	5.00	3.00	1.50
7	Mike Piazza	12.00	9.00	4.75
8	Barry Bonds	8.00	6.00	3.25
9	Randy Johnson	2.00	1.50	.80

1912 Pirate Cigarettes (T215)

This set can be considerd a British version of the Red Cross set. Distributed by Pirate brand cigarettes of Bristol and London, England, the fronts of the cards are identical to the Type I Red Cross cards, but the green backs carry advertising for Pirate Cigarettes. It is believed that the Pirate cards were printed for distribution to U.S. servicemen in the South Seas. They are very rare in both England and the United States.

		NR MT	EX	VG
Complete Set:		14000.	7000.	4200.
Common Player:		100.00	50.00	30.00
(1)	Red Ames	100.00	50.00	30.00
(2)	Home Run Baker	300.00	150.00	90.00
(3)	Neal Ball	100.00	50.00	30.00
(4)	Chief Bender	300.00	150.00	90.00
(5)	Al Bridwell	100.00	50.00	30.00
(6)	Bobby Byrne	100.00	50.00	30.00
(7)	Howie Camnitz	100.00	50.00	30.00
(8)	Frank Chance	325.00	162.00	97.00
(9)	Hal Chase	100.00	50.00	30.00
(10)	Eddie Collins	325.00	162.00	97.00
(11)	Doc Crandall	100.00	50.00	30.00
(12)	Sam Crawford	300.00	150.00	90.00
(13)	Birdie Cree	100.00	50.00	30.00
(14)	Harry Davis	100.00	50.00	30.00
(15)	Josh Devore	100.00	50.00	30.00
(16)	Mike Donlin	100.00	50.00	30.00
(17)	Mickey Doolan (batting)	100.00	50.00	30.00
(18)	Mickey Doolan (fielding)	100.00	50.00	30.00
(19)	Patsy Dougherty	100.00	50.00	30.00
(20)	Larry Doyle (batting)	100.00	50.00	30.00
(21)	Larry Doyle (portrait)	100.00	50.00	30.00
(22)	Jean Dubuc	100.00	50.00	30.00
(23)	Kid Elberfeld	100.00	50.00	30.00
(24)	Steve Evans	100.00	50.00	30.00
(25)	Johnny Evers	300.00	150.00	90.00
(26)	Russ Ford	100.00	50.00	30.00
(27)	Art Fromme	100.00	50.00	30.00
(28)	Clark Griffith	300.00	150.00	90.00
(29)	Bob Groom	100.00	50.00	30.00
(30)	Topsy Hartsel	100.00	50.00	30.00
(31)	Buck Herzog	100.00	50.00	30.00
(32)	Dick Hoblitzell	100.00	50.00	30.00
(33)	Solly Hofman	100.00	50.00	30.00
(34)	Del Howard	100.00	50.00	30.00
(35)	Miller Huggins (hands at mouth)	300.00	150.00	90.00
(36)	Miller Huggins (portrait)	300.00	150.00	90.00
(37)	John Hummel	100.00	50.00	30.00
(38)	Hughie Jennings (both hands showing)	300.00	150.00	90.00
(39)	Hughie Jennings (one hand showing)	300.00	150.00	90.00
(40)	Walter Johnson	500.00	250.00	150.00
(41)	Joe Kelley	300.00	150.00	90.00
(42)	Ed Konetchy	100.00	50.00	30.00
(43)	Harry Krause	100.00	50.00	30.00
(44)	Nap Lajoie	400.00	200.00	120.00
(45)	Joe Lake	100.00	50.00	30.00
(46)	Lefty Leifield	100.00	50.00	30.00
(47)	Harry Lord	100.00	50.00	30.00
(48)	Sherry Magee	100.00	50.00	30.00
(49)	Rube Marquard (pitching)	300.00	150.00	90.00
(50)	Rube Marquard (portrait)	300.00	150.00	90.00
(51)	Joe McGinnity	300.00	150.00	90.00
(52)	John McGraw (glove at side)	300.00	150.00	90.00
(53)	John McGraw (portrait)	300.00	150.00	90.00
(54)	Harry McIntyre (Chicago)	100.00	50.00	30.00
(55)	Harry McIntyre (Brooklyn & Chicago)	100.00	50.00	30.00
(56)	Larry McLean	100.00	50.00	30.00
(57)	Fred Merkle	100.00	50.00	30.00
(58)	Chief Meyers	100.00	50.00	30.00
(59)	Mike Mitchell	100.00	50.00	30.00
(60)	Mike Mowrey	100.00	50.00	30.00
(61)	George Mullin	100.00	50.00	30.00
(62)	Danny Murphy	100.00	50.00	30.00
(63)	Red Murray	100.00	50.00	30.00
(64)	Rebel Oakes	100.00	50.00	30.00
(65)	Rube Oldring	100.00	50.00	30.00
(66)	Charley O'Leary	100.00	50.00	30.00
(67)	Dode Paskert	100.00	50.00	30.00
(68)	Barney Pelty	100.00	50.00	30.00
(69)	Billy Purtell	100.00	50.00	30.00
(70)	Jack Quinn	100.00	50.00	30.00
(71)	Ed Reulbach	100.00	50.00	30.00
(72)	Nap Rucker	100.00	50.00	30.00
(73)	Germany Schaefer	100.00	50.00	30.00
(74)	Wildfire Schulte	100.00	50.00	30.00
(75)	Jimmy Sheckard	100.00	50.00	30.00
(76)	Frank Smith	100.00	50.00	30.00
(77)	Tris Speaker	375.00	187.00	112.00
(78)	Jake Stahl	100.00	50.00	30.00
(79)	Harry Steinfeldt	100.00	50.00	30.00
(80)	Gabby Street	100.00	50.00	30.00
(81)	Ed Summers	100.00	50.00	30.00
(82)	Jeff Sweeney	100.00	50.00	30.00
(83)	Lee Tannehill	100.00	50.00	30.00
(84)	Ira Thomas	100.00	50.00	30.00
(85)	Joe Tinker	300.00	150.00	90.00
(86)	Heinie Wagner	100.00	50.00	30.00
(87)	Jack Warhop	100.00	50.00	30.00
(88)	Zack Wheat (Brooklyn)	300.00	150.00	90.00
(89)	Ed Willetts (Willett)	100.00	50.00	30.00
(90)	Owen Wilson	100.00	50.00	30.00
(91)	Hooks Wiltse (pitching)	100.00	50.00	30.00
(92)	Hooks Wiltse (portrait)	100.00	50.00	30.00

1939 Play Ball

With the issuance of this card set by Gum Incorporated, a new era of baseball cards was born. Although the cards are black and white, the full-frame, actual photos on the card fronts are of better quality than previously seen, and the 2-1/2" by 3-1/8" size was larger and more popular than the smaller tobacco and caramel cards of the early 20th Century. Card backs featured player names and extensive biographies. There are 162 cards in the set, including superstars Joe DiMaggio and Ted Williams. Card number 126 was never issued. The complete set price does not include all back variations found in the low-numbered series. Most of the cards between numbers 2-115 can be found with the player name on back either in all capital letters, or in both upper and lower case letters. The latter are worth a premium of about 10% over the former.

		NR MT	EX	VG
Complete Set:		12500.	6250.	3750.
Common Player (1-115):		20.00	10.00	6.00
Common Player (116-162):		115.00	57.00	34.00
1	Alvin Jacob Powell	200.00	55.00	25.00
2a	Lee Theo Grissom (name in upper case letters)	25.00	9.00	5.50
2b	Lee Theo Grissom (name in upper and lower case)	35.00	12.50	7.50
3a	Charles Herbert Ruffing (name in upper case letters)	115.00	57.00	34.00
3b	Charles Herbert Ruffing (name in upper and lower case)	135.00	67.00	40.00
4a	Eldon LeRoy Auker (name in upper case letters)	20.00	10.00	6.00
4b	Eldon LeRoy Auker (name in upper and lower case)	22.00	11.00	6.50
5a	James Luther Sewell (name in upper case letters)	22.00	11.00	6.50
5b	James Luther Sewell (name in upper and lower case)	24.00	12.00	7.25
6a	Leo Ernest Durocher (name in upper case letters)	90.00	45.00	27.00
6b	Leo Ernest Durocher (name in upper and lower case)	115.00	57.00	34.00
7a	Robert Pershing Doerr (name in upper case letters)	90.00	45.00	27.00
7b	Robert Pershing Doerr (name in upper and lower case)	100.00	50.00	30.00
8	Henry Pippen	20.00	10.00	6.00
9a	James Tobin (name in upper case letters)	20.00	10.00	6.00
9b	James Tobin (name in upper and lower case)	22.00	11.00	6.50
10	James Brooklyn DeShong	20.00	10.00	6.00
11	John Costa Rizzo	20.00	10.00	6.00
12	Hershel Ray Martin (Herschel)	20.00	10.00	6.00
13a	Luke Daniel Hamlin (name in upper case letters)	20.00	10.00	6.00
13b	Luke Daniel Hamlin (name in upper and lower case)	22.00	11.00	6.50
14a	James R. Tabor ("...Tabor batted .295,...")	20.00	10.00	6.00
14b	James R. Tabor ("...Tabor batted 295,...")	22.00	11.00	6.50
15a	Paul Derringer (name in upper case letters)	22.00	11.00	6.50
15b	Paul Derringer (name in upper and lower case)	24.00	12.00	7.25
16	John Peacock	20.00	10.00	6.00
17	Emerson Dickman	20.00	10.00	6.00
18a	Harry Danning (name in upper case letters)	20.00	10.00	6.00
18b	Harry Danning (name in upper and lower case)	22.00	11.00	6.50
19	Paul Dean	35.00	17.50	10.50
20	Joseph Heving	20.00	10.00	6.00
21a	Emil Leonard (name in upper case letters)	20.00	10.00	6.00
21b	Emil Leonard (name in upper and lower case)	22.00	11.00	6.50
22a	William Henry Walters (name in upper case letters)	22.00	11.00	6.50
22b	William Henry Walters (name in upper and lower case)	24.00	12.00	7.25
23	Burgess U. Whitehead	20.00	10.00	6.00
24a	Richard S. Coffman (S. Richard) ("...Senators the same year.")	20.00	10.00	6.00
24b	Richard S. Coffman (S. Richard) ("...Browns the same year.")	35.00	17.50	10.50
25a	George Alexander Selkirk (name in upper case letters)	35.00	17.50	10.50
25b	George Alexander Selkirk (name in upper and lower case)	40.00	20.00	12.00
26a	Joseph Paul DiMaggio ("...206 hits in 1938 games...")	2000.	1000.	600.00
26b	Joseph Paul DiMaggio ("...206 hits in 138 games...")	2000.	1000.	600.00
27a	Fred Ray Ostermueller (name in upper case letters)	20.00	10.00	6.00
27b	Fred Ray Ostermueller (name in upper and lower case)	22.00	11.00	6.50
28	Sylvester Johnson	20.00	10.00	6.00
29a	John Francis Wilson (name in upper case letters)	20.00	10.00	6.00
29b	John Francis Wilson (name in upper and lower case)	22.00	11.00	6.50
30a	William Malcolm Dickey (name in upper case letters)	175.00	85.00	50.00
30b	William Malcolm Dickey (name in upper and lower case)	200.00	100.00	60.00
31a	Samuel West (name in upper case letters)	20.00	10.00	6.00
31b	Samuel West (name in upper and lower case)	22.00	11.00	6.50
32	Robert I. Seeds	20.00	10.00	6.00
33	Del Howard Young (name actually Del Edward)	20.00	10.00	6.00
34a	Frank Joseph Demaree (Joseph Franklin) (name in upper case letters)	20.00	10.00	6.00
34b	Frank Joseph Demaree (Joseph Franklin) (name in upper and lower case)	22.00	11.00	6.50
35a	William Frederick Jurges (name in upper case letters)	22.00	11.00	6.50
35b	William Frederick Jurges (name in upper and lower case)	24.00	12.00	7.25
36a	Frank Andrew McCormick (name in upper case letters)	20.00	10.00	6.00
36b	Frank Andrew McCormick (name in upper and lower case)	22.00	11.00	6.50
37	Virgil Lawrence Davis	20.00	10.00	6.00
38a	William Harrison Myers (name in upper case letters)	20.00	10.00	6.00
38b	William Harrison Myers (name in upper and lower case)	22.00	11.00	6.50
39a	Richard Benjamin Ferrell (name in upper case letters)	100.00	50.00	30.00
39b	Richard Benjamin Ferrell (name in upper and lower case)	115.00	57.00	34.00
40	James Charles Bagby Jr.	20.00	10.00	6.00
41a	Lonnie Warneke ("...the earned run department...")	20.00	10.00	6.00
41b	Lonnie Warneke ("...the earned-run department...")	22.00	11.00	6.50
42	Arndt Jorgens	24.00	12.00	7.25
43	Melo Almada	20.00	10.00	6.00
44	Donald Henry Heffner	20.00	10.00	6.00
45a	Merrill May (name in upper case letters)	20.00	10.00	6.00
45b	Merrill May (name in upper and lower case)	22.00	11.00	6.50
46a	Morris Arnovich (name in upper case letters)	20.00	10.00	6.00
46b	Morris Arnovich (name in upper and lower case)	22.00	11.00	6.50
47a	John Kelly Lewis, Jr. (name in upper case letters)	20.00	10.00	6.00
47b	John Kelly Lewis, Jr. (name in upper and lower case)	22.00	11.00	6.50
48a	Vernon Gomez (name in upper case letters)	175.00	85.00	50.00
48b	Vernon Gomez (name in upper and lower case)	200.00	100.00	60.00
49	Edward Miller	20.00	10.00	6.00
50a	Charles Len Gehringer (name actually Charles Leonard) (name in upper case letters)	175.00	85.00	50.00
50b	Charles Len Gehringer (name actually Charles Leonard) (name in upper & lower case)	200.00	100.00	60.00
51a	Melvin Thomas Ott (name in upper case)	175.00	85.00	50.00

51b	Melvin Thomas Ott (name in upper and lower case)	200.00	100.00	60.00
52a	Thomas D. Henrich (name in upper case letters)	40.00	20.00	12.00
52b	Thomas D. Henrich (name in upper and lower case)	45.00	22.00	13.50
53a	Carl Owen Hubbell (name in upper case letters)	175.00	85.00	50.00
53b	Carl Owen Hubbell (name in upper and lower case)	200.00	100.00	60.00
54a	Harry Edward Gumbert (name in upper case letters)	20.00	10.00	6.00
54b	Harry Edward Gumbert (name in upper and lower case)	22.00	11.00	6.50
55a	Floyd E. Vaugharr(Joseph Floyd) (name in upper case letters)	90.00	45.00	27.00
55b	Floyd E. Vaughan (Joseph Floyd) (name in upper and lower case)	100.00	50.00	30.00
56a	Henry Greenberg (name in upper case letters)	200.00	100.00	60.00
56b	Henry Greenberg (name in upper and lower case)	225.00	110.00	65.00
57a	John A. Hassett (name in upper case letters)	20.00	10.00	6.00
57b	John A. Hassett (name in upper and lower case)	22.00	11.00	6.50
58	Louis Peo Chiozza	20.00	10.00	6.00
59	Kendall Chase	20.00	10.00	6.00
60a	Lynwood Thomas Rowe (name in upper case letters)	22.00	11.00	6.50
60b	Lynwood Thomas Rowe (name in upper and lower case)	24.00	12.00	7.25
61a	Anthony F. Cuccinello (name in upper case letters)	20.00	10.00	6.00
61b	Anthony F. Cuccinello (name in upper and lower case)	22.00	11.00	6.50
62	Thomas Carey	20.00	10.00	6.00
63	Emmett Mueller	20.00	10.00	6.00
64a	Wallace Moses, Jr. (name in upper case letters)	20.00	10.00	6.00
64b	Wallace Moses, Jr. (name in upper and lower case)	22.00	11.00	6.50
65a	Harry Francis Craft (name in upper case letters)	20.00	10.00	6.00
65b	Harry Francis Craft (name in upper and lower case)	22.00	11.00	6.50
66	James A. Ripple	20.00	10.00	6.00
67	Edwin Joost	20.00	10.00	6.00
68	Fred Singleton	20.00	10.00	6.00
69	Elbert Preston Fletcher (Elburt)	20.00	10.00	6.00
70	Fred Maloy Frankhouse (Meloy)	20.00	10.00	6.00
71a	Marcellus Monte Pearson (name actually Montgomery Marcellus) (name in upper case)	24.00	12.00	7.25
71b	Marcellus Monte Pearson (name actually Montgomery Marcellus) (name in upper & lower)	35.00	17.50	10.50
72a	Debs Garms (Born: Bango, Tex.)	20.00	10.00	6.00
72b	Debs Garms (Born: Bangs, Tex.)	25.00	12.50	7.50
73a	Harold H. Schumacher (Born: Dolgville, N.Y.)	22.00	11.00	6.50
73b	Harold H. Schumacher (Born: Dolgeville, N.Y.)	40.00	20.00	12.00
74a	Harry A. Lavagetto (name in upper case letters)	24.00	12.00	7.25
74b	Harry A. Lavagetto (name in upper and lower case)	15.00	7.50	4.50
75a	Stanley Bordagaray (name in upper case letters)	20.00	10.00	6.00
75b	Stanley Bordagaray (name in upper and lower case)	22.00	11.00	6.50
76	Goodwin George Rosen	20.00	10.00	6.00
77	Lewis Sidney Riggs	20.00	10.00	6.00
78a	Julius Joseph Solters (name in upper case letters)	20.00	10.00	6.00
78b	Julius Joseph Solters (name in upper and lower case)	22.00	11.00	6.50
79a	Joseph Gregg Moore (given name is Joe) (Weight: 157 lbs.)	20.00	10.00	6.00
79b	Joseph Gregg Moore (given name is Joe) (Weight: 175 lbs.)	25.00	12.50	7.50
80a	Irwin Fox (Ervin) (Weight: 165 lbs.)	20.00	10.00	6.00
80b	Irwin Fox (Ervin) (Weight: 157 lbs.)	25.00	12.50	7.50
81a	Ellsworth Dahlgren (name in upper case letters)	24.00	12.00	7.25
81b	Ellsworth Dahlgren (name in upper and lower case)	35.00	17.50	10.50
82a	Charles Herbert Klein (name in upper case letters)	125.00	62.50	37.50
82b	Charles Herbert Klein (name in upper and lower case)	150.00	75.00	45.00
83a	August Richard Suhr (name in upper case letters)	20.00	10.00	6.00
83b	August Richard Suhr (name in upper and lower case)	22.00	11.00	6.50
84	Lamar Newsome	20.00	10.00	6.00
85	John Walter Cooney	20.00	10.00	6.00
86a	Adolph Camilli (Adolf) ("...start of the 1928 season,...")	22.00	11.00	6.50
86b	Adolph Camilli (Adolf) ("...start of the 1938 season,...")	35.00	17.50	10.50
87	Milburn G. Shoffner (middle initial actually J.)	20.00	10.00	6.00
88	Charles Keller	50.00	25.00	15.00
89a	Lloyd James Waner (name in upper case letters)	115.00	57.00	34.00
89b	Lloyd James Waner (name in upper and lower case)	120.00	60.00	36.00
90a	Robert H. Klinger (name in upper case letters)	20.00	10.00	6.00
90b	Robert H. Klinger (name in upper and lower case)	22.00	11.00	6.50
91a	John H. Knott (name in upper case letters)	20.00	10.00	6.00
91b	John H. Knott (name in upper and lower case)	22.00	11.00	6.50
92a	Ted Williams (name in upper case letters)	1800.	900.00	540.00
92b	Ted Williams (name in upper and lower case)	2000.	1000.	600.00
93	Charles M. Gelbert	20.00	10.00	6.00
94	Henry E. Manush	115.00	57.00	34.00
95a	Whitlow Wyatt (name in upper case letters)	22.00	11.00	6.50
95b	Whitlow Wyatt (name in upper and lower case)	24.00	12.00	7.25
96a	Ernest Gordon Phelps (name in upper case letters)	22.00	11.00	6.50
96b	Ernest Gordon Phelps (name in upper and lower case)	24.00	12.00	7.25
97a	Robert Lee Johnson (name in upper case letters)	20.00	10.00	6.00
97b	Robert Lee Johnson (name in upper and lower case)	22.00	11.00	6.50
98	Arthur Carter Whitney	20.00	10.00	6.00
99a	Walter Anton Berger (name in upper case letters)	22.00	11.00	6.50
99b	Walter Anton Berger (name in upper and lower case)	24.00	12.00	7.25
100a	Charles Solomon Myer (name in upper case letters)	20.00	10.00	6.00
100b	Charles Solomon Myer (name in upper and lower case)	22.00	11.00	6.50
101a	Roger M. Cramer ("...the Martinburg Club...")	20.00	10.00	6.00
101b	Roger M. Cramer ("...the Martinsburg Club...")	25.00	12.50	7.50
102a	Lemuel Floyd Young (name in upper case letters)	20.00	10.00	6.00
102b	Lemuel Floyd Young (name in upper and lower case)	22.00	11.00	6.50
103	Morris Berg	22.00	11.00	6.50
104a	Thomas Davis Bridges ("...280 games, winning 283,...")	22.00	11.00	6.50
104b	Thomas Davis Bridges ("...280 games, winning 133,...")	35.00	17.50	10.50
105a	Donald Eric McNair (name in upper case letters)	20.00	10.00	6.00
105b	Donald Eric McNair (name in upper and lower case)	22.00	11.00	6.50
106	Albert Stark	20.00	10.00	6.00
107	Joseph Franklin Vosmik	20.00	10.00	6.00
108a	Frank Witman Hayes (name in upper case letters)	20.00	10.00	6.00
108b	Frank Witman Hayes (name in upper and lower case)	22.00	11.00	6.50
109a	Myril Hoag (name in upper case letters)	20.00	10.00	6.00
109b	Myril Hoag (name in upper and lower case)	22.00	11.00	6.50
110	Fred L. Fitzsimmons	22.00	11.00	6.50
111a	Van Lingle Mungo (name in upper case letters)	35.00	17.50	10.50
111b	Van Lingle Mungo (name in upper and lower case)	40.00	20.00	12.00
112a	Paul Glee Waner ("...Waner, the older...")	115.00	57.00	34.00
112b	Paul Glee Waner ("...Waner, the elder...")	125.00	62.00	37.00
113	Al Schacht	25.00	12.50	7.50
114a	Cecil Howell Travis (name in upper case letters)	20.00	10.00	6.00
114b	Cecil Howell Travis (name in upper and lower case)	22.00	11.00	6.50
115a	Ralph Kress (name in upper case letters)	20.00	10.00	6.00
115b	Ralph Kress (name in upper and lower case)	22.00	11.00	6.50
116	Eugene A. Desautels	115.00	57.00	34.00
117	Wayne Ambler	115.00	57.00	34.00
118	Lynn Nelson	115.00	57.00	34.00
119	Willard McKee Hershberger	115.00	57.00	34.00
120	Harold Benton Warstler (middle name actually Burton)	115.00	57.00	34.00
121	William J. Posedel	115.00	57.00	34.00
122	George Hartley McQuinn	115.00	57.00	34.00
123	Ray T. Davis	115.00	57.00	34.00
124	Walter George Brown	115.00	57.00	34.00
125	Clifford George Melton	115.00	57.00	34.00
126	Not Issued			
127	Gilbert Herman Brack	115.00	57.00	34.00
128	Joseph Emil Bowman	115.00	57.00	34.00
129	William Swift	115.00	57.00	34.00
130	Wilbur Lee Brubaker	115.00	57.00	34.00
131	Morton Cecil Cooper	115.00	57.00	34.00
132	James Roberson Brown	115.00	57.00	34.00
133	Lynn Myers	115.00	57.00	34.00
134	Forrest Pressnell	115.00	57.00	34.00
135	Arnold Malcolm Owen	115.00	57.00	34.00
136	Roy Chester Bell	115.00	57.00	34.00
137	Peter William Appleton	115.00	57.00	34.00
138	George Washington Case Jr.	115.00	57.00	34.00
139	Vitautas C. Tamulis	115.00	57.00	34.00
140	Raymond Hall Hayworth	115.00	57.00	34.00
141	Peter Coscarart	115.00	57.00	34.00
142	Ira Kendall Hutchinson	115.00	57.00	34.00
143	Howard Earl Averill	275.00	140.00	85.00
144	Henry J. Bonura	115.00	57.00	34.00
145	Hugh Noyes Mulcahy	115.00	57.00	34.00
146	Thomas Sunkel	115.00	57.00	34.00
147	George D. Coffman	115.00	57.00	34.00
148	William Trotter	115.00	57.00	34.00
149	Max Edward West	115.00	57.00	34.00
150	James Elton Walkup	115.00	57.00	34.00
151	Hugh Thomas Casey	115.00	57.00	34.00
152	Roy Weatherly	115.00	57.00	34.00
153	Paul H. Trout	150.00	75.00	45.00
154	John W. Hudson	115.00	57.00	34.00
155	James Paul Outlaw (middle name actually Paulus)	115.00	57.00	34.00
156	Raymond Berres	115.00	57.00	34.00
157	Donald Willard Padgett (middle name actually Wilson)	115.00	57.00	34.00
158	Luther Baxter Thomas	115.00	57.00	34.00
159	Russell E. Evans	115.00	57.00	34.00
160	Eugene Moore Jr.	115.00	57.00	34.00
161	Linus Reinhard Frey	135.00	67.00	40.00
162	Lloyd Albert Moore	250.00	90.00	55.00

1940 Play Ball

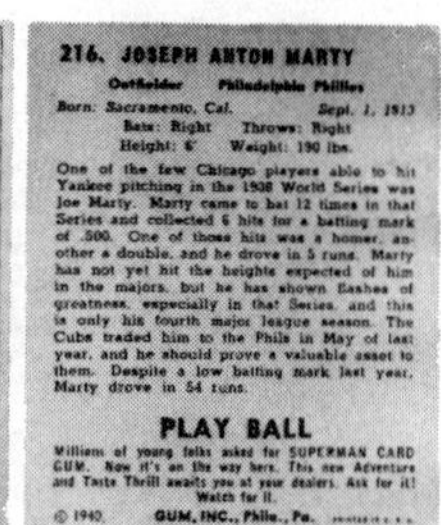

Following the success of their initial effort in 1939, Gum Incorporated issued a bigger and better set in 1940. The 240 black and white cards are once again in the 2-1/2" by 3-1/8" size, but the photos on the card fronts are enclosed by a frame which listed the player's name. Card backs again offer extensive biographies. Backs are also dated. A number of old-timers were issued along with the current day's players, and many Hall of Famers are included. The final 60 cards of the set are more difficult to obtain.

		NR MT	EX	VG
Complete Set:		19500.	9750.	5850.
Common Player (1-120):		22.00	8.50	4.25
Common Player (121-180):		25.00	9.75	4.75
Common Player (181-240):		80.00	31.00	15.00
1	Joe DiMaggio	2500.	900.00	550.00
2	"Art" Jorgens	25.00	9.75	4.75
3	"Babe" Dahlgren	25.00	9.75	4.75
4	"Tommy" Henrich	35.00	13.50	6.75
5	"Monte" Pearson	25.00	9.75	4.75
6	"Lefty" Gomez	200.00	78.00	38.00
7	"Bill" Dickey	200.00	78.00	38.00
8	"Twinkletoes" Selkirk	25.00	9.75	4.75
9	"Charley" Keller	35.00	13.50	6.75
10	"Red" Ruffing	75.00	29.00	14.00
11	"Jake" Powell	25.00	9.75	4.75
12	"Johnny" Schulte	25.00	9.75	4.75
13	"Jack" Knott	22.00	8.50	4.25
14	"Rabbit" McNair	22.00	8.50	4.25
15	George Case	22.00	8.50	4.25
16	Cecil Travis	22.00	8.50	4.25
17	"Buddy" Myer	22.00	8.50	4.25
18	"Charley" Gelbert	22.00	8.50	4.25
19	"Ken" Chase	22.00	8.50	4.25
20	"Buddy" Lewis	22.00	8.50	4.25
21	"Rick" Ferrell	55.00	21.00	10.50
22	"Sammy" West	22.00	8.50	4.25
23	"Dutch" Leonard	22.00	8.50	4.25
24	Frank "Blimp" Hayes	22.00	8.50	4.25
25	"Cherokee" Bob Johnson	22.00	8.50	4.25
26	"Wally" Moses	22.00	8.50	4.25
27	"Ted" Williams	1800.	702.00	342.00
28	"Gene" Desautels	22.00	8.50	4.25
29	"Doc" Cramer	22.00	8.50	4.25
30	"Moe" Berg	55.00	21.00	10.50
31	"Jack" Wilson	22.00	8.50	4.25
32	"Jim" Bagby	22.00	8.50	4.25
33	"Fritz" Ostermueller	22.00	8.50	4.25
34	John Peacock	22.00	8.50	4.25
35	"Joe" Heving	22.00	8.50	4.25
36	"Jim" Tabor	22.00	8.50	4.25
37	Emerson Dickman	22.00	8.50	4.25
38	"Bobby" Doerr	90.00	35.00	17.00
39	"Tom" Carey	22.00	8.50	4.25
40	"Hank" Greenberg	250.00	97.00	47.00
41	"Charley" Gehringer	125.00	49.00	24.00
42	"Bud" Thomas	22.00	8.50	4.25
43	Pete Fox	22.00	8.50	4.25
44	"Dizzy" Trout	25.00	9.75	4.75
45	"Red" Kress	22.00	8.50	4.25
46	Earl Averill	100.00	39.00	19.00
47	"Old Os" Vitt	22.00	8.50	4.25
48	"Luke" Sewell	25.00	9.75	4.75
49	"Stormy Weather" Weatherly	22.00	8.50	4.25
50	"Hal" Trosky	22.00	8.50	4.25
51	"Don" Heffner	22.00	8.50	4.25
52	Myril Hoag	22.00	8.50	4.25
53	"Mac" McQuinn	22.00	8.50	4.25
54	"Bill" Trotter	22.00	8.50	4.25
55	"Slick" Coffman	22.00	8.50	4.25
56	"Eddie" Miller	22.00	8.50	4.25
57	Max West	22.00	8.50	4.25
58	"Bill" Posedel	22.00	8.50	4.25
59	"Rabbit" Warstler	22.00	8.50	4.25
60	John Cooney	22.00	8.50	4.25
61	"Tony" Cuccinello	22.00	8.50	4.25
62	"Buddy" Hassett	22.00	8.50	4.25
63	"Pete" Cascarart	22.00	8.50	4.25
64	"Van" Mungo	30.00	11.50	5.75
65	"Fitz" Fitzsimmons	25.00	9.75	4.75

66	"Babe" Phelps	25.00	9.75	4.75
67	"Whit" Wyatt	25.00	9.75	4.75
68	"Dolph" Camilli	25.00	9.75	4.75
69	"Cookie" Lavagetto	25.00	9.75	4.75
70	"Hot Potato" Hamlin	22.00	8.50	4.25
71	"Mel" Almada	22.00	8.50	4.25
72	"Chuck" Dressen	25.00	9.75	4.75
73	"Bucky" Walters	25.00	9.75	4.75
74	"Duke" Derringer	25.00	9.75	4.75
75	"Buck" McCormick	22.00	8.50	4.25
76	"Lonny" Frey	22.00	8.50	4.25
77	"Bill" Hershberger	22.00	8.50	4.25
78	"Lew" Riggs	22.00	8.50	4.25
79	"Wildfire" Craft	22.00	8.50	4.25
80	"Bill" Myers	22.00	8.50	4.25
81	"Wally" Berger	25.00	9.75	4.75
82	"Hank" Gowdy	22.00	8.50	4.25
83	"Clif" Melton (Cliff)	22.00	8.50	4.25
84	"Jo-Jo" Moore	22.00	8.50	4.25
85	"Hal" Schumacher	25.00	9.75	4.75
86	Harry Gumbert	22.00	8.50	4.25
87	Carl Hubbell	200.00	78.00	38.00
88	"Mel" Ott	200.00	78.00	38.00
89	"Bill" Jurges	25.00	9.75	4.75
90	Frank Demaree	22.00	8.50	4.25
91	Bob "Suitcase" Seeds	22.00	8.50	4.25
92	"Whitey" Whitehead	22.00	8.50	4.25
93	Harry "The Horse" Danning	22.00	8.50	4.25
94	"Gus" Suhr	22.00	8.50	4.25
95	"Mul" Mulcahy	22.00	8.50	4.25
96	"Heinie" Mueller	22.00	8.50	4.25
97	"Morry" Arnovich	22.00	8.50	4.25
98	"Pinky" May	22.00	8.50	4.25
99	"Syl" Johnson	22.00	8.50	4.25
100	"Hersh" Martin	22.00	8.50	4.25
101	"Del" Young	22.00	8.50	4.25
102	"Chuck" Klein	150.00	58.00	28.00
103	"Elbie" Fletcher	22.00	8.50	4.25
104	"Big Poison" Waner	125.00	49.00	24.00
105	"Little Poison" Waner	125.00	49.00	24.00
106	"Pep" Young	22.00	8.50	4.25
107	"Arky" Vaughan	100.00	39.00	19.00
108	"Johnny" Rizzo	22.00	8.50	4.25
109	"Don" Padgett	22.00	8.50	4.25
110	"Tom" Sunkel	22.00	8.50	4.25
111	"Mickey" Owen	22.00	8.50	4.25
112	"Jimmy" Brown	22.00	8.50	4.25
113	"Mort" Cooper	22.00	8.50	4.25
114	"Lon" Warneke	22.00	8.50	4.25
115	"Mike" Gonzales (Gonzalez)	25.00	9.75	4.75
116	"Al" Schacht	25.00	9.75	4.75
117	"Dolly" Stark	22.00	8.50	4.25
118	"Schoolboy" Hoyt	100.00	39.00	19.00
119	"Ol Pete" Alexander	180.00	70.00	34.00
120	Walter "Big Train" Johnson	275.00	107.00	52.00
121	Atley Donald	25.00	9.75	4.75
122	"Sandy" Sundra	25.00	9.75	4.75
123	"Hildy" Hildebrand	25.00	9.75	4.75
124	"Colonel" Combs	115.00	45.00	22.00
125	"Art" Fletcher	25.00	9.75	4.75
126	"Jake" Solters	25.00	9.75	4.75
127	"Muddy" Ruel	25.00	9.75	4.75
128	"Pete" Appleton	25.00	9.75	4.75
129	"Bucky" Harris	100.00	39.00	19.00
130	"Deerfoot" Milan	25.00	9.75	4.75
131	"Zeke" Bonura	25.00	9.75	4.75
132	Connie Mack	240.00	94.00	46.00
133	"Jimmie" Foxx	275.00	107.00	52.00
134	"Joe" Cronin	125.00	49.00	24.00
135	"Line Drive" Nelson	25.00	9.75	4.75
136	"Cotton" Pippen	25.00	9.75	4.75
137	"Bing" Miller	25.00	9.75	4.75
138	"Beau" Bell	25.00	9.75	4.75
139	Elden Auker (Eldon)	25.00	9.75	4.75
140	"Dick" Coffman	25.00	9.75	4.75
141	"Casey" Stengel	175.00	68.00	33.00
142	"Highpockets" Kelly	100.00	39.00	19.00
143	"Gene" Moore	25.00	9.75	4.75
144	"Joe" Vosmik	25.00	9.75	4.75
145	"Vito" Tamulis	25.00	9.75	4.75
146	"Tot" Pressnell	25.00	9.75	4.75
147	"Johnny" Hudson	25.00	9.75	4.75
148	"Hugh" Casey	25.00	9.75	4.75
149	"Pinky" Shoffner	25.00	9.75	4.75
150	"Whitey" Moore	25.00	9.75	4.75
151	Edwin Joost	25.00	9.75	4.75
152	"Jimmy" Wilson	25.00	9.75	4.75
153	"Bill" McKechnie	90.00	35.00	17.00
154	"Jumbo" Brown	25.00	9.75	4.75
155	"Ray" Hayworth	25.00	9.75	4.75
156	"Daffy" Dean	30.00	11.50	5.75
157	"Lou" Chiozza	25.00	9.75	4.75
158	"Stonewall" Jackson	100.00	39.00	19.00
159	"Pancho" Snyder	25.00	9.75	4.75
160	"Hans" Lobert	25.00	9.75	4.75
161	"Debs" Garms	25.00	9.75	4.75
162	"Joe" Bowman	25.00	9.75	4.75
163	"Spud" Davis	25.00	9.75	4.75
164	"Ray" Berres	25.00	9.75	4.75
165	"Bob" Klinger	25.00	9.75	4.75
166	"Bill" Brubaker	25.00	9.75	4.75
167	"Frankie" Frisch	125.00	49.00	24.00
168	"Honus" Wagner	275.00	107.00	52.00
169	"Gabby" Street	25.00	9.75	4.75
170	"Tris" Speaker	250.00	97.00	47.00
171	Harry Heilmann	150.00	58.00	28.00
172	"Chief" Bender	125.00	49.00	24.00
173	"Larry" Lajoie	275.00	107.00	52.00
174	"Johnny" Evers	135.00	53.00	26.00
175	"Christy" Mathewson	275.00	107.00	52.00
176	"Heinie" Manush	125.00	49.00	24.00
177	Frank "Homerun" Baker	150.00	58.00	28.00
178	Max Carey	125.00	49.00	24.00
179	George Sisler	125.00	49.00	24.00
180	"Mickey" Cochrane	150.00	58.00	28.00
181	"Spud" Chandler	80.00	48.00	28.00
182	"Knick" Knickerbocker	80.00	48.00	28.00
183	Marvin Breuer	80.00	48.00	28.00
184	"Mule" Haas	80.00	48.00	28.00
185	"Joe" Kuhel	80.00	48.00	28.00
186	Taft Wright	80.00	48.00	28.00
187	"Jimmy" Dykes	60.00	36.00	21.00
188	"Joe" Krakauskas	80.00	48.00	28.00
189	"Jim" Bloodworth	80.00	48.00	28.00
190	"Charley" Berry	80.00	48.00	28.00
191	John Babich	80.00	48.00	28.00
192	"Dick" Siebert	80.00	48.00	28.00
193	"Chubby" Dean	80.00	48.00	28.00
194	"Sam" Chapman	80.00	48.00	28.00
195	"Dee" Miles	80.00	48.00	28.00
196	"Nonny" Nonnenkamp	80.00	48.00	28.00
197	"Lou" Finney	80.00	48.00	28.00
198	"Denny" Galehouse	80.00	48.00	28.00
199	"Pinky" Higgins	80.00	48.00	28.00
200	"Soupy" Campbell	80.00	48.00	28.00
201	Barney McCosky	80.00	48.00	28.00
202	"Al" Milnar	80.00	48.00	28.00
203	"Bad News" Hale	80.00	48.00	28.00
204	Harry Eisenstat	80.00	48.00	28.00
205	"Rollie" Hemsley	80.00	48.00	28.00
206	"Chet" Laabs	80.00	48.00	28.00
207	"Gus" Mancuso	80.00	48.00	28.00
208	Lee Gamble	80.00	48.00	28.00
209	"Hy" Vandenberg	80.00	48.00	28.00
210	"Bill" Lohrman	80.00	48.00	28.00
211	"Pop" Joiner	80.00	48.00	28.00
212	"Babe" Young	80.00	48.00	28.00
213	John Rucker	80.00	48.00	28.00
214	"Ken" O'Dea	80.00	48.00	28.00
215	"Johnnie" McCarthy	80.00	48.00	28.00
216	"Joe" Marty	80.00	48.00	28.00
217	Walter Beck	80.00	48.00	28.00
218	"Wally" Millies	80.00	48.00	28.00
219	"Russ" Bauers	80.00	48.00	28.00
220	Mace Brown	80.00	48.00	28.00
221	Lee Handley	80.00	48.00	28.00
222	"Max" Butcher	80.00	48.00	28.00
223	Hugh "Ee-Yah" Jennings	150.00	90.00	52.00
224	"Pie" Traynor	200.00	120.00	70.00
225	"Shoeless Joe" Jackson	2500.	1500.	875.00
226	Harry Hooper	125.00	75.00	44.00
227	"Pop" Haines	125.00	75.00	44.00
228	"Charley" Grimm	80.00	48.00	28.00
229	"Buck" Herzog	80.00	48.00	28.00
230	"Red" Faber	125.00	75.00	44.00
231	"Dolf" Luque	80.00	48.00	28.00
232	"Goose" Goslin	150.00	90.00	52.00
233	"Moose" Earnshaw	80.00	48.00	28.00
234	Frank "Husk" Chance	150.00	90.00	52.00
235	John J. McGraw	200.00	120.00	70.00
236	"Sunny Jim" Bottomley	125.00	75.00	44.00
237	"Wee Willie" Keeler	175.00	105.00	61.00
238	"Poosh 'Em Up Tony" Lazzeri	125.00	75.00	44.00
239	George Uhle	80.00	48.00	28.00
240	"Bill" Atwood	200.00	120.00	70.00

1941 Play Ball

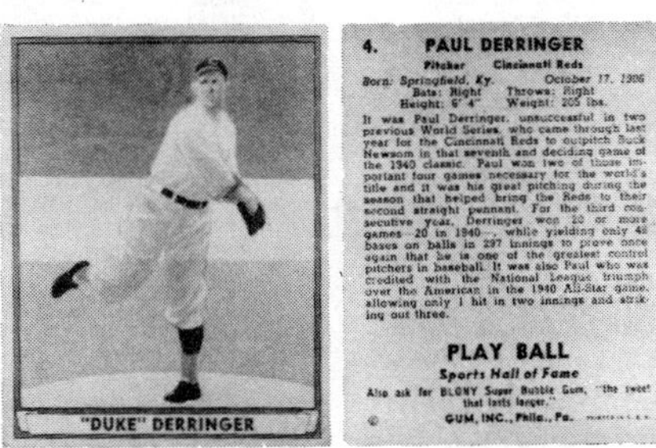

While the card backs are quite similar to the black and white cards Gum Incorporated issued in 1940, the card fronts in the 1941 set are printed in color. Many of the card photos, however, are just color versions of the player's 1940 card. The cards are still in the 2-1/2" by 3-1/8" size, but only 72 cards are included in the set. Joe DiMaggio and Ted Williams continue to be the key players in the set, while card numbers 49-72 are rarer than the lower-numbered cards. The cards were printed in sheets, and can still be found that way, or in paper strips, lacking the cardboard backing.

		NR MT	EX	VG
Complete Set (72):		11000.	5150.	2750.
Common Player (1-48):		55.00	26.00	13.50
Common Player (49-72):		75.00	35.00	18.50
1	"Eddie" Miller	200.00	94.00	50.00
2	Max West	55.00	26.00	13.50
3	"Bucky" Walters	55.00	26.00	13.50
4	"Duke" Derringer	65.00	31.00	16.00
5	"Buck" McCormick	55.00	26.00	13.50
6	Carl Hubbell	250.00	117.00	62.00
7	"The Horse" Danning	55.00	26.00	13.50
8	"Mel" Ott	300.00	141.00	75.00
9	"Pinky" May	55.00	26.00	13.50
10	"Arky" Vaughan	125.00	59.00	31.00
11	Debs Garms	55.00	26.00	13.50
12	"Jimmy" Brown	55.00	26.00	13.50
13	"Jimmie" Foxx	375.00	176.00	94.00
14	"Ted" Williams	2000.	940.00	500.00
15	"Joe" Cronin	175.00	82.00	44.00
16	"Hal" Trosky	55.00	26.00	13.50
17	"Stormy" Weatherly	55.00	26.00	13.50
18	"Hank" Greenberg	350.00	164.00	87.00
19	"Charley" Gehringer	250.00	117.00	62.00
20	"Red" Ruffing	175.00	82.00	44.00
21	"Charlie" Keller	65.00	31.00	16.00
22	"Indian Bob" Johnson	55.00	26.00	13.50
23	"Mac" McQuinn	55.00	26.00	13.50
24	"Dutch" Leonard	55.00	26.00	13.50
25	"Gene" Moore	55.00	26.00	13.50
26	Harry "Gunboat" Gumbert	55.00	26.00	13.50
27	"Babe" Young	55.00	26.00	13.50
28	"Joe" Marty	55.00	26.00	13.50
29	"Jack" Wilson	55.00	26.00	13.50
30	"Lou" Finney	55.00	26.00	13.50
31	"Joe" Kuhel	55.00	26.00	13.50
32	Taft Wright	55.00	26.00	13.50
33	"Happy" Milnar	55.00	26.00	13.50
34	"Rollie" Hemsley	55.00	26.00	13.50
35	"Pinky" Higgins	55.00	26.00	13.50
36	Barney McCosky	55.00	26.00	13.50
37	"Soupy" Campbell	55.00	26.00	13.50
38	Atley Donald	65.00	31.00	16.00
39	"Tommy" Henrich	65.00	31.00	16.00
40	"Johnny" Babich	55.00	26.00	13.50
41	Frank "Blimp" Hayes	55.00	26.00	13.50
42	"Wally" Moses	55.00	26.00	13.50
43	Albert "Bronk" Brancato	55.00	26.00	13.50
44	"Sam" Chapman	55.00	26.00	13.50
45	Elden Auker (Eldon)	55.00	26.00	13.50
46	"Sid" Hudson	55.00	26.00	13.50
47	"Buddy" Lewis	55.00	26.00	13.50
48	Cecil Travis	55.00	26.00	13.50
49	"Babe" Dahlgren	75.00	35.00	18.50
50	"Johnny" Cooney	75.00	35.00	18.50
51	"Dolph" Camilli	75.00	35.00	18.50
52	Kirby Higbe	75.00	35.00	18.50
53	Luke "Hot Potato" Hamlin	75.00	35.00	18.50
54	"Pee Wee" Reese	750.00	325.00	187.00
55	"Whit" Wyatt	75.00	35.00	18.50
56	"Vandy" Vander Meer	75.00	35.00	18.50
57	"Moe" Arnovich	75.00	35.00	18.50
58	"Frank" Demaree	75.00	35.00	18.50
59	"Bill" Jurges	75.00	35.00	18.50
60	"Chuck" Klein	250.00	117.00	62.00
61	"Vince" DiMaggio	200.00	94.00	50.00
62	"Elbie" Fletcher	75.00	35.00	18.50
63	"Dom" DiMaggio	200.00	94.00	50.00
64	"Bobby" Doerr	225.00	106.00	56.00
65	"Tommy" Bridges	75.00	35.00	18.50
66	Harland Clift (Harlond)	75.00	35.00	18.50
67	"Walt" Judnich	75.00	35.00	18.50
68	"Jack" Knott	75.00	35.00	18.50
69	George Case	75.00	35.00	18.50
70	"Bill" Dickey	550.00	258.00	137.00
71	"Joe" DiMaggio	2500.	1175.	700.00
72	"Lefty" Gomez	600.00	300.00	160.00

1976 Playboy Press Who Was Harry Steinfeldt?

This 12-card set was issued in 1976 by Playboy Press to promote author Bert Randolph Sugar's book "Who Was Harry Steinfeldt? & Other Baseball Trivia Questions." (Steinfeldt was the third baseman in the Cubs' famous infield that featured Hall of Famers Tinker, Evers and Chance). The black and white cards measure the standard 2-1/2" by 3-1/2" with a player photo on the front and a trivia question and ad for the book on the back.

		NR MT	EX	VG
Complete Set:		100.00	50.00	30.00
Common Player:		2.00	1.00	.60
(1)	Frankie Baumholtz	2.00	1.00	.60
(2)	Jim Bouton	3.00	1.50	.90
(3)	Tony Conigliaro	3.00	1.50	.90
(4)	Don Drysdale	7.00	3.50	2.00
(5)	Hank Greenberg	7.00	3.50	2.00
(6)	Walter Johnson	20.00	10.00	6.00
(7)	Billy Loes	2.00	1.00	.60
(8)	Johnny Mize	6.00	3.00	1.75
(9)	Frank "Lefty" O'Doul	2.00	1.00	.60
(10)	Babe Ruth	40.00	20.00	12.00
(11)	Johnny Sain	2.50	1.25	.70
(12)	Jim Thorpe	20.00	10.00	6.00

A player's name in italic type indicates a rookie card. An (FC) indicates a player's first card for that particular card company.

1910 Plow Boy Tobacco

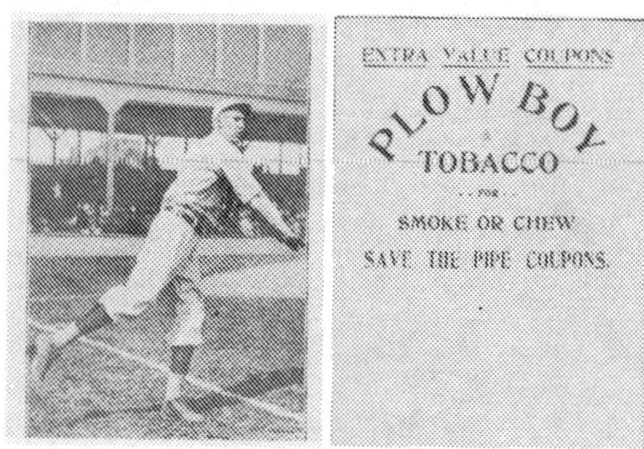

Plowboy Tobacco, a product of the Spaulding & Merrick Company, issued a set of bainet-size cards in the Chicago area featuring members of the Cubs and the White Sox. From the checklist of the 50 known cards, it appears that the bulk of the set was originally issued in 1910 with a few additional cards appearing over the next several years. The set appears to be complete at 25 Cubs and 25 White Sox players, although there is some speculation that other cards may still be discovered. Measuring approximately 5-3/4" by 8", the Plowboys are one of the largest tobacco cards of the 20th Century. They feature very nice sepia-toned player photos in poses not found on other tobacco issues. The player's name appears in the lower left corner, while the team name appears in the lower right. Two different backs are known to exist. One consists of a simple advertisement for Plowboy Tobacco, while a second more difficult variety includes a list of premiums available in exchange for coupons. The set is among the rarest of all 20th Century tobacco issues.

		NR MT	EX	VG
Complete Set (40):		14000.	7000.	4250.
Common Player:		300.00	150.00	90.00
(1)	Jimmy Archer	300.00	150.00	90.00
(2)	Ginger Beaumont	300.00	150.00	90.00
(3)	Lena Blackburne	300.00	150.00	90.00
(4)	Bruno Block	300.00	150.00	90.00
(5)	Ping Bodie	300.00	150.00	90.00
(6)	Mordecai Brown	700.00	350.00	210.00
(7)	Al Carson	300.00	150.00	90.00
(8)	Frank Chance	800.00	400.00	240.00
(9)	Ed Cicotte	400.00	200.00	120.00
(10)	King Cole	300.00	150.00	90.00
(11)	Eddie Collins	700.00	350.00	210.00
(12)	George Davis	300.00	150.00	90.00
(13)	Patsy Dougherty	300.00	150.00	90.00
(14)	Johnny Evers	700.00	350.00	210.00
(15)	Chick Gandel (Gandil)	400.00	200.00	120.00
(16)	Ed Hahn	300.00	150.00	90.00
(17)	Solly Hoffman (Hofman)	300.00	150.00	90.00
(18)	Del Howard	300.00	150.00	90.00
(19)	Bill Jones	300.00	150.00	90.00
(20)	Johnny Kling	300.00	150.00	90.00
(21)	Rube Kroh	300.00	150.00	90.00
(22)	Frank Lange	300.00	150.00	90.00
(23)	Fred Luderus	300.00	150.00	90.00
(24)	Harry McIntyre	300.00	150.00	90.00
(25)	Ward Miller	300.00	150.00	90.00
(26)	Charlie Mullen	300.00	150.00	90.00
(27)	Tom Needham	300.00	150.00	90.00
(28)	Fred Olmstead	300.00	150.00	90.00
(29)	Orval Overall	300.00	150.00	90.00
(30)	Fred Parent	300.00	150.00	90.00
(31)	Fred Payne	300.00	150.00	90.00
(32)	Francis "Big Jeff" Pfeffer	300.00	150.00	90.00
(33)	Jake Pfeister	300.00	150.00	90.00
(34)	Billy Purtell	300.00	150.00	90.00
(35)	Ed Reulbach	300.00	150.00	90.00
(36)	Lew Richie	300.00	150.00	90.00
(37)	Jimmy Scheckard (Sheckard)	300.00	150.00	90.00
(38)	Wildfire Schulte	300.00	150.00	90.00
(39a)	Jim Scot (name incorrect)	300.00	150.00	90.00
(39b)	Jim Scott (name correct)	300.00	150.00	90.00
(40)	Frank Smith	300.00	150.00	90.00
(41)	Harry Steinfeldt	300.00	150.00	90.00
(42)	Billy Sullivan	300.00	150.00	90.00
(43)	Lee Tannehill	300.00	150.00	90.00
(44)	Joe Tinker	700.00	350.00	210.00
(45)	Ed Walsh	700.00	350.00	210.00
(46)	Doc White	300.00	150.00	90.00
(47)	Irv Young	300.00	150.00	90.00
(48)	Rollie Zeider	300.00	150.00	90.00
(49)	Heinie Zimmerman	300.00	150.00	90.00

1912 Plow's Candy (E300)

An extremely rare candy issue, cards in this 1912 set measures 3" by 4" and feature sepia-toned photos surrounded by a rather wide border. The player's name and team appear in the border below the photo, while the words "Plow's Candy Collection" appear at the top. The backs are blank. Not even known to exist until the late 1960s, this set has been assigned the designation of E300.

		NR MT	EX	VG
Complete Set:		35000.	17500.	10000.
Common Player:		450.00	225.00	135.00
(1)	Babe Adams	450.00	225.00	135.00
(2)	Home Run Baker	1100.	550.00	330.00
(3)	Cy Barger	450.00	225.00	135.00
(4)	Jack Barry	450.00	225.00	135.00
(5)	Johnny Bates	450.00	225.00	135.00
(7)	Joe Benz	450.00	225.00	135.00
(8)	Cy Berger (Barger)	450.00	225.00	135.00
(9)	Roger Bresnahan	1100.	550.00	330.00
(10)	Mordecai Brown	1100.	550.00	330.00
(11)	Donie Bush	450.00	225.00	135.00
(12)	Bobby Byrne	450.00	225.00	135.00
(13)	Nixey Callahan	450.00	225.00	135.00
(14)	Hal Chase	700.00	350.00	210.00
(15)	Fred Clarke	1100.	550.00	330.00
(16)	Ty Cobb	4000.	2000.	1200.
(17)	King Cole	450.00	225.00	135.00
(18)	Eddie Collins	1100.	550.00	330.00
(19)	Jack Coombs	450.00	225.00	135.00
(20)	Bill Dahlen	450.00	225.00	135.00
(21)	Bert Daniels	450.00	225.00	135.00
(22)	Harry Davis	450.00	225.00	135.00
(23)	Jim Delehanty	450.00	225.00	135.00
(24)	Josh Devore	450.00	225.00	135.00
(25)	Wild Bill Donovan	450.00	225.00	135.00
(26)	Red Dooin	450.00	225.00	135.00
(27)	Johnny Evers	1100.	550.00	330.00
(28)	Russ Ford	450.00	225.00	135.00
(29)	Del Gainor	450.00	225.00	135.00
(30)	Vean Gregg	450.00	225.00	135.00
(31)	Bob Harmon	450.00	225.00	135.00
(32)	Arnold Hauser	450.00	225.00	135.00
(33)	Dick Hoblitzelle (Hoblitzell)	450.00	225.00	135.00
(34)	Solly Hofman	450.00	225.00	135.00
(35)	Miller Huggins	1100.	550.00	330.00
(36)	John Hummel	450.00	225.00	135.00
(37)	Walter Johnson	2000.	1000.	600.00
(38)	Johnny Kling	450.00	225.00	135.00
(39)	Nap Lajoie	1500.	750.00	450.00
(40)	Jack Lapp	450.00	225.00	135.00
(41)	Fred Luderus	450.00	225.00	135.00
(42)	Sherry Magee	450.00	225.00	135.00
(43)	Rube Marquard	1100.	550.00	330.00
(44)	Christy Mathewson	2000.	1000.	600.00
(45)	Stuffy McInnes (McInnis)	450.00	225.00	135.00
(46)	Larry McLean	450.00	225.00	135.00
(47)	Fred Merkle	450.00	225.00	135.00
(48)	Cy Morgan	450.00	225.00	135.00
(49)	George Moriarty	450.00	225.00	135.00
(50)	Mike Mowrey	450.00	225.00	135.00
(51)	Chief Myers (Meyers)	450.00	225.00	135.00
(52)	Rube Oldring	450.00	225.00	135.00
(53)	Marty O'Toole	450.00	225.00	135.00
(54)	Nap Rucker	450.00	225.00	135.00
(55)	Slim Sallee	450.00	225.00	135.00
(56)	Boss Schmidt	450.00	225.00	135.00
(57)	Jimmy Sheckard	450.00	225.00	135.00
(58)	Tris Speaker	1100.	550.00	330.00
(59)	Billy Sullivan	450.00	225.00	135.00
(60)	Ira Thomas	450.00	225.00	135.00
(61)	Joe Tinker	1100.	550.00	330.00
(62)	John Titus	450.00	225.00	135.00
(63)	Hippo Vaughan (Vaughn)	450.00	225.00	135.00
(64)	Honus Wagner	3000.	1500.	900.00
(65)	Ed Walsh	1100.	550.00	330.00
(66)	Bob Williams	450.00	225.00	135.00

Values quoted in this guide reflect the retail price of a card – the price a collector can expect to pay when buying a card from a dealer. The wholesale price – that which a collector can expect to receive from a dealer when selling cards – will be significantly lower, depending on desirability and condition.

1985 Polaroid J.C. Penney Indians

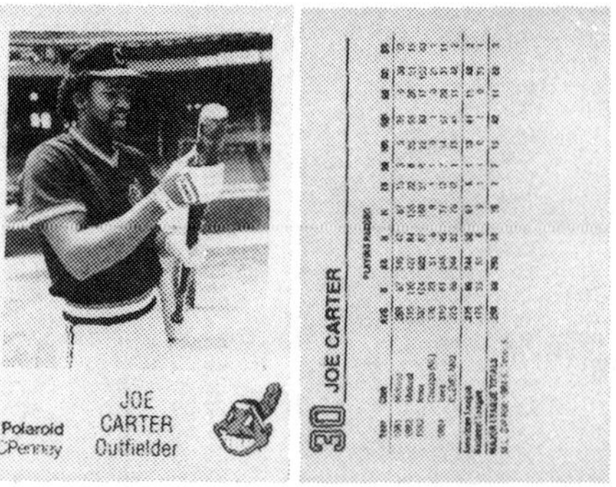

While the Cleveland Indians continued its four-year tradition of baseball card promotional game issues in 1985, the sponsor changed from Wheaties to Polaroid/J.C. Penney. The 32-card set features 30 player cards, a manager card and a group card of the coaching staff. Though produced in the "safety set" format - slightly oversize (2-13/16" by 4-1/8") with wide white borders - the Indians cards carry no safety message. Backs, once again numbered by uniform number, contain major and minor league stats.

		MT	NR MT	EX
Complete Set:		12.00	9.00	4.75
Common Player:		.25	.20	.10
2	Brett Butler	.50	.40	.20
4	Tony Bernazard	.25	.20	.10
8	Carmen Castillo	.25	.20	.10
10	Pat Tabler	.25	.20	.10
12	Benny Ayala	.25	.20	.10
13	Ernie Camacho	.25	.20	.10
14	Julio Franco	1.50	1.25	.60
16	Jerry Willard	.25	.20	.10
18	Pat Corrales	.30	.25	.12
20	Otis Nixon	.35	.25	.14
21	Mike Hargrove	.30	.25	.12
22	Mike Fischlin	.25	.20	.10
23	Chris Bando	.25	.20	.10
24	George Vukovich	.25	.20	.10
26	Brook Jacoby	.35	.25	.14
27	Mel Hall	.35	.25	.14
28	Bert Blyleven	.60	.45	.25
29	Andre Thornton	.30	.25	.12
30	Joe Carter	2.50	2.00	1.00
32	Rick Behenna	.25	.20	.10
33	Roy Smith	.25	.20	.10
35	Jerry Reed	.25	.20	.10
36	Jamie Easterly	.25	.20	.10
38	Dave Von Ohlen	.25	.20	.10
41	Rich Thompson	.25	.20	.10
43	Bryan Clark	.25	.20	.10
44	Neal Heaton	.30	.25	.12
48	Vern Ruhle	.25	.20	.10
49	Jeff Barkley	.25	.20	.10
50	Ramon Romero	.25	.20	.10
54	Tom Waddell	.25	.20	.10
----	Tribe Coaching Staff (Bobby Bonds, Johnny Goryl, Don McMahon, Ed Napolean, Dennis Sommers)	.35	.25	.14

1889 Police Gazette Cabinets

Issued in the late 1880s through early 1890s as a premium by Police Gazette, a popular newspaper of the day, these cabinet cards were only recently discovered and are very rare. The 4-1/2" by 6-1/2" cards consist of oval, sepia-toned photographs mounted on cardboard of various colors. Only about two dozen players are currently known. Some photographs correspond to those used in the S.F. Hess card series and some players are depicted in suit and tie, rather than baseball uniform. All of the cards display the name of the player next to his portrait, along with the signature of "Richard K. Fox" and a line identifying him as "Editor and Proprietor/Police Gazette/Franklin Sqaure, New York."

		NR MT	EX	VG
Common Player:		1600.	800.00	480.00
(1)	Hick Carpenter	1600.	800.00	480.00
(2)	Fred Carroll	1600.	800.00	480.00
(3)	Bob Clark	1600.	800.00	480.00
(4)	Roger Conner (Connor)	2400.	1200.	720.00

(5)	Pete Conway	1600.	800.00	480.00
(6)	John Corckhill	1600.	800.00	480.00
(7)	Jerry Denny	1600.	800.00	480.00
(8)	Buck Ewing	2400.	1200.	720.00
(9)	Bob Ferguson	1600.	800.00	480.00
(10)	Jocko Fields	1600.	800.00	480.00
(11)	Elmer Foster	1600.	800.00	480.00
(12)	Charlie Getzein	1600.	800.00	480.00
(13)	Pebbly Jack Glasscock	1600.	800.00	480.00
(14)	Bill Gleason	1600.	800.00	480.00
(15)	George Gore	1600.	800.00	480.00
(16)	Tim Keefe	2400.	1200.	720.00
(17)	Gus Krock	1600.	800.00	480.00
(18)	Tip O'Neil (O'Neill)	1800.	900.00	540.00
(19)	N. (Fred) Pfeffer	1600.	800.00	480.00
(20)	Danny Richardson	1600.	800.00	480.00
(21)	Elmer Smith	1600.	800.00	480.00
(22)	Harry Staley	1600.	800.00	480.00
(23)	George Tebeau	1600.	800.00	480.00
(24)	Curt Welch	1600.	800.00	480.00

1970 Police/Fire Safety Senators

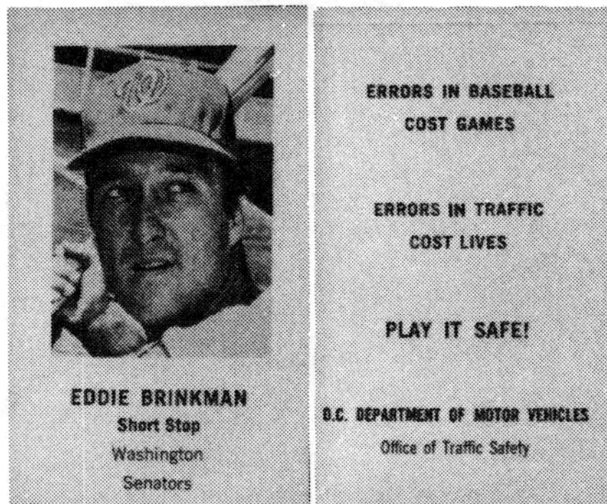

EDDIE BRINKMAN
Short Stop
Washington
Senators
A FAST BALL CAN GET
YOU "OUT" OF TROUBLE
A FAST CAR CAN GET
YOU "INTO" TROUBLE
ERRORS IN BASEBALL
COST GAMES
ERRORS IN TRAFFIC
COST LIVES
PLAY IT SAFE!
D.C. DEPARTMENT OF MOTOR VEHICLES
Office of Traffic Safety

Distributed in 1970 by the Washington, D.C. Department of Motor Vehicles, this regional set, promoting traffic safety, was one of the first police sets ever issued. Featuring black and white player photos of the Washington Senators, the cards measure 2-1/2" by 3-7/8" and have large borders surrounding the pictures with the player's name and position below. The team name appears in smaller type at the bottom. The 1970 set can be found on either pink card stock, used for the original print run, or on bright yellow stock, used for two subsequent printings. The additional print runs resulted in a scarce card of Dave Nelson, who replaced the traded Aurelio Rodriguez for the final printing. The Nelson card is found only on yellow stock, while the other players in the set can be found on both yellow and pink. The pink varieties carry a higher value. The backs of the cards offer traffic safety tips and identify the manufacturer of the sets as the "D.C. Department of Motor Vehicles/Office of Traffic Safety."

		NR MT	EX	VG
Complete Set: (pink stock)		125.00	62.00	37.00
Common Player: (pink stock)		7.00	3.50	2.00
Complete Set: (yellow stock)		300.00	150.00	90.00
Common Player: (yellow stock)		2.50	1.25	.70
(1a)	Dick Bosman (pink stock)	7.00	3.50	2.00
(1b)	Dick Bosman (yellow stock)	2.50	1.25	.70
(2a)	Eddie Brinkman (pink stock)	7.00	3.50	2.00
(2b)	Eddie Brinkman (yellow stock)	2.50	1.25	.70
(3a)	Paul Casanova (pink stock)	7.00	3.50	2.00
(3b)	Paul Casanova (yellow stock)	2.50	1.25	.70
(4a)	Mike Epstein (pink stock)	7.00	3.50	2.00
(4b)	Mike Epstein (yellow stock)	2.50	1.25	.70
(5a)	Frank Howard (pink stock)	18.00	9.00	5.50
(5b)	Frank Howard (yellow stock)	7.00	3.50	2.00
(6a)	Darold Knowles (pink stock)	7.00	3.50	2.00
(6b)	Darold Knowles (yellow stock)	2.50	1.25	.70
(7a)	Lee Maye (pink stock)	7.00	3.50	2.00
(7b)	Lee Maye (yellow stock)	2.50	1.25	.70
(8)	Dave Nelson	250.00	125.00	75.00
(9a)	Aurelio Rodriguez (pink stock)	7.00	3.50	2.00
(9b)	Aurelio Rodriguez (yellow stock)	5.00	2.50	1.50
(10a)	John Roseboro (pink stock)	7.00	3.50	2.00
(10b)	John Roseboro (yellow stock)	2.50	1.25	.70
(11a)	Ed Stroud (pink stock)	7.00	3.50	2.00
(11b)	Ed Stroud (yellow stock)	2.50	1.25	.70

1971 Police/Fire Safety Senators

The 1971 Senators safety set was again issued by the Washington, D.C., Department of Motor Vehicles and was similar in design and size (2-1/2" by 3-7/8") to the previous year, except that it was printed

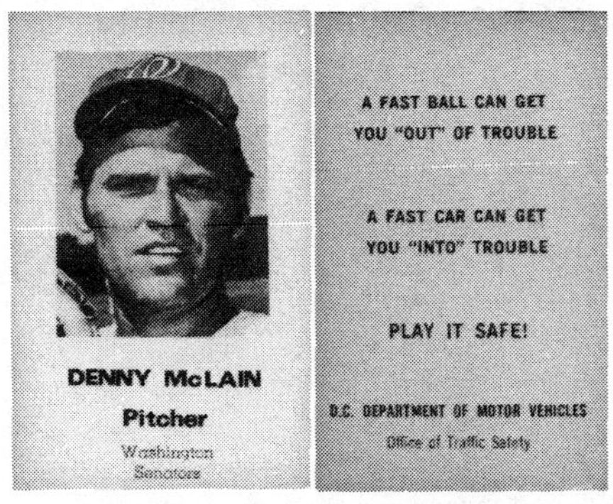

on a pale yellow stock. The set, which features several new players, including Denny McLain and Toby Harrah, contains no scarce cards. The backs contain traffic safety messages.

		NR MT	EX	VG
Complete Set:		12.00	6.00	3.50
Common Player:		1.25	.60	.40
(1)	Dick Bosman	1.25	.60	.40
(2)	Paul Casanova	1.25	.60	.40
(3)	Tim Cullen	1.25	.60	.40
(4)	Joe Foy	1.25	.60	.40
(5)	Toby Harrah	2.00	1.00	.60
(6)	Frank Howard	6.00	3.00	1.75
(7)	Elliott Maddox	1.25	.60	.40
(8)	Tom McCraw	1.25	.60	.40
(9)	Denny McLain	3.00	1.50	.90
(10)	Don Wert	1.25	.60	.40

1979 Police/Fire Safety Giants

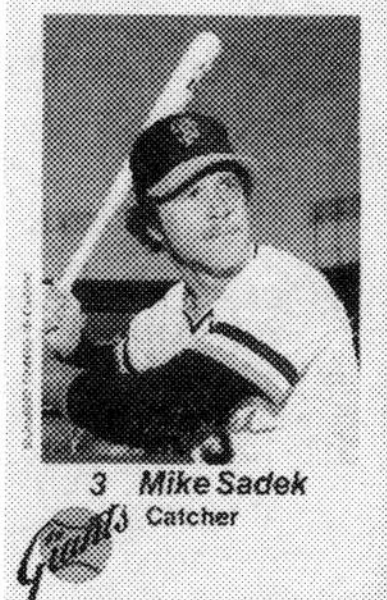

Each of the full-color cards measures 2-5/8" by 4-1/8" and is numbered by player uniform number. The set includes 20 Giants players and coaches. The player's name, position and facsimile autograph are on the card fronts, along with the Giants logo. Card backs have a "Tip from the Giants" and sponsor logos for the Giants and radio station KNBR, all printed the Giants' orange and black colors. Half of the set was distributed at a ballpark promotion during the 1979 season, while the other cards were available only from police agencies in several San Francisco Bay area counties.

		NR MT	EX	VG
Complete Set:		20.00	10.00	6.00
Common Player:		.40	.20	.12
1	Dave Bristol	.40	.20	.12
2	Marc Hill	.40	.20	.12
3	Mike Sadek	.40	.20	.12
5	Tom Haller	.40	.20	.12
6	Joe Altobelli	.50	.25	.15
8	Larry Shepard	.40	.20	.12
9	Heity Cruz	.40	.20	.12
10	Johnnie LeMaster	.40	.20	.12
12	Jim Davenport	.40	.20	.12
14	Vida Blue	.80	.40	.25
15	Mike Ivie	.40	.20	.12
16	Roger Metzger	.40	.20	.12
17	Randy Moffitt	.40	.20	.12
18	Bill Madlock	1.25	.60	.40
21	Rob Andrews	.40	.20	.12
22	Jack Clark	1.50	.70	.45
25	Dave Roberts	.40	.20	.12
26	John Montefusco	.40	.20	.12
28	Ed Halicki	.40	.20	.12
30	John Tamargo	.40	.20	.12
31	Larry Herndon	.40	.20	.12
36	Bill North	.40	.20	.12
39	Bob Knepper	.70	.35	.20
40	John Curtis	.40	.20	.12
41	Darrell Evans	1.50	.70	.45
43	Tom Griffin	.40	.20	.12
44	Willie McCovey	6.00	3.00	1.75
46	Gary Lavelle	.40	.20	.12
49	Max Venable	.40	.20	.12

1980 Police/Fire Safety Dodgers

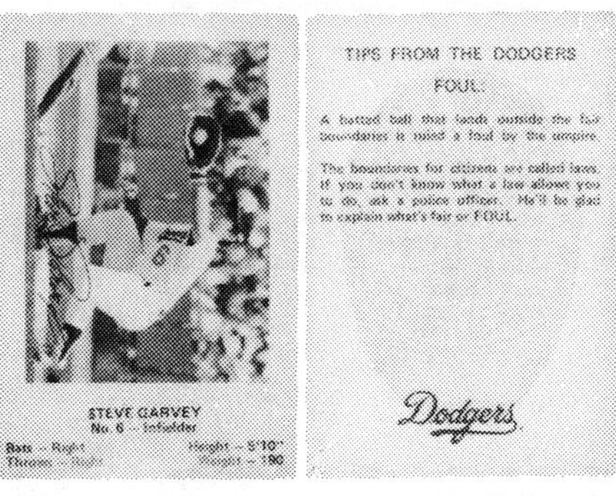

STEVE GARVEY
No. 6 - Infielder
TIPS FROM THE DODGERS
FOUL:
Dodgers

Producers of one of the most popular police and safety sets in baseball, the Los Angeles Dodgers began this successful promotion in 1980. The 2-13/16" by 4-1/8" cards feature attractive, full-color photos on the card fronts, along with brief personal statistics. Card backs include "Tips from the Dodgers" along with the team and Los Angeles Police Department logos. The 30 cards are numbered by player uniform number, with an unnumbered team card also included in the set.

		NR MT	EX	VG
Complete Set:		10.00	5.00	3.00
Common Player:		.30	.15	.09
5	Johnny Oates	.30	.15	.09
6	Steve Garvey	1.50	.70	.45
7	Steve Yeager	.30	.15	.09
8	Reggie Smith	.50	.25	.15
9	Gary Thomasson	.30	.15	.09
10	Ron Cey	.50	.25	.15
12	Dusty Baker	.40	.20	.12
13	Joe Ferguson	.30	.15	.09
15	Davey Lopes	.50	.25	.15
16	Rick Monday	.40	.20	.12
18	Bill Russell	.40	.20	.12
20	Don Sutton	.80	.40	.25
21	Jay Johnstone	.40	.20	.12
23	Teddy Martinez	.30	.15	.09
27	Joe Beckwith	.30	.15	.09
28	Pedro Guerrero	1.00	.50	.30
29	Don Stanhouse	.30	.15	.09
30	Derrel Thomas	.30	.15	.09
31	Doug Rau	.30	.15	.09
34	Ken Brett	.30	.15	.09
35	Bob Welch	.50	.25	.15
37	Robert Castillo	.30	.15	.09
38	Dave Goltz	.40	.20	.12
41	Jerry Reuss	.50	.25	.15
43	Rick Sutcliffe	.60	.30	.20
44	Mickey Hatcher	.40	.20	.12
46	Burt Hooton	.40	.20	.12
49	Charlie Hough	.40	.20	.12
51	Terry Forster	.40	.20	.12
----	Team Photo	.30	.15	.09

A card number in parentheses () indicates the set is unnumbered.

1980 Police/Fire Safety Giants

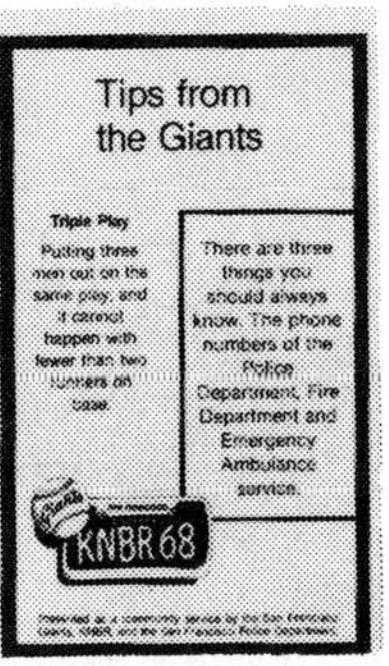

The 1980 Giants police set is virtually identical in format to its 1979 forerunner. Card design and colors are the same on both front and back, with radio station KNBR and the San Francisco Police Department once again co-sponsors. The 2-5/8" by 4-1/8" cards again feature fronts with full-color photos and facsimile autographs, while backs are in the team's orange and black colors. The set numbers 31 players and coaches, with each card numbered by uniform number. As in 1979, half the cards were distributed at a stadium promotion, with the remainder available only from police officers.

		NR MT	EX	VG
Complete Set:		12.00	6.00	3.50
Common Player:		.30	.15	.09
1	Dave Bristol	.30	.15	.09
2	Marc Hill	.30	.15	.09
3	Mike Sadek	.30	.15	.09
5	Jim Lefebvre	.40	.20	.12
6	Rennie Stennett	.30	.15	.09
7	Milt May	.30	.15	.09
8	Vern Benson	.30	.15	.09
9	Jim Wohlford	.30	.15	.09
10	Johnnie LeMaster	.30	.15	.09
12	Jim Davenport	.30	.15	.09
14	Vida Blue	.80	.40	.25
15	Mike Ivie	.30	.15	.09
16	Roger Metzger	.30	.15	.09
17	Randy Moffitt	.30	.15	.09
19	Al Holland	.30	.15	.09
20	Joe Strain	.30	.15	.09
22	Jack Clark	1.50	.70	.45
26	John Montefusco	.30	.15	.09
28	Ed Halicki	.30	.15	.09
31	Larry Herndon	.30	.15	.09
32	Ed Whitson	.30	.15	.09
36	Bill North	.30	.15	.09
38	Greg Minton	.30	.15	.09
39	Bob Knepper	.50	.25	.15
41	Darrell Evans	.90	.45	.25
42	John Van Ornum	.30	.15	.09
43	Tom Griffin	.30	.15	.09
44	Willie McCovey	4.00	2.00	1.25
45	Terry Whitfield	.30	.15	.09
46	Gary Lavelle	.30	.15	.09
47	Don McMahon	.30	.15	.09

1981 Police/Fire Safety Braves

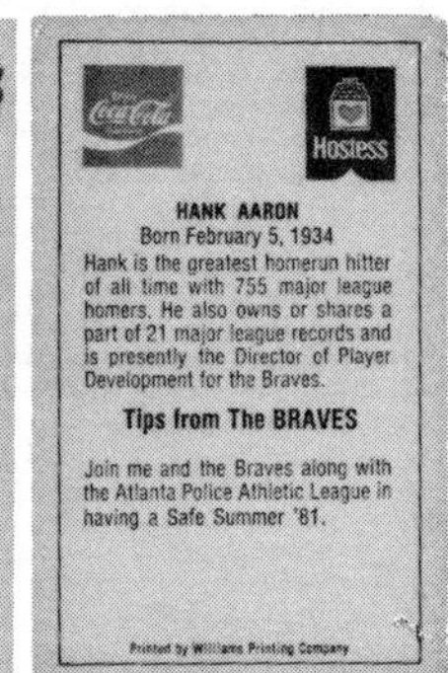

HANK AARON
Born February 5, 1934
Hank is the greatest homerun hitter of all time with 755 major league homers. He also owns or shares a part of 21 major league records and is presently the Director of Player Development for the Braves.
Tips from The BRAVES
Join me and the Braves along with the Atlanta Police Athletic League in having a Safe Summer '81.

The first Atlanta Braves police set was a cooperative effort of the team, Hostess, Coca-Cola and the Atlanta Police Department. Card fronts feature full-color photos of 27 different Braves and manager Bobby Cox. Police and team logos are on the card backs. Card backs offer capsule biographies of the players, along with a tip for youngsters. The 2-5/8" by 4-1/8" cards are numbered by uniform number. Terry Harper (#19) appears to be somewhat scarcer than the other cards in the set. Reportedly, 33,000 sets were printed.

		MT	NR MT	EX
Complete Set:		14.00	10.50	5.50
Common Player:		.30	.25	.12
1	Jerry Royster	.30	.25	.12
3	Dale Murphy	2.50	2.00	1.00
4	Biff Pocoroba	.30	.25	.12
5	Bob Horner	.60	.45	.25
6	Bob Cox	.40	.30	.15
9	Luis Gomez	.30	.25	.12
10	Chris Chambliss	.40	.30	.15
15	Bill Nahorodny	.30	.25	.12
16	Rafael Ramirez	.35	.25	.14
17	Glenn Hubbard	.35	.25	.14
18	Claudell Washington	.40	.30	.15
19	Terry Harper	.40	.30	.15
20	Bruce Benedict	.30	.25	.12
24	John Montefusco	.30	.25	.12
25	Rufino Linares	.30	.25	.12
26	Gene Garber	.30	.25	.12
30	Brian Asselstine	.30	.25	.12
34	Larry Bradford	.30	.25	.12
35	Phil Niekro	2.00	1.50	.80
37	Rick Camp	.30	.25	.12
39	Al Hrabosky	.35	.25	.14
40	Tommy Boggs	.30	.25	.12
42	Rick Mahler	.40	.30	.15
45	Ed Miller	.30	.25	.12
46	Gaylord Perry	3.00	2.25	1.25
49	Preston Hanna	.30	.25	.12
----	Hank Aaron	5.00	2.00	1.00

1981 Police/Fire Safety Dodgers

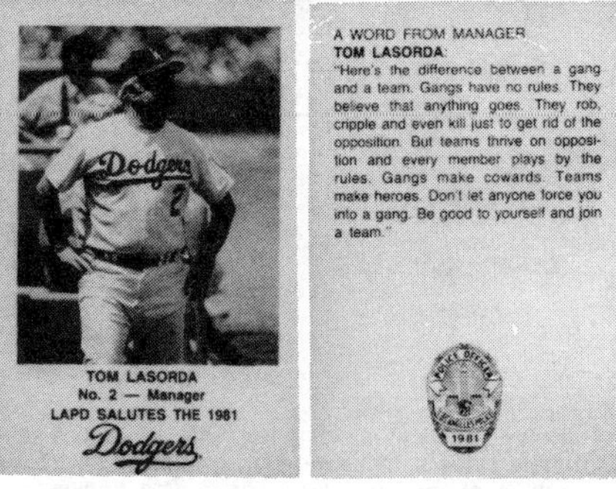

Very similar in format to their successful set of the year before, the Los Angeles Dodgers 1981 police set grew to 32 cards (from 30). This was due to the acquisitions of Ken Landreaux and Dave Stewart shortly before printing of the sets. These two cards may even have been added after the initial printing run, making them slightly more difficult to obtain. The full-color cards are again 2-13/16" by 4-1/8", with a safety tip on the card back. Each card front has the line "LAPD Salutes the 1981 Dodgers."

		MT	NR MT	EX
Complete Set:				
Common Player:		.20	.15	.08
2	Tom Lasorda	.40	.30	.15
3	Rudy Law	.20	.15	.08
6	Steve Garvey	1.25	.90	.50
7	Steve Yeager	.20	.15	.08
8	Reggie Smith	.40	.30	.15
10	Ron Cey	.40	.30	.15
12	Dusty Baker	.40	.30	.15
13	Joe Ferguson	.20	.15	.08
14	Mike Scioscia	.30	.25	.12
15	Davey Lopes	.35	.25	.14
16	Rick Monday	.30	.25	.12
18	Bill Russell	.30	.25	.12
21	Jay Johnstone	.25	.20	.10
26	Don Stanhouse	.20	.15	.08
27	Joe Beckwith	.20	.15	.08
28	Pete Guerrero	.50	.40	.20
30	Derrel Thomas	.20	.15	.08
34	Fernando Valenzuela	1.00	.70	.40
35	Bob Welch	.40	.30	.15
36	Pepe Frias	.20	.15	.08
37	Robert Castillo	.20	.15	.08
38	Dave Goltz	20.00	15.00	8.00
41	Jerry Reuss	.35	.25	.14
43	Rick Sutcliffe	.50	.40	.20
44a	Mickey Hatcher	.25	.20	.10
44b	Ken Landreaux	.30	.25	.12
46	Burt Hooton	.25	.20	.10
48	Dave Stewart	3.00	2.25	1.25
51	Terry Forster	.25	.20	.10
57	Steve Howe	.40	.30	.15
----	Coaching Staff (Monty Basgall, Mark Cresse, Tom Lasorda, Manny Mota, Danny Ozark, Ron Perranoski)	.20	.15	.08
----	Team Photo/Checklist	.20	.15	.08

1981 Police/Fire Safety Mariners

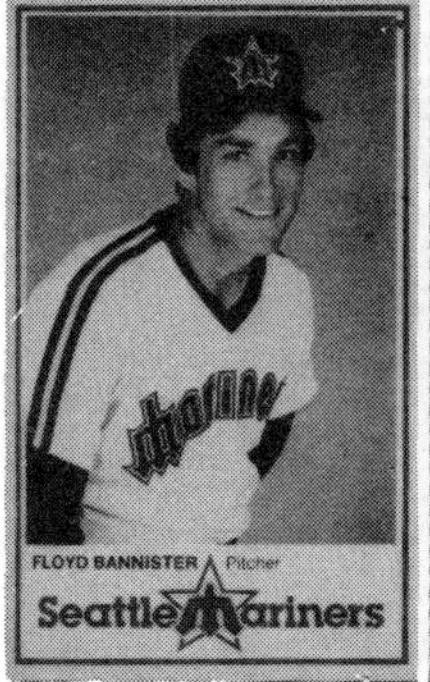

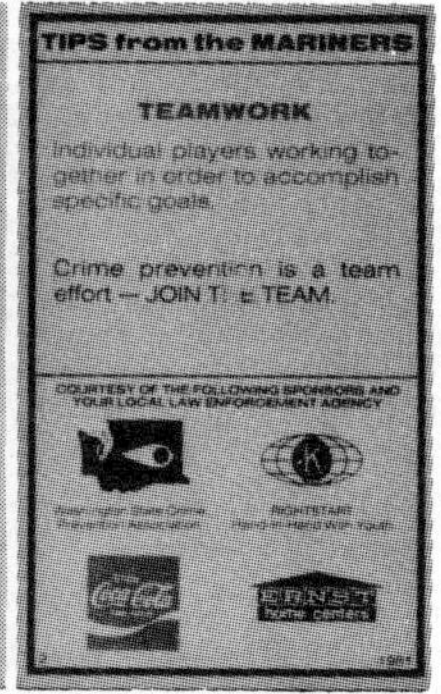

These 2-5/8" by 4-1/8" cards were co-sponsored by the Washington State Crime Prevention Assoc., Coca-Cola, Kiawanis and Ernst Home Centers. There are 16 players featured in this full-color set with each card numbered in the lower left of the card back. Card fronts list player name and position and have a team logo. Card backs are printed in blue and red and offer a "Tip from the Mariners" along with the four sponsor logos.

		MT	NR MT	EX
Complete Set:		5.00	3.75	2.00
Common Player:		.25	.20	.10
1	Jeff Burroughs	.35	.25	.14
2	Floyd Bannister	.35	.25	.14
3	Glenn Abbott	.25	.20	.10
4	Jim Anderson	.25	.20	.10
5	Danny Meyer	.25	.20	.10
6	Dave Edler	.25	.20	.10
7	Julio Cruz	.25	.20	.10
8	Kenny Clay	.25	.20	.10
9	Lenny Randle	.25	.20	.10
10	Mike Parrott	.25	.20	.10
11	Tom Paciorek	.25	.20	.10
12	Jerry Narron	.25	.20	.10
13	Richie Zisk	.35	.25	.14
14	Maury Wills	.50	.40	.20
15	Joe Simpson	.25	.20	.10
16	Shane Rawley	.35	.25	.14

1981 Police/Fire Safety Royals

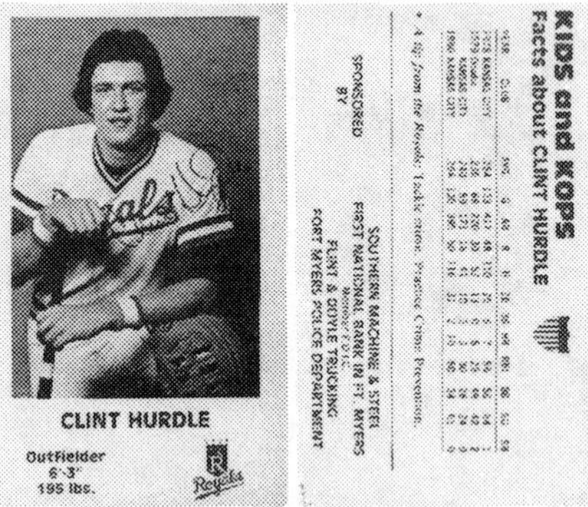

Ten of the most popular 1981 Kansas City players are featured in this 2-1/2" by 4-1/8" card set. Card fronts feature full-color photos with player name, position, facsimile autograph and team logo. Backs include player statistics, a tip from the Royals and list the four sponsoring organizations. Surprisingly, the set was issued by the Ft. Myers, Fla., police department near the Royals' spring training headquarters.

		MT	NR MT	EX
Complete Set:		30.00	22.00	12.00
Common Player:		1.50	1.25	.60
(1)	Willie Mays Aikens	1.50	1.25	.60
(2)	George Brett	18.00	13.50	7.25
(3)	Rich Gale	1.50	1.25	.60
(4)	Clint Hurdle	1.50	1.25	.60
(5)	Dennis Leonard	1.50	1.25	.60
(6)	Hal McRae	2.25	1.75	.90
(7)	Amos Otis	2.00	1.50	.80
(8)	U.L. Washington	1.50	1.25	.60
(9)	Frank White	2.00	1.50	.80
(10)	Willie Wilson	2.00	1.50	.80

1982 Police/Fire Safety Braves

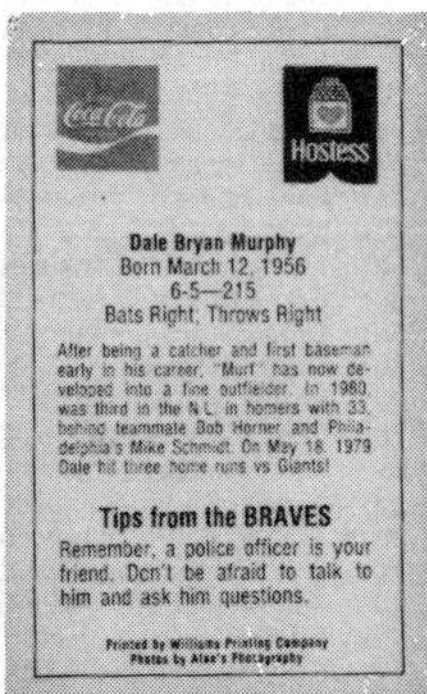

After their successful debut in 1981, the Atlanta Braves, the Atlanta Police Department, Coca-Cola and Hostess issued another card set in '82. This 30-card set is extremely close in format to the 1981 set and again measures 2-5/8" by 4-1/8". The full-color player photos are outstanding, and each card front also bears a statement marking the 1982 Braves' record-breaking 13-game win streak at the season's beginning. Card backs offer short biographies and

"Tips from the Braves." Sponsors logos are also included. Reportedly, only 8,000 of these sets were printed.

		MT	NR MT	EX
Complete Set:		15.00	11.00	6.00
Common Player:		.30	.25	.12
1	Jerry Royster	.30	.25	.12
3	Dale Murphy	3.50	2.75	1.50
4	Biff Pocoroba	.30	.25	.12
5	Bob Horner	.60	.45	.25
6	Randy Johnson	.30	.25	.12
8	Bob Watson	.45	.35	.20
9	Joe Torre	.60	.45	.25
10	Chris Chambliss	.40	.30	.15
15	Claudell Washington	.40	.30	.15
16	Rafael Ramirez	.35	.25	.14
17	Glenn Hubbard	.35	.25	.14
20	Bruce Benedict	.30	.25	.12
22	Brett Butler	.70	.50	.30
23	Tommie Aaron	.40	.30	.15
25	Rufino Linares	.30	.25	.12
26	Gene Garber	.30	.25	.12
27	Larry McWilliams	.30	.25	.12
28	Larry Whisenton	.30	.25	.12
32	Steve Bedrosian	1.00	.70	.40
35	Phil Niekro	2.00	1.50	.80
37	Rick Camp	.30	.25	.12
38	Joe Cowley	.30	.25	.12
39	Al Hrabosky	.35	.25	.14
42	Rick Mahler	.40	.30	.15
43	Bob Walk	.35	.25	.14
45	Bob Gibson	1.50	1.25	.60
49	Preston Hanna	.30	.25	.12
52	Joe Pignatano	.30	.25	.12
53	Dal Maxvill	.30	.25	.12
54	Rube Walker	.30	.25	.12

1982 Police/Fire Safety Brewers

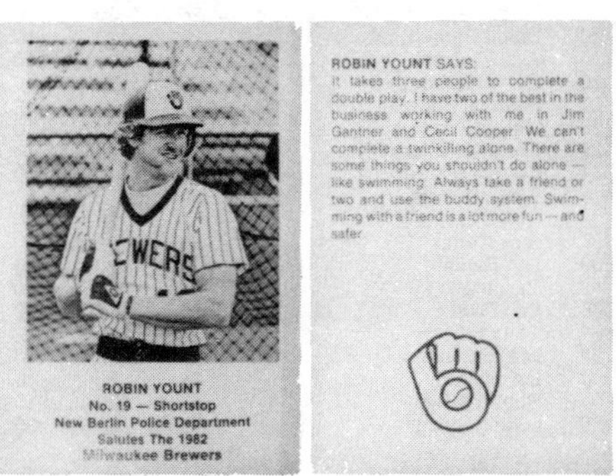

ROBIN YOUNT
No. 19 — Shortstop
New Berlin Police Department
Salutes The 1982
Milwaukee Brewers
ROBIN YOUNT SAYS:
It takes three people to complete a double play. I have two of the best in the business working with me in Jim Gantner and Cecil Cooper. We can't complete a twinkilling alone. There are some things you shouldn't do alone — like swimming. Always take a friend or two and use the buddy system. Swimming with a friend is a lot more fun — and safer.

The inaugural Milwaukee Brewers police set contains 30 cards in a 2-13/16" by 4-1/8" format. There are 26 players included in the set, which is numbered by player uniform number. Unnumbered cards were also issued for general manager Harry Dalton, manager Buck Rodgers, the coaches and a team card with checklist. The full-color photos are especially attractive, printed on the cards' crisp white stock. A number of Wisconsin law enforcement agencies distributed the cards and credit lines on the card fronts were changed accordingly.

		MT	NR MT	EX
Complete Set:		12.00	9.00	4.75
Common Player:		.25	.20	.10
4	Paul Molitor	1.50	1.25	.60
5	Ned Yost	.30	.25	.12
7	Don Money	.25	.20	.10
9	Larry Hisle	.25	.20	.10
10	Bob McClure	.25	.20	.10
11	Ed Romero	.25	.20	.10
13	Roy Howell	.25	.20	.10
15	Cecil Cooper	.50	.40	.20
17	Jim Gantner	.30	.25	.12
19	Robin Yount	3.00	2.25	1.25
20	Gorman Thomas	.30	.25	.12
22	Charlie Moore	.30	.25	.12
23	Ted Simmons	.50	.40	.20
24	Ben Oglivie	.30	.25	.12
26	Kevin Bass	.60	.45	.25
28	Jamie Easterly	.25	.20	.10
29	Mark Brouhard	.25	.20	.10
30	Moose Haas	.25	.20	.10
34	Rollie Fingers	1.50	1.25	.60
35	Randy Lerch	.25	.20	.10
37	Buck Rodgers	.25	.20	.10
41	Jim Slaton	.25	.20	.10
45	Doug Jones	.25	.20	.10
46	Jerry Augustine	.25	.20	.10
47	Dwight Bernard	.25	.20	.10
48	Mike Caldwell	.25	.20	.10
50	Pete Vuckovich	.30	.25	.12
----	Team Photo/Checklist	.25	.25	.12
----	Harry Dalton (general mgr.)	.30	.25	.12
----	Coaches Cards (Pat Dobson, Larry Haney, Ron Hansen, Cal McLish, Buck Rodgers, Harry Warner)	.30	.25	.12

1982 Police/Fire Safety Dodgers

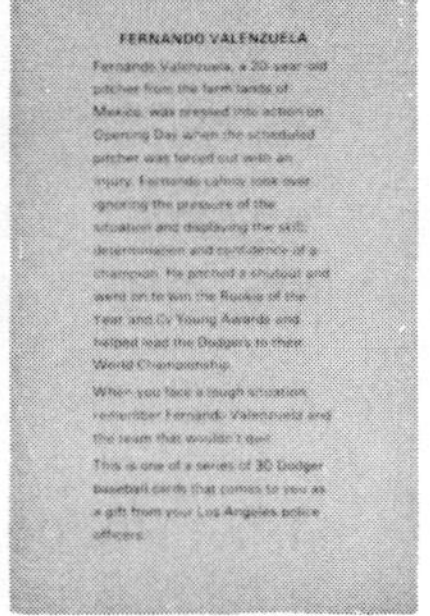

Again issued in the same 2-13/16" by 4-1/8" size of the '80 and '81 sets, the 1982 Los Angeles set commemorates the team's 1981 World Championship. In addition to the 26 cards numbered by uniform for players and manager Tom Lasorda, there are four unnumbered cards which feature the team winning the division, league and World Series titles, plus one of the World Series trophy. The full-color card photos are once again vivid portraits on a clean white card stock. Card backs offer brief biographies and stadium information in addition to a safety tip.

		MT	NR MT	EX
Complete Set:		7.00	5.25	2.75
Common Player:		.15	.11	.06
2	Tom Lasorda	.30	.25	.12
6	Steve Garvey	.90	.70	.35
7	Steve Yeager	.15	.11	.06
8	Mark Belanger	.20	.15	.08
10	Ron Cey	.30	.25	.12
12	Dusty Baker	.25	.20	.10
14	Mike Scioscia	.25	.20	.10
16	Rick Monday	.25	.20	.10
18	Bill Russell	.20	.15	.08
21	Jay Johnstone	.20	.15	.08
26	Alejandro Pena	.40	.30	.15
28	Pedro Guerrero	.40	.30	.15
30	Derrel Thomas	.15	.11	.06
31	Jorge Orta	.15	.11	.06
34	Fernando Valenzuela	.40	.30	.15
35	Bob Welch	.40	.30	.15
38	Dave Goltz	.15	.11	.06
40	Ron Roenicke	.15	.11	.06
41	Jerry Reuss	.25	.20	.10
44	Ken Landreaux	.15	.11	.06
46	Burt Hooton	.20	.15	.08
48	Dave Stewart	.90	.70	.35
49	Tom Niedenfuer	.35	.25	.14
51	Terry Forster	.20	.15	.08
52	Steve Sax	.40	.30	.15
57	Steve Howe	.30	.25	.12
----	Division Championship	.15	.11	.06
----	Trophy Card/Checklist	.15	.11	.06

1983 Police/Fire Safety Braves

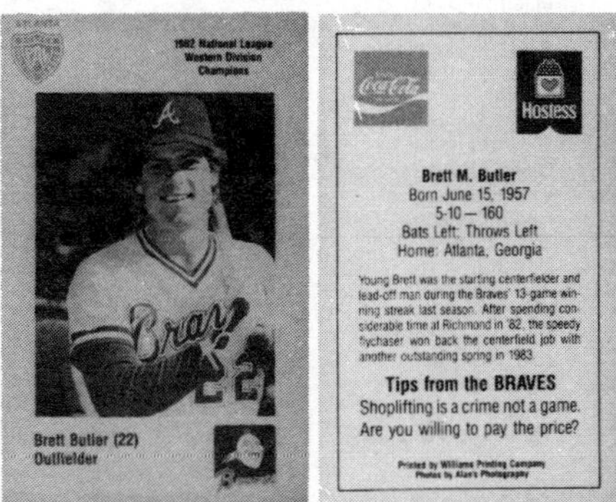

1982 National League
Western Division
Champions
Brett Butler (22)
Outfielder
Hostess
Brett M. Butler
Born June 15, 1957
5-10 — 160
Bats Left; Throws Left
Home: Atlanta, Georgia
Young Brett was the starting centerfielder and lead-off man during the Braves' 13-game winning streak last season. After spending considerable time at Richmond in '82, the speedy flychaser won back the centerfield job with another outstanding spring in 1983.
Tips from the BRAVES
Shoplifting is a crime not a game.
Are you willing to pay the price?

An almost exact replica of their 1982 set, the 1983 Atlanta Braves police set includes 30 cards numbered by uniform. Sponsors Hostess, Coca-Cola and the Atlanta Police Department returned for the third year. The cards are again 2-5/8" by 4-1/8", with full-color photos and police and team logos on the card fronts. A statement noting the team's 1982 National League Western Division title in the upper right corner is the key difference on the card fronts. As in 1982, 8,000 sets were reportedly printed.

		MT	NR MT	EX
Complete Set:		15.00	11.00	6.00
Common Player:		.30	.25	.12
1	Jerry Royster	.30	.25	.12
3	Dale Murphy	3.50	2.75	1.50
4	Biff Pocoroba	.30	.25	.12
5	Bob Horner	.45	.35	.20
6	Randy G. Johnson	.30	.25	.12
8	Bob Watson	.35	.25	.14
9	Joe Torre	.50	.40	.20
10	Chris Chambliss	.40	.30	.15
11	Ken Smith	.30	.25	.12
15	Claudell Washington	.40	.30	.15
16	Rafael Ramirez	.35	.25	.14
17	Glenn Hubbard	.35	.25	.14
19	Terry Harper	.30	.25	.12
20	Bruce Benedict	.30	.25	.12
22	Brett Butler	.40	.30	.15
24	Larry Owen	.30	.25	.12
26	Gene Garber	.30	.25	.12
27	Pascual Perez	.35	.25	.14
29	Craig McMurtry	.35	.25	.14
32	Steve Bedrosian	.60	.45	.25
33	Pete Falcone	.30	.25	.12
35	Phil Niekro	1.50	1.25	.60
36	Sonny Jackson	.30	.25	.12
37	Rick Camp	.30	.25	.12
45	Bob Gibson	1.50	1.25	.60
49	Rick Behenna	.30	.25	.12
51	Terry Forster	.35	.25	.14
52	Joe Pignatano	.30	.25	.12
53	Dal Maxvill	.30	.25	.12
54	Rube Walker	.30	.25	.12

1983 Police/Fire Safety Brewers

16 MARSHALL EDWARDS — OF
The Milwaukee Police Department
Presents The 1983
Milwaukee Brewers

MARSHALL EDWARDS SAYS:
Outfielders use judgement to play the game properly. We must judge fly balls and line drives and react quickly. Use good judgement when choosing your friends. Follow people who set a good example, someone you can learn from. If you get involved with bad friends, react quickly, get away from them before they get you in trouble.

Similar to 1982, a number of issuer variations exist for the 1983 Brewers police set, as law enforcement agencies throughout the state distributed the set with their own credit lines on the cards. At least 28 variations are known to exist, with those issued by smaller agencies being scarcest. Prices quoted below are for the most common variations, generally the Milwaukee police department and a few small-town departments whose entire supply of police cards seem to have fallen into dealers' hands. Some specialists are willing to pay a premium for the scarcer departments' issues. The 30 2-13/16" by 4-1/8" cards include 29 players and coaches, along with a team card (with a checklist back). The team card and group coaches' card are unnumbered, while the others are numbered by uniform number.

		MT	NR MT	EX
Complete Set:		10.00	7.50	4.00
Common Player:		.20	.15	.08
4	Paul Molitor	2.00	1.50	.80
5	Ned Yost	.20	.15	.08
7	Don Money	.25	.20	.10
8	Rob Picciolo	.20	.15	.08
10	Bob McClure	.20	.15	.08
11	Ed Romero	.20	.15	.08
13	Roy Howell	.20	.15	.08
15	Cecil Cooper	.50	.40	.20
16	Marshall Edwards	.20	.15	.08
17	Jim Gantner	.30	.25	.12
19	Robin Yount	3.00	2.25	1.25
20	Gorman Thomas	.25	.20	.10
21	Don Sutton	.90	.70	.35
22	Charlie Moore	.20	.15	.08
23	Ted Simmons	.50	.40	.20
24	Ben Oglivie	.30	.25	.12
26	Bob Skube	.20	.15	.08
27	Pete Ladd	.20	.15	.08
28	Jamie Easterly	.20	.15	.08
30	Moose Haas	.20	.15	.08
32	Harvey Kuenn	.30	.25	.12
34	Rollie Fingers	1.50	1.25	.60
40	Bob L. Gibson	.20	.15	.08
41	Jim Slaton	.20	.15	.08
42	Tom Tellmann	.20	.15	.08
46	Jerry Augustine	.20	.15	.08
48	Mike Caldwell	.25	.20	.10
50	Pete Vuckovich	.30	.25	.12
----	Team Photo/Checklist	.20	.15	.08
----	Coaches Card (Pat Dobson, Dave Garcia, Larry Haney, Ron Hansen)	.20	.15	.08

1983 Police/Fire Safety Dodgers

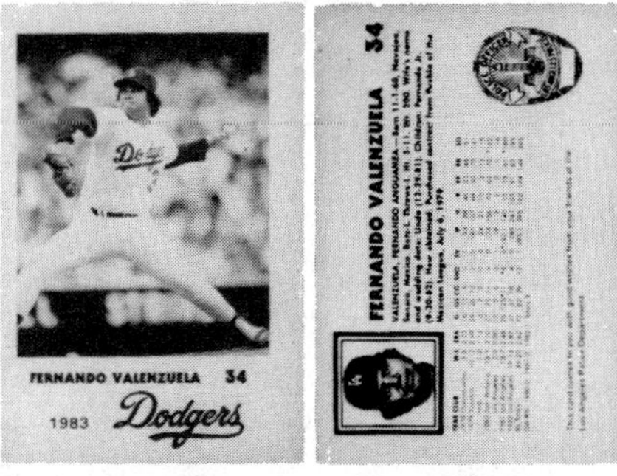

While these full-color cards remained 2-13/16" by 4-1/8" and card fronts were similar to those of previous years, the card backs are quite different. Card backs are in a horizontal design for the first time, and include a small head portrait photo of the player in the upper left corner. Fairly complete player statistics are included but there is no safety tip. The 30 cards are numbered by uniform number, with an unnumbered coaches card also included. Fronts include the year, team logo, player name and number.

		MT	NR MT	EX
Complete Set:		7.00	5.25	2.75
Common Player:		.15	.11	.06
2	Tom Lasorda	.30	.25	.12
3	Steve Sax	.40	.30	.15
5	Mike Marshall	.40	.30	.15
7	Steve Yeager	.15	.11	.06
12	Dusty Baker	.35	.25	.14
14	Mike Scioscia	.25	.20	.10
16	Rick Monday	.25	.20	.10
17	Greg Brock	.25	.20	.10
18	Bill Russell	.20	.15	.08
20	Candy Maldonado	.25	.20	.10
21	Ricky Wright	.15	.11	.06
22	Mark Bradley	.15	.11	.06
23	Dave Sax	.15	.11	.06
26	Alejandro Pena	.25	.20	.10
27	Joe Beckwith	.15	.11	.06
28	Pedro Guerrero	.40	.30	.15
30	Derrel Thomas	.15	.11	.06
34	Fernando Valenzuela	.40	.30	.15
35	Bob Welch	.30	.25	.12
38	Pat Zachry	.15	.11	.06
40	Ron Roenicke	.15	.11	.06
41	Jerry Reuss	.25	.20	.10
43	Jose Morales	.15	.11	.06
44	Ken Landreaux	.15	.11	.06
46	Burt Hooton	.20	.15	.08
47	Larry White	.15	.11	.06
48	Dave Stewart	.60	.45	.25
49	Tom Niedenfuer	.20	.15	.08
57	Steve Howe	.25	.20	.10
----	Coaches Card (Joe Amalfitano, Monty Basgall, Mark Cresse, Manny Mota, Ron Perranoski)	.15	.11	.06

1983 Police/Fire Safety Royals

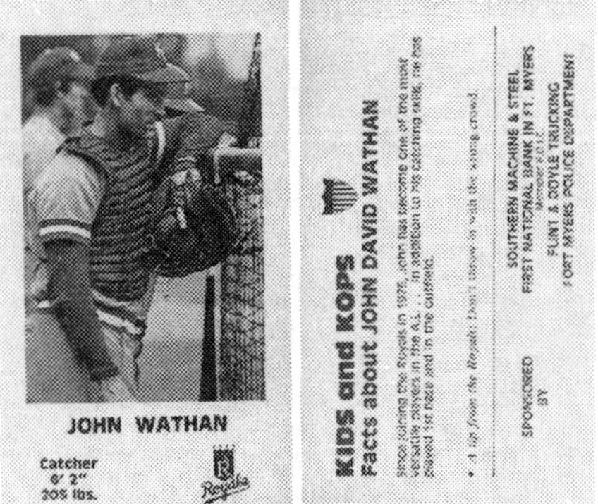

After skipping the 1982 season, the Ft. Myers, Fla., police department issued a Royals safety set in 1983 that is almost identical to their set of 1981. The set is again 2-1/2" by 4-1/8" and numbers just 10 players. Cards are unnumbered, with vertical fronts and horizontal backs. Card fronts have team logos, player name and position and facsimile autographs. Backs list the four sponsoring organizations, a "Tip from the Royals" and a "Kids and Cops Fact" about each player.

		MT	NR MT	EX
Complete Set:		30.00	22.00	12.00
Common Player:		1.00	.70	.40
(1)	Willie Mays Aikens	1.00	.70	.40
(2)	George Brett	18.00	13.50	7.25
(3)	Dennis Leonard	2.00	1.50	.80
(4)	Hal McRae	2.00	1.50	.80
(5)	Amos Otis	2.00	1.50	.80
(6)	Dan Quisenberry	3.00	2.25	1.25
(7)	U.L. Washington	1.00	.70	.40
(8)	John Wathan	2.00	1.50	.80
(9)	Frank White	3.00	2.25	1.25
(10)	Willie Wilson	3.00	2.25	1.25

1984 Police/Fire Safety Blue Jays

This 35-card set was issued in conjuction with the Toronto Sun newspaper and various Ontario area fire departments. The cards feature full-color action photos on the fronts, along with the player name, number and position. Rather than the customary wide white border on front, the Blue Jays fire safety set features bright blue borders. The card backs include brief player biographies and a fire safety tip. The 2-1/2" by 3-1/2" cards were distributed five at a time at two-week intervals during the summer of 1984.

		MT	NR MT	EX
Complete Set:		10.00	7.50	4.00
Common Player:		.20	.15	.08
1	Tony Fernandez	.50	.40	.20
3	Jimy Williams	.20	.15	.08
4	Alfredo Griffin	.30	.25	.12
5	Rance Mulliniks	.20	.15	.08
6	Bobby Cox	.30	.25	.12
7	Damaso Garcia	.30	.25	.12
8	John Sullivan	.20	.15	.08
9	Rick Leach	.20	.15	.08
10	Dave Collins	.25	.20	.10
11	George Bell	.80	.60	.30
12	Ernie Whitt	.30	.25	.12
13	Buck Martinez	.20	.15	.08
15	Lloyd Moseby	.30	.25	.12
16	Garth Iorg	.20	.15	.08
17	Kelly Gruber	.35	.25	.14
18	Jim Clancy	.30	.25	.12
23	Mitch Webster	.30	.25	.12
24	Willie Aikens	.20	.15	.08
25	Roy Lee Jackson	.20	.15	.08
26	Willie Upshaw	.30	.25	.12
27	Jimmy Key	1.00	.70	.40
29	Jesse Barfield	.40	.30	.15
31	Jim Acker	.20	.15	.08
33	Doyle Alexander	.30	.25	.12
34	Stan Clarke	.20	.15	.08
35	Bryan Clark	.20	.15	.08
37	Dave Stieb	.60	.45	.25
38	Jim Gott	.20	.15	.08
41	Al Widmar	.20	.15	.08
42	Billy Smith	.20	.15	.08
43	Cito Gaston	.40	.30	.15
44	Cliff Johnson	.20	.15	.08
48	Luis Leal	.20	.15	.08
53	Dennis Lamp	.20	.15	.08
----	Team Logo/Checklist	.20	.15	.08

1984 Police/Fire Safety Braves

A fourth annual effort by the Braves, the Atlanta Police Department, Coca-Cola and Hostess. This 30-card set continued to be printed in a 2-5/8" by 4-1/8" format, with full-color photos plus team and police logos on the card fronts. For the first time, the cards also have a large logo and date in the upper right corner. Hostess and Coke logos again are on the card backs, with brief player information and a safety tip. Two cards in the set (Pascual Perez and Rafael Ramirez) were issued in Spanish. Cards were distributed two per week by Atlanta police officers. As in 1982 and 1983, a reported 8,000 sets were printed.

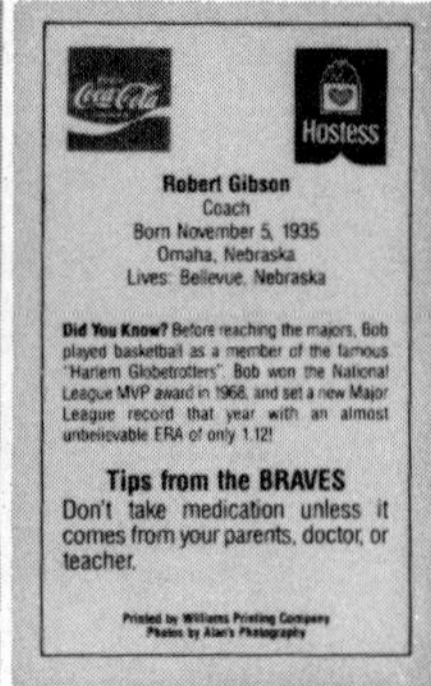

		MT	NR MT	EX
Complete Set:		12.00	9.00	4.75
Common Player:		.25	.20	.10
1	Jerry Royster	.25	.20	.10
3	Dale Murphy	3.50	2.75	1.50
5	Bob Horner	.60	.45	.25
6	Randy G. Johnson	.25	.20	.10
8	Bob Watson	.30	.25	.12
9	Joe Torre	.40	.30	.15
10	Chris Chambliss	.40	.30	.15
11	Mike Jorgensen	.25	.20	.10
15	Claudell Washington	.40	.30	.15
16	Rafael Ramirez	.30	.25	.12
17	Glenn Hubbard	.30	.25	.12
19	Terry Harper	.25	.20	.10
20	Bruce Benedict	.25	.20	.10
25	Alex Trevino	.25	.20	.10
26	Gene Garber	.25	.20	.10
27	Pascual Perez	.30	.25	.12
28	Gerald Perry	1.00	.70	.40
29	Craig McMurtry	.25	.20	.10
31	Donnie Moore	.25	.20	.10
32	Steve Bedrosian	.60	.45	.25
33	Pete Falcone	.25	.20	.10
37	Rick Camp	.25	.20	.10
39	Len Barker	.25	.20	.10
42	Rick Mahler	.25	.20	.10
45	Bob Gibson	1.50	1.25	.60
51	Terry Forster	.30	.25	.12
52	Joe Pignatano	.25	.20	.10
53	Dal Maxvill	.25	.20	.10
54	Rube Walker	.25	.20	.10
55	Luke Appling	.75	.60	.30

1984 Police/Fire Safety Brewers

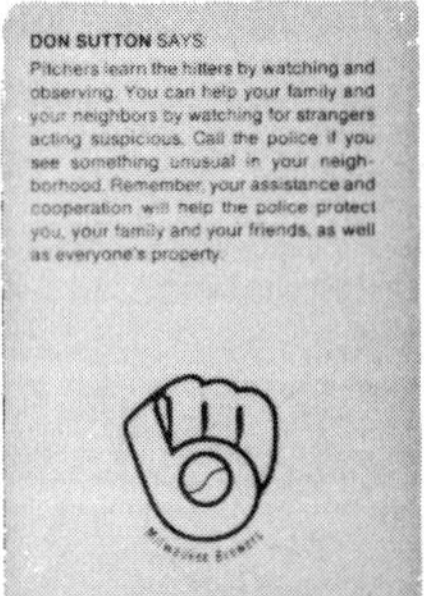

The king of the variations again in 1984, the Milwaukee Brewers set has been found with more than 50 different police agencies' credit lines on the front of the cards. Once again, law enforcement agencies statewide participated in distributing the sets. Some departments also include a badge of the participating agency on the card backs. The full-color cards measure 2-13/16" by 4-1/8". There are 28 numbered player and manager cards, along with an unnumbered coaches card and a team card. Player names, uniform numbers and positions are listed on each card front. Prices listed are for the most common variety (Milwaukee police department); sets issued by smaller departments may be worth a premium to specialists.

		MT	NR MT	EX
Complete Set:		8.00	6.00	3.25
Common Player:		.15	.11	.06
2	Randy Ready	.15	.11	.06
4	Paul Molitor	1.50	1.25	.60
8	Jim Sundberg	.15	.11	.06

9	Rene Lachemann	.15	.11	.06
10	Bob McClure	.15	.11	.06
11	Ed Romero	.15	.11	.06
13	Roy Howell	.15	.11	.06
14	Dion James	.25	.20	.10
15	Cecil Cooper	.40	.30	.15
17	Jim Gantner	.25	.20	.10
19	Robin Yount	2.50	2.00	1.00
20	Don Sutton	.60	.45	.25
21	Bill Schroeder	.15	.11	.06
22	Charlie Moore	.15	.11	.06
23	Ted Simmons	.40	.30	.15
24	Ben Oglivie	.25	.20	.10
25	Bobby Clark	.15	.11	.06
27	Pete Ladd	.15	.11	.06
28	Rick Manning	.15	.11	.06
29	Mark Brouhard	.15	.11	.06
30	Moose Haas	.15	.11	.06
34	Rollie Fingers	1.00	.70	.40
42	Tom Tellmann	.15	.11	.06
43	Chuck Porter	.15	.11	.06
46	Jerry Augustine	.15	.11	.06
47	Jaime Cocanower	.15	.11	.06
48	Mike Caldwell	.20	.15	.08
50	Pete Vuckovich	.25	.20	.10
----	Team Photo/Checklist	.15	.11	.06
----	Coaches Card (Pat Dobson, Dave Garcia, Larry Haney, Tom Trebelhorn)	.15	.11	.06

1984 Police/Fire Safety Dodgers

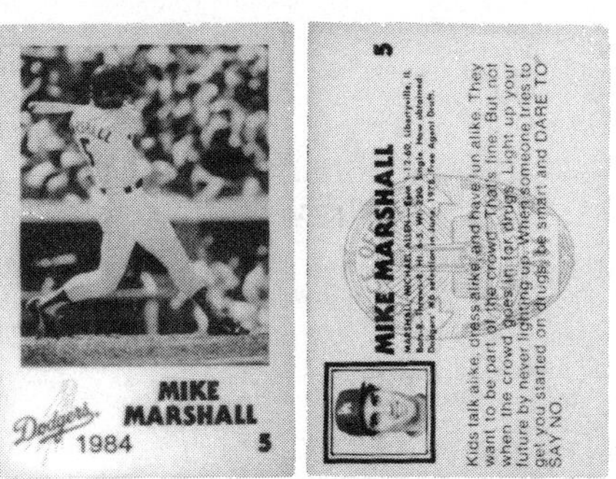

This was the fifth yearly effort of the Dodgers and the Los Angeles Police Department. There are 30 cards in the set, which remains 2-13/16" by 4-1/8". Card fronts are designed somewhat differently than previous years, with more posed photos, bolder player names and numbers and a different team logo. Card backs again feature a small portrait photo in the upper left corner, along with brief biographical information and an anti-drug tip. Card backs are in Dodger blue. Cards are numbered by uniform number, with an unnumbered coaches card also included.

		MT	NR MT	EX
	Complete Set:	8.00	6.00	3.25
	Common Player:	.15	.11	.06
2	Tom Lasorda	.30	.25	.12
3	Steve Sax	.40	.30	.15
5	Mike Marshall	.30	.25	.12
7	Steve Yeager	.15	.11	.06
9	Greg Brock	.20	.15	.08
10	Dave Anderson	.20	.15	.08
14	Mike Scioscia	.25	.20	.10
16	Rick Monday	.25	.20	.10
17	Rafael Landestoy	.15	.11	.06
18	Bill Russell	.20	.15	.08
20	Candy Maldonado	.25	.20	.10
21	Bob Bailor	.15	.11	.06
25	German Rivera	.15	.11	.06
26	Alejandro Pena	.25	.20	.10
27	Carlos Diaz	.15	.11	.06
28	Pedro Guerrero	.40	.30	.15
31	Jack Fimple	.15	.11	.06
34	Fernando Valenzuela	.40	.30	.15
35	Bob Welch	.30	.25	.12
38	Pat Zachry	.15	.11	.06
40	Rick Honeycutt	.25	.20	.10
41	Jerry Reuss	.25	.20	.10
43	Jose Morales	.15	.11	.06
44	Ken Landreaux	.15	.11	.06
45	Terry Whitfield	.15	.11	.06
46	Burt Hooton	.20	.15	.08
49	Tom Niedenfuer	.20	.15	.08
55	Orel Hershiser	2.50	2.00	1.00
56	Richard Rodas	.15	.11	.06
----	Coaches Card (Joe Amalfitano, Monty Basgall, Mark Cresse, Manny Mota, Ron Perranoski)	.15	.11	.06

1985 Police/Fire Safety Blue Jays

The Toronto Blue Jays issued a 35-card fire safety set for the second year in a row in 1985. Cards feature players, coaches, manager, checklist

and team picture. The full-color photos are on the card fronts with a blue border. The backs feature player stats and a safety tip. The cards measure 2-1/2" by 3-1/2" and were distributed throughout the Province of Ontario, Canada.

		MT	NR MT	EX
	Complete Set:	8.00	6.00	3.25
	Common Player:	.20	.15	.08
1	Tony Fernandez	.50	.40	.20
3	Jimy Williams	.20	.15	.08
4	Manny Lee	.25	.20	.10
5	Rance Mulliniks	.20	.15	.08
6	Bobby Cox	.35	.25	.14
7	Damaso Garcia	.30	.25	.12
8	John Sullivan	.20	.15	.08
11	George Bell	.60	.45	.25
12	Ernie Whitt	.30	.25	.12
13	Buck Martinez	.20	.15	.08
15	Lloyd Moseby	.25	.20	.10
16	Garth Iorg	.20	.15	.08
17	Kelly Gruber	.25	.20	.10
18	Jim Clancy	.30	.25	.12
22	Jimmy Key	.50	.40	.20
23	Mitch Webster	.25	.20	.10
24	Willie Aikens	.20	.15	.08
25	Len Matuszek	.20	.15	.08
26	Willie Upshaw	.30	.25	.12
28	Lou Thornton	.20	.15	.08
29	Jesse Barfield	.40	.30	.15
30	Ron Musselman	.20	.15	.08
31	Jim Acker	.20	.15	.08
33	Doyle Alexander	.30	.25	.12
36	Bill Caudill	.20	.15	.08
37	Dave Stieb	.30	.25	.12
41	Al Widmar	.20	.15	.08
42	Billy Smith	.20	.15	.08
43	Cito Gaston	.40	.30	.15
44	Jeff Burroughs	.20	.15	.08
46	Gary Lavelle	.20	.15	.08
48	Luis Leal	.20	.15	.08
50	Tom Henke	.40	.30	.15
53	Dennis Lamp	.20	.15	.08
----	Team Logo/Checklist, Team Photo/Schedule	.20	.15	.08

1985 Police/Fire Safety Braves

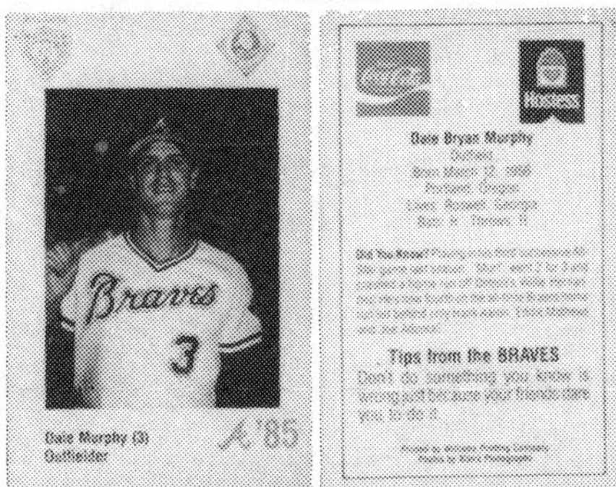

There are again 30 full-color cards in this fifth annual set. Hostess, Coca-Cola and the Atlanta Police Department joined the team as sponsors again for the 2-5/8" by 4-1/8" set. Card backs are similar to previous years, with the only difference on the fronts being a swap in position for the year and team logo. The cards are checklisted by uniform number.

		MT	NR MT	EX
	Complete Set:	12.00	9.00	4.75
	Common Player:	.25	.20	.10
2	Albert Hall	.25	.20	.10
3	Dale Murphy	3.00	2.25	1.25
5	Rick Cerone	.25	.20	.10
7	Bobby Wine	.25	.20	.10
10	Chris Chambliss	.35	.25	.14
11	Bob Horner	.60	.45	.25
12	Paul Runge	.30	.25	.12
15	Claudell Washington	.35	.25	.14
16	Rafael Ramirez	.30	.25	.12
17	Glenn Hubbard	.30	.25	.12
18	Paul Zuvella	.25	.20	.10
19	Terry Harper	.25	.20	.10
20	Bruce Benedict	.25	.20	.10
22	Eddie Haas	.25	.20	.10
24	Ken Oberkfell	.30	.25	.12
26	Gene Garber	.25	.20	.10
27	Pascual Perez	.40	.30	.15
28	Gerald Perry	.60	.45	.25
29	Craig McMurtry	.25	.20	.10
32	Steve Bedrosian	.50	.40	.20
33	Johnny Sain	.35	.25	.14
34	Zane Smith	.60	.45	.25
36	Brad Komminsk	.25	.20	.10
37	Rick Camp	.25	.20	.10
39	Len Barker	.25	.20	.10
40	Bruce Sutter	.70	.50	.30
42	Rick Mahler	.25	.20	.10
51	Terry Forster	.30	.25	.12
52	Leo Mazzone	.25	.20	.10
53	Bobby Dews	.25	.20	.10

1985 Police/Fire Safety Brewers

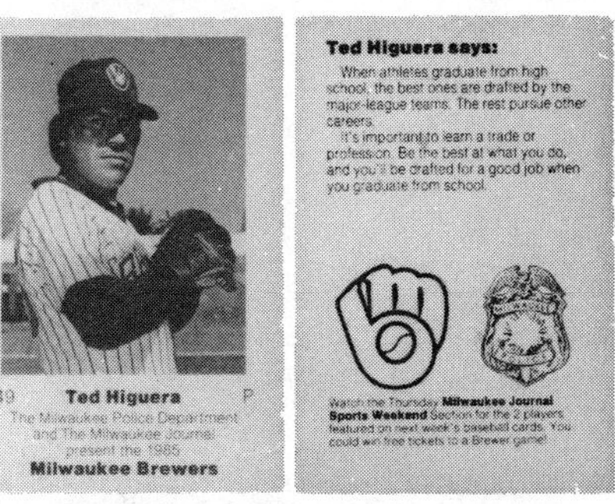

The Brewers changed the size of their annual police set in 1985, but almost imperceptibly. The full-color cards are 2-3/4" by 4-1/8", a slight 1/16" narrower than the four previous efforts. Player and team name on the card fronts are much bolder than in previous years. Once again, numerous area police groups distributed the sets, leading to nearly 60 variations, as each agency put their own credit line on the cards. Card backs include the Brewers logo, a safety tip and, in some cases, a badge of the participating law enforcement group. There are 27 numbered player cards (by uniform number) and three unnumbered cards - team roster, coaches and a newspaper carrier card. Prices are for the most common departments.

		MT	NR MT	EX
	Complete Set:	8.00	6.00	3.25
	Common Player:	.15	.11	.06
2	Randy Ready	.15	.11	.06
4	Paul Molitor	1.50	1.25	.60
5	Doug Loman	.15	.11	.06
7	Paul Householder	.15	.11	.06
10	Bob McClure	.15	.11	.06
11	Ed Romero	.15	.11	.06
14	Dion James	.25	.20	.10
15	Cecil Cooper	.40	.30	.15
17	Jim Gantner	.25	.20	.10
18	Danny Darwin	.20	.15	.08
19	Robin Yount	2.50	2.00	1.00
21	Bill Schroeder	.15	.11	.06
22	Charlie Moore	.15	.11	.06
23	Ted Simmons	.40	.30	.15
24	Ben Oglivie	.25	.20	.10
26	Brian Giles	.15	.11	.06
27	Pete Ladd	.15	.11	.06
28	Rick Manning	.15	.11	.06
29	Mark Brouhard	.15	.11	.06
30	Moose Haas	.15	.11	.06
31	George Bamberger	.15	.11	.06
34	Rollie Fingers	.90	.70	.35
40	Bob L. Gibson	.15	.11	.06
41	Ray Searage	.15	.11	.06
47	Jaime Cocanower	.15	.11	.06
48	Ray Burris	.15	.11	.06
49	Ted Higuera	.60	.45	.25
50	Pete Vuckovich	.25	.20	.10
----	Coaches Card (Andy Etchebarren, Larry Haney, Frank Howard, Tony Muser, Herm Starrette)	.15	.11	.06
----	Team Photo	.15	.11	.06

1985 Police/Fire Safety Phillies

This is a brilliantly colored 2-5/8" by 4-1/8" set, co-sponsored by the Phillies and Cigna Corporation. Card fronts include the player name, number, position and team logo. The 16 cards are numbered on

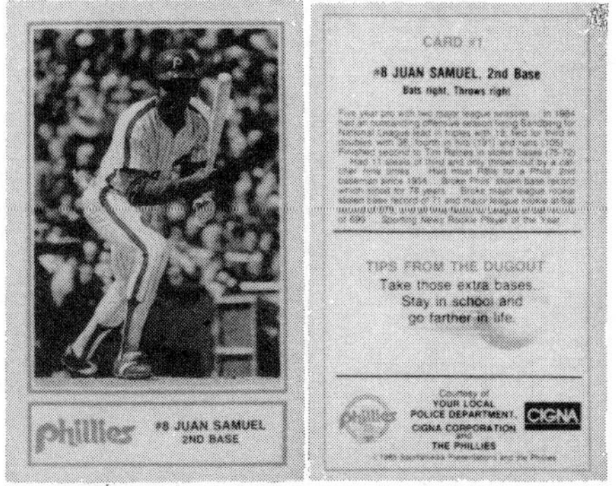

the back and include biographical information and a safety tip. The cards were distributed by several Philadelphia area police departments.

		MT	NR MT	EX
Complete Set:		8.00	6.00	3.25
Common Player:		.15	.11	.06
1	Juan Samuel	.50	.40	.20
2	Von Hayes	.25	.20	.10
3	Ozzie Virgil	.20	.15	.08
4	Mike Schmidt	2.50	2.00	1.00
5	Greg Gross	.15	.11	.06
6	Tim Corcoran	.15	.11	.06
7	Jerry Koosman	.25	.20	.10
8	Jeff Stone	.15	.11	.06
9	Glenn Wilson	.25	.20	.10
10	Steve Jeltz	.15	.11	.06
11	Garry Maddox	.20	.15	.08
12	Steve Carlton	1.25	.90	.50
13	John Denny	.15	.11	.06
14	Kevin Gross	.20	.15	.08
15	Shane Rawley	.20	.15	.08
16	Charlie Hudson	.15	.11	.06

1986 Police/Fire Safety Astros

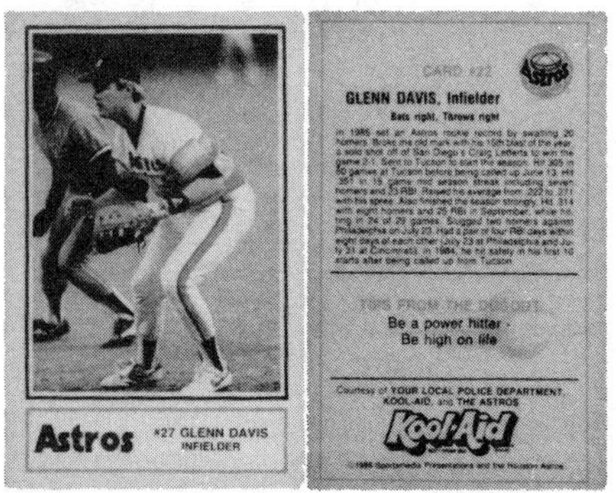

This full-color police safety set for the 1986 Houston Astros was issued by the Houston Police Department and sponsored by Kool-Aid. The 26-card set was distributed at the Astrodome on June 14, when 15,000 sets of the first 12 cards were given away. The balance of the set was distributed throughout the summer by the Houston police. The cards feature player photos on the fronts and a safety tip on the card backs. The cards measure 4-1/8" by 2-5/8".

		MT	NR MT	EX
Complete Set:		8.00	6.00	3.25
Common Player:		.20	.15	.08
1	Jim Pankovits	.20	.15	.08
2	Nolan Ryan	2.00	1.50	.80
3	Mike Scott	.30	.25	.12
4	Kevin Bass	.30	.25	.12
5	Bill Doran	.30	.25	.12
6	Hal Lanier	.20	.15	.08
7	Denny Walling	.20	.15	.08
8	Alan Ashby	.20	.15	.08
9	Phil Garner	.25	.20	.10
10	Charlie Kerfeld	.20	.15	.08
11	Dave Smith	.20	.15	.08
12	Jose Cruz	.35	.25	.14
13	Craig Reynolds	.20	.15	.08
14	Mark Bailey	.20	.15	.08
15	Bob Knepper	.30	.25	.12
16	Julio Solano	.20	.15	.08
17	Dickie Thon	.25	.20	.10
18	Mike Madden	.20	.15	.08
19	Jeff Calhoun	.20	.15	.08
20	Tony Walker	.20	.15	.08
21	Terry Puhl	.20	.15	.08
22	Glenn Davis	.40	.30	.15
23	Billy Hatcher	.40	.30	.15
24	Jim Deshaies	.40	.30	.15
25	Frank DiPino	.20	.15	.08
26	Coaching Staff (Yogi Berra, Matt Galante, Denis Menke, Les Moss, Gene Tenace)	.20	.15	.08

1986 Police/Fire Safety Blue Jays

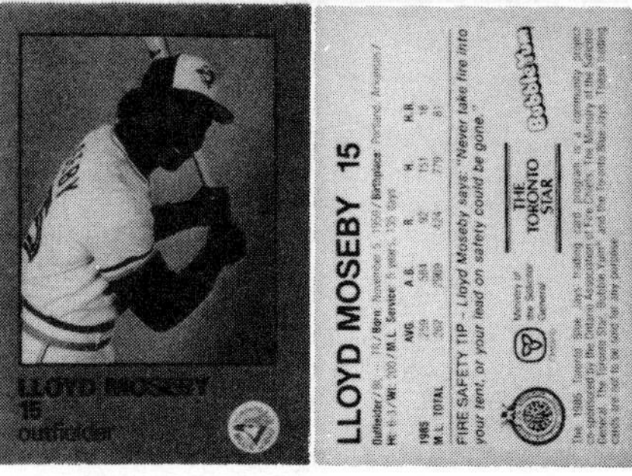

This was the third consecutive year the Toronto Blue Jays issued a fire safety set of 36 baseball cards. The cards were given out at many fire stations in Ontario, Canada. The cards are printed in full color and include players and other personnel. The set was co-sponsored by the local fire departments, Bubble Yum and the Toronto Star. The cards measure 2-1/2" by 3-1/2".

		MT	NR MT	EX
Complete Set:		10.00	7.50	4.00
Common Player:		.20	.15	.08
1	Tony Fernandez	.40	.30	.15
3	Jimy Williams	.20	.15	.08
5	Rance Mulliniks	.20	.15	.08
7	Damaso Garcia	.20	.15	.08
8	John Sullivan	.20	.15	.08
9	Rick Leach	.20	.15	.08
11	George Bell	.60	.45	.25
12	Ernie Whitt	.30	.25	.12
13	Buck Martinez	.20	.15	.08
15	Lloyd Moseby	.25	.20	.10
16	Garth Iorg	.20	.15	.08
17	Kelly Gruber	.30	.25	.12
18	Jim Clancy	.30	.25	.12
22	Jimmy Key	.50	.40	.20
23	Cecil Fielder	4.00	3.00	1.50
24	John McLaren	.20	.15	.08
25	Steve Davis	.20	.15	.08
26	Willie Upshaw	.30	.25	.12
29	Jesse Barfield	.40	.30	.15
31	Jim Acker	.20	.15	.08
33	Doyle Alexander	.30	.25	.12
36	Bill Caudill	.20	.15	.08
37	Dave Stieb	.30	.25	.12
38	Mark Eichhorn	.40	.30	.15
39	Don Gordon	.20	.15	.08
41	Al Widmar	.20	.15	.08
42	Billy Smith	.20	.15	.08
43	Cito Gaston	.40	.30	.15
44	Cliff Johnson	.20	.15	.08
46	Gary Lavelle	.20	.15	.08
49	Tom Filer	.20	.15	.08
50	Tom Henke	.40	.30	.15
53	Dennis Lamp	.20	.15	.08
54	Jeff Hearron	.20	.15	.08
----	Team Photo	.20	.15	.08

1986 Police/Fire Safety Braves

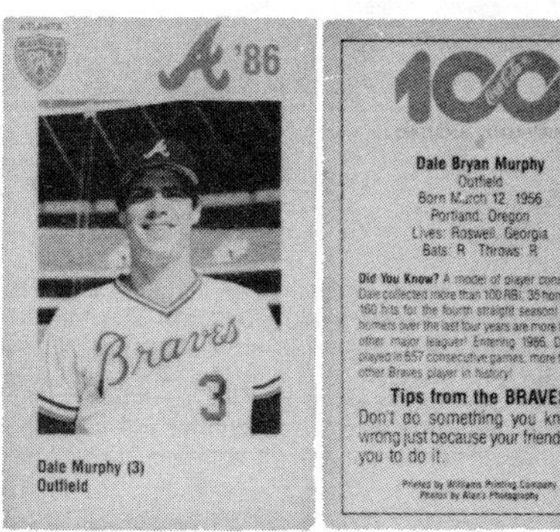

The Police Athletic League of Atlanta issued a 30-card full-color set featuring the Atlanta Braves players and personnel. The cards measure 2-5/8" by 4-1/8". Card fronts include player photos with name, uniform number and position below the photo. The cards backs offer the 100th Anniversary Coca-Cola logo, player information, statistics and a safety related tip. This was the sixth consecutive year that the Braves issued a safety set. The cards were available from police officers in Atlanta.

		MT	NR MT	EX
Complete Set:		11.00	8.25	4.50
Common Player:		.25	.20	.10
2	Russ Nixon	.25	.20	.10
3	Dale Murphy	2.50	2.00	1.00
4	Bob Skinner	.25	.20	.10
5	Billy Sample	.25	.20	.10
7	Chuck Tanner	.35	.25	.14
8	Willie Stargell	.80	.60	.30
9	Ozzie Virgil	.35	.25	.14
10	Chris Chambliss	.35	.25	.14
11	Bob Horner	.40	.30	.15
14	Andres Thomas	.25	.20	.10
15	Claudell Washington	.35	.25	.14
16	Rafael Ramirez	.30	.25	.12
17	Glenn Hubbard	.30	.25	.12
18	Omar Moreno	.25	.20	.10
19	Terry Harper	.25	.20	.10
20	Bruce Benedict	.25	.20	.10
23	Ted Simmons	.50	.40	.20
24	Ken Oberkfell	.30	.25	.12
26	Gene Garber	.25	.20	.10
29	Craig McMurtry	.25	.20	.10
30	Paul Assenmacher	.40	.30	.15
33	Johnny Sain	.30	.25	.12
34	Zane Smith	.40	.30	.15
38	Joe Johnson	.25	.20	.10
40	Bruce Sutter	.60	.45	.25
42	Rick Mahler	.25	.20	.10
46	David Palmer	.25	.20	.10
48	Duane Ward	.90	.70	.35
49	Jeff Dedmon	.25	.20	.10
52	Al Monchak	.25	.20	.10

1986 Police/Fire Safety Brewers

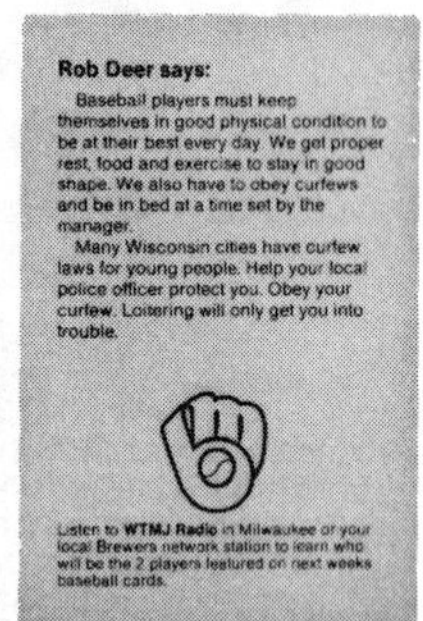

The Milwaukee Brewers, in conjunction with the Milwaukee Police Department, WTMJ Radio and Kinney Shoes, produced this attractive police safety set of 30 cards. The cards measure 2-13/16" by 4-1/2". A thin black border encloses a full-color Player photo on the front. The card backs give a safety tip and promos for the sponsor. The cards were distributed throughout the state of Wisconsin by numerous police departments; those of the smaller departments generally being scarcer than those issued in the big cities. Prices quoted below are for the most common departments' issues.

		MT	NR MT	EX
Complete Set:		7.00	5.25	2.75
Common Player:		.15	.11	.06
1	Ernest Riles	.30	.25	.12
2	Randy Ready	.15	.11	.06
3	Juan Castillo	.20	.15	.08
4	Paul Molitor	1.50	1.25	.60
7	Paul Householder	.15	.11	.06
10	Bob McClure	.15	.11	.06
11	Rick Cerone	.15	.11	.06
13	Billy Jo Robidoux	.15	.11	.06
15	Cecil Cooper	.40	.30	.15
16	Mike Felder	.30	.25	.12
17	Jim Gantner	.25	.20	.10
18	Danny Darwin	.20	.15	.08
19	Robin Yount	2.00	1.50	.80
20	Juan Nieves	.20	.15	.08
21	Bill Schroeder	.15	.11	.06
22	Charlie Moore	.15	.11	.06
24	Ben Oglivie	.25	.20	.10
25	Mark Clear	.15	.11	.06
28	Rick Manning	.15	.11	.06
31	George Bamberger	.15	.11	.06
37	Dan Plesac	.30	.25	.12
39	Tim Leary	.15	.11	.06
41	Ray Searage	.15	.11	.06
43	Chuck Porter	.15	.11	.06
45	Rob Deer	.20	.15	.08
46	Bill Wegman	.30	.25	.12
47	Jamie Cocanower	.15	.11	.06
49	Ted Higuera	.25	.20	.10
----	Coaches Card (Andy Etchebarren, Larry Haney, Frank Howard, Tony Muser, Herm Starrette)	.15	.11	.06
----	Team Photo/Roster	.15	.11	.06

1986 Police/Fire Safety Dodgers

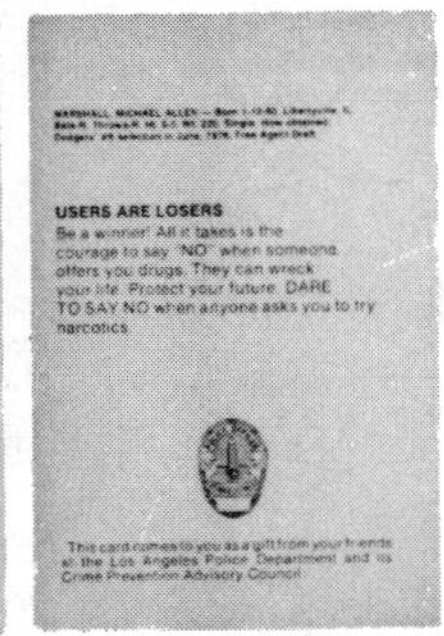

After skipping the 1985 season, the Los Angeles Dodgers once again issued baseball cards related to police safety. The club had issued sets from 1980-84. The 1986 set features 30 full-color glossy cards measuring 2-1/4" by 4-1/8". The cards are numbered according to player uniforms. The backs feature brief player data and a safety tip from the Los Angeles Police Department. The sets were given away May 18 during Baseball Card Day at Dodger Stadium.

		MT	NR MT	EX
	Complete Set:	7.00	5.25	2.75
	Common Player:	.15	.11	.06
2	Tom Lasorda	.25	.20	.10
3	Steve Sax	.25	.20	.10
5	Mike Marshall	.25	.20	.10
9	Greg Brock	.15	.11	.06
10	Dave Anderson	.15	.11	.06
12	Bill Madlock	.30	.25	.12
14	Mike Scioscia	.25	.20	.10
17	Len Matuszek	.15	.11	.06
18	Bill Russell	.20	.15	.08
22	Franklin Stubbs	.15	.11	.06
23	Enos Cabell	.15	.11	.06
25	Mariano Duncan	.60	.45	.25
26	Alejandro Pena	.25	.20	.10
27	Carlos Diaz	.15	.11	.06
28	Pedro Guerrero	.30	.25	.12
29	Alex Trevino	.15	.11	.06
31	Ed Vande Berg	.15	.11	.06
34	Fernando Valenzuela	.40	.30	.15
35	Bob Welch	.30	.25	.12
40	Rick Honeycutt	.15	.11	.06
41	Jerry Reuss	.25	.20	.10
43	Ken Howell	.20	.15	.08
44	Ken Landreaux	.15	.11	.06
45	Terry Whitfield	.15	.11	.06
48	Dennis Powell	.20	.15	.08
49	Tom Niedenfuer	.20	.15	.08
51	Reggie Williams	.20	.15	.08
55	Orel Hershiser	.40	.30	.15
----	Team Photo/Checklist	.15	.11	.06
----	Coaching Staff (Joe Amalfitano, Monty Basgall, Mark Cresse, Ben Hines, Don McMahon, Manny Mota, Ron Perranoski)	.15	.11	.06

1986 Police/Fire Safety Phillies

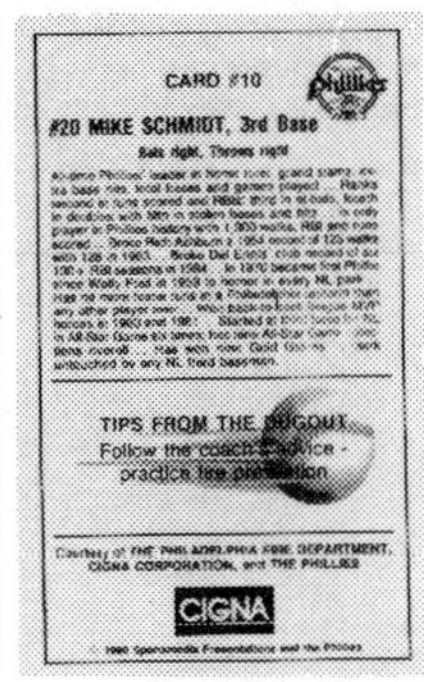

For the second straight year, the Philadelphia Phillies issued a 16-card safety set. However, in 1986 the set was issued in conjunction with the Philadelphia Fire Department rather than the police. Cigna Corporation remained a sponsor. The cards, which measure 2-5/8" by 4-1/8" in size, feature full color photos. Along with other pertinent information, the card backs contain a short player biography and a "Tips From The Dugout" fire safety hint.

		MT	NR MT	EX
	Complete Set:	6.00	4.50	2.50
	Common Player:	.15	.11	.06
1	Juan Samuel	.30	.25	.12
2	Don Carman	.20	.15	.08
3	Von Hayes	.20	.15	.08
4	Kent Tekulve	.20	.15	.08
5	Greg Gross	.15	.11	.06
6	Shane Rawley	.20	.15	.08
7	Darren Daulton	.20	.15	.08
8	Kevin Gross	.20	.15	.08
9	Steve Jeltz	.15	.11	.06
10	Mike Schmidt	1.50	1.25	.60
11	Steve Bedrosian	.35	.25	.14
12	Gary Redus	.30	.25	.12
13	Charles Hudson	.15	.11	.06
14	John Russell	.15	.11	.06
15	Fred Toliver	.15	.11	.06
16	Glenn Wilson	.20	.15	.08

1987 Police/Fire Safety Astros

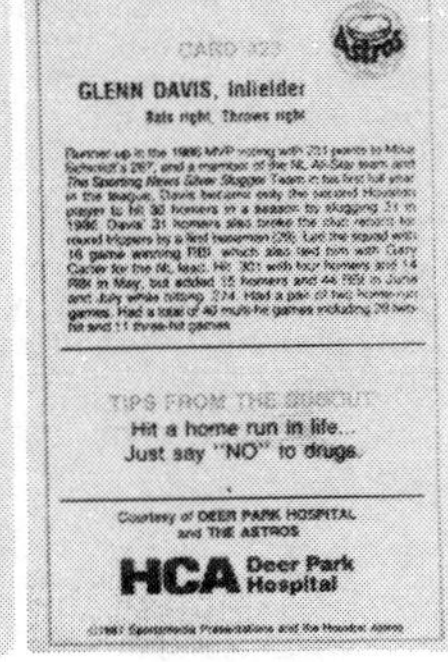

The 1987 Houston Astros safety set was produced through the combined efforts of the Astros, Deer Park Hospital and Sportsmedia Presentations. #'s 1-12 were handed out to youngsters 14 and under at the Astrodome on July 14th. The balancing of the distribution was handled by Deer Park Hospital. The cards, which measure 2-5/8" by 4-1/8", contain full-color photos. The backs offer a brief team/player history and a "Tips From The Dugout" anti-drug message.

		MT	NR MT	EX
	Complete Set:	8.00	6.00	3.25
	Common Player:	.20	.15	.08
1	Larry Andersen	.20	.15	.08
2	Mark Bailey	.20	.15	.08
3	Jose Cruz	.35	.25	.14
4	Danny Darwin	.25	.20	.10
5	Bill Doran	.25	.20	.10
6	Billy Hatcher	.40	.30	.15
7	Hal Lanier	.20	.15	.08
8	Davey Lopes	.30	.25	.12
9	Dave Meads	.20	.15	.08
10	Craig Reynolds	.20	.15	.08
11	Mike Scott	.30	.25	.12
12	Denny Walling	.20	.15	.08
13	Aurelio Lopez	.20	.15	.08
14	Dickie Thon	.25	.20	.10
15	Terry Puhl	.20	.15	.08
16	Nolan Ryan	2.00	1.50	.80
17	Dave Smith	.20	.15	.08
18	Julio Solano	.20	.15	.08
19	Jim Deshaies	.30	.25	.12
20	Bob Knepper	.30	.25	.12
21	Alan Ashby	.20	.15	.08
22	Kevin Bass	.40	.30	.15
23	Glenn Davis	.40	.30	.15
24	Phil Garner	.35	.25	.14
25	Jim Pankovits	.20	.15	.08
26	Coaching Staff (Yogi Berra, Matt Galante, Denis Menke, Les Moss, Gene Tenace)	.20	.15	.08

Definitions for grading conditions are located in the Introduction of this price guide.

1987 Police/Fire Safety Blue Jays

For the fourth consecutive year, the Toronto Blue Jays issued a fire safety set of 36 cards. As in 1986, the set was sponsored by the local fire departments and governing agencies, Bubble Yum and the Toronto Star. The card fronts feature a full-color photo surrounded by a white border. The backs carry a fire safety tip and logos of all sponsors, plus

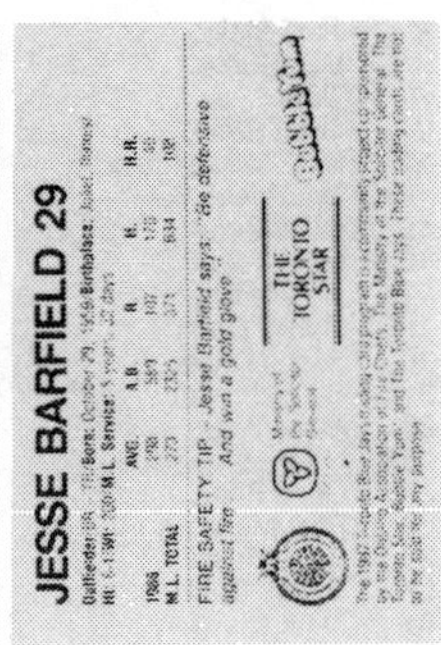

player personal data and statistics. Produced on thin stock, cards in the set are the standard 2-1/2" by 3-1/2" size.

		MT	NR MT	EX
	Complete Set:	9.00	6.75	3.50
	Common Player:	.15	.11	.06
1	Tony Fernandez	.35	.25	.14
3	Jimy Williams	.15	.11	.06
5	Rance Mulliniks	.15	.11	.06
8	John Sullivan	.15	.11	.06
9	Rick Leach	.15	.11	.06
10	Mike Sharperson	.20	.15	.08
11	George Bell	.60	.45	.25
12	Ernie Whitt	.25	.20	.10
15	Lloyd Moseby	.20	.15	.08
16	Garth Iorg	.15	.11	.06
17	Kelly Gruber	.25	.20	.10
18	Jim Clancy	.25	.20	.10
19	Fred McGriff	3.00	2.25	1.25
22	Jimmy Key	.40	.30	.15
23	Cecil Fielder	2.00	1.50	.80
24	John McLaren	.15	.11	.06
26	Willie Upshaw	.25	.20	.10
29	Jesse Barfield	.30	.25	.12
31	Duane Ward	.35	.25	.14
33	Joe Johnson	.15	.11	.06
35	Jeff Musselman	.20	.15	.08
37	Dave Stieb	.40	.30	.15
38	Mark Eichhorn	.20	.15	.08
40	Rob Ducey	.20	.15	.08
41	Al Widmar	.15	.11	.06
42	Billy Smith	.15	.11	.06
43	Cito Gaston	.30	.25	.12
45	Jose Nunez	.15	.11	.06
46	Gary Lavelle	.15	.11	.06
47	Matt Stark	.15	.11	.06
48	Craig McMurtry	.15	.11	.06
50	Tom Henke	.30	.25	.12
54	Jeff Hearron	.15	.11	.06
55	John Cerutti	.20	.15	.08
----	Logo/Won-Loss Record	.15	.11	.06
----	Team Photo/Checklist	.15	.11	.06

1987 Police/Fire Safety Brewers

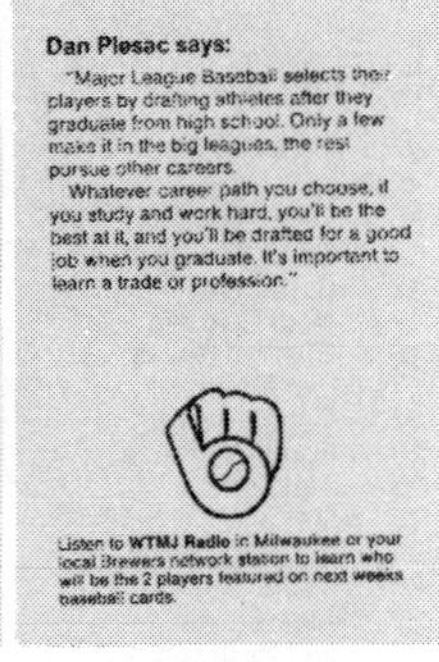

The Milwaukee Brewers issued a safety set in 1987 for the sixth consecutive year. As in the past, many local police departments throughout Wisconsin participated in the giveaway program. The Milwaukee version was sponsored by Kinney Shoe Stores and WTMJ Radio and was handed out to youngsters attending the Baseball Card Day at County Stadium on May 9th. The cards, which measure 2-1/4" by 4-1/8", feature full-color photos plus a safety tip on the backs. Chris Bosio can be found with a uniform number of 26 or 29. The card was corrected to #29 in later printings.

		MT	NR MT	EX
	Complete Set:	6.00	4.50	2.50
	Common Player:	.15	.11	.06
1	Ernest Riles	.15	.11	.06
2	Edgar Diaz	.15	.11	.06
3	Juan Castillo	.15	.11	.06

4	Paul Molitor	1.25	.90	.50
5	B.J. Surhoff	.40	.30	.15
7	Dale Sveum	.20	.15	.08
9	Greg Brock	.15	.11	.06
13	Billy Jo Robidoux	.15	.11	.06
14	Jim Paciorek	.15	.11	.06
15	Cecil Cooper	.30	.25	.12
16	Mike Felder	.15	.11	.06
17	Jim Gantner	.20	.15	.08
19	Robin Yount	2.00	1.50	.80
20	Juan Nieves	.20	.15	.08
21	Bill Schroeder	.15	.11	.06
25	Mark Clear	.15	.11	.06
26a	Glenn Braggs	.30	.25	.12
26b	Chris Bosio	.60	.45	.25
28	Rick Manning	.15	.11	.06
29	Chris Bosio	.60	.45	.25
32	Chuck Crim	.15	.11	.06
34	Mark Ciardi	.15	.11	.06
37	Dan Plesac	.20	.15	.08
38	John Henry Johnson	.15	.11	.06
40	Mike Birbeck	.25	.20	.10
42	Tom Trebelhorn	.20	.15	.08
45	Rob Deer	.20	.15	.08
46	Bill Wegman	.20	.15	.08
49	Ted Higuera	.20	.15	.08
----	Coaches Card (Andy Etchebarren, Larry Haney, Chuck Hartenstein, Dave Hilton, Tony Muser)	.15	.11	.06
----	Team Photo/Roster	.15	.11	.06

1987 Police/Fire Safety Dodgers

Producing a police set for the seventh time in eight years, the 1987 edition contains 30 cards which measure 2-13/16" by 4-1/8". The set includes a special Dodger Stadium 25th Anniversary card. The card fronts contain a full-color photo plus the Dodger Stadium 25th Anniversay logo. The photos are a mix of action and posed shots. The backs contain personal player data plus a police safety tip. The cards were given out April 24th at Dodger Stadium and were distributed by the Los Angeles police department at a rate of two cards per week.

		MT	NR MT	EX
	Complete Set:	6.00	4.50	2.50
	Common Player:	.15	.11	.06
2	Tom Lasorda	.25	.20	.10
3	Steve Sax	.25	.20	.10
5	Mike Marshall	.25	.20	.10
10	Dave Anderson	.15	.11	.06
12	Bill Madlock	.30	.25	.12
14	Mike Scioscia	.25	.20	.10
15	Gilberto Reyes	.15	.11	.06
17	Len Matuszek	.15	.11	.06
21	Reggie Williams	.15	.11	.06
22	Franklin Stubbs	.15	.11	.06
23	Tim Leary	.15	.11	.06
25	Mariano Duncan	.30	.25	.12
26	Alejandro Pena	.25	.20	.10
28	Pedro Guerrero	.40	.30	.15
29	Alex Trevino	.15	.11	.06
33	Jeff Hamilton	.35	.25	.14
34	Fernando Valenzuela	.40	.30	.15
35	Bob Welch	.30	.25	.12
36	Matt Young	.15	.11	.06
40	Rick Honeycutt	.15	.11	.06
41	Jerry Reuss	.25	.20	.10
43	Ken Howell	.15	.11	.06
44	Ken Landreaux	.15	.11	.06
46	Ralph Bryant	.25	.20	.10
47	Jose Gonzalez	.20	.15	.08
49	Tom Niedenfuer	.20	.15	.08
51	Brian Holton	.30	.25	.12
55	Orel Hershiser	.40	.30	.15
----	Coaching Staff (Joe Amalfitano, Mark Cresse, Tom Lasorda, Don McMahon, Manny Mota, Ron Perranoski, Bill Russell)	.15	.11	.06
----	Dodger Stadium/Checklist	.15	.11	.06

A player's name in italic type indicates a rookie card. An (FC) indicates a player's first card for that particular card company.

1988 Police/Fire Safety Astros

This set of 26 full-color cards highlighting the Houston Astros was produced by the team, in conjunction with Deer Park Hospital and Sportsmedia Promotions for distribution to fans 14 years and younger at a ballpark giveaway. The 2-5/8" by 4-1/8" cards feature full-color player photos framed by a narrow blue border with an orange player/team name block below the photo. The blue and white card backs have orange borders and list card numbers, player information, career highlights and anti-drug tips.

		MT	NR MT	EX
	Complete Set:	8.00	6.00	3.25
	Common Player:	.20	.15	.08
1	Juan Agosto	.20	.15	.08
2	Larry Andersen	.20	.15	.08
3	Joaquin Andujar	.30	.25	.12
4	Alan Ashby	.20	.15	.08
5	Mark Bailey	.20	.15	.08
6	Kevin Bass	.40	.30	.15
7	Danny Darwin	.25	.20	.10
8	Glenn Davis	.40	.30	.15
9	Jim Deshaies	.30	.25	.12
10	Bill Doran	.30	.25	.12
11	Billy Hatcher	.40	.30	.15
12	Jeff Heathcock	.20	.15	.08
13	Steve Henderson	.20	.15	.08
14	Chuck Jackson	.20	.15	.08
15	Bob Knepper	.30	.25	.12
16	Jim Pankovits	.20	.15	.08
17	Terry Puhl	.20	.15	.08
18	Rafael Ramirez	.20	.15	.08
19	Craig Reynolds	.20	.15	.08
20	Nolan Ryan	2.00	1.50	.80
21	Mike Scott	.30	.25	.12
22	Dave Smith	.30	.25	.12
23	Denny Walling	.20	.15	.08
24	Gerald Young	.60	.45	.25
25	Hal Lanier	.20	.15	.08
26	Coaching Staff (Yogi Berra, Gene Clines, Matt Galante, Marc Hill, Denis Menke, Les Moss)	.20	.15	.08

1988 Police/Fire Safety Blue Jays

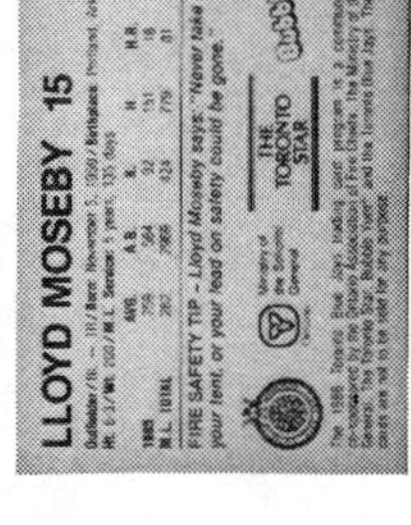

This 36-card set features full-color action photos on 3-1/2" by 5" cards with white borders and a thin black line framing the photos. Card numbers (player's uniform #) appear lower left, team logo lower right; player's name and position are printed bottom center. Card backs are blue on white and include personal and career info, 1987 and career stats, sponsor logos and a fire safety tip. The set includes 34 player cards, a team photo checklist card and a team logo card with a year-by-year won/loss record. The set was sponsored by the Ontario Fire Chief Association, Ontario's Solicitor General, The Toronto Star and Bubble Yum and was distributed free as part of a community service project.

		MT	NR MT	EX
	Complete Set:	7.00	5.25	2.75
	Common Player:	.15	.11	.06
1	Tony Fernandez	.35	.25	.14
2	Nelson Liriano	.15	.11	.06
3	Jimy Williams	.15	.11	.06
4	Manny Lee	.15	.11	.06
5	Rance Mulliniks	.15	.11	.06
6	Silvestre Campusuano	.20	.15	.08
7	John McLaren	.15	.11	.06
8	John Sullivan	.15	.11	.06
9	Rick Leach	.15	.11	.06
10	Pat Borders	.40	.30	.15
11	George Bell	.60	.45	.25
12	Ernie Whitt	.25	.20	.10
13	Jeff Musselman	.20	.15	.08
15	Lloyd Moseby	.20	.15	.08
16	Todd Stottlemyre	.60	.45	.25
17	Kelly Gruber	.20	.15	.08
18	Jim Clancy	.25	.20	.10
19	Fred McGriff	1.50	1.25	.60
21	Juan Beniquez	.15	.11	.06
22	Jimmy Key	.40	.30	.15
23	Cecil Fielder	1.00	.70	.40
29	Jesse Barfield	.30	.25	.12
31	Duane Ward	.35	.25	.14
36	David Wells	.25	.20	.10
37	Dave Stieb	.40	.30	.15
38	Mark Eichhorn	.20	.15	.08
40	Rob Ducey	.15	.11	.06
41	Al Widmar	.15	.11	.06
42	Billy Smith	.15	.11	.06
43	Cito Gaston	.30	.25	.12
46	Mike Flanagan	.25	.20	.10
50	Tom Henke	.25	.20	.10
55	John Cerutti	.20	.15	.08
57	Winston Llenas	.15	.11	.06
----	Team Photo	.15	.11	.06
----	Team Logo	.15	.11	.06

1988 Police/Fire Safety Brewers

This 30-card set is the 7th annual issue sponsored by the Milwaukee Police Department for local distribution during a crime prevention promotion. The full-color card fronts (2-3/4" by 4-1/8") feature the same design as the 1987 set with white borders and a black frame outling the player photo and name. Sponsor credits and the team name are listed below the photo. The vertical card backs are blue on white with messages from the player and sponsors. Two group photos - one of the team's five coaches and one of the team (with a checklist back) - are unnumbered and printed horizontally. Card numbers refer to the players uniform numbers.

		MT	NR MT	EX
	Complete Set:	6.00	4.50	2.50
	Common Player:	.15	.11	.06
1	Ernest Riles	.15	.11	.06
3	Juan Castillo	.15	.11	.06
4	Paul Molitor	1.00	.70	.40
5	B.J. Surhoff	.30	.25	.12
7	Dale Sveum	.15	.11	.06
9	Greg Brock	.15	.11	.06
11	Charlie O'Brien	.20	.15	.08
14	Jim Adduci	.15	.11	.06
16	Mike Felder	.15	.11	.06
17	Jim Gantner	.20	.15	.08
19	Robin Yount	1.50	1.25	.60
20	Juan Nieves	.15	.11	.06
21	Bill Schroeder	.15	.11	.06
23	Joey Meyer	.15	.11	.06
25	Mark Clear	.15	.11	.06
26	Glenn Braggs	.15	.11	.06
28	Odell Jones	.15	.11	.06
29	Chris Bosio	.15	.11	.06
30	Steve Kiefer	.15	.11	.06
32	Chuck Crim	.15	.11	.06
33	Jay Aldrich	.15	.11	.06
37	Dan Plesac	.15	.11	.06
40	Mike Birkbeck	.15	.11	.06
42	Tom Trebelhorn	.15	.11	.06
43	Dave Stapleton	.15	.11	.06

45	Rob Deer	.20	.15	.08
46	Bill Wegman	.20	.15	.08
49	Ted Higuera	.20	.15	.08
----	Coaches Card (Andy Etchebarren, Larry Haney, Chuck Hartenstein, Dave Hilton, Tony Muser)	.15	.11	.06
----	Team Photo	.15	.11	.06

1988 Police/Fire Safety Dodgers

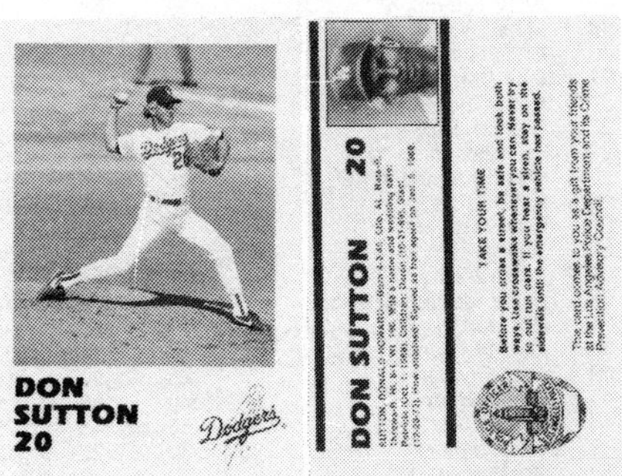

The Los Angeles police department sponsored this 30-card set (2-3/4" by 4-1/8") for use in a local crime prevention promotion. The sets include an unnumbered manager/coaches photo and three double-photo cards. The double cards feature posed closeups; the rest are action photos. The card fronts have white borders, with the team logo lower right and a bold black player name lower left. Card backs are black and white with a small closeup photo of the player, followed by personal and career info, a crime prevention tip and a LAPD badge logo. Card numbers refer to players' uniform numbers (the double-photo cards carry two numbers on both front and back).

		MT	NR MT	EX
Complete Set:		6.00	4.50	2.50
Common Player:		.15	.11	.06
2	Tom Lasorda	.25	.20	.10
3	Steve Sax	.25	.20	.10
5	Mike Marshall	.25	.20	.10
7	Alfredo Griffin	.20	.15	.08
9	Mickey Hatcher	.15	.11	.06
10	Dave Anderson	.15	.11	.06
12	Danny Heep	.15	.11	.06
14	Mike Scioscia	.20	.15	.08
1721	Tito Landrum, Len Matuszek	.15	.11	.06
20	Don Sutton	.40	.30	.15
22	Franklin Stubbs	.20	.15	.08
23	Kirk Gibson	.40	.30	.15
25	Mariano Duncan	.30	.25	.12
26	Alejandro Pena	.20	.15	.08
2752	Tim Crews, Mike Sharperson	.25	.20	.10
28	Pedro Guerrero	.25	.20	.10
29	Alex Trevino	.15	.11	.06
31	John Shelby	.15	.11	.06
33	Jeff Hamilton	.25	.20	.10
34	Fernando Valenzuela	.40	.30	.15
37	Mike Davis	.20	.15	.08
41	Brad Havens	.15	.11	.06
43	Ken Howell	.15	.11	.06
47	Jesse Orosco	.20	.15	.08
4957	Tim Belcher, Shawn Hillegas	.30	.25	.12
50	Jay Howell	.20	.15	.08
51	Brian Holton	.20	.15	.08
54	Tim Leary	.25	.20	.10
55	Orel Hershiser	.40	.30	.15
----	Manager/Coaches (Joe Amalfitano, Steve Boros, Mark Cresse, Joe Ferguson, Tom Lasorda, Manny Mota, Ron Perranoski, Bill Russell)	.15	.11	.06

1988 Police/Fire Safety Tigers

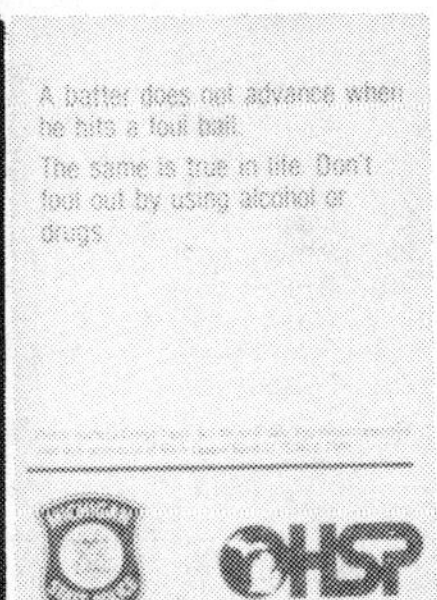

A batter does not advance when he hits a foul ball.
The same is true in life. Don't foul out by using alcohol or drugs.
OHSP

This unnumbered issue, sponsored by the Michigan State Police features 13 players and manager Sparky Anderson in full-color standard-size (2-1/2" by 3-1/2") cards. Player photos are framed by a blue border, with the Detroit logo upper left and a large name block that lists the player's name, position batting/throwing preference, height, weight and birthday beneath the photo. The backs carry an anti-drug or anti-crime message.

		MT	NR MT	EX
Complete Set:		9.00	6.75	3.50
Common Player:		.50	.40	.20
(1)	Doyle Alexander	.50	.40	.20
(2)	Sparky Anderson	.50	.40	.20
(3)	Dave Bergman	.50	.40	.20
(4)	Tom Brookens	.50	.40	.20
(5)	Darrell Evans	.60	.45	.25
(6)	Larry Herndon	.50	.40	.20
(7)	Chet Lemon	.50	.40	.20
(8)	Jack Morris	.80	.60	.30
(9)	Matt Nokes	.80	.60	.30
(10)	Jeff Robinson	.60	.45	.25
(11)	Frank Tanana	.40	.30	.15
(12)	Walt Terrell	.50	.40	.20
(13)	Alan Trammell	1.50	1.25	.60
(14)	Lou Whitaker	.90	.70	.35

1989 Police/Fire Safety Blue Jays

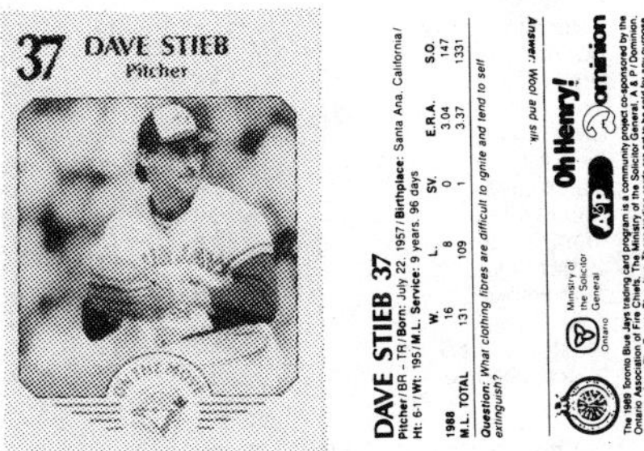

The 1989 Toronto Blue Jays safety set consisted of 34 standard-size cards co-sponsored by the Ontario Association of Fire Chiefs, Oh Henry! candy bars and A&P supermarkets. The card fronts feature color photos with the player's uniform number in large type in the upper left corner. His name and position are to the right above the photo. The Blue Jays "On the Move" logo is centered at the bottom. The backs of the cards include fire safety messages.

		MT	NR MT	EX
Complete Set:		6.00	4.50	2.50
Common Player:		.15	.11	.06
1	Tony Fernandez	.25	.20	.10
2	Nelson Liriano	.15	.11	.06
3	Jimy Williams	.15	.11	.06
4	Manny Lee	.15	.11	.06
5	Rance Mulliniks	.15	.11	.06
6	Silvestre Campusano	.15	.11	.06
7	John McLaren	.15	.11	.06
8	John Sullivan	.15	.11	.06
9	Bob Brenly	.15	.11	.06
10	Pat Borders	.30	.25	.12
11	George Bell	.60	.45	.25
12	Ernie Whitt	.25	.20	.10
13	Jeff Musselman	.15	.11	.06
15	Lloyd Moseby	.25	.20	.10
16	Greg Myers	.40	.30	.15
17	Kelly Gruber	.30	.25	.12
18	Tom Lawless	.15	.11	.06
19	Fred McGriff	1.50	1.25	.60
22	Jimmy Key	.25	.20	.10
25	Mike Squires	.15	.11	.06
26	Sal Butera	.15	.11	.06
29	Jesse Barfield	.20	.15	.08
30	Todd Stottlemyre	.40	.30	.15
31	Duane Ward	.25	.20	.10
36	David Wells	.20	.15	.08
37	Dave Steib	.40	.30	.15
40	Rob Ducey	.15	.11	.06
41	Al Widman	.15	.11	.06
43	Cito Gaston	.30	.25	.12
44	Frank Wills	.15	.11	.06
45	Jose Nunez	.15	.11	.06
46	Mike Flanagan	.20	.15	.08
50	Tom Henke	.20	.15	.08
55	John Cerutti	.15	.11	.06
----	Team Photo, Team Logo	.15	.11	.06

Values for recent cards and sets are listed in Mint (MT), Near Mint (NM), reflecting the fact that many cards from recent years have been preserved in top condition. Recent cards and sets in less than Excellent condition have little collector interest.

1989 Police/Fire Safety Brewers

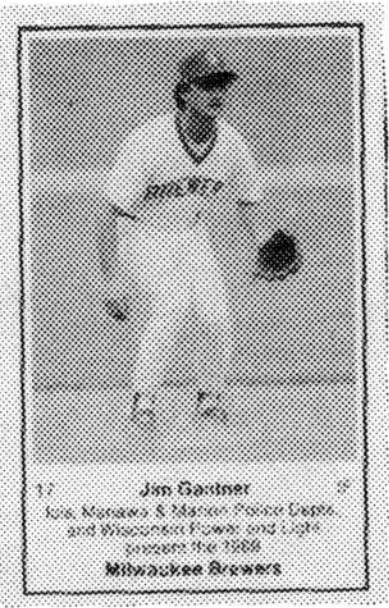

Jim Gantner says:

"Teamwork is very important in baseball. We know that we can't do it alone. Baseball players work together with their teammates and help each other. We develop strong friendships which last after our playing days are over. Your teammates are your family, your teachers, and your local police officers. They want to be your friends. Take advantage of their friendship and ask them for advice when needed. They'll work with you, help you, and be the friends you need to succeed in life."

Listen to WTMJ Radio in Milwaukee or your local Brewers network station to learn who will be the 2 players featured on next weeks baseball cards.

The Milwaukee Brewers, in conjunction with various corporate and civic sponsors, issued a 30-card police set in 1989, the eighth consecutive police set issued by the club. Some 95 law enforcement agencies in Wisconsin participated in the program, each releasing their own version of the same set. The cards measure 2-13/16" by 4-1/8" and feature full-color action photos with the player's name, uniform number and position below, along with the sponsoring agencies. The backs include the traditional safety messages. The cards were distributed in complete sets at a stadium promotion and also handed out individually over the course of the summer by uniformed police officers in various Wisconsin cities and counties.

		MT	NR MT	EX
Complete Set:		7.00	5.25	2.75
Common Player:		.15	.11	.06
1	Gary Sheffield	1.50	1.25	.60
4	Paul Molitor	1.00	.70	.40
5	B.J. Surhoff	.30	.25	.12
6	Bill Spiers	.30	.25	.12
7	Dale Sveum	.20	.15	.08
9	Greg Brock	.15	.11	.06
14	Gus Polidor	.15	.11	.06
16	Mike Felder	.15	.11	.06
17	Jim Gantner	.20	.15	.08
19	Robin Yount	1.50	1.25	.60
20	Juan Nieves	.15	.11	.06
22	Charlie O'Brien	.15	.11	.06
23	Joey Meyer	.15	.11	.06
25	Dave Engle	.15	.11	.06
26	Glenn Braggs	.25	.20	.10
27	Paul Mirabella	.15	.11	.06
29	Chris Bosio	.20	.15	.08
30	Terry Francona	.15	.11	.06
32	Chuck Crim	.15	.11	.06
37	Dan Plesac	.20	.15	.08
40	Mike Birkbeck	.15	.11	.06
41	Mark Knudson	.15	.11	.06
42	Tom Trebelhorn	.15	.11	.06
45	Rob Deer	.20	.15	.08
46	Bill Wegman	.20	.15	.08
48	Bryan Clutterbuck	.15	.11	.06
49	Teddy Higuera	.20	.15	.08
----	Team Photo, Coaching Staff	.15	.11	.06

A player's name in italic type indicates a rookie card. An (FC) indicates a player's first card for that particular card company.

1989 Police/Fire Safety Dodgers

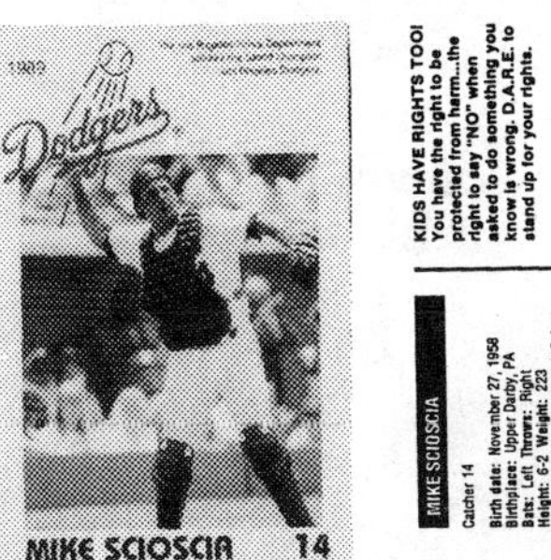

1989
Dodgers
MIKE SCIOSCIA 14
KIDS HAVE RIGHTS TOO!

The Los Angeles Dodgers and the L.A. Police Department teamed up in 1989 to produce a 30-card police set. The cards, which measure 4-1/4" by 2-5/8", feature color action photos with the player's name and uniform number below. The Dodgers logo and "1989" appear in the upper left. The backs include player information plus a safety message.

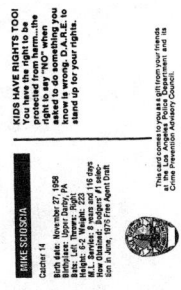

		MT	NR MT	EX
Complete Set:		6.00	4.50	2.50
Common Player:		.15	.11	.06
2	Tom Lasorda	.25	.20	.10
3	Jeff Hamilton	.15	.11	.06
5	Mike Marshall	.20	.15	.08
7	Alfredo Griffin	.15	.11	.06
9	Mickey Hatcher	.15	.11	.06
10	Dave Anderson	.15	.11	.06
12	Willie Randolph	.25	.20	.10
14	Mike Scioscia	.20	.15	.08
17	Rick Dempsey	.15	.11	.06
20	Mike Davis	.15	.11	.06
21	Tracy Woodson	.15	.11	.06
22	Franklin Stubbs	.15	.11	.06
23	Kirk Gibson	.40	.30	.15
25	Mariano Duncan	.30	.25	.12
26	Alejandro Pena	.20	.15	.08
27	Mike Sharperson	.20	.15	.08
29	Ricky Horton	.15	.11	.06
30	John Tudor	.15	.11	.06
31	John Shelby	.15	.11	.06
33	Eddie Murray	.75	.60	.30
34	Fernando Valenzuela	.40	.30	.15
36	Mike Morgan	.15	.11	.06
48	Ramon Martinez	1.50	1.25	.60
49	Tim Belcher	.30	.25	.12
50	Jay Howell	.20	.15	.08
52	Tim Crews	.15	.11	.06
54	Tim Leary	.15	.11	.06
55	Orel Hershiser	.60	.45	.25
57	Ray Searage	.15	.11	.06
----	Dodger Coaches	.15	.11	.06

1989 Police/Fire Safety Tigers

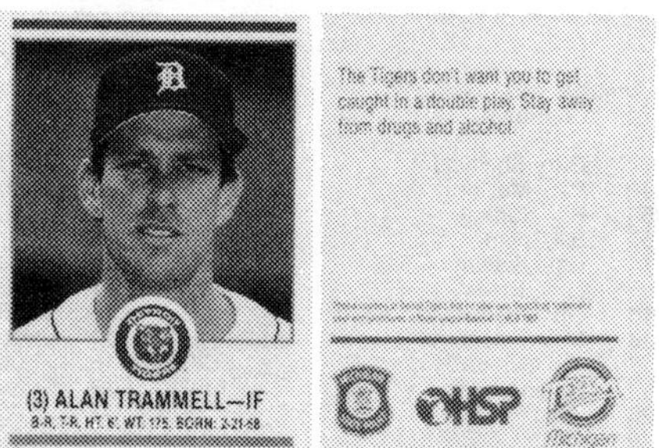

This unnumbered issue, distributed and sponsored by the Michigan State Police Department features 14 full-color 2-1/2" by 3-1/2" cards. Player photos are framed by a blue and orange border, with the team logo in the upper left and biographical information below the photo. The card backs featue anti-drug or anti-crime messages.

		MT	NR MT	EX
Complete Set:		6.00	4.50	2.50
Common Player:		.25	.20	.10
(1)	Doyle Alexander	.35	.25	.14
(2)	Sparky Anderson	.50	.40	.20
(3)	Dave Bergman	.25	.20	.10
(4)	Mike Henneman	.60	.45	.25
(5)	Guillermo Hernandez	.35	.25	.14
(6)	Chet Lemon	.35	.25	.14
(7)	Fred Lynn	.40	.30	.15
(8)	Jack Morris	.50	.40	.20
(9)	Matt Nokes	.50	.40	.20
(10)	Jeff Robinson	.40	.30	.15
(11)	Pat Sheridan	.25	.20	.10
(12)	Frank Tanana	.40	.30	.15
(13)	Alan Trammell	.90	.70	.35
(14)	Lou Whitaker	.60	.45	.25

1990 Police/Fire Safety Blue Jays

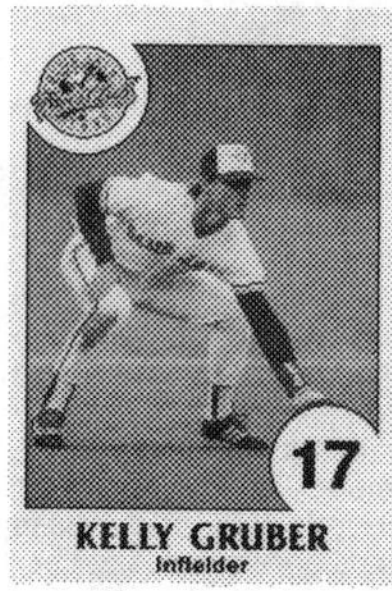

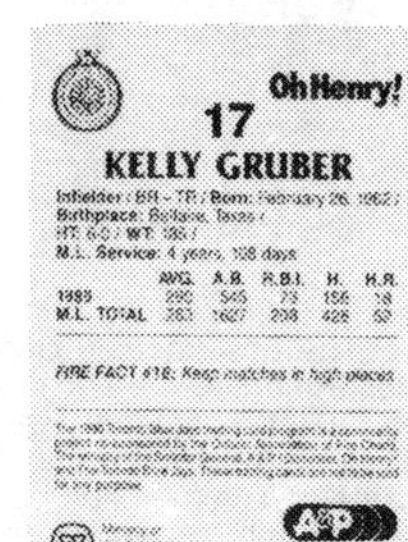

This 35-card set was co-sponsored by the Ontario Association of Fire Chiefs, The Ministry of the Solicitor General, A & P/Dominion, Oh Henry and the Toronto Blue Jays. The card fronts feature full-color photos on white stock and display a special Blue Jays fan club lougo in the upper left corner. The flip sides feature biographical information, statistics, and a fire fact. The cards are numbered according to the respective player or coaches' uniform number.

		MT	NR MT	EX
Complete Set:		8.00	6.00	3.25
Common Player:		.15	.11	.06
1	Tony Fernandez	.30	.25	.12
2	Nelson Liriano	.15	.11	.06
3	Mookie Wilson	.25	.20	.10
4	Manny Lee	.15	.11	.06
5	Rance Mulliniks	.15	.11	.06
7	John McLaren	.15	.11	.06
8	John Sullivan	.15	.11	.06
9	John Olerud	3.00	2.25	1.25
10	Pat Borders	.20	.15	.08
11	George Bell	.40	.30	.15
15	Gene Tenace	.15	.11	.06
18	Tom Lawless	.15	.11	.06
19	Fred McGriff	1.50	1.25	.60
21	Greg Myers	.25	.20	.10
22	Jimmy Key	.25	.20	.10
23	Alex Sanchez	.15	.11	.06
24	Glenallen Hill	.50	.40	.20
25	Mike Squires	.15	.11	.06
26	Ozzie Virgil	.15	.11	.06
27	Willie Blair	.15	.11	.06
28	Al Leiter	.15	.11	.06
30	Todd Stottlemyre	.25	.20	.10
31	Duane Ward	.35	.25	.14
34	Jim Acker	.15	.11	.06
36	David Wells	.15	.11	.06
37	Dave Steib	.35	.25	.14
39	Paul Kilgus	.15	.11	.06
42	Galen Cisco	.15	.11	.06
43	Cito Gaston	.25	.20	.10
44	Frank Wills	.15	.11	.06
47	Junior Felix	.70	.50	.30
50	Tom Henke	.20	.15	.08
55	John Cerutti	.15	.11	.06
----	Skydome/checklist	.15	.11	.06
----	Logo/Schedule	.15	.11	.06

1990 Police/Fire Safety Brewers

Blue borders are featured on the front of the 1990 Brewer Police/Fire Safety set. The cards are numbered according to uniform number and public service messages appear on the card backs. The oversized cards were distributed by Wisconsin police departments.

		MT	NR MT	EX
Complete Set:		6.00	4.50	2.50
Common Player:		.20	.15	.08
2	Edgar Diaz	.20	.15	.08
4	Paul Molitor	1.00	.70	.40
5	B. J. Surhoff	.35	.25	.14
7	Dale Sveum	.20	.15	.08
11	Gary Sheffield	.60	.45	.25
14	Gus Polidor	.20	.15	.08
16	Mike Felder	.20	.15	.08
17	Jim Gantner	.25	.20	.10
19	Robin Yount	1.50	1.25	.60
20	Juan Nieves	.20	.15	.08
22	Charlie O'Brien	.20	.15	.08
23	Greg Vaughn	.40	.30	.15
24	Darryl Hamilton	.30	.25	.12
26	Glenn Braggs	.25	.20	.10
27	Paul Mirabella	.20	.15	.08
28	Tom Filer	.20	.15	.08
29	Chris Bosio	.25	.20	.10
30	Terry Francona	.20	.15	.08
31	Jaime Navarro	.30	.25	.12
32	Chuck Crim	.20	.15	.08
34	Billy Bates	.20	.15	.08
36	Tony Fossas	.20	.15	.08
37	Dan Plesac	.20	.15	.08
38	Don August	.20	.15	.08
39	Dave Parker	.50	.40	.20
40	Mike Birkbeck	.20	.15	.08
41	Mark Knudson	.20	.15	.08
42	Tom Trebelhorn	.20	.15	.08
45	Rob Deer	.25	.20	.10
46	Bill Wegman	.25	.20	.10
47	Bill Krueger	.20	.15	.08
49	Ted Higuera	.25	.20	.10
----	Coaches	.20	.15	.08

1990 Police/Fire Safety Dodgers

This set honors the centennial celebration of the Los Angeles Dodgers. A special 100 Anniversary logo appears on the card fronts. The cards measure 2-3/4" by 4-1/4" and feature full-color photos. The card backs are printed horizontally and contain a special safety tip or anti-drug message along with player information. The L.A.P.D. logo is featured on the bottom of the card back.

		MT	NR MT	EX
Complete Set:		6.00	4.50	2.50
Common Player:		.15	.11	.06
2	Tommy Lasorda	.25	.20	.10
3	Jeff Hamilton	.15	.11	.06
7	Alfredo Griffin	.15	.11	.06
9	Mickey Hatcher	.15	.11	.06
10	Juan Samuel	.25	.20	.10
12	Willie Randolph	.25	.20	.10
14	Mike Scioscia	.20	.15	.08
15	Chris Gwynn	.15	.11	.06
17	Rick Dempsey	.15	.11	.06
21	Hubie Brooks	.20	.15	.08
22	Franklin Stubbs	.15	.11	.06
23	Kirk Gibson	.35	.25	.14
27	Mike Sharperson	.25	.20	.10
28	Kal Daniels	.25	.20	.10
29	Lenny Harris	.25	.20	.10
31	John Shelby	.15	.11	.06
33	Eddie Murray	.75	.60	.30
34	Fernando Valenzuela	.35	.25	.14
35	Jim Gott	.15	.11	.06
36	Mike Morgan	.15	.11	.06
38	Jose Gonzalez	.25	.20	.10
46	Mike Hartley	.40	.30	.15
48	Ramon Martinez	.60	.45	.25
49	Tim Belcher	.30	.25	.12
50	Jay Howell	.20	.15	.08
52	Tim Crews	.15	.11	.06
55	Orel Hershiser	.60	.45	.25
57	John Wetteland	.60	.45	.25
59	Ray Searage	.15	.11	.06
----	Coaches	.15	.11	.06

1991 Police/Fire Safety Brewers

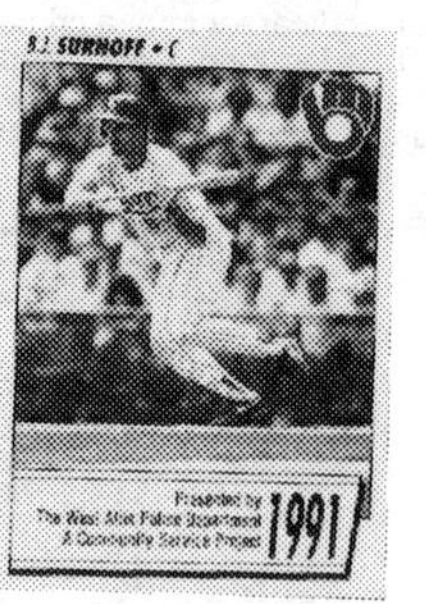

The Milwaukee Brewers are featured on a 1991 team set sponsored by several Milwaukee area police departments and Delicious Brand Cookies and Crackers. The 30-card set is in full color with light gray border on the front and the backs are unnumbered and contain safety tips from the players.

		MT	NR MT	EX
Complete Set:		6.00	4.50	2.50
Common Player:		.25	.20	.10
(1)	Robin Yount	1.00	.70	.40
(2)	Rick Dempsey	.25	.20	.10
(3)	Jamie Navarro	.25	.20	.10
(4)	Darryl Hamilton	.25	.20	.10
(5)	Bill Spiers	.25	.20	.10
(6)	Dante Bichette	.35	.25	.14
(7)	Dan Plesac	.25	.20	.10
(8)	Don August	.25	.20	.10
(9)	Willie Randolph	.25	.20	.10
(10)	Franklin Stubbs	.25	.20	.10
(11)	Julio Machado	.25	.20	.10
(12)	Greg Vaughn	.50	.40	.20
(13)	Chris Bosio	.35	.25	.14
(14)	Mark Knudson	.25	.20	.10
(15)	Paul Molitor	.75	.60	.30
(16)	Kevin Brown	.25	.20	.10
(17)	Ron Robinson	.25	.20	.10
(18)	Bill Wegman	.25	.20	.10
(19)	Teddy Higuera	.25	.20	.10
(20)	Mark Lee	.25	.20	.10
(21)	B.J. Surhoff	.30	.25	.12
(22)	Candy Maldonado	.25	.20	.10
(23)	Chuck Crim	.25	.20	.10
(24)	Dale Sveum	.25	.20	.10
(25)	Jim Gantner	.25	.20	.10
(26)	Greg Brock	.25	.20	.10
(27)	Gary Sheffield	.50	.40	.20
(28)	Edwin Nunez	.25	.20	.10
(29)	Coaches	.25	.20	.10
(30)	Tom Trebelhorn (Manager)	.25	.20	.10

The values quoted are intended to reflect the market price.

1992 Police/Fire Safety Brewers

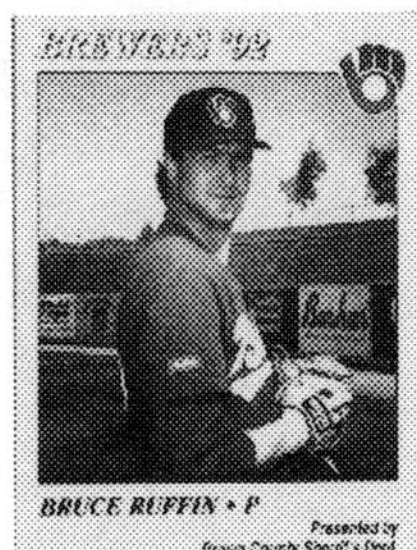

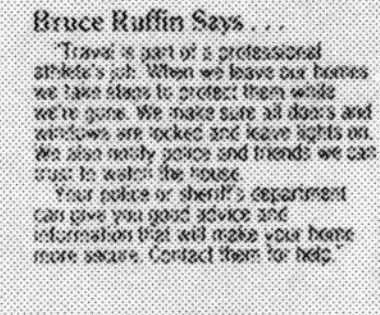

The 1992 Milwaukee Brewers Police set consists of 30-cards in the standard, 2-1/2" x 3-1/2" format. The yellow-bordered cards were produced by Delicious Brand Cookies and Crackers and distributed by local Wisconsin police departments in cooperation with the Brewers.

		MT	NR MT	EX
Complete Set:		6.00	4.50	2.50
Common Player:		.25	.20	.10
(1)	Andy Allanson	.25	.20	.10
(2)	James Austin	.25	.20	.10
(3)	Dante Bichette	.35	.25	.14
(4)	Ricky Bones	.35	.25	.14
(5)	Chris Bosio	.35	.25	.14
(6)	Mike Fetters	.25	.20	.10
(7)	Scott Fletcher	.30	.25	.12
(8)	Jim Gantner	.25	.20	.10
(9)	Phil Garner	.30	.25	.12
(10)	Darryl Hamilton	.25	.20	.10
(11)	Doug Henry	.25	.20	.10
(12)	Teddy Higuera	.25	.20	.10
(13)	Pat Listach	.50	.40	.20
(14)	Jamie Navarro	.25	.20	.10
(15)	Edwin Nunez	.25	.20	.10
(16)	Tim McIntosh	.25	.20	.10
(17)	Paul Molitor	.75	.60	.30
(18)	Jesse Orosco	.25	.20	.10
(19)	Dan Plesac	.25	.20	.10
(20)	Ron Robinson	.25	.20	.10
(21)	Bruce Ruffin	.25	.20	.10
(22)	Kevin Seitzer	.25	.20	.10
(23)	Bill Spiers	.25	.20	.10
(24)	Franklin Stubbs	.25	.20	.10
(25)	William Suero	.25	.20	.10
(26)	B.J. Surhoff	.30	.25	.12
(27)	Greg Vaughn	.35	.25	.14
(28)	Bill Wegman	.25	.20	.10
(29)	Robin Yount	1.00	.70	.40
(30)	Brewers Coaches	.25	.20	.10

1992 Police/Fire Safety Cardinals

The Cardinals were the subject of a set of 27 cards given out at Busch Stadium on April 25, 1992. Produced by Kansas City Life Insurance and distributed by Greater St. Louis law enforcement agencies, the cards are 2-1/2" x 4", and contain a special logo on the front which commemorates the team's 100th anniversary.

		MT	NR MT	EX
Complete Set:		6.00	4.50	2.50
Common Player:		.25	.20	.10
1	Ozzie Smith	1.00	.70	.40
7	Geronimo Pena	.30	.25	.12
9	Joe Torre	.35	.25	.14
10	Rex Hudler	.25	.20	.10
11	Jose Oquendo	.25	.20	.10
12	Craig Wilson	.25	.20	.10
16	Ray Lankford	.50	.40	.20
19	Tom Pagnozzi	.25	.20	.10
21	Gerald Perry	.25	.20	.10
23	Bernard Gilkey	.35	.25	.14
25	Milt Thompson	.25	.20	.10
26	Omar Olivares	.25	.20	.10
27	Todd Zeile	.40	.30	.15
28	Pedro Guerrero	.30	.25	.12
29	Rich Gedman	.25	.20	.10
32	Joe Magrane	.25	.20	.10
34	Felix Jose	.30	.25	.12
36	Bryn Smith	.25	.20	.10
37	Scott Terry	.25	.20	.10
38	Todd Worrell	.25	.20	.10
39	Bob Tewksbury	.30	.25	.12
41	Andres Galarraga	.60	.45	.25
44	Cris Carpenter	.25	.20	.10
47	Lee Smith	.40	.30	.15
48	Jose DeLeon	.25	.20	.10
49	Juan Agosto	.25	.20	.10
----	Checklist Card	.25	.20	.10

1992 Police/Fire Safety Dodgers

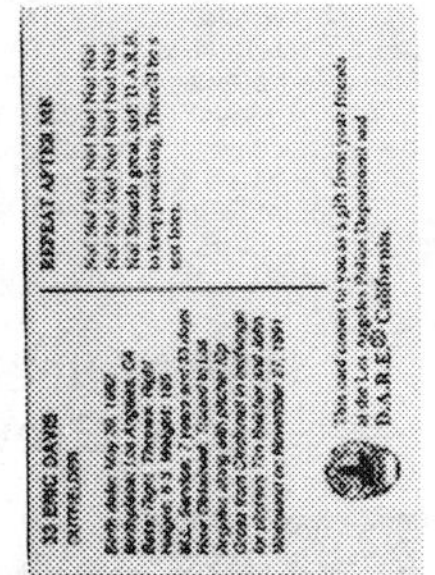

The 1992 Dodgers Police set consists of 30 cards numbered to correspond to the player's uniform number. The set includes a card of manager Tommy Lasorda and Dodgers coaches. They were given out at promotional dates at Dodger Stadium.

		MT	NR MT	EX
Complete Set:		5.00	3.75	2.00
Common Player:		.25	.20	.10
2	Tommy Lasorda	.35	.25	.14
3	Jeff Hamilton	.25	.20	.10
5	Stan Javier	.25	.20	.10
10	Juan Samuel	.50	.40	.20
14	Mike Scioscia	.30	.25	.12
15	Dave Hansen	.25	.20	.10
17	Bob Ojeda	.30	.25	.12
20	Mitch Webster	.25	.20	.10
22	Brett Butler	.30	.25	.12
23	Eric Karros	.75	.60	.30
27	Mike Sharperson	.30	.25	.12
28	Kal Daniels	.25	.20	.10
29	Lenny Harris	.25	.20	.10
30	Jose Offerman	.30	.25	.12
31	Roger McDowell	.30	.25	.12
33	Eric Davis	.35	.25	.14
35	Jim Gott	.25	.20	.10
36	Todd Benzinger	.30	.25	.12
38	Steve Wilson	.25	.20	.10
41	Carlos Hernandez	.50	.40	.20
44	Daryl Strawberry	.30	.25	.12
46	Kevin Gross	.25	.20	.10
48	Ramon Martinez	.35	.25	.14
49	Tom Candiotti	.25	.20	.10
50	Jay Howell	.25	.20	.10
52	Tim Crews	.25	.20	.10
54	John Candelaria	.25	.20	.10
55	Orel Hershiser	.35	.25	.14
57	Kip Gross	.25	.20	.10
----	Coaches (Joe Amalfitano, Mark Cresse, Joe Ferguson, Ben Hines, Tommy Lasorda, Manny Mota, Ron Perranoski, Ron Roenicke)	.25	.20	.10

1992 Police/Fire Safety Royals

The 1992 Kansas City Royals Police set was originally slated to by 27 cards, but two cards were pulled prior to its release. The cards of Kevin Seitzer (traded) and Kirk Gibson (released) were the ones withdrawn, though both names appear on the checklist. The cards are numbered to match the player's uniform numbers.

		MT	NR MT	EX
Complete Set:		7.00	5.25	2.75
Common Player:		.25	.20	.10
2	Bob Melvin	.25	.20	.10
3	Terry Shumpert	.30	.25	.12
5	George Brett	1.00	.70	.40
8	Jim Eisenreich	.35	.25	.14
9	Gregg Jefferies	.40	.30	.15
11	Hal McRae	.35	.25	.14
12	Wally Joyner	.40	.30	.15
13	David Howard	.30	.25	.12
15	Mike McFarlane	.30	.25	.12
16	Keith Miller	.25	.20	.10
21	Jeff Montgomery	.30	.25	.12
22	Kevin McReynolds	.30	.25	.12
23	Mark Gubicza	.30	.25	.12
24	Brent Mayne	.35	.25	.14
25	Gary Thomas	.25	.20	.10
27	Luis Aquino	.25	.20	.10
29	Chris Gwynn	.25	.20	.10
30	Kirk Gibson	.35	.25	.14
33	Kevin Seitzer	.25	.20	.10
36	Tom Gordon	.30	.25	.12
37	Joel Johnson	.25	.20	.10
48	Mark Davis	.25	.20	.10
52	Mike Boddicker	.25	.20	.10
55	Kevin Appier	.30	.25	.12
56	Brian McRae	.40	.30	.15
57	Mike Magnante	.25	.20	.10
----	Coaches (Glenn Ezell, Adrian Garrett, Guy Hansen, Lynn Jones, Bruce Kison, Lee May)	.25	.20	.10

1993 Police/Fire Safety Blue Jays

The Toronto Blue Jays produced a police set for the tenth year in a row in 1993. In the first year of offering the item as a boxed set, the cards feature a full-bleed color photo on the front, with the player's name printed in white over a blue stripe across the top of the card. The Blue Jay's 1992 World Champions logo appears in the upper left corner in the 35-card set.

		MT	NR MT	EX
Complete Set:		5.00	3.75	2.00
Common Player:		.25	.20	.10
(1)	Eddie Zosky	.30	.25	.12
(2)	Luis Sojo	.25	.20	.10
(3)	Bob Bailor	.25	.20	.10
(4)	Alfredo Griffin	.25	.20	.10
(5)	Domingo Martinez	.25	.20	.10
(6)	Rich Hacker	.25	.20	.10
(7)	John Sullivan	.25	.20	.10
(8)	John Olerud	.35	.25	.14
(9)	Pat Borders	.30	.25	.12
(10)	Darnell Coles	.25	.20	.10
(11)	Roberto Alomar	.50	.40	.20
(12)	Darrin Jackson	.30	.25	.12
(13)	Tom Quinlin	.25	.20	.10
(14)	Gene Tenace	.25	.20	.10
(15)	Paul Molitor	.60	.45	.25
(16)	Dick Schofield	.25	.20	.10
(17)	Turner Ward	.25	.20	.10
(18)	Devon White	.35	.25	.14
(19)	Randy Knorr	.25	.20	.10
(20)	Al Leiter	.25	.20	.10
(21)	Joe Carter	.50	.40	.20
(22)	Todd Stottlemyre	.30	.25	.12
(23)	Duane Ward	.30	.25	.12
(24)	Ed Sprague	.30	.25	.12
(25)	Dave Stewart	.35	.25	.14
(26)	Larry Hisle	.25	.20	.10
(27)	Mike Timlin	.25	.20	.10
(28)	Pat Hentgen	.30	.25	.12
(29)	Galen Cisco	.25	.20	.10
(30)	Cito Gaston	.30	.25	.12
(31)	Ken Davley	.25	.20	.10
(32)	Jack Morris	.30	.25	.12
(33)	Mark Eichhorn	.30	.25	.12
(34)	Danny Cox	.30	.25	.12
(35)	Juan Guzman	.35	.25	.14

1993 Police/Fire Safety Brewers

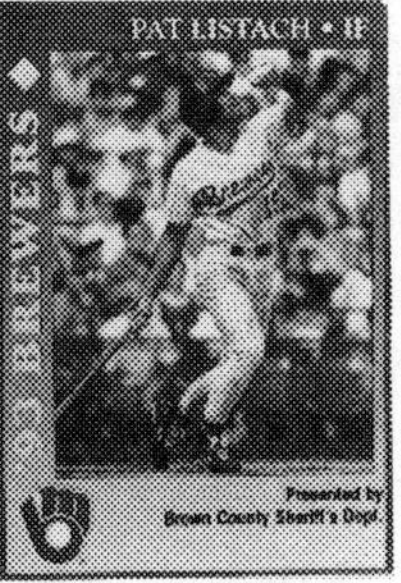

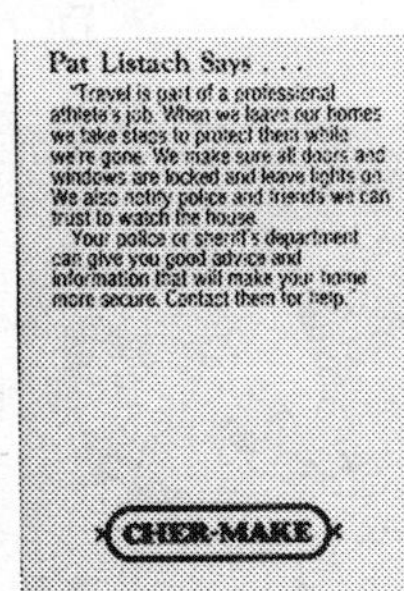

The 1993 Milwaukee Brewers Police set included 30 cards with a graduated blue border. The left side has a '93 Brewers flag along the border in yellow, with the player's name in the upper right corner in white. The backs, which are white with black print, feature quotes from the player pictured. The cards are not numbered and the set also includes a card commemorating Robin Yount's 3,000th hit.

		MT	NR MT	EX
Complete Set:		6.00	4.50	2.50
Common Player:		.25	.20	.10
(1)	Bernie Brewer	.25	.20	.10
(2)	Phil Garner	.30	.25	.12
(3)	Yount's 3000th hit	.50	.40	.20
(4)	Mark Kiefer	.25	.20	.10
(5)	Bill Spiers	.25	.20	.10
(6)	John Jaha	.30	.25	.12
(7)	Bill Wegman	.25	.20	.10
(8)	Ted Higuera	.25	.20	.10
(9)	Greg Vaughn	.30	.25	.12
(10)	Kevin Reimer	.25	.20	.10
(11)	Doug Henry	.25	.20	.10
(12)	William Suero	.25	.20	.10
(13)	Dave Nilsson	.25	.20	.10
(14)	James Austin	.25	.20	.10
(15)	Mike Fetters	.25	.20	.10
(16)	Ricky Bones	.25	.20	.10
(17)	Jaime Navarro	.25	.20	.10
(18)	Jesse Orosco	.25	.20	.10
(19)	Darryl Hamilton	.30	.25	.12
(20)	Cal Eldred	.30	.25	.12
(21)	Tim McIntosh	.25	.20	.10

(22)	Dickie Thon	.25	.20	.10
(23)	Graeme Lloyd	.35	.25	.14
(24)	Pat Listach	.35	.25	.14
(25)	Joe Kmak	.25	.20	.10
(26)	Alex Diaz	.25	.20	.10
(27)	Robin Yount	1.00	.70	.40
(28)	Tom Brunansky	.25	.20	.10
(29)	B.J. Surhoff	.30	.25	.12
(30)	Bill Doran	.30	.25	.12

1993 Police/Fire Safety Cardinals

The 1993 St. Louis Cardinals Kansas City Life Police Set featured 26 cards with a blue border and "Cardinals" printed in red at the top. The team logo appears in the lower left corner, while the player's name, position and number appear lower right. The card backs are printed in red on a white background with the player's biography and statistics listed above a safety message.

		MT	NR MT	EX
Complete Set:		6.00	4.50	2.50
Common Player:		.25	.20	.10
O	Omar Olivares	.25		
1	Ozzie Smith	.75	.60	.30
3	Brian Jordan	.50	.40	.20
5	Stan Royer	.50	.40	.20
9	Joe Tyrone	.25	.20	.10
11	Jose Oquendo	.25	.20	.10
16	Ray Lankford	.35	.25	.14
18	Luis Alicea	.25	.20	.10
19	Tom Pagnozzi	.25	.20	.10
21	Geronimo Pena	.30	.25	.12
23	Bernard Gilkey	.40	.30	.15
25	Gregg Jefferies	.40	.30	.15
26	Rob Murphy	.25	.20	.10
27	Todd Zeile	.35	.25	.14
28	Gerald Perry	.25	.20	.10
29	Hector Villanueva	.25	.20	.10
31	Donovan Osborne	.30	.25	.12
33	Rod Brewer	.25	.20	.10
39	Bob Tewksbury	.35	.25	.14
42	Mike Perez	.25	.20	.10
43	Rene Arocha	.30	.25	.12
46	Ozzie Canseco	.30	.25	.12
47	Lee Smith	.30	.25	.12
52	Rheal Cormier	.30	.25	.12
54	Tracy Woodson	.25	.20	.10
----	Checklist	.25	.20	.10

1993 Police/Fire Safety Dodgers

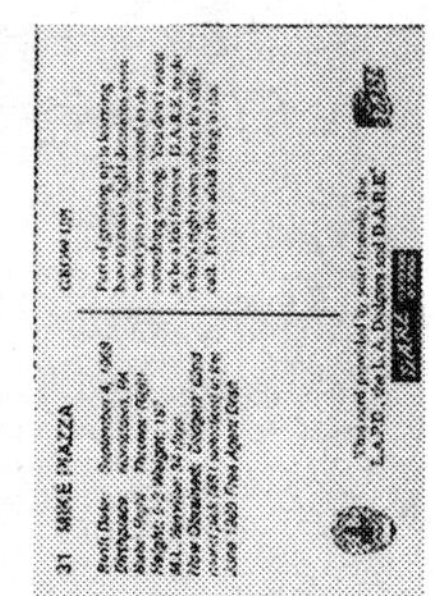

The 1993 Los Angeles Dodgers Police Set consisted of 29 cards, including cards of manager Tommy Lasorda and his coaches. The fronts of the cards have a photo surrounded by a blue border, with the Dodgers logo and the player's name on the bottom. The set is not numbered, but the player's uniform number does appear on the front of the cards.

		MT	NR MT	EX
Complete Set:		7.00	5.25	2.75
Common Player:		.25	.20	.10
2	Tommy Lasorda	.30	.25	.12
3	Jody Reed	.25	.20	.10
5	Dave Hansen	.25	.20	.10
12	Lance Parrish	.30	.25	.12
17	Roger McDowell	.30	.25	.12
20	Mitch Webster	.25	.20	.10
22	Brett Butler	.30	.25	.12
23	Eric Karros	.45	.35	.20
25	Tim Wallach	.30	.25	.12
26	Henry Rodriguez	.35	.25	.14
27	Mike Sharperson	.25	.20	.10
28	Cory Snyder	.30	.25	.12
29	Lenny Harris	.25	.20	.10
30	Jose Offerman	.30	.25	.12
31	Mike Piazza	2.00	1.50	.80
33	Eric Davis	.35	.25	.14
35	Jim Gott	.30	.25	.12
38	Todd Worrell	.25	.20	.10
41	Carlos Hernandez	.35	.25	.14
45	Pedro Martinez	.30	.25	.12
46	Kevin Gross	.25	.20	.10
47	Tom Goodwin	.30	.25	.12
48	Ramon Martinez	.30	.25	.12
49	Tom Candiotti	.25	.20	.10
50	Steve Wilson	.25	.20	.10
55	Orel Hershiser	.35	.25	.14
56	Pedro Astacio	.30	.25	.12
57	Kip Gross	.25	.20	.10
----	Coaches (Joe Amalfitano, Mark Cresse, Joe Ferguson, Ben Hines, Tommy Lasorda, Manny Mota, Ron Perranoski, Ron Roenicke)	.25	.20	.10

1994 Police/Fire Safety Brewers

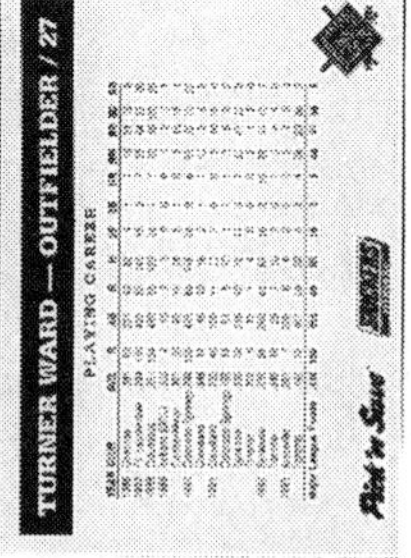

All youngsters attending the April 23 Brewers game received this 30-card set sponsored by Pick'n Save supermarkets and Snickers candy bar, whose logos appear on both front and back. Cards featured posed player photos in their new 25th anniversary uniforms, against a lime green fabric backdrop or game action photos. Two green border surround the photos. Navy blue bars above and below the photo have the player's name, team and uniform number. A 25th anniversary logo is at lower-right. The name of one of the many Wisconsin police agencies which distributed the cards is printed in black at bottom. Backs are printed in black-on-white and feature full major and minor league stats. The traditional safety message or anti-drug warning is not included on this issue. Cards are checklisted here by uniform number. Cards are inthe 2-1/2" x 3-1/2" format.

		MT	NR MT	EX
Complete Set (30):		5.00	3.75	2.00
Common Player:		.10	.08	.04
2	Jose Valentin	.10	.08	.04
3	Phil Garner	.15	.11	.06
5	B.J. Surhoff	.25	.20	.10
8	Jody Reed	.10	.08	.04
9	Bill Spiers	.10	.08	.04
11	Dave Nilsson	.15	.11	.06
12	Brian Harper	.15	.11	.06
16	Pat Listach	.15	.11	.06
18	Tom Brunansky	.10	.08	.04
20	Kevin Seitzer	.15	.11	.06
21	Cal Eldred	.25	.20	.10
23	Greg Vaughn	.50	.40	.20
24	Darryl Hamilton	.25	.20	.10
25	Ricky Bones	.15	.11	.06
27	Turner Ward	.15	.11	.06
28	Doug Henry	.10	.08	.04
29	Jeff Bronkey	.10	.08	.04
30	Matt Mieske	.10	.08	.04
31	Jaime Navarro	.15	.11	.06
32	John Jaha	.25	.20	.10
36	Mike Fetters	.10	.08	.04
37	Graeme Lloyd	.10	.08	.04
39	Bob Scanlan	.10	.08	.04
40	Mike Ignasiak	.10	.08	.04
43	Mark Kiefer	.10	.08	.04
46	Bill Wegman	.15	.11	.06
47	Jesse Orosco	.10	.08	.04
49	Teddy Higuera	.15	.11	.06
63	Jeff D'Amico, Kelly Wunsch	.50	.40	.20
----	Bernie Brewer (mascot)	.10	.08	.04

1994 Police/Fire Safety Dodgers

This 30-card set was distributed to all fans attending the Dodgers May 27 home game. Cards were produced in the form of a perforated sheet. Fronts have mostly game-action photos surrounded by a Dodger-blue border. The player's uniform number is in red in a baseball in the upper-left corner. At bottom is the team logo and the player's name in black on a yellow strip. Backs are in black on white, have a few career and biogrtaphical notes and an anti-drug message from the L.A.P.D. and the

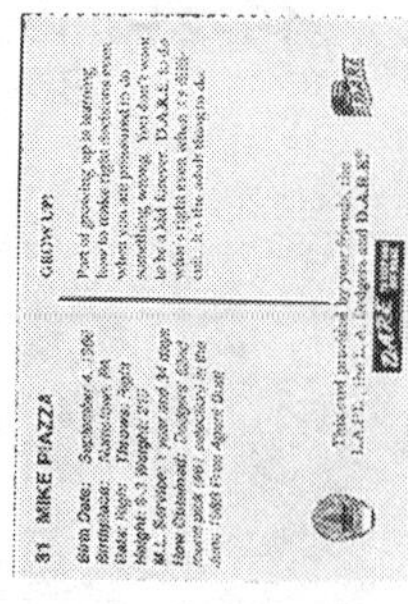

D.A.R.E. program. When removed from the sheet, cards measure the standard 2-1/2" x 3-1/2". They are checklisted here by uniform number.

		MT	NR MT	EX
Complete Set (30):		6.00	4.50	2.50
Common Player:		.10	.08	.04
2	Tommy Lasorda	.15	.11	.06
5	Dave Hansen	.10	.08	.04
7	Billy Ashley	.20	.15	.08
10	Chris Gwynn	.10	.08	.04
12	Jeff Treadway	.10	.08	.04
14	Delino DeShields	.25	.20	.10
15	Tom Prince	.10	.08	.04
17	Roger McDowell	.10	.08	.04
20	Mitch Webster	.10	.08	.04
21	Rafael Bournigal	.10	.08	.04
22	Brett Butler	.15	.11	.06
23	Eric Karros	.25	.20	.10
26	Carlos Hernandez	.15	.11	.06
28	Cory Snyder	.15	.11	.06
29	Tim Wallach	.25	.20	.10
30	Jose Offerman	.15	.11	.06
31	Mike Piazza	.50	.40	.20
35	Jim Gott	.10	.08	.04
37	Darren Dreifort	.15	.11	.06
38	Todd Worrell	.10	.08	.04
40	Henry Rodriguez	.25	.20	.10
43	Raul Mondesi	.25	.20	.10
46	Kevin Gross	.10	.08	.04
47	Garey Wayne	.10	.08	.04
48	Ramon Martinez	.15	.11	.06
49	Tom Candiotti	.10	.08	.04
55	Orel Hershiser	.10	.08	.04
56	Pedro Astacio	.10	.08	.04
61	Chan Ho Park	.50	.40	.20
----	Coaches (Mark Cresse, Manny Mota, Billy Russell, Reggie Smith, Joe Ferguson, Ron Perranoski, Tommy Lasorda, Joe Amalfitano)	.10	.08	.04

1914 Polo Grounds Game

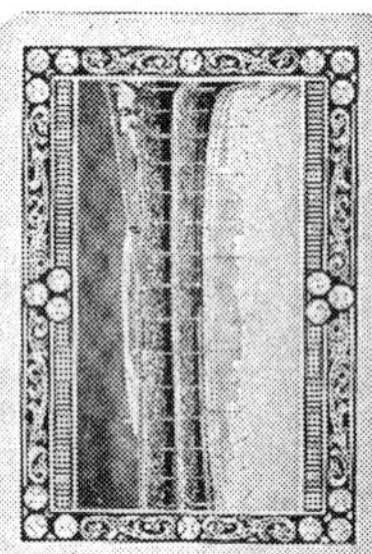

Some catalogers have attributed this set to 1910. Because many of the players depicted were not in the major leagues at that time, or had played only a handful of games, a more likely date of issue is 1914. The round-cornered 2-1/2" x 3-1/2" cards feature a green-and-white photo of the Polo Grounds on the back. Fronts have a black-and-white player photo and a baseball play scenario that is used to play a card game. The unnumbered cards are checklisted here alphabetically.

		NR MT	EX	VG
Complete Set (30):		1650.	825.00	480.00
Common Player:		25.00	12.50	7.50
(1)	Jimmy Archer	25.00	12.50	7.50
(2)	Frank Baker	50.00	25.00	15.00
(3)	Frank Chance	50.00	25.00	15.00
(4)	Larry Cheney	25.00	12.50	7.50
(5)	Ty Cobb	400.00	200.00	120.00
(6)	Eddie Collins	50.00	25.00	15.00
(7)	Larry Doyle	25.00	12.50	7.50
(8)	Art Fletcher	25.00	12.50	7.50
(9)	Claude Hendrix	25.00	12.50	7.50
(10)	Joe Jackson	400.00	200.00	120.00
(11)	Hughie Jennings	50.00	25.00	15.00

(12)	Nap Lajoie	80.00	40.00	24.00
(13)	Jimmy Lavender	25.00	12.50	7.50
(14)	Fritz Maisel	25.00	12.50	7.50
(15)	Rabbit Maranville	50.00	25.00	15.00
(16)	Rube Marquard	50.00	25.00	15.00
(17)	Christy Mathewson	125.00	62.00	37.00
(18)	John McGraw	50.00	25.00	15.00
(19)	Stuffy McInnis	25.00	12.50	7.50
(20)	Chief Meyers	25.00	12.50	7.50
(21)	Red Murray	25.00	12.50	7.50
(22)	Ed Plank	50.00	25.00	15.00
(23)	Nap Rucker	25.00	12.50	7.50
(24)	Reb Russell	25.00	12.50	7.50
(25)	Wildfire Schulte	25.00	12.50	7.50
(26)	Jim Scott	25.00	12.50	7.50
(27)	Tris Speaker	125.00	62.00	37.00
(28)	Honus Wagner	125.00	62.00	37.00
(29)	Ed Walsh	50.00	25.00	15.00
(30)	Joe Wood	25.00	12.50	7.50

1960 Post Cereal

These cards were issued on the backs of Grape Nuts cereal and measure an oversized 7" by 8-3/4". The nine cards in the set include five baseball players (Al Kaline, Mickey Mantle, Don Drysdale, Harmon Killebrew and Ed Mathews) as well as two football and two basketball players. The full-color photos were placed on a color background and bordered by a wood frame design. The cards covered the entire back of the cereal box and were blank backed. Card fronts also include the player's name and team and a facsimile autograph. A panel on the side of the box contains player biographical information. A scarce set, the cards are very difficult to obtain in mint condition.

		NR MT	EX	VG
Complete Set:		4500.	2250.	1350.
Common Player:		400.00	200.00	120.00
(1)	Bob Cousy	450.00	225.00	135.00
(2)	Don Drysdale	400.00	200.00	120.00
(3)	Frank Gifford	400.00	200.00	120.00
(4)	Al Kaline	450.00	225.00	135.00
(5)	Harmon Killebrew	400.00	200.00	120.00
(6)	Ed Mathews	400.00	200.00	120.00
(7)	Mickey Mantle	1500.	750.00	450.00
(8)	Bob Pettit	400.00	200.00	120.00
(9)	John Unitas	400.00	200.00	120.00

1961 Post Cereal

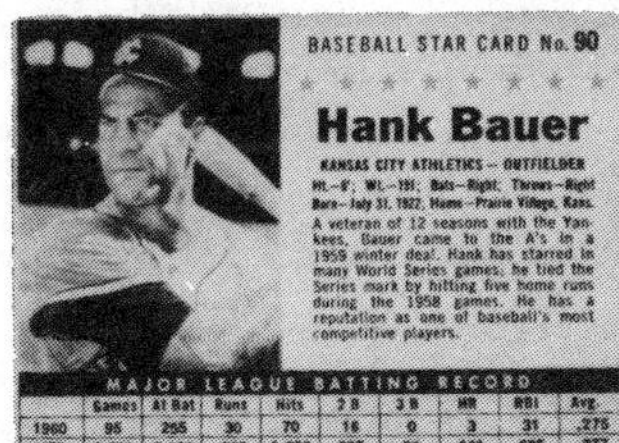

Two hundred different players are included in this set, but with variations the number of different cards exceeds 350. This was the first large-scale card set by the cereal company and it proved very popular with fans. Cards were issued both singly and in various panel sizes on the thick cardboard stock of cereal boxes, as well on thinner stock, in team sheets issued directly by Post via a mail-in offer. About 10 cards in the set were issued in significantly smaller quantities, making their prices much higher than other comparable players in the set. Individual cards measure a 3-1/2" by 2-1/2", and all cards are numbered in the upper left corner. Card fronts have full-color portait photos of the player, along with biographical information and 1960 and career statistics. Card backs are blank. The complete set price includes does not include the scarcer variations.

		NR MT	EX	VG
Complete Set:		2250.	1125.	675.00
Common Player:		3.00	1.50	.90
1a	Yogi Berra (box)	35.00	17.50	10.50
1b	Yogi Berra (company)	21.50	10.50	6.50
2a	Elston Howard (box)	7.50	3.75	2.25
2b	Elston Howard (company)	4.50	2.25	1.25
3a	Bill Skowron (box)	3.75	2.00	1.25
3b	Bill Skowron (company)	3.75	2.00	1.25
4a	Mickey Mantle (box)	125.00	62.00	37.00
4b	Mickey Mantle (company)	125.00	62.00	37.00
5	Bob Turley (company)	35.00	17.50	10.50
6a	Whitey Ford (box)	12.50	6.25	3.75
6b	Whitey Ford (company)	12.50	6.25	3.75
7a	Roger Maris (box)	35.00	17.50	10.50
7b	Roger Maris (company)	35.00	17.50	10.50
8a	Bobby Richardson (box)	4.50	2.25	1.25
8b	Bobby Richardson (company)	4.50	2.25	1.25
9a	Tony Kubek (box)	4.50	2.25	1.25
9b	Tony Kubek (company)	4.50	2.25	1.25
10	Gil McDougald (box)	50.00	25.00	15.00
11	Cletis Boyer (box)	3.00	1.50	.90
12a	Hector Lopez (box)	3.00	1.50	.90
12b	Hector Lopez (company)	3.00	1.50	.90
13	Bob Cerv (box)	3.00	1.50	.90
14	Ryne Duren (box)	3.00	1.50	.90
15	Bobby Shantz (box)	3.00	1.50	.90
16	Art Ditmar (box)	3.00	1.50	.90
17	Jim Coates (box)	3.00	1.50	.90
18	John Blanchard (box)	3.00	1.50	.90
19a	Luis Aparicio (box)	7.50	3.75	2.25
19b	Luis Aparicio (company)	7.50	3.75	2.25
20a	Nelson Fox (box)	6.00	3.00	1.75
20b	Nelson Fox (company)	6.00	3.00	1.75
21a	Bill Pierce (box)	9.00	4.50	2.75
21b	Bill Pierce (company)	3.50	1.75	1.00
22a	Early Wynn (box)	10.00	5.00	3.00
22b	Early Wynn (company)	35.00	17.50	10.50
23	Bob Shaw (box)	125.00	62.00	37.00
24a	Al Smith (box)	4.50	2.25	1.25
24b	Al Smith (company)	3.00	1.50	.90
25a	Minnie Minoso (box)	3.75	2.00	1.25
25b	Minnie Minoso (company)	3.75	2.00	1.25
26a	Roy Sievers (box)	3.50	1.75	1.00
26b	Roy Sievers (company)	3.50	1.75	1.00
27a	Jim Landis (box)	3.00	1.50	.90
27b	Jim Landis (company)	3.00	1.50	.90
28a	Sherman Lollar (box)	4.50	2.25	1.25
28b	Sherman Lollar (company)	3.00	1.50	.90
29	Gerry Staley (box)	3.00	1.50	.90
30a	Gene Freese (box, White Sox)	3.00	1.50	.90
30b	Gene Freese (company, Reds)	9.00	4.50	2.75
31	Ted Kluszewski (box)	4.50	2.25	1.25
32	Turk Lown (box)	3.00	1.50	.90
33a	Jim Rivera (box)	3.00	1.50	.90
33b	Jim Rivera (company)	3.00	1.50	.90
34	Frank Baumann (box)	3.00	1.50	.90
35a	Al Kaline (box)	30.00	15.00	9.00
35b	Al Kaline (company)	30.00	15.00	9.00
36a	Rocky Colavito (box)	9.00	4.50	2.75
36b	Rocky Colavito (company)	5.00	2.50	1.50
37a	Charley Maxwell (box)	6.00	3.00	1.75
37b	Charley Maxwell (company)	3.00	1.50	.90
38a	Frank Lary (box)	3.00	1.50	.90
38b	Frank Lary (company)	3.00	1.50	.90
39a	Jim Bunning (box)	6.00	3.00	1.75
39b	Jim Bunning (company)	6.00	3.00	1.75
40a	Norm Cash (box)	3.00	1.50	.90
40b	Norm Cash (company)	3.00	1.50	.90
41a	Frank Bolling (box, Tigers)	8.00	4.00	2.50
41b	Frank Bolling (company, Braves)	7.50	3.75	2.25
42a	Don Mossi (box)	3.00	1.50	.90
42b	Don Mossi (company)	3.00	1.50	.90
43a	Lou Berberet (box)	3.00	1.50	.90
43b	Lou Berberet (company)	3.00	1.50	.90
44	Dave Sisler (box)	3.00	1.50	.90
45	Ed Yost (box)	3.00	1.50	.90
46	Pete Burnside (box)	3.00	1.50	.90
47a	Pete Runnels (box)	4.50	2.25	1.25
47b	Pete Runnnels (company)	3.50	1.75	1.00
48a	Frank Malzone (box)	3.00	1.50	.90
48b	Frank Malzone (company)	3.00	1.50	.90
49a	Vic Wertz (box)	7.50	3.75	2.25
49b	Vic Wertz (company)	4.50	2.25	1.25
50a	Tom Brewer (box)	3.75	2.00	1.25
50b	Tom Brewer (company)	3.00	1.50	.90
51a	Willie Tasby (box, no sold line)	8.00	4.00	2.50
51b	Willie Tasby (company, sold line)	3.00	1.50	.90
52a	Russ Nixon (box)	3.00	1.50	.90
52b	Russ Nixon (company)	3.00	1.50	.90
53a	Don Buddin (box)	3.00	1.50	.90
53b	Don Buddin (company)	3.00	1.50	.90
54a	Bill Monbouquette (box)	3.00	1.50	.90
54b	Bill Monbouquette (company)	3.00	1.50	.90
55a	Frank Sullivan (box, Red Sox)	3.00	1.50	.90
55b	Frank Sullivan (company, Phillies)	35.00	17.50	10.50
56a	Haywood Sullivan (box)	3.00	1.50	.90
56b	Haywood Sullivan (company)	3.00	1.50	.90
57a	Harvey Kuenn (box, Indians)	4.50	2.25	1.25
57b	Harvey Kuenn (company, Giants)	9.00	4.50	2.75
58a	Gary Bell (box)	7.50	3.75	2.25
58b	Gary Bell (company)	3.50	1.75	1.00
59a	Jim Perry (box)	3.50	1.75	1.00
59b	Jim Perry (company)	3.50	1.75	1.00
60a	Jim Grant (box)	4.50	2.25	1.25
60b	Jim Grant (company)	3.50	1.75	1.00
61a	Johnny Temple (box)	3.00	1.50	.90
61b	Johnny Temple (company)	3.00	1.50	.90
62a	Paul Foytack (box)	3.00	1.50	.90
62b	Paul Foytack (company)	3.00	1.50	.90
63a	Vic Power (box)	3.00	1.50	.90
63b	Vic Power (company)	3.00	1.50	.90
64a	Tito Francona (box)	3.00	1.50	.90
64b	Tito Francona (company)	3.00	1.50	.90
65a	Ken Aspromonte (box, no sold line)	9.00	4.50	2.75
65b	Ken Aspromonte (company, sold line)	9.00	4.50	2.75
66	Bob Wilson (box)	3.00	1.50	.90
67a	John Romano (box)	3.00	1.50	.90
67b	John Romano (company)	3.00	1.50	.90
68a	Jim Gentile (box)	3.75	2.00	1.25
68b	Jim Gentile (company)	3.00	1.50	.90
69a	Gus Triandos (box)	4.50	2.25	1.25
69b	Gus Triandos (company)	3.00	1.50	.90
70	Gene Woodling (box)	20.00	10.00	6.00
71a	Milt Pappas (box)	4.50	2.25	1.25
71b	Milt Pappas (company)	3.00	1.50	.90
72a	Ron Hansen (box)	4.50	2.25	1.25
72b	Ron Hansen (company)	3.00	1.50	.90
73	Chuck Estrada (company)	125.00	62.00	37.00
74a	Steve Barber (box)	3.00	1.50	.90
74b	Steve Barber (company)	3.00	1.50	.90
75a	Brooks Robinson (box)	35.00	17.50	10.50
75b	Brooks Robinson (company)	35.00	17.50	10.50
76a	Jackie Brandt (box)	3.00	1.50	.90
76b	Jackie Brandt (company)	3.00	1.50	.90
77a	Marv Breeding (box)	3.00	1.50	.90
77b	Marv Breedding (company)	3.00	1.50	.90
78	Hal Brown (box)	3.00	1.50	.90
79	Billy Klaus (box)	3.00	1.50	.90
80a	Hoyt Wilhelm (box)	7.50	3.75	2.25
80b	Hoyt Wilhelm (company)	9.00	4.50	2.75
81a	Jerry Lumpe (box)	9.00	4.50	2.75
81b	Jerry Lumpe (company)	6.00	3.00	1.75
82a	Norm Siebern (box)	3.00	1.50	.90
82b	Norm Siebern (company)	3.00	1.50	.90
83a	Bud Daley (box)	3.50	1.75	1.00
83b	Bud Daley (company)	3.75	2.00	1.25
84a	Bill Tuttle (box)	3.00	1.50	.90
84b	Bill Tuttle (company)	3.00	1.50	.90
85a	Marv Throneberry (box)	3.75	2.00	1.25
85b	Marv Throneberry (company)	3.75	2.00	1.25
86a	Dick Williams (box)	3.50	1.75	1.00
86b	Dick Williams (company)	3.00	1.50	.90
87a	Ray Herbert (box)	3.00	1.50	.90
87b	Ray Herbert (company)	3.00	1.50	.90
88a	Whitey Herzog (box)	3.00	1.50	.90
88b	Whitey Herzog (company)	3.00	1.50	.90
89a	Ken Hamlin (box, no sold line)	3.00	1.50	.90
89b	Ken Hamlin (company, sold line)	8.00	4.00	2.50
90a	Hank Bauer (box)	3.00	1.50	.90
90b	Hank Bauer (company)	3.00	1.50	.90
91a	Bob Allison (box, Minneapolis)	6.00	3.00	1.75
91b	Bob Allison (company, Minnesota)	7.50	3.75	2.25
92a	Harmon Killebrew (box, Minneapolis)	32.50	16.00	9.75
92b	Harmon Killebrew (company, Minnesota)	32.50	16.00	9.75
93a	Jim Lemon (box, Minneapolis)	60.00	30.00	18.00
93b	Jim Lemon (company, Minnesota)	7.50	3.75	2.25
94	Chuck Stobbs (company)	180.00	90.00	54.00
95a	Reno Bertoia (box, Minneapolis)	3.00	1.50	.90
95b	Reno Bertoia (company, Minnesota)	6.00	3.00	1.75
96a	Billy Gardner (box, Minneapolis)	3.00	1.50	.90
96b	Billy Gardner (company, Minnesota)	6.00	3.00	1.75
97a	Earl Battey (box, Minneapolis)	6.00	3.00	1.75
97b	Earl Battey (company, Minnesota)	6.00	3.00	1.75
98a	Pedro Ramos (box, Minneapolis)	3.00	1.50	.90
98b	Pedro Ramos (company, Minnesota)	6.00	3.00	1.75
99a	Camilio Pascual (Camilo) (box, Minneapolis)	3.00	1.50	.90
99b	Camilio Pascual (Camilo) (company, Minnesota)	6.00	3.00	1.75
100a	Billy Consolo (box, Minneapolis)	3.00	1.50	.90
100b	Billy Consolo (company, Minnesota)	6.00	3.00	1.75
101a	Warren Spahn (box)	21.00	10.50	6.25
101b	Warren Spahn (company)	12.00	6.00	3.50
102a	Lew Burdette (box)	3.75	2.00	1.25
102b	Lew Burdette (company)	3.75	2.00	1.25
103a	Bob Buhl (box)	3.00	1.50	.90
103b	Bob Buhl (company)	3.00	1.50	.90
104a	Joe Adcock (box)	6.00	3.00	1.75
104b	Joe Adcock (company)	3.75	2.00	1.25
105a	John Logan (box)	6.00	3.00	1.75
105b	John Logan (company)	3.50	1.75	1.00
106	Ed Mathews (company)	40.00	20.00	12.00
107a	Hank Aaron (box)	35.00	17.50	10.50
107b	Hank Aaron (company)	35.00	17.50	10.50
108a	Wes Covington (box)	3.00	1.50	.90
108b	Wes Covington (company)	3.00	1.50	.90
109a	Bill Bruton (box, Braves)	9.00	4.50	2.75
109b	Bill Bruton (company, Tigers)	8.00	4.00	2.50
110a	Del Crandall (box)	6.00	3.00	1.75
110b	Del Crandall (company)	3.50	1.75	1.00
111	Red Schoendienst (box)	7.50	3.75	2.25
112	Juan Pizarro (box)	3.00	1.50	.90
113	Chuck Cottier (box)	8.00	4.00	2.50
114	Al Spangler (box)	3.00	1.50	.90
115a	Dick Farrell (box)	9.00	4.50	2.75
115b	Dick Farrell (company)	6.00	3.00	1.75
116a	Jim Owens (box)	9.00	4.50	2.75
116b	Jim Owens (company)	6.00	3.00	1.75
117a	Robin Roberts (box)	9.00	4.50	2.75
117b	Robin Roberts (company)	9.00	4.50	2.75
118a	Tony Taylor (box)	3.00	1.50	.90
118b	Tony Taylor (company)	3.00	1.50	.90
119a	Lee Walls (box)	3.00	1.50	.90
119b	Lee Walls (company)	3.00	1.50	.90
120a	Tony Curry (box)	3.00	1.50	.90
120b	Tony Curry (company)	3.00	1.50	.90
121a	Pancho Herrera (box)	3.00	1.50	.90
121b	Pancho Herrera (company)	3.00	1.50	.90
122a	Ken Walters (box)	3.00	1.50	.90

122b	Ken Walters (company)	3.00	1.50	.90
123a	John Callison (box)	3.00	1.50	.90
123b	John Callison (company)	3.00	1.50	.90
124a	Gene Conley (box, Phillies)	3.00	1.50	.90
124b	Gene Conley (company, Red Sox)	20.00	10.00	6.00
125a	Bob Friend (box)	6.00	3.00	1.75
125b	Bob Friend (company)	3.00	1.50	.90
126a	Vernon Law (box)	6.00	3.00	1.75
126b	Vernon Law (company)	3.00	1.50	.90
127a	Dick Stuart (box)	3.00	1.50	.90
127b	Dick Stuart (company)	3.00	1.50	.90
128a	Bill Mazeroski (box)	3.75	2.00	1.25
128b	Bill Mazeroski (company)	3.75	2.00	1.25
129a	Dick Groat (box)	4.50	2.25	1.25
129b	Dick Groat (company)	3.00	1.50	.90
130a	Don Hoak (box)	3.00	1.50	.90
130b	Don Hoak (company)	3.00	1.50	.90
131a	Bob Skinner (box)	3.00	1.50	.90
131b	Bob Skinner (company)	3.00	1.50	.90
132a	Bob Clemente (box)	35.00	17.50	10.50
132b	Bob Clemente (company)	35.00	17.50	10.50
133	Roy Face (box)	4.50	2.25	1.25
134	Harvey Haddix (box)	3.50	1.75	1.00
135	Bill Virdon (box)	42.50	21.00	12.50
136a	Gino Cimoli (box)	3.00	1.50	.90
136b	Gino Cimoli (company)	3.00	1.50	.90
137	Rocky Nelson (box)	3.00	1.50	.90
138a	Smoky Burgess (box)	3.50	1.75	1.00
138b	Smoky Burgess (company)	3.50	1.75	1.00
139	Hal Smith (box)	3.00	1.50	.90
140	Wilmer Mizell (box)	3.00	1.50	.90
141a	Mike McCormick (box)	3.00	1.50	.90
141b	Mike McCormick (company)	3.00	1.50	.90
142a	John Antonelli (box, Giants)	4.50	2.25	1.25
142b	John Antonelli (company, Indians)	6.00	3.00	1.75
143a	Sam Jones (box)	6.00	3.00	1.75
143b	Sam Jones (company)	3.00	1.50	.90
144a	Orlando Cepeda (box)	7.50	3.75	2.25
144b	Orlando Cepeda (company)	7.50	3.75	2.25
145a	Willie Mays (box)	35.00	17.50	10.50
145b	Willie Mays (company)	35.00	17.50	10.50
146a	Willie Kirkland (box, Giants)	7.50	3.75	2.25
146b	Willie Kirkland (company, Indians)	7.50	3.75	2.25
147a	Willie McCovey (box)	7.00	3.50	2.00
147b	Willie McCovey (company)	30.00	15.00	9.00
148a	Don Blasingame (box)	3.00	1.50	.90
148b	Don Blasingame (company)	3.00	1.50	.90
149a	Jim Davenport (box)	3.00	1.50	.90
149b	Jim Davenport (company)	3.00	1.50	.90
150a	Hobie Landrith (box)	3.00	1.50	.90
150b	Hobie Landrith (company)	3.00	1.50	.90
151	Bob Schmidt (box)	3.00	1.50	.90
152a	Ed Bressoud (box)	3.00	1.50	.90
152b	Ed Bressoud (company)	3.00	1.50	.90
153a	Andre Rodgers (box, no traded line)	9.00	4.50	2.75
153b	Andre Rodgers (box, traded line)	3.00	1.50	.90
154	Jack Sanford (box)	3.00	1.50	.90
155	Billy O'Dell (box)	3.00	1.50	.90
156a	Norm Larker (box)	3.75	2.00	1.25
156b	Norm Larker (company)	3.75	2.00	1.25
157a	Charlie Neal (box)	3.00	1.50	.90
157b	Charlie Neal (company)	3.00	1.50	.90
158a	Jim Gilliam (box)	6.00	3.00	1.75
158b	Jim Gilliam (company)	3.75	2.00	1.25
159a	Wally Moon (box)	3.00	1.50	.90
159b	Wally Moon (company)	3.00	1.50	.90
160a	Don Drysdale (box)	7.00	3.50	2.00
160b	Don Drysdale (company)	8.00	4.00	2.50
161a	Larry Sherry (box)	3.00	1.50	.90
161b	Larry Sherry (company)	3.00	1.50	.90
162	Stan Williams (box)	7.50	3.75	2.25
163	Mel Roach (box)	60.00	30.00	18.00
164a	Maury Wills (box)	6.00	3.00	1.75
164b	Maury Wills (company)	6.00	3.00	1.75
165	Tom Davis (box)	3.00	1.50	.90
166a	John Roseboro (box)	3.00	1.50	.90
166b	John Roseboro (company)	3.00	1.50	.90
167a	Duke Snider (box)	8.00	4.00	2.50
167b	Duke Snider (company)	30.00	15.00	9.00
168a	Gil Hodges (box)	7.50	3.75	2.25
168b	Gil Hodges (company)	9.00	4.50	2.75
169	John Podres (box)	3.75	2.00	1.25
170	Ed Roebuck (box)	3.00	1.50	.90
171a	Ken Boyer (box)	9.00	4.50	2.75
171b	Ken Boyer (company)	6.00	3.00	1.75
172a	Joe Cunningham (box)	3.00	1.50	.90
172b	Joe Cunningham (company)	3.00	1.50	.90
173a	Daryl Spencer (box)	3.00	1.50	.90
173b	Daryl Spencer (company)	3.00	1.50	.90
174a	Larry Jackson (box)	3.00	1.50	.90
174b	Larry Jackson (company)	3.00	1.50	.90
175a	Lindy McDaniel (box)	3.00	1.50	.90
175b	Lindy McDaniel (company)	3.00	1.50	.90
176a	Bill White (box)	3.50	1.75	1.00
176b	Bill White (company)	3.50	1.75	1.00
177a	Alex Grammas (box)	3.00	1.50	.90
177b	Alex Grammas (company)	3.00	1.50	.90
178a	Curt Flood (box)	3.00	1.50	.90
178b	Curt Flood (company)	3.00	1.50	.90
179a	Ernie Broglio (box)	3.00	1.50	.90
179b	Ernie Broglio (company)	3.00	1.50	.90
180a	Hal Smith (box)	3.00	1.50	.90
180b	Hal Smith (company)	3.00	1.50	.90
181a	Vada Pinson (box)	3.75	2.00	1.25
181b	Vada Pinson (company)	3.75	2.00	1.25
182a	Frank Robinson (box)	30.00	15.00	9.00
182b	Frank Robinson (company)	30.00	15.00	9.00
183	Roy McMillan (box)	80.00	40.00	24.00
184a	Bob Purkey (box)	3.00	1.50	.90
184b	Bob Purkey (company)	3.00	1.50	.90
185a	Ed Kasko (box)	3.00	1.50	.90
185b	Ed Kasko (company)	3.00	1.50	.90
186a	Gus Bell (box)	3.00	1.50	.90
186b	Gus Bell (company)	3.00	1.50	.90
187a	Jerry Lynch (box)	3.00	1.50	.90
187b	Jerry Lynch (company)	3.00	1.50	.90
188a	Ed Bailey (box)	3.00	1.50	.90
188b	Ed Bailey (company)	3.00	1.50	.90
189a	Jim O'Toole (box)	3.00	1.50	.90
189b	Jim O'Toole (company)	3.00	1.50	.90
190a	Billy Martin (box, no sold line)	4.50	2.25	1.25
190b	Billy Martin (company, sold line)	9.00	4.50	2.75
191a	Ernie Banks (box)	9.00	4.50	2.75
191b	Ernie Banks (company)	9.00	4.50	2.75
192a	Richie Ashburn (box)	4.50	2.25	1.25
192b	Richie Ashburn (company)	4.50	2.25	1.25
193a	Frank Thomas (box)	40.00	20.00	12.00
193b	Frank Thomas (company)	7.50	3.75	2.25
194a	Don Cardwell (box)	3.00	1.50	.90
194b	Don Cardwell (company)	3.00	1.50	.90
195a	George Altman (box)	3.00	1.50	.90
195b	George Altman (company)	3.00	1.50	.90
196a	Ron Santo (box)	4.50	2.25	1.25
196b	Ron Santo (company)	4.50	2.25	1.25
197a	Glen Hobbie (box)	3.00	1.50	.90
197b	Glen Hobbie (company)	3.00	1.50	.90
198a	Sam Taylor (box)	3.00	1.50	.90
198b	Sam Taylor (company)	3.00	1.50	.90
199a	Jerry Kindall (box)	3.00	1.50	.90
199b	Jerry Kindall (company)	3.00	1.50	.90
200a	Don Elston (box)	4.50	2.25	1.25
200b	Don Elston (company)	4.50	2.25	1.25

1962 Post Cereal

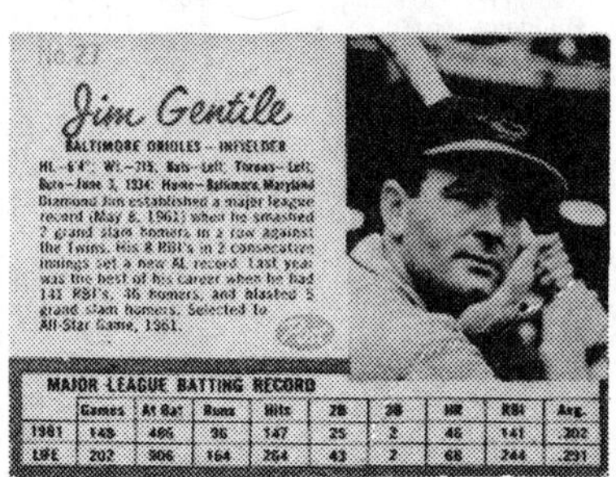

Like the 1961 Post set, there are 200 players pictured in the set of 3-1/2" by 2-1/2" cards. Differences include a Post logo on the card fronts and the player's name in script lettering. Cards are again blank backed and were issued in panels of five to seven cards on cereal boxes. American League players are numbered 1-100 and National League players 101-200. With variations there are 210 of the full-color cards known. A handful of the '62 cards were also issued in smaller quantities. The cards of Mickey Mantle and Roger Maris were reproduced in a special two-card panel for a Life magazine insert. the card stock for this insert is slightly thinner, with white margins. The 1962 Post Canadian and Jell-O sets have virtually the same checklist as this set. The complete set price does not include the scarcer variations.

		NR MT	EX	VG
Complete Set (200):		1750.	875.00	525.00
Common Player:		2.50	1.25	.70
1	Bill Skowron	5.00	2.50	1.50
2	Bobby Richardson	4.50	2.25	1.25
3	Cletis Boyer	3.00	1.50	.90
4	Tony Kubek	4.50	2.25	1.25
5a	Mickey Mantle (from box, no printing on back)	100.00	50.00	30.00
5b	Mickey Mantle (from ad, printing on back)	90.00	45.00	27.00
6a	Roger Maris (from box, no printing on back)	20.00	10.00	6.00
6b	Roger Maris (from ad, printing on back)	15.00	7.50	4.50
7	Yogi Berra	15.00	7.50	4.50
8	Elston Howard	4.50	2.25	1.25
9	Whitey Ford	10.00	5.00	3.00
10	Ralph Terry	3.00	1.50	.90
11	John Blanchard	3.00	1.50	.90
12	Luis Arroyo	3.00	1.50	.90
13	Bill Stafford	3.00	1.50	.90
14a	Norm Cash (Throws: Right)	3.00	1.50	.90
14b	Norm Cash (Throws: Left)	6.50	3.25	2.00
15	Jake Wood	2.50	1.25	.70
16	Steve Boros	2.50	1.25	.70
17	Chico Fernandez	2.50	1.25	.70
18	Bill Bruton	2.50	1.25	.70
19	Rocky Colavito	4.50	2.25	1.25
20	Al Kaline	10.00	5.00	3.00
21	Dick Brown	2.50	1.25	.70
22	Frank Lary	2.50	1.25	.70
23	Don Mossi	2.50	1.25	.70
24	Phil Regan	2.50	1.25	.70
25	Charley Maxwell	2.50	1.25	.70
26	Jim Bunning	4.50	2.25	1.25
27a	Jim Gentile (Home: Baltimore)	2.50	1.25	.70
27b	Jim Gentile (Home: San Lorenzo)	6.50	3.25	2.00
28	Marv Breeding	2.50	1.25	.70
29	Brooks Robinson	10.00	5.00	3.00
30	Ron Hansen	2.50	1.25	.70
31	Jackie Brandt	2.50	1.25	.70
32	Dick Williams	3.00	1.50	.90
33	Gus Triandos	2.50	1.25	.70
34	Milt Pappas	2.50	1.25	.70
35	Hoyt Wilhelm	7.50	3.75	2.25
36	Chuck Estrada	6.50	3.25	2.00
37	Vic Power	2.50	1.25	.70
38	Johnny Temple	2.50	1.25	.70
39	Bubba Phillips	2.50	1.25	.70
40	Tito Francona	2.50	1.25	.70
41	Willie Kirkland	2.50	1.25	.70
42	John Romano	2.50	1.25	.70
43	Jim Perry	3.00	1.50	.90
44	Woodie Held	2.50	1.25	.70
45	Chuck Essegian	2.50	1.25	.70
46	Roy Sievers	3.00	1.50	.90
47	Nellie Fox	6.00	3.00	1.75
48	Al Smith	2.50	1.25	.70
49	Luis Aparicio	9.00	4.50	2.75
50	Jim Landis	2.50	1.25	.70
51	Minnie Minoso	4.50	2.25	1.25
52	Andy Carey	2.50	1.25	.70
53	Sherman Lollar	2.50	1.25	.70
54	Bill Pierce	3.00	1.50	.90
55	Early Wynn	40.00	20.00	12.00
56	Chuck Schilling	2.50	1.25	.70
57	Pete Runnels	2.50	1.25	.70
58	Frank Malzone	2.50	1.25	.70
59	Don Buddin	2.50	1.25	.70
60	Gary Geiger	2.50	1.25	.70
61	Carl Yastrzemski	45.00	22.00	13.50
62	Jackie Jensen	4.50	2.25	1.25
63	Jim Pagliaroni	2.50	1.25	.70
64	Don Schwall	2.50	1.25	.70
65	Dale Long	2.50	1.25	.70
66	Chuck Cottier	2.50	1.25	.70
67	Billy Klaus	2.50	1.25	.70
68	Coot Veal	2.50	1.25	.70
69	Marty Keough	40.00	20.00	12.00
70	Willie Tasby	2.50	1.25	.70
71	Gene Woodling	3.50	1.75	1.00
72	Gene Green	2.50	1.25	.70
73	Dick Donovan	2.50	1.25	.70
74	Steve Bilko	2.50	1.25	.70
75	Rocky Bridges	2.50	1.25	.70
76	Eddie Yost	2.50	1.25	.70
77	Leon Wagner	2.50	1.25	.70
78	Albie Pearson	2.50	1.25	.70
79	Ken Hunt	2.50	1.25	.70
80	Earl Averill	2.50	1.25	.70
81	Ryne Duren	2.50	1.25	.70
82	Ted Kluszewski	4.50	2.25	1.25
83	Bob Allison	35.00	17.50	10.50
84	Billy Martin	4.50	2.25	1.25
85	Harmon Killebrew	10.00	5.00	3.00
86	Zoilo Versalles	2.50	1.25	.70
87	Lenny Green	2.50	1.25	.70
88	Bill Tuttle	2.50	1.25	.70
89	Jim Lemon	2.50	1.25	.70
90	Earl Battey	2.50	1.25	.70
91	Camilo Pascual	2.50	1.25	.70
92	Norm Siebern	60.00	30.00	18.00
93	Jerry Lumpe	2.50	1.25	.70
94	Dick Howser	3.00	1.50	.90
95a	Gene Stephens (Born: Jan. 5)	2.50	1.25	.70
95b	Gene Stephens (Born: Jan. 20)	6.50	3.25	2.00
96	Leo Posada	2.50	1.25	.70
97	Joe Pignatano	2.50	1.25	.70
98	Jim Archer	2.50	1.25	.70
99	Haywood Sullivan	2.50	1.25	.70
100	Art Ditmar	2.50	1.25	.70
101	Gil Hodges	65.00	32.00	19.50
102	Charlie Neal	2.50	1.25	.70
103	Daryl Spencer	25.00	12.50	7.50
104	Maury Wills	5.00	2.50	1.50
105	Tommy Davis	3.00	1.50	.90
106	Willie Davis	3.00	1.50	.90
107	John Roseboro	2.50	1.25	.70
108	John Podres	3.50	1.75	1.00
109a	Sandy Koufax (blue lines around stats)	40.00	20.00	12.00
109b	Sandy Koufax (red lines around stats)	25.00	12.50	7.50
110	Don Drysdale	10.00	5.00	3.00
111	Larry Sherry	2.50	1.25	.70
112	Jim Gilliam	3.50	1.75	1.00
113	Norm Larker	40.00	20.00	12.00
114	Duke Snider	12.00	6.00	3.50
115	Stan Williams	2.50	1.25	.70
116	Gordy Coleman	80.00	40.00	24.00
117	Don Blasingame	2.50	1.25	.70
118	Gene Freese	2.50	1.25	.70
119	Ed Kasko	2.50	1.25	.70
120	Gus Bell	2.50	1.25	.70
121	Vada Pinson	3.50	1.75	1.00
122	Frank Robinson	25.00	12.50	7.50
123	Bob Purkey	2.50	1.25	.70
124a	Joey Jay (blue lines around stats)	8.00	4.00	2.50
124b	Joey Jay (red lines around stats)	2.50	1.25	.70
125	Jim Brosnan	25.00	12.50	7.50
126	Jim O'Toole	2.50	1.25	.70
127	Jerry Lynch	60.00	30.00	18.00
128	Wally Post	2.50	1.25	.70
129	Ken Hunt	2.50	1.25	.70
130	Jerry Zimmerman	2.50	1.25	.70
131	Willie McCovey	80.00	40.00	24.00
132	Jose Pagan	2.50	1.25	.70
133	Felipe Alou	3.00	1.50	.90
134	Jim Davenport	2.50	1.25	.70
135	Harvey Kuenn	3.00	1.50	.90
136	Orlando Cepeda	4.50	2.25	1.25
137	Ed Bailey	2.50	1.25	.70
138	Sam Jones	2.50	1.25	.70
139	Mike McCormick	2.50	1.25	.70
140	Juan Marichal	80.00	40.00	24.00

141	Jack Sanford	2.50	1.25	.70
142	Willie Mays	35.00	17.50	10.50
143	Stu Miller (photo actually Chuck Hiller)	6.00	3.00	1.75
144	Joe Amalfitano	15.00	7.50	4.50
145a	Joe Adock (name incorrect)	40.00	20.00	12.00
145b	Joe Adcock (name correct)	3.00	1.50	.90
146	Frank Bolling	2.50	1.25	.70
147	Ed Mathews	10.00	5.00	3.00
148	Roy McMillan	2.50	1.25	.70
149	Hank Aaron	45.00	22.00	13.50
150	Gino Cimoli	2.50	1.25	.70
151	Frank Thomas	2.50	1.25	.70
152	Joe Torre	4.50	2.25	1.25
153	Lou Burdette	3.50	1.75	1.00
154	Bob Buhl	2.50	1.25	.70
155	Carlton Willey	2.50	1.25	.70
156	Lee Maye	2.50	1.25	.70
157	Al Spangler	2.50	1.25	.70
158	Bill White	45.00	22.00	13.50
159	Ken Boyer	4.50	2.25	1.25
160	Joe Cunningham	2.50	1.25	.70
161	Carl Warwick	2.50	1.25	.70
162	Carl Sawatski	2.50	1.25	.70
163	Lindy McDaniel	2.50	1.25	.70
164	Ernie Broglio	2.50	1.25	.70
165	Larry Jackson	2.50	1.25	.70
166	Curt Flood	3.50	1.75	1.00
167	Curt Simmons	2.50	1.25	.70
168	Alex Grammas	2.50	1.25	.70
169	Dick Stuart	3.50	1.75	1.00
170	Bill Mazeroski	5.00	2.50	1.50
171	Don Hoak	2.50	1.25	.70
172	Dick Groat	3.00	1.50	.90
173a	Roberto Clemente (blue lines around stats)	40.00	20.00	12.00
173b	Roberto Clemente (red lines around stats)	25.00	12.50	7.50
174	Bob Skinner	2.50	1.25	.70
175	Bill Virdon	3.00	1.50	.90
176	Smoky Burgess	3.00	1.50	.90
177	Elroy Face	3.00	1.50	.90
178	Bob Friend	2.50	1.25	.70
179	Vernon Law	2.50	1.25	.70
180	Harvey Haddix	2.50	1.25	.70
181	Hal Smith	2.50	1.25	.70
182	Ed Bouchee	2.50	1.25	.70
183	Don Zimmer	2.50	1.25	.70
184	Ron Santo	3.50	1.75	1.00
185	Andre Rodgers	2.50	1.25	.70
186	Richie Ashburn	5.00	2.50	1.50
187a	George Altman (last line is "...1955.)")	2.50	1.25	.70
187b	George Altman (last line is "...1955.")	4.50	2.25	1.25
188	Ernie Banks	15.00	7.50	4.50
189	Sam Taylor	2.50	1.25	.70
190	Don Elston	2.50	1.25	.70
191	Jerry Kindall	2.50	1.25	.70
192	Pancho Herrera	2.50	1.25	.70
193	Tony Taylor	2.50	1.25	.70
194	Ruben Amaro	2.50	1.25	.70
195	Don Demeter	2.50	1.25	.70
196	Bobby Gene Smith	2.50	1.25	.70
197	Clay Dalrymple	2.50	1.25	.70
198	Robin Roberts	10.00	5.00	3.00
199	Art Mahaffey	2.50	1.25	.70
200	John Buzhardt	3.50	1.75	1.00

1962 Post Cereal - Canadian

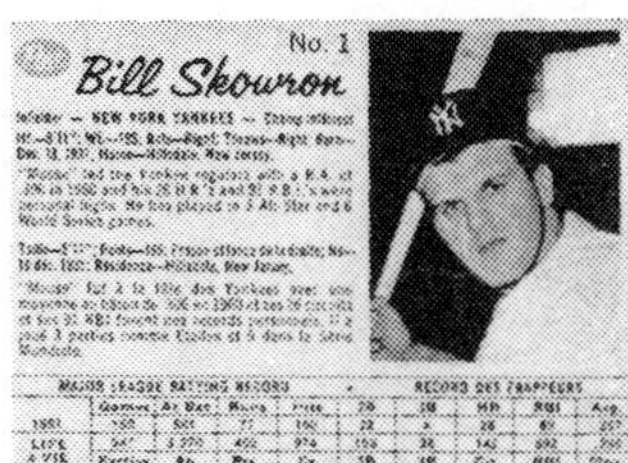

This Canadian set of cards is scarce due to the much more limited distribution in Canada. The cards were printed on the back of the cereal box itself and contains a full-color player photo with biography and statistics given in both French and English. The card backs are blank. Cards measure 3-1/2" by 2-1/2". This 200-card set is very similar to the Post Cereal cards printed in the United States. the Post logo appears at the upper left corner in the Canadian issue. Several cards are scarce because of limited distribution and there are two Whitey Ford cards, the corrected version being the most scarce. The complete set price does not include the scarcer variations.

		NR MT	EX	VG
Complete Set (200):		3000.	1500.	900.00
Common Player:		3.50	1.75	1.00
1	Bill Skowron	9.50	4.75	2.75
2	Bobby Richardson	7.00	3.50	2.00
3	Cletis Boyer	4.25	2.25	1.25
4	Tony Kubek	7.00	3.50	2.00
5a	Mickey Mantle (script name large)	200.00	100.00	60.00
5b	Mickey Mantle (script name small)	125.00	62.00	37.00
6	Roger Maris	40.00	20.00	12.00
7	Yogi Berra	25.00	12.50	7.50
8	Elston Howard	5.00	2.50	1.50
9a	Whitey Ford (Dodgers)	30.00	15.00	9.00
9b	Whitey Ford (Yankees)	55.00	27.00	16.50
10	Ralph Terry	35.00	17.50	10.50
11	John Blanchard	4.25	2.25	1.25
12	Luis Arroyo	4.25	2.25	1.25
13	Bill Stafford	4.25	2.25	1.25
14	Norm Cash	5.00	2.50	1.50
15	Jake Wood	3.50	1.75	1.00
16	Steve Boros	3.50	1.75	1.00
17	Chico Fernandez	3.50	1.75	1.00
18	Bill Bruton	3.50	1.75	1.00
19a	Rocky Colavito (script name large)	12.00	6.00	3.50
19b	Rocky Colavito (script name small)	12.00	6.00	3.50
20	Al Kaline	25.00	12.50	7.50
21	Dick Brown	8.50	4.25	2.50
22a	Frank Lary (French bio variation)	11.00	5.50	3.25
22b	Frank Lary (French bio variation)	11.00	5.50	3.25
23	Don Mossi	3.50	1.75	1.00
24	Phil Regan	3.50	1.75	1.00
25	Charley Maxwell	3.50	1.75	1.00
26	Jim Bunning	7.00	3.50	2.00
27a	Jim Gentile (French bio variation)	9.00	4.50	2.75
27b	Jim Gentile (French bio variation)	9.00	4.50	2.75
28	Marv Breeding	3.50	1.75	1.00
29	Brooks Robinson	35.00	17.50	10.50
30	Ron Hansen	3.50	1.75	1.00
31	Jackie Brandt	3.50	1.75	1.00
32	Dick Williams	35.00	17.50	10.50
33	Gus Triandos	3.50	1.75	1.00
34	Milt Pappas	4.25	2.25	1.25
35	Hoyt Wilhelm	25.00	12.50	7.50
36	Chuck Estrada	3.50	1.75	1.00
37	Vic Power	3.50	1.75	1.00
38	Johnny Temple	3.50	1.75	1.00
39	Bubba Phillips	35.00	17.50	10.50
40	Tito Francona	9.00	4.50	2.75
41	Willie Kirkland	8.50	4.25	2.50
42	John Romano	8.50	4.25	2.50
43	Jim Perry	5.00	2.50	1.50
44	Woodie Held	3.50	1.75	1.00
45	Chuck Essegian	3.50	1.75	1.00
46	Roy Sievers	4.25	2.25	1.25
47	Nellie Fox	7.00	3.50	2.00
48	Al Smith	3.50	1.75	1.00
49	Luis Aparicio	35.00	17.50	10.50
50	Jim Landis	3.50	1.75	1.00
51	Minnie Minoso	35.00	17.50	10.50
52	Andy Carey	8.50	4.25	2.50
53	Sherman Lollar	3.50	1.75	1.00
54	Bill Pierce	4.25	2.25	1.25
55	Early Wynn	20.00	10.00	6.00
56	Chuck Schilling	3.50	1.75	1.00
57	Pete Runnels	4.25	2.25	1.25
58	Frank Malzone	3.50	1.75	1.00
59	Don Buddin	8.50	4.25	2.50
60	Gary Geiger	3.50	1.75	1.00
61	Carl Yastrzemski	50.00	25.00	15.00
62	Jackie Jensen	9.00	4.50	2.75
63	Jim Pagliaroni	3.50	1.75	1.00
64	Don Schwall	9.00	4.50	2.75
65	Dale Long	3.50	1.75	1.00
66	Chuck Cottier	3.50	1.75	1.00
67	Billy Klaus	3.50	1.75	1.00
68	Coot Veal	3.50	1.75	1.00
69	Marty Keough	3.50	1.75	1.00
70	Willie Tasby	35.00	17.50	10.50
71	Gene Woodling (photo reversed)	4.25	2.25	1.25
72	Gene Green	3.50	1.75	1.00
73	Dick Donovan	3.50	1.75	1.00
74	Steve Bilko	3.50	1.75	1.00
75	Rocky Bridges	7.00	3.50	2.00
76	Eddie Yost	3.50	1.75	1.00
77	Leon Wagner	35.00	17.50	10.50
78	Albie Pearson	8.50	4.25	2.50
79	Ken Hunt	3.50	1.75	1.00
80	Earl Averill	3.50	1.75	1.00
81	Ryne Duren	5.00	2.50	1.50
82	Ted Kluszewski	11.00	5.50	3.25
83	Bob Allison	4.25	2.25	1.25
84	Billy Martin	9.00	4.50	2.75
85	Harmon Killebrew	20.00	10.00	6.00
86	Zoilo Versalles	3.50	1.75	1.00
87	Lenny Green	35.00	17.50	10.50
88	Bill Tuttle	3.50	1.75	1.00
89	Jim Lemon	3.50	1.75	1.00
90	Earl Battey	3.50	1.75	1.00
91	Camilo Pascual	4.25	2.25	1.25
92	Norm Siebern	3.50	1.75	1.00
93	Jerry Lumpe	3.50	1.75	1.00
94	Dick Howser	35.00	17.50	10.50
95	Gene Stephens	3.50	1.75	1.00
96	Leo Posada	3.50	1.75	1.00
97	Joe Pignatano	3.50	1.75	1.00
98	Jim Archer	3.50	1.75	1.00
99	Haywood Sullivan	35.00	17.50	10.50
100	Art Ditmar	35.00	17.50	10.50
101	Gil Hodges	20.00	10.00	6.00
102	Charlie Neal	3.50	1.75	1.00
103	Daryl Spencer	3.50	1.75	1.00
104	Maury Wills	12.00	6.00	3.50
105	Tommy Davis	12.00	6.00	3.50
106	Willie Davis	5.00	2.50	1.50
107	John Roseboro	4.25	2.25	1.25
108	John Podres	5.00	2.50	1.50
109	Sandy Koufax	30.00	15.00	9.00
110	Don Drysdale	25.00	12.50	7.50
111	Larry Sherry	35.00	17.50	10.50
112	Jim Gilliam	35.00	17.50	10.50
113	Norm Larker	3.50	1.75	1.00
114	Duke Snider	35.00	17.50	10.50
115	Stan Williams	3.50	1.75	1.00
116	Gordy Coleman	3.50	1.75	1.00
117	Don Blasingame	35.00	17.50	10.50
118	Gene Freese	8.50	4.25	2.50
119	Ed Kasko	3.50	1.75	1.00
120	Gus Bell	3.50	1.75	1.00
121	Vada Pinson	6.00	3.00	1.75
122	Frank Robinson	25.00	12.50	7.50
123	Bob Purkey	35.00	17.50	10.50
124	Joey Jay	3.50	1.75	1.00
125	Jim Brosnan	4.25	2.25	1.25
126	Jim O'Toole	3.50	1.75	1.00
127	Jerry Lynch	3.50	1.75	1.00
128	Wally Post	70.00	35.00	21.00
129	Ken Hunt	3.50	1.75	1.00
130	Jerry Zimmerman	3.50	1.75	1.00
131	Willie McCovey	25.00	12.50	7.50
132	Jose Pagan	3.50	1.75	1.00
133	Felipe Alou	4.25	2.25	1.25
134	Jim Davenport	3.50	1.75	1.00
135	Harvey Kuenn	5.00	2.50	1.50
136	Orlando Cepeda	7.00	3.50	2.00
137	Ed Bailey	35.00	17.50	10.50
138	Sam Jones	35.00	17.50	10.50
139	Mike McCormick	3.50	1.75	1.00
140	Juan Marichal	25.00	12.50	7.50
141	Jack Sanford	3.50	1.75	1.00
142a	Willie Mays (big head)	60.00	30.00	18.00
142b	Willie Mays (small head)	80.00	40.00	24.00
143	Stu Miller	3.50	1.75	1.00
144	Joe Amalfitano	35.00	17.50	10.50
145	Joe Adcock	5.00	2.50	1.50
146	Frank Bolling	3.50	1.75	1.00
147	Ed Mathews	20.00	10.00	6.00
148	Roy McMillan	3.50	1.75	1.00
149a	Hank Aaron (script name large)	50.00	25.00	15.00
149b	Hank Aaron (script name small)	50.00	25.00	15.00
150	Gino Cimoli	3.50	1.75	1.00
151	Frank J. Thomas	3.50	1.75	1.00
152	Joe Torre	8.00	4.00	2.50
153	Lou Burdette	6.00	3.00	1.75
154	Bob Buhl	4.25	2.25	1.25
155	Carlton Willey	3.50	1.75	1.00
156	Lee Maye	3.50	1.75	1.00
157	Al Spangler	3.50	1.75	1.00
158	Bill White	4.25	2.25	1.25
159	Ken Boyer	30.00	15.00	9.00
160	Joe Cunningham	3.50	1.75	1.00
161	Carl Warwick	8.50	4.25	2.50
162	Carl Sawatski	3.50	1.75	1.00
163	Lindy McDaniel	3.50	1.75	1.00
164	Ernie Broglio	3.50	1.75	1.00
165	Larry Jackson	3.50	1.75	1.00
166	Curt Flood	5.00	2.50	1.50
167	Curt Simmons	9.50	4.75	2.75
168	Alex Grammas	3.50	1.75	1.00
169	Dick Stuart	4.25	2.25	1.25
170	Bill Mazeroski	35.00	17.50	10.50
171	Don Hoak	3.50	1.75	1.00
172	Dick Groat	9.00	4.50	2.75
173	Roberto Clemente	45.00	22.00	13.50
174	Bob Skinner	3.50	1.75	1.00
175	Bill Virdon	5.00	2.50	1.50
176	Smoky Burgess	9.50	4.75	2.75
177	Elroy Face	9.50	4.75	2.75
178	Bob Friend	4.25	2.25	1.25
179	Vernon Law	4.25	2.25	1.25
180	Harvey Haddix	4.25	2.25	1.25
181	Hal Smith	35.00	17.50	10.50
182	Ed Bouchee	3.50	1.75	1.00
183	Don Zimmer	5.00	2.50	1.50
184	Ron Santo	6.00	3.00	1.75
185	Andre Rodgers	3.50	1.75	1.00
186	Richie Ashburn	7.00	3.50	2.00
187	George Altman	3.50	1.75	1.00
188	Ernie Banks	35.00	17.50	10.50
189	Sam Taylor	3.50	1.75	1.00
190	Don Elston	3.50	1.75	1.00
191	Jerry Kindall	3.50	1.75	1.00
192	Pancho Herrera	3.50	1.75	1.00
193	Tony Taylor	3.50	1.75	1.00
194	Ruben Amaro	3.50	1.75	1.00
195	Don Demeter	35.00	17.50	10.50
196	Bobby Gene Smith	3.50	1.75	1.00
197	Clay Dalrymple	3.50	1.75	1.00
198	Robin Roberts	20.00	10.00	6.00
199	Art Mahaffey	3.50	1.75	1.00
200	John Buzhardt	6.00	3.00	1.75

1963 Post Cereal

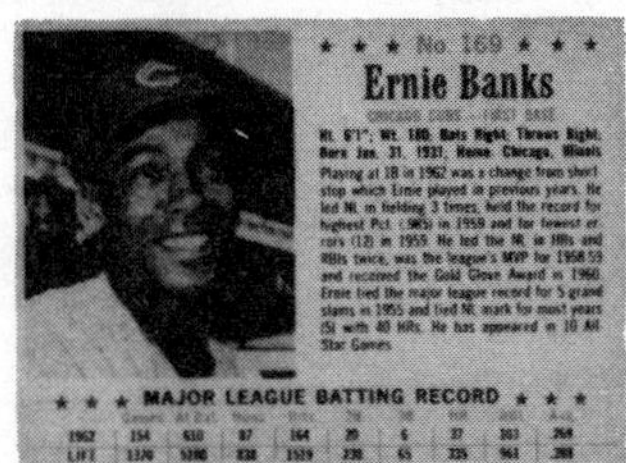

Another 200-player, 3-1/2" by 2-1/2" set that, with variations, totals more than 205 cards. Numerous color variations also exist due to the different cereal boxes on which the cards were printed. As many as 25 cards in the set are considered scarce, making it much more difficult to complete than the other major Post sets. Star cards also command higher prices than in the '61 or '62 Post cards. The 1963 Post cards are almost identical to the '63 Jell-O set, which is a slight 1/4" narrower. Cards are still blank backed, with a color player photo, biographies and statistics on the numbered card fronts. No Post logo appears on the '63 cards. The complete set price does not include the scarcer variations.

		NR MT	EX	VG
Complete Set (200):		3900.	1950.	1170.
Common Player:		3.00	1.50	.90
1	Vic Power	4.50	2.25	1.25
2	Bernie Allen	3.00	1.50	.90
3	Zoilo Versalles	3.00	1.50	.90
4	Rich Rollins	3.00	1.50	.90
5	Harmon Killebrew	12.00	6.00	3.50
6	Lenny Green	35.00	17.50	10.50
7	Bob Allison	3.00	1.50	.90
8	Earl Battey	3.00	1.50	.90
9	Camilo Pascual	3.00	1.50	.90
10	Jim Kaat	4.00	2.00	1.25
11	Jack Kralick	3.00	1.50	.90
12	Bill Skowron	3.50	1.75	1.00
13	Bobby Richardson	4.00	2.00	1.25
14	Cletis Boyer	3.50	1.75	1.00
15	Mickey Mantle	325.00	162.00	97.00
16	Roger Maris	150.00	75.00	45.00
17	Yogi Berra	15.00	7.50	4.50
18	Elston Howard	4.00	2.00	1.25
19	Whitey Ford	10.00	5.00	3.00
20	Ralph Terry	3.50	1.75	1.00
21	John Blanchard	3.50	1.75	1.00
22	Bill Stafford	3.50	1.75	1.00
23	Tom Tresh	3.50	1.75	1.00
24	Steve Bilko	3.00	1.50	.90
25	Bill Moran	3.00	1.50	.90
26a	Joe Koppe (1962 Avg. is .277)	3.00	1.50	.90
26b	Joe Koppe (1962 Avg. is .227)	12.00	6.00	3.50
27	Felix Torres	3.00	1.50	.90
28a	Leon Wagner (lifetime Avg. is .278)	3.00	1.50	.90
28b	Leon Wagner (lifetime Avg. is .272)	12.00	6.00	3.50
29	Albie Pearson	3.00	1.50	.90
30	Lee Thomas (photo actually George Thomas)	70.00	35.00	21.00
31	Bob Rodgers	3.00	1.50	.90
32	Dean Chance	3.00	1.50	.90
33	Ken McBride	3.00	1.50	.90
34	George Thomas (photo actually Lee Thomas)	3.00	1.50	.90
35	Joe Cunningham	3.00	1.50	.90
36a	Nelson Fox (no bat showing)	4.50	2.25	1.25
36b	Nelson Fox (part of bat showing)	10.00	5.00	3.00
37	Luis Aparicio	9.00	4.50	2.75
38	Al Smith	25.00	12.50	7.50
39	Floyd Robinson	80.00	40.00	24.00
40	Jim Landis	3.00	1.50	.90
41	Charlie Maxwell	3.00	1.50	.90
42	Sherman Lollar	3.00	1.50	.90
43	Early Wynn	7.50	3.75	2.25
44	Juan Pizarro	3.00	1.50	.90
45	Ray Herbert	3.00	1.50	.90
46	Norm Cash	4.00	2.00	1.25
47	Steve Boros	3.00	1.50	.90
48	Dick McAuliffe	25.00	12.50	7.50
49	Bill Bruton	3.00	1.50	.90
50	Rocky Colavito	5.00	2.50	1.50
51	Al Kaline	10.00	5.00	3.00
52	Dick Brown	3.00	1.50	.90
53	Jim Bunning	110.00	55.00	33.00
54	Hank Aguirre	3.00	1.50	.90
55	Frank Lary	3.00	1.50	.90
56	Don Mossi	3.00	1.50	.90
57	Jim Gentile	3.00	1.50	.90
58	Jackie Brandt	3.00	1.50	.90
59	Brooks Robinson	10.00	5.00	3.00
60	Ron Hansen	3.00	1.50	.90
61	Jerry Adair	150.00	75.00	45.00
62	John (Boog) Powell	4.00	2.00	1.25
63	Russ Snyder	3.00	1.50	.90
64	Steve Barber	3.00	1.50	.90
65	Milt Pappas	3.00	1.50	.90
66	Robin Roberts	7.50	3.75	2.25
67	Tito Francona	3.00	1.50	.90
68	Jerry Kindall	3.00	1.50	.90
69	Woodie Held	3.00	1.50	.90
70	Bubba Phillips	15.00	7.50	4.50
71	Chuck Essegian	3.00	1.50	.90
72	Willie Kirkland	3.00	1.50	.90
73	Al Luplow	3.00	1.50	.90
74	Ty Cline	3.00	1.50	.90
75	Dick Donovan	3.00	1.50	.90
76	John Romano	3.00	1.50	.90
77	Pete Runnels	3.00	1.50	.90
78	Ed Bressoud	3.00	1.50	.90
79	Frank Malzone	3.00	1.50	.90
80	Carl Yastrzemski	325.00	162.00	97.00
81	Gary Geiger	3.00	1.50	.90
82	Lou Clinton	3.00	1.50	.90
83	Earl Wilson	3.00	1.50	.90
84	Bill Monbouquette	3.00	1.50	.90
85	Norm Siebern	3.00	1.50	.90
86	Jerry Lumpe	80.00	40.00	24.00
87	Manny Jimenez	80.00	40.00	24.00
88	Gino Cimoli	3.00	1.50	.90
89	Ed Charles	3.00	1.50	.90
90	Ed Rakow	3.00	1.50	.90
91	Bob Del Greco	3.00	1.50	.90
92	Haywood Sullivan	3.00	1.50	.90
93	Chuck Hinton	3.00	1.50	.90
94	Ken Retzer	3.00	1.50	.90
95	Harry Bright	3.00	1.50	.90
96	Bob Johnson	3.00	1.50	.90
97	Dave Stenhouse	15.00	7.50	4.50
98	Chuck Cottier	25.00	12.50	7.50
99	Tom Cheney	3.00	1.50	.90
100	Claude Osteen	15.00	7.50	4.50
101	Orlando Cepeda	4.00	2.00	1.25
102	Charley Hiller	3.00	1.50	.90
103	Jose Pagan	3.00	1.50	.90
104	Jim Davenport	3.00	1.50	.90
105	Harvey Kuenn	3.50	1.75	1.00
106	Willie Mays	25.00	12.50	7.50
107	Felipe Alou	4.00	2.00	1.25
108	Tom Haller	110.00	55.00	33.00
109	Juan Marichal	9.00	4.50	2.75
110	Jack Sanford	3.00	1.50	.90
111	Bill O'Dell	3.00	1.50	.90
112	Willie McCovey	10.00	5.00	3.00
113	Lee Walls	3.00	1.50	.90
114	Jim Gilliam	4.00	2.00	1.25
115	Maury Wills	4.00	2.00	1.25
116	Ron Fairly	3.00	1.50	.90
117	Tommy Davis	3.50	1.75	1.00
118	Duke Snider	10.00	5.00	3.00
119	Willie Davis	150.00	75.00	45.00
120	John Roseboro	3.00	1.50	.90
121	Sandy Koufax	15.00	7.50	4.50
122	Stan Williams	3.00	1.50	.90
123	Don Drysdale	12.00	6.00	3.50
124a	Daryl Spencer (no arm showing)	3.00	1.50	.90
124b	Daryl Spencer (part of arm showing)	10.00	5.00	3.00
125	Gordy Coleman	3.00	1.50	.90
126	Don Blasingame	3.00	1.50	.90
127	Leo Cardenas	3.00	1.50	.90
128	Eddie Kasko	150.00	75.00	45.00
129	Jerry Lynch	15.00	7.50	4.50
130	Vada Pinson	3.50	1.75	1.00
131a	Frank Robinson (no stripes on hat)	10.00	5.00	3.00
131b	Frank Robinson (stripes on hat)	15.00	7.50	4.50
132	John Edwards	3.00	1.50	.90
133	Joey Jay	3.00	1.50	.90
134	Bob Purkey	3.00	1.50	.90
135	Marty Keough	15.00	7.50	4.50
136	Jim O'Toole	3.00	1.50	.90
137	Dick Stuart	3.50	1.75	1.00
138	Bill Mazeroski	5.00	2.50	1.50
139	Dick Groat	3.50	1.75	1.00
140	Don Hoak	30.00	15.00	9.00
141	Bob Skinner	15.00	7.50	4.50
142	Bill Virdon	3.50	1.75	1.00
143	Roberto Clemente	25.00	12.50	7.50
144	Smoky Burgess	3.00	1.50	.90
145	Bob Friend	3.00	1.50	.90
146	Al McBean	3.00	1.50	.90
147	El Roy Face (Elroy)	3.50	1.75	1.00
148	Joe Adcock	3.50	1.75	1.00
149	Frank Bolling	3.00	1.50	.90
150	Roy McMillan	3.00	1.50	.90
151	Eddie Mathews	10.00	5.00	3.00
152	Hank Aaron	70.00	35.00	21.00
153	Del Crandall	30.00	15.00	9.00
154a	Bob Shaw (third sentence has "In 1959" twice)	10.00	5.00	3.00
154b	Bob Shaw (third sentence has "In 1959" once)	3.00	1.50	.90
155	Lew Burdette	3.50	1.75	1.00
156	Joe Torre	4.00	2.00	1.25
157	Tony Cloninger	3.00	1.50	.90
158	Bill White	3.50	1.75	1.00
159	Julian Javier	3.00	1.50	.90
160	Ken Boyer	4.00	2.00	1.25
161	Julio Gotay	3.00	1.50	.90
162	Curt Flood	110.00	55.00	33.00
163	Charlie James	3.00	1.50	.90
164	Gene Oliver	3.00	1.50	.90
165	Ernie Broglio	3.00	1.50	.90
166	Bob Gibson	10.00	5.00	3.00
167a	Lindy McDaniel (asterisk before trade line)	3.00	1.50	.90
167b	Lindy McDaniel (no asterisk before trade line)	6.50	3.25	2.00
168	Ray Washburn	3.00	1.50	.90
169	Ernie Banks	10.00	5.00	3.00
170	Ron Santo	3.50	1.75	1.00
171	George Altman	3.00	1.50	.90
172	Billy Williams	110.00	55.00	33.00
173	Andre Rodgers	7.50	3.75	2.25
174	Ken Hubbs	20.00	10.00	6.00
175	Don Landrum	3.00	1.50	.90
176	Dick Bertell	15.00	7.50	4.50
177	Roy Sievers	3.00	1.50	.90
178	Tony Taylor	3.00	1.50	.90
179	John Callison	3.00	1.50	.90
180	Don Demeter	3.00	1.50	.90
181	Tony Gonzalez	3.00	1.50	.90
182	Wes Covington	20.00	10.00	6.00
183	Art Mahaffey	3.00	1.50	.90
184	Clay Dalrymple	3.00	1.50	.90
185	Al Spangler	3.00	1.50	.90
186	Roman Mejias	3.00	1.50	.90
187	Bob Aspromonte	325.00	162.00	97.00
188	Norm Larker	30.00	15.00	9.00
189	Johnny Temple	3.00	1.50	.90
190	Carl Warwick	3.00	1.50	.90
191	Bob Lillis	3.00	1.50	.90
192	Dick Farrell	3.00	1.50	.90
193	Gil Hodges	9.00	4.50	2.75
194	Marv Throneberry	4.00	2.00	1.25
195	Charlie Neal	10.00	5.00	3.00
196	Frank Thomas	150.00	75.00	45.00
197	Richie Ashburn	20.00	10.00	6.00
198	Felix Mantilla	3.00	1.50	.90
199	Rod Kanehl	20.00	10.00	6.00
200	Roger Craig	4.00	2.00	1.25

1990 Post Cereal

Post Cereal returned in 1990 with a 30-card set. The card fronts feature borders in white, red and blue, with the post logo in the upper left and the Major League Baseball logo in the upper right. Below the full-color shot of the player is his name in red. Backs of the cards show complete major league statistics; underneath is a facsimile autograph. The player photos do not display team logos. Cards were included three per box, inside Alpha-Bits cereal. Considered a difficult set to complete, the insert offer was only available for a limited time.

		MT	NR MT	EX
Complete Set (30):		12.00	9.00	4.75
Common Player:		.30	.25	.12
1	Don Mattingly	.80	.60	.30
2	Roger Clemens	.50	.40	.20
3	Kirby Puckett	.60	.45	.25
4	George Brett	.90	.70	.35
5	Tony Gwynn	.50	.40	.20
6	Ozzie Smith	.50	.40	.20
7	Will Clark	.80	.60	.30
8	Orel Hershiser	.40	.30	.15
9	Ryne Sandberg	1.00	.70	.40
10	Darryl Strawberry	.40	.30	.15
11	Nolan Ryan	1.50	1.25	.60
12	Mark McGwire	.40	.30	.15
13	Jim Abbott	.40	.30	.15
14	Bo Jackson	.80	.60	.30
15	Kevin Mitchell	.40	.30	.15
16	Jose Canseco	.90	.70	.35
17	Wade Boggs	.80	.60	.30
18	Dale Murphy	.60	.45	.25
19	Mark Grace	.40	.30	.15
20	Mike Scott	.30	.25	.12
21	Cal Ripken, Jr.	1.00	.70	.40
22	Pedro Guerrero	.30	.25	.12
23	Ken Griffey, Jr.	1.50	1.25	.60
24	Eric Davis	.60	.45	.25
25	Rickey Henderson	.80	.60	.30
26	Robin Yount	.60	.45	.25
27	Von Hayes	.30	.25	.12
28	Alan Trammell	.40	.30	.15
29	Dwight Gooden	.60	.45	.25
30	Joe Carter	.40	.30	.15

1991 Post Cereal

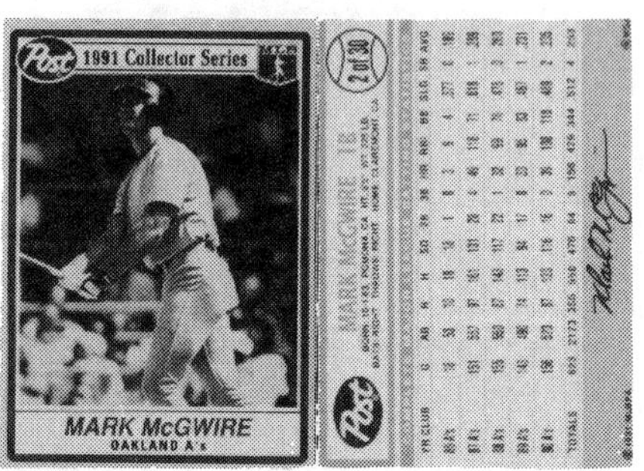

These superstar trading cards were inserted in Post Honeycomb, Super Golden Crisp, Cocoa Pebbles, Fruity Pebbles, Alpha-Bits and Marshmallow Alpha-Bits children's cereals. The complete set features 30 cards of baseball's top players. The cards were produced by Mike Schechter Associates, Inc. and are authorized by The Major League Baseball Players Association. The card fronts feature a player photo, the Post logo and the MLBPA logo. The flip sides feature statistics and a facsimile autograph.

		MT	NR MT	EX
Complete Set (30):		12.00	9.00	4.75
Common Player:		.30	.25	.12
1	Dave Justice	.50	.40	.20
2	Mark McGwire	.40	.30	.15
3	Will Clark	.80	.60	.30

		MT	NR MT	EX
4	Jose Canseco	.80	.60	.30
5	Vince Coleman	.30	.25	.12
6	Sandy Alomar, Jr.	.30	.25	.12
7	Darryl Strawberry	.40	.30	.15
8	Len Dykstra	.40	.30	.15
9	Gregg Jefferies	.40	.30	.15
10	Tony Gwynn	.40	.30	.15
11	Ken Griffey, Jr.	1.50	1.25	.60
12	Roger Clemens	.60	.45	.25
13	Chris Sabo	.30	.25	.12
14	Bobby Bonilla	.40	.30	.15
15	Gary Sheffield	.40	.30	.15
16	Ryne Sandberg	1.00	.70	.40
17	Nolan Ryan	1.50	1.25	.60
18	Barry Larkin	.40	.30	.15
19	Cal Ripken, Jr.	1.00	.70	.40
20	Jim Abbott	.40	.30	.15
21	Barry Bonds	.80	.60	.30
22	Mark Grace	.40	.30	.15
23	Cecil Fielder	.60	.45	.25
24	Kevin Mitchell	.40	.30	.15
25	Todd Zeile	.40	.30	.15
26	George Brett	.80	.60	.30
27	Rickey Henderson	.80	.60	.30
28	Kirby Puckett	.60	.45	.25
29	Don Mattingly	.80	.60	.30
30	Kevin Maas	.30	.25	.12

1991 Post Cereal - Canadian

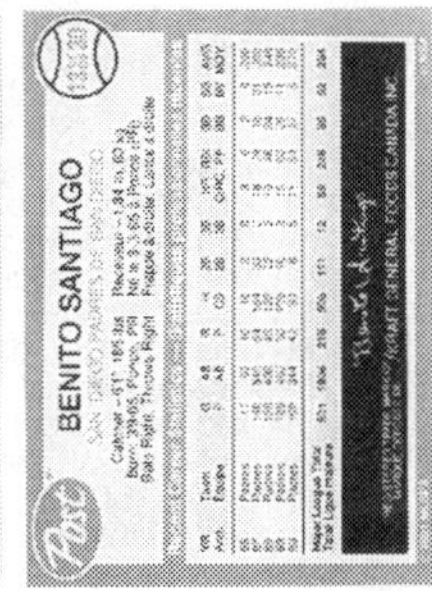

Specially-marked Post cereal boxes sold in Canada included one of 30 cards from a 1991 Super Star series of cards that featured 14 National League and 16 American League players. The cards are bilingual, and include player statistics and biographical information on the backs. The major league logos are airbrushed from the player's caps and uniforms. American Leaguer's cards have blue stripes above and below the photo on front and as a back border color; National Leaguers are in red.

		MT	NR MT	EX
Complete Set (30):		20.00	15.00	8.00
Common Player:		.50	.40	.20
1	Delino DeShields	.65	.50	.25
2	Tim Wallach	.50	.40	.20
3	Andres Galarraga	.65	.50	.25
4	Dave Magadan	.50	.40	.20
5	Barry Bonds	1.50	1.25	.60
6	Len Dykstra	.65	.50	.25
7	Andre Dawson	.75	.60	.30
8	Ozzie Smith	.75	.60	.30
9	Will Clark	1.00	.70	.40
10	Chris Sabo	.50	.40	.20
11	Eddie Murray	.75	.60	.30
12	Dave Justice	.65	.50	.25
13	Benito Santiago	.50	.40	.20
14	Glenn Davis	.50	.40	.20
15	Kelly Gruber	.50	.40	.20
16	Dave Stieb	.50	.40	.20
17	John Olerud	.65	.50	.25
18	Roger Clemens	.75	.60	.30
19	Cecil Fielder	.90	.70	.35
20	Kevin Maas	.50	.40	.20
21	Robin Yount	1.50	1.25	.60
22	Cal Ripken, Jr.	3.00	2.25	1.25
23	Sandy Alomar	.50	.40	.20
24	Rickey Henderson	1.00	.70	.40
25	Bobby Thigpen	.50	.40	.20
26	Ken Griffey, Jr.	4.00	3.00	1.50
27	Nolan Ryan	4.00	3.00	1.50
28	Dave Winfield	1.50	1.25	.60
29	George Brett	1.50	1.25	.60
30	Kirby Puckett	1.00	.70	.40

1992 Post Cereal

The addition of a back photo is notable on Post's 1992 30-card set. Again packaged at the rate of three cards in specially marked boxes, a complete set was available via a mail-in offer. Front photos had a blue strip at top with the Post logo at upper-left. A red stripe at bottom has the player's name and the logo of the Major League Baseball Player's Association. The absence of a Major League Baseball logo, and the airbrushing of uniform logos on all photos identifies this set as the work of Mike Schechter Associates. Backs have a small photo at

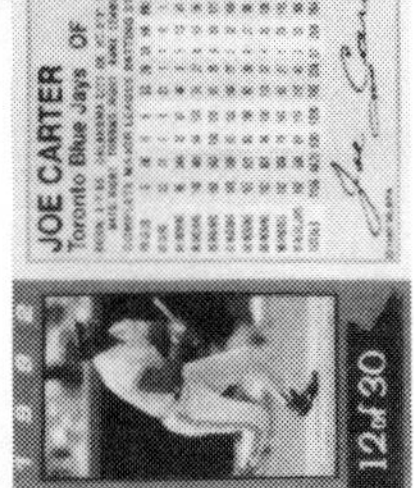

left, bordered in red. At right are biographical details, career stats and a facsimile autograph. The cards of 1991 Rookies of the Year Jeff Bagwell and Chuck Knoblauch are designated with a "Rookie Star" banner over the front photo.

		MT	NR MT	EX
Complete Set (30):		12.00	9.00	4.75
Common Player:		.25	.20	.10
1	Jeff Bagwell	.35	.25	.14
2	Ryne Sandberg	.75	.60	.30
3	Don Mattingly	.45	.35	.20
4	Wally Joyner	.30	.25	.12
5	Dwight Gooden	.30	.25	.12
6	Chuck Knoblauch	.30	.25	.12
7	Kirby Puckett	.40	.30	.15
8	Ozzie Smith	.40	.30	.15
9	Cal Ripken, Jr.	.75	.60	.30
10	Darryl Strawberry	.35	.25	.14
11	George Brett	.50	.40	.20
12	Joe Carter	.30	.25	.12
13	Cecil Fielder	.35	.25	.14
14	Will Clark	.35	.25	.14
15	Barry Bonds	.40	.30	.15
16	Roger Clemens	.30	.25	.12
17	Paul Molitor	.35	.25	.14
18	Scott Erickson	.25	.20	.10
19	Wade Boggs	.40	.30	.15
20	Ken Griffey, Jr.	.80	.60	.30
21	Bobby Bonilla	.30	.25	.12
22	Terry Pendleton	.25	.20	.10
23	Barry Larkin	.30	.25	.12
24	Frank Thomas	.80	.60	.30
25	Jose Canseco	.35	.25	.14
26	Tony Gwynn	.30	.25	.12
27	Nolan Ryan	.80	.60	.30
28	Howard Johnson	.30	.25	.12
29	Dave Justice	.35	.25	.14
30	Danny Tartabull	.30	.25	.12

1992 Post Cereal - Canadian

For the second year in a row Post Cereal of Canada issued a set of cards, this time 18 cards that were inserted in cereal boxes. The 1992 cards have a player photo on front (with airbrushed cap) and information on the reverse in both English and French. The back of the card also contains an action photo, which has a pop-up tab which when opened stands up, revealing a statistical base.

		MT	NR MT	EX
Complete Set (18):		18.00	13.50	7.25
Common Player:		.50	.40	.20
1	Dennis Martinez	.50	.40	.20
2	Benito Santiago	.60	.45	.25
3	Will Clark	1.00	.70	.40
4	Ryne Sandberg	4.00	3.00	1.50
5	Tim Wallach	.50	.40	.20
6	Ozzie Smith	.90	.70	.35
7	Darryl Strawberry	.75	.60	.30
8	Brett Butler	.50	.40	.20
9	Barry Bonds	1.25	.90	.50
10	Roger Clemens	.75	.60	.30
11	Sandy Alomar	.50	.40	.20
12	Cecil Fielder	1.00	.70	.40
13	Roberto Alomar	1.00	.70	.40
14	Kelly Gruber	.50	.40	.20
15	Cal Ripken, Jr.	4.00	3.00	1.50
16	Jose Canseco	.90	.70	.35
17	Kirby Puckett	1.50	1.25	.60
18	Rickey Henderson	1.00	.70	.40

1993 Post Cereal

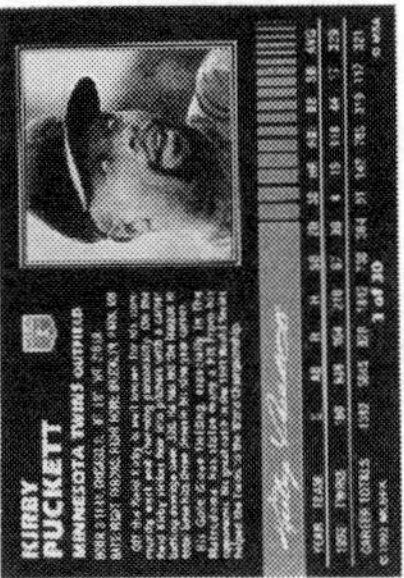

Post Cereal issued a 30-card set in 1993 of many of the top players in the game. The Post Cereal Collectors Series features a black border which runs along the bottom and the right side of the card, with the Post symbol located in the top right-hand corner and the player's name, team and position along the bottom. Team logos have been airbrushed from the uniforms. Backs have a black background, a color player portrait photo, personal data, a career summary, 1992 and career stats, and a red strip with a white facsimile autograph.

		MT	NR MT	EX
Complete Set (30):		9.00	6.75	3.50
Common Player:		.25	.20	.10
1	Dave Fleming	.25	.20	.10
2	Will Clark	.75	.60	.30
3	Kirby Puckett	.75	.60	.30
4	Roger Clemens	.35	.25	.14
5	Fred McGriff	.30	.25	.12
6	Eric Karros	.35	.25	.14
7	Ken Griffey, Jr.	1.00	.70	.40
8	Tony Gwynn	.40	.30	.15
9	Cal Ripken, Jr.	.80	.60	.30
10	Cecil Fielder	.40	.30	.15
11	Gary Sheffield	.30	.25	.12
12	Don Mattingly	.75	.60	.30
13	Ryne Sandberg	.80	.60	.30
14	Frank Thomas	1.00	.70	.40
15	Barry Bonds	.75	.60	.30
16	Paul Molitor	.40	.30	.15
17	Terry Pendleton	.25	.20	.10
18	Darren Daulton	.25	.20	.10
19	Mark McGwire	.35	.25	.14
20	Nolan Ryan	1.00	.70	.40
21	Tom Glavine	.25	.20	.10
22	Roberto Alomar	.35	.25	.14
23	Juan Gonzalez	.75	.60	.30
24	Bobby Bonilla	.30	.25	.12
25	George Brett	.75	.60	.30
26	Ozzie Smith	.50	.40	.20
27	Andy Van Slyke	.30	.25	.12
28	Barry Larkin	.30	.25	.12
29	John Kruk	.25	.20	.10
30	Robin Yount	.50	.40	.20

1993 Post Cereal - Canadian

For the third consecutive year, Post Canada produced a set of cards of Major League players. The 1993 set of 18 cards features a two-sided card with one side containing a special pop-up feature, much the same as their 1992 offering. There are 18 black-bordered and gold-lettered cards in the set. The cards were available in specially-marked boxes of cereal.

		MT	NR MT	EX
Complete Set (18):		18.00	13.50	7.25
Common Player:		.50	.40	.20
1	Pat Borders	.50	.40	.20
2	Juan Guzman	.50	.40	.20
3	Roger Clemens	.75	.60	.30
4	Joe Carter	.60	.45	.25
5	Roberto Alomar	1.00	.70	.40
6	Robin Yount	1.50	1.25	.60
7	Cal Ripken, Jr.	4.00	3.00	1.50
8	Kirby Puckett	1.50	1.25	.60
9	Ken Griffey, Jr.	4.00	3.00	1.50
10	Darren Daulton	.50	.40	.20
11	Andy Van Slyke	.50	.40	.20
12	Bobby Bonilla	.50	.40	.20
13	Larry Walker	.50	.40	.20
14	Ryne Sandberg	4.00	3.00	1.50
15	Barry Larkin	.50	.40	.20
16	Gary Sheffield	.50	.40	.20
17	Ozzie Smith	.75	.60	.30
18	Terry Pendleton	.50	.40	.20

1994 Post Cereal

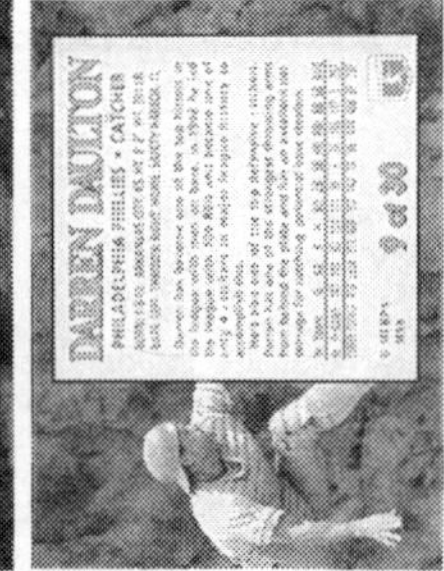

Post Cereal, makers of several popular, relatively large sets in the 1960s, returned to the baseball card arena in 1990, this time issuing smaller sets that concentrate on the top players in the game. In 1994, that means a 30-card set that was issued three cards at a time in cellophane packages in Post cereals.

		MT	NR MT	EX
Complete Set (22):		9.00	6.75	3.50
Common Player:		.25	.20	.10
1	Mike Piazza	.50	.40	.20
2	Don Mattingly	.60	.45	.25
3	Juan Gonzalez	.75	.60	.30
4	Kirby Puckett	.60	.45	.25
5	Gary Sheffield	.40	.30	.15
6	David Justice	.45	.35	.20
7	Jack McDowell	.25	.20	.10
8	Mo Vaughn	.35	.25	.14
9	Darren Daulton	.25	.20	.10
10	Bobby Bonilla	.25	.20	.10
11	Barry Bonds	.75	.60	.30
12	Barry Larkin	.35	.25	.14
13	Tony Gwynn	.40	.30	.15
14	Mark Grace	.35	.25	.14
15	Ken Griffey, Jr.	.80	.60	.30
16	Tom Glavine	.25	.20	.10
17	Cecil Fielder	.35	.25	.14
18	Roberto Alomar	.35	.25	.14
19	Mark Whiten	.25	.20	.10
20	Lenny Dykstra	.35	.25	.14
21	Frank Thomas	.80	.60	.30
22	Will Clark	.60	.45	.25
23	Andres Galarraga	.40	.30	.15
24	John Olerud	.35	.25	.14
25	Cal Ripken, Jr.	.75	.60	.30
26	Tim Salmon	.50	.40	.20
27	Albert Belle	.35	.25	.14
28	Greg Jefferies	.35	.25	.14
29	Jeff Bagwell	.35	.25	.14
30	Orlando Merced	.25	.20	.10

1994 Post Cereal - Canadian

		MT	NR MT	EX
Complete Set (18):		15.00	11.00	6.00
Common Player:		.25	.20	.10
1	Joe Carter	3.00	2.25	1.25
2	Paul Molitor	1.00	.70	.40
3	Roberto Alomar	.80	.60	.30
4	John Olerud	.60	.45	.25
5	Dave Stewart	.35	.25	.14
6	Juan Guzman	.25	.20	.10
7	Pat Borders	.25	.20	.10
8	Larry Walker	.25	.20	.10
9	Moises Alou	.35	.25	.14
10	Ken Griffey, Jr.	2.50	2.00	1.00
11	Barry Bonds	.80	.60	.30
12	Frank Thomas	2.50	2.00	1.00
13	Cal Ripken, Jr.	1.25	.90	.50
14	Mike Piazza	.50	.40	.20
15	Juan Gonzalez	.60	.45	.25
16	Lenny Dykstra	.35	.25	.14
17	David Justice	.40	.30	.15
18	Kirby Puckett	.60	.45	.25

1986 Provigo Expos

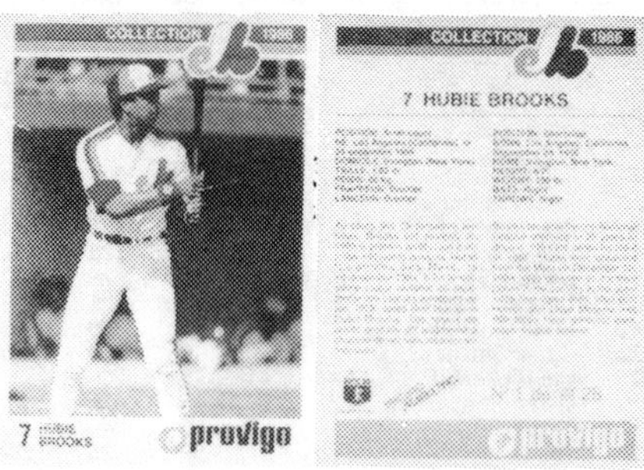

This 28-card set was issued in three-card panels of 7-1/2" by 3-3/8". Each card measures 2-1/2" by 3-3/8", and each panel includes two players and an advertising card. Panels are perforated to allow for separation, if desired. Card fronts have high quality game-action color photos with the player's name, uniform number and Expos and Provigo logos. Card backs include biographical information in both French and English and list the card's number within the set. There are 24 player, one manager and two coaches cards, along with a card of the Expos mascot, Youppi.

		MT	NR MT	EX
Complete Panel Set:		15.00	11.00	6.00
Complete Singles Set:		5.00	3.75	2.00
Common Panel:		.35	.25	.14
Common Single Player:		.15	.11	.06
	Panel 1	.80	.60	.30
1	Hubie Brooks	.50	.40	.20
2	Dann Bilardello	.15	.11	.06
----	Checklist	.03	.02	.01
	Panel 2	.35	.25	.14
3	Buck Rodgers	.15	.11	.06
4	Andy McGaffigan	.15	.11	.06
----	Album Offer	.03	.02	.01
	Panel 3	.60	.45	.25
5	Mitch Webster	.15	.11	.06
6	Jim Wohlford	.15	.11	.06
----	Album Offer	.03	.02	.01
	Panel 4	2.00	1.50	.80
7	Tim Raines	1.00	.70	.40
8	Jay Tibbs	.15	.11	.06
----	Album Offer	.03	.02	.01
	Panel 5	3.50	2.75	1.50
9	Andre Dawson	1.50	1.25	.60
10	Andres Galarraga	1.50	1.25	.60
----	Album Offer	.03	.02	.01
	Panel 6	.70	.50	.30
11	Tim Wallach	.40	.30	.15
12	Dan Schatzeder	.15	.11	.06
----	Checklist	.03	.02	.01
	Panel 7	.50	.40	.20
13	Jeff Reardon	.30	.25	.12
14	Expos' Coaching Staff (Larry Bearnarth, Joe Kerrigan, Bobby Winkles)	.15	.11	.06
----	Album Offer	.03	.02	.01
	Panel 8	.35	.25	.14
15	Jason Thompson	.15	.11	.06
16	Bert Roberge	.15	.11	.06
----	$1 Expos Ticket Coupon	.03	.02	.01
	Panel 9	.35	.25	.14
17	Al Newman	.15	.11	.06
18	Tim Burke	.25	.20	.10
----	Album Offer	.03	.02	.01
	Panel 10	.35	.25	.14
19	Bryn Smith	.15	.11	.06
20	Wayne Krenchicki	.15	.11	.06
----	Album Offer	.03	.02	.01
	Panel 11	.35	.25	.14
21	Joe Hesketh	.15	.11	.06
22	Herman Winningham	.15	.11	.06
----	Album Offer	.03	.02	.01
	Panel 12	.60	.45	.25
23	Vance Law	.15	.11	.06
24	Floyd Youmans	.15	.11	.06
----	Album Offer	.03	.02	.01
	Panel 13	.50	.40	.20
25	Jeff Parrett	.15	.11	.06
26	Mike Fitzgerald	.15	.11	.06
----	Album Offer	.03	.02	.01
	Panel 14	.35	.25	.14
27	Youppi (Team Mascot)	.15	.11	.06
28	Expos' Coaching Staff (Ron Hansen, Ken Macha, Rick Renick)	.15	.11	.06
----	Album Offer	.03	.02	.01

1972 Puerto Rican League Stickers

Often mistakenly called "minor league" cards, this issue consists of 231 ungummed stickers pertinent to the Puerto Rican winter baseball league. A colorful album was available in which to paste the stickers, though obviously stickers that have evidence of glue or torn paper have little collector value. Besides individual player photos, there are stickers of "old-timers" and groups of stickers which make up composite photos of all-star teams and of the island's god of baseball, Roberto Clemente. Team emblem stickers are also included. Many big league stars who were either beginning or ending their pro careers can be found in the set, including some current and future Hall of Famers. Stickers have color photos on the front, with backs printed in Spanish. They measure 2-1/4" x 3".

		NR MT	EX	VG
Complete Set w/Album:		1500.	750.00	450.00
Common Player:		5.00	2.50	1.50
1	Santurce All-Star Team Composite Photo	10.00	5.00	3.00
2	Santurce All-Star Team Composite Photo	10.00	5.00	3.00
3	Santurce All-Star Team Composite Photo	10.00	5.00	3.00
4	Santurce All-Star Team Composite Photo	10.00	5.00	3.00
5	Santurce All-Star Team Composite Photo	10.00	5.00	3.00
6	Santurce All-Star Team Composite Photo	10.00	5.00	3.00
7	Santurce All-Star Team Composite Photo	10.00	5.00	3.00
8	Santurce All-Star Team Composite Photo	10.00	5.00	3.00
9	Santurce All-Star Team Composite Photo	10.00	5.00	3.00
10	Ponce All-Star Team Composite Photo	10.00	5.00	3.00
11	Ponce All-Star Team Composite Photo	10.00	5.00	3.00
12	Ponce All-Star Team Composite Photo	10.00	5.00	3.00
13	Ponce All-Star Team Composite Photo	10.00	5.00	3.00
14	Ponce All-Star Team Composite Photo	10.00	5.00	3.00
15	Ponce All-Star Team Composite Photo	10.00	5.00	3.00
16	Ponce All-Star Team Composite Photo	10.00	5.00	3.00
17	Ponce All-Star Team Composite Photo	10.00	5.00	3.00
18	Ponce All-Star Team Composite Photo	10.00	5.00	3.00
19	Arecibo Team Emblem	5.00	2.50	1.50
20	Caguas-Guayana Team Emblem	5.00	2.50	1.50
21	Mayaguez Team Emblem	5.00	2.50	1.50
22	Ponce Team Emblem	5.00	2.50	1.50
23	San Juan Team Emblem	5.00	2.50	1.50
24	Santurce Team Emblem	5.00	2.50	1.50
25	Steve Boros	5.00	2.50	1.50
26	Luis Isaac	5.00	2.50	1.50
27	Emmanuel Toledo	5.00	2.50	1.50
28	Gregorio Perez	5.00	2.50	1.50
29	Rosario Llanos	5.00	2.50	1.50
30	Jose Geigel	5.00	2.50	1.50
31	Eduardo Figueroa	5.00	2.50	1.50
32	Julian Muniz	5.00	2.50	1.50
33	Fernando Gonzalez	5.00	2.50	1.50
34	Bennie Ayala	5.00	2.50	1.50
35	Miguel Villaran	5.00	2.50	1.50
36	Efrain Vazquez	5.00	2.50	1.50
37	Ramon Ariles	5.00	2.50	1.50
38	Angel Alcaraz	5.00	2.50	1.50

39	Henry Cruz	5.00	2.50	1.50
40	Jose Silva	5.00	2.50	1.50
41	Jose Alcaide	5.00	2.50	1.50
42	Pepe Mangual	5.00	2.50	1.50
43	Mike Jackson	5.00	2.50	1.50
44	Lynn McGlothen	5.00	2.50	1.50
45	Frank Ortenzio	5.00	2.50	1.50
46	Norm Angelini	5.00	2.50	1.50
47	Richard Coggins	5.00	2.50	1.50
48	Lance Clemons	5.00	2.50	1.50
49	Mike Kelleher	5.00	2.50	1.50
50	Ken Wright	5.00	2.50	1.50
51	Buck Martinez	5.00	2.50	1.50
52	Billy De Mars	5.00	2.50	1.50
53	Elwood Huyke	5.00	2.50	1.50
54	Pedro Garcia	5.00	2.50	1.50
55	Bob Boone	20.00	10.00	6.00
56	Jose Laboy	5.00	2.50	1.50
57	Eduardo Rodriguez	5.00	2.50	1.50
58	Jesus Hernaiz	5.00	2.50	1.50
59	Joaquin Quintana	5.00	2.50	1.50
60	Domingo Figueroa	5.00	2.50	1.50
61	Juan Lopez	5.00	2.50	1.50
62	Luiz Alvarado	5.00	2.50	1.50
63	Otoniel Velez	5.00	2.50	1.50
64	Mike Schmidt	500.00	250.00	150.00
65	Felix Millan	5.00	2.50	1.50
66	Guillermo Montanez	5.00	2.50	1.50
67	Ivan de Jesus	7.50	3.75	2.25
68	Sixto Lezcano	5.00	2.50	1.50
69	Jerry Morales	5.00	2.50	1.50
70	Bombo Rivera	5.00	2.50	1.50
71	Mike Ondina	5.00	2.50	1.50
72	Grant Jackson	5.00	2.50	1.50
73	Roger Freed	5.00	2.50	1.50
74	Steve Rogers	5.00	2.50	1.50
75	Mac Scarce	5.00	2.50	1.50
76	Mike Jorgensen	5.00	2.50	1.50
77	Jerry Crider	5.00	2.50	1.50
78	Fred Beene	5.00	2.50	1.50
79	Carl Ermer	5.00	2.50	1.50
80	Luis Marquez	5.00	2.50	1.50
81	Hector Valle	5.00	2.50	1.50
82	Ramon Vega	5.00	2.50	1.50
83	Cirito Cruz	5.00	2.50	1.50
84	Fernando Vega	5.00	2.50	1.50
85	Porfiro Sanchez	5.00	2.50	1.50
86	Jose Sevillano	5.00	2.50	1.50
87	Felix Roque	5.00	2.50	1.50
88	Enrique Rivera	5.00	2.50	1.50
89	Wildredo Rios	5.00	2.50	1.50
90	Javier Andino	5.00	2.50	1.50
91	Milton Ramirez	5.00	2.50	1.50
92	Max Oliveras	5.00	2.50	1.50
93	Jose Calero	5.00	2.50	1.50
94	Esteban Vazquez	5.00	2.50	1.50
95	Hector Cruz	5.00	2.50	1.50
96	Felix Arce	5.00	2.50	1.50
97	Gilberto Rivera	5.00	2.50	1.50
98	Rafael Rodriguez	5.00	2.50	1.50
99	Julio Gonzalez	5.00	2.50	1.50
100	Rosendo Cedeno	5.00	2.50	1.50
101	Pedro Cintron	5.00	2.50	1.50
102	Osvaldo Ortiz	5.00	2.50	1.50
103	Frank Verdi	5.00	2.50	1.50
104	Carlos Santiago	5.00	2.50	1.50
105	Ramon Conde	5.00	2.50	1.50
106	Pat Corrales	5.00	2.50	1.50
107	Jose Morales	5.00	2.50	1.50
108	Jack Whillock	5.00	2.50	1.50
109	Raul Mercado	5.00	2.50	1.50
110	Bonifacio Aponte	5.00	2.50	1.50
111	Angel Alicea	5.00	2.50	1.50
112	Santos Alomar	10.00	5.00	3.00
113	Francisco Libran	5.00	2.50	1.50
114	Edwin Pacheco	5.00	2.50	1.50
115	Luis Gonzalez	5.00	2.50	1.50
116	Juan Rios	5.00	2.50	1.50
117	Jorge Roque	5.00	2.50	1.50
118	Carlos Velez	5.00	2.50	1.50
119	David Gonzalez	5.00	2.50	1.50
120	Jose Cruz	7.50	3.75	2.25
121	Luis Melendez	5.00	2.50	1.50
122	Jose Ortiz	5.00	2.50	1.50
123	David Rosello	5.00	2.50	1.50
124	Juan Veintidos	5.00	2.50	1.50
125	Arnaldo Nazario	5.00	2.50	1.50
126	Dave Lemonds	5.00	2.50	1.50
127	Jim Magnuson	5.00	2.50	1.50
128	Tom Kelley	7.50	3.75	2.25
129	Chris Zachary	5.00	2.50	1.50
130	Hal Breeden	5.00	2.50	1.50
131	Jackie Hernandez	5.00	2.50	1.50
132	Rick Gossage	15.00	7.50	4.50
133	Frank Luchessi	5.00	2.50	1.50
134	Nino Escalera	5.00	2.50	1.50
135	Julio Navarro	5.00	2.50	1.50
136	Manny Sanguillen	7.50	3.75	2.25
137	Bob Johnson	5.00	2.50	1.50
138	Chuck Coggins	5.00	2.50	1.50
139	Orlando Gomez	5.00	2.50	1.50
140	William Melendez	5.00	2.50	1.50
141	Jose Del Moral	5.00	2.50	1.50
142	Jacinto Camacho	5.00	2.50	1.50
143	Emiliano Rivera	5.00	2.50	1.50
144	Luis Peraza	5.00	2.50	1.50
145	Carlos Velazquez	5.00	2.50	1.50
146	Luis Raul Garcia	5.00	2.50	1.50
147	Eliseo Rodriguez	5.00	2.50	1.50
148	Santiago Rosario	5.00	2.50	1.50
149	Ruben Castillo	5.00	2.50	1.50
150	Sergio Ferrer	5.00	2.50	1.50
151	Jose Pagan	5.00	2.50	1.50
152	Raul Colon	5.00	2.50	1.50
153	Robert Rauch	5.00	2.50	1.50
154	Luis Rosado	5.00	2.50	1.50
155	Francisco Lopez	5.00	2.50	1.50
156	Richard Zisk	5.00	2.50	1.50
157	Orlando Alvarez	5.00	2.50	1.50
158	Jaime Rosario	5.00	2.50	1.50
159	Rosendo Torres	5.00	2.50	1.50
160	Jim McKee	5.00	2.50	1.50
161	Mike Nagy	5.00	2.50	1.50
162	Brent Strom	5.00	2.50	1.50
163	Tom Walker	5.00	2.50	1.50
164	Angel Davila	5.00	2.50	1.50
165	Jose Cruz	5.00	2.50	1.50
166	Frank Robinson	25.00	12.50	7.50
167	German Rivera	5.00	2.50	1.50
168	Reinaldo Oliver	5.00	2.50	1.50
169	Geraldo Rodriguez	5.00	2.50	1.50
170	Elrod Hendricks	5.00	2.50	1.50
171	Gilberto Flores	5.00	2.50	1.50
172	Ruben Gomez	5.00	2.50	1.50
173	Juan Pizarro	5.00	2.50	1.50
174	William De Jesus	5.00	2.50	1.50
175	Rogelio Morel	5.00	2.50	1.50
176	Victor Agosto	5.00	2.50	1.50
177	Esteban Texidor	5.00	2.50	1.50
178	Ramon Hernandez	5.00	2.50	1.50
179	Gilberto Rondon Olivo	5.00	2.50	1.50
180	Juan Beniquez	5.00	2.50	1.50
181	Arturo Miranda	5.00	2.50	1.50
182	Manuel Ruiz	5.00	2.50	1.50
183	Julio Gotay	5.00	2.50	1.50
184	Arsenio Rodriguez	5.00	2.50	1.50
185	Luis Delgado	5.00	2.50	1.50
186	Jorge Rivera	5.00	2.50	1.50
187	Willie Crawford	5.00	2.50	1.50
188	Angel Mangual	5.00	2.50	1.50
189	Mike Strahler	5.00	2.50	1.50
190	Doyle Alexander	5.00	2.50	1.50
191	Bob Reynolds	5.00	2.50	1.50
192	Ron Cey	10.00	5.00	3.00
193	Jerr Da Vanon	5.00	2.50	1.50
194	Don Baylor	20.00	10.00	6.00
195	Tony Perez	20.00	10.00	6.00
196	Lloyd Allen	5.00	2.50	1.50
197	Orlando Cepeda	20.00	10.00	6.00
198	Roberto Clemente Composite Photo	25.00	12.50	7.50
199	Roberto Clemente Composite Photo	25.00	12.50	7.50
200	Roberto Clemente Composite Photo	25.00	12.50	7.50
201	Roberto Clemente Composite Photo	25.00	12.50	7.50
202	Roberto Clemente Composite Photo	25.00	12.50	7.50
203	Roberto Clemente Composite Photo	25.00	12.50	7.50
204	Roberto Clemente Composite Photo	25.00	12.50	7.50
205	Roberto Clemente Composite Photo	25.00	12.50	7.50
206	Roberto Clemente Composite Photo	25.00	12.50	7.50
207	Jaime Almendro	5.00	2.50	1.50
208	Jose R. Santiago	5.00	2.50	1.50
209	Luis Cabrera	5.00	2.50	1.50
210	Jorge Tirado	5.00	2.50	1.50
211	Radames Lopez	5.00	2.50	1.50
212	Juan Vargas	5.00	2.50	1.50
213	Francisco Coimbre	5.00	2.50	1.50
214	Freddie Thon	5.00	2.50	1.50
215	Manuel Alvarez	5.00	2.50	1.50
216	Luis Olmo	5.00	2.50	1.50
217	Jose Santiago	7.50	3.75	2.25
218	Hiram Bithorn	7.50	3.75	2.25
219	Willard Brown	7.50	3.75	2.25
220	Robert Thurman	7.50	3.75	2.25
221	Buster Clarkson	7.50	3.75	2.25
222	Satchel Paige	25.00	12.50	7.50
223	Raymond Brown	7.50	3.75	2.25
224	Alonso Perry	7.50	3.75	2.25
225	Quincy Trouppe	10.00	5.00	3.00
226	Santiago Muratti	5.00	2.50	1.50
227	Johnny Davis	5.00	2.50	1.50
228	Lino Suarez	5.00	2.50	1.50
229	Demetrio Pesante	5.00	2.50	1.50
230	Luis Arroyo	5.00	2.50	1.50
231	Jose Garcia	5.00	2.50	1.50

Grading Guide

Mint (MT): A perfect card. Well-centered with all corners sharp and square. No creases, stains, edge nicks, surface marks, yellowing or fading.

Near Mint (NM): A nearly perfect card. At first glance, a NM card appears to be perfect. May be slightly off-center. No surface marks, creases or loss of gloss.

Excellent (EX): Corners are still fairly sharp with only moderate wear. Borders may be off-center. No creases or stains on fronts or backs, but may show slight loss of surface luster.

Very Good (VG): Shows obvious handling. May have rounded corners, minor creases, major gum or wax stains. No major creases, tape marks, writing, etc.

Good (G): A well-worn card, but exhibits no intentional damage. May have major or multiple creases. Corners may be rounded well beyond card border.

1986 Quaker Oats

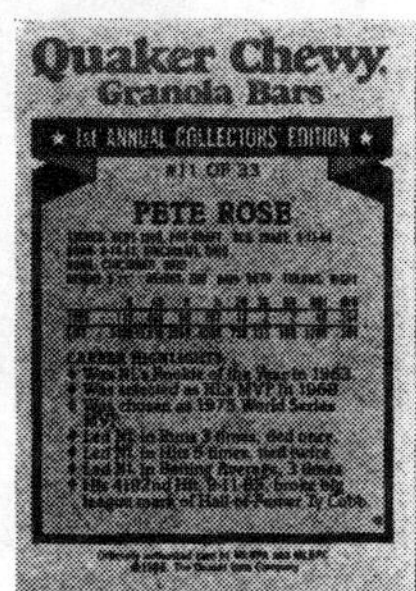

The Quaker Company, in conjunction with Topps, produced this 33-card set of current baseball stars for packaging in groups of three in Chewy Granola Bars packages. The cards are noted as the "1st Annual Collectors Edition." They are numbered and measure 2-1/2" by 3-1/2". Card fronts feature full-color player photos with the product name at the top and the player name, team and position below the photo. The complete set was offered via mail order by the Quaker Company.

		MT	NR MT	EX
Complete Set (33):		9.00	6.75	3.50
Common Player:		.15	.11	.06
1	Willie McGee	.15	.11	.06
2	Dwight Gooden	.40	.30	.15
3	Vince Coleman	.30	.25	.12
4	Gary Carter	.25	.20	.10
5	Jack Clark	.15	.11	.06
6	Steve Garvey	.25	.20	.10
7	Tony Gwynn	.35	.25	.14
8	Dale Murphy	.40	.30	.15
9	Dave Parker	.35	.25	.14
10	Tim Raines	.25	.20	.10
11	Pete Rose	.80	.60	.30
12	Nolan Ryan	2.00	1.50	.80
13	Ryne Sandberg	1.00	.70	.40
14	Mike Schmidt	.80	.60	.30
15	Ozzie Smith	.40	.30	.15
16	Darryl Strawberry	.20	.15	.08
17	Fernando Valenzuela	.20	.15	.08
18	Don Mattingly	.80	.60	.30
19	Bret Saberhagen	.20	.15	.08
20	Ozzie Guillen	.15	.11	.06
21	Bert Blyleven	.15	.11	.06
22	Wade Boggs	.80	.60	.30
23	George Brett	.80	.60	.30
24	Darrell Evans	.15	.11	.06
25	Rickey Henderson	.80	.60	.30
26	Reggie Jackson	.40	.30	.15
27	Eddie Murray	.30	.25	.12
28	Phil Niekro	.20	.15	.08
29	Dan Quisenberry	.15	.11	.06
30	Jim Rice	.25	.20	.10
31	Cal Ripken, Jr.	1.00	.70	.40
32	Tom Seaver	.40	.30	.15
33	Dave Winfield	.50	.40	.20
----	Offer Card	.03	.02	.01

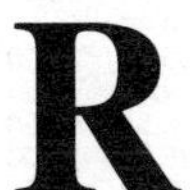

1936 R311 Glossy Finish

The cards in this 28-card set, which was available as a premium in 1936, measure 6" by 8" and were printed on a glossy cardboard. The photos are either black and white or sepia-toned and include a facsimile autograph. The unnumbered set includes individual players and team photos. The Boston Red Sox team card can be found in two varieties; one shows the sky above the building on the card's right side, while the other does not. Some of the cards are

scarcer than others in the set and command a premium. Babe Ruth is featured on the Boston Braves team card.

		NR MT	EX	VG
Complete Set (28):		1250.	625.00	375.00
Common Player:		25.00	12.50	7.50
(1)	Earl Averill	45.00	22.00	13.50
(2)	James L. "Jim" Bottomley	45.00	22.00	13.50
(3)	Gordon S. "Mickey" Cochrane	45.00	22.00	13.50
(4)	Joe Cronin	45.00	22.00	13.50
(5)	Jerome "Dizzy" Dean	75.00	37.00	22.00
(6)	Jimmy Dykes	30.00	15.00	9.00
(7)	Jimmy Foxx	70.00	35.00	21.00
(8)	Frankie Frisch	45.00	22.00	13.50
(9)	Henry "Hank" Greenberg	45.00	22.00	13.50
(10)	Mel Harder	25.00	12.50	7.50
(11)	Ken Keltner	25.00	12.50	7.50
(12)	Pepper Martin	35.00	17.50	10.50
(13)	Lynwood "Schoolboy" Rowe	25.00	12.50	7.50
(14)	William "Bill" Terry	45.00	22.00	13.50
(15)	Harold "Pie" Traynor	45.00	22.00	13.50
(16)	American League All-Stars - 1935	75.00	37.00	22.00
(17)	American League Pennant Winners - 1934 (Detroit Tigers)	45.00	22.00	13.50
(18)	Boston Braves - 1935	200.00	100.00	60.00
(19)	Boston Red Sox	45.00	22.00	13.50
(20)	Brooklyn Dodgers - 1935	100.00	50.00	30.00
(21)	Chicago White Sox - 1935	45.00	22.00	13.50
(22)	Columbus Red Birds (1934 Pennant Winners of American Association)	30.00	15.00	9.00
(23)	National League All-Stars - 1934	75.00	37.00	22.00
(24)	National League Champions - 1935 (Chicago Cubs)	45.00	22.00	13.50
(25)	New York Yankees - 1935	150.00	75.00	45.00
(26)	Pittsburgh Pirates - 1935	45.00	22.00	13.50
(27)	St. Louis Browns - 1935	45.00	22.00	13.50
(28)	The World Champions, 1934 (St. Louis Cardinals)	45.00	22.00	13.50

1936 R311 Leather Finish

This set of 15 unnumbered cards, issued as a premium in 1936, is distinctive because of its uneven, leather-like surface. The cards measure 6" by 8" and display a facsimilie autograph on the black and white photo surrounded by a plain border. The cards are unnumbered and include individual player photos, multi-player photos and team photos of the 1935 pennant winners.

		NR MT	EX	VG
Complete Set (15):		1000.	500.00	300.00
Common Player:		25.00	12.50	7.50
(1)	Frank Crosetti, Joe DiMaggio, Tony Lazzeri	225.00	112.00	67.00
(2)	Paul Derringer	25.00	12.50	7.50
(3)	Wes Ferrell	25.00	12.50	7.50
(4)	Jimmy Foxx	100.00	50.00	30.00
(5)	Charlie Gehringer	50.00	25.00	15.00
(6)	Mel Harder	25.00	12.50	7.50
(7)	Gabby Hartnett	50.00	25.00	15.00
(8)	Rogers Hornsby	100.00	50.00	30.00
(9)	Connie Mack	70.00	35.00	21.00
(10)	Van Mungo	25.00	12.50	7.50
(11)	Steve O'Neill	25.00	12.50	7.50
(12)	Charles Ruffing	50.00	25.00	15.00
(13)	Arky Vaughan, Honus Wagner	100.00	50.00	30.00
(14)	American League Pennant Winners - 1935 (Detroit Tigers)	40.00	20.00	12.00
(15)	National League Pennant Winners - 1935 (Chicago Cubs)	40.00	20.00	12.00

Regional interest may affect the value of a card.

1936 R312

The 50 cards in this set are black and white photos that have been tinted in soft pastel colors. The set includes 25 individual player portraits, 14 multi-player cards and 11 action photos. Six of the action

photos include facsimilie autographs, while the other five have printed legends. The Allen card is more scarce than the others in the set.

		NR MT	EX	VG
Complete Set (50):		2800.	1400.	850.00
Common Player:		40.00	20.00	12.00
(1)	John Thomas Allen	60.00	30.00	18.00
(2)	Nick Altrock, Al Schact	40.00	20.00	12.00
(3)	Ollie Bejma, Rolly Hemsley	40.00	20.00	12.00
(4)	Les Bell, Zeke Bonura	40.00	20.00	12.00
(5)	Cy Blanton	40.00	20.00	12.00
(6)	Cliff Bolton, Earl Whitehill	40.00	20.00	12.00
(7)	Frenchy Bordagaray, George Earnshaw	40.00	20.00	12.00
(8)	Mace Brown	40.00	20.00	12.00
(9)	Dolph Camilli	40.00	20.00	12.00
(10)	Phil Cavaretta (Cavarretta, Frank Demaree, Augie Galan, Stan Hack, Gabby Hartnett, Billy Herman, Billy Jurges, Chuck Klein, Fred Lindstrom)	80.00	40.00	24.00
(11)	Phil Cavaretta (Cavarretta, Stan Hack, Billy Herman, Billy Jurges)	50.00	25.00	15.00
(12)	Gordon Cochrane	80.00	40.00	24.00
(13)	Jim Collins, Stan Hack	40.00	20.00	12.00
(14)	Rip Collins	40.00	20.00	12.00
(15)	Joe Cronin, Buckey Harris	80.00	40.00	24.00
(16)	Alvin Crowder	40.00	20.00	12.00
(17)	Kiki Cuyler	80.00	40.00	24.00
(18)	Kiki Cuyler, Tris Speaker, Danny Taylor	80.00	40.00	24.00
(19)	"Bill" Dickey	40.00	20.00	12.00
(20)	Joe DiMagio (DiMaggio)	550.00	275.00	165.00
(21)	"Chas." Dressen	40.00	20.00	12.00
(22)	Rick Ferrell, Russ Van Atta	80.00	40.00	24.00
(23)	Pete Fox, Goose Goslin, "Jo Jo" White	70.00	35.00	21.00
(24)	Jimmey Foxx (Jimmie, Luke Sewell)	100.00	50.00	30.00
(25)	Benny Frey	40.00	20.00	12.00
(26)	Augie Galan, "Pie" Traynor	70.00	35.00	21.00
(27)	Lefty Gomez, Myril Hoag	70.00	35.00	21.00
(28)	"Hank" Greenberg	80.00	40.00	24.00
(29)	Lefty Grove, Connie Mack	150.00	75.00	45.00
(30)	Muel Haas (Mule, Mike Kreevich, Dixie Walker)	40.00	20.00	12.00
(31)	Mel Harder	40.00	20.00	12.00
(32)	Gabby Hartnett (Mickey Cochrane, Frank Demaree, Ernie Quigley (ump) in photo)	70.00	35.00	21.00
(33)	Gabby Hartnett, Lonnie Warnecke (Warneke)	60.00	30.00	18.00
(34)	Roger Hornsby (Rogers)	150.00	75.00	45.00
(35)	Rogers Hornsby, Allen Sothoren	80.00	40.00	24.00
(36)	Ernie Lombardi	80.00	40.00	24.00
(37)	Al Lopez	80.00	40.00	24.00
(38)	Pepper Martin	50.00	25.00	15.00
(39)	"Johnny" Mize	80.00	40.00	24.00
(40)	Van L. Mungo	40.00	20.00	12.00
(41)	Bud Parmelee	40.00	20.00	12.00
(42)	Schoolboy Rowe	40.00	20.00	12.00
(43)	Chas. Ruffing	80.00	40.00	24.00
(44)	Eugene Schott	40.00	20.00	12.00
(45)	Casey Stengel	125.00	62.00	37.00
(46)	Bill Sullivan	40.00	20.00	12.00
(47)	Bill Swift	40.00	20.00	12.00
(48)	Floyd Vaughan, Hans Wagner	100.00	50.00	30.00
(49)	L. Waner, P. Waner, Big Jim Weaver	90.00	45.00	27.00
(50)	Ralph Winegarner	40.00	20.00	12.00

The values quoted are intended to reflect the market price.

1928 R315

Issued in 1928, the 58 cards in this set can be found in either black and white or yellow and black. The unnumbered, blank-backed cards measure 3-1/4" by 5-1/4" and feature both portraits and action photos. The set includes several different types of cards, depending in the caption. Cards can be found with the player's name and team inside a white box in a lower corner; other cards add the position and team in small type in the bottom border; a third type

has the player's name in hand lettering near the bottom; and the final type includes the position and team printed in small type along the bottom border.

		NR MT	EX	VG
Complete Set (46):		1600.	800.00	480.00
Common Player:		20.00	10.00	6.00
(1)	Earl Averill	40.00	20.00	12.00
(2)	"Benny" Bengough	20.00	10.00	6.00
(3)	Laurence Benton (Lawrence)	20.00	10.00	6.00
(4)	"Max" Bishop	20.00	10.00	6.00
(5)	"Sunny Jim" Bottomley	40.00	20.00	12.00
(6)	Bill Cissell	20.00	10.00	6.00
(7)	Bud Clancey (Clancy)	20.00	10.00	6.00
(8)	"Freddy" Fitzsimmons	20.00	10.00	6.00
(9)	"Jimmy" Foxx	60.00	30.00	18.00
(10)	"Johnny" Fredericks (Frederick)	20.00	10.00	6.00
(11)	Frank Frisch	50.00	25.00	15.00
(12)	"Lou" Gehrig	350.00	175.00	100.00
(13)	"Goose" Goslin	40.00	20.00	12.00
(14)	Burleigh Grimes	40.00	20.00	12.00
(15)	"Lefty" Grove	50.00	25.00	15.00
(16)	"Mule" Haas	20.00	10.00	6.00
(17)	Harvey Hendricks (Hendrick)	20.00	10.00	6.00
(18)	"Babe" Herman	24.00	12.00	7.25
(19)	"Roger" Hornsby (Rogers)	60.00	30.00	18.00
(20)	Karl Hubbell (Carl)	40.00	20.00	12.00
(21)	"Stonewall" Jackson	40.00	20.00	12.00
(22)	Smead Jolley	20.00	10.00	6.00
(23)	"Chuck" Klein	40.00	20.00	12.00
(24)	Mark Koenig	20.00	10.00	6.00
(25)	"Tony" Lazerri (Lazzeri)	40.00	20.00	12.00
(26)	Fred Leach	20.00	10.00	6.00
(27)	"Freddy" Lindstrom	40.00	20.00	12.00
(28)	Fred Marberry	20.00	10.00	6.00
(29)	"Bing" Miller	20.00	10.00	6.00
(30)	"Bob" O'Farrell	20.00	10.00	6.00
(31)	Frank O'Doul	24.00	12.00	7.25
(32)	"Herbie" Pennock	40.00	20.00	12.00
(33)	George Pipgras	20.00	10.00	6.00
(34)	Andrew Reese	20.00	10.00	6.00
(35)	Carl Reynolds	20.00	10.00	6.00
(36)	"Babe" Ruth	400.00	200.00	120.00
(37)	"Bob" Shawkey	24.00	12.00	7.25
(38)	Art Shires	20.00	10.00	6.00
(39)	"Al" Simmons	40.00	20.00	12.00
(40)	"Riggs" Stephenson	24.00	12.00	7.25
(41)	"Bill" Terry	50.00	25.00	15.00
(42)	"Pie" Traynor	40.00	20.00	12.00
(43)	"Dazzy" Vance	40.00	20.00	12.00
(44)	Paul Waner	40.00	20.00	12.00
(45)	"Hack" Wilson	40.00	20.00	12.00
(46)	"Tom" Zachary	20.00	10.00	6.00

1932 R337

Issued circa 1932, little is known about the origin of this 24-card set, which is numbered from 401 through 424. The cards measure 2-5/16" by 2-13/16", and the design is similar to the M.P. & Co. sets with a crude drawing of the player on the front. The back of the card displays the card number at the top followed by the player's name, team and a brief write-up. Card numbers 403, 413, and 414 are missing and probably correspond to the three unnumbered cards in the set (Foxx, Johnson and Traynor).

		NR MT	EX	VG
Complete Set (24):		1500.	750.00	450.00
Common Player:		35.00	17.50	10.50
401	Johnny Vergez	35.00	17.50	10.50
402	Babe Ruth	450.00	225.00	135.00
403	Not Issued			
404	George Pipgras	35.00	17.50	10.50
405	Bill Terry	60.00	30.00	18.00
406	George Connally	35.00	17.50	10.50
407	Watson Clark	35.00	17.50	10.50
408	"Lefty" Grove	70.00	35.00	21.00
409	Henry Johnson	35.00	17.50	10.50
410	Jimmy Dykes	35.00	17.50	10.50
411	Henry Hine Schuble	35.00	17.50	10.50
412	Bucky Harris	50.00	25.00	15.00
413	Not Issued			
414	Not Issued			
415	Al Simmons	50.00	25.00	15.00
416	Henry "Heinie" Manush	50.00	25.00	15.00
417	Glen Myatt	35.00	17.50	10.50
418	Babe Herman	40.00	20.00	12.00
419	Frank Frisch	60.00	30.00	18.00
420	Tony Lazzeri	40.00	20.00	12.00
421	Paul Waner	50.00	25.00	15.00
422	Jimmy Wilson	35.00	17.50	10.50
423	Charles Grimm	35.00	17.50	10.50
424	Dick Bartell	35.00	17.50	10.50
----	Jimmy Fox (Foxx)	100.00	50.00	30.00
----	Roy Johnson	35.00	17.50	10.50
----	Pie Traynor	50.00	25.00	15.00

1947 R346 Blue Tint

Issued circa 1947-49, the cards in this 48-card set derive their name from the distinctive blue coloring used to tint the black and white photos. The cards have blank backs and measure 2" by 2-5/8". The set, which has a high percentage of New York players, was originally issued in strips of six or eight cards each and therefore would be more appropriately cataloged as a "W" strip card set, although collectors still commonly refer to it by the R346 designation. The set includes two major variations: Leo Durocher can be found as both a Dodger and a Giant; and Mel Ott can be found as a Giant or with no team designation. The complete set price does not include the variations.

		NR MT	EX	VG
Complete Set (48):		1200.	600.00	360.00
Common Player:		12.00	6.00	3.50
1	Bill Johnson	12.00	6.00	3.50
2a	Leo Durocher (Brooklyn)	25.00	12.50	7.50
2b	Leo Durocher (New York)	25.00	12.50	7.50
3	Marty Marion	15.00	7.50	4.50
4	Ewell Blackwell	15.00	7.50	4.50
5	John Lindell	12.00	6.00	3.50
6	Larry Jansen	12.00	6.00	3.50
7	Ralph Kiner	25.00	12.50	7.50
8	Chuck Dressen	12.00	6.00	3.50
9	Bobby Brown	15.00	7.50	4.50
10	Luke Appling	25.00	12.50	7.50
11	Bill Nicholson	12.00	6.00	3.50
12	Phil Masi	12.00	6.00	3.50
13	Frank Shea	12.00	6.00	3.50
14	Bob Dillinger	12.00	6.00	3.50
15	Pete Suder	12.00	6.00	3.50
16	Joe DiMaggio	200.00	100.00	60.00
17	John Corriden	12.00	6.00	3.50
18a	Mel Ott (New York)	30.00	15.00	9.00
18b	Mel Ott (no team designation)	30.00	15.00	9.00
19	Warren Rosar	12.00	6.00	3.50
20	Warren Spahn	25.00	12.50	7.50
21	Allie Reynolds	18.00	9.00	5.50
22	Lou Boudreau	25.00	12.50	7.50
23	Harry Majeski	12.00	6.00	3.50
24	Frank Crosetti	15.00	7.50	4.50
25	Gus Niarhos	12.00	6.00	3.50
26	Bruce Edwards	12.00	6.00	3.50
27	Rudy York	12.00	6.00	3.50
28	Don Black	12.00	6.00	3.50
29	Lou Gehrig	200.00	100.00	60.00
30	Johnny Mize	25.00	12.50	7.50
31	Ed Stanky	15.00	7.50	4.50
32	Vic Raschi	15.00	7.50	4.50
33	Cliff Mapes	12.00	6.00	3.50
34	Enos Slaughter	25.00	12.50	7.50
35	Hank Greenberg	30.00	15.00	9.00
36	Jackie Robinson	100.00	50.00	30.00
37	Frank Hiller	12.00	6.00	3.50
38	Bob Elliot (Elliott)	12.00	6.00	3.50
39	Harry Walker	12.00	6.00	3.50
40	Ed Lopat	15.00	7.50	4.50
41	Bobby Thomson	15.00	7.50	4.50
42	Tommy Henrich	18.00	9.00	5.50
43	Bobby Feller	30.00	15.00	9.00
44	Ted Williams	100.00	50.00	30.00
45	Dixie Walker	12.00	6.00	3.50
46	Johnnie Vander Meer	15.00	7.50	4.50
47	Clint Hartung	12.00	6.00	3.50
48	Charlie Keller	18.00	9.00	5.50

1950 R423

These tiny (3/4" by 5/8") cards are numbered from 1 through 120, although many numbers are still unknown or were never issued. The cards were available in long perforated strips from vending machines in the 1950s. The cards are printed on thin stock and include the player's name beneath his photo. The backs display a rough drawing of a baseball infield with tiny figures at the various positions. It appears the cards were intended to be used to play a game of baseball.

		NR MT	EX	VG
Complete Set (120):		150.00	75.00	45.00
Common Player:		1.00	.50	.30
(1)	Richie Ashburn	2.00	1.00	.60
(2)	Unknown			
(3)	Frank Baumholtz	1.00	.50	.30
(4)	Ralph Branca	1.00	.50	.30
(5)	Unknown			
(6)	Unknown			
(7)	Unknown			
(8)	Harry Brecheen	1.00	.50	.30
(9)	Chico Carrasquel	1.00	.50	.30
(10)	Jerry Coleman	1.00	.50	.30
(11)	Walker Cooper	1.00	.50	.30
(12)	Unknown			
(13)	Phil Cavaretta (Cavarretta)	1.00	.50	.30
(14)	Ty Cobb	10.00	5.00	3.00
(15)	Unknown			
(16)	Unknown			
(17)	Frank Crosetti	1.00	.50	.30
(18)	Larry Doby	1.75	.90	.50
(19)	Walter Dropo	1.00	.50	.30
(20)	Unknown			
(21)	Dizzy Dean	5.00	2.50	1.50
(22)	Bill Dickey	5.00	2.50	1.50
(23)	Murray Dickson (Murry)	1.00	.50	.30
(24)	Dom DiMaggio	1.75	.90	.50
(25)	Joe DiMaggio	12.00	6.00	3.50
(26)	Unknown			
(27)	Unknown			
(28)	Bob Elliott	1.00	.50	.30
(29)	Unknown			
(30)	Unknown			
(31)	Bob Feller	3.00	1.50	.90
(32)	Frank Frisch	2.00	1.00	.60
(33)	Unknown			
(34)	Unknown			
(35)	Lou Gehrig	12.00	6.00	3.50
(36)	Joe Gordon	1.00	.50	.30
(37)	Unknown			
(38)	Hank Greenberg	2.50	1.25	.70
(39)	Lefty Grove	2.50	1.25	.70
(40)	Unknown			
(41)	Unknown			
(42)	Ken Heintzelman	1.00	.50	.30
(43)	Unknown			
(44)	Jim Hearn	1.00	.50	.30
(45)	Unknown			
(46)	Harry Heilman (Heilmann)	1.75	.90	.50
(47)	Tommy Henrich	1.00	.50	.30
(48)	Roger Hornsby (Rogers)	2.00	1.00	.60
(49)	Unknown			
(50)	Edwin Joost	1.00	.50	.30
(51)	Unknown			
(52)	Unknown			
(53)	Nippy Jones	1.00	.50	.30
(54)	Walter Johnson	4.00	2.00	1.25
(55)	Ellis Kinder	1.00	.50	.30
(56)	Jim Konstanty	1.00	.50	.30
(57)	Unknown			
(58)	Ralph Kiner	2.00	1.00	.60
(59)	Bob Lemon	1.75	.90	.50
(60)	Unknown			
(61)	Unknown			
(62)	Unknown			
(63)	Cass Michaels	1.00	.50	.30
(64)	Unknown			
(65)	Unknown			
(66)	Clyde McCullough	1.00	.50	.30
(67)	Connie Mack	2.00	1.00	.60
(68)	Christy Mathewson	2.50	1.25	.70
(69)	Joe Medwick	1.75	.90	.50
(70)	Johnny Mize	2.00	1.00	.60
(71)	Terry Moore	1.00	.50	.30
(72)	Stan Musial	5.00	2.50	1.50
(73)	Hal Newhouser	1.75	.90	.50
(74)	Don Newcombe	1.00	.50	.30
(75)	Lefty O'Doul	1.00	.50	.30
(76)	Unknown			
(77)	Mel Parnell	1.00	.50	.30
(78)	Unknown			
(79)	Gerald Priddy	1.00	.50	.30
(80)	Dave Philley	1.00	.50	.30
(81)	Bob Porterfield	1.00	.50	.30
(82)	Andy Pafko	1.00	.50	.30
(83)	Howie Pollet	1.00	.50	.30
(84)	Herb Pennock	1.00	.50	.30
(85)	Al Rosen	1.75	.90	.50
(86)	Pee Wee Reese	3.50	1.75	1.00
(87)	Del Rice	1.00	.50	.30
(88)	Unknown			
(89)	Unknown			
(90)	Unknown			
(91)	Unknown			
(92)	Babe Ruth	18.00	9.00	5.50
(93)	Casey Stengel	2.25	1.25	.70
(94)	Vern Stephens	1.00	.50	.30
(95)	Duke Snider	2.25	1.25	.70
(96)	Enos Slaughter	1.75	.90	.50
(97)	Al Schoendienst	1.75	.90	.50
(98)	Gerald Staley	1.00	.50	.30
(99)	Clyde Shoun	1.00	.50	.30
(100)	Unknown			
(101)	Unknown			
(102)	Al Simmons	1.75	.90	.50
(103)	George Sisler	1.75	.90	.50
(104)	Tris Speaker	2.50	1.25	.70
(105)	Ed Stanky	1.00	.50	.30
(106)	Virgil Trucks	1.00	.50	.30
(107)	Henry Thompson	1.00	.50	.30
(108)	Unknown			
(109)	Dazzy Vance	1.75	.90	.50
(110)	Lloyd Waner	1.75	.90	.50
(111)	Paul Waner	1.75	.90	.50
(112)	Gene Woodling	1.00	.50	.30
(113)	Ted Williams	10.00	5.00	3.00
(114)	Unknown			
(115)	Wes Westrum	1.00	.50	.30
(116)	Johnny Wyrostek	1.00	.50	.30
(117)	Eddie Yost	1.00	.50	.30
(118)	Allen Zarilla	1.00	.50	.30
(119)	Gus Zernial	1.00	.50	.30
(120)	Sam Zoldack (Zoldak)	1.00	.50	.30

1989 Rainier Farms Super Stars Discs

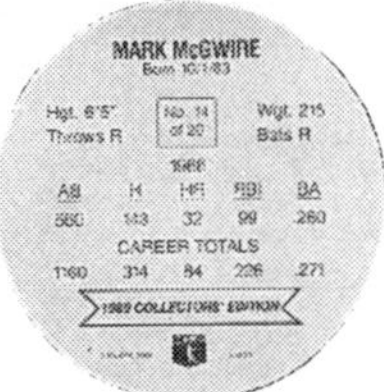

This set is one of the scarcer late-1980s disc issues produced by Michael Schecter Associates for various local businesses. The bakery began distribution of the discs by placing them directly in the cello wrapper with a loaf of bread. This resulted in those cards being severely grease stained and often creased. It also resulted in problems with public health officials who halted the distribution. Since the bakery could not economically and sanitarily package the cards they dropped the promotion and sold the remainder cards into the hobby. Discs measure 2-3/4" in diameter and have a color player photo (with team logos airbrushed away) at center with a white border. A Rainier Farms Homestyle logo is at top in red and black. Backs are printed in dark blue and feature a few stats, biographical details and a card number.

		MT	NR MT	EX
Complete Set (20):		50.00	37.00	20.00
Common Player:		2.00	1.50	.80
1	Wally Joyner	2.50	2.00	1.00
2	Wade Boggs	6.00	4.50	2.50
3	Ozzie Smith	4.00	3.00	1.50
4	Don Mattingly	7.50	5.75	3.00
5	Jose Canseco	7.50	5.75	3.00
6	Tony Gwynn	3.00	2.25	1.25
7	Eric Davis	2.00	1.50	.80
8	Kirby Puckett	4.00	3.00	1.50
9	Kevin Seitzer	2.00	1.50	.80
10	Darryl Strawberry	2.50	2.00	1.00
11	Gregg Jefferies	2.50	2.00	1.00
12	Mark Grace	2.00	1.50	.80
13	Matt Nokes	2.00	1.50	.80
14	Mark McGwire	3.00	2.25	1.25
15	Bobby Bonilla	2.50	2.00	1.00
16	Roger Clemens	2.50	2.00	1.00
17	Frank Viola	2.00	1.50	.80
18	Orel Hershiser	2.00	1.50	.80
19	Dave Cone	2.00	1.50	.80
20	Kirk Gibson	2.00	1.50	.80

1984 Ralston Purina

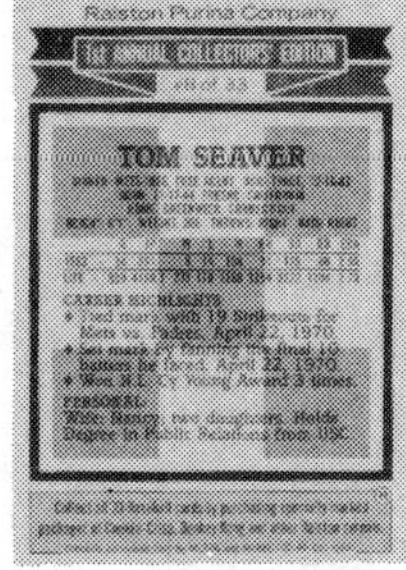

This set, produced in conjunction with Topps, has 33 of the game's top players, and is titled "1st Annual Collector's Edition." The full-color photos on the 2-1/2" by 3-1/2" cards are all close-up poses. Topps' logo appears only on the card fronts, and the backs are completely different from Topps' regular issue of 1984. Card backs feature a checkerboard look, coinciding with the well-known Ralston Purina logo. Cards are numbered 1-33, with odd numbers for American Leaguers and even numbered cards for National League players. Four cards were packed in boxes of Cookie Crisp and Donkey Kong Junior brand cereals, and the complete set was available via a mail-in offer.

		MT	NR MT	EX
Complete Set (86):		6.00	4.50	2.50
Common Player:		.10	.08	.04
1	Eddie Murray	.30	.25	.12
2	Ozzie Smith	.30	.25	.12
3	Ted Simmons	.10	.08	.04
4	Pete Rose	.80	.60	.30
5	Greg Luzinski	.10	.08	.04
6	Andre Dawson	.25	.20	.10
7	Dave Winfield	.35	.25	.14
8	Tom Seaver	.35	.25	.14
9	Jim Rice	.25	.20	.10
10	Fernando Valenzuela	.20	.15	.08
11	Wade Boggs	.60	.45	.25
12	Dale Murphy	.35	.25	.14
13	George Brett	.40	.30	.15
14	Nolan Ryan	.80	.60	.30
15	Rickey Henderson	.60	.45	.25
16	Steve Carlton	.30	.25	.12
17	Rod Carew	.30	.25	.12
18	Steve Garvey	.25	.20	.10
19	Reggie Jackson	.30	.25	.12
20	Dave Concepcion	.10	.08	.04
21	Robin Yount	.40	.30	.15
22	Mike Schmidt	.40	.30	.15
23	Jim Palmer	.20	.15	.08
24	Bruce Sutter	.10	.08	.04
25	Dan Quisenberry	.10	.08	.04
26	Bill Madlock	.10	.08	.04
27	Cecil Cooper	.10	.08	.04
28	Gary Carter	.25	.20	.10
29	Fred Lynn	.15	.11	.06
30	Pedro Guerrero	.15	.11	.06
31	Ron Guidry	.15	.11	.06
32	Keith Hernandez	.15	.11	.06
33	Carlton Fisk	.20	.15	.08

1987 Ralston Purina

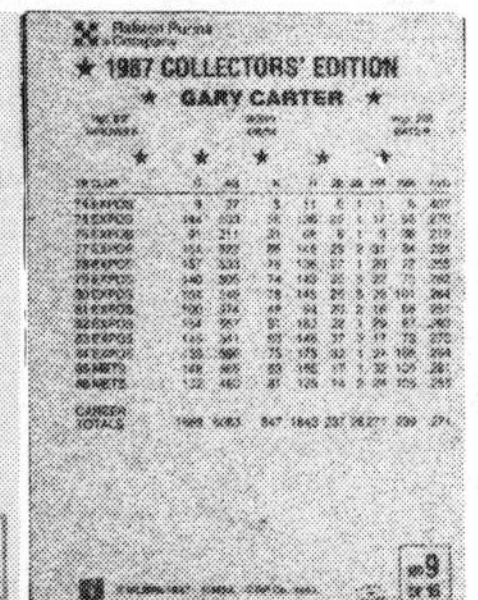

The Ralston Purina Company, in conjunction with Mike Schecter Associates, issued a 15-card set in specially marked boxes of Cookie Crisp and Honey Graham Chex brands of cereal. Three different cards, each measuring 2-1/2" by 3-1/2" and wrapped in cellophane, were inserted in each box. The card fronts contain a full-color photo with the team insignia airbrushed away. Above the photo are two yellow crossed bats and a star, with the player's uniform number inside the star. The card backs are grey with red printing and contain the set name, card number, player's name, personal information and career major league statistics. As part of the Ralston Purina promotion, the company advertised an uncut sheet of cards which was available by finding an "instant-winner" game card or sending $1 plus two non-winning cards. Cards on the uncut sheet are identical in design to the single cards, save the omission of the words "1987 Collectors Edition" in the upper right corner. A complete uncut sheet in mint condition is valued at $10.

		MT	NR MT	EX
Complete Set (15):		15.00	11.00	6.00
Common Player:		1.00	.70	.40
1	Nolan Ryan	2.00	1.50	.80
2	Steve Garvey	1.25	.90	.50
3	Wade Boggs	1.25	.90	.50
4	Dave Winfield	1.25	.90	.50
5	Don Mattingly	1.50	1.25	.60
6	Don Sutton	1.00	.70	.40
7	Dave Parker	1.25	.90	.50
8	Eddie Murray	1.25	.90	.50
9	Gary Carter	1.25	.90	.50
10	Roger Clemens	1.50	1.25	.60
11	Fernando Valenzuela	1.00	.70	.40
12	Cal Ripken Jr.	1.75	1.25	.70
13	Ozzie Smith	1.25	.90	.50
14	Mike Schmidt	1.50	1.25	.60
15	Ryne Sandberg	1.75	1.25	.70

1987 Ralston Purina Collectors' Sheet

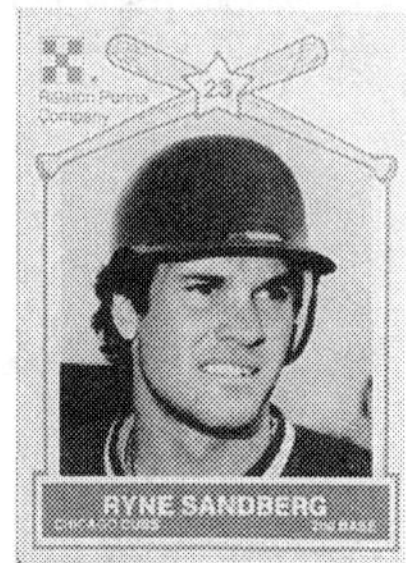

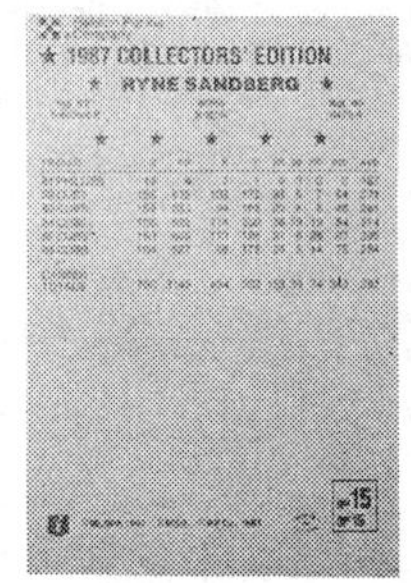

		MT	NR MT	EX
Complete Panel Set:		10.00	7.50	4.00
Complete Singles Set:		3.50	2.75	1.50
Common Single Player:		.10	.08	.04
1	Nolan Ryan	.90	.70	.35
2	Steve Garvey	.20	.15	.08
3	Wade Boggs	.40	.30	.15
4	Dave Winfield	.40	.30	.15
5	Don Mattingly	.60	.45	.25
6	Don Sutton	.10	.08	.04
7	Dave Parker	.20	.15	.08
8	Eddie Murray	.20	.15	.08
9	Gary Carter	.20	.15	.08
10	Roger Clemens	.30	.25	.12
11	Fernando Valenzuela	.15	.11	.06
12	Cal Ripken Jr.	.60	.45	.25
13	Ozzie Smith	.25	.20	.10
14	Mike Schmidt	.40	.30	.15
15	Ryne Sandberg	.60	.45	.25

1989 Ralston Purina

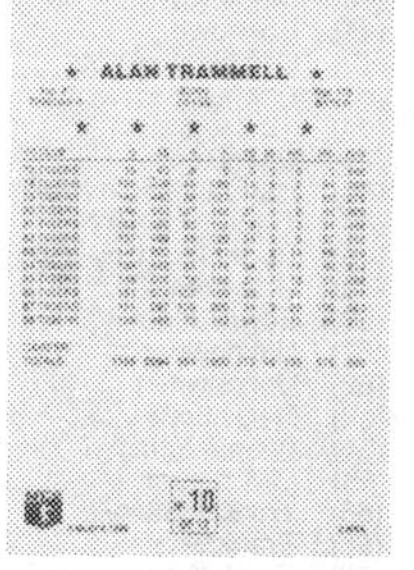

The Ralston Purina Co., in conjunction with Mike Schechter Associates, issued a 12-card "Superstars" set in 1989. As part of a late-spring and early-summer promotion, the standard-size cards were inserted, two per box, in specially-marked boxes of Crisp Crunch, Honey Nut O's, Fruit Rings and Frosted Flakes in most parts of the country. Ads on cereal boxes also offered complete sets through a mail-in offer. The fronts of the cards feature full-color player photos flanked by stars in all four corners. "Super Stars" appears at the top; the player's name and position are at the bottom. The backs include player stats and data, the card number and copyright line.

		MT	NR MT	EX
Complete Set (12):		8.00	6.00	3.25
Common Player:		.80	.60	.30
1	Ozzie Smith	.90	.70	.35
2	Andre Dawson	.80	.60	.30
3	Darryl Strawberry	.90	.70	.35
4	Mike Schmidt	1.25	.90	.50
5	Orel Hershiser	.80	.60	.30
6	Tim Raines	.80	.60	.30
7	Roger Clemens	1.25	.90	.50
8	Kirby Puckett	1.00	.70	.40
9	George Brett	1.00	.70	.40
10	Alan Trammell	.80	.60	.30
11	Don Mattingly	.90	.70	.35
12	Jose Canseco	1.25	.90	.50

1955 Rawlings Stan Musial

Though missing from Topps and Bowman card sets from 1954-57, Cardinals superstar Stan Musial wasn't entirely unavailable on baseball cards. About 1955 he appeared on a series of six cards found on boxes of Rawlings baseball gloves carrying Musial's endorsement. The cards feature black-and-white photos of Musial set against a blue background. Because the cards were part of a display box, they are blank-backed. Depending on the position on the box, the cards measure approximately 2" x 3" (#1A and 2A) or 2-1/2" x 3-3/4" (#1-4). Cards are numbered in a yellow star at upper left.

		NR MT	EX	VG
Complete Set (6):		1200.	600.00	350.00
Common Card:		200.00	100.00	60.00
1	Stan Musial (portrait)	200.00	100.00	60.00
1A	Stan Musial (portrait with bat)	200.00	100.00	60.00
2	Stan Musial (kneeling)	200.00	100.00	60.00
2A	Stan Musial (portrait)	200.00	100.00	60.00
3	Stan Musial (swinging, horizontal)	200.00	100.00	60.00
4	Stan Musial (batting pose)	200.00	100.00	60.00

1910 Red Cross Cigarettes Type 1 (T215)

The T215 set issued by Red Cross Tobacco is another of the Louisana area sets closely related to the popular T206 "White Border" tobacco cards. Very similar to the T213 Coupon cards, the Red Cross Tobacco cards are found in two distinct types, both featuring color player lithographs and measuring approximately 1-1/2" by 2-5/8", the standard tobacco card size. Type I Red Cross cards, issued from 1910 to 1912, have brown captions; while Type II cards, most of which appear to be from 1912, have blue printing. The backs of both types are identical, displaying the Red Cross name and emblem which can be used to positively identify the set and differentiate it from the other Louisana sets of the same period. Numerous variations have been found, most of them involving caption changes.

		NR MT	EX	VG
Complete Set (86):		10000.	5000.	3000.
Common Player:		125.00	62.00	37.00
(1)	Red Ames	125.00	62.00	37.00
(2)	Home Run Baker	700.00	350.00	210.00
(3)	Neal Ball	125.00	62.00	37.00
(4)	Chief Bender (no trees in background)	700.00	350.00	210.00
(5)	Chief Bender (trees in background)	700.00	350.00	210.00
(6)	Al Bridwell	125.00	62.00	37.00
(7)	Bobby Byrne	125.00	62.00	37.00
(8)	Howie Camnitz	125.00	62.00	37.00
(9)	Frank Chance	700.00	350.00	210.00
(10)	Hal Chase	125.00	62.00	37.00
(11)	Ty Cobb	2000.	1000.	600.00
(12)	Eddie Collins	700.00	350.00	210.00
(13)	Wid Conroy	125.00	62.00	37.00
(14)	Doc Crandall	125.00	62.00	37.00
(15)	Sam Crawford	700.00	350.00	210.00
(16)	Birdie Cree	125.00	62.00	37.00
(17)	Harry Davis	125.00	62.00	37.00
(18)	Josh Devore	125.00	62.00	37.00
(19)	Mike Donlin	125.00	62.00	37.00
(20)	Mickey Doolan	125.00	62.00	37.00
(21)	Patsy Dougherty	125.00	62.00	37.00
(22)	Larry Doyle (batting)	125.00	62.00	37.00
(23)	Larry Doyle (portrait)	125.00	62.00	37.00
(24)	Kid Elberfeld	125.00	62.00	37.00
(25)	Russ Ford	125.00	62.00	37.00
(26)	Art Fromme	125.00	62.00	37.00
(27)	Clark Griffith	700.00	350.00	210.00
(28)	Topsy Hartsel	125.00	62.00	37.00
(29)	Dick Hoblitzell	125.00	62.00	37.00
(30)	Solly Hofman	125.00	62.00	37.00
(31)	Del Howard	125.00	62.00	37.00
(32)	Miller Huggins	700.00	350.00	210.00
(33)	John Hummel	125.00	62.00	37.00
(34)	Hughie Jennings (both hands showing)	700.00	350.00	210.00
(35)	Hughie Jennings (one hand showing)	700.00	350.00	210.00
(36)	Walter Johnson	800.00	400.00	240.00
(37)	Ed Konetchy	125.00	62.00	37.00
(38)	Harry Krause	125.00	62.00	37.00
(39)	Nap Lajoie	700.00	350.00	210.00
(40)	Arlie Latham	125.00	62.00	37.00
(41)	Tommy Leach	125.00	62.00	37.00
(42)	Lefty Leifield	125.00	62.00	37.00
(43)	Harry Lord	125.00	62.00	37.00
(44)	Sherry Magee	125.00	62.00	37.00
(45)	Rube Marquard (pitching)	700.00	350.00	210.00
(46)	Rube Marquard (portrait)	700.00	350.00	210.00
(47)	Christy Mathewson (dark cap)	800.00	400.00	240.00
(48)	Christy Mathewson (white cap)	800.00	400.00	240.00
(49)	Joe McGinnity	700.00	350.00	210.00
(50)	John McGraw (glove at hip)	500.00	250.00	150.00
(51)	John McGraw (portrait)	500.00	250.00	150.00
(52)	Harry McIntyre	125.00	62.00	37.00
(53)	Fred Merkle	125.00	62.00	37.00
(54)	Chief Meyers	125.00	62.00	37.00
(55)	Dots Miller	125.00	62.00	37.00
(56)	Danny Murphy	125.00	62.00	37.00
(57)	Red Murray	125.00	62.00	37.00
(58)	Rebel Oakes	125.00	62.00	37.00
(59)	Charley O'Leary	125.00	62.00	37.00
(60)	Dode Paskert	125.00	62.00	37.00
(61)	Barney Pelty	125.00	62.00	37.00
(62)	Jack Quinn	125.00	62.00	37.00
(63)	Ed Reulbach	125.00	62.00	37.00
(64)	Nap Rucker	125.00	62.00	37.00
(65)	Germany Schaefer	125.00	62.00	37.00
(66)	Wildfire Schulte	125.00	62.00	37.00
(67)	Jimmy Sheckard	125.00	62.00	37.00
(68a)	Frank Smith	125.00	62.00	37.00
(68b)	Frank Smither (Smith)	125.00	62.00	37.00
(69)	Tris Speaker	650.00	325.00	195.00
(70)	Jake Stahl	125.00	62.00	37.00
(71)	Harry Steinfeldt	125.00	62.00	37.00
(72)	Gabby Street (catching)	125.00	62.00	37.00
(73)	Gabby Street (portrait)	125.00	62.00	37.00
(74)	Jeff Sweeney	125.00	62.00	37.00
(75)	Lee Tannehill	125.00	62.00	37.00
(76)	Joe Tinker (bat off shoulder)	700.00	350.00	210.00
(77)	Joe Tinker (bat on shoulder)	700.00	350.00	210.00
(78)	Heinie Wagner	125.00	62.00	37.00
(79)	Jack Warhop	125.00	62.00	37.00
(80)	Zach Wheat	700.00	350.00	210.00
(81)	Doc White	125.00	62.00	37.00
(82)	Ed Willetts (Willett)	125.00	62.00	37.00
(83)	Owen Wilson	125.00	62.00	37.00
(84)	Hooks Wiltse (pitching)	125.00	62.00	37.00
(85)	Hooks Wiltse (portrait)	125.00	62.00	37.00
(86)	Cy Young	700.00	350.00	210.00

Values for recent cards and sets are listed in Mint (MT), Near Mint (NM), reflecting the fact that many cards from recent years have been preserved in top condition. Recent cards and sets in less than Excellent condition have little collector interest.

1912 Red Cross Cigarettes Type 2 (T215)

		NR MT	EX	VG
Complete Set (77):		15000.	7500.	4500.
Common Player:		125.00	62.00	37.00
(1)	Red Ames	125.00	62.00	37.00
(2)	Chief Bender (no trees in background)	400.00	200.00	120.00
(3)	Chief Bender (trees in background)	400.00	200.00	120.00
(4)	Roger Bresnahan	325.00	162.00	97.00
(5)	Mordecai Brown	325.00	162.00	97.00
(6)	Bobby Byrne	125.00	62.00	37.00
(7)	Howie Camnitz	125.00	62.00	37.00
(8)	Frank Chance	325.00	162.00	97.00
(9)	Ty Cobb	2000.	1000.	600.00
(10)	Eddie Collins	325.00	162.00	97.00
(11)	Doc Crandall	125.00	62.00	37.00
(12)	Birdie Cree	125.00	62.00	37.00
(13)	Harry Davis	125.00	62.00	37.00
(14)	Josh Devore	125.00	62.00	37.00
(15)	Mike Donlin	125.00	62.00	37.00
(16)	Mickey Doolan (batting)	125.00	62.00	37.00
(17)	Mickey Doolan (fielding)	125.00	62.00	37.00
(18)	Patsy Dougherty	125.00	62.00	37.00
(19)	Larry Doyle (batting)	125.00	62.00	37.00
(20)	Larry Doyle (portrait)	125.00	62.00	37.00
(21)	Jean Dubuc	125.00	62.00	37.00
(22)	Kid Elberfeld	125.00	62.00	37.00
(23)	Johnny Evers	325.00	162.00	97.00
(24)	Russ Ford	125.00	62.00	37.00
(25)	Art Fromme	125.00	62.00	37.00
(26)	Clark Griffith	325.00	162.00	97.00
(27)	Bob Groom	125.00	62.00	37.00
(28)	Topsy Hartsel	125.00	62.00	37.00
(29)	Buck Herzog	125.00	62.00	37.00
(30)	Dick Hoblitzell	125.00	62.00	37.00
(31)	Solly Hofman	125.00	62.00	37.00
(32)	Miller Huggins (hands at mouth)	325.00	162.00	97.00
(33)	Miller Huggins (portrait)	325.00	162.00	97.00
(34)	John Hummel	125.00	62.00	37.00
(35)	Hughie Jennings	325.00	162.00	97.00
(36)	Walter Johnson	800.00	400.00	240.00
(37)	Joe Kelley	325.00	162.00	97.00
(38)	Ed Konetchy	125.00	62.00	37.00
(39)	Harry Krause	125.00	62.00	37.00
(40)	Nap Lajoie	225.00	112.00	67.00
(41)	Joe Lake	125.00	62.00	37.00
(42)	Tommy Leach	125.00	62.00	37.00
(43)	Lefty Leifield	125.00	62.00	37.00
(44)	Harry Lord	125.00	62.00	37.00
(45)	Rube Marquard	325.00	162.00	97.00
(46)	Christy Mathewson	800.00	400.00	240.00
(47)	John McGraw (glove at side)	350.00	175.00	105.00
(48)	John McGraw (portrait)	350.00	175.00	105.00
(49)	Larry McLean	125.00	62.00	37.00
(50)	Dots Miller	125.00	62.00	37.00
(51)	Mike Mitchell	125.00	62.00	37.00
(52)	Mike Mowrey	125.00	62.00	37.00
(53)	George Mullin	125.00	62.00	37.00
(54)	Danny Murphy	125.00	62.00	37.00
(55)	Red Murray	125.00	62.00	37.00
(56)	Rebel Oakes	125.00	62.00	37.00
(57)	Rube Oldring	125.00	62.00	37.00
(58)	Charley O'Leary	125.00	62.00	37.00
(59)	Dode Paskert	125.00	62.00	37.00
(60)	Barney Pelty	125.00	62.00	37.00
(61)	Billy Purtell	125.00	62.00	37.00
(62)	Ed Reulbach	125.00	62.00	37.00
(63)	Nap Rucker	125.00	62.00	37.00
(64a)	Germany Schaefer (Chicago)	125.00	62.00	37.00
(64b)	Germany Schaefer (Washington)	125.00	62.00	37.00
(65)	Wildfire Schulte	125.00	62.00	37.00
(66a)	Frank Smith	125.00	62.00	37.00
(66b)	Frank Smither (Smith)	125.00	62.00	37.00
(67)	Tris Speaker	600.00	300.00	175.00
(68)	Jake Stahl	125.00	62.00	37.00
(69)	Harry Steinfeldt	150.00	75.00	45.00
(70)	Ed Summers	125.00	62.00	37.00
(71)	Jeff Sweeney	125.00	62.00	37.00
(72)	Joe Tinker	325.00	162.00	97.00
(73)	Heinie Wagner	125.00	62.00	37.00
(74)	Jack Warhop	125.00	62.00	37.00
(75)	Doc White	125.00	62.00	37.00
(76)	Hooks Wiltse (pitching)	125.00	62.00	37.00
(77)	Hooks Wiltse (portrait)	125.00	62.00	37.00

1954 Red Heart Dog Food

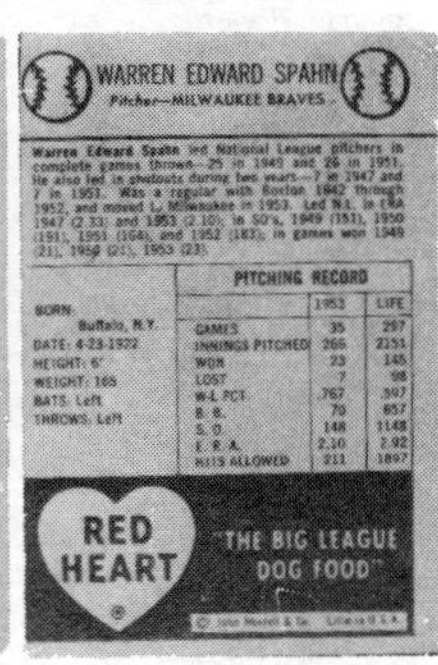

This set of 33 cards was issued in three color-coded series by the Red Heart Dog Food Co. Card fronts feature hand-colored photos on either a blue, green or red background. The 11 red-background cards are scarcer than the 11-card blue or green series. Backs of the 2-5/8" by 3-3/4" cards contain biographical and statistical information along with a Red Heart ad. Each 11-card series was available via a mail-in offer. As late as the early 1970s, the company was still sending cards to collectors who requested them.

		NR MT	EX	VG
Complete Set (33):		2200.	1100.	650.00
Common Player:		30.00	15.00	9.00
(1)	Richie Ashburn	50.00	25.00	15.00
(2)	Frankie Baumholtz	35.00	17.50	10.50
(3)	Gus Bell	30.00	15.00	9.00
(4)	Billy Cox	35.00	17.50	10.50
(5)	Alvin Dark	35.00	17.50	10.50
(6)	Carl Erskine	40.00	20.00	12.00
(7)	Ferris Fain	30.00	15.00	9.00
(8)	Dee Fondy	30.00	15.00	9.00
(9)	Nelson Fox	40.00	20.00	12.00
(10)	Jim Gilliam	40.00	20.00	12.00
(11)	Jim Hegan	35.00	17.50	10.50
(12)	George Kell	40.00	20.00	12.00
(13)	Ted Kluszewski	40.00	20.00	12.00
(14)	Ralph Kiner	55.00	27.00	16.50
(15)	Harvey Kuenn	35.00	17.50	10.50
(16)	Bob Lemon	55.00	27.00	16.50
(17)	Sherman Lollar	30.00	15.00	9.00
(18)	Mickey Mantle	550.00	275.00	165.00
(19)	Billy Martin	55.00	27.00	16.50
(20)	Gil McDougald	40.00	20.00	12.00
(21)	Roy McMillan	30.00	15.00	9.00
(22)	Minnie Minoso	35.00	17.50	10.50
(23)	Stan Musial	400.00	200.00	120.00
(24)	Billy Pierce	35.00	17.50	10.50
(25)	Al Rosen	40.00	20.00	12.00
(26)	Hank Sauer	30.00	15.00	9.00
(27)	Red Schoendienst	40.00	20.00	12.00
(28)	Enos Slaughter	40.00	20.00	12.00
(29)	Duke Snider	125.00	62.00	37.00
(30)	Warren Spahn	60.00	30.00	18.00
(31)	Sammy White	30.00	15.00	9.00
(32)	Eddie Yost	30.00	15.00	9.00
(33)	Gus Zernial	30.00	15.00	9.00

1982 Red Lobster Cubs

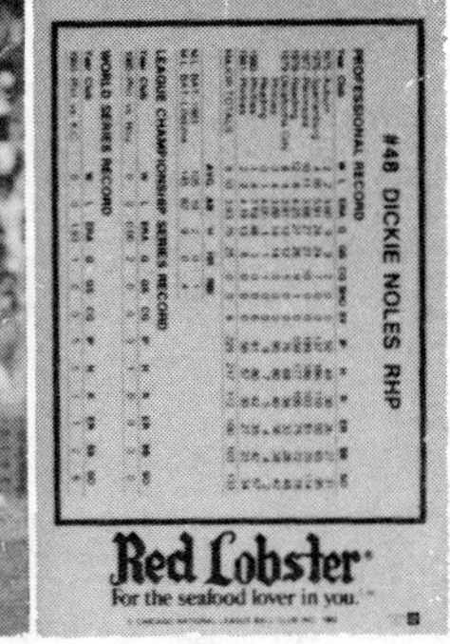

This 28-card set was co-sponsored by the team and a seafood restaurant chain for distribution at a 1982 Cubs promotional game. Card fronts are unbordered color photos, with player name, number, position and a superimposed facsimile autograph. The set includes 25 players on the 2-1/4" by 3-1/2" cards, along with a card for manager Lee Elia, an unnumbered card for the coaching staff and a team picture. Card backs have complete player statistics and a Red Lobster ad.

		MT	NR MT	EX
Complete Set (28):		20.00	15.00	8.00
Common Player:		.20	.15	.08
1	Larry Bowa	.40	.30	.15
4	Lee Elia	.20	.15	.08
6	Keith Moreland	.25	.20	.10
7	Jody Davis	.25	.20	.10
10	Leon Durham	.25	.20	.10
15	Junior Kennedy	.20	.15	.08
17	Bump Wills	.20	.15	.08
18	Scot Thompson	.20	.15	.08
21	Jay Johnstone	.25	.20	.10
22	Bill Buckner	.25	.20	.10
23	Ryne Sandberg	12.00	9.00	4.75
24	Jerry Morales	.20	.15	.08
25	Gary Woods	.20	.15	.08
28	Steve Henderson	.20	.15	.08
29	Bob Molinaro	.20	.15	.08
31	Fergie Jenkins	2.00	1.50	.80
33	Al Ripley	.20	.15	.08
34	Randy Martz	.20	.15	.08
36	Mike Proly	.20	.15	.08
37	Ken Kravec	.20	.15	.08
38	Willie Hernandez	.30	.25	.12
39	Bill Campbell	.20	.15	.08
41	Dick Tidrow	.20	.15	.08
46	Lee Smith	1.50	1.25	.60
47	Doug Bird	.20	.15	.08
48	Dickie Noles	.20	.15	.08
----	Team Photo	.20	.15	.08
----	Coaching Staff (Billy Connors, Tom Harmon, Gordy MacKenzie, John Vuckovich, Billy Williams)	.25	.20	.10

1952 Red Man Tobacco

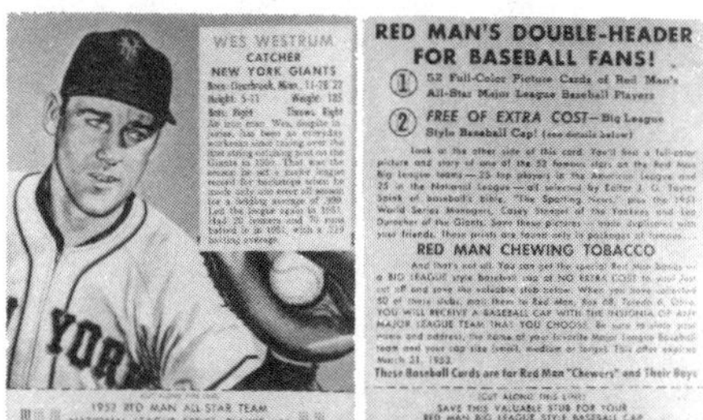

This was the first national set of tobacco cards produced since the golden days of tobacco sets in the early part of the century. There are 52 cards in the set, with 25 top players and one manager from each league. Player selection was made by editor J.G. Taylor Spink of The Sporting News. Cards measure 3-1/2"by 4", including a 1/2" tab at the bottom of each card. These tabs were redeemable for a free baseball cap from Red Man. Cards are harder to find with tabs intact, and thus more valuable in that form. Values quoted here are for cards with tabs. Cards with the tabs removed would be valued about 35-40 percent of the quoted figures. Card fronts are full color paintings of each player with biographical information inset in the portrait area. Card backs contain company advertising. Cards are numbered and dated only on the tabs.

		NR MT	EX	VG
Complete Set (52):		2500.	1250.	750.00
Common Player:		20.00	10.00	6.00
1A	Casey Stengel	65.00	32.00	19.50
1N	Leo Durocher	50.00	25.00	15.00
2A	Roberto Avila	30.00	15.00	9.00
2N	Richie Ashburn	40.00	20.00	12.00
3A	Larry "Yogi" Berra	90.00	45.00	27.00
3N	Ewell Blackwell	30.00	15.00	9.00
4A	Gil Coan	20.00	10.00	6.00
4N	Cliff Chambers	20.00	10.00	6.00
5A	Dom DiMaggio	35.00	17.50	10.50
5N	Murry Dickson	20.00	10.00	6.00
6A	Larry Doby	35.00	17.50	10.50
6N	Sid Gordon	20.00	10.00	6.00
7A	Ferris Fain	30.00	15.00	9.00
7N	Granny Hamner	20.00	10.00	6.00
8A	Bob Feller	80.00	40.00	24.00
8N	Jim Hearn	20.00	10.00	6.00
9A	Nelson Fox	40.00	20.00	12.00
9N	Monte Irvin	60.00	30.00	18.00
10A	Johnny Groth	20.00	10.00	6.00
10N	Larry Jansen	20.00	10.00	6.00
11A	Jim Hegan	20.00	10.00	6.00
11N	Willie Jones	20.00	10.00	6.00
12A	Eddie Joost	20.00	10.00	6.00
12N	Ralph Kiner	60.00	30.00	18.00
13A	George Kell	60.00	30.00	18.00
13N	Whitey Lockman	20.00	10.00	6.00
14A	Gil McDougald	35.00	17.50	10.50
14N	Sal Maglie	30.00	15.00	9.00
15A	Orestes Minoso	30.00	15.00	9.00
15N	Willie Mays	175.00	87.00	52.00
16A	Bill Pierce	30.00	15.00	9.00
16N	Stan Musial	175.00	87.00	52.00
17A	Bob Porterfield	20.00	10.00	6.00
17N	Pee Wee Reese	85.00	42.00	25.00
18A	Eddie Robinson	20.00	10.00	6.00
18N	Robin Roberts	60.00	30.00	18.00
19A	Saul Rogovin	20.00	10.00	6.00
19N	Al Schoendienst	35.00	17.50	10.50
20A	Bobby Shantz	30.00	15.00	9.00
20N	Enos Slaughter	60.00	30.00	18.00
21A	Vern Stephens	20.00	10.00	6.00
21N	Duke Snider	115.00	57.00	34.00
22A	Vic Wertz	20.00	10.00	6.00
22N	Warren Spahn	60.00	30.00	18.00
23A	Ted Williams	175.00	87.00	52.00
23N	Eddie Stanky	30.00	15.00	9.00
24A	Early Wynn	60.00	30.00	18.00
24N	Bobby Thomson	35.00	17.50	10.50
25A	Eddie Yost	20.00	10.00	6.00
25N	Earl Torgeson	20.00	10.00	6.00
26A	Gus Zernial	20.00	10.00	6.00
26N	Wes Westrum	20.00	10.00	6.00

1953 Red Man Tobacco

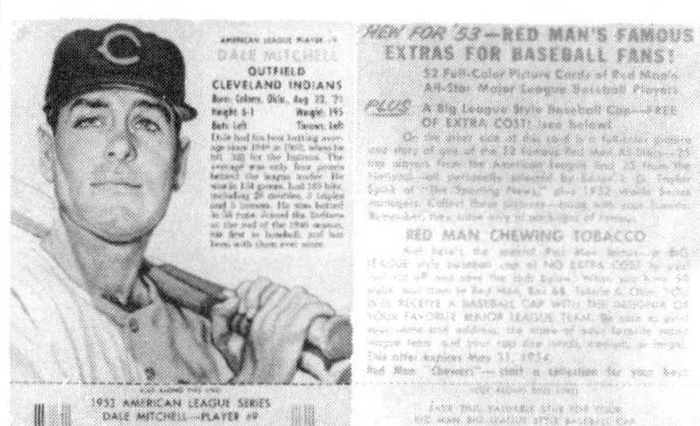

This was the chewing tobacco company's second annual set of 3-1/2" by 4" cards, including the tabs at the bottom of the cards. Formats for both the fronts and backs are similar to the '52 edition. The 1953 Red Man cards, however, include card numbers within the player biographical section, and the card backs are headlined "New for '53." Once again, cards with intact tabs (which were redeemable for a free cap) are more valuable. Prices below are for cards with tabs. Cards with tabs removed are worth about 35-40 percent of the stated values. Each league is represented by 25 players and a manager on the full-color cards, a total of 52.

		NR MT	EX	VG
Complete Set (52):		2250.	1100.	650.00
Common Player:		20.00	10.00	6.00
1A	Casey Stengel	55.00	27.00	16.50
1N	Charlie Dressen	27.50	13.50	8.25
2A	Hank Bauer	27.50	13.50	8.25
2N	Bobby Adams	20.00	10.00	6.00
3A	Larry "Yogi" Berra	80.00	40.00	24.00
3N	Richie Ashburn	40.00	20.00	12.00
4A	Walt Dropo	20.00	10.00	6.00
4N	Joe Black	27.50	13.50	8.25
5A	Nelson Fox	40.00	20.00	12.00
5N	Roy Campanella	85.00	42.00	25.00
6A	Jackie Jensen	27.50	13.50	8.25
6N	Ted Kluszewski	32.50	16.00	9.75
7A	Eddie Joost	20.00	10.00	6.00
7N	Whitey Lockman	20.00	10.00	6.00
8A	George Kell	55.00	27.00	16.50
8N	Sal Maglie	27.50	13.50	8.25
9A	Dale Mitchell	20.00	10.00	6.00
9N	Andy Pafko	27.50	13.50	8.25
10A	Phil Rizzuto	65.00	32.00	19.50
10N	Pee Wee Reese	75.00	37.00	22.00
11A	Eddie Robinson	20.00	10.00	6.00
11N	Robin Roberts	55.00	27.00	16.50
12A	Gene Woodling	27.50	13.50	8.25
12N	Red Schoendienst	55.00	27.00	16.50
13A	Gus Zernial	20.00	10.00	6.00
13N	Enos Slaughter	55.00	27.00	16.50
14A	Early Wynn	55.00	27.00	16.50
14N	Edwin "Duke" Snider	100.00	50.00	30.00
15A	Joe Dobson	20.00	10.00	6.00
15N	Ralph Kiner	55.00	27.00	16.50
16A	Billy Pierce	27.50	13.50	8.25
16N	Hank Sauer	20.00	10.00	6.00
17A	Bob Lemon	55.00	27.00	16.50
17N	Del Ennis	20.00	10.00	6.00
18A	Johnny Mize	55.00	27.00	16.50
18N	Granny Hamner	20.00	10.00	6.00
19A	Bob Porterfield	20.00	10.00	6.00
19N	Warren Spahn	60.00	30.00	18.00
20A	Bobby Shantz	27.50	13.50	8.25
20N	Wes Westrum	20.00	10.00	6.00
21A	"Mickey" Vernon	27.50	13.50	8.25
21N	Hoyt Wilhelm	55.00	27.00	16.50
22A	Dom DiMaggio	32.50	16.00	9.75
22N	Murry Dickson	20.00	10.00	6.00
23A	Gil McDougald	32.50	16.00	9.75
23N	Warren Hacker	20.00	10.00	6.00
24A	Al Rosen	32.50	16.00	9.75
24N	Gerry Staley	20.00	10.00	6.00
25A	Mel Parnell	20.00	10.00	6.00
25N	Bobby Thomson	27.50	13.50	8.25
26A	Roberto Avila	20.00	10.00	6.00
26N	Stan Musial	150.00	75.00	45.00

A player's name in italic type indicates a rookie card. An (FC) indicates a player's first card for that particular card company.

1954 Red Man Tobacco

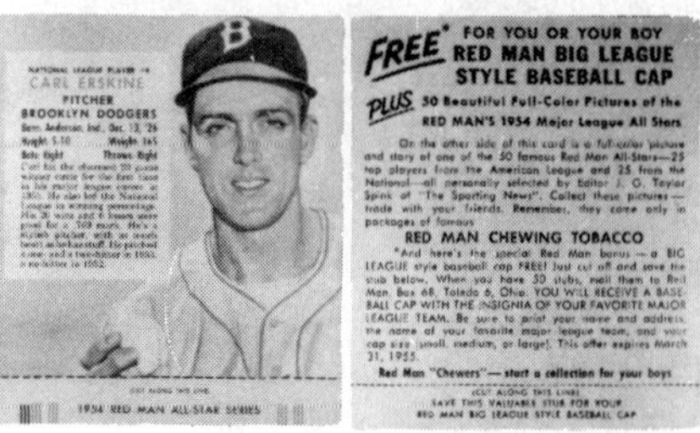

In 1954, the Red Man set eliminated managers from the set, and issued only 25 player cards for each league. There are, however, four variations which bring the total set size to 54 full-color cards. Two cards exist for Gus Bell and Enos Slaughter, while American Leaguers George Kell, Sam Mele and Dave Philley are each shown with two different teams. Complete set prices quoted below do not include the scarcer of the variation pairs. Cards still measure 3-1/2" by 4" with tabs intact. Cards without tabs are worth about 35-40 per cent of the values quoted below. Formats for the cards remain virtually unchanged, with card numbers included within the player information boxes as well as on the tabs.

		NR MT	EX	VG
Complete Set:		2500.	1250.	750.00
Common Player:		20.00	10.00	6.00
1A	Bobby Avila	20.00	10.00	6.00
1N	Richie Ashburn	45.00	22.00	13.50
2A	Jim Busby	20.00	10.00	6.00
2N	Billy Cox	30.00	15.00	9.00
3A	Nelson Fox	45.00	22.00	13.50
3N	Del Crandall	30.00	15.00	9.00
4Aa	George Kell (Boston)	80.00	40.00	24.00
4Ab	George Kell (Chicago)	90.00	45.00	27.00
4N	Carl Erskine	37.50	18.50	11.00
5A	Sherman Lollar	20.00	10.00	6.00
5N	Monte Irvin	60.00	30.00	18.00
6Aa	Sam Mele (Baltimore)	60.00	30.00	18.00
6Ab	Sam Mele (Chicago)	90.00	45.00	27.00
6N	Ted Kluszewski	37.50	18.50	11.00
7A	Orestes Minoso	30.00	15.00	9.00
7N	Don Mueller	20.00	10.00	6.00
8A	Mel Parnell	20.00	10.00	6.00
8N	Andy Pafko	30.00	15.00	9.00
9Aa	Dave Philley (Cleveland)	60.00	30.00	18.00
9Ab	Dave Philley (Philadelphia)	90.00	45.00	27.00
9N	Del Rice	20.00	10.00	6.00
10A	Billy Pierce	30.00	15.00	9.00
10N	Al Schoendienst	37.50	18.50	11.00
11A	Jim Piersall	30.00	15.00	9.00
11N	Warren Spahn	75.00	37.00	22.00
12A	Al Rosen	37.50	18.50	11.00
12N	Curt Simmons	30.00	15.00	9.00
13A	"Mickey" Vernon	30.00	15.00	9.00
13N	Roy Campanella	80.00	40.00	24.00
14A	Sammy White	20.00	10.00	6.00
14N	Jim Gilliam	37.50	18.50	11.00
15A	Gene Woodling	30.00	15.00	9.00
15N	"Pee Wee" Reese	90.00	45.00	27.00
16A	Ed "Whitey" Ford	80.00	40.00	24.00
16N	Edwin "Duke" Snider	100.00	50.00	30.00
17A	Phil Rizzuto	75.00	37.00	22.00
17N	Rip Repulski	20.00	10.00	6.00
18A	Bob Porterfield	20.00	10.00	6.00
18N	Robin Roberts	60.00	30.00	18.00
19A	Al "Chico" Carrasquel	20.00	10.00	6.00
19Na	Enos Slaughter	110.00	55.00	33.00
19Nb	Gus Bell	110.00	55.00	33.00
20A	Larry "Yogi" Berra	80.00	40.00	24.00
20N	Johnny Logan	20.00	10.00	6.00
21A	Bob Lemon	60.00	30.00	18.00
21N	Johnny Antonelli	30.00	15.00	9.00
22A	Ferris Fain	30.00	15.00	9.00
22N	Gil Hodges	70.00	35.00	21.00
23A	Hank Bauer	30.00	15.00	9.00
23N	Eddie Mathews	70.00	35.00	21.00
24A	Jim Delsing	20.00	10.00	6.00
24N	Lew Burdette	37.50	18.50	11.00
25A	Gil McDougald	37.50	18.50	11.00
25N	Willie Mays	150.00	75.00	45.00

The values quoted are intended to reflect the market price.

1955 Red Man Tobacco

These 50 cards are quite similar to the 1954 edition, with card fronts virtually unchanged except for the data in the biographical box on the color picture area. This set of the 3-1/2" by 4" cards includes 25 players from each league, with no known variations. As with all Red Man sets, those cards complete with the redeemable tabs are more valuable. Values

quoted below are for cards with tabs. Cards with the tabs removed are worth about 35-40 percent of those figures.

		NR MT	EX	VG
Complete Set (50):		2000.	1000.	600.00
Common Player:		22.00	11.00	6.50
1A	Ray Boone	22.00	11.00	6.50
1N	Richie Ashburn	40.00	20.00	12.00
2A	Jim Busby	22.00	11.00	6.50
2N	Del Crandall	30.00	15.00	9.00
3A	Ed "Whitey" Ford	65.00	32.00	19.50
3N	Gil Hodges	65.00	32.00	19.50
4A	Nelson Fox	40.00	20.00	12.00
4N	Brooks Lawrence	22.00	11.00	6.50
5A	Bob Grim	22.00	11.00	6.50
5N	Johnny Logan	22.00	11.00	6.50
6A	Jack Harshman	22.00	11.00	6.50
6N	Sal Maglie	30.00	15.00	9.00
7A	Jim Hegan	22.00	11.00	6.50
7N	Willie Mays	150.00	75.00	45.00
8A	Bob Lemon	50.00	25.00	15.00
8N	Don Mueller	22.00	11.00	6.50
9A	Irv Noren	22.00	11.00	6.50
9N	Bill Sarni	22.00	11.00	6.50
10A	Bob Porterfield	22.00	11.00	6.50
10N	Warren Spahn	60.00	30.00	18.00
11A	Al Rosen	35.00	17.50	10.50
11N	Henry Thompson	22.00	11.00	6.50
12A	"Mickey" Vernon	30.00	15.00	9.00
12N	Hoyt Wilhelm	60.00	30.00	18.00
13A	Vic Wertz	22.00	11.00	6.50
13N	Johnny Antonelli	30.00	15.00	9.00
14A	Early Wynn	60.00	30.00	18.00
14N	Carl Erskine	35.00	17.50	10.50
15A	Bobby Avila	22.00	11.00	6.50
15N	Granny Hamner	22.00	11.00	6.50
16A	Larry "Yogi" Berra	80.00	40.00	24.00
16N	Ted Kluszewski	35.00	17.50	10.50
17A	Joe Coleman	22.00	11.00	6.50
17N	Pee Wee Reese	75.00	37.00	22.00
18A	Larry Doby	35.00	17.50	10.50
18N	Al Schoendienst	35.00	17.50	10.50
19A	Jackie Jensen	30.00	15.00	9.00
19N	Duke Snider	100.00	50.00	30.00
20A	Pete Runnels	22.00	11.00	6.50
20N	Frank Thomas	22.00	11.00	6.50
21A	Jim Piersall	30.00	15.00	9.00
21N	Ray Jablonski	22.00	11.00	6.50
22A	Hank Bauer	30.00	15.00	9.00
22N	James "Dusty" Rhodes	22.00	11.00	6.50
23A	"Chico" Carrasquel	22.00	11.00	6.50
23N	Gus Bell	22.00	11.00	6.50
24A	Orestes Minoso	30.00	15.00	9.00
24N	Curt Simmons	30.00	15.00	9.00
25A	Sandy Consuegra	22.00	11.00	6.50
25N	Marvin Grissom	22.00	11.00	6.50

1977 Redpath Sugar Expos

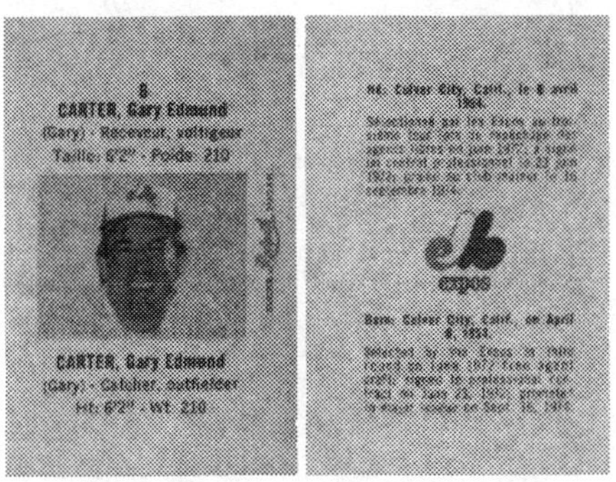

One of the more obscure regional Canadian issues, this 30-player set features members of the Expos and was printed on sugar packets distributed in the Montreal area in 1977. The front of the packet features a color photo of the player with his name, uniform number, position, height and weight listed in both English and French. A line identifying Redpath Sugar appears alongside the photo. The backs display the Expos logo and brief player highlights (again printed in both French and English). The set has been seen in uncut sheets, revealing that the packets of Steve Rogers and David Cash, Jr. were double printed.

		NR MT	EX	VG
Complete Set (30):		50.00	25.00	15.00
Common Player:		1.00	.50	.30
1	Osvaldo Jose Virgil	1.00	.50	.30
2	James Thomas Brewer	1.00	.50	.30
3	James Barton Vernon	1.00	.50	.30
4	Chris Edward Speier	1.00	.50	.30
5	Peter Mackanin Jr.	1.00	.50	.30
6	William Frederick Gardner	1.00	.50	.30
8	Gary Edmund Carter	8.00	4.00	2.50
9	Barry Clifton Foote	1.00	.50	.30
10	Andre Dawson	10.00	5.00	3.00
11	Ronald Wayne Garrett	1.00	.50	.30
14	Samuel Elias Mejias	1.00	.50	.30
15	Larry Alton Parrish	2.00	1.00	.60
16	Michael Jorgensen	1.00	.50	.30
17	Ellis Clarence Valentine	1.00	.50	.30
18	Joseph Thomas Kerrigan	1.00	.50	.30
20	William Henry McEnaney	1.00	.50	.30
23	Richard Hirshfield Williams	1.25	.60	.40
24	Atanasio Rigal Perez	3.00	1.50	.90
25	Delbert Bernard Unser	1.00	.50	.30
26	Donald Joseph Stanhouse	1.00	.50	.30
30	David Cash, Jr.	1.00	.50	.30
31	Jackie Gene Brown	1.00	.50	.30
34	Jose Manual Morales	1.00	.50	.30
35	Gerald Ellis Hannahs	1.00	.50	.30
38	Jesus Maria Frias (Andujar)	1.00	.50	.30
39	Daniel Dean Warthen	1.00	.50	.30
42	William Cecil Glenn Atkinson	1.00	.50	.30
45	Stephen Douglas Rogers	1.50	.70	.45
48	Jeffrey Michael Terpko	1.00	.50	.30
49	Warren Livingston Cromartie	1.00	.50	.30

1886 Red Stocking Cigars

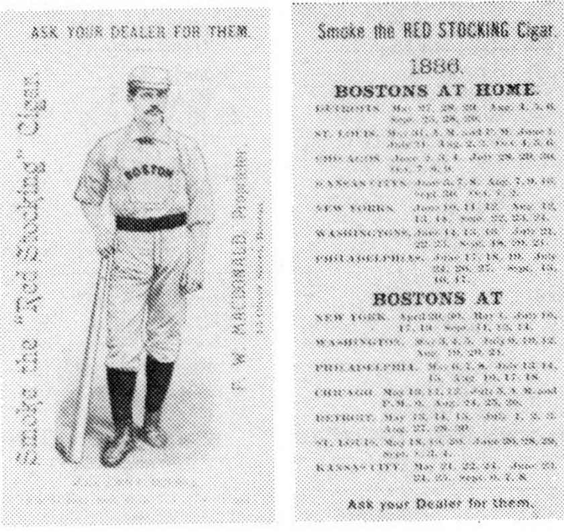

This set of Boston Red Stockings schedule cards was issued in 1886, and the three known cards measure 6-1/2" by 3-3/4". The cards were printed in black and red. One side carries the 1886 Boston schedule, while the other side features a full-length player drawing. Both sides include advertising for "Red Stocking" cigars. Only three different players are known.

		NR MT	EX	VG
Complete Set (3):		12000.	6000.	3250.
Common Player:		3750.	1875.	1125.
(1)	C.G. Buffington	3750.	1875.	1125.
(2)	Capt. John F. Morrill	3750.	1875.	1125.
(3)	Charles Radbourn	5000.	2500.	1500.

1988 Revco

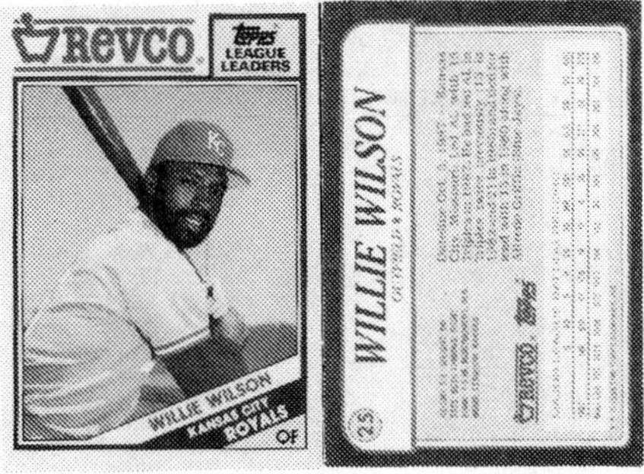

This super-glossy boxed set of 33 standard-size cards was produced by Topps for exclusive distribution by Revco stores east of the Mississippi River. Card fronts feature a large blue Revco logo in the upper left corner opposite a yellow and black boxed "Topps League Leader" label. Player photos are framed in black and orange with a diagonal player name banner in the lower right corner that lists the player's name, team and position on white, orange and gold stripes. The numbered card backs are horizontal, printed in red and black on white stock and include the player name, followed by personal biographical data, batting/pitching stats and a brief career summary.

		MT	NR MT	EX
Complete Set (33):		5.00	3.75	2.00
Common Player:		.05	.04	.02
1	Tony Gwynn	.25	.20	.10
2	Andre Dawson	.15	.11	.06
3	Vince Coleman	.15	.11	.06
4	Jack Clark	.10	.08	.04
5	Tim Raines	.25	.20	.10
6	Tim Wallach	.10	.08	.04
7	Juan Samuel	.10	.08	.04
8	Nolan Ryan	.80	.60	.30
9	Rick Sutcliffe	.10	.08	.04
10	Kent Tekulve	.05	.04	.02
11	Steve Bedrosian	.10	.08	.04
12	Orel Hershiser	.10	.08	.04
13	Rick Rueschel	.07	.05	.03
14	Fernando Valenzuela	.10	.08	.04
15	Bob Welch	.10	.08	.04
16	Wade Boggs	.50	.40	.20
17	Mark McGwire	.40	.30	.15
18	George Bell	.20	.15	.08
19	Harold Reynolds	.05	.04	.02
20	Paul Molitor	.25	.20	.10
21	Kirby Puckett	.25	.20	.10
22	Kevin Seitzer	.05	.04	.02
23	Brian Downing	.05	.04	.02
24	Dwight Evans	.10	.08	.04
25	Willie Wilson	.07	.05	.03
26	Danny Tartabull	.10	.08	.04
27	Jimmy Key	.07	.05	.03
28	Roger Clemens	.35	.25	.14
29	Dave Stewart	.25	.20	.10
30	Mark Eichhorn	.05	.04	.02
31	Tom Henke	.05	.04	.02
32	Charlie Hough	.05	.04	.02
33	Mark Langston	.10	.08	.04

The values quoted are intended to reflect the market price.

1935 Rice-Stix

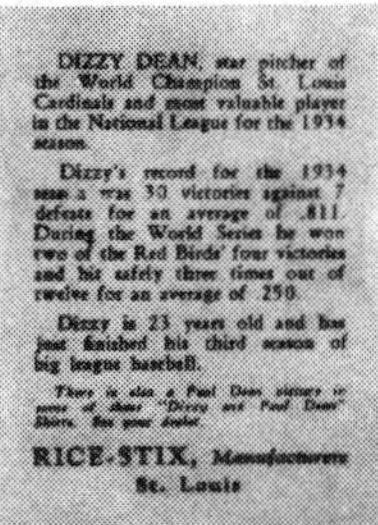

This two-card set was distributed in packages of shirts from a St. Louis firm. Measuring about 2-1/4" x 3", the cards feature color painting of the pitchers on front, along with a facsimile autograph and photo credits. Backs have a short career summary and an ad for the issuer.

(1)	Dizzy Dean	600.00	300.00	180.00
(2)	Paul Dean	400.00	200.00	120.00

1988 Rite Aid

This premiere edition was produced by Topps for distribution by Rite Aid drug and discount stores in the Eastern United States. The boxed set includes 33 standard-size full-color cards with at least one card for each major league team. Four cards in the set highlight MVP's from the 1987 season. Card fronts have white borders and carry a yellow "Team MVP's" header above the player photo which is outlined in red and blue. A large Rite Aid logo appears upper left; the players name appears bottom center.

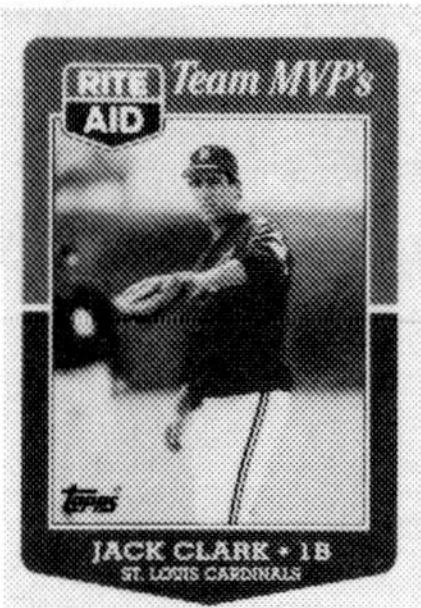

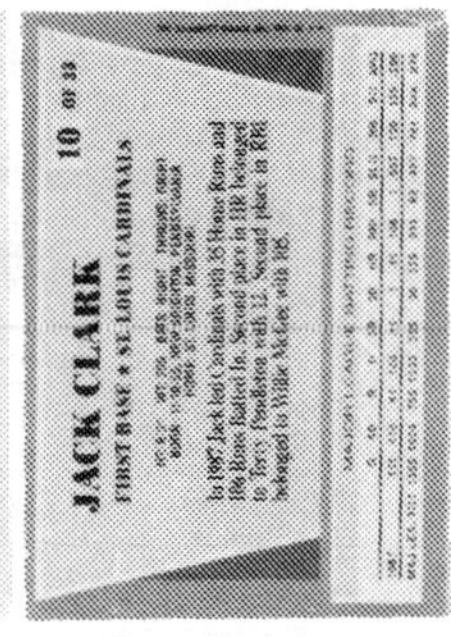

The numbered card backs are black on blue and white card stock in a horizontal layout containing the player name, biography and statistics.

		MT	NR MT	EX
Complete Set (33):		4.00	3.00	1.50
Common Player:		.05	.04	.02
1	Dale Murphy	.20	.15	.08
2	Andre Dawson	.20	.15	.08
3	Eric Davis	.10	.08	.04
4	Mike Scott	.10	.08	.04
5	Pedro Guerrero	.10	.08	.04
6	Tim Raines	.20	.15	.08
7	Darryl Strawberry	.20	.15	.08
8	Mike Schmidt	.40	.30	.15
9	Mike Dunne	.05	.04	.02
10	Jack Clark	.10	.08	.04
11	Tony Gwynn	.25	.20	.10
12	Will Clark	.60	.45	.25
13	Cal Ripken, Jr.	.75	.60	.30
14	Wade Boggs	.60	.45	.25
15	Wally Joyner	.20	.15	.08
16	Harold Baines	.12	.09	.05
17	Joe Carter	.20	.15	.08
18	Alan Trammell	.15	.11	.06
19	Kevin Seitzer	.10	.08	.04
20	Paul Molitor	.30	.25	.12
21	Kirby Puckett	.30	.25	.12
22	Don Mattingly	.60	.45	.25
23	Mark McGwire	.35	.25	.14
24	Alvin Davis	.05	.04	.02
25	Ruben Sierra	.35	.25	.14
26	George Bell	.10	.08	.04
27	Jack Morris	.10	.08	.04
28	Jeff Reardon	.07	.05	.03
29	John Tudor	.05	.04	.02
30	Rick Rueschel	.05	.04	.02
31	Gary Gaetti	.12	.09	.05
32	Jeffrey Leonard	.05	.04	.02
33	Frank Viola	.12	.09	.05

1933 Rittenhouse Candy (E285)

Designed to resemble a set of playing cards, this set, issued circa 1933 by the Rittenhouse Candy Company of Philadelphia, carries the ACC designation E285 and is generally considered to be the last of the E-card issues. Each card measures 2-1/4" by 1-7/16" and features a small player photo in the center of the playing card design. The backs of the cards usually consist of just one large letter and were part of a promotion in which collectors were instructed to find enough different letters to spell "Rittenhouse Candy Co." Other backs explaining the contest and the prizes available have also been found. Because it was designed as a deck of playing cards, the set is complete at 52 cards, featuring 46 different players (six are pictured on two cards each). Cards have been found in red, green and blue.

		NR MT	EX	VG
Complete Set (52):		5000.	2500.	1500.
Common Player:		50.00	25.00	15.00
(1)	Dick Bartell	50.00	25.00	15.00
(2)	Walter Berger	50.00	25.00	15.00
(3)	Max Bishop	50.00	25.00	15.00
(4)	James Bottomley	100.00	50.00	30.00
(5)	Fred Brickell	50.00	25.00	15.00
(6)	Sugar Cain	50.00	25.00	15.00
(7)	Ed. Cihocki	50.00	25.00	15.00
(8)	Phil Collins	50.00	25.00	15.00
(9)	Roger Cramer	50.00	25.00	15.00
(10)	Hughie Critz	50.00	25.00	15.00
(11)	Joe Cronin	110.00	55.00	33.00
(12)	Hazen (Kiki) Cuyler	100.00	50.00	30.00
(13)	Geo. Davis	50.00	25.00	15.00
(14)	Spud Davis	50.00	25.00	15.00
(15)	Jimmy Dykes	55.00	27.00	16.50
(16)	George Earnshaw	50.00	25.00	15.00
(17)	Jumbo Elliot	50.00	25.00	15.00
(18)	Lou Finney	50.00	25.00	15.00
(19)	Jimmy Foxx	150.00	75.00	45.00
(20)	Frankie Frisch (3 of Spades)	100.00	50.00	30.00
(21)	Frankie Frisch (7 of Spades)	100.00	50.00	30.00
(22)	Robert (Lefty) Grove	125.00	62.00	37.00
(23)	Mule Haas	50.00	25.00	15.00
(24)	Chick Hafey	100.00	50.00	30.00
(25)	Chas. Leo Hartnett	100.00	50.00	30.00
(26)	Babe Herman	55.00	27.00	16.50
(27)	Wm. Herman	100.00	50.00	30.00
(28)	Kid Higgins	50.00	25.00	15.00
(29)	Rogers Hornsby	125.00	62.00	37.00
(30)	Don Hurst (Jack of Diamonds)	50.00	25.00	15.00
(31)	Don Hurst (6 of Spades)	50.00	25.00	15.00
(32)	Chuck Klein	100.00	50.00	30.00
(33)	Leroy Mahaffey	50.00	25.00	15.00
(34)	Gus Mancuso	50.00	25.00	15.00
(35)	Rabbit McNair	50.00	25.00	15.00
(36)	Bing Miller	50.00	25.00	15.00
(37)	Frank (Lefty) O'Doul	60.00	30.00	18.00
(38)	Mel Ott	110.00	55.00	33.00
(39)	Babe Ruth (Ace of Spades)	1000.	500.00	300.00
(40)	Babe Ruth (King of Clubs)	1000.	500.00	300.00
(41)	Al Simmons	100.00	50.00	30.00
(42)	Bill Terry	110.00	55.00	33.00
(43)	Pie Traynor	100.00	50.00	30.00
(44)	Rube Wallberg (Walberg)	50.00	25.00	15.00
(45)	Lloyd Waner	100.00	50.00	30.00
(46)	Paul Waner	100.00	50.00	30.00
(47)	Lloyd Warner (Waner)	100.00	50.00	30.00
(48)	Paul Warner (Warner)	100.00	50.00	30.00
(49)	Pinkey Whitney	50.00	25.00	15.00
(50)	Dib Williams	50.00	25.00	15.00
(51)	Hack Wilson (9 of Spades)	100.00	50.00	30.00
(52)	Hack Wilson (9 of Clubs)	100.00	50.00	30.00

Regional interest may affect the value of a card.

1911 Rochester Baking Philadelphia A's (D359)

The 1911 Rochester Baking set, an 18-card Philadelphia Athletics set, is among the scarcest of early 20th Century bakery issues. The set commemorates the Athletics' 1910 Championship season, and, except for pitcher Jack Coombs, the checklist includes nearly all key members of the club, including manager Connie Mack. The cards are the standard size for the era, 1-1/2" by 2-5/8". The front of each card features a player portrait set against a colored background. The player's name and the word "Athletics" appear at the bottom, while "World's Champions 1910" is printed along the top. The backs of the cards advertise the set as the "Athletics Series." Collectors should be aware that the same checklist was used for a similar Athletics set issued by Williams Baking and Cullivan's Firesdie tobacco (T208), and also that blank-backed versions are also known to exist, but these are classified as E104 cards in the American Card Catalog.

		NR MT	EX	VG
Complete Set (18):		13000.	6500.	3900.
Common Player:		500.00	250.00	150.00
(1)	Home Run Baker	1500.	750.00	450.00
(2)	Jack Barry	500.00	250.00	150.00
(3)	Chief Bender	1500.	750.00	450.00
(4)	Eddie Collins	1500.	750.00	450.00
(5)	Harry Davis	500.00	250.00	150.00
(6)	Jimmy Dygert	500.00	250.00	150.00
(7)	Topsy Hartsel	500.00	250.00	150.00
(8)	Harry Krause	500.00	250.00	150.00
(9)	Jack Lapp	500.00	250.00	150.00
(10)	Paddy Livingstone (Livingston)	500.00	250.00	150.00
(11)	Bris Lord	500.00	250.00	150.00
(12)	Connie Mack	2000.	1000.	600.00
(13)	Cy Morgan	500.00	250.00	150.00
(14)	Danny Murphy	500.00	250.00	150.00
(15)	Rube Oldring	500.00	250.00	150.00
(16)	Eddie Plank	2000.	1000.	600.00
(17)	Amos Strunk	500.00	250.00	150.00
(18)	Ira Thomas	500.00	250.00	150.00

1955 Rodeo Meats Athletics

This set of 2-1/2" by 3-1/2" color cards was issued by a local meat company to commemorate the first year of the Athletics in Kansas City. There are 38 different players included in the set, with nine players known to apppear in two different variations for a total of 47 cards in the set. Most variations are in background colors, although Bobby Shantz is also listed incorrectly as "Schantz" on one variation. The cards are unnumbered, with the Rodeo logo and player name on the fronts, and an ad for a scrapbook album listed on the backs.

		NR MT	EX	VG
Complete Set (46):		4500.	2250.	1350.
Common Player:		90.00	45.00	27.00
(1)	Joe Astroth	90.00	45.00	27.00
(2)	Harold Bevan	125.00	62.00	37.00
(3)	Charles Bishop	125.00	62.00	37.00
(4)	Don Bollweg	125.00	62.00	37.00
(5)	Lou Boudreau	250.00	125.00	75.00
(6)	Cloyd Boyer (blue background)	125.00	62.00	37.00
(7)	Cloyd Boyer (pink background)	90.00	45.00	27.00
(8)	Ed Burtschy	125.00	62.00	37.00
(9)	Art Ceccarelli	90.00	45.00	27.00
(10)	Joe DeMaestri (pea green background)	125.00	62.00	37.00
(11)	Joe DeMaestri (light green background)	90.00	45.00	27.00
(12)	Art Ditmar	90.00	45.00	27.00
(13)	John Dixon	125.00	62.00	37.00
(14)	Jim Finigan	90.00	45.00	27.00
(15)	Marion Fricano	125.00	62.00	37.00
(16)	John Gray	125.00	62.00	37.00
(17)	Tom Gorman	90.00	45.00	27.00
(18)	Ray Herbert	90.00	45.00	27.00
(19)	Forest "Spook" Jacobs (Forrest)	125.00	62.00	37.00
(20)	Alex Kellner	125.00	62.00	37.00
(21)	Harry Kraft (Craft)	90.00	45.00	27.00
(22)	Jack Littrell	90.00	45.00	27.00
(23)	Hector Lopez	100.00	50.00	30.00
(24)	Oscar Melillo	90.00	45.00	27.00
(25)	Arnold Portocarrero (purple background)	125.00	62.00	37.00
(26)	Arnold Portocarrero (grey background)	90.00	45.00	27.00
(27)	Vic Power (pink background)	125.00	62.00	37.00
(28)	Vic Power (yellow background)	100.00	50.00	30.00
(29)	Vic Raschi	125.00	62.00	37.00
(30)	Bill Renna (dark pink background)	125.00	62.00	37.00
(31)	Bill Renna (light pink background)	90.00	45.00	27.00
(32)	Al Robertson	125.00	62.00	37.00
(33)	Johnny Sain	125.00	62.00	37.00
(34a)	Bobby Schantz (incorrect spelling)	250.00	125.00	75.00
(34b)	Bobby Shantz (correct spelling)	125.00	62.00	37.00
(35)	Wilmer Shantz (orange background)	125.00	62.00	37.00
(36)	Wilmer Shantz (purple background)	90.00	45.00	27.00
(37)	Harry Simpson	90.00	45.00	27.00
(38)	Enos Slaughter	300.00	150.00	90.00
(39)	Lou Sleater	90.00	45.00	27.00
(40)	George Susce	90.00	45.00	27.00
(41)	Bob Trice	125.00	62.00	37.00
(42)	Elmer Valo (yellow background)	125.00	62.00	37.00
(43)	Elmer Valo (green background)	90.00	45.00	27.00
(44)	Bill Wilson (yellow background)	125.00	62.00	37.00
(45)	Bill Wilson (purple background)	90.00	45.00	27.00
(46)	Gus Zernial	100.00	50.00	30.00

Values for recent cards and sets are listed in Mint (MT), Near Mint (NM), reflecting the fact that many cards from recent years have been preserved in top condition. Recent cards and sets in less than Excellent condition have little collector interest.

1956 Rodeo Meats Athletics

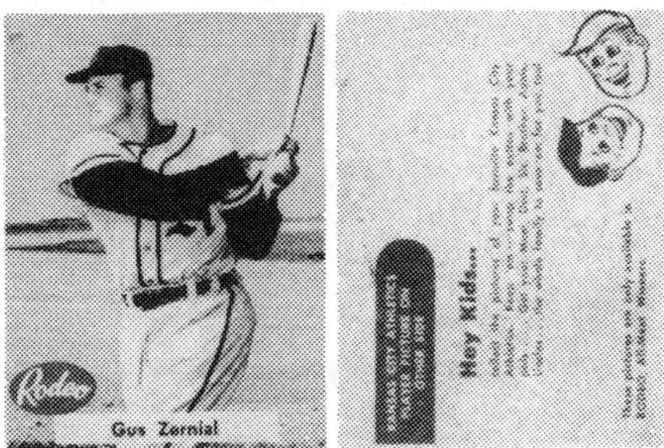

Rodeo Meats issued another Kansas City Athletics set in 1956, but this one was a much smaller 13-card set. The 2-1/2" by 3-1/2" cards are again unnumbered, with the player name and Rodeo logo on the fronts. Card backs feature some of the same graphics and copy as the 1955 cards, but the album offer is omitted. The full-color cards were only available in packages of Rodeo hot dogs.

		NR MT	EX	VG
Complete Set (12):		1250.	625.00	375.00
Common Player:		90.00	45.00	27.00
(1)	Joe Astroth	90.00	45.00	27.00
(2)	Lou Boudreau	250.00	125.00	75.00
(3)	Joe DeMaestri	90.00	45.00	27.00
(4)	Art Ditmar	90.00	45.00	27.00
(5)	Jim Finigan	90.00	45.00	27.00
(6)	Hector Lopez	100.00	50.00	30.00
(7)	Vic Power	100.00	50.00	30.00
(8)	Bobby Shantz	125.00	62.00	37.00
(9)	Harry Simpson	90.00	45.00	27.00
(10)	Enos Slaughter	250.00	125.00	75.00
(11)	Elmer Valo	90.00	45.00	27.00
(12)	Gus Zernial	100.00	50.00	30.00

1993 Rolaids Relief Pitcher Set

The Chicago Cubs issued a four-card All-Time Cubs Relief Pitchers set as a giveaway at the Sept. 4, 1993 game at Wrigley Field The four were selected by Cubs fans in a ballot conducted by Rolaids. The standard-sized cards have white borders with a color photo in a design similar to the NFL GameDay cards. The card backs include the player's name, years in which he pitched for the Cubs, the Rolaids logo and an explanation of the card set's purpose.

		MT	NR MT	EX
Complete Set (4):		4.50	3.50	1.75
Common Player:		1.00	.70	.40
(1)	Randy Myers	1.00	.70	.40
(2)	Lee Smith	1.50	.70	.45
(3)	Bruce Sutter	1.00	.70	.40
(4)	Mitch Williams	1.00	.70	.40

1970 Rold Gold Pretzels

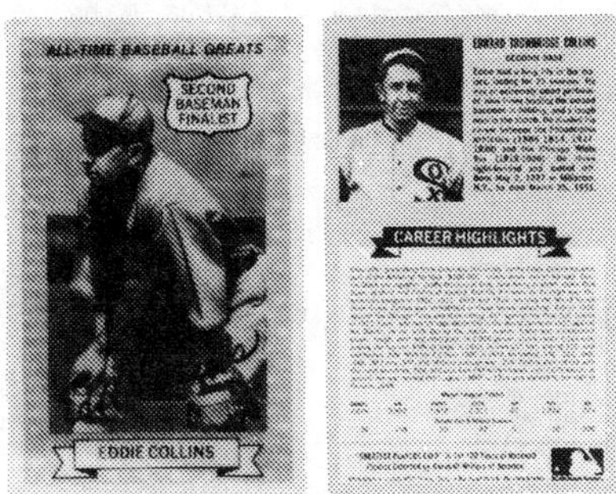

The 1970 Rold Gold Pretzels set of 15 cards honors the "Greatest Players Ever" in the first 100 years of baseball as chosen by the Baseball Writers of America. The cards, which measure 2-1/4" by 3-1/2" in size, feature a simulated 3-D effect. The set was re-released in 1972 by Kellogg's in packages of Danish-Go-Rounds. Rold Gold cards can be differentiated from the Kellogg's cards of 1972 by the 1970 copyright date found on the card reverse.

		NR MT	EX	VG
Complete Set (15):		50.00	25.00	15.00
Common Player:		1.00	.50	.30
1	Walter Johnson	2.50	1.25	.70
2	Rogers Hornsby	1.50	.70	.45
3	John McGraw	1.00	.50	.30
4	Mickey Cochrane	1.00	.50	.30
5	George Sisler	1.00	.50	.30
6	Babe Ruth	15.00	7.50	4.50
7	Robert "Lefty" Grove	1.50	.70	.45
8	Harold "Pie" Traynor	1.00	.50	.30
9	Honus Wagner	1.75	.90	.50
10	Eddie Collins	1.00	.50	.30
11	Tris Speaker	1.50	.70	.45
12	Cy Young	2.50	1.25	.70
13	Lou Gehrig	8.00	4.00	2.50
14	Babe Ruth	15.00	7.50	4.50
15	Ty Cobb	8.00	4.00	2.50

1950 Royal Desserts

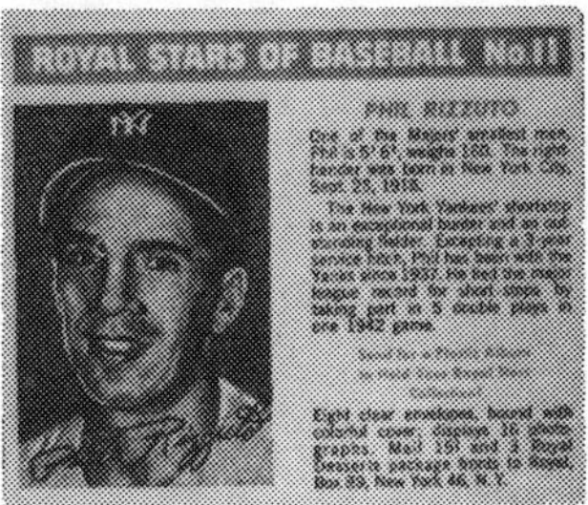

This set of 24 cards was issued one per box on the backs of various Royal Dessert products over a period of three years. The basic set contains 24 players, however a number of variations create the much higher total for the set. In 1950, Royal issued cards with two different tints - black and white with red, or blue and white with red. Over the next two years, various sentences of the cards' biographies were updated up to three times in some cases. Some players from the set left the majors after 1950 and others were apparently never updated, but the 23 biography updates that do exist, added to the original 24 cards issued in 1950, give the set a total of 47 cards. The 2-1/2" by 3-1/2" cards are blank-backed with personal and playing biographies alongside the card front photos.

		NR MT	EX	VG
Complete Set:		1750.	875.00	525.00
Common Player:		30.00	15.00	9.00
1a	Stan Musial (2nd paragraph begins "Musial's 207...")	125.00	62.00	37.00
1b	Stan Musial (2nd paragraph begins "Musial batted...")	125.00	62.00	37.00
2a	Pee Wee Reese (2nd paragraph begins "Pee Wee's...")	100.00	50.00	30.00
2b	Pee Wee Reese (2nd paragraph begins "Captain...")	100.00	50.00	30.00
3a	George Kell (2nd paragraph ends "...in 1945, '46.")	50.00	25.00	15.00
3b	George Kell (2nd paragraph ends "...two base hits, 56.")	50.00	25.00	15.00
4a	Dom DiMaggio (2nd paragraph ends "...during 1947.")	40.00	20.00	12.00
4b	Dom DiMaggio (2nd paragraph ends "...with 11.")	40.00	20.00	12.00
5a	Warren Spahn (2nd paragraph ends "...shutouts 7.")	75.00	37.00	22.00
5b	Warren Spahn (2nd paragraph ends "...with 191.")	75.00	37.00	22.00
6a	Andy Pafko (2nd paragraph ends "...7 games.")	35.00	17.50	10.50
6b	Andy Pafko (2nd paragraph ends "...National League.")	35.00	17.50	10.50
6c	Andy Pafko (2nd paragraph ends "...weighs 190.")	35.00	17.50	10.50
7a	Andy Seminick (2nd paragraph ends "...as outfield.")	30.00	15.00	9.00
7b	Andy Seminick (2nd paragraph ends "...since 1916.")	30.00	15.00	9.00
7c	Andy Seminick (2nd paragraph ends "...in the outfield.")	30.00	15.00	9.00
7d	Andy Seminick (2nd paragraph ends "...right handed.")	30.00	15.00	9.00
8a	Lou Brissie (2nd paragraph ends "...when pitching.")	30.00	15.00	9.00
8b	Lou Brissie (2nd paragraph ends "...weighs 215.")	30.00	15.00	9.00
9a	Ewell Blackwell (2nd paragraph begins "Despite recent illness...")	35.00	17.50	10.50
9b	Ewell Blackwell (2nd paragraph begins "Blackwell's...")	35.00	17.50	10.50
10a	Bobby Thomson (2nd paragraph begins "In 1949...")	35.00	17.50	10.50
10b	Bobby Thomson (2nd paragraph begins "Thomson is...")	35.00	17.50	10.50
11a	Phil Rizzuto (2nd paragraph ends "...one 1942 game.")	90.00	45.00	27.00
11b	Phil Rizzuto (2nd paragraph ends "...Most Valuable Player.")	90.00	45.00	27.00
12	Tommy Henrich	40.00	20.00	12.00
13	Joe Gordon	35.00	17.50	10.50
14a	Ray Scarborough (Senators)	30.00	15.00	9.00
14b	Ray Scarborough (White Sox, 2nd paragraph ends "...military service.")	30.00	15.00	9.00
14c	Ray Scarborough (White Sox, 2nd paragraph ends "...the season.")	30.00	15.00	9.00
14d	Ray Scarborough (Red Sox)	30.00	15.00	9.00
15a	Stan Rojek (Pirates)	30.00	15.00	9.00
15b	Stan Rojek (Browns)	30.00	15.00	9.00
16	Luke Appling	40.00	20.00	12.00
17	Willard Marshall	30.00	15.00	9.00
18	Alvin Dark	40.00	20.00	12.00
19a	Dick Sisler (2nd paragraph ends "...service record.")	30.00	15.00	9.00
19b	Dick Sisler (2nd paragraph ends "...National League flag.")	30.00	15.00	9.00
19c	Dick Sisler (2nd paragraph ends "...Nov. 2, 1920.")	30.00	15.00	9.00
19d	Dick Sisler (2nd paragraph ends "...from '46 to '48.")	30.00	15.00	9.00
20	Johnny Ostrowski	30.00	15.00	9.00
21a	Virgil Trucks (2nd paragraph ends "...in military service.")	35.00	17.50	10.50
21b	Virgil Trucks (2nd paragraph ends "...that year.")	35.00	17.50	10.50
21c	Virgil Trucks (2nd paragraph ends "...for military service.")	35.00	17.50	10.50
22	Eddie Robinson	30.00	15.00	9.00
23	Nanny Fernandez	30.00	15.00	9.00
24	Ferris Fain	35.00	17.50	10.50

1952 Royal Desserts

This set, issued as a premium by Royal Desserts in 1952, consists of 16 unnumbered black and white cards, each measuring 5" by 7". The cards include the inscription "To A Royal Fan" along with the player's facsimile autograph.

		NR MT	EX	VG
Complete Set (16):		700.00	350.00	210.00
Common Player:		25.00	12.50	7.50
(1)	Ewell Blackwell	30.00	15.00	9.00
(2)	Leland V. Brissie Jr.	25.00	12.50	7.50
(3)	Alvin Dark	30.00	15.00	9.00
(4)	Dom DiMaggio	40.00	20.00	12.00
(5)	Ferris Fain	25.00	12.50	7.50
(6)	George Kell	28.00	14.00	8.50
(7)	Stan Musial	120.00	60.00	36.00
(8)	Andy Pafko	30.00	15.00	9.00
(9)	Pee Wee Reese	65.00	32.00	19.50
(10)	Phil Rizzuto	65.00	32.00	19.50
(11)	Eddie Robinson	25.00	12.50	7.50
(12)	Ray Scarborough	25.00	12.50	7.50
(13)	Andy Seminick	25.00	12.50	7.50
(14)	Dick Sisler	25.00	12.50	7.50
(15)	Warren Spahn	65.00	32.00	19.50
(16)	Bobby Thomson	40.00	20.00	12.00

Grading Guide

Mint (MT): A perfect card. Well-centered with all corners sharp and square. No creases, stains, edge nicks, surface marks, yellowing or fading.

Near Mint (NM): A nearly perfect card. At first glance, a NM card appears to be perfect. May be slightly off-center. No surface marks, creases or loss of gloss.

Excellent (EX): Corners are still fairly sharp with only moderate wear. Borders may be off-center. No creases or stains on fronts or backs, but may show slight loss of surface luster.

Very Good (VG): Shows obvious handling. May have rounded corners, minor creases, major gum or wax stains. No major creases, tape marks, writing, etc.

Good (G): A well-worn card, but exhibits no intentional damage. May have major or multiple creases. Corners may be rounded well beyond card border.

1928 George Ruth Candy Co.

When you have a complete set of 6 (six) Pictures Nos. 1, 2, 3, 4, 5 and 6, send them to The Geo. H. Ruth Candy Co., Cleveland, Ohio, and you will receive a Baseball with Babe Ruth's genuine signature on it FREE OF CHARGE.

This obscure six-card set, issued circa 1928, features sepia-toned photos of Babe Ruth, and, according to the back of the cards, was actually issued by the Geo. H. Ruth Candy Co. The cards measure 1-7/8" by 4" and picture Ruth during a 1924 promotional West Coast tour and in scenes from the movie "Babe Comes Home." The cards are numbered and include photo captions at the bottom. the backs of the card contain an offer to exchange the six cards for an autographed baseball, which may explain their scarcity today.

		NR MT	EX	VG
Complete Set (6):		5000.	2500.	1500.
Common Player:		800.00	400.00	240.00
1	"Babe" Ruth (King of them all. Home Run Candy Bar. His Candy Helped Him.)	800.00	400.00	240.00
2	"Babe" Ruth (Knocked out 60 Home Runs in 1927. His Candy Helped Him.)	800.00	400.00	240.00
3	"Babe" Ruth (The only player who broke his own record. His Candy Helped Him.)	800.00	400.00	240.00
4	"Babe" Ruth (The Popular Bambino eating his Home Run Candy. His Candy Helped Him.)	800.00	400.00	240.00
5	"Babe" Ruth (A favorite with the Kiddies. Babe Ruth's Own Candy.)	800.00	400.00	240.00
6	"Babe" Ruth (The King of Swat. Babe Ruth's Own Candy.)	800.00	400.00	240.00

S

1936 S and S Game

Small black-and-white player photos are featured on the fronts of this 52-card game set. Measuring about 2-1/4" x 3-1/2", with rounded corners, the cards feature plain green backs. Besides the player photo on front, there are a few biographical details and stats, and a pair of game scenarios. The cards are unnumbered and are checklisted here alphabetically.

		NR MT	EX	VG
Complete Set (52):		600.00	300.00	180.00
Common Player:		10.00	5.00	3.00
(1)	Luke Appling	30.00	15.00	9.00
(2)	Earl Averill	30.00	15.00	9.00
(3)	Zeke Bonura	10.00	5.00	3.00
(4)	Dolph Camilli	10.00	5.00	3.00
(5)	Ben Cantwell	10.00	5.00	3.00
(6)	Phil Cavarretta	15.00	7.50	4.50
(7)	Rip Collins	10.00	5.00	3.00
(8)	Joe Cronin	30.00	15.00	9.00
(9)	Frank Crosetti	15.00	7.50	4.50
(10)	Kiki Cuyler	30.00	15.00	9.00
(11)	Virgil Davis	10.00	5.00	3.00
(12)	Frank Demaree	10.00	5.00	3.00
(13)	Paul Derringer	10.00	5.00	3.00
(14)	Bill Dickey	30.00	15.00	9.00
(15)	Woody English	10.00	5.00	3.00
(16)	Fred Fitzsimmons	10.00	5.00	3.00
(17)	Rick Ferrell	30.00	15.00	9.00
(18)	Pete Fox	10.00	5.00	3.00
(19)	Jimmy Foxx	30.00	15.00	9.00
(20)	Larry French	10.00	5.00	3.00
(21)	Frank Frisch	30.00	15.00	9.00
(22)	August Galan	10.00	5.00	3.00
(23)	Charlie Gehringer	30.00	15.00	9.00
(24)	John Gill	10.00	5.00	3.00
(25)	Charles Grimm	15.00	7.50	4.50
(26)	Mule Haas	10.00	5.00	3.00
(27)	Stan Hack	15.00	7.50	4.50
(28)	Bill Hallahan	10.00	5.00	3.00
(29)	Mel Harder	10.00	5.00	3.00
(30)	Gabby Hartnett	30.00	15.00	9.00
(31)	Ray Hayworth	10.00	5.00	3.00
(32)	Ralston Hemsley	10.00	5.00	3.00
(33)	Bill Herman	30.00	15.00	9.00
(34)	Frank Higgins	10.00	5.00	3.00
(35)	Carl Hubbell	30.00	15.00	9.00
(36)	Bill Jurges	10.00	5.00	3.00
(37)	Vernon Kennedy	10.00	5.00	3.00
(38)	Chuck Klein	30.00	15.00	9.00
(39)	Mike Kreevich	10.00	5.00	3.00
(40)	Bill Lee	10.00	5.00	3.00
(41)	Joe Medwick	30.00	15.00	9.00
(42)	Van Mungo	10.00	5.00	3.00
(43)	James O'Dea	10.00	5.00	3.00
(44)	Mel Ott	30.00	15.00	9.00
(45)	Rip Radcliff	10.00	5.00	3.00
(46)	Pie Traynor	30.00	15.00	9.00
(47)	Arky Vaughn	30.00	15.00	9.00
(48)	Joe Vosmik	10.00	5.00	3.00
(49)	Lloyd Waner	30.00	15.00	9.00
(50)	Paul Waner	30.00	15.00	9.00
(51)	Lon Warneke	10.00	5.00	3.00
(52)	Floyd Young	10.00	5.00	3.00

1909 S74 Silks - White

PIRATES
BASEBALL-ACTRESS SERIES ON SATIN
Useful in making pillow covers and other fancy articles for home decoration.
To remove satin from this paper back, loosen at corner and pull gently—moistening if necessary.
OLD MILL CIGARETTES.

Designated as S74 in Jefferson Burdick's American Card Catalog, these small, delicate fabric collectibles are growing in popularity among advanced collectors. Another tobacco issue from the 1910-1911 period, the silks were issued as premiums with three different brands of cigarettes: Turkey Red, Old Mill and Helmar. The satin-like silks can be found in two different styles, either "white" or "colored." The white silks measure 1 7/8" by 3" and were originally issued with a brown paper backing that carried an advertisement for one of the three cigarette brands mentioned above. The backing also advised that the silks were "useful in making pillow covers and other fancy articles for home decoration." Many undoubtedly were used for such purposes, making silks with the paper backing still intact more difficult to find. White silks must, however, have the backing intact to command top value. Although similar, the S74 "colored" silks, as their name indicates, were issued in a variety of colors. They are also slightly larger, measuring 1-7/8" by 3-1/2", and were issued without a paper backing. The colored silks, therefore, contained the cigarette brand name on the lower front of the fabric, either "Old Mill Cigarettes" or "Turkey Red Cigarettes." (No colored silks advertising the Helmar brand are known to exist.) There are 121 different players reported: six have been found in two poses, resulting in 127 different subjects. Ninety-two subjects are known in the "white" silk, while 120 have been found in the "colored." The silks feature the same players pictured in the popular T205 Gold Border tobacco card set.

		NR MT	EX	VG
Complete Set (92):		22500.	11000.	6500.
Common Player:		135.00	67.00	40.00
(1)	Home Run Baker	300.00	150.00	90.00
(2)	Cy Barger	135.00	67.00	40.00
(3)	Jack Barry	135.00	67.00	40.00
(4)	Johnny Bates	135.00	67.00	40.00
(5)	Fred Beck	135.00	67.00	40.00
(6)	Beals Becker	135.00	67.00	40.00
(7)	George Bell	135.00	67.00	40.00
(8)	Chief Bender	300.00	150.00	90.00
(9)	Roger Bresnahan	300.00	150.00	90.00
(10)	Al Bridwell	135.00	67.00	40.00
(11)	Mordecai Brown	300.00	150.00	90.00
(12)	Bobby Byrne	135.00	67.00	40.00
(13)	Howie Camnitz	135.00	67.00	40.00
(14)	Bill Carrigan	135.00	67.00	40.00
(15)	Frank Chance	375.00	187.00	112.00
(16)	Hal Chase	190.00	95.00	57.00
(17)	Fred Clarke	300.00	150.00	90.00
(18)	Ty Cobb	2100.	1000.	600.00
(19)	Eddie Collins	300.00	150.00	90.00
(20)	Doc Crandall	135.00	67.00	40.00
(21)	Lou Criger	135.00	67.00	40.00
(22)	Jim Delahanty	135.00	67.00	40.00
(23)	Art Devlin	135.00	67.00	40.00
(24)	Red Dooin	135.00	67.00	40.00
(25)	Mickey Doolan	135.00	67.00	40.00
(26)	Larry Doyle	135.00	67.00	40.00
(27)	Jimmy Dygert	135.00	67.00	40.00
(28)	Kid Elberfield (Elberfeld)	135.00	67.00	40.00
(29)	Steve Evans	135.00	67.00	40.00
(30)	Johnny Evers	300.00	150.00	90.00
(31)	Bob Ewing	135.00	67.00	40.00
(32)	Art Fletcher	135.00	67.00	40.00
(33)	John Flynn	135.00	67.00	40.00
(34)	Bill Foxen	135.00	67.00	40.00
(35)	George Gibson	135.00	67.00	40.00
(36)	Peaches Graham (Cubs)	135.00	67.00	40.00
(37)	Peaches Graham (Rustlers)	135.00	67.00	40.00
(38)	Clark Griffith	300.00	150.00	90.00
(39)	Topsy Hartsel	135.00	67.00	40.00
(40)	Arnold Hauser	135.00	67.00	40.00
(41)	Charlie Hemphill	135.00	67.00	40.00
(42)	Tom Jones	135.00	67.00	40.00
(43)	Jack Knight	135.00	67.00	40.00
(44)	Ed Konetchy	135.00	67.00	40.00
(45)	Harry Krause	135.00	67.00	40.00
(46)	Tommy Leach	135.00	67.00	40.00
(47)	Rube Marquard	300.00	150.00	90.00
(48)	Christy Mathewson	675.00	337.00	202.00
(49)	Al Mattern	135.00	67.00	40.00
(50)	Amby McConnell	135.00	67.00	40.00
(51)	John McGraw	375.00	187.00	112.00
(52)	Harry McIntire (McIntyre)	135.00	67.00	40.00
(53)	Fred Merkle	150.00	75.00	45.00
(54)	Chief Meyers	135.00	67.00	40.00
(55)	Dots Miller	135.00	67.00	40.00
(56)	Danny Murphy	135.00	67.00	40.00
(57)	Red Murray	135.00	67.00	40.00
(58)	Tom Needham	135.00	67.00	40.00
(59)	Rebel Oakes	135.00	67.00	40.00
(60)	Rube Oldring	135.00	67.00	40.00
(61)	Orval Overall	135.00	67.00	40.00
(62)	Fred Parent	135.00	67.00	40.00
(63)	Fred Payne	135.00	67.00	40.00
(64)	Barney Pelty	135.00	67.00	40.00
(65)	Deacon Phillippe	135.00	67.00	40.00
(66)	Jack Quinn	135.00	67.00	40.00
(67)	Bugs Raymond	135.00	67.00	40.00
(68)	Ed Reulbach	135.00	67.00	40.00
(69)	Doc Scanlon (Scanlan)	135.00	67.00	40.00
(70)	Germany Schaefer	135.00	67.00	40.00
(71)	Admiral Schlei	135.00	67.00	40.00
(72)	Wildfire Schulte	135.00	67.00	40.00
(73)	Dave Shean	135.00	67.00	40.00
(74)	Jimmy Sheckard	135.00	67.00	40.00
(75)	Hap Smith (Superbas)	135.00	67.00	40.00
(76)	Harry Smith (Rustlers)	525.00	262.00	157.00
(77)	Fred Snodgrass	135.00	67.00	40.00
(78)	Tris Speaker	450.00	225.00	135.00
(79)	Harry Steinfeldt (Cubs)	150.00	75.00	45.00
(80)	Harry Steinfeldt (Rustlers)	150.00	75.00	45.00
(81)	George Stone	135.00	67.00	40.00
(82)	Gabby Street	135.00	67.00	40.00
(83)	Ed Summers	135.00	67.00	40.00
(84)	Lee Tannehill	135.00	67.00	40.00
(85)	Joe Tinker	300.00	150.00	90.00
(86)	John Titus	135.00	67.00	40.00
(87)	Terry Turner	135.00	67.00	40.00
(88)	Bobby Wallace	300.00	150.00	90.00
(89)	Doc White	135.00	67.00	40.00
(90)	Ed Willett	135.00	67.00	40.00
(91)	Art Wilson	135.00	67.00	40.00
(92)	Harry Wolter	135.00	67.00	40.00

Values quoted in this guide reflect the retail price of a card – the price a collector can expect to pay when buying a card from a dealer. The wholesale price – that which a collector can expect to receive from a dealer when selling cards – will be significantly lower, depending on desirability and condition.

1910 S74 Silks - Colored

		NR MT	EX	VG
Complete Set (120):		22000.	11000.	6750.
Common Player:		125.00	62.00	37.00
(1)	Red Ames	125.00	62.00	37.00
(2)	Jimmy Archer	125.00	62.00	37.00
(3)	Home Run Baker	250.00	125.00	75.00
(4)	Cy Barger	125.00	62.00	37.00
(5)	Jack Barry	125.00	62.00	37.00
(6)	Johnny Bates	125.00	62.00	37.00
(7)	Beals Becker	125.00	62.00	37.00
(8)	George Bell	125.00	62.00	37.00
(9)	Chief Bender	250.00	125.00	75.00
(10)	Bill Bergen	125.00	62.00	37.00
(11)	Bob Bescher	125.00	62.00	37.00
(12)	Roger Bresnahan (mouth closed)	335.00	167.00	100.00
(13)	Roger Bresnahan (mouth open)	335.00	167.00	100.00
(14)	Al Bridwell	125.00	62.00	37.00
(15)	Mordecai Brown	250.00	125.00	75.00
(16)	Bobby Byrne	125.00	62.00	37.00
(17)	Howie Camnitz	125.00	62.00	37.00
(18)	Bill Carrigan	125.00	62.00	37.00
(19)	Frank Chance	335.00	167.00	100.00
(20)	Hal Chase	200.00	100.00	60.00
(21)	Ed Cicotte	175.00	87.00	52.00
(22)	Fred Clarke	250.00	125.00	75.00
(23)	Ty Cobb	1600.	800.00	480.00
(24)	Eddie Collins	250.00	125.00	75.00
(25)	Doc Crandall	125.00	62.00	37.00
(26)	Bill Dahlen	125.00	62.00	37.00
(27)	Jake Daubert	175.00	87.00	52.00
(28)	Jim Delahanty	125.00	62.00	37.00
(29)	Art Devlin	125.00	62.00	37.00
(30)	Josh Devore	125.00	62.00	37.00
(31)	Red Dooin	125.00	62.00	37.00
(32)	Mickey Doolan	125.00	62.00	37.00
(33)	Tom Downey	125.00	62.00	37.00
(34)	Larry Doyle	125.00	62.00	37.00
(35)	Hugh Duffy	250.00	125.00	75.00
(36)	Jimmy Dygert	125.00	62.00	37.00
(37)	Kid Elberfield (Elberfeld)	125.00	62.00	37.00
(38)	Steve Evans	125.00	62.00	37.00
(39)	Johnny Evers	250.00	125.00	75.00
(40)	Bob Ewing	125.00	62.00	37.00
(41)	Art Fletcher	125.00	62.00	37.00
(42)	John Flynn	125.00	62.00	37.00
(43)	Russ Ford	125.00	62.00	37.00
(44)	Bill Foxen	125.00	62.00	37.00
(45)	Art Fromme	125.00	62.00	37.00
(46)	George Gibson	125.00	62.00	37.00
(47)	Peaches Graham	125.00	62.00	37.00
(48)	Eddie Grant	125.00	62.00	37.00
(49)	Clark Griffith	250.00	125.00	75.00
(50)	Topsy Hartsel	125.00	62.00	37.00
(51)	Arnold Hauser	125.00	62.00	37.00
(52)	Charlie Hemphill	125.00	62.00	37.00
(53)	Dick Hoblitzell	125.00	62.00	37.00
(54)	Miller Huggins	250.00	125.00	75.00
(55)	John Hummel	125.00	62.00	37.00
(56)	Walter Johnson	675.00	337.00	202.00
(57)	Davy Jones	125.00	62.00	37.00
(58)	Johnny Kling	125.00	62.00	37.00
(59)	Jack Knight	125.00	62.00	37.00
(60)	Ed Konetchy	125.00	62.00	37.00
(61)	Harry Krause	125.00	62.00	37.00
(62)	Tommy Leach	125.00	62.00	37.00
(63)	Lefty Leifield	125.00	62.00	37.00
(64)	Hans Lobert	125.00	62.00	37.00
(65)	Rube Marquard	250.00	125.00	75.00
(66)	Christy Mathewson	675.00	337.00	202.00
(67)	Al Mattern	125.00	62.00	37.00
(68)	Amby McConnell	125.00	62.00	37.00
(69)	John McGraw	335.00	167.00	100.00
(70)	Harry McIntire (McIntyre)	125.00	62.00	37.00
(71)	Fred Merkle	175.00	87.00	52.00
(72)	Chief Meyers	125.00	62.00	37.00
(73)	Dots Miller	125.00	62.00	37.00
(74)	Mike Mitchell	125.00	62.00	37.00
(75)	Pat Moran	125.00	62.00	37.00
(76)	George Moriarty	125.00	62.00	37.00
(77)	George Mullin	125.00	62.00	37.00
(78)	Danny Murphy	125.00	62.00	37.00
(79)	Red Murray	125.00	62.00	37.00
(80)	Tom Needham	125.00	62.00	37.00
(81)	Rebel Oakes	125.00	62.00	37.00
(82)	Rube Oldring	125.00	62.00	37.00
(83)	Orval Overall	125.00	62.00	37.00
(84)	Fred Parent	125.00	62.00	37.00
(85)	Dode Paskert	125.00	62.00	37.00
(86)	Billy Payne	125.00	62.00	37.00
(87)	Barney Pelty	125.00	62.00	37.00
(88)	Deacon Phillippe	125.00	62.00	37.00
(89)	Jack Quinn	125.00	62.00	37.00
(90)	Bugs Raymond	125.00	62.00	37.00
(91)	Ed Reulbach	125.00	62.00	37.00
(92)	Jack Rowan	125.00	62.00	37.00
(93)	Nap Rucker	125.00	62.00	37.00
(94)	Doc Scanlon (Scanlan)	125.00	62.00	37.00
(95)	Germany Schaefer	125.00	62.00	37.00
(96)	Admiral Schlei	125.00	62.00	37.00
(97)	Wildfire Schulte	125.00	62.00	37.00
(98)	Dave Shean	125.00	62.00	37.00
(99)	Jimmy Sheckard	125.00	62.00	37.00
(100)	Happy Smith	125.00	62.00	37.00
(101)	Fred Snodgrass	125.00	62.00	37.00
(102)	Tris Speaker	500.00	250.00	150.00
(103)	Jake Stahl	125.00	62.00	37.00
(104)	Harry Steinfeldt	175.00	87.00	52.00
(105)	George Stone	125.00	62.00	37.00
(106)	Gabby Street	125.00	62.00	37.00
(107)	Ed Summers	125.00	62.00	37.00
(108)	Lee Tannehill	125.00	62.00	37.00
(109)	Joe Tinker	250.00	125.00	75.00
(110)	John Titus	125.00	62.00	37.00
(111)	Terry Turner	125.00	62.00	37.00
(112)	Bobby Wallace	250.00	125.00	75.00
(113)	Zack Wheat	250.00	125.00	75.00
(114)	Doc White (White Sox)	125.00	62.00	37.00
(115)	Kirby White (Pirates)	125.00	62.00	37.00
(116)	Ed Willett	125.00	62.00	37.00
(117)	Owen Wilson	125.00	62.00	37.00
(118)	Hooks Wiltse	125.00	62.00	37.00
(119)	Harry Wolter	125.00	62.00	37.00
(120)	Cy Young	675.00	337.00	202.00

1912 S81 Silks

The 1912 S81 "Silks," so-called because they featured pictures of baseball players on a satin-like fabric rather than paper or cardboard, are closely related to the better-known T3 Turkey Red cabinet cards of the same era. The silks, which featured 25 of the day's top baseball players among its other various subjects, were available as a premium with Helmar "Turkish Trophies" cigarettes. According to an advertising sheet, one silk could be obtained for 25 Helmar coupons. The silks measure 7" by 9" and, with a few exceptions, used the same pictures featured on the popular Turkey Red cards. Five players (Rube Marquard, Rube Benton, Marty O'Toole, Grover Alexander and Russ Ford) appear in the "Silks" set that were not included in the T3 set. In addition, an error involving the Frank Baker card was corrected for the "Silks" set. (In the T3 set, Baker's card actually pictured Jack Barry.) Several years ago a pair of New England collectors found a small stack of Christy Mathewson "Silks," making his, by far, the most common. Otherwise, the "Silks" are generally so rare that it is difficult to determine the relative scarcity of the others. Baseball enthusiasts are usually only attracted to the 25 baseball players in the "Silks" premium set, but it is interesting to note that the promotion also offered dozens of other subjects, including "beautiful women in bathing and athletic costumes, charming dancers in gorgeous attire, natiional flags and generals on horseback."

		NR MT	EX	VG
Complete Set (25):		47500.	24000.	14000.
Common Player:		975.00	487.00	292.00
90	Russ Ford	1100.	550.00	330.00
91	John McGraw	3250.	1625.	975.00
92	Nap Rucker	975.00	487.00	292.00
93	Mike Mitchell	975.00	487.00	292.00
94	Chief Bender	2600.	1300.	780.00
95	Home Run Baker	2600.	1300.	780.00
96	Nap Lajoie	3500.	1750.	1000.
97	Joe Tinker	2600.	1300.	780.00
98	Sherry Magee	975.00	487.00	292.00
99	Howie Camnitz	975.00	487.00	292.00
100	Eddie Collins	2600.	1300.	780.00
101	Red Dooin	975.00	487.00	292.00
102	Ty Cobb	8000.	4000.	2400.
103	Hugh Jennings	2600.	1300.	780.00
104	Roger Bresnahan	2600.	1300.	780.00
105	Jake Stahl	1100.	550.00	330.00
106	Tris Speaker	4200.	2100.	1250.
107	Ed Walsh	2600.	1300.	780.00
108	Christy Mathewson	2800.	1400.	800.00
109	Johnny Evers	2750.	1375.	825.00
110	Walter Johnson	4500.	2250.	1350.
111	Rube Marquard	2600.	1300.	780.00
112	Marty O'Toole	975.00	487.00	292.00
113	Rube Benton	975.00	487.00	292.00
114	Grover Alexander	2750.	1375.	825.00

1962 Salada-Junket Dessert Coins

These 1-3/8" diameter plastic coins were issued in packages of Salada Tea and Junket Pudding mix. There are 221 different players available, with variations bringing the total of different coins to 261. Each coin has a paper color photo inserted in the front which contains the player's name and position plus the coin number. The plastic rims come in six different colors, all color coded per team. (For example, the New York Yankees are found with light blue rims). Production began with 180 coins, but the addition of the New York Mets and Houston Colt .45's to the National League allowed the company to expand the set's size. Twenty expansion players were added along with 21 other players. Several players' coins were dropped after the initial 180 run, causing some scarcities. A Gary Geiger coin with a "BO" instead of a "B" on his cap is sometimes found on collectors' want lists. However, most Salada experts do not consider this coin to be a legitimate variation. The mark, which somewhat resembles an "O", is merely a printing smear and not an intended cap emblem. It has also been determined by Salada experts that a Jim Lemon coin with red shirt buttons does not exist.

		NR MT	EX	VG
Complete Set: (without variations)		3250.	1600.	975.00
Complete Set: (with variations)		8000.	4000.	2400.
Common Player (1-180):		4.00	2.00	1.25
Common Player (181-221):		8.00	4.00	2.50
1	Jim Gentile	5.50	2.75	1.75
2	Bill Pierce	125.00	62.00	37.00
3	Chico Fernandez	4.00	2.00	1.25
4	Tom Brewer	35.00	17.50	10.50
5	Woody Held	4.00	2.00	1.25
6	Ray Herbert	35.00	17.50	10.50
7a	Ken Aspromonte (Angels)	16.50	8.25	5.00
7b	Ken Aspromonte (Indians)	5.50	2.75	1.75
8	Whitey Ford	29.00	14.50	8.75
9	Jim Lemon	5.00	2.50	1.50
10	Billy Klaus	4.00	2.00	1.25
11	Steve Barber	35.00	17.50	10.50
12	Nellie Fox	15.00	7.50	4.50
13	Jim Bunning	11.00	5.50	3.25
14	Frank Malzone	5.00	2.50	1.50
15	Tito Francona	4.00	2.00	1.25
16	Bobby Del Greco	4.00	2.00	1.25
17a	Steve Bilko (red shirt buttons)	8.25	4.25	2.50
17b	Steve Bilko (white shirt buttons)	5.50	2.75	1.75
18	Tony Kubek	60.00	30.00	18.00
19	Earl Battey	5.00	2.50	1.50
20	Chuck Cottier	4.00	2.00	1.25
21	Willie Tasby	4.00	2.00	1.25
22	Bob Allison	5.50	2.75	1.75
23	Roger Maris	35.00	17.50	10.50
24a	Earl Averill (red shirt buttons)	8.25	4.25	2.50
24b	Earl Averill (white shirt buttons)	5.50	2.75	1.75
25	Jerry Lumpe	4.00	2.00	1.25
26	Jim Grant	35.00	17.50	10.50
27	Carl Yastrzemski	75.00	37.00	22.00
28	Rocky Colavito	12.00	6.00	3.50
29	Al Smith	4.00	2.00	1.25
30	Jim Busby	35.00	17.50	10.50
31	Dick Howser	4.00	2.00	1.25
32	Jim Perry	4.00	2.00	1.25
33	Yogi Berra	35.00	17.50	10.50
34a	Ken Hamlin (red shirt buttons)	9.00	4.50	2.75
34b	Ken Hamlin (white shirt buttons)	5.50	2.75	1.75
35	Dale Long	4.00	2.00	1.25
36	Harmon Killebrew	25.00	12.50	7.50
37	Dick Brown	4.00	2.00	1.25
38	Gary Geiger	4.00	2.00	1.25
39a	Minnie Minoso (White Sox)	35.00	17.50	10.50
39b	Minnie Minoso (Cardinals)	20.00	10.00	6.00
40	Brooks Robinson	42.50	21.00	12.50
41	Mickey Mantle	130.00	65.00	39.00
42	Bennie Daniels	4.00	2.00	1.25
43	Billy Martin	12.50	6.25	3.75
44	Vic Power	5.00	2.50	1.50
45	Joe Pignatano	4.00	2.00	1.25
46a	Ryne Duren (red shirt buttons)	8.25	4.25	2.50
46b	Ryne Duren (white shirt buttons)	5.50	2.75	1.75
47a	Pete Runnels (2B)	12.50	6.25	3.75
47b	Pete Runnels (1B)	6.00	3.00	1.75
48a	Dick Williams (name on right)	1000.	500.00	300.00

48b	Dick Williams (name on left)	6.00	3.00	1.75
49	Jim Landis	4.00	2.00	1.25
50	Steve Boros	4.00	2.00	1.25
51a	Zoilo Versalles (red shirt buttons)	8.25	4.25	2.50
51b	Zoilo Versalles (white shirt buttons)	5.50	2.75	1.75
52a	Johnny Temple (Indians)	20.00	10.00	6.00
52b	Johnny Temple (Orioles)	5.50	2.75	1.75
53a	Jackie Brandt (Oriole)	6.00	3.00	1.75
53b	Jackie Brandt (Orioles)	850.00	425.00	255.00
54	Joe McClain	4.00	2.00	1.25
55	Sherm Lollar	5.00	2.50	1.50
56	Gene Stephens	4.00	2.00	1.25
57a	Leon Wagner (red shirt buttons)	8.25	4.25	2.50
57b	Leon Wagner (white shirt buttons)	5.50	2.75	1.75
58	Frank Lary	4.00	2.00	1.25
59	Bill Skowron	8.50	4.25	2.50
60	Vic Wertz	4.00	2.00	1.25
61	Willie Kirkland	4.00	2.00	1.25
62	Leo Posada	4.00	2.00	1.25
63a	Albie Pearson (red shirt buttons)	11.00	5.50	3.25
63b	Albie Pearson (white shirt buttons)	5.50	2.75	1.75
64	Bobby Richardson	11.00	5.50	3.25
65a	Marv Breeding (SS)	22.00	11.00	6.50
65b	Marv Breeding (2B)	5.50	2.75	1.75
66	Roy Sievers	85.00	42.00	25.00
67	Al Kaline	37.50	18.50	11.00
68a	Don Buddin (Red Sox)	20.00	10.00	6.00
68b	Don Buddin (Colts)	10.00	5.00	3.00
69a	Lenny Green (red shirt buttons)	8.25	4.25	2.50
69B	Lenny Green (white shirt buttons)	5.50	2.75	1.75
70	Gene Green	40.00	20.00	12.00
71	Luis Aparicio	19.00	9.50	5.75
72	Norm Cash	9.00	4.50	2.75
73	Jackie Jensen	45.00	22.00	13.50
74	Bubba Phillips	4.00	2.00	1.25
75	Jim Archer	4.00	2.00	1.25
76a	Ken Hunt (red shirt buttons)	11.00	5.50	3.25
76b	Ken Hunt (white shirt buttons)	5.50	2.75	1.75
77	Ralph Terry	6.00	3.00	1.75
78	Camilo Pascual	4.00	2.00	1.25
79	Marty Keough	40.00	20.00	12.00
80	Cletis Boyer	5.50	2.75	1.75
81	Jim Pagliaroni	4.00	2.00	1.25
82a	Gene Leek (red shirt buttons)	8.25	4.25	2.50
82b	Gene Leek (white shirt buttons)	5.50	2.75	1.75
83	Jake Wood	4.00	2.00	1.25
84	Coot Veal	35.00	17.50	10.50
85	Norm Siebern	5.00	2.50	1.50
86a	Andy Carey (White Sox)	50.00	25.00	15.00
86b	Andy Carey (Phillies)	9.00	4.50	2.75
87a	Bill Tuttle (red shirt buttons)	8.25	4.25	2.50
87b	Bill Tuttle (white shirt buttons)	5.50	2.75	1.75
88a	Jimmy Piersall (Indians)	17.50	8.75	5.25
88b	Jimmy Piersall (Senators)	9.00	4.50	2.75
89	Ron Hansen	45.00	22.00	13.50
90a	Chuck Stobbs (red shirt buttons)	9.50	4.75	2.75
90b	Chuck Stobbs (white shirt buttons)	5.50	2.75	1.75
91a	Ken McBride (red shirt buttons)	8.25	4.25	2.50
91b	Ken McBride (white shirt buttons)	5.50	2.75	1.75
92	Bill Bruton	4.00	2.00	1.25
93	Gus Triandos	4.00	2.00	1.25
94	John Romano	4.00	2.00	1.25
95	Elston Howard	9.00	4.50	2.75
96	Gene Woodling	6.00	3.00	1.75
97a	Early Wynn (pitching pose)	75.00	37.00	22.00
97b	Early Wynn (portrait)	30.00	15.00	9.00
98	Milt Pappas	5.00	2.50	1.50
99	Bill Monbouquette	4.00	2.00	1.25
100	Wayne Causey	4.00	2.00	1.25
101	Don Elston	4.00	2.00	1.25
102a	Charlie Neal (Dodgers)	16.50	8.25	5.00
102b	Charlie Neal (Mets)	7.00	3.50	2.00
103	Don Blasingame	4.00	2.00	1.25
104	Frank Thomas	40.00	20.00	12.00
105	Wes Covington	5.00	2.50	1.50
106	Chuck Hiller	4.00	2.00	1.25
107	Don Hoak	5.00	2.50	1.50
108a	Bob Lillis (Cardinals)	35.00	17.50	10.50
108b	Bob Lillis (Colts)	7.00	3.50	2.00
109	Sandy Koufax	45.00	22.00	13.50
110	Gordy Coleman	4.00	2.00	1.25
111	Ed Matthews (Mathews)	20.00	10.00	6.00
112	Art Mahaffey	4.00	2.00	1.25
113a	Ed Bailey (red period above "i" in Giants)	11.00	5.50	3.25
113b	Ed Bailey (white period)	4.00	2.00	1.25
114	Smoky Burgess	5.50	2.75	1.75
115	Bill White	5.00	2.50	1.50
116	Ed Bouchee	35.00	17.50	10.50
117	Bob Buhl	4.00	2.00	1.25
118	Vada Pinson	6.00	3.00	1.75
119	Carl Sawatski	4.00	2.00	1.25
120	Dick Stuart	4.00	2.00	1.25
121	Harvey Kuenn	60.00	30.00	18.00
122	Pancho Herrera	4.00	2.00	1.25
123a	Don Zimmer (Cubs)	15.00	7.50	4.50
123b	Don Zimmer (Mets)	7.00	3.50	2.00
124	Wally Moon	5.00	2.50	1.50
125	Joe Adcock	5.50	2.75	1.75
126	Joey Jay	4.00	2.00	1.25
127a	Maury Wills (blue "3" on shirt)	20.00	10.00	6.00
127b	Maury Wills (red "3" on shirt)	7.00	3.50	2.00
128	George Altman	4.00	2.00	1.25
129a	John Buzhardt (Phillies)	20.00	10.00	6.00
129b	John Buzhardt (White Sox)	7.00	3.50	2.00
130	Felipe Alou	6.00	3.00	1.75
131	Bill Mazeroski	10.00	5.00	3.00
132	Ernie Broglio	4.00	2.00	1.25
133	John Roseboro	5.00	2.50	1.50
134	Mike McCormick	4.00	2.00	1.25
135a	Chuck Smith (Phillies)	20.00	10.00	6.00
135b	Chuck Smith (White Sox)	7.00	3.50	2.00
136	Ron Santo	8.00	4.00	2.40
137	Gene Freese	4.00	2.00	1.25
138	Dick Groat	6.00	3.00	1.75
139	Curt Flood	7.00	3.50	2.00
140	Frank Bolling	4.00	2.00	1.25
141	Clay Dalrymple	4.00	2.00	1.25
142	Willie McCovey	42.50	21.00	12.50
143	Bob Skinner	5.00	2.50	1.50
144	Lindy McDaniel	4.00	2.00	1.25
145	Glen Hobbie	4.00	2.00	1.25
146a	Gil Hodges (Dodgers)	55.00	27.00	16.50
146b	Gil Hodges (Mets)	35.00	17.50	10.50
147	Eddie Kasko	4.00	2.00	1.25
148	Gino Cimoli	45.00	22.00	13.50
149	Willie Mays	80.00	40.00	24.00
150	Roberto Clemente	80.00	40.00	24.00
151	Red Schoendienst	7.50	3.75	2.25
152	Joe Torre	5.50	2.75	1.75
153	Bob Purkey	4.00	2.00	1.25
154a	Tommy Davis (3B)	11.00	5.50	3.30
154b	Tommy Davis (OF)	6.00	3.00	1.75
155a	Andre Rogers (incorrect spelling)	13.50	6.75	4.00
155b	Andre Rodgers (correct spelling)	5.50	2.75	1.75
156	Tony Taylor	4.00	2.00	1.25
157	Bob Friend	4.00	2.00	1.25
158a	Gus Bell (Redlegs)	12.00	6.00	7.25
158b	Gus Bell (Mets)	7.00	3.50	2.00
159	Roy McMillan	4.00	2.00	1.25
160	Carl Warwick	4.00	2.00	1.25
161	Willie Davis	5.50	2.75	1.75
162	Sam Jones	65.00	32.00	19.50
163	Ruben Amaro	4.00	2.00	1.25
164	Sam Taylor	4.00	2.00	1.25
165	Frank Robinson	35.00	17.50	10.50
166	Lou Burdette	5.00	2.50	1.50
167	Ken Boyer	7.00	3.50	2.00
168	Bill Virdon	6.00	3.00	1.75
169	Jim Davenport	4.00	2.00	1.25
170	Don Demeter	4.00	2.00	1.25
171	Richie Ashburn	55.00	27.00	16.50
172	John Podres	5.50	2.75	1.75
173a	Joe Cunningham (Cardinals)	55.00	27.00	16.50
173b	Joe Cunningham (White Sox)	25.00	12.50	7.50
174	ElRoy Face	7.00	3.50	2.00
175	Orlando Cepeda	9.00	4.50	2.75
176a	Bobby Gene Smith (Phillies)	20.00	10.00	6.00
176b	Bobby Gene Smith (Mets)	7.00	3.50	2.00
177a	Ernie Banks (OF)	55.00	27.00	16.50
177b	Ernie Banks (SS)	25.00	12.50	7.50
178a	Daryl Spencer (3B)	18.00	9.00	5.50
178b	Daryl Spencer (1B)	7.00	3.50	2.00
179	Bob Schmidt	35.00	17.50	10.50
180	Hank Aaron	80.00	40.00	24.00
181	Hobie Landrith	10.00	5.00	3.00
182a	Ed Broussard	400.00	200.00	120.00
182b	Ed Bressoud	35.00	17.50	10.50
183	Felix Mantilla	10.00	5.00	3.00
184	Dick Farrell	10.00	5.00	3.00
185	Bob Miller	10.00	5.00	3.00
186	Don Taussig	10.00	5.00	3.00
187	Pumpsie Green	11.00	5.50	3.25
188	Bobby Shantz	12.00	6.00	3.50
189	Roger Craig	12.00	6.00	3.50
190	Hal Smith	10.00	5.00	3.00
191	John Edwards	8.00	4.00	2.50
192	John DeMerit	10.00	5.00	3.00
193	Joe Amalfitano	10.00	5.00	3.00
194	Norm Larker	10.00	5.00	3.00
195	Al Heist	10.00	5.00	3.00
196	Al Spangler	10.00	5.00	3.00
197	Alex Grammas	8.00	4.00	2.50
198	Gerry Lynch	8.00	4.00	2.50
199	Jim McKnight	8.00	4.00	2.50
200	Jose Pagen (Pagan)	8.00	4.00	2.50
201	Junior Gilliam	22.00	11.00	6.50
202	Art Ditmar	8.00	4.00	2.50
203	Pete Daley	8.00	4.00	2.50
204	Johnny Callison	24.00	12.00	7.25
205	Stu Miller	8.00	4.00	2.50
206	Russ Snyder	8.00	4.00	2.50
207	Billy Williams	32.00	16.00	9.50
208	Walter Bond	8.00	4.00	2.50
209	Joe Koppe	8.00	4.00	2.50
210	Don Schwall	30.00	15.00	9.00
211	Billy Gardner	15.00	7.50	4.50
212	Chuck Estrada	8.00	4.00	2.50
213	Gary Bell	8.00	4.00	2.50
214	Floyd Robinson	8.00	4.00	2.50
215	Duke Snider	55.00	27.00	16.50
216	Lee Maye	8.00	4.00	2.50
217	Howie Bedell	8.00	4.00	2.50
218	Bob Will	8.00	4.00	2.50
219	Dallas Green	11.00	5.50	3.25
220	Carroll Hardy	16.00	8.00	4.75
221	Danny O'Connell	11.00	5.50	3.25

1963 Salada-Junket Dessert Coins

A much smaller set of baseball coins was issued by Salada/Junket in 1963. The 63 coins issued were called "All-Star Baseball Coins" and included most the top players of the day. Unlike 1962, the coins were made of metal and measured a slightly larger 1-1/2" diameter. American League players have blue rims on their coins, while National Leaguers are rimmed in red. Coin fronts contain no printing on the full-color player photos, while backs list coin number, player name, team and position, along with brief statistics and the sponsors' logos.

		NR MT	EX	VG
Complete Set (63):		950.00	475.00	275.00
Common Player:		5.00	2.50	1.50
1	Don Drysdale	18.00	9.00	5.50
2	Dick Farrell	5.00	2.50	1.50
3	Bob Gibson	18.00	9.00	5.50
4	Sandy Koufax	30.00	15.00	9.00
5	Juan Marichal	18.00	9.00	5.50
6	Bob Purkey	5.00	2.50	1.50
7	Bob Shaw	5.00	2.50	1.50
8	Warren Spahn	18.00	9.00	5.50
9	Johnny Podres	5.00	2.50	1.50
10	Art Mahaffey	5.00	2.50	1.50
11	Del Crandall	6.50	3.25	2.00
12	John Roseboro	6.50	3.25	2.00
13	Orlando Cepeda	7.00	3.50	2.00
14	Bill Mazeroski	11.00	5.50	3.25
15	Ken Boyer	8.00	4.00	2.50
16	Dick Groat	7.00	3.50	2.00
17	Ernie Banks	25.00	12.50	7.50
18	Frank Bolling	5.00	2.50	1.50
19	Jim Davenport	5.00	2.50	1.50
20	Maury Wills	7.00	3.50	2.00
21	Tommy Davis	6.50	3.25	2.00
22	Willie Mays	65.00	32.00	19.50
23	Roberto Clemente	65.00	32.00	19.50
24	Henry Aaron	65.00	32.00	19.50
25	Felipe Alou	6.50	3.25	2.00
26	Johnny Callison	6.50	3.25	2.00
27	Richie Ashburn	9.00	4.50	2.75
28	Eddie Mathews	20.00	10.00	6.00
29	Frank Robinson	22.50	11.00	6.75
30	Billy Williams	18.00	9.00	5.50
31	George Altman	5.00	2.50	1.50
32	Hank Aguirre	5.00	2.50	1.50
33	Jim Bunning	9.00	4.50	2.75
34	Dick Donovan	5.00	2.50	1.50
35	Bill Monbouquette	5.00	2.50	1.50
36	Camilo Pascual	6.50	3.25	2.00
37	David Stenhouse	5.00	2.50	1.50
38	Ralph Terry	6.50	3.25	2.00
39	Hoyt Wilhelm	18.00	9.00	5.50
40	Jim Kaat	11.00	5.50	3.25
41	Ken McBride	5.00	2.50	1.50
42	Ray Herbert	5.00	2.50	1.50
43	Milt Pappas	6.50	3.25	2.00
44	Earl Battey	5.00	2.50	1.50
45	Elston Howard	9.00	4.50	2.75
46	John Romano	5.00	2.50	1.50
47	Jim Gentile	5.00	2.50	1.50
48	Billy Moran	5.00	2.50	1.50
49	Rich Rollins	5.00	2.50	1.50
50	Luis Aparicio	18.00	9.00	5.50
51	Norm Siebern	5.00	2.50	1.50
52	Bobby Richardson	15.00	7.50	4.50
53	Brooks Robinson	30.00	15.00	9.00
54	Tom Tresh	11.00	5.50	3.25
55	Leon Wagner	5.00	2.50	1.50
56	Mickey Mantle	140.00	70.00	42.00
57	Roger Maris	40.00	20.00	12.00
58	Rocky Colavito	11.00	5.50	3.25
59	Lee Thomas	5.00	2.50	1.50
60	Jim Landis	5.00	2.50	1.50
61	Pete Runnels	6.50	3.25	2.00
62	Yogi Berra	30.00	15.00	9.00
63	Al Kaline	30.00	15.00	9.00

1958 San Francisco Call-Bulletin Giants

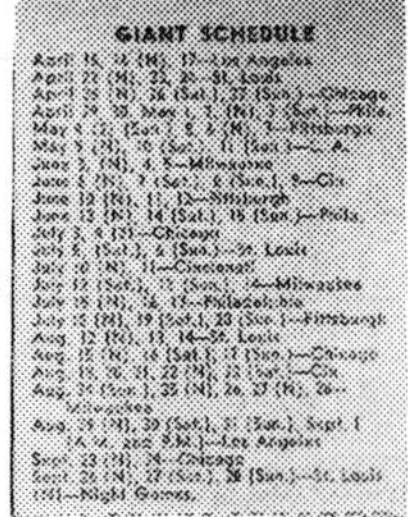

These unnumbered cards, picturing members of the San Francisco Giants, were inserted in copies of the San Francisco Call-Bulletin newspaper as part of a promotional contest. The 25 cards in the set measure 2" by 4" and were printed on orange paper. The top of the card contains a black and white player photo, while the bottom contains a perforated stub with a serial number used to win prizes. (Cards without the stub intact are approximately 50 percent of the prices listed.) The contest name, "Giant Payoff", appears prominently on both sides of the stub. The back of the card contains a 1958 Giants schedule.

		NR MT	EX	VG
Complete Set (25):		1200.	600.00	360.00
Common Player:		10.00	5.00	3.00
(1)	Johnny Antonelli	15.00	7.50	4.50
(2)	Curt Barclay	10.00	5.00	3.00
(3)	Tom Bowers	500.00	250.00	150.00
(4)	Ed Bressoud	90.00	45.00	27.00
(5)	Orlando Cepeda	90.00	45.00	27.00
(6)	Ray Crone	10.00	5.00	3.00
(7)	Jim Davenport	15.00	7.50	4.50
(8)	Paul Giel	10.00	5.00	3.00
(9)	Ruben Gomez	10.00	5.00	3.00
(10)	Marv Grissom	10.00	5.00	3.00
(11)	Ray Jablonski	90.00	45.00	27.00
(12)	Willie Kirkland	100.00	50.00	30.00
(13)	Whitey Lockman	15.00	7.50	4.50
(14)	Willie Mays	300.00	150.00	90.00
(15)	Mike McCormick	15.00	7.50	4.50
(16)	Stu Miller	15.00	7.50	4.50
(17)	Ramon Monzant	10.00	5.00	3.00
(18)	Danny O'Connell	10.00	5.00	3.00
(19)	Bill Rigney	15.00	7.50	4.50
(20)	Hank Sauer	15.00	7.50	4.50
(21)	Bob Schmidt	10.00	5.00	3.00
(22)	Daryl Spencer	10.00	5.00	3.00
(23)	Valmy Thomas	10.00	5.00	3.00
(24)	Bobby Thomson	30.00	15.00	9.00
(25)	Allan Worthington	10.00	5.00	3.00

1986 Schnucks Milk Cardinals

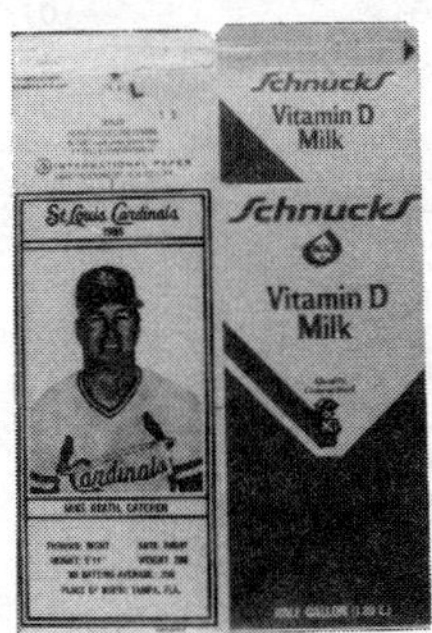

These milk carton panels were issued by Schnucks supermarkets in the St. Louis and southwestern Illinois areas. The 3-3/4" by 7-1/2" blank-backed panels feature black and white photos of 24 different St. Louis players along with personal information and 1985 playing statistics. A mascot and schedule card were also included in the set.

		MT	NR MT	EX
Complete Set (26):		30.00	22.00	12.00
Common Player:		.60	.45	.25
(1)	Jack Clark	2.00	1.50	.80
(2)	Vince Coleman	2.00	1.50	.80
(3)	Tim Conroy	.60	.45	.25
(4)	Danny Cox	.60	.45	.25
(5)	Ken Dayley	.60	.45	.25
(6)	Bob Forsch	.60	.45	.25
(7)	Mike Heath	.60	.45	.25
(8)	Tom Herr	.80	.60	.30
(9)	Rick Horton	.60	.45	.25
(10)	Clint Hurdle	.60	.45	.25
(11)	Kurt Kepshire	.60	.45	.25
(12)	Jeff Lahti	.60	.45	.25
(13)	Tito Landrum	.60	.45	.25
(14)	Mike Lavalliere	.90	.70	.35
(15)	Tom Lawless	.60	.45	.25
(16)	Willie McGee	2.50	2.00	1.00
(17)	Jose Oquendo	.90	.70	.35
(18)	Rick Ownbey	.60	.45	.25
(19)	Terry Pendleton	4.00	3.00	1.50
(20)	Pat Perry	.60	.45	.25
(21)	Ozzie Smith	8.00	6.00	3.25
(22)	John Tudor	.80	.60	.30
(23)	Andy Van Slyke	2.50	2.00	1.00
(24)	Todd Worrell	1.00	.70	.40
(25)	Fred Bird (mascot)	.60	.45	.25
(26)	1986 Cardinals Schedule	.60	.45	.25

1935 Schutter-Johnson (R332)

This 50-card set was issued by the Schutter-Johnson Candy Corp. of Chicago and Brooklyn circa 1930 and features drawings of major league players offering baseball playing tips. The cards measure 2-1/4" by 2-7/8". The drawings on the front are set

against a red background while the backs are titled "Major League Secrets" and give the player's advice on some aspect of the game. The Scutter-Johnson name appears at the bottom.

		NR MT	EX	VG
Complete Set (50):		3500.	1750.	1050.
Common Player:		35.00	17.50	10.50
1	Al Simmons	50.00	25.00	15.00
2	Lloyd Waner	50.00	25.00	15.00
3	Kiki Cuyler	50.00	25.00	15.00
4	Frank Frisch	60.00	30.00	18.00
5	Chick Hafey	50.00	25.00	15.00
6	Bill Klem (umpire)	50.00	25.00	15.00
7	Rogers Hornsby	90.00	45.00	27.00
8	Carl Mays	35.00	17.50	10.50
9	Chas. Wrigley (umpire)	35.00	17.50	10.50
10	Christy Mathewson	90.00	45.00	27.00
11	Bill Dickey	70.00	35.00	21.00
12	Walter Berger	35.00	17.50	10.50
13	George Earnshaw	35.00	17.50	10.50
14	"Hack" Wilson	50.00	25.00	15.00
15	Charley Grimm	35.00	17.50	10.50
16	Lloyd Waner, Paul Waner	50.00	25.00	15.00
17	Chuck Klein	50.00	25.00	15.00
18	Woody English	35.00	17.50	10.50
19	Grover Alexander	70.00	35.00	21.00
20	Lou Gehrig	300.00	150.00	90.00
21	Wes Ferrell	35.00	17.50	10.50
22	Carl Hubbell	60.00	30.00	18.00
23	Pie Traynor	50.00	25.00	15.00
24	Gus Mancuso	35.00	17.50	10.50
25	Ben Cantwell	35.00	17.50	10.50
26	Babe Ruth	450.00	225.00	135.00
27	"Goose" Goslin	50.00	25.00	15.00
28	Earle Combs	50.00	25.00	15.00
29	"Kiki" Cuyler	50.00	25.00	15.00
30	Jimmy Wilson	35.00	17.50	10.50
31	Dizzy Dean	100.00	50.00	30.00
32	Mickey Cochrane	60.00	30.00	18.00
33	Ted Lyons	50.00	25.00	15.00
34	Si Johnson	35.00	17.50	10.50
35	Dizzy Dean	100.00	50.00	30.00
36	Pepper Martin	40.00	20.00	12.00
37	Joe Cronin	50.00	25.00	15.00
38	Gabby Hartnett	50.00	25.00	15.00
39	Oscar Melillo	35.00	17.50	10.50
40	Ben Chapman	35.00	17.50	10.50
41	John McGraw	70.00	35.00	21.00
42	Babe Ruth	250.00	125.00	75.00
43	"Red" Lucas	35.00	17.50	10.50
44	Charley Root	35.00	17.50	10.50
45	Dazzy Vance	50.00	25.00	15.00
46	Hugh Critz	35.00	17.50	10.50
47	"Firpo" Marberry	35.00	17.50	10.50
48	Grover Alexander	70.00	35.00	21.00
49	Lefty Grove	70.00	35.00	21.00
50	Heinie Meine	35.00	17.50	10.50

1988 Score

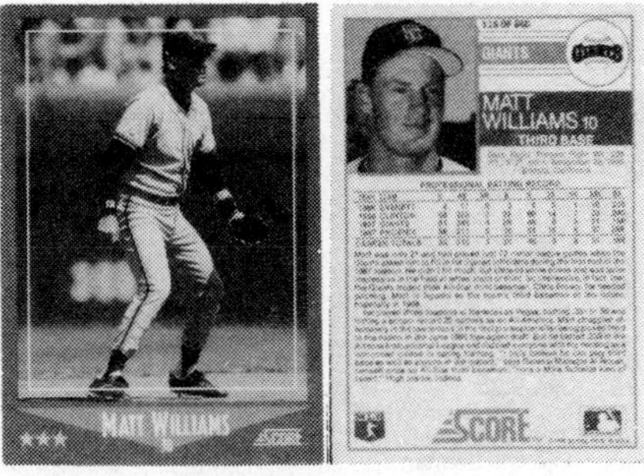

A fifth member joined the group of nationally distributed baseball cards in 1988. Titled "Score," the cards are characterized by extremely sharp and excellent full-color photography and printing. Card backs are full-color also and carry a player headshot, along with a brief biography and player personal and statistical information. The 660 cards in the set each measure 2-1/2" by 3-1/2" in size. The fronts come with one of six different border colors - blue, red, green, purple, orange and gold - which are equally divided at 110 cards per color. The Score set was produced by Major League Marketing, the same company that marketed the "triple-action" Sportflics card sets.

		MT	NR MT	EX
Complete Set (660):		20.00	15.00	8.00
Common Player:		.04	.03	.02
1	Don Mattingly	.30	.25	.12
2	Wade Boggs	.25	.15	.08
3	Tim Raines	.08	.06	.03
4	Andre Dawson	.20	.15	.08
5	Mark McGwire	.35	.20	.10
6	Kevin Seitzer	.08	.06	.03
7	Wally Joyner	.10	.08	.04
8	Jesse Barfield	.10	.08	.04
9	Pedro Guerrero	.15	.11	.06
10	Eric Davis	.12	.08	.04
11	George Brett	.35	.25	.14
12	Ozzie Smith	.15	.11	.06
13	Rickey Henderson	.25	.15	.08
14	Jim Rice	.08	.06	.03
15	*Matt Nokes*	.25	.15	.08
16	Mike Schmidt	.40	.30	.15
17	Dave Parker	.12	.09	.05
18	Eddie Murray	.25	.20	.10
19	Andres Galarraga	.20	.15	.08
20	Tony Fernandez	.10	.08	.04
21	Kevin McReynolds	.12	.09	.05
22	B.J. Surhoff	.10	.08	.04
23	Pat Tabler	.06	.05	.02
24	Kirby Puckett	.40	.25	.15
25	Benny Santiago	.12	.08	.04
26	Ryne Sandberg	.40	.30	.15
27	Kelly Downs	.08	.06	.03
28	Jose Cruz	.06	.05	.02
29	Pete O'Brien	.06	.05	.02
30	Mark Langston	.10	.08	.04
31	Lee Smith	.08	.06	.03
32	Juan Samuel	.10	.08	.04
33	Kevin Bass	.06	.05	.02
34	R.J. Reynolds	.04	.03	.02
35	Steve Sax	.12	.09	.05
36	John Kruk	.12	.08	.04
37	Alan Trammell	.08	.06	.03
38	Chris Bosio	.06	.05	.02
39	Brook Jacoby	.08	.06	.03
40	Willie McGee	.10	.08	.04
41	Dave Magadan	.10	.08	.04
42	Fred Lynn	.10	.08	.04
43	Kent Hrbek	.12	.09	.05
44	Brian Downing	.06	.05	.02
45	Jose Canseco	.35	.20	.10
46	Jim Presley	.08	.06	.03
47	Mike Stanley	.10	.08	.04
48	Tony Pena	.06	.05	.02
49	David Cone	.20	.15	.08
50	Rick Sutcliffe	.08	.06	.03
51	Doug Drabek	.10	.08	.04
52	Bill Doran	.06	.05	.02
53	Mike Scioscia	.06	.05	.02
54	Candy Maldonado	.06	.05	.02
55	Dave Winfield	.35	.25	.14
56	Lou Whitaker	.08	.06	.03
57	Tom Henke	.06	.05	.02
58	Ken Gerhart	.06	.05	.02
59	Glenn Braggs	.08	.06	.03
60	Julio Franco	.08	.06	.03
61	Charlie Leibrandt	.06	.05	.02
62	Gary Gaetti	.10	.08	.04
63	Bob Boone	.06	.05	.02
64	*Luis Polonia*	.20	.15	.08
65	Dwight Evans	.10	.08	.04
66	Phil Bradley	.08	.06	.03
67	Mike Boddicker	.06	.05	.02
68	Vince Coleman	.08	.06	.03
69	Howard Johnson	.08	.06	.03
70	Tim Wallach	.08	.06	.03
71	Keith Moreland	.06	.05	.02
72	Barry Larkin	.20	.15	.08
73	Alan Ashby	.04	.03	.02
74	Rick Rhoden	.06	.05	.02
75	Darrell Evans	.08	.06	.03
76	Dave Stieb	.08	.06	.03
77	Dan Plesac	.08	.06	.03
78	Will Clark	.40	.25	.15
79	Frank White	.06	.05	.02
80	Joe Carter	.25	.20	.10
81	Mike Witt	.06	.05	.02
82	Terry Steinbach	.10	.08	.04
83	Alvin Davis	.10	.08	.04
84	Tom Herr	.06	.05	.02
85	Vance Law	.06	.05	.02
86	Kal Daniels	.15	.11	.06
87	Rick Honeycutt	.04	.03	.02
88	Alfredo Griffin	.06	.05	.02
89	Bret Saberhagen	.10	.08	.04
90	Bert Blyleven	.10	.08	.04
91	Jeff Reardon	.08	.06	.03
92	Cory Snyder	.06	.05	.02
93	Greg Walker	.06	.05	.02
94	*Joe Magrane*	.10	.08	.04
95	Rob Deer	.06	.05	.02
96	Ray Knight	.06	.05	.02
97	Casey Candaele	.04	.03	.02
98	John Cerutti	.06	.05	.02
99	Buddy Bell	.08	.06	.03
100	Jack Clark	.12	.09	.05
101	Eric Bell	.06	.05	.02
102	Willie Wilson	.08	.06	.03
103	Dave Schmidt	.04	.03	.02
104	Dennis Eckersley	.10	.08	.04
105	Don Sutton	.12	.09	.05
106	Danny Tartabull	.10	.08	.04

107	Fred McGriff	.40	.25	.15
108	*Les Straker*	.15	.11	.06
109	Lloyd Moseby	.06	.05	.02
110	Roger Clemens	.35	.20	.10
111	Glenn Hubbard	.04	.03	.02
112	*Ken Williams*	.08	.06	.03
113	Ruben Sierra	.30	.20	.10
114	Stan Jefferson	.06	.05	.02
115	Milt Thompson	.04	.03	.02
116	Bobby Bonilla	.20	.15	.08
117	Wayne Tolleson	.04	.03	.02
118	*Matt Williams*	1.50	1.25	.60
119	Chet Lemon	.06	.05	.02
120	Dale Sveum	.06	.05	.02
121	Dennis Boyd	.06	.05	.02
122	Brett Butler	.06	.05	.02
123	Terry Kennedy	.06	.05	.02
124	Jack Howell	.06	.05	.02
125	Curt Young	.06	.05	.02
126a	Dale Valle (first name incorrect)	.25	.20	.10
126b	Dave Valle (correct spelling)	.06	.05	.02
127	Curt Wilkerson	.04	.03	.02
128	Tim Teufel	.04	.03	.02
129	Ozzie Virgil	.04	.03	.02
130	Brian Fisher	.06	.05	.02
131	Lance Parrish	.12	.09	.05
132	Tom Browning	.08	.06	.03
133a	Larry Anderson (incorrect spelling)	.25	.20	.10
133b	Larry Andersen (correct spelling)	.06	.05	.02
134a	Bob Brenley (incorrect spelling)	.25	.20	.10
134b	Bob Brenly (correct spelling)	.06	.05	.02
135	Mike Marshall	.10	.08	.04
136	Gerald Perry	.08	.06	.03
137	Bobby Meacham	.04	.03	.02
138	Larry Herndon	.04	.03	.02
139	*Fred Manrique*	.06	.05	.02
140	Charlie Hough	.06	.05	.02
141	Ron Darling	.10	.08	.04
142	Herm Winningham	.04	.03	.02
143	Mike Diaz	.06	.05	.02
144	*Mike Jackson*	.06	.05	.02
145	Denny Walling	.04	.03	.02
146	Rob Thompson	.06	.05	.02
147	Franklin Stubbs	.06	.05	.02
148	Albert Hall	.04	.03	.02
149	Bobby Witt	.08	.06	.03
150	Lance McCullers	.06	.05	.02
151	Scott Bradley	.04	.03	.02
152	Mark McLemore	.04	.03	.02
153	Tim Laudner	.04	.03	.02
154	Greg Swindell	.15	.11	.06
155	Marty Barrett	.06	.05	.02
156	Mike Heath	.04	.03	.02
157	Gary Ward	.06	.05	.02
158a	Lee Mazilli (incorrect spelling)	.25	.20	.10
158b	Lee Mazzilli (correct spelling)	.08	.06	.03
159	Tom Foley	.04	.03	.02
160	Robin Yount	.35	.25	.14
161	Steve Bedrosian	.10	.08	.04
162	Bob Walk	.04	.03	.02
163	Nick Esasky	.06	.05	.02
164	*Ken Caminiti*	.25	.20	.10
165	Jose Uribe	.04	.03	.02
166	Dave Anderson	.04	.03	.02
167	Ed Whitson	.04	.03	.02
168	Ernie Whitt	.06	.05	.02
169	Cecil Cooper	.08	.06	.03
170	Mike Pagliarulo	.08	.06	.03
171	Pat Sheridan	.04	.03	.02
172	Chris Bando	.04	.03	.02
173	Lee Lacy	.04	.03	.02
174	Steve Lombardozzi	.04	.03	.02
175	Mike Greenwell	.12	.08	.04
176	Greg Minton	.04	.03	.02
177	Moose Haas	.04	.03	.02
178	Mike Kingery	.04	.03	.02
179	Greg Harris	.04	.03	.02
180	Bo Jackson	.30	.20	.10
181	Carmelo Martinez	.06	.05	.02
182	Alex Trevino	.04	.03	.02
183	Ron Oester	.04	.03	.02
184	Danny Darwin	.04	.03	.02
185	Mike Krukow	.06	.05	.02
186	Rafael Palmeiro	.40	.25	.15
187	Tim Burke	.04	.03	.02
188	Roger McDowell	.08	.06	.03
189	Garry Templeton	.06	.05	.02
190	Terry Pendleton	.12	.08	.04
191	Larry Parrish	.06	.05	.02
192	Rey Quinones	.04	.03	.02
193	Joaquin Andujar	.06	.05	.02
194	Tom Brunansky	.08	.06	.03
195	Donnie Moore	.04	.03	.02
196	Dan Pasqua	.08	.06	.03
197	Jim Gantner	.04	.03	.02
198	Mark Eichhorn	.06	.05	.02
199	John Grubb	.04	.03	.02
200	*Bill Ripken*	.08	.06	.03
201	*Sam Horn*	.08	.06	.03
202	Todd Worrell	.08	.06	.03
203	Terry Leach	.04	.03	.02
204	Garth Iorg	.04	.03	.02
205	Brian Dayett	.04	.03	.02
206	Bo Diaz	.06	.05	.02
207	Craig Reynolds	.04	.03	.02
208	Brian Holton	.08	.06	.03
209	Marvelle Wynne (Marvell)	.04	.03	.02
210	Dave Concepcion	.06	.05	.02
211	Mike Davis	.06	.05	.02
212	Devon White	.15	.11	.06
213	Mickey Brantley	.04	.03	.02
214	Greg Gagne	.04	.03	.02
215	Oddibe McDowell	.06	.05	.02
216	Jimmy Key	.08	.06	.03
217	Dave Bergman	.04	.03	.02
218	Calvin Schiraldi	.04	.03	.02
219	Larry Sheets	.06	.05	.02
220	Mike Easler	.06	.05	.02
221	Kurt Stillwell	.08	.06	.03
222	*Chuck Jackson*	.06	.05	.02
223	Dave Martinez	.08	.06	.03
224	Tim Leary	.06	.05	.02
225	Steve Garvey	.12	.08	.04
226	Greg Mathews	.06	.05	.02
227	Doug Sisk	.04	.03	.02
228	Dave Henderson	.08	.06	.03
229	Jimmy Dwyer	.04	.03	.02
230	Larry Owen	.04	.03	.02
231	Andre Thornton	.06	.05	.02
232	Mark Salas	.04	.03	.02
233	Tom Brookens	.04	.03	.02
234	Greg Brock	.06	.05	.02
235	Rance Mulliniks	.04	.03	.02
236	Bob Brower	.06	.05	.02
237	Joe Niekro	.06	.05	.02
238	Scott Bankhead	.04	.03	.02
239	Doug DeCinces	.06	.05	.02
240	Tommy John	.12	.09	.05
241	Rich Gedman	.06	.05	.02
242	Ted Power	.04	.03	.02
243	*Dave Meads*	.12	.09	.05
244	Jim Sundberg	.06	.05	.02
245	Ken Oberkfell	.04	.03	.02
246	Jimmy Jones	.08	.06	.03
247	Ken Landreaux	.04	.03	.02
248	Jose Oquendo	.04	.03	.02
249	*John Mitchell*	.06	.05	.02
250	Don Baylor	.08	.06	.03
251	Scott Fletcher	.06	.05	.02
252	Al Newman	.04	.03	.02
253	Carney Lansford	.08	.06	.03
254	Johnny Ray	.06	.05	.02
255	Gary Pettis	.04	.03	.02
256	Ken Phelps	.06	.05	.02
257	Rick Leach	.04	.03	.02
258	Tim Stoddard	.04	.03	.02
259	Ed Romero	.04	.03	.02
260	Sid Bream	.06	.05	.02
261a	Tom Neidenfuer (incorrect spelling)	.25	.20	.10
261b	Tom Niedenfuer (correct spelling)	.06	.05	.02
262	Rick Dempsey	.06	.05	.02
263	Lonnie Smith	.06	.05	.02
264	Bob Forsch	.06	.05	.02
265	Barry Bonds	.60	.45	.25
266	Willie Randolph	.06	.05	.02
267	Mike Ramsey	.04	.03	.02
268	Don Slaught	.04	.03	.02
269	Mickey Tettleton	.10	.08	.04
270	Jerry Reuss	.06	.05	.02
271	Marc Sullivan	.04	.03	.02
272	Jim Morrison	.04	.03	.02
273	Steve Balboni	.06	.05	.02
274	Dick Schofield	.04	.03	.02
275	John Tudor	.08	.06	.03
276	*Gene Larkin*	.15	.11	.06
277	Harold Reynolds	.06	.05	.02
278	Jerry Browne	.06	.05	.02
279	Willie Upshaw	.06	.05	.02
280	Ted Higuera	.08	.06	.03
281	Terry McGriff	.04	.03	.02
282	Terry Puhl	.04	.03	.02
283	*Mark Wasinger*	.06	.05	.02
284	Luis Salazar	.04	.03	.02
285	Ted Simmons	.08	.06	.03
286	John Shelby	.04	.03	.02
287	*John Smiley*	.20	.15	.08
288	Curt Ford	.04	.03	.02
289	Steve Crawford	.04	.03	.02
290	Dan Quisenberry	.06	.05	.02
291	Alan Wiggins	.04	.03	.02
292	Randy Bush	.04	.03	.02
293	John Candelaria	.06	.05	.02
294	Tony Phillips	.04	.03	.02
295	Mike Morgan	.04	.03	.02
296	Bill Wegman	.04	.03	.02
297a	Terry Franconia (incorrect spelling)	.25	.20	.10
297b	Terry Francona (correct spelling)	.06	.05	.02
298	Mickey Hatcher	.04	.03	.02
299	Andres Thomas	.06	.05	.02
300	Bob Stanley	.04	.03	.02
301	*Alfredo Pedrique*	.06	.05	.02
302	Jim Lindeman	.06	.05	.02
303	Wally Backman	.06	.05	.02
304	Paul O'Neill	.06	.05	.02
305	Hubie Brooks	.08	.06	.03
306	Steve Buechele	.04	.03	.02
307	Bobby Thigpen	.08	.06	.03
308	George Hendrick	.06	.05	.02
309	John Moses	.04	.03	.02
310	Ron Guidry	.12	.09	.05
311	Bill Schroeder	.04	.03	.02
312	*Jose Nunez*	.06	.05	.02
313	Bud Black	.04	.03	.02
314	Joe Sambito	.04	.03	.02
315	Scott McGregor	.06	.05	.02
316	Rafael Santana	.04	.03	.02
317	Frank Williams	.04	.03	.02
318	Mike Fitzgerald	.04	.03	.02
319	Rick Mahler	.04	.03	.02
320	Jim Gott	.04	.03	.02
321	Mariano Duncan	.04	.03	.02
322	Jose Guzman	.06	.05	.02
323	Lee Guetterman	.04	.03	.02
324	Dan Gladden	.04	.03	.02
325	Gary Carter	.10	.08	.04
326	Tracy Jones	.10	.08	.04
327	Floyd Youmans	.04	.03	.02
328	Bill Dawley	.04	.03	.02
329	*Paul Noce*	.06	.05	.02
330	Angel Salazar	.04	.03	.02
331	Goose Gossage	.12	.09	.05
332	George Frazier	.04	.03	.02
333	Ruppert Jones	.04	.03	.02
334	Billy Jo Robidoux	.04	.03	.02
335	Mike Scott	.10	.08	.04
336	Randy Myers	.10	.08	.04
337	Bob Sebra	.04	.03	.02
338	Eric Show	.06	.05	.02
339	Mitch Williams	.06	.05	.02
340	Paul Molitor	.20	.15	.08
341	Gus Polidor	.04	.03	.02
342	Steve Trout	.04	.03	.02
343	Jerry Don Gleaton	.04	.03	.02
344	Bob Knepper	.06	.05	.02
345	Mitch Webster	.06	.05	.02
346	John Morris	.04	.03	.02
347	Andy Hawkins	.04	.03	.02
348	Dave Leiper	.04	.03	.02
349	Ernest Riles	.04	.03	.02
350	Dwight Gooden	.10	.08	.04
351	Dave Righetti	.12	.09	.05
352	Pat Dodson	.04	.03	.02
353	John Habyan	.04	.03	.02
354	Jim Deshaies	.06	.05	.02
355	Butch Wynegar	.04	.03	.02
356	Bryn Smith	.04	.03	.02
357	Matt Young	.04	.03	.02
358	*Tom Pagnozzi*	.10	.08	.04
359	Floyd Rayford	.04	.03	.02
360	Darryl Strawberry	.20	.15	.08
361	Sal Butera	.04	.03	.02
362	Domingo Ramos	.04	.03	.02
363	Chris Brown	.06	.05	.02
364	Jose Gonzalez	.04	.03	.02
365	Dave Smith	.06	.05	.02
366	Andy McGaffigan	.04	.03	.02
367	Stan Javier	.04	.03	.02
368	Henry Cotto	.04	.03	.02
369	Mike Birkbeck	.06	.05	.02
370	Len Dykstra	.15	.11	.06
371	Dave Collins	.06	.05	.02
372	Spike Owen	.04	.03	.02
373	Geno Petralli	.04	.03	.02
374	Ron Karkovice	.04	.03	.02
375	Shane Rawley	.06	.05	.02
376	*DeWayne Buice*	.06	.05	.02
377	*Bill Pecota*	.06	.05	.02
378	Leon Durham	.06	.05	.02
379	Ed Olwine	.04	.03	.02
380	Bruce Hurst	.08	.06	.03
381	Bob McClure	.04	.03	.02
382	Mark Thurmond	.04	.03	.02
383	Buddy Biancalana	.04	.03	.02
384	Tim Conroy	.04	.03	.02
385	Tony Gwynn	.25	.20	.10
386	Greg Gross	.04	.03	.02
387	*Barry Lyons*	.06	.05	.02
388	Mike Felder	.04	.03	.02
389	Pat Clements	.04	.03	.02
390	Ken Griffey	.06	.05	.02
391	Mark Davis	.04	.03	.02
392	Jose Rijo	.06	.05	.02
393	Mike Young	.04	.03	.02
394	Willie Fraser	.06	.05	.02
395	Dion James	.06	.05	.02
396	*Steve Shields*	.06	.05	.02
397	Randy St. Claire	.04	.03	.02
398	Danny Jackson	.12	.09	.05
399	Cecil Fielder	.20	.15	.08
400	Keith Hernandez	.15	.11	.06
401	Don Carman	.06	.05	.02
402	*Chuck Crim*	.08	.06	.03
403	Rob Woodward	.04	.03	.02
404	Junior Ortiz	.04	.03	.02
405	Glenn Wilson	.06	.05	.02
406	Ken Howell	.04	.03	.02
407	Jeff Kunkel	.04	.03	.02
408	Jeff Reed	.04	.03	.02
409	Chris James	.10	.08	.04
410	Zane Smith	.06	.05	.02
411	Ken Dixon	.04	.03	.02
412	Ricky Horton	.06	.05	.02
413	Frank DiPino	.04	.03	.02
414	*Shane Mack*	.25	.20	.10
415	Danny Cox	.06	.05	.02
416	Andy Van Slyke	.12	.08	.04
417	Danny Heep	.04	.03	.02
418	John Cangelosi	.04	.03	.02
419a	John Christiansen (incorrect spelling)	.25	.20	.10
419b	John Christensen (correct spelling)	.06	.05	.02
420	*Joey Cora*	.12	.09	.05
421	Mike LaValliere	.06	.05	.02
422	Kelly Gruber	.08	.06	.03
423	Bruce Benedict	.04	.03	.02
424	Len Matuszek	.04	.03	.02
425	Kent Tekulve	.06	.05	.02
426	Rafael Ramirez	.04	.03	.02
427	Mike Flanagan	.06	.05	.02
428	Mike Gallego	.04	.03	.02
429	Juan Castillo	.04	.03	.02
430	Neal Heaton	.04	.03	.02
431	Phil Garner	.04	.03	.02
432	*Mike Dunne*	.12	.09	.05
433	Wallace Johnson	.04	.03	.02
434	Jack O'Connor	.04	.03	.02
435	Steve Jeltz	.04	.03	.02
436	*Donnell Nixon*	.06	.05	.02
437	Jack Lazorko	.04	.03	.02
438	*Keith Comstock*	.06	.05	.02
439	Jeff Robinson	.04	.03	.02
440	Graig Nettles	.08	.06	.03
441	Mel Hall	.06	.05	.02
442	*Gerald Young*	.08	.06	.03
443	Gary Redus	.04	.03	.02
444	Charlie Moore	.04	.03	.02
445	Bill Madlock	.08	.06	.03
446	Mark Clear	.04	.03	.02
447	Greg Booker	.04	.03	.02
448	Rick Schu	.04	.03	.02
449	Ron Kittle	.06	.05	.02

450	Dale Murphy	.10	.08	.04
451	Bob Dernier	.04	.03	.02
452	Dale Mohorcic	.06	.05	.02
453	Rafael Belliard	.04	.03	.02
454	Charlie Puleo	.04	.03	.02
455	Dwayne Murphy	.06	.05	.02
456	Jim Eisenreich	.04	.03	.02
457	David Palmer	.04	.03	.02
458	Dave Stewart	.08	.06	.03
459	Pascual Perez	.06	.05	.02
460	Glenn Davis	.12	.09	.05
461	Dan Petry	.06	.05	.02
462	Jim Winn	.04	.03	.02
463	Darrell Miller	.04	.03	.02
464	Mike Moore	.04	.03	.02
465	Mike LaCoss	.04	.03	.02
466	Steve Farr	.04	.03	.02
467	Jerry Mumphrey	.04	.03	.02
468	Kevin Gross	.06	.05	.02
469	Bruce Bochy	.04	.03	.02
470	Orel Hershiser	.08	.06	.03
471	Eric King	.06	.05	.02
472	*Ellis Burks*	.30	.20	.10
473	Darren Daulton	.20	.15	.08
474	Mookie Wilson	.06	.05	.02
475	Frank Viola	.12	.09	.05
476	Ron Robinson	.04	.03	.02
477	Bob Melvin	.04	.03	.02
478	Jeff Musselman	.06	.05	.02
479	Charlie Kerfeld	.04	.03	.02
480	Richard Dotson	.06	.05	.02
481	Kevin Mitchell	.15	.11	.06
482	Gary Roenicke	.04	.03	.02
483	Tim Flannery	.04	.03	.02
484	Rich Yett	.04	.03	.02
485	Pete Incaviglia	.12	.09	.05
486	Rick Cerone	.04	.03	.02
487	Tony Armas	.06	.05	.02
488	Jerry Reed	.04	.03	.02
489	Davey Lopes	.06	.05	.02
490	Frank Tanana	.06	.05	.02
491	Mike Loynd	.04	.03	.02
492	Bruce Ruffin	.06	.05	.02
493	Chris Speier	.04	.03	.02
494	Tom Hume	.04	.03	.02
495	Jesse Orosco	.06	.05	.02
496	*Robby Wine, Jr.*	.06	.05	.02
497	*Jeff Montgomery*	.60	.40	.20
498	Jeff Dedmon	.04	.03	.02
499	Luis Aguayo	.04	.03	.02
500	Reggie Jackson (1968-75)	.20	.15	.08
501	Reggie Jackson (1976)	.20	.15	.08
502	Reggie Jackson (1977-81)	.20	.15	.08
503	Reggie Jackson (1982-86)	.20	.15	.08
504	Reggie Jackson (1987)	.20	.15	.08
505	Billy Hatcher	.06	.05	.02
506	Ed Lynch	.04	.03	.02
507	Willie Hernandez	.06	.05	.02
508	Jose DeLeon	.06	.05	.02
509	Joel Youngblood	.04	.03	.02
510	Bob Welch	.08	.06	.03
511	Steve Ontiveros	.04	.03	.02
512	Randy Ready	.04	.03	.02
513	Juan Nieves	.06	.05	.02
514	Jeff Russell	.04	.03	.02
515	Von Hayes	.06	.05	.02
516	Mark Gubicza	.10	.08	.04
517	Ken Dayley	.04	.03	.02
518	Don Aase	.04	.03	.02
519	Rick Reuschel	.08	.06	.03
520	*Mike Henneman*	.25	.20	.10
521	Rick Aguilera	.04	.03	.02
522	Jay Howell	.06	.05	.02
523	Ed Correa	.04	.03	.02
524	Manny Trillo	.06	.05	.02
525	Kirk Gibson	.15	.11	.06
526	*Wally Ritchie*	.06	.05	.02
527	Al Nipper	.04	.03	.02
528	Atlee Hammaker	.04	.03	.02
529	Shawon Dunston	.08	.06	.03
530	Jim Clancy	.06	.05	.02
531	Tom Paciorek	.04	.03	.02
532	Joel Skinner	.04	.03	.02
533	Scott Garrelts	.04	.03	.02
534	Tom O'Malley	.04	.03	.02
535	John Franco	.08	.06	.03
536	*Paul Kilgus*	.08	.06	.03
537	Darrell Porter	.06	.05	.02
538	Walt Terrell	.06	.05	.02
539	*Bill Long*	.06	.05	.02
540	George Bell	.12	.08	.04
541	Jeff Sellers	.06	.05	.02
542	*Joe Boever*	.08	.06	.03
543	Steve Howe	.06	.05	.02
544	Scott Sanderson	.04	.03	.02
545	Jack Morris	.10	.08	.04
546	*Todd Benzinger*	.20	.15	.08
547	Steve Henderson	.04	.03	.02
548	Eddie Milner	.04	.03	.02
549	*Jeff Robinson*	.10	.08	.04
550	Cal Ripken, Jr.	.40	.30	.15
551	Jody Davis	.06	.05	.02
552	Kirk McCaskill	.06	.05	.02
553	Craig Lefferts	.04	.03	.02
554	Darnell Coles	.06	.05	.02
555	Phil Niekro	.15	.11	.06
556	Mike Aldrete	.06	.05	.02
557	Pat Perry	.04	.03	.02
558	Juan Agosto	.04	.03	.02
559	Rob Murphy	.06	.05	.02
560	Dennis Rasmussen	.08	.06	.03
561	Manny Lee	.04	.03	.02
562	*Jeff Blauser*	.40	.25	.15
563	Bob Ojeda	.06	.05	.02
564	Dave Dravecky	.06	.05	.02
565	Gene Garber	.04	.03	.02
566	Ron Roenicke	.04	.03	.02
567	*Tommy Hinzo*	.06	.05	.02
568	*Eric Nolte*	.06	.05	.02
569	Ed Hearn	.04	.03	.02
570	*Mark Davidson*	.08	.06	.03
571	*Jim Walewander*	.06	.05	.02
572	Donnie Hill	.04	.03	.02
573	Jamie Moyer	.06	.05	.02
574	Ken Schrom	.04	.03	.02
575	Nolan Ryan	.60	.45	.25
576	Jim Acker	.04	.03	.02
577	Jamie Quirk	.04	.03	.02
578	*Jay Aldrich*	.06	.05	.02
579	Claudell Washington	.06	.05	.02
580	Jeff Leonard	.06	.05	.02
581	Carmen Castillo	.04	.03	.02
582	Daryl Boston	.04	.03	.02
583	*Jeff DeWillis*	.06	.05	.02
584	*John Marzano*	.08	.06	.03
585	Bill Gullickson	.06	.05	.02
586	Andy Allanson	.08	.06	.03
587	Lee Tunnell	.04	.03	.02
588	Gene Nelson	.04	.03	.02
589	Dave LaPoint	.04	.03	.02
590	Harold Baines	.10	.08	.04
591	Bill Buckner	.08	.06	.03
592	Carlton Fisk	.20	.15	.08
593	Rick Manning	.04	.03	.02
594	*Doug Jones*	.20	.15	.08
595	Tom Candiotti	.04	.03	.02
596	Steve Lake	.04	.03	.02
597	*Jose Lind*	.15	.11	.06
598	*Ross Jones*	.06	.05	.02
599	Gary Matthews	.06	.05	.02
600	Fernando Valezuela	.08	.06	.03
601	Dennis Martinez	.06	.05	.02
602	*Les Lancaster*	.15	.11	.06
603	Ozzie Guillen	.06	.05	.02
604	Tony Bernazard	.04	.03	.02
605	Chili Davis	.06	.05	.02
606	Roy Smalley	.04	.03	.02
607	Ivan Calderon	.08	.06	.03
608	Jay Tibbs	.04	.03	.02
609	Guy Hoffman	.04	.03	.02
610	Doyle Alexander	.06	.05	.02
611	Mike Bielecki	.04	.03	.02
612	*Shawn Hillegas*	.06	.05	.02
613	Keith Atherton	.04	.03	.02
614	Eric Plunk	.04	.03	.02
615	Sid Fernandez	.08	.06	.03
616	Dennis Lamp	.04	.03	.02
617	Dave Engle	.04	.03	.02
618	Harry Spilman	.04	.03	.02
619	Don Robinson	.06	.05	.02
620	*John Farrell*	.08	.06	.03
621	*Nelson Liriano*	.06	.05	.02
622	Floyd Bannister	.06	.05	.02
623	*Randy Milligan*	.25	.15	.08
624	*Kevin Elster*	.06	.05	.02
625	*Jody Reed*	.25	.15	.08
626	*Shawn Abner*	.08	.06	.03
627	*Kirt Manwaring*	.15	.11	.06
628	*Pete Stanicek*	.08	.06	.03
629	*Rob Ducey*	.08	.06	.03
630	Steve Kiefer	.04	.03	.02
631	*Gary Thurman*	.08	.06	.03
632	*Darrel Akerfelds*	.12	.09	.05
633	Dave Clark	.06	.05	.02
634	*Roberto Kelly*	.60	.40	.20
635	*Keith Hughes*	.08	.06	.03
636	*John Davis*	.08	.06	.03
637	*Mike Devereaux*	.80	.60	.30
638	*Tom Glavine*	2.00	1.50	.80
639	*Keith Miller*	.20	.15	.08
640	*Chris Gwynn*	.20	.15	.08
641	*Tim Crews*	.08	.06	.03
642	*Mackey Sasser*	.08	.06	.03
643	*Vicente Palacios*	.08	.06	.03
644	Kevin Romine	.06	.05	.02
645	*Gregg Jefferies*	2.00	1.50	.80
646	*Jeff Treadway*	.10	.08	.04
647	*Ron Gant*	1.50	.90	.50
648	Rookie Sluggers (Mark McGwire, Matt Nokes)	.20	.15	.08
649	Speed and Power (Eric Davis, Tim Raines)	.25	.20	.10
650	Game Breakers (Jack Clark, Don Mattingly)	.20	.15	.08
651	Super Shortstops (Tony Fernandez, Cal Ripken, Jr., Alan Trammell)	.20	.15	.08
652	Vince Coleman (Highlight)	.08	.06	.03
653	Kirby Puckett (Highlight)	.20	.15	.08
654	Benito Santiago (Highlight)	.10	.08	.04
655	Juan Nieves (Highlight)	.06	.05	.02
656	Steve Bedrosian (Highlight)	.06	.05	.02
657	Mike Schmidt (Highlight)	.20	.15	.08
658	Don Mattingly (Highlight)	.30	.25	.12
659	Mark McGwire (Highlight)	.15	.11	.06
660	Paul Molitor (Highlight)	.15	.11	.06

1988 Score Box Panels

This 18-card set, produced by Major League Marketing and manufactured by Optigraphics, is the premiere box-bottom set issued under the Score trademark. The set features 1987 major league All-star players in full-color action poses, framed by a white border. A "1987 All-Star" banner (red or purple) curves above an orange player name block beneath the player photo. Card backs are printed in red, blue, gold and black and carry the card number,

player name and position and league logo. Six colorful "Great Moments in Baseball" trivia cards are also included in this set. Each trivia card highlights an historical event at a famous ballpark.

		MT	NR MT	EX
Complete Panel Set:		8.00	6.00	3.25
Complete Singles Set:		3.00	2.25	1.25
Common Panel:		1.50	1.25	.60
Common Single Player:		.15	.11	.06
	Panel	1.50	1.25	.60
1	Terry Kennedy	.15	.11	.06
3	Willie Randolph	.15	.11	.06
15	Eric Davis	.40	.30	.15
	Panel	1.75	1.25	.70
3	Don Mattingly	.60	.45	.25
5	Cal Ripken, Jr.	.75	.60	.30
11	Jack Clark	.15	.11	.06
	Panel	2.00	1.50	.80
4	Wade Boggs	.50	.40	.20
9	Bret Saberhagen	.20	.15	.08
12	Ryne Sandberg	.75	.60	.30
	Panel	1.75	1.25	.60
6	George Bell	.25	.20	.10
13	Mike Schmidt	.60	.45	.25
18	Mike Scott	.15	.11	.06
	Panel	1.75	1.50	.80
7	Rickey Henderson	.60	.45	.25
16	Andre Dawson	.25	.20	.10
17	Darryl Strawberry	.20	.15	.08
	Panel	2.00	1.25	.60
8	Dave Winfield	.40	.30	.15
10	Gary Carter	.20	.15	.08
14	Ozzie Smith	.35	.25	.14

1988 Score Traded

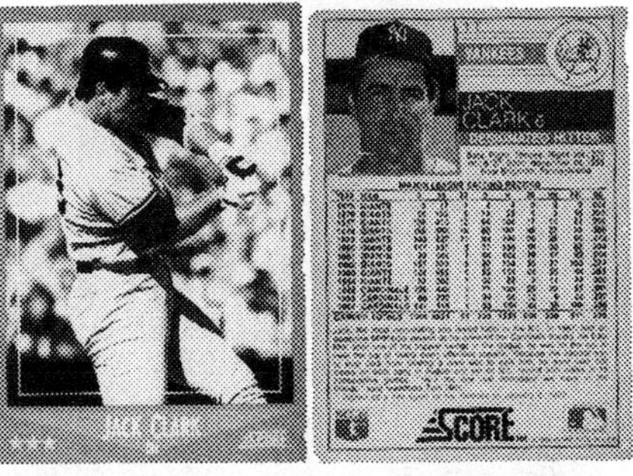

This 110-card set featuring new rookies and traded veterans is similar in design to the 1988 Score set, except for a change in border color. Individual standard-size player cards (2-1/2" by 3-1/2") feature a bright orange border framing full-figure action photos highlighted by a thin white outline. The player name (in white) is centered in the bottom margin, flanked by three yellow stars lower left and a yellow Score logo lower right. The backs carry full-color player close-ups on a cream-colored background, followed by card number, team name and logo, player personal information and a purple stats chart that lists year-by-year and major league totals. A brief player profile follows the stats chart and, on some cards, information is included about the player's trade or acquisition. The update set also includes 10 Magic Motion 3-D trivia cards.

		MT	NR MT	EX
Complete Set (110):		100.00	75.00	40.00
Common Player:		.08	.06	.03
1T	Jack Clark	.10	.08	.04
2T	Danny Jackson	.10	.08	.04
3T	Brett Butler	.25	.15	.08
4T	Kurt Stillwell	.12	.09	.05
5T	Tom Brunansky	.15	.11	.06
6T	Dennis Lamp	.08	.06	.03
7T	Jose DeLeon	.10	.08	.04
8T	Tom Herr	.12	.09	.05

9T	Keith Moreland	.10	.08	.04
10T	Kirk Gibson	.20	.15	.08
11T	Bud Black	.08	.06	.03
12T	Rafael Ramirez	.08	.06	.03
13T	Luis Salazar	.08	.06	.03
14T	Goose Gossage	.15	.11	.06
15T	Bob Welch	.15	.11	.06
16T	Vance Law	.10	.08	.04
17T	Ray Knight	.10	.08	.04
18T	Dan Quisenberry	.10	.08	.04
19T	Don Slaught	.08	.06	.03
20T	Lee Smith	1.00	.70	.40
21T	Rick Cerone	.08	.06	.03
22T	Pat Tabler	.10	.08	.04
23T	Larry McWilliams	.08	.06	.03
24T	Rick Horton	.10	.08	.04
25T	Graig Nettles	.12	.09	.05
26T	Dan Petry	.10	.08	.04
27T	Joe Rijo	.50	.30	.15
28T	Chili Davis	.10	.08	.04
29T	Dickie Thon	.10	.08	.04
30T	Mackey Sasser	.25	.15	.08
31T	Mickey Tettleton	.75	.60	.30
32T	Rick Dempsey	.08	.06	.03
33T	Ron Hassey	.08	.06	.03
34T	Phil Bradley	.12	.09	.05
35T	Jay Howell	.10	.08	.04
36T	Bill Buckner	.12	.09	.05
37T	Alfredo Griffin	.10	.08	.04
38T	Gary Pettis	.08	.06	.03
39T	Calvin Schiraldi	.08	.06	.03
40T	John Candelaria	.10	.08	.04
41T	Joe Orsulak	.08	.06	.03
42T	Willie Upshaw	.10	.08	.04
43T	Herm Winningham	.08	.06	.03
44T	Ron Kittle	.12	.09	.05
45T	Bob Dernier	.08	.06	.03
46T	Steve Balboni	.10	.08	.04
47T	Steve Shields	.08	.06	.03
48T	Henry Cotto	.08	.06	.03
49T	Dave Henderson	.10	.08	.04
50T	Dave Parker	.15	.11	.06
51T	Mike Young	.08	.06	.03
52T	Mark Salas	.08	.06	.03
53T	Mike Davis	.08	.06	.03
54T	Rafael Santana	.08	.06	.03
55T	Don Baylor	.15	.11	.06
56T	Dan Pasqua	.12	.09	.05
57T	Ernest Riles	.08	.06	.03
58T	Glenn Hubbard	.08	.06	.03
59T	Mike Smithson	.08	.06	.03
60T	Richard Dotson	.10	.08	.04
61T	Jerry Reuss	.10	.08	.04
62T	Mike Jackson	.10	.08	.04
63T	Floyd Bannister	.10	.08	.04
64T	Jesse Orosco	.10	.08	.04
65T	Larry Parrish	.10	.08	.04
66T	Jeff Bittiger (FC)	.10	.08	.04
67T	Ray Hayward (FC)	.10	.08	.04
68T	Ricky Jordan (FC)	.10	.08	.04
69T	Tommy Gregg (FC)	.12	.09	.05
70T	Brady Anderson (FC)	5.00	4.50	2.50
71T	Jeff Montgomery	4.00	1.50	.80
72T	Darryl Hamilton (FC)	3.00	2.25	1.25
73T	Cecil Espy (FC)	.10	.08	.04
74T	Greg Briley (FC)	.50	.40	.20
75T	Joey Meyer (FC)	.10	.08	.04
76T	Mike Macfarlane (FC)	.20	.15	.08
77T	Oswald Peraza (FC)	.10	.08	.04
78T	Jack Armstrong (FC)	.20	.15	.08
79T	Don Heinkel (FC)	.10	.08	.04
80T	Mark Grace (FC)	15.00	11.00	6.00
81T	Steve Curry (FC)	.10	.08	.04
82T	Damon Berryhill (FC)	.20	.15	.08
83T	Steve Ellsworth (FC)	.10	.08	.04
84T	Pete Smith (FC)	.20	.15	.08
85T	Jack McDowell	15.00	11.00	6.00
86T	Rob Dibble (FC)	1.50	1.25	.60
87T	Brian Harvey (FC)	6.00	3.00	1.50
88T	John Dopson (FC)	.25	.20	.10
89T	Dave Gallagher (FC)	.25	.20	.10
90T	Todd Stottlemyre (FC)	1.50	1.25	.60
91T	Mike Schooler (FC)	.20	.15	.08
92T	Don Gordon (FC)	.08	.06	.03
93T	Sil Campusano (FC)	.10	.08	.04
94T	Jeff Pico (FC)	.10	.08	.04
95T	Jay Buhner (FC)	7.00	3.00	1.50
96T	Nelson Santovenia (FC)	.10	.08	.04
97T	Al Leiter (FC)	.10	.08	.04
98T	Luis Alicea (FC)	.20	.15	.08
99T	Pat Borders (FC)	.75	.60	.30
100T	Chris Sabo (FC)	3.00	2.25	1.25
101T	Tim Belcher (FC)	.70	.50	.30
102T	Walt Weiss (FC)	.80	.60	.30
103T	Craig Biggio (FC)	7.50	5.50	3.00
104T	Don August (FC)	.10	.08	.04
105T	Roberto Alomar (FC)	55.00	41.00	22.00
106T	Todd Burns (FC)	.20	.15	.08
107T	John Costello (FC)	.20	.15	.08
108T	Melido Perez (FC)	1.00	.70	.40
109T	Darrin Jackson (FC)	2.00	1.50	.80
110T	Orestes Destrade (FC)	3.00	2.25	1.25

1988 Score Young Superstar Series I

This 40-card standard-size set (2-1/2" by 3-1/2" cards) from Optigraphics was divided into five separate 8-card sets. Similar to the company's regular issue, these cards are distinguished by excellent full-color photography on both front and back. The glossy player photos, with team logo in the lower

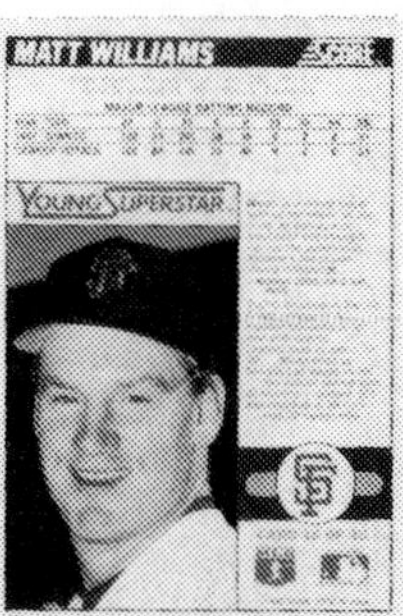

right corner, are centered on a white background and framed by a vivid blue and green border. A player name banner beneath the photo includes the name, position and uniform number. The card backs feature ful-color player closeups beneath a hot pink player name/Score logo banner. Hot pink also frames the personal stats (in green), career stats (in black) and career biography (in blue). The backs also include quotes from well-known baseball authorities discussing player performance. This set was distributed via a write-in offer printed on 1988 Score 17-card package wrappers.

		MT	NR MT	EX
Complete Set (40):		8.00	6.00	3.25
Common Player:		.10	.08	.04
1	Mark McGwire	.70	.50	.30
2	Benito Santiago	.30	.25	.12
3	Sam Horn	.10	.08	.04
4	Chris Bosio	.10	.08	.04
5	Matt Nokes	.15	.11	.06
6	Ken Williams	.10	.08	.04
7	Dion James	.10	.08	.04
8	B.J. Surhoff	.15	.11	.06
9	Joe Margrane	.20	.15	.08
10	Kevin Seitzer	.10	.08	.04
11	Stanley Jefferson	.10	.08	.04
12	Devon White	.30	.25	.12
13	Nelson Liriano	.10	.08	.04
14	Chris James	.10	.08	.04
15	Mike Henneman	.15	.11	.06
16	Terry Steinbach	.20	.15	.08
17	John Kruk	.25	.20	.10
18	Matt Williams	.60	.45	.25
19	Kelly Downs	.10	.08	.04
20	Bill Ripken	.10	.08	.04
21	Ozzie Guillen	.10	.08	.04
22	Luis Polonia	.10	.08	.04
23	Dave Magadan	.40	.30	.15
24	Mike Greenwell	.50	.40	.20
25	Will Clark	1.00	.70	.40
26	Mike Dunne	.10	.08	.04
27	Wally Joyner	.50	.40	.20
28	Robby Thompson	.30	.25	.12
29	Ken Caminiti	.20	.15	.08
30	Jose Canseco	1.00	.70	.40
31	Todd Benzinger	.30	.25	.12
32	Pete Incaviglia	.20	.15	.08
33	John Farrell	.10	.08	.04
34	Casey Candaele	.10	.08	.04
35	Mike Aldrete	.10	.08	.04
36	Ruben Sierra	.40	.30	.15
37	Ellis Burks	.40	.30	.15
38	Tracy Jones	.10	.08	.04
39	Kal Daniels	.10	.08	.04
40	Cory Snyder	.10	.08	.04

1988 Score Young Superstar Series II

This set of 40 standard-size cards (2-1/2" by 3-1/2") and five Magic trivia cards is part of a double series issued by Score. Each series is divided into five smaller sets of eight baseball cards and one trivia card. The design on both series is similar, except for border color. Series I has blue and green borders. Series II has red and blue borders framing full-color player photos with the player name and team logo printed beneath the photo. The card backs carry full-color head shots and stats in a variety of colors. Young Superstar series were offered via a write-in offer on the backs of 1988 Score card package wrappers. For each 8-card subset, collectors were instructed to send two Score wrappers and $1. Complete sets were offered by a number of hobby dealers nationwide.

		MT	NR MT	EX
Complete Set (40):		7.00	5.25	2.75
Common Player:		.10	.08	.04
1	Don Mattingly	1.00	.70	.40
2	Glenn Braggs	.15	.11	.06
3	Dwight Gooden	.30	.25	.12
4	Jose Lind	.10	.08	.04
5	Danny Tartabull	.30	.25	.12
6	Tony Fernandez	.15	.11	.06
7	Julio Franco	.15	.11	.06
8	Andres Galarraga	.15	.11	.06
9	Bobby Bonilla	.40	.30	.15
10	Eric Davis	.20	.15	.08
11	Gerald Young	.10	.08	.04
12	Barry Bonds	.75	.60	.30
13	Jerry Browne	.10	.08	.04
14	Jeff Blauser	.10	.08	.04
15	Mickey Brantley	.10	.08	.04
16	Floyd Youmans	.10	.08	.04
17	Bret Saberhagen	.25	.20	.10
18	Shawon Dunston	.20	.15	.08
19	Len Dykstra	.35	.25	.14
20	Darryl Strawberry	.20	.15	.08
21	Rick Aguilera	.10	.08	.04
22	Ivan Calderon	.10	.08	.04
23	Roger Clemens	.50	.40	.20
24	Vince Coleman	.30	.25	.12
25	Gary Thurman	.10	.08	.04
26	Jeff Treadway	.10	.08	.04
27	Oddibe McDowell	.10	.08	.04
28	Fred McGriff	.50	.40	.20
29	Mark McLemore	.10	.08	.04
30	Jeff Musselman	.10	.08	.04
31	Mitch Williams	.10	.08	.04
32	Dan Plesac	.10	.08	.04
33	Juan Nieves	.10	.08	.04
34	Barry Larkin	.30	.25	.12
35	Greg Mathews	.10	.08	.04
36	Shane Mack	.20	.15	.08
37	Scott Bankhead	.10	.08	.04
38	Eric Bell	.10	.08	.04
39	Greg Swindell	.15	.11	.06
40	Kevin Elster	.10	.08	.04

1989 Score

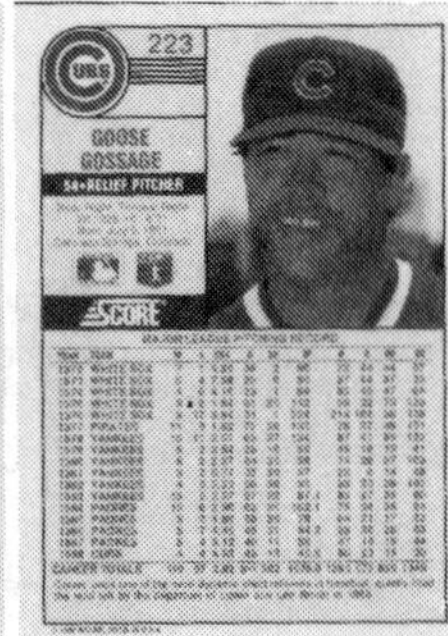

This set of 660 cards plus 56 Magic Motion trivia cards is the second annual basic issue from Score. Full-color player photos highlight 651 individual players and 9 season highlights, including the first Wrigley Field night game. Action photos are framed by thin brightly colored borders (green, cyan blue, purple, orange, red, royal blue) with a baseball diamond logo/player name beneath the photo. Full-color player close-ups (1-5/16" by 1-5/8") are printed on the pastel-colored backs, along with the card number, personal information, stats and career highlights. The cards measure 2-1/2" by 3-1/2" in size.

		MT	NR MT	EX
Complete Set (660):		15.00	11.00	6.00
Common Player:		.03	.02	.01
1	Jose Canseco	.35	.25	.14
2	Andre Dawson	.15	.11	.06
3	Mark McGwire	.30	.25	.12
4	Benny Santiago	.12	.09	.05
5	Rick Reuschel	.08	.06	.03
6	Fred McGriff	.35	.25	.14
7	Kal Daniels	.12	.09	.05
8	Gary Gaetti	.12	.09	.05
9	Ellis Burks	.08	.05	.02
10	Darryl Strawberry	.15	.11	.06
11	Julio Franco	.08	.06	.03
12	Lloyd Moseby	.06	.05	.02
13	*Jeff Pico*	.06	.05	.02
14	Johnny Ray	.06	.05	.02
15	Cal Ripken, Jr.	.40	.30	.15
16	Dick Schofield	.03	.02	.01
17	Mel Hall	.06	.05	.02
18	Bill Ripken	.06	.05	.02
19	Brook Jacoby	.08	.06	.03
20	Kirby Puckett	.35	.25	.14
21	Bill Doran	.06	.05	.02
22	Pete O'Brien	.06	.05	.02
23	Matt Nokes	.15	.11	.06
24	Brian Fisher	.06	.05	.02
25	Jack Clark	.12	.09	.05
26	Gary Pettis	.03	.02	.01
27	Dave Valle	.03	.02	.01
28	Willie Wilson	.08	.06	.03
29	Curt Young	.06	.05	.02
30	Dale Murphy	.10	.06	.03
31	Barry Larkin	.15	.10	.05
32	Dave Stewart	.08	.06	.03
33	Mike LaValliere	.06	.05	.02
34	Glen Hubbard	.03	.02	.01
35	Ryne Sandberg	.40	.30	.15
36	Tony Pena	.06	.05	.02

37	Greg Walker	.06	.05	.02
38	Von Hayes	.08	.06	.03
39	Kevin Mitchell	.08	.05	.02
40	Tim Raines	.08	.05	.02
41	Keith Hernandez	.20	.15	.08
42	Keith Moreland	.06	.05	.02
43	Ruben Sierra	.20	.12	.06
44	Chet Lemon	.06	.05	.02
45	Willie Randolph	.06	.05	.02
46	Andy Allanson	.03	.02	.01
47	Candy Maldonado	.06	.05	.02
48	Sid Bream	.06	.05	.02
49	Denny Walling	.03	.02	.01
50	Dave Winfield	.30	.25	.12
51	Alvin Davis	.10	.08	.04
52	Cory Snyder	.15	.11	.06
53	Hubie Brooks	.08	.06	.03
54	Chili Davis	.06	.05	.02
55	Kevin Seitzer	.12	.09	.05
56	Jose Uribe	.03	.02	.01
57	Tony Fernandez	.10	.08	.04
58	Tim Teufel	.03	.02	.01
59	Oddibe McDowell	.06	.05	.02
60	Les Lancaster	.06	.05	.02
61	Billy Hatcher	.06	.05	.02
62	Dan Gladden	.03	.02	.01
63	Marty Barrett	.06	.05	.02
64	Nick Esasky	.06	.05	.02
65	Wally Joyner	.08	.05	.02
66	Mike Greenwell	.08	.05	.02
67	Ken Williams	.06	.05	.02
68	Bob Horner	.08	.06	.03
69	Steve Sax	.12	.09	.05
70	Rickey Henderson	.20	.12	.06
71	Mitch Webster	.06	.05	.02
72	Rob Deer	.06	.05	.02
73	Jim Presley	.06	.05	.02
74	Albert Hall	.03	.02	.01
75a	George Brett (“"At age 33 ...")	1.00	.70	.40
75b	George Brett (“At age 35 ...")	.30	.25	.12
76	Brian Downing	.06	.05	.02
77	Dave Martinez	.06	.05	.02
78	Scott Fletcher	.06	.05	.02
79	Phil Bradley	.08	.06	.03
80	Ozzie Smith	.15	.11	.06
81	Larry Sheets	.06	.05	.02
82	Mike Aldrete	.06	.05	.02
83	Darnell Coles	.06	.05	.02
84	Len Dykstra	.12	.08	.04
85	Jim Rice	.08	.05	.02
86	Jeff Treadway	.10	.08	.04
87	Jose Lind	.08	.06	.03
88	Willie McGee	.10	.08	.04
89	Mickey Brantley	.03	.02	.01
90	Tony Gwynn	.20	.15	.08
91	R.J. Reynolds	.03	.02	.01
92	Milt Thompson	.03	.02	.01
93	Kevin McReynolds	.12	.09	.05
94	Eddie Murray	.15	.10	.05
95	Lance Parrish	.12	.09	.05
96	Ron Kittle	.06	.05	.02
97	Gerald Young	.10	.08	.04
98	Ernie Whitt	.06	.05	.02
99	Jeff Reed	.03	.02	.01
100	Don Mattingly	.20	.12	.06
101	Gerald Perry	.08	.06	.03
102	Vance Law	.06	.05	.02
103	John Shelby	.03	.02	.01
104	*Chris Sabo*	.40	.30	.15
105	Danny Tartabull	.15	.11	.06
106	Glenn Wilson	.06	.05	.02
107	Mark Davidson	.06	.05	.02
108	Dave Parker	.10	.08	.04
109	Eric Davis	.08	.05	.02
110	Alan Trammell	.15	.11	.06
111	Ozzie Virgil	.03	.02	.01
112	Frank Tanana	.06	.05	.02
113	Rafael Ramirez	.03	.02	.01
114	Dennis Martinez	.06	.05	.02
115	Jose DeLeon	.06	.05	.02
116	Bob Ojeda	.06	.05	.02
117	Doug Drabek	.06	.05	.02
118	Andy Hawkins	.03	.02	.01
119	Greg Maddux (FC)	.30	.25	.12
120	Cecil Fielder (reversed negative)	.25	.15	.08
121	Mike Scioscia	.06	.05	.02
122	Dan Petry	.06	.05	.02
123	Terry Kennedy	.06	.05	.02
124	Kelly Downs	.08	.06	.03
125	Greg Gross	.20	.15	.08
126	Fred Lynn	.10	.08	.04
127	Barry Bonds	.50	.30	.15
128	Harold Baines	.10	.08	.04
129	Doyle Alexander	.06	.05	.02
130	Kevin Elster	.08	.06	.03
131	Mike Heath	.03	.02	.01
132	Teddy Higuera	.08	.06	.03
133	Charlie Leibrandt	.06	.05	.02
134	Tim Laudner	.03	.02	.01
135a	Ray Knight (photo reversed)	.60	.45	.25
135b	Ray Knight (correct photo)	.08	.06	.03
136	Howard Johnson	.08	.06	.03
137	Terry Pendleton	.12	.08	.04
138	Andy McGaffigan	.03	.02	.01
139	Ken Oberkfell	.03	.02	.01
140	Butch Wynegar	.03	.02	.01
141	Rob Murphy	.03	.02	.01
142	*Rich Renteria* (FC)	.06	.05	.02
143	Jose Guzman	.08	.06	.03
144	Andres Galarraga	.15	.11	.06
145	Rick Horton	.06	.05	.02
146	Frank DiPino	.03	.02	.01
147	Glenn Braggs	.06	.05	.02
148	John Kruk	.12	.08	.04
149	Mike Schmidt	.35	.25	.14
150	Lee Smith	.08	.06	.03
151	Robin Yount	.30	.25	.12
152	Mark Eichhorn	.06	.05	.02
153	DeWayne Buice	.04	.03	.02
154	B.J. Surhoff	.08	.06	.03
155	Vince Coleman	.08	.06	.03
156	Tony Phillips	.03	.02	.01
157	Willie Fraser	.03	.02	.01
158	Lance McCullers	.06	.05	.02
159	Greg Gagne	.03	.02	.01
160	Jesse Barfield	.08	.06	.03
161	Mark Langston	.08	.06	.03
162	Kurt Stillwell	.06	.05	.02
163	Dion James	.03	.02	.01
164	Glenn Davis	.12	.09	.05
165	Walt Weiss	.10	.06	.03
166	Dave Concepcion	.08	.06	.03
167	Alfredo Griffin	.06	.05	.02
168	*Don Heinkel*	.03	.02	.01
169	Luis Rivera (FC)	.03	.02	.01
170	Shane Rawley	.06	.05	.02
171	Darrell Evans	.08	.06	.03
172	Robby Thompson	.06	.05	.02
173	Jody Davis	.06	.05	.02
174	Andy Van Slyke	.12	.09	.05
175	Wade Boggs	.20	.12	.06
176	Garry Templeton	.06	.05	.02
177	Gary Redus	.03	.02	.01
178	Craig Lefferts	.03	.02	.01
179	Carney Lansford	.06	.05	.02
180	Ron Darling	.10	.08	.04
181	Kirk McCaskill	.06	.05	.02
182	Tony Armas	.06	.05	.02
183	Steve Farr	.03	.02	.01
184	Tom Brunansky	.10	.08	.04
185	*Bryan Harvey*	.25	.20	.10
186	Mike Marshall	.10	.08	.04
187	Bo Diaz	.06	.05	.02
188	Willie Upshaw	.06	.05	.02
189	Mike Pagliarulo	.08	.06	.03
190	Mike Krukow	.06	.05	.02
191	Tommy Herr	.06	.05	.02
192	Jim Pankovits	.03	.02	.01
193	Dwight Evans	.10	.08	.04
194	Kelly Gruber	.03	.02	.01
195	Bobby Bonilla	.15	.10	.05
196	Wallace Johnson	.03	.02	.01
197	Dave Stieb	.08	.06	.03
198	*Pat Borders*	.25	.20	.10
199	Rafael Palmeiro	.15	.11	.06
200	Dwight Gooden	.08	.05	.02
201	Pete Incaviglia	.08	.06	.03
202	Chris James	.08	.06	.03
203	Marvell Wynne	.03	.02	.01
204	Pat Sheridan	.03	.02	.01
205	Don Baylor	.08	.06	.03
206	Paul O'Neill	.03	.02	.01
207	Pete Smith	.08	.06	.03
208	Mark McLemore	.03	.02	.01
209	Henry Cotto	.03	.02	.01
210	Kirk Gibson	.08	.05	.02
211	Claudell Washington	.06	.05	.02
212	Randy Bush	.03	.02	.01
213	Joe Carter	.25	.15	.08
214	Bill Buckner	.08	.06	.03
215	Bert Blyleven	.25	.20	.10
216	Brett Butler	.06	.05	.02
217	Lee Mazzilli	.06	.05	.02
218	Spike Owen	.03	.02	.01
219	Bill Swift	.03	.02	.01
220	Tim Wallach	.08	.06	.03
221	David Cone	.10	.06	.03
222	Don Carman	.06	.05	.02
223	Rich Gossage	.10	.08	.04
224	Bob Walk	.03	.02	.01
225	Dave Righetti	.10	.08	.04
226	Kevin Bass	.06	.05	.02
227	Kevin Gross	.06	.05	.02
228	Tim Burke	.03	.02	.01
229	Rick Mahler	.03	.02	.01
230	Lou Whitaker	.15	.11	.06
231	*Luis Alicea*	.10	.06	.03
232	Roberto Alomar	1.00	.70	.40
233	Bob Boone	.06	.05	.02
234	Dickie Thon	.03	.02	.01
235	Shawon Dunston	.08	.06	.03
236	Pete Stanicek	.08	.06	.03
237	*Craig Biggio*	.50	.40	.20
238	Dennis Boyd	.06	.05	.02
239	Tom Candiotti	.03	.02	.01
240	Gary Carter	.15	.11	.06
241	Mike Stanley	.03	.02	.01
242	Ken Phelps	.06	.05	.02
243	Chris Bosio	.03	.02	.01
244	Les Straker	.06	.05	.02
245	Dave Smith	.06	.05	.02
246	John Candelaria	.06	.05	.02
247	Joe Orsulak	.03	.02	.01
248	Storm Davis	.08	.06	.03
249	Floyd Bannister	.06	.05	.02
250	Jack Morris	.12	.09	.05
251	Bret Saberhagen	.12	.09	.05
252	Tom Niedenfuer	.06	.05	.02
253	Neal Heaton	.03	.02	.01
254	Eric Show	.06	.05	.02
255	Juan Samuel	.10	.08	.04
256	Dale Sveum	.06	.05	.02
257	Jim Gott	.03	.02	.01
258	Scott Garrelts	.03	.02	.01
259	Larry McWilliams	.03	.02	.01
260	Steve Bedrosian	.08	.06	.03
261	Jack Howell	.06	.05	.02
262	Jay Tibbs	.03	.02	.01
263	Jamie Moyer	.03	.02	.01
264	Doug Sisk	.03	.02	.01
265	Todd Worrell	.08	.06	.03
266	John Farrell	.08	.06	.03
267	Dave Collins	.06	.05	.02
268	Sid Fernandez	.08	.06	.03
269	Tom Brookens	.03	.02	.01
270	Shane Mack	.06	.05	.02
271	Paul Kilgus	.08	.06	.03
272	Chuck Crim	.03	.02	.01
273	Bob Knepper	.06	.05	.02
274	Mike Moore	.03	.02	.01
275	Guillermo Hernandez	.06	.05	.02
276	Dennis Eckersley	.10	.08	.04
277	Graig Nettles	.10	.08	.04
278	Rich Dotson	.06	.05	.02
279	Larry Herndon	.03	.02	.01
280	Gene Larkin	.08	.06	.03
281	Roger McDowell	.08	.06	.03
282	Greg Swindell	.10	.08	.04
283	Juan Agosto	.03	.02	.01
284	Jeff Robinson	.06	.05	.02
285	Mike Dunne	.08	.06	.03
286	Greg Mathews	.06	.05	.02
287	Kent Tekulve	.06	.05	.02
288	Jerry Mumphrey	.03	.02	.01
289	Jack McDowell (FC)	.40	.30	.15
290	Frank Viola	.12	.09	.05
291	Mark Gubicza	.08	.06	.03
292	Dave Schmidt	.03	.02	.01
293	Mike Henneman	.08	.06	.03
294	Jimmy Jones	.03	.02	.01
295	Charlie Hough	.06	.05	.02
296	Rafael Santana	.03	.02	.01
297	Chris Speier	.03	.02	.01
298	Mike Witt	.06	.05	.02
299	Pascual Perez	.06	.05	.02
300	Nolan Ryan	.50	.40	.20
301	Mitch Williams	.06	.05	.02
302	Mookie Wilson	.06	.05	.02
303	Mackey Sasser	.06	.05	.02
304	John Cerutti	.06	.05	.02
305	Jeff Reardon	.08	.06	.03
306	Randy Myers	.08	.06	.03
307	Greg Brock	.06	.05	.02
308	Bob Welch	.08	.06	.03
309	Jeff Robinson	.12	.09	.05
310	Harold Reynolds	.06	.05	.02
311	Jim Walewander	.03	.02	.01
312	Dave Magadan	.08	.06	.03
313	Jim Gantner	.03	.02	.01
314	Walt Terrell	.06	.05	.02
315	Wally Backman	.06	.05	.02
316	Luis Salazar	.03	.02	.01
317	Rick Rhoden	.06	.05	.02
318	Tom Henke	.06	.05	.02
319	*Mike Macfarlane*	.15	.10	.05
320	Dan Plesac	.08	.06	.03
321	Calvin Schiraldi	.03	.02	.01
322	Stan Javier	.03	.02	.01
323	Devon White	.10	.08	.04
324	Scott Bradley	.03	.02	.01
325	Bruce Hurst	.08	.06	.03
326	Manny Lee	.03	.02	.01
327	Rick Aguilera	.03	.02	.01
328	Bruce Ruffin	.03	.02	.01
329	Ed Whitson	.03	.02	.01
330	Bo Jackson	.30	.20	.10
331	Ivan Calderon	.06	.05	.02
332	Mickey Hatcher	.03	.02	.01
333	Barry Jones (FC)	.03	.02	.01
334	Ron Hassey	.03	.02	.01
335	Bill Wegman	.03	.02	.01
336	Damon Berryhill	.15	.11	.06
337	Steve Ontiverso	.03	.02	.01
338	Dan Pasqua	.08	.06	.03
339	Bill Pecota	.06	.05	.02
340	Greg Cadaret	.06	.05	.02
341	Scott Bankhead	.03	.02	.01
342	Ron Guidry	.12	.09	.05
343	Danny Heep	.03	.02	.01
344	Bob Brower	.03	.02	.01
345	Rich Gedman	.06	.05	.02
346	*Nelson Santovenia*	.06	.04	.02
347	George Bell	.08	.05	.02
348	Ted Power	.03	.02	.01
349	Mark Grant	.03	.02	.01
350a	Roger Clemens (778 wins)	3.00	2.25	1.25
350b	Roger Clemens (78 wins)	.40	.30	.15
351	Bill Long	.06	.05	.02
352	Jay Bell (FC)	.06	.05	.02
353	Steve Balboni	.06	.05	.02
354	Bob Kipper	.03	.02	.01
355	Steve Jeltz	.03	.02	.01
356	Jesse Orosco	.06	.05	.02
357	Bob Dernier	.03	.02	.01
358	Mickey Tettleton	.03	.02	.01
359	Duane Ward (FC)	.03	.02	.01
360	Darrin Jackson (FC)	.08	.06	.03
361	Rey Quinones	.03	.02	.01
362	Mark Grace (FC)	.80	.60	.30
363	Steve Lake	.03	.02	.01
364	Pat Perry	.03	.02	.01
365	Terry Steinbach	.08	.06	.03
366	Alan Ashby	.03	.02	.01
367	Jeff Montgomery	.06	.05	.02
368	Steve Buechele	.03	.02	.01
369	Chris Brown	.06	.05	.02
370	Orel Hershiser	.08	.05	.02
371	Todd Benzinger	.10	.08	.04
372	Ron Gant	.40	.30	.15
373	Paul Assenmacher (FC)	.03	.02	.01
374	Joey Meyer	.08	.06	.03
375	Neil Allen	.03	.02	.01
376	Mike Davis	.06	.05	.02
377	Jeff Parrett (FC)	.08	.06	.03
378	Jay Howell	.06	.05	.02
379	Rafael Belliard	.03	.02	.01
380	Luis Polonia	.06	.05	.02
381	Keith Atherton	.03	.02	.01
382	Kent Hrbek	.15	.11	.06
383	Bob Stanley	.03	.02	.01
384	Dave LaPoint	.06	.05	.02
385	Rance Mulliniks	.03	.02	.01
386	Melido Perez	.08	.06	.03
387	Doug Jones	.10	.08	.04

388 Steve Lyons .03 .02 .01
389 Alejandro Pena .06 .05 .02
390 Frank White .06 .05 .02
391 Pat Tabler .06 .05 .02
392 Eric Plunk (FC) .03 .02 .01
393 Mike Maddux (FC) .03 .02 .01
394 Allan Anderson (FC) .06 .05 .02
395 Bob Brenly .03 .02 .01
396 Rick Cerone .03 .02 .01
397 Scott Terry (FC) .08 .06 .03
398 Mike Jackson .06 .05 .02
399 Bobby Thigpen .08 .06 .03
400 Don Sutton .08 .05 .02
401 Cecil Espy .06 .05 .02
402 Junior Ortiz .03 .02 .01
403 Mike Smithson .03 .02 .01
404 Bud Black .03 .02 .01
405 Tom Foley .03 .02 .01
406 Andres Thomas .06 .05 .02
407 Rick Sutcliffe .08 .06 .03
408 Brian Harper .03 .02 .01
409 John Smiley .10 .08 .04
410 Juan Nieves .06 .05 .02
411 Shawn Abner .08 .06 .03
412 Wes Gardner (FC) .06 .05 .02
413 Darren Daulton .15 .10 .05
414 Juan Berenguer .03 .02 .01
415 Charles Hudson .03 .02 .01
416 Rick Honeycutt .03 .02 .01
417 Greg Booker .03 .02 .01
418 Tim Belcher .08 .06 .03
419 Don August .08 .06 .03
420 Dale Mohorcic .03 .02 .01
421 Steve Lombardozzi .03 .02 .01
422 Atlee Hammaker .03 .02 .01
423 Jerry Don Gleaton .03 .02 .01
424 Scott Bailes (FC) .03 .02 .01
425 Bruce Sutter .08 .06 .03
426 Randy Ready .03 .02 .01
427 Jerry Reed .03 .02 .01
428 Bryn Smith .03 .02 .01
429 Tim Leary .06 .05 .02
430 Mark Clear .03 .02 .01
431 Terry Leach .03 .02 .01
432 John Moses .03 .02 .01
433 Ozzie Guillen .06 .05 .02
434 Gene Nelson .03 .02 .01
435 Gary Ward .06 .05 .02
436 Luis Aguayo .03 .02 .01
437 Fernando Valenzuela .15 .11 .06
438 Jeff Russell .03 .02 .01
439 Cecilio Guante .03 .02 .01
440 Don Robinson .03 .02 .01
441 Rick Anderson (FC) .03 .02 .01
442 Tom Glavine .50 .40 .20
443 Daryl Boston .03 .02 .01
444 Joe Price .03 .02 .01
445 Stewart Cliburn .03 .02 .01
446 Manny Trillo .03 .02 .01
447 Joel Skinner .03 .02 .01
448 Charlie Puleo .03 .02 .01
449 Carlton Fisk .12 .09 .05
450 Will Clark .50 .40 .20
451 Otis Nixon .03 .02 .01
452 Rick Schu .03 .02 .01
453 Todd Stottlemyre (FC) .15 .11 .06
454 Tim Birtsas .03 .02 .01
455 *Dave Gallagher* .08 .05 .02
456 Barry Lyons .03 .02 .01
457 Fred Manrique .06 .05 .02
458 Ernest Riles .03 .02 .01
459 *Doug Jennings* (FC) .06 .04 .02
460 Joe Magrane .08 .06 .03
461 Jamie Quirk .03 .02 .01
462 *Jack Armstrong* .10 .06 .03
463 Bobby Witt .08 .06 .03
464 Keith Miller .06 .05 .02
465 *Todd Burns* .08 .06 .03
466 *John Dopson* .08 .06 .03
467 Rich Yett .03 .02 .01
468 Craig Reynolds .03 .02 .01
469 Dave Bergman .03 .02 .01
470 Rex Hudler .03 .02 .01
471 Eric King .03 .02 .01
472 Joaquin Andujar .06 .05 .02
473 *Sil Campusano* .06 .05 .02
474 Terry Mulholland (FC) .03 .02 .01
475 Mike Flanagan .06 .05 .02
476 Greg Harris .03 .02 .01
477 Tommy John .10 .08 .04
478 Dave Anderson .03 .02 .01
479 Fred Toliver .03 .02 .01
480 Jimmy Key .08 .06 .03
481 Donell Nixon .03 .02 .01
482 Mark Portugal (FC) .03 .02 .01
483 Tom Pagnozzi .06 .05 .02
484 Jeff Kunkel .03 .02 .01
485 Frank Williams .03 .02 .01
486 Jody Reed .10 .08 .04
487 Roberto Kelly .12 .08 .04
488 Shawn Hillegas .06 .05 .02
489 Jerry Reuss .06 .05 .02
490 Mark Davis .03 .02 .01
491 Jeff Sellers .03 .02 .01
492 Zane Smith .06 .05 .02
493 Al Newman (FC) .03 .02 .01
494 Mike Young .03 .02 .01
495 Larry Parrish .06 .05 .02
496 Herm Winningham .03 .02 .01
497 Carmen Castillo .03 .02 .01
498 Joe Hesketh .03 .02 .01
499 Darrell Miller .03 .02 .01
500 Mike LaCoss .03 .02 .01
501 Charlie Lea .03 .02 .01
502 Bruce Benedict .03 .02 .01
503 Chuck Finley (FC) .03 .02 .01
504 Brad Wellman (FC) .03 .02 .01
505 Tim Crews .06 .05 .02
506 Ken Gerhart .06 .05 .02
507a Brian Holton (Born: 1/25/65, Denver) .20 .15 .08
507b Brian Holton (Born: 11/29/59, McKeesport) .03 .02 .01
508 Dennis Lamp .03 .02 .01
509 Bobby Meacham .20 .15 .08
510 Tracy Jones .08 .06 .03
511 Mike Fitzgerald .03 .02 .01
512 *Jeff Bittiger* .06 .05 .02
513 Tim Flannery .03 .02 .01
514 Ray Hayward (FC) .03 .02 .01
515 Dave Leiper .03 .02 .01
516 Rod Scurry .03 .02 .01
517 Carmelo Martinez .03 .02 .01
518 Curtis Wilkerson .03 .02 .01
519 Stan Jefferson .03 .02 .01
520 Dan Quisenberry .06 .05 .02
521 Lloyd McClendon (FC) .03 .02 .01
522 Steve Trout .03 .02 .01
523 Larry Andersen .03 .02 .01
524 Don Aase .03 .02 .01
525 Bob Forsch .06 .05 .02
526 Geno Petralli .03 .02 .01
527 Angel Salazar .03 .02 .01
528 *Mike Schooler* .08 .06 .03
529 Jose Oquendo .03 .02 .01
530 Jay Buhner (FC) .15 .10 .05
531 Tom Bolton (FC) .06 .05 .02
532 Al Nipper .03 .02 .01
533 Dave Henderson .08 .06 .03
534 *John Costello* (FC) .06 .05 .02
535 Donnie Moore .03 .02 .01
536 Mike Laga .03 .02 .01
537 Mike Gallego .03 .02 .01
538 Jim Clancy .06 .05 .02
539 Joel Youngblood .03 .02 .01
540 Rick Leach .03 .02 .01
541 Kevin Romine .03 .02 .01
542 Mark Salas .03 .02 .01
543 Greg Minton .03 .02 .01
544 Dave Palmer .03 .02 .01
545 Dwayne Murphy .06 .05 .02
546 Jim Deshaies .03 .02 .01
547 Don Gordon (FC) .03 .02 .01
548 *Ricky Jordan* .10 .06 .03
549 Mike Boddicker .06 .05 .02
550 Mike Scott .10 .08 .04
551 Jeff Ballard (FC) .08 .06 .03
552a Jose Rijo (uniform number #24 on card back) .20 .15 .08
552b Jose Rijo (uniform number #27 on card back) .08 .06 .03
553 Danny Darwin .03 .02 .01
554 Tom Browning .08 .06 .03
555 Danny Jackson .12 .09 .05
556 Rick Dempsey .06 .05 .02
557 Jeffrey Leonard .06 .05 .02
558 Jeff Musselman .06 .05 .02
559 Ron Robinson .03 .02 .01
560 John Tudor .08 .06 .03
561 Don Slaught .03 .02 .01
562 Dennis Rasmussen .08 .06 .03
563 *Brady Anderson* .40 .30 .15
564 Pedro Guerrero .12 .09 .05
565 Paul Molitor .20 .12 .06
566 *Terry Clark* (FC) .06 .05 .02
567 Terry Puhl .03 .02 .01
568 Mike Campbell (FC) .08 .06 .03
569 Paul Mirabella .03 .02 .01
570 Jeff Hamilton (FC) .06 .05 .02
571 *Oswald Peraza* .08 .06 .03
572 Bob McClure .03 .02 .01
573 *Jose Bautista* (FC) .15 .11 .06
574 Alex Trevino .03 .02 .01
575 John Franco .08 .06 .03
576 *Mark Parent* (FC) .06 .05 .02
577 Nelson Liriano .06 .05 .02
578 Steve Shields .03 .02 .01
579 Odell Jones .03 .02 .01
580 Al Leiter .15 .11 .06
581 Dave Stapleton (FC) .06 .05 .02
582 1988 World Series (Jose Canseco, Kirk Gibson, Orel Hershiser, Dave Stewart) .10 .06 .03
583 Donnie Hill .03 .02 .01
584 Chuck Jackson .06 .05 .02
585 Rene Gonzales (FC) .06 .05 .02
586 Tracy Woodson (FC) .08 .06 .03
587 Jim Adduci (FC) .03 .02 .01
588 Mario Soto .06 .05 .02
589 Jeff Blauser .08 .06 .03
590 Jim Traber .06 .05 .02
591 Jon Perlman (FC) .03 .02 .01
592 Mark Williamson (FC) .06 .05 .02
593 Dave Meads .03 .02 .01
594 Jim Eisenreich .03 .02 .01
595 *Paul Gibson* (FC) .06 .05 .02
596 Mike Birkbeck .03 .02 .01
597 Terry Francona .03 .02 .01
598 Paul Zuvella (FC) .03 .02 .01
599 Franklin Stubbs .03 .02 .01
600 Gregg Jefferies .30 .25 .12
601 John Cangelosi .03 .02 .01
602 Mike Sharperson (FC) .03 .02 .01
603 Mike Diaz .06 .05 .02
604 *Gary Varsho* (FC) .06 .04 .02
605 *Terry Blocker* (FC) .08 .06 .03
606 Charlie O'Brien (FC) .03 .02 .01
607 Jim Eppard (FC) .06 .05 .02
608 John Davis .03 .02 .01
609 Ken Griffey, Sr. .08 .06 .03
610 Buddy Bell .06 .05 .02
611 Ted Simmons .08 .06 .03
612 Matt Williams .25 .15 .08
613 Danny Cox .06 .05 .02
614 Al Pedrique .03 .02 .01
615 Ron Oester .03 .02 .01
616 *John Smoltz* .60 .45 .25
617 Bob Melvin .03 .02 .01
618 *Rob Dibble* .20 .12 .06
619 Kirt Manwaring .10 .08 .04
620 Felix Fermin (FC) .06 .05 .02
621 *Doug Dascenzo* (FC) .08 .05 .02
622 *Bill Brennan* (FC) .06 .05 .02
623 *Carlos Quintana* .12 .08 .03
624 *Mike Harkey* .25 .20 .10
625 *Gary Sheffield* 1.25 .75 .50
626 *Tom Prince* (FC) .08 .06 .03
627 *Steve Searcy* (FC) .15 .11 .06
628 *Charlie Hayes* .50 .30 .15
629 *Felix Jose* .35 .20 .10
630 *Sandy Alomar* .30 .25 .12
631 *Derek Lilliquist* .15 .11 .06
632 Geronimo Berroa (FC) .06 .05 .02
633 *Luis Medina* .06 .05 .02
634 *Tom Gordon* .10 .06 .03
635 *Ramon Martinez* .60 .45 .25
636 *Craig Worthington* (FC) .08 .05 .02
637 Edgar Martinez (FC) .20 .12 .06
638 *Chad Krueter* .15 .11 .06
639 *Ron Jones* .08 .05 .02
640 *Van Snider* .06 .05 .02
641 *Lance Blankenship* .15 .11 .06
642 *Dwight Smith* .10 .08 .04
643 *Cameron Drew* .03 .02 .01
644 *Jerald Clark* .20 .12 .06
645 *Randy Johnson* .75 .50 .25
646 *Norm Charlton* .30 .25 .12
647 Todd Frohwirth (FC) .08 .06 .03
648 *Luis de los Santos* .06 .05 .02
649 *Tim Jones* (FC) .06 .05 .02
650 *Dave West* .20 .15 .08
651 *Bob Milacki* .10 .06 .03
652 1988 HL (Wrigley Field) .06 .05 .02
653 1988 HL (Orel Hershiser) .10 .08 .04
654a 1988 HL (Wade Boggs) ("...sixth consecutive seaason..." on back) 3.00 2.25 1.25
654b 1988 HL (Wade Boggs) ("season" corrected) .10 .06 .03
655 1988 HL (Jose Canseco) .25 .20 .10
656 1988 HL (Doug Jones) .06 .05 .02
657 1988 HL (Rickey Henderson) .12 .09 .05
658 1988 HL (Tom Browning) .06 .05 .02
659 1988 HL (Mike Greenwell) .15 .11 .06
660 1988 HL (Joe Morgan) (A.L. Win Streak) .06 .05 .02

1989 Score Traded

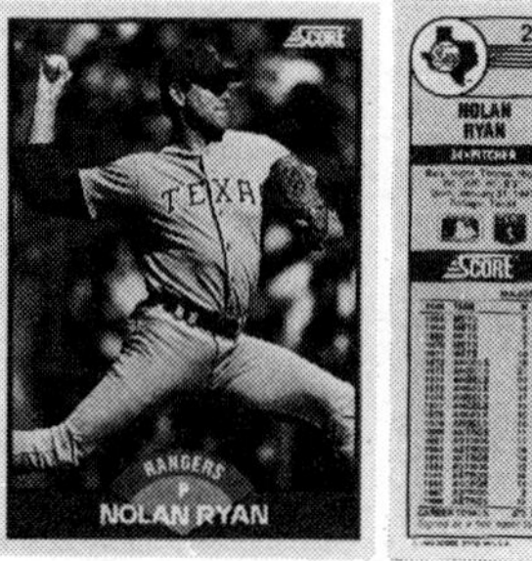

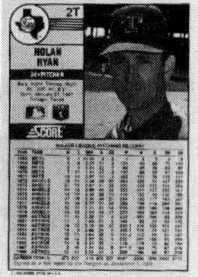

Score issued its second consecutive traded set in 1989 to supplement and update its regular set. The 110-card traded set features the same basic card design as the regular 1989 Score set. The set consists of rookies and traded players pictured with correct teams. The set was sold by hobby dealers in a special box that included an assortment of "Magic Motion" trivia cards.

	MT	NR MT	EX
Complete Set (110):	10.00	6.00	3.00
Common Player:	.06	.05	.02

1T Rafael Palmeiro .20 .15 .08
2T Nolan Ryan 1.50 1.25 .60
3T Jack Clark .10 .08 .04
4T Dave LaPoint .06 .05 .02
5T Mike Moore .08 .06 .03
6T Pete O'Brien .06 .05 .02
7T Jeffrey Leonard .06 .05 .02
8T Rob Murphy .06 .05 .02
9T Tom Herr .06 .05 .02
10T Claudell Washington .06 .05 .02
11T Mike Pagliarulo .06 .05 .02
12T Steve Lake .06 .05 .02
13T Spike Owen .06 .05 .02
14T Andy Hawkins .06 .05 .02
15T Todd Benzinger .06 .05 .02
16T Mookie Wilson .06 .05 .02
17T Bert Blyleven .08 .06 .03
18T Jeff Treadway .06 .05 .02
19T Bruce Hurst .08 .06 .03
20T Steve Sax .12 .09 .05
21T Juan Samuel .06 .05 .02
22T Jesse Barfield .06 .05 .02
23T Carmelo Castillo .06 .05 .02
24T Terry Leach .06 .05 .02
25T Mark Langston .12 .09 .05
26T Eric King .06 .05 .02
27T Steve Balboni .06 .05 .02
28T Len Dykstra .15 .11 .06
29T Keith Moreland .06 .05 .02
30T Terry Kennedy .06 .05 .02

31T	Eddie Murray	.15	.11	.06
32T	Mitch Williams	.10	.08	.04
33T	Jeff Parrett	.06	.05	.02
34T	Wally Backman	.06	.05	.02
35T	Julio Franco	.10	.08	.04
36T	Lance Parrish	.06	.05	.02
37T	Nick Esasky	.06	.05	.02
38T	Luis Polonia	.06	.05	.02
39T	Kevin Gross	.06	.05	.02
40T	John Dopson	.06	.05	.02
41T	Willie Randolph	.08	.06	.03
42T	Jim Clancy	.06	.05	.02
43T	Tracy Jones	.06	.05	.02
44T	Phil Bradley	.06	.05	.02
45T	Milt Thompson	.06	.05	.02
46T	Chris James	.06	.05	.02
47T	Scott Fletcher	.06	.05	.02
48T	Kal Daniels	.08	.06	.03
49T	Steve Bedrosian	.06	.05	.02
50T	Rickey Henderson	.50	.40	.20
51T	Dion James	.06	.05	.02
52T	Tim Leary	.06	.05	.02
53T	Roger McDowell	.06	.05	.02
54T	Mel Hall	.06	.05	.02
55T	Dickie Thon	.06	.05	.02
56T	Zane Smith	.06	.05	.02
57T	Danny Heep	.06	.05	.02
58T	Bob McClure	.06	.05	.02
59T	Brian Holton	.06	.05	.02
60T	Randy Ready	.06	.05	.02
61T	Bob Melvin	.06	.05	.02
62T	Harold Baines	.08	.06	.03
63T	Lance McCullers	.06	.05	.02
64T	Jody Davis	.06	.05	.02
65T	Darrell Evans	.06	.05	.02
66T	Joel Youngblood	.08	.06	.03
67T	Frank Viola	.08	.06	.03
68T	Mike Aldrete	.06	.05	.02
69T	Greg Cadaret	.06	.05	.02
70T	John Kruk	.12	.09	.05
71T	Pat Sheridan	.06	.05	.02
72T	Oddibe McDowell	.06	.05	.02
73T	Tom Brookens	.06	.05	.02
74T	Bob Boone	.08	.06	.03
75T	Walt Terrell	.06	.05	.02
76T	Joel Skinner	.06	.05	.02
77T	Randy Johnson	.60	.45	.25
78T	Felix Fermin	.06	.05	.02
79T	Rick Mahler	.06	.05	.02
80T	Rich Dotson	.06	.05	.02
81T	Cris Carpenter (FC)	.20	.15	.08
82T	Bill Spiers (FC)	.12	.09	.05
83T	Junior Felix (FC)	.25	.20	.10
84T	Joe Girardi (FC)	.20	.15	.08
85T	Jerome Walton (FC)	.25	.20	.10
86T	Greg Litton (FC)	.25	.20	.10
87T	Greg Harris (FC)	.20	.15	.08
88T	Jim Abbott (FC)	1.50	1.25	.60
89T	Kevin Brown (FC)	.20	.15	.08
90T	John Wetteland (FC)	.20	.15	.08
91T	Gary Wayne (FC)	.15	.11	.06
92T	Rich Monteleone (FC)	.15	.11	.06
93T	Bob Geren (FC)	.20	.15	.08
94T	Clay Parker (FC)	.15	.11	.06
95T	Steve Finley (FC)	.30	.25	.12
96T	Gregg Olson (FC)	.35	.25	.14
97T	Ken Patterson (FC)	.15	.11	.06
98T	Ken Hill (FC)	.50	.40	.20
99T	Scott Scudder (FC)	.15	.11	.06
100T	Ken Griffey, Jr. (FC)	6.00	4.50	2.50
101T	Jeff Brantley (FC)	.25	.20	.10
102T	Donn Pall (FC)	.15	.11	.06
103T	Carlos Martinez (FC)	.20	.15	.08
104T	Joe Oliver (FC)	.30	.25	.12
105T	Omar Vizquel (FC)	.15	.11	.06
106T	Albert Belle	4.50	3.50	1.75
107T	Kenny Rogers (FC)	.20	.15	.08
108T	Mark Carreon (FC)	.15	.11	.06
109T	Rolando Roomes (FC)	.15	.11	.06
110T	Pete Harnsisch (FC)	.35	.25	.14

1989 Score Young Superstar Series I

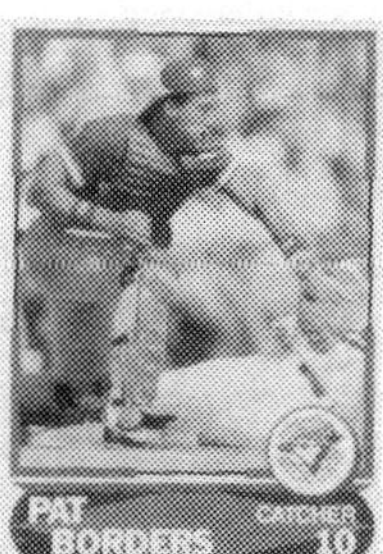

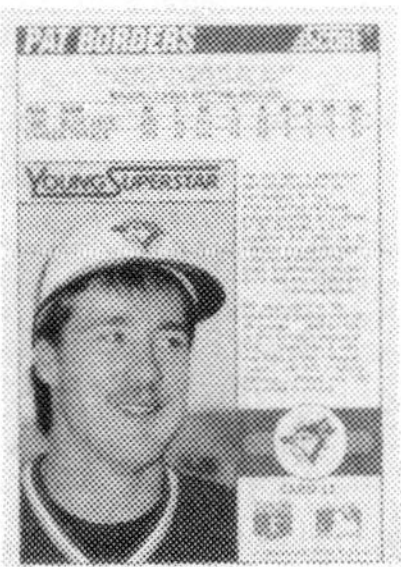

This standard-size card set (2-1/2" by 3-1/2") displays full-color action photos with a high gloss finish. The card fronts feature a red and blue border surrounding the photo with the team logo in the lower right. A red band beneath the photo provided the setting for the player ID including name, position, and team number. The flip side features a red "Young Superstar" headline above a close-up photo. Above the headline, appears the player's personal information and statistics in orange and black ink respectively. The top of the flip side highlights the player's name and the Score logo in white within a purple band. To the right of the close-up photo a condensed scouting report and career hightlights are revealed. The card number and related logos appear on the bottom portion. Five trivia cards featuring "A Year to Remember" accompanied the series. Each trivia card relates to a highlight from the past 56 years. This set was distributed via a write-in offer with Score card wrappers.

		MT	NR MT	EX
Complete Set (42):		9.00	6.75	3.50
Common Player:		.10	.08	.04
1	Gregg Jefferies	.40	.30	.15
2	Jody Reed	.10	.08	.04
3	Mark Grace	.40	.30	.15
4	Dave Gallagher	.15	.11	.06
5	Bo Jackson	.80	.60	.30
6	Jay Buhner	.30	.25	.12
7	Melido Perez	.10	.08	.04
8	Bobby Witt	.10	.08	.04
9	David Cone	.15	.11	.06
10	Chris Sabo	.15	.11	.06
11	Pat Borders	.10	.08	.04
12	Mark Grant	.10	.08	.04
13	Mike Macfarlane	.10	.08	.04
14	Mike Jackson	.10	.08	.04
15	Ricky Jordan	.20	.15	.08
16	Ron Gant	.50	.40	.20
17	Al Leiter	.10	.08	.04
18	Jeff Parrett	.10	.08	.04
19	Pete Smith	.10	.08	.04
20	Walt Weiss	.15	.11	.06
21	Doug Drabek	.12	.09	.05
22	Kirt Manwaring	.15	.11	.06
23	Keith Miller	.10	.08	.04
24	Damon Berryhill	.10	.08	.04
25	Gary Sheffield	.60	.45	.25
26	Brady Anderson	.30	.25	.12
27	Mitch Williams	.15	.11	.06
28	Roberto Alomar	.60	.45	.25
29	Bobby Thigpen	.12	.09	.05
30	Bryan Harvey	.10	.08	.04
31	Jose Rijo	.25	.20	.10
32	Dave West	.10	.08	.04
33	Joey Meyer	.10	.08	.04
34	Allan Anderson	.12	.09	.05
35	Rafael Palmeiro	.60	.45	.25
36	Tim Belcher	.30	.25	.12
37	John Smiley	.15	.11	.06
38	Mackey Sasser	.10	.08	.04
39	Greg Maddux	.40	.30	.15
40	Ramon Martinez	.30	.25	.12
41	Randy Myers	.12	.09	.05
42	Scott Bankhead	.15	.11	.06

1989 Score Young Superstar Series II

Score followed up with a second series of Young Superstars in 1989. The second series also included 42 cards and featured the same design as the first series. The set was also distributed via a write-in offer with Score card wrappers.

		MT	NR MT	EX
Complete Set (42):		5.00	3.75	2.00
Common Player:		.10	.08	.04
1	Sandy Alomar	.20	.15	.08
2	Tom Gordon	.20	.15	.08
3	Ron Jones	.10	.08	.04
4	Todd Burns	.10	.08	.04
5	Paul O'Neill	.40	.30	.15
6	Gene Larkin	.10	.08	.04
7	Eric King	.10	.08	.04
8	Jeff Robinson	.10	.08	.04
9	Bill Wegman	.10	.08	.04
10	Cecil Espy	.10	.08	.04
11	Jose Guzman	.10	.08	.04
12	Kelly Gruber	.20	.15	.08
13	Duane Ward	.20	.15	.08
14	Mark Gubicza	.25	.20	.10
15	Norm Charlton	.20	.15	.08
16	Jose Oquendo	.10	.08	.04
17	Geronimo Berroa	.10	.08	.04
18	Dwight Smith	.20	.15	.08
19	Lance McCullers	.10	.08	.04
20	Jimmy Jones	.10	.08	.04
21	Craig Worthington	.10	.08	.04
22	Mike Devereaux	.25	.20	.10
23	Bob Milacki	.15	.11	.06
24	Dale Sveum	.10	.08	.04
25	Carlos Quintana	.20	.15	.08
26	Luis Medina	.10	.08	.04
27	Steve Searcy	.10	.08	.04
28	Don August	.10	.08	.04
29	Shawn Hillegas	.10	.08	.04
30	Mike Campbell	.10	.08	.04
31	Mike Harkey	.10	.08	.04
32	Randy Johnson	.30	.25	.12
33	Craig Biggio	.35	.25	.14
34	Mike Schooler	.12	.09	.05
35	Andres Thomas	.10	.08	.04
36	Van Snider	.10	.08	.04
37	Cameron Drew	.10	.08	.04
38	Kevin Mitchell	.40	.30	.15
39	Lance Johnson	.20	.15	.08
40	Chad Kreuter	.10	.08	.04
41	Danny Jackson	.10	.08	.04
42	Kurt Stillwell	.10	.08	.04

1989 Score Rising Star

Similar in design to the Score Superstar set, this 100-card set showcased a host of rookies including Gary Sheffield and Gregg Jefferies. The full-color action photos are surrounded by a bright blue border with a green inner highlight line. The Score logo appears in the upper left in green and white. The player's name, position and team are found at the bottom. The flip sides display a full-color close-up of the player above his name and career highlights. The card number and player's rookie year are featured to the right. A "Rising Star" headline highlights the top border. Like the "Score Superstar" the Score "Rising Star" set was marketed as a combination with a related magazine: "1988-89 Baseball's 100 Hottest Rookies". The set also includes six Magic Motion baseball trivia cards featuring "Rookies to Remember." The magazine/card sets were available at a select group of retailers.

		MT	NR MT	EX
Complete Set (100):		10.00	7.50	4.00
Common Player:		.07	.05	.03
1	Gregg Jefferies	.40	.30	.15
2	Vicente Palacios	.07	.05	.03
3	Cameron Drew	.07	.05	.03
4	Doug Dascenzo	.12	.09	.05
5	Luis Medina	.07	.05	.03
6	Craig Worthington	.07	.05	.03
7	Rob Ducey	.07	.05	.03
8	Hal Morris	.60	.45	.25
9	Bill Brennan	.07	.05	.03
10	Gary Sheffield	.40	.30	.15
11	Mike Devereaux	.20	.15	.08
12	Hensley Meulens	.10	.08	.04
13	Carlos Quintana	.10	.08	.04
14	Todd Frohwirth	.07	.05	.03
15	Scott Lusader	.09	.07	.04
16	Mark Carreon	.15	.11	.06
17	Torey Lovullo	.20	.15	.08
18	Randy Velarde	.12	.09	.05
19	Billy Bean	.07	.05	.03
20	Lance Blankenship	.15	.11	.06
21	Chris Gwynn	.07	.05	.03
22	Felix Jose	.20	.15	.08
23	Derek Lilliquist	.10	.08	.04
24	Gary Thurman	.07	.05	.03
25	Ron Jones	.07	.05	.03
26	Dave Justice	1.00	.70	.40
27	Johnny Paredes	.07	.05	.03
28	Tim Jones	.07	.05	.03
29	Jose Gonzalez	.07	.05	.03
30	Geronimo Berroa	.15	.11	.06
31	Trevor Wilson	.12	.09	.05
32	Morris Madden	.07	.05	.03
33	Lance Johnson	.35	.25	.14
34	Marvin Freeman	.07	.05	.03
35	Jose Cecena	.07	.05	.03
36	Jim Corsi	.07	.05	.03
37	Rolando Roomes	.07	.05	.03
38	Scott Medvin	.07	.05	.03
39	Charlie Hayes	.20	.15	.08

#	Player	MT	NR MT	EX
40	Edgar Martinez	.15	.11	.06
41	Van Snider	.07	.05	.03
42	John Fishel	.07	.05	.03
43	Bruce Fields	.07	.05	.03
44	Darryl Hamilton	.09	.07	.04
45	Tom Prince	.09	.07	.04
46	Kirt Manwaring	.20	.15	.08
47	Steve Searcy	.12	.09	.05
48	Mike Harkey	.20	.15	.08
49	German Gonzalez	.07	.05	.03
50	Tony Perezchica	.07	.05	.03
51	Chad Kreuter	.15	.11	.06
52	Luis de los Santos	.07	.05	.03
53	Steve Curry	.07	.05	.03
54	Greg Bailey	.07	.05	.03
55	Ramon Martinez	.30	.25	.12
56	Ron Tingley	.07	.05	.03
57	Randy Kramer	.07	.05	.03
58	Alex Madrid	.07	.05	.03
59	Kevin Reimer	.07	.05	.03
60	Dave Otto	.07	.05	.03
61	Ken Patterson	.07	.05	.03
62	Keith Miller	.07	.05	.03
63	Randy Johnson	.40	.30	.15
64	Dwight Smith	.20	.15	.08
65	Eric Yelding	.20	.15	.08
66	Bob Geren	.07	.05	.03
67	Shane Turner	.07	.05	.03
68	Tom Gordon	.15	.11	.06
69	Jeff Huson	.30	.25	.12
70	Marty Brown	.07	.05	.03
71	Nelson Santovenia	.07	.05	.03
72	Roberto Alomar	.80	.60	.30
73	Mike Schooler	.15	.11	.06
74	Pete Smith	.10	.08	.04
75	John Costello	.07	.05	.03
76	Chris Sabo	.20	.15	.08
77	Damon Berryhill	.07	.05	.03
78	Mark Grace	.40	.30	.15
79	Melido Perez	.07	.05	.03
80	Al Leiter	.07	.05	.03
81	Todd Stottlemyre	.20	.15	.08
82	Mackey Sasser	.07	.05	.03
83	Don August	.07	.05	.03
84	Jeff Treadway	.07	.05	.03
85	Jody Reed	.07	.05	.03
86	Mike Campbell	.07	.05	.03
87	Ron Gant	.60	.45	.25
88	Ricky Jordan	.30	.25	.12
89	Terry Clark	.07	.05	.03
90	Roberto Kelly	.40	.30	.15
91	Pat Borders	.20	.15	.08
92	Bryan Harvey	.20	.15	.08
93	Joey Meyer	.07	.05	.03
94	Tim Belcher	.10	.08	.04
95	Walt Weiss	.15	.11	.06
96	Dave Gallagher	.15	.11	.06
97	Mike Macfarlane	.07	.05	.03
98	Craig Biggio	.30	.25	.12
99	Jack Armstrong	.15	.11	.06
100	Todd Burns	.07	.05	.03

1989 Score Superstar

This 100-card set features full-color action photos of baseball's superstars, and also includes six Magic Motion "Rookies to Remember" baseball trivia cards. The card fronts contain a bright red border with a blue line inside highlighting the photo. The Score logo appears in the bottom left corner. The player ID is displayed in unique fashion using overlapping triangles in white, green, and yellow. The flip side features a full-color player close-up directly beneath a bright red "Superstar" headline. The set was marketed along with the magazine "1989 Baseball's 100 Hottest Players". The magazine/card set combo was available at select retailers.

		MT	NR MT	EX
	Complete Set (100):	8.00	6.00	3.25
	Common Player:	.06	.05	.02
1	Jose Canseco	.60	.45	.25
2	David Cone	.15	.11	.06
3	Dave Winfield	.40	.30	.15
4	George Brett	.40	.30	.15
5	Frank Viola	.09	.07	.04
6	Cory Snyder	.06	.05	.02
7	Alan Trammell	.15	.11	.06
8	Dwight Evans	.09	.07	.04
9	Tim Leary	.06	.05	.02
10	Don Mattingly	.80	.60	.30

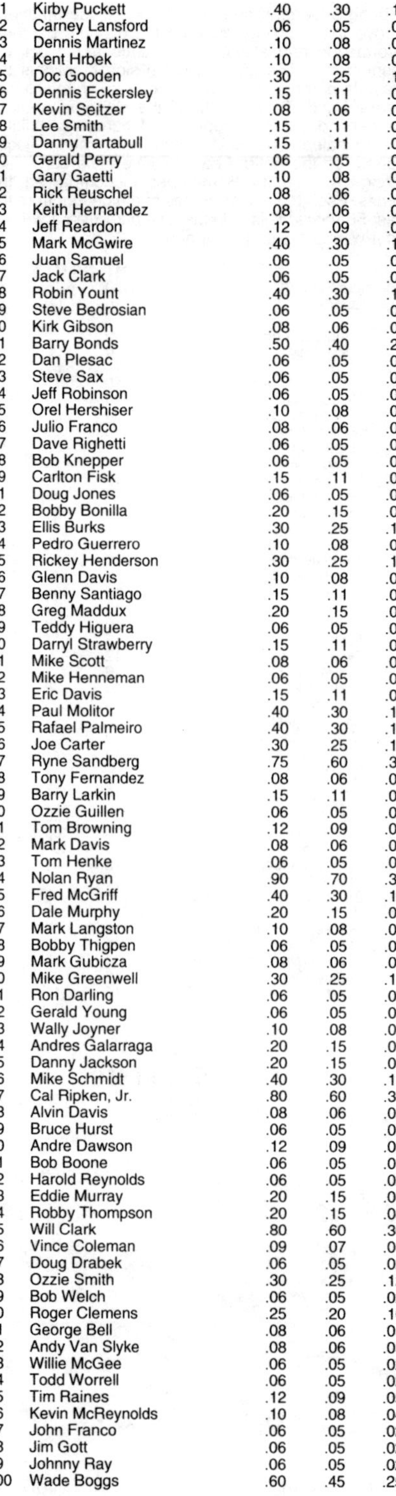

#	Player	MT	NR MT	EX
11	Kirby Puckett	.40	.30	.15
12	Carney Lansford	.06	.05	.02
13	Dennis Martinez	.10	.08	.04
14	Kent Hrbek	.10	.08	.04
15	Doc Gooden	.30	.25	.12
16	Dennis Eckersley	.15	.11	.06
17	Kevin Seitzer	.08	.06	.03
18	Lee Smith	.15	.11	.06
19	Danny Tartabull	.15	.11	.06
20	Gerald Perry	.06	.05	.02
21	Gary Gaetti	.10	.08	.04
22	Rick Reuschel	.08	.06	.03
23	Keith Hernandez	.08	.06	.03
24	Jeff Reardon	.12	.09	.05
25	Mark McGwire	.40	.30	.15
26	Juan Samuel	.06	.05	.02
27	Jack Clark	.06	.05	.02
28	Robin Yount	.40	.30	.15
29	Steve Bedrosian	.06	.05	.02
30	Kirk Gibson	.08	.06	.03
31	Barry Bonds	.50	.40	.20
32	Dan Plesac	.06	.05	.02
33	Steve Sax	.06	.05	.02
34	Jeff Robinson	.06	.05	.02
35	Orel Hershiser	.10	.08	.04
36	Julio Franco	.08	.06	.03
37	Dave Righetti	.06	.05	.02
38	Bob Knepper	.06	.05	.02
39	Carlton Fisk	.15	.11	.06
41	Doug Jones	.06	.05	.02
42	Bobby Bonilla	.20	.15	.08
43	Ellis Burks	.30	.25	.12
44	Pedro Guerrero	.10	.08	.04
45	Rickey Henderson	.30	.25	.12
46	Glenn Davis	.10	.08	.04
47	Benny Santiago	.15	.11	.06
48	Greg Maddux	.20	.15	.08
49	Teddy Higuera	.06	.05	.02
50	Darryl Strawberry	.15	.11	.06
51	Mike Scott	.08	.06	.03
52	Mike Henneman	.06	.05	.02
53	Eric Davis	.15	.11	.06
54	Paul Molitor	.40	.30	.15
55	Rafael Palmeiro	.40	.30	.15
56	Joe Carter	.30	.25	.12
57	Ryne Sandberg	.75	.60	.30
58	Tony Fernandez	.08	.06	.03
59	Barry Larkin	.15	.11	.06
60	Ozzie Guillen	.06	.05	.02
61	Tom Browning	.12	.09	.05
62	Mark Davis	.08	.06	.03
63	Tom Henke	.06	.05	.02
64	Nolan Ryan	.90	.70	.35
65	Fred McGriff	.40	.30	.15
66	Dale Murphy	.20	.15	.08
67	Mark Langston	.10	.08	.04
68	Bobby Thigpen	.06	.05	.02
69	Mark Gubicza	.08	.06	.03
70	Mike Greenwell	.30	.25	.12
71	Ron Darling	.06	.05	.02
72	Gerald Young	.06	.05	.02
73	Wally Joyner	.10	.08	.04
74	Andres Galarraga	.20	.15	.08
75	Danny Jackson	.20	.15	.08
76	Mike Schmidt	.40	.30	.15
77	Cal Ripken, Jr.	.80	.60	.30
78	Alvin Davis	.08	.06	.03
79	Bruce Hurst	.06	.05	.02
80	Andre Dawson	.12	.09	.05
81	Bob Boone	.06	.05	.02
82	Harold Reynolds	.06	.05	.02
83	Eddie Murray	.20	.15	.08
84	Robby Thompson	.20	.15	.08
85	Will Clark	.80	.60	.30
86	Vince Coleman	.09	.07	.04
87	Doug Drabek	.06	.05	.02
88	Ozzie Smith	.30	.25	.12
89	Bob Welch	.06	.05	.02
90	Roger Clemens	.25	.20	.10
91	George Bell	.08	.06	.03
92	Andy Van Slyke	.08	.06	.03
93	Willie McGee	.06	.05	.02
94	Todd Worrell	.06	.05	.02
95	Tim Raines	.12	.09	.05
96	Kevin McReynolds	.10	.08	.04
97	John Franco	.06	.05	.02
98	Jim Gott	.06	.05	.02
99	Johnny Ray	.06	.05	.02
100	Wade Boggs	.60	.45	.25

1989 Scoremasters

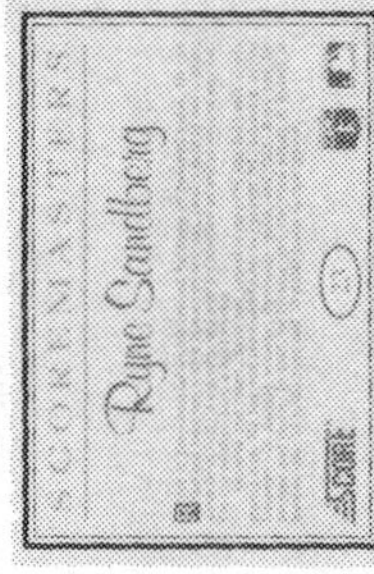

This unique 42-card boxed set from Score was reproduced from original artwork done by sports artist Jeffrey Rubin. The paintings are reproduced on a standard-size, white, glossy stock, and the set includes the top stars of the game, plus selected rookies such as Jefferies and Griffey Jr.

		MT	NR MT	EX
	Complete Set (42):	12.00	9.00	4.75
	Common Player:	.20	.15	.08
1	Bo Jackson	.75	.60	.30
2	Jerome Walton	.20	.15	.08
3	Cal Ripken, Jr.	1.00	.70	.40
4	Mike Scott	.20	.15	.08
5	Nolan Ryan	1.50	1.25	.60
6	Don Mattingly	.90	.70	.35
7	Tom Gordon	.20	.15	.08
8	Jack Morris	.20	.15	.08
9	Carlton Fisk	.30	.25	.12
10	Will Clark	.90	.70	.35
11	George Brett	1.00	.70	.40
12	Kevin Mitchell	.30	.25	.12
13	Mark Langston	.30	.25	.12
14	Dave Stewart	.30	.25	.12
15	Dale Murphy	.30	.25	.12
16	Gary Gaetti	.20	.15	.08
17	Wade Boggs	.70	.50	.30
18	Eric Davis	.20	.15	.08
19	Kirby Puckett	.60	.45	.25
20	Roger Clemens	.60	.45	.25
21	Orel Hershiser	.30	.25	.12
22	Mark Grace	.40	.30	.15
23	Ryne Sandberg	1.00	.70	.40
24	Barry Larkin	.40	.30	.15
25	Ellis Burks	.30	.25	.12
26	Dwight Gooden	.40	.30	.15
27	Ozzie Smith	.40	.30	.15
28	Andre Dawson	.30	.25	.12
29	Julio Franco	.20	.15	.08
30	Ken Griffey, Jr.	2.00	1.50	.80
31	Ruben Sierra	.60	.45	.25
32	Mark McGwire	.40	.30	.15
33	Andres Galarraga	.30	.25	.12
34	Joe Carter	.30	.25	.12
35	Vince Coleman	.20	.15	.08
36	Mike Greenwell	.25	.20	.10
37	Tony Gwynn	.40	.30	.15
38	Andy Van Slyke	.25	.20	.10
39	Gregg Jefferies	.50	.40	.20
40	Jose Canseco	.90	.70	.35
41	Dave Winfield	.40	.30	.15
42	Darryl Strawberry	.40	.30	.15

1989 Score Yankees

This 33-card New York Yankee team set was produced by Score as an in-stadium promotion in 1989 and was distributed to fans attending the July 29 game at Yankee Stadium. The standard-size cards include a full-color player photo with a line drawing of the famous Yankee Stadium facade running along the top of the card. The player's name, "New York Yankees" and position appear below the photo. A second full-color photo is included on the back of the card, along with stats, data and a brief player profile. The set includes a special Thurman Munson commemorative card.

		MT	NR MT	EX
	Complete Set (33):	8.00	6.00	3.25
	Common Player:	.15	.11	.06
1	Don Mattingly	1.75	1.25	.70
2	Steve Sax	.30	.25	.12
3	Alvaro Espinoza	.25	.20	.10
4	Luis Polonia	.40	.30	.15
5	Jesse Barfield	.25	.20	.10
6	Dave Righetti	.25	.20	.10
7	Dave Winfield	.80	.60	.30
8	John Candelaria	.15	.11	.06
9	Wayne Tolleson	.15	.11	.06
10	Ken Phelps	.15	.11	.06
11	Rafael Santana	.15	.11	.06
12	Don Slaught	.15	.11	.06
13	Mike Pagliarulo	.20	.15	.08
14	Lance McCullers	.15	.11	.06
15	Dave LaPoint	.15	.11	.06
16	Dale Mohorcic	.15	.11	.06
17	Steve Balboni	.15	.11	.06
18	Roberto Kelly	.60	.45	.25
19	Andy Hawkins	.25	.20	.10

20	Mel Hall	.20	.15	.08
21	Tom Brookens	.15	.11	.06
22	Deion Sanders	.80	.60	.30
23	Richard Dotson	.15	.11	.06
24	Lee Guetterman	.15	.11	.06
25	Bob Geren	.30	.25	.12
26	Jimmy Jones	.15	.11	.06
27	Chuck Cary	.15	.11	.06
28	Ron Guidry	.25	.20	.10
29	Hal Morris	1.00	.70	.40
30	Clay Parker	.25	.20	.10
31	Dallas Green	.20	.15	.08
32	Thurman Munson	.70	.50	.30
33	Sponsor Card	.15	.11	.06

1990 Score

The regular Score set increased to 704 cards in 1990. Included were a series of cards picturing first-round draft picks, an expanded subset of rookie cards, four World Series specials, five Highlight cards, and a 13-card "Dream Team" series featuring the game's top players pictured on old tobacco-style cards. For the first time in a Score set, team logos are displayed on the card fronts in the lower right corner. Card backs again include a full-color portrait photo with player data. A one-paragraph write-up of each player was again provided by former Sports Illustrated editor Les Woodcock. The Score set was again distributed with "Magic Motion" triva cards, this year using "Baseball's Most Valuable Players" as its theme.

		MT	NR MT	EX
	Complete Set (704):	20.00	15.00	8.00
	Common Player:	.04	.03	.02
1	Don Mattingly	.35	.25	.14
2	Cal Ripken, Jr.	.40	.30	.15
3	Dwight Evans	.08	.06	.03
4	Barry Bonds	.50	.40	.20
5	Kevin McReynolds	.12	.09	.05
6	Ozzie Guillen	.05	.04	.02
7	Terry Kennedy	.04	.03	.02
8	Bryan Harvey	.06	.05	.02
9	Alan Trammell	.09	.07	.04
10	Cory Snyder	.09	.07	.04
11	Jody Reed	.05	.04	.02
12	Roberto Alomar	.30	.25	.12
13	Pedro Guerrero	.09	.07	.04
14	Gary Redus	.04	.03	.02
15	Marty Barrett	.05	.04	.02
16	Ricky Jordan	.20	.15	.08
17	Joe Magrane	.07	.05	.03
18	Sid Fernandez	.07	.05	.03
19	Rich Dotson	.04	.03	.02
20	Jack Clark	.09	.07	.04
21	Bob Walk	.05	.04	.02
22	Ron Karkovice	.04	.03	.02
23	Lenny Harris (FC)	.10	.08	.04
24	Phil Bradley	.06	.05	.02
25	Andres Galarraga	.15	.11	.06
26	Brian Downing	.06	.05	.02
27	Dave Martinez	.06	.05	.02
28	Eric King	.04	.03	.02
29	Barry Lyons	.04	.03	.02
30	Dave Schmidt	.04	.03	.02
31	Mike Boddicker	.06	.05	.02
32	Tom Foley	.04	.03	.02
33	Brady Anderson	.07	.05	.03
34	Jim Presley	.05	.04	.02
35	Lance Parrish	.06	.05	.02
36	Von Hayes	.09	.07	.03
37	Lee Smith	.06	.05	.02
38	Herm Winningham	.04	.03	.02
39	Alejandro Pena	.04	.03	.02
40	Mike Scott	.09	.07	.04
41	Joe Orsulak	.04	.03	.02
42	Rafael Ramirez	.05	.04	.02
43	Gerald Young	.05	.04	.02
44	Dick Schofield	.05	.04	.02
45	Dave Smith	.06	.05	.02
46	Dave Magadan	.07	.05	.03
47	Dennis Martinez	.06	.05	.02
48	Greg Minton	.04	.03	.02
49	Milt Thompson	.04	.03	.02
50	Orel Hershiser	.12	.09	.05
51	Bip Roberts	.10	.07	.04
52	Jerry Browne	.09	.07	.04
53	Bob Ojeda	.05	.04	.02
54	Fernando Valenzuela	.09	.07	.04
55	Matt Nokes	.09	.07	.04
56	Brook Jacoby	.08	.06	.03
57	Frank Tanana	.05	.04	.02
58	Scott Fletcher	.05	.04	.02
59	Ron Oester	.05	.04	.02
60	Bob Boone	.08	.06	.03
61	Dan Gladden	.08	.06	.03
62	Darnell Coles	.04	.03	.02
63	Gregg Olson	.10	.07	.04
64	Todd Burns	.05	.04	.02
65	Todd Benzinger	.07	.05	.03
66	Dale Murphy	.12	.09	.05
67	Mike Flanagan	.06	.05	.02
68	Jose Oquendo	.06	.05	.02
69	Cecil Espy	.08	.06	.03
70	Chris Sabo	.10	.08	.04
71	Shane Rawley	.05	.04	.02
72	Tom Brunansky	.08	.06	.03
73	Vance Law	.05	.04	.02
74	B.J. Surhoff	.08	.06	.03
75	Lou Whitaker	.09	.07	.04
76	Ken Caminiti	.09	.07	.04
77	Nelson Liriano	.04	.03	.02
78	Tommy Gregg	.09	.07	.04
79	Don Slaught	.05	.04	.02
80	Eddie Murray	.12	.09	.05
81	Joe Boever	.08	.06	.03
82	Charlie Leibrandt	.06	.05	.02
83	Jose Lind	.06	.05	.02
84	Tony Phillips	.05	.04	.02
85	Mitch Webster	.04	.03	.02
86	Dan Plesac	.07	.05	.02
87	Rick Mahler	.05	.04	.02
88	Steve Lyons	.05	.04	.02
89	Tony Fernandez	.09	.07	.04
90	Ryne Sandberg	.30	.25	.12
91	Nick Esasky	.09	.07	.04
92	Luis Salazar	.04	.03	.02
93	Pete Incaviglia	.08	.06	.03
94	Ivan Calderon	.06	.05	.02
95	Jeff Treadway	.06	.05	.02
96	Kurt Stillwell	.06	.05	.02
97	Gary Sheffield	.25	.20	.10
98	Jeffrey Leonard	.07	.05	.03
99	Andres Thomas	.05	.04	.02
100	Roberto Kelly	.15	.11	.06
101	Alvaro Espinoza (FC)	.06	.05	.02
102	Greg Gagne	.05	.04	.02
103	John Farrell	.05	.04	.02
104	Willie Wilson	.05	.04	.02
105	Glenn Braggs	.08	.06	.03
106	Chet Lemon	.06	.05	.02
107	Jamie Moyer	.06	.05	.02
108	Chuck Crim	.04	.03	.02
109	Dave Valle	.04	.03	.02
110	Walt Weiss	.10	.08	.04
111	Larry Sheets	.04	.03	.02
112	Don Robinson	.05	.04	.02
113	Danny Heep	.04	.03	.02
114	Carmelo Martinez	.06	.05	.02
115	Dave Gallagher	.08	.06	.03
116	Mike LaValliere	.05	.04	.02
117	Bob McClure	.04	.03	.02
118	Rene Gonzales	.04	.03	.02
119	Mark Parent	.05	.04	.02
120	Wally Joyner	.15	.11	.06
121	Mark Gubicza	.09	.07	.04
122	Tony Pena	.08	.06	.03
123	Carmen Castillo	.04	.03	.02
124	Howard Johnson	.07	.05	.03
125	Steve Sax	.10	.08	.04
126	Tim Belcher	.10	.08	.04
127	Tim Burke	.06	.05	.02
128	Al Newman	.04	.03	.02
129	Dennis Rasmussen	.05	.04	.02
130	Doug Jones	.06	.05	.02
131	Fred Lynn	.09	.07	.04
132	Jeff Hamilton	.06	.05	.02
133	German Gonzalez	.05	.04	.02
134	John Morris	.05	.04	.02
135	Dave Parker	.10	.08	.04
136	Gary Pettis	.05	.04	.02
137	Dennis Boyd	.07	.05	.02
138	Candy Maldonado	.06	.05	.02
139	Rick Cerone	.04	.03	.02
140	George Brett	.25	.20	.10
141	Dave Clark	.05	.04	.02
142	Dickie Thon	.05	.04	.02
143	Junior Ortiz	.04	.03	.02
144	Don August	.06	.05	.02
145	Gary Gaetti	.10	.08	.04
146	Kirt Manwaring	.12	.09	.05
147	Jeff Reed	.04	.03	.02
148	Jose Alvarez (FC)	.04	.03	.02
149	Mike Schooler	.08	.06	.03
150	Mark Grace	.25	.20	.10
151	Geronimo Berroa	.08	.06	.03
152	Barry Jones	.04	.03	.02
153	Geno Petralli	.05	.04	.02
154	Jim Deshaies	.08	.06	.03
155	Barry Larkin	.12	.09	.05
156	Alfredo Griffin	.05	.04	.02
157	Tom Henke	.06	.05	.02
158	Mike Jeffcoat (FC)	.04	.03	.02
159	Bob Welch	.09	.07	.04
160	Julio Franco	.10	.08	.04
161	Henry Cotto	.04	.03	.02
162	Terry Steinbach	.10	.08	.04
163	Damon Berryhill	.08	.06	.03
164	Tim Crews	.04	.03	.02
165	Tom Browning	.09	.07	.04
166	Frd Manrique	.04	.03	.02
167	Harold Reynolds	.09	.07	.04
168	Ron Hassey	.05	.04	.02
169	Shawon Dunston	.08	.06	.03
170	Bobby Bonilla	.15	.11	.06
171	Tom Herr	.07	.05	.03
172	Mike Heath	.04	.03	.02
173	Rich Gedman	.05	.04	.02
174	Bill Ripken	.05	.04	.02
175	Pete O'Brien	.07	.05	.03
176a	Lloyd McClendon (uniform number 1 on back)	1.00	.70	.40
176b	Lloyd McClendon (uniform number 10 on back)	.20	.15	.08
177	Brian Holton	.05	.04	.02
178	Jeff Blauser	.05	.04	.02
179	Jim Eisenreich	.05	.04	.02
180	Bert Blyleven	.09	.07	.04
181	Rob Murphy	.05	.04	.02
182	Bill Doran	.07	.05	.03
183	Curt Ford	.04	.03	.02
184	Mike Henneman	.06	.05	.02
185	Eric Davis	.12	.09	.05
186	Lance McCullers	.06	.05	.02
187	*Steve Davis*	.08	.06	.03
188	Bill Wegman	.05	.04	.02
189	Brian Harper	.06	.05	.02
190	Mike Moore	.09	.07	.04
191	Dale Mohorcic	.04	.03	.02
192	Tim Wallach	.09	.07	.04
193	Keith Hernandez	.09	.07	.04
194	Dave Righetti	.07	.05	.03
195a	Bret Saberhagen ("joke" on card back)	.25	.20	.10
195b	Bret Saberhagen ("joker" on card back)	.30	.25	.12
196	Paul Kilgus	.04	.03	.02
197	Bud Black	.05	.04	.02
198	Juan Samuel	.09	.07	.04
199	Kevin Seitzer	.15	.11	.06
200	Darryl Strawberry	.12	.09	.05
201	Dave Steib	.09	.07	.04
202	Charlie Hough	.06	.05	.02
203	Jack Morris	.08	.06	.03
204	Rance Mulliniks	.04	.03	.02
205	Alvin Davis	.10	.08	.04
206	Jack Howell	.06	.05	.02
207	Ken Patterson (FC)	.06	.05	.02
208	Terry Pendleton	.10	.07	.04
209	Craig Lefferts	.06	.05	.02
210	Kevin Brown (FC)	.10	.08	.04
211	Dan Petry	.04	.03	.02
212	Dave Leiper	.06	.05	.02
213	Daryl Boston	.04	.03	.02
214	Kevin Hickey (FC)	.04	.03	.02
215	Mike Krukow	.06	.05	.02
216	Terry Francona	.04	.03	.02
217	Kirk McCaskill	.08	.06	.03
218	Scott Bailes	.05	.04	.02
219	Bob Forsch	.04	.03	.02
220	Mike Aldrete	.05	.04	.02
221	Steve Buechele	.06	.05	.02
222	Jesse Barfield	.09	.07	.05
223	Juan Berenguer	.06	.05	.02
224	Andy McGaffigan	.06	.05	.02
225	Pete Smith	.09	.07	.04
226	Mike Witt	.06	.05	.02
227	Jay Howell	.08	.06	.03
228	Scott Bradley	.05	.04	.02
229	*Jerome Walton*	.08	.06	.03
230	Greg Swindell	.15	.11	.06
231	Atlee Hammaker	.04	.03	.02
232	Mike Devereaux	.09	.07	.04
233	Ken Hill (FC)	.25	.20	.10
234	Craig Worthington	.15	.11	.06
235	Scott Terry	.08	.06	.03
236	Brett Butler	.09	.07	.04
237	Doyle Alexander	.07	.05	.03
238	Dave Anderson	.04	.03	.02
239	Bob Milacki	.10	.08	.04
240	Dwight Smith	.08	.06	.03
241	Otis Nixon	.04	.03	.02
242	Pat Tabler	.06	.05	.02
243	Derek Lilliquist	.12	.09	.05
244	Danny Tartabull	.15	.11	.06
245	Wade Boggs	.20	.15	.08
246	Scott Garrelts	.08	.06	.03
247	Spike Owen	.04	.03	.02
248	Norm Charlton	.12	.09	.05
249	Gerald Perry	.06	.05	.02
250	Nolan Ryan	.60	.45	.25
251	Kevin Gross	.07	.05	.03
252	Randy Milligan	.07	.05	.03
253	Mike LaCoss	.05	.04	.02
254	Dave Bergman	.04	.03	.02
255	Tony Gwynn	.35	.25	.12
256	Felix Fermin	.04	.03	.02
257	Greg Harris	.10	.08	.04
258	*Junior Felix*	.10	.08	.04
259	Mark Davis	.09	.07	.04
260	Vince Coleman	.15	.11	.06
261	Paul Gibson	.10	.08	.04
262	Mitch Williams	.10	.08	.04
263	Jeff Russell	.08	.06	.03
264	*Omar Vizquel*	.10	.07	.04
265	Andre Dawson	.12	.09	.05
266	Storm Davis	.08	.06	.03
267	Guillermo Hernandez	.04	.03	.02
268	Mike Felder	.05	.04	.02
269	Tom Candiotti	.05	.04	.02
270	Bruce Hurst	.09	.07	.04
271	Fred McGriff	.30	.25	.12
272	Glenn Davis	.15	.11	.60
273	John Franco	.09	.07	.04
274	Rich Yett	.04	.03	.02
275	Craig Biggio	.15	.11	.06
276	Gene Larkin	.05	.04	.02
277	Rob Dibble	.15	.11	.06
278	Randy Bush	.05	.04	.02
279	Kevin Bass	.08	.06	.03
280a	Bo Jackson ("Watham" on back)	.60	.45	.25
280b	Bo Jackson ("Wathan" on back)	1.00	.70	.40
281	Wally Backman	.06	.05	.02
282	Larry Andersen	.04	.03	.02
283	Chris Bosio	.09	.07	.04
284	Juan Agosto	.04	.03	.02

285	Ozzie Smith	.15	.11	.06
286	George Bell	.10	.08	.04
287	Rex Hudler	.05	.04	.02
288	Pat Borders	.10	.08	.04
289	Danny Jackson	.07	.05	.03
290	Carlton Fisk	.09	.07	.04
291	Tracy Jones	.05	.04	.02
292	Allan Anderson	.07	.05	.03
293	Johnny Ray	.07	.05	.03
294	Lee Guetterman	.04	.03	.02
295	Paul O'Neill	.09	.07	.05
296	Carney Lansford	.08	.06	.03
297	Tom Brookens	.04	.03	.02
298	Claudell Washington	.08	.06	.03
299	Hubie Brooks	.08	.06	.03
300	Will Clark	.35	.25	.14
301	*Kenny Rogers*	.20	.15	.08
302	Darrell Evans	.07	.05	.03
303	Greg Briley	.08	.06	.03
304	Donn Pall	.09	.07	.04
305	Teddy Higuera	.09	.07	.04
306	Dan Pasqua	.07	.05	.02
307	Dave Winfield	.20	.15	.08
308	Dennis Powell	.04	.03	.02
309	Jose DeLeon	.08	.06	.03
310	Roger Clemens	.25	.20	.10
311	Melido Perez	.09	.07	.04
312	Devon White	.09	.07	.04
313	Dwight Gooden	.08	.06	.03
314	*Carlos Martinez*	.08	.06	.03
315	Dennis Eckersley	.08	.06	.03
316	Clay Parker	.12	.09	.05
317	Rick Honeycutt	.05	.04	.02
318	Tim Laudner	.05	.04	.02
319	Joe Carter	.20	.15	.08
320	Robin Yount	.25	.20	.10
321	Felix Jose	.30	.25	.15
322	Mickey Tettleton	.09	.07	.04
323	Mike Gallego	.04	.03	.02
324	Edgar Martinez	.09	.07	.04
325	Dave Henderson	.09	.07	.04
326	Chili Davis	.09	.07	.04
327	Steve Balboni	.05	.04	.02
328	Jody Davis	.04	.03	.02
329	Shawn Hillegas	.04	.03	.02
330	Jim Abbott	.20	.15	.08
331	John Dopson	.10	.08	.04
332	Mark Williamson	.04	.03	.02
333	Jeff Robinson	.08	.06	.03
334	John Smiley	.09	.07	.04
335	Bobby Thigpen	.07	.05	.03
336	Garry Templeton	.05	.04	.02
337	Marvell Wynne	.05	.04	.02
338a	Ken Griffey, Sr. (uniform number 25 on card back)	.25	.20	.10
338b	Ken Griffey, Sr. (uniform number 30 on card back)	3.00	2.25	1.25
339	*Steve Finley*	.25	.20	.10
340	Ellis Burks	.08	.06	.03
341	Frank Williams	.04	.03	.02
342	Mike Morgan	.05	.04	.02
343	Kevin Mitchell	.08	.06	.03
344	Joel Youngblood	.04	.03	.02
345	Mike Greenwell	.10	.08	.04
346	Glenn Wilson	.05	.04	.02
347	John Costello	.05	.04	.02
348	Wes Gardner	.04	.03	.02
349	Jeff Ballard	.09	.07	.04
350	Mark Thurmond	.04	.03	.02
351	Randy Myers	.07	.05	.03
352	Shawn Abner	.07	.05	.03
353	Jesse Orosco	.04	.03	.02
354	Greg Walker	.05	.04	.02
355	Pete Harnisch	.15	.11	.06
356	Steve Farr	.05	.04	.02
357	Dave LaPoint	.05	.04	.02
358	Willie Fraser	.05	.04	.02
359	Mickey Hatcher	.04	.03	.02
360	Rickey Henderson	.20	.15	.08
361	Mike Fitzgerald	.04	.03	.02
362	Bill Schroeder	.04	.03	.02
363	Mark Carreon	.10	.08	.04
364	Ron Jones	.10	.08	.04
365	Jeff Montgomery	.06	.05	.02
366	Bill Krueger (FC)	.04	.03	.02
367	John Cangelosi	.04	.03	.02
368	Jose Gonzalez	.10	.08	.04
369	*Greg Hibbard* (FC)	.15	.11	.06
370	John Smoltz	.15	.11	.06
371	*Jeff Brantley*	.08	.06	.03
372	Frank White	.08	.06	.03
373	Ed Whitson	.06	.05	.02
374	Willie McGee	.09	.07	.04
375	Jose Canseco	.25	.20	.10
376	Randy Ready	.04	.03	.02
377	Don Aase	.04	.03	.02
378	Tony Armas	.05	.04	.02
379	Steve Bedrosian	.07	.05	.03
380	Chuck Finley	.07	.05	.03
381	Kent Hrbek	.12	.09	.05
382	Jim Gantner	.06	.05	.02
383	Mel Hall	.06	.05	.02
384	Mike Marshall	.07	.05	.03
385	Mark McGwire	.20	.15	.08
386	Wayne Tolleson	.04	.03	.02
387	Brian Holton	.05	.04	.02
388	*John Wetteland*	.20	.15	.08
389	Darren Daulton	.04	.03	.02
390	Rob Deer	.07	.05	.03
391	John Moses	.04	.03	.02
392	Todd Worrell	.07	.05	.03
393	Chuck Cary (FC)	.10	.08	.04
394	Stan Javier	.05	.04	.02
395	Willie Randolph	.09	.07	.04
396	Bill Buckner	.06	.05	.02
397	Robby Thompson	.07	.05	.02
398	Mike Scioscia	.07	.05	.03
399	Lonnie Smith	.09	.07	.04
400	Kirby Puckett	.40	.30	.15
401	Mark Langston	.15	.11	.06
402	Danny Darwin	.04	.03	.02
403	Greg Maddux	.20	.15	.08
404	Lloyd Moseby	.07	.05	.02
405	Rafael Palmeiro	.15	.07	.04
406	Chad Kreuter	.10	.08	.04
407	Jimmy Key	.09	.07	.05
408	Tim Birtsas	.04	.03	.02
409	Tim Raines	.10	.08	.04
410	Dave Stewart	.09	.07	.04
411	*Eric Yelding*	.15	.11	.06
412	*Kent Anderson* (FC)	.06	.05	.02
413	Les Lancaster	.05	.04	.02
414	Rick Dempsey	.04	.03	.02
415	Randy Johnson	.12	.09	.05
416	Gary Carter	.07	.05	.03
417	Rolando Roomes	.15	.11	.06
418	Dan Schatzeder	.04	.03	.02
419	Bryn Smith	.07	.05	.03
420	Ruben Sierra	.15	.11	.06
421	Steve Jeltz	.04	.03	.02
422	Ken Oberkfell	.04	.03	.02
423	Sid Bream	.04	.03	.02
424	Jim Clancy	.04	.03	.02
425	Kelly Gruber	.09	.07	.04
426	Rick Leach	.04	.03	.02
427	Lenny Dykstra	.07	.05	.03
428	Jeff Pico	.06	.05	.02
429	John Cerutti	.06	.05	.02
430	David Cone	.15	.11	.06
431	Jeff Kunkel	.04	.03	.02
432	Luis Aquino	.05	.04	.02
433	Ernie Whitt	.05	.04	.02
434	Bo Diaz	.05	.04	.02
435	Steve Lake	.04	.03	.02
436	Pat Perry	.04	.03	.02
437	Mike Davis	.05	.04	.02
438	Cecilio Guante	.04	.03	.02
439	Duane Ward	.04	.03	.02
440	Andy Van Slyke	.10	.08	.04
441	Gene Nelson	.04	.03	.02
442	Luis Polonia	.06	.05	.02
443	Kevin Elster	.06	.05	.02
444	Keith Moreland	.06	.05	.02
445	Roger McDowell	.06	.05	.02
446	Ron Darling	.08	.06	.03
447	Ernest Riles	.04	.03	.02
448	Mookie Wilson	.08	.06	.03
449a	*Bill Spiers* (66 missing for year of birth)	1.25	.90	.50
449b	*Bill Spiers* (1966 for birth year)	.30	.25	.12
450	Rick Sutcliffe	.07	.05	.03
451	Nelson Santovenia	.10	.08	.04
452	Andy Allanson	.04	.03	.02
453	Bob Melvin	.04	.03	.02
454	Benny Santiago	.12	.09	.05
455	Jose Uribe	.05	.04	.02
456	Bill Landrum (FC)	.08	.06	.03
457	Bobby Witt	.07	.05	.03
458	Kevin Romine	.07	.05	.03
459	Lee Mazzilli	.04	.03	.02
460	Paul Molitor	.20	.15	.08
461	*Ramon Martinez*	.15	.10	.05
462	Frank DiPino	.04	.03	.02
463	Walt Terrell	.06	.05	.02
464	*Bob Geren*	.10	.08	.04
465	Rick Reuchel	.09	.07	.04
466	Mark Grant	.06	.05	.02
467	John Kruk	.07	.05	.03
468	Gregg Jefferies	.25	.20	.10
469	R.J. Reynolds	.04	.03	.02
470	Harold Baines	.09	.07	.04
471	Dennis Lamp	.04	.03	.02
472	Tom Gordon	.20	.15	.08
473	Terry Puhl	.04	.03	.02
474	Curtis Wilkerson	.04	.03	.02
475	Dan Quisenberry	.05	.04	.02
476	Oddibe McDowell	.07	.05	.03
477	Zane Smith	.04	.03	.02
478	Franklin Stubbs	.04	.03	.02
479	Wallace Johnson	.04	.03	.02
480	Jay Tibbs	.04	.03	.02
481	Tom Glavine	.15	.07	.03
482	Manny Lee	.05	.04	.02
483	Joe Hesketh	.04	.03	.02
484	Mike Bielecki	.07	.05	.03
485	Greg Brock	.06	.05	.02
486	Pascual Perez	.06	.05	.02
487	Kirk Gibson	.09	.07	.04
488	Scott Sanderson	.05	.04	.02
489	Domingo Ramos	.04	.03	.02
490	Kal Daniels	.10	.08	.04
491a	David Wells (reversed negative on back photo)	3.00	2.25	1.25
491b	David Wells (corrected)	.05	.04	.02
492	Jerry Reed	.04	.03	.02
493	Eric Show	.06	.05	.02
494	Mike Pagliarulo	.06	.05	.02
495	Ron Robinson	.05	.04	.02
496	Brad Komminsk	.04	.03	.02
497	*Greg Litton*	.08	.06	.03
498	Chris James	.07	.05	.02
499	Luis Quinones (FC)	.05	.04	.02
500	Frank Viola	.10	.08	.04
501	Tim Teufel	.05	.04	.02
502	Terry Leach	.04	.03	.02
503	Matt Williams	.20	.15	.08
504	Tim Leary	.06	.05	.02
505	Doug Drabek	.06	.05	.02
506	Mariano Duncan	.06	.05	.02
507	Charlie Hayes	.10	.08	.04
508	*Albert Belle*	1.25	.90	.50
509	Pat Sheridan	.05	.04	.02
510	Mackey Sasser	.05	.04	.02
511	Jose Rijo	.09	.07	.04
512	Mike Smithson	.04	.03	.02
513	Gary Ward	.04	.03	.02
514	Dion James	.06	.05	.02
515	Jim Gott	.06	.05	.02
516	Drew Hall (FC)	.04	.03	.02
517	Doug Bair	.04	.03	.02
518	*Scott Scudder*	.10	.08	.04
519	Rick Aguilera	.06	.05	.02
520	Rafael Belliard	.05	.04	.02
521	Jay Buhner	.10	.08	.04
522	Jeff Reardon	.06	.05	.02
523	Steve Rosenberg (FC)	.06	.05	.02
524	Randy Velarde (FC)	.09	.07	.04
525	Jeff Musselman	.06	.05	.02
526	Bill Long	.06	.05	.02
527	*Gary Wayne*	.06	.05	.02
528	*Dave Johnson* (FC)	.06	.05	.02
529	Ron Kittle	.08	.06	.03
530	Erik Hanson (FC)	.20	.15	.08
531	Steve Wilson (FC)	.20	.15	.08
532	Joey Meyer	.04	.03	.02
533	Curt Young	.04	.03	.02
534	Kelly Downs	.06	.05	.02
535	Joe Girardi	.20	.15	.08
536	Lance Blankenship	.09	.07	.04
537	Greg Mathews	.05	.04	.02
538	Donell Nixon	.04	.03	.02
539	Mark Knudson (FC)	.06	.05	.02
540	*Jeff Wetherby* (FC)	.10	.08	.04
541	Darrin Jackson	.04	.03	.02
542	Terry Mulholland	.09	.07	.03
543	Eric Hetzel (FC)	.08	.06	.03
544	*Rick Reed* (FC)	.08	.06	.03
545	Dennis Cook (FC)	.10	.08	.04
546	Mike Jackson	.05	.04	.02
547	Brian Fisher	.06	.05	.02
548	*Gene Harris* (FC)	.10	.08	.04
549	Jeff King (FC)	.20	.15	.08
550	Dave Dravecky (Salute)	.10	.08	.04
551	Randy Kutcher (FC)	.08	.06	.03
552	Mark Portugal	.06	.05	.02
553	*Jim Corsi* (FC)	.12	.09	.05
554	Todd Stottlemyre	.12	.09	.05
555	Scott Bankhead	.09	.07	.04
556	Ken Dayley	.05	.04	.02
557	*Rick Wrona* (FC)	.15	.11	.06
558	*Sammy Sosa*	.60	.45	.25
559	Keith Miller	.08	.06	.03
560	Ken Griffey, Jr.	2.00	1.50	.80
561a	Ryne Sandberg (HL, 3B on front)	10.00	7.50	4.00
561b	Ryne Sandberg (HL, no position)	.50	.40	.20
562	Billy Hatcher	.06	.05	.02
563	Jay Bell (FC)	.09	.07	.04
564	*Jack Daugherty*	.06	.05	.02
565	*Rich Monteleone*	.08	.06	.03
566	Bo Jackson (AS-MVP)	.30	.25	.12
567	*Tony Fossas* (FC)	.06	.05	.02
568	*Roy Smith* (FC)	.06	.05	.02
569	*Jaime Navarro*	.15	.10	.05
570	Lance Johnson	.15	.11	.06
571	*Mike Dyer*	.06	.05	.02
572	*Kevin Ritz* (FC)	.10	.08	.04
573	Dave West	.15	.11	.06
574	*Gary Mielke*	.08	.06	.03
575	Scott Lusader (FC)	.09	.07	.04
576	*Joe Oliver*	.10	.08	.04
577	Sandy Alomar, Jr.	.10	.08	.04
578	Andy Benes	.30	.25	.12
579	Tim Jones	.07	.05	.03
580	*Randy McCament* (FC)	.06	.05	.02
581	Curt Schilling (FC)	.15	.11	.06
582	*John Orton*	.08	.06	.03
583a	*Milt Cuyler* (998 games)	2.00	1.50	.80
583b	*Milt Cuyler* (98 games)	.15	.11	.06
584	*Eric Anthony*	.30	.25	.12
585	*Greg Vaughn*	.40	.30	.15
586	*Deion Sanders*	.50	.40	.20
587	Jose DeJesus (FC)	.06	.05	.02
588	*Chip Hale* (FC)	.15	.11	.06
589	*John Olerud*	1.50	1.25	.60
590	*Steve Olin*	.08	.06	.03
591	*Marquis Grissom*	.60	.45	.25
592	*Moises Alou*	.60	.45	.25
593	Mark Lemke (FC)	.06	.05	.02
594	*Dean Palmer*	.50	.40	.20
595	*Robin Ventura*	.75	.50	.25
596	*Tino Martinez*	.10	.07	.04
597	*Mike Huff*	.08	.06	.03
598	*Scott Hemond*	.08	.06	.03
599	*Wally Whitehurst* (FC)	.20	.15	.08
600	*Todd Zeile*	.20	.15	.08
601	*Glenallen Hill*	.10	.08	.04
602	Hal Morris (FC)	.15	.11	.06
603	Juan Bell (FC)	.15	.11	.06
604	*Bobby Rose*	.08	.06	.03
605	*Matt Merullo* (FC)	.20	.15	.08
606	*Kevin Maas*	.08	.06	.03
607	*Randy Nosek* (FC)	.15	.11	.06
608	*Billy Bates* (FC)	.06	.05	.02
609	*Mike Stanton*	.10	.07	.04
610	*Goose Gozzo* (FC)	.10	.08	.04
611	*Charles Nagy* (FC)	.20	.15	.08
612	*Scott Coolbaugh* (FC)	.08	.06	.03
613	*Jose Vizcaino* (FC)	.25	.20	.10
614	*Greg Smith* (FC)	.08	.06	.03
615	*Jeff Huson*	.10	.08	.04
616	*Mickey Weston* (FC)	.08	.06	.03
617	*John Pawlowski* (FC)	.08	.06	.03
618a	*Joe Skalski* (FC) (uniform #27)	.15	.11	.06
618b	*Joe Skalski* (FC) (uniform #67)	2.00	1.50	.80
619	*Bernie Williams*	.25	.20	.10
620	*Shawn Holman*	.06	.05	.02
621	*Gary Eave*	.06	.05	.02
622	*Darrin Fletcher*	.20	.15	.08
623	*Pat Combs*	.10	.08	.04
624	*Mike Blowers*	.08	.06	.03
625	*Kevin Appier*	.30	.25	.12
626	*Pat Austin*	.08	.06	.03
627	*Kelly Mann*	.06	.05	.02

628	*Matt Kinzer*	.08	.06	.03
629	*Chris Hammond*	.25	.20	.10
630	*Dean Wilkins* (FC)	.08	.06	.03
631	*Larry Walker*	1.00	.45	.25
632	*Blaine Beatty*	.20	.15	.08
633a	Tom Barrett (FC) (uniform #29)	.15	.11	.06
633b	Tom Barrett (FC) (uniform #14)	4.00	3.00	1.50
634	*Stan Belinda* (FC)	.10	.08	.04
635	*Tex Smith* (FC)	.06	.05	.02
636	*Hensley Meulens*	.08	.06	.03
637	*Juan Gonzalez*	2.50	2.00	1.00
638	*Lenny Webster*	.10	.08	.04
639	*Mark Gardner*	.10	.08	.04
640	*Tommy Greene*	.20	.15	.08
641	*Mike Hartley* (FC)	.08	.06	.03
642	*Phil Stephenson* (FC)	.06	.05	.02
643	*Kevin Mmahat* (FC)	.15	.11	.06
644	*Ed Whited* (FC)	.08	.06	.03
645	*Delino DeShields*	.40	.30	.15
646	Kevin Blankenship (FC)	.15	.11	.06
647	*Paul Sorrento*	.20	.15	.08
648	*Mike Roesler* (FC)	.15	.11	.06
649	*Jason Grimsley*	.10	.08	.04
650	*Dave Justice*	2.00	1.50	.80
651	*Scott Cooper*	.40	.30	.15
652	Dave Eiland (FC)	.08	.06	.03
653	*Mike Munoz* (FC)	.08	.06	.03
654	*Jeff Fischer* (FC)	.08	.06	.03
655	*Terry Jorgenson* (FC)	.06	.05	.02
656	*George Canale* (FC)	.06	.05	.02
657	*Brian DuBois*	.08	.06	.03
658	Carlos Quintana	.10	.08	.04
659	Luis de los Santos	.06	.05	.02
660	Jerald Clark	.10	.08	.04
661	*Donald Harris* (1st Round Pick)	.12	.09	.05
662	*Paul Coleman* (1st Round Pick)	.20	.15	.08
663	*Frank Thomas* (1st Round Pick)	7.00	5.25	2.75
664	*Brent Mayne* (1st Round Pick)	.12	.09	.05
665	*Eddie Zosky* (1st Round Pick)	.10	.07	.04
666	*Steve Hosey* (1st Round Pick)	.20	.15	.08
667	*Scott Bryant* (1st Round Pick)	.10	.07	.04
668	*Tom Goodwin* (1st Round Pick)	.10	.07	.04
669	*Cal Eldred* (1st Round Pick)	.25	.20	.10
670	*Earl Cunningham* (1st Round Pick)	.10	.07	.04
671	*Alan Zinter* (1st Round Pick)	.25	.20	.10
672	*Chuck Knoblauch* (1st Round Pick)	.35	.25	.14
673	*Kyle Abbott* (1st Round Pick)	.10	.07	.04
674	*Roger Salkeld* (1st Round Pick)	.25	.20	.10
675	*Mo Vaughn* (1st Round Pick)	1.25	.90	.50
676	*Kiki Jones* (1st Round Pick)	.12	.09	.05
677	*Tyler Houston* (1st Round Pick)	.12	.09	.05
678	*Jeff Jackson* (1st Round Pick)	.12	.09	.05
679	*Greg Gohr* (1st Round Pick)	.10	.07	.04
680	*Ben McDonald* (1st Round Pick)	.75	.60	.30
681	*Greg Blosser* (1st Round Pick)	.25	.20	.10
682	*Willie Green* ((Greene) 1st Round Pick)	.15	.10	.05
683	Wade Boggs (Dream Team)	.10	.07	.04
684	Will Clark (Dream Team)	.20	.15	.08
685	Tony Gwynn (Dream Team)	.20	.15	.08
686	Rickey Henderson (Dream Team)	.10	.07	.04
687	Bo Jackson (Dream Team)	.30	.25	.12
688	Mark Langston (Dream Team)	.10	.07	.04
689	Barry Larkin (Dream Team)	.12	.09	.05
690	Kirby Puckett (Dream Team)	.20	.15	.08
691	Ryne Sandberg (Dream Team)	.30	.25	.12
692	Mike Scott (Dream Team)	.10	.07	.04
693	Terry Steinbach (Dream Team)	.10	.07	.04
694	Bobby Thigpen (Dream Team)	.08	.06	.03
695	Mitch Williams (Dream Team)	.10	.07	.04
696	Nolan Ryan (HL)	.60	.45	.25
697	Bo Jackson (FB/BB)	1.50	1.25	.60
698	Rickey Henderson (ALCS MVP)	.12	.09	.05
699	Will Clark (NLCS MVP)	.15	.11	.06
700	World Series Games 1-2 (Dave Stewart/Mike Moore)	.10	.07	.04
701	Lights Out: Candlestick	.12	.09	.05
702	World Series Game 3	.12	.09	.05
703	World Series Wrap-up	.30	.25	.12
704	Wade Boggs (HL)	.10	.07	.04

1990 Score Dream Team

This 10 card "Dream Team" set, in the same format as those found in the regular issue 1990 Score, were available only in factory sets for the hobby trade. Factory sets for general retail outlets did not include these cards, nor were they available in Score packs. Cards carry a "B" prefix to their numbers.

		MT	NR MT	EX
	Complete Set (10):	8.00	6.00	3.25
	Common Player:	.25	.15	.10
1	A. Bartlett Giamatti	1.00	.75	.40
2	Pat Combs	.25	.15	.10
3	Todd Zeile	1.50	1.00	.60
4	Luis de los Santos	.25	.15	.10
5	Mark Lemke	.25	.20	.10
6	Robin Ventura	5.00	3.75	2.00
7	Jeff Huson	.25	.15	.10
8	Greg Vaughn	1.00	.70	.40
9	Marquis Grissom	1.50	1.00	.60
10	Eric Anthony	.60	.45	.25

1990 Score McDonald's

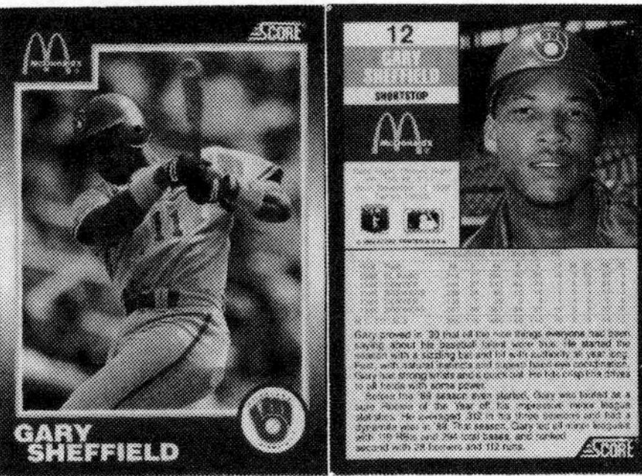

This 25-card set was released exclusively in the Boise, Idaho area. The set features baseball all-stars and was very limited in production. The cards are styled after the regular 1990 Score issue. The McDonald's logo appears on the front and back of the cards.

		MT	NR MT	EX
	Complete Set (25):	200.00	150.00	80.00
	Common Player:	4.00	3.00	1.50
1	Will Clark	25.00	18.50	10.00
2	Sandy Alomar, Jr.	5.00	3.75	2.00
3	Julio Franco	5.00	3.75	2.00
4	Carlton Fisk	10.00	7.50	4.00
5	Rickey Henderson	20.00	15.00	8.00
6	Matt Williams	7.00	5.25	2.75
7	John Franco	4.00	3.00	1.50
8	Ryne Sandberg	25.00	18.50	10.00
9	Kelly Gruber	4.00	3.00	1.50
10	Andre Dawson	8.00	6.00	3.25
11	Barry Bonds	25.00	18.50	10.00
12	Gary Sheffield	12.00	9.00	4.75
13	Ramon Martinez	5.00	3.75	2.00
14	Len Dykstra	5.00	3.75	2.00
15	Benito Santiago	4.00	3.00	1.50
16	Cecil Fielder	15.00	11.00	6.00
17	John Olerud	8.00	6.00	3.25
18	Roger Clemens	15.00	11.00	6.00
19	George Brett	20.00	15.00	8.00
20	George Bell	4.00	3.00	1.50
21	Ozzie Guillen	4.00	3.00	1.50
22	Steve Sax	4.00	3.00	1.50
23	Dave Stewart	5.00	3.75	2.00
24	Ozzie Smith	10.00	7.50	4.00
25	Robin Yount	15.00	11.00	6.00

1990 Score Rising Stars

For the second consecutive year Score produced a 100-card "Rising Stars" set. The 1990 Score Rising Stars were made available as a boxed set and were also marketed with a related magazine like the 1989 issue. Magic Motion trivia cards featuring past MVP's accompany the card set. The cards feature full-color action photos on the front and posed shots on the flip sides.

		MT	NR MT	EX
	Complete Set (100):	12.00	9.00	4.75
	Common Player:	.08	.06	.03
1	Tom Gordon	.12	.09	.05
2	Jerome Walton	.12	.09	.05
3	Ken Griffey, Jr.	3.00	2.25	1.25
4	Dwight Smith	.12	.09	.05
5	Jim Abbott	.25	.20	.10
6	Todd Zeile	.40	.30	.15
7	Donn Pall	.08	.06	.03
8	Rick Reed	.08	.06	.03
9	Joey Belle	.60	.45	.25
10	Gregg Jefferies	.35	.25	.14
11	Kevin Ritz	.10	.08	.04
12	Charlie Hayes	.15	.11	.06
13	Kevin Appier	.30	.25	.12
14	Jeff Huson	.15	.11	.06
15	Gary Wayne	.08	.06	.03
16	Eric Yelding	.15	.11	.06
17	Clay Parker	.08	.06	.03
18	Junior Felix	.30	.25	.12
19	Derek Lilliquist	.08	.06	.03
20	Gary Sheffield	.30	.25	.12
21	Craig Worthington	.08	.06	.03
22	Jeff Brantley	.10	.08	.04
23	Eric Hetzel	.10	.08	.04
24	Greg Harris	.08	.06	.03
25	John Wetteland	.20	.15	.08
26	Joe Oliver	.15	.11	.06
27	Kevin Maas	.30	.25	.12
28	Kevin Brown	.10	.08	.04
29	Mike Stanton	.15	.11	.06
30	Greg Vaughn	.40	.30	.15
31	Ron Jones	.08	.06	.03
32	Gregg Olson	.20	.15	.08
33	Joe Girardi	.10	.08	.04
34	Ken Hill	.08	.06	.03
35	Sammy Sosa	.35	.25	.14
36	Geronimo Berroa	.08	.06	.03
37	Omar Vizquel	.10	.08	.04
38	Dean Palmer	.10	.08	.04
39	John Olerud	.70	.50	.30
40	Deion Sanders	.50	.40	.20
41	Randy Kramer	.08	.06	.03
42	Scott Lusader	.08	.06	.03
43	Dave Johnson	.08	.06	.03
44	Jeff Wetherby	.08	.06	.03
45	Eric Anthony	.30	.25	.12
46	Kenny Rogers	.10	.08	.04
47	Matt Winters	.08	.06	.03
48	Goose Gozzo	.10	.08	.04
49	Carlos Quintana	.15	.11	.06
50	Bob Geren	.10	.08	.04
51	Chad Kreuter	.08	.06	.03
52	Randy Johnson	.25	.20	.10
53	Hensley Meulens	.15	.11	.06
54	Gene Harris	.10	.08	.04
55	Bill Spiers	.10	.08	.04
56	Kelly Mann	.15	.11	.06
57	Tom McCarthy	.08	.06	.03
58	Steve Finley	.10	.08	.04
59	Ramon Martinez	.30	.25	.12
60	Greg Briley	.08	.06	.03
61	Jack Daugherty	.10	.08	.04
62	Tim Jones	.08	.06	.03
63	Doug Strange	.08	.06	.03
64	John Orton	.08	.06	.03
65	Scott Scudder	.15	.11	.06
66	Mark Gardner	.20	.15	.08
67	Mark Carreon	.08	.06	.03
68	Bob Milacki	.08	.06	.03
69	Andy Benes	.20	.15	.08
70	Carlos Martinez	.10	.08	.04
71	Jeff King	.15	.11	.06
72	Brad Arnsberg	.08	.06	.03
73	Rick Wrona	.08	.06	.03
74	Cris Carpenter	.08	.06	.03
75	Dennis Cook	.08	.06	.03
76	Pete Harnisch	.10	.08	.04
77	Greg Hibbard	.15	.11	.06
78	Ed Whited	.08	.06	.03
79	Scott Coolbaugh	.08	.06	.03
80	Billy Bates	.08	.06	.03
81	German Gonzalez	.08	.06	.03
82	Lance Blankenship	.08	.06	.03
83	Lenny Harris	.10	.08	.04
84	Milt Cuyler	.20	.15	.08
85	Erik Hanson	.20	.15	.08
86	Kent Anderson	.08	.06	.03
87	Hal Morris	.40	.30	.15
88	Mike Brumley	.08	.06	.03
89	Ken Patterson	.08	.06	.03
90	Mike Devereaux	.08	.06	.03
91	Greg Litton	.10	.08	.04
92	Rolando Roomes	.08	.06	.03
93	Ben McDonald	.60	.45	.25
94	Curt Schilling	.10	.08	.04
95	Jose DeJesus	.15	.11	.06
96	Robin Ventura	.40	.30	.15
97	Steve Searcy	.08	.06	.03
98	Chip Hale	.10	.08	.04
99	Marquis Grissom	.40	.30	.15
100	Luis de los Santos	.10	.08	.04

Definitions for grading conditions are located in the Introduction of this price guide.

1990 Score Superstar

100 of the game's top players are featured in this set. The card fronts feature full-color action photos and are similar in style to the past Score Superstar set. The set was marketed as a boxed set and with a special magazine devoted to baseball's 100 hottest

players. Each set includes a series of Magic Motion cards honoring past MVP winners. The player cards measure 2-1/2" by 3-1/2" in size.

		MT	NR MT	EX
Complete Set (100):		8.00	6.00	3.25
Common Player:		.08	.06	.03
1	Kirby Puckett	.40	.30	.15
2	Steve Sax	.10	.08	.04
3	Tony Gwynn	.15	.11	.06
4	Willie Randolph	.08	.06	.03
5	Jose Canseco	.70	.50	.30
6	Ozzie Smith	.30	.25	.12
7	Rick Reuschel	.08	.06	.03
8	Bill Doran	.08	.06	.03
9	Mickey Tettleton	.20	.15	.08
10	Don Mattingly	.50	.40	.20
11	Greg Swindell	.08	.06	.03
12	Bert Blyleven	.10	.08	.04
13	Dave Stewart	.15	.11	.06
14	Andres Galarraga	.20	.15	.08
15	Darryl Strawberry	.15	.11	.06
16	Ellis Burks	.20	.15	.08
17	Paul O'Neill	.20	.15	.08
18	Bruce Hurst	.08	.06	.03
19	Dave Smith	.08	.06	.03
20	Carney Lansford	.08	.06	.03
21	Robby Thompson	.15	.11	.06
22	Gary Gaetti	.10	.08	.04
23	Jeff Russell	.08	.06	.03
24	Chuck Finley	.10	.08	.04
25	Mark McGwire	.35	.25	.14
26	Alvin Davis	.10	.08	.04
27	George Bell	.10	.08	.04
28	Cory Snyder	.08	.06	.03
29	Keith Hernandez	.08	.06	.03
30	Will Clark	.40	.30	.15
31	Steve Bedrosian	.08	.06	.03
32	Ryne Sandberg	.60	.45	.25
33	Tom Browning	.08	.06	.03
34	Tim Burke	.08	.06	.03
35	John Smoltz	.10	.08	.04
36	Phil Bradley	.08	.06	.03
37	Bobby Bonilla	.15	.11	.06
38	Kirk McCaskill	.08	.06	.03
39	Dave Righetti	.10	.08	.04
40	Bo Jackson	.50	.40	.20
41	Alan Trammell	.20	.15	.08
42	Mike Moore	.08	.06	.03
43	Harold Reynolds	.08	.06	.03
44	Nolan Ryan	.80	.60	.30
45	Fred McGriff	.25	.20	.10
46	Brian Downing	.08	.06	.03
47	Brett Butler	.08	.06	.03
48	Mike Scioscia	.08	.06	.03
49	John Franco	.08	.06	.03
50	Kevin Mitchell	.30	.25	.12
51	Mark Davis	.08	.06	.03
52	Glenn Davis	.10	.08	.04
53	Barry Bonds	.60	.45	.25
54	Dwight Evans	.10	.08	.04
55	Terry Steinbach	.08	.06	.03
56	Dave Gallagher	.08	.06	.03
57	Roberto Kelly	.20	.15	.08
58	Rafael Palmeiro	.20	.15	.08
59	Joe Carter	.20	.15	.08
60	Mark Grace	.20	.15	.08
61	Pedro Guerrero	.10	.08	.04
62	Von Hayes	.08	.06	.03
63	Benny Santiago	.15	.11	.06
64	Dale Murphy	.20	.15	.08
65	John Smiley	.08	.06	.03
66	Cal Ripken,Jr.	.60	.45	.25
67	Mike Greenwell	.25	.20	.10
68	Devon White	.20	.15	.08
69	Ed Whitson	.08	.06	.03
70	Carlton Fisk	.20	.15	.08
71	Lou Whitaker	.15	.11	.06
72	Danny Tartabull	.10	.08	.04
73	Vince Coleman	.10	.08	.04
74	Andre Dawson	.15	.11	.06
75	Tim Raines	.10	.08	.04
76	George Brett	.60	.45	.25
77	Tom Herr	.08	.06	.03
78	Andy Van Slyke	.10	.08	.04
79	Roger Clemens	.30	.25	.12
80	Wade Boggs	.40	.30	.15
81	Wally Joyner	.10	.08	.04
82	Lonnie Smith	.08	.06	.03
83	Howard Johnson	.15	.11	.06
84	Julio Franco	.15	.11	.06
85	Ruben Sierra	.20	.15	.08
86	Dan Plesac	.08	.06	.03
87	Bobby Thigpen	.08	.06	.03
88	Kevin Seitzer	.10	.08	.04
89	Dave Steib	.10	.08	.04
90	Rickey Henderson	.40	.30	.15
91	Jeffrey Leonard	.08	.06	.03
92	Robin Yount	.40	.30	.15
93	Mitch Williams	.10	.08	.04
94	Orel Hershiser	.20	.15	.08
95	Eric Davis	.15	.11	.06
96	Mark Langston	.10	.08	.04
97	Mike Scott	.08	.06	.03
98	Paul Molitor	.30	.25	.12
99	Dwight Gooden	.25	.20	.10
100	Kevin Bass	.08	.06	.03

1990 Score Traded

This 110-card set features players with new teams as well as 1990 Major League rookies. The cards feature full-color action photos framed in yellow with an orange border. The player's name and position appear in green print below the photo. The team logo is displayed next to the player's name. The card backs feature posed player photos and follow the style of the regular 1990 Score issue. The cards are numbered 1T-110T. Young hockey phenom Eric Lindros is featured trying out for the Toronto Blue Jays.

		MT	NR MT	EX
Complete Set (110):		12.00	9.00	4.75
Common Player:		.06	.05	.02
1T	Dave Winfield	.20	.15	.08
2T	Kevin Bass	.06	.05	.02
3T	Nick Esasky	.06	.05	.02
4T	Mitch Webster	.06	.05	.02
5T	Pascual Perez	.06	.05	.02
6T	Gary Pettis	.06	.05	.02
7T	Tony Pena	.08	.06	.03
8T	Candy Maldonado	.08	.06	.03
9T	Cecil Fielder	.30	.25	.12
10T	Carmelo Martinez	.06	.05	.02
11T	Mark Langston	.08	.06	.03
12T	Dave Parker	.15	.11	.06
13T	Don Slaught	.06	.05	.02
14T	Tony Phillips	.06	.05	.02
15T	John Franco	.08	.06	.03
16T	Randy Myers	.08	.06	.03
17T	Jeff Reardon	.08	.06	.03
18T	Sandy Alomar, Jr.	.20	.15	.08
19T	Joe Carter	.20	.15	.08
20T	Fred Lynn	.06	.05	.02
21T	Storm Davis	.06	.05	.02
22T	Craig Lefferts	.06	.05	.02
23T	Pete O'Brien	.06	.05	.02
24T	Dennis Boyd	.06	.05	.02
25T	Lloyd Moseby	.06	.05	.02
26T	Mark Davis	.06	.05	.02
27T	Tim Leary	.06	.05	.02
28T	Gerald Perry	.06	.05	.02
29T	Don Aase	.06	.05	.02
30T	Ernie Whitt	.06	.05	.02
31T	Dale Murphy	.10	.08	.04
32T	Alejandro Pena	.06	.05	.02
33T	Juan Samuel	.08	.06	.03
34T	Hubie Brooks	.08	.06	.03
35T	Gary Carter	.10	.08	.04
36T	Jim Presley	.06	.05	.02
37T	Wally Backman	.06	.05	.02
38T	Matt Nokes	.06	.05	.02
39T	Dan Petry	.06	.05	.02
40T	Franklin Stubbs	.06	.05	.02
41T	Jeff Huson	.15	.11	.06
42T	Billy Hatcher	.06	.05	.02
43T	Terry Leach	.06	.05	.02
44T	Phil Bradley	.06	.05	.02
45T	Claudell Washington	.06	.05	.02
46T	Luis Polonia	.06	.05	.02
47T	Daryl Boston	.06	.05	.02
48T	Lee Smith	.08	.06	.03
49T	Tom Brunansky	.08	.06	.03
50T	Mike Witt	.06	.05	.02
51T	Willie Randolph	.08	.06	.03
52T	Stan Javier	.06	.05	.02
53T	Brad Komminsk	.06	.05	.02
54T	John Candelaria	.06	.05	.02
55T	Bryn Smith	.06	.05	.02
56T	Glenn Braggs	.06	.05	.02
57T	Keith Hernandez	.08	.06	.03
58T	Ken Oberkfell	.06	.05	.02
59T	Steve Jeltz	.06	.05	.02
60T	Chris James	.06	.05	.02
61T	Scott Sanderson	.06	.05	.02
62T	Bill Long	.06	.05	.02
63T	Rick Cerone	.06	.05	.02
64T	Scott Bailes	.06	.05	.02
65T	Larry Sheets	.06	.05	.02
66T	Junior Ortiz	.06	.05	.02
67T	Francisco Cabrera (FC)	.06	.05	.02
68T	Gary DiSarcina (FC)	.15	.11	.06
69T	Greg Olson (FC)	.08	.06	.03
70T	Beau Allred (FC)	.06	.05	.02
71T	Oscar Azocar (FC)	.10	.07	.04
72T	Kent Mercker (FC)	.30	.25	.12
73T	John Burkett (FC)	.40	.30	.15
74T	Carlos Baerga (FC)	2.00	1.50	.80
75T	Dave Hollins (FC)	.75	.60	.30
76T	Todd Hundley (FC)	.20	.15	.08
77T	Rick Parker (FC)	.08	.06	.03
78T	Steve Cummings (FC)	.08	.06	.03
79T	Bill Sampen (FC)	.08	.06	.03
80T	Jerry Kutzler (FC)	.08	.06	.03
81T	Derek Bell (FC)	.35	.25	.14
82T	Kevin Tapani (FC)	.30	.25	.12
83T	Jim Leyritz (FC)	.25	.20	.10
84T	Ray Lankford (FC)	1.25	.90	.50
85T	Wayne Edwards (FC)	.15	.11	.06
86T	Frank Thomas	7.00	5.25	2.75
87T	Tim Naehring (FC)	.20	.15	.08
88T	Willie Blair (FC)	.15	.11	.06
89T	Alan Mills (FC)	.12	.09	.05
90T	Scott Radinsky (FC)	.08	.06	.03
91T	Howard Farmer (FC)	.08	.06	.03
92T	Julio Machado (FC)	.06	.05	.02
93T	Rafael Valdez (FC)	.06	.05	.02
94T	Shawn Boskie (FC)	.25	.20	.10
95T	David Segui (FC)	.20	.15	.08
96T	Chris Hoiles (FC)	.40	.30	.15
97T	D.J. Dozier (FC)	.08	.06	.03
98T	Hector Villanueva (FC)	.08	.06	.03
99T	Eric Gunderson (FC)	.10	.08	.04
100T	Eric Lindros (FC)	5.00	3.75	2.00
101T	Dave Otto (FC)	.12	.09	.05
102T	Dana Kiecker (FC)	.10	.08	.04
103T	Tim Drummond (FC)	.08	.06	.03
104T	Mickey Pina (FC)	.06	.05	.02
105T	Craig Grebeck (FC)	.10	.08	.04
106T	Bernard Gilkey (FC)	.50	.40	.20
107T	Tim Layana (FC)	.10	.07	.04
108T	Scott Chiamparino (FC)	.10	.08	.04
109T	Steve Avery (FC)	1.00	.70	.40
110T	Terry Shumpert (FC)	.10	.08	.04

1990 Score Young Superstars Set I

For the third consecutive year, Score produced Young Superstars boxed sets. The 1990 versions contain 42 player cards plus five Magic-Motion trivia cards. The cards are similar to previous Score Young Superstar sets, with action photography on the front and a glossy finish. Card backs have a color portrait, major league statistics and scouting reports. Besides the boxed set, cards from Set I were inserted into rak packs.

		MT	NR MT	EX
Complete Set (42):		8.00	6.00	3.25
Common Player:		.15	.11	.06
1	Bo Jackson	.25	.20	.10
2	Dwight Smith	.15	.11	.06
3	Joey Belle	1.25	.90	.50
4	Gregg Olson	.15	.11	.06
5	Jim Abbott	.45	.35	.20
6	Felix Fermin	.15	.11	.06
7	Brian Holman	.15	.11	.06
8	Clay Parker	.15	.11	.06
9	Junior Felix	.15	.11	.06
10	Joe Oliver	.25	.20	.10
11	Steve Finley	.25	.20	.10
12	Greg Briley	.15	.11	.06
13	Greg Vaughn	.25	.20	.10
14	Bill Spiers	.15	.11	.06
15	Eric Yelding	.15	.11	.06
16	Jose Gonzalez	.15	.11	.06
17	Mark Carreon	.15	.11	.06
18	Greg Harris	.15	.11	.06
19	Felix Jose	.25	.20	.10
20	Bob Milacki	.15	.11	.06
21	Kenny Rogers	.15	.11	.06
22	Rolando Roomes	.15	.11	.06
23	Bip Roberts	.15	.11	.06
24	Jeff Brantley	.15	.11	.06
25	Jeff Ballard	.15	.11	.06
26	John Dopson	.15	.11	.06
27	Ken Patterson	.15	.11	.06
28	Omar Vizquel	.25	.20	.10
29	Kevin Brown	.15	.11	.06
30	Derek Lilliquist	.15	.11	.06
31	David Wells	.15	.11	.06
32	Ken Hill	.15	.11	.06
33	Greg Litton	.15	.11	.06
34	Rob Ducey	.15	.11	.06
35	Carlos Martinez	.15	.11	.06
36	John Smoltz	.45	.35	.20
37	Lenny Harris	.15	.11	.06
38	Charlie Hayes	.25	.20	.10
39	Tommy Gregg	.15	.11	.06
40	John Wetteland	.25	.20	.10
41	Jeff Huson	.15	.11	.06
42	Eric Anthony	.25	.20	.10

1990 Score Young Superstars Set II

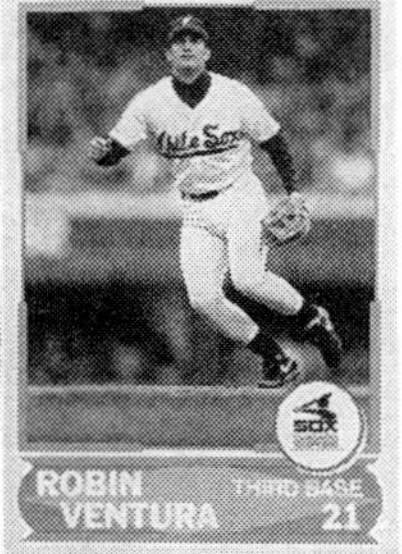

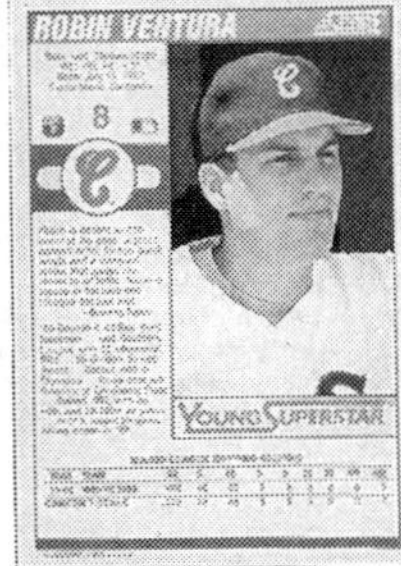

Available only as a boxed set via a mail-order offer, Set II of 1990 Score Young Superstars is identical in format to Set I, with the exception that the graphic elements on the front of Set II cards are in red and green, while in Set I they are in blue and magenta.

		MT	NR MT	EX
Complete Set (42):		8.00	6.00	3.25
Common Player:		.15	.11	.06
1	Todd Zeile	.25	.20	.10
2	Ben McDonald	.25	.20	.10
3	Delino DeShields	.25	.20	.10
4	Pat Combs	.15	.11	.06
5	John Olerud	.75	.60	.30
6	Marquis Grissom	.45	.35	.20
7	Mike Stanton	.15	.11	.06
8	Robin Ventura	.45	.35	.20
9	Larry Walker	.25	.20	.10
10	Dante Bichette	.15	.11	.06
11	Jack Armstrong	.15	.11	.06
12	Jay Bell	.15	.11	.06
13	Andy Benes	.25	.20	.10
14	Joey Cora	.15	.11	.06
15	Rob Dibble	.15	.11	.06
16	Jeff King	.35	.25	.14
17	Jeff Hamilton	.15	.11	.06
18	Erik Hanson	.15	.11	.06
19	Pete Harnisch	.15	.11	.06
20	Greg Hibbard	.15	.11	.06
21	Stan Javier	.15	.11	.06
22	Mark Lemke	.15	.11	.06
23	Steve Olin	.15	.11	.06
24	Tommy Greene	.25	.20	.10
25	Sammy Sosa	.25	.20	.10
26	Gary Wayne	.15	.11	.06
27	Deion Sanders	.60	.45	.25
28	Steve Wilson	.15	.11	.06
29	Joe Girardi	.25	.20	.10
30	John Orton	.15	.11	.06
31	Kevin Tapani	.15	.11	.06
32	Carlos Baerga	1.25	.90	.50
33	Glenallen Hill	.15	.11	.06
34	Mike Blowers	.15	.11	.06
35	Dave Hollins	.45	.35	.20
36	Lance Blankenship	.15	.11	.06
37	Hal Morris	.15	.11	.06
38	Lance Johnson	.15	.11	.06
39	Chris Gwynn	.15	.11	.06
40	Doug Dascenzo	.15	.11	.06
41	Jerald Clark	.15	.11	.06
42	Carlos Quintana	.15	.11	.06

1991 Score

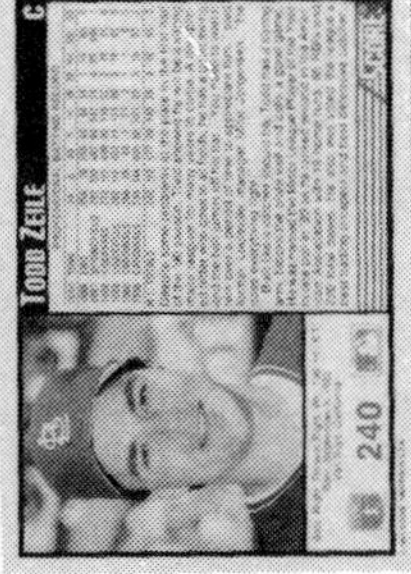

Score introduced a two series format in 1991. The first series includes cards 1-441. Score cards once again feature multiple border colors within the set, several subsets (Master Blaster, K-Man, Highlights and Rifleman), full-color action photos on the front, posed photos on the flip side. Score eliminated providing the player's uniform number on the 1991 cards. Card number 441 of Series I features a Jose Canseco Vanity Fair photo. All of the 1991 Dream Team cards feature this style. Prospects and #1 Draft Picks highlight the 1991 set. The second series was released in February of 1991.

		MT	NR MT	EX
Complete Set (893):		20.00	15.00	8.00
Common Player:		.04	.03	.02
1	Jose Canseco	.15	.10	.05
2	Ken Griffey, Jr.	1.00	.75	.40
3	Ryne Sandberg	.20	.15	.08
4	Nolan Ryan	.40	.30	.15
5	Bo Jackson	.25	.20	.10
6	Bret Saberhagen	.12	.09	.05
7	Will Clark	.20	.15	.08
8	Ellis Burks	.15	.11	.06
9	Joe Carter	.20	.15	.08
10	Rickey Henderson	.25	.20	.10
11	Ozzie Guillen	.10	.08	.04
12	Wade Boggs	.20	.15	.08
13	Jerome Walton	.08	.06	.03
14	John Franco	.10	.08	.04
15	Ricky Jordan	.08	.06	.03
16	Wally Backman	.04	.03	.02
17	Rob Dibble	.10	.08	.04
18	Glenn Braggs	.05	.04	.02
19	Cory Snyder	.10	.08	.04
20	Kal Daniels	.10	.08	.04
21	Mark Langston	.10	.08	.04
22	Kevin Gross	.06	.05	.02
23	Don Mattingly	.30	.25	.12
24	Dave Righetti	.08	.06	.03
25	Roberto Alomar	.30	.25	.12
26	Robby Thompson	.06	.05	.02
27	Jack McDowell	.08	.06	.03
28	Bip Roberts	.08	.06	.03
29	Jay Howell	.05	.04	.02
30	Dave Steib	.08	.06	.03
31	Johnny Ray	.04	.03	.02
32	Steve Sax	.10	.08	.04
33	Terry Mulholland	.08	.06	.03
34	Lee Guetterman	.04	.03	.02
35	Tim Raines	.12	.09	.05
36	Scott Fletcher	.04	.03	.02
37	Lance Parrish	.08	.06	.03
38	Tony Phillips	.05	.04	.02
39	Todd Stottlemyre	.06	.05	.02
40	Alan Trammell	.08	.06	.03
41	Todd Burns	.04	.03	.02
42	Mookie Wilson	.06	.05	.02
43	Chris Bosio	.05	.04	.02
44	Jeffrey Leonard	.06	.05	.02
45	Doug Jones	.08	.06	.03
46	Mike Scott	.08	.06	.03
47	Andy Hawkins	.05	.04	.02
48	Harold Reynolds	.08	.06	.03
49	Paul Molitor	.15	.11	.06
50	John Farrell	.05	.04	.02
51	Danny Darwin	.06	.05	.02
52	Jeff Blauser	.04	.03	.02
53	John Tudor	.05	.04	.02
54	Milt Thompson	.04	.03	.02
55	Dave Justice	.30	.25	.12
56	*Greg Olson*	.12	.09	.05
57	*Willie Blair*	.12	.09	.05
58	*Rick Parker*	.10	.08	.04
59	*Shawn Boskie*	.15	.11	.06
60	Kevin Tapani	.10	.08	.04
61	*Dave Hollins*	.20	.15	.08
62	*Scott Radinsky*	.12	.09	.05
63	Francisco Cabrera	.10	.08	.04
64	*Tim Layana*	.12	.09	.05
65	*Jim Leyritz*	.12	.09	.05
66	Wayne Edwards	.08	.06	.03
67	Lee Stevens (FC)	.15	.11	.06
68	*Bill Sampen*	.15	.11	.06
69	*Craig Grebeck*	.10	.08	.04
70	John Burkett	.15	.11	.06
71	*Hector Villanueva*	.15	.11	.06
72	*Oscar Azocar*	.15	.11	.06
73	*Alan Mills*	.15	.11	.06
74	*Carlos Baerga*	.25	.20	.10
75	Charles Nagy	.08	.06	.03
76	Tim Drummond	.08	.06	.03
77	*Dana Kiecker*	.15	.11	.06
78	*Tom Edens* (FC)	.10	.08	.04
79	Kent Mercker	.10	.08	.04
80	Steve Avery	.20	.15	.08
81	Lee Smith	.08	.06	.03
82	Dave Martinez	.05	.04	.02
83	Dave Winfield	.12	.09	.05
84	Bill Spiers	.06	.05	.02
85	Dan Pasqua	.05	.04	.02
86	Randy Milligan	.06	.05	.02
87	Tracy Jones	.04	.03	.02
88	Greg Myers (FC)	.06	.05	.02
89	Keith Hernandez	.06	.05	.02
90	Todd Benzinger	.06	.05	.02
91	Mike Jackson	.05	.04	.02
92	Mike Stanley	.04	.03	.02
93	Candy Maldonado	.06	.05	.02
94	John Kruk	.05	.04	.02
95	Cal Ripken, Jr.	.30	.25	.12
96	Willie Fraser	.04	.03	.02
97	Mike Felder	.04	.03	.02
98	Bill Landrum	.05	.04	.02
99	Chuck Crim	.04	.03	.02
100	Chuck Finley	.08	.06	.03
101	Kirt Manwaring	.06	.05	.02
102	Jaime Navarro	.08	.06	.03
103	Dickie Thon	.04	.03	.02
104	Brian Downing	.05	.04	.02
105	Jim Abbott	.12	.09	.05
106	Tom Brookens	.04	.03	.02
107	Darryl Hamilton	.06	.05	.02
108	Bryan Harvey	.06	.05	.02
109	Greg Harris	.04	.03	.02
110	Greg Swindell	.08	.06	.03
111	Juan Berenguer	.04	.03	.02
112	Mike Heath	.04	.03	.02
113	Scott Bradley	.04	.03	.02
114	Jack Morris	.08	.06	.03
115	Barry Jones	.05	.04	.02
116	Kevin Romine	.04	.03	.02
117	Garry Templeton	.05	.04	.02
118	Scott Sanderson	.05	.04	.02
119	Roberto Kelly	.08	.06	.03
120	George Brett	.20	.15	.08
121	Oddibe McDowell	.05	.04	.02
122	Jim Acker	.04	.03	.02
123	Bill Swift	.05	.04	.02
124	Eric King	.05	.04	.02
125	Jay Buhner	.06	.05	.02
126	Matt Young	.04	.03	.02
127	Alvaro Espinoza	.05	.04	.02
128	Greg Hibbard	.08	.06	.03
129	Jeff Robinson	.05	.04	.02
130	Mike Greenwell	.15	.11	.06
131	Dion James	.04	.03	.02
132	Donn Pall	.04	.03	.02
133	Lloyd Moseby	.06	.05	.02
134	Randy Velarde	.04	.03	.02
135	Allan Anderson	.05	.04	.02
136	Mark Davis	.06	.05	.02
137	Eric Davis	.08	.06	.03
138	Phil Stephenson	.04	.03	.02
139	Felix Fermin	.04	.03	.02
140	Pedro Guerrero	.08	.06	.03
141	Charlie Hough	.05	.04	.02
142	Mike Henneman	.06	.05	.02
143	Jeff Montgomery	.06	.05	.02
144	Lenny Harris	.06	.05	.02
145	Bruce Hurst	.06	.05	.02
146	Eric Anthony	.15	.11	.06
147	Paul Assenmacher	.04	.03	.02
148	Jesse Barfield	.06	.05	.02
149	Carlos Quintana	.08	.06	.03
150	Dave Stewart	.12	.09	.05
151	Roy Smith	.04	.03	.02
152	Paul Gibson	.04	.03	.02
153	Mickey Hatcher	.04	.03	.02
154	Jim Eisenreich	.04	.03	.02
155	Kenny Rogers	.06	.05	.02
156	Dave Schmidt	.04	.03	.02
157	Lance Johnson	.06	.05	.02
158	Dave West	.05	.04	.02
159	Steve Balboni	.04	.03	.02
160	Jeff Brantley	.08	.06	.03
161	Craig Biggio	.06	.05	.02
162	Brook Jacoby	.06	.05	.02
163	Dan Gladden	.05	.04	.02
164	Jeff Reardon	.08	.06	.03
165	Mark Carreon	.05	.04	.02
166	Mel Hall	.05	.04	.02
167	Gary Mielke	.06	.05	.02
168	Cecil Fielder	.25	.20	.10
169	Darrin Jackson	.04	.03	.02
170	Rick Aguilera	.06	.05	.02
171	Walt Weiss	.06	.05	.02
172	Steve Farr	.05	.04	.02
173	Jody Reed	.06	.05	.02
174	Mike Jeffcoat	.04	.03	.02
175	Mark Grace	.15	.11	.06
176	Larry Sheets	.04	.03	.02
177	Bill Gullickson	.05	.04	.02
178	Chris Gwynn	.06	.05	.02
179	Melido Perez	.06	.05	.02
180	Sid Fernandez	.08	.06	.03
181	Tim Burke	.06	.05	.02
182	Gary Pettis	.05	.04	.02
183	Rob Murphy	.04	.03	.02
184	Craig Lefferts	.06	.05	.02
185	Howard Johnson	.07	.05	.03
186	Ken Caminiti	.05	.04	.02
187	Tim Belcher	.06	.05	.02
188	Greg Cadaret	.04	.03	.02
189	Matt Williams	.12	.09	.05
190	Dave Magadan	.08	.06	.03
191	Geno Petralli	.04	.03	.02
192	Jeff Robinson	.05	.04	.02
193	Jim Deshaies	.05	.04	.02
194	Willie Randolph	.06	.05	.02
195	George Bell	.10	.08	.04
196	Hubie Brooks	.10	.08	.04
197	Tom Gordon	.10	.08	.04
198	Mike Fitzgerald	.04	.03	.02
199	Mike Pagliarulo	.05	.04	.02
200	Kirby Puckett	.15	.11	.06
201	Shawon Dunston	.08	.06	.03
202	Dennis Boyd	.05	.04	.02
203	Junior Felix	.08	.06	.03
204	Alejandro Pena	.04	.03	.02
205	Pete Smith	.05	.04	.02
206	Tom Glavine	.06	.05	.02
207	Luis Salazar	.04	.03	.02
208	John Smoltz	.08	.06	.03
209	Doug Dascenzo	.05	.04	.02
210	Tim Wallach	.08	.06	.03
211	Greg Gagne	.05	.04	.02
212	Mark Gubicza	.08	.06	.03
213	Mark Parent	.04	.03	.02
214	Ken Oberkfell	.04	.03	.02
215	Gary Carter	.08	.06	.03
216	Rafael Palmeiro	.10	.08	.04
217	Tom Niedenfuer	.04	.03	.02
218	Dave LaPoint	.05	.04	.02
219	Jeff Treadway	.05	.04	.02
220	Mitch Williams	.06	.05	.02
221	Jose DeLeon	.05	.04	.02
222	Mike LaValliere	.05	.04	.02
223	Darrel Akerfelds	.04	.03	.02
224	Kent Anderson	.05	.04	.02
225	Dwight Evans	.08	.06	.03
226	Gary Redus	.04	.03	.02

227	Paul O'Neill	.06	.05	.02
228	Marty Barrett	.05	.04	.02
229	Tom Browning	.06	.05	.02
230	Terry Pendleton	.06	.05	.02
231	Jack Armstrong	.08	.06	.03
232	Mike Boddicker	.06	.05	.02
233	Neal Heaton	.05	.04	.02
234	Marquis Grissom	.10	.08	.04
235	Bert Blyleven	.08	.06	.03
236	Curt Young	.05	.04	.02
237	Don Carman	.05	.04	.02
238	Charlie Hayes	.06	.05	.02
239	Mark Knudson	.04	.03	.02
240	Todd Zeile	.10	.08	.04
241	Larry Walker	.10	.08	.04
242	Jerald Clark	.06	.05	.02
243	Jeff Ballard	.05	.04	.02
244	Jeff King	.06	.05	.02
245	Tom Brunansky	.08	.06	.03
246	Darren Daulton	.06	.05	.02
247	Scott Terry	.04	.03	.02
248	Rob Deer	.06	.05	.02
249	Brady Anderson	.04	.03	.02
250	Len Dykstra	.08	.06	.03
251	Greg Harris	.06	.05	.02
252	Mike Hartley	.08	.06	.03
253	Joey Cora	.04	.03	.02
254	Ivan Calderon	.08	.06	.03
255	Ted Power	.04	.03	.02
256	Sammy Sosa	.15	.11	.06
257	Steve Buechele	.05	.04	.02
258	Mike Devereaux	.05	.04	.02
259	Brad Komminsk	.04	.03	.02
260	Teddy Higuera	.08	.06	.03
261	Shawn Abner	.05	.04	.02
262	Dave Valle	.05	.04	.02
263	Jeff Huson	.06	.05	.02
264	Edgar Martinez	.06	.05	.02
265	Carlton Fisk	.10	.08	.04
266	Steve Finley	.06	.05	.02
267	John Wetteland	.06	.05	.02
268	Kevin Appier	.08	.06	.03
269	Steve Lyons	.04	.03	.02
270	Mickey Tettleton	.05	.04	.02
271	Luis Rivera	.04	.03	.02
272	Steve Jeltz	.04	.03	.02
273	R.J. Reynolds	.04	.03	.02
274	Carlos Martinez	.05	.04	.02
275	Dan Plesac	.06	.05	.02
276	Mike Morgan	.04	.03	.02
277	Jeff Russell	.06	.05	.02
278	Pete Incaviglia	.06	.05	.02
279	Kevin Seitzer	.08	.06	.03
280	Bobby Thigpen	.08	.06	.03
281	Stan Javier	.04	.03	.02
282	Henry Cotto	.04	.03	.02
283	Gary Wayne	.05	.04	.02
284	Shane Mack	.05	.04	.02
285	Brian Holman	.06	.05	.02
286	Gerald Perry	.05	.04	.02
287	Steve Crawford	.04	.03	.02
288	Nelson Liriano	.04	.03	.02
289	Don Aase	.04	.03	.02
290	Randy Johnson	.06	.05	.02
291	Harold Baines	.08	.06	.03
292	Kent Hrbek	.08	.06	.03
293	Les Lancaster	.04	.03	.02
294	Jeff Musselman	.04	.03	.02
295	Kurt Stillwell	.06	.05	.02
296	Stan Belinda	.06	.05	.02
297	Lou Whitaker	.08	.06	.03
298	Glenn Wilson	.05	.04	.02
299	Omar Vizquel	.04	.03	.02
300	Ramon Martinez	.15	.11	.06
301	Dwight Smith	.06	.05	.02
302	Tim Crews	.04	.03	.02
303	Lance Blankenship	.05	.04	.02
304	Sid Bream	.06	.05	.02
305	Rafael Ramirez	.04	.03	.02
306	Steve Wilson	.06	.05	.02
307	Mackey Sasser	.06	.05	.02
308	Franklin Stubbs	.06	.05	.02
309	Jack Daugherty	.06	.05	.02
310	Eddie Murray	.10	.08	.04
311	Bob Welch	.08	.06	.03
312	Brian Harper	.06	.05	.02
313	Lance McCullers	.04	.03	.02
314	Dave Smith	.06	.05	.02
315	Bobby Bonilla	.10	.08	.04
316	Jerry Don Gleaton	.04	.03	.02
317	Greg Maddux	.08	.06	.03
318	Keith Miller	.05	.04	.03
319	Mark Portugal	.04	.03	.02
320	Robin Ventura	.20	.15	.10
321	Bob Ojeda	.04	.03	.02
322	Mike Harkey	.08	.06	.03
323	Jay Bell	.06	.05	.02
324	Mark McGwire	.10	.08	.04
325	Gary Gaetti	.10	.08	.04
326	Jeff Pico	.04	.03	.02
327	Kevin McReynolds	.08	.06	.03
328	Frank Tanana	.05	.04	.02
329	Eric Yelding	.06	.05	.02
330	Barry Bonds	.40	.30	.15
331	*Brian McRae* (FC)	.10	.08	.04
332	*Pedro Munoz* (FC)	.08	.06	.03
333	*Daryl Irvine* (FC)	.08	.06	.03
334	*Chris Hoiles*	.20	.15	.10
335	*Thomas Howard* (FC)	.08	.06	.03
336	*Jeff Schulz* (FC)	.08	.06	.03
337	Jeff Manto (FC)	.08	.06	.03
338	Beau Allred	.10	.08	.04
339	*Mike Bordick* (FC)	.08	.06	.03
340	*Todd Hundley*	.06	.04	.02
341	*Jim Vatcher* (FC)	.06	.04	.02
342	Luis Sojo (FC)	.10	.08	.04
343	*Jose Offerman*	.20	.15	.08
344	*Pete Coachman* (FC)	.15	.11	.06

345	Mike Benjamin (FC)	.10	.08	.04
346	*Ozzie Canseco* (FC)	.08	.06	.03
347	Tim McIntosh (FC)	.08	.06	.03
348	*Phil Plantier*	.40	.30	.15
349	*Terry Shumpert*	.10	.08	.06
350	*Darren Lewis*	.30	.25	.12
351	*David Walsh* (FC)	.10	.08	.04
352	*Scott Chiamparino*	.15	.11	.06
353	*Julio Valera* (FC)	.08	.06	.03
354	*Anthony Telford* (FC)	.08	.06	.03
355	Kevin Wickander (FC)	.10	.08	.04
356	*Tim Naehring*	.08	.06	.03
357	*Jim Poole* (FC)	.08	.06	.03
358	*Mark Whiten*	.25	.20	.10
359	*Terry Wells*	.10	.08	.04
360	*Rafael Valdez*	.10	.08	.04
361	*Mel Stottlemyre* (FC)	.15	.11	.06
362	*David Segui*	.20	.15	.08
363	Paul Abbott	.15	.11	.06
364	*Steve Howard* (FC)	.15	.11	.06
365	*Karl Rhodes*	.15	.11	.06
366	*Rafael Novoa*	.10	.06	.03
367	*Joe Grahe*	.15	.11	.06
368	*Darren Reed* (FC)	.15	.11	.06
369	Jeff McKnight (FC)	.10	.08	.04
370	Scott Leius (FC)	.10	.08	.04
371	*Mark Dewey*	.10	.06	.03
372	*Mark Lee*	.10	.06	.03
373	*Rosario Rodriguez*	.15	.11	.06
374	Chuck McElroy (FC)	.10	.08	.04
375	*Mike Bell*	.10	.06	.03
376	Mickey Morandini (FC)	.10	.08	.04
377	*Bill Haselman*	.12	.10	.06
378	*Dave Pavlas*	.10	.06	.03
379	*Derrick May*	.25	.20	.10
380	*Jeromy Burnitz,*	.50	.40	.20
381	*Donald Peters* (1st Draft Pick)	.10	.08	.04
382	*Alex Fernandez,*	.50	.40	.20
383	*Mike Mussina,*	1.00	.75	.40
384	*Daniel Smith* (1st Draft Pick)	.12	.09	.05
385	*Lance Dickson* (1st Draft Pick)	.10	.08	.04
386	*Carl Everett,*	.25	.20	.10
387	*Thomas Nevers* (1st Draft Pick)	.15	.10	.05
388	*Adam Hyzdu* (1st Draft Pick)	.15	.10	.05
389	*Todd Van Poppel,*	.30	.25	.12
390	*Rondell White,*	.75	.45	.25
391	*Marc Newfield,*	.40	.30	.15
392	Julio Franco (AS)	.10	.08	.04
393	Wade Boggs (AS)	.12	.09	.05
394	Ozzie Guillen (AS)	.10	.08	.04
395	Cecil Fielder (AS)	.15	.10	.08
396	Ken Griffey,Jr. (AS)	.40	.30	.15
397	Rickey Henderson (AS)	.15	.10	.08
398	Jose Canseco (AS)	.10	.08	.04
399	Roger Clemens (AS)	.15	.11	.06
400	Sandy Alomar,Jr. (AS)	.10	.08	.04
401	Bobby Thigpen (AS)	.10	.08	.04
402	Bobby Bonilla (Master Blaster)	.10	.08	.04
403	Eric Davis (Master Blaster)	.10	.08	.04
404	Fred McGriff (Master Blaster)	.15	.08	.04
405	Glenn Davis (Master Blaster)	.10	.08	.04
406	Kevin Mitchell (Master Blaster)	.10	.08	.04
407	Rob Dibble (K-Man)	.10	.08	.04
408	Ramon Martinez (K-Man)	.15	.11	.06
409	David Cone (K-Man)	.10	.08	.04
410	Bobby Witt (K-Man)	.10	.08	.04
411	Mark Langston (K-Man)	.10	.08	.04
412	Bo Jackson (Rifleman)	.20	.15	.12
413	Shawon Dunston (Rifleman)	.10	.08	.04
414	Jesse Barfield (Rifleman)	.08	.06	.03
415	Ken Caminiti (Rifleman)	.08	.06	.03
416	Benito Santiago (Rifleman)	.10	.08	.04
417	Nolan Ryan (HL)	.35	.25	.14
418	Bobby Thigpen (HL)	.10	.08	.04
419	Ramon Martinez (HL)	.15	.11	.06
420	Bo Jackson (HL)	.20	.15	.08
421	Carlton Fisk (HL)	.10	.08	.04
422	Jimmy Key	.06	.05	.02
423	Junior Noboa (FC)	.05	.04	.02
424	Al Newman	.04	.03	.02
425	Pat Borders	.05	.04	.02
426	Von Hayes	.08	.06	.03
427	Tim Teufel	.04	.03	.02
428	Eric Plunk	.04	.03	.02
429	John Moses	.04	.03	.02
430	Mike Witt	.05	.04	.02
431	Otis Nixon	.04	.03	.02
432	Tony Fernandez	.08	.06	.03
433	Rance Mulliniks	.04	.03	.02
434	Dan Petry	.04	.03	.02
435	Bob Geren	.05	.04	.02
436	Steve Frey (FC)	.06	.05	.02
437	Jamie Moyer	.05	.04	.02
438	Junior Ortiz	.04	.03	.02
439	Tom O'Malley	.04	.03	.02
440	Pat Combs	.06	.05	.02
441	Jose Canseco (Dream Team)	.50	.30	.15
442	Alfredo Griffin	.04	.03	.02
443	Andres Galarraga	.08	.06	.03
444	Bryn Smith	.04	.03	.02
445	Andre Dawson	.12	.09	.05
446	Juan Samuel	.06	.05	.02
447	Mike Aldrete	.04	.03	.02
448	Ron Gant	.12	.09	.05
449	Fernando Valenzuela	.08	.06	.03
450	Vince Coleman	.08	.06	.03
451	Kevin Mitchell	.15	.11	.06
452	Spike Owen	.04	.03	.02
453	Mike Bielecki	.04	.03	.02
454	Dennis Martinez	.08	.06	.03
455	Brett Butler	.08	.06	.03
456	Ron Darling	.06	.05	.02
457	Dennis Rasmussen	.04	.03	.02
458	Ken Howell	.04	.03	.02
459	Steve Bedrosian	.05	.04	.02
460	Frank Viola	.12	.09	.05
461	Jose Lind	.04	.03	.02
462	Chris Sabo	.08	.06	.03

463	Dante Bichette	.05	.04	.02
464	Rick Mahler	.04	.03	.02
465	John Smiley	.06	.05	.02
466	Devon White	.06	.05	.02
467	John Orton	.04	.03	.02
468	Mike Stanton	.08	.06	.03
469	Billy Hatcher	.04	.03	.02
470	Wally Joyner	.12	.09	.05
471	Gene Larkin	.05	.04	.02
472	Doug Drabek	.08	.06	.03
473	Gary Sheffield	.15	.11	.06
474	David Wells	.04	.03	.02
475	Andy Van Slyke	.08	.06	.03
476	Mike Gallego	.05	.04	.02
477	B.J. Surhoff	.08	.06	.03
478	Gene Nelson	.04	.03	.02
479	Mariano Duncan	.05	.04	.02
480	Fred McGriff	.20	.15	.05
481	Jerry Browne	.04	.03	.02
482	Alvin Davis	.06	.05	.02
483	Bill Wegman	.05	.04	.02
484	Dave Parker	.08	.06	.03
485	Dennis Eckersley	.12	.09	.05
486	Erik Hanson	.12	.09	.05
487	Bill Ripken	.04	.03	.02
488	Tom Candiotti	.05	.04	.02
489	Mike Schooler	.06	.05	.02
490	Gregg Olson	.12	.09	.05
491	Chris James	.05	.04	.02
492	Pete Harnisch	.06	.05	.02
493	Julio Franco	.10	.08	.04
494	Greg Briley	.05	.04	.02
495	Ruben Sierra	.15	.11	.06
496	Steve Olin	.05	.04	.02
497	Mike Fetters	.05	.04	.02
498	Mark Williamson	.04	.03	.02
499	Bob Tewksbury	.04	.03	.02
500	Tony Gwynn	.15	.11	.06
501	Randy Myers	.08	.06	.03
502	Keith Comstock	.04	.03	.02
503	Craig Worthington	.08	.06	.03
504	Mark Eichhorn	.04	.03	.02
505	Barry Larkin	.12	.09	.05
506	Dave Johnson	.04	.03	.02
507	Bobby Witt	.06	.05	.02
508	Joe Orsulak	.04	.03	.02
509	Pete O'Brien	.04	.03	.02
510	Brad Arnsberg	.05	.04	.02
511	Storm Davis	.05	.04	.02
512	Bob Milacki	.05	.04	.02
513	Bill Pecota	.05	.04	.02
514	Glenallen Hill	.08	.06	.03
515	Danny Tartabull	.10	.08	.04
516	Mike Moore	.05	.04	.02
517	Ron Robinson	.04	.03	.02
518	Mark Gardner	.08	.06	.03
519	Rick Wrona	.04	.03	.02
520	Mike Scioscia	.06	.05	.02
521	Frank Wills	.04	.03	.02
522	Greg Brock	.04	.03	.02
523	Jack Clark	.08	.06	.03
524	Bruce Ruffin	.05	.04	.02
525	Robin Yount	.15	.11	.06
526	Tom Foley	.04	.03	.02
527	Pat Perry	.04	.03	.02
528	Greg Vaughn	.10	.08	.06
529	Wally Whitehurst	.06	.05	.02
530	Norm Charlton	.06	.05	.02
531	Marvell Wynne	.04	.03	.02
532	Jim Gantner	.05	.04	.02
533	Greg Litton	.04	.03	.02
534	Manny Lee	.05	.04	.02
535	Scott Bailes	.04	.03	.02
536	Charlie Leibrandt	.04	.03	.02
537	Roger McDowell	.05	.04	.02
538	Andy Benes	.12	.09	.06
539	Rick Honeycutt	.04	.03	.02
540	Dwight Gooden	.08	.06	.03
541	Scott Garrelts	.04	.03	.02
542	Dave Clark	.04	.03	.02
543	Lonnie Smith	.04	.03	.02
544	Rick Rueschel	.05	.04	.02
545	Delino DeShields	.20	.15	.08
546	Mike Sharperson	.04	.03	.02
547	Mike Kingery	.04	.03	.02
548	Terry Kennedy	.04	.03	.02
549	David Cone	.08	.06	.03
550	Orel Hershiser	.12	.09	.05
551	Matt Nokes	.06	.05	.02
552	Eddie Williams	.04	.03	.02
553	Frank DiPino	.04	.03	.02
554	Fred Lynn	.05	.04	.02
555	Alex Cole (FC)	.10	.08	.06
556	Terry Leach	.04	.03	.02
557	Chet Lemon	.04	.03	.02
558	Paul Mirabella	.04	.03	.02
559	Bill Long	.04	.03	.02
560	Phil Bradley	.05	.04	.02
561	Duane Ward	.05	.04	.02
562	Dave Bergman	.04	.03	.02
563	Eric Show	.04	.03	.02
564	Xavier Hernandez (FC)	.08	.06	.03
565	Jeff Parrett	.04	.03	.02
566	Chuck Cary	.04	.03	.02
567	Ken Hill	.06	.05	.02
568	Bob Welch	.08	.06	.03
569	John Mitchell	.04	.03	.02
570	*Travis Fryman* (FC)	.60	.45	.25
571	Derek Lilliquist	.04	.03	.02
572	Steve Lake	.04	.03	.02
573	*John Barfield* (FC)	.10	.08	.04
574	Randy Bush	.04	.03	.02
575	Joe Magrane	.06	.05	.02
576	Edgar Diaz	.04	.03	.02
577	Casy Candaele	.04	.03	.02
578	Jesse Orosco	.04	.03	.02
579	Tom Henke	.06	.05	.02
580	Rick Cerone	.04	.03	.02

581	Drew Hall	.04	.03	.02
582	Tony Castillo	.04	.03	.02
583	Jimmy Jones	.04	.03	.02
584	Rick Reed	.04	.03	.02
585	Joe Girardi	.05	.04	.02
586	*Jeff Gray* (FC)	.15	.11	.06
587	Luis Polonia	.06	.05	.02
588	Joe Klink (FC)	.08	.06	.03
589	Rex Hudler	.05	.04	.02
590	Kirk McCaskill	.06	.05	.02
591	Juan Agosto	.04	.03	.02
592	Wes Gardner	.04	.03	.02
593	*Rich Rodriguez* (FC)	.12	.09	.05
594	Mitch Webster	.04	.03	.02
595	Kelly Gruber	.12	.09	.05
596	Dale Mohorcic	.04	.03	.02
597	Willie McGee	.08	.06	.03
598	Bill Krueger	.05	.04	.02
599	Bob Walk	.04	.03	.02
600	Kevin Maas	.10	.08	.04
601	Danny Jackson	.06	.05	.02
602	Craig McMurtry	.04	.03	.02
603	Curtis Wilkerson	.04	.03	.02
604	Adam Peterson	.04	.03	.02
605	Sam Horn	.06	.05	.02
606	Tommy Gregg	.04	.03	.02
607	Ken Dayley	.04	.03	.02
608	Carmelo Castillo	.04	.03	.02
609	John Shelby	.04	.03	.02
610	Don Slaught	.04	.03	.02
611	Calvin Schiraldi	.04	.03	.02
612	Dennis Lamp	.04	.03	.02
613	Andres Thomas	.04	.03	.02
614	Jose Gonzales	.04	.03	.02
615	Randy Ready	.04	.03	.02
616	Kevin Bass	.06	.05	.02
617	Mike Marshall	.05	.04	.02
618	Daryl Boston	.04	.03	.02
619	Andy McGaffigan	.04	.03	.02
620	Joe Oliver	.06	.05	.02
621	Jim Gott	.04	.03	.02
622	Jose Oquendo	.04	.03	.02
623	Jose DeJesus	.06	.05	.02
624	Mike Brumley	.04	.03	.02
625	John Olerud	.50	.40	.20
626	Ernest Riles	.04	.03	.02
627	Gene Harris	.05	.04	.02
628	Jose Uribe	.04	.03	.02
629	Darnell Coles	.04	.03	.02
630	Carney Lansford	.06	.05	.02
631	Tim Leary	.05	.04	.02
632	Tim Hulett	.04	.03	.02
633	Kevin Elster	.06	.05	.02
634	Tony Fossas	.04	.03	.02
635	Francisco Oliveras	.04	.03	.02
636	Bob Patterson	.04	.03	.02
637	Gary Ward	.04	.03	.02
638	Rene Gonzales	.04	.03	.02
639	Don Robinson	.04	.03	.02
640	Darryl Strawberry	.12	.10	.08
641	Dave Anderson	.04	.03	.02
642	Scott Scudder	.06	.05	.02
643	*Reggie Harris* (FC)	.20	.15	.08
644	Dave Henderson	.08	.06	.03
645	Ben McDonald	.10	.08	.04
646	Bob Kipper	.04	.03	.02
647	Hal Morris	.15	.11	.06
648	Tim Birtsas	.04	.03	.02
649	Steve Searcy	.04	.03	.02
650	Dale Murphy	.12	.09	.05
651	Ron Oester	.04	.03	.02
652	Mike LaCoss	.04	.03	.02
653	Ron Jones	.05	.04	.02
654	Kelly Downs	.04	.03	.02
655	Roger Clemens	.20	.15	.08
656	Herm Winningham	.04	.03	.02
657	Trevor Wilson	.06	.05	.02
658	Jose Rijo	.08	.06	.03
659	Dann Bilardello	.04	.03	.02
660	Gregg Jefferies	.15	.11	.06
661	Doug Drabek (AS)	.08	.06	.03
662	Randy Myers (AS)	.06	.05	.02
663	Benito Santiago (AS)	.08	.06	.03
664	Will Clark (AS)	.15	.11	.06
665	Ryne Sandberg (AS)	.15	.11	.06
666	Barry Larkin (AS)	.08	.06	.03
667	Matt Williams (AS)	.10	.06	.03
668	Barry Bonds (AS)	.20	.15	.05
669	Eric Davis	.12	.09	.05
670	Bobby Bonilla (AS)	.08	.06	.03
671	*Chipper Jones,*	.50	.40	.20
672	*Eric Christopherson,*	.15	.11	.06
673	*Robbie Beckett,*	.15	.11	.06
674	*Shane Andrews,*	.20	.15	.08
675	*Steve Karsay,*	.50	.40	.20
676	*Aaron Holbert* (1st Draft Pick)	.10	.07	.04
677	*Donovan Osborne,*	.15	.11	.06
678	*Todd Ritchie,*	.15	.11	.06
679	*Ron Walden* (1st Draft Pick)	.10	.08	.04
680	*Tim Costo,*	.20	.15	.08
681	*Dan Wilson,*	.15	.11	.06
682	*Kurt Miller,*	.15	.11	.06
683	*Mike Lieberthal,*	.25	.20	.10
684	*Roger Clemens* (K-Man)	.15	.11	.06
685	Dwight Gooden (K-Man)	.15	.11	.06
686	Nolan Ryan (K-Man)	.30	.25	.12
687	Frank Viola (K-Man)	.08	.06	.03
688	Erik Hanson (K-Man)	.08	.06	.03
689	Matt Williams (Master Blaster)	.10	.08	.04
690	Jose Canseco (Master Blaster)	.10	.08	.04
691	Darryl Strawberry (Master Blaster)	.10	.08	.06
692	Bo Jackson (Master Blaster)	.20	.15	.12
693	Cecil Fielder (Master Blaster)	.20	.15	.08
694	Sandy Alomar, Jr. (Rifleman)	.08	.06	.03
695	Cory Snyder (Rifleman)	.05	.04	.02
696	Eric Davis (Rifleman)	.08	.06	.03
697	Ken Griffey,Jr. (Rifleman)	.50	.40	.20
698	Andy Van Slyke (Rifleman)	.08	.06	.03
699	Langston/Witt (No-hitter)	.08	.06	.03
700	Randy Johnson (No-hitter)	.08	.06	.03
701	Nolan Ryan (No-hitter)	.30	.25	.12
702	Dave Stewart (No-hitter)	.08	.06	.03
703	Fernando Valenzuela (No-hitter)	.06	.05	.02
704	Andy Hawkins (No-hitter)	.04	.03	.02
705	Melido Perez (No-hitter)	.04	.03	.02
706	Terry Mulholland (No-hitter)	.06	.05	.02
707	Dave Stieb (No-hitter)	.06	.05	.02
708	*Brian Barnes*	.20	.15	.08
709	*Bernard Gilkey*	.30	.25	.12
710	*Steve Decker* (FC)	.10	.08	.04
711	*Paul Faries* (FC)	.12	.09	.05
712	*Paul Marak* (FC)	.10	.08	.04
713	*Wes Chamberlain* (FC)	.20	.10	.05
714	*Kevin Belcher* (FC)	.10	.08	.04
715	Dan Boone (FC)	.05	.04	.02
716	*Steve Adkins* (FC)	.10	.08	.04
717	*Geronimo Pena* (FC)	.10	.08	.04
718	*Howard Farmer*	.08	.06	.03
719	*Mark Leonard* (FC)	.10	.08	.04
720	Tom Lampkin	.04	.03	.02
721	*Mike Gardiner* (FC)	.10	.06	.03
722	*Jeff Conine* (FC)	.30	.15	.06
723	*Efrain Valdez* (FC)	.10	.08	.04
724	Chuck Malone (FC)	.08	.06	.03
725	*Leo Gomez* (FC)	.12	.09	.05
726	*Paul McClellan* (FC)	.15	.11	.06
727	*Mark Leiter* (FC)	.10	.08	.04
728	*Rich DeLucia* (FC)	.15	.11	.06
729	Mel Rojas (FC)	.08	.06	.03
730	*Hector Wagner* (FC)	.10	.08	.04
731	*Ray Lankford*	.25	.20	.15
732	*Turner Ward*	.15	.11	.06
733	*Gerald Alexander* (FC)	.10	.08	.04
734	*Scott Anderson* (FC)	.10	.08	.04
735	Tony Perezchica (FC)	.05	.04	.02
736	Jimmy Kremers (FC)	.08	.06	.03
737	American Flag	.30	.25	.12
738	*Mike York* (FC)	.10	.08	.04
739	Mike Rochford (FC)	.06	.05	.02
740	Scott Aldred (FC)	.08	.06	.03
741	*Rico Brogna* (FC)	.10	.08	.04
742	*Dave Burba* (FC)	.10	.08	.04
743	*Ray Stephens* (FC)	.10	.08	.04
744	*Eric Gunderson*	.08	.06	.03
745	*Troy Afenir* (FC)	.08	.06	.03
746	Jeff Shaw (FC)	.08	.06	.03
747	*Orlando Merced*	.15	.11	.06
748	*Omar Oliveras* (FC)	.10	.08	.04
749	Jerry Kutzler (FC)	.06	.05	.02
750	Mo Vaughn	.50	.40	.20
751	*Matt Stark* (FC)	.10	.08	.04
752	*Randy Hennis* (FC)	.10	.08	.04
753	*Andujar Cedeno*	.35	.25	.14
754	Kelvin Torve (FC)	.08	.06	.03
755	Joe Kraemer (FC)	.08	.06	.03
756	*Phil Clark* (FC)	.15	.11	.06
757	*Ed Vosberg* (FC)	.10	.08	.04
758	*Mike Perez* (FC)	.10	.08	.04
759	*Scott Lewis* (FC)	.10	.08	.04
760	*Steve Chitren* (FC)	.10	.08	.04
761	*Ray Young* (FC)	.10	.08	.04
762	*Andres Santana* (FC)	.15	.11	.06
763	*Rodney McCray* (FC)	.10	.08	.04
764	*Sean Berry* (FC)	.10	.08	.04
765	Brent Mayne	.08	.06	.03
766	*Mike Simms* (FC)	.15	.11	.06
767	*Glenn Sutko* (FC)	.10	.08	.04
768	Gary Disarcina	.06	.05	.02
769	George Brett (HL)	.20	.15	.08
770	Cecil Fielder (HL)	.08	.06	.03
771	Jim Presley	.05	.04	.02
772	John Dopson	.05	.04	.02
773	Bo Jackson (Breaker)	.35	.25	.14
774	Brent Knackert (FC)	.08	.06	.03
775	Bill Doran	.06	.05	.02
776	Dick Schofield	.04	.03	.02
777	Nelson Santovenia	.04	.03	.02
778	Mark Guthrie (FC)	.08	.06	.03
779	Mark Lemke	.08	.06	.03
780	Terry Steinbach	.06	.05	.02
781	Tom Bolton	.05	.04	.02
782	*Randy Tomlin* (FC)	.10	.06	.03
783	Jeff Kunkel	.04	.03	.02
784	Felix Jose	.10	.08	.04
785	Rick Sutcliffe	.05	.04	.02
786	John Cerutti	.04	.03	.02
787	Jose Vizcaino	.05	.04	.02
788	Curt Schilling	.06	.05	.02
789	Ed Whitson	.05	.04	.02
790	Tony Pena	.06	.05	.02
791	John Candelaria	.04	.03	.02
792	Carmelo Martinez	.04	.03	.02
793	Sandy Alomar, Jr.	.08	.06	.03
794	*Jim Neidlinger* (FC)	.08	.06	.03
795	Red's October	.08	.06	.03
796	Paul Sorrento	.05	.04	.02
797	Tom Pagnozzi	.06	.05	.02
798	Tino Martinez	.10	.08	.06
799	Scott Ruskin (FC)	.08	.06	.03
800	Kirk Gibson	.08	.06	.03
801	Walt Terrell	.04	.03	.02
802	John Russell	.04	.03	.02
803	Chili Davis	.08	.06	.03
804	Chris Nabholz (FC)	.08	.06	.03
805	Juan Gonzalez	.60	.45	.25
806	Ron Hassey	.04	.03	.02
807	Todd Worrell	.06	.05	.02
808	Tommy Greene	.06	.05	.02
809	Joel Skinner	.04	.03	.02
810	Benito Santiago	.08	.06	.03
811	Pat Tabler	.04	.03	.02
812	*Scott Erickson* (FC)	.10	.08	.04
813	Moises Alou	.25	.15	.10
814	Dale Sveum	.04	.03	.02
815	Ryne Sandberg (Man of the Year)	.20	.15	.08
816	Rick Dempsey	.04	.03	.02
817	Scott Bankhead	.05	.04	.02
818	Jason Grimsley	.05	.04	.02
819	Doug Jennings	.04	.03	.02
820	Tom Herr	.05	.04	.02
821	Rob Ducey	.04	.03	.02
822	Luis Quinones	.04	.03	.02
823	Greg Minton	.04	.03	.02
824	Mark Grant	.04	.03	.02
825	Ozzie Smith	.10	.08	.04
826	Dave Eiland	.04	.03	.02
827	Danny Heep	.04	.03	.02
828	Hensley Meulens	.08	.06	.03
829	Charlie O'Brien	.04	.03	.02
830	Glenn Davis	.08	.06	.03
831	John Marzano	.04	.03	.02
832	Steve Ontiveros	.04	.03	.02
833	Ron Karkovice	.04	.03	.02
834	Jerry Goff (FC)	.08	.06	.03
835	Ken Griffey, Sr.	.08	.06	.03
836	Kevin Reimer (FC)	.10	.08	.04
837	Randy Kutcher	.04	.03	.02
838	Mike Blowers	.05	.04	.02
839	Mike Macfarlane	.05	.04	.02
840	Frank Thomas	1.25	.90	.50
841	Ken Griffey, Jr. & Sr.	.50	.30	.15
842	Jack Howell	.04	.03	.02
843	Mauro Gozzo (FC)	.06	.05	.02
844	Gerald Young	.04	.03	.02
845	Zane Smith	.05	.04	.02
846	Kevin Brown	.05	.04	.02
847	Sil Campusano	.04	.03	.02
848	Larry Andersen	.04	.03	.02
849	Cal Ripken, Jr. (Franchise)	.12	.09	.05
850	Roger Clemens (Franchise)	.12	.09	.05
851	Sandy Alomar, Jr. (Franchise)	.08	.06	.03
852	Alan Trammell (Franchise)	.08	.06	.03
853	George Brett (Franchise)	.15	.11	.06
854	Robin Yount (Franchise)	.10	.07	.04
855	Kirby Puckett (Franchise)	.12	.06	.03
856	Don Mattingly (Franchise)	.12	.06	.03
857	Rickey Henderson (Franchise)	.12	.10	.06
858	Ken Griffey, Jr. (Franchise)	.50	.40	.20
859	Ruben Sierra (Franchise)	.10	.08	.04
860	John Olerud (Franchise)	.20	.15	.08
861	Dave Justice (Franchise)	.15	.10	.05
862	Ryne Sandberg (Franchise)	.15	.11	.06
863	Eric Davis (Franchise)	.08	.06	.03
864	Darryl Strawberry (Franchise)	.08	.06	.03
865	Tim Wallach (Franchise)	.05	.04	.02
866	Dwight Gooden (Franchise)	.08	.06	.03
867	Len Dykstra (Franchise)	.10	.07	.04
868	Barry Bonds (Franchise)	.25	.15	.10
869	Todd Zeile (Franchise)	.10	.08	.04
870	Benito Santiago (Franchise)	.08	.06	.03
871	Will Clark (Franchise)	.12	.10	.08
872	Craig Biggio (Franchise)	.08	.06	.03
873	Wally Joyner (Franchise)	.08	.06	.03
874	Frank Thomas (Franchise)	.75	.45	.25
875	Rickey Henderson (MVP)	.10	.08	.04
876	Barry Bonds (MVP)	.25	.08	.04
877	Bob Welch (Cy Young)	.05	.04	.02
878	Doug Drabek (Cy Young)	.06	.05	.03
879	Sandy Alomar, Jr. (ROY)	.08	.06	.03
880	Dave Justice (ROY)	.25	.20	.10
881	Damon Berryhill	.05	.04	.02
882	Frank Viola (Dream Team)	.10	.08	.04
883	Dave Stewart (Dream Team)	.10	.08	.04
884	Doug Jones (Dream Team)	.05	.04	.02
885	Randy Myers (Dream Team)	.06	.05	.02
886	Will Clark (Dream Team)	.30	.25	.12
887	Roberto Alomar (Dream Team)	.40	.30	.20
888	Barry Larkin (Dream Team)	.12	.09	.05
889	Wade Boggs (Dream Team)	.20	.15	.08
890	Rickey Henderson (Dream Team)	.20	.15	.08
891	Kirby Puckett (Dream Team)	.20	.15	.08
892	Ken Griffey,Jr. (Dream Team)	1.50	1.25	.60
893	Benito Santiago (Dream Team)	.10	.08	.04

The values quoted are intended to reflect the market price.

1991 Score Cooperstown

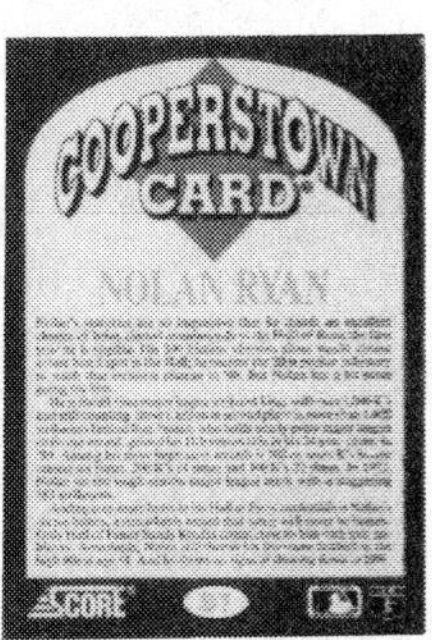

These standard-size cards were available as a seven-card set, one per every factory set. The card fronts are white, with a player portrait inside an oval. "Cooperstown Card" is written across the top in yellow along with a yellow stripe. A yellow stripe also appears at the bottom, along with the player's name in yellow. The backs have green borders surrounding a yellow background which contains a summary of the player's career. Cards are numbered B1-B7.

		MT	NR MT	EX
Complete Set (7):		8.00	6.00	3.25
Common Player:		.50	.40	.20
1	Wade Boggs	1.00	.70	.40
2	Barry Larkin	.50	.40	.20
3	Ken Griffey Jr.	3.50	2.75	1.50
4	Rickey Henderson	1.00	.70	.40
5	George Brett	1.25	.90	.50
6	Will Clark	1.00	.70	.40
7	Nolan Ryan	3.00	2.25	1.25

1991 Score Hot Rookies

These standard-size cards were inserted one per every 100-card 1991 Score blister pack. Action photos with white borders are featured on the front, and "Hot Rookie" is written in yellow at the top. The background is shaded from yellow to orange. The backs are numbered and each has a color mug shot and a career summary.

		MT	NR MT	EX
Complete Set (10):		22.00	16.50	8.75
Common Card:		.75	.60	.30
1	Dave Justice	3.00	2.25	1.25
2	Kevin Maas	.75	.60	.30
3	Hal Morris	.75	.60	.30
4	Frank Thomas	11.00	8.25	4.50
5	Jeff Conine	2.00	1.50	.80
6	Sandy Alomar Jr.	.75	.60	.30
7	Ray Lankford	1.25	.90	.50
8	Steve Decker	.75	.60	.30
9	Juan Gonzalez	11.00	8.25	4.50
10	Jose Offerman	.75	.60	.30

1991 Score Mickey Mantle

These standard-size cards recall Mickey Mantle's career as a Yankee. Card fronts are glossy and have red and white borders. The card's caption appears at the bottom in a blue stripe. The backs have a photo and a summary of the caption, plus the card number and serial number. Dealers and media members who were on Score's mailing list received the seven-card sets, which were limited to 5,000 sets produced.

		MT	NR MT	EX
Complete Set (7):		300.00	250.00	140.00
Common Card:		50.00	40.00	20.00
Autographed Card:		500.00	370.00	200.00
1	The Rookie	50.00	37.00	20.00
2	Triple Crown	50.00	37.00	20.00
3	World Series	50.00	37.00	20.00
4	Going, Going, Gone	50.00	37.00	20.00
5	Speed and Grace	50.00	37.00	20.00
6	A True Yankee	50.00	37.00	20.00
7	Twilight	50.00	37.00	20.00

1991 Score Rising Star

Marketed along with 1990-91 "Baseball's Hottest Rookies" magazine, this 100-card set features top rookies and young players such as Alex Fernandez and Frank Thomas. The cards are similar in design to the Score Superstar set. The magazine/card sets were available to a select group of retailers.

		MT	NR MT	EX
Complete Set (100):		10.00	7.50	4.00
Common Player:		.08	.06	.03
1	Sandy Alomar,Jr.	.10	.08	.04
2	Tom Edens	.08	.06	.03
3	Terry Shumpert	.10	.08	.04
4	Shawn Boskie	.10	.08	.04
5	Steve Avery	.70	.50	.30
6	Deion Sanders	.30	.25	.12
7	John Burkett	.20	.15	.08
8	Stan Belinda	.08	.06	.03
9	Thomas Howard	.10	.08	.04
10	Wayne Edwards	.08	.06	.03
11	Rick Parker	.08	.06	.03
12	Randy Veres	.08	.06	.03
13	Alex Cole	.10	.08	.04
14	Scott Chaimparino	.10	.08	.04
15	Greg Olson	.08	.06	.03
16	Jose DeJesus	.10	.08	.04
17	Mike Blowers	.08	.06	.03
18	Jeff Huson	.08	.06	.03
19	Willie Blair	.10	.08	.04
20	Howard Farmer	.10	.08	.04
21	Larry Walker	.15	.11	.06
22	Scott Hemond	.08	.06	.03
23	Mel Stottlemyre	.10	.08	.04
24	Mark Whiten	.25	.20	.10
25	Jeff Schulz	.10	.08	.04
26	Gary Disarcina	.08	.06	.03
27	George Canale	.08	.06	.03
28	Dean Palmer	.10	.08	.04
29	Jim Leyritz	.20	.15	.08
30	Carlos Baerga	.60	.45	.25
31	Rafael Valdez	.08	.06	.03
32	Derek Bell	.20	.15	.08
33	Francisco Cabrera	.08	.06	.03
34	Chris Hoiles	.20	.15	.08
35	Craig Grebeck	.08	.06	.03
36	Scott Coolbaugh	.08	.06	.03
37	Kevin Wickander	.10	.08	.04
38	Marquis Grissom	.25	.20	.10
39	Chip Hale	.08	.06	.03
40	Kevin Maas	.20	.15	.08
41	Juan Gonzalez	1.25	.90	.50
42	Eric Anthony	.25	.20	.10
43	Luis Sojo	.10	.08	.04
44	Paul Sorrento	.20	.15	.08
45	Dave Justice	1.00	.70	.40
46	Oscar Azocar	.08	.06	.03
47	Charles Nagy	.08	.06	.03
48	Robin Ventura	.30	.25	.12
49	Reggie Harris	.10	.08	.04
50	Ben McDonald	.30	.25	.12
51	Hector Villanueva	.10	.08	.04
52	Kevin Tapani	.15	.11	.06
53	Brian Bohanon	.08	.06	.03
54	Tim Layana	.10	.08	.04
55	Delino DeShields	.25	.20	.10
56	Beau Allred	.08	.06	.03
57	Eric Gunderson	.08	.06	.03
58	Kent Mercker	.10	.08	.04
59	Juan Bell	.10	.08	.04
60	Glenallen Hill	.10	.08	.04
61	David Segui	.15	.11	.06
62	Alan Mills	.15	.11	.06
63	Mike Harkey	.15	.11	.06
64	Bill Sampen	.15	.11	.06
65	Greg Vaughn	.20	.15	.08
66	Alex Fernandez	.50	.40	.20
67	Mike Hartley	.08	.06	.03
68	Travis Fryman	.40	.30	.15
69	Dave Rohde	.10	.08	.04
70	Tom Lampkin	.08	.06	.03
71	Mark Gardner	.15	.11	.06
72	Pat Combs	.10	.08	.04
73	Kevin Appier	.15	.11	.06
74	Mike Fetters	.08	.06	.03
75	Greg Myers	.08	.06	.03
76	Steve Searcy	.08	.06	.03
77	Tim Naehring	.25	.20	.10
78	Frank Thomas	2.50	2.00	1.00
79	Todd Hundley	.10	.08	.04
80	Ed Vosburg	.15	.11	.06
81	Todd Zeile	.20	.15	.08
82	Lee Stevens	.10	.08	.04
83	Scott Radinsky	.10	.08	.04
84	Hensley Meulens	.10	.08	.04
85	Brian DuBois	.08	.06	.03
86	Steve Olin	.08	.06	.03
87	Julio Machado	.10	.08	.04
88	Jose Vizcaino	.10	.08	.04
89	Mark Lemke	.08	.06	.03
90	Felix Jose	.10	.08	.04
91	Wally Whitehurst	.08	.06	.03
92	Dana Kiecker	.10	.08	.04
93	Mike Munoz	.08	.06	.03
94	Adam Peterson	.08	.06	.03
95	Tim Drummond	.08	.06	.03
96	Dave Hollins	.40	.30	.15
97	Craig Wilson	.10	.08	.04
98	Hal Morris	.20	.15	.08
99	Jose Offerman	.30	.25	.12
100	John Olerud	.30	.25	.12

Definitions for grading conditions are located in the Introduction of this price guide.

1991 Score Superstar

This 100-card set features full-color action photos on the card fronts and posed shots on the flip sides. The set was marketed along with the magazine "1991 Baseball's Hottest Players". The cards feature red, white, and blue borders and display the player's name and position below the photo on the card front. The backs contain brief career highlights of the player. The magazine/card set combo was available to select retailers.

		MT	NR MT	EX
Complete Set (100):		10.00	7.50	4.00
Common Player:		.08	.06	.03
1	Jose Canseco	.50	.40	.20
2	Bo Jackson	.30	.25	.12
3	Wade Boggs	.20	.15	.08
4	Will Clark	.35	.25	.14
5	Ken Griffey,Jr.	1.50	1.25	.60
6	Doug Drabek	.10	.08	.04
7	Kirby Puckett	.30	.25	.12
8	Joe Orsulak	.08	.06	.03
9	Eric Davis	.15	.11	.06
10	Rickey Henderson	.30	.25	.12
11	Lenny Dykstra	.20	.15	.08
12	Ruben Sierra	.20	.15	.08
13	Paul Molitor	.30	.25	.12
14	Ron Gant	.35	.25	.14
15	Ozzie Guillen	.10	.08	.04
16	Ramon Martinez	.20	.15	.08
17	Edgar Martinez	.08	.06	.03
18	Ozzie Smith	.20	.15	.08
19	Charlie Hayes	.08	.06	.03
20	Barry Larkin	.15	.11	.06
21	Cal Ripken,Jr.	.50	.40	.20
22	Andy Van Slyke	.10	.08	.04
23	Don Mattingly	.35	.25	.14
24	Dave Stewart	.15	.11	.06
25	Nolan Ryan	.60	.45	.25
26	Barry Bonds	.50	.40	.20
27	Gregg Olson	.10	.08	.04
28	Chris Sabo	.10	.08	.04
29	John Franco	.10	.08	.04
30	Gary Sheffield	.20	.15	.08
31	Jeff Treadway	.08	.06	.03
32	Tom Browning	.08	.06	.03
33	Jose Lind	.08	.06	.03
34	Dave Magadan	.10	.08	.04
35	Dale Murphy	.20	.15	.08
36	Tom Candiotti	.08	.06	.03
37	Willie McGee	.10	.08	.04
38	Robin Yount	.30	.25	.12
39	Mark McGwire	.20	.15	.08
40	George Bell	.10	.08	.04
41	Carlton Fisk	.15	.11	.06
42	Bobby Bonilla	.10	.08	.04
43	Randy Milligan	.08	.06	.03
44	Dave Parker	.20	.15	.08
45	Shawon Dunston	.10	.08	.04
46	Brian Harper	.15	.11	.06
47	John Tudor	.08	.06	.03
48	Ellis Burks	.15	.11	.06
49	Bob Welch	.10	.08	.04
50	Roger Clemens	.30	.25	.12
51	Mike Henneman	.10	.08	.04
52	Eddie Murray	.25	.20	.10
53	Kal Daniels	.10	.08	.04
54	Doug Jones	.10	.08	.04
55	Craig Biggio	.10	.08	.04
56	Rafael Palmeiro	.20	.15	.08
57	Wally Joyner	.10	.08	.04
58	Tim Wallach	.10	.08	.04
59	Bret Saberhagen	.15	.11	.06
60	Ryne Sandberg	.60	.45	.25
61	Benito Santiago	.10	.08	.04
62	Darryl Strawberry	.15	.11	.06
63	Alan Trammell	.20	.15	.08
64	Kelly Gruber	.15	.11	.06
65	Dwight Gooden	.20	.15	.08
66	Dave Winfield	.35	.25	.14
67	Rick Aguilera	.08	.06	.03
68	Dave Righetti	.10	.08	.04
69	Jim Abbott	.20	.15	.08
70	Frank Viola	.15	.11	.06
71	Fred McGriff	.20	.15	.08
72	Steve Sax	.10	.08	.04
73	Dennis Eckersley	.15	.11	.06
74	Cory Snyder	.08	.06	.03
75	Mackey Sasser	.08	.06	.03
76	Candy Maldonado	.08	.06	.03
77	Matt Williams	.25	.20	.10
78	Kent Hrbek	.10	.08	.04

79	Randy Myers	.10	.08	.04
80	Gregg Jefferies	.20	.15	.08
81	Joe Carter	.20	.15	.08
82	Mike Greenwell	.15	.11	.06
83	Jack Armstrong	.10	.08	.04
84	Julio Franco	.10	.08	.04
85	George Brett	.60	.45	.25
86	Howard Johnson	.10	.08	.04
87	Andre Dawson	.25	.20	.10
88	Cecil Fielder	.35	.25	.14
89	Tim Raines	.15	.11	.06
90	Chuck Finley	.10	.08	.04
91	Mark Grace	.15	.11	.06
92	Brook Jacoby	.10	.08	.04
93	Dave Steib	.10	.08	.04
94	Tony Gwynn	.25	.20	.10
95	Bobby Thigpen	.10	.08	.04
96	Roberto Kelly	.20	.15	.08
97	Kevin Seitzer	.10	.08	.04
98	Kevin Mitchell	.15	.11	.06
99	Dwight Evans	.10	.08	.04
100	Roberto Alomar	.30	.25	.12

1991 Score Rookies

This 40-card boxed set did not receive much attention in the hobby world, but features some of the top young players of 1991. The card fronts feature full-color action photos with a "Rookies" banner along the the side border of the card. The backs feature statistics and a player profile. This set was available through hobby dealers and is Score's first release of its kind.

		MT	NR MT	EX
Complete Set (40):		8.00	6.00	3.25
Common Player:		.10	.08	.04
1	Mel Rojas	.20	.15	.08
2	Ray Lankford	.30	.25	.12
3	Scott Aldred	.10	.08	.04
4	Turner Ward	.20	.15	.08
5	Omar Olivares	.10	.08	.04
6	Mo Vaughn	.50	.40	.20
7	Phil Clark	.15	.11	.06
8	Brent Mayne	.10	.08	.04
9	Scott Lewis	.15	.11	.06
10	Brian Barnes	.20	.15	.08
11	Bernard Gilkey	.20	.15	.08
12	Steve Decker	.20	.15	.08
13	Paul Marak	.15	.11	.06
14	Wes Chamberlain	.30	.25	.12
15	Kevin Belcher	.10	.08	.04
16	Steve Adkins	.10	.08	.04
17	Geronimo Pena	.20	.15	.08
18	Mark Leonard	.15	.11	.06
19	Jeff Conine	.20	.15	.08
20	Leo Gomez	.20	.15	.08
21	Chuck Malone	.10	.08	.04
22	Beau Allred	.10	.08	.04
23	Todd Hundley	.20	.15	.08
24	Lance Dickson	.20	.15	.08
25	Mike Benjamin	.10	.08	.04
26	Jose Offerman	.25	.20	.10
27	Terry Shumpert	.10	.08	.04
28	Darren Lewis	.25	.20	.10
29	Scott Chiamparino	.10	.08	.04
30	Tim Naehring	.20	.15	.08
31	David Segui	.15	.11	.06
32	Karl Rhodes	.15	.11	.06
33	Mickey Morandini	.15	.11	.06
34	Chuck McElroy	.10	.08	.04
35	Tim McIntosh	.10	.08	.04
36	Derrick May	.30	.25	.12
37	Rich DeLucia	.10	.08	.04
38	Tino Martinez	.20	.15	.08
39	Hensley Meulens	.15	.11	.06
40	Andujar Cedeno	.30	.25	.12

The values quoted are intended to reflect the market price.

1991 Score Traded

This 110-card set features players with new teams as well as 1991 Major League rookies. The cards are designed in the same style as the regular 1991 Score issue. The cards once again feature a

"T" designation along with the card number. The complete set was sold at hobby shops in a special box.

		MT	NR MT	EX
Complete Set (110):		6.00	4.50	2.50
Common Player:		.06	.05	.02
1	Bo Jackson	.35	.25	.14
2	Mike Flanagan	.06	.05	.02
3	Pete Incaviglia	.08	.06	.03
4	Jack Clark	.10	.08	.04
5	Hubie Brooks	.08	.06	.03
6	Ivan Calderon	.12	.09	.05
7	Glenn Davis	.12	.09	.05
8	Wally Backman	.06	.05	.02
9	Dave Smith	.08	.06	.03
10	Tim Raines	.15	.11	.06
11	Joe Carter	.15	.11	.06
12	Sid Bream	.08	.06	.03
13	George Bell	.12	.09	.05
14	Steve Bedrosian	.06	.05	.02
15	Willie Wilson	.06	.05	.02
16	Darryl Strawberry	.12	.10	.05
17	Danny Jackson	.06	.05	.02
18	Kirk Gibson	.08	.06	.03
19	Willie McGee	.10	.08	.04
20	Junior Felix	.08	.06	.03
21	Steve Farr	.06	.05	.02
22	Pat Tabler	.06	.05	.02
23	Brett Butler	.10	.08	.04
24	Danny Darwin	.06	.05	.02
25	Mikey Tettleton	.08	.06	.03
26	Gary Carter	.10	.08	.04
27	Mitch Williams	.08	.06	.03
28	Candy Maldonado	.08	.06	.03
29	Otis Nixon	.08	.06	.03
30	Brian Downing	.06	.05	.02
31	Tom Candiotti	.06	.05	.02
32	John Candelaria	.06	.05	.02
33	Rob Murphy	.06	.05	.02
34	Deion Sanders	.20	.15	.08
35	Willie Randolph	.08	.06	.03
36	Pete Harnisch	.08	.06	.03
37	Dante Bichette	.06	.05	.02
38	Garry Templeton	.08	.06	.03
39	Gary Gaetti	.08	.06	.03
40	John Cerutti	.06	.05	.02
41	Rick Cerone	.06	.05	.02
42	Mike Pagliarulo	.06	.05	.02
43	Ron Hassey	.06	.05	.02
44	Roberto Alomar	.30	.25	.12
45	Mike Boddicker	.08	.06	.03
46	Bud Black	.06	.05	.02
47	Rob Deer	.06	.05	.02
48	Devon White	.08	.06	.03
49	Luis Sojo	.06	.05	.02
50	Terry Pendleton	.08	.06	.03
51	Kevin Gross	.06	.05	.02
52	Mike Huff	.08	.06	.03
53	Dave Righetti	.08	.06	.03
54	Matt Young	.06	.05	.02
55	Ernest Riles	.06	.05	.02
56	Bill Gullickson	.08	.06	.03
57	Vince Coleman	.10	.08	.04
58	Fred McGriff	.20	.15	.08
59	Franklin Stubbs	.06	.05	.02
60	Eric King	.06	.05	.02
61	Cory Snyder	.06	.05	.02
62	Dwight Evans	.08	.06	.03
63	Gerald Perry	.06	.05	.02
64	Eric Show	.06	.05	.02
65	Shawn Hillegas	.06	.05	.02
66	Tony Fernandez	.08	.06	.03
67	Tim Teufel	.06	.05	.02
68	Mitch Webster	.06	.05	.02
69	Mike Heath	.06	.05	.02
70	Chili Davis	.08	.06	.03
71	Larry Andersen	.06	.05	.02
72	Gary Varsho	.06	.05	.02
73	Juan Berenguer	.06	.05	.02
74	Jack Morris	.08	.06	.03
75	Barry Jones	.06	.05	.02
76	Rafael Belliard	.06	.05	.02
77	Steve Buechele	.06	.05	.02
78	Scott Sanderson	.06	.05	.02
79	Bob Ojeda	.06	.05	.02
80	Curt Schilling	.06	.05	.02
81	Brian Drahman (FC)	.15	.11	.06
82	Ivan Rodriguez (FC)	1.00	.70	.40
83	David Howard (FC)	.10	.08	.04
84	Heath Slocumb (FC)	.10	.08	.06
85	Mike Timlin (FC)	.20	.15	.08
86	Darruyl Kile (FC)	.25	.15	.08
87	Pete Schourek (FC)	.10	.08	.04
88	Bruce Walton (FC)	.12	.09	.05
89	Al Osuna (FC)	.15	.11	.06
90	Gary Scott (FC)	.10	.08	.04
91	Doug Simons (FC)	.15	.11	.06
92	Chris Jones (FC)	.10	.08	.04
93	Chuck Knoblauch	.25	.20	.15
94	Dana Allison (FC)	.15	.11	.06
95	Erik Pappas (FC)	.20	.15	.08
96	Jeff Bagwell (FC)	1.50	1.25	.60
97	Kirk Dressendorfer (FC)	.10	.08	.04
98	Freddie Benavides (FC)	.20	.15	.08
99	Luis Gonzalez (FC)	.40	.30	.15
100	Wade Taylor (FC)	.20	.15	.08
101	Ed Sprague (FC)	.15	.11	.06
102	Bob Scanlan (FC)	.10	.08	.06
103	Rick Wilkins (FC)	.30	.25	.12
104	Chris Donnels (FC)	.10	.08	.04
105	Joe Slusarski (FC)	.10	.08	.04
106	Mark Lewis (FC)	.10	.08	.04
107	Pat Kelly (FC)	.25	.20	.10
108	John Briscoe (FC)	.15	.11	.06
109	Luis Lopez (FC)	.10	.08	.04
110	Jeff Johnson (FC)	.25	.20	.10

1992 Score

Score used a two series format for the second consecutive year in 1992. Cards 1-442 are featured in the first series. The card fronts feature full-color game action photos. The player's name, in white lettering, is across the top with the team logo on the upper-right corner. The player's position is across the bottom. Four-color borders are used. Card backs feature color head shots of the players, team logo and career stats on a vertical layout. Several subsets are included in 1992, including a five-card Joe DiMaggio set. DiMaggio autographed cards were also inserted into random packs. Cards 736-772 can be found with or without a "Rookie Prospects" banner on the card front.

		MT	NR MT	EX
Complete Set (893):		20.00	15.00	8.00
Common Player:		.04	.03	.02
1	Ken Griffey, Jr.	.75	.60	.30
2	Nolan Ryan	.60	.45	.25
3	Will Clark	.25	.20	.10
4	Dave Justice	.30	.25	.12
5	Dave Henderson	.08	.06	.03
6	Bret Saberhagen	.08	.06	.03
7	Fred McGriff	.15	.11	.06
8	Erik Hanson	.08	.06	.03
9	Darryl Strawberry	.10	.08	.04
10	Dwight Gooden	.12	.09	.05
11	Juan Gonzalez	.75	.60	.30
12	Mark Langston	.08	.06	.03
13	Lonnie Smith	.04	.03	.02
14	Jeff Montgomery	.05	.04	.02
15	Roberto Alomar	.25	.20	.10
16	Delino DeShields	.08	.06	.03
17	Steve Bedrosian	.04	.03	.02
18	Terry Pendleton	.08	.06	.03
19	Mark Carreon	.04	.03	.02
20	Mark McGwire	.10	.07	.04
21	Roger Clemens	.15	.11	.06
22	Chuck Crim	.04	.03	.02
23	Don Mattingly	.20	.15	.08
24	Dickie Thon	.04	.03	.02
25	Ron Gant	.15	.11	.06
26	Milt Cuyler	.10	.08	.04
27	Mike Macfarlane	.05	.04	.02
28	Dan Gladden	.04	.03	.02
29	Melido Perez	.04	.03	.02
30	Willie Randolph	.05	.04	.02
31	Albert Belle	.20	.15	.08
32	Dave Winfield	.15	.11	.06
33	Jimmy Jones	.04	.03	.02
34	Kevin Gross	.04	.03	.02
35	Andres Galarraga	.06	.05	.02
36	Mike Devereaux	.05	.04	.02
37	Chris Bosio	.05	.04	.02
38	Mike LaValliere	.05	.04	.02
39	Gary Gaetti	.08	.06	.03
40	Felix Jose	.10	.08	.04
41	Alvaro Espinoza	.04	.03	.02
42	Rick Aguilera	.06	.05	.02
43	Mike Gallego	.04	.03	.02
44	Eric Davis	.12	.09	.05
45	George Bell	.08	.06	.03
46	Tom Brunansky	.06	.05	.02

47	Steve Farr	.04	.03	.02
48	Duane Ward	.05	.04	.02
49	David Wells	.04	.03	.02
50	Cecil Fielder	.20	.15	.08
51	Walt Weiss	.06	.05	.02
52	Todd Zeile	.10	.08	.04
53	Doug Jones	.04	.03	.02
54	Bob Walk	.04	.03	.02
55	Rafael Palmeiro	.08	.06	.03
56	Rob Deer	.04	.03	.02
57	Paul O'Neill	.08	.06	.03
58	Jeff Reardon	.08	.06	.03
59	Randy Ready	.04	.03	.02
60	Scott Erickson	.08	.06	.03
61	Paul Molitor	.12	.09	.05
62	Jack McDowell	.08	.06	.03
63	Jim Acker	.04	.03	.02
64	Jay Buhner	.06	.05	.02
65	Travis Fryman	.20	.15	.08
66	Marquis Grissom	.10	.08	.04
67	Mike Harkey	.05	.04	.02
68	Luis Polonia	.05	.04	.02
69	Ken Caminiti	.05	.04	.02
70	Chris Sabo	.08	.06	.03
71	Gregg Olson	.08	.06	.03
72	Carlton Fisk	.12	.09	.05
73	Juan Samuel	.06	.05	.02
74	Todd Stottlemyre	.06	.05	.02
75	Andre Dawson	.12	.09	.05
76	Alvin Davis	.06	.05	.02
77	Bill Doran	.06	.05	.02
78	B.J. Surhoff	.06	.05	.02
79	Kirk McCaskill	.06	.05	.02
80	Dale Murphy	.08	.06	.03
81	Jose DeLeon	.05	.04	.02
82	Alex Fernandez	.20	.15	.08
83	Ivan Calderon	.08	.06	.03
84	Brent Mayne	.06	.05	.02
85	Jody Reed	.06	.05	.02
86	Randy Tomlin	.06	.05	.02
87	Randy Milligan	.06	.05	.02
88	Pascual Perez	.04	.03	.02
89	Hensley Meulens	.08	.06	.03
90	Joe Carter	.10	.08	.04
91	Mike Moore	.05	.04	.02
92	Ozzie Guillen	.08	.06	.03
93	Shawn Hillegas	.04	.03	.02
94	Chili Davis	.08	.06	.03
95	Vince Coleman	.08	.06	.03
96	Jimmy Key	.06	.05	.02
97	Billy Ripken	.04	.03	.02
98	Dave Smith	.06	.05	.02
99	Tom Bolton	.04	.03	.02
100	Barry Larkin	.12	.09	.05
101	Kenny Rogers	.04	.03	.02
102	Mike Boddicker	.06	.05	.02
103	Kevin Elster	.04	.03	.02
104	Ken Hill	.06	.05	.02
105	Charlie Leibrandt	.04	.03	.02
106	Pat Combs	.06	.05	.02
107	Hubie Brooks	.06	.05	.02
108	Julio Franco	.10	.08	.04
109	Vicente Palacios	.04	.03	.02
110	Kal Daniels	.08	.06	.03
111	Bruce Hurst	.06	.05	.02
112	Willie McGee	.08	.06	.03
113	Ted Power	.04	.03	.02
114	Milt Thompson	.04	.03	.02
115	Doug Drabek	.08	.06	.03
116	Rafael Belliard	.04	.03	.02
117	Scott Garrelts	.04	.03	.02
118	Terry Mulholland	.06	.05	.02
119	Jay Howell	.05	.04	.02
120	Danny Jackson	.05	.04	.02
121	Scott Ruskin	.05	.04	.02
122	Robin Ventura	.15	.11	.06
123	Bip Roberts	.06	.05	.02
124	Jeff Russell	.05	.04	.02
125	Hal Morris	.08	.06	.03
126	Teddy Higuera	.06	.05	.02
127	Luis Sojo	.05	.04	.02
128	Carlos Baerga	.25	.20	.10
129	Jeff Ballard	.04	.03	.02
130	Tom Gordon	.08	.06	.03
131	Sid Bream	.06	.05	.02
132	Rance Mulliniks	.04	.03	.02
133	Andy Benes	.10	.08	.04
134	Mickey Tettleton	.08	.06	.03
135	Rich DeLucia	.06	.05	.02
136	Tom Pagnozzi	.06	.05	.02
137	Harold Baines	.08	.06	.03
138	Danny Darwin	.04	.03	.02
139	Kevin Bass	.06	.05	.02
140	Chris Nabholz	.06	.05	.02
141	Pete O'Brien	.04	.03	.02
142	Jeff Treadway	.05	.04	.02
143	Mickey Morandini	.08	.06	.03
144	Eric King	.04	.03	.02
145	Danny Tartabull	.08	.06	.03
146	Lance Johnson	.04	.03	.02
147	Casey Candaele	.04	.03	.02
148	Felix Fermin	.04	.03	.02
149	Rich Rodriguez	.06	.05	.02
150	Dwight Evans	.08	.06	.03
151	Joe Klink	.04	.03	.02
152	Kevin Reimer	.08	.06	.03
153	Orlando Merced	.10	.08	.04
154	Mel Hall	.05	.04	.02
155	Randy Myers	.06	.05	.02
156	Greg Harris	.04	.03	.02
157	Jeff Brantley	.05	.04	.02
158	Jim Eisenreich	.05	.04	.02
159	Luis Rivera	.04	.03	.02
160	Cris Carpenter	.05	.04	.02
161	Bruce Ruffin	.04	.03	.02
162	Omar Vizquel	.04	.03	.02
163	Gerald Alexander	.05	.04	.02
164	Mark Guthrie	.06	.05	.02
165	Scott Lewis	.06	.05	.02
166	Bill Sampen	.06	.05	.02
167	Dave Anderson	.04	.03	.02
168	Kevin McReynolds	.08	.06	.03
169	Jose Vizcaino	.04	.03	.02
170	Bob Geren	.04	.03	.02
171	Mike Morgan	.05	.04	.02
172	Jim Gott	.04	.03	.02
173	Mike Pagliarulo	.05	.04	.02
174	Mike Jeffcoat	.04	.03	.02
175	Craig Lefferts	.05	.04	.02
176	Steve Finley	.08	.06	.03
177	Wally Backman	.04	.03	.02
178	Kent Mercker	.06	.05	.02
179	John Cerutti	.04	.03	.02
180	Jay Bell	.06	.05	.02
181	Dale Sveum	.04	.03	.02
182	Greg Gagne	.04	.03	.02
183	Donnie Hill	.04	.03	.02
184	Rex Hudler	.04	.03	.02
185	Pat Kelly	.08	.06	.03
186	Jeff Robinson	.04	.03	.02
187	Jeff Gray	.08	.06	.03
188	Jerry Willard	.04	.03	.02
189	Carlos Quintana	.08	.06	.03
190	Dennis Eckersley	.08	.06	.03
191	Kelly Downs	.04	.03	.02
192	Gregg Jefferies	.12	.09	.05
193	Darrin Fletcher	.05	.04	.02
194	Mike Jackson	.05	.04	.02
195	Eddie Murray	.12	.09	.05
196	Billy Landrum	.04	.03	.02
197	Eric Yelding	.04	.03	.02
198	Devon White	.06	.05	.02
199	Larry Walker	.08	.06	.03
200	Ryne Sandberg	.20	.15	.08
201	Dave Magadan	.08	.06	.03
202	Steve Chitren	.06	.05	.02
203	Scott Fletcher	.04	.03	.02
204	Dwayne Henry	.04	.03	.02
205	Scott Coolbaugh	.06	.05	.02
206	Tracy Jones	.04	.03	.02
207	Von Hayes	.06	.05	.02
208	Bob Melvin	.04	.03	.02
209	Scott Scudder	.05	.04	.02
210	Luis Gonzalez	.08	.06	.03
211	Scott Sanderson	.05	.04	.02
212	*Chris Donnels*	.05	.04	.02
213	*Heath Slocumb*	.08	.06	.03
214	Mike Timlin	.12	.09	.05
215	Brian Harper	.06	.05	.02
216	Juan Berenguer	.04	.03	.02
217	Mike Henneman	.06	.05	.02
218	Bill Spiers	.04	.03	.02
219	Scott Terry	.04	.03	.02
220	Frank Viola	.12	.09	.05
221	Mark Eichhorn	.04	.03	.02
222	Ernest Riles	.04	.03	.02
223	Ray Lankford	.10	.08	.04
224	Pete Harnisch	.06	.05	.02
225	Bobby Bonilla	.12	.09	.05
226	Mike Scioscia	.05	.04	.02
227	Joel Skinner	.04	.03	.02
228	Brian Holman	.05	.04	.02
229	Gilberto Reyes (FC)	.06	.05	.02
230	Matt Williams	.15	.11	.06
231	Jaime Navarro	.06	.05	.02
232	Jose Rijo	.08	.06	.03
233	Atlee Hammaker	.04	.03	.02
234	Tim Teufel	.04	.03	.02
235	John Kruk	.08	.06	.03
236	Kurt Stillwell	.05	.04	.02
237	Dan Pasqua	.05	.04	.02
238	Tim Crews	.04	.03	.02
239	Dave Gallagher	.05	.04	.02
240	Leo Gomez	.08	.06	.03
241	Steve Avery	.25	.20	.10
242	Bill Gullickson	.06	.05	.02
243	Mark Portugal	.04	.03	.02
244	Lee Guetterman	.04	.03	.02
245	Benny Santiago	.08	.06	.03
246	Jim Gantner	.04	.03	.02
247	Robby Thompson	.05	.04	.02
248	Terry Shumpert	.04	.03	.02
249	*Mike Bell* (FC)	.15	.11	.06
250	Harold Reynolds	.06	.05	.02
251	Mike Felder	.04	.03	.02
252	Bill Pecota	.04	.03	.02
253	Bill Krueger	.04	.03	.02
254	Alfredo Griffin	.04	.03	.02
255	Lou Whitaker	.08	.06	.03
256	Roy Smith	.04	.03	.02
257	Jerald Clark	.05	.04	.02
258	Sammy Sosa	.08	.06	.03
259	Tim Naehring	.10	.08	.04
260	Dave Righetti	.08	.06	.03
261	Paul Gibson	.04	.03	.02
262	Chris James	.05	.04	.02
263	Larry Andersen	.04	.03	.02
264	Storm Davis	.05	.04	.02
265	Jose Lind	.04	.03	.02
266	Greg Hibbard	.06	.05	.02
267	Norm Charlton	.06	.05	.02
268	Paul Kilgus	.04	.03	.02
269	Greg Maddux	.06	.05	.02
270	Ellis Burks	.12	.09	.05
271	Frank Tanana	.05	.04	.02
272	Gene Larkin	.05	.04	.02
273	Ron Hassey	.04	.03	.02
274	Jeff Robinson	.04	.03	.02
275	Steve Howe	.05	.04	.02
276	Daryl Boston	.04	.03	.02
277	Mark Lee	.04	.03	.02
278	*Jose Segura* (FC)	.12	.09	.05
279	Lance Blankenship	.04	.03	.02
280	Don Slaught	.04	.03	.02
281	Russ Swan	.08	.06	.03
282	Bob Tewksbury	.04	.03	.02
283	Geno Petralli	.04	.03	.02
284	Shane Mack	.08	.06	.03
285	Bob Scanlan	.10	.08	.04
286	Tim Leary	.05	.04	.02
287	John Smoltz	.15	.11	.06
288	Pat Borders	.05	.04	.02
289	Mark Davidson	.04	.03	.02
290	Sam Horn	.06	.05	.02
291	Lenny Harris	.05	.04	.02
292	Franklin Stubbs	.04	.03	.02
293	Thomas Howard	.05	.04	.02
294	Steve Lyons	.04	.03	.02
295	Francisco Oliveras	.04	.03	.02
296	Terry Leach	.04	.03	.02
297	Barry Jones	.04	.03	.02
298	Lance Parrish	.08	.06	.03
299	Wally Whitehurst	.06	.05	.02
300	Bob Welch	.06	.05	.02
301	Charlie Hayes	.05	.04	.02
302	Charlie Hough	.05	.04	.02
303	Gary Redus	.04	.03	.02
304	Scott Bradley	.04	.03	.02
305	Jose Oquendo	.04	.03	.02
306	Pete Incaviglia	.06	.05	.02
307	Marvin Freeman	.04	.03	.02
308	Gary Pettis	.04	.03	.02
309	Joe Slusarski	.10	.08	.04
310	Kevin Seitzer	.05	.04	.02
311	Jeff Reed	.04	.03	.02
312	Pat Tabler	.04	.03	.02
313	Mike Maddux	.04	.03	.02
314	Bob Milacki	.04	.03	.02
315	Eric Anthony	.10	.08	.04
316	Dante Bichette	.05	.04	.02
317	Steve Decker	.10	.08	.04
318	Jack Clark	.08	.06	.03
319	Doug Dascenzo	.04	.03	.02
320	Scott Leius	.10	.08	.04
321	Jim Lindeman	.04	.03	.02
322	Bryan Harvey	.08	.06	.03
323	Spike Owen	.04	.03	.02
324	Roberto Kelly	.10	.08	.04
325	Stan Belinda	.05	.04	.02
326	Joey Cora	.04	.03	.02
327	Jeff Innis	.04	.03	.02
328	Willie Wilson	.05	.04	.02
329	Juan Agosto	.04	.03	.02
330	Charles Nagy	.10	.08	.04
331	Scott Bailes	.04	.03	.02
332	*Pete Schourek*	.08	.06	.03
333	Mike Flanagan	.04	.03	.02
334	Omar Olivares	.10	.08	.04
335	Dennis Lamp	.04	.03	.02
336	Tommy Greene	.06	.05	.02
337	Randy Velarde	.04	.03	.02
338	Tom Lampkin	.04	.03	.02
339	John Russell	.04	.03	.02
340	Bob Kipper	.04	.03	.02
341	Todd Burns	.04	.03	.02
342	Ron Jones	.05	.04	.02
343	Dave Valle	.04	.03	.02
344	Mike Heath	.04	.03	.02
345	John Olerud	.25	.20	.10
346	Gerald Young	.04	.03	.02
347	Ken Patterson	.04	.03	.02
348	Les Lancaster	.04	.03	.02
349	Steve Crawford	.04	.03	.02
350	John Candelaria	.04	.03	.02
351	Mike Aldrete	.04	.03	.02
352	Mariano Duncan	.05	.04	.02
353	Julio Machado	.04	.03	.02
354	Ken Williams	.04	.03	.02
355	Walt Terrell	.04	.03	.02
356	Mitch Williams	.08	.06	.03
357	Al Newman	.04	.03	.02
358	Bud Black	.05	.04	.02
359	Joe Hesketh	.04	.03	.02
360	Paul Assenmacher	.05	.04	.02
361	Bo Jackson	.25	.20	.10
362	Jeff Blauser	.04	.03	.02
363	Mike Brumley	.04	.03	.02
364	Jim Deshaies	.04	.03	.02
365	Brady Anderson	.04	.03	.02
366	Chuck McElroy	.04	.03	.02
367	Matt Merullo	.04	.03	.02
368	Tim Belcher	.06	.05	.02
369	Luis Aquino	.04	.03	.02
370	Joe Oliver	.05	.04	.02
371	Greg Swindell	.08	.06	.03
372	Lee Stevens	.10	.08	.04
373	Mark Knudson	.04	.03	.02
374	Bill Wegman	.05	.04	.02
375	Jerry Don Gleaton	.04	.03	.02
376	Pedro Guerrero	.10	.08	.04
377	Randy Bush	.04	.03	.02
378	Greg Harris	.04	.03	.02
379	Eric Plunk	.04	.03	.02
380	Jose DeJesus	.08	.06	.03
381	Bobby Witt	.06	.05	.02
382	Curtis Wilkerson	.04	.03	.02
383	Gene Nelson	.04	.03	.02
384	Wes Chamberlain	.10	.08	.04
385	Tom Henke	.06	.05	.02
386	Mark Lemke	.06	.05	.02
387	Greg Briley	.04	.03	.02
388	Rafael Ramirez	.04	.03	.02
389	Tony Fossas	.04	.03	.02
390	Henry Cotto	.04	.03	.02
391	Tim Hulett	.04	.03	.02
392	Dean Palmer	.25	.20	.10
393	Glenn Braggs	.05	.04	.02
394	Mark Salas	.04	.03	.02
395	*Rusty Meacham* (FC)	.08	.06	.03
396	*Andy Ashby* (FC)	.08	.06	.03
397	*Jose Melendez* (FC)	.10	.08	.04
398	*Warren Newson* (FC)	.08	.06	.03
399	*Frank Castillo* (FC)	.15	.11	.06
400	*Chito Martinez* (FC)	.10	.08	.04

401	Bernie Williams	.10	.08	.04
402	Derek Bell (FC)	.12	.09	.05
403	*Javier Ortiz* (FC)	.10	.08	.04
404	*Tim Sherrill* (FC)	.08	.06	.03
405	*Rob MacDonald* (FC)	.10	.08	.04
406	Phil Plantier	.15	.11	.06
407	Troy Afenir	.10	.08	.04
408	*Gino Minutelli* (FC)	.10	.08	.04
409	*Reggie Jefferson* (FC)	.10	.08	.04
410	*Mike Remlinger* (FC)	.15	.11	.06
411	*Carlos Rodriguez* (FC)	.10	.08	.04
412	*Joe Redfield* (FC)	.20	.15	.08
413	Alonzo Powell (FC)	.08	.06	.03
414	*Scott Livingstone* (FC)	.08	.06	.03
415	*Scott Kamieniecki* (FC)	.08	.06	.03
416	*Tim Spehr* (FC)	.10	.08	.04
417	*Brian Hunter* (FC)	.10	.08	.04
418	*Ced Landrum* (FC)	.10	.08	.04
419	*Bret Barberie* (FC)	.08	.06	.03
420	Kevin Morton (FC)	.08	.06	.03
421	*Doug Henry* (FC)	.10	.08	.04
422	*Doug Piatt* (FC)	.08	.06	.03
423	*Pat Rice* (FC)	.15	.11	.06
424	*Juan Guzman* (FC)	.20	.15	.08
425	Nolan Ryan (No-Hit)	.30	.25	.12
426	Tommy Greene (No-Hit)	.10	.08	.04
427	Bob Milacki (No-Hit, Mike Flanagan, Mark Williamson, Gregg Olson)	.10	.08	.04
428	Wilson Alvarez (No-Hit)	.08	.06	.03
429	Otis Nixon (Highlight)	.08	.06	.03
430	Rickey Henderson (Highlight)	.10	.08	.04
431	Cecil Fielder (AS)	.10	.08	.04
432	Julio Franco (AS)	.08	.06	.03
433	Cal Ripken, Jr. (AS)	.15	.11	.06
434	Wade Boggs (AS)	.10	.08	.04
435	Joe Carter (AS)	.10	.08	.04
436	Ken Griffey, Jr. (AS)	.40	.30	.15
437	Ruben Sierra (AS)	.10	.08	.04
438	Scott Erickson (AS)	.15	.11	.06
439	Tom Henke (AS)	.05	.04	.02
440	Terry Steinbach (AS)	.05	.04	.02
441	Rickey Henderson (Dream Team)	.25	.20	.10
442	Ryne Sandberg (Dream Team)	.35	.25	.14
443	Otis Nixon	.06	.05	.02
444	Scott Radinsky	.04	.03	.02
445	Mark Grace	.08	.06	.03
446	Tony Pena	.06	.05	.02
447	Billy Hatcher	.04	.03	.02
448	Glenallen Hill	.06	.05	.02
449	Chris Gwynn	.04	.03	.02
450	Tom Glavine	.08	.06	.03
451	John Habyan	.04	.03	.02
452	Al Osuna	.04	.03	.02
453	Tony Phillips	.06	.05	.02
454	Greg Cadaret	.04	.03	.02
455	Rob Dibble	.08	.06	.03
456	Rick Honeycutt	.04	.03	.02
457	Jerome Walton	.04	.03	.02
458	Mookie Wilson	.04	.03	.02
459	Mark Gubicza	.04	.03	.02
460	Craig Biggio	.08	.06	.03
461	Dave Cochrane	.04	.03	.02
462	Keith Miller	.04	.03	.02
463	Alex Cole	.06	.05	.02
464	Pete Smith	.04	.03	.02
465	Brett Butler	.06	.05	.02
466	Jeff Huson	.04	.03	.02
467	Steve Lake	.04	.03	.02
468	Lloyd Moseby	.04	.03	.02
469	Tim McIntosh	.04	.03	.02
470	Dennis Martinez	.06	.05	.02
471	Greg Myers	.04	.03	.02
472	Mackey Sasser	.04	.03	.02
473	Junior Ortiz	.04	.03	.02
474	Greg Olson	.04	.03	.02
475	Steve Sax	.06	.05	.02
476	Ricky Jordan	.06	.05	.02
477	Max Venable	.04	.03	.02
478	Brian McRae	.10	.08	.04
479	Doug Simons	.04	.03	.02
480	Rickey Henderson	.15	.11	.06
481	Gary Varsho	.04	.03	.02
482	Carl Willis	.04	.03	.02
483	*Rick Wilkins*	.10	.08	.04
484	Donn Pall	.04	.03	.02
485	Edgar Martinez	.08	.06	.03
486	Tom Foley	.08	.06	.03
487	Mark Williamson	.08	.06	.03
488	Jack Armstrong	.08	.06	.03
489	Gary Carter	.08	.06	.03
490	Ruben Sierra	.15	.11	.06
491	Gerald Perry	.04	.03	.02
492	Rob Murphy	.04	.03	.02
493	Zane Smith	.04	.03	.02
494	*Darryl Kile*	.10	.08	.04
495	Kelly Gruber	.06	.05	.02
496	Jerry Browne	.04	.03	.02
497	Darryl Hamilton	.06	.05	.02
498	Mike Stanton	.04	.03	.02
499	Mark Leonard	.04	.03	.02
500	Jose Canseco	.12	.09	.05
501	Dave Martinez	.04	.03	.02
502	Jose Guzman	.04	.03	.02
503	Terry Kennedy	.04	.03	.02
504	*Ed Sprague*	.08	.06	.03
505	Frank Thomas	1.00	.70	.40
506	Darren Daulton	.06	.05	.02
507	Kevin Tapani	.06	.05	.02
508	Luis Salazar	.04	.03	.02
509	Paul Faries	.04	.03	.02
510	Sandy Alomar, Jr.	.08	.06	.03
511	Jeff King	.04	.03	.02
512	Gary Thurman	.04	.03	.02
513	Chris Hammond	.06	.05	.02
514	*Pedro Munoz*	.15	.11	.06
515	Alan Trammell	.08	.06	.03
516	Geronimo Pena	.06	.05	.02
517	Rodney McCray	.04	.03	.02
518	Manny Lee	.04	.03	.02
519	Junior Felix	.06	.05	.02
520	Kirk Gibson	.06	.05	.02
521	Darrin Jackson	.06	.05	.02
522	John Burkett	.06	.05	.02
523	Jeff Johnson	.06	.05	.02
524	Jim Corsi	.04	.03	.02
525	Robin Yount	.12	.09	.05
526	Jamie Quirk	.04	.03	.02
527	Bob Ojeda	.04	.03	.02
528	Mark Lewis	.10	.08	.04
529	Bryn Smith	.04	.03	.02
530	Kent Hrbek	.06	.05	.02
531	Dennis Boyd	.04	.03	.02
532	Ron Karkovice	.04	.03	.02
533	Don August	.04	.03	.02
534	Todd Frohwirth	.04	.03	.02
535	Wally Joyner	.08	.06	.03
536	Dennis Rasmussen	.04	.03	.02
537	Andy Allanson	.04	.03	.02
538	Rich Gossage	.04	.03	.02
539	John Marzano	.04	.03	.02
540	Cal Ripken, Jr.	.20	.15	.08
541	Bill Swift	.06	.05	.02
542	Kevin Appier	.06	.05	.02
543	Dave Bergman	.04	.03	.02
544	Bernard Gilkey	.10	.08	.04
545	Mike Greenwell	.08	.06	.03
546	Jose Uribe	.04	.03	.02
547	Jesse Orosco	.04	.03	.02
548	Bob Patterson	.04	.03	.02
549	Mike Stanley	.04	.03	.02
550	Howard Johnson	.08	.06	.03
551	Joe Orsulak	.04	.03	.02
552	Dick Schofield	.04	.03	.02
553	Dave Hollins	.08	.06	.03
554	David Segui	.06	.05	.02
555	Barry Bonds	.30	.25	.12
556	Mo Vaughn	.20	.15	.08
557	Craig Wilson	.06	.05	.02
558	Bobby Rose	.04	.03	.02
559	Rod Nichols	.04	.03	.02
560	Len Dykstra	.12	.09	.05
561	Craig Grebeck	.04	.03	.02
562	Darren Lewis	.10	.08	.04
563	Todd Benzinger	.04	.03	.02
564	Ed Whitson	.04	.03	.02
565	Jesse Barfield	.04	.03	.02
566	Lloyd McClendon	.04	.03	.02
567	Dan Plesac	.04	.03	.02
568	Danny Cox	.04	.03	.02
569	Skeeter Barnes	.04	.03	.02
570	Bobby Thigpen	.08	.06	.03
571	Deion Sanders	.10	.08	.04
572	Chuck Knoblauch	.10	.08	.04
573	Matt Nokes	.06	.05	.02
574	Herm Winningham	.04	.03	.02
575	Tom Candiotti	.06	.05	.02
576	*Jeff Bagwell*	.35	.25	.14
577	Brook Jacoby	.04	.03	.02
578	Chico Walker	.04	.03	.02
579	Brian Downing	.04	.03	.02
580	Dave Stewart	.06	.05	.02
581	Francisco Cabrera	.04	.03	.02
582	Rene Gonzales	.04	.03	.02
583	Stan Javier	.04	.03	.02
584	Randy Johnson	.06	.05	.02
585	Chuck Finley	.06	.05	.02
586	Mark Gardner	.04	.03	.02
587	Mark Whiten	.10	.08	.04
588	Garry Templeton	.04	.03	.02
589	Gary Sheffield	.20	.15	.08
590	Ozzie Smith	.08	.06	.03
591	Candy Maldonado	.04	.03	.02
592	Mike Sharperson	.04	.03	.02
593	Carlos Martinez	.04	.03	.02
594	Scott Bankhead	.04	.03	.02
595	Tim Wallach	.06	.05	.02
596	Tino Martinez	.08	.06	.03
597	Roger McDowell	.04	.03	.02
598	Cory Snyder	.06	.05	.02
599	Andujar Cedeno	.10	.08	.04
600	Kirby Puckett	.15	.11	.06
601	Rick Parker	.04	.03	.02
602	Todd Hundley	.08	.06	.03
603	Greg Litton	.04	.03	.02
604	Dave Johnson	.04	.03	.02
605	John Franco	.04	.03	.02
606	Mike Fetters	.04	.03	.02
607	Luis Alicea	.04	.03	.02
608	Trevor Wilson	.04	.03	.02
609	Rob Ducey	.04	.03	.02
610	Ramon Martinez	.08	.06	.03
611	Dave Burba	.04	.03	.02
612	Dwight Smith	.04	.03	.02
613	Kevin Maas	.08	.06	.03
614	John Costello	.04	.03	.02
615	Glenn Davis	.06	.05	.02
616	Shawn Abner	.04	.03	.02
617	Scott Hemond	.04	.03	.02
618	Tom Prince	.04	.03	.02
619	Wally Ritchie	.04	.03	.02
620	Jim Abbott	.08	.06	.03
621	Charlie O'Brien	.04	.03	.02
622	Jack Daugherty	.04	.03	.02
623	Tommy Gregg	.04	.03	.02
624	Jeff Shaw	.04	.03	.02
625	Tony Gwynn	.15	.11	.06
626	Mark Leiter	.04	.03	.02
627	Jim Clancy	.04	.03	.02
628	Tim Layana	.04	.03	.02
629	Jeff Schaefer	.04	.03	.02
630	Lee Smith	.06	.05	.02
631	Wade Taylor	.06	.05	.02
632	Mike Simms	.06	.05	.02
633	Terry Steinbach	.04	.03	.02
634	Shawon Dunston	.06	.05	.02
635	Tim Raines	.06	.05	.02
636	Kirt Manwaring	.04	.03	.02
637	Warren Cromartie	.04	.03	.02
638	Luis Quinones	.04	.03	.02
639	Greg Vaughn	.08	.06	.03
640	Kevin Mitchell	.08	.06	.03
641	Chris Hoiles	.10	.08	.04
642	Tom Browning	.04	.03	.02
643	Mitch Webster	.04	.03	.02
644	Steve Olin	.06	.05	.02
645	Tony Fernandez	.06	.05	.02
646	Juan Bell	.04	.03	.02
647	Joe Boever	.04	.03	.02
648	Carney Lansford	.06	.05	.02
649	Mike Benjamin	.04	.03	.02
650	George Brett	.12	.09	.05
651	Tim Burke	.04	.03	.02
652	Jack Morris	.06	.05	.02
653	Orel Hershiser	.06	.05	.02
654	Mike Schooler	.04	.03	.02
655	Andy Van Slyke	.08	.06	.03
656	Dave Stieb	.06	.05	.02
657	Dave Clark	.04	.03	.02
658	Ben McDonald	.10	.08	.04
659	John Smiley	.06	.05	.02
660	Wade Boggs	.12	.09	.05
661	Eric Bullock	.04	.03	.02
662	Eric Show	.04	.03	.02
663	Lenny Webster	.06	.05	.02
664	Mike Huff	.04	.03	.02
665	Rick Sutcliffe	.06	.05	.02
666	Jeff Manto	.04	.03	.02
667	Mike Fitzgerald	.04	.03	.02
668	Matt Young	.04	.03	.02
669	Dave West	.04	.03	.02
670	Mike Hartley	.04	.03	.02
671	Curt Schilling	.06	.05	.02
672	Brian Bohanon	.04	.03	.02
673	Cecil Espy	.04	.03	.02
674	Joe Grahe	.04	.03	.02
675	Sid Fernandez	.06	.05	.02
676	Edwin Nunez	.04	.03	.02
677	Hector Villanueva	.04	.03	.02
678	Sean Berry	.06	.05	.02
679	Dave Eiland	.04	.03	.02
680	David Cone	.08	.06	.03
681	Mike Bordick	.06	.05	.02
682	Tony Castillo	.04	.03	.02
683	John Barfield	.04	.03	.02
684	Jeff Hamilton	.04	.03	.02
685	Ken Dayley	.04	.03	.02
686	Carmelo Martinez	.04	.03	.02
687	Mike Capel	.04	.03	.02
688	Scott Chiamparino	.04	.03	.02
689	Rich Gedman	.04	.03	.02
690	Rich Monteleone	.04	.03	.02
691	Alejandro Pena	.04	.03	.02
692	Oscar Azocar	.04	.03	.02
693	Jim Poole	.04	.03	.02
694	Mike Gardiner	.04	.03	.02
695	Steve Buechele	.04	.03	.02
696	Rudy Seanez	.04	.03	.02
697	Paul Abbott	.04	.03	.02
698	Steve Searcy	.04	.03	.02
699	Jose Offerman	.06	.05	.02
700	*Ivan Rodriguez*	.30	.25	.12
701	Joe Girardi	.04	.03	.02
702	Tony Perezchica	.04	.03	.02
703	Paul McClellan	.05	.04	.02
704	*David Howard*	.06	.05	.02
705	Dan Petry	.04	.03	.02
706	Jack Howell	.04	.03	.02
707	Jose Mesa	.04	.03	.02
708	Randy St. Claire	.04	.03	.02
709	Kevin Brown	.06	.05	.02
710	Ron Darling	.06	.05	.02
711	Jason Grimsley	.04	.03	.02
712	John Orton	.04	.03	.02
713	Shawn Boskie	.04	.03	.02
714	Pat Clements	.04	.03	.02
715	Brian Barnes	.06	.05	.02
716	*Luis Lopez* (FC)	.08	.06	.03
717	Bob McClure	.04	.03	.02
718	Mark Davis	.04	.03	.02
719	Dann Billardello	.04	.03	.02
720	Tom Edens	.04	.03	.02
721	Willie Fraser	.04	.03	.02
722	Curt Young	.04	.03	.02
723	Neal Heaton	.04	.03	.02
724	Craig Worthington	.04	.03	.02
725	Mel Rojas	.04	.03	.02
726	Daryl Irvine	.04	.03	.02
727	Roger Mason	.04	.03	.02
728	Kirk Dressendorfer	.08	.06	.03
729	Scott Aldred	.04	.03	.02
730	Willie Blair	.04	.03	.02
731	Allan Anderson	.04	.03	.02
732	Dana Kiecker	.04	.03	.02
733	Jose Gonzalez	.04	.03	.02
734	Brian Drahman	.04	.03	.02
735	Brad Komminsk	.04	.03	.02
736	*Arthur Rhodes* (FC)	.15	.11	.06
737	*Terry Mathews* (FC)	.10	.08	.04
738	*Jeff Fassero* (FC)	.08	.06	.03
739	*Mike Magnante* (FC)	.08	.06	.03
740	*Kip Gross* (FC)	.08	.06	.03
741	*Jim Hunter* (FC)	.06	.05	.02
742	*Jose Mota* (FC)	.08	.06	.03
743	Joe Bitker	.04	.03	.02
744	*Tim Mauser* (FC)	.08	.06	.03
745	*Ramon Garcia* (FC)	.08	.06	.03
746	*Rod Beck* (FC)	.10	.08	.04
747	*Jim Austin* (FC)	.08	.06	.03
748	*Keith Mitchell* (FC)	.10	.08	.04
749	*Wayne Rosenthal* (FC)	.06	.05	.02
750	*Bryan Hickerson* (FC)	.08	.06	.03
751	*Bruce Egloff* (FC)	.08	.06	.03
752	*John Wehner* (FC)	.08	.06	.03
753	Darren Holmes (FC)	.05	.04	.02

754 Dave Hansen .06 .05 .02
755 Mike Mussina (FC) .20 .15 .08
756 *Anthony Young* (FC) .10 .08 .04
757 Ron Tingley .04 .03 .02
758 *Ricky Bones* (FC) .10 .08 .04
759 *Mark Wohlers* (FC) .10 .08 .04
760 Wilson Alvarez (FC) .08 .06 .03
761 *Harvey Pulliam* (FC) .08 .06 .03
762 *Ryan Bowen* (FC) .10 .08 .04
763 Terry Bross (FC) .04 .03 .02
764 *Joel Johnston* (FC) .08 .06 .03
765 *Terry McDaniel* (FC) .10 .08 .04
766 *Esteban Beltre* (FC) .08 .06 .03
767 *Rob Maurer* (FC) .10 .08 .04
768 Ted Wood .10 .08 .04
769 *Mo Sanford* (FC) .10 .08 .04
770 *Jeff Carter* (FC) .08 .06 .03
771 *Gil Heredia* (FC) .08 .06 .03
772 Monty Fariss (FC) .08 .06 .03
773 Will Clark (AS) .10 .08 .04
774 Ryne Sandberg (AS) .10 .08 .04
775 Barry Larkin (AS) .08 .06 .03
776 Howard Johnson (AS) .08 .06 .03
777 Barry Bonds (AS) .15 .11 .06
778 Brett Butler (AS) .06 .05 .02
779 Tony Gwynn (AS) .10 .08 .04
780 Ramon Martinez (AS) .06 .05 .02
781 Lee Smith (AS) .06 .05 .02
782 Mike Scioscia (AS) .04 .03 .02
783 Dennis Martinez (Highlight) .04 .03 .02
784 Dennis Martinez (No-Hit) .04 .03 .02
785 Mark Gardner (No-Hit) .04 .03 .02
786 Bret Saberhagen (No-Hit) .06 .05 .02
787 Kent Mercker (No-Hit, Mark Wohlers, Alejandro Pena) .06 .05 .02
788 Cal Ripken (MVP) .10 .08 .04
789 Terry Pendleton (MVP) .08 .06 .03
790 Roger Clemens (CY) .10 .08 .04
791 Tom Glavine (CY) .08 .06 .03
792 Chuck Knoblauch (ROY) .10 .08 .04
793 Jeff Bagwell (ROY) .15 .11 .06
794 Cal Ripken, Jr. (Man of the Year) .08 .06 .03
795 David Cone (Highlight) .06 .05 .02
796 Kirby Puckett (Highlight) .08 .06 .03
797 Steve Avery (Highlight) .10 .08 .04
798 Jack Morris (Highlight) .06 .05 .02
799 *Allen Watson* (FC) .50 .40 .20
800 *Manny Ramirez* 1.50 1.25 .60
801 *Cliff Floyd* 2.00 1.50 .80
802 *Al Shirley* (FC) .10 .08 .04
803 *Brian Barber* (FC) .20 .15 .08
804 *John Farrell* (FC) .20 .15 .08
805 *Brent Gates* (FC) .50 .40 .20
806 *Scott Ruffcorn* (FC) .20 .15 .08
807 *Tyrone Hill* (FC) .30 .25 .12
808 *Benji Gil* (FC) .30 .25 .12
809 *Aaron Sele* (FC) 1.25 .90 .50
810 *Tyler Green* .25 .20 .10
811 Chris Jones .04 .03 .02
812 Steve Wilson .04 .03 .02
813 *Cliff Young* .08 .06 .03
814 *Don Wakamatsu* .08 .06 .03
815 *Mike Humphreys* .08 .06 .03
816 *Scott Servais* .08 .06 .03
817 *Rico Rossy* .08 .06 .03
818 *John Ramos* .08 .06 .03
819 Rob Mallicoat .06 .05 .02
820 *Milt Hill* .08 .06 .03
821 Carlos Carcia .06 .05 .02
822 Stan Royer .06 .05 .02
823 *Jeff Plympton* (FC) .15 .11 .06
824 *Braulio Castillo* .15 .11 .06
825 *David Haas* (FC) .08 .06 .03
826 *Luis Mercedes* (FC) .10 .08 .04
827 *Eric Karros* (FC) .25 .20 .10
828 *Shawn Hare* (FC) .10 .08 .04
829 *Reggie Sanders* (FC) .30 .25 .12
830 Tom Goodwin .10 .08 .04
831 *Dan Gakeler* (FC) .08 .06 .03
832 *Stacy Jones* (FC) .08 .06 .03
833 *Kim Batiste* .08 .06 .03
834 Cal Eldred .08 .06 .03
835 *Chris George* (FC) .10 .08 .04
836 *Wayne Housie* (FC) .10 .08 .04
837 *Mike Ignasiak* (FC) .10 .08 .04
838 *Josias Manzanillo* (FC) .10 .08 .04
839 *Jim Olander* (FC) .10 .08 .04
840 *Gary Cooper* (FC) .10 .08 .04
841 *Royce Clayton* (FC) .20 .15 .08
842 *Hector Fajardo* (FC) .20 .15 .08
843 Blaine Beatty .04 .03 .02
844 *Jorge Pedre* (FC) .10 .08 .04
845 *Kenny Lofton* (FC) .50 .40 .20
846 *Scott Brosius* (FC) .08 .06 .03
847 *Chris Cron* (FC) .08 .06 .03
848 Denis Boucher .06 .05 .02
849 Kyle Abbott .10 .08 .04
850 *Bob Zupcic* (FC) .30 .25 .12
851 *Rheal Cormier* (FC) .15 .11 .06
852 *Jim Lewis* (FC) .08 .06 .03
853 Anthony Telford .04 .03 .02
854 *Cliff Brantley* (FC) .10 .08 .04
855 *Kevin Campbell* (FC) .10 .08 .04
856 *Craig Shipley* (FC) .08 .06 .03
857 Chuck Carr .04 .03 .02
858 *Tony Eusebio* (FC) .10 .08 .04
859 *Jim Thome* (FC) .20 .15 .08
860 *Vinny Castilla* (FC) .10 .08 .04
861 Dann Howitt .04 .03 .02
862 *Kevin Ward* (FC) .10 .08 .04
863 *Steve Wapnick* (FC) .08 .06 .03
864 Rod Brewer .08 .06 .03
865 Todd Van Poppel .20 .15 .08
866 *Jose Hernandez* (FC) .10 .08 .04
867 *Amalio Carreno* (FC) .10 .08 .04
868 *Calvin Jones* (FC) .10 .08 .04
869 *Jeff Gardner* (FC) .10 .08 .04
870 *Jarvis Brown* (FC) .10 .08 .04
871 *Eddie Taubensee* (FC) .20 .15 .08
872 *Andy Mota* (FC) .08 .06 .03
873 Chris Haney .06 .05 .02
874 Roberto Hernandez .10 .08 .04
875 *Laddie Renfroe* (FC) .10 .08 .04
876 Scott Cooper .08 .06 .03
877 *Armando Reynoso* (FC) .10 .08 .04
878 Ty Cobb (Memorabilia) .30 .25 .12
879 Babe Ruth (Memorabilia) .40 .30 .15
880 Honus Wagner (Memorabilia) .20 .15 .08
881 Lou Gehrig (Memorabilia) .30 .25 .12
882 Satchel Paige (Memorabilia) .20 .15 .08
883 Will Clark (Dream Team) .20 .15 .08
884 Cal Ripken, Jr. (Dream Team) .30 .25 .12
885 Wade Boggs (Dream Team) .20 .15 .08
886 Kirby Puckett (Dream Team) .20 .15 .08
887 Tony Gwynn (Dream Team) .20 .15 .08
889 Scott Erickson (Dream Team) .08 .06 .03
890 Tom Glavine (Dream Team) .15 .11 .06
891 Rob Dibble (Dream Team) .08 .06 .03
892 Mitch Williams (Dream Team) .06 .05 .02
893 Frank Thomas (Dream Team) .80 .60 .30

1992 Score Joe DiMaggio

Colorized vintage photos are featured on the front and back of each of five Joe DiMaggio tribute cards which were issued as random inserts in 1992 Score Series I packs. A limited number of each card were autographed.

	MT	NR MT	EX
Complete Set (5):	100.00	75.00	40.00
Common Card:	20.00	15.00	8.00
Autographed Card:	450.00	350.00	175.00

		MT	NR MT	EX
1	Joe DiMaggio (The Minors)	20.00	15.00	8.00
2	Joe DiMaggio (The Rookie)	20.00	15.00	8.00
3	Joe DiMaggio (The MVP)	20.00	15.00	8.00
4	Joe DiMaggio (The Streak)	20.00	15.00	8.00
5	Joe DiMaggio (The Legend)	20.00	15.00	8.00

1992 Score Factory Inserts

Available exclusively in factory sets these 17 cards are divided into four subsets commemorating the 1991 World Series, potential future Hall of Famers, the career of Joe DiMaggio and Carl Yastrzemski's 1967 Triple Crown season. Cards carry a "B" prefix to the card number.

	MT	NR MT	EX
Complete Set (17):	10.00	7.50	4.50
Common World Series (1-7):	.20	.15	.08
Common Cooperstown (8-11):	1.00	.70	.40
Common DiMaggio (12-14):	.50	.40	.20
Common Yastrzemski (15-17):	.25	.20	.10

		MT	NR MT	EX
1	World Series Game 1 (Greg Gagne)	.20	.15	.08
2	World Series Game 2 (Scott Leius)	.20	.15	.08
3	World Series Game 3 (David Justice/Brian Harper)	.20	.15	.08
4	World Series Game 4 (Lonnie Smith/Brian Harper)	.20	.15	.08
5	World Series Game 5 (David Justice)	.40	.30	.15
6	World Series Game 6 (Kirby Puckett)	.50	.40	.20
7	World Series Game 7 (Gene Larkin)	.20	.15	.08
8	Carlton Fisk (Cooperstown)	1.00	.70	.40
9	Ozzie Smith (Cooperstown)	1.50	1.25	.60
10	Dave Winfield (Cooperstown)	2.00	1.50	.80
11	Robin Yount (Cooperstown)	3.50	2.75	1.50
12	Joe DiMaggio (The Hard Hitter)	.50	.40	.20
13	Joe DiMaggio (The Stylish Fielder)	.50	.40	.20
14	Joe DiMaggio (The Champion Player)	.50	.40	.20
15	Carl Yastrzemski (The Impossible Dream)	.25	.20	.10
16	Carl Yastrzemski (The Triple Crown)	.25	.20	.10
17	Carl Yastrzemski (The World Series)	.25	.20	.10

1992 Score The Franchise

This four-card set, in both autographed and unautographed form, was a random insert in various premium packaging of Score's 1992 Series II cards. Each of the four cards was produced in an edition of 150,000, with 2,000 of each play's card being autographed and 500 of the triple-player card carrying the autographs of all three superstars.

	MT	NR MT	EX
Complete Set (4):	30.00	22.50	12.00
Common Player:	8.00	6.00	3.25
Musial autograph:	250.00	175.00	100.00
Mantle autograph:	500.00	375.00	200.00
Yastrzemski autograph:	150.00	110.00	60.00
Triple autograph:	1000.	750.00	400.00

		MT	NR MT	EX
1	Stan Musial	8.00	6.00	3.25
2	Mickey Mantle	12.00	9.00	4.75
3	Carl Yastrzemski	8.00	6.00	3.25
4	Musial/Mantle/Yastrzemski	9.00	6.75	3.50

1992 Score Hot Rookies

This 10-card rookie issue was produced as an insert in special blister packs of 1992 Score cards sold at retail outlets. Action photos on front and portraits on back are set against white backgrounds with orange highlights. Cards are standard 2-1/2" x 3-1/2".

	MT	NR MT	EX
Complete Set (10):	10.00	7.50	4.00
Common Player:	.30	.25	.12

		MT	NR MT	EX
1	Cal Eldred	2.00	1.50	.75
2	Royce Clayton	1.50	1.00	.60
3	Kenny Lofton	4.00	3.00	1.50
4	Todd Van Poppel	1.50	1.00	.60
5	Scott Cooper	1.25	.95	.50
6	Todd Hundley	.30	.25	.12
7	Tino Martinez	.30	.25	.12
8	Anthony Telford	.30	.25	.12
9	Derek Bell	1.00	.75	.40
10	Reggie Jefferson	1.00	.75	.40

1992 Score Impact Players

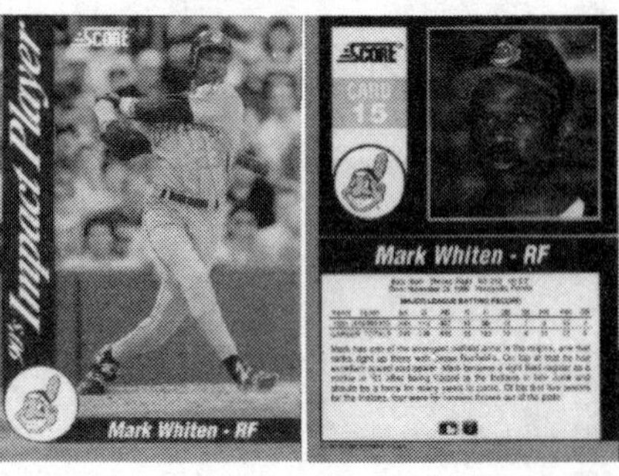

Jumbo packs of 1992 Score Series I and II cards contained five of these special inserts labeled "90's Impact Players". The designation and the player's name and position are printed on team color-coated stripes at the left and bottom of the card front, along with a team logo. Front action photos contrast with portrait photos on the backs, which are again color-coded by team. Cards #1-45 were packaged with Series I, cards 46-90 were included in Series II packs.

		MT	NR MT	EX
Complete Set (90):		20.00	15.00	8.00
Common Player:		.10	.08	.04
1	Chuck Knoblauch	.25	.20	.10
2	Jeff Bagwell	.60	.45	.25
3	Juan Guzman	.20	.15	.08
4	Milt Cuyler	.10	.08	.04
5	Ivan Rodriguez	.25	.20	.10
6	Rich DeLucia	.10	.08	.04
7	Orlando Merced	.15	.11	.06
8	Ray Lankford	.20	.15	.08
9	Brian Hunter	.10	.08	.04
10	Roberto Alomar	.60	.45	.25
11	Wes Chamberlain	.10	.08	.04
12	Steve Avery	.35	.25	.14
13	Scott Erickson	.10	.08	.04
14	Jim Abbott	.15	.11	.06
15	Mark Whiten	.10	.08	.04
16	Leo Gomez	.15	.11	.06
17	Doug Henry	.10	.08	.04
18	Brent Mayne	.10	.08	.04
19	Charles Nagy	.15	.11	.06
20	Phil Plantier	.20	.15	.08
21	Mo Vaughn	.40	.30	.15
22	Craig Biggio	.10	.08	.04
23	Derek Bell	.15	.11	.06
24	Royce Clayton	.20	.15	.08
25	Gary Cooper	.10	.08	.04
26	Scott Cooper	.25	.20	.10
27	Juan Gonzalez	2.00	1.50	.80
28	Ken Griffey, Jr.	4.00	3.00	1.50
29	Larry Walker	.20	.15	.08
30	John Smoltz	.20	.15	.08
31	Todd Hundley	.10	.08	.04
32	Kenny Lofton	1.25	.90	.50
33	Andy Mota	.10	.08	.04
34	Todd Zeile	.10	.08	.04
35	Arthur Rhodes	.10	.08	.04
36	Jim Thome	.50	.40	.20
37	Todd Van Poppel	.15	.11	.06
38	Mark Wohlers	.10	.08	.04
39	Anthony Young	.10	.08	.04
40	Sandy Alomar Jr.	.10	.08	.04
41	John Olerud	.60	.45	.25
42	Robin Ventura	.25	.20	.10
43	Frank Thomas	4.00	3.00	1.50
44	Dave Justice	.50	.40	.20
45	Hal Morris	.10	.08	.04
46	Ruben Sierra	.15	.11	.06
47	Travis Fryman	.60	.45	.25
48	Mike Mussina	.60	.45	.25
49	Tom Glavine	.25	.20	.10
50	Barry Larkin	.15	.11	.06
51	Will Clark	.60	.45	.25
52	Jose Canseco	.60	.45	.25
53	Bo Jackson	.25	.20	.10
54	Dwight Gooden	.15	.11	.06
55	Barry Bonds	.90	.70	.35
56	Fred McGriff	.35	.25	.14
57	Roger Clemens	.30	.25	.12
58	Benito Santiago	.10	.08	.04
59	Darryl Strawberry	.15	.11	.06
60	Cecil Fielder	.30	.25	.12
61	John Franco	.10	.08	.04
62	Matt Williams	.20	.15	.08
63	Marquis Grissom	.20	.15	.08
64	Danny Tartabull	.10	.08	.04
65	Ron Gant	.15	.11	.06
66	Paul O'Neill	.20	.15	.08
67	Devon White	.15	.11	.06
68	Rafael Palmeiro	.25	.20	.10
69	Tom Gordon	.10	.08	.04
70	Shawon Dunston	.10	.08	.04
71	Rob Dibble	.10	.08	.04
72	Eddie Zosky	.10	.08	.04
73	Jack McDowell	.15	.11	.06
74	Len Dykstra	.20	.15	.08
75	Ramon Martinez	.10	.08	.04
76	Reggie Sanders	.30	.25	.12
77	Greg Maddux	.25	.20	.10
78	Ellis Burks	.10	.08	.04
79	John Smiley	.10	.08	.04
80	Roberto Kelly	.20	.15	.08
81	Ben McDonald	.15	.11	.06
82	Mark Lewis	.10	.08	.04
83	Jose Rijo	.10	.08	.04
84	Ozzie Guillen	.10	.08	.04
85	Lance Dickson	.10	.08	.04
86	Kim Batiste	.10	.08	.04
87	Gregg Olson	.10	.08	.04
88	Andy Benes	.20	.15	.08
89	Cal Eldred	.20	.15	.08
90	David Cone	.10	.08	.04

1992 Score Procter & Gamble

In 1992 Score and Procter and Gamble combined to produce an 18-card All-Star set. Printed by the Score Group Inc., of Dallas, the company reportedly ordered two million cards, making 101,000 sets. It was offered to collectors originally for $1.49 along with proof of purchase symbols from P & G products. Card fronts feature a color player action photo set against a background of blue star and pink-to-purple diagonal stripes (American Leaguers) or red star and green stripes (National Leaguers). The All-Star logo appears in the lower-left corner. Player names and positions are in a yellow-orange stripe at lower-right. Back designs include a color player portrait photo at upper-right, with personal data, career

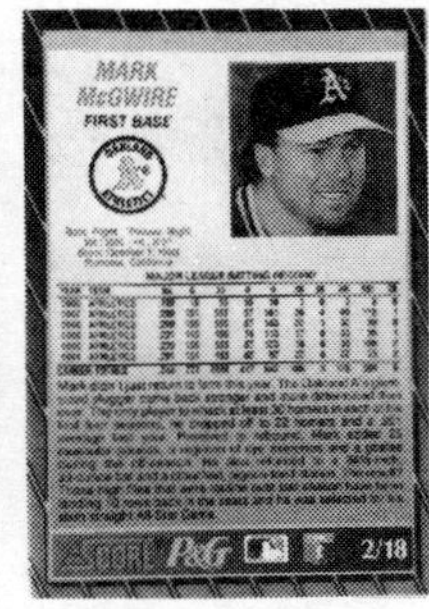

stats and highlights in a shaded central area that flows from yellow to red. Appropriate logos and card number complete the design, which is bordered in color striping similar to the front background.

		MT	NR MT	EX
Complete Set (18):		8.00	6.00	3.25
Common Player:		.25	.20	.10
1	Sandy Alomar Jr.	.25	.20	.10
2	Mark McGwire	.50	.40	.20
3	Roberto Alomar	.50	.40	.20
4	Wade Boggs	.75	.60	.30
5	Cal Ripken, Jr.	1.00	.70	.40
6	Kirby Puckett	.75	.60	.30
7	Ken Griffey, Jr.	1.50	1.25	.60
8	Jose Canseco	.50	.40	.20
9	Kevin Brown	.25	.20	.10
10	Benito Santiago	.25	.20	.10
11	Fred McGriff	.40	.30	.15
12	Ryne Sandberg	1.00	.70	.40
13	Terry Pendleton	.25	.20	.10
14	Ozzie Smith	.50	.40	.20
15	Barry Bonds	.75	.60	.30
16	Tony Gwynn	.50	.40	.20
17	Andy Van Slyke	.25	.20	.10
18	Tom Glavine	.25	.20	.10

1992 Score Rookie & Traded

This 110-card set features traded players, free agents and top rookies from 1992. The cards are styled after the regular 1992 Score cards. Cards 80-110 feature the rookies. The set was released as a boxed set and was available at hobby shops and through hobby dealers.

		MT	NR MT	EX
Complete Set (110):		30.00	22.00	12.00
Common Player:		.05	.04	.02
1	Gary Sheffield	.50	.40	.20
2	Kevin Seitzer	.05	.04	.02
3	Danny Tartabull	.08	.06	.03
4	Steve Sax	.06	.05	.02
5	Bobby Bonilla	.20	.15	.08
6	Frank Viola	.08	.06	.03
7	Dave Winfield	.60	.45	.25
8	Rick Sutcliffe	.08	.06	.03
9	Jose Canseco	.90	.70	.35
10	Greg Swindell	.08	.06	.03
11	Eddie Murray	.40	.30	.15
12	Randy Myers	.06	.05	.02
13	Wally Joyner	.08	.06	.03
14	Kenny Lofton	2.00	1.50	.80
15	Jack Morris	.25	.20	.10
16	Charlie Hayes	.20	.15	.08
17	Pete Incaviglia	.06	.05	.02
18	Kevin Mitchell	.08	.06	.03
19	Kurt Stillwell	.05	.04	.02
20	Bret Saberhagen	.08	.06	.03
21	Steve Buechele	.05	.04	.02
22	John Smiley	.06	.05	.02
23	Sammy Sosa	.50	.40	.20
24	George Bell	.08	.06	.03
25	Curt Schilling	.08	.06	.03
26	Dick Schofield	.05	.04	.02
27	David Cone	.08	.06	.03
28	Dan Gladden	.05	.04	.02
29	Kirk McCaskill	.05	.04	.02
30	Mike Gallego	.05	.04	.02
31	Kevin McReynolds	.06	.05	.02
32	Bill Swift	.06	.05	.02
33	Dave Martinez	.05	.04	.02
34	Storm Davis	.05	.04	.02
35	Willie Randolph	.06	.05	.02
36	Melido Perez	.05	.04	.02
37	Mark Carreon	.05	.04	.02
38	Doug Jones	.05	.04	.02
39	Gregg Jefferies	.30	.25	.12
40	Mike Jackson	.05	.04	.02
41	Dickie Thon	.05	.04	.02
42	Eric King	.05	.04	.02
43	Herm Winningham	.05	.04	.02
44	Derek Lilliquist	.05	.04	.02
45	Dave Anderson	.05	.04	.02
46	Jeff Reardon	.08	.06	.03
47	Scott Bankhead	.05	.04	.02
48	Cory Snyder	.05	.04	.02
49	Al Newman	.05	.04	.02
50	Keith Miller	.05	.04	.02
51	Dave Burba	.05	.04	.02
52	Bill Pecota	.05	.04	.02
53	Chuck Crim	.05	.04	.02
54	Mariano Duncan	.15	.11	.06
55	Dave Gallagher	.05	.04	.02
56	Chris Gwynn	.05	.04	.02
57	Scott Ruskin	.05	.04	.02
58	Jack Armstrong	.05	.04	.02
59	Gary Carter	.20	.15	.08
60	Andres Galarraga	.40	.30	.15
61	Ken Hill	.20	.15	.08
62	Eric Davis	.20	.15	.08
63	Ruben Sierra	.30	.25	.12
64	Darrin Fletcher	.05	.04	.02
65	Tim Belcher	.06	.05	.02
66	Mike Morgan	.06	.05	.02
67	Scott Scudder	.05	.04	.02
68	Tom Candiotti	.05	.04	.02
69	Hubie Brooks	.05	.04	.02
70	Kal Daniels	.05	.04	.02
71	Bruce Ruffin	.05	.04	.02
72	Billy Hatcher	.08	.06	.03
73	Bob Melvin	.05	.04	.02
74	Lee Guetterman	.05	.04	.02
75	Rene Gonzales	.05	.04	.02
76	Kevin Bass	.05	.04	.02
77	Tom Bolton	.05	.04	.02
78	John Wetteland	.20	.15	.08
79	Bip Roberts	.08	.06	.03
80	Pat Listach (FC)	.40	.30	.15
81	John Doherty (FC)	.20	.15	.08
82	Sam Militello (FC)	.25	.20	.10
83	Brian Jordan (FC)	.60	.45	.25
84	Jeff Kent (FC)	1.50	1.25	.60
85	Dave Fleming (FC)	1.00	.70	.40
86	Jeff Tackett (FC)	.12	.09	.05
87	Chad Curtis (FC)	1.50	1.25	.60
88	Eric Fox	.12	.09	.05
89	Denny Neagle (FC)	.12	.09	.05
90	Donovan Osborne (FC)	.50	.40	.20
91	Carlos Hernandez (FC)	.12	.09	.05
92	Tim Wakefield (FC)	.30	.25	.12
93	Tim Salmon (FC)	20.00	15.00	8.00
94	Dave Nilsson (FC)	.75	.60	.30
95	Mike Perez (FC)	.12	.09	.05
96	Pat Hentgen (FC)	1.00	.70	.40
97	Frank Seminara (FC)	.12	.09	.05
98	Ruben Amaro, Jr. (FC)	.12	.09	.05
99	Archi Cianfrocco (FC)	.20	.15	.08
100	Andy Stankiewicz (FC)	.20	.15	.08
101	Jim Bullinger (FC)	.12	.09	.05
102	Pat Mahomes (FC)	.20	.15	.08
103	Hipolito Pichardo (FC)	.12	.09	.05
104	Bret Boone (FC)	1.50	1.25	.60
105	John Vander Wal (FC)	.12	.09	.05
106	Vince Horsman (FC)	.10	.08	.04
107	James Austin (FC)	.10	.08	.04
108	Brian Williams (FC)	.12	.09	.05
109	Dan Walters (FC)	.12	.09	.05
110	Wil Cordero (FC)	1.50	1.25	.60

1992 Score Rising Stars

Sold in a blister pack with a book and a handful of "Magic Motion" trivia cards this 100-card set features baseball's top young players. The color player action photo is bordered in shades of green and yellow, with the player's name in a blue stripe beneath the photo and his position and team in white at the bottom. "Rising Star" is in white with a yellow star at top. Backs have a similar color scheme and feature a player portrait, a career summary and team, league and card company logos.

		MT	NR MT	EX
Complete Set (100):		7.00	5.25	2.75
Common Player:		.05	.04	.02
1	Milt Cuyler	.05	.04	.02
2	David Howard	.05	.04	.02
3	Brian Hunter	.05	.04	.02
4	Darryl Kile	.05	.04	.02
5	Pat Kelly	.05	.04	.02
6	Luis Gonzalez	.05	.04	.02
7	Mike Benjamin	.05	.04	.02
8	Eric Anthony	.05	.04	.02
9	Moises Alou	.10	.08	.04
10	Darren Lewis	.05	.04	.02

		MT	NR MT	EX
11	Chuck Knoblauch	.10	.08	.04
12	Geronimo Pena	.05	.04	.02
13	Jeff Plympton	.05	.04	.02
14	Bret Barberie	.05	.04	.02
15	Chris Haney	.05	.04	.02
16	Rick Wilkins	.10	.08	.04
17	Julio Valera	.05	.04	.02
18	Joe Slusarski	.05	.04	.02
19	Jose Melendez	.05	.04	.02
20	Pete Schourek	.05	.04	.02
21	Jeff Conine	.05	.04	.02
22	Paul Faries	.05	.04	.02
23	Scott Kamieniecki	.05	.04	.02
24	Bernard Gilkey	.10	.08	.04
25	Wes Chamberlain	.05	.04	.02
26	Charles Nagy	.05	.04	.02
27	Juan Guzman	.10	.08	.04
28	Heath Slocumb	.05	.04	.02
29	Eddie Taubensee	.05	.04	.02
30	Cedric Landrum	.05	.04	.02
31	Jose Offerman	.10	.08	.04
32	Andres Santana	.05	.04	.02
33	David Segui	.05	.04	.02
34	Bernie Williams	.10	.08	.04
35	Jeff Bagwell	.20	.15	.08
36	Kevin Morton	.05	.04	.02
37	Kirk Dressendorfer	.10	.08	.04
38	Mike Fetters	.05	.04	.02
39	Darren Holmes	.05	.04	.02
40	Jeff Johnson	.05	.04	.02
41	Scott Aldred	.05	.04	.02
42	Kevin Ward	.05	.04	.02
43	Ray Lankford	.10	.08	.04
44	Terry Shumpert	.05	.04	.02
45	Wade Taylor	.05	.04	.02
46	Rob MacDonald	.05	.04	.02
47	Jose Mota	.05	.04	.02
48	Reggie Harris	.05	.04	.02
49	Mike Remlinger	.05	.04	.02
50	Mark Lewis	.05	.04	.02
51	Tino Martinez	.10	.08	.04
52	Ed Sprague	.10	.08	.04
53	Freddie Benavides	.10	.08	.04
54	Rich DeLucia	.05	.04	.02
55	Brian Drahman	.05	.04	.02
56	Steve Decker	.05	.04	.02
57	Scott Livingstone	.10	.08	.04
58	Mike Timlin	.05	.04	.02
59	Bob Scanlan	.05	.04	.02
60	Dean Palmer	.20	.15	.08
61	Frank Castillo	.05	.04	.02
62	Mark Leonard	.05	.04	.02
63	Chuck McElroy	.05	.04	.02
64	Derek Bell	.20	.15	.08
65	Andujar Cedeno	.30	.25	.12
66	Leo Gomez	.20	.15	.08
67	Rusty Meacham	.05	.04	.02
68	Dann Howitt	.05	.04	.02
69	Chris Jones	.05	.04	.02
70	Dave Cochrane	.05	.04	.02
71	Carlos Martinez	.05	.04	.02
72	Hensley Meulens	.05	.04	.02
73	Rich Reed	.05	.04	.02
74	Pedro Munoz	.05	.04	.02
75	Orlando Merced	.10	.08	.04
76	Chito Martinez	.10	.08	.04
77	Ivan Rodriguez	.20	.15	.08
78	Brian Barnes	.05	.04	.02
79	Chris Donnels	.05	.04	.02
80	Todd Hundley	.05	.04	.02
81	Gary Scott	.05	.04	.02
82	John Wehner	.05	.04	.02
83	Al Osuna	.05	.04	.02
84	Luis Lopez	.05	.04	.02
85	Brent Mayne	.05	.04	.02
86	Phil Plantier	.40	.30	.15
87	Joe Bitker	.05	.04	.02
88	Scott Cooper	.30	.25	.12
89	Chris Hammond	.05	.04	.02
90	Tim Sherrill	.05	.04	.02
91	Doug Simons	.05	.04	.02
92	Kip Gross	.05	.04	.02
93	Tim McIntosh	.05	.04	.02
94	Larry Casian	.05	.04	.02
95	Mike Dalton	.05	.04	.02
96	Lance Dickson	.05	.04	.02
97	Joe Grahe	.05	.04	.02
98	Glenn Sutko	.05	.04	.02
99	Gerald Alexander	.05	.04	.02
100	Mo Vaughn	.60	.45	.25

Values quoted in this guide reflect the retail price of a card – the price a collector can expect to pay when buying a card from a dealer. The wholesale price – that which a collector can expect to receive from a dealer when selling cards – will be significantly lower, depending on desirability and condition.

1992 Score Superstars

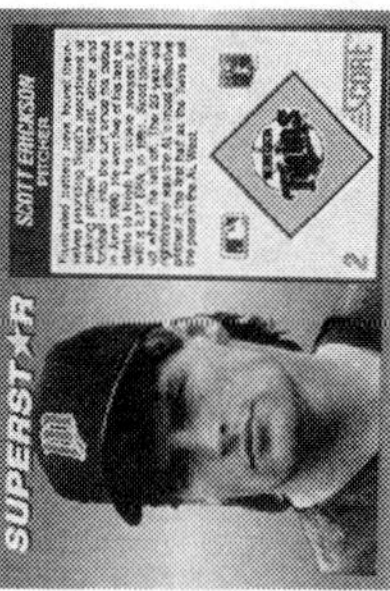

Available in a blister pack with a book and six "Magic Motion" trivia cards, this 100-card set spotlights the games top veteran stars. Red and yellow borders surround a player action photo. A white and yellow "Superstar" logo appears above, while the player's name is in a blue stripe below. The player's position and team are in white at the bottom. Backs have a similar color scheme and are dominated by a player portrait photo. There is a short career summary, along with team, league and card company logos.

		MT	NR MT	EX
	Complete Set (100):	9.00	6.75	3.50
	Common Player:	.05	.04	.02
1	Ken Griffey, Jr.	1.00	.70	.40
2	Scott Erickson	.05	.04	.02
3	John Smiley	.05	.04	.02
4	Rick Aguilera	.10	.08	.04
5	Jeff Reardon	.10	.08	.04
6	Chuck Finley	.05	.04	.02
7	Kirby Puckett	.60	.45	.25
8	Paul Molitor	.60	.45	.25
9	Dave Winfield	.60	.45	.25
10	Mike Greenwell	.30	.25	.12
11	Bret Saberhagen	.20	.15	.08
12	Pete Harnisch	.10	.08	.04
13	Ozzie Guillen	.05	.04	.02
14	Hal Morris	.10	.08	.04
15	Tom Glavine	.10	.08	.04
16	David Cone	.10	.08	.04
17	Edgar Martinez	.05	.04	.02
18	Willie McGee	.05	.04	.02
19	Jim Abbott	.20	.15	.08
20	Mark Grace	.20	.15	.08
21	George Brett	.60	.45	.25
22	Jack McDowell	.10	.08	.04
23	Don Mattingly	.60	.45	.25
24	Will Clark	.60	.45	.25
25	Dwight Gooden	.30	.25	.12
26	Barry Bonds	.60	.45	.25
27	Rafael Palmeiro	.30	.25	.12
28	Lee Smith	.20	.15	.08
29	Wally Joyner	.10	.08	.04
30	Wade Boggs	.50	.40	.20
31	Tom Henke	.05	.04	.02
32	Mark Langston	.05	.04	.02
33	Robin Ventura	.30	.25	.12
34	Steve Avery	.10	.08	.04
35	Joe Carter	.20	.15	.08
36	Benito Santiago	.15	.11	.06
37	Dave Stieb	.05	.04	.02
38	Julio Franco	.05	.04	.02
39	Albert Belle	.40	.30	.15
40	Dale Murphy	.40	.30	.15
41	Rob Dibble	.05	.04	.02
42	Dave Justice	.40	.30	.15
43	Jose Rijo	.20	.15	.08
44	Eric Davis	.15	.11	.06
45	Terry Pendleton	.15	.11	.06
46	Kevin Maas	.05	.04	.02
47	Ozzie Smith	.25	.20	.10
48	Andre Dawson	.25	.20	.10
49	Sandy Alomar, Jr.	.05	.04	.02
50	Nolan Ryan	1.00	.70	.40
51	Frank Thomas	1.00	.70	.40
52	Craig Biggio	.05	.04	.02
53	Doug Drabek	.05	.04	.02
54	Bobby Thigpen	.05	.04	.02
55	Darryl Strawberry	.20	.15	.08
56	Dennis Eckersley	.20	.15	.08
57	John Franco	.05	.04	.02
58	Paul O'Neill	.20	.15	.08
59	Scott Sanderson	.05	.04	.02
60	Dave Stewart	.05	.04	.02
61	Ivan Calderon	.05	.04	.02
62	Frank Viola	.05	.04	.02
63	Mark McGwire	.30	.25	.12
64	Kelly Gruber	.05	.04	.02
65	Fred McGriff	.30	.25	.12
66	Cecil Fielder	.40	.30	.15
67	Jose Canseco	.60	.45	.25
68	Howard Johnson	.10	.08	.04
69	Juan Gonzalez	.60	.45	.25
70	Tim Wallach	.10	.08	.04
71	John Olerud	.30	.25	.12
72	Carlton Fisk	.25	.20	.10
73	Otis Nixon	.05	.04	.02
74	Roger Clemens	.35	.25	.14
75	Ramon Martinez	.15	.11	.06
76	Ron Gant	.20	.15	.08
77	Barry Larkin	.15	.11	.06
78	Eddie Murray	.25	.20	.10
79	Vince Coleman	.05	.04	.02
80	Bobby Bonilla	.10	.08	.04
81	Tony Gwynn	.30	.25	.12
82	Roberto Alomar	.35	.25	.14
83	Ellis Burks	.20	.15	.08
84	Robin Yount	.50	.40	.20
85	Ryne Sandberg	.80	.60	.30
86	Len Dykstra	.15	.11	.06
87	Ruben Sierra	.15	.11	.06
88	George Bell	.05	.04	.02
89	Cal Ripken, Jr.	.80	.60	.30
90	Danny Tartabull	.15	.11	.06
91	Gregg Olson	.05	.04	.02
92	Dave Henderson	.05	.04	.02
93	Kevin Mitchell	.10	.08	.04
94	Ben McDonald	.10	.08	.04
95	Matt Williams	.15	.11	.06
96	Roberto Kelly	.15	.11	.06
97	Dennis Martinez	.05	.04	.02
98	Kent Hrbek	.10	.08	.04
99	Felix Jose	.05	.04	.02
100	Rickey Henderson	.50	.40	.20

1993 Score

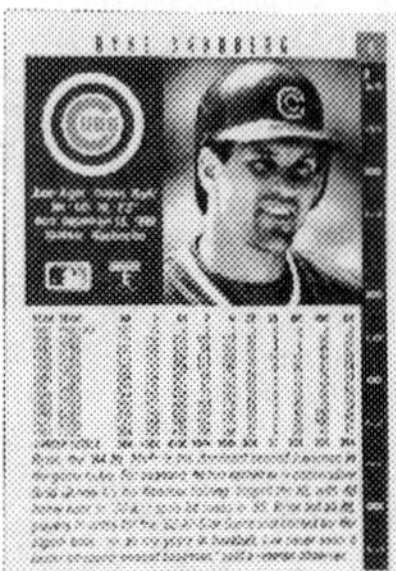

Score's 1993 cards have white borders surrounding color action photographs. The player's name is at the bottom of the card, while his team's name and position appears on the left side in a color band. Score's logo is in the upper right. Backs have color portraits, statistics and text. Subsets feature rookies, award winners, draft picks, highlights, World Series highlights, all-star caricatures, dream team players, and the Man of the Year (Kirby Puckett). Insert sets include: Boys of Summer, the Franchise and Stat Leaders, which feature Select's card design.

		MT	NR MT	EX
	Complete Set (660):	20.00	15.00	8.00
	Common Player:	.04	.03	.02
1	Ken Griffey, Jr.	.50	.40	.20
2	Gary Sheffield	.15	.11	.06
3	Frank Thomas	.80	.60	.30
4	Ryne Sandberg	.20	.15	.08
5	Larry Walker	.10	.08	.04
6	Cal Ripken, Jr.	.25	.20	.10
7	Roger Clemens	.10	.08	.04
8	Bobby Bonilla	.08	.06	.03
9	Carlos Baerga	.20	.15	.08
10	Darren Daulton	.08	.06	.03
11	Travis Fryman	.10	.08	.04
12	Andy Van Slyke	.08	.06	.03
13	Jose Canseco	.15	.11	.06
14	Roberto Alomar	.20	.15	.08
15	Tom Glavine	.10	.08	.04
16	Barry Larkin	.08	.06	.03
17	Gregg Jefferies	.08	.06	.03
18	Craig Biggio	.04	.03	.02
19	Shane Mack	.04	.03	.02
20	Brett Butler	.04	.03	.02
21	Dennis Eckersley	.08	.06	.03
22	Will Clark	.20	.15	.08
23	Don Mattingly	.20	.15	.08
24	Tony Gwynn	.15	.11	.06
25	Ivan Rodriguez	.15	.11	.06
26	Shawon Dunston	.04	.03	.02
27	Mike Mussina	.10	.08	.04
28	Marquis Grissom	.10	.08	.04
29	Charles Nagy	.04	.03	.02
30	Len Dykstra	.10	.08	.04
31	Cecil Fielder	.20	.15	.08
32	Jay Bell	.08	.06	.03
33	B.J. Surhoff	.04	.03	.02
34	Bob Tewksbury	.04	.03	.02
35	Danny Tartabull	.04	.03	.02
36	Terry Pendleton	.08	.06	.03
37	Jack Morris	.04	.03	.02
38	Hal Morris	.04	.03	.02
39	Luis Polonia	.04	.03	.02
40	Ken Caminiti	.04	.03	.02
41	Robin Ventura	.15	.11	.06
42	Darryl Strawberry	.08	.06	.03
43	Wally Joyner	.10	.08	.04
44	Fred McGriff	.15	.11	.06
45	Kevin Tapani	.04	.03	.02
46	Matt Williams	.10	.08	.04
47	Robin Yount	.20	.15	.08
48	Ken Hill	.04	.03	.02
49	Edgar Martinez	.08	.06	.03
50	Mark Grace	.08	.06	.03
51	Juan Gonzalez	.50	.40	.20
52	Curt Schilling	.04	.03	.02
53	Dwight Gooden	.08	.06	.03

54	Chris Hoiles	.04	.03	.02
55	Frank Viola	.04	.03	.02
56	Ray Lankford	.04	.03	.02
57	George Brett	.25	.20	.10
58	Kenny Lofton	.15	.11	.06
59	Nolan Ryan	.50	.40	.20
60	Mickey Tettleton	.04	.03	.02
61	John Smoltz	.04	.03	.02
62	Howard Johnson	.08	.06	.03
63	Eric Karros	.15	.11	.06
64	Rick Aguilera	.04	.03	.02
65	Steve Finley	.04	.03	.02
66	Mark Langston	.04	.03	.02
67	Bill Swift	.04	.03	.02
68	John Olerud	.15	.11	.06
69	Kevin McReynolds	.04	.03	.02
70	Jack McDowell	.08	.06	.03
71	Rickey Henderson	.20	.15	.08
72	Brian Harper	.04	.03	.02
73	Mike Morgan	.04	.03	.02
74	Rafael Palmeiro	.10	.08	.04
75	Dennis Martinez	.04	.03	.02
76	Tino Martinez	.04	.03	.02
77	Eddie Murray	.12	.09	.05
78	Ellis Burks	.08	.06	.03
79	John Kruk	.08	.06	.03
80	Gregg Olson	.04	.03	.02
81	Bernard Gilkey	.04	.03	.02
82	Milt Cuyler	.04	.03	.02
83	Mike LaValliere	.04	.03	.02
84	Albert Belle	.10	.08	.04
85	Bip Roberts	.08	.06	.03
86	Melido Perez	.04	.03	.02
87	Otis Nixon	.06	.05	.02
88	Bill Spiers	.04	.03	.02
89	Jeff Bagwell	.15	.11	.06
90	Orel Hershiser	.10	.08	.04
91	Andy Benes	.10	.08	.04
92	Devon White	.08	.06	.03
93	Willie McGee	.06	.05	.02
94	Ozzie Guillen	.06	.05	.02
95	Ivan Calderon	.04	.03	.02
96	Keith Miller	.04	.03	.02
97	Steve Buechele	.04	.03	.02
98	Kent Hrbek	.10	.08	.04
99	Dave Hollins	.04	.03	.02
100	Mike Bordick	.04	.03	.02
101	Randy Tomlin	.04	.03	.02
102	Omar Vizquel	.04	.03	.02
103	Lee Smith	.08	.06	.03
104	Leo Gomez	.04	.03	.02
105	Jose Rijo	.08	.06	.03
106	Mark Whiten	.06	.05	.02
107	Dave Justice	.20	.15	.08
108	Eddie Taubensee	.04	.03	.02
109	Lance Johnson	.08	.06	.03
110	Felix Jose	.04	.03	.02
111	Mike Harkey	.04	.03	.02
112	Randy Milligan	.06	.05	.02
113	Anthony Young	.04	.03	.02
114	Rico Brogna	.04	.03	.02
115	Bret Saberhagen	.08	.06	.03
116	Sandy Alomar, Jr.	.04	.03	.02
117	Terry Mulholland	.04	.03	.02
118	Darryl Hamilton	.04	.03	.02
119	Todd Zeile	.08	.06	.03
120	Bernie Williams	.04	.03	.02
121	Zane Smith	.04	.03	.02
122	Derek Bell	.04	.03	.02
123	Deion Sanders	.10	.08	.04
124	Luis Sojo	.04	.03	.02
125	Joe Oliver	.06	.05	.02
126	Craig Grebeck	.04	.03	.02
127	Andujar Cedeno	.04	.03	.02
128	Brian McRae	.06	.05	.02
129	Jose Offerman	.04	.03	.02
130	Pedro Munoz	.04	.03	.02
131	Bud Black	.04	.03	.02
132	Mo Vaughn	.08	.06	.03
133	Bruce Hurst	.04	.03	.02
134	Dave Henderson	.04	.03	.02
135	Tom Pagnozzi	.04	.03	.02
136	Erik Hanson	.04	.03	.02
137	Orlando Merced	.04	.03	.02
138	Dean Palmer	.08	.06	.03
139	John Franco	.04	.03	.02
140	Brady Anderson	.06	.05	.02
141	Ricky Jordan	.04	.03	.02
142	Jeff Blauser	.04	.03	.02
143	Sammy Sosa	.08	.06	.03
144	Bob Walk	.04	.03	.02
145	Delino DeShields	.08	.06	.03
146	Kevin Brown	.04	.03	.02
147	Mark Lemke	.04	.03	.02
148	Chuck Knoblauch	.08	.06	.03
149	Chris Sabo	.06	.05	.02
150	Bobby Witt	.04	.03	.02
151	Luis Gonzalez	.04	.03	.02
152	Ron Karkovice	.04	.03	.02
153	Jeff Brantley	.04	.03	.02
154	Kevin Appier	.04	.03	.02
155	Darrin Jackson	.04	.03	.02
156	Kelly Gruber	.04	.03	.02
157	Royce Clayton	.08	.06	.03
158	Chuck Finley	.04	.03	.02
159	Jeff King	.04	.03	.02
160	Greg Vaughn	.08	.06	.03
161	Geronimo Pena	.04	.03	.02
162	Steve Farr	.04	.03	.02
163	Jose Oquendo	.04	.03	.02
164	Mark Lewis	.04	.03	.02
165	John Wetteland	.06	.05	.02
166	Mike Henneman	.04	.03	.02
167	Todd Hundley	.04	.03	.02
168	Wes Chamberlain	.04	.03	.02
169	Steve Avery	.10	.08	.04
170	Mike Devereaux	.04	.03	.02
171	Reggie Sanders	.08	.06	.03
172	Jay Buhner	.08	.06	.03
173	Eric Anthony	.04	.03	.02
175	Tom Candiotti	.04	.03	.02
176	Phil Plantier	.08	.06	.03
177	Doug Henry	.04	.03	.02
178	Scott Leius	.04	.03	.02
179	Kirt Manwaring	.04	.03	.02
180	Jeff Parrett	.04	.03	.02
181	Don Slaught	.04	.03	.02
182	Scott Radinsky	.04	.03	.02
183	Luis Alicea	.04	.03	.02
184	Tom Gordon	.04	.03	.02
185	Rick Wilkins	.04	.03	.02
186	Todd Stottlemyre	.04	.03	.02
187	Moises Alou	.08	.06	.03
188	Joe Grahe	.04	.03	.02
189	Jeff Kent	.04	.03	.02
190	Bill Wegman	.04	.03	.02
191	Kim Batiste	.04	.03	.02
192	Matt Nokes	.04	.03	.02
193	Mark Wohlers	.04	.03	.02
194	Paul Sorrento	.04	.03	.02
195	Chris Hammond	.04	.03	.02
196	Scott Livingstone	.04	.03	.02
197	Doug Jones	.04	.03	.02
198	Scott Cooper	.04	.03	.02
199	Ramon Martinez	.04	.03	.02
200	Dave Valle	.04	.03	.02
201	Mariano Duncan	.04	.03	.02
202	Ben McDonald	.10	.08	.04
203	Darren Lewis	.04	.03	.02
204	Kenny Rogers	.04	.03	.02
205	Manuel Lee	.04	.03	.02
206	Scott Erickson	.06	.05	.02
207	Dan Gladden	.04	.03	.02
208	Bob Welch	.04	.03	.02
209	Greg Olson	.04	.03	.02
210	Dan Pasqua	.04	.03	.02
211	Tim Wallach	.04	.03	.02
212	Jeff Montgomery	.04	.03	.02
213	Derrick May	.04	.03	.02
214	Ed Sprague	.04	.03	.02
215	David Haas	.04	.03	.02
216	Darrin Fletcher	.04	.03	.02
217	Brian Jordan	.08	.06	.03
218	Jaime Navarro	.04	.03	.02
219	Randy Velarde	.04	.03	.02
220	Ron Gant	.10	.08	.04
221	Paul Quantrill	.04	.03	.02
222	*Damion Easley*	.15	.11	.06
223	Charlie Hough	.04	.03	.02
224	*Brad Brink*	.04	.03	.02
225	*Barry Manual*	.08	.06	.03
226	*Kevin Koslofski*	.04	.03	.02
227	*Ryan Thompson*	.15	.11	.06
228	*Mike Munoz*	.04	.03	.02
229	*Dan Wilson*	.08	.06	.03
230	*Peter Hoy*	.08	.06	.03
231	*Pedro Astacio*	.15	.11	.06
232	*Matt Stairs*	.04	.03	.02
233	*Jeff Reboulet*	.04	.03	.02
234	*Manny Alexander*	.08	.06	.03
235	*Willie Banks*	.08	.06	.03
236	*John Jaha*	.20	.15	.08
237	*Scooter Tucker*	.06	.05	.02
238	*Russ Springer*	.06	.05	.02
239	*Paul Miller*	.06	.05	.02
240	*Dan Peltier*	.06	.05	.02
241	*Ozzie Canseco*	.06	.05	.02
242	*Ben Rivera*	.06	.05	.02
243	*John Valentin*	.15	.11	.06
244	*Henry Rodriguez*	.08	.06	.03
245	*Derek Parks*	.08	.06	.03
246	*Carlos Garcia*	.10	.08	.04
247	*Tim Pugh* (FC)	.15	.11	.06
248	*Melvin Nieves*	.35	.25	.14
249	*Rich Amaral*	.08	.06	.03
250	*Willie Greene*	.08	.06	.03
251	*Tim Scott*	.08	.06	.03
252	*Dave Silvestri*	.08	.06	.03
253	*Rob Mallicoat*	.08	.06	.03
254	*Donald Harris*	.10	.08	.04
255	*Craig Colbert*	.08	.06	.03
256	Jose Guzman	.04	.03	.02
257	*Domingo Martinez* (FC)	.25	.20	.10
258	*William Suero*	.06	.05	.02
259	*Juan Guerrero*	.06	.05	.02
260	*J.T. Snow*	.60	.45	.25
261	Tony Pena	.04	.03	.02
262	*Tim Fortugno*	.06	.05	.02
263	*Tom Marsh*	.06	.05	.02
264	*Kurt Knudsen*	.08	.06	.03
265	*Tim Costo*	.08	.06	.03
266	*Steve Shifflett*	.06	.05	.02
267	*Billy Ashley*	.20	.15	.08
268	Jerry Nielsen	.06	.05	.02
269	*Pete Young*	.04	.03	.02
270	*Johnny Guzman*	.08	.06	.03
271	*Greg Colbrunn*	.08	.06	.03
272	*Jeff Nelson*	.08	.06	.03
273	*Kevin Young*	.20	.15	.08
274	*Jeff Frye*	.08	.06	.03
275	*J.T. Bruett*	.08	.06	.03
276	*Todd Pratt*	.08	.06	.03
277	*Mike Butcher*	.08	.06	.03
278	*John Flaherty*	.10	.08	.04
279	*John Patterson*	.08	.06	.03
280	*Eric Hillman*	.08	.06	.03
281	*Bien Figueros*	.08	.06	.03
282	*Shane Reynolds*	.10	.08	.04
283	*Rich Rowland*	.08	.06	.03
284	*Steve Foster*	.08	.06	.03
285	*Dave Mlicki*	.08	.06	.03
286	*Mike Piazza*	2.50	2.00	1.00
287	*Mike Trombley*	.08	.06	.03
288	*Jim Pena*	.08	.06	.03
289	*Bob Ayrault*	.08	.06	.03
290	*Henry Meroedee*	.06	.05	.02
291	Bob Wickman	.30	.25	.12
292	*Jacob Brumfield*	.08	.06	.03
293	*David Hulse*	.10	.08	.04
294	Ryan Klesko	.40	.25	.12
295	Doug Linton	.08	.06	.03
296	Steve Cooke	.04	.03	.02
297	Eddie Zosky	.04	.03	.02
298	*Gerald Williams*	.08	.06	.03
299	*Jonathan Hurst*	.08	.06	.03
300	*Larry Carter*	.06	.05	.02
301	*William Pennyfeather*	.06	.05	.02
302	*Cesar Hernandez*	.06	.05	.02
303	*Steve Hosey*	.15	.11	.06
304	*Blas Minor*	.10	.08	.04
305	*Jeff Grotewold*	.06	.05	.02
306	*Bernardo Brito*	.06	.05	.02
307	*Rafael Bournigal*	.08	.06	.03
308	*Jeff Branson*	.06	.05	.02
309	*Tom Quinlan*	.06	.05	.02
310	*Pat Gomez*	.08	.06	.03
311	*Sterling Hitchcock*	.30	.25	.12
312	*Kent Bottenfield*	.06	.05	.02
313	Alan Trammell	.04	.03	.02
314	*Cris Colon*	.06	.05	.02
315	*Paul Wagner*	.06	.05	.02
316	*Matt Maysey*	.06	.05	.02
317	Mike Stanton	.04	.03	.02
318	*Rick Tricek*	.06	.05	.02
319	*Kevin Rogers*	.06	.05	.02
320	*Mark Clark*	.06	.05	.02
321	*Pedro Martinez*	.12	.09	.05
322	*Al Martin* (FC)	.30	.25	.12
323	Mike Macfarlane	.04	.03	.02
324	*Rey Sanchez*	.06	.05	.02
325	*Roger Pavlik*	.06	.05	.02
326	*Troy Neel*	.20	.15	.08
327	*Kerry Woodson*	.06	.05	.02
328	*Wayne Kirby*	.08	.06	.03
329	*Ken Ryan* (FC)	.20	.15	.08
330	*Jesse Levis*	.06	.05	.02
331	James Austin	.04	.03	.02
332	Dan Walters	.04	.03	.02
333	Brian Williams	.04	.03	.02
334	Wil Cordero	.12	.09	.05
335	*Bret Boone*	.20	.15	.08
336	Hipolito Pichardo	.04	.03	.02
337	Pat Mahomes	.06	.05	.02
338	Andy Stankiewicz	.06	.05	.02
339	Jim Bullinger	.04	.03	.02
341	Ruben Amaro, Jr.	.06	.05	.02
342	Frank Seminara	.04	.03	.02
343	Pat Hentgen	.08	.06	.03
344	Dave Nilsson	.04	.03	.02
345	Mike Perez	.04	.03	.02
346	*Tim Salmon*	1.50	1.25	.60
347	*Tim Wakefield*	.10	.08	.04
348	Carlos Hernandez	.04	.03	.02
349	Donovan Osborne	.06	.05	.02
350	Denny Naegle	.04	.03	.02
351	Sam Militello	.06	.05	.02
352	Eric Fox	.04	.03	.02
353	John Doherty	.04	.03	.02
354	Chad Curtis	.08	.06	.03
355	Jeff Tackett	.04	.03	.02
356	Dave Fleming	.06	.05	.02
357	*Pat Listach*	.12	.09	.05
358	Kevin Wickander	.04	.03	.02
359	John VanderWal	.04	.03	.02
360	Arthur Rhodes	.06	.05	.02
361	Bob Scanlan	.04	.03	.02
362	Bob Zupcic	.04	.03	.02
363	Mel Rojas	.04	.03	.02
364	Jim Thome	.10	.08	.04
365	Bill Pecota	.04	.03	.02
366	Mark Carreon	.04	.03	.02
367	Mitch Williams	.04	.03	.02
368	Cal Eldred	.08	.06	.03
369	Stan Belinda	.04	.03	.02
370	Pat Kelly	.04	.03	.02
371	Pheal Cormier	.04	.03	.02
372	Juan Guzman	.10	.08	.04
373	Damon Berryhill	.04	.03	.02
374	Gary DiSarcina	.04	.03	.02
375	Norm Charlton	.04	.03	.02
376	Roberto Hernandez	.04	.03	.02
377	Scott Kamieniecki	.04	.03	.02
378	Rusty Meacham	.04	.03	.02
379	Kurt Stillwell	.04	.03	.02
380	Lloyd McClendon	.04	.03	.02
381	Mark Leonard	.04	.03	.02
382	Jerry Browne	.04	.03	.02
383	Glenn Davis	.04	.03	.02
384	Randy Johnson	.06	.05	.02
385	Mike Greenwell	.08	.06	.03
386	Scott Chiamparino	.04	.03	.02
387	George Bell	.06	.05	.02
388	Steve Olin	.04	.03	.02
389	Chuck McElroy	.04	.03	.02
390	Mark Gardner	.04	.03	.02
391	Rod Beck	.06	.05	.02
392	Dennis Rasmussen	.04	.03	.02
393	Charlie Leibrandt	.04	.03	.02
394	Julio Franco	.04	.03	.02
395	Pete Harnisch	.04	.03	.02
396	Sid Bream	.04	.03	.02
397	Milt Thompson	.04	.03	.02
398	Glenallen Hill	.04	.03	.02
399	Chico Walker	.04	.03	.02
400	Alex Cole	.04	.03	.02
401	Trevor Wilson	.04	.03	.02
402	Jeff Conine	.06	.05	.02
403	Kyle Abbott	.06	.05	.02
404	Tom Browning	.04	.03	.02
405	Jerald Clark	.04	.03	.02
406	Vince Horsman	.04	.03	.02
407	Kevin Mitchell	.08	.06	.03
408	Pete Smith	.04	.03	.02
409	Jeff Innis	.04	.03	.02

410	Mike Timlin	.04	.03	.02
411	Charlie Hayes	.06	.05	.02
412	Alex Fernandez	.06	.05	.02
413	Jeff Russell	.04	.03	.02
414	Jody Reed	.04	.03	.02
415	Mickey Morandini	.04	.03	.02
416	Darnell Coles	.04	.03	.02
417	Xavier Hernandez	.04	.03	.02
418	Steve Sax	.04	.03	.02
419	Joe Girardi	.04	.03	.02
420	Mike Fetters	.04	.03	.02
421	Danny Jackson	.04	.03	.02
422	Jim Gott	.04	.03	.02
423	Tim Belcher	.04	.03	.02
424	Jose Mesa	.04	.03	.02
425	Junior Felix	.04	.03	.02
426	Thomas Howard	.04	.03	.02
427	Julio Valera	.04	.03	.02
428	Dante Bichette	.06	.05	.02
429	Mike Sharperson	.04	.03	.02
430	Darryl Kile	.06	.05	.02
431	Lonnie Smith	.04	.03	.02
432	Monty Fariss	.06	.05	.02
433	Reggie Jefferson	.04	.03	.02
434	Bob McClure	.04	.03	.02
435	Craig lefferts	.04	.03	.02
436	Duane Ward	.04	.03	.02
437	Shawn Abner	.04	.03	.02
438	Roberto Kelly	.06	.05	.02
439	Paul O'Neill	.08	.06	.03
440	Alan Mills	.06	.05	.02
441	Roger Mason	.04	.03	.02
442	Gary Pettis	.04	.03	.02
443	Steve Lake	.04	.03	.02
444	Gene Larkin	.04	.03	.02
445	Larry Anderson	.04	.03	.02
446	Doug Dascenzo	.04	.03	.02
447	Daryl Boston	.04	.03	.02
448	John Candelaria	.04	.03	.02
449	Storm Davis	.04	.03	.02
450	Tom Edens	.04	.03	.02
451	Mike Maddux	.04	.03	.02
452	Tim Naehring	.04	.03	.02
453	John Orton	.04	.03	.02
454	Joey Cora	.04	.03	.02
455	Chuck Crim	.04	.03	.02
456	Dan Plesac	.04	.03	.02
457	Mike Bielecki	.04	.03	.02
458	*Terry Jorgensen*	.04	.03	.02
459	John Habyan	.04	.03	.02
460	Pete O'Brien	.04	.03	.02
461	Jeff Treadway	.04	.03	.02
462	Frank Castillo	.04	.03	.02
463	Jimmy Jones	.04	.03	.02
464	Tommy Greene	.04	.03	.02
465	Tracy Woddson	.06	.05	.02
466	Rich Rodriguez	.04	.03	.02
467	Joe Hesketh	.04	.03	.02
468	Greg Myers	.04	.03	.02
469	Kirk McCaskill	.04	.03	.02
470	Ricky Bones	.04	.03	.02
471	Lenny Webster	.04	.03	.02
472	Francisco Cabrera	.04	.03	.02
473	Turner Ward	.04	.03	.02
474	Dwayne Henry	.04	.03	.02
475	Al Osuna	.04	.03	.02
476	Craig Wilson	.04	.03	.02
477	Chris Nabholz	.04	.03	.02
478	Rafael Belliard	.04	.03	.02
479	Terry Leach	.04	.03	.02
480	Tim Teufel	.04	.03	.02
481	Dennis Eckersley (Award Winner)	.06	.05	.02
482	Barry Bonds (Award Winner)	.10	.08	.04
483	Dennis Eckersley (Award Winner)	.06	.05	.02
484	Greg Maddux (Award Winner)	.08	.06	.03
485	Pat Listach (ROY)	.10	.08	.04
486	Eric Karros (ROY)	.12	.09	.05
487	*Jamie Arnold* (FC)	.20	.15	.08
488	*B.J. Wallace* (FC)	.35	.25	.14
489	*Derek Jeter* (FC)	.45	.35	.20
490	*Jason Kendall* (FC)	.25	.20	.10
491	*Rick Helling* (FC)	.20	.15	.08
492	*Derek Wallace* (FC)	.20	.15	.08
493	*Sean Lowe* (FC)	.20	.15	.08
494	*Shannon Stewart* (FC)	.20	.15	.08
495	*Benji Grigsby* (FC)	.20	.15	.08
496	*Todd Steverson* (FC)	.20	.15	.08
497	*Dan Serafini* (FC)	.25	.20	.10
498	*Michael Tucker* (FC)	.50	.40	.20
499	Chris Roberts (Draft Pick)	.08	.06	.03
500	Pete Janicki (Draft Pick)	.08	.06	.03
501	*Jeff Schmidt* (FC)	.20	.15	.08
502	Edgar Martinez (Draft Pick)	.04	.03	.02
503	Omar Vizquel (AS)	.04	.03	.02
504	Ken Griffey, Jr. (AS)	.30	.25	.12
505	Kirby Puckett (AS)	.10	.08	.04
506	Joe Carter (AS)	.10	.08	.04
507	Ivan Rodriguez (AS)	.06	.05	.02
508	Jack Morris (AS)	.04	.03	.02
509	Dennis Eckersley (AS)	.04	.03	.02
510	Frank Thomas (AS)	.35	.25	.14
511	Roberto Alomar (AS)	.10	.08	.04
512	Mickey Morandini (Highlight)	.04	.03	.02
513	Dennis Eckersley (Highlight)	.06	.05	.02
514	Jeff Reardon (Highlight)	.04	.03	.02
515	Danny Tartabull (Hightlight)	.04	.03	.02
516	Bip Roberts (Highlight)	.04	.03	.02
517	George Brett (Highlight)	.08	.06	.03
518	Robin Yount (Highlight)	.15	.11	.06
519	Kevin Gross (Highlight)	.04	.03	.02
520	Ed Sprague (World Series Highlight)	.04	.03	.02
521	Dave Winfield (World Series Highlight)	.10	.07	.04
522	Ozzie Smith (AS)	.08	.06	.03
523	Barry Bonds (AS)	.15	.11	.06
524	Andy Van Slyke (AS)	.04	.03	.02
525	Tony Gwynn (AS)	.08	.06	.03
526	Darren Daulton (AS)	.06	.05	.02
527	Greg Maddux (AS)	.08	.06	.03
528	Fred McGriff (AS)	.08	.06	.03
529	Lee Smith (AS)	.04	.03	.02
530	Ryne Sandberg (AS)	.10	.08	.04
531	Gary Sheffield (AS)	.06	.05	.03
532	Ozzie Smith (Dream Team)	.06	.05	.02
533	Kirby Puckett (Dream Team)	.08	.06	.03
534	Gary Sheffield (Dream Team)	.06	.05	.02
535	Andy Van Slyke (Dream Team)	.04	.03	.02
536	Ken Griffey, Jr. (Dream Team)	.25	.20	.10
537	Ivan Rodriguez (Dream Team)	.08	.06	.03
538	Charles Nagy (Dream Team)	.04	.03	.02
539	Tom Glavine (Dream Team)	.10	.08	.04
540	Dennis Eckersley (Dream Team)	.06	.05	.02
541	Frank Thomas (Dream Team)	.40	.30	.15
542	Roberto Alomar (Dream Team)	.10	.08	.04
543	Sean Barry	.04	.03	.02
544	Mike Schooler	.04	.03	.02
545	Chuck Carr	.04	.03	.02
546	Lenny Harris	.04	.03	.02
547	Gary Scott	.04	.03	.02
548	Derek Lilliquist	.04	.03	.02
549	Brian Hunter	.04	.03	.02
550	Kirby Puckett (MOY)	.10	.08	.04
551	Jim Eisenreich	.04	.03	.02
552	Andre Dawson	.06	.05	.02
553	*David Nied*	.75	.60	.30
554	Spike Owen	.04	.03	.02
555	Greg Gagne	.06	.05	.02
556	Sid Fernandez	.04	.03	.02
557	Mark McGwire	.20	.15	.08
558	Bryan Harvey	.06	.05	.02
559	Harold Reynolds	.04	.03	.02
560	Barry Bonds	.30	.25	.12
561	*Eric Wedge* (FC)	.25	.20	.10
562	Ozzie Smith	.12	.09	.05
563	Rick Sutcliffe	.04	.03	.02
564	Jeff Reardon	.04	.03	.02
565	*Alex Arias*	.04	.03	.02
566	Greg Swindell	.04	.03	.02
567	Brook Jacoby	.04	.03	.02
568	Pete Incaviglia	.04	.03	.02
569	*Butch Henry*	.06	.05	.02
570	Eric Davis	.08	.06	.03
571	Kevin Seitzer	.04	.03	.02
572	Tony Fernandez	.04	.03	.02
573	*Steve Reed*	.08	.06	.03
574	Cory Snyder	.04	.03	.02
575	Joe Carter	.12	.09	.05
576	Greg Maddux	.15	.11	.06
577	Bert Blyleven	.08	.06	.03
578	Kevin Bass	.04	.03	.02
579	Carlton Fisk	.12	.09	.05
580	Doug Drabek	.08	.06	.03
581	Mark Gubicza	.06	.05	.02
582	Bobby Thigpen	.04	.03	.02
583	Chili Davis	.08	.06	.03
584	Scott Bankhead	.04	.03	.02
585	Harold Baines	.06	.05	.02
586	*Eric Young*	.06	.05	.02
587	Lance Parrish	.04	.03	.02
588	Juan Bell	.04	.03	.02
589	Bob Ojeda	.04	.03	.02
590	Joe Orsulak	.04	.03	.02
591	Benito Santiago	.06	.05	.02
592	Wade Boggs	.20	.15	.08
593	Robby Thompson	.06	.05	.02
594	Erik Plunk	.04	.03	.02
595	Hensley Meulens	.04	.03	.02
596	Lou Whitaker	.10	.08	.04
597	Dale Murphy	.20	.15	.08
598	Paul Molitor	.20	.15	.08
599	Greg W. Harris	.04	.03	.02
600	Darren Holmes	.04	.03	.02
601	Dave Martinez	.04	.03	.02
602	Tom Henke	.04	.03	.02
603	Mike Benjamin	.04	.03	.02
604	Rene Gonzales	.04	.03	.02
605	Roger McDowell	.04	.03	.02
606	Kirby Puckett	.20	.15	.08
607	Randy Myers	.04	.03	.02
608	Ruben Sierra	.10	.08	.04
609	Wilson Alvarez	.04	.03	.02
610	Dave Segui	.04	.03	.02
611	Juan Samuel	.04	.03	.02
612	Tom Brunansky	.04	.03	.02
613	Willie Randolph	.04	.03	.02
614	Tony Phillips	.04	.03	.02
615	Candy Maldonado	.04	.03	.02
616	Chris Bosio	.04	.03	.02
617	Bret Barberie	.06	.05	.02
618	Scott Sanderson	.04	.03	.02
619	Ron Darling	.04	.03	.02
620	Dave Winfield	.15	.11	.06
621	Mike Felder	.04	.03	.02
622	Greg Hibbard	.04	.03	.02
623	Mike Scioscia	.04	.03	.02
624	John Smiley	.04	.03	.02
625	Alejandro Pena	.04	.03	.02
626	Terry Steinbach	.08	.06	.03
627	Freddie Benavides	.04	.03	.02
628	Kevin Reimer	.04	.03	.02
629	Braulio Castillo	.04	.03	.02
630	Dave Stieb	.04	.03	.02
631	Dave Magadan	.08	.06	.03
632	Scott Fletcher	.04	.03	.02
633	Cris Carpenter	.04	.03	.02
634	Kevin Maas	.06	.05	.02
635	Todd Worrell	.04	.03	.02
636	Rob Deer	.04	.03	.02
637	Dwight Smith	.04	.03	.02
638	Chito Martinez	.04	.03	.02
639	Jimmy Key	.04	.03	.02
640	Greg Harris	.04	.03	.02
641	Mike Moore	.04	.03	.02
642	Pat Borders	.04	.03	.02
643	Bill Gullickson	.06	.05	.02
644	Gary Gaetti	.04	.03	.02
645	David Howard	.04	.03	.02
646	Jim Abbott	.10	.08	.04
647	Willie Wilson	.04	.03	.02
648	David Wells	.04	.03	.02
649	Andres Galarraga	.08	.06	.03
650	Vince Coleman	.06	.05	.02
651	Rob Dibble	.06	.05	.02
652	Frank Tanana	.04	.03	.02
653	Steve Decker	.04	.03	.02
654	David Cone	.06	.05	.02
655	Jack Armstrong	.04	.03	.02
656	Dave Stewart	.08	.06	.03
657	Billy Hatcher	.06	.05	.02
658	Tim Raines	.08	.06	.03
659	Walt Weiss	.06	.05	.02
660	Jose Lind	.06	.05	.02

1993 Score Boys of Summer

These cards were available as inserts only in Score 35-card Super Packs, about one in every four packs. Borderless fronts have a color action photo of the player superimposed over the sun. The player's name is in black script in a green strip at bottom, along with a subset logo. On back is a player portrait, again with the sun as a background. Subset, company, team and major league logos are in color on the right, and there is a short career summary on the green background at bottom.

		MT	NR MT	EX
Complete Set (30):		75.00	56.00	30.00
Common Player:		.75	.60	.30
1	Billy Ashley	4.00	3.00	1.50
2	Tim Salmon	18.00	13.50	7.25
3	Pedro Martinez	1.25	.90	.50
4	Luis Mercedes	.75	.60	.30
5	Mike Piazza	25.00	18.50	10.00
6	Troy Neel	1.50	1.25	.60
7	Melvin Nieves	2.50	2.00	1.00
8	Ryan Klesko	4.50	3.50	1.75
9	Ryan Thompson	.90	.70	.35
10	Kevin Young	2.00	1.50	.80
11	Gerald Williams	.75	.60	.30
12	Willie Greene	1.50	1.25	.60
13	John Patterson	.75	.60	.30
14	Carlos Garcia	1.50	1.25	.60
15	Eddie Zosky	.75	.60	.30
16	Sean Berry	.75	.60	.30
17	Rico Brogna	1.25	.90	.50
18	Larry Carter	1.00	.70	.40
19	Bobby Ayala	1.00	.70	.40
20	Alan Embree	1.00	.70	.40
21	Donald Harris	.75	.60	.30
22	Sterling Hitchcock	2.00	1.50	.80
23	David Nied	3.50	2.75	1.50
24	Henry Mercedes	1.00	.70	.40
25	Ozzie Canseco	.75	.60	.30
26	David Hulse	1.50	1.25	.60
27	Al Martin	3.00	2.25	1.25
28	Dan Wilson	.75	.60	.30
29	Paul Miller	1.00	.70	.40
30	Rich Rowland	.75	.60	.30

Grading Guide

Mint (MT): A perfect card. Well-centered with all corners sharp and square. No creases, stains, edge nicks, surface marks, yellowing or fading.

Near Mint (NM): A nearly perfect card. At first glance, a NM card appears to be perfect. May be slightly off-center. No surface marks, creases or loss of gloss.

Excellent (EX): Corners are still fairly sharp with only moderate wear. Borders may be off-center. No creases or stains on fronts or backs, but may show slight loss of surface luster.

Very Good (VG): Shows obvious handling. May have rounded corners, minor creases, major gum or wax stains. No major creases, tape marks, writing, etc.

Good (G): A well-worn card, but exhibits no intentional damage. May have major or multiple creases. Corners may be rounded well beyond card border.

1993 Score The Franchise

These glossy inserts have full-bleed color action photos against a darkened background so that the player stands out. Cards could be found in 16-card packs only; odds of finding one are 1 in every 24 packs. The fronts have a gold foil stamping which says Franchise.

		MT	NR MT	EX
Complete Set (28):		80.00	60.00	32.00
Common Player:		1.00	.70	.40
1	Cal Ripken, Jr.	7.00	5.25	2.75
2	Roger Clemens	5.00	3.75	2.00
3	Mark Langston	1.00	.70	.40
4	Frank Thomas	18.00	13.50	7.25
5	Carlos Baerga	5.00	3.75	2.00
6	Cecil Fielder	3.50	2.75	1.50
7	Gregg Jefferies	1.00	.70	.40
8	Robin Yount	4.00	3.00	1.50
9	Kirby Puckett	6.00	4.50	2.50
10	Don Mattingly	3.00	2.25	1.25
11	Dennis Eckersley	1.00	.70	.40
12	Ken Griffey, Jr.	14.00	10.50	5.50
13	Juan Gonzalez	14.00	10.50	5.50
14	Roberto Alomar	6.00	4.50	2.50
15	Terry Pendleton	1.00	.70	.40
16	Ryne Sandberg	6.00	4.50	2.50
17	Barry Larkin	1.00	.70	.40
18	Jeff Bagwell	3.00	2.25	1.25
19	Brett Butler	1.00	.70	.40
20	Larry Walker	1.50	1.25	.60
21	Bobby Bonilla	1.00	.70	.40
22	Darren Daulton	2.00	1.50	.80
23	Andy Van Slyke	1.00	.70	.40
24	Ray Lankford	1.00	.70	.40
25	Gary Sheffield	2.00	1.50	.80
26	Will Clark	2.50	2.00	1.00
27	Bryan Harvey	1.00	.70	.40
28	David Nied	3.50	2.75	1.50

1993 Score Gold Dream Team

This 11-player insert set consists of the same players in the regular set's Dream Team subset, except the cards are gold foil stamped. There is an unnumbered header card in the set, which was available only via a mail-in offer.

		MT	NR MT	EX
Complete Set (12):		15.00	10.00	5.00
Common Player:		.50	.30	.15
1	Ozzie Smith	1.00	.60	.30
2	Kirby Puckett	2.00	1.50	.75
3	Gary Sheffield	1.50	1.00	.50
4	Andy Van Slyke	.50	.40	.20
5	Ken Griffey, Jr.	4.00	3.00	1.50
6	Ivan Rodriguez	1.00	.60	.30
7	Charles Nagy	.50	.40	.20
8	Tom Glavine	1.50	1.00	.60
9	Dennis Eckersley	.75	.60	.30
10	Frank Thomas	5.00	3.00	1.50
11	Roberto Alomar	2.50	1.50	.75
----	Header card	.05	.04	.02

1993 Score Procter & Gamble Rookies

This 10-card set was available via a mail-in offer in the summer of 1993. Ten proofs of purchase from Procter & Gamble products were required along with a small amount of cash for postage and handling. Fronts feature a player action photo in a diamond at center with the name, position and team logo in a home plate device at the bottom of the photo. At bottom center is a color photo of the player's home stadium, flanked by silver-foil stripes on a dark green background. Above the player photo are gold-foil Score and P&G logos on a dark green background.

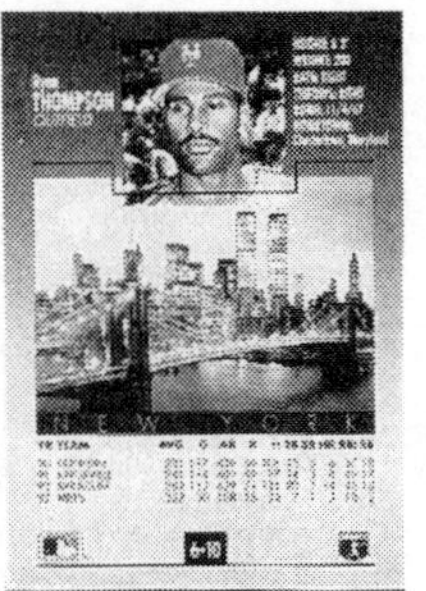

A center bar in gold foil has the word "ROOKIE" in green. Backs have a small player portrait photo at top against a dark green background. His name and position are in white at left and personal data at right. At center is a large color photo of the player's hometeam skyline, with the city name in gold type in a green stripe below. At bottom are complete major and minor league stats, MLB and MLBPA logos and the card number.

		MT	NR MT	EX
Complete Set (10):		5.00	3.75	2.00
Common Player:		.50	.40	.20
1	Wil Cordero	.75	.50	.30
2	Pedro Martinez	.50	.40	.20
3	Bret Boone	.50	.40	.20
4	Melvin Nieves	.75	.50	.30
5	Ryan Klesko	.75	.50	.30
6	Ryan Thompson	.50	.40	.20
7	Kevin Young	.75	.50	.30
8	Willie Greene	.50	.40	.20
9	Eric Wedge	.50	.40	.20
10	David Nied	.75	.50	.30

1993 Score Select

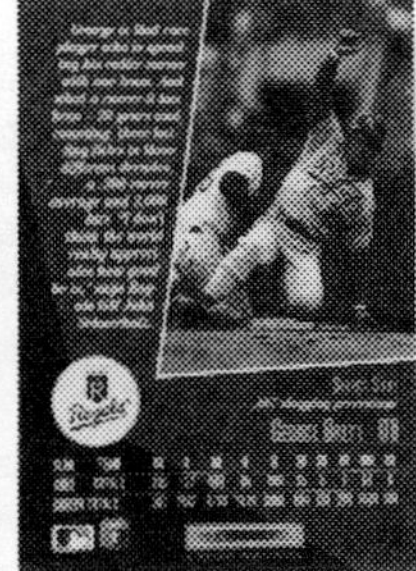

This 400-card set from Score is designed for the mid-priced card market. The card fronts feature green borders on two sides of the card with the photo filling the remaining portion of the card front. "Score Select" appears within the photo. The backs feature an additional photo, player information and statistics. Cards numbered 271-360 are devoted to rookies and draft picks. Several cards from this set are printed horizontally. The cards are UV coated on both sides.

		MT	NR MT	EX
Complete Set (405):		32.00	24.00	15.00
Common Player:		.06	.05	.02
1	Barry Bonds	.75	.60	.30
2	Ken Griffey, Jr.	1.50	1.25	.60
3	Will Clark	.25	.20	.10
4	Kirby Puckett	.35	.25	.14
5	Tony Gwynn	.20	.15	.08
6	Frank Thomas	3.00	2.25	1.25
7	Tom Glavine	.25	.20	.10
8	Roberto Alomar	.40	.30	.15
9	Andre Dawson	.15	.11	.06
10	Ron Darling	.08	.06	.03
11	Bobby Bonilla	.12	.09	.05
12	Danny Tartabull	.12	.09	.05
13	Darren Daulton	.12	.09	.05
14	Roger Clemens	.40	.30	.15
15	Ozzie Smith	.25	.20	.10
16	Mark McGwire	.15	.11	.06
17	Terry Pendleton	.15	.11	.06
18	Cal Ripken, Jr.	.60	.45	.25
19	Fred McGriff	.25	.20	.10
20	Cecil Fielder	.25	.20	.10
21	Darryl Strawberry	.12	.09	.05
22	Robin Yount	.35	.25	.14
23	Barry Larkin	.15	.11	.06
24	Don Mattingly	.30	.25	.12
25	Craig Biggio	.10	.08	.04
26	Sandy Alomar Jr.	.15	.11	.06
27	Larry Walker	.15	.11	.06
28	Junior Felix	.06	.05	.02
29	Eddie Murray	.12	.09	.05
30	Robin Ventura	.15	.11	.06
31	Greg Maddux	.20	.15	.08
32	Dave Winfield	.25	.20	.10
33	John Kruk	.12	.09	.05
34	Wally Joyner	.12	.09	.05
35	Andy Van Slyke	.12	.09	.05
36	Chuck Knoblauch	.12	.09	.05
37	Tom Pagnozzi	.08	.06	.03
38	Dennis Eckersley	.12	.09	.05
39	Dave Justice	.50	.40	.20
40	Juan Gonzalez	1.50	1.25	.60
41	Gary Sheffield	.25	.20	.10
42	Paul Molitor	.25	.20	.10
43	Delino DeShields	.12	.09	.05
44	Travis Fryman	.25	.20	.10
45	Hal Morris	.10	.08	.04
46	Gregg Olson	.10	.08	.04
47	Ken Caminiti	.08	.06	.03
48	Wade Boggs	.20	.15	.08
49	Orel Hershiser	.12	.09	.05
50	Albert Belle	.40	.30	.15
51	Bill Swift	.08	.06	.03
52	Mark Langston	.12	.09	.05
53	Joe Girardi	.06	.05	.02
54	Keith Miller	.06	.05	.02
55	Gary Carter	.12	.09	.05
56	Brady Anderson	.15	.11	.06
57	Dwight Gooden	.15	.11	.06
58	Julio Franco	.10	.08	.04
59	Len Dykstra	.15	.11	.06
60	Mickey Tettleton	.10	.08	.04
61	Randy Tomlin	.10	.08	.04
62	B.J. Surhoff	.08	.06	.03
63	Todd Zeile	.08	.06	.03
64	Roberto Kelly	.10	.08	.04
65	Rob Dibble	.10	.08	.04
66	Leo Gomez	.10	.08	.04
67	Doug Jones	.06	.05	.02
68	Ellis Burks	.12	.09	.05
69	Mike Scioscia	.06	.05	.02
70	Charles Nagy	.20	.15	.08
71	Cory Snyder	.06	.05	.02
72	Devon White	.08	.06	.03
73	Mark Grace	.12	.09	.05
74	Luis Polonia	.06	.05	.02
75	John Smiley	.08	.06	.03
76	Carlton Fisk	.15	.11	.06
77	Luis Sojo	.06	.05	.02
78	George Brett	.40	.30	.15
79	Mitch Williams	.10	.08	.04
80	Kent Hrbek	.10	.08	.04
81	Jay Bell	.10	.08	.04
82	Edgar Martinez	.15	.11	.06
83	Lee Smith	.10	.08	.04
84	Deion Sanders	.25	.20	.10
85	Bill Gullickson	.08	.06	.03
86	Paul O'Neill	.08	.06	.03
87	Kevin Seitzer	.08	.06	.03
88	Steve Finley	.08	.06	.03
89	Mel Hall	.08	.06	.03
90	Nolan Ryan	1.50	1.25	.60
91	Eric Davis	.15	.11	.06
92	Mike Mussina	.40	.30	.15
93	Tony Fernandez	.08	.06	.03
94	Frank Viola	.12	.09	.05
95	Matt Williams	.12	.09	.05
96	Joe Carter	.25	.20	.10
97	Ryne Sandberg	.50	.40	.20
98	Jim Abbott	.15	.11	.06
99	Marquis Grissom	.15	.11	.06
100	George Bell	.10	.07	.04
101	Howard Johnson	.10	.08	.04
102	Kevin Appier	.12	.09	.05
103	Dale Murphy	.12	.09	.05
104	Shane Mack	.10	.08	.04
105	Jose Lind	.08	.06	.03
106	Rickey Henderson	.30	.25	.12
107	Bob Tewksbury	.08	.06	.03
108	Kevin Mitchell	.12	.09	.05
109	Steve Avery	.20	.15	.08
110	Candy Maldonado	.08	.06	.03
111	Bip Roberts	.10	.08	.04
112	Lou Whitaker	.10	.08	.04
113	Jeff Bagwell	.35	.25	.14
114	Dante Bichette	.06	.05	.02
115	Brett Butler	.10	.08	.04
116	Melido Perez	.06	.05	.02
117	Andy Benes	.12	.09	.05
118	Randy Johnson	.08	.06	.03
119	Willie McGee	.08	.06	.03
120	Jody Reed	.08	.06	.03
121	Shawon Dunston	.08	.06	.03
122	Carlos Baerga	.40	.30	.15
123	Bret Saberhagen	.12	.09	.05
124	John Olerud	.40	.30	.15
125	Ivan Calderon	.08	.06	.03
126	Bryan Harvey	.10	.08	.04
127	Terry Mulholland	.08	.06	.03
128	Ozzie Guillen	.10	.08	.04
129	Steve Buechele	.08	.06	.03
130	Kevin Tapani	.08	.06	.03
131	Felix Jose	.12	.09	.05
132	Terry Steinbach	.08	.06	.03
133	Ron Gant	.12	.09	.05
134	Harold Reynolds	.08	.06	.03
135	Chris Sabo	.10	.08	.04
136	Ivan Rodriguez	.15	.11	.06
137	Eric Anthony	.08	.06	.03
138	Mike Henneman	.08	.06	.03
139	Robby Thompson	.08	.06	.03
140	Scott Fletcher	.06	.05	.02
141	Bruce Hurst	.08	.06	.03
142	Kevin Maas	.08	.06	.03
143	Tom Candiotti	.08	.06	.03
144	Chris Hoiles	.15	.11	.06

145	Mike Morgan	.08	.06	.03
146	Mark Whiten	.12	.09	.05
147	Dennis Martinez	.10	.08	.04
148	Tony Pena	.08	.06	.03
149	Dave Magadan	.08	.06	.03
150	Mark Lewis	.10	.08	.04
151	Mariano Duncan	.06	.05	.02
152	Gregg Jefferies	.15	.11	.06
153	Doug Drabek	.12	.09	.05
154	Brian Harper	.12	.09	.05
155	Ray Lankford	.15	.11	.06
156	Carney Lansford	.08	.06	.03
157	Mike Sharperson	.08	.06	.03
158	Jack Morris	.15	.11	.06
159	Otis Nixon	.10	.08	.04
160	Steve Sax	.10	.08	.04
161	Mark Lemke	.08	.06	.03
162	Rafael Palmeiro	.12	.09	.05
163	Jose Rijo	.12	.09	.05
164	Omar Vizquel	.06	.05	.02
165	Sammy Sosa	.10	.07	.04
166	Milt Cuyler	.08	.06	.03
167	John Franco	.08	.06	.03
168	Darryl Hamilton	.08	.06	.03
169	Ken Hill	.10	.08	.04
170	Mike Devereaux	.10	.08	.04
171	Don Slaught	.06	.05	.02
172	Steve Farr	.06	.05	.02
173	Bernard Gilkey	.10	.08	.04
174	Mike Fetters	.06	.05	.02
175	Vince Coleman	.08	.06	.03
176	Kevin McReynolds	.10	.08	.04
177	John Smoltz	.12	.09	.05
178	Greg Gagne	.08	.06	.03
179	Greg Swindell	.15	.11	.06
180	Juan Guzman	.12	.09	.05
181	Kal Daniels	.08	.06	.03
182	Rick Sutcliffe	.12	.09	.05
183	Orlando Merced	.12	.09	.05
184	Bill Wegman	.08	.06	.03
185	Mark Gardner	.08	.06	.03
186	Rob Deer	.08	.06	.03
187	Dave Hollins	.15	.11	.06
188	Jack Clark	.08	.06	.03
189	Brian Hunter	.10	.08	.04
190	Tim Wallach	.08	.06	.03
191	Tim Belcher	.08	.06	.03
192	Walt Weiss	.08	.06	.03
193	Kurt Stillwell	.06	.05	.02
194	Charlie Hayes	.08	.06	.03
195	Willie Randolph	.08	.06	.03
196	Jack McDowell	.15	.11	.06
197	Jose Offerman	.10	.08	.04
198	Chuck Finley	.10	.08	.04
199	Darrin Jackson	.08	.06	.03
200	Kelly Gruber	.08	.06	.03
201	John Wetteland	.12	.09	.05
202	Jay Buhner	.08	.06	.03
203	Mike LaValliere	.06	.05	.02
204	Kevin Brown	.12	.09	.05
205	Luis Gonzalez	.12	.09	.05
206	Rick Aguilera	.12	.09	.05
207	Norm Charlton	.12	.09	.05
208	Mike Bordick	.12	.09	.05
209	Charlie Leibrandt	.06	.05	.02
210	Tom Brunansky	.08	.06	.03
211	Tom Henke	.10	.08	.04
212	Randy Milligan	.06	.05	.02
213	Ramon Martinez	.15	.11	.06
214	Mo Vaughn	.08	.06	.03
215	Randy Myers	.08	.06	.03
216	Greg Hibbard	.08	.06	.03
217	Wes Chamberlain	.10	.08	.04
218	Tony Phillips	.10	.08	.04
219	Pete Harnisch	.10	.08	.04
220	Mike Gallego	.06	.05	.02
221	Bud Black	.06	.05	.02
222	Greg Vaughn	.10	.08	.04
223	Milt Thompson	.06	.05	.02
224	Ben McDonald	.25	.20	.10
225	Billy Hatcher	.06	.05	.02
226	Paul Sorrento	.08	.06	.03
227	Mark Gubicza	.08	.06	.03
228	Mike Greenwell	.08	.06	.03
229	Curt Schilling	.08	.06	.03
230	Alan Trammell	.10	.08	.04
231	Zane Smith	.08	.06	.03
232	Bobby Thigpen	.10	.08	.04
233	Greg Olson	.06	.05	.02
234	Joe Orsulak	.06	.05	.02
235	Joe Oliver	.06	.05	.02
236	Tim Raines	.12	.09	.05
237	Juan Samuel	.06	.05	.02
238	Chili Davis	.08	.06	.03
239	Spike Owen	.06	.05	.02
240	Dave Stewart	.12	.09	.05
241	Jim Eisenreich	.06	.05	.02
242	Phil Plantier	.20	.15	.08
243	Sid Fernandez	.10	.08	.04
244	Dan Gladden	.06	.05	.02
245	Mickey Morandini	.12	.09	.05
246	Tino Martinez	.12	.09	.05
247	Kirt Manwaring	.06	.05	.02
248	Dean Palmer	.12	.09	.05
249	Tom Browning	.08	.06	.03
250	Brian McRae	.12	.09	.05
251	Scott Leius	.08	.06	.03
252	Bert Blyleven	.08	.06	.03
253	Scott Erickson	.10	.08	.04
254	Bob Welch	.10	.08	.04
255	Pat Kelly	.10	.08	.04
256	Felix Fermin	.06	.05	.02
257	Harold Baines	.12	.09	.05
258	Duane Ward	.08	.06	.03
259	Bill Spiers	.08	.06	.03
260	Jaime Navarro	.10	.08	.04
261	Scott Sanderson	.08	.06	.03
262	Gary Gaetti	.08	.06	.03
263	Bob Ojeda	.06	.05	.02
264	Jeff Montgomery	.08	.06	.03
265	Scott Bankhead	.08	.06	.03
266	Lance Johnson	.08	.06	.03
267	Rafael Belliard	.06	.05	.02
268	Kevin Reimer	.08	.06	.03
269	Benito Santiago	.12	.09	.05
270	Mike Moore	.08	.06	.03
271	Dave Fleming	.12	.09	.05
272	Moises Alou	.20	.15	.08
273	Pat Listach	.12	.09	.05
274	Reggie Sanders	.12	.09	.05
275	Kenny Lofton	.40	.30	.15
276	Donovan Osborne	.15	.11	.06
277	Rusty Meacham	.20	.15	.08
278	Eric Karros	.15	.11	.06
279	Andy Stankiewicz	.15	.11	.06
280	Brian Jordan	.15	.11	.06
281	Gary DiSarcina	.08	.06	.03
282	Mark Wohlers	.08	.06	.03
283	Dave Nilsson	.20	.15	.08
284	Anthony Young	.10	.08	.04
285	Jim Bullinger	.12	.09	.05
286	Derek Bell	.12	.09	.05
287	Brian Williams	.15	.11	.06
288	Julio Valera	.15	.11	.06
289	Dan Walters	.15	.11	.06
290	Chad Curtis	.15	.11	.06
291	Michael Tucker	.80	.60	.30
292	Bob Zupcic	.15	.11	.06
293	Todd Hundley	.15	.11	.06
294	Jeff Tackett	.15	.11	.06
295	Greg Colbrunn	.15	.11	.06
296	Cal Eldred	.15	.11	.06
297	Chris Roberts	.20	.15	.08
298	John Doherty	.20	.15	.08
299	Denny Neagle	.12	.09	.05
300	Arthur Rhodes	.15	.11	.06
301	Mark Clark	.20	.15	.08
302	Scott Cooper	.20	.15	.08
303	*Jamie Arnold*	.20	.15	.08
304	Jim Thome	.40	.30	.15
305	Frank Seminara	.12	.09	.05
306	Kurt Knudsen	.12	.09	.05
307	Tim Wakefield	.12	.09	.05
308	John Jaha	.12	.09	.05
309	Pat Hentgen	.20	.15	.08
310	B.J. Wallace	.20	.15	.08
311	Roberto Hernandez	.15	.11	.06
312	Hipolito Pichardo	.20	.15	.08
313	Eric Fox	.15	.11	.06
314	Willie Banks	.15	.11	.06
315	Sam Millitello	.12	.09	.05
316	Vince Horsman	.12	.09	.05
317	Carlos Hernandez	.12	.09	.05
318	Jeff Kent	.20	.15	.08
319	Mike Perez	.12	.09	.05
320	Scott Livingstone	.12	.09	.05
321	Jeff Conine	.15	.11	.06
322	James Austin	.15	.11	.06
323	John Vander Wal	.15	.11	.06
324	Pat Mahomes	.10	.08	.04
325	Pedro Astacio	.12	.09	.05
326	Bret Boone	.12	.09	.05
327	Matt Stairs	.15	.11	.06
328	Damion Easley	.12	.09	.05
329	Ben Rivera	.20	.15	.08
330	Reggie Jefferson	.12	.09	.05
331	Luis Mercedes	.20	.15	.08
332	Kyle Abbott	.12	.09	.05
333	Eddie Taubensee	.12	.09	.05
334	Tim McIntosh	.10	.08	.04
335	Phil Clark	.10	.08	.04
336	Wil Cordero	.12	.09	.05
337	Russ Springer	.12	.09	.05
338	Craig Colbert	.10	.08	.04
339	Tim Salmon	2.00	1.50	.80
340	Braulio Castillo	.20	.15	.08
341	Donald Harris	.12	.09	.05
342	Eric Young	.15	.11	.06
343	Bob Wickman	.12	.09	.05
344	John Valentin	.12	.09	.05
345	Dan Wilson	.15	.11	.06
346	Steve Hosey	.12	.09	.05
347	Mike Piazza	4.00	3.00	1.50
348	Willie Greene	.12	.09	.05
349	Tom Goodwin	.10	.08	.04
350	Eric Hillman	.15	.11	.06
351	Steve Reed	.12	.09	.05
352	*Dan Serafini*	.25	.20	.10
353	*Todd Steverson*	.25	.20	.10
354	Benji Grigsby	.15	.11	.06
355	Shannon Stewart	.25	.20	.10
356	Sean Lowe	.25	.20	.10
357	Derek Wallace	.25	.20	.10
358	Rick Helling	.25	.20	.10
359	*Jason Kendall*	.25	.20	.10
360	*Derek Jeter*	1.00	.70	.40
361	David Cone	.15	.11	.06
362	Jeff Reardon	.15	.11	.06
363	Bobby Witt	.08	.06	.03
364	Jose Canseco	.25	.20	.10
365	Jeff Russell	.08	.06	.03
366	Ruben Sierra	.15	.11	.06
367	Alan Mills	.06	.05	.02
368	Matt Nokes	.08	.06	.03
369	Pat Borders	.08	.06	.03
370	Pedro Munoz	.12	.09	.05
371	Danny Jackson	.06	.05	.02
372	Geronimo Pena	.10	.08	.04
373	Craig Lefferts	.08	.06	.03
374	Joe Grahe	.08	.06	.03
375	Roger McDowell	.06	.05	.02
376	Jimmy Key	.10	.08	.04
377	Steve Olin	.10	.08	.04
378	Glenn Davis	.10	.08	.04
379	Rene Gonzales	.06	.05	.02
380	Manuel Lee	.06	.05	.02
381	Ron Karkovice	.06	.05	.02
382	Sid Bream	.06	.05	.02
383	Gerald Williams	.12	.09	.05
384	Lenny Harris	.06	.05	.02
385	*J.T. Snow*	.50	.40	.20
386	Dave Stieb	.08	.06	.03
387	Kirk McCaskill	.08	.06	.03
388	Lance Parrish	.08	.06	.03
389	Craig Greback	.06	.05	.02
390	Rick Wilkins	.12	.09	.05
391	Manny Alexander	.15	.11	.06
392	Mike Schooler	.06	.05	.02
393	Bernie Williams	.12	.09	.05
394	Kevin Koslofski	.20	.15	.08
395	Willie Wilson	.08	.06	.03
396	Jeff Parrett	.06	.05	.02
397	Mike Harkey	.08	.06	.03
398	Frank Tanana	.08	.06	.03
399	Doug Henry	.08	.06	.03
400	Royce Clayton	.12	.09	.05
401	Eric Wedge	.12	.09	.05
402	Derrick May	.12	.09	.05
403	Carlos Garcia	.12	.09	.05
404	Henry Rodriguez	.12	.09	.05
405	Ryan Klesko	1.00	.75	.40

1993 Score Select Aces

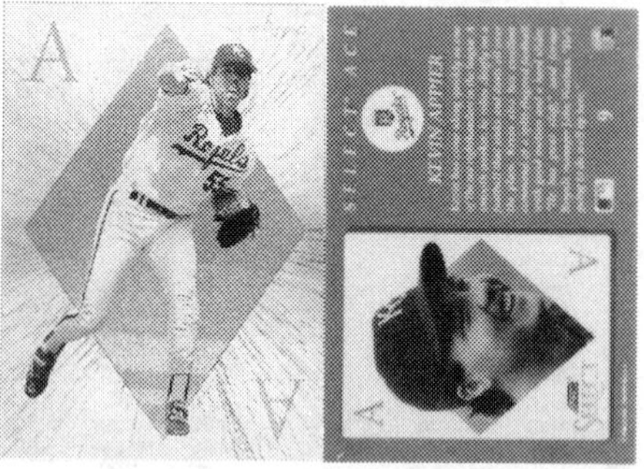

Cards from this set feature 24 of the top pitchers from 1992 and were included one per every 27-card Super Pack. The fronts have a picture of the player in action against an Ace card background. Backs have text and a portrait in the middle of a card suit for an Ace.

		MT	NR MT	EX
Complete Set (24):		70.00	52.00	28.00
Common Player:		3.00	2.25	1.25
1	Roger Clemens	12.00	9.00	4.75
2	Tom Glavine	6.00	4.50	2.50
3	Jack McDowell	4.00	3.00	1.50
4	Greg Maddux	7.50	5.75	3.00
5	Jack Morris	3.00	2.25	1.25
6	Dennis Martinez	3.00	2.25	1.25
7	Kevin Brown	3.00	2.25	1.25
8	Dwight Gooden	3.00	2.25	1.25
9	Kevin Appier	3.50	2.75	1.50
10	Mike Morgan	3.00	2.25	1.25
11	Juan Guzman	4.00	3.00	1.50
12	Charles Nagy	3.00	2.25	1.25
13	John Smiley	3.00	2.25	1.25
14	Ken Hill	3.00	2.25	1.25
15	Bob Tewksbury	3.00	2.25	1.25
16	Doug Drabek	3.00	2.25	1.25
17	John Smoltz	3.50	2.75	1.50
18	Greg Swindell	3.00	2.25	1.25
19	Bruce Hurst	3.00	2.25	1.25
20	Mike Mussina	9.00	6.75	3.50
21	Cal Eldred	3.00	2.25	1.25
22	Melido Perez	3.00	2.25	1.25
23	Dave Fleming	3.00	2.25	1.25
24	Kevin Tapani	4.00	3.00	1.50

1993 Score Select Chase Rookies

Top newcomers in 1992 are featured in this 21-card insert set. Cards were randomly inserted in 15-card hobby packs. The fronts have a Score Select Rookies logo on the front. The backs have text and a player portrait.

		MT	NR MT	EX
Complete Set (21):		245.00	184.00	98.00
Common Player:		6.00	4.50	2.50
1	Pat Listach	6.00	4.50	2.50
2	Moises Alou	18.00	13.50	7.25
3	Reggie Sanders	15.00	11.00	6.00
4	Kenny Lofton	40.00	30.00	15.00
5	Eric Karros	10.00	7.50	4.00
6	Brian Williams	6.00	4.50	2.50
7	Donovan Osborne	7.00	5.25	2.75
8	Sam Militello	6.00	4.50	2.50
9	Chad Curtis	10.00	7.50	4.00
10	Bob Zupcic	6.00	4.50	2.50
11	Tim Salmon	65.00	49.00	26.00
12	Jeff Conine	15.00	11.00	6.00
13	Pedro Astacio	12.00	9.00	4.75
14	Arthur Rhodes	6.00	4.50	2.50
15	Cal Eldred	10.00	7.50	4.00
16	Tim Wakefield	6.00	4.50	2.50
17	Andy Stankiewicz	6.00	4.50	2.50
18	Wil Cordero	16.00	12.00	6.50
19	Todd Hundley	6.00	4.50	2.50
20	Dave Fleming	10.00	7.50	4.00
21	Bret Boone	13.00	9.75	5.25

1993 Score Select Chase Stars

The top 24 players from 1992 are featured in this insert set. Cards were randomly inserted in 15-card retail packs.

		MT	NR MT	EX
Complete Set (24):		150.00	110.00	60.00
Common Player:		2.50	2.00	1.00
1	Fred McGriff	7.00	5.50	3.00
2	Ryne Sandberg	12.00	9.00	4.75
3	Ozzie Smith	6.00	4.50	2.50
4	Gary Sheffield	4.00	3.00	1.50
5	Darren Daulton	5.00	3.75	2.00
6	Andy Van Slyke	2.50	2.00	1.00
7	Barry Bonds	13.00	3.00	12.00
8	Tony Gwynn	6.00	4.50	2.50
9	Greg Maddux	7.50	5.50	3.00
10	Tom Glavine	6.00	4.50	2.50
11	John Franco	2.50	2.00	1.00
12	Lee Smith	2.50	2.00	1.00
13	Cecil Fielder	6.00	4.50	2.50
14	Roberto Alomar	12.00	9.00	4.75
15	Cal Ripken, Jr.	15.00	11.00	6.00
16	Edgar Martinez	2.50	2.00	1.00
17	Ivan Rodriguez	4.50	3.50	1.75
18	Kirby Puckett	15.00	11.00	6.00
19	Ken Griffey, Jr.	45.00	34.00	18.00
20	Joe Carter	8.00	6.00	3.25
21	Roger Clemens	12.00	9.00	4.75
22	Dave Fleming	3.50	2.75	1.50
23	Paul Molitor	8.00	6.00	3.25
24	Dennis Eckersley	2.50	2.00	1.00

Values for recent cards and sets are listed in Mint (MT), Near Mint (NM), reflecting the fact that many cards from recent years have been preserved in top condition. Recent cards and sets in less than Excellent condition have little collector interest.

1993 Score Select Stat Leaders

This 90-card set features 1992 American League and National League leaders in various statistical categories. Each card front indicates the league and the category the player finished at or near the top in. The backs have a list of the leaders; the pictured player's name is in larger type size. Backs use the special Dufex foil printing process. Cards were inserted one per foil pack.

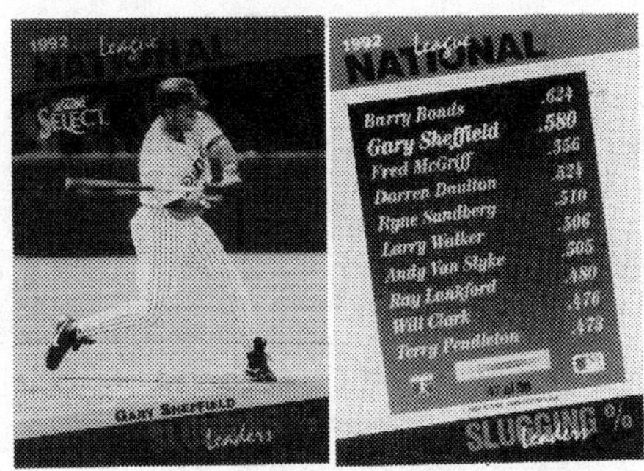

		MT	NR MT	EX
Complete Set (90):		12.00	9.00	4.75
Common Player:		.10	.08	.04
1	Edgar Martinez	.20	.15	.08
2	Kirby Puckett	.50	.40	.20
3	Frank Thomas	1.25	.90	.50
4	Gary Sheffield	.15	.11	.06
5	Andy Van Slyke	.10	.08	.04
6	John Kruk	.20	.15	.08
7	Kirby Puckett	.50	.40	.20
8	Carlos Baerga	.35	.25	.14
9	Paul Molitor	.25	.20	.10
10	Terry Pendleton/Andy Van Slyke	.10	.08	.04
11	Ryne Sandberg	.40	.30	.15
12	Mark Grace	.20	.15	.08
13	Frank Thomas	.75	.60	.30
14	Don Mattingly	.25	.20	.10
15	Ken Griffey, Jr.	1.00	.70	.40
16	Andy Van Slyke	.10	.08	.04
17	Mariano Duncan/Jerald Clark/Ray Lankford	.10	.08	.04
18	Marquis Grissom/Terry Pendleton	.10	.08	.04
19	Lance Johnson	.10	.08	.04
20	Mike Devereaux	.10	.08	.04
21	Brady Anderson	.10	.08	.04
22	Deion Sanders	.20	.15	.08
23	Steve Finley	.10	.08	.04
24	Andy Van Slyke	.10	.08	.04
25	Juan Gonzalez	.75	.60	.30
26	Mark McGwire	.20	.15	.08
27	Cecil Fielder	.20	.15	.08
28	Fred McGriff	.20	.15	.08
29	Barry Bonds	.40	.30	.15
30	Gary Sheffield	.20	.15	.08
31	Cecil Fielder	.20	.15	.08
32	Joe Carter	.20	.15	.08
33	Frank Thomas	1.25	.90	.50
34	Darren Daulton	.10	.08	.04
35	Terry Pendleton	.10	.08	.04
36	Fred McGriff	.20	.15	.08
37	Tony Phillips	.10	.08	.04
38	Frank Thomas	1.25	.90	.50
39	Roberto Alomar	.35	.25	.14
40	Barry Bonds	.40	.30	.15
41	Dave Hollins	.10	.08	.04
42	Andy Van Slyke	.10	.08	.04
43	Mark McGwire	.40	.30	.15
44	Edgar Martinez	.20	.15	.08
45	Frank Thomas	1.25	.90	.50
46	Barry Bonds	.40	.30	.15
47	Gary Sheffield	.20	.15	.08
48	Fred McGriff	.20	.15	.08
49	Frank Thomas	1.25	.90	.50
50	Danny Tartabull	.10	.08	.04
51	Roberto Alomar	.30	.25	.12
52	Barry Bonds	.40	.30	.15
53	John Kruk	.15	.11	.06
54	Brett Butler	.10	.08	.04
55	Kenny Lofton	.10	.08	.04
56	Pat Listach	.10	.08	.04
57	Brady Anderson	.10	.08	.04
58	Marquis Grissom	.10	.08	.04
59	Delino DeShields	.15	.11	.06
60	Steve Finley	.10	.08	.04
61	Jack McDowell	.10	.08	.04
62	Kevin Brown	.10	.08	.04
63	Melido Perez	.10	.08	.04
64	Terry Mulholland	.10	.08	.04
65	Curt Schilling	.10	.08	.04
66	Doug Drabek/Greg Maddux/John Smoltz	.10	.08	.04
67	Dennis Eckersley	.15	.11	.06
68	Rick Aguilera	.10	.08	.04
69	Jeff Montgomery	.10	.08	.04
70	Lee Smith	.15	.11	.06
71	Randy Myers	.10	.08	.04
72	John Wetteland	.10	.08	.04
73	Randy Johnson	.10	.08	.04
74	Melido Perez	.10	.08	.04
75	Roger Clemens	.30	.25	.12
76	John Smoltz	.10	.08	.04
77	David Cone	.10	.08	.04
78	Greg Maddux	.15	.11	.06
79	Roger Clemens	.30	.25	.12
80	Kevin Appier	.10	.08	.04
81	Mike Mussina	.10	.08	.04
82	Bill Swift	.10	.08	.04
83	Bob Tewksbury	.10	.08	.04
84	Greg Maddux	.15	.11	.06
85	Kevin Brown	.10	.08	.04
86	Jack McDowell	.10	.08	.04
87	Roger Clemens	.30	.25	.12
88	Tom Glavine	.10	.08	.04
89	Ken Hill/Bob Tewksbury	.10	.08	.04
90	Mike Morgan/Ramon Martinez	.10	.08	.04

1993 Score Select Triple Crown

This three-card set commemorates the Triple Crown seasons of Hall of Famers: Mickey Mantle, Frank Robinson and Carl Yastrzemski. Cards were randomly inserted in 15-card hobby packs. Card fronts have a green metallic-look textured border, with the player's name at top in gold, and "Triple Crown" in gold at bottom. There are other silver and green highlights around the photo, which features the player set against a metallized background. Dark green backs have a player photo and information on his Triple Crown season.

		MT	NR MT	EX
Complete Set (3):		100.00	75.00	40.00
Common Player:		30.00	22.00	12.00
1	Mickey Mantle	75.00	56.00	30.00
2	Frank Robinson	30.00	22.00	12.00
3	Carl Yastrzemski	30.00	22.00	12.00

1993 Score Select Update

Production of this 150-card set was limited to 1,950 numbered cases. Several future Hall of Famers and six dozen top rookies are featured in the set. Cards were available in packs rather than collated sets and include randomly inserted FX cards, which feature Nolan Ryan (two per 24-box case), Tim Salmon and Mike Piazza (one per 576 packs) and All-Star Rookie Team members (one per 36 packs).

		MT	NR MT	EX
Complete Set (150):		60.00	45.00	24.00
Common Player:		.25	.20	.10
1	Rickey Henderson	1.25	.90	.50
2	Rob Deer	.25	.20	.10
3	Tim Belcher	.25	.20	.10
4	Gary Sheffield	.60	.45	.25
5	Fred McGriff	1.75	1.25	.70
6	Mark Whiten	.25	.20	.10
7	Jeff Russell	.25	.20	.10
8	Harold Baines	.25	.20	.10
9	Dave Winfield	1.75	1.25	.70
10	Ellis Burks	.25	.20	.10
11	Andre Dawson	.25	.20	.10
12	Gregg Jefferies	.60	.45	.25
13	Jimmy Key	.25	.20	.10
14	Harold Reynolds	.25	.20	.10
15	Tom Henke	.25	.20	.10
16	Paul Molitor	1.75	1.25	.70
17	Wade Boggs	.75	.60	.30
18	David Cone	.25	.20	.10
19	Tony Fernandez	.25	.20	.10
20	Roberto Kelly	.25	.20	.10
21	Paul O'Neill	.25	.20	.10
22	Jose Lind	.25	.20	.10
23	Barry Bonds	3.00	2.25	1.25
24	Dave Stewart	.25	.20	.10
25	Randy Myers	.25	.20	.10
26	Benito Santiago	.25	.20	.10
27	Tim Wallach	.25	.20	.10
28	Greg Gagne	.25	.20	.10
29	Kevin Mitchell	.25	.20	.10
30	Jim Abbott	.30	.25	.12
31	Lee Smith	.25	.20	.10
32	*Bobby Munoz*	.75	.60	.30
33	*Mo Sanford*	.75	.60	.30
34	John Roper	.75	.60	.30
35	*David Hulse*	1.00	.70	.40
36	Pedro Martinez	2.00	1.50	.80
37	*Chuck Carr*	.50	.40	.20
38	*Armando Reynoso*	.60	.45	.25
39	Ryan Thompson	1.00	.70	.40
40	*Carlos Garcia*	1.00	.70	.40
41	Matt Whiteside	.25	.20	.10
42	*Benji Gil*	3.00	2.25	1.25
43	*Rodney Bolton*	.50	.40	.20
44	J.T. Snow	1.00	.75	.40

45	David McCarty	1.00	.75	.40
46	*Paul Quantrill*	.40	.30	.15
47	Al Martin	1.25	.90	.50
48	*Lance Painter*	.60	.45	.25
49	*Lou Frazier*	.50	.40	.20
50	*Eduardo Perez*	2.00	1.50	.80
51	*Kevin Young*	1.50	1.25	.60
52	Mike Trombley	.25	.20	.10
53	*Sterling Hitchcock*	1.50	1.25	.60
54	*Tim Bogar*	.40	.30	.15
55	*Hilly Hathaway*	1.00	.70	.40
56	*Wayne Kirby*	.60	.45	.25
57	*Craig Paquette*	.40	.30	.15
58	Bret Boone	1.50	1.25	.60
59	*Greg McMichael*	1.25	.90	.50
60	*Mike Lansing*	1.50	1.25	.60
61	*Brent Gates*	3.00	2.25	1.25
62	*Rene Arocha*	1.25	.90	.50
63	*Ricky Gutierrez*	.60	.45	.25
64	*Kevin Rogers*	.40	.30	.15
65	*Ken Ryan*	.60	.45	.25
66	*Phil Hiatt*	1.25	.90	.50
67	*Pat Meares*	.60	.45	.25
68	*Troy Neel*	1.50	1.25	.60
69	*Steve Cooke*	.60	.45	.25
70	*Sherman Obando*	1.00	.70	.40
71	*Blas Minor*	.75	.60	.30
72	*Angel Miranda*	.40	.30	.15
73	*Tom Kramer*	.40	.30	.15
74	*Chip Hale*	.60	.45	.25
75	*Brad Pennington*	.40	.30	.15
76	*Graeme Lloyd*	.50	.40	.20
77	*Darrell Whitmore*	1.25	.90	.50
78	David Nied	1.50	1.25	.60
79	Todd Van Poppel	.60	.45	.25
80	*Chris Gomez*	.40	.30	.15
81	*Jason Bere*	7.00	5.25	2.75
82	Jeffrey Hammonds	5.00	3.75	2.00
83	*Brad Ausmus*	.40	.30	.15
84	*Kevin Stocker*	2.00	1.50	.80
85	*Jeromy Burnitz*	1.00	.70	.40
86	*Aaron Sele*	5.00	3.50	2.00
87	*Roberto Mejia*	1.50	1.25	.60
88	*Kirk Rueter*	5.50	4.00	2.25
89	*Kevin Roberson*	2.50	2.00	1.00
90	*Allen Watson*	1.50	1.25	.60
91	Charlie Leibrandt	.25	.20	.10
92	Eric Davis	.25	.20	.10
93	Jody Reed	.25	.20	.10
94	Danny Jackson	.25	.20	.10
95	Gary Gaetti	.25	.20	.10
96	Norm Charlton	.25	.20	.10
97	Doug Drabek	.25	.20	.10
98	Scott Fletcher	.25	.20	.10
99	Greg Swindell	.25	.20	.10
100	John Smiley	.25	.20	.10
101	Kevin Reimer	.25	.20	.10
102	Andres Galarraga	.25	.20	.10
103	Greg Hibbard	.25	.20	.10
104	Chris Hammond	.25	.20	.10
105	Darnell Coles	.25	.20	.10
106	Mike Felder	.25	.20	.10
107	Jose Guzman	.25	.20	.10
108	Chris Bosio	.25	.20	.10
109	Spike Owen	.25	.20	.10
110	Felix Jose	.25	.20	.10
111	Cory Snyder	.25	.20	.10
112	Craig Lefferts	.25	.20	.10
113	David Wells	.25	.20	.10
114	Pete Incaviglia	.25	.20	.10
115	Mike Pagliarulo	.25	.20	.10
116	Dave Magadan	.25	.20	.10
117	Charlie Hough	.25	.20	.10
118	Ivan Calderon	.25	.20	.10
119	Manuel Lee	.25	.20	.10
120	Bob Patterson	.25	.20	.10
121	Bob Ojeda	.25	.20	.10
122	Scott Bankhead	.25	.20	.10
123	Greg Maddux	1.00	.70	.40
124	Chili Davis	.25	.20	.10
125	Milt Thompson	.25	.20	.10
126	Dave Martinez	.25	.20	.10
127	Frank Tanana	.25	.20	.10
128	Phil Plantier	.60	.45	.25
129	Juan Samuel	.25	.20	.10
130	Eric Young	.30	.25	.12
131	Joe Orsulak	.25	.20	.10
132	Derek Bell	.30	.25	.12
133	Darrin Jackson	.25	.20	.10
134	Tom Brunansky	.25	.20	.10
135	Jeff Reardon	.25	.20	.10
136	*Kevin Higgins*	.30	.25	.12
137	*Joel Johnston*	.40	.30	.15
138	*Rick Trlicek*	.40	.30	.15
139	*Richie Lewis*	1.00	.70	.40
140	*Jeff Gardner*	.30	.25	.12
141	*Jack Voigt*	.50	.40	.20
142	*Rod Correia*	.60	.45	.25
143	*Billy Brewer*	.30	.25	.12
144	*Terry Jorgensen*	.30	.25	.12
145	*Rich Amaral*	.30	.25	.12
146	*Sean Berry*	.40	.30	.15
147	*Dan Peltier*	.40	.30	.15
148	*Paul Wagner*	.50	.40	.20
149	*Damon Buford*	.40	.30	.15
150	Wil Cordero	1.00	.70	.40

Values for recent cards and sets are listed in Mint (MT), Near Mint (NM), reflecting the fact that many cards from recent years have been preserved in top condition. Recent cards and sets in less than Excellent condition have little collector interest.

1993 Score Select All-Star Rookies

These cards were randomly inserted into the Score Select Rookie/Traded packs, making them among the scarcest of the year's many "chase" cards.

		MT	NR MT	EX
Complete Set (10):		350.00	260.00	140.00
Common Player:		20.00	15.00	8.00
1	Jeff Conine	20.00	15.00	8.00
2	Brent Gates	20.00	15.00	8.00
3	Mike Lansing	40.00	30.00	15.00
4	Kevin Stocker	45.00	35.00	15.00
5	Mike Piazza	100.00	75.00	40.00
6	Jeffrey Hammonds	55.00	40.00	22.00
7	David Hulse	30.00	22.50	12.00
8	Tim Salmon	80.00	60.00	30.00
9	Rene Arocha	35.00	25.00	12.00
10	Greg McMichael	20.00	15.00	8.00

1993 Score Select Rookie/Traded Inserts

Three cards honoring the 1993 Rookies of the Year and retiring superstar Nolan Ryan were issued as random inserts in the Select Rookie/Traded packs.

		MT	NR MT	EX
1NR	Nolan Ryan	150.00	110.00	60.00
1ROY	Tim Salmon	100.00	75.00	40.00
2ROY	Mike Piazza	200.00	150.00	80.00

1994 Score

Score's 1994 set, with a new design and UV coating, was issued in two series of 330 cards each. The cards, which use more action photos than before, have dark blue borders with the player's name in a team color-coded strip at the bottom. A special Gold Rush card, done for each card in the set, is included in every pack. These cards are actually printed on foil, rather than simply being foil stamped. Series I includes American League checklists, which are printed on the backs of cards depicting panoramic views of each team's ballpark. Series II has the National League team checklists. Insert sets include Dream Team players, and National (Series I packs) and American League Gold Stars (Series II packs), which use the Gold Rush process and appear once every 18 packs.

		MT	NR MT	EX
Complete Set (660):		30.00	22.00	12.00
Common Player:		.04	.03	.02
1	Barry Bonds	.50	.40	.20
2	John Olerud	.25	.20	.10
3	Ken Griffey, Jr.	.75	.60	.30
4	Jeff Bagwell	.20	.15	.08
5	John Burkett	.04	.03	.02
6	Jack McDowell	.10	.08	.04
7	Albert Belle	.25	.20	.10
8	Andres Galarraga	.08	.06	.03
9	Mike Mussina	.15	.11	.06
10	Will Clark	.20	.15	.08
11	Travis Fryman	.25	.20	.10
12	Tony Gwynn	.20	.15	.08
13	Robin Yount	.20	.15	.08
14	Dave Magadan	.04	.03	.02
15	Paul O'Neill	.04	.03	.02
16	Ray Lankford	.04	.03	.02
17	Damion Easley	.04	.03	.02
18	Andy Van Slyke	.04	.03	.02
19	Brian McRae	.04	.03	.02
20	Ryne Sandberg	.25	.20	.10
21	Kirby Puckett	.25	.20	.10
22	Dwight Gooden	.04	.03	.02
23	Don Mattingly	.25	.20	.10
24	Kevin Mitchell	.04	.03	.02
25	Roger Clemens	.15	.11	.06
26	Eric Karros	.10	.07	.04
27	Juan Gonzalez	.75	.60	.30
28	John Kruk	.10	.08	.04
29	Gregg Jefferies	.04	.03	.02
30	Tom Glavine	.15	.11	.06
31	Ivan Rodriguez	.15	.11	.06
32	Jay Bell	.04	.03	.02
33	Randy Johnson	.04	.03	.02
34	Darren Daulton	.04	.03	.02
35	Rickey Henderson	.10	.08	.04
36	Eddie Murray	.04	.03	.02
37	Brian Harper	.04	.03	.02
38	Delino DeShields	.08	.06	.03
39	Jose Lind	.04	.03	.02
40	Benito Santiago	.04	.03	.02
41	Frank Thomas	1.00	.70	.40
42	Mark Grace	.10	.08	.04
43	Roberto Alomar	.15	.11	.06
44	Andy Benes	.04	.03	.02
45	Luis Polonia	.04	.03	.02
46	Brett Butler	.04	.03	.02
47	Terry Steinbach	.04	.03	.02
48	Craig Biggio	.04	.03	.02
49	Greg Vaughn	.04	.03	.02
50	Charlie Hayes	.04	.03	.02
51	Mickey Tettleton	.04	.03	.02
52	Jose Rijo	.04	.03	.02
53	Carlos Baerga	.15	.11	.06
54	Jeff Blauser	.04	.03	.02
55	Leo Gomez	.04	.03	.02
56	Bob Tewksbury	.04	.03	.02
57	Mo Vaughn	.04	.03	.02
58	Orlando Merced	.04	.03	.02
59	Tino Martinez	.04	.03	.02
60	Len Dykstra	.10	.08	.04
61	Jose Canseco	.10	.08	.04
62	Tony Fernandez	.04	.03	.02
63	Donovan Osborne	.04	.03	.02
64	Ken Hill	.04	.03	.02
65	Kent Hrbek	.04	.03	.02
66	Bryan Harvey	.04	.03	.02
67	Wally Joyner	.04	.03	.02
68	Derrick May	.04	.03	.02
69	Lance Johnson	.04	.03	.02
70	Willie McGee	.04	.03	.02
71	Mark Langston	.04	.03	.02
72	Terry Pendleton	.04	.03	.02
73	Joe Carter	.10	.08	.04
74	Barry Larkin	.04	.03	.02
75	Jimmy Key	.04	.03	.02
76	Joe Girardi	.04	.03	.02
77	B.J. Surhoff	.04	.03	.02
78	Pete Harnisch	.04	.03	.02
79	Lou Whitaker	.04	.03	.02
80	Cory Snyder	.04	.03	.02
81	Kenny Lofton	.10	.08	.04
82	Fred McGriff	.10	.08	.04
83	Mike Greenwell	.04	.03	.02
84	Mike Perez	.04	.03	.02
85	Cal Ripken, Jr.	.25	.20	.10
86	Don Slaught	.04	.03	.02
87	Omar Vizquel	.04	.03	.02
88	Curt Schilling	.04	.03	.02
89	Chuck Knoblauch	.04	.03	.02
90	Moises Alou	.04	.03	.02
91	Greg Gagne	.04	.03	.02
92	Bret Saberhagen	.04	.03	.02
93	Ozzie Guillen	.04	.03	.02
94	Matt Williams	.04	.03	.02
95	Chad Curtis	.04	.03	.02
96	Mike Harkey	.04	.03	.02
97	Devon White	.04	.03	.02
98	Walt Weiss	.04	.03	.02
99	Kevin Brown	.04	.03	.02
100	Gary Sheffield	.10	.08	.04
101	Wade Boggs	.10	.08	.04
102	Orel Hershiser	.04	.03	.02
103	Tony Phillips	.04	.03	.02
104	Andujar Cedeno	.04	.03	.02
105	Bill Spiers	.04	.03	.02
106	Otis Nixon	.04	.03	.02
107	Felix Fermin	.04	.03	.02
108	Bip Roberts	.04	.03	.02
109	Dennis Eckersley	.04	.03	.02
110	Dante Bichette	.04	.03	.02
111	Ben McDonald	.04	.03	.02
112	Jim Poole	.04	.03	.02
113	John Dopson	.04	.03	.02
114	Rob Dibble	.04	.03	.02
115	Jeff Treadway	.04	.03	.02
116	Ricky Jordan	.04	.03	.02
117	Mike Henneman	.04	.03	.02
118	Willie Blair	.04	.03	.02
119	Doug Henry	.04	.03	.02
120	Gerald Perry	.04	.03	.02
121	Greg Myers	.04	.03	.02
122	John Franco	.04	.03	.02
123	Roger Mason	.04	.03	.02
124	Chris Hammond	.04	.03	.02
125	Hubie Brooks	.04	.03	.02

126	Kent Mercker	.04	.03	.02
127	Jim Abbott	.04	.03	.02
128	Kevin Bass	.04	.03	.02
129	Rick Aguilera	.04	.03	.02
130	Mitch Webster	.04	.03	.02
131	Eric Plunk	.04	.03	.02
132	Mark Carreon	.04	.03	.02
133	Dave Stewart	.04	.03	.02
134	Willie Wilson	.04	.03	.02
135	Dave Fleming	.04	.03	.02
136	Jeff Tackett	.04	.03	.02
137	Geno Petralli	.04	.03	.02
138	Gene Harris	.04	.03	.02
139	Scott Bankhead	.04	.03	.02
140	Trevor Wilson	.04	.03	.02
141	Alvaro Espinoza	.04	.03	.02
142	Ryan Bowen	.04	.03	.02
143	Mike Moore	.04	.03	.02
144	Bill Pecota	.04	.03	.02
145	Jaime Navarro	.04	.03	.02
146	Jack Daugherty	.04	.03	.02
147	Bob Wickman	.04	.03	.02
148	Chris Jones	.04	.03	.02
149	Todd Stottlemyre	.04	.03	.02
150	Brian Williams	.04	.03	.02
151	Chuck Finley	.04	.03	.02
152	Lenny Harris	.04	.03	.02
153	Alex Fernandez	.08	.06	.03
154	Candy Maldonado	.04	.03	.02
155	Jeff Montgomery	.04	.03	.02
156	David West	.04	.03	.02
157	Mark Williamson	.04	.03	.02
158	Milt Thompson	.04	.03	.02
159	Ron Darling	.04	.03	.02
160	Stan Belinda	.04	.03	.02
161	Henry Cotto	.04	.03	.02
162	Mel Rojas	.04	.03	.02
163	Doug Strange	.04	.03	.02
164	Rene Arocha (1993 Rookie)	.10	.08	.04
165	Tim Hulett	.04	.03	.02
166	Steve Avery	.10	.08	.04
167	Jim Thome	.10	.08	.04
168	Tom Browning	.04	.03	.02
169	Mario Diaz	.04	.03	.02
170	Steve Reed (1993 Rookie)	.04	.03	.02
171	Scott Livingstone	.04	.03	.02
172	Chris Donnels	.04	.03	.02
173	John Jaha	.10	.08	.04
174	Carlos Hernandez	.04	.03	.02
175	Dion James	.04	.03	.02
176	Bud Black	.04	.03	.02
177	Tony Castillo	.04	.03	.02
178	Jose Guzman	.04	.03	.02
179	Torey Lovullo	.04	.03	.02
180	John Vander Wal	.04	.03	.02
181	Mike LaValliere	.04	.03	.02
182	Sid Fernandez	.04	.03	.02
183	Brent Mayne	.04	.03	.02
184	Terry Mulholland	.04	.03	.02
185	Willie Banks	.04	.03	.02
186	Steve Cooke (1993 Rookie)	.04	.03	.02
187	Brent Gates (1993 Rookie)	.15	.11	.06
188	Erik Pappas (1993 Rookie)	.15	.11	.06
189	Bill Haselman (1993 Rookie)	.04	.03	.02
190	Fernando Valenzuela	.04	.03	.02
191	Gary Redus	.04	.03	.02
192	Danny Darwin	.04	.03	.02
193	Mark Portugal	.04	.03	.02
194	Derek Lilliquist	.04	.03	.02
195	Charlie O'Brien	.04	.03	.02
196	Matt Nokes	.04	.03	.02
197	Danny Sheaffer	.04	.03	.02
198	Bill Gullickson	.04	.03	.02
199	Alex Arias (1993 Rookie)	.10	.08	.04
200	Mike Fetters	.04	.03	.02
201	Brian Jordan	.04	.03	.02
202	Joe Grahe	.04	.03	.02
203	Tom Candiotti	.04	.03	.02
204	Jeremy Stanton	.04	.03	.02
205	Mike Stanton	.04	.03	.02
206	David Howard	.04	.03	.02
207	Darren Holmes	.04	.03	.02
208	Rick Honeycutt	.04	.03	.02
209	Danny Jackson	.04	.03	.02
210	Rich Amaral (1993 Rookie)	.04	.03	.02
211	Blas Minor (1993 Rookie)	.10	.08	.04
212	Kenny Rogers	.04	.03	.02
213	Jim Leyritz	.04	.03	.02
214	Mike Morgan	.04	.03	.02
215	Dan Gladden	.04	.03	.02
216	Randy Velarde	.04	.03	.02
217	Mitch Williams	.04	.03	.02
218	Hipolito Pichardo	.04	.03	.02
219	Dave Burba	.04	.03	.02
220	Wilson Alvarez	.04	.03	.02
221	Bob Zupcic	.04	.03	.02
222	Francisco Cabrera	.04	.03	.02
223	Julio Valera	.04	.03	.02
224	Paul Assenmacher	.04	.03	.02
225	Jeff Branson	.04	.03	.02
226	Todd Frohwirth	.04	.03	.02
227	Armando Reynoso	.04	.03	.02
228	Rich Rowland (1993 Rookie)	.04	.03	.02
229	Freddie Benavides	.04	.03	.02
230	Wayne Kirby (1993 Rookie)	.04	.03	.02
231	Darryl Kile	.04	.03	.02
232	Skeeter Barnes	.04	.03	.02
233	Ramon Martinez	.04	.03	.02
234	Tom Gordon	.04	.03	.02
235	Dave Gallagher	.04	.03	.02
236	Ricky Bones	.04	.03	.02
237	Larry Andersen	.04	.03	.02
238	Pat Meares (1993 Rookie)	.08	.06	.03
239	Zane Smith	.04	.03	.02
240	Tim Leary	.04	.03	.02
241	Phil Clark	.08	.06	.03
242	Danny Cox	.04	.03	.02
243	Mike Jackson	.04	.03	.02
244	Mike Gallego	.04	.03	.02
245	Lee Smith	.04	.03	.02
246	Todd Jones (1993 Rookie)	.04	.03	.02
247	Steve Bedrosian	.04	.03	.02
248	Troy Neel	.10	.08	.04
249	Jose Bautista	.04	.03	.02
250	Steve Frey	.04	.03	.02
251	Jeff Reardon	.04	.03	.02
252	Stan Javier	.04	.03	.02
253	Mo Sanford (1993 Rookie)	.04	.03	.02
254	Steve Sax	.04	.03	.02
255	Luis Aquino	.04	.03	.02
256	Domingo Jean (1993 Rookie)	.10	.08	.04
257	Scott Servais	.04	.03	.02
258	Brad Pennington (1993 Rookie)	.08	.06	.03
259	Dave Hansen	.04	.03	.02
260	Goose Gossage	.04	.03	.02
261	Jeff Fassero	.04	.03	.02
262	Junior Ortiz	.04	.03	.02
263	Anthony Young	.04	.03	.02
264	Chris Bosio	.04	.03	.02
265	Ruben Amaro, Jr.	.04	.03	.02
266	Mark Eichhorn	.04	.03	.02
267	Dave Clark	.04	.03	.02
268	Gary Thurman	.04	.03	.02
269	Les Lancaster	.04	.03	.02
270	Jamie Moyer	.04	.03	.02
271	Ricky Gutierrez (1993 Rookie)	.04	.03	.02
272	Greg Harris	.04	.03	.02
273	Mike Benjamin	.04	.03	.02
274	Gene Nelson	.04	.03	.02
275	Damon Berryhill	.04	.03	.02
276	Scott Radinsky	.04	.03	.02
277	Mike Aldrete	.04	.03	.02
278	Jerry DiPoto (1993 Rookie)	.04	.03	.02
279	Chris Haney	.04	.03	.02
280	Richie Lewis (1993 Rookie)	.04	.03	.02
281	Jarvis Brown	.04	.03	.02
282	Juan Bell	.04	.03	.02
283	Joe Klink	.04	.03	.02
284	Graeme Lloyd (1993 Rookie)	.08	.06	.03
285	Casey Candaele	.04	.03	.02
286	Bob MacDonald	.04	.03	.02
287	Mike Sharperson	.04	.03	.02
288	Gene Larkin	.04	.03	.02
289	Brian Barnes	.04	.03	.02
290	David McCarty (1993 Rookie)	.08	.06	.03
291	Jeff Innis	.04	.03	.02
292	Bob Patterson	.04	.03	.02
293	Ben Rivera	.04	.03	.02
294	John Habyan	.04	.03	.02
295	Rich Rodriguez	.04	.03	.02
296	Edwin Nunez	.04	.03	.02
297	Rod Brewer	.04	.03	.02
298	Mike Timlin	.04	.03	.02
299	Jesse Orosco	.04	.03	.02
300	Gary Gaetti	.04	.03	.02
301	Todd Benzinger	.04	.03	.02
302	Jeff Nelson	.04	.03	.02
303	Rafael Belliard	.04	.03	.02
304	Matt Whiteside	.04	.03	.02
305	Vinny Castilla	.04	.03	.02
306	Matt Turner	.04	.03	.02
307	Eduardo Perez	.15	.11	.06
308	Joel Johnston	.04	.03	.02
309	Chris Gomez	.15	.11	.06
310	Pat Rapp	.04	.03	.02
311	Jim Tatum	.10	.08	.04
312	*Kirk Rueter*	.80	.60	.30
313	John Flaherty	.10	.08	.04
314	Tom Kramer	.10	.07	.04
315	Mark Whiten (Highlights)	.04	.03	.02
316	Chris Bosio (Highlights)	.04	.03	.02
317	Orioles Checklist	.04	.03	.02
318	Red Sox Checklist	.04	.03	.02
319	Angels Checklist	.04	.03	.02
320	White Sox Checklist	.04	.03	.02
321	Indians Checklist	.04	.03	.02
322	Tigers Checklist	.04	.03	.02
323	Royals Checklist	.04	.03	.02
324	Brewers Checklist	.04	.03	.02
325	Twins Checklist	.04	.03	.02
326	Yankees Checklist	.04	.03	.02
327	Athletics Checklist	.04	.03	.02
328	Mariners Checklist	.04	.03	.02
329	Rangers Checklist	.04	.03	.02
330	Blue Jays Checklist	.04	.03	.02
331	Frank Viola	.04	.03	.02
332	Ron Gant	.05	.04	.02
333	Charles Nagy	.04	.03	.02
334	Roberto Kelly	.04	.03	.02
335	Brady Anderson	.04	.03	.02
336	Alex Cole	.04	.03	.02
337	Alan Trammell	.06	.05	.02
338	Derek Bell	.05	.04	.02
339	Bernie Williams	.04	.03	.02
340	Jose Offerman	.05	.04	.02
341	Bill Wegman	.04	.03	.02
342	Ken Caminiti	.04	.03	.02
343	Pat Borders	.04	.03	.02
344	Kirt Manwaring	.04	.03	.02
345	Chili Davis	.04	.03	.02
346	Steve Buechele	.04	.03	.02
347	Robin Ventura	.08	.06	.03
348	Teddy Higuera	.04	.03	.02
349	Jerry Browne	.04	.03	.02
350	Scott Kamieniecki	.04	.03	.02
351	Kevin Tapani	.04	.03	.02
352	Marquis Grissom	.07	.05	.03
353	Jay Buhner	.04	.03	.02
354	Dave Hollins	.08	.06	.03
355	Dan Wilson	.04	.03	.02
356	Bob Walk	.04	.03	.02
357	Chris Hoiles	.06	.05	.02
358	Todd Zeile	.05	.04	.02
359	Kevin Appier	.04	.03	.02
360	Chris Sabo	.04	.03	.02
361	David Segui	.04	.03	.02
362	Jerald Clark	.04	.03	.02
363	Tony Pena	.04	.03	.02
364	Steve Finley	.04	.03	.02
365	Roger Pavlik	.04	.03	.02
366	John Smoltz	.07	.05	.03
367	Scott Fletcher	.04	.03	.02
368	Jody Reed	.04	.03	.02
369	David Wells	.04	.03	.02
370	Jose Vizcaino	.04	.03	.02
371	Pat Listach	.05	.04	.02
372	Orestes Destrade	.06	.05	.02
373	Danny Tartabull	.05	.04	.02
374	Greg W. Harris	.04	.03	.02
375	Juan Guzman	.08	.06	.03
376	Larry Walker	.08	.06	.03
377	Gary DiSarcina	.05	.04	.02
378	Bobby Bonilla	.06	.05	.02
379	Tim Raines	.05	.04	.02
380	Tommy Greene	.04	.03	.02
381	Chris Gwynn	.04	.03	.02
382	Jeff King	.04	.03	.02
383	Shane Mack	.04	.03	.02
384	Ozzie Smith	.15	.11	.06
385	*Eddie Zambrano*	.15	.11	.06
386	Mike Devereaux	.04	.03	.02
387	Erik Hanson	.04	.03	.02
388	Scott Cooper	.06	.05	.02
389	Dean Palmer	.05	.04	.02
390	John Wetteland	.05	.04	.02
391	Reggie Jefferson	.04	.03	.02
392	Mark Lemke	.04	.03	.02
393	Cecil Fielder	.15	.11	.06
394	Reggie Sanders	.07	.05	.03
395	Darryl Hamilton	.04	.03	.02
396	Daryl Boston	.04	.03	.02
397	Pat Kelly	.04	.03	.02
398	Joe Orsulak	.04	.03	.02
399	Ed Sprague	.04	.03	.02
400	Eric Anthony	.04	.03	.02
401	Scott Sanderson	.04	.03	.02
402	Jim Gott	.04	.03	.02
403	Ron Karkovice	.04	.03	.02
404	Phil Plantier	.06	.05	.02
405	David Cone	.04	.03	.02
406	Robby Thompson	.04	.03	.02
407	Dave Winfield	.15	.11	.06
408	Dwight Smith	.04	.03	.02
409	Ruben Sierra	.08	.06	.03
410	Jack Armstrong	.04	.03	.02
411	Mike Felder	.04	.03	.02
412	Wil Cordero	.05	.04	.02
413	Julio Franco	.04	.03	.02
414	Howard Johnson	.04	.03	.02
415	Mark McLemore	.04	.03	.02
416	Pete Incaviglia	.04	.03	.02
417	John Valentin	.04	.03	.02
418	Tim Wakefield	.04	.03	.02
419	Jose Mesa	.04	.03	.02
420	Bernard Gilkey	.05	.04	.02
421	Kirk Gibson	.05	.04	.02
422	Dave Justice	.20	.15	.08
423	Tom Brunansky	.04	.03	.02
424	John Smiley	.04	.03	.02
425	Kevin Maas	.04	.03	.02
426	Doug Drabek	.04	.03	.02
427	Paul Molitor	.15	.11	.06
428	Darryl Strawberry	.05	.04	.02
429	Tim Naehring	.06	.05	.02
430	Bill Swift	.04	.03	.02
431	Ellis Burks	.04	.03	.02
432	Greg Hibbard	.04	.03	.02
433	Felix Jose	.04	.03	.02
434	Bret Barberie	.04	.03	.02
435	Pedro Munoz	.05	.04	.02
436	Darrin Fletcher	.05	.04	.02
437	Bobby Witt	.04	.03	.02
438	Wes Chamberlain	.04	.03	.02
439	Mackey Sasser	.04	.03	.02
440	Mark Whiten	.04	.03	.02
441	Harold Reynolds	.04	.03	.02
442	Greg Olson	.04	.03	.02
443	Billy Hatcher	.04	.03	.02
444	Joe Oliver	.04	.03	.02
445	Sandy Alomar Jr.	.04	.03	.02
446	Tim Wallach	.04	.03	.02
447	Karl Rhodes	.06	.05	.02
448	Royce Clayton	.06	.05	.02
449	Cal Eldred	.07	.05	.03
450	Rick Wilkins	.04	.03	.02
451	Mike Stanley	.05	.04	.02
452	Charlie Hough	.04	.03	.02
453	Jack Morris	.04	.03	.02
454	*Jon Ratliff*	.15	.11	.06
455	Rene Gonzales	.05	.04	.02
456	Eddie Taubensee	.04	.03	.02
457	Roberto Hernandez	.04	.03	.02
458	Todd Hundley	.08	.06	.03
459	Mike MacFarlane	.05	.04	.02
460	Mickey Morandini	.04	.03	.02
461	Scott Erickson	.04	.03	.02
462	Lonnie Smith	.04	.03	.02
463	Dave Henderson	.04	.03	.02
464	Ryan Klesko	.40	.30	.15
465	Edgar Martinez	.04	.03	.02
466	Tom Pagnozzi	.04	.03	.02
467	Charlie Leibrandt	.04	.03	.02
468	Brian Anderson	.04	.03	.02
469	Harold Baines	.05	.04	.02
470	Tim Belcher	.04	.03	.02
471	Andre Dawson	.06	.05	.02
472	Eric Young	.04	.03	.02
473	Paul Sorrento	.04	.03	.02
474	Luis Gonzalez	.05	.04	.02
475	Rob Deer	.04	.03	.02
476	Mike Piazza	1.00	.70	.40
477	Kevin Reimer	.04	.03	.02
478	Jeff Gardner	.04	.03	.02
479	Melido Perez	.04	.03	.02

480	Darren Lewis	.04	.03	.02
481	Duane Ward	.04	.03	.02
482	Rey Sanchez	.04	.03	.02
483	Mark Lewis	.04	.03	.02
484	Jeff Conine	.04	.03	.02
485	Joey Cora	.04	.03	.02
486	*Trot Nixon*	1.75	1.25	.70
487	Kevin McReynolds	.04	.03	.02
488	Mike Lansing	.06	.05	.02
489	Mike Pagliarulo	.04	.03	.02
490	Mariano Duncan	.04	.03	.02
491	Mike Bordick	.04	.03	.02
492	Kevin Young	.04	.03	.02
493	Dave Valle	.04	.03	.02
494	*Wayne Gomes*	.15	.11	.06
495	Rafael Palmeiro	.08	.06	.03
496	Deion Sanders	.15	.11	.06
497	Rick Sutcliffe	.04	.03	.02
498	Randy Milligan	.04	.03	.02
499	Carlos Quintana	.04	.03	.02
500	Chris Turner	.04	.03	.02
501	Thomas Howard	.04	.03	.02
502	Greg Swindell	.04	.03	.02
503	Chad Kreuter	.04	.03	.02
504	Eric Davis	.05	.04	.02
505	Dickie Thon	.04	.03	.02
506	*Matt Drews*	.15	.11	.06
507	Spike Owen	.04	.03	.02
508	Rod Beck	.05	.04	.02
509	Pat Hentgen	.06	.05	.02
510	Sammy Sosa	.06	.05	.02
511	J.T. Snow	.08	.06	.03
512	Chuck Carr	.04	.03	.02
513	Bo Jackson	.15	.11	.06
514	Dennis Martinez	.04	.03	.02
515	Phil Hiatt	.06	.05	.02
516	Jeff Kent	.15	.11	.06
517	*Brooks Kieschnick*	.75	.60	.30
518	*Kirk Presley*	.35	.25	.14
519	Kevin Seitzer	.04	.03	.02
520	Carlos Garcia	.05	.04	.02
521	Mike Blowers	.04	.03	.02
522	Luis Alicea	.04	.03	.02
523	David Hulse	.05	.04	.02
524	Greg Maddux	.15	.11	.06
525	Gregg Olson	.04	.03	.02
526	Hal Morris	.04	.03	.02
527	Daron Kirkreit	.15	.11	.06
528	David Nied	.05	.04	.02
529	Jeff Russell	.04	.03	.02
530	Kevin Gross	.04	.03	.02
531	John Doherty	.04	.03	.02
532	*Matt Brunson*	.15	.11	.06
533	Dave Nilsson	.04	.03	.02
534	Randy Myers	.04	.03	.02
535	Steve Farr	.04	.03	.02
536	*Billy Wagner*	.20	.15	.08
537	Darnell Coles	.04	.03	.02
538	Frank Tanana	.04	.03	.02
539	Tim Salmon	.50	.40	.20
540	Kim Batiste	.04	.03	.02
541	George Bell	.04	.03	.02
542	Tom Henke	.04	.03	.02
543	Sam Horn	.04	.03	.02
544	Doug Jones	.04	.03	.02
545	Scott Leius	.04	.03	.02
546	Al Martin	.05	.04	.02
547	Bob Welch	.04	.03	.02
548	*Scott Christman*	.15	.11	.06
549	Norm Charlton	.04	.03	.02
550	Mark McGwire	.15	.11	.06
551	Greg McMichael	.08	.06	.03
552	Tim Costo	.05	.04	.02
553	Rodney Bolton	.05	.04	.02
554	Pedro Martinez	.05	.04	.02
555	Marc Valdes	.08	.06	.03
556	Darrell Whitmore	.08	.06	.03
557	Tim Bogar	.05	.04	.02
558	Steve Karsay	.35	.25	.14
559	Danny Bautista	.04	.03	.02
560	Jeffrey Hammonds	.40	.30	.15
561	Aaron Sele	.40	.30	.15
562	Russ Springer	.06	.05	.02
563	Jason Bere	.40	.30	.15
564	Billy Brewer	.04	.03	.02
565	Sterling Hitchcock	.04	.03	.02
566	Bobby Munoz	.04	.03	.02
567	Craig Paquette	.04	.03	.02
568	Bret Boone	.04	.03	.02
569	Dan Peltier	.04	.03	.02
570	Jeromy Burnitz	.04	.03	.02
571	*John Wasdin*	.15	.11	.06
572	Chipper Jones	.20	.15	.08
573	*Jamey Wright*	.15	.11	.06
574	Jeff Granger	.15	.11	.06
575	*Jay Powell*	.15	.11	.06
576	Ryan Thompson	.04	.03	.02
577	Lou Frazier	.04	.03	.02
578	Paul Wagner	.04	.03	.02
579	Brad Ausmus	.04	.03	.02
580	Jack Voigt	.04	.03	.02
581	Kevin Rogers	.04	.03	.02
582	Damon Buford	.04	.03	.02
583	Paul Quantrill	.04	.03	.02
584	Marc Newfield	.15	.11	.06
585	*Derek Lee*	.15	.11	.06
586	Shane Reynolds	.04	.03	.02
587	Cliff Floyd	.60	.45	.25
588	Jeff Schwarz	.04	.03	.02
589	*Ross Powell*	.15	.11	.06
590	Gerald Williams	.04	.03	.02
591	Mike Trombley	.05	.04	.02
592	Ken Ryan	.04	.03	.02
593	John O'Donoghue	.04	.03	.02
594	Rod Correia	.04	.03	.02
595	Darrell Sherman	.04	.03	.02
596	Steve Scarsone	.05	.04	.02
597	Sherman Obando	.05	.04	.02
598	Kurt Abbott	.04	.03	.02
599	Dave Telgheder	.04	.03	.02
600	Rick Trlicek	.04	.03	.02
601	Carl Everett	.08	.06	.03
602	Luis Ortiz	.04	.03	.02
603	*Larry Luebbers*	.15	.11	.06
604	Kevin Roberson	.10	.08	.04
605	Butch Huskey	.08	.06	.03
606	Benji Gil	.10	.08	.04
607	Todd Van Poppel	.04	.03	.02
608	Mark Hutton	.04	.03	.02
609	Chip Hale	.04	.03	.02
610	Matt Maysey	.04	.03	.02
611	Scott Ruffcorn	.20	.15	.08
612	Hilly Hathaway	.05	.04	.02
613	Allen Watson	.15	.11	.06
614	Carlos Delgado	.75	.60	.30
615	Roberto Mejia	.15	.11	.06
616	Turk Wendell	.04	.03	.02
617	Tony Tarasco	.25	.20	.10
618	Raul Mondesi	.10	.08	.04
619	Kevin Stocker	.15	.11	.06
620	Javier Lopez	.40	.30	.15
621	*Keith Kessinger*	.15	.11	.06
622	Bob Hamelin	.04	.03	.02
623	John Roper	.05	.04	.02
624	Len Dykstra	.06	.05	.02
625	Joe Carter	.10	.08	.04
626	Jim Abbott	.05	.04	.02
627	Lee Smith	.04	.03	.02
628	Ken Griffey Jr.	.50	.40	.20
629	Dave Winfield	.08	.06	.03
630	Darryl Kile	.05	.04	.02
631	Frank Thomas (MVP)	.50	.40	.20
632	Barry Bonds (MVP)	.25	.20	.10
633	Jack McDowell (Cy Young)	.06	.05	.02
634	Greg Maddux (Cy Young)	.08	.06	.03
635	Tim Salmon (ROY)	.25	.20	.10
636	Mike Piazza (ROY)	.50	.40	.20
637	*Brian Turang*	.20	.15	.08
638	Rondell White	.25	.20	.10
639	Nigel Wilson	.08	.06	.03
640	*Torii Hunter*	.20	.15	.08
641	Salomon Torres	.20	.15	.08
642	Kevin Higgins	.05	.04	.02
643	Eric Wedge	.05	.04	.02
644	Roger Salkeld	.05	.04	.02
645	Manny Ramirez	.50	.40	.20
646	Jeff McNeely	.05	.04	.02
647	Atlanta Braves	.08	.06	.03
648	Chicago Cubs	.08	.06	.03
649	Cincinnati Reds	.08	.06	.03
650	Colorado Rockies	.08	.06	.03
651	Florida Marlins	.08	.06	.03
652	Houston Astros	.08	.06	.03
653	Los Angeles Dodgers	.08	.06	.03
654	Montreal Expos	.08	.06	.03
655	New York Mets	.08	.06	.03
656	Philadelphia Phillies	.08	.06	.03
657	Pittsburgh Pirates	.08	.06	.03
658	St. Louis Cardinals	.08	.06	.03
659	San Diego Padres	.08	.06	.03
660	San Francisco Giants	.08	.06	.03

1994 Score The Cycle

Leaders in the previous season's production of singles, doubles, triples and home runs are featured in this insert set which was packaged with Series II Score. Player action photos pop out of a circle at center and are surrounded by dark blue borders. "The Cycle" in printed in green at top. The player's name is in gold foil at bottom, printed over an infield diagram in a green strip. The stat which earned the player inclusion in the set is in gold foil at bottom right. On back are the rankings for the statistical category. Cards are numbered with a "TC" prefix.

		MT	NR MT	EX
Complete Set (20):		250.00	185.00	100.00
Common Player:		6.00	4.50	2.50
1	Brett Butler	6.00	4.50	2.50
2	Kenny Lofton	15.00	11.00	6.00
3	Paul Molitor	12.00	9.00	4.75
4	Carlos Baerga	18.00	13.50	7.25
5	Gregg Jefferies, Tony Phillips	6.00	4.50	2.50
6	John Olerud	15.00	11.00	6.00
7	Charlie Hayes	6.00	4.50	2.50
8	Len Dykstra	10.00	7.50	4.00
9	Dante Bichette	7.50	5.50	3.00
10	Devon White	7.00	5.25	2.75
11	Lance Johnson	6.00	4.50	2.50
12	Joey Cora, Steve Finley	6.00	4.50	2.50
13	Tony Fernandez	6.00	4.50	2.50
14	David Hulse, Brett Butler	6.00	4.50	2.50
15	Jay Bell, Brian McRae, Mickey Morandini	6.00	4.50	2.50
16	Juan Gonzalez, Barry Bonds	35.00	26.00	14.00
17	Ken Griffey Jr.	50.00	37.00	20.00
18	Frank Thomas	50.00	37.00	20.00
19	Dave Justice	18.00	13.50	7.25
20	Matt Williams, Albert Belle	18.00	13.50	7.25

1994 Score Dream Team

Score's 1994 "Dream Team," one top player at each position, was featured in a 10-card insert set. The stars were decked out in vintage uniforms and equipment for the photos. Green and black bars at top and bottom frame the photo, and all printing on the front is in gold foil. Backs have a white background with green highlights. A color player portrait photo is featured, along with a brief justification for the player's selection to the squad. Cards are UV coated on both sides. Stated odds of finding a Dream Team insert were given as one per 72 packs.

		MT	NR MT	EX
Complete Set (10):		90.00	67.00	36.00
Common Player:		4.00	3.00	1.50
1	Mike Mussina	12.00	9.00	4.75
2	Tom Glavine	8.00	6.00	3.25
3	Don Mattingly	15.00	11.00	6.00
4	Carlos Baerga	18.00	13.50	7.25
5	Barry Larkin	5.00	3.75	2.00
6	Matt Williams	4.50	3.50	1.75
7	Juan Gonzalez	30.00	22.00	12.00
8	Andy Van Slyke	4.00	3.00	1.50
9	Larry Walker	4.50	3.50	1.75
10	Mike Stanley	4.00	3.00	1.50

1994 Score Gold Stars

Limited to inclusion in hobby packs, Score 60-card "Gold Stars" insert set features 30 National League players, found in Series I packs, and 30 American Leaguers inserted with Series II. Stated odds of finding a Gold Stars card were listed on the wrapper as one in 18 packs. A notation on the cards' back indicates that no more than 6,500 sets of Gold Stars were produced. The high-tech cards feature a color player action photo, the full-bleed background of which has been converted to metallic tones. Backs have a graduated gold background with a portrait-style color player photo.

		MT	NR MT	EX
Complete Set (60):		275.00	210.00	100.00
Common Player:		2.00	1.50	.80
1	Barry Bonds	20.00	15.00	8.00
2	Orlando Merced	2.00	1.50	.80
3	Mark Grace	3.00	2.25	1.25
4	Darren Daulton	3.50	2.75	1.50
5	Jeff Blauser	2.00	1.50	.80
6	Deion Sanders	7.00	5.25	2.75
7	John Kruk	3.00	2.25	1.25
8	Jeff Bagwell	10.00	7.50	4.00
9	Gregg Jefferies	3.00	2.25	1.25

		MT	NR MT	EX
10	Matt Williams	5.00	3.75	2.00
11	Andres Galarraga	4.50	3.50	1.75
12	Jay Bell	2.00	1.50	.80
13	Mike Piazza	30.00	22.00	12.00
14	Ron Gant	3.00	2.25	1.25
15	Barry Larkin	2.50	2.00	1.00
16	Tom Glavine	6.00	4.50	2.50
17	Len Dykstra	6.00	4.50	2.50
18	Fred McGriff	6.00	4.50	2.50
19	Andy Van Slyke	2.00	1.50	.80
20	Gary Sheffield	4.00	3.00	1.50
21	John Burkett	2.00	1.50	.80
22	Dante Bichette	2.00	1.50	.80
23	Tony Gwynn	5.00	3.75	2.00
24	Dave Justice	10.00	7.50	4.00
25	Marquis Grissom	2.00	1.50	.80
26	Bobby Bonilla	2.50	2.00	1.00
27	Larry Walker	2.00	1.50	.80
28	Brett Butler	2.00	1.50	.80
29	Robby Thompson	2.00	1.50	.80
30	Jeff Conine	3.50	2.75	1.50
31	Joe Carter	6.00	4.50	2.50
32	Ken Griffey, Jr.	35.00	26.00	14.00
33	Juan Gonzalez	20.00	15.00	8.00
34	Rickey Henderson	4.00	3.00	1.50
35	Bo Jackson	4.00	3.00	1.50
36	Cal Ripken, Jr.	16.00	12.00	6.50
37	John Olerud	8.00	6.00	3.25
38	Carlos Baerga	8.00	6.00	3.25
39	Jack McDowell	2.50	2.00	1.00
40	Cecil Fielder	4.00	3.00	1.50
41	Kenny Lofton	7.50	5.50	3.00
42	Roberto Alomar	8.00	6.00	3.25
43	Randy Johnson	2.00	1.50	.80
44	Tim Salmon	10.00	7.50	4.00
45	Frank Thomas	35.00	26.00	14.00
46	Albert Belle	10.00	7.50	4.00
47	Greg Vaughn	2.00	1.50	.80
48	Travis Fryman	6.00	4.50	2.50
49	Don Mattingly	8.00	6.00	3.25
50	Wade Boggs	4.00	3.00	1.50
51	Mo Vaughn	4.00	3.00	1.50
52	Kirby Puckett	15.00	11.00	6.00
53	Devon White	2.50	2.00	1.00
54	Tony Phillips	2.00	1.50	.80
55	Brian Harper	2.00	1.50	.80
56	Chad Curtis	3.00	2.25	1.25
57	Paul Molitor	6.00	4.50	2.50
58	Ivan Rodriguez	3.00	2.25	1.25
59	Rafael Palmeiro	4.00	3.00	1.50
60	Brian McRae	2.00	1.50	.80

1994 Score Boys of Summer

A heavy emphasis on rookies and recent rookies is noted in this 1994 Score insert set, released in two series, cards #1-30 with Score's Series I and 31-60 packaged with Series II. Card fronts feature a color action photo on which the background has been rendered in a blurred watercolor effect. A hot-color aura separates the player from the background. The player's name appears vertically in gold foil. Score and "Boys of Summer" logos appear in the upper corners. Backs have backgrounds in reds and orange with a portrait-style player photo on one side and a large "Boys of Summer" logo on the other. A short description of the player's talents appears at center.

	MT	NR MT	EX
Complete Set (60):	120.00	90.00	47.50
Complete Series 1 (30):	55.00	41.00	22.00
Complete Series 2 (30):	55.00	41.00	22.00
Common Player:	1.00	.75	.40

		MT	NR MT	EX
1	Jeff Conine	2.50	2.00	1.00
2	Aaron Sele	4.00	3.00	1.50
3	Kevin Stocker	3.00	2.25	1.25
4	Pat Meares	1.00	.75	.40
5	Jeromy Burnitz	2.00	1.50	.80
6	Mike Piazza	15.00	11.00	6.00
7	Allen Watson	3.00	2.25	1.25
8	Jeffrey Hammonds	6.00	4.50	2.50
9	Kevin Roberson	2.50	2.00	1.00
10	Hilly Hathaway	2.00	1.50	.80
11	Kirk Reuter	6.00	4.50	2.50
12	Eduardo Perez	3.00	2.25	1.25
13	Ricky Gutierrez	1.50	1.25	.60
14	Domingo Jean	1.50	1.25	.60
15	David Nied	2.00	1.50	.80
16	Wayne Kirby	1.00	.75	.40
17	Mike Lansing	2.50	2.00	1.00
18	Jason Bere	4.00	3.00	1.50
19	Brent Gates	3.00	2.25	1.25
20	Javier Lopez	5.00	3.75	2.00
21	Greg McMichael	1.50	1.25	.60
22	David Hulse	1.00	.75	.40
23	Roberto Mejia	2.00	1.50	.80
24	Tim Salmon	9.00	6.75	3.50
25	Rene Arocha	1.50	1.25	.60
26	Bret Boone	1.50	1.25	.60
27	David McCarty	1.50	1.25	.60
28	Todd Van Poppel	1.50	1.25	.60
29	Lance Painter	1.00	.75	.40
30	Erik Pappas	1.25	.90	.50
31	Chuck Carr	1.75	1.25	.70
32	Mark Hutton	1.25	.90	.50
33	Jeff McNeely	1.25	.90	.50
34	Willie Greene	1.75	1.25	.70
35	Nigel Wilson	2.00	1.50	.80
36	Rondell White	4.00	3.00	1.50
37	Brian Turang	1.50	1.25	.60
38	Manny Ramirez	5.00	3.75	2.00
39	Salomon Torres	2.00	1.50	.80
40	Melvin Nieves	1.75	1.25	.70
41	Ryan Klesko	2.50	2.00	1.00
42	Keith Kessinger	1.00	.75	.40
43	Eric Wedge	1.50	1.25	.60
44	Bob Hamelin	1.25	.90	.50
45	Carlos Delgado	6.00	4.50	2.50
46	Marc Newfield	2.00	1.50	.80
47	Raul Mondesi	2.50	2.00	1.00
48	Tim Costo	1.25	.90	.50
49	Pedro Martinez	2.00	1.50	.80
50	Steve Karsay	1.75	1.25	.70
51	Danny Bautista	1.00	.75	.40
52	Butch Huskey	1.50	1.25	.60
53	Kurt Abbott	1.00	.75	.40
54	Darrell Sherman	1.00	.75	.40
55	Damon Buford	1.00	.75	.40
56	Ross Powell	1.00	.75	.40
57	Darrell Whitmore	1.50	1.25	.60
58	Chipper Jones	3.50	2.75	1.50
59	Jeff Granger	1.25	.90	.50
60	Cliff Floyd	10.00	7.50	4.00

1994 Score Gold Rush

Opting to include one insert card in each pack of its 1994 product, Score created a "Gold Rush" version of each card in its regular set. Gold Rush cards are basically the same as their counterparts with a few enhancements. Card fronts are printed on foil with a gold border and a Score Gold Rush logo in one of the upper corners. The background of the photo has been metalized, allowing the color player portion to stand out in sharp contrast. Backs are identical to the regular cards except for the appearance of a large Gold Rush logo under the typography at left.

	MT	NR MT	EX
Complete Set (660):	250.00	187.00	100.00
Common Player:	.25	.20	.10

Gold Rush cards valued at 5X same card in 1994 Score

1994 Score Cal Ripken, Jr.

Although the cards themselves do not indicate it, this nine-card issue was co-sponsored by Burger King and Coke, and distributed in BK restaurants in the Baltimore-Washington area. Cards were available in three-card packs for 25 cents with the purchase of a Coke product. Each pack contains two regular cards and a gold card. Each of the nine cards could be found in a regular and gold version. Cards feature color photos with a semi-circular heavy black border at top or left. "Score '94" appears in orange in one of the upper corners, along with an Orioles logo. Cal Ripken, Jr.'s name appears at the bottom. On the gold premium version, there is a gold-foil circle around the Orioles logo and Ripken's name appears in gold, rather than white. Backs have a smaller color photo, again meeting at a semi-circular edge with the black border at left and bottom. In the black are another Score logo, a card number, an Orioles logo, a headline and a few career details and/or stats. Cards are UV coated on each side. Several hundred of the cards were personally autographed by Ripken and distributed in a drawing.

	MT	NR MT	EX
Complete Set (9):	2.00	1.50	.80
Complete Set, Gold (9):	6.00	4.50	2.50
Common Card:	.25	.20	.10
Common Card, Gold:	.75	.60	.30
Autographed Card:	300.00	225.00	120.00

		MT	NR MT	EX
1	Double Honors	.25	.20	.10
1a	Double Honors (gold)	.75	.60	.30
2	Perennial All-Star	.25	.20	.10
2a	Perennial All-Star (gold)	.75	.60	.30
3	Peerless Power	.25	.20	.10
3a	Peerless Power (gold)	.75	.60	.30
4	Fitness Fan	.25	.20	.10
4a	Fitness Fan (gold)	.75	.60	.30
5	Prime Concerns	.25	.20	.10
5a	Prime Concerns (gold)	.75	.60	.30
6	Home Run Club	.25	.20	.10
6a	Home Run Club (gold)	.75	.60	.30
7	The Iron Man	.25	.20	.10
7a	The Iron Man (gold)	.75	.60	.30
8	Heavy Hitter	.25	.20	.10
8a	Heavy Hitter (gold)	.75	.60	.30
9	Gold Glover	.25	.20	.10
9a	Gold Glover (gold)	.75	.60	.30

1994 Score Select Promos

To introduce its 1994 offering to dealers and collectors, Score Select created an eight-card promo set. Cards are identical in format to regular-issue cards with the exception of the word "SAMPLE" overprinted diagonally on front and back. The promos included five of the regular-run cards, a Rookie Prospect card and one each of its Rookie Surge '94 and Crown Contenders insert sets. The promos were cello-packaged with a header card describing the set and chase cards.

	MT	NR MT	EX
Complete Set (8):	35.00	26.00	14.00
Common Player:	3.00	2.25	1.25

		MT	NR MT	EX
3	Paul Molitor	6.00	4.50	2.50
17	Kirby Puckett	6.00	4.50	2.50
19	Randy Johnson	3.00	2.25	1.25
24	John Kruk	4.00	3.00	1.50
51	Jose Lind	3.00	2.25	1.25
197	Ryan Klesko (Rookie Prospect)	6.00	4.50	2.50
1CC	Lenny Dykstra (Crown Contenders)	6.00	4.50	2.50
1RS	Cliff Floyd (Rookie Surge '94)	12.00	9.00	4.75
----	Header card	.10	.08	.04

1994 Score Select

The first series of this premium brand from the Score/Pinnacle lineup offered 210 regular cards and a trio of special insert sets. The announced press run for Series I was 4,950 20-box, 36-pack cases. Cards have a horizontal format with a color action photo at right and a second action photo at left done in a single team color-coded hue. The player's last

name is dropped out of a vertical gold-foil strip between the two photos, with his first name in white at top-center. Backs are vertically oriented with yet another color action photo at center. In a vertical bar at right, matching the color-coding on front and printed over the photo are 1993 and career stats, a "Select Stat," and a few sentences about the player. The card number is in white at upper-right. The player's name and position are printed in white on a black photo overprint at left. The appropriate logos and Pinnacle's optical-variable counterfeiting device are at bottom-center. Thirty of the final 33 cards in the series are a "1994 Rookie Prospect" subset, so noted in a special gold-foil logo on front.

		MT	NR MT	EX
Complete Set (210):		30.00	22.00	12.00
Common Player:		.15	.11	.06
1	Ken Griffey, Jr.	5.00	3.75	2.00
2	Greg Maddux	.35	.25	.14
3	Paul Molitor	.40	.30	.15
4	Mike Piazza	3.00	2.25	1.25
5	Jay Bell	.15	.11	.06
6	Frank Thomas	5.00	3.75	2.00
7	Barry Larkin	.20	.15	.08
8	Paul O'Neill	.15	.11	.06
9	Darren Daulton	.15	.11	.06
10	Mike Greenwell	.15	.11	.06
11	Chuck Carr	.15	.11	.06
12	Joe Carter	.35	.25	.14
13	Lance Johnson	.15	.11	.06
14	Jeff Blauser	.15	.11	.06
15	Chris Hoiles	.15	.11	.06
16	Rick Wilkins	.15	.11	.06
17	Kirby Puckett	.75	.60	.30
18	Larry Walker	.20	.15	.08
19	Randy Johnson	.15	.11	.06
20	Bernard Gilkey	.15	.11	.06
21	Devon White	.15	.11	.06
22	Randy Myers	.15	.11	.06
23	Don Mattingly	.60	.45	.25
24	John Kruk	.20	.15	.08
25	Ozzie Guillen	.15	.11	.06
26	Jeff Conine	.20	.15	.08
27	Mike Macfarlane	.15	.11	.06
28	Dave Hollins	.20	.15	.08
29	Chuck Knoblauch	.15	.11	.06
30	Ozzie Smith	.30	.25	.12
31	Harold Baines	.15	.11	.06
32	Ryne Sandberg	.75	.60	.30
33	Ron Karkovice	.15	.11	.06
34	Terry Pendleton	.15	.11	.06
35	Wally Joyner	.15	.11	.06
36	Mike Mussina	.40	.30	.15
37	Felix Jose	.15	.11	.06
38	Derrick May	.15	.11	.06
39	Scott Cooper	.15	.11	.06
40	Jose Rijo	.15	.11	.06
41	Robin Ventura	.30	.25	.12
42	Charlie Hayes	.15	.11	.06
43	Jimmy Key	.15	.11	.06
44	Eric Karros	.15	.11	.06
45	Ruben Sierra	.20	.15	.08
46	Ryan Thompson	.15	.11	.06
47	Brian McRae	.15	.11	.06
48	Pat Hentgen	.15	.11	.06
49	John Valentin	.15	.11	.06
50	Al Martin	.20	.15	.08
51	Jose Lind	.15	.11	.06
52	Kevin Stocker	.25	.20	.10
53	Mike Gallego	.15	.11	.06
54	Dwight Gooden	.15	.11	.06
55	Brady Anderson	.15	.11	.06
56	Jeff King	.15	.11	.06
57	Mark McGwire	.25	.20	.10
58	Sammy Sosa	.20	.15	.08
59	Ryan Bowen	.15	.11	.06
60	Mark Lemke	.15	.11	.06
61	Roger Clemens	.50	.40	.20
62	Brian Jordan	.15	.11	.06
63	Andres Galarraga	.15	.11	.06
64	Kevin Appier	.15	.11	.06
65	Don Slaught	.15	.11	.06
66	Mike Blowers	.15	.11	.06
67	Wes Chamberlain	.15	.11	.06
68	Troy Neel	.15	.11	.06
69	John Wetteland	.15	.11	.06
70	Joe Girardi	.15	.11	.06
71	Reggie Sanders	.15	.11	.06
72	Edgar Martinez	.15	.11	.06
73	Todd Hundley	.15	.11	.06
74	Pat Borders	.15	.11	.06
75	Roberto Mejia	.25	.20	.10
76	David Cone	.15	.11	.06
77	Tony Gwynn	.35	.25	.14
78	Jim Abbott	.20	.15	.08
79	Jay Buhner	.15	.11	.06
80	Mark McLemore	.15	.11	.06
81	Wil Cordero	.20	.15	.08
82	Pedro Astacio	.15	.11	.06
83	Bob Tewksbury	.15	.11	.06
84	Dave Winfield	.25	.20	.10
85	Jeff Kent	.15	.11	.06
86	Todd Van Poppel	.20	.15	.08
87	Steve Avery	.30	.25	.12
88	Mike Lansing	.20	.15	.08
89	Len Dykstra	.25	.20	.10
90	Jose Guzman	.15	.11	.06
91	Brian Hunter	.15	.11	.06
92	Tim Raines	.15	.11	.06
93	Andre Dawson	.20	.15	.08
94	Joe Orsulak	.15	.11	.06
95	Ricky Jordan	.15	.11	.06
96	Billy Hatcher	.15	.11	.06
97	Jack McDowell	.25	.20	.10
98	Tom Pagnozzi	.15	.11	.06
99	Darryl Strawberry	.20	.15	.08
100	Mike Stanley	.15	.11	.06
101	Bret Saberhagen	.15	.11	.06
102	Willie Greene	.15	.11	.06
103	Bryan Harvey	.15	.11	.06
104	Tim Bogar	.15	.11	.06
105	Jack Voight	.15	.11	.06
106	Brad Ausmus	.15	.11	.06
107	Ramon Martinez	.15	.11	.06
108	Mike Perez	.15	.11	.06
109	Jeff Montgomery	.15	.11	.06
110	Danny Darwin	.15	.11	.06
111	Wilson Alvarez	.20	.15	.08
112	Kevin Mitchell	.20	.15	.08
113	David Nied	.30	.25	.12
114	Rich Amaral	.15	.11	.06
115	Stan Javier	.15	.11	.06
116	Mo Vaughn	.25	.20	.10
117	Ben McDonald	.25	.20	.10
118	Tom Gordon	.15	.11	.06
119	Carlos Garcia	.15	.11	.06
120	Phil Plantier	.15	.11	.06
121	Mike Morgan	.15	.11	.06
122	Pat Meares	.15	.11	.06
123	Kevin Young	.15	.11	.06
124	Jeff Fassero	.15	.11	.06
125	Gene Harris	.15	.11	.06
126	Bob Welch	.15	.11	.06
127	Walt Weiss	.15	.11	.06
128	Bobby Witt	.15	.11	.06
129	Andy Van Slyke	.15	.11	.06
130	Steve Cooke	.15	.11	.06
131	Mike Devereaux	.15	.11	.06
132	Joey Cora	.15	.11	.06
133	Bret Barberie	.15	.11	.06
134	Orel Hershiser	.15	.11	.06
135	Ed Sprague	.15	.11	.06
136	Shawon Dunston	.15	.11	.06
137	Alex Arias	.15	.11	.06
138	Archi Cianfrocco	.15	.11	.06
139	Tim Wallach	.15	.11	.06
140	Bernie Williams	.15	.11	.06
141	Karl Rhodes	.15	.11	.06
142	Pat Kelly	.15	.11	.06
143	Dave Magadan	.15	.11	.06
144	Kevin Tapani	.15	.11	.06
145	Eric Young	.15	.11	.06
146	Derek Bell	.15	.11	.06
147	Dante Bichette	.20	.15	.08
148	Geronimo Pena	.15	.11	.06
149	Joe Oliver	.15	.11	.06
150	Orestes Destrade	.15	.11	.06
151	Tim Naehring	.20	.15	.08
152	Ray Lankford	.15	.11	.06
153	Phil Clark	.15	.11	.06
154	David McCarty	.20	.15	.08
155	Tommy Greene	.15	.11	.06
156	Wade Boggs	.30	.25	.12
157	Kevin Gross	.15	.11	.06
158	Hal Morris	.15	.11	.06
159	Moises Alou	.20	.15	.08
160	Rick Aguilera	.15	.11	.06
161	Curt Schilling	.15	.11	.06
162	Chip Hale	.15	.11	.06
163	Tino Martinez	.15	.11	.06
164	Mark Whiten	.15	.11	.06
165	Dave Stewart	.15	.11	.06
166	Steve Buechele	.15	.11	.06
167	Bobby Jones	.15	.11	.06
168	Darrin Fletcher	.15	.11	.06
169	John Smiley	.15	.11	.06
170	Cory Snyder	.15	.11	.06
171	Scott Erickson	.15	.11	.06
172	Kirk Rueter	.75	.60	.30
173	Dave Fleming	.15	.11	.06
174	John Smoltz	.20	.15	.08
175	Ricky Gutierrez	.15	.11	.06
176	Mike Bordick	.15	.11	.06
177	Chan Ho Park	1.00	.75	.40
178	Alex Gonzalez	1.00	.75	.40
179	Steve Karsay	.40	.30	.15
180	Jeffrey Hammonds	.75	.60	.30
181	Manny Ramirez	1.50	1.25	.60
182	Salomon Torres	.20	.15	.08
183	Raul Mondesi	1.00	.75	.40
184	James Mouton	.50	.40	.20
185	Cliff Floyd	1.50	1.25	.60
186	Danny Bautista	.15	.11	.06
187	Kurt Abbott	.20	.15	.08
188	Javier Lopez	.75	.60	.30
189	John Patterson	.15	.11	.06
190	Greg Blosser	.15	.11	.06
191	Bob Hamelin	.20	.15	.08
192	Tony Eusebio	.15	.11	.06
193	Carlos Delgado	.75	.60	.30
194	Chris Gomez	.25	.20	.10
195	Kelly Stinnett	.15	.11	.06
196	Shane Reynolds	.15	.11	.06
197	Ryan Klesko	1.00	.75	.40
198	Jim Edmonds	.20	.15	.08
199	James Hurst	.15	.11	.06
200	Dave Staton	.20	.15	.08
201	Rondell White	.50	.40	.20
202	Keith Mitchell	.15	.11	.06
203	Darren Oliver	.15	.11	.06
204	Mike Matheny	.20	.15	.08
205	Chris Turner	.15	.11	.06
206	Matt Mieske	.20	.15	.08
207	NL Team Checklist	.15	.11	.06
208	NL Team Checklist	.15	.11	.06
209	AL Team Checklist	.15	.11	.06
210	AL Team Checklist	.15	.11	.06

1994 Score Select Crown Contenders

Candidates for the major baseball annual awards are featured in this subset. Horizontal-format cards have a color player photo printed on a holographic foil background. Backs are vertically oriented with a player portrait photo and justification for the player's inclusion in the set. Cards are numbered with a "CC" prefix and feature a special optical-variable anti-counterfeiting device at bottom-center. According to stated odds of one card on average in every 24 packs it has been estimated that fewer than 12,000 of each Crown Contenders card was produced.

		MT	NR MT	EX
Complete Set (10):		160.00	120.00	65.00
Common Player:		5.00	3.75	2.00
1	Greg Maddux	7.50	5.50	3.00
2	Roger Clemens	9.00	6.75	3.50
3	Randy Johnson	5.00	3.75	2.00
4	Frank Thomas	40.00	30.00	15.00
5	Barry Bonds	20.00	15.00	8.00
6	Juan Gonzalez	25.00	18.00	10.00
7	John Olerud	8.00	6.00	3.25
8	Mike Piazza	28.00	21.00	11.00
9	Ken Griffey, Jr.	40.00	30.00	15.00
10	Len Dykstra	5.00	3.75	2.00

1994 Score Select Rookie Surge

Top rookies are featured in this insert set. Metallic foil printing technology is utilized on the front of the card in a dazzling color display, over which the player photo is printed, also on metallic foil. Approximately the bottom one-third of the card is occupied by a "Rookie S urge '94" logo. The player's name is virtually hidden in the border beyond the upper-right corner of the player photo. Backs are horizontally oriented and feature the same wild coloring, though produced in standard offset printing. A player portrait photo appears at right, with a few words and stats at left. Cards are numbered with an "RS" prefix. Stated odds of finding one of these chase cards were approximately one per 48 packs, indicating a print run of about 6,600 of each card.

		MT	NR MT	EX
Complete Set (9):		85.00	64.00	34.00
Common Player:		4.00	3.00	1.50
1	Cliff Floyd	15.00	11.00	6.00
2	Bob Hamelin	4.00	3.00	1.50
3	Ryan Klesko	18.00	13.50	7.25
4	Carlos Delgado	15.00	11.00	6.00
5	Jeffrey Hammonds	10.00	7.50	4.00
6	Rondell White	8.00	6.00	3.25
7	Salomon Torres	4.00	3.00	1.50
8	Steve Karsay	7.00	5.50	3.00
9	Javier Lopez	15.00	11.00	6.00

1994 Score Select Salute

With odds of finding one of these cards stated at one per 360 packs, it is estimated that only about 4,000 of each of this two-card chase set were produced.

		MT	NR MT	EX
Complete Set (2):		200.00	150.00	80.00
1	Cal Ripken, Jr.	150.00	110.00	60.00
2	Dave Winfield	75.00	56.00	30.00

1888 Scrapps Tobacco

The origin of these die-cut, embossed player busts is not known, but they were apparently part of a book of "punch-outs" issued in the late 1880s. When out of their original album, they apparently resembled scraps of paper, presumably leading to their unusual name. An earlier theory that they were issued by "Scrapps Tobacco" has since been discounted after research indicated there never was such a company. The die-cuts include 18 different players - nine members of the American Association St. Louis Browns and nine from the National League Detroit Wolverines. Although they vary slightly in size, the player busts are generally about 2" wide and 3" high. The drawings for the St. Louis player busts were taken from the Old Judge "Brown's Champions" set. The player's name appears along the bottom.

		NR MT	EX	VG
Complete Set (18):		6500.	3250.	1900.
Common Player:		250.00	125.00	75.00
(1)	C.W. Bennett	250.00	125.00	75.00
(2)	D. Brouthers	500.00	250.00	150.00
(3)	A.J. Bushong	250.00	125.00	75.00
(4)	Robert L. Caruthers	250.00	125.00	75.00
(5)	Charles Comiskey	600.00	300.00	175.00
(6)	F. Dunlap	300.00	150.00	90.00
(7)	David L. Foutz	250.00	125.00	75.00
(8)	C.H. Getzen (Geitzen)	300.00	150.00	90.00
(9)	Wm. Gleason	250.00	125.00	75.00
(10)	E. Hanlon	300.00	150.00	90.00
(11)	Walter A. Latham	250.00	125.00	75.00
(12)	James O'Neill	250.00	125.00	75.00
(13)	H. Richardson	300.00	150.00	90.00
(14)	Wm. Robinson	500.00	250.00	150.00
(15)	J.C. Rowe	300.00	150.00	90.00
(16)	S. Thompson	500.00	250.00	150.00
(17)	Curtis Welch	250.00	125.00	75.00
(18)	J.L. White	300.00	150.00	90.00

1949 Sealtest Phillies

This regional Phillies set was issued in the Philadelphia area in 1949 by Sealtest Dairy. It consisted of 12 large (3-1/2" by 4-1/4") sticker cards with peel-

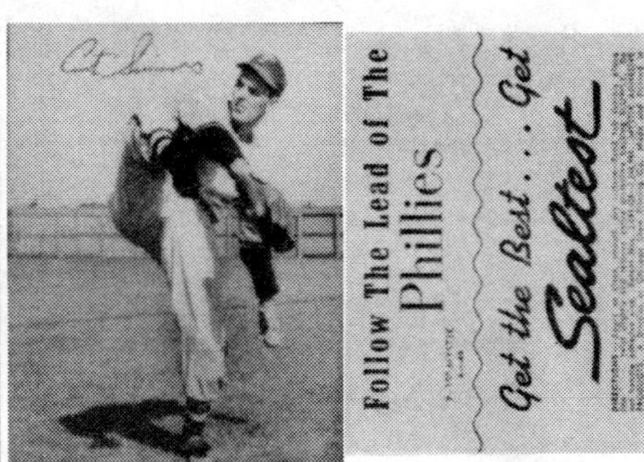

off backs. The front of the unnumbered cards featured an action photo with facsimilie autograph, while the back has an advertisement for Sealtest products. The same format, photos and checklist were also used for the Lummis Peanut Butter card set issued in Philadelphia the same year.

		NR MT	EX	VG
Complete Set (12):		700.00	350.00	210.00
Common Player:		45.00	22.00	13.50
(1)	Rich Ashburn	110.00	55.00	33.00
(2)	Hank Borowy	45.00	22.00	13.50
(3)	Del Ennis	75.00	37.00	22.00
(4)	Granny Hamner	45.00	22.00	13.50
(5)	Puddinhead Jones	45.00	22.00	13.50
(6)	Russ Meyer	45.00	22.00	13.50
(7)	Bill Nicholson	45.00	22.00	13.50
(8)	Robin Roberts	150.00	75.00	45.00
(9)	"Schoolboy" Rowe	45.00	22.00	13.50
(10)	Andy Seminick	45.00	22.00	13.50
(11)	Curt Simmons	75.00	37.00	22.00
(12)	Eddie Waitkus	45.00	22.00	13.50

1983 7-11 Slurpee Coins

This first production of player coins by 7-Eleven stores was distributed only in the Los Angeles area. The test promotion, which awarded a coin to every purchaser of a large Slurpee drink, must have proved successful, as it was expanded nationally in subsequent years. Six California Angels and six Los Angeles Dodgers are included in the full-color set, with Angels players in red backgrounds and the Dodgers in blue. The 1-3/4" diameter plastic coins feature both an action and a portrait photo of the player, which can be alternately seen by moving the coin slightly from side to side. The 12 coin backs are numbered and include brief statistics and the company logo.

		MT	NR MT	EX
Complete Set (12):		12.00	9.00	4.75
Common Player:		.50	.40	.20
1	Rod Carew	2.50	2.00	1.00
2	Steve Sax	.60	.45	.25
3	Fred Lynn	.75	.60	.30
4	Pedro Guerrero	.50	.40	.20
5	Reggie Jackson	3.50	2.75	1.50
6	Dusty Baker	.60	.45	.25
7	Doug DeCinces	.50	.40	.20
8	Fernando Valenzuela	.75	.60	.30
9	Tommy John	1.00	.70	.40
10	Rick Monday	.50	.40	.20
11	Bobby Grich	.50	.40	.20
12	Greg Brock	.50	.40	.20

1984 7-11 Slurpee Coins Eastern Region

The 7-Eleven coins were distributed nationally in 1984, with different players displayed on 72 total coins. The coins, called "Slurpee Discs," were issued in three different regional sets of 24 coins

each. East, West, and Central regional series were distributed, with players on teams in those areas of the country dominating the region's set. George Brett, Andre Dawson, Dale Murphy, Eddie Murray, Mike Schmidt and Robin Yount appear in all three of the full-color sets. At least one player appears from every major league team. The formats are very similar to the 1983 coins, with double-image photos on the fronts and statistics and coin numbers on the backs.

		MT	NR MT	EX
Complete Set (24):		70.00	52.00	28.00
Common Player:		.60	.45	.25
1	Andre Dawson	1.50	1.25	.60
2	Robin Yount	3.00	2.25	1.25
3	Dale Murphy	1.50	1.25	.60
4	Mike Schmidt	3.00	2.25	1.25
5	George Brett	1.50	1.25	.60
6	Eddie Murray	1.00	.70	.40
7	Dave Winfield	1.00	.70	.40
8	Tom Seaver	2.50	2.00	1.00
9	Mike Boddicker	.60	.45	.25
10	Wade Boggs	2.00	1.50	.80
11	Bill Madlock	.60	.45	.25
12	Steve Carlton	2.50	2.00	1.00
13	Dave Stieb	.60	.45	.25
14	Cal Ripken, Jr.	3.00	2.25	1.25
15	Jim Rice	.75	.60	.30
16	Ron Guidry	.75	.60	.30
17	Darryl Strawberry	.90	.70	.35
18	Tony Pena	.60	.45	.25
19	John Denny	.60	.45	.25
20	Tim Raines	.75	.60	.30
21	Rick Dempsey	.60	.45	.25
22	Rich Gossage	.80	.60	.30
23	Gary Matthews	.60	.45	.25
24	Keith Hernandez	.75	.60	.30

1984 7-11 Slurpee Coins Central Region

1	Andre Dawson	1.50	1.25	.60
2	Robin Yount	3.00	2.25	1.25
3	Dale Murphy	1.50	1.25	.60
4	Mike Schmidt	3.00	2.25	1.25
5	George Brett	1.50	1.25	.60
6	Eddie Murray	1.00	.70	.40
7	Bruce Sutter	.60	.45	.25
8	Cecil Cooper	.60	.45	.25
9	Willie McGee	.75	.60	.30
10	Mike Hargrove	.60	.45	.25
11	Kent Hrbek	.75	.60	.30
12	Carlton Fisk	1.00	.70	.40
13	Mario Soto	.60	.45	.25
14	Lonnie Smith	.60	.45	.25
15	Gary Carter	.90	.70	.35
16	Lou Whitaker	.80	.60	.30
17	Ron Kittle	.60	.45	.25
18	Paul Molitor	1.00	.70	.40
19	Ozzie Smith	.80	.60	.30
20	Fergie Jenkins	.90	.70	.35
21	Ted Simmons	.70	.50	.30
22	Pete Rose	2.50	2.00	1.00
23	LaMarr Hoyt	.60	.45	.25
24	Dan Quisenberry	.60	.45	.25

1984 7-11 Slurpee Coins Western Region

1	Andre Dawson	1.50	1.25	.60
2	Robin Yount	3.00	2.25	1.25
3	Dale Murphy	1.50	1.25	.60
4	Mike Schmidt	3.00	2.25	1.25
5	George Brett	1.50	1.25	.60
6	Eddie Murray	1.00	.70	.40
7	Steve Garvey	1.00	.70	.40
8	Rod Carew	2.50	2.00	1.00
9	Fernando Valenzuela	.70	.50	.30
10	Bob Horner	.70	.50	.30
11	Buddy Bell	.60	.45	.25
12	Reggie Jackson	3.00	2.25	1.25
13	Nolan Ryan	4.00	3.00	1.50
14	Pedro Guerrero	.70	.50	.30
15	Atlee Hammaker	.60	.45	.25
16	Fred Lynn	.80	.60	.30
17	Terry Kennedy	.60	.45	.25
18	Dusty Baker	.70	.50	.30
19	Jose Cruz	.60	.45	.25

20	Steve Rogers	.60	.45	.25
21	Rickey Henderson	2.50	2.00	1.00
22	Steve Sax	.70	.50	.30
23	Dickie Thon	.60	.45	.25
24	Matt Young	.60	.45	.25

1985 7-11 Twins

The Minnesota Twins, in co-operation with 7-Eleven and the Fire Marshall's Association, issued this set of 13 baseball fire safety cards. The card fronts feature full-color pictures of Twins players. A fire safety tip and short player history appear on the back. The cards were given out at all 7-Eleven stores in the state and at the Twins June 3 baseball game. Each fan received one baseball card with a poster which told how to collect the other cards in the set. Twelve cards feature players and the 13th card has an artist's rendering of Twins players on the front and a checklist of the set on the back. A group of 50,000 cards was distributed to fifth graders throughout the state by the fire departments.

		MT	NR MT	EX
Complete Set (13):		6.00	4.50	2.50
Common Player:		.20	.15	.08
1	Kirby Puckett	2.00	1.50	.80
2	Frank Viola	.50	.40	.20
3	Mickey Hatcher	.20	.15	.08
4	Kent Hrbek	.75	.60	.30
5	John Butcher	.20	.15	.08
6	Roy Smalley	.20	.15	.08
7	Tom Brunansky	.25	.20	.10
8	Ron Davis	.20	.15	.08
9	Gary Gaetti	1.00	.70	.40
10	Tim Teufel	.30	.25	.12
11	Mike Smithson	.20	.15	.08
12	Tim Laudner	.30	.25	.12
----	Checklist	.10	.08	.04

1985 7-11 Slurpee Coins Eastern Region

In 1985, the "Slurpee Disc" promotion was further expanded to a total of 94 full-color coins. The formats were very similar to the previous two years, but there were six different regional sets. Five of these regional series contain 16 coins, with a Detroit series totaling 14. The other five regions are: East, West, Great Lakes, Central and Southeast. The coins are again 1-1/4" in diameter, printed on plastic with double-image photos. All coins are numbered. No player appears in all regions. although several are in two or more.

		MT	NR MT	EX
Complete Set (16):		80.00	60.00	32.00
Common Player:		.60	.45	.25
1	Eddie Murray	1.00	.70	.40
2	George Brett	1.50	1.25	.60
3	Steve Carlton	2.00	1.50	.80
4	Jim Rice	.75	.60	.30
5	Dave Winfield	1.00	.70	.40
6	Mike Boddicker	.60	.45	.25
7	Wade Boggs	1.75	1.25	.70
8	Dwight Evans	.70	.50	.30
9	Dwight Gooden	.90	.70	.35
10	Keith Hernandez	.70	.50	.30
11	Bill Madlock	.60	.45	.25
12	Don Mattingly	2.00	1.50	.80
13	Dave Righetti	.70	.50	.30
14	Cal Ripken, Jr.	3.00	2.25	1.25
15	Juan Samuel	.70	.50	.30
16	Mike Schmidt	3.00	2.25	1.25

1985 7-11 Slurpee Coins Southeastern Region

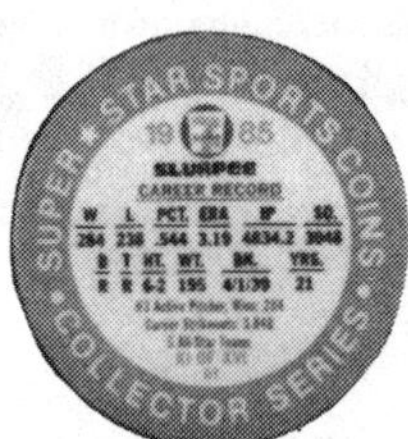

1	Dale Murphy	1.25	.90	.50
2	Steve Carlton	2.00	1.50	.80
3	Nolan Ryan	4.00	3.00	1.50
4	Bruce Sutter	.60	.45	.25
5	Dave Winfield	2.00	1.50	.80
6	Steve Bedrosian	.60	.45	.25
7	Andre Dawson	1.00	.70	.40
8	Kirk Gibson	.80	.60	.30
9	Fred Lynn	.75	.60	.30
10	Gary Matthews	.60	.45	.25
11	Phil Niekro	.70	.50	.30
12	Tim Raines	.75	.60	.30
13	Darryl Strawberry	.90	.70	.35
14	Dave Stieb	.60	.45	.25
15	Willie Upshaw	.60	.45	.25
16	Lou Whitaker	.70	.50	.30

1985 7-11 Slurpee Coins Great Lakes Region

1	Willie Hernandez	.60	.45	.25
2	George Brett	1.50	1.25	.60
3	Dave Winfield	1.00	.70	.40
4	Eddie Murray	1.00	.70	.40
5	Bruce Sutter	.60	.45	.25
6	Harold Baines	.75	.60	.30
7	Bert Blyleven	.60	.45	.25
8	Leon Durham	.60	.45	.25
9	Chet Lemon	.60	.45	.25
10	Pete Rose	2.00	1.50	.80
11	Ryne Sandberg	4.00	3.00	1.50
12	Tom Seaver	3.00	2.25	1.25
13	Mario Soto	.60	.45	.25
14	Rick Sutcliffe	.60	.45	.25
15	Alan Trammell	.90	.70	.35
16	Robin Yount	2.50	2.00	1.00

A player's name in italic type indicates a rookie card. An (FC) indicates a player's first card for that particular card company.

Values quoted in this guide reflect the retail price of a card – the price a collector can expect to pay when buying a card from a dealer. The wholesale price – that which a collector can expect to receive from a dealer when selling cards – will be significantly lower, depending on desirability and condition.

1985 7-11 Slurpee Coins Southwest/Central Region

1	Nolan Ryan	4.00	3.00	1.50
2	George Brett	1.50	1.25	.60
3	Dave Winfield	1.00	.70	.40
4	Mike Schmidt	3.00	2.25	1.25
5	Bruce Sutter	.60	.45	.25
6	Joaquin Andujar	.60	.45	.25
7	Willie Hernandez	.60	.45	.25
8	Wade Boggs	1.75	1.25	.70
9	Gary Carter	.75	.60	.30
10	Jose Cruz	.60	.45	.25
11	Kent Hrbek	.70	.50	.30
12	Reggie Jackson	3.00	2.25	1.25
13	Lance Parrish	.70	.50	.30
14	Terry Puhl	.60	.45	.25
15	Dan Quisenberry	.60	.45	.25
16	Ozzie Smith	.90	.70	.35

1985 7-11 Slurpee Coins Western Region

1	Mike Schmidt	3.00	2.25	1.25
2	Jim Rice	.75	.60	.30
3	Dale Murphy	1.25	.90	.50
4	Eddie Murray	1.00	.70	.40
5	Dave Winfield	1.00	.70	.40
6	Rod Carew	2.00	1.50	.80
7	Alvin Davis	.60	.45	.25
8	Steve Garvey	.80	.60	.30
9	Rich Gossage	.60	.45	.25
10	Pedro Guerrero	.60	.45	.25
11	Tony Gwynn	.80	.60	.30
12	Rickey Henderson	2.00	1.50	.80
13	Reggie Jackson	3.00	2.25	1.25
14	Jeff Leonard	.60	.45	.25
15	Alejandro Pena	.60	.45	.25
16	Fernando Valenzuela	.75	.60	.30

1985 7-11 Slurpee Coins Tigers

		MT	NR MT	EX
Complete Set (14):		10.00	7.50	4.00
Common Player:		.60		
1	Sparky Anderson	.75	.60	.30
2	Darrell Evans	.75	.60	.30
3	Kirk Gibson	.75	.60	.30

4	Willie Hernandez	.60	.45	.25
5	Larry Herndon	.60	.45	.25
6	Chet Lemon	.60	.45	.25
7	Aurelio Lopez	.60	.45	.25
8	Jack Morris	.80	.60	.30
9	Lance Parrish	.80	.60	.30
10	Dan Petry	.60	.45	.25
11	Dave Rozema	.60	.45	.25
12	Alan Trammell	2.00	1.50	.80
13	Lou Whitaker	1.50	1.25	.60
14	Milt Wilcox	.60	.45	.25

1986 7-11 Slurpee Coins Eastern Region

This marked the fourth year of production for these coins, issued with the purchase of a large Slurpee drink at 7-Eleven stores. Once again, there are different regional issues, with 16 coins issued for four different regions in 1986. The 1-3/4" diameter plastic coins each feature three different players' pictures, which can be seen alternately by tilting from side to side. Eight of the coins are the same in every region. Each coin is numbered on the back, along with brief player information.

	MT	NR MT	EX
Complete Set:	70.00	52.00	28.00
Common Player:	.40	.30	.15

1	Dwight Gooden	.75	.60	.30
2	Batting Champs (Wade Boggs, George Brett, Pete Rose)	2.00	1.50	.80
3	MVP's (Keith Hernandez, Don Mattingly, Cal Ripken, Jr.)	2.00	1.50	.80
4	Slugging Champs (Harold Baines, Pedro Guerrero, Dave Parker)	.60	.45	.25
5	Home Run Champs (Dale Murphy, Jim Rice, Mike Schmidt)	2.00	1.50	.80
6	Cy Young Winners (Ron Guidry, Bret Saberhagen, Fernando Valenzuela)	.70	.50	.30
7	Bullpen Aces (Rich Gossage, Dan Quisenberry, Bruce Sutter)	.50	.40	.20
8	Strikeout Kings (Steve Carlton, Nolan Ryan, Tom Seaver)	3.00	2.25	1.25
9	1985 Rookies (Steve Lyons, Rick Schu, Larry Sheets)	.40	.30	.15
10	Bullpen Aces (Jeff Reardon, Dave Righetti, Bob Stanley)	.50	.40	.20
11	Power Hitters (George Bell, Darryl Strawberry, Dave Winfield)	1.00	.70	.40
12	Base Stealers (Rickey Henderson, Tim Raines, Juan Samuel)	1.00	.70	.40
13	Home Run Hitters (Andre Dawson, Dwight Evans, Eddie Murray)	.80	.60	.30
14	Ace Pitchers (Mike Boddicker, Ron Darling, Dave Stieb)	.40	.30	.15
15	1985 Bullpen Rookies (Tim Burke, Brian Fisher, Roger McDowell)	.50	.40	.20
16	Sluggers (Jesse Barfield, Gary Carter, Fred Lynn)	.60	.45	.25

1986 7-11 Slurpee Coins Mideastern Region

1	Dwight Gooden	.75	.60	.30
2	Batting Champs (Wade Boggs, George Brett, Pete Rose)	2.00	1.50	.80
3	MVP's (Keith Hernandez, Don Mattingly, Cal Ripken)	2.00	1.50	.80
4	Slugging Champs (Harold Baines, Pedro Guerrero, Dave Parker)	.60	.45	.25
5	Home Run Champs (Dale Murphy, Jim Rice, Mike Schmidt)	2.00	1.50	.80
6	Cy Young Winners (Ron Guidry, Bret Saberhagen, Fernando Valenzuela)	.70	.50	.30
7	Bullpen Aces (Rich Gossage, Dan Quisenberry, Bruce Sutter)	.50	.40	.20
8	Strikeout Kings (Steve Carlton, Nolan Ryan, Tom Seaver)	3.00	2.25	1.25
9	MVP's (Willie Hernandez, Ryne Sandberg, Robin Yount)	2.00	1.50	.80
10	Ace Pitchers (Bert Blyleven, Jack Morris, Rick Sutcliffe)	.50	.40	.20
11	Bullpen Aces (Rollie Fingers, Bob James, Lee Smith)	.75	.60	.30
12	All-Star Catchers (Carlton Fisk, Lance Parrish, Tony Pena)	.75	.60	.30
13	1985 Rookies (Shawon Dunston, Ozzie Guillen, Ernest Riles)	.40	.30	.15
14	Star Outfielders (Brett Butler, Chet Lemon, Willie Wilson)	.40	.30	.15
15	Home Run Hitters (Tom Brunansky, Cecil Cooper, Darrell Evans)	.40	.30	.15
16	Big Hitters (Kirk Gibson, Paul Molitor, Greg Walker)	.80	.60	.30

1986 7-11 Slurpee Coins Midwestern Region

1	Dwight Gooden	.75	.60	.30
2	Batting Champs (Wade Boggs, George Brett, Pete Rose)	2.00	1.50	.80
3	MVP's (Keith Hernandez, Don Mattingly, Cal Ripken, Jr.)	2.00	1.50	.80
4	Slugging Champs (Harold Baines, Pedro Guerrero, Dave Parker)	.60	.45	.25
5	Home Run Champs (Dale Murphy, Jim Rice, Mike Schmidt)	2.00	1.50	.80
6	Cy Young Winners (Ron Guidry, Bret Saberhagen, Fernando Valenzuela)	.70	.50	.30
7	Bullpen Aces (Rich Gossage, Dan Quisenberry, Bruce Sutter)	.50	.40	.20
8	Strikeout Kings (Steve Carlton, Nolan Ryan, Tom Seaver)	3.00	2.25	1.25
9	1985 Rookies (Vince Coleman, Glenn Davis, Oddibe McDowell)	1.00	.70	.40
10	Gold Glovers (Buddy Bell, Ozzie Smith, Lou Whitaker)	.60	.45	.25
11	Ace Pitchers (Mike Scott, Mario Soto, John Tudor)	.40	.30	.15
12	Bullpen Aces (Jeff Lahti, Ted Power, Dave Smith)	.40	.30	.15
13	Big Hitters (Jack Clark, Jose Cruz, Bob Horner)	.40	.30	.15
14	Star Second Basemen (Bill Doran, Tommy Herr, Ron Oester)	.40	.30	.15
15	1985 Rookie Pitchers (Tom Browning, Joe Hesketh, Todd Worrell)	.40	.30	.15
16	Top Switch-Hitters (Willie McGee, Jerry Mumphrey, Pete Rose)	.75	.60	.30

1986 7-11 Slurpee Coins Western Region

1	Dwight Gooden	.75	.60	.30
2	Batting Champs (Wade Boggs, George Brett, Pete Rose)	2.00	1.50	.80
3	MVP's (Keith Hernandez, Don Mattingly, Cal Ripken, Jr.)	2.00	1.50	.80
4	Slugging Champs (Harold Baines, Pedro Guerrero, Dave Parker)	.60	.45	.25
5	Home Run Champs (Dale Murphy, Jim Rice, Mike Schmidt)	2.00	1.50	.80
6	Cy Young Winners (Ron Guidry, Bret Saberhagen, Fernando Valenzuela)	.70	.50	.30
7	Bullpen Aces (Rich Gossage, Dan Quisenberry, Bruce Sutter)	.50	.40	.20
8	Strikeout Kings (Steve Carlton, Nolan Ryan, Tom Seaver)	3.00	2.25	1.25
9	Home Run Champs (Reggie Jackson, Dave Kingman, Gorman Thomas)	1.00	.70	.40
10	Batting Champs (Rod Carew, Tony Gwynn, Carney Lansford)	1.00	.70	.40
11	Sluggers (Phil Bradley, Mike Marshall, Graig Nettles)	.50	.40	.20
12	Ace Pitchers (Andy Hawkins, Orel Hershiser, Mike Witt)	.50	.40	.20
13	1985 Rookies (Chris Brown, Ivan Calderon, Mariano Duncan)	.40	.30	.15
14	Big Hitters (Steve Garvey, Bill Madlock, Jim Presley)	.40	.30	.15
15	Bullpen Aces (Jay Howell, Donnie Moore, Ed Nunez)	.40	.30	.15
16	1985 Bullpen Rookies (Karl Best, Stewart Cliburn, Steve Ontiveros)	.40	.30	.15

Regional interest may affect the value of a card.

1987 7-11 Slurpee Coins Eastern Region

Continuing with a tradition started in 1983, 7-Eleven stores offered a free "Super Star Sports Coin" with the purchase of a Slurpee drink. Five different regional sets of Slurpee coins were issued for 1987, a total of 75 coins. Each coin measures 1-3/4" in diameter and features a multiple image effect which allows three different pictures to be seen, depending on how the coin is tilted. The coin reverses contain career records and personal player information.

	MT	NR MT	EX
Complete Set:	45.00	34.00	18.00
Common Player:	.40	.30	.15

1	Gary Carter	.60	.45	.25
2	Don Baylor	.50	.40	.20
3	Rickey Henderson	1.50	1.25	.60
4	Lenny Dykstra	.70	.50	.30
5	Wade Boggs	1.75	1.25	.70
6	Mike Pagliarulo	.40	.30	.15
7	Dwight Gooden	.60	.45	.25
8	Roger Clemens	.75	.60	.30
9	Dave Righetti	.60	.45	.25
10	Keith Hernandez	.50	.40	.20
11	Pat Dodson	.50	.40	.20
12	Don Mattingly	2.00	1.50	.80
13	Darryl Strawberry	.75	.60	.30
14	Jim Rice	.60	.45	.25
15	Dave Winfield	1.00	.70	.40

1987 7-11 Slurpee Coins Mideastern Region

1	Gary Carter	.60	.45	.25
2	Marty Barrett	.40	.30	.15
3	Jody Davis	.40	.30	.15
4	Don Aase	.40	.30	.15
5	Lenny Dykstra	.70	.50	.30
6	Wade Boggs	1.25	.90	.50
7	Keith Moreland	.40	.30	.15
8	Mike Boddicker	.40	.30	.15
9	Dwight Gooden	.75	.60	.30
10	Roger Clemens	1.25	.90	.50
11	Ryne Sandberg	3.00	2.25	1.25
12	Eddie Murray	.90	.70	.35
13	Keith Hernandez	.50	.40	.20
14	Jim Rice	.60	.45	.25
15	Lee Smith	.60	.45	.25
16	Cal Ripken, Jr.	3.00	2.25	1.25

1987 7-11 Slurpee Coins Great Lakes Region

1	Harold Baines	.60	.45	.25
2	Jody Davis	.40	.30	.15
3	John Cangelosi	.40	.30	.15
4	Shawon Dunston	.70	.50	.30
5	Dave Cochrane	.40	.30	.15
6	Leon Durham	.40	.30	.15
7	Carlton Fisk	.70	.50	.30
8	Dennis Eckersley	.75	.60	.30
9	Ozzie Guillen	.50	.40	.20
10	Gary Matthews	.40	.30	.15
11	Ron Karkovice	.50	.40	.20
12	Keith Moreland	.40	.30	.15
13	Bobby Thigpen	.40	.30	.15
14	Ryne Sandberg	3.00	2.25	1.25
15	Greg Walker	.40	.30	.15
16	Lee Smith	.60	.45	.25

1987 7-11 Slurpee Coins Western Region

1	Doug DeCinces	.50	.40	.20
2	Mariano Duncan	.50	.40	.20
3	Wally Joyner	.75	.60	.30
4	Pedro Guerrero	.40	.30	.15
5	Kirk McCaskill	.40	.30	.15
6	Orel Hershiser	.60	.45	.25
7	Gary Pettis	.40	.30	.15
8	Mike Marshall	.50	.40	.20

9	Dick Schofield	.40	.30	.15
10	Steve Sax	.50	.40	.20
11	Don Sutton	.80	.60	.30
12	Mike Scioscia	.40	.30	.15
13	Devon White	.70	.50	.30
14	Franklin Stubbs	.40	.30	.15
15	Mike Witt	.50	.40	.20
16	Fernando Valenzuela	.50	.40	.20

1987 7-11 Slurpee Coins Tigers

		MT	NR MT	EX
Complete Set (12):		6.00	4.50	2.50
Common Player:		.40	.30	.15
1	Darnell Coles	.40	.30	.15
2	Darrell Evans	.60	.45	.25
3	Kirk Gibson	.70	.50	.30
4	Willie Hernandez	.50	.40	.20
5	Larry Herndon	.40	.30	.15
6	Chet Lemon	.40	.30	.15
7	Dwight Lowry	.40	.30	.15
8	Jack Morris	.90	.70	.35
9	Dan Petry	.50	.40	.20
10	Frank Tanana	.40	.30	.15
11	Alan Trammell	.90	.70	.35
12	Lou Whitaker	.70	.50	.30

1992 7-11 Slurpee Superstar Action Coins

After a four-year lay-off, Slurpee baseball 3-D coins returned to 7-11 stores on a very limited basis in 1992. A 26-piece set of the plastic coins (one for each major league team) was produced by Score in the familiar 1-3/4" diameter format. The coins feature a maroon border on which is printed in white the player's name, team, position and uniform number. At center is a 1-1/4" circle with "flasher" portrait and action photos of the player. Backs have a black border with the player name in yellow at the top, a few career stats, 7-11 and Score logos and a coin number in a pale yellow center circle. At bottom in green is "Superstar Action Coin".

		MT	NR MT	EX
Complete Set (26):		30.00	22.00	12.00
Common Player:		.50	.40	.20
1	Dwight Gooden	.75	.60	.30
2	Don Mattingly	2.00	1.50	.80
3	Roger Clemens	.75	.60	.30
4	Ivan Calderon	.50	.40	.20
5	Roberto Alomar	1.50	1.25	.60
6	Sandy Alomar, Jr.	.50	.40	.20
7	Andy Van Slyke	.50	.40	.20
8	Lenny Dykstra	.75	.60	.30
9	Cal Ripken, Jr.	2.50	2.00	1.00
10	Dave Justice	1.00	.70	.40
11	Nolan Ryan	3.00	2.25	1.25
12	Craig Biggio	.50	.40	.20
13	Barry Larkin	.75	.60	.30
14	Ozzie Smith	1.00	.70	.40
15	Ryne Sandberg	2.50	2.00	1.00
16	Frank Thomas	3.00	2.25	1.25
17	Robin Yount	2.00	1.50	.80
18	Kirby Puckett	1.50	1.25	.60
19	Cecil Fielder	1.50	1.25	.60
20	Will Clark	1.50	1.25	.60
21	Jose Canseco	2.00	1.50	.80
22	Jim Abbott	.75	.60	.30
23	Tony Gwynn	1.00	.70	.40
24	Darryl Strawberry	.75	.60	.30
25	George Brett	2.00	1.50	.80
26	Ken Griffey, Jr.	3.00	2.25	1.25

1984 7-Up Cubs

The Chicago Cubs and 7-Up issued this 28-card set featuring full-color game-action photos on a 2-1/4" by 3-1/2" borderless front. The backs have the player's stats and personal information. This was the

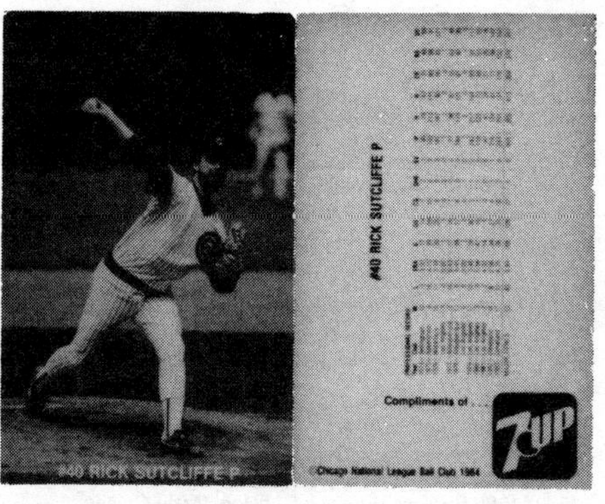

third consecutive year the Cubs issued this type of set as a giveaway at a "Baseball Card Day" promotional game.

		MT	NR MT	EX
Complete Set (28):		12.00	9.00	4.75
Common Player:		.20	.15	.08
1	Larry Bowa	.40	.30	.15
6	Keith Moreland	.20	.15	.08
7	Jody Davis	.20	.15	.08
10	Leon Durham	.20	.15	.08
11	Ron Cey	.40	.30	.15
15	Ron Hassey	.20	.15	.08
18	Richie Hebner	.20	.15	.08
19	Dave Owen	.20	.15	.08
20	Bob Dernier	.20	.15	.08
21	Jay Johnstone	.25	.20	.10
23	Ryne Sandberg	4.00	3.00	1.50
24	Scott Sanderson	.35	.25	.14
25	Gary Woods	.20	.15	.08
27	Thad Bosley	.20	.15	.08
28	Henry Cotto	.25	.20	.10
34	Steve Trout	.25	.20	.10
36	Gary Matthews	.30	.25	.12
39	George Frazier	.20	.15	.08
40	Rick Sutcliffe	.80	.60	.30
41	Warren Brusstar	.20	.15	.08
42	Rich Bordi	.20	.15	.08
43	Dennis Eckersley	1.25	.90	.50
44	Dick Ruthven	.20	.15	.08
46	Lee Smith	.75	.60	.30
47	Rick Reuschel	.30	.25	.12
49	Tim Stoddard	.20	.15	.08
----	Jim Frey	.20	.15	.08
----	Cubs Coaches (Ruben Amaro, Billy Connors, Johnny Oates, John Vukovich, Don Zimmer)	.20	.15	.08

1985 7-Up Cubs

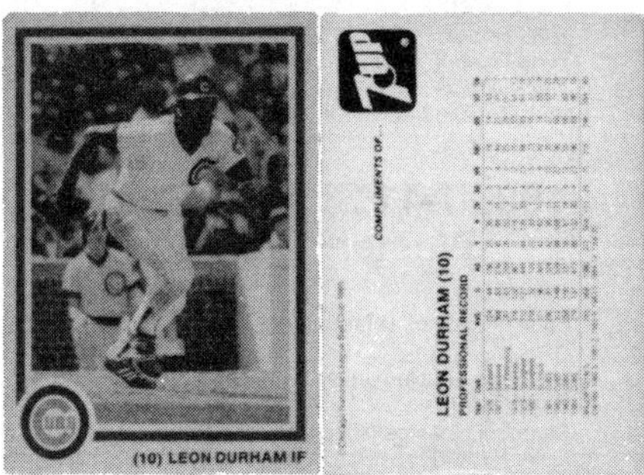

This was the second year a Chicago Cubs card set was released with 7-Up as the sponsor. The set has 28 unnumbered cards in the standard 2-1/2" by 3-1/2" size. They were distributed to fans attending the Cubs game on August 14 at Wrigley Field. They feature full-color game-action photos of the players. Card backs contain the player's professional stats.

		MT	NR MT	EX
Complete Set (28):		8.00	6.00	3.25
Common Player:		.10	.08	.04
1	Larry Bowa	.25	.20	.10
6	Keith Moreland	.10	.08	.04
7	Jody Davis	.10	.08	.04
10	Leon Durham	.10	.08	.04
11	Ron Cey	.30	.25	.12
15	Davey Lopes	.25	.20	.10
16	Steve Lake	.10	.08	.04
18	Richie Hebner	.10	.08	.04
20	Bob Dernier	.10	.08	.04
21	Scott Sanderson	.25	.20	.10
22	Billy Hatcher	.30	.25	.12
23	Ryne Sandberg	3.00	2.25	1.25
24	Brian Dayett	.10	.08	.04
25	Gary Woods	.10	.08	.04
27	Thad Bosley	.10	.08	.04
28	Chris Speier	.10	.08	.04
31	Ray Fontenot	.10	.08	.04
34	Steve Trout	.10	.08	.04
36	Gary Matthews	.15	.11	.06
39	George Frazier	.10	.08	.04
40	Rick Sutcliffe	.50	.40	.20
41	Warren Brusstar	.10	.08	.04
42	Lary Sorensen	.10	.08	.04
43	Dennis Eckersley	1.00	.70	.40
44	Dick Ruthven	.10	.08	.04
46	Lee Smith	.45	.35	.20
----	Jim Frey	.10	.08	.04
----	Coaching Staff (Ruben Amaro, Billy Connors, Johnny Oates, John Vukovich, Don Zimmer)	.10	.08	.04

1992 Silver Star Holograms

This collectors' issue consists of seven player hologram cards and accompanying "Authentickets" plus a hologram header card depicting the Gold Glove Award. The Gold Glove card has a black back on which is printed a serial number in gold foil. The player holograms are standard 2-1/2" x 3-1/2". The player's name is featured in the upper-left corner, with "Silver Star Holograms" in the upper-right. Some holograms have a card title (Non-Stop shortstop, Pride of Texas, etc.) in the lower-right corner. Backs are printed in team colors and feature a player portrait photo and some 1991 stats and season highlights. The player's position and uniform number are in the upper corners. The 5-3/8" x 2-1/16" Authenticket sold with each hologram contains a serial number, player photo, 1991 season highlights and a black panel at left with "Silver Star" in silver prismatic foil. This piece is blank-backed. The checklist is presented here by uniform number. Values given are for player hologram/Authenticket combinations. Holograms alone are worth about half the values shown; unaccompanied Authentickets have little collector value.

		MT	NR MT	EX
Complete Set (8):		30.00	22.00	12.00
Common Player:		2.00	1.50	.80
8	Cal Ripken, Jr.	6.00	4.50	2.50
21	Roger Clemens	5.00	3.75	2.00
22	Will Clark	5.00	3.75	2.00
23	Dave Justice	5.00	3.75	2.00
24	Rickey Henderson	2.00	1.50	.80
34	Nolan Ryan	8.00	6.00	3.25
44	Darryl Strawberry	2.50	2.00	1.00
----	Rawlings Gold Glove Award	3.00	2.25	1.25

1984 Smokey Bear Angels

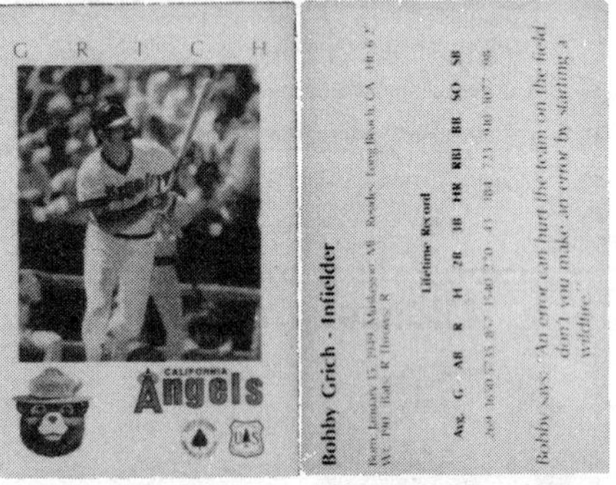

This 32-card set was distributed at a June home game to fans 14 and under. Cards measure 2-1/2" by 3-1/2". The full-color card fronts list the player name along with the team logo and Forestry service logos commemorating the 40th birthday of Smokey the the Bear. The black and white card backs list tips for preventing forest fires.

		MT	NR MT	EX
Complete Set (32):		8.00	6.00	3.25
Common Player:		.20	.15	.08
(1)	Don Aase	.20	.15	.08
(2)	Juan Beniquez	.20	.15	.08
(3)	Bob Boone	.30	.25	.12

(4)	Rick Burleson	.30	.25	.12
(5)	Rod Carew	1.00	.70	.40
(6)	John Curtis	.20	.15	.08
(7)	Doug DeCinces	.30	.25	.12
(8)	Brian Downing	.30	.25	.12
(9)	Ken Forsch	.20	.15	.08
(10)	Bobby Grich	.30	.25	.12
(11)	Reggie Jackson	1.25	.90	.50
(12)	Ron Jackson	.20	.15	.08
(13)	Tommy John	.60	.45	.25
(14)	Curt Kaufman	.20	.15	.08
(15)	Bruce Kison	.20	.15	.08
(16)	Frank LaCorte	.20	.15	.08
(17)	Fred Lynn	.60	.45	.25
(18)	John McNamara	.20	.15	.08
(19)	Jerry Narron	.20	.15	.08
(20)	Gary Pettis	.40	.30	.15
(21)	Robert Picciolo	.20	.15	.08
(22)	Ron Romanick	.20	.15	.08
(23)	Luis Sanchez	.20	.15	.08
(24)	Dick Schofield	.30	.25	.12
(25)	Daryl Sconiers	.20	.15	.08
(26)	Jim Slaton	.20	.15	.08
(27)	Ellis Valentine	.20	.15	.08
(28)	Robert Wilfong	.20	.15	.08
(29)	Mike Witt	.50	.40	.20
(30)	Geoff Zahn	.20	.15	.08
----	Forestry Dept. Logo Card	.10	.08	.04
----	Smokey Logo Card	.10	.08	.04

1984 Smokey Bear Jackson Mets In Majors

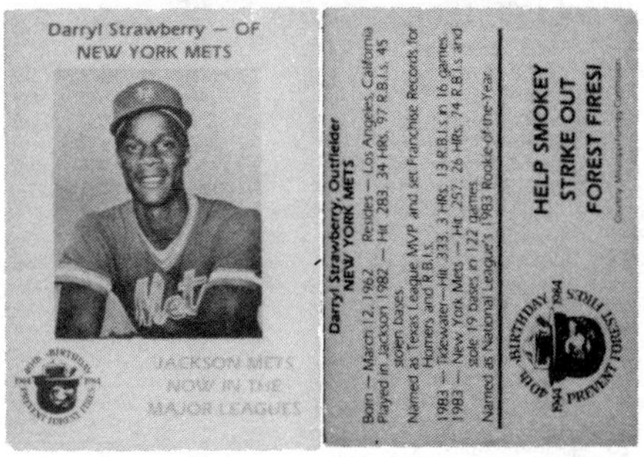

This set, issued in conjunction with the Mississippi Forestry Commission, features big leaguers who played for the Mets' Double-A farm club. The fifteen 3" by 4" cards have a black and white portrait photo on the front with the name, position and major league team shown in blue. A Smokey the Bear logo is also included. Card backs feature player information and career highlights.

		MT	NR MT	EX
Complete Set (15):		30.00	22.00	12.00
Common Player:		1.00	.70	.40
(1)	Neil Allen	1.00	.70	.40
(2)	Wally Backman	2.00	1.50	.80
(3)	Hubie Brooks	2.00	1.50	.80
(4)	Jody Davis	2.00	1.50	.80
(5)	Brian Giles	1.00	.70	.40
(6)	Dave Johnson	2.00	1.50	.80
(7)	Tim Leary	2.00	1.50	.80
(8)	Lee Mazzilli	1.00	.70	.40
(9)	Jesse Orosco	1.00	.70	.40
(10)	Jeff Reardon	3.00	2.25	1.25
(11)	Doug Sisk	1.00	.70	.40
(12)	Darryl Strawberry	10.00	7.50	4.00
(13)	Mookie Wilson	2.00	1.50	.80
(14)	Marvel Wynne (Marvell)	1.00	.70	.40
(15)	Ned Yost	1.00	.70	.40

1984 Smokey Bear Dodgers

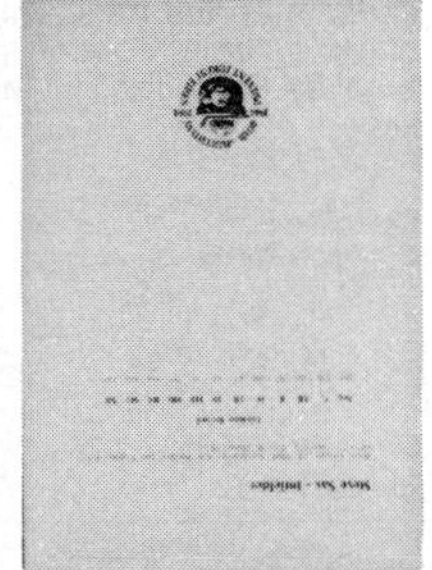

Unlike the California Angels and San Diego Padres sets issued in conjunction with the Forestry Service in 1984, the Los Angeles Dodgers set contains only three players, pictured on much larger 5" by 7" cards. Ken Landreaux, Tom Niedenfuer and Steve Sax (plus a Smokey the Bear card) are pictured on the cards. Each player is pictured in a forest scene on the full-color fronts. Backs of the unnumbered cards have brief biographical information and lifetime statistics. The cards were distributed at a Dodgers home game.

		MT	NR MT	EX
Complete Set (4):		8.00	6.00	3.25
Common Player:		2.50	2.00	1.00
(1)	Ken Landreaux	2.50	2.00	1.00
(2)	Tom Niedenfuer	2.50	2.00	1.00
(3)	Steve Sax	3.50	2.75	1.50
(4)	Smokey Bear	.50	.40	.20

1984 Smokey Bear Padres

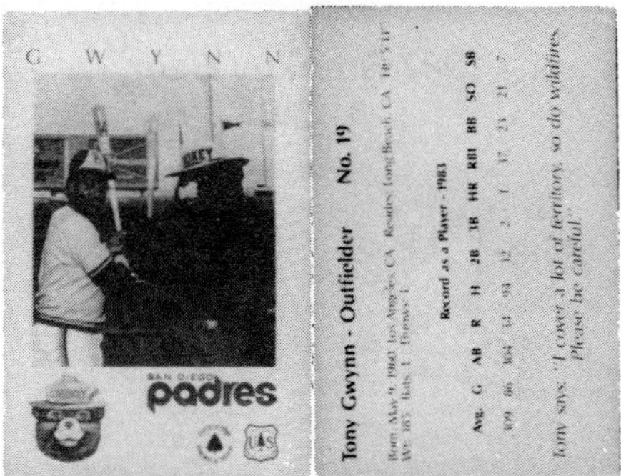

This set of 28 full-color cards is very similar in format to the Angels set of the same year. San Diego Padres players are posed in photos with Smokey the Bear. Forestry Department and team logos are also pictured on the card fronts. The Padres cards feature players, coaches, broadcasters and the Famous Chicken, all posing with Smokey. The backs of the cards which were distributed at a Padres home game, offer brief player information and a fire prevention tip.

		MT	NR MT	EX
Complete Set (28):		10.00	7.50	4.00
Common Player:		.25	.20	.10
1	Garry Templeton	.40	.30	.15
2	Alan Wiggins	.25	.20	.10
4	Luis Salazar	.25	.20	.10
6	Steve Garvey	1.25	.90	.50
7	Kurt Bevacqua	.25	.20	.10
10	Doug Gwosdz	.25	.20	.10
11	Tim Flannery	.25	.20	.10
16	Terry Kennedy	.30	.25	.12
18	Kevin McReynolds	1.50	1.25	.60
19	Tony Gwynn	2.00	1.50	.80
20	Bobby Brown	.25	.20	.10
30	Eric Show	.40	.30	.15
31	Ed Whitson	.25	.20	.10
35	Luis DeLeon	.25	.20	.10
38	Mark Thurmond	.25	.20	.10
42	Sid Monge	.25	.20	.10
43	Dave Dravecky	.40	.30	.15
48	Tim Lollar	.25	.20	.10
----	Smokey Logo Card: Dave Campbell (broadcaster), Jerry Coleman (broadcaster), Harry Dunlop (coach), Harold (Doug) Harvey (umpire), Jack Krol (coach), Jack McKeon (vice-president), Norm Sherry (coach), Ozzie Virgil (coach), Dick Williams (manager)	.25	.20	.10

1985 Smokey Bear Angels

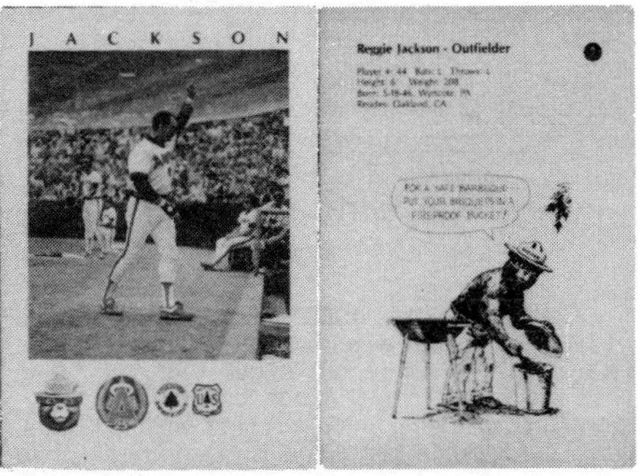

The California Forestry Service and the California Angels gave this full-color set of oversized baseball cards to fans attending the July 14 game at Anaheim Stadium. The 24 cards feature player photos on the fronts with their last name at the top of the cards above the picture. On the card bottoms are the logos for Smokey Bear, the Angels, the State Forestry Service and the U.S. Forestry Service. The cards measure 4-1/4" by 6". On the card backs, printed in black and white, are personal data, limited playing stats and a wildfire safety tip from Smokey the Bear.

		MT	NR MT	EX
Complete Set (24):		7.00	5.25	2.75
Common Player:		.20	.15	.08
1	Mike Witt	.50	.40	.20
2	Reggie Jackson	1.25	.90	.50
3	Bob Boone	.30	.25	.12
4	Mike Brown	.20	.15	.08
5	Rod Carew	1.00	.70	.40
6	Doug DeCinces	.30	.25	.12
7	Brian Downing	.30	.25	.12
8	Ken Forsch	.20	.15	.08
9	Gary Pettis	.20	.15	.08
10	Jerry Narron	.20	.15	.08
11	Ron Romanick	.20	.15	.08
12	Bobby Grich	.30	.25	.12
13	Dick Schofield	.30	.25	.12
14	Juan Beniquez	.20	.15	.08
15	Geoff Zahn	.20	.15	.08
16	Luis Sanchez	.20	.15	.08
17	Jim Slaton	.20	.15	.08
18	Doug Corbett	.20	.15	.08
19	Ruppert Jones	.20	.15	.08
20	Rob Wilfong	.20	.15	.08
21	Donnie Moore	.20	.15	.08
22	Pat Clements	.20	.15	.08
23	Tommy John	.60	.45	.25
24	Gene Mauch	.30	.25	.12

1986 Smokey Bear Angels

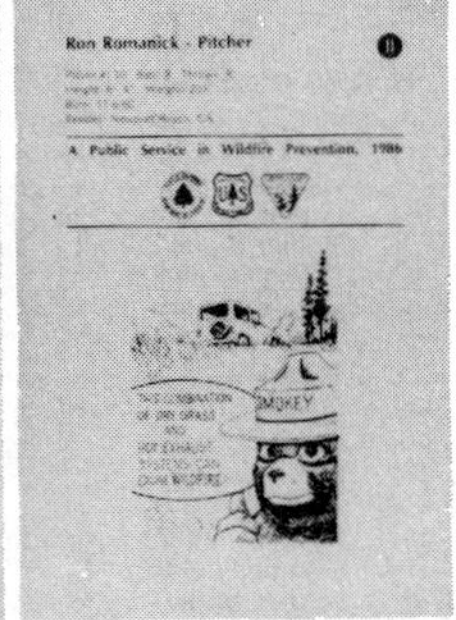

The California Angels, in conjuction with the Forestry Service, issued this 24-card set of Wildfire Prevention baseball cards. The cards measure 4-1/4" by 6" and offer a full-color front with the player's picture placed in an oval frame. The card backs have player stats with a drawing and slogan for fire prevention. The sets were given out on August 9th at the Angels game in Anaheim Stadium.

		MT	NR MT	EX
Complete Set (24):		6.00	4.50	2.50
Common Player:		.20	.15	.08
1	Mike Witt	.30	.25	.12
2	Reggie Jackson	1.25	.90	.50
3	Bob Boone	.30	.25	.12
4	Don Sutton	.60	.45	.25
5	Kirk McCaskill	.50	.40	.20
6	Doug DeCinces	.30	.25	.12
7	Brian Downing	.30	.25	.12
8	Doug Corbett	.20	.15	.08
9	Gary Pettis	.20	.15	.08
10	Jerry Narron	.20	.15	.08
11	Ron Romanick	.20	.15	.08
12	Bobby Grich	.30	.25	.12
13	Dick Schofield	.30	.25	.12
14	George Hendrick	.30	.25	.12
15	Rick Burleson	.30	.25	.12
16	John Candelaria	.30	.25	.12
17	Jim Slaton	.20	.15	.08
18	Darrell Miller	.30	.25	.12
19	Ruppert Jones	.20	.15	.08
20	Rob Wilfong	.20	.15	.08
21	Donnie Moore	.20	.15	.08
22	Wally Joyner	.75	.60	.30
23	Terry Forster	.30	.25	.12
24	Gene Mauch	.30	.25	.12

1987 Smokey Bear

The U.S. Forestry Service and Major League Baseball united in an effort to promote National Smokey the Bear Day. Two perforated sheets of baseball cards, one each for the American and National Leagues, were produced by the Forestry Service. The sheet of American Leaguers measures 18" by 24" and contains 16 full-color cards. The National League sheet measures 20" by 18" and contains 15 cards. Each individual card is 4" by 6" and contains a fire prevention tip on the back. An average number of 25,000 sets was sent to all teams.

		MT	NR MT	EX
Complete Set:		8.00	6.00	3.25
Common Player:		.20	.15	.08
1A	Jose Canseco	1.50	1.25	.60
1N	Steve Sax	.40	.30	.15
2A	Dennis "Oil Can" Boyd	.20	.15	.08
2Na	Dale Murphy (shirttail out)	5.00	3.75	2.00
2Nb	Dale Murphy (shirttail in)	.80	.60	.30
3A	John Candelaria	.20	.15	.08
3Na	Jody Davis (standing)	3.50	2.75	1.50
3Nb	Jody Davis (kneeling)	.25	.20	.10
4A	Harold Baines	.30	.25	.12
4N	Bill Gullickson	.20	.15	.08
5A	Joe Carter	.50	.40	.20
5N	Mike Scott	.30	.25	.12
6A	Jack Morris	.40	.30	.15
6N	Roger McDowell	.25	.20	.10
7A	Buddy Biancalana	.20	.15	.08
7N	Steve Bedrosian	.30	.25	.12
8A	Kirby Puckett	.90	.70	.35
8N	Johnny Ray	.20	.15	.08
9A	Mike Pagliarulo	.25	.20	.10
9N	Ozzie Smith	.50	.40	.20
10A	Larry Sheets	.20	.15	.08
10N	Steve Garvey	.60	.45	.25
11A	Mike Moore	.20	.15	.08
11N	Smokey Bear Logo Card	.05	.04	.02
12A	Charlie Hough	.20	.15	.08
12N	Mike Krukow	.20	.15	.08
13A	Smokey Bear Logo Card	.05	.04	.02
13N	Smokey Bear	.05	.04	.02
14A	Tom Henke	.20	.15	.08
14N	Mike Fitzgerald	.20	.15	.08
15A	Jim Gantner	.20	.15	.08
15N	National League Logo Card	.05	.04	.02
16A	American League Logo Card	.05	.04	.02

1987 Smokey Bear A's

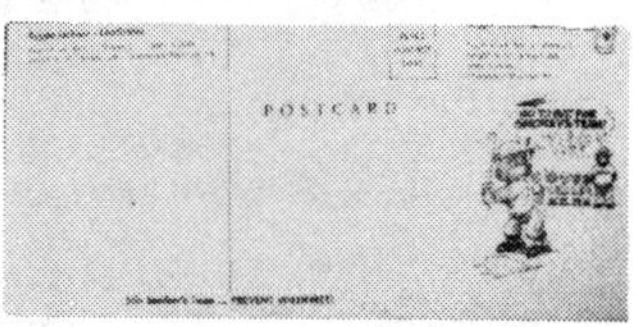

The 1987 Smokey Bear A's set is not comparable to any other Smokey Bear issue produced in 1987 or before. The 12 cards in the set are bound together in a book titled "Smokey Bear's Fire Prevention Color-Grams." The Color-Gram cards feature two cards in one. A near-standard size (2-1/2" by 3-3/4") black and white card is attached to a large perforated (3-3/4" by 6") card, also black and white. The large card, which has a postcard back, features a caricature photo of the player and is intended to be colored and then mailed. The card backs contain personal and statistical information and carry a Smokey the Bear cartoon message. The books were distributed at an Oakland A's game during the 1987 season.

		MT	NR MT	EX
Complete Book:		6.00	4.50	2.50
Complete Singles Set:		3.00	2.25	1.25
Common Single Player:		.15	.11	.06
(1)	Joaquin Andujar	.15	.11	.06
(2)	Jose Canseco	1.50	1.25	.60
(3)	Mike Davis	.15	.11	.06
(4)	Alfredo Griffin	.15	.11	.06
(5)	Moose Haas	.15	.11	.06
(6)	Jay Howell	.25	.20	.10
(7)	Reggie Jackson	1.00	.70	.40
(8)	Carney Lansford	.20	.15	.08
(9)	Dwayne Murphy	.15	.11	.06
(10)	Tony Phillips	.15	.11	.06
(11)	Dave Stewart	.60	.45	.25
(12)	Curt Young	.30	.25	.12

1987 Smokey Bear Angels

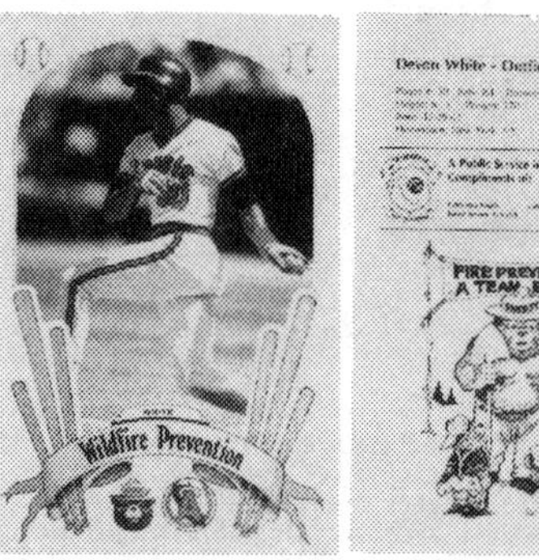

A 24-card set featuring the California Angels and produced by the U.S. Forestry Service was distributed to 25,000 fans in attendance at Anaheim Stadium on August 1st. The full-color cards measure 4" x 6". The card fronts carry a unique design with baseballs and bats framing the player photo. Only the player's last name is given on the card fronts. The backs contain the player's name, position and personal statistics along with a Smokey Bear cartoon and a fire prevention tip.

		MT	NR MT	EX
Complete Set:		8.00	6.00	3.25
Common Player:		.20	.15	.08
1	John Candelaria	.30	.25	.12
2	Don Sutton	.60	.45	.25
3	Mike Witt	.30	.25	.12
4	Gary Lucas	.20	.15	.08
5	Kirk McCaskill	.30	.25	.12
6	Chuck Finley	.30	.25	.12
7	Willie Fraser	.30	.25	.12
8	Donnie Moore	.20	.15	.08
9	Urbano Lugo	.20	.15	.08
10	Butch Wynegar	.20	.15	.08
11	Darrell Miller	.20	.15	.08
12	Wally Joyner	.50	.40	.20
13	Mark McLemore	.30	.25	.12
14	Mark Ryal	.20	.15	.08
15	Dick Schofield	.25	.20	.10
16	Jack Howell	.30	.25	.12
17	Doug DeCinces	.30	.25	.12
18	Gus Polidor	.20	.15	.08
19	Brian Downing	.30	.25	.12
20	Gary Pettis	.20	.15	.08
21	Ruppert Jones	.20	.15	.08
22	George Hendrick	.25	.20	.10
23	Devon White	1.50	1.25	.60
----	Smokey Bear Logo Card/Checklist	.10	.08	.04

The values quoted are intended to reflect the market price.

1987 Smokey Bear Braves

Cards from the 1987 Smokey Bear Atlanta Braves set were given out at several different Braves games, with about 25,000 sets in all being distributed. The 4" by 6" cards feature Atlanta players in an oval frame, bordered in red, white and blue. Only the player's last name is listed on the card fronts. Card backs contain the player's name, position and personal data plus a Smokey Bear cartoon with a fire safety message.

		MT	NR MT	EX
Complete Set:		7.00	5.25	2.75
Common Player:		.20	.15	.08
1	Zane Smith	.40	.30	.15
2	Charlie Puleo	.20	.15	.08
3	Randy O'Neal	.20	.15	.08
4	David Palmer	.20	.15	.08
5	Rick Mahler	.20	.15	.08
6	Ed Olwine	.20	.15	.08
7	Jeff Dedmon	.20	.15	.08
8	Paul Assenmacher	.30	.25	.12
9	Gene Garber	.20	.15	.08
10	Jim Acker	.20	.15	.08
11	Bruce Benedict	.20	.15	.08
12	Ozzie Virgil	.20	.15	.08
13	Ted Simmons	.40	.30	.15
14	Dale Murphy	1.75	1.25	.70
15	Graig Nettles	.40	.30	.15
16	Ken Oberkfell	.20	.15	.08
17	Gerald Perry	.60	.45	.25
18	Rafael Ramirez	.20	.15	.08
19	Ken Griffey	.30	.25	.12
20	Andres Thomas	.20	.15	.08
21	Glenn Hubbard	.20	.15	.08
22	Damaso Garcia	.20	.15	.08
23	Gary Roenicke	.20	.15	.08
24	Dion James	.20	.15	.08
25	Albert Hall	.20	.15	.08
26	Chuck Tanner	.20	.15	.08
----	Smokey Bear Logo Card/Checklist	.10	.08	.04

1987 Smokey Bear Cardinals

Approximately 25,000 fans in attendance at Busch Stadium on August 24th received a 25-card set featuring the St. Louis Cardinals. Produced by the U.S. Forestry Service, the cards measure 4" by 6". The card fronts feature a full-color photo set inside an oval frame. Only the player's last name appears on the front. The card reverse carries the player's name, position and personal data plus a Smokey Bear cartoon with a fire prevention message.

		MT	NR MT	EX
Complete Set:		.20	5.25	2.75
Common Player:		.20	.15	.08
1	Ray Soff	.20	.15	.08
2	Todd Worrell	.30	.25	.12
3	John Tudor	.25	.20	.10
4	Pat Perry	.20	.15	.08
5	Rick Horton	.20	.15	.08
6	Dan Cox	.35	.25	.14
7	Bob Forsch	.30	.25	.12
8	Greg Mathews	.25	.20	.10
9	Bill Dawley	.20	.15	.08
10	Steve Lake	.20	.15	.08
11	Tony Pena	.30	.25	.12
12	Tom Pagnozzi	.30	.25	.12
13	Jack Clark	.50	.40	.20
14	Jim Lindeman	.35	.25	.14

15	Mike Laga	.20	.15	.08
16	Terry Pendleton	.75	.60	.30
17	Ozzie Smith	.90	.70	.35
18	Jose Oquendo	.20	.15	.08
19	Tom Lawless	.20	.15	.08
20	Tom Herr	.20	.15	.08
21	Curt Ford	.20	.15	.08
22	Willie McGee	.60	.45	.25
23	Tito Landrum	.20	.15	.08
24	Vince Coleman	.60	.45	.25
25	Whitey Herzog	.30	.25	.12

1987 Smokey Bear Dodgers

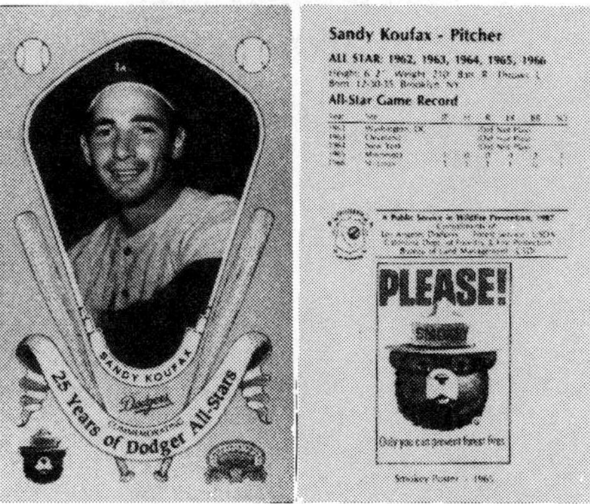

The 40-card Smokey Bear Dodgers set features "25 Years of Dodger All-Stars." The cards, which measure 2-1/2" by 3-3/4", were given out to fans 14 years of age and younger at the September 18th game at Dodgers Stadium. The card fronts contain full-color photos set in the shape of Dodger Stadium and have attractive silver borders. The backs carry the player's All-Star Game record plus a fire prevention message. Many of the photos used in the set were from team-issued picture packs sold by the Dodgers in the past.

		MT	NR MT	EX
Complete Set:		10.00	7.50	4.00
Common Player:		.20	.15	.08
(1)	Walt Alston	.40	.30	.15
(2)	Dusty Baker	.25	.20	.10
(3)	Jim Brewer	.20	.15	.08
(4)	Ron Cey	.30	.25	.12
(5)	Tommy Davis	.25	.20	.10
(6)	Willie Davis	.25	.20	.10
(7)	Don Drysdale	.80	.60	.30
(8)	Steve Garvey	.80	.60	.30
(9)	Bill Grabarkewitz	.20	.15	.08
(10)	Pedro Guerrero	.30	.25	.12
(11)	Tom Haller	.20	.15	.08
(12)	Orel Hershiser	.60	.45	.25
(13)	Burt Hooton	.20	.15	.08
(14)	Steve Howe	.25	.20	.10
(15)	Tommy John	.50	.40	.20
(16)	Sandy Koufax	1.25	.90	.50
(17)	Tom Lasorda	.30	.25	.12
(18)	Jim Lefebvre	.20	.15	.08
(19)	Davey Lopes	.25	.20	.10
(20)	Mike Marshall (outfielder)	.30	.25	.12
(21)	Mike Marshall (pitcher)	.25	.20	.10
(22)	Andy Messersmith	.20	.15	.08
(23)	Rick Monday	.25	.20	.10
(24)	Manny Mota	.25	.20	.10
(25)	Claude Osteen	.20	.15	.08
(26)	Johnny Podres	.30	.25	.12
(27)	Phil Regan	.20	.15	.08
(28)	Jerry Reuss	.25	.20	.10
(29)	Rick Rhoden	.25	.20	.10
(30)	John Roseboro	.25	.20	.10
(31)	Bill Russell	.25	.20	.10
(32)	Steve Sax	.30	.25	.12
(33)	Bill Singer	.20	.15	.08
(34)	Reggie Smith	.25	.20	.10
(35)	Don Sutton	.60	.45	.25
(36)	Fernando Valenzuela	.50	.40	.20
(37)	Bob Welch	.30	.25	.12
(38)	Maury Wills	.40	.30	.15
(39)	Jim Wynn	.20	.15	.08
(40)	Logo Card/Checklist	.10	.08	.04

1987 Smokey Bear Rangers

The 1987 Smokey Bear Rangers set is made up of 32 full-color cards. Co-sponsored by the Texas Rangers, U.S. Forest Service and Texas Forest Service, the set was given out to fans at special promotions at Arlington Stadium. The cards measure 4-1/4" by 6" and feature full-color photos on the fronts. The backs contain brief player personal information, along with the card number and a Smokey the Bear

message. Cards of Mike Mason and Tom Paciorek were withdrawn from the sets given out by the Rangers and are quite scarce.

		MT	NR MT	EX
Complete Set:		60.00	45.00	24.00
Common Player:		.30	.25	.12
1	Charlie Hough	.60	.45	.25
2	Greg Harris	.30	.25	.12
3	Jose Guzman	.40	.30	.15
4	Mike Mason	25.00	18.50	10.00
5	Dale Mohorcic	.40	.30	.15
6	Bobby Witt	.60	.45	.25
7	Mitch Williams	.50	.40	.20
8	Geno Petralli	.30	.25	.12
9	Don Slaught	.40	.30	.15
10	Darrell Porter	.30	.25	.12
11	Steve Beuchele	.40	.30	.15
12	Pete O'Brien	.40	.30	.15
13	Scott Fletcher	.40	.30	.15
14	Tom Paciorek	25.00	18.50	10.00
15	Pete Incaviglia	.80	.60	.30
16	Oddibe McDowell	.60	.45	.25
17	Ruben Sierra	1.50	1.25	.60
18	Larry Parrish	.40	.30	.15
19	Bobby Valentine	.40	.30	.15
20	Tom House	.30	.25	.12
21	Tom Robson	.30	.25	.12
22	Edwin Correa	.30	.25	.12
23	Mike Stanley	.60	.45	.25
24	Joe Ferguson	.30	.25	.12
25	Art Howe	.30	.25	.12
26	Bob Brower	.40	.30	.15
27	Mike Loynd	.30	.25	.12
28	Curtis Wilkerson	.30	.25	.12
29	Tim Foli	.30	.25	.12
30	Dave Oliver	.30	.25	.12
31	Jerry Browne	.50	.40	.20
32	Jeff Russell	.30	.25	.12

1988 Smokey Bear Angels

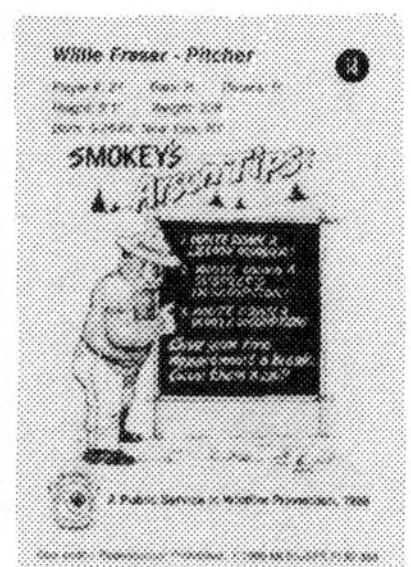

This set includes 25 borderless full-color cards (2-1/2" by 3-1/2") that are highlighted by a thin white inset outline on the card fronts. The player name, team logo and a Smokey Bear picture logo appear in the lower right corner. The backs are black and white and include personal information and a large cartoon-style fire prevention logo. The set also includes a team logo checklist card. Part of the U.S. Forest Service fire prevention campaign, the cards were distributed in three separate in-stadium giveaways during August and September, 1988 games.

		MT	NR MT	EX
Complete Set:		9.00	6.75	3.50
Common Player:		.30	.25	.12
1	Cookie Rojas	.30	.25	.12
2	Johnny Ray	.30	.25	.12
3	Jack Howell	.40	.30	.15
4	Mike Witt	.40	.30	.15
5	Tony Armas	.40	.30	.15
6	Gus Polidor	.30	.25	.12
7	DeWayne Buice	.40	.30	.15
8	Dan Petry	.40	.30	.15
9	Bob Boone	.50	.40	.20
10	Chili Davis	.60	.45	.25
11	Greg Minton	.30	.25	.12
12	Kirk McCaskill	.40	.30	.15
13	Devon White	.80	.60	.30
14	Willie Fraser	.30	.25	.12
15	Chuck Finley	.30	.25	.12
16	Dick Schofield	.30	.25	.12
17	Wally Joyner	.60	.45	.25
18	Brian Downing	.40	.30	.15
19	Stewart Cliburn	.30	.25	.12
20	Donnie Moore	.30	.25	.12
21	Bryan Harvey	.50	.40	.20
22	Mark McLemore	.40	.30	.15
23	Butch Wynegar	.30	.25	.12
24	George Hendrick	.40	.30	.15
----	Team Logo/Checklist	.30	.25	.12

1988 Smokey Bear Cardinals

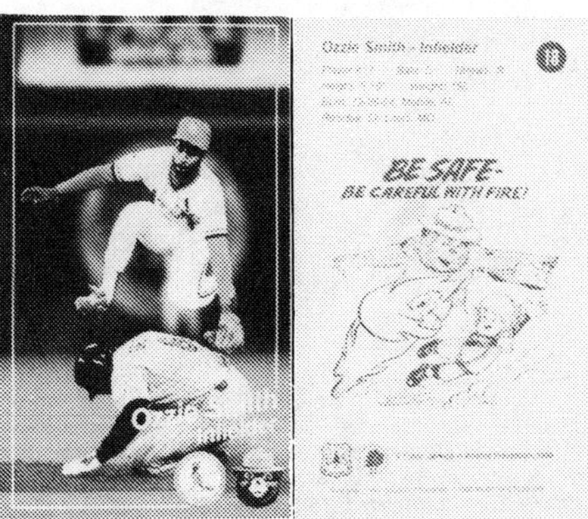

This set of 25 oversized (3" by 5") cards features full-color action photos that fill the entire card fronts. A thin white line frames the player photo. The player name, team logo and Smokey Bear picture logo are printed in the lower right corner. The black and white cards backs contain player information and a Smokey Bear fire prevention cartoon. The card sets were distributed to young St. Louis fans as part of a Forest Service fire prevention campaign. The National Association of State Foresters co-sponsored this set.

		MT	NR MT	EX
Complete Set:		8.00	6.00	3.25
Common Player:		.20	.15	.08
1	Whitey Herzog	.30	.25	.12
2	Danny Cox	.30	.25	.12
3	Ken Dayley	.20	.15	.08
4	Jose DeLeon	.30	.25	.12
5	Bob Forsch	.20	.15	.08
6	Joe Magrane	.40	.30	.15
7	Greg Mathews	.20	.15	.08
8	Scott Terry	.20	.15	.08
9	John Tudor	.20	.15	.08
10	Todd Worrell	.50	.40	.20
11	Steve Lake	.20	.15	.08
12	Tom Pagnozzi	.20	.15	.08
13	Tony Pena	.30	.25	.12
14	Bob Horner	.35	.25	.14
15	Tom Lawless	.20	.15	.08
16	Jose Oquendo	.20	.15	.08
17	Terry Pendleton	.60	.45	.25
18	Ozzie Smith	.80	.60	.30
19	Vince Coleman	.60	.45	.25
20	Curt Ford	.20	.15	.08
21	Willie McGee	.60	.45	.25
22	Larry McWilliams	.20	.15	.08
23	Steve Peters	.30	.25	.12
24	Luis Alicea	.30	.25	.12
25	Tom Brunansky	.30	.25	.12

Grading Guide

Mint (MT): A perfect card. Well-centered with all corners sharp and square. No creases, stains, edge nicks, surface marks, yellowing or fading.

Near Mint (NM): A nearly perfect card. At first glance, a NM card appears to be perfect. May be slightly off-center. No surface marks, creases or loss of gloss.

Excellent (EX): Corners are still fairly sharp with only moderate wear. Borders may be off-center. No creases or stains on fronts or backs, but may show slight loss of surface luster.

Very Good (VG): Shows obvious handling. May have rounded corners, minor creases, major gum or wax stains. No major creases, tape marks, writing, etc.

Good (G): A well-worn card, but exhibits no intentional damage. May have major or multiple creases. Corners may be rounded well beyond card border.

1988 Smokey Bear Cubs

		MT	NR MT	EX
Complete Set:		7.00	5.25	2.75
Common Card:		1.00	.70	.40
1	Vance Law (with Smokey)	2.00	1.50	.80
2	Vance Law (fielding)	2.00	1.50	.80
3	Vance Law (batting)	2.00	1.50	.80
4	Smokey Bear	1.00	.70	.40

1988 Smokey Bear Dodgers

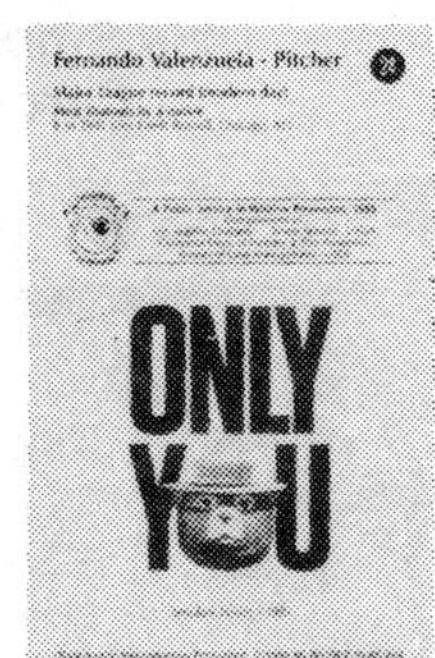

Record-breaking Dodgers from the past three decades are featured on this 32-card perforated sheet. Individual cards measure 2-1/2" by 4" and are printed on a light blue background in a design similar to the 1987 Smokey Bear Dodgers All-Star set. The black and white card backs contain the player name, a brief summary of the player's record-breaking performance and a reproduction of one of a number of Smokey Bear fire prevention posters printed during the 1950s through the 1980s. The sheets were distributed to fans in Dodger Stadium. Sponsors the Piedmont brand of the Liggert & Meyers Tobacco Co., the stamps include the Forest Service, California Dept. of Forestry and the Bureau of Land Management.

		MT	NR MT	EX
Complete Set:		10.00	7.50	4.00
Common Player:		.20	.15	.08
1	Walter Alston	.40	.30	.15
2	John Roseboro	.25	.20	.10
3	Frank Howard	.40	.30	.15
4	Sandy Koufax	1.25	.90	.50
5	Manny Mota	.25	.20	.10
6	Record Pitchers (Sandy Koufax, Jerry Reuss, Bill Singer)	.50	.40	.20
7	Maury Wills	.40	.30	.15
8	Tommy Davis	.25	.20	.10
9	Phil Regan	.20	.15	.08
10	Wes Parker	.20	.15	.08
11	Don Drysdale	.80	.60	.30
12	Willie Davis	.25	.20	.10
13	Bill Russell	.25	.20	.10
14	Jim Brewer	.20	.15	.08
15	Record Fielders (Ron Cey, Steve Garvey, Davey Lopes, Bill Russell)	.30	.25	.12
16	Mike Marshall (pitcher)	.25	.20	.10
17	Steve Garvey	.80	.60	.30
18	Davey Lopes	.25	.20	.10
19	Burt Hooton	.20	.15	.08
20	Jim Wynn	.20	.15	.08
21	Record Hitters (Dusty Baker, Ron Cey, Steve Garvey, Reggie Smith)	.30	.25	.12
22	Dusty Baker	.25	.20	.10
23	Tom Lasorda	.30	.25	.12
24	Fernando Valenzuela	.40	.30	.15
25	Steve Sax	.30	.25	.12
26	Dodger Stadium	.20	.15	.08
27	Ron Cey	.30	.25	.12
28	Pedro Guerrero	.30	.25	.12
29	Mike Marshall (outfielder)	.40	.30	.15
30	Don Sutton	.60	.45	.25
----	Logo Card/Checklist	.20	.15	.08
----	Smokey Bear	.20	.15	.08

1988 Smokey Bear Padres

This 33-card oversized (3" by 5") set was produced in conjunction with the U.S. Forest Service as a fire prevention campaign promotion. A full-color player photo, framed by a thin white line, fills the card face. The player number and position and Smokey Bear logo appear lower right. The black and white card backs are printed in horizontal postcard format, with player info and a Smokey Bear cartoon on the left half of the card back. The set was available for purchase at the Padres Gift Shop. Cards of

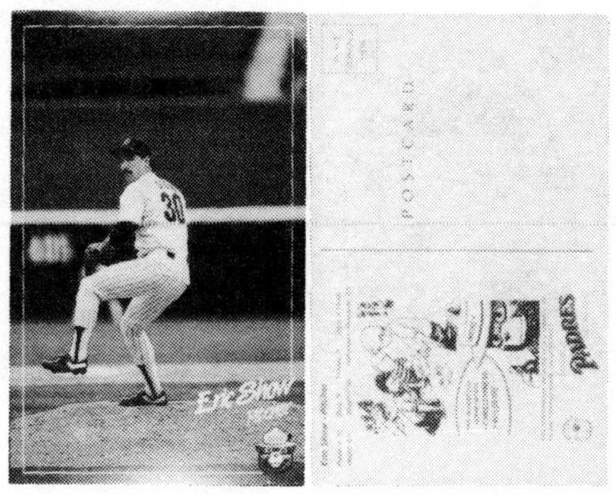

Candy Sierra and Larry Bowa were not released by the Padres and are quite rare. The complete set price does not include the two rare cards.

		MT	NR MT	EX
Complete Set:		13.00	9.75	5.25
Common Player:		.30	.25	.12
(1)	Shawn Abner	.30	.25	.12
(2)	Roberto Alomar	3.00	2.25	1.25
(3)	Sandy Alomar	.30	.25	.12
(4)	Greg Booker	.30	.25	.12
(5)	Larry Bowa	10.00	7.50	4.00
(6)	Chris Brown	.40	.30	.15
(7)	Mark Davis	.30	.25	.12
(8)	Pat Dobson	.30	.25	.12
(9)	Tim Flannery	.30	.25	.12
(10)	Mark Grant	.30	.25	.12
(11)	Tony Gwynn	1.50	1.25	.60
(12)	Andy Hawkins	.30	.25	.12
(13)	Stan Jefferson	.30	.25	.12
(14)	Jimmy Jones	.30	.25	.12
(15)	John Kruk	.80	.60	.30
(16)	Dave Leiper	.30	.25	.12
(17)	Shane Mack	.50	.40	.20
(18)	Carmelo Martinez	.40	.30	.15
(19)	Lance McCullers	.40	.30	.15
(20)	Keith Moreland	.30	.25	.12
(21)	Eric Nolte	.30	.25	.12
(22)	Amos Otis	.30	.25	.12
(23)	Mark Parent	.30	.25	.12
(24)	Randy Ready	.30	.25	.12
(25)	Greg Riddoch	.30	.25	.12
(26)	Benito Santiago	.80	.60	.30
(27)	Eric Show	.30	.25	.12
(28)	Candy Sierra	10.00	7.50	4.00
(29)	Denny Sommers	.30	.25	.12
(30)	Garry Templeton	.40	.30	.15
(31)	Dickie Thon	.30	.25	.12
(32)	Ed Whitson	.30	.25	.12
(33)	Marvell Wynne	.30	.25	.12

1988 Smokey Bear Rangers

This 21-card oversized (3-1/2" by 5") set was distributed to Rangers' fans at Smokey Bear Game Day on August 7th. The card fronts feature full-color action photos framed in an oval blue and red border on a white background. A nameplate above the photo identifies the player and a "Wildfire Prevention" logo is printed beneath the photo. Rangers (left) and Smokey (right) logos fill the upper corners of the card face. The card backs are black and white and include player info., U.S. and Texas Forest Service logos, and fire prevention tips.

		MT	NR MT	EX
Complete Set:		8.00	6.00	3.25
Common Player:		.30	.25	.12
1	Tom O'Malley	.30	.25	.12
2	Pete O'Brien	.40	.30	.15
3	Geno Petralli	.30	.25	.12
4	Pete Incaviglia	.50	.40	.20
5	Oddibe McDowell	.35	.25	.14
6	Dale Mohorcic	.30	.25	.12
7	Bobby Witt	.35	.25	.14
8	Bobby Valentine	.40	.30	.15
9	Ruben Sierra	1.00	.70	.40
10	Scott Fletcher	.40	.30	.15
11	Mike Stanley	.40	.30	.15
12	Steve Buechele	.40	.30	.15
13	Charlie Hough	.50	.40	.20
14	Larry Parrish	.40	.30	.15
15	Jerry Browne	.40	.30	.15
16	Bob Brower	.30	.25	.12
17	Jeff Russell	.40	.30	.15
18	Edwin Correa	.30	.25	.12
19	Mitch Williams	.40	.30	.15
20	Jose Guzman	.30	.25	.12
21	Curtis Wilkerson	.30	.25	.12

1988 Smokey Bear Royals

This 28-card set featuring full-color player caricatures by K.K. Goodale was produced for an in-stadium promotion on August 14, 1988. The 3" by 5" cards depict players, manager and coaches in action poses against a white background with a Royals logo upper left, opposite the Smokey Bear logo. The backs are black and white and contain brief player data and a Smokey cartoon.

		MT	NR MT	EX
Complete Set:		10.00	7.50	4.00
Common Player:		.20	.15	.08
1	John Wathan	.30	.25	.12
2	Royals Coaches (Frank Funk, Adrian Garrett, Mike Lum, Ed Napolean, Bob Schaefer, Jim Schaefer)	.20	.15	.08
3	Willie Wilson	.40	.30	.15
4	Danny Tartabull	.70	.50	.30
5	Bo Jackson	.90	.70	.35
6	Gary Thurman	.30	.25	.12
7	Jerry Don Gleaton	.20	.15	.08
8	Floyd Bannister	.20	.15	.08
9	Buddy Black	.40	.30	.15
10	Steve Farr	.20	.15	.08
11	Gene Garber	.20	.15	.08
12	Mark Gubicza	.50	.40	.20
13	Charlie Liebrandt	.30	.25	.12
14	Ted Power	.20	.15	.08
15	Dan Quisenberry	.30	.25	.12
16	Bret Saberhagen	.70	.50	.30
17	Mike Macfarlane	.40	.30	.15
18	Scotti Madison	.30	.25	.12
19	Jamie Quirk	.20	.15	.08
20	George Brett	1.25	.90	.50
21	Kevin Seitzer	.35	.25	.14
22	Bill Pecota	.20	.15	.08
23	Kurt Stillwell	.35	.25	.14
24	Brad Wellman	.20	.15	.08
25	Frank White	.30	.25	.12
26	Jim Eisenreich	.25	.20	.10
27	Smokey Bear	.20	.15	.08
----	Checklist	.20	.15	.08

Values for recent cards and sets are listed in Mint (MT), Near Mint (NM), reflecting the fact that many cards from recent years have been preserved in top condition. Recent cards and sets in less than Excellent condition have little collector interest.

1988 Smokey Bear Twins

This 8-1/4" by 3-3/4" booklet contains a dozen postcards called Color-Grams featuring caricatures (suitable for coloring) of star players from the Minnesota Twins. Postcards are attached along a perforated edge to a baseball card-size stub with a black and white photo of the featured player. The backs of the postcards include the player name and personal information. The card stubs include the same information, along with a fire prevention tip. Twins Color-

Grams were produced as a public service by the U.S. Forest Service and Dept. of Agriculture and were distributed to fans at the Metrodome.

		MT	NR MT	EX
Complete Set:		12.00	9.00	4.75
Common Player:		.70	.50	.30
(1)	Bert Blyleven	1.00	.70	.40
(2)	Randy Bush	.70	.50	.30
(3)	Gary Gaetti	1.00	.70	.40
(4)	Greg Gagne	1.00	.70	.40
(5)	Dan Gladden	.70	.50	.30
(6)	Kent Hrbek	1.50	1.25	.60
(7)	Gene Larkin	.70	.50	.30
(8)	Tim Laudner	.70	.50	.30
(9)	Al Newman	.70	.50	.30
(10)	Kirby Puckett	3.00	2.25	1.25
(11)	Jeff Reardon	1.50	1.25	.60
(12)	Frank Viola	1.75	1.25	.70

1989 Smokey Bear Angels All-Stars

The U.S. Forest Service, in conjunction with the California Angels, issued a 20-card set of "Angels All-Stars" in 1989. The standard-size cards are printed on a silver background and the player photos are bordered in red. Beneath the photo a banner stretches across homeplate, reading "Angels All-Stars," along with the player's name and position, which are flanked by Smokey Bear on the left and the Angels 1989 All-Star Game logo on the right. Card backs highlight the player's career with the Angels and include an illustrated fire prevention tip.

		MT	NR MT	EX
Complete Set:		8.00	6.00	3.25
Common Player:		.20	.15	.08
1	Bill Rigney	.20	.15	.08
2	Dean Chance	.35	.25	.14
3	Jim Fregosi	.40	.30	.15
4	Bobby Knoop	.20	.15	.08
5	Don Mincher	.20	.15	.08
6	Clyde Wright	.20	.15	.08
7	Nolan Ryan	3.00	2.25	1.25
8	Frank Robinson	1.00	.70	.40
9	Frank Tanana	.20	.15	.08
10	Rod Carew	.75	.60	.30
11	Bobby Grich	.20	.15	.08
12	Brian Downing	.20	.15	.08
13	Don Baylor	.35	.25	.14
14	Fred Lynn	.35	.25	.14
15	Reggie Jackson	1.00	.70	.40
16	Doug DeCinces	.20	.15	.08
17	Bob Boone	.35	.25	.14
18	Wally Joyner	.40	.30	.15
19	Mike Witt	.20	.15	.08
20	Johnny Ray	.20	.15	.08

Definitions for grading conditions are located in the Introduction of this price guide.

1989 Smokey Bear Cardinals

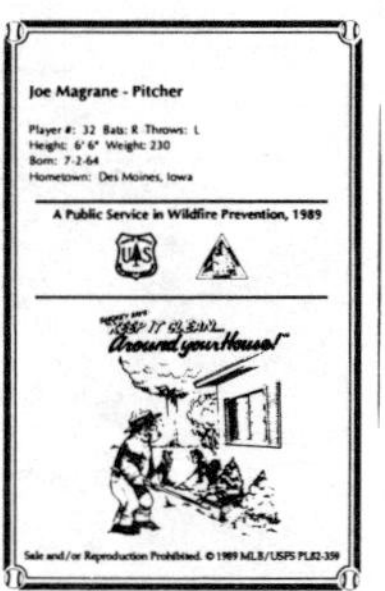

This 25-card set featuring action player photos was issued by the U.S. Forest Service to promote fire safety. The cards measure 4" by 6" and include the player's name, team logo and a small picture of Smokey Bear beneath the player photo.

		MT	NR MT	EX
Complete Set:		8.00	6.00	3.25
Common Player:		.20	.15	.08
(1)	Tom Brunansky	.20	.15	.08
(2)	Cris Carpenter	.20	.15	.08
(3)	Vince Coleman	.60	.45	.25
(4)	John Costello	.30	.25	.12
(5)	Ken Dayley	.20	.15	.08
(6)	Jose DeLeon	.25	.20	.10
(7)	Frank DiPino	.20	.15	.08
(8)	Whitey Herzog	.30	.25	.12
(9)	Ken Hill	.80	.60	.30
(10)	Pedro Guerrero	.50	.40	.20
(11)	Tim Jones	.30	.25	.12
(12)	Jim Lindeman	.20	.15	.08
(13)	Joe Magrane	.30	.25	.12
(14)	Willie McGee	.50	.40	.20
(15)	John Morris	.30	.25	.12
(16)	Jose Oquendo	.30	.25	.12
(17)	Tom Pagnozzi	.20	.15	.08
(18)	Tony Pena	.30	.25	.12
(19)	Terry Pendleton	.50	.40	.20
(20)	Dan Quisenberry	.30	.25	.12
(21)	Ozzie Smith	.80	.60	.30
(22)	Scott Terry	.30	.25	.12
(23)	Milt Thompson	.30	.25	.12
(24)	Denny Walling	.20	.15	.08
(25)	Todd Worrell	.50	.40	.20

1990 Smokey Bear Angels

This 20-card set was released by the U.S. Forestry Service in conjunction with the California Angels. The sets were distributed at a 1990 Angels home game. (May 27) The cards feature full-color action photos surrounded by metallic looking silver borders. Both California Angels and Smokey Bear logos appear on the fronts. Card backs contain player data and a cartoon Smokey Bear message urging the prevention of forest fires.

		MT	NR MT	EX
Complete Set:		5.00	3.75	2.00
Common Player:		.20	.15	.08
1	Jim Abbott	.50	.40	.20
2	Bert Blyleven	.40	.30	.15
3	Chili Davis	.30	.25	.12
4	Brian Downing	.20	.15	.08
5	Chuck Finley	.30	.25	.12
6	Willie Fraser	.20	.15	.08
7	Bryan Harvey	.30	.25	.12
8	Jack Howell	.20	.15	.08
9	Wally Joyner	.40	.30	.15
10	Mark Langston	.30	.25	.12
11	Kirk McCaskill	.25	.20	.10
12	Mark McLemore	.20	.15	.08
13	Lance Parrish	.30	.25	.12
14	Johnny Ray	.20	.15	.08
15	Dick Schofield	.20	.15	.08
16	Mike Witt	.20	.15	.08
17	Claudell Washington	.20	.15	.08
18	Devon White	.20	.15	.08
19	Scott Bailes	.20	.15	.08
20	Bob McClure	.20	.15	.08

1991 Smokey Bear Angels

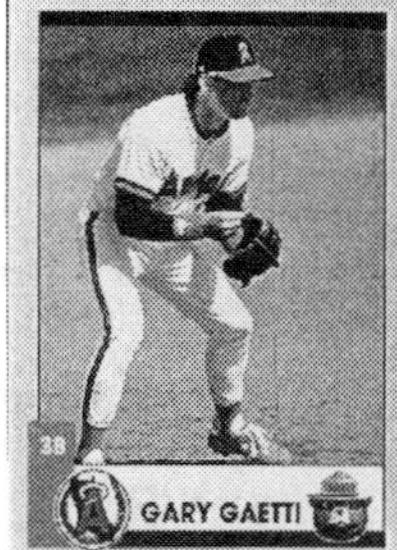

This 20-card set was sponsored by the California Department of Forestry. The card fronts feature gray borders surrounding full-color action photos. The flip sides feature a fire safety cartoon and biographical information. The cards are numbered on the back.

		MT	NR MT	EX
Complete Set:		5.00	3.75	2.00
Common Player:		.25	.20	.10
1	Luis Polonia	.35	.25	.14
2	Junior Felix	.35	.25	.14
3	Dave Winfield	.60	.45	.25
4	Dave Parker	.40	.30	.15
5	Lance Parrish	.35	.25	.14
6	Wally Joyner	.60	.45	.25
7	Jim Abbott	.60	.45	.25
8	Mark Langston	.40	.30	.15
9	Chuck Finley	.35	.25	.14
10	Kirk McCaskill	.30	.25	.12
11	Jack Howell	.25	.20	.10
12	Donnie Hill	.25	.20	.10
13	Gary Gaetti	.35	.25	.14
14	Dick Schofield	.25	.20	.10
15	Luis Sojo	.25	.20	.10
16	Mark Eichhorn	.25	.20	.10
17	Bryan Harvey	.35	.25	.14
18	Jeff Robinson	.25	.20	.10
19	Scott Lewis	.25	.20	.10
20	John Orton	.25	.20	.10

1992 Smokey Bear Padres Postcards

The Padres issued a 36-card postcard set in 1992, sponsored by Smokey the Bear. The backs of the cards contain the usual fire safety messages, but they are also translated into Spanish. Fronts have full-bleed color photos with the player's name and position in orange in a dark blue box at bottom center. A color Smokey logo appears in one of the upper corners. The unnumbered cards are checklisted here alphabetically.

		MT	NR MT	EX
Complete Set (36):		16.00	12.00	6.50
Common Player:		.25	.20	.10
(1)	Larry Andersen	.25	.20	.10
(2)	Oscar Azocar	.25	.20	.10
(3)	Andy Benes	1.00	.70	.40
(4)	Dan Bilardello	.25	.20	.10
(5)	Jerald Clark	.25	.20	.10
(6)	Pat Clements	.25	.20	.10

(7)	Dave Eiland	.25	.20	.10
(8)	Tony Fernandez	.50	.40	.20
(9)	Tony Gwynn	1.50	1.25	.60
(10)	Gene Harris	.25	.20	.10
(11)	Greg Harris	.25	.20	.10
(12)	Jeremy Hernandez	.40	.30	.15
(13)	Bruce Hurst	.25	.20	.10
(14)	Darrin Jackson	.50	.40	.20
(15)	Tom Lampkin	.25	.20	.10
(16)	Bruce Kimm	.25	.20	.10
(17)	Craig Lefferts	.35	.25	.14
(18)	Mike Maddux	.25	.20	.10
(19)	Fred McGriff	2.00	1.50	.80
(20)	Jose Melendez	.25	.20	.10
(21)	Randy Myers, Craig Shipley	.35	.25	.14
(22)	Gary Pettis	.25	.20	.10
(23)	Rob Picciolo	.25	.20	.10
(24)	Merv Rettenmund	.25	.20	.10
(25)	Greg Riddoch	.25	.20	.10
(26)	Mike Roarke	.25	.20	.10
(27)	Rich Rodriguez	.75	.60	.30
(28)	Benito Santiago	.75	.60	.30
(29)	Frank Seminara	.25	.20	.10
(30)	Gary Sheffield	1.00	.70	.40
(32)	Jim Snyder	.25	.20	.10
(33)	Dave Staton	1.00	.70	.40
(34)	Kurt Stillwell	.25	.20	.10
(35)	Tim Teufel	.25	.20	.10
(36)	Kevin Ward	.25	.20	.10

1957 Sohio Gas Indians/Reds

In 1957 Sohio (Standard Oil of Ohio) gas stations in Ohio issued sets of Cleveland Indians and Cincinnati Reds photocards and team albums. The blank-backed cards are 5" x 7" and printed in black-and-white with one perforated edge. The cards have a facsimile autograph as the only identification. The unnumbered cards are checklisted here alphabetically within team.

		NR MT	EX	VG
Complete Set (36):		600.00	300.00	180.00
Common Player:		9.00	4.50	2.75
	CLEVELAND INDIANS			
(1)	Bob Avila	12.00	6.00	3.50
(2)	Jim Busby	9.00	4.50	2.75
(3)	Chico Carrasquel	9.00	4.50	2.75
(4)	Rocky Colavito	50.00	25.00	15.00
(5)	Mike Garcia	12.00	6.00	3.50
(6)	Jim Hegan	9.00	4.50	2.75
(7)	Bob Lemon	24.00	12.00	7.25
(8)	Roger Maris	200.00	100.00	60.00
(9)	Don Mossi	9.00	4.50	2.75
(10)	Ray Narleski	9.00	4.50	2.75
(11)	Russ Nixon	9.00	4.50	2.75
(12)	Herb Score	12.00	6.00	3.50
(13)	Al Smith	9.00	4.50	2.75
(14)	George Strickland	9.00	4.50	2.75
(15)	Bob Usher	9.00	4.50	2.75
(16)	Vic Wertz	9.00	4.50	2.75
(17)	Gene Woodling	9.00	4.50	2.75
(18)	Early Wynn	24.00	12.00	7.25
----	Cleveland Indians album	60.00	30.00	18.00
	CINCINNATI REDS			
(1)	Ed Bailey	9.00	4.50	2.75
(2)	Gus Bell	12.00	4.50	2.75
(3)	Rocky Bridges	9.00	4.50	2.75
(4)	Smoky Burgess	12.00	4.50	2.75
(5)	Hersh Freeman	9.00	4.50	2.75
(6)	Alex Grammas	9.00	4.50	2.75
(7)	Don Gross	9.00	4.50	2.75
(8)	Warren Hacker	9.00	4.50	2.75
(9)	Don Hoak	9.00	4.50	2.75
(10)	Hal Jeffcoat	9.00	4.50	2.75
(11)	Johnny Klippstein	9.00	4.50	2.75
(12)	Ted Kluszewski	40.00	4.50	2.75
(13)	Brooks Lawrence	9.00	4.50	2.75
(14)	Roy McMillan	9.00	4.50	2.75
(15)	Joe Nuxhall	9.00	4.50	2.75
(16)	Wally Post	9.00	4.50	2.75
(17)	Frank Robinson	65.00	4.50	2.75
(18)	Johnny Temple	9.00	4.50	2.75
----	Cincinnati Redlegs album	60.00	30.00	18.00

The values quoted are intended to reflect the market price.

1994 Spectrum 1969 Miracle Mets

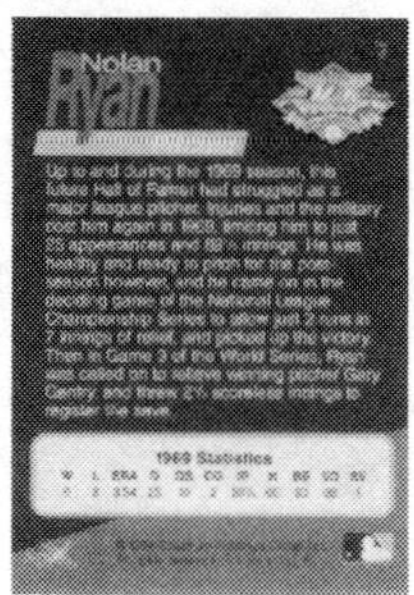

The 1969 Miracle Mets card set, produced by Spectrum Holdings Group of Birmingham, Mich. was part of what the company called "an integrated memorabilia program, with the 1969 Mets card set as the centerpiece." The 70-card set measures the standard 2-1/2" x 3-1/2", complete with UV coating on both sides and gold foil on the fronts, was sold complete at $24.95, and limited to 25,000 sets. A total of 750 numbered sets were signed by all 25 living players, including Hall of Famer Tom Seaver and future Cooperstown resident Nolan Ryan.

		MT	NR MT	EX
Complete Set (69):		25.00	20.00	10.00
Common Player:		.25	.20	.10
1	Commemorative Card	.25	.20	.10
2	Team Photo	.25	.20	.10
3	Tom Seaver	3.00	2.25	1.25
4	Jerry Koosman	.45	.35	.20
5	Tommie Agee	.25	.20	.10
6	Bud Harrelson	.25	.20	.10
7	Nolan Ryan	6.00	4.50	2.50
8	Jerry Grote	.25	.20	.10
9	Ron Swoboda	.25	.20	.10
10	Donn Clendenon	.25	.20	.10
11	Art Shamsky	.25	.20	.10
12	Tug McGraw	.35	.25	.14
13	Ed Kranepool	.35	.25	.14
14	Cleon Jones	.35	.25	.14
15	Ron Taylor	.25	.20	.10
16	Gary Gentry	.25	.20	.10
17	Ken Boswell	.25	.20	.10
18	Ed Charles	.25	.20	.10
19	J.C. Martin	.25	.20	.10
20	Al Weis	.25	.20	.10
21	Jack DiLauro	.25	.20	.10
22	Duffy Dyer	.25	.20	.10
23	Wayne Garrett	.25	.20	.10
24	Jim McAndrew	.25	.20	.10
25	Rod Gaspar	.25	.20	.10
26	Don Cardwell	.25	.20	.10
27	Bob Pfeil	.25	.20	.10
28	Cal Koonce	.25	.20	.10
29	Gil Hodges	2.00	1.50	.80
30	Yogi Berra	2.50	2.00	1.00
31	Joe Pignatano	.25	.20	.10
32	Rube Walker	.25	.20	.10
33	Eddie Yost	.25	.20	.10
34	First-ever Met Game	.25	.20	.10
35	Opening Day 1969	.25	.20	.10
36	Kranepool Breaks Home Run Record	.25	.20	.10
37	Koosman Sets Club Strikeout Record	.25	.20	.10
38	Mets Trade for Clendenon	.25	.20	.10
39	Koosman's 23 Scoreless Innings	.25	.20	.10
40	Mets Begin 7-Game Winning Streak	.25	.20	.10
41	Mets vs. Division Leading Cubs	.25	.20	.10
42	Seaver's Near Perfect Game	.25	.20	.10
43	Mets Trail by 3-1/2	.25	.20	.10
44	All-Star Break	.25	.20	.10
45	All-Star Game	.25	.20	.10
46	Mets Sweep Atlanta	.25	.20	.10
47	Mets Sweep Padres	.25	.20	.10
48	Mets Defeat Cubs, Koosman Strikes Out 13	.25	.20	.10
49	Mets Defeat Cubs 1/2 Game Back	.25	.20	.10
50	First Place!	.25	.20	.10
51	Mets Continue Nine Game Winning Streak	.25	.20	.10
52	Seaver Earns 22nd Victory	.25	.20	.10
53	Mets Win, Carlton Strikes Out 19	.25	.20	.10
54	Koosman Pitches 15th Complete Game	.25	.20	.10
55	Eastern Division Champs!	.25	.20	.10
56	100th Victory	.25	.20	.10
57	Final Game, Mets Prepare for Braves	.25	.20	.10
58	N.L. Championship Series, Game 1	.25	.20	.10
59	N.L. Championship Series, Game 2	.25	.20	.10
60	N.L. Championship Series, Game 3	.25	.20	.10
61	World Series, Game 1	.25	.20	.10
62	World Series, Game 2	.25	.20	.10
63	World Series, Game 3	.25	.20	.10
64	World Series, Game 4	.25	.20	.10
65	World Series, Game 5	.25	.20	.10
66	World Champions	.25	.20	.10
67	World Champions	.25	.20	.10
68	World Champions	.25	.20	.10
69	World Champions	.25	.20	.10
----	Checklist	.25	.20	.10

1953 Spic and Span Braves

The first of several regional issues from a Milwaukee dry cleaner, the 1953-54 Spic and Span Braves set consists of 27 cards, each measuring 3-1/4" by 5-1/2". The fronts of the card have a facsimilie autograph beneath the player photo. Cards are found with blank backs or with a Spic and Span advertising message on the back.

		NR MT	EX	VG
Complete Set:		800.00	400.00	240.00
Common Player:		25.00	12.50	7.50
(1)	Joe Adcock	35.00	17.50	10.50
(2)	John Antonelli	25.00	12.50	7.50
(3)	Vern Bickford	25.00	12.50	7.50
(4)	Bill Bruton	30.00	15.00	9.00
(5)	Bob Buhl	25.00	12.50	7.50
(6)	Lew Burdette	30.00	15.00	9.00
(7)	Dick Cole	25.00	12.50	7.50
(8)	Walker Cooper	25.00	12.50	7.50
(9)	Del Crandall	30.00	15.00	9.00
(10)	George Crowe	25.00	12.50	7.50
(11)	Jack Dittmer	25.00	12.50	7.50
(12)	Sid Gordon	25.00	12.50	7.50
(13)	Ernie Johnson	25.00	12.50	7.50
(14)	Dave Jolly	25.00	12.50	7.50
(15)	Don Liddle	25.00	12.50	7.50
(16)	John Logan	30.00	15.00	9.00
(17)	Ed Mathews	100.00	50.00	30.00
(18)	Dan O'Connell	25.00	12.50	7.50
(19)	Andy Pafko	30.00	15.00	9.00
(20)	Jim Pendleton	25.00	12.50	7.50
(21)	Ebba St. Claire	25.00	12.50	7.50
(22)	Warren Spahn	100.00	50.00	30.00
(23)	Max Surkont	25.00	12.50	7.50
(24)	Bob Thomson	30.00	15.00	9.00
(25)	Bob Thorpe	25.00	12.50	7.50
(26)	Roberto Vargas	25.00	12.50	7.50
(27)	Jim Wilson	25.00	12.50	7.50

1953 Spic and Span Braves 7x10 Photos

This regional set was issued by Spic and Span Dry Cleaners of Milwaukee over a four-year period and consiste of 13 large (7" by 10") photos of Braves players. Of all the various Spic and Span sets, this one seems to be the easiest to find. The fronts feature a player photo with a facsimilie autograph below. The Spic and Span logo also appears on the fronts, while the backs are blank. A photo of Milwaukee County Stadium also exists but is not generally considered to be part of the set.

		NR MT	EX	VG
Complete Set:		225.00	112.00	67.00
Common Player:		10.00	5.00	3.00
(1)	Joe Adcock	15.00	7.50	4.50
(2)	Bill Bruton	10.00	5.00	3.00
(3)	Bob Buhl	10.00	5.00	3.00
(4)	Lew Burdette	15.00	7.50	4.50
(5)	Del Crandall	15.00	7.50	4.50
(6)	Jack Dittmer	10.00	5.00	3.00
(7)	John Logan	15.00	7.50	4.50
(8)	Ed Mathews	50.00	25.00	15.00
(9)	Chet Nichols	10.00	5.00	3.00
(10)	Dan O'Connell	10.00	5.00	3.00
(11)	Andy Pafko	15.00	7.50	4.50
(12)	Warren Spahn	50.00	25.00	15.00
(13)	Bob Thomson	15.00	7.50	4.50

1954 Spic and Span Braves

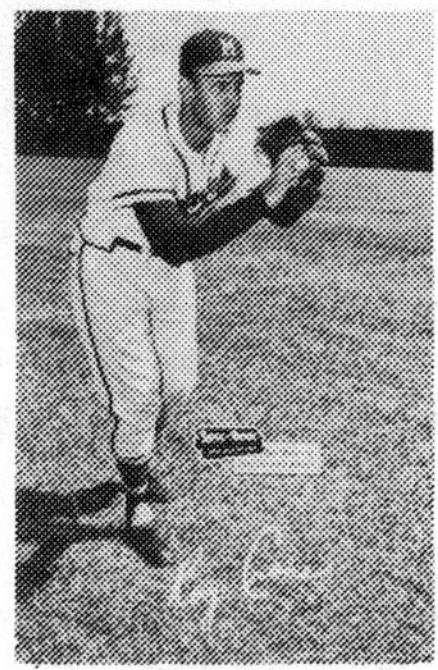

Issued during the three-year period from 1954-1956, this Spic and Span set consists of 18 postcard-size (4" by 6") cards. The front of the cards include a facsimilie autograph printed in white and the Spic and Span logo.

		NR MT	EX	VG
Complete Set:		500.00	250.00	150.00
Common Player:		12.00	6.00	3.50
(1)	Hank Aaron	180.00	90.00	54.00
(2)	Joe Adcock	20.00	10.00	6.00
(3)	Bill Bruton	12.00	6.00	3.50
(4)	Bob Buhl	12.00	6.00	3.50
(5)	Lew Burdette	15.00	7.50	4.50
(6)	Gene Conley	12.00	6.00	3.50
(7)	Del Crandall	15.00	7.50	4.50
(8)	Ray Crone	12.00	6.00	3.50
(9)	Jack Dittmer	12.00	6.00	3.50
(10)	Ernie Johnson	12.00	6.00	3.50
(11)	Dave Jolly	12.00	6.00	3.50
(12)	John Logan	15.00	7.50	4.50
(13)	Ed Mathews	80.00	40.00	24.00
(14)	Chet Nichols	12.00	6.00	3.50
(15)	Dan O'Connell	12.00	6.00	3.50
(16)	Andy Pafko	15.00	7.50	4.50
(17)	Warren Spahn	80.00	40.00	24.00
(18)	Bob Thomson	15.00	7.50	4.50

1955 Spic and Span Braves Die-cuts

This 17-card, die-cut set is the rarest of all the Spic and Span issues. The stand-ups, which measure approximately 7-1/2" by 7", picture the players in action poses and were designed to be punched out, allowing them to stand up. Most cards were used in this fashion, making better-condition cards very rare today. The front of the card includes a facsimilie autograph and the Spic and Span logo.

		NR MT	EX	VG
Complete Set:		3500.	1750.	1050.
Common Player:		125.00	62.00	37.00
(1)	Hank Aaron	800.00	400.00	240.00
(2)	Joe Adcock	175.00	87.00	52.00
(3)	Bill Bruton	125.00	62.00	37.00
(4)	Bob Buhl	125.00	62.00	37.00
(5)	Lew Burdette	150.00	75.00	45.00
(6)	Gene Conley	125.00	62.00	37.00
(7)	Del Crandall	150.00	75.00	45.00
(8)	Jack Dittmer	125.00	62.00	37.00
(9)	Ernie Johnson	125.00	62.00	37.00
(10)	Dave Jolly	125.00	62.00	37.00
(11)	John Logan	150.00	75.00	45.00
(12)	Ed Mathews	350.00	175.00	105.00
(13)	Chet Nichols	125.00	62.00	37.00
(14)	Dan O'Connell	125.00	62.00	37.00
(15)	Andy Pafko	150.00	75.00	45.00
(16)	Warren Spahn	350.00	175.00	105.00
(17)	Bob Thomson	150.00	75.00	45.00
(18)	Jim Wilson	125.00	62.00	37.00

1957 Spic and Span Braves

This 20-card set was issued in 1957, the year the Braves were World Champions and is a highly desirable set. The cards measure 4" by 5" and have a wide, white border surrounding the player photo. A blue Spic and Span logo appears in the extreme lower right corner, and the card includes a salutation and facsimilie autograph, also in blue.

		NR MT	EX	VG
Complete Set:		450.00	225.00	135.00
Common Player:		12.00	6.00	3.50
(1)	Hank Aaron	125.00	62.00	37.00
(2)	Joe Adcock	20.00	10.00	6.00
(3)	Bill Bruton	12.00	6.00	3.50
(4)	Bob Buhl	12.00	6.00	3.50
(5)	Lew Burdette	15.00	7.50	4.50
(6)	Gene Conley	12.00	6.00	3.50
(7)	Wes Covington	12.00	6.00	3.50
(8)	Del Crandall	20.00	10.00	6.00
(9)	Ray Crone	12.00	6.00	3.50
(10)	Fred Haney	12.00	6.00	3.50
(11)	Ernie Johnson	12.00	6.00	3.50
(12)	Felix Mantilla	15.00	7.50	4.50
(13)	Ed Mathews	60.00	30.00	18.00
(14)	John Logan	15.00	7.50	4.50
(15)	Dan O'Connell	12.00	6.00	3.50
(16)	Andy Pafko	15.00	7.50	4.50
(17)	Red Schoendienst	40.00	20.00	12.00
(18)	Warren Spahn	60.00	30.00	18.00
(19)	Bob Thomson	15.00	7.50	4.50
(20)	Bob Trowbridge	12.00	6.00	3.50

1960 Spic and Span Braves

Spic and Span's final Milwaukee Braves issue consisted of 26 cards, each mesauring 2-3/4" by 3-1/8". The fronts contain a white-bordered photo with no printing, while the backs include a facsimilie autograph and the words "Photographed and Autographed Exclusively for Spic and Span." The 1960 set includes the only known variation in the Spic and Span sets. A "flopped" negative error showing catcher Del Crandell batting left-handed was later corrected.

		NR MT	EX	VG
Complete Set:		550.00	275.00	165.00
Common Player:		12.00	6.00	3.50
(1)	Hank Aaron	125.00	62.00	37.00
(2)	Joe Adcock	20.00	10.00	6.00
(3)	Bill Bruton	12.00	6.00	3.50
(4)	Bob Buhl	12.00	6.00	3.50
(5)	Lew Burdette	20.00	10.00	6.00
(6)	Chuck Cottier	12.00	6.00	3.50
(7a)	Del Crandall (photo reversed)	25.00	12.50	7.50
(7b)	Del Crandall (correct photo)	25.00	12.50	7.50
(8)	Chuck Dressen	12.00	6.00	3.50
(9)	Joey Jay	12.00	6.00	3.50
(10)	John Logan	15.00	7.50	4.50
(11)	Felix Mantilla	12.00	6.00	3.50
(12)	Ed Mathews	60.00	30.00	18.00
(13)	Lee Maye	12.00	6.00	3.50
(14)	Don McMahon	12.00	6.00	3.50
(15)	George Myatt	12.00	6.00	3.50
(16)	Andy Pafko	15.00	7.50	4.50
(17)	Juan Pizarro	12.00	6.00	3.50
(18)	Mel Roach	12.00	6.00	3.50
(19)	Bob Rush	12.00	6.00	3.50
(20)	Bob Scheffing	12.00	6.00	3.50
(21)	Red Schoendienst	35.00	17.50	10.50
(22)	Warren Spahn	60.00	30.00	18.00
(23)	Al Spangler	12.00	6.00	3.50
(24)	Frank Torre	12.00	6.00	3.50
(25)	Carl Willey	12.00	6.00	3.50
(26)	Whit Wyatt	12.00	6.00	3.50

1977 - 79 Sportscaster

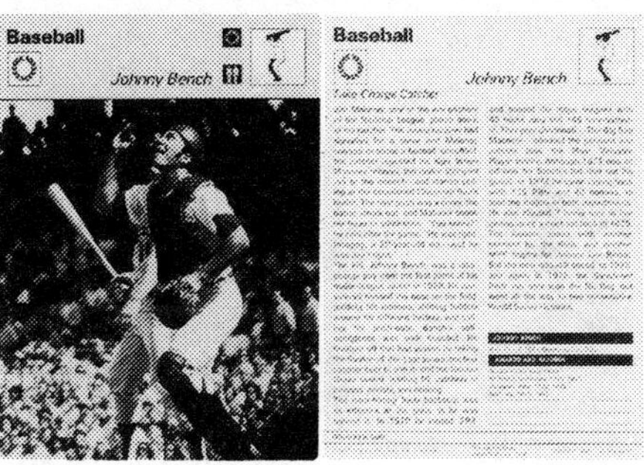

This massive set of full-color cards, which includes players from dozens of different sports - some of them very obscure - contains more than 2,000 different subjects, making it one of the biggest sets of trading cards ever issued. Available by mail subscription from 1977 through 1979, the Sportscaster cards are large, measuring 6-1/4" by 4-3/4". Subscribers were mailed one series of 24 cards each for $1.89 plus postage every month or so. The cards are not numbered, making it very difficult to assemble a complete set. The set has an international flavor to it, including such sports as rugby, soccer, lawn bowling, fencing, karate, bicycling, curling, skiing, bullfighting, auto racing, mountain climbing, hang gliding, yachting, sailing, badminton, bobsledding, etc. Each card has a series of legends in the upper right corner to assist collectors in the various methods of sorting. Most popular among American collectors are the baseball, football and basketball stars in the set, which includes the 140 baseball subjects listed here. The checklist includes many Hall of Famers and future Hall of Famers. The card backs contain detailed write-ups of the player featured. Because the set was issued in series, and many collectors dropped out of the program before the end, cards in the higher series are especially scarce. This accounts for prices on some of the superstar cards, issued in early series, being lower than for some of the lesser-known players.

		NR MT	EX	VG
Complete Set (Baseball Only):		550.00	275.00	165.00
Common Player:		2.00	1.00	.60
(1)	Henry Aaron	8.00	4.00	2.50
(2)	Danny Ainge	2.00	1.00	.60
(3)	Emmett Ashford (umpire)	5.00	2.50	1.50
(4)	Ernie Banks	7.00	3.50	2.00
(5)	Johnny Bench	7.00	3.50	2.00
(6)	Vida Blue	6.00	3.00	1.75
(7)	Bert Blyleven	3.00	1.50	.90
(8)	Bobby Bonds	6.00	3.00	1.75
(9)	Lyman Bostock	2.00	1.00	.60
(10)	George Brett	12.00	6.00	3.50
(11)	Lou Brock	4.00	2.00	1.25
(12)	Jeff Burroughs	2.00	1.00	.60
(13)	Roy Campanella	21.00	10.50	6.25
(14)	John Candelaria	3.50	1.75	1.00
(15)	Rod Carew	5.00	2.50	1.50
(16)	Steve Carlton	6.00	3.00	1.75
(17)	Ron Cey	2.00	1.00	.60
(18)	Roberto Clemente	35.00	17.50	10.50
(19)	Steve Dembowski	9.00	4.50	2.75
(20)	Joe DiMaggio	15.00	7.50	4.50
(21)	Dennis Eckersley	6.00	3.00	1.75
(22)	Mark Fidrych	3.00	1.50	.90

(23)	Carlton Fisk	2.00	1.00	.60
(24)	Mike Flanagan	9.00	4.50	2.75
(25)	Steve Garvey	12.00	6.00	3.50
(26)	Ron Guidry	15.00	7.50	4.50
(27)	Gil Hodges	15.00	7.50	4.50
(28)	Catfish Hunter	3.00	1.50	.90
(29)	Tommy John	3.25	1.75	1.00
(30)	Randy Jones	2.00	1.00	.60
(31)	Dave Kingman	2.00	1.00	.60
(32)	Sandy Koufax	9.00	4.50	2.75
(33)	Tommy Lasorda	10.00	5.00	3.00
(34)	Ron LeFlore	2.00	1.00	.60
(35)	Greg Luzinski	2.00	1.00	.60
(36)	Billy Martin	10.00	5.00	3.00
(37)	Willie Mays	9.00	4.50	2.75
(38)	Lee Mazzilli	8.00	4.00	2.50
(39)	Willie McCovey	15.00	7.50	4.50
(40)	Joe Morgan	6.00	3.00	1.75
(41)	Thurman Munson	5.00	2.50	1.50
(42)	Stan Musial	10.00	5.00	3.00
(43)	Phil Niekro	11.00	5.50	3.25
(44)	Jim Palmer	6.00	3.00	1.75
(45)	Dave Parker	4.00	2.00	1.25
(46)	Freddie Patek	2.00	1.00	.60
(47)	Gaylord Perry	2.00	1.00	.60
(48)	Jim Piersall	2.00	1.00	.60
(49)	Vada Pinson	2.00	1.00	.60
(50)	Rick Reuschel	2.00	1.00	.60
(51)	Jim Rice	3.00	1.50	.90
(52)	J.R. Richard	11.00	5.50	3.25
(53)	Brooks Robinson	8.00	4.00	2.50
(54)	Frank Robinson	12.00	6.00	3.50
(55)	Jackie Robinson	8.00	4.00	2.50
(56)	Pete Rose	5.00	2.50	1.50
(57)	Joe Rudi	2.00	1.00	.60
(58)	Babe Ruth	11.00	5.50	3.25
(59)	Nolan Ryan	35.00	17.50	10.50
(60)	Tom Seaver	9.00	4.50	2.75
(61)	Warren Spahn	6.00	3.00	1.75
(62)	Monty Stratton	5.00	2.50	1.50
(63)	Craig Swan	7.00	3.50	2.00
(64)	Frank Tanana	2.00	1.00	.60
(65)	Ron Taylor	9.00	4.50	2.75
(66)	Garry Templeton	2.00	1.00	.60
(67)	Gene Tenace	2.00	1.00	.60
(68)	Bobby Thomson	2.00	1.00	.60
(69)	Andre Thornton	2.00	1.00	.60
(70)	Johnny VanderMeer	2.00	1.00	.60
(71)	Ted Williams	8.00	4.00	2.50
(72)	Maury Wills	3.00	1.50	.90
(73)	Hack Wilson	2.00	1.00	.60
(74)	Dave Winfield (hitting)	15.00	7.50	4.50
(75)	Dave Winfield (portrait)	10.00	5.00	3.00
(76)	Cy Young	5.00	2.50	1.50
(77)	The 1927 Yankees	5.00	2.50	1.50
(78)	1969 Mets	6.00	3.00	1.75
(79)	All-Star Game (Steve Garvey, Joe Morgan)	12.00	6.00	3.50
(80)	Amateur Draft (Rick Monday)	2.00	1.00	.60
(81)	At-A-Glance Reference (Tom Seaver)	5.00	2.50	1.50
(82)	Babe Ruth Baseball (Ed Figueroa)	10.00	5.00	3.00
(83)	Baltimore Memorial Stadium	11.00	5.50	3.25
(84)	Boston's Fenway Park	6.00	3.00	1.75
(85)	Brother vs. Brother (Joe Niekro)	8.00	4.00	2.50
(86)	Busch Memorial Stadium	11.00	5.50	3.25
(87)	Candlestick Park	6.00	3.00	1.75
(88)	Cape Cod League (Jim Beattie)	2.00	1.00	.60
(89)	A Century and a Half of Baseball (Johnny Bench)	5.00	2.50	1.50
(90)	Cy Young Award (Tom Seaver)	5.00	2.50	1.50
(91)	The Dean Brothers (Dizzy Dean, Paul Dean)	10.00	5.00	3.00
(92)	Designated Hitter (Rusty Staub)	8.00	4.00	2.50
(93)	Dodger Stadium	8.00	4.00	2.50
(94)	Perfect Game (Don Larsen)	8.00	4.00	2.50
(95)	The Double Steal (Davey Lopes)	2.00	1.00	.60
(96)	Fenway Park	8.00	4.00	2.50
(97)	The Firemen (Goose Gossage)	11.00	5.50	3.25
(98)	Forever Blowing Bubbles (Davey Lopes)	6.00	3.00	1.75
(99)	The Forsch Brothers (Bob Forsch, Ken Forsch)	2.00	1.00	.60
(100)	Four Home Runs In A Game (Mike Schmidt)	7.00	3.50	2.00
(101)	400-Homer Club (Duke Snider)	7.00	3.50	2.00
(102)	Great Moments (Bob Gibson)	6.00	3.00	1.75
(103)	Great Moments (Ferguson Jenkins)	3.00	1.50	.90
(104)	Great Moments (Mickey Lolich)	3.00	1.50	.90
(105)	Great Moments (Carl Yastrzemski)	7.00	3.50	2.00
(106)	Hidden Ball Trick (Carl Yastrzemski)	3.00	1.50	.90
(107)	Hit And Run (George Foster)	2.00	1.00	.60
(108)	Hitting The Cutoff Man	2.00	1.00	.60
(109)	Hitting Pitchers (Don Drysdale)	10.00	5.00	3.00
(110)	Infield Fly Rule (Bobby Grich)	2.00	1.00	.60
(111)	Instruction (Rod Carew)	4.50	2.25	1.25
(112)	Interference (Johnny Bench)	7.00	3.50	2.00
(113)	Iron Mike (Pitching Machine)	2.00	1.00	.60
(114)	Keeping Score	2.00	1.00	.60
(115)	Like Father, Like Son (Roy Smalley)	5.00	2.50	1.50
(116)	Lingo I (Gary Carter)	4.00	2.00	1.25
(117)	Lingo II (Earl Weaver)	3.00	1.50	.90
(118)	Little Leagues To Big Leagues (Hector Torres)	2.00	1.00	.60
(119)	Maris and Mantle (Mickey Mantle, Roger Maris)	8.00	4.00	2.50
(120)	Measurements (Memorial Stadium)	2.00	1.00	.60
(121)	The Money Game (Dennis Eckersley)	12.00	6.00	3.50
(122)	NCAA Tournament (Aggies-Longhorns	4.00	2.00	1.25
(123)	The Oakland A's, 1971-75	6.00	3.00	1.75
(124)	The Perfect Game (Sandy Koufax)	6.00	3.00	1.75
125	Pickoff (.00 Tiant)	2.00	1.00	.60
(126)	The Presidential Ball (William Howard Taft)	5.00	2.50	1.50
(127)	Relief Pitching (Mike Marshall)	3.00	1.50	.90
(128)	The Rules (Hank Aaron)	9.00	4.50	2.75
(129)	Rundown	2.00	1.00	.60
(130)	7th Game of the World Series (Bert Campaneris)	7.00	3.50	2.00
(131)	Shea Stadium	2.00	1.00	.60
(132)	The 3000 Hit Club (Roberto Clemente)	20.00	10.00	6.00
(133)	Training Camps (Orioles	5.00	2.50	1.50
(134)	Triple Crown (Carl Yastrzemski)	12.00	6.00	3.50
(135)	Triple Play (Rick Burleson)	9.00	4.50	2.75
(136)	Triple Play (Bill Wambsganss)	3.00	1.50	.90
(137)	Umpires Strike	5.00	2.50	1.50
(138)	Veterans Stadium	9.00	4.50	2.75
(139)	Wrigley Marathon (Mike Schmidt)	7.00	3.50	2.00
(140)	Yankee Stadium	2.00	1.00	.60

1986 Sportflics

The premiere issue from Sportflics was distributed nationally by Amurol Division of Wrigley Gum Company. These high quality, three-phase "Magic Motion" cards depict three different photos per card, with each visible separately as the card is tilted. The 1986 issue features 200 full-color baseball cards plus 133 trivia cards. The cards come in the standard 2-1/2" by 3-1/2" size with the backs containing player stats and personal information. There are three different types of picture cards: 1) Tri-Star cards - 50 cards feature three players on one card; 2) Big Six cards - 10 cards which have six players in special categories; and 3) the Big Twelve card of 12 World Series players from the Kansas City Royals. The trivia cards are 1-3/4" by 2" and do not have player photos.

		MT	NR MT	EX
Complete Set (200):		40.00	30.00	16.00
Common Player:		.10	.08	.04
1	George Brett	2.00	1.50	.80
2	Don Mattingly	2.00	1.50	.80
3	Wade Boggs	1.50	1.25	.60
4	Eddie Murray	.60	.45	.25
5	Dale Murphy	.50	.40	.20
6	Rickey Henderson	1.00	.70	.40
7	Harold Baines	.20	.15	.08
8	Cal Ripken, Jr.	2.00	1.50	.80
9	Orel Hershiser	.25	.20	.10
10	Bret Saberhagen	.15	.11	.06
11	Tim Raines	.20	.15	.08
12	Fernando Valenzuela	.15	.11	.06
13	Tony Gwynn	.45	.35	.20
14	Pedro Guerrero	.15	.11	.06
15	Keith Hernandez	.15	.11	.06
16	Ernest Riles	.10	.08	.04
17	Jim Rice	.30	.25	.12
18	Ron Guidry	.15	.11	.06
19	Willie McGee	.25	.20	.10
20	Ryne Sandberg	2.00	1.50	.80
21	Kirk Gibson	.20	.15	.08
22	Ozzie Guillen	.30	.25	.12
23	Dave Parker	.60	.45	.25
24	Vince Coleman	.35	.25	.14
25	Tom Seaver	.75	.60	.30
26	Brett Butler	.10	.08	.04
27	Steve Carlton	.75	.60	.30
28	Gary Carter	.35	.25	.14
29	Cecil Cooper	.10	.08	.04
30	Jose Cruz	.10	.08	.04
31	Alvin Davis	.10	.08	.04
32	Dwight Evans	.15	.11	.06
33	Julio Franco	.15	.11	.06
34	Damaso Garcia	.10	.08	.04
35	Steve Garvey	.40	.30	.15
36	Kent Hrbek	.25	.20	.10
37	Reggie Jackson	1.00	.70	.40
38	Fred Lynn	.20	.15	.08
39	Paul Molitor	.60	.45	.25
40	Jim Presley	.10	.08	.04
41	Dave Righetti	.20	.15	.08
42a	Robin Yount (Yankees logo on back)	150.00	125.00	60.00
42b	Robin Yount (Brewers logo)	1.25	.90	.50
43	Nolan Ryan	2.00	1.50	.80
44	Mike Schmidt	1.25	.90	.50
45	Lee Smith	.15	.11	.06
46	Rick Sutcliffe	.15	.11	.06
47	Bruce Sutter	.15	.11	.06
48	Lou Whitaker	.20	.15	.08
49	Dave Winfield	.60	.45	.25
50	Pete Rose	1.50	1.25	.60
51	N.L. MVPs (Steve Garvey, Pete Rose, Ryne Sandberg)	.70	.50	.30
52	Slugging Stars (Harold Baines, George Brett, Jim Rice)	.35	.25	.14
53	No-Hitters (Phil Niekro, Jerry Reuss, Mike Witt)	.15	.11	.06
54	Big Hitters (Don Mattingly, Cal Ripken, Jr., Robin Yount)	1.25	.90	.50
55	Bullpen Aces (Goose Gossage, Dan Quisenberry, Lee Smith)	.10	.08	.04
56	Rookies of the Year (Pete Rose, Steve Sax, Darryl Strawberry)	.80	.60	.30
57	A.L. MVPs (Don Baylor, Reggie Jackson, Cal Ripken, Jr.)	.35	.25	.14
58	Repeat Batting Champs (Bill Madlock, Dave Parker, Pete Rose)	.60	.45	.25
59	Cy Young Winners (Mike Flanagan, Ron Guidry, LaMarr Hoyt)	.10	.08	.04
60	Double Award Winners (Tom Seaver, Rick Sutcliffe, Fernando Valenzuela)	.20	.15	.08
61	Home Run Champs (Tony Armas, Reggie Jackson, Jim Rice)	.25	.20	.10
62	N.L. MVPs (Keith Hernandez, Dale Murphy, Mike Schmidt)	.50	.40	.20
63	A.L. MVPs (George Brett, Fred Lynn, Robin Yount)	.30	.25	.12
64	Comeback Players (Bert Blyleven, John Denny, Jerry Koosman)	.10	.08	.04
65	Cy Young Relievers (Rollie Fingers, Willie Hernandez, Bruce Sutter)	.15	.11	.06
66	Rookies of the Year (Andre Dawson, Bob Horner, Gary Matthews)	.30	.20	.10
67	Rookies of the Year (Carlton Fisk, Ron Kittle, Tom Seaver)	.15	.11	.06
68	Home Run Champs (George Foster, Dave Kingman, Mike Schmidt)	.30	.25	.12
69	Double Award Winners (Rod Carew, Cal Ripken, Jr., Pete Rose)	1.00	.70	.40
70	Cy Young Winners (Steve Carlton, Tom Seaver, Rick Sutcliffe)	.25	.20	.10
71	Top Sluggers (Reggie Jackson, Fred Lynn, Robin Yount)	.30	.25	.12
72	Rookies of the Year (Dave Righetti, Rick Sutcliffe, Fernando Valenzuela)	.15	.11	.06
73	Rookies of the Year (Fred Lynn, Eddie Murray, Cal Ripken, Jr.)	.25	.20	.10
74	Rookies of the Year (Rod Carew, Alvin Davis, Lou Whitaker)	.20	.15	.08
75	Batting Champs (Wade Boggs, Carney Lansford, Don Mattingly)	1.50	1.25	.60
76	Jesse Barfield	.15	.11	.06
77	Phil Bradley	.15	.11	.06
78	Chris Brown	.10	.08	.04
79	Tom Browning	.30	.25	.12
80	Tom Brunansky	.15	.11	.06
81	Bill Buckner	.10	.08	.04
82	Chili Davis	.15	.11	.06
83	Mike Davis	.10	.08	.04
84	Rich Gedman	.10	.08	.04
85	Willie Hernandez	.10	.08	.04
86	Ron Kittle	.10	.08	.04
87	Lee Lacy	.10	.08	.04
88	Bill Madlock	.15	.11	.06
89	Mike Marshall	.15	.11	.06
90	Keith Moreland	.10	.08	.04
91	Graig Nettles	.15	.11	.06
92	Lance Parrish	.20	.15	.08
93	Kirby Puckett	2.00	1.50	.80
94	Juan Samuel	.15	.11	.06
95	Steve Sax	.15	.11	.06
96	Dave Stieb	.10	.08	.04
97	Darryl Strawberry	1.00	.70	.40
98	Willie Upshaw	.10	.08	.04
99	Frank Viola	.25	.20	.10
100	Dwight Gooden	2.00	1.50	.80
101	Joaquin Andujar	.10	.08	.04
102	George Bell	.20	.15	.08
103	Bert Blyleven	.15	.11	.06
104	Mike Boddicker	.10	.08	.04
105	Britt Burns	.10	.08	.04
106	Rod Carew	1.25	.90	.50
107	Jack Clark	.15	.11	.06
108	Danny Cox	.10	.08	.04
109	Ron Darling	.15	.11	.06
110	Andre Dawson	.25	.20	.10
111	Leon Durham	.10	.08	.04
112	Tony Fernandez	.15	.11	.06
113	Tom Herr	.10	.08	.04
114	Teddy Higuera	.10	.08	.04
115	Bob Horner	.15	.11	.06
116	Dave Kingman	.15	.11	.06
117	Jack Morris	.15	.11	.06
118	Dan Quisenberry	.10	.08	.04
119	Jeff Reardon	.15	.11	.06
120	Bryn Smith	.10	.08	.04
121	Ozzie Smith	.25	.20	.10
122	John Tudor	.10	.08	.04
123	Tim Wallach	.15	.11	.06
124	Willie Wilson	.15	.11	.06
125	Carlton Fisk	.25	.20	.10
126	RBI Sluggers (Gary Carter, George Foster, Al Oliver)	.15	.11	.06
127	Run Scorers (Keith Hernandez, Tim Raines, Ryne Sandberg)	.25	.20	.10
128	Run Scorers (Paul Molitor, Cal Ripken, Jr., Willie Wilson)	.20	.15	.08
129	No-Hitters (John Candelaria, Dennis Eckersley, Bob Forsch)	.10	.08	.04
130	World Series MVPs (Ron Cey, Rollie Fingers, Pete Rose)	.50	.40	.20

No.	Player	MT	NR MT	EX
131	All-Star Game MVPs (Dave Concepcion, George Foster, Bill Madlock)	.10	.08	.04
132	Cy Young Winners (Vida Blue, John Denny, Fernando Valenzuela)	.15	.11	.06
133	Comeback Players (Doyle Alexander, Joaquin Andujar, Richard Dotson)	.10	.08	.04
134	Big Winners (John Denny, Tom Seaver, Rick Sutcliffe)	.15	.11	.06
135	Veteran Pitchers (Phil Niekro, Tom Seaver, Don Sutton)	.25	.20	.10
136	Rookies of the Year (Vince Coleman, Dwight Gooden, Alfredo Griffin)	.80	.60	.30
137	All-Star Game MVPs (Gary Carter, Steve Garvey, Fred Lynn)	.20	.15	.08
138	Veteran Hitters (Tony Perez, Pete Rose, Rusty Staub)	.50	.40	.20
139	Power Hitters (George Foster, Jim Rice, Mike Schmidt)	.30	.25	.12
140	Batting Champs (Bill Buckner, Tony Gwynn, Al Oliver)	.20	.15	.08
141	No-Hitters (Jack Morris, Dave Righetti, Nolan Ryan)	.20	.15	.08
142	No-Hitters (Vida Blue, Bert Blyleven, Tom Seaver)	.15	.11	.06
143	Strikeout Kings (Dwight Gooden, Nolan Ryan, Fernando Valenzuela)	1.25	.90	.50
144	Base Stealers (Dave Lopes, Tim Raines, Willie Wilson)	.15	.11	.06
145	RBI Sluggers (Tony Armas, Cecil Cooper, Eddie Murray)	.15	.11	.06
146	A.L. MVPs (Rod Carew, Rollie Fingers, Jim Rice)	.25	.20	.10
147	World Series MVPs (Rick Dempsey, Reggie Jackson, Alan Trammell)	.25	.20	.10
148	World Series MVPs (Pedro Guerrero, Darrell Porter, Mike Schmidt)	.20	.15	.08
149	ERA Leaders (Mike Boddicker, Ron Guidry, Rick Sutcliffe)	.10	.08	.04
150	Comeback Players (Reggie Jackson, Dave Kingman, Fred Lynn)	.20	.15	.08
151	Buddy Bell	.15	.11	.06
152	Dennis Boyd	.10	.08	.04
153	Dave Concepcion	.15	.11	.06
154	Brian Downing	.10	.08	.04
155	Shawon Dunston	.15	.11	.06
156	John Franco	.15	.11	.06
157	Scott Garrelts	.10	.08	.04
158	Bob James	.10	.08	.04
159	Charlie Leibrandt	.10	.08	.04
160	Oddibe McDowell	.10	.08	.04
161	Roger McDowell	.15	.11	.06
162	Mike Moore	.10	.08	.04
163	Phil Niekro	.25	.20	.10
164	Al Oliver	.15	.11	.06
165	Tony Pena	.10	.08	.04
166	Ted Power	.10	.08	.04
167	Mike Scioscia	.10	.08	.04
168	Mario Soto	.10	.08	.04
169	Bob Stanley	.10	.08	.04
170	Garry Templeton	.10	.08	.04
171	Andre Thornton	.10	.08	.04
172	Alan Trammell	.30	.25	.12
173	Doug DeCinces	.10	.08	.04
174	Greg Walker	.10	.08	.04
175	Don Sutton	.25	.20	.10
176	1985 Award Winners (Vince Coleman, Dwight Gooden, Ozzie Guillen, Don Mattingly, Wille McGee, Bret Saberhagen)	1.00	.70	.40
177	1985 Hot Rookies (Stewart Cliburn, Brian Fisher, Joe Hesketh, Joe Orsulak, Mark Salas, Larry Sheets)	.20	.15	.08
178 a	Future Stars (Jose Canseco (FC), Mark Funderburk, Mike Greenwell, Steve Lombardozzi, Billy Joe Robidoux, Danny Tartabull)	8.00	4.00	2.00
178b	Future Stars (Jose Canseco, Mike Greenwell, Steve Lombardozzi, Billy Joe Robidoux, Danny Tartabull, Jim Wilson)	60.00	45.00	24.00
179	Gold Glove (George Brett, Ron Guidry, Keith Hernandez, Don Mattingly, Willie McGee, Dale Murphy)	1.25	.90	.50
180	.300 (Wade Boggs, George Brett, Rod Carew, Cecil Cooper, Don Mattingly, Willie Wilson)	1.25	.90	.50
181	.300 (Pedro Guerrero, Tony Gwynn, Keith Hernandez, Bill Madlock, Dave Parker, Pete Rose)	.70	.50	.30
182	1985 Milestones (Rod Carew, Phil Niekro, Pete Rose, Nolan Ryan, Tom Seaver, Matt Tallman)	1.50	1.25	.60
183	1985 Triple Crown (Wade Boggs, Darrell Evans, Don Mattingly, Willie McGee, Dale Murphy, Dave Parker)	1.25	.90	.50
184	1985 HL (Wade Boggs, Dwight Gooden, Rickey Henderson, Don Mattingly, Willie McGee, John Tudor)	1.50	1.25	.60
185	1985 20-Game Winners (Joaquin Andujar, Tom Browning, Dwight Gooden, Ron Guidry, Bret Saberhagen, John Tudor)	.60	.45	.25
186	World Series Champs (Steve Balboni, George Brett, Dane Iorg, Danny Jackson, Charlie Leibrandt, Darryl Motley, Dan Quisenberry, Bret Saberhagen, Lonnie Smith, Jim Sundberg, Frank White, Willie Wilson)	.40	.30	.15
187	Hubie Brooks	.10	.08	.04
188	Glenn Davis	.15	.11	.06
189	Darrell Evans	.10	.08	.04
190	Rich Gossage	.15	.11	.06
191	Andy Hawkins	.10	.08	.04
192	Jay Howell	.10	.08	.04
193	LaMarr Hoyt	.10	.08	.04
194	Davey Lopes	.10	.08	.04
195	Mike Scott	.20	.15	.08
196	Ted Simmons	.15	.11	.06
197	Gary Ward	.10	.08	.04
198	Bob Welch	.15	.11	.06
199	Mike Young	.10	.08	.04
200	Buddy Biancalana	.10	.08	.04

1986 Sportflics Decade Greats

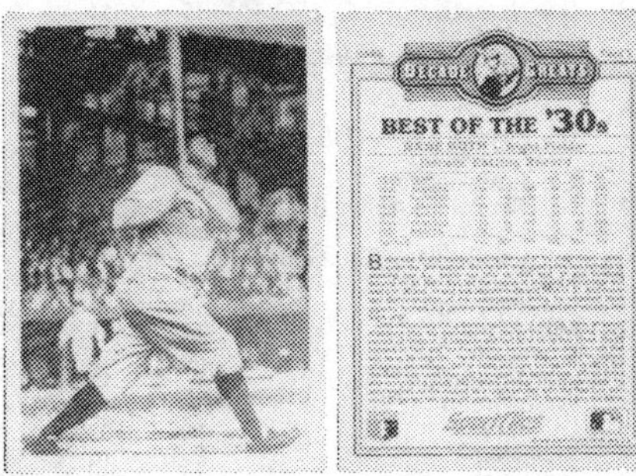

This set, produced by Sportflics, features outstanding players, by position, from the 1930s to the 1980s by decades. The card fronts are printed in sepia-toned photos or full-color with the Sportflics three-phase "Magic Motion" animation. The complete set contains 75 cards with 59 single player cards and 16 multi-player cards. Biographies appear on the card backs which are printed in full-color and color-coded by decade. The set was distributed only through hobby dealers and is in the popular 2-1/2" by 3-1/2" size.

		MT	NR MT	EX
	Complete Set:	15.00	11.00	6.00
	Common Player:	.15	.11	.06
1	Babe Ruth	3.50	2.75	1.50
2	Jimmie Foxx	.40	.30	.15
3	Lefty Grove	.30	.25	.12
4	Hank Greenberg	.30	.25	.12
5	Al Simmons	.15	.11	.06
6	Carl Hubbell	.30	.25	.12
7	Joe Cronin	.25	.20	.10
8	Mel Ott	.30	.25	.12
9	Lefty Gomez	.30	.25	.12
10	Lou Gehrig	1.50	1.25	.60
11	Pie Traynor	.15	.11	.06
12	Charlie Gehringer	.30	.25	.12
13	Catchers (Mickey Cochrane, Bill Dickey, Gabby Hartnett)	.30	.25	.12
14	Pitchers (Dizzy Dean, Paul Derringer, Red Ruffing)	.30	.25	.12
15	Outfielders (Earl Averill, Joe Medwick, Paul Waner)	.15	.11	.06
16	Bob Feller	.60	.45	.25
17	Lou Boudreau	.15	.11	.06
18	Enos Slaughter	.25	.20	.10
19	Hal Newhouser	.15	.11	.06
20	Joe DiMaggio	1.50	1.25	.60
21	Pee Wee Reese	.40	.30	.15
22	Phil Rizzuto	.30	.25	.12
23	Ernie Lombardi	.15	.11	.06
24	Infielders (Joe Cronin, George Kell, Johnny Mize)	.15	.11	.06
25	Ted Williams	1.25	.90	.50
26	Mickey Mantle	3.50	2.75	1.50
27	Warren Spahn	.30	.25	.12
28	Jackie Robinson	1.00	.70	.40
29	Ernie Banks	.30	.25	.12
30	Stan Musial	1.00	.70	.40
31	Yogi Berra	.60	.45	.25
32	Duke Snider	.70	.50	.30
33	Roy Campanella	.70	.50	.30
34	Eddie Mathews	.30	.25	.12
35	Ralph Kiner	.30	.25	.12
36	Early Wynn	.25	.20	.10
37	Double Play Duo (Luis Aparicio, Nellie Fox)	.25	.20	.10
38	First Basemen (Gil Hodges, Ted Kluszewski, Mickey Vernon)	.25	.20	.10
40	Henry Aaron	1.00	.70	.40
41	Frank Robinson	.30	.25	.12
42	Bob Gibson	.30	.25	.12
43	Roberto Clemente	1.00	.70	.40
44	Whitey Ford	.40	.30	.15
45	Brooks Robinson	.50	.40	.20
46	Juan Marichal	.25	.20	.10
47	Carl Yastrzemski	1.00	.70	.40
48	First Basemen (Orlando Cepeda, Harmon Killebrew, Willie McCovey)	.30	.25	.12
49	Catchers (Bill Freehan, Elston Howard, Joe Torre)	.15	.11	.06
50	Willie Mays	1.00	.70	.40
51	Outfielders (Al Kaline, Tony Oliva, Billy Williams)	.30	.25	.12
52	Tom Seaver	.60	.45	.25
53	Reggie Jackson	.70	.50	.30
54	Steve Carlton	.40	.30	.15
55	Mike Schmidt	.70	.50	.30
56	Joe Morgan	.25	.20	.10
57	Jim Rice	.40	.30	.15
58	Jim Palmer	.30	.25	.12
59	Lou Brock	.30	.25	.12
60	Pete Rose	1.25	.90	.50
61	Steve Garvey	.40	.30	.15
62	Catchers (Carlton Fisk, Thurman Munson, Ted Simmons)	.25	.20	.10
63	Pitchers (Vida Blue, Catfish Hunter, Nolan Ryan)	.30	.25	.12
64	George Brett	.80	.60	.30
65	Don Mattingly	1.25	.90	.50
66	Fernando Valenzuela	.30	.25	.12
67	Dale Murphy	.80	.60	.30
68	Wade Boggs	1.50	1.25	.60
69	Rickey Henderson	.60	.45	.25
70	Eddie Murray	.60	.45	.25
71	Ron Guidry	.25	.20	.10
72	Catchers (Gary Carter, Lance Parrish, Tony Pena)	.30	.25	.12
73	Infielders (Cal Ripken, Jr., Lou Whitaker, Robin Yount)	.30	.25	.12
74	Outfielders (Pedro Guerrero, Tim Raines, Dave Winfield)	.30	.25	.12
75	Dwight Gooden	1.00	.70	.40

1986 Sportflics Rookies

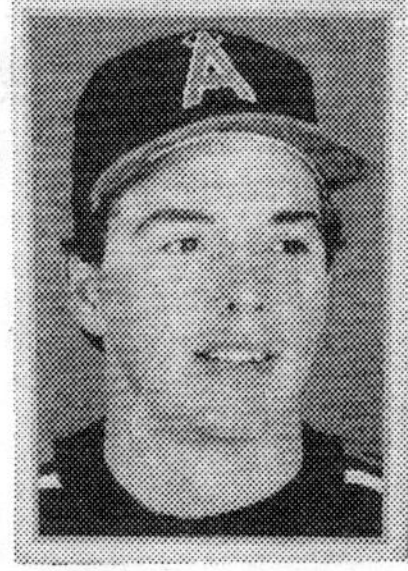

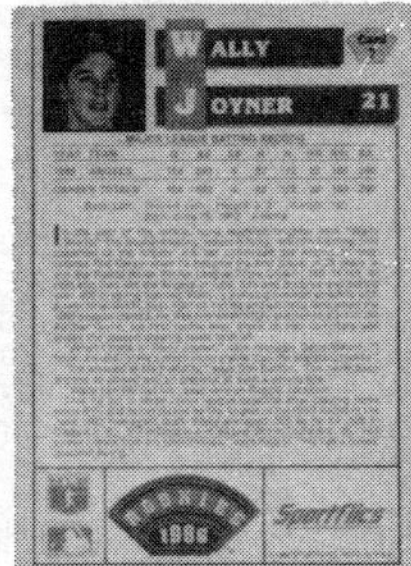

The 1986 Rookies set issued by Sportflics offers 50 cards and features 47 individual rookie players. In addition, there are two Tri-Star cards; one highlights former Rookies of the Year and the other features three prominent players. There is one "Big Six" card featuring six superstars. The full-color photos on the 2-1/2" by 3-1/2" cards use Sportflics three-phase "Magic Motion" animation. The set was packaged in an attractive collector box which also contained 34 trivia cards that measure 1-3/4" by 2". The set was distributed only by hobby dealers. For its second season in the national baseball card

		MT	NR MT	EX
	Complete Set:	16.00	12.00	6.50
	Common Player:	.20	.15	.08
1	John Kruk	.80	.60	.30
2	Edwin Correa	.20	.15	.08
3	Pete Incaviglia	.25	.20	.10
4	Dale Sveum	.20	.15	.08
5	Juan Nieves	.20	.15	.08
6	Will Clark	3.00	2.25	1.25
7	Wally Joyner	.80	.60	.30
8	Lance McCullers	.20	.15	.08
9	Scott Bailes	.20	.15	.08
10	Dan Plesac	.20	.15	.08
11	Jose Canseco	3.00	2.25	1.25
12	Bobby Witt	.40	.30	.15
13	Barry Bonds	3.00	2.25	1.25
14	Andres Thomas	.20	.15	.08
15	Jim Deshaies	.30	.25	.12
16	Ruben Sierra	1.50	1.25	.60
17	Steve Lombardozzi	.20	.15	.08
18	Cory Snyder	.25	.20	.10
19	Reggie Williams	.20	.15	.08
20	Mitch Williams	.25	.20	.10
21	Glenn Braggs	.20	.15	.08
22	Danny Tartabull	.80	.60	.30
23	Charlie Kerfeld	.20	.15	.08
24	Paul Assenmacher	.20	.15	.08
25	Robby Thompson	.50	.40	.20
26	Bobby Bonilla	.60	.45	.25
27	Andres Galarraga	.60	.45	.25
28	Billy Jo Robidoux	.20	.15	.08
29	Bruce Ruffin	.20	.15	.08
30	Greg Swindell	.40	.30	.15
31	John Cangelosi	.20	.15	.08
32	Jim Traber	.20	.15	.08
33	Russ Morman	.20	.15	.08
34	Barry Larkin	.75	.60	.30
35	Todd Worrell	.25	.20	.10
36	John Cerutti	.20	.15	.08
37	Mike Kingery	.20	.15	.08
38	Mark Eichhorn	.20	.15	.08
39	Scott Bankhead	.20	.15	.08
40	Bo Jackson	1.00	.70	.40
41	Greg Mathews	.30	.25	.12
42	Eric King	.20	.15	.08
43	Kal Daniels	.20	.15	.08
44	Calvin Schiraldi	.20	.15	.08
45	Mickey Brantley	.20	.15	.08
46	Outstanding Rookie Seasons (Fred Lynn, Willie Mays, Pete Rose)	.40	.30	.15
47	Outstanding Rookie Seasons (Dwight Gooden, Tom Seaver, Fernando Valenzuela)	.40	.30	.15
48	Outstanding Rookie Seasons (Eddie Murray, Dave Righetti, Cal Ripken, Jr., Steve Sax, Darryl Strawberry, Lou Whitaker)	.60	.45	.25
49	Kevin Mitchell	.60	.45	.25
50	Mike Diaz	.20	.15	.08

Regional interest may affect the value of a card.

1987 Sportflics

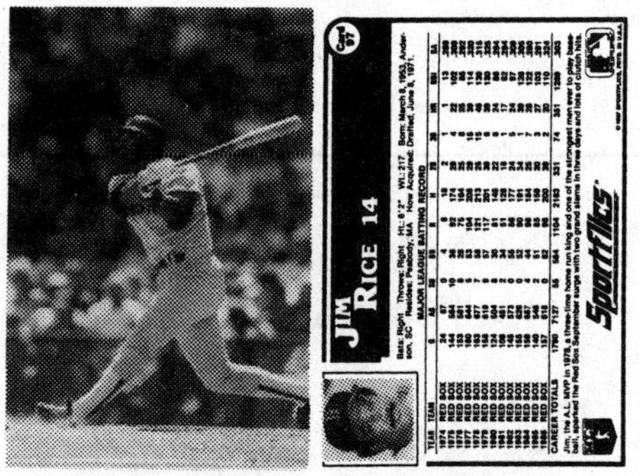

In its second year in the national market, Sportflics' basic issue was again a 200-card set of 2-1/2" by 3-1/2" "Magic Motion" cards, which offer three different photos on the same card, each visible in turn as the card is moved from top to bottom or side to side. Besides single-player cards, the '87 Sportflics set includes several three- and six-player cards, though not as many as in the 1986 set. The card backs feature a small player portrait photo on the single-player cards, an innovation for 1987.

		MT	NR MT	EX
Complete Set (200):		30.00	22.00	12.00
Common Player:		.10	.08	.04
1	Don Mattingly	2.00	1.50	.80
2	Wade Boggs	1.50	1.25	.60
3	Dale Murphy	.50	.40	.20
4	Rickey Henderson	1.00	.70	.40
5	George Brett	2.00	1.50	.80
6	Eddie Murray	.50	.40	.20
7	Kirby Puckett	.90	.70	.35
8	Ryne Sandberg	3.00	2.25	1.25
9	Cal Ripken, Jr.	3.00	2.25	1.25
10	Roger Clemens	1.00	.70	.40
11	Ted Higuera	.15	.11	.06
12	Steve Sax	.10	.08	.04
13	Chris Brown	.10	.08	.04
14	Jesse Barfield	.15	.11	.06
15	Kent Hrbek	.20	.15	.08
16	Robin Yount	1.50	1.25	.60
17	Glenn Davis	.10	.08	.04
18	Hubie Brooks	.10	.08	.04
19	Mike Scott	.15	.11	.06
20	Darryl Strawberry	.45	.35	.20
21	Alvin Davis	.15	.11	.06
22	Eric Davis	.35	.25	.14
23	Danny Tartabull	.30	.25	.12
24a	Cory Snyder (Pat Tabler photo on back)	2.00	1.50	.80
24b	Cory Snyder (Pat Tabler photo on back (facing front), 1/4 swing on front)	2.00	1.50	.80
24c	Cory Snyder (Snyder photo on back (facing to side))	1.00	.70	.40
25	Pete Rose	1.00	.70	.40
26	Wally Joyner	.40	.30	.15
27	Pedro Guerrero	.20	.15	.08
28	Tom Seaver	.75	.60	.30
29	Bob Knepper	.10	.08	.04
30	Mike Schmidt	1.00	.70	.40
31	Tony Gwynn	.50	.40	.20
32	Don Slaught	.10	.08	.04
33	Todd Worrell	.30	.25	.12
34	Tim Raines	.20	.15	.08
35	Dave Parker	.40	.30	.15
36	Bob Ojeda	.10	.08	.04
37	Pete Incaviglia	.20	.15	.08
38	Bruce Hurst	.15	.11	.06
39	Bobby Witt	.20	.15	.08
40	Steve Garvey	.40	.30	.15
41	Dave Winfield	.90	.70	.35
42	Jose Cruz	.10	.08	.04
43	Orel Hershiser	.30	.25	.12
44	Reggie Jackson	1.00	.70	.40
45	Chili Davis	.10	.08	.04
46	Robby Thompson	.20	.15	.08
47	Dennis Boyd	.10	.08	.04
48	Kirk Gibson	.20	.15	.08
49	Fred Lynn	.20	.15	.08
50	Gary Carter	.30	.25	.12
51	George Bell	.15	.11	.06
52	Pete O'Brien	.10	.08	.04
53	Ron Darling	.15	.11	.06
54	Paul Molitor	.60	.45	.25
55	Mike Pagliarulo	.15	.11	.06
56	Mike Boddicker	.10	.08	.04
57	Dave Righetti	.20	.15	.08
58	Len Dykstra (FC)	.30	.25	.12
59	Mike Witt	.10	.08	.04
60	Tony Bernazard	.10	.08	.04
61	John Kruk	.30	.25	.12
62	Mike Krukow	.10	.08	.04
63	Sid Fernandez	.15	.11	.06
64	Gary Gaetti	.20	.15	.08
65	Vince Coleman	.30	.25	.12
66	Pat Tabler	.10	.08	.04
67	Mike Scioscia	.10	.08	.04
68	Scott Garrelts	.10	.08	.04
69	Brett Butler	.10	.08	.04
70	Bill Buckner	.10	.08	.04
71a	Dennis Rasmussen (John Montefusco photo on back)	.25	.20	.10
71b	Dennis Rasmussen (Rasmussen photo on back)	.15	.11	.06
72	Tim Wallach	.15	.11	.06
73	Bob Horner	.15	.11	.06
74	Willie McGee	.15	.11	.06
75	A.L. First Basemen (Wally Joyner, Don Mattingly, Eddie Murray)	.50	.40	.20
76	Jesse Orosco	.10	.08	.04
77	N.L. Relief Pitchers (Jeff Reardon, Dave Smith, Todd Worrell)	.15	.11	.06
78	Candy Maldonado	.10	.08	.04
79	N.L. Shortstops (Hubie Brooks, Shawon Dunston, Ozzie Smith)	.15	.11	.06
80	A.L. Left Fielders (George Bell, Jose Canseco, Jim Rice)	.50	.40	.20
81	Bert Blyleven	.15	.11	.06
82	Mike Marshall	.15	.11	.06
83	Ron Guidry	.20	.15	.08
84	Julio Franco	.15	.11	.06
85	Willie Wilson	.15	.11	.06
86	Lee Lacy	.10	.08	.04
87	Jack Morris	.20	.15	.08
88	Ray Knight	.10	.08	.04
89	Phil Bradley	.15	.11	.06
90	Jose Canseco	2.00	1.50	.80
91	Gary Ward	.10	.08	.04
92	Mike Easler	.10	.08	.04
93	Tony Pena	.10	.08	.04
94	Dave Smith	.10	.08	.04
95	Will Clark	2.00	1.50	.80
96	Lloyd Moseby	.10	.08	.04
97	Jim Rice	.20	.15	.08
98	Shawon Dunston	.15	.11	.06
99	Don Sutton	.40	.30	.15
100	Dwight Gooden	.50	.40	.20
101	Lance Parrish	.20	.15	.08
102	Mark Langston	.15	.11	.06
103	Floyd Youmans	.10	.08	.04
104	Lee Smith	.25	.20	.10
105	Willie Hernandez	.10	.08	.04
106	Doug DeCinces	.10	.08	.04
107	Ken Schrom	.10	.08	.04
108	Don Carman	.10	.08	.04
109	Brook Jacoby	.15	.11	.06
110	Steve Bedrosian	.15	.11	.06
111	A.L. Pitchers (Roger Clemens, Teddy Higuera, Jack Morris)	.25	.20	.10
112	A.L. Second Basemen (Marty Barrett, Tony Bernazard, Lou Whitaker)	.10	.08	.04
113	A.L. Shortstops (Tony Fernandez, Scott Fletcher, Cal Ripken, Jr.)	.25	.20	.10
114	A.L. Third Basemen (Wade Boggs, George Brett, Gary Gaetti)	.60	.45	.25
115	N.L. Third Basemen (Chris Brown, Mike Schmidt, Tim Wallach)	.35	.25	.14
116	N.L. Second Basemen (Bill Doran, Johnny Ray, Ryne Sandberg)	.15	.11	.06
117	N.L. Right Fielders (Kevin Bass, Tony Gwynn, Dave Parker)	.25	.20	.10
118	Hot Rookie Prospects (David Clark, Pat Dodson, Ty Gainey, Phil Lombardi, Benito Santiago, Terry Steinbach)	1.00	.70	.40
119	1986 Season Highlights (Dave Righetti, Mike Scott, Fernando Valenzuela)	.15	.11	.06
120	N.L. Pitchers (Dwight Gooden, Mike Scott, Fernando Valenzuela)	.25	.20	.10
121	Johnny Ray	.10	.08	.04
122	Keith Moreland	.10	.08	.04
123	Juan Samuel	.15	.11	.06
124	Wally Backman	.10	.08	.04
125	Nolan Ryan	2.00	1.50	.80
126	Greg Harris	.10	.08	.04
127	Kirk McCaskill	.10	.08	.04
128	Dwight Evans	.15	.11	.06
129	Rick Rhoden	.10	.08	.04
130	Bill Madlock	.15	.11	.06
131	Oddibe McDowell	.10	.08	.04
132	Darrell Evans	.10	.08	.04
133	Keith Hernandez	.15	.11	.06
134	Tom Brunansky	.15	.11	.06
135	Kevin McReynolds	.20	.15	.08
136	Scott Fletcher	.10	.08	.04
137	Lou Whitaker	.20	.15	.08
138	Carney Lansford	.10	.08	.04
139	Andre Dawson	.35	.25	.14
140	Carlton Fisk	.35	.25	.14
141	Buddy Bell	.15	.11	.06
142	Ozzie Smith	.35	.25	.14
143	Dan Pasqua	.15	.11	.06
144	Kevin Mitchell	.20	.15	.08
145	Bret Saberhagen	.25	.20	.10
146	Charlie Kerfeld	.10	.08	.04
147	Phil Niekro	.25	.20	.10
148	John Candelaria	.10	.08	.04
149	Rich Gedman	.10	.08	.04
150	Fernando Valenzuela	.15	.11	.06
151	N.L. Catchers (Gary Carter, Tony Pena, Mike Scioscia)	.15	.11	.06
152	N.L. Left Fielders (Vince Coleman, Jose Cruz, Tim Raines)	.20	.15	.08
153	A.L. Right Fielders (Harold Baines, Jesse Barfield, Dave Winfield)	.25	.20	.10
154	A.L. Catchers (Rich Gedman, Lance Parrish, Don Slaught)	.10	.08	.04
155	N.L. Center Fielders (Eric Davis, Kevin McReynolds, Dale Murphy)	.30	.25	.12
156	'86 Highlights (Jim Deshaies, Mike Schmidt, Don Sutton)	.30	.25	.12
157	A.L. Speedburners (John Cangelosi, Rickey Henderson, Gary Pettis)	.25	.20	.10
158	Hot Rookie Prospects (Randy Asadoor, Casey Candaele, Dave Cochrane, Rafael Palmeiro, Tim Pyznarski, Kevin Seitzer)	1.25	.90	.50
159	The Best of the Best (Roger Clemens, Dwight Gooden, Rickey Henderson, Don Mattingly, Dale Murphy, Eddie Murray)	1.25	.90	.50
160	Roger McDowell	.15	.11	.06
161	Brian Downing	.10	.08	.04
162	Bill Doran	.10	.08	.04
163	Don Baylor	.15	.11	.06
164	Alfredo Griffin	.10	.08	.04
165	Don Aase	.10	.08	.04
166	Glenn Wilson	.10	.08	.04
167	Dan Quisenberry	.10	.08	.04
168	Frank White	.10	.08	.04
169	Cecil Cooper	.15	.11	.06
170	Jody Davis	.10	.08	.04
171	Harold Baines	.20	.15	.08
172	Rob Deer	.10	.08	.04
173	John Tudor	.15	.11	.06
174	Larry Parrish	.10	.08	.04
175	Kevin Bass	.10	.08	.04
176	Joe Carter	.35	.25	.14
177	Mitch Webster	.10	.08	.04
178	Dave Kingman	.15	.11	.06
179	Jim Presley	.15	.11	.06
180	Mel Hall	.10	.08	.04
181	Shane Rawley	.10	.08	.04
182	Marty Barrett	.10	.08	.04
183	Damaso Garcia	.10	.08	.04
184	Bobby Grich	.10	.08	.04
185	Leon Durham	.10	.08	.04
186	Ozzie Guillen	.15	.11	.06
187	Tony Fernandez	.15	.11	.06
188	Alan Trammell	.30	.25	.12
189	Jim Clancy	.10	.08	.04
190	Bo Jackson	1.00	.70	.40
191	Bob Forsch	.10	.08	.04
192	John Franco	.10	.08	.04
193	Von Hayes	.10	.08	.04
194	A.L. Relief Pitchers (Don Aase, Mark Eichhorn, Dave Righetti)	.10	.08	.04
195	N.L. First Basemen (Will Clark, Glenn Davis, Keith Hernandez)	.50	.40	.20
196	'86 Highlights (Roger Clemens, Joe Cowley, Bob Horner)	.35	.25	.14
197	The Best of the Best (Wade Boggs, George Brett, Hubie Brooks, Tony Gwynn, Tim Raines, Ryne Sandberg)	.80	.60	.30
198	A.L. Center Fielders (Rickey Henderson, Fred Lynn, Kirby Puckett)	.25	.20	.10
199	N.L. Speedburners (Vince Coleman, Eric Davis, Tim Raines)	.35	.25	.14
200	Steve Carlton	.75	.60	.30

1987 Sportflics Rookie Discs

The 1987 Sportflics Rookie Discs set consists of seven discs which measure 4" in diameter. The front of the discs offer three "Magic Motion" photos in full color, encompassed by a blue border. The disc backs are printed in red, blue, yellow and green and include the team logo, player statistics, player biography and the disc number. The set was issued with Cooperstown Timeless Trivia Cards.

		MT	NR MT	EX
Complete Set:		12.00	9.00	4.75
Common Player:		1.00	.70	.40
1	Casey Candaele	1.00	.70	.40
2	Mark McGwire	3.00	2.25	1.25
3	Kevin Seitzer	1.00	.70	.40
4	Joe Magrane	1.50	1.25	.60
5	Benito Santiago	2.50	2.00	1.00
6	Dave Magadan	1.50	1.25	.60
7	Devon White	2.50	2.00	1.00

1987 Sportflics Rookie Prospects

The 1987 Sportflics Rookie Prospects set consists of 10 cards that are the standard 2-1/2" by 3-1/2" size. The card fronts feature Sportflics' "Magic Motion" process. Card backs contain a player photo plus a short biography and player personal and statistical information. The set was offered in two separately wrapped mylar packs of five cards to hobby

dealers purchasing cases of Sportflics' Team Preview set. Twenty-four packs of "Rookie Prospects" cards were included with each case.

		MT	NR MT	EX
Complete Set:		6.00	4.50	2.50
Common Player:		.50	.40	.20
1	Terry Steinbach	.70	.50	.30
2	Rafael Palmeiro	2.00	1.50	.80
3	Dave Magadan	.70	.50	.30
4	Marvin Freeman	.50	.40	.20
5	Brick Smith	.50	.40	.20
6	B.J. Surhoff	.70	.50	.30
7	John Smiley	.70	.50	.30
8	Alonzo Powell	.50	.40	.20
9	Benny Santiago	.80	.60	.30
10	Devon White	.70	.50	.30

1987 Sportflics Rookies

The 1987 Sportflics Rookies set was issued in two series of 25 cards. The first was released in July with the second series following in October. The cards, which are the standard 2-1/2" by 3-1/2", feature Sportflics' special "Magic Motion" process. The card fronts contain a full-color photo and present three different pictures, depending on how the card is held. The backs also contain a full-color photo along with player statistics and a biography.

		MT	NR MT	EX
Complete Set:		12.00	9.00	4.75
Common Player:		.20	.15	.08
1	Eric Bell	.20	.15	.08
2	Chris Bosio	.20	.15	.08
3	Bob Brower	.20	.15	.08
4	Jerry Browne	.30	.25	.12
5	Ellis Burks	.80	.60	.30
6	Casey Candaele	.20	.15	.08
7	Joey Cora	.20	.15	.08
8	Ken Gerhart	.20	.15	.08
9	Mike Greenwell	1.00	.70	.40
10	Stan Jefferson	.20	.15	.08
11	Dave Magadan	.70	.50	.30
12	Joe Magrane	.30	.25	.12
13	Fred McGriff	2.00	1.50	.80
14	Mark McGwire	2.00	1.50	.80
15	Mark McLemore	.30	.25	.12
16	Jeff Musselman	.20	.15	.08
17	Matt Nokes	.40	.30	.15
18	Paul O'Neill	.60	.45	.25
19	Luis Polonia	.30	.25	.12
20	Benny Santiago	.80	.60	.30
21	Kevin Seitzer	.20	.15	.08
22	Terry Steinbach	.30	.25	.12
23	B.J. Surhoff	.40	.30	.15
24	Devon White	.80	.60	.30
25	Matt Williams	.90	.70	.35
26	DeWayne Buice	.20	.15	.08
27	Willie Fraser	.20	.15	.08
28	Bill Ripken	.20	.15	.08
29	Mike Henneman	.30	.25	.12
30	Shawn Hillegas	.20	.15	.08
31	Shane Mack	.40	.30	.15
32	Rafael Palmeiro	1.50	1.25	.60
33	Mike Jackson	.20	.15	.08
34	Gene Larkin	.20	.15	.08
35	Jimmy Jones	.20	.15	.08
36	Gerald Young	.20	.15	.08
37	Ken Caminiti	.30	.25	.12
38	Sam Horn	.30	.25	.12
39	David Cone	.70	.50	.30
40	Mike Dunne	.30	.25	.12
41	Ken Williams	.20	.15	.08
42	John Morris	.20	.15	.08
43	Jim Lindeman	.20	.15	.08
44	Todd Benzinger	.30	.25	.12
45	Mike Stanley	.30	.25	.12
46	Les Straker	.20	.15	.08
47	Jeff Robinson	.30	.25	.12
48	Jeff Blauser	.30	.25	.12
49	John Marzano	.20	.15	.08
50	Keith Miller	.20	.15	.08

1987 Sportflics Superstar Discs

Released in three series of six discs and numbered 1 through 18, the 1987 Sportflics Superstar Disc set features the special "Magic Motion" process. Each disc, which measures 4-1/2" in diameter, contains three different player photos, depending which way it is tilted. A red border, containing eleven stars, the player's name and uniform number, surrounds the photo. The backs have a turquoise border which carries the words "Superstar Disc Collector Series." The backs also include the team logo, player statistics, player biography and the disc number. The discs were issued with eighteen 1-3/4" by 2-1/2" Cooperstown Timeless Trivia Cards.

		MT	NR MT	EX
Complete Set:		50.00	37.00	20.00
Common Player:		2.00	1.50	.80
1	Jose Canseco	4.00	3.00	1.50
2	Mike Scott	2.00	1.50	.80
3	Ryne Sandberg	5.00	3.75	2.00
4	Mike Schmidt	4.00	3.00	1.50
5	Dale Murphy	2.50	2.00	1.00
6	Fernando Valenzuela	2.00	1.50	.80
7	Tony Gwynn	3.50	2.75	1.50
8	Cal Ripken, Jr.	5.00	3.75	2.00
9	Gary Carter	2.00	1.50	.80
10	Cory Snyder	2.00	1.50	.80
11	Kirby Puckett	4.00	3.00	1.50
12	George Brett	5.00	3.75	2.00
13	Keith Hernandez	2.00	1.50	.80
14	Rickey Henderson	3.00	2.25	1.25
15	Tim Raines	2.50	2.00	1.00
16	Bo Jackson	2.50	2.00	1.00
17	Pete Rose	3.00	2.25	1.25
18	Eric Davis	2.00	1.50	.80

1987 Sportflics Team Preview

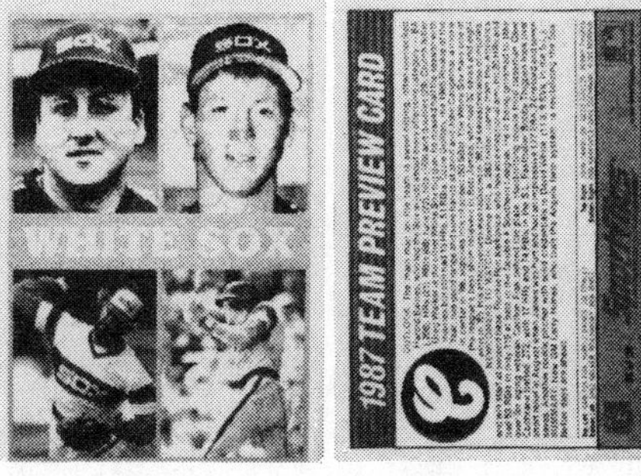

The 1987 Sportflics Team Preview set appeared to be a good idea, but never caught on with collectors. The intent of the set is to provide a pre-season look at each of the 26 major league clubs. The card backs contain three categories of the team preview: Outlook, Newcomers to Watch and Summary. Using the "Magic Motion" process, 12 different players are featured on the card fronts. Four of the different player photos can be made visible at once. The cards, which measure 2-1/2" by 3-1/2", were issued with team logo/trivia cards in a specially designed box.

		MT	NR MT	EX
Complete Set:		8.00	6.00	3.25
Common Team:		.50	.40	.20
1	Texas Rangers (Scott Fletcher, Greg Harris, Charlie Hough, Pete Incaviglia, Mike Loynd, Oddibe McDowell, Pete O'Brien, Larry Parrish, Ruben Sierra, Don Slaught, Mitch Williams, Bobby Witt)	.50	.40	.20
2	New York Mets (Wally Backman, Gary Carter, Ron Darling, Lenny Dykstra, Sid Fernandez, Dwight Gooden, Keith Hernandez, Dave Magadan, Kevin McReynolds, Randy Myers, Bob Ojeda, Darryl Strawberry)	.70	.50	.30
3	Cleveland Indians (Tony Bernazard, Brett Butler, Tom Candiotti, Joe Carter, Julio Franco, Mel Hall, Brook Jacoby, Phil Niekro, Ken Schrom, Cory Snyder, Greg Swindell, Pat Tabler)	.50	.40	.20
4	Cincinnati Reds (Buddy Bell, Tom Browning, Kal Daniels, Eric Davis, John Franco, Bill Gullickson, Tracy Jones, Barry Larkin, Rob Murphy, Paul O'Neill, Dave Parker, Pete Rose)	.50	.40	.20
5	Toronto Blue Jays (Jesse Barfield, George Bell, John Cerutti, Mark Eichhorn, Tony Fernandez, Tom Henke, Glenallen Hill, Jimmy Key, Fred McGriff, Lloyd Moseby, Dave Stieb, Willie Upshaw)	.50	.40	.20
6	Philadelphia Phillies (Steve Bedrosian, Don Carman, Marvin Freeman, Kevin Gross, Von Hayes, Shane Rawley, Bruce Ruffin, Juan Samuel, Mike Schmidt, Kent Tekulve, Milt Thompson, Glenn Wilson)	.50	.40	.20
7	New York Yankees (Rickey Henderson, Phil Lombardi, Don Mattingly, Mike Pagliarulo, Dan Pasqua, Willie Randolph, Dennis Rasmussen, Rick Rhoden, Dave Righetti, Joel Skinner, Bob Tewksbury, Dave Winfield)	.80	.60	.30
8	Houston Astros (Kevin Bass, Jose Cruz, Glenn Davis, Jim Deshaies, Bill Doran, Ty Gainey, Charlie Kerfeld, Bob Knepper, Nolan Ryan, Mike Scott, Dave Smith, Robby Wine)	.60	.45	.25
9	Boston Red Sox (Marty Barrett, Don Baylor, Wade Boggs, Dennis Boyd, Roger Clemens, Pat Dodson, Dwight Evans, Mike Greenwell, Dave Henderson, Bruce Hurst, Jim Rice, Calvin Schiraldi)	.50	.40	.20
10	San Francisco Giants (Bob Brenly, Chris Brown, Will Clark, Chili Davis, Kelly Downs, Scott Garrelts, Mark Grant, Mike Krukow, Jeff Leonard, Candy Maldonado, Terry Mulholland, Robby Thompson)	.50	.40	.20
11	California Angels (John Candelaria, Doug DeCinces, Brian Downing, Ruppert Jones, Wally Joyner, Kirk McCaskill, Darrell Miller, Donnie Moore, Gary Pettis, Don Sutton, Devon White, Mike Witt)	.50	.40	.20
12	St. Louis Cardinals (Jack Clark, Vince Coleman, Danny Cox, Bob Forsch, Tom Herr, Joe Magrane, Willie McGee, Terry Pendleton, Ozzie Smith, John Tudor, Andy Van Slyke, Todd Worrell)	.50	.40	.20
13	Kansas City Royals (George Brett, Mark Gubicza, Bo Jackson, Charlie Leibrandt, Hal McRae, Dan Quisenberry, Bret Saberhagen, Kevin Seitzer, Lonnie Smith, Danny Tartabull, Frank White, Willie Wilson)	.60	.45	.25
14	Los Angeles Dodgers (Ralph Bryant, Mariano Duncan, Jose Gonzalez, Pedro Guerrero, Orel Hershiser, Mike Marshall, Steve Sax, Mike Scioscia, Franklin Stubbs, Fernando Valenzuela, Reggie Williams, Matt Young)	.50	.40	.20
15	Detroit Tigers (Darnell Coles, Darrell Evans, Kirk Gibson, Willie Hernandez, Eric King, Chet Lemon, Dwight Lowry, Jack Morris, Dan Petry, Frank Tanana, Alan Trammell, Lou Whitaker)	.50	.40	.20
16	San Diego Padres (Randy Asadoor, Steve Garvey, Tony Gwynn, Andy Hawkins, Jim Jones, John Kruk, Craig Lefferts, Shane Mack, Lance McCullers, Kevin Mitchell, Benny Santiago, Ed Wojna)	.50	.40	.20
17	Minnesota Twins (Bert Blyleven, Tom Brunansky, Gary Gaetti, Greg Gagne, Kent Hrbek, Joe Klink, Steve Lombardozzi, Kirby Puckett, Jeff Reardon, Mark Salas, Roy Smalley, Frank Viola)	.50	.40	.20
18	Pittsburgh Pirates (Barry Bonds, Bobby Bonilla, Sid Bream, Mike Diaz, Brian Fisher, Jim Morrison, Joe Orsulak, Bob Patterson, Tony Pena, Johnny Ray, R.J. Reynolds, John Smiley)	.60	.45	.25
19	Milwaukee Brewers (Glenn Braggs, Rob Deer, Teddy Higuera, Paul Molitor, Juan Nieves, Dan Plesac, Tim Pyznarski, Ernest Riles, Billy Jo Robidoux, B.J. Surhoff, Dale Sveum, Robin Yount)	.50	.40	.20
20	Montreal Expos (Hubie Brooks, Tim Burke, Casey Candaele, Dave Collins, Mike Fitzgerald, Andres Galarraga, Billy Moore, Alonzo Powell, Randy St. Claire, Tim Wallach, Mitch Webster, Floyd Youmans)	.50	.40	.20
21	Baltimore Orioles (Don Aase, Eric Bell, Mike Boddicker, Ken Gerhardt, Terry Kennedy, Ray Knight, Lee Lacy, Fred Lynn, Eddie Murray, Cal Ripken, Jr., Larry Sheets, Jim Traber)	.50	.40	.20
22	Chicago Cubs (Jody Davis, Shawon Dunston, Leon Durham, Dennis Eckersley, Greg Maddux, Dave Martinez, Keith Moreland, Jerry Mumphrey, Rafael Palmeiro, Ryne Sandberg, Scott Sanderson, Lee Smith)	.50	.40	.20
23	Oakland Athletics (Jose Canseco, Mike Davis, Alfredo Griffin, Reggie Jackson, Carney Lansford, Mark McGwire, Dwayne Murphy, Rob Nelson, Tony Phillips, Jose Rijo, Terry Steinbach, Curt Young)	.70	.50	.30

		MT	NR MT	EX
24	Atlanta Braves (Paul Assenmacher, Gene Garber, Tom Glavine, Ken Griffey, Glenn Hubbard, Dion James, Rick Mahler, Dale Murphy, Ken Oberkfell, David Palmer, Zane Smith, Andres Thomas)	.50	.40	.20
25	Seattle Mariners (Scott Bankhead, Phil Bradley, Scott Bradley, Mickey Brantley, Alvin Davis, Steve Fireovid, Mark Langston, Mike Moore, Donell Nixon, Ken Phelps, Jim Presley, Dave Valle)	.50	.40	.20
26	Chicago White Sox (Harold Baines, John Cangelosi, Dave Cochrane, Joe Cowley, Carlton Fisk, Ozzie Guillen, Ron Hassey, Bob James, Ron Karkovice, Russ Mormon, Bobby Thigpen, Greg Walker)	.50	.30	.15

1988 Sportflics

The design of the 1988 Sportflics set differs greatly from the previous two years. Besides increasing the number of cards in the set to 225, Sportflics included the player name, team and uniform number on the card front. The triple-action color photos are surrounded by a red border. The backs are re-designed, also. Full-color action photos, plus extensive statistics and informative biographies are utilized. Three highlights cards and three rookie prospects card are included in the set. The cards are the standard 2-1/2" by 3-1/2".

		MT	NR MT	EX
Complete Set (225):		30.00	22.00	12.00
Common Player:		.10	.08	.04
1	Don Mattingly	1.00	.70	.40
2	Tim Raines	.35	.25	.14
3	Andre Dawson	.25	.20	.10
4	George Bell	.30	.25	.12
5	Joe Carter	.15	.11	.06
6	Matt Nokes	.20	.15	.08
7	Dave Winfield	.75	.60	.30
8	Kirby Puckett	1.00	.70	.40
9	Will Clark	1.00	.70	.40
10	Eric Davis	.30	.25	.12
11	Rickey Henderson	.75	.60	.30
12	Ryne Sandberg	1.50	1.25	.60
13	Jesse Barfield	.15	.11	.06
14	Ozzie Guillen	.10	.08	.04
15	Bret Saberhagen	.20	.15	.08
16	Tony Gwynn	.40	.30	.15
17	Kevin Seitzer	.30	.25	.12
18	Jack Clark	.20	.15	.08
19	Danny Tartabull	.30	.25	.12
20	Ted Higuera	.15	.11	.06
21	Charlie Leibrandt, Jr.	.10	.08	.04
22	Benny Santiago	.50	.40	.20
23	Fred Lynn	.15	.11	.06
24	Rob Thompson	.10	.08	.04
25	Alan Trammell	.25	.20	.10
26	Tony Fernandez	.15	.11	.06
27	Rick Sutcliffe	.15	.11	.06
28	Gary Carter	.25	.20	.10
29	Cory Snyder	.20	.15	.08
30	Lou Whitaker	.20	.15	.08
31	Keith Hernandez	.25	.20	.10
32	Mike Witt	.10	.08	.04
33	Harold Baines	.15	.11	.06
34	Robin Yount	1.00	.70	.40
35	Mike Schmidt	1.00	.70	.40
36	Dion James	.10	.08	.04
37	Tom Candiotti	.10	.08	.04
38	Tracy Jones	.15	.11	.06
39	Nolan Ryan	2.00	1.50	.80
40	Fernando Valenzuela	.15	.11	.06
41	Vance Law	.10	.08	.04
42	Roger McDowell	.10	.08	.04
43	Carlton Fisk	.25	.20	.10
44	Scott Garrelts	.10	.08	.04
45	Lee Guetterman	.10	.08	.04
46	Mark Langston	.15	.11	.06
47	Willie Randolph	.10	.08	.04
48	Bill Doran	.10	.08	.04
49	Larry Parrish	.10	.08	.04
50	Wade Boggs	.90	.70	.35
51	Shane Rawley	.10	.08	.04
52	Alvin Davis	.15	.11	.06
53	Jeff Reardon	.15	.11	.06
54	Jim Presley	.10	.08	.04
55	Kevin Bass	.10	.08	.04
56	Kevin McReynolds	.20	.15	.08
57	B.J. Surhoff	.15	.11	.06
58	Julio Franco	.15	.11	.06
59	Eddie Murray	.40	.30	.15
60	Jody Davis	.10	.08	.04
61	Todd Worrell	.15	.11	.06
62	Von Hayes	.10	.08	.04
63	Billy Hatcher	.10	.08	.04
64	John Kruk	.25	.20	.10
65	Tom Henke	.10	.08	.04
66	Mike Scott	.15	.11	.06
67	Vince Coleman	.20	.15	.08
68	Ozzie Smith	.40	.30	.15
69	Ken Williams	.10	.08	.04
70	Steve Bedrosian	.15	.11	.06
71	Luis Polonia	.10	.08	.04
72	Brook Jacoby	.15	.11	.06
73	Ron Darling	.15	.11	.06
74	Lloyd Moseby	.10	.08	.04
75	Wally Joyner	.50	.40	.20
76	Dan Quisenberry	.10	.08	.04
77	Scott Fletcher	.10	.08	.04
78	Kirk McCaskill	.10	.08	.04
79	Paul Molitor	.75	.60	.30
80	Mike Aldrete	.10	.08	.04
81	Neal Heaton	.10	.08	.04
82	Jeffrey Leonard	.10	.08	.04
83	Dave Magadan	.15	.11	.06
84	Danny Cox	.10	.08	.04
85	Lance McCullers	.10	.08	.04
86	Jay Howell	.10	.08	.04
87	Charlie Hough	.10	.08	.04
88	Gene Garber	.10	.08	.04
89	Jesse Orosco	.10	.08	.04
90	Don Robinson	.10	.08	.04
91	Willie McGee	.15	.11	.06
92	Bert Blyleven	.15	.11	.06
93	Phil Bradley	.15	.11	.06
94	Terry Kennedy	.10	.08	.04
95	Kent Hrbek	.20	.15	.08
96	Juan Samuel	.15	.11	.06
97	Pedro Guerrero	.20	.15	.08
98	Sid Bream	.10	.08	.04
99	Devon White	.30	.25	.12
100	Mark McGwire	.50	.40	.20
101	Dave Parker	.60	.45	.25
102	Glenn Davis	.10	.08	.04
103	Greg Walker	.10	.08	.04
104	Rick Rhoden	.10	.08	.04
105	Mitch Webster	.10	.08	.04
106	Lenny Dykstra	.20	.15	.08
107	Gene Larkin	.15	.11	.06
108	Floyd Youmans	.10	.08	.04
109	Andy Van Slyke	.15	.11	.06
110	Mike Scioscia	.10	.08	.04
111	Kirk Gibson	.25	.20	.10
112	Kal Daniels	.10	.08	.04
113	Ruben Sierra	.50	.40	.20
114	Sam Horn	.10	.08	.04
115	Ray Knight	.10	.08	.04
116	Jimmy Key	.10	.08	.04
117	Bo Diaz	.10	.08	.04
118	Mike Greenwell	.60	.45	.25
119	Barry Bonds	1.00	.70	.40
120	Reggie Jackson	1.00	.70	.40
121	Mike Pagliarulo	.15	.11	.06
122	Tommy John	.20	.15	.08
123	Bill Madlock	.15	.11	.06
124	Ken Caminiti	.30	.25	.12
125	Gary Ward	.10	.08	.04
126	Candy Maldonado	.10	.08	.04
127	Harold Reynolds	.10	.08	.04
128	Joe Magrane	.10	.08	.04
129	Mike Henneman	.15	.11	.06
130	Jim Gantner	.10	.08	.04
131	Bobby Bonilla	.40	.30	.15
132	John Farrell	.10	.08	.04
133	Frank Tanana	.10	.08	.04
134	Zane Smith	.10	.08	.04
135	Dave Righetti	.20	.15	.08
136	Rick Reuschel	.10	.08	.04
137	Dwight Evans	.15	.11	.06
138	Howard Johnson	.15	.11	.06
139	Terry Leach	.10	.08	.04
140	Casey Candaele	.10	.08	.04
141	Tom Herr	.10	.08	.04
142	Tony Pena	.10	.08	.04
143	Lance Parrish	.20	.15	.08
144	Ellis Burks	.50	.40	.20
145	Pete O'Brien	.10	.08	.04
146	Mike Boddicker	.10	.08	.04
147	Buddy Bell	.10	.08	.04
148	Bo Jackson	.60	.45	.25
149	Frank White	.10	.08	.04
150	George Brett	1.00	.70	.40
151	Tim Wallach	.10	.08	.04
152	Cal Ripken, Jr.	1.50	1.25	.60
153	Brett Butler	.10	.08	.04
154	Gary Gaetti	.15	.11	.06
155	Darryl Strawberry	.40	.30	.15
156	Alfredo Griffin	.10	.08	.04
157	Marty Barrett	.10	.08	.04
158	Jim Rice	.15	.11	.06
159	Terry Pendleton	.40	.30	.15
160	Orel Hershiser	.30	.25	.12
161	Larry Sheets	.10	.08	.04
162	Dave Stewart	.10	.08	.04
163	Shawon Dunston	.15	.11	.06
164	Keith Moreland	.10	.08	.04
165	Ken Oberkfell	.10	.08	.04
166	Ivan Calderon	.10	.08	.04
167	Bob Welch	.15	.11	.06
168	Fred McGriff	.50	.40	.20
169	Pete Incaviglia	.15	.11	.06
170	Dale Murphy	.50	.40	.20
171	Mike Dunne	.10	.08	.04
172	Chili Davis	.30	.25	.12
173	Milt Thompson	.10	.08	.04
174	Terry Steinbach	.15	.11	.06
175	Oddibe McDowell	.10	.08	.04
176	Jack Morris	.20	.15	.08
177	Sid Fernandez	.15	.11	.06
178	Ken Griffey	.10	.08	.04
179	Lee Smith	.10	.08	.04
180	1987 Highlights (Juan Nieves, Kirby Puckett, Mike Schmidt)	.25	.20	.10
181	Brian Downing	.10	.08	.04
182	Andres Galarraga	.50	.40	.20
183	Rob Deer	.10	.08	.04
184	Greg Brock	.10	.08	.04
185	Doug DeCinces	.10	.08	.04
186	Johnny Ray	.10	.08	.04
187	Hubie Brooks	.10	.08	.04
188	Darrell Evans	.10	.08	.04
189	Mel Hall	.10	.08	.04
190	Jim Deshaies	.10	.08	.04
191	Dan Plesac	.15	.11	.06
192	Willie Wilson	.15	.11	.06
193	Mike LaValliere	.10	.08	.04
194	Tom Brunansky	.15	.11	.06
195	John Franco	.15	.11	.06
196	Frank Viola	.20	.15	.08
197	Bruce Hurst	.10	.08	.04
198	John Tudor	.10	.08	.04
199	Bob Forsch	.10	.08	.04
200	Dwight Gooden	.30	.25	.12
201	Jose Canseco	1.50	1.25	.60
202	Carney Lansford	.10	.08	.04
203	Kelly Downs	.10	.08	.04
204	Glenn Wilson	.10	.08	.04
205	Pat Tabler	.10	.08	.04
206	Mike Davis	.10	.08	.04
207	Roger Clemens	.90	.70	.35
208	Dave Smith	.10	.08	.04
209	Curt Young	.10	.08	.04
210	Mark Eichhorn	.10	.08	.04
211	Juan Nieves	.10	.08	.04
212	Bob Boone	.10	.08	.04
213	Don Sutton	.20	.15	.08
214	Willie Upshaw	.10	.08	.04
215	Jim Clancy	.10	.08	.04
216	Bill Ripken	.10	.08	.04
217	Ozzie Virgil	.10	.08	.04
218	Dave Concepcion	.10	.08	.04
219	Alan Ashby	.10	.08	.04
220	Mike Marshall	.15	.11	.06
221	'87 Highlights (Vince Coleman, Mark McGwire, Paul Molitor)	.50	.40	.20
222	'87 Highlights (Steve Bedrosian, Don Mattingly, Benito Santiago)	.50	.40	.20
223	Hot Rookie Prospects (Shawn Abner, Jay Buhner, Gary Thurman)	.20	.15	.08
224	Hot Rookie Prospects (Tim Crews, John Davis, Vincente Palacios)	.10	.08	.04
225	Hot Rookie Prospects (Keith Miller, Jody Reed, Jeff Treadway)	.20	.15	.08

1988 Sportflics Gamewinners

This set of 25 standard-size cards (2-1/2" by 3-1/2"), featuring star players in the Sportflics patented 3-D Magic Motion design, was issued by Weiser Card Co. of Plainsboro, N.J., for use as a youth organizational fundraiser. (Weiser's president is former Yankees outfielder Bobby Murcer.) A limited number of sets was produced for test marketing in the Northwestern U.S., with plans for a 1989 set to be marketed nationwide. A green-and-yellow Gamewinners logo banner spans the upper border of the cards face, with a matching player name (with uniform number and position) below the full-color triple photo. The card backs carry large full-color player photos (1-3/4" by 1-3/4"), along with stats, personal information and career high-lights.

		MT	NR MT	EX
Complete Set:		10.00	7.50	4.00
Common Player:		.20	.15	.08
1	Don Mattingly	2.00	1.50	.80
2	Mark McGwire	.80	.60	.30
3	Wade Boggs	.80	.60	.30
4	Will Clark	1.00	.70	.40
5	Eric Davis	.40	.30	.15
6	Willie Randolph	.20	.15	.08
7	Dave Winfield	.80	.60	.30
8	Rickey Henderson	.60	.45	.25
9	Dwight Gooden	.60	.45	.25
10	Benny Santiago	.20	.15	.08
11	Keith Hernandez	.20	.15	.08
12	Juan Samuel	.20	.15	.08
13	Kevin Seitzer	.20	.15	.08

14	Gary Carter	.30	.25	.12
15	Darryl Strawberry	.40	.30	.15
16	Rick Rhoden	.20	.15	.08
17	Howard Johnson	.25	.20	.10
18	Matt Nokes	.25	.20	.10
19	Dave Righetti	.30	.25	.12
20	Roger Clemens	.80	.60	.30
21	Mike Schmidt	1.00	.70	.40
22	Kevin McReynolds	.30	.25	.12
23	Mike Pagliarulo	.20	.15	.08
24	Kevin Elster	.20	.15	.08
25	Jack Clark	.20	.15	.08

1989 Sportflics

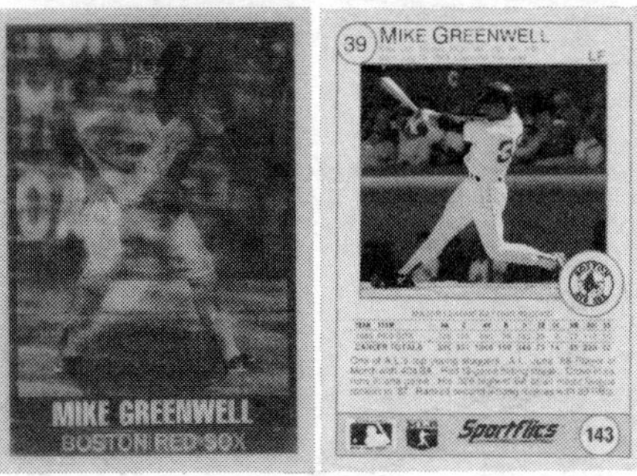

This basic issue includes 225 standard-size player cards (2-1/2" by 3-1/2") and 153 trivia cards, all featuring the patented Magic Motion design. A 5-card sub-set of triple photo cards called "Tri-Star" features a mix of veterans and rookies. The card fronts feature a white outer border and double color inner border in one of six color schemes (i.e. red, blue, purple). The inner border color changes when the card is tilted and the bottom border carries a double stripe of colors. The player name appears in the top border, player postition and uniform number appear, alternately, in the bottom border. The card backs contain crisp 1-7/8" by 1-3/4" player action shots, along with personal information, stats and career highlights. "The Unforgettables" trivia cards in this set salute members of the Hall of Fame.

		MT	NR MT	EX
Complete Set (225):		30.00	22.00	12.50
Common Player:		.10	.08	.04
1	Jose Canseco	.60	.45	.25
2	Wally Joyner	.40	.30	.15
3	Roger Clemens	.60	.45	.25
4	Greg Swindell	.15	.11	.06
5	Jack Morris	.20	.15	.08
6	Mickey Brantley	.10	.08	.04
7	Jim Presley	.15	.11	.06
8	Pete O'Brien	.10	.08	.04
9	Jesse Barfield	.15	.11	.06
10	Frank Viola	.20	.15	.08
11	Kevin Bass	.10	.08	.04
12	Glenn Wilson	.10	.08	.04
13	Chris Sabo	.60	.45	.25
14	Fred McGriff	.50	.40	.20
15	Mark Grace	.20	.15	.08
16	Devon White	.20	.15	.08
17	Juan Samuel	.15	.11	.06
18	Lou Whitaker	.25	.20	.10
19	Greg Walker	.10	.08	.04
20	Roberto Alomar	.50	.40	.20
21	Mike Schmidt	.60	.45	.25
22	Benny Santiago	.25	.20	.10
23	Dave Stewart	.10	.08	.04
24	Dave Winfield	.35	.25	.14
25	George Bell	.30	.25	.12
26	Jack Clark	.20	.15	.08
27	Doug Drabek	.10	.08	.04
28	Ron Gant	.15	.11	.06
29	Glenn Braggs	.10	.08	.04
30	Rafael Palmeiro	.20	.15	.08
31	Brett Butler	.10	.08	.04
32	Ron Darling	.15	.11	.06
33	Alvin Davis	.15	.11	.06
34	Bob Walk	.10	.08	.04
35	Dave Stieb	.15	.11	.06
36	Orel Hershiser	.40	.30	.15
37	John Farrell	.15	.11	.06
38	Doug Jones	.10	.08	.04
39	Kelly Downs	.10	.08	.04
40	Bob Boone	.10	.08	.04
41	Gary Sheffield	.80	.60	.30
42	Doug Dascenzo	.30	.25	.12
43	Chad Krueter	.20	.15	.08
44	Ricky Jordan	.50	.40	.20
45	Dave West	.30	.25	.12
46	Danny Tartabull	.30	.25	.12
47	Teddy Higuera	.15	.11	.06
48	Gary Gaetti	.15	.11	.06
49	Dave Parker	.15	.11	.06
50	Don Mattingly	.80	.60	.30
51	David Cone	.25	.20	.10
52	Kal Daniels	.25	.20	.10
53	Carney Lansford	.10	.08	.04
54	Mike Marshall	.15	.11	.06
55	Kevin Seitzer	.30	.25	.12
56	Mike Henneman	.10	.08	.04
57	Bill Doran	.10	.08	.04
58	Steve Sax	.20	.15	.08
59	Lance Parrish	.15	.11	.06
60	Keith Hernandez	.25	.20	.10
61	Jose Uribe	.10	.08	.04
62	Jose Lind	.15	.11	.06
63	Steve Bedrosian	.15	.11	.06
64	George Brett	.60	.45	.25
65	Kirk Gibson	.25	.20	.10
66	Cal Ripken, Jr.	.60	.45	.25
67	Mitch Webster	.10	.08	.04
68	Fred Lynn	.15	.11	.06
69	Eric Davis	.50	.40	.20
70	Bo Jackson	1.00	.70	.40
71	Kevin Elster	.15	.11	.06
72	Rick Reuschel	.10	.08	.04
73	Tim Burke	.10	.08	.04
74	Mark Davis	.10	.08	.04
75	Claudell Washington	.10	.08	.04
76	Lance McCullers	.10	.08	.04
77	Mike Moore	.10	.08	.04
78	Robby Thompson	.10	.08	.04
79	Roger McDowell	.10	.08	.04
80	Danny Jackson	.15	.11	.06
81	Tim Leary	.10	.08	.04
82	Bobby Witt	.15	.11	.06
83	Jim Gott	.10	.08	.04
84	Andy Hawkins	.10	.08	.04
85	Ozzie Guillen	.10	.08	.04
86	John Tudor	.15	.11	.06
87	Todd Burns	.25	.20	.10
88	Dave Gallagher	.25	.20	.10
89	Jay Buhner	.15	.11	.06
90	Gregg Jefferies	.40	.30	.15
91	Bob Welch	.15	.11	.06
92	Charlie Hough	.10	.08	.04
93	Tony Fernandez	.15	.11	.06
94	Ozzie Virgil	.10	.08	.04
95	Andre Dawson	.25	.20	.10
96	Hubie Brooks	.10	.08	.04
97	Kevin McReynolds	.20	.15	.08
98	Mike LaValliere	.10	.08	.04
99	Terry Pendleton	.10	.08	.04
100	Wade Boggs	.60	.45	.25
101	Dennis Eckersley	.15	.11	.06
102	Mark Gubicza	.15	.11	.06
103	Frank Tanana	.10	.08	.04
104	Joe Carter	.15	.11	.06
105	Ozzie Smith	.20	.15	.08
106	Dennis Martinez	.10	.08	.04
107	Jeff Treadway	.15	.11	.06
108	Greg Maddux	.15	.11	.06
109	Bret Saberhagen	.20	.15	.08
110	Dale Murphy	.40	.30	.15
111	Rob Deer	.10	.08	.04
112	Pete Incaviglia	.15	.11	.06
113	Vince Coleman	.20	.15	.08
114	Tim Wallach	.15	.11	.06
115	Nolan Ryan	1.00	.70	.40
116	Walt Weiss	.35	.25	.14
117	Brian Downing	.10	.08	.04
118	Melido Perez	.15	.11	.06
119	Terry Steinbach	.15	.11	.06
120	Mike Scott	.15	.11	.06
121	Tim Belcher	.15	.11	.06
122	Mike Boddicker	.10	.08	.04
123	Len Dykstra	.10	.08	.04
124	Fernando Valenzuela	.25	.20	.10
125	Gerald Young	.15	.11	.06
126	Tom Henke	.10	.08	.04
127	Dave Henderson	.10	.08	.04
128	Dan Plesac	.15	.11	.06
129	Chili Davis	.10	.08	.04
130	Bryan Harvey	.25	.20	.10
131	Don August	.15	.11	.06
132	Mike Harkey	.50	.40	.20
133	Luis Polonia	.10	.08	.04
134	Craig Worthington	.25	.20	.10
135	Joey Meyer	.15	.11	.06
136	Barry Larkin	.25	.20	.10
137	Glenn Davis	.20	.15	.08
138	Mike Scioscia	.10	.08	.04
139	Andres Galarraga	.20	.15	.08
140	Doc Gooden	.40	.30	.15
141	Keith Moreland	.10	.08	.04
142	Kevin Mitchell	.10	.08	.04
143	Mike Greenwell	.20	.15	.08
144	Mel Hall	.10	.08	.04
145	Rickey Henderson	.50	.40	.20
146	Barry Bonds	.20	.15	.08
147	Eddie Murray	.40	.30	.15
148	Lee Smith	.10	.08	.04
149	Julio Franco	.15	.11	.06
150	Tim Raines	.35	.25	.14
151	Mitch Williams	.10	.08	.04
152	Tim Laudner	.10	.08	.04
153	Mike Pagliarulo	.15	.11	.06
154	Floyd Bannister	.10	.08	.04
155	Gary Carter	.25	.20	.10
156	Kirby Puckett	.40	.30	.15
157	Harold Baines	.20	.15	.08
158	Dave Righetti	.20	.15	.08
159	Mark Langston	.15	.11	.06
160	Tony Gwynn	.50	.40	.20
161	Tom Brunansky	.15	.11	.06
162	Vance Law	.10	.08	.04
163	Kelly Gruber	.10	.08	.04
164	Gerald Perry	.15	.11	.06
165	Harold Reynolds	.10	.08	.04
166	Andy Van Slyke	.15	.11	.06
167	Jimmy Key	.15	.11	.06
168	Jeff Reardon	.15	.11	.06
169	Milt Thompson	.10	.08	.04
170	Will Clark	.80	.60	.30
171	Chet Lemon	.10	.08	.04
172	Pat Tabler	.10	.08	.04
173	Jim Rice	.30	.25	.12
174	Billy Hatcher	.10	.08	.04
175	Bruce Hurst	.15	.11	.06
176	John Franco	.15	.11	.06
177	Van Snider	.25	.20	.10
178	Ron Jones	.25	.20	.10
179	Jerald Clark	.30	.25	.12
180	Tom Browning	.15	.11	.06
181	Von Hayes	.10	.08	.04
182	Bobby Bonilla	.15	.11	.06
183	Todd Worrell	.15	.11	.06
184	John Kruk	.15	.11	.06
185	Scott Fletcher	.10	.08	.04
186	Willie Wilson	.15	.11	.06
187	Jody Davis	.10	.08	.04
188	Kent Hrbek	.20	.15	.08
189	Ruben Sierra	.35	.25	.14
190	Shawon Dunston	.15	.11	.06
191	Ellis Burks	.50	.40	.20
192	Brook Jacoby	.15	.11	.06
193	Jeff Robinson	.15	.11	.06
194	Rich Dotson	.10	.08	.04
195	Johnny Ray	.10	.08	.04
196	Cory Snyder	.25	.20	.10
197	Mike Witt	.10	.08	.04
198	Marty Barrett	.10	.08	.04
199	Robin Yount	.30	.25	.12
200	Mark McGwire	.50	.40	.20
201	Ryne Sandberg	.80	.60	.30
202	John Candelaria	.10	.08	.04
203	Matt Nokes	.20	.15	.08
204	Dwight Evans	.15	.11	.06
205	Darryl Strawberry	.60	.45	.25
206	Willie McGee	.15	.11	.06
207	Bobby Thigpen	.15	.11	.06
208	B.J. Surhoff	.15	.11	.06
209	Paul Molitor	.40	.30	.15
210	Jody Reed	.15	.11	.06
211	Doyle Alexander	.10	.08	.04
212	Dennis Rasmussen	.15	.11	.06
213	Kevin Gross	.10	.08	.04
214	Kirk McCaskill	.10	.08	.04
215	Alan Trammell	.30	.25	.12
216	Damon Berryhill	.15	.11	.06
217	Rick Sutcliffe	.15	.11	.06
218	Don Slaught	.10	.08	.04
219	Carlton Fisk	.30	.25	.12
220	Allan Anderson	.10	.08	.04
221	'88 Highlights (Wade Boggs, Jose Canseco, Mike Greenwell)	1.50	1.25	.60
222	'88 Highlights (Tom Browning, Dennis Eckersley, Orel Hershiser)	.25	.20	.10
223	Hot Rookie Prospects (Sandy Alomar, Gregg Jefferies, Gary Sheffield)	4.00	3.00	1.50
224	Hot Rookie Prospects (Randy Johnson, Ramon Martinez, Bob Milacki)	1.50	1.25	.60
225	Hot Rookie Prospects (Geronimo Berroa, Cameron Drew, Ron Jones)	.10	.08	.04

1990 Sportflics

The Sportflics set for 1990 again contained 225 cards. The cards feature the unique "Magic Motion" effect which displays either of two different photos depending on how the card is tilted. (Previous years' sets had used three photos per card.) The two-photo "Magic Motion" sequence is designed to depict sequential game-action, showing a batter following through on his swing, a pitcher completing his motion, etc. Sportflics also added a moving red and yellow "marquee" border on the cards to compliment the animation effect. The player's name, which appears below the animation, remains stationary. The set includes 19 special rookie cards. The backs contain a color player photo, team logo, player information and stats. The cards were distributed in non-transparent mylar packs with small MVP trivia cards.

		MT	NR MT	EX
Complete Set (225):		25.00	20.00	10.00
Common Player:		.10	.08	.04
1	Kevin Mitchell	.20	.15	.08
2	Wade Boggs	.50	.40	.20
3	Cory Snyder	.10	.08	.04
4	Paul O'Neill	.20	.15	.08
5	Will Clark	.20	.15	.08
6	Tony Fernandez	.10	.08	.04
7	Ken Griffey, Jr.	3.00	2.25	1.25
8	Nolan Ryan	1.00	.70	.40
9	Rafael Palmeiro	.10	.08	.04
10	Jesse Barfield	.10	.08	.04
11	Kirby Puckett	.40	.30	.15
12	Steve Sax	.10	.08	.04

13	Fred McGriff	.40	.30	.15
14	Gregg Jefferies	.30	.25	.12
15	Mark Grace	.20	.15	.08
16	Devon White	.10	.08	.04
17	Juan Samuel	.15	.11	.06
18	Robin Yount	.50	.40	.20
19	Glenn Davis	.10	.08	.04
20	Jeffrey Leonard	.10	.08	.04
21	Chili Davis	.10	.08	.04
22	Craig Biggio	.70	.50	.30
23	Jose Canseco	.50	.40	.20
24	Derek Lilliquist	.20	.15	.08
25	Chris Bosio	.10	.08	.04
26	Dave Steib	.10	.08	.04
27	Bobby Thigpen	.10	.08	.04
28	Jack Clark	.10	.08	.04
29	Kevin Ritz	.10	.08	.04
30	Tom Gordon	.10	.08	.04
31	Bryan Harvey	.10	.08	.04
32	Jim Deshaies	.10	.08	.04
33	Terry Steinbach	.15	.11	.06
34	Tom Glavine	.15	.11	.06
35	Bob Welch	.10	.08	.04
36	Charlie Hayes	.20	.15	.08
37	Jeff Reardon	.10	.08	.04
38	Joe Orsulak	.10	.08	.04
39	Scott Garrelts	.10	.08	.04
40	Bob Boone	.10	.08	.04
41	Scott Bankhead	.10	.08	.04
42	Tom Henke	.10	.08	.04
43	Greg Briley	.15	.11	.06
44	Teddy Higuera	.10	.08	.04
45	Pat Borders	.10	.08	.04
46	Kevin Seitzer	.15	.11	.06
47	Bruce Hurst	.15	.11	.06
48	Ozzie Guillen	.10	.08	.04
49	Wally Joyner	.30	.25	.12
50	Mike Greenwell	.20	.15	.08
51	Gary Gaetti	.12	.09	.05
52	Gary Sheffield	.20	.15	.08
53	Dennis Martinez	.10	.08	.04
54	Ryne Sandberg	.80	.60	.30
55	Mike Scott	.12	.09	.05
56	Todd Benzinger	.10	.08	.04
57	Kelly Gruber	.15	.11	.06
58	Jose Lind	.10	.08	.04
59	Allan Anderson	.10	.08	.04
60	Robby Thompson	.10	.08	.04
61	John Smoltz	.30	.25	.12
62	Mark Davis	.12	.09	.05
63	Tom Herr	.10	.08	.04
64	Randy Johnson	.20	.15	.08
65	Lonnie Smith	.10	.08	.04
66	Pedro Guerrero	.15	.11	.06
67	Jerome Walton	.10	.08	.04
68	Ramon Martinez	.15	.11	.06
69	Tim Raines	.12	.09	.05
70	Matt Williams	.20	.15	.08
71	Joe Oliver	.20	.15	.08
72	Nick Esasky	.12	.09	.05
73	Kevin Brown	.25	.20	.10
74	Walt Weiss	.12	.09	.05
75	Roger McDowell	.10	.08	.04
76	Jose DeLeon	.10	.08	.04
77	Brian Downing	.10	.08	.04
78	Jay Howell	.10	.08	.04
79	Jose Uribe	.10	.08	.04
80	Ellis Burks	.30	.25	.12
81	Sammy Sosa	.30	.25	.12
82	Johnny Ray	.20	.15	.08
83	Danny Darwin	.10	.08	.04
84	Carney Lansford	.12	.09	.05
85	Jose Oquendo	.10	.08	.04
86	John Cerutti	.10	.08	.04
87	Dave Winfield	.15	.11	.06
88	Dave Righetti	.10	.08	.04
89	Danny Jackson	.10	.08	.04
90	Andy Benes	.30	.25	.12
91	Tom Browning	.10	.08	.04
92	Pete O'Brien	.10	.08	.04
93	Roberto Alomar	.15	.11	.06
94	Bret Saberhagen	.15	.11	.06
95	Phil Bradley	.10	.08	.04
96	Doug Jones	.10	.08	.04
97	Eric Davis	.40	.30	.15
98	Tony Gwynn	.40	.30	.15
99	Jim Abbott	.40	.30	.15
100	Cal Ripken, Jr.	.80	.60	.30
101	Andy Van Slyke	.12	.09	.05
102	Dan Plesac	.10	.08	.04
103	Lou Whitaker	.10	.08	.04
104	Steve Bedrosian	.10	.08	.04
105	Dave Gallagher	.10	.08	.04
106	Keith Hernandez	.10	.08	.04
107	Duane Ward	.10	.08	.04
108	Andre Dawson	.15	.11	.06
109	Howard Johnson	.20	.15	.08
110	Mark Langston	.12	.09	.05
111	Jerry Browne	.10	.08	.04
112	Alvin Davis	.10	.08	.04
113	Sid Fernandez	.10	.08	.04
114	Mike Devereaux	.10	.08	.04
115	Benny Santiago	.12	.09	.05
116	Bip Roberts	.10	.08	.04
117	Craig Worthington	.15	.11	.06
118	Kevin Elster	.10	.08	.04
119	Harold Reynolds	.10	.08	.04
120	Joe Carter	.15	.11	.06
121	Brian Harper	.10	.08	.04
122	Frank Viola	.15	.11	.06
123	Jeff Ballard	.10	.08	.04
124	John Kruk	.10	.08	.04
125	Harold Baines	.10	.08	.04
126	Tom Candiotti	.10	.08	.04
127	Kevin McReynolds	.15	.11	.06
128	Mookie Wilson	.10	.08	.04
129	Danny Tartabull	.12	.09	.05
130	Craig Lefferts	.10	.08	.04
131	Jose DeJesus	.15	.11	.06
132	John Orton	.10	.08	.04
133	Curt Schilling	.20	.15	.08
134	Marquis Grissom	.20	.15	.08
135	Greg Vaughn	.20	.15	.08
136	Brett Butler	.10	.08	.04
137	Rob Deer	.10	.08	.04
138	John Franco	.10	.08	.04
139	Keith Moreland	.10	.08	.04
140	Dave Smith	.10	.08	.04
141	Mark McGwire	.60	.45	.25
142	Vince Coleman	.15	.11	.06
143	Barry Bonds	.15	.11	.06
144	Mike Henneman	.10	.08	.04
145	Doc Gooden	.30	.25	.12
146	Darryl Strawberry	.50	.40	.20
147	Von Hayes	.10	.08	.04
148	Andres Galarraga	.12	.09	.05
149	Roger Clemens	.25	.20	.10
150	Don Mattingly	.80	.60	.30
151	Joe Magrane	.10	.08	.04
152	Dwight Smith	.15	.11	.06
153	Ricky Jordan	.10	.08	.04
154	Alan Trammell	.10	.08	.04
155	Brook Jacoby	.10	.08	.04
156	Lenny Dykstra	.10	.08	.04
157	Mike LaValliere	.10	.08	.04
158	Julio Franco	.12	.09	.05
159	Joey Belle	.80	.60	.30
160	Barry Larkin	.15	.11	.06
161	Rick Reuschel	.10	.08	.04
162	Nelson Santovenia	.10	.08	.04
163	Mike Scioscia	.10	.08	.04
164	Damon Berryhill	.10	.08	.04
165	Todd Worrell	.10	.08	.04
166	Jim Eisenreich	.10	.08	.04
167	Ivan Calderon	.10	.08	.04
168	Goose Gozzo	.25	.20	.10
169	Kirk McCaskill	.10	.08	.04
170	Dennis Eckersley	.10	.08	.04
171	Mickey Tettleton	.12	.09	.05
172	Chuck Finley	.10	.08	.04
173	Dave Magadan	.10	.08	.04
174	Terry Pendleton	.10	.08	.04
175	Willie Randolph	.10	.08	.04
176	Jeff Huson	.25	.20	.10
177	Todd Zeile	.30	.25	.12
178	Steve Olin	.10	.08	.04
179	Eric Anthony	.15	.11	.06
180	Scott Coolbaugh	.10	.08	.04
181	Rick Sutcliffe	.10	.08	.04
182	Tim Wallach	.10	.08	.04
183	Paul Molitor	.12	.09	.05
184	Roberto Kelly	.12	.09	.05
185	Mike Moore	.10	.08	.04
186	Junior Felix	.15	.11	.06
187	Mike Schooler	.10	.08	.04
188	Ruben Sierra	.40	.30	.15
189	Dale Murphy	.12	.09	.05
190	Dan Gladden	.10	.08	.04
191	John Smiley	.10	.08	.04
192	Jeff Russell	.10	.08	.04
193	Bert Blyleven	.10	.08	.04
194	Dave Stewart	.12	.09	.05
195	Bobby Bonilla	.12	.09	.05
196	Mitch Williams	.10	.08	.04
197	Orel Hershiser	.20	.15	.08
198	Kevin Bass	.10	.08	.04
199	Tim Burke	.10	.08	.04
200	Bo Jackson	.75	.60	.30
201	David Cone	.12	.09	.05
202	Gary Pettis	.10	.08	.04
203	Kent Hrbek	.10	.08	.04
204	Carlton Fisk	.10	.08	.04
205	Bob Geren	.20	.15	.08
206	Bill Spiers	.25	.20	.10
207	Oddibe McDowell	.10	.08	.04
208	Rickey Henderson	.40	.30	.15
209	Ken Caminiti	.10	.08	.04
210	Devon White	.10	.08	.04
211	Greg Maddux	.15	.11	.06
212	Ed Whitson	.10	.08	.04
213	Carlos Martinez	.10	.08	.04
214	George Brett	.60	.20	.10
215	Gregg Olson	.15	.11	.06
216	Kenny Rogers	.20	.15	.08
217	Dwight Evans	.10	.08	.04
218	Pat Tabler	.10	.08	.04
219	Jeff Treadway	.10	.08	.04
220	Scott Fletcher	.10	.08	.04
221	Deion Sanders	.70	.50	.30
222	Robin Ventura	.30	.25	.12
223	Chip Hale	.20	.15	.08
224	Tommy Greene	.20	.15	.08
225	Dean Palmer	.20	.15	.08

The values quoted are intended to reflect the market price.

1994 Sportflics 2000 Promos

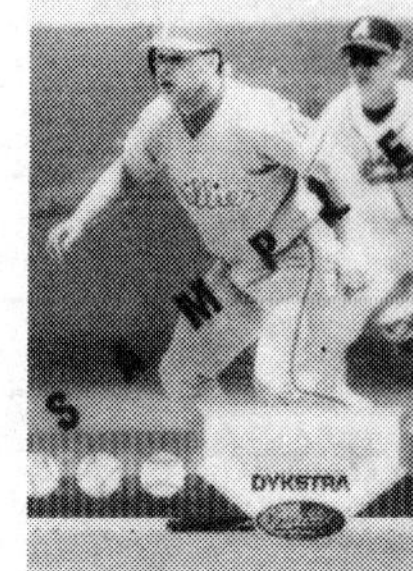

To reintroduce its "Magic Motion" baseball cards to the hobby (last produced by Score in 1990), Pinnacle Brands produced a three-card promo set which it sent to dealers along with a header card explaining the issue. In the same format as the regular issue, though some different photos were used, the promos feature on front what Sportflics calls "state-of-the-art lenticular technology" to create an action effect when the card is moved. Backs are produced by standard printing techniques and are gold-foil highlighted and UV-coated. Each of the promo cards has a large black "SAMPLE" overprinted diagonally across front and back.

		MT	NR MT	EX
Complete Set (3):		8.00	6.00	3.25
Common Player:		2.00	1.50	.80
1	Lenny Dykstra	2.00	1.50	.80
193	Greg Maddux (Starflics)	2.00	1.50	.80
7	Javy Lopez (Shakers)	4.00	3.00	1.50
----	Header card	.10	.08	.04

1994 Sportflics 2000

The concept of "Magic Motion" baseball cards returned to the hobby in 1994 after a three-year hiatus. Pinnacle Brands refined its "state-of-the-art lenticular technology" to produce cards which show alternating pictures when viewed from different angles on the basic cards, and to create a striking 3-D effect on its "Starflics" A.L. and N.L. all-star team subset. Backs use conventional printing techniques and are UV-coated and gold-foil highlighted, featuring a player photo and recent stats. Cards were sold in eight-card foil packs with a suggested retail price of $2.49.

		MT	NR MT	EX
Complete Set (193):		22.00	16.50	8.75
Common Player:		.10	.08	.04
1	Len Dykstra	.20	.15	.08
2	Mike Stanley	.10	.08	.04
3	Alex Fernandez	.15	.11	.06
4	Mark McGwire	.25	.20	.10
5	Eric Karros	.10	.08	.04
6	Dave Justice	.35	.25	.14
7	Jeff Bagwell	.20	.15	.08
8	Darren Lewis	.10	.08	.04
9	David McCarty	.15	.11	.06
10	Albert Belle	.35	.25	.14
11	Ben McDonald	.20	.15	.08
12	Joe Carter	.25	.20	.10
13	Benito Santiago	.10	.08	.04
14	Rob Dibble	.10	.08	.04
15	Roger Clemens	.25	.20	.10
16	Travis Fryman	.25	.20	.10
17	Doug Drabek	.10	.08	.04
18	Jay Buhner	.10	.08	.04
19	Orlando Merced	.10	.08	.04
20	Ryan Klesko	.50	.40	.20
21	Chuck Finley	.10	.08	.04
22	Dante Bichette	.10	.08	.04
23	Wally Joyner	.10	.08	.04
24	Robin Yount	.25	.20	.10
25	Tony Gwynn	.25	.20	.10
26	Allen Watson	.25	.20	.10
27	Rick Wilkins	.10	.08	.04
28	Gary Sheffield	.15	.11	.06
29	John Burkett	.10	.08	.04
30	Randy Johnson	.10	.08	.04
31	Roberto Alomar	.40	.30	.15
32	Fred McGriff	.20	.15	.08
33	Ozzie Guillen	.10	.08	.04
34	Jimmy Key	.10	.08	.04
35	Juan Gonzalez	1.50	1.25	.60
36	Wil Cordero	.10	.08	.04
37	Aaron Sele	.60	.45	.25
38	Mark Langston	.10	.08	.04

39	David Cone	.10	.08	.04
40	John Jaha	.10	.08	.04
41	Ozzie Smith	.20	.15	.08
42	Kirby Puckett	.35	.25	.14
43	Kenny Lofton	.20	.15	.08
44	Mike Mussina	.20	.15	.08
45	Ryne Sandberg	.35	.25	.14
46	Robby Thompson	.10	.08	.04
47	Bryan Harvey	.10	.08	.04
48	Marquis Grissom	.15	.11	.06
49	Bobby Bonilla	.15	.11	.06
50	Dennis Eckersley	.10	.08	.04
51	Curt Schilling	.10	.08	.04
52	Andy Benes	.10	.08	.04
53	Greg Maddux	.10	.08	.04
54	Bill Swift	.10	.08	.04
55	Andres Galarraga	.10	.08	.04
56	Tony Phillips	.10	.08	.04
57	Darryl Hamilton	.10	.08	.04
58	Duane Ward	.10	.08	.04
59	Bernie Williams	.10	.08	.04
60	Steve Avery	.10	.08	.04
61	Eduardo Perez	.10	.08	.04
62	Jeff Conine	.10	.08	.04
63	Dave Winfield	.10	.08	.04
64	Phil Plantier	.10	.08	.04
65	Ray Lankford	.10	.08	.04
66	Robin Ventura	.10	.08	.04
67	Mike Piazza	.10	.08	.04
68	Jason Bere	.10	.08	.04
69	Cal Ripken Jr	.10	.08	.04
70	Frank Thomas	.10	.08	.04
71	Carlos Baerga	.10	.08	.04
72	Darryl Kile	.10	.08	.04
73	Ruben Sierra	.10	.08	.04
74	Gregg Jefferies	.10	.08	.04
75	John Olerud	.10	.08	.04
76	Andy Van Slyke	.10	.08	.04
77	Larry Walker	.10	.08	.04
78	Cecil Fielder	.10	.08	.04
79	Andre Dawson	.10	.08	.04
80	Tom Glavine	.10	.08	.04
81	Sammy Sosa	.10	.08	.04
82	Charlie Hayes	.10	.08	.04
83	Chuck Knoblauch	.10	.08	.04
84	Kevin Appier	.10	.08	.04
85	Dean Palmer	.10	.08	.04
86	Royce Clayton	.10	.08	.04
87	Moises Alou	.10	.08	.04
88	Ivan Rodriguez	.10	.08	.04
89	Tim Salmon	.10	.08	.04
90	Ron Gant	.10	.08	.04
91	Barry Bonds	.10	.08	.04
92	Jack McDowell	.10	.08	.04
93	Alan Trammell	.10	.08	.04
94	Doc Gooden	.10	.08	.04
95	Jay Bell	.10	.08	.04
96	Devon White	.10	.08	.04
97	Wilson Alvarez	.10	.08	.04
98	Jim Thome	.10	.08	.04
99	Ramon Martinez	.10	.08	.04
100	Kent Hrbek	.10	.08	.04
101	John Kruk	.10	.08	.04
102	Wade Boggs	.10	.08	.04
103	Greg Vaughn	.10	.08	.04
104	Tom Henke	.10	.08	.04
105	Brian Jordan	.10	.08	.04
106	Paul Molitor	.10	.08	.04
107	Cal Eldred	.10	.08	.04
108	Deion Sanders	.10	.08	.04
109	Barry Larkin	.10	.08	.04
110	Mike Greenwell	.10	.08	.04
111	Jeff Blauser	.10	.08	.04
112	Jose Rijo	.10	.08	.04
113	Pete Harnisch	.10	.08	.04
114	Chris Hoiles	.10	.08	.04
115	Edgar Martinez	.10	.08	.04
116	Juan Guzman	.10	.08	.04
117	Todd Zeile	.10	.08	.04
118	Danny Tartabull	.10	.08	.04
119	Chad Curtis	.10	.08	.04
120	Mark Grace	.10	.08	.04
121	J.T. Snow	.10	.08	.04
122	Mo Vaughn	.10	.08	.04
123	Lance Johnson	.10	.08	.04
124	Eric Davis	.10	.08	.04
125	Orel Hershiser	.10	.08	.04
126	Kevin Mitchell	.10	.08	.04
127	Don Mattingly	.10	.08	.04
128	Darren Daulton	.10	.08	.04
129	Rod Beck	.10	.08	.04
130	Charles Nagy	.10	.08	.04
131	Mickey Tettleton	.10	.08	.04
132	Kevin Brown	.10	.08	.04
133	Pat Hentgen	.10	.08	.04
134	Terry Mulholland	.10	.08	.04
135	Steve Finley	.10	.08	.04
136	John Smoltz	.10	.08	.04
137	Frank Viola	.10	.08	.04
138	Jim Abbott	.10	.08	.04
139	Matt Williams	.10	.08	.04
140	Bernard Gilkey	.10	.08	.04
141	Jose Canseco	.10	.08	.04
142	Mark Whiten	.10	.08	.04
143	Ken Griffey Jr.	.10	.08	.04
144	Rafael Palmeiro	.10	.08	.04
145	Dave Hollins	.10	.08	.04
146	Will Clark	.10	.08	.04
147	Paul O'Neill	.10	.08	.04
148	Bobby Jones	.10	.08	.04
149	Butch Huskey	.10	.08	.04
150	Jeffrey Hammonds	.10	.08	.04
151	Manny Ramirez	.10	.08	.04
152	Bob Hamelin	.10	.08	.04
153	Kurt Abbott	.10	.08	.04
154	Scott Stahoviak	.10	.08	.04
155	Steve Hosey	.10	.08	.04
156	Salomon Torres	.10	.08	.04
157	Sterling Hitchcock	.10	.08	.04
158	Nigel Wilson	.10	.08	.04
159	Luis Lopez	.10	.08	.04
160	Chipper Jones	.10	.08	.04
161	Norberto Martin	.10	.08	.04
162	Raul Mondesi	.10	.08	.04
163	Steve Karsay	.10	.08	.04
164	J.R. Phillips	.10	.08	.04
165	Marc Newfield	.10	.08	.04
166	Mark Hutton	.10	.08	.04
167	Curtis Pride	.10	.08	.04
168	Carl Everett	.10	.08	.04
169	Scott Ruffcorn	.10	.08	.04
170	Turk Wendell	.10	.08	.04
171	Jeff McNeely	.10	.08	.04
172	Javier Lopez	.10	.08	.04
173	Cliff Floyd	.10	.08	.04
174	Rondell White	.10	.08	.04
175	Scott Lydy	.10	.08	.04
176	Frank Thomas	.10	.08	.04
177	Roberto Alomar	.10	.08	.04
178	Travis Fryman	.10	.08	.04
179	Cal Ripken Jr.	.10	.08	.04
180	Chris Hoiles	.10	.08	.04
181	Ken Griffey Jr.	.10	.08	.04
182	Juan Gonzalez	.10	.08	.04
183	Joe Carter	.10	.08	.04
184	Jack McDowell	.10	.08	.04
185	Fred McGriff	.10	.08	.04
186	Robby Thompson	.10	.08	.04
187	Matt Williams	.10	.08	.04
188	Jay Bell	.10	.08	.04
189	Mike Piazza	.10	.08	.04
190	Barry Bonds	.10	.08	.04
191	Lenny Dykstra	.10	.08	.04
192	Dave Justice	.10	.08	.04
193	Greg Maddux	.10	.08	.04

1994 Sportflics 2000 Movers

A dozen top veteran ballplayers were featured in the "Movers" insert set produced for inclusion in retail packaging of Sportflics 2000. The inserts feature the same Magic Motion features as the regular cards, showing different images on the card front when the card is viewed from different angles. The UV-coated, gold-foil highlighted backs are printed conventionally. A special "Movers" logo is found on both front and back. Stated odds of finding a Movers card are one in 24 packs.

		MT	NR MT	EX
Complete Set:		35.00	26.00	14.00
Common Player:		3.00	2.25	1.25
1	Gregg Jefferies	3.00	2.25	1.25
2	Ryne Sandberg	6.00	4.50	2.50
3	Cecil Fielder	4.00	3.00	1.50
4	Kirby Puckett	4.00	3.00	1.50
5	Tony Gwynn	3.00	2.25	1.25
6	Andres Galarraga	3.00	2.25	1.25
7	Sammy Sosa	3.00	2.25	1.25
8	Rickey Henderson	4.00	3.00	1.50
9	Don Mattingly	4.00	3.00	1.50
10	Joe Carter	3.00	2.25	1.25
11	Carlos Baerga	3.00	2.25	1.25
12	Lenny Dykstra	3.00	2.25	1.25

1994 Sportflics 2000 Shakers

Hobby packs are the exclusive source for this 12-card insert set of top rookies, found on average once every 24 packs. The chase cards utilize the Sportflics Magic Motion technology to create two different images on the card front when the card is viewed from different angles. Backs are printed conventionally but feature UV-coating and gold-foil highlights. The "Shakers" logo appears on both front and back.

		MT	NR MT	EX
Complete Set:		35.00	26.00	14.00
Common Player:		3.00	2.25	1.25
1	Kenny Lofton	3.00	2.25	1.25
2	Tim Salmon	4.00	3.00	1.50
3	Jeff Bagwell	3.00	2.25	1.25
4	Jason Bere	3.00	2.25	1.25
5	Salomon Torres	3.00	2.25	1.25
6	Rondell White	4.00	3.00	1.50
7	Javier Lopez	4.00	3.00	1.50
8	Dean Palmer	3.00	2.25	1.25
9	Jim Thome	3.00	2.25	1.25
10	J.T. Snow	3.00	2.25	1.25
11	Mike Piazza	5.00	3.75	2.00
12	Manny Ramirez	4.00	3.00	1.50

1994 Sportflics Commemoratives

A pair of extra-rare commemorative chase cards were produced for the Sportflics 2000 set honoring Canada's veteran superstar Paul Molitor and its hottest rookie, Cliff Floyd. Cards, utilizing Magic Motion technology to alternate card-front pictures when the viewing angle changes, were inserted on average once in every 360 packs.

		MT	NR MT	EX
Complete Set (2):		80.00	60.00	32.00
1	Paul Molitor	40.00	30.00	16.00
2	Cliff Floyd	50.00	37.00	20.00

1906 Sporting Life Team Composites (W601)

Originally sold as a string-bound "Premier Art Portfolio" containing 24 major and minor league team composite pictures, single pieces from this premium issue are not uncommonly found. The individual pieces measure 14" x 14" and are printed in black-and-white on heavy enameled paper. Individual player pictures are arranged around a baseball containing the manager's picture. Each player is identified beneath his photo by name and position.

		NR MT	EX	VG
Complete Set (24):		7500.	3750.	2200.
Common Major League Team:		400.00	200.00	120.00
Common Minor League Team:		250.00	125.00	75.00
(1)	Boston, National League	600.00	300.00	180.00
(2)	Brooklyn, National League	500.00	250.00	150.00
(3)	Chicago, National League	600.00	300.00	180.00
(4)	Cincinnati, National League	400.00	200.00	120.00
(5)	New York, National League	600.00	300.00	180.00
(6)	Philadelphia, National League	500.00	250.00	150.00
(7)	Pittsburg, National League	600.00	300.00	180.00
(8)	St. Louis, National League	400.00	200.00	120.00
(9)	National League President, Managers	600.00	300.00	180.00
(10)	Boston, American League	600.00	300.00	180.00
(11)	Chicago, American League	500.00	250.00	150.00
(12)	Cleveland, American League	900.00	450.00	270.00
(13)	Detroit, American League	900.00	450.00	270.00
(14)	New York, American League	600.00	300.00	180.00
(15)	Philadelphia, American League	600.00	300.00	180.00
(16)	St. Louis, American League	400.00	200.00	120.00
(17)	Washington, American League	400.00	200.00	120.00
(18)	American League President, Managers	600.00	300.00	180.00
(19)	A. J. & G, New York State League (Amsterdam, Johnstown and Gloversville)	250.00	125.00	75.00
(20)	Columbus, American Association	350.00	175.00	105.00
(21)	Concord, New England League	250.00	125.00	75.00
(22)	Macon, South Atlantic League	250.00	125.00	75.00
(23)	New Orleans, Southern League	250.00	125.00	75.00
(24)	Providence, Eastern League	250.00	125.00	75.00

1911 Sporting Life (M116)

This set of 1-1/2" by 2-3/4" cards was offered to subscribers of Sporting Life, a major competitor of The Sporting News in the early part of the century. The cards were issued in 24 series of 12 cards each. Specialists consider the set complete at 310 different cards, including variations on which the background is in blue, rather than pastel colors. Each of the 16 major league teams are represented by 13 to 21 players, with nine minor leaguers also included. The card fronts are black and white photos that have been hand colored and carry the player's name and

Livingstone, Philadelphia Amer.

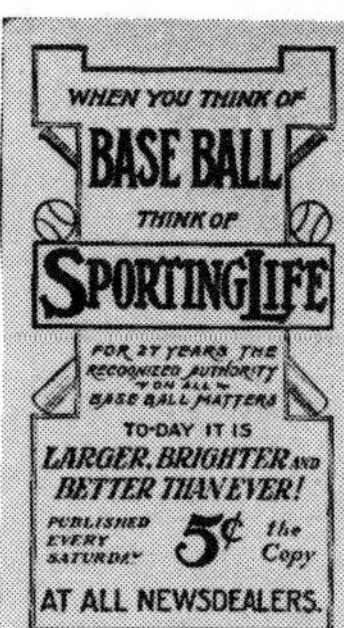
WHEN YOU THINK OF
BASE BALL
THINK OF
SPORTING LIFE
FOR 27 YEARS THE RECOGNIZED AUTHORITY ON ALL BASE BALL MATTERS
TO-DAY IT IS
LARGER, BRIGHTER AND BETTER THAN EVER!
PUBLISHED EVERY SATURDAY
5¢ the Copy
AT ALL NEWSDEALERS.

team. The card backs show various ads for the magazine. The last 72 cards issued are scarcer than the earlier series.

	NR MT	EX	VG
Complete Set:	17750.	8750.	5250.
Common Player:	110.00	55.00	33.00
(1) Ed Abbaticchio	110.00	55.00	33.00
(2) Babe Adams	275.00	137.00	82.00
(3) Red Ames	275.00	137.00	82.00
(4) Jimmy Archer	275.00	137.00	82.00
(5) Frank Arrelanes (Arellanes)	110.00	55.00	33.00
(6) Tommy Atkins	275.00	137.00	82.00
(7) Jimmy Austin	275.00	137.00	82.00
(8) Les Bachman (Backman)	110.00	55.00	33.00
(9) Bill Bailey	110.00	55.00	33.00
(10) Home Run Baker	350.00	175.00	105.00
(11) Cy Barger	110.00	55.00	33.00
(12) Jack Barry	110.00	55.00	33.00
(13) Johnny Bates	110.00	55.00	33.00
(14) Ginger Beaumont	110.00	55.00	33.00
(15) Fred Beck	110.00	55.00	33.00
(16) Heinie Beckendorf	110.00	55.00	33.00
(17) Fred Beebe	110.00	55.00	33.00
(18) George Bell	110.00	55.00	33.00
(19) Harry Bemis	110.00	55.00	33.00
(20a) Chief Bender (blue background)	650.00	325.00	195.00
(20b) Chief Bender (pastel background)	350.00	175.00	105.00
(21) Bill Bergen	110.00	55.00	33.00
(22) Heinie Berger	110.00	55.00	33.00
(23) Bob Bescher	110.00	55.00	33.00
(24) Joe Birmingham	110.00	55.00	33.00
(25) Lena Blackburn (Blackburne)	110.00	55.00	33.00
(26) John Bliss	275.00	137.00	82.00
(27) Bruno Block	275.00	137.00	82.00
(28) Bill Bradley	110.00	55.00	33.00
(29) Kitty Bransfield	110.00	55.00	33.00
(30) Roger Bresnahan	500.00	250.00	150.00
(31) Al Bridwell	110.00	55.00	33.00
(32) Buster Brown (Boston N.L.)	110.00	55.00	33.00
(33a) Mordecai Brown (blue background, Chicago N.L.)	650.00	325.00	195.00
(33b) Mordecai Brown (pastel background, Chicago N.L.)	350.00	175.00	105.00
(34) Al Burch	110.00	55.00	33.00
(35) Donie Bush	110.00	55.00	33.00
(36) Bobby Byrne	110.00	55.00	33.00
(37) Howie Camnitz	110.00	55.00	33.00
(38) Vin Campbell	275.00	137.00	82.00
(39) Bill Carrigan	110.00	55.00	33.00
(40a) Frank Chance (blue background)	650.00	325.00	195.00
(40b) Frank Chance (pastel background)	350.00	175.00	105.00
(41) Chappy Charles	110.00	55.00	33.00
(42a) Hal Chase (blue)	500.00	250.00	150.00
(42b) Hal Chase (pastel)	250.00	125.00	75.00
(43) Ed Cicotte	200.00	90.00	40.00
(44) Fred Clarke (Pittsburgh)	400.00	200.00	120.00
(45) Nig Clarke (Cleveland)	110.00	55.00	33.00
(46) Tommy Clarke (Cincinnati)	275.00	137.00	82.00
(47a) Ty Cobb (blue background)	3200.	1600.	975.00
(47b) Ty Cobb (pastel background)	1775.	875.00	525.00
(48a) Eddie Collins (blue background)	700.00	350.00	210.00
(48b) Eddie Collins (pastel background)	425.00	212.00	127.00
(49) Ray Collins	275.00	137.00	82.00
(50) Wid Conroy	110.00	55.00	33.00
(51) Jack Coombs	125.00	62.00	37.00
(52) Frank Corridon	110.00	55.00	33.00
(53) Harry Coveleskie (Coveleski)	350.00	175.00	105.00
(54) Doc Crandall	110.00	55.00	33.00
(55a) Sam Crawford (blue background)	650.00	325.00	195.00
(55b) Sam Crawford (pastel background)	350.00	175.00	105.00
(56) Birdie Cree	110.00	55.00	33.00
(57) Lou Criger	110.00	55.00	33.00
(58) Dode Criss	275.00	137.00	82.00
(59) Cliff Curtis	275.00	137.00	82.00
(60) Bill Dahlen	110.00	55.00	33.00
(61) Bill Davidson	275.00	137.00	82.00
(62a) Harry Davis (blue)	275.00	137.00	82.00
(62b) Harry Davis (pastel background)	110.00	55.00	33.00
(63) Jim Delehanty (Delahanty)	110.00	55.00	33.00
(64) Ray Demmitt	275.00	137.00	82.00
(65) Rube Dessau	275.00	137.00	82.00
(66) Art Devlin	110.00	55.00	33.00
(67) Josh Devore	275.00	137.00	82.00
(68) Pat Donahue	110.00	55.00	33.00
(69) Patsy Donovan	275.00	137.00	82.00
(70) Wild Bill Donovan	110.00	55.00	33.00
(71a) Red Dooin (blue)	275.00	137.00	82.00
(71b) Red Dooin (pastel)	110.00	55.00	33.00
(72) Mickey Doolan	110.00	55.00	33.00
(73) Patsy Dougherty	110.00	55.00	33.00
(74) Tom Downey	110.00	55.00	33.00
(75) Jim Doyle	110.00	55.00	33.00
(76a) Larry Doyle (blue)	275.00	137.00	82.00
(76b) Larry Doyle (pastel)	110.00	55.00	33.00
(77) Hugh Duffy	425.00	212.00	127.00
(78) Jimmy Dygert	110.00	55.00	33.00
(79) Dick Eagan (Egan)	110.00	55.00	33.00
(80) Kid Elberfeld	110.00	55.00	33.00
(81) Rube Ellis	110.00	55.00	33.00
(82) Clyde Engle	110.00	55.00	33.00
(83) Tex Erwin	275.00	137.00	82.00
(84) Steve Evans	275.00	137.00	82.00
(85) Johnny Evers	350.00	175.00	105.00
(86) Bob Ewing	110.00	55.00	33.00
(87) Cy Falkenberg	110.00	55.00	33.00
(88) George Ferguson	110.00	55.00	33.00
(89) Art Fletcher	275.00	137.00	82.00
(90) Elmer Flick	350.00	175.00	105.00
(91) John Flynn	275.00	137.00	82.00
(92) Russ Ford	275.00	137.00	82.00
(93) Eddie Foster	350.00	175.00	105.00
(94) Bill Foxen	110.00	55.00	33.00
(95) John Frill	350.00	175.00	105.00
(96) Sam Frock	275.00	137.00	82.00
(97) Art Fromme	110.00	55.00	33.00
(98) Earl Gardner (New York A.L.)	275.00	137.00	82.00
(99) Larry Gardner (Boston A.L.)	275.00	137.00	82.00
(100) Harry Gaspar	275.00	137.00	82.00
(101) Doc Gessler	110.00	55.00	33.00
(102a) George Gibson (blue background)	275.00	137.00	82.00
(102b) George Gibson (pastel background)	110.00	55.00	33.00
(103) Bill Graham (St. Louis A.L.)	110.00	55.00	33.00
(104) Peaches Graham (Boston)	110.00	55.00	33.00
(105) Eddie Grant	110.00	55.00	33.00
(106) Clark Griffith	350.00	175.00	105.00
(107) Ed Hahn	110.00	55.00	33.00
(108) Charley Hall	110.00	55.00	33.00
(109) Bob Harmon	275.00	137.00	82.00
(110) Topsy Hartsel	110.00	55.00	33.00
(111) Roy Hartzell	110.00	55.00	33.00
(112) Heinie Heitmuller	110.00	55.00	33.00
(113) Buck Herzog	110.00	55.00	33.00
(114) Dick Hoblitzel (Hoblitzell)	110.00	55.00	33.00
(115) Danny Hoffman	110.00	55.00	33.00
(116) Solly Hofman	110.00	55.00	33.00
(117) Harry Hooper	500.00	250.00	150.00
(118) Harry Howell	110.00	55.00	33.00
(119) Miller Huggins	425.00	212.00	127.00
(120) Long Tom Hughes	350.00	175.00	105.00
(121) Rudy Hulswitt	110.00	55.00	33.00
(122) John Hummel	110.00	55.00	33.00
(123) George Hunter	110.00	55.00	33.00
(124) Ham Hyatt	110.00	55.00	33.00
(125) Fred Jacklitsch	110.00	55.00	33.00
(126a) Hughie Jennings (blue background)	700.00	350.00	210.00
(126b) Hughie Jennings (pastel background)	425.00	212.00	127.00
(127) Walter Johnson	1000.	500.00	300.00
(128) Davy Jones	110.00	55.00	33.00
(129) Tom Jones	110.00	55.00	33.00
(130a) Tim Jordan (blue background)	275.00	137.00	82.00
(130b) Tim Jordan (pastel background)	110.00	55.00	33.00
(131) Addie Joss	450.00	225.00	135.00
(132) Johnny Kane	110.00	55.00	33.00
(133) Ed Karger	110.00	55.00	33.00
(134) Red Killifer (Killefer)	275.00	137.00	82.00
(135) Johnny Kling	110.00	55.00	33.00
(136) Otto Knabe	110.00	55.00	33.00
(137) John Knight	275.00	137.00	82.00
(138) Ed Konetchy	110.00	55.00	33.00
(139) Harry Krause	110.00	55.00	33.00
(140) Rube Kroh	110.00	55.00	33.00
(141) Art Krueger	350.00	175.00	105.00
(142a) Nap Lajoie (blue background)	1000.	500.00	300.00
(142b) Nap Lajoie (pastel)	600.00	300.00	180.00
(143) Fred Lake (Boston N.L.)	110.00	55.00	33.00
(144) Joe Lake (St. Louis A.L.)	275.00	137.00	82.00
(145) Frank LaPorte	110.00	55.00	33.00
(146) Jack Lapp	275.00	137.00	82.00
(147) Chick Lathers	275.00	137.00	82.00
(148a) Tommy Leach (blue background)	275.00	137.00	82.00
(148b) Tommy Leach (pastel background)	110.00	55.00	33.00
(149) Sam Leever	110.00	55.00	33.00
(150) Lefty Leifield	110.00	55.00	33.00
(151) Ed Lennox	110.00	55.00	33.00
(152) Fred Linke (Link)	275.00	137.00	82.00
(153) Paddy Livingstone (ston)	110.00	55.00	33.00
(154) Hans Lobert	110.00	55.00	33.00
(155) Bris Lord (Cleveland)	110.00	55.00	33.00
(156a) Harry Lord (blue background, Boston A.L.)	275.00	137.00	82.00
(156b) Harry Lord (pastel background, Boston A.L.)	110.00	55.00	33.00
(157) Johnny Lush	110.00	55.00	33.00
(158) Connie Mack	650.00	325.00	195.00
(159) Tom Madden	275.00	137.00	82.00
(160) Nick Maddox	110.00	55.00	33.00
(161) Sherry Magee	125.00	62.00	37.00
(162a) Christy Mathewson (blue background)	1775.	875.00	525.00
162b Christy Mathewson (pastel background)	1100.	550.00	325.00
(163) Al Mattern	110.00	55.00	33.00
(164) Jimmy McAleer	110.00	55.00	33.00
(165) George McBride	275.00	137.00	82.00
(166a) Amby McConnell (Boston)	110.00	55.00	33.00
(166b) Amby McConnell (Chicago A.L.)	3200.	1600.	975.00
(167) Pryor McElveen	110.00	55.00	33.00
(168) John McGraw	500.00	250.00	150.00
(169) Deacon McGuire	110.00	55.00	33.00
(170) Stuffy McInnes (McInnis)	275.00	137.00	82.00
(171) Harry McIntire (McIntyre)	110.00	55.00	33.00
(172) Matty McIntyre	110.00	55.00	33.00
(173) Larry McLean	110.00	55.00	33.00
(174) Tommy McMillan	110.00	55.00	33.00
(175a) George McQuillan (blue background, Philadelphia N.L.)	275.00	137.00	82.00
(175b) George McQuillan (pastel background, Philadelphia N.L.)	110.00	55.00	33.00
(175c) George McQuillan (Cincinnati)	3200.	1600.	975.00
(176) Paul Meloan	275.00	137.00	82.00
(177) Fred Merkle	110.00	55.00	33.00
(178) Clyde Milan	110.00	55.00	33.00
(179) Dots Miller (Pittsburgh)	110.00	55.00	33.00
(180) Warren Miller (Washington)	275.00	137.00	82.00
(181) Fred Mitchell	350.00	175.00	105.00
(182) Mike Mitchell	110.00	55.00	33.00
(183) Earl Moore	110.00	55.00	33.00
(184) Pat Moran	110.00	55.00	33.00
(185) Lew Moren	110.00	55.00	33.00
(186) Cy Morgan	110.00	55.00	33.00
(187) George Moriarty	110.00	55.00	33.00
(188) Mike Mowrey	275.00	137.00	82.00
(189) George Mullin	110.00	55.00	33.00
(190) Danny Murphy	110.00	55.00	33.00
(191) Red Murray	110.00	55.00	33.00
(192) Chief Myers (Meyers)	275.00	137.00	82.00
(193) Tom Needham	110.00	55.00	33.00
(194) Harry Niles	110.00	55.00	33.00
(195) Rebel Oakes	275.00	137.00	82.00
(196) Jack O'Connor	110.00	55.00	33.00
(197) Paddy O'Connor	110.00	55.00	33.00
(198) Bill O'Hara	350.00	175.00	105.00
(199) Rube Oldring	110.00	55.00	33.00
(200) Charley O'Leary	110.00	55.00	33.00
(201) Orval Overall	110.00	55.00	33.00
(202) Freddy Parent	110.00	55.00	33.00
(203) Dode Paskert	275.00	137.00	82.00
(204) Fred Payne	275.00	137.00	82.00
(205) Barney Pelty	110.00	55.00	33.00
(206) Hub Pernoll	275.00	137.00	82.00
(207) George Perring	350.00	175.00	105.00
(208) Big Jeff Pfeffer	275.00	137.00	82.00
(209) Jack Pfiester	110.00	55.00	33.00
(210) Art Phelan	275.00	137.00	82.00
(211) Ed Phelps	110.00	55.00	33.00
(212) Deacon Phillippe	110.00	55.00	33.00
(213) Eddie Plank	650.00	325.00	195.00
(214) Jack Powell	110.00	55.00	33.00
(215) Billy Purtell	110.00	55.00	33.00
(216) Farmer Ray	350.00	175.00	105.00
(217) Bugs Raymond	110.00	55.00	33.00
(218) Doc Reisling	110.00	55.00	33.00
(219) Ed Reulbach	110.00	55.00	33.00
(220) Lew Richie	110.00	55.00	33.00
(221) Jack Rowan	110.00	55.00	33.00
(222) Nap Rucker	110.00	55.00	33.00
(223) Slim Sallee	110.00	55.00	33.00
(224) Doc Scanlon	110.00	55.00	33.00
(225) Germany Schaefer	110.00	55.00	33.00
(226) Lou Schettler	275.00	137.00	82.00
(227) Admiral Schlei	110.00	55.00	33.00
(228) Boss Schmidt	110.00	55.00	33.00
(229) Wildfire Schulte	110.00	55.00	33.00
(230) Al Schweitzer	110.00	55.00	33.00
(231) Jim Scott	275.00	137.00	82.00
(232) Cy Seymour	110.00	55.00	33.00
(233) Tillie Shafer	110.00	55.00	33.00
(234) Bud Sharpe	275.00	137.00	82.00
(235) Dave Shean	275.00	137.00	82.00
(236) Jimmy Sheckard	110.00	55.00	33.00
(237) Mike Simon	275.00	137.00	82.00
(238) Charlie Smith (Boston N.L.)	275.00	137.00	82.00
(239) Frank Smith (Chicago A.L.)	110.00	55.00	33.00
(240) Harry Smith (Boston N.L.)	110.00	55.00	33.00
(241) Fred Snodgrass	110.00	55.00	33.00
(242) Bob Spade	110.00	55.00	33.00
(243) Tully Sparks	110.00	55.00	33.00
(244) Tris Speaker	1100.	550.00	325.00
(245) Jake Stahl	110.00	55.00	33.00
(246) George Stallings	110.00	55.00	33.00
(247) Oscar Stanage	110.00	55.00	33.00
(248) Harry Steinfeldt	125.00	62.00	37.00
(249) Jim Stephens	110.00	55.00	33.00
(250) George Stone	110.00	55.00	33.00
(251) George Stovall	110.00	55.00	33.00
(252) Gabby Street	110.00	55.00	33.00
(253) Sailor Stroud	275.00	137.00	82.00
(254) Amos Strunk	275.00	137.00	82.00
(255) George Suggs	110.00	55.00	33.00
(256) Billy Sullivan	110.00	55.00	33.00
(257) Ed Summers	110.00	55.00	33.00
(258) Bill Sweeney (Boston N.L.)	110.00	55.00	33.00
(259) Jeff Sweeney (New York)	275.00	137.00	82.00
(260) Lee Tannehill	110.00	55.00	33.00
(261a) Fred Tenney (blue background)	275.00	137.00	82.00
(261b) Fred Tenney (pastel background)	110.00	55.00	33.00
(262a) Ira Thomas (blue)	275.00	137.00	82.00
(262b) Ira Thomas (pastel background)	110.00	55.00	33.00
(263) Jack Thoney	110.00	55.00	33.00
(264) Joe Tinker	350.00	175.00	105.00
(265) John Titus	275.00	137.00	82.00
(266) Terry Turner	110.00	55.00	33.00
(267) Bob Unglaub	110.00	55.00	33.00
(268) Rube Waddell	450.00	225.00	135.00
(269a) Hans Wagner (blue background, Pittsburgh)	2150.	1000.	600.00
(269b) Hans Wagner (pastel background, Pittsburgh)	1250.	625.00	375.00
(270) Heinie Wagner (Boston A.L.)	110.00	55.00	33.00
(271) Bobby Wallace	400.00	200.00	120.00
(272) Ed Walsh (Chicago A.L.)	500.00	250.00	150.00
(273a) Jimmy Walsh (grey background)	425.00	212.00	127.00
(273b) Jimmy Walsh (white background)	425.00	212.00	127.00
(274) Doc White	110.00	55.00	33.00
(275) Kaiser Wilhelm	110.00	55.00	33.00
(276) Ed Willett	110.00	55.00	33.00
(277) Vic Willis	110.00	55.00	33.00
(278) Art Wilson (New York N.L.)	110.00	55.00	33.00
(279) Owen Wilson (Pittsburgh)	110.00	55.00	33.00
(280) Hooks Wiltse	110.00	55.00	33.00

(281)	Harry Wolter	110.00	55.00	33.00
(282)	Smoky Joe Wood	275.00	137.00	82.00
(283)	Ralph Works	110.00	55.00	33.00
(284)	Cy Young (Cleveland)	675.00	325.00	200.00
(285)	Irv Young (Chicago A.L.)	110.00	55.00	33.00
(286)	Heinie Zimmerman	275.00	137.00	82.00
(287)	Dutch Zwilling	275.00	137.00	82.00

1915 The Sporting News (M101-5)

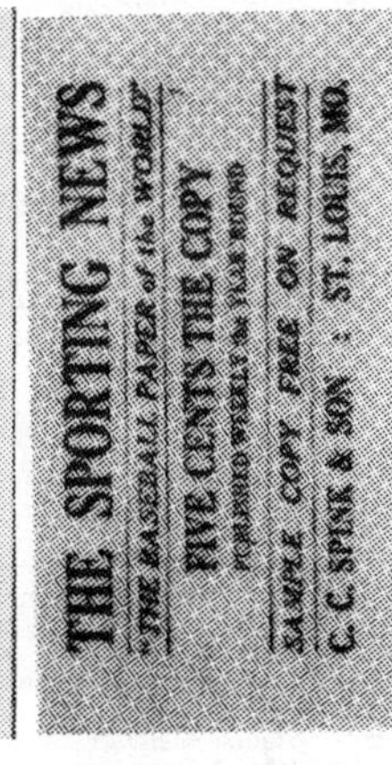

This 200-card set was issued as a premium by The Sporting News and was also used by Weil Baking, the Globe Stores, and several other regional advertisers. The 1-5/8" by 3" cards contain bordered black and white photos on the fronts, with the player name, position and team, as well as a card number. Card backs are in a horizontal format and show an advertisement for the sponsoring sports weekly. Most of the day's top players and many Hall of Famers are included in the set, with the Babe Ruth card carrying the highest value. The complete set price includes all variations.

		NR MT	EX	VG
Complete Set:		14500.	7250.	4250.
Common Player:		30.00	15.00	9.00
1	Babe Adams	50.00	25.00	15.00
2	Sam Agnew	30.00	15.00	9.00
3	Eddie Ainsmith	30.00	15.00	9.00
4	Grover Alexander	90.00	45.00	27.00
5	Leon Ames	30.00	15.00	9.00
6	Jimmy Archer	30.00	15.00	9.00
7	Jimmy Austin	30.00	15.00	9.00
8	J. Franklin Baker	65.00	32.00	19.50
9	Dave Bancroft	65.00	32.00	19.50
10	Jack Barry	30.00	15.00	9.00
11	Zinn Beck	30.00	15.00	9.00
12	Lute Boone	30.00	15.00	9.00
13	Joe Benz	30.00	15.00	9.00
14	Bob Bescher	30.00	15.00	9.00
15	Al Betzel	30.00	15.00	9.00
16	Roger Bresnahan	75.00	37.00	22.00
17	Eddie Burns	30.00	15.00	9.00
18	Geo. J. Burns	30.00	15.00	9.00
19	Joe Bush	35.00	17.50	10.50
20	Owen Bush	35.00	17.50	10.50
21	Art Butler	30.00	15.00	9.00
22	Bobbie Byrne	30.00	15.00	9.00
23a	Forrest Cady	90.00	45.00	27.00
23b	Mordecai Brown	75.00	37.00	22.00
24	Jimmy Callahan	30.00	15.00	9.00
25	Ray Caldwell	30.00	15.00	9.00
26	Max Carey	65.00	32.00	19.50
27	George Chalmers	30.00	15.00	9.00
28	Frank Chance	80.00	40.00	24.00
29	Ray Chapman	40.00	20.00	12.00
30	Larry Cheney	30.00	15.00	9.00
31	Eddie Cicotte	45.00	22.00	13.50
32	Tom Clarke	30.00	15.00	9.00
33	Eddie Collins	75.00	37.00	22.00
34	"Shauno" Collins	30.00	15.00	9.00
35	Charles Comisky (Comiskey)	80.00	40.00	24.00
36	Joe Connolly	30.00	15.00	9.00
37	Luther Cook	30.00	15.00	9.00
38	Jack Coombs	30.00	15.00	9.00
39	Dan Costello	30.00	15.00	9.00
40	Harry Coveleskie (Coveleski)	30.00	15.00	9.00
41	Gavvy Cravath	30.00	15.00	9.00
42	Sam Crawford	65.00	32.00	19.50
43	Jean Dale	30.00	15.00	9.00
44	Jake Daubert	30.00	15.00	9.00
45	Geo. A. Davis Jr.	35.00	17.50	10.50
46	Charles Deal	30.00	15.00	9.00
47	Al Demaree	30.00	15.00	9.00
48	William Doak	30.00	15.00	9.00
49	Bill Donovan	30.00	15.00	9.00
50	Charles Dooin	30.00	15.00	9.00
51	Mike Doolan	30.00	15.00	9.00
52	Larry Doyle	35.00	17.50	10.50
53	Jean Dubuc	30.00	15.00	9.00
54	Oscar Dugey	30.00	15.00	9.00
55	Johnny Evers	65.00	32.00	19.50
56	Urban Faber	65.00	32.00	19.50
57	"Hap" Felsch	45.00	22.00	13.50
58	Bill Fischer	30.00	15.00	9.00
59	Ray Fisher	30.00	15.00	9.00
60	Max Flack	30.00	15.00	9.00
61	Art Fletcher	30.00	15.00	9.00
62	Eddie Foster	30.00	15.00	9.00
63	Jacques Fournier	30.00	15.00	9.00
64	Del Gainer (Gainor)	30.00	15.00	9.00
65	Larry Gardner	30.00	15.00	9.00
66	Joe Gedeon	30.00	15.00	9.00
67	Gus Getz	30.00	15.00	9.00
68	Geo. Gibson	30.00	15.00	9.00
69	Wilbur Good	30.00	15.00	9.00
70	Hank Gowdy	30.00	15.00	9.00
71	John Graney	30.00	15.00	9.00
72	Tom Griffith	30.00	15.00	9.00
73	Heinie Groh	30.00	15.00	9.00
74	Earl Hamilton	30.00	15.00	9.00
75	Bob Harmon	30.00	15.00	9.00
76	Roy Hartzell	30.00	15.00	9.00
77	Claude Hendrix	30.00	15.00	9.00
78	Olaf Henriksen	30.00	15.00	9.00
79	John Henry	30.00	15.00	9.00
80	"Buck" Herzog	30.00	15.00	9.00
81	Hugh High	30.00	15.00	9.00
82	Dick Hoblitzell	30.00	15.00	9.00
83	Harry Hooper	65.00	32.00	19.50
84	Ivan Howard	30.00	15.00	9.00
85	Miller Huggins	65.00	32.00	19.50
86	Joe Jackson	2500.	1250.	750.00
87	William James	30.00	15.00	9.00
88	Harold Janvrin	30.00	15.00	9.00
89	Hugh Jennings	65.00	32.00	19.50
90	Walter Johnson	300.00	150.00	90.00
91	Fielder Jones	30.00	15.00	9.00
92	Bennie Kauff	30.00	15.00	9.00
93	Wm. Killefer Jr.	30.00	15.00	9.00
94	Ed. Konetchy	30.00	15.00	9.00
95	Napoleon Lajoie	275.00	137.00	82.00
96	Jack Lapp	30.00	15.00	9.00
97a	John Lavan (correct spelling)	40.00	20.00	12.00
97b	John Lavin (incorrect spelling)	40.00	20.00	12.00
98	Jimmy Lavender	30.00	15.00	9.00
99	"Nemo" Leibold	30.00	15.00	9.00
100	H.B. Leonard	30.00	15.00	9.00
101	Duffy Lewis	35.00	17.50	10.50
102	Hans Lobert	30.00	15.00	9.00
103	Tom Long	30.00	15.00	9.00
104	Fred Luderus	30.00	15.00	9.00
105	Connie Mack	100.00	50.00	30.00
106	Lee Magee	30.00	15.00	9.00
107	Al. Mamaux	30.00	15.00	9.00
108	Leslie Mann	30.00	15.00	9.00
109	"Rabbit" Maranville	65.00	32.00	19.50
110	Rube Marquard	65.00	32.00	19.50
111	Armando Marsans	40.00	20.00	12.00
112	J. Erskine Mayer	30.00	15.00	9.00
113	George McBride	30.00	15.00	9.00
114	John J. McGraw	80.00	40.00	24.00
115	Jack McInnis	30.00	15.00	9.00
116	Fred Merkle	35.00	17.50	10.50
117	Chief Meyers	30.00	15.00	9.00
118	Clyde Milan	30.00	15.00	9.00
119	Otto Miller	30.00	15.00	9.00
120	Willie Mitchel (Mitchell)	30.00	15.00	9.00
121	Fred Mollwitz	30.00	15.00	9.00
122	J. Herbert Moran	35.00	17.50	10.50
123	Pat Moran	30.00	15.00	9.00
124	Ray Morgan	30.00	15.00	9.00
125	Geo. Moriarty	30.00	15.00	9.00
126	Guy Morton	30.00	15.00	9.00
127	Ed. Murphy (photo actually Danny Murphy)	35.00	17.50	10.50
128	John Murray	30.00	15.00	9.00
129	"Hy" Myers	30.00	15.00	9.00
130	J.A. Niehoff	30.00	15.00	9.00
131	Leslie Nunamaker	30.00	15.00	9.00
132	Rube Oldring	30.00	15.00	9.00
133	Oliver O'Mara	30.00	15.00	9.00
134	Steve O'Neill	30.00	15.00	9.00
135	"Dode" Paskert	30.00	15.00	9.00
136	Roger Peckinpaugh (photo actually Gavvy Cravath)	35.00	17.50	10.50
137	E.J. Pfeffer (photo actually Jeff Pfeffer)	35.00	17.50	10.50
138	Geo. Pierce (Pearce)	30.00	15.00	9.00
139	Walter Pipp	45.00	22.00	13.50
140	Derril Pratt (Derrill)	30.00	15.00	9.00
141	Bill Rariden	30.00	15.00	9.00
142	Eppa Rixey	65.00	32.00	19.50
143	Davey Robertson	30.00	15.00	9.00
144	Wilbert Robertson	65.00	32.00	19.50
145	Bob Roth	30.00	15.00	9.00
146	Ed. Roush	65.00	32.00	19.50
147	Clarence Rowland	30.00	15.00	9.00
148	"Nap" Rucker	30.00	15.00	9.00
149	Dick Rudolph	30.00	15.00	9.00
150	Reb Russell	30.00	15.00	9.00
151	Babe Ruth	3500.	1750.	1050.
152	Vic Saier	30.00	15.00	9.00
153	"Slim" Sallee	30.00	15.00	9.00
154	"Germany" Schaefer	30.00	15.00	9.00
155	Ray Schalk	65.00	32.00	19.50
156	Walter Schang	30.00	15.00	9.00
157	Chas. Schmidt	30.00	15.00	9.00
158	Frank Schulte	30.00	15.00	9.00
159	Jim Scott	30.00	15.00	9.00
160	Everett Scott	30.00	15.00	9.00
161	Tom Seaton	30.00	15.00	9.00
162	Howard Shanks	30.00	15.00	9.00
163	Bob Shawkey (photo actually Jack McInnis)	35.00	17.50	10.50
164	Ernie Shore	30.00	15.00	9.00
165	Burt Shotton	30.00	15.00	9.00
166	George Sisler	75.00	37.00	22.00
167	J. Carlisle Smith	30.00	15.00	9.00
168	Fred Snodgrass	30.00	15.00	9.00
169	Geo. Stallings	30.00	15.00	9.00
170	Oscar Stanage (photo actually Chas. Schmidt)	35.00	17.50	10.50
171	Charles Stengel	275.00	137.00	82.00
172	Milton Stock	30.00	15.00	9.00
173	Amos Strunk (photo actually Olaf Henriksen)	35.00	17.50	10.50
174	Billy Sullivan	30.00	15.00	9.00
175	Chas. Tesreau	30.00	15.00	9.00
176	Jim Thorpe	3500.	1750.	1050.
177	Joe Tinker	65.00	32.00	19.50
178	Fred Toney	30.00	15.00	9.00
179	Terry Turner	30.00	15.00	9.00
180	Jim Vaughn	30.00	15.00	9.00
181	Bob Veach	30.00	15.00	9.00
182	James Voix	30.00	15.00	9.00
183	Oscar Vitt	30.00	15.00	9.00
184	Hans Wagner	300.00	150.00	90.00
185	Clarence Walker (photo not Walker)	35.00	17.50	10.50
186	Zach Wheat	65.00	32.00	19.50
187	Ed. Walsh	65.00	32.00	19.50
188	Buck Weaver	45.00	22.00	13.50
189	Carl Weilman	30.00	15.00	9.00
190	Geo. Whitted	30.00	15.00	9.00
191	Fred Williams	35.00	17.50	10.50
192	Art Wilson	30.00	15.00	9.00
193	J. Owen Wilson	30.00	15.00	9.00
194	Ivy Wingo	30.00	15.00	9.00
195	"Mel" Wolfgang	30.00	15.00	9.00
196	Joe Wood	35.00	17.50	10.50
197	Steve Yerkes	30.00	15.00	9.00
198	Rollie Zeider	30.00	15.00	9.00
199	Heiny Zimmerman	30.00	15.00	9.00
200	Ed. Zwilling	40.00	20.00	12.00

1916 The Sporting News (M101-4)

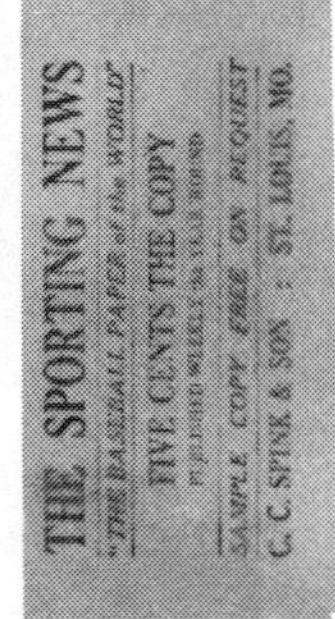

This set, which is quite similar to the M101-5 The Sporting News issue, was also issued as a promotional premium by The Sporting News. The 200 black and white cards once again are printed with player photo, name, position, team and card number on and advertising on the backs. The set checklist is the same as for sets issued by Morehouse Baking and Standard Baking. Most of the players included in the 1-5/8" by 3" set also appear in the prior The Sporting News edition. The complete set price includes all variations.

		NR MT	EX	VG
Complete Set:		12750.	6250.	3750.
Common Player:		30.00	15.00	9.00
1	Babe Adams	40.00	20.00	12.00
2	Sam Agnew	30.00	15.00	9.00
3	Eddie Ainsmith	30.00	15.00	9.00
4	Grover Alexander	90.00	45.00	27.00
5	Leon Ames	30.00	15.00	9.00
6	Jimmy Archer	30.00	15.00	9.00
7	Jimmy Austin	30.00	15.00	9.00
8	H.D. Baird	30.00	15.00	9.00
9	J. Franklin Baker	65.00	32.00	19.50
10	Dave Bancroft	65.00	32.00	19.50
11	Jack Barry	30.00	15.00	9.00
12	Zinn Beck	30.00	15.00	9.00
13	"Chief" Bender	65.00	32.00	19.50
14	Joe Benz	30.00	15.00	9.00
15	Bob Bescher	30.00	15.00	9.00
16	Al Betzel	30.00	15.00	9.00
17	Mordecai Brown	65.00	32.00	19.50
18	Eddie Burns	30.00	15.00	9.00
19	George Burns	35.00	17.50	10.50
20	Geo. J. Burns	30.00	15.00	9.00
21	Joe Bush	35.00	17.50	10.50
22	"Donie" Bush	30.00	15.00	9.00
23	Art Butler	30.00	15.00	9.00
24	Bobbie Byrne	30.00	15.00	9.00
25	Forrest Cady	30.00	15.00	9.00
26	Jimmy Callahan	30.00	15.00	9.00
27	Ray Caldwell	30.00	15.00	9.00
28	Max Carey	65.00	32.00	19.50
29	George Chalmers	30.00	15.00	9.00
30	Ray Chapman	40.00	20.00	12.00
31	Larry Cheney	30.00	15.00	9.00
32	Eddie Cicotte	45.00	22.00	13.50
33	Tom Clarke	30.00	15.00	9.00
34	Eddie Collins	75.00	37.00	22.00
35	"Shauno" Collins	30.00	15.00	9.00
36	Charles Comiskey	75.00	37.00	22.00

37	Joe Connolly	30.00	15.00	9.00
38	Ty Cobb	1200.	600.00	360.00
39	Harry Coveleskie (Coveleski)	30.00	15.00	9.00
40	Gavvy Cravath	30.00	15.00	9.00
41	Sam Crawford	65.00	32.00	19.50
42	Jean Dale	30.00	15.00	9.00
43	Jake Daubert	35.00	17.50	10.50
44	Charles Deal	30.00	15.00	9.00
45	Al Demaree	30.00	15.00	9.00
46	Josh Devore	35.00	17.50	10.50
47	William Doak	30.00	15.00	9.00
48	Bill Donovan	30.00	15.00	9.00
49	Charles Dooin	30.00	15.00	9.00
50	Mike Doolan	30.00	15.00	9.00
51	Larry Doyle	35.00	17.50	10.50
52	Jean Dubuc	30.00	15.00	9.00
53	Oscar Dugey	30.00	15.00	9.00
54	Johnny Evers	65.00	32.00	19.50
55	Urban Faber	65.00	32.00	19.50
56	"Hap" Felsch	45.00	22.00	13.50
57	Bill Fischer	30.00	15.00	9.00
58	Ray Fisher	30.00	15.00	9.00
59	Max Flack	30.00	15.00	9.00
60	Art Fletcher	30.00	15.00	9.00
61	Eddie Foster	30.00	15.00	9.00
62	Jacques Fournier	30.00	15.00	9.00
63	Del Gainer (Gainor)	30.00	15.00	9.00
64	"Chic" Gandil	65.00	32.00	19.50
65	Larry Gardner	30.00	15.00	9.00
66	Joe Gedeon	30.00	15.00	9.00
67	Gus Getz	30.00	15.00	9.00
68	Geo. Gibson	30.00	15.00	9.00
69	Wilbur Good	30.00	15.00	9.00
70	Hank Gowdy	30.00	15.00	9.00
71	John Graney	30.00	15.00	9.00
72	Clark Griffith	75.00	37.00	22.00
73	Tom Griffith	30.00	15.00	9.00
74	Heinie Groh	30.00	15.00	9.00
75	Earl Hamilton	30.00	15.00	9.00
76	Bob Harmon	30.00	15.00	9.00
77	Roy Hartzell	30.00	15.00	9.00
78	Claude Hendrix	30.00	15.00	9.00
79	Olaf Henriksen	30.00	15.00	9.00
80	John Henry	30.00	15.00	9.00
81	"Buck" Herzog	30.00	15.00	9.00
82	Hugh High	30.00	15.00	9.00
83	Dick Hoblitzell	30.00	15.00	9.00
84	Harry Hooper	65.00	32.00	19.50
85	Ivan Howard	30.00	15.00	9.00
86	Miller Huggins	65.00	32.00	19.50
87	Joe Jackson	2000.	1000.	600.00
88	William James	30.00	15.00	9.00
89	Harold Janvrin	30.00	15.00	9.00
90	Hugh Jennings	65.00	32.00	19.50
91	Walter Johnson	250.00	125.00	75.00
92	Fielder Jones	30.00	15.00	9.00
93	Joe Judge	35.00	17.50	10.50
94	Bennie Kauff	30.00	15.00	9.00
95	Wm. Killefer Jr.	30.00	15.00	9.00
96	Ed. Konetchy	30.00	15.00	9.00
97	Napoleon Lajoie	80.00	40.00	24.00
98	Jack Lapp	30.00	15.00	9.00
99	John Lavan	30.00	15.00	9.00
100	Jimmy Lavender	30.00	15.00	9.00
101	"Nemo" Leibold	30.00	15.00	9.00
102	H.B. Leonard	30.00	15.00	9.00
103	Duffy Lewis	35.00	17.50	10.50
104	Hans Lobert	30.00	15.00	9.00
105	Tom Long	30.00	15.00	9.00
106	Fred Luderus	30.00	15.00	9.00
107	Connie Mack	80.00	40.00	24.00
108	Lee Magee	30.00	15.00	9.00
109	Sherwood Magee	30.00	15.00	9.00
110	Al. Mamaux	30.00	15.00	9.00
111	Leslie Mann	30.00	15.00	9.00
112	"Rabbit" Maranville	65.00	32.00	19.50
113	Rube Marquard	65.00	32.00	19.50
114	J. Erskine Mayer	30.00	15.00	9.00
115	George McBride	30.00	15.00	9.00
116	John J. McGraw	65.00	32.00	19.50
117	Jack McInnis	30.00	15.00	9.00
118	Fred Merkle	35.00	17.50	10.50
119	Chief Meyers	30.00	15.00	9.00
120	Clyde Milan	30.00	15.00	9.00
121	John Miller	30.00	15.00	9.00
122	Otto Miller	30.00	15.00	9.00
123	Willie Mitchell	30.00	15.00	9.00
124	Fred Mollwitz	30.00	15.00	9.00
125	Pat Moran	30.00	15.00	9.00
126	Ray Morgan	30.00	15.00	9.00
127	Geo. Moriarty	30.00	15.00	9.00
128	Guy Morton	30.00	15.00	9.00
129	Mike Mowrey	30.00	15.00	9.00
130	Ed. Murphy	30.00	15.00	9.00
131	"Hy" Myers	30.00	15.00	9.00
132	J.A. Niehoff	30.00	15.00	9.00
133	Rube Oldring	30.00	15.00	9.00
134	Oliver O'Mara	30.00	15.00	9.00
135	Steve O'Neill	30.00	15.00	9.00
136	"Dode" Paskert	30.00	15.00	9.00
137	Roger Peckinpaugh	35.00	17.50	10.50
138	Walter Pipp	45.00	22.00	13.50
139	Derril Pratt (Derrill)	30.00	15.00	9.00
140	Pat Ragan	30.00	15.00	9.00
141	Bill Rariden	30.00	15.00	9.00
142	Eppa Rixey	65.00	32.00	19.50
143	Davey Robertson	30.00	15.00	9.00
144	Wilbert Robinson	65.00	32.00	19.50
145	Bob Roth	30.00	15.00	9.00
146	Ed. Roush	65.00	32.00	19.50
147	Clarence Rowland	30.00	15.00	9.00
148	"Nap" Rucker	30.00	15.00	9.00
149	Dick Rudolph	30.00	15.00	9.00
150	Reb Russell	30.00	15.00	9.00
151	Babe Ruth	3200.	1600.	960.00
152	Vic Saier	30.00	15.00	9.00
153	"Slim" Sallee	30.00	15.00	9.00
154	Ray Schalk	65.00	32.00	19.50
155	Walter Schang	30.00	15.00	9.00
156	Frank Schulte	30.00	15.00	9.00
157	Everett Scott	30.00	15.00	9.00
158	Jim Scott	30.00	15.00	9.00
159	Tom Seaton	30.00	15.00	9.00
160	Howard Shanks	30.00	15.00	9.00
161	Bob Shawkey	35.00	17.50	10.50
162	Ernie Shore	30.00	15.00	9.00
163	Burt Shotton	35.00	17.50	10.50
164	Geo. Sisler	75.00	37.00	22.00
165	J. Carlisle Smith	30.00	15.00	9.00
166	Fred Snodgrass	30.00	15.00	9.00
167	Geo. Stallings	30.00	15.00	9.00
168a	Oscar Stanage (catching)	40.00	20.00	12.00
168b	Oscar Stanage (portrait to waist)	40.00	20.00	12.00
169	Charles Stengel	150.00	75.00	45.00
170	Milton Stock	30.00	15.00	9.00
171	Amos Strunk	30.00	15.00	9.00
172	Billy Sullivan	30.00	15.00	9.00
173	"Jeff" Tesreau	30.00	15.00	9.00
174	Joe Tinker	65.00	32.00	19.50
175	Fred Toney	30.00	15.00	9.00
176	Terry Turner	30.00	15.00	9.00
177	George Tyler	30.00	15.00	9.00
178	Jim Vaughn	30.00	15.00	9.00
179	Bob Veach	30.00	15.00	9.00
180	James Viox	30.00	15.00	9.00
181	Oscar Vitt	30.00	15.00	9.00
182	Hans Wagner	250.00	125.00	75.00
183	Clarence Walker	30.00	15.00	9.00
184	Ed. Walsh	65.00	32.00	19.50
185	W. Wambsganss (photo actually Fritz Coumbe)	40.00	20.00	12.00
186	Buck Weaver	45.00	22.00	13.50
187	Carl Weilman	30.00	15.00	9.00
188	Zach Wheat	65.00	32.00	19.50
189	Geo. Whitted	30.00	15.00	9.00
190	Fred Williams	40.00	20.00	12.00
191	Art Wilson	30.00	15.00	9.00
192	J. Owen Wilson	30.00	15.00	9.00
193	Ivy Wingo	30.00	15.00	9.00
194	"Mel" Wolfgang	30.00	15.00	9.00
195	Joe Wood	35.00	17.50	10.50
196	Steve Yerkes	30.00	15.00	9.00
197	"Pep" Young	30.00	15.00	9.00
198	Rollie Zeider	30.00	15.00	9.00
199	Heiny Zimmerman	30.00	15.00	9.00
200	Ed. Zwilling	40.00	20.00	12.00

1919 Sporting News Supplements (M101-6)

This set of glossy black-and-white player photos is generally attributed to The Sporting News, even though the only clue to the issuer are the initials "F.M." beneath the copyright logo. The photos measure 4-1/2" x 6-1/2" and feature action shots of the player whose name, position and team appear at the bottom of the borderless cards. Four of the players in the checklist appear with two different teams, but since the trades spanned the years 1915-20, it gives rise to speculation these photos were issued over a period of several seasons, rather than the generally attributed 1919. The Sporting News itself carries no advertisements for these photos in its 1919 issues.

		NR MT	EX	VG
	Complete Set:	8500.	4250.	2550.
	Common Player:	45.00	22.00	13.50
(1)	Grover C. Alexander (Philadelphia)	90.00	45.00	27.00
(2)	Grover C. Alexander (Chicago)	90.00	45.00	27.00
(3)	Jim Bagby	45.00	22.00	13.50
(4)	Franklin Baker	75.00	37.00	22.00
(5)	Dave Bancroft	75.00	37.00	22.00
(6)	Jack Barry	45.00	22.00	13.50
(7)	Johnny Bates	45.00	22.00	13.50
(8)	Carson Bigbee	45.00	22.00	13.50
(9)	George Burns	45.00	22.00	13.50
(10)	Owen Bush	45.00	22.00	13.50
(11)	Max Carey	75.00	37.00	22.00
(12)	Ray Chapman	50.00	25.00	15.00
(13)	Hal Chase	50.00	25.00	15.00
(14)	Eddie Cicotte	65.00	32.00	19.50
(15)	Ty Cobb	1000.	500.00	300.00
(16)	Eddie Collins	75.00	37.00	22.00
(17)	"Gavvy" Cravath	45.00	22.00	13.50
(18)	Walton Cruise	45.00	22.00	13.50
(19)	George Cutshaw	45.00	22.00	13.50
(20)	George Dauss	45.00	22.00	13.50
(21)	Dave Davenport	45.00	22.00	13.50
(22)	Bill Doak	45.00	22.00	13.50
(23)	Larry Doyle	45.00	22.00	13.50
(24)	Howard Ehmke	45.00	22.00	13.50
(25)	Urban Faber	75.00	37.00	22.00
(26)	Happy Felsch	65.00	32.00	19.50
(27)	Del Gainer (Gainor)	45.00	22.00	13.50
(28)	Chick Gandil	75.00	37.00	22.00
(29)	Larry Gardner	45.00	22.00	13.50
(30)	Mike Gonzales	45.00	22.00	13.50
(31)	Jack Graney	45.00	22.00	13.50
(32)	Heinie Groh	45.00	22.00	13.50
(33)	Earl Hamilton	45.00	22.00	13.50
(34)	Harry Heilmann	75.00	37.00	22.00
(35)	Hugh High (New York, photo actually Bob Shawkey)	45.00	22.00	13.50
(36)	Hugh High (Detroit, correct photo)	45.00	22.00	13.50
(37)	Bill Hinchman	45.00	22.00	13.50
(38)	Walter Holke (New York)	45.00	22.00	13.50
(39)	Walter Holke (Boston)	45.00	22.00	13.50
(40)	Harry Hooper	75.00	37.00	22.00
(41)	Rogers Hornsby	200.00	100.00	60.00
(42)	Joe Jackson	1250.	625.00	375.00
(43)	Bill Jacobson	45.00	22.00	13.50
(44)	Walter Johnson	300.00	150.00	90.00
(45)	Sam Jones	45.00	22.00	13.50
(46)	Joe Judge	45.00	22.00	13.50
(47)	Benny Kauff	45.00	22.00	13.50
(48)	Ed Konetchy (Boston)	45.00	22.00	13.50
(49)	Ed Konetchy (Brooklyn)	45.00	22.00	13.50
(50)	Nemo Leibold	45.00	22.00	13.50
(51)	Duffy Lewis	45.00	22.00	13.50
(52)	Fred Luderas (Luderus)	45.00	22.00	13.50
(53)	Les Mann	45.00	22.00	13.50
(54)	"Rabbit" Maranville	75.00	37.00	22.00
(55)	John McGraw	90.00	45.00	27.00
(56)	Fred Merkle	50.00	25.00	15.00
(57)	Clyde Milan	45.00	22.00	13.50
(58)	Otto Miller	45.00	22.00	13.50
(59)	Guy Morton	45.00	22.00	13.50
(60)	Hy Myers	45.00	22.00	13.50
(61)	Greasy Neale	50.00	25.00	15.00
(62)	Dode Paskert	45.00	22.00	13.50
(63)	Roger Peckinpaugh	45.00	22.00	13.50
(64)	Jeff Pfeffer	45.00	22.00	13.50
(65)	Walter Pipp	60.00	30.00	18.00
(66)	Johnny Rawlings	45.00	22.00	13.50
(67)	Sam Rice	75.00	37.00	22.00
(68)	Ed Roush	75.00	37.00	22.00
(69)	Dick Rudolph	45.00	22.00	13.50
(70)	Babe Ruth (Red Sox)	1500.	750.00	450.00
(71)	Babe Ruth (New York)	1350.	675.00	405.00
(72)	Ray Schalk	75.00	37.00	22.00
(73)	Hank Severeid	45.00	22.00	13.50
(74)	Burt Shotton	45.00	22.00	13.50
(75)	George Sisler	75.00	37.00	22.00
(76)	Jack Smith	45.00	22.00	13.50
(77)	Frank Snyder	45.00	22.00	13.50
(78)	Tris Speaker	90.00	45.00	27.00
(79)	Oscar Stanage	45.00	22.00	13.50
(80)	Casey Stengel	90.00	45.00	27.00
(81)	Amos Strunk	45.00	22.00	13.50
(82)	Fred Toney	45.00	22.00	13.50
(83)	Jim Vaughn	45.00	22.00	13.50
(84)	Bobby Veach	45.00	22.00	13.50
(85)	Oscar Vitt	45.00	22.00	13.50
(86)	"Honus" Wagner	250.00	125.00	75.00
(87)	Tilly Walker	45.00	22.00	13.50
(88)	Bill Wambsganss	45.00	22.00	13.50
(89)	"Buck" Weaver	65.00	32.00	19.50
(90)	Zack Wheat	75.00	37.00	22.00
(91)	George Whitted	45.00	22.00	13.50
(92)	Cy Williams	45.00	22.00	13.50
(93)	Ivy Wingo	45.00	22.00	13.50
(94)	Pep ("Pep" Young)	45.00	22.00	13.50
(95)	Heinie Zimmerman	45.00	22.00	13.50

1926 Sporting News Supplements (M101-7)

This set of 11 player photos was issued as a supplement by The Sporting News in 1926. The sepia-toned portrait photos were enclosed inside an oval on the 7" x 10" supplements. The player's name and team are printed at the bottom, while a line indentifying The Sporting News and the date appear in the upper left corner. The unnumbered set includes a half-dozen Hall of Famers.

		NR MT	EX	VG
Complete Set:		1350.	675.00	405.00
Common Player:		40.00	20.00	12.00
(1)	Hazen "Kiki" Cuyler	125.00	62.00	37.00
(2)	Rogers Hornsby	150.00	75.00	45.00
(3)	Tony Lazzeri	125.00	62.00	37.00
(4)	Harry E. Manush	110.00	55.00	33.00
(5)	John Mostil	40.00	20.00	12.00
(6)	Harry Rice	40.00	20.00	12.00
(7)	George Herman Ruth	600.00	300.00	180.00
(8)	Al Simmons	110.00	55.00	33.00
(9)	Harold "Pie" Traynor	110.00	55.00	33.00
(10)	George Uhle	40.00	20.00	12.00
(11)	Glenn Wright	40.00	20.00	12.00

1981 Sporting News Conlon Collection

This set of 100 cards was sold directly into the hobby by The Sporting News in a slip-cover case for $50. The blank-backed cards measure 4x5" and feature a sepi-toned photo surrounded by a 1/4" white border. The photos were the first of several uses on baseball cards of TSN's archives of ballplayer photos taken by Charles Martin Conlon between 1915-1935. The paper's logo appears at the top of the card. At bottom are the player's or players' names(s), team at the time the photo was taken, and position or positions played for the season indicated. A card number appears at lower-right.

		MT	NR MT	EX
Complete Set:		100.00	75.00	40.00
Common Player:		1.00	.70	.40
1	Ty Cobb	10.00	7.50	4.00
2	Hughie Jennings	1.00	.70	.40
3	Miller Huggins	1.00	.70	.40
4	Babe Ruth	13.00	9.75	5.25
5	Lou Gehrig	10.00	7.50	4.00
6	John McGraw	1.00	.70	.40
7	Bill Terry	1.00	.70	.40
8	Stan Baumgartner	1.00	.70	.40
9	Christy Mathewson	5.00	3.75	2.00
10	Grover Alexander	2.00	1.50	.80
11	Tony Lazzeri	1.00	.70	.40
12	Frank Chance, Joe Tinker	2.00	1.50	.80
13	Johnny Evers	1.00	.70	.40
14	Tris Speaker	2.00	1.50	.80
15	Harry Hooper	1.00	.70	.40
16	Duffy Lewis	1.00	.70	.40
17	Joe Wood	1.00	.70	.40
18	Hugh Duffy	1.00	.70	.40
19	Rogers Hornsby	5.00	3.75	2.00
20	Earl Averill	1.00	.70	.40
21	Dizzy Dean	2.00	1.50	.80
22	Daffy Dean	1.00	.70	.40
23	Frankie Frisch	2.00	1.50	.80
24	Pepper Martin	1.00	.70	.40
25	Blondie Ryan	1.00	.70	.40
26	Hank Gowdy	1.00	.70	.40
27	Fred Merkle	1.00	.70	.40
28	Ernie Lombardi	1.00	.70	.40
29	Greasy Neale	1.00	.70	.40
30	Morris Badgro	1.00	.70	.40
31	Jim Thorpe	5.00	3.75	2.00
32	Roy Johnson	1.00	.70	.40
33	Bob Johnson	1.00	.70	.40
34	Mule Solters	1.00	.70	.40
35	Specs Toporcer	1.00	.70	.40
36	Jackie Hayes	1.00	.70	.40
37	Walter Johnson	5.00	3.75	2.00
38	Lefty Grove	1.00	.70	.40
39	Eddie Collins	1.00	.70	.40
40	Buck Weaver	4.00	3.00	1.50
41	Cozy Dolan	1.00	.70	.40
42	Emil Meusel	1.00	.70	.40
43	Bob Meusel	1.00	.70	.40
44	Lefty Gomez	1.00	.70	.40
45	Rube Marquard	1.00	.70	.40
46	Jeff Tesreau	1.00	.70	.40
47	Joe Heving	1.00	.70	.40
48	John Heving	1.00	.70	.40
49	Rick Ferrell	1.00	.70	.40
50	Wes Ferrell	1.00	.70	.40
51	Bill Wambsganss	1.00	.70	.40
52	Ben Chapman	1.00	.70	.40
53	Joe Sewell	1.00	.70	.40
54	Luke Sewell	1.00	.70	.40
55	Odell Hale	1.00	.70	.40
56	Sammy Hale	1.00	.70	.40
57	Earle Mack	1.00	.70	.40
58	Connie Mack	1.00	.70	.40
59	Rube Walberg	1.00	.70	.40
60	Mule Haas	1.00	.70	.40
61	Paul Waner	1.00	.70	.40
62	Lloyd Waner	1.00	.70	.40
63	Pie Traynor	1.00	.70	.40
64	Honus Wagner	2.00	1.50	.80
65	Joe Cronin	1.00	.70	.40
66	Joe Harris	1.00	.70	.40
67	Dave Harris	1.00	.70	.40
68	Bucky Harris	1.00	.70	.40
69	Alex Gaston	1.00	.70	.40
70	Milt Gaston	1.00	.70	.40
71	Casey Stengel	2.00	1.50	.80
72	Amos Rusie	1.00	.70	.40
73	Mickey Welch	1.00	.70	.40
74	Roger Bresnaham	1.00	.70	.40
75	Jesse Burkett	1.00	.70	.40
76	Harry Heilmann	1.00	.70	.40
77	Heinie Manush	1.00	.70	.40
78	Charlie Gehringer	1.00	.70	.40
79	Hank Greenberg	2.00	1.50	.80
80	Jimmie Foxx	4.00	3.00	1.50
81	Al Simmons	1.00	.70	.40
82	Eddie Plank	1.00	.70	.40
83	George Sisler	1.00	.70	.40
84	Joe Medwick	1.00	.70	.40
85	Mel Ott	1.00	.70	.40
86	Hack Wilson	1.00	.70	.40
87	Jimmy Wilson	1.00	.70	.40
88	Chuck Klein	1.00	.70	.40
89	Gabby Hartnett	1.00	.70	.40
90	Henie Groh	1.00	.70	.40
91	Ping Bodie	1.00	.70	.40
92	Ted Lyons	1.00	.70	.40
93	Jack Quinn	1.00	.70	.40
94	Oscar Roettger	1.00	.70	.40
95	Wally Roettger	1.00	.70	.40
96	Bubbles Hargrave	1.00	.70	.40
97	Pinky Hargrave	1.00	.70	.40
98	Sam Crawford	1.00	.70	.40
99	Gee Walker	1.00	.70	.40
100	Homer Summa	1.00	.70	.40

1984 Sporting News Conlon Collection

This 60-card set, mostly Hall of Famers, was produced in conjunction with the Smithsonian Institution's "Baseball Immortals" photo exhibition of the work of Charles Martin Conlon. The oversize (4-1/4" x 6-1/8") cards have sepia-toned photos on front; backs are printed in black-and-white. The issue was initially sold only as a complete set.

		MT	NR MT	EX
Complete Set:		20.00	15.00	8.00
Common Player:		.10	.08	.04
1	Grover Cleveland Alexander	.25	.20	.10
2	Chief Bender	.15	.11	.06
3	Fred Clarke	.15	.11	.06
4	Ty Cobb	.75	.60	.30
5	Ty Cobb	.75	.60	.30
6	Ty Cobb	.75	.60	.30
7	Ty Cobb	.75	.60	.30
8	Mickey Cochrane	.15	.11	.06
9	Jack Coombs	.10	.08	.04
10	Charles & Margie Conlon	.10	.08	.04
11	Charles Conlon	.10	.08	.04
12	Joe Cronin	.15	.11	.06
13	Dizzy Dean	.25	.20	.10
14	Leo Durocher	.15	.11	.06
15	Jimmie Foxx	.15	.11	.06
16	The Gashouse Gang (Frank Frisch, Mike Gonzalez, Buzzy Wares)	.10	.08	.04
17	Lou Gehrig	.75	.60	.30
18	Lou Gehrig	.75	.60	.30
19	Lou Gehrig	.75	.60	.30
20	Lou Gehrig	.75	.60	.30
21	Charlie Gehringer	.15	.11	.06
22	Lefty Gomez	.15	.11	.06
23	Lefty Grove	.15	.11	.06
24	Bucky Harris	.15	.11	.06
25	Harry Heilmann	.15	.11	.06
26	Rogers Hornsby	.25	.20	.10
27	Waite Hoyt	.15	.11	.06
28	Carl Hubbell	.15	.11	.06
29	Miller Huggins	.15	.11	.06
30	Walter Johnson	.25	.20	.10
31	Bill Klem	.15	.11	.06
32	Connie Mack	.15	.11	.06
33	Heinie Manush	.15	.11	.06
34	Rube Marquard	.15	.11	.06
35	Pepper Martin	.15	.11	.06
36	Christy Mathewson	.25	.20	.10
37	Christy Mathewson	.25	.20	.10
38	Christy Mathewson	.25	.20	.10
39	Joe McCarthy	.15	.11	.06
40	John McGraw	.15	.11	.06
41	Fred Merkle	.10	.08	.04
42	Mel Ott	.15	.11	.06
43	Roger Peckinpaugh	.10	.08	.04
44	Herb Pennock	.15	.11	.06
45	Babe Ruth	1.00	.70	.40
46	Babe Ruth	1.00	.70	.40
47	Babe Ruth	1.00	.70	.40
48	Babe Ruth	1.00	.70	.40
49	Babe Ruth	1.00	.70	.40
50	Babe Ruth	1.00	.70	.40
51	Al Simmons	.15	.11	.06
52	Tris Speaker	.25	.20	.10
53	Casey Stengel	.25	.20	.10
54	Bill Terry	.15	.11	.06
55	Pie Traynor	.15	.11	.06
56	Rube Waddell	.15	.11	.06
57	Honus Wagner	.35	.25	.14
58	Lloyd Waner, Paul Waner	.15	.11	.06
59	Paul Waner	.15	.11	.06
60	Hack Wilson	.15	.11	.06

1888 Sporting Times (M117)

Examples of these cards, issued in 1888 and 1889 by the Sporting Times weekly newspaper, are very rare. The complete set price includes all variations. The cabinet-size cards (7-1/4" by 4-1/2") feature line drawings of players in action poses on soft cardboard stock. The cards came in a variety of pastel colors surrounded by a 1/4" white border. The player's last name is printed on each drawing, as are the words "Courtesy Sporting Times New York." A pair of crossed bats and a baseball appear along the bottom of the card. Twenty-seven different players are known to exist. The drawing of Cap Anson is the same one used in the N28 Allen & Ginter series, and some of the other drawings are based on photos used in the popular Old Judge series. The Sporting Times set has an American Card Catalog number of M117.

		NR MT	EX	VG
Complete Set:		20000.	10000.	6000.
Common Player:		500.00	250.00	150.00
(1)	Cap Anson	2500.	1250.	750.00
(2)	Jersey Bakely	500.00	250.00	150.00
(3)	Dan Brouthers	1000.	500.00	300.00
(4)	Doc Bushong	500.00	250.00	150.00
(5)	Jack Clements	500.00	250.00	150.00
(6)	Commy Comiskey	1000.	500.00	300.00
(7)	Jerry Denny	500.00	250.00	150.00
(8)	Buck Ewing	1000.	500.00	300.00
(9)	Dude Esterbrook	500.00	250.00	150.00
(10)	Jay Faatz	500.00	250.00	150.00
(11)	Pud Galvin	1000.	500.00	300.00
(12)	Pebbly Jack Glasscock	500.00	250.00	150.00
(13)	Tim Keefe	1000.	500.00	300.00
(14)	King Kelly	1000.	500.00	300.00
(15)	Matt Kilroy	500.00	250.00	150.00
(16)	Arlie Latham	500.00	250.00	150.00
(17)	Doggie Miller	500.00	250.00	150.00
(18)	Hank O'Day	500.00	250.00	150.00
(19)	Fred Pfeffer	500.00	250.00	150.00
(20)	Henry Porter	500.00	250.00	150.00
(21)	Toad Ramsey	500.00	250.00	150.00
(22)	Long John Reilly	500.00	250.00	150.00
(23)	Mike Smith	500.00	250.00	150.00
(24)	Harry Stovey	500.00	250.00	150.00
(25)	Big Sam Thompson	1000.	500.00	300.00
(26)	Monte Ward	1000.	500.00	300.00
(27)	Mickey Welch	1000.	500.00	300.00

1933 Sport Kings

This 48-card set was issued by the Goudey Gum Company. Participants in 18 different sports are included in the set, which honors the top sports figures of the era. Three baseball players are pictured on the 2-3/8" by 2-7/8" cards. The card fronts are

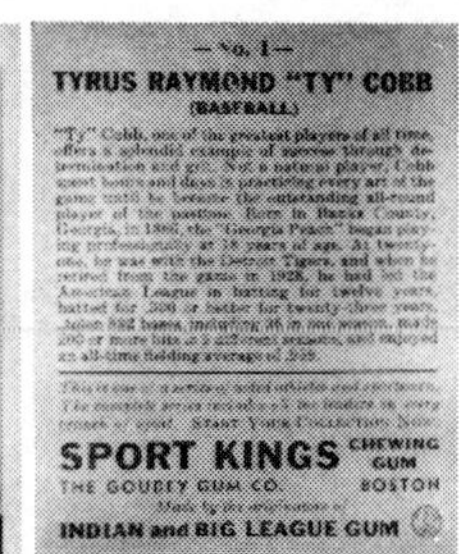

color portraits and include the player's name and silhouette representations of the respective sport. The card backs are numbered and list biographical information and a company ad.

		NR MT	EX	VG
Complete Set (48):		19000.	9500.	5750.
Common Player (1-24):		100.00	50.00	30.00
Common Player (25-48):		200.00	100.00	60.00
1	Ty Cobb	2500.	1250.	750.00
2	Babe Ruth	5250.	2625.	1575.
3	Nat Holman (basketball)	400.00	200.00	120.00
4	Red Grange (football)	1175.	587.00	352.00
5	Ed Wachter (basketball)	200.00	100.00	60.00
6	Jim Thorpe (football)	1000.	500.00	300.00
7	Bobby Walthour, Sr. (bicycling)	100.00	50.00	30.00
8	Walter Hagen (golf)	450.00	225.00	135.00
9	Ed Blood (skiiing)	175.00	87.00	52.00
10	Anston Lekang (skiing)	100.00	50.00	30.00
11	Charles Jewtraw (ice skating)	100.00	50.00	30.00
12	Bobby McLean (ice skating)	100.00	50.00	30.00
13	Laverne Fator (jockey)	100.00	50.00	30.00
14	Jim Londos (wrestling)	100.00	50.00	30.00
15	Reggie McNamara (bicycling)	100.00	50.00	30.00
16	Bill Tilden (tennis)	125.00	62.00	37.00
17	Jack Dempsey (boxing)	450.00	225.00	135.00
18	Gene Tunney (boxing)	400.00	200.00	120.00
19	Eddie Shore (hockey)	375.00	187.00	112.00
20	Duke Kahanamoku (surfing/swimming)	300.00	150.00	90.00
21	Johnny Weissmuller (swimming "Tarzan")	350.00	175.00	105.00
22	Gene Sarazen (golf)	400.00	200.00	120.00
23	Vincent Richards (tennis)	300.00	150.00	90.00
24	Howie Morenz (hockey)	600.00	300.00	180.00
25	Ralph Snoddy (speedboating)	200.00	100.00	60.00
26	James Wedell (aviator)	200.00	100.00	60.00
27	Roscoe Turner (aviator)	200.00	100.00	60.00
28	James Doolittle (aviator)	400.00	200.00	120.00
29	Ace Bailey (hockey)	350.00	175.00	105.00
30	Irvin Johnson (hockey)	350.00	175.00	105.00
31	Bobby Walthour, Jr. (bicycling)	200.00	100.00	60.00
32	Joe Lopchick (basketball)	300.00	150.00	90.00
33	Eddie Burke (basketball)	200.00	100.00	60.00
34	Irving Jaffee (ice skating)	200.00	100.00	60.00
35	Knute Rockne (football)	950.00	475.00	285.00
36	Willie Hoppe (billiards)	600.00	300.00	180.00
37	Helene Madison (swimming)	200.00	100.00	60.00
38	Bobby Jones (golf)	700.00	350.00	210.00
39	Jack Westrope (jockey)	200.00	100.00	60.00
40	Don George (wrestling)	200.00	100.00	60.00
41	Jim Browning (wrestling)	200.00	100.00	60.00
42	Carl Hubbell	600.00	300.00	180.00
43	Primo Carnera (boxing)	300.00	150.00	90.00
44	Max Baer (boxing)	400.00	200.00	120.00
45	Babe Didrickson (track)	1200.	600.00	360.00
46	Ellsworth Vines (tennis)	200.00	100.00	60.00
47	J.H. Stevens (bobsled)	200.00	100.00	60.00
48	Leonard Seppala (dog sled)	200.00	100.00	60.00

1946 - 49 Sports Exchange (W603)

Produced and sold by "The Trading Post," one of the first card collectors' publications, over a period which spanned several years in the late 1940s, this 113-card set was issued in 12 series. Most of the series were nine cards each, printed in black-and-white, unnumbered and blank-backed in a 7" x 10" format. The first 27 cards carry no series designation but were evidently offered as Series 1A and 1B and Series 2. Series 3 features 11 cards and is printed in sepia tones rather than black-and-white. The fourth series is also unmarked. The final two series consist of 12 cards each, printed two per sheet in smaller format. The photos are labeled as originating with the International News Service. Most of the same players and photos appearing in this set are also found in the Sports Exchange Baseball Miniatures set. Because this was one of the first baseball card sets issued after World War II, it contains cards of several players not found in other issues. The set carries a W603 designation in the "American Card Catalog." Cards are listed alphabetically within series in the checklist which follows.

		NR MT	EX	VG
Complete Set (113):		2250.	1125.	675.00
Common Card:		10.00	5.00	3.00
	SERIES 1A			
(1)	Phil Cavaretta	12.00	6.00	3.50
(2)	Walker Cooper	10.00	5.00	3.00
(3)	Dave Ferriss	10.00	5.00	3.00
(4)	Les Fleming	10.00	5.00	3.00
(5)	Whitey Kurowski	10.00	5.00	3.00
(6)	Marty Marion	12.00	6.00	3.50
(7)	Rip Sewell	10.00	5.00	3.00
(8)	Eddie Stanky	12.00	6.00	3.50
(9)	Dixie Walker	10.00	5.00	3.00
	SERIES 1B			
(10)	Bill Dickey	25.00	12.50	7.50
(11)	Bobby Doerr	20.00	10.00	6.00
(12)	Bob Feller	25.00	12.50	7.50
(13)	Hank Greenberg	30.00	15.00	9.00
(14)	George McQuinn	10.00	5.00	3.00
(15)	Ray Mueller	10.00	5.00	3.00
(16)	Hal Newhouser	20.00	10.00	6.00
(17)	Dick Wakefield	10.00	5.00	3.00
(18)	Ted Williams	100.00	50.00	30.00
	SERIES 2			
(19)	Al Benton	10.00	5.00	3.00
(20)	Lou Boudreau	20.00	10.00	6.00
(21)	Spud Chandler	10.00	5.00	3.00
(22)	Jeff Heath	10.00	5.00	3.00
(23)	Kirby Higbe	10.00	5.00	3.00
(24)	Tex Hughson	10.00	5.00	3.00
(25)	Stan Musial	90.00	45.00	27.00
(26)	Howie Pollet	10.00	5.00	3.00
(27)	Enos Slaughter	20.00	10.00	6.00
	SERIES 3			
(28)	Harry Brecheen	10.00	5.00	3.00
(29)	Dom DiMaggio	15.00	7.50	4.50
(30)	Del Ennis	10.00	5.00	3.00
(31)	Al Evans	10.00	5.00	3.00
(32)	Johnny Lindell	10.00	5.00	3.00
(33)	Johnny Mize	20.00	10.00	6.00
(34)	Johnny Pesky	10.00	5.00	3.00
(35)	Pete Reiser	10.00	5.00	3.00
(36)	Aaron Robinson	10.00	5.00	3.00
(37)	1946 Boston Red Sox Team	15.00	7.50	4.50
(38)	1946 St. Louis Cardinals Team	15.00	7.50	4.50
	SERIES 4			
(39)	Jimmie Foxx	30.00	15.00	9.00
(40)	Frank Frisch	25.00	12.50	7.50
(41)	Lou Gehrig	150.00	75.00	45.00
(42)	Lefty Grove	25.00	12.50	7.50
(43)	Bill Hallahan	10.00	5.00	3.00
(44)	Rogers Hornsby	40.00	20.00	12.00
(45)	Carl Hubbell	40.00	20.00	12.00
(46)	Babe Ruth	250.00	125.00	75.00
(47)	Hack Wilson	20.00	10.00	6.00
	SERIES 5			
(48)	Eddie Dyer	10.00	5.00	3.00
(49)	Charlie Grimm	12.00	6.00	3.50
(50)	Billy Herman	20.00	10.00	6.00
(51)	Ted Lyons	20.00	10.00	6.00
(52)	Lefty O'Doul	15.00	7.50	4.50
(53)	Steve O'Neill	10.00	5.00	3.00
(54)	Herb Pennock	20.00	10.00	6.00
(55)	Luke Sewell	10.00	5.00	3.00
(56)	Billy Southworth	10.00	5.00	3.00
	SERIES 6			
(57)	Ewell Blackwell	12.00	6.00	3.50
(58)	Jimmy Outlaw	10.00	5.00	3.00
(59)	Andy Pafko	12.00	6.00	3.50
(60)	Pee Wee Reese	30.00	15.00	9.00
(61)	Phil Rizzuto	30.00	15.00	9.00
(62)	Buddy Rosar	10.00	5.00	3.00
(63)	Johnny Sain	15.00	7.50	4.50
(64)	Dizzy Trout	12.00	6.00	3.50
(65)	Harry Walker	10.00	5.00	3.00
	SERIES 7			
(66)	Floyd Bevens	10.00	5.00	3.00
(67)	Hugh Casey	10.00	5.00	3.00
(68)	Sam Chapman	10.00	5.00	3.00
(69)	Joe DiMaggio	150.00	75.00	45.00
(70)	Tommy Henrich	10.00	5.00	3.00
(71)	Ralph Kiner	20.00	10.00	6.00
(72)	Cookie Lavagetto	10.00	5.00	3.00
(73)	Vic Lombardi	10.00	5.00	3.00
(74)	Cecil Travis	10.00	5.00	3.00
	SERIES 8			
(75)	Nick Altrock	10.00	5.00	3.00
(76)	Mark Christman	10.00	5.00	3.00
(77)	Earle Combs	20.00	10.00	6.00
(78)	Travis Jackson	20.00	10.00	6.00
(79)	Bob Muncrief	10.00	5.00	3.00
(80)	Earl Neale	12.00	6.00	3.50
(81)	Joe Page	12.00	6.00	3.50
(82)	Honus Wagner	40.00	20.00	12.00
(83)	Mickey Witek	10.00	5.00	3.00
	SERIES 9			
(84)	George Case	10.00	5.00	3.00
(85)	Jake Early	10.00	5.00	3.00
(86)	Carl Furillo	15.00	7.50	4.50
(87)	Augie Galan	10.00	5.00	3.00
(88)	Bert Haas	10.00	5.00	3.00
(89)	Johnny Hopp	10.00	5.00	3.00
(90)	Ray Lamanno	10.00	5.00	3.00
(91)	Buddy Kelly	10.00	5.00	3.00
(92)	Warren Spahn	25.00	12.50	7.50
	SERIES 10			
(93)	Lu Blue	10.00	5.00	3.00
(94)	Bruce Edwards	10.00	5.00	3.00
(95)	Elbie Fletcher	10.00	5.00	3.00
(96)	Joe Gordon	10.00	5.00	3.00
(97)	Tommy Holmes	10.00	5.00	3.00
(98)	Billy Johnson	10.00	5.00	3.00
(99)	Phil Masi	10.00	5.00	3.00
(100)	Red Munger	10.00	5.00	3.00
(101)	Vern Stephens	10.00	5.00	3.00
	SERIES 11			
(102)	Ralph Branca, Ken Keltner	15.00	7.50	4.50
(103)	Mickey Cochrane, Bob Dillinger	20.00	10.00	6.00
(104)	Dizzy Dean, Eddie Joost	40.00	20.00	12.00
(105)	Joe Jackson, Wally Westlake	300.00	150.00	90.00
(106)	Larry Jansen, Yogi Berra	40.00	20.00	12.00
(107)	Peanuts Lowrey, Heinie Manush	20.00	10.00	6.00
	SERIES 12			
(108)	Gene Bearden, Dale Mitchell	25.00	12.50	7.50
(109)	Steve Gromek, Earl Torgeson	25.00	12.50	7.50
(110)	Jim Hegan, Mickey Vernon	25.00	12.50	7.50
(111)	Bob Lemon, Red Rolfe	40.00	20.00	12.00
(112)	Billy Meyer, Ben Chapman	25.00	12.50	7.50
(113)	Sibbi Sisti, Zach Taylor	25.00	12.50	7.50

1947 Sports Exchange Baseball Miniatures (W602)

Produced and sold by one of the hobby's first periodicals, "The Trading Post," this 118 card set was released in three series, designated by red, green and gold borders. The blank-back, unnumbered cards are printed in black and white and were sold in sheets of six. When cut from the sheets, individual cards in the red- and green-bordered series measure 2-1/2" x 3," while the gold-bordered cards measure 2-1/2" x 3-1/8". The set is checklisted here alphabetically within series. The set carries an "American Card Catalog" designation of W602.

		NR MT	EX	VG
Complete Set (108):		2000.	1000.	600.00
Common Player:		10.00	5.00	3.00
	GREEN BORDER SERIES			
(1)	Nick Altrock	10.00	5.00	3.00
(2)	Floyd Bevens	10.00	5.00	3.00
(3)	Ewell Blackwell	10.00	5.00	3.00
(4)	Lou Boudreau	20.00	10.00	6.00
(5)	Harry Brecheen	10.00	5.00	3.00
(6)	Hugh Casey	10.00	5.00	3.00
(7)	Phil Cavaretta	12.00	6.00	3.50
(8)	Sam Chapman	10.00	5.00	3.00
(9)	Mark Christman	10.00	5.00	3.00
(10)	Bill Dickey	25.00	12.50	7.50
(11)	Dom DiMaggio	15.00	7.50	4.50
(12)	Joe DiMaggio	150.00	75.00	45.00
(13)	Eddie Dyer	10.00	5.00	3.00
(14)	Frank Frisch	25.00	12.50	7.50
(15)	Lou Gehrig	150.00	75.00	45.00
(16)	Charlie Grimm	12.00	6.00	3.50
(17)	Lefty Grove	25.00	12.50	7.50
(18)	Tommy Henrich	12.00	6.00	3.50
(19)	Ralph Kiner	20.00	10.00	6.00
(20)	Cookie Lavagetto	10.00	5.00	3.00
(21)	Vic Lombardi	10.00	5.00	3.00
(22)	Ted Lyons	20.00	10.00	6.00
(23)	Bob Muncrief	10.00	5.00	3.00
(24)	Stan Musial	90.00	45.00	27.00
(25)	Steve O'Neill	10.00	5.00	3.00
(26)	Jimmy Outlaw	10.00	5.00	3.00
(27)	Joe Page	12.00	6.00	3.50
(28)	Pee Wee Reese	30.00	15.00	9.00
(29)	Phil Rizzuto	30.00	15.00	9.00
(30)	Buddy Rosar	10.00	5.00	3.00
(31)	Johnny Sain	15.00	7.50	4.50
(32)	Billy Southworth	10.00	5.00	3.00
(33)	Cecil Travis	10.00	5.00	3.00
(34)	Honus Wagner	40.00	20.00	12.00
(35)	Harry Walker	10.00	5.00	3.00
(36)	Mickey Witek	10.00	5.00	3.00

	RED BORDER SERIES			
(37)	Yogi Berra	40.00	20.00	12.00
(38)	Lu Blue	10.00	5.00	3.00
(39)	Ben Chapman	12.00	6.00	3.50
(40)	Mickey Cochrane	20.00	10.00	6.00
(41)	Earle Combs	20.00	10.00	6.00
(42)	Dizzy Dean	50.00	25.00	15.00
(43)	Bob Dillinger	10.00	5.00	3.00
(44)	Bobby Doerr	20.00	10.00	6.00
(45)	Al Evans	10.00	5.00	3.00
(46)	Jimmie Foxx	30.00	15.00	9.00
(47)	Joe Gordon	10.00	5.00	3.00
(48)	Bill Hallahan	10.00	5.00	3.00
(49)	Tommy Holmes	10.00	5.00	3.00
(50)	Rogers Hornsby	40.00	20.00	12.00
(51)	Carl Hubbell	40.00	20.00	12.00
(52)	Travis Jackson	20.00	10.00	6.00
(53)	Bill Johnson	10.00	5.00	3.00
(54)	Ken Keltner	10.00	5.00	3.00
(55)	Whitey Kurowski	10.00	5.00	3.00
(56)	Ray Lamanno	10.00	5.00	3.00
(57)	Johnny Lindell	10.00	5.00	3.00
(58)	Peanuts Lowrey	10.00	5.00	3.00
(59)	Phil Masi	10.00	5.00	3.00
(60)	Earl Neale	12.00	6.00	3.50
(61)	Hal Newhouser	20.00	10.00	6.00
(62)	Lefty O'Doul	15.00	7.50	4.50
(63)	Herb Pennock	20.00	10.00	6.00
(64)	Red Rolfe	20.00	10.00	6.00
(65)	Babe Ruth	250.00	125.00	75.00
(66)	Luke Sewell	10.00	5.00	3.00
(67)	Rip Sewell	10.00	5.00	3.00
(68)	Warren Spahn	25.00	12.50	7.50
(69)	Vern Stephens	10.00	5.00	3.00
(70)	Dizzy Trout	12.00	6.00	3.50
(71)	Wally Westlake	10.00	5.00	3.00
(72)	Hack Wilson	20.00	10.00	6.00
	GOLD BORDER SERIES			
(73)	Al Benton	10.00	5.00	3.00
(74)	Ralph Branca	12.00	6.00	3.50
(75)	George Case	10.00	5.00	3.00
(76)	Spud Chandler	10.00	5.00	3.00
(77)	Jake Early	10.00	5.00	3.00
(78)	Bruce Edwards	10.00	5.00	3.00
(79)	Del Ennis	10.00	5.00	3.00
(80)	Bob Feller	25.00	12.50	7.50
(81)	Dave Ferriss	10.00	5.00	3.00
(82)	Les Fleming	10.00	5.00	3.00
(83)	Carl Furillo	15.00	7.50	4.50
(84)	Augie Galan	10.00	5.00	3.00
(85)	Hank Greenberg	30.00	15.00	9.00
(86)	Bert Haas	10.00	5.00	3.00
(87)	Jeff Heath	10.00	5.00	3.00
(88)	Billy Herman	20.00	10.00	6.00
(89)	Kirby Higbe	10.00	5.00	3.00
(90)	Tex Hughson	10.00	5.00	3.00
(91)	Johnny Hopp	10.00	5.00	3.00
(92)	Joe Jackson	300.00	150.00	90.00
(93)	Larry Jansen	10.00	5.00	3.00
(94)	Eddie Joost	10.00	5.00	3.00
(95)	Buddy Lewis	10.00	5.00	3.00
(96)	Heinie Manush	20.00	10.00	6.00
(97)	Marty Marion	12.00	6.00	3.50
(98)	George McQuinn	10.00	5.00	3.00
(99)	Johnny Mize	20.00	10.00	6.00
(100)	Red Munger	10.00	5.00	3.00
(101)	Andy Pafko	12.00	6.00	3.50
(102)	Johnny Pesky	10.00	5.00	3.00
(103)	Howie Pollet	10.00	5.00	3.00
(104)	Pete Reiser	10.00	5.00	3.00
(105)	Aaron Robinson	10.00	5.00	3.00
(106)	Enos Slaughter	20.00	10.00	6.00
(107)	Dixie Howell	10.00	5.00	3.00
(108)	Ted Williams (photo actually Bobby Doerr)	100.00	50.00	30.00

1948 Sport Thrills

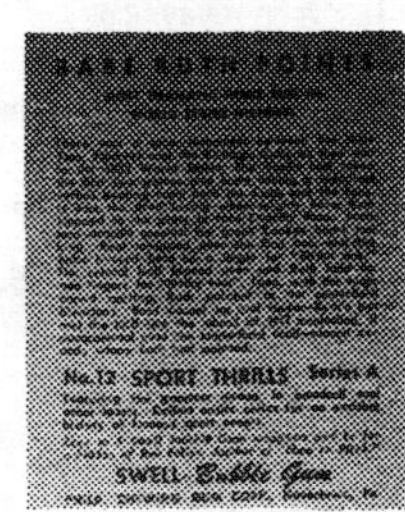

This is a set of black and white cards which depict memorable events in baseball history. The cards measure 2-1/2" by 3" and have a picture frame border and event title on the card fronts. The card backs describe the event in detail. Twenty cards were produced in this set by the Swell Gum Company of Philadelphia. Each card is numbered, and card numbers 9, 11, 16 and 20 are considered more difficult to obtain.

	NR MT	EX	VG
Complete Set:	1250.	625.00	375.00
Common Player:	25.00	12.50	7.50

1	Greatest Single Inning (Mickey Cochrane, Jimmy Foxx, George Haas, Bing Miller, Al Simmons)	65.00	32.00	19.50
2	Amazing Record (Pete Reiser)	25.00	12.50	7.50
3	Dramatic Debut (Jackie Robinson)	145.00	72.00	43.00
4	Greatest Pitcher (Walter Johnson)	80.00	40.00	24.00
5	Three Strikes Not Out! (Tommy Henrich, Mickey Owen)	25.00	12.50	7.50
6	Home Run Wins Series (Bill Dickey)	30.00	15.00	9.00
7	Never Say Die Pitcher (Hal Schumacher)	25.00	12.50	7.50
8	Five Strikeouts! (Carl Hubbell)	30.00	15.00	9.00
9	Greatest Catch! (Al Gionfriddo)	65.00	32.00	19.50
10	No Hits! No Runs! (Johnny Vander Meer)	25.00	12.50	7.50
11	Bases Loaded! (Tony Lazzeri, Bob O'Farrell)	65.00	32.00	19.50
12	Most Dramatic Home Run (Lou Gehrig, Babe Ruth)	225.00	112.00	67.00
13	Winning Run (Tommy Bridges, Mickey Cochrane, Goose Goslin)	25.00	12.50	7.50
14	Great Slugging (Lou Gehrig)	225.00	112.00	67.00
15	Four Men to Stop Him! (Jim Bagby, Al Smith)	25.00	12.50	7.50
16	Three Run Homer in Ninth! (Joe DiMaggio, Joe Gordon, Ted Williams)	225.00	112.00	67.00
17	Football Block! (Whitey Kurowski, Johnny Lindell)	25.00	12.50	7.50
18	Home Run to Fame (Pee Wee Reese)	65.00	32.00	19.50
19	Strikout Record! (Bob Feller)	80.00	40.00	24.00
20	Rifle Arm! (Carl Furillo)	80.00	40.00	24.00

1981 Spot-bilt George Brett

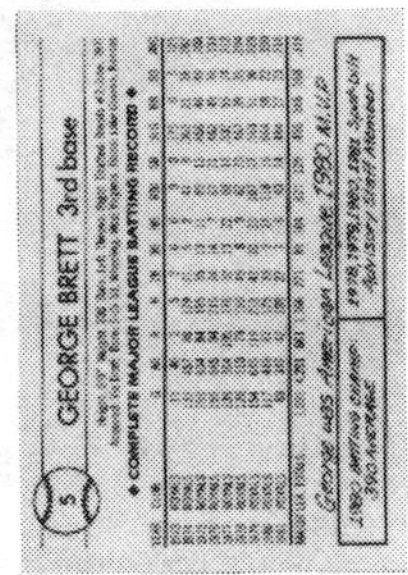

This one-card set was released in both 1981 and 1982 (see stats on back to differentiate) in boxes of turf baseball shoes, for which Brett served on the athletic advisory staff. Cards are standard 2-1/2x3-1/2". Despite the card number 5 on the back, there are no other players in the series. Brett wore uniform #5.

5	George Brett	5.00	3.75	2.00

1986 Springhill Papers

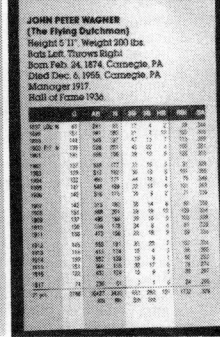

An obscure "old-timers" issue, this five-card set was available through a mail-in offer advertising in printing trade publications in 1986. The four player cards, and a header card which advertises the company's paper stock, are printed on thin cardboard and measure 2-3/4" x 4-1/8". Card fronts have a blue-and-white duo-tone portrait of the player set in a 1-3/4" red circle. The player's name and position are in white above and below the portrait. A light blue pin-striped background behind the circle is framed by an orange diamond, which in turn is surrounded by a blue background. Two of the four orange circles in the corners have logos of the paper brand and its parent company - International Paper. Backs have a black border, blue interior and player biographical data and career stats printed in black. The set was packaged in a white paper envelope with logos similar to the header card.

	MT	NR MT	EX
Complete Set (5):	5.00	3.75	2.00
Common Player:	2.00	1.50	.80

(1)	Grover Alexander	2.00	1.50	.80
(2)	John McGraw	2.00	1.50	.80
(3)	Honus Wagner	2.00	1.50	.80
(4)	Cy Young	2.00	1.50	.80
(5)	Header card	.05	.04	.02

1981 Squirt

These cards, issued in conjunction with Topps, were issued as two-card panels in eight-pack cartons of the soft drink. Individual cards measure the standard 2-1/2" by 3-1/2", while the vertical panels measure 2-1/2" by 10-1/2", with a promotional card reading "Free Topps 1981 Baseball Cards" attached. The promotional card is blank-backed, while the player card backs are similar to Topps' regular issue, though re-numbered for inclusion in this 33-card set. Most of the game's top players are included. There are only 22 different two-card panels, as card numbers 1-11 appear in two different bottom panel combinations. Card fronts feature a color player portrait photo within a baseball design, team and position designation, and the Squirt logo.

	MT	NR MT	EX
Complete Panel Set:	25.00	18.50	10.00
Complete Singles Set:	15.00	11.00	6.00
Common Panel:	.50	.40	.20
Common Single Player:	.15	.11	.06

	Panel 1	2.00	1.50	.80
1	George Brett	1.00	.70	.40
12	Garry Templeton	.25	.20	.10
	Panel 2	2.00	1.50	.80
1	George Brett	1.00	.70	.40
23	Jerry Mumphrey	.25	.20	.10
	Panel 3	.50	.40	.20
2	George Foster	.25	.20	.10
13	Rick Burleson	.25	.20	.10
	Panel 4	.50	.40	.20
2	George Foster	.25	.20	.10
24	Tony Armas	.25	.20	.10
	Panel 5	.50	.40	.20
3	Ben Oglivie	.15	.11	.06
14	Dave Kingman	.15	.11	.06
	Panel 6	.50	.40	.20
3	Ben Oglivie	.15	.11	.06
25	Fred Lynn	.15	.11	.06
	Panel 7	2.00	1.50	.80
4	Steve Garvey	.50	.40	.20
15	Eddie Murray	.75	.60	.30
	Panel 8	1.50	1.25	.60
4	Steve Garvey	.50	.40	.20

26	Ron LeFlore	.25	.20	.10
	Panel 9	2.50	1.50	.80
5	Reggie Jackson	1.00	.70	.40
16	Don Sutton	.50	.40	.20
	Panel 10	1.50	1.25	.60
5	Reggie Jackson	1.00	.70	.40
27	Steve Kemp	.15	.11	.06
	Panel 11	.50	.40	.20
6	Bill Buckner	.15	.11	.06
17	Dusty Baker	.25	.20	.10
	Panel 12	4.00	3.00	1.50
6	Bill Buckner	.15	.11	.06
28	Rickey Henderson	3.00	2.25	1.25
	Panel 13	.60	.45	.25
7	Jim Rice	.15	.11	.06
18	Jack Clark	.15	.11	.06
	Panel 14	.50	.40	.20
7	Jim Rice	.15	.11	.06
29	John Castino	.25	.20	.10
	Panel 15	3.00	2.25	1.25
8	Mike Schmidt	1.00	.70	.40
19	Dave Winfield	1.00	.70	.40
	Panel 16	1.25	.90	.50
8	Mike Schmidt	1.00	.70	.40
30	Cecil Cooper	.20	.15	.08
	Panel 17	3.00	2.25	1.25
9	Rod Carew	1.00	.70	.40
20	Johnny Bench	1.00	.70	.40
	Panel 18	1.25	.90	.50
9	Rod Carew	1.00	.70	.40
31	Bruce Bochte	.25	.20	.10
	Panel 19	1.00	.70	.40
10	Dave Parker	.50	.40	.20
21	Lee Mazzilli	.25	.20	.10
	Panel 20	1.00	.70	.40
10	Dave Parker	.50	.40	.20
32	Joe Charboneau	.25	.20	.10
	Panel 21	2.00	1.50	.80
11	Pete Rose	1.25	.90	.50
22	Al Oliver	.30	.25	.12
	Panel 22	2.00	1.50	.80
11	Pete Rose	1.25	.90	.50
33	Chet Lemon	.25	.20	.10

1982 Squirt

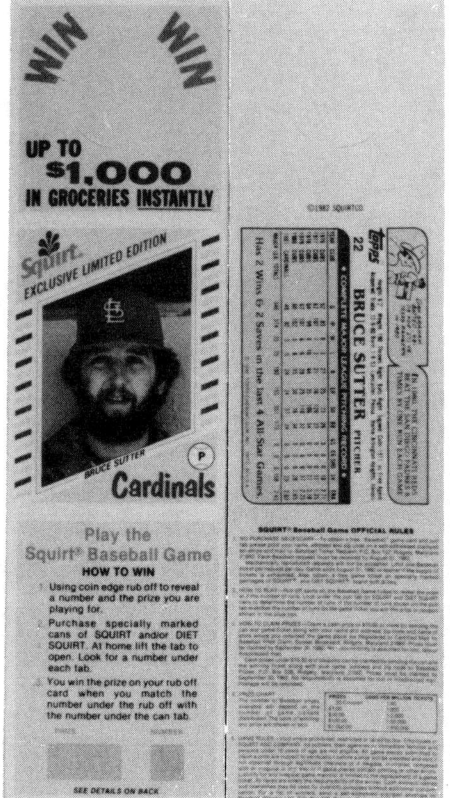

This set was again prepared in conjunction with Topps, but the 1982 Squirt cards are completely different from Topps' regular issue. Only 22 players are included in the full-color set, with the 2-1/2" by 3-1/2" player cards available on one- or two-player panels. Card panels come in four variations, with free grocery contest and scratch-off game cards taking one or two of the positions on the three-card panels. Card backs are numbered and list player statistics.

		MT	NR MT	EX
Complete Set:		8.00	6.00	3.25
Common Player:		.15	.11	.06
1	Cecil Cooper	.25	.20	.10
2	Jerry Remy	.15	.11	.06
3	George Brett	1.00	.70	.40
4	Alan Trammell	.60	.45	.25
5	Reggie Jackson	1.00	.70	.40
6	Kirk Gibson	.35	.25	.14
7	Dave Winfield	1.00	.70	.40
8	Carlton Fisk	.40	.30	.15
9	Ron Guidry	.30	.25	.12
10	Dennis Leonard	.15	.11	.06
11	Rollie Fingers	.60	.45	.25
12	Pete Rose	1.00	.70	.40
13	Phil Garner	.15	.11	.06
14	Mike Schmidt	1.00	.70	.40
15	Dave Concepcion	.20	.15	.08
16	George Hendrick	.15	.11	.06
17	Andre Dawson	.35	.25	.14
18	George Foster	.20	.15	.08
19	Gary Carter	.40	.30	.15
20	Fernando Valenzuela	.40	.30	.15
21	Tom Seaver	.50	.40	.20
22	Bruce Sutter	.25	.20	.10

1975 SSPC

This set, issued by the Sport Star Publishing Company in 1976 as a collectors' issue, was withdrawn from the market because of legal entanglements. Because SSPC agreed never to reprint the issue, some collectors feel it has an air of legitimacy. The complete set contains 630 full-color cards, each 2-1/2" by 3-1/2" in size. The cards look similar to 1953 Bowmans, with only the player picture (no identification) on the fronts. Card backs are in a vertical format, with personal stats, brief biographies and card numbers.

		NR MT	EX	VG
Complete Set:		100.00	50.00	30.00
Common Player:		.12	.06	.04
1	Lee William (Buzz) Capra	.20	.10	.06
2	Thomas Ross House	.12	.06	.04
3	Maximino Leon	.12	.06	.04
4	Carl Wendle Morton	.12	.06	.04
5	Philip Henry Niekro	1.50	.70	.45
6	Michael Wayne Thompson	.12	.06	.04
7	Elias Sosa (Martinez)	.12	.06	.04
8	Larvell Blanks	.12	.06	.04
9	Darrell Wayne Evans	.40	.20	.12
10	Rodney Joe Gilbreath	.12	.06	.04
11	Michael Ken-Wai Lum	.12	.06	.04
12	Craig George Robinson	.12	.06	.04
13	Earl Craig Williams, Jr.	.12	.06	.04
14	Victor Crosby Correll	.12	.06	.04
15	Biff Pocoroba	.12	.06	.04
16	Johnny B. (Dusty) Baker, Jr.	.20	.10	.06
17	Ralph Allen Garr	.15	.08	.05
18	Clarence Edward (Cito) Gaston	.25	.13	.08
19	David LaFrance May	.12	.06	.04
20	Rowland Johnnie Office	.12	.06	.04
21	Robert Brooks Beall	.12	.06	.04
22	George Lee (Sparky) Anderson	.20	.10	.06
23	John Eugene Billingham	.12	.06	.04
24	Pedro Rodriguez Borbon	.12	.06	.04
25	Clay Palmer Carroll	.15	.08	.05
26	Patrick Leonard Darcy	.12	.06	.04
27	Donald Edward Gullett	.15	.08	.05
28	Clayton Laws Kirby	.12	.06	.04
29	Gary Lynn Nolan	.12	.06	.04
30	Fredie Hubert Norman	.12	.06	.04
31	Johnny Lee Bench	8.00	4.00	2.50
32	William Francis Plummer	.12	.06	.04
33	Darrel Lee Chaney	.12	.06	.04
34	David Ismael Concepcion	.30	.15	.09
35	Terrence Michael Crowley	.12	.06	.04
36	Daniel Driessen	.15	.08	.05
37	Robert Douglas Flynn, Jr.	.12	.06	.04
38	Joe Leonard Morgan	3.00	1.50	.90
39	Atanasio Rigal (Tony) Perez	.80	.40	.25
40	George Kenneth (Ken) Griffey	.30	.15	.09
41	Peter Edward Rose	12.00	6.00	3.50
42	Edison Rosanda Armbrister	.12	.06	.04
43	John Christopher Vukovich	.12	.06	.04
44	George Arthur Foster	.40	.20	.12
45	Cesar Francisco Geronimo	.12	.06	.04
46	Mervin Weldon Rettenmund	.12	.06	.04
47	James Frederick Crawford	.12	.06	.04
48	Kenneth Roth Forsch	.12	.06	.04
49	Douglas James Konieczny	.12	.06	.04
50	Joseph Franklin Niekro	.25	.13	.08
51	Clifford Johnson	.12	.06	.04
52	Alfred Henry (Skip) Jutze	.12	.06	.04
53	Milton Scott May	.12	.06	.04
54	Robert Patrick Andrews	.12	.06	.04
55	Kenneth George Boswell	.12	.06	.04
56	Tommy Vann Helms	.12	.06	.04
57	Roger Henry Metzger	.12	.06	.04
58	Lawrence William Milbourne	.12	.06	.04
59	Douglas Lee Rader	.12	.06	.04
60	Robert Jose Watson	.15	.08	.05
61	Enos Milton Cabell, Jr.	.12	.06	.04
62	Jose Delan Cruz	.30	.15	.09
63	Cesar Cedeno	.30	.15	.09
64	Gregory Eugene Gross	.12	.06	.04
65	Wilbur Leon Howard	.12	.06	.04
66	Alphonso Erwin Downing	.12	.06	.04
67	Burt Carlton Hooton	.15	.08	.05
68	Charles Oliver Hough	.20	.10	.06
69	Thomas Edward John	.80	.40	.25
70	John Alexander Messersmith	.15	.08	.05
71	Douglas James Rau	.12	.06	.04
72	Richard Alan Rhoden	.25	.13	.08
73	Donald Howard Sutton	.80	.40	.25
74	Frederick Steven Auerbach	.12	.06	.04
75	Ronald Charles Cey	.25	.13	.08
76	Ivan De Jesus	.12	.06	.04
77	Steven Patrick Garvey	3.00	1.50	.90
78	Leonadus Lacy	.15	.08	.05
79	David Earl Lopes	.20	.10	.06
80	Kenneth Lee McMullen	.12	.06	.04
81	Joseph Vance Ferguson	.12	.06	.04
82	Paul Ray Powell	.12	.06	.04
83	Stephen Wayne Yeager	.12	.06	.04
84	Willie Murphy Crawford	.12	.06	.04
85	Henry Cruz	.12	.06	.04
86	Charles Fuqua Manuel	.12	.06	.04
87	Manuel Mota	.20	.10	.06
88	Thomas Marian Paciorek	.12	.06	.04
89	James Sherman Wynn	.20	.10	.06
90	Walter Emmons Alston	.60	.30	.20
91	William Joseph Buckner	.20	.10	.06
92	James Leland Barr	.12	.06	.04
93	Ralph Michael (Mike) Caldwell	.12	.06	.04
94	John Francis D'Acquisto	.12	.06	.04
95	David Wallace Heaverlo	.12	.06	.04
96	Gary Robert Lavelle	.12	.06	.04
97	John Joseph Montefusco, Jr.	.12	.06	.04
98	Charles Prosek Williams	.12	.06	.04
99	Christopher Paul Arnold	.12	.06	.04
100	Mark Kevin Hill (Marc)	.12	.06	.04
101	David Martin Rader	.12	.06	.04
102	Charles Bruce Miller	.12	.06	.04
103	Guillermo Naranjo (Willie) Montanez	.15	.08	.05
104	Steven Robert Ontiveros	.12	.06	.04
105	Chris Edward Speier	.15	.08	.05
106	Derrel Osbon Thomas	.12	.06	.04
107	Gary Leah Thomasson	.12	.06	.04
108	Glenn Charles Adams	.12	.06	.04
109	Von Everett Joshua	.12	.06	.04
110	Gary Nathaniel Matthews	.20	.10	.06
111	Bobby Ray Murcer	.25	.13	.08
112	Horace Arthur Speed III	.12	.06	.04
113	Wesley Noreen Westrum	.12	.06	.04
114	Richard Nevin Folkers	.12	.06	.04
115	Alan Benton Foster	.12	.06	.04
116	David James Freisleben	.12	.06	.04
117	Daniel Vincent Frisella	.12	.06	.04
118	Randall Leo Jones	.15	.08	.05
119	Daniel Ray Spillner	.12	.06	.04
120	Howard Lawrence (Larry) Hardy	.12	.06	.04
121	Cecil Randolph (Randy) Hundley	.12	.06	.04
122	Fred Lyn Kendall	.12	.06	.04
123	John Francis McNamara	.12	.06	.04
124	Rigoberto (Tito) Fuentes	.12	.06	.04
125	Enzo Octavio Hernandez	.12	.06	.04
126	Stephen Michael Huntz	.12	.06	.04
127	Michael Wilson Ivie	.12	.06	.04
128	Hector Epitacio Torres	.12	.06	.04
129	Theodore Rodger Kubiak	.12	.06	.04
130	John Maywood Grubb, Jr.	.12	.06	.04
131	John Henry Scott	.12	.06	.04
132	Robert Tolan	.15	.08	.05
133	David Mark Winfield	8.00	4.00	2.50
134	William Joseph Gogolewski	.12	.06	.04
135	Danny L. Osborn	.12	.06	.04
136	James Lee Kaat	.50	.25	.15
137	Claude Wilson Osteen	.15	.08	.05
138	Cecil Lee Upshaw, Jr.	.12	.06	.04
139	Wilbur Forrester Wood, Jr.	.15	.08	.05
140	Lloyd Cecil Allen	.12	.06	.04
141	Brian Jay Downing	.20	.10	.06
142	James Sarkis Essian, Jr.	.12	.06	.04
143	Russell Earl (Bucky) Dent	.25	.13	.08
144	Jorge Orta	.12	.06	.04
145	Lee Edward Richard	.12	.06	.04
146	William Allen Stein	.12	.06	.04
147	Kenneth Joseph Henderson	.12	.06	.04
148	Carlos May	.15	.08	.05
149	Nyls Wallace Rex Nyman	.12	.06	.04
150	Robert Pasquali Coluccio, Jr.	.12	.06	.04
151	Charles William Tanner, Jr.	.20	.10	.06
152	Harold Patrick (Pat) Kelly	.12	.06	.04
153	Jerry Wayne Hairston	.12	.06	.04
154	Richard Fred (Pete) Varney, Jr.	.12	.06	.04
155	William Edwin Melton	.15	.08	.05
156	Richard Michael Gossage	.60	.30	.20
157	Terry Jay Forster	.15	.08	.05
158	Richard Michael Hinton	.12	.06	.04
159	Nelson Kelley Briles	.12	.06	.04
160	Alan James Fitzmorris	.12	.06	.04
161	Stephen Bernard Mingori	.12	.06	.04
162	Martin William Pattin	.12	.06	.04
163	Paul William Splittorff, Jr.	.15	.08	.05
164	Dennis Patrick Leonard	.15	.08	.05
165	John Albert (Buck) Martinez	.12	.06	.04
166	Gorrell Robert (Bob) Stinson III	.12	.06	.04
167	George Howard Brett	12.00	6.00	3.50
168	Harmon Clayton Killebrew, Jr.	6.00	3.00	1.75
169	John Claiborn Mayberry	.15	.08	.05

170 Freddie Joe Patek .12 .06 .04
171 Octavio (Cookie) Rojas .12 .06 .04
172 Rodney Darrell Scott .12 .06 .04
173 Tolia (Tony) Solaita .12 .06 .04
174 Frank White, Jr. .20 .10 .06
175 Alfred Edward Cowens, Jr. .12 .06 .04
176 Harold Abraham McRae .25 .13 .08
177 Amos Joseph Otis .15 .08 .05
178 Vada Edward Pinson, Jr. .40 .20 .12
179 James Eugene Wohlford .12 .06 .04
180 James Douglas Bird .12 .06 .04
181 Mark Alan Littell .12 .06 .04
182 Robert McClure .12 .06 .04
183 Steven Lee Busby .15 .08 .05
184 Francis Xavier Healy .12 .06 .04
185 Dorrel Norman Elvert (Whitey) Herzog .20 .10 .06
186 Andrew Earl Hassler .12 .06 .04
187 Lynn Nolan Ryan, Jr. 15.00 7.50 4.50
188 William Robert Singer .12 .06 .04
189 Frank Daryl Tanana .20 .10 .06
190 Eduardo Figueroa .12 .06 .04
191 David S. Collins .15 .08 .05
192 Richard Hirshfeld Williams .15 .08 .05
193 Eliseo Rodriguez .12 .06 .04
194 David Lee Chalk .12 .06 .04
195 Winston Enriquillo Llenas .12 .06 .04
196 Rudolph Bart Meoli .12 .06 .04
197 Orlando Ramirez .12 .06 .04
198 Gerald Peter Remy .12 .06 .04
199 Billy Edward Smith .12 .06 .04
200 Bruce Anton Bochte .12 .06 .04
201 Joseph Michael Lahoud, Jr. .12 .06 .04
202 Morris Nettles, Jr. .12 .06 .04
203 John Milton (Mickey) Rivers .15 .08 .05
204 Leroy Bobby Stanton .12 .06 .04
205 Victor Albury .12 .06 .04
206 Thomas Henry Burgmeier .12 .06 .04
207 William Franklin Butler .12 .06 .04
208 William Richard Campbell .12 .06 .04
209 Alton Ray Corbin .12 .06 .04
210 George Henry (Joe) Decker, Jr. .12 .06 .04
211 James Michael Hughes .12 .06 .04
212 Edward Norman Bane (photo actually Mike Pazik) .12 .06 .04
213 Glenn Dennis Borgmann .12 .06 .04
214 Rodney Cline Carew 8.00 4.00 2.50
215 Stephen Robert Brye .12 .06 .04
216 Darnell Glenn (Dan) Ford .12 .06 .04
217 Antonio Oliva .50 .25 .15
218 David Allan Goltz .15 .08 .05
219 Rikalbert Blyleven .60 .30 .20
220 Larry Eugene Hisle .15 .08 .05
221 Stephen Russell Braun, III .12 .06 .04
222 Jerry Wayne Terrell .12 .06 .04
223 Eric Thane Soderholm .12 .06 .04
224 Philip Anthony Roof .12 .06 .04
225 Danny Leon Thompson .12 .06 .04
226 James William Colborn .12 .06 .04
227 Thomas Andrew Murphy .12 .06 .04
228 Eduardo Rodriguez .12 .06 .04
229 James Michael Slaton .12 .06 .04
230 Edward Nelson Sprague .12 .06 .04
231 Charles William Moore, Jr. .12 .06 .04
232 Darrell Ray Porter .15 .08 .05
233 Kurt Anthony Bevacqua .12 .06 .04
234 Pedro Garcia .12 .06 .04
235 James Michael (Mike) Hegan .12 .06 .04
236 Donald Wayne Money .15 .08 .05
237 George C. Scott, Jr. .15 .08 .05
238 Robin R. Yount 12.00 6.00 3.50
239 Henry Louis Aaron 12.00 6.00 3.50
240 Robert Walker Ellis .12 .06 .04
241 Sixto Lezcano .12 .06 .04
242 Robert Vance Mitchell .12 .06 .04
243 James Gorman Thomas, III .20 .10 .06
244 William Edward Travers .12 .06 .04
245 Peter Sven Broberg .12 .06 .04
246 William Howard Sharp .12 .06 .04
247 Arthur Bobby Lee Darwin .12 .06 .04
248 Rick Gerald Austin (photo actually Larry Anderson) .12 .06 .04
249 Lawrence Dennis Anderson (photo actually Rick Austin) .12 .06 .04
250 Thomas Antony Bianco .12 .06 .04
251 DeLancy LaFayette Currence .12 .06 .04
252 Steven Raymond Foucault .12 .06 .04
253 William Alfred Hands, Jr. .12 .06 .04
254 Steven Lowell Hargan .12 .06 .04
255 Ferguson Arthur Jenkins .60 .30 .20
256 Bob Mitchell Sheldon .12 .06 .04
257 James Umbarger .12 .06 .04
258 Clyde Wright .12 .06 .04
259 William Roger Fahey .12 .06 .04
260 James Howard Sundberg .15 .08 .05
261 Leonardo Alfonso Cardenas .12 .06 .04
262 James Louis Fregosi .20 .10 .06
263 Dudley Michael (Mike) Hargrove .15 .08 .05
264 Colbert Dale (Toby) Harrah .20 .10 .06
265 Roy Lee Howell .12 .06 .04
266 Leonard Shenoff Randle .12 .06 .04
267 Roy Frederick Smalley III .15 .08 .05
268 James Lloyd Spencer .12 .06 .04
269 Jeffrey Alan Burroughs .15 .08 .05
270 Thomas Alan Grieve .12 .06 .04
271 Joseph Lovitto, Jr. .12 .06 .04
272 Frank Joseph Lucchesi .12 .06 .04
273 David Earl Nelson .12 .06 .04
274 Ted Lyle Simmons .40 .20 .12
275 Louis Clark Brock 4.00 2.00 1.25
276 Ronald Ray Fairly .15 .08 .05
277 Arnold Ray (Bake) McBride .12 .06 .04
278 Carl Reginald (Reggie) Smith .25 .13 .08
279 William Henry Davis .20 .10 .06
280 Kenneth John Reitz .12 .06 .04
281 Charles William (Buddy) Bradford .12 .06 .04
282 Luis Antonio Melendez .12 .06 .04
283 Michael Ray Tyson .12 .06 .04
284 Ted Crawford Sizemore .12 .06 .04
285 Mario Miguel Guerrero .12 .06 .04
286 Larry Lintz .12 .06 .04
287 Kenneth Victor Rudolph .12 .06 .04
288 Richard Arlin Billings .12 .06 .04
289 Jerry Wayne Mumphrey .20 .10 .06
290 Michael Sherman Wallace .12 .06 .04
291 Alan Thomas Hrabosky .15 .08 .05
292 Kenneth Lee Reynolds .12 .06 .04
293 Michael Douglas Garman .12 .06 .04
294 Robert Herbert Forsch .20 .10 .06
295 John Allen Denny .15 .08 .05
296 Harold R. Rasmussen .12 .06 .04
297 Lynn Everratt McGlothen (Everett) .12 .06 .04
298 Michael Roswell Barlow .12 .06 .04
299 Gregory John Terlecky .12 .06 .04
300 Albert Fred (Red) Schoendienst .20 .10 .06
301 Ricky Eugene Reuschel .25 .13 .08
302 Steven Michael Stone .15 .08 .05
303 William Gordon Bonham .12 .06 .04
304 Oscar Joseph Zamora .12 .06 .04
305 Kenneth Douglas Frailing .12 .06 .04
306 Milton Edward Wilcox .15 .08 .05
307 Darold Duane Knowles .12 .06 .04
308 Rufus James (Jim) Marshall .12 .06 .04
309 Bill Madlock, Jr. .50 .25 .15
310 Jose Domec Cardenal .15 .08 .05
311 Robert James (Rick) Monday, Jr. .20 .10 .06
312 Julio Ruben (Jerry) Morales .12 .06 .04
313 Timothy Kenneth Hosley .12 .06 .04
314 Gene Taylor Hiser .12 .06 .04
315 Donald Eulon Kessinger .15 .08 .05
316 Jesus Manuel (Manny) Trillo .20 .10 .06
317 Ralph Pierre (Pete) LaCock, Jr. .12 .06 .04
318 George Eugene Mitterwald .12 .06 .04
319 Steven Eugene Swisher .12 .06 .04
320 Robert Walter Sperring .12 .06 .04
321 Victor Lanier Harris .12 .06 .04
322 Ronald Ray Dunn .12 .06 .04
323 Jose Manuel Morales .12 .06 .04
324 Peter MacKanin, Jr. .12 .06 .04
325 James Charles Cox .12 .06 .04
326 Larry Alton Parrish .25 .13 .08
327 Michael Jorgensen .12 .06 .04
328 Timothy John Foli .12 .06 .04
329 Harold Noel Breeden .12 .06 .04
330 Nathan Colbert, Jr. .12 .06 .04
331 Jesus Maria (Pepe) Frias .12 .06 .04
332 James Patrick (Pat) Scanlon .12 .06 .04
333 Robert Sherwood Bailey .12 .06 .04
334 Gary Edmund Carter 3.50 1.75 1.00
335 Jose Mauel (Pepe) Mangual .12 .06 .04
336 Lawrence David Biittner .12 .06 .04
337 James Lawrence Lyttle, Jr. .12 .06 .04
338 Gary Roenicke .15 .08 .05
339 Anthony Scott .12 .06 .04
340 Jerome Cardell White .12 .06 .04
341 James Edward Dwyer .12 .06 .04
342 Ellis Clarence Valentine .12 .06 .04
343 Frederick John Scherman, Jr. .12 .06 .04
344 Dennis Herman Blair .12 .06 .04
345 Woodrow Thompson Fryman .15 .08 .05
346 Charles Gilbert Taylor .12 .06 .04
347 Daniel Dean Warthen .12 .06 .04
348 Donald George Carrithers .12 .06 .04
349 Stephen Douglas Rogers .15 .08 .05
350 Dale Albert Murray .12 .06 .04
351 Edwin Donald (Duke) Snider 8.00 4.00 2.50
352 Ralph George Houk .15 .08 .05
353 John Frederick Hiller .15 .08 .05
354 Michael Stephen Lolich .40 .20 .12
355 David Lawrence Lemancyzk .12 .06 .04
356 Lerrin Harris LaGrow .12 .06 .04
357 Fred Arroyo .12 .06 .04
358 Joseph Howard Coleman .12 .06 .04
359 Benjamin A. Oglivie .15 .08 .05
360 Willie Wattison Horton .20 .10 .06
361 John Clinton Knox .12 .06 .04
362 Leon Kauffman Roberts .12 .06 .04
363 Ronald LeFlore .20 .10 .06
364 Gary Lynn Sutherland .12 .06 .04
365 Daniel Thomas Meyer .12 .06 .04
366 Aurelio Rodriguez .15 .08 .05
367 Thomas Martin Veryzer .12 .06 .04
368 Lavern Jack Pierce .12 .06 .04
369 Eugene Richard Michael .12 .06 .04
370 Robert (Billy) Baldwin .12 .06 .04
371 William James Gates Brown .12 .06 .04
372 Mitchell Jack (Mickey) Stanley .15 .08 .05
373 Terryal Gene Humphrey .12 .06 .04
374 Doyle Lafayette Alexander .25 .13 .08
375 Miguel Angel (Mike) Cuellar .20 .10 .06
376 Marcus Wayne Garland .12 .06 .04
377 Ross Albert Grimsley III .15 .08 .05
378 Grant Dwight Jackson .12 .06 .04
379 Dyar K. Miller .12 .06 .04
380 James Alvin Palmer 7.00 3.50 2.00
381 Michael Augustine Torrez .15 .08 .05
382 Michael Henry Willis .12 .06 .04
383 David Edwin Duncan .12 .06 .04
384 Elrod Jerome Hendricks .12 .06 .04
385 James Neamon Hutto Jr. .12 .06 .04
386 Robert Michael Bailor .12 .06 .04
387 Douglas Vernon DeCinces .20 .10 .06
388 Robert Anthony Grich .20 .10 .06
389 Lee Andrew May .15 .08 .05
390 Anthony Joseph Muser .12 .06 .04
391 Timothy C. Nordbrook .12 .06 .04
392 Brooks Calbert Robinson, Jr. 9.00 4.50 2.75
393 Royle Stillman .12 .06 .04
394 Don Edward Baylor .30 .15 .09
395 Paul L.D. Blair .15 .08 .05
396 Alonza Benjamin Bumbry .15 .08 .05
397 Larry Duane Harlow .12 .06 .04
398 Herman Thomas (Tommy) Davis, Jr. .20 .10 .06
399 James Thomas Northrup .15 .08 .05
400 Kenneth Wayne Singleton .25 .13 .08
401 Thomas Michael Shopay .12 .06 .04
402 Fredrick Michael Lynn .80 .40 .25
403 Carlton Ernest Fisk 3.00 1.50 .90
404 Cecil Celester Cooper .40 .20 .12
405 James Edward Rice .80 .40 .25
406 Juan Jose Beniquez .12 .06 .04
407 Robert Dennis Doyle .12 .06 .04
408 Dwight Michael Evans .40 .20 .12
409 Carl Michael Yastrzemski 8.00 4.00 2.50
410 Richard Paul Burleson .15 .08 .05
411 Bernardo Carbo .12 .06 .04
412 Douglas Lee Griffin, Jr. .12 .06 .04
413 Americo P. Petrocelli .15 .08 .05
414 Robert Edward Montgomery .12 .06 .04
415 Timothy P. Blackwell .12 .06 .04
416 Richard Alan Miller .12 .06 .04
417 Darrell Dean Johnson .12 .06 .04
418 Jim Scott Burton .12 .06 .04
419 James Arthur Willoughby .12 .06 .04
420 Rogelio (Roger) Moret .12 .06 .04
421 William Francis Lee, III .15 .08 .05
422 Richard Anthony Drago .12 .06 .04
423 Diego Pablo Segui .12 .06 .04
424 Luis Clemente Tiant .30 .15 .09
425 James Augustus (Catfish) Hunter 3.00 1.50 .90
426 Richard Clyde Sawyer .12 .06 .04
427 Rudolph May Jr. .15 .08 .05
428 Richard William Tidrow .12 .06 .04
429 Albert Walter (Sparky) Lyle .25 .13 .08
430 George Francis (Doc) Medich .12 .06 .04
431 Patrick Edward Dobson, Jr. .15 .08 .05
432 David Percy Pagan .12 .06 .04
433 Thurman Lee Munson 4.00 2.00 1.25
434 Carroll Christopher Chambliss .20 .10 .06
435 Roy Hilton White .25 .13 .08
436 Walter Allen Williams .12 .06 .04
437 Graig Nettles .60 .30 .20
438 John Rikard (Rick) Dempsey .15 .08 .05
439 Bobby Lee Bonds .25 .13 .08
440 Edward Martin Hermann (Herrmann) .12 .06 .04
441 Santos Alomar .12 .06 .04
442 Frederick Blair Stanley .12 .06 .04
443 Terry Bertland Whitfield .12 .06 .04
444 Richard Alan Bladt .12 .06 .04
445 Louis Victor Piniella .25 .13 .08
446 Richard Allen Coggins .12 .06 .04
447 Edwin Albert Brinkman .15 .08 .05
448 James Percy Mason .12 .06 .04
449 Larry Murray .12 .06 .04
450 Ronald Mark Blomberg .15 .08 .05
451 Elliott Maddox .12 .06 .04
452 Kerry Dineen .12 .06 .04
453 Alfred Manuel (Billy) Martin .30 .15 .09
454 Dave Bergman .12 .06 .04
455 Otoniel Velez .12 .06 .04
456 Joseph Walter Hoerner .12 .06 .04
457 Frank Edwin (Tug) McGraw, Jr. .25 .13 .08
458 Henry Eugene (Gene) Garber .12 .06 .04
459 Steven Norman Carlton 7.00 3.50 2.00
460 Larry Richard Christenson .12 .06 .04
461 Thomas Gerald Underwood .12 .06 .04
462 James Reynold Lonborg .15 .08 .05
463 John William (Jay) Johnstone, Jr. .15 .08 .05
464 Lawrence Robert Bowa .25 .13 .08
465 David Cash, Jr. .12 .06 .04
466 Ollie Lee Brown .12 .06 .04
467 Gregory Michael Luzinski .25 .13 .08
468 Johnny Lane Oates .12 .06 .04
469 Michael Allen Anderson .12 .06 .04
470 Michael Jack Schmidt 8.00 4.00 2.50
471 Robert Raymond Boone .15 .08 .05
472 Thomas George Hutton .12 .06 .04
473 Richard Anthony Allen .30 .15 .09
474 Antonio Taylor .12 .06 .04
475 Jerry Lindsey Martin .12 .06 .04
476 Daniel Leonard Ozark .12 .06 .04
477 Richard David Ruthven .12 .06 .04
478 James Richard Todd, Jr. .12 .06 .04
479 Paul Aaron Lindblad .12 .06 .04
480 Roland Glen Fingers 3.00 1.50 .90
481 Vida Blue, Jr. .30 .15 .09
482 Kenneth Dale Holtzman .15 .08 .05
483 Richard Allen Bosman .12 .06 .04
484 Wilfred Charles (Sonny) Siebert .12 .06 .04
485 William Glenn Abbott .12 .06 .04
486 Stanley Raymond Bahnsen .12 .06 .04
487 Michael Norris .12 .06 .04
488 Alvin Ralph Dark .15 .08 .05
489 Claudell Washington .20 .10 .06
490 Joseph Oden Rudi .20 .10 .06
491 William Alex North .12 .06 .04
492 Dagoberto Blanco (Bert) Campaneris .25 .13 .08
493 Fury Gene Tenace .15 .08 .05
494 Reginald Martinez Jackson 8.00 4.00 2.50
495 Philip Mason Garner .15 .08 .05
496 Billy Leo Williams 5.00 2.50 1.50
497 Salvatore Leonard Bando .20 .10 .06
498 James William Holt .12 .06 .04
499 Teodoro Noel Martinez .12 .06 .04
500 Raymond Earl Fosse .12 .06 .04
501 Matthew Alexander .12 .06 .04
502 Wallace Larry Haney .12 .06 .04
503 Angel Luis Mangual .12 .06 .04
504 Fred Ray Beene .12 .06 .04
505 Thomas William Buskey .12 .06 .04
506 Dennis Lee Eckersley .20 .10 .06
507 Roric Edward Harrison .12 .06 .04
508 Donald Harris Hood .12 .06 .04
509 James Lester Kern .12 .06 .04
510 David Eugene LaRoche .12 .06 .04
511 Fred Ingels (Fritz) Peterson .12 .06 .04
512 James Michael Strickland .12 .06 .04
513 Michael Richard (Rick) Waits .12 .06 .04
514 Alan Dean Ashby .12 .06 .04

515	John Charles Ellis	.12	.06	.04
516	Rick Cerone	.15	.08	.05
517	David Gus (Buddy) Bell	.30	.15	.09
518	John Anthony Brohamer, Jr.	.12	.06	.04
519	Ricardo Adolfo Jacobo Carty	.20	.10	.06
520	Edward Carlton Crosby	.12	.06	.04
521	Frank Thomas Duffy	.12	.06	.04
522	Duane Eugene Kuiper (photo actually Rick Manning)	.12	.06	.04
523	Joseph Anthony Lis	.12	.06	.04
524	John Wesley (Boog) Powell	.50	.25	.15
525	Frank Robinson	7.00	3.50	2.00
526	Oscar Charles Gamble	.15	.08	.05
527	George Andrew Hendrick	.15	.08	.05
528	John Lee Lowenstein	.12	.06	.04
529	Richard Eugene Manning (photo actually Duane Kuiper)	.12	.06	.04
530	Tommy Alexander Smith	.12	.06	.04
531	Leslie Charles (Charlie) Spikes	.12	.06	.04
532	Steve Jack Kline	.12	.06	.04
533	Edward Emil Kranepool	.15	.08	.05
534	Michael Vail	.12	.06	.04
535	Delbert Bernard Unser	.12	.06	.04
536	Felix Bernardo Martinez Millan	.12	.06	.04
537	Daniel Joseph (Rusty) Staub	.40	.20	.12
538	Jesus Maria Rojas Alou	.15	.08	.05
539	Ronald Wayne Garrett	.12	.06	.04
540	Michael Dwaine Phillips	.12	.06	.04
541	Joseph Paul Torre	.40	.20	.12
542	David Arthur Kingman	.30	.15	.09
543	Eugene Anthony Clines	.12	.06	.04
544	Jack Seale Heidemann	.12	.06	.04
545	Derrel McKinley (Bud) Harrelson	.15	.08	.05
546	John Hardin Stearns	.12	.06	.04
547	John David Milner	.12	.06	.04
548	Robert John Apodaca	.12	.06	.04
549	Claude Edward (Skip) Lockwood Jr.	.12	.06	.04
550	Kenneth George Sanders	.12	.06	.04
551	George Thomas (Tom) Seaver	9.00	4.50	2.75
552	Ricky Alan Baldwin	.12	.06	.04
553	Jonathan Trumpbour Matlack	.15	.08	.05
554	Henry Gaylon Webb	.12	.06	.04
555	Randall Lee Tate	.12	.06	.04
556	Tom Edward Hall	.12	.06	.04
557	George Heard Stone Jr.	.12	.06	.04
558	Craig Steven Swan	.12	.06	.04
559	Gerald Allen Cram	.12	.06	.04
560	Roy J. Staiger	.12	.06	.04
561	Kenton C. Tekulve	.20	.10	.06
562	Jerry Reuss	.20	.10	.06
563	John R. Candelaria	.25	.13	.08
564	Lawrence C. Demery	.12	.06	.04
565	David John Giusti Jr.	.12	.06	.04
566	James Phillip Rooker	.12	.06	.04
567	Ramon Gonzalez Hernandez	.12	.06	.04
568	Bruce Eugene Kison	.12	.06	.04
569	Kenneth Alven Brett (Alvin)	.15	.08	.05
570	Robert Ralph Moose Jr.	.12	.06	.04
571	Manuel Jesus Sanguillen	.15	.08	.05
572	David Gene Parker	3.00	1.50	.90
573	Wilver Dornel Stargell	5.00	2.50	1.50
574	Richard Walter Zisk	.15	.08	.05
575	Renaldo Antonio Stennett	.12	.06	.04
576	Albert Oliver Jr.	.60	.30	.20
577	William Henry Robinson Jr.	.12	.06	.04
578	Robert Eugene Robertson	.12	.06	.04
579	Richard Joseph Hebner	.12	.06	.04
580	Edgar Leon Kirkpatrick	.12	.06	.04
581	Don Robert (Duffy) Dyer	.12	.06	.04
582	Craig Reynolds	.12	.06	.04
583	Franklin Fabian Taveras	.12	.06	.04
584	William Larry Randolph	.40	.20	.12
585	Arthur H. Howe	.12	.06	.04
586	Daniel Edward Murtaugh	.15	.08	.05
587	Charles Richard (Rich) McKinney	.12	.06	.04
588	James Edward Goodson	.12	.06	.04
589	George Brett, Al Cowans/Checklist	1.75	.90	.50
590	Keith Hernandez, Lou Brock/Checklist	1.75	.90	.50
591	Jerry Koosman, Duke Snider/Checklist	.60	.30	.20
592	John Knox, Maury Wills/Checklist	.20	.10	.06
593a	Catfish Hunter, Noland Ryan/Checklist	15.00	7.50	4.50
593b	Catfish Hunter, Nolan Ryan/Checklist	1.00	.50	.30
594	Ralph Branca, Carl Erskine, Pee Wee Reese/Checklist	.50	.25	.15
595	Willie Mays, Herb Score/Checklist	1.50	.70	.45
596	Larry Eugene Cox	.12	.06	.04
597	Eugene William Mauch	.15	.08	.05
598	William Frederick (Whitey) Wietelmann	.12	.06	.04
599	Wayne Kirby Simpson	.12	.06	.04
600	Melvin Erskine Thomason	.12	.06	.04
601	Issac Bernard (Ike) Hampton	.12	.06	.04
602	Kenneth S. Crosby	.12	.06	.04
603	Ralph Emanuel Rowe	.12	.06	.04
604	James Vernon Tyrone	.12	.06	.04
605	Michael Dennis Kelleher	.12	.06	.04
606	Mario Mendoza	.12	.06	.04
607	Michael George Rogodzinski	.12	.06	.04
608	Robert Collins Gallagher	.12	.06	.04
609	Jerry Martin Koosman	.25	.13	.08
610	Joseph Filmore Frazier	.12	.06	.04
611	Karl Kuehl	.12	.06	.04
612	Frank J. LaCorte	.12	.06	.04
613	Raymond Douglas Bare	.12	.06	.04
614	Billy Arnold Muffett	.12	.06	.04
615	William Harry Laxton	.12	.06	.04
616	Willie Howard Mays	12.00	6.00	3.50
617	Philip Joseph Cavaretta (Cavarretta)	.15	.08	.05
618	Theodore Bernard Kluszewski	.30	.15	.09
619	Elston Gene Howard	.30	.15	.09
620	Alexander Peter Grammas	.12	.06	.04
621	James Barton (Mickey) Vernon	.15	.08	.05
622	Richard Allan Sisler	.12	.06	.04
623	Harvey Haddix, Jr.	.15	.08	.05
624	Bobby Brooks Winkles	.12	.06	.04
625	John Michael Pesky	.15	.08	.05
626	James Houston Davenport	.12	.06	.04
627	David Allen Tomlin	.12	.06	.04
628	Roger Lee Craig	.15	.08	.05
629	John Joseph Amalfitano	.12	.06	.04
630	James Harrison Reese	.40	.20	.12

1953 Stahl-Meyer Franks

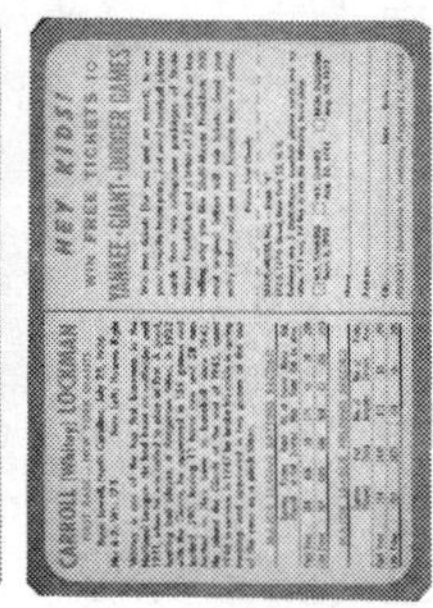

These nine cards, issued in packages of hot dogs by a New York area meat company, feature three players from each of the New York teams of the day - Dodgers Giants and Yankees. Cards in the set measure 3-1/4" by 4-1/2". The card fronts in this unnumbered set feature color photos with player name and facsimile autograph. The backs list both biographical and statistical information on half the card and a ticket offer promotion on the other half. The card corners are cut diagonally, although some cards (apparently cut from sheets) with square corners have been seen. Cards are white-bordered.

		NR MT	EX	VG
Complete Set:		4250.	2125.	1275.
Common Player:		125.00	62.00	37.00
(1)	Hank Bauer	150.00	75.00	45.00
(2)	Roy Campanella	550.00	275.00	165.00
(3)	Gil Hodges	300.00	150.00	90.00
(4)	Monte Irvin	200.00	100.00	60.00
(5)	Whitey Lockman	125.00	62.00	37.00
(6)	Mickey Mantle	2000.	1000.	600.00
(7)	Phil Rizzuto	350.00	175.00	105.00
(8)	Duke Snider	550.00	275.00	165.00
(9)	Bobby Thompson	150.00	75.00	45.00

1954 Stahl-Meyer Franks

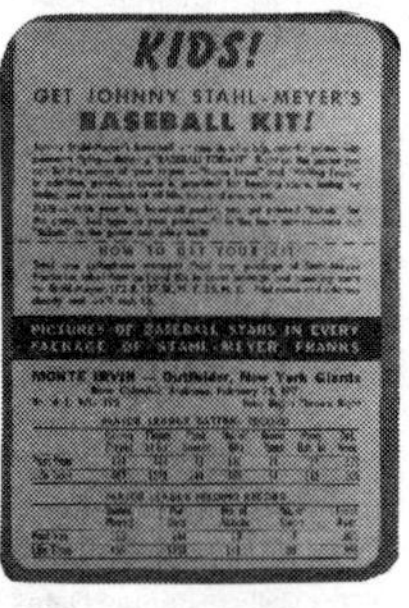

The 1954 set of Stahl-Meyer Franks was increased to 12 cards which retained the 3-1/4" by 4-1/2" size. The most prominent addition to the '54 set was New York Giants slugger Willie Mays. The card fronts are identical in format to the previous year's set. However, the backs are different as they are designed on a vertical format. The backs also contain an advertisement for a "Johnny Stahl-Meyer Baseball Kit." The cards in the set are unnumbered.

		NR MT	EX	VG
Complete Set:		6250.	3125.	1875.
Common Player:		125.00	62.00	37.00
(1)	Hank Bauer	150.00	75.00	45.00
(2)	Carl Erskine	150.00	75.00	45.00
(3)	Gil Hodges	300.00	150.00	90.00
(4)	Monte Irvin	200.00	100.00	60.00
(5)	Whitey Lockman	125.00	62.00	37.00
(6)	Gil McDougald	150.00	75.00	45.00
(7)	Mickey Mantle	2500.	1250.	750.00
(8)	Willie Mays	1500.	750.00	450.00
(9)	Don Mueller	125.00	62.00	37.00
(10)	Don Newcombe	150.00	75.00	45.00
(11)	Phil Rizzuto	350.00	175.00	105.00
(12)	Duke Snider	550.00	275.00	165.00

1955 Stahl-Meyer Franks

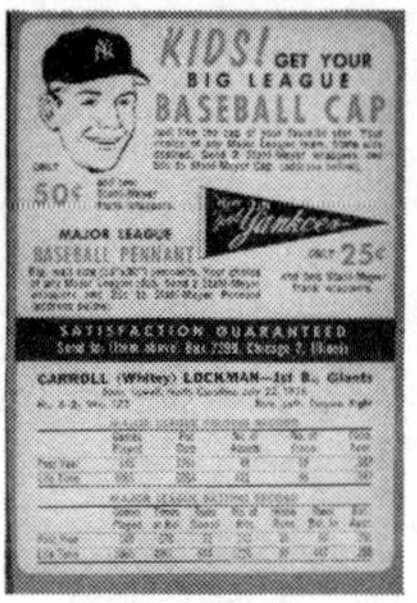

Eleven of the 12 players in the 1955 set are the same as those featured in 1954. The exception is the New York Giants Dusty Rhodes, who replaced Willie Mays on the 3-1/4" by 4-1/2" cards. The card fronts are again full-color photos bordered in yellow with diagonal corners, and four players from each of the three New York teams are featured. The backs offer a new promotion, with a drawing of Mickey Mantle and advertisements selling pennants and caps. Player statistics are still included on the vertical card backs. The cards in the set are unnumbered.

		NR MT	EX	VG
Complete Set:		4850.	2425.	1455.
Common Player:		125.00	62.00	37.00
(1)	Hank Bauer	150.00	75.00	45.00
(2)	Carl Erskine	150.00	75.00	45.00
(3)	Gil Hodges	300.00	150.00	90.00
(4)	Monte Irvin	200.00	100.00	60.00
(5)	Whitey Lockman	125.00	62.00	37.00
(6)	Mickey Mantle	2500.	1250.	750.00
(7)	Gil McDougald	150.00	75.00	45.00
(8)	Don Mueller	125.00	62.00	37.00
(9)	Don Newcombe	150.00	75.00	45.00
(10)	Jim Rhodes	125.00	62.00	37.00
(11)	Phil Rizzuto	350.00	175.00	105.00
(12)	Duke Snider	550.00	275.00	165.00

1910 Standard Caramel Co. (E93)

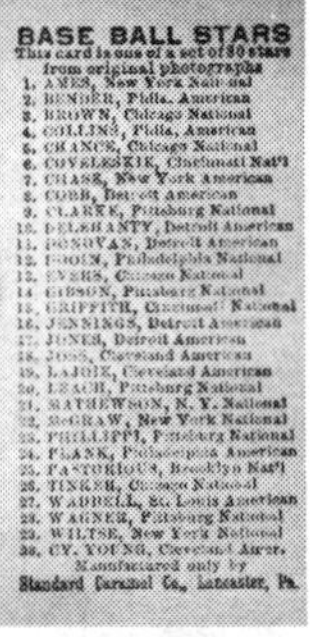

This 30-card set issued in 1910 by Standard Caramel Co. of Lancaster, Pa., is closely related to several other candy sets from this period which share the same format and, in many cases, the same player poses. The cards measure 1-1/2" by 2-3/4" and contain tinted black and white player photos. The back of each card contains an alphabetical checklist of the set plus a line indicating it was manufactured by Standard Caramel Co., Lancaster, Pa. The set carries the ACC designation of E93.

		NR MT	EX	VG
Complete Set (30):		18000.	9000.	5400.
Common Player:		175.00	87.00	52.00
(1)	Red Ames	175.00	87.00	52.00
(2)	Chief Bender	575.00	287.00	172.00
(3)	Mordecai Brown	575.00	287.00	172.00
(4)	Frank Chance	625.00	312.00	187.00
(5)	Hal Chase	275.00	137.00	82.00
(6)	Fred Clarke	575.00	287.00	172.00
(7)	Ty Cobb	4500.	2000.	1150.
(8)	Eddie Collins	575.00	287.00	172.00
(9)	Harry Coveleskie (Coveleski)	175.00	87.00	52.00
(10)	Jim Delehanty	175.00	87.00	52.00
(11)	Wild Bill Donovan	175.00	87.00	52.00
(12)	Red Dooin	175.00	87.00	52.00

(13)	Johnny Evers	575.00	287.00	172.00
(14)	George Gibson	175.00	87.00	52.00
(15)	Clark Griffith	575.00	287.00	172.00
(16)	Hugh Jennings	575.00	287.00	172.00
(17)	Davy Jones	175.00	87.00	52.00
(18)	Addie Joss	575.00	287.00	172.00
(19)	Nap Lajoie	875.00	437.00	262.00
(20)	Tommy Leach	175.00	87.00	52.00
(21)	Christy Mathewson	1150.	575.00	345.00
(22)	John McGraw	700.00	350.00	210.00
(23)	Jim Pastorious	175.00	87.00	52.00
(24)	Deacon Phillippi (Phillippe)	175.00	87.00	52.00
(25)	Eddie Plank	750.00	375.00	225.00
(26)	Joe Tinker	575.00	287.00	172.00
(27)	Honus Wagner	1700.	850.00	510.00
(28)	Rube Waddell	575.00	287.00	172.00
(29)	Hooks Wiltse	175.00	87.00	52.00
(30)	Cy Young	1150.	575.00	345.00

1928 Star Player Candy

This somewhat confusing issue can be dated to 1928, although little is known about its origin. The producer of the set is not identified, but experienced collectors generally refer to it as the Star Player Candy set, apparently because it was distributed with a product of that name. The cards measure 1-7/8" by 2-7/8", are sepia-toned and blank-backed. The player's name (but no team designation) appears in the border below the photo in brown capital letters. To date the checklist of baseball players numbers 72, but more may exist, and cards of football players have also been found.

		NR MT	EX	VG
Complete Set:		8500.	4250.	2550.
Common Player:		60.00	30.00	18.00
(1)	Dave Bancroft	125.00	62.00	37.00
(2)	Emile Barnes	60.00	30.00	18.00
(3)	L.A. Blue	60.00	30.00	18.00
(4)	Garland Buckeye	60.00	30.00	18.00
(5)	George Burns	60.00	30.00	18.00
(6)	Guy T. Bush	60.00	30.00	18.00
(7)	Owen T. Carroll	60.00	30.00	18.00
(8)	Chalmer Cissell	60.00	30.00	18.00
(9)	Ty Cobb	1500.	750.00	450.00
(10)	Gordon Cochrane	125.00	62.00	37.00
(11)	Richard Coffman	60.00	30.00	18.00
(12)	Eddie Collins	125.00	62.00	37.00
(13)	Stanley Coveleskie (Coveleski)	125.00	62.00	37.00
(14)	Hugh Critz	60.00	30.00	18.00
(15)	Hazen Cuyler	125.00	62.00	37.00
(16)	Charles Dressen	70.00	35.00	21.00
(17)	Joe Dugan	70.00	35.00	21.00
(18)	Elwood English	60.00	30.00	18.00
(19)	Bib Falk (Bibb)	60.00	30.00	18.00
(20)	Ira Flagstead	60.00	30.00	18.00
(21)	Bob Fothergill	60.00	30.00	18.00
(22)	Frank T. Frisch	125.00	62.00	37.00
(23)	Foster Ganzel	60.00	30.00	18.00
(24)	Lou Gehrig	1500.	750.00	450.00
(25)	Chas. Gihringer (Gehringer)	125.00	62.00	37.00
(26)	George Gerken	60.00	30.00	18.00
(27)	Grant Gillis	60.00	30.00	18.00
(28)	Miguel Gonzales	70.00	35.00	21.00
(29)	Sam Gray	60.00	30.00	18.00
(30)	Chas. J. Grimm	70.00	35.00	21.00
(31)	Robert M. Grove	150.00	75.00	45.00
(32)	Chas. J. Hafey	125.00	62.00	37.00
(33)	Jesse Haines	125.00	62.00	37.00
(34)	Chas. L. Hartnett	125.00	62.00	37.00
(35)	Clifton HHeathcote	60.00	30.00	18.00
(36)	Harry Heilmann	125.00	62.00	37.00
(37)	John Heving	60.00	30.00	18.00
(38)	Waite Hoyt	125.00	62.00	37.00
(39)	Chas. Jamieson	60.00	30.00	18.00
(40)	Joe Judge	60.00	30.00	18.00
(41)	Willie Kamm	60.00	30.00	18.00
(42)	George Kelly	125.00	62.00	37.00
(43)	Tony Lazzeri	125.00	62.00	37.00
(44)	Adolfo Luque	60.00	30.00	18.00
(45)	Ted Lyons	125.00	62.00	37.00
(46)	Hugh McMullen	60.00	30.00	18.00
(47)	Bob Meusel	70.00	35.00	21.00
(48)	Wilcey Moore (Wilcy)	60.00	30.00	18.00
(49)	Ed C. Morgan	60.00	30.00	18.00
(50)	Herb Pennock	125.00	62.00	37.00
(51)	Everett Purdy	60.00	30.00	18.00
(52)	William Regan	60.00	30.00	18.00
(53)	Eppa Rixey	125.00	62.00	37.00
(54)	Charles Root	70.00	35.00	21.00
(55)	Jack Rothrock	60.00	30.00	18.00
(56)	Harold Ruel (Herold)	60.00	30.00	18.00
(57)	Babe Ruth	1750.	875.00	525.00
(58)	Wally Schang	60.00	30.00	18.00
(59)	Joe Sewell	125.00	62.00	37.00
(60)	Luke Sewell	60.00	30.00	18.00
(61)	Joe Shaute	60.00	30.00	18.00
(62)	George Sisler	125.00	62.00	37.00
(63)	Tris Speaker	175.00	87.00	52.00
(64)	Riggs Stephenson	75.00	37.00	22.00
(65)	Jack Tavener	60.00	30.00	18.00
(66)	Al Thomas	60.00	30.00	18.00
(67)	Harold J. Traynor	125.00	62.00	37.00
(68)	George Uhle	60.00	30.00	18.00
(69)	Dazzy Vance	125.00	62.00	37.00
(70)	Cy Williams	70.00	35.00	21.00
(71)	Ken Williams	70.00	35.00	21.00
(72)	Lewis R. Wilson	125.00	62.00	37.00

1983 Star Co. Mike Schmidt

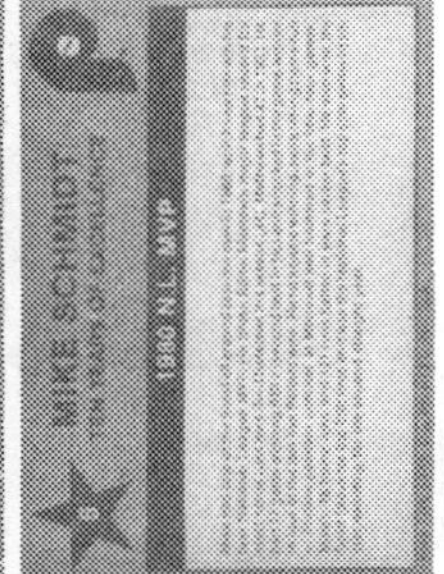

The first issue offered by the Star Company, this 15-card set was produced in 1983 and spotlights Mike Schmidt. Subtitled "Ten Years of Excellence", the cards measure the standard 2-1/2" by 3-1/2" and feature full-color photos showing Schmidt in various action and portrait poses surrounded by a bright red border. The backs contain statistics and biographical information. The set was available only through hobby dealers. (Star Co. cards are generally collected only as complete sets, and cards are rarely bought or sold individually.)

	MT	NR MT	EX
Complete Set:	40.00	30.00	16.00

1984 Star Co. George Brett

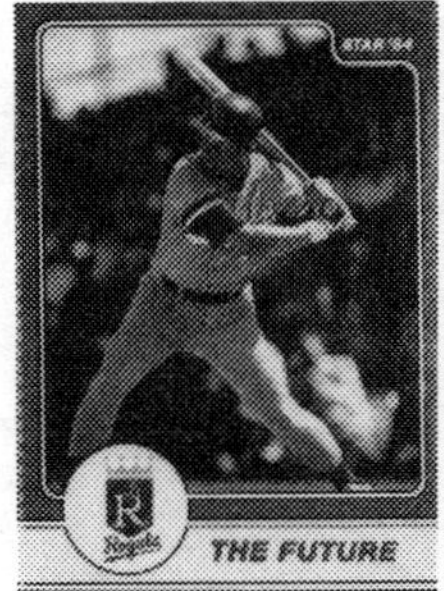

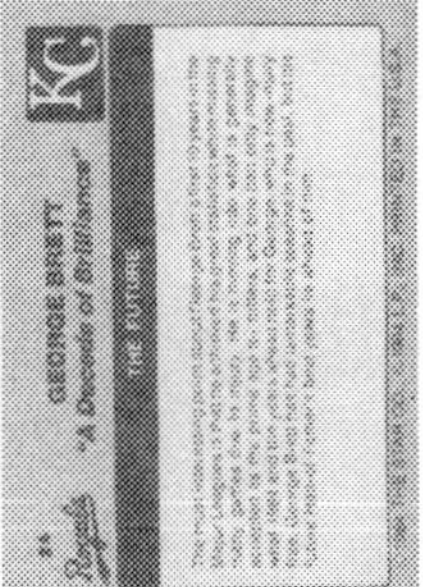

Issued by the Star Co. in 1984, this 24-card set features Royals star George Brett and was subtitled "A Decade of Brilliance". Bordered in blue, the cards are standard size and were issued in eight three-card, perforated panels. The Royals' logo appears in the lower left corner.

	MT	NR MT	EX
Complete Set:	15.00	11.00	6.00

Values for recent cards and sets are listed in Mint (MT), Near Mint (NM), reflecting the fact that many cards from recent years have been preserved in top condition. Recent cards and sets in less than Excellent condition have little collector interest.

1984 Star Co. Steve Carlton

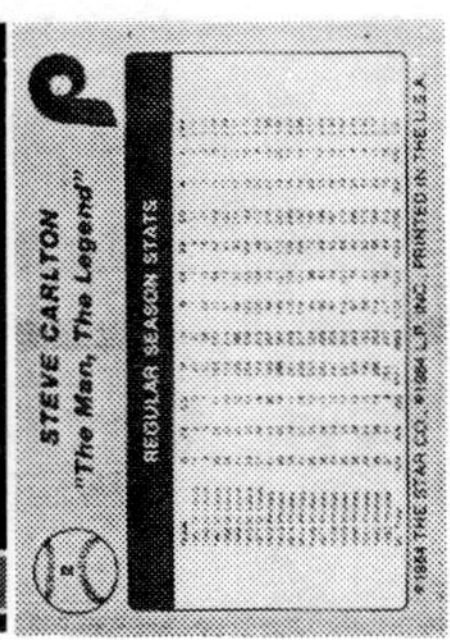

This 24-card set featuring Steve Carlton was issued by the Star Co. in 1984. Like all Star Co. issues, the set was available only from hobby dealers. It was issued in eight perforated panels of three cards each. The photos picture Carlton in various stages of his career, both as a Phillie and as a Cardinal, and the cards display the corresponding team logo in the lower left corner. The backs contain statistics and career highlights.

	MT	NR MT	EX
Complete Set:	40.00	30.00	16.00

1984 Star Co. Steve Garvey

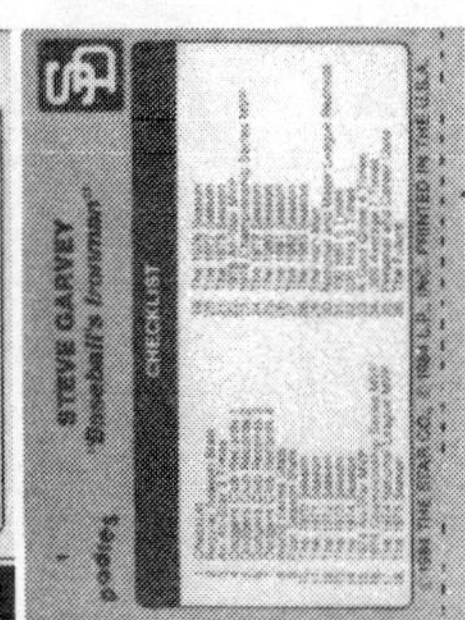

The 36-card Steve Garvey set consists of 12 three-card panels. The full-color photos, surrounded by either a blue or a yellow border, show Garvey as a member of both the Dodgers and the Padres, and the cards display the appropriate team logo in the lower left corner. The backs contain highlights and statistics.

	MT	NR MT	EX
Complete Set:	15.00	11.00	6.00

1984 Star Co. Darryl Strawberry

The Star Co. honored Darryl Strawberry with a 36-card set in 1984. Issued in 12 perforated panels of three cards each, the blue-bordered cards display the Mets logo in the lower left corner. Some of the backs contain biographical and statistical information, while others are puzzle backs.

	MT	NR MT	EX
Complete Set:	20.00	15.00	8.00

1984 Star Co. Carl Yastrzemski

Red Sox star Carl Yastrzemski was featured in a 24-card set issued by the Star Co. in 1984. Following the same style as the 1984 Star Co. sets, the cards were issued in three-card panels and feature

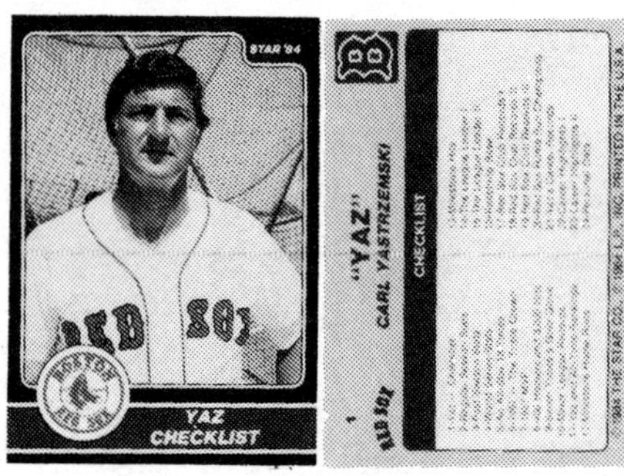

the team logo in the lower left corner. (Star Co. cards are generally collected as complete sets, and cards are rarely bought or sold individually.)

	MT	NR MT	EX
Complete Set:	15.00	11.00	6.00

1985 Star Co. Reggie Jackson

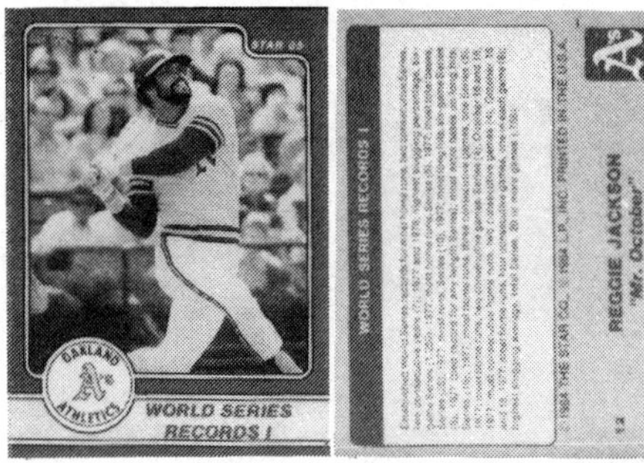

This 36-card set featuring Reggie Jackson was issued by the Star Co. in 1985 and pictures the slugger as a member of the A's, Orioles, Yankees and Angels. It was issued in 12 panels of three cards each.

	MT	NR MT	EX
Complete Set:	15.00	11.00	6.00

1986 Star Co. Wade Boggs

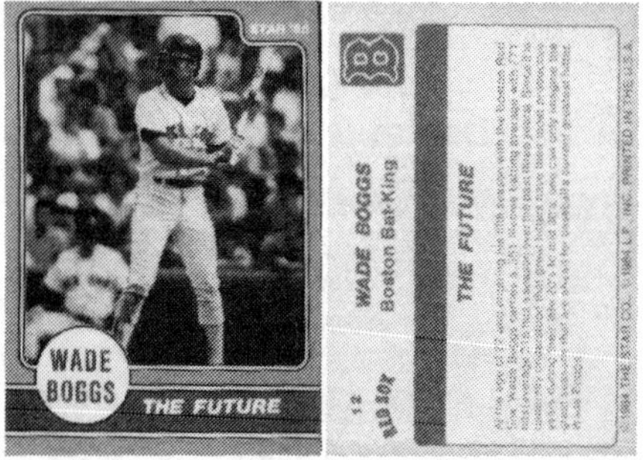

This 24-card set, produced by the Star Co. in 1986, features photos of Wade Boggs, whose name appears inside a circle in the lower left corner of the red-bordered cards. The set was issued in three-card panels and was also available in a special, limited-edition glossy format which commands a value about three times that of the regular set.

	MT	NR MT	EX
Complete Set:	12.00	9.00	4.75

A player's name in italic type indicates a rookie card. An (FC) indicates a player's first card for that particular card company.

Values quoted in this guide reflect the retail price of a card – the price a collector can expect to pay when buying a card from a dealer. The wholesale price – that which a collector can expect to receive from a dealer when selling cards – will be significantly lower, depending on desirability and condition.

1986 Star Co. Jose Canseco

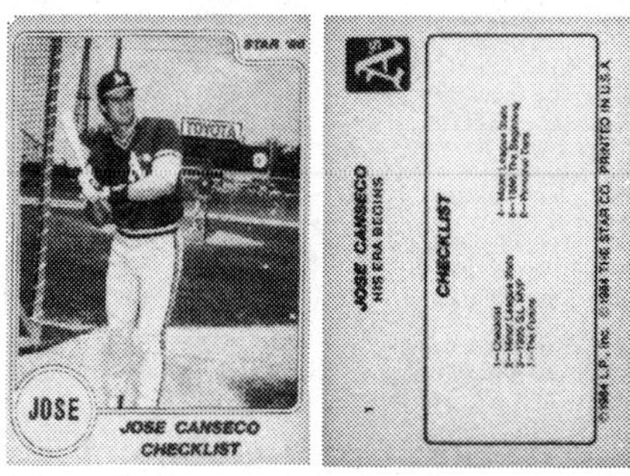

Oakland slugger Jose Canseco was featured in a 15-card set issued by the Star Co. in 1986. The yellow-bordered cards display the name "Jose" in the lower left corner. Eight of the

	MT	NR MT	EX
Complete Set:	30.00	22.00	12.00

1986 Star Co. Rod Carew

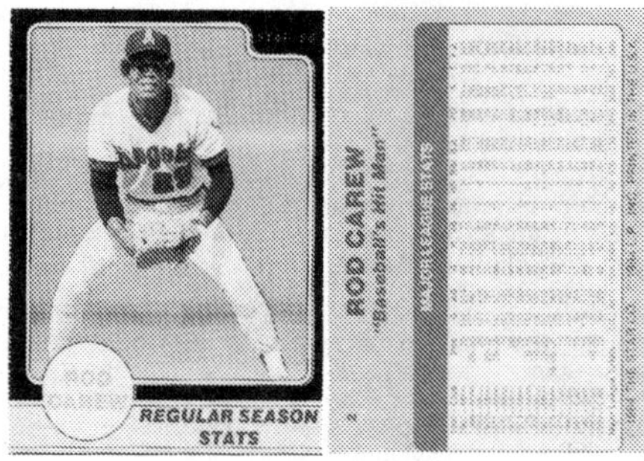

Subtitled "Baseball's Hit Man", this 24-card set of Rod Carew was issued by the Star Co. in 1986 and pictures Carew as both a Twin and an Angel. It was issued in eight perforated panels of three cards each.

	MT	NR MT	EX
Complete Set:	12.00	9.00	4.75

1986 Star Co. Wally Joyner

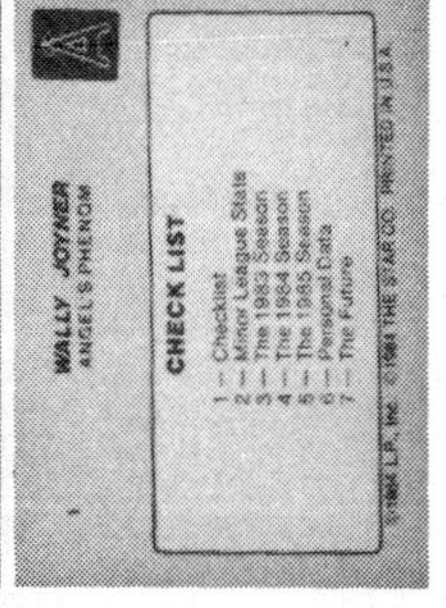

This 15-card set, issued by the Star Co. in 1986, features Wally Joyner and follows the same format as other Star Co. issues. It was also available in a limited-edition glossy version which is valued about four times the price of a regular set.

	MT	NR MT	EX
Complete Set:	10.00	7.50	4.00

1986 Star Co. Don Mattingly

Yankees superstar Don Mattingly was featured in a 24-card set by the Star Co. in 1986. The set, which follows the same format as other Star Co. issues, was also available in a limited-edition glossy version valued about three times the price of the

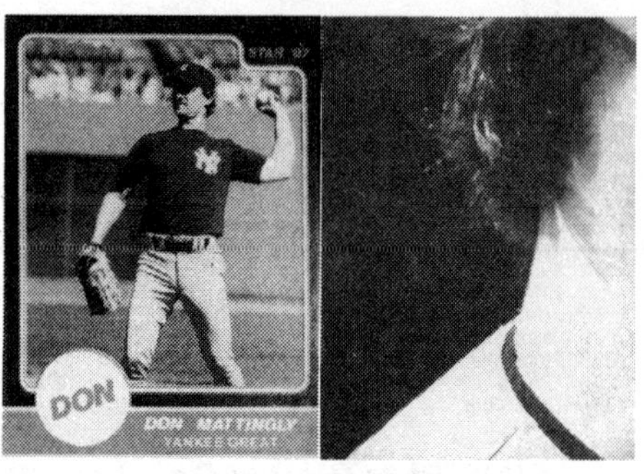

regular set. (Star Co. cards are generally collected only as complete sets, and cards are rarely bought or sold individually.)

	MT	NR MT	EX
Complete Set:	14.00	10.50	5.50

1986 Star Co. Dale Murphy

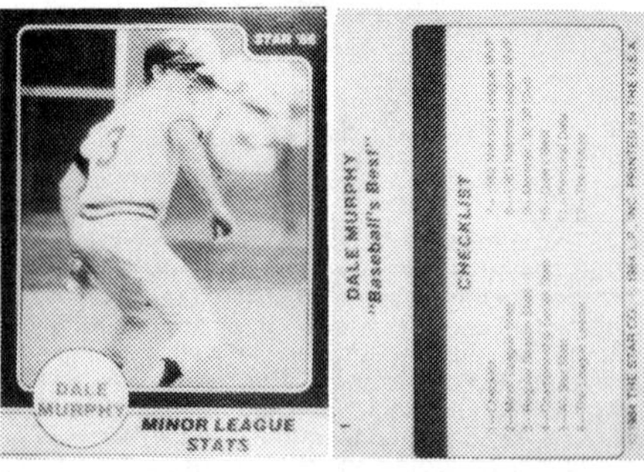

Issued by the Star Co. in 1986, this 24-card set of Braves star Dale Murphy was issued in eight three-card panels. The backs contain statistics and career highlights.

	MT	NR MT	EX
Complete Set:	12.00	9.00	4.75

1986 Star Co. Jim Rice

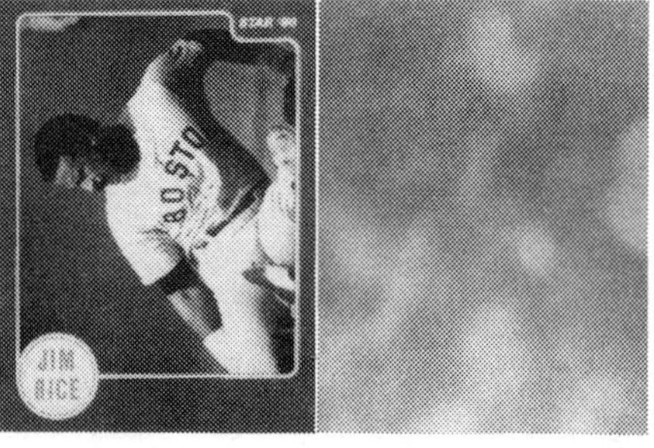

This 24-card set featuring Jim Rice was issued in three-card panels by the Star Co. in 1986. A limited-edition glossy version generally sells for about four times the price of a regular set.

	MT	NR MT	EX
Complete Set:	7.00	5.25	2.75

Grading Guide

Mint (MT): A perfect card. Well-centered with all corners sharp and square. No creases, stains, edge nicks, surface marks, yellowing or fading.

Near Mint (NM): A nearly perfect card. At first glance, a NM card appears to be perfect. May be slightly off-center. No surface marks, creases or loss of gloss.

Excellent (EX): Corners are still fairly sharp with only moderate wear. Borders may be off-center. No creases or stains on fronts or backs, but may show slight loss of surface luster.

Very Good (VG): Shows obvious handling. May have rounded corners, minor creases, major gum or wax stains. No major creases, tape marks, writing, etc.

Good (G): A well-worn card, but exhibits no intentional damage. May have major or multiple creases. Corners may be rounded well beyond card border.

1986 Star Co. Nolan Ryan

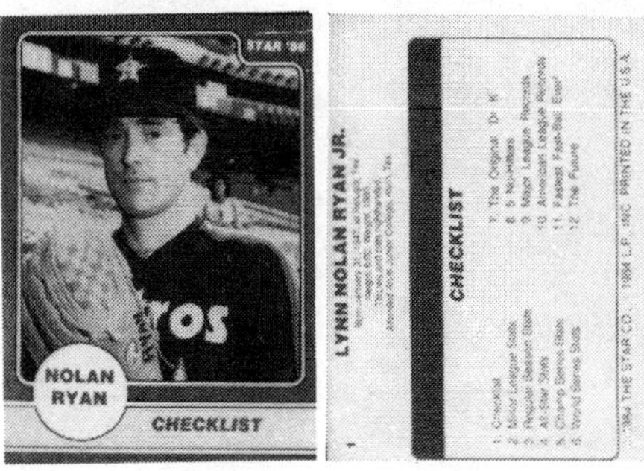

This 1986 set from the Star Co. pictures Noln Ryan as a member of the Angels and Astros. The 24-card set was issued in eight three-card panels with bright green borders. Twelve of the card backs form a puzzle.

	MT	NR MT	EX
Complete Set:	30.00	22.00	12.00

1986 Star Co. Tom Seaver

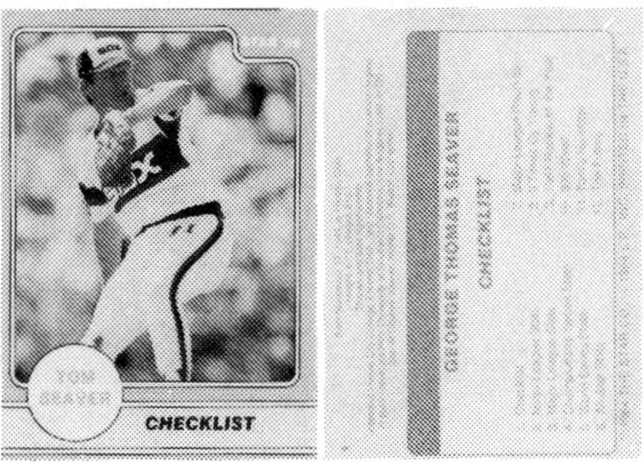

Issued in 1986, this 24-card set was also issued in eight panels of three cards each and pictures Seaver as a member of the Reds, Mets and White Sox. The cards have light blue borders and twelve of the backs form a puzzle.

	MT	NR MT	EX
Complete Set:	15.00	11.00	6.00

1987 Star Co. Gary Carter

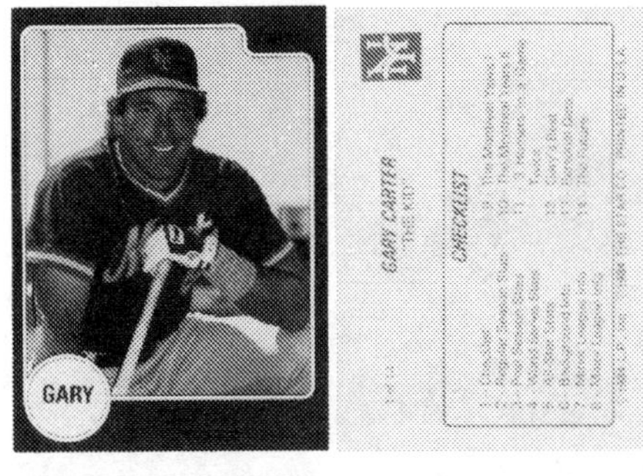

Subtitled "The Kid", this 14-card set features Gary Carter and displays the name "Gary" in the lower left corner of the bluebordered cards. A limited-edition glossy version of the set was also printed and commands a value about twice that of the regular edition. (Star Co. cards are generally collected only as complete sets, and cards are rarely bought or sold individually.)

	MT	NR MT	EX
Complete Set:	7.00	5.25	2.75

1987 Star Co. Roger Clemens

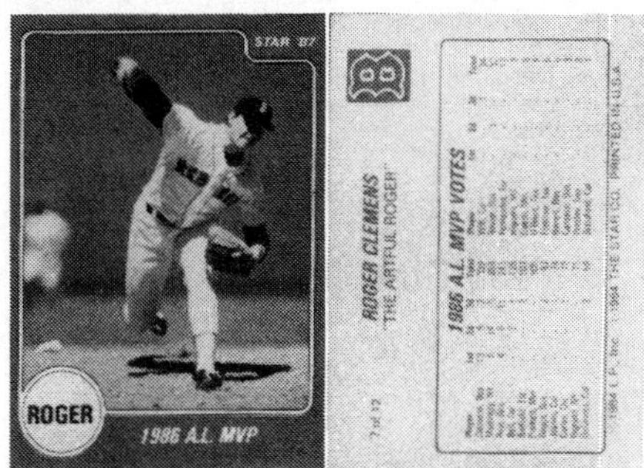

This 12-card set featuring Red Sox pitcher Roger Clemens, issued by the Star Co. in 1987, was subtitled "The Artful Roger" and featured bright red borders. A limited number of sets were also produced in a special glossy format, which command a value about two to three times the price of a regular set.

	MT	NR MT	EX
Complete Set:	12.00	9.00	4.75

1987 Star Co. Roger Clemens Update

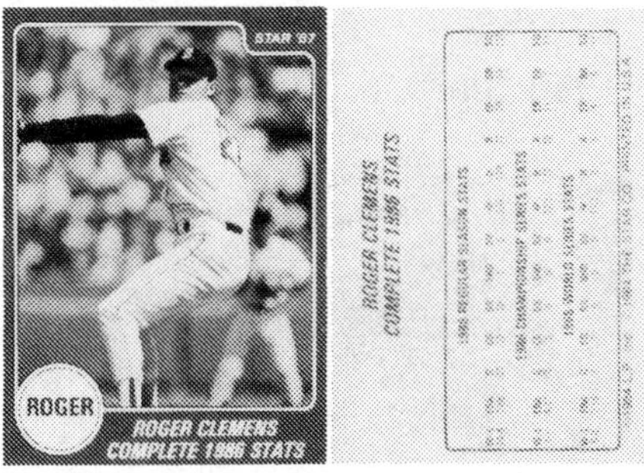

Late in 1987, the Star Co. issued a second set featuring Roger Clemens to update its earlier set devoted to the Boston hurler. Consisting of just five cards, the set had pinkish-colored borders and followed the same design as other Star Co. sets. A special limited-edition glossy version was available and is worth about twice the value of a regular set.

	MT	NR MT	EX
Complete Set:	9.00	6.75	3.50

1987 Star Co. Keith Hernandez

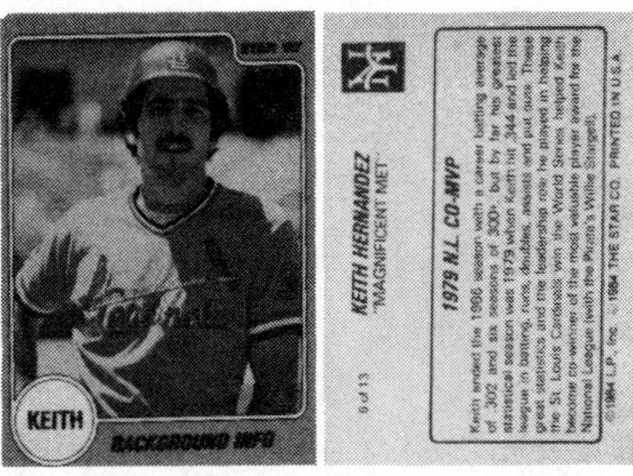

This 13-card set featuring Keith Hernandez was issued by the Star Co. in 1987. The orange-bordered cards are subtitled "Magnificient Met" and display the name "Keith" in the lower left corner. It was also printed in a limited-edition glossy version which is valued at between two and three times the price of a regular set.

	MT	NR MT	EX
Complete Set:	6.00	4.50	2.50

1987 Star Co. Tim Raines

Subtitled "Expo Expert", this 12-card set of Tim Raines was issued by the Star Co. in 1987 and has bright blue borders. A limited number of glossy sets were also available and are generally worth about two to three times the value of a regular set.

	MT	NR MT	EX
Complete Set:	8.00	6.00	3.25

1987 Star Co. Fernando Valenzuela

Complete at 13 cards, this 1987 Star Co. set features Fernando Valenzuela. The blue-bordered cards display the Dodgers logo in the lower left corner. Similar in design to other Star Co. issues, the set was also available in a limited-edition glossy version worth about two to three times the value of a regular set. (Star Co. cards are generally collected only as complete sets, and cards are rarely bought or sold individually.)

	MT	NR MT	EX
Complete Set:	6.00	4.50	2.50

1988 Star Co. "Baseball's Best"

This 11-card Star Co. set is titled "Baseball's Best" and features both Roger Clemens and Dwight Gooden. There are five cards of each hurler, plus one combination card picturing both. A limited-edition glossy version of the set was available and sells for about twice the value of a regular set.

	MT	NR MT	EX
Complete Set:	10.00	7.50	4.50

1988 Star Co. "Baseball's Best" Limited Edition

Issued in both a regular edition and a limited-edition glossy format, this 11-card set pictures Blue Jays star George Bell and was issued by the Star Co. in 1988. The glossy edition is worth about two to three times the value of a regular set.

	MT	NR MT	EX
Complete Set:	7.00	5.25	2.75

1988 Star Co. "Best of '87"

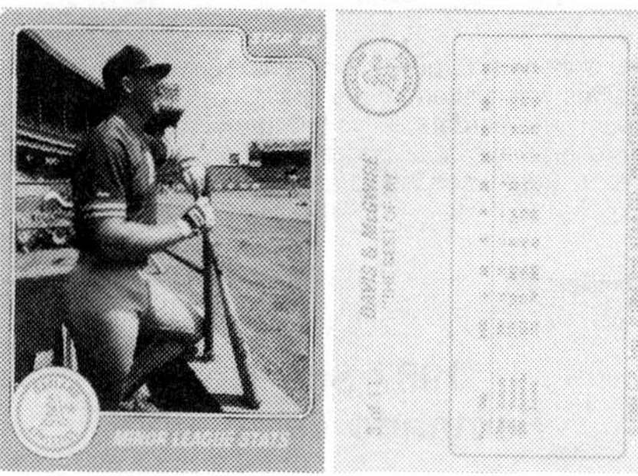

This 11-card set, issued by the Star Co. in 1988, features cards of both Eric Davis and Mark McGwire. There are five cards of each player, plus one combination card picturing both sluggers. The set was also issued in a limited-edition glossy format worth about twice the value of the regular set.

	MT	NR MT	EX
Complete Set:	8.00	6.00	3.25

1988 Star Co. Wade Boggs

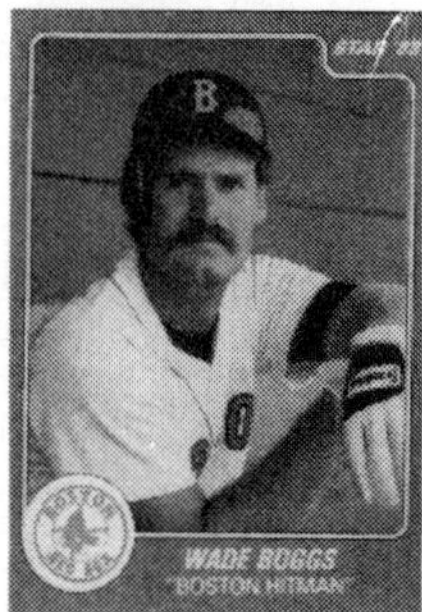

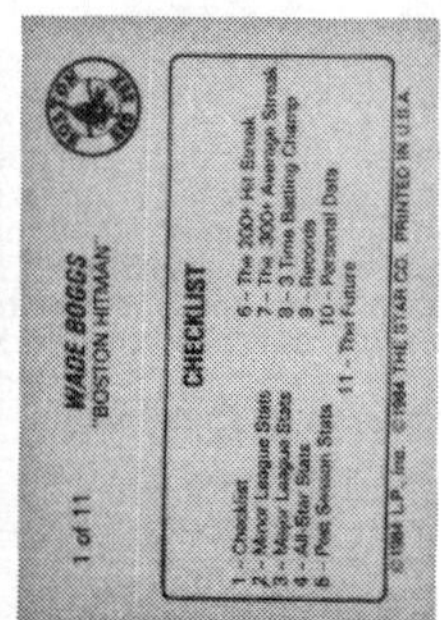

An 11-card issue subtitled "Boston Hit Man", this aqua-bordered set was issued by the Star Co. in 1988 and was the second Star Co. set featuring Wade Boggs. It was also available in a limited-edition glossy format, which is generally valued at about two times the price of a regular set.

	MT	NR MT	EX
Complete Set:	7.00	5.25	2.75

1988 Star Co. Gary Carter

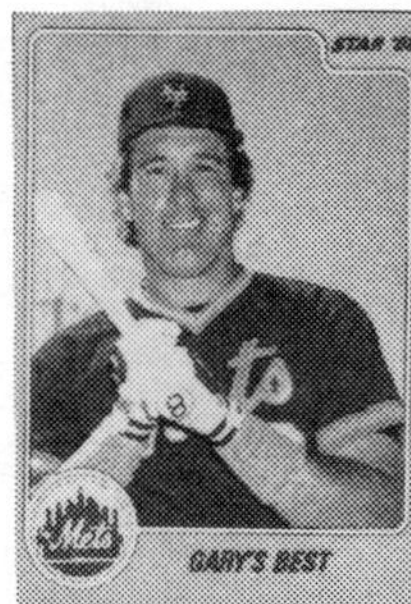

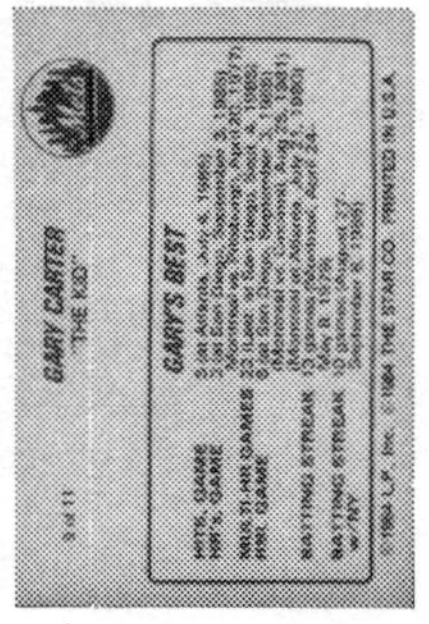

The Star Co. issued a second set featuring Gary Carter in 1988. Again titled "The Kid", the 11-card set has orange borders and displays the Mets logo in the lower left corner. A limited-edition glossy version of the set was available and is generally worth about twice the value of the regular set. (Star Co. cards are generally collected only as complete sets, and cards are rarely bought or sold individually.)

	MT	NR MT	EX
Complete Set:	6.00	4.50	2.50

1988 Star Co. Will Clark

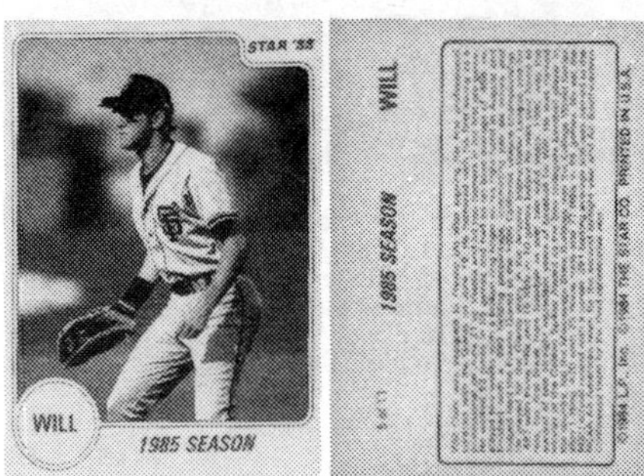

A 1988 issue from the Star Co., the yellow-bordered Will Clark set contains 11 cards. It was also available in a limited-edition glossy format that generally sells for about two to three times the value of a regular set.

	MT	NR MT	EX
Complete Set:	10.00	7.50	4.00

1988 Star Co. Andre Dawson

After the winning the N.L. Most Valuable Player Award in 1987, Andre Dawson was honored by the Star Co. with an 11-card set in 1988. Subtitled "The Hawk", the cards have pinkish-colored borders and display the Cubs logo in the lower left corner. A limited-edition glossy version of the set was available and generally is worth about twice the value of a regular set.

	MT	NR MT	EX
Complete Set:	7.00	5.25	2.75

1988 Star Co. Eric Davis

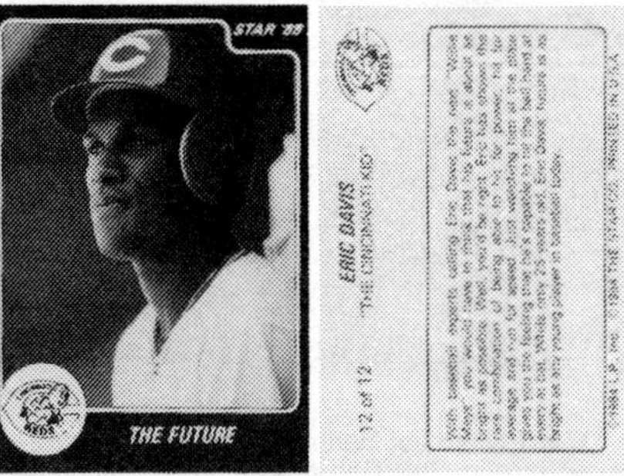

Subtitled "The Cincinnati Kid", this 12-card set featuring Eric Davis was issued by the Star Co. in 1988. The red-bordered set was also issued in a limited-edition glossy version, which commands a value about twice that of a regular set.

	MT	NR MT	EX
Complete Set:	6.00	4.50	2.50

1988 Star Co. Dwight Gooden

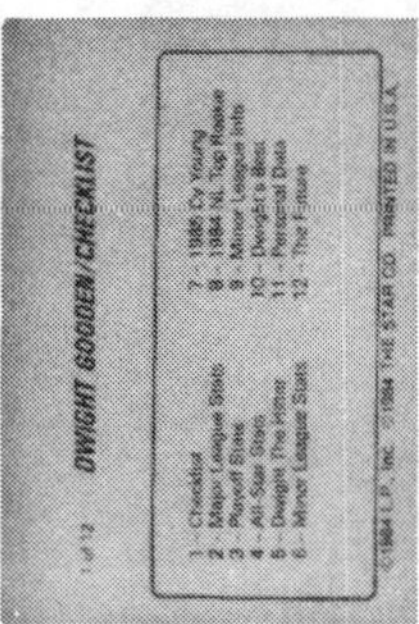

Mets pitching ace Dwight Gooden was featured in an 11-card Star Co. set in 1988. The blue-bordered cards display the name "Dwight" in the lower left corner. The set was also printed in a limited-edition glossy version which commands a value about twice that of a regular set.

	MT	NR MT	EX
Complete Set:	7.00	5.25	2.75

1988 Star Co. Tony Gwynn

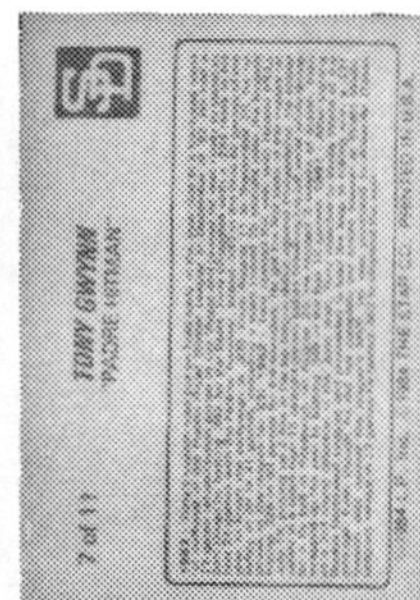

Padres star Tony Gwynn was featured in an 11-card set issued by the Star Co. in 1988. The cards have light brown borders and display the Padres logo in the lower left corner. Similar in design to other Star Co. issues, the set was also available in a limited-edition glossy format which commands a value about twice that of a regular set. (Star Co. cards are generally collected only as complete sets, and cards are rarely bought and sold individually.)

	MT	NR MT	EX
Complete Set:	8.00	6.00	3.25

1988 Star Co. "Hits 'R Us"

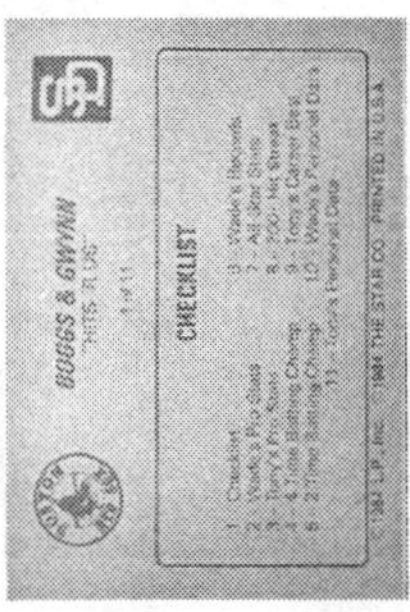

This 11-card set, issued by the Star Co. in 1988, features batting leaders Wade Boggs and Tony Gwynn. There are five cards of each player, plus one combination card picturing both superstars. Their respective team logos are displayed in the lower left corner. The set was also printed in a limited-edition glossy version which is worth about twice the value of a regular set.

	MT	NR MT	EX
Complete Set:	8.00	6.00	3.25

1988 Star Co. Bo Jackson

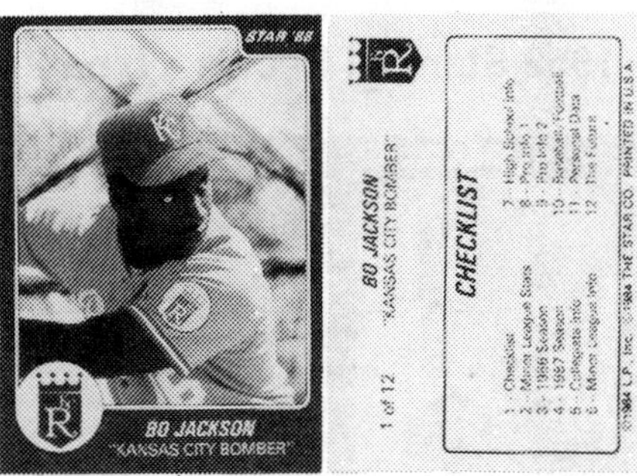

Royals star Bo Jackson was featured in a 12-card set issued by the Star Co. in 1988. The blue-bordered cards display the Royals logo in the lower left corner and are subtitled "Kansas City Bomber". In addition to the 12 regular cards picturing Jackson with the Royals, the Star Co. also released four additional unnumbered, blank-backed cards highlighting Jackson's collegiate football career at Auburn. The set was also issued in a limited-edition glossy format which is worth about twice the value of a regular set.

	MT	NR MT	EX
Complete Set:	10.00	7.50	4.00

1988 Star Co. Don Mattingly

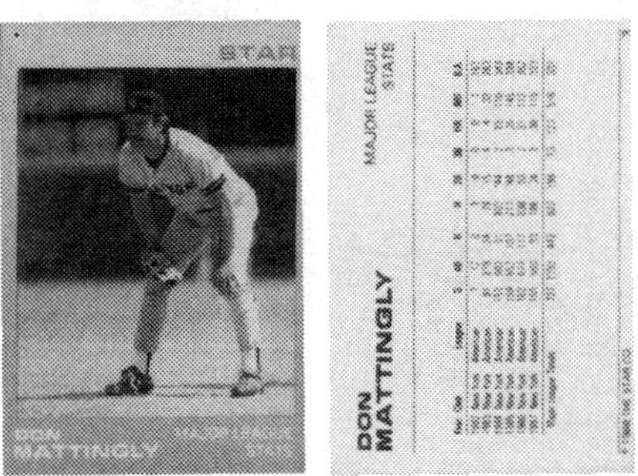

Yankees' star Don Mattingly was featured in his second Star Co. issue in 1988 with an 11-card set. The gray-bordered set, subtitled "Yankee Hit Man", was also available in a glossy format which is valued at about two times the price of a regular set.

	MT	NR MT	EX
Complete Set:	9.00	6.75	3.50

1988 Star Co. Mark McGwire

This 12-card set, issued by the Star Co. in 1988, features photos of A's slugger Mark McGwire and is subtitled "Oakland Power King". The yellow-bordered cards were also available in a limited-edition glossy version worth about twice the value of a regular set.

	MT	NR MT	EX
Complete Set:	8.00	6.00	3.25

1988 Star Co. Mark McGwire #2

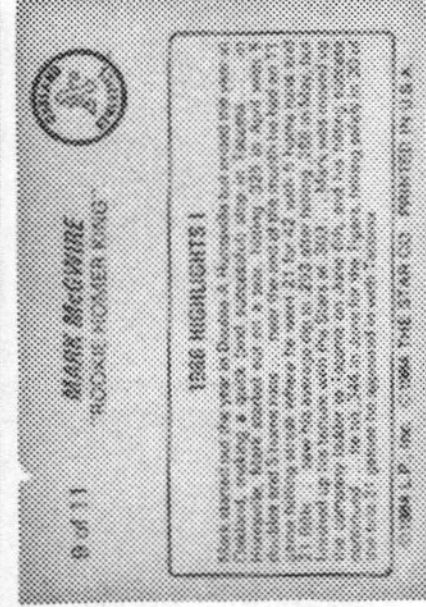

Oakland slugger Mark McGwire was featured in a second 11-card set by the Star Co. in 1988. Subtitled "Rookie Homer King", the cards feature aqua-colored borders. The set follows the same basic format as other Star Co. issues and was also available in a limited-edition glossy version which is valued at about twice the price of the regular set.

	MT	NR MT	EX
Complete Set:	8.00	6.00	3.25

1988 Star Co. Mark McGwire #3

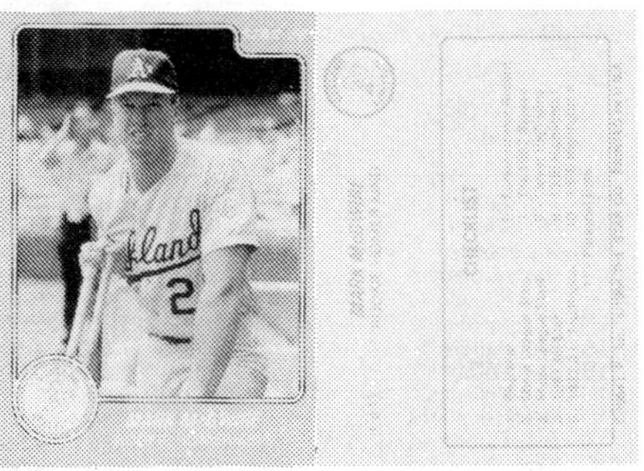

Capitalizing on the popularity of Mark McGwire, the Star Co. issued a third set featuring the A's slugger in 1988. Again titled "Rookie Homer King", the 11-card set has green borders and was also available in a limited-edition glossy version which commands a value about twice that of a regular set. (Star Co. cards are generally collected only as complete sets, and cards are rarely bought or sold individually.)

	MT	NR MT	EX
Complete Set:	7.00	5.25	2.75

1988 Star Co. Mike Scott

Mike Scott was featured in an 11-card Star Co. set in 1988. The green-bordered cards display the name "Mike" in the lower left corner and were also issued in a limited-edition glossy version, which are worth twice as much as a regular set.

	MT	NR MT	EX
Complete Set:	6.00	4.50	2.50

1988 Star Co. Kevin Seitzer

Subtitled "Kansas City Hitman", this 11-card set features Kevin Seitzer. The cards have blue borders with yellow accents and display the Royals logo in the lower left corner. The set was also issued in a limited-edition glossy version which generally sells for about twice the value of the regular set.

	MT	NR MT	EX
Complete Set:	6.00	4.50	2.50

1988 Star Co. Cory Snyder

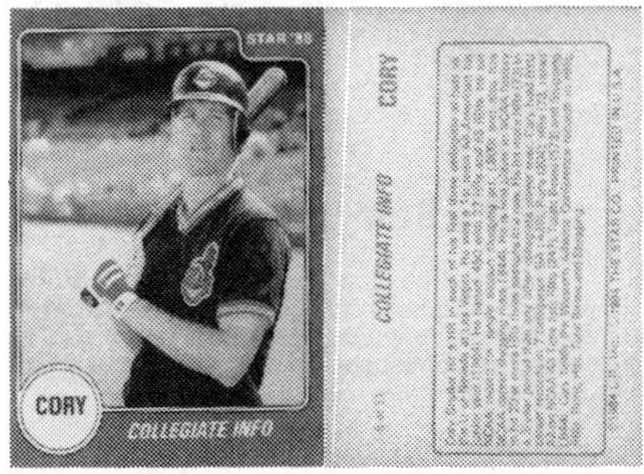

The Star Co. honored Cory Snyder with an 11-card set in 1988. The red-bordered set was issued in a regular edition, a glossy edition and a special "sticker" back version. The special editions are generally worth about two to three times the value of a regular set.

	MT	NR MT	EX
Complete Set:	6.00	4.50	2.50

1988 Star Co. Dave Winfield

The Star Co. honored Dave Winfield with a 12-card set in 1988. The gray-bordered cards display the name "Dave" in the lower left corner. The set was also issued in a limited-edition glossy version which is generally worth about two times the value of a regular set. (Star Co. cards are generally collected only as complete sets, and cards are rarely bought or sold individually.)

	MT	NR MT	EX
Complete Set:	8.00	6.00	3.25

1988 Star Co. Platinum

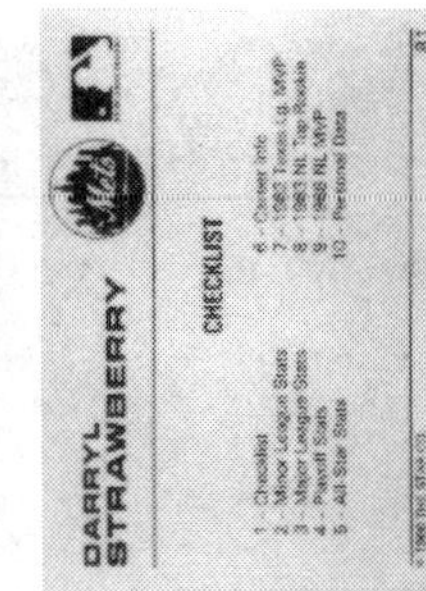

Twelve single-player subsets make up the 1988 Star Platinum set. Ten cards were devoted to each player. The card numbers are displayed in the value list below. 1,000 total sets were issued.

	MT	NR MT	EX
Complete Set:	400.00	300.00	160.00

1989 Star Co. Gold Edition

This 180-card set was actually released at the end of 1988 and into 1989. Twenty single-player subsets are included. The high quality photographs feature a special gold embossing. The cards devoted to each player are noted by number in the corresponding value list.

	MT	NR MT	EX
Complete Set:	350.00	260.00	140.00

1989 Star Co. Platinum

Fourteen of baseball's top players are featured in this 140-card set. Cards 21-30 were devoted to Gregg Jefferies, but a contract dispute prevented its release. The corresponding card numbers are provided for each player.

	MT	NR MT	EX
Complete Set:	350.00	260.00	140.00

1989 Star Co. Silver Series

This 90-card set features ten player subsets including young superstar Ken Griffey, Jr. Only 2,000 sets were printed and each is serial numbered. The card subsets were released in pairs, one established player and one future star. The corresponding card numbers are provided in the value list for the respective player.

	MT	NR MT	EX
Complete Set:	200.00	150.00	80.00

1990 Star Sophomore Stars

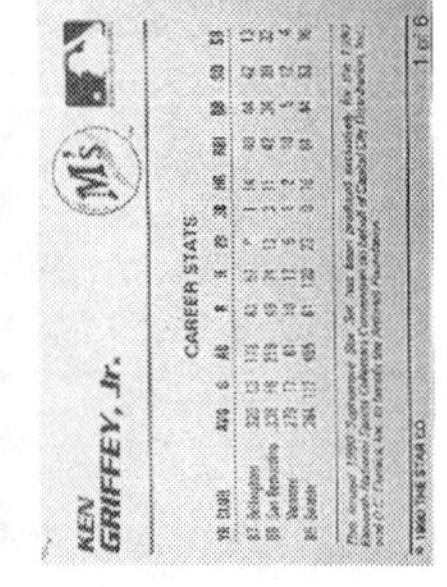

This special six-card set was distributed only at the 1990 Arlington 11th National Sports Collectors Convention. The set came polybagged with a DC comic book in exchange for a donation to the Arthritis Foundation. The 2-1/2" x 3-1/2" cards feature a border that changes from dark blue at the top to red at the bottom. Backs are printed in blue-on-white and include team and MLB logos along with major and minor league career stats.

		MT	NR MT	EX
	Complete Set (6):	8.00	6.00	3.25
	Common Player:	.50	.40	.20
1	Ken Girffey, Jr. (batting cage)	3.00	2.25	1.20
2	Ken Griffey, Jr. (sitting)	3.00	2.25	1.20
3	Gary Sheffield (portrait)	1.00	.75	.40
4	Gary Sheffield (batting)	1.00	.75	.40
5	Jerome Walton (portrait)	.50	.40	.20
6	Jerome Walton (batting)	.50	.40	.20

1952 Star-Cal Decals - Type I

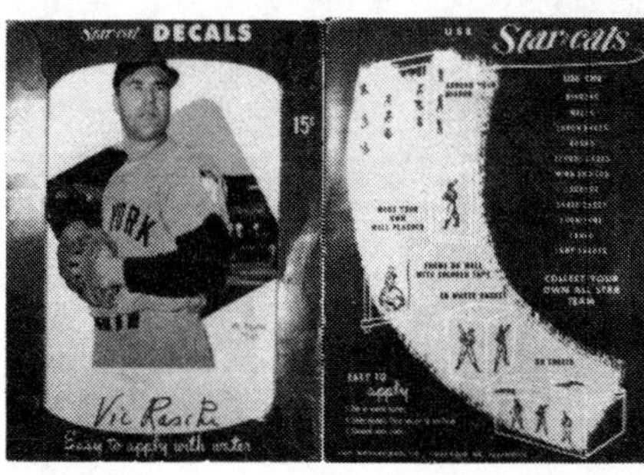

The Meyercord Co., of Chicago issued two sets of baseball player decals in 1952. The Type I Star-Cal Decal set consists of 68 different major leaguers, each pictured on a large (4-1/8" x 6-1/8") decal. The player's name and facsimile autograph appear on the decal, along with the decal number listed on the checklist here. Values shown are for decals complete with outer directions envelope.

		NR MT	EX	VG
	Complete Set (68):	2800.	1400.	840.00
	Common Player:	15.00	7.50	4.50
70A	Allie Reynolds	18.00	9.00	5.50
70B	Ed Lopat	15.00	7.50	4.50
70C	Yogi Berra	50.00	25.00	15.00
70D	Vic Raschi	15.00	7.50	4.50
70E	Jerry Coleman	15.00	7.50	4.50
70F	Phil Rizzuto	45.00	22.00	13.50
70G	Mickey Mantle	450.00	225.00	135.00
71A	Mel Parnell	15.00	7.50	4.50
71B	Ted Williams	175.00	85.00	50.00
71C	Ted Williams	175.00	85.00	50.00
71D	Vern Stephens	15.00	7.50	4.50
71E	Billy Goodman	15.00	7.50	4.50
71F	Dom DiMaggio	18.00	9.00	5.50
71G	Dick Gernert	15.00	7.50	4.50
71H	Hoot Evers	15.00	7.50	4.50
72A	George Kell	25.00	12.50	7.50
72B	Hal Newhouser	25.00	12.50	7.50
72C	Hoot Evers	15.00	7.50	4.50
72D	Vic Wertz	15.00	7.50	4.50
72E	Fred Hutchinson	15.00	7.50	4.50
72F	Johnny Groth	15.00	7.50	4.50
73A	Al Zarilla	15.00	7.50	4.50
73B	Billy Pierce	18.00	9.00	5.50
73C	Eddie Robinson	15.00	7.50	4.50
73D	Chico Carrasquel	15.00	7.50	4.50
73E	Minnie Minoso	20.00	10.00	6.00
73F	Jim Busby	15.00	7.50	4.50
73G	Nellie Fox	20.00	10.00	6.00
73H	Sam Mele	15.00	7.50	4.50
74A	Larry Doby	18.00	9.00	5.50
74B	Al Rosen	18.00	9.00	5.50
74C	Bob Lemon	25.00	12.50	7.50
74D	Jim Hegan	15.00	7.50	4.50
74E	Bob Feller	40.00	20.00	12.00
74F	Dale Mitchell	15.00	7.50	4.50
75A	Ned Garver	15.00	7.50	4.50
76A	Gus Zernial	15.00	7.50	4.50
76B	Ferris Fain	15.00	7.50	4.50
76C	Bobby Shantz	18.00	9.00	5.50
77A	Richie Ashburn	25.00	12.50	7.50
77B	Ralph Kiner	25.00	12.50	7.50
77C	Curt Simmons	15.00	7.50	4.50
78A	Bobby Thomson	18.00	9.00	5.50
78B	Alvin Dark	15.00	7.50	4.50
78C	Sal Maglie	15.00	7.50	4.50
78D	Larry Jansen	15.00	7.50	4.50
78E	Willie Mays	275.00	135.00	85.00
78F	Monte Irvin	25.00	12.50	7.50
78G	Whitey Lockman	15.00	7.50	4.50
79A	Gil Hodges	30.00	15.00	9.00
79B	Pee Wee Reese	40.00	20.00	12.00
79C	Roy Campanella	50.00	25.00	15.00
79D	Don Newcombe	18.00	9.00	5.50
79E	Duke Snider	75.00	37.50	22.00
79F	Preacher Roe	15.00	7.50	4.50
79G	Jackie Robinson	150.00	75.00	45.00
80A	Eddie Miksis	15.00	7.50	4.50
80B	Dutch Leonard	15.00	7.50	4.50
80C	Randy Jackson	15.00	7.50	4.50
80D	Bob Rush	15.00	7.50	4.50
80E	Hank Sauer	15.00	7.50	4.50
80F	Phil Cavarretta	15.00	7.50	4.50
80G	Warren Hacker	15.00	7.50	4.50
81A	Red Schoendienst	25.00	12.50	7.50
81B	Wally Westlake	15.00	7.50	4.50
81C	Cliff Chambers	15.00	7.50	4.50
81D	Enos Slaughter	25.00	12.50	7.50
81E	Stan Musial	150.00	75.00	45.00
81F	Stan Musial	150.00	75.00	45.00
81G	Jerry Staley	15.00	7.50	4.50

1952 Star-Cal Decals - Type 2

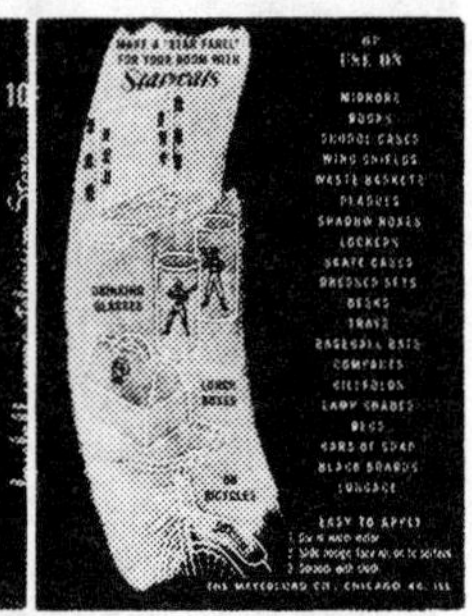

Also produced by Chicago's Meyercord Company in 1952, these Star-cal decals are similar to the Type I variety, except the decal sheets are smaller, measuring 4-1/8" by 3-1/16", and each sheet features two players instead of one.

		NR MT	EX	VG
	Complete Set:	1250.	625.00	375.00
	Common Player:	12.00	6.00	3.50
84A	Vic Raschi	18.00	9.00	5.50
84A	Allie Reynolds	18.00	9.00	5.50
84B	Yogi Berra	50.00	25.00	15.00
84B	Ed Lopat	50.00	25.00	15.00
84C	Jerry Coleman	40.00	20.00	12.00
84C	Phil Rizzuto	40.00	20.00	12.00
85A	Ted Williams	175.00	87.00	52.00
85A	Ted Williams	175.00	87.00	52.00
85B	Dom DiMaggio	15.00	7.50	4.50
85B	Mel Parnell	15.00	7.50	4.50
85C	Billy Goodman	12.00	6.00	3.50
85C	Vern Stephens	12.00	6.00	3.50
86A	George Kell	25.00	12.50	7.50
86A	Hal Newhouser	25.00	12.50	7.50
86B	Hoot Evers	12.00	6.00	3.50
86B	Vic Wertz	12.00	6.00	3.50
86C	Bill Groth	12.00	6.00	3.50
86C	Fred Hutchinson	12.00	6.00	3.50
87A	Eddie Robinson	12.00	6.00	3.50
87A	Eddie Robinson	12.00	6.00	3.50
87B	Chico Carrasquel	15.00	7.50	4.50
87B	Minnie Minoso	15.00	7.50	4.50
87C	Nellie Fox	18.00	9.00	5.50
87C	Billy Pierce	18.00	9.00	5.50
87D	Jim Busby	12.00	6.00	3.50
87D	Al Zarilla	12.00	6.00	3.50
88A	Jim Hegan	20.00	10.00	6.00
88A	Bob Lemon	20.00	10.00	6.00
88B	Larry Doby	50.00	25.00	15.00
88B	Bob Feller	50.00	25.00	15.00
88C	Dale Mitchell	15.00	7.50	4.50
88C	Al Rosen	15.00	7.50	4.50
89A	Ned Garver	12.00	6.00	3.50
89A	Ned Garver	12.00	6.00	3.50
89B	Ferris Fain	12.00	6.00	3.50
89B	Gus Zernial	12.00	6.00	3.50
89C	Richie Ashburn	20.00	10.00	6.00
89C	Richie Ashburn	20.00	10.00	6.00
89D	Ralph Kiner	25.00	12.50	7.50
89D	Ralph Kiner	25.00	12.50	7.50
90A	Monty Irvin	225.00	112.00	67.00
90A	Willie Mays	225.00	112.00	67.00
90B	Larry Jansen	12.00	6.00	3.50
90B	Sal Maglie	12.00	6.00	3.50
90C	Al Dark	15.00	7.50	4.50
90C	Bobby Thomson	15.00	7.50	4.50
91A	Gil Hodges	50.00	25.00	15.00
91A	Pee Wee Reese	50.00	25.00	15.00
91B	Roy Campanella	125.00	62.00	37.00
91B	Jackie Robinson	125.00	62.00	37.00
91C	Preacher Roe	60.00	30.00	18.00
91C	Duke Snider	60.00	30.00	18.00
92A	Phil Cavarretta	12.00	6.00	3.50
92A	Dutch Leonard	12.00	6.00	3.50
92B	Randy Jackson	12.00	6.00	3.50
92B	Eddie Miksis	12.00	6.00	3.50
92C	Bob Rush	12.00	6.00	3.50
92C	Hank Sauer	12.00	6.00	3.50
93A	Stan Musial	125.00	62.00	37.00
93A	Stan Musial	125.00	62.00	37.00
93B	Red Schoendienst	20.00	10.00	6.00
93B	Enos Slaughter	20.00	10.00	6.00
93C	Cliff Chambers	12.00	6.00	3.50
93C	Wally Westlake	12.00	6.00	3.50

1989 Starline Prototypes

Prior to its first major baseball card issue, Starline produced five variations of a prototype issue. The seven-card sets feature game-action photos on the front, surrounded by colorful borders and with a combination of up to three logos in the bottom border. Cards were produced with just the Starline logo, with the Starline and Coca-Cola logos and with the card company and soft drink logos in conjunction

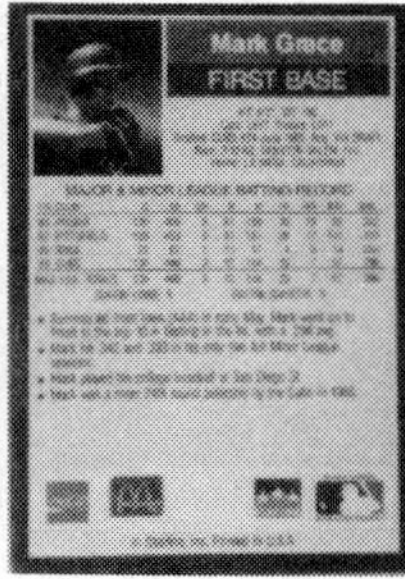

with those of McDonald's, 7-11 or Dominos pizza. Backs repeat the logos at bottom, along with that of Major League Baseball. At top is a color player photo, along with biographical data, complete major and minor league stats and career highlights. The unnumbered cards are checklisted here alphabetically.

		MT	NR MT	EX
Complete Set (7):		250.00	187.00	100.00
Common Player:		35.00	26.00	14.00
(1)	Eric Davis	35.00	26.00	14.00
(2)	Mark Grace	35.00	26.00	14.00
(3)	Tony Gwynn	60.00	45.00	24.00
(4)	Gregg Jefferies	50.00	37.00	20.00
(5)	Don Mattingly	75.00	56.00	30.00
(6)	Mark McGwire	50.00	37.00	20.00
(7)	Darryl Strawberry	50.00	37.00	20.00

1990 Starline

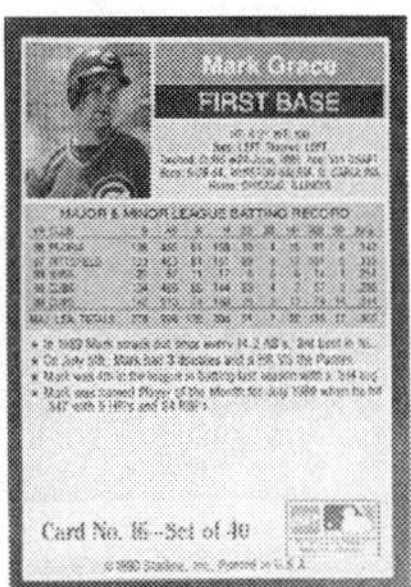

Five-card packs of this Coca-Cola sponsored issue were given away with the purchase of a soft drink at Long John Silver fish restaurants. Cards feature game-action photos on front, bordered in team colors. Backs repeat the team-color scheme and feature a portrait photo along with major league stats and career highlights. Most of the players had two or more cards in the 40-card issue.

		MT	NR MT	EX
Complete Set (40):		12.00	9.00	4.75
Common Player:		.25	.20	.10
1	Don Mattingly	.75	.60	.30
2	Mark Grace	.50	.40	.20
3	Eric Davis	.35	.25	.14
4	Tony Gwynn	.45	.35	.20
5	Bobby Bonilla	.35	.25	.14
6	Wade Boggs	.60	.45	.25
7	Frank Viola	.25	.20	.10
8	Ruben Sierra	.35	.25	.14
9	Mark McGwire	.40	.30	.15
10	Alan Trammell	.40	.30	.15
11	Mark McGwire	.40	.30	.15
12	Gregg Jefferies	.35	.25	.14
13	Nolan Ryan	1.25	.90	.50
14	John Smoltz	.40	.30	.15
15	Glenn Davis	.25	.20	.10
16	Mark Grace	.50	.40	.20
17	Wade Boggs	.60	.45	.25
18	Frank Viola	.25	.20	.10
19	Bret Saberhagen	.25	.20	.10
20	Chris Sabo	.25	.20	.10
21	Darryl Strawberry	.35	.25	.14
22	Wade Boggs	.60	.45	.25
23	Tim Raines	.35	.25	.14
24	Alan Trammell	.40	.30	.15
25	Chris Sabo	.25	.20	.10
26	Nolan Ryan	1.25	.90	.50
27	Mark McGwire	.40	.30	.15
28	Don Mattingly	.75	.60	.30
29	Tony Gwynn	.40	.30	.15
30	Glenn Davis	.25	.20	.10
31	Bobby Bonilla	.35	.25	.14
32	Gregg Jefferies	.35	.25	.14
33	Ruben Sierra	.35	.25	.14
34	John Smoltz	.35	.25	.14
35	Don Mattingly	.75	.60	.30
36	Bret Saberhagen	.25	.20	.10
37	Darryl Strawberry	.35	.25	.14
38	Eric Davis	.35	.25	.14
39	Tim Raines	.35	.25	.14
40	Mark Grace	.50	.40	.20

1988 Starting Lineup Talking Baseball

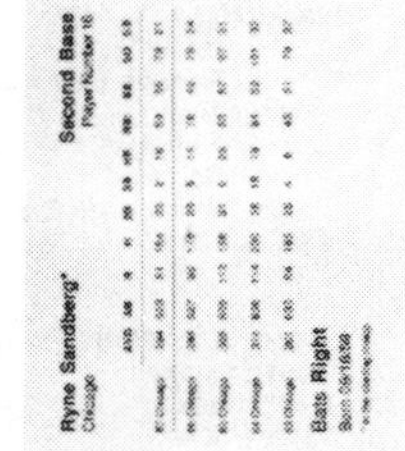

Measuring 2-5/8" by 3", these cards were part of the Starting Lineup Talking Baseball game produced by Kenner Parker Toys Inc. The electronic game, with a computer memory and keyboard to respond to a particular baseball game situation, retailed for more than $100. However, several hobby dealers sold the cards separately from the game. The set includes seven instruction cards that do not picture players.

		MT	NR MT	EX
Complete Set:		60.00	45.00	24.00
Common Player:		.75	.60	.30
11a	Terry Kennedy	.75	.60	.30
11b	Gary Carter	1.50	1.25	.60
12a	Carlton Fisk	1.00	.70	.40
12b	Steve Sax	1.00	.70	.40
13a	Eddie Murray	2.00	1.50	.80
13b	Jack Clark	1.00	.70	.40
14a	Don Mattingly	6.00	4.50	2.50
14b	Keith Hernandez	1.25	.90	.50
15a	Willie Randolph	.75	.60	.30
15b	Buddy Bell	.75	.60	.30
16a	Cal Ripken	2.25	1.75	.90
16b	Ryne Sandberg	1.50	1.25	.60
17a	Lou Whitaker	1.00	.70	.40
17b	Ozzie Smith	1.00	.70	.40
18a	Wade Boggs	4.00	3.00	1.50
18b	Dale Murphy	2.50	2.00	1.00
19a	George Brett	2.50	2.00	1.00
19b	Mike Schmidt	2.50	2.00	1.00
20a	Alan Trammell	1.25	.90	.50
20b	Eric Davis	3.25	2.50	1.25
21a	Kirby Puckett	2.00	1.50	.80
21b	Tony Gwynn	2.25	1.75	.90
22a	George Bell	1.50	1.25	.60
22b	Darryl Strawberry	3.25	2.50	1.25
23a	Rickey Henderson	2.25	1.75	.90
23b	Tim Raines	1.75	1.25	.70
24a	Dave Winfield	2.00	1.50	.80
24b	Andre Dawson	1.25	.90	.50
25a	Jack Morris	1.00	.70	.40
25b	Mike Scott	.75	.60	.30
26a	Robin Yount	1.25	.90	.50
26b	Jody Davis	.75	.60	.30
27a	Roger Clemens	3.50	2.75	1.50
27b	Todd Worrell	1.00	.70	.40
28a	Bret Saberhagen	1.25	.90	.50
28b	Fernando Valenzuela	1.25	.90	.50
29a	Dave Righetti	1.00	.70	.40
29b	Dwight Gooden	3.50	2.75	1.50
30a	Dan Quisenberry	.75	.60	.30
30b	Nolan Ryan	1.50	1.25	.60

1983 Stuart Expos

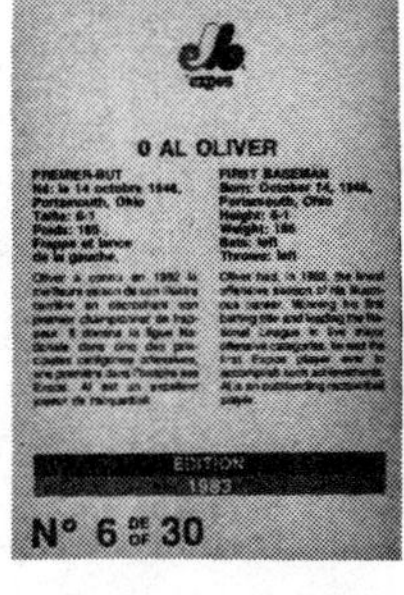

This set of Montreal Expos players and coaches was issued by a Montreal area baking company for inclusion in packages of snack cakes. The 30 cards feature full-color player photos, with the player name, number and team logo also on the card fronts. The backs list brief player biographies in both English and French. Twenty-five players are pictured on the 2-1/2" by 3-1/2" cards.

		MT	NR MT	EX
Complete Set (30):		13.00	9.75	5.25
Common Player:		.25	.20	.10
1	Bill Virdon	.25	.20	.10
2	Woodie Fryman	.25	.20	.10
3	Vern Rapp	.25	.20	.10
4	Andre Dawson	3.00	2.25	1.25
5	Jeff Reardon	1.00	.70	.40
6	Al Oliver	.50	.40	.20
7	Doug Flynn	.25	.20	.10
8	Gary Carter	1.00	.70	.40
9	Tim Raines	1.50	1.25	.60
10	Steve Rogers	.30	.25	.12
11	Billy DeMars	.25	.20	.10
12	Tim Wallach	1.00	.70	.40
13	Galen Cisco	.25	.20	.10
14	Terry Francona	.25	.20	.10
15	Bill Gullickson	.25	.20	.10
16	Ray Burris	.25	.20	.10
17	Scott Sanderson	.35	.25	.14
18	Warren Cromartie	.25	.20	.10
19	Jerry White	.25	.20	.10
20	Bobby Ramos	.25	.20	.10
21	Jim Wolhford	.25	.20	.10
22	Dan Schatzeder	.25	.20	.10
23	Charlie Lea	.25	.20	.10
24	Bryan Little	.25	.20	.10
25	Mel Wright	.25	.20	.10
26	Tim Blackwell	.25	.20	.10
27	Chris Speier	.25	.20	.10
28	Randy Lerch	.25	.20	.10
29	Bryn Smith	.35	.25	.14
30	Brad Mills	.25	.20	.10

1984 Stuart Expos

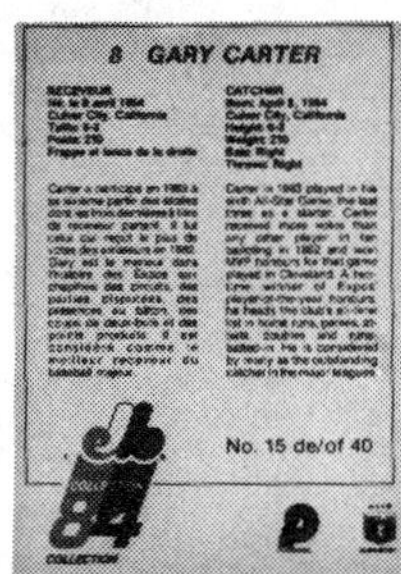

For the second year in a row, Stuart Cakes issued a full-color card set of the Montreal Expos. The 2-1/2" by 3-1/2" cards again list the player name and number along with the team and company logos on the card fronts. The backs are bilingual with biographical information in both English and French. The 40-card set was issued in two series. Card numbers 21-40, issued late in the summer, are more difficult to find than the first 20 cards. The 40 cards include players, the manager, coaches and team mascot.

		MT	NR MT	EX
Complete Set:		20.00	15.00	8.00
Common Player (1-20):		.25	.20	.10
Common Player (21-40):		.50	.40	.20
1	Youppi! (mascot)	.25	.20	.10
2	Bill Virdon	.25	.20	.10
3	Billy DeMars	.25	.20	.10
4	Galen Cisco	.25	.20	.10
5	Russ Nixon	.25	.20	.10
6	Felipe Alou	.45	.35	.20
7	Dan Schatzeder	.25	.20	.10
8	Charlie Lea	.25	.20	.10
9	Bobby Ramos	.25	.20	.10
10	Bob James	.25	.20	.10
11	Andre Dawson	2.00	1.50	.80
12	Gary Lucas	.25	.20	.10
13	Jeff Reardon	.75	.60	.30
14	Tim Wallach	1.00	.70	.40
15	Gary Carter	2.00	1.50	.80
16	Bill Gullickson	.25	.20	.10
17	Pete Rose	4.00	3.00	1.50
18	Terry Francona	.25	.20	.10
19	Steve Rogers	.30	.25	.12
20	Tim Raines	1.25	.90	.50
21	Bryn Smith	.50	.40	.20
22	Greg Harris	.50	.40	.20
23	David Palmer	.50	.40	.20
24	Jim Wohlford	.50	.40	.20
25	Miguel Dilone	.50	.40	.20
26	Mike Stenhouse	.50	.40	.20
27	Chris Speier	.50	.40	.20
28	Derrel Thomas	.50	.40	.20

29	Doug Flynn	.50	.40	.20
30	Bryan Little	.50	.40	.20
31	Argenis Salazar	.50	.40	.20
32	Mike Fuentes	.50	.40	.20
33	Joe Kerrigan	.50	.40	.20
34	Andy McGaffigan	.45	.35	.20
35	Fred Breining	.50	.40	.20
36	Expos 1983 All-Stars (Gary Carter, Andre Dawson, Tim Raines, Steve Rogers)	1.25	.90	.50
37	Co-Players Of The Year (Andre Dawson, Tim Raines)	1.25	.90	.50
38	Expos' Coaching Staff (Felipe Alou, Galen Cisco, Billy DeMars, Joe Kerrigan, Russ Nixon, Bill Virdon)	.50	.40	.20
39	Team Photo	.50	.40	.20
40	Checklist	.50	.40	.20

1987 Stuart

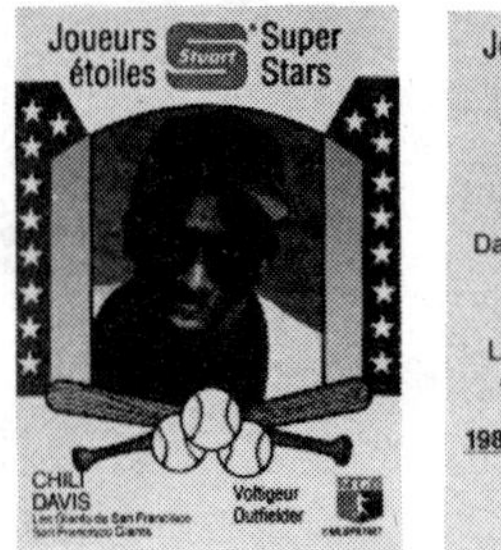

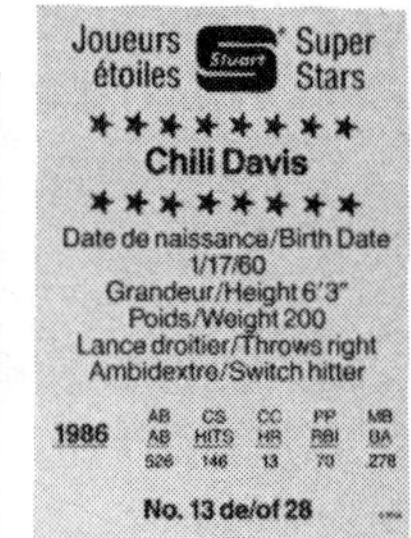

Twenty-eight four-part folding panels make up the 1987 Stuart Super Stars set, which was issued only in Canada. Three player cards and a sweepstakes entry form card comprise each panel. All 26 major league teams are included with the Montreal Expos and Toronto Blue Jays being represented twice. The cards, which are full color and measure 2-1/2" by 3-1/2", are written in both English and French. The card backs contain the player's previous year's statistics. All team insignias have been airbrushed away.

		MT	NR MT	EX
Complete Panel Set:		50.00	37.00	20.00
Complete Singles Set:		25.00	18.50	10.00
Common Panel:		.80	.60	.30
Common Single Player:		.10	.08	.04
	Panel (New York Mets)	2.00	1.50	.80
1a	Gary Carter	.30	.25	.12
1b	Keith Hernandez	.20	.15	.08
1c	Darryl Strawberry	.30	.25	.12
	Panel (Atlanta Braves)	2.25	1.75	.90
2a	Bruce Benedict	.10	.08	.04
2b	Ken Griffey	.15	.11	.06
2c	Dale Murphy	.60	.45	.25
	Panel (Chicago Cubs)	1.50	1.25	.60
3a	Jody Davis	.15	.11	.06
3b	Andre Dawson	.30	.25	.12
3c	Leon Durham	.15	.11	.06
	Panel (Cincinnati Reds)	2.00	1.50	.80
4a	Buddy Bell	.15	.11	.06
4b	Eric Davis	.30	.25	.12
4c	Dave Parker	.40	.30	.15
	Panel (Houston Astros)	3.00	2.25	1.25
5a	Glenn Davis	.10	.08	.04
5b	Nolan Ryan	1.50	1.25	.60
5c	Mike Scott	.25	.20	.10
	Panel (Los Angeles Dodgers)	1.50	1.25	.60
6a	Pedro Guerrero	.20	.15	.08
6b	Mike Marshall	.20	.15	.08
6c	Fernando Valenzuela	.20	.15	.08
	Panel (Montreal Expos)	1.75	1.25	.70
7a	Tim Raines	.40	.30	.15
7b	Tim Wallach	.20	.15	.08
7c	Mitch Webster	.10	.08	.04
	Panel (Montreal Expos)	.80	.60	.30
8a	Hubie Brooks	.15	.11	.06
8b	Bryn Smith	.10	.08	.04
8c	Floyd Youmans	.10	.08	.04
	Panel (Philadelphia Phillies)	2.25	1.75	.90
9a	Shane Rawley	.10	.08	.04
9b	Juan Samuel	.20	.15	.08
9c	Mike Schmidt	.80	.60	.30
	Panel (Pittsburgh Pirates)	.80	.60	.30
10a	Jim Morrison	.10	.08	.04
10b	Johnny Ray	.15	.11	.06
10c	R.J. Reynolds	.10	.08	.04
	Panel (St. Louis Cardinals)	2.00	1.50	.80
11a	Jack Clark	.15	.11	.06
11b	Vince Coleman	.30	.25	.12
11c	Ozzie Smith	.40	.30	.15
	Panel (San Diego Padres)	3.50	2.75	1.50
12a	Steve Garvey	.40	.30	.15
12b	Tony Gwynn	.50	.40	.20
12c	John Kruk	.30	.25	.12
	Panel (San Francisco Giants)	1.50	1.25	.60
13a	Chili Davis	.20	.15	.08
13b	Jeffrey Leonard	.10	.08	.04
13c	Robbie Thompson	.20	.15	.08
	Panel (Baltimore Orioles)	4.00	3.00	1.50
14a	Fred Lynn	.25	.20	.10
14b	Eddie Murray	.50	.40	.20
14c	Cal Ripken, Jr.	1.00	.70	.40
	Panel (Boston Red Sox)	4.00	3.00	1.50
15a	Don Baylor	.15	.11	.06
15b	Wade Boggs	.80	.60	.30
15c	Roger Clemens	.60	.45	.25
	Panel (California Angels)	2.00	1.50	.80
16a	Doug DeCinces	.10	.08	.04
16b	Wally Joyner	.60	.45	.25
16c	Mike Witt	.10	.08	.04
	Panel (Chicago White Sox)	1.50	1.25	.60
17a	Harold Baines	.20	.15	.08
17b	Carlton Fisk	.25	.20	.10
17c	Ozzie Guillen	.15	.11	.06
	Panel (Cleveland Indians)	1.25	.90	.50
18a	Joe Carter	.30	.25	.12
18b	Julio Franco	.15	.11	.06
18c	Pat Tabler	.10	.08	.04
	Panel (Detroit Tigers)	2.00	1.50	.80
19a	Kirk Gibson	.20	.15	.08
19b	Jack Morris	.25	.20	.10
19c	Alan Trammell	.40	.30	.15
	Panel (Kansas City Royals)	2.50	2.00	1.00
20a	George Brett	.80	.60	.30
20b	Bret Saberhagen	.20	.15	.08
20c	Willie Wilson	.15	.11	.06
	Panel (Milwaukee Brewers)	3.50	2.75	1.50
21a	Cecil Cooper	.15	.11	.06
21b	Paul Molitor	.40	.30	.15
21c	Robin Yount	.75	.60	.30
	Panel (Minnesota Twins)	2.50	2.00	1.00
22a	Tom Brunansky	.20	.15	.08
22b	Kent Hrbek	.30	.25	.12
22c	Kirby Puckett	.60	.45	.25
	Panel (New York Yankees)	6.00	4.50	2.50
23a	Rickey Henderson	.75	.60	.30
23b	Don Mattingly	1.00	.70	.40
23c	Dave Winfield	.75	.60	.30
	Panel (Oakland A's)	3.00	2.25	1.25
24a	Jose Canseco	1.25	.90	.50
24b	Alfredo Griffin	.10	.08	.04
24c	Carney Lansford	.10	.08	.04
	Panel 25 (Seattle Mariners)	1.50	1.25	.60
25a	Phil Bradley	.15	.11	.06
25b	Alvin Davis	.15	.11	.06
25c	Mark Langston	.25	.20	.10
	Panel (Texas Rangers)	1.50	1.25	.60
26a	Pete Incaviglia	.20	.15	.08
26b	Pete O'Brien	.10	.08	.04
26c	Larry Parrish	.10	.08	.04
	Panel (Toronto Blue Jays)	2.00	1.50	.80
27a	Jesse Barfield	.20	.15	.08
27b	George Bell	.30	.25	.12
27c	Tony Fernandez	.20	.15	.08
	Panel (Toronto Blue Jays)	.80	.60	.30
28a	Lloyd Moseby	.10	.08	.04
28b	Dave Stieb	.15	.11	.06
28c	Ernie Whitt	.10	.08	.04

A card number in parentheses () indicates the set is unnumbered.

1991 Studio Preview

Each 1991 Donruss set packaged for the retail trade included a pack of four cards previewing the debut Studio set. The cards are in the same format as the regular set, 2-1/2" x 3-1/2" with evocative black-and-white photos bordered in maroon on front, and a biographical write-up on the back.

		MT	NR MT	EX
Complete Set (18):		24.00	18.00	9.50
Common Card:		1.00	.70	.40
1	Juan Bell	1.00	.70	.40
2	Roger Clemens	4.00	3.00	1.50
3	Dave Parker	2.00	1.50	.80
4	Tim Raines	1.50	1.25	.60
5	Kevin Seitzer	1.00	.70	.40
6	Teddy Higuera	1.00	.70	.40
7	Bernie Williams	1.50	1.25	.60
8	Harold Baines	1.20	.90	.50
9	Gary Pettis	1.00	.70	.40
10	Dave Justice	4.00	3.00	1.50
11	Eric Davis	1.50	1.25	.60
12	Andujar Cedeno	1.50	1.25	.60
13	Tom Foley	1.00	.70	.40
14	Dwight Gooden	2.00	1.50	.80
15	Doug Drabek	1.20	.90	.50
16	Steve Decker	1.00	.70	.40
17	Joe Torre	1.00	.70	.40
18	Header card	1.00	.70	.40

1991 Studio

Donruss introduced this 264-card set in 1991. The cards feature maroon borders surrounding black and white posed player photos. The card backs are printed in black and white and feature personal data, career highlights, hobbies and interests and the player's hero. The cards were released in foil packs only and feature a special Rod Carew puzzle.

		MT	NR MT	EX
Complete Set (264):		20.00	15.00	8.00
Common Player:		.12	.09	.05
1	Glenn Davis	.15	.11	.06
2	Dwight Evans	.15	.11	.06
3	Leo Gomez	.40	.30	.15
4	Chris Hoiles	.25	.20	.10
5	Sam Horn	.12	.09	.05
6	Ben McDonald	.20	.15	.08
7	Randy Milligan	.12	.09	.05
8	Gregg Olson	.15	.11	.06
9	Cal Ripken, Jr.	.80	.60	.30
10	David Segui	.20	.15	.08
11	Wade Boggs	.30	.25	.12
12	Ellis Burks	.25	.20	.10
13	Jack Clark	.12	.09	.05
14	Roger Clemens	.75	.60	.30
15	Mike Greenwell	.20	.15	.08
16	Tim Naehring	.15	.11	.06
17	Tony Pena	.12	.09	.05
18	*Phil Plantier*	.75	.60	.30
19	Jeff Reardon	.15	.11	.06
20	Mo Vaughn	1.00	.75	.40
21	Jimmy Reese	.15	.11	.06
22	Jim Abbott	.30	.25	.12
23	Bert Blyleven	.15	.11	.06
24	Chuck Finley	.20	.15	.08
25	Gary Gaetti	.12	.09	.05
26	Wally Joyner	.30	.25	.12
27	Mark Langston	.25	.20	.10
28	Kirk McCaskill	.12	.09	.05
29	Lance Parrish	.15	.11	.06
30	Dave Winfield	.25	.20	.10
31	Alex Fernandez	.30	.25	.12
32	Carlton Fisk	.15	.11	.06
33	Scott Fletcher	.12	.09	.05
34	Greg Hibbard	.12	.09	.05
35	Charlie Hough	.12	.09	.05
36	Jack McDowell	.25	.20	.10
37	Tim Raines	.25	.20	.10
38	Sammy Sosa	.60	.45	.25
39	Bobby Thigpen	.25	.20	.10
40	Frank Thomas	5.00	3.75	2.00
41	Sandy Alomar	.30	.25	.12
42	John Farrell	.12	.09	.05
43	Glenallen Hill	.15	.11	.06
44	Brook Jacoby	.12	.09	.05
45	Chris James	.12	.09	.05
46	Doug Jones	.12	.09	.05
47	Eric King	.12	.09	.05
48	Mark Lewis	.15	.11	.06
49	Greg Swindell	.15	.11	.06
50	Mark Whiten	.50	.40	.20
51	Milt Cuyler	.15	.11	.06
52	Rob Deer	.12	.09	.05
53	Cecil Fielder	.35	.25	.14
54	Travis Fryman	1.25	.90	.50
55	Bill Gullickson	.12	.09	.05
56	Lloyd Moseby	.12	.09	.05
57	Frank Tanana	.12	.09	.05
58	Mickey Tettleton	.20	.15	.08
59	Alan Trammell	.25	.20	.10
60	Lou Whitaker	.20	.15	.08
61	Mike Boddicker	.12	.09	.05
62	George Brett	.40	.30	.15
63	Jeff Conine	1.00	.75	.40
64	Warren Cromartie	.12	.09	.05
65	Storm Davis	.12	.09	.05
66	Kirk Gibson	.20	.15	.08
67	Mark Gubicza	.15	.11	.06
68	Brian McRae	.40	.30	.15
69	Bret Saberhagen	.15	.11	.06
70	Kurt Stillwell	.12	.09	.05
71	Tim McIntosh	.15	.11	.06
72	Candy Maldonado	.12	.09	.05
73	Paul Molitor	.50	.40	.20
74	Willie Randolph	.12	.09	.05
75	Ron Robinson	.12	.09	.05
76	Gary Sheffield	.30	.25	.12
77	Franklin Stubbs	.12	.09	.05
78	B.J. Surhoff	.12	.09	.05
79	Greg Vaughn	.20	.15	.08

80	Robin Yount	.35	.25	.14
81	Rick Aguilera	.12	.09	.05
82	Steve Bedrosian	.12	.09	.05
83	Scott Erickson	.15	.11	.06
84	Greg Gagne	.12	.09	.05
85	Dan Gladden	.12	.09	.05
86	Brian Harper	.15	.11	.06
87	Kent Hrbek	.15	.11	.06
88	Shane Mack	.25	.20	.10
89	Jack Morris	.20	.15	.08
90	Kirby Puckett	.30	.25	.12
91	Jesse Barfield	.12	.09	.05
92	Steve Farr	.12	.09	.05
93	Steve Howe	.12	.09	.05
94	Roberto Kelly	.20	.15	.08
95	Tim Leary	.12	.09	.05
96	Kevin Maas	.15	.11	.06
97	Don Mattingly	.50	.40	.20
98	Hensley Meulens	.20	.15	.08
99	Scott Sanderson	.12	.09	.05
100	Steve Sax	.15	.11	.06
101	Jose Canseco	.50	.40	.20
102	Dennis Eckersley	.15	.11	.06
103	Dave Henderson	.15	.11	.06
104	Rickey Henderson	.30	.25	.12
105	Rick Honeycutt	.12	.09	.05
106	Mark McGwire	.30	.25	.12
107	Dave Stewart	.20	.15	.08
108	Eric Show	.12	.09	.05
109	*Todd Van Poppel*	.35	.25	.14
110	Bob Welch	.15	.11	.06
111	Alvin Davis	.12	.09	.05
112	Ken Griffey, Jr.	4.00	3.00	1.50
113	Ken Griffey, Sr.	.12	.09	.05
114	Erik Hanson	.15	.11	.06
115	Brian Holman	.12	.09	.05
116	Randy Johnson	.25	.20	.10
117	Edgar Martinez	.15	.11	.06
118	Tino Martinez	.15	.11	.06
119	Harold Reynolds	.15	.11	.06
120	David Valle	.12	.09	.05
121	Kevin Belcher	.12	.09	.05
122	Scott Chiamparino	.12	.09	.05
123	Julio Franco	.20	.15	.08
124	Juan Gonzalez	2.50	2.00	1.00
125	Rich Gossage	.15	.11	.06
126	Jeff Kunkel	.12	.09	.05
127	Rafael Palmeiro	.25	.20	.10
128	Nolan Ryan	1.25	.90	.50
129	Ruben Sierra	.15	.11	.06
130	Bobby Witt	.15	.11	.06
131	Roberto Alomar	.60	.45	.25
132	Tom Candiotti	.12	.09	.05
133	Joe Carter	.20	.15	.08
134	Ken Dayley	.12	.09	.05
135	Kelly Gruber	.15	.11	.06
136	John Olerud	1.00	.75	.40
137	Dave Stieb	.15	.11	.06
138	Turner Ward	.15	.11	.06
139	Devon White	.15	.11	.06
140	Mookie Wilson	.12	.09	.05
141	Steve Avery	.25	.20	.10
142	Sid Bream	.12	.09	.05
143	Nick Esasky	.12	.09	.05
144	Ron Gant	.20	.15	.08
145	Tom Glavine	.20	.15	.08
146	Dave Justice	1.00	.75	.40
147	Kelly Mann	.12	.09	.05
148	Terry Pendleton	.15	.11	.06
149	John Smoltz	.20	.15	.08
150	Jeff Treadway	.12	.09	.05
151	George Bell	.20	.15	.08
152	Shawn Boskie	.12	.09	.05
153	Andre Dawson	.20	.15	.08
154	Lance Dickson	.12	.09	.05
155	Shawon Dunston	.12	.09	.05
156	Joe Girardi	.12	.09	.05
157	Mark Grace	.25	.20	.10
158	Ryne Sandberg	.80	.60	.30
159	Gary Scott	.15	.11	.06
160	Dave Smith	.12	.09	.05
161	Tom Browning	.15	.11	.06
162	Eric Davis	.30	.25	.12
163	Rob Dibble	.20	.15	.08
164	Mariano Duncan	.12	.09	.05
165	Chris Hammond	.12	.09	.05
166	Billy Hatcher	.12	.09	.05
167	Barry Larkin	.20	.15	.08
168	Hal Morris	.15	.11	.06
169	Paul O'Neill	.15	.11	.06
170	Chris Sabo	.15	.11	.06
171	Eric Anthony	.15	.11	.06
172	*Jeff Bagwell*	3.00	2.25	1.25
173	Craig Biggio	.20	.15	.08
174	Ken Caminitti	.15	.11	.06
175	Jim Deshaies	.12	.09	.05
176	Steve Finley	.15	.11	.06
177	Pete Harnisch	.15	.11	.06
178	Darryl Kile	.20	.15	.08
179	Curt Schilling	.12	.09	.05
180	Mike Scott	.12	.09	.05
181	Brett Butler	.15	.11	.06
182	Gary Carter	.15	.11	.06
183	Orel Hershiser	.20	.15	.08
184	Ramon Martinez	.15	.11	.06
185	Eddie Murray	.30	.25	.12
186	Jose Offerman	.15	.11	.06
187	Bob Ojeda	.12	.09	.05
188	Juan Samuel	.12	.09	.05
189	Mike Scioscia	.12	.09	.05
190	Darryl Strawberry	.20	.15	.08
191	Moises Alou	.75	.60	.30
192	Brian Barnes	.12	.09	.05
193	Oil Can Boyd	.12	.09	.05
194	Ivan Calderon	.12	.09	.05
195	Delino DeShields	.20	.15	.08
196	Mike Fitzgerald	.12	.09	.05
197	Andres Galarraga	.15	.11	.06
198	Marquis Grissom	.20	.15	.08
199	Bill Sampen	.12	.09	.05
200	Tim Wallach	.12	.09	.05
201	Daryl Boston	.12	.09	.05
202	Vince Coleman	.15	.11	.06
203	John Franco	.15	.11	.06
204	Dwight Gooden	.30	.25	.12
205	Tom Herr	.12	.09	.05
206	Gregg Jefferies	.25	.20	.10
207	Howard Johnson	.20	.15	.08
208	Dave Magadan	.20	.15	.08
209	Kevin McReynolds	.15	.11	.06
210	Frank Viola	.15	.11	.06
211	Wes Chamberlain	.30	.25	.12
212	Darren Daulton	.12	.09	.05
213	Len Dykstra	.20	.15	.08
214	Charlie Hayes	.15	.11	.06
215	Ricky Jordan	.15	.11	.06
216	Steve Lake	.12	.09	.05
217	Roger McDowell	.12	.09	.05
218	Mickey Morandini	.15	.11	.06
219	Terry Mulholland	.15	.11	.06
220	Dale Murphy	.20	.15	.08
221	Jay Bell	.15	.11	.06
222	Barry Bonds	1.00	.75	.40
223	Bobby Bonilla	.20	.15	.08
224	Doug Drabek	.15	.11	.06
225	Bill Landrum	.12	.09	.05
226	Mike LaValliere	.12	.09	.05
227	Jose Lind	.12	.09	.05
228	Don Slaught	.12	.09	.05
229	John Smiley	.15	.11	.06
230	Andy Van Slyke	.15	.11	.06
231	Bernard Gilkey	.30	.25	.12
232	Pedro Guerrero	.20	.15	.08
233	Rex Hudler	.12	.09	.05
234	Ray Lankford	.35	.25	.14
235	Joe Magrane	.12	.09	.05
236	Jose Oquendo	.12	.09	.05
237	Lee Smith	.15	.11	.06
238	Ozzie Smith	.25	.20	.10
239	Milt Thompson	.12	.09	.05
240	Todd Zeile	.15	.11	.06
241	Larry Andersen	.12	.09	.05
242	Andy Benes	.15	.11	.06
243	Paul Faries	.12	.09	.05
244	Tony Fernandez	.12	.09	.05
245	Tony Gwynn	.20	.15	.08
246	Atlee Hammaker	.12	.09	.05
247	Fred McGriff	.20	.15	.08
248	Bip Roberts	.12	.09	.05
249	Benito Santiago	.15	.11	.06
250	Ed Whitson	.12	.09	.05
251	Dave Anderson	.12	.09	.05
252	Mike Benjamin	.15	.11	.06
253	John Burkett	.15	.11	.06
254	Will Clark	.40	.30	.15
255	Scott Garrelts	.12	.09	.05
256	Willie McGee	.15	.11	.06
257	Kevin Mitchell	.15	.11	.06
258	Dave Righetti	.15	.11	.06
259	Matt Williams	.30	.25	.12
260	Black & Decker	.20	.15	.08
261	Checklist	.10	.08	.04
262	Checklist	.10	.08	.04
263	Checklist	.10	.08	.04
264	Checklist	.10	.08	.04

1992 Studio Preview

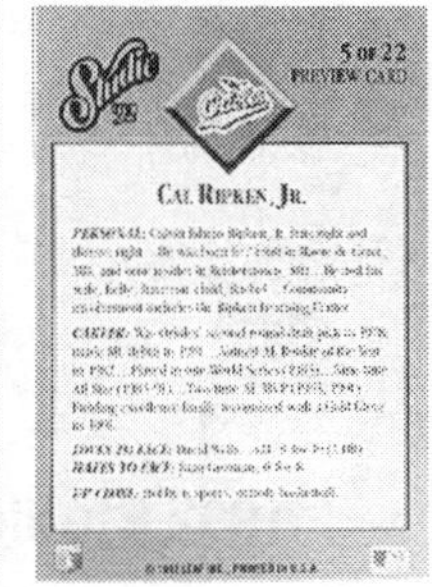

To introduce its 1992 Studio brand, Leaf included four-card packs of preview cards in its retail factory sets of 1992 Donruss. Twenty-two preview cards were produced in format virtually identical to the issued versions of the same cards. The only differences are the appearance of the word "PREVIEW" in the lower-right corner of the card front, in place of the player's position, and the number "X of 22 / Preview Card" on the back where regular cards have the card number in the upper-right corner.

		MT	NR MT	EX
Complete Set (22):		80.00		
Common Player:		2.00	1.50	.80
1	Ruben Sierra	2.50	2.00	1.00
2	Kirby Puckett	4.00	3.00	1.50
3	Ryne Sandberg	6.00	4.50	2.50
4	John Kruk	2.50	2.00	1.00
5	Cal Ripken, Jr.	6.00	4.50	2.50
6	Robin Yount	5.00	3.75	2.00
7	Dwight Gooden	2.50	2.00	1.00
8	David Justice	4.00	3.00	1.50
9	Don Mattingly	4.00	3.00	1.50
10	Wally Joyner	2.50	2.00	1.00
11	Will Clark	4.00	3.00	1.50
12	Rob Dibble	2.00	1.50	.80
13	Roberto Alomar	4.00	3.00	1.50
14	Wade Boggs	3.00	2.25	1.25
15	Barry Bonds	5.00	3.75	2.00
16	Jeff Bagwell	2.50	2.00	1.00
17	Mark McGwire	3.00	2.25	1.25
18	Frank Thomas	9.00	6.75	3.50
19	Brett Butler	2.00	1.50	.80
20	Ozzie Smith	4.00	3.00	1.50
21	Jim Abbott	3.00	2.25	1.25
22	Tony Gwynn	2.50	2.00	1.00

1992 Studio

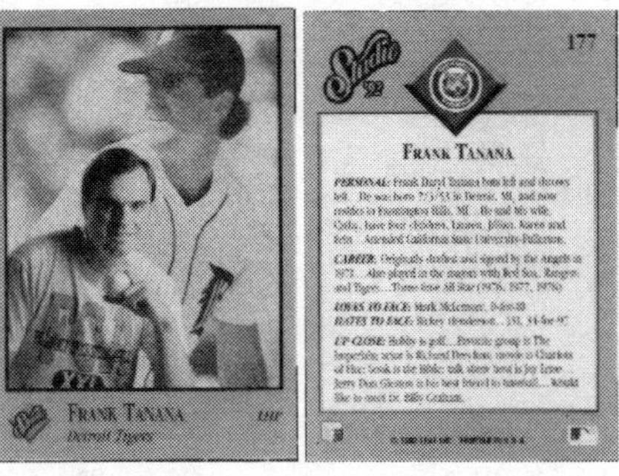

Donruss introduced the Studio line in 1991 and released another 264-card set entitled Leaf Studio for 1992. The cards feature a color player closeup with a large black and white photo behind the player. Tan borders surround the photos. The cards were only released in foil packs. Special Heritage insert cards featuring top players could be found in foil packs. Eight Heritage cards were released.

		MT	NR MT	EX
Complete Set (264):		15.00	15.00	8.00
Common Player:		.10	.08	.04
1	Steve Avery	.25	.20	.10
2	Sid Bream	.10	.08	.04
3	Ron Gant	.15	.11	.06
4	Tom Glavine	.20	.15	.08
5	Dave Justice	.25	.20	.10
6	Mark Lemke	.10	.08	.04
7	Greg Olson	.10	.08	.04
8	Terry Pendleton	.15	.11	.06
9	Deion Sanders	.30	.25	.12
10	John Smoltz	.15	.11	.06
11	Doug Dascenzo	.10	.08	.04
12	Andre Dawson	.20	.15	.08
13	Joe Girardi	.10	.08	.04
14	Mark Grace	.15	.11	.06
15	Greg Maddux	.25	.20	.10
16	Chuck McElroy	.10	.08	.04
17	Mike Morgan	.10	.08	.04
18	Ryne Sandberg	.50	.40	.20
19	Gary Scott	.10	.08	.04
20	Sammy Sosa	.25	.20	.10
21	Norm Charlton	.12	.09	.05
22	Rob Dibble	.15	.11	.06
23	Barry Larkin	.25	.20	.10
24	Hal Morris	.10	.08	.04
25	Paul O'Neill	.15	.11	.06
26	Jose Rijo	.12	.09	.05
27	Bip Roberts	.15	.11	.06
28	Chris Sabo	.15	.11	.06
29	Reggie Sanders	.20	.15	.08
30	Greg Swindell	.15	.11	.06
31	Jeff Bagwell	.30	.25	.12
32	Craig Biggio	.15	.11	.06
33	Ken Caminiti	.10	.08	.04
34	Andujar Cedeno	.15	.11	.06
35	Steve Finley	.15	.11	.06
36	Pete Harnisch	.12	.09	.05
37	Butch Henry	.10	.08	.04
38	Doug Jones	.10	.08	.04
39	Darryl Kile	.15	.11	.06
40	Eddie Taubensee	.10	.08	.04
41	Brett Butler	.12	.09	.05
42	Tom Candiotti	.10	.08	.04
43	Eric Davis	.15	.11	.06
44	Orel Hershiser	.15	.11	.06
45	Eric Karros	.25	.20	.10
46	Ramon Martinez	.15	.11	.06
47	Jose Offerman	.15	.11	.06
48	Mike Scioscia	.10	.08	.04
49	Mike Sharperson	.10	.08	.04
50	Darryl Strawberry	.15	.11	.06
51	Bret Barbarie	.15	.11	.06
52	Ivan Calderon	.10	.08	.04
53	Gary Carter	.15	.11	.06
54	Delino DeShields	.15	.11	.06
55	Marquis Grissom	.20	.15	.08
56	Ken Hill	.10	.08	.04
57	Dennis Martinez	.12	.09	.05
58	Spike Owen	.10	.08	.04
59	Larry Walker	.15	.11	.06
60	Tim Wallach	.12	.09	.05
61	Bobby Bonilla	.15	.11	.06
62	Tim Burke	.10	.08	.04
63	Vince Coleman	.15	.11	.06

64	John Franco	.10	.08	.04
65	Dwight Gooden	.25	.20	.10
66	Todd Hundley	.10	.08	.04
67	Howard Johnson	.15	.11	.06
68	Eddie Murray	.15	.11	.06
69	Bret Saberhagen	.15	.11	.06
70	Anthony Young	.10	.08	.04
71	Kim Batiste	.10	.08	.04
72	Wes Chamberlain	.10	.08	.04
73	Darren Daulton	.15	.11	.06
74	Mariano Duncan	.10	.08	.04
75	Len Dykstra	.15	.11	.06
76	John Kruk	.15	.11	.06
77	Mickey Morandini	.15	.11	.06
78	Terry Mulholland	.10	.08	.04
79	Dale Murphy	.20	.15	.08
80	Mitch Williams	.15	.11	.06
81	Jay Bell	.15	.11	.06
82	Barry Bonds	.60	.45	.25
83	Steve Buechele	.10	.08	.04
84	Doug Drabek	.15	.11	.06
85	Mike LaValliere	.10	.08	.04
86	Jose Lind	.10	.08	.04
87	Denny Neagle	.10	.08	.04
88	Randy Tomlin	.10	.08	.04
89	Andy Van Slyke	.10	.08	.04
90	Gary Varsho	.10	.08	.04
91	Pedro Guererro	.10	.08	.04
92	Rex Hudler	.10	.08	.04
93	Brian Jordan	.25	.20	.10
94	Felix Jose	.12	.09	.05
95	Donovan Osborne	.20	.15	.08
96	Tom Pagnozzi	.10	.08	.04
97	Lee Smith	.15	.11	.06
98	Ozzie Smith	.25	.20	.10
99	Todd Worrell	.10	.08	.04
100	Todd Zeile	.15	.11	.06
101	Andy Benes	.15	.11	.06
102	Jerald Clark	.10	.08	.04
103	Tony Fernandez	.10	.08	.04
104	Tony Gwynn	.20	.15	.08
105	Greg Harris	.10	.08	.04
106	Fred McGriff	.25	.20	.10
107	Benito Santiago	.15	.11	.06
108	Gary Sheffield	.30	.25	.12
109	Kurt Stillwell	.10	.08	.04
110	Tim Teufel	.10	.08	.04
111	Kevin Bass	.10	.08	.04
112	Jeff Brantley	.10	.08	.04
113	John Burkett	.10	.08	.04
114	Will Clark	.30	.25	.12
115	Royce Clayton	.15	.11	.06
116	Mike Jackson	.10	.08	.04
117	Darren Lewis	.12	.09	.05
118	Bill Swift	.10	.08	.04
119	Robby Thompson	.10	.08	.04
120	Matt Williams	.15	.11	.06
121	Brady Anderson	.20	.15	.08
122	Glenn Davis	.10	.08	.04
123	Mike Devereaux	.10	.08	.04
124	Chris Hoiles	.15	.11	.06
125	Sam Horn	.10	.08	.04
126	Ben McDonald	.15	.11	.06
127	Mike Mussina	.30	.25	.12
128	Gregg Olson	.15	.11	.06
129	Cal Ripken, Jr.	.50	.40	.20
130	Rick Sutcliffe	.15	.11	.06
131	Wade Boggs	.30	.25	.12
132	Roger Clemens	.40	.30	.15
133	Greg Harris	.10	.08	.04
134	Tim Naehring	.10	.08	.04
135	Tony Pena	.10	.08	.04
136	Phil Plantier	.15	.11	.06
137	Jeff Reardon	.15	.11	.06
138	Jody Reed	.10	.08	.04
139	Mo Vaughn	.35	.25	.14
140	Frank Viola	.20	.15	.08
141	Jim Abbott	.20	.15	.08
142	Hubie Brooks	.10	.08	.04
143	Chad Curtis	.60	.45	.25
144	Gary DiSarcina	.10	.08	.04
145	Chuck Finley	.15	.11	.06
146	Bryan Harvey	.15	.11	.06
147	Von Hayes	.10	.08	.04
148	Mark Langston	.15	.11	.06
149	Lance Parrish	.10	.08	.04
150	Lee Stevens	.10	.08	.04
151	George Bell	.15	.11	.06
152	Alex Fernandez	.15	.11	.06
153	Greg Hibbard	.10	.08	.04
154	Lance Johnson	.10	.08	.04
155	Kirk McCaskill	.10	.08	.04
156	Tim Raines	.15	.11	.06
157	Steve Sax	.10	.08	.04
158	Bobby Thigpen	.10	.08	.04
159	Frank Thomas	3.00	2.25	1.25
160	Robin Ventura	.25	.20	.10
161	Sandy Alomar, Jr.	.15	.11	.06
162	Jack Armstrong	.10	.08	.04
163	Carlos Baerga	.50	.40	.20
164	Albert Belle	.60	.45	.25
165	Alex Cole	.10	.08	.04
166	Glenallen Hill	.10	.08	.04
167	Mark Lewis	.15	.11	.06
168	Kenny Lofton	.30	.25	.12
169	Paul Sorrento	.10	.08	.04
170	Mark Whiten	.15	.11	.06
171	Milt Cuyler (color photo actually Lou Whitaker)	.10	.08	.04
172	Rob Deer	.10	.08	.04
173	Cecil Fielder	.30	.25	.12
174	Travis Fryman	.30	.25	.12
175	Mike Henneman	.10	.08	.04
176	Tony Phillips	.10	.08	.04
177	Frank Tanana	.10	.08	.04
178	Mickey Tettleton	.15	.11	.06
179	Alan Trammell	.20	.15	.08
180	Lou Whitaker	.15	.11	.06
181	George Brett	.50	.40	.20
182	Tom Gordon	.10	.08	.04
183	Mark Gubicza	.10	.08	.04
184	Gregg Jefferies	.20	.15	.08
185	Wally Joyner	.20	.15	.08
186	Brent Mayne	.10	.08	.04
187	Brian McRae	.15	.11	.06
188	Kevin McReynolds	.15	.11	.06
189	Keith Miller	.10	.08	.04
190	Jeff Montgomery	.10	.08	.04
191	Dante Bichette	.10	.08	.04
192	Ricky Bones	.10	.08	.04
193	Scott Fletcher	.10	.08	.04
194	Paul Molitor	.30	.25	.12
195	Jaime Navarro	.15	.11	.06
196	Franklin Stubbs	.10	.08	.04
197	B.J. Surhoff	.10	.08	.04
198	Greg Vaughn	.10	.08	.04
199	Bill Wegman	.10	.08	.04
200	Robin Yount	.50	.40	.20
201	Rick Aguilera	.10	.08	.04
202	Scott Erickson	.15	.11	.06
203	Greg Gagne	.10	.08	.04
204	Brian Harper	.10	.08	.04
205	Kent Hrbek	.15	.11	.06
206	Scott Leius	.10	.08	.04
207	Shane Mack	.15	.11	.06
208	Pat Mahomes	.10	.08	.04
209	Kirby Puckett	.50	.40	.20
210	John Smiley	.10	.08	.04
211	Mike Gallego	.10	.08	.04
212	Charlie Hayes	.10	.08	.04
213	Pat Kelly	.12	.09	.05
214	Roberto Kelly	.15	.11	.06
215	Kevin Maas	.10	.08	.04
216	Don Mattingly	.30	.25	.12
217	Matt Nokes	.10	.08	.04
218	Melido Perez	.10	.08	.04
219	Scott Sanderson	.10	.08	.04
220	Danny Tartabull	.15	.11	.06
221	Harold Baines	.15	.11	.06
222	Jose Canseco	.35	.25	.14
223	Dennis Eckersley	.20	.15	.08
224	Dave Henderson	.10	.08	.04
225	Carney Lansford	.10	.08	.04
226	Mark McGwire	.30	.25	.12
227	Mike Moore	.10	.08	.04
228	Randy Ready	.10	.08	.04
229	Terry Steinbach	.10	.08	.04
230	Dave Stewart	.15	.11	.06
231	Jay Buhner	.10	.08	.04
232	Ken Griffey, Jr.	2.50	2.00	1.00
233	Erik Hanson	.10	.08	.04
234	Randy Johnson	.15	.11	.06
235	Edgar Martinez	.15	.11	.06
236	Tino Martinez	.10	.08	.04
237	Kevin Mitchell	.15	.11	.06
238	Pete O'Brien	.10	.08	.04
239	Harold Reynolds	.15	.11	.06
240	David Valle	.10	.08	.04
241	Julio Franco	.15	.11	.06
242	Juan Gonzalez	1.50	1.25	.60
243	Jose Guzman	.15	.11	.06
244	Rafael Palmeiro	.25	.20	.10
245	Dean Palmer	.20	.15	.08
246	Ivan Rodriguez	.30	.25	.12
247	Jeff Russell	.10	.08	.04
248	Nolan Ryan	1.50	1.25	.60
249	Ruben Sierra	.15	.11	.06
250	Dickie Thon	.10	.08	.04
251	Roberto Alomar	.50	.40	.20
252	Derek Bell	.20	.15	.08
253	Pat Borders	.10	.08	.04
254	Joe Carter	.25	.20	.10
255	Kelly Gruber	.10	.08	.04
256	Juan Guzman	.15	.11	.06
257	Jack Morris	.15	.11	.06
258	John Olerud	.40	.30	.15
259	Devon White	.15	.11	.06
260	Dave Winfield	.30	.25	.12
261	Checklist	.10	.08	.04
262	Checklist	.10	.08	.04
263	Checklist	.10	.08	.04
264	History Card	.10	.08	.04

1992 Studio Heritage

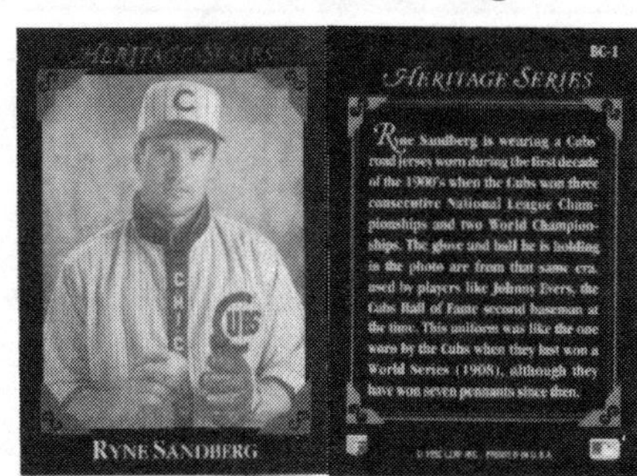

Superstars of 1992 were photographed in vintage-style uniforms in this 14-card insert set found in packages of Studio's 1992 issue. Cards #1-8 could be found in standard foil packs while 9-14 were inserted in Studio jumbos. Cards featured a sepia-tone photo bordered in turquoise and highlighted with copper foil. Cards carry a BC prefix to the card number on back.

		MT	NR MT	EX
Complete Set (14):		20.00	15.00	8.00
Common Player:		1.00	.70	.40
1	Ryne Sandberg	3.00	2.25	1.25
2	Carlton Fisk	1.00	.70	.40
3	Wade Boggs	1.00	.70	.40
4	Jose Canseco	1.50	1.25	.60
5	Don Mattingly	3.00	2.25	1.25
6	Darryl Strawberry	1.00	.70	.40
7	Cal Ripken, Jr.	3.00	2.25	1.25
8	Will Clark	2.00	1.50	.80
9	Andre Dawson	1.00	.70	.40
10	Andy Van Slyke	1.00	.70	.40
11	Paul Molitor	2.00	1.50	.80
12	Jeff Bagwell	1.00	.70	.40
13	Darren Daulton	1.00	.70	.40
14	Kirby Puckett	1.50	1.25	.60

1993 Studio

This 220-card set features full-bleed photos. The player's portrait appears against one of several backgrounds featuring his team's uniform. His signature and the Studio logo are also stamped on in gold foild. Backs have a partial portrait of the player and insights into his personality.

		MT	NR MT	EX
Complete Set (220):		24.00	18.00	9.50
Common Player:		.10	.08	.04
1	Dennis Eckersley	.10	.08	.04
2	Chad Curtis	.40	.30	.15
3	Eric Anthony	.10	.08	.04
4	Roberto Alomar	.60	.45	.25
5	Steve Avery	.50	.40	.20
6	Cal Eldred	.15	.11	.06
7	Bernard Gilkey	.10	.08	.04
8	Steve Buechele	.08	.06	.03
9	Brett Butler	.08	.06	.03
10	Terry Mulholland	.08	.06	.03
11	Moises Alou	.15	.11	.06
12	Barry Bonds	1.00	.70	.40
13	Sandy Alomar Jr.	.08	.06	.03
14	Chris Bosio	.08	.06	.03
15	Scott Sanderson	.08	.06	.03
16	Bobby Bonilla	.15	.11	.06
17	Brady Anderson	.10	.08	.04
18	Derek Bell	.15	.11	.06
19	Wes Chamberlain	.08	.06	.03
20	Jay Bell	.08	.06	.03
21	Kevin Brown	.08	.06	.03
22	Roger Clemens	.40	.30	.15
23	Roberto Kelly	.10	.08	.04
24	Dante Bichette	.10	.08	.04
25	George Brett	.40	.30	.15
26	Rob Deer	.08	.06	.03
27	Brian Harper	.10	.08	.04
28	George Bell	.10	.08	.04
29	Jim Abbott	.12	.09	.05
30	Dave Henderson	.08	.06	.03
31	Wade Boggs	.20	.15	.08
32	Chili Davis	.08	.06	.03
33	Ellis Burks	.08	.06	.03
34	Jeff Bagwell	.40	.30	.15
35	Kent Hrbek	.08	.06	.03
36	Pat Borders	.08	.06	.03
37	Cecil Fielder	.30	.25	.12
38	Sid Bream	.08	.06	.03
39	Greg Gagne	.08	.06	.03
40	Darryl Hamilton	.10	.08	.04
41	Jerald Clark	.08	.06	.03
42	Mark Grace	.15	.11	.06
43	Barry Larkin	.20	.15	.08
44	John Burkett	.08	.06	.03
45	Scott Cooper	.08	.06	.03
46	*Mike Lansing*	.50	.40	.20
47	Jose Canseco	.35	.25	.14
48	Will Clark	.40	.30	.15
49	Carlos Garcia	.15	.11	.06
50	Carlos Baerga	.70	.50	.30
51	Darren Daulton	.30	.25	.12
52	Jay Buhner	.10	.08	.04
53	Andy Benes	.10	.08	.04
54	Jeff Conine	.08	.06	.03
55	Mike Devereaux	.08	.06	.03
56	Vince Coleman	.08	.06	.03
57	Terry Steinbach	.08	.06	.03

58	*J.T. Snow*	.60	.45	.25
59	Greg Swindell	.08	.06	.03
60	Devon White	.10	.08	.04
61	John Smoltz	.15	.11	.06
62	Todd Zeile	.10	.08	.04
63	Rick Wilkins	.10	.08	.04
64	Tim Wallach	.08	.06	.03
65	John Wetteland	.08	.06	.03
66	Matt Williams	.40	.30	.15
67	Paul Sorrento	.10	.08	.04
68	David Valle	.08	.06	.03
69	Walt Weiss	.08	.06	.03
70	John Franco	.08	.06	.03
71	Nolan Ryan	2.00	1.50	.80
72	Frank Viola	.08	.06	.03
73	Chris Sabo	.08	.06	.03
74	David Nied	.75	.60	.30
75	Kevin McReynolds	.08	.06	.03
76	Lou Whitaker	.10	.08	.04
77	Dave Winfield	.40	.30	.15
78	Robin Ventura	.50	.40	.20
79	Spike Owen	.08	.06	.03
80	Cal Ripken, Jr.	.80	.60	.30
81	Dan Walter	.08	.06	.03
82	Mitch Williams	.10	.08	.04
83	Tim Wakefield	.15	.11	.06
84	Rickey Henderson	.20	.15	.08
85	Gary DiSarcina	.10	.08	.04
86	Craig Biggio	.10	.08	.04
87	Joe Carter	.30	.25	.12
88	Ron Gant	.15	.11	.06
89	John Jaha	.15	.11	.06
90	Gregg Jefferies	.10	.08	.04
91	Jose Guzman	.10	.08	.04
92	Eric Karros	.25	.20	.10
93	Wil Cordero	.15	.11	.06
94	Royce Clayton	.10	.08	.04
95	Albert Belle	.80	.60	.30
96	Ken Griffey, Jr.	4.00	3.00	1.50
97	Orestes Destrade	.10	.08	.04
98	Tony Fernandez	.08	.06	.03
99	Leo Gomez	.08	.06	.03
100	Tony Gwynn	.20	.15	.08
101	Len Dykstra	.15	.11	.06
102	Jeff King	.10	.08	.04
103	Julio Franco	.08	.06	.03
104	Andre Dawson	.15	.11	.06
105	Randy Milligan	.08	.06	.03
106	Alex Cole	.08	.06	.03
107	Phil Hiatt	.50	.40	.20
108	Travis Fryman	.50	.40	.20
109	Chuck Knoblauch	.12	.09	.05
110	Bo Jackson	.30	.25	.12
111	Pat Kelly	.08	.06	.03
112	Bret Saberhagen	.08	.06	.03
113	Ruben Sierra	.15	.11	.06
114	Tim Salmon	3.00	2.25	1.25
115	Doug Jones	.08	.06	.03
116	Ed Sprague	.08	.06	.03
117	Terry Pendleton	.12	.09	.05
118	Robin Yount	.35	.25	.14
119	Mark Whiten	.10	.08	.04
120	Checklist	.08	.06	.03
121	Sammy Sosa	.12	.09	.05
122	Darryl Strawberry	.12	.09	.05
123	Larry Walker	.30	.25	.12
124	Robby Thompson	.10	.08	.04
125	Carlos Martinez	.08	.06	.03
126	Edgar Martinez	.10	.08	.04
127	Benito Santiago	.10	.08	.04
128	Howard Johnson	.08	.06	.03
129	Harold Reynolds	.08	.06	.03
130	Craig Shipley	.08	.06	.03
131	Curt Schilling	.10	.08	.04
132	Andy Van Slyke	.12	.09	.05
133	Ivan Rodriguez	.40	.30	.15
134	Mo Vaughn	.30	.25	.12
135	Bip Roberts	.08	.06	.03
136	Charlie Hayes	.12	.09	.05
137	Brian McRae	.10	.08	.04
138	Mickey Tettleton	.10	.08	.04
139	Frank Thomas	4.00	3.00	1.50
140	Paul O'Neill	.08	.06	.03
141	Mark McGwire	.25	.20	.10
142	Damion Easley	.25	.20	.10
143	Ken Caminiti	.08	.06	.03
144	Juan Guzman	.30	.25	.12
145	Tom Glavine	.40	.30	.15
146	Pat Listach	.20	.15	.08
147	Lee Smith	.10	.08	.04
148	Derrick May	.10	.08	.04
149	Ramon Martinez	.10	.08	.04
150	Delino DeShields	.15	.11	.06
151	Kirt Manwaring	.08	.06	.03
152	Reggie Jefferson	.08	.06	.03
153	Randy Johnson	.15	.11	.06
154	Dave Magadan	.08	.06	.03
155	Dwight Gooden	.10	.08	.04
156	Chris Hoiles	.10	.08	.04
157	Fred McGriff	.30	.25	.12
158	Dave Hollins	.20	.15	.08
159	Al Martin	.50	.40	.20
160	Juan Gonzalez	2.50	2.00	1.00
161	Mike Greenwell	.08	.06	.03
162	Kevin Mitchell	.10	.08	.04
163	Andres Galarraga	.20	.15	.08
164	Wally Joyner	.08	.06	.03
165	Kirk Gibson	.08	.06	.03
166	Pedro Munoz	.08	.06	.03
167	Ozzie Guillen	.08	.06	.03
168	Jimmy Key	.10	.08	.04
169	Kevin Seitzer	.08	.06	.03
170	Luis Polonia	.08	.06	.03
171	Luis Gonzalez	.10	.08	.04
172	Paul Molitor	.20	.15	.08
173	Dave Justice	.75	.60	.30
174	B.J. Surhoff	.08	.06	.03
175	Ray Lankford	.20	.15	.08
176	Ryne Sandberg	.80	.60	.30
177	Jody Reed	.08	.06	.03
178	Marquis Grissom	.25	.20	.10
179	Willie McGee	.10	.08	.04
180	Kenny Lofton	.80	.60	.30
181	Junior Felix	.08	.06	.03
182	Jose Offerman	.10	.08	.04
183	John Kruk	.20	.15	.08
184	Orlando Merced	.12	.09	.05
185	Rafael Palmeiro	.20	.15	.08
186	Billy Hatcher	.08	.06	.03
187	Joe Oliver	.08	.06	.03
188	Joe Girardi	.08	.06	.03
189	Jose Lind	.08	.06	.03
190	Harold Baines	.10	.08	.04
191	Mike Pagliarulo	.08	.06	.03
192	Lance Johnson	.08	.06	.03
193	Don Mattingly	.30	.25	.12
194	Doug Drabek	.10	.08	.04
195	John Olerud	.40	.30	.15
196	Greg Maddux	.20	.15	.08
197	Greg Vaughn	.12	.09	.05
198	Tom Pagnozzi	.08	.06	.03
199	Willie Wilson	.08	.06	.03
200	Jack McDowell	.25	.20	.10
201	Mike Piazza	5.00	3.75	2.00
202	Mike Mussina	.50	.40	.20
203	Charles Nagy	.08	.06	.03
204	Tino Martinez	.08	.06	.03
205	Charlie Hough	.08	.06	.03
206	Todd Hundley	.08	.06	.03
207	Gary Sheffield	.25	.20	.10
208	Mickey Morandini	.08	.06	.03
209	Don Slaught	.08	.06	.03
210	Dean Palmer	.25	.20	.10
211	Jose Rijo	.10	.08	.04
212	Vinny Castilla	.08	.06	.03
213	Tony Phillips	.08	.06	.03
214	Kirby Puckett	.70	.50	.30
215	Tim Raines	.12	.09	.05
216	Otis Nixon	.10	.08	.04
217	Ozzie Smith	.25	.20	.10
218	Jose Vizcaino	.08	.06	.03
220	Checklist	.08	.06	.03

1993 Studio Heritage

All types of 1993 Leaf Studio packs were candidates for having one of 12 Heritage cards inserted in them. The fronts feature the player posing in an old-time uniform. The picture has a frame and says Heritage Series at the top. The backs have a mug shot surrounded by an ornate frame and tell what year the uniform on the front is from. Team trivia is also included.

		MT	NR MT	EX
Complete Set (12):		20.00	15.00	8.00
Common Player:		1.00	.70	.40
1	George Brett	3.00	2.25	1.25
2	Juan Gonzalez	6.00	4.50	2.50
3	Roger Clemens	2.00	1.50	.80
4	Mark McGwire	1.50	1.25	.60
5	Mark Grace	1.00	.70	.40
6	Ozzie Smith	1.00	.70	.40
7	Barry Larkin	1.00	.70	.40
8	Frank Thomas	6.00	4.50	2.50
9	Carlos Baerga	1.50	1.25	.60
10	Eric Karros	1.00	.70	.40
11	J.T. Snow	1.00	.70	.40
12	John Kruk	1.00	.70	.40

Values for recent cards and sets are listed in Mint (MT), Near Mint (NM), reflecting the fact that many cards from recent years have been preserved in top condition. Recent cards and sets in less than Excellent condition have little collector interest.

1993 Studio Silhouettes

These insert cards were randomly included in jumbo packs only. The card fronts feature a ghosted image of the player against an action silhouette on a

gray background. The player's name is in bronze foil at bottom. Backs have a player action photo and description of a career highlights.

		MT	NR MT	EX
Complete Set (10):		30.00	22.00	12.00
Common Player:		1.00	.70	.40
1	Frank Thomas	6.00	4.50	2.50
2	Barry Bonds	4.00	3.00	1.50
3	Jeff Bagwell	1.50	1.25	.60
4	Juan Gonzalez	5.00	3.75	2.00
5	Travis Fryman	1.00	.70	.40
6	J.T. Snow	1.00	.70	.40
7	John Kruk	1.00	.70	.40
8	Jeff Blauser	1.00	.70	.40
9	Mike Piazza	8.00	6.00	3.25
10	Nolan Ryan	7.00	5.25	2.75

1993 Studio Superstars on Canvas

Ten players are featured on these insert cards, which were availalbe in hobby and retail packs. The cards show player portraits which mix photography and artwork.

		MT	NR MT	EX
Complete Set (10):		20.00	15.00	8.00
Common Player:		1.00	.70	.40
1	Ken Griffey, Jr.	6.00	4.50	2.50
2	Jose Canseco	2.00	1.50	.80
3	Mark McGwire	1.00	.70	.40
4	Mike Mussina	1.00	.70	.40
5	Joe Carter	1.00	.70	.40
6	Frank Thomas	6.00	4.50	2.50
7	Darren Daulton	1.00	.70	.40
8	Mark Grace	1.00	.70	.40
9	Andres Galarraga	1.00	.70	.40
10	Barry Bonds	3.00	2.25	1.25

A player's name in italic type indicates a rookie card. An (FC) indicates a player's first card for that particular card company.

1993 Studio Frank Thomas

This five-card set is devoted to Frank Thomas. Cards were randomly included in all types of 1993 Leaf Studio packs. Topics covered on the cards include Thomas' childhood, his baseball memories, his family, his performance and being a role model.

		MT	NR MT	EX
Complete Set (5):		20.00	15.00	8.00
Common Player:		4.00	3.00	1.50
1	Childhood	4.00	3.00	1.50
2	Baseball Memories	4.00	3.00	1.50
3	Importance of Family	4.00	3.00	1.50
4	Performance	4.00	3.00	1.50
5	On Being a Role Model	4.00	3.00	1.50

1962 Sugardale Weiners

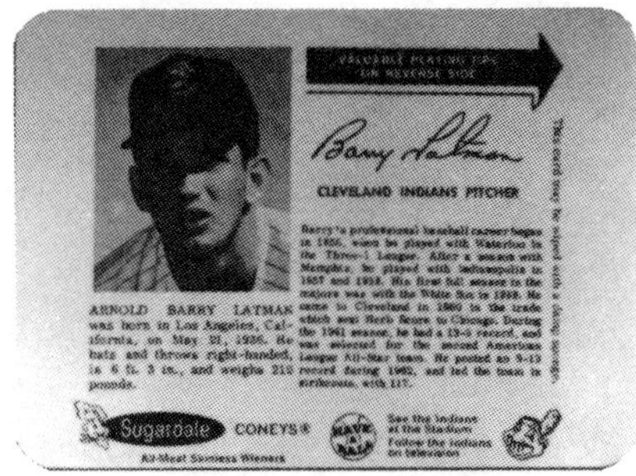

The Sugardale Meats set of black and white cards measure 5-1/8" by 3-3/4". The 22-card set includes 18 Cleveland Indians and four Pittsburgh Pirates players. The Indians cards are numbered from 1-19 with card number 6 not issued. The Pirates cards are lettered from A to D. The card fronts contain a relatively small player photo, with biographical information and Sugardale logo. The backs are printed in red and offer playing tips and another company logo. Card number 10 (Bob Nieman) is considerably more scarce than other cards in the set.

		NR MT	EX	VG
Complete Set:		1900.	950.00	570.00
Common Player:		40.00	20.00	12.00
A	Dick Groat	70.00	35.00	21.00
B	Roberto Clemente	750.00	375.00	225.00
C	Don Hoak	55.00	27.00	16.50
D	Dick Stuart	55.00	27.00	16.50
1	Barry Latman	40.00	20.00	12.00
2	Gary Bell	45.00	22.00	13.50
3	Dick Donovan	40.00	20.00	12.00
4	Frank Funk	40.00	20.00	12.00
5	Jim Perry	60.00	30.00	18.00
6	Not issued			
7	Johnny Romano	40.00	20.00	12.00
8	Ty Cline	40.00	20.00	12.00
9	Tito Francona	45.00	22.00	13.50
10	Bob Nieman	300.00	150.00	90.00
11	Willie Kirkland	40.00	20.00	12.00
12	Woodie Held	45.00	22.00	13.50
13	Jerry Kindall	40.00	20.00	12.00
14	Bubba Phillips	40.00	20.00	12.00
15	Mel Harder	45.00	22.00	13.50
16	Salty Parker	40.00	20.00	12.00
17	Ray Katt	40.00	20.00	12.00
18	Mel McGaha	40.00	20.00	12.00
19	Pedro Ramos	40.00	20.00	12.00

1963 Sugardale Weiners

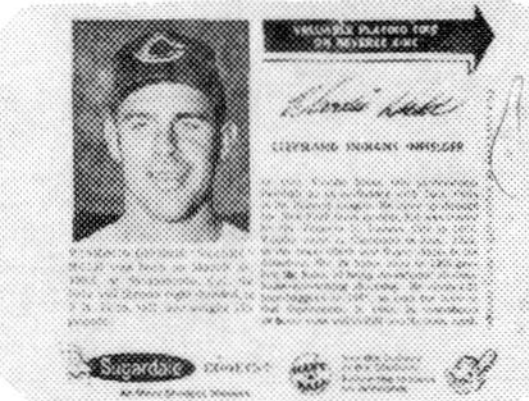

Sugardale Meats again featured Cleveland and Pittsburgh players in its 1963 set, which grew to 31 cards. The black and white cards again measure 5-1/8" by 3-3/4", and consist of 28 Indians and five Pirates players. Card formats are virtually identical to the 1962 cards, with the only real difference being the information included in the player biographies. The cards are numbered 1-38, with numbers 6, 21, 22 and 29-32 not issued. Cards for Bob Skinner (#35) and Jim Perry (#5) are scarce as these two players were traded during the season and their cards withdrawn from distribution. The red card backs again offer playing tips.

		NR MT	EX	VG
Complete Set:		2250.	1125.	675.00
Common Player:		40.00	20.00	12.00
A	Don Cardwell	40.00	20.00	12.00
B	Robert R. Skinner	200.00	100.00	60.00
C	Donald B. Schwall	40.00	20.00	12.00
D	Jim Pagliaroni	40.00	20.00	12.00
E	Dick Schofield	45.00	22.00	13.50
1	Barry Latman	40.00	20.00	12.00
2	Gary Bell	45.00	22.00	13.50
3	Dick Donovan	40.00	20.00	12.00
4	Joe Adcock	60.00	30.00	18.00
5	Jim Perry	175.00	87.00	52.00
6	Not issued			
7	Johnny Romano	40.00	20.00	12.00
8	Mike De La Hoz	40.00	20.00	12.00
9	Tito Francona	45.00	22.00	13.50
10	Gene Green	40.00	20.00	12.00
11	Willie Kirkland	40.00	20.00	12.00
12	Woodie Held	45.00	22.00	13.50
13	Jerry Kindall	40.00	20.00	12.00
14	Max Alvis	45.00	22.00	13.50
15	Mel Harder	45.00	22.00	13.50
16	George Strickland	40.00	20.00	12.00
17	Elmer Valo	40.00	20.00	12.00
18	Birdie Tebbetts	45.00	22.00	13.50
19	Pedro Ramos	40.00	20.00	12.00
20	Al Luplow	40.00	20.00	12.00
21	Not issued			
22	Not issued			
23	Jim Grant	45.00	22.00	13.50
24	Victor Davalillo	45.00	22.00	13.50
25	Jerry Walker	40.00	20.00	12.00
26	Sam McDowell	60.00	30.00	18.00
27	Fred Whitfield	40.00	20.00	12.00
28	Jack Kralick	40.00	20.00	12.00
29	Not issued			
30	Not issued			
31	Not issued			
32	Not issued			
33	Bob Allen	40.00	20.00	12.00

1957 Swift Meats

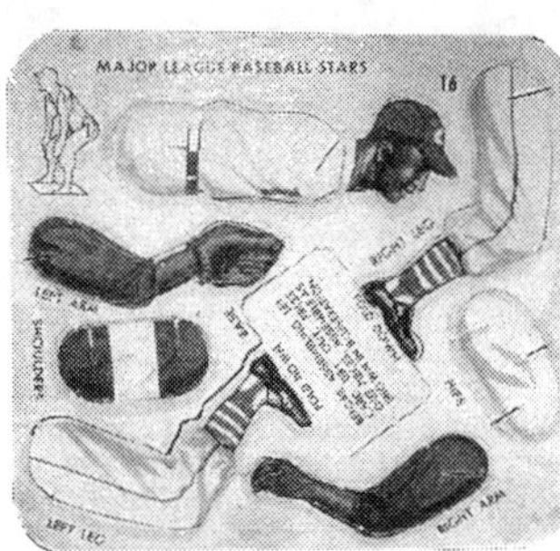

One of the really different baseball card issues of the Fifties was the set of 18 3-D baseball player figures which could be punched out and assembled from cards included in packages of hot dogs. The unpunched cards measure approximately 3-1/2" x 4". Prices below are for unpunched cards. Values for assembled figures are problematical.

		NR MT	EX	VG
Complete Set (18):		2000.	1000.	600.00
Common Player:		75.00	37.00	22.00
1	John Podres	100.00	50.00	30.00
2	Gus Triandos	75.00	37.00	22.00
3	Dale Long	75.00	37.00	22.00
4	Billy Pierce	75.00	37.00	22.00
5	Ed Bailey	75.00	37.00	22.00
6	Vic Wertz	75.00	37.00	22.00
7	Nelson Fox	150.00	75.00	45.00
8	Ken Boyer	100.00	50.00	30.00
9	Gil McDougald	100.00	50.00	30.00
10	Junior Gilliam	100.00	50.00	30.00
11	Eddie Yost	75.00	37.00	22.00
12	Johnny Logan	75.00	37.00	22.00
13	Hank Aaron	300.00	150.00	90.00
14	Bill Tuttle	75.00	37.00	22.00
15	Jackie Jensen	75.00	37.00	22.00
16	Frank Robinson	200.00	100.00	60.00
17	Richie Ashburn	150.00	75.00	45.00
18	Rocky Colavito	100.00	50.00	30.00

Definitions for grading conditions are located in the Introduction of this price guide.

T

1911 Turkey Red (T3)

Turkey Reds are the only cabinet cards the average collector can have a realistic chance to complete. Obtained by mailing in coupons found in Turkey Red, Fez and Old Mill brand cigarettes, the Turkey Reds measure 5-3/4" by 8", a size known to collectors as "cabinet cards." Turkey Reds feature full color lithograph fronts with wide gray frames. Backs carried either a numbered ordering list or an ad for Turkey Red cigarettes. The Turkey Red series consists of 25 boxers and 100 baseball players. Despite their cost, Turkey Reds remain very popular today as the most attractive of the cabinet sets.

		NR MT	EX	VG
Complete (Baseball) Set:		55000.	25000.	15000.
Common Player:		325.00	162.00	97.00
1	Mordecai Brown	1000.	500.00	300.00
2	Bill Bergen	325.00	162.00	97.00
3	Tommy Leach	325.00	162.00	97.00
4	Roger Bresnahan	1200.	600.00	360.00
5	Sam Crawford	1200.	600.00	360.00
6	Hal Chase	450.00	225.00	135.00
7	Howie Camnitz	325.00	162.00	97.00
8	Fred Clarke	1000.	500.00	300.00
9	Ty Cobb	8500.	4250.	2550.
10	Art Devlin	325.00	162.00	97.00
11	Bill Dahlen	325.00	162.00	97.00
12	Wild Bill Donovan	325.00	162.00	97.00
13	Larry Doyle	350.00	175.00	105.00
14	Red Dooin	325.00	162.00	97.00
15	Kid Elberfeld	325.00	162.00	97.00
16	Johnny Evers	1200.	600.00	360.00
17	Clark Griffith	1100.	550.00	330.00
18	Hughie Jennings	1100.	550.00	330.00
19	Addie Joss	1800.	900.00	540.00
20	Tim Jordan	325.00	162.00	97.00
21	Red Kleinow	325.00	162.00	97.00
22	Harry Krause	325.00	162.00	97.00
23	Nap Lajoie	2250.	1125.	675.00
24	Mike Mitchell	325.00	162.00	97.00
25	Matty McIntyre	325.00	162.00	97.00
26	John McGraw	1200.	600.00	360.00
27	Christy Mathewson	3500.	1750.	1050.
28a	Harry McIntyre (Brooklyn)	325.00	162.00	97.00
28b	Harry McIntyre (Brooklyn and Chicago)	350.00	175.00	105.00
29	Amby McConnell	325.00	162.00	97.00
30	George Mullin	325.00	162.00	97.00
31	Sherry Magee	325.00	162.00	97.00
32	Orval Overall	325.00	162.00	97.00
33	Jake Pfeister	325.00	162.00	97.00
34	Nap Rucker	325.00	162.00	97.00
35	Joe Tinker	1200.	600.00	360.00
36	Tris Speaker	2800.	1400.	840.00
37	Slim Sallee	325.00	162.00	97.00
38	Jake Stahl	325.00	162.00	97.00
39	Rube Waddell	1000.	500.00	300.00
40a	Vic Willis (Pittsburg)	325.00	162.00	97.00
40b	Vic Willis (Pittsburg and St. Louis)	350.00	175.00	105.00
41	Hooks Wiltse	325.00	162.00	97.00
42	Cy Young	3500.	1750.	1050.
43	Out At Third	200.00	100.00	60.00
44	Trying To Catch Him Napping	200.00	100.00	60.00
45	Jordan & Herzog At First	325.00	162.00	97.00
46	Safe At Third	200.00	100.00	60.00
47	Frank Chance At Bat	1000.	500.00	300.00
48	Jack Murray At Bat	325.00	162.00	97.00
49	A Close Play At Second	325.00	162.00	97.00
50	Chief Myers At Bat	325.00	162.00	97.00
77	Red Ames	325.00	162.00	97.00
78	Home Run Baker	1100.	550.00	330.00
79	George Bell	325.00	162.00	97.00
80	Chief Bender	1000.	500.00	300.00
81	Bob Bescher	325.00	162.00	97.00
82	Kitty Bransfield	325.00	162.00	97.00
83	Al Bridwell	325.00	162.00	97.00
84	George Browne	325.00	162.00	97.00
85	Bill Burns	325.00	162.00	97.00
86	Bill Carrigan	325.00	162.00	97.00
87	Eddie Collins	1000.	500.00	300.00
88	Harry Coveleski	325.00	162.00	97.00
89	Lou Criger	325.00	162.00	97.00
90a	Mickey Doolin (name incorrect)	500.00	250.00	150.00

90b	Mickey Doolan (name correct)	325.00	162.00	97.00
91	Tom Downey	325.00	162.00	97.00
92	Jimmy Dygert	325.00	162.00	97.00
93	Art Fromme	325.00	162.00	97.00
94	George Gibson	325.00	162.00	97.00
95	Peaches Graham	325.00	162.00	97.00
96	Bob Groom	325.00	162.00	97.00
97	Dick Hoblitzell	325.00	162.00	97.00
98	Solly Hofman	325.00	162.00	97.00
99	Walter Johnson	3500.	1750.	1050.
100	Davy Jones	325.00	162.00	97.00
101	Wee Willie Keeler	500.00	250.00	150.00
102	Johnny Kling	325.00	162.00	97.00
103	Ed Konetchy	325.00	162.00	97.00
104	Ed Lennox	325.00	162.00	97.00
105	Hans Lobert	325.00	162.00	97.00
106	Harry Lord	325.00	162.00	97.00
107	Rube Manning	325.00	162.00	97.00
108	Fred Merkle	325.00	162.00	97.00
109	Pat Moran	325.00	162.00	97.00
110	George McBride	325.00	162.00	97.00
111	Harry Niles	325.00	162.00	97.00
112a	Dode Paskert (Cincinnati)	350.00	175.00	105.00
112b	Dode Paskert (Cincinnati and Philadelphia)	325.00	162.00	97.00
113	Bugs Raymond	325.00	162.00	97.00
114	Bob Rhoades (Rhoads)	350.00	175.00	105.00
115	Admiral Schlei	325.00	162.00	97.00
116	Boss Schmidt	325.00	162.00	97.00
117	Wildfire Schulte	325.00	162.00	97.00
118	Frank Smith	325.00	162.00	97.00
119	George Stone	325.00	162.00	97.00
120	Gabby Street	325.00	162.00	97.00
121	Billy Sullivan	325.00	162.00	97.00
122a	Fred Tenney (New York)	325.00	162.00	97.00
122b	Fred Tenney (New York and Boston)	325.00	162.00	97.00
123	Ira Thomas	325.00	162.00	97.00
124	Bobby Wallace	1000.	500.00	300.00
125	Ed Walsh	1200.	600.00	360.00
126	Owen Wilson	325.00	162.00	97.00

1911 T5 Pinkerton

Because they were photographs affixed to a cardboard backing, the cards in the 1911 T5 Pinkerton set are considered by today's advanced collectors to be "true" cabinet cards. The Pinkerton cabinets are a rather obscure issue, and because of their original method of distribution, it would be virtually impossible to assemble a complete set today. It has never actually been determined how many subjects in the set even exist. Pinkerton, the parent of Red Man and other tobacco products, offered the cabinets in exchange for coupons found in cigarette packages. According to an original advertising sheet, some 376 different photos were available. A consumer could exchange ten coupons for the cabinet card of his choice. The photos available included players from the 16 major league teams plus five teams from the American Association (Indianapolis, Columbus, Toledo, Kansas City and Minneapolis). Pinkerton cabinet cards have been found to vary in both size and type of mount. The most desirable combination is a 3-3/8" by 5-1/2" photograph affixed to a thick, cardboard mount measuring approximately 4-3/4" by 7-3/4". But original Pinkerton cabinets have also been found in slightly different sizes with less substantial backings. The most attractive mounts are embossed around the picture, but some Pinkertons have been found with a white border surrounding the photograph. Prices listed are for cards with cardboard mounts. Cards with paper mounts are worth about 3/4 of listed prices. Collectors should be aware that some of the Pinkerton photos were reproduced in postcard size issues in later years. Because of the rarity of the T5s, no complete set price is given.

		NR MT	EX	VG
Common Player:		150.00	75.00	45.00
101	Jim Stephens	150.00	75.00	45.00
102	Bobby Wallace	500.00	250.00	150.00
103	Joe Lake	150.00	75.00	45.00
104	George Stone	150.00	75.00	45.00
105	Jack O'Connor	150.00	75.00	45.00
106	Bill Abstein	150.00	75.00	45.00
107	Rube Waddell	500.00	250.00	150.00
108	Roy Hartzell	150.00	75.00	45.00
109	Danny Hoffman	150.00	75.00	45.00
110	Dode Cris	150.00	75.00	45.00
111	Al Schweitzer	150.00	75.00	45.00
112	Art Griggs	150.00	75.00	45.00
113	Bill Bailey	150.00	75.00	45.00
114	Pat Newman	150.00	75.00	45.00
115	Harry Howell	150.00	75.00	45.00
117	Hobe Ferris	150.00	75.00	45.00
118	John McAleese	150.00	75.00	45.00
119	Ray Demmitt	150.00	75.00	45.00
120	Red Fisher	150.00	75.00	45.00
121	Frank Truesdale	150.00	75.00	45.00
122	Barney Pelty	150.00	75.00	45.00
123	Ed Killifer (Killefer)	150.00	75.00	45.00
151	Matty McIntyre	150.00	75.00	45.00
152	Jim Delahanty	150.00	75.00	45.00
153	Hughey Jennings	500.00	250.00	150.00
154	Ralph Works	150.00	75.00	45.00
155	George Moriarity (Moriarty)	150.00	75.00	45.00
156	Sam Crawford	500.00	250.00	150.00
157	Boss Schmidt	150.00	75.00	45.00
158	Owen Bush	150.00	75.00	45.00
159	Ty Cobb	3250.	1600.	975.00
160	Bill Donovan	150.00	75.00	45.00
161	Oscar Stanage	150.00	75.00	45.00
162	George Mullin	150.00	75.00	45.00
163	Davy Jones	150.00	75.00	45.00
164	Charley O'Leary	150.00	75.00	45.00
165	Tom Jones	150.00	75.00	45.00
166	Joe Casey	150.00	75.00	45.00
167	Ed Willetts (Willett)	150.00	75.00	45.00
168	Ed Lafeite (Lafitte)	150.00	75.00	45.00
169	Ty Cobb	3250.	1600.	975.00
170	Ty Cobb	3250.	1600.	975.00
201	John Evers	500.00	250.00	150.00
202	Mordecai Brown	500.00	250.00	150.00
203	King Cole	150.00	75.00	45.00
204	Johnny Cane	150.00	75.00	45.00
205	Heinie Zimmerman	150.00	75.00	45.00
206	Wildfire Schulte	150.00	75.00	45.00
207	Frank Chance	500.00	250.00	150.00
208	Joe Tinker	500.00	250.00	150.00
209	Orvall Overall	150.00	75.00	45.00
210	Jimmy Archer	150.00	75.00	45.00
211	Johnny Kling	150.00	75.00	45.00
212	Jimmy Sheckard	150.00	75.00	45.00
213	Harry McIntyre	150.00	75.00	45.00
214	Lew Richie	150.00	75.00	45.00
215	Ed Ruelbach	150.00	75.00	45.00
216	Artie Hoffman (Hofman)	150.00	75.00	45.00
217	Jake Pfeister	150.00	75.00	45.00
218	Harry Steinfeldt	150.00	75.00	45.00
219	Tom Needham	150.00	75.00	45.00
220	Ginger Beaumont	150.00	75.00	45.00
251	Christy Mathewson	1300.	650.00	400.00
252	Fred Merkle	150.00	75.00	45.00
253	Hooks Wiltsie	150.00	75.00	45.00
254	Art Devlin	150.00	75.00	45.00
255	Fred Snodgrass	150.00	75.00	45.00
256	Josh Devore	150.00	75.00	45.00
257	Red Murray	150.00	75.00	45.00
258	Cy Seymour	150.00	75.00	45.00
259	Al Bridwell	150.00	75.00	45.00
260	Larry Doyle	150.00	75.00	45.00
261	Bugs Raymond	150.00	75.00	45.00
262	Doc Crandall	150.00	75.00	45.00
263	Admiral Schlei	150.00	75.00	45.00
264	Chief Myers (Meyers)	150.00	75.00	45.00
265	Bill Dahlen	150.00	75.00	45.00
266	Beals Becker	150.00	75.00	45.00
267	Louis Drucke	150.00	75.00	45.00
301	Fred Luderus	150.00	75.00	45.00
302	John Titus	150.00	75.00	45.00
303	Red Dooin	150.00	75.00	45.00
304	Eddie Stack	150.00	75.00	45.00
305	Kitty Bransfield	150.00	75.00	45.00
306	Sherry Magee	150.00	75.00	45.00
307	Otto Knabe	150.00	75.00	45.00
308	Jimmy "Runt" Walsh	150.00	75.00	45.00
309	Earl Moore	150.00	75.00	45.00
310	Mickey Doolan	150.00	75.00	45.00
311	Ad Brennan	150.00	75.00	45.00
312	Bob Ewing	150.00	75.00	45.00
313	Lou Schettler	150.00	75.00	45.00
351	Joe Willis	150.00	75.00	45.00
352	Rube Ellis	150.00	75.00	45.00
353	Steve Evans	150.00	75.00	45.00
354	Miller Huggins	500.00	250.00	150.00
355	Arnold Hauser	150.00	75.00	45.00
356	Frank Corridon	150.00	75.00	45.00
357	Roger Bresnahan	500.00	250.00	150.00
358	Slim Sallee	150.00	75.00	45.00
359	Mike Mowrey	150.00	75.00	45.00
360	Ed Konetchy	150.00	75.00	45.00
361	Beckman	150.00	75.00	45.00
362	Rebel Oakes	150.00	75.00	45.00
363	Johnny Lush	150.00	75.00	45.00
364	Eddie Phelps	150.00	75.00	45.00
365	Robert Harmon	150.00	75.00	45.00
401	Lew Moren	150.00	75.00	45.00
402	George McQuillian (McQuillan)	150.00	75.00	45.00
403	Johnny Bates	150.00	75.00	45.00
404	Eddie Grant	150.00	75.00	45.00
405	Tommy McMillan	150.00	75.00	45.00
406	Tommy Clark (Clarke)	150.00	75.00	45.00
407	Jack Rowan	150.00	75.00	45.00
408	Bob Bescher	150.00	75.00	45.00
409	Fred Beebe	150.00	75.00	45.00
410	Tom Downey	150.00	75.00	45.00
411	George Suggs	150.00	75.00	45.00
412	Hans Lobert	150.00	75.00	45.00
413	Jimmy Phelan	150.00	75.00	45.00
414	Dode Paskert	150.00	75.00	45.00
415	Ward Miller	150.00	75.00	45.00
416	Dick Egan	150.00	75.00	45.00
417	Art Fromme	150.00	75.00	45.00
418	Bill Burns	150.00	75.00	45.00
419	Clark Griffith	500.00	250.00	150.00
420	Dick Hoblitzell	150.00	75.00	45.00
421	Harry Gasper	150.00	75.00	45.00
422	Dave Altizer	150.00	75.00	45.00
423	Larry McLean	150.00	75.00	45.00
424	Mike Mitchell	150.00	75.00	45.00
451	John Hummel	150.00	75.00	45.00
452	Tony Smith	150.00	75.00	45.00
453	Bill Davidson	150.00	75.00	45.00
454	Ed Lennox	150.00	75.00	45.00
455	Zach Wheat	500.00	250.00	150.00
457	Elmer Knetzer	150.00	75.00	45.00
458	Rube Dessau	150.00	75.00	45.00
459	George Bell	150.00	75.00	45.00
460	Jake Daubert	150.00	75.00	45.00
461	Doc Scanlan	150.00	75.00	45.00
462	Nap Rucker	150.00	75.00	45.00
463	Cy Barger	150.00	75.00	45.00
464	Kaiser Wilhelm	150.00	75.00	45.00
465	Bill Bergen	150.00	75.00	45.00
466	Tex Erwin	150.00	75.00	45.00
501	Chief Bender	500.00	250.00	150.00
502	John Coombs	150.00	75.00	45.00
503	Eddie Plank	500.00	250.00	150.00
504	Amos Strunk	150.00	75.00	45.00
505	Connie Mack	650.00	325.00	195.00
506	Ira Thomas	150.00	75.00	45.00
507	Biscoe Lord (Briscoe)	150.00	75.00	45.00
508	Stuffy McInnis	150.00	75.00	45.00
509	Jimmy Dygert	150.00	75.00	45.00
510	Rube Oldring	150.00	75.00	45.00
511	Eddie Collins	500.00	250.00	150.00
512	Home Run Baker	500.00	250.00	150.00
513	Harry Krause	150.00	75.00	45.00
514	Harry Davis	150.00	75.00	45.00
515	Jack Barry	150.00	75.00	45.00
516	Jack Lapp	150.00	75.00	45.00
517	Cy Morgan	150.00	75.00	45.00
518	Danny Murphy	150.00	75.00	45.00
519	Topsy Hartsell	150.00	75.00	45.00
520	Paddy Livingston	150.00	75.00	45.00
521	P. Adkins	150.00	75.00	45.00
522	Eddie Collins	500.00	250.00	150.00
523	Paddy Livingston	150.00	75.00	45.00
551	Doc Gessler	150.00	75.00	45.00
552	Bill Cunningham	150.00	75.00	45.00
554	John Henry	150.00	75.00	45.00
555	Jack Lelivelt	150.00	75.00	45.00
556	Bobby Groome	150.00	75.00	45.00
557	Doc Ralston	150.00	75.00	45.00
558	Kid Elberfelt (Elberfeld)	150.00	75.00	45.00
559	Doc Reisling	150.00	75.00	45.00
560	Herman Schaefer	150.00	75.00	45.00
561	Walter Johnson	1300.	650.00	400.00
562	Dolly Gray	150.00	75.00	45.00
563	Wid Conroy	150.00	75.00	45.00
564	Charley Street	150.00	75.00	45.00
565	Bob Unglaub	150.00	75.00	45.00
566	Clyde Milan	150.00	75.00	45.00
567	George Browne	150.00	75.00	45.00
568	George McBride	150.00	75.00	45.00
569	Red Killifer (Killefer)	150.00	75.00	45.00
601	Addie Joss	500.00	250.00	150.00
602	Addie Joss	500.00	250.00	150.00
603	Napoleon Lajoie	800.00	400.00	240.00
604	Nig Clark (Clarke)	150.00	75.00	45.00
605	Cy Falkenberg	150.00	75.00	45.00
606	Harry Bemis	150.00	75.00	45.00
607	George Stovall	150.00	75.00	45.00
608	Fred Blanding	150.00	75.00	45.00
609	Elmer Koestner	150.00	75.00	45.00
610	Ted Easterly	150.00	75.00	45.00
611	Willie Mitchell	150.00	75.00	45.00
612	Hornhorst	150.00	75.00	45.00
613	Elmer Flick	500.00	250.00	150.00
614	Speck Harkness	150.00	75.00	45.00
615	Tuck Turner	150.00	75.00	45.00
616	Joe Jackson	5000.	2500.	1500.
617	Grover Land	150.00	75.00	45.00
618	Gladstone Graney	150.00	75.00	45.00
619	Dave Callahan	150.00	75.00	45.00
620	Ben DeMott	150.00	75.00	45.00
621	Neill Ball (Neal)	150.00	75.00	45.00
622	Dode Birmingham	150.00	75.00	45.00
623	George Kaler (Kahler)	150.00	75.00	45.00
624	Sid Smith	150.00	75.00	45.00
625	Bert Adams	150.00	75.00	45.00
626	Bill Bradley	150.00	75.00	45.00
627	Napoleon Lajoie	650.00	325.00	195.00
651	Bill Corrigan (Carrigan)	150.00	75.00	45.00
652	Joe Wood	150.00	75.00	45.00
653	Heinie Wagner	150.00	75.00	45.00
654	Billy Purtell	150.00	75.00	45.00
655	Frank Smith	150.00	75.00	45.00
656	Harry Lord	150.00	75.00	45.00
657	Patsy Donovan	150.00	75.00	45.00
658	Duffy Lewis	150.00	75.00	45.00
659	Jack Kleinow	150.00	75.00	45.00
660	Ed Karger	150.00	75.00	45.00
661	Clyde Engle	150.00	75.00	45.00
662	Ben Hunt	150.00	75.00	45.00
663	Charlie Smith	150.00	75.00	45.00
664	Tris Speaker	900.00	450.00	270.00
665	Tom Madden	150.00	75.00	45.00
666	Larry Gardner	150.00	75.00	45.00
667	Harry Hooper	500.00	250.00	150.00
668	Marty McHale	150.00	75.00	45.00
669	Ray Collins	150.00	75.00	45.00
670	Jake Stahl	150.00	75.00	45.00
701	Dave Shean	150.00	75.00	45.00
702	Roy Miller	150.00	75.00	45.00
703	Fred Beck	150.00	75.00	45.00
704	Bill Collings (Collins)	150.00	75.00	45.00
705	Bill Sweeney	150.00	75.00	45.00
706	Buck Herzog	150.00	75.00	45.00
707	Bud Sharp (Sharpe)	150.00	75.00	45.00
708	Cliff Curtis	150.00	75.00	45.00
709	Al Mattern	150.00	75.00	45.00
710	Buster Brown	150.00	75.00	45.00
711	Bill Rariden	150.00	75.00	45.00
712	Grant	150.00	75.00	45.00
713	Ed Abbaticchio	150.00	75.00	45.00
714	Cecil Ferguson	150.00	75.00	45.00
715	Billy Burke	150.00	75.00	45.00

716	Sam Frock	150.00	75.00	45.00
717	Wilbur Goode (Good)	150.00	75.00	45.00
751	Charlie French	150.00	75.00	45.00
752	Patsy Dougherty	150.00	75.00	45.00
753	Shano Collins	150.00	75.00	45.00
754	Fred Parent	150.00	75.00	45.00
755	Willis Cole	150.00	75.00	45.00
756	Billy Sullivan	150.00	75.00	45.00
757	Rube Sutor (Suter)	150.00	75.00	45.00
758	Chick Gandil	150.00	75.00	45.00
759	Jim Scott	150.00	75.00	45.00
760	Ed Walsh	500.00	250.00	150.00
761	Gavvy Cravath	150.00	75.00	45.00
762	Bobby Messenger	150.00	75.00	45.00
763	Doc White	150.00	75.00	45.00
764	Rollie Zeider	150.00	75.00	45.00
765	Fred Payne	150.00	75.00	45.00
766	Lee Tannehill	150.00	75.00	45.00
767	Eddie Hahn	150.00	75.00	45.00
768	Hugh Duffy	500.00	250.00	150.00
769	Fred Olmstead	150.00	75.00	45.00
770	Lena Blackbourne (Blackburne)	150.00	75.00	45.00
771	Young "Cy" Young	150.00	75.00	45.00
801	Lew Brockett	150.00	75.00	45.00
802	Frank Laporte (LaPorte)	150.00	75.00	45.00
803	Bert Daniels	150.00	75.00	45.00
804	Walter Blair	150.00	75.00	45.00
805	Jack Knight	150.00	75.00	45.00
806	Jimmy Austin	150.00	75.00	45.00
807	Hal Chase	175.00	87.00	52.00
808	Birdie Cree	150.00	75.00	45.00
809	Jack Quinn	150.00	75.00	45.00
810	Walter Manning	150.00	75.00	45.00
811	Jack Warhop	150.00	75.00	45.00
812	Jeff Sweeney	150.00	75.00	45.00
813	Charley Hemphill	150.00	75.00	45.00
814	Harry Wolters	150.00	75.00	45.00
815	Tom Hughes	150.00	75.00	45.00
816	Earl Gardiner (Gardner)	150.00	75.00	45.00
851	John Flynn	150.00	75.00	45.00
852	Bill Powell	150.00	75.00	45.00
853	Honus Wagner	1800.	900.00	550.00
854	Bill Powell	150.00	75.00	45.00
855	Fred Clarke	500.00	250.00	150.00
856	Owen Wilson	150.00	75.00	45.00
857	George Gibson	150.00	75.00	45.00
858	Mike Simon	150.00	75.00	45.00
859	Tommy Leach	150.00	75.00	45.00
860	Lefty Leifeld (Leifield)	150.00	75.00	45.00
861	Nick Maddox	150.00	75.00	45.00
862	Dots Miller	150.00	75.00	45.00
863	Howard Camnitz	150.00	75.00	45.00
864	Deacon Phillippi (Phillippe)	150.00	75.00	45.00
865	Babe Adams	150.00	75.00	45.00
866	Ed Abbaticchio	150.00	75.00	45.00
867	Paddy O'Connor	150.00	75.00	45.00
868	Bobby Byrne	150.00	75.00	45.00
869	Vin Campbell	150.00	75.00	45.00
870	Ham Hyatt	150.00	75.00	45.00
871	Sam Leever	150.00	75.00	45.00
872	Hans Wagner	1800.	900.00	550.00
873	Hans Wagner	1800.	900.00	550.00
874	Bill McKecknie (McKechnie)	500.00	250.00	150.00
875	Kirby White	150.00	75.00	45.00
901	Jimmie Burke	150.00	75.00	45.00
902	Charlie Carr	150.00	75.00	45.00
903	Larry Cheney	150.00	75.00	45.00
904	Chet Chadbourne	150.00	75.00	45.00
905	Dan Howley	150.00	75.00	45.00
906	Jimmie Burke	150.00	75.00	45.00
907	Ray Mowe	150.00	75.00	45.00
908	Billy Milligan	150.00	75.00	45.00
909	Frank Oberlin	150.00	75.00	45.00
910	Ralph Glaze	150.00	75.00	45.00
911	O'Day	150.00	75.00	45.00
912	Kerns	150.00	75.00	45.00
913	Jim Duggan	150.00	75.00	45.00
914	Simmy Murch	150.00	75.00	45.00
915	Frank Delehanty	150.00	75.00	45.00
916	Craig	150.00	75.00	45.00
917	Jack Coffee (Coffey)	150.00	75.00	45.00
918	Lefty George	150.00	75.00	45.00
919	Otto Williams	150.00	75.00	45.00
920	M. Hayden	150.00	75.00	45.00
951	Joe Cantillion	150.00	75.00	45.00
952	Smith	150.00	75.00	45.00
953	Claud Rossman (Claude)	150.00	75.00	45.00
1001	Tony James	150.00	75.00	45.00
1002	Jack Powell	150.00	75.00	45.00
1003	Wm. J. Harbeau	150.00	75.00	45.00
1004	Homer Smoot	150.00	75.00	45.00
1051	Bill Friel	150.00	75.00	45.00
1052	Bill Friel	150.00	75.00	45.00
1053	Fred Odwell	150.00	75.00	45.00
1054	Alex Reilley	150.00	75.00	45.00
1055	Eugene Packard	150.00	75.00	45.00
1056	Irve Wrattan	150.00	75.00	45.00
1057	"Red" Nelson	150.00	75.00	45.00
1058	George Perring	150.00	75.00	45.00
1059	Glen Liebhardt	150.00	75.00	45.00
1060	Jimmie O'Rourke	150.00	75.00	45.00
1061	Fred Cook	150.00	75.00	45.00
1062	Charles Arbogast	150.00	75.00	45.00
1063	Jerry Downs	150.00	75.00	45.00
1064	"Bunk" Congalton	150.00	75.00	45.00
1065	Fred Carisch	150.00	75.00	45.00
1066	"Red" Sitton	150.00	75.00	45.00
1067	George Kaler (Kahler)	150.00	75.00	45.00
1068	Arthur Kruger	150.00	75.00	45.00
1102	Earl Yingling	150.00	75.00	45.00
1103	Jerry Freeman	150.00	75.00	45.00
1104	Harry Hinchman	150.00	75.00	45.00
1105	Jim Baskette	150.00	75.00	45.00
1106	Denny Sullivan	150.00	75.00	45.00
1107	Carl Robinson	150.00	75.00	45.00
1108	Bill Rodgers	150.00	75.00	45.00
1109	Hi West	150.00	75.00	45.00
1110	Billy Hallman	150.00	75.00	45.00
1111	Wm. Elwert	150.00	75.00	45.00
1112	Piano Legs Hickman	150.00	75.00	45.00
1113	Joe McCarthy	350.00	175.00	105.00
1114	Fred Abbott	150.00	75.00	45.00
1115	Jack Gilligan	150.00	75.00	45.00

1911 T201 Mecca Double Folders

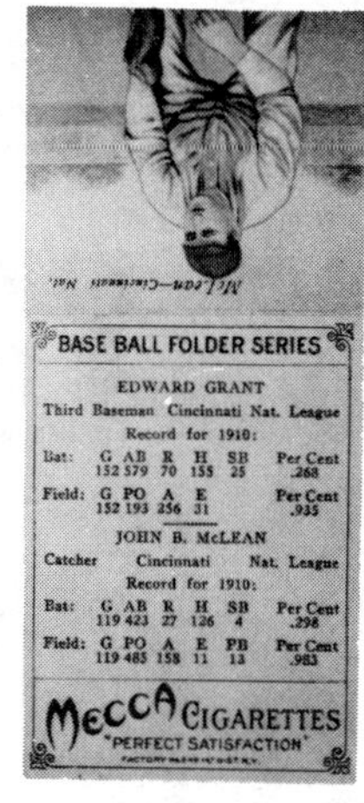

These cards found in packages of Mecca cigarettes feature one player when the card is open, and another when the card is folded; two players sharing the same pair of legs. Mecca Double Folders measure 2-1/4" by 4-11/16." The fronts are color lithographs with the player's name appearing in black script in the upper left. The backs are printed in red and contain an innovation in the form of player statistics. The 50-card set contains 100 different players including a number of Hall of Famers. The Mecca Double Folders, with two players (Topps "borrowed" the idea in 1955) and statistics, were one of the most innovative of the tobacco card era.

		NR MT	EX	VG
	Complete Set (50):	9000.	4500.	2700.
	Common Player:	67.50	34.00	20.00
(1)	William Abstein, John Butler	67.50	34.00	20.00
(2)	Frank Baker, Edward Collins	360.00	180.00	108.00
(3)	Harry Baker, Thomas Downie (Downey)	67.50	34.00	20.00
(4)	James Barrett, Grant McGlynn	67.50	34.00	20.00
(5)	John Barry, John Lapp	67.50	34.00	20.00
(6)	Charles Bender, Reuben Oldring	225.00	112.00	67.00
(7)	William Bergen, Zack Wheat	225.00	112.00	67.00
(8)	Walter Blair, Roy Hartzell	67.50	34.00	20.00
(9)	Roger Bresnahan, Miller Huggins	450.00	225.00	135.00
(10)	Albert Bridwell, Christy Matthewson (Mathewson)	700.00	350.00	210.00
(11)	Mordecai Brown, Arthur Hofman	225.00	112.00	67.00
(12)	Robert Byrne, Fred Clarke	180.00	90.00	54.00
(13)	Frank Chance, John Evers	400.00	200.00	120.00
(14)	Harold Chase, Edward Sweeney	115.00	57.00	34.00
(15)	Edward Cicotte, John Thoney	90.00	45.00	27.00
(16)	Thomas Clarke, Harry Gaspar	67.50	34.00	20.00
(17)	Ty Cobb, Sam Crawford	1750.	875.00	525.00
(18)	Leonard Cole, John Kling	67.50	34.00	20.00
(19)	John Coombs, Ira Thomas	67.50	34.00	20.00
(20)	Jake Daubert, Nap Rucker	90.00	45.00	27.00
(21)	Bill Donovan, Ralph Stroud, Bill Donovan	67.50	34.00	20.00
(22)	Charles Dooin, John Titus	67.50	34.00	20.00
(23)	Patsy Dougherty, Harry Lord	380.00	190.00	110.00
(24)	Jerry Downs, Fred Odwell	67.50	34.00	20.00
(25)	Larry Doyle, Chief Meyers	67.50	34.00	20.00
(26)	James Dygert, Cy Seymour	67.50	34.00	20.00
(27)	Norman Elberfeld, George McBride	67.50	34.00	20.00
(28)	Fred Falkenberg, Napoleon Lajoie	450.00	225.00	135.00
(29)	Edward Fitzpatrick, Ed Killian	67.50	34.00	20.00
(30)	Russell Ford, Otis Johnson	67.50	34.00	20.00
(31)	Edward Foster, Joseph Ward	67.50	34.00	20.00
(32)	Earl Gardner, Tris Speaker	135.00	67.00	40.00
(33)	George Gibson, Thomas Leach	67.50	34.00	20.00
(34)	George Graham, Al Mattern	67.50	34.00	20.00
(35)	Edward Grant, John McLean	67.50	34.00	20.00
(36)	Arnold Hauser, Ernest Lush	67.50	34.00	20.00
(37)	Charles Herzog, Roy Miller	67.50	34.00	20.00
(38)	Charles Hickman, Harry Hinchman	67.50	34.00	20.00
(39)	Hugh Jennings, Edgar Summers	225.00	112.00	67.00
(40)	Walter Johnson, Charles Street	700.00	350.00	210.00
(41)	Frank LaPorte, James Stephens	67.50	34.00	20.00
(42)	Joseph Lake, Robert Wallace	180.00	90.00	54.00
(43)	Albert Leifield, Mike Simon	67.50	34.00	20.00
(44)	John Lobert, Earl Moore	67.50	34.00	20.00
(45)	Arthur McCabe, Charles Starr	67.50	34.00	20.00
(46)	Lewis McCarty, Joseph McGinnity	180.00	90.00	54.00
(47)	Fred Merkle, George Wiltse	90.00	45.00	27.00
(48)	Grederick Payne, Edward Walsh	225.00	112.00	67.00
(49)	George Stovall, Torrence Turner	67.50	34.00	20.00
(50)	Pttp Williams, Orville Woodruff	67.50	34.00	20.00

1912 T202 Hassan Triple Folders

Measuring 5-1/2" by 2-1/4", Hassan cigarette cards carried the concept of multiple-player cards even further than the innovative Mecca set of the previous year. Scored so that the two end cards - which are full-color and very close to exact duplicates of T205 "Gold Borders" - can fold over the black and white center panel, the Hassan Triple Folder appears like a booklet when closed. The two end cards are individual player cards, while the larger center panel contains an action scene. Usually the two player cards are not related to the action scene. The unique Hassan Triple Folders feature player biographies on the back of the two individual cards with a description of the action on the back of the center panel. Values depend on the player featured in the center panel, as well as the players featured on the end cards.

		NR MT	EX	VG
	Complete Set (132):	37500.	18750.	11250.
	Common Player:	200.00	100.00	60.00
(1a)	A Close Play At The Home Plate (LaPorte, Wallace)	225.00	112.00	67.00
(1b)	A Close Play At The Home Plate (Pelty, Wallace)	215.00	107.00	64.00
(2)	A Desperate Slide For Third (Ty Cobb, O'Leary)	2225.	1112.	667.00
(3a)	A Great Batsman (Barger, Bergen)	200.00	100.00	60.00
(3b)	A Great Batsman (Bergen, Rucker)	200.00	100.00	60.00
(4)	Ambrose McConnell At Bat (Blair, Quinn)	200.00	100.00	60.00
(5)	A Wide Throw Saves Crawford (Mullin, Stanage)	200.00	100.00	60.00
(6)	Baker Gets His Man (Baker, Collins)	425.00	212.00	127.00
(7)	Birmingham Gets To Third (Johnson, Street)	675.00	337.00	202.00
(8)	Birmingham's Home Run (Birmingham, Turner)	675.00	337.00	202.00
(9)	Bush Just Misses Austin (Magee, Moran)	200.00	100.00	60.00
(10a)	Carrigan Blocks His Man (Gaspar, McLean)	200.00	100.00	60.00
(10b)	Carrigan Blocks His Man (Carrigan, Wagner)	200.00	100.00	60.00
(11)	Catching Him Napping (Bresnahan, Oakes)	300.00	150.00	90.00
(12)	Caught Asleep Off First (Bresnahan, Harmon)	350.00	175.00	105.00
(13a)	Chance Beats Out A Hit (Chance, Foxen)	350.00	175.00	105.00
(13b)	Chance Beats Out A Hit (Archer, McIntyre)	200.00	100.00	60.00
(13c)	Chance Beats Out A Hit (Archer, Overall)	200.00	100.00	60.00
(13d)	Chance Beats Out A Hit (Archer, Rowan)	200.00	100.00	60.00
(13e)	Chance Beats Out A Hit (Chance, Shean)	350.00	175.00	105.00
(14a)	Chase Dives Into Third (Chase, Wolter)	200.00	100.00	60.00
(14b)	Chase Dives Into Third (Clarke, Gibson)	225.00	112.00	67.00
(14c)	Chase Dives Into Third (Gibson, Phillippe)	200.00	100.00	60.00
(15a)	Chase Gets Ball Too Late (Egan, Mitchell)	200.00	100.00	60.00
(15b)	Chase Gets Ball Too Late (Chase, Wolter)	200.00	100.00	60.00
(16a)	Chase Guarding First (Chase, Wolter)	200.00	100.00	60.00
(16b)	Chase Guarding First (Clarke, Gibson)	225.00	112.00	67.00
(16c)	Chase Guarding First (Gibson, Leifield)	200.00	100.00	60.00
(17)	Chase Ready For The Squeeze Play (Magee, Paskert)	200.00	100.00	60.00
(18)	Chase Safe At Third (Baker, Barry)	350.00	175.00	105.00
(19)	Chief Bender Waiting For A Good One (Bender, Thomas)	350.00	175.00	105.00

		NR MT	EX	VG
(20)	Clarke Hikes For Home (Bridwell, Kling)	200.00	100.00	60.00
(21)	Close At First (Ball, Stovall)	200.00	100.00	60.00
(22a)	Close At The Plate (Payne, Walsh)	350.00	175.00	105.00
(22b)	Close At The Plate (Payne, White)	200.00	100.00	60.00
(23)	Close At Third - Speaker (Speaker, Wood)	450.00	225.00	135.00
(24)	Close At Third - Wagner (Carrigan, Wagner)	200.00	100.00	60.00
(25a)	Collins Easily Safe (Byrne, Clarke)	275.00	137.00	82.00
(25b)	Collins Easily Safe (Baker, Collins)	450.00	225.00	135.00
(25c)	Collins Easily Safe (Collins, Murphy)	350.00	175.00	105.00
(26)	Crawford About To Smash One (Stanage, Summers)	200.00	100.00	60.00
(27)	Cree Rolls Home (Daubert, Hummel)	200.00	100.00	60.00
(28)	Davy Jones' Great Slide (Delahanty, Jones)	200.00	100.00	60.00
(29a)	Devlin Gets His Man (Devlin (Giants), Mathewson)	1000.	500.00	300.00
(29b)	Devlin Gets His Man (Devlin (Rustlers), Mathewson)	575.00	287.00	172.00
(29c)	Devlin Gets His Man (Fletcher, Mathewson)	575.00	287.00	172.00
(29d)	Devlin Gets His Man (Mathewson, Meyers)	575.00	287.00	172.00
(30a)	Donlin Out At First (Camnitz, Gibson)	200.00	100.00	60.00
(30b)	Donlin Out At First (Doyle, Merlke)	200.00	100.00	60.00
(30c)	Donlin Out At First (Leach, Wilson)	200.00	100.00	60.00
(30d)	Donlin Out At First (Dooin, Magee)	200.00	100.00	60.00
(30e)	Donlin Out At First (Gibson, Phillippe)	200.00	100.00	60.00
(31a)	Dooin Gets His Man (Dooin, Doolan)	200.00	100.00	60.00
(31b)	Dooin Gets His Man (Dooin, Lobert)	200.00	100.00	60.00
(31c)	Dooin Gets His Man (Dooin, Titus)	200.00	100.00	60.00
(32)	Easy For Larry (Doyle, Merlke)	200.00	100.00	60.00
(33)	Elberfeld Beats The Throw (Elberfeld, Milan)	200.00	100.00	60.00
(34)	Elberfeld Gets His Man (Elberfeld, Milan)	200.00	100.00	60.00
(35)	Engle In A Close Play (Engle, Speaker)	400.00	200.00	120.00
(36a)	Evers Makes A Safe Slide (Archer, Evers)	350.00	175.00	105.00
(36b)	Evers Makes A Safe Slide (Chance, Evers)	450.00	225.00	135.00
(36c)	Evers Makes A Safe Slide (Archer, Overall)	200.00	100.00	60.00
(36d)	Evers Makes A Safe Slide (Archer, Reulbach)	200.00	100.00	60.00
(36e)	Evers Makes A Safe Slide (Chance, Tinker)	500.00	250.00	150.00
(37)	Fast Work At Third (Cobb, O'Leary)	2225.	1112.	667.00
(38a)	Ford Putting Over A Spitter (Ford, Vaughn)	200.00	100.00	60.00
(38b)	Ford Putting Over A Spitter (Sweeney, Ford)	200.00	100.00	60.00
(39)	Good Play At Third (Cobb, Moriarity)	2225.	1112.	667.00
(40)	Grant Gets His Man (Grant, Hoblitzell)	200.00	100.00	60.00
(41a)	Hal Chase Too Late (McConnell, McIntyre)	200.00	100.00	60.00
(41b)	Hal Chase Too Late (McLean, Suggs)	200.00	100.00	60.00
(42)	Harry Lord At Third (Lennox, Tinker)	350.00	175.00	105.00
(43)	Hartzell Covering Third (Dahlen, Scanlan)	200.00	100.00	60.00
(44)	Hartsel Strikes Out (Gray, Groom)	200.00	100.00	60.00
(45)	Held At Third (Lord, Tannehill)	200.00	100.00	60.00
(46)	Jake Stahl Guarding First (Cicotte, Stahl)	200.00	100.00	60.00
(47)	Jim Delahanty At Bat (Delahanty, Jones)	200.00	100.00	60.00
(48a)	Just Before The Battle (Ames, Meyers)	200.00	100.00	60.00
(48b)	Just Before The Battle (Bresnahan, McGraw)	450.00	225.00	135.00
(48c)	Just Before The Battle (Crandall, Meyers)	200.00	100.00	60.00
(48d)	Just Before The Battle (Becker, Devore)	200.00	100.00	60.00
(48e)	Just Before The Battle (Fletcher, Mathewson)	575.00	287.00	172.00
(48f)	Just Before The Battle (Marquard, Meyers)	350.00	175.00	105.00
(48g)	Just Before The Battle (Jennings, McGraw)	500.00	250.00	150.00
(48h)	Just Before The Battle (Mathewson, Meyers)	575.00	287.00	172.00
(48i)	Just Before The Battle (Murray, Snodgrass)	200.00	100.00	60.00
(48j)	Just Before The Battle (Meyers, Wiltse)	200.00	100.00	60.00
(49)	Knight Catches A Runner (Johnson, Knight)	650.00	325.00	195.00
(50a)	Lobert Almost Caught (Bridwell, Kling)	200.00	100.00	60.00
(50b)	Lobert Almost Caught (Kling, Young)	500.00	250.00	150.00
(50c)	Lobert Almost Caught (Kling, Mattern)	200.00	100.00	60.00
(50d)	Lobert Almost Caught (Kling, Steinfeldt)	200.00	100.00	60.00
(51)	Lobert Gets Tenney (Dooin, Lobert)	200.00	100.00	60.00
(52)	Lord Catches His Man (Lord, Tannehil)	200.00	100.00	60.00
(53)	McConnell Caught (Needham, Richie)	200.00	100.00	60.00
(54)	McIntyre At Bat (McConnell, McIntyre)	200.00	100.00	60.00
(55)	Moriarty Spiked (Stanage, Willett)	200.00	100.00	60.00
(56)	Nearly Caught (Bates, Bescher)	200.00	100.00	60.00
(57)	Oldring Almost Home (Lord, Oldring)	200.00	100.00	60.00
(58)	Schaefer On First (McBride, Milan)	200.00	100.00	60.00
(59)	Schaefer Steals Second (Clark Griffith, McBride)	300.00	150.00	90.00
(60)	Scoring From Second (Lord, Oldring)	200.00	100.00	60.00
(61a)	Scrambling Back To First (Barger, Bergen)	200.00	100.00	60.00
(61b)	Scrambling Back To First (Chase, Wolter)	200.00	100.00	60.00
(62)	Speaker Almost Caught (Clarke, Miller)	275.00	137.00	82.00
(63)	Speaker Rounding Third (Speaker, Wood)	450.00	225.00	135.00
(64)	Speaker Scores (Engle, Speaker)	450.00	225.00	135.00
(65)	Stahl Safe (Austin, Stovall)	200.00	100.00	60.00
(66)	Stone About To Swing (Schulte, Sheckard)	200.00	100.00	60.00
(67a)	Sullivan Puts Up A High One (Evans, Huggins)	350.00	175.00	105.00
(67b)	Sullivan Puts Up A High One (Gray, Groom)	200.00	100.00	60.00
(68a)	Sweeney Gets Stahl (Ford, Vaughn)	200.00	100.00	60.00
(68b)	Sweeney Gets Stahl (Ford, Sweeney)	200.00	100.00	60.00
(69)	Tenney Lands Safely (Latham, Raymond)	200.00	100.00	60.00
(70a)	The Athletic Infield (Baker, Barry)	350.00	175.00	105.00
(70b)	The Athletic Infield (Brown, Graham)	350.00	175.00	105.00
(70c)	The Athletic Infield (Hauser, Konetchy)	200.00	100.00	60.00
(70d)	The Athletic Infield (Krause, Thomas)	200.00	100.00	60.00
(71)	The Pinch Hitter (Egan, Hoblitzell)	250.00	125.00	75.00
(72)	The Scissors Slide (Birmingham, Turner)	200.00	100.00	60.00
(73a)	Tom Jones At Bat (Fromme, McLean)	200.00	100.00	60.00
(73b)	Tom Jones At Bat (Gaspar, McLean)	200.00	100.00	60.00
(74a)	Too Late For Devlin (Ames, Meyers)	200.00	100.00	60.00
(74b)	Too Late For Devlin (Crandall, Meyers)	200.00	100.00	60.00
(74c)	Too Late For Devlin (Devlin (Giants), Mathewson)	800.00	400.00	240.00
(74d)	Too Late For Devlin (Devlin (Rustlers), Mathewson)	575.00	287.00	172.00
(74e)	Too Late For Devlin (Marquard, Meyers)	350.00	175.00	105.00
(74f)	Too Late For Devlin (Meyers, Wiltse)	200.00	100.00	60.00
(75a)	Ty Cobb Steals Third (Cobb, Jennings)	2500.	1250.	750.00
(75b)	Ty Cobb Steals Third (Cobb, Moriarty)	2500.	1250.	750.00
(75c)	Ty Cobb Steals Third (Austin, Stoval)	1075.	537.00	322.00
(76)	Wheat Strikes Out (Dahlen, Wheat)	375.00	187.00	112.00

1909 T204 Ramly

While issued with both Ramly and T.T.T. brand Turkish tobacco cigarettes, the 121 cards in this set take their name from the more common of the two brands. By any name, the set is one of the more interesting and attractive of the early 20th Century. The 2-1/2" by 2-1/2" cards carry black and white oval photographic portraits with impressive gold embossed frames and borders on the front. Toward the bottom appears the player's last name, position, team and league. The backs carry only the most basic information on the cigarette company. Due to their scarcity, the Ramly set is not widely collected. The complete set price does not include the scarce variations.

		NR MT	EX	VG
	Complete Set (121):	65000.	32500.	19500.
	Common Player:	400.00	200.00	120.00
(1)	Whitey Alperman	400.00	200.00	120.00
(2)	John Anderson	400.00	200.00	120.00
(3)	Jimmy Archer	400.00	200.00	120.00
(4)	Frank Arrelanes (Arellanes)	400.00	200.00	120.00
(5)	Jim Ball	400.00	200.00	120.00
(6)	Neal Ball	400.00	200.00	120.00
(7a)	Frank C. Bancroft (photo inside oval frame)	400.00	200.00	120.00
(7b)	Frank C. Bancroft (photo inside square frame)	1500.	750.00	450.00
(8)	Johnny Bates	400.00	200.00	120.00
(9)	Fred Beebe	400.00	200.00	120.00
(10)	George Bell	400.00	200.00	120.00
(11)	Chief Bender	1700.	850.00	510.00
(12)	Walter Blair	400.00	200.00	120.00
(13)	Cliff Blankenship	400.00	200.00	120.00
(14)	Frank Bowerman	400.00	200.00	120.00
(15a)	Wm. Bransfield (photo inside oval frame)	400.00	200.00	120.00
(15b)	Wm. Bransfield (photo inside square frame)	1750.	875.00	525.00
(16)	Roger Bresnahan	750.00	375.00	225.00
(17)	Al Bridwell	400.00	200.00	120.00
(18)	Mordecai Brown	1700.	850.00	510.00
(19)	Fred Burchell	400.00	200.00	120.00
(20a)	Jesse C. Burkett (photo inside oval frame)	1500.	750.00	450.00
(20b)	Jesse C. Burkett (photo inside square frame)	2200.	1100.	660.00
(21)	Bobby Byrnes (Byrne)	400.00	200.00	120.00
(22)	Bill Carrigan	400.00	200.00	120.00
(23)	Frank Chance	1500.	750.00	450.00
(24)	Charlie Chech	400.00	200.00	120.00
(25)	Ed Cicolte (Cicotte)	550.00	275.00	165.00
(26)	Bill Clymer	400.00	200.00	120.00
(27)	Andy Coakley	400.00	200.00	120.00
(28)	Jimmy Collins	1500.	750.00	450.00
(29)	Ed. Collins	2200.	1100.	660.00
(30)	Wid Conroy	400.00	200.00	120.00
(31)	Jack Coombs	400.00	200.00	120.00
(32)	Doc Crandall	400.00	200.00	120.00
(33)	Lou Criger	400.00	200.00	120.00
(34)	Harry Davis	400.00	200.00	120.00
(35)	Art Devlin	400.00	200.00	120.00
(36a)	Wm. H. Dineen (Dinneen) (photo inside oval frame)	400.00	200.00	120.00
(36b)	Wm. H. Dineen (Dinneen) (photo inside square frame)	1000.	500.00	300.00
(37)	Jiggs Donahue	400.00	200.00	120.00
(38)	Mike Donlin	400.00	200.00	120.00
(39)	Wild Bill Donovan	400.00	200.00	120.00
(40)	Gus Dorner	400.00	200.00	120.00
(41)	Joe Dunn	400.00	200.00	120.00
(42)	Kid Elberfield (Elberfeld)	400.00	200.00	120.00
(43)	Johnny Evers	1700.	850.00	510.00
(44)	Bob Ewing	400.00	200.00	120.00
(45)	Cecil Ferguson	400.00	200.00	120.00
(46)	Hobe Ferris	400.00	200.00	120.00
(47)	Jerry Freeman	400.00	200.00	120.00
(48)	Art Fromme	400.00	200.00	120.00
(49)	Bob Ganley	400.00	200.00	120.00
(50)	Doc Gessler	400.00	200.00	120.00
(51)	Peaches Graham	400.00	200.00	120.00
(52)	Clark Griffith	1500.	750.00	450.00
(53)	Roy Hartzell	400.00	200.00	120.00
(54)	Charlie Hemphill	400.00	200.00	120.00
(55)	Dick Hoblitzel (Hoblitzell)	400.00	200.00	120.00
(56)	Geo. Howard	400.00	200.00	120.00
(57)	Harry Howell	400.00	200.00	120.00
(58)	Miller Huggins	1700.	850.00	510.00
(59)	John Hummell (Hummel)	400.00	200.00	120.00
(60)	Walter Johnson	8500.	4250.	2550.
(61)	Thos. Jones	400.00	200.00	120.00
(62)	Mike Kahoe	400.00	200.00	120.00
(63)	Ed Kargar	400.00	200.00	120.00
(64)	Wee Willie Keeler	2200.	1100.	660.00
(65)	Red Kleinon (Kleinow)	400.00	200.00	120.00
(66)	Jack Knight	400.00	200.00	120.00
(67)	Ed Konetchey (Konetchy)	400.00	200.00	120.00
(68)	Vive Lindaman	400.00	200.00	120.00
(69)	Hans Loebert (Lobert)	400.00	200.00	120.00
(70)	Harry Lord	400.00	200.00	120.00
(71)	Harry Lumley	400.00	200.00	120.00
(72)	Johnny Lush	400.00	200.00	120.00
(73)	Rube Manning	400.00	200.00	120.00
(74)	Jimmy McAleer	400.00	200.00	120.00
(75)	Amby McConnell	400.00	200.00	120.00
(76)	Moose McCormick	400.00	200.00	120.00
(77)	Harry McIntyre	400.00	200.00	120.00
(78)	Larry McLean	400.00	200.00	120.00
(79)	Fred Merkle	400.00	200.00	120.00
(80)	Clyde Milan	400.00	200.00	120.00
(81)	Mike Mitchell	400.00	200.00	120.00
(82a)	Pat Moran (photo inside oval frame)	400.00	200.00	120.00
(82b)	Pat Moran (photo inside square frame)	400.00	200.00	120.00
(83)	Cy Morgan	400.00	200.00	120.00
(84)	Tim Murname (Murnane)	400.00	200.00	120.00
(85)	Danny Murphy	400.00	200.00	120.00
(86)	Red Murray	400.00	200.00	120.00
(87)	Doc Newton	400.00	200.00	120.00
(88)	Simon Nichols (Nicholls)	400.00	200.00	120.00
(89)	Harry Niles	400.00	200.00	120.00
(90)	Bill O'Hare (O'Hara)	400.00	200.00	120.00
(91)	Charley O'Leary	400.00	200.00	120.00
(92)	Dode Paskert	400.00	200.00	120.00
(93)	Barney Pelty	400.00	200.00	120.00

No.	Player	NR MT	EX	VG
(94)	Jake Pfeister	400.00	200.00	120.00
(95)	Ed Plank	3000.	1500.	900.00
(96)	Jack Powell	400.00	200.00	120.00
(97)	Bugs Raymond	400.00	200.00	120.00
(98)	Tom Reilly	400.00	200.00	120.00
(99)	Claude Ritchey	400.00	200.00	120.00
(100)	Nap Rucker	400.00	200.00	120.00
(101)	Ed Ruelbach (Reulbach)	400.00	200.00	120.00
(102)	Slim Sallee	400.00	200.00	120.00
(103)	Germany Schaefer	400.00	200.00	120.00
(104)	Jimmy Schekard (Sheckard)	400.00	200.00	120.00
(105)	Admiral Schlei	400.00	200.00	120.00
(106)	Wildfire Schulte	400.00	200.00	120.00
(107)	Jimmy Sebring	400.00	200.00	120.00
(108)	Bill Shipke	400.00	200.00	120.00
(109)	Charlie Smith	400.00	200.00	120.00
(110)	Tubby Spencer	400.00	200.00	120.00
(111)	Jake Stahl	400.00	200.00	120.00
(112)	Jim Stephens	400.00	200.00	120.00
(113)	Harry Stienfeldt (Steinfeldt)	400.00	200.00	120.00
(114)	Gabby Street	400.00	200.00	120.00
(115)	Bill Sweeney	400.00	200.00	120.00
(116)	Fred Tenney	400.00	200.00	120.00
(117)	Ira Thomas	400.00	200.00	120.00
(118)	Joe Tinker	1500.	750.00	450.00
(119)	Bob Unclane (Unglaub)	400.00	200.00	120.00
(120)	Heinie Wagner	400.00	200.00	120.00
(121)	Bobby Wallace	1500.	750.00	450.00

1911 T205 Gold Border

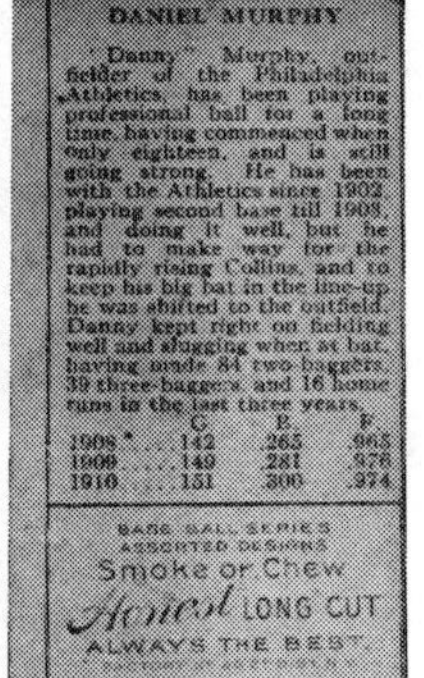

Taking their hobby nickname from their border color, these cards were issued in a number of different cigarette brands. The cards measure 1-1/2" by 2-5/8". American League cards feature a color lithograph of the player inside a stylized baseball diamond. National League cards have head- and-shoulders portraits and a plain background, plus the first ever use of a facsimile autograph in a major card set. The 12 minor league players in the set feature three-quarter length portraits or action pictures in an elaborate frame of columns and other devices. Card backs of the major leaguers carry the player's full name (a first) and statistics. Card backs of the minor leaguers lack the statistics. The complete set price does not include the scarcer variations.

		NR MT	EX	VG
Complete Set:		40000.	20000.	12000.
Common Player:		90.00	45.00	24.00
(1)	Edward J. Abbaticchio	90.00	45.00	24.00
(2)	Doc Adkins	300.00	150.00	81.00
(3)	Leon K. Ames	90.00	45.00	24.00
(4)	Jas. P. Archer	90.00	45.00	24.00
(5)	Jimmy Austin	90.00	45.00	24.00
(6)	Bill Bailey	90.00	45.00	24.00
(7)	Home Run Baker	350.00	175.00	94.00
(8)	Neal Ball	90.00	45.00	24.00
(9)	E.B. Barger (full "B" on cap)	90.00	45.00	24.00
(10)	E.B. Barger (partial "B" on cap)	450.00	225.00	121.00
(11)	Jack Barry	90.00	45.00	24.00
(12)	Emil Batch	300.00	150.00	81.00
(13)	John W. Bates	90.00	45.00	24.00
(14)	Fred Beck	90.00	45.00	24.00
(15)	B. Becker	90.00	45.00	24.00
(16)	George G. Bell	90.00	45.00	24.00
(17)	Chas. Bender	500.00	250.00	135.00
(18)	William Bergen	90.00	45.00	24.00
(19)	Bob Bescher	90.00	45.00	24.00
(20)	Joe Birmingham	90.00	45.00	24.00
(21)	Lena Blackburne	90.00	45.00	24.00
(22)	William E. Bransfield	90.00	45.00	24.00
(23)	Roger P. Bresnahan (mouth closed)	600.00	300.00	162.00
(24)	Roger P. Bresnahan (mouth open)	575.00	287.00	155.00
(25)	A.H. Bridwell	90.00	45.00	24.00
(26)	Mordecai Brown	400.00	200.00	108.00
(27)	Robert Byrne	90.00	45.00	24.00
(28)	Hick Cady	300.00	150.00	81.00
(29)	H. Camnitz	90.00	45.00	24.00
(30)	Bill Carrigan	90.00	45.00	24.00
(31)	Frank J. Chance	400.00	200.00	108.00
(32a)	Hal Chase (both ears show, gold diamond frame extends below shoulders)	150.00	75.00	40.00
(32b)	Hal Chase (both ears show, gold diamond frame ends at shoulders)	150.00	75.00	40.00
(33)	Hal Chase (only left ear shows)	475.00	237.00	128.00
(34)	Ed Cicotte	125.00	62.00	34.00
(35)	Fred C. Clarke	275.00	137.00	74.00
(36)	Ty Cobb	5000.	2500.	1350.
(37)	Eddie Collins (mouth closed)	500.00	250.00	135.00
(38)	Eddie Collins (mouth open)	575.00	287.00	155.00
(39)	Jimmy Collins	600.00	300.00	162.00
(40)	Frank J. Corridon	90.00	45.00	24.00
(41a)	Otis Crandall ("t" not crossed in name)	90.00	45.00	24.00
(41b)	Otis Crandall ("t" crossed in name)	90.00	45.00	24.00
(42)	Lou Criger	90.00	45.00	24.00
(43)	W.F. Dahlen	250.00	125.00	67.00
(44)	Jake Daubert	95.00	47.00	26.00
(45)	Jim Delahanty	90.00	45.00	24.00
(46)	Arthur Devlin	90.00	45.00	24.00
(47)	Josh Devore	90.00	45.00	24.00
(48)	W.R. Dickson	90.00	45.00	24.00
(49)	Jiggs Donohue (Donahue)	400.00	200.00	108.00
(50)	Chas. S. Dooin	90.00	45.00	24.00
(51)	Michael J. Doolan	90.00	45.00	24.00
(52a)	Patsy Dougherty (red sock for team emblem)	90.00	45.00	24.00
(52b)	Patsy Dougherty (white sock for team emblem)	275.00	137.00	74.00
(53)	Thomas Downey	90.00	45.00	24.00
(54)	Larry Doyle	90.00	45.00	24.00
(55)	Hugh Duffy	450.00	225.00	121.00
(56)	Jack Dunn	325.00	162.00	88.00
(57)	Jimmy Dygert	90.00	45.00	24.00
(58)	R. Egan	90.00	45.00	24.00
(59)	Kid Elberfeld	90.00	45.00	24.00
(60)	Clyde Engle	90.00	45.00	24.00
(61)	Louis Evans	90.00	45.00	24.00
(62)	John J. Evers	450.00	225.00	121.00
(63)	Robert Ewing	90.00	45.00	24.00
(64)	G.C. Ferguson	90.00	45.00	24.00
(65)	Ray Fisher	350.00	175.00	94.00
(66)	Arthur Fletcher	90.00	45.00	24.00
(67)	John A. Flynn	90.00	45.00	24.00
(68)	Russ Ford (black cap)	90.00	45.00	24.00
(69)	Russ Ford (white cap)	325.00	162.00	88.00
(70)	Wm. A. Foxen	90.00	45.00	24.00
(71)	Jimmy Frick	300.00	150.00	81.00
(72)	Arthur Fromme	90.00	45.00	24.00
(73)	Earl Gardner	90.00	45.00	24.00
(74)	H.L. Gaspar	90.00	45.00	24.00
(75)	George Gibson	90.00	45.00	24.00
(76)	Wilbur Goode	90.00	45.00	24.00
(77)	George F. Graham (Rustlers)	90.00	45.00	24.00
(78)	George F. Graham (Cubs)	450.00	225.00	121.00
(79)	Edward L. Grant	325.00	162.00	88.00
(80a)	Dolly Gray (no stats on back)	90.00	45.00	24.00
(80b)	Dolly Gray (stats on back)	200.00	100.00	54.00
(81)	Clark Griffith	400.00	200.00	108.00
(82)	Bob Groom	90.00	45.00	24.00
(83)	Charlie Hanford	300.00	150.00	81.00
(84)	Bob Harmon (both ears show)	90.00	45.00	24.00
(85)	Bob Harmon (only left ear shows)	450.00	225.00	121.00
(86)	Topsy Hartsel	90.00	45.00	24.00
(87)	Arnold J. Hauser	90.00	45.00	24.00
(88)	Charlie Hemphill	90.00	45.00	24.00
(89)	C.L. Herzog	90.00	45.00	24.00
(90a)	R. Hoblitzell (no stats on back)	600.00	300.00	162.00
(90b)	R. Hoblitzell ("Cin." after 2nd 1908 in stats)	225.00	112.00	61.00
(90c)	R. Hoblitzel (name incorrect, no "Cin." after 1908 in stats)	90.00	45.00	24.00
(90d)	R. Hoblitzell (name correct, no "Cin." after 1908 in stats)	225.00	112.00	61.00
(91)	Danny Hoffman	90.00	45.00	24.00
(92)	Miller J. Huggins	300.00	150.00	81.00
(93)	John E. Hummel	90.00	45.00	24.00
(94)	Fred Jacklitsch	90.00	45.00	24.00
(95)	Hughie Jennings	600.00	300.00	162.00
(96)	Walter Johnson	1600.	800.00	432.00
(97)	D. Jones	90.00	45.00	24.00
(98)	Tom Jones	90.00	45.00	24.00
(99)	Addie Joss	600.00	300.00	162.00
(100)	Ed Karger	300.00	150.00	81.00
(101)	Ed Killian	90.00	45.00	24.00
(102)	Red Kleinow	300.00	150.00	81.00
(103)	John G. Kling	90.00	45.00	24.00
(104)	Jack Knight	90.00	45.00	24.00
(105)	Ed Konetchy	90.00	45.00	24.00
(106)	Harry Krause	90.00	45.00	24.00
(107)	Floyd M. Kroh	90.00	45.00	24.00
(108)	Frank LaPorte	90.00	45.00	24.00
(109)	Frank Lang (Lange)	90.00	45.00	24.00
(110a)	A. Latham (A. Latham on back)	90.00	45.00	24.00
(110b)	A. Latham (W.A. Latham on back)	90.00	45.00	24.00
(111)	Thomas W. Leach	90.00	45.00	24.00
(112)	Watty Lee	300.00	150.00	81.00
(113)	Sam Leever	90.00	45.00	24.00
(114a)	A. Leifield (initial "A." on front)	90.00	45.00	24.00
(114b)	A.P. Leifield (initials "A.P." on front)	90.00	45.00	24.00
(115)	Edgar Lennox	90.00	45.00	24.00
(116)	Paddy Livingston	90.00	45.00	24.00
(117)	John B. Lobert	90.00	45.00	24.00
(118)	Bris Lord (Athletics)	90.00	45.00	24.00
(119)	Harry Lord (White Sox)	90.00	45.00	24.00
(120)	Jno. C. Lush	90.00	45.00	24.00
(121)	Nick Maddox	90.00	45.00	24.00
(122)	Sherwood R. Magee	90.00	45.00	24.00
(123)	R.W. Marquard	400.00	200.00	108.00
(124)	C. Mathewson	1350.	675.00	364.00
(125)	A.A. Mattern	90.00	45.00	24.00
(126)	Sport McAllister	300.00	150.00	81.00
(127)	George McBride	90.00	45.00	24.00
(128)	Amby McConnell	90.00	45.00	24.00
(129)	P.M. McElveen	90.00	45.00	24.00
(130)	J.J. McGraw	500.00	250.00	135.00
(131)	Harry McIntyre (Cubs)	90.00	45.00	24.00
(132)	Matty McIntyre (White Sox)	90.00	45.00	24.00
(133)	M.A. McLean (initials actually J.B.)	90.00	45.00	24.00
(134)	Fred Merkle	95.00	47.00	26.00
(135)	George Merritt	300.00	150.00	81.00
(136)	J.T. Meyers	90.00	45.00	24.00
(137)	Clyde Milan	90.00	45.00	24.00
(138)	J.D. Miller	90.00	45.00	24.00
(139)	M.F. Mitchell	90.00	45.00	24.00
(140a)	P.J. Moran (stray line of type below stats)	90.00	45.00	24.00
(140b)	P.J. Moran (no stray line)	90.00	45.00	24.00
(141)	George Moriarty	90.00	45.00	24.00
(142)	George Mullin	90.00	45.00	24.00
(143)	Danny Murphy	90.00	45.00	24.00
(144)	Jack Murray	90.00	45.00	24.00
(145)	John Nee	300.00	150.00	81.00
(146)	Thomas J. Needham	90.00	45.00	24.00
(147)	Rebel Oakes	90.00	45.00	24.00
(148)	Rube Oldring	90.00	45.00	24.00
(149)	Charley O'Leary	90.00	45.00	24.00
(150)	Fred Olmstead	90.00	45.00	24.00
(151)	Orval Overall	90.00	45.00	24.00
(152)	Freddy Parent	90.00	45.00	24.00
(153)	George Paskert	90.00	45.00	24.00
(154)	Billy Payne	90.00	45.00	24.00
(155)	Barney Pelty	90.00	45.00	24.00
(156)	John Pfeister	90.00	45.00	24.00
(157)	Jimmy Phelan	300.00	150.00	81.00
(158)	E.J. Phelps	90.00	45.00	24.00
(159)	C. Phillippe	90.00	45.00	24.00
(160)	Jack Quinn	90.00	45.00	24.00
(161)	A.L. Raymond	400.00	200.00	108.00
(162)	E.M. Reulbach	90.00	45.00	24.00
(163)	Lewis Richie	90.00	45.00	24.00
(164)	John A. Rowan	300.00	150.00	81.00
(165)	George N. Rucker	90.00	45.00	24.00
(166)	W.D. Scanlan	300.00	150.00	81.00
(167)	Germany Schaefer	90.00	45.00	24.00
(168)	George Schlei	90.00	45.00	24.00
(169)	Boss Schmidt	90.00	45.00	24.00
(170)	F.M. Schulte	90.00	45.00	24.00
(171)	Jim Scott	90.00	45.00	24.00
(172)	B.H. Sharpe	90.00	45.00	24.00
(173)	David Shean (Rustlers)	90.00	45.00	24.00
(174)	David Shean (Cubs)	450.00	225.00	121.00
(175)	Jas. T. Sheckard	90.00	45.00	24.00
(176)	Hack Simmons	90.00	45.00	24.00
(177)	Tony Smith	90.00	45.00	24.00
(178)	Fred C. Snodgrass	90.00	45.00	24.00
(179)	Tris Speaker	550.00	275.00	148.00
(180)	Jake Stahl	90.00	45.00	24.00
(181)	Oscar Stanage	90.00	45.00	24.00
(182)	Harry Steinfeldt	95.00	47.00	26.00
(183)	George Stone	90.00	45.00	24.00
(184)	George Stovall	90.00	45.00	24.00
(185)	Gabby Street	90.00	45.00	24.00
(186)	George F. Suggs	450.00	225.00	121.00
(187)	Ed Summers	90.00	45.00	24.00
(188)	Jeff Sweeney	300.00	150.00	81.00
(189)	Lee Tannehill	90.00	45.00	24.00
(190)	Ira Thomas	90.00	45.00	24.00
(191)	Joe Tinker	450.00	225.00	121.00
(192)	John Titus	90.00	45.00	24.00
(193)	Terry Turner	450.00	225.00	121.00
(194)	James Vaughn	90.00	45.00	24.00
(195)	Heinie Wagner	300.00	150.00	81.00
(196)	Bobby Wallace (with cap)	300.00	150.00	81.00
(197a)	Bobby Wallace (no cap, one line of 1910 stats)	600.00	300.00	162.00
(197b)	Bobby Wallace (no cap, two lines of 1910 stats)	450.00	225.00	121.00
(198)	Ed Walsh	475.00	237.00	128.00
(199)	Z.D. Wheat	450.00	225.00	121.00
(200)	Doc White (White Sox)	90.00	45.00	24.00
(201)	Kirb. White (Pirates)	300.00	150.00	81.00
(202)	Irvin K. Wilhelm	450.00	225.00	121.00
(203)	Ed Willett	90.00	45.00	24.00
(204)	J. Owen Wilson	90.00	45.00	24.00
(205)	George R. Wiltse (both ears show)	90.00	45.00	24.00
(206)	George R. Wiltse (only right ear shows)	450.00	225.00	121.00
(207)	Harry Wolter	90.00	45.00	24.00
(208)	Cy Young	1200.	600.00	324.00

1909 - 11 T206 White Border

The nearly 525 cards which make up the T206 set are the most popular of the early tobacco card issues. Players are depicted in a color lithograph against a variety of colorful backgrounds, surrounded by a white border. The player names on the 1-1/2" by 2-5/8" cards appear at the bottom with the city and league, when a city had more than one team. Backs contain an ad for one of 16 brands of cigarettes. There are 389 major leaguer cards and 134 minor leaguer cards in the set, but with front/back varieties the number of potentially different cards runs into the thousands. The set features many expensive cards including a number of pose and/or team variations, along with the very scarce Eddie Plank card and the "King of Baseball Cards," the T206 Honus Wagner, the most avidly sought of

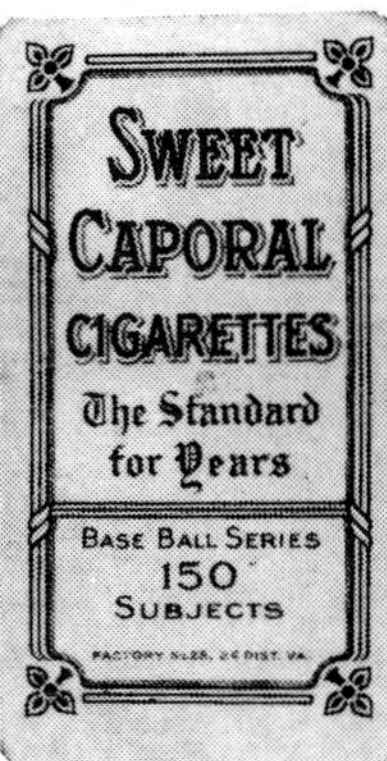

all baseball cards. The complete set price does not include the Ty Cobb card with Ty Cobb brand back, Doyle (N.Y. Nat'l.), Magie, Plank and Wagner cards.

		NR MT	EX	VG
	Complete Set:	80000.	40000.	24000.
	Common Player:	70.00	35.00	21.00
	Common Minor Leaguer:	75.00	37.00	22.00
	Common Southern Leaguer:	175.00	87.00	52.00
(1)	Ed Abbaticchio (blue sleeves)	115.00	57.00	34.00
(2)	Ed Abbaticchio (brown sleeves)	75.00	37.00	22.00
(3)	Fred Abbott	80.00	40.00	24.00
(4)	Bill Abstein	75.00	37.00	22.00
(5)	Doc Adkins	80.00	40.00	24.00
(6)	Whitey Alperman	95.00	47.00	28.00
(7)	Red Ames (hands at chest)	95.00	47.00	28.00
(8)	Red Ames (hands above head)	95.00	47.00	28.00
(9)	Red Ames (portrait)	75.00	37.00	22.00
(10)	John Anderson	80.00	40.00	24.00
(11)	Frank Arellanes	75.00	37.00	22.00
(12)	Herman Armbruster	80.00	40.00	24.00
(13)	Harry Arndt	80.00	40.00	24.00
(14)	Jake Atz	75.00	37.00	22.00
(15)	Home Run Baker	450.00	225.00	135.00
(16)	Neal Ball (New York)	95.00	47.00	28.00
(17)	Neal Ball (Cleveland)	75.00	37.00	22.00
(18)	Jap Barbeau	95.00	47.00	28.00
(19)	Cy Barger	80.00	40.00	24.00
(20)	Jack Barry (Philadelphia)	75.00	37.00	22.00
(21)	Shad Barry (Milwaukee)	80.00	40.00	24.00
(22)	Jack Bastian	175.00	87.00	52.00
(23)	Emil Batch	80.00	40.00	24.00
(24)	Johnny Bates	95.00	47.00	28.00
(25)	Harry Bay	225.00	112.00	67.00
(26)	Ginger Beaumont	95.00	47.00	28.00
(27)	Fred Beck	75.00	37.00	22.00
(28)	Beals Becker	75.00	37.00	22.00
(29)	Jake Beckley	295.00	147.00	88.00
(30)	George Bell (hands above head)	95.00	47.00	28.00
(31)	George Bell (pitching follow thru)	75.00	37.00	22.00
(32)	Chief Bender (pitching, no trees in background)	350.00	175.00	105.00
(33)	Chief Bender (pitching, trees in background)	350.00	175.00	105.00
(34)	Chief Bender (portrait)	360.00	180.00	108.00
(35)	Bill Bergen (batting)	95.00	47.00	28.00
(36)	Bill Bergen (catching)	80.00	40.00	24.00
(37)	Heinie Berger	75.00	37.00	22.00
(38)	Bill Bernhard	175.00	87.00	52.00
(39)	Bob Bescher (hands in air)	75.00	37.00	22.00
(40)	Bob Bescher (portrait)	75.00	37.00	22.00
(41)	Joe Birmingham	100.00	50.00	30.00
(42)	Lena Blackburne	80.00	40.00	24.00
(43)	Jack Bliss	75.00	37.00	22.00
(44)	Frank Bowerman	95.00	47.00	28.00
(45)	Bill Bradley (portrait)	95.00	47.00	28.00
(46)	Bill Bradley (with bat)	75.00	37.00	22.00
(47)	Dave Brain	80.00	40.00	24.00
(48)	Kitty Bransfield	95.00	47.00	28.00
(49)	Roy Brashear	80.00	40.00	24.00
(50)	Ted Breitenstein	175.00	87.00	52.00
(51)	Roger Bresnahan (portrait)	400.00	200.00	120.00
(52)	Roger Bresnahan (with bat)	375.00	187.00	112.00
(53)	Al Bridwell (portrait, no cap)	75.00	37.00	22.00
(54)	Al Bridwell (portrait, with cap)	95.00	47.00	28.00
(55a)	George Brown (Browne) (Chicago)	95.00	47.00	28.00
(55b)	George Brown (Browne) (Washington)	750.00	375.00	225.00
(56)	Mordecai Brown (Chicago on shirt)	300.00	150.00	90.00
(57)	Mordecai Brown (Cubs on shirt)	400.00	200.00	120.00
(58)	Mordecai Brown (portrait)	350.00	175.00	105.00
(59)	Al Burch (batting)	200.00	100.00	60.00
(60)	Al Burch (fielding)	75.00	37.00	22.00
(61)	Fred Burchell	80.00	40.00	24.00
(62)	Jimmy Burke	80.00	40.00	24.00
(63)	Bill Burns	75.00	37.00	22.00
(64)	Donie Bush	75.00	37.00	22.00
(65)	John Butler	80.00	40.00	24.00
(66)	Bobby Byrne	75.00	37.00	22.00
(67)	Howie Camnitz (arm at side)	75.00	37.00	22.00
(68)	Howie Camnitz (arms folded)	95.00	47.00	28.00
(69)	Howie Camnitz (hands above head)	75.00	37.00	22.00
(70)	Billy Campbell	75.00	37.00	22.00
(71)	Scoops Carey	130.00	65.00	39.00
(72)	Charley Carr	80.00	40.00	24.00
(73)	Bill Carrigan	75.00	37.00	22.00
(74)	Doc Casey	80.00	40.00	24.00
(75)	Peter Cassidy	80.00	40.00	24.00
(76)	Frank Chance (batting)	300.00	150.00	90.00
(77)	Frank Chance (portrait, red background)	400.00	200.00	120.00
(78)	Frank Chance (portrait, yellow background)	350.00	175.00	105.00
(79)	Bill Chappelle	80.00	40.00	24.00
(80)	Chappie Charles	75.00	37.00	22.00
(81)	Hal Chase (holding trophy)	200.00	100.00	60.00
(82)	Hal Chase (portrait, blue background)	150.00	75.00	45.00
(83)	Hal Chase (portrait, pink background)	275.00	137.00	82.00
(84)	Hal Chase (throwing, dark cap)	175.00	87.00	52.00
(85)	Hal Chase (throwing, white cap)	350.00	175.00	105.00
(86)	Jack Chesbro	370.00	185.00	111.00
(87)	Ed Cicotte	200.00	100.00	60.00
(88)	Bill Clancy (Clancey)	80.00	40.00	24.00
(89)	Josh Clark (Clarke) (Columbus)	80.00	40.00	24.00
(90)	Fred Clarke (Pittsburg, holding bat)	300.00	150.00	90.00
(91)	Fred Clarke (Pittsburg, portrait)	350.00	175.00	105.00
(92)	Nig Clarke (Cleveland)	95.00	47.00	28.00
(93)	Bill Clymer	80.00	40.00	24.00
(94)	Ty Cobb (portrait, green background)	2750.	1375.	825.00
(95a)	Ty Cobb (portrait, red background)	1950.	975.00	585.00
(95b)	Ty Cobb (portrait, red background, Ty Cobb brand back)	60000.	30000.	18000.
(96)	Ty Cobb (bat off shoulder)	2800.	1400.	840.00
(97)	Ty Cobb (bat on shoulder)	2400.	1200.	720.00
(98)	Cad Coles	175.00	87.00	52.00
(99)	Eddie Collins (Philadelphia)	375.00	187.00	112.00
(100)	Jimmy Collins (Minneapolis)	325.00	162.00	97.00
(101)	Bunk Congalton	80.00	40.00	24.00
(102)	Wid Conroy (fielding)	95.00	47.00	28.00
(103)	Wid Conroy (with bat)	75.00	37.00	22.00
(104)	Harry Covaleski (Coveleski)	95.00	47.00	28.00
(105)	Doc Crandall (portrait, no cap)	95.00	47.00	28.00
(106)	Doc Crandall (portrait, with cap)	75.00	37.00	22.00
(107)	Bill Cranston	190.00	95.00	57.00
(108)	Gavvy Cravath	125.00	62.00	37.00
(109)	Sam Crawford (throwing)	375.00	187.00	112.00
(110)	Sam Crawford (with bat)	350.00	175.00	105.00
(111)	Birdie Cree	75.00	37.00	22.00
(112)	Lou Criger	95.00	47.00	28.00
(113)	Dode Criss	95.00	47.00	28.00
(114)	Monte Cross	80.00	40.00	24.00
(115a)	Bill Dahlen (Boston)	100.00	50.00	30.00
(115b)	Bill Dahlen (Brooklyn)	425.00	212.00	127.00
(116)	Paul Davidson	80.00	40.00	24.00
(117)	George Davis (Chicago)	95.00	47.00	28.00
(118)	Harry Davis (Philadelphia, Davis on front)	75.00	37.00	22.00
(119)	Harry Davis (Philadelphia, H. Davis on front)	95.00	47.00	28.00
(120)	Frank Delehanty (Delahanty) (Louisville)	80.00	40.00	24.00
(121)	Jim Delehanty (Delahanty) (Washington)	95.00	47.00	28.00
(122a)	Ray Demmitt (New York)	75.00	37.00	22.00
(122b)	Ray Demmitt (St. Louis)	6000.	3000.	1800.
(123)	Rube Dessau	80.00	40.00	24.00
(124)	Art Devlin	95.00	47.00	28.00
(125)	Josh Devore	75.00	37.00	22.00
(126)	Bill Dineen (Dinneen)	75.00	37.00	22.00
(127)	Mike Donlin (fielding)	250.00	125.00	75.00
(128)	Mike Donlin (seated)	95.00	47.00	28.00
(129)	Mike Donlin (with bat)	75.00	37.00	22.00
(130)	Jiggs Donohue (Donahue)	95.00	47.00	28.00
(131)	Wild Bill Donovan (portrait)	95.00	47.00	28.00
(132)	Wild Bill Donovan (throwing)	75.00	37.00	22.00
(133)	Red Dooin	95.00	47.00	28.00
(134)	Mickey Doolan (batting)	75.00	37.00	22.00
(135)	Mickey Doolan (fielding)	75.00	37.00	22.00
(136)	Mickey Doolin (Doolan)	95.00	47.00	28.00
(137)	Gus Dorner	80.00	40.00	24.00
(138)	Patsy Dougherty (arm in air)	75.00	37.00	22.00
(139)	Patsy Dougherty (portrait)	95.00	47.00	28.00
(140)	Tom Downey (batting)	75.00	37.00	22.00
(141)	Tom Downey (fielding)	75.00	37.00	22.00
(142)	Jerry Downs	80.00	40.00	24.00
(143a)	Joe Doyle (N.Y. Nat'l., hands above head)	22500.	11250.	6750.
(143b)	Joe Doyle (N.Y., hands above head)	75.00	37.00	22.00
(144)	Larry Doyle (N.Y. Nat'l., portrait)	95.00	47.00	28.00
(145)	Larry Doyle (N.Y. Nat'l., throwing)	125.00	62.00	37.00
(146)	Larry Doyle (N.Y. Nat'l., with bat)	95.00	47.00	28.00
(147)	Jean Dubuc	75.00	37.00	22.00
(148)	Hugh Duffy	300.00	150.00	90.00
(149)	Jack Dunn (Baltimore)	80.00	40.00	24.00
(150)	Joe Dunn (Brooklyn)	75.00	37.00	22.00
(151)	Bull Durham	100.00	50.00	30.00
(152)	Jimmy Dygert	75.00	37.00	22.00
(153)	Ted Easterly	75.00	37.00	22.00
(154)	Dick Egan	75.00	37.00	22.00
(155a)	Kid Elberfeld (New York)	95.00	47.00	28.00
(155b)	Kid Elberfeld (Washington, portrait)	1875.	937.00	562.00
(156)	Kid Elberfeld (Washington, fielding)	75.00	37.00	22.00
(157)	Roy Ellam	175.00	87.00	52.00
(158)	Clyde Engle	75.00	37.00	22.00
(159)	Steve Evans	75.00	37.00	22.00
(160)	Johnny Evers (portrait)	475.00	237.00	142.00
(161)	Johnny Evers (with bat, Chicago on shirt)	300.00	150.00	90.00
(162)	Johnny Evers (with bat, Cubs on shirt)	375.00	187.00	112.00
(163)	Bob Ewing	95.00	47.00	28.00
(164)	Cecil Ferguson	75.00	37.00	22.00
(165)	Hobe Ferris	95.00	47.00	28.00
(166)	Lou Fiene (portrait)	75.00	37.00	22.00
(167)	Lou Fiene (throwing)	75.00	37.00	22.00
(168)	Steamer Flanagan	80.00	40.00	24.00
(169)	Art Fletcher	75.00	37.00	22.00
(170)	Elmer Flick	325.00	162.00	97.00
(171)	Russ Ford	75.00	37.00	22.00
(172)	Ed Foster	175.00	87.00	52.00
(173)	Jerry Freeman	80.00	40.00	24.00
(174)	John Frill	75.00	37.00	22.00
(175)	Charlie Fritz	175.00	87.00	52.00
(176)	Art Fromme	75.00	37.00	22.00
(177)	Chick Gandil	200.00	100.00	60.00
(178)	Bob Ganley	95.00	47.00	28.00
(179)	John Ganzel	80.00	40.00	24.00
(180)	Harry Gasper	75.00	37.00	22.00
(181)	Rube Geyer	75.00	37.00	22.00
(182)	George Gibson	95.00	47.00	28.00
(183)	Billy Gilbert	95.00	47.00	28.00
(184)	Wilbur Goode (Good)	95.00	47.00	28.00
(185)	Bill Graham (St. Louis)	75.00	37.00	22.00
(186)	Peaches Graham (Boston)	75.00	37.00	22.00
(187)	Dolly Gray	75.00	37.00	22.00
(188)	Ed Greminger	175.00	87.00	52.00
(189)	Clark Griffith (batting)	275.00	137.00	82.00
(190)	Clark Griffith (portrait)	425.00	212.00	127.00
(191)	Moose Grimshaw	80.00	40.00	24.00
(192)	Bob Groom	75.00	37.00	22.00
(193)	Tom Guiheen	200.00	100.00	60.00
(194)	Ed Hahn	95.00	47.00	28.00
(195)	Bob Hall	80.00	40.00	24.00
(196)	Bill Hallman	80.00	40.00	24.00
(197)	Jack Hannifan (Hannifin)	80.00	40.00	24.00
(198)	Bill Hart (Little Rock)	225.00	112.00	67.00
(199)	Jimmy Hart (Montgomery)	190.00	95.00	57.00
(200)	Topsy Hartsel	75.00	37.00	22.00
(201)	Jack Hayden	80.00	40.00	24.00
(202)	J. Ross Helm	175.00	87.00	52.00
(203)	Charlie Hemphill	95.00	47.00	28.00
(204)	Buck Herzog (Boston)	75.00	37.00	22.00
(205)	Buck Herzog (New York)	95.00	47.00	28.00
(206)	Gordon Hickman	175.00	87.00	52.00
(207)	Bill Hinchman (Cleveland)	95.00	47.00	28.00
(208)	Harry Hinchman (Toledo)	80.00	40.00	24.00
(209)	Dick Hoblitzell	75.00	37.00	22.00
(210)	Danny Hoffman (St. Louis)	75.00	37.00	22.00
(211)	Izzy Hoffman (Providence)	80.00	40.00	24.00
(212)	Solly Hofman	75.00	37.00	22.00
(213)	Bock Hooker	175.00	87.00	52.00
(214)	Del Howard (Chicago)	75.00	37.00	22.00
(215)	Ernie Howard (Savannah)	175.00	87.00	52.00
(216)	Harry Howell (hand at waist)	75.00	37.00	22.00
(217)	Harry Howell (portrait)	75.00	37.00	22.00
(218)	Miller Huggins (hands at mouth)	300.00	150.00	90.00
(219)	Miller Huggins (portrait)	375.00	187.00	112.00
(220)	Rudy Hulswitt	75.00	37.00	22.00
(221)	John Hummel	75.00	37.00	22.00
(222)	George Hunter	75.00	37.00	22.00
(223)	Frank Isbell	100.00	50.00	30.00
(224)	Fred Jacklitsch	100.00	50.00	30.00
(225)	Jimmy Jackson	80.00	40.00	24.00
(226)	Hughie Jennings (one hand showing)	300.00	150.00	90.00
(227)	Hughie Jennings (both hands showing)	300.00	150.00	90.00
(228)	Hughie Jennings (portrait)	275.00	137.00	82.00
(229)	Walter Johnson (hands at chest)	950.00	475.00	285.00
(230)	Walter Johnson (portrait)	1200.	600.00	360.00
(231)	Fielder Jones (Chicago, hands at hips)	95.00	47.00	28.00
(232)	Fielder Jones (Chicago, portrait)	95.00	47.00	28.00
(233)	Davy Jones (Detroit)	75.00	37.00	22.00
(234)	Tom Jones (St. Louis)	95.00	47.00	28.00
(235)	Dutch Jordan (Atlanta)	175.00	87.00	52.00
(236)	Tim Jordan (Brooklyn, batting)	75.00	37.00	22.00
(237)	Tim Jordan (Brooklyn, portrait)	95.00	47.00	28.00
(238)	Addie Joss (hands at chest)	350.00	175.00	105.00
(239)	Addie Joss (portrait)	425.00	212.00	127.00
(240)	Ed Karger	95.00	47.00	28.00
(241)	Willie Keeler (portrait)	550.00	275.00	165.00
(242)	Willie Keeler (with bat)	525.00	262.00	157.00
(243)	Joe Kelley	225.00	112.00	67.00
(244)	J.F. Kiernan	175.00	87.00	52.00
(245)	Ed Killian (hands at chest)	75.00	37.00	22.00
(246)	Ed Killian (portrait)	95.00	47.00	28.00
(247)	Frank King	175.00	87.00	52.00
(248)	Rube Kisinger (Kissinger)	80.00	40.00	24.00
(249a)	Red Kleinow (Boston)	800.00	400.00	240.00
(249b)	Red Kleinow (New York, catching)	75.00	37.00	22.00
(250)	Red Kleinow (New York, with bat)	95.00	47.00	28.00
(251)	Johnny Kling	95.00	47.00	28.00
(252)	Otto Knabe	75.00	37.00	22.00
(253)	Jack Knight (portrait)	75.00	37.00	22.00
(254)	Jack Knight (with bat)	75.00	37.00	22.00
(255)	Ed Konetchy (glove above head)	95.00	47.00	28.00
(256)	Ed Konetchy (glove near ground)	75.00	37.00	22.00
(257)	Harry Krause (pitching)	75.00	37.00	22.00
(258)	Harry Krause (portrait)	75.00	37.00	22.00
(259)	Rube Kroh	75.00	37.00	22.00
(260)	Otto Kruger (Krueger)	80.00	40.00	24.00
(261)	James Lafitte	175.00	87.00	52.00

(262) Nap Lajoie (portrait) 950.00 475.00 285.00
(263) Nap Lajoie (throwing) 500.00 250.00 150.00
(264) Nap Lajoie (with bat) 500.00 250.00 150.00
(265) Joe Lake (New York) 95.00 47.00 28.00
(266) Joe Lake (St. Louis, ball in hand) 75.00 37.00 22.00
(267) Joe Lake (St. Louis, no ball in hand) 75.00 37.00 22.00
(268) Frank LaPorte 75.00 37.00 22.00
(269) Arlie Latham 75.00 37.00 22.00
(270) Bill Lattimore 80.00 40.00 24.00
(271) Jimmy Lavender 80.00 40.00 24.00
(272) Tommy Leach (bending over) 75.00 37.00 22.00
(273) Tommy Leach (portrait) 95.00 47.00 28.00
(274) Lefty Leifield (batting) 75.00 37.00 22.00
(275) Lefty Leifield (pitching) 95.00 47.00 28.00
(276) Ed Lennox 75.00 37.00 22.00
(277) Harry Lentz (Sentz) 175.00 87.00 52.00
(278) Glenn Liebhardt 95.00 47.00 28.00
(279) Vive Lindaman 95.00 47.00 28.00
(280) Perry Lipe 175.00 87.00 52.00
(281) Paddy Livingstone (Livingston) 75.00 37.00 22.00
(282) Hans Lobert 95.00 47.00 28.00
(283) Harry Lord 75.00 37.00 22.00
(284) Harry Lumley 95.00 47.00 28.00
(285a)Carl Lundgren (Chicago) 550.00 275.00 165.00
(285b)Carl Lundgren (Kansas City) 80.00 40.00 24.00
(286) Nick Maddox 75.00 37.00 22.00
(287a)Sherry Magie (Magee) 22500. 11250. 6750.
(287b)Sherry Magee (portrait) 125.00 62.00 37.00
(288) Sherry Magee (with bat) 95.00 47.00 28.00
(289) Bill Malarkey 80.00 40.00 24.00
(290) Billy Maloney 80.00 40.00 24.00
(291) George Manion 175.00 87.00 52.00
(292) Rube Manning (batting) 95.00 47.00 28.00
(293) Rube Manning (pitching) 75.00 37.00 22.00
(294) Rube Marquard (hands at thighs) 375.00 187.00 112.00
(295) Rube Marquard (pitching follow thru) 350.00 175.00 105.00
(296) Rube Marquard (portrait) 400.00 200.00 120.00
(297) Doc Marshall 75.00 37.00 22.00
(298) Christy Mathewson (dark cap) 600.00 300.00 180.00
(299) Christy Mathewson (portrait) 1200. 600.00 360.00
(300) Christy Mathewson (white cap) 900.00 450.00 270.00
(301) Al Mattern 75.00 37.00 22.00
(302) John McAleese 75.00 37.00 22.00
(303) George McBride 75.00 37.00 22.00
(304) Pat McCauley 175.00 87.00 52.00
(305) Moose McCormick 75.00 37.00 22.00
(306) Pryor McElveen 75.00 37.00 22.00
(307) Dan McGann 80.00 40.00 24.00
(308) Jim McGinley 80.00 40.00 24.00
(309) Iron Man McGinnity 250.00 125.00 75.00
(310) Stoney McGlynn 80.00 40.00 24.00
(311) John McGraw (finger in air) 345.00 175.00 100.00
(312) John McGraw (glove at hip) 345.00 175.00 100.00
(313) John McGraw (portrait, no cap) 400.00 200.00 120.00
(314) John McGraw (portrait, with cap) 295.00 145.00 87.50
(315) Harry McIntyre (Brooklyn) 95.00 47.00 28.00
(316) Harry McIntyre (Brooklyn & Chicago) 75.00 37.00 22.00
(317) Matty McIntyre (Detroit) 75.00 37.00 22.00
(318) Larry McLean 75.00 37.00 22.00
(319) George McQuillan (ball in hand) 95.00 47.00 28.00
(320) George McQuillan (with bat) 75.00 37.00 22.00
(321) Fred Merkle (portrait) 125.00 62.00 37.00
(322) Fred Merkle (throwing) 95.00 47.00 28.00
(323) George Merritt 80.00 40.00 24.00
(324) Chief Meyers 75.00 37.00 22.00
(325) Clyde Milan 75.00 37.00 22.00
(326) Dots Miller (Pittsburg) 75.00 37.00 22.00
(327) Molly Miller (Dallas) 175.00 87.00 52.00
(328) Bill Milligan 80.00 40.00 24.00
(329) Fred Mitchell (Toronto) 80.00 40.00 24.00
(330) Mike Mitchell (Cincinnati) 75.00 37.00 22.00
(331) Dan Moeller 80.00 40.00 24.00
(332) Carlton Molesworth 175.00 87.00 52.00
(333) Herbie Moran (Providence) 80.00 40.00 24.00
(334) Pat Moran (Chicago) 75.00 37.00 22.00
(335) George Moriarty 75.00 37.00 22.00
(336) Mike Mowrey 75.00 37.00 22.00
(337) Dom Mullaney 175.00 87.00 52.00
(338) George Mullen (Mullin) 75.00 37.00 22.00
(339) George Mullin (throwing) 95.00 47.00 28.00
(340) George Mullin (with bat) 75.00 37.00 22.00
(341) Danny Murphy (batting) 75.00 37.00 22.00
(342) Danny Murphy (throwing) 95.00 47.00 28.00
(343) Red Murray (batting) 75.00 37.00 22.00
(344) Red Murray (portrait) 75.00 37.00 22.00
(345) Chief Myers (Meyers) (batting) 75.00 37.00 22.00
(346) Chief Myers (Meyers) (fielding) 75.00 37.00 22.00
(347) Billy Nattress 80.00 40.00 24.00
(348) Tom Needham 75.00 37.00 22.00
(349) Simon Nicholls (hands on knees) 95.00 47.00 28.00
(350) Simon Nichols (Nicholls) (batting) 75.00 37.00 22.00
(351) Harry Niles 95.00 47.00 28.00
(352) Rebel Oakes 75.00 37.00 22.00
(353) Frank Oberlin 80.00 40.00 24.00
(354) Peter O'Brien 80.00 40.00 24.00
(355a)Bill O'Hara (New York) 75.00 37.00 22.00
(355b)Bill O'Hara (St. Louis) 5500. 2750. 1650.
(356) Rube Oldring (batting) 75.00 37.00 22.00
(357) Rube Oldring (fielding) 95.00 47.00 28.00
(358) Charley O'Leary (hands on knees) 75.00 37.00 22.00
(359) Charley O'Leary (portrait) 95.00 47.00 28.00
(360) William J. O'Neil 80.00 40.00 24.00
(361) Al Orth 175.00 87.00 52.00
(362) William Otey 175.00 87.00 52.00
(363) Orval Overall (hand face level) 75.00 37.00 22.00
(364) Orval Overall (hands waist level) 75.00 37.00 22.00
(365) Orval Overall (portrait) 95.00 47.00 28.00
(366) Frank Owen 95.00 47.00 28.00
(367) George Paige 175.00 87.00 52.00
(368) Fred Parent 95.00 47.00 28.00
(369) Dode Paskert 75.00 37.00 22.00
(370) Jim Pastorius 95.00 47.00 28.00
(371) Harry Pattee 400.00 200.00 120.00
(372) Billy Payne 75.00 37.00 22.00
(373) Barney Pelty (horizontal photo) 250.00 125.00 75.00
(374) Barney Pelty (vertical photo) 75.00 37.00 22.00
(375) Hub Perdue 175.00 87.00 52.00
(376) George Perring 75.00 37.00 22.00
(377) Arch Persons 175.00 87.00 52.00
(378) Francis (Big Jeff) Pfeffer 75.00 37.00 22.00
(379) Jake Pfeister (Pfiester) (seated) 75.00 37.00 22.00
(380) Jake Pfeister (Pfiester) (throwing) 75.00 37.00 22.00
(381) Jimmy Phelan 80.00 40.00 24.00
(382) Eddie Phelps 75.00 37.00 22.00
(383) Deacon Phillippe 75.00 37.00 22.00
(384) Ollie Pickering 80.00 40.00 24.00
(385) Eddie Plank 25000. 12500. 7500.
(386) Phil Poland 80.00 40.00 24.00
(387) Jack Powell 95.00 47.00 28.00
(388) Mike Powers 260.00 130.00 78.00
(389) Billy Purtell 75.00 37.00 22.00
(390) Ambrose Puttman (Puttmann) 80.00 40.00 24.00
(391) Lee Quillen (Quillin) 80.00 40.00 24.00
(392) Jack Quinn 75.00 37.00 22.00
(393) Newt Randall 80.00 40.00 24.00
(394) Bugs Raymond 75.00 37.00 22.00
(395) Ed Reagan 175.00 87.00 52.00
(396) Ed Reulbach (glove showing) 200.00 100.00 60.00
(397) Ed Reulbach (no glove showing) 75.00 37.00 22.00
(398) Dutch Revelle 175.00 87.00 52.00
(399) Bob Rhoades (Rhoads) (hands at chest) 75.00 37.00 22.00
(400) Bob Rhoades (Rhoads) (right arm extended) 75.00 37.00 22.00
(401) Charlie Rhodes 75.00 37.00 22.00
(402) Claude Ritchey 95.00 47.00 28.00
(403) Lou Ritter 80.00 40.00 24.00
(404) Ike Rockenfeld 175.00 87.00 52.00
(405) Claude Rossman 75.00 37.00 22.00
(406) Nap Rucker (portrait) 95.00 47.00 28.00
(407) Nap Rucker (throwing) 75.00 37.00 22.00
(408) Dick Rudolph 80.00 40.00 24.00
(409) Ray Ryan 175.00 87.00 52.00
(410) Germany Schaefer (Detroit) 95.00 47.00 28.00
(411) Germany Schaefer (Washington) 75.00 37.00 22.00
(412) George Schirm 80.00 40.00 24.00
(413) Larry Schlafly 80.00 40.00 24.00
(414) Admiral Schlei (batting) 75.00 37.00 22.00
(415) Admiral Schlei (catching) 95.00 47.00 28.00
(416) Admiral Schlei (portrait) 75.00 37.00 22.00
(417) Boss Schmidt (portrait) 75.00 37.00 22.00
(418) Boss Schmidt (throwing) 95.00 47.00 28.00
(419) Ossee Schreck (Schreckengost) 80.00 40.00 24.00
(420) Wildfire Schulte (front view) 95.00 47.00 28.00
(421) Wildfire Schulte (back view) 75.00 37.00 22.00
(422) Jim Scott 75.00 37.00 22.00
(423) Charles Seitz 175.00 87.00 52.00
(424) Cy Seymour (batting) 95.00 47.00 28.00
(425) Cy Seymour (portrait) 75.00 37.00 22.00
(426) Cy Seymour (throwing) 75.00 37.00 22.00
(427) Spike Shannon 80.00 40.00 24.00
(428) Bud Sharpe 80.00 40.00 24.00
(429) Shag Shaughnessy 175.00 87.00 52.00
(430) Al Shaw (St. Louis) 95.00 47.00 28.00
(431) Hunky Shaw (Providence) 80.00 40.00 24.00
(432) Jimmy Sheckard (glove showing) 75.00 37.00 22.00
(433) Jimmy Sheckard (no glove showing) 95.00 47.00 28.00
(434) Bill Shipke 95.00 47.00 28.00
(435) Jimmy Slagle 80.00 40.00 24.00
(436) Carlos Smith (Shreveport) 175.00 87.00 52.00
(437) Frank Smith (Chicago, F. Smith on front) 185.00 92.00 55.00
(438a)Frank Smith (Chicago, white cap) 75.00 37.00 22.00
(438b)Frank Smith (Chicago & Boston) 950.00 475.00 285.00
(439) "Happy" Smith (Brooklyn) 75.00 37.00 22.00
(440) Heinie Smith (Buffalo) 80.00 40.00 24.00
(441) Sid Smith (Atlanta) 175.00 87.00 52.00
(442) Fred Snodgrass (batting) 95.00 47.00 28.00
(443) Fred Snodgrass (catching) 95.00 47.00 28.00
(444) Bob Spade 75.00 37.00 22.00
(445) Tris Speaker 750.00 375.00 225.00
(446) Tubby Spencer 95.00 47.00 28.00
(447) Jake Stahl (glove shows) 75.00 37.00 22.00
(448) Jake Stahl (no glove shows) 95.00 47.00 28.00
(449) Oscar Stanage 75.00 37.00 22.00
(450) Dolly Stark 175.00 87.00 52.00
(451) Charlie Starr 75.00 37.00 22.00
(452) Harry Steinfeldt (portrait) 125.00 62.00 37.00
(453) Harry Steinfeldt (with bat) 95.00 47.00 28.00
(454) Jim Stephens 75.00 37.00 22.00
(455) George Stone 95.00 47.00 28.00
(456) George Stovall (batting) 75.00 37.00 22.00
(457) George Stovall (portrait) 95.00 47.00 28.00
(458) Sam Strang 80.00 40.00 24.00
(459) Gabby Street (catching) 75.00 37.00 22.00
(460) Gabby Street (portrait) 75.00 37.00 22.00
(461) Billy Sullivan 95.00 47.00 28.00
(462) Ed Summers 75.00 37.00 22.00
(463) Bill Sweeney (Boston) 75.00 37.00 22.00
(464) Jeff Sweeney (New York) 75.00 37.00 22.00
(465) Jesse Tannehill (Washington) 75.00 37.00 22.00
(466) Lee Tannehill (Chicago, L. Tannehill on front) 95.00 47.00 28.00
(467) Lee Tannehill (Chicago, Tannehill on front) 75.00 37.00 22.00
(468) Dummy Taylor 80.00 40.00 24.00
(469) Fred Tenney 95.00 47.00 28.00
(470) Tony Thebo 175.00 87.00 52.00
(471) Jake Thielman 80.00 40.00 24.00
(472) Ira Thomas 75.00 37.00 22.00
(473) Woodie Thornton 175.00 87.00 52.00
(474) Joe Tinker (bat off shoulder) 325.00 162.00 97.00
(475) Joe Tinker (bat on shoulder) 325.00 162.00 97.00
(476) Joe Tinker (hands on knees) 350.00 175.00 105.00
(477) Joe Tinker (portrait) 375.00 187.00 112.00
(478) John Titus 75.00 37.00 22.00
(479) Terry Turner 95.00 47.00 28.00
(480) Bob Unglaub 75.00 37.00 22.00
(481) Juan Violat (Viola) 175.00 87.00 52.00
(482) Rube Waddell (portrait) 375.00 187.00 112.00
(483) Rube Waddell (throwing) 375.00 187.00 112.00
(484) Heinie Wagner (bat on left shoulder) 95.00 47.00 28.00
(485) Heinie Wagner (bat on right shoulder) 75.00 37.00 22.00
(486) Honus Wagner 400,000. 160,000. 100,000.
(487) Bobby Wallace 350.00 175.00 105.00
(488) Ed Walsh 400.00 200.00 120.00
(489) Jack Warhop 75.00 37.00 22.00
(490) Jake Weimer 95.00 47.00 28.00
(491) James Westlake 175.00 87.00 52.00
(492) Zack Wheat 350.00 175.00 105.00
(493) Doc White (Chicago, pitching) 75.00 37.00 22.00
(494) Doc White (Chicago, portrait) 95.00 47.00 28.00
(495) Foley White (Houston) 175.00 87.00 52.00
(496) Jack White (Buffalo) 80.00 40.00 24.00
(497) Kaiser Wilhelm (hands at chest) 95.00 47.00 28.00
(498) Kaiser Wilhelm (with bat) 75.00 37.00 22.00
(499) Ed Willett 75.00 37.00 22.00
(500) Ed Willetts (Willett) 75.00 37.00 22.00
(501) Jimmy Williams 95.00 47.00 28.00
(502) Vic Willis (Pittsburg) 75.00 37.00 22.00
(503) Vic Willis (St. Louis, throwing) 75.00 37.00 22.00
(504) Vic Willis (St. Louis, with bat) 75.00 37.00 22.00
(505) Owen Wilson 75.00 37.00 22.00
(506) Hooks Wiltse (pitching) 80.00 40.00 24.00
(507) Hooks Wiltse (portrait, no cap) 95.00 47.00 28.00
(508) Hooks Wiltse (portrait, with cap) 75.00 37.00 22.00
(509) Lucky Wright 80.00 40.00 24.00
(510) Cy Young (Cleveland, glove shows) 600.00 300.00 180.00
(511) Cy Young (Cleveland, bare hand shows) 600.00 300.00 180.00
(512) Cy Young (Cleveland, portrait) 1200. 600.00 360.00
(513) Irv Young (Minneapolis) 80.00 40.00 24.00
(514) Heinie Zimmerman 75.00 37.00 22.00

1912 T207 Brown Background

LORD-CHICAGO-AMER.
Harry Lord
Harry Lord, the brilliant White Sox third baseman, came to Chicago in one of the queerest baseball deals ever recorded. Lord first achieved success in the New England League, where, in 1908, he was lifted to the Boston Americans. Although rated as a wonderful ball player, he fell out with the club management and was traded to Comiskey, who secured a star. Lord played wonderful ball in 1911 and is rated by many as the greatest third baseman now playing—a worthy successor to Bradley and Collins. Last season he batted .321, fielded .941 and led his club with stolen bases.

These 1-1/2" by 2-5/8" cards take their name from the background color which frames the rather drab sepia and white player drawings. They have tan borders making them less colorful than the more popular issues of their era. Player pictures are also on the dull side, with a white strip containing the player's last name, team and league. The card backs have the player's full name, a baseball biography and an ad for one of several brands of cigarettes. The set features 200 players including stars and three classic rarities: Irving Lewis (Boston-Nat.), Ward Miller (Chicago-Nat.) and Louis Lowdermilk (St. Louis-Nat.). There are a number of other scarce cards in the set, including a higher than usual number of obscure players.

	NR MT	EX	VG
Complete Set:	30000.	15000.	9000.
Common Player:	75.00	37.00	22.00
(1) John B. Adams	110.00	55.00	33.00
(2) Edward Ainsmith	75.00	37.00	22.00
(3) Rafael Almeida	110.00	55.00	33.00
(4a) James Austin (insignia on shirt)	125.00	62.00	37.00
(4b) James Austin (no insignia on shirt)	110.00	55.00	33.00

No.	Player	NR MT	EX	VG
(5)	Neal Ball	75.00	37.00	22.00
(6)	Eros Barger	75.00	37.00	22.00
(7)	Jack Barry	75.00	37.00	22.00
(8)	Charles Bauman	110.00	55.00	33.00
(9)	Beals Becker	75.00	37.00	22.00
(10)	Chief (Albert) Bender	500.00	250.00	150.00
(11)	Joseph Benz	110.00	55.00	33.00
(12)	Robert Bescher	75.00	37.00	22.00
(13)	Joe Birmingham	110.00	55.00	33.00
(14)	Russell Blackburne	110.00	55.00	33.00
(15)	Fred Blanding	110.00	55.00	33.00
(16)	Jimmy Block	75.00	37.00	22.00
(17)	Ping Bodie	75.00	37.00	22.00
(18)	Hugh Bradley	75.00	37.00	22.00
(19)	Roger Bresnahan	550.00	275.00	165.00
(20)	J.F. Bushelman	110.00	55.00	33.00
(21)	Henry (Hank) Butcher	110.00	55.00	33.00
(22)	Robert M. Byrne	75.00	37.00	22.00
(23)	John James Callahan	75.00	37.00	22.00
(24)	Howard Camnitz	75.00	37.00	22.00
(25)	Max Carey	375.00	187.00	112.00
(26)	William Carrigan	75.00	37.00	22.00
(27)	George Chalmers	75.00	37.00	22.00
(28)	Frank Leroy Chance	550.00	275.00	165.00
(29)	Edward Cicotte	110.00	55.00	33.00
(30)	Tom Clarke	75.00	37.00	22.00
(31)	Leonard Cole	75.00	37.00	22.00
(32)	John Collins	110.00	55.00	33.00
(33)	Robert Coulson	75.00	37.00	22.00
(34)	Tex Covington	75.00	37.00	22.00
(35)	Otis Crandall	75.00	37.00	22.00
(36)	William Cunningham	110.00	55.00	33.00
(37)	Dave Danforth	75.00	37.00	22.00
(38)	Bert Daniels	75.00	37.00	22.00
(39)	John Daubert	110.00	55.00	33.00
(40a)	Harry Davis (brown "C" on cap)	125.00	62.00	37.00
(40b)	Harry Davis (blue "C" on cap)	125.00	62.00	37.00
(41)	Jim Delehanty	75.00	37.00	22.00
(42)	Claude Derrick	75.00	37.00	22.00
(43)	Arthur Devlin	75.00	37.00	22.00
(44)	Joshua Devore	75.00	37.00	22.00
(45)	Mike Donlin	110.00	55.00	33.00
(46)	Edward Donnelly	110.00	55.00	33.00
(47)	Charles Dooin	75.00	37.00	22.00
(48)	Tom Downey	110.00	55.00	33.00
(49)	Lawrence Doyle	75.00	37.00	22.00
(50)	Del Drake	75.00	37.00	22.00
(51)	Ted Easterly	75.00	37.00	22.00
(52)	George Ellis	75.00	37.00	22.00
(53)	Clyde Engle	75.00	37.00	22.00
(54)	R.E. Erwin	75.00	37.00	22.00
(55)	Louis Evans	75.00	37.00	22.00
(56)	John Ferry	75.00	37.00	22.00
(57a)	Ray Fisher (blue cap)	125.00	62.00	37.00
(57b)	Ray Fisher (white cap)	125.00	62.00	37.00
(58)	Arthur Fletcher	75.00	37.00	22.00
(59)	Jacques Fournier	110.00	55.00	33.00
(60)	Arthur Fromme	75.00	37.00	22.00
(61)	Del Gainor	75.00	37.00	22.00
(62)	William Lawrence Gardner	75.00	37.00	22.00
(63)	Lefty George	75.00	37.00	22.00
(64)	Roy Golden	75.00	37.00	22.00
(65)	Harry Gowdy	75.00	37.00	22.00
(66)	George Graham	110.00	55.00	33.00
(67)	J.G. Graney	75.00	37.00	22.00
(68)	Vean Gregg	110.00	55.00	33.00
(69)	Casey Hageman	75.00	37.00	22.00
(70)	Charlie Hall	75.00	37.00	22.00
(71)	E.S. Hallinan	75.00	37.00	22.00
(72)	Earl Hamilton	75.00	37.00	22.00
(73)	Robert Harmon	75.00	37.00	22.00
(74)	Grover Hartley	110.00	55.00	33.00
(75)	Olaf Henriksen	75.00	37.00	22.00
(76)	John Henry	110.00	55.00	33.00
(77)	Charles Herzog	110.00	55.00	33.00
(78)	Robert Higgins	75.00	37.00	22.00
(79)	Chester Hoff	110.00	55.00	33.00
(80)	William Hogan	75.00	37.00	22.00
(81)	Harry Hooper	650.00	325.00	200.00
(82)	Ben Houser	110.00	55.00	33.00
(83)	Hamilton Hyatt	110.00	55.00	33.00
(84)	Walter Johnson	1200.	600.00	360.00
(85)	George Kaler	75.00	37.00	22.00
(86)	William Kelly	110.00	55.00	33.00
(87)	Jay Kirke	110.00	55.00	33.00
(88)	John Kling	75.00	37.00	22.00
(89)	Otto Knabe	75.00	37.00	22.00
(90)	Elmer Knetzer	75.00	37.00	22.00
(91)	Edward Konetchy	75.00	37.00	22.00
(92)	Harry Krause	75.00	37.00	22.00
(93)	"Red" Kuhn	110.00	55.00	33.00
(94)	Joseph Kutina	110.00	55.00	33.00
(95)	F.H. (Bill) Lange	110.00	55.00	33.00
(96)	Jack Lapp	75.00	37.00	22.00
(97)	W. Arlington Latham	75.00	37.00	22.00
(98)	Thomas W. Leach	75.00	37.00	22.00
(99)	Albert Leifield	75.00	37.00	22.00
(100)	Edgar Lennox	75.00	37.00	22.00
(101)	Duffy Lewis	75.00	37.00	22.00
(102a)	Irving Lewis (no emblem on sleeve)	2000.	1000.	600.00
(102b)	Irving Lewis (emblem on sleeve)	1800.	900.00	540.00
(103)	Jack Lively	75.00	37.00	22.00
(104a)	Paddy Livingston ("A" on shirt)	550.00	275.00	165.00
(104b)	Paddy Livingston (big "C" on shirt)	550.00	275.00	165.00
(104c)	Paddy Livingston (little "C" on shirt)	125.00	62.00	37.00
(105)	Briscoe Lord (Philadelphia)	75.00	37.00	22.00
(106)	Harry Lord (Chicago)	75.00	37.00	22.00
(107)	Louis Lowdermilk	4000.	2000.	1200.
(108)	Richard Marquard	500.00	250.00	150.00
(109)	Armando Marsans	75.00	37.00	22.00
(110)	George McBride	75.00	37.00	22.00
(111)	Alexander McCarthy	125.00	62.00	37.00
(112)	Edward McDonald	75.00	37.00	22.00
(113)	John J. McGraw	650.00	325.00	195.00
(114)	Harry McIntire (McIntyre)	75.00	37.00	22.00
(115)	Matthew McIntyre	75.00	37.00	22.00
(116)	William McKechnie	400.00	200.00	120.00
(117)	Larry McLean	75.00	37.00	22.00
(118)	Clyde Milan	75.00	37.00	22.00
(119)	John B. Miller (Pittsburg)	75.00	37.00	22.00
(120)	Otto Miller (Brooklyn)	110.00	55.00	33.00
(121)	Roy Miller (Boston)	110.00	55.00	33.00
(122)	Ward Miller (Chicago)	2000.	1000.	600.00
(123)	Mike Mitchell (Cleveland, front depicts Willie Mitchell)	110.00	55.00	33.00
(124)	Mike Mitchell (Cincinnati)	75.00	37.00	22.00
(125)	Geo. Mogridge	110.00	55.00	33.00
(126)	Earl Moore	110.00	55.00	33.00
(127)	Patrick J. Moran	75.00	37.00	22.00
(128)	Cy Morgan (Philadelphia)	75.00	37.00	22.00
(129)	Ray Morgan (Washington)	75.00	37.00	22.00
(130)	George Moriarty	110.00	55.00	33.00
(131a)	George Mullin ("D" on cap)	125.00	62.00	37.00
(131b)	George Mullin (no "D" on cap)	125.00	62.00	37.00
(132)	Thomas Needham	75.00	37.00	22.00
(133)	Red Nelson	110.00	55.00	33.00
(134)	Herbert Northen	75.00	37.00	22.00
(135)	Leslie Nunamaker	75.00	37.00	22.00
(136)	Rebel Oakes	75.00	37.00	22.00
(137)	Buck O'Brien	75.00	37.00	22.00
(138)	Rube Oldring	75.00	37.00	22.00
(139)	Ivan Olson	75.00	37.00	22.00
(140)	Martin J. O'Toole	75.00	37.00	22.00
(141)	George Paskart (Paskert)	75.00	37.00	22.00
(142)	Barney Pelty	110.00	55.00	33.00
(143)	Herbert Perdue	75.00	37.00	22.00
(144)	O.C. Peters	110.00	55.00	33.00
(145)	Arthur Phelan	110.00	55.00	33.00
(146)	Jack Quinn	75.00	37.00	22.00
(147)	Don Carlos Ragan	225.00	112.00	67.00
(148)	Arthur Rasmussen	225.00	112.00	67.00
(149)	Morris Rath	110.00	55.00	33.00
(150)	Edward Reulbach	75.00	37.00	22.00
(151)	Napoleon Rucker	75.00	37.00	22.00
(152)	J.B. Ryan	110.00	55.00	33.00
(153)	Victor Saier	750.00	375.00	225.00
(154)	William Scanlon	75.00	37.00	22.00
(155)	Germany Schaefer	75.00	37.00	22.00
(156)	Wilbur Schardt	75.00	37.00	22.00
(157)	Frank Schulte	75.00	37.00	22.00
(158)	Jim Scott	75.00	37.00	22.00
(159)	Henry Severoid (Severeid)	75.00	37.00	22.00
(160)	Mike Simon	75.00	37.00	22.00
(161)	Frank E. Smith (Cincinnati)	75.00	37.00	22.00
(162)	Wallace Smith (St. Louis)	75.00	37.00	22.00
(163)	Fred Snodgrass	75.00	37.00	22.00
(164)	Tristam Speaker	2000.	1000.	600.00
(165)	Harry Lee Spratt	75.00	37.00	22.00
(166)	Edward Stack	75.00	37.00	22.00
(167)	Oscar Stanage	75.00	37.00	22.00
(168)	William Steele	75.00	37.00	22.00
(169)	Harry Steinfeldt	75.00	37.00	22.00
(170)	George Stovall	75.00	37.00	22.00
(171)	Charles (Gabby) Street	75.00	37.00	22.00
(172)	Amos Strunk	75.00	37.00	22.00
(173)	William Sullivan	75.00	37.00	22.00
(174)	William J. Sweeney	110.00	55.00	33.00
(175)	Leeford Tannehill	75.00	37.00	22.00
(176)	C.D. Thomas	75.00	37.00	22.00
(177)	Joseph Tinker	500.00	250.00	150.00
(178)	Bert Tooley	75.00	37.00	22.00
(179)	Terence Turner (Terrence)	75.00	37.00	22.00
(180)	George Tyler	300.00	150.00	90.00
(181)	Jim Vaughn	75.00	37.00	22.00
(182)	Chas. (Heinie) Wagner	75.00	37.00	22.00
(183)	Ed (Dixie) Walker	75.00	37.00	22.00
(184)	Robert Wallace	375.00	187.00	112.00
(185)	John Warhop	75.00	37.00	22.00
(186)	George Weaver	400.00	200.00	120.00
(187)	Zach Wheat	450.00	225.00	135.00
(188)	G. Harris White	110.00	55.00	33.00
(189)	Ernest Wilie	110.00	55.00	33.00
(190)	Bob Williams	75.00	37.00	22.00
(191)	Arthur Wilson (New York)	110.00	55.00	33.00
(192)	Owen Wilson (Pittsburg)	75.00	37.00	22.00
(193)	George Wiltse	75.00	37.00	22.00
(194)	Ivey Wingo	75.00	37.00	22.00
(195)	Harry Wolverton	75.00	37.00	22.00
(196)	Joe Wood	110.00	55.00	33.00
(197)	Eugene Woodburn	110.00	55.00	33.00
(198)	Ralph Works	110.00	55.00	33.00
(199)	Stanley Yerkes	75.00	37.00	22.00
(200)	Rollie Zeider	110.00	55.00	33.00

1914 T216 Kotton

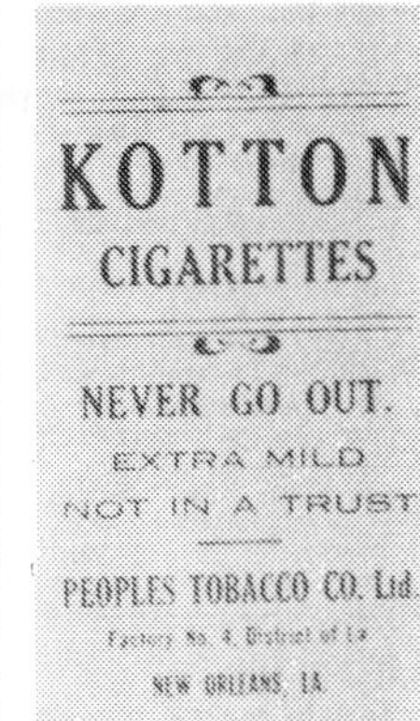

The T216 baseball card set, issued by several brands of the Peoples Tobacco Co., is the last of the Louisana area tobacco sets and the most confusing. Apparently issued over a period of several years between 1911 and 1916, the set emplys the same pictures in the E90-1 and E92 caramel card sets and is also closely related to the E106 American Caramal and D303 General Baking sets. Exact identification of cards from this era is often complicated by the fact that it was common for the same picture to be used in several different sets. Positive identification can usually be determined by the back of the cards. The Peoples Tobacco cards carry advertising for one of three brands of cigarettes: Kotton, Mino or Virginia Extra. The Kotton brand are the most common, while the Virginia Extra and Mino backs command a 50-100" premium. T216 cards are found in two types; one has a glossy card stock, while a second scarcer type is printed on a thin paper. The thin paper cards command an additional 15" premium. There are 73 poses known to exist plus 29 variations, mostly involving caption changes. The cards represent players from both major leagues and the Federal League. Of the 73 poses identified, 23 were taken from the E90-1 set, 38 originated in the E92 set and a dozen appeared in both of the earlier caramel sets.

		NR MT	EX	VG
	Complete Set:	18000.	9000.	5400.
	Common Player:	100.00	50.00	30.00
(1)	Jack Barry (batting)	100.00	50.00	30.00
(2)	Jack Barry (fielding)	100.00	50.00	30.00
(3)	Harry Bemis	100.00	50.00	30.00
(4a)	Chief Bender (Philadelphia, striped cap)	250.00	125.00	75.00
(4b)	Chief Bender (Baltimore, striped cap)	250.00	125.00	75.00
(5a)	Chief Bender (Philadelphia, white cap)	250.00	125.00	75.00
(5b)	Chief Bender (Baltimore, white cap)	250.00	125.00	75.00
(6)	Bill Bergen	100.00	50.00	30.00
(7a)	Bob Bescher (Cincinnati)	100.00	50.00	30.00
(7b)	Bob Bescher (St. Louis)	100.00	50.00	30.00
(8)	Roger Bresnahan	250.00	125.00	75.00
(9)	Al Bridwell (batting)	100.00	50.00	30.00
(10a)	Al Bridwell (New York, sliding)	100.00	50.00	30.00
(10b)	Al Bridwell (St. Louis, sliding)	100.00	50.00	30.00
(11)	Donie Bush	100.00	50.00	30.00
(12)	Doc Casey	100.00	50.00	30.00
(13)	Frank Chance	250.00	125.00	75.00
(14a)	Hal Chase (New York, fielding)	65.00	32.00	19.50
(14b)	Hal Chase (Buffalo, fielding)	65.00	32.00	19.50
(15)	Hal Chase (portrait)	65.00	32.00	19.50
(16a)	Ty Cobb (Detroit Am., standing)	2000.	1000.	600.00
(16b)	Ty Cobb (Detroit Americans, standing)	2000.	1000.	600.00
(17)	"Ty" Cobb (batting)	2000.	1000.	600.00
(18a)	Eddie Collins (Phila. Am.)	250.00	125.00	75.00
(18b)	Eddie Collins (Phila. Amer.)	250.00	125.00	75.00
(19)	Eddie Collins (Chicago)	250.00	125.00	75.00
(20)	Sam Crawford	250.00	125.00	75.00
(21)	Harry Davis	100.00	50.00	30.00
(22)	Ray Demmitt	100.00	50.00	30.00
(23a)	Wild Bill Donovan (Detroit)	100.00	50.00	30.00
(23b)	Wild Bill Donovan (New York)	100.00	50.00	30.00
(24a)	Red Dooin (Philadelphia)	100.00	50.00	30.00
(24b)	Red Dooin (Cincinnati)	100.00	50.00	30.00
(25a)	Mickey Doolan (Philadelphia)	100.00	50.00	30.00
(25b)	Mickey Doolan (Baltimore)	100.00	50.00	30.00
(26)	Patsy Dougherty	100.00	50.00	30.00
(27a)	Larry Doyle (N.Y. Nat'l, batting)	100.00	50.00	30.00
(27a)	Larry Doyle (New York Nat'l, batting)	100.00	50.00	30.00
(28)	Larry Doyle (throwing)	100.00	50.00	30.00
(29)	Clyde Engle	100.00	50.00	30.00
(30a)	Johnny Evers (Chicago)	250.00	125.00	75.00
(30b)	Johnny Evers (Boston)	250.00	125.00	75.00
(31)	Art Fromme	100.00	50.00	30.00
(32a)	George Gibson (Pittsburg Nat'l, back view)	100.00	50.00	30.00
(32b)	George Gibson (Pittsburgh Nat'l., back view)	100.00	50.00	30.00
(33a)	George Gibson (Pittsburg Nat'l, front view)	100.00	50.00	30.00
(33b)	George Gibson (Pittsburgh Nat'l., front view)	100.00	50.00	30.00
(34a)	Topsy Hartsel (Phila. Am.)	100.00	50.00	30.00
(34b)	Topsy Hartsel (Phila. Amer.)	100.00	50.00	30.00
(35)	Roy Hartzell (batting)	100.00	50.00	30.00
(36)	Roy Hartzell (catching)	100.00	50.00	30.00
(37a)	Fred Jacklitsch (Philadelphia)	100.00	50.00	30.00
(37b)	Fred Jacklitsch (Baltimore)	100.00	50.00	30.00
(38a)	Hughie Jennings (orange background)	250.00	125.00	75.00
(38b)	Hughie Jennings (red background)	250.00	125.00	75.00
(39)	Red Kleinow	100.00	50.00	30.00
(40a)	Otto Knabe (Philadelphia)	100.00	50.00	30.00
(40b)	Otto Knabe (Baltimore)	100.00	50.00	30.00
(41)	Jack Knight	100.00	50.00	30.00
(42a)	Nap Lajoie (Philadelphia, fielding)	400.00	200.00	120.00

		NR MT	EX	VG
(42b)	Nap Lajoie (Cleveland, fielding)	400.00	200.00	120.00
(43)	Nap Lajoie (portrait)	400.00	200.00	120.00
(44a)	Hans Lobert (Cincinnati)	100.00	50.00	30.00
(44b)	Hans Lobert (New York)	100.00	50.00	30.00
(45)	Sherry Magee	55.00	27.00	16.50
(46)	Rube Marquard	250.00	125.00	75.00
(47a)	Christy Matthewson (Mathewson) (large print)	600.00	300.00	180.00
(47b)	Christy Matthewson (Mathewson) (small print)	600.00	300.00	180.00
(48a)	John McGraw (large print)	90.00	45.00	27.00
(48b)	John McGraw (small print)	90.00	45.00	27.00
(49)	Larry McLean	100.00	50.00	30.00
(50)	George McQuillan	100.00	50.00	30.00
(51)	Dots Miller (batting)	100.00	50.00	30.00
(52a)	Dots Miller (Pittsburg, fielding)	100.00	50.00	30.00
(52b)	Dots Miller (St. Louis, fielding)	100.00	50.00	30.00
(53a)	Danny Murphy (Philadelphia)	100.00	50.00	30.00
(53b)	Danny Murphy (Brooklyn)	100.00	50.00	30.00
(54)	Rebel Oakes	100.00	50.00	30.00
(55)	Bill O'Hara	100.00	50.00	30.00
(56)	Eddie Plank	250.00	125.00	75.00
(57a)	Germany Schaefer (Washington)	100.00	50.00	30.00
(57b)	Germany Schaefer (Newark)	100.00	50.00	30.00
(58)	Admiral Schlei	100.00	50.00	30.00
(59)	Boss Schmidt	100.00	50.00	30.00
(60)	Johnny Seigle	100.00	50.00	30.00
(61)	Dave Shean	100.00	50.00	30.00
(62)	Boss Smith (Schmidt)	100.00	50.00	30.00
(63)	Tris Speaker	500.00	250.00	150.00
(64)	Oscar Stanage	100.00	50.00	30.00
(65)	George Stovall	100.00	50.00	30.00
(66)	Jeff Sweeney	100.00	50.00	30.00
(67a)	Joe Tinker (Chicago Nat'l, batting)	250.00	125.00	75.00
(67b)	Joe Tinker (Chicago Feds, batting)	250.00	125.00	75.00
(68)	Joe Tinker (portrait)	250.00	125.00	75.00
(69a)	Honus Wagner (batting, S.S.)	1000.	500.00	300.00
(69b)	Honus Wagner (batting, 2b.)	1000.	500.00	300.00
(70a)	Honus Wagner (throwing, S.S.)	1000.	500.00	300.00
(70b)	Honus Wagner (throwing, 2b.)	1000.	500.00	300.00
(71)	Hooks Wiltse	100.00	50.00	30.00
(72)	Cy Young	225.00	112.00	67.00
(73a)	Heinie Zimmerman (2b.)	100.00	50.00	30.00
(73b)	Heinie Zimmerman (3b.)	100.00	50.00	30.00

1912 T227 Series Of Champions

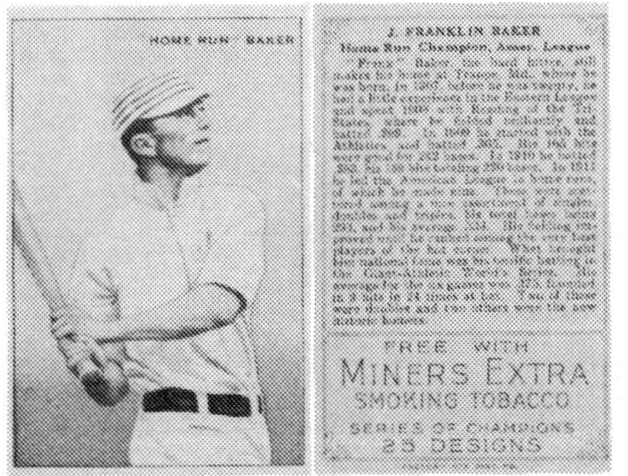

The 1912 "Series of Champions" card set issued by the "Honest Long Cut" and "Miners Extra" tobacco brands features several baseball stars among its 25 famous athletes of the day. Larger than a standard-size tobacco issue, each card in the "Champions" series measures 3-3/8" by 2-5/16". The back includes a relatively lengthy player biography, while the front features a lithograph of the player in action. Although the set includes only four baseball players, these attractive cards are popular among collectors because of the stature of the four players selected. The "Champions" series holds additional significance because it includes the only known baseball cards issued under the "Miners Extra" brand name. The set carries the American Card Catalog designation of T227.

		NR MT	EX	VG
Complete Set (4):		6000.	3000.	1800.
Common Player:		900.00	450.00	270.00
(1)	"Home Run" Baker	900.00	450.00	270.00
(2)	"Chief" Bender	900.00	450.00	270.00
(3)	Ty Cobb	3600.	1800.	1050.
(4)	R. Marquard	900.00	450.00	270.00

1988 T & M Sports Umpires

This special set of 4 oversize cards (approximately 3-7/8" by 5-1/2") was produced on a single perforated sheet for distribution to fans as part of a U.S. Forest Service fire prevention campaign. The card fronts feature full-color photos framed by blue and pink vertical borders and a light blue player name at the bottom margin. Cubs and Smokey logos flank the name and "Chicago Cubs" is printed in red, following the curved top of the card photo. The backs carry brief player information and a large wildfire prevention cartoon message.

		MT	NR MT	EX
Complete Set (64):		12.00	9.00	4.75
Common Player:		.15	.11	.06
1	Doug Harvey	.15	.11	.06
2	Lee Weyer	.15	.11	.06
3	Billy Williams	.15	.11	.06
4	John Kibler	.15	.11	.06
5	Bob Engel	.15	.11	.06
6	Harry Wendelstedt	.15	.11	.06
7	Larry Barnett	.15	.11	.06
8	Don Denkinger	.15	.11	.06
9	Dave Phillips	.15	.11	.06
10	Larry McCoy	.15	.11	.06
11	Bruce Froemming	.15	.11	.06
12	John McSherry	.15	.11	.06
13	Jim Evans	.15	.11	.06
14	Frank Pulli	.15	.11	.06
15	Joe Brinkman	.15	.11	.06
16	Terry Tata	.15	.11	.06
17	Paul Runge	.15	.11	.06
18	Dutch Rennert	.15	.11	.06
19	Nick Bremigan	.15	.11	.06
20	Jim McKean	.15	.11	.06
21	Terry Cooney	.15	.11	.06
22	Rich Garcia	.15	.11	.06
23	Dale Ford	.15	.11	.06
24	Al Clark	.15	.11	.06
25	Greg Kosc	.15	.11	.06
26	Jim Quick	.15	.11	.06
27	Ed Montague	.15	.11	.06
28	Jerry Crawford	.15	.11	.06
29	Steve Palermo	.15	.11	.06
30	Durwood Merrill	.15	.11	.06
31	Ken Kaiser	.15	.11	.06
32	Vic Voltaggio	.15	.11	.06
33	Mike Reilly	.15	.11	.06
34	Eric Gregg	.15	.11	.06
35	Ted Hendry	.15	.11	.06
36	Joe West	.15	.11	.06
37	Dave Pallone	.15	.11	.06
38	Fred Brocklander	.15	.11	.06
39	John Shulock	.15	.11	.06
40	Derryl Cousins	.15	.11	.06
41	Charlie Williams	.15	.11	.06
42	Rocky Roe	.15	.11	.06
43	Randy Marsh	.15	.11	.06
44	Bob Davidson	.15	.11	.06
45	Drew Coble	.15	.11	.06
46	Tim McClelland	.15	.11	.06
47	Dan Morrison	.15	.11	.06
48	Rick Reed	.15	.11	.06
49	Steve Rippley	.15	.11	.06
50	John Hirshbeck	.15	.11	.06
51	Mark Johnson	.15	.11	.06
52	Gerry Davis	.15	.11	.06
53	Dana DeMuth	.15	.11	.06
54	Larry Young	.15	.11	.06
55	Tim Welke	.15	.11	.06
56	Greg Bonin	.15	.11	.06
57	Tom Hallion	.15	.11	.06
58	Dale Scott	.15	.11	.06
59	Tim Tschida	.15	.11	.06
60	Dick Stello	.15	.11	.06
61	1987 All-Star Game (Derryl Cousins, Bob Davidson, Don Denkinger, Dick Stello, Vic Voltaggio, Joe West)	.15	.11	.06
62	1987 World Series (Ken Kaiser, Greg Kosc, John McSherry, Dave Phillips, Terry Tata, Lee Weyer)	.15	.11	.06
63	Jocko Conlan	.30	.25	.12
64	Checklist	.15	.11	.06

1989 T & M Sports Senior League

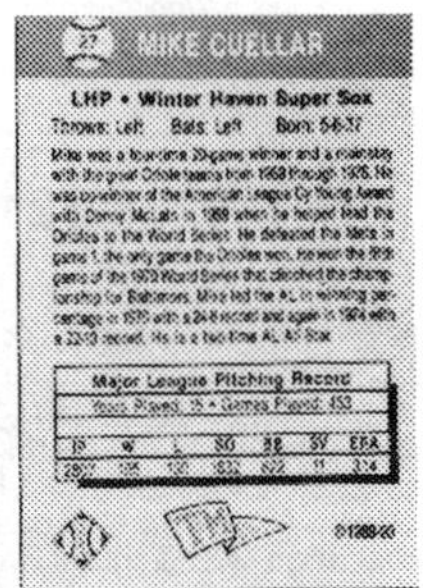

The 120-card 1989-90 T&M Sports Senior League set featured a full-color photo of the player on the front on a borderless card. A red stripe separates the photo from the black bottom with the player's name, team logo and position. The cards were printed on heavy, white cardboard stock and sold as a boxed set. The backs have a red border across the top and bio and career notes, along with a summary of the player's career. Included in the set are eight static-cling puzzle pieces which, when put together, show a drawing of a prominent player from each team.

		MT	NR MT	EX
Complete Set (120):		5.00	3.75	2.00
Common Player:		.05	.04	.02
1	Curt Flood (Commissioner)	.10	.08	.04
2	Willie Aikens	.05	.04	.02
3	Gary Allenson	.05	.04	.02
4	Stan Bahnsen	.05	.04	.02
5	Alan Bannister	.05	.04	.02
6	Juan Beniquez	.05	.04	.02
7	Jim Bibby	.05	.04	.02
8	Paul Blair	.05	.04	.02
9	Vida Blue	.10	.08	.04
10	Bobby Bonds	.15	.11	.06
11	Pedro Borbon	.05	.04	.02
12	Clete Boyer	.05	.04	.02
13	Gates Brown	.05	.04	.02
14	Al Bumbry	.05	.04	.02
15	Sal Butera	.05	.04	.02
16	Bert Campaneris	.10	.08	.04
17	Bill Campbell	.05	.04	.02
18	Bernie Carbo	.05	.04	.02
19	Dave Cash	.05	.04	.02
20	Cesar Cedeno	.05	.04	.02
21	Gene Clines	.05	.04	.02
22	Dave Collins	.05	.04	.02
23	Cecil Cooper	.05	.04	.02
24	Doug Corbett	.05	.04	.02
25	Al Cowens	.05	.04	.02
26	Jose Cruz	.05	.04	.02
27	Mike Cuellar	.05	.04	.02
28	Pat Dobson	.05	.04	.02
29	Dick Drago	.05	.04	.02
30	Dan Driessen	.05	.04	.02
31	Jamie Easterly	.05	.04	.02
32	Juan Eichelberger	.05	.04	.02
33	Dock Ellis	.05	.04	.02
34	Ed Figueroa	.05	.04	.02
35	Rollie Fingers	.50	.40	.20
36	George Foster	.15	.11	.06
37	Oscar Gamble	.05	.04	.02
38	Wayne Garland	.05	.04	.02
39	Wayne Garrett	.05	.04	.02
40	Ross Grimsley	.05	.04	.02
41	Jerry Grote	.05	.04	.02
42	Johnny Grubb	.05	.04	.02
43	Mario Guerrero	.05	.04	.02
44	Toby Harrah	.05	.04	.02
45	Steve Henderson	.05	.04	.02
46	George Hendrick	.05	.04	.02
47	Butch Hobson	.05	.04	.02
48	Roy Howell	.05	.04	.02
49	Al Hrabosky	.05	.04	.02
50	Clint Hurdle	.05	.04	.02
51	Garth Iorg	.05	.04	.02
52	Tim Ireland	.05	.04	.02
53	Grant Jackson	.05	.04	.02
54	Ron Jackson	.05	.04	.02
55	Ferguson Jenkins	.50	.40	.20
56	Odell Jones	.05	.04	.02
57	Mike Kekich	.05	.04	.02
58	Steve Kemp	.05	.04	.02
59	Dave Kingman	.05	.04	.02
60	Bruce Kison	.05	.04	.02
61	Lee Lacy	.05	.04	.02
62	Rafael Landestoy	.05	.04	.02
63	Ken Landreaux	.05	.04	.02
64	Tito Landrum	.05	.04	.02
65	Dave LaRoche	.05	.04	.02
66	Bill Lee	.05	.04	.02
67	Ron LeFlore	.05	.04	.02
68	Dennis Leonard	.05	.04	.02
69	Bill Madlock	.10	.08	.04
70	Mickey Mahler	.05	.04	.02
71	Rick Manning	.05	.04	.02
72	Tippy Martinez	.05	.04	.02
73	Jon Matlack	.05	.04	.02
74	Bake McBride	.05	.04	.02
75	Steve McCarty	.05	.04	.02
76	Hal McRae	.10	.08	.04
77	Dan Meyer	.05	.04	.02
78	Felix Millan	.05	.04	.02
79	Paul Mirabella	.05	.04	.02
80	Omar Moreno	.05	.04	.02
81	Jim Morrison	.05	.04	.02
82	Graig Nettles	.05	.04	.02
83	Al Oliver	.10	.08	.04
84	Amos Otis	.05	.04	.02
85	Tom Paciorek	.05	.04	.02
86	Lowell Plamer	.05	.04	.02
87	Pat Putnam	.05	.04	.02
88	Lenny Randle	.05	.04	.02
89	Ken Reitz	.05	.04	.02
90	Gene Richards	.05	.04	.02
91	Mickey Rivers	.05	.04	.02
92	Leon Roberts	.05	.04	.02
93	Joe Sambito	.05	.04	.02
94	Rodney Scott	.05	.04	.02
95	Bob Shirley	.05	.04	.02
96	Jim Slaton	.05	.04	.02
97	Elias Sosa	.05	.04	.02
98	Fred Stanley	.05	.04	.02
99	Bill Stein	.05	.04	.02
100	Rennie Stennett	.05	.04	.02
101	Sammy Stewart	.05	.04	.02
102	Tim Stoddard	.05	.04	.02
103	Champ Summers	.05	.04	.02
104	Derrell Thomas	.05	.04	.02
105	Luis Tiant	.10	.08	.04
106	Bobby Tolan	.05	.04	.02
107	Bill Travers	.05	.04	.02

108	Ton Underwood	.05	.04	.02
109	Rick Waits	.05	.04	.02
110	Ron Washington	.05	.04	.02
111	U.L. Washington	.05	.04	.02
112	Earl Weaver	.15	.11	.06
113	Jerry White	.05	.04	.02
114	Milt Wilcox	.05	.04	.02
115	Dick Williams	.05	.04	.02
116	Walt Williams	.05	.04	.02
117	Rick Wise	.05	.04	.02
118	Favorite Suns (Luis Tiant, Cesar Cedeno)	.05	.04	.02
119	Home Run Legends (George Foster, Bobby Bonds)	.05	.04	.02
120	Sunshine Skippers (Earl Weaver, Dick Williams)	.05	.04	.02

1916 Tango Eggs

Ask your grocer for
"TANGO BRAND EGGS"
Every one guaranteed
to be of
"FINEST QUALITY"
Packed only by
L. FRANK & COMPANY
NEW ORLEANS, LA.

Unknown until the discovery of a hoard of "fewer than 500" cards in 1991, this 20-card set was produced for L. Frank & Company of New Orleans to be distributed in an as-yet unknown manner in connection with its Tango brand eggs. Similar in size (1-1/2" by 2-3/4") and format to contemporary caramel cards, the Tango set features familiar player pictures from those issues. In fact, several of the Tango cards have player designations which differ from the same pictures used in the E106 American Caramel issue of 1915. The Tango cards feature a glossy front surface, and are brightly colored. The hoard varied greatly in the number of each player's card. Some were found in quantities of five or fewer, while some were represented by more than 50 specimens. Prices show in the alphabetized checklist below reflect the scarcity of known examples.

		NR MT	EX	VG
Complete Set (20):		9750.	4875.	2925.
Common Player:		175.00	87.00	52.00
(1)	Bob Bescher	175.00	87.00	52.00
(2)	Roger Bresnahan	275.00	137.00	82.00
(3)	Al Bridwell	450.00	225.00	135.00
(4)	Hal Chase	500.00	250.00	150.00
(5)	Ty Cobb	500.00	250.00	150.00
(6)	Eddie Collins	1550.	775.00	465.00
(7)	Sam Crawford	1550.	775.00	465.00
(8)	Red Dooin	275.00	137.00	82.00
(9)	Johnny Evers	275.00	137.00	82.00
(10)	Happy Felsch (picture actually Ray Demmitt)	275.00	137.00	82.00
(11)	Hughie Jennings	575.00	287.00	172.00
(12)	George McQuillen	275.00	137.00	82.00
(13)	Billy Meyer (picture actually Fred Jacklitsch)	275.00	137.00	82.00
(14)	Ray Morgan (picture actually Red Dooin)	275.00	137.00	82.00
(15)	Danny Murphy	350.00	175.00	105.00
(16)	Germany Schaefer	350.00	175.00	105.00
(17)	Joe Tinker	350.00	175.00	105.00
(18)	Honus Wagner	350.00	175.00	105.00
(19)	Buck Weaver (picture actually Joe Tinker)	1550.	775.00	465.00
(20)	Heinie Zimmerman	475.00	237.00	142.00

1990 Target Dodgers

Virtually every player who appeared in the uniform of the Brooklyn/Los Angeles Dodgers between 1890-1990 was included in this 1,100-card issue. Quality of the photo varies wildly from sharp to barely identifiable. Cards measure 2-1/16" x 3" and are perforated on two, three or four sides, depending where they were positioned on the 15-card perforated sheets in which the cards were distributed at various Dodgers home games. Player photos are in dark blue and white, bordered in speckled blue. Name and position appear in black in a light blue banner at top. At lower-left is the Dodgers 100th anniversary logo, with the Target stores logo at lower-right. On back the player's name and position reappear at top, with the logos below and the card number in a banner at bottom. Cards were numbered roughly alphabetically, though many are out of order. Some cards have duplicated numbers and there were some numbers skipped in the issue. All back printing is in blue on white. Career major league stats and the years in which the player was with the Dodgers are also noted on back.

		MT	NR MT	EX
Complete Set:		100.00	75.00	40.00
Common Player:		.10	.08	.04
1	Bert Abbey	.10	.08	.04
2	Cal Abrams	.10	.08	.04
3	Hank Aguirre	.10	.08	.04
4	Eddie Ainsmith	.10	.08	.04
5	Ed Albosta	.10	.08	.04
6	Luis Alcaraz	.10	.08	.04
7	Doyle Alexander	.10	.08	.04
8	Dick Allen	.15	.11	.06
9	Frank Allen	.10	.08	.04
10	Johnny Allen	.10	.08	.04
11	Mel Almada	.10	.08	.04
12	Walter Alston	.20	.15	.08
13	Ed Amelung	.10	.08	.04
14	Sandy Amoros	.12	.09	.05
15	Dave Anderson	.10	.08	.04
16	Ferrell Anderson	.10	.08	.04
17	John Anderson	.10	.08	.04
18	Stan Andrews	.10	.08	.04
19	Bill Antonello	.10	.08	.04
20	Jimmy Archer	.10	.08	.04
21	Bob Aspromonte	.10	.08	.04
22	Rick Auerbach	.10	.08	.04
23	Charlie Babb	.10	.08	.04
24	Johnny Babich	.10	.08	.04
25	Bob Bailey	.10	.08	.04
26	Bob Bailor	.10	.08	.04
27	Dusty Baker	.12	.09	.05
28	Tom Baker	.10	.08	.04
29	Dave Bancroft	.15	.11	.06
30	Dan Bankhead	.12	.09	.05
31	Jack Banta	.10	.08	.04
32	Jim Barbieri	.10	.08	.04
33	Red Barkley	.10	.08	.04
34	Jesse Barnes	.10	.08	.04
35	Rex Barney	.10	.08	.04
36	Billy Barnie	.10	.08	.04
37	Bob Barrett	.10	.08	.04
38	Jim Baxes	.10	.08	.04
39	Billy Bean	.10	.08	.04
40	Boom Boom Beck	.10	.08	.04
41	Joe Beckwith	.10	.08	.04
42	Hank Behrman	.10	.08	.04
43	Mark Belanger	.10	.08	.04
44	Wayne Belardi	.10	.08	.04
45	Tim Belcher	.10	.08	.04
46	George Bell	.10	.08	.04
47	Ray Benge	.10	.08	.04
48	Moe Berg	.15	.11	.06
49	Bill Bergen	.10	.08	.04
50	Ray Berres	.10	.08	.04
51	Don Bessent	.10	.08	.04
52	Steve Bilko	.10	.08	.04
53	Jack Billingham	.10	.08	.04
54	Babe Birrer	.10	.08	.04
55	Del Bissonette	.10	.08	.04
56	Joe Black	.12	.09	.05
57	Lu Blue	.10	.08	.04
58	George Boehler	.10	.08	.04
59	Sammy Bohne	.10	.08	.04
60	John Boiling	.10	.08	.04
61	Ike Boone	.10	.08	.04
62	Frenchy Bordagaray	.10	.08	.04
63	Ken Boyer	.12	.09	.05
64	Buzz Boyle	.10	.08	.04
65	Mark Bradley	.10	.08	.04
66	Bobby Bragan	.10	.08	.04
67	Ralph Branca	.15	.11	.06
68	Ed Brandt	.10	.08	.04
69	Sid Bream	.10	.08	.04
70	Marv Breeding	.10	.08	.04
71	Tom Brennan	.10	.08	.04
72	William Brennan	.10	.08	.04
73	Rube Bressler	.10	.08	.04
74	Ken Brett	.10	.08	.04
75	Jim Brewer	.10	.08	.04
76	Tony Brewer	.10	.08	.04
77	Rocky Bridges	.10	.08	.04
78	Greg Brock	.10	.08	.04
79	Dan Brouthers	.15	.11	.06
80	Eddie Brown	.10	.08	.04
81	Elmer Brown	.10	.08	.04
82	Lindsay Brown	.10	.08	.04
83	Lloyd Brown	.10	.08	.04
84	Mace Brown	.10	.08	.04
85	Tommy Brown	.10	.08	.04
86	Pete Browning	.10	.08	.04
87	Ralph Bryant	.10	.08	.04
88	Jim Bucher	.10	.08	.04
89	Bill Buckner	.12	.09	.05
90	Jim Bunning	.15	.11	.06
91	Jack Burdock	.10	.08	.04
92	Glenn Burke	.10	.08	.04
93	Buster Burrell	.10	.08	.04
94	Larry Burright	.10	.08	.04
95	Doc Bushong	.10	.08	.04
96	Max Butcher	.10	.08	.04
97	Johnny Butler	.10	.08	.04
98	Enos Cabell	.10	.08	.04
99	Leon Cadore	.10	.08	.04
100	Bruce Caldwell	.10	.08	.04
101	Dick Calmus	.10	.08	.04
102	Dolf Camilli	.10	.08	.04
103	Doug Camilli	.10	.08	.04
104	Roy Campanella	1.00	.70	.40
105	Al Campanis	.10	.08	.04
106	Jim Campanis	.10	.08	.04
107A	Leo Callahan	.10	.08	.04
107B	Gilly Campbell	.10	.08	.04
108	Jimmy Canavan	.10	.08	.04
109	Chris Cannizzaro	.10	.08	.04
110	Guy Cantrell	.10	.08	.04
111	Ben Cantwell	.10	.08	.04
112	Andy Carey	.10	.08	.04
113	Max Carey	.15	.11	.06
114	Tex Carleton	.10	.08	.04
115	Ownie Carroll	.10	.08	.04
116	Bob Caruthers	.10	.08	.04
117	Doc Casey	.10	.08	.04
118	Hugh Casey	.10	.08	.04
119	Bobby Castillo	.10	.08	.04
120	Cesar Cedeno	.10	.08	.04
121	Ron Cey	.15	.11	.06
122	Ed Chandler	.10	.08	.04
123	Ben Chapman	.10	.08	.04
124	Larry Cheney	.10	.08	.04
125	Bob Chipman	.10	.08	.04
126	Chuck Churn	.10	.08	.04
127	Gino Cimoli	.10	.08	.04
128	Moose Clabaugh	.10	.08	.04
129	Bud Clancy	.10	.08	.04
130	Bob Clark	.10	.08	.04
131	Watty Clark	.10	.08	.04
132	Alta Cohen	.10	.08	.04
133	Rocky Colavito	.25	.20	.10
134	Jackie Collum	.10	.08	.04
135	Chuck Connors	.75	.60	.30
136	Jack Coombs	.10	.08	.04
137	Johnny Cooney	.10	.08	.04
138	Tommy Corcoran	.10	.08	.04
139	Pop Corkhill	.10	.08	.04
140	John Corriden	.10	.08	.04
141	Pete Coscarart	.10	.08	.04
142	Wes Covington	.10	.08	.04
143	Billy Cox	.10	.08	.04
144	Roger Craig	.12	.09	.05
145	Not issued			
146	Willie Crawford	.10	.08	.04
147	Tim Crews	.10	.08	.04
148	John Cronin	.10	.08	.04
149	Lave Cross	.10	.08	.04
150	Bill Crouch	.10	.08	.04
151	Don Crow	.10	.08	.04
152	Henry Cruz	.10	.08	.04
153	Tony Cuccinello	.10	.08	.04
154	Roy Cullenbine	.10	.08	.04
155	George Culver	.10	.08	.04
156	Nick Cullop	.10	.08	.04
157	George Cutshaw	.10	.08	.04
158	Kiki Cuyler	.15	.11	.06
159	Bill Dahlen	.10	.08	.04
160	Babe Dahlgren	.10	.08	.04
161	Jack Dalton	.10	.08	.04
162	Tom Daly	.10	.08	.04
163	Cliff Dapper	.10	.08	.04
164	Bob Darnell	.10	.08	.04
165	Bobby Darwin	.10	.08	.04
166	Jake Daubert	.10	.08	.04
167	Vic Davalillo	.10	.08	.04
168	Curt Davis	.10	.08	.04
169	Mike Davis	.10	.08	.04
170	Ron Davis	.10	.08	.04
171	Tommy Davis	.12	.09	.05
172	Willie Davis	.12	.09	.05
173	Pea Ridge Day	.10	.08	.04
174	Tommy Dean	.10	.08	.04
175	Hank DeBerry	.10	.08	.04
176	Art Decatur	.10	.08	.04
177	Raoul Dedeaux	.10	.08	.04
178	Ivan DeJesus	.10	.08	.04
179	Don Demeter	.10	.08	.04
180	Gene DeMontreville	.10	.08	.04
181	Rick Dempsey	.10	.08	.04
182	Eddie Dent	.10	.08	.04
183	Mike Devereaux	.12	.09	.05
184	Carlos Diaz	.10	.08	.04
185	Dick Dietz	.10	.08	.04
186	Pop Dillon	.10	.08	.04
187	Bill Doak	.10	.08	.04
188	John Dobbs	.10	.08	.04
189	George Dockins	.10	.08	.04
190	Cozy Dolan	.10	.08	.04
191	Patsy Donovan	.10	.08	.04
192	Wild Bill Donovan	.10	.08	.04
193	Mickey Doolan	.10	.08	.04
194	Jack Doscher	.10	.08	.04
195	Phil Douglas	.10	.08	.04
196	Snooks Dowd	.10	.08	.04
197	Al Downing	.10	.08	.04
198	Red Downs	.10	.08	.04
199	Jack Doyle	.10	.08	.04
200	Solly Drake	.10	.08	.04
201	Tom Drake	.10	.08	.04
202	Chuck Dressen	.10	.08	.04
203	Don Drysdale	.50	.40	.20
204	Clise Dudley	.10	.08	.04

205	Mariano Duncan	.10	.08	.04
206	Jack Dunn	.10	.08	.04
207	Bull Durham	.10	.08	.04
208	Leo Durocher	.20	.15	.08
209	Billy Earle	.10	.08	.04
210	George Earnshaw	.10	.08	.04
211	Ox Eckhardt	.10	.08	.04
212	Bruce Edwards	.10	.08	.04
213	Hank Edwards	.10	.08	.04
214	Dick W. Egan	.10	.08	.04
215	Harry Eisenstat	.10	.08	.04
216	Kid Elberfeld	.10	.08	.04
217	Jumbo Elliot	.10	.08	.04
218	Don Elston	.10	.08	.04
219	Gil English	.10	.08	.04
220	Johnny Enzmann	.10	.08	.04
221	Al Epperly	.10	.08	.04
222	Carl Erskine	.12	.09	.05
223	Tex Erwin	.10	.08	.04
224	Cecil Espy	.10	.08	.04
225	Chuck Essegian	.10	.08	.04
226	Dude Esterbrook	.10	.08	.04
227	Red Evans	.10	.08	.04
228	Bunny Fabrique	.10	.08	.04
229	Jim Fairey	.10	.08	.04
230	Ron Fairly	.12	.09	.05
231	George Fallon	.10	.08	.04
232	Turk Farrell	.10	.08	.04
233	Duke Farrel	.10	.08	.04
234	Jim Faulkner	.10	.08	.04
235	Alex Ferguson	.10	.08	.04
236	Joe Ferguson	.10	.08	.04
237	Chico Fernandez	.10	.08	.04
238	Sid Fernandez	.10	.08	.04
239	Al Ferrara	.10	.08	.04
240	Wes Ferrell	.10	.08	.04
241	Lou Fette	.10	.08	.04
242	Chick Fewster	.10	.08	.04
243	Jack Fimple	.10	.08	.04
244	Neal "Mickey" Finn	.10	.08	.04
245	Bob Fisher	.10	.08	.04
246	Freddie Fitzsimmons	.10	.08	.04
247	Tim Flood	.10	.08	.04
248	Jake Flowers	.10	.08	.04
249	Hod Ford	.10	.08	.04
250	Terry Forster	.10	.08	.04
251	Alan Foster	.10	.08	.04
252	Jack Fournier	.10	.08	.04
253	Dave Foutz	.10	.08	.04
254	Art Fowler	.10	.08	.04
255	Fred Frankhouse	.10	.08	.04
256	Herman Franks	.10	.08	.04
257	Johnny Frederick	.10	.08	.04
258	Larry French	.10	.08	.04
259	Lonny Frey	.10	.08	.04
260	Pepe Frias	.10	.08	.04
261	Charlie Fuchs	.10	.08	.04
262	Carl Furillo	.20	.15	.08
263	Len Gabrielson	.10	.08	.04
264	Augie Galan	.10	.08	.04
265	Joe Gallagher	.10	.08	.04
266	Phil Gallivan	.10	.08	.04
267	Balvino Galvez	.10	.08	.04
268	Mike Garman	.10	.08	.04
269	Phil Garner	.10	.08	.04
270	Steve Garvey	.15	.11	.06
271	Ned Garvin	.10	.08	.04
272	Hank Gastright	.10	.08	.04
273	Sid Gautreaux	.10	.08	.04
274	Jim Gentile	.10	.08	.04
275	Greek George	.10	.08	.04
276	Ben Geraghty	.10	.08	.04
277	Gus Getz	.10	.08	.04
278	Bob Giallombardo	.10	.08	.04
279	Kirk Gibson	.12	.09	.05
280	Charlie Gilbert	.10	.08	.04
281	Jim Gilliam	.12	.09	.05
282	Al Gionfriddo	.10	.08	.04
283	Tony Giuliani	.10	.08	.04
284	Al Glossop	.10	.08	.04
285	John Gochnaur	.10	.08	.04
286	Jim Golden	.10	.08	.04
287	Dave Goltz	.10	.08	.04
288	Jose Gonzalez	.10	.08	.04
289	Johnny Gooch	.10	.08	.04
290	Ed Goodson	.10	.08	.04
291	Bill Grabarkewitz	.10	.08	.04
292	Jack Graham	.10	.08	.04
293	Mudcat Grant	.10	.08	.04
294	Dick Gray	.10	.08	.04
295	Kent Greenfield	.10	.08	.04
296	Hal Gregg	.10	.08	.04
297	Alfredo Griffin	.10	.08	.04
298	Mike Griffin	.10	.08	.04
299	Derrell Griffith	.10	.08	.04
300	Tommy Griffith	.10	.08	.04
301	Burleigh Grimes	.15	.11	.06
302	Lee Grissom	.10	.08	.04
303	Jerry Grote	.10	.08	.04
304	Pedro Guerrero	.12	.09	.05
305	Brad Gulden	.10	.08	.04
306	Ad Gumbert	.10	.08	.04
307	Chris Gwynn	.10	.08	.04
308	Bert Haas	.10	.08	.04
309	John Hale	.10	.08	.04
310	Tom Haller	.10	.08	.04
311	Bill Hallman	.10	.08	.04
312	Jeff Hamilton	.10	.08	.04
313	Luke Hamlin	.10	.08	.04
314	Ned Hanlon	.10	.08	.04
315	Gerald Hannahs	.10	.08	.04
316	Charlie Hargreaves	.10	.08	.04
317	Tim Harkness	.10	.08	.04
318	Harry Harper	.10	.08	.04
319	Joe Harris	.10	.08	.04
320	Lenny Harris	.10	.08	.04
321	Bill F. Hart	.10	.08	.04
322	Buddy Hassett	.10	.08	.04
323	Mickey Hatcher	.10	.08	.04
324	Joe Hatten	.10	.08	.04
325	Phil Haugstad	.10	.08	.04
326	Brad Havens	.10	.08	.04
327	Ray Hayworth	.10	.08	.04
328	Ed Head	.10	.08	.04
329	Danny Heep	.10	.08	.04
330	Fred Heimach	.10	.08	.04
331	Harvey Hendrick	.10	.08	.04
332	Weldon Henley	.10	.08	.04
333	Butch Henline	.10	.08	.04
334	Dutch Henry	.10	.08	.04
335	Roy Henshaw	.10	.08	.04
336	Babe Herman	.12	.09	.05
337	Billy Herman	.15	.11	.06
338	Gene Hermanski	.10	.08	.04
339	Enzo Hernandez	.10	.08	.04
340	Art Herring	.10	.08	.04
341	Orel Hershiser	.15	.11	.06
342	Dave J. Hickman	.10	.08	.04
343	Jim Hickman	.10	.08	.04
344	Kirby Higbe	.10	.08	.04
345	Andy High	.10	.08	.04
346	George Hildebrand	.10	.08	.04
347	Hunkey Hines	.10	.08	.04
348	Don Hoak	.10	.08	.04
349	Oris Hockett	.10	.08	.04
350	Gil Hodges	.25	.20	.10
351	Glenn Hoffman	.10	.08	.04
352	Al Hollingsworth	.10	.08	.04
353	Tommy Holmes	.10	.08	.04
354	Brian Holton	.10	.08	.04
355	Rick Honeycutt	.10	.08	.04
356	Burt Hooton	.10	.08	.04
357	Gail Hopkins	.10	.08	.04
358	Johnny Hopp	.10	.08	.04
359	Charlie Hough	.12	.09	.05
360	Frank Howard	.12	.09	.05
361	Steve Howe	.12	.09	.05
362	Dixie Howell	.10	.08	.04
363	Harry Howell	.10	.08	.04
364	Jay Howell	.10	.08	.04
365	Ken Howell	.10	.08	.04
366	Waite Hoyt	.15	.11	.06
367	Johnny Hudson	.10	.08	.04
368	Jim J. Hughes	.10	.08	.04
369	Jim R. Hughes	.10	.08	.04
370	Mickey Hughes	.10	.08	.04
371	John Hummel	.10	.08	.04
372	Ron Hunt	.10	.08	.04
373	Willard Hunter	.10	.08	.04
374	Ira Hutchinson	.10	.08	.04
375	Tom Hutton	.10	.08	.04
376	Charlie Irwin	.10	.08	.04
377	Fred Jacklitsch	.10	.08	.04
378	Randy Jackson	.10	.08	.04
379	Merwin Jacobson	.10	.08	.04
380	Cleo James	.10	.08	.04
381	Hal Janvrin	.10	.08	.04
382	Roy Jarvis	.10	.08	.04
383	George Jeffcoat	.10	.08	.04
384	Jack Jenkins	.10	.08	.04
385	Hughie Jennings	.15	.11	.06
386	Tommy John	.12	.09	.05
387	Lou Johnson	.10	.08	.04
388	Fred Ivy Johnston	.10	.08	.04
389	Jimmy Johnston	.10	.08	.04
390	Jay Johnstone	.12	.09	.05
391	Fielder Jones	.10	.08	.04
392	Oscar Jones	.10	.08	.04
393	Tim Jordan	.10	.08	.04
394	Spider Jorgensen	.10	.08	.04
395	Von Joshua	.10	.08	.04
396	Bill Joyce	.10	.08	.04
397	Joe Judge	.10	.08	.04
398	Alex Kampouris	.10	.08	.04
399	Willie Keeler	.15	.11	.06
400	Mike Kekich	.10	.08	.04
401	John Kelleher	.10	.08	.04
402	Frank Kellert	.10	.08	.04
403	Joe Kelley	.10	.08	.04
404	George Kelly	.15	.11	.06
405	Bob Kennedy	.10	.08	.04
406	Brickyard Kennedy	.10	.08	.04
407	John Kennedy	.10	.08	.04
408	Not issued			
409	Newt Kimball	.10	.08	.04
410	Clyde King	.10	.08	.04
411	Enos Kirkpatrick	.10	.08	.04
412	Frank Kitson	.10	.08	.04
413	Johnny Klippstein	.10	.08	.04
414	Elmer Klumpp	.10	.08	.04
415	Len Koenecke	.10	.08	.04
416	Ed Konetchy	.10	.08	.04
417	Andy Kosco	.10	.08	.04
418	Sandy Koufax	.75	.60	.30
419	Ernie Koy	.10	.08	.04
420	Charlie Kress	.10	.08	.04
421	Bill Krueger	.10	.08	.04
422	Ernie Krueger	.10	.08	.04
423	Clem Labine	.12	.09	.05
424	Candy LaChance	.10	.08	.04
425	Lee Lacy	.10	.08	.04
426	Lerrin LaGrow	.10	.08	.04
427	Bill Lamar	.10	.08	.04
428	Wayne LaMaster	.10	.08	.04
429	Ray Lamb	.10	.08	.04
430	Rafael Landestoy	.10	.08	.04
431	Ken Landreaux	.10	.08	.04
432	Tito Landrum	.10	.08	.04
433	Norm Larker	.12	.09	.05
434	Lyn Lary	.10	.08	.04
435	Tom Lasorda	.20	.15	.08
436	Cookie Lavagetto	.10	.08	.04
437	Rudy Law	.10	.08	.04
438	Tony Lazzeri	.15	.11	.06
439	Tim Leary	.10	.08	.04
440	Bob Lee	.10	.08	.04
441	Hall Lee	.10	.08	.04
442	Leron Lee	.10	.08	.04
443	Jim Lefebvre	.10	.08	.04
444	Ken Lehman	.10	.08	.04
445	Don LeJohn	.10	.08	.04
446	Steve Lembo	.10	.08	.04
447	Ed Lennox	.10	.08	.04
448	Dutch Leonard	.10	.08	.04
449	Jeffery Leonard	.10	.08	.04
450	Not issued			
451	Dennis Lewallyn	.10	.08	.04
452	Bob Lillis	.10	.08	.04
453	Jim Lindsey	.10	.08	.04
454	Fred Lindstrom	.15	.11	.06
455	Billy Loes	.10	.08	.04
456	Bob Logan	.10	.08	.04
457	Bill Lohrman	.10	.08	.04
458	Not issued			
459	Vic Lombardi	.10	.08	.04
460	Davey Lopes	.12	.09	.05
461	Al Lopez	.15	.11	.06
462	Ray Lucas	.10	.08	.04
463	Not issued			
464	Harry Lumley	.10	.08	.04
465	Don Lund	.10	.08	.04
466	Dolf Luque	.10	.08	.04
467	Jim Lyttle	.10	.08	.04
468	Max Macon	.10	.08	.04
469	Bill Madlock	.12	.09	.05
470	Lee Magee	.10	.08	.04
471	Sal Maglie	.10	.08	.04
472	George Magoon	.10	.08	.04
473	Duster Mails	.10	.08	.04
474	Candy Maldonado	.10	.08	.04
475	Tony Malinosky	.10	.08	.04
476	Lew Malone	.10	.08	.04
477	Al Mamaux	.10	.08	.04
478	Gus Mancuso	.10	.08	.04
479	Charlie Manuel	.10	.08	.04
480	Heinie Manush	.15	.11	.06
481	Rabbit Maranville	.15	.11	.06
482	Juan Marichal	.20	.15	.08
483	Rube Marquard	.15	.11	.06
484	Bill Marriott	.10	.08	.04
485	Buck Marrow	.10	.08	.04
486	Mike A. Marshall	.10	.08	.04
487	Mike G. Marshall	.10	.08	.04
488	Morrie Martin	.10	.08	.04
489	Ramon Martinez	.12	.09	.05
490	Teddy Martinez	.10	.08	.04
491	Earl Mattingly	.10	.08	.04
492	Len Matuszek	.10	.08	.04
493	Gene Mauch	.10	.08	.04
494	Al Maul	.10	.08	.04
495	Carmen Mauro	.10	.08	.04
496	Alvin McBean	.10	.08	.04
497	Bill McCarren	.10	.08	.04
498	Jack McCarthy	.10	.08	.04
499	Tommy McCarthy	.15	.11	.06
500	Lew McCarty	.10	.08	.04
501	Mike J. McCormick	.10	.08	.04
502	Judge McCreedie	.10	.08	.04
503	Tom McCreery	.10	.08	.04
504	Danny McDevitt	.10	.08	.04
505	Chappie McFarland	.10	.08	.04
506	Joe McGinnity	.15	.11	.06
507	Bob McGraw	.10	.08	.04
508	Deacon McGuire	.10	.08	.04
509	Bill McGunnigle	.10	.08	.04
510	Harry McIntyre	.10	.08	.04
511	Cal McLish	.10	.08	.04
512	Ken McMullen	.10	.08	.04
513	Dough McWeeny	.10	.08	.04
514	Joe Medwick	.15	.11	.06
515	Rube Melton	.10	.08	.04
516	Fred Merkle	.10	.08	.04
517	Orlando Mercado	.10	.08	.04
518	Andy Messersmith	.10	.08	.04
519	Irish Meusel	.10	.08	.04
520	Benny Meyer	.10	.08	.04
521	Russ Meyer	.10	.08	.04
522	Chief Meyers	.10	.08	.04
523	Gene Michael	.10	.08	.04
524	Pete Mikkelsen	.10	.08	.04
525	Eddie Miksis	.10	.08	.04
526	Johnny Miljus	.10	.08	.04
527	Bob Miller	.10	.08	.04
528	Larry Miller	.10	.08	.04
529	Otto Miller	.10	.08	.04
530	Ralph Miller	.10	.08	.04
531	Walt Miller	.10	.08	.04
532	Wally Millies	.10	.08	.04
533	Bob Milliken	.10	.08	.04
534	Buster Mills	.10	.08	.04
535	Paul Minner	.10	.08	.04
536	Bobby Mitchell	.10	.08	.04
537	Clarence Mitchell	.10	.08	.04
538	Dale Mitchell	.10	.08	.04
539	Fred Mitchell	.10	.08	.04
540	Johnny Mitchell	.10	.08	.04
541	Joe Moeller	.10	.08	.04
542	Rick Monday	.10	.08	.04
543	Wally Moon	.10	.08	.04
544	Cy Moore	.10	.08	.04
545	Dee Moore	.10	.08	.04
546	Eddie Moore	.10	.08	.04
547	Gene Moore	.10	.08	.04
548	Randy Moore	.10	.08	.04
549	Ray Moore	.10	.08	.04
550	Jose Morales	.10	.08	.04
551	Bobby Morgan	.10	.08	.04
552	Eddie Morgan	.10	.08	.04
553	Mike Morgan	.10	.08	.04
554	Johnny Morrison	.10	.08	.04
555	Walt Moryn	.10	.08	.04
556	Ray Moss	.10	.08	.04
557	Manny Mota	.12	.09	.05
558	Joe Mulvey	.10	.08	.04

559	Van Lingle Mungo	.10	.08	.04
560	Les Munns	.10	.08	.04
561	Mike Munoz	.10	.08	.04
562	Simmy Murch	.10	.08	.04
563	Eddie Murray	.20	.15	.08
564	Hy Myers	.10	.08	.04
565	Sam Nahem	.10	.08	.04
566	Earl Naylor	.10	.08	.04
567	Charlie Neal	.10	.08	.04
568	Ron Negray	.10	.08	.04
569	Bernie Neis	.10	.08	.04
570	Rocky Nelson	.10	.08	.04
571	Dick Nen	.10	.08	.04
572	Don Newcombe	.15	.11	.06
573	Bobo Newsom	.10	.08	.04
574	Doc Newton	.10	.08	.04
575	Tom Niedenfuer	.10	.08	.04
576	Otho Nitcholas	.10	.08	.04
577	Al Nixon	.10	.08	.04
578	Jerry Nops	.10	.08	.04
579	Irv Noren	.10	.08	.04
580	Fred Norman	.10	.08	.04
581	Bill North	.10	.08	.04
582	Johnny Oates	.10	.08	.04
583	Bob O'Brien	.10	.08	.04
584	John O'Brien	.10	.08	.04
585	Lefty O'Doul	.12	.09	.05
586	Joe Oeschger	.10	.08	.04
587	Al Oliver	.12	.09	.05
588	Nate Oliver	.10	.08	.04
589	Luis Olmo	.10	.08	.04
590	Ivy Olson	.10	.08	.04
591	Mickey O'Neil	.10	.08	.04
592	Joe Orengo	.10	.08	.04
593	Jesse Orosco	.10	.08	.04
594	Frank O'Rourke	.10	.08	.04
595	Jorge Orta	.10	.08	.04
596	Phil Ortega	.10	.08	.04
597	Claude Osteen	.10	.08	.04
598	Fritz Ostermueller	.10	.08	.04
599	Mickey Owen	.10	.08	.04
600	Tom Paciorek	.10	.08	.04
601	Don Padgett	.10	.08	.04
602	Andy Pafko	.10	.08	.04
603	Erv Palica	.10	.08	.04
604	Ed Palmquist	.10	.08	.04
605	Wes Parker	.10	.08	.04
606	Jay Partridge	.10	.08	.04
607	Camilo Pascual	.10	.08	.04
608	Kevin Pasley	.10	.08	.04
609	Dave Patterson	.10	.08	.04
610	Harley Payne	.10	.08	.04
611	Johnny Peacock	.10	.08	.04
612	Hal Peck	.10	.08	.04
613	Stu Pederson	.10	.08	.04
614	Alejandro Pena	.10	.08	.04
615	Jose Pena	.10	.08	.04
616	Jack Perconte	.10	.08	.04
617	Charlie Perkins	.10	.08	.04
618	Ron Perranoski	.12	.09	.05
619	Jim Peterson	.10	.08	.04
620	Jesse Petty	.10	.08	.04
621	Jeff Pfeffer	.10	.08	.04
622	Babe Phelps	.10	.08	.04
623	Val Picinich	.10	.08	.04
624	Joe Pignatano	.10	.08	.04
625	George Pinckney	.10	.08	.04
626	Ed Pipgras	.10	.08	.04
627	Bud Podbielan	.10	.08	.04
628	Johnny Podres	.15	.11	.06
629	Boots Poffenberger	.10	.08	.04
630	Nick Polly	.10	.08	.04
631	Paul Popovich	.10	.08	.04
632	Bill Posedel	.10	.08	.04
633	Boog Powell	.12	.09	.05
634	Dennis Powell	.10	.08	.04
635	Paul Ray Powell	.10	.08	.04
636	Ted Power	.10	.08	.04
637	Tot Pressnell	.10	.08	.04
638	John Purdin	.10	.08	.04
639	Jack Quinn	.10	.08	.04
640	Marv Rackley	.10	.08	.04
641	Jack Radtke	.10	.08	.04
642	Pat Ragan	.10	.08	.04
643	Ed Rakow	.10	.08	.04
644	Bob Ramazzotti	.10	.08	.04
645	Willie Ramsdell	.10	.08	.04
646	Mike James Ramsey	.10	.08	.04
647	Mike Jeffery Ramsey	.10	.08	.04
648	Willie Randolph	.10	.08	.04
649	Doug Rau	.10	.08	.04
650	Lance Rautzhan	.10	.08	.04
651	Howie Reed	.10	.08	.04
652	Pee Wee Reese	1.00	.70	.40
653	Phil Regan	.10	.08	.04
654	Bill Reidy	.10	.08	.04
655	Bobby Reis	.10	.08	.04
656	Pete Reiser	.12	.09	.05
657	Rip Repulski	.10	.08	.04
658	Ed Reulbach	.10	.08	.04
659	Jerry Reuss	.12	.09	.05
660	R.J. Reynolds	.10	.08	.04
661	Billy Rhiel	.10	.08	.04
662	Rick Rhoden	.10	.08	.04
663	Paul Richards	.10	.08	.04
664	Danny Richardson	.10	.08	.04
665	Pete Richert	.10	.08	.04
666	Harry Riconda	.10	.08	.04
667	Joe Riggert	.10	.08	.04
668	Lew Riggs	.10	.08	.04
669	Jimmy Ripple	.10	.08	.04
670	Lou Ritter	.10	.08	.04
671	German Rivera	.10	.08	.04
672	Johnny Rizzo	.10	.08	.04
673	Jim Roberts	.10	.08	.04
674	Earl Robinson	.10	.08	.04
675	Frank Robinson	.35	.25	.14
676	Jackie Robinson	1.50	1.25	.60
677A	Wilbert Robinson	.10	.08	.04
678	Rich Rodas	.10	.08	.04
678B	Sergio Robles	.10	.08	.04
679	Ellie Rodriguez	.10	.08	.04
680	Preacher Roe	.12	.09	.05
681	Ed Roebuck	.10	.08	.04
682	Ron Roenicke	.10	.08	.04
683	Oscar Roettger	.10	.08	.04
684	Lee Rogers	.10	.08	.04
685	Packy Rogers	.10	.08	.04
686	Stan Rojek	.10	.08	.04
687	Vicente Romo	.10	.08	.04
688	Johnny Roseboro	.12	.09	.05
689	Goody Rosen	.10	.08	.04
690	Don Ross	.10	.08	.04
691	Ken Rowe	.10	.08	.04
692	Schoolboy Rowe	.10	.08	.04
693	Luther Roy	.10	.08	.04
694	Jerry Royster	.10	.08	.04
695	Nap Rucker	.10	.08	.04
696	Dutch Ruether	.10	.08	.04
697	Bill Russell	.12	.09	.05
698	Jim Russell	.10	.08	.04
699	John Russell	.10	.08	.04
700	Johnny Rutherford	.10	.08	.04
701	John Ryan	.10	.08	.04
702	Rosy Ryan	.10	.08	.04
703	Mike Sandlock	.10	.08	.04
704	Ted Savage	.10	.08	.04
705	Dave Sax	.10	.08	.04
706	Steve Sax	.12	.09	.05
707	Bill Sayles	.10	.08	.04
708	Bill Schardt	.10	.08	.04
709	Johnny Schmitz	.10	.08	.04
710	Dick Schofield	.10	.08	.04
711	Howie Schultz	.10	.08	.04
712	Ferdie Schupp	.10	.08	.04
713	Mike Scioscia	.12	.09	.05
714	Dick Scott	.10	.08	.04
715	Tom Seats	.10	.08	.04
716	Jimmy Sebring	.10	.08	.04
717	Larry See	.10	.08	.04
718	Dave Sells	.10	.08	.04
719	Greg Shanahan	.10	.08	.04
720	Mike Sharperson	.10	.08	.04
721	Joe Shaute	.10	.08	.04
722	Merv Shea	.10	.08	.04
723	Jimmy Sheckhard	.10	.08	.04
724	Jack Sheehan	.10	.08	.04
725	John Shelby	.10	.08	.04
726	Vince Sherlock	.10	.08	.04
727	Larry Sherry	.12	.09	.05
728	Norm Sherry	.12	.09	.05
729	Bill Shindle	.10	.08	.04
730	Craig Shipley	.10	.08	.04
731	Bart Shirley	.10	.08	.04
732	Steve Shirley	.10	.08	.04
733	Burt Shotton	.10	.08	.04
734	George Shuba	.10	.08	.04
735	Dick Siebert	.10	.08	.04
736	Joe Simpson	.10	.08	.04
737	Duke Sims	.10	.08	.04
738	Bill Singer	.10	.08	.04
739	Fred Sington	.10	.08	.04
740	Ted Sizemore	.10	.08	.04
741	Frank Skaff	.10	.08	.04
742	Bill Skowron	.15	.11	.06
743	Gordon Slade	.10	.08	.04
744	Dwain Lefty Sloat	.10	.08	.04
745	Charley Smith	.10	.08	.04
746	Dick Smith	.10	.08	.04
747	George Smith	.10	.08	.04
748	Germany Smith	.10	.08	.04
749	Jack Smith	.10	.08	.04
750	Reggie Smith	.12	.09	.05
751	Sherry Smith	.10	.08	.04
752	Harry Smythe	.10	.08	.04
753	Duke Snider	1.00	.70	.40
754	Eddie Solomon	.10	.08	.04
755	Elias Sosa	.10	.08	.04
756	Daryl Spencer	.10	.08	.04
757	Roy Spencer	.10	.08	.04
758	Karl Spooner	.10	.08	.04
759	Eddie Stack	.10	.08	.04
760	Tuck Stainback	.10	.08	.04
761	George Stallings	.10	.08	.04
762	Jerry Standaert	.10	.08	.04
763	Don Stanhouse	.10	.08	.04
764	Eddie Stanky	.10	.08	.04
765	Dolly Stark	.10	.08	.04
766	Jigger Statz	.10	.08	.04
767	Casey Stengel	.20	.15	.08
768	Jerry Stephenson	.10	.08	.04
769	Ed Stevens	.10	.08	.04
770	Dave Stewart	.12	.09	.05
771	Stuffy Stewart	.10	.08	.04
772	Bob Stinson	.10	.08	.04
773	Milt Stock	.10	.08	.04
774	Harry Stovey	.10	.08	.04
775	Mike Strahler	.10	.08	.04
776	Sammy Strang	.10	.08	.04
777	Elmer Stricklett	.10	.08	.04
778	Joe Stripp	.10	.08	.04
779	Dick Stuart	.10	.08	.04
780	Franklin Stubbs	.10	.08	.04
781	Bill Sudakis	.10	.08	.04
782	Clyde Sukeforth	.10	.08	.04
783	Billy Sullivan	.10	.08	.04
784	Tom Sunkel	.10	.08	.04
785	Rick Sutcliffe	.12	.09	.05
786	Don Sutton	.15	.11	.06
787	Bill Swift	.10	.08	.04
788	Vito Tamulis	.10	.08	.04
789	Danny Taylor	.10	.08	.04
790	Harry Taylor	.10	.08	.04
791	Zack Taylor	.10	.08	.04
792	Not issued			
793	Chuck Templeton	.10	.08	.04
794	Wayne Terwilliger	.10	.08	.04
795	Derrel Thomas	.10	.08	.04
796	Fay Thomas	.10	.08	.04
797	Gary Thomasson	.10	.08	.04
798	Don Thompson	.10	.08	.04
799	Fresco Thompson	.10	.08	.04
800	Tim Thompson	.10	.08	.04
801	Hank Thormahlen	.10	.08	.04
802	Sloppy Thurston	.10	.08	.04
803	Cotton Tierney	.10	.08	.04
804	Al Todd	.10	.08	.04
805	Bert Tooley	.10	.08	.04
806	Jeff Torborg	.10	.08	.04
807	Dick Tracewski	.10	.08	.04
808	Nick Tremark	.10	.08	.04
809	Alex Trevino	.10	.08	.04
810	Tommy Tucker	.10	.08	.04
811	John Tudor	.10	.08	.04
812	Mike Vail	.10	.08	.04
813	Rene Valdes	.10	.08	.04
814	Bobby Valentine	.10	.08	.04
815	Fernando Valenzuela	.15	.11	.06
816	Elmer Valo	.10	.08	.04
817	Dazzy Vance	.15	.11	.06
818	Sandy Vance	.10	.08	.04
819	Chris Van Cuyk	.10	.08	.04
820	Ed VandeBerg	.10	.08	.04
821	Arky Vaughan	.15	.11	.06
822	Zoilo Versalles	.10	.08	.04
823	Joe Vosmik	.10	.08	.04
824	Ben Wade	.10	.08	.04
825	Dixie Walker	.10	.08	.04
826	Rube Walker	.10	.08	.04
827	Stan Wall	.10	.08	.04
828	Lee Walls	.10	.08	.04
829	Danny Walton	.10	.08	.04
830	Lloyd Waner	.15	.11	.06
831	Paul Waner	.15	.11	.06
832	Chuck Ward	.10	.08	.04
833	John Monte Ward	.15	.11	.06
834	Preston Ward	.10	.08	.04
835	Jack Warner	.10	.08	.04
836	Tommy Warren	.10	.08	.04
837	Carl Warwick	.10	.08	.04
838	Jimmy Wasdell	.10	.08	.04
839	Ron Washington	.10	.08	.04
840	George Watkins	.10	.08	.04
841	Hank Webb	.10	.08	.04
842	Les Webber	.10	.08	.04
843	Gary Weiss	.10	.08	.04
844	Bob Welch	.12	.09	.05
845	Brad Wellman	.10	.08	.04
846	John Werhas	.10	.08	.04
847	Max West	.10	.08	.04
848	Gus Weyhing	.10	.08	.04
849	Mack Wheat	.10	.08	.04
850	Zack Wheat	.15	.11	.06
851	Ed Wheeler	.10	.08	.04
852	Larry White	.10	.08	.04
853	Myron White	.10	.08	.04
854	Terry Whitfield	.10	.08	.04
855	Dick Whitman	.10	.08	.04
856	Possum Whitted	.10	.08	.04
857	Kemp Wicker	.10	.08	.04
858	Hoyt Wilhelm	.15	.11	.06
859	Kaiser Wilhelm	.10	.08	.04
860	Nick Willhite	.10	.08	.04
861	Dick Williams	.12	.09	.05
862	Reggie Williams	.10	.08	.04
863	Stan Williams	.10	.08	.04
864	Woody Williams	.10	.08	.04
865	Maury Wills	.15	.11	.06
866	Hack Wilson	.15	.11	.06
867	Robert Wilson	.10	.08	.04
868	Gordon Windhorn	.10	.08	.04
869	Jim Winford	.10	.08	.04
870	Lave Winham	.10	.08	.04
871	Tom Winsett	.10	.08	.04
872	Hank Winston	.10	.08	.04
873	Whitey Witt	.10	.08	.04
874	Pete Wojey	.10	.08	.04
875	Tracy Woodson	.10	.08	.04
876	Clarence Wright	.10	.08	.04
877	Glenn Wright	.10	.08	.04
878	Ricky Wright	.10	.08	.04
879	Whit Wyatt	.10	.08	.04
880	Jimmy Wynn	.10	.08	.04
881	Joe Yeager	.10	.08	.04
882	Steve Yeager	.10	.08	.04
883	Matt Young	.10	.08	.04
884	Tom Zachary	.10	.08	.04
885	Pat Zachry	.10	.08	.04
886	Geoff Zahn	.10	.08	.04
887	Don Zimmer	.12	.09	.05
888	Morrie Aderholt	.10	.08	.04
889	Raleigh Aitchison	.10	.08	.04
890	Whitey Alperman	.10	.08	.04
891	Orlando Alvarez	.10	.08	.04
892	Pat Ankeman	.10	.08	.04
893	Ed Appleton	.10	.08	.04
894	Doug Baird	.10	.08	.04
895	Lady Baldwin	.10	.08	.04
896	Win Ballou	.10	.08	.04
897	Bob Barr	.10	.08	.04
898	Boyd Bartley	.10	.08	.04
899	Eddie Basinski	.10	.08	.04
900	Erve Beck	.10	.08	.04
901	Ralph Birkofer	.10	.08	.04
902	Not issued			
903	Joe Bradshaw	.10	.08	.04
904	Bruce Brubaker	.10	.08	.04
905	Oyster Burns	.10	.08	.04
906	John Butler	.10	.08	.04
907	Not issued			
908	Kid Carsey	.10	.08	.04
909	Pete Cassidy	.10	.08	.04
910	Tom Catterson	.10	.08	.04
911	Glenn Chapman	.10	.08	.04

912	Paul Chervinko	.10	.08	.04
913	George Cisar	.10	.08	.04
914	Wally Clement	.10	.08	.04
915	Bill Collins	.10	.08	.04
916	Chuck Corgan	.10	.08	.04
917	Dick Cox	.10	.08	.04
918	George Crable	.10	.08	.04
919	Sam Crane	.10	.08	.04
920	Cliff Curtis	.10	.08	.04
921	Fats Dantonio	.10	.08	.04
922	Con Daily	.10	.08	.04
923	Jud Daley	.10	.08	.04
924	Jake Daniel	.10	.08	.04
925	Kal Daniels	.10	.08	.04
926	Dan Daub	.10	.08	.04
927	Lindsay Deal	.10	.08	.04
928	Artie Dede	.10	.08	.04
929	Pat Deisel	.10	.08	.04
930	Bert Delmas	.10	.08	.04
931	Rube Dessau	.10	.08	.04
932	Leo Dickerman	.10	.08	.04
933	John Douglas	.10	.08	.04
934	Red Downey	.10	.08	.04
935	Carl Doyle	.10	.08	.04
936	John Duffie	.10	.08	.04
937	Dick Durning	.10	.08	.04
938	Red Durrett	.10	.08	.04
939	Mal Eason	.10	.08	.04
940	Charlie Ebbetts	.12	.09	.05
941	Rube Ehardt	.10	.08	.04
942	Rowdy Elliot	.10	.08	.04
943	Bones Ely	.10	.08	.04
944	Woody English	.10	.08	.04
945	Roy Evans	.10	.08	.04
946	Gus Felix	.10	.08	.04
947	Bill Fischer	.10	.08	.04
948	Jeff Fischer	.10	.08	.04
949	Chauncey Fisher	.10	.08	.04
950	Tom Fitzsimmons	.10	.08	.04
951	Darrin Fletcher	.10	.08	.04
952	Wes Flowers	.10	.08	.04
953	Howard Freigau	.10	.08	.04
954	Nig Fuller	.10	.08	.04
955	John Gaddy	.10	.08	.04
956	Welcome Gaston	.10	.08	.04
957	Frank Gatins	.10	.08	.04
958	Pete Gilbert	.10	.08	.04
959	Wally Wilbert	.10	.08	.04
960	Carden Gillenwater	.10	.08	.04
961	Roy Gleason	.10	.08	.04
962	Harvey Green	.10	.08	.04
963	Nelson Greene	.10	.08	.04
964	John Grim	.10	.08	.04
965	Dan Griner	.10	.08	.04
967	Bill Hall	.10	.08	.04
968	Johnny Hall	.10	.08	.04
969	Not issued			
970	Pat Hanifin	.10	.08	.04
971	Bill Harris	.10	.08	.04
972	Bill W. Hart	.10	.08	.04
973	Chris Hartje	.10	.08	.04
974	Mike Hartley	.10	.08	.04
975	Gil Hatfield	.10	.08	.04
976	Chris Haughey	.10	.08	.04
977	Hugh Hearne	.10	.08	.04
978	Mike Hechinger	.10	.08	.04
979	Jake Hehl	.10	.08	.04
980	Bob Higgins	.10	.08	.04
981	Still Bill Hill	.10	.08	.04
982	Shawn Hillegas	.10	.08	.04
983	Wally Hood	.10	.08	.04
984	Lefty Hopper	.10	.08	.04
985	Ricky Horton	.10	.08	.04
986	Ed Householder	.10	.08	.04
987	Bill Hubbell	.10	.08	.04
988	Al Humphrey	.10	.08	.04
989	Bernie Hungling	.10	.08	.04
990	George Hunter	.10	.08	.04
991	Pat Hurley	.10	.08	.04
992	Joe Hutcheson	.10	.08	.04
993	Roy Hutson	.10	.08	.04
994	Bert Inks	.10	.08	.04
995	Dutch Jordan	.10	.08	.04
996	Not issued			
997	Frank Kane	.10	.08	.04
998	Chet Kehn	.10	.08	.04
999	Maury Kent	.10	.08	.04
1000	Tom Kinslow	.10	.08	.04
1001	Fred Kipp	.10	.08	.04
1002	Joe Klugman	.10	.08	.04
1003	Elmer Knetzer	.10	.08	.04
1004	Barney Koch	.10	.08	.04
1005	Jim Korwan	.10	.08	.04
1006	Joe Koukalik	.10	.08	.04
1007	Lou Koupal	.10	.08	.04
1008	Joe Kustus	.10	.08	.04
1009	Frank Lamanske	.10	.08	.04
1010	Tacks Latimer	.10	.08	.04
1011	Bill Leard	.10	.08	.04
1012	Phil Lewis	.10	.08	.04
1013	Mickey Livingston	.10	.08	.04
1014	Dick Loftus	.10	.08	.04
1015	Charlie Loudenslager	.10	.08	.04
1016	Tom Lovett	.10	.08	.04
1017	Charlie Malay	.10	.08	.04
1018	Mal Mallett	.10	.08	.04
1019	Ralph Mauriello	.10	.08	.04
1020	Bill McCabe	.10	.08	.04
1021	Gene McCann	.10	.08	.04
1022	Mike W. McCormick	.10	.08	.04
1023	Terry McDermott	.10	.08	.04
1024	John McDougal	.10	.08	.04
1025	Pryor McElveen	.10	.08	.04
1026	Dan McGann	.10	.08	.04
1027	Pat McGlothin	.10	.08	.04
1028	Doc McJames	.10	.08	.04
1029	Kit McKenna	.10	.08	.04
1030	Sadie McMahon	.10	.08	.04
1031	Not issued			
1032	Tommy McMillan	.10	.08	.04
1033	Glenn Mickens	.10	.08	.04
1034	Don Miles	.10	.08	.04
1035	Hack Miller	.10	.08	.04
1036	John Miller	.10	.08	.04
1037	Lemmie Miller	.10	.08	.04
1038	George Mohart	.10	.08	.04
1039	Gary Moore	.10	.08	.04
1040	Herbie Moran	.10	.08	.04
1041	Earl Mossor	.10	.08	.04
1042	Glen Moulder	.10	.08	.04
1043	Billy Mullen	.10	.08	.04
1045	Curly Onis	.10	.08	.04
1046	Tiny Osbourne	.10	.08	.04
1047	Jim Pastorius	.10	.08	.04
1048	Art Parks	.10	.08	.04
1049	Chink Outen	.10	.08	.04
1050	Jimmy Pattison	.10	.08	.04
1051	Norman Pitt	.10	.08	.04
1052	Doc Reisling	.10	.08	.04
1053	Gilberto Reyes	.10	.08	.04
1054	Not issued			
1055	Lou Rochelli	.10	.08	.04
1056	Jim Romano	.10	.08	.04
1057	Max Rosenfeld	.10	.08	.04
1058	Andy Rush	.10	.08	.04
1059	Jack Ryan	.10	.08	.04
1060	Jack Savage	.10	.08	.04
1061	Not issued			
1062	Ray Schmandt	.10	.08	.04
1063	Henry Schmidt	.10	.08	.04
1064	Charlie Schmutz	.10	.08	.04
1065	Joe Schultz	.10	.08	.04
1066	Ray Searage	.10	.08	.04
1067	Elmer Sexauer	.10	.08	.04
1068	George Sharrott	.10	.08	.04
1069	Tommy Sheehan	.10	.08	.04
1071	George Shoch	.10	.08	.04
1072	Broadway Aleck Smith	.10	.08	.04
1073	Hap Smith	.10	.08	.04
1074	Red Smith	.10	.08	.04
1075	Tony Smith	.10	.08	.04
1076	Gene Snyder	.10	.08	.04
1077	Denny Sothern	.10	.08	.04
1078	Bill Steele	.10	.08	.04
1080	Farmer Steelman	.10	.08	.04
1081	Dutch Stryker	.10	.08	.04
1082	Tommy Tatum	.10	.08	.04
1084	Adonis Terry	.10	.08	.04
1085	Ray Thomas	.10	.08	.04
1086	George Treadway	.10	.08	.04
1087	Overton Tremper	.10	.08	.04
1088	Ty Tyson	.10	.08	.04
1089	Rube Vickers	.10	.08	.04
1090	Jose Vizcaino	.10	.08	.04
1091	Bull Wagner	.10	.08	.04
1092	Butts Wagner	.10	.08	.04
1093	Rube Ward	.10	.08	.04
1094	John Wetteland	.12	.09	.05
1095	Eddie Wilson	.10	.08	.04
1096	Tex Wilson	.10	.08	.04
1097	Zeke Wrigley	.10	.08	.04
1098	Not issued			
1099	Rube Yarrison	.10	.08	.04
1100	Earl Yingling	.10	.08	.04
1101	Chink Zachary	.10	.08	.04
1102	Lefty Davis	.10	.08	.04
1103	Bob Hall	.10	.08	.04
1104	Darby O'Brien	.10	.08	.04
1105	Larry LeJeune	.10	.08	.04
1144	Hub Northern	.10	.08	.04

1984 Tastykake Phillies

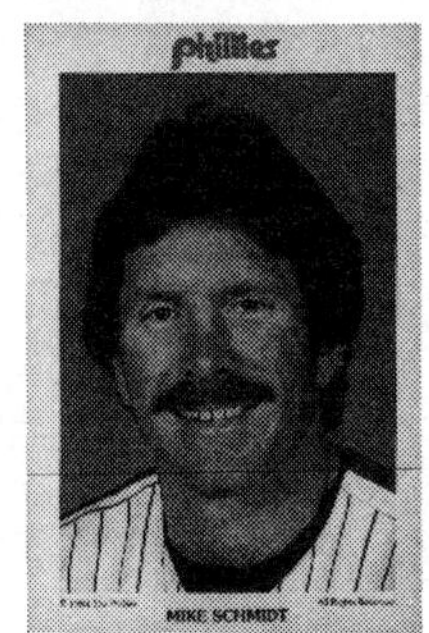

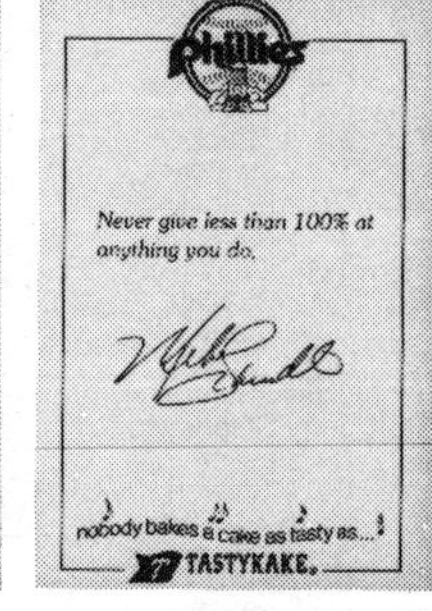

Phillies
Never give less than 100% at anything you do.
nobody bakes a cake as tasty as...!
TASTYKAKE

This 40-card regional set featuring the Philadelphia Phillies was issued as a promotion by Tastykake in 1984 and was distributed as a complete set to fans attending the April 21st game at Philadelphia's Veterans Stadium. The large (3-1/2" by 5-1/4") full-color cards have a white border surrounding the photo with "Phillies" at the top and the player's name at the bottom. A 1984 Phillies copyright line appears in the lower left corner. The backs display facsimile autographs, a brief inspirational message and the Tastykake and Phillies logos. The set includes special cards featuring the club's broadcasters, manager and coaches, a team photo, logo/checklist card and two action photos of Mike Schmidt and Steve Carlton, labeled "Future Hall of Famers".

		MT	NR MT	EX
Complete Set (44):		10.00	7.50	4.00
Common Player:		.20	.15	.08
(1)	Luis Aguayo	.20	.15	.08
(2)	Larry Andersen	.20	.15	.08
(3)	Dave Bristol	.20	.15	.08
(4)	Marty Bystrom	.20	.15	.08
(5)	Bill Campbell	.20	.15	.08
(6)	Steve Carlton	2.00	1.50	.80
(7)	Future Hall of Famer (Steve Carlton)	1.50	1.25	.60
(8)	Don Carman	.60	.45	.25
(9)	Tim Corcoran	.20	.15	.08
(10)	Ivan DeJesus	.20	.15	.08
(11)	John Denny	.25	.20	.10
(12)	Bo Diaz	.20	.15	.08
(13)	John Felske	.20	.15	.08
(14)	Kiko Garcia	.20	.15	.08
(15)	Tony Ghelfi	.20	.15	.08
(16)	Greg Gross	.20	.15	.08
(17)	Kevin Gross	.20	.15	.08
(18)	Von Hayes	.25	.20	.10
(19)	Al Holland	.20	.15	.08
(20)	Charles Hudson	.20	.15	.08
(21)	Deron Johnson	.20	.15	.08
(22)	Jerry Koosman	.25	.20	.10
(23)	Joe Lefebvre	.20	.15	.08
(24)	Sixto Lezcano	.20	.15	.08
(25)	Garry Maddox	.25	.20	.10
(26)	Len Matuszek	.20	.15	.08
(27)	Tug McGraw	.40	.30	.15
(28)	Claude Osteen	.20	.15	.08
(29)	Paul Owens	.20	.15	.08
(30)	John Russell	.20	.15	.08
(31)	Mike Ryan	.20	.15	.08
(32)	Juan Samuel	.40	.30	.15
(33)	Mike Schmidt	4.00	3.00	1.50
(34)	Future Hall of Famer (Mike Schmidt)	3.00	2.25	1.25
(35)	Jeff Stone	.20	.15	.08
(36)	Ozzie Virgil	.25	.20	.10
(37)	Dave Wehrmeister	.20	.15	.08
(38)	Glenn Wilson	.25	.20	.10
(39)	John Wockenfuss	.20	.15	.08
(40)	Phillie Phanatic	.20	.15	.08
(41)	Phillies Broadcasters (Richie Ashburn, Harry Kalas, Andy Musser, Chris Wheeler)	.50	.40	.20
(42)	Veterans Stadium	.20	.15	.08
(43)	Team Photo	.20	.15	.08
(44)	Checklist	.20	.15	.08

1985 Tastykake Phillies

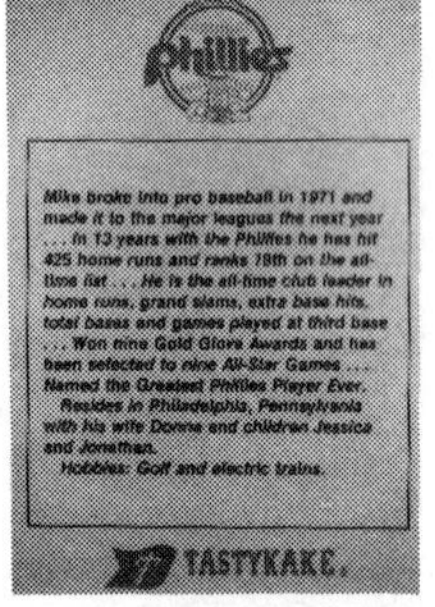

This regional set of Phillies cards, sponsored by Tastykake, was given away at a stadium promotion on April 21st at Philadelphia's Veterans Stadium. The 47 full-color cards measure a large 3" by 5" and are numbered according to the player's uniform number. In addition to player's from the 1985 Phillies roster, the set includes the manager, coaches, group photos, and cards of 14 promising minor leaguers in the club's farm system. The full-color cards are printed on a white, glossy stock and surrrounded by a white border. The player's uniform number, name and position appear below, with a 1985 Phillies copyright in the lower right corner. The backs of the cards display the Phillies and Tastykake logos at the top and bottom respectively, with player information in the center.

		MT	NR MT	EX
Complete Set (47):		12.00	9.00	4.75
Common Player:		.20	.15	.08
(1)	Checklist	.20	.15	.08
(2)	John Felske	.20	.15	.08
(3)	Dave Bristol	.20	.15	.08
(4)	Lee Elia	.20	.15	.08
(5)	Claude Osteen	.20	.15	.08
(6)	Mike Ryan	.20	.15	.08
(7)	Del Unser	.20	.15	.08
(8)	Phillies Coaching Staff (Dave Bristol, Lee Elia, John Felske, Hank King, Claude Osteen, Mike Ryan, Del Unser)	.20	.15	.08
(9)	Phillies Pitchers (Larry Andersen, Bill Campbell, Steve Carlton, Don Carman, John Denny, Kevin Gross, Al Holland, Charles Hudson, Jerry Koosman, Shane Rawley, Pat Zachry)	.30	.25	.12
(10)	Phillies Catchers (Darren Daulton, Bo Diaz, Ozzie Virgil)	.20	.15	.08
(11)	Phillies Infielders (Luis Aguayo, Ivan De Jesus, Steve Jeltz, John Russell, Juan Samuel, Mike Schmidt)	.50	.40	.20

		MT	NR MT	EX
(12)	Phillies Outfielders (Tim Corcoran, Greg Gross, Von Hayes, Jeff Stone, Glenn Wilson)	.25	.20	.10
(13)	Larry Andersen	.20	.15	.08
(14)	Steve Carlton	2.00	1.50	.80
(15)	Don Carman	.20	.15	.08
(16)	John Denny	.20	.15	.08
(17)	Tony Ghelfi	.20	.15	.08
(18)	Kevin Gross	.20	.15	.08
(19)	Al Holland	.20	.15	.08
(20)	Charles Hudson	.20	.15	.08
(21)	Jerry Koosman	.25	.20	.10
(22)	Shane Rawley	.30	.25	.12
(23)	Pat Zachry	.20	.15	.08
(24)	Darren Daulton	2.00	1.50	.80
(25)	Bo Diaz	.25	.20	.10
(26)	Ozzie Virgil	.25	.20	.10
(27)	John Wockenfuss	.20	.15	.08
(28)	Luis Aguayo	.20	.15	.08
(29)	Kiko Garcia	.20	.15	.08
(30)	Steve Jeltz	.20	.15	.08
(31)	John Russell	.20	.15	.08
(32)	Juan Samuel	.30	.25	.12
(33)	Mike Schmidt	3.00	2.25	1.25
(34)	Tim Corcoran	.20	.15	.08
(35)	Greg Gross	.20	.15	.08
(36)	Von Hayes	.30	.25	.12
(37)	Joe Lefebvre	.20	.15	.08
(38)	Garry Maddox	.25	.20	.10
(40)	Glenn Wilson	.20	.15	.08
(41)	Future Phillies (Ramon Caraballo, Mike Diaz)	.20	.15	.08
(42)	Future Phillies (Rodger Cole, Mike Maddux)	.20	.15	.08
(43)	Future Phillies (Chris James, Rick Schu)	.50	.40	.20
(44)	Future Phillies (Ken Jackson, Francisco Melendez)	.25	.20	.10
(45)	Future Phillies (Rocky Childress, Randy Salava)	.25	.20	.10
(46)	Future Phillies (Ralph Citarella, Rich Surhoff)	.25	.20	.10
(47)	Team Photo	.20	.15	.08

1986 Tastykake Phillies

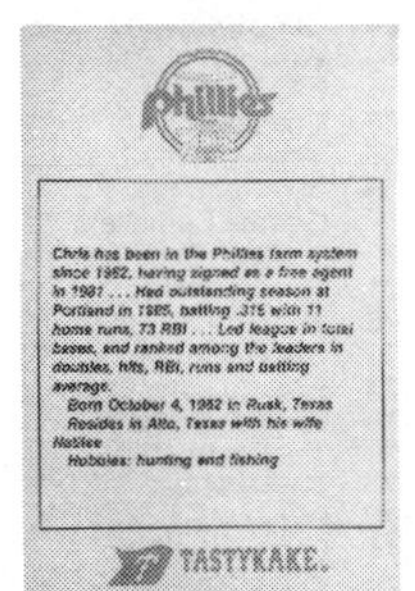

The 1986 Tastykake Phillies set consists of 49 cards that measure 3-1/2" by 5-1/4" in size. The cards were given away at the Phillies' annual baseball card day promotion. The card fronts feature a full-color photo along with the player's name, uniform number and position. The card backs are printed in red and black and carry a brief player biography. Five cards commemorating past Phillies' pennants were included in the set.

		MT	NR MT	EX
Complete Set (49):		12.00	9.00	4.75
Common Player:		.15	.11	.06
2	Jim Davenport	.15	.11	.06
3	Claude Osteen	.15	.11	.06
4	Lee Elia	.15	.11	.06
5	Mike Ryan	.15	.11	.06
6	John Russell	.15	.11	.06
7	John Felske	.15	.11	.06
8	Juan Samuel	.30	.25	.12
9	Von Hayes	.25	.20	.10
10	Darren Daulton	1.50	1.25	.60
11	Tom Foley	.15	.11	.06
12	Glenn Wilson	.15	.11	.06
14	Jeff Stone	.15	.11	.06
15	Rick Schu	.15	.11	.06
16	Luis Aguayo	.15	.11	.06
20	Mike Schmidt	3.00	2.25	1.25
21	Greg Gross	.15	.11	.06
22	Gary Redus	.15	.11	.06
23	Joe Lefebvre	.15	.11	.06
24	Milt Thompson	.30	.25	.12
25	Del Unser	.15	.11	.06
26	Chris James	.50	.40	.20
27	Kent Tekulve	.20	.15	.08
28	Shane Rawley	.20	.15	.08
29	Ronn Reynolds	.15	.11	.06
30	Steve Jeltz	.15	.11	.06
31	Garry Maddox	.25	.20	.10
32	Steve Carlton	2.00	1.50	.80
33	Dave Shipanoff	.15	.11	.06
35	Randy Lerch	.15	.11	.06
36	Robin Roberts	.60	.45	.25
39	Dave Rucker	.15	.11	.06
40	Steve Bedrosian	.40	.30	.15
41	Tom Hume	.15	.11	.06
42	Don Carman	.15	.11	.06
43	Fred Toliver	.15	.11	.06
46	Kevin Gross	.15	.11	.06
47	Larry Andersen	.15	.11	.06
48	Dave Stewart	.50	.40	.20
49	Charles Hudson	.20	.15	.08
50	Rocky Childress	.20	.15	.08
----	Future Phillies (Ramon Caraballo, Joe Cipolloni)	.20	.15	.08
----	Future Phillies (Arturo Gonzalez, Mike Maddux)	.40	.30	.15
----	Future Phillies (Ricky Jordan, Francisco Melendez)	.20	2.25	1.25
----	Future Phillies (Randy Day, Kevin Ward)	.20	.15	.08
----	The 1915 Phillies	.15	.11	.06
----	The 1950 Phillies	.15	.11	.06
----	The 1980 Phillies	.15	.11	.06
----	The 1983 Phillies	.15	.11	.06
----	June 11, 1985 - A Night To Remember	.15	.11	.06

1987 Tastykake Phillies

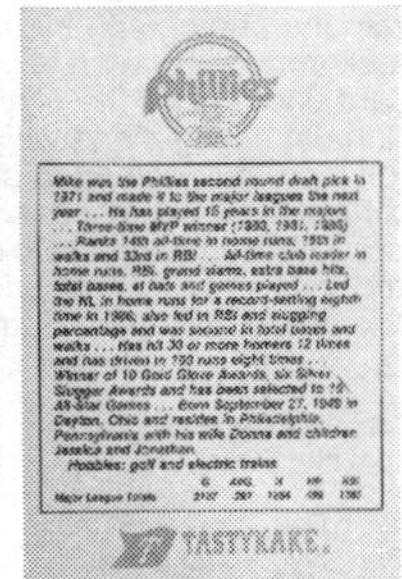

A 46-card set featuring the Philadelphia Phillies and sponsored by Tastykake was given out to fans present at Veterans Stadium for the Phillies' April 12th baseball card day promotion. The cards measure 3-1/2" by 5-1/4" with fronts that feature a full-color player photo framed with a white border. The player's number, name and position appear below the photo. Card backs are printed in red and black and contain a brief biography. The set was available for $4 via a mail-in offer to the Phillies ball club.

		MT	NR MT	EX
Complete Set (46):		10.00	7.50	4.00
Common Player:		.15	.11	.06
6	John Russell	.15	.11	.06
7	John Felske	.15	.11	.06
8	Juan Samuel	.30	.25	.12
10	Darren Daulton	.15	.11	.06
11	Greg Legg	.15	.11	.06
12	Glenn Wilson	.15	.11	.06
13	Lance Parrish	.30	.25	.12
14	Jeff Stone	.15	.11	.06
15	Rick Schu	.15	.11	.06
16	Luis Aguayo	.15	.11	.06
17	Ron Roenicke	.15	.11	.06
18	Chris James	.50	.40	.20
20	Mike Schmidt	3.00	2.25	1.25
21	Greg Gross	.15	.11	.06
23	Joe Cipolloni	.15	.11	.06
24	Milt Thompson	.20	.15	.08
27	Kent Tekulve	.20	.15	.08
28	Shane Rawley	.20	.15	.08
29	Ronn Reynolds	.15	.11	.06
30	Steve Jeltz	.15	.11	.06
33	Mike Jackson	.20	.15	.08
34	Mike Easler	.20	.15	.08
35	Dan Schatzeder	.15	.11	.06
37	Ken Dowell	.15	.11	.06
38	Jim Olander	.15	.11	.06
39a	Joe Cowley	.15	.11	.06
39b	Bob Scanlan	.15	.11	.06
40	Steve Bedrosian	.40	.30	.15
41	Tom Hume	.15	.11	.06
42	Don Carman	.15	.11	.06
43	Freddie Toliver	.15	.11	.06
44	Mike Maddux	.15	.11	.06
45	Greg Jelks	.15	.11	.06
46	Kevin Gross	.25	.20	.10
47	Bruce Ruffin	.20	.15	.08
48	Marvin Freeman	.20	.15	.08
49	Len Watts	.15	.11	.06
50	Tom Newell	.15	.11	.06
51	Ken Jackson	.15	.11	.06
52	Todd Frohwirth	.30	.25	.12
58	Doug Bair	.15	.11	.06
----	Shawn Burton, Rick Lundblade	.20	.15	.08
----	Jeff Kaye, Darren Loy	.20	.15	.08
----	Phillies Coaches (Jim Davenport, Lee Elia, Claude Osteen, Mike Ryan, Del Unser)	.15	.11	.06
----	Phillie Phanatic	.15	.11	.06
----	Team Photo	.15	.11	.06

1988 Tastykake Phillies

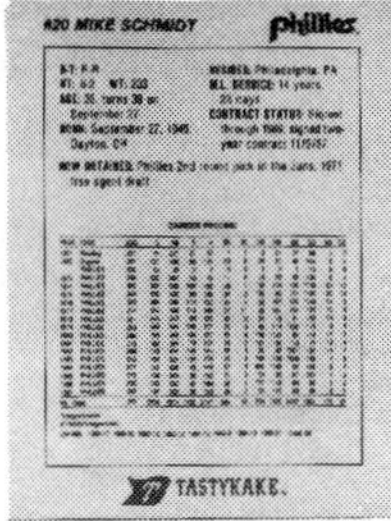

This 39-card set was co-produced by Tastykake and the Phillies. The semi-glossy oversize cards, 4-7/8" by 6-1/4", feature full-color action photos with white borders. The coaching staff, young player prospects, the team mascot and a full team photo are included in the set. The card backs carry personal data and career stats in black letters, with the Phillies and Tastykake logos in red. Card numbers correspond to player uniform numbers. The cards were available upon request from individual players and were not made available as a set. Nine cards (#'s 4, 6, 7, 11, 15 Gutierrez, 16 Bowa, 17, 33 and Broadcasters) were added later in the year. These cards have blank backs.

		MT	NR MT	EX
Complete Set (39):		10.00	7.50	4.00
Common Player:		.15	.11	.06
4a	Lee Elia (vertical format)	.15	.11	.06
4b	Lee Elia (horizontal format)	.15	.11	.06
6	John Russell	.15	.11	.06
7	John Vukovich	.15	.11	.06
8	Juan Samuel	.30	.25	.12
9	Von Hayes	.25	.20	.10
10	Darren Daulton	.50	.40	.20
11	Keith Miller	.20	.15	.08
13	Lance Parrish	.25	.20	.10
15a	Bill Almon	.15	.11	.06
15b	Jackie Gutierrez	.15	.11	.06
16a	Luis Aguayo	.15	.11	.06
16b	Larry Bowa	.20	.15	.08
17	Ricky Jordan	.40	.30	.15
18	Chris James	.20	.15	.08
19	Mike Young	.15	.11	.06
20	Mike Schmidt	2.00	1.50	.80
21	Greg Gross	.15	.11	.06
22	Bob Dernier	.15	.11	.06
24	Milt Thompson	.20	.15	.08
27	Kent Tekulve	.25	.20	.10
28	Shane Rawley	.25	.20	.10
29	Phil Bradley	.20	.15	.08
30	Steve Jeltz	.15	.11	.06
31	Jeff Calhoun	.15	.11	.06
33	Greg Harris	.15	.11	.06
38	Wally Ritchie	.15	.11	.06
40	Steve Bedrosian	.35	.25	.14
42	Don Carman	.15	.11	.06
44	Mike Maddux	.15	.11	.06
45	David Palmer	.15	.11	.06
46	Kevin Gross	.15	.11	.06
47	Bruce Ruffin	.15	.11	.06
52	Todd Frohwirth	.20	.15	.08
----	Coaching Staff (Dave Bristol, Claude Osteen, Mike Ryan, Tony Taylor, Del Unser, John Vukovich)	.15	.11	.06
----	Phillies Prospects (Tom Barrett, Brad Brink, Steve DeAngelis, Ron Jones, Keith Miller, Brad Moore, Howard Nichols, Shane Turner)	.40	.30	.15
----	Phillie Phanatic	.15	.11	.06
----	Team Photo	.15	.11	.06
----	Broadcasters (Richie Ashburn, Harry Kalas, Garry Maddox, Andy Musser, Chris Wheeler)	.15	.11	.06

1989 Tastykake Phillies

These oversize (approximately 4" by 6") cards feature very nice borderless action photos of the Philadelphia Phillies. The 36-card set was sponsored by Tastykake (whose logo appears on the bottom of the card backs) and was given to fans attending the May 13 Phillies game as a stadium promotion. The backs include player information and complete stats.

		MT	NR MT	EX
Complete Set (36):		15.00	11.00	6.00
Common Player:		.15	.11	.06
2	Larry Bowa	.15	.11	.06
3	Darold Knowles	.15	.11	.06
4a	Lenny Dykstra	.50	.40	.20
4b	Denis Menke	.15	.11	.06
5	Mike Ryan	.15	.11	.06
6	Dwayne Murphy	.15	.11	.06
7	John Vuckovich	.15	.11	.06
8a	Juan Samuel	.30	.25	.12
8b	Charlie Hayes	.25	.20	.10
9	Von Hayes	.20	.15	.08
10	Darren Daulton	.60	.45	.25
11	John Kruk	.75	.60	.30
12	Tony Taylor	.15	.11	.06
13	Roger McDowell	.25	.20	.10
15	Floyd Youmans	.15	.11	.06
16	Nick Leyva	.20	.15	.08
17	Ricky Jordan	.40	.30	.15
18	Jim Adduci (Update Card)	.25	.20	.10
19	Tom Nieto	.15	.11	.06
20	Mike Schmidt	2.00	1.50	.80
21	Dickie Thon	.15	.11	.06
22	Bob Dernier	.15	.11	.06
23	Randy Ready (Update Card)	.25	.20	.10
24	Curt Ford	.15	.11	.06
25	Steve Lake	.15	.11	.06
26	Chris James	.30	.25	.12
27	Randy O'Neal	.15	.11	.06
28	Tom Herr	.15	.11	.06
30	Steve Jeltz	.15	.11	.06
31	Mark Ryal	.15	.11	.06
33	Greg Harris	.15	.11	.06
34	Alex Madrid	.20	.15	.08
35	Eric Bullock (Update Card)	.25	.20	.10
39	Dennis Cook (Update Card)	.25	.20	.10
40	Steve Bedrosian	.35	.25	.14
41	Steve Ontiveros	.15	.11	.06
42	Don Carman	.15	.11	.06
43	Ken Howell	.15	.11	.06
44	Mike Maddux	.15	.11	.06
45	Terry Mulholland (Update Card)	.25	.20	.10
46	Larry McWilliams	.15	.11	.06
47	Bruce Ruffin	.15	.11	.06
49	Jeff Parrett	.20	.15	.08
52	Todd Frohwirth	.20	.15	.08
----	Sponsor Card	.15	.11	.06

1990 Tastykake Phillies

Identical in format to the prior year's issue, these borderless large-format (4-1/8" x 6") cards have the player's name in white on a red strip. Black-and-white backs have complete major and minor league stats, along with the Phillies logo, a few biographical details and information on the player's acquisition. Besides the current manager, players and coaches, the set included several stars of the past. The set is checklisted here alphabetically.

		MT	NR MT	EX
Complete Set (36):		10.00	7.50	4.00
Common Player:		.15	.11	.06
(1)	Darrel Ackerfelds	.15	.11	.06
(2)	Richie Ashburn	1.50	1.25	.60
(3)	Rod Booker	.15	.11	.06
(4)	Sil Campusano	.15	.11	.06
(5)	Steve Carlton	1.50	1.25	.60
(6)	Don Carman	.15	.11	.06
(7)	Pat Combs	.15	.11	.06
(8)	Dennis Cook	.15	.11	.06
(9)	Darren Daulton	.35	.25	.14
(10)	Lenny Dykstra	.45	.35	.20
(11)	Curt Ford	.15	.11	.06
(12)	Jason Grimsley	.20	.15	.08
(13)	Charlie Hayes	.20	.15	.08
(14)	Von Hayes	.20	.15	.08
(15)	Tommy Herr	.15	.11	.06
(16)	Dave Hollins	.60	.45	.25
(17)	Ken Howell	.15	.11	.06
(18)	Ron Jones	.15	.11	.06
(19)	Ricky Jordan	.35	.25	.14
(20)	John Kruk	.50	.40	.20
(21)	Steve Lake	.15	.11	.06
(22)	Nick Levya	.15	.11	.06
(23)	Carmelo Martinez	.15	.11	.06
(24)	Roger McDowell	.15	.11	.06
(25)	Chuck McElroy	.15	.11	.06
(26)	Terry Mulholland	.25	.20	.10
(27)	Jeff Parrett	.15	.11	.06
(28)	Randy Ready	.15	.11	.06
(29)	Robin Roberts	1.25	.90	.50
(30)	Bruce Ruffin	.15	.11	.06
(31)	Mike Schmidt	2.00	1.50	.80
(32)	Dickie Thon	.15	.11	.06
33	Phillie Phanatic (mascot)	.15	.11	.06
(34)	Coaches (Larry Bowa, Darold Knowles, Hal Lanier, Denis Menke, Mike Ryan, John Vukovich)	.15	.11	.06
(35)	Broadcasters (Richie Ashburn, Harry Kalas, Andy Musser, Chris Wheeler)	.20	.15	.08
(36)	Broadcasters (Jim Barniak, Garry Maddox, Mike Schmidt)	.50	.40	.20

1933 Tattoo Orbit

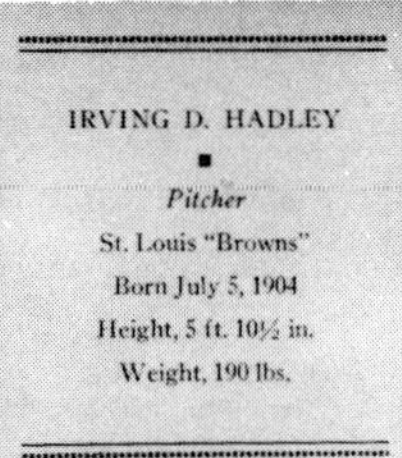

IRVING D. HADLEY
Pitcher
St. Louis "Browns"
Born July 5, 1904
Height, 5 ft. 10½ in.
Weight, 190 lbs.

Found in 1¢ packages of Tattoo gum, these 2" by 2-1/4" cards were produced by the Orbit Gum Company of Chicago, Illinois. The fronts feature a photograph which is tinted to give skin some color. Stylized baseball park backgrounds are separated from the photograph by a black line. The rest of the background is printed in vivid red, yellow and green. Card backs have the player's name, team, position, birth date, height and weight. The 60-card set is not common, but their interesting format does not seem to have struck a responsive chord in today's collectors. Cards of Bump Hadley and George Blaeholder are the most elusive, followed by those of Ivy Andrews and Rogers Hornsby.

		NR MT	EX	VG
Complete Set (60):		4500.	2250.	1350.
Common Player:		60.00	30.00	18.00
(1)	Dale Alexander	120.00	60.00	36.00
(2)	Ivy Paul Andrews	250.00	125.00	75.00
(3)	Earl Averill	120.00	60.00	36.00
(4)	Richard Bartell	60.00	30.00	18.00
(5)	Walter Berger	60.00	30.00	18.00
(6)	George F. Blaeholder	170.00	85.00	51.00
(7)	Irving J. Burns	60.00	30.00	18.00
(8)	Guy T. Bush	60.00	30.00	18.00
(9)	Bruce D. Campbell	60.00	30.00	18.00
(10)	William Cissell	60.00	30.00	18.00
(11)	Lefty Clark	60.00	30.00	18.00
(12)	Mickey Cochrane	120.00	60.00	36.00
(13)	Phil Collins	60.00	30.00	18.00
(14)	Hazen Kiki Cuyler	120.00	60.00	36.00
(15)	Dizzy Dean	250.00	125.00	75.00
(16)	Jimmy Dykes	70.00	35.00	21.00
(17)	George L. Earnshaw	60.00	30.00	18.00
(18)	Woody English	60.00	30.00	18.00
(19)	Lewis A. Fonseca	70.00	35.00	21.00
(20)	Jimmy Foxx	200.00	100.00	60.00
(21)	Burleigh A. Grimes	120.00	60.00	36.00
(22)	Charles John Grimm	70.00	35.00	21.00
(23)	Robert M. Grove	120.00	60.00	36.00
(24)	Frank Grube	60.00	30.00	18.00
(25)	George W. Haas	60.00	30.00	18.00
(26)	Irving D. Hadley	170.00	85.00	51.00
(27)	Chick Hafey	120.00	60.00	36.00
(28)	Jesse Joseph Haines	120.00	60.00	36.00
(29)	William Hallahan	60.00	30.00	18.00
(30)	Melvin Harder	60.00	30.00	18.00
(31)	Gabby Hartnett	120.00	60.00	36.00
(32)	Babe Herman	70.00	35.00	21.00
(33)	William Herman	120.00	60.00	36.00
(34)	Rogers Hornsby	340.00	170.00	102.00
(35)	Roy C. Johnson	60.00	30.00	18.00
(36)	J. Smead Jolley	60.00	30.00	18.00
(37)	William Jurges	60.00	30.00	18.00
(38)	William Kamm	60.00	30.00	18.00
(39)	Mark A. Koenig	60.00	30.00	18.00
(40)	James J. Levey	60.00	30.00	18.00
(41)	Ernie Lombardi	120.00	60.00	36.00
(42)	Red Lucas	60.00	30.00	18.00
(43)	Ted Lyons	120.00	60.00	36.00
(44)	Connie Mack	200.00	100.00	60.00
(45)	Pat Malone	60.00	30.00	18.00
(46)	Pepper Martin	70.00	35.00	21.00
(47)	Marty McManus	60.00	30.00	18.00
(48)	Frank J. O'Doul	70.00	35.00	21.00
(49)	Richard Porter	60.00	30.00	18.00
(50)	Carl N. Reynolds	60.00	30.00	18.00
(51)	Charles Henry Root	60.00	30.00	18.00
(52)	Robert Seeds	60.00	30.00	18.00
(53)	Al H. Simmons	120.00	60.00	36.00
(54)	Jackson Riggs Stepheson	70.00	35.00	21.00
(55)	Bud Tinning	60.00	30.00	18.00
(56)	Joe Vosmik	60.00	30.00	18.00
(57)	Rube Walberg	60.00	30.00	18.00
(58)	Paul Waner	120.00	60.00	36.00
(59)	Lonnie Warneke	60.00	30.00	18.00
(60)	Arthur C. Whitney	60.00	30.00	18.00

Definitions for grading conditions are located in the Introduction of this price guide.

1933 Tatoo Orbit (R308)

This obscure set of cards, issued by Tatoo Orbit, is numbered from 151 through 207, with a few of the numbers still unknown. The tiny cards measure just

1-7/8" by 1-1/4" and were considered more of a novelty item because the crude player drawings on the cards actually "developed" when moistened and exposed to light.

		NR MT	EX	VG
Complete Set:		2400.	1200.	720.00
Common Player:		30.00	15.00	9.00
151	Vernon Gomez	75.00	37.00	22.00
152	Kiki Cuyler	75.00	37.00	22.00
153	Jimmy Foxx	112.50	56.00	34.00
154	Al Simmons	75.00	37.00	22.00
155	Chas. J. Grimm	33.00	16.50	10.00
156	William Jurges	30.00	15.00	9.00
157	Chuck Klein	75.00	37.00	22.00
158	Richard Bartell	30.00	15.00	9.00
159	Pepper Martin	45.00	22.00	13.50
160	Earl Averill	75.00	37.00	22.00
161	William Dickey	90.00	45.00	27.00
162	Wesley Ferrell	30.00	15.00	9.00
163	Oral Hildebrand	30.00	15.00	9.00
164	Wm. Kamm	30.00	15.00	9.00
165	Earl Whitehill	30.00	15.00	9.00
166	Charles Fullis	30.00	15.00	9.00
167	Jimmy Dykes	33.00	16.50	10.00
168	Ben Cantwell	30.00	15.00	9.00
169	George Earnshaw	30.00	15.00	9.00
170	Jackson Stephenson	33.00	16.50	10.00
171	Randolph Moore	30.00	15.00	9.00
172	Ted Lyons	75.00	37.00	22.00
173	Goose Goslin	75.00	37.00	22.00
174	E. Swanson	30.00	15.00	9.00
175	Lee Roy Mahaffey	30.00	15.00	9.00
176	Joe Cronin	75.00	37.00	22.00
177	Tom Bridges	30.00	15.00	9.00
178	Henry Manush	75.00	37.00	22.00
179	Walter Stewart	30.00	15.00	9.00
180	Frank Pytlak	30.00	15.00	9.00
181	Dale Alexander	30.00	15.00	9.00
182	Robert Grove	90.00	45.00	27.00
183	Charles Gehringer	75.00	37.00	22.00
184	Lewis Fonseca	30.00	15.00	9.00
185	Alvin Crowder	30.00	15.00	9.00
186	Mickey Cochrane	75.00	37.00	22.00
187	Max Bishop	30.00	15.00	9.00
188	Connie Mack	90.00	45.00	27.00
189	Guy Bush	30.00	15.00	9.00
190	Charlie Root	30.00	15.00	9.00
191a	Burleigh Grimes	75.00	37.00	22.00
191b	Gabby Hartnett	75.00	37.00	22.00
192	Pat Malone	30.00	15.00	9.00
193	Woody English	30.00	15.00	9.00
194	Lonnie Warneke	30.00	15.00	9.00
195	Babe Herman	33.00	16.50	10.00
196	Unknown			
197	Unknown			
198	Unknown			
199	Unknown			
200	Gabby Hartnett	75.00	37.00	22.00
201	Paul Waner	75.00	37.00	22.00
202	Dizzy Dean	150.00	75.00	45.00
203	Unknown			
204	Unknown			
205	Jim Bottomley	75.00	37.00	22.00
206	Unknown			
207	Charles Hafey	75.00	37.00	22.00
208	Unknown			
209	Unknown			
210	Unknown			

A player's name in italic type indicates a rookie card. An (FC) indicates a player's first card for that particular card company.

1986 Texas Gold Ice Cream Reds

One of the last regional baseball card sets produced during the 1986 season was a 28-card team set sponsored by a Cincinnati-area ice cream company and given to fans attending a September 19th game. Photos on the 2-1/2" by 3-1/2" cards are game-action shots, and include three different cards

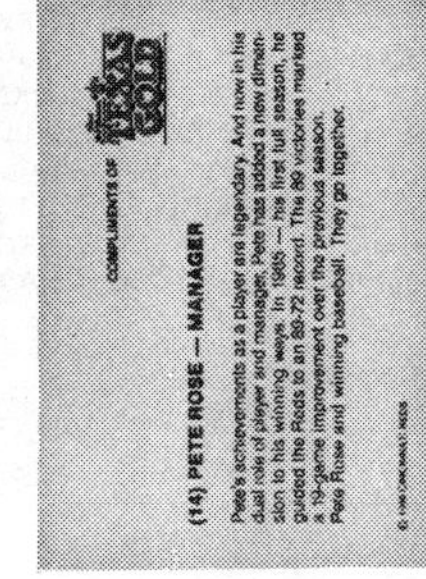

of playing manager Pete Rose. The set is also notable for the inclusion of first cards of some of the Reds' young stars.

		MT	NR MT	EX
Complete Set (28):		15.00	11.00	6.00
Common Player:		.25	.20	.10
6	Bo Diaz	.25	.20	.10
9	Max Venable	.25	.20	.10
11	Kurt Stillwell	.30	.25	.12
12	Nick Esasky	.30	.25	.12
13	Dave Concepcion	.50	.40	.20
14a	Pete Rose (commemorative)	2.00	1.50	.80
14b	Pete Rose (infield)	2.00	1.50	.80
14c	Pete Rose (manager)	2.00	1.50	.80
16	Ron Oester	.25	.20	.10
20	Eddie Milner	.25	.20	.10
22	Sal Butera	.25	.20	.10
24	Tony Perez	.70	.50	.30
25	Buddy Bell	.35	.25	.14
28	Kal Daniels	.75	.60	.30
29	Tracy Jones	.40	.30	.15
31	John Franco	.80	.60	.30
32	Tom Browning	.60	.45	.25
33	Ron Robinson	.35	.25	.14
34	Bill Gullickson	.25	.20	.10
36	Mario Soto	.35	.25	.14
39	Dave Parker	1.00	.70	.40
40	John Denny	.25	.20	.10
44	Eric Davis	.80	.60	.30
45	Chris Welsh	.25	.20	.10
48	Ted Power	.25	.20	.10
49	Joe Price	.25	.20	.10
----	Coaches Card (Scott Breeden, Billy DeMars, Tommy Helms, Bruce Kimm, Jim Lett, George Scherger)	.25	.20	.10
----	Logo/Coupon Card	.10	.08	.04

1914 Texas Tommy Type I (E224)

Little is known about the origin of this 50-card set issued in 1914 and designated as E224 in the American Card Catalog. Measuring 2-3/8" by 3-1/2", the front of the cards feature sepia-toned action photos with the player's name in capital letters and his team below in parenthesis. The back carries a rather lengthy player biography and most cards, although not all, include year-by-year statistics at the bottom. The words "Texas Tommy" appear at the top, apparently referring to the sponsor of the set, although it is still unclear who or what "Texas Tommy" was, and despite its name, most examples of this set have been found in northern California. There is also a second variety of the set, smaller in size (1-7/8" by 3"), which are borderless pictures with a glossy finish.

		NR MT	EX	VG
Complete Set (50):		24500.	12250.	7350.
Common Player:		225.00	112.00	67.00
(1)	Jimmy Archer	225.00	112.00	67.00
(2)	Jimmy Austin	225.00	112.00	67.00
(3)	Home Run Baker	800.00	400.00	240.00
(4)	Chief Bender	800.00	400.00	240.00
(5)	Bob Bescher	225.00	112.00	67.00
(6)	Ping Bodie	225.00	112.00	67.00
(7)	Donie Bush	225.00	112.00	67.00
(8)	Bobby Byrne	225.00	112.00	67.00
(9)	Nixey Callahan (Callahan)	225.00	112.00	67.00
(10)	Howie Camnitz	225.00	112.00	67.00
(11)	Frank Chance	800.00	400.00	240.00
(12)	Hal Chase	500.00	250.00	150.00
(13)	Ty Cobb	3500.	1750.	1050.
(14)	Jack Coombs	225.00	112.00	67.00
(15)	Sam Crawford	800.00	400.00	240.00
(16)	Birdie Cree	225.00	112.00	67.00
(17)	Al DeMaree (Demaree)	225.00	112.00	67.00
(18)	Red Dooin	225.00	112.00	67.00
(19)	Larry Doyle	225.00	112.00	67.00
(20)	Johnny Evers	800.00	400.00	240.00
(21)	Vean Gregg	225.00	112.00	67.00
(22)	Bob Harmon	225.00	112.00	67.00
(23)	Shoeless Joe Jackson	4500.	2250.	1350.
(24)	Walter Johnson	1250.	625.00	375.00
(25)	Otto Knabe	225.00	112.00	67.00
(26)	Nap Lajoie	900.00	450.00	270.00
(27)	Harry Lord	225.00	112.00	67.00
(28)	Connie Mack	850.00	425.00	255.00
(29)	Armando Marsans	225.00	112.00	67.00
(30)	Christy Mathewson	1200.	600.00	360.00
(31)	George McBride	225.00	112.00	67.00
(32)	John McGraw	800.00	400.00	240.00
(33)	Stuffy McInnis	225.00	112.00	67.00
(34)	Chief Meyers	225.00	112.00	67.00
(35)	Earl Moore	225.00	112.00	67.00
(36)	Mike Mowrey	225.00	112.00	67.00
(37)	Marty O'Toole	225.00	112.00	67.00
(38)	Eddie Plank	800.00	400.00	240.00
(39)	Bud Ryan	225.00	112.00	67.00
(40)	Tris Speaker	1000.	500.00	300.00
(41)	Jake Stahl	225.00	112.00	67.00
(42)	Oscar Strange (Stanage)	225.00	112.00	67.00
(43)	Bill Sweeney	225.00	112.00	67.00
(44)	Honus Wagner	2000.	1000.	600.00
(45)	Ed Walsh	800.00	400.00	240.00
(46)	Zach Wheat	800.00	400.00	240.00
(47)	Harry Wolter	225.00	112.00	67.00
(48)	Joe Wood	450.00	225.00	135.00
(49)	Steve Yerkes	225.00	112.00	67.00
(50)	Heinie Zimmerman	225.00	112.00	67.00

1914 Texas Tommy Type II (E224)

		NR MT	EX	VG
Complete Set (14):		9000.	4500.	2700.
Common Player:		250.00	125.00	75.00
(1)	Ping Bodie	250.00	125.00	75.00
(2)	Larry Doyle	250.00	125.00	75.00
(3)	Vean Gregg	250.00	125.00	75.00
(4)	Harry Hooper	800.00	400.00	240.00
(5)	Walter Johnson	1250.	625.00	375.00
(6)	Connie Mack	850.00	425.00	255.00
(7)	Rube Marquard	800.00	400.00	240.00
(8)	Christy Mathewson	1200.	600.00	360.00
(9)	John McGraw	800.00	400.00	240.00
(10)	Chief Meyers	250.00	125.00	75.00
(11)	Jake Stahl	250.00	125.00	75.00
(12)	Honus Wagner	2200.	1100.	660.00
(13)	Joe Wood	275.00	137.00	82.00
(14)	Steve Yerkes	250.00	125.00	75.00

A card number in parentheses () indicates the set is unnumbered.

1928 Tharp's Ice Cream

Sharing the same format and checklist with several other contemporary ice cream sets this 60-card set includes all of the top stars of the day. Cards are printed in black and white on a 1-3/8" x 2-1/2" format. The player's name and a card number appear either in a strip within the frame of the photo, or printed in the border beneath the photo. Card backs

have a redemption offer that includes an ice cream bar in exchange for a Babe Ruth card, or a gallon of ice cream for a complete set of 60.

		NR MT	EX	VG
Complete Set (60):		2900.	1450.	870.00
Common Player:		25.00	12.50	7.50
1	Burleigh Grimes	40.00	20.00	12.00
2	Walter Reuther	25.00	12.50	7.50
3	Joe Dugan	25.00	12.50	7.50
4	Red Faber	40.00	20.00	12.00
5	Gabby Hartnett	40.00	20.00	12.00
6	Babe Ruth	650.00	325.00	195.00
7	Bob Meusel	25.00	12.50	7.50
8	Herb Pennock	40.00	20.00	12.00
9	George Burns	25.00	12.50	7.50
10	Joe Sewell	40.00	20.00	12.00
11	George Uhle	25.00	12.50	7.50
12	Bob O'Farrell	25.00	12.50	7.50
13	Rogers Hornsby	125.00	62.00	37.00
14	"Pie" Traynor	40.00	20.00	12.00
15	Clarence Mitchell	25.00	12.50	7.50
16	Eppa Rixey	40.00	20.00	12.00
17	Carl Mays	25.00	12.50	7.50
18	Adolfo Luque	25.00	12.50	7.50
19	Dave Bancroft	40.00	20.00	12.00
20	George Kelly	40.00	20.00	12.00
21	Earl (Earle) Combs	40.00	20.00	12.00
22	Harry Heilmann	40.00	20.00	12.00
23	Ray W. Schalk	40.00	20.00	12.00
24	Johnny Mostil	25.00	12.50	7.50
25	Hack Wilson	40.00	20.00	12.00
26	Lou Gehrig	400.00	200.00	120.00
27	Ty Cobb	400.00	200.00	120.00
28	Tris Speaker	55.00	27.00	16.50
29	Tony Lazzeri	40.00	20.00	12.00
30	Waite Hoyt	40.00	20.00	12.00
31	Sherwood Smith	25.00	12.50	7.50
32	Max Carey	40.00	20.00	12.00
33	Eugene Hargrave	25.00	12.50	7.50
34	Miguel L. Gonzalez	25.00	12.50	7.50
35	Joe Judge	25.00	12.50	7.50
36	E.C. (Sam) Rice	40.00	20.00	12.00
37	Earl Sheely	25.00	12.50	7.50
38	Sam Jones	25.00	12.50	7.50
39	Bib (Bibb) A. Falk	25.00	12.50	7.50
40	Willie Kamm	25.00	12.50	7.50
41	Stanley Harris	40.00	20.00	12.00
42	John J. McGraw	40.00	20.00	12.00
43	Artie Nehf	25.00	12.50	7.50
44	Grover Alexander	55.00	27.00	16.50
45	Paul Waner	40.00	20.00	12.00
46	William H. Terry	40.00	20.00	12.00
47	Glenn Wright	25.00	12.50	7.50
48	Earl Smith	25.00	12.50	7.50
49	Leon (Goose) Goslin	40.00	20.00	12.00
50	Frank Frisch	40.00	20.00	12.00
51	Joe Harris	25.00	12.50	7.50
52	Fred (Cy) Williams	25.00	12.50	7.50
53	Eddie Roush	40.00	20.00	12.00
54	George Sisler	40.00	20.00	12.00
55	Ed. Rommel	25.00	12.50	7.50
56	Roger Peckinpaugh	25.00	12.50	7.50
57	Stanley Coveleskie (Coveleski)	40.00	20.00	12.00
58	Lester Bell	25.00	12.50	7.50
59	Lloyd Waner	40.00	20.00	12.00
60	John P. McInnis	25.00	12.50	7.50

The values quoted are intended to reflect the market price.

1985 Thom McAn Discs

One of the more obscure 1985 issues, this 47-card set of "Pro Player Discs" was issued by Thom McAn as a promotion for its "Jox" tennis shoes, which are advertised on the back of the cards. The discs, which measure 2-3/4" in diameter, feature black and white player photos against a background of either gold, yellow, red, pink, green or blue. Although not included in the "official" checklist

released by the company, cards of George Brett have also been reported. The discs are unnumbered.

		MT	NR MT	EX
Complete Set (47):		70.00	52.00	28.00
Common Player:		1.00	.70	.40
(1)	Benny Ayala	1.00	.70	.40
(2)	Buddy Bell	1.25	.90	.50
(3)	Juan Beniquez	1.00	.70	.40
(4)	Tony Bernazard	1.00	.70	.40
(5)	Mike Boddicker	1.00	.70	.40
(6)	George Brett	8.00	6.00	3.25
(7)	Bill Buckner	1.25	.90	.50
(8)	Rod Carew	4.00	3.00	1.50
(9)	Steve Carlton	4.00	3.00	1.50
(10)	Caesar Cedeno (Cesar)	1.25	.90	.50
(11)	Onix Concepcion	1.00	.70	.40
(12)	Cecil Cooper	1.00	.70	.40
(13)	Al Cowens	1.00	.70	.40
(14)	Jose Cruz	1.00	.70	.40
(15)	Ivan DeJesus	1.00	.70	.40
(16)	Luis DeLeon	1.00	.70	.40
(17)	Rich Gossage	1.25	.90	.50
(18)	Pedro Guerrero	1.50	1.25	.60
(19)	Ron Guidry	1.50	1.25	.60
(20)	Tony Gwynn	4.00	3.00	1.50
(21)	Mike Hargrove	1.00	.70	.40
(22)	Keith Hernandez	1.25	.90	.50
(23)	Bob Horner	1.00	.70	.40
(24)	Kent Hrbek	2.25	1.75	.90
(25)	Rick Langford	1.00	.70	.40
(26)	Jeff Leonard	1.00	.70	.40
(27)	Willie McGee	1.50	1.25	.60
(28)	Jack Morris	1.50	1.25	.60
(29)	Jesse Orosco	1.00	.70	.40
(30)	Junior Ortiz	1.00	.70	.40
(31)	Terry Puhl	1.00	.70	.40
(32)	Dan Quisenberry	1.25	.90	.50
(33)	Johnny Ray	1.00	.70	.40
(34)	Cal Ripken	6.00	4.50	2.50
(35)	Ed Romero	1.00	.70	.40
(36)	Ryne Sandberg	6.00	4.50	2.50
(37)	Mike Schmidt	6.00	4.50	2.50
(38)	Tom Seaver	4.00	3.00	1.50
(39)	Rick Sutcliffe	1.25	.90	.50
(40)	Bruce Sutter	1.25	.90	.50
(41)	Alan Trammell	2.00	1.50	.80
(42)	Fernando Valenzuela	1.25	.90	.50
(43)	Ozzie Virgil	1.00	.70	.40
(44)	Greg Walker	1.00	.70	.40
(45)	Willie Wilson	1.00	.70	.40
(46)	Dave Winfield	4.00	3.00	1.50
(47)	Geoff Zahn	1.00	.70	.40

1983 Thorn Apple Valley Cubs

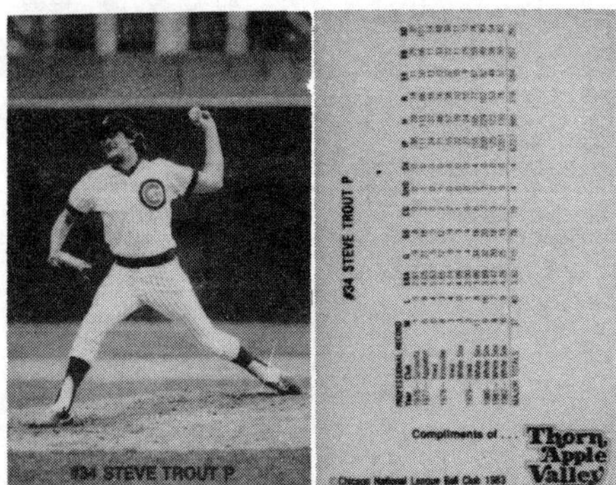

This set of 27 cards was issued in conjuction with a "Baseball Card Day" promotion at Wrigley Field in 1983. Thorn Apple Valley was the meat company which produced the hot dogs sold at the ballpark. The cards feature borderless color photos with the player's name, uniform number (also the card's number in the checklist) and an abbreviation for their position. Card backs feature annual statistics. Of the 27 cards, which measure 2-1/4" by 3-1/2", 25 feature players, one is a team card, and one features the manager and coaches.

		MT	NR MT	EX
Complete Set (27):		15.00	11.00	6.00
Common Player:		.20	.15	.08
1	Larry Bowa	.25	.20	.10
6	Keith Moreland	.25	.20	.10
7	Jody Davis	.25	.20	.10
10	Leon Durham	.25	.20	.10
11	Ron Cey	.25	.20	.10
16	Steve Lake	.20	.15	.08
20	Thad Bosley	.20	.15	.08
21	Jay Johnstone	.35	.25	.14
22	Bill Buckner	.40	.30	.15
23	Ryne Sandberg	6.00	4.50	2.50
24	Jerry Morales	.20	.15	.08
25	Gary Woods	.20	.15	.08
27	Mel Hall	.20	.15	.08
29	Tom Veryzer	.20	.15	.08
30	Chuck Rainey	.20	.15	.08
31	Fergie Jenkins	1.00	.70	.40
32	Craig Lefferts	.30	.25	.12
33	Joe Carter	6.00	4.50	2.50
34	Steve Trout	.25	.20	.10
36	Mike Proly	.20	.15	.08
39	Bill Campbell	.20	.15	.08
41	Warren Brusstar	.20	.15	.08
44	Dick Ruthven	.20	.15	.08
46	Lee Smith	.80	.60	.30
48	Dickie Noles	.20	.15	.08
----	Coaching Staff (Ruben Amaro, Billy Connors, Duffy Dyer, Lee Elia, Fred Koenig, John Vukovich)	.20	.15	.08
----	Team Photo	.20	.15	.08

1910 Tip-Top Bread Pittsburgh Pirates

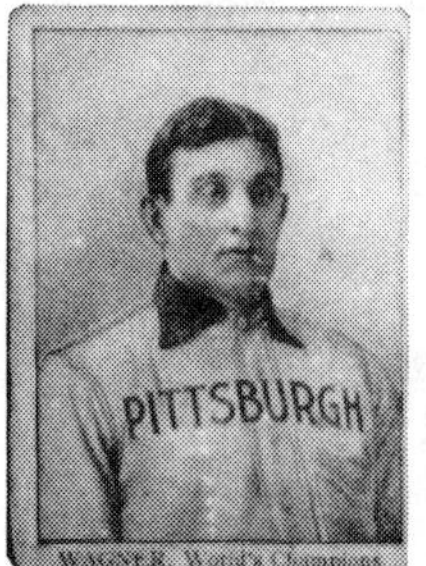

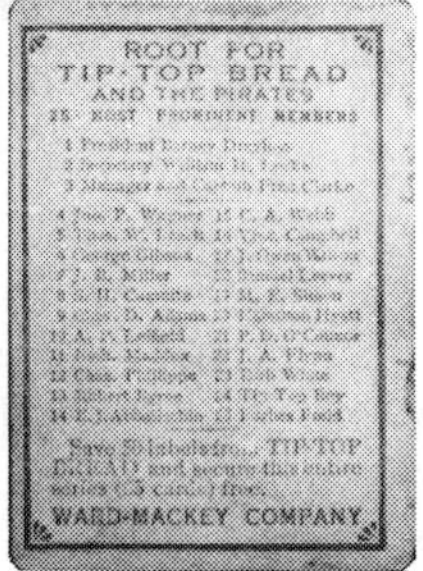

		NR MT	EX	VG
Complete Set (25):		3000.	1500.	900.00
Common Player:		100.00	50.00	30.00
1	Barney Dreyfuss (President)	200.00	100.00	60.00
2	William H. Locke (Secretary)	100.00	50.00	30.00
3	Fred Clarke	250.00	125.00	75.00
4	Honus Wagner	800.00	400.00	240.00
5	Tom Leach	100.00	50.00	30.00
6	George Gibson	100.00	50.00	30.00
7	Dots Miller	100.00	50.00	30.00
8	Howie Camnitz	100.00	50.00	30.00
9	Babe Adams	100.00	50.00	30.00
10	Lefty Leifield	100.00	50.00	30.00
11	Nick Maddox	100.00	50.00	30.00
12	Deacon Philippe	100.00	50.00	30.00
13	Bobby Byrne	100.00	50.00	30.00
14	Ed Abbaticchio	100.00	50.00	30.00
15	Lefty Webb	100.00	50.00	30.00
16	Vin Campbell	100.00	50.00	30.00
17	Owen Wilson	100.00	50.00	30.00
18	Sam Leever	100.00	50.00	30.00
19	Mike Simon	100.00	50.00	30.00
20	Ham Hyatt	100.00	50.00	30.00
21	Paddy O'Connor	100.00	50.00	30.00
22	John Flynn	100.00	50.00	30.00
23	Kirby White	100.00	50.00	30.00
24	Tip Top Boy Mascot	100.00	50.00	30.00
25	Forbes Field	100.00	50.00	30.00

1947 Tip Top Bread

This 163-card set actually consists of a group of regional issues, some of which are more scarce then others. The 2-1/4" by 3" cards are borderless with a black and white player photo below which is a white strip containing the player's name, position, city name and league. Backs carry an advertisement. The set is known for a quantity of obscure players, many of whom played during the talent-lean World War II seasons. Overall it is a scarce set, with a number of interesting cards including first-issues of Yogi Berra and Joe Garagiola.

		NR MT	EX	VG
Complete Set (163):		12000.	6000.	3500.
Common Player:		35.00	17.50	10.50
(1)	Bill Ayers	35.00	17.50	10.50
(2)	Floyd Baker	50.00	25.00	15.00
(3)	Charles Barrett	50.00	25.00	15.00
(4)	Eddie Basinski	35.00	17.50	10.50
(5)	John Berardino	50.00	25.00	15.00
(6)	Larry Berra	400.00	200.00	120.00
(7)	Bill Bevens	50.00	25.00	15.00
(8)	Robert Blattner	35.00	17.50	10.50
(9)	Ernie Bonham	35.00	17.50	10.50
(10)	Bob Bragan	45.00	22.00	13.50
(11)	Ralph Branca	70.00	35.00	21.00
(12)	Alpha Brazle	35.00	17.50	10.50
(13)	Bobbie Brown	60.00	30.00	18.00
(14)	Mike Budnick	35.00	17.50	10.50
(15)	Ken Burkhart	35.00	17.50	10.50
(16)	Thomas Byrne	50.00	25.00	15.00
(17)	Earl Caldwell	50.00	25.00	15.00
(18)	"Hank" Camelli	50.00	25.00	15.00
(19)	Hugh Casey	45.00	22.00	13.50
(20)	Phil Cavarretta	65.00	32.00	19.50
(21)	Bob Chipman	50.00	25.00	15.00
(22)	Lloyd Christopher	50.00	25.00	15.00
(23)	Bill Cox	35.00	17.50	10.50
(24)	Bernard Creger	35.00	17.50	10.50
(25)	Frank Crosetti	65.00	32.00	19.50
(26)	Joffre Cross	35.00	17.50	10.50
(27)	Leon Culberson	50.00	25.00	15.00
(28)	Dick Culler	50.00	25.00	15.00
(29)	Dom DiMaggio	200.00	100.00	60.00
(30)	George Dickey	60.00	30.00	18.00
(31)	Chas. E. Diering	35.00	17.50	10.50
(32)	Joseph Dobson	50.00	25.00	15.00
(33)	Bob Doerr	275.00	137.00	82.00
(34)	Ervin Dusak	35.00	17.50	10.50
(35)	Bruce Edwards	40.00	20.00	12.00
(36)	Walter "Hoot" Evers	50.00	25.00	15.00
(37)	Clifford Fannin	35.00	17.50	10.50
(38)	"Nanny" Fernandez	50.00	25.00	15.00
(39)	Dave "Boo" Ferriss	50.00	25.00	15.00
(40)	Elbie Fletcher	35.00	17.50	10.50
(41)	Dennis Galehouse	35.00	17.50	10.50
(42)	Joe Garagiola	200.00	100.00	60.00
(43)	Sid Gordon	35.00	17.50	10.50
(44)	John Gorsica	50.00	25.00	15.00
(45)	Hal Gregg	40.00	20.00	12.00
(46)	Frank Gustine	35.00	17.50	10.50
(47)	Stanley Hack	65.00	32.00	19.50
(48)	Mickey Harris	50.00	25.00	15.00
(49)	Clinton Hartung	35.00	17.50	10.50
(50)	Joe Hatten	40.00	20.00	12.00
(51)	Frank Hayes	50.00	25.00	15.00
(52)	"Jeff" Heath	35.00	17.50	10.50
(53)	Tom Henrich	70.00	35.00	21.00
(54)	Gene Hermanski	40.00	20.00	12.00
(55)	Kirby Higbe	35.00	17.50	10.50
(56)	Ralph Hodgin	50.00	25.00	15.00
(57)	Tex Hughson	50.00	25.00	15.00
(58)	Fred Hutchinson	70.00	35.00	21.00
(59)	LeRoy Jarvis	35.00	17.50	10.50
(60)	"Si" Johnson	50.00	25.00	15.00
(61)	Don Johnson	50.00	25.00	15.00
(62)	Earl Johnson	50.00	25.00	15.00
(63)	John Jorgensen	40.00	20.00	12.00
(64)	Walter Judnick (Judnich)	35.00	17.50	10.50
(65)	Tony Kaufmann	35.00	17.50	10.50
(66)	George Kell	400.00	200.00	120.00
(67)	Charlie Keller	65.00	32.00	19.50
(68)	Bob Kennedy	50.00	25.00	15.00
(69)	Montia Kennedy	35.00	17.50	10.50
(70)	Ralph Kiner	80.00	40.00	24.00
(71)	Dave Koslo	35.00	17.50	10.50
(72)	Jack Kramer	35.00	17.50	10.50
(73)	Joe Kuhel	50.00	25.00	15.00
(74)	George Kurowski	35.00	17.50	10.50
(75)	Emil Kush	50.00	25.00	15.00
(76)	"Eddie" Lake	50.00	25.00	15.00
(77)	Harry Lavagetto	45.00	22.00	13.50
(78)	Bill Lee	50.00	25.00	15.00
(79)	Thornton Lee	50.00	25.00	15.00
(80)	Paul Lehner	35.00	17.50	10.50
(81)	John Lindell	50.00	25.00	15.00
(82)	Danny Litwhiler	50.00	25.00	15.00
(83)	"Mickey" Livingston	50.00	25.00	15.00
(84)	Carroll Lockman	35.00	17.50	10.50
(85)	Jack Lohrke	35.00	17.50	10.50
(86)	Ernie Lombardi	80.00	40.00	24.00
(87)	Vic Lombardi	40.00	20.00	12.00
(88)	Edmund Lopat	65.00	32.00	19.50
(89)	Harry Lowrey	50.00	25.00	15.00
(90)	Marty Marion	50.00	25.00	15.00
(91)	Willard Marshall	35.00	17.50	10.50
(92)	Phil Masi	50.00	25.00	15.00
(93)	Edward J. Mayo	50.00	25.00	15.00
(94)	Clyde McCullough	50.00	25.00	15.00
(95)	Frank Melton	40.00	20.00	12.00
(96)	Cass Michaels	50.00	25.00	15.00
(97)	Ed Miksis	40.00	20.00	12.00
(98)	Arthur Mills	50.00	25.00	15.00
(99)	Johnny Mize	80.00	40.00	24.00
(100)	Lester Moss	35.00	17.50	10.50
(101)	"Pat" Mullin	50.00	25.00	15.00
(102)	"Bob" Muncrief	35.00	17.50	10.50
(103)	George Munger	35.00	17.50	10.50
(104)	Fritz Ostermueller	35.00	17.50	10.50
(105)	James P. Outlaw	50.00	25.00	15.00
(106)	Frank "Stub" Overmire	50.00	25.00	15.00
(107)	Andy Pafko	60.00	30.00	18.00

(108)	Joe Page	50.00	25.00	15.00
(109)	Roy Partee	50.00	25.00	15.00
(110)	Johnny Pesky	60.00	30.00	18.00
(111)	Nelson Potter	35.00	17.50	10.50
(112)	Mel Queen	50.00	25.00	15.00
(113)	Marion Rackley	40.00	20.00	12.00
(114)	Al Reynolds	70.00	35.00	21.00
(115)	Del Rice	35.00	17.50	10.50
(116)	Marv Rickert	50.00	25.00	15.00
(117)	John Rigney	50.00	25.00	15.00
(118)	Aaron Robinson	50.00	25.00	15.00
(119)	"Preacher" Roe	45.00	22.00	13.50
(120)	Carvel Rowell	50.00	25.00	15.00
(121)	Jim Russell	35.00	17.50	10.50
(122)	Rip Russell	50.00	25.00	15.00
(123)	Phil Rizzuto	200.00	100.00	60.00
(124)	Connie Ryan	50.00	25.00	15.00
(125)	John Sain	90.00	45.00	27.00
(126)	Ray Sanders	50.00	25.00	15.00
(127)	Fred Sanford	35.00	17.50	10.50
(128)	Johnny Schmitz	50.00	25.00	15.00
(129)	Joe Schultz	35.00	17.50	10.50
(130)	"Rip" Sewell	35.00	17.50	10.50
(131)	Dick Sisler	35.00	17.50	10.50
(132)	"Sibby" Sisti	50.00	25.00	15.00
(133)	Enos Slaughter	80.00	40.00	24.00
(134)	"Billy" Southworth	50.00	25.00	15.00
(135)	Warren Spahn	400.00	200.00	120.00
(136)	Verne Stephens (Vern)	35.00	17.50	10.50
(137)	George Sternweiss (Stirnweiss)	50.00	25.00	15.00
(138)	Ed Stevens	40.00	20.00	12.00
(139)	Nick Strincevich	35.00	17.50	10.50
(140)	"Bobby" Sturgeon	50.00	25.00	15.00
(141)	Robt. "Bob" Swift	50.00	25.00	15.00
(142)	Geo. "Birdie" Tibbetts (Tebbetts)	55.00	27.00	16.50
(143)	"Mike" Tresh	55.00	27.00	16.50
(144)	Ken Trinkle	35.00	17.50	10.50
(145)	Paul "Diz" Trout	55.00	27.00	16.50
(146)	Virgil "Fire" Trucks	55.00	27.00	16.50
(147)	Thurman Tucker	50.00	25.00	15.00
(148)	Bill Voiselle	35.00	17.50	10.50
(149)	Hal Wagner	50.00	25.00	15.00
(150)	Honus Wagner	200.00	100.00	60.00
(151)	Eddy Waitkus	50.00	25.00	15.00
(152)	Richard "Dick" Wakefield	50.00	25.00	15.00
(153)	Jack Wallaesa	50.00	25.00	15.00
(154)	Charles Wensloff	50.00	25.00	15.00
(155)	Ted Wilks	35.00	17.50	10.50
(156)	Mickey Witek	35.00	17.50	10.50
(157)	"Jerry" Witte	35.00	17.50	10.50
(158)	Ed Wright	50.00	25.00	15.00
(159)	Taft Wright	50.00	25.00	15.00
(160)	Henry Wyse	50.00	25.00	15.00
(161)	"Rudy" York	55.00	27.00	16.50
(162)	Al Zarilla	35.00	17.50	10.50
(163)	Bill Zuber	50.00	25.00	15.00

1952 Tip Top Bread Labels

This unnumbered set of bread end-labels consists of 48 different labels, including two of Phil Rizzuto. The player's photo, name and team appear inside a star, with the words "Tip Top" printed above. The labels measure approximately 2-1/2" by 2-3/4".

		NR MT	EX	VG
Complete Set (48):		5500.	2750.	1650.
Common Player:		65.00	32.00	19.50
(1)	Hank Bauer	80.00	40.00	24.00
(2)	Yogi Berra	200.00	100.00	60.00
(3)	Ralph Branca	55.00	27.00	16.50
(4)	Lou Brissie	65.00	32.00	19.50
(5)	Roy Campanella	250.00	125.00	75.00
(6)	Phil Cavarreta (Cavarretta)	65.00	32.00	19.50
(7)	Murray Dickson (Murry)	65.00	32.00	19.50
(8)	Ferris Fain	65.00	32.00	19.50
(9)	Carl Furillo	80.00	40.00	24.00
(10)	Ned Garver	65.00	32.00	19.50
(11)	Sid Gordon	65.00	32.00	19.50
(12)	John Groth	65.00	32.00	19.50
(13)	Gran Hamner	65.00	32.00	19.50
(14)	Jim Hearn	65.00	32.00	19.50
(15)	Gene Hermanski	65.00	32.00	19.50
(16)	Gil Hodges	110.00	55.00	33.00
(17)	Larry Jansen	65.00	32.00	19.50
(18)	Eddie Joost	65.00	32.00	19.50
(19)	George Kell	100.00	50.00	30.00
(20)	Dutch Leonard	65.00	32.00	19.50
(21)	Whitey Lockman	65.00	32.00	19.50
(22)	Ed Lopat	80.00	40.00	24.00
(23)	Sal Maglie	55.00	27.00	16.50
(24)	Mickey Mantle	1500.	750.00	450.00
(25)	Gil McDougald	80.00	40.00	24.00
(26)	Dale Mitchell	65.00	32.00	19.50
(27)	Don Mueller	65.00	32.00	19.50
(28)	Andy Pafko	55.00	27.00	16.50
(29)	Bob Porterfield	65.00	32.00	19.50
(30)	Ken Raffensberger	65.00	32.00	19.50
(31)	Allie Reynolds	80.00	40.00	24.00
(32a)	Phil Rizutto (Rizzuto) ("NY" shows on shirt)	110.00	55.00	33.00
(32b)	Phil Rizutto (Rizzuto) (no "NY" visible on shirt)	110.00	55.00	33.00
(33)	Robin Roberts	100.00	50.00	30.00
(34)	Saul Rogovin	65.00	32.00	19.50
(35)	Ray Scarborough	65.00	32.00	19.50
(36)	Red Schoendienst	80.00	40.00	24.00
(37)	Dick Sisler	65.00	32.00	19.50
(38)	Enos Slaughter	80.00	40.00	24.00
(39)	Duke Snider	150.00	75.00	45.00
(40)	Warren Spahn	90.00	45.00	27.00
(41)	Vern Stephens	65.00	32.00	19.50
(42)	Earl Torgeson	65.00	32.00	19.50
(43)	Mickey Vernon	65.00	32.00	19.50
(44)	Ed Waitkus	65.00	32.00	19.50
(45)	Wes Westrum	65.00	32.00	19.50
(46)	Eddie Yost	65.00	32.00	19.50
(47)	Al Zarilla	65.00	32.00	19.50

1887 Tobin Lithographs (H891)

The Tobin lithographs, measuring 3" by 4-1/2", were typical of the various "trade" cards that were popular advertising vehicles cin the late 19th Century. Found in both black and white and color, the Tobin "lithos" include 10 cards depicting caricature action drawings of popular baseball players of the 1887-1888 era. Each cartoon-like drawing is accompanied by a colorful caption along with the player's name in parenthesis below. The team affiliation is printed in the upper left corner, while a large space in the upper right corner was left blank to accomodate advertising messages. As a result, Tobin cards have been found with this space displaying ads for various cigarettes and other products or left blank. Similarly the backs of te cards are also found either blank or with advertising. The set takes its name from the manufacturer, whose name ("Tobin N.Y." appears in the lower right corner of each card.

		NR MT	EX	VG
Complete Set:		2250.	1125.	675.00
Common Player:		150.00	75.00	45.00
(1)	"Go It Old Boy" (Ed Andrews)	150.00	75.00	45.00
(2)	"Oh, Come Off!" (Cap Anson)	550.00	275.00	165.00
(3)	"Watch Me Soak it" (Dan Brouthers)	250.00	125.00	75.00
(4)	"Not Onto It" (Charlie Ferguson)	150.00	75.00	45.00
(5)	"Struck By A Cyclone" (Pebbly Jack Glasscock)	150.00	75.00	45.00
(6)	"An Anxious Moment" (Paul Hines)	150.00	75.00	45.00
(7)	"Where'l You Have It?" (Tim Keefe)	250.00	125.00	75.00
(8)	"The Flower Of The Flock" (Our Own Kelly)	250.00	125.00	75.00
(9)	"A Slide For Home" (Jim M'Cormick) (McCormick)	150.00	75.00	45.00
(10)	"Ain't It A Daisy?" (Smiling Mickey Welch)	250.00	150.00	90.00

1994 Tombstone Pizza

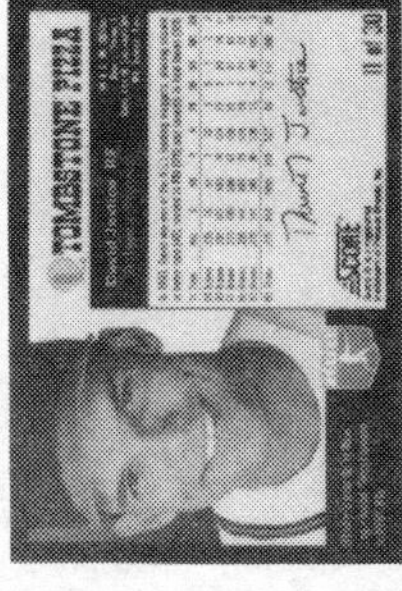

Score produced a special 30-card set which could be obtained by eating a lot of frozen pizzas (one card per pizza) or by sending in a dollar and five proofs of purchase. Titled "'94 Tombstone Super-Pro Series," the cards are black-bordered and UV coated on both front and back. Because the set is licensed only by the players' union and not by Major League Baseball, the uniform logos on the front action photos and back portraits have been airbrushed away. Cards feature the Tombstone logo on both front and back. Backs have recent and career stats, a facsimile autograph and a card number.

		MT	NR MT	EX
Complete Set (30):		10.00	7.50	4.00
Common Player:		.25	.20	.10
1	Jeff Bagwell	.35	.25	.14
2	Jay Bell	.25	.20	.10
3	Barry Bonds	.75	.60	.30
4	Bobby Bonilla	.25	.20	.10
5	Andres Galarraga	.35	.25	.14
6	Mark Grace	.35	.25	.14
7	Marquis Grissom	.25	.20	.10
8	Tony Gwynn	.35	.25	.14
9	Bryan Harvey	.25	.20	.10
10	Gregg Jefferies	.35	.25	.14
11	David Justice	.45	.35	.20
12	John Kruk	.35	.25	.14
13	Barry Larkin	.25	.20	.10
14	Greg Maddux	.35	.25	.14
15	Mike Piazza	.75	.60	.30
16	Jim Abbott	.35	.25	.14
17	Albert Belle	.35	.25	.14
18	Cecil Fielder	.45	.35	.20
19	Juan Gonzalez	.75	.60	.30
20	Mike Greenwell	.25	.20	.10
21	Ken Griffey, Jr.	1.25	.90	.50
22	Jack McDowell	.25	.20	.10
23	Jeff Montgomery	.25	.20	.10
24	John Olerud	.35	.25	.14
25	Kirby Puckett	.45	.35	.20
26	Cal Ripken, Jr.	1.00	.70	.40
27	Tim Salmon	.50	.40	.20
28	Ruben Sierra	.25	.20	.10
29	Frank Thomas	1.25	.90	.50
30	Robin Yount	.75	.60	.30

1948 Topps Magic Photos

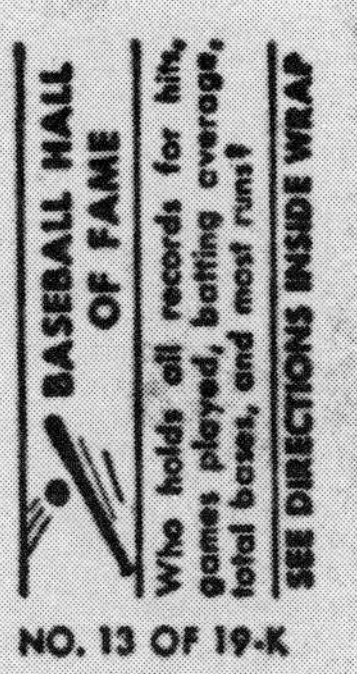

The first Topps baseball cards appeared as a subset of 19 cards from an issue of 252 "Magic Photos." The set takes its name from the self-developing nature of the cards. The cards were blank on the front when first taken from the wrapper. By spitting on the wrapper and holding it to the card while exposing it to light the black and white photo appeared. Measuring 7/8" by 1-1/2," the cards are very similar to Topps 1956 "Hocus Focus" issue.

		NR MT	EX	VG
Complete Set (19):		2000.	1000.	600.00
Common Player:		50.00	25.00	15.00
1	Lou Boudreau	100.00	50.00	30.00
2	Cleveland Indians	50.00	25.00	15.00
3	Bob Eliott	50.00	25.00	15.00
4	Cleveland Indians 4-3	50.00	25.00	15.00
5	Cleveland Indians 4-1 (Lou Boudreau Scoring)	75.00	37.00	22.00
6	Babe Ruth (714)	400.00	200.00	120.00
7	Tris Speaker (793)	125.00	62.00	37.00
8	Rogers Hornsby	150.00	75.00	45.00
9	Connie Mack	125.00	62.00	37.00
10	Christy Mathewson	150.00	75.00	45.00
11	Hans Wagner	150.00	75.00	45.00
12	Grover Alexander	125.00	62.00	37.00
13	Ty Cobb	200.00	100.00	60.00
14	Lou Gehrig	300.00	150.00	90.00
15	Walter Johnson	150.00	75.00	45.00
16	Cy Young	125.00	62.00	37.00
17	George Sisler (257)	100.00	50.00	30.00
18	Tinker and Evers	100.00	50.00	30.00
19	Third Base Cleveland Indians	50.00	25.00	15.00

1951 Topps Red Backs

Like the Blue Backs, the Topps Red Backs which were sold at the same time, came two to a package for 1¢. Their black and white photographs appear on a red, white, blue and yellow background. The back printing is red on white. Their 2" by 2-5/8" size is the same as Blue Backs. Also identical is the set size (52 cards) and the game situations to be found on the fronts of the cards, for use in playing a card game of baseball. Red Backs are more common than the Blue Backs by virtue of a recent discovery of a large hoard of unopened boxes.

		NR MT	EX	VG
Complete Set (52):		650.00	325.00	195.00
Common Player:		10.00	5.00	3.00
1	Yogi Berra	75.00	38.00	23.50
2	Sid Gordon	11.00	5.50	3.25
3	Ferris Fain	10.00	5.00	3.00
4	Vern Stephens	10.00	5.00	3.00
5	Phil Rizzuto	40.00	20.00	12.00
6	Allie Reynolds	15.00	7.50	4.50
7	Howie Pollet	10.00	5.00	3.00
8	Early Wynn	25.00	12.50	7.50
9	Roy Sievers	10.00	5.00	3.00
10	Mel Parnell	10.00	5.00	3.00
11	Gene Hermanski	10.00	5.00	3.00
12	Jim Hegan	10.00	5.00	3.00
13	Dale Mitchell	10.00	5.00	3.00
14	Wayne Terwilliger	10.00	5.00	3.00
15	Ralph Kiner	25.00	12.50	7.50
16	Preacher Roe	12.00	6.00	3.50
17	Gus Bell	12.00	6.00	3.50
18	Gerry Coleman	12.50	6.25	3.75
19	Dick Kokos	10.00	5.00	3.00
20	Dom DiMaggio	12.50	6.25	3.75
21	Larry Jansen	10.00	5.00	3.00
22	Bob Feller	45.00	22.50	13.50
23	Ray Boone	10.00	5.00	3.00
24	Hank Bauer	15.00	7.50	4.50
25	Cliff Chambers	10.00	5.00	3.00
26	Luke Easter	10.00	5.00	3.00
27	Wally Westlake	10.00	5.00	3.00
28	Elmer Valo	10.00	5.00	3.00
29	Bob Kennedy	10.00	5.00	3.00
30	Warren Spahn	45.00	22.50	13.50
31	Gil Hodges	40.00	20.00	12.00
32	Henry Thompson	10.00	5.00	3.00
33	William Werle	10.00	5.00	3.00
34	Grady Hatton	10.00	5.00	3.00
35	Al Rosen	11.00	5.50	3.25
36a	Gus Zernial (Chicago in bio)	20.00	10.00	6.00
36b	Gus Zernial (Philadelphia in bio)	20.00	10.00	6.00
37	Wes Westrum	10.00	5.00	3.00
38	Duke Snider	50.00	25.00	15.00
39	Ted Kluszewski	15.00	7.50	4.50
40	Mike Garcia	10.00	5.00	3.00
41	Whitey Lockman	10.00	5.00	3.00
42	Ray Scarborough	10.00	5.00	3.00
43	Maurice McDermott	10.00	5.00	3.00
44	Sid Hudson	10.00	5.00	3.00
45	Andy Seminick	10.00	5.00	3.00
46	Billy Goodman	10.00	5.00	3.00
47	Tommy Glaviano	10.00	5.00	3.00
48	Eddie Stanky	11.00	5.50	3.25
49	Al Zarilla	10.00	5.00	3.00
50	Monte Irvin	40.00	20.00	12.00
51	Eddie Robinson	10.00	5.00	3.00
52a	Tommy Holmes (Boston in bio)	20.00	10.00	6.00
52b	Tommy Holmes (Hartford in bio)	24.00	12.00	7.25

1951 Topps Blue Backs

Sold two cards in a package with a piece of candy for 1¢, the Topps Blue Backs are considerably scarcer than their Red Back counterparts. The 2" by 2-5/8" cards carry a black and white player photograph on a red, white, yellow and green background along with the player's name and other information including their 1950 record on the front. The back is printed in blue on a white background. The 52-card set has varied baseball situations on them, making the playing of a rather elementary game of baseball possible. Although scarce, Blue Backs were printed on thick cardboard and have survived quite well over the years. There are, however, few stars (Johnny Mize and Enos Slaughter are two) in the set. Despite being a Topps product, Blue Backs do not currently enjoy great popularity.

		NR MT	EX	VG
Complete Set (52):		1950.	975.00	575.00
Common Player:		40.00	20.00	12.00
1	Eddie Yost	40.00	20.00	12.00
2	Henry Majeski	40.00	20.00	12.00
3	Richie Ashburn	55.00	27.00	16.50
4	Del Ennis	40.00	20.00	12.00
5	Johnny Pesky	40.00	20.00	12.00
6	Red Schoendienst	60.00	30.00	18.00
7	Gerry Staley	40.00	20.00	12.00
8	Dick Sisler	40.00	20.00	12.00
9	Johnny Sain	42.50	21.00	12.50
10	Joe Page	45.00	22.50	13.50
11	Johnny Groth	40.00	20.00	12.00
12	Sam Jethroe	40.00	20.00	12.00
13	Mickey Vernon	40.00	20.00	12.00
14	Red Munger	40.00	20.00	12.00
15	Eddie Joost	40.00	20.00	12.00
16	Murry Dickson	40.00	20.00	12.00
17	Roy Smalley	40.00	20.00	12.00
18	Ned Garver	40.00	20.00	12.00
19	Phil Masi	40.00	20.00	12.00
20	Ralph Branca	45.00	22.50	13.50
21	Billy Johnson	40.00	20.00	12.00
22	Bob Kuzava	40.00	20.00	12.00
23	Dizzy Trout	40.00	20.00	12.00
24	Sherman Lollar	40.00	20.00	12.00
25	Sam Mele	40.00	20.00	12.00
26	Chico Carrasquel	40.00	20.00	12.00
27	Andy Pafko	40.00	20.00	12.00
28	Harry (The Cat) Brecheen	40.00	20.00	12.00
29	Granny Hamner	40.00	20.00	12.00
30	Enos Slaughter	60.00	30.00	18.00
31	Lou Brissie	40.00	20.00	12.00
32	Bob Elliott	40.00	20.00	12.00
33	Don Lenhardt	40.00	20.00	12.00
34	Earl Torgeson	40.00	20.00	12.00
35	Tommy Byrne	42.50	21.00	12.50
36	Cliff Fannin	40.00	20.00	12.00
37	Bobby Doerr	60.00	30.00	18.00
38	Irv Noren	40.00	20.00	12.00
39	Ed Lopat	42.50	21.00	12.50
40	Vic Wertz	40.00	20.00	12.00
41	Johnny Schmitz	40.00	20.00	12.00
42	Bruce Edwards	40.00	20.00	12.00
43	Willie Jones	40.00	20.00	12.00
44	Johnny Wyrostek	40.00	20.00	12.00
45	Bill Pierce	40.00	20.00	12.00
46	Gerry Priddy	40.00	20.00	12.00
47	Herman Wehmeier	40.00	20.00	12.00
48	Billy Cox	42.50	21.00	12.50
49	Hank Sauer	40.00	20.00	12.00
50	Johnny Mize	60.00	30.00	18.00
51	Eddie Waitkus	40.00	20.00	12.00
52	Sam Chapman	40.00	20.00	12.00

1951 Topps Connie Mack's All-Stars

A set of die-cut, 2-1/16" by 5-1/4" cards, all eleven players are Hall of Famers. The cards feature a black and white photograph of the player printed on a red background with a red, white, blue, yellow and black plaque underneath. Like the "Current All-Stars," with which they were issued, the background could be removed making it possible for the card to stand up. This practice, however, resulted in the card's mutilation and lowers its condition in the eyes of today's collectors. Connie Mack All-Stars are scarce today and, despite being relatively expensive, retain a certain popularity as one of Topps first issues.

		NR MT	EX	VG
Complete Set (11):		8750.	4375.	2600.
Common Player:		350.00	150.00	60.00
(1)	Grover Cleveland Alexander	500.00	250.00	150.00
(2)	Mickey Cochrane	350.00	175.00	105.00
(3)	Eddie Collins	350.00	150.00	60.00
(4)	Jimmy Collins	350.00	150.00	60.00
(5)	Lou Gehrig	2000.	1000.	350.00
(6)	Walter Johnson	750.00	325.00	150.00
(7)	Connie Mack	350.00	175.00	105.00
(8)	Christy Mathewson	700.00	350.00	210.00
(9)	Babe Ruth	2250.	1150.	450.00
(10)	Tris Speaker	550.00	275.00	165.00
(11)	Honus Wagner	600.00	300.00	180.00

1951 Topps Current All-Stars

The Topps Current All-Stars are very similar to the Connie Mack All-Stars of the same year. The 2-1/16 by 5-1/4" cards have a black and white photograph on a red die-cut background. Most of the background could be folded over or removed so that the card would stand up. A plaque at the base carries brief biographical information. The set was to contain 11 cards, but only eight were actually issued in gum packs. Those of Jim Konstanty, Robin Roberts and Eddie Stanky were not released and are very rare. A big problem with the set is that if the card was used as it was intended it was folded and, thus, damaged from a collector's viewpoint. That makes top quality examples of any players difficult to find and quite expensive.

		NR MT	EX	VG
Complete Set (11):		32500.	16000.	7500.
Common Player:		500.00	250.00	100.00
(1)	Yogi Berra	1500.	750.00	450.00
(2)	Larry Doby	750.00	375.00	150.00
(3)	Walt Dropo	750.00	375.00	150.00
(4)	"Hoot" Evers	500.00	250.00	100.00
(5)	George Kell	900.00	450.00	275.00
(6)	Ralph Kiner	900.00	450.00	275.00
(7)	Jim Konstanty	8500.	4250.	2000.
(8)	Bob Lemon	900.00	450.00	275.00
(9)	Phil Rizzuto	1200.	600.00	225.00
(10)	Robin Roberts	9500.	4750.	2250.
(11)	Ed Stanky	8500.	4250.	2000.

1951 Topps Teams

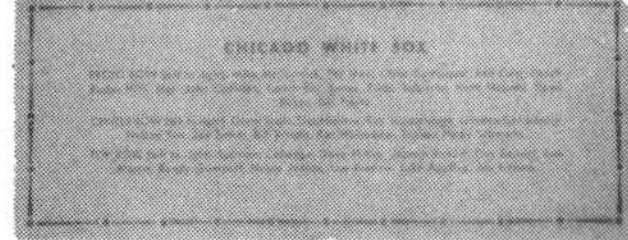

An innovative issue for 1951, the Topps team cards were a nine-card set, 5-1/4" by 2-1/16," which carried a black and white picture of a major league team surrounded by a yellow border on the front. The back identifies team members with red printing on white cardboard. There are two versions of each card, with and without the date "1950" in the banner that carries the team name. Undated versions are valued slightly higher than the cards with dates. Strangely only nine teams were issued. Scarcity varies, with the Cardinals and Red Sox being the most difficult to obtain. The complete set price does not include the scarcer variations.

		NR MT	EX	VG
Complete Set (Dated):		1900.	950.00	575.00
Common Card:		185.00	92.00	55.00
(1a)	Boston Red Sox (1950)	300.00	150.00	90.00
(1b)	Boston Red Sox (undated)	375.00	187.00	112.00
(2a)	Brooklyn Dodgers (1950)	400.00	200.00	120.00
(2b)	Brooklyn Dodgers (undated)	450.00	225.00	135.00
(3a)	Chicago White Sox (1950)	185.00	92.00	55.00
(3b)	Chicago White Sox (undated)	250.00	125.00	75.00
(4a)	Cincinnati Reds (1950)	185.00	92.00	55.00
(4b)	Cincinnati Reds (undated)	250.00	125.00	75.00
(5a)	New York Giants (1950)	300.00	150.00	90.00
(5b)	New York Giants (undated)	375.00	187.00	112.00
(6a)	Philadelphia Athletics (1950)	185.00	92.00	55.00
(6b)	Philadelphia Athletics (undated)	250.00	125.00	75.00
(7a)	Philadelphia Phillies (1950)	185.00	92.00	55.00
(7b)	Philadelphia Phillies (undated)	250.00	125.00	75.00
(8a)	St. Louis Cardinals (1950)	185.00	92.00	55.00
(8b)	St. Louis Cardinals (undated)	250.00	125.00	75.00
(9a)	Washington Senators (1950)	200.00	100.00	60.00
(9b)	Washington Senators (undated)	250.00	125.00	75.00

1952 Topps

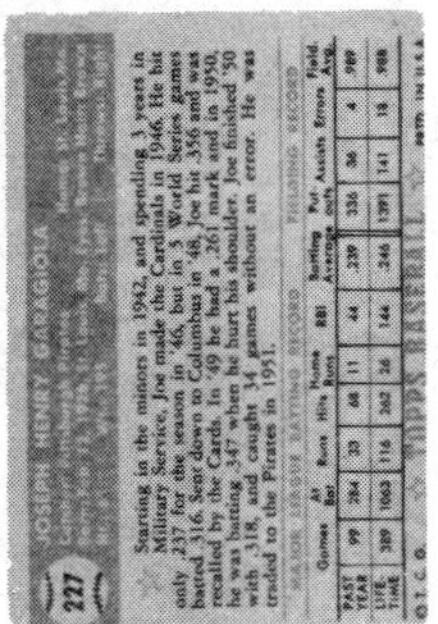

At 407 cards, the 1952 Topps set was the largest set of its day, both in number of cards and physical dimensions of the cards. Cards are 2-5/8" by 3-3/4" with a hand-colored black and white photo on front. Major baseball card innovations presented in the set include the first-ever use of color team logos as part of the design, and the inclusion of stats for the previous season and overall career on the backs. A major variety in the set is that first 80 cards can be found with backs printed entirely in black or black and red. Backs entirely in black command a $10-15 premium. Card numbers 311-407 were printed in limited supplies and are extremely rare.

		NR MT	EX	VG
Complete Set (407):		54250.	25000.	14500.
Common Player (1-80):		55.00	22.00	8.25
Common Player (81-250):		30.00	12.00	4.50
Common Player (251-310):		50.00	20.00	7.50
Common Player (311-407):		250.00	100.00	65.00
1	Andy Pafko	1200.	400.00	65.00
2	*Pete Runnels*	60.00	24.00	9.00
3	Hank Thompson	55.00	22.00	8.25
4	Don Lenhardt	55.00	22.00	8.25
5	Larry Jansen	55.00	22.00	8.25
6	Grady Hatton	55.00	22.00	8.25
7	Wayne Terwilliger	60.00	24.00	9.00
8	Fred Marsh	55.00	22.00	8.25
9	Bobby Hogue	65.00	26.00	9.75
10	Al Rosen	80.00	32.00	12.00
11	Phil Rizzuto	250.00	100.00	37.00
12	Monty Basgall	55.00	22.00	8.25
13	Johnny Wyrostek	55.00	22.00	8.25
14	Bob Elliott	55.00	22.00	8.25
15	Johnny Pesky	55.00	22.00	8.25
16	Gene Hermanski	55.00	22.00	8.25
17	Jim Hegan	55.00	22.00	8.25
18	Merrill Combs	55.00	22.00	8.25
19	Johnny Bucha	55.00	22.00	8.25
20	*Billy Loes*	95.00	38.00	14.00
21	Ferris Fain	55.00	22.00	8.25
22	Dom DiMaggio	90.00	36.00	13.50
23	Billy Goodman	55.00	22.00	8.25
24	Luke Easter	55.00	22.00	8.25
25	Johnny Groth	55.00	22.00	8.25
26	Monte Irvin	100.00	40.00	15.00
27	Sam Jethroe	55.00	22.00	8.25
28	Jerry Priddy	55.00	22.00	8.25
29	Ted Kluszewski	100.00	40.00	15.00
30	Mel Parnell	55.00	22.00	8.25
31	Gus Zernial	55.00	22.00	8.25
32	Eddie Robinson	55.00	22.00	8.25
33	Warren Spahn	250.00	100.00	37.00
34	Elmer Valo	55.00	22.00	8.25
35	Hank Sauer	55.00	22.00	8.25
36	Gil Hodges	175.00	70.00	26.00
37	Duke Snider	275.00	110.00	41.00
38	Wally Westlake	55.00	22.00	8.25
39	"Dizzy" Trout	55.00	22.00	8.25
40	Irv Noren	55.00	22.00	8.25
41	Bob Wellman	55.00	22.00	8.25
42	Lou Kretlow	55.00	22.00	8.25
43	Ray Scarborough	55.00	22.00	8.25
44	Con Dempsey	55.00	22.00	8.25
45	Eddie Joost	55.00	22.00	8.25
46	Gordon Goldsberry	55.00	22.00	8.25
47	Willie Jones	55.00	22.00	8.25
48a	Joe Page (Johnny Sain back)	300.00	120.00	45.00
48b	Joe Page (Joe Page back)	80.00	32.00	12.00
49a	Johnny Sain (Joe Page back)	350.00	140.00	52.00
49b	Johnny Sain (Johnny Sain back)	80.00	32.00	12.00
50	Marv Rickert	55.00	22.00	8.25
51	Jim Russell	60.00	24.00	9.00
52	Don Mueller	55.00	22.00	8.25
53	Chris Van Cuyk	60.00	24.00	9.00
54	Leo Kiely	55.00	22.00	8.25
55	Ray Boone	60.00	24.00	9.00
56	Tommy Glaviano	55.00	22.00	8.25
57	Ed Lopat	75.00	30.00	11.00
58	Bob Mahoney	55.00	22.00	8.25
59	Robin Roberts	125.00	50.00	18.50
60	Sid Hudson	55.00	22.00	8.25
61	"Tookie" Gilbert	55.00	22.00	8.25
62	Chuck Stobbs	55.00	22.00	8.25
63	Howie Pollet	55.00	22.00	8.25
64	Roy Sievers	55.00	22.00	8.25
65	Enos Slaughter	100.00	40.00	15.00
66	Preacher Roe	90.00	36.00	13.50
67	Allie Reynolds	90.00	36.00	13.50
68	Cliff Chambers	55.00	22.00	8.25
69	Virgil Stallcup	55.00	22.00	8.25
70	Al Zarilla	55.00	22.00	8.25
71	Tom Upton	55.00	22.00	8.25
72	Karl Olson	55.00	22.00	8.25
73	William Werle	55.00	22.00	8.25
74	Andy Hansen	55.00	22.00	8.25
75	Wes Westrum	55.00	22.00	8.25
76	Eddie Stanky	55.00	22.00	8.25
77	Bob Kennedy	55.00	22.00	8.25
78	Ellis Kinder	55.00	22.00	8.25
79	Gerald Staley	55.00	22.00	8.25
80	Herman Wehmeier	55.00	22.00	8.25
81	Vernon Law	30.00	12.00	4.50
82	Duane Pillette	30.00	12.00	4.50
83	Billy Johnson	30.00	12.00	4.50
84	Vern Stephens	30.00	12.00	4.50
85	Bob Kuzava	40.00	16.00	6.00
86	Ted Gray	30.00	12.00	4.50
87	Dale Coogan	30.00	12.00	4.50
88	Bob Feller	175.00	70.00	26.00
89	Johnny Lipon	30.00	12.00	4.50
90	Mickey Grasso	30.00	12.00	4.50
91	Red Schoendienst	80.00	32.00	12.00
92	Dale Mitchell	30.00	12.00	4.50
93	Al Sima	30.00	12.00	4.50
94	Sam Mele	30.00	12.00	4.50
95	Ken Holcombe	30.00	12.00	4.50
96	Willard Marshall	30.00	12.00	4.50
97	Earl Torgeson	30.00	12.00	4.50
98	Bill Pierce	30.00	12.00	4.50
99	Gene Woodling	50.00	20.00	7.50
100	Del Rice	30.00	12.00	4.50
101	Max Lanier	30.00	12.00	4.50
102	Bill Kennedy	30.00	12.00	4.50
103	Cliff Mapes	30.00	12.00	4.50
104	Don Kolloway	30.00	12.00	4.50
105	John Pramesa	30.00	12.00	4.50
106	Mickey Vernon	30.00	12.00	4.50
107	Connie Ryan	30.00	12.00	4.50
108	Jim Konstanty	30.00	12.00	4.50
109	Ted Wilks	30.00	12.00	4.50
110	Dutch Leonard	30.00	12.00	4.50
111	Harry Lowrey	30.00	12.00	4.50
112	Henry Majeski	30.00	12.00	4.50
113	Dick Sisler	30.00	12.00	4.50
114	Willard Ramsdell	30.00	12.00	4.50
115	George Munger	30.00	12.00	4.50
116	Carl Scheib	30.00	12.00	4.50
117	Sherman Lollar	30.00	12.00	4.50
118	Ken Raffensberger	30.00	12.00	4.50
119	Maurice McDermott	30.00	12.00	4.50
120	Bob Chakales	30.00	12.00	4.50
121	Gus Niarhos	30.00	12.00	4.50
122	Jack Jensen	65.00	26.00	9.75
123	Eddie Yost	30.00	12.00	4.50
124	Monte Kennedy	30.00	12.00	4.50
125	Bill Rigney	30.00	12.00	4.50
126	Fred Hutchinson	30.00	12.00	4.50
127	Paul Minner	30.00	12.00	4.50
128	Don Bollweg	40.00	16.00	6.00
129	Johnny Mize	80.00	32.00	12.00
130	Sheldon Jones	30.00	12.00	4.50
131	Morrie Martin	30.00	12.00	4.50
132	Clyde Kluttz	30.00	12.00	4.50
133	Al Widmar	30.00	12.00	4.50
134	Joe Tipton	30.00	12.00	4.50
135	Dixie Howell	30.00	12.00	4.50
136	Johnny Schmitz	35.00	14.00	5.25
137	*Roy McMillan*	30.00	12.00	4.50
138	Bill MacDonald	30.00	12.00	4.50
139	Ken Wood	30.00	12.00	4.50
140	John Antonelli	30.00	12.00	4.50
141	Clint Hartung	30.00	12.00	4.50
142	Harry Perkowski	30.00	12.00	4.50
143	Les Moss	30.00	12.00	4.50
144	Ed Blake	30.00	12.00	4.50
145	Joe Haynes	30.00	12.00	4.50
146	Frank House	30.00	12.00	4.50
147	Bob Young	30.00	12.00	4.50
148	Johnny Klippstein	30.00	12.00	4.50
149	Dick Kryhoski	30.00	12.00	4.50
150	Ted Beard	30.00	12.00	4.50
151	Wally Post	30.00	12.00	4.50
152	Al Evans	30.00	12.00	4.50
153	Bob Rush	30.00	12.00	4.50
154	Joe Muir	30.00	12.00	4.50
155	Frank Overmire	40.00	16.00	6.00
156	Frank Hiller	30.00	12.00	4.50
157	Bob Usher	30.00	12.00	4.50
158	Eddie Waitkus	30.00	12.00	4.50
159	Saul Rogovin	30.00	12.00	4.50
160	Owen Friend	30.00	12.00	4.50
161	Bud Byerly	30.00	12.00	4.50
162	Del Crandall	30.00	12.00	4.50
163	Stan Rojek	30.00	12.00	4.50
164	Walt Dubiel	30.00	12.00	4.50
165	Eddie Kazak	30.00	12.00	4.50
166	Paul LaPalme	30.00	12.00	4.50
167	Bill Howerton	30.00	12.00	4.50
168	*Charlie Silvera*	40.00	16.00	6.00
169	Howie Judson	30.00	12.00	4.50
170	Gus Bell	30.00	12.00	4.50
171	Ed Erautt	30.00	12.00	4.50
172	Eddie Miksis	30.00	12.00	4.50
173	Roy Smalley	30.00	12.00	4.50
174	Clarence Marshall	30.00	12.00	4.50
175	*Billy Martin*	300.00	120.00	45.00
176	Hank Edwards	30.00	12.00	4.50
177	Bill Wight	30.00	12.00	4.50
178	Cass Michaels	30.00	12.00	4.50
179	Frank Smith	30.00	12.00	4.50
180	*Charley Maxwell*	30.00	12.00	4.50
181	Bob Swift	30.00	12.00	4.50
182	Billy Hitchcock	30.00	12.00	4.50
183	Erv Dusak	30.00	12.00	4.50
184	Bob Ramazzotti	30.00	12.00	4.50
185	Bill Nicholson	30.00	12.00	4.50
186	Walt Masterson	30.00	12.00	4.50
187	Bob Miller	30.00	12.00	4.50
188	Clarence Podbielan	35.00	14.00	5.25
189	Pete Reiser	30.00	12.00	4.50
190	Don Johnson	30.00	12.00	4.50
191	Yogi Berra	300.00	120.00	45.00
192	Myron Ginsberg	30.00	12.00	4.50
193	Harry Simpson	30.00	12.00	4.50
194	Joe Hatten	30.00	12.00	4.50
195	*Minnie Minoso*	125.00	50.00	18.50
196	Solly Hemus	30.00	12.00	4.50
197	George Strickland	30.00	12.00	4.50
198	Phil Haugstad	35.00	14.00	5.25
199	George Zuverink	30.00	12.00	4.50
200	Ralph Houk	65.00	26.00	9.75
201	Alex Kellner	30.00	12.00	4.50
202	Joe Collins	40.00	16.00	6.00
203	Curt Simmons	30.00	12.00	4.50
204	Ron Northey	30.00	12.00	4.50
205	Clyde King	35.00	14.00	5.25
206	Joe Ostrowski	40.00	16.00	6.00
207	Mickey Harris	30.00	12.00	4.50
208	Marlin Stuart	30.00	12.00	4.50
209	Howie Fox	30.00	12.00	4.50
210	Dick Fowler	30.00	12.00	4.50
211	Ray Coleman	30.00	12.00	4.50
212	Ned Garver	30.00	12.00	4.50
213	Nippy Jones	30.00	12.00	4.50
214	Johnny Hopp	40.00	16.00	6.00
215	Hank Bauer	50.00	20.00	7.50
216	Richie Ashburn	110.00	44.00	16.50
217	George Stirnweiss	30.00	12.00	4.50
218	Clyde McCullough	30.00	12.00	4.50
219	Bobby Shantz	30.00	12.00	4.50
220	Joe Presko	30.00	12.00	4.50
221	Granny Hamner	30.00	12.00	4.50
222	"Hoot" Evers	30.00	12.00	4.50
223	Del Ennis	30.00	12.00	4.50
224	Bruce Edwards	30.00	12.00	4.50
225	Frank Baumholtz	30.00	12.00	4.50
226	Dave Philley	30.00	12.00	4.50
227	Joe Garagiola	75.00	30.00	11.00
228	Al Brazle	30.00	12.00	4.50
229	Gene Bearden	30.00	12.00	4.50
230	Matt Batts	30.00	12.00	4.50
231	Sam Zoldak	30.00	12.00	4.50
232	Billy Cox	45.00	18.00	6.75
233	*Bob Friend*	30.00	12.00	4.50
234	Steve Souchock	30.00	12.00	4.50
235	Walt Dropo	30.00	12.00	4.50
236	Ed Fitz Gerald	30.00	12.00	4.50
237	Jerry Coleman	40.00	16.00	6.00
238	Art Houtteman	30.00	12.00	4.50
239	*Rocky Bridges*	35.00	14.00	5.25
240	Jack Phillips	30.00	12.00	4.50
241	Tommy Byrne	30.00	12.00	4.50
242	Tom Poholsky	30.00	12.00	4.50
243	Larry Doby	45.00	18.00	6.75
244	Vic Wertz	30.00	12.00	4.50
245	Sherry Robertson	30.00	12.00	4.50
246	George Kell	80.00	32.00	12.00
247	Randy Gumpert	30.00	12.00	4.50
248	Frank Shea	30.00	12.00	4.50
249	Bobby Adams	30.00	12.00	4.50
250	Carl Erskine	60.00	24.00	9.00
251	Chico Carrasquel	50.00	20.00	7.50
252	Vern Bickford	50.00	20.00	7.50
253	Johnny Berardino	60.00	24.00	9.00
254	Joe Dobson	50.00	20.00	7.50
255	Clyde Vollmer	50.00	20.00	7.50
256	Pete Suder	50.00	20.00	7.50
257	Bobby Avila	60.00	24.00	9.00
258	Steve Gromek	50.00	20.00	7.50
259	Bob Addis	50.00	20.00	7.50
260	Pete Castiglione	50.00	20.00	7.50
261	Willie Mays	2650.	1300.	550.00
262	Virgil Trucks	50.00	20.00	7.50
263	Harry Brecheen	50.00	20.00	7.50
264	Roy Hartsfield	50.00	20.00	7.50
265	Chuck Diering	50.00	20.00	7.50
266	Murry Dickson	50.00	20.00	7.50
267	Sid Gordon	50.00	20.00	7.50
268	Bob Lemon	150.00	60.00	22.00
269	Willard Nixon	50.00	20.00	7.50
270	Lou Brissie	50.00	20.00	7.50
271	Jim Delsing	50.00	20.00	7.50
272	Mike Garcia	50.00	20.00	7.50
273	Erv Palica	55.00	22.00	8.25
274	Ralph Branca	75.00	30.00	11.00
275	Pat Mullin	50.00	20.00	7.50

276	Jim Wilson	50.00	20.00	7.50
277	Early Wynn	160.00	64.00	24.00
278	Al Clark	50.00	20.00	7.50
279	Ed Stewart	50.00	20.00	7.50
280	Cloyd Boyer	50.00	20.00	7.50
281	Tommy Brown	50.00	20.00	7.50
282	Birdie Tebbetts	50.00	20.00	7.50
283	Phil Masi	50.00	20.00	7.50
284	Hank Arft	50.00	20.00	7.50
285	Cliff Fannin	50.00	20.00	7.50
286	Joe DeMaestri	50.00	20.00	7.50
287	Steve Bilko	50.00	20.00	7.50
288	Chet Nichols	50.00	20.00	7.50
289	Tommy Holmes	50.00	20.00	7.50
290	Joe Astroth	50.00	20.00	7.50
291	Gil Coan	50.00	20.00	7.50
292	Floyd Baker	50.00	20.00	7.50
293	Sibby Sisti	50.00	20.00	7.50
294	Walker Cooper	50.00	20.00	7.50
295	Phil Cavarretta	50.00	20.00	7.50
296	Red Rolfe	50.00	20.00	7.50
297	Andy Seminick	50.00	20.00	7.50
298	Bob Ross	50.00	20.00	7.50
299	Ray Murray	50.00	20.00	7.50
300	Barney McCosky	50.00	20.00	7.50
301	Bob Porterfield	50.00	20.00	7.50
302	Max Surkont	50.00	20.00	7.50
303	Harry Dorish	50.00	20.00	7.50
304	Sam Dente	50.00	20.00	7.50
305	Paul Richards	50.00	20.00	7.50
306	Lou Sleator	50.00	20.00	7.50
307	Frank Campos	50.00	20.00	7.50
308	Luis Aloma	50.00	20.00	7.50
309	Jim Busby	50.00	20.00	7.50
310	George Metkovich	50.00	20.00	7.50
311	Mickey Mantle	18000.	9000.	4600.
312	Jackie Robinson	1450.	725.00	425.00
313	Bobby Thomson	250.00	125.00	75.00
314	Roy Campanella	1750.	875.00	525.00
315	Leo Durocher	600.00	300.00	180.00
316	Davey Williams	250.00	125.00	75.00
317	Connie Marrero	250.00	125.00	75.00
318	Hal Gregg	250.00	125.00	75.00
319	Al Walker	240.00	120.00	72.00
320	John Rutherford	250.00	125.00	75.00
321	*Joe Black*	275.00	137.00	82.00
322	Randy Jackson	250.00	125.00	75.00
323	Bubba Church	250.00	125.00	75.00
324	Warren Hacker	250.00	125.00	75.00
325	Bill Serena	250.00	125.00	75.00
326	George Shuba	240.00	120.00	72.00
327	Archie Wilson	250.00	125.00	75.00
328	Bob Borkowski	250.00	125.00	75.00
329	Ike Delock	250.00	125.00	75.00
330	Turk Lown	250.00	125.00	75.00
331	Tom Morgan	250.00	125.00	75.00
332	Tony Bartirome	250.00	125.00	75.00
333	Pee Wee Reese	1200.	600.00	360.00
334	Wilmer Mizell	250.00	125.00	75.00
335	Ted Lepcio	250.00	125.00	75.00
336	Dave Koslo	250.00	125.00	75.00
337	Jim Hearn	250.00	125.00	75.00
338	Sal Yvars	250.00	125.00	75.00
339	Russ Meyer	250.00	125.00	75.00
340	Bob Hooper	250.00	125.00	75.00
341	Hal Jeffcoat	250.00	125.00	75.00
342	*Clem Labine*	275.00	137.00	82.00
343	Dick Gernert	250.00	125.00	75.00
344	Ewell Blackwell	250.00	125.00	75.00
345	Sam White	250.00	125.00	75.00
346	George Spencer	250.00	125.00	75.00
347	Joe Adcock	250.00	125.00	75.00
348	Bob Kelly	250.00	125.00	75.00
349	Bob Cain	250.00	125.00	75.00
350	Cal Abrams	250.00	125.00	75.00
351	Al Dark	250.00	125.00	75.00
352	Karl Drews	250.00	125.00	75.00
353	Bob Del Greco	250.00	125.00	75.00
354	Fred Hatfield	250.00	125.00	75.00
355	Bobby Morgan	250.00	125.00	75.00
356	Toby Atwell	250.00	125.00	75.00
357	Smoky Burgess	250.00	125.00	75.00
358	John Kucab	250.00	125.00	75.00
359	Dee Fondy	250.00	125.00	75.00
360	George Crowe	250.00	125.00	75.00
361	Bill Posedel	250.00	125.00	75.00
362	Ken Heintzelman	250.00	125.00	75.00
363	Dick Rozek	250.00	125.00	75.00
364	Clyde Sukeforth	250.00	125.00	75.00
365	Cookie Lavagetto	250.00	125.00	75.00
366	Dave Madison	250.00	125.00	75.00
367	Bob Thorpe	250.00	125.00	75.00
368	Ed Wright	250.00	125.00	75.00
369	*Dick Groat*	350.00	175.00	105.00
370	Billy Hoeft	250.00	125.00	75.00
371	Bob Hofman	250.00	125.00	75.00
372	*Gil McDougald*	350.00	175.00	105.00
373	Jim Turner	250.00	125.00	75.00
374	Al Benton	250.00	125.00	75.00
375	Jack Merson	250.00	125.00	75.00
376	Faye Throneberry	250.00	125.00	75.00
377	Chuck Dressen	240.00	120.00	72.00
378	Les Fusselman	250.00	125.00	75.00
379	Joe Rossi	250.00	125.00	75.00
380	Clem Koshorek	250.00	125.00	75.00
381	Milton Stock	250.00	125.00	75.00
382	Sam Jones	250.00	125.00	75.00
383	Del Wilber	250.00	125.00	75.00
384	Frank Crosetti	260.00	130.00	78.00
385	Herman Franks	250.00	125.00	75.00
386	Eddie Yuhas	250.00	125.00	75.00
387	Billy Meyer	250.00	125.00	75.00
388	Bob Chipman	250.00	125.00	75.00
389	Ben Wade	240.00	120.00	72.00
390	Rocky Nelson	240.00	120.00	72.00
391	Ben Chapman (photo actually Sam Chapman)	250.00	125.00	75.00
392	*Hoyt Wilhelm*	700.00	350.00	210.00
393	Ebba St. Claire	250.00	125.00	75.00
394	Billy Herman	265.00	132.00	79.00
395	Jake Pitler	240.00	120.00	72.00
396	*Dick Williams*	275.00	137.00	82.00
397	Forrest Main	250.00	125.00	75.00
398	Hal Rice	250.00	125.00	75.00
399	Jim Fridley	250.00	125.00	75.00
400	Bill Dickey	600.00	300.00	180.00
401	Bob Schultz	250.00	125.00	75.00
402	Earl Harrist	250.00	125.00	75.00
403	Bill Miller	250.00	125.00	75.00
404	Dick Brodowski	250.00	125.00	75.00
405	Eddie Pellagrini	250.00	125.00	75.00
406	*Joe Nuxhall*	275.00	137.00	82.00
407	*Eddie Mathews*	3000.	1200.	600.00

1953 Topps

The 1953 Topps set reflects the company's continuing legal battles with Bowman. The set, originally intended to consist of 280 cards, is lacking six numbers (#'s 253, 261, 267, 268, 271 and 275) which probably represent players whose contracts were lost to the competition. The 2-5/8" by 3-3/4" cards feature painted player pictures. A color team logo appears at a bottom panel (red for American Leauge and black for National.) Card backs contain the first baseball trivia questions along with brief statistics and player biographies. In the red panel at the top which lists the player's personal data, cards from the 2nd Series (#'s 86-165 plus 10, 44, 61, 72 and 81) can be found with that data printed in either black or white, black being the scarcer variety. Cards 221-280 are the scarce high numbers, with even scarcer short-printed cards interspersed in the series.

	NR MT	EX	VG
Complete Set (274):	15000.	7500.	3450.
Common Player (1-165):	22.00	11.00	5.00
Common Player (166-220):	17.50	8.75	4.00
Common Player (221-280):	45.00	22.00	10.50
Short-print Player (221-280):	85.00	42.00	19.50

1	Jackie Robinson	550.00	275.00	126.00
2	Luke Easter	22.00	11.00	5.00
3	George Crowe	22.00	11.00	5.00
4	Ben Wade	26.00	13.00	6.00
5	Joe Dobson	22.00	11.00	5.00
6	Sam Jones	22.00	11.00	5.00
7	Bob Borkowski	22.00	11.00	5.00
8	Clem Koshorek	22.00	11.00	5.00
9	Joe Collins	30.00	15.00	7.00
10	Smoky Burgess	40.00	20.00	9.25
11	Sal Yvars	22.00	11.00	5.00
12	Howie Judson	22.00	11.00	5.00
13	Connie Marrero	22.00	11.00	5.00
14	Clem Labine	30.00	15.00	7.00
15	Bobo Newsom	22.00	11.00	5.00
16	Harry Lowrey	22.00	11.00	5.00
17	Billy Hitchcock	22.00	11.00	5.00
18	Ted Lepcio	22.00	11.00	5.00
19	Mel Parnell	22.00	11.00	5.00
20	Hank Thompson	22.00	11.00	5.00
21	Billy Johnson	22.00	11.00	5.00
22	Howie Fox	22.00	11.00	5.00
23	Toby Atwell	22.00	11.00	5.00
24	Ferris Fain	22.00	11.00	5.00
25	Ray Boone	22.00	11.00	5.00
26	Dale Mitchell	22.00	11.00	5.00
27	Roy Campanella	200.00	100.00	46.00
28	Eddie Pellagrini	22.00	11.00	5.00
29	Hal Jeffcoat	22.00	11.00	5.00
30	Willard Nixon	22.00	11.00	5.00
31	Ewell Blackwell	35.00	17.50	8.00
32	Clyde Vollmer	22.00	11.00	5.00
33	Bob Kennedy	22.00	11.00	5.00
34	George Shuba	26.00	13.00	6.00
35	Irv Noren	30.00	15.00	7.00
36	Johnny Groth	22.00	11.00	5.00
37	Eddie Mathews	90.00	45.00	21.00
38	Jim Hearn	22.00	11.00	5.00
39	Eddie Miksis	22.00	11.00	5.00
40	John Lipon	22.00	11.00	5.00
41	Enos Slaughter	80.00	40.00	18.50
42	Gus Zernial	22.00	11.00	5.00
43	Gil McDougald	40.00	20.00	9.25
44	Ellis Kinder	30.00	15.00	7.00
45	Grady Hatton	22.00	11.00	5.00
46	Johnny Klippstein	22.00	11.00	5.00
47	Bubba Church	22.00	11.00	5.00
48	Bob Del Greco	22.00	11.00	5.00
49	Faye Throneberry	22.00	11.00	5.00
50	Chuck Dressen	26.00	13.00	6.00
51	Frank Campos	22.00	11.00	5.00
52	Ted Gray	22.00	11.00	5.00
53	Sherman Lollar	22.00	11.00	5.00
54	Bob Feller	110.00	55.00	25.00
55	Maurice McDermott	22.00	11.00	5.00
56	Gerald Staley	22.00	11.00	5.00
57	Carl Scheib	22.00	11.00	5.00
58	George Metkovich	22.00	11.00	5.00
59	Karl Drews	22.00	11.00	5.00
60	Cloyd Boyer	22.00	11.00	5.00
61	Early Wynn	90.00	45.00	21.00
62	Monte Irvin	80.00	40.00	18.50
63	Gus Niarhos	22.00	11.00	5.00
64	Dave Philley	22.00	11.00	5.00
65	Earl Harrist	22.00	11.00	5.00
66	Minnie Minoso	40.00	20.00	9.25
67	Roy Sievers	25.00	12.50	5.75
68	Del Rice	22.00	11.00	5.00
69	Dick Brodowski	22.00	11.00	5.00
70	Ed Yuhas	22.00	11.00	5.00
71	Tony Bartirome	22.00	11.00	5.00
72	Fred Hutchinson	22.00	11.00	5.00
73	Eddie Robinson	22.00	11.00	5.00
74	Joe Rossi	22.00	11.00	5.00
75	Mike Garcia	22.00	11.00	5.00
76	Pee Wee Reese	150.00	75.00	34.00
77	Johnny Mize	80.00	40.00	18.50
78	Red Schoendienst	80.00	40.00	18.50
79	Johnny Wyrostek	22.00	11.00	5.00
80	Jim Hegan	22.00	11.00	5.00
81	Joe Black	60.00	30.00	14.00
82	Mickey Mantle	3250.	1625.	747.00
83	Howie Pollet	22.00	11.00	5.00
84	Bob Hooper	22.00	11.00	5.00
85	Bobby Morgan	26.00	13.00	6.00
86	Billy Martin	100.00	50.00	23.00
87	Ed Lopat	30.00	15.00	7.00
88	Willie Jones	22.00	11.00	5.00
89	Chuck Stobbs	22.00	11.00	5.00
90	Hank Edwards	22.00	11.00	5.00
91	Ebba St. Claire	22.00	11.00	5.00
92	Paul Minner	22.00	11.00	5.00
93	Hal Rice	22.00	11.00	5.00
94	William Kennedy	22.00	11.00	5.00
95	Willard Marshall	22.00	11.00	5.00
96	Virgil Trucks	22.00	11.00	5.00
97	Don Kolloway	22.00	11.00	5.00
98	Cal Abrams	22.00	11.00	5.00
99	Dave Madison	22.00	11.00	5.00
100	Bill Miller	30.00	15.00	7.00
101	Ted Wilks	22.00	11.00	5.00
102	Connie Ryan	22.00	11.00	5.00
103	Joe Astroth	22.00	11.00	5.00
104	Yogi Berra	250.00	125.00	57.00
105	Joe Nuxhall	25.00	12.50	5.75
106	Johnny Antonelli	24.00	12.00	5.50
107	Danny O'Connell	22.00	11.00	5.00
108	Bob Porterfield	22.00	11.00	5.00
109	Alvin Dark	22.00	11.00	5.00
110	Herman Wehmeier	22.00	11.00	5.00
111	Hank Sauer	22.00	11.00	5.00
112	Ned Garver	22.00	11.00	5.00
113	Jerry Priddy	22.00	11.00	5.00
114	Phil Rizzuto	125.00	62.00	29.00
115	George Spencer	22.00	11.00	5.00
116	Frank Smith	22.00	11.00	5.00
117	Sid Gordon	22.00	11.00	5.00
118	Gus Bell	22.00	11.00	5.00
119	Johnny Sain	40.00	20.00	9.25
120	Davey Williams	22.00	11.00	5.00
121	Walt Dropo	22.00	11.00	5.00
122	Elmer Valo	22.00	11.00	5.00
123	Tommy Byrne	22.00	11.00	5.00
124	Sibby Sisti	22.00	11.00	5.00
125	Dick Williams	28.00	14.00	6.50
126	Bill Connelly	22.00	11.00	5.00
127	Clint Courtney	22.00	11.00	5.00
128	Wilmer Mizell	22.00	11.00	5.00
129	Keith Thomas	22.00	11.00	5.00
130	Turk Lown	22.00	11.00	5.00
131	Harry Byrd	22.00	11.00	5.00
132	Tom Morgan	30.00	15.00	7.00
133	Gil Coan	22.00	11.00	5.00
134	Rube Walker	26.00	13.00	6.00
135	Al Rosen	27.00	13.50	6.25
136	Ken Heintzelman	22.00	11.00	5.00
137	John Rutherford	26.00	13.00	6.00
138	George Kell	75.00	37.00	17.00
139	Sammy White	22.00	11.00	5.00
140	Tommy Glaviano	22.00	11.00	5.00
141	Allie Reynolds	35.00	17.50	8.00
142	Vic Wertz	22.00	11.00	5.00
143	Billy Pierce	24.00	12.00	5.50
144	Bob Schultz	22.00	11.00	5.00
145	Harry Dorish	22.00	11.00	5.00
146	Granny Hamner	22.00	11.00	5.00
147	Warren Spahn	150.00	75.00	34.00
148	Mickey Grasso	22.00	11.00	5.00
149	Dom DiMaggio	35.00	17.50	8.00
150	Harry Simpson	22.00	11.00	5.00
151	Hoyt Wilhelm	75.00	37.00	17.00
152	Bob Adams	22.00	11.00	5.00
153	Andy Seminick	22.00	11.00	5.00
154	Dick Groat	32.50	16.00	7.50
155	Dutch Leonard	22.00	11.00	5.00
156	Jim Rivera	22.00	11.00	5.00
157	Bob Addis	22.00	11.00	5.00
158	*Johnny Logan*	25.00	12.50	5.75
159	Wayne Terwilliger	22.00	11.00	5.00
160	Bob Young	22.00	11.00	5.00
161	Vern Bickford	22.00	11.00	5.00
162	Ted Kluszewski	50.00	25.00	11.50
163	Fred Hatfield	22.00	11.00	5.00
164	Frank Shea	22.00	11.00	5.00
165	Billy Hoeft	22.00	11.00	5.00
166	Bill Hunter	22.00	11.00	5.00
167	Art Schult	25.00	12.50	5.75
168	Willard Schmidt	17.50	8.75	4.00
169	Dizzy Trout	17.50	8.75	4.00

170	Bill Werle	17.50	8.75	4.00
171	Bill Glynn	17.50	8.75	4.00
172	Rip Repulski	17.50	8.75	4.00
173	Preston Ward	17.50	8.75	4.00
174	Billy Loes	22.00	11.00	5.00
175	Ron Kline	17.50	8.75	4.00
176	*Don Hoak*	28.00	14.00	6.50
177	Jim Dyck	17.50	8.75	4.00
178	Jim Waugh	17.50	8.75	4.00
179	Gene Hermanski	17.50	8.75	4.00
180	Virgil Stallcup	17.50	8.75	4.00
181	Al Zarilla	17.50	8.75	4.00
182	Bob Hofman	17.50	8.75	4.00
183	*Stu Miller*	17.50	8.75	4.00
184	*Hal Brown*	17.50	8.75	4.00
185	*Jim Pendleton*	17.50	8.75	4.00
186	Charlie Bishop	17.50	8.75	4.00
187	Jim Fridley	17.50	8.75	4.00
188	*Andy Carey*	25.00	12.50	5.75
189	Ray Jablonski	17.50	8.75	4.00
190	Dixie Walker	17.50	8.75	4.00
191	Ralph Kiner	70.00	35.00	16.00
192	Wally Westlake	17.50	8.75	4.00
193	Mike Clark	17.50	8.75	4.00
194	Eddie Kazak	17.50	8.75	4.00
195	Ed McGhee	17.50	8.75	4.00
196	Bob Keegan	17.50	8.75	4.00
197	Del Crandall	17.50	8.75	4.00
198	Forrest Main	17.50	8.75	4.00
199	Marion Fricano	17.50	8.75	4.00
200	Gordon Goldsberry	17.50	8.75	4.00
201	Paul LaPalme	17.50	8.75	4.00
202	Carl Sawatski	17.50	8.75	4.00
203	Cliff Fannin	17.50	8.75	4.00
204	Dick Bokelmann	17.50	8.75	4.00
205	Vern Benson	17.50	8.75	4.00
206	*Ed Bailey*	20.00	10.00	4.50
207	Whitey Ford	135.00	67.00	31.00
208	Jim Wilson	17.50	8.75	4.00
209	Jim Greengrass	17.50	8.75	4.00
210	*Bob Cerv*	25.00	12.50	5.75
211	J.W. Porter	17.50	8.75	4.00
212	Jack Dittmer	17.50	8.75	4.00
213	Ray Scarborough	25.00	12.50	5.75
214	*Bill Bruton*	17.50	8.75	4.00
215	*Gene Conley*	17.50	8.75	4.00
216	Jim Hughes	22.00	11.00	5.00
217	Murray Wall	17.50	8.75	4.00
218	Les Fusselman	17.50	8.75	4.00
219	Pete Runnels (picture actually Don Johnson)	17.50	8.75	4.00
220	Satchel Paige	450.00	225.00	103.00
221	Bob Milliken	95.00	47.00	22.00
222	Vic Janowicz	50.00	25.00	11.50
223	John O'Brien	45.00	22.00	10.50
224	Lou Sleater	45.00	22.00	10.50
225	Bobby Shantz	90.00	45.00	21.00
226	Ed Erautt	85.00	42.00	19.50
227	Morris Martin	45.00	22.00	10.50
228	Hal Newhouser	150.00	75.00	34.00
229	Rocky Krsnich	85.00	42.00	19.50
230	Johnny Lindell	45.00	22.00	10.50
231	Solly Hemus	45.00	22.00	10.50
232	Dick Kokos	85.00	42.00	19.50
233	Al Aber	85.00	42.00	19.50
234	Ray Murray	45.00	22.00	10.50
235	John Hetki	45.00	22.00	10.50
236	Harry Perkowski	45.00	22.00	10.50
237	Clarence Podbielan	45.00	22.00	10.50
238	Cal Hogue	45.00	22.00	10.50
239	Jim Delsing	85.00	42.00	19.50
240	Freddie Marsh	45.00	22.00	10.50
241	Al Sima	45.00	22.00	10.50
242	*Charlie Silvera*	100.00	50.00	23.00
243	Carlos Bernier	45.00	22.00	10.50
244	Willie Mays	2600.	1300.	598.00
245	Bill Norman	85.00	42.00	19.50
246	*Roy Face*	75.00	37.00	17.00
247	Mike Sandlock	45.00	22.00	10.50
248	Gene Stephens	45.00	22.00	10.50
249	Ed O'Brien	85.00	42.00	19.50
250	Bob Wilson	85.00	42.00	19.50
251	Sid Hudson	85.00	42.00	19.50
252	Henry Foiles	85.00	42.00	19.50
253	Not Issued			
254	Preacher Roe	75.00	37.00	17.00
255	Dixie Howell	95.00	47.00	22.00
256	Les Peden	85.00	42.00	19.50
257	Bob Boyd	85.00	42.00	19.50
258	*Jim Gilliam*	300.00	150.00	69.00
259	Roy McMillan	45.00	22.00	10.50
260	Sam Calderone	85.00	42.00	19.50
261	Not Issued			
262	Bob Oldis	85.00	42.00	19.50
263	*Johnny Podres*	250.00	125.00	57.00
264	Gene Woodling	65.00	32.00	15.00
265	Jackie Jensen	125.00	62.00	29.00
266	Bob Cain	85.00	42.00	19.50
267	Not Issued			
268	Not Issued			
269	Duane Pillette	85.00	42.00	19.50
270	Vern Stephens	85.00	42.00	19.50
271	Not Issued			
272	Bill Antonello	95.00	47.00	22.00
273	*Harvey Haddix*	150.00	75.00	34.00
274	John Riddle	85.00	42.00	19.50
275	Not Issued			
276	Ken Raffensberger	85.00	42.00	19.50
277	Don Lund	85.00	42.00	19.50
278	Willie Miranda	85.00	42.00	19.50
279	Joe Coleman	45.00	22.00	10.50
280	Milt Bolling	300.00	45.00	27.00

The values quoted are intended to reflect the market price.

1954 Topps

The first issue to use two player pictures on the front, the 1954 Topps set is very popular today. Solid color backgrounds frame both color head- and-shoulders and black and white action pictures of the player. The player's name, position, team and team logo appear at the top. Backs include an "Inside Baseball" cartoon regarding the player as well as statistics and biography. The 250-card, 2-5/8" by 3-3/4", set includes manager and coaches cards, and the first use by Topps of two players together on a card; the players were, appropriately, the O'Brien twins.

	NR MT	EX	VG
Complete Set (250):	9000.	4500.	2700.
Common Player (1-50):	15.00	7.50	4.50
Common Player (51-75):	30.00	15.00	9.00
Common player (76-250):	15.00	7.50	4.50

1	Ted Williams	650.00	200.00	125.00
2	Gus Zernial	15.00	7.50	4.50
3	Monte Irvin	35.00	17.50	10.50
4	Hank Sauer	15.00	7.50	4.50
5	Ed Lopat	20.00	10.00	6.00
6	Pete Runnels	15.00	7.50	4.50
7	Ted Kluszewski	30.00	15.00	9.00
8	Bobby Young	15.00	7.50	4.50
9	Harvey Haddix	15.00	7.50	4.50
10	Jackie Robinson	260.00	130.00	78.00
11	Paul Smith	15.00	7.50	4.50
12	Del Crandall	15.00	7.50	4.50
13	Billy Martin	75.00	37.00	22.00
14	Preacher Roe	25.00	12.50	7.50
15	Al Rosen	18.00	9.00	5.50
16	Vic Janowicz	18.00	9.00	5.50
17	Phil Rizzuto	70.00	35.00	21.00
18	Walt Dropo	15.00	7.50	4.50
19	Johnny Lipon	15.00	7.50	4.50
20	Warren Spahn	100.00	50.00	30.00
21	Bobby Shantz	18.00	9.00	5.50
22	Jim Greengrass	15.00	7.50	4.50
23	Luke Easter	15.00	7.50	4.50
24	Granny Hamner	15.00	7.50	4.50
25	*Harvey Kuenn*	35.00	17.50	10.50
26	Ray Jablonski	15.00	7.50	4.50
27	Ferris Fain	15.00	7.50	4.50
28	Paul Minner	15.00	7.50	4.50
29	Jim Hegan	15.00	7.50	4.50
30	Eddie Mathews	85.00	42.00	25.00
31	Johnny Klippstein	15.00	7.50	4.50
32	Duke Snider	140.00	70.00	42.00
33	Johnny Schmitz	15.00	7.50	4.50
34	Jim Rivera	15.00	7.50	4.50
35	Junior Gilliam	27.50	13.50	8.25
36	Hoyt Wilhelm	45.00	22.00	13.50
37	Whitey Ford	100.00	50.00	30.00
38	Eddie Stanky	15.00	7.50	4.50
39	Sherm Lollar	15.00	7.50	4.50
40	Mel Parnell	15.00	7.50	4.50
41	Willie Jones	15.00	7.50	4.50
42	Don Mueller	15.00	7.50	4.50
43	Dick Groat	15.00	7.50	4.50
44	Ned Garver	15.00	7.50	4.50
45	Richie Ashburn	40.00	20.00	12.00
46	Ken Raffensberger	15.00	7.50	4.50
47	Ellis Kinder	15.00	7.50	4.50
48	Billy Hunter	15.00	7.50	4.50
49	Ray Murray	15.00	7.50	4.50
50	Yogi Berra	225.00	110.00	65.00
51	Johnny Lindell	30.00	15.00	9.00
52	Vic Power	30.00	15.00	9.00
53	Jack Dittmer	30.00	15.00	9.00
54	Vern Stephens	30.00	15.00	9.00
55	Phil Cavarretta	30.00	15.00	9.00
56	Willie Miranda	35.00	17.50	10.50
57	Luis Aloma	30.00	15.00	9.00
58	Bob Wilson	30.00	15.00	9.00
59	Gene Conley	30.00	15.00	9.00
60	Frank Baumholtz	30.00	15.00	9.00
61	Bob Cain	30.00	15.00	9.00
62	Eddie Robinson	35.00	17.50	10.50
63	Johnny Pesky	30.00	15.00	9.00
64	Hank Thompson	30.00	15.00	9.00
65	Bob Swift	30.00	15.00	9.00
66	Ted Lepcio	30.00	15.00	9.00
67	Jim Willis	30.00	15.00	9.00
68	Sam Calderone	30.00	15.00	9.00
69	Bud Podbielan	30.00	15.00	9.00
70	Larry Doby	60.00	30.00	18.00
71	Frank Smith	30.00	15.00	9.00
72	Preston Ward	30.00	15.00	9.00
73	Wayne Terwilliger	30.00	15.00	9.00
74	Bill Taylor	30.00	15.00	9.00
75	Fred Haney	30.00	15.00	9.00
76	Bob Scheffing	15.00	7.50	4.50
77	Ray Boone	15.00	7.50	4.50
78	Ted Kazanski	15.00	7.50	4.50
79	Andy Pafko	15.00	7.50	4.50
80	Jackie Jensen	18.00	9.00	5.50
81	Dave Hoskins	15.00	7.50	4.50
82	Milt Bolling	15.00	7.50	4.50
83	Joe Collins	20.00	10.00	6.00
84	Dick Cole	15.00	7.50	4.50
85	*Bob Turley*	18.00	9.00	5.50
86	Billy Herman	40.00	20.00	12.00
87	Roy Face	15.00	7.50	4.50
88	Matt Batts	15.00	7.50	4.50
89	Howie Pollet	15.00	7.50	4.50
90	Willie Mays	550.00	275.00	135.00
91	Bob Oldis	15.00	7.50	4.50
92	Wally Westlake	15.00	7.50	4.50
93	Sid Hudson	15.00	7.50	4.50
94	*Ernie Banks*	750.00	375.00	200.00
95	Hal Rice	15.00	7.50	4.50
96	Charlie Silvera	20.00	10.00	6.00
97	Jerry Lane	15.00	7.50	4.50
98	Joe Black	20.00	10.00	6.00
99	Bob Hofman	15.00	7.50	4.50
100	Bob Keegan	15.00	7.50	4.50
101	Gene Woodling	20.00	10.00	6.00
102	Gil Hodges	85.00	42.00	25.00
103	*Jim Lemon*	18.00	9.00	5.50
104	Mike Sandlock	15.00	7.50	4.50
105	Andy Carey	20.00	10.00	6.00
106	Dick Kokos	15.00	7.50	4.50
107	Duane Pillette	15.00	7.50	4.50
108	Thornton Kipper	15.00	7.50	4.50
109	Bill Bruton	15.00	7.50	4.50
110	Harry Dorish	15.00	7.50	4.50
111	Jim Delsing	15.00	7.50	4.50
112	Bill Renna	15.00	7.50	4.50
113	Bob Boyd	15.00	7.50	4.50
114	Dean Stone	15.00	7.50	4.50
115	"Rip" Repulski	15.00	7.50	4.50
116	Steve Bilko	15.00	7.50	4.50
117	Solly Hemus	15.00	7.50	4.50
118	Carl Scheib	15.00	7.50	4.50
119	Johnny Antonelli	15.00	7.50	4.50
120	Roy McMillan	15.00	7.50	4.50
121	Clem Labine	20.00	10.00	6.00
122	Johnny Logan	15.00	7.50	4.50
123	Bobby Adams	15.00	7.50	4.50
124	Marion Fricano	15.00	7.50	4.50
125	Harry Perkowski	15.00	7.50	4.50
126	Ben Wade	18.00	9.00	5.50
127	Steve O'Neill	15.00	7.50	4.50
128	*Hank Aaron*	1600.	800.00	450.00
129	Forrest Jacobs	15.00	7.50	4.50
130	Hank Bauer	30.00	15.00	9.00
131	Reno Bertoia	15.00	7.50	4.50
132	*Tom Lasorda*	150.00	75.00	45.00
133	Del Baker	15.00	7.50	4.50
134	Cal Hogue	15.00	7.50	4.50
135	Joe Presko	15.00	7.50	4.50
136	Connie Ryan	15.00	7.50	4.50
137	*Wally Moon*	25.00	12.50	7.50
138	Bob Borkowski	15.00	7.50	4.50
139	Ed & Johnny O'Brien	45.00	22.00	13.50
140	Tom Wright	15.00	7.50	4.50
141	*Joe Jay*	15.00	7.50	4.50
142	Tom Poholsky	15.00	7.50	4.50
143	Rollie Hemsley	15.00	7.50	4.50
144	Bill Werle	15.00	7.50	4.50
145	Elmer Valo	15.00	7.50	4.50
146	Don Johnson	15.00	7.50	4.50
147	John Riddle	15.00	7.50	4.50
148	Bob Trice	15.00	7.50	4.50
149	Jim Robertson	15.00	7.50	4.50
150	Dick Kryhoski	15.00	7.50	4.50
151	Alex Grammas	15.00	7.50	4.50
152	Mike Blyzka	15.00	7.50	4.50
153	Rube Walker	18.00	9.00	5.50
154	Mike Fornieles	15.00	7.50	4.50
155	Bob Kennedy	15.00	7.50	4.50
156	Joe Coleman	15.00	7.50	4.50
157	Don Lenhardt	15.00	7.50	4.50
158	Peanuts Lowrey	15.00	7.50	4.50
159	Dave Philley	15.00	7.50	4.50
160	Red Kress	15.00	7.50	4.50
161	John Hetki	15.00	7.50	4.50
162	Herman Wehmeier	15.00	7.50	4.50
163	Frank House	15.00	7.50	4.50
164	Stu Miller	15.00	7.50	4.50
165	Jim Pendleton	15.00	7.50	4.50
166	Johnny Podres	30.00	15.00	9.00
167	Don Lund	15.00	7.50	4.50
168	Morrie Martin	15.00	7.50	4.50
169	Jim Hughes	18.00	9.00	5.50
170	*Dusty Rhodes*	15.00	7.50	4.50
171	Leo Kiely	15.00	7.50	4.50
172	Hal Brown	15.00	7.50	4.50
173	Jack Harshman	15.00	7.50	4.50
174	Tom Qualters	15.00	7.50	4.50
175	Frank Leja	20.00	10.00	6.00
176	Bob Keely	15.00	7.50	4.50
177	Bob Milliken	18.00	9.00	5.50
178	Bill Gylnn (Glynn)	15.00	7.50	4.50
179	Gair Allie	15.00	7.50	4.50
180	Wes Westrum	15.00	7.50	4.50
181	Mel Roach	15.00	7.50	4.50
182	Chuck Harmon	15.00	7.50	4.50
183	Earle Combs	35.00	17.50	10.50
184	Ed Bailey	15.00	7.50	4.50
185	Chuck Stobbs	15.00	7.50	4.50
186	Karl Olson	15.00	7.50	4.50
187	Heinie Manush	35.00	17.50	10.50
188	Dave Jolly	15.00	7.50	4.50
189	Bob Ross	15.00	7.50	4.50
190	Ray Herbert	15.00	7.50	4.50
191	*Dick Schofield*	18.00	9.00	5.50

192	Cot Deal	15.00	7.50	4.50
193	Johnny Hopp	15.00	7.50	4.50
194	Bill Sarni	15.00	7.50	4.50
195	Bill Consolo	15.00	7.50	4.50
196	Stan Jok	15.00	7.50	4.50
197	Schoolboy Rowe	15.00	7.50	4.50
198	Carl Sawatski	15.00	7.50	4.50
199	Rocky Nelson	15.00	7.50	4.50
200	Larry Jansen	15.00	7.50	4.50
201	*Al Kaline*	750.00	375.00	220.00
202	*Bob Purkey*	15.00	7.50	4.50
203	Harry Brecheen	15.00	7.50	4.50
204	Angel Scull	15.00	7.50	4.50
205	Johnny Sain	30.00	15.00	9.00
206	Ray Crone	15.00	7.50	4.50
207	Tom Oliver	15.00	7.50	4.50
208	Grady Hatton	15.00	7.50	4.50
209	Charlie Thompson	18.00	9.00	5.50
210	*Bob Buhl*	15.00	7.50	4.50
211	Don Hoak	18.00	9.00	5.50
212	Mickey Micelotta	15.00	7.50	4.50
213	John Fitzpatrick	15.00	7.50	4.50
214	Arnold Portocarrero	15.00	7.50	4.50
215	Ed McGhee	15.00	7.50	4.50
216	Al Sima	15.00	7.50	4.50
217	Paul Schreiber	15.00	7.50	4.50
218	Fred Marsh	15.00	7.50	4.50
219	Charlie Kress	15.00	7.50	4.50
220	Ruben Gomez	15.00	7.50	4.50
221	Dick Brodowski	15.00	7.50	4.50
222	Bill Wilson	15.00	7.50	4.50
223	Joe Haynes	15.00	7.50	4.50
224	Dick Weik	15.00	7.50	4.50
225	Don Liddle	15.00	7.50	4.50
226	Jehosie Heard	15.00	7.50	4.50
227	Buster Mills	15.00	7.50	4.50
228	Gene Hermanski	15.00	7.50	4.50
229	Bob Talbot	15.00	7.50	4.50
230	Bob Kuzava	20.00	10.00	6.00
231	Roy Smalley	15.00	7.50	4.50
232	Lou Limmer	15.00	7.50	4.50
233	Augie Galan	15.00	7.50	4.50
234	*Jerry Lynch*	15.00	7.50	4.50
235	Vern Law	15.00	7.50	4.50
236	Paul Penson	15.00	7.50	4.50
237	Mike Ryba	15.00	7.50	4.50
238	Al Aber	15.00	7.50	4.50
239	*Bill Skowron*	85.00	42.00	25.00
240	Sam Mele	15.00	7.50	4.50
241	Bob Miller	15.00	7.50	4.50
242	Curt Roberts	15.00	7.50	4.50
243	Ray Blades	15.00	7.50	4.50
244	Leroy Wheat	15.00	7.50	4.50
245	Roy Sievers	15.00	7.50	4.50
246	Howie Fox	15.00	7.50	4.50
247	Eddie Mayo	15.00	7.50	4.50
248	*Al Smith*	15.00	7.50	4.50
249	Wilmer Mizell	15.00	7.50	4.50
250	Ted Williams	700.00	225.00	110.00

1955 Topps

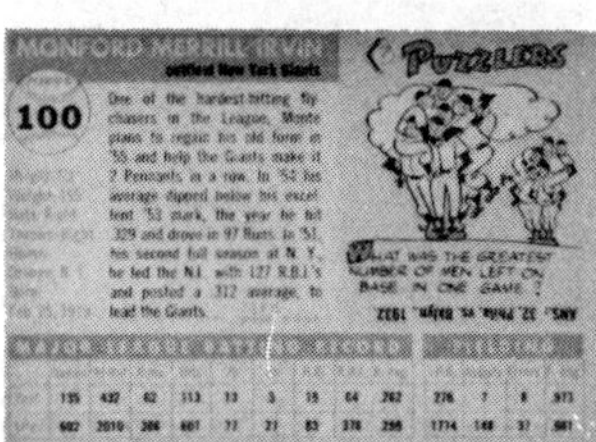

The 1955 Topps set is numerically the smallest of the regular issue Topps sets. The 3-3/4" by 2-5/8" cards mark the first time that Topps used a horizontal format. While that format was new, the design was not; they are very similar to the 1954 cards to the point many pictures appeared in both years. Although it was slated for a 210-card set, the 1955 Topps set turned out to be only 206 cards with numbers 175, 186, 203 and 209 never being released. The scarce high numbers in this set begin with #161.

		NR MT	EX	VG
Complete Set (206):		7750.	3825.	2300.
Common Player (1-150):		9.00	4.50	2.75
Common Player (151-160):		18.00	9.00	5.50
Common Player (161-210):		29.00	14.50	8.75
1	Dusty Rhodes	40.00	15.00	9.00
2	Ted Williams	375.00	187.00	112.00
3	Art Fowler	9.00	4.50	2.75
4	Al Kaline	175.00	87.50	52.50
5	Jim Gilliam	12.00	6.00	3.50
6	Stan Hack	9.00	4.50	2.75
7	Jim Hegan	9.00	4.50	2.75
8	Hal Smith	9.00	4.50	2.75
9	Bob Miller	9.00	4.50	2.75
10	Bob Keegan	9.00	4.50	2.75
11	15. (Ferris Fain)	9.00	4.50	2.75
12	"Jake" Thies	9.00	4.50	2.75
13	Fred Marsh	9.00	4.50	2.75
14	Jim Finigan	9.00	4.50	2.75
15	Jim Pendleton	9.00	4.50	2.75
16	Roy Sievers	10.00	5.00	3.00
17	Bobby Hofman	9.00	4.50	2.75
18	Russ Kemmerer	9.00	4.50	2.75
19	Billy Herman	12.00	6.00	3.50
20	Andy Carey	15.00	7.50	4.50
21	Alex Grammas	9.00	4.50	2.75
22	Bill Skowron	18.00	9.00	5.50
23	Jack Parks	9.00	4.50	2.75
24	Hal Newhouser	24.00	12.00	7.25
25	Johnny Podres	15.00	7.50	4.50
26	Dick Groat	12.00	6.00	3.50
27	Billy Gardner	9.00	4.50	2.75
28	Ernie Banks	225.00	110.00	65.00
29	Herman Wehmeier	9.00	4.50	2.75
30	Vic Power	9.00	4.50	2.75
31	Warren Spahn	80.00	40.00	24.00
32	Ed McGhee	9.00	4.50	2.75
33	Tom Qualters	9.00	4.50	2.75
34	Wayne Terwilliger	9.00	4.50	2.75
35	Dave Jolly	9.00	4.50	2.75
36	Leo Kiely	9.00	4.50	2.75
37	*Joe Cunningham*	9.00	4.50	2.75
38	Bob Turley	15.00	7.50	4.50
39	Bill Glynn	9.00	4.50	2.75
40	Don Hoak	12.00	6.00	3.50
41	Chuck Stobbs	9.00	4.50	2.75
42	Windy McCall	9.00	4.50	2.75
43	Harvey Haddix	9.00	4.50	2.75
44	Corky Valentine	9.00	4.50	2.75
45	Hank Sauer	9.00	4.50	2.75
46	Ted Kazanski	9.00	4.50	2.75
47	Hank Aaron	325.00	162.00	97.00
48	Bob Kennedy	9.00	4.50	2.75
49	J.W. Porter	9.00	4.50	2.75
50	Jackie Robinson	225.00	112.00	67.00
51	Jim Hughes	12.00	6.00	3.50
52	Bill Tremel	9.00	4.50	2.75
53	Bill Taylor	9.00	4.50	2.75
54	Lou Limmer	9.00	4.50	2.75
55	"Rip" Repulski	9.00	4.50	2.75
56	Ray Jablonski	9.00	4.50	2.75
57	*Billy O'Dell*	9.00	4.50	2.75
58	Jim Rivera	9.00	4.50	2.75
59	Gair Allie	9.00	4.50	2.75
60	Dean Stone	9.00	4.50	2.75
61	"Spook" Jacobs	9.00	4.50	2.75
62	Thornton Kipper	9.00	4.50	2.75
63	Joe Collins	15.00	7.50	4.50
64	*Gus Triandos*	10.00	5.00	3.00
65	Ray Boone	9.00	4.50	2.75
66	Ron Jackson	9.00	4.50	2.75
67	Wally Moon	9.00	4.50	2.75
68	Jim Davis	9.00	4.50	2.75
69	Ed Bailey	9.00	4.50	2.75
70	Al Rosen	11.00	5.50	3.25
71	Ruben Gomez	9.00	4.50	2.75
72	Karl Olson	9.00	4.50	2.75
73	Jack Shepard	9.00	4.50	2.75
74	Bob Borkowski	9.00	4.50	2.75
75	*Sandy Amoros*	15.00	7.50	4.50
76	Howie Pollet	9.00	4.50	2.75
77	Arnold Portocarrero	9.00	4.50	2.75
78	Gordon Jones	9.00	4.50	2.75
79	Danny Schell	9.00	4.50	2.75
80	Bob Grim	15.00	7.50	4.50
81	Gene Conley	9.00	4.50	2.75
82	Chuck Harmon	9.00	4.50	2.75
83	Tom Brewer	9.00	4.50	2.75
84	*Camilo Pascual*	9.00	4.50	2.75
85	*Don Mossi*	9.00	4.50	2.75
86	Bill Wilson	9.00	4.50	2.75
87	Frank House	9.00	4.50	2.75
88	*Bob Skinner*	9.00	4.50	2.75
89	*Joe Frazier*	9.00	4.50	2.75
90	*Karl Spooner*	12.00	6.00	3.50
91	Milt Bolling	9.00	4.50	2.75
92	*Don Zimmer*	35.00	17.50	10.50
93	Steve Bilko	9.00	4.50	2.75
94	Reno Bertoia	9.00	4.50	2.75
95	Preston Ward	9.00	4.50	2.75
96	Charlie Bishop	9.00	4.50	2.75
97	Carlos Paula	9.00	4.50	2.75
98	Johnny Riddle	9.00	4.50	2.75
99	Frank Leja	15.00	7.50	4.50
100	Monte Irvin	30.00	15.00	9.00
101	Johnny Gray	9.00	4.50	2.75
102	Wally Westlake	9.00	4.50	2.75
103	Charlie White	9.00	4.50	2.75
104	Jack Harshman	9.00	4.50	2.75
105	Chuck Diering	9.00	4.50	2.75
106	*Frank Sullivan*	9.00	4.50	2.75
107	Curt Roberts	9.00	4.50	2.75
108	Rube Walker	12.00	6.00	3.50
109	Ed Lopat	15.00	7.50	4.50
110	Gus Zernial	9.00	4.50	2.75
111	Bob Milliken	12.00	6.00	3.50
112	Nelson King	9.00	4.50	2.75
113	Harry Brecheen	9.00	4.50	2.75
114	Lou Ortiz	9.00	4.50	2.75
115	Ellis Kinder	9.00	4.50	2.75
116	Tom Hurd	9.00	4.50	2.75
117	Mel Roach	9.00	4.50	2.75
118	Bob Purkey	9.00	4.50	2.75
119	Bob Lennon	9.00	4.50	2.75
120	Ted Kluszewski	25.00	12.50	7.50
121	Bill Renna	9.00	4.50	2.75
122	Carl Sawatski	9.00	4.50	2.75
123	*Sandy Koufax*	1000.	500.00	300.00
124	*Harmon Killebrew*	300.00	150.00	90.00
125	*Ken Boyer*	75.00	37.00	22.00
126	*Dick Hall*	9.00	4.50	2.75
127	*Dale Long*	9.00	4.50	2.75
128	Ted Lepcio	9.00	4.50	2.75
129	Elvin Tappe	9.00	4.50	2.75
130	Mayo Smith	9.00	4.50	2.75
131	Grady Hatton	9.00	4.50	2.75
132	Bob Trice	9.00	4.50	2.75
133	Dave Hoskins	9.00	4.50	2.75
134	Joe Jay	9.00	4.50	2.75
135	Johnny O'Brien	9.00	4.50	2.75
136	"Bunky" Stewart	9.00	4.50	2.75
137	Harry Elliott	9.00	4.50	2.75
138	Ray Herbert	9.00	4.50	2.75
139	Steve Kraly	15.00	7.50	4.50
140	Mel Parnell	9.00	4.50	2.75
141	Tom Wright	9.00	4.50	2.75
142	Jerry Lynch	9.00	4.50	2.75
143	Dick Schofield	9.00	4.50	2.75
144	Joe Amalfitano	9.00	4.50	2.75
145	Elmer Valo	9.00	4.50	2.75
146	*Dick Donovan*	9.00	4.50	2.75
147	Laurin Pepper	9.00	4.50	2.75
148	Hal Brown	9.00	4.50	2.75
149	Ray Crone	9.00	4.50	2.75
150	Mike Higgins	9.00	4.50	2.75
151	Red Kress	18.00	9.00	5.50
152	*Harry Agganis*	55.00	27.00	16.50
153	Bud Podbielan	18.00	9.00	5.50
154	Willie Miranda	18.00	9.00	5.50
155	Eddie Mathews	90.00	45.00	27.00
156	Joe Black	20.00	10.00	6.00
157	Bob Miller	18.00	9.00	5.50
158	Tom Carroll	22.50	11.00	6.75
159	Johnny Schmitz	18.00	9.00	5.50
160	Ray Narleski	18.00	9.00	5.50
161	*Chuck Tanner*	30.00	15.00	9.00
162	Joe Coleman	29.00	14.50	8.75
163	Faye Throneberry	29.00	14.50	8.75
164	*Roberto Clemente*	1675.	825.00	475.00
165	Don Johnson	29.00	14.50	8.75
166	Hank Bauer	35.00	17.50	10.50
167	Tom Casagrande	29.00	14.50	8.75
168	Duane Pillette	29.00	14.50	8.75
169	Bob Oldis	29.00	14.50	8.75
170	Jim Pearce	29.00	14.50	8.75
171	Dick Brodowski	29.00	14.50	8.75
172	Frank Baumholtz	29.00	14.50	8.75
173	Bob Kline	29.00	14.50	8.75
174	Rudy Minarcin	29.00	14.50	8.75
175	Not Issued			
176	Norm Zauchin	29.00	14.50	8.75
177	Jim Robertson	29.00	14.50	8.75
178	Bobby Adams	29.00	14.50	8.75
179	Jim Bolger	29.00	14.50	8.75
180	Clem Labine	35.00	17.50	10.50
181	Roy McMillan	29.00	14.50	8.75
182	Humberto Robinson	29.00	14.50	8.75
183	Tony Jacobs	29.00	14.50	8.75
184	Harry Perkowski	29.00	14.50	8.75
185	Don Ferrarese	29.00	14.50	8.75
186	Not Issued			
187	Gil Hodges	150.00	75.00	45.00
188	Charlie Silvera	35.00	17.50	10.50
189	Phil Rizzuto	150.00	75.00	45.00
190	Gene Woodling	29.00	14.50	8.75
191	Ed Stanky	29.00	14.50	8.75
192	Jim Delsing	29.00	14.50	8.75
193	Johnny Sain	40.00	20.00	12.00
194	Willie Mays	475.00	237.00	142.00
195	Ed Roebuck	32.50	16.00	9.75
196	Gale Wade	29.00	14.50	8.75
197	Al Smith	29.00	14.50	8.75
198	Yogi Berra	180.00	90.00	54.00
199	Bert Hamric	32.50	16.00	9.75
200	Jack Jensen	35.00	17.50	10.50
201	Sherm Lollar	29.00	14.50	8.75
202	Jim Owens	29.00	14.50	8.75
203	Not Issued			
204	Frank Smith	29.00	14.50	8.75
205	Gene Freese	29.00	14.50	8.75
206	Pete Daley	29.00	14.50	8.75
207	Bill Consolo	29.00	14.50	8.75
208	Ray Moore	29.00	14.50	8.75
209	Not Issued			
210	Duke Snider	425.00	210.00	125.00

1955 Topps Doubleheaders

This set is a throwback to the 1911 T201 Mecca Double Folders. The cards were perforated allowing them to be folded. Open, there is a color painting of a player set against a ballpark background. When folded, a different stadium and player appears, although both share the same lower legs and feet. Back gives abbreviated career histories. Placed side by side in reverse numerical order, the backgrounds form a continuous stadium scene. When open, the cards measure 2-1/16" by 4-7/8." The 66 cards in the set mean 132 total players, all of whom also appeared in the lower number regular 1955 Topps set.

		NR MT	EX	VG
Complete Set (66):		3600.	1800.	1075.
Common Player:		30.00	15.00	9.00
1	Al Rosen			
2	Chuck Diering	30.00	15.00	9.00
3	Monte Irvin			
4	Russ Kemmerer	30.00	15.00	9.00
5	Ted Kazanski			
6	Gordon Jones	30.00	15.00	9.00
7	Bill Taylor			
8	Billy O'Dell	30.00	15.00	9.00
9	J.W. Porter			
10	Thornton Kipper	30.00	15.00	9.00
11	Curt Roberts			
12	Arnie Portocarrero	30.00	15.00	9.00
13	Wally Westlake			
14	Frank House	30.00	15.00	9.00
15	"Rube" Walker			
16	Lou Limmer	30.00	15.00	9.00
17	Dean Stone			
18	Charlie White	30.00	15.00	9.00
19	Karl Spooner			
20	Jim Hughes	30.00	15.00	9.00
21	Bill Skowron			
22	Frank Sullivan	30.00	15.00	9.00
23	Jack Shepard			
24	Stan Hack	30.00	15.00	9.00
25	Jackie Robinson			
26	Don Hoak	260.00	130.00	78.00
27	"Dusty" Rhodes			
28	Jim Davis	30.00	15.00	9.00
29	Vic Power			
30	Ed Bailey	30.00	15.00	9.00
31	Howie Pollet			
32	Ernie Banks	150.00	75.00	45.00
33	Jim Pendleton			
34	Gene Conley	30.00	15.00	9.00
35	Karl Olson			
36	Andy Carey	30.00	15.00	9.00
37	Wally Moon			
38	Joe Cunningham	30.00	15.00	9.00
39	Fred Marsh			
40	"Jake" Thies	30.00	15.00	9.00
41	Ed Lopat			
42	Harvey Haddix	30.00	15.00	9.00
43	Leo Kiely			
44	Chuck Stobbs	30.00	15.00	9.00
45	Al Kaline			
46	"Corky" Valentine	280.00	140.00	84.00
47	"Spook" Jacobs			
48	Johnny Gray	30.00	15.00	9.00
49	Ron Jackson			
50	Jim Finigan	30.00	15.00	9.00
51	Ray Jablonski			
52	Bob Keegan	30.00	15.00	9.00
53	Billy Herman			
54	Sandy Amoros	30.00	15.00	9.00
55	Chuck Harmon			
56	Bob Skinner	30.00	15.00	9.00
57	Dick Hall			
58	Bob Grim	30.00	15.00	9.00
59	Billy Glynn			
60	Bob Miller	30.00	15.00	9.00
61	Billy Gardner			
62	John Hetki	30.00	15.00	9.00
63	Bob Borkowski			
64	Bob Turley	30.00	15.00	9.00
65	Joe Collins			
66	Jack Harshman	30.00	15.00	9.00
67	Jim Hegan			
68	Jack Parks	30.00	15.00	9.00
69	Ted Williams			
70	Hal Smith	300.00	150.00	90.00
71	Gair Allie			
72	Grady Hatton	30.00	15.00	9.00
73	Jerry Lynch			
74	Harry Brecheen	30.00	15.00	9.00
75	Tom Wright			
76	"Bunky" Stewart	30.00	15.00	9.00
77	Dave Hoskins			
78	Ed McGhee	30.00	15.00	9.00
79	Roy Sievers			
80	Art Fowler	30.00	15.00	9.00
81	Danny Schell			
82	Gus Triandos	30.00	15.00	9.00
83	Joe Frazier			
84	Don Mossi	30.00	15.00	9.00
85	Elmer Valo			
86	Hal Brown	30.00	15.00	9.00
87	Bob Kennedy			
88	"Windy" McCall	30.00	15.00	9.00
89	Ruben Gomez			
90	Jim Rivera	30.00	15.00	9.00
91	Lou Ortiz			
92	Milt Bolling	30.00	15.00	9.00
93	Carl Sawatski			
94	Elvin Tappe	30.00	15.00	9.00
95	Dave Jolly			
96	Bobby Hofman	30.00	15.00	9.00
97	Preston Ward			
98	Don Zimmer	30.00	15.00	9.00
99	Bill Renna			
100	Dick Groat	30.00	15.00	9.00
101	Bill Wilson			
102	Bill Tremel	30.00	15.00	9.00
103	Hank Sauer			
104	Camilo Pascual	30.00	15.00	9.00
105	Hank Aaron			
106	Ray Herbert	400.00	200.00	120.00
107	Alex Grammas			
108	Tom Qualters	30.00	15.00	9.00
109	Hal Newhouser			
110	Charlie Bishop	30.00	15.00	9.00
111	Harmon Killebrew			
112	John Podres	225.00	110.00	65.00
113	Ray Boone			
114	Bob Purkey	30.00	15.00	9.00
115	Dale Long			
116	Ferris Fain	30.00	15.00	9.00
117	Steve Bilko			
118	Bob Milliken	30.00	15.00	9.00
119	Mel Parnell			
120	Tom Hurd	30.00	15.00	9.00
121	Ted Kluszewski			
122	Jim Owens	30.00	15.00	9.00
123	Gus Zernial			
124	Bob Trice	30.00	15.00	9.00
125	"Rip" Repulski			
126	Ted Lepcio	30.00	15.00	9.00
127	Warren Spahn			
128	Tom Brewer	150.00	75.00	45.00
129	Jim Gilliam			
130	Ellis Kinder	30.00	15.00	9.00
131	Herm Wehmeier			
132	Wayne Terwilliger	30.00	15.00	9.00

1955 Topps Test Stamps

An extremely rare and enigmatic test issue, only two specimens have been cataloged to date. The stamps are the same size as Topps' 1955 card issue and have a blank, gummed back. Each of the two specimens currently known is imperforate along one of the sides. Because of their rarity, no valuations are possible.

(1) Bobby Hofman
(2) Charlie White

1956 Topps

This 340-card set is quite similar in design to the 1955 Topps set, again using both a portrait and an "action" picture. Some portraits are the same as those used in 1955 (and even 1954). Innovations found in the 1956 Topps set of 2-5/8" by 3-3/4" cards include team cards introduced as part of a regular set. Additionally, there are two unnumbered checklist cards (the complete set price quoted below does not include the checklist cards). Finally, there are cards of the two league presidents, William Harridge and Warren Giles. On the backs, a three-panel cartoon depicts big moments from the player's career while biographical information appears above the cartoon and the statistics below. Card backs for numbers 1-180 can be found with either white or grey cardboard. Some dealers charge a premium for grey backs (#'s 1-100) and white backs (#'s 101-180).

		NR MT	EX	VG
Complete Set (340):		7450.	3725.	2235.
Common Player (1-100):		8.50	4.25	2.50
Common Player (101-180):		11.00	5.50	3.25
Common Player (181-260):		14.00	7.00	4.25
Common Player (261-340):		11.00	5.50	3.25
1	William Harridge	100.00	35.00	20.00
2	Warren Giles	18.00	9.00	5.50
3	Elmer Valo	8.50	4.25	2.50
4	Carlos Paula	8.50	4.25	2.50
5	Ted Williams	300.00	150.00	90.00
6	Ray Boone	9.00	4.50	2.75
7	Ron Negray	8.50	4.25	2.50
8	Walter Alston	40.00	20.00	12.00
9	Ruben Gomez	8.50	4.25	2.50
10	Warren Spahn	65.00	32.00	19.50
11a	Cubs Team (with date)	75.00	37.00	22.00
11b	Cubs Team (no date, name centered)	25.00	12.50	7.50
11c	Cubs Team (no date, name at left)	35.00	17.50	10.50
12	Andy Carey	10.00	5.00	3.00
13	Roy Face	9.00	4.50	2.75
14	Ken Boyer	14.00	7.00	4.25
15	Ernie Banks	90.00	45.00	27.00
16	*Hector Lopez*	10.00	5.00	3.00
17	Gene Conley	12.00	6.00	3.50
18	Dick Donovan	8.50	4.25	2.50
19	Chuck Diering	8.50	4.25	2.50
20	Al Kaline	105.00	52.00	31.00
21	Joe Collins	10.00	5.00	3.00
22	Jim Finigan	8.50	4.25	2.50
23	Freddie Marsh	8.50	4.25	2.50
24	Dick Groat	10.50	5.25	3.25
25	Ted Kluszewski	20.00	10.00	6.00
26	Grady Hatton	8.50	4.25	2.50
27	Nelson Burbrink	8.50	4.25	2.50
28	Bobby Hofman	8.50	4.25	2.50
29	Jack Harshman	8.50	4.25	2.50
30	Jackie Robinson	135.00	67.00	40.00
31	Hank Aaron	250.00	125.00	75.00
32	Frank House	8.50	4.25	2.50
33	Roberto Clemente	415.00	200.00	120.00
34	Tom Brewer	8.50	4.25	2.50
35	Al Rosen	12.00	6.00	3.50
36	Rudy Minarcin	8.50	4.25	2.50
37	Alex Grammas	8.50	4.25	2.50
38	Bob Kennedy	8.50	4.25	2.50
39	Don Mossi	12.00	6.00	3.50
40	Bob Turley	12.00	6.00	3.50
41	Hank Sauer	8.50	4.25	2.50
42	Sandy Amoros	11.00	5.50	3.25
43	Ray Moore	8.50	4.25	2.50
44	"Windy" McCall	8.50	4.25	2.50
45	Gus Zernial	12.00	6.00	3.50
46	Gene Freese	8.50	4.25	2.50
47	Art Fowler	8.50	4.25	2.50
48	Jim Hegan	8.50	4.25	2.50
49	*Pedro Ramos*	12.00	6.00	3.50
50	"Dusty" Rhodes	12.00	6.00	3.50
51	Ernie Oravetz	8.50	4.25	2.50
52	Bob Grim	10.00	5.00	3.00
53	Arnold Portocarrero	8.50	4.25	2.50
54	Bob Keegan	8.50	4.25	2.50
55	Wally Moon	12.00	6.00	3.50
56	Dale Long	12.00	6.00	3.50
57	"Duke" Maas	8.50	4.25	2.50
58	Ed Roebuck	12.00	6.00	3.50
59	Jose Santiago	8.50	4.25	2.50
60	Mayo Smith	8.50	4.25	2.50
61	Bill Skowron	12.50	6.25	3.75
62	Hal Smith	8.50	4.25	2.50
63	*Roger Craig*	30.00	15.00	9.00
64	Luis Arroyo	8.50	4.25	2.50
65	Johnny O'Brien	8.50	4.25	2.50
66	Bob Speake	8.50	4.25	2.50
67	Vic Power	8.50	4.25	2.50
68	Chuck Stobbs	8.50	4.25	2.50
69	Chuck Tanner	9.00	4.50	2.75
70	Jim Rivera	8.50	4.25	2.50
71	Frank Sullivan	8.50	4.25	2.50
72a	Phillies Team (with date)	75.00	37.00	22.00
72b	Phillies Team (no date, name centered)	32.50	16.00	9.75
72c	Philadelphia Phillies (no date, name at left)	35.00	17.50	10.50
73	Wayne Terwilliger	8.50	4.25	2.50
74	Jim King	8.50	4.25	2.50
75	Roy Sievers	12.00	6.00	3.50
76	Ray Crone	8.50	4.25	2.50
77	Harvey Haddix	12.00	6.00	3.50
78	Herman Wehmeier	8.50	4.25	2.50
79	Sandy Koufax	360.00	175.00	100.00
80	Gus Triandos	9.50	4.75	2.75
81	Wally Westlake	8.50	4.25	2.50
82	Bill Renna	8.50	4.25	2.50
83	Karl Spooner	10.00	5.00	3.00
84	Babe Birrer	8.50	4.25	2.50
85a	Indians Team (with date)	75.00	37.00	22.00
85b	Indians Team (no date, name centered)	24.00	12.00	7.25
85c	Indians Team (no date, name at left)	35.00	17.50	10.50
86	Ray Jablonski	8.50	4.25	2.50
87	Dean Stone	8.50	4.25	2.50
88	Johnny Kucks	10.00	5.00	3.00
89	Norm Zauchin	8.50	4.25	2.50
90a	Redlegs Team (with date)	75.00	37.00	22.00
90b	Redlegs Team (no date, name centered)	24.00	12.00	7.25

90c	Redlegs Team (no date, name at left)	35.00	17.50	10.50
91	Gail Harris	8.50	4.25	2.50
92	"Red" Wilson	8.50	4.25	2.50
93	George Susce, Jr.	8.50	4.25	2.50
94	Ronnie Kline	8.50	4.25	2.50
95a	Braves Team (with date)	75.00	37.00	22.00
95b	Braves Team (no date, name centered)	40.00	20.00	12.00
95c	Braves Team (no date, name at left)	45.00	22.00	13.50
96	Bill Tremel	8.50	4.25	2.50
97	Jerry Lynch	8.50	4.25	2.50
98	Camilo Pascual	9.00	4.50	2.75
99	Don Zimmer	15.00	7.50	4.50
100a	Orioles Team (with date)	40.00	20.00	12.00
100b	Orioles Team (no date, name centered)	32.50	16.00	9.75
100c	Orioles Team (no date, name at left)	32.50	16.00	9.75
101	Roy Campanella	130.00	65.00	39.00
102	Jim Davis	12.00	6.00	3.50
103	Willie Miranda	12.00	6.00	3.50
104	Bob Lennon	12.00	6.00	3.50
105	Al Smith	12.00	6.00	3.50
106	Joe Astroth	12.00	6.00	3.50
107	Eddie Mathews	50.00	25.00	15.00
108	Laurin Pepper	12.00	6.00	3.50
109	Enos Slaughter	30.00	15.00	9.00
110	Yogi Berra	120.00	60.00	36.00
111	Red Sox Team	35.00	17.50	10.50
112	Dee Fondy	12.00	6.00	3.50
113	Phil Rizzuto	55.00	27.00	16.50
114	Jim Owens	12.00	6.00	3.50
115	Jackie Jensen	15.00	7.50	4.50
116	Eddie O'Brien	12.00	6.00	3.50
117	Virgil Trucks	12.00	6.00	3.50
118	Nellie Fox	35.00	17.50	10.50
119	*Larry Jackson*	12.00	6.00	3.50
120	Richie Ashburn	35.00	17.50	10.50
121	Pirates Team	35.00	17.50	10.50
122	Willard Nixon	12.00	6.00	3.50
123	Roy McMillan	12.00	6.00	3.50
124	Don Kaiser	12.00	6.00	3.50
125	Minnie Minoso	20.00	10.00	6.00
126	Jim Brady	12.00	6.00	3.50
127	Willie Jones	12.00	6.00	3.50
128	Eddie Yost	12.00	6.00	3.50
129	Jake Martin	12.00	6.00	3.50
130	Willie Mays	350.00	175.00	105.00
131	Bob Roselli	12.00	6.00	3.50
132	Bobby Avila	12.00	6.00	3.50
133	Ray Narleski	12.00	6.00	3.50
134	Cardinals Team	28.00	14.00	8.50
135	Mickey Mantle	1125.	562.00	300.00
136	Johnny Logan	12.00	6.00	3.50
137	Al Silvera	12.00	6.00	3.50
138	Johnny Antonelli	12.00	6.00	3.50
139	Tommy Carroll	12.00	6.00	3.50
140	*Herb Score*	40.00	20.00	12.00
141	Joe Frazier	12.00	6.00	3.50
142	Gene Baker	12.00	6.00	3.50
143	Jim Piersall	12.00	6.00	3.50
144	Leroy Powell	12.00	6.00	3.50
145	Gil Hodges	50.00	25.00	15.00
146	Nationals Team	35.00	17.50	10.50
147	Earl Torgeson	12.00	6.00	3.50
148	Alvin Dark	12.00	6.00	3.50
149	Dixie Howell	12.00	6.00	3.50
150	Duke Snider	130.00	65.00	39.00
151	Spook Jacobs	12.00	6.00	3.50
152	Billy Hoeft	12.00	6.00	3.50
153	Frank J. Thomas	12.00	6.00	3.50
154	Dave Pope	12.00	6.00	3.50
155	Harvey Kuenn	18.00	9.00	5.50
156	Wes Westrum	12.00	6.00	3.50
157	Dick Brodowski	12.00	6.00	3.50
158	Wally Post	12.00	6.00	3.50
159	Clint Courtney	12.00	6.00	3.50
160	Billy Pierce	15.00	7.50	4.50
161	Joe DeMaestri	12.00	6.00	3.50
162	Gus Bell	12.00	6.00	3.50
163	Gene Woodling	14.00	7.00	4.25
164	Harmon Killebrew	125.00	62.00	37.00
165	Red Schoendienst	25.00	12.50	7.50
166	Dodgers Team	190.00	95.00	57.00
167	Harry Dorish	12.00	6.00	3.50
168	Sammy White	12.00	6.00	3.50
169	Bob Nelson	12.00	6.00	3.50
170	Bill Virdon	17.50	8.75	5.25
171	Jim Wilson	12.00	6.00	3.50
172	*Frank Torre*	12.00	6.00	3.50
173	Johnny Podres	17.50	8.75	5.25
174	Glen Gorbous	12.00	6.00	3.50
175	Del Crandall	12.00	6.00	3.50
176	Alex Kellner	12.00	6.00	3.50
177	Hank Bauer	15.00	7.50	4.50
178	Joe Black	12.00	6.00	3.50
179	Harry Chiti	12.00	6.00	3.50
180	Robin Roberts	30.00	15.00	9.00
181	Billy Martin	85.00	42.00	25.00
182	Paul Minner	17.50	8.75	5.25
183	Stan Lopata	17.50	8.75	5.25
184	Don Bessent	20.00	10.00	6.00
185	Bill Bruton	17.50	8.75	5.25
186	Ron Jackson	17.50	8.75	5.25
187	Early Wynn	35.00	17.50	10.50
188	White Sox Team	35.00	17.50	10.50
189	Ned Garver	17.50	8.75	5.25
190	Carl Furillo	25.00	12.50	7.50
191	Frank Lary	17.50	8.75	5.25
192	Smoky Burgess	17.50	8.75	5.25
193	Wilmer Mizell	17.50	8.75	5.25
194	Monte Irvin	32.50	16.00	9.75
195	George Kell	32.50	16.00	9.75
196	Tom Poholsky	17.50	8.75	5.25
197	Granny Hamner	17.50	8.75	5.25
198	Ed Fitzgerald (Fitz Gerald)	17.50	8.75	5.25
199	Hank Thompson	17.50	8.75	5.25
200	Bob Feller	115.00	55.00	32.50
201	Rip Repulski	17.50	8.75	5.25
202	Jim Hearn	17.50	8.75	5.25
203	Bill Tuttle	17.50	8.75	5.25
204	Art Swanson	17.50	8.75	5.25
205	"Whitey" Lockman	17.50	8.75	5.25
206	Erv Palica	17.50	8.75	5.25
207	Jim Small	17.50	8.75	5.25
208	Elston Howard	35.00	17.50	10.50
209	Max Surkont	17.50	8.75	5.25
210	Mike Garcia	17.50	8.75	5.25
211	Murry Dickson	17.50	8.75	5.25
212	Johnny Temple	17.50	8.75	5.25
213	Tigers Team	55.00	27.00	16.50
214	Bob Rush	17.50	8.75	5.25
215	Tommy Byrne	20.00	10.00	6.00
216	Jerry Schoonmaker	17.50	8.75	5.25
217	Billy Klaus	17.50	8.75	5.25
218	Joe Nuxall (Nuxhall)	20.00	10.00	6.00
219	Lew Burdette	19.00	9.50	5.75
220	Del Ennis	17.50	8.75	5.25
221	Bob Friend	17.50	8.75	5.25
222	Dave Philley	17.50	8.75	5.25
223	Randy Jackson	20.00	10.00	6.00
224	Bud Podbielan	17.50	8.75	5.25
225	Gil McDougald	27.50	13.50	8.25
226	Giants Team	65.00	32.00	19.50
227	Russ Meyer	17.50	8.75	5.25
228	Mickey Vernon	17.50	8.75	5.25
229	Harry Brecheen	17.50	8.75	5.25
230	Chico Carrasquel	19.00	9.50	5.75
231	Bob Hale	17.50	8.75	5.25
232	Toby Atwell	17.50	8.75	5.25
233	Carl Erskine	26.00	13.00	8.00
234	Pete Runnels	17.50	8.75	5.25
235	Don Newcombe	40.00	20.00	12.00
236	Athletics Team	35.00	17.50	10.50
237	Jose Valdivielso	17.50	8.75	5.25
238	Walt Dropo	17.50	8.75	5.25
239	Harry Simpson	17.50	8.75	5.25
240	Whitey Ford	120.00	60.00	36.00
241	Don Mueller	17.50	8.75	5.25
242	Hershell Freeman	17.50	8.75	5.25
243	Sherm Lollar	17.50	8.75	5.25
244	Bob Buhl	17.50	8.75	5.25
245	Billy Goodman	17.50	8.75	5.25
246	Tom Gorman	17.50	8.75	5.25
247	Bill Sarni	17.50	8.75	5.25
248	Bob Porterfield	17.50	8.75	5.25
249	Johnny Klippstein	17.50	8.75	5.25
250	Larry Doby	22.00	11.00	6.50
251	Yankees Team	185.00	92.00	55.00
252	Vernon Law	17.50	8.75	5.25
253	Irv Noren	22.00	11.00	6.50
254	George Crowe	17.50	8.75	5.25
255	Bob Lemon	35.00	17.50	10.50
256	Tom Hurd	17.50	8.75	5.25
257	Bobby Thomson	21.00	10.50	6.25
258	Art Ditmar	17.50	8.75	5.25
259	Sam Jones	17.50	8.75	5.25
260	Pee Wee Reese	125.00	62.00	37.00
261	Bobby Shantz	15.00	7.50	4.50
262	Howie Pollet	12.00	6.00	3.50
263	Bob Miller	12.00	6.00	3.50
264	Ray Monzant	12.00	6.00	3.50
265	Sandy Consuegra	12.00	6.00	3.50
266	Don Ferrarese	12.00	6.00	3.50
267	Bob Nieman	12.00	6.00	3.50
268	Dale Mitchell	12.00	6.00	3.50
269	Jack Meyer	12.00	6.00	3.50
270	Billy Loes	19.00	9.50	5.75
271	Foster Castleman	12.00	6.00	3.50
272	Danny O'Connell	12.00	6.00	3.50
273	Walker Cooper	12.00	6.00	3.50
274	Frank Baumholtz	12.00	6.00	3.50
275	Jim Greengrass	12.00	6.00	3.50
276	George Zuverink	12.00	6.00	3.50
277	Daryl Spencer	12.00	6.00	3.50
278	Chet Nichols	12.00	6.00	3.50
279	Johnny Groth	12.00	6.00	3.50
280	Jim Gilliam	27.50	13.50	8.25
281	Art Houtteman	12.00	6.00	3.50
282	Warren Hacker	12.00	6.00	3.50
283	Hal Smith	12.00	6.00	3.50
284	Ike Delock	12.00	6.00	3.50
285	Eddie Miksis	12.00	6.00	3.50
286	Bill Wight	12.00	6.00	3.50
287	Bobby Adams	12.00	6.00	3.50
288	Bob Cerv	29.00	14.50	8.75
289	Hal Jeffcoat	12.00	6.00	3.50
290	Curt Simmons	12.00	6.00	3.50
291	Frank Kellert	12.00	6.00	3.50
292	*Luis Aparicio*	120.00	60.00	36.00
293	Stu Miller	12.00	6.00	3.50
294	Ernie Johnson	12.00	6.00	3.50
295	Clem Labine	20.00	10.00	6.00
296	Andy Seminick	12.00	6.00	3.50
297	Bob Skinner	12.00	6.00	3.50
298	Johnny Schmitz	12.00	6.00	3.50
299	Charley Neal	25.00	12.50	7.50
300	Vic Wertz	12.00	6.00	3.50
301	Marv Grissom	12.00	6.00	3.50
302	Eddie Robinson	20.00	10.00	6.00
303	Jim Dyck	12.00	6.00	3.50
304	Frank Malzone	12.00	6.00	3.50
305	Brooks Lawrence	12.00	6.00	3.50
306	Curt Roberts	12.00	6.00	3.50
307	Hoyt Wilhelm	28.00	14.00	8.50
308	Chuck Harmon	12.00	6.00	3.50
309	*Don Blasingame*	12.00	6.00	3.50
310	Steve Gromek	12.00	6.00	3.50
311	Hal Naragon	12.00	6.00	3.50
312	Andy Pafko	12.00	6.00	3.50
313	Gene Stephens	12.00	6.00	3.50
314	Hobie Landrith	12.00	6.00	3.50
315	Milt Bolling	12.00	6.00	3.50
316	Jerry Coleman	22.50	11.00	6.75
317	Al Aber	12.00	6.00	3.50
318	Fred Hatfield	12.00	6.00	3.50
319	Jack Crimian	12.00	6.00	3.50
320	Joe Adcock	12.00	6.00	3.50
321	Jim Konstanty	20.00	10.00	6.00
322	Karl Olson	12.00	6.00	3.50
323	Willard Schmidt	12.00	6.00	3.50
324	"Rocky" Bridges	12.00	6.00	3.50
325	Don Liddle	12.00	6.00	3.50
326	Connie Johnson	12.00	6.00	3.50
327	Bob Wiesler	12.00	6.00	3.50
328	Preston Ward	12.00	6.00	3.50
329	Lou Berberet	12.00	6.00	3.50
330	Jim Busby	12.00	6.00	3.50
331	Dick Hall	12.00	6.00	3.50
332	Don Larsen	42.50	21.00	12.50
333	Rube Walker	20.00	10.00	6.00
334	Bob Miller	12.00	6.00	3.50
335	Don Hoak	12.00	6.00	3.50
336	Ellis Kinder	12.00	6.00	3.50
337	Bobby Morgan	12.00	6.00	3.50
338	Jim Delsing	12.00	6.00	3.50
339	Rance Pless	12.00	6.00	3.50
340	Mickey McDermott	42.50	15.00	7.50
----	Checklist 1/3	200.00	100.00	60.00
----	Checklist 2/4	200.00	100.00	60.00

1956 Topps Hocus Focus Large

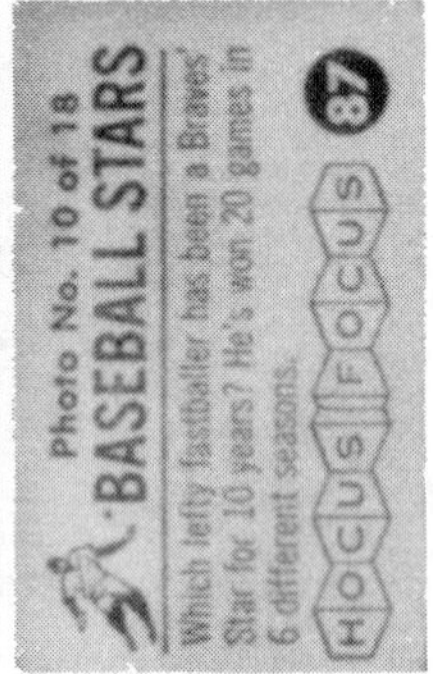

These sets are a direct descendant of the 1948 "Topps Magic Photo" issue. Again, the baseball players were part of a larger overall series covering several topical areas. There are two distinct issues of Hocus Focus cards in 1956. The "large" cards, measuring 1" by 1-5/8," consists of 18 players. The "small" cards, 7/8 by 1-3/8," state on the back that they are a series of 23, though only 13 are known. Besides players on the cards themselves, the easiest way to distinguish Hocus Focus cards of 1956 from the Magic Photos series of 1948 is to remember that the 1956 cards actually have the words "Hocus Focus" on the back. The photos on these cards were developed by wetting the cards surface and exposing to light. Prices below are for cards with well- developed pictures. Cards with poorly developed photos are worth significantly less.

		NR MT	EX	VG
Complete Set (18):		3000.	1500.	900.00
Common Player:		90.00	45.00	27.00
1	Dick Groat	195.00	97.00	58.00
2	Ed Lopat	125.00	62.00	37.00
3	Hank Sauer	90.00	45.00	27.00
4	"Dusty" Rhodes	90.00	45.00	27.00
5	Ted Williams	800.00	400.00	240.00
6	Harvey Haddix	90.00	45.00	27.00
7	Ray Boone	90.00	45.00	27.00
8	Al Rosen	125.00	62.00	37.00
9	Mayo Smith	90.00	45.00	27.00
10	Warren Spahn	300.00	150.00	90.00
11	Jim Rivera	90.00	45.00	27.00
12	Ted Kluszewski	195.00	97.00	58.00
13	Gus Zernial	90.00	45.00	27.00
14	Jackie Robinson	800.00	400.00	240.00
15	Hal Smith	90.00	45.00	27.00
16	Johnny Schmitz	90.00	45.00	27.00
17	"Spook" Jacobs	90.00	45.00	27.00
18	Mel Parnell	90.00	45.00	27.00

1956 Topps Hocus Focus Small

		NR MT	EX	VG
Complete Set (13):		3300.	1650.	990.00
Common Player:		85.00	42.00	25.00
1	Babe Ruth	950.00	475.00	285.00
2	Unknown			
3	Dick Groat	125.00	62.00	37.00
4	Unknown			
5	Unknown			
6	"Dusty" Rhodes	85.00	42.00	25.00
7	Ted Williams	800.00	400.00	240.00
8	Harvey Haddix	85.00	42.00	25.00

9	Ray Boone	85.00	42.00	25.00
10	Unknown			
11	Unknown			
12	Warren Spahn	300.00	150.00	90.00
13	Jim Rivera	85.00	42.00	25.00
14	Ted Kluszewski	195.00	97.00	58.00
15	Gus Zernial	85.00	42.00	25.00
16	Unknown			
17	Unknown			
18	Johnny Schmitz	85.00	42.00	25.00
19	Unknown			
20	Karl Spooner	125.00	62.00	37.00
21	Ed Mathews	325.00	162.00	97.00
22	Unknown			
23	Unknown			

1956 Topps Pins

One of Topps first specialty issues, the 60-pin set of ballplayers issued in 1956 contains a high percentage of big-name stars which, combined with the scarcity of the pins, makes collecting a complete set extremely challenging. Compounding the situation is the fact that some pins are seen far less often than others, though the reason is unknown. Chuck Stobbs, Hector Lopez and Chuck Diering are unaccountably scarce. Measuring 1-1/8" in diameter, the pins utilize the same portraits found on 1956 Topps baseball cards. The photos are set against a solid color background.

		NR MT	EX	VG
Complete Set (60):		2750.	1350.	825.00
Common Player:		17.50	8.75	5.25
(1)	Hank Aaron	120.00	60.00	35.00
(2)	Sandy Amoros	17.50	8.75	5.25
(3)	Luis Arroyo	17.50	8.75	5.25
(4)	Ernie Banks	60.00	30.00	18.00
(5)	Yogi Berra	80.00	40.00	24.00
(6)	Joe Black	17.50	8.75	5.25
(7)	Ray Boone	17.50	8.75	5.25
(8)	Ken Boyer	20.00	10.00	6.00
(9)	Joe Collins	17.50	8.75	5.25
(10)	Gene Conley	17.50	8.75	5.25
(11)	Chuck Diering	225.00	112.00	67.00
(12)	Dick Donovan	17.50	8.75	5.25
(13)	Jim Finigan	17.50	8.75	5.25
(14)	Art Fowler	17.50	8.75	5.25
(15)	Ruben Gomez	17.50	8.75	5.25
(16)	Dick Groat	20.00	10.00	6.00
(17)	Harvey Haddix	17.50	8.75	5.25
(18)	Jack Harshman	17.50	8.75	5.25
(19)	Grady Hatton	17.50	8.75	5.25
(20)	Jim Hegan	17.50	8.75	5.25
(21)	Gil Hodges	40.00	20.00	12.00
(22)	Bobby Hofman	17.50	8.75	5.25
(23)	Frank House	17.50	8.75	5.25
(24)	Jackie Jensen	20.00	10.00	6.00
(25)	Al Kaline	65.00	32.00	19.50
(26)	Bob Kennedy	17.50	8.75	5.25
(27)	Ted Kluszewski	25.00	12.50	7.50
(28)	Dale Long	17.50	8.75	5.25
(29)	Hector Lopez	200.00	100.00	60.00
(30)	Ed Mathews	50.00	25.00	15.00
(31)	Willie Mays	120.00	60.00	35.00
(32)	Roy McMillan	17.50	8.75	5.25
(33)	Willie Miranda	17.50	8.75	5.25
(34)	Wally Moon	17.50	8.75	5.25
(35)	Don Mossi	17.50	8.75	5.25
(36)	Ron Negray	17.50	8.75	5.25
(37)	Johnny O'Brien	17.50	8.75	5.25
(38)	Carlos Paula	17.50	8.75	5.25
(39)	Vic Power	17.50	8.75	5.25
(40)	Jim Rivera	17.50	8.75	5.25
(41)	Phil Rizzuto	40.00	20.00	12.00
(42)	Jackie Robinson	100.00	50.00	30.00
(43)	Al Rosen	25.00	12.50	7.50
(44)	Hank Sauer	17.50	8.75	5.25
(45)	Roy Sievers	17.50	8.75	5.25
(46)	Bill Skowron	20.00	10.00	6.00
(47)	Al Smith	17.50	8.75	5.25
(48)	Hal Smith	17.50	8.75	5.25
(49)	Mayo Smith	17.50	8.75	5.25
(50)	Duke Snider	75.00	37.00	22.00
(51)	Warren Spahn	60.00	30.00	18.00
(52)	Karl Spooner	17.50	8.75	5.25
(53)	Chuck Stobbs	175.00	87.00	52.00
(54)	Frank Sullivan	17.50	8.75	5.25
(55)	Bill Tremel	17.50	8.75	5.25
(56)	Gus Triandos	17.50	8.75	5.25
(57)	Bob Turley	20.00	10.00	6.00
(58)	Herman Wehmeier	17.50	8.75	5.25
(59)	Ted Williams	125.00	62.50	37.50
(60)	Gus Zernial	17.50	8.75	5.25

1957 Topps

For 1957, Topps reduced the size of its cards to the now-standard 2-1/2" by 3-1/2." Set size was increased to 407 cards. Another change came in the form of the use of real color photographs as opposed to the hand-colored black and whites of previous years. For the first time since 1954, there were also cards with more than one player. The two, "Dodger Sluggers" and "Yankees' Power Hitters" began a trend toward the increased use of mulitple-player cards. Another first-time innovation, found on the backs, is complete players statistics. The scarce cards in the set are not the highest numbers, but rather numbers 265-352. Four unnumbered checklist cards were issued along with the set. They are quite expensive and are not included in the complete set prices quoted below.

		NR MT	EX	VG
Complete Set (407):		7500.	3750.	2250.
Common Player (1-176):		7.50	3.75	2.25
Common Player (177-264):		5.00	2.50	1.50
Common Player (265-352):		18.00	9.00	5.50
Common Player (353-407):		7.50	3.75	2.25
1	Ted Williams	400.00	200.00	120.00
2	Yogi Berra	115.00	55.00	32.50
3	Dale Long	7.50	3.75	2.25
4	Johnny Logan	7.50	3.75	2.25
5	Sal Maglie	9.00	4.50	2.75
6	Hector Lopez	7.50	3.75	2.25
7	Luis Aparicio	35.00	17.50	10.50
8	Don Mossi	7.50	3.75	2.25
9	Johnny Temple	7.50	3.75	2.25
10	Willie Mays	200.00	75.00	45.00
11	George Zuverink	7.50	3.75	2.25
12	Dick Groat	8.00	4.00	2.50
13	Wally Burnette	7.50	3.75	2.25
14	Bob Nieman	7.50	3.75	2.25
15	Robin Roberts	25.00	12.50	7.50
16	Walt Moryn	7.50	3.75	2.25
17	Billy Gardner	7.50	3.75	2.25
18	*Don Drysdale*	240.00	120.00	72.50
19	Bob Wilson	7.50	3.75	2.25
20	Hank Aaron (negative reversed)	200.00	100.00	60.00
21	Frank Sullivan	7.50	3.75	2.25
22	Jerry Snyder (photo actually Ed Fitz Gerald)	7.50	3.75	2.25
23	Sherm Lollar	7.50	3.75	2.25
24	*Bill Mazeroski*	65.00	32.00	19.50
25	Whitey Ford	55.00	27.00	16.50
26	Bob Boyd	7.50	3.75	2.25
27	Ted Kazanski	7.50	3.75	2.25
28	Gene Conley	7.50	3.75	2.25
29	*Whitey Herzog*	32.00	16.00	9.50
30	Pee Wee Reese	65.00	32.00	19.50
31	Ron Northey	7.50	3.75	2.25
32	Hersh Freeman	7.50	3.75	2.25
33	Jim Small	7.50	3.75	2.25
34	Tom Sturdivant	8.00	4.00	2.50
35	*Frank Robinson*	250.00	125.00	65.00
36	Bob Grim	8.00	4.00	2.50
37	Frank Torre	7.50	3.75	2.25
38	Nellie Fox	20.00	10.00	6.00
39	Al Worthington	7.50	3.75	2.25
40	Early Wynn	22.00	11.00	6.50
41	Hal Smith	7.50	3.75	2.25
42	Dee Fondy	7.50	3.75	2.25
43	Connie Johnson	7.50	3.75	2.25
44	Joe DeMaestri	7.50	3.75	2.25
45	Carl Furillo	12.50	6.25	3.75
46	Bob Miller	7.50	3.75	2.25
47	Don Blasingame	7.50	3.75	2.25
48	Bill Bruton	7.50	3.75	2.25
49	Daryl Spencer	7.50	3.75	2.25
50	Herb Score	7.50	3.75	2.25
51	Clint Courtney	7.50	3.75	2.25
52	Lee Walls	7.50	3.75	2.25
53	Clem Labine	8.00	4.00	2.50
54	Elmer Valo	7.50	3.75	2.25
55	Ernie Banks	110.00	55.00	33.00
56	Dave Sisler	7.50	3.75	2.25
57	Jim Lemon	7.50	3.75	2.25
58	Ruben Gomez	7.50	3.75	2.25
59	Dick Williams	8.00	4.00	2.50
60	Billy Hoeft	7.50	3.75	2.25
61	Dusty Rhodes	7.50	3.75	2.25
62	Billy Martin	45.00	22.00	13.50
63	Ike Delock	7.50	3.75	2.25
64	Pete Runnels	7.50	3.75	2.25
65	Wally Moon	7.50	3.75	2.25
66	Brooks Lawrence	7.50	3.75	2.25
67	Chico Carrasquel	7.50	3.75	2.25
68	Ray Crone	7.50	3.75	2.25
69	Roy McMillan	7.50	3.75	2.25
70	Richie Ashburn	25.00	12.50	7.50
71	Murry Dickson	7.50	3.75	2.25
72	Bill Tuttle	7.50	3.75	2.25
73	George Crowe	7.50	3.75	2.25
74	Vito Valentinetti	7.50	3.75	2.25
75	Jim Piersall	8.00	4.00	2.50
76	Roberto Clemente	215.00	107.00	64.00
77	Paul Foytack	7.50	3.75	2.25
78	Vic Wertz	7.50	3.75	2.25
79	*Lindy McDaniel*	8.00	4.00	2.50
80	Gil Hodges	47.50	24.00	14.00
81	Herm Wehmeier	7.50	3.75	2.25
82	Elston Howard	20.00	10.00	6.00
83	Lou Skizas	7.50	3.75	2.25
84	Moe Drabowsky	7.50	3.75	2.25
85	Larry Doby	10.00	5.00	3.00
86	Bill Sarni	7.50	3.75	2.25
87	Tom Gorman	7.50	3.75	2.25
88	Harvey Kuenn	8.00	4.00	2.50
89	Roy Sievers	7.50	3.75	2.25
90	Warren Spahn	60.00	30.00	18.00
91	Mack Burk	7.50	3.75	2.25
92	Mickey Vernon	7.50	3.75	2.25
93	Hal Jeffcoat	7.50	3.75	2.25
94	Bobby Del Greco	7.50	3.75	2.25
95	Mickey Mantle	1100.	550.00	225.00
96	*Hank Aguirre*	7.50	3.75	2.25
97	Yankees Team	60.00	30.00	18.00
98	Al Dark	8.00	4.00	2.50
99	Bob Keegan	7.50	3.75	2.25
100	League Presidents (Warren Giles, William Harridge)	9.00	4.50	2.75
101	Chuck Stobbs	7.50	3.75	2.25
102	Ray Boone	7.50	3.75	2.25
103	Joe Nuxhall	9.00	4.50	2.75
104	Hank Foiles	7.50	3.75	2.25
105	Johnny Antonelli	7.50	3.75	2.25
106	Ray Moore	7.50	3.75	2.25
107	Jim Rivera	7.50	3.75	2.25
108	Tommy Byrne	8.00	4.00	2.50
109	Hank Thompson	7.50	3.75	2.25
110	Bill Virdon	8.00	4.00	2.50
111	Hal Smith	7.50	3.75	2.25
112	Tom Brewer	7.50	3.75	2.25
113	Wilmer Mizell	7.50	3.75	2.25
114	Braves Team	15.00	7.50	4.50
115	Jim Gilliam	12.00	6.00	3.50
116	Mike Fornieles	7.50	3.75	2.25
117	Joe Adcock	7.50	3.75	2.25
118	Bob Porterfield	7.50	3.75	2.25
119	Stan Lopata	7.50	3.75	2.25
120	Bob Lemon	18.00	9.00	5.25
121	*Cletis Boyer*	15.00	7.50	4.50
122	Ken Boyer	8.00	4.00	2.50
123	Steve Ridzik	7.50	3.75	2.25
124	Dave Philley	7.50	3.75	2.25
125	Al Kaline	85.00	42.00	25.00
126	Bob Wiesler	7.50	3.75	2.25
127	Bob Buhl	7.50	3.75	2.25
128	Ed Bailey	7.50	3.75	2.25
129	Saul Rogovin	7.50	3.75	2.25
130	Don Newcombe	12.50	6.25	3.75
131	Milt Bolling	7.50	3.75	2.25
132	Art Ditmar	8.00	4.00	2.50
133	Del Crandall	8.00	4.00	2.50
134	Don Kaiser	7.50	3.75	2.25
135	Bill Skowron	13.50	6.75	4.00
136	Jim Hegan	7.50	3.75	2.25
137	Bob Rush	7.50	3.75	2.25
138	Minnie Minoso	8.00	4.00	2.50
139	Lou Kretlow	7.50	3.75	2.25
140	Frank J. Thomas	7.50	3.75	2.25
141	Al Aber	7.50	3.75	2.25
142	Charley Thompson	7.50	3.75	2.25
143	Andy Pafko	7.50	3.75	2.25
144	Ray Narleski	7.50	3.75	2.25
145	Al Smith	7.50	3.75	2.25
146	Don Ferrarese	7.50	3.75	2.25
147	Al Walker	8.00	4.00	2.50
148	Don Mueller	7.50	3.75	2.25
149	Bob Kennedy	7.50	3.75	2.25
150	Bob Friend	7.50	3.75	2.25
151	Willie Miranda	7.50	3.75	2.25
152	Jack Harshman	7.50	3.75	2.25
153	Karl Olson	7.50	3.75	2.25
154	Red Schoendienst	18.00	9.00	5.50
155	Jim Brosnan	7.50	3.75	2.25
156	Gus Triandos	7.50	3.75	2.25
157	Wally Post	7.50	3.75	2.25
158	Curt Simmons	7.50	3.75	2.25
159	Solly Drake	7.50	3.75	2.25
160	Billy Pierce	8.00	4.00	2.50
161	Pirates Team	12.50	6.25	3.75
162	Jack Meyer	7.50	3.75	2.25
163	Sammy White	7.50	3.75	2.25
164	Tommy Carroll	8.00	4.00	2.50
165	Ted Kluszewski	35.00	17.50	10.50
166	Roy Face	7.50	3.75	2.25
167	Vic Power	7.50	3.75	2.25
168	Frank Lary	7.50	3.75	2.25
169	Herb Plews	7.50	3.75	2.25
170	Duke Snider	90.00	45.00	27.00
171	Red Sox Team	12.00	6.00	3.50
172	Gene Woodling	7.50	3.75	2.25
173	Roger Craig	12.50	6.25	3.75
174	Willie Jones	7.50	3.75	2.25
175	Don Larsen	15.00	7.50	4.50
176	Gene Baker	7.50	3.75	2.25
177	Eddie Yost	5.00	2.50	1.50
178	Don Bessent	8.00	4.00	2.50

179	Ernie Oravetz	5.00	2.50	1.50
180	Gus Bell	5.00	2.50	1.50
181	Dick Donovan	5.00	2.50	1.50
182	Hobie Landrith	5.00	2.50	1.50
183	Cubs Team	15.00	7.50	4.50
184	*Tito Francona*	5.00	2.50	1.50
185	Johnny Kucks	8.00	4.00	2.50
186	Jim King	5.00	2.50	1.50
187	Virgil Trucks	5.00	2.50	1.50
188	Felix Mantilla	5.00	2.50	1.50
189	Willard Nixon	5.00	2.50	1.50
190	Randy Jackson	8.00	4.00	2.50
191	Joe Margoneri	5.00	2.50	1.50
192	Jerry Coleman	9.00	4.50	2.75
193	Del Rice	5.00	2.50	1.50
194	Hal Brown	5.00	2.50	1.50
195	Bobby Avila	5.00	2.50	1.50
196	Larry Jackson	5.00	2.50	1.50
197	Hank Sauer	5.00	2.50	1.50
198	Tigers Team	15.00	7.50	4.50
199	Vernon Law	5.00	2.50	1.50
200	Gil McDougald	15.00	7.50	4.50
201	Sandy Amoros	9.00	4.50	2.75
202	Dick Gernert	5.00	2.50	1.50
203	Hoyt Wilhelm	20.00	10.00	6.00
204	Athletics Team	15.00	7.50	4.50
205	Charley Maxwell	5.00	2.50	1.50
206	Willard Schmidt	5.00	2.50	1.50
207	Billy Hunter	5.00	2.50	1.50
208	Lew Burdette	5.00	2.50	1.50
209	Bob Skinner	5.00	2.50	1.50
210	Roy Campanella	100.00	50.00	30.00
211	Camilo Pascual	5.00	2.50	1.50
212	*Rocky Colavito*	125.00	62.50	37.50
213	Les Moss	5.00	2.50	1.50
214	Phillies Team	12.00	6.00	3.50
215	Enos Slaughter	22.00	11.00	6.50
216	Marv Grissom	5.00	2.50	1.50
217	Gene Stephens	5.00	2.50	1.50
218	Ray Jablonski	5.00	2.50	1.50
219	Tom Acker	5.00	2.50	1.50
220	Jackie Jensen	8.00	4.00	2.50
221	Dixie Howell	5.00	2.50	1.50
222	Alex Grammas	5.00	2.50	1.50
223	Frank House	5.00	2.50	1.50
224	Marv Blaylock	5.00	2.50	1.50
225	Harry Simpson	5.00	2.50	1.50
226	Preston Ward	5.00	2.50	1.50
227	Jerry Staley	5.00	2.50	1.50
228	Smoky Burgess	5.00	2.50	1.50
229	George Susce	5.00	2.50	1.50
230	George Kell	18.00	9.00	5.50
231	Solly Hemus	5.00	2.50	1.50
232	Whitey Lockman	5.00	2.50	1.50
233	Art Fowler	5.00	2.50	1.50
234	Dick Cole	5.00	2.50	1.50
235	Tom Poholsky	5.00	2.50	1.50
236	Joe Ginsberg	5.00	2.50	1.50
237	Foster Castleman	5.00	2.50	1.50
238	Eddie Robinson	5.00	2.50	1.50
239	Tom Morgan	5.00	2.50	1.50
240	Hank Bauer	10.00	5.00	3.00
241	Joe Lonnett	5.00	2.50	1.50
242	Charley Neal	8.00	4.00	2.50
243	Cardinals Team	15.00	7.50	4.50
244	Billy Loes	5.00	2.50	1.50
245	Rip Repulski	5.00	2.50	1.50
246	Jose Valdivielso	5.00	2.50	1.50
247	Turk Lown	5.00	2.50	1.50
248	Jim Finigan	5.00	2.50	1.50
249	Dave Pope	5.00	2.50	1.50
250	Eddie Mathews	40.00	20.00	12.00
251	Orioles Team	15.00	7.50	4.50
252	Carl Erskine	12.00	6.00	3.50
253	Gus Zernial	5.00	2.50	1.50
254	Ron Negray	5.00	2.50	1.50
255	Charlie Silvera	5.00	2.50	1.50
256	Ronnie Kline	5.00	2.50	1.50
257	Walt Dropo	5.00	2.50	1.50
258	Steve Gromek	5.00	2.50	1.50
259	Eddie O'Brien	5.00	2.50	1.50
260	Del Ennis	5.00	2.50	1.50
261	Bob Chakales	5.00	2.50	1.50
262	Bobby Thomson	5.00	2.50	1.50
263	George Strickland	5.00	2.50	1.50
264	Bob Turley	8.00	4.00	2.50
265	Harvey Haddix	20.00	10.00	6.00
266	Ken Kuhn	18.00	9.00	5.50
267	Danny Kravitz	18.00	9.00	5.50
268	Jackie Collum	18.00	9.00	5.50
269	Bob Cerv	18.00	9.00	5.50
270	Senators Team	30.00	15.00	9.00
271	Danny O'Connell	18.00	9.00	5.50
272	Bobby Shantz	27.50	13.50	8.25
273	Jim Davis	18.00	9.00	5.50
274	Don Hoak	18.00	9.00	5.50
275	Indians Team	40.00	20.00	12.00
276	Jim Pyburn	18.00	9.00	5.50
277	Johnny Podres	50.00	25.00	15.00
278	Fred Hatfield	18.00	9.00	5.50
279	Bob Thurman	18.00	9.00	5.50
280	Alex Kellner	18.00	9.00	5.50
281	Gail Harris	18.00	9.00	5.50
282	Jack Dittmer	18.00	9.00	5.50
283	*Wes Covington*	18.00	9.00	5.50
284	Don Zimmer	25.00	12.50	7.50
285	Ned Garver	18.00	9.00	5.50
286	*Bobby Richardson*	105.00	57.50	31.50
287	Sam Jones	18.00	9.00	5.50
288	Ted Lepcio	18.00	9.00	5.50
289	Jim Bolger	18.00	9.00	5.50
290	Andy Carey	22.00	11.00	6.50
291	Windy McCall	18.00	9.00	5.50
292	Billy Klaus	18.00	9.00	5.50
293	Ted Abernathy	18.00	9.00	5.50
294	Rocky Bridges	18.00	9.00	5.50
295	Joe Collins	22.00	11.00	6.50
296	Johnny Klippstein	18.00	9.00	5.50
297	Jack Crimian	18.00	9.00	5.50
298	Irv Noren	18.00	9.00	5.50
299	Chuck Harmon	18.00	9.00	5.50
300	Mike Garcia	18.00	9.00	5.50
301	Sam Esposito	18.00	9.00	5.50
302	Sandy Koufax	325.00	162.50	97.50
303	Billy Goodman	18.00	9.00	5.50
304	Joe Cunningham	18.00	9.00	5.50
305	Chico Fernandez	18.00	9.00	5.50
306	Darrell Johnson	22.00	11.00	6.50
307	Jack Phillips	18.00	9.00	5.50
308	Dick Hall	18.00	9.00	5.50
309	Jim Busby	18.00	9.00	5.50
310	Max Surkont	18.00	9.00	5.50
311	Al Pilarcik	18.00	9.00	5.50
312	*Tony Kubek*	95.00	47.00	28.00
313	Mel Parnell	18.00	9.00	5.50
314	Ed Bouchee	18.00	9.00	5.50
315	Lou Berberet	18.00	9.00	5.50
316	Billy O'Dell	18.00	9.00	5.50
317	Giants Team	60.00	30.00	18.00
318	Mickey McDermott	18.00	9.00	5.50
319	Gino Cimoli	20.00	10.00	6.00
320	Neil Chrisley	18.00	9.00	5.50
321	Red Murff	18.00	9.00	5.50
322	Redlegs Team	50.00	25.00	15.00
323	Wes Westrum	18.00	9.00	5.50
324	Dodgers Team	110.00	55.00	33.00
325	Frank Bolling	18.00	9.00	5.50
326	Pedro Ramos	18.00	9.00	5.50
327	Jim Pendleton	18.00	9.00	5.50
328	*Brooks Robinson*	325.00	160.00	95.00
329	White Sox Team	45.00	22.00	13.50
330	Jim Wilson	18.00	9.00	5.50
331	Ray Katt	18.00	9.00	5.50
332	Bob Bowman	18.00	9.00	5.50
333	Ernie Johnson	18.00	9.00	5.50
334	Jerry Schoonmaker	18.00	9.00	5.50
335	Granny Hamner	18.00	9.00	5.50
336	*Haywood Sullivan*	18.00	9.00	5.50
337	Rene Valdes	20.00	10.00	6.00
338	*Jim Bunning*	125.00	62.00	37.00
339	Bob Speake	18.00	9.00	5.50
340	Bill Wight	18.00	9.00	5.50
341	Don Gross	18.00	9.00	5.50
342	Gene Mauch	20.00	10.00	6.00
343	Taylor Phillips	18.00	9.00	5.50
344	Paul LaPalme	18.00	9.00	5.50
345	Paul Smith	18.00	9.00	5.50
346	Dick Littlefield	18.00	9.00	5.50
347	Hal Naragon	18.00	9.00	5.50
348	Jim Hearn	18.00	9.00	5.50
349	Nelson King	18.00	9.00	5.50
350	Eddie Miksis	18.00	9.00	5.50
351	Dave Hillman	18.00	9.00	5.50
352	Ellis Kinder	18.00	9.00	5.50
353	Cal Neeman	7.50	3.75	2.25
354	Rip Coleman	7.50	3.75	2.25
355	Frank Malzone	7.50	3.75	2.25
356	Faye Throneberry	7.50	3.75	2.25
357	Earl Torgeson	7.50	3.75	2.25
358	Jerry Lynch	7.50	3.75	2.25
359	Tom Cheney	7.50	3.75	2.25
360	Johnny Groth	7.50	3.75	2.25
361	Curt Barclay	7.50	3.75	2.25
362	Roman Mejias	7.50	3.75	2.25
363	Eddie Kasko	7.50	3.75	2.25
364	Cal McLish	7.50	3.75	2.25
365	Ossie Virgil	7.50	3.75	2.25
366	Ken Lehman	8.00	4.00	2.50
367	Ed Fitz Gerald	7.50	3.75	2.25
368	Bob Purkey	7.50	3.75	2.25
369	Milt Graff	7.50	3.75	2.25
370	Warren Hacker	7.50	3.75	2.25
371	Bob Lennon	7.50	3.75	2.25
372	Norm Zauchin	7.50	3.75	2.25
373	Pete Whisenant	7.50	3.75	2.25
374	Don Cardwell	7.50	3.75	2.25
375	*Jim Landis*	7.50	3.75	2.25
376	Don Elston	8.00	4.00	2.50
377	Andre Rodgers	7.50	3.75	2.25
378	Elmer Singleton	7.50	3.75	2.25
379	Don Lee	7.50	3.75	2.25
380	Walker Cooper	7.50	3.75	2.25
381	Dean Stone	7.50	3.75	2.25
382	Jim Brideweser	7.50	3.75	2.25
383	*Juan Pizarro*	7.50	3.75	2.25
384	Bobby Gene Smith	7.50	3.75	2.25
385	Art Houtteman	7.50	3.75	2.25
386	Lyle Luttrell	7.50	3.75	2.25
387	*Jack Sanford*	7.50	3.75	2.25
388	Pete Daley	7.50	3.75	2.25
389	Dave Jolly	7.50	3.75	2.25
390	Reno Bertoia	7.50	3.75	2.25
391	*Ralph Terry*	10.00	5.00	3.00
392	Chuck Tanner	7.50	3.75	2.25
393	Raul Sanchez	7.50	3.75	2.25
394	Luis Arroyo	7.50	3.75	2.25
395	Bubba Phillips	7.50	3.75	2.25
396	Casey Wise	7.50	3.75	2.25
397	Roy Smalley	7.50	3.75	2.25
398	Al Cicotte	7.50	3.75	2.25
399	Billy Consolo	7.50	3.75	2.25
400	Roy Campanella, Carl Furillo, Gil Hodges, Duke Snider)	200.00	100.00	60.00
401	*Earl Battey*	8.00	4.00	2.50
402	Jim Pisoni	7.50	3.75	2.25
403	Dick Hyde	7.50	3.75	2.25
404	Harry Anderson	7.50	3.75	2.25
405	Duke Maas	7.50	3.75	2.25
406	Bob Hale	7.50	3.75	2.25
407	Yankees' Power Hitters (Mickey Mantle, Yogi Berra)	350.00	175.00	105.00
----	Checklist Series 1-2 (Big Blony ad on back)	175.00	87.00	52.00
----	Checklist Series 1-2 (Bazooka ad on back)	175.00	87.00	52.00
----	Checklist Series 2-3 (Big Blony ad on back)	300.00	150.00	90.00
----	Checklist Series 2-3 (Bazooka ad on back)	300.00	150.00	90.00
----	Checklist Series 3-4 (Big Blony ad on back)	500.00	250.00	150.00
----	Checklist Series 3-4 (Bazooka ad on back)	500.00	250.00	150.00
----	Checklist Series 4-5 (Big Blony ad on back)	750.00	325.00	225.00
----	Checklist Series 4-5 (Bazooka ad on back)	750.00	325.00	225.00
----	Contest May 4	40.00	30.00	15.00
----	Contest May 25	40.00	30.00	15.00
----	Contest June 22	50.00	35.00	20.00
----	Contest July 19	60.00	40.00	20.00
----	Lucky Penny Insert Card	15.00	7.50	4.50

1958 Topps

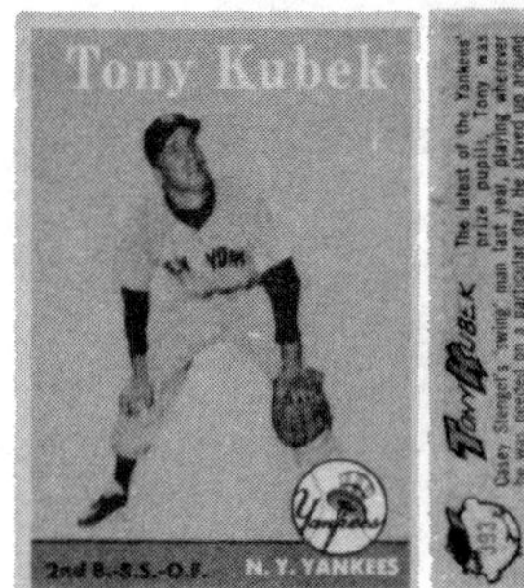

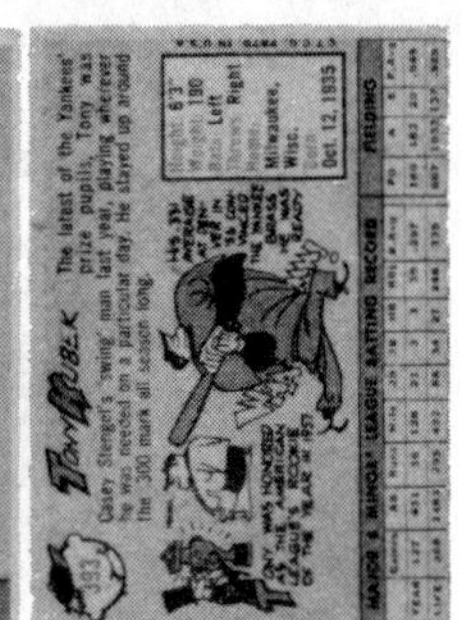

Topps continued to expand its set size in 1958 with the release of a 494-card set. One card (#145) was not issued after Ed Bouchee was suspended from baseball. Cards retained the 2-1/2" by 3-1/2" size. There are a number of variations, including yellow or white lettering on 33 cards between numbers 2-108 (higher priced yellow letter variations checklisted below are not included in the complete set prices). The number of multiple-player cards was increased. A major innovation is the addition of 20 "All-Star" cards. For the first time, checklists were incorporated into the numbered series, as the backs of team cards.

	NR MT	EX	VG
Complete Set (494):	5500.	2750.	1650.
Common Player (1-110):	7.50	3.75	2.25
Common Player (111-198):	6.50	3.25	2.00
Common Player (199-352):	5.50	2.75	1.65
Common Player (353-474):	4.00	2.00	1.25
Common Player (475-495):	5.50	2.75	1.65

1	Ted Williams	350.00	175.00	100.00
2a	Bob Lemon (yellow team letters)	35.00	17.50	10.50
2b	Bob Lemon (white team letters)	12.00	6.00	3.50
3	Alex Kellner	7.50	3.75	2.25
4	Hank Foiles	7.50	3.75	2.25
5	Willie Mays	195.00	95.00	55.00
6	George Zuverink	7.50	3.75	2.25
7	Dale Long	7.50	3.75	2.25
8a	Eddie Kasko (yellow name)	25.00	12.50	7.50
8b	Eddie Kasko (white name)	7.50	3.75	2.25
9	Hank Bauer	12.00	6.00	3.50
10	Lou Burdette	7.50	3.75	2.25
11a	Jim Rivera (yellow team letters)	25.00	12.50	7.50
11b	Jim Rivera (white team letters)	7.50	3.75	2.25
12	George Crowe	7.50	3.75	2.25
13a	Billy Hoeft (yellow name)	25.00	12.50	7.50
13b	Billy Hoeft (white name, orange triangle by foot)	7.50	3.75	2.25
13c	Billy Hoeft (white name, red triangle by foot)	7.50	3.75	2.25
14	Rip Repulski	7.50	3.75	2.25
15	Jim Lemon	7.50	3.75	2.25
16	Charley Neal	7.50	3.75	2.25
17	Felix Mantilla	7.50	3.75	2.25
18	Frank Sullivan	7.50	3.75	2.25
19	Giants Team/Checklist 1-88	22.00	11.00	6.50
20a	Gil McDougald (yellow name)	30.00	15.00	9.00
20b	Gil McDougald (white name)	9.00	4.50	2.75
21	Curt Barclay	7.50	3.75	2.25
22	Hal Naragon	7.50	3.75	2.25
23a	Bill Tuttle (yellow name)	25.00	12.50	7.50
23b	Bill Tuttle (white name)	7.50	3.75	2.25
24a	Hobie Landrith (yellow name)	25.00	12.50	7.50
24b	Hobie Landrith (white name)	7.50	3.75	2.25
25	Don Drysdale	75.00	37.00	22.00
26	Ron Jackson	7.50	3.75	2.25
27	Bud Freeman	7.50	3.75	2.25
28	Jim Busby	7.50	3.75	2.25
29	Ted Lepcio	7.50	3.75	2.25
30a	Hank Aaron (yellow name)	300.00	150.00	90.00
30b	Hank Aaron (white name)	175.00	87.00	52.00
31	Tex Clevenger	7.50	3.75	2.25
32a	J.W. Porter (yellow name)	25.00	12.50	7.50
32b	J.W. Porter (white name)	7.50	3.75	2.25
33a	Cal Neeman (yellow team letters)	25.00	12.50	7.50
33b	Cal Neeman (white team letters)	7.50	3.75	2.25
34	Bob Thurman	7.50	3.75	2.25
35a	Don Mossi (yellow team letters)	25.00	12.50	7.50
35b	Don Mossi (white team letters)	7.50	3.75	2.25
36	Ted Kazanski	7.50	3.75	2.25
37	*Mike McCormick* (photo actually Ray Monzant)	7.50	3.75	2.25
38	Dick Gernert	7.50	3.75	2.25
39	Bob Martyn	7.50	3.75	2.25
40	George Kell	15.00	7.50	4.50

41	Dave Hillman	7.50	3.75	2.25
42	*John Roseboro*	9.00	4.50	2.75
43	Sal Maglie	10.00	5.00	3.00
44	Senators Team/Checklist 1-88	15.00	7.50	4.50
45	Dick Groat	7.50	3.75	2.25
46a	Lou Sleater (yellow name)	25.00	12.50	7.50
46b	Lou Sleater (white name)	7.50	3.75	2.25
47	*Roger Maris*	415.00	200.00	120.00
48	Chuck Harmon	7.50	3.75	2.25
49	Smoky Burgess	7.50	3.75	2.25
50a	Billy Pierce (yellow team letters)	25.00	12.50	7.50
50b	Billy Pierce (white team letters)	7.50	3.75	2.25
51	Del Rice	7.50	3.75	2.25
52a	Roberto Clemente (yellow team letters)	375.00	185.00	110.00
52b	Roberto Clemente (white team letters)	225.00	112.00	55.00
53a	Morrie Martin (yellow name)	25.00	12.50	7.50
53b	Morrie Martin (white name)	7.50	3.75	2.25
54	*Norm Siebern*	9.00	4.50	2.75
55	Chico Carrasquel	7.50	3.75	2.25
56	Bill Fischer	7.50	3.75	2.25
57a	Tim Thompson (yellow name)	25.00	12.50	7.50
57b	Tim Thompson (white name)	7.50	3.75	2.25
58a	Art Schult (yellow team letters)	25.00	12.50	7.50
58b	Art Schult (white team letters)	7.50	3.75	2.25
59	Dave Sisler	7.50	3.75	2.25
60a	Del Ennis (yellow name)	25.00	12.50	7.50
60b	Del Ennis (white name)	7.50	3.75	2.25
61a	Darrell Johnson (yellow name)	30.00	15.00	9.00
61b	Darrell Johnson (white name)	9.00	4.50	2.75
62	Joe DeMaestri	7.50	3.75	2.25
63	Joe Nuxhall	7.50	3.75	2.25
64	Joe Lonnett	7.50	3.75	2.25
65a	Von McDaniel (yellow name)	25.00	12.50	7.50
65b	Von McDaniel (white name)	7.50	3.75	2.25
66	Lee Walls	7.50	3.75	2.25
67	Joe Ginsberg	7.50	3.75	2.25
68	Daryl Spencer	7.50	3.75	2.25
69	Wally Burnette	7.50	3.75	2.25
70a	Al Kaline (yellow name)	200.00	100.00	60.00
70b	Al Kaline (white name)	70.00	35.00	21.00
71	Dodgers Team	30.00	15.00	9.00
72	Bud Byerly	7.50	3.75	2.25
73	Pete Daley	7.50	3.75	2.25
74	Roy Face	7.50	3.75	2.25
75	Gus Bell	7.50	3.75	2.25
76a	Dick Farrell (yellow team letters)	25.00	12.50	7.50
76b	Dick Farrell (white team letters)	7.50	3.75	2.25
77a	Don Zimmer (yellow team letters)	30.00	15.00	9.00
77b	Don Zimmer (white team letters)	9.00	4.50	2.75
78a	Ernie Johnson (yellow name)	25.00	12.50	7.50
78b	Ernie Johnson (white name)	7.50	3.75	2.25
79a	Dick Williams (yellow team letters)	25.00	12.50	7.50
79b	Dick Williams (white team letters)	7.50	3.75	2.25
80	Dick Drott	7.50	3.75	2.25
81a	*Steve Boros* (yellow team letters)	25.00	12.50	7.50
81b	*Steve Boros* (white team letters)	7.50	3.75	2.25
82	Ronnie Kline	7.50	3.75	2.25
83	*Bob Hazle*	7.50	3.75	2.25
84	Billy O'Dell	7.50	3.75	2.25
85a	Luis Aparicio (yellow team letters)	60.00	30.00	18.00
85b	Luis Aparicio (white team letters)	25.00	12.50	7.50
86	Valmy Thomas	7.50	3.75	2.25
87	Johnny Kucks	8.00	4.00	2.50
88	Duke Snider	70.00	35.00	21.00
89	Billy Klaus	7.50	3.75	2.25
90	Robin Roberts	21.00	10.50	6.25
91	Chuck Tanner	7.50	3.75	2.25
92a	Clint Courtney (yellow name)	25.00	12.50	7.50
92b	Clint Courtney (white name)	7.50	3.75	2.25
93	Sandy Amoros	7.50	3.75	2.25
94	Bob Skinner	7.50	3.75	2.25
95	Frank Bolling	7.50	3.75	2.25
96	Joe Durham	7.50	3.75	2.25
97a	Larry Jackson (yellow name)	25.00	12.50	7.50
97b	Larry Jackson (white name)	7.50	3.75	2.25
98a	Billy Hunter (yellow name)	25.00	12.50	7.50
98b	Billy Hunter (white name)	7.50	3.75	2.25
99	Bobby Adams	7.50	3.75	2.25
100a	Early Wynn (yellow team letters)	40.00	20.00	12.00
100b	Early Wynn (white team letters)	17.50	8.75	5.25
101a	Bobby Richardson (yellow name)	45.00	22.00	13.50
101b	Bobby Richardson (white name)	18.00	9.00	5.50
102	George Strickland	7.50	3.75	2.25
103	Jerry Lynch	7.50	3.75	2.25
104	Jim Pendleton	7.50	3.75	2.25
105	Billy Gardner	7.50	3.75	2.25
106	Dick Schofield	7.50	3.75	2.25
107	Ossie Virgil	7.50	3.75	2.25
108a	Jim Landis (yellow team letters)	25.00	12.50	7.50
108b	Jim Landis (white team letters)	7.50	3.75	2.25
109	Herb Plews	7.50	3.75	2.25
110	Johnny Logan	7.50	3.75	2.25
111	Stu Miller	6.50	3.25	2.00
112	Gus Zernial	6.50	3.25	2.00
113	Jerry Walker	6.50	3.25	2.00
114	Irv Noren	6.50	3.25	2.00
115	Jim Bunning	25.00	12.50	7.50
116	Dave Philley	6.50	3.25	2.00
117	Frank Torre	6.50	3.25	2.00
118	Harvey Haddix	6.50	3.25	2.00
119	Harry Chiti	6.50	3.25	2.00
120	Johnny Podres	7.50	3.75	2.25
121	Eddie Miksis	6.50	3.25	2.00
122	Walt Moryn	6.50	3.25	2.00
123	Dick Tomanek	6.50	3.25	2.00
124	Bobby Usher	6.50	3.25	2.00
125	Al Dark	6.50	3.25	2.00
126	Stan Palys	6.50	3.25	2.00
127	Tom Sturdivant	7.50	3.75	2.25
128	*Willie Kirkland*	6.50	3.25	2.00
129	Jim Derrington	6.50	3.25	2.00
130	Jackie Jensen	7.50	3.75	2.25
131	Bob Henrich	6.50	3.25	2.00
132	Vernon Law	6.50	3.25	2.00
133	Russ Nixon	6.50	3.25	2.00
134	Phillies Team/Checklist 89-176	12.00	6.00	3.50
135	Mike Drabowsky	6.50	3.25	2.00
136	Jim Finingan	6.50	3.25	2.00
137	Russ Kemmerer	6.50	3.25	2.00
138	Earl Torgeson	6.50	3.25	2.00
139	George Brunet	6.50	3.25	2.00
140	Wes Covington	6.50	3.25	2.00
141	Ken Lehman	6.50	3.25	2.00
142	Enos Slaughter	25.00	12.50	7.50
143	Billy Muffett	6.50	3.25	2.00
144	Bobby Morgan	6.50	3.25	2.00
145	Not Issued			
146	Dick Gray	6.50	3.25	2.00
147	*Don McMahon*	6.50	3.25	2.00
148	Billy Consolo	6.50	3.25	2.00
149	Tom Acker	6.50	3.25	2.00
150	Mickey Mantle	600.00	300.00	160.00
151	Buddy Pritchard	6.50	3.25	2.00
152	Johnny Antonelli	6.50	3.25	2.00
153	Les Moss	6.50	3.25	2.00
154	Harry Byrd	6.50	3.25	2.00
155	Hector Lopez	6.50	3.25	2.00
156	Dick Hyde	6.50	3.25	2.00
157	Dee Fondy	6.50	3.25	2.00
158	Indians Team/Checklist 177-264	12.50	6.25	3.75
159	Taylor Phillips	6.50	3.25	2.00
160	Don Hoak	6.50	3.25	2.00
161	Don Larsen	9.00	4.50	2.75
162	Gil Hodges	25.00	12.50	7.50
163	Jim Wilson	6.50	3.25	2.00
164	Bob Taylor	6.50	3.25	2.00
165	Bob Nieman	6.50	3.25	2.00
166	Danny O'Connell	6.50	3.25	2.00
167	Frank Baumann	6.50	3.25	2.00
168	Joe Cunningham	6.50	3.25	2.00
169	Ralph Terry	6.50	3.25	2.00
170	Vic Wertz	6.50	3.25	2.00
171	Harry Anderson	6.50	3.25	2.00
172	Don Gross	6.50	3.25	2.00
173	Eddie Yost	6.50	3.25	2.00
174	A's Team/Checklist 89-176	12.00	6.00	3.50
175	*Marv Throneberry*	12.00	6.00	3.50
176	Bob Buhl	6.50	3.25	2.00
177	Al Smith	6.50	3.25	2.00
178	Ted Kluszewski	9.00	4.50	2.75
179	Willy Miranda	6.50	3.25	2.00
180	Lindy McDaniel	6.50	3.25	2.00
181	Willie Jones	6.50	3.25	2.00
182	Joe Caffie	6.50	3.25	2.00
183	Dave Jolly	6.50	3.25	2.00
184	Elvin Tappe	6.50	3.25	2.00
185	Ray Boone	6.50	3.25	2.00
186	Jack Meyer	6.50	3.25	2.00
187	Sandy Koufax	180.00	90.00	54.00
188	Milt Bolling (photo actually Lou Berberet)	6.50	3.25	2.00
189	George Susce	6.50	3.25	2.00
190	Red Schoendienst	17.50	8.75	5.25
191	Art Ceccarelli	6.50	3.25	2.00
192	Milt Graff	6.50	3.25	2.00
193	*Jerry Lumpe*	7.00	3.50	2.00
194	Roger Craig	8.00	4.00	2.50
195	Whitey Lockman	6.50	3.25	2.00
196	Mike Garcia	6.50	3.25	2.00
197	Haywood Sullivan	6.50	3.25	2.00
198	Bill Virdon	6.50	3.25	2.00
199	Don Blasingame	5.50	2.75	1.75
200	Bob Keegan	5.50	2.75	1.75
201	Jim Bolger	5.50	2.75	1.75
202	*Woody Held*	5.50	2.75	1.75
203	Al Walker	5.50	2.75	1.75
204	Leo Kiely	5.50	2.75	1.75
205	Johnny Temple	5.50	2.75	1.75
206	Bob Shaw	5.50	2.75	1.75
207	Solly Hemus	5.50	2.75	1.75
208	Cal McLish	5.50	2.75	1.75
209	Bob Anderson	5.50	2.75	1.75
210	Wally Moon	5.50	2.75	1.75
211	Pete Burnside	5.50	2.75	1.75
212	Bubba Phillips	5.50	2.75	1.75
213	Red Wilson	5.50	2.75	1.75
214	Willard Schmidt	5.50	2.75	1.75
215	Jim Gilliam	7.50	3.75	2.25
216	Cards Team/Checklist 177-264	13.50	6.75	4.00
217	Jack Harshman	5.50	2.75	1.75
218	Dick Rand	5.50	2.75	1.75
219	Camilo Pascual	5.50	2.75	1.75
220	Tom Brewer	5.50	2.75	1.75
221	Jerry Kindall	5.50	2.75	1.75
222	Bud Daley	5.50	2.75	1.75
223	Andy Pafko	5.50	2.75	1.75
224	Bob Grim	8.00	4.00	2.50
225	Billy Goodman	5.50	2.75	1.75
226	Bob Smith (photo actually Bobby Gene Smith)	5.50	2.75	1.75
227	Gene Stephens	5.50	2.75	1.75
228	Duke Maas	5.50	2.75	1.75
229	Frank Zupo	5.50	2.75	1.75
230	Richie Ashburn	12.00	6.00	3.50
231	Lloyd Merritt	5.50	2.75	1.75
232	Reno Bertoia	5.50	2.75	1.75
233	Mickey Vernon	5.50	2.75	1.75
234	Carl Sawatski	5.50	2.75	1.75
235	Tom Gorman	5.50	2.75	1.75
236	Ed Fitz Gerald	5.50	2.75	1.75
237	Bill Wight	5.50	2.75	1.75
238	Bill Mazeroski	15.00	7.50	4.50
239	Chuck Stobbs	5.50	2.75	1.75
240	Moose Skowron	10.00	5.00	3.00
241	Dick Littlefield	5.50	2.75	1.75
242	Johnny Klippstein	5.50	2.75	1.75
243	Larry Raines	5.50	2.75	1.75
244	*Don Demeter*	5.50	2.75	1.75
245	*Frank Lary*	5.50	2.75	1.75
246	Yankees Team	40.00	20.00	12.00
247	Casey Wise	5.50	2.75	1.75
248	Herm Wehmeier	5.50	2.75	1.75
249	Ray Moore	5.50	2.75	1.75
250	Roy Sievers	5.50	2.75	1.75
251	Warren Hacker	5.50	2.75	1.75
252	Bob Trowbridge	5.50	2.75	1.75
253	Don Mueller	5.50	2.75	1.75
254	Alex Grammas	5.50	2.75	1.75
255	Bob Turley	7.00	3.50	2.00
256	White Sox Team/Checklist 265-352	12.00	6.00	3.50
257	Hal Smith	5.50	2.75	1.75
258	Carl Erskine	7.00	3.50	2.00
259	Al Pilarcik	5.50	2.75	1.75
260	Frank Malzone	5.50	2.75	1.75
261	Turk Lown	5.50	2.75	1.75
262	Johnny Groth	5.50	2.75	1.75
263	Eddie Bressoud	5.50	2.75	1.75
264	Jack Sanford	5.50	2.75	1.75
265	Pete Runnels	5.50	2.75	1.75
266	Connie Johnson	5.50	2.75	1.75
267	Sherm Lollar	5.50	2.75	1.75
268	Granny Hamner	5.50	2.75	1.75
269	Paul Smith	5.50	2.75	1.75
270	Warren Spahn	45.00	22.00	13.50
271	Billy Martin	12.00	6.00	3.50
272	Ray Crone	5.50	2.75	1.75
273	Hal Smith	5.50	2.75	1.75
274	Rocky Bridges	5.50	2.75	1.75
275	Elston Howard	8.00	4.00	2.50
276	Bobby Avila	5.50	2.75	1.75
277	Virgil Trucks	5.50	2.75	1.75
278	Mack Burk	5.50	2.75	1.75
279	Bob Boyd	5.50	2.75	1.75
280	Jim Piersall	6.00	3.00	1.75
281	Sam Taylor	5.50	2.75	1.75
282	Paul Foytack	5.50	2.75	1.75
283	Ray Shearer	5.50	2.75	1.75
284	Ray Katt	5.50	2.75	1.75
285	Frank Robinson	75.00	37.00	22.00
286	Gino Cimoli	5.50	2.75	1.75
287	Sam Jones	5.50	2.75	1.75
288	Harmon Killebrew	70.00	35.00	21.00
289	Series Hurling Rivals (Lou Burdette, Bobby Shantz)	8.00	4.00	2.50
290	Dick Donovan	5.50	2.75	1.75
291	Don Landrum	5.50	2.75	1.75
292	Ned Garver	5.50	2.75	1.75
293	Gene Freese	5.50	2.75	1.75
294	Hal Jeffcoat	5.50	2.75	1.75
295	Minnie Minoso	7.00	3.50	2.00
296	*Ryne Duren*	12.00	6.00	3.50
297	Don Buddin	5.50	2.75	1.75
298	Jim Hearn	5.50	2.75	1.75
299	Harry Simpson	7.00	3.50	2.00
300	League Presidents (Warren Giles, William Harridge)	9.00	4.50	2.75
301	Randy Jackson	5.50	2.75	1.75
302	Mike Baxes	5.50	2.75	1.75
303	Neil Chrisley	5.50	2.75	1.75
304	Tigers' Big Bats (Al Kaline, Harvey Kuenn)	17.50	8.75	5.25
305	Clem Labine	7.00	3.50	2.00
306	Whammy Douglas	5.50	2.75	1.75
307	Brooks Robinson	90.00	45.00	27.00
308	Paul Giel	5.50	2.75	1.75
309	Gail Harris	5.50	2.75	1.75
310	Ernie Banks	80.00	40.00	24.00
311	Bob Purkey	5.50	2.75	1.75
312	Red Sox Team	12.00	6.00	3.50
313	Bob Rush	5.50	2.75	1.75
314	Dodgers' Boss & Power (Duke Snider, Walter Alston)	17.50	8.75	5.25
315	Bob Friend	5.50	2.75	1.75
316	Tito Francona	5.50	2.75	1.75
317	*Albie Pearson*	6.00	3.00	1.75
318	Frank House	5.50	2.75	1.75
319	Lou Skizas	5.50	2.75	1.75
320	Whitey Ford	35.00	17.50	10.50
321	Sluggers Supreme (Ted Kluszewski, Ted Williams)	50.00	25.00	15.00
322	Harding Peterson	5.50	2.75	1.75
323	Elmer Valo	5.50	2.75	1.75
324	Hoyt Wilhelm	15.00	7.50	4.50
325	Joe Adcock	5.50	2.75	1.75
326	Bob Miller	5.50	2.75	1.75
327	Cubs Team/Checklist 265-352	12.50	6.25	3.75
328	Ike Delock	5.50	2.75	1.75
329	Bob Cerv	5.50	2.75	1.75
330	Ed Bailey	5.50	2.75	1.75
331	Pedro Ramos	5.50	2.75	1.75
332	Jim King	5.50	2.75	1.75
333	Andy Carey	7.50	3.75	2.25
334	Mound Aces (Bob Friend, Billy Pierce)	9.00	4.50	2.75
335	Ruben Gomez	5.50	2.75	1.75
336	Bert Hamric	5.50	2.75	1.75
337	Hank Aguirre	5.50	2.75	1.75
338	Walt Dropo	5.50	2.75	1.75
339	Fred Hatfield	5.50	2.75	1.75
340	Don Newcombe	7.50	3.75	2.25
341	Pirates Team/Checklist 265-352	12.50	6.25	3.75
342	Jim Brosnan	5.50	2.75	1.75
343	*Orlando Cepeda*	80.00	40.00	24.00

#	Player	NR MT	EX	VG
344	Bob Porterfield	5.50	2.75	1.75
345	Jim Hegan	5.50	2.75	1.75
346	Steve Bilko	5.50	2.75	1.75
347	Don Rudolph	5.50	2.75	1.75
348	Chico Fernandez	5.50	2.75	1.75
349	Murry Dickson	5.50	2.75	1.75
350	Ken Boyer	5.50	2.75	1.75
351	Braves' Fence Busters (Hank Aaron, Joe Adcock, Del Crandall, Eddie Mathews)	30.00	15.00	9.00
352	Herb Score	5.50	2.75	1.75
353	Stan Lopata	4.00	2.00	1.25
354	Art Ditmar	7.50	3.75	2.25
355	Bill Bruton	4.00	2.00	1.25
356	Bob Malkmus	4.00	2.00	1.25
357	Danny McDevitt	4.00	2.00	1.25
358	Gene Baker	4.00	2.00	1.25
359	Billy Loes	4.00	2.00	1.25
360	Roy McMillan	4.00	2.00	1.25
361	Mike Fornieles	4.00	2.00	1.25
362	Ray Jablonski	4.00	2.00	1.25
363	Don Elston	4.00	2.00	1.25
364	Earl Battey	4.00	2.00	1.25
365	Tom Morgan	4.00	2.00	1.25
366	Gene Green	4.00	2.00	1.25
367	Jack Urban	4.00	2.00	1.25
368	Rocky Colavito	30.00	15.00	9.00
369	Ralph Lumenti	4.00	2.00	1.25
370	Yogi Berra	90.00	45.00	27.00
371	Marty Keough	4.00	2.00	1.25
372	Don Cardwell	4.00	2.00	1.25
373	Joe Pignatano	4.00	2.00	1.25
374	Brooks Lawrence	4.00	2.00	1.25
375	Pee Wee Reese	55.00	27.00	16.50
376	Charley Rabe	4.00	2.00	1.25
377a	Braves Team (alphabetical checklist on back)	15.00	7.50	4.50
377b	Braves Team (numerical checklist on back)	65.00	32.00	19.50
377b	Braves Team	60.00	30.00	18.00
378	Hank Sauer	4.00	2.00	1.25
379	Ray Herbert	4.00	2.00	1.25
380	Charley Maxwell	4.00	2.00	1.25
381	Hal Brown	4.00	2.00	1.25
382	Al Cicotte	7.00	3.50	2.00
383	Lou Berberet	4.00	2.00	1.25
384	John Goryl	4.00	2.00	1.25
385	Wilmer Mizell	4.00	2.00	1.25
386	Birdie's Young Sluggers (Ed Bailey, Frank Robinson, Birdie Tebbetts)	12.00	6.00	3.50
387	Wally Post	4.00	2.00	1.25
388	Billy Moran	4.00	2.00	1.25
389	Bill Taylor	4.00	2.00	1.25
390	Del Crandall	6.00	3.00	1.75
391	Dave Melton	4.00	2.00	1.25
392	Bennie Daniels	4.00	2.00	1.25
393	Tony Kubek	15.00	7.50	4.50
394	*Jim Grant*	6.00	3.00	1.75
395	Willard Nixon	4.00	2.00	1.25
396	Dutch Dotterer	4.00	2.00	1.25
397a	Tigers Team (alphabetical checklist on back)	15.00	7.50	4.50
397b	Tigers Team (checklist on back)	65.00	32.00	19.50
397b	Tigers Team (numerical)	60.00	30.00	18.00
398	Gene Woodling	4.00	2.00	1.25
399	Marv Grissom	4.00	2.00	1.25
400	Nellie Fox	15.00	7.50	4.50
401	Don Bessent	4.00	2.00	1.25
402	Bobby Gene Smith	4.00	2.00	1.25
403	Steve Korcheck	4.00	2.00	1.25
404	Curt Simmons	4.00	2.00	1.25
405	Ken Aspromonte	4.00	2.00	1.25
406	Vic Power	4.00	2.00	1.25
407	Carlton Willey	4.00	2.00	1.25
408a	Orioles Team (alphabetical checklist on back)	12.00	6.00	3.50
408b	Orioles Team (checklist on back)	65.00	32.00	19.50
408b	Orioles Team (numerical)	60.00	30.00	18.00
409	Frank J. Thomas	4.00	2.00	1.25
410	Murray Wall	4.00	2.00	1.25
411	*Tony Taylor*	4.00	2.00	1.25
412	Jerry Staley	4.00	2.00	1.25
413	*Jim Davenport*	4.00	2.00	1.25
414	Sammy White	4.00	2.00	1.25
415	Bob Bowman	4.00	2.00	1.25
416	Foster Castleman	4.00	2.00	1.25
417	Carl Furillo	9.00	4.50	2.75
418	World Series Foes (Hank Aaron, Mickey Mantle)	175.00	87.00	52.00
419	Bobby Shantz	7.50	3.75	2.25
420	*Vada Pinson*	30.00	15.00	9.00
421	Dixie Howell	5.50	2.75	1.75
422	Norm Zauchin	5.50	2.75	1.75
423	Phil Clark	5.50	2.75	1.75
424	Larry Doby	5.50	2.75	1.75
425	Sam Esposito	5.50	2.75	1.75
426	Johnny O'Brien	5.50	2.75	1.75
427	Al Worthington	5.50	2.75	1.75
428a	Redlegs Team	50.00	25.00	15.00
428b	Redlegs Team (numerical checklist on back)	65.00	32.00	19.50
429	Gus Triandos	5.50	2.75	1.75
430	Bobby Thomson	6.00	3.00	1.75
431	Gene Conley	5.50	2.75	1.75
432	John Powers	5.50	2.75	1.75
433	Pancho Herrera	5.50	2.75	1.75
434	Harvey Kuenn	6.00	3.00	1.75
435	Ed Roebuck	5.50	2.75	1.75
436	Rival Fence Busters (Willie Mays, Duke Snider)	65.00	32.00	19.50
437	Bob Speake	5.50	2.75	1.75
438	Whitey Herzog	7.50	3.75	2.25
439	Ray Narleski	5.50	2.75	1.75
440	Eddie Mathews	30.00	15.00	9.00
441	Jim Marshall	4.00	2.00	1.25
442	Phil Paine	4.00	2.00	1.25
443	Billy Harrell	7.50	3.75	2.25
444	Danny Kravitz	4.00	2.00	1.25
445	Bob Smith	4.00	2.00	1.25
446	Carroll Hardy	7.50	3.75	2.25
447	Ray Monzant	4.00	2.00	1.25
448	*Charlie Lau*	5.50	2.75	1.75
449	Gene Fodge	4.00	2.00	1.25
450	Preston Ward	7.50	3.75	2.25
451	Joe Taylor	4.00	2.00	1.25
452	Roman Mejias	4.00	2.00	1.25
453	Tom Qualters	4.00	2.00	1.25
454	Harry Hanebrink	4.00	2.00	1.25
455	Hal Griggs	4.00	2.00	1.25
456	Dick Brown	4.00	2.00	1.25
457	*Milt Pappas*	5.50	2.75	1.75
458	Julio Becquer	4.00	2.00	1.25
459	Ron Blackburn	4.00	2.00	1.25
460	Chuck Essegian	4.00	2.00	1.25
461	Ed Mayer	4.00	2.00	1.25
462	Gary Geiger	7.50	3.75	2.25
463	Vito Valentinetti	4.00	2.00	1.25
464	*Curt Flood*	22.00	11.00	5.50
465	Arnie Portocarrero	4.00	2.00	1.25
466	Pete Whisenant	4.00	2.00	1.25
467	Glen Hobbie	4.00	2.00	1.25
468	Bob Schmidt	4.00	2.00	1.25
469	Don Ferrarese	4.00	2.00	1.25
470	R.C. Stevens	4.00	2.00	1.25
471	Lenny Green	4.00	2.00	1.25
472	Joe Jay	4.00	2.00	1.25
473	Bill Renna	4.00	2.00	1.25
474	Roman Semproch	4.00	2.00	1.25
475	All-Star Managers (Fred Haney, Casey Stengel)	18.00	9.00	5.50
476	Stan Musial (All-Star)	32.00	16.00	9.50
477	Bill Skowron (All-Star)	6.00	3.00	1.75
478	Johnny Temple (All-Star)	7.00	3.50	2.00
479	Nellie Fox (All-Star)	10.00	5.00	3.00
480	Eddie Mathews (All-Star)	13.50	6.75	4.00
481	Frank Malzone (All-Star)	7.00	3.50	2.00
482	Ernie Banks (All-Star)	25.00	12.50	7.50
483	Luis Aparicio (All-Star)	12.00	6.00	3.50
484	Frank Robinson (All-Star)	25.00	12.50	7.50
485	Ted Williams (All-Star)	65.00	32.00	19.50
486	Willie Mays (All-Star)	50.00	25.00	15.00
487	Mickey Mantle (All-Star)	115.00	57.00	34.00
488	Hank Aaron (All-Star)	50.00	25.00	15.00
489	Jackie Jensen (All-Star)	7.00	3.50	2.00
490	Ed Bailey (All-Star)	7.00	3.50	2.00
491	Sherm Lollar (All-Star)	7.00	3.50	2.00
492	Bob Friend (All-Star)	7.00	3.50	2.00
493	Bob Turley (All-Star)	7.50	3.75	2.25
494	Warren Spahn (All-Star)	17.50	8.75	5.25
495	Herb Score (All-Star)	7.50	3.75	2.25
----	Contest Card (All-Star Game, July 8)	15.00	7.50	4.50
----	Felt Emblems Insert Card	15.00	7.50	4.50

1959 Topps

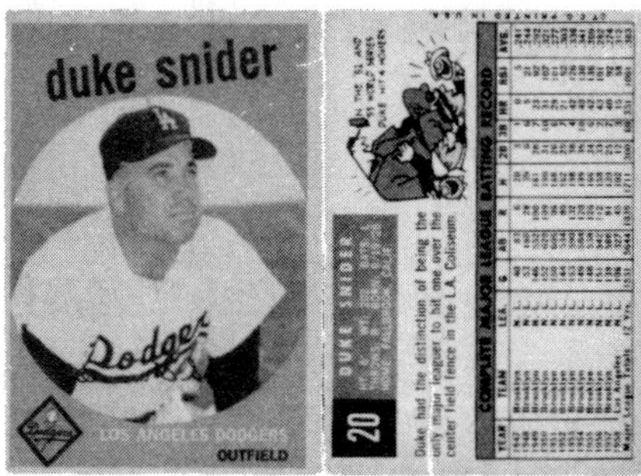

These 2-1/2" by 3-1/2" cards have a round photograph at the center of the front with a solid-color background and white border. A facsimile autograph is found across the photo. The 572- card set marks the largest set issued to that time. Card numbers below 507 have red and green printing with the card number in white in a green box. On high number cards beginning with #507, the printing is black and red and the card number is in a black box. Specialty cards include multiple-player cards, team cards with checklists, "All-Star" cards, highlights from previous season, and 31 "Rookie Stars." There is also a card of the commissioner, Ford Frick, and one of Roy Campanella in a wheelchair. A handful of cards can be found with and without lines added to the biographies on back indicating trades or demotions; those without the added lines are considerably more rare and valuable and are not included in the complete set price. Card numbers 199-286 can be found with either white or grey backs, with the grey stock being the less common.

	NR MT	EX	VG
Complete Set (572):	5000.	2500.	1500.
Common Player (1-110):	6.00	3.00	1.75
Common Player (111-506):	4.00	2.00	1.25
Common Player (507-572):	15.00	7.50	4.50

#	Player	NR MT	EX	VG
1	Ford Frick	70.00	25.00	12.00
2	Eddie Yost	6.00	3.00	1.75
3	Don McMahon	6.00	3.00	1.75
4	Albie Pearson	6.00	3.00	1.75
5	Dick Donovan	6.00	3.00	1.75
6	Alex Grammas	6.00	3.00	1.75
7	Al Pilarcik	6.00	3.00	1.75
8	Phillies Team	30.00	15.00	9.00
9	Paul Giel	6.00	3.00	1.75
10	Mickey Mantle	500.00	250.00	150.00
11	Billy Hunter	6.00	3.00	1.75
12	Vern Law	6.00	3.00	1.75
13	Dick Gernert	6.00	3.00	1.75
14	Pete Whisenant	6.00	3.00	1.75
15	Dick Drott	6.00	3.00	1.75
16	Joe Pignatano	6.00	3.00	1.75
17	Danny's All-Stars (Ted Kluszewski, Danny Murtaugh, Frank J. Thomas)	9.00	4.50	2.75
18	Jack Urban	6.00	3.00	1.75
19	Ed Bressoud	6.00	3.00	1.75
20	Duke Snider	65.00	32.00	19.50
21	Connie Johnson	6.00	3.00	1.75
22	Al Smith	6.00	3.00	1.75
23	Murry Dickson	7.00	3.50	2.00
24	Red Wilson	6.00	3.00	1.75
25	Don Hoak	6.00	3.00	1.75
26	Chuck Stobbs	6.00	3.00	1.75
27	Andy Pafko	6.00	3.00	1.75
28	Red Worthington	6.00	3.00	1.75
29	Jim Bolger	6.00	3.00	1.75
30	Nellie Fox	20.00	10.00	6.00
31	Ken Lehman	6.00	3.00	1.75
32	Don Buddin	6.00	3.00	1.75
33	Ed Fitz Gerald	6.00	3.00	1.75
34	Pitchers Beware (Al Kaline, Charlie Maxwell)	12.00	6.00	3.50
35	Ted Kluszewski	10.00	5.00	3.00
36	Hank Aguirre	6.00	3.00	1.75
37	Gene Green	6.00	3.00	1.75
38	Morrie Martin	6.00	3.00	1.75
39	Ed Bouchee	6.00	3.00	1.75
40	Warren Spahn	50.00	25.00	15.00
41	Bob Martyn	6.00	3.00	1.75
42	Murray Wall	6.00	3.00	1.75
43	Steve Bilko	6.00	3.00	1.75
44	Vito Valentinetti	6.00	3.00	1.75
45	Andy Carey	7.00	3.50	2.00
46	Bill Henry	6.00	3.00	1.75
47	Jim Finigan	6.00	3.00	1.75
48	Orioles Team/Checklist 1-88	20.00	10.00	6.00
49	Bill Hall	6.00	3.00	1.75
50	Willie Mays	145.00	70.00	42.00
51	Rip Coleman	6.00	3.00	1.75
52	Coot Veal	6.00	3.00	1.75
53	Stan Williams	6.00	3.00	1.75
54	Mel Roach	6.00	3.00	1.75
55	Tom Brewer	6.00	3.00	1.75
56	Carl Sawatski	6.00	3.00	1.75
57	Al Cicotte	6.00	3.00	1.75
58	Eddie Miksis	6.00	3.00	1.75
59	Irv Noren	6.00	3.00	1.75
60	Bob Turley	7.00	3.50	2.00
61	Dick Brown	6.00	3.00	1.75
62	Tony Taylor	6.00	3.00	1.75
63	Jim Hearn	6.00	3.00	1.75
64	Joe DeMaestri	6.00	3.00	1.75
65	Frank Torre	6.00	3.00	1.75
66	Joe Ginsberg	6.00	3.00	1.75
67	Brooks Lawrence	6.00	3.00	1.75
68	Dick Schofield	6.00	3.00	1.75
69	Giants Team/Checklist 89-176	24.00	12.00	7.25
70	Harvey Kuenn	9.00	4.50	2.75
71	Don Bessent	6.00	3.00	1.75
72	Bill Renna	6.00	3.00	1.75
73	Ron Jackson	6.00	3.00	1.75
74	Directing the Power (Cookie Lavagetto, Jim Lemon, Roy Sievers)	9.00	4.50	2.75
75	Sam Jones	6.00	3.00	1.75
76	Bobby Richardson	17.50	8.75	5.25
77	John Goryl	6.00	3.00	1.75
78	Pedro Ramos	6.00	3.00	1.75
79	Harry Chiti	6.00	3.00	1.75
80	Minnie Minoso	7.50	3.75	2.25
81	Hal Jeffcoat	6.00	3.00	1.75
82	Bob Boyd	6.00	3.00	1.75
83	Bob Smith	6.00	3.00	1.75
84	Reno Bertoia	6.00	3.00	1.75
85	Harry Anderson	6.00	3.00	1.75
86	Bob Keegan	6.00	3.00	1.75
87	Danny O'Connell	6.00	3.00	1.75
88	Herb Score	6.00	3.00	1.75
89	Billy Gardner	6.00	3.00	1.75
90	Bill Skowron	12.50	6.25	3.75
91	Herb Moford	6.00	3.00	1.75
92	Dave Philley	6.00	3.00	1.75
93	Julio Becquer	6.00	3.00	1.75
94	W. Sox Team	20.00	10.00	6.00
95	Carl Willey	6.00	3.00	1.75
96	Lou Berberet	6.00	3.00	1.75
97	Jerry Lynch	6.00	3.00	1.75
98	Arnie Portocarrero	6.00	3.00	1.75
99	Ted Kazanski	6.00	3.00	1.75
100	Bob Cerv	6.00	3.00	1.75
101	Alex Kellner	6.00	3.00	1.75
102	*Felipe Alou*	30.00	15.00	9.00
103	Billy Goodman	6.00	3.00	1.75
104	Del Rice	6.00	3.00	1.75
105	Lee Walls	6.00	3.00	1.75
106	Hal Woodeshick	6.00	3.00	1.75
107	Norm Larker	6.00	3.00	1.75
108	Zack Monroe	7.00	3.50	2.00
109	Bob Schmidt	6.00	3.00	1.75
110	George Witt	6.00	3.00	1.75
111	Redlegs Team,	17.50	8.75	5.25
112	Billy Consolo	4.00	2.00	1.25
113	Taylor Phillips	4.00	2.00	1.25
114	Earl Battey	4.00	2.00	1.25
115	Mickey Vernon	4.00	2.00	1.25
116	*Bob Allison*	7.00	3.50	2.00
117	*John Blanchard*	5.00	2.50	1.50
118	John Buzhardt	4.00	2.00	1.25
119	*John Callison*	6.00	3.00	1.75

No.	Player			
120	Chuck Coles	4.00	2.00	1.25
121	Bob Conley	4.00	2.00	1.25
122	Bennie Daniels	4.00	2.00	1.25
123	Don Dillard	4.00	2.00	1.25
124	Dan Dobbek	4.00	2.00	1.25
125	*Ron Fairly*	5.00	2.50	1.50
126	Eddie Haas	4.00	2.00	1.25
127	Kent Hadley	4.00	2.00	1.25
128	Bob Hartman	4.00	2.00	1.25
129	Frank Herrera	4.00	2.00	1.25
130	Lou Jackson	4.00	2.00	1.25
131	*Deron Johnson*	5.00	2.50	1.50
132	Don Lee	4.00	2.00	1.25
133	*Bob Lillis*	5.00	2.50	1.50
134	Jim McDaniel	4.00	2.00	1.25
135	Gene Oliver	4.00	2.00	1.25
136	*Jim O'Toole*	5.00	2.50	1.50
137	Dick Ricketts	4.00	2.00	1.25
138	John Romano	4.00	2.00	1.25
139	Ed Sadowski	4.00	2.00	1.25
140	Charlie Secrest	4.00	2.00	1.25
141	Joe Shipley	4.00	2.00	1.25
142	Dick Stigman	4.00	2.00	1.25
143	Willie Tasby	4.00	2.00	1.25
144	Jerry Walker	4.00	2.00	1.25
145	Dom Zanni	4.00	2.00	1.25
146	Jerry Zimmerman	4.00	2.00	1.25
147	Cubs' Clubbers (Ernie Banks, Dale Long, Walt Moryn)	16.00	8.00	4.75
148	Mike McCormick	4.00	2.00	1.25
149	Jim Bunning	15.00	7.50	4.50
150	Stan Musial	135.00	65.00	40.00
151	Bob Malkmus	4.00	2.00	1.25
152	Johnny Klippstein	4.00	2.00	1.25
153	Jim Marshall	4.00	2.00	1.25
154	Ray Herbert	4.00	2.00	1.25
155	Enos Slaughter	18.00	9.00	5.50
156	Ace Hurlers (Billy Pierce, Robin Roberts)	5.00	2.50	1.50
157	Felix Mantilla	4.00	2.00	1.25
158	Walt Dropo	4.00	2.00	1.25
159	Bob Shaw	4.00	2.00	1.25
160	Dick Groat	4.00	2.00	1.25
161	Frank Baumann	4.00	2.00	1.25
162	Bobby G. Smith	4.00	2.00	1.25
163	Sandy Koufax	145.00	70.00	42.50
164	Johnny Groth	4.00	2.00	1.25
165	Bill Bruton	4.00	2.00	1.25
166	Destruction Crew (Rocky Colavito, Larry Doby, Minnie Minoso)	5.00	2.50	1.50
167	Duke Maas	5.00	2.50	1.50
168	Carroll Hardy	4.00	2.00	1.25
169	Ted Abernathy	4.00	2.00	1.25
170	Gene Woodling	4.00	2.00	1.25
171	Willard Schmidt	4.00	2.00	1.25
172	A's Team/Checklist 177-242	12.00	6.00	3.50
173	*Bill Monbouquette*	4.00	2.00	1.25
174	Jim Pendleton	4.00	2.00	1.25
175	Dick Farrell	4.00	2.00	1.25
176	Preston Ward	4.00	2.00	1.25
177	Johnny Briggs	4.00	2.00	1.25
178	Ruben Amaro	4.00	2.00	1.25
179	Don Rudolph	4.00	2.00	1.25
180	Yogi Berra	75.00	37.00	22.00
181	Bob Porterfield	4.00	2.00	1.25
182	Milt Graff	4.00	2.00	1.25
183	Stu Miller	4.00	2.00	1.25
184	Harvey Haddix	4.00	2.00	1.25
185	Jim Busby	4.00	2.00	1.25
186	Mudcat Grant	4.00	2.00	1.25
187	Bubba Phillips	4.00	2.00	1.25
188	Juan Pizarro	4.00	2.00	1.25
189	Neil Chrisley	4.00	2.00	1.25
190	Bill Virdon	4.00	2.00	1.25
191	Russ Kemmerer	4.00	2.00	1.25
192	Charley Beamon	4.00	2.00	1.25
193	Sammy Taylor	4.00	2.00	1.25
194	Jim Brosnan	4.00	2.00	1.25
195	Rip Repulski	4.00	2.00	1.25
196	Billy Moran	4.00	2.00	1.25
197	Ray Semproch	4.00	2.00	1.25
198	Jim Davenport	4.00	2.00	1.25
199	Leo Kiely	4.00	2.00	1.25
200	Warren Giles	5.00	2.50	1.50
201	Tom Acker	4.00	2.00	1.25
202	Roger Maris	120.00	60.00	36.00
203	Ozzie Virgil	4.00	2.00	1.25
204	Casey Wise	4.00	2.00	1.25
205	Don Larsen	7.00	3.50	2.00
206	Carl Furillo	7.00	3.50	2.00
207	George Strickland	4.00	2.00	1.25
208	Willie Jones	4.00	2.00	1.25
209	Lenny Green	4.00	2.00	1.25
210	Ed Bailey	4.00	2.00	1.25
211	Bob Blaylock	4.00	2.00	1.25
212	Fence Busters (Hank Aaron, Eddie Mathews)	60.00	30.00	18.00
213	Jim Rivera	4.00	2.00	1.25
214	Marcelino Solis	4.00	2.00	1.25
215	Jim Lemon	4.00	2.00	1.25
216	Andre Rodgers	4.00	2.00	1.25
217	Carl Erskine	6.00	3.00	1.75
218	Roman Mejias	4.00	2.00	1.25
219	George Zuverink	4.00	2.00	1.25
220	Frank Malzone	4.00	2.00	1.25
221	Bob Bowman	4.00	2.00	1.25
222	Bobby Shantz	6.00	3.00	1.75
223	Cards Team/Checklist 265-352	12.00	6.00	3.50
224	*Claude Osteen*	4.00	2.00	1.25
225	Johnny Logan	4.00	2.00	1.25
226	Art Ceccarelli	4.00	2.00	1.25
227	Hal Smith	4.00	2.00	1.25
228	Don Gross	4.00	2.00	1.25
229	Vic Power	4.00	2.00	1.25
230	Bill Fischer	4.00	2.00	1.25
231	Ellis Burton	4.00	2.00	1.25
232	Eddie Kasko	4.00	2.00	1.25
233	Paul Foytack	4.00	2.00	1.25
234	Chuck Tanner	4.00	2.00	1.25
235	Valmy Thomas	4.00	2.00	1.25
236	Ted Bowsfield	4.00	2.00	1.25
237	Run Preventers (Gil McDougald, Bobby Richardson, Bob Turley)	9.00	4.50	2.75
238	Gene Baker	4.00	2.00	1.25
239	Bob Trowbridge	4.00	2.00	1.25
240	Hank Bauer	7.00	3.50	2.00
241	Billy Muffett	4.00	2.00	1.25
242	Ron Samford	4.00	2.00	1.25
243	Marv Grissom	4.00	2.00	1.25
244	Dick Gray	4.00	2.00	1.25
245	Ned Garver	4.00	2.00	1.25
246	J.W. Porter	4.00	2.00	1.25
247	Don Ferrarese	4.00	2.00	1.25
248	Red Sox Team/Checklist 177-264	12.50	6.25	3.75
249	Bobby Adams	4.00	2.00	1.25
250	Billy O'Dell	4.00	2.00	1.25
251	Cletis Boyer	6.00	3.00	1.75
252	Ray Boone	4.00	2.00	1.25
253	Seth Morehead	4.00	2.00	1.25
254	Zeke Bella	4.00	2.00	1.25
255	Del Ennis	4.00	2.00	1.25
256	Jerry Davie	4.00	2.00	1.25
257	*Leon Wagner*	4.00	2.00	1.25
258	Fred Kipp	4.00	2.00	1.25
259	Jim Pisoni	4.00	2.00	1.25
260	Early Wynn	15.00	7.50	4.50
261	Gene Stephens	4.00	2.00	1.25
262	Hitters' Foes (Don Drysdale, Clem Labine, Johnny Podres)	12.00	6.00	3.50
263	Buddy Daley	4.00	2.00	1.25
264	Chico Carrasquel	4.00	2.00	1.25
265	Ron Kline	4.00	2.00	1.25
266	Woody Held	4.00	2.00	1.25
267	John Romonosky	4.00	2.00	1.25
268	Tito Francona	4.00	2.00	1.25
269	Jack Meyer	4.00	2.00	1.25
270	Gil Hodges	20.00	10.00	6.00
271	*Orlando Pena*	4.00	2.00	1.25
272	Jerry Lumpe	5.00	2.50	1.50
273	Joe Jay	4.00	2.00	1.25
274	Jerry Kindall	4.00	2.00	1.25
275	Jack Sanford	4.00	2.00	1.25
276	Pete Daley	4.00	2.00	1.25
277	Turk Lown	4.00	2.00	1.25
278	Chuck Essegian	4.00	2.00	1.25
279	Ernie Johnson	4.00	2.00	1.25
280	Frank Bolling	4.00	2.00	1.25
281	Walt Craddock	4.00	2.00	1.25
282	R.C. Stevens	4.00	2.00	1.25
283	Russ Heman	4.00	2.00	1.25
284	Steve Korcheck	4.00	2.00	1.25
285	Joe Cunningham	4.00	2.00	1.25
286	Dean Stone	4.00	2.00	1.25
287	Don Zimmer	5.00	2.50	1.50
288	Dutch Dotterer	4.00	2.00	1.25
289	Johnny Kucks	5.00	2.50	1.50
290	Wes Covington	4.00	2.00	1.25
291	Pitching Partners (Camilo Pascual, Pedro Ramos)	5.00	2.50	1.50
292	Dick Williams	4.00	2.00	1.25
293	Ray Moore	4.00	2.00	1.25
294	Hank Foiles	4.00	2.00	1.25
295	Billy Martin	12.50	6.25	3.75
296	*Ernie Broglio*	4.00	2.00	1.25
297	*Jackie Brandt*	4.00	2.00	1.25
298	Tex Clevenger	4.00	2.00	1.25
299	Billy Klaus	4.00	2.00	1.25
300	Richie Ashburn	20.00	10.00	6.00
301	Earl Averill	4.00	2.00	1.25
302	Don Mossi	4.00	2.00	1.25
303	Marty Keough	4.00	2.00	1.25
304	Cubs Team/Checklist 265-352	12.00	6.00	3.50
305	Curt Raydon	4.00	2.00	1.25
306	Jim Gilliam	6.00	3.00	1.75
307	Curt Barclay	4.00	2.00	1.25
308	Norm Siebern	5.00	2.50	1.50
309	Sal Maglie	4.00	2.00	1.25
310	Luis Aparicio	15.00	7.50	4.50
311	Norm Zauchin	4.00	2.00	1.25
312	Don Newcombe	6.00	3.00	1.75
313	Frank House	4.00	2.00	1.25
314	Don Cardwell	4.00	2.00	1.25
315	Joe Adcock	4.00	2.00	1.25
316a	Ralph Lumenti (no optioned statement)	90.00	45.00	27.00
316b	Ralph Lumenti (optioned statement)	4.00	2.00	1.25
317	N.L. Hitting Kings (Richie Ashburn, Willie Mays)	35.00	17.50	10.50
318	Rocky Bridges	4.00	2.00	1.25
319	Dave Hillman	4.00	2.00	1.25
320	Bob Skinner	4.00	2.00	1.25
321a	Bob Giallombardo (no optioned statement)	90.00	45.00	27.00
321b	Bob Giallombardo (optioned statement)	4.00	2.00	1.25
322a	Harry Hanebrink (no trade statement)	80.00	40.00	24.00
322b	Harry Hanebrink (trade statement)	4.00	2.00	1.25
323	Frank Sullivan	4.00	2.00	1.25
324	Don Demeter	4.00	2.00	1.25
325	Ken Boyer	10.00	5.00	3.00
326	Marv Throneberry	6.00	3.00	1.75
327	*Gary Bell*	4.00	2.00	1.25
328	Lou Skizas	4.00	2.00	1.25
329	Tigers Team/Checklist 353-429	12.50	6.25	3.75
330	Gus Triandos	4.00	2.00	1.25
331	Steve Boros	4.00	2.00	1.25
332	Ray Monzant	4.00	2.00	1.25
333	Harry Simpson	4.00	2.00	1.25
334	Glen Hobbie	4.00	2.00	1.25
335	Johnny Temple	4.00	2.00	1.25
336a	Billy Loes (no trade statement)	80.00	40.00	24.00
336b	Billy Loes (trade statement)	4.00	2.00	1.25
337	George Crowe	4.00	2.00	1.25
338	*Sparky Anderson*	65.00	32.00	19.50
339	Roy Face	4.00	2.00	1.25
340	Roy Sievers	4.00	2.00	1.25
341	Tom Qualters	4.00	2.00	1.25
342	Ray Jablonski	4.00	2.00	1.25
343	Billy Hoeft	4.00	2.00	1.25
344	Russ Nixon	4.00	2.00	1.25
345	Gil McDougald	7.00	3.50	2.00
346	Batter Bafflers (Tom Brewer, Dave Sisler)	5.00	2.50	1.50
347	Bob Buhl	5.00	2.50	1.50
348	Ted Lepcio	4.00	2.00	1.25
349	Hoyt Wilhelm	15.00	7.50	4.50
350	Ernie Banks	70.00	35.00	21.00
351	Earl Torgeson	4.00	2.00	1.25
352	Robin Roberts	15.00	7.50	4.50
353	Curt Flood	4.00	2.00	1.25
354	Pete Burnside	4.00	2.00	1.25
355	Jim Piersall	4.00	2.00	1.25
356	Bob Mabe	4.00	2.00	1.25
357	*Dick Stuart*	6.00	3.00	1.75
358	Ralph Terry	4.00	2.00	1.25
359	*Bill White*	30.00	15.00	9.00
360	Al Kaline	60.00	30.00	18.00
361	Willard Nixon	4.00	2.00	1.25
362a	Dolan Nichols (no optioned statement)	90.00	45.00	27.00
362b	Dolan Nichols (optioned statement)	4.00	2.00	1.25
363	Bobby Avila	4.00	2.00	1.25
364	Danny McDevitt	4.00	2.00	1.25
365	Gus Bell	4.00	2.00	1.25
366	Humberto Robinson	4.00	2.00	1.25
367	Cal Neeman	4.00	2.00	1.25
368	Don Mueller	4.00	2.00	1.25
369	Dick Tomanek	4.00	2.00	1.25
370	Pete Runnels	4.00	2.00	1.25
371	Dick Brodowski	4.00	2.00	1.25
372	Jim Hegan	4.00	2.00	1.25
373	Herb Plews	4.00	2.00	1.25
374	Art Ditmar	4.00	2.00	1.25
375	Bob Nieman	4.00	2.00	1.25
376	Hal Naragon	4.00	2.00	1.25
377	Johnny Antonelli	4.00	2.00	1.25
378	Gail Harris	4.00	2.00	1.25
379	Bob Miller	4.00	2.00	1.25
380	Hank Aaron	110.00	55.00	33.00
381	Mike Baxes	4.00	2.00	1.25
382	Curt Simmons	4.00	2.00	1.25
383	Words of Wisdom (Don Larsen, Casey Stengel)	9.00	4.50	2.75
384	Dave Sisler	4.00	2.00	1.25
385	Sherm Lollar	4.00	2.00	1.25
386	Jim Delsing	4.00	2.00	1.25
387	Don Drysdale	40.00	20.00	12.00
388	Bob Will	4.00	2.00	1.25
389	Joe Nuxhall	4.00	2.00	1.25
390	Orlando Cepeda	20.00	10.00	6.00
391	Milt Pappas	4.00	2.00	1.25
392	Whitey Herzog	6.00	3.00	1.75
393	Frank Lary	4.00	2.00	1.25
394	Randy Jackson	4.00	2.00	1.25
395	Elston Howard	7.00	3.50	2.00
396	Bob Rush	4.00	2.00	1.25
397	Senators Team/Checklist 430-495	12.00	6.00	3.50
398	Wally Post	4.00	2.00	1.25
399	Larry Jackson	4.00	2.00	1.25
400	Jackie Jensen	4.00	2.00	1.25
401	Ron Blackburn	4.00	2.00	1.25
402	Hector Lopez	4.00	2.00	1.25
403	Clem Labine	4.00	2.00	1.25
404	Hank Sauer	4.00	2.00	1.25
405	Roy McMillan	4.00	2.00	1.25
406	Solly Drake	4.00	2.00	1.25
407	Moe Drabowsky	4.00	2.00	1.25
408	Keystone Combo (Luis Aparicio, Nellie Fox)	12.00	6.00	3.50
409	Gus Zernial	4.00	2.00	1.25
410	Billy Pierce	4.00	2.00	1.25
411	Whitey Lockman	4.00	2.00	1.25
412	Stan Lopata	4.00	2.00	1.25
413	Camillo (Camilo) Pascual	4.00	2.00	1.25
414	Dale Long	4.00	2.00	1.25
415	Bill Mazeroski	8.00	4.00	2.50
416	Haywood Sullivan	4.00	2.00	1.25
417	Virgil Trucks	4.00	2.00	1.25
418	Gino Cimoli	4.00	2.00	1.25
419	Braves Team/Checklist 353-429	14.00	7.00	4.25
420	Rocky Colavito	25.00	12.50	7.50
421	Herm Wehmeier	4.00	2.00	1.25
422	Hobie Landrith	4.00	2.00	1.25
423	Bob Grim	4.00	2.00	1.25
424	Ken Aspromonte	4.00	2.00	1.25
425	Del Crandall	4.00	2.00	1.25
426	Jerry Staley	4.00	2.00	1.25
427	Charlie Neal	4.00	2.00	1.25
428	Buc Hill Aces (Roy Face, Bob Friend, Ron Kline, Vern Law)	5.00	2.50	1.50
429	Bobby Thomson	4.00	2.00	1.25
430	Whitey Ford	30.00	15.00	9.00
431	Whammy Douglas	4.00	2.00	1.25
432	Smoky Burgess	4.00	2.00	1.25
433	Billy Harrell	4.00	2.00	1.25
434	Hal Griggs	4.00	2.00	1.25
435	Frank Robinson	40.00	20.00	12.00
436	Granny Hamner	4.00	2.00	1.25
437	Ike Delock	4.00	2.00	1.25
438	Sam Esposito	4.00	2.00	1.25
439	Brooks Robinson	50.00	25.00	15.00
440	Lou Burdette	6.00	3.00	1.75
441	John Roseboro	4.00	2.00	1.25
442	Ray Narleski	4.00	2.00	1.25
443	Daryl Spencer	4.00	2.00	1.25
444	*Ronnie Hansen*	5.00	2.50	1.50

445	Cal McLish	4.00	2.00	1.25
446	Rocky Nelson	4.00	2.00	1.25
447	Bob Anderson	4.00	2.00	1.25
448	Vada Pinson	6.00	3.00	1.75
449	Tom Gorman	4.00	2.00	1.25
450	Eddie Mathews	30.00	15.00	9.00
451	Jimmy Constable	4.00	2.00	1.25
452	Chico Fernandez	4.00	2.00	1.25
453	Les Moss	4.00	2.00	1.25
454	Phil Clark	4.00	2.00	1.25
455	Larry Doby	4.00	2.00	1.25
456	Jerry Casale	4.00	2.00	1.25
457	Dodgers Team	24.00	12.00	7.25
458	Gordon Jones	4.00	2.00	1.25
459	Bill Tuttle	4.00	2.00	1.25
460	Bob Friend	4.00	2.00	1.25
461	Mantle Hits 42nd Homer For Crown (Mickey Mantle)	40.00	20.00	12.00
462	Colavito's Great Catch Saves Game (Rocky Colavito)	10.00	5.00	3.00
463	Kaline Becomes Youngest Batting Champ (Al Kaline)	12.00	6.00	3.50
464	Mays' Catch Makes Series History (Willie Mays)	25.00	12.50	7.50
465	Sievers Sets Homer Mark (Roy Sivers)	5.00	2.50	1.50
466	Pierce All-Star Starter (Billy Pierce)	5.00	2.50	1.50
467	Aaron Clubs World Series Homer (Hank Aaron)	25.00	12.50	7.50
468	Snider's Play Brings L.A. Victory (Duke Snider)	12.50	6.25	3.75
469	Hustler Banks Wins M.V.P. Award (Ernie Banks)	14.00	7.00	4.25
470	Musial Raps Out 3,000th Hit (Stan Musial)	18.00	9.00	5.50
471	Tom Sturdivant	5.00	2.50	1.50
472	Gene Freese	4.00	2.00	1.25
473	Mike Fornieles	4.00	2.00	1.25
474	Moe Thacker	4.00	2.00	1.25
475	Jack Harshman	4.00	2.00	1.25
476	Indians Team/Checklist 496-572	12.00	6.00	3.50
477	Barry Latman	4.00	2.00	1.25
478	Roberto Clemente	125.00	62.50	37.50
479	Lindy McDaniel	4.00	2.00	1.25
480	Red Schoendienst	15.00	7.50	4.50
481	Charley Maxwell	4.00	2.00	1.25
482	Russ Meyer	4.00	2.00	1.25
483	Clint Courtney	4.00	2.00	1.25
484	Willie Kirkland	4.00	2.00	1.25
485	Ryne Duren	6.00	3.00	1.75
486	Sammy White	4.00	2.00	1.25
487	Hal Brown	4.00	2.00	1.25
488	Walt Moryn	4.00	2.00	1.25
489	John C. Powers	4.00	2.00	1.25
490	Frank J. Thomas	4.00	2.00	1.25
491	Don Blasingame	4.00	2.00	1.25
492	Gene Conley	4.00	2.00	1.25
493	Jim Landis	4.00	2.00	1.25
494	Don Pavletich	4.00	2.00	1.25
495	Johnny Podres	6.00	3.00	1.75
496	Wayne Terwilliger	4.00	2.00	1.25
497	Hal R. Smith	4.00	2.00	1.25
498	Dick Hyde	4.00	2.00	1.25
499	Johnny O'Brien	4.00	2.00	1.25
500	Vic Wertz	4.00	2.00	1.25
501	Bobby Tiefenauer	4.00	2.00	1.25
502	Al Dark	4.00	2.00	1.25
503	Jim Owens	4.00	2.00	1.25
504	Ossie Alvarez	4.00	2.00	1.25
505	Tony Kubek	8.00	4.00	2.50
506	Bob Purkey	4.00	2.00	1.25
507	Bob Hale	15.00	7.50	4.50
508	Art Fowler	15.00	7.50	4.50
509	*Norm Cash*	65.00	32.00	19.50
510	Yankees Team	70.00	35.00	21.00
511	George Susce	15.00	7.50	4.50
512	George Altman	15.00	7.50	4.50
513	Tom Carroll	15.00	7.50	4.50
514	*Bob Gibson*	350.00	175.00	100.00
515	Harmon Killebrew	160.00	80.00	48.00
516	Mike Garcia	15.00	7.50	4.50
517	Joe Koppe	15.00	7.50	4.50
518	*Mike Cueller*	20.00	10.00	6.00
519	Infield Power (Dick Gernert, Frank Malzone, Pete Runnels)	18.00	9.00	5.50
520	Don Elston	15.00	7.50	4.50
521	Gary Geiger	15.00	7.50	4.50
522	Gene Snyder	15.00	7.50	4.50
523	Harry Bright	15.00	7.50	4.50
524	Larry Osborne	15.00	7.50	4.50
525	Jim Coates	16.00	8.00	4.75
526	Bob Speake	15.00	7.50	4.50
527	Solly Hemus	15.00	7.50	4.50
528	Pirates Team	45.00	22.00	13.50
529	*George Bamberger*	16.00	8.00	4.75
530	Wally Moon	16.00	8.00	4.75
531	Ray Webster	15.00	7.50	4.50
532	Mark Freeman	15.00	7.50	4.50
533	Darrell Johnson	16.00	8.00	4.75
534	Faye Throneberry	15.00	7.50	4.50
535	Ruben Gomez	15.00	7.50	4.50
536	Dan Kravitz	15.00	7.50	4.50
537	Rodolfo Arias	15.00	7.50	4.50
538	Chick King	15.00	7.50	4.50
539	Gary Blaylock	15.00	7.50	4.50
540	Willy Miranda	15.00	7.50	4.50
541	Bob Thurman	15.00	7.50	4.50
542	*Jim Perry*	20.00	10.00	6.00
543	Corsair Outfield Trio (Roberto Clemente, Bob Skinner, Bill Virdon)	80.00	40.00	24.00
544	Lee Tate	15.00	7.50	4.50
545	Tom Morgan	15.00	7.50	4.50
546	Al Schroll	15.00	7.50	4.50
547	Jim Baxes	15.00	7.50	4.50
548	Elmer Singleton	15.00	7.50	4.50
549	Howie Nunn	15.00	7.50	4.50
550	Roy Campanella	175.00	80.00	48.00
551	Fred Haney (All-Star)	25.00	12.50	7.50
552	Casey Stengel (All-Star)	35.00	17.50	10.50
553	Orlando Cepeda (All-Star)	29.00	14.50	8.75
554	Bill Skowron (All-Star)	25.00	12.50	7.50
555	Bill Mazeroski (All-Star)	29.00	14.50	8.75
556	Nellie Fox (All-Star)	25.00	12.50	7.50
557	Ken Boyer (All-Star)	25.00	12.50	7.50
558	Frank Malzone (All-Star)	23.00	11.50	7.00
559	Ernie Banks (All-Star)	55.00	27.00	16.50
560	Luis Aparicio (All-Star)	30.00	15.00	9.00
561	Hank Aaron (All-Star)	130.00	65.00	39.00
562	Al Kaline (All-Star)	55.00	27.00	16.50
563	Willie Mays (All-Star)	130.00	65.00	39.00
564	Mickey Mantle (All-Star)	310.00	155.00	93.00
565	Wes Covington (All-Star)	23.00	11.50	7.00
566	Roy Sievers (All-Star)	23.00	11.50	7.00
567	Del Crandall (All-Star)	23.00	11.50	7.00
568	Gus Triandos (All-Star)	23.00	11.50	7.00
569	Bob Friend (All-Star)	23.00	11.50	7.00
570	Bob Turley (All-Star)	25.00	12.50	7.50
571	Warren Spahn (All-Star)	40.00	20.00	12.00
572	Billy Pierce (All-Star)	30.00	11.50	7.00
----	Elect Your Favorite Rookie Insert (paper stock, September 29 date on back)	15.00	7.50	4.50
----	Felt Pennants Insert (paper stock)	15.00	7.50	4.50

1960 Topps

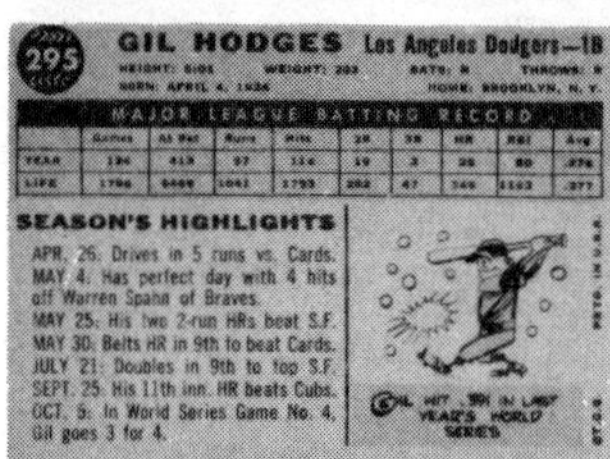

In 1960, Topps returned to a horizontal format (3-1/2" by 2-1/2") with a color portrait and a black and white "action" photograph on the front. The backs returned to the use of just the previous year and lifetime statistics along with a cartoon and short career summary or previous season highlights. Specialty cards in the 572-card set are multi-player cards, managers and coaches cards, and highlights of the 1959 World Series. Two groups of rookie cards are included. The first are numbers 117-148, which are the Sport Magazine rookies. The second group is called "Topps All-Star Rookies." Finally, there is a continuation of the All-Star cards to close out the set in the scarcer high numbers. Card #'s 375-440 can be found with backs printed on either white or grey cardboard, with the white stock being the less common.

	NR MT	EX	VG
Complete Set (572):	3900.	1900.	1150.
Common Player (1-110):	4.00	2.00	1.25
Common Player (111-286):	4.00	2.00	1.25
Common Player (287-440):	4.00	2.00	1.25
Common Player (441-506):	5.50	2.75	1.75
Common Player (507-572):	12.00	6.00	3.50

		NR MT	EX	VG
1	Early Wynn	25.00	11.00	6.60
2	Roman Mejias	4.00	2.00	1.25
3	Joe Adcock	4.00	2.00	1.25
4	Bob Purkey	4.00	2.00	1.25
5	Wally Moon	4.00	2.00	1.25
6	Lou Berberet	4.00	2.00	1.25
7	Master and Mentor (Willie Mays, Bill Rigney)	19.00	9.50	5.75
8	Bud Daley	4.00	2.00	1.25
9	Faye Throneberry	4.00	2.00	1.25
10	Ernie Banks	50.00	25.00	15.00
11	Norm Siebern	4.00	2.00	1.25
12	Milt Pappas	4.00	2.00	1.25
13	Wally Post	4.00	2.00	1.25
14	Jim Grant	4.00	2.00	1.25
15	Pete Runnels	4.00	2.00	1.25
16	Ernie Broglio	4.00	2.00	1.25
17	Johnny Callison	4.00	2.00	1.25
18	Dodgers Team/Checklist 1-88	15.00	7.50	4.50
19	Felix Mantilla	4.00	2.00	1.25
20	Roy Face	4.00	2.00	1.25
21	Dutch Dotterer	4.00	2.00	1.25
22	Rocky Bridges	4.00	2.00	1.25
23	Eddie Fisher	4.00	2.00	1.25
24	Dick Gray	4.00	2.00	1.25
25	Roy Sievers	4.00	2.00	1.25
26	Wayne Terwilliger	4.00	2.00	1.25
27	Dick Drott	4.00	2.00	1.25
28	Brooks Robinson	50.00	25.00	15.00
29	Clem Labine	4.00	2.00	1.25
30	Tito Francona	4.00	2.00	1.25
31	Sammy Esposito	4.00	2.00	1.25
32	Sophomore Stalwarts (Jim O'Toole, Vada Pinson)	6.00	3.00	1.75
33	Tom Morgan	4.00	2.00	1.25
34	Sparky Anderson	15.00	7.50	4.50
35	Whitey Ford	35.00	17.50	10.50
36	Russ Nixon	4.00	2.00	1.25
37	Bill Bruton	4.00	2.00	1.25
38	Jerry Casale	4.00	2.00	1.25
39	Earl Averill	4.00	2.00	1.25
40	Joe Cunningham	4.00	2.00	1.25
41	Barry Latman	4.00	2.00	1.25
42	Hobie Landrith	4.00	2.00	1.25
43	Senators Team/Checklist 1-88	10.00	5.00	3.00
44	Bobby Locke	4.00	2.00	1.25
45	Roy McMillan	4.00	2.00	1.25
46	Jack Fisher	4.00	2.00	1.25
47	Don Zimmer	4.00	2.00	1.25
48	Hal Smith	4.00	2.00	1.25
49	Curt Raydon	4.00	2.00	1.25
50	Al Kaline	40.00	20.00	12.00
51	Jim Coates	4.00	2.00	1.25
52	Dave Philley	4.00	2.00	1.25
53	Jackie Brandt	4.00	2.00	1.25
54	Mike Fornieles	4.00	2.00	1.25
55	Bill Mazeroski	5.00	2.50	1.50
56	Steve Korcheck	4.00	2.00	1.25
57	Win-Savers (Turk Lown, Gerry Staley)	4.50	2.25	1.25
58	Gino Cimoli	4.00	2.00	1.25
59	Juan Pizarro	4.00	2.00	1.25
60	Gus Triandos	4.00	2.00	1.25
61	Eddie Kasko	4.00	2.00	1.25
62	Roger Craig	4.00	2.00	1.25
63	George Strickland	4.00	2.00	1.25
64	Jack Meyer	4.00	2.00	1.25
65	Elston Howard	6.00	3.00	1.75
66	Bob Trowbridge	4.00	2.00	1.25
67	*Jose Pagan*	4.00	2.00	1.25
68	Dave Hillman	4.00	2.00	1.25
69	Billy Goodman	4.00	2.00	1.25
70	Lou Burdette	4.00	2.00	1.25
71	Marty Keough	4.00	2.00	1.25
72	Tigers Team/Checklist 89-176	12.00	6.00	3.50
73	Bob Gibson	50.00	25.00	15.00
74	Walt Moryn	4.00	2.00	1.25
75	Vic Power	4.00	2.00	1.25
76	Bill Fischer	4.00	2.00	1.25
77	Hank Foiles	4.00	2.00	1.25
78	Bob Grim	4.00	2.00	1.25
79	Walt Dropo	4.00	2.00	1.25
80	Johnny Antonelli	4.00	2.00	1.25
81	Russ Snyder	4.00	2.00	1.25
82	Ruben Gomez	4.00	2.00	1.25
83	Tony Kubek	4.50	2.25	1.25
84	Hal Smith	4.00	2.00	1.25
85	Frank Lary	4.00	2.00	1.25
86	Dick Gernert	4.00	2.00	1.25
87	John Romonosky	4.00	2.00	1.25
88	John Roseboro	4.00	2.00	1.25
89	Hal Brown	4.00	2.00	1.25
90	Bobby Avila	4.00	2.00	1.25
91	Bennie Daniels	4.00	2.00	1.25
92	Whitey Herzog	4.50	2.25	1.25
93	Art Schult	4.00	2.00	1.25
94	Leo Kiely	4.00	2.00	1.25
95	Frank J. Thomas	4.00	2.00	1.25
96	Ralph Terry	4.00	2.00	1.25
97	Ted Lepcio	4.00	2.00	1.25
98	Gordon Jones	4.00	2.00	1.25
99	Lenny Green	4.00	2.00	1.25
100	Nellie Fox	7.00	3.50	2.00
101	Bob Miller	4.00	2.00	1.25
102	Kent Hadley	4.00	2.00	1.25
103	Dick Farrell	4.00	2.00	1.25
104	Dick Schofield	4.00	2.00	1.25
105	Larry Sherry	4.00	2.00	1.25
106	Billy Gardner	4.00	2.00	1.25
107	Carl Willey	4.00	2.00	1.25
108	Pete Daley	4.00	2.00	1.25
109	Cletis Boyer	4.00	2.00	1.25
110	Cal McLish	4.00	2.00	1.25
111	Vic Wertz	3.00	1.50	.90
112	Jack Harshman	3.00	1.50	.90
113	Bob Skinner	3.00	1.50	.90
114	Ken Aspromonte	3.00	1.50	.90
115	Fork and Knuckler (Roy Face, Hoyt Wilhelm)	6.00	3.00	1.75
116	Jim Rivera	3.00	1.50	.90
117	Tom Borland	3.00	1.50	.90
118	Bob Bruce	3.00	1.50	.90
119	*Chico Cardenas*	3.00	1.50	.90
120	Duke Carmel	3.00	1.50	.90
121	Camilo Carreon	3.00	1.50	.90
122	Don Dillard	3.00	1.50	.90
123	Dan Dobbek	3.00	1.50	.90
124	Jim Donohue	3.00	1.50	.90
125	*Dick Ellsworth*	3.00	1.50	.90
126	*Chuck Estrada*	3.00	1.50	.90
127	Ronnie Hansen	3.00	1.50	.90
128	Bill Harris	3.00	1.50	.90
129	Bob Hartman	3.00	1.50	.90
130	Frank Herrera	3.00	1.50	.90
131	Ed Hobaugh	3.00	1.50	.90
132	*Frank Howard*	20.00	10.00	6.00
133	*Manuel Javier*	3.00	1.50	.90
134	Deron Johnson	5.00	2.50	1.50
135	Ken Johnson	3.00	1.50	.90
136	*Jim Kaat*	38.00	19.00	11.00
137	Lou Klimchock	3.00	1.50	.90
138	*Art Mahaffey*	3.00	1.50	.90
139	Carl Mathias	3.00	1.50	.90
140	Julio Navarro	3.00	1.50	.90
141	Jim Proctor	3.00	1.50	.90

142 Bill Short 5.00 2.50 1.50
143 Al Spangler 3.00 1.50 .90
144 Al Stieglitz 3.00 1.50 .90
145 Jim Umbricht 3.00 1.50 .90
146 Ted Wieand 3.00 1.50 .90
147 Bob Will 3.00 1.50 .90
148 *Carl Yastrzemski* 200.00 100.00 60.00
149 Bob Nieman 3.00 1.50 .90
150 Billy Pierce 3.00 1.50 .90
151 Giants Team/Checklist 177-264 9.00 4.50 2.75
152 Gail Harris 3.00 1.50 .90
153 Bobby Thomson 3.00 1.50 .90
154 Jim Davenport 3.00 1.50 .90
155 Charlie Neal 3.00 1.50 .90
156 Art Ceccarelli 3.00 1.50 .90
157 Rocky Nelson 3.00 1.50 .90
158 Wes Covington 3.00 1.50 .90
159 Jim Piersall 3.00 1.50 .90
160 Rival All-Stars (Ken Boyer, Mickey Mantle) 55.00 27.00 16.50
161 Ray Narleski 3.00 1.50 .90
162 Sammy Taylor 3.00 1.50 .90
163 Hector Lopez 3.00 1.50 .90
164 Reds Team/Checklist 89-176 9.00 4.50 2.75
165 Jack Sanford 3.00 1.50 .90
166 Chuck Essegian 3.00 1.50 .90
167 Valmy Thomas 3.00 1.50 .90
168 Alex Grammas 3.00 1.50 .90
169 Jake Striker 3.00 1.50 .90
170 Del Crandall 3.00 1.50 .90
171 Johnny Groth 3.00 1.50 .90
172 Willie Kirkland 3.00 1.50 .90
173 Billy Martin 10.00 5.00 3.00
174 Indians Team/Checklist 89-176 9.00 4.50 2.75
175 Pedro Ramos 3.00 1.50 .90
176 Vada Pinson 3.00 1.50 .90
177 Johnny Kucks 3.00 1.50 .90
178 Woody Held 3.00 1.50 .90
179 Rip Coleman 3.00 1.50 .90
180 Harry Simpson 3.00 1.50 .90
181 Billy Loes 3.00 1.50 .90
182 Glen Hobbie 3.00 1.50 .90
183 Eli Grba 3.00 1.50 .90
184 Gary Geiger 3.00 1.50 .90
185 Jim Owens 3.00 1.50 .90
186 Dave Sisler 3.00 1.50 .90
187 Jay Hook 3.00 1.50 .90
188 Dick Williams 3.00 1.50 .90
189 Don McMahon 3.00 1.50 .90
190 Gene Woodling 3.00 1.50 .90
191 Johnny Klippstein 3.00 1.50 .90
192 Danny O'Connell 3.00 1.50 .90
193 Dick Hyde 3.00 1.50 .90
194 Bobby Gene Smith 3.00 1.50 .90
195 Lindy McDaniel 3.00 1.50 .90
196 Andy Carey 3.00 1.50 .90
197 Ron Kline 3.00 1.50 .90
198 Jerry Lynch 3.00 1.50 .90
199 Dick Donovan 3.00 1.50 .90
200 Willie Mays 115.00 55.00 33.00
201 Larry Osborne 3.00 1.50 .90
202 Fred Kipp 3.00 1.50 .90
203 Sammy White 3.00 1.50 .90
204 Ryne Duren 4.50 2.25 1.25
205 Johnny Logan 3.00 1.50 .90
206 Claude Osteen 3.00 1.50 .90
207 Bob Boyd 3.00 1.50 .90
208 White Sox Team/Checklist 177-264 9.00 4.50 2.75
209 Ron Blackburn 3.00 1.50 .90
210 Harmon Killebrew 25.00 12.50 7.50
211 Taylor Phillips 3.00 1.50 .90
212 Walt Alston 9.00 4.50 2.75
213 Chuck Dressen 3.00 1.50 .90
214 Jimmie Dykes 3.00 1.50 .90
215 Bob Elliott 3.00 1.50 .90
216 Joe Gordon 3.00 1.50 .90
217 Charley Grimm 3.00 1.50 .90
218 Solly Hemus 3.00 1.50 .90
219 Fred Hutchinson 3.00 1.50 .90
220 Billy Jurges 3.00 1.50 .90
221 Cookie Lavagetto 3.00 1.50 .90
222 Al Lopez 5.50 2.75 1.75
223 Danny Murtaugh 3.00 1.50 .90
224 Paul Richards 3.00 1.50 .90
225 Bill Rigney 3.00 1.50 .90
226 Eddie Sawyer 3.00 1.50 .90
227 Casey Stengel 15.00 7.50 4.50
228 Ernie Johnson 3.00 1.50 .90
229 Joe M. Morgan 3.00 1.50 .90
230 Mound Magicians (Bob Buhl, Lou Burdette, Warren Spahn) 9.00 4.50 2.75
231 Hal Naragon 3.00 1.50 .90
232 Jim Busby 3.00 1.50 .90
233 Don Elston 3.00 1.50 .90
234 Don Demeter 3.00 1.50 .90
235 Gus Bell 3.00 1.50 .90
236 Dick Ricketts 3.00 1.50 .90
237 Elmer Valo 3.00 1.50 .90
238 Danny Kravitz 3.00 1.50 .90
239 Joe Shipley 3.00 1.50 .90
240 Luis Aparicio 12.00 6.00 3.50
241 Albie Pearson 3.00 1.50 .90
242 Cards Team/Checklist 265-352 9.00 4.50 2.75
243 Bubba Phillips 3.00 1.50 .90
244 Hal Griggs 3.00 1.50 .90
245 Eddie Yost 3.00 1.50 .90
246 Lee Maye 3.00 1.50 .90
247 Gil McDougald 5.00 2.50 1.50
248 Del Rice 3.00 1.50 .90
249 *Earl Wilson* 3.00 1.50 .90
250 Stan Musial 115.00 55.00 33.00
251 Bobby Malkmus 3.00 1.50 .90
252 Ray Herbert 3.00 1.50 .90
253 Eddie Bressoud 3.00 1.50 .90
254 Arnie Portocarrero 3.00 1.50 .90
255 Jim Gilliam 5.00 2.50 1.50
256 Dick Brown 3.00 1.50 .90
257 Gordy Coleman 3.00 1.50 .90
258 Dick Groat 4.50 2.25 1.25
259 George Altman 3.00 1.50 .90
260 Power Plus (Rocky Colavito, Tito Francona) 6.00 3.00 1.75
261 Pete Burnside 3.00 1.50 .90
262 Hank Bauer 3.00 1.50 .90
263 Darrell Johnson 3.00 1.50 .90
264 Robin Roberts 14.00 7.00 4.25
265 Rip Repulski 3.00 1.50 .90
266 Joe Jay 3.00 1.50 .90
267 Jim Marshall 3.00 1.50 .90
268 Al Worthington 3.00 1.50 .90
269 Gene Green 3.00 1.50 .90
270 Bob Turley 4.50 2.25 1.25
271 Julio Becquer 3.00 1.50 .90
272 Fred Green 3.00 1.50 .90
273 Neil Chrisley 3.00 1.50 .90
274 Tom Acker 3.00 1.50 .90
275 Curt Flood 3.00 1.50 .90
276 Ken McBride 3.00 1.50 .90
277 Harry Bright 3.00 1.50 .90
278 Stan Williams 3.00 1.50 .90
279 Chuck Tanner 3.00 1.50 .90
280 Frank Sullivan 3.00 1.50 .90
281 Ray Boone 3.00 1.50 .90
282 Joe Nuxhall 3.00 1.50 .90
283 John Blanchard 4.50 2.25 1.25
284 Don Gross 3.00 1.50 .90
285 Harry Anderson 3.00 1.50 .90
286 Ray Semproch 3.00 1.50 .90
287 Felipe Alou 6.00 3.00 1.75
288 Bob Mabe 4.00 2.00 1.25
289 Willie Jones 4.00 2.00 1.25
290 Jerry Lumpe 4.00 2.00 1.25
291 Bob Keegan 4.00 2.00 1.25
292 Dodger Backstops (Joe Pignatano, John Roseboro) 6.00 3.00 1.75
293 Gene Conley 4.00 2.00 1.25
294 Tony Taylor 4.00 2.00 1.25
295 Gil Hodges 20.00 10.00 6.00
296 Nelson Chittum 4.00 2.00 1.25
297 Reno Bertoia 4.00 2.00 1.25
298 George Witt 4.00 2.00 1.25
299 Earl Torgeson 4.00 2.00 1.25
300 Hank Aaron 105.00 52.50 31.00
301 Jerry Davie 4.00 2.00 1.25
302 Phillies Team/Checklist 353-429 10.00 5.00 3.00
303 Billy O'Dell 4.00 2.00 1.25
304 Joe Ginsberg 4.00 2.00 1.25
305 Richie Ashburn 10.00 5.00 3.00
306 Frank Baumann 4.00 2.00 1.25
307 Gene Oliver 4.00 2.00 1.25
308 Dick Hall 4.00 2.00 1.25
309 Bob Hale 4.00 2.00 1.25
310 Frank Malzone 4.00 2.00 1.25
311 Raul Sanchez 4.00 2.00 1.25
312 Charlie Lau 4.50 2.25 1.25
313 Turk Lown 4.00 2.00 1.25
314 Chico Fernandez 4.00 2.00 1.25
315 Bobby Shantz 5.00 2.50 1.50
316 *Willie McCovey* 185.00 92.50 55.00
317 Pumpsie Green 4.00 2.00 1.25
318 Jim Baxes 4.00 2.00 1.25
319 Joe Koppe 4.00 2.00 1.25
320 Bob Allison 4.00 2.00 1.25
321 Ron Fairly 4.00 2.00 1.25
322 Willie Tasby 4.00 2.00 1.25
323 Johnny Romano 4.00 2.00 1.25
324 Jim Perry 4.00 2.00 1.25
325 Jim O'Toole 4.00 2.00 1.25
326 Roberto Clemente 130.00 65.00 40.00
327 *Ray Sadecki* 4.00 2.00 1.25
328 Earl Battey 4.00 2.00 1.25
329 Zack Monroe 4.00 2.00 1.25
330 Harvey Kuenn 4.50 2.25 1.25
331 Henry Mason 4.00 2.00 1.25
332 Yankees Team/Checklist 265-352 28.00 14.00 8.25
333 Danny McDevitt 4.00 2.00 1.25
334 Ted Abernathy 4.00 2.00 1.25
335 Red Schoendienst 10.00 5.00 3.00
336 Ike Delock 4.00 2.00 1.25
337 Cal Neeman 4.00 2.00 1.25
338 Ray Monzant 4.00 2.00 1.25
339 Harry Chiti 4.00 2.00 1.25
340 Harvey Haddix 4.00 2.00 1.25
341 Carroll Hardy 4.00 2.00 1.25
342 Casey Wise 4.00 2.00 1.25
343 Sandy Koufax 125.00 62.00 37.00
344 Clint Courtney 4.00 2.00 1.25
345 Don Newcombe 4.00 2.00 1.25
346 J.C. Martin (photo actually Gary Peters) 4.00 2.00 1.25
347 Ed Bouchee 4.00 2.00 1.25
348 Barry Shetrone 4.00 2.00 1.25
349 Moe Drabowsky 4.00 2.00 1.25
350 Mickey Mantle 400.00 200.00 120.00
351 Don Nottebart 4.00 2.00 1.25
352 Cincy Clouters (Gus Bell, Jerry Lynch, Frank Robinson) 9.00 4.50 2.75
353 Don Larsen 4.50 2.25 1.25
354 Bob Lillis 4.00 2.00 1.25
355 Bill White 4.50 2.25 1.25
356 Joe Amalfitano 4.00 2.00 1.25
357 Al Schroll 4.00 2.00 1.25
358 Joe DeMaestri 4.00 2.00 1.25
359 Buddy Gilbert 4.00 2.00 1.25
360 Herb Score 4.00 2.00 1.25
361 Bob Oldis 4.00 2.00 1.25
362 Russ Kemmerer 4.00 2.00 1.25
363 Gene Stephens 4.00 2.00 1.25
364 Paul Foytack 4.00 2.00 1.25
365 Minnie Minoso 4.50 2.25 1.25
366 *Dallas Green* 4.50 2.25 1.25
367 Bill Tuttle 4.00 2.00 1.25
368 Daryl Spencer 4.00 2.00 1.25
369 Billy Hoeft 4.00 2.00 1.25
370 Bill Skowron 6.00 3.00 1.75
371 Bud Byerly 4.00 2.00 1.25
372 Frank House 4.00 2.00 1.25
373 Don Hoak 4.00 2.00 1.25
374 Bob Buhl 4.00 2.00 1.25
375 Dale Long 4.00 2.00 1.25
376 Johnny Briggs 4.00 2.00 1.25
377 Roger Maris 100.00 50.00 30.00
378 Stu Miller 4.00 2.00 1.25
379 Red Wilson 4.00 2.00 1.25
380 Bob Shaw 4.00 2.00 1.25
381 Braves Team/Checklist 353-429 10.00 5.00 3.00
382 Ted Bowsfield 4.00 2.00 1.25
383 Leon Wagner 4.00 2.00 1.25
384 Don Cardwell 4.00 2.00 1.25
385 World Series Game 1 (Neal Steals Second) 6.00 3.00 1.75
386 World Series Game 2 (Neal Belts 2nd Homer) 6.00 3.00 1.75
387 World Series Game 3 (Furillo Breaks Up Game) 8.00 4.00 2.50
388 World Series Game 4 (Hodges' Winning Homer) 8.00 4.00 2.50
389 World Series Game 5 (Luis Swipes Base) 8.00 4.00 2.50
390 World Series Game 6 (Scrambling After Ball) 6.00 3.00 1.75
391 World Series Summary (The Champs Celebrate) 7.00 3.50 2.00
392 Tex Clevenger 4.00 2.00 1.25
393 Smoky Burgess 4.00 2.00 1.25
394 Norm Larker 4.00 2.00 1.25
395 Hoyt Wilhelm 12.00 6.00 3.50
396 Steve Bilko 4.00 2.00 1.25
397 Don Blasingame 4.00 2.00 1.25
398 Mike Cuellar 4.00 2.00 1.25
399 Young Hill Stars (Jack Fisher, Milt Pappas, Jerry Walker) 5.00 2.50 1.50
400 Rocky Colavito 15.00 7.50 4.50
401 Bob Duliba 4.00 2.00 1.25
402 Dick Stuart 4.50 2.25 1.25
403 Ed Sadowski 4.00 2.00 1.25
404 Bob Rush 4.00 2.00 1.25
405 Bobby Richardson 6.00 3.00 1.75
406 Billy Klaus 4.00 2.00 1.25
407 *Gary Peters* (photo actually J.C. Martin) 4.00 2.00 1.25
408 Carl Furillo 7.50 3.75 2.25
409 Ron Samford 4.00 2.00 1.25
410 Sam Jones 4.00 2.00 1.25
411 Ed Bailey 4.00 2.00 1.25
412 Bob Anderson 4.00 2.00 1.25
413 A's Team/Checklist 430-495 10.00 5.00 3.00
414 Don Williams 4.00 2.00 1.25
415 Bob Cerv 4.00 2.00 1.25
416 Humberto Robinson 4.00 2.00 1.25
417 Chuck Cottier 4.00 2.00 1.25
418 Don Mossi 4.00 2.00 1.25
419 George Crowe 4.00 2.00 1.25
420 Eddie Mathews 30.00 15.00 9.00
421 Duke Maas 4.00 2.00 1.25
422 Johnny Powers 4.00 2.00 1.25
423 Ed Fitz Gerald 4.00 2.00 1.25
424 Pete Whisenant 4.00 2.00 1.25
425 Johnny Podres 4.50 2.25 1.25
426 Ron Jackson 4.00 2.00 1.25
427 Al Grunwald 4.00 2.00 1.25
428 Al Smith 4.00 2.00 1.25
429 American League Kings (Nellie Fox, Harvey Kuenn) 6.00 3.00 1.75
430 Art Ditmar 4.00 2.00 1.25
431 Andre Rodgers 4.00 2.00 1.25
432 Chuck Stobbs 4.00 2.00 1.25
433 Irv Noren 4.00 2.00 1.25
434 Brooks Lawrence 4.00 2.00 1.25
435 Gene Freese 4.00 2.00 1.25
436 Marv Throneberry 4.00 2.00 1.25
437 Bob Friend 4.00 2.00 1.25
438 Jim Coker 4.00 2.00 1.25
439 Tom Brewer 4.00 2.00 1.25
440 Jim Lemon 4.00 2.00 1.25
441 Gary Bell 5.50 2.75 1.75
442 Joe Pignatano 5.50 2.75 1.75
443 Charlie Maxwell 5.50 2.75 1.75
444 Jerry Kindall 5.50 2.75 1.75
445 Warren Spahn 45.00 22.50 13.50
446 Ellis Burton 5.50 2.75 1.75
447 Ray Moore 5.50 2.75 1.75
448 *Jim Gentile* 5.50 2.75 1.75
449 Jim Brosnan 5.50 2.75 1.75
450 Orlando Cepeda 20.00 10.00 6.00
451 Curt Simmons 5.50 2.75 1.75
452 Ray Webster 5.50 2.75 1.75
453 Vern Law 5.50 2.75 1.75
454 Hal Woodeshick 5.50 2.75 1.75
455 Orioles Coaches (Harry Brecheen, Lum Harris, Eddie Robinson) 5.50 2.75 1.75
456 Red Sox Coaches (Del Baker, Billy Herman, Sal Maglie, Rudy York) 6.50 3.25 2.00
457 Cubs Coaches (Lou Klein, Charlie Root, Elvin Tappe) 5.50 2.75 1.75
458 White Sox Coaches (Ray Berres, Johnny Cooney, Tony Cuccinello, Don Gutteridge) 5.50 2.75 1.75
459 Reds Coaches (Cot Deal, Wally Moses, Reggie Otero) 5.50 2.75 1.75
460 Indians Coaches (Mel Harder, Red Kress, Bob Lemon, Jo-Jo White) 6.50 3.25 2.00
461 Tigers Coaches (Luke Appling, Tom Ferrick, Billy Hitchcock) 6.50 3.25 2.00
462 A's Coaches (Walker Cooper, Fred Fitzsimmons, Don Heffner) 5.50 2.75 1.75
463 Dodgers Coaches (Joe Becker, Bobby Bragan, Greg Mulleavy, Pete Reiser) 5.50 2.75 1.75
464 Braves Coaches (George Myatt, Andy Pafko, Bob Scheffing, Whitlow Wyatt) 5.50 2.75 1.75

		NR MT	EX	VG
465	Yankees Coaches (Frank Crosetti, Bill Dickey, Ralph Houk, Ed Lopat)	12.00	6.00	3.50
466	Phillies Coaches (Dick Carter, Andy Cohen, Ken Silvestri)	5.50	2.75	1.75
467	Pirates Coaches (Bill Burwell, Sam Narron, Frank Oceak, Mickey Vernon)	5.50	2.75	1.75
468	Cardinals Coaches (Ray Katt, Johnny Keane, Howie Pollet, Harry Walker)	5.50	2.75	1.75
469	Giants Coaches (Salty Parker, Bill Posedel, Wes Westrum)	5.50	2.75	1.75
470	Senators Coaches (Ellis Clary, Sam Mele, Bob Swift)	5.50	2.75	1.75
471	Ned Garver	5.50	2.75	1.75
472	Al Dark	5.50	2.75	1.75
473	Al Cicotte	5.50	2.75	1.75
474	Haywood Sullivan	5.50	2.75	1.75
475	Don Drysdale	40.00	20.00	12.00
476	Lou Johnson	5.50	2.75	1.75
477	Don Ferrarese	5.50	2.75	1.75
478	Frank Torre	5.50	2.75	1.75
479	Georges Maranda	5.50	2.75	1.75
480	Yogi Berra	75.00	37.00	22.00
481	Wes Stock	5.50	2.75	1.75
482	Frank Bolling	5.50	2.75	1.75
483	Camilo Pascual	5.50	2.75	1.75
484	Pirates Team/Checklist 430-495	25.00	12.50	7.50
485	Ken Boyer	8.00	4.00	3.25
486	Bobby Del Greco	5.50	2.75	1.75
487	Tom Sturdivant	5.50	2.75	1.75
488	Norm Cash	6.00	3.00	1.75
489	Steve Ridzik	5.50	2.75	1.75
490	Frank Robinson	48.00	24.00	14.00
491	Mel Roach	5.50	2.75	1.75
492	Larry Jackson	5.50	2.75	1.75
493	Duke Snider	48.00	24.00	14.00
494	Orioles Team/Checklist 496-572	10.00	5.00	3.00
495	Sherm Lollar	5.50	2.75	1.75
496	Bill Virdon	5.50	2.75	1.75
497	John Tsitouris	5.50	2.75	1.75
498	Al Pilarcik	5.50	2.75	1.75
499	Johnny James	5.50	2.75	1.75
500	Johnny Temple	5.50	2.75	1.75
501	Bob Schmidt	5.50	2.75	1.75
502	Jim Bunning	12.00	6.00	3.50
503	Don Lee	5.50	2.75	1.75
504	Seth Morehead	5.50	2.75	1.75
505	Ted Kluszewski	9.00	4.50	2.75
506	Lee Walls	5.50	2.75	1.75
507	Dick Stigman	12.00	6.00	3.50
508	Billy Consolo	12.00	6.00	3.50
509	*Tommy Davis*	25.00	12.50	7.50
510	Jerry Staley	12.00	6.00	3.50
511	Ken Walters	12.00	6.00	3.50
512	Joe Gibbon	12.00	6.00	3.50
513	Cubs Team/Checklist 496-572	30.00	15.00	9.00
514	*Steve Barber*	12.00	6.00	3.50
515	Stan Lopata	12.00	6.00	3.50
516	Marty Kutyna	12.00	6.00	3.50
517	Charley James	12.00	6.00	3.50
518	*Tony Gonzalez*	12.00	6.00	3.50
519	Ed Roebuck	12.00	6.00	3.50
520	Don Buddin	12.00	6.00	3.50
521	Mike Lee	12.00	6.00	3.50
522	Ken Hunt	12.00	6.00	3.50
523	*Clay Dalrymple*	12.00	6.00	3.50
524	Bill Henry	12.00	6.00	3.50
525	Marv Breeding	12.00	6.00	3.50
526	Paul Giel	12.00	6.00	3.50
527	Jose Valdivielso	12.00	6.00	3.50
528	Ben Johnson	12.00	6.00	3.50
529	Norm Sherry	12.00	6.00	3.50
530	Mike McCormick	12.00	6.00	3.50
531	Sandy Amoros	12.00	6.00	3.50
532	Mike Garcia	12.00	6.00	3.50
533	Lu Clinton	12.00	6.00	3.50
534	Ken MacKenzie	12.00	6.00	3.50
535	Whitey Lockman	12.00	6.00	3.50
536	Wynn Hawkins	12.00	6.00	3.50
537	Red Sox Team/Checklist 496-572	30.00	15.00	9.00
538	Frank Barnes	12.00	6.00	3.50
539	Gene Baker	12.00	6.00	3.50
540	Jerry Walker	12.00	6.00	3.50
541	Tony Curry	12.00	6.00	3.50
542	Ken Hamlin	12.00	6.00	3.50
543	Elio Chacon	12.00	6.00	3.50
544	Bill Monbouquette	12.00	6.00	3.50
545	Carl Sawatski	12.00	6.00	3.50
546	Hank Aguirre	12.00	6.00	3.50
547	*Bob Aspromonte*	12.00	6.00	3.50
548	*Don Mincher*	12.00	6.00	3.50
549	John Buzhardt	12.00	6.00	3.50
550	Jim Landis	12.00	6.00	3.50
551	Ed Rakow	12.00	6.00	3.50
552	Walt Bond	12.00	6.00	3.50
553	Bill Skowron (All-Star)	20.00	10.00	6.00
554	Willie McCovey (All-Star)	50.00	25.00	15.00
555	Nellie Fox (All-Star)	25.00	12.50	7.50
556	Charlie Neal (All-Star)	20.00	10.00	6.00
557	Frank Malzone (All-Star)	20.00	10.00	6.00
558	Eddie Mathews (All-Star)	35.00	17.50	10.50
559	Luis Aparicio (All-Star)	25.00	12.50	7.50
560	Ernie Banks (All-Star)	55.00	27.00	16.50
561	Al Kaline (All-Star)	55.00	27.00	16.50
562	Joe Cunningham (All-Star)	20.00	10.00	6.00
563	Mickey Mantle (All-Star)	250.00	125.00	75.00
564	Willie Mays (All-Star)	130.00	65.00	40.00
565	Roger Maris (All-Star)	100.00	50.00	30.00
566	Hank Aaron (All-Star)	125.00	62.50	37.50
567	Sherm Lollar (All-Star)	20.00	10.00	6.00
568	Del Crandall (All-Star)	20.00	10.00	6.00
569	Camilo Pascual (All-Star)	20.00	10.00	6.00
570	Don Drysdale (All-Star)	30.00	15.00	9.00
571	Billy Pierce (All-Star)	20.00	10.00	6.00
572	Johnny Antonelli (All-Star)	30.00	15.00	9.00
----	Elect Your Favorite Rookie Insert (paper stock, no date on back)	15.00	7.50	4.50
----	Hot Iron Transfer Insert (paper stock)	15.00	7.50	4.50

1960 Topps Baseball Tattoos

Probably the least popular of all Topps products among parents and teachers, the Topps Tattoos were delightful little items on the reverse of the wrappers of Topps "Tattoo Bubble Gum." The entire wrapper was 1-9/16" by 3-1/2." The happy owner simply moistened his skin and applied the back of the wrapper to the wet spot. Presto, out came a "tattoo" in color (although often blurred by running colors). The set offered 96 tattoo possibilities of which 55 were players, 16 teams, 15 action shots and 10 autographed balls. Surviving specimens are very rare today.

		NR MT	EX	VG
Complete Set (96):		1000.	500.00	300.00
Common Player:		9.00	4.50	2.75
Common Non-player:		6.00	3.00	1.75
(1)	Hank Aaron	37.50	18.50	11.00
(2)	Bob Allison	11.00	5.50	3.25
(3)	John Antonelli	9.00	4.50	2.75
(4)	Richie Ashburn	17.50	8.75	5.25
(5)	Ernie Banks	20.00	10.00	6.00
(6)	Yogi Berra	25.00	12.50	7.50
(7)	Lew Burdette	9.00	4.50	2.75
(8)	Orlando Cepeda	11.00	5.50	3.25
(9)	Rocky Colavito	15.00	7.50	4.50
(10)	Joe Cunningham	9.00	4.50	2.75
(11)	Buddy Daley	9.00	4.50	2.75
(12)	Don Drysdale	24.00	12.00	7.25
(13)	Ryne Duren	11.00	5.50	3.25
(14)	Roy Face	11.00	5.50	3.25
(15)	Whitey Ford	17.50	8.75	5.25
(16)	Nellie Fox	13.50	6.75	4.00
(17)	Tito Francona	9.00	4.50	2.75
(18)	Gene Freese	9.00	4.50	2.75
(19)	Jim Gilliam	12.00	6.00	3.50
(20)	Dick Groat	12.00	6.00	3.50
(21)	Ray Herbert	9.00	4.50	2.75
(22)	Glen Hobbie	9.00	4.50	2.75
(23)	Jackie Jensen	12.00	6.00	3.50
(24)	Sam Jones	9.00	4.50	2.75
(25)	Al Kaline	25.00	12.50	7.50
(26)	Harmon Killebrew	25.00	12.50	7.50
(27)	Harvey Kuenn (Harvey)	12.00	6.00	3.50
(28)	Frank Lary	9.00	4.50	2.75
(29)	Vernon Law	11.00	5.50	3.25
(30)	Frank Malzone	9.00	4.50	2.75
(31)	Mickey Mantle	125.00	62.00	37.00
(32)	Roger Maris	30.00	15.00	9.00
(33)	Ed Mathews	20.00	10.00	6.00
(34)	Willie Mays	37.50	18.50	11.00
(35)	Cal Mclish	9.00	4.50	2.75
(36)	Wally Moon	11.00	5.50	3.25
(37)	Walt Moryn	9.00	4.50	2.75
(38)	Don Mossi	9.00	4.50	2.75
(39)	Stan Musial	37.50	18.50	11.00
(40)	Charlie Neal	9.00	4.50	2.75
(41)	Don Newcombe	12.00	6.00	3.50
(42)	Milt Pappas	11.00	5.50	3.25
(43)	Camilo Pascual	11.00	5.50	3.25
(44)	Billie (Billy) Pierce	11.00	5.50	3.25
(45)	Robin Roberts	22.00	11.00	6.50
(46)	Frank Robinson	24.00	12.00	7.25
(47)	Pete Runnels	9.00	4.50	2.75
(48)	Herb Score	11.00	5.50	3.25
(49)	Warren Spahn	20.00	10.00	6.00
(50)	Johnny Temple	9.00	4.50	2.75
(51)	Gus Triandos	9.00	4.50	2.75
(52)	Jerry Walker	9.00	4.50	2.75
(53)	Bill White	11.00	5.50	3.25
(54)	Gene Woodling	11.00	5.50	3.25
(55)	Early Wynn	20.00	10.00	6.00
(56)	Chicago Cubs Logo	7.00	3.50	2.00
(57)	Cincinnati Reds Logo	7.00	3.50	2.00
(58)	Los Angeles Dodgers Logo	9.00	4.50	2.75
(59)	Milwaukee Braves Logo	7.00	3.50	2.00
(60)	Philadelphia Phillies Logo	7.00	3.50	2.00
(61)	Pittsburgh Pirates Logo	9.00	4.50	2.75
(62)	San Francisco Giants Logo	7.00	3.50	2.00
(63)	St. Louis Cardinals Logo	7.00	3.50	2.00
(64)	Baltimore Orioles Logo	7.00	3.50	2.00
(65)	Boston Red Sox Logo	7.00	3.50	2.00
(66)	Chicago White Sox Logo	7.00	3.50	2.00
(67)	Cleveland Indians Logo	7.00	3.50	2.00
(68)	Detroit Tigers Logo	7.00	3.50	2.00
(69)	Kansas City Athletics Logo	7.00	3.50	2.00
(70)	New York Yankees Logo	11.00	5.50	3.25
(71)	Washington Senators Logo	7.00	3.50	2.00
(72)	Autograph (Richie Ashburn)	12.00	6.00	3.50
(73)	Autograph (Rocky Colavito)	15.00	7.50	4.50
(74)	Autograph (Roy Face)	9.00	4.50	2.75
(75)	Autograph (Jackie Jensen)	11.00	5.50	3.25
(76)	Autograph (Harmon Killebrew)	20.00	10.00	6.00
(77)	Autograph (Mickey Mantle)	50.00	25.00	15.00
(78)	Autograph (Willie Mays)	25.00	12.50	7.50
(79)	Autograph (Stan Musial)	25.00	12.50	7.50
(80)	Autograph (Billy Pierce)	9.00	4.50	2.75
(81)	Autograph (Jerry Walker)	9.00	4.50	2.75
(82)	Run-Down	6.00	3.00	1.75
(83)	Out At First	6.00	3.00	1.75
(84)	The Final Word	6.00	3.00	1.75
(85)	Twisting Foul	6.00	3.00	1.75
(86)	Out At Home	6.00	3.00	1.75
(87)	Circus Catch	6.00	3.00	1.75
(88)	Great Catch	6.00	3.00	1.75
(89)	Stolen Base	6.00	3.00	1.75
(90)	Grand Slam Homer	6.00	3.00	1.75
(91)	Double Play	6.00	3.00	1.75
(92)	Right-Handed Follow-Thru (no caption)	6.00	3.00	1.75
(93)	Right-Handed High Leg Kick (no caption)	6.00	3.00	1.75
(94)	Left-Handed Pitcher (no caption)	6.00	3.00	1.75
(95)	Right-Handed Batter (no caption)	6.00	3.00	1.75
(96)	Left-Handed Batter (no caption)	6.00	3.00	1.75

1961 Topps

Except for some of the specialty cards, Topps returned to a vertical format with their 1961 cards. The set is numbered through 598, however only 587 cards were printed. No numbers 426, 587 and 588 were issued. Two cards numbered 463 exist (one a Braves team card and one a player card of Jack Fisher). Actually, the Braves team card is checklisted as #426. Designs for 1961 are basically large color portraits; the backs return to extensive statistics. A three-panel cartoon highlighting the player's career appears on the card backs. Innovations include numbered checklists, cards for statistical leaders, and 10 "Baseball Thrills" cards. The scarce high numbers are card numbers 523-589.

		NR MT	EX	VG
Complete Set (587):		6000.	2850.	1700.
Common Player (1-446):		2.50	1.25	.70
Common Player (447-522):		4.50	2.25	1.25
Common Player (523-589):		35.00	17.50	10.50
1	Dick Groat	20.00	9.00	4.00
2	Roger Maris	160.00	80.00	48.00
3	John Buzhardt	2.50	1.25	.70
4	Lenny Green	2.50	1.25	.70
5	Johnny Romano	2.50	1.25	.70
6	Ed Roebuck	2.50	1.25	.70
7	White Sox Team	6.00	3.00	1.75
8	Dick Williams	4.50	2.25	1.25
9	Bob Purkey	2.50	1.25	.70
10	Brooks Robinson	30.00	15.00	9.00
11	Curt Simmons	2.50	1.25	.70
12	Moe Thacker	2.50	1.25	.70
13	Chuck Cottier	2.50	1.25	.70
14	Don Mossi	2.50	1.25	.70
15	Willie Kirkland	2.50	1.25	.70
16	Billy Muffett	2.50	1.25	.70
17	Checklist 1-88	7.00	3.50	2.00
18	Jim Grant	2.50	1.25	.70
19	Cletis Boyer	2.50	1.25	.70
20	Robin Roberts	10.00	5.00	3.00
21	*Zorro Versalles*	3.50	1.75	1.00
22	Clem Labine	2.50	1.25	.70
23	Don Demeter	2.50	1.25	.70
24	Ken Johnson	2.50	1.25	.70
25	Reds' Heavy Artillery (Gus Bell, Vada Pinson, Frank Robinson)	8.00	4.00	2.50
26	Wes Stock	2.50	1.25	.70
27	Jerry Kindall	2.50	1.25	.70
28	Hector Lopez	2.50	1.25	.70
29	Don Nottebart	2.50	1.25	.70
30	Nellie Fox	6.00	3.00	1.75
31	Bob Schmidt	2.50	1.25	.70
32	Ray Sadecki	2.50	1.25	.70
33	Gary Geiger	2.50	1.25	.70
34	Wynn Hawkins	2.50	1.25	.70
35	*Ron Santo*	65.00	32.00	19.50
36	Jack Kralick	2.50	1.25	.70
37	Charlie Maxwell	2.50	1.25	.70
38	Bob Lillis	2.50	1.25	.70
39	Leo Posada	2.50	1.25	.70
40	Bob Turley	3.00	1.50	.90

41 N.L. Batting Leaders (Roberto Clemente, Dick Groat, Norm Larker, Willie Mays) 8.00 4.00 2.50
42 A.L. Batting Leaders (Minnie Minoso, Pete Runnels, Bill Skowron, Al Smith) 6.00 3.00 1.75
43 N.L. Home Run Leaders (Hank Aaron, Ernie Banks, Ken Boyer, Eddie Mathews) 9.00 4.50 2.75
44 A.L. Home Run Leaders (Rocky Colavito, Jim Lemon, Mickey Mantle, Roger Maris) 35.00 17.50 10.50
45 N.L. E.R.A. Leaders (Ernie Broglio, Don Drysdale, Bob Friend, Mike McCormick, Stan Williams) 6.00 3.00 1.75
46 A.L. E.R.A. Leaders (Frank Baumann, Hal Brown, Jim Bunning, Art Ditmar) 6.00 3.00 1.75
47 N.L. Pitching Leaders (Ernie Broglio, Lou Burdette, Vern Law, Warren Spahn) 6.00 3.00 1.75
48 A.L. Pitching Leaders (Bud Daley, Art Ditmar, Chuck Estrada, Frank Lary, Milt Pappas, Jim Perry) 6.00 3.00 1.75
49 N.L. Strikeout Leaders (Ernie Broglio, Don Drysdale, Sam Jones, Sandy Koufax) 8.00 4.00 2.50
50 A.L. Strikeout Leaders (Jim Bunning, Frank Lary, Pedro Ramos, Early Wynn) 6.00 3.00 1.75
51 Tigers Team 7.50 3.75 2.25
52 George Crowe 2.50 1.25 .70
53 Russ Nixon 2.50 1.25 .70
54 Earl Francis 2.50 1.25 .70
55 Jim Davenport 2.50 1.25 .70
56 Russ Kemmerer 2.50 1.25 .70
57 Marv Throneberry 2.50 1.25 .70
58 Joe Schaffernoth 2.50 1.25 .70
59 Jim Woods 2.50 1.25 .70
60 Woodie Held 2.50 1.25 .70
61 Ron Piche 2.50 1.25 .70
62 Al Pilarcik 2.50 1.25 .70
63 Jim Kaat 7.50 3.75 2.25
64 Alex Grammas 2.50 1.25 .70
65 Ted Kluszewski 7.50 3.75 2.25
66 Bill Henry 2.50 1.25 .70
67 Ossie Virgil 2.50 1.25 .70
68 Deron Johnson 2.50 1.25 .70
69 Earl Wilson 2.50 1.25 .70
70 Bill Virdon 2.50 1.25 .70
71 Jerry Adair 2.50 1.25 .70
72 Stu Miller 2.50 1.25 .70
73 Al Spangler 2.50 1.25 .70
74 Joe Pignatano 2.50 1.25 .70
75 Lindy Shows Larry (Larry Jackson, Lindy McDaniel) 5.00 2.50 1.50
76 Harry Anderson 2.50 1.25 .70
77 Dick Stigman 2.50 1.25 .70
78 Lee Walls 2.50 1.25 .70
79 Joe Ginsberg 2.50 1.25 .70
80 Harmon Killebrew 23.00 11.50 7.00
81 Tracy Stallard 2.50 1.25 .70
82 Joe Christopher 2.50 1.25 .70
83 Bob Bruce 2.50 1.25 .70
84 Lee Maye 2.50 1.25 .70
85 Jerry Walker 2.50 1.25 .70
86 Dodgers Team 7.50 3.75 2.25
87 Joe Amalfitano 2.50 1.25 .70
88 Richie Ashburn 8.00 4.00 2.50
89 Billy Martin 8.00 4.00 2.50
90 Jerry Staley 2.50 1.25 .70
91 Walt Moryn 2.50 1.25 .70
92 Hal Naragon 2.50 1.25 .70
93 Tony Gonzalez 2.50 1.25 .70
94 Johnny Kucks 2.50 1.25 .70
95 Norm Cash 3.50 1.75 1.00
96 Billy O'Dell 2.50 1.25 .70
97 Jerry Lynch 2.50 1.25 .70
98a Checklist 89-176 (word "Checklist" in red on front) 9.00 4.50 2.75
98b Checklist 89-176 ("Checklist" in yellow, 98 on back in black) 6.00 3.00 1.75
98c Checklist 89-176 ("Checklist" in yellow, 98 on back in white) 9.00 4.50 2.75
99 Don Buddin 2.50 1.25 .70
100 Harvey Haddix 2.50 1.25 .70
101 Bubba Phillips 2.50 1.25 .70
102 Gene Stephens 2.50 1.25 .70
103 Ruben Amaro 2.50 1.25 .70
104 John Blanchard 2.50 1.25 .70
105 Carl Willey 2.50 1.25 .70
106 Whitey Herzog 4.00 2.00 1.25
107 Seth Morehead 2.50 1.25 .70
108 Dan Dobbek 2.50 1.25 .70
109 Johnny Podres 3.50 1.75 1.00
110 Vada Pinson 6.00 3.00 1.75
111 Jack Meyer 2.50 1.25 .70
112 Chico Fernandez 2.50 1.25 .70
113 Mike Fornieles 2.50 1.25 .70
114 Hobie Landrith 2.50 1.25 .70
115 Johnny Antonelli 2.50 1.25 .70
116 Joe DeMaestri 2.50 1.25 .70
117 Dale Long 2.50 1.25 .70
118 Chris Cannizzaro 2.50 1.25 .70
119 A's Big Armor (Hank Bauer, Jerry Lumpe, Norm Siebern) 5.00 2.50 1.50
120 Eddie Mathews 26.00 13.00 8.00
121 Eli Grba 2.50 1.25 .70
122 Cubs Team 6.00 3.00 1.75
123 Billy Gardner 2.50 1.25 .70
124 J.C. Martin 2.50 1.25 .70
125 Steve Barber 2.50 1.25 .70
126 Dick Stuart 3.00 1.50 .90
127 Ron Kline 2.50 1.25 .70
128 Rip Repulski 2.50 1.25 .70
129 Ed Hobaugh 2.50 1.25 .70
130 Norm Larker 2.50 1.25 .70
131 Paul Richards 2.50 1.25 .70
132 Al Lopez 5.00 2.50 1.50
133 Ralph Houk 5.00 2.50 1.50
134 Mickey Vernon 2.50 1.25 .70
135 Fred Hutchinson 2.50 1.25 .70
136 Walt Alston 5.00 2.50 1.50
137 Chuck Dressen 2.50 1.25 .70
138 Danny Murtaugh 2.50 1.25 .70
139 Solly Hemus 2.50 1.25 .70
140 Gus Triandos 2.50 1.25 .70
141 *Billy Williams* 85.00 35.00 22.00
142 Luis Arroyo 2.50 1.25 .70
143 Russ Snyder 2.50 1.25 .70
144 Jim Coker 2.50 1.25 .70
145 Bob Buhl 2.50 1.25 .70
146 Marty Keough 2.50 1.25 .70
147 Ed Rakow 2.50 1.25 .70
148 Julian Javier 2.50 1.25 .70
149 Bob Oldis 2.50 1.25 .70
150 Willie Mays 120.00 60.00 36.00
151 Jim Donohue 2.50 1.25 .70
152 Earl Torgeson 2.50 1.25 .70
153 Don Lee 2.50 1.25 .70
154 Bobby Del Greco 2.50 1.25 .70
155 Johnny Temple 2.50 1.25 .70
156 Ken Hunt 2.50 1.25 .70
157 Cal McLish 2.50 1.25 .70
158 Pete Daley 2.50 1.25 .70
159 Orioles Team 6.00 3.00 1.75
160 Whitey Ford 40.00 20.00 12.00
161 Sherman Jones (photo actually Eddie Fisher) 2.50 1.25 .70
162 Jay Hook 2.50 1.25 .70
163 Ed Sadowski 2.50 1.25 .70
164 Felix Mantilla 2.50 1.25 .70
165 Gino Cimoli 2.50 1.25 .70
166 Danny Kravitz 2.50 1.25 .70
167 Giants Team 6.00 3.00 1.75
168 Tommy Davis 5.00 2.50 1.50
169 Don Elston 2.50 1.25 .70
170 Al Smith 2.50 1.25 .70
171 Paul Foytack 2.50 1.25 .70
172 Don Dillard 2.50 1.25 .70
173 Beantown Bombers (Jackie Jensen, Frank Malzone, Vic Wertz) 6.00 3.00 1.75
174 Ray Semproch 2.50 1.25 .70
175 Gene Freese 2.50 1.25 .70
176 Ken Aspromonte 2.50 1.25 .70
177 Don Larsen 2.50 1.25 .70
178 Bob Nieman 2.50 1.25 .70
179 Joe Koppe 2.50 1.25 .70
180 Bobby Richardson 6.00 3.00 1.75
181 Fred Green 2.50 1.25 .70
182 Dave Nicholson 2.50 1.25 .70
183 Andre Rodgers 2.50 1.25 .70
184 Steve Bilko 2.50 1.25 .70
185 Herb Score 2.50 1.25 .70
186 Elmer Valo 2.50 1.25 .70
187 Billy Klaus 2.50 1.25 .70
188 Jim Marshall 2.50 1.25 .70
189 Checklist 177-264 6.00 3.00 1.75
190 Stan Williams 2.50 1.25 .70
191 Mike de la Hoz 2.50 1.25 .70
192 Dick Brown 2.50 1.25 .70
193 Gene Conley 2.50 1.25 .70
194 Gordy Coleman 2.50 1.25 .70
195 Jerry Casale 2.50 1.25 .70
196 Ed Bouchee 2.50 1.25 .70
197 Dick Hall 2.50 1.25 .70
198 Carl Sawatski 2.50 1.25 .70
199 Bob Boyd 2.50 1.25 .70
200 Warren Spahn 30.00 15.00 9.00
201 Pete Whisenant 2.50 1.25 .70
202 Al Neiger 2.50 1.25 .70
203 Eddie Bressoud 2.50 1.25 .70
204 Bob Skinner 2.50 1.25 .70
205 Bill Pierce 2.50 1.25 .70
206 Gene Green 2.50 1.25 .70
207 Dodger Southpaws (Sandy Koufax, Johnny Podres) 22.00 11.00 6.50
208 Larry Osborne 2.50 1.25 .70
209 Ken McBride 2.50 1.25 .70
210 Pete Runnels 2.50 1.25 .70
211 Bob Gibson 35.00 17.50 10.50
212 Haywood Sullivan 2.50 1.25 .70
213 *Bill Stafford* 4.50 2.25 1.25
214 Danny Murphy 2.50 1.25 .70
215 Gus Bell 2.50 1.25 .70
216 Ted Bowsfield 2.50 1.25 .70
217 Mel Roach 2.50 1.25 .70
218 Hal Brown 2.50 1.25 .70
219 Gene Mauch 2.50 1.25 .70
220 Al Dark 2.50 1.25 .70
221 Mike Higgins 2.50 1.25 .70
222 Jimmie Dykes 2.50 1.25 .70
223 Bob Scheffing 2.50 1.25 .70
224 Joe Gordon 2.50 1.25 .70
225 Bill Rigney 2.50 1.25 .70
226 Harry Lavagetto 2.50 1.25 .70
227 Juan Pizarro 2.50 1.25 .70
228 Yankees Team 33.00 16.00 9.75
229 Rudy Hernandez 2.50 1.25 .70
230 Don Hoak 2.50 1.25 .70
231 Dick Drott 2.50 1.25 .70
232 Bill White 4.50 2.25 1.25
233 Joe Jay 2.50 1.25 .70
234 Ted Lepcio 2.50 1.25 .70
235 Camilo Pascual 2.50 1.25 .70
236 Don Gile 2.50 1.25 .70
237 Billy Loes 2.50 1.25 .70
238 Jim Gilliam 4.50 2.25 1.25
239 Dave Sisler 2.50 1.25 .70
240 Ron Hansen 2.50 1.25 .70
241 Al Cicotte 2.50 1.25 .70
242 Hal W. Smith 2.50 1.25 .70
243 Frank Lary 2.50 1.25 .70
244 Chico Cardenas 2.50 1.25 .70
245 Joe Adcock 2.50 1.25 .70
246 Bob Davis 2.50 1.25 .70
247 Billy Goodman 2.50 1.25 .70
248 Ed Keegan 2.50 1.25 .70
249 Reds Team 6.00 3.00 1.75
250 Buc Hill Aces (Roy Face, Vern Law) 6.00 3.00 1.75
251 Bill Bruton 2.50 1.25 .70
252 Bill Short 2.50 1.25 .70
253 Sammy Taylor 2.50 1.25 .70
254 Ted Sadowski 2.50 1.25 .70
255 Vic Power 2.50 1.25 .70
256 Billy Hoeft 2.50 1.25 .70
257 Carroll Hardy 2.50 1.25 .70
258 Jack Sanford 2.50 1.25 .70
259 John Schaive 2.50 1.25 .70
260 Don Drysdale 35.00 17.50 10.50
261 Charlie Lau 2.50 1.25 .70
262 Tony Curry 2.50 1.25 .70
263 Ken Hamlin 2.50 1.25 .70
264 Glen Hobbie 2.50 1.25 .70
265 Tony Kubek 5.00 2.50 1.50
266 Lindy McDaniel 2.50 1.25 .70
267 Norm Siebern 2.50 1.25 .70
268 Ike DeLock (Delock) 2.50 1.25 .70
269 Harry Chiti 2.50 1.25 .70
270 Bob Friend 2.50 1.25 .70
271 Jim Landis 2.50 1.25 .70
272 Tom Morgan 2.50 1.25 .70
273 Checklist 265-352 6.00 3.00 1.75
274 Gary Bell 2.50 1.25 .70
275 Gene Woodling 2.50 1.25 .70
276 Ray Rippelmeyer 2.50 1.25 .70
277 Hank Foiles 2.50 1.25 .70
278 Don McMahon 2.50 1.25 .70
279 Jose Pagan 2.50 1.25 .70
280 Frank Howard 4.00 2.00 1.25
281 Frank Sullivan 2.50 1.25 .70
282 Faye Throneberry 2.50 1.25 .70
283 Bob Anderson 2.50 1.25 .70
284 Dick Gernert 2.50 1.25 .70
285 Sherm Lollar 2.50 1.25 .70
286 George Witt 2.50 1.25 .70
287 Carl Yastrzemski 75.00 37.00 22.00
288 Albie Pearson 2.50 1.25 .70
289 Ray Moore 2.50 1.25 .70
290 Stan Musial 105.00 50.00 30.00
291 Tex Clevenger 2.50 1.25 .70
292 Jim Baumer 2.50 1.25 .70
293 Tom Sturdivant 2.50 1.25 .70
294 Don Blasingame 2.50 1.25 .70
295 Milt Pappas 2.50 1.25 .70
296 Wes Covington 2.50 1.25 .70
297 Athletics Team 6.00 3.00 1.75
298 Jim Golden 2.50 1.25 .70
299 Clay Dalrymple 2.50 1.25 .70
300 Mickey Mantle 400.00 200.00 120.00
301 Chet Nichols 2.50 1.25 .70
302 Al Heist 2.50 1.25 .70
303 Gary Peters 2.50 1.25 .70
304 Rocky Nelson 2.50 1.25 .70
305 Mike McCormick 2.50 1.25 .70
306 World Series Game 1 (Virdon Saves Game) 7.50 3.75 2.25
307 World Series Game 2 (Mantle Slams 2 Homers) 45.00 22.00 13.50
308 World Series Game 3 (Richardson is Hero) 7.50 3.75 2.25
309 World Series Game 4 (Cimoli is Safe in Crucial Play) 7.50 3.75 2.25
310 World Series Game 5 (Face Saves the Day) 7.50 3.75 2.25
311 World Series Game 6 (Ford Pitches Second Shutout) 7.50 3.75 2.25
312 World Series Game 7 (Mazeroski's Homer Wins It!) 12.00 6.00 3.50
313 World Series Summary (The Winners Celebrate) 7.50 3.75 2.25
314 Bob Miller 2.50 1.25 .70
315 Earl Battey 2.50 1.25 .70
316 Bobby Gene Smith 2.50 1.25 .70
317 *Jim Brewer* 2.50 1.25 .70
318 Danny O'Connell 2.50 1.25 .70
319 Valmy Thomas 2.50 1.25 .70
320 Lou Burdette 2.50 1.25 .70
321 Marv Breeding 2.50 1.25 .70
322 Bill Kunkel 2.50 1.25 .70
323 Sammy Esposito 2.50 1.25 .70
324 Hank Aguirre 2.50 1.25 .70
325 Wally Moon 2.50 1.25 .70
326 Dave Hillman 2.50 1.25 .70
327 *Matty Alou* 4.00 2.00 1.25
328 Jim O'Toole 2.50 1.25 .70
329 Julio Becquer 2.50 1.25 .70
330 Rocky Colavito 5.00 2.50 1.50
331 Ned Garver 2.50 1.25 .70
332 Dutch Dotterer (photo actually Tommy Dotterer) 2.50 1.25 .70
333 Fritz Brickell 3.00 1.50 .90
334 Walt Bond 2.50 1.25 .70
335 Frank Bolling 2.50 1.25 .70
336 Don Mincher 2.50 1.25 .70
337 Al's Aces (Al Lopez, Herb Score, Early Wynn) 7.50 3.75 2.25
338 Don Landrum 2.50 1.25 .70
339 Gene Baker 2.50 1.25 .70
340 Vic Wertz 2.50 1.25 .70
341 Jim Owens 2.50 1.25 .70
342 Clint Courtney 2.50 1.25 .70
343 Earl Robinson 2.50 1.25 .70
344 Sandy Koufax 85.00 42.00 25.00
345 Jim Piersall 2.50 1.25 .70
346 Howie Nunn 2.50 1.25 .70
347 Cardinals Team 6.00 3.00 1.75
348 Steve Boros 2.50 1.25 .70
349 Danny McDevitt 2.50 1.25 .70
350 Ernie Banks 36.00 18.00 10.75
351 Jim King 2.50 1.25 .70
352 Bob Shaw 2.50 1.25 .70
353 Howie Bedell 2.50 1.25 .70
354 Billy Harrell 2.50 1.25 .70
355 Bob Allison 2.50 1.25 .70
356 Ryne Duren 3.50 1.75 1.00
357 Daryl Spencer 2.50 1.25 .70
358 Earl Averill 2.50 1.25 .70
359 Dallas Green 3.50 1.75 1.00
360 Frank Robinson 35.00 17.50 10.50
361a Checklist 353-429 ("Topps Baseball" in black on front) 6.00 3.00 1.75
361b Checklist 353-429 ("Topps Baseball" in yellow) 7.00 3.50 2.00
362 Frank Funk 2.50 1.25 .70
363 John Roseboro 2.50 1.25 .70
364 Moe Drabowsky 2.50 1.25 .70
365 Jerry Lumpe 2.50 1.25 .70
366 Eddie Fisher 2.50 1.25 .70
367 Jim Rivera 2.50 1.25 .70
368 Bennie Daniels 2.50 1.25 .70
369 Dave Philley 2.50 1.25 .70

370	Roy Face	2.50	1.25	.70
371	Bill Skowron (SP)	15.00	7.50	4.50
372	Bob Hendley	2.50	1.25	.70
373	Red Sox Team	8.00	4.00	2.50
374	Paul Giel	2.50	1.25	.70
375	Ken Boyer	6.00	3.00	1.75
376	Mike Roarke	2.50	1.25	.70
377	Ruben Gomez	2.50	1.25	.70
378	Wally Post	2.50	1.25	.70
379	Bobby Shantz	5.00	2.50	1.50
380	Minnie Minoso	6.00	3.00	1.75
381	Dave Wickersham	2.50	1.25	.70
382	Frank J. Thomas	2.50	1.25	.70
383	Frisco First Liners (Mike McCormick, Billy O'Dell, Jack Sanford)	6.00	3.00	1.75
384	Chuck Essegian	2.50	1.25	.70
385	Jim Perry	2.50	1.25	.70
386	Joe Hicks	2.50	1.25	.70
387	Duke Maas	2.50	1.25	.70
388	Roberto Clemente	105.00	50.00	30.00
389	Ralph Terry	5.00	2.50	1.50
390	Del Crandall	2.50	1.25	.70
391	Winston Brown	2.50	1.25	.70
392	Reno Bertoia	2.50	1.25	.70
393	Batter Bafflers (Don Cardwell, Glen Hobbie)	2.50	1.25	.70
394	Ken Walters	2.50	1.25	.70
395	Chuck Estrada	2.50	1.25	.70
396	Bob Aspromonte	2.50	1.25	.70
397	Hal Woodeshick	2.50	1.25	.70
398	Hank Bauer	4.00	2.00	1.20
399	Cliff Cook	2.50	1.25	.70
400	Vern Law	2.50	1.25	.70
401	Babe Ruth Hits 60th Homer	35.00	17.50	10.50
402	Larsen Pitches Perfect Game	15.00	7.50	4.50
403	Brooklyn-Boston Play 26-Inning Tie	2.50	1.25	.70
404	Hornsby Tops N.L. with .424 Average	5.00	2.50	1.50
405	After 2,130 Games, Gehrig Benched	25.00	12.50	7.50
406	Mantle Blasts 565 ft. Home Run	45.00	22.00	13.50
407	Jack Chesbro Wins 41st Game	2.50	1.25	.70
408	Mathewson Strikes Out 267 Batters	6.00	3.00	1.75
409	Johnson Hurls 3rd Shutout in 4 Days	7.00	3.50	2.00
410	Haddix Pitches 12 Perfect Innings	6.00	3.00	1.75
411	Tony Taylor	2.50	1.25	.70
412	Larry Sherry	2.50	1.25	.70
413	Eddie Yost	2.50	1.25	.70
414	Dick Donovan	2.50	1.25	.70
415	Hank Aaron	110.00	55.00	33.00
416	*Dick Howser*	6.00	3.00	1.75
417	*Juan Marichal*	135.00	65.00	40.00
418	Ed Bailey	2.50	1.25	.70
419	Tom Borland	2.50	1.25	.70
420	Ernie Broglio	2.50	1.25	.70
421	Ty Cline (SP)	7.50	3.75	2.25
422	Bud Daley	2.50	1.25	.70
423	Charlie Neal	2.50	1.25	.70
424	Turk Lown	2.50	1.25	.70
425	Yogi Berra	70.00	35.00	21.00
426	Not Issued			
427	Dick Ellsworth	2.50	1.25	.70
428	Ray Barker (SP)	7.50	3.75	2.25
429	Al Kaline	40.00	20.00	12.00
430	Bill Mazeroski	45.00	22.00	13.50
431	Chuck Stobbs	2.50	1.25	.70
432	Coot Veal	2.50	1.25	.70
433	Art Mahaffey	2.50	1.25	.70
434	Tom Brewer	2.50	1.25	.70
435	Orlando Cepeda	10.00	5.00	3.00
436	*Jim Maloney*	2.50	1.25	.70
437a	Checklist 430-506 (#440 is Louis Aparicio)	11.00	5.50	3.25
437b	Checklist 430-506 (#440 is Luis Aparicio)	11.00	5.50	3.25
438	Curt Flood	3.50	1.75	1.00
439	*Phil Regan*	2.50	1.25	.70
440	Luis Aparicio	14.00	7.00	4.25
441	Dick Bertell	2.50	1.25	.70
442	Gordon Jones	2.50	1.25	.70
443	Duke Snider	40.00	20.00	12.00
444	Joe Nuxhall	2.50	1.25	.70
445	Frank Malzone	2.50	1.25	.70
446	Bob "Hawk" Taylor	2.50	1.25	.70
447	Harry Bright	4.50	2.25	1.25
448	Del Rice	4.50	2.25	1.25
449	*Bobby Bolin*	4.50	2.25	1.25
450	Jim Lemon	4.50	2.25	1.25
451	Power For Ernie (Ernie Broglio, Daryl Spencer, Bill White)	5.00	2.50	1.50
452	Bob Allen	4.50	2.25	1.25
453	Dick Schofield	4.50	2.25	1.25
454	Pumpsie Green	4.50	2.25	1.25
455	Early Wynn	12.00	6.00	3.50
456	Hal Bevan	4.50	2.25	1.25
457	Johnny James	4.50	2.25	1.25
458	Willie Tasby	4.50	2.25	1.25
459	Terry Fox	4.50	2.25	1.25
460	Gil Hodges	18.00	9.00	5.50
461	Smoky Burgess	4.50	2.25	1.25
462	Lou Klimchock	4.50	2.25	1.25
463a	Braves Team (should be card #426)	8.00	4.00	2.50
463b	Jack Fisher	4.50	2.25	1.25
464	*Leroy Thomas*	4.50	2.25	1.25
465	Roy McMillan	4.50	2.25	1.25
466	Ron Moeller	4.50	2.25	1.25
467	Indians Team	8.00	4.00	2.50
468	Johnny Callison	4.50	2.25	1.25
469	Ralph Lumenti	4.50	2.25	1.25
470	Roy Sievers	4.50	2.25	1.25
471	Phil Rizzuto (MVP)	12.00	6.00	3.50
472	Yogi Berra (MVP)	45.00	22.00	13.50
473	Bobby Shantz (MVP)	7.50	3.75	2.25
474	Al Rosen (MVP)	7.50	3.75	2.25
475	Mickey Mantle (MVP)	125.00	62.00	37.00
476	Jackie Jensen (MVP)	7.50	3.75	2.25
477	Nellie Fox (MVP)	9.00	4.50	2.75
478	Roger Maris (MVP)	50.00	25.00	15.00
479	Jim Konstanty	7.50	3.75	2.25
480	Roy Campanella (MVP)	35.00	17.50	10.50
481	Hank Sauer	7.50	3.75	2.25
482	Willie Mays	40.00	20.00	12.00
483	Don Newcombe (MVP)	9.00	4.50	2.75
484	Hank Aaron (MVP)	40.00	20.00	12.00
485	Ernie Banks (MVP)	35.00	17.50	10.50
486	Dick Groat (MVP)	7.50	3.75	2.25
487	Gene Oliver	4.50	2.25	1.25
488	Joe McClain	4.50	2.25	1.25
489	Walt Dropo	4.50	2.25	1.25
490	Jim Bunning	8.00	4.00	2.50
491	Phillies Team	9.00	4.50	2.75
492	Ron Fairly	4.50	2.25	1.25
493	Don Zimmer	4.50	2.25	1.25
494	Tom Cheney	4.50	2.25	1.25
495	Elston Howard	6.00	3.00	1.75
496	Ken MacKenzie	4.50	2.25	1.25
497	Willie Jones	4.50	2.25	1.25
498	Ray Herbert	4.50	2.25	1.25
499	Chuck Schilling	4.50	2.25	1.25
500	Harvey Kuenn	5.00	2.50	1.50
501	John DeMerit	4.50	2.25	1.25
502	Clarence Coleman	4.50	2.25	1.25
503	Tito Francona	4.50	2.25	1.25
504	Billy Consolo	4.50	2.25	1.25
505	Red Schoendienst	12.50	6.25	3.75
506	*Willie Davis*	12.00	6.00	3.50
507	Pete Burnside	4.50	2.25	1.25
508	Rocky Bridges	4.50	2.25	1.25
509	Camilo Carreon	4.50	2.25	1.25
510	Art Ditmar	4.50	2.25	1.25
511	Joe M. Morgan	4.50	2.25	1.25
512	Bob Will	4.50	2.25	1.25
513	Jim Brosnan	4.50	2.25	1.25
514	Jake Wood	4.50	2.25	1.25
515	Jackie Brandt	4.50	2.25	1.25
516	Checklist 507-587	12.00	6.00	3.50
517	Willie McCovey	45.00	22.00	13.50
518	Andy Carey	4.50	2.25	1.25
519	Jim Pagliaroni	4.50	2.25	1.25
520	Joe Cunningham	4.50	2.25	1.25
521	Brother Battery (Larry Sherry, Norm Sherry)	6.00	3.00	1.75
522	Dick Farrell	4.50	2.25	1.25
523	Joe Gibbon	35.00	17.50	10.50
524	Johnny Logan	35.00	17.50	10.50
525	*Ron Perranoski*	40.00	20.00	12.00
526	R.C. Stevens	35.00	17.50	10.50
527	Gene Leek	35.00	17.50	10.50
528	Pedro Ramos	35.00	17.50	10.50
529	Bob Roselli	35.00	17.50	10.50
530	Bobby Malkmus	35.00	17.50	10.50
531	Jim Coates	35.00	17.50	10.50
532	Bob Hale	35.00	17.50	10.50
533	Jack Curtis	35.00	17.50	10.50
534	Eddie Kasko	35.00	17.50	10.50
535	Larry Jackson	35.00	17.50	10.50
536	Bill Tuttle	35.00	17.50	10.50
537	Bobby Locke	35.00	17.50	10.50
538	Chuck Hiller	35.00	17.50	10.50
539	Johnny Klippstein	35.00	17.50	10.50
540	Jackie Jensen	35.00	17.50	10.50
541	Roland Sheldon	35.00	17.50	10.50
542	Twins Team	70.00	35.00	21.00
543	Roger Craig	40.00	20.00	12.00
544	George Thomas	35.00	17.50	10.50
545	Hoyt Wilhelm	60.00	30.00	18.00
546	Marty Kutyna	35.00	17.50	10.50
547	Leon Wagner	35.00	17.50	10.50
548	Ted Wills	35.00	17.50	10.50
549	Hal R. Smith	35.00	17.50	10.50
550	Frank Baumann	35.00	17.50	10.50
551	George Altman	35.00	17.50	10.50
552	Jim Archer	35.00	17.50	10.50
553	Bill Fischer	35.00	17.50	10.50
554	Pirates Team	60.00	30.00	18.00
555	Sam Jones	35.00	17.50	10.50
556	Ken R. Hunt	35.00	17.50	10.50
557	Jose Valdivielso	35.00	17.50	10.50
558	Don Ferrarese	35.00	17.50	10.50
559	Jim Gentile	35.00	17.50	10.50
560	Barry Latman	35.00	17.50	10.50
561	Charley James	35.00	17.50	10.50
562	Bill Monbouquette	35.00	17.50	10.50
563	Bob Cerv	35.00	17.50	10.50
564	Don Cardwell	35.00	17.50	10.50
565	Felipe Alou	45.00	22.00	13.50
566	Paul Richards (All-Star)	35.00	17.50	10.50
567	Danny Murtaugh (All-Star)	35.00	17.50	10.50
568	Bill Skowron (All-Star)	40.00	20.00	12.00
569	Frank Herrera (All-Star)	35.00	17.50	10.50
570	Nellie Fox (All-Star)	45.00	22.00	13.50
571	Bill Mazeroski (All-Star)	45.00	22.00	13.50
572	Brooks Robinson (All-Star)	65.00	32.00	19.50
573	Ken Boyer (All-Star)	40.00	20.00	12.00
574	Luis Aparicio (All-Star)	45.00	22.00	13.50
575	Ernie Banks (All-Star)	85.00	42.00	25.00
576	Roger Maris (All-Star)	130.00	65.00	40.00
577	Hank Aaron (All-Star)	140.00	70.00	42.00
578	Mickey Mantle (All-Star)	400.00	200.00	120.00
579	Willie Mays (All-Star)	150.00	75.00	45.00
580	Al Kaline (All-Star)	90.00	45.00	27.00
581	Frank Robinson (All-Star)	85.00	42.00	25.00
582	Earl Battey (All-Star)	35.00	17.50	10.50
583	Del Crandall (All-Star)	35.00	17.50	10.50
584	Jim Perry (All-Star)	35.00	17.50	10.50
585	Bob Friend (All-Star)	35.00	17.50	10.50
586	Whitey Ford (All-Star)	85.00	42.00	25.00
587	Not Issued			
588	Not Issued			
589	Warren Spahn (All-Star)	120.00	60.00	36.00

1961 Topps Dice Game

One of the more obscure Topps test issues that may have never actually been issued is the 1961 Topps Dice Game. Eighteen black and white cards, each measuring 2-1/2" by 3-1/2" in size, comprise the set. Interestingly, there are no identifying marks, such as copyrights or trademarks, to indicate the set was produced by Topps. The card backs contain various baseball plays that occur when a certain pitch is called and a specific number of the dice is rolled.

		NR MT	EX	VG
Complete Set (18):		7500.	3750.	2250.
Common Player:		100.00	50.00	30.00
(1)	Earl Battey	100.00	50.00	30.00
(2)	Del Crandall	100.00	50.00	30.00
(3)	Jim Davenport	100.00	50.00	30.00
(4)	Don Drysdale	400.00	200.00	120.00
(5)	Dick Groat	150.00	75.00	45.00
(6)	Al Kaline	600.00	300.00	175.00
(7)	Tony Kubek	150.00	75.00	45.00
(8)	Mickey Mantle	2500.	1250.	750.00
(9)	Willie Mays	1000.	500.00	300.00
(10)	Bill Mazeroski	200.00	100.00	60.00
(11)	Stan Musial	800.00	400.00	240.00
(12)	Camilo Pascual	100.00	50.00	30.00
(13)	Bobby Richardson	150.00	75.00	45.00
(14)	Brooks Robinson	400.00	200.00	120.00
(15)	Frank Robinson	350.00	175.00	105.00
(16)	Norm Siebern	100.00	50.00	30.00
(17)	Leon Wagner	100.00	50.00	30.00
(18)	Bill White	100.00	50.00	30.00

1961 Topps Magic Rub-Offs

Not too different in concept from the tattoos of the previous year, the Topps Magic Rub-Off was designed to leave impressions of team themes or individual players when properly applied. Measuring 2-1/16" by 3-1/16," the Magic Rub-Off was not designed specifically for application to the owner's skin. The set of 36 Rub-Offs seems to almost be a tongue-in-cheek product as the team themes were a far cry from official logos, and the players seem to have been included for their nicknames. Among the players (one representing each team) the best known and most valuable are Yogi Berra and Ernie Banks.

		NR MT	EX	VG
Complete Set (36):		130.00	65.00	40.00
Common Player:		3.50	1.75	1.00
(1)	Baltimore Orioles Pennant	3.50	1.75	1.00
(2)	Ernie "Bingo" Banks	15.00	7.50	4.50
(3)	Yogi Berra	20.00	10.00	6.00
(4)	Boston Red Sox Pennant	3.50	1.75	1.00
(5)	Jackie "Ozark" Brandt	3.50	1.75	1.00
(6)	Jim "Professor" Brosnan	3.50	1.75	1.00
(7)	Chicago Cubs Pennant	3.50	1.75	1.00
(8)	Chicago White Sox Pennant	3.50	1.75	1.00
(9)	Cincinnati Red Legs Pennant	3.50	1.75	1.00
(10)	Cleveland Indians Pennant	3.50	1.75	1.00
(11)	Detroit Tigers Pennant	3.50	1.75	1.00

(12)	Henry "Dutch" Dotterer	3.50	1.75	1.00
(13)	Joe "Flash" Gordon	3.50	1.75	1.00
(14)	Harvey "The Kitten" Haddix	3.50	1.75	1.00
(15)	Frank "Pancho" Hererra	3.50	1.75	1.00
(16)	Frank "Tower" Howard	5.00	2.50	1.50
(17)	"Sad" Sam Jones	3.50	1.75	1.00
(18)	Kansas City Athletics Pennant	3.50	1.75	1.00
(19)	Los Angeles Angels Pennant	3.50	1.75	1.00
(20)	Los Angeles Dodgers Pennant	3.50	1.75	1.00
(21)	Omar "Turk" Lown	3.50	1.75	1.00
(22)	Billy "The Kid" Martin	8.00	4.00	2.50
(23)	Duane "Duke" Mass (Maas)	3.50	1.75	1.00
(24)	Charlie "Paw Paw" Maxwell	3.50	1.75	1.00
(25)	Milwaukee Braves Pennant	3.50	1.75	1.00
(26)	Minnesota Twins Pennant	3.50	1.75	1.00
(27)	"Farmer" Ray Moore	3.50	1.75	1.00
(28)	Walt "Moose" Moryn	3.50	1.75	1.00
(29)	New York Yankees Pennant	4.00	2.00	1.25
(30)	Philadelphia Phillies Pennant	3.50	1.75	1.00
(31)	Pittsburgh Pirates Pennant	3.50	1.75	1.00
(32)	John "Honey" Romano	3.50	1.75	1.00
(33)	"Pistol Pete" Runnels	3.50	1.75	1.00
(34)	St. Louis Cardinals Pennant	3.50	1.75	1.00
(35)	San Francisco Giants Pennant	3.50	1.75	1.00
(36)	Washington Senators Pennant	3.50	1.75	1.00

1961 Topps Stamps

Issued as an added insert to 1961 Topps wax packs these 1-3/8" by 1-3/16" stamps were desigend to be collected and placed in an album which could be bought for an additional 10¢. Packs of cards contained two stamps. There are 208 stamps in a complete set which depict 207 different players (Al Kaline appears twice). There are 104 players on brown stamps and 104 on green. While there are many Hall of Famers on the stamps, prices remain low because there is relatively little interest in what is a non-card set.

	NR MT	EX	VG
Complete Set:	225.00	112.00	67.00
Stamp Album:	35.00	17.50	10.50
Common Player:	1.00	.50	.30

(1)	Hank Aaron	12.00	6.00	3.50
(2)	Joe Adcock	1.00	.50	.30
(3)	Hank Aguirre	1.00	.50	.30
(4)	Bob Allison	1.00	.50	.30
(5)	George Altman	1.00	.50	.30
(6)	Bob Anderson	1.00	.50	.30
(7)	Johnny Antonelli	1.00	.50	.30
(8)	Luis Aparicio	4.50	2.25	1.25
(9)	Luis Arroyo	1.00	.50	.30
(10)	Richie Ashburn	3.00	1.50	.90
(11)	Ken Aspromonte	1.00	.50	.30
(12)	Ed Bailey	1.00	.50	.30
(13)	Ernie Banks	6.50	3.25	2.00
(14)	Steve Barber	1.00	.50	.30
(15)	Earl Battey	1.00	.50	.30
(16)	Hank Bauer	1.00	.50	.30
(17)	Gus Bell	1.00	.50	.30
(18)	Yogi Berra	8.00	4.00	2.50
(19)	Reno Bertoia	1.00	.50	.30
(20)	John Blanchard	1.00	.50	.30
(21)	Don Blasingame	1.00	.50	.30
(22)	Frank Bolling	1.00	.50	.30
(23)	Steve Boros	1.00	.50	.30
(24)	Ed Bouchee	1.00	.50	.30
(25)	Bob Boyd	1.00	.50	.30
(26)	Cletis Boyer	1.00	.50	.30
(27)	Ken Boyer	1.50	.70	.45
(28)	Jackie Brandt	1.00	.50	.30
(29)	Marv Breeding	1.00	.50	.30
(30)	Eddie Bressoud	1.00	.50	.30
(31)	Jim Brewer	1.00	.50	.30
(32)	Tom Brewer	1.00	.50	.30
(33)	Jim Brosnan	1.00	.50	.30
(34)	Bill Bruton	1.00	.50	.30
(35)	Bob Buhl	1.00	.50	.30
(36)	Jim Bunning	1.50	.70	.45
(37)	Smoky Burgess	1.00	.50	.30
(38)	John Buzhardt	1.00	.50	.30
(39)	Johnny Callison	1.00	.50	.30
(40)	Chico Cardenas	1.00	.50	.30
(41)	Andy Carey	1.00	.50	.30
(42)	Jerry Casale	1.00	.50	.30
(43)	Norm Cash	2.00	1.00	.60
(44)	Orlando Cepeda	2.00	1.00	.60
(45)	Bob Cerv	1.00	.50	.30
(46)	Harry Chiti	1.00	.50	.30
(47)	Gene Conley	1.00	.50	.30
(48)	Wes Covington	1.00	.50	.30
(49)	Del Crandall	1.00	.50	.30
(50)	Tony Curry	1.00	.50	.30
(51)	Bud Daley	1.00	.50	.30
(52)	Pete Daley	1.00	.50	.30
(53)	Clay Dalrymple	1.00	.50	.30
(54)	Jim Davenport	1.00	.50	.30
(55)	Tommy Davis	1.00	.50	.30
(56)	Bobby Del Greco	1.00	.50	.30
(57)	Ike Delock	1.00	.50	.30
(58)	Art Ditmar	1.00	.50	.30
(59)	Dick Donovan	1.00	.50	.30
(60)	Don Drysdale	6.50	3.25	2.00
(61)	Dick Ellsworth	1.00	.50	.30
(62)	Don Elston	1.00	.50	.30
(63)	Chuck Estrada	1.00	.50	.30
(64)	Roy Face	1.00	.50	.30
(65)	Dick Farrell	1.00	.50	.30
(66)	Chico Fernandez	1.00	.50	.30
(67)	Curt Flood	1.00	.50	.30
(68)	Whitey Ford	5.00	2.50	1.50
(69)	Tito Francona	1.00	.50	.30
(70)	Gene Freese	1.00	.50	.30
(71)	Bob Friend	1.00	.50	.30
(72)	Billy Gardner	1.00	.50	.30
(73)	Ned Garver	1.00	.50	.30
(74)	Gary Geiger	1.00	.50	.30
(75)	Jim Gentile	1.00	.50	.30
(76)	Dick Gernert	1.00	.50	.30
(77)	Tony Gonzalez	1.00	.50	.30
(78)	Alex Grammas	1.00	.50	.30
(79)	Jim Grant	1.00	.50	.30
(80)	Dick Groat	1.00	.50	.30
(81)	Dick Hall	1.00	.50	.30
(82)	Ron Hansen	1.00	.50	.30
(83)	Bob Hartman	1.00	.50	.30
(84)	Woodie Held	1.00	.50	.30
(85)	Ray Herbert	1.00	.50	.30
(86)	Frank Herrera	1.00	.50	.30
(87)	Whitey Herzog	1.50	.70	.45
(88)	Don Hoak	1.00	.50	.30
(89)	Elston Howard	2.00	1.00	.60
(90)	Frank Howard	2.00	1.00	.60
(91)	Ken Hunt	1.00	.50	.30
(92)	Larry Jackson	1.00	.50	.30
(93)	Julian Javier	1.00	.50	.30
(94)	Joe Jay	1.00	.50	.30
(95)	Jackie Jensen	1.00	.50	.30
(96)	Jim Kaat	1.50	.70	.45
(97a)	Al Kaline (green)	8.50	4.25	2.75
(97b)	Al Kaline (brown)	7.00	3.50	2.00
(98)	Eddie Kasko	1.00	.50	.30
(99)	Russ Kemmerer	1.00	.50	.30
(100)	Harmon Killebrew	8.50	4.25	2.75
(101)	Billy Klaus	1.00	.50	.30
(102)	Ron Kline	1.00	.50	.30
(103)	Johnny Klippstein	1.00	.50	.30
(104)	Ted Kluszewski	3.00	1.50	.90
(105)	Tony Kubek	2.00	1.00	.60
(106)	Harvey Kuenn	1.50	.70	.45
(107)	Jim Landis	1.00	.50	.30
(108)	Hobie Landrith	1.00	.50	.30
(109)	Norm Larker	1.00	.50	.30
(110)	Frank Lary	1.00	.50	.30
(111)	Barry Latman	1.00	.50	.30
(112)	Vern Law	1.00	.50	.30
(113)	Jim Lemon	1.00	.50	.30
(114)	Sherm Lollar	1.00	.50	.30
(115)	Dale Long	1.00	.50	.30
(116)	Jerry Lumpe	1.00	.50	.30
(117)	Jerry Lynch	1.00	.50	.30
(118)	Art Mahaffey	1.00	.50	.30
(119)	Frank Malzone	1.00	.50	.30
(120)	Felix Mantilla	1.00	.50	.30
(121)	Mickey Mantle	50.00	25.00	15.00
(122)	Juan Marichal	5.00	2.50	1.50
(123)	Roger Maris	13.50	6.50	4.00
(124)	Billy Martin	2.00	1.00	.60
(125)	J.C. Martin	1.00	.50	.30
(126)	Ed Mathews	6.00	3.00	1.75
(127)	Charlie Maxwell	1.00	.50	.30
(128)	Willie Mays	12.00	6.00	3.50
(129)	Bill Mazeroski	4.00	2.00	1.25
(130)	Mike McCormick	1.00	.50	.30
(131)	Willie McCovey	6.00	3.00	1.75
(132)	Lindy McDaniel	1.00	.50	.30
(133)	Roy McMillan	1.00	.50	.30
(134)	Minnie Minoso	1.50	.70	.45
(135)	Bill Monbouquette	1.00	.50	.30
(136)	Wally Moon	1.00	.50	.30
(137)	Stan Musial	12.00	6.00	3.50
(138)	Charlie Neal	1.00	.50	.30
(139)	Rocky Nelson	1.00	.50	.30
(140)	Russ Nixon	1.00	.50	.30
(141)	Billy O'Dell	1.00	.50	.30
(142)	Jim O'Toole	1.00	.50	.30
(143)	Milt Pappas	1.00	.50	.30
(144)	Camilo Pascual	1.00	.50	.30
(145)	Jim Perry	1.00	.50	.30
(146)	Bubba Phillips	1.00	.50	.30
(147)	Bill Pierce	1.00	.50	.30
(148)	Jim Piersall	1.50	.70	.45
(149)	Vada Pinson	1.50	.70	.45
(150)	Johnny Podres	1.50	.70	.45
(151)	Wally Post	1.00	.50	.30
(152)	Vic Powers (Power)	1.00	.50	.30
(153)	Pedro Ramos	1.00	.50	.30
(154)	Robin Roberts	3.00	1.50	.90
(155)	Brooks Robinson	6.00	3.00	1.75
(156)	Frank Robinson	6.00	3.00	1.75
(157)	Ed Roebuck	1.00	.50	.30
(158)	John Romano	1.00	.50	.30
(159)	John Roseboro	1.00	.50	.30
(160)	Pete Runnels	1.00	.50	.30
(161)	Ed Sadowski	1.00	.50	.30
(162)	Jack Sanford	1.00	.50	.30
(163)	Ron Santo	1.00	.50	.30
(164)	Ray Semproch	1.00	.50	.30
(165)	Bobby Shantz	1.50	.70	.45
(166)	Bob Shaw	1.00	.50	.30
(167)	Larry Sherry	1.00	.50	.30
(168)	Norm Siebern	1.00	.50	.30
(169)	Roy Sievers	1.00	.50	.30
(170)	Curt Simmons	1.00	.50	.30
(171)	Dave Sisler	1.00	.50	.30
(172)	Bob Skinner	1.00	.50	.30
(173)	Al Smith	1.00	.50	.30
(174)	Hal Smith	1.00	.50	.30
(175)	Hal Smith	1.00	.50	.30
(176)	Duke Snider	6.00	3.00	1.75
(177)	Warren Spahn	6.00	3.00	1.75
(178)	Daryl Spencer	1.00	.50	.30
(179)	Bill Stafford	1.00	.50	.30
(180)	Jerry Staley	1.00	.50	.30
(181)	Gene Stephens	1.00	.50	.30
(182)	Chuck Stobbs	1.00	.50	.30
(183)	Dick Stuart	1.00	.50	.30
(184)	Willie Tasby	1.00	.50	.30
(185)	Sammy Taylor	1.00	.50	.30
(186)	Tony Taylor	1.00	.50	.30
(187)	Johnny Temple	1.00	.50	.30
(188)	Marv Throneberry	1.00	.50	.30
(189)	Gus Triandos	1.00	.50	.30
(190)	Bob Turley	1.00	.50	.30
(191)	Bill Tuttle	1.00	.50	.30
(192)	Zorro Versalles	1.00	.50	.30
(193)	Bill Virdon	1.00	.50	.30
(194)	Lee Walls	1.00	.50	.30
(195)	Vic Wertz	1.00	.50	.30
(196)	Pete Whisenant	1.00	.50	.30
(197)	Bill White	1.50	.70	.45
(198)	Hoyt Wilhelm	3.00	1.50	.90
(199)	Bob Will	1.00	.50	.30
(200)	Carl Willey	1.00	.50	.30
(201)	Billy Williams	4.50	2.25	1.25
(202)	Dick Williams	1.00	.50	.30
(203)	Stan Williams	1.00	.50	.30
(204)	Gene Woodling	1.00	.50	.30
(205)	Early Wynn	3.00	1.50	.90
(206)	Carl Yastrzemski	7.00	3.50	2.00
(207)	Eddie Yost	1.00	.50	.30

1962 Topps

The 1962 Topps set established another plateau for set size with 598 cards. The 2-1/2" by 3-1/2" cards feature a photograph set against a woodgrain background. The lower righthand corner has been made to look like it is curling away. Many established specialty cards dot the set including statistical leaders, multi-player cards, team cards, checklists, World Series cards and All-Stars. Of note is that 1962 was the first year of the multi-player rookie card. There is a 9-card "In Action" subset and a 10-card run of special Babe Ruth cards. Photo variations of several cards in the 2nd Series (#'s 110-196) exist. All cards in the 2nd Series can be found with two distinct printing variations, an early printing with the cards containing a very noticeable greenish tint, having been corrected to clear photos in subsequent print runs. The complete set price in the checklist that follows does not include the higher-priced variations. Among the high numbers (#523-598) certain cards were "short-printed," produced in lesser quantities. These cards carry a higher value and are indicated in the checklist by the notation (SP) after the player name.

	NR MT	EX	VG
Complete Set (598):	5000.	2500.	1500.
Common Player (1-370):	3.50	1.75	1.00
Common Player (371-446):	5.00	2.50	1.50
Common Player (447-522):	7.50	3.75	2.25
Common Player (523-598):	20.00	10.00	6.00

1	Roger Maris	205.00	100.00	60.00
2	Jim Brosnan	3.50	1.75	1.00
3	Pete Runnels	3.50	1.75	1.00
4	John DeMerit	3.50	1.75	1.00
5	Sandy Koufax	120.00	60.00	36.00
6	Marv Breeding	3.50	1.75	1.00
7	Frank J. Thomas	3.50	1.75	1.00
8	Ray Herbert	3.50	1.75	1.00
9	Jim Davenport	3.50	1.75	1.00
10	Roberto Clemente	110.00	55.00	33.00
11	Tom Morgan	3.50	1.75	1.00
12	Harry Craft	3.50	1.75	1.00
13	Dick Howser	3.50	1.75	1.00
14	Bill White	4.50	2.25	1.25
15	Dick Donovan	3.50	1.75	1.00

16	Darrell Johnson	3.50	1.75	1.00
17	Johnny Callison	3.50	1.75	1.00
18	Managers' Dream (Mickey Mantle, Willie Mays)	110.00	55.00	33.00
19	*Ray Washburn*	3.50	1.75	1.00
20	Rocky Colavito	8.00	4.00	2.50
21	Jim Kaat	5.00	2.50	1.50
22a	Checklist 1-88 (numbers 121-176 on back)	7.00	3.50	2.00
22b	Checklist 1-88 (numbers 33-88 on back)	7.00	3.50	2.00
23	Norm Larker	3.50	1.75	1.00
24	Tigers Team	7.50	3.75	2.25
25	Ernie Banks	40.00	20.00	12.00
26	Chris Cannizzaro	3.50	1.75	1.00
27	Chuck Cottier	3.50	1.75	1.00
28	Minnie Minoso	5.00	2.50	1.50
29	Casey Stengel	20.00	10.00	6.00
30	Eddie Mathews	20.00	10.00	6.00
31	*Tom Tresh*	13.00	6.50	4.00
32	John Roseboro	3.50	1.75	1.00
33	Don Larsen	3.50	1.75	1.00
34	Johnny Temple	3.50	1.75	1.00
35	*Don Schwall*	3.50	1.75	1.00
36	Don Leppert	3.50	1.75	1.00
37	Tribe Hill Trio (Barry Latman, Jim Perry, Dick Stigman)	5.00	2.50	1.50
38	Gene Stephens	3.50	1.75	1.00
39	Joe Koppe	3.50	1.75	1.00
40	Orlando Cepeda	9.00	4.50	2.75
41	Cliff Cook	3.50	1.75	1.00
42	Jim King	3.50	1.75	1.00
43	Dodgers Team	7.50	3.75	2.25
44	Don Taussig	3.50	1.75	1.00
45	Brooks Robinson	30.00	15.00	9.00
46	*Jack Baldschun*	3.50	1.75	1.00
47	Bob Will	3.50	1.75	1.00
48	Ralph Terry	4.00	2.00	1.25
49	Hal Jones	3.50	1.75	1.00
50	Stan Musial	100.00	50.00	30.00
51	A.L. Batting Leaders (Norm Cash, Elston Howard, Al Kaline, Jim Piersall)	8.00	4.00	2.50
52	N.L. Batting Leaders (Ken Boyer, Bob Clemente, Wally Moon, Vada Pinson)	8.00	4.00	2.50
53	A.L. Home Run Leaders (Jim Gentile, Harmon Killebrew, Mickey Mantle, Roger Maris)	55.00	27.00	16.50
54	N.L. Home Run Leaders (Orlando Cepeda, Willie Mays, Frank Robinson)	12.00	6.00	3.50
55	A.L. E.R.A. Leaders (Dick Donovan, Don Mossi, Milt Pappas, Bill Stafford)	8.00	4.00	2.50
56	N.L. E.R.A. Leaders (Mike McCormick, Jim O'Toole, Curt Simmons, Warren Spahn)	8.00	4.00	2.50
57	A.L. Win Leaders (Steve Barber, Jim Bunning, Whitey Ford, Frank Lary)	8.00	4.00	2.50
58	N.L. Win Leaders (Joe Jay, Jim O'Toole, Warren Spahn)	8.00	4.00	2.50
59	A.L. Strikeout Leaders (Jim Bunning, Whitey Ford, Camilo Pascual, Juan Pizzaro)	8.00	4.00	2.50
60	N.L. Strikeout Leaders (Don Drysdale, Sandy Koufax, Jim O'Toole, Stan Williams)	9.00	4.50	2.75
61	Cardinals Team	7.50	3.75	2.25
62	Steve Boros	3.50	1.75	1.00
63	*Tony Cloninger*	3.50	1.75	1.00
64	Russ Snyder	3.50	1.75	1.00
65	Bobby Richardson	6.00	3.00	1.75
66	Cuno Barragon (Barragan)	3.50	1.75	1.00
67	Harvey Haddix	3.50	1.75	1.00
68	Ken L. Hunt	3.50	1.75	1.00
69	Phil Ortega	3.50	1.75	1.00
70	Harmon Killebrew	18.00	9.00	5.50
71	Dick LeMay	3.50	1.75	1.00
72	Bob's Pupils (Steve Boros, Bob Scheffing, Jake Wood)	4.50	2.25	1.25
73	Nellie Fox	8.00	4.00	2.50
74	Bob Lillis	3.50	1.75	1.00
75	Milt Pappas	3.50	1.75	1.00
76	Howie Bedell	3.50	1.75	1.00
77	Tony Taylor	3.50	1.75	1.00
78	Gene Green	3.50	1.75	1.00
79	Ed Hobaugh	3.50	1.75	1.00
80	Vada Pinson	5.00	2.50	1.50
81	Jim Pagliaroni	3.50	1.75	1.00
82	Deron Johnson	3.50	1.75	1.00
83	Larry Jackson	3.50	1.75	1.00
84	Lenny Green	3.50	1.75	1.00
85	Gil Hodges	17.50	8.75	5.25
86	*Donn Clendenon*	3.50	1.75	1.00
87	Mike Roarke	3.50	1.75	1.00
88	Ralph Houk	3.50	1.75	1.00
89	Barney Schultz	3.50	1.75	1.00
90	Jim Piersall	3.50	1.75	1.00
91	J.C. Martin	3.50	1.75	1.00
92	Sam Jones	3.50	1.75	1.00
93	John Blanchard	3.50	1.75	1.00
94	Jay Hook	3.50	1.75	1.00
95	Don Hoak	3.50	1.75	1.00
96	Eli Grba	3.50	1.75	1.00
97	Tito Francona	3.50	1.75	1.00
98	Checklist 89-176	7.00	3.50	2.00
99	*Boog Powell*	29.00	14.50	8.75
100	Warren Spahn	27.50	13.50	8.25
101	Carroll Hardy	3.50	1.75	1.00
102	Al Schroll	3.50	1.75	1.00
103	Don Blasingame	3.50	1.75	1.00
104	Ted Savage	3.50	1.75	1.00
105	Don Mossi	3.50	1.75	1.00
106	Carl Sawatski	3.50	1.75	1.00
107	Mike McCormick	3.50	1.75	1.00
108	Willie Davis	5.00	2.50	1.50
109	Bob Shaw	3.50	1.75	1.00
110	Bill Skowron	5.00	2.50	1.50
111	Dallas Green	4.50	2.25	1.25
112	Hank Foiles	3.50	1.75	1.00
113	White Sox Team	7.50	3.75	2.25
114	Howie Koplitz	3.50	1.75	1.00
115	Bob Skinner	3.50	1.75	1.00
116	Herb Score	3.50	1.75	1.00
117	Gary Geiger	3.50	1.75	1.00
118	Julian Javier	3.50	1.75	1.00
119	Danny Murphy	3.50	1.75	1.00
120	Bob Purkey	3.50	1.75	1.00
121	Billy Hitchcock	3.50	1.75	1.00
122	Norm Bass	3.50	1.75	1.00
123	Mike de la Hoz	3.50	1.75	1.00
124	Bill Pleis	3.50	1.75	1.00
125	Gene Woodling	3.50	1.75	1.00
126	Al Cicotte	3.50	1.75	1.00
127	Pride of the A's (Hank Bauer, Jerry Lumpe, Norm Siebern)	5.00	2.50	1.50
128	Art Fowler	3.50	1.75	1.00
129a	Lee Walls (facing left)	30.00	15.00	9.00
129b	Lee Walls (facing right)	3.50	1.75	1.00
130	Frank Bolling	3.50	1.75	1.00
131	*Pete Richert*	3.50	1.75	1.00
132a	Angels Team (with inset photos)	30.00	15.00	9.00
132b	Angels Team (no inset photos)	8.00	4.00	2.50
133	Felipe Alou	5.00	2.50	1.50
134a	Billy Hoeft (green sky)	25.00	12.50	7.50
134b	Billy Hoeft (blue sky)	3.50	1.75	1.00
135	Babe As A Boy	15.00	7.50	4.50
136	Babe Joins Yanks	15.00	7.50	4.50
137	Babe and Mgr. Huggins	15.00	7.50	4.50
138	The Famous Slugger	17.50	8.75	5.25
139a	Hal Reniff (pitching)	40.00	20.00	12.00
139b	Hal Reniff (portrait)	20.00	10.00	6.00
139c	Babe Hits 60	20.00	10.00	6.00
140	Gehrig and Ruth	20.00	10.00	6.00
141	Twilight Years	11.00	5.50	3.25
142	Coaching for the Dodgers	11.00	5.50	3.25
143	Greatest Sports Hero	11.00	5.50	3.25
144	Farewell Speech	11.00	5.50	3.25
145	Barry Latman	3.50	1.75	1.00
146	Don Demeter	3.50	1.75	1.00
147a	Bill Kunkel (pitching)	22.00	11.00	6.50
147b	Bill Kunkel (portrait)	3.50	1.75	1.00
148	Wally Post	3.50	1.75	1.00
149	Bob Duliba	3.50	1.75	1.00
150	Al Kaline	30.00	15.00	9.00
151	Johnny Klippstein	3.50	1.75	1.00
152	Mickey Vernon	3.50	1.75	1.00
153	Pumpsie Green	3.50	1.75	1.00
154	Lee Thomas	3.50	1.75	1.00
155	Stu Miller	3.50	1.75	1.00
156	Merritt Ranew	3.50	1.75	1.00
157	Wes Covington	3.50	1.75	1.00
158	Braves Team	7.50	3.75	2.25
159	Hal Reniff	3.50	1.75	1.00
160	Dick Stuart	3.50	1.75	1.00
161	Frank Baumann	3.50	1.75	1.00
162	Sammy Drake	3.50	1.75	1.00
163	Hot Corner Guardians (Cletis Boyer, Billy Gardner)	5.00	2.50	1.50
164	Hal Naragon	3.50	1.75	1.00
165	Jackie Brandt	3.50	1.75	1.00
166	Don Lee	3.50	1.75	1.00
167	*Tim McCarver*	26.00	13.00	7.75
168	Leo Posada	3.50	1.75	1.00
169	Bob Cerv	3.50	1.75	1.00
170	Ron Santo	12.00	6.00	3.50
171	Dave Sisler	3.50	1.75	1.00
172	Fred Hutchinson	3.50	1.75	1.00
173	Chico Fernandez	3.50	1.75	1.00
174a	Carl Willey (with cap)	22.00	11.00	6.50
174b	Carl Willey (no cap)	3.50	1.75	1.00
175	Frank Howard	5.00	2.50	1.50
176a	Eddie Yost (batting)	22.00	11.00	6.50
176b	Eddie Yost (portrait)	3.50	1.75	1.00
177	Bobby Shantz	4.50	2.25	1.25
178	Camilo Carreon	3.50	1.75	1.00
179	Tom Sturdivant	3.50	1.75	1.00
180	Bob Allison	3.50	1.75	1.00
181	Paul Brown	3.50	1.75	1.00
182	Bob Nieman	3.50	1.75	1.00
183	Roger Craig	5.00	2.50	1.50
184	Haywood Sullivan	3.50	1.75	1.00
185	Roland Sheldon	3.50	1.75	1.00
186	*Mack Jones*	3.50	1.75	1.00
187	Gene Conley	3.50	1.75	1.00
188	Chuck Hiller	3.50	1.75	1.00
189	Dick Hall	3.50	1.75	1.00
190a	Wally Moon (with cap)	24.00	12.00	7.25
190b	Wally Moon (no cap)	3.50	1.75	1.00
191	Jim Brewer	3.50	1.75	1.00
192a	Checklist 177-264 (192 is Check List, 3)	7.00	3.50	2.00
192b	Checklist 177-264 (192 is Check List 3)	6.00	3.00	1.75
193	Eddie Kasko	3.50	1.75	1.00
194	*Dean Chance*	5.00	2.50	1.50
195	Joe Cunningham	3.50	1.75	1.00
196	Terry Fox	3.50	1.75	1.00
197	Daryl Spencer	3.50	1.75	1.00
198	Johnny Keane	3.50	1.75	1.00
199	*Gaylord Perry*	110.00	55.00	33.00
200	Mickey Mantle	525.00	260.00	155.00
201	Ike Delock	3.50	1.75	1.00
202	Carl Warwick	3.50	1.75	1.00
203	Jack Fisher	3.50	1.75	1.00
204	Johnny Weekly	3.50	1.75	1.00
205	Gene Freese	3.50	1.75	1.00
206	Senators Team	7.50	3.75	2.25
207	Pete Burnside	3.50	1.75	1.00
208	Billy Martin	6.00	3.00	1.75
209	*Jim Fregosi*	10.00	5.00	3.00
210	Roy Face	3.50	1.75	1.00
211	Midway Masters (Frank Bolling, Roy McMillan)	4.50	2.25	1.25
212	Jim Owens	3.50	1.75	1.00
213	Richie Ashburn	6.00	3.00	1.75
214	Dom Zanni	3.50	1.75	1.00
215	Woody Held	3.50	1.75	1.00
216	Ron Kline	3.50	1.75	1.00
217	Walt Alston	5.00	2.50	1.50
218	*Joe Torre*	27.00	13.50	8.00
219	*Al Downing*	4.50	2.25	1.25
220	Roy Sievers	3.50	1.75	1.00
221	Bill Short	3.50	1.75	1.00
222	Jerry Zimmerman	3.50	1.75	1.00
223	Alex Grammas	3.50	1.75	1.00
224	Don Rudolph	3.50	1.75	1.00
225	Frank Malzone	3.50	1.75	1.00
226	Giants Team	7.50	3.75	2.25
227	Bobby Tiefenauer	3.50	1.75	1.00
228	Dale Long	3.50	1.75	1.00
229	Jesus McFarlane	3.50	1.75	1.00
230	Camlio Pascual	3.50	1.75	1.00
231	Ernie Bowman	3.50	1.75	1.00
232	World Series Game 1 (Yanks Win Opener)	7.00	3.50	2.00
233	World Series Game 2 (Jay Ties It Up)	7.00	3.50	2.00
234	World Series Game 3 (Maris Wins It In The 9th)	12.00	6.00	3.50
235	World Series Game 4 (Ford Sets New Mark)	9.00	4.50	2.75
236	World Series Game 5 (Yanks Crush Reds In Finale)	9.00	4.50	2.75
237	World Series Summary (The Winners Celebrate)	7.00	3.50	2.00
238	Norm Sherry	3.50	1.75	1.00
239	Cecil Butler	3.50	1.75	1.00
240	George Altman	3.50	1.75	1.00
241	Johnny Kucks	3.50	1.75	1.00
242	Mel McGaha	3.50	1.75	1.00
243	Robin Roberts	15.00	7.50	4.50
244	Don Gile	3.50	1.75	1.00
245	Ron Hansen	3.50	1.75	1.00
246	Art Ditmar	3.50	1.75	1.00
247	Joe Pignatano	3.50	1.75	1.00
248	Bob Aspromonte	3.50	1.75	1.00
249	Ed Keegan	3.50	1.75	1.00
250	Norm Cash	7.00	3.50	2.00
251	Yankees Team	25.00	12.50	7.50
252	Earl Francis	3.50	1.75	1.00
253	Harry Chiti	3.50	1.75	1.00
254	Gordon Windhorn	3.50	1.75	1.00
255	Juan Pizarro	3.50	1.75	1.00
256	Elio Chacon	3.50	1.75	1.00
257	Jack Spring	3.50	1.75	1.00
258	Marty Keough	3.50	1.75	1.00
259	Lou Klimchock	3.50	1.75	1.00
260	Bill Pierce	3.50	1.75	1.00
261	George Alusik	3.50	1.75	1.00
262	Bob Schmidt	3.50	1.75	1.00
263	The Right Pitch (Joe Jay, Bob Purkey, Jim Turner)	4.50	2.25	1.25
264	Dick Ellsworth	3.50	1.75	1.00
265	Joe Adcock	3.50	1.75	1.00
266	John Anderson	3.50	1.75	1.00
267	Dan Dobbek	3.50	1.75	1.00
268	Ken McBride	3.50	1.75	1.00
269	Bob Oldis	3.50	1.75	1.00
270	Dick Groat	3.50	1.75	1.00
271	Ray Rippelmeyer	3.50	1.75	1.00
272	Earl Robinson	3.50	1.75	1.00
273	Gary Bell	3.50	1.75	1.00
274	Sammy Taylor	3.50	1.75	1.00
275	Norm Siebern	3.50	1.75	1.00
276	Hal Kostad	3.50	1.75	1.00
277	Checklist 265-352	7.00	3.50	2.00
278	Ken Johnson	3.50	1.75	1.00
279	Hobie Landrith	3.50	1.75	1.00
280	Johnny Podres	4.50	2.25	1.25
281	*Jake Gibbs*	3.50	1.75	1.00
282	Dave Hillman	3.50	1.75	1.00
283	Charlie Smith	3.50	1.75	1.00
284	Ruben Amaro	3.50	1.75	1.00
285	Curt Simmons	3.50	1.75	1.00
286	Al Lopez	5.00	2.50	1.50
287	George Witt	3.50	1.75	1.00
288	Billy Williams	24.00	12.00	7.25
289	Mike Krsnich	3.50	1.75	1.00
290	Jim Gentile	3.50	1.75	1.00
291	Hal Stowe	3.50	1.75	1.00
292	Jerry Kindall	3.50	1.75	1.00
293	Bob Miller	3.50	1.75	1.00
294	Phillies Team	7.50	3.75	2.25
295	Vern Law	3.50	1.75	1.00
296	Ken Hamlin	3.50	1.75	1.00
297	Ron Perranoski	3.50	1.75	1.00
298	Bill Tuttle	3.50	1.75	1.00
299	*Don Wert*	3.50	1.75	1.00
300	Willie Mays	140.00	70.00	42.00
301	Galen Cisco	3.50	1.75	1.00
302	*John Edwards*	3.50	1.75	1.00
303	Frank Torre	3.50	1.75	1.00
304	Dick Farrell	3.50	1.75	1.00
305	Jerry Lumpe	3.50	1.75	1.00
306	Redbird Rippers (Larry Jackson, Lindy McDaniel)	4.50	2.25	1.25
307	Jim Grant	3.50	1.75	1.00
308	Neil Chrisley	3.50	1.75	1.00
309	Moe Morhardt	3.50	1.75	1.00
310	Whitey Ford	32.00	16.00	9.50
311	Kubek Makes The Double Play	6.00	3.00	1.75
312	Spahn Show No-Hit Form	8.00	4.00	2.50
313	Maris Blasts 61st	20.00	10.00	6.00
314	Colavito's Power	7.00	3.50	2.00
315	Ford Tosses a Curve	8.00	4.00	2.50
316	Killebrew Send One into Orbit	20.00	10.00	6.00
317	Musial Plays 21st Season	30.00	15.00	9.00
318	The Switch Hitter Connects, Mickey Mantle	60.00	30.00	18.00
319	McCormick Shows His Stuff	5.00	2.50	1.50
320	Hank Aaron	140.00	70.00	42.00
321	Lee Stange	3.50	1.75	1.00
322	Al Dark	3.50	1.75	1.00
323	Don Landrum	3.50	1.75	1.00
324	Joe McClain	3.50	1.75	1.00
325	Luis Aparicio	18.00	9.00	5.50
326	Tom Parsons	3.50	1.75	1.00

327 Ozzie Virgil 3.50 1.75 1.00
328 Ken Walters 3.50 1.75 1.00
329 Bob Bolin 3.50 1.75 1.00
330 Johnny Romano 3.50 1.75 1.00
331 Moe Drabowsky 3.50 1.75 1.00
332 Don Buddin 3.50 1.75 1.00
333 Frank Cipriani 3.50 1.75 1.00
334 Red Sox Team 7.50 3.75 2.25
335 Bill Bruton 3.50 1.75 1.00
336 Billy Muffett 3.50 1.75 1.00
337 Jim Marshall 3.50 1.75 1.00
338 Billy Gardner 3.50 1.75 1.00
339 Jose Valdivielso 3.50 1.75 1.00
340 Don Drysdale 40.00 20.00 12.00
341 Mike Hershberger 3.50 1.75 1.00
342 Ed Rakow 3.50 1.75 1.00
343 Albie Pearson 3.50 1.75 1.00
344 Ed Bauta 3.50 1.75 1.00
345 Chuck Schilling 3.50 1.75 1.00
346 Jack Kralick 3.50 1.75 1.00
347 Chuck Hinton 3.50 1.75 1.00
348 Larry Burright 3.50 1.75 1.00
349 Paul Foytack 3.50 1.75 1.00
350 Frank Robinson 45.00 22.00 13.50
351 Braves' Backstops (Del Crandall, Joe Torre)
5.00 2.50 1.50
352 Frank Sullivan 3.50 1.75 1.00
353 Bill Mazeroski 8.00 4.00 2.50
354 Roman Mejias 3.50 1.75 1.00
355 Steve Barber 3.50 1.75 1.00
356 Tom Haller 3.50 1.75 1.00
357 Jerry Walker 3.50 1.75 1.00
358 Tommy Davis 5.00 2.50 1.50
359 Bobby Locke 3.50 1.75 1.00
360 Yogi Berra 70.00 35.00 21.00
361 Bob Hendley 3.50 1.75 1.00
362 Ty Cline 3.50 1.75 1.00
363 Bob Roselli 3.50 1.75 1.00
364 Ken Hunt 3.50 1.75 1.00
365 Charley Neal 3.50 1.75 1.00
366 Phil Regan 3.50 1.75 1.00
367 Checklist 353-429 7.00 3.50 2.00
368 Bob Tillman 3.50 1.75 1.00
369 Ted Bowsfield 3.50 1.75 1.00
370 Ken Boyer 5.00 2.50 1.50
371 Earl Battey 5.00 2.50 1.50
372 Jack Curtis 5.00 2.50 1.50
373 Al Heist 5.00 2.50 1.50
374 Gene Mauch 5.00 2.50 1.50
375 Ron Fairly 5.00 2.50 1.50
376 Bud Daley 5.00 2.50 1.50
377 Johnny Orsino 5.00 2.50 1.50
378 Bennie Daniels 5.00 2.50 1.50
379 Chuck Essegian 5.00 2.50 1.50
380 Lou Burdette 5.00 2.50 1.50
381 Chico Cardenas 5.00 2.50 1.50
382 Dick Williams 6.00 3.00 1.75
383 Ray Sadecki 5.00 2.50 1.50
384 Athletics Team 9.00 4.50 2.75
385 Early Wynn 18.00 9.00 5.50
386 Don Mincher 5.00 2.50 1.50
387 *Lou Brock* 190.00 95.00 57.00
388 Ryne Duren 5.00 2.50 1.50
389 Smoky Burgess 5.00 2.50 1.50
390 Orlando Cepeda (All-Star) 7.50 3.75 2.25
391 Bill Mazeroski (All-Star) 7.50 3.75 2.25
392 Ken Boyer (All-Star) 7.00 3.50 2.00
393 Roy McMillan (All-Star) 6.00 3.00 1.75
394 Hank Aaron (All-Star) 37.50 18.50 11.00
395 Willie Mays (All-Star) 37.50 18.50 11.00
396 Frank Robinson (All-Star) 20.00 10.00 6.00
397 John Roseboro (All-Star) 6.00 3.00 1.75
398 Don Drysdale (All-Star) 13.00 6.50 4.00
399 Warren Spahn (All-Star) 13.00 6.50 4.00
400 Elston Howard 7.00 3.50 2.00
401 AL & NL Homer Kings (Roger Maris, Orlando Cepeda) 40.00 20.00 12.00
402 Gino Cimoli 5.00 2.50 1.50
403 Chet Nichols 5.00 2.50 1.50
404 Tim Harkness 5.00 2.50 1.50
405 Jim Perry 5.00 2.50 1.50
406 Bob Taylor 5.00 2.50 1.50
407 Hank Aguirre 5.00 2.50 1.50
408 Gus Bell 5.00 2.50 1.50
409 Pirates Team 9.00 4.50 2.75
410 Al Smith 5.00 2.50 1.50
411 Danny O'Connell 5.00 2.50 1.50
412 Charlie James 5.00 2.50 1.50
413 Matty Alou 5.00 2.50 1.50
414 Joe Gaines 5.00 2.50 1.50
415 Bill Virdon 5.00 2.50 1.50
416 Bob Scheffing 5.00 2.50 1.50
417 Joe Azcue 5.00 2.50 1.50
418 Andy Carey 5.00 2.50 1.50
419 Bob Bruce 5.00 2.50 1.50
420 Gus Triandos 5.00 2.50 1.50
421 Ken MacKenzie 5.00 2.50 1.50
422 Steve Bilko 5.00 2.50 1.50
423 Rival League Relief Aces (Roy Face, Hoyt Wilhelm)
7.50 3.75 2.25
424 Al McBean 5.00 2.50 1.50
425 Carl Yastrzemski 155.00 75.00 45.00
426 Bob Farley 5.00 2.50 1.50
427 Jake Wood 5.00 2.50 1.50
428 Joe Hicks 5.00 2.50 1.50
429 Bill O'Dell 5.00 2.50 1.50
430 Tony Kubek 8.00 4.00 2.50
431 *Bob Rodgers* 7.00 3.50 2.00
432 Jim Pendleton 5.00 2.50 1.50
433 Jim Archer 5.00 2.50 1.50
434 Clay Dalrymple 5.00 2.50 1.50
435 Larry Sherry 5.00 2.50 1.50
436 Felix Mantilla 5.00 2.50 1.50
437 Ray Moore 5.00 2.50 1.50
438 Dick Brown 5.00 2.50 1.50
439 Jerry Buchek 5.00 2.50 1.50
440 Joe Jay 5.00 2.50 1.50
441 Checklist 430-506 8.00 4.00 2.50
442 Wes Stock 5.00 2.50 1.50
443 Del Crandall 5.00 2.50 1.50
444 Ted Wills 5.00 2.50 1.50
445 Vic Power 5.00 2.50 1.50
446 Don Elston 5.00 2.50 1.50
447 Willie Kirkland 7.50 3.75 2.25
448 Joe Gibbon 7.50 3.75 2.25
449 Jerry Adair 7.50 3.75 2.25
450 Jim O'Toole 7.50 3.75 2.25
451 *Jose Tartabull* 7.50 3.75 2.25
452 Earl Averill 7.50 3.75 2.25
453 Cal McLish 7.50 3.75 2.25
454 Floyd Robinson 7.50 3.75 2.25
455 Luis Arroyo 7.50 3.75 2.25
456 Joe Amalfitano 7.50 3.75 2.25
457 Lou Clinton 7.50 3.75 2.25
458a Bob Buhl ("M" on cap) 7.50 3.75 2.25
458b Bob Buhl (plain cap) 65.00 32.00 19.50
459 Ed Bailey 7.50 3.75 2.25
460 Jim Bunning 9.00 4.50 2.75
461 *Ken Hubbs* 22.00 11.00 6.60
462a Willie Tasby ("W" on cap) 7.50 3.75 2.25
462b Willie Tasby (plain cap) 65.00 32.00 19.50
463 Hank Bauer 7.50 3.75 2.25
464 *Al Jackson* 7.50 3.75 2.25
465 Reds Team 7.50 3.75 2.25
466 Norm Cash (All-Star) 8.00 4.00 2.50
467 Chuck Schilling (All-Star) 7.50 3.75 2.25
468 Brooks Robinson (All-Star) 20.00 10.00 6.00
469 Luis Aparicio (All-Star) 9.00 4.50 2.75
470 Al Kaline (All-Star) 20.00 10.00 6.00
471 Mickey Mantle (All-Star) 145.00 72.00 43.00
472 Rocky Colavito (All-Star) 12.00 6.00 3.50
473 Elston Howard (All-Star) 8.00 4.00 2.50
474 Frank Lary (All-Star) 7.50 3.75 2.25
475 Whitey Ford (All-Star) 10.00 5.00 3.00
476 Orioles Team 12.00 6.00 3.50
477 Andre Rodgers 7.50 3.75 2.25
478 Don Zimmer 7.50 3.75 2.25
479 *Joel Horlen* 7.50 3.75 2.25
480 Harvey Kuenn 7.50 3.75 2.25
481 Vic Wertz 7.50 3.75 2.25
482 Sam Mele 7.50 3.75 2.25
483 Don McMahon 7.50 3.75 2.25
484 Dick Schofield 7.50 3.75 2.25
485 Pedro Ramos 7.50 3.75 2.25
486 Jim Gilliam 7.50 3.75 2.25
487 Jerry Lynch 7.50 3.75 2.25
488 Hal Brown 7.50 3.75 2.25
489 Julio Gotay 7.50 3.75 2.25
490 Clete Boyer 7.50 3.75 2.25
491 Leon Wagner 7.50 3.75 2.25
492 Hal Smith 7.50 3.75 2.25
493 Danny McDevitt 7.50 3.75 2.25
494 Sammy White 7.50 3.75 2.25
495 Don Cardwell 7.50 3.75 2.25
496 Wayne Causey 7.50 3.75 2.25
497 Ed Bouchee 7.50 3.75 2.25
498 Jim Donohue 7.50 3.75 2.25
499 Zoilo Versalles 7.50 3.75 2.25
500 Duke Snider 40.00 20.00 12.00
501 Claude Osteen 7.50 3.75 2.25
502 Hector Lopez 7.50 3.75 2.25
503 Danny Murtaugh 7.50 3.75 2.25
504 Eddie Bressoud 7.50 3.75 2.25
505 Juan Marichal 35.00 17.50 10.50
506 Charley Maxwell 7.50 3.75 2.25
507 Ernie Broglio 7.50 3.75 2.25
508 Gordy Coleman 7.50 3.75 2.25
509 *Dave Giusti* 7.50 3.75 2.25
510 Jim Lemon 7.50 3.75 2.25
511 Bubba Phillips 7.50 3.75 2.25
512 Mike Fornieles 7.50 3.75 2.25
513 Whitey Herzog 7.50 3.75 2.25
514 Sherm Lollar 7.50 3.75 2.25
515 Stan Williams 7.50 3.75 2.25
516 Checklist 507-598 9.00 4.50 2.75
517 Dave Wickersham 7.50 3.75 2.25
518 Lee Maye 7.50 3.75 2.25
519 Bob Johnson 7.50 3.75 2.25
520 Bob Friend 7.50 3.75 2.25
521 Jacke Davis 7.50 3.75 2.25
522 Lindy McDaniel 7.50 3.75 2.25
523 Russ Nixon (SP) 24.00 12.00 7.25
524 Howie Nunn (SP) 24.00 12.00 7.25
525 George Thomas 20.00 10.00 6.00
526 Hal Woodeshick (SP) 24.00 12.00 7.25
527 *Dick McAuliffe* 20.00 10.00 6.00
528 Turk Lown 20.00 10.00 6.00
529 John Schaive (SP) 24.00 12.00 7.25
530 Bob Gibson 175.00 87.00 52.00
531 Bobby G. Smith 20.00 10.00 6.00
532 Dick Stigman 20.00 10.00 6.00
533 Charley Lau (SP) 24.00 12.00 7.25
534 Tony Gonzalez (SP) 24.00 12.00 7.25
535 Ed Roebuck 20.00 10.00 6.00
536 Dick Gernert 20.00 10.00 6.00
537 Indians Team 40.00 20.00 12.00
538 Jack Sanford 20.00 10.00 6.00
539 Billy Moran 20.00 10.00 6.00
540 Jim Landis (SP) 24.00 12.00 7.25
541 Don Nottebart (SP) 24.00 12.00 7.25
542 Dave Philley 20.00 10.00 6.00
543 Bob Allen (SP) 24.00 12.00 7.25
544 Willie McCovey (SP) 130.00 65.00 39.00
545 Hoyt Wilhelm (SP) 55.00 27.00 16.50
546 Moe Thacker (SP) 24.00 12.00 7.25
547 Don Ferrarese 20.00 10.00 6.00
548 Bobby Del Greco 20.00 10.00 6.00
549 Bill Rigney (SP) 26.00 13.00 7.75
550 Art Mahaffey (SP) 24.00 12.00 7.25
551 Harry Bright 20.00 10.00 6.00
552 Cubs Team 30.00 15.00 9.00
553 Jim Coates 20.00 10.00 6.00
554 Bubba Morton (SP) 24.00 12.00 7.25
555 John Buzhardt (SP) 24.00 12.00 7.25
556 Al Spangler 20.00 10.00 6.00
557 Bob Anderson (SP) 24.00 12.00 7.25
558 John Goryl 20.00 10.00 6.00
559 Mike Higgins 20.00 10.00 6.00
560 Chuck Estrada (SP) 24.00 12.00 7.25
561 Gene Oliver (SP) 24.00 12.00 7.25
562 Bill Henry 20.00 10.00 6.00
563 Ken Aspromonte 20.00 10.00 6.00
564 Bob Grim 20.00 10.00 6.00
565 Jose Pagan 20.00 10.00 6.00
566 Marty Kutyna (SP) 24.00 12.00 7.25
567 Tracy Stallard (SP) 24.00 12.00 7.25
568 Jim Golden 20.00 10.00 6.00
569 Ed Sadowski (SP) 24.00 12.00 7.25
570 Bill Stafford 20.00 10.00 6.00
571 Billy Klaus (SP) 24.00 12.00 7.25
572 Bob Miller 20.00 10.00 6.00
573 Johnny Logan 20.00 10.00 6.00
574 Dean Stone 20.00 10.00 6.00
575 Red Schoendienst 35.00 17.50 10.50
576 Russ Kemmerer (SP) 24.00 12.00 7.25
577 Dave Nicholson (SP) 24.00 12.00 7.25
578 Jim Duffalo 20.00 10.00 6.00
579 Jim Schaffer (SP) 24.00 12.00 7.25
580 Bill Monbouquette 20.00 10.00 6.00
581 Mel Roach 20.00 10.00 6.00
582 Ron Piche 20.00 10.00 6.00
583 Larry Osborne 20.00 10.00 6.00
584 Twins Team 35.00 17.50 10.50
585 Glen Hobbie (SP) 24.00 12.00 7.25
586 Sammy Esposito (SP) 24.00 12.00 7.25
587 Frank Funk (SP) 24.00 12.00 7.25
588 Birdie Tebbetts 20.00 10.00 6.00
589 Bob Turley 20.00 10.00 6.00
590 Curt Flood 20.00 10.00 6.00
591 Rookie Parade Pitchers (*Sam McDowell*, Ron Nischwitz, Art Quirk, Dick Radatz, Ron Taylor)
60.00 30.00 18.00
592 Rookie Parade Pitchers (*Bo Belinsky*, Joe Bonikowski, Jim Bouton, Dan Pfister, Dave Stenhouse) 60.00 30.00 18.00
593 Rookie Parade Pitchers (Craig Anderson, Jack Hamilton, Jack Lamabe, Bob Moorhead, Bob Veale)
25.00 12.50 7.50
594 Rookie Parade Catchers (Doug Camilli, Doc Edwards, Don Pavletich, Ken Retzer, Bob Uecker)
85.00 42.00 25.00
595 Rookie Parade Infielders (*Ed Charles*, Marlin Coughtry, Bob Sadowski, Felix Torres)
30.00 15.00 9.00
596 Rookie Parade Infielders (*Bernie Allen*, Phil Linz, Joe Pepitone, Rich Rollins) 65.00 32.00 19.50
597 Rookie Parade Infielders (Rod Kanehl, Jim McKnight, Denis Menke, Amado Samuel)
30.00 15.00 9.00
598 Rookie Parade Outfielders (Howie Goss, Jim Hickman, Manny Jimenez, Al Luplow, Ed Olivares)
65.00 15.00 7.50

1962 Topps Baseball Bucks

Issued in their own 1¢ package, the 1962 Topps "Baseball Bucks" were another in the growing list of specialty Topps items. The 96 Baseball Bucks in the set measure 4-1/8" by 1-3/4," and were designed to look vaguely like dollar bills. The center player portrait has a banner underneath with the player's name. His home park is shown on the right and there is some biographical information on the left. The back features a large denomination, with the player's league and team logo on either side.

		NR MT	EX	VG
Complete Set:		900.00	450.00	270.00
Common Player:		4.00	2.00	1.25
(1)	Hank Aaron	32.50	16.00	9.75
(2)	Joe Adcock	4.00	2.00	1.25
(3)	George Altman	4.00	2.00	1.25
(4)	Jim Archer	4.00	2.00	1.25
(5)	Richie Ashburn	12.00	6.00	3.50
(6)	Ernie Banks	24.00	12.00	7.25
(7)	Earl Battey	4.00	2.00	1.25
(8)	Gus Bell	4.00	2.00	1.25
(9)	Yogi Berra	20.00	10.00	6.00
(10)	Ken Boyer	4.00	2.00	1.25
(11)	Jackie Brandt	4.00	2.00	1.25
(12)	Jim Bunning	6.00	3.00	1.75
(13)	Lou Burdette	4.00	2.00	1.25
(14)	Don Cardwell	4.00	2.00	1.25
(15)	Norm Cash	4.00	2.00	1.25
(16)	Orlando Cepeda	6.00	3.00	1.75
(17)	Roberto Clemente	32.50	16.00	9.75
(18)	Rocky Colavito	8.00	4.00	2.50
(19)	Chuck Cottier	4.00	2.00	1.25

(20)	Roger Craig	6.00	3.00	1.75
(21)	Bennie Daniels	4.00	2.00	1.25
(22)	Don Demeter	4.00	2.00	1.25
(23)	Don Drysdale	15.00	7.50	4.50
(24)	Chuck Estrada	4.00	2.00	1.25
(25)	Dick Farrell	4.00	2.00	1.25
(26)	Whitey Ford	22.00	11.00	6.50
(27)	Nellie Fox	6.00	3.00	1.75
(28)	Tito Francona	4.00	2.00	1.25
(29)	Bob Friend	4.00	2.00	1.25
(30)	Jim Gentile	4.00	2.00	1.25
(31)	Dick Gernert	4.00	2.00	1.25
(32)	Lenny Green	4.00	2.00	1.25
(33)	Dick Groat	4.00	2.00	1.25
(34)	Woody Held	4.00	2.00	1.25
(35)	Don Hoak	4.00	2.00	1.25
(36)	Gil Hodges	8.00	4.00	2.50
(37)	Frank Howard	7.00	3.50	2.00
(38)	Elston Howard	6.00	3.00	1.75
(39)	Dick Howser	4.00	2.00	1.25
(40)	Ken Hunt	4.00	2.00	1.25
(41)	Larry Jackson	4.00	2.00	1.25
(42)	Joe Jay	4.00	2.00	1.25
(43)	Al Kaline	15.00	7.50	4.50
(44)	Harmon Killebrew	15.00	7.50	4.50
(45)	Sandy Koufax	26.00	13.00	8.00
(46)	Harvey Kuenn	6.00	3.00	1.75
(47)	Jim Landis	4.00	2.00	1.25
(48)	Norm Larker	4.00	2.00	1.25
(49)	Frank Lary	4.00	2.00	1.25
(50)	Jerry Lumpe	4.00	2.00	1.25
(51)	Art Mahaffey	4.00	2.00	1.25
(52)	Frank Malzone	4.00	2.00	1.25
(53)	Felix Mantilla	4.00	2.00	1.25
(54)	Mickey Mantle	130.00	65.00	40.00
(55)	Roger Maris	24.00	12.00	7.25
(56)	Ed Mathews	18.00	9.00	5.50
(57)	Willie Mays	30.00	15.00	9.00
(58)	Ken McBride	4.00	2.00	1.25
(59)	Mike McCormick	4.00	2.00	1.25
(60)	Minnie Minoso	7.00	3.50	2.00
(61)	Wally Moon	4.00	2.00	1.25
(62)	Stu Miller	4.00	2.00	1.25
(63)	Stan Musial	35.00	17.50	10.50
(64)	Danny O'Connell	4.00	2.00	1.25
(65)	Jim O'Toole	4.00	2.00	1.25
(66)	Camilo Pascual	4.00	2.00	1.25
(67)	Jim Perry	4.00	2.00	1.25
(68)	Jimmy Piersall	4.00	2.00	1.25
(69)	Vada Pinson	5.00	2.50	1.50
(70)	Juan Pizarro	4.00	2.00	1.25
(71)	Johnny Podres	4.00	2.00	1.25
(72)	Vic Power	4.00	2.00	1.25
(73)	Bob Purkey	4.00	2.00	1.25
(74)	Pedro Ramos	4.00	2.00	1.25
(75)	Brooks Robinson	20.00	10.00	6.00
(76)	Floyd Robinson	4.00	2.00	1.25
(77)	Frank Robinson	18.00	9.00	5.50
(78)	Johnny Romano	4.00	2.00	1.25
(79)	Pete Runnels	4.00	2.00	1.25
(80)	Don Schwall	4.00	2.00	1.25
(81)	Bobby Shantz	4.00	2.00	1.25
(82)	Norm Siebern	4.00	2.00	1.25
(83)	Roy Sievers	4.00	2.00	1.25
(84)	Hal (W.) Smith	4.00	2.00	1.25
(85)	Warren Spahn	15.00	7.50	4.50
(86)	Dick Stuart	4.00	2.00	1.25
(87)	Tony Taylor	4.00	2.00	1.25
(88)	Lee Thomas	4.00	2.00	1.25
(89)	Gus Triandos	4.00	2.00	1.25
(90)	Leon Wagner	4.00	2.00	1.25
(91)	Jerry Walker	4.00	2.00	1.25
(92)	Bill White	4.00	2.00	1.25
(93)	Billy Williams	15.00	7.50	4.50
(94)	Gene Woodling	4.00	2.00	1.25
(95)	Early Wynn	15.00	7.50	4.50
(96)	Carl Yastrzemski	22.00	11.00	6.50

1962 Topps Stamps

An artistic improvement over the somewhat drab Topps stamps of the previous year, the 1962 stamps, 1-3/8" by 1-7/8," had color player photographs set on red or yellow backgrounds. As in 1961, they were issued in two-stamp panels as insert with Topps baseball cards. A change from 1961 was the inclusion of team emblems in the set. A complete set consists of 201 stamps; Roy Sievers was originally portrayed on the wrong team - Athletics - and was later corrected to the Phillies.

		NR MT	EX	VG
	Complete Set (200):	220.00	110.00	66.00
	Stamp Album:	35.00	17.50	10.50
	Common Player:	1.00	.50	.30
(1)	Hank Aaron	12.50	6.25	3.75
(2)	Jerry Adair	1.00	.50	.30
(3)	Joe Adcock	1.00	.50	.30
(4)	Bob Allison	1.00	.50	.30
(5)	Felipe Alou	2.00	1.00	.60
(6)	George Altman	1.00	.50	.30
(7)	Joe Amalfitano	1.00	.50	.30
(8)	Ruben Amaro	1.00	.50	.30
(9)	Luis Aparicio	3.00	1.50	.90
(10)	Jim Archer	1.00	.50	.30
(11)	Bob Aspromonte	1.00	.50	.30
(12)	Ed Bailey	1.00	.50	.30
(13)	Jack Baldschun	1.00	.50	.30
(14)	Ernie Banks	9.00	4.50	2.75
(15)	Earl Battey	1.00	.50	.30
(16)	Gus Bell	1.00	.50	.30
(17)	Yogi Berra	9.00	4.50	2.75
(18)	Dick Bertell	1.00	.50	.30
(19)	Steve Bilko	1.00	.50	.30
(20)	Frank Bolling	1.00	.50	.30
(21)	Steve Boros	1.00	.50	.30
(22)	Ted Bowsfield	1.00	.50	.30
(23)	Clete Boyer	1.00	.50	.30
(24)	Ken Boyer	1.50	.70	.45
(25)	Jackie Brandt	1.00	.50	.30
(26)	Bill Bruton	1.00	.50	.30
(27)	Jim Bunning	1.50	.70	.45
(28)	Lou Burdette	1.00	.50	.30
(29)	Smoky Burgess	1.00	.50	.30
(30)	Johnny Callizon (Callison)	1.00	.50	.30
(31)	Don Cardwell	1.00	.50	.30
(32)	Camilo Carreon	1.00	.50	.30
(33)	Norm Cash	1.50	.70	.45
(34)	Orlando Cepeda	2.00	1.00	.60
(35)	Roberto Clemente	13.00	6.50	4.00
(36)	Ty Cline	1.00	.50	.30
(37)	Rocky Colavito	4.00	2.00	1.20
(38)	Gordon Coleman	1.00	.50	.30
(39)	Chuck Cottier	1.00	.50	.30
(40)	Roger Craig	1.50	.70	.45
(41)	Del Crandall	1.00	.50	.30
(42)	Pete Daley	1.00	.50	.30
(43)	Clay Dalrymple	1.00	.50	.30
(44)	Bennie Daniels	1.00	.50	.30
(45)	Jim Davenport	1.00	.50	.30
(46)	Don Demeter	1.00	.50	.30
(47)	Dick Donovan	1.00	.50	.30
(48)	Don Drysdale	9.00	4.50	2.75
(49)	John Edwards	1.00	.50	.30
(50)	Dick Ellsworth	1.00	.50	.30
(51)	Chuck Estrada	1.00	.50	.30
(52)	Roy Face	1.00	.50	.30
(53)	Ron Fairly	1.00	.50	.30
(54)	Dick Farrell	1.00	.50	.30
(55)	Whitey Ford	7.00	3.50	2.00
(56)	Mike Fornieles	1.00	.50	.30
(57)	Nellie Fox	4.00	2.00	1.20
(58)	Tito Francona	1.00	.50	.30
(59)	Gene Freese	1.00	.50	.30
(60)	Bob Friend	1.00	.50	.30
(61)	Gary Geiger	1.00	.50	.30
(62)	Jim Gentile	1.00	.50	.30
(63)	Tony Gonzalez	1.00	.50	.30
(64)	Lenny Green	1.00	.50	.30
(65)	Dick Groat	1.00	.50	.30
(66)	Ron Hansen	1.00	.50	.30
(67)	Al Heist	1.00	.50	.30
(68)	Woody Held	1.00	.50	.30
(69)	Ray Herbert	1.00	.50	.30
(70)	Chuck Hinton	1.00	.50	.30
(71)	Don Hoak	1.00	.50	.30
(72)	Glen Hobbie	1.00	.50	.30
(73)	Gil Hodges	5.00	2.50	1.50
(74)	Jay Hook	1.00	.50	.30
(75)	Elston Howard	3.00	1.50	.90
(76)	Frank Howard	1.50	.70	.45
(77)	Dick Howser	1.00	.50	.30
(78)	Ken Hunt	1.00	.50	.30
(79)	Larry Jackson	1.00	.50	.30
(80)	Julian Javier	1.00	.50	.30
(81)	Joe Jay	1.00	.50	.30
(82)	Bob Johnson	1.00	.50	.30
(83)	Sam Jones	1.00	.50	.30
(84)	Al Kaline	9.00	4.50	2.75
(85)	Eddie Kasko	1.00	.50	.30
(86)	Harmon Killebrew	8.00	4.00	2.50
(87)	Sandy Koufax	12.00	6.00	3.50
(88)	Jack Kralick	1.00	.50	.30
(89)	Tony Kubek	2.00	1.00	.60
(90)	Harvey Kuenn	1.50	.70	.45
(91)	Jim Landis	1.00	.50	.30
(92)	Hobie Landrith	1.00	.50	.30
(93)	Frank Lary	1.00	.50	.30
(94)	Barry Latman	1.00	.50	.30
(95)	Jerry Lumpe	1.00	.50	.30
(96)	Art Mahaffey	1.00	.50	.30
(97)	Frank Malzone	1.00	.50	.30
(98)	Felix Mantilla	1.00	.50	.30
(99)	Mickey Mantle	45.00	22.00	13.50
(100)	Juan Marichal	5.00	2.50	1.50
(101)	Roger Maris	7.00	3.50	2.00
(102)	J.C. Martin	1.00	.50	.30
(103)	Ed Mathews	6.00	3.00	1.75
(104)	Willie Mays	13.00	6.50	4.00
(105)	Bill Mazeroski	2.00	1.00	.60
(106)	Ken McBride	1.00	.50	.30
(107)	Tim McCarver	1.50	.70	.45
(108)	Joe McClain	1.00	.50	.30
(109)	Mike McCormick	1.00	.50	.30
(110)	Lindy McDaniel	1.00	.50	.30
(111)	Roy McMillan	1.00	.50	.30
(112)	Bob L. Miller	1.00	.50	.30
(113)	Stu Miller	1.00	.50	.30
(114)	Minnie Minoso	3.00	1.50	.90
(115)	Bill Monbouquette	1.00	.50	.30
(116)	Wally Moon	1.00	.50	.30
(117)	Don Mossi	1.00	.50	.30
(118)	Stan Musial	12.00	6.00	3.50
(119)	Russ Nixon	1.00	.50	.30
(120)	Danny O'Connell	1.00	.50	.30
(121)	Jim O'Toole	1.00	.50	.30
(122)	Milt Pappas	1.00	.50	.30
(123)	Camilo Pascual	1.00	.50	.30
(124)	Albie Pearson	1.00	.50	.30
(125)	Jim Perry	1.00	.50	.30
(126)	Bubba Phillips	1.00	.50	.30
(127)	Jimmy Piersall	1.00	.50	.30
(128)	Vada Pinson	1.50	.70	.45
(129)	Juan Pizarro	1.00	.50	.30
(130)	Johnny Podres	1.00	.50	.30
(131)	Leo Posada	1.00	.50	.30
(132)	Vic Power	1.00	.50	.30
(133)	Bob Purkey	1.00	.50	.30
(134)	Pedro Ramos	1.00	.50	.30
(135)	Bobby Richardson	1.50	.70	.45
(136)	Brooks Robinson	8.00	4.00	2.50
(137)	Floyd Robinson	1.00	.50	.30
(138)	Frank Robinson	7.00	3.50	2.00
(139)	Bob Rodgers	1.00	.50	.30
(140)	Johnny Romano	1.00	.50	.30
(141)	John Roseboro	1.00	.50	.30
(142)	Pete Runnels	1.00	.50	.30
(143)	Ray Sadecki	1.00	.50	.30
(144)	Ron Santo	1.50	.70	.45
(145)	Chuck Schilling	1.00	.50	.30
(146)	Barney Schultz	1.00	.50	.30
(147)	Don Schwall	1.00	.50	.30
(148)	Bobby Shantz	1.50	.70	.45
(149)	Bob Shaw	1.00	.50	.30
(150)	Norm Siebern	1.00	.50	.30
(151a)	Roy Sievers (Kansas City)	1.00	.50	.30
(151b)	Roy Sievers (Philadelphia)	1.00	.50	.30
(152)	Bill Skowron	1.50	.70	.45
(153)	Hal (W.) Smith	1.00	.50	.30
(154)	Duke Snider	9.00	4.50	2.75
(155)	Warren Spahn	7.00	3.50	2.00
(156)	Al Spangler	1.00	.50	.30
(157)	Daryl Spencer	1.00	.50	.30
(158)	Gene Stephens	1.00	.50	.30
(159)	Dick Stuart	1.00	.50	.30
(160)	Haywood Sullivan	1.00	.50	.30
(161)	Tony Taylor	1.00	.50	.30
(162)	George Thomas	1.00	.50	.30
(163)	Lee Thomas	1.00	.50	.30
(164)	Bob Tiefenauer	1.00	.50	.30
(165)	Joe Torre	1.00	.50	.30
(166)	Gus Triandos	1.00	.50	.30
(167)	Bill Tuttle	1.00	.50	.30
(168)	Zoilo Versalles	1.00	.50	.30
(169)	Bill Virdon	1.00	.50	.30
(170)	Leon Wagner	1.00	.50	.30
(171)	Jerry Walker	1.00	.50	.30
(172)	Lee Walls	1.00	.50	.30
(173)	Bill White	1.50	.70	.45
(174)	Hoyt Wilhelm	4.00	2.00	1.25
(175)	Billy Williams	6.00	3.00	1.75
(176)	Jake Wood	1.00	.50	.30
(177)	Gene Woodling	1.00	.50	.30
(178)	Early Wynn	4.00	2.00	1.25
(179)	Carl Yastrzemski	7.00	3.50	2.00
(180)	Don Zimmer	1.00	.50	.30
(181)	Baltimore Orioles Logo	1.00	.50	.30
(182)	Boston Red Sox Logo	1.00	.50	.30
(183)	Chicago Cubs Logo	1.00	.50	.30
(184)	Chicago White Sox Logo	1.00	.50	.30
(185)	Cincinnati Reds Logo	1.00	.50	.30
(186)	Cleveland Indians Logo	1.00	.50	.30
(187)	Detroit Tigers Logo	1.00	.50	.30
(188)	Houston Colts Logo	1.00	.50	.30
(189)	Kansas City Athletics Logo	1.00	.50	.30
(190)	Los Angeles Angels Logo	1.00	.50	.30
(191)	Los Angeles Dodgers Logo	1.00	.50	.30
(192)	Milwaukee Braves Logo	1.00	.50	.30
(193)	Minnesota Twins Logo	1.00	.50	.30
(194)	New York Mets Logo	1.00	.50	.30
(195)	New York Yankees Logo	2.00	1.00	.60
(196)	Philadelphia Phillies Logo	1.00	.50	.30
(197)	Pittsburgh Pirates Logo	1.00	.50	.30
(198)	St. Louis Cardinals Logo	1.00	.50	.30
(199)	San Francisco Giants Logo	1.00	.50	.30
(200)	Washington Senators Logo	1.00	.50	.30

1963 Topps

Although the number of cards dropped to 576, the 1963 Topps set is among the most popular of the 1960s. A color photo dominates the 2-1/2" by 3-1/2" card, but a colored circle at the bottom carries a black and white portrait as well. A colored band gives the player's name, team and position. The backs again feature career statistics and a cartoon, career summary and brief biographical details. The set is somewhat unlike those immediately preceding it in that there are fewer specialty cards. The major groupings are statistical leaders, World Series highlights and rookies. It is one rookie which makes the set special - Pete Rose. As one of most avidly

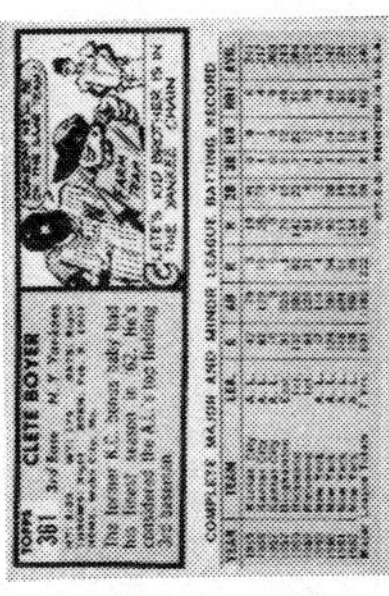

sought cards in history and a high-numbered card at that, the Rose rookie card accounts for much of the value of a complete set.

	NR MT	EX	VG
Complete Set (576):	5500.	2750.	1650.
Common Player (1-283):	3.25	1.75	1.00
Common Player (284-446):	4.50	2.25	1.25
Common Player (447-522):	16.00	8.00	4.75
Common Player (523-576):	10.00	5.00	3.00

1	N.L. Batting Leaders (Hank Aaron, Bill White, Frank Robinson, Tommy Davis, Stan Musial)	35.00	17.50	10.50
2	A.L. Batting Leaders (Chuck Hinton, Mickey Mantle, Floyd Robinson, Pete Runnels, Norm Siebern)	27.00	13.50	8.00
3	N.L. Home Run Leaders (Hank Aaron, Ernie Banks, Orlando Cepeda, Willie Mays, Frank Robinson)	26.00	13.00	7.75
4	A.L. Home Run Leaders (Norm Cash, Rocky Colavito, Harmon Killebrew, Roger Maris, Leon Wagner)	9.00	4.50	2.75
5	N.L. E.R.A. Leaders (Don Drysdale, Bob Gibson, Sandy Koufax)	12.00	6.00	3.50
6	A.L. E.R.A. Leaders (Whitey Ford, Hank Aguirre, Eddie Fisher, Robin Roberts)	6.50	3.25	2.00
7	N.L. Pitching Leaders (Don Drysdale, Joe Jay, Art Mahaffey, Billy O'Dell, Bob Purkey, Jack Sanford)	7.50	3.75	2.25
8	A.L. Pitching Leaders (Jim Bunning, Dick Donovan, Ray Herbert, Camilo Pascual, Ralph Terry)	5.75	3.00	1.75
9	N.L. Strikeout Leaders (Don Drysdale, Dick Farrell, Bob Gibson, Sandy Koufax, Billy O'Dell)	12.00	6.00	3.50
10	A.L. Strikeout Leaders (Jim Bunning, Jim Kaat, Camilo Pascual, Ralph Terry)	5.50	2.75	1.75
11	Lee Walls	3.25	1.75	1.00
12	Steve Barber	3.25	1.75	1.00
13	Phillies Team	5.00	2.50	1.50
14	Pedro Ramos	3.25	1.75	1.00
15	Ken Hubbs	6.00	3.00	1.75
16	Al Smith	3.25	1.75	1.00
17	Ryne Duren	3.25	1.75	1.00
18	Buc Blasters (Smoky Burgess, Roberto Clemente, Bob Skinner, Dick Stuart)	21.00	10.50	6.25
19	Pete Burnside	3.25	1.75	1.00
20	Tony Kubek	6.00	3.00	1.75
21	Marty Keough	3.25	1.75	1.00
22	Curt Simmons	3.25	1.75	1.00
23	Ed Lopat	3.25	1.75	1.00
24	Bob Bruce	3.25	1.75	1.00
25	Al Kaline	31.00	15.50	9.25
26	Ray Moore	3.25	1.75	1.00
27	Choo Choo Coleman	3.25	1.75	1.00
28	Mike Fornieles	3.25	1.75	1.00
29a	1962 Rookie Stars (Sammy Ellis)	9.00	4.50	2.75
29a	1962 Rookie Stars (Ray Culp)	9.00	4.50	2.75
29a	1962 Rookie Stars (*John Boozer*)	9.00	4.50	2.75
29a	1962 Rookie Stars (Jesse Gonder)	9.00	4.50	2.75
29b	1963 Rookie Stars (Sammy Ellis)	3.25	1.75	1.00
29b	1963 Rookie Stars (*Ray Culp*)			
29b	1963 Rookie Stars (John Boozer)	3.25	1.75	1.00
29b	1963 Rookie Stars (Jesse Gonder)	3.25	1.75	1.00
30	Harvey Kuenn	3.50	1.75	1.00
31	Cal Koonce	3.25	1.75	1.00
32	Tony Gonzalez	3.25	1.75	1.00
33	Bo Belinsky	3.25	1.75	1.00
34	Dick Schofield	3.25	1.75	1.00
35	John Buzhardt	3.25	1.75	1.00
36	Jerry Kindall	3.25	1.75	1.00
37	Jerry Lynch	3.25	1.75	1.00
38	Bud Daley	3.25	1.75	1.00
39	Angels Team	5.00	2.50	1.50
40	Vic Power	3.25	1.75	1.00
41	Charlie Lau	3.25	1.75	1.00
42	Stan Williams	3.25	1.75	1.00
43	Veteran Masters (Casey Stengel, Gene Woodling)	5.00	2.50	1.50
44	Terry Fox	3.25	1.75	1.00
45	Bob Aspromonte	3.25	1.75	1.00
46	*Tommie Aaron*	5.00	2.50	1.50
47	Don Lock	3.25	1.75	1.00
48	Birdie Tebbetts	3.25	1.75	1.00
49	*Dal Maxvill*	3.25	1.75	1.00
50	Bill Pierce	3.25	1.75	1.00
51	George Alusik	3.25	1.75	1.00
52	Chuck Schilling	3.25	1.75	1.00
53	Joe Moeller	3.25	1.75	1.00
54a	1962 Rookie Stars (*Nelson Mathews*)			
	(*Harry Fanok*)			
	(*Jack Cullen*)			
	(*Dave DeBusschere*)	15.00	7.50	4.50
54b	1963 Rookie Stars (*Jack Cullen*)			
	(*Dave DeBusschere*)			
	(Harry Fanok)			
	(Nelson Mathews)	5.50	2.75	1.75
55	Bill Virdon	3.25	1.75	1.00
56	Dennis Bennett	3.25	1.75	1.00
57	Billy Moran	3.25	1.75	1.00
58	Bob Will	3.25	1.75	1.00
59	Craig Anderson	3.25	1.75	1.00
60	Elston Howard	6.00	3.00	1.75
61	Ernie Bowman	3.25	1.75	1.00
62	Bob Hendley	3.25	1.75	1.00
63	Reds Team	5.00	2.50	1.50
64	Dick McAuliffe	3.25	1.75	1.00
65	Jackie Brandt	3.25	1.75	1.00
66	Mike Joyce	3.25	1.75	1.00
67	Ed Charles	3.25	1.75	1.00
68	Friendly Foes (Gil Hodges, Duke Snider)	16.50	8.25	5.00
69	Bud Zipfel	3.25	1.75	1.00
70	Jim O'Toole	3.25	1.75	1.00
71	*Bobby Wine*	3.25	1.75	1.00
72	Johnny Romano	3.25	1.75	1.00
73	Bobby Bragan	3.25	1.75	1.00
74	*Denver Lemaster*	3.25	1.75	1.00
75	Bob Allison	3.25	1.75	1.00
76	Earl Wilson	3.25	1.75	1.00
77	Al Spangler	3.25	1.75	1.00
78	Marv Throneberry	3.25	1.75	1.00
79	Checklist 1-88	8.00	4.00	2.50
80	Jim Gilliam	4.50	2.25	1.25
81	Jimmie Schaffer	3.25	1.75	1.00
82	Ed Rakow	3.25	1.75	1.00
83	Charley James	3.25	1.75	1.00
84	Ron Kline	3.25	1.75	1.00
85	Tom Haller	3.25	1.75	1.00
86	Charley Maxwell	3.25	1.75	1.00
87	Bob Veale	3.25	1.75	1.00
88	Ron Hansen	3.25	1.75	1.00
89	Dick Stigman	3.25	1.75	1.00
90	Gordy Coleman	3.25	1.75	1.00
91	Dallas Green	3.25	1.75	1.00
92	Hector Lopez	3.25	1.75	1.00
93	Galen Cisco	3.25	1.75	1.00
94	Bob Schmidt	3.25	1.75	1.00
95	Larry Jackson	3.25	1.75	1.00
96	Lou Clinton	3.25	1.75	1.00
97	Bob Duliba	3.25	1.75	1.00
98	George Thomas	3.25	1.75	1.00
99	Jim Umbricht	3.25	1.75	1.00
100	Joe Cunningham	3.25	1.75	1.00
101	Joe Gibbon	3.25	1.75	1.00
102a	Checklist 89-176 ("Checklist" in red on front)	9.00	4.50	2.75
102b	Checklist 89-176 ("Checklist" in white)	10.00	5.00	3.00
103	Chuck Essegian	3.25	1.75	1.00
104	Lew Krausse	3.25	1.75	1.00
105	Ron Fairly	3.25	1.75	1.00
106	Bob Bolin	3.25	1.75	1.00
107	Jim Hickman	3.25	1.75	1.00
108	Hoyt Wilhelm	10.00	5.00	3.00
109	Lee Maye	3.25	1.75	1.00
110	Rich Rollins	3.25	1.75	1.00
111	Al Jackson	3.25	1.75	1.00
112	Dick Brown	3.25	1.75	1.00
113	Don Landrum (photo actally Ron Santo)	3.25	1.75	1.00
114	Dan Osinski	3.25	1.75	1.00
115	Carl Yastrzemski	45.00	22.00	13.50
116	Jim Brosnan	3.25	1.75	1.00
117	Jacke Davis	3.25	1.75	1.00
118	Sherm Lollar	3.25	1.75	1.00
119	Bob Lillis	3.25	1.75	1.00
120	Roger Maris	45.00	22.00	13.50
121	Jim Hannan	3.25	1.75	1.00
122	Julio Gotay	3.25	1.75	1.00
123	Frank Howard	3.50	1.75	1.00
124	Dick Howser	3.25	1.75	1.00
125	Robin Roberts	10.00	5.00	3.00
126	Bob Uecker	15.00	7.50	4.50
127	Bill Tuttle	3.25	1.75	1.00
128	Matty Alou	3.25	1.75	1.00
129	Gary Bell	3.25	1.75	1.00
130	Dick Groat	3.25	1.75	1.00
131	Senators Team	5.00	2.50	1.50
132	Jack Hamilton	3.25	1.75	1.00
133	Gene Freese	3.25	1.75	1.00
134	Bob Scheffing	3.25	1.75	1.00
135	Richie Ashburn	10.00	5.00	3.00
136	Ike Delock	3.25	1.75	1.00
137	Mack Jones	3.25	1.75	1.00
138	Pride of N.L. (Willie Mays, Stan Musial)	40.00	20.00	12.00
139	Earl Averill	3.25	1.75	1.00
140	Frank Lary	3.25	1.75	1.00
141	*Manny Mota*	7.00	3.50	2.00
142	World Series Game 1 (Yanks' Ford Wins Series Opener)	7.00	3.50	2.00
143	World Series Game 2 (Sanford Flashes Shutout Magic	5.00	2.50	1.50
144	World Series Game 3 (Maris Sparks Yankee Rally)	6.00	3.00	1.75
145	World Series Game 4 (Hiller Blasts Grand Slammer)	5.00	2.50	1.50
146	World Series Game 5 (Tresh's Homer Defeats) Giants	5.00	2.50	1.50
147	World Series Game 6 (Pierce Stars In 3-Hit Victory)	5.00	2.50	1.50
148	World Series Game 7 (Yanks Celebrate As Terry Wins)	5.00	2.50	1.50
149	Marv Breeding	3.25	1.75	1.00
150	Johnny Podres	4.50	2.25	1.25
151	Pirates Team	5.00	2.50	1.50
152	Ron Nischwitz	3.25	1.75	1.00
153	Hal Smith	3.25	1.75	1.00
154	Walt Alston	5.00	2.50	1.50
155	Bill Stafford	3.25	1.75	1.00
156	Roy McMillan	3.25	1.75	1.00
157	*Diego Segui*	3.25	1.75	1.00
158	1963 Rookie Stars (Rogelio Alvarez, Tommy Harper, Dave Roberts, Bob Saverine)	4.00	2.00	1.25
159	Jim Pagliaroni	3.25	1.75	1.00
160	Juan Pizarro	3.25	1.75	1.00
161	Frank Torre	3.25	1.75	1.00
162	Twins Team	5.00	2.50	1.50
163	Don Larsen	3.25	1.75	1.00
164	Bubba Morton	3.25	1.75	1.00
165	Jim Kaat	6.00	3.00	1.75
166	Johnny Keane	3.25	1.75	1.00
167	Jim Fregosi	4.00	2.00	1.25
168	Russ Nixon	3.25	1.75	1.00
169	1963 Rookie Stars (Dick Egan, Julio Navarro, Gaylord Perry, Tommie Sisk)	25.00	12.50	7.50
170	Joe Adcock	3.25	1.75	1.00
171	Steve Hamilton	3.25	1.75	1.00
172	Gene Oliver	3.25	1.75	1.00
173	Bombers' Best (Tom Tresh, Mickey Mantle, Bobby Richardson)	85.00	42.00	25.00
174	Larry Burright	3.25	1.75	1.00
175	Bob Buhl	3.25	1.75	1.00
176	Jim King	3.25	1.75	1.00
177	Bubba Phillips	3.25	1.75	1.00
178	Johnny Edwards	3.25	1.75	1.00
179	Ron Piche	3.25	1.75	1.00
180	Bill Skowron	4.50	2.25	1.25
181	Sammy Esposito	3.25	1.75	1.00
182	Albie Pearson	3.25	1.75	1.00
183	Joe Pepitone	4.00	2.00	1.25
184	Vern Law	3.25	1.75	1.00
185	Chuck Hiller	3.25	1.75	1.00
186	Jerry Zimmerman	3.25	1.75	1.00
187	Willie Kirkland	3.25	1.75	1.00
188	Eddie Bressoud	3.25	1.75	1.00
189	Dave Giusti	3.25	1.75	1.00
190	Minnie Minoso	4.00	2.00	1.25
191	Checklist 177-264	9.00	4.50	2.75
192	Clay Dalrymple	3.25	1.75	1.00
193	Andre Rodgers	3.25	1.75	1.00
194	Joe Nuxhall	3.25	1.75	1.00
195	Manny Jimenez	3.25	1.75	1.00
196	Doug Camilli	3.25	1.75	1.00
197	Roger Craig	4.50	2.25	1.25
198	Lenny Green	3.25	1.75	1.00
199	Joe Amalfitano	3.25	1.75	1.00
200	Mickey Mantle	450.00	225.00	135.00
201	Cecil Butler	3.25	1.75	1.00
202	Red Sox Team	6.00	3.00	1.75
203	Chico Cardenas	3.25	1.75	1.00
204	Don Nottebart	3.25	1.75	1.00
205	Luis Aparicio	12.00	6.00	3.50
206	Ray Washburn	3.25	1.75	1.00
207	Ken Hunt	3.25	1.75	1.00
208	1963 Rookie Stars (Ron Herbel, John Miller, Ron Taylor, Wally Wolf)	3.25	1.75	1.00
209	Hobie Landrith	3.25	1.75	1.00
210	Sandy Koufax	130.00	65.00	39.00
211	Fred Whitfield	3.25	1.75	1.00
212	Glen Hobbie	3.25	1.75	1.00
213	Billy Hitchcock	3.25	1.75	1.00
214	Orlando Pena	3.25	1.75	1.00
215	Bob Skinner	3.25	1.75	1.00
216	Gene Conley	3.25	1.75	1.00
217	Joe Christopher	3.25	1.75	1.00
218	Tiger Twirlers (Jim Bunning, Frank Lary, Don Mossi)	6.00	3.00	1.75
219	Chuck Cottier	3.25	1.75	1.00
220	Camilo Pascual	3.25	1.75	1.00
221	*Cookie Rojas*	3.25	1.75	1.00
222	Cubs Team	6.00	3.00	1.75
223	Eddie Fisher	3.25	1.75	1.00
224	Mike Roarke	3.25	1.75	1.00
225	Joe Jay	3.25	1.75	1.00
226	Julian Javier	3.25	1.75	1.00
227	Jim Grant	3.25	1.75	1.00
228	1963 Rookie Stars (Max Alvis, Bob Bailey, Ed Kranepool, Tony Oliva	45.00	22.00	13.50
229	Willie Davis	3.50	1.75	1.00
230	Pete Runnels	3.25	1.75	1.00
231	Eli Grba (photo actually Ryne Duren)	3.25	1.75	1.00
232	Frank Malzone	3.25	1.75	1.00
233	Casey Stengel	16.00	8.00	4.75
234	Dave Nicholson	3.25	1.75	1.00
235	Billy O'Dell	3.25	1.75	1.00
236	Bill Bryan	3.25	1.75	1.00
237	Jim Coates	3.25	1.75	1.00
238	Lou Johnson	3.25	1.75	1.00
239	Harvey Haddix	3.25	1.75	1.00
240	Rocky Colavito	12.00	6.00	3.50
241	Billy Smith	3.25	1.75	1.00
242	Power Plus (Hank Aaron, Ernie Banks)	30.00	15.00	9.00
243	Don Leppert	3.25	1.75	1.00
244	John Tsitouris	3.25	1.75	1.00
245	Gil Hodges	17.00	8.50	5.00
246	Lee Stange	3.25	1.75	1.00
247	Yankees Team	20.00	10.00	6.00
248	Tito Francona	3.25	1.75	1.00
249	Leo Burke	3.25	1.75	1.00
250	Stan Musial	85.00	42.00	25.00
251	Jack Lamabe	3.25	1.75	1.00
252	Ron Santo	4.50	2.25	1.25
253	1963 Rookie Stars (Len Gabrielson, Pete Jernigan, Deacon Jones, John Wojcik)	3.25	1.75	1.00

254 Mike Hershberger 3.25 1.75 1.00
255 Bob Shaw 3.25 1.75 1.00
256 Jerry Lumpe 3.25 1.75 1.00
257 Hank Aguirre 3.25 1.75 1.00
258 Alvin Dark 3.25 1.75 1.00
259 Johnny Logan 3.25 1.75 1.00
260 Jim Gentile 3.25 1.75 1.00
261 Bob Miller 3.25 1.75 1.00
262 Ellis Burton 3.25 1.75 1.00
263 Dave Stenhouse 3.25 1.75 1.00
264 Phil Linz 3.25 1.75 1.00
265 Vada Pinson 5.00 2.50 1.50
266 Bob Allen 3.25 1.75 1.00
267 Carl Sawatski 3.25 1.75 1.00
268 Don Demeter 3.25 1.75 1.00
269 Don Mincher 3.25 1.75 1.00
270 Felipe Alou 6.00 3.00 1.75
271 Dean Stone 3.25 1.75 1.00
272 Danny Murphy 3.25 1.75 1.00
273 Sammy Taylor 3.25 1.75 1.00
274 Checklist 265-352 8.00 4.00 2.50
275 Eddie Mathews 20.00 10.00 6.00
276 Barry Shetrone 3.25 1.75 1.00
277 Dick Farrell 3.25 1.75 1.00
278 Chico Fernandez 3.25 1.75 1.00
279 Wally Moon 3.25 1.75 1.00
280 Bob Rodgers 3.25 1.75 1.00
281 Tom Sturdivant 3.25 1.75 1.00
282 Bob Del Greco 3.25 1.75 1.00
283 Roy Sievers 3.25 1.75 1.00
284 Dave Sisler 4.50 2.25 1.25
285 Dick Stuart 4.50 2.25 1.25
286 Stu Miller 4.50 2.25 1.25
287 Dick Bertell 4.50 2.25 1.25
288 White Sox Team 5.00 2.50 1.50
289 Hal Brown 4.50 2.25 1.25
290 Bill White 4.50 2.25 1.25
291 Don Rudolph 4.50 2.25 1.25
292 Pumpsie Green 4.50 2.25 1.25
293 Bill Pleis 4.50 2.25 1.25
294 Bill Rigney 4.50 2.25 1.25
295 Ed Roebuck 4.50 2.25 1.25
296 Doc Edwards 4.50 2.25 1.25
297 Jim Golden 4.50 2.25 1.25
298 Don Dillard 4.50 2.25 1.25
299 1963 Rookie Stars (Tom Butters, Bob Dustal, Dave Morehead, Dan Schneider) 4.50 2.25 1.25
300 Willie Mays 160.00 80.00 48.00
301 Bill Fischer 4.50 2.25 1.25
302 Whitey Herzog 4.50 2.25 1.25
303 Earl Francis 4.50 2.25 1.25
304 Harry Bright 4.50 2.25 1.25
305 Don Hoak 4.50 2.25 1.25
306 Star Receivers (Earl Battey, Elston Howard) 4.50 2.25 1.25
307 Chet Nichols 4.50 2.25 1.25
308 Camilo Carreon 4.50 2.25 1.25
309 Jim Brewer 4.50 2.25 1.25
310 Tommy Davis 4.50 2.25 1.25
311 Joe McClain 4.50 2.25 1.25
312 Colt .45s Team 19.00 9.50 5.75
313 Ernie Broglio 4.50 2.25 1.25
314 John Goryl 4.50 2.25 1.25
315 Ralph Terry 4.50 2.25 1.25
316 Norm Sherry 4.50 2.25 1.25
317 Sam McDowell 4.50 2.25 1.25
318 Gene Mauch 4.50 2.25 1.25
319 Joe Gaines 4.50 2.25 1.25
320 Warren Spahn 35.00 17.50 10.50
321 Gino Cimoli 4.50 2.25 1.25
322 Bob Turley 4.50 2.25 1.25
323 Bill Mazeroski 8.00 4.00 2.50
324 1963 Rookie Stars (*Vic Davalillo*, Phil Roof, Pete Ward, George Williams) 5.00 2.50 1.50
325 Jack Sanford 4.50 2.25 1.25
326 Hank Foiles 4.50 2.25 1.25
327 Paul Foytack 4.50 2.25 1.25
328 Dick Williams 4.00 2.00 1.25
329 Lindy McDaniel 4.50 2.25 1.25
330 Chuck Hinton 4.50 2.25 1.25
331 Series Foes (Bill Pierce, Bill Stafford) 4.00 2.00 1.25
332 Joel Horlen 4.50 2.25 1.25
333 Carl Warwick 4.50 2.25 1.25
334 Wynn Hawkins 4.50 2.25 1.25
335 Leon Wagner 4.50 2.25 1.25
336 Ed Bauta 4.50 2.25 1.25
337 Dodgers Team 13.00 6.50 4.00
338 Russ Kemmerer 4.50 2.25 1.25
339 Ted Bowsfield 4.50 2.25 1.25
340 Yogi Berra 55.00 27.00 16.50
341 Jack Baldschun 4.50 2.25 1.25
342 Gene Woodling 4.50 2.25 1.25
343 Johnny Pesky 4.50 2.25 1.25
344 Don Schwall 4.50 2.25 1.25
345 Brooks Robinson 55.00 27.00 16.50
346 Billy Hoeft 4.50 2.25 1.25
347 Joe Torre 9.00 4.50 2.75
348 Vic Wertz 4.50 2.25 1.25
349 Zoilo Versalles 4.50 2.25 1.25
350 Bob Purkey 4.50 2.25 1.25
351 Al Luplow 4.50 2.25 1.25
352 Ken Johnson 4.50 2.25 1.25
353 Billy Williams 25.00 12.50 7.50
354 Dom Zanni 4.50 2.25 1.25
355 Dean Chance 4.50 2.25 1.25
356 John Schaive 4.50 2.25 1.25
357 George Altman 4.50 2.25 1.25
358 Milt Pappas 4.50 2.25 1.25
359 Haywood Sullivan 4.50 2.25 1.25
360 Don Drysdale 37.00 18.50 11.00
361 Clete Boyer 4.50 2.25 1.25
362 Checklist 353-429 9.00 4.50 2.75
363 Dick Radatz 3.75 2.00 1.25
364 Howie Goss 4.50 2.25 1.25
365 Jim Bunning 10.00 5.00 3.00
366 Tony Taylor 4.50 2.25 1.25
367 Tony Cloninger 4.50 2.25 1.25
368 Ed Bailey 4.50 2.25 1.25

369 Jim Lemon 4.50 2.25 1.25
370 Dick Donovan 4.50 2.25 1.25
371 Rod Kanehl 4.50 2.25 1.25
372 Don Lee 4.50 2.25 1.25
373 Jim Campbell 4.50 2.25 1.25
374 Claude Osteen 4.50 2.25 1.25
375 Ken Boyer 7.00 3.50 2.00
376 Johnnie Wyatt 4.50 2.25 1.25
377 Orioles Team 9.00 4.50 2.75
378 Bill Henry 4.50 2.25 1.25
379 Bob Anderson 4.50 2.25 1.25
380 Ernie Banks 60.00 30.00 18.00
381 Frank Baumann 4.50 2.25 1.25
382 Ralph Houk 4.50 2.25 1.25
383 Pete Richert 4.50 2.25 1.25
384 Bob Tillman 4.50 2.25 1.25
385 Art Mahaffey 4.50 2.25 1.25
386 1963 Rookie Stars (*John Bateman*, Larry Bearnarth, Ed Kirkpatrick, Garry Roggenburk) 4.50 2.25 1.25
387 Al McBean 4.50 2.25 1.25
388 Jim Davenport 4.50 2.25 1.25
389 Frank Sullivan 4.50 2.25 1.25
390 Hank Aaron 130.00 65.00 39.00
391 Bill Dailey 4.50 2.25 1.25
392 Tribe Thumpers (Tito Francona, Johnny Romano) 4.00 2.00 1.25
393 Ken MacKenzie 4.50 2.25 1.25
394 Tim McCarver 4.00 2.00 1.25
395 Don McMahon 4.50 2.25 1.25
396 Joe Koppe 4.50 2.25 1.25
397 Athletics Team 9.00 4.50 2.75
398 Boog Powell 22.00 11.00 6.50
399 Dick Ellsworth 4.50 2.25 1.25
400 Frank Robinson 45.00 22.00 13.50
401 Jim Bouton 10.00 5.00 3.00
402 Mickey Vernon 4.50 2.25 1.25
403 Ron Perranoski 4.50 2.25 1.25
404 Bob Oldis 4.50 2.25 1.25
405 Floyd Robinson 4.50 2.25 1.25
406 Howie Koplitz 4.50 2.25 1.25
407 1963 Rookie Stars (Larry Elliot, Frank Kostro, Chico Ruiz, Dick Simpson) 4.50 2.25 1.25
408 Billy Gardner 4.50 2.25 1.25
409 Roy Face 4.50 2.25 1.25
410 Earl Battey 4.50 2.25 1.25
411 Jim Constable 4.50 2.25 1.25
412 Dodgers' Big Three (Johnny Podres, Don Drysdale, Sandy Koufax) 35.00 17.50 10.50
413 Jerry Walker 4.50 2.25 1.25
414 Ty Cline 4.50 2.25 1.25
415 Bob Gibson 45.00 22.00 13.50
416 Alex Grammas 4.50 2.25 1.25
417 Giants Team 9.00 4.50 2.75
418 Johnny Orsino 4.50 2.25 1.25
419 Tracy Stallard 4.50 2.25 1.25
420 Bobby Richardson 11.00 5.50 3.25
421 Tom Morgan 4.50 2.25 1.25
422 Fred Hutchinson 4.50 2.25 1.25
423 Ed Hobaugh 4.50 2.25 1.25
424 Charley Smith 4.50 2.25 1.25
425 Smoky Burgess 4.50 2.25 1.25
426 Barry Latman 4.50 2.25 1.25
427 Bernie Allen 4.50 2.25 1.25
428 Carl Boles 4.50 2.25 1.25
429 Lou Burdette 4.50 2.25 1.25
430 Norm Siebern 4.50 2.25 1.25
431a Checklist 430-506 ("Checklist" in black on front) 7.00 3.50 2.00
431b Checklist 430-506 ("Checklist" in white) 11.00 5.50 3.25
432 Roman Mejias 4.50 2.25 1.25
433 Denis Menke 4.50 2.25 1.25
434 Johnny Callison 4.50 2.25 1.25
435 Woody Held 4.50 2.25 1.25
436 Tim Harkness 4.50 2.25 1.25
437 Bill Bruton 4.50 2.25 1.25
438 Wes Stock 4.50 2.25 1.25
439 Don Zimmer 5.00 2.50 1.50
440 Juan Marichal 30.00 15.00 9.00
441 Lee Thomas 4.50 2.25 1.25
442 J.C. Hartman 4.50 2.25 1.25
443 Jim Piersall 6.00 3.00 1.75
444 Jim Maloney 6.50 3.25 2.00
445 Norm Cash 7.00 3.50 2.00
446 Whitey Ford 35.00 17.50 10.50
447 Felix Mantilla 16.00 8.00 4.75
448 Jack Kralick 16.00 8.00 4.75
449 Jose Tartabull 16.00 8.00 4.75
450 Bob Friend 16.00 8.00 4.75
451 Indians Team 30.00 15.00 9.00
452 Barney Schultz 16.00 8.00 4.75
453 Jake Wood 16.00 8.00 4.75
454a Art Fowler (card # on orange background) 16.00 8.00 4.75
454b Art Fowler (card # on white background) 25.00 12.50 7.50
455 Ruben Amaro 16.00 8.00 4.75
456 Jim Coker 16.00 8.00 4.75
457 Tex Clevenger 16.00 8.00 4.75
458 Al Lopez 17.50 8.75 5.25
459 Dick LeMay 16.00 8.00 4.75
460 Del Crandall 16.00 8.00 4.75
461 Norm Bass 16.00 8.00 4.75
462 Wally Post 16.00 8.00 4.75
463 Joe Schaffernoth 16.00 8.00 4.75
464 Ken Aspromonte 16.00 8.00 4.75
465 Chuck Estrada 16.00 8.00 4.75
466 1963 Rookie Stars (*Bill Freehan*, Tony Martinez, Nate Oliver, Jerry Robinson) 60.00 30.00 18.00
467 Phil Ortega 16.00 8.00 4.75
468 Carroll Hardy 16.00 8.00 4.75
469 Jay Hook 16.00 8.00 4.75
470 Tom Tresh 60.00 30.00 18.00
471 Ken Retzer 16.00 8.00 4.75
472 Lou Brock 115.00 57.00 34.00
473 Mets Team 115.00 57.00 34.00
474 Jack Fisher 16.00 8.00 4.75
475 Gus Triandos 16.00 8.00 4.75

476 Frank Funk 16.00 8.00 4.75
477 Donn Clendenon 16.00 8.00 4.75
478 Paul Brown 16.00 8.00 4.75
479 *Ed Brinkman* 16.00 8.00 4.75
480 Bill Monbouquette 16.00 8.00 4.75
481 Bob Taylor 16.00 8.00 4.75
482 Felix Torres 16.00 8.00 4.75
483 Jim Owens 16.00 8.00 4.75
484 Dale Long 16.00 8.00 4.75
485 Jim Landis 16.00 8.00 4.75
486 Ray Sadecki 16.00 8.00 4.75
487 John Roseboro 16.00 8.00 4.75
488 Jerry Adair 16.00 8.00 4.75
489 Paul Toth 16.00 8.00 4.75
490 Willie McCovey 110.00 55.00 33.00
491 Harry Craft 16.00 8.00 4.75
492 Dave Wickersham 16.00 8.00 4.75
493 Walt Bond 16.00 8.00 4.75
494 Phil Regan 16.00 8.00 4.75
495 Frank J. Thomas 22.00 11.00 6.50
496 1963 Rookie Stars (Carl Bouldin, Steve Dalkowski, Fred Newman, Jack Smith) 16.00 8.00 4.75
497 Bennie Daniels 16.00 8.00 4.75
498 Eddie Kasko 16.00 8.00 4.75
499 J.C. Martin 16.00 8.00 4.75
500 Harmon Killebrew 120.00 60.00 36.00
501 Joe Azcue 16.00 8.00 4.75
502 Daryl Spencer 16.00 8.00 4.75
503 Braves Team 35.00 17.50 10.50
504 Bob Johnson 16.00 8.00 4.75
505 Curt Flood 18.00 9.00 5.50
506 Gene Green 16.00 8.00 4.75
507 Roland Sheldon 16.00 8.00 4.75
508 Ted Savage 16.00 8.00 4.75
509a Checklist 507-576 (copyright centered) 18.00 9.00 5.50
509b Checklist 509-576 (copyright to right) 18.00 9.00 5.50
510 Ken McBride 16.00 8.00 4.75
511 Charlie Neal 16.00 8.00 4.75
512 Cal McLish 16.00 8.00 4.75
513 Gary Geiger 16.00 8.00 4.75
514 Larry Osborne 16.00 8.00 4.75
515 Don Elston 16.00 8.00 4.75
516 Purnal Goldy 16.00 8.00 4.75
517 Hal Woodeshick 16.00 8.00 4.75
518 Don Blasingame 16.00 8.00 4.75
519 Claude Raymond 17.50 8.75 5.25
520 Orlando Cepeda 22.00 11.00 6.50
521 Dan Pfister 16.00 8.00 4.75
522 1963 Rookie Stars (Mel Nelson, Gary Peters, Art Quirk, Jim Roland) 16.00 8.00 4.75
523 Bill Kunkel 11.00 5.50 3.25
524 Cardinals Team 22.00 11.00 6.50
525 Nellie Fox 25.00 12.50 7.50
526 Dick Hall 11.00 5.50 3.25
527 Ed Sadowski 11.00 5.50 3.25
528 Carl Willey 11.00 5.50 3.25
529 Wes Covington 11.00 5.50 3.25
530 Don Mossi 11.00 5.50 3.25
531 Sam Mele 11.00 5.50 3.25
532 Steve Boros 11.00 5.50 3.25
533 Bobby Shantz 12.50 6.25 3.75
534 Ken Walters 11.00 5.50 3.25
535 Jim Perry 11.00 5.50 3.25
536 Norm Larker 11.00 5.50 3.25
537 1963 Rookie Stars (Pedro Gonzalez, Ken McMullen, Pete Rose, Al Weis) 920.00 460.00 276.00
538 George Brunet 11.00 5.50 3.25
539 Wayne Causey 11.00 5.50 3.25
540 Roberto Clemente 265.00 132.00 79.00
541 Ron Moeller 11.00 5.50 3.25
542 Lou Klimchock 11.00 5.50 3.25
543 Russ Snyder 11.00 5.50 3.25
544 1963 Rookie Stars (Duke Carmel, Bill Haas, Dick Phillips, Rusty Staub) 40.00 20.00 12.00
545 Jose Pagan 11.00 5.50 3.25
546 Hal Reniff 11.00 5.50 3.25
547 Gus Bell 11.00 5.50 3.25
548 Tom Satriano 11.00 5.50 3.25
549 1963 Rookie Stars (*Marcelino Lopez*, Pete Lovrich, Elmo Plaskett, Paul Ratliff) 11.00 5.50 3.25
550 Duke Snider 70.00 35.00 21.00
551 Billy Klaus 11.00 5.50 3.25
552 Tigers Team 35.00 17.50 10.50
553 1963 Rookie Stars (Brock Davis, Jim Gosger, John Herrnstein, Willie Stargell) 180.00 90.00 54.00
554 Hank Fischer 11.00 5.50 3.25
555 John Blanchard 11.00 5.50 3.25
556 Al Worthington 11.00 5.50 3.25
557 Cuno Barragan 11.00 5.50 3.25
558 1963 Rookie Stars (Bill Faul, Ron Hunt, Bob Lipski, Al Moran) 12.50 6.25 3.75
559 Danny Murtaugh 11.00 5.50 3.25
560 Ray Herbert 11.00 5.50 3.25
561 Mike de la Hoz 11.00 5.50 3.25
562 1963 Rookie Stars (Randy Cardinal, Dave McNally, Don Rowe, Ken Rowe) 20.00 10.00 6.00
563 Mike McCormick 11.00 5.50 3.25
564 George Banks 11.00 5.50 3.25
565 Larry Sherry 11.00 5.50 3.25
566 Cliff Cook 11.00 5.50 3.25
567 Jim Duffalo 11.00 5.50 3.25
568 Bob Sadowski 11.00 5.50 3.25
569 Luis Arroyo 11.00 5.50 3.25
570 Frank Bolling 11.00 5.50 3.25
571 Johnny Klippstein 11.00 5.50 3.25
572 Jack Spring 11.00 5.50 3.25
573 Coot Veal 11.00 5.50 3.25
574 Hal Kolstad 11.00 5.50 3.25
575 Don Cardwell 11.00 5.50 3.25
576 Johnny Temple 17.00 8.00 4.75

1963 Topps Peel-Offs

Measuring 1-1/4" by 2-3/4," Topps Peel-Offs were an insert with 1963 Topps baseball cards. There are 46 players in the unnumbered set, each pictured in a color photo inside an oval with the player's name, team and position in a band below. The back of the Peel-Off is removable, leaving a sticky surface that made the Peel-Off a popular decorative item among youngsters of the day. Naturally, that makes them quite scarce today, but as a non-card Topps issue, demand is not particularly strong.

		NR MT	EX	VG
Complete Set (46):		225.00	110.00	65.00
Common Player:		2.50	1.25	.70
(1)	Hank Aaron	10.00	5.00	3.00
(2)	Luis Aparicio	4.50	2.25	1.25
(3)	Richie Ashburn	4.00	2.00	1.20
(4)	Bob Aspromonte	2.50	1.25	.70
(5)	Ernie Banks	7.00	3.50	2.00
(6)	Ken Boyer	3.50	1.75	1.00
(7)	Jim Bunning	4.00	2.00	1.20
(8)	Johnny Callison	2.50	1.25	.70
(9)	Orlando Cepeda	4.00	2.00	1.20
(10)	Roberto Clemente	10.00	5.00	3.00
(11)	Rocky Colavito	6.00	3.00	1.75
(12)	Tommy Davis	3.50	1.75	1.00
(13)	Dick Donovan	2.50	1.25	.70
(14)	Don Drysdale	9.00	4.50	2.75
(15)	Dick Farrell	2.50	1.25	.70
(16)	Jim Gentile	2.50	1.25	.70
(17)	Ray Herbert	2.50	1.25	.70
(18)	Chuck Hinton	2.50	1.25	.70
(19)	Ken Hubbs	3.50	1.75	1.00
(20)	Al Jackson	2.50	1.25	.70
(21)	Al Kaline	8.00	4.00	2.50
(22)	Harmon Killebrew	7.00	3.50	2.00
(23)	Sandy Koufax	8.00	4.00	2.50
(24)	Jerry Lumpe	2.50	1.25	.70
(25)	Art Mahaffey	2.50	1.25	.70
(26)	Mickey Mantle	50.00	25.00	15.00
(27)	Willie Mays	10.00	5.00	3.00
(28)	Bill Mazeroski	5.00	2.50	1.50
(29)	Bill Monbouquette	2.50	1.25	.70
(30)	Stan Musial	10.00	5.00	3.00
(31)	Camilo Pascual	2.50	1.25	.70
(32)	Bob Purkey	2.50	1.25	.70
(33)	Bobby Richardson	3.00	1.50	.90
(34)	Brooks Robinson	8.00	4.00	2.50
(35)	Floyd Robinson	2.50	1.25	.70
(36)	Frank Robinson	8.00	4.00	2.50
(37)	Bob Rodgers	2.50	1.25	.70
(38)	Johnny Romano	2.50	1.25	.70
(39)	Jack Sanford	2.50	1.25	.70
(40)	Norm Siebern	2.50	1.25	.70
(41)	Warren Spahn	7.00	3.50	2.00
(42)	Dave Stenhouse	2.50	1.25	.70
(43)	Ralph Terry	2.50	1.25	.70
(44)	Lee Thomas	2.50	1.25	.70
(45)	Bill White	3.00	1.50	.90
(46)	Carl Yastrzemski	10.00	5.00	3.00

1964 Topps

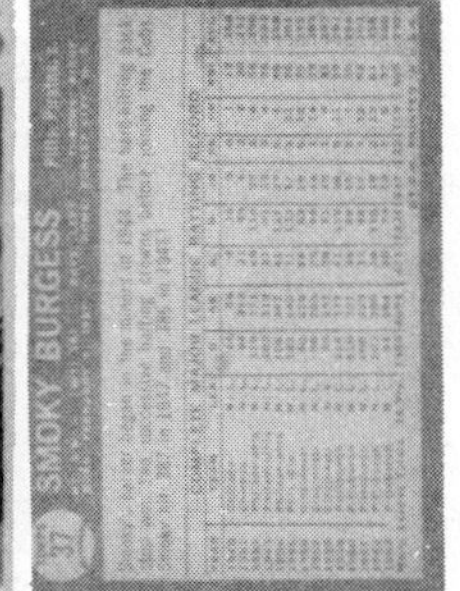

The 1964 Topps set is a 587-card issue of 2-1/2" by 3-1/2" cards which is considered by many as being among the company's best efforts. Card fronts feature a large color photo which blends into a top panel which contains the team name, while a panel below the picture carries the player's name and position. An interesting innovation on the back is a baseball quiz question which required the rubbing of a white panel to reveal the answer. As in 1963, specialty cards remained modest in number with a 12-card set of statistical leaders, a few multi-player cards, rookies and World Series highlights. An interesting card is an "In Memoriam" card for Ken Hubbs who was killed in an airplane crash.

		NR MT	EX	VG
Complete Set (587):		2750.	1375.	825.00
Common Player (1-370):		2.50	1.25	.70
Common Player (371-522):		5.00	2.50	1.50
Common Player (523-587):		9.50	4.75	2.75
1	N.L. E.R.A. Leaders (Dick Ellsworth, Bob Friend, Sandy Koufax)	16.00	8.00	4.75
2	A.L. E.R.A. Leaders (Camilo Pascual, Gary Peters, Juan Pizarro)	5.00	2.50	1.50
3	N.L. Pitching Leaders (Sandy Koufax, Jim Maloney, Juan Marichal, Warren Spahn)	12.00	6.00	3.50
4a	A.L. Pitching Leaders (Jim Bouton) (apostrophe after "Pitching" on back)	9.50	4.75	2.75
4a	A.L. Pitching Leaders (Whitey Ford) (apostrophe after "Pitching" on back)	9.50	4.75	2.75
4a	A.L. Pitching Leaders (Camilo Pascual) (apostrophe after "Pitching" on back)	9.50	4.75	2.75
4b	A.L. Pitching Leaders (Jim Bouton) (no apostrophe)	5.00	2.50	1.50
4b	A.L. Pitching Leaders (Whitey Ford) (no apostrophe)	5.00	2.50	1.50
4b	A.L. Pitching Leaders (Camilo Pascual) (no apostrophe)	5.00	2.50	1.50
5	N.L. Strikeout Leaders (Don Drysdale, Sandy Koufax, Jim Maloney)	10.00	5.00	3.00
6	A.L. Strikeout Leaders (Jim Bunning, Camilo Pascual, Dick Stigman)	5.00	2.50	1.50
7	N.L. Batting Leaders (Hank Aaron, Roberto Clemente, Tommy Davis, Dick Groat)	11.00	5.50	3.25
8	A.L. Batting Leaders (Al Kaline, Rich Rollins, Carl Yastrzemski)	9.50	4.75	2.75
9	N.L. Home Run Leaders (Hank Aaron, Orlando Cepeda, Willie Mays, Willie McCovey)	16.00	8.00	4.75
10	A.L. Home Run Leaders (Bob Allison, Harmon Killebrew, Dick Stuart)	5.00	2.50	1.50
11	N.L. R.B.I. Leaders (Hank Aaron, Ken Boyer, Bill White)	8.00	4.00	2.50
12	A.L. R.B.I. Leaders (Al Kaline, Harmon Killebrew, Dick Stuart)	8.00	4.00	2.50
13	Hoyt Wilhelm	8.00	4.00	2.50
14	Dodgers Rookies (Dick Nen, Nick Willhite)	2.50	1.25	.70
15	Zoilo Versalles	2.50	1.25	.70
16	John Boozer	2.50	1.25	.70
17	Willie Kirkland	2.50	1.25	.70
18	Billy O'Dell	2.50	1.25	.70
19	Don Wert	2.50	1.25	.70
20	Bob Friend	2.50	1.25	.70
21	Yogi Berra	35.00	17.50	10.50
22	Jerry Adair	2.50	1.25	.70
23	Chris Zachary	2.50	1.25	.70
24	Carl Sawatski	2.50	1.25	.70
25	Bill Monbouquette	2.50	1.25	.70
26	Gino Cimoli	2.50	1.25	.70
27	Mets Team	5.00	2.50	1.50
28	Claude Osteen	2.50	1.25	.70
29	Lou Brock	35.00	17.50	10.50
30	Ron Perranoski	2.50	1.25	.70
31	Dave Nicholson	2.50	1.25	.70
32	Dean Chance	3.00	1.50	.90
33	Reds Rookies (Sammy Ellis, Mel Queen)	2.50	1.25	.70
34	Jim Perry	2.50	1.25	.70
35	Eddie Mathews	20.00	10.00	6.00
36	Hal Reniff	2.50	1.25	.70
37	Smoky Burgess	2.50	1.25	.70
38	*Jim Wynn*	5.00	2.50	1.50
39	Hank Aguirre	2.50	1.25	.70
40	Dick Groat	3.00	1.50	.90
41	Friendly Foes (Willie McCovey, Leon Wagner)	5.00	2.50	1.50
42	Moe Drabowsky	2.50	1.25	.70
43	Roy Sievers	2.50	1.25	.70
44	Duke Carmel	2.50	1.25	.70
45	Milt Pappas	2.50	1.25	.70
46	Ed Brinkman	2.50	1.25	.70
47	Giants Rookies (*Jesus Alou*, Ron Herbel)	3.50	1.75	1.00
48	Bob Perry	2.50	1.25	.70
49	Bill Henry	2.50	1.25	.70
50	Mickey Mantle	300.00	150.00	90.00
51	Pete Richert	2.50	1.25	.70
52	Chuck Hinton	2.50	1.25	.70
53	Denis Menke	2.50	1.25	.70
54	Sam Mele	2.50	1.25	.70
55	Ernie Banks	30.00	15.00	9.00
56	Hal Brown	2.50	1.25	.70
57	Tim Harkness	2.50	1.25	.70
58	Don Demeter	2.50	1.25	.70
59	Ernie Broglio	2.50	1.25	.70
60	Frank Malzone	2.50	1.25	.70
61	Angel Backstops (Bob Rodgers, Ed Sadowski)	3.50	1.75	1.00
62	Ted Savage	2.50	1.25	.70
63	Johnny Orsino	2.50	1.25	.70
64	Ted Abernathy	2.50	1.25	.70
65	Felipe Alou	5.50	2.75	1.75
66	Eddie Fisher	2.50	1.25	.70
67	Tigers Team	5.00	2.50	1.50
68	Willie Davis	3.50	1.75	1.00
69	Clete Boyer	3.50	1.75	1.00
70	Joe Torre	2.50	1.25	.70
71	Jack Spring	2.50	1.25	.70
72	Chico Cardenas	2.50	1.25	.70
73	*Jimmie Hall*	2.50	1.25	.70
74	Pirates Rookies (Tom Butters, Bob Priddy)	2.50	1.25	.70
75	Wayne Causey	2.50	1.25	.70
76	Checklist 1-88	8.00	4.00	2.50
77	Jerry Walker	2.50	1.25	.70
78	Merritt Ranew	2.50	1.25	.70
79	Bob Heffner	2.50	1.25	.70
80	Vada Pinson	3.50	1.75	1.00
81	All-Star Vets (Nellie Fox, Harmon Killebrew)	9.50	4.75	2.75
82	Jim Davenport	2.50	1.25	.70
83	Gus Triandos	2.50	1.25	.70
84	Carl Willey	2.50	1.25	.70
85	Pete Ward	2.50	1.25	.70
86	Al Downing	3.00	1.50	.90
87	Cardinals Team	9.50	4.75	2.75
88	John Roseboro	2.50	1.25	.70
89	Boog Powell	6.00	3.00	1.75
90	Earl Battey	2.50	1.25	.70
91	Bob Bailey	2.50	1.25	.70
92	Steve Ridzik	2.50	1.25	.70
93	Gary Geiger	2.50	1.25	.70
94	Braves Rookies (Jim Britton, Larry Maxie)	2.50	1.25	.70
95	George Altman	2.50	1.25	.70
96	Bob Buhl	2.50	1.25	.70
97	Jim Fregosi	3.00	1.50	.90
98	Bill Bruton	2.50	1.25	.70
99	Al Stanek	2.50	1.25	.70
100	Elston Howard	4.00	2.00	1.25
101	Walt Alston	5.00	2.50	1.50
102	Checklist 89-176	5.00	2.50	1.50
103	Curt Flood	3.50	1.75	1.00
104	Art Mahaffey	2.50	1.25	.70
105	Woody Held	2.50	1.25	.70
106	Joe Nuxhall	2.50	1.25	.70
107	White Sox Rookies (Bruce Howard, Frank Kreutzer)	2.50	1.25	.70
108	John Wyatt	2.50	1.25	.70
109	Rusty Staub	9.00	4.50	2.75
110	Albie Pearson	2.50	1.25	.70
111	Don Elston	2.50	1.25	.70
112	Bob Tillman	2.50	1.25	.70
113	Grover Powell	2.50	1.25	.70
114	Don Lock	2.50	1.25	.70
115	Frank Bolling	2.50	1.25	.70
116	Twins Rookies (Tony Oliva, Jay Ward)	14.00	7.00	4.25
117	Earl Francis	2.50	1.25	.70
118	John Blanchard	2.50	1.25	.70
119	Gary Kolb	2.50	1.25	.70
120	Don Drysdale	20.00	10.00	6.00
121	Pete Runnels	2.50	1.25	.70
122	Don McMahon	2.50	1.25	.70
123	Jose Pagan	2.50	1.25	.70
124	Orlando Pena	2.50	1.25	.70
125	Pete Rose	145.00	72.00	43.00
126	Russ Snyder	2.50	1.25	.70
127	Angels Rookies (Aubrey Gatewood, Dick Simpson)	2.50	1.25	.70
128	*Mickey Lolich*	14.00	7.00	4.25
129	Amado Samuel	2.50	1.25	.70
130	Gary Peters	2.50	1.25	.70
131	Steve Boros	2.50	1.25	.70
132	Braves Team	5.50	2.75	1.75
133	Jim Grant	2.50	1.25	.70
134	Don Zimmer	3.50	1.75	1.00
135	Johnny Callison	2.50	1.25	.70
136	Koufax Strikes Out 15	15.00	7.50	4.50
137	World Series Game 2 (Davis Sparks Rally)	3.50	1.75	1.00
138	World Series Game 3 (L.A. Takes 3rd Straight)	3.50	1.75	1.00
139	World Series Game 4 (Sealing Yanks' Doom)	4.75	2.50	1.50
140	World Series Summary (The Dodgers Celebrate)	3.50	1.75	1.00
141	Danny Murtaugh	2.50	1.25	.70
142	John Bateman	2.50	1.25	.70
143	Bubba Phillips	2.50	1.25	.70
144	Al Worthington	2.50	1.25	.70
145	Norm Siebern	2.50	1.25	.70
146	Indians Rookies (Bob Chance, Tommy John)	55.00	27.00	16.50
147	Ray Sadecki	2.50	1.25	.70
148	J.C. Martin	2.50	1.25	.70
149	Paul Foytack	2.50	1.25	.70
150	Willie Mays	100.00	50.00	30.00
151	Athletics Team	5.50	2.75	1.75
152	Denver Lemaster	2.50	1.25	.70
153	Dick Williams	3.00	1.50	.90
154	Dick Tracewski	2.50	1.25	.70
155	Duke Snider	27.50	13.50	8.25
156	Bill Dailey	2.50	1.25	.70
157	Gene Mauch	2.50	1.25	.70
158	Ken Johnson	2.50	1.25	.70
159	Charlie Dees	2.50	1.25	.70
160	Ken Boyer	6.00	3.00	1.75
161	Dave McNally	2.50	1.25	.70
162	Hitting Area (Vada Pinson, Dick Sisler)	3.50	1.75	1.00
163	Donn Clendenon	2.50	1.25	.70
164	Bud Daley	2.50	1.25	.70
165	Jerry Lumpe	2.50	1.25	.70
166	Marty Keough	2.50	1.25	.70
167	Senators Rookies (Mike Brumley, Lou Piniella)	30.00	15.00	9.00
168	Al Weis	2.50	1.25	.70
169	Del Crandall	2.50	1.25	.70
170	Dick Radatz	2.50	1.25	.70
171	Ty Cline	2.50	1.25	.70
172	Indians Team	5.50	2.75	1.75
173	Ryne Duren	2.50	1.25	.70
174	Doc Edwards	2.50	1.25	.70
175	Billy Williams	15.00	7.50	4.50

176	Tracy Stallard	2.50	1.25	.70
177	Harmon Killebrew	22.00	11.00	6.50
178	Hank Bauer	2.50	1.25	.70
179	Carl Warwick	2.50	1.25	.70
180	Tommy Davis	5.00	2.50	1.50
181	Dave Wickersham	2.50	1.25	.70
182	Sox Sockers (Chuck Schilling, Carl Yastrzemski)	12.00	6.00	3.50
183	Ron Taylor	2.50	1.25	.70
184	Al Luplow	2.50	1.25	.70
185	Jim O'Toole	2.50	1.25	.70
186	Roman Mejias	2.50	1.25	.70
187	Ed Roebuck	2.50	1.25	.70
188	Checklist 177-264	8.00	4.00	2.50
189	Bob Hendley	2.50	1.25	.70
190	Bobby Richardson	7.50	3.75	2.25
191	Clay Dalrymple	2.50	1.25	.70
192	Cubs Rookies (John Boccabella, Billy Cowan)	2.50	1.25	.70
193	Jerry Lynch	2.50	1.25	.70
194	John Goryl	2.50	1.25	.70
195	Floyd Robinson	2.50	1.25	.70
196	Jim Gentile	2.50	1.25	.70
197	Frank Lary	2.50	1.25	.70
198	Len Gabrielson	2.50	1.25	.70
199	Joe Azcue	2.50	1.25	.70
200	Sandy Koufax	95.00	47.00	28.00
201	Orioles Rookies (Sam Bowens, Wally Bunker)	2.50	1.25	.70
202	Galen Cisco	2.50	1.25	.70
203	John Kennedy	2.50	1.25	.70
204	Matty Alou	2.50	1.25	.70
205	Nellie Fox	7.00	3.50	2.00
206	Steve Hamilton	2.50	1.25	.70
207	Fred Hutchinson	2.50	1.25	.70
208	Wes Covington	2.50	1.25	.70
209	Bob Allen	2.50	1.25	.70
210	Carl Yastrzemski	50.00	25.00	15.00
211	Jim Coker	2.50	1.25	.70
212	Pete Lovrich	2.50	1.25	.70
213	Angels Team	5.50	2.75	1.75
214	Ken McMullen	2.50	1.25	.70
215	Ray Herbert	2.50	1.25	.70
216	Mike de la Hoz	2.50	1.25	.70
217	Jim King	2.50	1.25	.70
218	Hank Fischer	2.50	1.25	.70
219	Young Aces (Jim Bouton, Al Downing)	5.00	2.50	1.50
220	Dick Ellsworth	2.50	1.25	.70
221	Bob Saverine	2.50	1.25	.70
222	Bill Pierce	2.50	1.25	.70
223	George Banks	2.50	1.25	.70
224	Tommie Sisk	2.50	1.25	.70
225	Roger Maris	65.00	32.00	19.50
226	Colts Rookies (*Gerald Grote*, Larry Yellen)	3.50	1.75	1.00
227	Barry Latman	2.50	1.25	.70
228	Felix Mantilla	2.50	1.25	.70
229	Charley Lau	2.50	1.25	.70
230	Brooks Robinson	35.00	17.50	10.50
231	Dick Calmus	2.50	1.25	.70
232	Al Lopez	5.00	2.50	1.50
233	Hal Smith	2.50	1.25	.70
234	Gary Bell	2.50	1.25	.70
235	Ron Hunt	2.50	1.25	.70
236	Bill Faul	2.50	1.25	.70
237	Cubs Team	5.50	2.75	1.75
238	Roy McMillan	2.50	1.25	.70
239	Herm Starrette	2.50	1.25	.70
240	Bill White	3.50	1.75	1.00
241	Jim Owens	2.50	1.25	.70
242	Harvey Kuenn	3.50	1.75	1.00
243	Phillies Rookies (*Richie Allen*, John Herrnstein)	32.50	16.00	9.75
244	*Tony LaRussa*	35.00	17.50	10.50
245	Dick Stigman	2.50	1.25	.70
246	Manny Mota	3.00	1.50	.90
247	Dave DeBusschere	5.00	2.50	1.50
248	Johnny Pesky	2.50	1.25	.70
249	Doug Camilli	2.50	1.25	.70
250	Al Kaline	32.50	16.00	9.75
251	Choo Choo Coleman	2.50	1.25	.70
252	Ken Aspromonte	2.50	1.25	.70
253	Wally Post	2.50	1.25	.70
254	Don Hoak	2.50	1.25	.70
255	Lee Thomas	2.50	1.25	.70
256	Johnny Weekly	2.50	1.25	.70
257	Giants Team	5.50	2.75	1.75
258	Garry Roggenburk	2.50	1.25	.70
259	Harry Bright	2.50	1.25	.70
260	Frank Robinson	30.00	15.00	9.00
261	Jim Hannan	2.50	1.25	.70
262	Cardinals Rookies (Harry Fanok, Mike Shannon)	4.00	2.00	1.25
263	Chuck Estrada	2.50	1.25	.70
264	Jim Landis	2.50	1.25	.70
265	Jim Bunning	7.00	3.50	2.00
266	Gene Freese	2.50	1.25	.70
267	*Wilbur Wood*	5.00	2.50	1.50
268	Bill's Got It (Danny Murtaugh, Bill Virdon)	4.00	2.00	1.25
269	Ellis Burton	2.50	1.25	.70
270	Rich Rollins	2.50	1.25	.70
271	Bob Sadowski	2.50	1.25	.70
272	Jake Wood	2.50	1.25	.70
273	Mel Nelson	2.50	1.25	.70
274	Checklist 265-352	8.00	4.00	2.50
275	John Tsitouris	2.50	1.25	.70
276	Jose Tartabull	2.50	1.25	.70
277	Ken Retzer	2.50	1.25	.70
278	Bobby Shantz	3.00	1.50	.90
279	Joe Koppe	2.50	1.25	.70
280	Juan Marichal	13.00	6.50	4.00
281	Yankees Rookies (Jake Gibbs, Tom Metcalf)	5.00	2.50	1.50
282	Bob Bruce	2.50	1.25	.70
283	*Tommy McCraw*	2.50	1.25	.70
284	Dick Schofield	2.50	1.25	.70
285	Robin Roberts	10.00	5.00	3.00
286	Don Landrum	2.50	1.25	.70
287	Red Sox Rookies (*Tony Conigliaro*, Bill Spanswick)	35.00	17.50	10.50
288	Al Moran	2.50	1.25	.70
289	Frank Funk	2.50	1.25	.70
290	Bob Allison	2.50	1.25	.70
291	Phil Ortega	2.50	1.25	.70
292	Mike Roarke	2.50	1.25	.70
293	Phillies Team	5.50	2.75	1.75
294	Ken Hunt	2.50	1.25	.70
295	Roger Craig	3.50	1.75	1.00
296	Ed Kirkpatrick	2.50	1.25	.70
297	Ken MacKenzie	2.50	1.25	.70
298	Harry Craft	2.50	1.25	.70
299	Bill Stafford	2.50	1.25	.70
300	Hank Aaron	115.00	57.00	34.00
301	Larry Brown	2.50	1.25	.70
302	Dan Pfister	2.50	1.25	.70
303	Jim Campbell	2.50	1.25	.70
304	Bob Johnson	2.50	1.25	.70
305	Jack Lamabe	2.50	1.25	.70
306	Giant Gunners (Orlando Cepeda, Willie Mays)	22.00	11.00	6.50
307	Joe Gibbon	2.50	1.25	.70
308	Gene Stephens	2.50	1.25	.70
309	Paul Toth	2.50	1.25	.70
310	Jim Gilliam	3.50	1.75	1.00
311	Tom Brown	2.50	1.25	.70
312	Tigers Rookies (Fritz Fisher, Fred Gladding)	2.50	1.25	.70
313	Chuck Hiller	2.50	1.25	.70
314	Jerry Buchek	2.50	1.25	.70
315	Bo Belinsky	2.50	1.25	.70
316	Gene Oliver	2.50	1.25	.70
317	Al Smith	2.50	1.25	.70
318	Twins Team	5.50	2.75	1.75
319	Paul Brown	2.50	1.25	.70
320	Rocky Colavito	7.00	3.50	2.00
321	Bob Lillis	2.50	1.25	.70
322	George Brunet	2.50	1.25	.70
323	John Buzhardt	2.50	1.25	.70
324	Casey Stengel	17.50	8.75	5.25
325	Hector Lopez	2.50	1.25	.70
326	Ron Brand	2.50	1.25	.70
327	Don Blasingame	2.50	1.25	.70
328	Bob Shaw	2.50	1.25	.70
329	Russ Nixon	2.50	1.25	.70
330	Tommy Harper	2.50	1.25	.70
331	A.L. Bombers (Norm Cash, Al Kaline, Mickey Mantle, Roger Maris)	130.00	65.00	39.00
332	Ray Washburn	2.50	1.25	.70
333	Billy Moran	2.50	1.25	.70
334	Lew Krausse	2.50	1.25	.70
335	Don Mossi	2.50	1.25	.70
336	Andre Rodgers	2.50	1.25	.70
337	Dodgers Rookies (*Al Ferrara*, Jeff Torborg)	6.00	3.00	1.75
338	Jack Kralick	2.50	1.25	.70
339	Walt Bond	2.50	1.25	.70
340	Joe Cunningham	2.50	1.25	.70
341	Jim Roland	2.50	1.25	.70
342	Willie Stargell	40.00	20.00	12.00
343	Senators Team	5.50	2.75	1.75
344	Phil Linz	3.00	1.50	.90
345	Frank J. Thomas	2.50	1.25	.70
346	Joe Jay	2.50	1.25	.70
347	Bobby Wine	2.50	1.25	.70
348	Ed Lopat	2.50	1.25	.70
349	Art Fowler	2.50	1.25	.70
350	Willie McCovey	22.50	11.00	6.75
351	Dan Schneider	2.50	1.25	.70
352	Eddie Bressoud	2.50	1.25	.70
353	Wally Moon	2.50	1.25	.70
354	Dave Giusti	2.50	1.25	.70
355	Vic Power	2.50	1.25	.70
356	Reds Rookies (Bill McCool, Chico Ruiz)	2.50	1.25	.70
357	Charley James	2.50	1.25	.70
358	Ron Kline	2.50	1.25	.70
359	Jim Schaffer	2.50	1.25	.70
360	Joe Pepitone	4.00	2.00	1.25
361	Jay Hook	2.50	1.25	.70
362	Checklist 353-429	8.00	4.00	2.50
363	Dick McAuliffe	2.50	1.25	.70
364	Joe Gaines	2.50	1.25	.70
365	Cal McLish	2.50	1.25	.70
366	Nelson Mathews	2.50	1.25	.70
367	Fred Whitfield	2.50	1.25	.70
368	White Sox Rookies (Fritz Ackley, Don Buford)	3.50	1.75	1.00
369	Jerry Zimmerman	2.50	1.25	.70
370	Hal Woodeshick	2.50	1.25	.70
371	Frank Howard	6.00	3.00	1.75
372	Howie Koplitz	5.00	2.50	1.50
373	Pirates Team	10.00	5.00	3.00
374	Bobby Bolin	5.00	2.50	1.50
375	Ron Santo	7.00	3.50	2.00
376	Dave Morehead	5.00	2.50	1.50
377	Bob Skinner	5.00	2.50	1.50
378	Braves Rookies (Jack Smith, Woody Woodward)	5.00	2.50	1.50
379	Tony Gonzalez	5.00	2.50	1.50
380	Whitey Ford	24.00	12.00	7.25
381	Bob Taylor	5.00	2.50	1.50
382	Wes Stock	5.00	2.50	1.50
383	Bill Rigney	5.00	2.50	1.50
384	Ron Hansen	5.00	2.50	1.50
385	Curt Simmons	5.00	2.50	1.50
386	Lenny Green	5.00	2.50	1.50
387	Terry Fox	5.00	2.50	1.50
388	Athletics Rookies (John O'Donoghue, George Williams)	5.00	2.50	1.50
389	Jim Umbricht	5.00	2.50	1.50
390	Orlando Cepeda	9.00	4.50	2.75
391	Sam McDowell	6.00	3.00	1.75
392	Jim Pagliaroni	5.00	2.50	1.50
393	Casey Teaches (Ed Kranepool, Casey Stengel)	9.50	4.75	2.75
394	Bob Miller	5.00	2.50	1.50
395	Tom Tresh	6.00	3.00	1.75
396	Dennis Bennett	5.00	2.50	1.50
397	Chuck Cottier	5.00	2.50	1.50
398	Mets Rookies (Bill Haas, Dick Smith)	5.00	2.50	1.50
399	Jackie Brandt	5.00	2.50	1.50
400	Warren Spahn	35.00	17.50	10.50
401	Charlie Maxwell	5.00	2.50	1.50
402	Tom Sturdivant	5.00	2.50	1.50
403	Reds Team	9.00	4.50	2.75
404	Tony Martinez	5.00	2.50	1.50
405	Ken McBride	5.00	2.50	1.50
406	Al Spangler	5.00	2.50	1.50
407	Bill Freehan	5.00	2.50	1.50
408	Cubs Rookies (Fred Burdette, Jim Stewart)	5.00	2.50	1.50
409	Bill Fischer	5.00	2.50	1.50
410	Dick Stuart	5.50	2.75	1.75
411	Lee Walls	5.00	2.50	1.50
412	Ray Culp	5.00	2.50	1.50
413	Johnny Keane	5.00	2.50	1.50
414	Jack Sanford	5.00	2.50	1.50
415	Tony Kubek	7.00	3.50	2.00
416	Lee Maye	5.00	2.50	1.50
417	Don Cardwell	5.00	2.50	1.50
418	Orioles Rookies (*Darold Knowles*, Les Narum)	5.50	2.75	1.75
419	*Ken Harrelson*	7.00	3.50	2.00
420	Jim Maloney	5.00	2.50	1.50
421	Camilo Carreon	5.00	2.50	1.50
422	Jack Fisher	5.00	2.50	1.50
423	Tops in N.L. (Hank Aaron, Willie Mays)	130.00	65.00	39.00
424	Dick Bertell	5.00	2.50	1.50
425	Norm Cash	6.00	3.00	1.75
426	Bob Rodgers	5.00	2.50	1.50
427	Don Rudolph	5.00	2.50	1.50
428	Red Sox Rookies (Archie Skeen, Pete Smith)	5.00	2.50	1.50
429	Tim McCarver	8.00	4.00	2.50
430	Juan Pizarro	5.00	2.50	1.50
431	George Alusik	5.00	2.50	1.50
432	Ruben Amaro	5.00	2.50	1.50
433	Yankees Team	11.00	5.50	3.25
434	Don Nottebart	5.00	2.50	1.50
435	Vic Davalillo	5.00	2.50	1.50
436	Charlie Neal	5.00	2.50	1.50
437	Ed Bailey	5.00	2.50	1.50
438	Checklist 430-506	13.00	6.50	4.00
439	Harvey Haddix	5.00	2.50	1.50
440	Roberto Clemente	170.00	85.00	51.00
441	Bob Duliba	5.00	2.50	1.50
442	Pumpsie Green	5.00	2.50	1.50
443	Chuck Dressen	5.00	2.50	1.50
444	Larry Jackson	5.00	2.50	1.50
445	Bill Skowron	6.00	3.00	1.75
446	Julian Javier	5.00	2.50	1.50
447	Ted Bowsfield	5.00	2.50	1.50
448	Cookie Rojas	5.00	2.50	1.50
449	Deron Johnson	5.00	2.50	1.50
450	Steve Barber	5.00	2.50	1.50
451	Joe Amalfitano	5.00	2.50	1.50
452	Giants Rookies (Gil Garrido, Jim Hart)	5.50	2.75	1.75
453	Frank Baumann	5.00	2.50	1.50
454	Tommie Aaron	5.50	2.75	1.75
455	Bernie Allen	5.00	2.50	1.50
456	Dodgers Rookies (*Wes Parker*, John Werhas)	5.00	2.50	1.50
457	Jesse Gonder	5.00	2.50	1.50
458	Ralph Terry	5.00	2.50	1.50
459	Red Sox Rookies (Pete Charton, Dalton Jones)	5.00	2.50	1.50
460	Bob Gibson	30.00	15.00	9.00
461	George Thomas	5.00	2.50	1.50
462	Birdie Tebbetts	5.00	2.50	1.50
463	Don Leppert	5.00	2.50	1.50
464	Dallas Green	5.50	2.75	1.75
465	Mike Hershberger	5.00	2.50	1.50
466	Athletics Rookies (*Dick Green*, Aurelio Monteagudo)	5.50	2.75	1.75
467	Bob Aspromonte	5.00	2.50	1.50
468	Gaylord Perry	42.50	21.00	12.50
469	Cubs Rookies (Fred Norman, Sterling Slaughter)	5.00	2.50	1.50
470	Jim Bouton	6.00	3.00	1.75
471	*Gates Brown*	5.50	2.75	1.75
472	Vern Law	5.00	2.50	1.50
473	Orioles Team	9.00	4.50	2.75
474	Larry Sherry	5.00	2.50	1.50
475	Ed Charles	5.00	2.50	1.50
476	*Rico Carty*, Dick Kelley)	9.50	4.75	2.75
477	Mike Joyce	5.00	2.50	1.50
478	Dick Howser	5.00	2.50	1.50
479	Cardinals Rookies (Dave Bakenhaster, Johnny Lewis)	5.00	2.50	1.50
480	Bob Purkey	5.00	2.50	1.50
481	Chuck Schilling	5.00	2.50	1.50
482	Phillies Rookies (*John Briggs*, Danny Cater)	5.50	2.75	1.75
483	Fred Valentine	5.00	2.50	1.50
484	Bill Pleis	5.00	2.50	1.50
485	Tom Haller	5.00	2.50	1.50
486	Bob Kennedy	5.00	2.50	1.50
487	Mike McCormick	5.00	2.50	1.50
488	Yankees Rookies (Bob Meyer, Pete Mikkelsen)	5.00	2.50	1.50
489	Julio Navarro	5.00	2.50	1.50
490	Ron Fairly	5.00	2.50	1.50
491	Ed Rakow	5.00	2.50	1.50
492	Colts Rookies (Jim Beauchamp, Mike White)	5.00	2.50	1.50
493	Don Lee	5.00	2.50	1.50
494	Al Jackson	5.00	2.50	1.50
495	Bill Virdon	5.00	2.50	1.50
496	White Sox Team	9.00	4.50	2.75
497	Jeoff Long	5.00	2.50	1.50
498	Dave Stenhouse	5.00	2.50	1.50

499	Indians Rookies (Chico Salmon, Gordon Seyfried)	5.00	2.50	1.50
500	Camilo Pascual	5.00	2.50	1.50
501	Bob Veale	5.00	2.50	1.50
502	Angels Rookies (*Bobby Knoop*, Bob Lee)	5.50	2.75	1.75
503	Earl Wilson	5.00	2.50	1.50
504	Claude Raymond	5.00	2.50	1.50
505	Stan Williams	5.00	2.50	1.50
506	Bobby Bragan	5.00	2.50	1.50
507	John Edwards	5.00	2.50	1.50
508	Diego Segui	5.00	2.50	1.50
509	Pirates Rookies (*Gene Alley*, Orlando McFarlane)	5.50	2.75	1.75
510	Lindy McDaniel	5.00	2.50	1.50
511	Lou Jackson	5.00	2.50	1.50
512	*Willie Horton*, Joe Sparma	14.00	7.00	4.25
513	Don Larsen	5.00	2.50	1.50
514	Jim Hickman	5.00	2.50	1.50
515	Johnny Romano	5.00	2.50	1.50
516	Twins Rookies (Jerry Arrigo, Dwight Siebler)	5.00	2.50	1.50
517a	Checklist 507-587 (wrong numbering on back)	9.50	4.75	2.75
517b	Checklist 507-587 (correct numbering on back)	9.50	4.75	2.75
518	Carl Bouldin	5.00	2.50	1.50
519	Charlie Smith	5.00	2.50	1.50
520	Jack Baldschun	5.00	2.50	1.50
521	Tom Satriano	5.00	2.50	1.50
522	Bobby Tiefenauer	5.00	2.50	1.50
523	Lou Burdette	9.50	4.75	2.75
524	Reds Rookies (Jim Dickson, Bobby Klaus)	9.50	4.75	2.75
525	Al McBean	9.50	4.75	2.75
526	Lou Clinton	9.50	4.75	2.75
527	Larry Bearnarth	9.50	4.75	2.75
528	Athletics Rookies (*Dave Duncan*, Tom Reynolds)	9.50	4.75	2.75
529	Al Dark	9.50	4.75	2.75
530	Leon Wagner	9.50	4.75	2.75
531	Dodgers Team	20.00	10.00	6.00
532	Twins Rookies (Bud Bloomfield, Joe Nossek)	9.50	4.75	2.75
533	Johnny Klippstein	9.50	4.75	2.75
534	Gus Bell	9.50	4.75	2.75
535	Phil Regan	9.50	4.75	2.75
536	Mets Rookies (Larry Elliot, John Stephenson)	9.50	4.75	2.75
537	Dan Osinski	9.50	4.75	2.75
538	Minnie Minoso	11.00	5.50	3.25
539	Roy Face	9.50	4.75	2.75
540	Luis Aparicio	15.00	7.50	4.50
541	Braves Rookies (*Phil Niekro*, Phil Roof)	175.00	87.00	52.00
542	Don Mincher	9.50	4.75	2.75
543	Bob Uecker	45.00	22.00	13.50
544	Colts Rookies (Steve Hertz, Joe Hoerner)	9.50	4.75	2.75
545	Max Alvis	9.50	4.75	2.75
546	Joe Christopher	9.50	4.75	2.75
547	Gil Hodges	16.00	8.00	4.75
548	N.L. Rookies (Wayne Schurr, Paul Speckenbach)	9.50	4.75	2.75
549	Joe Moeller	9.50	4.75	2.75
550	Ken Hubbs	30.00	15.00	9.00
551	Billy Hoeft	9.50	4.75	2.75
552	Indians Rookies (Tom Kelley, Sonny Siebert)	9.50	4.75	2.75
553	Jim Brewer	9.50	4.75	2.75
554	Hank Foiles	9.50	4.75	2.75
555	Lee Stange	9.50	4.75	2.75
556	Mets Rookies (Steve Dillon, Ron Locke)	9.50	4.75	2.75
557	Leo Burke	9.50	4.75	2.75
558	Don Schwall	9.50	4.75	2.75
559	Dick Phillips	9.50	4.75	2.75
560	Dick Farrell	9.50	4.75	2.75
561	Phillies Rookies (Dave Bennett, Rick Wise)	15.00	7.50	4.50
562	Pedro Ramos	9.50	4.75	2.75
563	Dal Maxvill	9.50	4.75	2.75
564	A.L. Rookies (Joe McCabe, Jerry McNertney)	9.50	4.75	2.75
565	Stu Miller	9.50	4.75	2.75
566	Ed Kranepool	9.50	4.75	2.75
567	Jim Kaat	13.00	6.50	4.00
568	N.L. Rookies (Phil Gagliano, Cap Peterson)	9.50	4.75	2.75
569	Fred Newman	9.50	4.75	2.75
570	Bill Mazeroski	13.00	6.50	4.00
571	Gene Conley	9.50	4.75	2.75
572	A.L. Rookies (Dick Egan, Dave Gray)	9.50	4.75	2.75
573	Jim Duffalo	9.50	4.75	2.75
574	Manny Jimenez	9.50	4.75	2.75
575	Tony Cloninger	9.50	4.75	2.75
576	Mets Rookies (Jerry Hinsley, Bill Wakefield)	9.50	4.75	2.75
577	Gordy Coleman	9.50	4.75	2.75
578	Glen Hobbie	9.50	4.75	2.75
579	Red Sox Team	18.00	9.00	5.50
580	Johnny Podres	11.00	5.50	3.25
581	Yankees Rookies (Pedro Gonzalez, Archie Moore)	9.50	4.75	2.75
582	Rod Kanehl	9.50	4.75	2.75
583	Tito Francona	9.50	4.75	2.75
584	Joel Horlen	9.50	4.75	2.75
585	Tony Taylor	9.50	4.75	2.75
586	Jim Piersall	9.00	4.50	2.75
587	Bennie Daniels	12.00	4.50	2.75

Definitions for grading conditions are located in the Introduction of this price guide.

1964 Topps Coins

The 164 metal coins in this set were issued by Topps as inserts in the company's baseball card wax packs. The series is divided into two principal types, 120 "regular" coins and 44 All-Star coins. The 1 1/2" diameter coins feature a full-color background for the player photos in the "regular" series, while the players in the All-Star series are featured against plain red or blue backgrounds. There are two variations each of the Mantle, Causey and Hinton coins among the All-Star subset.

		NR MT	EX	VG
Complete Set:		700.00	350.00	210.00
Common Player:		2.00	1.00	.60
1	Don Zimmer	3.00	1.50	.90
2	Jim Wynn	2.00	1.00	.60
3	Johnny Orsino	2.00	1.00	.60
4	Jim Bouton	3.00	1.50	.90
5	Dick Groat	3.00	1.50	.90
6	Leon Wagner	2.00	1.00	.60
7	Frank Malzone	2.00	1.00	.60
8	Steve Barber	2.00	1.00	.60
9	Johnny Romano	2.00	1.00	.60
10	Tom Tresh	3.00	1.50	.90
11	Felipe Alou	3.00	1.50	.90
12	Dick Stuart	2.00	1.00	.60
13	Claude Osteen	2.00	1.00	.60
14	Juan Pizarro	2.00	1.00	.60
15	Donn Clendenon	2.00	1.00	.60
16	Jimmie Hall	2.00	1.00	.60
17	Larry Jackson	2.00	1.00	.60
18	Brooks Robinson	12.50	6.25	3.75
19	Bob Allison	2.00	1.00	.60
20	Ed Roebuck	2.00	1.00	.60
21	Pete Ward	2.00	1.00	.60
22	Willie McCovey	8.00	4.00	2.50
23	Elston Howard	3.00	1.50	.90
24	Diego Segui	2.00	1.00	.60
25	Ken Boyer	3.00	1.50	.90
26	Carl Yastrzemski	15.00	7.50	4.50
27	Bill Mazeroski	4.00	2.00	1.25
28	Jerry Lumpe	2.00	1.00	.60
29	Woody Held	2.00	1.00	.60
30	Dick Radatz	2.00	1.00	.60
31	Luis Aparicio	8.00	4.00	2.50
32	Dave Nicholson	2.00	1.00	.60
33	Ed Mathews	12.00	6.00	3.50
34	Don Drysdale	15.00	7.50	4.50
35	Ray Culp	2.00	1.00	.60
36	Juan Marichal	8.00	4.00	2.50
37	Frank Robinson	12.50	6.25	3.75
38	Chuck Hinton	2.00	1.00	.60
39	Floyd Robinson	2.00	1.00	.60
40	Tommy Harper	2.00	1.00	.60
41	Ron Hansen	2.00	1.00	.60
42	Ernie Banks	15.00	7.50	4.50
43	Jesse Gonder	2.00	1.00	.60
44	Billy Williams	8.00	4.00	2.50
45	Vada Pinson	3.00	1.50	.90
46	Rocky Colavito	4.00	2.00	1.25
47	Bill Monbouquette	2.00	1.00	.60
48	Max Alvis	2.00	1.00	.60
49	Norm Siebern	2.00	1.00	.60
50	John Callison	2.00	1.00	.60
51	Rich Rollins	2.00	1.00	.60
52	Ken McBride	2.00	1.00	.60
53	Don Lock	2.00	1.00	.60
54	Ron Fairly	2.00	1.00	.60
55	Roberto Clemente	25.00	12.50	7.50
56	Dick Ellsworth	2.00	1.00	.60
57	Tommy Davis	2.00	1.00	.60
58	Tony Gonzalez	2.00	1.00	.60
59	Bob Gibson	12.00	6.00	3.50
60	Jim Maloney	2.00	1.00	.60
61	Frank Howard	3.00	1.50	.90
62	Jim Pagliaroni	2.00	1.00	.60
63	Orlando Cepeda	4.00	2.00	1.25
64	Ron Perranoski	2.00	1.00	.60
65	Curt Flood	2.50	1.25	.70
66	Al McBean	2.00	1.00	.60
67	Dean Chance	2.00	1.00	.60
68	Ron Santo	2.50	1.25	.70
69	Jack Baldschun	2.00	1.00	.60
70	Milt Pappas	2.00	1.00	.60
71	Gary Peters	2.00	1.00	.60
72	Bobby Richardson	2.50	1.25	.70
73	Lee Thomas	2.00	1.00	.60
74	Hank Aguirre	2.00	1.00	.60
75	Carl Willey	2.00	1.00	.60
76	Camilo Pascual	2.00	1.00	.60
77	Bob Friend	2.00	1.00	.60
78	Bill White	2.50	1.25	.70
79	Norm Cash	3.00	1.50	.90
80	Willie Mays	25.00	12.50	7.50
81	Duke Carmel	2.00	1.00	.60
82	Pete Rose	20.00	10.00	6.00
83	Hank Aaron	25.00	12.50	7.50
84	Bob Aspromonte	2.00	1.00	.60
85	Jim O'Toole	2.00	1.00	.60
86	Vic Davalillo	2.00	1.00	.60
87	Bill Freehan	2.00	1.00	.60
88	Warren Spahn	12.00	6.00	3.50
89	Ron Hunt	2.00	1.00	.60
90	Denis Menke	2.00	1.00	.60
91	Turk Farrell	2.00	1.00	.60
92	Jim Hickman	2.00	1.00	.60
93	Jim Bunning	3.00	1.50	.90
94	Bob Hendley	2.00	1.00	.60
95	Ernie Broglio	2.00	1.00	.60
96	Rusty Staub	3.00	1.50	.90
97	Lou Brock	8.00	4.00	2.50
98	Jim Fregosi	2.50	1.25	.70
99	Jim Grant	2.00	1.00	.60
100	Al Kaline	15.00	7.50	4.50
101	Earl Battey	2.00	1.00	.60
102	Wayne Causey	2.00	1.00	.60
103	Chuck Schilling	2.00	1.00	.60
104	Boog Powell	3.50	1.75	1.00
105	Dave Wickersham	2.00	1.00	.60
106	Sandy Koufax	18.00	9.00	5.50
107	John Bateman	2.00	1.00	.60
108	Ed Brinkman	2.00	1.00	.60
109	Al Downing	2.00	1.00	.60
110	Joe Azcue	2.00	1.00	.60
111	Albie Pearson	2.00	1.00	.60
112	Harmon Killebrew	12.00	6.00	3.50
113	Tony Taylor	2.00	1.00	.60
114	Alvin Jackson	2.00	1.00	.60
115	Billy O'Dell	2.00	1.00	.60
116	Don Demeter	2.00	1.00	.60
117	Ed Charles	2.00	1.00	.60
118	Joe Torre	2.50	1.25	.70
119	Don Nottebart	2.00	1.00	.60
120	Mickey Mantle	45.00	22.00	13.50
121	Joe Pepitone (All-Star)	2.00	1.00	.60
122	Dick Stuart (All-Star)	3.00	1.50	.90
123	Bobby Richardson (All-Star)	2.50	1.25	.70
124	Jerry Lumpe (All-Star)	2.00	1.00	.60
125	Brooks Robinson (All-Star)	12.50	6.25	3.75
126	Frank Malzone (All-Star)	2.00	1.00	.60
127	Luis Aparicio (All-Star)	8.00	4.00	2.50
128	Jim Fregosi (All-Star)	2.50	1.25	.70
129	Al Kaline (All-Star)	15.00	7.50	4.50
130	Leon Wagner (All-Star)	2.00	1.00	.60
131a	Mickey Mantle (All-Star, left handed)	45.00	22.00	13.50
131b	Mickey Mantle (All-Star, right handed)	45.00	22.00	13.50
132	Albie Pearson (All-Star)	2.00	1.00	.60
133	Harmon Killebrew (All-Star)	12.00	6.00	3.50
134	Carl Yastrzemski (All-Star)	15.00	7.50	4.50
135	Elston Howard (All-Star)	3.00	1.50	.90
136	Earl Battey (All-Star)	2.00	1.00	.60
137	Camilo Pascual (All-Star)	2.00	1.00	.60
138	Jim Bouton (All-Star)	3.00	1.50	.90
139	Whitey Ford (All-Star)	12.00	6.00	3.50
140	Gary Peters (All-Star)	2.00	1.00	.60
141	Bill White (All-Star)	2.50	1.25	.70
142	Orlando Cepeda (All-Star)	3.00	1.50	.90
143	Bill Mazeroski (All-Star)	4.00	2.00	1.25
144	Tony Taylor (All-Star)	2.00	1.00	.60
145	Ken Boyer (All-Star)	3.00	1.50	.90
146	Ron Santo (All-Star)	2.50	1.25	.70
147	Dick Groat (All-Star)	2.00	1.00	.60
148	Roy McMillan (All-Star)	2.00	1.00	.60
149	Hank Aaron (All-Star)	25.00	12.50	7.50
150	Roberto Clemente (All-Star)	25.00	12.50	7.50
151	Willie Mays (All-Star)	25.00	12.50	7.50
152	Vada Pinson (All-Star)	3.00	1.50	.90
153	Tommy Davis (All-Star)	2.00	1.00	.60
154	Frank Robinson (All-Star)	12.50	6.25	3.75
155	Joe Torre (All-Star)	2.50	1.25	.70
156	Tim McCarver (All-Star)	2.50	1.25	.70
157	Juan Marichal (All-Star)	8.00	4.00	2.50
158	Jim Maloney (All-Star)	2.00	1.00	.60
159	Sandy Koufax (All-Star)	18.00	9.00	5.50
160	Warren Spahn (All-Star)	12.00	6.00	3.50
161a	Wayne Causey (All-Star, A.L. on back)	15.00	7.50	4.50
161b	Wayne Causey (All-Star, A.L. on back)	2.00	1.00	.60
162a	Chuck Hinton (All-Star, N.L. on back)	15.00	7.50	4.50
162b	Chuck Hinton (All-Star, A.L. on back)	2.00	1.00	.60
163	Bob Aspromonte (All-Star)	2.00	1.00	.60
164	Ron Hunt (All-Star)	2.00	1.00	.60

1964 Topps Giants

Measuring 3-1/8" by 5-1/4" the Topps Giants were the company's first postcard-size issue. The cards feature large color photographs surrounded by white borders with a white baseball containing the player's name, position and team. Card backs carry another photo of the player surrounded by a newspaper-style explanation of the depicted career highlight. The 60-card set contains primarily stars which means it's an excellent place to find inexpensive cards of Hall of Famers. The '64 Giants were not

printed in equal quantity and seven of the cards, including Sandy Koufax and Willie Mays, are significantly scarcer than the remainder of the set.

		NR MT	EX	VG
Complete Set:		150.00	75.00	45.00
Common Player:		1.00	.50	.30
1	Gary Peters	1.00	.50	.30
2	Ken Johnson	1.00	.50	.30
3	Sandy Koufax	18.00	9.00	5.50
4	Bob Bailey	1.00	.50	.30
5	Milt Pappas	1.00	.50	.30
6	Ron Hunt	1.00	.50	.30
7	Whitey Ford	3.00	1.50	.90
8	Roy McMillan	1.00	.50	.30
9	Rocky Colavito	2.00	1.00	.60
10	Jim Bunning	1.50	.70	.45
11	Roberto Clemente	5.00	2.50	1.50
12	Al Kaline	3.00	1.50	.90
13	Nellie Fox	2.00	1.00	.60
14	Tony Gonzalez	1.00	.50	.30
15	Jim Gentile	1.00	.50	.30
16	Dean Chance	1.00	.50	.30
17	Dick Ellsworth	1.00	.50	.30
18	Jim Fregosi	1.00	.50	.30
19	Dick Groat	1.00	.50	.30
20	Chuck Hinton	1.00	.50	.30
21	Elston Howard	1.50	.70	.45
22	Dick Farrell	1.00	.50	.30
23	Albie Pearson	1.00	.50	.30
24	Frank Howard	1.50	.70	.45
25	Mickey Mantle	18.00	9.00	5.50
26	Joe Torre	1.00	.50	.30
27	Ed Brinkman	1.00	.50	.30
28	Bob Friend	4.00	2.00	1.25
29	Frank Robinson	3.00	1.50	.90
30	Bill Freehan	1.00	.50	.30
31	Warren Spahn	3.00	1.50	.90
32	Camilo Pascual	1.00	.50	.30
33	Pete Ward	1.00	.50	.30
34	Jim Maloney	1.00	.50	.30
35	Dave Wickersham	1.00	.50	.30
36	Johnny Callison	1.00	.50	.30
37	Juan Marichal	3.00	1.50	.90
38	Harmon Killebrew	3.00	1.50	.90
39	Luis Aparicio	3.00	1.50	.90
40	Dick Radatz	1.00	.50	.30
41	Bob Gibson	3.00	1.50	.90
42	Dick Stuart	4.00	2.00	1.25
43	Tommy Davis	1.00	.50	.30
44	Tony Oliva	1.50	.70	.45
45	Wayne Causey	4.00	2.00	1.25
46	Max Alvis	1.00	.50	.30
47	Galen Cisco	4.00	2.00	1.25
48	Carl Yastrzemski	3.00	1.50	.90
49	Hank Aaron	5.00	2.50	1.50
50	Brooks Robinson	3.00	1.50	.90
51	Willie Mays	18.00	9.00	5.50
52	Billy Williams	3.00	1.50	.90
53	Juan Pizarro	1.00	.50	.30
54	Leon Wagner	1.00	.50	.30
55	Orlando Cepeda	2.00	1.00	.60
56	Vada Pinson	1.50	.70	.45
57	Ken Boyer	1.50	.70	.45
58	Ron Santo	1.50	.70	.45
59	John Romano	1.00	.50	.30
60	Bill Skowron	4.00	2.00	1.25

1964 Topps Photo Tatoos

Apparently not content to leave the skin of American children without adornment, Topps jumped back into the tattoo field in 1964 with the release of a new series. Measuring 1-9/16" by 3-1/2," there were 75 tattoos in a complete set. The picture side for the 20 team tattoos gives the team logo and name. For the player tattoos, the picture side has the player's face, name and team.

		NR MT	EX	VG
Complete Set:		750.00	375.00	225.00
Common Player:		6.50	3.25	2.00
(1)	Hank Aaron	50.00	25.00	15.00
(2)	Hank Aguirre	6.50	3.25	2.00
(3)	Max Alvis	6.50	3.25	2.00
(4)	Ernie Banks	32.00	16.00	9.50
(5)	Steve Barber	6.50	3.25	2.00
(6)	Ken Boyer	6.50	3.25	2.00
(7)	Johnny Callison	7.50	3.75	2.25
(8)	Norm Cash	6.50	3.25	2.00
(9)	Wayne Causey	6.50	3.25	2.00
(10)	Orlando Cepeda	9.00	4.50	2.75
(11)	Rocky Colavito	9.00	4.50	2.75
(12)	Ray Culp	6.50	3.25	2.00
(13)	Vic Davalillo	6.50	3.25	2.00
(14)	Moe Drabowsky	6.50	3.25	2.00
(15)	Dick Ellsworth	6.50	3.25	2.00
(16)	Curt Flood	6.50	3.25	2.00
(17)	Bill Freehan	7.50	3.75	2.25
(18)	Jim Fregosi	7.50	3.75	2.25
(19)	Bob Friend	7.50	3.75	2.25
(20)	Dick Groat	7.50	3.75	2.25
(21)	Woody Held	6.50	3.25	2.00
(22)	Frank Howard	6.50	3.25	2.00
(23)	Al Jackson	6.50	3.25	2.00
(24)	Larry Jackson	6.50	3.25	2.00
(25)	Ken Johnson	6.50	3.25	2.00
(26)	Al Kaline	32.00	16.00	9.50
(27a)	Harmon Killebrew (green background)	32.00	16.00	9.50
(27b)	Harmon Killebrew (red background)	32.00	16.00	9.50
(28)	Sandy Koufax	45.00	22.00	13.50
(29)	Don Lock	6.50	3.25	2.00
(30)	Frank Malzone	6.50	3.25	2.00
(31)	Mickey Mantle	125.00	62.00	37.00
(32)	Eddie Mathews	20.00	10.00	6.00
(33a)	Willie Mays (yellow background encompasses entire head)	50.00	25.00	15.00
(33b)	Willie Mays (yellow background covers one-half of head)	50.00	25.00	15.00
(34)	Bill Mazeroski	6.50	3.25	2.00
(35)	Ken McBride	6.50	3.25	2.00
(36)	Bill Monbouquette	6.50	3.25	2.00
(37)	Dave Nicholson	6.50	3.25	2.00
(38)	Claude Osteen	7.50	3.75	2.25
(39)	Milt Pappas	7.50	3.75	2.25
(40)	Camilio Pascual	7.50	3.75	2.25
(41)	Albie Pearson	6.50	3.25	2.00
(42)	Ron Perranoski	6.50	3.25	2.00
(43)	Gary Peters	6.50	3.25	2.00
(44)	Boog Powell	6.50	3.25	2.00
(45)	Frank Robinson	25.00	12.50	7.50
(46)	John Romano	6.50	3.25	2.00
(47)	Norm Siebern	6.50	3.25	2.00
(48)	Warren Spahn	20.00	10.00	6.00
(49)	Dick Stuart	7.50	3.75	2.25
(50)	Lee Thomas	6.50	3.25	2.00
(51)	Joe Torre	6.50	3.25	2.00
(52)	Pete Ward	6.50	3.25	2.00
(53)	Carlton Willey	6.50	3.25	2.00
(54)	Billy Williams	32.00	16.00	9.50
(55)	Carl Yastrzemski	65.00	32.00	19.50
(56)	Baltimore Orioles Logo	6.50	3.25	2.00
(57)	Boston Red Sox Logo	6.50	3.25	2.00
(58)	Chicago Cubs Logo	6.50	3.25	2.00
(59)	Chicago White Sox Logo	6.50	3.25	2.00
(60)	Cincinnati Reds Logo	6.50	3.25	2.00
(61)	Cleveland Indians Logo	6.50	3.25	2.00
(62)	Detroit Tigers Logo	6.50	3.25	2.00
(63)	Houston Colts Logo	6.50	3.25	2.00
(64)	Kansas City Athletics Logo	6.50	3.25	2.00
(65)	Los Angeles Angels Logo	6.50	3.25	2.00
(66)	Los Angeles Dodgers Logo	6.50	3.25	2.00
(67)	Milwaukee Braves Logo	6.50	3.25	2.00
(68)	Minnesota Twins Logo	6.50	3.25	2.00
(69)	New York Mets Logo	6.50	3.25	2.00
(70)	New York Yankees Logo	7.50	3.75	2.25
(71)	Philadelphia Phillies Logo	6.50	3.25	2.00
(72)	Pittsburgh Pirates Logo	6.50	3.25	2.00
(73)	St. Louis Cardinals Logo	6.50	3.25	2.00
(74)	San Francisco Giants Logo	6.50	3.25	2.00
(75)	Washington Senators Logo	6.50	3.25	2.00

Definitions for grading conditions are located in the Introduction of this price guide.

1964 Topps Stand-Ups

These 2-1/2" by 3-1/2" cards were the first since the All-Star sets of 1951 to be die-cut. This made it possible for a folded card to stand on display. The 77-cards in the set feature color photographs of the player with yellow and green backgrounds. Directions for folding are on the yellow top background, and when folded only the green background remains. Of the 77 cards, 55 were double-printed while 22 were single-printed, making them twice as

scarce. Included in the single-printed group are Warren Spahn, Don Drysdale, Juan Marichal, Willie McCovey and Carl Yastrzemski.

		NR MT	EX	VG
Complete Set:		2000.	1000.	600.00
Common Player:		7.50	3.75	2.25
(1)	Hank Aaron	120.00	60.00	36.00
(2)	Hank Aguirre	7.50	3.75	2.25
(3)	George Altman	7.50	3.75	2.25
(4)	Max Alvis	7.50	3.75	2.25
(5)	Bob Aspromonte	7.50	3.75	2.25
(6)	Jack Baldschun (SP)	25.00	12.50	7.50
(7)	Ernie Banks	45.00	22.00	13.50
(8)	Steve Barber	7.50	3.75	2.25
(9)	Earl Battey	7.50	3.75	2.25
(10)	Ken Boyer	12.50	6.25	3.75
(11)	Ernie Broglio	7.50	3.75	2.25
(12)	Johnny Callison	7.50	3.75	2.25
(13)	Norm Cash (SP)	25.00	12.50	7.50
(14)	Wayne Causey	7.50	3.75	2.25
(15)	Orlando Cepeda	12.00	6.00	3.50
(16)	Ed Charles	7.50	3.75	2.25
(17)	Roberto Clemente	55.00	27.00	16.50
(18)	Donn Clendenon (SP)	25.00	12.50	7.50
(19)	Rocky Colavito	9.00	4.50	2.75
(20)	Ray Culp (SP)	25.00	12.50	7.50
(21)	Tommy Davis	9.00	4.50	2.75
(22)	Don Drysdale (SP)	135.00	67.50	40.00
(23)	Dick Ellsworth	7.50	3.75	2.25
(24)	Dick Farrell	7.50	3.75	2.25
(25)	Jim Fregosi	7.50	3.75	2.25
(26)	Bob Friend	7.50	3.75	2.25
(27)	Jim Gentile	8.00	4.00	2.50
(28)	Jesse Gonder (SP)	25.00	12.50	7.50
(29)	Tony Gonzalez (SP)	30.00	15.00	9.00
(30)	Dick Groat	9.00	4.50	2.75
(31)	Woody Held	7.50	3.75	2.25
(32)	Chuck Hinton	7.50	3.75	2.25
(33)	Elston Howard	9.00	4.50	2.75
(34)	Frank Howard (SP)	25.00	12.50	7.50
(35)	Ron Hunt	7.50	3.75	2.25
(36)	Al Jackson	7.50	3.75	2.25
(37)	Ken Johnson	7.50	3.75	2.25
(38)	Al Kaline	40.00	20.00	12.00
(39)	Harmon Killebrew	40.00	20.00	12.00
(40)	Sandy Koufax	80.00	40.00	24.00
(41)	Don Lock (SP)	25.00	12.50	7.50
(42)	Jerry Lumpe (SP)	28.00	14.00	8.50
(43)	Jim Maloney	7.50	3.75	2.25
(44)	Frank Malzone	7.50	3.75	2.25
(45)	Mickey Mantle	350.00	175.00	105.00
(46)	Juan Marichal (SP)	125.00	62.00	37.00
(47)	Ed Mathews (SP)	125.00	62.00	37.00
(48)	Willie Mays	125.00	62.50	37.50
(49)	Bill Mazeroski	9.00	4.50	2.75
(50)	Ken McBride	7.50	3.75	2.25
(51)	Willie McCovey (SP)	125.00	62.00	37.00
(52)	Claude Osteen	7.50	3.75	2.25
(53)	Jim O'Toole	7.50	3.75	2.25
(54)	Camilo Pascual	7.50	3.75	2.25
(55)	Albie Pearson (SP)	25.00	12.50	7.50
(56)	Gary Peters	7.50	3.75	2.25
(57)	Vada Pinson	9.00	4.50	2.75
(58)	Juan Pizarro	7.50	3.75	2.25
(59)	Boog Powell	9.00	4.50	2.75
(60)	Bobby Richardson	9.00	4.50	2.75
(61)	Brooks Robinson	50.00	25.00	15.00
(62)	Floyd Robinson	7.50	3.75	2.25
(63)	Frank Robinson	50.00	25.00	15.00
(64)	Ed Roebuck (SP)	25.00	12.50	7.50
(65)	Rich Rollins	7.50	3.75	2.25
(66)	Johnny Romano	7.50	3.75	2.25
(67)	Ron Santo (SP)	25.00	12.50	7.50
(68)	Norm Siebern	7.50	3.75	2.25
(69)	Warren Spahn (SP)	125.00	62.00	37.00
(70)	Dick Stuart (SP)	25.00	12.50	7.50
(71)	Lee Thomas	7.50	3.75	2.25
(72)	Joe Torre	22.00	11.00	6.50
(73)	Pete Ward	7.50	3.75	2.25
(74)	Bill White (SP)	30.00	15.00	9.00
(75)	Billy Williams (SP)	125.00	62.00	37.00
(76)	Hal Woodeshick (SP)	30.00	15.00	9.00
(77)	Carl Yastrzemski (SP)	400.00	200.00	120.00

1965 Topps

The 1965 Topps set features a large color photograph of the player which was surrounded by a colored, round-cornered frame and a white border.

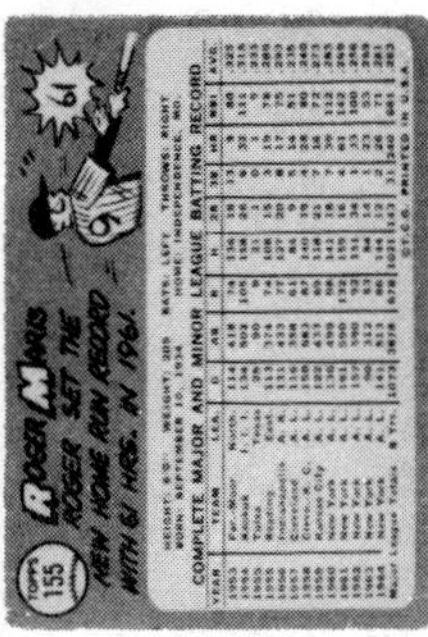

The bottom of the 2-1/2" by 3-1/2" cards include a pennant with a color team logo and name over the left side of a rectangle which features the player's name and position. Backs feature statistics and, if space allowed, a cartoon and headline about the player. There are no multi-player cards in the 1965 set other than the usual team cards and World Series highlights. Rookie cards include team, as well as league groupings from two to four players per card. Also present in the 598-card set are statistical leaders. Certain cards in the high-number series (#523-598) were produced in lesser quantities than the rest of the series. Known as "short-prints," and valued somewhat higher than the other high numbers, they are indicated in the checklist by an (SP) after the player name.

	NR MT	EX	VG
Complete Set (598):	3750.	1875.	1125.
Common Player (1-283):	2.50	1.25	.70
Common Player (284-370):	3.50	1.75	1.00
Common Player (371-598):	7.00	3.50	2.00

#	Player	NR MT	EX	VG
1	A.L. Batting Leaders (Elston Howard, Tony Oliva, Brooks Robinson)	15.00	7.50	4.50
2	N.L. Batting Leaders (Hank Aaron, Rico Carty, Roberto Clemente)	15.00	7.50	4.50
3	A.L. Home Run Leaders (Harmon Killebrew, Mickey Mantle, Boog Powell)	18.00	9.00	5.50
4	N.L. Home Run Leaders (Johnny Callison, Orlando Cepeda, Jim Hart, Willie Mays, Billy Williams)	15.00	7.50	4.50
5	A.L. RBI Leaders (Harmon Killebrew, Mickey Mantle, Brooks Robinson, Dick Stuart)	27.50	13.50	8.25
6	N.L. RBI Leaders (Ken Boyer, Willie Mays, Ron Santo)	12.00	6.00	3.50
7	A.L. ERA Leaders (Dean Chance, Joel Horlen)	7.00	3.50	2.00
8	N.L. ERA Leaders (Don Drysdale, Sandy Koufax)	9.00	4.50	2.75
9	A.L. Pitching Leaders (Wally Bunker, Dean Chance, Gary Peters, Juan Pizarro, Dave Wickersham)	6.00	3.00	1.75
10	N.L. Pitching Leaders (Larry Jackson, Juan Marichal, Ray Sadecki)	6.00	3.00	1.75
11	A.L. Strikeout Leaders (Dean Chance, Al Downing, Camilo Pascual)	6.00	3.00	1.75
12	N.L. Strikeout Leaders (Don Drysdale, Bob Gibson, Bob Veale)	7.00	3.50	2.00
13	Pedro Ramos	2.50	1.25	.70
14	Len Gabrielson	2.50	1.25	.70
15	Robin Roberts	9.75	5.00	3.00
16	Astros Rookies (*Sonny Jackson*, Joe Morgan)	85.00	42.00	25.00
17	Johnny Romano	2.50	1.25	.70
18	Bill McCool	2.50	1.25	.70
19	Gates Brown	2.50	1.25	.70
20	Jim Bunning	5.00	2.50	1.50
21	Don Blasingame	2.50	1.25	.70
22	Charlie Smith	2.50	1.25	.70
23	Bob Tiefenauer	2.50	1.25	.70
24	Twins Team	5.00	2.50	1.50
25	Al McBean	2.50	1.25	.70
26	Bobby Knoop	2.50	1.25	.70
27	Dick Bertell	2.50	1.25	.70
28	Barney Schultz	2.50	1.25	.70
29	Felix Mantilla	2.50	1.25	.70
30	Jim Bouton	5.00	2.50	1.50
31	Mike White	2.50	1.25	.70
32	Herman Franks	2.50	1.25	.70
33	Jackie Brandt	2.50	1.25	.70
34	Cal Koonce	2.50	1.25	.70
35	Ed Charles	2.50	1.25	.70
36	Bobby Wine	2.50	1.25	.70
37	Fred Gladding	2.50	1.25	.70
38	Jim King	2.50	1.25	.70
39	Gerry Arrigo	2.50	1.25	.70
40	Frank Howard	5.00	2.50	1.50
41	White Sox Rookies (Bruce Howard, Marv Staehle)	2.50	1.25	.70
42	Earl Wilson	2.50	1.25	.70
43	Mike Shannon	2.50	1.25	.70
44	Wade Blasingame	2.50	1.25	.70
45	Roy McMillan	2.50	1.25	.70
46	Bob Lee	2.50	1.25	.70
47	Tommy Harper	2.50	1.25	.70
48	Claude Raymond	2.50	1.25	.70
49	Orioles Rookies (*Curt Blefary*, John Miller)	4.50	2.25	1.25
50	Juan Marichal	12.00	6.00	3.50
51	Billy Bryan	2.50	1.25	.70
52	Ed Roebuck	2.50	1.25	.70
53	Dick McAuliffe	2.50	1.25	.70
54	Joe Gibbon	2.50	1.25	.70
55	Tony Conigliaro	7.00	3.50	2.00
56	Ron Kline	2.50	1.25	.70
57	Cardinals Team	5.00	2.50	1.50
58	Fred Talbot	2.50	1.25	.70
59	Nate Oliver	2.50	1.25	.70
60	Jim O'Toole	2.50	1.25	.70
61	Chris Cannizzaro	2.50	1.25	.70
62	Jim Katt (Kaat)	5.00	2.50	1.50
63	Ty Cline	2.50	1.25	.70
64	Lou Burdette	2.50	1.25	.70
65	Tony Kubek	4.50	2.25	1.25
66	Bill Rigney	2.50	1.25	.70
67	Harvey Haddix	2.50	1.25	.70
68	Del Crandall	2.50	1.25	.70
69	Bill Virdon	2.50	1.25	.70
70	Bill Skowron	2.50	1.25	.70
71	John O'Donoghue	2.50	1.25	.70
72	Tony Gonzalez	2.50	1.25	.70
73	Dennis Ribant	2.50	1.25	.70
74	Red Sox Rookies (*Rico Petrocelli*, Jerry Stephenson)	7.00	3.50	2.00
75	Deron Johnson	2.50	1.25	.70
76	Sam McDowell	2.50	1.25	.70
77	Doug Camilli	2.50	1.25	.70
78	Dal Maxvill	2.50	1.25	.70
79a	Checklist 1-88 (61 is C. Cannizzaro)	4.50	2.25	1.25
79b	Checklist 1-88 (61 is Cannizzaro)	7.00	3.50	2.00
80	Turk Farrell	2.50	1.25	.70
81	Don Buford	2.50	1.25	.70
82	Braves Rookies (*Santos Alomar*, John Braun)	4.50	2.25	1.25
83	George Thomas	2.50	1.25	.70
84	Ron Herbel	2.50	1.25	.70
85	Willie Smith	2.50	1.25	.70
86	Les Narum	2.50	1.25	.70
87	Nelson Mathews	2.50	1.25	.70
88	Jack Lamabe	2.50	1.25	.70
89	Mike Hershberger	2.50	1.25	.70
90	Rich Rollins	2.50	1.25	.70
91	Cubs Team	5.00	2.50	1.50
92	Dick Howser	2.50	1.25	.70
93	Jack Fisher	2.50	1.25	.70
94	Charlie Lau	2.50	1.25	.70
95	Bill Mazeroski	7.00	3.50	2.00
96	Sonny Siebert	2.50	1.25	.70
97	Pedro Gonzalez	2.50	1.25	.70
98	Bob Miller	2.50	1.25	.70
99	Gil Hodges	7.50	3.75	2.25
100	Ken Boyer	5.00	2.50	1.50
101	Fred Newman	2.50	1.25	.70
102	Steve Boros	2.50	1.25	.70
103	Harvey Kuenn	4.00	2.00	1.25
104	Checklist 89-176	4.50	2.25	1.25
105	Chico Salmon	2.50	1.25	.70
106	Gene Oliver	2.50	1.25	.70
107	Phillies Rookies (*Pat Corrales*, Costen Shockley)	4.50	2.25	1.25
108	Don Mincher	2.50	1.25	.70
109	Walt Bond	2.50	1.25	.70
110	Ron Santo	4.50	2.25	1.25
111	Lee Thomas	2.50	1.25	.70
112	Derrell Griffith	2.50	1.25	.70
113	Steve Barber	2.50	1.25	.70
114	Jim Hickman	2.50	1.25	.70
115	Bobby Richardson	5.00	2.50	1.50
116	Cardinals Rookies (Dave Dowling, Bob Tolan)	2.50	1.25	.70
117	Wes Stock	2.50	1.25	.70
118	*Hal Lanier*	2.50	1.25	.70
119	John Kennedy	2.50	1.25	.70
120	Frank Robinson	30.00	15.00	9.00
121	Gene Alley	2.50	1.25	.70
122	Bill Pleis	2.50	1.25	.70
123	Frank J. Thomas	2.50	1.25	.70
124	Tom Satriano	2.50	1.25	.70
125	Juan Pizarro	2.50	1.25	.70
126	Dodgers Team	7.00	3.50	2.00
127	Frank Lary	2.50	1.25	.70
128	Vic Davalillo	2.50	1.25	.70
129	Bennie Daniels	2.50	1.25	.70
130	Al Kaline	27.00	13.50	8.00
131	Johnny Keane	2.50	1.25	.70
132	World Series Game 1 (Cards Take Opener)	5.00	2.50	1.50
133	World Series Game 2 (Stottlemyre Wins)	5.00	2.50	1.50
134	World Series Game 3 (Mantle's Clutch HR)	40.00	20.00	12.00
135	World Series Game 4 (Boyer's Grand-Slam)	7.00	3.50	2.00
136	World Series Game 5 (10th Inning Triumph)	5.00	2.50	1.50
137	World Series Game 6 (Bouton Wins Again)	5.00	2.50	1.50
138	World Series Game 7 (Gibson Wins Finale)	7.00	3.50	2.00
139	World Series Summary (The Cards Celebrate)	5.00	2.50	1.50
140	Dean Chance	2.50	1.25	.70
141	Charlie James	2.50	1.25	.70
142	Bill Monbouquette	2.50	1.25	.70
143	Pirates Rookies (John Gelnar, Jerry May)	2.50	1.25	.70
144	Ed Kranepool	2.50	1.25	.70
145	*Luis Tiant*	18.00	9.00	5.50
146	Ron Hansen	2.50	1.25	.70
147	Dennis Bennett	2.50	1.25	.70
148	Willie Kirkland	2.50	1.25	.70
149	Wayne Schurr	2.50	1.25	.70
150	Brooks Robinson	23.00	11.50	7.00
151	Athletics Team	5.00	2.50	1.50
152	Phil Ortega	2.50	1.25	.70
153	Norm Cash	4.00	2.00	1.25
154	Bob Humphreys	2.50	1.25	.70
155	Roger Maris	55.00	27.00	16.50
156	Bob Sadowski	2.50	1.25	.70
157	Zoilo Versalles	2.50	1.25	.70
158	Dick Sisler	2.50	1.25	.70
159	Jim Duffalo	2.50	1.25	.70
160	Roberto Clemente	80.00	40.00	24.00
161	Frank Baumann	2.50	1.25	.70
162	Russ Nixon	2.50	1.25	.70
163	John Briggs	2.50	1.25	.70
164	Al Spangler	2.50	1.25	.70
165	Dick Ellsworth	2.50	1.25	.70
166	Indians Rookies (*Tommie Agee*, George Culver)	4.50	2.25	1.25
167	Bill Wakefield	2.50	1.25	.70
168	Dick Green	2.50	1.25	.70
169	Dave Vineyard	2.50	1.25	.70
170	Hank Aaron	85.00	42.00	25.00
171	Jim Roland	2.50	1.25	.70
172	Jim Piersall	2.50	1.25	.70
173	Tigers Team	5.00	2.50	1.50
174	Joe Jay	2.50	1.25	.70
175	Bob Aspromonte	2.50	1.25	.70
176	Willie McCovey	17.00	8.50	5.00
177	Pete Mikkelsen	2.50	1.25	.70
178	Dalton Jones	2.50	1.25	.70
179	Hal Woodeshick	2.50	1.25	.70
180	Bob Allison	2.50	1.25	.70
181	Senators Rookies (Don Loun, Joe McCabe)	2.50	1.25	.70
182	Mike de la Hoz	2.50	1.25	.70
183	Dave Nicholson	2.50	1.25	.70
184	John Boozer	2.50	1.25	.70
185	Max Alvis	2.50	1.25	.70
186	Billy Cowan	2.50	1.25	.70
187	Casey Stengel	15.00	7.50	4.50
188	Sam Bowens	2.50	1.25	.70
189	Checklist 177-264	4.50	2.25	1.25
190	Bill White	4.00	2.00	1.25
191	Phil Regan	2.50	1.25	.70
192	Jim Coker	2.50	1.25	.70
193	Gaylord Perry	17.50	8.75	5.25
194	Angels Rookies (Bill Kelso, Rick Reichardt)	2.50	1.25	.70
195	Bob Veale	2.50	1.25	.70
196	Ron Fairly	2.50	1.25	.70
197	Diego Segui	2.50	1.25	.70
198	Smoky Burgess	2.50	1.25	.70
199	Bob Heffner	2.50	1.25	.70
200	Joe Torre	4.50	2.25	1.25
201	Twins Rookies (*Cesar Tovar*, Sandy Valdespino)	2.50	1.25	.70
202	Leo Burke	2.50	1.25	.70
203	Dallas Green	3.50	1.75	1.00
204	Russ Snyder	2.50	1.25	.70
205	Warren Spahn	20.00	10.00	6.00
206	Willie Horton	2.50	1.25	.70
207	Pete Rose	145.00	72.00	43.00
208	Tommy John	10.00	5.00	3.00
209	Pirates Team	5.00	2.50	1.50
210	Jim Fregosi	2.50	1.25	.70
211	Steve Ridzik	2.50	1.25	.70
212	Ron Brand	2.50	1.25	.70
213	Jim Davenport	2.50	1.25	.70
214	Bob Purkey	2.50	1.25	.70
215	Pete Ward	2.50	1.25	.70
216	Al Worthington	2.50	1.25	.70
217	Walt Alston	5.00	2.50	1.50
218	Dick Schofield	2.50	1.25	.70
219	Bob Meyer	2.50	1.25	.70
220	Billy Williams	12.50	6.25	3.75
221	John Tsitouris	2.50	1.25	.70
222	Bob Tillman	2.50	1.25	.70
223	Dan Osinski	2.50	1.25	.70
224	Bob Chance	2.50	1.25	.70
225	Bo Belinsky	2.50	1.25	.70
226	Yankees Rookies (Jake Gibbs, Elvio Jimenez)	2.50	1.25	.70
227	Bobby Klaus	2.50	1.25	.70
228	Jack Sanford	2.50	1.25	.70
229	Lou Clinton	2.50	1.25	.70
230	Ray Sadecki	2.50	1.25	.70
231	Jerry Adair	2.50	1.25	.70
232	*Steve Blass*	2.50	1.25	.70
233	Don Zimmer	2.50	1.25	.70
234	White Sox Team	5.00	2.50	1.50
235	Chuck Hinton	2.50	1.25	.70
236	*Dennis McLain*	27.00	13.50	8.00
237	Bernie Allen	2.50	1.25	.70
238	Joe Moeller	2.50	1.25	.70
239	Doc Edwards	2.50	1.25	.70
240	Bob Bruce	2.50	1.25	.70
241	Mack Jones	2.50	1.25	.70
242	George Brunet	2.50	1.25	.70
243	Reds Rookies (Ted Davidson, Tommy Helms)	2.50	1.25	.70
244	Lindy McDaniel	2.50	1.25	.70
245	Joe Pepitone	2.50	1.25	.70
246	Tom Butters	2.50	1.25	.70
247	Wally Moon	2.50	1.25	.70
248	Gus Triandos	2.50	1.25	.70
249	Dave McNally	2.50	1.25	.70
250	Willie Mays	100.00	50.00	30.00
251	Billy Herman	5.00	2.50	1.50
252	Pete Richert	2.50	1.25	.70
253	Danny Cater	2.50	1.25	.70
254	Roland Sheldon	2.50	1.25	.70
255	Camilo Pascual	2.50	1.25	.70
256	Tito Francona	2.50	1.25	.70
257	Jim Wynn	2.50	1.25	.70
258	Larry Bearnarth	2.50	1.25	.70
259	Tigers Rookies (*Jim Northrup*, Ray Oyler)	2.50	1.25	.70
260	Don Drysdale	20.00	10.00	6.00
261	Duke Carmel	2.50	1.25	.70
262	Bud Daley	2.50	1.25	.70
263	Marty Keough	2.50	1.25	.70
264	Bob Buhl	2.50	1.25	.70
265	Jim Pagliaroni	2.50	1.25	.70

266 *Bert Campaneris* 7.00 3.50 2.00
267 Senators Team 5.00 2.50 1.50
268 Ken McBride 2.50 1.25 .70
269 Frank Bolling 2.50 1.25 .70
270 Milt Pappas 2.50 1.25 .70
271 Don Wert 2.50 1.25 .70
272 Chuck Schilling 2.50 1.25 .70
273 Checklist 265-352 2.50 1.25 .70
274 Lum Harris 2.50 1.25 .70
275 Dick Groat 2.50 1.25 .70
276 Hoyt Wilhelm 8.00 4.00 2.50
277 Johnny Lewis 2.50 1.25 .70
278 Ken Retzer 2.50 1.25 .70
279 Dick Tracewski 2.50 1.25 .70
280 Dick Stuart 2.50 1.25 .70
281 Bill Stafford 2.50 1.25 .70
282 Giants Rookies (Dick Estelle, Masanori Murakami) 17.00 8.50 5.00
283 Fred Whitfield 2.50 1.25 .70
284 Nick Willhite 3.50 1.75 1.00
285 Ron Hunt 3.50 1.75 1.00
286 Athletic Rookies (Jim Dickson, Aurelio Monteagudo) 3.50 1.75 1.00
287 Gary Kolb 3.50 1.75 1.00
288 Jack Hamilton 3.50 1.75 1.00
289 Gordy Coleman 3.50 1.75 1.00
290 Wally Bunker 3.50 1.75 1.00
291 Jerry Lynch 3.50 1.75 1.00
292 Larry Yellen 3.50 1.75 1.00
293 Angels Team 5.00 2.50 1.50
294 Tim McCarver 4.50 2.25 1.25
295 Dick Radatz 3.50 1.75 1.00
296 Tony Taylor 3.50 1.75 1.00
297 Dave DeBusschere 5.00 2.50 1.50
298 Jim Stewart 3.50 1.75 1.00
299 Jerry Zimmerman 3.50 1.75 1.00
300 Sandy Koufax 125.00 62.00 37.00
301 Birdie Tebbetts 3.50 1.75 1.00
302 Al Stanek 3.50 1.75 1.00
303 Johnny Orsino 3.50 1.75 1.00
304 Dave Stenhouse 3.50 1.75 1.00
305 Rico Carty 3.50 1.75 1.00
306 Bubba Phillips 3.50 1.75 1.00
307 Barry Latman 3.50 1.75 1.00
308 Mets Rookies (*Cleon Jones*, Tom Parsons) 5.00 2.50 1.50
309 Steve Hamilton 3.50 1.75 1.00
310 Johnny Callison 3.50 1.75 1.00
311 Orlando Pena 3.50 1.75 1.00
312 Joe Nuxhall 3.50 1.75 1.00
313 Jimmie Schaffer 3.50 1.75 1.00
314 Sterling Slaughter 3.50 1.75 1.00
315 Frank Malzone 3.50 1.75 1.00
316 Reds Team 5.00 2.50 1.50
317 Don McMahon 3.50 1.75 1.00
318 Matty Alou 3.50 1.75 1.00
319 Ken McMullen 3.50 1.75 1.00
320 Bob Gibson 32.00 16.00 9.50
321 Rusty Staub 5.00 2.50 1.50
322 Rick Wise 3.50 1.75 1.00
323 Hank Bauer 3.50 1.75 1.00
324 Bobby Locke 3.50 1.75 1.00
325 Donn Clendenon 3.50 1.75 1.00
326 Dwight Siebler 3.50 1.75 1.00
327 Denis Menke 3.50 1.75 1.00
328 Eddie Fisher 3.50 1.75 1.00
329 Hawk Taylor 3.50 1.75 1.00
330 Whitey Ford 25.00 12.50 7.50
331 Dodgers Rookies (Al Ferrara, John Purdin) 3.50 1.75 1.00
332 Ted Abernathy 3.50 1.75 1.00
333 Tommie Reynolds 3.50 1.75 1.00
334 Vic Roznovsky 3.50 1.75 1.00
335 Mickey Lolich 4.50 2.25 1.25
336 Woody Held 3.50 1.75 1.00
337 Mike Cuellar 3.50 1.75 1.00
338 Phillies Team 5.00 2.50 1.50
339 Ryne Duren 3.50 1.75 1.00
340 Tony Oliva 15.00 7.50 4.50
341 Bobby Bolin 3.50 1.75 1.00
342 Bob Rodgers 3.50 1.75 1.00
343 Mike McCormick 3.50 1.75 1.00
344 Wes Parker 3.50 1.75 1.00
345 Floyd Robinson 3.50 1.75 1.00
346 Bobby Bragan 3.50 1.75 1.00
347 Roy Face 3.50 1.75 1.00
348 George Banks 3.50 1.75 1.00
349 Larry Miller 3.50 1.75 1.00
350 Mickey Mantle 500.00 250.00 150.00
351 Jim Perry 3.50 1.75 1.00
352 *Alex Johnson* 3.50 1.75 1.00
353 Jerry Lumpe 3.50 1.75 1.00
354 Cubs Rookies (Billy Ott, Jack Warner) 3.50 1.75 1.00
355 Vada Pinson 6.00 3.00 1.75
356 Bill Spanswick 3.50 1.75 1.00
357 Carl Warwick 3.50 1.75 1.00
358 Albie Pearson 3.50 1.75 1.00
359 Ken Johnson 3.50 1.75 1.00
360 Orlando Cepeda 7.50 3.75 2.25
361 Checklist 353-429 4.50 2.25 1.25
362 Don Schwall 3.50 1.75 1.00
363 Bob Johnson 3.50 1.75 1.00
364 Galen Cisco 3.50 1.75 1.00
365 Jim Gentile 3.50 1.75 1.00
366 Dan Schneider 3.50 1.75 1.00
367 Leon Wagner 3.50 1.75 1.00
368 White Sox Rookies (*Ken Berry*, Joel Gibson) 3.50 1.75 1.00
369 Phil Linz 3.50 1.75 1.00
370 Tommy Davis 4.00 2.00 1.25
371 Frank Kreutzer 7.00 3.50 2.00
372 Clay Dalrymple 7.00 3.50 2.00
373 Curt Simmons 7.00 3.50 2.00
374 Angels Rookies (*Jose Cardenal*, Dick Simpson) 7.00 3.50 2.00
375 Dave Wickersham 7.00 3.50 2.00
376 Jim Landis 7.00 3.50 2.00
377 Willie Stargell 20.00 10.00 6.00
378 Chuck Estrada 7.00 3.50 2.00
379 Giants Team 7.00 3.50 2.00
380 Rocky Colavito 10.00 5.00 3.00
381 Al Jackson 7.00 3.50 2.00
382 J.C. Martin 7.00 3.50 2.00
383 Felipe Alou 7.00 3.50 2.00
384 Johnny Klippstein 7.00 3.50 2.00
385 Carl Yastrzemski 65.00 32.00 19.50
386 Cubs Rookies (Paul Jaeckel, Fred Norman) 7.00 3.50 2.00
387 Johnny Podres 7.00 3.50 2.00
388 John Blanchard 7.00 3.50 2.00
389 Don Larsen 7.00 3.50 2.00
390 Bill Freehan 7.00 3.50 2.00
391 Mel McGaha 7.00 3.50 2.00
392 Bob Friend 7.00 3.50 2.00
393 Ed Kirkpatrick 7.00 3.50 2.00
394 Jim Hannan 7.00 3.50 2.00
395 Jim Hart 7.00 3.50 2.00
396 Frank Bertaina 7.00 3.50 2.00
397 Jerry Buchek 7.00 3.50 2.00
398 Reds Rookies (Dan Neville, Art Shamsky) 7.00 3.50 2.00
399 Ray Herbert 7.00 3.50 2.00
400 Harmon Killebrew 30.00 15.00 9.00
401 Carl Willey 7.00 3.50 2.00
402 Joe Amalfitano 7.00 3.50 2.00
403 Red Sox Team 7.50 3.75 2.25
404 Stan Williams 7.00 3.50 2.00
405 John Roseboro 7.00 3.50 2.00
406 Ralph Terry 7.00 3.50 2.00
407 Lee Maye 7.00 3.50 2.00
408 Larry Sherry 7.00 3.50 2.00
409 Astros Rookies (Jim Beauchamp, Larry Dierker) 7.00 3.50 2.00
410 Luis Aparicio 9.00 4.50 2.75
411 Roger Craig 7.00 3.50 2.00
412 Bob Bailey 7.00 3.50 2.00
413 Hal Reniff 7.00 3.50 2.00
414 Al Lopez 7.00 3.50 2.00
415 Curt Flood 7.00 3.50 2.00
416 Jim Brewer 7.00 3.50 2.00
417 Ed Brinkman 7.00 3.50 2.00
418 Johnny Edwards 7.00 3.50 2.00
419 Ruben Amaro 7.00 3.50 2.00
420 Larry Jackson 7.00 3.50 2.00
421 Twins Rookies (Gary Dotter, Jay Ward) 7.00 3.50 2.00
422 Aubrey Gatewood 7.00 3.50 2.00
423 Jesse Gonder 7.00 3.50 2.00
424 Gary Bell 7.00 3.50 2.00
425 Wayne Causey 7.00 3.50 2.00
426 Braves Team 7.00 3.50 2.00
427 Bob Saverine 7.00 3.50 2.00
428 Bob Shaw 7.00 3.50 2.00
429 Don Demeter 7.00 3.50 2.00
430 Gary Peters 7.00 3.50 2.00
431 Cardinals Rookies (*Nelson Briles*, Wayne Spiezio) 7.00 3.50 2.00
432 Jim Grant 7.00 3.50 2.00
433 John Bateman 7.00 3.50 2.00
434 Dave Morehead 7.00 3.50 2.00
435 Willie Davis 7.00 3.50 2.00
436 Don Elston 7.00 3.50 2.00
437 Chico Cardenas 7.00 3.50 2.00
438 Harry Walker 7.00 3.50 2.00
439 Moe Drabowsky 7.00 3.50 2.00
440 Tom Tresh 7.00 3.50 2.00
441 Denver Lemaster 7.00 3.50 2.00
442 Vic Power 7.00 3.50 2.00
443 Checklist 430-506 8.00 4.00 2.50
444 Bob Hendley 7.00 3.50 2.00
445 Don Lock 7.00 3.50 2.00
446 Art Mahaffey 7.00 3.50 2.00
447 Julian Javier 7.00 3.50 2.00
448 Lee Stange 7.00 3.50 2.00
449 Mets Rookies (Jerry Hinsley, Gary Kroll) 7.00 3.50 2.00
450 Elston Howard 7.00 3.50 2.00
451 Jim Owens 7.00 3.50 2.00
452 Gary Geiger 7.00 3.50 2.00
453 Dodgers Rookies (*Willie Crawford*, John Werhas) 7.00 3.50 2.00
454 Ed Rakow 7.00 3.50 2.00
455 Norm Siebern 7.00 3.50 2.00
456 Bill Henry 7.00 3.50 2.00
457 Bob Kennedy 7.00 3.50 2.00
458 John Buzhardt 7.00 3.50 2.00
459 Frank Kostro 7.00 3.50 2.00
460 Richie Allen 15.00 7.50 4.50
461 Braves Rookies (*Clay Carroll*, Phil Niekro) 45.00 22.00 13.50
462 Lew Krausse (photo actually Pete Lovrich) 7.00 3.50 2.00
463 Manny Mota 7.00 3.50 2.00
464 Ron Piche 7.00 3.50 2.00
465 Tom Haller 7.00 3.50 2.00
466 Senators Rookies (Pete Craig, Dick Nen) 7.00 3.50 2.00
467 Ray Washburn 7.00 3.50 2.00
468 Larry Brown 7.00 3.50 2.00
469 Don Nottebart 7.00 3.50 2.00
470 Yogi Berra 50.00 25.00 15.00
471 Billy Hoeft 7.00 3.50 2.00
472 Don Pavletich 7.00 3.50 2.00
473 Orioles Rookies (*Paul Blair*, Dave Johnson) 15.00 7.50 4.50
474 Cookie Rojas 7.00 3.50 2.00
475 Clete Boyer 7.00 3.50 2.00
476 Billy O'Dell 7.00 3.50 2.00
477 Cardinals Rookies (Fritz Ackley, Steve Carlton) 415.00 207.00 124.00
478 Wilbur Wood 7.00 3.50 2.00
479 Ken Harrelson 7.00 3.50 2.00
480 Joel Horlen 7.00 3.50 2.00
481 Indians Team 9.00 4.50 2.75
482 Bob Priddy 7.00 3.50 2.00
483 George Smith 7.00 3.50 2.00
484 Ron Perranoski 7.00 3.50 2.00
485 Nellie Fox 14.00 7.00 4.25
486 Angels Rookies (Tom Egan, Pat Rogan) 7.00 3.50 2.00
487 Woody Woodward 7.00 3.50 2.00
488 Ted Wills 7.00 3.50 2.00
489 Gene Mauch 7.00 3.50 2.00
490 Earl Battey 7.00 3.50 2.00
491 Tracy Stallard 7.00 3.50 2.00
492 Gene Freese 7.00 3.50 2.00
493 Tigers Rookies (Bruce Brubaker, Bill Roman) 7.00 3.50 2.00
494 Jay Ritchie 7.00 3.50 2.00
495 Joe Christopher 7.00 3.50 2.00
496 Joe Cunningham 7.00 3.50 2.00
497 Giants Rookies (*Ken Henderson*, Jack Hiatt) 7.00 3.50 2.00
498 Gene Stephens 7.00 3.50 2.00
499 Stu Miller 7.00 3.50 2.00
500 Eddie Mathews 32.50 16.00 9.75
501 Indians Rookies (Ralph Gagliano, Jim Rittwage) 7.00 3.50 2.00
502 Don Cardwell 7.00 3.50 2.00
503 Phil Gagliano 7.00 3.50 2.00
504 Jerry Grote 7.00 3.50 2.00
505 Ray Culp 7.00 3.50 2.00
506 Sam Mele 7.00 3.50 2.00
507 Sammy Ellis 7.00 3.50 2.00
508a Checklist 507-598 (large print on front) 7.50 3.75 2.25
508b Checklist 507-598 (small print on front) 7.00 3.50 2.00
509 Red Sox Rookies (Bob Guindon, Gerry Vezendy) 7.00 3.50 2.00
510 Ernie Banks 65.00 32.00 19.50
511 Ron Locke 7.00 3.50 2.00
512 Cap Peterson 7.00 3.50 2.00
513 Yankees Team 25.00 12.50 7.50
514 Joe Azcue 7.00 3.50 2.00
515 Vern Law 7.00 3.50 2.00
516 Al Weis 7.00 3.50 2.00
517 Angels Rookies (Paul Schaal, Jack Warner) 7.00 3.50 2.00
518 Ken Rowe 7.00 3.50 2.00
519 Bob Uecker 30.00 15.00 9.00
520 Tony Cloninger 7.00 3.50 2.00
521 Phillies Rookies (Dave Bennett, Morrie Stevens) 7.00 3.50 2.00
522 Hank Aguirre 7.00 3.50 2.00
523 Mike Brumley (SP) 10.00 5.00 3.00
524 Dave Giusti (SP) 10.00 5.00 3.00
525 Eddie Bressoud 7.00 3.50 2.00
526 *Catfish Hunter*, Rene Lachemann, Skip Lockwood, Johnny Odom 100.00 50.00 30.00
527 Jeff Torborg 10.00 5.00 3.00
528 George Altman 7.00 3.50 2.00
529 Jerry Fosnow (SP) 10.00 5.00 3.00
530 Jim Maloney 7.00 3.50 2.00
531 Chuck Hiller 7.00 3.50 2.00
532 Hector Lopez 7.00 3.50 2.00
533 Mets Rookies (Jim Bethke, Tug McGraw, Dan Napolean, Ron Swoboda) 28.00 14.00 8.50
534 John Herrnstein 7.00 3.50 2.00
535 Jack Kralick (SP) 10.00 5.00 3.00
536 Andre Rodgers (SP) 10.00 5.00 3.00
537 Angels Rookies (Marcelino Lopez, Rudy May, Phil Roof) 7.00 3.50 2.00
538 Chuck Dressen (SP) 10.00 5.00 3.00
539 Herm Starrette 7.00 3.50 2.00
540 Lou Brock 40.00 20.00 12.00
541 White Sox Rookies (Greg Bollo, Bob Locker) 7.00 3.50 2.00
542 Lou Klimchock 7.00 3.50 2.00
543 Ed Connolly (SP) 10.00 5.00 3.00
544 Howie Reed 7.00 3.50 2.00
545 Jesus Alou (SP) 10.00 5.00 3.00
546 Indians Rookies (Ray Barker, Bill Davis, Mike Hedlund, Floyd Weaver) 7.00 3.50 2.00
547 Jake Wood (SP) 10.00 5.00 3.00
548 Dick Stigman 7.00 3.50 2.00
549 Cubs Rookies (*Glenn Beckert*, Roberto Pena) 19.00 9.50 5.75
550 *Mel Stottlemyre* 27.50 13.50 8.25
551 Mets Team 23.00 11.50 7.00
552 Julio Gotay 7.00 3.50 2.00
553 Houston Rookies (Dan Coombs, Jack McClure, Gene Ratliff) 7.00 3.50 2.00
554 Chico Ruiz (SP) 10.00 5.00 3.00
555 Jack Baldschun (SP) 10.00 5.00 3.00
556 Red Schoendienst 15.00 7.50 4.50
557 Jose Santiago 7.00 3.50 2.00
558 Tommie Sisk 7.00 3.50 2.00
559 Ed Bailey (SP) 10.00 5.00 3.00
560 Boog Powell 20.00 10.00 6.00
561 Dodgers Rookies (Dennis Daboll, Mike Kekich, Jim Lefebvre, Hector Valle) 12.00 6.00 3.50
562 Billy Moran 7.00 3.50 2.00
563 Julio Navarro 7.00 3.50 2.00
564 Mel Nelson 7.00 3.50 2.00
565 Ernie Broglio (SP) 10.00 5.00 3.00
566 Yankees Rookies (Gil Blanco) (SP, Art Lopez, Ross Moschitto) 12.00 6.00 3.50
567 Tommie Aaron 7.00 3.50 2.00
568 Ron Taylor (SP) 10.00 5.00 3.00
569 Gino Cimoli (SP) 10.00 5.00 3.00
570 Claude Osteen (SP) 10.00 5.00 3.00
571 Ossie Virgil (SP) 10.00 5.00 3.00
572 Orioles Team 22.00 11.00 6.50
573 Red Sox Rookies (*Jim Lonborg*, Gerry Moses, Mike Ryan, Bill Schlesinger) 22.00 11.00 6.50
574 Roy Sievers 7.00 3.50 2.00
575 Jose Pagan 7.00 3.50 2.00
576 Terry Fox (SP) 10.00 5.00 3.00
577 A.L. Rookies (Jim Buschhorn) (SP, Darold Knowles, Richie Scheinblum) 10.00 5.00 3.00
578 Camilo Carreon (SP) 10.00 5.00 3.00
579 Dick Smith (SP) 10.00 5.00 3.00

580	Jimmie Hall (SP)	10.00	5.00	3.00
581	N.L. Rookies (Kevin Collins, Tony Perez, Dave Ricketts)	115.00	57.00	34.00
582	Bob Schmidt (SP)	10.00	5.00	3.00
583	Wes Covington (SP)	10.00	5.00	3.00
584	Harry Bright	7.00	3.50	2.00
585	Hank Fischer	7.00	3.50	2.00
586	Tommy McCraw (SP)	10.00	5.00	3.00
587	Joe Sparma	7.00	3.50	2.00
588	Lenny Green	7.00	3.50	2.00
589	Giants Rookies (Frank Linzy) (SP, Bob Schroder)	10.00	5.00	3.00
590	Johnnie Wyatt	7.00	3.50	2.00
591	Bob Skinner (SP)	10.00	5.00	3.00
592	Frank Bork (SP)	10.00	5.00	3.00
593	Tigers Rookies (Jackie Moore, John Sullivan)	9.00	4.50	2.75
594	Joe Gaines	7.00	3.50	2.00
595	Don Lee	7.00	3.50	2.00
596	Don Landrum (SP)	10.00	5.00	3.00
597	Twins Rookies (Joe Nossek, Dick Reese, John Sevcik)	7.50	3.75	2.25
598	Al Downing	15.00	5.00	3.00

1965 Topps Embossed

Inserted in regular packs, the 2-1/8" by 3-1/2" Topps Embossed cards are one of the more fascinating issues of the company. The fronts feature an embossed profile portrait on gold foil-like cardboard (some collectors report finding the cards with silver cardboard). The player's name, team and position are below the portrait - which is good, because most of the embossed portraits are otherwise unrecognizeable. There is a gold border with American players framed in blue and National Leaguers in red. The set contains 72 cards divided equally bewteen the leagues. The set provides an inexpensive way to add some interesting cards to a collection. Being special cards, many stars appear in the set.

		NR MT	EX	VG
Complete Set:		150.00	75.00	45.00
Common Player:		2.00	1.00	.60
1	Carl Yastrzemski	5.00	2.50	1.50
2	Ron Fairly	2.00	1.00	.60
3	Max Alvis	2.00	1.00	.60
4	Jim Ray Hart	2.00	1.00	.60
5	Bill Skowron	3.00	1.50	.90
6	Ed Kranepool	2.00	1.00	.60
7	Tim McCarver	3.00	1.50	.90
8	Sandy Koufax	5.00	2.50	1.50
9	Donn Clendenon	2.00	1.00	.60
10	John Romano	2.00	1.00	.60
11	Mickey Mantle	25.00	12.50	7.50
12	Joe Torre	2.50	1.25	.70
13	Al Kaline	5.00	2.50	1.50
14	Al McBean	2.00	1.00	.60
15	Don Drysdale	5.00	2.50	1.50
16	Brooks Robinson	5.00	2.50	1.50
17	Jim Bunning	2.50	1.25	.70
18	Gary Peters	2.00	1.00	.60
19	Roberto Clemente	7.50	3.75	2.25
20	Milt Pappas	2.00	1.00	.60
21	Wayne Causey	2.00	1.00	.60
22	Frank Robinson	5.00	2.50	1.50
23	Bill Mazeroski	3.00	1.50	.90
24	Diego Segui	2.00	1.00	.60
25	Jim Bouton	2.50	1.25	.70
26	Ed Mathews	5.00	2.50	1.50
27	Willie Mays	7.50	3.75	2.25
28	Ron Santo	2.50	1.25	.70
29	Boog Powell	2.50	1.25	.70
30	Ken McBride	2.00	1.00	.60
31	Leon Wagner	2.00	1.00	.60
32	John Callison	2.00	1.00	.60
33	Zoilo Versalles	2.00	1.00	.60
34	Jack Baldschun	2.00	1.00	.60
35	Ron Hunt	2.00	1.00	.60
36	Richie Allen	2.50	1.25	.70
37	Frank Malzone	2.00	1.00	.60
38	Bob Allison	2.00	1.00	.60
39	Jim Fregosi	2.00	1.00	.60
40	Billy Williams	5.00	2.50	1.50
41	Bill Freehan	2.00	1.00	.60
42	Vada Pinson	2.50	1.25	.70
43	Bill White	2.50	1.25	.70
44	Roy McMillan	2.00	1.00	.60
45	Orlando Cepeda	3.00	1.50	.90
46	Rocky Colavito	3.00	1.50	.90
47	Ken Boyer	2.50	1.25	.70
48	Dick Radatz	2.00	1.00	.60
49	Tommy Davis	2.00	1.00	.60
50	Walt Bond	2.00	1.00	.60
51	John Orsino	2.00	1.00	.60
52	Joe Christopher	2.00	1.00	.60
53	Al Spangler	2.00	1.00	.60
54	Jim King	2.00	1.00	.60
55	Mickey Lolich	2.50	1.25	.70
56	Harmon Killebrew	5.00	2.50	1.50
57	Bob Shaw	2.00	1.00	.60
58	Ernie Banks	5.00	2.50	1.50
59	Hank Aaron	7.50	3.75	2.25
60	Chuck Hinton	2.00	1.00	.60
61	Bob Aspromonte	2.00	1.00	.60
62	Lee Maye	2.00	1.00	.60
63	Joe Cunningham	2.00	1.00	.60
64	Pete Ward	2.00	1.00	.60
65	Bobby Richardson	2.50	1.25	.70
66	Dean Chance	2.00	1.00	.60
67	Dick Ellsworth	2.00	1.00	.60
68	Jim Maloney	2.00	1.00	.60
69	Bob Gibson	5.00	2.50	1.50
70	Earl Battey	2.00	1.00	.60
71	Tony Kubek	2.50	1.25	.70
72	Jack Kralick	2.00	1.00	.60

1965 Topps Transfers

Issued as strips of three players each as inserts in 1965, the Topps Transfers were 2" by 3" portraits of players. The transfers have blue or red bands at the top and bottom with the team name and position in the top band and the player's name in the bottom. As is so often the case, the superstars in the transfer set can be quite expensive, but like many of Topps non-card products, the transfers are neither terribly expensive or popular today.

		NR MT	EX	VG
Complete Set:		400.00	200.00	120.00
Common Player:		5.00	2.50	1.50
(1)	Hank Aaron	25.00	12.50	7.50
(2)	Richie Allen	5.00	2.50	1.50
(3)	Bob Allison	5.00	2.50	1.50
(4)	Max Alvis	5.00	2.50	1.50
(5)	Luis Aparicio	6.00	3.00	1.75
(6)	Bob Aspromonte	5.00	2.50	1.50
(7)	Walt Bond	5.00	2.50	1.50
(8)	Jim Bouton	5.00	2.50	1.50
(9)	Ken Boyer	5.00	2.50	1.50
(10)	Jim Bunning	5.00	2.50	1.50
(11)	John Callison	5.00	2.50	1.50
(12)	Rico Carty	5.00	2.50	1.50
(13)	Wayne Causey	5.00	2.50	1.50
(14)	Orlando Cepeda	6.00	3.00	1.75
(15)	Bob Chance	5.00	2.50	1.50
(16)	Dean Chance	5.00	2.50	1.50
(17)	Joe Christopher	5.00	2.50	1.50
(18)	Roberto Clemente	25.00	12.50	7.50
(19)	Rocky Colavito	6.00	3.00	1.75
(20)	Tony Conigliaro	5.00	2.50	1.50
(21)	Tommy Davis	5.00	2.50	1.50
(22)	Don Drysdale	10.00	5.00	3.00
(23)	Bill Freehan	5.00	2.50	1.50
(24)	Jim Fregosi	5.00	2.50	1.50
(25)	Bob Gibson	10.00	5.00	3.00
(26)	Dick Groat	5.00	2.50	1.50
(27)	Tom Haller	5.00	2.50	1.50
(28)	Chuck Hinton	5.00	2.50	1.50
(29)	Elston Howard	5.00	2.50	1.50
(30)	Ron Hunt	5.00	2.50	1.50
(31)	Al Jackson	5.00	2.50	1.50
(32)	Al Kaline	10.00	5.00	3.00
(33)	Harmon Killebrew	10.00	5.00	3.00
(34)	Jim King	5.00	2.50	1.50
(35)	Ron Kline	5.00	2.50	1.50
(36)	Bobby Knoop	5.00	2.50	1.50
(37)	Sandy Koufax	10.00	5.00	3.00
(38)	Ed Kranepool	5.00	2.50	1.50
(39)	Jim Maloney	5.00	2.50	1.50
(40)	Mickey Mantle	60.00	30.00	18.00
(41)	Juan Marichal	10.00	5.00	3.00
(42)	Lee Maye	5.00	2.50	1.50
(43)	Willie Mays	25.00	12.50	7.50
(44)	Bill Mazeroski	6.00	3.00	1.75
(45)	Tony Oliva	6.00	3.00	1.75
(46)	Jim O'Toole	5.00	2.50	1.50
(47)	Milt Pappas	5.00	2.50	1.50
(48)	Camilo Pascual	5.00	2.50	1.50
(49)	Gary Peters	5.00	2.50	1.50
(50)	Vada Pinson	5.00	2.50	1.50
(51)	Juan Pizarro	5.00	2.50	1.50
(52)	Boog Powell	5.00	2.50	1.50
(53)	Dick Radatz	5.00	2.50	1.50
(54)	Bobby Richardson	5.00	2.50	1.50
(55)	Brooks Robinson	10.00	5.00	3.00
(56)	Frank Robinson	10.00	5.00	3.00
(57)	Bob Rodgers	5.00	2.50	1.50
(58)	John Roseboro	5.00	2.50	1.50
(59)	Ron Santo	5.00	2.50	1.50
(60)	Diego Segui	5.00	2.50	1.50
(61)	Bill Skowron	5.00	2.50	1.50
(62)	Al Spangler	5.00	2.50	1.50
(63)	Dick Stuart	5.00	2.50	1.50
(64)	Luis Tiant	5.00	2.50	1.50
(65)	Joe Torre	5.00	2.50	1.50
(66)	Bob Veale	5.00	2.50	1.50
(67)	Leon Wagner	5.00	2.50	1.50
(68)	Pete Ward	5.00	2.50	1.50
(69)	Bill White	5.00	2.50	1.50
(70)	Dave Wickersham	5.00	2.50	1.50
(71)	Billy Williams	10.00	5.00	3.00
(72)	Carl Yastrzemski	25.00	12.50	7.50

1966 Topps

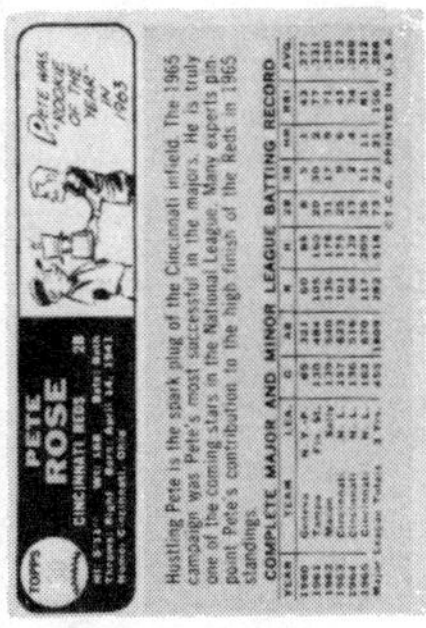

In 1966, Topps produced another 598-card set. The 2-1/2" by 3-1/2" cards feature the almost traditional color photograph with a diagonal strip in the upper left-hand corner carrying the team name. A band at the bottom carries the player's name and position. Multi-player cards returned in 1966 after having had a year's hiatus. The statistical leader cards feature the categorical leader and two runners-up. Most team managers have cards as well. The 1966 set features a handful of cards found with without a notice of the player's sale or trade to another team. Cards without the notice bring higher prices not included in the complete set prices below. Some cards in the high series (#523-598) were short-printed - produced in lesser quantities than the rest of the series. They are valued somewhat higher than the others and are indicated in the checklist by a (SP) notation following the player name.

		NR MT	EX	VG
Complete Set (598):		4750.	2375.	1425.
Common Player (1-196):		1.50	.70	.45
Common Player (197-370):		2.00	1.00	.60
Common Player (371-446):		4.00	2.00	1.25
Common Player (447-522):		8.00	4.00	2.50
Common Player (523-598):		16.00	8.00	4.75
1	Willie Mays	125.00	62.00	37.00
2	Ted Abernathy	1.50	.70	.45
3	Sam Mele	1.50	.70	.45
4	Ray Culp	1.50	.70	.45
5	Jim Fregosi	1.50	.70	.45
6	Chuck Schilling	1.50	.70	.45
7	Tracy Stallard	1.50	.70	.45
8	Floyd Robinson	1.50	.70	.45
9	Clete Boyer	2.00	1.00	.60
10	Tony Cloninger	1.50	.70	.45
11	Senators Rookies (Brant Alyea, Pete Craig)	1.50	.70	.45
12	John Tsitouris	1.50	.70	.45
13	Lou Johnson	1.50	.70	.45
14	Norm Siebern	1.50	.70	.45
15	Vern Law	1.50	.70	.45
16	Larry Brown	1.50	.70	.45
17	Johnny Stephenson	1.50	.70	.45
18	Roland Sheldon	1.50	.70	.45
19	Giants Team	5.00	2.50	1.50
20	Willie Horton	1.50	.70	.45
21	Don Nottebart	1.50	.70	.45
22	Joe Nossek	1.50	.70	.45
23	Jack Sanford	1.50	.70	.45
24	*Don Kessinger*	2.00	1.00	.60
25	Pete Ward	1.50	.70	.45
26	Ray Sadecki	1.50	.70	.45
27	Orioles Rookies (*Andy Etchebarren*, Darold Knowles)	2.00	1.00	.60
28	Phil Niekro	14.00	7.00	4.25
29	Mike Brumley	1.50	.70	.45
30	Pete Rose	40.00	20.00	12.00
31	Jack Cullen	1.50	.70	.45
32	Adolfo Phillips	1.50	.70	.45
33	Jim Pagliaroni	1.50	.70	.45
34	Checklist 1-88	5.00	2.50	1.50
35	Ron Swoboda	1.50	.70	.45
36	Catfish Hunter	18.00	9.00	5.50
37	Billy Herman	5.00	2.50	1.50
38	Ron Nischwitz	1.50	.70	.45
39	Ken Henderson	1.50	.70	.45

40	Jim Grant	1.50	.70	.45
41	Don LeJohn	1.50	.70	.45
42	Aubrey Gatewood	1.50	.70	.45
43	Don Landrum	1.50	.70	.45
44	Indians Rookies (Bill Davis, Tom Kelley)	1.50	.70	.45
45	Jim Gentile	1.50	.70	.45
46	Howie Koplitz	1.50	.70	.45
47	J.C. Martin	1.50	.70	.45
48	Paul Blair	1.50	.70	.45
49	Woody Woodward	1.50	.70	.45
50	Mickey Mantle	200.00	100.00	60.00
51	Gordon Richardson	1.50	.70	.45
52	Power Plus (Johnny Callison, Wes Covington)	2.50	1.25	.70
53	Bob Duliba	1.50	.70	.45
54	Jose Pagan	1.50	.70	.45
55	Ken Harrelson	1.50	.70	.45
56	Sandy Valdespino	1.50	.70	.45
57	Jim Lefebvre	2.00	1.00	.60
58	Dave Wickersham	1.50	.70	.45
59	Reds Team	5.00	2.50	1.50
60	Curt Flood	1.50	.70	.45
61	Bob Bolin	1.50	.70	.45
62a	Merritt Ranew (no sold statement)	36.00	18.00	11.00
62b	Merritt Ranew (with sold statement)	1.50	.70	.45
63	Jim Stewart	1.50	.70	.45
64	Bob Bruce	1.50	.70	.45
65	Leon Wagner	1.50	.70	.45
66	Al Weis	1.50	.70	.45
67	Mets Rookies (Cleon Jones, Dick Selma)	1.50	.70	.45
68	Hal Reniff	1.50	.70	.45
69	Ken Hamlin	1.50	.70	.45
70	Carl Yastrzemski	35.00	17.50	10.50
71	Frank Carpin	1.50	.70	.45
72	Tony Perez	25.00	12.50	7.50
73	Jerry Zimmerman	1.50	.70	.45
74	Don Mossi	1.50	.70	.45
75	Tommy Davis	2.50	1.25	.70
76	Red Schoendienst	5.00	2.50	1.50
77	Johnny Orsino	1.50	.70	.45
78	Frank Linzy	1.50	.70	.45
79	Joe Pepitone	2.00	1.00	.60
80	Richie Allen	3.00	1.50	.90
81	Ray Oyler	1.50	.70	.45
82	Bob Hendley	1.50	.70	.45
83	Albie Pearson	1.50	.70	.45
84	Braves Rookies (Jim Beauchamp, Dick Kelley)	1.50	.70	.45
85	Eddie Fisher	1.50	.70	.45
86	John Bateman	1.50	.70	.45
87	Dan Napoleon	1.50	.70	.45
88	Fred Whitfield	1.50	.70	.45
89	Ted Davidson	1.50	.70	.45
90	Luis Aparicio	7.50	3.75	2.25
91a	Bob Uecker (no trade statement)	65.00	32.00	19.50
91b	Bob Uecker (with trade statement)	15.00	7.50	4.50
92	Yankees Team	7.50	3.75	2.25
93	Jim Lonborg	1.50	.70	.45
94	Matty Alou	1.50	.70	.45
95	Pete Richert	1.50	.70	.45
96	Felipe Alou	2.50	1.25	.70
97	Jim Merritt	1.50	.70	.45
98	Don Demeter	1.50	.70	.45
99	Buc Belters (Donn Clendenon, Willie Stargell)	5.00	2.50	1.50
100	Sandy Koufax	95.00	47.00	28.00
101a	Checklist 89-176 (115 is Spahn)	12.00	6.00	3.50
101b	Checklist 89-176 (115 is Henry)	4.00	2.00	1.25
102	Ed Kirkpatrick	1.50	.70	.45
103a	Dick Groat (no trade statement)	25.00	12.50	7.50
103b	Dick Groat (with trade statement)	3.00	1.50	.90
104a	Alex Johnson (no trade statement)	32.00	16.00	9.50
104b	Alex Johnson (with trade statement)	1.50	.70	.45
105	Milt Pappas	1.50	.70	.45
106	Rusty Staub	3.00	1.50	.90
107	Athletics Rookies (Larry Stahl, Ron Tompkins)	1.50	.70	.45
108	Bobby Klaus	1.50	.70	.45
109	Ralph Terry	1.50	.70	.45
110	Ernie Banks	25.00	12.50	7.50
111	Gary Peters	2.00	1.00	.60
112	Manny Mota	2.00	1.00	.60
113	Hank Aguirre	2.00	1.00	.60
114	Jim Gosger	2.00	1.00	.60
115	Bill Henry	2.00	1.00	.60
116	Walt Alston	5.00	2.50	1.50
117	Jake Gibbs	2.00	1.00	.60
118	Mike McCormick	2.00	1.00	.60
119	Art Shamsky	2.00	1.00	.60
120	Harmon Killebrew	20.00	10.00	6.00
121	Ray Herbert	2.00	1.00	.60
122	Joe Gaines	2.00	1.00	.60
123	Pirates Rookies (Frank Bork, Jerry May)	2.00	1.00	.60
124	Tug McGraw	3.00	1.50	.90
125	Lou Brock	18.00	9.00	5.50
126	*Jim Palmer*	155.00	77.00	46.00
127	Ken Berry	2.00	1.00	.60
128	Jim Landis	2.00	1.00	.60
129	Jack Kralick	2.00	1.00	.60
130	Joe Torre	2.25	1.25	.70
131	Angels Team	3.00	1.50	.90
132	Orlando Cepeda	8.00	4.00	2.50
133	Don McMahon	2.00	1.00	.60
134	Wes Parker	2.00	1.00	.60
135	Dave Morehead	2.00	1.00	.60
136	Woody Held	2.00	1.00	.60
137	Pat Corrales	2.00	1.00	.60
138	Roger Repoz	2.00	1.00	.60
139	Cubs Rookies (Byron Browne, Don Young)	2.00	1.00	.60
140	Jim Maloney	2.00	1.00	.60
141	Tom McCraw	2.00	1.00	.60
142	Don Dennis	2.00	1.00	.60
143	Jose Tartabull	2.00	1.00	.60
144	Don Schwall	2.00	1.00	.60
145	Bill Freehan	2.00	1.00	.60
146	George Altman	2.00	1.00	.60
147	Lum Harris	2.00	1.00	.60
148	Bob Johnson	2.00	1.00	.60
149	Dick Nen	2.00	1.00	.60
150	Rocky Colavito	8.00	4.00	2.50
151	Gary Wagner	2.00	1.00	.60
152	Frank Malzone	2.00	1.00	.60
153	Rico Carty	2.50	1.25	.70
154	Chuck Hiller	2.00	1.00	.60
155	Marcelino Lopez	2.00	1.00	.60
156	D P Combo (Hal Lanier, Dick Schofield)	2.50	1.25	.70
157	Rene Lachemann	2.00	1.00	.60
158	Jim Brewer	2.00	1.00	.60
159	Chico Ruiz	2.00	1.00	.60
160	Whitey Ford	22.00	11.00	6.50
161	Jerry Lumpe	2.00	1.00	.60
162	Lee Maye	2.00	1.00	.60
163	Tito Francona	2.00	1.00	.60
164	White Sox Rookies (Tommie Agee, Marv Staehle)	2.00	1.00	.60
165	Don Lock	2.00	1.00	.60
166	Chris Krug	2.00	1.00	.60
167	Boog Powell	4.00	2.00	1.25
168	Dan Osinski	2.00	1.00	.60
169	Duke Sims	2.00	1.00	.60
170	Cookie Rojas	2.00	1.00	.60
171	Nick Willhite	2.00	1.00	.60
172	Mets Team	7.00	3.50	2.00
173	Al Spangler	2.00	1.00	.60
174	Ron Taylor	2.00	1.00	.60
175	Bert Campaneris	3.00	1.50	.90
176	Jim Davenport	2.00	1.00	.60
177	Hector Lopez	2.00	1.00	.60
178	Bob Tillman	2.00	1.00	.60
179	Cardinals Rookies (Dennis Aust, Bob Tolan)	2.00	1.00	.60
180	Vada Pinson	2.50	1.25	.70
181	Al Worthington	2.00	1.00	.60
182	Jerry Lynch	2.00	1.00	.60
183a	Checklist 177-264 (large print on front)	4.00	2.00	1.25
183b	Checklist 177-264 (small print on front)	8.00	4.00	2.50
184	Denis Menke	2.00	1.00	.60
185	Bob Buhl	2.00	1.00	.60
186	Ruben Amaro	2.00	1.00	.60
187	Chuck Dressen	2.00	1.00	.60
188	Al Luplow	2.00	1.00	.60
189	John Roseboro	2.00	1.00	.60
190	Jimmie Hall	2.00	1.00	.60
191	Darrell Sutherland	2.00	1.00	.60
192	Vic Power	2.00	1.00	.60
193	Dave McNally	2.00	1.00	.60
194	Senators Team	8.00	4.00	2.50
195	Joe Morgan	29.00	14.50	8.75
196	Don Pavletich	2.00	1.00	.60
197	Sonny Siebert	2.00	1.00	.60
198	*Mickey Stanley*	2.00	1.00	.60
199	Chisox Clubbers (Floyd Robinson, Johnny Romano, Bill Skowron)	2.50	1.25	.70
200	Eddie Mathews	20.00	10.00	6.00
201	Jim Dickson	2.00	1.00	.60
202	Clay Dalrymple	2.00	1.00	.60
203	Jose Santiago	2.00	1.00	.60
204	Cubs Team	8.00	4.00	2.50
205	Tom Tresh	4.00	2.00	1.25
206	Alvin Jackson	2.00	1.00	.60
207	Frank Quilici	2.00	1.00	.60
208	Bob Miller	2.00	1.00	.60
209	Tigers Rookies (Fritz Fisher, John Hiller)	2.00	1.00	.60
210	Bill Mazeroski	4.25	2.25	1.25
211	Frank Kreutzer	2.00	1.00	.60
212	Ed Kranepool	2.00	1.00	.60
213	Fred Newman	2.00	1.00	.60
214	Tommy Harper	2.00	1.00	.60
215	N.L. Batting Leaders (Hank Aaron, Roberto Clemente, Willie Mays)	20.00	10.00	6.00
216	A.L. Batting Leaders (Vic Davalillo, Tony Oliva, Carl Yastrzemski)	8.00	4.00	2.50
217	N.L. Home Run Leaders (Willie Mays, Willie McCovey, Billy Williams)	7.50	3.75	2.25
218	A.L. Home Run Leaders (Norm Cash, Tony Conigliaro, Willie Horton)	4.00	2.00	1.25
219	N.L. RBI Leaders (Deron Johnson, Willie Mays, Frank Robinson)	7.00	3.50	2.00
220	A.L. RBI Leaders (Rocky Colavito, Willie Horton, Tony Oliva)	4.00	2.00	1.25
221	N.L. ERA Leaders (Sandy Koufax, Vern Law, Juan Marichal)	8.00	4.00	2.50
222	A.L. ERA Leaders (Eddie Fisher, Sam McDowell, Sonny Siebert)	4.00	2.00	1.25
223	N.L. Pitching Leaders (Tony Cloninger, Don Drysdale, Sandy Koufax)	8.00	4.00	2.50
224	A.L. Pitching Leaders (Jim Grant, Jim Kaat, Mel Stottlemyre)	4.00	2.00	1.25
225	N.L. Strikeout Leaders (Bob Gibson, Sandy Koufax, Bob Veale)	8.00	4.00	2.50
226	A.L. Strikeout Leaders (Mickey Lolich, Sam McDowell, Denny McLain, Sonny Siebert)	4.00	2.00	1.25
227	Russ Nixon	2.00	1.00	.60
228	Larry Dierker	2.00	1.00	.60
229	Hank Bauer	2.00	1.00	.60
230	Johnny Callison	2.00	1.00	.60
231	Floyd Weaver	2.00	1.00	.60
232	Glenn Beckert	2.00	1.00	.60
233	Dom Zanni	2.00	1.00	.60
234	Yankees Rookies (Rich Beck, Roy White)	5.00	2.50	1.50
235	Don Cardwell	2.00	1.00	.60
236	Mike Hershberger	2.00	1.00	.60
237	Billy O'Dell	2.00	1.00	.60
238	Dodgers Team	8.00	4.00	2.50
239	Orlando Pena	2.00	1.00	.60
240	Earl Battey	2.00	1.00	.60
241	Dennis Ribant	2.00	1.00	.60
242	Jesus Alou	2.00	1.00	.60
243	Nelson Briles	2.00	1.00	.60
244	Astros Rookies (Chuck Harrison, Sonny Jackson)	2.00	1.00	.60
245	John Buzhardt	2.00	1.00	.60
246	Ed Bailey	2.00	1.00	.60
247	Carl Warwick	2.00	1.00	.60
248	Pete Mikkelsen	2.00	1.00	.60
249	Bill Rigney	2.00	1.00	.60
250	Sam Ellis	2.00	1.00	.60
251	Ed Brinkman	2.00	1.00	.60
252	Denver Lemaster	2.00	1.00	.60
253	Don Wert	2.00	1.00	.60
254	Phillies Rookies (*Fergie Jenkins*, Bill Sorrell)	100.00	50.00	30.00
255	Willie Stargell	18.00	9.00	5.50
256	Lew Krausse	2.00	1.00	.60
257	Jeff Torborg	2.00	1.00	.60
258	Dave Giusti	2.00	1.00	.60
259	Red Sox Team	8.00	4.00	2.50
260	Bob Shaw	2.00	1.00	.60
261	Ron Hansen	2.00	1.00	.60
262	Jack Hamilton	2.00	1.00	.60
263	Tom Egan	2.00	1.00	.60
264	Twins Rookies (Andy Kosco, Ted Uhlaender)	2.00	1.00	.60
265	Stu Miller	2.00	1.00	.60
266	Pedro Gonzalez	2.00	1.00	.60
267	Joe Sparma	2.00	1.00	.60
268	John Blanchard	2.00	1.00	.60
269	Don Heffner	2.00	1.00	.60
270	Claude Osteen	2.00	1.00	.60
271	Hal Lanier	2.00	1.00	.60
272	Jack Baldschun	2.00	1.00	.60
273	Astro Aces (Bob Aspromonte, Rusty Staub)	7.50	3.75	2.25
274	Buster Narum	2.00	1.00	.60
275	Tim McCarver	2.50	1.25	.70
276	Jim Bouton	3.00	1.50	.90
277	George Thomas	2.00	1.00	.60
278	Calvin Koonce	2.00	1.00	.60
279a	Checklist 265-352 (player's cap black)	8.00	4.00	2.50
279b	Checklist 265-352 (player's cap red)	4.00	2.00	1.25
280	Bobby Knoop	2.00	1.00	.60
281	Bruce Howard	2.00	1.00	.60
282	Johnny Lewis	2.00	1.00	.60
283	Jim Perry	2.00	1.00	.60
284	Bobby Wine	2.00	1.00	.60
285	Luis Tiant	4.00	2.00	1.25
286	Gary Geiger	2.00	1.00	.60
287	Jack Aker	2.00	1.00	.60
288	Dodgers Rookies (*Bill Singer*, Don Sutton)	105.00	52.00	31.00
289	Larry Sherry	2.00	1.00	.60
290	Ron Santo	5.00	2.50	1.50
291	Moe Drabowsky	2.00	1.00	.60
292	Jim Coker	2.00	1.00	.60
293	Mike Shannon	2.00	1.00	.60
294	Steve Ridzik	2.00	1.00	.60
295	Jim Hart	2.00	1.00	.60
296	Johnny Keane	2.00	1.00	.60
297	Jim Owens	2.00	1.00	.60
298	Rico Petrocelli	3.00	1.50	.90
299	Lou Burdette	2.00	1.00	.60
300	Roberto Clemente	100.00	50.00	30.00
301	Greg Bollo	2.00	1.00	.60
302	Ernie Bowman	2.00	1.00	.60
303	Indians Team	8.00	4.00	2.50
304	John Herrnstein	2.00	1.00	.60
305	Camilo Pascual	2.00	1.00	.60
306	Ty Cline	2.00	1.00	.60
307	Clay Carroll	2.00	1.00	.60
308	Tom Haller	2.00	1.00	.60
309	Diego Segui	2.00	1.00	.60
310	Frank Robinson	33.00	16.50	10.00
311	Reds Rookies (Tommy Helms, Dick Simpson)	2.00	1.00	.60
312	Bob Saverine	2.00	1.00	.60
313	Chris Zachary	2.00	1.00	.60
314	Hector Valle	2.00	1.00	.60
315	Norm Cash	4.00	2.00	1.25
316	Jack Fisher	2.00	1.00	.60
317	Dalton Jones	2.00	1.00	.60
318	Harry Walker	2.00	1.00	.60
319	Gene Freese	2.00	1.00	.60
320	Bob Gibson	22.00	11.00	6.50
321	Rick Reichardt	2.00	1.00	.60
322	Bill Faul	2.00	1.00	.60
323	Ray Barker	2.00	1.00	.60
324	John Boozer	2.00	1.00	.60
325	Vic Davalillo	2.00	1.00	.60
326	Braves Team	8.00	4.00	2.50
327	Bernie Allen	2.00	1.00	.60
328	Jerry Grote	2.00	1.00	.60
329	Pete Charton	2.00	1.00	.60
330	Ron Fairly	2.00	1.00	.60
331	Ron Herbel	2.00	1.00	.60
332	Billy Bryan	2.00	1.00	.60
333	Senators Rookies (*Joe Coleman*, Jim French)	2.00	1.00	.60
334	Marty Keough	2.00	1.00	.60
335	Juan Pizarro	2.00	1.00	.60
336	Gene Alley	2.00	1.00	.60
337	Fred Gladding	2.00	1.00	.60
338	Dal Maxvill	2.00	1.00	.60

#	Player	NR MT	EX	VG
339	Del Crandall	2.00	1.00	.60
340	Dean Chance	2.00	1.00	.60
341	Wes Westrum	2.00	1.00	.60
342	Bob Humphreys	2.00	1.00	.60
343	Joe Christopher	2.00	1.00	.60
344	Steve Blass	2.00	1.00	.60
345	Bob Allison	2.00	1.00	.60
346	Mike de la Hoz	2.00	1.00	.60
347	Phil Regan	2.00	1.00	.60
348	Orioles Team	8.00	4.00	2.50
349	Cap Peterson	2.00	1.00	.60
350	Mel Stottlemyre	3.50	1.75	1.00
351	Fred Valentine	2.00	1.00	.60
352	Bob Aspromonte	2.00	1.00	.60
353	Al McBean	2.00	1.00	.60
354	Smoky Burgess	2.00	1.00	.60
355	Wade Blasingame	2.00	1.00	.60
356	Red Sox Rookies (Owen Johnson, Ken Sanders)	2.00	1.00	.60
357	Gerry Arrigo	2.00	1.00	.60
358	Charlie Smith	2.00	1.00	.60
359	Johnny Briggs	2.00	1.00	.60
360	Ron Hunt	2.00	1.00	.60
361	Tom Satriano	2.00	1.00	.60
362	Gates Brown	2.00	1.00	.60
363	Checklist 353-429	6.00	3.00	1.75
364	Nate Oliver	2.00	1.00	.60
365	Roger Maris	55.00	27.00	16.50
366	Wayne Causey	2.00	1.00	.60
367	Mel Nelson	2.00	1.00	.60
368	Charlie Lau	2.00	1.00	.60
369	Jim King	2.00	1.00	.60
370	Chico Cardenas	2.00	1.00	.60
371	Lee Stange	4.00	2.00	1.25
372	Harvey Kuenn	4.00	2.00	1.25
373	Giants Rookies (Dick Estelle, Jack Hiatt)	4.00	2.00	1.25
374	Bob Locker	4.00	2.00	1.25
375	Donn Clendenon	4.00	2.00	1.25
376	Paul Schaal	4.00	2.00	1.25
377	Turk Farrell	4.00	2.00	1.25
378	Dick Tracewski	4.00	2.00	1.25
379	Cardinals Team	8.00	4.00	2.50
380	Tony Conigliaro	6.00	3.00	1.75
381	Hank Fischer	4.00	2.00	1.25
382	Phil Roof	4.00	2.00	1.25
383	Jackie Brandt	4.00	2.00	1.25
384	Al Downing	4.00	2.00	1.25
385	Ken Boyer	4.00	2.00	1.25
386	Gil Hodges	8.00	4.00	2.50
387	Howie Reed	4.00	2.00	1.25
388	Don Mincher	4.00	2.00	1.25
389	Jim O'Toole	4.00	2.00	1.25
390	Brooks Robinson	31.00	15.50	9.25
391	Chuck Hinton	4.00	2.00	1.25
392	Cubs Rookies (*Bill Hands*, Randy Hundley)	4.00	2.00	1.25
393	George Brunet	4.00	2.00	1.25
394	Ron Brand	4.00	2.00	1.25
395	Len Gabrielson	4.00	2.00	1.25
396	Jerry Stephenson	4.00	2.00	1.25
397	Bill White	4.00	2.00	1.25
398	Danny Cater	4.00	2.00	1.25
399	Ray Washburn	4.00	2.00	1.25
400	Zoilo Versalles	4.00	2.00	1.25
401	Ken McMullen	4.00	2.00	1.25
402	Jim Hickman	4.00	2.00	1.25
403	Fred Talbot	4.00	2.00	1.25
404	Pirates Team	8.00	4.00	2.50
405	Elston Howard	8.00	4.00	2.50
406	Joe Jay	4.00	2.00	1.25
407	John Kennedy	4.00	2.00	1.25
408	Lee Thomas	4.00	2.00	1.25
409	Billy Hoeft	4.00	2.00	1.25
410	Al Kaline	25.00	12.50	7.50
411	Gene Mauch	4.00	2.00	1.25
412	Sam Bowens	4.00	2.00	1.25
413	John Romano	4.00	2.00	1.25
414	Dan Coombs	4.00	2.00	1.25
415	Max Alvis	4.00	2.00	1.25
416	Phil Ortega	4.00	2.00	1.25
417	Angels Rookies (Jim McGlothlin, Ed Sukla)	4.00	2.00	1.25
418	Phil Gagliano	4.00	2.00	1.25
419	Mike Ryan	4.00	2.00	1.25
420	Juan Marichal	8.00	4.00	2.50
421	Roy McMillan	4.00	2.00	1.25
422	Ed Charles	4.00	2.00	1.25
423	Ernie Broglio	4.00	2.00	1.25
424	*Lee May*, Darrell Osteen	8.50	4.25	2.50
425	Bob Veale	4.00	2.00	1.25
426	White Sox Team	8.00	4.00	2.50
427	John Miller	4.00	2.00	1.25
428	Sandy Alomar	4.00	2.00	1.25
429	Bill Monbouquette	4.00	2.00	1.25
430	Don Drysdale	22.00	11.00	6.50
431	Walt Bond	4.00	2.00	1.25
432	Bob Heffner	4.00	2.00	1.25
433	Alvin Dark	4.00	2.00	1.25
434	Willie Kirkland	4.00	2.00	1.25
435	Jim Bunning	8.00	4.00	2.50
436	Julian Javier	4.00	2.00	1.25
437	Al Stanek	4.00	2.00	1.25
438	Willie Smith	4.00	2.00	1.25
439	Pedro Ramos	4.00	2.00	1.25
440	Deron Johnson	4.00	2.00	1.25
441	Tommie Sisk	4.00	2.00	1.25
442	Orioles Rookies (Ed Barnowski, Eddie Watt)	4.00	2.00	1.25
443	Bill Wakefield	4.00	2.00	1.25
444a	Checklist 430-506 (456 is R. Sox Rookies)	4.00	2.00	1.25
444b	Checklist 430-506 (456 is Red Sox Rookies)	8.00	4.00	2.50
445	Jim Kaat	8.00	4.00	2.50
446	Mack Jones	4.00	2.00	1.25
447	Dick Ellsworth (photo actually Ken Hubbs)	7.50	3.75	2.25
448	Eddie Stanky	7.50	3.75	2.25
449	Joe Moeller	7.50	3.75	2.25
450	Tony Oliva	9.00	4.50	2.75
451	Barry Latman	7.50	3.75	2.25
452	Joe Azcue	7.50	3.75	2.25
453	Ron Kline	7.50	3.75	2.25
454	Jerry Buchek	7.50	3.75	2.25
455	Mickey Lolich	9.00	4.50	2.75
456	Red Sox Rookies (Darrell Brandon, Joe Foy)	7.50	3.75	2.25
457	Joe Gibbon	7.50	3.75	2.25
458	Manny Jiminez (Jimenez)	7.50	3.75	2.25
459	Bill McCool	7.50	3.75	2.25
460	Curt Blefary	7.50	3.75	2.25
461	Roy Face	7.50	3.75	2.25
462	Bob Rodgers	7.50	3.75	2.25
463	Phillies Team	11.00	5.50	3.25
464	Larry Bearnarth	7.50	3.75	2.25
465	Don Buford	7.50	3.75	2.25
466	Ken Johnson	7.50	3.75	2.25
467	Vic Roznovsky	7.50	3.75	2.25
468	Johnny Podres	9.00	4.50	2.75
469	Yankees Rookies (*Bobby Murcer*, Dooley Womack)	30.00	15.00	9.00
470	Sam McDowell	7.50	3.75	2.25
471	Bob Skinner	7.50	3.75	2.25
472	Terry Fox	7.50	3.75	2.25
473	Rich Rollins	7.50	3.75	2.25
474	Dick Schofield	7.50	3.75	2.25
475	Dick Radatz	7.50	3.75	2.25
476	Bobby Bragan	7.50	3.75	2.25
477	Steve Barber	7.50	3.75	2.25
478	Tony Gonzalez	7.50	3.75	2.25
479	Jim Hannan	7.50	3.75	2.25
480	Dick Stuart	7.50	3.75	2.25
481	Bob Lee	7.50	3.75	2.25
482	Cubs Rookies (John Boccabella, Dave Dowling)	7.50	3.75	2.25
483	Joe Nuxhall	7.50	3.75	2.25
484	Wes Covington	7.50	3.75	2.25
485	Bob Bailey	7.50	3.75	2.25
486	Tommy John	13.00	6.50	4.00
487	Al Ferrara	7.50	3.75	2.25
488	George Banks	7.50	3.75	2.25
489	Curt Simmons	7.50	3.75	2.25
490	Bobby Richardson	12.00	6.00	3.50
491	Dennis Bennett	7.50	3.75	2.25
492	Athletics Team	12.50	6.25	3.75
493	Johnny Klippstein	7.50	3.75	2.25
494	Gordon Coleman	7.50	3.75	2.25
495	Dick McAuliffe	7.50	3.75	2.25
496	Lindy McDaniel	7.50	3.75	2.25
497	Chris Cannizzaro	7.50	3.75	2.25
498	Pirates Rookies (*Woody Fryman*, Luke Walker)	7.50	3.75	2.25
499	Wally Bunker	7.50	3.75	2.25
500	Hank Aaron	100.00	50.00	30.00
501	John O'Donoghue	7.50	3.75	2.25
502	Lenny Green	7.50	3.75	2.25
503	Steve Hamilton	7.50	3.75	2.25
504	Grady Hatton	7.50	3.75	2.25
505	Jose Cardenal	7.50	3.75	2.25
506	Bo Belinsky	7.50	3.75	2.25
507	John Edwards	7.50	3.75	2.25
508	*Steve Hargan*	7.50	3.75	2.25
509	Jake Wood	7.50	3.75	2.25
510	Hoyt Wilhelm	13.50	6.75	4.00
511	Giants Rookies (Bob Barton, Tito Fuentes)	7.50	3.75	2.25
512	Dick Stigman	7.50	3.75	2.25
513	Camilo Carreon	7.50	3.75	2.25
514	Hal Woodeshick	7.50	3.75	2.25
515	Frank Howard	10.00	5.00	3.00
516	Eddie Bressoud	7.50	3.75	2.25
517a	Checklist 507-598 (529 is W. Sox Rookies)	9.00	4.50	2.75
517b	Checklist 506-598 (529 is White Sox Rookies)	10.00	5.00	3.00
518	Braves Rookies (Herb Hippauf, Arnie Umbach)	7.50	3.75	2.25
519	Bob Friend	7.50	3.75	2.25
520	Jim Wynn	7.50	3.75	2.25
521	John Wyatt	7.50	3.75	2.25
522	Phil Linz	7.50	3.75	2.25
523	Bob Sadowski	19.00	9.50	5.75
524	Giants Rookies (Ollie Brown) (SP, Don Mason)	24.00	12.00	7.25
525	Gary Bell (SP)	24.00	12.00	7.25
526	Twins Team	67.00	33.00	20.00
527	Julio Navarro	19.00	9.50	5.75
528	Jesse Gonder (SP)	24.00	12.00	7.25
529	White Sox Rookies (*Lee Elia*, Dennis Higgins, Bill Voss)	19.00	9.50	5.75
530	Robin Roberts	42.00	21.00	12.50
531	Joe Cunningham	19.00	9.50	5.75
532	Aurelio Monteagudo (SP)	24.00	12.00	7.25
533	Jerry Adair (SP)	24.00	12.00	7.25
534	Mets Rookies (Dave Eilers, Rob Gardner)	19.00	9.50	5.75
535	Willie Davis	30.00	15.00	9.00
536	Dick Egan	19.00	9.50	5.75
537	Herman Franks	19.00	9.50	5.75
538	Bob Allen (SP)	24.00	12.00	7.25
539	Astros Rookies (Bill Heath, Carroll Sembera)	19.00	9.50	5.75
540	Denny McLain	50.00	25.00	15.00
541	Gene Oliver (SP)	24.00	12.00	7.25
542	George Smith	19.00	9.50	5.75
543	Roger Craig	45.00	22.00	13.50
544	Cardinals Rookies (Joe Hoerner) (SP, George Kernek, Jimmy Williams)	24.00	12.00	7.25
545	Dick Green (SP)	24.00	12.00	7.25
546	Dwight Siebler	19.00	9.50	5.75
547	*Horace Clarke* (SP)	42.00	21.00	12.50
548	Gary Kroll (SP)	24.00	12.00	7.25
549	Senators Rookies (Al Closter, Casey Cox)	19.00	9.50	5.75
550	Willie McCovey	115.00	57.00	34.00
551	Bob Purkey (SP)	24.00	12.00	7.25
552	Birdie Tebbetts (SP)	24.00	12.00	7.25
553	Major League Rookies (Pat Garrett, Jackie Warner)	19.00	9.50	5.75
554	Jim Northrup (SP)	24.00	12.00	7.25
555	Ron Perranoski (SP)	24.00	12.00	7.25
556	Mel Queen (SP)	24.00	12.00	7.25
557	Felix Mantilla (SP)	24.00	12.00	7.25
558	Red Sox Rookies (Guido Grilli, Pete Magrini, George Scott)	30.00	15.00	9.00
559	Roberto Pena (SP)	24.00	12.00	7.25
560	Joel Horlen	19.00	9.50	5.75
561	Choo Choo Coleman	32.00	16.00	9.50
562	Russ Snyder	19.00	9.50	5.75
563	Twins Rookies (Pete Cimino, Cesar Tovar)	19.00	9.50	5.75
564	Bob Chance (SP)	24.00	12.00	7.25
565	Jimmy Piersall	35.00	17.50	10.50
566	Mike Cuellar	30.00	15.00	9.00
567	Dick Howser	30.00	15.00	9.00
568	Athletics Rookies (Paul Lindblad, Ron Stone)	19.00	9.50	5.75
569	Orlando McFarlane (SP)	24.00	12.00	7.25
570	Art Mahaffey (SP)	24.00	12.00	7.25
571	Dave Roberts (SP)	24.00	12.00	7.25
572	Bob Priddy	19.00	9.50	5.75
573	Derrell Griffith	19.00	9.50	5.75
574	Mets Rookies (Bill Hepler, Bill Murphy)	19.00	9.50	5.75
575	Earl Wilson	19.00	9.50	5.75
576	Dave Nicholson (SP)	24.00	12.00	7.25
577	Jack Lamabe (SP)	24.00	12.00	7.25
578	Chi Chi Olivo (SP)	24.00	12.00	7.25
579	Orioles Rookies (Frank Bertaina, Gene Brabender, Dave Johnson)	17.50	8.75	5.25
580	Billy Williams	80.00	40.00	24.00
581	Tony Martinez	19.00	9.50	5.75
582	Garry Roggenburk	19.00	9.50	5.75
583	Tigers Team	150.00	75.00	45.00
584	Yankees Rookies (Frank Fernandez, Fritz Peterson)	19.00	9.50	5.75
585	Tony Taylor	19.00	9.50	5.75
586	Claude Raymond (SP)	24.00	12.00	7.25
587	Dick Bertell	19.00	9.50	5.75
588	Athletics Rookies (Chuck Dobson, Ken Suarez)	19.00	9.50	5.75
589	Lou Klimchock	26.00	13.00	7.75
590	Bill Skowron	35.00	17.50	10.50
591	N.L. Rookies (*Grant Jackson*, Bart Shirley)	26.00	13.00	7.75
592	Andre Rodgers	19.00	9.50	5.75
593	Doug Camilli (SP)	24.00	12.00	7.25
594	Chico Salmon	19.00	9.50	5.75
595	Larry Jackson	19.00	9.50	5.75
596	Astros Rookies (*Nate Colbert*, Greg Sims)	25.00	12.50	7.50
597	John Sullivan	19.00	9.50	5.75
598	Gaylord Perry	225.00	112.00	67.00

1966 Topps Rub-Offs

Returning to a concept last tried in 1961, Topps tried an expanded version of Rub-Offs in 1966. Measuring 2-1/16" by 3," the Rub-Offs are in vertical format for the 100 players and horizontal for the 20 team pennants. The player Rub-Offs feature a color photo.

		NR MT	EX	VG
	Complete Set:	400.00	200.00	120.00
	Common Player:	2.00	1.00	.60
(1)	Hank Aaron	10.00	5.00	3.00
(2)	Jerry Adair	2.00	1.00	.60
(3)	Richie Allen	2.50	1.25	.70
(4)	Jesus Alou	2.00	1.00	.60
(5)	Max Alvis	2.00	1.00	.60
(6)	Bob Aspromonte	2.00	1.00	.60
(7)	Ernie Banks	6.00	3.00	1.75
(8)	Earl Battey	2.00	1.00	.60
(9)	Curt Blefary	2.00	1.00	.60
(10)	Ken Boyer	2.50	1.25	.70
(11)	Bob Bruce	2.00	1.00	.60
(12)	Jim Bunning	3.50	1.75	1.00
(13)	Johnny Callison	2.00	1.00	.60
(14)	Bert Campaneris	2.50	1.25	.70
(15)	Jose Cardenal	2.00	1.00	.60
(16)	Dean Chance	2.00	1.00	.60
(17)	Ed Charles	2.00	1.00	.60
(18)	Bob Clemente	10.00	5.00	3.00
(19)	Tony Cloninger	2.00	1.00	.60
(20)	Rocky Colavito	4.00	2.00	1.25
(21)	Tony Conigliaro	2.50	1.25	.70
(22)	Vic Davalillo	2.00	1.00	.60

(23)	Willie Davis	2.00	1.00	.60
(24)	Don Drysdale	5.00	2.50	1.50
(25)	Sammy Ellis	2.00	1.00	.60
(26)	Dick Ellsworth	2.00	1.00	.60
(27)	Ron Fairly	2.00	1.00	.60
(28)	Dick Farrell	2.00	1.00	.60
(29)	Eddie Fisher	2.00	1.00	.60
(30)	Jack Fisher	2.00	1.00	.60
(31)	Curt Flood	2.00	1.00	.60
(32)	Whitey Ford	5.00	2.50	1.50
(33)	Bill Freehan	2.00	1.00	.60
(34)	Jim Fregosi	2.00	1.00	.60
(35)	Bob Gibson	5.00	2.50	1.50
(36)	Jim Grant	2.00	1.00	.60
(37)	Jimmie Hall	2.00	1.00	.60
(38)	Ken Harrelson	2.00	1.00	.60
(39)	Jim Hart	2.00	1.00	.60
(40)	Joel Horlen	2.00	1.00	.60
(41)	Willie Horton	2.00	1.00	.60
(42)	Frank Howard	2.50	1.25	.70
(43)	Deron Johnson	2.00	1.00	.60
(44)	Al Kaline	6.00	3.00	1.75
(45)	Harmon Killebrew	5.00	2.50	1.50
(46)	Bobby Knoop	2.00	1.00	.60
(47)	Sandy Koufax	7.00	3.50	2.00
(48)	Ed Kranepool	2.00	1.00	.60
(49)	Gary Kroll	2.00	1.00	.60
(50)	Don Landrum	2.00	1.00	.60
(51)	Vernon Law	2.00	1.00	.60
(52)	Johnny Lewis	2.00	1.00	.60
(53)	Don Lock	2.00	1.00	.60
(54)	Mickey Lolich	2.50	1.25	.70
(55)	Jim Maloney	2.00	1.00	.60
(56)	Felix Mantilla	2.00	1.00	.60
(57)	Mickey Mantle	40.00	20.00	12.00
(58)	Juan Marichal	5.00	2.50	1.50
(59)	Ed Mathews	6.00	3.00	1.75
(60)	Willie Mays	10.00	5.00	3.00
(61)	Bill Mazeroski	3.00	1.50	.90
(62)	Dick McAuliffe	2.00	1.00	.60
(63)	Tim McCarver	2.50	1.25	.70
(64)	Willie McCovey	6.00	3.00	1.75
(65)	Sammy McDowell	2.00	1.00	.60
(66)	Ken McMullen	2.00	1.00	.60
(67)	Denis Menke	2.00	1.00	.60
(68)	Bill Monbouquette	2.00	1.00	.60
(69)	Joe Morgan	5.00	2.50	1.50
(70)	Fred Newman	2.00	1.00	.60
(71)	John O'Donoghue	2.00	1.00	.60
(72)	Tony Oliva	2.50	1.25	.70
(73)	Johnny Orsino	2.00	1.00	.60
(74)	Phil Ortega	2.00	1.00	.60
(75)	Milt Pappas	2.00	1.00	.60
(76)	Dick Radatz	2.00	1.00	.60
(77)	Bobby Richardson	2.50	1.25	.70
(78)	Pete Richert	2.00	1.00	.60
(79)	Brooks Robinson	6.00	3.00	1.75
(80)	Floyd Robinson	2.00	1.00	.60
(81)	Frank Robinson	6.00	3.00	1.75
(82)	Cookie Rojas	2.00	1.00	.60
(83)	Pete Rose	20.00	10.00	6.00
(84)	John Roseboro	2.00	1.00	.60
(85)	Ron Santo	2.50	1.25	.70
(86)	Bill Skowron	2.50	1.25	.70
(87)	Willie Stargell	6.00	3.00	1.75
(88)	Mel Stottlemyre	2.00	1.00	.60
(89)	Dick Stuart	2.00	1.00	.60
(90)	Ron Swoboda	2.00	1.00	.60
(91)	Fred Talbot	2.00	1.00	.60
(92)	Ralph Terry	2.00	1.00	.60
(93)	Joe Torre	2.00	1.00	.60
(94)	Tom Tresh	2.00	1.00	.60
(95)	Bob Veale	2.00	1.00	.60
(96)	Pete Ward	2.00	1.00	.60
(97)	Bill White	2.50	1.25	.70
(98)	Billy Williams	5.00	2.50	1.50
(99)	Jim Wynn	2.00	1.00	.60
(100)	Carl Yastrzemski	6.00	3.00	1.75
(101)	Angels Pennant	2.00	1.00	.60
(102)	Astros Pennant	2.00	1.00	.60
(103)	Athletics Pennant	2.00	1.00	.60
(104)	Braves Pennant	2.00	1.00	.60
(105)	Cards Pennant	2.00	1.00	.60
(106)	Cubs Pennant	2.00	1.00	.60
(107)	Dodgers Pennant	2.00	1.00	.60
(108)	Giants Pennant	2.00	1.00	.60
(109)	Indians Pennant	2.00	1.00	.60
(110)	Mets Pennant	2.00	1.00	.60
(111)	Orioles Pennant	2.00	1.00	.60
(112)	Phillies Pennant	2.00	1.00	.60
(113)	Pirates Pennant	2.00	1.00	.60
(114)	Red Sox Pennant	2.00	1.00	.60
(115)	Reds Pennant	2.00	1.00	.60
(116)	Senators Pennant	2.00	1.00	.60
(117)	Tigers Pennant	2.00	1.00	.60
(118)	Twins Pennant	2.00	1.00	.60
(119)	White Sox Pennant	2.00	1.00	.60
(120)	Yankees Pennant	2.00	1.00	.60

1967 Topps

This 609-card set of 2-1/2" by 3-1/2" cards marked the largest set up to that time for Topps. Card fronts feature large color photographs bordered by white. The player's name and position are printed at the top with the team at the bottom. Across the front of the card with the exception of #254 (Milt Pappas) there is a facsimile autograph. The backs were the first to be done vertically, although they continued to carry familiar statistical and biographical information. The only subsets are statistical leaders and World Series highlights. Rookie cards are done by team or league with two players per card. The high numbers (#'s 534-609) in '67 are quite scarce, and while it is known that some are even scarcer, by virtue of having been short-printed in relation to the rest of the series, there is no general agreement on which cards are involved. Cards in the high series which are generally believed to have been double-printed - and thus worth somewhat less than the other cards in the series - and indicated in the checklist by a (DP) notation following the player name.

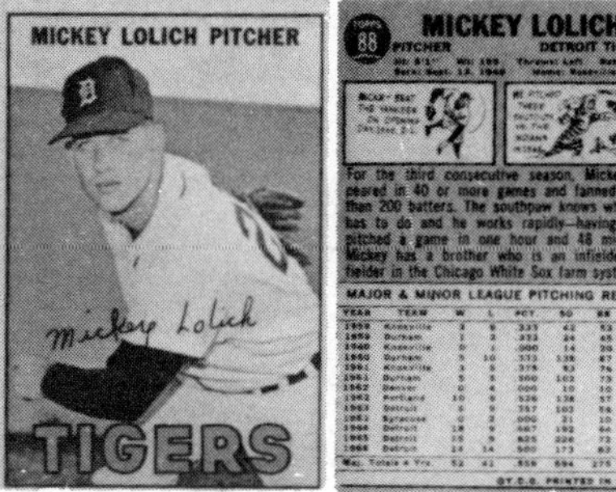

	NR MT	EX	VG
Complete Set (609):	5500.	2750.	1650.
Common Player (1-196):	1.50	.70	.45
Common Player (197-370):	2.00	1.00	.60
Common Player (371-457):	3.00	1.50	.90
Common Player (458-533):	7.00	3.50	2.00
Common Player (534-609):	12.00	6.00	3.50

		NR MT	EX	VG
1	The Champs (Hank Bauer, Brooks Robinson, Frank Robinson)	20.00	10.00	6.00
2	Jack Hamilton	1.50	.70	.45
3	Duke Sims	1.50	.70	.45
4	Hal Lanier	1.50	.70	.45
5	Whitey Ford	17.00	8.50	5.00
6	Dick Simpson	1.50	.70	.45
7	Don McMahon	1.50	.70	.45
8	Chuck Harrison	1.50	.70	.45
9	Ron Hansen	1.50	.70	.45
10	Matty Alou	1.50	.70	.45
11	Barry Moore	1.50	.70	.45
12	Dodgers Rookies (Jimmy Campanis, Bill Singer)	2.50	1.25	.70
13	Joe Sparma	1.50	.70	.45
14	Phil Linz	1.50	.70	.45
15	Earl Battey	1.50	.70	.45
16	Bill Hands	1.50	.70	.45
17	Jim Gosger	1.50	.70	.45
18	Gene Oliver	1.50	.70	.45
19	Jim McGlothlin	1.50	.70	.45
20	Orlando Cepeda	10.00	5.00	3.00
21	Dave Bristol	1.50	.70	.45
22	Gene Brabender	1.50	.70	.45
23	Larry Elliot	1.50	.70	.45
24	Bob Allen	1.50	.70	.45
25	Elston Howard	3.00	1.50	.90
26a	Bob Priddy (no trade statement)	35.00	17.50	10.50
26b	Bob Priddy (with trade statement)	1.50	.70	.45
27	Bob Saverine	1.50	.70	.45
28	Barry Latman	1.50	.70	.45
29	Tommy McCraw	1.50	.70	.45
30	Al Kaline	15.00	7.50	4.50
31	Jim Brewer	1.50	.70	.45
32	Bob Bailey	1.50	.70	.45
33	*Sal Bando*, Randy Schwartz	4.50	2.25	1.25
34	Pete Cimino	1.50	.70	.45
35	Rico Carty	1.50	.70	.45
36	Bob Tillman	1.50	.70	.45
37	Rick Wise	1.50	.70	.45
38	Bob Johnson	1.50	.70	.45
39	Curt Simmons	1.50	.70	.45
40	Rick Reichardt	1.50	.70	.45
41	Joe Hoerner	1.50	.70	.45
42	Mets Team	5.00	2.50	1.50
43	Chico Salmon	1.50	.70	.45
44	Joe Nuxhall	1.50	.70	.45
45a	Roger Maris (Cards on front)	35.00	17.50	10.50
45b	Roger maris (Yankees on front, blank-back proof)	500.00	250.00	150.00
46	Lindy McDaniel	1.50	.70	.45
47	Ken McMullen	1.50	.70	.45
48	Bill Freehan	1.50	.70	.45
49	Roy Face	1.50	.70	.45
50	Tony Oliva	4.00	2.00	1.25
51	Astros Rookies (Dave Adlesh, Wes Bales)	1.50	.70	.45
52	Dennis Higgins	1.50	.70	.45
53	Clay Dalrymple	1.50	.70	.45
54	Dick Green	1.50	.70	.45
55	Don Drysdale	13.50	6.75	4.00
56	Jose Tartabull	1.50	.70	.45
57	*Pat Jarvis*	1.50	.70	.45
58	Paul Schaal	1.50	.70	.45
59	Ralph Terry	1.50	.70	.45
60	Luis Aparicio	6.00	3.00	1.75
61	Gordy Coleman	1.50	.70	.45
62	Checklist 1-109 (Frank Robinson)	5.00	2.50	1.50
63	Cards Clubbers (Lou Brock, Curt Flood)	13.00	6.50	4.00
64	Fred Valentine	1.50	.70	.45
65	Tom Haller	1.50	.70	.45
66	Manny Mota	1.50	.70	.45
67	Ken Berry	1.50	.70	.45
68	Bob Buhl	1.50	.70	.45
69	Vic Davalillo	1.50	.70	.45
70	Ron Santo	2.00	1.00	.60
71	Camilo Pascual	1.50	.70	.45
72	Tigers Rookies (George Korince, John Matchick)	1.50	.70	.45
73	Rusty Staub	2.50	1.25	.70
74	Wes Stock	1.50	.70	.45
75	George Scott	2.50	1.25	.70
76	Jim Barbieri	1.50	.70	.45
77	Dooley Womack	1.50	.70	.45
78	Pat Corrales	1.50	.70	.45
79	Bubba Morton	1.50	.70	.45
80	Jim Maloney	1.50	.70	.45
81	Eddie Stanky	1.50	.70	.45
82	Steve Barber	1.50	.70	.45
83	Ollie Brown	1.50	.70	.45
84	Tommie Sisk	1.50	.70	.45
85	Johnny Callison	1.50	.70	.45
86a	Mike McCormick (no trade statement)	20.00	10.00	6.00
86b	Mike McCormick (with trade statement)	1.50	.70	.45
87	George Altman	1.50	.70	.45
88	Mickey Lolich	4.00	2.00	1.25
89	*Felix Millan*	1.50	.70	.45
90	Jim Nash	1.50	.70	.45
91	Johnny Lewis	1.50	.70	.45
92	Ray Washburn	1.50	.70	.45
93	Yankees Rookies (*Stan Bahnsen*, Bobby Murcer)	3.50	1.75	1.00
94	Ron Fairly	1.50	.70	.45
95	Sonny Siebert	1.50	.70	.45
96	Art Shamsky	1.50	.70	.45
97	Mike Cuellar	1.50	.70	.45
98	Rich Rollins	1.50	.70	.45
99	Lee Stange	1.50	.70	.45
100	Frank Robinson	18.00	9.00	5.50
101	Ken Johnson	1.50	.70	.45
102	Phillies Team	5.00	2.50	1.50
103a	Checklist 110-196 (Mickey Mantle) (170 is D McAuliffe)	15.00	7.50	4.50
103b	Checklist 110-196 (Mickey mantle) (170 is D. McAuliffe)	10.00	5.00	3.00
104	Minnie Rojas	1.50	.70	.45
105	Ken Boyer	2.00	1.00	.60
106	Randy Hundley	1.50	.70	.45
107	Joel Horlen	1.50	.70	.45
108	Alex Johnson	1.50	.70	.45
109	Tribe Thumpers (Rocky Colavito, Leon Wagner)	2.50	1.25	.70
110	Jack Aker	1.50	.70	.45
111	John Kennedy	2.50	1.25	.70
112	Dave Wickersham	2.50	1.25	.70
113	Dave Nicholson	2.50	1.25	.70
114	Jack Baldschun	2.50	1.25	.70
115	Paul Casanova	2.50	1.25	.70
116	Herman Franks	2.50	1.25	.70
117	Darrell Brandon	2.50	1.25	.70
118	Bernie Allen	2.50	1.25	.70
119	Wade Blasingame	2.50	1.25	.70
120	Floyd Robinson	2.50	1.25	.70
121	Ed Bressoud	2.50	1.25	.70
122	George Brunet	2.50	1.25	.70
123	Pirates Rookies (Jim Price, Luke Walker)	2.50	1.25	.70
124	Jim Stewart	2.50	1.25	.70
125	Moe Drabowsky	2.50	1.25	.70
126	Tony Taylor	2.50	1.25	.70
127	John O'Donoghue	2.50	1.25	.70
128	Ed Spiezio	2.50	1.25	.70
129	Phil Roof	2.50	1.25	.70
130	Phil Regan	2.50	1.25	.70
131	Yankees Team	7.50	3.75	2.25
132	Ozzie Virgil	2.50	1.25	.70
133	Ron Kline	2.50	1.25	.70
134	Gates Brown	2.50	1.25	.70
135	Deron Johnson	2.50	1.25	.70
136	Carroll Sembera	2.50	1.25	.70
137	Twins Rookies (Ron Clark, Jim Ollom)	2.50	1.25	.70
138	Dick Kelley	2.50	1.25	.70
139	Dalton Jones	2.50	1.25	.70
140	Willie Stargell	20.00	10.00	6.00
141	John Miller	2.50	1.25	.70
142	Jackie Brandt	2.50	1.25	.70
143	Sox Sockers (Don Buford, Pete Ward)	3.00	1.50	.90
144	Bill Hepler	2.50	1.25	.70
145	Larry Brown	2.50	1.25	.70
146	Steve Carlton	100.00	50.00	30.00
147	Tom Egan	2.50	1.25	.70
148	Adolfo Phillips	2.50	1.25	.70
149	Joe Moeller	2.50	1.25	.70
150	Mickey Mantle	250.00	125.00	75.00
151	World Series Game 1 (Moe Mows Down 11)	3.50	1.75	1.00
152	World Series Game 2 (Palmer Blanks Dodgers)	5.00	2.50	1.50
153	World Series Game 3 (Blair's Homer Defeats L.A.)	3.50	1.75	1.00
154	World Series Game 4 (Orioles Win 4th Straight)	3.50	1.75	1.00
155	World Series Summary (The Winners Celebrate)	3.50	1.75	1.00
156	Ron Herbel	2.50	1.25	.70
157	Danny Cater	2.50	1.25	.70
158	Jimmy Coker	2.50	1.25	.70
159	Bruce Howard	2.50	1.25	.70
160	Willie Davis	2.50	1.25	.70
161	Dick Williams	2.50	1.25	.70
162	Billy O'Dell	2.50	1.25	.70
163	Vic Roznovsky	2.50	1.25	.70
164	Dwight Siebler	2.50	1.25	.70
165	Cleon Jones	2.50	1.25	.70

166	Eddie Mathews	10.00	5.00	3.00
167	Senators Rookies (Joe Coleman, Tim Cullen)	2.50	1.25	.70
168	Ray Culp	2.50	1.25	.70
169	Horace Clarke	2.50	1.25	.70
170	Dick McAuliffe	2.50	1.25	.70
171	Calvin Koonce	2.50	1.25	.70
172	Bill Heath	2.50	1.25	.70
173	Cardinals Team	5.00	2.50	1.50
174	Dick Radatz	2.50	1.25	.70
175	Bobby Knoop	2.50	1.25	.70
176	Sammy Ellis	2.50	1.25	.70
177	Tito Fuentes	2.50	1.25	.70
178	John Buzhardt	2.50	1.25	.70
179	Braves Rookies (Cecil Upshaw, Chas. Vaughn)	2.50	1.25	.70
180	Curt Blefary	2.50	1.25	.70
181	Terry Fox	2.50	1.25	.70
182	Ed Charles	2.50	1.25	.70
183	Jim Pagliaroni	2.50	1.25	.70
184	George Thomas	2.50	1.25	.70
185	*Ken Holtzman*	2.50	1.25	.70
186	Mets Maulers (Ed Kranepool, Ron Swoboda)	3.00	1.50	.90
187	Pedro Ramos	2.50	1.25	.70
188	Ken Harrelson	2.50	1.25	.70
189	Chuck Hinton	2.50	1.25	.70
190	Turk Farrell	2.50	1.25	.70
191a	Checklist 197-283 (Willie Mays) (214 is Dick Kelley)	12.00	6.00	3.50
191b	Checklist 197-283 (Willie Mays) (214 is Tom Kelley)	12.00	6.00	3.50
192	Fred Gladding	2.50	1.25	.70
193	Jose Cardenal	2.50	1.25	.70
194	Bob Allison	2.50	1.25	.70
195	Al Jackson	2.50	1.25	.70
196	Johnny Romano	2.50	1.25	.70
197	Ron Perranoski	2.50	1.25	.70
198	Chuck Hiller	2.50	1.25	.70
199	Billy Hitchcock	2.50	1.25	.70
200	Willie Mays	90.00	45.00	27.00
201	Hal Reniff	2.50	1.25	.70
202	Johnny Edwards	2.50	1.25	.70
203	Al McBean	2.50	1.25	.70
204	Orioles Rookies (*Mike Epstein*, Tom Phoebus)	2.50	1.25	.70
205	Dick Groat	2.50	1.25	.70
206	Dennis Bennett	2.50	1.25	.70
207	John Orsino	2.50	1.25	.70
208	Jack Lamabe	2.50	1.25	.70
209	Joe Nossek	2.50	1.25	.70
210	Bob Gibson	18.00	9.00	5.50
211	Twins Team	5.00	2.50	1.50
212	Chris Zachary	2.50	1.25	.70
213	*Jay Johnstone*	2.00	1.00	.60
214	Tom Kelley	3.00	1.50	.90
215	Ernie Banks	20.00	10.00	6.00
216	Bengal Belters (Norm Cash, Al Kaline)	7.50	3.75	2.25
217	Rob Gardner	2.50	1.25	.70
218	Wes Parker	2.50	1.25	.70
219	Clay Carroll	2.50	1.25	.70
220	Jim Hart	2.50	1.25	.70
221	Woody Fryman	2.50	1.25	.70
222	Reds Rookies (Lee May, Darrell Osteen)	2.50	1.25	.70
223	Mike Ryan	2.50	1.25	.70
224	Walt Bond	2.50	1.25	.70
225	Mel Stottlemyre	2.50	1.25	.70
226	Julian Javier	2.50	1.25	.70
227	Paul Lindblad	2.50	1.25	.70
228	Gil Hodges	5.00	2.50	1.50
229	Larry Jackson	2.50	1.25	.70
230	Boog Powell	2.50	1.25	.70
231	John Bateman	2.50	1.25	.70
232	Don Buford	2.50	1.25	.70
233	A.L. ERA Leaders (Steve Hargan, Joel Horlen, Gary Peters)	3.00	1.50	.90
234	N.L. ERA Leaders (Mike Cuellar, Sandy Koufax, Juan Marichal)	12.00	6.00	3.50
235	A.L. Pitching Leaders (Jim Kaat, Denny McLain, Earl Wilson)	3.00	1.50	.90
236	N.L. Pitching Leaders (Bob Gibson, Sandy Koufax, Juan Marichal, Gaylord Perry)	12.00	6.00	3.50
237	A.L. Strikeout Leaders (Jim Kaat, Sam McDowell, Earl Wilson)	3.00	1.50	.90
238	N.L. Strikeout Leaders (Jim Bunning, Sandy Koufax, Bob Veale)	12.00	6.00	3.50
239	A.L. Batting Leaders (Al Kaline, Tony Oliva, Frank Robinson)	12.00	6.00	3.50
240	N.L. Batting Leaders (Felipe Alou, Matty Alou, Rico Carty)	3.00	1.50	.90
241	A.L. RBI Leaders (Harmon Killebrew, Boog Powell, Frank Robinson)	4.50	2.25	1.25
242	N.L. RBI Leaders (Hank Aaron, Richie Allen, Bob Clemente)	12.00	6.00	3.50
243	A.L. Home Run Leaders (Harmon Killebrew, Boog Powell, Frank Robinson)	6.00	3.00	1.75
244	N.L. Home Run Leaders (Hank Aaron, Richie Allen, Willie Mays)	12.00	6.00	3.50
245	Curt Flood	2.50	1.25	.70
246	Jim Perry	2.50	1.25	.70
247	Jerry Lumpe	2.50	1.25	.70
248	Gene Mauch	2.50	1.25	.70
249	Nick Willhite	2.50	1.25	.70
250	Hank Aaron	80.00	40.00	24.00
251	Woody Held	2.50	1.25	.70
252	Bob Bolin	2.50	1.25	.70
253	Indians Rookies (Bill Davis, Gus Gil)	2.50	1.25	.70
254	Milt Pappas	2.50	1.25	.70
255	Frank Howard	3.00	1.50	.90
256	Bob Hendley	2.50	1.25	.70
257	Charley Smith	2.50	1.25	.70
258	Lee Maye	2.50	1.25	.70
259	Don Dennis	2.50	1.25	.70
260	Jim Lefebvre	2.50	1.25	.70
261	John Wyatt	2.50	1.25	.70
262	Athletics Team	5.00	2.50	1.50
263	Hank Aguirre	2.50	1.25	.70
264	Ron Swoboda	2.50	1.25	.70
265	Lou Burdette	2.50	1.25	.70
266	Pitt Power (Donn Clendenon, Willie Stargell)	5.00	2.50	1.50
267	Don Schwall	2.50	1.25	.70
268	John Briggs	2.50	1.25	.70
269	Don Nottebart	2.50	1.25	.70
270	Zoilo Versalles	2.50	1.25	.70
271	Eddie Watt	2.50	1.25	.70
272	Cubs Rookies (Bill Connors, Dave Dowling)	2.50	1.25	.70
273	Dick Lines	2.50	1.25	.70
274	Bob Aspromonte	2.50	1.25	.70
275	Fred Whitfield	2.50	1.25	.70
276	Bruce Brubaker	2.50	1.25	.70
277	Steve Whitaker	2.50	1.25	.70
278	Checklist 284-370 (Jim Kaat)	5.00	2.50	1.50
279	Frank Linzy	2.50	1.25	.70
280	Tony Conigliaro	3.50	1.75	1.00
281	Bob Rodgers	2.50	1.25	.70
282	Johnny Odom	2.50	1.25	.70
283	Gene Alley	2.50	1.25	.70
284	Johnny Podres	3.50	1.75	1.00
285	Lou Brock	20.00	10.00	6.00
286	Wayne Causey	2.50	1.25	.70
287	Mets Rookies (Greg Goossen, Bart Shirley)	2.50	1.25	.70
288	Denver Lemaster	2.50	1.25	.70
289	Tom Tresh	3.50	1.75	1.00
290	Bill White	2.50	1.25	.70
291	Jim Hannan	2.50	1.25	.70
292	Don Pavletich	2.50	1.25	.70
293	Ed Kirkpatrick	2.50	1.25	.70
294	Walt Alston	5.00	2.50	1.50
295	Sam McDowell	2.50	1.25	.70
296	Glenn Beckert	2.50	1.25	.70
297	Dave Morehead	2.50	1.25	.70
298	Ron Davis	2.50	1.25	.70
299	Norm Siebern	2.50	1.25	.70
300	Jim Kaat	9.00	4.50	2.75
301	Jesse Gonder	2.50	1.25	.70
302	Orioles Team	5.00	2.50	1.50
303	Gil Blanco	2.50	1.25	.70
304	Phil Gagliano	2.50	1.25	.70
305	Earl Wilson	2.50	1.25	.70
306	*Bud Harrelson*	2.50	1.25	.70
307	Jim Beauchamp	2.50	1.25	.70
308	Al Downing	2.50	1.25	.70
309	Hurlers Beware (Richie Allen, Johnny Callison)	4.00	2.00	1.25
310	Gary Peters	2.50	1.25	.70
311	Ed Brinkman	2.50	1.25	.70
312	Don Mincher	2.50	1.25	.70
313	Bob Lee	2.50	1.25	.70
314	Red Sox Rookies (*Mike Andrews*, Reggie Smith)	7.50	3.75	2.25
315	Billy Williams	12.00	6.00	3.50
316	Jack Kralick	2.50	1.25	.70
317	Cesar Tovar	2.50	1.25	.70
318	Dave Giusti	2.50	1.25	.70
319	Paul Blair	2.50	1.25	.70
320	Gaylord Perry	14.00	7.00	4.25
321	Mayo Smith	2.50	1.25	.70
322	Jose Pagan	2.50	1.25	.70
323	Mike Hershberger	2.50	1.25	.70
324	Hal Woodeshick	2.50	1.25	.70
325	Chico Cardenas	2.50	1.25	.70
326	Bob Uecker	20.00	10.00	6.00
327	Angels Team	5.00	2.50	1.50
328	Clete Boyer	2.50	1.25	.70
329	Charlie Lau	2.50	1.25	.70
330	Claude Osteen	2.50	1.25	.70
331	Joe Foy	2.50	1.25	.70
332	Jesus Alou	2.50	1.25	.70
333	Fergie Jenkins	25.00	12.50	7.50
334	Twin Terrors (Bob Allison, Harmon Killebrew)	4.50	2.25	1.25
335	Bob Veale	2.50	1.25	.70
336	Joe Azcue	2.50	1.25	.70
337	Joe Morgan	18.00	9.00	5.50
338	Bob Locker	2.50	1.25	.70
339	Chico Ruiz	2.50	1.25	.70
340	Joe Pepitone	2.50	1.25	.70
341	Giants Rookies (*Dick Dietz*, Bill Sorrell)	2.50	1.25	.70
342	Hank Fischer	2.50	1.25	.70
343	Tom Satriano	2.50	1.25	.70
344	Ossie Chavarria	2.50	1.25	.70
345	Stu Miller	2.50	1.25	.70
346	Jim Hickman	2.50	1.25	.70
347	Grady Hatton	2.50	1.25	.70
348	Tug McGraw	2.50	1.25	.70
349	Bob Chance	2.50	1.25	.70
350	Joe Torre	2.50	1.25	.70
351	Vern Law	2.50	1.25	.70
352	Ray Oyler	2.50	1.25	.70
353	Bill McCool	2.50	1.25	.70
354	Cubs Team	5.00	2.50	1.50
355	Carl Yastrzemski	65.00	32.00	19.50
356	Larry Jaster	2.50	1.25	.70
357	Bill Skowron	3.50	1.75	1.00
358	Ruben Amaro	2.50	1.25	.70
359	Dick Ellsworth	2.50	1.25	.70
360	Leon Wagner	2.50	1.25	.70
361	Checklist 371-457 (Roberto Clemente)	13.00	6.50	4.00
362	Darold Knowles	2.50	1.25	.70
363	Dave Johnson	2.50	1.25	.70
364	Claude Raymond	2.50	1.25	.70
365	John Roseboro	2.50	1.25	.70
366	Andy Kosco	2.50	1.25	.70
367	Angels Rookies (Bill Kelso, Don Wallace)	2.50	1.25	.70
368	Jack Hiatt	2.50	1.25	.70
369	Catfish Hunter	15.00	7.50	4.50
370	Tommy Davis	2.50	1.25	.70
371	Jim Lonborg	3.00	1.50	.90
372	Mike de la Hoz	3.00	1.50	.90
373	White Sox Rookies (Duane Josephson, Fred Klages)	3.00	1.50	.90
374	Mel Queen	3.00	1.50	.90
375	Jake Gibbs	3.00	1.50	.90
376	Don Lock	3.00	1.50	.90
377	Luis Tiant	3.00	1.50	.90
378	Tigers Team	5.00	2.50	1.50
379	Jerry May	3.00	1.50	.90
380	Dean Chance	3.00	1.50	.90
381	Dick Schofield	3.00	1.50	.90
382	Dave McNally	3.00	1.50	.90
383	Ken Henderson	3.00	1.50	.90
384	Cardinals Rookies (Jim Cosman, Dick Hughes)	3.00	1.50	.90
385	Jim Fregosi	3.00	1.50	.90
386	Dick Selma	3.00	1.50	.90
387	Cap Peterson	3.00	1.50	.90
388	Arnold Earley	3.00	1.50	.90
389	Al Dark	3.00	1.50	.90
390	Jim Wynn	3.00	1.50	.90
391	Wilbur Wood	3.00	1.50	.90
392	Tommy Harper	3.00	1.50	.90
393	Jim Bouton	3.00	1.50	.90
394	Jake Wood	3.00	1.50	.90
395	Chris Short	3.00	1.50	.90
396	Atlanta Aces (Tony Cloninger, Denis Menke)	3.00	1.50	.90
397	Willie Smith	3.00	1.50	.90
398	Jeff Torborg	3.00	1.50	.90
399	Al Worthington	3.00	1.50	.90
400	Roberto Clemente	85.00	42.00	25.00
401	Jim Coates	3.00	1.50	.90
402	Phillies Rookies (Grant Jackson, Billy Wilson)	3.00	1.50	.90
403	Dick Nen	3.00	1.50	.90
404	Nelson Briles	3.00	1.50	.90
405	Russ Snyder	3.00	1.50	.90
406	Lee Elia	3.00	1.50	.90
407	Reds Team	5.00	2.50	1.50
408	Jim Northrup	3.00	1.50	.90
409	Ray Sadecki	3.00	1.50	.90
410	Lou Johnson	3.00	1.50	.90
411	Dick Howser	3.00	1.50	.90
412	Astros Rookies (Norm Miller, Doug Rader)	3.00	1.50	.90
413	Jerry Grote	3.00	1.50	.90
414	Casey Cox	3.00	1.50	.90
415	Sonny Jackson	3.00	1.50	.90
416	Roger Repoz	3.00	1.50	.90
417a	Bob Bruce (RBAVES on back)	18.00	9.00	5.50
417b	Bob Bruce (corrected)	3.00	1.50	.90
418	Sam Mele	3.00	1.50	.90
419	Don Kessinger	3.00	1.50	.90
420	Denny McLain	7.50	3.75	2.25
421	Dal Maxvill	3.00	1.50	.90
422	Hoyt Wilhelm	12.50	6.25	3.75
423	Fence Busters (Willie Mays, Willie McCovey)	25.00	12.50	7.50
424	Pedro Gonzalez	3.00	1.50	.90
425	Pete Mikkelsen	3.00	1.50	.90
426	Lou Clinton	3.00	1.50	.90
427	Ruben Gomez	3.00	1.50	.90
428	Dodgers Rookies (Tom Hutton, Gene Michael)	3.00	1.50	.90
429	Garry Roggenburk	3.00	1.50	.90
430	Pete Rose	70.00	35.00	21.00
431	Ted Uhlaender	3.00	1.50	.90
432	Jimmie Hall	3.00	1.50	.90
433	Al Luplow	3.00	1.50	.90
434	Eddie Fisher	3.00	1.50	.90
435	Mack Jones	3.00	1.50	.90
436	Pete Ward	3.00	1.50	.90
437	Senators Team	5.00	2.50	1.50
438	Chuck Dobson	3.00	1.50	.90
439	Byron Browne	3.00	1.50	.90
440	Steve Hargan	3.00	1.50	.90
441	Jim Davenport	3.00	1.50	.90
442	Yankees Rookies (*Bill Robinson*, Joe Verbanic)	3.00	1.50	.90
443	Tito Francona	3.00	1.50	.90
444	George Smith	3.00	1.50	.90
445	Don Sutton	24.00	12.00	7.25
446	Russ Nixon	3.00	1.50	.90
447	Bo Belinsky	3.00	1.50	.90
448	Harry Walker	3.00	1.50	.90
449	Orlando Pena	3.00	1.50	.90
450	Richie Allen	5.00	2.50	1.50
451	Fred Newman	3.00	1.50	.90
452	Ed Kranepool	3.00	1.50	.90
453	Aurelio Monteagudo	3.00	1.50	.90
454a	Checklist 458-533 (Juan Marichal) (left ear shows)	12.00	6.00	3.50
454b	Checklist 458-533 (Juan Marichal) (no left ear)	12.00	6.00	3.50
455	Tommie Agee	3.00	1.50	.90
456	Phil Niekro	12.00	6.00	3.50
457	Andy Etchebarren	3.00	1.50	.90
458	Lee Thomas	7.00	3.50	2.00
459	Senators Rookies (*Dick Bosman*, Pete Craig)	7.00	3.50	2.00
460	Harmon Killebrew	40.00	20.00	12.00
461	Bob Miller	7.00	3.50	2.00
462	Bob Barton	7.00	3.50	2.00
463	Hill Aces (Sam McDowell, Sonny Siebert)	11.00	5.50	3.25
464	Dan Coombs	7.00	3.50	2.00
465	Willie Horton	9.00	4.50	2.75
466	Bobby Wine	7.00	3.50	2.00
467	Jim O'Toole	7.00	3.50	2.00
468	Ralph Houk	9.00	4.50	2.75
469	Len Gabrielson	7.00	3.50	2.00
470	Bob Shaw	7.00	3.50	2.00
471	Rene Lachemann	7.00	3.50	2.00
472	Pirates Rookies (John Gelnar, George Spriggs)	7.00	3.50	2.00
473	Jose Santiago	7.00	3.50	2.00
474	Bob Tolan	7.00	3.50	2.00
475	Jim Palmer	85.00	42.00	25.00
476	Tony Perez	65.00	32.00	19.50

477	Braves Team	12.00	6.00	3.50
478	Bob Humphreys	7.00	3.50	2.00
479	Gary Bell	7.00	3.50	2.00
480	Willie McCovey	32.00	16.00	9.50
481	Leo Durocher	13.00	6.50	4.00
482	Bill Monbouquette	7.00	3.50	2.00
483	Jim Landis	7.00	3.50	2.00
484	Jerry Adair	7.00	3.50	2.00
485	Tim McCarver	13.00	6.50	4.00
486	Twins Rookies (Rich Reese, Bill Whitby)	7.00	3.50	2.00
487	Tom Reynolds	7.00	3.50	2.00
488	Gerry Arrigo	7.00	3.50	2.00
489	Doug Clemens	7.00	3.50	2.00
490	Tony Cloninger	7.00	3.50	2.00
491	Sam Bowens	7.00	3.50	2.00
492	Pirates Team	12.00	6.00	3.50
493	Phil Ortega	7.00	3.50	2.00
494	Bill Rigney	7.00	3.50	2.00
495	Fritz Peterson	9.00	4.50	2.75
496	Orlando McFarlane	7.00	3.50	2.00
497	Ron Campbell	7.00	3.50	2.00
498	Larry Dierker	7.00	3.50	2.00
499	Indians Rookies (George Culver, Jose Vidal)	7.00	3.50	2.00
500	Juan Marichal	24.00	12.00	7.25
501	Jerry Zimmerman	7.00	3.50	2.00
502	Derrell Griffith	7.00	3.50	2.00
503	Dodgers Team	13.00	6.50	4.00
504	Orlando Martinez	7.00	3.50	2.00
505	Tommy Helms	7.00	3.50	2.00
506	Smoky Burgess	8.00	4.00	2.50
507	Orioles Rookies (Ed Barnowski, Larry Haney)	7.00	3.50	2.00
508	Dick Hall	7.00	3.50	2.00
509	Jim King	7.00	3.50	2.00
510	Bill Mazeroski	13.00	6.50	4.00
511	Don Wert	7.00	3.50	2.00
512	Red Schoendienst	15.00	7.50	4.50
513	Marcelino Lopez	7.00	3.50	2.00
514	John Werhas	7.00	3.50	2.00
515	Bert Campaneris	9.00	4.50	2.75
516	Giants Team	12.00	6.00	3.50
517	Fred Talbot	7.00	3.50	2.00
518	Denis Menke	7.00	3.50	2.00
519	Ted Davidson	7.00	3.50	2.00
520	Max Alvis	7.00	3.50	2.00
521	Bird Bombers (Curt Blefary, Boog Powell)	13.00	6.50	4.00
522	John Stephenson	7.00	3.50	2.00
523	Jim Merritt	7.00	3.50	2.00
524	Felix Mantilla	7.00	3.50	2.00
525	Ron Hunt	7.00	3.50	2.00
526	Tigers Rookies (*Pat Dobson*, George Korince)	9.00	4.50	2.75
527	Dennis Ribant	7.00	3.50	2.00
528	Rico Petrocelli	9.00	4.50	2.75
529	Gary Wagner	7.00	3.50	2.00
530	Felipe Alou	12.00	6.00	3.50
531	Checklist 534-609 (Brooks Robinson)	12.00	6.00	3.50
532	Jim Hicks	7.00	3.50	2.00
533	Jack Fisher	7.00	3.50	2.00
534	Hank Bauer	12.00	6.00	3.50
535	Donn Clendenon	15.00	7.50	4.50
536	*Joe Niekro*, Paul Popovich)	35.00	17.50	10.50
537	Chuck Estrada	12.00	6.00	3.50
538	J.C. Martin	15.00	7.50	4.50
539	Dick Egan	12.00	6.00	3.50
540	Norm Cash	35.00	17.50	10.50
541	Joe Gibbon	15.00	7.50	4.50
542	*Rick Monday*, Tony Pierce)	15.00	7.50	4.50
543	Dan Schneider	15.00	7.50	4.50
544	Indians Team	22.00	11.00	6.50
545	Jim Grant	15.00	7.50	4.50
546	Woody Woodward	15.00	7.50	4.50
547	Red Sox Rookies (Russ Gibson, Bill Rohr)	12.00	6.00	3.50
548	Tony Gonzalez	12.00	6.00	3.50
549	Jack Sanford	15.00	7.50	4.50
550	Vada Pinson	18.00	9.00	5.50
551	Doug Camilli	12.00	6.00	3.50
552	Ted Savage	15.00	7.50	4.50
553	Yankees Rookies (Mike Hegan, Thad Tillotson)	18.00	9.00	5.50
554	Andre Rodgers	12.00	6.00	3.50
555	Don Cardwell	15.00	7.50	4.50
556	Al Weis	12.00	6.00	3.50
557	Al Ferrara	15.00	7.50	4.50
558	*Mark Belanger*, Bill Dillman	35.00	17.50	10.50
559	Dick Tracewski	12.00	6.00	3.50
560	Jim Bunning	50.00	25.00	15.00
561	Sandy Alomar	15.00	7.50	4.50
562	Steve Blass	12.00	6.00	3.50
563	Joe Adcock	15.00	7.50	4.50
564	Astros Rookies (Alonzo Harris, Aaron Pointer)	12.00	6.00	3.50
565	Lew Krausse	15.00	7.50	4.50
566	Gary Geiger	12.00	6.00	3.50
567	Steve Hamilton	15.00	7.50	4.50
568	John Sullivan	15.00	7.50	4.50
569	A.L. Rookies (Hank Allen, Rod Carew)	375.00	187.00	112.00
570	Maury Wills	80.00	40.00	24.00
571	Larry Sherry	15.00	7.50	4.50
572	Don Demeter	15.00	7.50	4.50
573	White Sox Team	22.00	11.00	6.50
574	Jerry Buchek	15.00	7.50	4.50
575	*Dave Boswell*	15.00	7.50	4.50
576	N.L. Rookies (Norm Gigon, Ramon Hernandez)	15.00	7.50	4.50
577	Bill Short	15.00	7.50	4.50
578	John Boccabella	15.00	7.50	4.50
579	Bill Henry	15.00	7.50	4.50
580	Rocky Colavito	75.00	37.00	22.00
581	Mets Rookies (Bill Denehy, Tom Seaver)	900.00	450.00	270.00
582	Jim Owens	12.00	6.00	3.50
583	Ray Barker	15.00	7.50	4.50
584	Jim Piersall	20.00	10.00	6.00
585	Wally Bunker	15.00	7.50	4.50
586	Manny Jimenez	15.00	7.50	4.50
587	N.L. Rookies (Don Shaw, Gary Sutherland)	15.00	7.50	4.50
588	Johnny Klippstein	12.00	6.00	3.50
589	Dave Ricketts	12.00	6.00	3.50
590	Pete Richert	15.00	7.50	4.50
591	Ty Cline	15.00	7.50	4.50
592	N.L. Rookies (Jim Shellenback, Ron Willis)	15.00	7.50	4.50
593	Wes Westrum	15.00	7.50	4.50
594	Dan Osinski	15.00	7.50	4.50
595	Cookie Rojas	15.00	7.50	4.50
596	Galen Cisco	12.00	6.00	3.50
597	Ted Abernathy	15.00	7.50	4.50
598	White Sox Rookies (Ed Stroud, Walt Williams)	15.00	7.50	4.50
599	Bob Duliba	12.00	6.00	3.50
600	Brooks Robinson	225.00	112.00	67.00
601	Bill Bryan	12.00	6.00	3.50
602	Juan Pizarro	15.00	7.50	4.50
603	Athletics Rookies (Tim Talton, Ramon Webster)	15.00	7.50	4.50
604	Red Sox Team	100.00	50.00	30.00
605	Mike Shannon	35.00	17.50	10.50
606	Ron Taylor	15.00	7.50	4.50
607	Mickey Stanley	15.00	7.50	4.50
608	Cubs Rookies (Rich Nye, John Upham)	12.00	6.00	3.50
609	Tommy John	100.00	50.00	30.00

1967 Topps Pin-Ups

The 5" by 7" "All Star Pin-ups" were inserts to regular 1967 Topps baseball cards. They feature a full color picture with the player's name, position and team in a circle on the lower left side of the front. The numbered set consists of 32 players (generally big names). Even so, they are rather inexpensive. Because the large paper pin-ups had to be folded several times to fit into the wax packs, they are almost never found in true "Mint" condition.

		NR MT	EX	VG
Complete Set:		80.00	40.00	24.00
Common Player:		1.00	.50	.30
1	Boog Powell	1.50	.70	.45
2	Bert Campaneris	1.50	.70	.45
3	Brooks Robinson	6.00	3.00	1.75
4	Tommie Agee	1.00	.50	.30
5	Carl Yastrzemski	6.00	3.00	1.75
6	Mickey Mantle	20.00	10.00	6.00
7	Frank Howard	1.50	.70	.45
8	Sam McDowell	1.00	.50	.30
9	Orlando Cepeda	2.50	1.25	.70
10	Chico Cardenas	1.00	.50	.30
11	Roberto Clemente	10.00	5.00	3.00
12	Willie Mays	10.00	5.00	3.00
13	Cleon Jones	1.00	.50	.30
14	John Callison	1.00	.50	.30
15	Hank Aaron	10.00	5.00	3.00
16	Don Drysdale	6.00	3.00	1.75
17	Bobby Knoop	1.00	.50	.30
18	Tony Oliva	1.50	.70	.45
19	Frank Robinson	6.00	3.00	1.75
20	Denny McLain	1.50	.70	.45
21	Al Kaline	6.00	3.00	1.75
22	Joe Pepitone	1.00	.50	.30
23	Harmon Killebrew	5.00	2.50	1.50
24	Leon Wagner	1.00	.50	.30
25	Joe Morgan	4.00	2.00	1.25
26	Ron Santo	1.00	.50	.30
27	Joe Torre	1.00	.50	.30
28	Juan Marichal	4.00	2.00	1.25
29	Matty Alou	1.00	.50	.30
30	Felipe Alou	2.00	1.00	.60
31	Ron Hunt	1.00	.50	.30
32	Willie McCovey	5.00	2.50	1.50

1967 Topps Stand-Ups

Never actually issued, no more than a handful of each of these rare test issues has made their way into the hobby market. Designed so that the color photo of the player's head could be popped out of the black background, and the top folded over to create a stand-up display, examples of these 3-1/8" by 5-1/4" cards can be found either die-cut around the portrait or without the cutting. Blank-backed, there are 24 cards in the set, numbered on the front at bottom left. The cards are popular with advanced superstar collectors.

		NR MT	EX	VG
Complete Set:		6750.	3375.	2025.
Common Player:		65.00	32.00	19.50
1	Pete Rose	700.00	350.00	210.00
2	Gary Peters	65.00	32.00	19.50
3	Frank Robinson	200.00	100.00	60.00
4	Jim Lonborg	65.00	32.00	19.50
5	Ron Swoboda	65.00	32.00	19.50
6	Harmon Killebrew	200.00	100.00	60.00
7	Roberto Clemente	800.00	400.00	240.00
8	Mickey Mantle	1500.	750.00	450.00
9	Jim Fregosi	75.00	37.00	22.00
10	Al Kaline	300.00	150.00	90.00
11	Don Drysdale	250.00	125.00	75.00
12	Dean Chance	65.00	32.00	19.50
13	Orlando Cepeda	75.00	37.00	22.00
14	Tim McCarver	75.00	37.00	22.00
15	Frank Howard	75.00	37.00	22.00
16	Max Alvis	65.00	32.00	19.50
17	Rusty Staub	75.00	37.00	22.00
18	Richie Allen	75.00	37.00	22.00
19	Willie Mays	800.00	400.00	240.00
20	Hank Aaron	800.00	400.00	240.00
21	Carl Yastrzemski	400.00	200.00	120.00
22	Ron Santo	75.00	37.00	22.00
23	Catfish Hunter	200.00	100.00	60.00
24	Jim Wynn	65.00	32.00	19.50

1967 Topps Stickers Pirates

Considered a "test" issue, this 33-sticker set of 2-1/2" by 3-1/2" stickers is very similar to the Red Sox stickers which were produced the same year. Player stickers have a color picture (often just the player's head) and the player's name in large "comic book" letters. Besides the players, there are other topics such as "I Love the Pirates," "Bob Clemente for Mayor," and a number of similar sentiments. The stickers have blank backs and are rather scarce.

		NR MT	EX	VG
Complete Set:		225.00	112.00	67.00
Common Player:		3.00	1.50	.90
1	Gene Alley	3.00	1.50	.90
2	Matty Alou	7.00	3.50	2.00
3	Dennis Ribant	3.00	1.50	.90
4	Steve Blass	3.00	1.50	.90
5	Juan Pizarro	3.00	1.50	.90
6	Bob Clemente	75.00	37.00	22.00
7	Donn Clendenon	5.00	2.50	1.50
8	Roy Face	5.00	2.50	1.50
9	Woody Fryman	3.00	1.50	.90
10	Jesse Gonder	3.00	1.50	.90
11	Vern Law	5.00	2.50	1.50
12	Al McBean	3.00	1.50	.90
13	Jerry May	3.00	1.50	.90
14	Bill Mazeroski	12.00	6.00	3.50
15	Pete Mikkelsen	3.00	1.50	.90
16	Manny Mota	5.00	2.50	1.50
17	Billy O'Dell	3.00	1.50	.90
18	Jose Pagan	3.00	1.50	.90

		NR MT	EX	VG
19	Jim Pagliaroni	3.00	1.50	.90
20	Johnny Pesky	3.00	1.50	.90
21	Tommie Sisk	3.00	1.50	.90
22	Willie Stargell	40.00	20.00	12.00
23	Bob Veale	3.00	1.50	.90
24	Harry Walker	3.00	1.50	.90
25	I Love The Pirates	3.00	1.50	.90
26	Let's Go Pirates	3.00	1.50	.90
27	Bob Clemente For Mayor	25.00	12.50	7.50
28	National League Batting Champion (Matty Alou)	4.00	2.00	1.25
29	Happiness Is A Pirate Win	3.00	1.50	.90
30	Donn Clendenon Is My Hero	4.00	2.00	1.25
31	Pirates' Home Run Champion (Willie Stargell)	15.00	7.50	4.50
32	Pirates Logo	3.00	1.50	.90
33	Pirates Pennant	3.00	1.50	.90

1967 Topps Stickers Red Sox

Like the 1967 Pirates Stickers, the Red Sox Stickers were part of the same test procedure. The Red Sox Stickers have the same 2-1/2" by 3-1/2" dimensions, color picture and large player's name on the front. A set is complete at 33 stickers. The majority are players, but themes such as "Let's Go Red Sox" are also included.

		NR MT	EX	VG
Complete Set:		275.00	137.00	82.00
Common Player:		5.00	2.50	1.50
1	Dennis Bennett	5.00	2.50	1.50
2	Darrell Brandon	5.00	2.50	1.50
3	Tony Conigliaro	35.00	17.50	10.50
4	Don Demeter	5.00	2.50	1.50
5	Hank Fischer	5.00	2.50	1.50
6	Joe Foy	5.00	2.50	1.50
7	Mike Andrews	5.00	2.50	1.50
8	Dalton Jones	5.00	2.50	1.50
9	Jim Lonborg	12.00	6.00	3.50
10	Don McMahon	5.00	2.50	1.50
11	Dave Morehead	5.00	2.50	1.50
12	George Smith	5.00	2.50	1.50
13	Rico Petrocelli	10.00	5.00	3.00
14	Mike Ryan	5.00	2.50	1.50
15	Jose Santiago	5.00	2.50	1.50
16	George Scott	10.00	5.00	3.00
17	Sal Maglie	9.00	4.50	2.75
18	Reggie Smith	11.00	5.50	3.25
19	Lee Stange	5.00	2.50	1.50
20	Jerry Stephenson	5.00	2.50	1.50
21	Jose Tartabull	5.00	2.50	1.50
22	George Thomas	5.00	2.50	1.50
23	Bob Tillman	5.00	2.50	1.50
24	Johnnie Wyatt	5.00	2.50	1.50
25	Carl Yastrzemski	75.00	37.00	22.00
26	Dick Williams	11.00	5.50	3.25
27	I Love The Red Sox	9.00	4.50	2.75
28	Let's Go Red Sox	9.00	4.50	2.75
29	Carl Yastrzemski For Mayor	35.00	17.50	10.50
30	Tony Conigliaro Is My Hero	12.00	6.00	3.50
31	Happiness Is A Boston Win	9.00	4.50	2.75
32	Red Sox Logo	9.00	4.50	2.75
33	Red Sox Pennant	9.00	4.50	2.75

1968 Topps

In 1968, Topps returned to a 598-card set of 2-1/2" by 3-1/2" cards. It is not, however, more of the same by way of appearance as the cards feature a color photograph on a background of what appears to be a burlap fabric. The player's name is below the photo but on the unusual background. A colored circle on the lower right carries the team and position. Backs were also changed. While retaining the vertical format introduced the previous year, with stats in the middle and cartoon at the bottom. The set features many of the old favorite subsets, including statistical leaders, World Series highlights, multi-player cards, checklists, rookie cards and the return of All-Star cards.

		NR MT	EX	VG
Complete Set (598):		3500.	1750.	1050.
Common Player (1-457):		1.50	.70	.45
Common Player (458-533):		2.50	1.25	.70
Common Player (534-598):		3.00	1.50	.90
1	N.L. Batting Leaders (Matty Alou, Roberto Clemente, Tony Gonzalez)	17.50	8.75	5.25
2	A.L. Batting Leaders (Al Kaline, Frank Robinson, Carl Yastrzemski)	8.00	4.00	2.50
3	N.L. RBI Leaders (Hank Aaron, Orlando Cepeda, Roberto Clemente)	9.00	4.50	2.75
4	A.L. RBI Leaders (Harmon Killebrew, Frank Robinson, Carl Yastrzemski)	8.00	4.00	2.50
5	N.L. Home Run Leaders (Hank Aaron, Willie McCovey, Ron Santo, Jim Wynn)	8.00	4.00	2.50
6	A.L. Home Run Leaders (Frank Howard, Harmon Killebrew, Carl Yastrzemski)	8.00	4.00	2.50
7	N.L. ERA Leaders (Jim Bunning, Phil Niekro, Chris Short)	3.50	1.75	1.00
8	A.L. ERA Leaders (Joe Horlen, Gary Peters, Sonny Siebert)	3.00	1.50	.90
9	N.L. Pitching Leaders (Jim Bunning, Fergie Jenkins, Mike McCormick, Claude Osteen)	3.50	1.75	1.00
10a	A.L. Pitching Leaders (Dean Chance) ("Lonberg" on back)	3.50	1.75	1.00
10a	A.L. Pitching Leaders (Jim Lonborg) ("Lonberg" on back)	3.50	1.75	1.00
10a	A.L. Pitching Leaders (Earl Wilson) ("Lonberg" on back)	3.50	1.75	1.00
10b	A.L. Pitching Leaders (Dean Chance) ("Lonborg" on back)	3.00	1.50	.90
10b	A.L. Pitching Leaders (Jim Lonborg) ("Lonborg" on back)	3.00	1.50	.90
10b	A.L. Pitching Leaders (Earl Wilson) ("Lonborg" on back)	3.00	1.50	.90
11	N.L. Strikeout Leaders (Jim Bunning, Fergie Jenkins, Gaylord Perry)	4.50	2.25	1.25
12	A.L. Strikeout Leaders (Dean Chance, Jim Lonborg, Sam McDowell)	3.00	1.50	.90
13	Chuck Hartenstein	1.50	.70	.45
14	Jerry McNertney	1.50	.70	.45
15	Ron Hunt	1.50	.70	.45
16	*Lou Piniella*, Richie Scheinblum	3.50	1.75	1.00
17	Dick Hall	1.50	.70	.45
18	Mike Hershberger	1.50	.70	.45
19	Juan Pizarro	1.50	.70	.45
20	Brooks Robinson	21.00	10.50	6.25
21	Ron Davis	1.50	.70	.45
22	Pat Dobson	1.50	.70	.45
23	Chico Cardenas	1.50	.70	.45
24	Bobby Locke	1.50	.70	.45
25	Julian Javier	1.50	.70	.45
26	Darrell Brandon	1.50	.70	.45
27	Gil Hodges	6.00	3.00	1.75
28	Ted Uhlaender	1.50	.70	.45
29	Joe Verbanic	1.50	.70	.45
30	Joe Torre	1.50	.70	.45
31	Ed Stroud	1.50	.70	.45
32	Joe Gibbon	1.50	.70	.45
33	Pete Ward	1.50	.70	.45
34	Al Ferrara	1.50	.70	.45
35	Steve Hargan	1.50	.70	.45
36	Pirates Rookies (Bob Moose, Bob Robertson)	1.50	.70	.45
37	Billy Williams	7.00	3.50	2.00
38	Tony Pierce	1.50	.70	.45
39	Cookie Rojas	1.50	.70	.45
40	Denny McLain	3.00	1.50	.90
41	Julio Gotay	1.50	.70	.45
42	Larry Haney	1.50	.70	.45
43	Gary Bell	1.50	.70	.45
44	Frank Kostro	1.50	.70	.45
45	Tom Seaver	125.00	62.00	37.00
46	Dave Ricketts	1.50	.70	.45
47	Ralph Houk	1.50	.70	.45
48	Ted Davidson	1.50	.70	.45
49a	Ed Brinkman (yellow team)	75.00	37.00	22.00
49b	Ed Brinkman (white team)	1.50	.70	.45
50	Willie Mays	65.00	32.00	19.50
51	Bob Locker	1.50	.70	.45
52	Hawk Taylor	1.50	.70	.45
53	Gene Alley	1.50	.70	.45
54	Stan Williams	1.50	.70	.45
55	Felipe Alou	2.50	1.25	.70
56	Orioles Rookies (Dave Leonhard, Dave May)	1.50	.70	.45
57	Dan Schneider	1.50	.70	.45
58	Eddie Mathews	10.00	5.00	3.00
59	Don Lock	1.50	.70	.45
60	Ken Holtzman	1.50	.70	.45
61	Reggie Smith	2.50	1.25	.70
62	Chuck Dobson	1.50	.70	.45
63	Dick Kenworthy	1.50	.70	.45
64	Jim Merritt	1.50	.70	.45
65	John Roseboro	1.50	.70	.45
66a	Casey Cox (yellow team)	75.00	37.00	22.00
66b	Casey Cox (white team)	1.50	.70	.45
67	Checklist 1-109 (Jim Kaat)	3.00	1.50	.90
68	Ron Willis	1.50	.70	.45
69	Tom Tresh	2.50	1.25	.70
70	Bob Veale	1.50	.70	.45
71	Vern Fuller	1.50	.70	.45
72	Tommy John	5.00	2.50	1.50
73	Jim Hart	1.50	.70	.45
74	Milt Pappas	1.50	.70	.45
75	Don Mincher	1.50	.70	.45
76	Braves Rookies (Jim Britton, Ron Reed)	2.50	1.25	.70
77	*Don Wilson*	1.50	.70	.45
78	Jim Northrup	1.50	.70	.45
79	Ted Kubiak	1.50	.70	.45
80	Rod Carew	90.00	45.00	27.00
81	Larry Jackson	1.50	.70	.45
82	Sam Bowens	1.50	.70	.45
83	John Stephenson	1.50	.70	.45
84	Bob Tolan	1.50	.70	.45
85	Gaylord Perry	9.00	4.50	2.75
86	Willie Stargell	8.00	4.00	2.50
87	Dick Williams	2.00	1.00	.60
88	Phil Regan	1.50	.70	.45
89	Jake Gibbs	1.50	.70	.45
90	Vada Pinson	3.00	1.50	.90
91	Jim Ollom	1.50	.70	.45
92	Ed Kranepool	1.50	.70	.45
93	Tony Cloninger	1.50	.70	.45
94	Lee Maye	1.50	.70	.45
95	Bob Aspromonte	1.50	.70	.45
96	Senators Rookies (Frank Coggins, Dick Nold)	1.50	.70	.45
97	Tom Phoebus	1.50	.70	.45
98	Gary Sutherland	1.50	.70	.45
99	Rocky Colavito	3.00	1.50	.90
100	Bob Gibson	20.00	10.00	6.00
101	Glenn Beckert	1.50	.70	.45
102	Jose Cardenal	1.50	.70	.45
103	Don Sutton	8.00	4.00	2.50
104	Dick Dietz	1.50	.70	.45
105	Al Downing	2.00	1.00	.60
106	Dalton Jones	1.50	.70	.45
107	Checklist 110-196 (Juan Marichal)	3.50	1.75	1.00
108	Don Pavletich	1.50	.70	.45
109	Bert Campaneris	2.00	1.00	.60
110	Hank Aaron	65.00	32.00	19.50
111	Rich Reese	1.50	.70	.45
112	Woody Fryman	1.50	.70	.45
113	Tigers Rookies (Tom Matchick, Daryl Patterson)	1.50	.70	.45
114	Ron Swoboda	1.50	.70	.45
115	Sam McDowell	1.50	.70	.45
116	Ken McMullen	1.50	.70	.45
117	Larry Jaster	1.50	.70	.45
118	Mark Belanger	2.00	1.00	.60
119	Ted Savage	1.50	.70	.45
120	Mel Stottlemyre	2.00	1.00	.60
121	Jimmie Hall	1.50	.70	.45
122	Gene Mauch	1.50	.70	.45
123	Jose Santiago	1.50	.70	.45
124	Nate Oliver	1.50	.70	.45
125	Joe Horlen	1.50	.70	.45
126	Bobby Etheridge	1.50	.70	.45
127	Paul Lindblad	1.50	.70	.45
128	Astros Rookies (Tom Dukes, Alonzo Harris)	1.50	.70	.45
129	Mickey Stanley	1.50	.70	.45
130	Tony Perez	8.00	4.00	2.50
131	Frank Bertaina	1.50	.70	.45
132	Bud Harrelson	1.50	.70	.45
133	Fred Whitfield	1.50	.70	.45
134	Pat Jarvis	1.50	.70	.45
135	Paul Blair	1.50	.70	.45
136	Randy Hundley	1.50	.70	.45
137	Twins Team	4.00	2.00	1.25
138	Ruben Amaro	1.50	.70	.45
139	Chris Short	1.50	.70	.45
140	Tony Conigliaro	3.00	1.50	.90
141	Dal Maxvill	1.50	.70	.45
142	White Sox Rookies (Buddy Bradford, Bill Voss)	1.50	.70	.45
143	Pete Cimino	1.50	.70	.45
144	Joe Morgan	15.00	7.50	4.50
145	Don Drysdale	12.00	6.00	3.50
146	Sal Bando	1.50	.70	.45
147	Frank Linzy	1.50	.70	.45
148	Dave Bristol	1.50	.70	.45
149	Bob Saverine	1.50	.70	.45
150	Roberto Clemente	65.00	32.00	19.50
151	World Series Game 1 (Brock Socks 4-Hits in Opener)	4.00	2.00	1.25
152	World Series Game 2, Yaz Smashes Two Homers)	6.00	3.00	1.75
153	World Series Game 3 (Briles Cools Off Boston)	3.00	1.50	.90
154	World Series Game 4, Gibson Hurls Shutout!)	8.00	4.00	2.50
155	World Series Game 5 (Lonborg Wins Again!)	3.00	1.50	.90
156	World Series Game 6 (Petrocelli Socks Two Homers)	3.00	1.50	.90
157	World Series Game 7 (St. Louis Wins It!)	3.00	1.50	.90
158	World Series Summary (The Cardinals Celebrate!)	3.00	1.50	.90
159	Don Kessinger	1.50	.70	.45
160	Earl Wilson	1.50	.70	.45
161	Norm Miller	1.50	.70	.45
162	Cardinals Rookies (Hal Gilson, Mike Torrez)	2.00	1.00	.60
163	Gene Brabender	1.50	.70	.45
164	Ramon Webster	1.50	.70	.45
165	Tony Oliva	2.50	1.25	.70
166	Claude Raymond	1.50	.70	.45
167	Elston Howard	2.50	1.25	.70
168	Dodgers Team	4.00	2.00	1.25
169	Bob Bolin	1.50	.70	.45
170	Jim Fregosi	2.00	1.00	.60
171	Don Nottebart	1.50	.70	.45
172	Walt Williams	1.50	.70	.45
173	John Boozer	1.50	.70	.45
174	Bob Tillman	1.50	.70	.45
175	Maury Wills	2.50	1.25	.70

176 Bob Allen 1.50 .70 .45
177 Mets Rookies (*Jerry Koosman*, Nolan Ryan)
1400. 700.00 420.00
178 Don Wert 1.50 .70 .45
179 Bill Stoneman 1.50 .70 .45
180 Curt Flood 1.50 .70 .45
181 Jerry Zimmerman 1.50 .70 .45
182 Dave Giusti 1.50 .70 .45
183 Bob Kennedy 1.50 .70 .45
184 Lou Johnson 1.50 .70 .45
185 Tom Haller 1.50 .70 .45
186 Eddie Watt 1.50 .70 .45
187 Sonny Jackson 1.50 .70 .45
188 Cap Peterson 1.50 .70 .45
189 Bill Landis 1.50 .70 .45
190 Bill White 2.50 1.25 .70
191 Dan Frisella 1.50 .70 .45
192a Checklist 197-283 (Carl Yastrzemski) ("To increase the..." on back) 4.50 2.25 1.25
192b Checklist 197-283 (Carl yastrzemski) ("To increase your..." on back) 6.00 3.00 1.75
193 Jack Hamilton 1.50 .70 .45
194 Don Buford 1.50 .70 .45
195 Joe Pepitone 1.50 .70 .45
196 Gary Nolan 1.50 .70 .45
197 Larry Brown 1.50 .70 .45
198 Roy Face 1.50 .70 .45
199 A's Rookies (Darrell Osteen, Roberto Rodriguez)
1.50 .70 .45
200 Orlando Cepeda 4.00 2.00 1.25
201 *Mike Marshall* 3.00 1.50 .90
202 Adolfo Phillips 1.50 .70 .45
203 Dick Kelley 1.50 .70 .45
204 Andy Etchebarren 1.50 .70 .45
205 Juan Marichal 8.00 4.00 2.50
206 Cal Ermer 1.50 .70 .45
207 Carroll Sembera 1.50 .70 .45
208 Willie Davis 1.50 .70 .45
209 Tim Cullen 1.50 .70 .45
210 Gary Peters 1.50 .70 .45
211 J.C. Martin 1.50 .70 .45
212 Dave Morehead 1.50 .70 .45
213 Chico Ruiz 1.50 .70 .45
214 Yankees Rookies (Stan Bahnsen, Frank Fernandez)
2.00 1.00 .60
215 Jim Bunning 4.00 2.00 1.25
216 Bubba Morton 1.50 .70 .45
217 Turk Farrell 1.50 .70 .45
218 Ken Suarez 1.50 .70 .45
219 Rob Gardner 1.50 .70 .45
220 Harmon Killebrew 12.50 6.25 3.75
221 Braves Team 4.00 2.00 1.25
222 Jim Hardin 1.50 .70 .45
223 Ollie Brown 1.50 .70 .45
224 Jack Aker 1.50 .70 .45
225 Richie Allen 2.50 1.25 .70
226 Jimmie Price 1.50 .70 .45
227 Joe Hoerner 1.50 .70 .45
228 Dodgers Rookies (*Jack Billingham*, Jim Fairey)
1.50 .70 .45
229 Fred Klages 1.50 .70 .45
230 Pete Rose 32.00 16.00 9.50
231 Dave Baldwin 1.50 .70 .45
232 Denis Menke 1.50 .70 .45
233 George Scott 1.50 .70 .45
234 Bill Monbouquette 1.50 .70 .45
235 Ron Santo 4.00 2.00 1.25
236 Tug McGraw 1.50 .70 .45
237 Alvin Dark 1.50 .70 .45
238 Tom Satriano 1.50 .70 .45
239 Bill Henry 1.50 .70 .45
240 Al Kaline 20.00 10.00 6.00
241 Felix Millan 1.50 .70 .45
242 Moe Drabowsky 1.50 .70 .45
243 Rich Rollins 1.50 .70 .45
244 John Donaldson 1.50 .70 .45
245 Tony Gonzalez 1.50 .70 .45
246 Fritz Peterson 1.50 .70 .45
247 *Johnny Bench*, Ron Tompkins
215.00 107.00 64.00
248 Fred Valentine 1.50 .70 .45
249 Bill Singer 1.50 .70 .45
250 Carl Yastrzemski 26.00 13.00 7.75
251 *Manny Sanguillen* 1.50 .70 .45
252 Angels Team 4.00 2.00 1.25
253 Dick Hughes 1.50 .70 .45
254 Cleon Jones 1.50 .70 .45
255 Dean Chance 1.50 .70 .45
256 Norm Cash 3.00 1.50 .90
257 Phil Niekro 5.00 2.50 1.50
258 Cubs Rookies (Jose Arcia, Bill Schlesinger)
1.50 .70 .45
259 Ken Boyer 3.00 1.50 .90
260 Jim Wynn 1.50 .70 .45
261 Dave Duncan 1.50 .70 .45
262 Rick Wise 1.50 .70 .45
263 Horace Clarke 1.50 .70 .45
264 Ted Abernathy 1.50 .70 .45
265 Tommy Davis 1.50 .70 .45
266 Paul Popovich 1.50 .70 .45
267 Herman Franks 1.50 .70 .45
268 Bob Humphreys 1.50 .70 .45
269 Bob Tiefenauer 1.50 .70 .45
270 Matty Alou 1.50 .70 .45
271 Bobby Knoop 1.50 .70 .45
272 Ray Culp 1.50 .70 .45
273 Dave Johnson 1.50 .70 .45
274 Mike Cuellar 1.50 .70 .45
275 Tim McCarver 2.50 1.25 .70
276 Jim Roland 1.50 .70 .45
277 Jerry Buchek 1.50 .70 .45
278a Checklist 284-370 (Orlando cepeda) (copyright at right) 3.00 1.50 .90
278b Checklist 284-370 (Orlando Cepeda) (copyright at left) 5.00 2.50 1.50
279 Bill Hands 1.50 .70 .45
280 Mickey Mantle 230.00 115.00 69.00
281 Jim Campanis 1.50 .70 .45
282 Rick Monday 1.50 .70 .45
283 Mel Queen 1.50 .70 .45
284 John Briggs 1.50 .70 .45
285 Dick McAuliffe 1.50 .70 .45
286 Cecil Upshaw 1.50 .70 .45
287 White Sox Rookies (Mickey Abarbanel, Cisco Carlos) 1.50 .70 .45
288 Dave Wickersham 1.50 .70 .45
289 Woody Held 1.50 .70 .45
290 Willie McCovey 10.00 5.00 3.00
291 Dick Lines 1.50 .70 .45
292 Art Shamsky 1.50 .70 .45
293 Bruce Howard 1.50 .70 .45
294 Red Schoendienst 4.00 2.00 1.25
295 Sonny Siebert 1.50 .70 .45
296 Byron Browne 1.50 .70 .45
297 Russ Gibson 1.50 .70 .45
298 Jim Brewer 1.50 .70 .45
299 Gene Michael 1.50 .70 .45
300 Rusty Staub 2.00 1.00 .60
301 Twins Rookies (George Mitterwald, Rick Renick)
1.50 .70 .45
302 Gerry Arrigo 1.50 .70 .45
303 Dick Green 1.50 .70 .45
304 Sandy Valdespino 1.50 .70 .45
305 Minnie Rojas 1.50 .70 .45
306 Mike Ryan 1.50 .70 .45
307 John Hiller 1.50 .70 .45
308 Pirates Team 4.00 2.00 1.25
309 Ken Henderson 1.50 .70 .45
310 Luis Aparicio 5.00 2.50 1.50
311 Jack Lamabe 1.50 .70 .45
312 Curt Blefary 1.50 .70 .45
313 Al Weis 1.50 .70 .45
314 Red Sox Rookies (Bill Rohr, George Spriggs)
1.50 .70 .45
315 Zoilo Versalles 1.50 .70 .45
316 Steve Barber 1.50 .70 .45
317 Ron Brand 1.50 .70 .45
318 Chico Salmon 1.50 .70 .45
319 George Culver 1.50 .70 .45
320 Frank Howard 2.50 1.25 .70
321 Leo Durocher 2.25 1.25 .70
322 Dave Boswell 1.50 .70 .45
323 Deron Johnson 1.50 .70 .45
324 Jim Nash 1.50 .70 .45
325 Manny Mota 1.50 .70 .45
326 Dennis Ribant 1.50 .70 .45
327 Tony Taylor 1.50 .70 .45
328 Angels Rookies (Chuck Vinson, Jim Weaver)
1.50 .70 .45
329 Duane Josephson 1.50 .70 .45
330 Roger Maris 40.00 20.00 12.00
331 Dan Osinski 1.50 .70 .45
332 Doug Rader 1.50 .70 .45
333 Ron Herbel 1.50 .70 .45
334 Orioles Team 4.00 2.00 1.25
335 Bob Allison 1.50 .70 .45
336 John Purdin 1.50 .70 .45
337 Bill Robinson 1.50 .70 .45
338 Bob Johnson 1.50 .70 .45
339 Rich Nye 1.50 .70 .45
340 Max Alvis 1.50 .70 .45
341 Jim Lemon 1.50 .70 .45
342 Ken Johnson 1.50 .70 .45
343 Jim Gosger 1.50 .70 .45
344 Donn Clendenon 1.50 .70 .45
345 Bob Hendley 1.50 .70 .45
346 Jerry Adair 1.50 .70 .45
347 George Brunet 1.50 .70 .45
348 Phillies Rookies (Larry Colton, Dick Thoenen)
1.50 .70 .45
349 Ed Spiezio 1.50 .70 .45
350 Hoyt Wilhelm 6.00 3.00 1.75
351 Bob Barton 1.50 .70 .45
352 Jackie Hernandez 1.50 .70 .45
353 Mack Jones 1.50 .70 .45
354 Pete Richert 1.50 .70 .45
355 Ernie Banks 24.00 12.00 7.25
356 Checklist 371-457 (Ken Holtzman)
3.00 1.50 .90
357 Len Gabrielson 1.50 .70 .45
358 Mike Epstein 1.50 .70 .45
359 Joe Moeller 1.50 .70 .45
360 Willie Horton 1.50 .70 .45
361 Harmon Killebrew (All-Star) 5.00 2.50 1.50
362 Orlando Cepeda (All-Star) 2.75 1.50 .80
363 Rod Carew (All-Star) 7.00 3.50 2.00
364 Joe Morgan (All-Star) 3.00 1.50 .90
365 Brooks Robinson (All-Star) 6.00 3.00 1.75
366 Ron Santo (All-Star) 3.50 1.75 1.00
367 Jim Fregosi (All-Star) 3.00 1.50 .90
368 Gene Alley (All-Star) 3.00 1.50 .90
369 Carl Yastrzemski (All-Star) 7.00 3.50 2.00
370 Hank Aaron (All-Star) 15.00 7.50 4.50
371 Tony Oliva (All-Star) 3.50 1.75 1.00
372 Lou Brock (All-Star) 6.00 3.00 1.75
373 Frank Robinson (All-Star) 8.00 4.00 2.50
374 Roberto Clemente (All-Star) 15.00 7.50 4.50
375 Bill Freehan (All-Star) 3.00 1.50 .90
376 Tim McCarver (All-Star) 3.50 1.75 1.00
377 Joe Horlen (All-Star) 3.00 1.50 .90
378 Bob Gibson (All-Star) 7.00 3.50 2.00
379 Gary Peters (All-Star) 3.00 1.50 .90
380 Ken Holtzman (All-Star) 3.00 1.50 .90
381 Boog Powell 3.00 1.50 .90
382 Ramon Hernandez 1.50 .70 .45
383 Steve Whitaker 1.50 .70 .45
384 Red Rookies (Bill Henry, Hal McRae)
12.00 6.00 3.50
385 Catfish Hunter 8.00 4.00 2.50
386 Greg Goossen 1.50 .70 .45
387 Joe Foy 1.50 .70 .45
388 Ray Washburn 1.50 .70 .45
389 Jay Johnstone 1.50 .70 .45
390 Bill Mazeroski 4.00 2.00 1.25
391 Bob Priddy 1.50 .70 .45
392 Grady Hatton 1.50 .70 .45
393 Jim Perry 1.50 .70 .45
394 Tommie Aaron 1.50 .70 .45
395 Camilo Pascual 1.50 .70 .45
396 Bobby Wine 1.50 .70 .45
397 Vic Davalillo 1.50 .70 .45
398 Jim Grant 1.50 .70 .45
399 Ray Oyler 1.50 .70 .45
400a Mike McCormick (white team) 80.00 40.00 24.00
400b Mike McCormick (yellow team) 1.50 .70 .45
401 Mets Team 4.50 2.25 1.25
402 Mike Hegan 1.50 .70 .45
403 John Buzhardt 1.50 .70 .45
404 Floyd Robinson 1.50 .70 .45
405 Tommy Helms 1.50 .70 .45
406 Dick Ellsworth 1.50 .70 .45
407 Gary Kolb 1.50 .70 .45
408 Steve Carlton 50.00 25.00 15.00
409 Orioles Rookies (Frank Peters, Ron Stone)
1.50 .70 .45
410 Fergie Jenkins 20.00 10.00 6.00
411 Ron Hansen 1.50 .70 .45
412 Clay Carroll 1.50 .70 .45
413 Tommy McCraw 1.50 .70 .45
414 Mickey Lolich 2.75 1.50 .80
415 Johnny Callison 1.50 .70 .45
416 Bill Rigney 1.50 .70 .45
417 Willie Crawford 1.50 .70 .45
418 Eddie Fisher 1.50 .70 .45
419 Jack Hiatt 1.50 .70 .45
420 Cesar Tovar 1.50 .70 .45
421 Ron Taylor 1.50 .70 .45
422 Rene Lachemann 1.50 .70 .45
423 Fred Gladding 1.50 .70 .45
424 White Sox Team 4.00 2.00 1.25
425 Jim Maloney 1.50 .70 .45
426 Hank Allen 1.50 .70 .45
427 Dick Calmus 1.50 .70 .45
428 Vic Roznovsky 1.50 .70 .45
429 Tommie Sisk 1.50 .70 .45
430 Rico Petrocelli 1.50 .70 .45
431 Dooley Womack 1.50 .70 .45
432 Indians Rookies (Bill Davis, Jose Vidal)
1.50 .70 .45
433 Bob Rodgers 1.50 .70 .45
434 Ricardo Joseph 1.50 .70 .45
435 Ron Perranoski 1.50 .70 .45
436 Hal Lanier 1.50 .70 .45
437 Don Cardwell 1.50 .70 .45
438 Lee Thomas 1.50 .70 .45
439 Luman Harris 1.50 .70 .45
440 Claude Osteen 1.50 .70 .45
441 Alex Johnson 1.50 .70 .45
442 Dick Bosman 1.50 .70 .45
443 Joe Azcue 1.50 .70 .45
444 Jack Fisher 1.50 .70 .45
445 Mike Shannon 1.50 .70 .45
446 Ron Kline 1.50 .70 .45
447 Tigers Rookies (George Korince, Fred Lasher)
1.50 .70 .45
448 Gary Wagner 1.50 .70 .45
449 Gene Oliver 1.50 .70 .45
450 Jim Kaat 6.00 3.00 1.75
451 Al Spangler 1.50 .70 .45
452 Jesus Alou 1.50 .70 .45
453 Sammy Ellis 1.50 .70 .45
454 Checklist 458-533 (Frank Robinson)
4.00 2.00 1.25
455 Rico Carty 1.50 .70 .45
456 John O'Donoghue 1.50 .70 .45
457 Jim Lefebvre 1.50 .70 .45
458 Lew Krausse 2.50 1.25 .70
459 Dick Simpson 2.50 1.25 .70
460 Jim Lonborg 2.50 1.25 .70
461 Chuck Hiller 2.50 1.25 .70
462 Barry Moore 2.50 1.25 .70
463 Jimmie Schaffer 2.50 1.25 .70
464 Don McMahon 2.50 1.25 .70
465 Tommie Agee 2.50 1.25 .70
466 Bill Dillman 2.50 1.25 .70
467 Dick Howser 2.50 1.25 .70
468 Larry Sherry 2.50 1.25 .70
469 Ty Cline 2.50 1.25 .70
470 Bill Freehan 2.50 1.25 .70
471 Orlando Pena 2.50 1.25 .70
472 Walt Alston 4.00 2.00 1.25
473 Al Worthington 2.50 1.25 .70
474 Paul Schaal 2.50 1.25 .70
475 Joe Niekro 2.50 1.25 .70
476 Woody Woodward 2.50 1.25 .70
477 Phillies Team 4.00 2.00 1.25
478 Dave McNally 2.50 1.25 .70
479 Phil Gagliano 2.50 1.25 .70
480 Manager's Dream (Chico Cardenas, Roberto Clemente, Tony Oliva) 25.00 12.50 7.50
481 John Wyatt 2.50 1.25 .70
482 Jose Pagan 2.50 1.25 .70
483 Darold Knowles 2.50 1.25 .70
484 Phil Roof 2.50 1.25 .70
485 Ken Berry 2.50 1.25 .70
486 Cal Koonce 2.50 1.25 .70
487 Lee May 2.50 1.25 .70
488 Dick Tracewski 2.50 1.25 .70
489 Wally Bunker 2.50 1.25 .70
490 Super Stars (Harmon Killebrew, Mickey Mantle, Willie Mays) 100.00 50.00 30.00
491 Denny Lemaster 2.50 1.25 .70
492 Jeff Torborg 2.50 1.25 .70
493 Jim McGlothlin 2.50 1.25 .70
494 Ray Sadecki 2.50 1.25 .70
495 Leon Wagner 2.50 1.25 .70
496 Steve Hamilton 2.50 1.25 .70
497 Cards Team 4.00 2.00 1.25
498 Bill Bryan 2.50 1.25 .70
499 Steve Blass 2.50 1.25 .70
500 Frank Robinson 22.00 11.00 6.50
501 John Odom 2.50 1.25 .70
502 Mike Andrews 2.50 1.25 .70
503 Al Jackson 2.50 1.25 .70
504 Russ Snyder 2.50 1.25 .70
505 Joe Sparma 2.50 1.25 .70
506 Clarence Jones 2.50 1.25 .70

		NR MT	EX	VG
507	Wade Blasingame	2.50	1.25	.70
508	Duke Sims	2.50	1.25	.70
509	Dennis Higgins	2.50	1.25	.70
510	Ron Fairly	2.50	1.25	.70
511	Bill Kelso	2.50	1.25	.70
512	Grant Jackson	2.50	1.25	.70
513	Hank Bauer	2.50	1.25	.70
514	Al McBean	2.50	1.25	.70
515	Russ Nixon	2.50	1.25	.70
516	Pete Mikkelsen	2.50	1.25	.70
517	Diego Segui	2.50	1.25	.70
518a	Checklist 534-598 (Clete Boyer) (539 is Maj. L. Rookies)	3.00	1.50	.90
518b	Checklist 534-598 (Clete Boyer) (539 is Amer. L. Rookies)	5.00	2.50	1.50
519	Jerry Stephenson	2.50	1.25	.70
520	Lou Brock	20.00	10.00	6.00
521	Don Shaw	2.50	1.25	.70
522	Wayne Causey	2.50	1.25	.70
523	John Tsitouris	2.50	1.25	.70
524	Andy Kosco	2.50	1.25	.70
525	Jim Davenport	2.50	1.25	.70
526	Bill Denehy	2.50	1.25	.70
527	Tito Francona	2.50	1.25	.70
528	Tigers Team	65.00	32.00	19.50
529	Bruce Von Hoff	2.50	1.25	.70
530	Bird Belters (Brooks Robinson, Frank Robinson)	10.00	5.00	3.00
531	Chuck Hinton	2.50	1.25	.70
532	Luis Tiant	2.50	1.25	.70
533	Wes Parker	2.50	1.25	.70
534	Bob Miller	3.00	1.50	.90
535	Danny Cater	3.00	1.50	.90
536	Bill Short	3.00	1.50	.90
537	Norm Siebern	3.00	1.50	.90
538	Manny Jimenez	3.00	1.50	.90
539	Major League Rookies (Mike Ferraro, Jim Ray)	3.00	1.50	.90
540	Nelson Briles	3.00	1.50	.90
541	Sandy Alomar	3.00	1.50	.90
542	John Boccabella	3.00	1.50	.90
543	Bob Lee	3.00	1.50	.90
544	Mayo Smith	3.00	1.50	.90
545	Lindy McDaniel	3.00	1.50	.90
546	Roy White	3.00	1.50	.90
547	Dan Coombs	3.00	1.50	.90
548	Bernie Allen	3.00	1.50	.90
549	Orioles Rookies (Curt Motton, Roger Nelson)	3.00	1.50	.90
550	Clete Boyer	3.00	1.50	.90
551	Darrell Sutherland	3.00	1.50	.90
552	Ed Kirkpatrick	3.00	1.50	.90
553	Hank Aguirre	3.00	1.50	.90
554	A's Team	6.00	3.00	1.75
555	Jose Tartabull	3.00	1.50	.90
556	Dick Selma	3.00	1.50	.90
557	Frank Quilici	3.00	1.50	.90
558	John Edwards	3.00	1.50	.90
559	Pirates Rookies (Carl Taylor, Luke Walker)	3.00	1.50	.90
560	Paul Casanova	3.00	1.50	.90
561	Lee Elia	3.00	1.50	.90
562	Jim Bouton	3.50	1.75	1.00
563	Ed Charles	3.00	1.50	.90
564	Eddie Stanky	3.00	1.50	.90
565	Larry Dierker	3.00	1.50	.90
566	Ken Harrelson	3.00	1.50	.90
567	Clay Dalrymple	3.00	1.50	.90
568	Willie Smith	3.00	1.50	.90
569	N.L. Rookies (Ivan Murrell, Les Rohr)	3.00	1.50	.90
570	Rick Reichardt	3.00	1.50	.90
571	Tony LaRussa	4.00	2.00	1.25
572	Don Bosch	3.00	1.50	.90
573	Joe Coleman	3.00	1.50	.90
574	Reds Team	6.00	3.00	1.75
575	Jim Palmer	45.00	22.00	13.50
576	Dave Adlesh	3.00	1.50	.90
577	Fred Talbot	3.00	1.50	.90
578	Orlando Martinez	3.00	1.50	.90
579	N.L. Rookies (*Larry Hisle*, Mike Lum)	3.00	1.50	.90
580	Bob Bailey	3.00	1.50	.90
581	Garry Roggenburk	3.00	1.50	.90
582	Jerry Grote	3.00	1.50	.90
583	Gates Brown	3.00	1.50	.90
584	Larry Shepard	3.00	1.50	.90
585	Wilbur Wood	3.00	1.50	.90
586	Jim Pagliaroni	3.00	1.50	.90
587	Roger Repoz	3.00	1.50	.90
588	Dick Schofield	3.00	1.50	.90
589	Twins Rookies (Ron Clark, Moe Ogier)	3.00	1.50	.90
590	Tommy Harper	3.00	1.50	.90
591	Dick Nen	3.00	1.50	.90
592	John Bateman	3.00	1.50	.90
593	Lee Stange	3.00	1.50	.90
594	Phil Linz	3.00	1.50	.90
595	Phil Ortega	3.00	1.50	.90
596	Charlie Smith	3.00	1.50	.90
597	Bill McCool	3.00	1.50	.90
598	Jerry May	9.00	4.50	2.75

1968 Topps Action All-Star Stickers

Still another of the many Topps test issues of the late 1960s, the Action All-Star stickers were sold in a strip of three, with bubblegum, for 10¢. The strip is comprised of three 3-1/4" by 5-1/4" panels, perforated at the joints for separation. The central panel which is numbered, contains a large color picture of a star player. The top and bottom panels contains smaller pictures of three players each. While there are 16 numbered center panels, only 12 of them are different; panels 13-16 show players previously used. Similarly, the triple-player panels at top and bottom of stickers 13-16 repeat panels from #'s 1-4. Prices below are for stickers which have all three panels still joined. Individual panels are priced significantly lower.

	NR MT	EX	VG
Complete Set:	1300.	650.00	390.00
Common Player:	18.00	9.00	5.50

		NR MT	EX	VG
1	Orlando Cepeda, Joe Horlen, Al Kaline, Bill Mazeroski, Claude Osteen, Mel Stottlemyre, Carl Yastrzemski	100.00	50.00	30.00
2	Don Drysdale, Harmon Killebrew, Mike McCormick, Tom Phoebus, George Scott, Ron Swoboda, Pete Ward	30.00	15.00	9.00
3	Hank Aaron, Paul Casanova, Jim Maloney, Joe Pepitone, Rick Reichardt, Frank Robinson, Tom Seaver	35.00	17.50	10.50
4	Bob Aspromonte, Johnny Callison, Dean Chance, Jim Lefebvre, Jim Lonborg, Frank Robinson, Ron Santo	50.00	25.00	15.00
5	Bert Campaneris, Al Downing, Willie Horton, Ed Kranepool, Willie Mays, Pete Rose, Ron Santo	200.00	100.00	60.00
6	Max Alvis, Ernie Banks, Al Kaline, Tim McCarver, Rusty Staub, Walt Williams, Carl Yastrzemski	70.00	35.00	21.00
7	Rod Carew, Tony Gonzalez, Steve Hargan, Mickey Mantle, Willie McCovey, Rick Monday, Billy Williams	300.00	150.00	90.00
8	Clete Boyer, Jim Bunning, Tony Conigliaro, Mike Cuellar, Joe Horlen, Ken McMullen, Don Mincher	18.00	9.00	5.50
9	Orlando Cepeda, Bob Clemente, Jim Fregosi, Harmon Killebrew, Willie Mays, Chris Short, Earl Wilson	40.00	20.00	12.00
10	Hank Aaron, Bob Gibson, Bud Harrelson, Jim Hunter, Mickey Mantle, Gary Peters, Vada Pinson	100.00	50.00	30.00
11	Don Drysdale, Bill Freehan, Frank Howard, Ferguson Jenkins, Tony Oliva, Bob Veale, Jim Wynn	60.00	30.00	18.00
12	Richie Allen, Bob Clemente, Sam McDowell, Jim McGlothlin, Tony Perez, Brooks Robinson, Joe Torre	100.00	50.00	30.00
13	Dean Chance, Don Drysdale, Jim Lefebvre, Tom Phoebus, Frank Robinson, George Scott, Carl Yastrzemski	100.00	50.00	30.00
14	Paul Casanova, Orlando Cepeda, Joe Horlen, Harmon Killebrew, Bill Mazeroski, Rick Reichardt, Tom Seaver	30.00	15.00	9.00
15	Bob Aspromonte, Johnny Callison, Jim Lonborg, Mike McCormick, Frank Robinson, Ron Swoboda, Pete Ward	30.00	15.00	9.00
16	Hank Aaron, Al Kaline, Jim Maloney, Claude Osteen, Joe Pepitone, Ron Santo, Mel Stottlemyre	60.00	30.00	18.00

1968 Topps Deckle Edge Test Proofs

While most Topps proofs are so rare as to preclude their listing in this catalog, the 1968 Deckle Edge test set is an exception. Usually found in the form of a 7-3/4"x11" uncut sheet of nine black-and-white cards, single cards are sometimes encountered. The blank-backed sheet and cards can be found with the players' facsimile autographs printed in red, black or blue. Unnumbered cards are checklisted here alphabetically.

		NR MT	EX	VG
Complete Set:		200.00	100.00	60.00
Uncut Sheet:		250.00	125.00	75.00
Common Player:		20.00	10.00	6.00
(1)	Dave Adlesh	20.00	10.00	6.00
(2)	Hank Aguire	20.00	10.00	6.00
(3)	Sandy Alomar	20.00	10.00	6.00
(4)	Sonny Jackson	20.00	10.00	6.00
(5)	Bob Johnson	20.00	10.00	6.00
(6)	Claude Osteen	20.00	10.00	6.00
(7)	Juan Pizarro	20.00	10.00	6.00
(8)	Hal Woodeshick	20.00	10.00	6.00
(9)	Carl Yastrzemski	75.00	37.00	22.00

1968 Topps Discs

One of the scarcest of all Topps collectibles, this 28-player set was apparently a never-completed test issue. These full-color, cardboard discs, which measure approximately 2-1/8" in diameter, were apparantly intended to be made into a "pin" set, but for some reason, production was never completed and no actual "pins" are known to exist. Uncut sheets of the player discs have been found, however. The discs include a player portrait photo with the name beneath and the city and team nickname along the sides. The set includes eight Hall of Famers.

		NR MT	EX	VG
Complete Set:		3250.	1750.	1050.
Common Player:		40.00	20.00	12.00
(1)	Hank Aaron	300.00	150.00	90.00
(2)	Richie Allen	45.00	22.00	13.50
(3)	Gene Alley	40.00	20.00	12.00
(4)	Rod Carew	300.00	150.00	90.00
(5)	Orlando Cepeda	60.00	30.00	18.00
(6)	Dean Chance	40.00	20.00	12.00
(7)	Roberto Clemente	300.00	150.00	90.00

		NR MT	EX	VG
(8)	Tommy Davis	40.00	20.00	12.00
(9)	Bill Freehan	40.00	20.00	12.00
(10)	Jim Fregosi	40.00	20.00	12.00
(11)	Steve Hargan	40.00	20.00	12.00
(12)	Frank Howard	45.00	22.00	13.50
(13)	Al Kaline	200.00	100.00	60.00
(14)	Harmon Killebrew	150.00	75.00	45.00
(15)	Mickey Mantle	600.00	300.00	180.00
(16)	Willie Mays	300.00	150.00	90.00
(17)	Mike McCormick	40.00	20.00	12.00
(18)	Rick Monday	40.00	20.00	12.00
(19)	Claude Osteen	40.00	20.00	12.00
(20)	Gary Peters	40.00	20.00	12.00
(21)	Brooks Robinson	200.00	100.00	60.00
(22)	Frank Robinson	200.00	100.00	60.00
(23)	Pete Rose	350.00	175.00	105.00
(24)	Ron Santo	60.00	30.00	18.00
(25)	Rusty Staub	60.00	30.00	18.00
(26)	Joe Torre	40.00	20.00	12.00
(27)	Carl Yastrzemski	200.00	100.00	60.00
(28)	Bob Veale	40.00	20.00	12.00

1968 Topps Game

A throwback to the Red and Blue Back sets of 1951, the 33-cards in the 1968 Topps Game set, inserted into packs of regular '68 Topps cards or purchases as a complete boxed set, enable the owner to play a game of baseball based on the game situations on each card. Also on the 2-1/4" by 3-1/4" cards were a color photograph of a player and his facsimile autograph. One redeeming social value of the set (assuming you're not mesmerized by the game) is that it affords an inexpensive way to get big-name cards as the set is loaded with stars, but not at all popular with collectors.

		NR MT	EX	VG
Complete Set:		80.00	40.00	24.00
Common Player:		2.00	1.00	.60
1	Mateo Alou	2.00	1.00	.60
2	Mickey Mantle	25.00	12.50	7.50
3	Carl Yastrzemski	6.00	3.00	1.75
4	Henry Aaron	10.00	5.00	3.00
5	Harmon Killebrew	4.00	2.00	1.25
6	Roberto Clemente	10.00	5.00	3.00
7	Frank Robinson	6.00	3.00	1.75
8	Willie Mays	10.00	5.00	3.00
9	Brooks Robinson	6.00	3.00	1.75
10	Tommy Davis	2.00	1.00	.60
11	Bill Freehan	2.00	1.00	.60
12	Claude Osteen	2.00	1.00	.60
13	Gary Peters	2.00	1.00	.60
14	Jim Lonborg	2.00	1.00	.60
15	Steve Hargan	2.00	1.00	.60
16	Dean Chance	2.00	1.00	.60
17	Mike McCormick	2.00	1.00	.60
18	Tim McCarver	3.00	1.50	.90
19	Ron Santo	3.00	1.50	.90
20	Tony Gonzalez	2.00	1.00	.60
21	Frank Howard	3.00	1.50	.90
22	George Scott	2.00	1.00	.60
23	Rich Allen	3.00	1.50	.90
24	Jim Wynn	2.00	1.00	.60
25	Gene Alley	2.00	1.00	.60
26	Rick Monday	2.00	1.00	.60
27	Al Kaline	6.00	3.00	1.75
28	Rusty Staub	3.00	1.50	.90
29	Rod Carew	6.00	3.00	1.75
30	Pete Rose	12.00	6.00	3.50
31	Joe Torre	2.00	1.00	.60
32	Orlando Cepeda	4.00	2.00	1.25
33	Jim Fregosi	2.00	1.00	.60

1968 Topps Plaks

Among the scarcest of the Topps test issues of the late 1960s, the "All Star Baseball Plaks" were plastic busts of two dozen stars of the era which came packaged like model airplane parts. The busts had to be snapped off a sprue and could be inserted into a base which carried the player's name. Packed with the plastic plaks was one of two checklist cards which featured six color photos per side. The 2-1/8" by 4" checklist cards are popular with superstar collectors and are considerably easier to find today than the actual plaks.

		NR MT	EX	VG
Complete Set:		2300.	1150.	690.00
Common Player:		20.00	10.00	6.00
1	Max Alvis	20.00	10.00	6.00
2	Frank Howard	30.00	15.00	9.00
3	Dean Chance	20.00	10.00	6.00
4	Catfish Hunter	50.00	25.00	15.00
5	Jim Fregosi	25.00	12.50	7.50
6	Al Kaline	60.00	30.00	18.00
7	Harmon Killebrew	60.00	30.00	18.00
8	Gary Peters	20.00	10.00	6.00
9	Jim Lonborg	20.00	10.00	6.00
10	Frank Robinson	60.00	30.00	18.00
11	Mickey Mantle	800.00	400.00	240.00
12	Carl Yastrzemski	75.00	37.00	22.00
13	Hank Aaron	100.00	50.00	30.00
14	Roberto Clemente	100.00	50.00	30.00
15	Richie Allen	30.00	15.00	9.00
16	Tommy Davis	25.00	12.50	7.50
17	Orlando Cepeda	40.00	20.00	12.00
18	Don Drysdale	60.00	30.00	18.00
19	Willie Mays	100.00	50.00	30.00
20	Rusty Staub	30.00	15.00	9.00
21	Tim McCarver	30.00	15.00	9.00
22	Pete Rose	200.00	100.00	60.00
23	Ron Santo	30.00	15.00	9.00
24	Jim Wynn	20.00	10.00	6.00
----	Checklist Card 1-12	400.00	200.00	120.00
----	Checklist Card 13-24	400.00	200.00	120.00

1968 Topps Posters

Yet another innovation from the creative minds at Topps appeared in 1968; a set of color player posters. Measuring 9-3/4" by 18-1/8," each poster was sold separately with its own piece of gum, rather than as an insert. The posters feature a large color photograph with a star at the bottom containing the player's name, position and team. There are 24 different posters which were folded numerous times to fit into the package they were sold in.

		NR MT	EX	VG
Complete Set:		350.00	175.00	105.00
Common Player:		6.00	3.00	1.75
1	Dean Chance	6.00	3.00	1.75
2	Max Alvis	6.00	3.00	1.75
3	Frank Howard	8.00	4.00	2.50
4	Jim Fregosi	6.00	3.00	1.75
5	Catfish Hunter	12.00	6.00	3.50
6	Roberto Clemente	30.00	15.00	9.00
7	Don Drysdale	15.00	7.50	4.50
8	Jim Wynn	6.00	3.00	1.75
9	Al Kaline	20.00	10.00	6.00
10	Harmon Killebrew	20.00	10.00	6.00
11	Jim Lonborg	6.00	3.00	1.75
12	Orlando Cepeda	8.00	4.00	2.50
13	Gary Peters	6.00	3.00	1.75
14	Hank Aaron	30.00	15.00	9.00
15	Richie Allen	8.00	4.00	2.50
16	Carl Yastrzemski	20.00	10.00	6.00
17	Ron Swoboda	6.00	3.00	1.75
18	Mickey Mantle	60.00	30.00	18.00
19	Tim McCarver	8.00	4.00	2.50
20	Willie Mays	30.00	15.00	9.00
21	Ron Santo	8.00	4.00	2.50
22	Rusty Staub	8.00	4.00	2.50
23	Pete Rose	40.00	20.00	12.00
24	Frank Robinson	20.00	10.00	6.00

1968 Topps Punch-outs

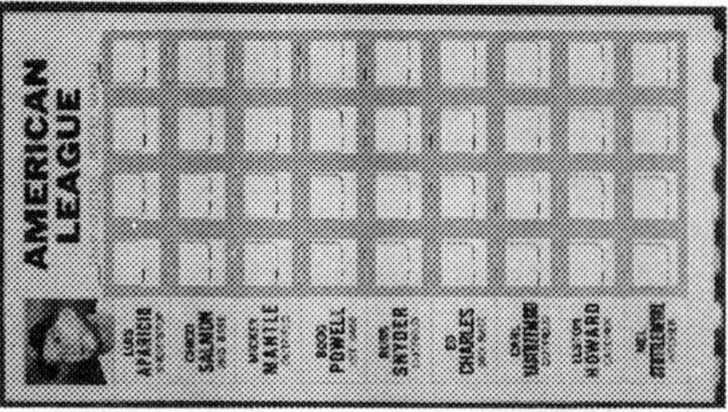

This little-known Topps test issue was reportedly issued around Maryland in cello packs containing two perforated strips of three game cards each. Cards are printed in black, white and red and measure 2-1/2" x 4-2/3". Backs have instructions on how to play a baseball game by punching out the small squares. Only the "Team Captain" is pictured on the card, and the same captain can be found with different line-ups on his team, creating a large number of collectible variations. Cropping variations in some player photos have been noted, also. The unnumbered issue is checklisted here in alphabetical order.

		NR MT	EX	VG
Complete Set:		4950.	2475.	1475.
Common Player:		50.00	25.00	15.00
(1)	Hank Aaron	200.00	100.00	60.00
(2)	Richie Allen	80.00	40.00	24.00
(3)	Gene Alley	50.00	25.00	15.00
(4)	Felipe Alou	50.00	25.00	15.00
(5)	Matty Alou	50.00	25.00	15.00
(6)	Max Alvis	50.00	25.00	15.00
(7)	Luis Aparicio	75.00	37.00	22.00
(8)	Steve Barber	50.00	25.00	15.00
(9)	Earl Battey	50.00	25.00	15.00
(10)	Clete Boyer	50.00	25.00	15.00
(11)	Ken Boyer	60.00	30.00	18.00
(12)	Lou Brock	65.00	32.00	19.50
(13)	Jim Bunning	60.00	30.00	18.00
(14)	Johnny Callison	50.00	25.00	15.00
(15)	Bert Campaneris	50.00	25.00	15.00
(16)	Leo Cardenas	50.00	25.00	15.00
(17)	Rico Carty	50.00	25.00	15.00
(18)	Norm Cash	50.00	25.00	15.00
(19)	Orlando Cepeda	65.00	32.00	19.50
(20)	Ed Charles	50.00	25.00	15.00
(21)	Roberto Clemente	100.00	50.00	30.00
(22)	Donn Clendenon	50.00	25.00	15.00
(23)	Rocky Colavito	60.00	30.00	18.00
(24)	Tony Conigliaro	60.00	30.00	18.00
(25)	Willie Davis	50.00	25.00	15.00
(26)	Johnny Edwards	50.00	25.00	15.00
(27)	Andy Etchebarren	50.00	25.00	15.00
(28)	Curt Flood	50.00	25.00	15.00
(29)	Bill Freehan	50.00	25.00	15.00
(30)	Jim Fregosi	50.00	25.00	15.00
(31)	Bob Gibson	75.00	37.00	22.00
(32)	Dick Green	50.00	25.00	15.00
(33)	Dick Groat	50.00	25.00	15.00
(34)	Tom Haller	50.00	25.00	15.00
(35)	Jim Ray Hart	50.00	25.00	15.00
(36)	Mike Hershberger	50.00	25.00	15.00
(37)	Elston Howard	80.00	40.00	24.00
(38)	Frank Howard	80.00	40.00	24.00
(39)	Ron Hunt	50.00	25.00	15.00
(40)	Sonny Jackson	50.00	25.00	15.00
(41)	Cleon Jones	50.00	25.00	15.00
(42)	Jim Kaat	60.00	30.00	18.00
(43)	Al Kaline	125.00	62.00	37.00
(44)	Harmon Killebrew	90.00	45.00	27.00
(45)	Bobby Knoop	50.00	25.00	15.00
(46)	Sandy Koufax	250.00	125.00	75.00
(47)	Ed Kranepool	50.00	25.00	15.00
(48)	Jim Lefebvre	50.00	25.00	15.00
(49)	Don Lock	50.00	25.00	15.00
(50)	Jerry Lumpe	50.00	25.00	15.00
(51)	Mickey Mantle	350.00	175.00	105.00
(52)	Juan Marichal	65.00	32.00	19.50
(53)	Willie Mays	200.00	100.00	60.00
(54)	Bill Mazeroski	60.00	30.00	18.00
(55)	Dick McAuliffe	50.00	25.00	15.00
(56)	Tim McCarver	60.00	30.00	18.00
(57)	Denny McLain	50.00	25.00	15.00
(58)	Roy McMillan	50.00	25.00	15.00
(59)	Denis Menke	50.00	25.00	15.00
(60)	Joe Morgan	65.00	32.00	19.50
(61)	Tony Oliva	60.00	30.00	18.00
(62)	Joe Pepitone	50.00	25.00	15.00
(63)	Gaylord Perry	60.00	30.00	18.00
(64)	Vada Pinson	50.00	25.00	15.00
(65)	Boog Powell	60.00	30.00	18.00
(66)	Rick Reichardt	50.00	25.00	15.00
(67)	Brooks Robinson	125.00	62.00	37.00
(68)	Floyd Robinson	50.00	25.00	15.00
(69)	Frank Robinson	100.00	50.00	30.00
(70)	Johnny Romano	50.00	25.00	15.00
(71)	Pete Rose	150.00	75.00	45.00
(72)	John Roseboro	50.00	25.00	15.00

No.	Player	NR MT	EX	VG
(73)	Ron Santo	50.00	25.00	15.00
(74)	Chico Salmon	50.00	25.00	15.00
(75)	George Scott	50.00	25.00	15.00
(76)	Sonny Siebert	50.00	25.00	15.00
(77)	Russ Snyder	50.00	25.00	15.00
(78)	Willie Stargell	75.00	37.00	22.00
(79)	Mel Stottlemyre	50.00	25.00	15.00
(80)	Joe Torre	50.00	25.00	15.00
(81)	Cesar Tovar	50.00	25.00	15.00
(82)	Tom Tresh	50.00	25.00	15.00
(83)	Zoilo Versalles	50.00	25.00	15.00
(84)	Leon Wagner	50.00	25.00	15.00
(85)	Bill White	60.00	30.00	18.00
(86)	Fred Whitfield	50.00	25.00	15.00
(87)	Billy Williams	100.00	50.00	30.00
(88)	Jimmy Wynn	50.00	25.00	15.00
(89)	Carl Yastrzemski	150.00	75.00	45.00

1968 Topps 3-D

These are very rare pioneer issues on the part of Topps. The cards measure 2-1/4" by 3-1/2" and were specially printed to simulate a three-dimensional effect. Backgrounds are a purposely blurred stadium scene, in front of which was a normally sharp color player photograph. The outer layer is a thin coating of ribbed plastic. The special process gives the picture the illusion of depth when the card is moved or tilted. As this was done two years before Kellogg's began its 3-D cards, this 12-card test issue really was breaking new ground. Unfortunately, production and distribution were limited making the cards very tough to find.

		NR MT	EX	VG
Complete Set:		9000.	4500.	2500.
Common Player:		350.00	175.00	105.00
(1)	Bob Clemente	2500.	1250.	750.00
(2)	Willie Davis	400.00	200.00	125.00
(3)	Ron Fairly	400.00	200.00	125.00
(4)	Curt Flood	400.00	200.00	125.00
(5)	Jim Lonborg	400.00	200.00	125.00
(6)	Jim Maloney	350.00	175.00	105.00
(7)	Tony Perez	600.00	300.00	175.00
(8)	Boog Powell	500.00	250.00	150.00
(9)	Bill Robinson	350.00	175.00	105.00
(10)	Rusty Staub	450.00	230.00	135.00
(11)	Mel Stottlemyre	400.00	200.00	120.00
(12)	Ron Swoboda	350.00	175.00	105.00

1969 Topps

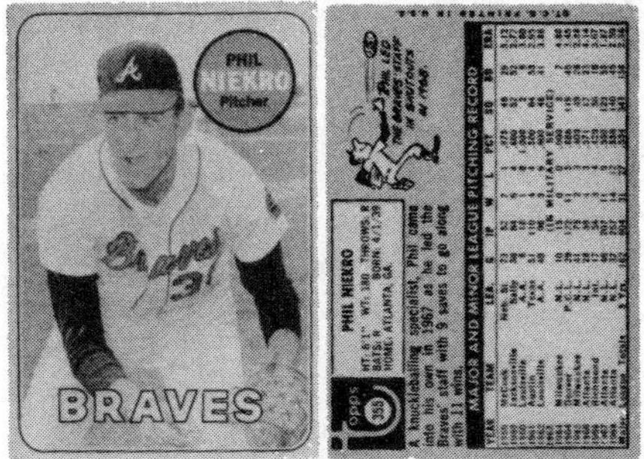

The 1969 Topps set broke yet another record for quantity as the issue is officially a whopping 664 cards. With substantial numbers of variations, the number of possible cards runs closer to 700. The design of the 2-1/2" by 3-1/2" cards in the set feature a color photo with the team name printed in block letters underneath. A circle contains the player's name and position. Card backs returned to a horizontal format. Despite the size of the set, it contains no teamcards. It does, however, have multi-player cards, All-Stars, statistical leaders, and World Series highlights. Most significant among the varieties are white and yellow letter cards from the run of #'s 440-511. The complete set prices below do not include the scarcer and more expensive "white letter" variations.

	NR MT	EX	VG
Complete Set (664):	2800.	1400.	840.00
Common Player (1-218):	1.00	.50	.30
Common Player (219-327):	1.50	.70	.45
Common Player (328-512):	1.00	.50	.30
Common Player (513-588):	1.50	.70	.45
Common Player (589-664):	2.50	1.25	.70

No.	Player	NR MT	EX	VG
1	A.L. Batting Leaders (Danny Cater, Tony Oliva, Carl Yastrzemski)	10.00	5.00	3.00
2	N.L. Batting Leaders (Felipe Alou, Matty Alou, Pete Rose)	4.00	2.00	1.25
3	A.L. RBI Leaders (Ken Harrelson, Frank Howard, Jim Northrup)	2.00	1.00	.60
4	N.L. RBI Leaders (Willie McCovey, Ron Santo, Billy Williams)	4.00	2.00	1.25
5	A.L. Home Run Leaders (Ken Harrelson, Willie Horton, Frank Howard)	2.00	1.00	.60
6	N.L. Home Run Leaders (Richie Allen, Ernie Banks, Willie McCovey)	4.00	2.00	1.25
7	A.L. ERA Leaders (Sam McDowell, Dave McNally, Luis Tiant)	2.00	1.00	.60
8	N.L. ERA Leaders (Bobby Bolin, Bob Gibson, Bob Veale)	3.00	1.50	.90
9	A.L. Pitching Leaders (Denny McLain, Dave McNally, Mel Stottlemyre, Luis Tiant)	2.50	1.25	.70
10	N.L. Pitching Leaders (Bob Gibson, Fergie Jenkins, Juan Marichal)	3.50	1.75	1.00
11	A.L. Strikeout Leaders (Sam McDowell, Denny McLain, Luis Tiant)	2.50	1.25	.70
12	N.L. Strikeout Leaders (Bob Gibson, Fergie Jenkins, Bill Singer)	3.00	1.50	.90
13	Mickey Stanley	1.00	.50	.30
14	Al McBean	1.00	.50	.30
15	Boog Powell	2.00	1.00	.60
16	Giants Rookies (Cesar Gutierrez, Rich Robertson)	1.00	.50	.30
17	Mike Marshall	1.00	.50	.30
18	Dick Schofield	1.00	.50	.30
19	Ken Suarez	1.00	.50	.30
20	Ernie Banks	20.00	10.00	6.00
21	Jose Santiago	1.00	.50	.30
22	Jesus Alou	1.00	.50	.30
23	Lew Krausse	1.00	.50	.30
24	Walt Alston	3.00	1.50	.90
25	Roy White	1.00	.50	.30
26	Clay Carroll	1.00	.50	.30
27	Bernie Allen	1.00	.50	.30
28	Mike Ryan	1.00	.50	.30
29	Dave Morehead	1.00	.50	.30
30	Bob Allison	1.00	.50	.30
31	Mets Rookies (*Gary Gentry*, Amos Otis)	1.50	.70	.45
32	Sammy Ellis	1.00	.50	.30
33	Wayne Causey	1.00	.50	.30
34	Gary Peters	1.00	.50	.30
35	Joe Morgan	10.00	5.00	3.00
36	Luke Walker	1.00	.50	.30
37	Curt Motton	1.00	.50	.30
38	Zoilo Versalles	1.00	.50	.30
39	Dick Hughes	1.00	.50	.30
40	Mayo Smith	1.00	.50	.30
41	Bob Barton	1.00	.50	.30
42	Tommy Harper	1.00	.50	.30
43	Joe Niekro	1.50	.70	.45
44	Danny Cater	1.00	.50	.30
45	Maury Wills	2.00	1.00	.60
46	Fritz Peterson	1.00	.50	.30
47a	Paul Popovich (emblem visible thru airbrush)	25.00	12.50	7.50
47b	Paul Popovich (helmet emblem completely airbrushed)	1.00	.50	.30
48	Brant Alyea	1.00	.50	.30
49a	Royals Rookies (Steve Jones) (Rodriquez on front)	27.00	13.50	8.00
49a	Royals Rookies (Eliseo Rodriquez) (Rodriquez on front)	27.00	13.50	8.00
49b	Royals Rookies (Steve Jones) (Rodriguez on front)	1.00	.50	.30
49b	Royals Rookies (Eliseo Rodriguez) (Rodriguez on front)	1.00	.50	.30
50	Roberto Clemente	50.00	25.00	15.00
51	Woody Fryman	1.00	.50	.30
52	Mike Andrews	1.00	.50	.30
53	Sonny Jackson	1.00	.50	.30
54	Cisco Carlos	1.00	.50	.30
55	Jerry Grote	1.00	.50	.30
56	Rich Reese	1.00	.50	.30
57	Checklist 1-109 (Denny McLain)	3.00	1.50	.90
58	Fred Gladding	1.00	.50	.30
59	Jay Johnstone	1.00	.50	.30
60	Nelson Briles	1.00	.50	.30
61	Jimmie Hall	1.00	.50	.30
62	Chico Salmon	1.00	.50	.30
63	Jim Hickman	1.00	.50	.30
64	Bill Monbouquette	1.00	.50	.30
65	Willie Davis	1.00	.50	.30
66	Orioles Rookies (Mike Adamson, Merv Rettenmund)	1.00	.50	.30
67	Bill Stoneman	1.00	.50	.30
68	Dave Duncan	1.00	.50	.30
69	Steve Hamilton	1.00	.50	.30
70	Tommy Helms	1.00	.50	.30
71	Steve Whitaker	1.00	.50	.30
72	Ron Taylor	1.00	.50	.30
73	Johnny Briggs	1.00	.50	.30
74	Preston Gomez	1.00	.50	.30
75	Luis Aparicio	5.00	2.50	1.50
76	Norm Miller	1.00	.50	.30
77a	Ron Perranoski (LA visible thru airbrush)	25.00	12.50	7.50
77b	Ron Perranoski (cap emblem completely airbrushed)	1.00	.50	.30
78	Tom Satriano	1.00	.50	.30
79	Milt Pappas	1.00	.50	.30
80	Norm Cash	1.75	.90	.50
81	Mel Queen	1.00	.50	.30
82	Pirates Rookies (*Rich Hebner*, Al Oliver)	12.00	6.00	3.50
83	Mike Ferraro	1.00	.50	.30
84	Bob Humphreys	1.00	.50	.30
85	Lou Brock	22.00	11.00	6.50
86	Pete Richert	1.00	.50	.30
87	Horace Clarke	1.00	.50	.30
88	Rich Nye	1.00	.50	.30
89	Russ Gibson	1.00	.50	.30
90	Jerry Koosman	2.00	1.00	.60
91	Al Dark	1.00	.50	.30
92	Jack Billingham	1.00	.50	.30
93	Joe Foy	1.00	.50	.30
94	Hank Aguirre	1.00	.50	.30
95	Johnny Bench	100.00	50.00	30.00
96	Denver Lemaster	1.00	.50	.30
97	Buddy Bradford	1.00	.50	.30
98	Dave Giusti	1.00	.50	.30
99a	Twins Rookies (Danny Morris) (black loop above "Twins")	20.00	10.00	6.00
99a	Twins Rookies (*Graig Nettles*) (black loop above "Twins")	20.00	10.00	6.00
99b	Twins Rookies (Danny Morris) (no black loop)	20.00	10.00	6.00
99b	*Graig Nettles*	20.00	10.00	6.00
100	Hank Aaron	65.00	32.00	19.50
101	Daryl Patterson	1.00	.50	.30
102	Jim Davenport	1.00	.50	.30
103	Roger Repoz	1.00	.50	.30
104	Steve Blass	1.00	.50	.30
105	Rick Monday	1.00	.50	.30
106	Jim Hannan	1.00	.50	.30
107a	Checklist 110-218 (Bob Gibson) (161 is Jim Purdin)	3.00	1.50	.90
107b	Checklist 110-218 (Bob gibson) (161 is John Purdin)	6.00	3.00	1.75
108	Tony Taylor	1.00	.50	.30
109	Jim Lonborg	1.25	.60	.40
110	Mike Shannon	1.00	.50	.30
111	Johnny Morris	1.00	.50	.30
112	J.C. Martin	1.00	.50	.30
113	Dave May	1.00	.50	.30
114	Yankees Rookies (Alan Closter, John Cumberland)	1.00	.50	.30
115	Bill Hands	1.00	.50	.30
116	Chuck Harrison	1.00	.50	.30
117	Jim Fairey	1.00	.50	.30
118	Stan Williams	1.00	.50	.30
119	Doug Rader	1.00	.50	.30
120	Pete Rose	35.00	17.50	10.50
121	Joe Grzenda	1.00	.50	.30
122	Ron Fairly	1.00	.50	.30
123	Wilbur Wood	1.25	.60	.40
124	Hank Bauer	1.00	.50	.30
125	Ray Sadecki	1.00	.50	.30
126	Dick Tracewski	1.00	.50	.30
127	Kevin Collins	1.00	.50	.30
128	Tommie Aaron	1.00	.50	.30
129	Bill McCool	1.00	.50	.30
130	Carl Yastrzemski	18.00	9.00	5.50
131	Chris Cannizzaro	1.00	.50	.30
132	Dave Baldwin	1.00	.50	.30
133	Johnny Callison	1.00	.50	.30
134	Jim Weaver	1.00	.50	.30
135	Tommy Davis	1.00	.50	.30
136	Cards Rookies (Steve Huntz, Mike Torrez)	1.00	.50	.30
137	Wally Bunker	1.00	.50	.30
138	John Bateman	1.00	.50	.30
139	Andy Kosco	1.00	.50	.30
140	Jim Lefebvre	1.00	.50	.30
141	Bill Dillman	1.00	.50	.30
142	Woody Woodward	1.00	.50	.30
143	Joe Nossek	1.00	.50	.30
144	Bob Hendley	1.00	.50	.30
145	Max Alvis	1.00	.50	.30
146	Jim Perry	1.00	.50	.30
147	Leo Durocher	2.00	1.00	.60
148	Lee Stange	1.00	.50	.30
149	Ollie Brown	1.00	.50	.30
150	Denny McLain	2.00	1.00	.60
151a	Clay Dalrymple (Phillies)	25.00	12.50	7.50
151b	Clay Dalrymple (Orioles)	1.00	.50	.30
152	Tommie Sisk	1.00	.50	.30
153	Ed Brinkman	1.00	.50	.30
154	Jim Britton	1.00	.50	.30
155	Pete Ward	1.00	.50	.30
156	Astros Rookies (Hal Gilson, Leon McFadden)	1.00	.50	.30
157	Bob Rodgers	1.00	.50	.30
158	Joe Gibbon	1.00	.50	.30
159	Jerry Adair	1.00	.50	.30
160	Vada Pinson	2.00	1.00	.60
161	John Purdin	1.00	.50	.30
162	World Series Game 1 (Gibson Fans 17; Sets New Record)	4.00	2.00	1.25
163	World Series Game 2 (Tiger Homers Deck The Cards)	3.00	1.50	.90
164	World Series Game 3 (McCarver's Homer Puts St. Louis Ahead)	3.50	1.75	1.00
165	World Series Game 4 (Brock's Lead-Off HR Starts Cards' Romp)	3.50	1.75	1.00
166	World Series Game 5 (Kaline's Key Hit Sparks Tiger Rally)	4.00	2.00	1.25
167	World Series Game 6 (Tiger 10-Run Inning Ties Mark)	3.50	1.75	1.00
168	World Series Game 7 (Lolich Series Hero Outduels Gibson)	3.50	1.75	1.00
169	World Series Summary (Tigers Celebrate Their Victory)	3.50	1.75	1.00
170	Frank Howard	1.50	.70	.45
171	Glenn Beckert	1.00	.50	.30
172	Jerry Stephenson	1.00	.50	.30
173	White Sox Rookies (Bob Christian, Gerry Nyman)	1.00	.50	.30
174	Grant Jackson	1.00	.50	.30

175 Jim Bunning 4.00 2.00 1.25
176 Joe Azcue 1.00 .50 .30
177 Ron Reed 1.00 .50 .30
178 Ray Oyler 1.00 .50 .30
179 Don Pavletich 1.00 .50 .30
180 Willie Horton 1.00 .50 .30
181 Mel Nelson 1.00 .50 .30
182 Bill Rigney 1.00 .50 .30
183 Don Shaw 1.00 .50 .30
184 Roberto Pena 1.00 .50 .30
185 Tom Phoebus 1.00 .50 .30
186 John Edwards 1.00 .50 .30
187 Leon Wagner 1.00 .50 .30
188 Rick Wise 1.00 .50 .30
189 Red Sox Rookies (Joe Lahoud, John Thibdeau) 1.00 .50 .30
190 Willie Mays 65.00 32.00 19.50
191 Lindy McDaniel 1.00 .50 .30
192 Jose Pagan 1.00 .50 .30
193 Don Cardwell 1.00 .50 .30
194 Ted Uhlaender 1.00 .50 .30
195 John Odom 1.00 .50 .30
196 Lum Harris 1.00 .50 .30
197 Dick Selma 1.00 .50 .30
198 Willie Smith 1.00 .50 .30
199 Jim French 1.00 .50 .30
200 Bob Gibson 12.50 6.25 3.75
201 Russ Snyder 1.00 .50 .30
202 Don Wilson 1.00 .50 .30
203 Dave Johnson 1.00 .50 .30
204 Jack Hiatt 1.00 .50 .30
205 Rick Reichardt 1.00 .50 .30
206 Phillies Rookies (Larry Hisle, Barry Lersch) 1.00 .50 .30
207 Roy Face 1.00 .50 .30
208a Donn Clendenon (Expos) 18.00 9.00 5.50
208b Donn Clendenon (Houston) 1.00 .50 .30
209 Larry Haney (photo reversed) 1.00 .50 .30
210 Felix Millan 1.00 .50 .30
211 Galen Cisco 1.00 .50 .30
212 Tom Tresh 1.50 .70 .45
213 Gerry Arrigo 1.00 .50 .30
214 Checklist 219-327 2.50 1.25 .70
215 Rico Petrocelli 1.25 .60 .40
216 Don Sutton 4.00 2.00 1.25
217 John Donaldson 1.00 .50 .30
218 John Roseboro 1.00 .50 .30
219 *Freddie Patek* 2.00 1.00 .60
220 Sam McDowell 1.50 .70 .45
221 Art Shamsky 1.50 .70 .45
222 Duane Josephson 1.50 .70 .45
223 Tom Dukes 1.50 .70 .45
224 Angels Rookies (Bill Harrelson, Steve Kealey) 1.50 .70 .45
225 Don Kessinger 1.50 .70 .45
226 Bruce Howard 1.50 .70 .45
227 Frank Johnson 1.50 .70 .45
228 Dave Leonhard 1.50 .70 .45
229 Don Lock 1.50 .70 .45
230 Rusty Staub 2.50 1.25 .70
231 Pat Dobson 1.50 .70 .45
232 Dave Ricketts 1.50 .70 .45
233 Steve Barber 1.50 .70 .45
234 Dave Bristol 1.50 .70 .45
235 Catfish Hunter 12.00 6.00 3.50
236 Manny Mota 1.50 .70 .45
237 *Bobby Cox* 1.50 .70 .45
238 Ken Johnson 1.50 .70 .45
239 Bob Taylor 1.50 .70 .45
240 Ken Harrelson 2.00 1.00 .60
241 Jim Brewer 1.50 .70 .45
242 Frank Kostro 1.50 .70 .45
243 Ron Kline 1.50 .70 .45
244 Indians Rookies (*Ray Fosse*, George Woodson) 1.50 .70 .45
245 Ed Charles 1.50 .70 .45
246 Joe Coleman 1.50 .70 .45
247 Gene Oliver 1.50 .70 .45
248 Bob Priddy 1.50 .70 .45
249 Ed Spiezio 1.50 .70 .45
250 Frank Robinson 26.00 13.00 7.75
251 Ron Herbel 1.50 .70 .45
252 Chuck Cottier 1.50 .70 .45
253 Jerry Johnson 1.50 .70 .45
254 Joe Schultz 1.50 .70 .45
255 Steve Carlton 45.00 22.00 13.50
256 Gates Brown 1.50 .70 .45
257 Jim Ray 1.50 .70 .45
258 Jackie Hernandez 1.50 .70 .45
259 Bill Short 1.50 .70 .45
260 *Reggie Jackson* 550.00 275.00 165.00
261 Bob Johnson 1.50 .70 .45
262 Mike Kekich 1.50 .70 .45
263 Jerry May 1.50 .70 .45
264 Bill Landis 1.50 .70 .45
265 Chico Cardenas 1.50 .70 .45
266 Dodgers Rookies (Alan Foster, Tom Hutton) 1.50 .70 .45
267 Vicente Romo 1.50 .70 .45
268 Al Spangler 1.50 .70 .45
269 Al Weis 1.50 .70 .45
270 Mickey Lolich 3.50 1.75 1.00
271 Larry Stahl 1.50 .70 .45
272 Ed Stroud 1.50 .70 .45
273 Ron Willis 1.50 .70 .45
274 Clyde King 1.50 .70 .45
275 Vic Davalillo 1.50 .70 .45
276 Gary Wagner 1.50 .70 .45
277 *Rod Hendricks* 1.50 .70 .45
278 Gary Geiger 1.50 .70 .45
279 Roger Nelson 1.50 .70 .45
280 Alex Johnson 1.50 .70 .45
281 Ted Kubiak 1.50 .70 .45
282 Pat Jarvis 1.50 .70 .45
283 Sandy Alomar 1.50 .70 .45
284 Expos Rookies (Jerry Robertson, Mike Wegener) 1.50 .70 .45
285 Don Mincher 1.50 .70 .45
286 *Dock Ellis* 1.50 .70 .45
287 Jose Tartabull 1.50 .70 .45
288 Ken Holtzman 1.50 .70 .45
289 Bart Shirley 1.50 .70 .45
290 Jim Kaat 4.50 2.25 1.25
291 Vern Fuller 1.50 .70 .45
292 Al Downing 1.50 .70 .45
293 Dick Dietz 1.50 .70 .45
294 Jim Lemon 1.50 .70 .45
295 Tony Perez 10.00 5.00 3.00
296 *Andy Messersmith* 1.50 .70 .45
297 Deron Johnson 1.50 .70 .45
298 Dave Nicholson 1.50 .70 .45
299 Mark Belanger 1.50 .70 .45
300 Felipe Alou 2.50 1.25 .70
301 Darrell Brandon 1.50 .70 .45
302 Jim Pagliaroni 1.50 .70 .45
303 Cal Koonce 1.50 .70 .45
304 Padres Rookies (Bill Davis, Cito Gaston) 15.00 7.50 4.50
305 Dick McAuliffe 1.50 .70 .45
306 Jim Grant 1.50 .70 .45
307 Gary Kolb 1.50 .70 .45
308 Wade Blasingame 1.50 .70 .45
309 Walt Williams 1.50 .70 .45
310 Tom Haller 1.50 .70 .45
311 *Sparky Lyle* 12.50 6.25 3.75
312 Lee Elia 1.50 .70 .45
313 Bill Robinson 1.50 .70 .45
314 Checklist 328-425 (Don Drysdale) 3.50 1.75 1.00
315 Eddie Fisher 1.50 .70 .45
316 Hal Lanier 1.50 .70 .45
317 Bruce Look 1.50 .70 .45
318 Jack Fisher 1.50 .70 .45
319 Ken McMullen 1.50 .70 .45
320 Dal Maxvill 1.50 .70 .45
321 Jim McAndrew 1.50 .70 .45
322 Jose Vidal 1.50 .70 .45
323 Larry Miller 1.50 .70 .45
324 Tigers Rookies (Les Cain, Dave Campbell) 1.50 .70 .45
325 Jose Cardenal 1.50 .70 .45
326 Gary Sutherland 1.50 .70 .45
327 Willie Crawford 1.50 .70 .45
328 Joe Horlen 1.00 .50 .30
329 Rick Joseph 1.00 .50 .30
330 Tony Conigliaro 1.50 .70 .45
331 Braves Rookies (Gil Garrido, Tom House) 1.00 .50 .30
332 Fred Talbot 1.00 .50 .30
333 Ivan Murrell 1.00 .50 .30
334 Phil Roof 1.00 .50 .30
335 Bill Mazeroski 2.50 1.25 .70
336 Jim Roland 1.00 .50 .30
337 Marty Martinez 1.00 .50 .30
338 *Del Unser* 1.00 .50 .30
339 Reds Rookies (Steve Mingori, Jose Pena) 1.00 .50 .30
340 Dave McNally 1.00 .50 .30
341 Dave Adlesh 1.00 .50 .30
342 Bubba Morton 1.00 .50 .30
343 Dan Frisella 1.00 .50 .30
344 Tom Matchick 1.00 .50 .30
345 Frank Linzy 1.00 .50 .30
346 Wayne Comer 1.00 .50 .30
347 Randy Hundley 1.00 .50 .30
348 Steve Hargan 1.00 .50 .30
349 Dick Williams 1.25 .60 .40
350 Richie Allen 2.00 1.00 .60
351 Carroll Sembera 1.00 .50 .30
352 Paul Schaal 1.00 .50 .30
353 Jeff Torborg 1.00 .50 .30
354 Nate Oliver 1.00 .50 .30
355 Phil Niekro 7.00 3.50 2.00
356 Frank Quilici 1.00 .50 .30
357 Carl Taylor 1.00 .50 .30
358 Athletics Rookies (George Lauzerique, Roberto Rodriguez) 1.00 .50 .30
359 Dick Kelley 1.00 .50 .30
360 Jim Wynn 1.00 .50 .30
361 Gary Holman 1.00 .50 .30
362 Jim Maloney 1.00 .50 .30
363 Russ Nixon 1.00 .50 .30
364 Tommie Agee 1.00 .50 .30
365 Jim Fregosi 1.00 .50 .30
366 Bo Belinsky 1.00 .50 .30
367 Lou Johnson 1.00 .50 .30
368 Vic Roznovsky 1.00 .50 .30
369 Bob Skinner 1.00 .50 .30
370 Juan Marichal 7.00 3.50 2.00
371 Sal Bando 1.25 .60 .40
372 Adolfo Phillips 1.00 .50 .30
373 Fred Lasher 1.00 .50 .30
374 Bob Tillman 1.00 .50 .30
375 Harmon Killebrew 20.00 10.00 6.00
376 Royals Rookies (Mike Fiore, Jim Rooker) 1.00 .50 .30
377 Gary Bell 1.00 .50 .30
378 Jose Herrera 1.00 .50 .30
379 Ken Boyer 1.50 .70 .45
380 Stan Bahnsen 1.00 .50 .30
381 Ed Kranepool 1.00 .50 .30
382 Pat Corrales 1.00 .50 .30
383 Casey Cox 1.00 .50 .30
384 Larry Shepard 1.00 .50 .30
385 Orlando Cepeda 4.00 2.00 1.25
386 Jim McGlothlin 1.00 .50 .30
387 Bobby Klaus 1.00 .50 .30
388 Tom McCraw 1.00 .50 .30
389 Dan Coombs 1.00 .50 .30
390 Bill Freehan 1.00 .50 .30
391 Ray Culp 1.00 .50 .30
392 Bob Burda 1.00 .50 .30
393 Gene Brabender 1.00 .50 .30
394 *Lou Piniella*, Marv Staehle 2.00 1.00 .60
395 Chris Short 1.00 .50 .30
396 Jim Campanis 1.00 .50 .30
397 Chuck Dobson 1.00 .50 .30
398 Tito Francona 1.00 .50 .30
399 Bob Bailey 1.00 .50 .30
400 Don Drysdale 10.00 5.00 3.00
401 Jake Gibbs 1.00 .50 .30
402 Ken Boswell 1.00 .50 .30
403 Bob Miller 1.00 .50 .30
404 Cubs Rookies (Vic LaRose, Gary Ross) 1.00 .50 .30
405 Lee May 1.00 .50 .30
406 Phil Ortega 1.00 .50 .30
407 Tom Egan 1.00 .50 .30
408 Nate Colbert 1.00 .50 .30
409 Bob Moose 1.00 .50 .30
410 Al Kaline 18.00 9.00 5.50
411 Larry Dierker 1.00 .50 .30
412 Checklist 426-512 (Mickey Mantle) 9.00 4.50 2.75
413 Roland Sheldon 1.00 .50 .30
414 Duke Sims 1.00 .50 .30
415 Ray Washburn 1.00 .50 .30
416 Willie McCovey (All-Star) 3.50 1.75 1.00
417 Ken Harrelson (All-Star) 1.00 .50 .30
418 Tommy Helms (All-Star) 1.00 .50 .30
419 Rod Carew (All-Star) 8.00 4.00 2.50
420 Ron Santo (All-Star) 1.50 .70 .45
421 Brooks Robinson (All-Star) 4.00 2.00 1.25
422 Don Kessinger (All-Star) 1.00 .50 .30
423 Bert Campaneris (All-Star) 1.00 .50 .30
424 Pete Rose (All-Star) 12.00 6.00 3.50
425 Carl Yastrzemski (All-Star) 8.00 4.00 2.50
426 Curt Flood (All-Star) 1.00 .50 .30
427 Tony Oliva (All-Star) 1.50 .70 .45
428 Lou Brock (All-Star) 5.00 2.50 1.50
429 Willie Horton (All-Star) 1.00 .50 .30
430 Johnny Bench (All-Star) 12.00 6.00 3.50
431 Bill Freehan (All-Star) 1.00 .50 .30
432 Bob Gibson (All-Star) 5.00 2.50 1.50
433 Denny McLain (All-Star) 1.50 .70 .45
434 Jerry Koosman (All-Star) 1.00 .50 .30
435 Sam McDowell (All-Star) 1.00 .50 .30
436 Gene Alley 1.00 .50 .30
437 Luis Alcaraz 1.00 .50 .30
438 Gary Waslewski 1.00 .50 .30
439 White Sox Rookies (Ed Herrmann, Dan Lazar) 1.00 .50 .30
440a Willie McCovey (last name in white) 120.00 60.00 36.00
440b Willie McCovey (last name in yellow) 15.00 7.50 4.50
441a Dennis Higgins (last name in white) 30.00 15.00 9.00
441b Dennis Higgins (last name in yellow) 1.00 .50 .30
442 Ty Cline 1.00 .50 .30
443 Don Wert 1.00 .50 .30
444a Joe Moeller (last name in white) 30.00 15.00 9.00
444b Joe Moeller (last name in yellow) 1.00 .50 .30
445 Bobby Knoop 1.00 .50 .30
446 Claude Raymond 1.00 .50 .30
447a Ralph Houk (last name in white) 40.00 20.00 12.00
447b Ralph Houk (last name in yellow) 1.50 .70 .45
448 Bob Tolan 1.00 .50 .30
449 Paul Lindblad 1.00 .50 .30
450 Billy Williams 6.00 3.00 1.75
451a Rich Rollins (first name in white) 30.00 15.00 9.00
451b Rich Rollins (first name in yellow) 1.25 .60 .40
452a Al Ferrara (first name in white) 30.00 15.00 9.00
452b Al Ferrara (first name in yellow) 1.00 .50 .30
453 Mike Cuellar 1.00 .50 .30
454a Phillies Rookies (Larry Colton) (*Don Money*) (names in white) 30.00 15.00 9.00
454b Phillies Rookies (Larry Colton) (*Don Money*) (names in yellow) 1.25 .60 .40
455 Sonny Siebert 1.00 .50 .30
456 Bud Harrelson 1.00 .50 .30
457 Dalton Jones 1.00 .50 .30
458 Curt Blefary 1.00 .50 .30
459 Dave Boswell 1.00 .50 .30
460 Joe Torre 1.00 .50 .30
461a Mike Epstein (last name in white) 30.00 15.00 9.00
461b Mike Epstein (last name in yellow) 1.00 .50 .30
462 Red Schoendienst 3.00 1.50 .90
463 Dennis Ribant 1.00 .50 .30
464a Dave Marshall (last name in white) 30.00 15.00 9.00
464b Dave Marshall (last name in yellow) 1.00 .50 .30
465 Tommy John 4.00 2.00 1.25
466 John Boccabella 1.00 .50 .30
467 Tom Reynolds 1.00 .50 .30
468a Pirates Rookies (Bruce Dal Canton) (Bob Robertson) (names in white) 30.00 15.00 9.00
468b Pirates Rookies (Bruce Dal Canton) (Bob Robertson) (names in yellow) 1.00 .50 .30
469 Chico Ruiz 1.00 .50 .30
470a Mel Stottlemyre (last name in white) 40.00 20.00 12.00
470b Mel Stottlemyre (last name in yellow) 1.50 .70 .45
471a Ted Savage (last name in white) 30.00 15.00 9.00
471b Ted Savage (last name in yellow) 1.00 .50 .30
472 Jim Price 1.00 .50 .30
473a Jose Arcia (first name in white) 30.00 15.00 9.00
473b Jose Arcia (first name in yellow) 1.00 .50 .30

#	Player	NR MT	EX	VG
474	Tom Murphy	1.00	.50	.30
475	Tim McCarver	1.50	.70	.45
476a	Red Sox Rookies (*Ken Brett*, Gerry Moses) (names in white)	30.00	15.00	9.00
476b	Red Sox Rookies (*Ken Brett*, Gerry Moses) (names in yellow)	1.00	.50	.30
477	Jeff James	1.00	.50	.30
478	Don Buford	1.00	.50	.30
479	Richie Scheinblum	1.00	.50	.30
480	Tom Seaver	85.00	42.00	25.00
481	*Bill Melton*	1.25	.60	.40
482a	Jim Gosger (first name in white)	30.00	15.00	9.00
482b	Jim Gosger (first name in yellow)	1.25	.60	.40
483	Ted Abernathy	1.00	.50	.30
484	Joe Gordon	1.00	.50	.30
485a	Gaylord Perry (last name in white)	125.00	62.00	37.00
485b	Gaylord Perry (last name in yellow)	10.00	5.00	3.00
486a	Paul Casanova (last name in white)	30.00	15.00	9.00
486b	Paul Casanova (last name in yellow)	1.00	.50	.30
487	Denis Menke	1.00	.50	.30
488	Joe Sparma	1.00	.50	.30
489	Clete Boyer	1.00	.50	.30
490	Matty Alou	1.00	.50	.30
491a	Twins Rookies (Jerry Crider, George Mitterwald) (names in white)	30.00	15.00	9.00
491b	Twins Rookies (Jerry Crider, George Mitterwald) (names in yellow)	1.00	.50	.30
492	Tony Cloninger	1.00	.50	.30
493a	Wes Parker (last name in white)	30.00	15.00	9.00
493b	Wes Parker (last name in yellow)	1.00	.50	.30
494	Ken Berry	1.00	.50	.30
495	Bert Campaneris	1.00	.50	.30
496	Larry Jaster	1.00	.50	.30
497	Julian Javier	1.00	.50	.30
498	Juan Pizarro	1.00	.50	.30
499	Astros Rookies (Don Bryant, Steve Shea)	1.00	.50	.30
500a	Mickey Mantle (last name in white)	750.00	375.00	225.00
500b	Mickey Mantle (last name in yellow)	265.00	132.00	79.00
501a	Tony Gonzalez (first name in white)	30.00	15.00	9.00
501b	Tony Gonzalez (first name in yellow)	1.00	.50	.30
502	Minnie Rojas	1.00	.50	.30
503	Larry Brown	1.00	.50	.30
504	Checklist 513-588 (Brooks Robinson)	4.00	2.00	1.25
505a	Bobby Bolin (last name in white)	30.00	15.00	9.00
505b	Bobby Bolin (last name in yellow)	1.00	.50	.30
506	Paul Blair	1.00	.50	.30
507	Cookie Rojas	1.00	.50	.30
508	Moe Drabowsky	1.00	.50	.30
509	Manny Sanguillen	1.00	.50	.30
510	Rod Carew	55.00	27.00	16.50
511a	Diego Segui (first name in white)	30.00	15.00	9.00
511b	Diego Segui (first name in yellow)	1.00	.50	.30
512	Cleon Jones	1.00	.50	.30
513	Camilo Pascual	1.50	.70	.45
514	Mike Lum	1.50	.70	.45
515	Dick Green	1.50	.70	.45
516	Earl Weaver	8.00	4.00	2.50
517	Mike McCormick	1.50	.70	.45
518	Fred Whitfield	1.50	.70	.45
519	Yankees Rookies (Len Boehmer, Gerry Kenney)	1.50	.70	.45
520	Bob Veale	1.50	.70	.45
521	George Thomas	1.50	.70	.45
522	Joe Hoerner	1.50	.70	.45
523	Bob Chance	1.50	.70	.45
524	Expos Rookies (Jose Laboy, Floyd Wicker)	1.50	.70	.45
525	Earl Wilson	1.50	.70	.45
526	Hector Torres	1.50	.70	.45
527	Al Lopez	3.00	1.50	.90
528	Claude Osteen	1.50	.70	.45
529	Ed Kirkpatrick	1.50	.70	.45
530	Cesar Tovar	1.50	.70	.45
531	Dick Farrell	1.50	.70	.45
532	Bird Hill Aces (Mike Cuellar, Jim Hardin, Dave McNally, Tom Phoebus)	3.00	1.50	.90
533	Nolan Ryan	500.00	250.00	150.00
534	Jerry McNertney	1.50	.70	.45
535	Phil Regan	1.50	.70	.45
536	Padres Rookies (Danny Breeden, Dave Roberts)	1.50	.70	.45
537	Mike Paul	1.50	.70	.45
538	Charlie Smith	1.50	.70	.45
539	Ted Shows How (Mike Epstein, Ted Williams)	3.25	1.75	1.00
540	Curt Flood	2.00	1.00	.60
541	Joe Verbanic	1.50	.70	.45
542	Bob Aspromonte	1.50	.70	.45
543	Fred Newman	1.50	.70	.45
544	Tigers Rookies (Mike Kilkenny, Ron Woods)	1.50	.70	.45
545	Willie Stargell	10.00	5.00	3.00
546	Jim Nash	1.50	.70	.45
547	Billy Martin	5.00	2.50	1.50
548	Bob Locker	1.50	.70	.45
549	Ron Brand	1.50	.70	.45
550	Brooks Robinson	20.00	10.00	6.00
551	Wayne Granger	1.50	.70	.45
552	Dodgers Rookies (*Ted Sizemore*, Bill Sudakis)	1.75	.90	.50
553	Ron Davis	1.50	.70	.45
554	Frank Bertaina	1.50	.70	.45
555	Jim Hart	1.50	.70	.45
556	A's Stars (Sal Bando, Bert Campaneris, Danny Cater)	2.50	1.25	.70
557	Frank Fernandez	1.50	.70	.45
558	*Tom Burgmeier*	1.50	.70	.45
559	Cards Rookies (Joe Hague, Jim Hicks)	1.50	.70	.45
560	Luis Tiant	2.50	1.25	.70
561	Ron Clark	1.50	.70	.45
562	*Bob Watson*	1.50	.70	.45
563	Marty Pattin	1.50	.70	.45
564	Gil Hodges	6.00	3.00	1.75
565	Hoyt Wilhelm	7.00	3.50	2.00
566	Ron Hansen	1.50	.70	.45
567	Pirates Rookies (Elvio Jimenez, Jim Shellenback)	1.50	.70	.45
568	Cecil Upshaw	1.50	.70	.45
569	Billy Harris	1.50	.70	.45
570	Ron Santo	2.00	1.00	.60
571	Cap Peterson	1.50	.70	.45
572	Giants Heroes (Juan Marichal, Willie McCovey)	15.00	7.50	4.50
573	Jim Palmer	35.00	17.50	10.50
574	George Scott	1.50	.70	.45
575	Bill Singer	1.50	.70	.45
576	Phillies Rookies (Ron Stone, Bill Wilson)	1.50	.70	.45
577	Mike Hegan	1.50	.70	.45
578	Don Bosch	1.50	.70	.45
579	*Dave Nelson*	1.50	.70	.45
580	Jim Northrup	1.50	.70	.45
581	Gary Nolan	1.50	.70	.45
582a	Checklist 589-664 (Tony Oliva) (red circle on back)	3.50	1.75	1.00
582b	Checklist 589-664 (Tony oliva) (white circle on back)	2.50	1.25	.70
583	*Clyde Wright*	1.50	.70	.45
584	Don Mason	1.50	.70	.45
585	Ron Swoboda	1.50	.70	.45
586	Tim Cullen	1.50	.70	.45
587	*Joe Rudi*	2.00	1.00	.60
588	Bill White	2.50	1.25	.70
589	Joe Pepitone	3.50	1.75	1.00
590	Rico Carty	2.50	1.25	.70
591	Mike Hedlund	2.50	1.25	.70
592	Padres Rookies (Rafael Robles, Al Santorini)	2.50	1.25	.70
593	Don Nottebart	2.50	1.25	.70
594	Dooley Womack	2.50	1.25	.70
595	Lee Maye	2.50	1.25	.70
596	Chuck Hartenstein	2.50	1.25	.70
597	A.L. Rookies (Larry Burchart, Rollie Fingers, Bob Floyd)	75.00	37.00	22.00
598	Ruben Amaro	2.50	1.25	.70
599	John Boozer	2.50	1.25	.70
600	Tony Oliva	4.50	2.25	1.25
601	Tug McGraw	2.50	1.25	.70
602	Cubs Rookies (Alec Distaso, Jim Qualls, Don Young)	2.50	1.25	.70
603	Joe Keough	2.50	1.25	.70
604	Bobby Etheridge	2.50	1.25	.70
605	Dick Ellsworth	2.50	1.25	.70
606	Gene Mauch	2.50	1.25	.70
607	Dick Bosman	2.50	1.25	.70
608	Dick Simpson	2.50	1.25	.70
609	Phil Gagliano	2.50	1.25	.70
610	Jim Hardin	2.50	1.25	.70
611	Braves Rookies (Bob Didier, Walt Hriniak, Gary Neibauer)	2.50	1.25	.70
612	Jack Aker	2.50	1.25	.70
613	Jim Beauchamp	2.50	1.25	.70
614	Astros Rookies (Tom Griffin, Skip Guinn)	2.50	1.25	.70
615	Len Gabrielson	2.50	1.25	.70
616	Don McMahon	2.50	1.25	.70
617	Jesse Gonder	2.50	1.25	.70
618	Ramon Webster	2.50	1.25	.70
619	Royals Rookies (Bill Butler, Pat Kelly, Juan Rios)	2.50	1.25	.70
620	Dean Chance	2.50	1.25	.70
621	Bill Voss	2.50	1.25	.70
622	Dan Osinski	2.50	1.25	.70
623	Hank Allen	2.50	1.25	.70
624	N.L. Rookies (Darrel Chaney, Duffy Dyer, Terry Harmon)	2.50	1.25	.70
625	Mack Jones	2.50	1.25	.70
626	Gene Michael	2.50	1.25	.70
627	George Stone	2.50	1.25	.70
628	Red Sox Rookies (*Bill Conigliaro*, Syd O'Brien, Fred Wenz)	2.50	1.25	.70
629	Jack Hamilton	2.50	1.25	.70
630	*Bobby Bonds*	45.00	22.00	13.50
631	John Kennedy	2.50	1.25	.70
632	Jon Warden	2.50	1.25	.70
633	Harry Walker	2.50	1.25	.70
634	Andy Etchebarren	2.50	1.25	.70
635	George Culver	2.50	1.25	.70
636	Woodie Held	2.50	1.25	.70
637	Padres Rookies (Jerry DaVanon, Clay Kirby, Frank Reberger)	2.50	1.25	.70
638	Ed Sprague	2.50	1.25	.70
639	Barry Moore	2.50	1.25	.70
640	Fergie Jenkins	20.00	10.00	6.00
641	N.L. Rookies (Bobby Darwin, Tommy Dean, John Miller)	2.50	1.25	.70
642	John Hiller	2.50	1.25	.70
643	Billy Cowan	2.50	1.25	.70
644	Chuck Hinton	2.50	1.25	.70
645	George Brunet	2.50	1.25	.70
646	Expos Rookies (Dan McGinn, Carl Morton)	2.50	1.25	.70
647	Dave Wickersham	2.50	1.25	.70
648	Bobby Wine	2.50	1.25	.70
649	Al Jackson	2.50	1.25	.70
650	Ted Williams	12.00	6.00	3.50
651	Gus Gil	2.50	1.25	.70
652	Eddie Watt	2.50	1.25	.70
653	*Aurelio Rodriguez* (photo actually batboy Leonard Garcia)	3.50	1.75	1.00
654	White Sox Rookies (*Carlos May*, Rich Morales, Don Secrist)	2.50	1.25	.70
655	Mike Hershberger	2.50	1.25	.70
656	Dan Schneider	2.50	1.25	.70
657	Bobby Murcer	3.00	1.50	.90
658	A.L. Rookies (Bill Burbach, Tom Hall, Jim Miles)	2.50	1.25	.70
659	Johnny Podres	3.00	1.50	.90
660	Reggie Smith	2.50	1.25	.70
661	Jim Merritt	2.50	1.25	.70
662	Royals Rookies (Dick Drago, Bob Oliver, George Spriggs)	2.50	1.25	.70
663	Dick Radatz	2.50	1.25	.70
664	Ron Hunt	2.50	1.25	.70

1969 Topps Decals

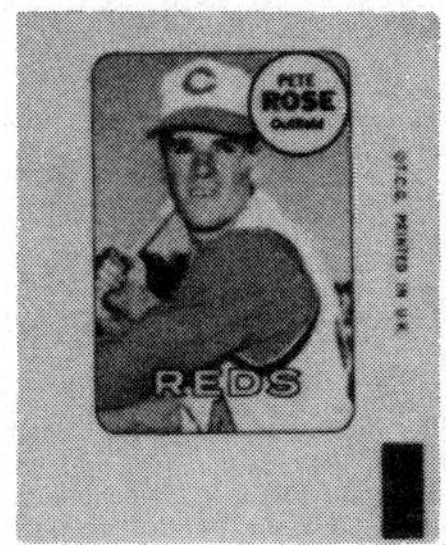

Designed as an insert for 1969 regular issue card packs, these decals are virtually identical in format to the '69 cards. The 48 decals in the set measure 1" by 2-1/2," although they are mounted on white paper backing which measures 1-3/4" by 2-1/8."

		NR MT	EX	VG
	Complete Set:	500.00	250.00	150.00
	Common Player:	4.00	2.00	1.25
(1)	Hank Aaron	45.00	22.00	13.50
(2)	Richie Allen	9.00	4.50	2.75
(3)	Felipe Alou	9.00	4.50	2.75
(4)	Matty Alou	4.00	2.00	1.25
(5)	Luis Aparicio	12.00	6.00	3.50
(6)	Bob Clemente	50.00	25.00	15.00
(7)	Donn Clendenon	4.00	2.00	1.25
(8)	Tommy Davis	4.00	2.00	1.25
(9)	Don Drysdale	12.00	6.00	3.50
(10)	Joe Foy	4.00	2.00	1.25
(11)	Jim Fregosi	4.00	2.00	1.25
(12)	Bob Gibson	12.00	6.00	3.50
(13)	Tony Gonzalez	4.00	2.00	1.25
(14)	Tom Haller	4.00	2.00	1.25
(15)	Ken Harrelson	4.00	2.00	1.25
(16)	Tommy Helms	4.00	2.00	1.25
(17)	Willie Horton	4.00	2.00	1.25
(18)	Frank Howard	6.00	3.00	1.75
(19)	Reggie Jackson	95.00	47.00	28.00
(20)	Fergie Jenkins	12.00	6.00	3.50
(21)	Harmon Killebrew	12.00	6.00	3.50
(22)	Jerry Koosman	4.00	2.00	1.25
(23)	Mickey Mantle	95.00	47.00	28.00
(24)	Willie Mays	50.00	25.00	15.00
(25)	Tim McCarver	7.50	3.75	2.25
(26)	Willie McCovey	12.00	6.00	3.50
(27)	Sam McDowell	4.00	2.00	1.25
(28)	Denny McLain	6.00	3.00	1.75
(29)	Dave McNally	4.00	2.00	1.25
(30)	Don Mincher	4.00	2.00	1.25
(31)	Rick Monday	4.00	2.00	1.25
(32)	Tony Oliva	6.00	3.00	1.75
(33)	Camilo Pascual	4.00	2.00	1.25
(34)	Rick Reichardt	4.00	2.00	1.25
(35)	Frank Robinson	12.00	6.00	3.50
(36)	Pete Rose	30.00	15.00	9.00
(37)	Ron Santo	6.00	3.00	1.75
(38)	Tom Seaver	45.00	22.00	13.50
(39)	Dick Selma	4.00	2.00	1.25
(40)	Chris Short	4.00	2.00	1.25
(41)	Rusty Staub	6.00	3.00	1.75
(42)	Mel Stottlemyre	4.00	2.00	1.25
(43)	Luis Tiant	6.00	3.00	1.75
(44)	Pete Ward	4.00	2.00	1.25
(45)	Hoyt Wilhelm	10.00	5.00	3.00
(46)	Maury Wills	6.00	3.00	1.75
(47)	Jim Wynn	4.00	2.00	1.25
(48)	Carl Yastrzemski	20.00	10.00	6.00

1969 Topps Deckle Edge

These 2-1/4" by 3-1/4" inch cards take their name from their interesting borders which have a scalloped effect. The fronts have a black and white picture of the player along with a blue facsimile autograph. Backs have the player's name and the card number in light blue ink in a small box at the bottom

of the card. Technically, there are only 33 numbered cards, but there are actually 35 possible players; both Jim Wynn and Hoyt Wilhelm cards are found as #11 while cards of Joe Foy and Rusty Staub can be found as #22. Many of the players in the set are stars.

		NR MT	EX	VG
Complete Set:		100.00	50.00	30.00
Common Player:		1.00	.50	.30
1	Brooks Robinson	15.00	7.50	4.50
2	Boog Powell	2.50	1.25	.70
3	Ken Harrelson	1.00	.50	.30
4	Carl Yastrzemski	15.00	7.50	4.50
5	Jim Fregosi	1.00	.50	.30
6	Luis Aparicio	5.00	2.50	1.50
7	Luis Tiant	2.00	1.00	.60
8	Denny McLain	2.50	1.25	.70
9	Willie Horton	1.00	.50	.30
10	Bill Freehan	1.00	.50	.30
11a	Hoyt Wilhelm	10.00	5.00	3.00
11b	Jim Wynn	10.00	5.00	3.00
12	Rod Carew	15.00	7.50	4.50
13	Mel Stottlemyre	1.00	.50	.30
14	Rick Monday	1.00	.50	.30
15	Tommy Davis	1.00	.50	.30
16	Frank Howard	2.00	1.00	.60
17	Felipe Alou	2.50	1.25	.70
18	Don Kessinger	1.00	.50	.30
19	Ron Santo	2.50	1.25	.70
20	Tommy Helms	1.00	.50	.30
21	Pete Rose	10.00	5.00	3.00
22a	Rusty Staub	2.25	1.25	.70
22b	Joe Foy	7.00	3.50	2.00
23	Tom Haller	1.00	.50	.30
24	Maury Wills	2.00	1.00	.60
25	Jerry Koosman	1.00	.50	.30
26	Richie Allen	2.00	1.00	.60
27	Roberto Clemente	20.00	10.00	6.00
28	Curt Flood	1.00	.50	.30
29	Bob Gibson	10.00	5.00	3.00
30	Al Ferrara	1.00	.50	.30
31	Willie McCovey	10.00	5.00	3.00
32	Juan Marichal	7.00	3.50	2.00
33	Willie Mays	15.00	7.50	4.50

1969 Topps 4-On-1 Mini Stickers

Another in the long line of Topps test issues, the 4-on-1s are 2-1/2" by 3-1/2" cards with blank backs featuring a quartet of miniature stickers in the design of the same cards from the 1969 Topps regular set. There are 25 different cards, for a total of 100 different stickers. As they are not common, Mint cards bring fairly strong prices on today's market. As the set was drawn from the 3rd Series of the regular cards, it includes some rookie stickers and World Series highlight stickers.

		NR MT	EX	VG
Complete Set:		950.00	475.00	285.00
Common Player:		15.00	7.50	4.50
(1)	Jerry Adair, Willie Mays, Johnny Morris, Don Wilson	100.00	50.00	30.00
(2)	Tommie Aaron, Jim Britton, Donn Clendenon, Woody Woodward	15.00	7.50	4.50
(3)	World Series Game 4, Tommy Davis, Don Pavletich, Vada Pinson	20.00	10.00	6.00
(4)	Max Alvis, Glenn Beckert, Ron Fairly, Rick Wise	15.00	7.50	4.50
(5)	Johnny Callison, Jim French, Lum Harris, Dick Selma	15.00	7.50	4.50
(6)	World Series Game 3, Bob Gibson, Larry Haney, Rick Reichardt	40.00	20.00	12.00
(7)	Houston Rookie Stars, Wally Bunker, Don Cardwell, Joe Gibbon	15.00	7.50	4.50
(8)	Ollie Brown, Jim Bunning, Andy Kosco, Ron Reed	20.00	10.00	6.00
(9)	Bill Dillman, Jim Lefebvre, John Purdin, John Roseboro	15.00	7.50	4.50
(10)	Bill Hands, Chuck Harrison, Lindy McDaniel, Felix Millan	15.00	7.50	4.50
(11)	Jack Hiatt, Dave Johnson, Mel Nelson, Tommie Sisk	18.00	9.00	5.50
(12)	Clay Dalrymple, Leo Durocher, John Odom, Wilbur Wood	18.00	9.00	5.50
(13)	Hank Bauer, Kevin Collins, Ray Oyler, Russ Snyder	15.00	7.50	4.50
(14)	Red Sox Rookie Stars, World Series Game 7, Gerry Arrigo, Jim Perry	18.00	9.00	5.50
(15)	World Series Game 2, Bill McCool, Roberto Pena, Doug Rader	15.00	7.50	4.50
(16)	Ed Brinkman, Roy Face, Willie Horton, Bob Rodgers	18.00	9.00	5.50
(17)	Dave Baldwin, J.C. Martin, Dave May, Ray Sadecki	15.00	7.50	4.50
(18)	World Series Game 1, Jose Pagan, Tom Phoebus, Mike Shannon	15.00	7.50	4.50
(19)	Pete Rose, Lee Stange, Don Sutton, Ted Uhlaender	275.00	137.00	82.00
(20)	Joe Grzenda, Frank Howard, Dick Tracewski, Jim Weaver	20.00	10.00	6.00
(21)	White Sox Rookie Stars, Joe Azcue, Grant Jackson, Denny McLain	20.00	10.00	6.00
(22)	John Edwards, Jim Fairey, Phillies Rookies, Stan Williams	15.00	7.50	4.50
(23)	World Series Summary, John Bateman, Willie Smith, Leon Wagner	15.00	7.50	4.50
(24)	World Series Game 5, Yankees Rookies, Chris Cannizzaro, Bob Hendley	15.00	7.50	4.50
(25)	Cardinals Rookie Stars, Joe Nossek, Rico Petrocelli, Carl Yastrzemski	175.00	87.00	52.00

1969 Topps Stamps

Topps continued to refine its efforts at baseball stamps in 1969 with the release of 240 player stamps, each measuring 1" by 1-7/16." Each stamp has a color photo along with the player's name, position and team. Unlike prior stamp issues, the 1969 stamps have 24 separate albums (one per team). The stamps were issued in strips of 12.

		NR MT	EX	VG
Complete Sheet Set:		500.00	250.00	150.00
Common Sheet:		3.00	1.50	.90
Complete Stamp Album Set:		28.00	14.00	8.50
Single Stamp Album:		1.00	.50	.30
(1)	Tommie Agee, Sandy Alomar, Jose Cardenal, Dean Chance, Joe Foy, Jim Grant, Don Kessinger, Mickey Mantle, Jerry May, Bob Rodgers, Cookie Rojas, Gary Sutherland	40.00	20.00	12.00
(2)	Jesus Alou, Mike Andrews, Larry Brown, Moe Drabowsky, Alex Johnson, Lew Krausse, Jim Lefebvre, Dal Maxvill, John Odom, Claude Osteen, Rick Reichardt, Luis Tiant	3.00	1.50	.90
(3)	Hank Aaron, Matty Alou, Max Alvis, Nelson Briles, Eddie Fisher, Bud Harrelson, Willie Horton, Randy Hundley, Larry Jaster, Jim Kaat, Gary Peters, Pete Ward	15.00	7.50	4.50
(4)	Don Buford, John Callison, Tommy Davis, Jackie Hernandez, Fergie Jenkins, Lee May, Denny McLain, Bob Oliver, Roberto Pena, Tony Perez, Joe Torre, Tom Tresh	6.00	3.00	1.75
(5)	Jim Bunning, Dean Chance, Joe Foy, Sonny Jackson, Don Kessinger, Rick Monday, Gaylord Perry, Roger Repoz, Cookie Rojas, Mel Stottlemyre, Leon Wagner, Jim Wynn	6.00	3.00	1.75
(6)	Felipe Alou, Gerry Arrigo, Bob Aspromonte, Gary Bell, Clay Dalrymple, Jim Fregosi, Tony Gonzalez, Duane Josephson, Dick McAuliffe, Tony Oliva, Brooks Robinson, Willie Stargell	12.00	6.00	3.50
(7)	Steve Barber, Donn Clendenon, Joe Coleman, Vic Davalillo, Russ Gibson, Jerry Grote, Tom Haller, Andy Kosco, Willie McCovey, Don Mincher, Joe Morgan, Don Wilson	8.00	4.00	2.50
(8)	George Brunet, Don Buford, John Callison, Danny Cater, Tommy Davis, Willie Davis, John Edwards, Jim Hart, Mickey Lolich, Willie Mays, Roberto Pena, Mickey Stanley	15.00	7.50	4.50
(9)	Ernie Banks, Glenn Beckert, Ken Berry, Horace Clarke, Roberto Clemente, Larry Dierker, Len Gabrielson, Jake Gibbs, Jerry Koosman, Sam McDowell, Tom Satriano, Bill Singer	7.00	3.50	2.00
(10)	Gene Alley, Lou Brock, Larry Brown, Moe Drabowsky, Frank Howard, Tommie John, Roger Nelson, Claude Osteen, Phil Regan, Rick Reichardt, Tony Taylor, Roy White	8.00	4.00	2.50
(11)	Bob Allison, John Bateman, Don Drysdale, Dave Johnson, Harmon Killebrew, Jim Maloney, Bill Mazeroski, Gerry McNertney, Ron Perranoski, Rico Petrocelli, Pete Rose, Billy Williams	40.00	20.00	12.00
(12)	Bernie Allen, Jose Arcia, Stan Bahnsen, Sal Bando, Jim Davenport, Tito Francona, Dick Green, Ron Hunt, Mack Jones, Vada Pinson, George Scott, Don Wert	3.00	1.50	.90
(13)	Gerry Arrigo, Bob Aspromonte, Joe Azcue, Curt Blefary, Orlando Cepeda, BIll Freehan, Jim Fregosi, Dave Giusti, Duane Josephson, Tim McCarver, Jose Santiago, Bob Tolan	4.00	2.00	1.25
(14)	Jerry Adair, Johnny Bench, Clete Boyer, John Briggs, Bert Campaneris, Woody Fryman, Ron Kline, Bobby Knoop, Ken McMullen, Adolfo Phillips, John Roseboro, Tom Seaver	15.00	7.50	4.50
(15)	Norm Cash, Ron Fairly, Bob Gibson, Bill Hands, Cleon Jones, Al Kaline, Paul Schaal, Mike Shannon, Duke Sims, Reggie Smith, Steve Whitaker, Carl Yastrzemski	25.00	12.50	7.50
(16)	Steve Barber, Paul Casanova, Dick Dietz, Russ Gibson, Jerry Grote, Tom Haller, Ed Kranepool, Juan Marichal, Denis Menke, Jim Nash, Bill Robinson, Frank Robinson	8.00	4.00	2.50
(17)	Bobby Bolin, Ollie Brown, Rod Carew, Mike Epstein, Bud Harrelson, Larry Jaster, Dave McNally, Willie Norton, Milt Pappas, Gary Peters, Paul Popovich, Stan Williams	12.00	6.00	3.50
(18)	Ted Abernathy, Bob Allison, Ed Brinkman, Don Drysdale, Jim Hardin, Julian Javier, Hal Lanier, Jim McGlothlin, Ron Perranoski, Rich Rollins, Ron Santo, Billy Williams	6.00	3.00	1.75
(19)	Richie Allen, Luis Aparicio, Wally Bunker, Curt Flood, Ken Harrelson, Catfish Hunter, Denver Lemaster, Felix Millan, Jim Northrop (Northrup), Art Shamsky, Larry Stahl, Ted Uhlaender	6.00	3.00	1.75
(20)	Bob Bailey, Johnny Bench, Woody Fryman, Jim Hannan, Ron Kline, Al McBean, Camilo Pascual, Joe Pepitone, Doug Rader, Ron Reed, John Roseboro, Sonny Siebert	6.00	3.00	1.75
(21)	Jack Aker, Tommy Harper, Tommy Helms, Dennis Higgins, Jim Hunter, Don Lock, Lee Maye, Felix Millan, Jim Northrop (Northrup), Larry Stahl, Don Sutton, Zoilo Versalles	6.00	3.00	1.75
(22)	Norm Cash, Ed Charles, Joe Horlen, Pat Jarvis, Jim Lonborg, Manny Mota, Boog Powell, Dick Selma, Mike Shannon, Duke Sims, Steve Whitaker, Hoyt Wilhelm	6.00	3.00	1.75
(23)	Bernie Allen, Ray Culp, Al Ferrara, Tito Francona, Dick Green, Ron Hunt, Ray Oyler, Tom Phoebus, Rusty Staub, Bob Veale, Maury Wills, Wilbur Wood	4.00	2.00	1.25
(24)	Ernie Banks, Mark Belanger, Steve Blass, Horace Clarke, Bob Clemente, Larry Dierker, Dave Duncan, Chico Salmon, Chris Short, Ron Swoboda, Cesar Tovar, Rick Wise	7.00	3.50	2.00

1969 Topps Super

These 2-1/4" by 3-1/4" cards are not the bigger "Super" cards which would be seen in following years. Rather, what enabled Topps to dub them "Super Baseball Cards" is their high-gloss finish which enhances the bright color photograph used on their fronts. The only other design element on the front is a facsimile autograph. The backs contain a box at the the bottom which carries the player's name, team, position, a copyright line and the card number. Another unusual feature is that the cards have rounded corners. The 66-card set saw limited production, meaning supplies are tight today. Considering the quality of the cards and the fact that many big names are represented, it's easy to understand why the set is quite expensive and desirable.

		NR MT	EX	VG
Complete Set:		6500.	3250.	1950.
Common Player:		25.00	12.50	7.50
1	Dave McNally	25.00	12.50	7.50
2	Frank Robinson	350.00	175.00	105.00
3	Brooks Robinson	350.00	175.00	105.00
4	Ken Harrelson	25.00	12.50	7.50
5	Carl Yastrzemski	600.00	300.00	180.00
6	Ray Culp	25.00	12.50	7.50
7	James Fregosi	25.00	12.50	7.50
8	Rick Reichardt	25.00	12.50	7.50
9	Vic Davalillo	25.00	12.50	7.50
10	Luis Aparicio	100.00	50.00	30.00
11	Pete Ward	25.00	12.50	7.50
12	Joe Horlen	25.00	12.50	7.50
13	Luis Tiant	30.00	15.00	9.00
14	Sam McDowell	25.00	12.50	7.50
15	Jose Cardenal	25.00	12.50	7.50
16	Willie Horton	25.00	12.50	7.50
17	Denny McLain	30.00	15.00	9.00
18	Bill Freehan	25.00	12.50	7.50
19	Harmon Killebrew	275.00	137.00	82.00
20	Tony Oliva	30.00	15.00	9.00
21	Dean Chance	25.00	12.50	7.50
22	Joe Foy	25.00	12.50	7.50
23	Roger Nelson	25.00	12.50	7.50
24	Mickey Mantle	1250.	625.00	375.00
25	Mel Stottlemyre	25.00	12.50	7.50
26	Roy White	25.00	12.50	7.50
27	Rick Monday	25.00	12.50	7.50
28	Reggie Jackson	750.00	375.00	225.00
29	Bert Campaneris	25.00	12.50	7.50
30	Frank Howard	30.00	15.00	9.00
31	Camilo Pascual	25.00	12.50	7.50
32	Tommy Davis	25.00	12.50	7.50
33	Don Mincher	25.00	12.50	7.50
34	Henry Aaron	600.00	300.00	180.00
35	Felipe Alou	45.00	22.00	13.50
36	Joe Torre	25.00	12.50	7.50
37	Fergie Jenkins	100.00	50.00	30.00
38	Ronald Santo	25.00	12.50	7.50
39	Billy Williams	100.00	50.00	30.00
40	Tommy Helms	25.00	12.50	7.50
41	Pete Rose	500.00	250.00	150.00
42	Joe Morgan	150.00	75.00	45.00
43	Jim Wynn	25.00	12.50	7.50
44	Curt Blefary	25.00	12.50	7.50
45	Willie Davis	25.00	12.50	7.50
46	Don Drysdale	250.00	125.00	75.00
47	Tom Haller	25.00	12.50	7.50
48	Rusty Staub	25.00	12.50	7.50
49	Maurice Wills	25.00	12.50	7.50
50	Cleon Jones	25.00	12.50	7.50
51	Jerry Koosman	25.00	12.50	7.50
52	Tom Seaver	700.00	350.00	210.00
53	Rich Allen	40.00	20.00	12.00
54	Chris Short	25.00	12.50	7.50
55	Cookie Rojas	25.00	12.50	7.50
56	Mateo Alou	25.00	12.50	7.50
57	Steve Blass	25.00	12.50	7.50
58	Roberto Clemente	600.00	300.00	180.00
59	Curt Flood	25.00	12.50	7.50
60	Bob Gibson	150.00	75.00	45.00
61	Tim McCarver	40.00	20.00	12.00
62	Dick Selma	25.00	12.50	7.50
63	Ollie Brown	25.00	12.50	7.50
64	Juan Marichal	150.00	75.00	45.00
65	Willie Mays	600.00	300.00	180.00
66	Willie McCovey	150.00	75.00	45.00

1969 Topps Team Posters

Picking up where the 1968 posters left off, the 1969 poster is larger at about 12" by 20." The posters, 24 in number like the previous year, are very different in style. Each has a team focus with a large pennant carrying the team name, along with nine or ten photos of players. Each of the photos carries a name and a facsimile autograph. Unfortunately, the bigger size of 1969 posters meant they had to be folded to fit in their packages as was the case in 1968. That means that collectors today will have a tough job finding them without fairly heavy creases from the folding.

		NR MT	EX	VG
Complete Set:		1500.	750.00	450.00
Common Poster:		40.00	20.00	12.00
1	Detroit Tigers (Norm Cash, Bill Freehan, Willie Horton, Al Kaline, Mickey Lolich, Dick McAuliffe, Denny McLain, Jim Northrup, Mickey Stanley, Don Wert, Earl Wilson)	80.00	40.00	24.00
2	Atlanta Braves (Hank Aaron, Felipe Alou, Clete Boyer, Rico Carty, Tito Francona, Sonny Jackson, Pat Jarvis, Felix Millan, Phil Niekro, Milt Pappas, Joe Torre)	80.00	40.00	24.00
3	Boston Red Sox (Mike Andrews, Tony Conigliaro, Ray Culp, Russ Gibson, Ken Harrelson, Jim Lonborg, Rico Petrocelli, Jose Santiago, George Scott, Reggie Smith, Carl Yastrzemski)	100.00	50.00	30.00
4	Chicago Cubs (Ernie Banks, Glenn Beckert, Bill Hands, Jim Hickman, Ken Holtzman, Randy Hundley, Fergie Jenkins, Don Kessinger, Adolfo Phillips, Ron Santo, Billy Williams)	80.00	40.00	24.00
5	Baltimore Orioles (Mark Belanger, Paul Blair, Don Buford, Andy Etchebarren, Jim Hardin, Dave Johnson, Dave McNally, Tom Phoebus, Boog Powell, Brooks Robinson, Frank Robinson)	80.00	40.00	24.00
6	Houston Astros (Curt Blefary, Donn Clendenon, Larry Dierker, John Edwards, Denny Lemaster, Denis Menke, Norm Miller, Joe Morgan, Doug Rader, Don Wilson, Jim Wynn)	40.00	20.00	12.00
7	Kansas City Royals (Jerry Adair, Wally Bunker, Mike Fiore, Joe Foy, Jackie Hernandez, Pat Kelly, Dave Morehead, Roger Nelson, Dave Nicholson, Eliseo Rodriguez, Steve Whitaker)	40.00	20.00	12.00
8	Philadelphia Phillies (Richie Allen, Johnny Callison, Woody Fryman, Larry Hisle, Don Money, Cookie Rojas, Mike Ryan, Chris Short, Tony Taylor, Bill White, Rick Wise)	40.00	20.00	12.00
9	Seattle Pilots (Jack Aker, Steve Barber, Gary Bell, Tommy Davis, Jim Gosger, Tommy Harper, Gerry McNertney, Don Mincher, Ray Oyler, Rich Rollins, Chico Salmon)	90.00	45.00	27.00
10	Montreal Expos (Bob Bailey, John Bateman, Jack Billingham, Jim Grant, Larry Jaster, Mack Jones, Manny Mota, Rusty Staub, Gary Sutherland, Jim Williams, Maury Wills)	40.00	20.00	12.00
11	Chicago White Sox (Sandy Alomar, Luis Aparicio, Ken Berry, Buddy Bradford, Joe Horlen, Tommy John, Duane Josephson, Tom McCraw, Bill Melton, Pete Ward, Wilbur Wood)	50.00	25.00	15.00
12	San Diego Padres (Jose Arcia, Danny Breeden, Ollie Brown, Bill Davis, Ron Davis, Tony Gonzalez, Dick Kelley, Al McBean, Roberto Pena, Dick Selma, Ed Spiezio)	40.00	20.00	12.00
13	Cleveland Indians (Max Alvis, Joe Azcue, Jose Cardenal, Vern Fuller, Lou Johnson, Sam McDowell, Sonny Siebert, Duke Sims, Russ Snyder, Luis Tiant, Zoilo Versalles)	40.00	20.00	12.00
14	San Francisco Giants (Bobby Bolin, Jim Davenport, Dick Dietz, Jim Hart, Ron Hunt, Hal Lanier, Juan Marichal, Willie Mays, Willie McCovey, Gaylord Perry, Charlie Smith)	80.00	40.00	24.00
15	Minnesota Twins (Bob Allison, Chico Cardenas, Rod Carew, Dean Chance, Jim Kaat, Harmon Killebrew, Tony Oliva, Jim Perry, John Roseboro, Cesar Tovar, Ted Uhlaender)	80.00	40.00	24.00
16	Pittsburgh Pirates (Gene Alley, Matty Alou, Steve Blass, Jim Bunning, Bob Clemente, Rich Hebner, Jerry May, Bill Mazeroski, Bob Robertson, Willie Stargell, Bob Veale)	80.00	40.00	24.00
17	California Angels (Ruben Amaro, George Brunet, Bob Chance, Vic Davalillo, Jim Fregosi, Bobby Knoop, Jim McGlothlin, Rick Reichardt, Roger Repoz, Bob Rodgers, Hoyt Wilhelm)	40.00	20.00	12.00
18	St. Louis Cardinals (Nelson Briles, Lou Brock, Orlando Cepeda, Curt Flood, Bob Gibson, Julian Javier, Dal Maxvill, Tim McCarver, Vada Pinson, Mike Shannon, Ray Washburn)	70.00	35.00	21.00
19	New York Yankees (Stan Bahnsen, Horace Clarke, Bobby Cox, Jake Gibbs, Mickey Mantle, Joe Pepitone, Fritz Peterson, Bill Robinson, Mel Stottlemyre, Tom Tresh, Roy White)	125.00	62.00	37.00
20	Cincinnati Reds (Gerry Arrigo, Johnny Bench, Tommy Helms, Alex Johnson, Jim Maloney, Lee May, Gary Nolan, Tony Perez, Pete Rose, Bob Tolan, Woody Woodward)	100.00	50.00	30.00
21	Oakland Athletics (Sal Bando, Bert Campaneris, Danny Cater, Dick Green, Mike Hershberger, Jim Hunter, Reggie Jackson, Rick Monday, Jim Nash, John Odom, Jim Pagliaroni)	100.00	50.00	30.00
22	Los Angeles Dodgers (Willie Crawford, Willie Davis, Don Drysdale, Ron Fairly, Tom Haller, Andy Kosco, Jim Lefebvre, Claude Osteen, Paul Popovich, Bill Singer, Bill Sudakis)	70.00	35.00	21.00
23	Washington Senators (Bernie Allen, Brant Alyea, Ed Brinkman, Paul Casanova, Joe Coleman, Mike Epstein, Jim Hannan, Frank Howard, Ken McMullen, Camilo Pascual, Del Unser)	40.00	20.00	12.00
24	New York Mets (Tommie Agee, Ken Boswell, Ed Charles, Jerry Grote, Bud Harrelson, Cleon Jones, Jerry Koosman, Ed Kranepool, Jim McAndrew, Tom Seaver, Ron Swoboda)	150.00	75.00	45.00

A player's name in italic type indicates a rookie card. An (FC) indicates a player's first card for that particular card company.

1970 Topps

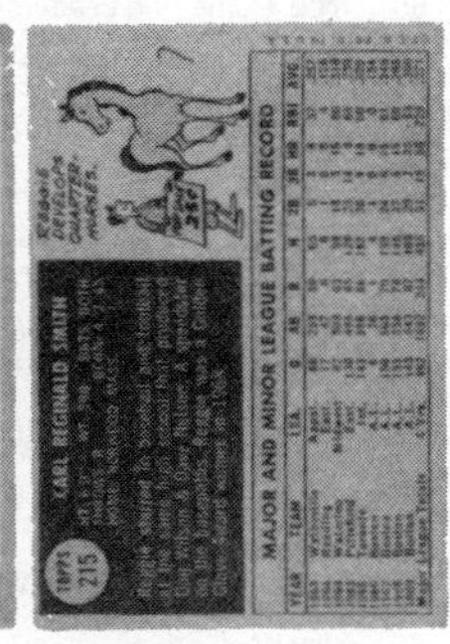

Topps established another set size record by coming out with 720 cards in 1970. The 2-1/2" by 3-1/2" cards have a color photo with a thin white frame. The photo have the player's team overprinted at the top, while the player's name in script and his position are at the bottom. A gray border surrounds the front. Card backs follows the normal design pattern, although they are more readable than some issues of the past. Team cards returned and were joined with many of the usual specialty cards. The World Series highlights were joined by cards with playoff highlights. Statistical leaders and All-Stars are also included in the set. High-numbered cards provide the most expensive cards in the set.

		NR MT	EX	VG
Complete Set (720):		2250.	1125.	675.00
Common Player (1-372):		.90	.45	.25
Common Player (373-546):		1.50	.70	.45
Common Player (547-633):		3.00	1.50	.90
Common Player (634-720):		6.00	3.00	1.75
1	World Champions (Mets Team)	12.00	6.00	3.50
2	Diego Segui	.90	.45	.25
3	Darrel Chaney	.90	.45	.25
4	Tom Egan	.90	.45	.25
5	Wes Parker	.90	.45	.25
6	Grant Jackson	.90	.45	.25
7	Indians Rookies (Gary Boyd, Russ Nagelson)	.90	.45	.25
8	Jose Martinez	.90	.45	.25
9	Checklist 1-132	3.50	1.75	1.00
10	Carl Yastrzemski	20.00	10.00	6.00
11	Nate Colbert	.90	.45	.25
12	John Hiller	.90	.45	.25
13	Jack Hiatt	.90	.45	.25
14	Hank Allen	.90	.45	.25
15	Larry Dierker	.90	.45	.25
16	Charlie Metro	.90	.45	.25
17	Hoyt Wilhelm	4.00	2.00	1.25
18	Carlos May	.90	.45	.25
19	John Boccabella	.90	.45	.25
20	Dave McNally	.90	.45	.25
21	*Vida Blue*, Gene Tenace	6.00	3.00	1.75
22	Ray Washburn	.90	.45	.25
23	Bill Robinson	.90	.45	.25
24	Dick Selma	.90	.45	.25
25	Cesar Tovar	.90	.45	.25
26	Tug McGraw	.90	.45	.25
27	Chuck Hinton	.90	.45	.25
28	Billy Wilson	.90	.45	.25
29	Sandy Alomar	.90	.45	.25
30	Matty Alou	.90	.45	.25
31	Marty Pattin	.90	.45	.25
32	Harry Walker	[illegible]	.45	.25
33	Don Wert	[illegible]	.45	.25
34	Willie Crawford	.90	.45	.25
35	Joe Horlen	.90	.45	.25
36	Reds Rookies (Danny Breeden, Bernie Carbo)	.90	.45	.25
37	Dick Drago	.90	.45	.25
38	Mack Jones	.90	.45	.25
39	Mike Nagy	.90	.45	.25
40	Rich Allen	2.00	1.00	.60
41	George Lauzerique	.90	.45	.25
42	Tito Fuentes	.90	.45	.25
43	Jack Aker	.90	.45	.25
44	Roberto Pena	.90	.45	.25
45	Dave Johnson	.90	.45	.25
46	Ken Rudolph	.90	.45	.25
47	Bob Miller	.90	.45	.25
48	Gill Garrido (Gil)	.90	.45	.25
49	Tim Cullen	.90	.45	.25
50	Tommie Agee	.90	.45	.25
51	Bob Christian	.90	.45	.25
52	Bruce Dal Canton	.90	.45	.25
53	John Kennedy	.90	.45	.25
54	Jeff Torborg	.90	.45	.25
55	John Odom	.90	.45	.25
56	Phillies Rookies (Joe Lis, Scott Reid)	.90	.45	.25
57	Pat Kelly	.90	.45	.25
58	Dave Marshall	.90	.45	.25
59	Dick Ellsworth	.90	.45	.25
60	Jim Wynn	.90	.45	.25
61	N.L. Batting Leaders (Roberto Clemente, Cleon Jones, Pete Rose)	5.50	2.75	1.75
62	A.L. Batting Leaders (Rod Carew, Tony Oliva, Reggie Smith)	3.50	1.75	1.00
63	N.L. RBI Leaders (Willie McCovey, Tony Perez, Ron Santo)	3.75	2.00	1.25

64 A.L. RBI Leaders (Reggie Jackson, Harmon Killebrew, Boog Powell) 5.00 2.50 1.50
65 N.L. Home Run Leaders (Hank Aaron, Lee May, Willie McCovey) 5.00 2.50 1.50
66 A.L. Home Run Leaders (Frank Howard, Reggie Jackson, Harmon Killebrew) 5.00 2.50 1.50
67 N.L. ERA Leaders (Steve Carlton, Bob Gibson, Juan Marichal) 4.00 2.00 1.25
68 A.L. ERA Leaders (Dick Bosman, Mike Cuellar, Jim Palmer) 3.50 1.75 1.00
69 N.L. Pitching Leaders (Fergie Jenkins, Juan Marichal, Phil Niekro, Tom Seaver) 5.00 2.50 1.50
70 A.L. Pitching Leaders (Dave Boswell, Mike Cuellar, Dennis McLain, Dave McNally, Jim Perry, Mel Stottlemyre) 3.50 1.75 1.00
71 N.L. Strikeout Leaders (Bob Gibson, Fergie Jenkins, Bill Singer) 4.00 2.00 1.25
72 A.L. Strikeout Leaders (Mickey Lolich, Sam McDowell, Andy Messersmith) 3.50 1.75 1.00
73 Wayne Granger .90 .45 .25
74 Angels Rookies (Greg Washburn, Wally Wolf) .90 .45 .25
75 Jim Kaat 3.00 1.50 .90
76 Carl Taylor .90 .45 .25
77 Frank Linzy .90 .45 .25
78 Joe Lahoud .90 .45 .25
79 Clay Kirby .90 .45 .25
80 Don Kessinger .90 .45 .25
81 Dave May .90 .45 .25
82 Frank Fernandez .90 .45 .25
83 Don Cardwell .90 .45 .25
84 Paul Casanova .90 .45 .25
85 Max Alvis .90 .45 .25
86 Lum Harris .90 .45 .25
87 Steve Renko .90 .45 .25
88 Pilots Rookies (Dick Baney, Miguel Fuentes) .90 .45 .25
89 Juan Rios .90 .45 .25
90 Tim McCarver 1.00 .50 .30
91 Rich Morales .90 .45 .25
92 George Culver .90 .45 .25
93 Rick Renick .90 .45 .25
94 Fred Patek .90 .45 .25
95 Earl Wilson .90 .45 .25
96 Cards Rookies (Leron Lee, Jerry Reuss) 3.00 1.50 .90
97 Joe Moeller .90 .45 .25
98 Gates Brown .90 .45 .25
99 Bobby Pfeil .90 .45 .25
100 Mel Stottlemyre .90 .45 .25
101 Bobby Floyd .90 .45 .25
102 Joe Rudi .90 .45 .25
103 Frank Reberger .90 .45 .25
104 Gerry Moses .90 .45 .25
105 Tony Gonzalez .90 .45 .25
106 Darold Knowles .90 .45 .25
107 Bobby Etheridge .90 .45 .25
108 Tom Burgmeier .90 .45 .25
109 Expos Rookies (Garry Jestadt, Carl Morton) .90 .45 .25
110 Bob Moose .90 .45 .25
111 Mike Hegan .90 .45 .25
112 Dave Nelson .90 .45 .25
113 Jim Ray .90 .45 .25
114 Gene Michael .90 .45 .25
115 Alex Johnson .90 .45 .25
116 Sparky Lyle 1.50 .70 .45
117 Don Young .90 .45 .25
118 George Mitterwald .90 .45 .25
119 Chuck Taylor .90 .45 .25
120 Sal Bando .90 .45 .25
121 Orioles Rookies (Fred Beene, Terry Crowley) .90 .45 .25
122 George Stone .90 .45 .25
123 Don Gutteridge .90 .45 .25
124 Larry Jaster .90 .45 .25
125 Deron Johnson .90 .45 .25
126 Marty Martinez .90 .45 .25
127 Joe Coleman .90 .45 .25
128a Checklist 133-263 (226 is R Perranoski) 3.00 1.50 .90
128b Checklist 133-263 (226 is R. Perranoski) 3.50 1.75 1.00
129 Jimmie Price .90 .45 .25
130 Ollie Brown .90 .45 .25
131 Dodgers Rookies (Ray Lamb, Bob Stinson) .90 .45 .25
132 Jim McGlothlin .90 .45 .25
133 Clay Carroll .90 .45 .25
134 Danny Walton, Mantle's Clutch HR .90 .45 .25
135 Dick Dietz .90 .45 .25
136 Steve Hargan .90 .45 .25
137 Art Shamsky .90 .45 .25
138 Joe Foy .90 .45 .25
139 Rich Nye .90 .45 .25
140 Reggie Jackson 150.00 75.00 45.00
141 Pirates Rookies (*Dave Cash*, Johnny Jeter) .90 .45 .25
142 Fritz Peterson .90 .45 .25
143 Phil Gagliano .90 .45 .25
144 Ray Culp .90 .45 .25
145 Rico Carty .90 .45 .25
146 Danny Murphy .90 .45 .25
147 Angel Hermoso .90 .45 .25
148 Earl Weaver 1.75 .90 .50
149 Billy Champion .90 .45 .25
150 Harmon Killebrew 8.00 4.00 2.50
151 Dave Roberts .90 .45 .25
152 Ike Brown .90 .45 .25
153 Gary Gentry .90 .45 .25
154 Senators Rookies (Jan Dukes, Jim Miles) .90 .45 .25
155 Denis Menke .90 .45 .25
156 Eddie Fisher .90 .45 .25
157 Manny Mota .90 .45 .25
158 Jerry McNertney .90 .45 .25
159 Tommy Helms .90 .45 .25
160 Phil Niekro 3.50 1.75 1.00
161 Richie Scheinblum .90 .45 .25
162 Jerry Johnson .90 .45 .25
163 Syd O'Brien .90 .45 .25
164 Ty Cline .90 .45 .25
165 Ed Kirkpatrick .90 .45 .25
166 Al Oliver 2.50 1.25 .70
167 Bill Burbach .90 .45 .25
168 Dave Watkins .90 .45 .25
169 Tom Hall .90 .45 .25
170 Billy Williams 6.00 3.00 1.75
171 Jim Nash .90 .45 .25
172 Braves Rookies (*Ralph Garr*, Garry Hill) 1.50 .70 .45
173 Jim Hicks .90 .45 .25
174 Ted Sizemore .90 .45 .25
175 Dick Bosman .90 .45 .25
176 Jim Hart .90 .45 .25
177 Jim Northrup .90 .45 .25
178 Denny Lemaster .90 .45 .25
179 Ivan Murrell .90 .45 .25
180 Tommy John 3.00 1.50 .90
181 Sparky Anderson 3.00 1.50 .90
182 Dick Hall .90 .45 .25
183 Jerry Grote .90 .45 .25
184 Ray Fosse .90 .45 .25
185 Don Mincher .90 .45 .25
186 Rick Joseph .90 .45 .25
187 Mike Hedlund .90 .45 .25
188 Manny Sanguillen .90 .45 .25
189 Yankees Rookies (Dave McDonald, Thurman Munson) 90.00 45.00 27.00
190 Joe Torre .90 .45 .25
191 Vicente Romo .90 .45 .25
192 Jim Qualls .90 .45 .25
193 Mike Wegener .90 .45 .25
194 Chuck Manuel .90 .45 .25
195 N.L.C.S. Game 1 15.00 7.50 4.50
196 N.L.C.S. Game 2 (Mets Show Muscle!) 4.00 2.00 1.25
197 N.L.C.S. Game 3 25.00 12.50 7.50
198 N.L. Playoffs Summary (We're Number One!) 4.00 2.00 1.25
199 A.L.C.S. Game 1 (Orioles Win A Squeaker!) 5.00 2.50 1.50
200 A.L.C.S. Game 2 (Powell Scores Winning Run!) 5.00 2.50 1.50
201 A.L.C.S. Game 3 (Birds Wrap It Up!) 5.00 2.50 1.50
202 A.L.C.S. Summary (Sweep Twins In Three!) 5.00 2.50 1.50
203 Rudy May .90 .45 .25
204 Len Gabrielson .90 .45 .25
205 Bert Campaneris .90 .45 .25
206 Clete Boyer .90 .45 .25
207 Tigers Rookies (Norman McRae, Bob Reed) .90 .45 .25
208 Fred Gladding .90 .45 .25
209 Ken Suarez .90 .45 .25
210 Juan Marichal 8.00 4.00 2.50
211 Ted Williams 10.00 5.00 3.00
212 Al Santorini .90 .45 .25
213 Andy Etchebarren .90 .45 .25
214 Ken Boswell .90 .45 .25
215 Reggie Smith 1.00 .50 .30
216 Chuck Hartenstein .90 .45 .25
217 Ron Hansen .90 .45 .25
218 Ron Stone .90 .45 .25
219 Jerry Kenney .90 .45 .25
220 Steve Carlton 32.50 16.00 9.75
221 Ron Brand .90 .45 .25
222 Jim Rooker .90 .45 .25
223 Nate Oliver .90 .45 .25
224 Steve Barber .90 .45 .25
225 Lee May .90 .45 .25
226 Ron Perranoski .90 .45 .25
227 Astros Rookies (*John Mayberry*, Bob Watkins) 1.50 .70 .45
228 Aurelio Rodriguez .90 .45 .25
229 Rich Robertson .90 .45 .25
230 Brooks Robinson 12.00 6.00 3.50
231 Luis Tiant 1.25 .60 .40
232 Bob Didier .90 .45 .25
233 Lew Krausse .90 .45 .25
234 Tommy Dean .90 .45 .25
235 Mike Epstein .90 .45 .25
236 Bob Veale .90 .45 .25
237 Russ Gibson .90 .45 .25
238 Jose Laboy .90 .45 .25
239 Ken Berry .90 .45 .25
240 Fergie Jenkins 8.00 4.00 2.50
241 Royals Rookies (Al Fitzmorris, Scott Northey) .90 .45 .25
242 Walter Alston 3.50 1.75 1.00
243 Joe Sparma .90 .45 .25
244a Checklist 264-372 (red bat on front) 3.00 1.50 .90
244b Checklist 264-372 (brown bat on front) 3.50 1.75 1.00
245 Leo Cardenas .90 .45 .25
246 Jim McAndrew .90 .45 .25
247 Lou Klimchock .90 .45 .25
248 Jesus Alou .90 .45 .25
249 Bob Locker .90 .45 .25
250 Willie McCovey 8.00 4.00 2.50
251 Dick Schofield .90 .45 .25
252 Lowell Palmer .90 .45 .25
253 Ron Woods .90 .45 .25
254 Camilo Pascual .90 .45 .25
255 *Jim Spencer* .90 .45 .25
256 Vic Davalillo .90 .45 .25
257 Dennis Higgins .90 .45 .25
258 Paul Popovich .90 .45 .25
259 Tommie Reynolds .90 .45 .25
260 Claude Osteen .90 .45 .25
261 Curt Motton .90 .45 .25
262 Padres Rookies (Jerry Morales, Jim Williams) .90 .45 .25
263 Duane Josephson .90 .45 .25
264 Rich Hebner .90 .45 .25
265 Randy Hundley .90 .45 .25
266 Wally Bunker .90 .45 .25
267 Twins Rookies (Herman Hill, Paul Ratliff) .90 .45 .25
268 Claude Raymond .90 .45 .25
269 Cesar Gutierrez .90 .45 .25
270 Chris Short .90 .45 .25
271 Greg Goossen .90 .45 .25
272 Hector Torres .90 .45 .25
273 Ralph Houk 1.00 .50 .30
274 Gerry Arrigo .90 .45 .25
275 Duke Sims .90 .45 .25
276 Ron Hunt .90 .45 .25
277 Paul Doyle .90 .45 .25
278 Tommie Aaron .90 .45 .25
279 *Bill Lee* .90 .45 .25
280 Donn Clendenon .90 .45 .25
281 Casey Cox .90 .45 .25
282 Steve Huntz .90 .45 .25
283 Angel Bravo .90 .45 .25
284 Jack Baldschun .90 .45 .25
285 Paul Blair .90 .45 .25
286 *Bill Buckner*, Jack Jenkins 6.00 3.00 1.75
287 Fred Talbot .90 .45 .25
288 Larry Hisle .90 .45 .25
289 Gene Brabender .90 .45 .25
290 Rod Carew 35.00 17.50 10.50
291 Leo Durocher 1.75 .90 .50
292 Eddie Leon .90 .45 .25
293 Bob Bailey .90 .45 .25
294 Jose Azcue .90 .45 .25
295 Cecil Upshaw .90 .45 .25
296 Woody Woodward .90 .45 .25
297 Curt Blefary .90 .45 .25
298 Ken Henderson .90 .45 .25
299 Buddy Bradford .90 .45 .25
300 Tom Seaver 70.00 35.00 21.00
301 Chico Salmon .90 .45 .25
302 Jeff James .90 .45 .25
303 Brant Alyea .90 .45 .25
304 *Bill Russell* 3.00 1.50 .90
305 World Series Game 1 (Buford Belts Leadoff Homer!) 4.00 2.00 1.25
306 World Series Game 2 (Clendenon's HR Breaks Ice!) 4.00 2.00 1.25
307 World Series Game 3 (Agee's Catch Saves The Day!) 4.00 2.00 1.25
308 World Series Game 4 (Martin's Bunt Ends Deadlock!) 4.00 2.00 1.25
309 World Series Game 5 (Koosman Shuts The Door! 4.00 2.00 1.25
310 World Series Summary (Mets Whoop It Up! 4.00 2.00 1.25
311 Dick Green .90 .45 .25
312 Mike Torrez .90 .45 .25
313 Mayo Smith .90 .45 .25
314 Bill McCool .90 .45 .25
315 Luis Aparicio 4.50 2.25 1.25
316 Skip Guinn .90 .45 .25
317 Red Sox Rookies (Luis Alvarado, Billy Conigliaro) .90 .45 .25
318 Willie Smith .90 .45 .25
319 Clayton Dalrymple .90 .45 .25
320 Jim Maloney .90 .45 .25
321 Lou Piniella 1.50 .70 .45
322 Luke Walker .90 .45 .25
323 Wayne Comer .90 .45 .25
324 Tony Taylor .90 .45 .25
325 Dave Boswell .90 .45 .25
326 Bill Voss .90 .45 .25
327 Hal King .90 .45 .25
328 George Brunet .90 .45 .25
329 Chris Cannizzaro .90 .45 .25
330 Lou Brock 10.00 5.00 3.00
331 Chuck Dobson .90 .45 .25
332 Bobby Wine .90 .45 .25
333 Bobby Murcer .90 .45 .25
334 Phil Regan .90 .45 .25
335 Bill Freehan .90 .45 .25
336 Del Unser .90 .45 .25
337 Mike McCormick .90 .45 .25
338 Paul Schaal .90 .45 .25
339 Johnny Edwards .90 .45 .25
340 Tony Conigliaro 1.75 .90 .50
341 Bill Sudakis .90 .45 .25
342 Wilbur Wood .90 .45 .25
343a Checklist 373-459 (red bat on front) 3.50 1.75 1.00
343b Checklist 373-459 (brown bat on front) 3.00 1.50 .90
344 Marcelino Lopez .90 .45 .25
345 Al Ferrara .90 .45 .25
346 Red Schoendienst 1.75 .90 .50
347 Russ Snyder .90 .45 .25
348 Mets Rookies (Jesse Hudson, Mike Jorgensen) .90 .45 .25
349 Steve Hamilton .90 .45 .25
350 Roberto Clemente 52.50 26.00 15.50
351 Tom Murphy .90 .45 .25
352 Bob Barton .90 .45 .25
353 Stan Williams .90 .45 .25
354 Amos Otis .90 .45 .25
355 Doug Rader .90 .45 .25
356 Fred Lasher .90 .45 .25
357 Bob Burda .90 .45 .25
358 *Pedro Borbon* 1.00 .50 .30
359 Phil Roof .90 .45 .25
360 Curt Flood .90 .45 .25
361 Ray Jarvis .90 .45 .25
362 Joe Hague .90 .45 .25
363 Tom Shopay .90 .45 .25
364 Dan McGinn .90 .45 .25
365 Zoilo Versalles .90 .45 .25
366 Barry Moore .90 .45 .25
367 Mike Lum .90 .45 .25
368 Ed Herrmann .90 .45 .25
369 Alan Foster .90 .45 .25
370 Tommy Harper .90 .45 .25
371 Rod Gaspar .90 .45 .25
372 Dave Giusti .90 .45 .25
373 Roy White 1.50 .70 .45
374 Tommie Sisk 1.50 .70 .45
375 Johnny Callison 1.50 .70 .45
376 Lefty Phillips 1.50 .70 .45
377 Bill Butler 1.50 .70 .45
378 Jim Davenport 1.50 .70 .45
379 Tom Tischinski 1.50 .70 .45
380 Tony Perez 3.00 1.50 .90
381 Athletics Rookies (Bobby Brooks, Mike Olivo) 1.50 .70 .45

382	Jack DiLauro	1.50	.70	.45
383	Mickey Stanley	1.50	.70	.45
384	Gary Neibauer	1.50	.70	.45
385	George Scott	1.50	.70	.45
386	Bill Dillman	1.50	.70	.45
387	Orioles Team	3.00	1.50	.90
388	Byron Browne	1.50	.70	.45
389	Jim Shellenback	1.50	.70	.45
390	Willie Davis	1.75	.90	.50
391	Larry Brown	1.50	.70	.45
392	Walt Hriniak	1.50	.70	.45
393	John Gelnar	1.50	.70	.45
394	Gil Hodges	4.00	2.00	1.25
395	Walt Williams	1.50	.70	.45
396	Steve Blass	1.50	.70	.45
397	Roger Repoz	1.50	.70	.45
398	Bill Stoneman	1.50	.70	.45
399	Yankees Team	5.00	2.50	1.50
400	Denny McLain	2.50	1.25	.70
401	Giants Rookies (John Harrell, Bernie Williams)	1.50	.70	.45
402	Ellie Rodriguez	1.50	.70	.45
403	Jim Bunning	3.25	1.75	1.00
404	Rich Reese	1.50	.70	.45
405	Bill Hands	1.50	.70	.45
406	Mike Andrews	1.50	.70	.45
407	Bob Watson	1.50	.70	.45
408	Paul Lindblad	1.50	.70	.45
409	Bob Tolan	1.50	.70	.45
410	Boog Powell	2.50	1.25	.70
411	Dodgers Team	4.00	2.00	1.25
412	Larry Burchart	1.50	.70	.45
413	Sonny Jackson	1.50	.70	.45
414	Paul Edmondson	1.50	.70	.45
415	Julian Javier	1.50	.70	.45
416	Joe Verbanic	1.50	.70	.45
417	John Bateman	1.50	.70	.45
418	John Donaldson	1.50	.70	.45
419	Ron Taylor	1.50	.70	.45
420	Ken McMullen	1.50	.70	.45
421	Pat Dobson	1.50	.70	.45
422	Royals Team	3.00	1.50	.90
423	Jerry May	1.50	.70	.45
424	Mike Kilkenny	1.50	.70	.45
425	Bobby Bonds	2.00	1.00	.60
426	Bill Rigney	1.50	.70	.45
427	Fred Norman	1.50	.70	.45
428	Don Buford	1.50	.70	.45
429	Cubs Rookies (Randy Bobb, Jim Cosman)	1.50	.70	.45
430	Andy Messersmith	1.50	.70	.45
431	Ron Swoboda	1.50	.70	.45
432a	Checklist 460-546 ("Baseball" on front in yellow)	4.00	2.00	1.25
432b	Checklist 460-546 ("Baseball" on front in white)	3.50	1.75	1.00
433	Ron Bryant	1.50	.70	.45
434	Felipe Alou	2.50	1.25	.70
435	Nelson Briles	1.50	.70	.45
436	Phillies Team	3.00	1.50	.90
437	Danny Cater	1.50	.70	.45
438	Pat Jarvis	1.50	.70	.45
439	Lee Maye	1.50	.70	.45
440	Bill Mazeroski	3.00	1.50	.90
441	John O'Donoghue	1.50	.70	.45
442	Gene Mauch	1.75	.90	.50
443	Al Jackson	1.50	.70	.45
444	White Sox Rookies (Bill Farmer, John Matias)	1.50	.70	.45
445	Vada Pinson	2.00	1.00	.60
446	*Billy Grabarkewitz*	1.50	.70	.45
447	Lee Stange	1.50	.70	.45
448	Astros Team	3.00	1.50	.90
449	Jim Palmer	16.00	8.00	4.75
450	Willie McCovey (All-Star)	5.00	2.50	1.50
451	Boog Powell (All-Star)	1.50	.70	.45
452	Felix Millan (All-Star)	1.50	.70	.45
453	Rod Carew (All-Star)	6.00	3.00	1.75
454	Ron Santo (All-Star)	1.50	.70	.45
455	Brooks Robinson (All-Star)	8.00	4.00	2.50
456	Don Kessinger (All-Star)	1.50	.70	.45
457	Rico Petrocelli (All-Star)	1.50	.70	.45
458	Pete Rose (All-Star)	12.00	6.00	3.50
459	Reggie Jackson (All-Star)	25.00	12.00	7.50
460	Matty Alou (All-Star)	1.50	.70	.45
461	Carl Yastrzemski (All-Star)	8.00	4.00	2.50
462	Hank Aaron (All-Star)	15.00	7.50	4.50
463	Frank Robinson (All-Star)	8.00	4.00	2.50
464	Johnny Bench (All-Star)	10.00	5.00	3.00
465	Bill Freehan (All-Star)	1.50	.70	.45
466	Juan Marichal (All-Star)	5.00	2.50	1.50
467	Denny McLain (All-Star)	1.50	.70	.45
468	Jerry Koosman (All-Star)	1.50	.70	.45
469	Sam McDowell (All-Star)	1.50	.70	.45
470	Willie Stargell	7.00	3.50	2.00
471	Chris Zachary	1.50	.70	.45
472	Braves Team	3.00	1.50	.90
473	Don Bryant	1.50	.70	.45
474	Dick Kelley	1.50	.70	.45
475	Dick McAuliffe	1.50	.70	.45
476	Don Shaw	1.50	.70	.45
477	Orioles Rookies (Roger Freed, Al Severinsen)	1.50	.70	.45
478	Bob Heise	1.50	.70	.45
479	Dick Woodson	1.50	.70	.45
480	Glenn Beckert	1.50	.70	.45
481	Jose Tartabull	1.50	.70	.45
482	Tom Hilgendorf	1.50	.70	.45
483	Gail Hopkins	1.50	.70	.45
484	Gary Nolan	1.50	.70	.45
485	Jay Johnstone	1.50	.70	.45
486	Terry Harmon	1.50	.70	.45
487	Cisco Carlos	1.50	.70	.45
488	J.C. Martin	1.50	.70	.45
489	Eddie Kasko	1.50	.70	.45
490	Bill Singer	1.50	.70	.45
491	Graig Nettles	3.00	1.50	.90
492	Astros Rookies (Keith Lampard, Scipio Spinks)	1.50	.70	.45
493	Lindy McDaniel	1.50	.70	.45
494	Larry Stahl	1.50	.70	.45
495	Dave Morehead	1.50	.70	.45
496	Steve Whitaker	1.50	.70	.45
497	Eddie Watt	1.50	.70	.45
498	Al Weis	1.50	.70	.45
499	Skip Lockwood	1.50	.70	.45
500	Hank Aaron	50.00	25.00	15.00
501	White Sox Team	3.00	1.50	.90
502	Rollie Fingers	22.00	11.00	6.50
503	Dal Maxvill	1.50	.70	.45
504	Don Pavletich	1.50	.70	.45
505	Ken Holtzman	1.50	.70	.45
506	Ed Stroud	1.50	.70	.45
507	Pat Corrales	1.50	.70	.45
508	Joe Niekro	2.00	1.00	.60
509	Expos Team	3.00	1.50	.90
510	Tony Oliva	2.50	1.25	.70
511	Joe Hoerner	1.50	.70	.45
512	Billy Harris	1.50	.70	.45
513	Preston Gomez	1.50	.70	.45
514	Steve Hovley	1.50	.70	.45
515	Don Wilson	1.50	.70	.45
516	Yankees Rookies (John Ellis, Jim Lyttle)	1.50	.70	.45
517	Joe Gibbon	1.50	.70	.45
518	Bill Melton	1.50	.70	.45
519	Don McMahon	1.50	.70	.45
520	Willie Horton	1.75	.90	.50
521	Cal Koonce	1.50	.70	.45
522	Angels Team	3.00	1.50	.90
523	Jose Pena	1.50	.70	.45
524	Alvin Dark	1.50	.70	.45
525	Jerry Adair	1.50	.70	.45
526	Ron Herbel	1.50	.70	.45
527	Don Bosch	1.50	.70	.45
528	Elrod Hendricks	1.50	.70	.45
529	Bob Aspromonte	1.50	.70	.45
530	Bob Gibson	10.00	5.00	3.00
531	Ron Clark	1.50	.70	.45
532	Danny Murtaugh	1.50	.70	.45
533	Buzz Stephen	1.50	.70	.45
534	Twins Team	3.00	1.50	.90
535	Andy Kosco	1.50	.70	.45
536	Mike Kekich	1.50	.70	.45
537	Joe Morgan	10.00	5.00	3.00
538	Bob Humphreys	1.50	.70	.45
539	*Larry Bowa*, Dennis Doyle	3.00	1.50	.90
540	Gary Peters	1.50	.70	.45
541	Bill Heath	1.50	.70	.45
542a	Checklist 547-633 (grey bat on front)	3.50	1.75	1.00
542b	Checklist 547-633 (brown bat on front)	3.50	1.75	1.00
543	Clyde Wright	1.50	.70	.45
544	Reds Team	3.00	1.50	.90
545	Ken Harrelson	1.50	.70	.45
546	Ron Reed	1.50	.70	.45
547	Rick Monday	3.00	1.50	.90
548	Howie Reed	3.00	1.50	.90
549	Cardinals Team	7.00	3.50	2.00
550	Frank Howard	4.50	2.25	1.25
551	Dock Ellis	3.00	1.50	.90
552	Royals Rookies (Don O'Riley, Dennis Paepke, Fred Rico)	3.00	1.50	.90
553	Jim Lefebvre	3.50	1.75	1.00
554	Tom Timmermann	3.00	1.50	.90
555	Orlando Cepeda	4.50	2.25	1.25
556	Dave Bristol	3.00	1.50	.90
557	Ed Kranepool	3.00	1.50	.90
558	Vern Fuller	3.00	1.50	.90
559	Tommy Davis	4.00	2.00	1.25
560	Gaylord Perry	9.00	4.50	2.75
561	Tom McCraw	3.00	1.50	.90
562	Ted Abernathy	3.00	1.50	.90
563	Red Sox Team	7.00	3.50	2.00
564	Johnny Briggs	3.00	1.50	.90
565	Catfish Hunter	11.00	5.50	3.25
566	Gene Alley	3.00	1.50	.90
567	Bob Oliver	3.00	1.50	.90
568	Stan Bahnsen	3.00	1.50	.90
569	Cookie Rojas	3.00	1.50	.90
570	Jim Fregosi	3.50	1.75	1.00
571	Jim Brewer	3.00	1.50	.90
572	Frank Quilici	3.00	1.50	.90
573	Padres Rookies (Mike Corkins, Rafael Robles, Ron Slocum)	3.00	1.50	.90
574	Bobby Bolin	3.00	1.50	.90
575	Cleon Jones	3.00	1.50	.90
576	Milt Pappas	3.00	1.50	.90
577	Bernie Allen	3.00	1.50	.90
578	Tom Griffin	3.00	1.50	.90
579	Tigers Team	7.00	3.50	2.00
580	Pete Rose	60.00	30.00	18.00
581	Tom Satriano	3.00	1.50	.90
582	Mike Paul	3.00	1.50	.90
583	Hal Lanier	3.00	1.50	.90
584	Al Downing	3.00	1.50	.90
585	Rusty Staub	4.50	2.25	1.25
586	Rickey Clark	3.00	1.50	.90
587	Jose Arcia	3.00	1.50	.90
588a	Checklist 634-720 (666 is Adolpho Phillips)	4.50	2.25	1.25
588b	Checklist 634-720 (666 is Adolfo Phillips)	4.00	2.00	1.25
589	Joe Keough	3.00	1.50	.90
590	Mike Cuellar	3.50	1.75	1.00
591	Mike Ryan	3.00	1.50	.90
592	Daryl Patterson	3.00	1.50	.90
593	Cubs Team	7.00	3.50	2.00
594	Jake Gibbs	3.00	1.50	.90
595	Maury Wills	4.00	2.00	1.25
596	Mike Hershberger	3.00	1.50	.90
597	Sonny Siebert	3.00	1.50	.90
598	Joe Pepitone	3.00	1.50	.90
599	Senators Rookies (Gene Martin, Dick Stelmaszek, Dick Such)	3.00	1.50	.90
600	Willie Mays	65.00	32.00	19.50
601	Pete Richert	3.00	1.50	.90
602	Ted Savage	3.00	1.50	.90
603	Ray Oyler	3.00	1.50	.90
604	Cito Gaston	4.50	2.25	1.25
605	Rick Wise	3.00	1.50	.90
606	Chico Ruiz	3.00	1.50	.90
607	Gary Waslewski	3.00	1.50	.90
608	Pirates Team	7.00	3.50	2.00
609	*Buck Martinez*	3.00	1.50	.90
610	Jerry Koosman	3.00	1.50	.90
611	Norm Cash	4.00	2.00	1.25
612	Jim Hickman	3.00	1.50	.90
613	Dave Baldwin	3.00	1.50	.90
614	Mike Shannon	3.00	1.50	.90
615	Mark Belanger	3.00	1.50	.90
616	Jim Merritt	3.00	1.50	.90
617	Jim French	3.00	1.50	.90
618	Billy Wynne	3.00	1.50	.90
619	Norm Miller	3.00	1.50	.90
620	Jim Perry	3.00	1.50	.90
621	*Darrell Evans*, Rick Kester, Mike McQueen	20.00	10.00	6.00
622	Don Sutton	7.00	3.50	2.00
623	Horace Clarke	3.00	1.50	.90
624	Clyde King	3.00	1.50	.90
625	Dean Chance	3.00	1.50	.90
626	Dave Ricketts	3.00	1.50	.90
627	Gary Wagner	3.00	1.50	.90
628	Wayne Garrett	3.00	1.50	.90
629	Merv Rettenmund	3.00	1.50	.90
630	Ernie Banks	36.00	18.00	11.00
631	Athletics Team	7.00	3.50	2.00
632	Gary Sutherland	3.00	1.50	.90
633	Roger Nelson	3.00	1.50	.90
634	Bud Harrelson	7.00	3.50	2.00
635	Bob Allison	6.00	3.00	1.75
636	Jim Stewart	6.00	3.00	1.75
637	Indians Team	9.00	4.50	2.75
638	Frank Bertaina	6.00	3.00	1.75
639	Dave Campbell	6.00	3.00	1.75
640	Al Kaline	50.00	25.00	15.00
641	Al McBean	6.00	3.00	1.75
642	Angels Rookies (Greg Garrett, Gordon Lund, Jarvis Tatum)	6.00	3.00	1.75
643	Jose Pagan	6.00	3.00	1.75
644	Gerry Nyman	6.00	3.00	1.75
645	Don Money	6.00	3.00	1.75
646	Jim Britton	6.00	3.00	1.75
647	Tom Matchick	6.00	3.00	1.75
648	Larry Haney	6.00	3.00	1.75
649	Jimmie Hall	6.00	3.00	1.75
650	Sam McDowell	7.00	3.50	2.00
651	Jim Gosger	6.00	3.00	1.75
652	Rich Rollins	6.00	3.00	1.75
653	Moe Drabowsky	6.00	3.00	1.75
654	N.L. Rookies (Boots Day, Oscar Gamble, Angel Mangual)	6.00	3.00	1.75
655	John Roseboro	6.00	3.00	1.75
656	Jim Hardin	6.00	3.00	1.75
657	Padres Team	9.00	4.50	2.75
658	Ken Tatum	6.00	3.00	1.75
659	Pete Ward	6.00	3.00	1.75
660	Johnny Bench	125.00	62.50	37.50
661	Jerry Robertson	6.00	3.00	1.75
662	Frank Lucchesi	6.00	3.00	1.75
663	Tito Francona	6.00	3.00	1.75
664	Bob Robertson	6.00	3.00	1.75
665	Jim Lonborg	7.00	3.50	2.00
666	Adolfo Phillips	6.00	3.00	1.75
667	Bob Meyer	6.00	3.00	1.75
668	Bob Tillman	6.00	3.00	1.75
669	White Sox Rookies (Bart Johnson, Dan Lazar, Mickey Scott)	6.00	3.00	1.75
670	Ron Santo	7.50	3.75	2.25
671	Jim Campanis	6.00	3.00	1.75
672	Leon McFadden	6.00	3.00	1.75
673	Ted Uhlaender	6.00	3.00	1.75
674	Dave Leonhard	6.00	3.00	1.75
675	Jose Cardenal	6.00	3.00	1.75
676	Senators Team	9.00	4.50	2.75
677	Woodie Fryman	6.00	3.00	1.75
678	Dave Duncan	6.00	3.00	1.75
679	Ray Sadecki	6.00	3.00	1.75
680	Rico Petrocelli	7.00	3.50	2.00
681	Bob Garibaldi	6.00	3.00	1.75
682	Dalton Jones	6.00	3.00	1.75
683	Reds Rookies (Vern Geishert, Hal McRae, Wayne Simpson)	7.00	3.50	2.00
684	Jack Fisher	6.00	3.00	1.75
685	Tom Haller	6.00	3.00	1.75
686	Jackie Hernandez	6.00	3.00	1.75
687	Bob Priddy	6.00	3.00	1.75
688	Ted Kubiak	6.00	3.00	1.75
689	Frank Tepedino	6.00	3.00	1.75
690	Ron Fairly	6.00	3.00	1.75
691	Joe Grzenda	6.00	3.00	1.75
692	Duffy Dyer	6.00	3.00	1.75
693	Bob Johnson	6.00	3.00	1.75
694	Gary Ross	6.00	3.00	1.75
695	Bobby Knoop	6.00	3.00	1.75
696	Giants Team	9.00	4.50	2.75
697	Jim Hannan	6.00	3.00	1.75
698	Tom Tresh	7.00	3.50	2.00
699	Hank Aguirre	6.00	3.00	1.75
700	Frank Robinson	50.00	25.00	15.00
701	Jack Billingham	6.00	3.00	1.75
702	A.L. Rookies (Bob Johnson, Ron Klimkowski, Bill Zepp)	6.00	3.00	1.75
703	Lou Marone	6.00	3.00	1.75
704	Frank Baker	6.00	3.00	1.75
705	Tony Cloninger	6.00	3.00	1.75
706	John McNamara	6.00	3.00	1.75
707	Kevin Collins	6.00	3.00	1.75
708	Jose Santiago	6.00	3.00	1.75
709	Mike Fiore	6.00	3.00	1.75
710	Felix Millan	6.00	3.00	1.75
711	Ed Brinkman	6.00	3.00	1.75
712	Nolan Ryan	500.00	250.00	150.00
713	Pilots Team	25.00	12.50	7.50
714	Al Spangler	6.00	3.00	1.75
715	Mickey Lolich	7.00	3.50	2.00
716	Cards Rookies (Sal Campisi, Reggie Cleveland, Santiago Guzman)	6.00	3.00	1.75
717	Tom Phoebus	6.00	3.00	1.75
718	Ed Spiezio	6.00	3.00	1.75
719	Jim Roland	6.00	3.00	1.75
720	Rick Reichardt	6.00	3.00	1.75

1970 Topps Candy Lids

The 1970 Topps Candy Lids are a test issue that was utilized again in 1973. The set is made up of 24 lids that measure 1-7/8" in diameter and were the tops of small 1.1 oz. tubs of "Baseball Stars Candy." Unlike the 1973 versions, the 1970 lids have no border surrounding the full-color photos. Frank Howard, Tom Seaver and Carl Yastrzemski photos are found on the bottom (inside) of the candy lid.

		NR MT	EX	VG
Complete Set:		2000.	1000.	600.00
Common Player:		30.00	15.00	9.00
(1)	Hank Aaron	200.00	100.00	60.00
(2)	Rich Allen	50.00	25.00	15.00
(3)	Luis Aparicio	80.00	40.00	24.00
(4)	Johnny Bench	200.00	100.00	60.00
(5)	Ollie Brown	30.00	15.00	9.00
(6)	Willie Davis	30.00	15.00	9.00
(7)	Jim Fregosi	30.00	15.00	9.00
(8)	Mike Hegan	30.00	15.00	9.00
(9)	Frank Howard	50.00	25.00	15.00
(10)	Reggie Jackson	200.00	100.00	60.00
(11)	Fergie Jenkins	60.00	30.00	18.00
(12)	Harmon Killebrew	100.00	50.00	30.00
(13)	Juan Marichal	100.00	50.00	30.00
(14)	Bill Mazeroski	50.00	25.00	15.00
(15)	Tim McCarver	50.00	25.00	15.00
(16)	Sam McDowell	30.00	15.00	9.00
(17)	Denny McLain	50.00	25.00	15.00
(18)	Lou Piniella	50.00	25.00	15.00
(19)	Frank Robinson	100.00	50.00	30.00
(20)	Tom Seaver	175.00	87.00	52.00
(21)	Rusty Staub	50.00	25.00	15.00
(22)	Mel Stottlemyre	50.00	25.00	15.00
(23)	Jim Wynn	30.00	15.00	9.00
(24)	Carl Yastrzemski	150.00	75.00	45.00

1970 Topps Cloth Stickers

The earliest and rarest of the Topps cloth sticker test issues, only 15 subjects are known, and only a single specimen apiece is known for many of them. In the same 2-1/2" x 3-1/2" size, and with the same design as the 1970 Topps baseball cards, the stickers are blank-backed. The stickers of Denny Lemaster, Dennis Higgins and Rich Nye use photos that are different from their '70 Topps cards. It is quite likely that the checklist presented here is incomplete. The stickers are unnumbered and are checklisted alphabetically.

		NR MT	EX	VG
Common Player:		50.00	25.00	15.00
(1)	A.L. Playoff Game 2 (Boog Powell)	50.00	25.00	15.00
(2)	Bill Burbach	50.00	25.00	15.00
(3)	Chuck Hartenstein	50.00	25.00	15.00
(4)	Dennis Higgins	50.00	25.00	15.00
(5)	Jose Laboy	50.00	25.00	15.00
(6)	Denny Lemaster	50.00	25.00	15.00
(7)	Juan Marichal	150.00	75.00	45.00
(8)	Jerry McNertney	50.00	25.00	15.00
(9)	Ivan Murrell	50.00	25.00	15.00
(10)	N.L. Playoff Game 3 (Nolan Ryan)	300.00	150.00	90.00
(11)	Phil Niekro	60.00	30.00	18.00
(12)	Jim Northrup	50.00	25.00	15.00
(13)	Rich Nye	50.00	25.00	15.00
(14)	Ron Perranoski	50.00	25.00	15.00
(15)	Al Santorini	50.00	25.00	15.00

1970 Topps Posters

Helping to ease a price increase, Topps included extremely fragile 8-11/16" by 9-5/8" posters in packs of regular cards. The posters feature color portraits and a smaller black and white "action" pose as well as the player's name, team and position at the top. Although there are Hall of Famers in the 24-poster set, all the top names are not represented. Once again, due to folding, heavy creases are a fact of life for today's collector.

		NR MT	EX	VG
Complete Set:		60.00	30.00	18.00
Common Player:		1.50	.70	.45
1	Joe Horlen	1.50	.70	.45
2	Phil Niekro	3.00	1.50	.90
3	Willie Davis	2.00	1.00	.60
4	Lou Brock	4.00	2.00	1.25
5	Ron Santo	2.50	1.25	.70
6	Ken Harrelson	2.00	1.00	.60
7	Willie McCovey	6.00	3.00	1.75
8	Rick Wise	1.50	.70	.45
9	Andy Messersmith	1.50	.70	.45
10	Ron Fairly	1.50	.70	.45
11	Johnny Bench	8.00	4.00	2.50
12	Frank Robinson	6.00	3.00	1.75
13	Tommie Agee	1.50	.70	.45
14	Roy White	2.00	1.00	.60
15	Larry Dierker	1.50	.70	.45
16	Rod Carew	6.00	3.00	1.75
17	Don Mincher	1.50	.70	.45
18	Ollie Brown	1.50	.70	.45
19	Ed Kirkpatrick	1.50	.70	.45
20	Reggie Smith	1.50	.70	.45
21	Roberto Clemente	10.00	5.00	3.00
22	Frank Howard	2.50	1.25	.70
23	Bert Campaneris	1.50	.70	.45
24	Denny McLain	2.50	1.25	.70

1970 Topps Scratch-Offs

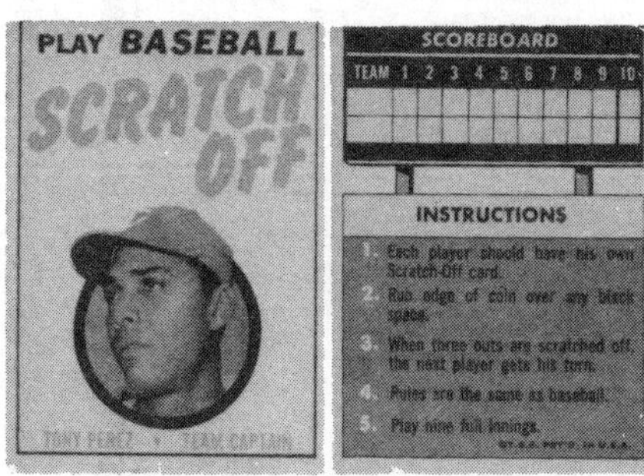

Needing inserts, and having not given up on the idea of a game which could be played with baseball cards, Topps provided a new game - the baseball scratch-off. The set consists of 24 cards. Unfolded, they measure 3-3/8" by 5," and reveal a baseball game of sorts which was played by rubbing the black ink off playing squares which then determined the "action." Fronts of the cards have a player picture as "captain," while backs have instructions and a scoreboard. Inserts with white centers are from 1970 while those with red centers are from 1971.

		NR MT	EX	VG
Complete Set:		35.00	17.50	10.50
Common Player:		1.00	.50	.30
(1)	Hank Aaron	5.00	2.50	1.50
(2)	Rich Allen	1.50	.70	.45
(3)	Luis Aparicio	2.50	1.25	.70
(4)	Sal Bando	1.00	.50	.30
(5)	Glenn Beckert	1.00	.50	.30
(6)	Dick Bosman	1.00	.50	.30
(7)	Nate Colbert	1.00	.50	.30
(8)	Mike Hegan	1.00	.50	.30
(9)	Mack Jones	1.00	.50	.30
(10)	Al Kaline	3.00	1.50	.90
(11)	Harmon Killebrew	3.00	1.50	.90
(12)	Juan Marichal	2.00	1.00	.60
(13)	Tim McCarver	1.50	.70	.45
(14)	Sam McDowell	1.00	.50	.30
(15)	Claude Osteen	1.00	.50	.30
(16)	Tony Perez	1.25	.60	.40
(17)	Lou Piniella	1.00	.50	.30
(18)	Boog Powell	1.25	.60	.40
(19)	Tom Seaver	3.00	1.50	.90
(20)	Jim Spencer	1.00	.50	.30
(21)	Willie Stargell	3.00	1.50	.90
(22)	Mel Stottlemyre	1.00	.50	.30
(23)	Jim Wynn	1.00	.50	.30
(24)	Carl Yastrzemski	4.00	2.00	1.25

1970 Topps Story Booklets

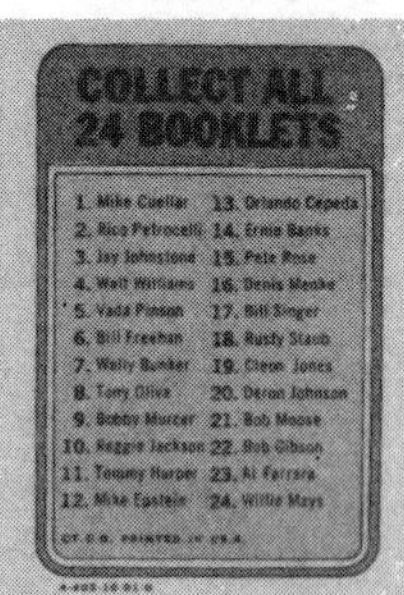

Measuring 2-1/2" by 3-7/16," the Topps Story Booklet was a 1970 regular pack insert. The booklet feature a photo, title and booklet number on the "cover." Inside are six pages of comic book story. The backs give a checklist of other available booklets. Not every star had a booklet as the set is only 24 in number.

		NR MT	EX	VG
Complete Set:		40.00	20.00	12.00
Common Player:		1.00	.50	.30
1	Mike Cuellar	1.00	.50	.30
2	Rico Petrocelli	1.00	.50	.30
3	Jay Johnstone	1.00	.50	.30
4	Walt Williams	1.00	.50	.30
5	Vada Pinson	1.50	.70	.45
6	Bill Freehan	1.00	.50	.30
7	Wally Bunker	1.00	.50	.30
8	Tony Oliva	1.50	.70	.45
9	Bobby Murcer	1.00	.50	.30
10	Reggie Jackson	5.00	2.50	1.50
11	Tommy Harper	6.00	3.00	1.75
12	Mike Epstein	1.00	.50	.30
13	Orlando Cepeda	2.00	1.00	.60
14	Ernie Banks	4.00	2.00	1.25
15	Pete Rose	8.00	4.00	2.50
16	Denis Menke	1.00	.50	.30
17	Bill Singer	1.00	.50	.30
18	Rusty Staub	1.50	.70	.45
19	Cleon Jones	1.00	.50	.30
20	Deron Johnson	1.00	.50	.30
21	Bob Moose	1.00	.50	.30
22	Bob Gibson	4.00	2.00	1.25
23	Al Ferrara	1.00	.50	.30
24	Willie Mays	7.00	3.50	2.00

1970 Topps Super

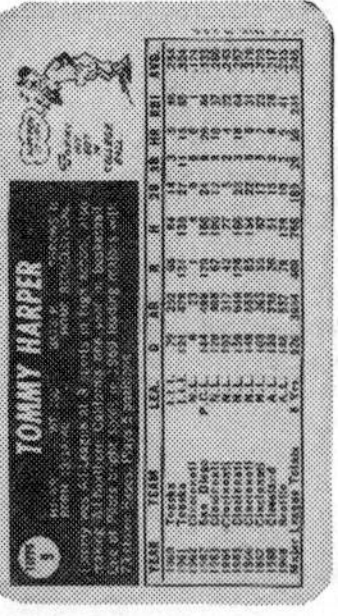

Representing a refinement of the concept begun in 1969, the 1970 Topps Supers had a new 3-1/8" by 5-1/4" postcard size. Printed on heavy stock with rounded corners, card fronts feature a borderless color photograph and facsimile autograph. Card backs are simply an enlarged back from the player's regular 1970 Topps card. The Topps Supers set numbers 42 cards. Probably due to the press sheet configuration eight of the 42 had smaller printings. The most elusive is card #38 (Boog Powell). The set was more widely produced than was the case in 1969, meaning collectors stand a much better chance of affording it.

		NR MT	EX	VG
Complete Set:		250.00	125.00	75.00
Common Player:		2.00	1.00	.60
1	Claude Osteen	3.00	1.50	.90
2	Sal Bando	3.50	1.75	1.00
3	Luis Aparicio	4.00	2.00	1.25
4	Harmon Killebrew	6.00	3.00	1.75
5	Tom Seaver	25.00	12.50	7.50
6	Larry Dierker	2.00	1.00	.60
7	Bill Freehan	2.00	1.00	.60
8	Johnny Bench	15.00	7.50	4.50
9	Tommy Harper	2.00	1.00	.60
10	Sam McDowell	2.00	1.00	.60
11	Lou Brock	6.00	3.00	1.75
12	Roberto Clemente	15.00	7.50	4.50
13	Willie McCovey	6.00	3.00	1.75
14	Rico Petrocelli	2.00	1.00	.60
15	Phil Niekro	3.00	1.50	.90
16	Frank Howard	2.50	1.25	.70
17	Denny McLain	2.50	1.25	.70
18	Willie Mays	15.00	7.50	4.50
19	Willie Stargell	6.00	3.00	1.75
20	Joe Horlen	2.00	1.00	.60
21	Ron Santo	2.50	1.25	.70
22	Dick Bosman	2.00	1.00	.60
23	Tim McCarver	2.50	1.25	.70
24	Henry Aaron	15.00	7.50	4.50
25	Andy Messersmith	2.00	1.00	.60
26	Tony Oliva	2.50	1.25	.70
27	Mel Stottlemyre	2.00	1.00	.60
28	Reggie Jackson	25.00	12.50	7.50
29	Carl Yastrzemski	12.00	6.00	3.50
30	James Fregosi	2.00	1.00	.60
31	Vada Pinson	2.50	1.25	.70
32	Lou Piniella	2.00	1.00	.60
33	Robert Gibson	6.00	3.00	1.75
34	Pete Rose	25.00	12.50	7.50
35	Jim Wynn	2.00	1.00	.60
36	Ollie Brown	5.00	2.50	1.50
37	Frank Robinson	18.00	9.00	5.50
38	Boog Powell	65.00	32.00	19.50
39	Willie Davis	5.00	2.50	1.50
40	Billy Williams	12.00	6.00	3.50
41	Rusty Staub	2.00	1.00	.60
42	Tommie Agee	2.00	1.00	.60

1971 Topps

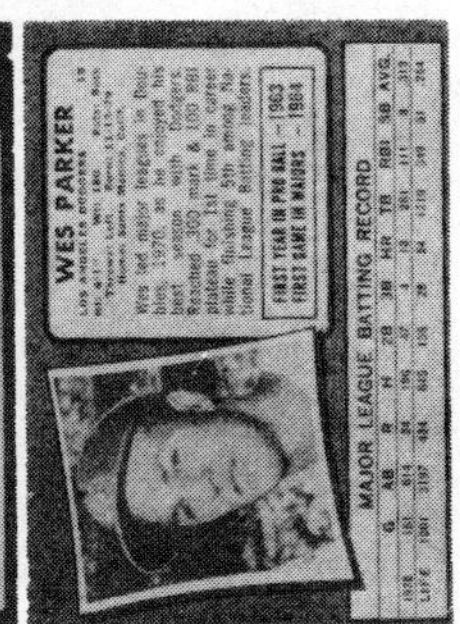

In 1971, Topps again increased the size of its set to 752 cards. These well-liked cards, measuring 2-1/2" by 3-1/2," feature a large color photo which has a thin white frame. Above the picture, in the card's overall black border, is the player's name, team and position. A facsimile autograph completes the front. Backs feature a major change as a black and white "snapshot" of the player appears. Abbreviated statistics, a line giving the player's first pro and major league games and a short biography complete the back of these innovative cards. Specialty cards in this issue are limited. There are statistical leaders as well as World Series and playoff highlights. High numbered cards #644-752 are scarce, with about half of the cards being short-printed.

		NR MT	EX	VG
Complete Set (752):		2250.	1125.	675.00
Common Player (1-393):		1.00	.50	.30
Common Player (394-523):		2.00	1.00	.60
Common Player (524-643):		3.50	1.75	1.00
Common Player (644-752):		4.50	2.25	1.25
1	World Champions (Orioles Team)	12.00	6.00	3.50
2	Dock Ellis	1.00	.50	.30
3	Dick McAuliffe	1.00	.50	.30
4	Vic Davalillo	1.00	.50	.30
5	Thurman Munson	30.00	15.00	9.00
6	Ed Spiezio	1.00	.50	.30
7	Jim Holt	1.00	.50	.30
8	Mike McQueen	1.00	.50	.30
9	George Scott	1.00	.50	.30
10	Claude Osteen	1.00	.50	.30
11	*Elliott Maddox*	1.00	.50	.30
12	Johnny Callison	1.00	.50	.30
13	White Sox Rookies (Charlie Brinkman, Dick Moloney)	1.00	.50	.30
14	*Dave Concepcion*	20.00	10.00	6.00
15	Andy Messersmith	1.00	.50	.30
16	*Ken Singleton*	3.50	1.75	1.00
17	Billy Sorrell	1.00	.50	.30
18	Norm Miller	1.00	.50	.30
19	Skip Pitlock	1.00	.50	.30
20	Reggie Jackson	90.00	45.00	27.00
21	Dan McGinn	1.00	.50	.30
22	Phil Roof	1.00	.50	.30
23	Oscar Gamble	1.00	.50	.30
24	Rich Hand	1.00	.50	.30
25	Cito Gaston	2.50	1.25	.70
26	*Bert Blyleven*	20.00	10.00	6.00
27	Pirates Rookies (Fred Cambria, Gene Clines)	1.00	.50	.30
28	Ron Klimkowski	1.00	.50	.30
29	Don Buford	1.00	.50	.30
30	Phil Niekro	3.25	1.75	1.00
31	Eddie Kasko	1.00	.50	.30
32	Jerry DaVanon	1.00	.50	.30
33	Del Unser	1.00	.50	.30
34	Sandy Vance	1.00	.50	.30
35	Lou Piniella	1.00	.50	.30
36	Dean Chance	1.00	.50	.30
37	Rich McKinney	1.00	.50	.30
38	*Jim Colborn*	1.00	.50	.30
39	Tigers Rookies (Gene Lamont, Lerrin LaGrow)	1.00	.50	.30
40	Lee May	1.00	.50	.30
41	Rick Austin	1.00	.50	.30
42	Boots Day	1.00	.50	.30
43	Steve Kealey	1.00	.50	.30
44	Johnny Edwards	1.00	.50	.30
45	Catfish Hunter	5.00	2.50	1.50
46	Dave Campbell	1.00	.50	.30
47	Johnny Jeter	1.00	.50	.30
48	Dave Baldwin	1.00	.50	.30
49	Don Money	1.00	.50	.30
50	Willie McCovey	7.00	3.50	2.00
51	Steve Kline	1.00	.50	.30
52	Braves Rookies (Oscar Brown, Earl Williams)	1.00	.50	.30
53	Paul Blair	1.00	.50	.30
54	Checklist 1-132	3.25	1.75	1.00
55	Steve Carlton	25.00	12.50	7.50
56	Duane Josephson	1.00	.50	.30
57	Von Joshua	1.00	.50	.30
58	Bill Lee	1.00	.50	.30
59	Gene Mauch	1.00	.50	.30
60	Dick Bosman	1.00	.50	.30
61	A.L. Batting Leaders (Alex Johnson, Tony Oliva, Carl Yastrzemski)	3.50	1.75	1.00
62	N.L. Batting Leaders (Rico Carty, Manny Sanguillen, Joe Torre)	1.50	.70	.45
63	A.L. RBI Leaders (Tony Conigliaro, Frank Howard, Boog Powell)	1.50	.70	.45
64	N.L. RBI Leaders (Johnny Bench, Tony Perez, Billy Williams)	3.50	1.75	1.00
65	A.L. Home Run Leaders (Frank Howard, Harmon Killebrew, Carl Yastrzemski)	3.50	1.75	1.00
66	N.L. Home Run Leaders (Johnny Bench, Tony Perez, Billy Williams)	3.50	1.75	1.00
67	A.L. ERA Leaders (Jim Palmer, Diego Segui, Clyde Wright)	1.50	.70	.45
68	N.L. ERA Leaders (Tom Seaver, Wayne Simpson, Luke Walker)	1.50	.70	.45
69	A.L. Pitching Leaders (Mike Cuellar, Dave McNally, Jim Perry)	1.50	.70	.45
70	N.L. Pitching Leaders (Bob Gibson, Fergie Jenkins, Gaylord Perry)	3.50	1.75	1.00
71	A.L. Strikeout Leaders (Bob Johnson, Mickey Lolich, Sam McDowell)	1.50	.70	.45
72	N.L. Strikeout Leaders (Bob Gibson, Fergie Jenkins, Tom Seaver)	3.50	1.75	1.00
73	George Brunet	1.00	.50	.30
74	Twins Rookies (Pete Hamm, Jim Nettles)	1.00	.50	.30
75	Gary Nolan	1.00	.50	.30
76	Ted Savage	1.00	.50	.30
77	Mike Compton	1.00	.50	.30
78	Jim Spencer	1.00	.50	.30
79	Wade Blasingame	1.00	.50	.30
80	Bill Melton	1.00	.50	.30
81	Felix Millan	1.00	.50	.30
82	Casey Cox	1.00	.50	.30
83	Mets Rookies (Randy Bobb, Tim Foli)	1.00	.50	.30
84	Marcel Lachemann	1.00	.50	.30
85	Billy Grabarkewitz	1.00	.50	.30
86	Mike Kilkenny	1.00	.50	.30
87	Jack Heidemann	1.00	.50	.30
88	Hal King	1.00	.50	.30
89	Ken Brett	1.00	.50	.30
90	Joe Pepitone	1.00	.50	.30
91	Bob Lemon	3.50	1.75	1.00
92	Fred Wenz	1.00	.50	.30
93	Senators Rookies (Norm McRae, Denny Riddleberger)	1.00	.50	.30
94	Don Hahn	1.00	.50	.30
95	Luis Tiant	1.50	.70	.45
96	Joe Hague	1.00	.50	.30
97	Floyd Wicker	1.00	.50	.30
98	Joe Decker	1.00	.50	.30
99	Mark Belanger	1.00	.50	.30
100	Pete Rose	35.00	17.50	10.50
101	Les Cain	1.00	.50	.30
102	Astros Rookies (*Ken Forsch*, Larry Howard)	1.00	.50	.30
103	Rich Severson	1.00	.50	.30
104	Dan Frisella	1.00	.50	.30
105	Tony Conigliaro	1.25	.60	.40
106	Tom Dukes	1.00	.50	.30
107	Roy Foster	1.00	.50	.30
108	John Cumberland	1.00	.50	.30
109	Steve Hovley	1.00	.50	.30
110	Bill Mazeroski	2.50	1.25	.70
111	Yankees Rookies (Loyd Colson, Bobby Mitchell)	1.00	.50	.30
112	Manny Mota	1.00	.50	.30
113	Jerry Crider	1.00	.50	.30
114	Billy Conigliaro	1.00	.50	.30
115	Donn Clendenon	1.00	.50	.30
116	Ken Sanders	1.00	.50	.30
117	*Ted Simmons*	22.00	11.00	6.50
118	Cookie Rojas	1.00	.50	.30
119	Frank Lucchesi	1.00	.50	.30
120	Willie Horton	1.00	.50	.30
121	Cubs Rookies (Jim Dunegan, Roe Skidmore)	1.00	.50	.30
122	Eddie Watt	1.00	.50	.30
123a	Checklist 133-263 (card # on right, orange helmet)	3.25	1.75	1.00
123b	Checklist 133-263 (card # on right, red helmet)	3.25	1.75	1.00
123c	Checklist 133-263 (card # centered)	3.50	1.75	1.00
124	*Don Gullett*	1.00	.50	.30
125	Ray Fosse	1.00	.50	.30
126	Danny Coombs	1.00	.50	.30
127	*Danny Thompson*	1.00	.50	.30
128	Frank Johnson	1.00	.50	.30
129	Aurelio Monteagudo	1.00	.50	.30
130	Denis Menke	1.00	.50	.30
131	Curt Blefary	1.00	.50	.30
132	Jose Laboy	1.00	.50	.30
133	Mickey Lolich	1.25	.60	.40
134	Jose Arcia	1.00	.50	.30
135	Rick Monday	1.00	.50	.30
136	Duffy Dyer	1.00	.50	.30
137	Marcelino Lopez	1.00	.50	.30
138	Phillies Rookies (Joe Lis, Willie Montanez)	1.00	.50	.30
139	Paul Casanova	1.00	.50	.30
140	Gaylord Perry	6.00	3.00	1.75
141	Frank Quilici	1.00	.50	.30
142	Mack Jones	1.00	.50	.30
143	Steve Blass	1.00	.50	.30
144	Jackie Hernandez	1.00	.50	.30
145	Bill Singer	1.00	.50	.30
146	Ralph Houk	1.00	.50	.30
147	Bob Priddy	1.00	.50	.30
148	John Mayberry	1.00	.50	.30
149	Mike Hershberger	1.00	.50	.30
150	Sam McDowell	1.00	.50	.30
151	Tommy Davis	1.00	.50	.30
152	Angels Rookies (Lloyd Allen, Winston Llenas)	1.00	.50	.30
153	Gary Ross	1.00	.50	.30
154	Cesar Gutierrez	1.00	.50	.30
155	Ken Henderson	1.00	.50	.30
156	Bart Johnson	1.00	.50	.30
157	Bob Bailey	1.00	.50	.30
158	Jerry Reuss	1.00	.50	.30
159	Jarvis Tatum	1.00	.50	.30
160	Tom Seaver	45.00	22.00	13.50
161	Coins Checklist	3.25	1.75	1.00
162	Jack Billingham	1.00	.50	.30
163	Buck Martinez	1.00	.50	.30
164	Reds Rookies (Frank Duffy, Milt Wilcox)	1.00	.50	.30
165	Cesar Tovar	1.00	.50	.30
166	Joe Hoerner	1.00	.50	.30
167	Tom Grieve	1.00	.50	.30
168	Bruce Dal Canton	1.00	.50	.30
169	Ed Herrmann	1.00	.50	.30
170	Mike Cuellar	1.00	.50	.30
171	Bobby Wine	1.00	.50	.30
172	Duke Sims	1.00	.50	.30
173	Gil Garrido	1.00	.50	.30
174	*Dave LaRoche*	1.00	.50	.30
175	Jim Hickman	1.00	.50	.30
176	Red Sox Rookies (Doug Griffin, Bob Montgomery)	1.00	.50	.30
177	Hal McRae	2.00	1.00	.60
178	Dave Duncan	1.00	.50	.30
179	Mike Corkins	1.00	.50	.30
180	Al Kaline	15.00	7.50	4.50
181	Hal Lanier	1.00	.50	.30
182	Al Downing	1.00	.50	.30
183	Gil Hodges	4.00	2.00	1.25
184	Stan Bahnsen	1.00	.50	.30
185	Julian Javier	1.00	.50	.30
186	Bob Spence	1.00	.50	.30
187	Ted Abernathy	1.00	.50	.30
188	Dodgers Rookies (Mike Strahler, Bob Valentine)	3.50	1.75	1.00
189	George Mitterwald	1.00	.50	.30
190	Bob Tolan	1.00	.50	.30
191	Mike Andrews	1.00	.50	.30
192	Billy Wilson	1.00	.50	.30
193	*Bob Grich*	3.50	1.75	1.00
194	Mike Lum	1.00	.50	.30
195	A.L. Playoff Game 1 (Powell Muscles Twins!)	2.00	1.00	.60
196	A.L. Playoff Game 2 (McNally Makes It Two Straight!)	2.00	1.00	.60
197	A.L. Playoff Game 3 (Palmer Mows 'Em Down!)	3.50	1.75	1.00
198	A.L. Playoffs Summary (A Team Effort!)	2.00	1.00	.60
199	N.L. Playoff Game 1 (Cline Pinch-Triple Decides It!)	2.00	1.00	.60
200	N.L. Playoff Game 2 (Tolan Scores For Third Time!)	2.00	1.00	.60
201	N.L. Playoff Game 3 (Cline Scores Winning Run!)	2.00	1.00	.60
202	N.L. Playoffs Summary (World Series Bound!)	2.00	1.00	.60
203	*Larry Gura*	1.00	.50	.30
204	Brewers Rookies (George Kopacz, Bernie Smith)	1.00	.50	.30
205	Gerry Moses	1.00	.50	.30

No.	Player	NR MT	EX	VG
206a	Checklist 264-393 (orange helmet)	3.25	1.75	1.00
206b	Checklist 264-393 (red helmet)	3.25	1.75	1.00
207	Alan Foster	1.00	.50	.30
208	Billy Martin	3.50	1.75	1.00
209	Steve Renko	1.00	.50	.30
210	Rod Carew	30.00	15.00	9.00
211	Phil Hennigan	1.00	.50	.30
212	Rich Hebner	1.00	.50	.30
213	Frank Baker	1.00	.50	.30
214	Al Ferrara	1.00	.50	.30
215	Diego Segui	1.00	.50	.30
216	Cards Rookies (Reggie Cleveland, Luis Melendez)	1.00	.50	.30
217	Ed Stroud	1.00	.50	.30
218	Tony Cloninger	1.00	.50	.30
219	Elrod Hendricks	1.00	.50	.30
220	Ron Santo	2.50	1.25	.70
221	Dave Morehead	1.00	.50	.30
222	Bob Watson	1.00	.50	.30
223	Cecil Upshaw	1.00	.50	.30
224	Alan Gallagher	1.00	.50	.30
225	Gary Peters	1.00	.50	.30
226	Bill Russell	2.00	1.00	.60
227	Floyd Weaver	1.00	.50	.30
228	Wayne Garrett	1.00	.50	.30
229	Jim Hannan	1.00	.50	.30
230	Willie Stargell	8.00	4.00	2.50
231	Indians Rookies (Vince Colbert, John Lowenstein)	1.00	.50	.30
232	John Strohmayer	1.00	.50	.30
233	Larry Bowa	2.00	1.00	.60
234	Jim Lyttle	1.00	.50	.30
235	Nate Colbert	1.00	.50	.30
236	Bob Humphreys	1.00	.50	.30
237	*Cesar Cedeno*	3.50	1.75	1.00
238	Chuck Dobson	1.00	.50	.30
239	Red Schoendienst	3.50	1.75	1.00
240	Clyde Wright	1.00	.50	.30
241	Dave Nelson	1.00	.50	.30
242	Jim Ray	1.00	.50	.30
243	Carlos May	1.00	.50	.30
244	Bob Tillman	1.00	.50	.30
245	Jim Kaat	2.50	1.25	.70
246	Tony Taylor	1.00	.50	.30
247	Royals Rookies (Jerry Cram, Paul Splittorff)	1.00	.50	.30
248	Hoyt Wilhelm	3.75	2.00	1.25
249	Chico Salmon	1.00	.50	.30
250	Johnny Bench	35.00	17.50	10.50
251	Frank Reberger	1.00	.50	.30
252	Eddie Leon	1.00	.50	.30
253	Bill Sudakis	1.00	.50	.30
254	Cal Koonce	1.00	.50	.30
255	Bob Robertson	1.00	.50	.30
256	Tony Gonzalez	1.00	.50	.30
257	Nelson Briles	1.00	.50	.30
258	Dick Green	1.00	.50	.30
259	Dave Marshall	1.00	.50	.30
260	Tommy Harper	1.00	.50	.30
261	Darold Knowles	1.00	.50	.30
262	Padres Rookies (Dave Robinson, Jim Williams)	1.00	.50	.30
263	John Ellis	1.00	.50	.30
264	Joe Morgan	10.00	5.00	3.00
265	Jim Northrup	1.00	.50	.30
266	Bill Stoneman	1.00	.50	.30
267	Rich Morales	1.00	.50	.30
268	Phillies Team	3.50	1.75	1.00
269	Gail Hopkins	1.00	.50	.30
270	Rico Carty	1.00	.50	.30
271	Bill Zepp	1.00	.50	.30
272	Tommy Helms	1.00	.50	.30
273	Pete Richert	1.00	.50	.30
274	Ron Slocum	1.00	.50	.30
275	Vada Pinson	2.00	1.00	.60
276	Giants Rookies (Mike Davison, George Foster)	7.50	3.75	2.25
277	Gary Waslewski	1.00	.50	.30
278	Jerry Grote	1.00	.50	.30
279	Lefty Phillips	1.00	.50	.30
280	Fergie Jenkins	8.00	4.00	2.50
281	Danny Walton	1.00	.50	.30
282	Jose Pagan	1.00	.50	.30
283	Dick Such	1.00	.50	.30
284	Jim Gosger	1.00	.50	.30
285	Sal Bando	1.00	.50	.30
286	Jerry McNertney	1.00	.50	.30
287	Mike Fiore	1.00	.50	.30
288	Joe Moeller	1.00	.50	.30
289	White Sox Team	3.50	1.75	1.00
290	Tony Oliva	1.50	.70	.45
291	George Culver	1.00	.50	.30
292	Jay Johnstone	1.00	.50	.30
293	Pat Corrales	1.00	.50	.30
294	Steve Dunning	1.00	.50	.30
295	Bobby Bonds	1.25	.60	.40
296	Tom Timmermann	1.00	.50	.30
297	Johnny Briggs	1.00	.50	.30
298	Jim Nelson	1.00	.50	.30
299	Ed Kirkpatrick	1.00	.50	.30
300	Brooks Robinson	20.00	10.00	6.00
301	Earl Wilson	1.00	.50	.30
302	Phil Gagliano	1.00	.50	.30
303	Lindy McDaniel	1.00	.50	.30
304	Ron Brand	1.00	.50	.30
305	Reggie Smith	1.50	.70	.45
306	Jim Nash	1.00	.50	.30
307	Don Wert	1.00	.50	.30
308	Cards Team	3.50	1.75	1.00
309	Dick Ellsworth	1.00	.50	.30
310	Tommie Agee	1.00	.50	.30
311	Lee Stange	1.00	.50	.30
312	Harry Walker	1.00	.50	.30
313	Tom Hall	1.00	.50	.30
314	Jeff Torborg	1.00	.50	.30
315	Ron Fairly	1.00	.50	.30
316	Fred Scherman	1.00	.50	.30
317	Athletics Rookies (Jim Driscoll, Angel Mangual)	1.00	.50	.30
318	Rudy May	1.00	.50	.30
319	Ty Cline	1.00	.50	.30
320	Dave McNally	1.00	.50	.30
321	Tom Matchick	1.00	.50	.30
322	Jim Beauchamp	1.00	.50	.30
323	Billy Champion	1.00	.50	.30
324	Graig Nettles	2.00	1.00	.60
325	Juan Marichal	6.00	3.00	1.75
326	Richie Scheinblum	1.00	.50	.30
327	World Series Game 1 (Powell Homers To Opposite Field!)	3.50	1.75	1.00
328	World Series Game 2 (Buford Goes 2-For-4!)	2.00	1.00	.60
329	World Series Game 3 (F. Robinson Shows Muscle!)	3.50	1.75	1.00
330	World Series Game 4 (Reds Stay Alive!)	2.00	1.00	.60
331	World Series Game 5 (B. Robinson Commits Robbery!)	3.50	1.75	1.00
332	World Series Summary (Convincing Performance!)	2.00	1.00	.60
333	Clay Kirby	1.00	.50	.30
334	Roberto Pena	1.00	.50	.30
335	Jerry Koosman	1.00	.50	.30
336	Tigers Team	3.50	1.75	1.00
337	Jesus Alou	1.00	.50	.30
338	Gene Tenace	1.00	.50	.30
339	Wayne Simpson	1.00	.50	.30
340	Rico Petrocelli	1.00	.50	.30
341	*Steve Garvey*	55.00	27.00	16.50
342	Frank Tepedino	1.00	.50	.30
343	Pirates Rookies (Ed Acosta, Milt May)	1.00	.50	.30
344	Ellie Rodriguez	1.00	.50	.30
345	Joe Horlen	1.00	.50	.30
346	Lum Harris	1.00	.50	.30
347	Ted Uhlaender	1.00	.50	.30
348	Fred Norman	1.00	.50	.30
349	Rich Reese	1.00	.50	.30
350	Billy Williams	8.00	4.00	2.50
351	Jim Shellenback	1.00	.50	.30
352	Denny Doyle	1.00	.50	.30
353	Carl Taylor	1.00	.50	.30
354	Don McMahon	1.00	.50	.30
355	Bud Harrelson	1.00	.50	.30
356	Bob Locker	1.00	.50	.30
357	Reds Team	3.50	1.75	1.00
358	Danny Cater	1.00	.50	.30
359	Ron Reed	1.00	.50	.30
360	Jim Fregosi	1.00	.50	.30
361	Don Sutton	3.50	1.75	1.00
362	Orioles Rookies (Mike Adamson, Roger Freed)	1.00	.50	.30
363	Mike Nagy	1.00	.50	.30
364	Tommy Dean	1.00	.50	.30
365	Bob Johnson	1.00	.50	.30
366	Ron Stone	1.00	.50	.30
367	Dalton Jones	1.00	.50	.30
368	Bob Veale	1.00	.50	.30
369a	Checklist 394-523 (orange helmet)	3.25	1.75	1.00
369b	Checklist 394-523 (red helmet, black line above ear)	3.25	1.75	1.00
369c	Checklist 394-523 (red helmet, no line)	3.25	1.75	1.00
370	Joe Torre	1.00	.50	.30
371	Jack Hiatt	1.00	.50	.30
372	Lew Krausse	1.00	.50	.30
373	Tom McCraw	1.00	.50	.30
374	Clete Boyer	1.00	.50	.30
375	Steve Hargan	1.00	.50	.30
376	Expos Rookies (Clyde Mashore, Ernie McAnally)	1.00	.50	.30
377	Greg Garrett	1.00	.50	.30
378	Tito Fuentes	1.00	.50	.30
379	Wayne Granger	1.00	.50	.30
380	Ted Williams	10.00	5.00	3.00
381	Fred Gladding	1.00	.50	.30
382	Jake Gibbs	1.00	.50	.30
383	Rod Gaspar	1.00	.50	.30
384	Rollie Fingers	7.50	3.75	2.25
385	Maury Wills	1.25	.60	.40
386	Red Sox Team	3.50	1.75	1.00
387	Ron Herbel	1.00	.50	.30
388	Al Oliver	1.50	.70	.45
389	Ed Brinkman	1.00	.50	.30
390	Glenn Beckert	1.00	.50	.30
391	Twins Rookies (Steve Brye, Cotton Nash)	1.00	.50	.30
392	Grant Jackson	1.00	.50	.30
393	Merv Rettenmund	1.00	.50	.30
394	Clay Carroll	2.00	1.00	.60
395	Roy White	2.00	1.00	.60
396	Dick Schofield	2.00	1.00	.60
397	Alvin Dark	2.00	1.00	.60
398	Howie Reed	2.00	1.00	.60
399	Jim French	2.00	1.00	.60
400	Hank Aaron	45.00	22.00	13.50
401	Tom Murphy	2.00	1.00	.60
402	Dodgers Team	3.50	1.75	1.00
403	Joe Coleman	2.00	1.00	.60
404	Astros Rookies (Buddy Harris, Roger Metzger)	2.00	1.00	.60
405	Leo Cardenas	2.00	1.00	.60
406	Ray Sadecki	2.00	1.00	.60
407	Joe Rudi	2.00	1.00	.60
408	Rafael Robles	2.00	1.00	.60
409	Don Pavletich	2.00	1.00	.60
410	Ken Holtzman	2.00	1.00	.60
411	George Spriggs	2.00	1.00	.60
412	Jerry Johnson	2.00	1.00	.60
413	Pat Kelly	2.00	1.00	.60
414	Woodie Fryman	2.00	1.00	.60
415	Mike Hegan	2.00	1.00	.60
416	Gene Alley	2.00	1.00	.60
417	Dick Hall	2.00	1.00	.60
418	Adolfo Phillips	2.00	1.00	.60
419	Ron Hansen	2.00	1.00	.60
420	Jim Merritt	2.00	1.00	.60
421	John Stephenson	2.00	1.00	.60
422	Frank Bertaina	2.00	1.00	.60
423	Tigers Rookies (Tim Marting, Dennis Saunders)	2.00	1.00	.60
424	Roberto Rodriquez (Rodriguez)	2.00	1.00	.60
425	Doug Rader	2.00	1.00	.60
426	Chris Cannizzaro	2.00	1.00	.60
427	Bernie Allen	2.00	1.00	.60
428	Jim McAndrew	2.00	1.00	.60
429	Chuck Hinton	2.00	1.00	.60
430	Wes Parker	2.00	1.00	.60
431	Tom Burgmeier	2.00	1.00	.60
432	Bob Didier	2.00	1.00	.60
433	Skip Lockwood	2.00	1.00	.60
434	Gary Sutherland	2.00	1.00	.60
435	Jose Cardenal	2.00	1.00	.60
436	Wilbur Wood	2.00	1.00	.60
437	Danny Murtaugh	2.00	1.00	.60
438	Mike McCormick	2.00	1.00	.60
439	*Greg Luzinski*, Scott Reid	6.00	3.00	1.75
440	Bert Campaneris	2.00	1.00	.60
441	Milt Pappas	2.00	1.00	.60
442	Angels Team	3.50	1.75	1.00
443	Rich Robertson	2.00	1.00	.60
444	Jimmie Price	2.00	1.00	.60
445	Art Shamsky	2.00	1.00	.60
446	Bobby Bolin	2.00	1.00	.60
447	*Cesar Geronimo*	2.00	1.00	.60
448	Dave Roberts	2.00	1.00	.60
449	Brant Alyea	2.00	1.00	.60
450	Bob Gibson	12.00	6.00	3.50
451	Joe Keough	2.00	1.00	.60
452	John Boccabella	2.00	1.00	.60
453	Terry Crowley	2.00	1.00	.60
454	Mike Paul	2.00	1.00	.60
455	Don Kessinger	2.25	1.25	.70
456	Bob Meyer	2.00	1.00	.60
457	Willie Smith	2.00	1.00	.60
458	White Sox Rookies (Dave Lemonds, Ron Lolich)	2.00	1.00	.60
459	Jim Lefebvre	2.50	1.25	.70
460	Fritz Peterson	2.00	1.00	.60
461	Jim Hart	2.00	1.00	.60
462	Senators Team	3.50	1.75	1.00
463	Tom Kelley	2.00	1.00	.60
464	Aurelio Rodriguez	2.00	1.00	.60
465	Tim McCarver	2.50	1.25	.70
466	Ken Berry	2.00	1.00	.60
467	Al Santorini	2.00	1.00	.60
468	Frank Fernandez	2.00	1.00	.60
469	Bob Aspromonte	2.00	1.00	.60
470	Bob Oliver	2.00	1.00	.60
471	Tom Griffin	2.00	1.00	.60
472	Ken Rudolph	2.00	1.00	.60
473	Gary Wagner	2.00	1.00	.60
474	Jim Fairey	2.00	1.00	.60
475	Ron Perranoski	2.00	1.00	.60
476	Dal Maxvill	2.00	1.00	.60
477	Earl Weaver	4.00	2.00	1.25
478	Bernie Carbo	2.00	1.00	.60
479	Dennis Higgins	2.00	1.00	.60
480	Manny Sanguillen	2.00	1.00	.60
481	Daryl Patterson	2.00	1.00	.60
482	Padres Team	3.50	1.75	1.00
483	Gene Michael	2.00	1.00	.60
484	Don Wilson	2.00	1.00	.60
485	Ken McMullen	2.00	1.00	.60
486	Steve Huntz	2.00	1.00	.60
487	Paul Schaal	2.00	1.00	.60
488	Jerry Stephenson	2.00	1.00	.60
489	Luis Alvarado	2.00	1.00	.60
490	Deron Johnson	2.00	1.00	.60
491	Jim Hardin	2.00	1.00	.60
492	Ken Boswell	2.00	1.00	.60
493	Dave May	2.00	1.00	.60
494	Braves Rookies (Ralph Garr, Rick Kester)	2.00	1.00	.60
495	Felipe Alou	3.50	1.75	1.00
496	Woody Woodward	2.00	1.00	.60
497	Horacio Pina	2.00	1.00	.60
498	John Kennedy	2.00	1.00	.60
499	Checklist 524-643	3.25	1.75	1.00
500	Jim Perry	2.00	1.00	.60
501	Andy Etchebarren	2.00	1.00	.60
502	Cubs Team	3.50	1.75	1.00
503	Gates Brown	2.00	1.00	.60
504	Ken Wright	2.00	1.00	.60
505	Ollie Brown	2.00	1.00	.60
506	Bobby Knoop	2.00	1.00	.60
507	George Stone	2.00	1.00	.60
508	Roger Repoz	2.00	1.00	.60
509	Jim Grant	2.00	1.00	.60
510	Ken Harrelson	2.00	1.00	.60
511	Chris Short	2.00	1.00	.60
512	Red Sox Rookies (Mike Garman, Dick Mills)	2.00	1.00	.60
513	Nolan Ryan	250.00	125.00	75.00
514	Ron Woods	2.00	1.00	.60
515	Carl Morton	2.00	1.00	.60
516	Ted Kubiak	2.00	1.00	.60
517	Charlie Fox	2.00	1.00	.60
518	Joe Grzenda	2.00	1.00	.60
519	Willie Crawford	2.00	1.00	.60
520	Tommy John	4.00	2.00	1.25
521	Leron Lee	2.00	1.00	.60
522	Twins Team	3.50	1.75	1.00
523	John Odom	2.00	1.00	.60
524	Mickey Stanley	3.50	1.75	1.00
525	Ernie Banks	30.00	15.00	9.00
526	Ray Jarvis	3.50	1.75	1.00
527	Cleon Jones	3.50	1.75	1.00
528	Wally Bunker	3.50	1.75	1.00
529	N.L. Rookies (Bill Buckner, Enzo Hernandez, Marty Perez)	4.00	2.00	1.25
530	Carl Yastrzemski	30.00	15.00	9.00
531	Mike Torrez	3.50	1.75	1.00
532	Bill Rigney	3.50	1.75	1.00
533	Mike Ryan	3.50	1.75	1.00
534	Luke Walker	3.50	1.75	1.00
535	Curt Flood	3.50	1.75	1.00
536	Claude Raymond	3.50	1.75	1.00
537	Tom Egan	3.50	1.75	1.00
538	Angel Bravo	3.50	1.75	1.00
539	Larry Brown	3.50	1.75	1.00
540	Larry Dierker	3.50	1.75	1.00
541	Bob Burda	3.50	1.75	1.00
542	Bob Miller	3.50	1.75	1.00

543	Yankees Team	7.50	3.75	2.25
544	Vida Blue	3.50	1.75	1.00
545	Dick Dietz	3.50	1.75	1.00
546	John Matias	3.50	1.75	1.00
547	Pat Dobson	3.50	1.75	1.00
548	Don Mason	3.50	1.75	1.00
549	Jim Brewer	3.50	1.75	1.00
550	Harmon Killebrew	20.00	10.00	6.00
551	Frank Linzy	3.50	1.75	1.00
552	Buddy Bradford	3.50	1.75	1.00
553	Kevin Collins	3.50	1.75	1.00
554	Lowell Palmer	3.50	1.75	1.00
555	Walt Williams	3.50	1.75	1.00
556	Jim McGlothlin	3.50	1.75	1.00
557	Tom Satriano	3.50	1.75	1.00
558	Hector Torres	3.50	1.75	1.00
559	A.L. Rookies (Terry Cox, Bill Gogolewski, Gary Jones)	3.50	1.75	1.00
560	Rusty Staub	4.00	2.00	1.25
561	Syd O'Brien	3.50	1.75	1.00
562	Dave Giusti	3.50	1.75	1.00
563	Giants Team	6.00	3.00	1.75
564	Al Fitzmorris	3.50	1.75	1.00
565	Jim Wynn	3.50	1.75	1.00
566	Tim Cullen	3.50	1.75	1.00
567	Walt Alston	4.00	2.00	1.25
568	Sal Campisi	3.50	1.75	1.00
569	Ivan Murrell	3.50	1.75	1.00
570	Jim Palmer	30.00	15.00	9.00
571	Ted Sizemore	3.50	1.75	1.00
572	Jerry Kenney	3.50	1.75	1.00
573	Ed Kranepool	3.50	1.75	1.00
574	Jim Bunning	4.00	2.00	1.25
575	Bill Freehan	3.50	1.75	1.00
576	Cubs Rookies (Brock Davis, Adrian Garrett, Garry Jestadt)	3.50	1.75	1.00
577	Jim Lonborg	4.00	2.00	1.25
578	Ron Hunt	3.50	1.75	1.00
579	Marty Pattin	3.50	1.75	1.00
580	Tony Perez	12.00	6.00	3.50
581	Roger Nelson	3.50	1.75	1.00
582	Dave Cash	3.50	1.75	1.00
583	Ron Cook	3.50	1.75	1.00
584	Indians Team	6.00	3.00	1.75
585	Willie Davis	3.50	1.75	1.00
586	Dick Woodson	3.50	1.75	1.00
587	Sonny Jackson	3.50	1.75	1.00
588	Tom Bradley	3.50	1.75	1.00
589	Bob Barton	3.50	1.75	1.00
590	Alex Johnson	3.50	1.75	1.00
591	Jackie Brown	3.50	1.75	1.00
592	Randy Hundley	3.50	1.75	1.00
593	Jack Aker	3.50	1.75	1.00
594	Cards Rookies (Bob Chlupsa, Al Hrabosky, Bob Stinson)	3.50	1.75	1.00
595	Dave Johnson	3.50	1.75	1.00
596	Mike Jorgensen	3.50	1.75	1.00
597	Ken Suarez	3.50	1.75	1.00
598	Rick Wise	3.50	1.75	1.00
599	Norm Cash	4.00	2.00	1.25
600	Willie Mays	80.00	40.00	24.00
601	Ken Tatum	3.50	1.75	1.00
602	Marty Martinez	3.50	1.75	1.00
603	Pirates Team	7.50	3.75	2.25
604	John Gelnar	3.50	1.75	1.00
605	Orlando Cepeda	6.00	3.00	1.75
606	Chuck Taylor	3.50	1.75	1.00
607	Paul Ratliff	3.50	1.75	1.00
608	Mike Wegener	3.50	1.75	1.00
609	Leo Durocher	3.50	1.75	1.00
610	Amos Otis	3.50	1.75	1.00
611	Tom Phoebus	3.50	1.75	1.00
612	Indians Rookies (Lou Camilli, Ted Ford, Steve Mingori)	3.50	1.75	1.00
613	Pedro Borbon	3.50	1.75	1.00
614	Billy Cowan	3.50	1.75	1.00
615	Mel Stottlemyre	3.50	1.75	1.00
616	Larry Hisle	3.50	1.75	1.00
617	Clay Dalrymple	3.50	1.75	1.00
618	Tug McGraw	3.50	1.75	1.00
619a	Checklist 644-752 (no copyright on back)	4.50	2.25	1.25
619b	Checklist 644-752 (with copyright, no wavy line on helmet brim)	3.50	1.75	1.00
619c	Checklist 644-752 (with copyright, wavy line on helmet brim)	3.50	1.75	1.00
620	Frank Howard	4.00	2.00	1.25
621	Ron Bryant	3.50	1.75	1.00
622	Joe Lahoud	3.50	1.75	1.00
623	Pat Jarvis	3.50	1.75	1.00
624	Athletics Team	6.00	3.00	1.75
625	Lou Brock	20.00	10.00	6.00
626	Freddie Patek	3.50	1.75	1.00
627	Steve Hamilton	3.50	1.75	1.00
628	John Bateman	3.50	1.75	1.00
629	John Hiller	3.50	1.75	1.00
630	Roberto Clemente	80.00	40.00	24.00
631	Eddie Fisher	3.50	1.75	1.00
632	Darrel Chaney	3.50	1.75	1.00
633	A.L. Rookies (Bobby Brooks, Pete Koegel, Scott Northey)	3.50	1.75	1.00
634	Phil Regan	3.50	1.75	1.00
635	Bobby Murcer	4.00	2.00	1.25
636	Denny Lemaster	3.50	1.75	1.00
637	Dave Bristol	3.50	1.75	1.00
638	Stan Williams	3.50	1.75	1.00
639	Tom Haller	3.50	1.75	1.00
640	Frank Robinson	35.00	17.50	10.50
641	Mets Team	8.00	4.00	2.50
642	Jim Roland	3.50	1.75	1.00
643	Rick Reichardt	3.50	1.75	1.00
644	Jim Stewart	6.00	3.00	1.75
645	Jim Maloney	6.00	3.00	1.75
646	Bobby Floyd	6.00	3.00	1.75
647	Juan Pizarro	4.50	2.25	1.25
648	Mets Rookies (Rich Folkers, Ted Martinez, Jon Matlack)	8.00	4.00	2.50
649	Sparky Lyle	8.00	4.00	2.50
650	Rich Allen	15.00	7.50	4.50
651	Jerry Robertson	6.00	3.00	1.75
652	Braves Team	5.00	2.50	1.50
653	Russ Snyder	6.00	3.00	1.75
654	Don Shaw	6.00	3.00	1.75
655	Mike Epstein	6.00	3.00	1.75
656	Gerry Nyman	6.00	3.00	1.75
657	Jose Azcue	4.50	2.25	1.25
658	Paul Lindblad	6.00	3.00	1.75
659	Byron Browne	6.00	3.00	1.75
660	Ray Culp	4.50	2.25	1.25
661	Chuck Tanner	6.00	3.00	1.75
662	Mike Hedlund	6.00	3.00	1.75
663	Marv Staehle	4.50	2.25	1.25
664	Major League Rookies (Archie Reynolds, Bob Reynolds, Ken Reynolds)	6.00	3.00	1.75
665	Ron Swoboda	8.00	4.00	2.50
666	Gene Brabender	6.00	3.00	1.75
667	Pete Ward	4.50	2.25	1.25
668	Gary Neibauer	4.50	2.25	1.25
669	Ike Brown	6.00	3.00	1.75
670	Bill Hands	4.50	2.25	1.25
671	Bill Voss	6.00	3.00	1.75
672	Ed Crosby	6.00	3.00	1.75
673	Gerry Janeski	6.00	3.00	1.75
674	Expos Team	5.00	2.50	1.50
675	Dave Boswell	4.50	2.25	1.25
676	Tommie Reynolds	4.50	2.25	1.25
677	Jack DiLauro	6.00	3.00	1.75
678	George Thomas	4.50	2.25	1.25
679	Don O'Riley	4.50	2.25	1.25
680	Don Mincher	6.00	3.00	1.75
681	Bill Butler	4.50	2.25	1.25
682	Terry Harmon	4.50	2.25	1.25
683	Bill Burbach	6.00	3.00	1.75
684	Curt Motton	4.50	2.25	1.25
685	Moe Drabowsky	4.50	2.25	1.25
686	Chico Ruiz	6.00	3.00	1.75
687	Ron Taylor	6.00	3.00	1.75
688	Sparky Anderson	25.00	12.50	7.50
689	Frank Baker	4.50	2.25	1.25
690	Bob Moose	4.50	2.25	1.25
691	Bob Heise	4.50	2.25	1.25
692	A.L. Rookies (Hal Haydel, Rogelio Moret, Wayne Twitchell)	6.00	3.00	1.75
693	Jose Pena	6.00	3.00	1.75
694	Rick Renick	6.00	3.00	1.75
695	Joe Niekro	5.00	2.50	1.50
696	Jerry Morales	4.50	2.25	1.25
697	Rickey Clark	6.00	3.00	1.75
698	Brewers Team	15.00	7.50	4.50
699	Jim Britton	4.50	2.25	1.25
700	Boog Powell	12.00	6.00	3.50
701	Bob Garibaldi	4.50	2.25	1.25
702	Milt Ramirez	4.50	2.25	1.25
703	Mike Kekich	4.50	2.25	1.25
704	J.C. Martin	6.00	3.00	1.75
705	Dick Selma	6.00	3.00	1.75
706	Joe Foy	6.00	3.00	1.75
707	Fred Lasher	4.50	2.25	1.25
708	Russ Nagelson	6.00	3.00	1.75
709	*Dusty Baker*, Don Baylor, Tom Paciorek	75.00	37.00	22.00
710	Sonny Siebert	4.50	2.25	1.25
711	Larry Stahl	6.00	3.00	1.75
712	Jose Martinez	4.50	2.25	1.25
713	Mike Marshall	6.00	3.00	1.75
714	Dick Williams	7.00	3.50	2.00
715	Horace Clarke	6.00	3.00	1.75
716	Dave Leonhard	4.50	2.25	1.25
717	Tommie Aaron	6.00	3.00	1.75
718	Billy Wynne	4.50	2.25	1.25
719	Jerry May	6.00	3.00	1.75
720	Matty Alou	4.50	2.25	1.25
721	John Morris	4.50	2.25	1.25
722	Astros Team	9.00	4.50	2.75
723	Vicente Romo	6.00	3.00	1.75
724	Tom Tischinski	6.00	3.00	1.75
725	Gary Gentry	6.00	3.00	1.75
726	Paul Popovich	4.50	2.25	1.25
727	Ray Lamb	6.00	3.00	1.75
728	N.L. Rookies (Keith Lampard, Wayne Redmond, Bernie Williams)	4.50	2.25	1.25
729	Dick Billings	4.50	2.25	1.25
730	Jim Rooker	4.50	2.25	1.25
731	Jim Qualls	6.00	3.00	1.75
732	Bob Reed	4.50	2.25	1.25
733	Lee Maye	6.00	3.00	1.75
734	Rob Gardner	6.00	3.00	1.75
735	Mike Shannon	6.00	3.00	1.75
736	Mel Queen	6.00	3.00	1.75
737	Preston Gomez	6.00	3.00	1.75
738	Russ Gibson	6.00	3.00	1.75
739	Barry Lersch	6.00	3.00	1.75
740	Luis Aparicio	15.00	7.50	4.50
741	Skip Guinn	4.50	2.25	1.25
742	Royals Team	9.00	4.50	2.75
743	John O'Donoghue	6.00	3.00	1.75
744	Chuck Manuel	6.00	3.00	1.75
745	Sandy Alomar	6.00	3.00	1.75
746	Andy Kosco	4.50	2.25	1.25
747	N.L. Rookies (Balor Moore, Al Severinsen, Scipio Spinks)	4.50	2.25	1.25
748	John Purdin	6.00	3.00	1.75
749	Ken Szotkiewicz	4.50	2.25	1.25
750	Denny McLain	15.00	7.50	4.50
751	Al Weis	6.00	3.00	1.75
752	Dick Drago	6.00	3.00	1.75

1971 Topps Coins

Measuring 1-1/2" in diameter, the latest edition of the Topps coins was a 153-piece set. The coins feature a color photograph surrounded by a colored band on the front. The band carries the player's name, team, position and several stars. Backs have a short biography, the coin number and encouragement to collect the entire set. Back colors differ, with #s 1-51 having a brass back, #s 52-102 chrome backs, and the rest have blue backs. Most of the stars of the period are included in the set.

		NR MT	EX	VG
	Complete Set:	400.00	200.00	120.00
	Common Player:	.90	.45	.25
1	Cito Gaston	1.50	.70	.45
2	Dave Johnson	1.25	.60	.40
3	Jim Bunning	2.00	1.00	.60
4	Jim Spencer	.90	.45	.25
5	Felix Millan	.90	.45	.25
6	Gerry Moses	.90	.45	.25
7	Fergie Jenkins	5.00	2.50	1.50
8	Felipe Alou	1.50	.70	.45
9	Jim McGlothlin	.90	.45	.25
10	Dick McAuliffe	.90	.45	.25
11	Joe Torre	1.50	.70	.45
12	Jim Perry	1.25	.60	.40
13	Bobby Bonds	1.50	.70	.45
14	Danny Cater	.90	.45	.25
15	Bill Mazeroski	3.00	1.50	.90
16	Luis Aparicio	5.00	2.50	1.50
17	Doug Rader	.90	.45	.25
18	Vada Pinson	1.50	.70	.45
19	John Bateman	.90	.45	.25
20	Lew Krausse	.90	.45	.25
21	Billy Grabarkewitz	.90	.45	.25
22	Frank Howard	1.50	.70	.45
23	Jerry Koosman	1.25	.60	.40
24	Rod Carew	8.00	4.00	2.50
25	Al Ferrara	.90	.45	.25
26	Dave McNally	.90	.45	.25
27	Jim Hickman	.90	.45	.25
28	Sandy Alomar	.90	.45	.25
29	Lee May	.90	.45	.25
30	Rico Petrocelli	1.25	.60	.40
31	Don Money	.90	.45	.25
32	Jim Rooker	.90	.45	.25
33	Dick Dietz	.90	.45	.25
34	Roy White	1.25	.60	.40
35	Carl Morton	.90	.45	.25
36	Walt Williams	.90	.45	.25
37	Phil Niekro	3.25	1.75	1.00
38	Bill Freehan	1.25	.60	.40
39	Julian Javier	.90	.45	.25
40	Rick Monday	.90	.45	.25
41	Don Wilson	.90	.45	.25
42	Ray Fosse	.90	.45	.25
43	Art Shamsky	.90	.45	.25
44	Ted Savage	.90	.45	.25
45	Claude Osteen	.90	.45	.25
46	Ed Brinkman	.90	.45	.25
47	Matty Alou	.90	.45	.25
48	Bob Oliver	.90	.45	.25
49	Danny Coombs	.90	.45	.25
50	Frank Robinson	7.00	3.50	2.00
51	Randy Hundley	.90	.45	.25
52	Cesar Tovar	.90	.45	.25
53	Wayne Simpson	.90	.45	.25
54	Bobby Murcer	1.25	.60	.40
55	Tony Taylor	.90	.45	.25
56	Tommy John	1.50	.70	.45
57	Willie McCovey	7.00	3.50	2.00
58	Carl Yastrzemski	12.00	6.00	3.50
59	Bob Bailey	.90	.45	.25
60	Clyde Wright	.90	.45	.25
61	Orlando Cepeda	2.00	1.00	.60
62	Al Kaline	7.00	3.50	2.00
63	Bob Gibson	7.00	3.50	2.00
64	Bert Campaneris	1.25	.60	.40
65	Ted Sizemore	.90	.45	.25
66	Duke Sims	.90	.45	.25
67	Bud Harrelson	.90	.45	.25
68	Jerry McNertney	.90	.45	.25
69	Jim Wynn	.90	.45	.25
70	Dick Bosman	.90	.45	.25
71	Roberto Clemente	15.00	7.50	4.50
72	Rich Reese	.90	.45	.25
73	Gaylord Perry	5.00	2.50	1.50
74	Boog Powell	1.50	.70	.45
75	Billy Williams	5.00	2.50	1.50
76	Bill Melton	.90	.45	.25
77	Nate Colbert	.90	.45	.25
78	Reggie Smith	1.25	.60	.40
79	Deron Johnson	.90	.45	.25
80	Catfish Hunter	5.00	2.50	1.50
81	Bob Tolan	.90	.45	.25
82	Jim Northrup	.90	.45	.25
83	Ron Fairly	.90	.45	.25
84	Alex Johnson	.90	.45	.25
85	Pat Jarvis	.90	.45	.25

86	Sam McDowell	.90	.45	.25
87	Lou Brock	6.00	3.00	1.75
88	Danny Walton	.90	.45	.25
89	Denis Menke	.90	.45	.25
90	Jim Palmer	7.00	3.50	2.00
91	Tommie Agee	.90	.45	.25
92	Duane Josephson	.90	.45	.25
93	Willie Davis	1.25	.60	.40
94	Mel Stottlemyre	1.25	.60	.40
95	Ron Santo	1.25	.60	.40
96	Amos Otis	.90	.45	.25
97	Ken Henderson	.90	.45	.25
98	George Scott	.90	.45	.25
99	Dock Ellis	.90	.45	.25
100	Harmon Killebrew	7.00	3.50	2.00
101	Pete Rose	25.00	12.50	7.50
102	Rick Reichardt	.90	.45	.25
103	Cleon Jones	.90	.45	.25
104	Ron Perranoski	.90	.45	.25
105	Tony Perez	2.50	1.25	.70
106	Mickey Lolich	1.25	.60	.40
107	Tim McCarver	1.25	.60	.40
108	Reggie Jackson	12.00	6.00	3.50
109	Chris Cannizzaro	.90	.45	.25
110	Steve Hargan	.90	.45	.25
111	Rusty Staub	1.50	.70	.45
112	Andy Messersmith	.90	.45	.25
113	Rico Carty	.90	.45	.25
114	Brooks Robinson	7.00	3.50	2.00
115	Steve Carlton	7.00	3.50	2.00
116	Mike Hegan	.90	.45	.25
117	Joe Morgan	5.00	2.50	1.50
118	Thurman Munson	4.00	2.00	1.25
119	Don Kessinger	.90	.45	.25
120	Joe Horlen	.90	.45	.25
121	Wes Parker	.90	.45	.25
122	Sonny Siebert	.90	.45	.25
123	Willie Stargell	5.00	2.50	1.50
124	Ellie Rodriguez	.90	.45	.25
125	Juan Marichal	5.00	2.50	1.50
126	Mike Epstein	.90	.45	.25
127	Tom Seaver	7.00	3.50	2.00
128	Tony Oliva	2.50	1.25	.70
129	Jim Merritt	.90	.45	.25
130	Willie Horton	.90	.45	.25
131	Rick Wise	.90	.45	.25
132	Sal Bando	.90	.45	.25
133	Ollie Brown	.90	.45	.25
134	Ken Harrelson	.90	.45	.25
135	Mack Jones	.90	.45	.25
136	Jim Fregosi	1.25	.60	.40
137	Hank Aaron	15.00	7.50	4.50
138	Fritz Peterson	.90	.45	.25
139	Joe Hague	.90	.45	.25
140	Tommy Harper	.90	.45	.25
141	Larry Dierker	.90	.45	.25
142	Tony Conigliaro	1.50	.70	.45
143	Glenn Beckert	.90	.45	.25
144	Carlos May	.90	.45	.25
145	Don Sutton	2.50	1.25	.70
146	Paul Casanova	.90	.45	.25
147	Bob Moose	.90	.45	.25
148	Leo Cardenas	.90	.45	.25
149	Johnny Bench	9.00	4.50	2.75
150	Mike Cuellar	1.25	.60	.40
151	Donn Clendenon	.90	.45	.25
152	Lou Piniella	1.25	.60	.40
153	Willie Mays	15.00	7.50	4.50

Definitions for grading conditions are located in the Introduction of this price guide.

1971 Topps Greatest Moments

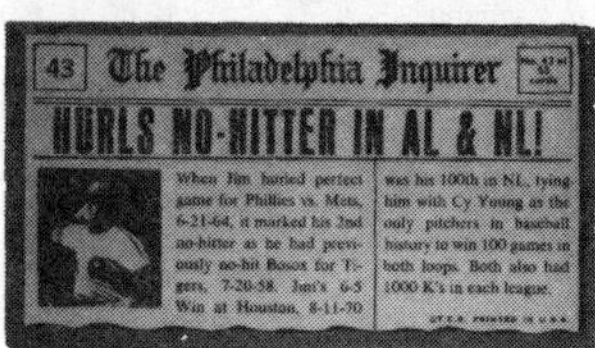

This 55-card set features a great moment from the careers of top players at the time. The front of the 2-1/2" by 4-3/4" cards features a portrait photo of the player at the left and deckle-edge action photo at the right. There is a small headline on the white border of the action photo. The player's name and "One of Baseball's Greatest Moments" along with a black border complete the front. The back features a detail from the front photo and the story of the event. The newspaper style presentation includes the name of real newspapers. Relatively scarce, virtually every card in this set is a star or at least an above-average player.

		NR MT	EX	VG
	Complete Set:	1650.	825.00	495.00
	Common Player:	5.00	2.50	1.50
1	Thurman Munson	60.00	30.00	18.00
2	Hoyt Wilhelm	35.00	17.50	10.50
3	Rico Carty	16.00	8.00	4.75
4	Carl Morton	5.00	2.50	1.50
5	Sal Bando	7.00	3.50	2.00
6	Bert Campaneris	7.00	3.50	2.00
7	Jim Kaat	27.50	13.50	8.25
8	Harmon Killebrew	90.00	45.00	27.00
9	Brooks Robinson	125.00	62.00	37.00
10	Jim Perry	20.00	10.00	6.00
11	Tony Oliva	35.00	17.50	10.50
12	Vada Pinson	32.50	16.00	9.75
13	Johnny Bench	200.00	100.00	60.00
14	Tony Perez	40.00	20.00	12.00
15	Pete Rose	90.00	45.00	27.00
16	Jim Fregosi	5.00	2.50	1.50
17	Alex Johnson	5.00	2.50	1.50
18	Clyde Wright	5.00	2.50	1.50
19	Al Kaline	35.00	17.50	10.50
20	Denny McLain	25.00	12.50	7.50
21	Jim Northrup	15.00	7.50	4.50
22	Bill Freehan	15.00	7.50	4.50
23	Mickey Lolich	24.00	12.00	7.25
24	Bob Gibson	24.00	12.00	7.25
25	Tim McCarver	10.00	5.00	3.00
26	Orlando Cepeda	10.00	5.00	3.00
27	Lou Brock	40.00	20.00	12.00
28	Nate Colbert	5.00	2.50	1.50
29	Maury Wills	25.00	12.50	7.50
30	Wes Parker	22.00	11.00	6.50
31	Jim Wynn	17.50	8.75	5.25
32	Larry Dierker	15.00	7.50	4.50
33	Bill Melton	15.00	7.50	4.50
34	Joe Morgan	60.00	30.00	18.00
35	Rusty Staub	30.00	15.00	9.00
36	Ernie Banks	32.50	16.00	9.75
37	Billy Williams	55.00	27.00	16.50
38	Lou Piniella	30.00	15.00	9.00
39	Rico Petrocelli	8.00	4.00	2.50
40	Carl Yastrzemski	60.00	30.00	18.00
41	Willie Mays	45.00	22.00	13.50
42	Tommy Harper	15.00	7.50	4.50
43	Jim Bunning	9.00	4.50	2.75
44	Fritz Peterson	25.00	12.50	7.50
45	Roy White	25.00	12.50	7.50
46	Bobby Murcer	30.00	15.00	9.00
47	Reggie Jackson	250.00	125.00	75.00
48	Frank Howard	30.00	15.00	9.00
49	Dick Bosman	15.00	7.50	4.50
50	Sam McDowell	8.00	4.00	2.50
51	Luis Aparicio	15.00	7.50	4.50
52	Willie McCovey	20.00	10.00	6.00
53	Joe Pepitone	24.00	12.00	7.25
54	Jerry Grote	25.00	12.50	7.50
55	Bud Harrelson	20.00	10.00	6.00

1971 Topps Super

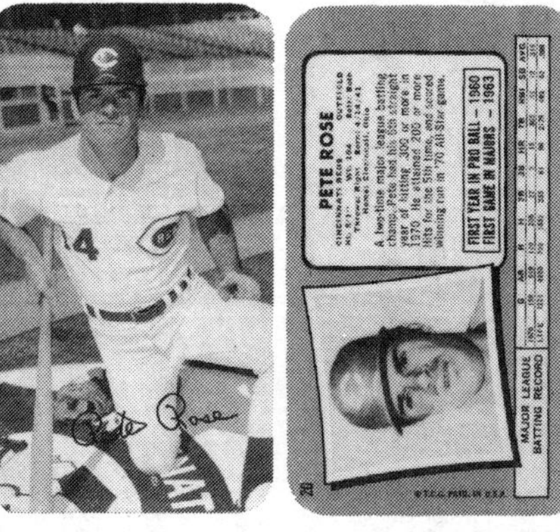

Topps continued to produce its special oversized cards in 1971. The cards, measuring 3-1/8" by 5-1/4," carry a large color photograph with a facsimile autograph on the front. Backs are basically enlargements of the player's regular Topps card. The set size was enlarged to 63 cards in 1971, so there are no short-printed cards as in 1970. Again, Topps included almost every major star who was active at the time, so the set of oversized cards with rounded corners remains an interesting source for those seeking the big names of the era.

		NR MT	EX	VG
	Complete Set:	200.00	100.00	60.00
	Common Player:	.80	.40	.25
1	Reggie Smith	1.00	.50	.30
2	Gaylord Perry	3.00	1.50	.90
3	Ted Savage	.80	.40	.25
4	Donn Clendenon	.80	.40	.25
5	Boog Powell	1.25	.60	.40
6	Tony Perez	1.75	.90	.50
7	Dick Bosman	.80	.40	.25
8	Alex Johnson	.80	.40	.25
9	Rusty Staub	1.25	.60	.40
10	Mel Stottlemyre	1.00	.50	.30
11	Tony Oliva	1.50	.70	.45
12	Bill Freehan	1.00	.50	.30
13	Fritz Peterson	.80	.40	.25
14	Wes Parker	.80	.40	.25
15	Cesar Cedeno	1.25	.60	.40
16	Sam McDowell	1.00	.50	.30
17	Frank Howard	1.50	.70	.45
18	Dave McNally	1.00	.50	.30
19	Rico Petrocelli	.80	.40	.25
20	Pete Rose	25.00	12.50	7.50
21	Luke Walker	.80	.40	.25
22	Nate Colbert	.80	.40	.25
23	Luis Aparicio	2.50	1.25	.70
24	Jim Perry	1.00	.50	.30
25	Louis Brock	4.50	2.25	1.25
26	Roy White	1.00	.50	.30
27	Claude Osteen	.80	.40	.25
28	Carl W. Morton	.80	.40	.25
29	Rico Carty	1.00	.50	.30
30	Larry Dierker	.80	.40	.25
31	Bert Campaneris	1.00	.50	.30
32	Johnny Bench	8.00	4.00	2.50
33	Felix Millan	.80	.40	.25
34	Tim McCarver	1.25	.60	.40
35	Ronald Santo	1.25	.60	.40
36	Tommie Agee	.80	.40	.25
37	Roberto Clemente	10.00	5.00	3.00
38	Reggie Jackson	15.00	7.50	4.50
39	Clyde Wright	.80	.40	.25
40	Rich Allen	1.50	.70	.45
41	Curt Flood	1.25	.60	.40
42	Fergie Jenkins	1.75	.90	.50
43	Willie Stargell	3.00	1.50	.90
44	Henry Aaron	10.00	5.00	3.00
45	Amos Otis	1.00	.50	.30
46	Willie McCovey	4.50	2.25	1.25
47	William Melton	.80	.40	.25
48	Bob Gibson	3.50	1.75	1.00
49	Carl Yastrzemski	15.00	7.50	4.50
50	Glenn Beckert	1.00	.50	.30
51	Ray Fosse	.80	.40	.25
52	Clarence Gaston	.80	.40	.25
53	Tom Seaver	8.00	4.00	2.50
54	Al Kaline	6.00	3.00	1.75
55	Jim Northrup	.80	.40	.25
56	Willie Mays	10.00	5.00	3.00
57	Sal Bando	1.00	.50	.30
58	Deron Johnson	.80	.40	.25
59	Brooks Robinson	7.00	3.50	2.00
60	Harmon Killebrew	6.00	3.00	1.75
61	Joseph Torre	1.75	.90	.50
62	Lou Piniella	1.25	.60	.40
63	Tommy Harper	.80	.40	.25

1971 Topps Baseball Tattoos

Topps once again produced baseball tattoos in 1971. This time, the tattoos came in a variety of sizes, shapes and themes. The sheets of tattoos measure 3-1/2" by 14-1/4." Each sheet contains an assortment of tattoos in two sizes, 1-3/4" by 2-3/8," or 1-3/16" by 1-3/4." There are players, facsimile autographed baseballs, team pennants and assorted baseball cartoon figures carried on the 16 different sheets. Listings below are for complete sheets; with the exception of the biggest-name stars, individual tattoos have little or no collector value.

		NR MT	EX	VG
	Complete Sheet Set:	250.00	125.00	75.00
	Common Sheet:	5.00	2.50	1.50
1	Brooks Robinson Autograph, Montreal Expos Pennant, San Francisco Giants Pennant, Sal Bando, Dick Bosman, Nate Colbert, Cleon Jones, Juan Marichal, B. Robinson	15.00	7.50	4.50
2	Boston Red Sox Pennant, Carl Yastrzemski Autograph, New York Mets Pennant, Glenn Beckert, Tommy Harper, Ken Henderson, Fritz Peterson, Bob Robertson, Carl Yastrzemski	25.00	12.50	7.50
3	Jim Fregosi Autograph, New York Yankees Pennant, Philadelphia Phillies Pennant, Orlando Cepeda, Jim Fregosi, Randy Hundley, Reggie Jackson, Jerry Koosman, Jim Palmer	22.00	11.00	6.50
4	Kansas City Royals Pennant, Oakland Athletics Pennant, Sam McDowell Autograph, Dick Dietz, Cito Gaston, Dave Johnson, Sam McDowell, Gary Nolan, Amos Otis	5.00	2.50	1.50
5	Al Kaline Autograph, Atlanta Braves Pennant, L.A. Dodgers Pennant, B. Grabarkewitz, Al Kaline, Lee May, Tom Murphy, Vada Pinson, Manny Sanguillen	15.00	7.50	4.50

6	Chicago Cubs Pennant, Cincinnati Reds Pennant, Harmon Killebrew Autograph, Luis Aparicio, Paul Blair, Chris Cannizzaro, Donn Clendenon, Larry Dieker, H. Killebrew	15.00	7.50	4.50
7	Boog Powell Autograph, Cleveland Indians Pennant, Milwaukee Brewers Pennant, Rich Allen, B. Campaneris, Don Money, Boog Powell, Ted Savage, Rusty Staub	7.50	3.75	2.25
8	Chicago White Sox Pennant, Frank Howard Autograph, San Diego Padres Pennant, Leo Cardenas, Bill Hands, Frank Howard, Wes Parker, Reggie Smith, Willie Stargell	7.50	3.75	2.25
9	Detroit Tigers Pennant, Henry Aaron Autograph, Hank Aaron, Tommy Agee, Jim Hunter, Dick McAuliffe, Tony Perez, Lou Piniella	22.00	11.00	6.50
10	Baltimore Orioles Pennant, Fergie Jenkins Autograph, Roberto Clemente, Tony Conigliaro, Fergie Jenkins, Thurman Munson, Gary Peters, Joe Torre	18.00	9.00	5.50
11	Johnny Bench Autograph, Washington Senators Pennant, Johnny Bench, Rico Carty, B. Mazeroski, Bob Oliver, R. Petrocelli, F. Robinson	15.00	7.50	4.50
12	Billy Williams Autograph, Houston Astros Pennant, Bill Freehan, Dave McNally, Felix Millan, M. Stottlemyre, Bob Tolan, Billy Williams	9.00	4.50	2.75
13	Pittsburgh Pirates Pennant, Willie McCovey Autograph, Ray Culp, Bud Harrelson, Mickey Lolich, W. McCovey, Ron Santo, Roy White	13.00	6.50	4.00
14	Minnesota Twins Pennant, Tom Seaver Autograph, Bill Melton, Jim Perry, Pete Rose, Tom Seaver, Maury Wills, Clyde Wright	35.00	17.50	10.50
15	Robert Gibson Autograph, St. Louis Cardinals Pennant, Rod Carew, Bob Gibson, Alex Johnson, Don Kessinger, Jim Merritt, Rick Monday	13.00	6.50	4.00
16	California Angels Pennant, Willie Mays Autograph, Larry Bowa, Mike Cuellar, Ray Fosse, Willie Mays, Carl Morton, Tony Oliva	22.00	11.00	6.50

1972 Topps

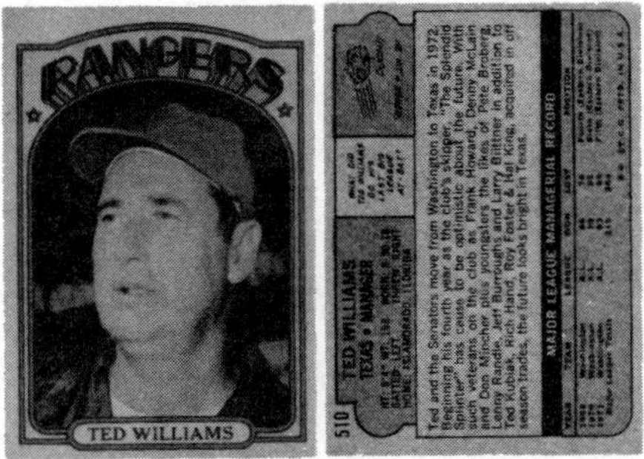

The largest Topps issue of its time appeared in 1972, with the set size reaching the 787 mark. The 2-1/2" by 3-1/2" cards are something special as well. Their fronts have a color photo which is shaped into an arch and surrounded by two different color borders, all of which is inside the overall white border. The player's name is in a white panel below the picture while the team name is above the picture in what might best be described as "superhero" type in a variety of colors. No mention of the player's position appears on the front. Cards backs are tame by comparison, featuring statistics and a trivia question. The set features a record number of specialty cards including more than six dozen "In Action" (shown as "IA" in checklists below) cards featuring action shots of popular players. There are the usual statistical leaders, playoff and World Series highlights. Other innovations are 16 "Boyhood Photo" cards which depict scrapbook black and white photos of 1972's top players, and a group of cards depicting the trophies which comprise baseball's major awards. Finally, a group of seven "Traded" cards was included which feature a large "Traded" across the front of the card.

	NR MT	EX	VG
Complete Set (787):	2300.	1150.	700.00
Common Player (1-394):	.75	.40	.25
Common Player (395-525):	1.00	.50	.30
Common Player (526-656):	2.00	1.00	.60
Common Player (657-787):	6.00	3.00	1.75

1	World Champions (Pirates Team)	8.00	4.00	2.50
2	Ray Culp	.75	.40	.25
3	Bob Tolan	.75	.40	.25
4	Checklist 1-132	4.00	2.00	1.25
5	John Bateman	.75	.40	.25
6	Fred Scherman	.75	.40	.25
7	Enzo Hernandez	.75	.40	.25
8	Ron Swoboda	.75	.40	.25
9	Stan Williams	.75	.40	.25
10	Amos Otis	.75	.40	.25
11	Bobby Valentine	.75	.40	.25
12	Jose Cardenal	.75	.40	.25
13	Joe Grzenda	.75	.40	.25
14	Phillies Rookies (Mike Anderson, Pete Koegel, Wayne Twitchell)	.75	.40	.25
15	Walt Williams	.75	.40	.25
16	Mike Jorgensen	.75	.40	.25
17	Dave Duncan	.75	.40	.25
18a	Juan Pizarro (green under "C" and "S")	3.50	1.75	1.00
18b	Juan Pizarro (yellow under "C" and "S")	.75	.40	.25
19	Billy Cowan	.75	.40	.25
20	Don Wilson	.75	.40	.25
21	Braves Team	3.50	1.75	1.00
22	Rob Gardner	.75	.40	.25
23	Ted Kubiak	.75	.40	.25
24	Ted Ford	.75	.40	.25
25	Bill Singer	.75	.40	.25
26	Andy Etchebarren	.75	.40	.25
27	Bob Johnson	.75	.40	.25
28	Twins Rookies (Steve Brye, Bob Gebhard, Hal Haydel)	.75	.40	.25
29a	Bill Bonham (green under "C" and "S")	3.50	1.75	1.00
29b	Bill Bonham (yellow under "C" and "S")	.75	.40	.25
30	Rico Petrocelli	.90	.45	.25
31	Cleon Jones	.75	.40	.25
32	Cleon Jones (In Action)	.75	.40	.25
33	Billy Martin	4.50	2.25	1.25
34	Billy Martin (In Action)	1.50	.70	.45
35	Jerry Johnson	.75	.40	.25
36	Jerry Johnson (In Action)	.75	.40	.25
37	Carl Yastrzemski	10.00	5.00	3.00
38	Carl Yastrzemski (In Action)	6.00	3.00	1.75
39	Bob Barton	.75	.40	.25
40	Bob Barton (In Action)	.75	.40	.25
41	Tommy Davis	.80	.40	.25
42	Tommy Davis (In Action)	.75	.40	.25
43	Rick Wise	.75	.40	.25
44	Rick Wise (In Action)	.75	.40	.25
45a	Glenn Beckert (green under "C" and "S")	3.50	1.75	1.00
45b	Glenn Beckert (yellow under "C" and "S")	.75	.40	.25
46	Glenn Beckert (In Action)	.75	.40	.25
47	John Ellis	.75	.40	.25
48	John Ellis (In Action)	.75	.40	.25
49	Willie Mays	30.00	15.00	9.00
50	Willie Mays (In Action)	15.00	7.50	4.50
51	Harmon Killebrew	6.00	3.00	1.75
52	Harmon Killebrew (In Action)	4.00	2.00	1.25
53	Bud Harrelson	.75	.40	.25
54	Bud Harrelson (In Action)	.75	.40	.25
55	Clyde Wright	.75	.40	.25
56	Rich Chiles	.75	.40	.25
57	Bob Oliver	.75	.40	.25
58	Ernie McAnally	.75	.40	.25
59	*Fred Stanley*	.90	.45	.25
60	Manny Sanguillen	.75	.40	.25
61	Cubs Rookies (Gene Hiser, Burt Hooton, Earl Stephenson)	1.00	.50	.30
62	Angel Mangual	.75	.40	.25
63	Duke Sims	.75	.40	.25
64	Pete Broberg	.75	.40	.25
65	Cesar Cedeno	1.00	.50	.30
66	Ray Corbin	.75	.40	.25
67	Red Schoendienst	3.00	1.50	.90
68	Jim York	.75	.40	.25
69	Roger Freed	.75	.40	.25
70	Mike Cuellar	.75	.40	.25
71	Angels Team	3.00	1.50	.90
72	*Bruce Kison*	.75	.40	.25
73	Steve Huntz	.75	.40	.25
74	Cecil Upshaw	.75	.40	.25
75	Bert Campaneris	.90	.45	.25
76	Don Carrithers	.75	.40	.25
77	Ron Theobald	.75	.40	.25
78	Steve Arlin	.75	.40	.25
79	Red Sox Rookies (*Cecil Cooper*, Carlton Fisk, Mike Garman)	100.00	50.00	30.00
80	Tony Perez	4.00	2.00	1.25
81	Mike Hedlund	.75	.40	.25
82	Ron Woods	.75	.40	.25
83	Dalton Jones	.75	.40	.25
84	Vince Colbert	.75	.40	.25
85	N.L. Batting Leaders (Glenn Beckert, Ralph Garr, Joe Torre)	2.00	1.00	.60
86	A.L. Batting Leaders (Bobby Murcer, Tony Oliva, Merv Rettenmund)	2.00	1.00	.60
87	N.L. R.B.I. Leaders (Hank Aaron, Willie Stargell, Joe Torre)	4.50	2.25	1.25
88	A.L. R.B.I. Leaders (Harmon Killebrew, Frank Robinson, Reggie Smith)	3.50	1.75	1.00
89	N.L. Home Run Leaders (Hank Aaron, Lee May, Willie Stargell)	4.50	2.25	1.25
90	A.L. Home Run Leaders (Norm Cash, Reggie Jackson, Bill Melton)	3.50	1.75	1.00
91	N.L. E.R.A. Leaders (Dave Roberts, Tom Seaver, Don Wilson)	3.00	1.50	.90
92	A.L. E.R.A. Leaders (Vida Blue, Jim Palmer, Wilbur Wood)	3.00	1.50	.90
93	N.L. Pitching Leaders (Steve Carlton, Al Downing, Fergie Jenkins, Tom Seaver)	3.50	1.75	1.00
94	A.L. Pitching Leaders (Vida Blue, Mickey Lolich, Wilbur Wood)	2.00	1.00	.60
95	N.L. Strikeout Leaders (Fergie Jenkins, Tom Seaver, Bill Stoneman)	3.00	1.50	.90
96	A.L. Strikeout Leaders (Vida Blue, Joe Coleman, Mickey Lolich)	2.00	1.00	.60
97	Tom Kelley	.75	.40	.25
98	Chuck Tanner	.70	.35	.20
99	*Ross Grimsley*	.80	.40	.25
100	Frank Robinson	6.00	3.00	1.75
101	Astros Rookies (Ray Busse, Bill Grief, J.R. Richard)	1.00	.50	.30
102	Lloyd Allen	.75	.40	.25
103	Checklist 133-263	3.00	1.50	.90
104	*Toby Harrah*	1.50	.70	.45
105	Gary Gentry	.75	.40	.25
106	Brewers Team	3.00	1.50	.90
107	*Jose Cruz*	2.50	1.25	.70
108	Gary Waslewski	.75	.40	.25
109	Jerry May	.75	.40	.25
110	Ron Hunt	.75	.40	.25
111	Jim Grant	.75	.40	.25
112	Greg Luzinski	1.00	.50	.30
113	Rogelio Moret	.75	.40	.25
114	Bill Buckner	1.25	.60	.40
115	Jim Fregosi	.75	.40	.25
116	*Ed Farmer*	.75	.40	.25
117a	Cleo James (green under "C" and "S")	3.50	1.75	1.00
117b	Cleo James (yellow under "C" and "S")	.75	.40	.25
118	Skip Lockwood	.75	.40	.25
119	Marty Perez	.75	.40	.25
120	Bill Freehan	.75	.40	.25
121	Ed Sprague	.75	.40	.25
122	Larry Biittner	.75	.40	.25
123	Ed Acosta	.75	.40	.25
124	Yankees Rookies (Alan Closter, Roger Hambright, Rusty Torres)	.75	.40	.25
125	Dave Cash	.75	.40	.25
126	Bart Johnson	.75	.40	.25
127	Duffy Dyer	.75	.40	.25
128	Eddie Watt	.75	.40	.25
129	Charlie Fox	.75	.40	.25
130	Bob Gibson	6.00	3.00	1.75
131	Jim Nettles	.75	.40	.25
132	Joe Morgan	5.00	2.50	1.50
133	Joe Keough	.75	.40	.25
134	Carl Morton	.75	.40	.25
135	Vada Pinson	1.00	.50	.30
136	Darrel Chaney	.75	.40	.25
137	Dick Williams	.75	.40	.25
138	Mike Kekich	.75	.40	.25
139	Tim McCarver	1.00	.50	.30
140	Pat Dobson	.75	.40	.25
141	Mets Rookies (Buzz Capra, Jon Matlack, Leroy Stanton)	.75	.40	.25
142	*Chris Chambliss*	3.00	1.50	.90
143	Garry Jestadt	.75	.40	.25
144	Marty Pattin	.75	.40	.25
145	Don Kessinger	.75	.40	.25
146	Steve Kealey	.75	.40	.25
147	*Dave Kingman*	5.00	2.50	1.50
148	Dick Billings	.75	.40	.25
149	Gary Neibauer	.75	.40	.25
150	Norm Cash	1.00	.50	.30
151	Jim Brewer	.75	.40	.25
152	Gene Clines	.75	.40	.25
153	Rick Auerbach	.75	.40	.25
154	Ted Simmons	1.00	.50	.30
155	Larry Dierker	.75	.40	.25
156	Twins Team	3.00	1.50	.90
157	Don Gullett	.75	.40	.25
158	Jerry Kenney	.75	.40	.25
159	John Boccabella	.75	.40	.25
160	Andy Messersmith	.75	.40	.25
161	Brock Davis	.75	.40	.25
162	Brewers Rookies (Jerry Bell) (Bell & Porter photos transposed, Darrell Porter, Bob Reynolds)	.75	.40	.25
163	Tug McGraw	.75	.40	.25
164	Tug McGraw (In Action)	.75	.40	.25
165	*Chris Speier*	1.00	.50	.30
166	Chris Speier (In Action)	.75	.40	.25
167	Deron Johnson	.75	.40	.25
168	Deron Johnson (In Action)	.75	.40	.25
169	Vida Blue	1.00	.50	.30
170	Vida Blue (In Action)	.75	.40	.25
171	Darrell Evans	1.00	.50	.30
172	Darrell Evans (In Action)	.75	.40	.25
173	Clay Kirby	.75	.40	.25
174	Clay Kirby (In Action)	.75	.40	.25
175	Tom Haller	.75	.40	.25
176	Tom Haller (In Action)	.75	.40	.25
177	Paul Schaal	.75	.40	.25
178	Paul Schaal (In Action)	.75	.40	.25
179	Dock Ellis	.75	.40	.25
180	Dock Ellis (In Action)	.75	.40	.25
181	Ed Kranepool	.75	.40	.25
182	Ed Kranepool (In Action)	.75	.40	.25
183	Bill Melton	.75	.40	.25
184	Bill Melton (In Action)	.75	.40	.25
185	Ron Bryant	.75	.40	.25
186	Ron Bryant (In Action)	.75	.40	.25
187	Gates Brown	.75	.40	.25
188	Frank Lucchesi	.75	.40	.25
189	Gene Tenace	.75	.40	.25
190	Dave Giusti	.75	.40	.25
191	*Jeff Burroughs*	1.00	.50	.30
192	Cubs Team	3.00	1.50	.90
193	*Kurt Bevacqua*	.75	.40	.25
194	Fred Norman	.75	.40	.25
195	Orlando Cepeda	2.00	1.00	.60
196	Mel Queen	.75	.40	.25
197	Johnny Briggs	.75	.40	.25
198	*Charlie Hough*, Bob O'Brien, Mike Strahler	7.00	3.50	2.00
199	Mike Fiore	.75	.40	.25
200	Lou Brock	6.00	3.00	1.75
201	Phil Roof	.75	.40	.25
202	Scipio Spinks	.75	.40	.25
203	*Ron Blomberg*	.75	.40	.25
204	Tommy Helms	.75	.40	.25
205	Dick Drago	.75	.40	.25
206	Dal Maxvill	.75	.40	.25
207	Tom Egan	.75	.40	.25
208	Milt Pappas	.75	.40	.25
209	Joe Rudi	.75	.40	.25
210	Denny McLain	1.00	.50	.30
211	Gary Sutherland	.75	.40	.25
212	Grant Jackson	.75	.40	.25
213	Angels Rookies (Art Kusnyer, Billy Parker, Tom Silverio)	.75	.40	.25
214	Mike McQueen	.75	.40	.25
215	Alex Johnson	.75	.40	.25
216	Joe Niekro	.75	.40	.25

217 Roger Metzger .75 .40 .25
218 Eddie Kasko .75 .40 .25
219 *Rennie Stennett* .75 .40 .25
220 Jim Perry .75 .40 .25
221 N.L. Playoffs (Bucs Champs! 2.00 1.00 .60
222 A.L. Playoffs (Orioles Champs! 2.00 1.00 .60
223 World Series Game 1 2.00 1.00 .60
224 World Series Game 2 2.00 1.00 .60
225 World Series Game 3 2.00 1.00 .60
226 World Series Game 4 2.00 1.00 .60
227 World Series Game 5 2.00 1.00 .60
228 World Series Game 6 2.00 1.00 .60
229 World Series Game 7 2.00 1.00 .60
230 World Series Summary (Series Celebration)
2.00 1.00 .60
231 Casey Cox .75 .40 .25
232 Giants Rookies (Chris Arnold, Jim Barr, Dave Rader)
.75 .40 .25
233 Jay Johnstone .75 .40 .25
234 Ron Taylor .75 .40 .25
235 Merv Rettenmund .75 .40 .25
236 Jim McGlothlin .75 .40 .25
237 Yankees Team 4.50 2.25 1.25
238 Leron Lee .75 .40 .25
239 Tom Timmermann .75 .40 .25
240 Rich Allen 2.00 1.00 .60
241 Rollie Fingers 6.00 3.00 1.75
242 Don Mincher .75 .40 .25
243 Frank Linzy .75 .40 .25
244 Steve Braun .75 .40 .25
245 Tommie Agee .75 .40 .25
246 Tom Burgmeier .75 .40 .25
247 Milt May .75 .40 .25
248 Tom Bradley .75 .40 .25
249 Harry Walker .75 .40 .25
250 Boog Powell 1.25 .60 .40
251a Checklist 264-394 (small print on front)
3.00 1.50 .90
251b Checklist 264-394 (large print on front)
3.00 1.50 .90
252 Ken Reynolds .75 .40 .25
253 Sandy Alomar .75 .40 .25
254 Boots Day .75 .40 .25
255 Jim Lonborg .90 .45 .25
256 George Foster 1.00 .50 .30
257 Tigers Rookies (Jim Foor, Tim Hosley, Paul Jata)
.75 .40 .25
258 Randy Hundley .75 .40 .25
259 Sparky Lyle 1.00 .50 .30
260 Ralph Garr .75 .40 .25
261 Steve Mingori .75 .40 .25
262 Padres Team 3.00 1.50 .90
263 Felipe Alou 2.00 1.00 .60
264 Tommy John 2.00 1.00 .60
265 Wes Parker .75 .40 .25
266 Bobby Bolin .75 .40 .25
267 Dave Concepcion 1.75 .90 .50
268 A's Rookies (Dwain Anderson, Chris Floethe)
.75 .40 .25
269 Don Hahn .75 .40 .25
270 Jim Palmer 10.00 5.00 3.00
271 Ken Rudolph .75 .40 .25
272 *Mickey Rivers* 1.00 .50 .30
273 Bobby Floyd .75 .40 .25
274 Al Severinsen .75 .40 .25
275 Cesar Tovar .75 .40 .25
276 Gene Mauch .75 .40 .25
277 Elliott Maddox .75 .40 .25
278 Dennis Higgins .75 .40 .25
279 Larry Brown .75 .40 .25
280 Willie McCovey 6.00 3.00 1.75
281 Bill Parsons .75 .40 .25
282 Astros Team 3.00 1.50 .90
283 Darrell Brandon .75 .40 .25
284 Ike Brown .75 .40 .25
285 Gaylord Perry 6.00 3.00 1.75
286 Gene Alley .75 .40 .25
287 Jim Hardin .75 .40 .25
288 Johnny Jeter .75 .40 .25
289 Syd O'Brien .75 .40 .25
290 Sonny Siebert .75 .40 .25
291 Hal McRae 1.00 .50 .30
292 Hal McRae (In Action) .75 .40 .25
293 Danny Frisella .75 .40 .25
294 Danny Frisella (In Action) .75 .40 .25
295 Dick Dietz .75 .40 .25
296 Dick Dietz (In Action) .75 .40 .25
297 Claude Osteen .75 .40 .25
298 Claude Osteen (In Action) .75 .40 .25
299 Hank Aaron 30.00 15.00 9.00
300 Hank Aaron (In Action) 15.00 7.50 4.50
301 George Mitterwald .75 .40 .25
302 George Mitterwald (In Action) .75 .40 .25
303 Joe Pepitone .75 .40 .25
304 Joe Pepitone (In Action) .75 .40 .25
305 Ken Boswell .75 .40 .25
306 Ken Boswell (In Action) .75 .40 .25
307 Steve Renko .75 .40 .25
308 Steve Renko (In Action) .75 .40 .25
309 Roberto Clemente 25.00 12.50 7.50
310 Roberto Clemente (In Action) 15.00 7.50 4.50
311 Clay Carroll .75 .40 .25
312 Clay Carroll (In Action) .75 .40 .25
313 Luis Aparicio 4.00 2.00 1.25
314 Luis Aparicio (In Action) 2.00 1.00 .60
315 Paul Splittorff .75 .40 .25
316 Cardinals Rookies (*Jim Bibby*, Santiago Guzman,
Jorge Roque) .70 .35 .20
317 Rich Hand .75 .40 .25
318 Sonny Jackson .75 .40 .25
319 Aurelio Rodriguez .75 .40 .25
320 Steve Blass .75 .40 .25
321 Joe Lahoud .75 .40 .25
322 Jose Pena .75 .40 .25
323 Earl Weaver 1.00 .50 .30
324 Mike Ryan .75 .40 .25
325 Mel Stottlemyre .75 .40 .25
326 Pat Kelly .75 .40 .25
327 *Steve Stone* 2.00 1.00 .60
328 Red Sox Team 4.00 2.00 1.25
329 Roy Foster .75 .40 .25
330 Catfish Hunter 3.50 1.75 1.00
331 Stan Swanson .75 .40 .25
332 Buck Martinez .75 .40 .25
333 Steve Barber .75 .40 .25
334 Rangers Rookies (Bill Fahey, Jim Mason, Tom
Ragland) .75 .40 .25
335 Bill Hands .75 .40 .25
336 Marty Martinez .75 .40 .25
337 Mike Kilkenny .75 .40 .25
338 Bob Grich .75 .40 .25
339 Ron Cook .75 .40 .25
340 Roy White .75 .40 .25
341 Boyhood Photo (Joe Torre) .75 .40 .25
342 Boyhood Photo (Wilbur Wood) .75 .40 .25
343 Boyhood Photo (Willie Stargell)
1.50 .70 .45
344 Boyhood Photo (Dave McNally) .75 .40 .25
345 Boyhood Photo (Rick Wise) .75 .40 .25
346 Boyhood Photo (Jim Fregosi) .75 .40 .25
347 Boyhood Photo (Tom Seaver) 4.00 2.00 1.25
348 Boyhood Photo (Sal Bando) .75 .40 .25
349 Al Fitzmorris .75 .40 .25
350 Frank Howard 1.00 .50 .30
351 Braves Rookies (Jimmy Britton, Tom House, Rick
Kester) .75 .40 .25
352 Dave LaRoche .75 .40 .25
353 Art Shamsky .75 .40 .25
354 Tom Murphy .75 .40 .25
355 Bob Watson .75 .40 .25
356 Gerry Moses .75 .40 .25
357 Woodie Fryman .75 .40 .25
358 Sparky Anderson 1.50 .70 .45
359 Don Pavletich .75 .40 .25
360 Dave Roberts .75 .40 .25
361 Mike Andrews .75 .40 .25
362 Mets Team 4.00 2.00 1.25
363 Ron Klimkowski .75 .40 .25
364 Johnny Callison .75 .40 .25
365 Dick Bosman .75 .40 .25
366 Jimmy Rosario .75 .40 .25
367 Ron Perranoski .75 .40 .25
368 Danny Thompson .75 .40 .25
369 Jim Lefebvre .75 .40 .25
370 Don Buford .75 .40 .25
371 Denny Lemaster .75 .40 .25
372 Royals Rookies (Lance Clemons, Monty
Montgomery) .75 .40 .25
373 Royals Rookies (John Mayberry) .75 .40 .25
374 Jack Heidemann .75 .40 .25
375 Reggie Cleveland .75 .40 .25
376 Andy Kosco .75 .40 .25
377 Terry Harmon .75 .40 .25
378 Checklist 395-525 3.00 1.50 .90
379 Ken Berry .75 .40 .25
380 Earl Williams .75 .40 .25
381 White Sox Team 3.00 1.50 .90
382 Joe Gibbon .75 .40 .25
383 Brant Alyea .75 .40 .25
384 Dave Campbell .75 .40 .25
385 Mickey Stanley .75 .40 .25
386 Jim Colborn .75 .40 .25
387 Horace Clarke .75 .40 .25
388 Charlie Williams .75 .40 .25
389 Bill Rigney .75 .40 .25
390 Willie Davis .75 .40 .25
391 Ken Sanders .75 .40 .25
392 Pirates Rookies (Fred Cambria, Richie Zisk)
1.00 .50 .30
393 Curt Motton .75 .40 .25
394 Ken Forsch .75 .40 .25
395 Matty Alou 1.00 .50 .30
396 Paul Lindblad 1.00 .50 .30
397 Phillies Team 4.00 2.00 1.25
398 Larry Hisle 1.00 .50 .30
399 Milt Wilcox 1.00 .50 .30
400 Tony Oliva 1.50 .70 .45
401 Jim Nash 1.00 .50 .30
402 Bobby Heise 1.00 .50 .30
403 John Cumberland 1.00 .50 .30
404 Jeff Torborg 1.00 .50 .30
405 Ron Fairly 1.00 .50 .30
406 *George Hendrick* 1.50 .70 .45
407 Chuck Taylor 1.00 .50 .30
408 Jim Northrup 1.00 .50 .30
409 Frank Baker 1.00 .50 .30
410 Fergie Jenkins 6.00 3.00 1.75
411 Bob Montgomery 1.00 .50 .30
412 Dick Kelley 1.00 .50 .30
413 White Sox Rookies (Don Eddy, Dave Lemonds)
1.00 .50 .30
414 Bob Miller 1.00 .50 .30
415 Cookie Rojas 1.00 .50 .30
416 Johnny Edwards 1.00 .50 .30
417 Tom Hall 1.00 .50 .30
418 Tom Shopay 1.00 .50 .30
419 Jim Spencer 1.00 .50 .30
420 Steve Carlton 15.00 7.50 4.50
421 Ellie Rodriguez 1.00 .50 .30
422 Ray Lamb 1.00 .50 .30
423 Oscar Gamble 1.00 .50 .30
424 Bill Gogolewski 1.00 .50 .30
425 Ken Singleton 1.00 .50 .30
426 Ken Singleton (In Action) 1.00 .50 .30
427 Tito Fuentes 1.00 .50 .30
428 Tito Fuentes (In Action) 1.00 .50 .30
429 Bob Robertson 1.00 .50 .30
430 Bob Robertson (In Action) 1.00 .50 .30
431 Cito Gaston 2.50 1.25 .70
432 Cito Gaston (In Action) 1.75 .90 .50
433 Johnny Bench 25.00 12.50 7.50
434 Johnny Bench (In Action) 15.00 7.50 4.50
435 Reggie Jackson 40.00 20.00 12.00
436 Reggie Jackson (In Action) 20.00 10.00 6.00
437 Maury Wills 1.50 .70 .45
438 Maury Wills (In Action) 1.00 .50 .30
439 Billy Williams 6.00 3.00 1.75
440 Billy Williams (In Action) 3.00 1.50 .90
441 Thurman Munson 15.00 7.50 4.50
442 Thurman Munson (In Action) 7.00 3.50 2.00
443 Ken Henderson 1.00 .50 .30
444 Ken Henderson (In Action) 1.00 .50 .30
445 Tom Seaver 24.00 12.00 7.25
446 Tom Seaver (In Action) 12.00 6.00 3.50
447 Willie Stargell 6.00 3.00 1.75
448 Willie Stargell (In Action) 3.00 1.50 .90
449 Bob Lemon 3.00 1.50 .90
450 Mickey Lolich 1.25 .60 .40
451 Tony LaRussa 1.25 .60 .40
452 Ed Herrmann 1.00 .50 .30
453 Barry Lersch 1.00 .50 .30
454 A's Team 4.00 2.00 1.25
455 Tommy Harper 1.00 .50 .30
456 Mark Belanger 1.00 .50 .30
457 Padres Rookies (Darcy Fast, Mike Ivie, Derrel
Thomas) 1.00 .50 .30
458 Aurelio Monteagudo 1.00 .50 .30
459 Rick Renick 1.00 .50 .30
460 Al Downing 1.00 .50 .30
461 Tim Cullen 1.00 .50 .30
462 Rickey Clark 1.00 .50 .30
463 Bernie Carbo 1.00 .50 .30
464 Jim Roland 1.00 .50 .30
465 Gil Hodges 3.00 1.50 .90
466 Norm Miller 1.00 .50 .30
467 Steve Kline 1.00 .50 .30
468 Richie Scheinblum 1.00 .50 .30
469 Ron Herbel 1.00 .50 .30
470 Ray Fosse 1.00 .50 .30
471 Luke Walker 1.00 .50 .30
472 Phil Gagliano 1.00 .50 .30
473 Dan McGinn 1.00 .50 .30
474 Orioles Rookies (Don Baylor, Roric Harrison, Johnny
Oates) 10.00 5.00 3.00
475 Gary Nolan 1.00 .50 .30
476 Lee Richard 1.00 .50 .30
477 Tom Phoebus 1.00 .50 .30
478a Checklist 526-656 (small print on front)
3.00 1.50 .90
478b Checklist 526-656 (large printing on front)
3.00 1.50 .90
479 Don Shaw 1.00 .50 .30
480 Lee May 1.00 .50 .30
481 Billy Conigliaro 1.00 .50 .30
482 Joe Hoerner 1.00 .50 .30
483 Ken Suarez 1.00 .50 .30
484 Lum Harris 1.00 .50 .30
485 Phil Regan 1.00 .50 .30
486 John Lowenstein 1.00 .50 .30
487 Tigers Team 4.00 2.00 1.25
488 Mike Nagy 1.00 .50 .30
489 Expos Rookies (Terry Humphrey, Keith Lampard)
1.00 .50 .30
490 Dave McNally 1.00 .50 .30
491 Boyhood Photo (Lou Piniella) 1.00 .50 .30
492 Boyhood Photo (Mel Stottlemyre)
1.00 .50 .30
493 Boyhood Photo (Bob Bailey) 1.00 .50 .30
494 Boyhood Photo (Willie Horton)
1.00 .50 .30
495 Boyhood Photo (Bill Melton) 1.00 .50 .30
496 Boyhood Photo (Bud Harrelson) 1.00 .50 .30
497 Boyhood Photo (Jim Perry) 1.00 .50 .30
498 Boyhood Photo (Brooks Robinson)
2.00 1.00 .60
499 Vicente Romo 1.00 .50 .30
500 Joe Torre 1.00 .50 .30
501 Pete Hamm 1.00 .50 .30
502 Jackie Hernandez 1.00 .50 .30
503 Gary Peters 1.00 .50 .30
504 Ed Spiezio 1.00 .50 .30
505 Mike Marshall 1.00 .50 .30
506 Indians Rookies (Terry Ley, Jim Moyer, Dick
Tidrow) 1.00 .50 .30
507 Fred Gladding 1.00 .50 .30
508 Ellie Hendricks 1.00 .50 .30
509 Don McMahon 1.00 .50 .30
510 Ted Williams 8.00 4.00 2.50
511 Tony Taylor 1.00 .50 .30
512 Paul Popovich 1.00 .50 .30
513 Lindy McDaniel 1.00 .50 .30
514 Ted Sizemore 1.00 .50 .30
515 Bert Blyleven 7.00 3.50 2.00
516 Oscar Brown 1.00 .50 .30
517 Ken Brett 1.00 .50 .30
518 Wayne Garrett 1.00 .50 .30
519 Ted Abernathy 1.00 .50 .30
520 Larry Bowa 1.25 .60 .40
521 Alan Foster 1.00 .50 .30
522 Dodgers Team 4.00 2.00 1.25
523 Chuck Dobson 1.00 .50 .30
524 Reds Rookies (Ed Armbrister, Mel Behney)
1.00 .50 .30
525 Carlos May 1.00 .50 .30
526 Bob Bailey 2.00 1.00 .60
527 Dave Leonhard 2.00 1.00 .60
528 Ron Stone 2.00 1.00 .60
529 Dave Nelson 2.00 1.00 .60
530 Don Sutton 4.00 2.00 1.25
531 Freddie Patek 2.00 1.00 .60
532 Fred Kendall 2.00 1.00 .60
533 Ralph Houk 2.00 1.00 .60
534 Jim Hickman 2.00 1.00 .60
535 Ed Brinkman 2.00 1.00 .60
536 Doug Rader 2.00 1.00 .60
537 Bob Locker 2.00 1.00 .60
538 Charlie Sands 2.00 1.00 .60
539 *Terry Forster* 2.00 1.00 .60
540 Felix Millan 2.00 1.00 .60
541 Roger Repoz 2.00 1.00 .60
542 Jack Billingham 2.00 1.00 .60
543 Duane Josephson 2.00 1.00 .60
544 Ted Martinez 2.00 1.00 .60
545 Wayne Granger 2.00 1.00 .60
546 Joe Hague 2.00 1.00 .60
547 Indians Team 6.00 3.00 1.75
548 Frank Reberger 2.00 1.00 .60

549	Dave May	2.00	1.00	.60
550	Brooks Robinson	20.00	10.00	6.00
551	Ollie Brown	2.00	1.00	.60
552	Ollie Brown (In Action)	2.00	1.00	.60
553	Wilbur Wood	2.00	1.00	.60
554	Wilbur Wood (In Action)	2.00	1.00	.60
555	Ron Santo	3.00	1.50	.90
556	Ron Santo (In Action)	2.00	1.00	.60
557	John Odom	2.00	1.00	.60
558	John Odom (In Action)	2.00	1.00	.60
559	Pete Rose	35.00	17.50	10.50
560	Pete Rose (In Action)	19.00	9.50	5.75
561	Leo Cardenas	2.00	1.00	.60
562	Leo Cardenas (In Action)	2.00	1.00	.60
563	Ray Sadecki	2.00	1.00	.60
564	Ray Sadecki (In Action)	2.00	1.00	.60
565	Reggie Smith	2.00	1.00	.60
566	Reggie Smith (In Action)	2.00	1.00	.60
567	Juan Marichal	6.00	3.00	1.75
568	Juan Marichal (In Action)	3.00	1.50	.90
569	Ed Kirkpatrick	2.00	1.00	.60
570	Ed Kirkpatrick (In Action)	2.00	1.00	.60
571	Nate Colbert	2.00	1.00	.60
572	Nate Colbert (In Action)	2.00	1.00	.60
573	Fritz Peterson	2.00	1.00	.60
574	Fritz Peterson (In Action)	2.00	1.00	.60
575	Al Oliver	3.00	1.50	.90
576	Leo Durocher	2.50	1.25	.70
577	Mike Paul	2.00	1.00	.60
578	Billy Grabarkewitz	2.00	1.00	.60
579	*Doyle Alexander*	2.00	1.00	.60
580	Lou Piniella	2.50	1.25	.70
581	Wade Blasingame	2.00	1.00	.60
582	Expos Team	5.00	2.50	1.50
583	Darold Knowles	2.00	1.00	.60
584	Jerry McNertney	2.00	1.00	.60
585	George Scott	2.00	1.00	.60
586	Denis Menke	2.00	1.00	.60
587	Billy Wilson	2.00	1.00	.60
588	Jim Holt	2.00	1.00	.60
589	Hal Lanier	2.00	1.00	.60
590	Graig Nettles	3.00	1.50	.90
591	Paul Casanova	2.00	1.00	.60
592	Lew Krausse	2.00	1.00	.60
593	Rich Morales	2.00	1.00	.60
594	Jim Beauchamp	2.00	1.00	.60
595	Nolan Ryan	250.00	125.00	75.00
596	Manny Mota	2.00	1.00	.60
597	Jim Magnuson	2.00	1.00	.60
598	Hal King	2.00	1.00	.60
599	Billy Champion	2.00	1.00	.60
600	Al Kaline	20.00	10.00	6.00
601	George Stone	2.00	1.00	.60
602	Dave Bristol	2.00	1.00	.60
603	Jim Ray	2.00	1.00	.60
604a	Checklist 657-787 (copyright on right)	3.50	1.75	1.00
604b	Checklist 657-787 (copyright on left)	5.00	2.50	1.50
605	Nelson Briles	2.00	1.00	.60
606	Luis Melendez	2.00	1.00	.60
607	Frank Duffy	2.00	1.00	.60
608	Mike Corkins	2.00	1.00	.60
609	Tom Grieve	2.00	1.00	.60
610	Bill Stoneman	2.00	1.00	.60
611	Rich Reese	2.00	1.00	.60
612	Joe Decker	2.00	1.00	.60
613	Mike Ferraro	2.00	1.00	.60
614	Ted Uhlaender	2.00	1.00	.60
615	Steve Hargan	2.00	1.00	.60
616	*Joe Ferguson*	2.00	1.00	.60
617	Royals Team	5.00	2.50	1.50
618	Rich Robertson	2.00	1.00	.60
619	Rich McKinney	2.00	1.00	.60
620	Phil Niekro	6.00	3.00	1.75
621	Commissioners Award	2.00	1.00	.60
622	MVP Award	2.00	1.00	.60
623	Cy Young Award	2.00	1.00	.60
624	Minor League Player Of The Year Award	2.00	1.00	.60
625	Rookie Of The Year Award	2.00	1.00	.60
626	Babe Ruth Award	2.00	1.00	.60
627	Moe Drabowsky	2.00	1.00	.60
628	Terry Crowley	2.00	1.00	.60
629	Paul Doyle	2.00	1.00	.60
630	Rich Hebner	2.00	1.00	.60
631	John Strohmayer	2.00	1.00	.60
632	Mike Hegan	2.00	1.00	.60
633	Jack Hiatt	2.00	1.00	.60
634	Dick Woodson	2.00	1.00	.60
635	Don Money	2.00	1.00	.60
636	Bill Lee	2.00	1.00	.60
637	Preston Gomez	2.00	1.00	.60
638	Ken Wright	2.00	1.00	.60
639	J.C. Martin	2.00	1.00	.60
640	Joe Coleman	2.00	1.00	.60
641	Mike Lum	2.00	1.00	.60
642	Denny Riddleberger	2.00	1.00	.60
643	Russ Gibson	2.00	1.00	.60
644	Bernie Allen	2.00	1.00	.60
645	Jim Maloney	2.00	1.00	.60
646	Chico Salmon	2.00	1.00	.60
647	Bob Moose	2.00	1.00	.60
648	Jim Lyttle	2.00	1.00	.60
649	Pete Richert	2.00	1.00	.60
650	Sal Bando	2.00	1.00	.60
651	Reds Team	6.00	3.00	1.75
652	Marcelino Lopez	2.00	1.00	.60
653	Jim Fairey	2.00	1.00	.60
654	Horacio Pina	2.00	1.00	.60
655	Jerry Grote	2.00	1.00	.60
656	Rudy May	2.00	1.00	.60
657	Bobby Wine	6.00	3.00	1.75
658	Steve Dunning	6.00	3.00	1.75
659	Bob Aspromonte	6.00	3.00	1.75
660	Paul Blair	6.00	3.00	1.75
661	Bill Virdon	6.00	3.00	1.75
662	Stan Bahnsen	6.00	3.00	1.75
663	Fran Healy	6.00	3.00	1.75
664	Bobby Knoop	6.00	3.00	1.75
665	Chris Short	6.00	3.00	1.75
666	Hector Torres	6.00	3.00	1.75
667	Ray Newman	6.00	3.00	1.75
668	Rangers Team	9.00	4.50	2.75
669	Willie Crawford	6.00	3.00	1.75
670	Ken Holtzman	6.00	3.00	1.75
671	Donn Clendenon	6.00	3.00	1.75
672	Archie Reynolds	6.00	3.00	1.75
673	Dave Marshall	6.00	3.00	1.75
674	John Kennedy	6.00	3.00	1.75
675	Pat Jarvis	6.00	3.00	1.75
676	Danny Cater	6.00	3.00	1.75
677	Ivan Murrell	6.00	3.00	1.75
678	Steve Luebber	6.00	3.00	1.75
679	Astros Rookies (Bob Fenwick, Bob Stinson)	6.00	3.00	1.75
680	Dave Johnson	6.00	3.00	1.75
681	Bobby Pfeil	6.00	3.00	1.75
682	Mike McCormick	6.00	3.00	1.75
683	Steve Hovley	6.00	3.00	1.75
684	Hal Breeden	6.00	3.00	1.75
685	Joe Horlen	6.00	3.00	1.75
686	Steve Garvey	40.00	20.00	12.00
687	Del Unser	6.00	3.00	1.75
688	Cardinals Team	12.00	6.00	3.50
689	Eddie Fisher	6.00	3.00	1.75
690	Willie Montanez	6.00	3.00	1.75
691	Curt Blefary	6.00	3.00	1.75
692	Curt Blefary (In Action)	6.00	3.00	1.75
693	Alan Gallagher	6.00	3.00	1.75
694	Alan Gallagher (In Action)	6.00	3.00	1.75
695	Rod Carew	75.00	37.00	22.00
696	Rod Carew (In Action)	35.00	17.50	10.50
697	Jerry Koosman	6.00	3.00	1.75
698	Jerry Koosman (In Action)	6.00	3.00	1.75
699	Bobby Murcer	6.00	3.00	1.75
700	Bobby Murcer (In Action)	6.00	3.00	1.75
701	Jose Pagan	6.00	3.00	1.75
702	Jose Pagan (In Action)	6.00	3.00	1.75
703	Doug Griffin	6.00	3.00	1.75
704	Doug Griffin (In Action)	6.00	3.00	1.75
705	Pat Corrales	6.00	3.00	1.75
706	Pat Corrales (In Action)	6.00	3.00	1.75
707	Tim Foli	6.00	3.00	1.75
708	Tim Foli (In Action)	6.00	3.00	1.75
709	Jim Kaat	9.00	4.50	2.75
710	Jim Kaat (In Action)	6.00	3.00	1.75
711	Bobby Bonds	12.00	6.00	3.50
712	Bobby Bonds (In Action)	7.00	3.50	2.00
713	Gene Michael	6.00	3.00	1.75
714	Gene Michael (In Action)	6.00	3.00	1.75
715	Mike Epstein	6.00	3.00	1.75
716	Jesus Alou	6.00	3.00	1.75
717	Bruce Dal Canton	6.00	3.00	1.75
718	Del Rice	6.00	3.00	1.75
719	Cesar Geronimo	6.00	3.00	1.75
720	Sam McDowell	6.00	3.00	1.75
721	Eddie Leon	6.00	3.00	1.75
722	Bill Sudakis	6.00	3.00	1.75
723	Al Santorini	6.00	3.00	1.75
724	A.L. Rookies (John Curtis, Rich Hinton, Mickey Scott)	6.00	3.00	1.75
725	Dick McAuliffe	6.00	3.00	1.75
726	Dick Selma	6.00	3.00	1.75
727	Jose Laboy	6.00	3.00	1.75
728	Gail Hopkins	6.00	3.00	1.75
729	Bob Veale	6.00	3.00	1.75
730	Rick Monday	6.00	3.00	1.75
731	Orioles Team	12.00	6.00	3.50
732	George Culver	6.00	3.00	1.75
733	Jim Hart	6.00	3.00	1.75
734	Bob Burda	6.00	3.00	1.75
735	Diego Segui	6.00	3.00	1.75
736	Bill Russell	6.00	3.00	1.75
737	*Lenny Randle*	6.00	3.00	1.75
738	Jim Merritt	6.00	3.00	1.75
739	Don Mason	6.00	3.00	1.75
740	Rico Carty	6.00	3.00	1.75
741	Major League Rookies (Tom Hutton, Rick Miller, John Milner)	6.00	3.00	1.75
742	Jim Rooker	6.00	3.00	1.75
743	Cesar Gutierrez	6.00	3.00	1.75
744	*Jim Slaton*	6.00	3.00	1.75
745	Julian Javier	6.00	3.00	1.75
746	Lowell Palmer	6.00	3.00	1.75
747	Jim Stewart	6.00	3.00	1.75
748	Phil Hennigan	6.00	3.00	1.75
749	Walter Alston	12.00	6.00	3.50
750	Willie Horton	6.00	3.00	1.75
751	Steve Carlton (Traded)	60.00	30.00	18.00
752	Joe Morgan (Traded)	40.00	20.00	12.00
753	Denny McLain (Traded)	10.00	5.00	3.00
754	Frank Robinson (Traded)	35.00	17.50	10.50
755	Jim Fregosi (Traded)	6.00	3.00	1.75
756	Rick Wise (Traded)	6.00	3.00	1.75
757	Jose Cardenal (Traded)	6.00	3.00	1.75
758	Gil Garrido	6.00	3.00	1.75
759	Chris Cannizzaro	6.00	3.00	1.75
760	Bill Mazeroski	12.00	6.00	3.50
761	A.L.-N.L. Rookies (*Ron Cey*, Ben Oglivie, Bernie Williams)	25.00	12.50	7.50
762	Wayne Simpson	6.00	3.00	1.75
763	Ron Hansen	6.00	3.00	1.75
764	Dusty Baker	12.00	6.00	3.50
765	Ken McMullen	6.00	3.00	1.75
766	Steve Hamilton	6.00	3.00	1.75
767	Tom McCraw	6.00	3.00	1.75
768	Denny Doyle	6.00	3.00	1.75
769	Jack Aker	6.00	3.00	1.75
770	Jim Wynn	6.00	3.00	1.75
771	Giants Team	9.00	4.50	2.75
772	Ken Tatum	6.00	3.00	1.75
773	Ron Brand	6.00	3.00	1.75
774	Luis Alvarado	6.00	3.00	1.75
775	Jerry Reuss	6.00	3.00	1.75
776	Bill Voss	6.00	3.00	1.75
777	Hoyt Wilhelm	16.00	8.00	4.75
778	Twins Rookies (Vic Albury, Rick Dempsey, Jim Strickland)	6.00	3.00	1.75
779	Tony Cloninger	6.00	3.00	1.75
780	Dick Green	6.00	3.00	1.75
781	Jim McAndrew	6.00	3.00	1.75
782	Larry Stahl	6.00	3.00	1.75
783	Les Cain	6.00	3.00	1.75
784	Ken Aspromonte	6.00	3.00	1.75
785	Vic Davalillo	6.00	3.00	1.75
786	Chuck Brinkman	6.00	3.00	1.75
787	Ron Reed	6.00	3.00	1.75

1972 Topps Cloth Stickers

Despite the fact they were never actually issued, examples of this test issue can readily be found within the hobby. The set of 33 contains stickers with designs identical to cards found in three contiguous rows of a regular Topps card sheet that year; thus the inclusion of a meaningless checklist card. Sometimes found in complete 33-sticker strips, individual stickers nominally measure 2-1/2" by 3-1/2," though dimensions vary according to the care with which they were cut. Stickers are unnumbered and blank-backed, and do not contain glue.

		NR MT	EX	VG
Complete Set:		350.00	175.00	100.00
Common Player:		6.00	3.00	1.75
(1)	Hank Aaron	65.00	32.00	19.50
(2)	Luis Aparicio (In Action)	20.00	10.00	6.00
(3)	Ike Brown	6.00	3.00	1.75
(4)	Johnny Callison	10.00	5.00	3.00
(5)	Checklist 264-319	6.00	3.00	1.75
(6)	Roberto Clemente (In Action)	80.00	40.00	24.00
(7)	Dave Concepcion	16.00	8.00	4.75
(8)	Ron Cook	6.00	3.00	1.75
(9)	Willie Davis	10.00	5.00	3.00
(10)	Al Fitzmorris	6.00	3.00	1.75
(11)	Bobby Floyd	6.00	3.00	1.75
(12)	Roy Foster	6.00	3.00	1.75
(13)	Jim Fregosi Boyhood Photo	8.00	4.00	2.50
(14)	Danny Frisella (In Action)	6.00	3.00	1.75
(15)	Woody Fryman	7.00	3.50	2.00
(16)	Terry Harmon	6.00	3.00	1.75
(17)	Frank Howard	14.00	7.00	4.25
(18)	Ron Klimkowski	6.00	3.00	1.75
(19)	Joe Lahoud	6.00	3.00	1.75
(20)	Jim Lefebvre	7.00	3.50	2.00
(21)	Elliott Maddox	6.00	3.00	1.75
(22)	Marty Martinez	6.00	3.00	1.75
(23)	Willie McCovey	35.00	17.50	10.50
(24)	Hal McRae	12.00	6.00	3.50
(25)	Syd O'Brien	6.00	3.00	1.75
(26)	Red Sox Team	8.00	4.00	2.50
(27)	Aurelio Rodriguez	7.00	3.50	2.00
(28)	Al Severinsen	6.00	3.00	1.75
(29)	Art Shamsky	6.00	3.00	1.75
(30)	Steve Stone	8.00	4.00	2.50
(31)	Stan Swanson	6.00	3.00	1.75
(32)	Bob Watson	7.00	3.50	2.00
(33)	Roy White	12.00	6.00	3.50

1972 Topps Posters

Issued as a separate set, rather than as a wax pack insert, the twenty-four 9-7/16" by 18" posters of 1972 feature a borderless full-color picture on the front with the player's name, team and position. Printed on very thin paper, the posters, as happened with earlier issues, were folded for packaging, causing large creases which cannot be removed. Even so, they are good display items for they feature many of stars of the period.

		NR MT	EX	VG
Complete Set:		500.00	250.00	150.00
Common Player:		10.00	5.00	3.00
1	Dave McNally	10.00	5.00	3.00
2	Carl Yastrzemski	50.00	25.00	15.00
3	Bill Melton	10.00	5.00	3.00
4	Ray Fosse	10.00	5.00	3.00
5	Mickey Lolich	12.00	6.00	3.50
6	Amos Otis	10.00	5.00	3.00
7	Tony Oliva	12.00	6.00	3.50
8	Vida Blue	12.00	6.00	3.50
9	Hank Aaron	40.00	20.00	12.00
10	Fergie Jenkins	16.00	8.00	4.75
11	Pete Rose	75.00	37.50	22.00
12	Willie Davis	12.00	6.00	3.50
13	Tom Seaver	30.00	15.00	9.00
14	Rick Wise	10.00	5.00	3.00
15	Willie Stargell	24.00	12.00	7.25
16	Joe Torre	14.00	7.00	4.25
17	Willie Mays	40.00	20.00	12.00
18	Andy Messersmith	10.00	5.00	3.00
19	Wilbur Wood	10.00	5.00	3.00
20	Harmon Killebrew	30.00	15.00	9.00
21	Billy Williams	24.00	12.00	7.25
22	Bud Harrelson	10.00	5.00	3.00
23	Roberto Clemente	40.00	20.00	12.00
24	Willie McCovey	30.00	15.00	9.00

1973 Topps

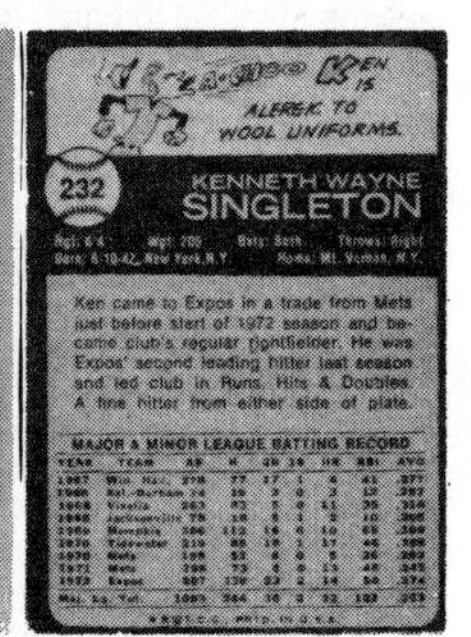

Topps cut back to 660 cards in 1973. The set is interesting for it marks the last time cards were issued by series, a procedure which had produced many a scarce high number card over the years. These 2-1/2" by 3-1/2" cards have a color photo, accented by a silhouette of a player on the front, indicative of his position. Card backs are vertical for the first time since 1968, with the usual statistical and biographical information. Specialty cards begin with card number 1, which depicted Ruth, Mays and Aaron as the all-time home run leaders. It was followed by statistical leaders, although there also were additional all-time leader cards. Also present are playoff and World Series highlights. From the age-and-youth department, the 1973 Topps set has coaches and managers as well as more "Boyhood Photos."

		NR MT	EX	VG
Complete Set (660):		1200.	600.00	360.00
Common Player (1-396):		.40	.20	.12
Common Player (397-528):		.70	.35	.20
Common Player (529-660):		2.00	1.00	.60
1	All Time Home Run Leaders (Hank Aaron, Willie Mays, Babe Ruth)	35.00	17.50	10.50
2	Rich Hebner	.40	.20	.12
3	Jim Lonborg	.50	.25	.15
4	John Milner	.40	.20	.12
5	Ed Brinkman	.40	.20	.12
6	Mac Scarce	.40	.20	.12
7	Rangers Team	3.00	1.50	.90
8	Tom Hall	.40	.20	.12
9	Johnny Oates	.40	.20	.12
10	Don Sutton	2.00	1.00	.60
11	Chris Chambliss	.40	.20	.12
12a	Padres Mgr./Coaches (Dave Garcia) (Coaches background brown)	.75	.40	.25
12a	Padres Mgr./Coaches (Johnny Podres) (Coaches background brown)	.75	.40	.25
12a	Padres Mgr./Coaches (Bob Skinner) (Coaches background brown)	.75	.40	.25
12a	Padres Mgr./Coaches (Whitey Wietelmann) (Coaches background brown)	.75	.40	.25
12a	Padres Mgr./Coaches (Don Zimmer) (Coaches background brown)	.75	.40	.25
12b	Padres Mgr./Coaches (Dave Garcia) (Coaches background orange)	.75	.40	.25
12b	Padres Mgr./Coaches (Johnny Podres) (Coaches background orange)	.75	.40	.25
12b	Padres Mgr./Coaches (Bob Skinner) (Coaches background orange)	.75	.40	.25
12b	Padres Mgr./Coaches (Whitey Wietelmann) (Coaches background orange)	.75	.40	.25
12b	Padres Mgr./Coaches (Don Zimmer) (Coaches background orange)	.75	.40	.25
13	George Hendrick	.40	.20	.12
14	Sonny Siebert	.40	.20	.12
15	Ralph Garr	.40	.20	.12
16	Steve Braun	.40	.20	.12
17	Fred Gladding	.40	.20	.12
18	Leroy Stanton	.40	.20	.12
19	Tim Foli	.40	.20	.12
20a	Stan Bahnsen (small gap in left border)	.70	.35	.20
20b	Stan Bahnsen (no gap)	.40	.20	.12
21	Randy Hundley	.40	.20	.12
22	Ted Abernathy	.40	.20	.12
23	Dave Kingman	.75	.40	.25
24	Al Santorini	.40	.20	.12
25	Roy White	.50	.25	.15
26	Pirates Team	3.00	1.50	.90
27	Bill Gogolewski	.40	.20	.12
28	Hal McRae	.75	.40	.25
29	Tony Taylor	.40	.20	.12
30	Tug McGraw	.40	.20	.12
31	*Buddy Bell*	4.00	2.00	1.25
32	Fred Norman	.40	.20	.12
33	Jim Breazeale	.40	.20	.12
34	Pat Dobson	.40	.20	.12
35	Willie Davis	.40	.20	.12
36	Steve Barber	.40	.20	.12
37	Bill Robinson	.40	.20	.12
38	Mike Epstein	.40	.20	.12
39	Dave Roberts	.40	.20	.12
40	Reggie Smith	.40	.20	.12
41	Tom Walker	.40	.20	.12
42	Mike Andrews	.40	.20	.12
43	*Randy Moffitt*	.40	.20	.12
44	Rick Monday	.40	.20	.12
45	Ellie Rodriguez (photo actually Paul Ratliff)	.40	.20	.12
46	Lindy McDaniel	.40	.20	.12
47	Luis Melendez	.40	.20	.12
48	Paul Splittorff	.40	.20	.12
49a	Twins Mgr./Coaches (Vern Morgan) (Coaches background brown)	.50	.25	.15
49a	Twins Mgr./Coaches (Frank Quilici) (Coaches background brown)	.50	.25	.15
49a	Twins Mgr./Coaches (Bob Rodgers) (Coaches background brown)	.50	.25	.15
49a	Twins Mgr./Coaches (Ralph Rowe) (Coaches background brown)	.50	.25	.15
49a	Twins Mgr./Coaches (Al Worthington) (Coaches background brown)	.50	.25	.15
49b	Twins Mgr./Coaches (Vern Morgan) (Coaches background orange)	.50	.25	.15
49b	Twins Mgr./Coaches (Frank Quilici) (Coaches background orange)	.50	.25	.15
49b	Twins Mgr./Coaches (Bob Rodgers) (Coaches background orange)	.50	.25	.15
49b	Twins Mgr./Coaches (Ralph Rowe) (Coaches background orange)	.50	.25	.15
49b	Twins Mgr./Coaches (Al Worthington) (Coaches background orange)	.50	.25	.15
50	Roberto Clemente	35.00	17.50	10.50
51	Chuck Seelbach	.40	.20	.12
52	Denis Menke	.40	.20	.12
53	Steve Dunning	.40	.20	.12
54	Checklist 1-132	2.00	1.00	.60
55	Jon Matlack	.40	.20	.12
56	Merv Rettenmund	.40	.20	.12
57	Derrel Thomas	.40	.20	.12
58	Mike Paul	.40	.20	.12
59	*Steve Yeager*	.80	.40	.25
60	Ken Holtzman	.40	.20	.12
61	Batting Leaders (Rod Carew, Billy Williams)	2.25	1.25	.70
62	Home Run Leaders (Dick Allen, Johnny Bench)	2.25	1.25	.70
63	Runs Batted In Leaders (Dick Allen, Johnny Bench)	2.25	1.25	.70
64	Stolen Base Leaders (Lou Brock, Bert Campaneris)	2.00	1.00	.60
65	Earned Run Average Leaders (Steve Carlton, Luis Tiant)	2.00	1.00	.60
66	Victory Leaders (Steve Carlton, Gaylord Perry, Wilbur Wood)	2.00	1.00	.60
67	Strikeout Leaders (Steve Carlton, Nolan Ryan)	18.00	9.00	5.50
68	Leading Firemen (Clay Carroll, Sparky Lyle)	.75	.40	.25
69	Phil Gagliano	.40	.20	.12
70	Milt Pappas	.40	.20	.12
71	Johnny Briggs	.40	.20	.12
72	Ron Reed	.40	.20	.12
73	Ed Herrmann	.40	.20	.12
74	Billy Champion	.40	.20	.12
75	Vada Pinson	.75	.40	.25
76	Doug Rader	.40	.20	.12
77	Mike Torrez	.40	.20	.12
78	Richie Scheinblum	.40	.20	.12
79	Jim Willoughby	.40	.20	.12
80	Tony Oliva	.75	.40	.25
81a	Cubs Mgr./Coaches (Hank Aguirre) (trees in Coaches background)	.90	.45	.25
81a	Cubs Mgr./Coaches (Ernie Banks) (trees in Coaches background)	.90	.45	.25
81a	Cubs Mgr./Coaches (Larry Jansen) (trees in Coaches background)	.90	.45	.25
81a	Cubs Mgr./Coaches (Whitey Lockman) (trees in Coaches background)	.90	.45	.25
81a	Cubs Mgr./Coaches (Pete Reiser) (trees in Coaches background)	.90	.45	.25
81b	Cubs Mgr./Coaches (Hank Aguirre) (orange, solid background)	.70	.35	.20
81b	Cubs Mgr./Coaches (Ernie banks) (orange, solid background)	.70	.35	.20
81b	Cubs Mgr./Coaches (Larry Jansen) (orange, solid background)	.70	.35	.20
81b	Cubs Mgr./Coaches (Whitey Lockman) (orange, solid background)	.70	.35	.20
81b	Cubs Mgr./Coaches (Pete Reiser) (orange, solid background)	.70	.35	.20
82	Fritz Peterson	.40	.20	.12
83	Leron Lee	.40	.20	.12
84	Rollie Fingers	5.00	2.50	1.50
85	Ted Simmons	1.50	.70	.45
86	Tom McCraw	.40	.20	.12
87	Ken Boswell	.40	.20	.12
88	Mickey Stanley	.40	.20	.12
89	Jack Billingham	.40	.20	.12
90	Brooks Robinson	7.50	3.75	2.25
91	Dodgers Team	4.00	2.00	1.25
92	Jerry Bell	.40	.20	.12
93	Jesus Alou	.40	.20	.12
94	Dick Billings	.40	.20	.12
95	Steve Blass	.40	.20	.12
96	Doug Griffin	.40	.20	.12
97	Willie Montanez	.40	.20	.12
98	Dick Woodson	.40	.20	.12
99	Carl Taylor	.40	.20	.12
100	Hank Aaron	25.00	12.50	7.50
101	Ken Henderson	.40	.20	.12
102	Rudy May	.40	.20	.12
103	Celerino Sanchez	.40	.20	.12
104	Reggie Cleveland	.40	.20	.12
105	Carlos May	.40	.20	.12
106	Terry Humphrey	.40	.20	.12
107	Phil Hennigan	.40	.20	.12
108	Bill Russell	.60	.30	.20
109	Doyle Alexander	.40	.20	.12
110	Bob Watson	.40	.20	.12
111	Dave Nelson	.40	.20	.12
112	Gary Ross	.40	.20	.12
113	Jerry Grote	.40	.20	.12
114	Lynn McGlothen	.40	.20	.12
115	Ron Santo	.75	.40	.25
116a	Yankees Mgr./Coaches (Jim Hegan) (Coaches background brown)	2.25	1.25	.70
116a	Yankees Mgr./Coaches (Ralph Houk) (Coaches background brown)	2.25	1.25	.70
116a	Yankees Mgr./Coaches (Elston Howard) (Coaches background brown)	2.25	1.25	.70
116a	Yankees Mgr./Coaches (Dick Howser) (Coaches background brown)	2.25	1.25	.70
116a	Yankees Mgr./Coaches (Jim Turner) (Coaches background brown)	2.25	1.25	.70
116b	Yankees Mgr./Coaches (Jim Hegan) (Coaches background orange)	.90	.45	.25
116b	Yankees Mgr./Coaches (Ralph Houk) (Coaches background orange)	.90	.45	.25
116b	Yankees Mgr./Coaches (Elston Howard) (Coaches background orange)	.90	.45	.25
116b	Yankees Mgr./Coaches (Dick Howser) (Coaches background orange)	.90	.45	.25
116b	Yankees Mgr./Coaches (Jim Turner) (Coaches background orange)	.90	.45	.25
117	Ramon Hernandez	.40	.20	.12
118	John Mayberry	.40	.20	.12
119	Larry Bowa	.75	.40	.25
120	Joe Coleman	.40	.20	.12
121	Dave Rader	.40	.20	.12
122	Jim Strickland	.40	.20	.12
123	Sandy Alomar	.40	.20	.12
124	Jim Hardin	.40	.20	.12
125	Ron Fairly	.40	.20	.12
126	Jim Brewer	.40	.20	.12
127	Brewers Team	3.00	1.50	.90
128	Ted Sizemore	.40	.20	.12
129	Terry Forster	.40	.20	.12
130	Pete Rose	20.00	10.00	6.00
131a	Red Sox Mgr./Coaches (Doug Camilli) (Coaches background brown)	.70	.35	.20
131a	Red Sox Mgr./Coaches (Eddie Kasko) (Coaches background brown)	.70	.35	.20
131a	Red Sox Mgr./Coaches (Don Lenhardt) (Coaches background brown)	.70	.35	.20
131a	Red Sox Mgr./Coaches (Eddie Popowski) (Coaches background brown)	.70	.35	.20
131a	Red Sox Mgr./Coaches (Lee Stange) (Coaches background brown)	.70	.35	.20
131b	Red Sox Mgr./Coaches (Doug Camilli) (Coaches background orange)	.50	.25	.15
131b	Red Sox Mgr./Coaches (Eddie Kasko) (Coaches background orange)	.50	.25	.15
131b	Red Sox Mgr./Coaches (Don Lenhardt) (Coaches background orange)	.50	.25	.15
131b	Red Sox Mgr./Coaches (Eddie Popowski) (Coaches background orange)	.50	.25	.15
131b	Red Sox Mgr./Coaches (Lee Stange) (Coaches background orange)	.50	.25	.15
132	Matty Alou	.40	.20	.12
133	Dave Roberts	.40	.20	.12
134	Milt Wilcox	.40	.20	.12
135	Lee May	.40	.20	.12
136a	Orioles Mgr./Coaches (George Bamberger) (Coaches background brown)	2.25	1.25	.70
136a	Orioles Mgr./Coaches (Jim Frey) (Coaches background brown)	2.25	1.25	.70
136a	Orioles Mgr./Coaches (Billy Hunter) (Coaches background brown)	2.25	1.25	.70
136a	Orioles Mgr./Coaches (George Staller) (Coaches background brown)	2.25	1.25	.70
136a	Orioles Mgr./Coaches (Earl Weaver) (Coaches background brown)	2.25	1.25	.70
136b	Orioles Mgr./Coaches (George Bamberger) (Coaches background orange)	.90	.45	.25
136b	Orioles Mgr./Coaches (Jim Frey) (Coaches background orange)	.90	.45	.25
136b	Orioles Mgr./Coaches (Billy Hunter) (Coaches background orange)	.90	.45	.25
136b	Orioles Mgr./Coaches (George Staller) (Coaches background orange)	.90	.45	.25
136b	Orioles Mgr./Coaches (Earl Weaver) (Coaches background orange)	.90	.45	.25
137	Jim Beauchamp	.40	.20	.12
138	Horacio Pina	.40	.20	.12
139	Carmen Fanzone	.40	.20	.12

140 Lou Piniella .60 .30 .20
141 Bruce Kison .40 .20 .12
142 Thurman Munson 10.00 5.00 3.00
143 John Curtis .40 .20 .12
144 Marty Perez .40 .20 .12
145 Bobby Bonds .90 .45 .25
146 Woodie Fryman .40 .20 .12
147 Mike Anderson .40 .20 .12
148 *Dave Goltz* .40 .20 .12
149 Ron Hunt .40 .20 .12
150 Wilbur Wood .40 .20 .12
151 Wes Parker .40 .20 .12
152 Dave May .40 .20 .12
153 Al Hrabosky .40 .20 .12
154 Jeff Torborg .40 .20 .12
155 Sal Bando .40 .20 .12
156 Cesar Geronimo .40 .20 .12
157 Denny Riddleberger .40 .20 .12
158 Astros Team 3.00 1.50 .90
159 Cito Gaston .75 .40 .25
160 Jim Palmer 10.00 5.00 3.00
161 Ted Martinez .40 .20 .12
162 Pete Broberg .40 .20 .12
163 Vic Davalillo .40 .20 .12
164 Monty Montgomery .40 .20 .12
165 Luis Aparicio 2.75 1.50 .80
166 Terry Harmon .40 .20 .12
167 Steve Stone .40 .20 .12
168 Jim Northrup .40 .20 .12
169 Ron Schueler .40 .20 .12
170 Harmon Killebrew 5.00 2.50 1.50
171 Bernie Carbo .40 .20 .12
172 Steve Kline .40 .20 .12
173 Hal Breeden .40 .20 .12
174 *Rich Gossage* 15.00 7.50 4.50
175 Frank Robinson 7.50 3.75 2.25
176 Chuck Taylor .40 .20 .12
177 Bill Plummer .40 .20 .12
178 Don Rose .40 .20 .12
179a A's Mgr./Coaches (Jerry Adair) (Coaches background brown) 1.00 .50 .30
179a A's Mgr./Coaches (Vern Hoscheit) (Coaches background brown) 1.00 .50 .30
179a A's Mgr./Coaches (Irv Noren) (Coaches background brown) 1.00 .50 .30
179a A's Mgr./Coaches (Wes Stock) (Coaches background brown) 1.00 .50 .30
179a A's Mgr./Coaches (Dick Williams) (Coaches background brown) 1.00 .50 .30
179b A's Mgr./Coaches (Jerry Adair) (Coaches background orange) .70 .35 .20
179b A's Mgr./Coaches (Vern Hoscheit) (Coaches background orange) .70 .35 .20
179b A's Mgr./Coaches (Irv Noren) (Coaches background orange) .70 .35 .20
179b A's Mgr./Coaches (Wes Stock) (Coaches background orange) .70 .35 .20
179b A's Mgr./Coaches (Dick Williams) (Coaches background orange) .70 .35 .20
180 Fergie Jenkins 4.00 2.00 1.25
181 Jack Brohamer .40 .20 .12
182 *Mike Caldwell* .40 .20 .12
183 Don Buford .40 .20 .12
184 Jerry Koosman .40 .20 .12
185 Jim Wynn .40 .20 .12
186 Bill Fahey .40 .20 .12
187 Luke Walker .40 .20 .12
188 Cookie Rojas .40 .20 .12
189 Greg Luzinski .90 .45 .25
190 Bob Gibson 5.00 2.50 1.50
191 Tigers Team 3.00 1.50 .90
192 Pat Jarvis .40 .20 .12
193 Carlton Fisk 30.00 15.00 9.00
194 *Jorge Orta* .40 .20 .12
195 Clay Carroll .40 .20 .12
196 Ken McMullen .40 .20 .12
197 Ed Goodson .40 .20 .12
198 Horace Clarke .40 .20 .12
199 Bert Blyleven 3.00 1.50 .90
200 Billy Williams 4.00 2.00 1.25
201 A.L. Playoffs (Hendrick Scores Winning Run.) 2.25 1.25 .70
202 N.L. Playoffs (Foster's Run Decides It.) 2.25 1.25 .70
203 World Series Game 1 (Tenace The Menace.) 2.25 1.25 .70
204 World Series Game 2 (A's Make It Two Straight.) 2.25 1.25 .70
205 World Series Game 3 (Reds Win Squeeker.) 2.25 1.25 .70
206 World Series Game 4 (Tenace Singles In Ninth.) 2.25 1.25 .70
207 World Series Game 5 (Odom Out At Plate.) 2.25 1.25 .70
208 World Series Game 6 (Reds' Slugging Ties Series.) 2.25 1.25 .70
209 World Series Game 7 (Campy Starts Winning Rally.) 2.25 1.25 .70
210 World Series Summary (World Champions.) 2.25 1.25 .70
211 Balor Moore .40 .20 .12
212 Joe Lahoud .40 .20 .12
213 Steve Garvey 7.50 3.75 2.25
214 Dave Hamilton .40 .20 .12
215 Dusty Baker .75 .40 .25
216 Toby Harrah .40 .20 .12
217 Don Wilson .40 .20 .12
218 Aurelio Rodriguez .40 .20 .12
219 Cardinals Team 3.00 1.50 .90
220 Nolan Ryan 95.00 47.00 28.00
221 Fred Kendall .40 .20 .12
222 Rob Gardner .40 .20 .12
223 Bud Harrelson .40 .20 .12
224 Bill Lee .40 .20 .12
225 Al Oliver .75 .40 .25
226 Ray Fosse .40 .20 .12
227 Wayne Twitchell .40 .20 .12
228 Bobby Darwin .40 .20 .12
229 Roric Harrison .40 .20 .12
230 Joe Morgan 5.00 2.50 1.50
231 Bill Parsons .40 .20 .12
232 Ken Singleton .40 .20 .12
233 Ed Kirkpatrick .40 .20 .12
234 *Bill North* .40 .20 .12
235 Catfish Hunter 4.00 2.00 1.25
236 Tito Fuentes .40 .20 .12
237a Braves Mgr./Coaches (Lew Burdette) (Coaches background brown) 2.50 1.25 .70
237a Braves Mgr./Coaches (Jim Busby) (Coaches background brown) 2.50 1.25 .70
237a Braves Mgr./Coaches (Roy Hartsfield) (Coaches background brown) 2.50 1.25 .70
237a Braves Mgr./Coaches (Eddie Mathews) 2.50 1.25 .70
237a Braves Mgr./Coaches (Ken Silvestri) (Coaches background brown) 2.50 1.25 .70
237b Braves Mgr./Coaches (Lew Burdette) (Coaches background orange) 2.25 1.25 .70
237b Braves Mgr./Coaches (Jim Busby) (Coaches background orange) 2.25 1.25 .70
237b Braves Mgr./Coaches (Roy Hartsfield) (Coaches background orange) 2.25 1.25 .70
237b Braves Mgr./Coaches (Eddie mathews) (Coaches background orange) 2.25 1.25 .70
237b Braves Mgr./Coaches (Ken Silvestri) (Coaches background orange) 2.25 1.25 .70
238 Tony Muser .40 .20 .12
239 Pete Richert .40 .20 .12
240 Bobby Murcer .60 .30 .20
241 Dwain Anderson .40 .20 .12
242 George Culver .40 .20 .12
243 Angels Team 3.00 1.50 .90
244 Ed Acosta .40 .20 .12
245 Carl Yastrzemski 15.00 7.50 4.50
246 Ken Sanders .40 .20 .12
247 Del Unser .40 .20 .12
248 Jerry Johnson .40 .20 .12
249 Larry Biittner .40 .20 .12
250 Manny Sanguillen .40 .20 .12
251 Roger Nelson .40 .20 .12
252a Giants Mgr./Coaches (Joe Amalfitano) (Coaches background brown) .70 .35 .20
252a Giants Mgr./Coaches (Charlie Fox) (Coaches background brown) .70 .35 .20
252a Giants Mgr./Coaches (Andy Gilbert) (Coaches background brown) .70 .35 .20
252a Giants Mgr./Coaches (Don McMahon) (Coaches background brown) .70 .35 .20
252a Giants Mgr./Coaches (John McNamara) (Coaches background brown) .70 .35 .20
252b Giants Mgr./Coaches (Joe Amalfitano) (Coaches background orange) .50 .25 .15
252b Giants Mgr./Coaches (Charlie Fox) (Coaches background orange) .50 .25 .15
252b Giants Mgr./Coaches (Andy Gilbert) (Coaches background orange) .50 .25 .15
252b Giants Mgr./Coaches (Don McMahon) (Coaches background orange) .50 .25 .15
252b Giants Mgr./Coaches (John McNamara) (Coaches background orange) .50 .25 .15
253 Mark Belanger .40 .20 .12
254 Bill Stoneman .40 .20 .12
255 Reggie Jackson 30.00 15.00 9.00
256 Chris Zachary .40 .20 .12
257a Mets Mgr./Coaches (Yogi Berra) (Coaches background brown) 3.00 1.50 .90
257a Mets Mgr./Coaches (Roy McMillan) (Coaches background brown) 3.00 1.50 .90
257a Mets Mgr./Coaches (Joe Pignatano) (Coaches background brown) 3.00 1.50 .90
257a Mets Mgr./Coaches (Rube Walker) (Coaches background brown) 3.00 1.50 .90
257a Mets Mgr./Coaches (Eddie Yost) (Coaches background brown) 3.00 1.50 .90
257b Mets Mgr./Coaches (Yogi berra) (Coaches background orange) 2.50 1.25 .70
257b Mets Mgr./Coaches (Roy McMillan) (Coaches background orange) 2.50 1.25 .70
257b Mets Mgr./Coaches (Joe Pignatano) (Coaches background orange) 2.50 1.25 .70
257b Mets Mgr./Coaches (Rube Walker) (Coaches background orange) 2.50 1.25 .70
257b Mets Mgr./Coaches (Eddie Yost) (Coaches background orange) 2.50 1.25 .70
258 Tommy John 2.00 1.00 .60
259 Jim Holt .40 .20 .12
260 Gary Nolan .40 .20 .12
261 Pat Kelly .40 .20 .12
262 Jack Aker .40 .20 .12
263 George Scott .40 .20 .12
264 Checklist 133-264 2.00 1.00 .60
265 Gene Michael .40 .20 .12
266 Mike Lum .40 .20 .12
267 Lloyd Allen .40 .20 .12
268 Jerry Morales .40 .20 .12
269 Tim McCarver .75 .40 .25
270 Luis Tiant .75 .40 .25
271 Tom Hutton .40 .20 .12
272 Ed Farmer .40 .20 .12
273 Chris Speier .40 .20 .12
274 Darold Knowles .40 .20 .12
275 Tony Perez 3.00 1.50 .90
276 Joe Lovitto .40 .20 .12
277 Bob Miller .40 .20 .12
278 Orioles Team 3.00 1.50 .90
279 Mike Strahler .40 .20 .12
280 Al Kaline 8.00 4.00 2.50
281 Mike Jorgensen .40 .20 .12
282 Steve Hovley .40 .20 .12
283 Ray Sadecki .40 .20 .12
284 Glenn Borgmann .40 .20 .12
285 Don Kessinger .40 .20 .12
286 Frank Linzy .40 .20 .12
287 Eddie Leon .40 .20 .12
288 Gary Gentry .40 .20 .12
289 Bob Oliver .40 .20 .12
290 Cesar Cedeno .40 .20 .12
291 Rogelio Moret .40 .20 .12
292 Jose Cruz .60 .30 .20
293 Bernie Allen .40 .20 .12
294 Steve Arlin .40 .20 .12
295 Bert Campaneris .75 .40 .25
296 Reds Mgr./Coaches (Sparky Anderson, Alex Grammas, Ted Kluszewski, George Scherger, Larry Shepard) 2.00 1.00 .60
297 Walt Williams .40 .20 .12
298 Ron Bryant .40 .20 .12
299 Ted Ford .40 .20 .12
300 Steve Carlton 15.00 7.50 4.50
301 Billy Grabarkewitz .40 .20 .12
302 Terry Crowley .40 .20 .12
303 Nelson Briles .40 .20 .12
304 Duke Sims .40 .20 .12
305 Willie Mays 35.00 17.50 10.50
306 Tom Burgmeier .40 .20 .12
307 Boots Day .40 .20 .12
308 Skip Lockwood .40 .20 .12
309 Paul Popovich .40 .20 .12
310 Dick Allen .75 .40 .25
311 Joe Decker .40 .20 .12
312 Oscar Brown .40 .20 .12
313 Jim Ray .40 .20 .12
314 Ron Swoboda .40 .20 .12
315 John Odom .40 .20 .12
316 Padres Team 3.00 1.50 .90
317 Danny Cater .40 .20 .12
318 Jim McGlothlin .40 .20 .12
319 Jim Spencer .40 .20 .12
320 Lou Brock 6.00 3.00 1.75
321 Rich Hinton .40 .20 .12
322 *Garry Maddox* 1.00 .50 .30
323 Tigers Mgr./Coaches (Art Fowler, Billy Martin, Joe Schultz, Charlie Silvera, Dick Tracewski) 1.50 .70 .45
324 Al Downing .40 .20 .12
325 Boog Powell .75 .40 .25
326 Darrell Brandon .40 .20 .12
327 John Lowenstein .40 .20 .12
328 Bill Bonham .40 .20 .12
329 Ed Kranepool .40 .20 .12
330 Rod Carew 10.00 5.00 3.00
331 Carl Morton .40 .20 .12
332 *John Felske* .40 .20 .12
333 Gene Clines .40 .20 .12
334 Freddie Patek .40 .20 .12
335 Bob Tolan .40 .20 .12
336 Tom Bradley .40 .20 .12
337 Dave Duncan .40 .20 .12
338 Checklist 265-396 2.00 1.00 .60
339 Dick Tidrow .40 .20 .12
340 Nate Colbert .40 .20 .12
341 Boyhood Photo (Jim Palmer) 2.00 1.00 .60
342 Boyhood Photo (Sam McDowell) .40 .20 .12
343 Boyhood Photo (Bobby Murcer) .40 .20 .12
344 Boyhood Photo (Catfish Hunter) 1.50 .70 .45
345 Boyhood Photo (Chris Speier) .40 .20 .12
346 Boyhood Photo (Gaylord Perry) 1.50 .70 .45
347 Royals Team 3.00 1.50 .90
348 Rennie Stennett .40 .20 .12
349 Dick McAuliffe .40 .20 .12
350 Tom Seaver 20.00 10.00 6.00
351 Jimmy Stewart .40 .20 .12
352 *Don Stanhouse* .40 .20 .12
353 Steve Brye .40 .20 .12
354 Billy Parker .40 .20 .12
355 Mike Marshall .40 .20 .12
356 White Sox Mgr./Coaches (Joe Lonnett, Jim Mahoney, Al Monchak, Johnny Sain, Chuck Tanner) .60 .30 .20
357 Ross Grimsley .40 .20 .12
358 Jim Nettles .40 .20 .12
359 Cecil Upshaw .40 .20 .12
360 Joe Rudi (photo actually Gene Tenace) .40 .20 .12
361 Fran Healy .40 .20 .12
362 Eddie Watt .40 .20 .12
363 Jackie Hernandez .40 .20 .12
364 Rick Wise .40 .20 .12
365 Rico Petrocelli .40 .20 .12
366 Brock Davis .40 .20 .12
367 Burt Hooton .40 .20 .12
368 Bill Buckner .60 .30 .20
369 Lerrin LaGrow .40 .20 .12
370 Willie Stargell 6.00 3.00 1.75
371 Mike Kekich .40 .20 .12
372 Oscar Gamble .40 .20 .12
373 Clyde Wright .40 .20 .12
374 Darrell Evans .40 .20 .12
375 Larry Dierker .40 .20 .12
376 Frank Duffy .40 .20 .12
377 Expos Mgr./Coaches (Dave Bristol, Larry Doby, Gene Mauch, Cal McLish, Jerry Zimmerman) .60 .30 .20
378 Lenny Randle .40 .20 .12
379 Cy Acosta .40 .20 .12
380 Johnny Bench 16.00 8.00 4.75
381 Vicente Romo .40 .20 .12
382 Mike Hegan .40 .20 .12
383 Diego Segui .40 .20 .12
384 Don Baylor 2.00 1.00 .60
385 Jim Perry .40 .20 .12
386 Don Money .40 .20 .12
387 Jim Barr .40 .20 .12
388 Ben Oglivie .40 .20 .12
389 Mets Team 3.00 1.50 .90
390 Mickey Lolich .75 .40 .25
391 *Lee Lacy* .40 .20 .12
392 Dick Drago .40 .20 .12
393 Jose Cardenal .40 .20 .12
394 Sparky Lyle .40 .20 .12

395 Roger Metzger .40 .20 .12
396 Grant Jackson .40 .20 .12
397 Dave Cash .70 .35 .20
398 Rich Hand .70 .35 .20
399 George Foster 1.50 .70 .45
400 Gaylord Perry 6.00 3.00 1.75
401 Clyde Mashore .70 .35 .20
402 Jack Hiatt .70 .35 .20
403 Sonny Jackson .70 .35 .20
404 Chuck Brinkman .70 .35 .20
405 Cesar Tovar .70 .35 .20
406 Paul Lindblad .70 .35 .20
407 Felix Millan .70 .35 .20
408 Jim Colborn .70 .35 .20
409 Ivan Murrell .70 .35 .20
410 Willie McCovey 6.00 3.00 1.75
411 Ray Corbin .70 .35 .20
412 Manny Mota .70 .35 .20
413 Tom Timmermann .70 .35 .20
414 Ken Rudolph .70 .35 .20
415 Marty Pattin .70 .35 .20
416 Paul Schaal .70 .35 .20
417 Scipio Spinks .70 .35 .20
418 Bobby Grich .70 .35 .20
419 Casey Cox .70 .35 .20
420 Tommie Agee .70 .35 .20
421 Angels Mgr./Coaches (Tom Morgan, Salty Parker, Jimmie Reese, John Roseboro, Bobby Winkles) .70 .35 .20
422 Bob Robertson .70 .35 .20
423 Johnny Jeter .70 .35 .20
424 Denny Doyle .70 .35 .20
425 Alex Johnson .70 .35 .20
426 Dave LaRoche .70 .35 .20
427 Rick Auerbach .70 .35 .20
428 Wayne Simpson .70 .35 .20
429 Jim Fairey .70 .35 .20
430 Vida Blue 1.00 .50 .30
431 Gerry Moses .70 .35 .20
432 Dan Frisella .70 .35 .20
433 Willie Horton .70 .35 .20
434 Giants Team 4.00 2.00 1.25
435 Rico Carty .70 .35 .20
436 Jim McAndrew .70 .35 .20
437 John Kennedy .70 .35 .20
438 Enzo Hernandez .70 .35 .20
439 Eddie Fisher .70 .35 .20
440 Glenn Beckert .70 .35 .20
441 Gail Hopkins .70 .35 .20
442 Dick Dietz .70 .35 .20
443 Danny Thompson .70 .35 .20
444 Ken Brett .70 .35 .20
445 Ken Berry .70 .35 .20
446 Jerry Reuss .70 .35 .20
447 Joe Hague .70 .35 .20
448 John Hiller .70 .35 .20
449a Indians Mgr./Coaches (Ken Aspromonte) (Spahn's ear pointed) 1.50 .70 .45
449a Indians Mgr./Coaches (Rocky colavito) (Spahn's ear pointed) 1.50 .70 .45
449a Indians Mgr./Coaches (Joe Lutz) (Spahn's ear pointed) 1.50 .70 .45
449a Indians Mgr./Coaches (Warren spahn) (Spahn's ear pointed) 1.50 .70 .45
449b Indians Mgr./Coaches (Ken Aspromonte) (Spahn's ear round) 2.00 1.00 .60
449b Indians Mgr./Coaches (Rocky Colavito) (Spahn's ear round) 2.00 1.00 .60
449b Indians Mgr./Coaches (Joe Lutz) (Spahn's ear round) 2.00 1.00 .60
449b Indians Mgr./Coaches (Warren Spahn) (Spahn's ear round) 2.00 1.00 .60
450 Joe Torre .70 .35 .20
451 John Vukovich .70 .35 .20
452 Paul Casanova .70 .35 .20
453 Checklist 397-528 2.25 1.25 .70
454 Tom Haller .70 .35 .20
455 Bill Melton .70 .35 .20
456 Dick Green .70 .35 .20
457 John Strohmayer .70 .35 .20
458 Jim Mason .70 .35 .20
459 Jimmy Howarth .70 .35 .20
460 Bill Freehan .70 .35 .20
461 Mike Corkins .70 .35 .20
462 Ron Blomberg .70 .35 .20
463 Ken Tatum .70 .35 .20
464 Cubs Team 4.00 2.00 1.25
465 Dave Giusti .70 .35 .20
466 Jose Arcia .70 .35 .20
467 Mike Ryan .70 .35 .20
468 Tom Griffin .70 .35 .20
469 Dan Monzon .70 .35 .20
470 Mike Cuellar .70 .35 .20
471 All-Time Hit Leader (Ty Cobb) 5.00 2.50 1.50
472 All-Time Grand Slam Leader (Lou Gehrig) 5.00 2.50 1.50
473 All-Time Total Base Leader (Hank Aaron) 5.00 2.50 1.50
474 All-Time RBI Leader (Babe Ruth) 10.00 5.00 3.00
475 All-Time Batting Leader (Ty Cobb) 5.00 2.50 1.50
476 All-Time Shutout Leader (Walter Johnson) 2.00 1.00 .60
477 All-Time Victory Leader (Cy Young) 2.00 1.00 .60
478 All-Time Strikeout Leader (Walter Johnson) 2.00 1.00 .60
479 Hal Lanier .70 .35 .20
480 Juan Marichal 6.00 3.00 1.75
481 White Sox Team 4.00 2.00 1.25
482 *Rick Reuschel* 1.50 .70 .45
483 Dal Maxvill .70 .35 .20
484 Ernie McAnally .70 .35 .20
485 Norm Cash 1.00 .50 .30
486a Phillies Mgr./Coaches (Carroll Berringer) (Coaches background brown-red) .90 .45 .25
486a Phillies Mgr./Coaches (Billy DeMars) (Coaches background brown-red) .90 .45 .25
486a Phillies Mgr./Coaches (Danny Ozark) (Coaches background brown-red) .90 .45 .25
486a Phillies Mgr./Coaches (Ray Rippelmeyer) (Coaches background brown-red) .90 .45 .25
486a Phillies Mgr./Coaches (Bobby Wine) (Coaches background brown-red) .90 .45 .25
486b Phillies Mgr./Coaches (Carroll Beringer) (Coaches background orange) .70 .35 .20
486b Phillies Mgr./Coaches (Billy DeMars) (Coaches background orange) .70 .35 .20
486b Phillies Mgr./Coaches (Danny Ozark) (Coaches background orange) .70 .35 .20
486b Phillies Mgr./Coaches (Ray Rippelmeyer) (Coaches background orange) .70 .35 .20
486b Phillies Mgr./Coaches (Bobby Wine) (Coaches background orange) .70 .35 .20
487 Bruce Dal Canton .70 .35 .20
488 Dave Campbell .70 .35 .20
489 Jeff Burroughs .70 .35 .20
490 Claude Osteen .70 .35 .20
491 Bob Montgomery .70 .35 .20
492 Pedro Borbon .70 .35 .20
493 Duffy Dyer .70 .35 .20
494 Rich Morales .70 .35 .20
495 Tommy Helms .70 .35 .20
496 Ray Lamb .70 .35 .20
497 Cardinals Mgr./Coaches (Vern Benson, George Kissell, Red Schoendienst, Barney Schultz) 1.25 .60 .40
498 Graig Nettles 1.00 .50 .30
499 Bob Moose .70 .35 .20
500 A's Team 4.00 2.00 1.25
501 Larry Gura .70 .35 .20
502 Bobby Valentine .70 .35 .20
503 Phil Niekro 5.00 2.50 1.50
504 Earl Williams .70 .35 .20
505 Bob Bailey .70 .35 .20
506 Bart Johnson .70 .35 .20
507 Darrel Chaney .70 .35 .20
508 Gates Brown .70 .35 .20
509 Jim Nash .70 .35 .20
510 Amos Otis .70 .35 .20
511 Sam McDowell .70 .35 .20
512 Dalton Jones .70 .35 .20
513 Dave Marshall .70 .35 .20
514 Jerry Kenney .70 .35 .20
515 Andy Messersmith .70 .35 .20
516 Danny Walton .70 .35 .20
517a Pirates Mgr./Coaches (Don Leppert) (Coaches background brown) 2.00 1.00 .60
517a Pirates Mgr./Coaches (Bill Mazeroski) (Coaches background brown) 2.00 1.00 .60
517a Pirates Mgr./Coaches (Dave Ricketts) (Coaches background brown) 2.00 1.00 .60
517a Pirates Mgr./Coaches (Bill Virdon) (Coaches background brown) 2.00 1.00 .60
517a Pirates Mgr./Coaches (Mel Wright) (Coaches background brown) 2.00 1.00 .60
517b Pirates Mgr./Coaches (Don Leppert) (Coaches background orange) .70 .35 .20
517b Pirates Mgr./Coaches (Bill Mazeroski) (Coaches background orange) .70 .35 .20
517b Pirates Mgr./Coaches (Dave Ricketts) (Coaches background orange) .70 .35 .20
517b Pirates Mgr./Coaches (Bill Virdon) (Coaches background orange) .70 .35 .20
517b Pirates Mgr./Coaches (Mel Wright) (Coaches background orange) .70 .35 .20
518 Bob Veale .70 .35 .20
519 John Edwards .70 .35 .20
520 Mel Stottlemyre .70 .35 .20
521 Braves Team 4.00 2.00 1.25
522 Leo Cardenas .70 .35 .20
523 Wayne Granger .70 .35 .20
524 Gene Tenace .70 .35 .20
525 Jim Fregosi .70 .35 .20
526 Ollie Brown .70 .35 .20
527 Dan McGinn .70 .35 .20
528 Paul Blair .70 .35 .20
529 Milt May 2.00 1.00 .60
530 Jim Kaat 4.00 2.00 1.25
531 Ron Woods 2.00 1.00 .60
532 Steve Mingori 2.00 1.00 .60
533 Larry Stahl 2.00 1.00 .60
534 Dave Lemonds 2.00 1.00 .60
535 John Callison 2.00 1.00 .60
536 Phillies Team 6.00 3.00 1.75
537 Bill Slayback 2.00 1.00 .60
538 Jim Hart 2.00 1.00 .60
539 Tom Murphy 2.00 1.00 .60
540 Cleon Jones 2.00 1.00 .60
541 Bob Bolin 2.00 1.00 .60
542 Pat Corrales 2.00 1.00 .60
543 Alan Foster 2.00 1.00 .60
544 Von Joshua 2.00 1.00 .60
545 Orlando Cepeda 4.00 2.00 1.25
546 Jim York 2.00 1.00 .60
547 Bobby Heise 2.00 1.00 .60
548 Don Durham 2.00 1.00 .60
549 Rangers Mgr./Coaches (Chuck Estrada, Whitey Herzog, Chuck Hiller, Jackie Moore) 2.50 1.25 .70
550 Dave Johnson 2.00 1.00 .60
551 Mike Kilkenny 2.00 1.00 .60
552 J.C. Martin 2.00 1.00 .60
553 Mickey Scott 2.00 1.00 .60
554 Dave Concepcion 2.50 1.25 .70
555 Bill Hands 2.00 1.00 .60
556 Yankees Team 7.50 3.75 2.25
557 Bernie Williams 2.00 1.00 .60
558 Jerry May 2.00 1.00 .60
559 Barry Lersch 2.00 1.00 .60
560 Frank Howard 2.00 1.00 .60
561 Jim Geddes 2.00 1.00 .60
562 Wayne Garrett 2.00 1.00 .60
563 Larry Haney 2.00 1.00 .60
564 Mike Thompson 2.00 1.00 .60
565 Jim Hickman 2.00 1.00 .60
566 Lew Krausse 2.00 1.00 .60
567 Bob Fenwick 2.00 1.00 .60
568 Ray Newman 2.00 1.00 .60
569 Dodgers Mgr./Coaches (Red Adams, Walt Alston, Monty Basgall, Jim Gillam, Tom Lasorda) 4.00 2.00 1.25
570 Bill Singer 2.00 1.00 .60
571 Rusty Torres 2.00 1.00 .60
572 Gary Sutherland 2.00 1.00 .60
573 Fred Beene 2.00 1.00 .60
574 Bob Didier 2.00 1.00 .60
575 Dock Ellis 2.00 1.00 .60
576 Expos Team 5.00 2.50 1.50
577 *Eric Soderholm* 2.00 1.00 .60
578 Ken Wright 2.00 1.00 .60
579 Tom Grieve 2.00 1.00 .60
580 Joe Pepitone 2.00 1.00 .60
581 Steve Kealey 2.00 1.00 .60
582 Darrell Porter 2.00 1.00 .60
583 Bill Greif 2.00 1.00 .60
584 Chris Arnold 2.00 1.00 .60
585 Joe Niekro 2.00 1.00 .60
586 Bill Sudakis 2.00 1.00 .60
587 Rich McKinney 2.00 1.00 .60
588 Checklist 529-660 2.00 1.00 .60
589 Ken Forsch 2.00 1.00 .60
590 Deron Johnson 2.00 1.00 .60
591 Mike Hedlund 2.00 1.00 .60
592 John Boccabella 2.00 1.00 .60
593 Royals Mgr./Coaches (Galen Cisco, Harry Dunlop, Charlie Lau, Jack McKeon) 2.25 1.25 .70
594 Vic Harris 2.00 1.00 .60
595 Don Gullett 2.00 1.00 .60
596 Red Sox Team 6.00 3.00 1.75
597 Mickey Rivers 2.00 1.00 .60
598 Phil Roof 2.00 1.00 .60
599 Ed Crosby 2.00 1.00 .60
600 Dave McNally 2.00 1.00 .60
601 Rookie Catchers (George Pena, Sergio Robles, Rick Stelmaszek) 2.00 1.00 .60
602 Rookie Pitchers (Mel Behney, Ralph Garcia, Doug Rau) 2.00 1.00 .60
603 Rookie Third Basemen (Terry Hughes, Bill McNulty, Ken Reitz) 2.00 1.00 .60
604 Rookie Pitchers (Jesse Jefferson, Dennis O'Toole, Bob Strampe) 2.00 1.00 .60
605 Rookie First Basemen (Pat Bourque, Enos Cabell, Gonzalo Marquez) 2.00 1.00 .60
606 Rookie Outfielders (*Gary Matthews*, Tom Paciorek, Jorge Roque) 2.25 1.25 .70
607 Rookie Shortstops (Ray Busse, Pepe Frias, Mario Guerrero) 2.00 1.00 .60
608 Rookie Pitchers (*Steve Busby*, Dick Colpaert, George Medich) 2.25 1.25 .70
609 Rookie Second Basemen (Larvell Blanks, Pedro Garcia, Dave Lopes) 4.00 2.00 1.25
610 Rookie Pitchers (Jimmy Freeman, Charlie Hough, Hank Webb) 2.25 1.25 .70
611 Rookie Outfielders (Rich Coggins, Jim Wohlford, Richie Zisk) 2.25 1.25 .70
612 Rookie Pitchers (Steve Lawson, Bob Reynolds, Brent Strom) 2.00 1.00 .60
613 Rookie Catchers (*Bob Boone*, Mike Ivie, Skip Jutze) 30.00 15.00 9.00
614 Rookie Outfielders (*Alonza Bumbry*, Dwight Evans, Charlie Spikes) 30.00 15.00 9.00
615 Rookie Third Basemen (Ron Cey, John Hilton, Mike Schmidt) 450.00 225.00 135.00
616 Rookie Pitchers (Norm Angelini, Steve Blateric, Mike Garman) 2.00 1.00 .60
617 Rich Chiles 2.00 1.00 .60
618 Andy Etchebarren 2.00 1.00 .60
619 Billy Wilson 2.00 1.00 .60
620 Tommy Harper 2.00 1.00 .60
621 Joe Ferguson 2.00 1.00 .60
622 Larry Hisle 2.00 1.00 .60
623 Steve Renko 2.00 1.00 .60
624 Astros Mgr./Coaches (Leo Durocher, Preston Gomez, Grady Hatton, Hub Kittle, Jim Owens) 2.25 1.25 .70
625 Angel Mangual 2.00 1.00 .60
626 Bob Barton 2.00 1.00 .60
627 Luis Alvarado 2.00 1.00 .60
628 Jim Slaton 2.00 1.00 .60
629 Indians Team 5.00 2.50 1.50
630 Denny McLain 3.00 1.50 .90
631 Tom Matchick 2.00 1.00 .60
632 Dick Selma 2.00 1.00 .60
633 Ike Brown 2.00 1.00 .60
634 Alan Closter 2.00 1.00 .60
635 Gene Alley 2.00 1.00 .60
636 Rick Clark 2.00 1.00 .60
637 Norm Niller 2.00 1.00 .60
638 Ken Reynolds 2.00 1.00 .60
639 Willie Crawford 2.00 1.00 .60
640 Dick Bosman 2.00 1.00 .60
641 Reds Team 6.00 3.00 1.75
642 Jose Laboy 2.00 1.00 .60
643 Al Fitzmorris 2.00 1.00 .60
644 Jack Heidemann 2.00 1.00 .60
645 Bob Locker 2.00 1.00 .60
646 Brewers Mgr./Coaches (Del Crandall, Harvey Kuenn, Joe Nossek, Bob Shaw, Jim Walton) 2.25 1.25 .70
647 George Stone 2.00 1.00 .60
648 Tom Egan 2.00 1.00 .60
649 Rich Folkers 2.00 1.00 .60
650 Felipe Alou 3.00 1.50 .90
651 Don Carrithers 2.00 1.00 .60
652 Ted Kubiak 2.00 1.00 .60
653 Joe Hoerner 2.00 1.00 .60
654 Twins Team 6.00 3.00 1.75
655 Clay Kirby 2.00 1.00 .60
656 John Ellis 2.00 1.00 .60
657 Bob Johnson 2.00 1.00 .60
658 Elliott Maddox 2.00 1.00 .60
659 Jose Pagan 2.00 1.00 .60
660 Fred Scherman 2.00 1.00 .60

1973 Topps Candy Lids

A bit out of the ordinary, the Topps Candy Lids were the top of a product called "Baseball Stars Bubble Gum." The bottom (inside) of the lids carry a color photo of a player with a ribbon which contains the name, position and team. The lids are 1-7/8" in diameter. A total of 55 different lids were made, featuring most of the stars of the day.

		NR MT	EX	VG
Complete Set:		600.00	300.00	180.00
Common Player:		5.00	2.50	1.50
(1)	Hank Aaron	30.00	15.00	9.00
(2)	Dick Allen	8.00	4.00	2.50
(3)	Dusty Baker	5.00	2.50	1.50
(4)	Sal Bando	7.00	3.50	2.00
(5)	Johnny Bench	20.00	10.00	6.00
(6)	Bobby Bonds	7.00	3.50	2.00
(7)	Dick Bosman	5.00	2.50	1.50
(8)	Lou Brock	25.00	12.50	7.50
(9)	Rod Carew	20.00	10.00	6.00
(10)	Steve Carlton	20.00	10.00	6.00
(11)	Nate Colbert	5.00	2.50	1.50
(12)	Willie Davis	7.00	3.50	2.00
(13)	Larry Dierker	5.00	2.50	1.50
(14)	Mike Epstein	5.00	2.50	1.50
(15)	Carlton Fisk	15.00	7.50	4.50
(16)	Tim Foli	5.00	2.50	1.50
(17)	Ray Fosse	5.00	2.50	1.50
(18)	Bill Freehan	7.00	3.50	2.00
(19)	Bob Gibson	25.00	12.50	7.50
(20)	Bud Harrelson	5.00	2.50	1.50
(21)	Catfish Hunter	16.00	8.00	4.75
(22)	Reggie Jackson	25.00	12.50	7.50
(23)	Fergie Jenkins	15.00	7.50	4.50
(24)	Al Kaline	25.00	12.50	7.50
(25)	Harmon Killebrew	25.00	12.50	7.50
(26)	Clay Kirby	5.00	2.50	1.50
(27)	Mickey Lolich	8.00	4.00	2.50
(28)	Greg Luzinski	7.00	3.50	2.00
(29)	Mike Marshall	5.00	2.50	1.50
(30)	Lee May	5.00	2.50	1.50
(31)	John Mayberry	5.00	2.50	1.50
(32)	Willie Mays	30.00	15.00	9.00
(33)	Willie McCovey	25.00	12.50	7.50
(34)	Thurman Munson	25.00	12.50	7.50
(35)	Bobby Murcer	7.00	3.50	2.00
(36)	Gary Nolan	5.00	2.50	1.50
(37)	Amos Otis	5.00	2.50	1.50
(38)	Jim Palmer	16.00	8.00	4.75
(39)	Gaylord Perry	16.00	8.00	4.75
(40)	Lou Piniella	7.00	3.50	2.00
(41)	Brooks Robinson	25.00	12.50	7.50
(42)	Frank Robinson	25.00	12.50	7.50
(43)	Ellie Rodriguez	5.00	2.50	1.50
(44)	Pete Rose	65.00	32.00	19.50
(45)	Nolan Ryan	40.00	20.00	12.00
(46)	Manny Sanguillen	5.00	2.50	1.50
(47)	George Scott	5.00	2.50	1.50
(48)	Tom Seaver	20.00	10.00	6.00
(49)	Chris Speier	5.00	2.50	1.50
(50)	Willie Stargell	25.00	12.50	7.50
(51)	Don Sutton	16.00	8.00	4.75
(52)	Joe Torre	8.00	4.00	2.50
(53)	Billy Williams	16.00	8.00	4.75
(54)	Wilbur Wood	5.00	2.50	1.50
(55)	Carl Yastrzemski	25.00	12.50	7.50

Values quoted in this guide reflect the retail price of a card – the price a collector can expect to pay when buying a card from a dealer. The wholesale price – that which a collector can expect to receive from a dealer when selling cards – will be significantly lower, depending on desirability and condition.

1973 Topps Comics

Strictly a test issue, if ever publicly distributed at all (most are found without any folding which would have occurred had they actually been used to wrap a piece of bubblegum), the 24 players in the 1973 Topps Comics issue appear on 4-5/8" by 3-7/16" waxed paper wrappers. The inside of the wrapper combines a color photo and facsimile autograph with a comic-style presentation of the player's career highlights. The Comics share a checklist with the 1973 Topps Pin-Ups, virtually all star players.

		NR MT	EX	VG
Complete Set:		3000.	1500.	900.00
Common Player:		70.00	35.00	21.00
(1)	Hank Aaron	200.00	100.00	60.00
(2)	Dick Allen	80.00	40.00	24.00
(3)	Johnny Bench	150.00	75.00	45.00
(4)	Steve Carlton	125.00	62.00	37.00
(5)	Nate Colbert	70.00	35.00	21.00
(6)	Willie Davis	80.00	40.00	24.00
(7)	Mike Epstein	70.00	35.00	21.00
(8)	Reggie Jackson	200.00	100.00	60.00
(9)	Harmon Killebrew	125.00	62.00	37.00
(10)	Mickey Lolich	80.00	40.00	24.00
(11)	Mike Marshall	70.00	35.00	21.00
(12)	Lee May	70.00	35.00	21.00
(13)	Willie McCovey	125.00	62.00	37.00
(14)	Bobby Murcer	80.00	40.00	24.00
(15)	Gaylord Perry	100.00	50.00	30.00
(16)	Lou Piniella	80.00	40.00	24.00
(17)	Brooks Robinson	125.00	62.00	37.00
(18)	Nolan Ryan	125.00	62.00	37.00
(19)	George Scott	70.00	35.00	21.00
(20)	Tom Seaver	150.00	75.00	45.00
(21)	Willie Stargell	100.00	50.00	30.00
(22)	Joe Torre	80.00	40.00	24.00
(23)	Billy Williams	100.00	50.00	30.00
(24)	Carl Yastrzemski	250.00	125.00	75.00

1973 Topps 1953 Reprints

Long before Topps reprinted virtually the entire 1953 set in its "Archives" program in 1991, selected cards from the '53 set had been reprinted in a rare eight-card issue. Some sources say the cards were produced as table favors at a Topps banquet, while at least one contemporary hobby periodical said they were sold on a test-issue basis in Brooklyn. It was said only 300 of the sets were made. Unlike the original cards in 2-5/8" x 3-3/4" format, the test issue cards are modern standard 2-1/2" x 3-1/2". Three of the players in the issue were misidentified. Card backs feature a career summary written as though in 1953; the backs are formatted differently than original 1953 Topps cards and are printed in black-and-white.

		NR MT	EX	VG
Complete Set (8):		600.00	300.00	180.00
Common Player:		24.00	12.00	7.25
1	Satchell Paige	225.00	112.00	67.00
2	Jackie Robinson	150.00	75.00	45.00
3	Carl Furillo (picture actually Bill Antonello)	40.00	20.00	12.00
4	Al Rosen (picture actually Jim Fridley)	30.00	15.00	9.00
5	Hal Newhouser	40.00	20.00	12.00
6	Clyde McCullough (picture actually Vic Janowicz)	24.00	12.00	7.25
7	"Peanuts Lowrey	24.00	12.00	7.25
8	Johnny Mize	65.00	32.00	19.50

1973 Topps Pin-Ups

Another test issue of 1973, the 24 Topps Pin-Ups include the same basic format and the same checklist of star-caliber players as the Comics test issue of the same year. The 3-7/16" by 4-5/8" Pin-Ups are actually the inside of a wrapper for a piece of bubblegum. The color player photo features a decorative lozenge inserted at bottom with the player's name, team and position. There is also a facsimile autograph. Curiously, neither the Pin-Ups nor the Comics of 1973 bear team logos on the players' caps.

		NR MT	EX	VG
Complete Set:		1250.	625.00	375.00
Common Player:		30.00	15.00	9.00
(1)	Hank Aaron	90.00	45.00	27.00
(2)	Dick Allen	35.00	17.50	10.50
(3)	Johnny Bench	70.00	35.00	21.00
(4)	Steve Carlton	60.00	30.00	18.00
(5)	Nate Colbert	30.00	15.00	9.00
(6)	Willie Davis	35.00	17.50	10.50
(7)	Mike Epstein	30.00	15.00	9.00
(8)	Reggie Jackson	90.00	45.00	27.00
(9)	Harmon Killebrew	50.00	25.00	15.00
(10)	Mickey Lolich	35.00	17.50	10.50
(11)	Mike Marshall	30.00	15.00	9.00
(12)	Lee May	30.00	15.00	9.00
(13)	Willie McCovey	50.00	25.00	15.00
(14)	Bobby Murcer	35.00	17.50	10.50
(15)	Gaylord Perry	45.00	22.00	13.50
(16)	Lou Piniella	35.00	17.50	10.50
(17)	Brooks Robinson	55.00	27.00	16.50
(18)	Nolan Ryan	55.00	27.00	16.50
(19)	George Scott	30.00	15.00	9.00
(20)	Tom Seaver	75.00	37.00	22.00
(21)	Willie Stargell	45.00	22.00	13.50
(22)	Joe Torre	35.00	17.50	10.50
(23)	Billy Williams	45.00	22.00	13.50
(24)	Carl Yastrzemski	110.00	55.00	33.00

The values quoted are intended to reflect the market price.

1973 Topps Team Checklists

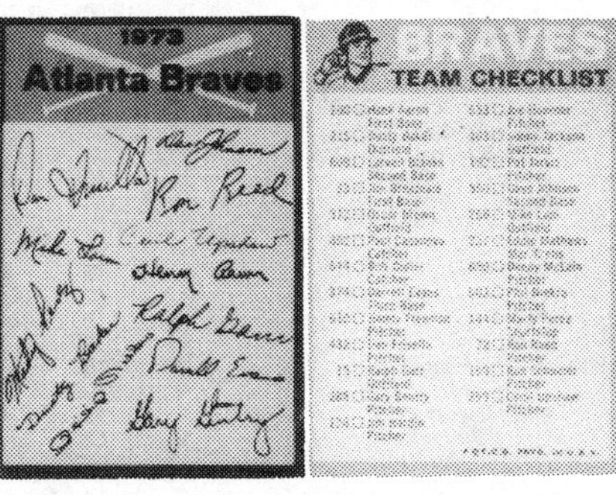

This is a 24-card unnumbered set of 2-1/2" by 3-1/2" cards that is generally believed to have been included with the high-numbered series in 1973, while also being made available in a mail-in offer. The front of the cards have the team name at the top and a white panel with various facsimile autographs takes up the rest of the space except for a blue border. Backs feature the team name and checklist. Relatively scarce, these somewhat mysterious cards are not included by many in their collections despite their obvious relationship to the regular set.

		NR MT	EX	VG
Complete Set:		75.00	37.00	22.00
Common Checklist:		3.00	1.50	.90
(1)	Atlanta Braves	3.00	1.50	.90
(2)	Baltimore Orioles	3.00	1.50	.90
(3)	Boston Red Sox	3.00	1.50	.90
(4)	California Angels	3.00	1.50	.90
(5)	Chicago Cubs	3.00	1.50	.90
(6)	Chicago White Sox	3.00	1.50	.90
(7)	Cincinnati Reds	3.00	1.50	.90
(8)	Cleveland Indians	3.00	1.50	.90
(9)	Detroit Tigers	3.50	1.75	1.00
(10)	Houston Astros	3.00	1.50	.90
(11)	Kansas City Royals	3.00	1.50	.90
(12)	Los Angeles Dodgers	3.00	1.50	.90
(13)	Milwaukee Brewers	3.00	1.50	.90
(14)	Minnesota Twins	3.00	1.50	.90
(15)	Montreal Expos	3.00	1.50	.90
(16)	New York Mets	3.50	1.75	1.00
(17)	New York Yankees	3.50	1.75	1.00
(18)	Oakland A's	3.50	1.75	1.00
(19)	Philadelphia Phillies	3.00	1.50	.90
(20)	Pittsburgh Pirates	3.00	1.50	.90
(21)	St. Louis Cardinals	3.00	1.50	.90
(22)	San Diego Padres	3.00	1.50	.90
(23)	San Francisco Giants	3.00	1.50	.90
(24)	Texas Rangers	3.00	1.50	.90

1974 Topps

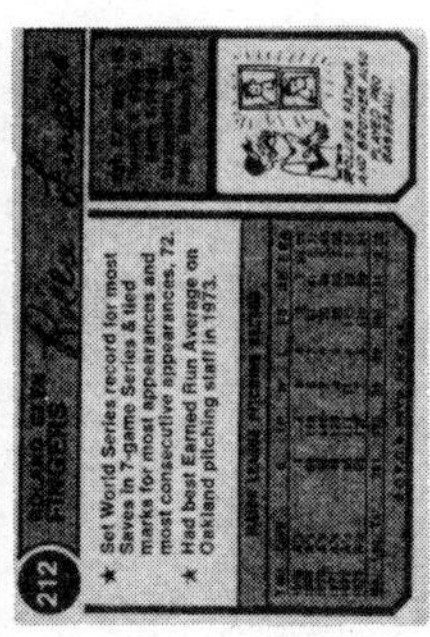

Issued all at once at the beginning of the year, rather than by series throughout the baseball season as had been done since 1952, this 660-card '74 Topps set features a famous group of error cards. At the time the cards were printed, it was uncertain whether the San Diego Padres would move to Washington, D.C., and by the time a decision was made some Padres cards had appeared with a "Washington, Nat'l League" designation on the front. A total of 15 cards were affected, and those with the Washington designation bring prices well in excess of regular cards of the same players (the Washington variations are not included in the complete set prices quoted below). The 2-1/2" by 3-1/2" cards feature color photos (frequently game-action shots) along with the player's name, team and position. Specialty cards abound, starting with a Hank Aaron tribute and running through the usual managers, statistical leaders, playoff and World Series highlights, multi-player rookie cards and All-Stars.

		NR MT	EX	VG
Complete Set (660):		650.00	325.00	195.00
Common Player:		.30	.15	.09
1	Hank Aaron (All-Time Home Run King)	30.00	15.00	9.00
2	Aaron Special 1954-57	4.00	2.00	1.25
3	Aaron Special 1958-61	4.00	2.00	1.25
4	Aaron Special 1962-65	4.00	2.00	1.25
5	Aaron Special 1966-69	4.00	2.00	1.25
6	Aaron Special 1970-73	4.00	2.00	1.25
7	Catfish Hunter	4.00	2.00	1.25
8	George Theodore	.30	.15	.09
9	Mickey Lolich	.60	.30	.20
10	Johnny Bench	15.00	7.50	4.50
11	Jim Bibby	.30	.15	.09
12	Dave May	.30	.15	.09
13	Tom Hilgendorf	.30	.15	.09
14	Paul Popovich	.30	.15	.09
15	Joe Torre	.30	.15	.09
16	Orioles Team	2.00	1.00	.60
17	Doug Bird	.30	.15	.09
18	Gary Thomasson	.30	.15	.09
19	Gerry Moses	.30	.15	.09
20	Nolan Ryan	80.00	40.00	24.00
21	Bob Gallagher	.30	.15	.09
22	Cy Acosta	.30	.15	.09
23	Craig Robinson	.30	.15	.09
24	John Hiller	.30	.15	.09
25	Ken Singleton	.30	.15	.09
26	*Bill Campbell*	.30	.15	.09
27	George Scott	.30	.15	.09
28	Manny Sanguillen	.30	.15	.09
29	Phil Niekro	2.00	1.00	.60
30	Bobby Bonds	.50	.25	.15
31	Astros Mgr./Coaches (Roger Craig, Preston Gomez, Grady Hatton, Hub Kittle, Bob Lillis)	.75	.40	.25
32a	John Grubb (Washington)	3.50	1.75	1.00
32b	John Grubb (San Diego)	.30	.15	.09
33	Don Newhauser	.30	.15	.09
34	Andy Kosco	.30	.15	.09
35	Gaylord Perry	4.00	2.00	1.25
36	Cardinals Team	2.00	1.00	.60
37	Dave Sells	.30	.15	.09
38	Don Kessinger	.30	.15	.09
39	Ken Suarez	.30	.15	.09
40	Jim Palmer	9.00	4.50	2.75
41	Bobby Floyd	.30	.15	.09
42	Claude Osteen	.30	.15	.09
43	Jim Wynn	.30	.15	.09
44	Mel Stottlemyre	.30	.15	.09
45	Dave Johnson	.30	.15	.09
46	Pat Kelly	.30	.15	.09
47	*Dick Ruthven*	.30	.15	.09
48	Dick Sharon	.30	.15	.09
49	Steve Renko	.30	.15	.09
50	Rod Carew	10.00	5.00	3.00
51	Bobby Heise	.30	.15	.09
52	Al Oliver	.75	.40	.25
53a	Fred Kendall (Washington)	3.50	1.75	1.00
53b	Fred Kendall (San Diego)	.30	.15	.09
54	*Elias Sosa*	.30	.15	.09
55	Frank Robinson	9.00	4.50	2.75
56	Mets Team	2.00	1.00	.60
57	Darold Knowles	.30	.15	.09
58	Charlie Spikes	.30	.15	.09
59	Ross Grimsley	.30	.15	.09
60	Lou Brock	5.00	2.50	1.50
61	Luis Aparicio	2.50	1.25	.70
62	Bob Locker	.30	.15	.09
63	Bill Sudakis	.30	.15	.09
64	Doug Rau	.30	.15	.09
65	Amos Otis	.30	.15	.09
66	Sparky Lyle	.30	.15	.09
67	Tommy Helms	.30	.15	.09
68	Grant Jackson	.30	.15	.09
69	Del Unser	.30	.15	.09
70	Dick Allen	.50	.25	.15
71	Danny Frisella	.30	.15	.09
72	Aurleio Rodriguez	.30	.15	.09
73	Mike Marshall	.30	.15	.09
74	Twins Team	2.00	1.00	.60
75	Jim Colborn	.30	.15	.09
76	Mickey Rivers	.30	.15	.09
77a	Rich Troedson (Washington)	3.50	1.75	1.00
77b	Rich Troedson (San Diego)	.30	.15	.09
78	Giants Mgr./Coaches (Joe Amalfitano, Charlie Fox, Andy Gilbert, Don McMahon, John McNamara)	.30	.15	.09
79	Gene Tenace	.30	.15	.09
80	Tom Seaver	15.00	7.50	4.50
81	Frank Duffy	.30	.15	.09
82	Dave Giusti	.30	.15	.09
83	Orlando Cepeda	2.00	1.00	.60
84	Rick Wise	.30	.15	.09
85	Joe Morgan	5.00	2.50	1.50
86	Joe Ferguson	.30	.15	.09
87	Fergie Jenkins	4.00	2.00	1.25
88	Freddie Patek	.30	.15	.09
89	Jackie Brown	.30	.15	.09
90	Bobby Murcer	.40	.20	.12
91	Ken Forsch	.30	.15	.09
92	Paul Blair	.30	.15	.09
93	Rod Gilbreath	.30	.15	.09
94	Tigers Team	2.00	1.00	.60
95	Steve Carlton	9.00	4.50	2.75
96	*Jerry Hairston*	.30	.15	.09
97	Bob Bailey	.30	.15	.09
98	Bert Blyleven	1.00	.50	.30
99	Brewers Mgr./Coaches (Del Crandall, Harvey Kuenn, Joe Nossek, Jim Walton, Al Widmar)	.30	.15	.09
100	Willie Stargell	6.00	3.00	1.75
101	Bobby Valentine	.30	.15	.09
102a	Bill Greif (Washington)	3.50	1.75	1.00
102b	Bill Greif (San Diego)	.30	.15	.09
103	Sal Bando	.30	.15	.09
104	Ron Bryant	.30	.15	.09
105	Carlton Fisk	12.50	6.25	3.75
106	Harry Parker	.30	.15	.09
107	Alex Johnson	.30	.15	.09
108	Al Hrabosky	.30	.15	.09
109	Bob Grich	.40	.20	.12
110	Billy Williams	6.00	3.00	1.75
111	Clay Carroll	.30	.15	.09
112	Dave Lopes	.40	.20	.12
113	Dick Drago	.30	.15	.09
114	Angels Team	2.00	1.00	.60
115	Willie Horton	.30	.15	.09
116	Jerry Reuss	.30	.15	.09
117	Ron Blomberg	.30	.15	.09
118	Bill Lee	.30	.15	.09
119	Phillies Mgr./Coaches (Carroll Beringer, Bill DeMars, Danny Ozark, Ray Ripplemeyer, Bobby Wine)	.30	.15	.09
120	Wilbur Wood	.30	.15	.09
121	Larry Lintz	.30	.15	.09
122	Jim Holt	.30	.15	.09
123	Nelson Briles	.30	.15	.09
124	Bob Coluccio	.30	.15	.09
125a	Nate Colbert (Washington)	3.50	1.75	1.00
125b	Nate Colbert (San Diego)	.30	.15	.09
126	Checklist 1-132	1.50	.70	.45
127	Tom Paciorek	.30	.15	.09
128	John Ellis	.30	.15	.09
129	Chris Speier	.30	.15	.09
130	Reggie Jackson	30.00	15.00	9.00
131	Bob Boone	2.50	1.25	.70
132	Felix Millan	.30	.15	.09
133	*David Clyde*	.30	.15	.09
134	Denis Menke	.30	.15	.09
135	Roy White	.40	.20	.12
136	Rick Reuschel	.30	.15	.09
137	Al Bumbry	.30	.15	.09
138	Ed Brinkman	.30	.15	.09
139	Aurelio Monteagudo	.30	.15	.09
140	Darrell Evans	.60	.30	.20
141	Pat Bourque	.30	.15	.09
142	Pedro Garcia	.30	.15	.09
143	Dick Woodson	.30	.15	.09
144	Dodgers Mgr./Coaches (Red Adams, Walter Alston, Monty Basgall, Jim Gilliam, Tom Lasorda)	1.50	.70	.45
145	Dock Ellis	.30	.15	.09
146	Ron Fairly	.30	.15	.09
147	Bart Johnson	.30	.15	.09
148a	Dave Hilton (Washington)	3.50	1.75	1.00
148b	Dave Hilton (San Diego)	.30	.15	.09
149	Mac Scarce	.30	.15	.09
150	John Mayberry	.30	.15	.09
151	Diego Segui	.30	.15	.09
152	Oscar Gamble	.30	.15	.09
153	Jon Matlack	.30	.15	.09
154	Astros Team	2.00	1.00	.60
155	Bert Campaneris	.30	.15	.09
156	Randy Moffitt	.30	.15	.09
157	Vic Harris	.30	.15	.09
158	Jack Billingham	.30	.15	.09
159	Jim Ray Hart	.30	.15	.09
160	Brooks Robinson	9.00	4.50	2.75
161	*Ray Burris*	.30	.15	.09
162	Bill Freehan	.30	.15	.09
163	Ken Berry	.30	.15	.09
164	Tom House	.30	.15	.09
165	Willie Davis	.30	.15	.09
166	Royals Mgr./Coaches (Galen Cisco, Harry Dunlop, Charlie Lau, Jack McKeon)	.45	.25	.14
167	Luis Tiant	.50	.25	.15
168	Danny Thompson	.30	.15	.09
169	*Steve Rogers*	.30	.15	.09
170	Bill Melton	.30	.15	.09
171	Eduardo Rodriguez	.30	.15	.09
172	Gene Clines	.30	.15	.09
173a	*Randy Jones* (Washington)	3.50	1.75	1.00
173b	*Randy Jones* (San Diego)	.30	.15	.09
174	Bill Robinson	.30	.15	.09
175	Reggie Cleveland	.30	.15	.09
176	John Lowenstein	.30	.15	.09
177	Dave Roberts	.30	.15	.09
178	Garry Maddox	.30	.15	.09
179	Mets Mgr./Coaches (Yogi Berra, Roy McMillan, Joe Pignatano, Rube Walker, Eddie Yost)	2.00	1.00	.60
180	Ken Holtzman	.30	.15	.09
181	Cesar Geronimo	.30	.15	.09
182	Lindy McDaniel	.30	.15	.09
183	Johnny Oates	.30	.15	.09
184	Rangers Team	2.00	1.00	.60
185	Jose Cardenal	.30	.15	.09
186	Fred Scherman	.30	.15	.09
187	Don Baylor	.50	.25	.15
188	Rudy Meoli	.30	.15	.09
189	Jim Brewer	.30	.15	.09
190	Tony Oliva	.50	.25	.15
191	Al Fitzmorris	.30	.15	.09
192	Mario Guerrero	.30	.15	.09
193	Tom Walker	.30	.15	.09
194	Darrell Porter	.30	.15	.09
195	Carlos May	.30	.15	.09
196	Jim Fregosi	.30	.15	.09
197a	Vicente Romo (Washington)	3.50	1.75	1.00
197b	Vicente Romo (San Diego)	.30	.15	.09
198	Dave Cash	.30	.15	.09
199	Mike Kekich	.30	.15	.09
200	Cesar Cedeno	.30	.15	.09
201	Batting Leaders (Rod Carew, Pete Rose)	4.00	2.00	1.25
202	Home Run Leaders (Reggie Jackson, Willie Stargell)	5.00	2.50	1.50
203	RBI Leaders (Reggie Jackson, Willie Stargell)	5.00	2.50	1.50
204	Stolen Base Leaders (Lou Brock, Tommy Harper)	1.50	.70	.45
205	Victory Leaders (Ron Bryant, Wilbur Wood)	1.50	.70	.45
206	Earned Run Average Leaders (Jim Palmer, Tom Seaver)	2.00	1.00	.60
207	Strikeout Leaders (Nolan Ryan, Tom Seaver)	15.00	7.50	4.50
208	Leading Firemen (John Hiller, Mike Marshall)	.50	.25	.15
209	Ted Sizemore	.30	.15	.09
210	Bill Singer	.30	.15	.09
211	Cubs Team	2.00	1.00	.60
212	Rollie Fingers	5.00	2.50	1.50
213	Dave Rader	.30	.15	.09
214	Billy Grabarkewitz	.30	.15	.09
215	Al Kaline	8.00	4.00	2.50
216	Ray Sadecki	.30	.15	.09
217	Tim Foli	.30	.15	.09
218	Johnny Briggs	.30	.15	.09
219	Doug Griffin	.30	.15	.09
220	Don Sutton	2.00	1.00	.60
221	White Sox Mgr./Coaches (Joe Lonnett, Jim Mahoney, Alex Monchak, Johnny Sain, Chuck Tanner)	.45	.25	.14
222	Ramon Hernandez	.30	.15	.09
223	Jeff Burroughs	.30	.15	.09
224	Roger Metzger	.30	.15	.09
225	Paul Splittorff	.30	.15	.09
226a	Washington Nat'l. Team	6.00	3.00	1.75
226b	Padres Team	2.00	1.00	.60
227	Mike Lum	.30	.15	.09
228	Ted Kubiak	.30	.15	.09
229	Fritz Peterson	.30	.15	.09
230	Tony Perez	1.25	.60	.40
231	Dick Tidrow	.30	.15	.09
232	Steve Brye	.30	.15	.09
233	Jim Barr	.30	.15	.09
234	John Milner	.30	.15	.09
235	Dave McNally	.30	.15	.09
236	Cardinals Mgr./Coaches (Vern Benson, George Kissell, Johnny Lewis, Red Schoendienst, Barney Schultz)	.75	.40	.25
237	Ken Brett	.30	.15	.09
238	Fran Healy	.30	.15	.09
239	Bill Russell	.30	.15	.09

240	Joe Coleman	.30	.15	.09
241a	Glenn Beckert (Washington)	3.50	1.75	1.00
241b	Glenn Beckert (San Diego)	3.50	1.75	1.00
242	Bill Gogolewski	.30	.15	.09
243	Bob Oliver	.30	.15	.09
244	Carl Morton	.30	.15	.09
245	Cleon Jones	.30	.15	.09
246	A's Team	2.00	1.00	.60
247	Rick Miller	.30	.15	.09
248	Tom Hall	.30	.15	.09
249	George Mitterwald	.30	.15	.09
250a	Willie McCovey (Washington)	25.00	12.50	7.50
250b	Willie McCovey (San Diego)	5.00	2.50	1.50
251	Graig Nettles	.30	.15	.09
252	*Dave Parker*	20.00	10.00	6.00
253	John Boccabella	.30	.15	.09
254	Stan Bahnsen	.30	.15	.09
255	Larry Bowa	.40	.20	.12
256	Tom Griffin	.30	.15	.09
257	Buddy Bell	.40	.20	.12
258	Jerry Morales	.30	.15	.09
259	Bob Reynolds	.30	.15	.09
260	Ted Simmons	.50	.25	.15
261	Jerry Bell	.30	.15	.09
262	Ed Kirkpatrick	.30	.15	.09
263	Checklist 133-264	1.50	.70	.45
264	Joe Rudi	.30	.15	.09
265	Tug McGraw	.30	.15	.09
266	Jim Northrup	.30	.15	.09
267	Andy Messersmith	.30	.15	.09
268	Tom Grieve	.30	.15	.09
269	Bob Johnson	.30	.15	.09
270	Ron Santo	.50	.25	.15
271	Bill Hands	.30	.15	.09
272	Paul Casanova	.30	.15	.09
273	Checklist 265-396	1.50	.70	.45
274	Fred Beene	.30	.15	.09
275	Ron Hunt	.30	.15	.09
276	Angels Mgr./Coaches (Tom Morgan, Salty Parker, Jimmie Reese, John Roseboro, Bobby Winkles)	.30	.15	.09
277	Gary Nolan	.30	.15	.09
278	Cookie Rojas	.30	.15	.09
279	Jim Crawford	.30	.15	.09
280	Carl Yastrzemski	15.00	7.50	4.50
281	Giants Team	2.00	1.00	.60
282	Doyle Alexander	.30	.15	.09
283	Mike Schmidt	75.00	37.00	22.00
284	Dave Duncan	.30	.15	.09
285	Reggie Smith	.30	.15	.09
286	Tony Muser	.30	.15	.09
287	Clay Kirby	.30	.15	.09
288	*Gorman Thomas*	.50	.25	.15
289	Rick Auerbach	.30	.15	.09
290	Vida Blue	.40	.20	.12
291	Don Hahn	.30	.15	.09
292	Chuck Seelbach	.30	.15	.09
293	Milt May	.30	.15	.09
294	Steve Foucault	.30	.15	.09
295	Rick Monday	.30	.15	.09
296	Ray Corbin	.30	.15	.09
297	Hal Breeden	.30	.15	.09
298	Roric Harrison	.30	.15	.09
299	Gene Michael	.30	.15	.09
300	Pete Rose	15.00	7.50	4.50
301	Bob Montgomery	.30	.15	.09
302	Rudy May	.30	.15	.09
303	George Hendrick	.30	.15	.09
304	Don Wilson	.30	.15	.09
305	Tito Fuentes	.30	.15	.09
306	Orioles Mgr./Coaches (George Bamberger, Jim Frey, Billy Hunter, George Staller, Earl Weaver)	1.50	.70	.45
307	Luis Melendez	.30	.15	.09
308	Bruce Dal Canton	.30	.15	.09
309a	Dave Roberts (Washington)	3.50	1.75	1.00
309b	Dave Roberts (San Diego)	.30	.15	.09
310	Terry Forster	.30	.15	.09
311	Jerry Grote	.30	.15	.09
312	Deron Johnson	.30	.15	.09
313	Berry Lersch	.30	.15	.09
314	Brewers Team	2.00	1.00	.60
315	Ron Cey	.60	.30	.20
316	Jim Perry	.30	.15	.09
317	Richie Zisk	.30	.15	.09
318	Jim Merritt	.30	.15	.09
319	Randy Hundley	.30	.15	.09
320	Dusty Baker	.40	.20	.12
321	Steve Braun	.30	.15	.09
322	Ernie McAnally	.30	.15	.09
323	Richie Scheinblum	.30	.15	.09
324	Steve Kline	.30	.15	.09
325	Tommy Harper	.30	.15	.09
326	Reds Mgr./Coaches (Sparky Anderson, Alex Grammas, Ted Kluszewski, George Scherger, Larry Shepard)	1.50	.70	.45
327	Tom Timmermann	.30	.15	.09
328	Skip Jutze	.30	.15	.09
329	Mark Belanger	.30	.15	.09
330	Juan Marichal	4.00	2.00	1.25
331	All-Star Catchers (Johnny Bench, Carlton Fisk)	5.00	2.50	1.50
332	All-Star First Basemen (Hank Aaron, Dick Allen)	5.00	2.50	1.50
333	All-Star Second Basemen (Rod Carew, Joe Morgan)	3.00	1.50	.90
334	All-Star Third Basemen (Brooks Robinson, Ron Santo)	3.00	1.50	.90
335	All-Star Shortstops (Bert Campaneris, Chris Speier)	.40	.20	.12
336	All-Star Left Fielders (Bobby Murcer, Pete Rose)	2.50	1.25	.70
337	All-Star Center Fielders (Cesar Cedeno, Amos Otis)	.40	.20	.12
338	All-Star Right Fielders (Reggie Jackson, Billy Williams)	5.00	2.50	1.50
339	All-Star Pitchers (Catfish Hunter, Rick Wise)	.80	.40	.25
340	Thurman Munson	5.00	2.50	1.50
341	*Dan Driessen*	.30	.15	.09
342	Jim Lonborg	.30	.15	.09
343	Royals Team	2.00	1.00	.60
344	Mike Caldwell	.30	.15	.09
345	Bill North	.30	.15	.09
346	Ron Reed	.30	.15	.09
347	Sandy Alomar	.30	.15	.09
348	Pete Richert	.30	.15	.09
349	John Vukovich	.30	.15	.09
350	Bob Gibson	6.00	3.00	1.75
351	Dwight Evans	5.00	2.50	1.50
352	Bill Stoneman	.30	.15	.09
353	Rich Coggins	.30	.15	.09
354	Cubs Mgr./Coaches (Hank Aguirre, Whitey Lockman, Jim Marshall, J.C. Martin, Al Spangler)	.30	.15	.09
355	Dave Nelson	.30	.15	.09
356	Jerry Koosman	.30	.15	.09
357	Buddy Bradford	.30	.15	.09
358	Dal Maxvill	.30	.15	.09
359	Brent Strom	.30	.15	.09
360	Greg Luzinski	.50	.25	.15
361	Don Carrithers	.30	.15	.09
362	Hal King	.30	.15	.09
363	Yankees Team	3.00	1.50	.90
364a	Cito Gaston (Washington)	4.50	2.25	1.25
364b	Cito Gaston (San Diego)	.75	.40	.25
365	Steve Busby	.30	.15	.09
366	Larry Hisle	.30	.15	.09
367	Norm Cash	.50	.25	.15
368	Manny Mota	.30	.15	.09
369	Paul Lindblad	.30	.15	.09
370	Bob Watson	.30	.15	.09
371	Jim Slaton	.30	.15	.09
372	Ken Reitz	.30	.15	.09
373	John Curtis	.30	.15	.09
374	Marty Perez	.30	.15	.09
375	Earl Williams	.30	.15	.09
376	Jorge Orta	.30	.15	.09
377	Ron Woods	.30	.15	.09
378	Burt Hooton	.30	.15	.09
379	Rangers Mgr./Coaches (Art Fowler, Frank Lucchesi, Billy Martin, Jackie Moore, Charlie Silvera)	1.00	.50	.30
380	Bud Harrelson	.30	.15	.09
381	Charlie Sands	.30	.15	.09
382	Bob Moose	.30	.15	.09
383	Phillies Team	2.00	1.00	.60
384	Chris Chambliss	.30	.15	.09
385	Don Gullett	.30	.15	.09
386	Gary Matthews	.30	.15	.09
387a	Rich Morales (Washington)	3.50	1.75	1.00
387b	Rich Morales (San Diego)	.30	.15	.09
388	Phil Roof	.30	.15	.09
389	Gates Brown	.30	.15	.09
390	Lou Piniella	.30	.15	.09
391	Billy Champion	.30	.15	.09
392	Dick Green	.30	.15	.09
393	Orlando Pena	.30	.15	.09
394	Ken Henderson	.30	.15	.09
395	Doug Rader	.30	.15	.09
396	Tommy Davis	.30	.15	.09
397	George Stone	.30	.15	.09
398	Duke Sims	.30	.15	.09
399	Mike Paul	.30	.15	.09
400	Harmon Killebrew	5.00	2.50	1.50
401	Elliott Maddox	.30	.15	.09
402	Jim Rooker	.30	.15	.09
403	Red Sox Mgr./Coaches (Don Bryant, Darrell Johnson, Eddie Popowski, Lee Stange, Don Zimmer)	.45	.25	.14
404	Jim Howarth	.30	.15	.09
405	Ellie Rodriguez	.30	.15	.09
406	Steve Arlin	.30	.15	.09
407	Jim Wohlford	.30	.15	.09
408	Charlie Hough	.40	.20	.12
409	Ike Brown	.30	.15	.09
410	Pedro Borbon	.30	.15	.09
411	Frank Baker	.30	.15	.09
412	Chuck Taylor	.30	.15	.09
413	Don Money	.30	.15	.09
414	Checklist 397-528	1.50	.70	.45
415	Gary Gentry	.30	.15	.09
416	White Sox Team	2.00	1.00	.60
417	Rich Folkers	.30	.15	.09
418	Walt Williams	.30	.15	.09
419	Wayne Twitchell	.30	.15	.09
420	Ray Fosse	.30	.15	.09
421	Dan Fife	.30	.15	.09
422	Gonzalo Marquez	.30	.15	.09
423	Fred Stanley	.30	.15	.09
424	Jim Beauchamp	.30	.15	.09
425	Pete Broberg	.30	.15	.09
426	Rennie Stennett	.30	.15	.09
427	Bobby Bolin	.30	.15	.09
428	Gary Sutherland	.30	.15	.09
429	Dick Lange	.30	.15	.09
430	Matty Alou	.30	.15	.09
431	*Gene Garber*	.30	.15	.09
432	Chris Arnold	.30	.15	.09
433	Lerrin LaGrow	.30	.15	.09
434	Ken McMullen	.30	.15	.09
435	Dave Concepcion	.50	.25	.15
436	Don Hood	.30	.15	.09
437	Jim Lyttle	.30	.15	.09
438	Ed Herrmann	.30	.15	.09
439	Norm Miller	.30	.15	.09
440	Jim Kaat	1.25	.60	.40
441	Tom Ragland	.30	.15	.09
442	Alan Foster	.30	.15	.09
443	Tom Hutton	.30	.15	.09
444	Vic Davalillo	.30	.15	.09
445	George Medich	.30	.15	.09
446	Len Randle	.30	.15	.09
447	Twins Mgr./Coaches (Vern Morgan, Frank Quilici, Bob Rodgers, Ralph Rowe)	.30	.15	.09
448	Ron Hodges	.30	.15	.09
449	Tom McCraw	.30	.15	.09
450	Rich Hebner	.30	.15	.09
451	Tommy John	1.00	.50	.30
452	Gene Hiser	.30	.15	.09
453	Balor Moore	.30	.15	.09
454	Kurt Bevacqua	.30	.15	.09
455	Tom Bradley	.30	.15	.09
456	*Dave Winfield*	225.00	112.00	67.00
457	Chuck Goggin	.30	.15	.09
458	Jim Ray	.30	.15	.09
459	Reds Team	.90	.45	.25
460	Boog Powell	.75	.40	.25
461	John Odom	.30	.15	.09
462	Luis Alvarado	.30	.15	.09
463	Pat Dobson	.30	.15	.09
464	Jose Cruz	.60	.30	.20
465	Dick Bosman	.30	.15	.09
466	Dick Billings	.30	.15	.09
467	Winston Llenas	.30	.15	.09
468	Pepe Frias	.30	.15	.09
469	Joe Decker	.30	.15	.09
470	A.L. Playoffs (Reggie Jackson)	6.00	3.00	1.75
471	N.L. Playoffs	.80	.40	.25
472	World Series Game 1	.80	.40	.25
473	World Series Game 2 (Willie Mays)	5.00	2.50	1.50
474	World Series Game 3	.80	.40	.25
475	World Series Game 4	.80	.40	.25
476	World Series Game 5	.80	.40	.25
477	World Series Game 6 (Reggie Jackson)	8.00	4.00	2.50
478	World Series Game 7	.80	.40	.25
479	World Series Summary (A's Celebrate)	.80	.40	.25
480	Willie Crawford	.30	.15	.09
481	Jerry Terrell	.30	.15	.09
482	Bob Didier	.30	.15	.09
483	Braves Team	2.00	1.00	.60
484	Carmen Fanzone	.30	.15	.09
485	Felipe Alou	.90	.45	.25
486	Steve Stone	.30	.15	.09
487	Ted Martinez	.30	.15	.09
488	Andy Etchebarren	.30	.15	.09
489	Pirates Mgr./Coaches (Don Leppert, Bill Mazeroski, Danny Murtaugh, Don Osborn, Bob Skinner)	.75	.40	.25
490	Vada Pinson	.60	.30	.20
491	Roger Nelson	.30	.15	.09
492	Mike Rogodzinski	.30	.15	.09
493	Joe Hoerner	.30	.15	.09
494	Ed Goodson	.30	.15	.09
495	Dick McAuliffe	.30	.15	.09
496	Tom Murphy	.30	.15	.09
497	Bobby Mitchell	.30	.15	.09
498	Pat Corrales	.30	.15	.09
499	Rusty Torres	.30	.15	.09
500	Lee May	.30	.15	.09
501	Eddie Leon	.30	.15	.09
502	Dave LaRoche	.30	.15	.09
503	Eric Soderholm	.30	.15	.09
504	Joe Niekro	.30	.15	.09
505	Bill Buckner	.30	.15	.09
506	Ed Farmer	.30	.15	.09
507	Larry Stahl	.30	.15	.09
508	Expos Team	2.00	1.00	.60
509	Jesse Jefferson	.30	.15	.09
510	Wayne Garrett	.30	.15	.09
511	Toby Harrah	.30	.15	.09
512	Joe Lahoud	.30	.15	.09
513	Jim Campanis	.30	.15	.09
514	Paul Schaal	.30	.15	.09
515	Willie Montanez	.30	.15	.09
516	Horacio Pina	.30	.15	.09
517	Mike Hegan	.30	.15	.09
518	Derrel Thomas	.30	.15	.09
519	Bill Sharp	.30	.15	.09
520	Tim McCarver	.45	.25	.14
521	Indians Mgr./Coaches (Ken Aspromonte, Clay Bryant, Tony Pacheco)	.30	.15	.09
522	J.R. Richard	.30	.15	.09
523	Cecil Cooper	.50	.25	.15
524	Bill Plummer	.30	.15	.09
525	Clyde Wright	.30	.15	.09
526	Frank Tepedino	.30	.15	.09
527	Bobby Darwin	.30	.15	.09
528	Bill Bonham	.30	.15	.09
529	Horace Clarke	.30	.15	.09
530	Mickey Stanley	.30	.15	.09
531	Expos Mgr./Coaches (Dave Bristol, Larry Doby, Gene Mauch, Cal McLish, Jerry Zimmerman)	.40	.20	.12
532	Skip Lockwood	.30	.15	.09
533	Mike Phillips	.30	.15	.09
534	Eddie Watt	.30	.15	.09
535	Bob Tolan	.30	.15	.09
536	Duffy Dyer	.30	.15	.09
537	Steve Mingori	.30	.15	.09
538	Cesar Tovar	.30	.15	.09
539	Lloyd Allen	.30	.15	.09
540	Bob Robertson	.30	.15	.09
541	Indians Team	2.00	1.00	.60
542	Rich Gossage	2.00	1.00	.60
543	Danny Cater	.30	.15	.09
544	Ron Schueler	.30	.15	.09
545	Billy Conigliaro	.30	.15	.09
546	Mike Corkins	.30	.15	.09
547	Glenn Borgmann	.30	.15	.09
548	Sonny Siebert	.30	.15	.09
549	Mike Jorgensen	.30	.15	.09
550	Sam McDowell	.30	.15	.09
551	Von Joshua	.30	.15	.09
552	Denny Doyle	.30	.15	.09
553	Jim Willoughby	.30	.15	.09
554	Tim Johnson	.30	.15	.09
555	Woodie Fryman	.30	.15	.09
556	Dave Campbell	.30	.15	.09
557	Jim McGlothlin	.30	.15	.09
558	Bill Fahey	.30	.15	.09
559	Darrel Chaney	.30	.15	.09
560	Mike Cuellar	.30	.15	.09
561	Ed Kranepool	.30	.15	.09

562	Jack Aker	.30	.15	.09
563	Hal McRae	.40	.20	.12
564	Mike Ryan	.30	.15	.09
565	Milt Wilcox	.30	.15	.09
566	Jackie Hernandez	.30	.15	.09
567	Red Sox Team	3.00	1.50	.90
568	Mike Torrez	.30	.15	.09
569	Rick Dempsey	.30	.15	.09
570	Ralph Garr	.30	.15	.09
571	Rich Hand	.30	.15	.09
572	Enzo Hernandez	.30	.15	.09
573	Mike Adams	.30	.15	.09
574	Bill Parsons	.30	.15	.09
575	Steve Garvey	7.00	3.50	2.00
576	Scipio Spinks	.30	.15	.09
577	Mike Sadek	.30	.15	.09
578	Ralph Houk	.30	.15	.09
579	Cecil Upshaw	.30	.15	.09
580	Jim Spencer	.30	.15	.09
581	Fred Norman	.30	.15	.09
582	*Bucky Dent*	.50	.25	.15
583	Marty Pattin	.30	.15	.09
584	Ken Rudolph	.30	.15	.09
585	Merv Rettenmund	.30	.15	.09
586	Jack Brohamer	.30	.15	.09
587	*Larry Christenson*	.30	.15	.09
588	Hal Lanier	.30	.15	.09
589	Boots Day	.30	.15	.09
590	Rogelio Moret	.30	.15	.09
591	Sonny Jackson	.30	.15	.09
592	Ed Bane	.30	.15	.09
593	Steve Yeager	.30	.15	.09
594	Leroy Stanton	.30	.15	.09
595	Steve Blass	.30	.15	.09
596	Rookie Pitchers (*Wayne Garland*, Fred Holdsworth, Mark Littell, Dick Pole)	.30	.15	.09
597	Rookie Shortstops (Dave Chalk, John Gamble, Pete Mackanin, Manny Trillo)	.80	.40	.25
598	Rookie Outfielders (Dave Augustine, Ken Griffey, Steve Ontiveros, Jim Tyrone)	15.00	7.50	4.50
599a	Rookie Pitchers (Ron Diorio) (Dave Freisleben) (Freisleben-Washington) (Frank Riccelli) (Greg Shanahan)	.80	.40	.25
599b	Rookie Pitchers (Ron Diorio) (Dave Freisleben) (Freisleben-San (Frank Riccelli) (Greg Shanahan)	3.50	1.75	1.00
599c	Rookie Pitchers (Ron Diorio) (Freisleben-San Diego	6.00	3.00	1.75
	(Dave Freisleben) (Freisleben-San Diego small print)	6.00	3.00	1.75
	(Frank Riccelli) (Freisleben-San	6.00	3.00	1.75
	(Greg Shanahan) (Freisleben-San	6.00	3.00	1.75
600	Rookie Infielders (Ron Cash, Jim Cox, Bill Madlock, Reggie J. Sanders)	5.00	2.50	1.50
601	Rookie Outfielders (Ed Armbrister, Rich Bladt, Brian Downing, Bake McBride)	4.50	2.25	1.25
602	Rookie Pitchers (Glenn Abbott, Rick Henninger, Craig Swan, Dan Vossler)	.30	.15	.09
603	Rookie Catchers (Barry Foote, Tom Lundstedt, Charlie Moore, Sergio Robles)	.30	.15	.09
604	Rookie Infielders (Terry Hughes, John Knox, Andy Thornton, Frank White)	4.00	2.00	1.25
605	Rookie Pitchers (Vic Albury, Ken Frailing, Kevin Kobel, Frank Tanana)	4.00	2.00	1.25
606	Rookie Outfielders (Jim Fuller, Wilbur Howard, Tommy Smith, Otto Velez)	.30	.15	.09
607	Rookie Shortstops (Leo Foster, Tom Heintzelman, Dave Rosello, Frank Taveras)	.30	.15	.09
608a	Rookie Pitchers (Bob Apodaco) (Dick Baney) (John D'Acquisto) (Mike Wallace)	2.00	1.00	.60
608b	Rookie Pitchers (Bob Apodaca) (Dick Baney) (John D'Acquisto) (Mike Wallace)	.30	.15	.09
609	Rico Petrocelli	.30	.15	.09
610	Dave Kingman	.45	.25	.14
611	Rick Stelmaszek	.30	.15	.09
612	Luke Walker	.30	.15	.09
613	Dan Monzon	.30	.15	.09
614	Adrian Devine	.30	.15	.09
615	Johnny Jeter	.30	.15	.09
616	Larry Gura	.30	.15	.09
617	Ted Ford	.30	.15	.09
618	Jim Mason	.30	.15	.09
619	Mike Anderson	.30	.15	.09
620	Al Downing	.30	.15	.09
621	Bernie Carbo	.30	.15	.09
622	Phil Gagliano	.30	.15	.09
623	Celerino Sanchez	.30	.15	.09
624	Bob Miller	.30	.15	.09
625	Ollie Brown	.30	.15	.09
626	Pirates Team	2.00	1.00	.60
627	Carl Taylor	.30	.15	.09
628	Ivan Murrell	.30	.15	.09
629	Rusty Staub	.60	.30	.20
630	Tommie Agee	.30	.15	.09
631	Steve Barber	.30	.15	.09
632	George Culver	.30	.15	.09
633	Dave Hamilton	.30	.15	.09
634	Braves Mgr./Coaches (Jim Busby, Eddie Mathews, Connie Ryan, Ken Silvestri, Herm Starrette)	1.50	.70	.45
635	John Edwards	.30	.15	.09
636	Dave Goltz	.30	.15	.09
637	Checklist 529-660	1.50	.70	.45
638	Ken Sanders	.30	.15	.09
639	Joe Lovitto	.30	.15	.09
640	Milt Pappas	.30	.15	.09
641	Chuck Brinkman	.30	.15	.09
642	Terry Harmon	.30	.15	.09
643	Dodgers Team	3.00	1.50	.90
644	Wayne Granger	.30	.15	.09
645	Ken Boswell	.30	.15	.09
646	George Foster	.75	.40	.25
647	*Juan Beniquez*	.30	.15	.09
648	Terry Crowley	.30	.15	.09
649	Fernando Gonzalez	.30	.15	.09
650	Mike Epstein	.30	.15	.09
651	Leron Lee	.30	.15	.09
652	Gail Hopkins	.30	.15	.09
653	Bob Stinson	.30	.15	.09
654a	Jesus Alou (no position)	5.00	2.50	1.50
654b	Jesus Alou ("Outfield")	.30	.15	.09
655	Mike Tyson	.30	.15	.09
656	Adrian Garrett	.30	.15	.09
657	Jim Shellenback	.30	.15	.09
658	Lee Lacy	.30	.15	.09
659	Joe Lis	.30	.15	.09
660	Larry Dierker	.30	.15	.09

1974 Topps Deckle Edge

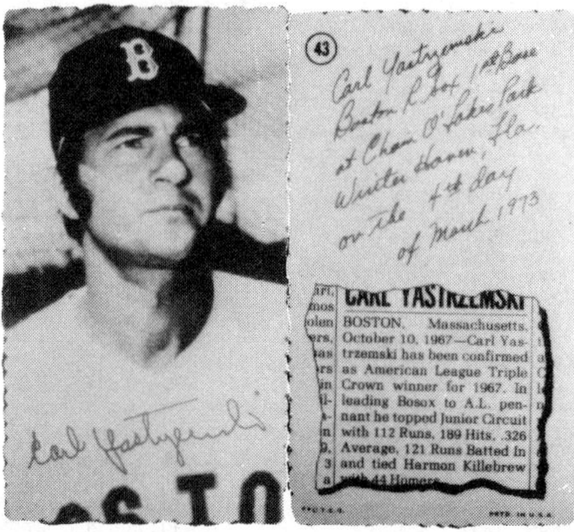

These borderless 2-7/8" by 5" cards feature a black and white photograph with a blue facsimile autograph on the front. The backs have in handwritten script the player's name, team, position and the date and location of the picture. Below is a mock newspaper clipping providing a detail from the player's career. The cards take their names from their specially cut edges which give them a scalloped appearance. The 72-card set was a test issue and received rather limited distribution around Massachusetts. The cards were sold three per pack for five cents, without gum.

		NR MT	EX	VG
	Complete Set:	2900.	1450.	900.00
	Common Player:	15.00	7.50	4.50
1	Amos Otis	15.00	7.50	4.50
2	Darrell Evans	25.00	12.50	7.50
3	Bob Gibson	125.00	62.50	37.50
4	David Nelson	15.00	7.50	4.50
5	Steve Carlton	150.00	75.00	45.00
6	Catfish Hunter	100.00	50.00	30.00
7	Thurman Munson	75.00	37.00	22.00
8	Bob Grich	25.00	12.50	7.50
9	Tom Seaver	150.00	75.00	45.00
10	Ted Simmons	25.00	12.50	7.50
11	Bobby Valentine	15.00	7.50	4.50
12	Don Sutton	25.00	12.50	7.50
13	Wilbur Wood	15.00	7.50	4.50
14	Doug Rader	15.00	7.50	4.50
15	Chris Chambliss	15.00	7.50	4.50
16	Pete Rose	200.00	100.00	60.00
17	John Hiller	15.00	7.50	4.50
18	Burt Hooton	15.00	7.50	4.50
19	Tim Foli	15.00	7.50	4.50
20	Lou Brock	100.00	50.00	30.00
21	Ron Bryant	15.00	7.50	4.50
22	Manuel Sanguillen	15.00	7.50	4.50
23	Bobby Tolan	15.00	7.50	4.50
24	Greg Luzinski	25.00	12.50	7.50
25	Brooks Robinson	125.00	62.50	37.50
26	Felix Millan	15.00	7.50	4.50
27	Luis Tiant	25.00	12.50	7.50
28	Willie McCovey	125.00	62.50	37.50
29	Chris Speier	15.00	7.50	4.50
30	George Scott	15.00	7.50	4.50
31	Willie Stargell	100.00	50.00	30.00
32	Rod Carew	125.00	62.50	37.50
33	Charlie Spikes	15.00	7.50	4.50
34	Nate Colbert	15.00	7.50	4.50
35	Richie Hebner	15.00	7.50	4.50
36	Bobby Bonds	25.00	12.50	7.50
37	Buddy Bell	25.00	12.50	7.50
38	Claude Osteen	15.00	7.50	4.50
39	Rich Allen	40.00	20.00	12.00
40	Bill Russell	15.00	7.50	4.50
41	Nolan Ryan	400.00	200.00	120.00
42	Willie Davis	25.00	12.50	7.50
43	Carl Yastrzemski	125.00	62.50	37.50
44	Jon Matlack	15.00	7.50	4.50
45	Jim Palmer	100.00	50.00	30.00
46	Bert Campaneris	25.00	12.50	7.50
47	Bert Blyleven	25.00	12.50	7.50
48	Jeff Burroughs	15.00	7.50	4.50
49	Jim Colborn	15.00	7.50	4.50
50	Dave Johnson	25.00	12.50	7.50
51	John Mayberry	15.00	7.50	4.50
52	Don Kessinger	15.00	7.50	4.50
53	Joe Coleman	15.00	7.50	4.50
54	Tony Perez	60.00	30.00	18.00
55	Jose Cardenal	15.00	7.50	4.50
56	Paul Splittorff	15.00	7.50	4.50
57	Henry Aaron	250.00	125.00	75.00
58	David May	15.00	7.50	4.50
59	Fergie Jenkins	100.00	50.00	30.00
60	Ron Blomberg	15.00	7.50	4.50
61	Reggie Jackson	250.00	125.00	75.00
62	Tony Oliva	40.00	20.00	12.00
63	Bobby Murcer	25.00	12.50	7.50
64	Carlton Fisk	50.00	25.00	15.00
65	Steve Rogers	15.00	7.50	4.50
66	Frank Robinson	125.00	62.50	37.50
67	Joe Ferguson	15.00	7.50	4.50
68	Bill Melton	15.00	7.50	4.50
69	Bob Watson	15.00	7.50	4.50
70	Larry Bowa	25.00	12.50	7.50
71	Johnny Bench	150.00	75.00	45.00
72	Willie Horton	15.00	7.50	4.50

1974 Topps Puzzles

One of many test issues by Topps in the mid-1970s, the 12-player jigsaw puzzle set was an innovation which never caught on with collectors. The 40-piece puzzles (4-3/4" by 7-1/2") feature color photos with a decorative lozenge at bottom naming the player, team and position. The puzzles came in individual wrappers.

		NR MT	EX	VG
	Complete Set:	1000.	500.00	300.00
	Common Player:	35.00	17.50	10.50
(1)	Hank Aaron	125.00	62.00	37.00
(2)	Dick Allen	50.00	25.00	15.00
(3)	Johnny Bench	110.00	55.00	33.00
(4)	Bobby Bonds	50.00	25.00	15.00
(5)	Bob Gibson	100.00	50.00	30.00
(6)	Reggie Jackson	150.00	75.00	45.00
(7)	Bobby Murcer	35.00	17.50	10.50
(8)	Jim Palmer	110.00	55.00	33.00
(9)	Nolan Ryan	200.00	100.00	60.00
(10)	Tom Seaver	110.00	55.00	33.00
(11)	Willie Stargell	100.00	50.00	30.00
(12)	Carl Yastrzemski	110.00	55.00	33.00

1974 Topps Stamps

Topps continued to market baseball stamps in 1974 through the release of 240 unnumbered stamps featuring color player portraits. The player's name, team and position are found in an oval at the bottom of the 1" by 1-1/2" stamps. The stamps, sold separately rather than issued as an insert, came in strips of six which were then pasted in an appropriate team album designed to hold 10 stamps.

	NR MT	EX	VG
Complete Sheet Set:	150.00	75.00	45.00
Common Sheet:	2.00	1.00	.60
Complete Stamp Album Set:	100.00	50.00	30.00
Single Stamp Album:	4.00	2.00	1.20

(1) Hank Aaron, Luis Aparicio, Bob Bailey, Johnny Bench, Ron Blomberg, Bob Boone, Lou Brock, Bud Harrelson, Randy Jones, Dave Rader, Nolan Ryan, Joe Torre 10.00 5.00 3.00

(2) Buddy Bell, Steve Braun, Jerry Grote, Tommy Helms, Bill Lee, Mike Lum, Dave May, Brooks Robinson, Bill Russell, Del Unser, Wilbur Wood, Carl Yastrzemski 10.00 5.00 3.00

(3) Jerry Bell, Jerry Bell, Jim Colborn, Toby Harrah, Ken Henderson, John Hiller, Randy Hundley, Don Kessinger, Jerry Koosman, Dave Lopes, Felix Millan, Thurman Munson, Ted Simmons 6.00 3.00 1.75

(4) Jerry Bell, Bill Buckner, Jim Colborn, Ken Henderson, Don Kessinger, Felix Millan, George Mitterwald, Dave Roberts, Ted Simmons, Jim Slaton, Charlie Spikes, Paul Splittorff 2.00 1.00 .60

(5) Glenn Beckert, Jim Bibby, Bill Buckner, Jim Lonborg, George Mitterwald, Dave Parker, Dave Roberts, Jim Slaton, Reggie Smith, Charlie Spikes, Paul Splittorff, Bob Watson 6.00 3.00 1.75

(6) Paul Blair, Bobby Bonds, Ed Brinkman, Norm Cash, Mike Epstein, Tommy Harper, Mike Marshall, Phil Niekro, Cookie Rojas, George Scott, Mel Stottlemyre, Jim Wynn 6.00 3.00 1.75

(7) Jack Billingham, Reggie Cleveland, Bobby Darwin, Dave Duncan, Tim Foli, Ed Goodson, Cleon Jones, Mickey Lolich, George Medich, John Milner, Rick Monday, Bobby Murcer 2.00 1.00 .60

(8) Steve Carlton, Orlando Cepeda, Joe Decker, Reggie Jackson, Dave Johnson, John Mayberry, Bill Melton, Roger Metzger, Dave Nelson, Jerry Reuss, Jim Spencer, Bobby Valentine 10.00 5.00 3.00

(9) Dan Driessen, Pedro Garcia, Grant Jackson, Al Kaline, Clay Kirby, Carlos May, Willie Montanez, Rogelio Moret, Jim Palmer, Doug Rader, J. R. Richard, Frank Robinson 6.00 3.00 1.75

(10) Pedro Garcia, Ralph Garr, Wayne Garrett, Ron Hunt, Al Kaline, Fred Kendall, Carlos May, Jim Palmer, Doug Rader, Frank Robinson, Rick Wise, Richie Zisk 6.00 3.00 1.75

(11) Dusty Baker, Larry Bowa, Steve Busby, Chris Chambliss, Dock Ellis, Cesar Geronimo, Fran Healy, Deron Johnson, Jorge Orta, Joe Rudi, Mickey Stanley, Rennie Stennett 6.00 3.00 1.75

(12) Bob Coluccio, Ray Corbin, John Ellis, Oscar Gamble, Dave Giusti, Bill Greif, Alex Johnson, Mike Jorgensen, Andy Messersmith, Elias Sosa, Willie Stargell 6.00 3.00 1.75

(13) Ron Bryant, Nate Colbert, Jose Cruz, Dan Driessen, Billy Grabarkewitz, Don Gullett, Willie Horton, Grant Jackson, Clay Kirby, Willie Montanez, Rogelio Moret, J. R. Richard 2.00 1.00 .60

(14) Carlton Fisk, Bill Freehan, Bobby Grich, Vic Harris, George Hendrick, Ed Herrmann, Jim Holt, Ken Holtzman, Fergie Jenkins, Lou Piniella, Steve Rogers, Ken Singleton 6.00 3.00 1.75

(15) Stan Bahnsen, Sal Bando, Mark Belanger, David Clyde, Willie Crawford, Burt Hooton, Jon Matlack, Tim McCarver, Joe Morgan, Gene Tenace, Dick Tidrow, Dave Winfield 8.00 4.00 2.50

(16) Hank Aaron, Stan Bahnsen, Bob Bailey, Johnny Bench, Bob Boone, Joe Matlack, Tim McCarver, Joe Morgan, Dave Rader, Gene Tenace, Dick Tidrow, Joe Torre 8.00 4.00 2.50

(17) John Boccabella, Frank Duffy, Darrell Evans, Sparky Lyle, Lee May, Don Money, Bill North, Ted Sizemore, Chris Speier, Wayne Twitchell, Billy Williams, Earl Williams 2.00 1.00 .60

(18) John Boccabella, Bobby Darwin, Frank Duffy, Dave Duncan, Tim Foli, Cleon Jones, Mickey Lolich, Sparky Lyle, Lee May, Rick Monday, Bill North, Billy Williams 2.00 1.00 .60

(19) Don Baylor, Vida Blue, Tom Bradley, Jose Cardenal, Ron Cey, Greg Luzinski, Johnny Oates, Tony Oliva, Al Oliver, Tony Perez, Darrell Porter, Roy White 6.00 3.00 1.75

(20) Pedro Borbon, Rod Carew, Roric Harrison, Jim Hunter, Ed Kirkpatrick, Garry Maddox, Gene Michael, Rick Miller, Claude Osteen, Amos Otis, Rich Reuschel, Mike Tyson 8.00 4.00 2.50

(21) Sandy Alomar, Bert Campaneris, Tommy Davis, Joe Ferguson, Tito Fuentes, Jerry Morales, Carl Morton, Gaylord Perry, Vada Pinson, Dave Roberts, Ellie Rodriguez 6.00 3.00 1.75

(22) Dick Allen, Jeff Burroughs, Joe Coleman, Terry Forster, Bob Gibson, Harmon Killebrew, Tug McGraw, Bob Oliver, Steve Renko, Pete Rose, Luis Tiant, Otto Velez 13.00 6.50 4.00

(23) Johnny Briggs, Willie Davis, Jim Fregosi, Rich Hebner, Pat Kelly, Dave Kingman, Willie McCovey, Graig Nettles, Freddie Patek, Marty Pattin, Manny Sanguillen, Richie Scheinblum 8.00 4.00 2.50

(24) Bert Blyleven, Nelson Briles, Cesar Cedeno, Ron Fairly, Johnny Grubb, Dave McNally, Aurelio Rodriguez, Ron Santo, Tom Seaver, Bill Singer, Bill Sudakis, Don Sutton 10.00 5.00 3.00

1974 Topps Team Checklists

This set is a repeat of the 1973 mystery set in the form of 24 unnumbered 2-1/2" by 3-1/2" checklist cards. As with the 1973 set, the 1974s feature a team name on the front at the top with a white panel and a number of facsimile autographs below. Backs

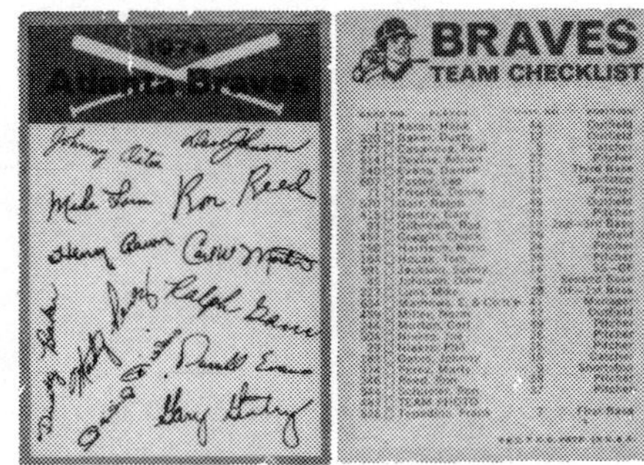

feature the team name and a checklist. The big difference between the 1973 and 1974 checklists is that the 1973s have blue borders while the 1974s have a red border. The 1974s were inserted into packages of the regular issue Topps cards.

		NR MT	EX	VG
Complete Set:		12.00	6.00	3.50
Common Checklist:		.50	.25	.15
(1)	Atlanta Braves	.50	.25	.15
(2)	Baltimore Orioles	.50	.25	.15
(3)	Boston Red Sox	.50	.25	.15
(4)	California Angels	.50	.25	.15
(5)	Chicago Cubs	.50	.25	.15
(6)	Chicago White Sox	.50	.25	.15
(7)	Cincinnati Reds	.50	.25	.15
(8)	Cleveland Indians	.50	.25	.15
(9)	Detroit Tigers	.50	.25	.15
(10)	Houston Astros	.50	.25	.15
(11)	Kansas City Royals	.50	.25	.15
(12)	Los Angeles Dodgers	.50	.25	.15
(13)	Milwaukee Brewers	.50	.25	.15
(14)	Minnesota Twins	.50	.25	.15
(15)	Montreal Expos	.50	.25	.15
(16)	New York Mets	.50	.25	.15
(17)	New York Yankees	.50	.25	.15
(18)	Oakland A's	.50	.25	.15
(19)	Philadelphia Phillies	.50	.25	.15
(20)	Pittsburgh Pirates	.50	.25	.15
(21)	St. Louis Cardinals	.50	.25	.15
(22)	San Diego Padres	.50	.25	.15
(23)	San Francisco Giants	.50	.25	.15
(24)	Texas Rangers	.50	.25	.15

1974 Topps Traded

Appearing late in the season, these 2-1/2" by 3-1/2" cards are basically the same as the regular issue Topps cards. The major change was that a big red panel with the word "Traded" was added below the player photo. Backs feature a "Baseball News" newspaper which contains the details of the trade. Card numbers correspond to the player's regular card number in 1974 except that the suffix "T" is added after the number. The set consists of 43 player cards and a checklist. In most cases, Topps did not obtain pictures of the players in their new uniforms. Instead the Topps artists simply provided the needed changes to existing photos.

		NR MT	EX	VG
Complete Set (44):		12.00	6.00	3.50
Common Player:		.25	.20	.10
23T	Craig Robinson	.25	.20	.10
42T	Claude Osteen	.25	.20	.10
43T	Jim Wynn	.40	.30	.15
51T	Bobby Heise	.25	.20	.10
59T	Ross Grimsley	.25	.20	.10
62T	Bob Locker	.25	.20	.10
63T	Bill Sudakis	.25	.20	.10
73T	Mike Marshall	.60	.45	.25
123T	Nelson Briles	.25	.20	.10
139T	Aurelio Monteagudo	.25	.20	.10
151T	Diego Segui	.25	.20	.10
165T	Willie Davis	.40	.30	.15
175T	Reggie Cleveland	.25	.20	.10
182T	Lindy McDaniel	.25	.20	.10
186T	Fred Scherman	.25	.20	.10
249T	George Mitterwald	.25	.20	.10
262T	Ed Kirkpatrick	.25	.20	.10
269T	Bob Johnson	.25	.20	.10
270T	Ron Santo	2.00	1.50	.80
313T	Barry Lersch	.12	.09	.05
319T	Randy Hundley	.25	.20	.10
330T	Juan Marichal	3.00	2.25	1.25
348T	Pete Richert	.25	.20	.10
373T	John Curtis	.25	.20	.10
390T	Lou Piniella	1.00	.70	.40
428T	Gary Sutherland	.25	.20	.10
454T	Kurt Bevacqua	.25	.20	.10
458T	Jim Ray	.25	.20	.10
485T	Felipe Alou	1.00	.70	.40
486T	Steve Stone	.40	.30	.15
496T	Tom Murphy	.25	.20	.10
516T	Horacio Pina	.25	.20	.10
534T	Eddie Watt	.25	.20	.10
538T	Cesar Tovar	.25	.20	.10
544T	Ron Schueler	.25	.20	.10
579T	Cecil Upshaw	.25	.20	.10
585T	Merv Rettenmund	.25	.20	.10
612T	Luke Walker	.25	.20	.10
616T	Larry Gura	.25	.20	.10
618T	Jim Mason	.25	.20	.10
630T	Tommie Agee	.25	.20	.10
648T	Terry Crowley	.25	.20	.10
649T	Fernando Gonzalez	.25	.20	.10
----	Traded Checklist	.70	.35	.20

1975 Topps

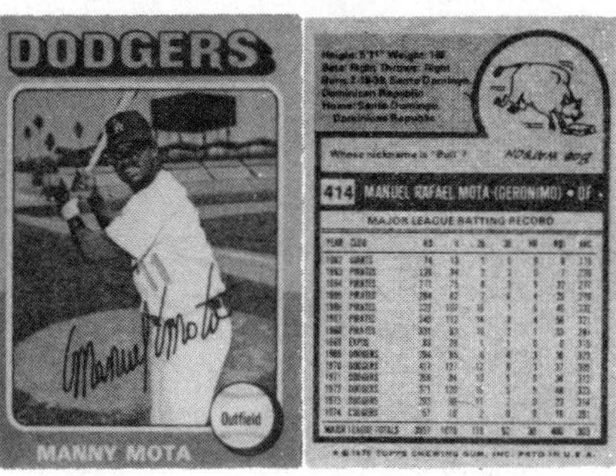

This year Topps produced another 660-card set, one which collectors either seem to like or despise. The 2-1/2" by 3-1/2" cards have a color photo which is framed by a round-cornered white frame. Around that is an eye-catching two-color border in bright colors. The team name appears at the top in bright letters while the player name is at the bottom and his position a baseball at the lower right. A facsimile autograph runs across the picture. The card backs are vertical feature normal statistical and biographical information along with a trivia quiz. Specialty cards include a new 24-card series on MVP winners going back to 1951. Other specialty cards include statistical leaders and post-season highlights. The real highlight of the set, however, are the rookie cards which include their numbers such names as George Brett, Gary Carter, Robin Yount, Jim Rice, Keith Hernandez and Fred Lynn. While the set was released at one time, card numbers 1-132 were printed in somewhat shorter supply than the remainder of the issue.

		NR MT	EX	VG
Complete Set (660):		900.00	450.00	275.00
Common Player (1-132):		.35	.20	.11
Common Player (133-660):		.30	.15	.09
Complete Mini Set:		1000.	500.00	300.00
Common Mini Player:		.40	.20	.12
1	'74 Highlights (Hank Aaron)	22.00	11.00	6.50
2	'74 Highlights (Lou Brock)	2.00	1.00	.60
3	'74 Highlights (Bob Gibson)	1.75	.90	.50
4	'74 Highlights (Al Kaline)	2.00	1.00	.60
5	'74 Highlights (Nolan Ryan)	28.00	14.00	8.50
6	'74 Highlights (Mike Marshall)	.40	.20	.12
7	'74 Highlights (Dick Bosman, Steve Busby, Nolan Ryan)	1.00	.50	.30
8	Rogelio Moret	.35	.20	.11
9	Frank Tepedino	.35	.20	.11
10	Willie Davis	.35	.20	.11
11	Bill Melton	.35	.20	.11
12	David Clyde	.35	.20	.11
13	Gene Locklear	.35	.20	.11
14	Milt Wilcox	.35	.20	.11
15	Jose Cardenal	.35	.20	.11
16	Frank Tanana	.35	.20	.11
17	Dave Concepcion	.45	.25	.14
18	Tigers Team (Ralph Houk)	2.00	1.00	.60
19	Jerry Koosman	.35	.20	.11
20	Thurman Munson	7.00	3.50	2.00
21	Rollie Fingers	5.00	2.50	1.50
22	Dave Cash	.35	.20	.11
23	Bill Russell	.35	.20	.11
24	Al Fitzmorris	.35	.20	.11
25	Lee May	.35	.20	.11
26	Dave McNally	.35	.20	.11
27	Ken Reitz	.35	.20	.11
28	Tom Murphy	.35	.20	.11

29 Dave Parker 8.00 4.00 2.50
30 Bert Blyleven 1.00 .50 .30
31 Dave Rader .35 .20 .11
32 Reggie Cleveland .35 .20 .11
33 Dusty Baker .40 .20 .12
34 Steve Renko .35 .20 .11
35 Ron Santo .50 .25 .15
36 Joe Lovitto .35 .20 .11
37 Dave Freisleben .35 .20 .11
38 Buddy Bell .35 .20 .11
39 Andy Thornton .40 .20 .12
40 Bill Singer .35 .20 .11
41 Cesar Geronimo .35 .20 .11
42 Joe Coleman .35 .20 .11
43 Cleon Jones .35 .20 .11
44 Pat Dobson .35 .20 .11
45 Joe Rudi .40 .20 .12
46 Phillies Team (Danny Ozark) 2.00 1.00 .60
47 Tommy John 1.25 .60 .40
48 Freddie Patek .35 .20 .11
49 Larry Dierker .35 .20 .11
50 Brooks Robinson 6.00 3.00 1.75
51 *Bob Forsch* .80 .40 .25
52 Darrell Porter .35 .20 .11
53 Dave Giusti .35 .20 .11
54 Eric Soderholm .35 .20 .11
55 Bobby Bonds .35 .20 .11
56 Rick Wise .35 .20 .11
57 Dave Johnson .35 .20 .11
58 Chuck Taylor .35 .20 .11
59 Ken Henderson .35 .20 .11
60 Fergie Jenkins 4.00 2.00 1.25
61 Dave Winfield 70.00 35.00 21.00
62 Fritz Peterson .35 .20 .11
63 Steve Swisher .35 .20 .11
64 Dave Chalk .35 .20 .11
65 Don Gullett .35 .20 .11
66 Willie Horton .35 .20 .11
67 Tug McGraw .35 .20 .11
68 Ron Blomberg .35 .20 .11
69 John Odom .35 .20 .11
70 Mike Schmidt 65.00 32.00 19.50
71 Charlie Hough .35 .20 .11
72 Royals Team (Jack McKeon) 2.00 1.00 .60
73 J.R. Richard .35 .20 .11
74 Mark Belanger .35 .20 .11
75 Ted Simmons .35 .20 .11
76 Ed Sprague .35 .20 .11
77 Richie Zisk .35 .20 .11
78 Ray Corbin .35 .20 .11
79 Gary Matthews .35 .20 .11
80 Carlton Fisk 15.00 7.50 4.50
81 Ron Reed .35 .20 .11
82 Pat Kelly .35 .20 .11
83 Jim Merritt .35 .20 .11
84 Enzo Hernandez .35 .20 .11
85 Bill Bonham .35 .20 .11
86 Joe Lis .35 .20 .11
87 George Foster .75 .40 .25
88 Tom Egan .35 .20 .11
89 Jim Ray .35 .20 .11
90 Rusty Staub .60 .30 .20
91 Dick Green .35 .20 .11
92 Cecil Upshaw .35 .20 .11
93 Dave Lopes .40 .20 .12
94 Jim Lonborg .35 .20 .11
95 John Mayberry .35 .20 .11
96 Mike Cosgrove .35 .20 .11
97 Earl Williams .35 .20 .11
98 Rich Folkers .35 .20 .11
99 Mike Hegan .35 .20 .11
100 Willie Stargell 6.00 3.00 1.75
101 Expos Team (Gene Mauch) 2.00 1.00 .60
102 Joe Decker .35 .20 .11
103 Rick Miller .35 .20 .11
104 Bill Madlock 1.25 .60 .40
105 Buzz Capra .35 .20 .11
106 *Mike Hargrove* .35 .20 .11
107 Jim Barr .35 .20 .11
108 Tom Hall .35 .20 .11
109 George Hendrick .35 .20 .11
110 Wilbur Wood .35 .20 .11
111 Wayne Garrett .35 .20 .11
112 Larry Hardy .35 .20 .11
113 Elliott Maddox .35 .20 .11
114 Dick Lange .35 .20 .11
115 Joe Ferguson .35 .20 .11
116 Lerrin LaGrow .35 .20 .11
117 Orioles Team (Earl Weaver) 2.50 1.25 .70
118 Mike Anderson .35 .20 .11
119 Tommy Helms .35 .20 .11
120 Steve Busby (photo actually Fran Healy) .35 .20 .11
121 Bill North .35 .20 .11
122 Al Hrabosky .35 .20 .11
123 Johnny Briggs .35 .20 .11
124 Jerry Reuss .35 .20 .11
125 Ken Singleton .35 .20 .11
126 Checklist 1-132 1.50 .70 .45
127 Glen Borgmann .35 .20 .11
128 Bill Lee .35 .20 .11
129 Rick Monday .35 .20 .11
130 Phil Niekro 1.50 .70 .45
131 Toby Harrah .35 .20 .11
132 Randy Moffitt .35 .20 .11
133 Dan Driessen .35 .20 .11
134 Ron Hodges .30 .15 .09
135 Charlie Spikes .30 .15 .09
136 Jim Mason .30 .15 .09
137 Terry Forster .30 .15 .09
138 Del Unser .30 .15 .09
139 Horacio Pina .30 .15 .09
140 Steve Garvey 5.00 2.50 1.50
141 Mickey Stanley .30 .15 .09
142 Bob Reynolds .30 .15 .09
143 *Cliff Johnson* .30 .15 .09
144 Jim Wohlford .30 .15 .09
145 Ken Holtzman .30 .15 .09
146 Padres Team (John McNamara) 2.00 1.00 .60
147 Pedro Garcia .30 .15 .09
148 Jim Rooker .30 .15 .09
149 Tim Foli .30 .15 .09
150 Bob Gibson 5.00 2.50 1.50
151 Steve Brye .30 .15 .09
152 Mario Guerrero .30 .15 .09
153 Rick Reuschel .30 .15 .09
154 Mike Lum .30 .15 .09
155 Jim Bibby .30 .15 .09
156 Dave Kingman .45 .25 .14
157 Pedro Borbon .30 .15 .09
158 Jerry Grote .30 .15 .09
159 Steve Arlin .30 .15 .09
160 Graig Nettles .45 .25 .14
161 Stan Bahnsen .30 .15 .09
162 Willie Montanez .30 .15 .09
163 Jim Brewer .30 .15 .09
164 Mickey Rivers .30 .15 .09
165 Doug Rader .30 .15 .09
166 Woodie Fryman .30 .15 .09
167 Rich Coggins .30 .15 .09
168 Bill Greif .30 .15 .09
169 Cookie Rojas .30 .15 .09
170 Bert Campaneris .40 .20 .12
171 Ed Kirkpatrick .30 .15 .09
172 Red Sox Team (Darrell Johnson)2.00 1.00 .60
173 Steve Rogers .30 .15 .09
174 Bake McBride .30 .15 .09
175 Don Money .30 .15 .09
176 Burt Hooton .30 .15 .09
177 Vic Correll .30 .15 .09
178 Cesar Tovar .30 .15 .09
179 Tom Bradley .30 .15 .09
180 Joe Morgan 5.00 2.50 1.50
181 Fred Beene .30 .15 .09
182 Don Hahn .30 .15 .09
183 Mel Stottlemyre .30 .15 .09
184 Jorge Orta .30 .15 .09
185 Steve Carlton 10.00 5.00 3.00
186 Willie Crawford .30 .15 .09
187 Denny Doyle .30 .15 .09
188 Tom Griffin .30 .15 .09
189 Yogi Berra (MVP, Roy Campanella) 2.00 1.00 .60
190 Hank Sauer (MVP, Bobby Shantz) .40 .20 .12
191 Roy Campanella (MVP, Al Rosen) .90 .45 .25
192 Yogi Berra (MVP, Willie Mays) 2.00 1.00 .60
193 Yogi Berra (MVP, Roy Campanella) 2.00 1.00 .60
194 Mickey Mantle (MVP, Don Newcombe) 6.00 3.00 1.75
195 Hank Aaron (MVP, Mickey Mantle) 10.00 5.00 3.00
196 Ernie Banks (MVP, Jackie Jensen) .90 .45 .25
197 Ernie Banks (MVP, Nellie Fox) .90 .45 .25
198 Dick Groat (MVP, Roger Maris) 1.25 .60 .40
199 Roger Maris (MVP, Frank Robinson) 1.50 .70 .45
200 Mickey Mantle (MVP, Maury Wills) 6.00 3.00 1.75
201 Elston Howard (MVP, Sandy Koufax) 1.50 .70 .45
202 Ken Boyer (MVP, Brooks Robinson) 1.25 .60 .40
203 Willie Mays (MVP, Zoilo Versalles) 1.50 .70 .45
204 Roberto Clemente (MVP, Frank Robinson) 1.50 .70 .45
205 Orlando Cepeda (MVP, Carl Yastrzemski) 1.25 .60 .40
206 Bob Gibson (MVP, Denny McLain) 1.25 .60 .40
207 Harmon Killebrew (MVP, Willie McCovey) 1.50 .70 .45
208 Johnny Bench (MVP, Boog Powell) 1.25 .60 .40
209 Vida Blue (MVP, Joe Torre) .50 .25 .15
210 Rich Allen (MVP, Johnny Bench) 1.25 .60 .40
211 Reggie Jackson (MVP, Pete Rose) 6.00 3.00 1.75
212 Jeff Burroughs (MVP, Steve Garvey) .75 .40 .25
213 Oscar Gamble .30 .15 .09
214 Harry Parker .30 .15 .09
215 Bobby Valentine .30 .15 .09
216 Giants Team (Wes Westrum) 2.00 1.00 .60
217 Lou Piniella .30 .15 .09
218 Jerry Johnson .30 .15 .09
219 Ed Herrmann .30 .15 .09
220 Don Sutton 1.50 .70 .45
221 Aurelio Rodriquez (Rodriguez) .30 .15 .09
222 Dan Spillner .30 .15 .09
223 *Robin Yount* 200.00 100.00 60.00
224 Ramon Hernandez .30 .15 .09
225 Bob Grich .30 .15 .09
226 Bill Campbell .30 .15 .09
227 Bob Watson .30 .15 .09
228 *George Brett* 220.00 110.00 65.00
229 Barry Foote .30 .15 .09
230 Catfish Hunter 2.00 1.00 .60
231 Mike Tyson .30 .15 .09
232 Diego Segui .30 .15 .09
233 Billy Grabarkewitz .30 .15 .09
234 Tom Grieve .30 .15 .09
235 Jack Billingham .30 .15 .09
236 Angels Team (Dick Williams) 2.00 1.00 .60
237 Carl Morton .30 .15 .09
238 Dave Duncan .30 .15 .09
239 George Stone .30 .15 .09
240 Garry Maddox .30 .15 .09
241 Dick Tidrow .30 .15 .09
242 Jay Johnstone .30 .15 .09
243 Jim Kaat 1.25 .60 .40
244 Bill Buckner .30 .15 .09
245 Mickey Lolich .40 .20 .12
246 Cardinals Team (Red Schoendienst) 2.00 1.00 .60
247 Enos Cabell .30 .15 .09
248 Randy Jones .30 .15 .09
249 Danny Thompson .30 .15 .09
250 Ken Brett .30 .15 .09
251 Fran Healy .30 .15 .09
252 Fred Scherman .30 .15 .09
253 Jesus Alou .30 .15 .09
254 Mike Torrez .30 .15 .09
255 Dwight Evans 4.00 2.00 1.25
256 Billy Champion .30 .15 .09
257 Checklist 133-264 1.50 .70 .45
258 Dave LaRoche .30 .15 .09
259 Len Randle .30 .15 .09
260 Johnny Bench 12.00 6.00 3.50
261 Andy Hassler .30 .15 .09
262 Rowland Office .30 .15 .09
263 Jim Perry .30 .15 .09
264 John Milner .30 .15 .09
265 Ron Bryant .30 .15 .09
266 Sandy Alomar .30 .15 .09
267 Dick Ruthven .30 .15 .09
268 Hal McRae .40 .20 .12
269 Doug Rau .30 .15 .09
270 Ron Fairly .30 .15 .09
271 Jerry Moses .30 .15 .09
272 Lynn McGlothen .30 .15 .09
273 Steve Braun .30 .15 .09
274 Vicente Romo .30 .15 .09
275 Paul Blair .30 .15 .09
276 White Sox Team (Chuck Tanner) 2.00 1.00 .60
277 Frank Taveras .30 .15 .09
278 Paul Lindblad .30 .15 .09
279 Milt May .30 .15 .09
280 Carl Yastrzemski 12.00 6.00 3.50
281 Jim Slaton .30 .15 .09
282 Jerry Morales .30 .15 .09
283 Steve Foucault .30 .15 .09
284 Ken Griffey .70 .35 .20
285 Ellie Rodriguez .30 .15 .09
286 Mike Jorgensen .30 .15 .09
287 Roric Harrison .30 .15 .09
288 Bruce Ellingsen .30 .15 .09
289 Ken Rudolph .30 .15 .09
290 Jon Matlack .30 .15 .09
291 Bill Sudakis .30 .15 .09
292 Ron Schueler .30 .15 .09
293 Dick Sharon .30 .15 .09
294 *Geoff Zahn* .30 .15 .09
295 Vada Pinson .45 .25 .14
296 Alan Foster .30 .15 .09
297 Craig Kusick .30 .15 .09
298 Johnny Grubb .30 .15 .09
299 Bucky Dent .40 .20 .12
300 Reggie Jackson 30.00 15.00 9.00
301 Dave Roberts .30 .15 .09
302 *Rick Burleson* .30 .15 .09
303 Grant Jackson .30 .15 .09
304 Pirates Team (Danny Murtaugh) 2.00 1.00 .60
305 Jim Colborn .30 .15 .09
306 Batting Leaders (Rod Carew, Ralph Garr) .80 .40 .25
307 Home Run Leaders (Dick Allen, Mike Schmidt) .90 .45 .25
308 Runs Batted In Leaders (Johnny Bench, Jeff Burroughs) .80 .40 .25
309 Stolen Base Leaders (Lou Brock, Bill North) .75 .40 .25
310 Victory Leaders (Jim Hunter, Fergie Jenkins, Andy Messersmith, Phil Niekro) .80 .40 .25
311 Earned Run Average Leaders (Buzz Capra, Catfish Hunter) .50 .25 .15
312 Strikeout Leaders (Steve Carlton, Nolan Ryan) 9.00 4.50 2.75
313 Leading Firemen (Terry Forster, Mike Marshall) .50 .25 .15
314 Buck Martinez .30 .15 .09
315 Don Kessinger .30 .15 .09
316 Jackie Brown .30 .15 .09
317 Joe Lahoud .30 .15 .09
318 Ernie McAnally .30 .15 .09
319 Johnny Oates .30 .15 .09
320 Pete Rose 20.00 10.00 6.00
321 Rudy May .30 .15 .09
322 Ed Goodson .30 .15 .09
323 Fred Holdsworth .30 .15 .09
324 Ed Kranepool .35 .20 .11
325 Tony Oliva .45 .25 .14
326 Wayne Twitchell .30 .15 .09
327 Jerry Hairston .30 .15 .09
328 Sonny Siebert .30 .15 .09
329 Ted Kubiak .30 .15 .09
330 Mike Marshall .30 .15 .09
331 Indians Team (Frank Robinson) 2.00 1.00 .60
332 Fred Kendall .30 .15 .09
333 Dick Drago .30 .15 .09
334 *Greg Gross* .30 .15 .09
335 Jim Palmer 8.00 4.00 2.50
336 Rennie Stennett .30 .15 .09
337 Kevin Kobel .30 .15 .09
338 Rick Stelmaszek .30 .15 .09
339 Jim Fregosi .30 .15 .09
340 Paul Splittorff .30 .15 .09
341 Hal Breeden .30 .15 .09
342 Leroy Stanton .30 .15 .09
343 Danny Frisella .30 .15 .09
344 Ben Oglivie .30 .15 .09
345 Clay Carroll .30 .15 .09
346 Bobby Darwin .30 .15 .09
347 Mike Caldwell .30 .15 .09
348 Tony Muser .30 .15 .09
349 Ray Sadecki .30 .15 .09

350	Bobby Murcer	.30	.15	.09
351	Bob Boone	.40	.20	.12
352	Darold Knowles	.30	.15	.09
353	Luis Melendez	.30	.15	.09
354	Dick Bosman	.30	.15	.09
355	Chris Cannizzaro	.30	.15	.09
356	Rico Petrocelli			
357	Ken Forsch	.30	.15	.09
358	Al Bumbry	.30	.15	.09
359	Paul Popovich	.30	.15	.09
360	George Scott	.30	.15	.09
361	Dodgers Team (Walter Alston)	3.00	1.50	.90
362	Steve Hargan	.30	.15	.09
363	Carmen Fanzone	.30	.15	.09
364	Doug Bird	.30	.15	.09
365	Bob Bailey	.30	.15	.09
366	Ken Sanders	.30	.15	.09
367	Craig Robinson	.30	.15	.09
368	Vic Albury	.30	.15	.09
369	Merv Rettenmund	.30	.15	.09
370	Tom Seaver	15.00	7.50	4.50
371	Gates Brown	.30	.15	.09
372	John D'Acquisto	.30	.15	.09
373	Bill Sharp	.30	.15	.09
374	Eddie Watt	.30	.15	.09
375	Roy White	.30	.15	.09
376	Steve Yeager	.30	.15	.09
377	Tom Hilgendorf	.30	.15	.09
378	Derrel Thomas	.30	.15	.09
379	Bernie Carbo	.30	.15	.09
380	Sal Bando	.30	.15	.09
381	John Curtis	.30	.15	.09
382	Don Baylor	.45	.25	.14
383	Jim York	.30	.15	.09
384	Brewers Team (Del Crandall)	2.00	1.00	.60
385	Dock Ellis	.30	.15	.09
386	Checklist 265-396	1.50	.70	.45
387	Jim Spencer	.30	.15	.09
388	Steve Stone	.30	.15	.09
389	Tony Solaita	.30	.15	.09
390	Ron Cey	.30	.15	.09
391	Don DeMola	.30	.15	.09
392	Bruce Bochte	.30	.15	.09
393	Gary Gentry	.30	.15	.09
394	Larvell Blanks	.30	.15	.09
395	Bud Harrelson	.30	.15	.09
396	Fred Norman	.30	.15	.09
397	Bill Freehan	.30	.15	.09
398	Elias Sosa	.30	.15	.09
399	Terry Harmon	.30	.15	.09
400	Dick Allen	.80	.40	.25
401	Mike Wallace	.30	.15	.09
402	Bob Tolan	.30	.15	.09
403	Tom Buskey	.30	.15	.09
404	Ted Sizemore	.30	.15	.09
405	John Montague	.30	.15	.09
406	Bob Gallagher	.30	.15	.09
407	*Herb Washington*	.35	.20	.11
408	Clyde Wright	.30	.15	.09
409	Bob Robertson	.30	.15	.09
410	Mike Cueller (Cuellar)	.30	.15	.09
411	George Mitterwald	.30	.15	.09
412	Bill Hands	.30	.15	.09
413	Marty Pattin	.30	.15	.09
414	Manny Mota	.30	.15	.09
415	John Hiller	.30	.15	.09
416	Larry Lintz	.30	.15	.09
417	Skip Lockwood	.30	.15	.09
418	Leo Foster	.30	.15	.09
419	Dave Goltz	.30	.15	.09
420	Larry Bowa	.40	.20	.12
421	Mets Team (Yogi Berra)	2.50	1.25	.70
422	Brian Downing	.30	.15	.09
423	Clay Kirby	.30	.15	.09
424	John Lowenstein	.30	.15	.09
425	Tito Fuentes	.30	.15	.09
426	George Medich	.30	.15	.09
427	Clarence Gaston	.30	.15	.09
428	Dave Hamilton	.30	.15	.09
429	*Jim Dwyer*	.30	.15	.09
430	Luis Tiant	.40	.20	.12
431	Rod Gilbreath	.30	.15	.09
432	Ken Berry	.30	.15	.09
433	Larry Demery	.30	.15	.09
434	Bob Locker	.30	.15	.09
435	Dave Nelson	.30	.15	.09
436	Ken Frailing	.30	.15	.09
437	*Al Cowens*	.30	.15	.09
438	Don Carrithers	.30	.15	.09
439	Ed Brinkman	.30	.15	.09
440	Andy Messersmith	.30	.15	.09
441	Bobby Heise	.30	.15	.09
442	Maximino Leon	.30	.15	.09
443	Twins Team (Frank Quilici)	2.00	1.00	.60
444	Gene Garber	.30	.15	.09
445	Felix Millan	.30	.15	.09
446	Bart Johnson	.30	.15	.09
447	Terry Crowley	.30	.15	.09
448	Frank Duffy	.30	.15	.09
449	Charlie Williams	.30	.15	.09
450	Willie McCovey	4.00	2.00	1.25
451	Rick Dempsey	.30	.15	.09
452	Angel Mangual	.30	.15	.09
453	Claude Osteen	.30	.15	.09
454	Doug Griffin	.30	.15	.09
455	Don Wilson	.30	.15	.09
456	Bob Coluccio	.30	.15	.09
457	Mario Mendoza	.30	.15	.09
458	Ross Grimsley	.30	.15	.09
459	A.L. Championships	.80	.40	.25
460	N.L. Championships (Steve Garvey)	.80	.40	.25
461	World Series Game 1 (Reggie Jackson)	2.00	1.00	.60
462	World Series Game 2	.80	.40	.25
463	World Series Game 3 (Rollie Fingers)	1.00	.50	.30
464	World Series Game 4	.80	.40	.25
465	World Series Game 5	.80	.40	.25
466	World Series Summary (A's Do It Again)	.80	.40	.25
467	Ed Halicki	.30	.15	.09
468	Bobby Mitchell	.30	.15	.09
469	Tom Dettore	.30	.15	.09
470	Jeff Burroughs	.30	.15	.09
471	Bob Stinson	.30	.15	.09
472	Bruce Dal Canton	.30	.15	.09
473	Ken McMullen	.30	.15	.09
474	Luke Walker	.30	.15	.09
475	Darrell Evans	.45	.25	.14
476	*Ed Figueroa*	.30	.15	.09
477	Tom Hutton	.30	.15	.09
478	Tom Burgmeier	.30	.15	.09
479	Ken Boswell	.30	.15	.09
480	Carlos May	.30	.15	.09
481	*Will McEnaney*	.30	.15	.09
482	Tom McCraw	.30	.15	.09
483	Steve Ontiveros	.30	.15	.09
484	Glenn Beckert	.30	.15	.09
485	Sparky Lyle	.30	.15	.09
486	Ray Fosse	.30	.15	.09
487	Astros Team (Preston Gomez)	2.00	1.00	.60
488	Bill Travers	.30	.15	.09
489	Cecil Cooper	.45	.25	.14
490	Reggie Smith	.30	.15	.09
491	Doyle Alexander	.30	.15	.09
492	Rich Hebner	.30	.15	.09
493	Don Stanhouse	.30	.15	.09
494	*Pete LaCock*	.30	.15	.09
495	Nelson Briles	.30	.15	.09
496	Pepe Frias	.30	.15	.09
497	Jim Nettles	.30	.15	.09
498	Al Downing	.30	.15	.09
499	Marty Perez	.30	.15	.09
500	Nolan Ryan	85.00	42.00	25.00
501	Bill Robinson	.30	.15	.09
502	Pat Bourque	.30	.15	.09
503	Fred Stanley	.30	.15	.09
504	Buddy Bradford	.30	.15	.09
505	Chris Speier	.30	.15	.09
506	Leron Lee	.30	.15	.09
507	Tom Carroll	.30	.15	.09
508	Bob Hansen	.30	.15	.09
509	Dave Hilton	.30	.15	.09
510	Vida Blue	.50	.25	.15
511	Rangers Team (Billy Martin)	2.00	1.00	.60
512	Larry Milbourne	.30	.15	.09
513	Dick Pole	.30	.15	.09
514	Jose Cruz	.30	.15	.09
515	Manny Sanguillen	.30	.15	.09
516	Don Hood	.30	.15	.09
517	Checklist 397-528	1.25	.60	.40
518	Leo Cardenas	.30	.15	.09
519	Jim Todd	.30	.15	.09
520	Amos Otis	.30	.15	.09
521	Dennis Blair	.30	.15	.09
522	Gary Sutherland	.30	.15	.09
523	Tom Paciorek	.30	.15	.09
524	John Doherty	.30	.15	.09
525	Tom House	.30	.15	.09
526	Larry Hisle	.30	.15	.09
527	Mac Scarce	.30	.15	.09
528	Eddie Leon	.30	.15	.09
529	Gary Thomasson	.30	.15	.09
530	Gaylord Perry	3.00	1.50	.90
531	Reds Team (Sparky Anderson)	3.00	1.50	.90
532	Gorman Thomas	.30	.15	.09
533	Rudy Meoli	.30	.15	.09
534	Alex Johnson	.30	.15	.09
535	Gene Tenace	.30	.15	.09
536	Bob Moose	.30	.15	.09
537	Tommy Harper	.30	.15	.09
538	Duffy Dyer	.30	.15	.09
539	Jesse Jefferson	.30	.15	.09
540	Lou Brock	4.00	2.00	1.25
541	Roger Metzger	.30	.15	.09
542	Pete Broberg	.30	.15	.09
543	Larry Biittner	.30	.15	.09
544	Steve Mingori	.30	.15	.09
545	Billy Williams	3.00	1.50	.90
546	John Knox	.30	.15	.09
547	Von Joshua	.30	.15	.09
548	Charlie Sands	.30	.15	.09
549	Bill Butler	.30	.15	.09
550	Ralph Garr	.30	.15	.09
551	Larry Christenson	.30	.15	.09
552	Jack Brohamer	.30	.15	.09
553	John Boccabella	.30	.15	.09
554	Rich Gossage	.45	.25	.14
555	Al Oliver	.60	.30	.20
556	Tim Johnson	.30	.15	.09
557	Larry Gura	.30	.15	.09
558	Dave Roberts	.30	.15	.09
559	Bob Montgomery	.30	.15	.09
560	Tony Perez	2.00	1.00	.60
561	A's Team (Alvin Dark)	2.00	1.00	.60
562	Gary Nolan	.30	.15	.09
563	Wilbur Howard	.30	.15	.09
564	Tommy Davis	.30	.15	.09
565	Joe Torre	.70	.35	.20
566	Ray Burris	.30	.15	.09
567	*Jim Sundberg*	.30	.15	.09
568	Dale Murray	.30	.15	.09
569	Frank White	.40	.20	.12
570	Jim Wynn	.35	.20	.11
571	Dave Lemanczyk	.30	.15	.09
572	Roger Nelson	.30	.15	.09
573	Orlando Pena	.30	.15	.09
574	Tony Taylor	.30	.15	.09
575	Gene Clines	.30	.15	.09
576	Phil Roof	.30	.15	.09
577	John Morris	.30	.15	.09
578	Dave Tomlin	.30	.15	.09
579	Skip Pitlock	.30	.15	.09
580	Frank Robinson	6.00	3.00	1.75
581	Darrel Chaney	.30	.15	.09
582	Eduardo Rodriguez	.30	.15	.09
583	Andy Etchebarren	.30	.15	.09
584	Mike Garman	.30	.15	.09
585	Chris Chambliss	.30	.15	.09
586	Tim McCarver	.45	.25	.14
587	Chris Ward	.30	.15	.09
588	Rick Auerbach	.30	.15	.09
589	Braves Team (Clyde King)	2.00	1.00	.60
590	Cesar Cedeno	.30	.15	.09
591	Glenn Abbott	.30	.15	.09
592	Balor Moore	.30	.15	.09
593	Gene Lamont	.30	.15	.09
594	Jim Fuller	.30	.15	.09
595	Joe Niekro	.30	.15	.09
596	Ollie Brown	.30	.15	.09
597	Winston Llenas	.30	.15	.09
598	Bruce Kison	.30	.15	.09
599	Nate Colbert	.30	.15	.09
600	Rod Carew	9.00	4.50	2.75
601	Juan Beniquez	.30	.15	.09
602	John Vukovich	.30	.15	.09
603	Lew Krausse	.30	.15	.09
604	Oscar Zamora	.30	.15	.09
605	John Ellis	.30	.15	.09
606	Bruce Miller	.30	.15	.09
607	Jim Holt	.30	.15	.09
608	Gene Michael	.30	.15	.09
609	Ellie Hendricks	.30	.15	.09
610	Ron Hunt	.30	.15	.09
611	Yankees Team (Bill Virdon)	3.00	1.50	.90
612	Terry Hughes	.30	.15	.09
613	Bill Parsons	.30	.15	.09
614	Rookie Pitchers (Jack Kucek, Dyar Miller, Vern Ruhle, Paul Siebert)	.30	.15	.09
615	Rookie Pitchers (Pat Darcy, Dennis Leonard, Tom Underwood, Hank Webb)	.30	.15	.09
616	Rookie Outfielders (Dave Augustine, Pepe Mangual, Jim Rice, John Scott)	18.00	9.00	5.50
617	Rookie Infielders (Mike Cubbage, Doug DeCinces, Reggie J. Sanders, Manny Trillo)	1.25	.60	.40
618	Rookie Pitchers (*Jamie Easterly*, Tom Johnson, Scott McGregor, Rick Rhoden)	2.25	1.25	.70
619	Rookie Outfielders (Benny Ayala, Nyls Nyman, Tommy Smith, Jerry Turner)	.30	.15	.09
620	*Gary Carter*, Marc Hill, Danny Meyer, Leon Roberts)	35.00	17.50	10.50
621	Rookie Pitchers (*John Denny*, Rawly Eastwick, Jim Kern, Juan Veintidos)	.60	.30	.20
622	Rookie Outfielders (Ed Armbrister, Fred Lynn, Tom Poquette, Terry Whitfield)	10.00	5.00	3.00
623	Rookie Infielders (*Phil Garner*, Keith Hernandez, Bob Sheldon, Tom Veryzer)	10.00	5.00	3.00
624	Rookie Pitchers (Doug Konieczny, Gary Lavelle, Jim Otten, Eddie Solomon)	.30	.15	.09
625	Boog Powell	.45	.25	.14
626	Larry Haney	.30	.15	.09
627	Tom Walker	.30	.15	.09
628	*Ron LeFlore*	.80	.40	.25
629	Joe Hoerner	.30	.15	.09
630	Greg Luzinski	.45	.25	.14
631	Lee Lacy	.30	.15	.09
632	Morris Nettles	.30	.15	.09
633	Paul Casanova	.30	.15	.09
634	Cy Acosta	.30	.15	.09
635	Chuck Dobson	.30	.15	.09
636	Charlie Moore	.30	.15	.09
637	Ted Martinez	.30	.15	.09
638	Cubs Team (Jim Marshall)	2.00	1.00	.60
639	Steve Kline	.30	.15	.09
640	Harmon Killebrew	5.00	2.50	1.50
641	Jim Northrup	.30	.15	.09
642	Mike Phillips	.30	.15	.09
643	Brent Strom	.30	.15	.09
644	Bill Fahey	.30	.15	.09
645	Danny Cater	.30	.15	.09
646	Checklist 529-660	1.50	.70	.45
647	*Claudell Washington*	1.00	.50	.30
648	Dave Pagan	.30	.15	.09
649	Jack Heidemann	.30	.15	.09
650	Dave May	.30	.15	.09
651	John Morlan	.30	.15	.09
652	Lindy McDaniel	.30	.15	.09
653	Lee Richards	.30	.15	.09
654	Jerry Terrell	.30	.15	.09
655	Rico Carty	.30	.15	.09
656	Bill Plummer	.30	.15	.09
657	Bob Oliver	.30	.15	.09
658	Vic Harris	.30	.15	.09
659	Bob Apodaca	.30	.15	.09
660	Hank Aaron	30.00	15.00	9.00

1975 Topps Mini

One of the most popular Topps sets of the 1970s is really a test issue. The Topps Minis measure 2-1/4" by 3-1/8," exactly 20 percent smaller than the regular card size. Other than their size, the Minis are in every way the same as the regular cards. The experiment primarily took place in parts of Michigan and the West Coast, where the Minis were snapped up quickly by collectors.

		NR MT	EX	VG
	Complete Set:	1200.	600.00	350.00
	Common Player:	.40	.20	.12
1	'74 Highlights (Hank Aaron)	25.00	12.50	7.50
2	'74 Highlights (Lou Brock)	3.50	1.75	1.00
3	'74 Highlights (Bob Gibson)	3.25	1.75	1.00
4	'74 Highlights (Al Kaline)	3.25	1.75	1.00
5	'74 Highlights (Nolan Ryan)	15.00	7.50	4.50
6	'74 Highlights (Mike Marshall)	.60	.30	.20
7	'74 Highlights (Dick Bosman, Steve Busby, Nolan Ryan)	.60	.30	.20
8	Rogelio Moret	.40	.20	.12
9	Frank Tepedino	.40	.20	.12
10	Willie Davis	.60	.30	.20
11	Bill Melton	.40	.20	.12
12	David Clyde	.40	.20	.12
13	Gene Locklear	.40	.20	.12
14	Milt Wilcox	.40	.20	.12
15	Jose Cardenal	.40	.20	.12
16	Frank Tanana	.60	.30	.20
17	Dave Concepcion	.90	.45	.25
18	Tigers Team (Ralph Houk)	1.25	.60	.40
19	Jerry Koosman	.40	.20	.12
20	Thurman Munson	10.00	5.00	3.00
21	Rollie Fingers	6.00	3.00	1.75
22	Dave Cash	.40	.20	.12
23	Bill Russell	.60	.30	.20
24	Al Fitzmorris	.40	.20	.12
25	Lee May	.60	.30	.20
26	Dave McNally	.60	.30	.20
27	Ken Reitz	.40	.20	.12
28	Tom Murphy	.40	.20	.12
29	Dave Parker	10.00	5.00	3.00
30	Bert Blyleven	2.00	1.00	.60
31	Dave Rader	.40	.20	.12
32	Reggie Cleveland	.40	.20	.12
33	Dusty Baker	.90	.45	.25
34	Steve Renko	.40	.20	.12
35	Ron Santo	.80	.40	.25
36	Joe Lovitto	.40	.20	.12
37	Dave Freisleben	.40	.20	.12
38	Buddy Bell	.75	.40	.25
39	Andy Thornton	.60	.30	.20
40	Bill Singer	.40	.20	.12
41	Cesar Geronimo	.40	.20	.12
42	Joe Coleman	.40	.20	.12
43	Cleon Jones	.40	.20	.12
44	Pat Dobson	.40	.20	.12
45	Joe Rudi	.60	.30	.20
46	Phillies Team (Danny Ozark)	1.25	.60	.40
47	Tommy John	2.50	1.25	.70
48	Freddie Patek	.40	.20	.12
49	Larry Dierker	.40	.20	.12
50	Brooks Robinson	10.00	5.00	3.00
51	Bob Forsch	1.25	.60	.40
52	Darrell Porter	.60	.30	.20
53	Dave Giusti	.40	.20	.12
54	Eric Soderholm	.40	.20	.12
55	Bobby Bonds	.80	.40	.25
56	Rick Wise	.60	.30	.20
57	Dave Johnson	1.25	.60	.40
58	Chuck Taylor	.40	.20	.12
59	Ken Henderson	.40	.20	.12
60	Fergie Jenkins	3.00	1.50	.90
61	Dave Winfield	60.00	30.00	18.00
62	Fritz Peterson	.40	.20	.12
63	Steve Swisher	.40	.20	.12
64	Dave Chalk	.40	.20	.12
65	Don Gullett	.40	.20	.12
66	Willie Horton	.60	.30	.20
67	Tug McGraw	.60	.30	.20
68	Ron Blomberg	.40	.20	.12
69	John Odom	.40	.20	.12
70	Mike Schmidt	60.00	30.00	18.00
71	Charlie Hough	.60	.30	.20
72	Royals Team (Jack McKeon)	1.25	.60	.40
73	J.R. Richard	.60	.30	.20
74	Mark Belanger	.60	.30	.20
75	Ted Simmons	.60	.30	.20
76	Ed Sprague	.40	.20	.12
77	Richie Zisk	.40	.20	.12
78	Ray Corbin	.40	.20	.12
79	Gary Matthews	.60	.30	.20
80	Carlton Fisk	12.00	6.00	3.50
81	Ron Reed	.40	.20	.12
82	Pat Kelly	.40	.20	.12
83	Jim Merritt	.40	.20	.12
84	Enzo Hernandez	.40	.20	.12
85	Bill Bonham	.40	.20	.12
86	Joe Lis	.40	.20	.12
87	George Foster	1.75	.90	.50
88	Tom Egan	.40	.20	.12
89	Jim Ray	.40	.20	.12
90	Rusty Staub	.90	.45	.25
91	Dick Green	.40	.20	.12
92	Cecil Upshaw	.40	.20	.12
93	Dave Lopes	.60	.30	.20
94	Jim Lonborg	.75	.40	.25
95	John Mayberry	.40	.20	.12
96	Mike Cosgrove	.40	.20	.12
97	Earl Williams	.40	.20	.12
98	Rich Folkers	.40	.20	.12
99	Mike Hegan	.40	.20	.12
100	Willie Stargell	7.00	3.50	2.00
101	Expos Team (Gene Mauch)	1.25	.60	.40
102	Joe Decker	.40	.20	.12
103	Rick Miller	.40	.20	.12
104	Bill Madlock	1.00	.50	.30
105	Buzz Capra	.40	.20	.12
106	Mike Hargrove	.60	.30	.20
107	Jim Barr	.40	.20	.12
108	Tom Hall	.40	.20	.12
109	George Hendrick	.40	.20	.12
110	Wilbur Wood	.40	.20	.12
111	Wayne Garrett	.40	.20	.12
112	Larry Hardy	.40	.20	.12
113	Elliott Maddox	.40	.20	.12
114	Dick Lange	.40	.20	.12
115	Joe Ferguson	.40	.20	.12
116	Lerrin LaGrow	.40	.20	.12
117	Orioles Team (Earl Weaver)	1.25	.60	.40
118	Mike Anderson	.40	.20	.12
119	Tommy Helms	.40	.20	.12
120	Steve Busby (photo actually Fran Healy)	.40	.20	.12
121	Bill North	.40	.20	.12
122	Al Hrabosky	.40	.20	.12
123	Johnny Briggs	.40	.20	.12
124	Jerry Reuss	.60	.30	.20
125	Ken Singleton	.60	.30	.20
126	Checklist 1-132	2.25	1.25	.70
127	Glen Borgmann	.40	.20	.12
128	Bill Lee	.60	.30	.20
129	Rick Monday	.60	.30	.20
130	Phil Niekro	4.00	2.00	1.25
131	Toby Harrah	.40	.20	.12
132	Randy Moffitt	.40	.20	.12
133	Dan Driessen	.60	.30	.20
134	Ron Hodges	.40	.20	.12
135	Charlie Spikes	.40	.20	.12
136	Jim Mason	.40	.20	.12
137	Terry Forster	.40	.20	.12
138	Del Unser	.40	.20	.12
139	Horacio Pina	.40	.20	.12
140	Steve Garvey	9.00	4.50	2.75
141	Mickey Stanley	.40	.20	.12
142	Bob Reynolds	.40	.20	.12
143	Cliff Johnson	.40	.20	.12
144	Jim Wohlford	.40	.20	.12
145	Ken Holtzman	.60	.30	.20
146	Padres Team (John McNamara)	1.25	.60	.40
147	Pedro Garcia	.40	.20	.12
148	Jim Rooker	.40	.20	.12
149	Tim Foli	.40	.20	.12
150	Bob Gibson	7.00	3.50	2.00
151	Steve Brye	.40	.20	.12
152	Mario Guerrero	.40	.20	.12
153	Rick Reuschel	.60	.30	.20
154	Mike Lum	.40	.20	.12
155	Jim Bibby	.40	.20	.12
156	Dave Kingman	.90	.45	.25
157	Pedro Borbon	.40	.20	.12
158	Jerry Grote	.40	.20	.12
159	Steve Arlin	.40	.20	.12
160	Graig Nettles	2.00	1.00	.60
161	Stan Bahnsen	.40	.20	.12
162	Willie Montanez	.40	.20	.12
163	Jim Brewer	.40	.20	.12
164	Mickey Rivers	.60	.30	.20
165	Doug Rader	.60	.30	.20
166	Woodie Fryman	.40	.20	.12
167	Rich Coggins	.40	.20	.12
168	Bill Greif	.40	.20	.12
169	Cookie Rojas	.40	.20	.12
170	Bert Campaneris	.60	.30	.20
171	Ed Kirkpatrick	.40	.20	.12
172	Red Sox Team (Darrell Johnson)	1.25	.60	.40
173	Steve Rogers	.40	.20	.12
174	Bake McBride	.40	.20	.12
175	Don Money	.40	.20	.12
176	Burt Hooton	.40	.20	.12
177	Vic Correll	.40	.20	.12
178	Cesar Tovar	.40	.20	.12
179	Tom Bradley	.40	.20	.12
180	Joe Morgan	10.00	5.00	3.00
181	Fred Beene	.40	.20	.12
182	Don Hahn	.40	.20	.12
183	Mel Stottlemyre	.60	.30	.20
184	Jorge Orta	.40	.20	.12
185	Steve Carlton	15.00	7.50	4.50
186	Willie Crawford	.40	.20	.12
187	Denny Doyle	.40	.20	.12
188	Tom Griffin	.40	.20	.12
189	1951-MVPs (Larry (Yogi) Berra, Roy Campanella)	2.25	1.25	.70
190	1952-MVPs (Hank Sauer, Bobby Shantz)	.60	.30	.20
191	1953-MVPs (Roy Campanella, Al Rosen)	1.25	.60	.40
192	1954-MVPs (Yogi Berra, Willie Mays)	2.25	1.25	.70
193	1955-MVPs (Yogi Berra, Roy Campanella)	2.25	1.25	.70
194	1956-MVPs (Mickey Mantle, Don Newcombe)	9.00	4.50	2.75
195	1957-MVPs (Hank Aaron, Mickey Mantle)	10.00	5.00	3.00
196	1958-MVPs (Ernie Banks, Jackie Jensen)	1.25	.60	.40
197	1959-MVPs (Ernie Banks, Nellie Fox)	1.25	.60	.40
198	1960-MVPs (Dick Groat, Roger Maris)	1.75	.90	.50
199	1961-MVPs (Roger Maris, Frank Robinson)	2.25	1.25	.70
200	1962-MVPs (Mickey Mantle, Maury Wills)	9.00	4.50	2.75
201	1963-MVPs (Elston Howard, Sandy Koufax)	2.25	1.25	.70
202	1964-MVPs (Ken Boyer, Brooks Robinson)	1.75	.90	.50
203	1965-MVPs (Willie Mays, Zoilo Versalles)	1.75	.90	.50
204	1966-MVPs (Roberto Clemente, Frank Robinson)	2.25	1.25	.70
205	1967-MVPs (Orlando Cepeda, Carl Yastrzemski)	1.75	.90	.50
206	1968-MVPs (Bob Gibson, Denny McLain)	1.75	.90	.50
207	1969-MVPs (Harmon Killebrew, Willie McCovey)	2.25	1.25	.70
208	1970-MVPs (Johnny Bench, Boog Powell)	1.75	.90	.50
209	1971-MVPs (Vida Blue, Joe Torre)	.80	.40	.25
210	1972-MVPs (Rich Allen, Johnny Bench)	1.75	.90	.50
211	1973-MVPs (Reggie Jackson, Pete Rose)	7.00	3.50	2.00
212	1974-MVPs (Jeff Burroughs, Steve Garvey)	1.25	.60	.40
213	Oscar Gamble	.40	.20	.12
214	Harry Parker	.40	.20	.12
215	Bobby Valentine	.40	.20	.12
216	Giants Team (Wes Westrum)	1.25	.60	.40
217	Lou Piniella	.80	.40	.25
218	Jerry Johnson	.40	.20	.12
219	Ed Herrmann	.40	.20	.12
220	Don Sutton	3.00	1.50	.90
221	Aurelio Rodriquez (Rodriguez)	.40	.20	.12
222	Dan Spillner	.40	.20	.12
223	Robin Yount	200.00	100.00	60.00
224	Ramon Hernandez	.40	.20	.12
225	Bob Grich	.60	.30	.20
226	Bill Campbell	.40	.20	.12
227	Bob Watson	.40	.20	.12
228	George Brett	250.00	125.00	75.00
229	Barry Foote	.40	.20	.12
230	Catfish Hunter	4.00	2.00	1.25
231	Mike Tyson	.40	.20	.12
232	Diego Segui	.40	.20	.12
233	Billy Grabarkewitz	.40	.20	.12
234	Tom Grieve	.40	.20	.12
235	Jack Billingham	.40	.20	.12
236	Angels Team (Dick Williams)	1.25	.60	.40
237	Carl Morton	.40	.20	.12
238	Dave Duncan	.40	.20	.12
239	George Stone	.40	.20	.12
240	Garry Maddox	.60	.30	.20
241	Dick Tidrow	.40	.20	.12
242	Jay Johnstone	.60	.30	.20
243	Jim Kaat	2.00	1.00	.60
244	Bill Buckner	.80	.40	.25
245	Mickey Lolich	.80	.40	.25
246	Cardinals Team (Red Schoendienst)	1.25	.60	.40
247	Enos Cabell	.40	.20	.12
248	Randy Jones	.40	.20	.12
249	Danny Thompson	.40	.20	.12
250	Ken Brett	.40	.20	.12
251	Fran Healy	.40	.20	.12
252	Fred Scherman	.40	.20	.12
253	Jesus Alou	.40	.20	.12
254	Mike Torrez	.40	.20	.12
255	Dwight Evans	1.50	.70	.45
256	Billy Champion	.40	.20	.12
257	Checklist 133-264	2.25	1.25	.70
258	Dave LaRoche	.40	.20	.12
259	Len Randle	.40	.20	.12
260	Johnny Bench	15.00	7.50	4.50
261	Andy Hassler	.40	.20	.12
262	Rowland Office	.40	.20	.12
263	Jim Perry	.60	.30	.20
264	John Milner	.40	.20	.12
265	Ron Bryant	.40	.20	.12
266	Sandy Alomar	.40	.20	.12
267	Dick Ruthven	.40	.20	.12
268	Hal McRae	.60	.30	.20
269	Doug Rau	.40	.20	.12
270	Ron Fairly	.60	.30	.20
271	Jerry Moses	.40	.20	.12
272	Lynn McGlothen	.40	.20	.12
273	Steve Braun	.40	.20	.12
274	Vicente Romo	.40	.20	.12
275	Paul Blair	.60	.30	.20
276	White Sox Team (Chuck Tanner)	1.25	.60	.40
277	Frank Taveras	.40	.20	.12
278	Paul Lindblad	.40	.20	.12
279	Milt May	.40	.20	.12
280	Carl Yastrzemski	10.00	5.00	3.00
281	Jim Slaton	.40	.20	.12
282	Jerry Morales	.40	.20	.12
283	Steve Foucault	.40	.20	.12
284	Ken Griffey	3.00	1.50	.90
285	Ellie Rodriguez	.40	.20	.12
286	Mike Jorgensen	.40	.20	.12
287	Roric Harrison	.40	.20	.12
288	Bruce Ellingsen	.40	.20	.12
289	Ken Rudolph	.40	.20	.12
290	Jon Matlack	.40	.20	.12
291	Bill Sudakis	.40	.20	.12
292	Ron Schueler	.40	.20	.12
293	Dick Sharon	.40	.20	.12
294	Geoff Zahn	.40	.20	.12
295	Vada Pinson	1.50	.70	.45
296	Alan Foster	.40	.20	.12
297	Craig Kusick	.40	.20	.12
298	Johnny Grubb	.40	.20	.12
299	Bucky Dent	.60	.30	.20
300	Reggie Jackson	30.00	15.00	9.00
301	Dave Roberts	.40	.20	.12
302	Rick Burleson	.80	.40	.25
303	Grant Jackson	.40	.20	.12
304	Pirates Team (Danny Murtaugh)	1.25	.60	.40
305	Jim Colborn	.40	.20	.12
306	Batting Leaders (Rod Carew, Ralph Garr)	1.25	.60	.40
307	Home Run Leaders (Dick Allen, Mike Schmidt)	1.25	.60	.40
308	Runs Batted In Leaders (Johnny Bench, Jeff Burroughs)	1.25	.60	.40

309 Stole Base Leaders (Lou Brock, Bill North) 1.25 .60 .40
310 Victory Leaders (Catfish Hunter, Fergie Jenkins, Andy Messersmith, Phil Niekro) 1.25 .60 .40
311 Earned Run Average Leaders (Buzz Capra, Catfish Hunter) .80 .40 .25
312 Strikeout Leaders (Steve Carlton, Nolan Ryan) 2.50 1.25 .70
313 Leading Firemen (Terry Forster, Mike Marshall) .80 .40 .25
314 Buck Martinez .40 .20 .12
315 Don Kessinger .40 .20 .12
316 Jackie Brown .40 .20 .12
317 Joe Lahoud .40 .20 .12
318 Ernie McAnally .40 .20 .12
319 Johnny Oates .40 .20 .12
320 Pete Rose 25.00 12.50 7.50
321 Rudy May .40 .20 .12
322 Ed Goodson .40 .20 .12
323 Fred Holdsworth .40 .20 .12
324 Ed Kranepool .40 .20 .12
325 Tony Oliva 2.50 1.25 .70
326 Wayne Twitchell .40 .20 .12
327 Jerry Hairston .40 .20 .12
328 Sonny Siebert .40 .20 .12
329 Ted Kubiak .40 .20 .12
330 Mike Marshall .60 .30 .20
331 Indians Team (Frank Robinson) 1.25 .60 .40
332 Fred Kendall .40 .20 .12
333 Dick Drago .40 .20 .12
334 Greg Gross .40 .20 .12
335 Jim Palmer 10.00 5.00 3.00
336 Rennie Stennett .40 .20 .12
337 Kevin Kobel .40 .20 .12
338 Rick Stelmaszek .40 .20 .12
339 Jim Fregosi .60 .30 .20
340 Paul Splittorff .40 .20 .12
341 Hal Breeden .40 .20 .12
342 Leroy Stanton .40 .20 .12
343 Danny Frisella .40 .20 .12
344 Ben Oglivie .60 .30 .20
345 Clay Carroll .40 .20 .12
346 Bobby Darwin .40 .20 .12
347 Mike Caldwell .40 .20 .12
348 Tony Muser .40 .20 .12
349 Ray Sadecki .40 .20 .12
350 Bobby Murcer .60 .30 .20
351 Bob Boone 2.00 1.00 .60
352 Darold Knowles .40 .20 .12
353 Luis Melendez .40 .20 .12
354 Dick Bosman .40 .20 .12
355 Chris Cannizzaro .40 .20 .12
356 Rico Petrocelli .40 .20 .12
357 Ken Forsch .40 .20 .12
358 Al Bumbry .40 .20 .12
359 Paul Popovich .40 .20 .12
360 George Scott .40 .20 .12
361 Dodgers Team (Walter Alston) 1.50 .70 .45
362 Steve Hargan .40 .20 .12
363 Carmen Fanzone .40 .20 .12
364 Doug Bird .40 .20 .12
365 Bob Bailey .40 .20 .12
366 Ken Sanders .40 .20 .12
367 Craig Robinson .40 .20 .12
368 Vic Albury .40 .20 .12
369 Merv Rettenmund .40 .20 .12
370 Tom Seaver 20.00 10.00 6.00
371 Gates Brown .40 .20 .12
372 John D'Acquisto .40 .20 .12
373 Bill Sharp .40 .20 .12
374 Eddie Watt .40 .20 .12
375 Roy White .60 .30 .20
376 Steve Yeager .40 .20 .12
377 Tom Hilgendorf .40 .20 .12
378 Derrel Thomas .40 .20 .12
379 Bernie Carbo .40 .20 .12
380 Sal Bando .60 .30 .20
381 John Curtis .40 .20 .12
382 Don Baylor .90 .45 .25
383 Jim York .40 .20 .12
384 Brewers Team (Del Crandall) 1.25 .60 .40
385 Dock Ellis .40 .20 .12
386 Checklist 265-396 2.25 1.25 .70
387 Jim Spencer .40 .20 .12
388 Steve Stone .60 .30 .20
389 Tony Solaita .40 .20 .12
390 Ron Cey .60 .30 .20
391 Don DeMola .40 .20 .12
392 Bruce Bochte .40 .20 .12
393 Gary Gentry .40 .20 .12
394 Larvell Blanks .40 .20 .12
395 Bud Harrelson .40 .20 .12
396 Fred Norman .40 .20 .12
397 Bill Freehan .60 .30 .20
398 Elias Sosa .40 .20 .12
399 Terry Harmon .40 .20 .12
400 Dick Allen 1.25 .60 .40
401 Mike Wallace .40 .20 .12
402 Bob Tolan .40 .20 .12
403 Tom Buskey .40 .20 .12
404 Ted Sizemore .40 .20 .12
405 John Montague .40 .20 .12
406 Bob Gallagher .40 .20 .12
407 Herb Washington .80 .40 .25
408 Clyde Wright .40 .20 .12
409 Bob Robertson .40 .20 .12
410 Mike Cueller (Cuellar) .60 .30 .20
411 George Mitterwald .40 .20 .12
412 Bill Hands .40 .20 .12
413 Marty Pattin .40 .20 .12
414 Manny Mota .60 .30 .20
415 John Hiller .40 .20 .12
416 Larry Lintz .40 .20 .12
417 Skip Lockwood .40 .20 .12
418 Leo Foster .40 .20 .12
419 Dave Goltz .40 .20 .12
420 Larry Bowa .60 .30 .20
421 Mets Team (Yogi Berra) 1.50 .70 .45
422 Brian Downing .60 .30 .20
423 Clay Kirby .40 .20 .12
424 John Lowenstein .40 .20 .12
425 Tito Fuentes .40 .20 .12
426 George Medich .40 .20 .12
427 Cito Gaston .75 .40 .25
428 Dave Hamilton .40 .20 .12
429 Jim Dwyer .40 .20 .12
430 Luis Tiant .80 .40 .25
431 Rod Gilbreath .40 .20 .12
432 Ken Berry .40 .20 .12
433 Larry Demery .40 .20 .12
434 Bob Locker .40 .20 .12
435 Dave Nelson .40 .20 .12
436 Ken Frailing .40 .20 .12
437 Al Cowens .40 .20 .12
438 Don Carrithers .40 .20 .12
439 Ed Brinkman .40 .20 .12
440 Andy Messersmith .60 .30 .20
441 Bobby Heise .40 .20 .12
442 Maximino Leon .40 .20 .12
443 Twins Team (Frank Quilici) 1.25 .60 .40
444 Gene Garber .40 .20 .12
445 Felix Millan .40 .20 .12
446 Bart Johnson .40 .20 .12
447 Terry Crowley .40 .20 .12
448 Frank Duffy .40 .20 .12
449 Charlie Williams .40 .20 .12
450 Willie McCovey 7.00 3.50 2.00
451 Rick Dempsey .60 .30 .20
452 Angel Mangual .40 .20 .12
453 Claude Osteen .40 .20 .12
454 Doug Griffin .40 .20 .12
455 Don Wilson .40 .20 .12
456 Bob Coluccio .40 .20 .12
457 Mario Mendoza .40 .20 .12
458 Ross Grimsley .40 .20 .12
459 A.L. Championships 1.25 .60 .40
460 N.L. Championships 1.25 .60 .40
461 World Series Game 1 2.25 1.25 .70
462 World Series Game 2 1.50 .70 .45
463 World Series Game 3 1.50 .70 .45
464 World Series Game 4 1.25 .60 .40
465 World Series Game 5 1.25 .60 .40
466 World Series Summary 1.25 .60 .40
467 Ed Halicki .40 .20 .12
468 Bobby Mitchell .40 .20 .12
469 Tom Dettore .40 .20 .12
470 Jeff Burroughs .40 .20 .12
471 Bob Stinson .40 .20 .12
472 Bruce Dal Canton .40 .20 .12
473 Ken McMullen .40 .20 .12
474 Luke Walker .40 .20 .12
475 Darrell Evans .90 .45 .25
476 Ed Figueroa .40 .20 .12
477 Tom Hutton .40 .20 .12
478 Tom Burgmeier .40 .20 .12
479 Ken Boswell .40 .20 .12
480 Carlos May .40 .20 .12
481 Will McEnaney .40 .20 .12
482 Tom McCraw .40 .20 .12
483 Steve Ontiveros .40 .20 .12
484 Glenn Beckert .40 .20 .12
485 Sparky Lyle .60 .30 .20
486 Ray Fosse .40 .20 .12
487 Astros Team (Preston Gomez) 1.25 .60 .40
488 Bill Travers .40 .20 .12
489 Cecil Cooper .75 .40 .25
490 Reggie Smith .60 .30 .20
491 Doyle Alexander .60 .30 .20
492 Rich Hebner .40 .20 .12
493 Doug Stanhouse .40 .20 .12
494 Pete LaCock .40 .20 .12
495 Nelson Briles .40 .20 .12
496 Pepe Frias .40 .20 .12
497 Jim Nettles .40 .20 .12
498 Al Downing .40 .20 .12
499 Marty Perez .40 .20 .12
500 Nolan Ryan 90.00 45.00 27.00
501 Bill Robinson .40 .20 .12
502 Pat Bourque .40 .20 .12
503 Fred Stanley .40 .20 .12
504 Buddy Bradford .40 .20 .12
505 Chris Speier .40 .20 .12
506 Leron Lee .40 .20 .12
507 Tom Carroll .40 .20 .12
508 Bob Hansen .40 .20 .12
509 Dave Hilton .40 .20 .12
510 Vida Blue .80 .40 .25
511 Rangers Team (Billy Martin) 1.25 .60 .40
512 Larry Milbourne .40 .20 .12
513 Dick Pole .40 .20 .12
514 Jose Cruz .80 .40 .25
515 Manny Sanguillen .40 .20 .12
516 Don Hood .40 .20 .12
517 Checklist 397-528 2.25 1.25 .70
518 Leo Cardenas .40 .20 .12
519 Jim Todd .40 .20 .12
520 Amos Otis .40 .20 .12
521 Dennis Blair .40 .20 .12
522 Gary Sutherland .40 .20 .12
523 Tom Paciorek .40 .20 .12
524 John Doherty .40 .20 .12
525 Tom House .40 .20 .12
526 Larry Hisle .40 .20 .12
527 Mac Scarce .40 .20 .12
528 Eddie Leon .40 .20 .12
529 Gary Thomasson .40 .20 .12
530 Gaylord Perry 6.00 3.00 1.75
531 Reds Team (Sparky Anderson) 1.50 .70 .45
532 Gorman Thomas .40 .20 .12
533 Rudy Meoli .40 .20 .12
534 Alex Johnson .40 .20 .12
535 Gene Tenace .40 .20 .12
536 Bob Moose .40 .20 .12
537 Tommy Harper .40 .20 .12
538 Duffy Dyer .40 .20 .12
539 Jesse Jefferson .40 .20 .12
540 Lou Brock 7.00 3.50 2.00
541 Roger Metzger .40 .20 .12
542 Pete Broberg .40 .20 .12
543 Larry Biittner .40 .20 .12
544 Steve Mingori .40 .20 .12
545 Billy Williams 6.00 3.00 1.75
546 John Knox .40 .20 .12
547 Von Joshua .40 .20 .12
548 Charlie Sands .40 .20 .12
549 Bill Butler .40 .20 .12
550 Ralph Garr .40 .20 .12
551 Larry Christenson .40 .20 .12
552 Jack Brohamer .40 .20 .12
553 John Boccabella .40 .20 .12
554 Rich Gossage 1.75 .90 .50
555 Al Oliver 1.25 .60 .40
556 Tim Johnson .40 .20 .12
557 Larry Gura .40 .20 .12
558 Dave Roberts .40 .20 .12
559 Bob Montgomery .40 .20 .12
560 Tony Perez 4.00 2.00 1.25
561 A's Team (Alvin Dark) 1.25 .60 .40
562 Gary Nolan .40 .20 .12
563 Wilbur Howard .40 .20 .12
564 Tommy Davis .60 .30 .20
565 Joe Torre 1.00 .50 .30
566 Ray Burris .40 .20 .12
567 Jim Sundberg .60 .30 .20
568 Dale Murray .40 .20 .12
569 Frank White .60 .30 .20
570 Jim Wynn .60 .30 .20
571 Dave Lemanczyk .40 .20 .12
572 Roger Nelson .40 .20 .12
573 Orlando Pena .40 .20 .12
574 Tony Taylor .40 .20 .12
575 Gene Clines .40 .20 .12
576 Phil Roof .40 .20 .12
577 John Morris .40 .20 .12
578 Dave Tomlin .40 .20 .12
579 Skip Pitlock .40 .20 .12
580 Frank Robinson 7.00 3.50 2.00
581 Darrel Chaney .40 .20 .12
582 Eduardo Rodriguez .40 .20 .12
583 Andy Etchebarren .40 .20 .12
584 Mike Garman .40 .20 .12
585 Chris Chambliss .60 .30 .20
586 Tim McCarver 1.25 .60 .40
587 Chris Ward .40 .20 .12
588 Rick Auerbach .40 .20 .12
589 Braves Team (Clyde King) 1.25 .60 .40
590 Cesar Cedeno .60 .30 .20
591 Glenn Abbott .40 .20 .12
592 Balor Moore .40 .20 .12
593 Gene Lamont .40 .20 .12
594 Jim Fuller .40 .20 .12
595 Joe Niekro .60 .30 .20
596 Ollie Brown .40 .20 .12
597 Winston Llenas .40 .20 .12
598 Bruce Kison .40 .20 .12
599 Nate Colbert .40 .20 .12
600 Rod Carew 12.00 6.00 3.50
601 Juan Beniquez .40 .20 .12
602 John Vukovich .40 .20 .12
603 Lew Krausse .40 .20 .12
604 Oscar Zamora .40 .20 .12
605 John Ellis .40 .20 .12
606 Bruce Miller .40 .20 .12
607 Jim Holt .40 .20 .12
608 Gene Michael .40 .20 .12
609 Ellie Hendricks .40 .20 .12
610 Ron Hunt .40 .20 .12
611 Yankees Team (Bill Virdon) 1.75 .90 .50
612 Terry Hughes .40 .20 .12
613 Bill Parsons .40 .20 .12
614 Rookie Pitchers (Jack Kucek, Dyar Miller, Vern Ruhle, Paul Siebert) .40 .20 .12
615 Rookie Pitchers (Pat Darcy, Dennis Leonard, Tom Underwood, Hank Webb) .90 .45 .25
616 Rookie Outfielders (Dave Augustine, Pepe Mangual, Jim Rice, John Scott) 50.00 25.00 15.00
617 Rookie Infielders (Mike Cubbage, Doug DeCinces, Reggie Sanders, Manny Trillo) 2.50 1.25 .70
618 Rookie Pitchers (Jamie Easterly, Tom Johnson, Scott McGregor, Rick Rhoden) 5.00 2.50 1.50
619 Rookie Outfielders (Benny Ayala, Nyls Nyman, Tommy Smith, Jerry Turner) .40 .20 .12
620 Rookie Catchers-Outfielders (Gary Carter, Marc Hill, Danny Meyer, Leon Roberts) 50.00 25.00 15.00
621 Rookie Pitchers (John Denny, Rawly Eastwick, Jim Kern, Juan Veintidos) .90 .45 .25
622 Rookie Outfielders (Ed Armbrister, Fred Lynn, Tom Poquette, Terry Whitfield) 15.00 7.50 4.50
623 Rookie Infielders (Phil Garner, Keith Hernandez, Bob Sheldon, Tom Veryzer) 40.00 20.00 12.00
624 Rookie Pitchers (Doug Konieczny, Gary Lavelle, Jim Otten, Eddie Solomon) .40 .20 .12
625 Boog Powell 2.00 1.00 .60
626 Larry Haney .40 .20 .12
627 Tom Walker .40 .20 .12
628 Ron LeFlore 1.25 .60 .40
629 Joe Hoerner .40 .20 .12
630 Greg Luzinski 2.00 1.00 .60
631 Lee Lacy .40 .20 .12
632 Morris Nettles .40 .20 .12
633 Paul Casanova .40 .20 .12
634 Cy Acosta .40 .20 .12
635 Chuck Dobson .40 .20 .12
636 Charlie Moore .40 .20 .12
637 Ted Martinez .40 .20 .12
638 Cubs Team (Jim Marshall) 1.25 .60 .40
639 Steve Kline .40 .20 .12
640 Harmon Killebrew 6.00 3.00 1.75
641 Jim Northrup .40 .20 .12
642 Mike Phillips .40 .20 .12
643 Brent Strom .40 .20 .12
644 Bill Fahey .40 .20 .12

645	Danny Cater	.40	.20	.12
646	Checklist 529-660	2.25	1.25	.70
647	Claudell Washington	2.00	1.00	.60
648	Dave Pagan	.40	.20	.12
649	Jack Heidemann	.40	.20	.12
650	Dave May	.40	.20	.12
651	John Morlan	.40	.20	.12
652	Lindy McDaniel	.40	.20	.12
653	Lee Richards	.40	.20	.12
654	Jerry Terrell	.40	.20	.12
655	Rico Carty	.60	.30	.20
656	Bill Plummer	.40	.20	.12
657	Bob Oliver	.40	.20	.12
658	Vic Harris	.40	.20	.12
659	Bob Apodaca	.40	.20	.12
660	Hank Aaron	35.00	17.50	10.50

1976 Topps

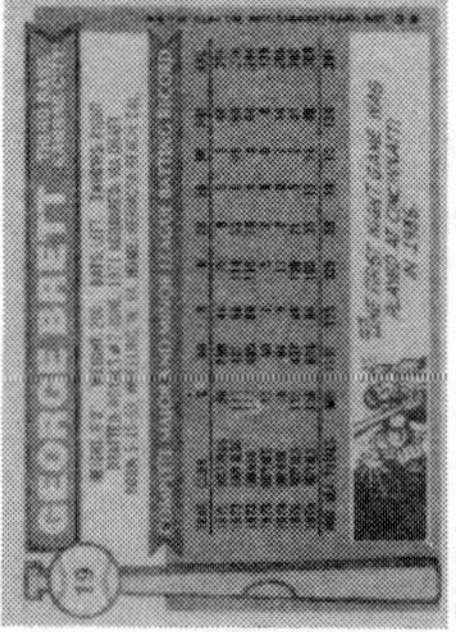

These 2-1/2" by 3-1/2" cards begin a design trend for Topps. The focus was more on the photo quality than in past years with a corresponding trend toward simplicity in the borders. The front of the cards has the player's name and team in two strips while his position is in the lower left corner under a drawing of a player representing that position. The backs have a bat and ball with the card number on the left; statistics and personal information and career highlights on the right. The 660-card set features a number of specialty sets including record-setting performances, statistical leaders, playoff and World Series highlights, the Sporting News All-Time All-Stars and father and son combinations.

		NR MT	EX	VG
	Complete Set (660):	450.00	225.00	135.00
	Common Player:	.25	.13	.08
1	Record Breaker (Hank Aaron)	15.00	7.50	4.50
2	Record Breaker (Bobby Bonds)	.40	.20	.12
3	Record Breaker (Mickey Lolich)	.35	.20	.11
4	Record Breaker (Dave Lopes)	.25	.13	.08
5	Record Breaker (Tom Seaver)	4.00	2.00	1.25
6	Record Breaker (Rennie Stennett)	.25	.13	.08
7	Jim Umbarger	.25	.13	.08
8	Tito Fuentes	.25	.13	.08
9	Paul Lindblad	.25	.13	.08
10	Lou Brock	4.00	2.00	1.25
11	Jim Hughes	.25	.13	.08
12	Richie Zisk	.25	.13	.08
13	Johnny Wockenfuss	.25	.13	.08
14	Gene Garber	.25	.13	.08
15	George Scott	.25	.13	.08
16	Bob Apodaca	.25	.13	.08
17	Yankees Team (Billy Martin)	1.25	.60	.40
18	Dale Murray	.25	.13	.08
19	George Brett	60.00	30.00	18.00
20	Bob Watson	.25	.13	.08
21	Dave LaRoche	.25	.13	.08
22	Bill Russell	.25	.13	.08
23	Brian Downing	.25	.13	.08
24	Cesar Geronimo	.25	.13	.08
25	Mike Torrez	.25	.13	.08
26	Andy Thornton	.25	.13	.08
27	Ed Figueroa	.25	.13	.08
28	Dusty Baker	1.50	.75	.45
29	Rick Burleson	.25	.13	.08
30	*John Montefusco*	.25	.13	.08
31	Len Randle	.25	.13	.08
32	Danny Frisella	.25	.13	.08
33	Bill North	.25	.13	.08
34	Mike Garman	.25	.13	.08
35	Tony Oliva	.40	.20	.12
36	Frank Taveras	.25	.13	.08
37	John Hiller	.25	.13	.08
38	Garry Maddox	.25	.13	.08
39	Pete Broberg	.25	.13	.08
40	Dave Kingman	.25	.13	.08
41	*Tippy Martinez*	.25	.13	.08
42	Barry Foote	.25	.13	.08
43	Paul Splittorff	.25	.13	.08
44	Doug Rader	.25	.13	.08
45	Boog Powell	.25	.13	.08
46	Dodgers Team (Walter Alston)	1.00	.50	.30
47	Jesse Jefferson	.25	.13	.08
48	Dave Concepcion	.40	.20	.12
49	Dave Duncan	.25	.13	.08
50	Fred Lynn	2.00	1.00	.60
51	Ray Burris	.25	.13	.08
52	Dave Chalk	.25	.13	.08
53	Mike Beard	.25	.13	.08
54	Dave Rader	.25	.13	.08
55	Gaylord Perry	3.00	1.50	.90
56	Bob Tolan	.25	.13	.08
57	Phil Garner	.25	.13	.08
58	Ron Reed	.25	.13	.08
59	Larry Hisle	.25	.13	.08
60	Jerry Reuss	.25	.13	.08
61	Ron LeFlore	.25	.13	.08
62	Johnny Oates	.25	.13	.08
63	Bobby Darwin	.25	.13	.08
64	Jerry Koosman	.25	.13	.08
65	Chris Chambliss	.25	.13	.08
66	Father & Son (Buddy Bell, Gus Bell)	.25	.13	.08
67	Father & Son (Bob Boone, Ray Boone)	.40	.20	.12
68	Father & Son (Joe Coleman, Joe Coleman, Jr.)	.25	.13	.08
69	Father & Son (Jim Hegan, Mike Hegan)	.25	.13	.08
70	Father & Son (Roy Smalley, Roy Smalley, Jr.)	.25	.13	.08
71	Steve Rogers	.25	.13	.08
72	Hal McRae	.40	.20	.12
73	Orioles Team (Earl Weaver)	1.00	.50	.30
74	Oscar Gamble	.25	.13	.08
75	Larry Dierker	.25	.13	.08
76	Willie Crawford	.25	.13	.08
77	Pedro Borbon	.25	.13	.08
78	Cecil Cooper	.50	.25	.15
79	Jerry Morales	.25	.13	.08
80	Jim Kaat	.90	.45	.25
81	Darrell Evans	.40	.20	.12
82	Von Joshua	.25	.13	.08
83	Jim Spencer	.25	.13	.08
84	Brent Strom	.25	.13	.08
85	Mickey Rivers	.25	.13	.08
86	Mike Tyson	.25	.13	.08
87	Tom Burgmeier	.25	.13	.08
88	Duffy Dyer	.25	.13	.08
89	Vern Ruhle	.25	.13	.08
90	Sal Bando	.25	.13	.08
91	Tom Hutton	.25	.13	.08
92	Eduardo Rodriguez	.25	.13	.08
93	Mike Phillips	.25	.13	.08
94	Jim Dwyer	.25	.13	.08
95	Brooks Robinson	5.00	2.50	1.50
96	Doug Bird	.25	.13	.08
97	Wilbur Howard	.25	.13	.08
98	*Dennis Eckersley*	45.00	22.00	13.50
99	Lee Lacy	.25	.13	.08
100	Catfish Hunter	3.00	1.50	.90
101	Pete LaCock	.25	.13	.08
102	Jim Willoughby	.25	.13	.08
103	Biff Pocoroba	.25	.13	.08
104	Reds Team (Sparky Anderson)	1.00	.50	.30
105	Gary Lavelle	.25	.13	.08
106	Tom Grieve	.25	.13	.08
107	Dave Roberts	.25	.13	.08
108	Don Kirkwood	.25	.13	.08
109	Larry Lintz	.25	.13	.08
110	Carlos May	.25	.13	.08
111	Danny Thompson	.25	.13	.08
112	*Kent Tekulve*	.75	.40	.25
113	Gary Sutherland	.25	.13	.08
114	Jay Johnstone	.25	.13	.08
115	Ken Holtzman	.25	.13	.08
116	Charlie Moore	.25	.13	.08
117	Mike Jorgensen	.25	.13	.08
118	Red Sox Team (Darrell Johnson)	.90	.45	.25
119	Checklist 1-132	1.25	.60	.40
120	Rusty Staub	.35	.20	.11
121	Tony Solaita	.25	.13	.08
122	Mike Cosgrove	.25	.13	.08
123	Walt Williams	.25	.13	.08
124	Doug Rau	.25	.13	.08
125	Don Baylor	.40	.20	.12
126	Tom Dettore	.25	.13	.08
127	Larvell Blanks	.25	.13	.08
128	Ken Griffey	.40	.20	.12
129	Andy Etchebarren	.25	.13	.08
130	Luis Tiant	.40	.20	.12
131	Bill Stein	.25	.13	.08
132	Don Hood	.25	.13	.08
133	Gary Matthews	.25	.13	.08
134	Mike Ivie	.25	.13	.08
135	Bake McBride	.25	.13	.08
136	Dave Goltz	.25	.13	.08
137	Bill Robinson	.25	.13	.08
138	Lerrin LaGrow	.25	.13	.08
139	Gorman Thomas	.25	.13	.08
140	Vida Blue	.40	.20	.12
141	*Larry Parrish*	.80	.40	.25
142	Dick Drago	.25	.13	.08
143	Jerry Grote	.25	.13	.08
144	Al Fitzmorris	.25	.13	.08
145	Larry Bowa	.35	.20	.11
146	George Medich	.25	.13	.08
147	Astros Team (Bill Virdon)	.80	.40	.25
148	Stan Thomas	.25	.13	.08
149	Tommy Davis	.25	.13	.08
150	Steve Garvey	4.00	2.00	1.25
151	Bill Bonham	.25	.13	.08
152	Leroy Stanton	.25	.13	.08
153	Buzz Capra	.25	.13	.08
154	Bucky Dent	.25	.13	.08
155	Jack Billingham	.25	.13	.08
156	Rico Carty	.25	.13	.08
157	Mike Caldwell	.25	.13	.08
158	Ken Reitz	.25	.13	.08
159	Jerry Terrell	.25	.13	.08
160	Dave Winfield	50.00	25.00	15.00
161	Bruce Kison	.25	.13	.08
162	Jack Pierce	.25	.13	.08
163	Jim Slaton	.25	.13	.08
164	Pepe Mangual	.25	.13	.08
165	Gene Tenace	.25	.13	.08
166	Skip Lockwood	.25	.13	.08
167	Freddie Patek	.25	.13	.08
168	Tom Hilgendorf	.25	.13	.08
169	Graig Nettles	1.00	.50	.30
170	Rick Wise	.25	.13	.08
171	Greg Gross	.25	.13	.08
172	Rangers Team (Frank Lucchesi)	.80	.40	.25
173	Steve Swisher	.25	.13	.08
174	Charlie Hough	.25	.13	.08
175	Ken Singleton	.25	.13	.08
176	Dick Lange	.25	.13	.08
177	Marty Perez	.25	.13	.08
178	Tom Buskey	.25	.13	.08
179	George Foster	1.00	.50	.30
180	Rich Gossage	1.50	.75	.45
181	Willie Montanez	.25	.13	.08
182	Harry Rasmussen	.25	.13	.08
183	Steve Braun	.25	.13	.08
184	Bill Greif	.25	.13	.08
185	Dave Parker	3.00	1.50	.90
186	Tom Walker	.25	.13	.08
187	Pedro Garcia	.25	.13	.08
188	Fred Scherman	.25	.13	.08
189	Claudell Washington	.25	.13	.08
190	Jon Matlack	.25	.13	.08
191	N.L. Batting Leaders (Bill Madlock, Manny Sanguillen, Ted Simmons)	1.00	.50	.30
192	A.L. Batting Leaders (Rod Carew, Fred Lynn, Thurman Munson)	2.00	1.00	.60
193	N.L. Home Run Leaders (Dave Kingman, Greg Luzinski, Mike Schmidt)	2.00	1.00	.60
194	A.L. Home Run Leaders (Reggie Jackson, John Mayberry, George Scott)	2.00	1.00	.60
195	N.L. RBI Leaders (Johnny Bench, Greg Luzinski, Tony Perez, N.L. RBI Leaders)	2.00	1.00	.60
196	A.L. RBI Leaders (Fred Lynn, John Mayberry, George Scott)	1.00	.50	.30
197	N.L. Stolen Base Leaders (Lou Brock, Dave Lopes, Joe Morgan)	1.00	.50	.30
198	A.L. Stolen Base Leaders (Amos Otis, Mickey Rivers, Claudell Washington)	1.00	.50	.30
199	N.L. Victory Leaders (Randy Jones, Andy Messersmith, Tom Seaver, N.L. Victory Leaders)	2.00	1.00	.60
200	A.L. Victory Leaders (Vida Blue, Catfish Hunter, Jim Palmer)	2.00	1.00	.60
201	N.L. ERA Leaders (Randy Jones, Andy Messersmith, Tom Seaver)	2.00	1.00	.60
202	A.L. ERA Leaders (Dennis Eckersley, Catfish Hunter, Jim Palmer)	5.00	2.50	1.50
203	N.L. Strikeout Leaders (Andy Messersmith, John Montefusco, Tom Seaver)	1.50	.75	.45
204	A.L. Strikeout Leaders (Bert Blyleven, Gaylord Perry, Frank Tanana)	1.00	.50	.30
205	Major League Leading Firemen (Rich Gossage, Al Hrabosky)	.40	.20	.12
206	Manny Trillo	.25	.13	.08
207	Andy Hassler	.25	.13	.08
208	Mike Lum	.25	.13	.08
209	Alan Ashby	.25	.13	.08
210	Lee May	.25	.13	.08
211	Clay Carroll	.25	.13	.08
212	Pat Kelly	.25	.13	.08
213	Dave Heaverlo	.25	.13	.08
214	Eric Soderholm	.25	.13	.08
215	Reggie Smith	.25	.13	.08
216	Expos Team (Karl Kuehl)	.80	.40	.25
217	Dave Freisleben	.25	.13	.08
218	John Knox	.25	.13	.08
219	Tom Murphy	.25	.13	.08
220	Manny Sanguillen	.25	.13	.08
221	Jim Todd	.25	.13	.08
222	Wayne Garrett	.25	.13	.08
223	Ollie Brown	.25	.13	.08
224	Jim York	.25	.13	.08
225	Roy White	.25	.13	.08
226	Jim Sundberg	.25	.13	.08
227	Oscar Zamora	.25	.13	.08
228	John Hale	.25	.13	.08
229	*Jerry Remy*	.25	.13	.08
230	Carl Yastrzemski	8.00	4.00	2.50
231	Tom House	.25	.13	.08
232	Frank Duffy	.25	.13	.08
233	Grant Jackson	.25	.13	.08
234	Mike Sadek	.25	.13	.08
235	Bert Blyleven	.50	.25	.15
236	Royals Team (Whitey Herzog)	.80	.40	.25
237	Dave Hamilton	.25	.13	.08
238	Larry Biittner	.25	.13	.08
239	John Curtis	.25	.13	.08
240	Pete Rose	12.00	6.00	3.50
241	Hector Torres	.25	.13	.08
242	Dan Meyer	.25	.13	.08
243	Jim Rooker	.25	.13	.08
244	Bill Sharp	.25	.13	.08
245	Felix Millan	.25	.13	.08
246	Cesar Tovar	.25	.13	.08
247	Terry Harmon	.25	.13	.08
248	Dick Tidrow	.25	.13	.08
249	Cliff Johnson	.25	.13	.08
250	Fergie Jenkins	3.00	1.50	.90
251	Rick Monday	.25	.13	.08
252	Tim Nordbrook	.25	.13	.08
253	Bill Buckner	.25	.13	.08
254	Rudy Meoli	.25	.13	.08
255	Fritz Peterson	.25	.13	.08
256	Rowland Office	.25	.13	.08
257	Ross Grimsley	.25	.13	.08
258	Nyls Nyman	.25	.13	.08
259	Darrel Chaney	.25	.13	.08
260	Steve Busby	.25	.13	.08
261	Gary Thomasson	.25	.13	.08
262	Checklist 133-264	1.50	.70	.45
263	*Lyman Bostock*	.80	.40	.25
264	Steve Renko	.25	.13	.08
265	Willie Davis	.25	.13	.08
266	Alan Foster	.25	.13	.08

267 Aurelio Rodriguez .25 .13 .08
268 Del Unser .25 .13 .08
269 Rick Austin .25 .13 .08
270 Willie Stargell 3.00 1.50 .90
271 Jim Lonborg .25 .13 .08
272 Rick Dempsey .25 .13 .08
273 Joe Niekro .25 .13 .08
274 Tommy Harper .25 .13 .08
275 *Rick Manning* .40 .20 .12
276 Mickey Scott .25 .13 .08
277 Cubs Team (Jim Marshall) .80 .40 .25
278 Bernie Carbo .25 .13 .08
279 Roy Howell .25 .13 .08
280 Burt Hooton .25 .13 .08
281 Dave May .25 .13 .08
282 Dan Osborn .25 .13 .08
283 Merv Rettenmund .25 .13 .08
284 Steve Ontiveros .25 .13 .08
285 Mike Cuellar .25 .13 .08
286 Jim Wohlford .25 .13 .08
287 Pete Mackanin .25 .13 .08
288 Bill Campbell .25 .13 .08
289 Enzo Hernandez .25 .13 .08
290 Ted Simmons .25 .13 .08
291 Ken Sanders .25 .13 .08
292 Leon Roberts .25 .13 .08
293 Bill Castro .25 .13 .08
294 Ed Kirkpatrick .25 .13 .08
295 Dave Cash .25 .13 .08
296 Pat Dobson .25 .13 .08
297 Roger Metzger .25 .13 .08
298 Dick Bosman .25 .13 .08
299 Champ Summers .25 .13 .08
300 Johnny Bench 10.00 5.00 3.00
301 Jackie Brown .25 .13 .08
302 Rick Miller .25 .13 .08
303 Steve Foucault .25 .13 .08
304 Angels Team (Dick Williams) .80 .40 .25
305 Andy Messersmith .25 .13 .08
306 Rod Gilbreath .25 .13 .08
307 Al Bumbry .25 .13 .08
308 Jim Barr .25 .13 .08
309 Bill Melton .25 .13 .08
310 Randy Jones .25 .13 .08
311 Cookie Rojas .25 .13 .08
312 Don Carrithers .25 .13 .08
313 *Dan Ford* .25 .13 .08
314 Ed Kranepool .25 .13 .08
315 Al Hrabosky .25 .13 .08
316 Robin Yount 55.00 27.00 16.50
317 *John Candelaria* 2.00 1.00 .60
318 Bob Boone .25 .13 .08
319 Larry Gura .25 .13 .08
320 Willie Horton .25 .13 .08
321 Jose Cruz .25 .13 .08
322 Glenn Abbott .25 .13 .08
323 Rob Sperring .25 .13 .08
324 Jim Bibby .25 .13 .08
325 Tony Perez 1.50 .70 .45
326 Dick Pole .25 .13 .08
327 Dave Moates .25 .13 .08
328 Carl Morton .25 .13 .08
329 Joe Ferguson .25 .13 .08
330 Nolan Ryan 70.00 35.00 21.00
331 Padres Team (John McNamara) .80 .40 .25
332 Charlie Williams .25 .13 .08
333 Bob Coluccio .25 .13 .08
334 Dennis Leonard .25 .13 .08
335 Bob Grich .25 .13 .08
336 Vic Albury .25 .13 .08
337 Bud Harrelson .25 .13 .08
338 Bob Bailey .25 .13 .08
339 John Denny .25 .13 .08
340 Jim Rice 6.00 3.00 1.75
341 Lou Gehrig (All Time 1B) 5.00 2.50 1.50
342 Rogers Hornsby (All Time 2B) 1.25 .60 .40
343 Pie Traynor (All Time 3B) .80 .40 .25
344 Honus Wagner (All Time SS) 1.25 .60 .40
345 Babe Ruth (All Time OF) 10.00 5.00 3.00
346 Ty Cobb (All Time OF) 5.00 2.50 1.50
347 Ted Williams (All Time OF) 7.50 3.75 2.25
348 Mickey Cochrane (All Time C) .80 .40 .25
349 Walter Johnson (All Time RHP) 1.25 .60 .40
350 Lefty Grove (All Time LHP) 1.00 .50 .30
351 Randy Hundley .25 .13 .08
352 Dave Giusti .25 .13 .08
353 *Sixto Lezcano* .25 .13 .08
354 Ron Blomberg .25 .13 .08
355 Steve Carlton 7.00 3.50 2.00
356 Ted Martinez .25 .13 .08
357 Ken Forsch .25 .13 .08
358 Buddy Bell .25 .13 .08
359 Rick Reuschel .30 .15 .09
360 Jeff Burroughs .25 .13 .08
361 Tigers Team (Ralph Houk) 1.00 .50 .30
362 Will McEnaney .25 .13 .08
363 *Dave Collins* .40 .20 .12
364 Elias Sosa .25 .13 .08
365 Carlton Fisk 9.00 4.50 2.75
366 Bobby Valentine .25 .13 .08
367 Bruce Miller .25 .13 .08
368 Wilbur Wood .25 .13 .08
369 Frank White .25 .13 .08
370 Ron Cey .25 .13 .08
371 Ellie Hendricks .25 .13 .08
372 Rick Baldwin .25 .13 .08
373 Johnny Briggs .25 .13 .08
374 Dan Warthen .25 .13 .08
375 Ron Fairly .25 .13 .08
376 Rich Hebner .25 .13 .08
377 Mike Hegan .25 .13 .08
378 Steve Stone .25 .13 .08
379 Ken Boswell .25 .13 .08
380 Bobby Bonds .25 .13 .08
381 Denny Doyle .25 .13 .08
382 Matt Alexander .25 .13 .08
383 John Ellis .25 .13 .08
384 Phillies Team (Danny Ozark) .80 .40 .25

385 Mickey Lolich .40 .20 .12
386 Ed Goodson .25 .13 .08
387 Mike Miley .25 .13 .08
388 Stan Perzanowski .25 .13 .08
389 Glenn Adams .25 .13 .08
390 Don Gullett .25 .13 .08
391 Jerry Hairston .25 .13 .08
392 Checklist 265-396 1.50 .70 .45
393 Paul Mitchell .25 .13 .08
394 Fran Healy .25 .13 .08
395 Jim Wynn .25 .13 .08
396 Bill Lee .25 .13 .08
397 Tim Foli .25 .13 .08
398 Dave Tomlin .25 .13 .08
399 Luis Melendez .25 .13 .08
400 Rod Carew 8.00 4.00 2.50
401 Ken Brett .25 .13 .08
402 Don Money .25 .13 .08
403 Geoff Zahn .25 .13 .08
404 Enos Cabell .25 .13 .08
405 Rollie Fingers 3.50 1.75 1.00
406 Ed Herrmann .25 .13 .08
407 Tom Underwood .25 .13 .08
408 Charlie Spikes .25 .13 .08
409 Dave Lemanczyk .25 .13 .08
410 Ralph Garr .25 .13 .08
411 Bill Singer .25 .13 .08
412 Toby Harrah .25 .13 .08
413 Pete Varney .25 .13 .08
414 Wayne Garland .25 .13 .08
415 Vada Pinson .40 .20 .12
416 Tommy John 1.00 .50 .30
417 Gene Clines .25 .13 .08
418 Jose Morales .25 .13 .08
419 Reggie Cleveland .25 .13 .08
420 Joe Morgan 6.00 3.00 1.75
421 A's Team .80 .40 .25
422 Johnny Grubb .25 .13 .08
423 Ed Halicki .25 .13 .08
424 Phil Roof .25 .13 .08
425 Rennie Stennett .25 .13 .08
426 Bob Forsch .25 .13 .08
427 Kurt Bevacqua .25 .13 .08
428 Jim Crawford .25 .13 .08
429 Fred Stanley .25 .13 .08
430 Jose Cardenal .25 .13 .08
431 Dick Ruthven .25 .13 .08
432 Tom Veryzer .25 .13 .08
433 Rick Waits .25 .13 .08
434 Morris Nettles .25 .13 .08
435 Phil Niekro 1.50 .70 .45
436 Bill Fahey .25 .13 .08
437 Terry Forster .25 .13 .08
438 Doug DeCinces .25 .13 .08
439 Rick Rhoden .25 .13 .08
440 John Mayberry .25 .13 .08
441 Gary Carter 8.00 4.00 2.50
442 Hank Webb .25 .13 .08
443 Giants Team .80 .40 .25
444 Gary Nolan .25 .13 .08
445 Rico Petrocelli .25 .13 .08
446 Larry Haney .25 .13 .08
447 Gene Locklear .25 .13 .08
448 Tom Johnson .25 .13 .08
449 Bob Robertson .25 .13 .08
450 Jim Palmer 6.00 3.00 1.75
451 Buddy Bradford .25 .13 .08
452 Tom Hausman .25 .13 .08
453 Lou Piniella .25 .13 .08
454 Tom Griffin .25 .13 .08
455 Dick Allen .40 .20 .12
456 Joe Coleman .25 .13 .08
457 Ed Crosby .25 .13 .08
458 Earl Williams .25 .13 .08
459 Jim Brewer .25 .13 .08
460 Cesar Cedeno .25 .13 .08
461 NL & AL Championships .80 .40 .25
462 1975 World Series .80 .40 .25
463 Steve Hargan .25 .13 .08
464 Ken Henderson .25 .13 .08
465 Mike Marshall .25 .13 .08
466 Bob Stinson .25 .13 .08
467 Woodie Fryman .25 .13 .08
468 Jesus Alou .25 .13 .08
469 Rawly Eastwick .25 .13 .08
470 Bobby Murcer .25 .13 .08
471 Jim Burton .25 .13 .08
472 Bob Davis .25 .13 .08
473 Paul Blair .25 .13 .08
474 Ray Corbin .25 .13 .08
475 Joe Rudi .25 .13 .08
476 Bob Moose .25 .13 .08
477 Indians Team (Frank Robinson) .80 .40 .25
478 Lynn McGlothen .25 .13 .08
479 Bobby Mitchell .25 .13 .08
480 Mike Schmidt 30.00 15.00 9.00
481 Rudy May .25 .13 .08
482 Tim Hosley .25 .13 .08
483 Mickey Stanley .25 .13 .08
484 Eric Raich .25 .13 .08
485 Mike Hargrove .25 .13 .08
486 Bruce Dal Canton .25 .13 .08
487 Leron Lee .25 .13 .08
488 Claude Osteen .25 .13 .08
489 Skip Jutze .25 .13 .08
490 Frank Tanana .25 .13 .08
491 Terry Crowley .25 .13 .08
492 Marty Pattin .25 .13 .08
493 Derrel Thomas .25 .13 .08
494 Craig Swan .25 .13 .08
495 Nate Colbert .25 .13 .08
496 Juan Beniquez .25 .13 .08
497 Joe McIntosh .25 .13 .08
498 Glenn Borgmann .25 .13 .08
499 Mario Guerrero .25 .13 .08
500 Reggie Jackson 24.00 12.00 7.25
501 Billy Champion .25 .13 .08
502 Tim McCarver .40 .20 .12

503 Elliott Maddox .25 .13 .08
504 Pirates Team (Danny Murtaugh) .80 .40 .25
505 Mark Belanger .25 .13 .08
506 George Mitterwald .25 .13 .08
507 Ray Bare .25 .13 .08
508 *Duane Kuiper* .25 .13 .08
509 Bill Hands .25 .13 .08
510 Amos Otis .25 .13 .08
511 Jamie Easterly .25 .13 .08
512 Ellie Rodriguez .25 .13 .08
513 Bart Johnson .25 .13 .08
514 Dan Driessen .25 .13 .08
515 Steve Yeager .25 .13 .08
516 Wayne Granger .25 .13 .08
517 John Milner .25 .13 .08
518 *Doug Flynn* .25 .13 .08
519 Steve Brye .25 .13 .08
520 Willie McCovey 3.00 1.50 .90
521 Jim Colborn .25 .13 .08
522 Ted Sizemore .25 .13 .08
523 Bob Montgomery .25 .13 .08
524 Pete Falcone .25 .13 .08
525 Billy Williams 2.25 1.25 .70
526 Checklist 397-528 1.50 .70 .45
527 Mike Anderson .25 .13 .08
528 Dock Ellis .25 .13 .08
529 Deron Johnson .25 .13 .08
530 Don Sutton 1.50 .70 .45
531 Mets Team (Joe Frazier) .90 .45 .25
532 Milt May .25 .13 .08
533 Lee Richard .25 .13 .08
534 Stan Bahnsen .25 .13 .08
535 Dave Nelson .25 .13 .08
536 Mike Thompson .25 .13 .08
537 Tony Muser .25 .13 .08
538 Pat Darcy .25 .13 .08
539 John Balaz .25 .13 .08
540 Bill Freehan .25 .13 .08
541 Steve Mingori .25 .13 .08
542 Keith Hernandez 3.00 1.50 .90
543 Wayne Twitchell .25 .13 .08
544 Pepe Frias .25 .13 .08
545 Sparky Lyle .25 .13 .08
546 Dave Rosello .25 .13 .08
547 Roric Harrison .25 .13 .08
548 Manny Mota .25 .13 .08
549 Randy Tate .25 .13 .08
550 Hank Aaron 25.00 12.50 7.50
551 Jerry DaVanon .25 .13 .08
552 Terry Humphrey .25 .13 .08
553 Randy Moffitt .25 .13 .08
554 Ray Fosse .25 .13 .08
555 Dyar Miller .25 .13 .08
556 Twins Team (Gene Mauch) .80 .40 .25
557 Dan Spillner .25 .13 .08
558 Cito Gaston .40 .20 .12
559 Clyde Wright .25 .13 .08
560 Jorge Orta .25 .13 .08
561 Tom Carroll .25 .13 .08
562 Adrian Garrett .25 .13 .08
563 Larry Demery .25 .13 .08
564 Bubble Gum Blowing Champ (Kurt Bevacqua) .30 .15 .09
565 Tug McGraw .25 .13 .08
566 Ken McMullen .25 .13 .08
567 George Stone .25 .13 .08
568 Rob Andrews .25 .13 .08
569 Nelson Briles .25 .13 .08
570 George Hendrick .25 .13 .08
571 Don DeMola .25 .13 .08
572 Rich Coggins .25 .13 .08
573 Bill Travers .25 .13 .08
574 Don Kessinger .25 .13 .08
575 Dwight Evans 2.00 1.00 .60
576 Maximino Leon .25 .13 .08
577 Marc Hill .25 .13 .08
578 Ted Kubiak .25 .13 .08
579 Clay Kirby .25 .13 .08
580 Bert Campaneris .25 .13 .08
581 Cardinals Team (Red Schoendienst) .80 .40 .25
582 Mike Kekich .25 .13 .08
583 Tommy Helms .25 .13 .08
584 Stan Wall .25 .13 .08
585 Joe Torre .25 .13 .08
586 Ron Schueler .25 .13 .08
587 Leo Cardenas .25 .13 .08
588 Kevin Kobel .25 .13 .08
589 Rookie Pitchers (Santo Alcala, Mike Flanagan, Joe Pactwa, Pablo Torrealba) 1.00 .50 .30
590 Rookie Outfielders (Henry Cruz, Chet Lemon, Ellis Valentine, Terry Whitfield) .75 .40 .25
591 Rookie Pitchers (Steve Grilli, Craig Mitchell, Jose Sosa, George Throop) .25 .13 .08
592 Rookie Infielders (Dave McKay, Willie Randolph, Jerry Royster, Roy Staiger) 6.00 3.00 1.75
593 Rookie Pitchers (Larry Anderson, Ken Crosby, Mark Littell, Butch Metzger) .25 .13 .08
594 Rookie Catchers & Outfielders (Andy Merchant, Ed Ott, Royle Stillman, Jerry White) .25 .13 .08
595 Rookie Pitchers (Steve Barr, Art DeFilippis, Randy Lerch, Sid Monge) .25 .13 .08
596 Rookie Infielders (Lamar Johnson, Johnny LeMaster, Jerry Manuel, Craig Reynolds) .25 .13 .08
597 Rookie Pitchers (*Don Aase*, Jack Kucek, Frank LaCorte, Mike Pazik) .25 .13 .08
598 Rookie Outfielders (Hector Cruz, Jamie Quirk, Jerry Turner, Joe Wallis) .25 .13 .08
599 Rookie Pitchers (Rob Dressler, Ron Guidry, Bob McClure, Pat Zachry) 6.00 3.00 1.75
600 Tom Seaver 12.00 6.00 3.50
601 Ken Rudolph .25 .13 .08
602 Doug Konieczny .25 .13 .08
603 Jim Holt .25 .13 .08
604 Joe Lovitto .25 .13 .08
605 Al Downing .25 .13 .08
606 Brewers Team (Alex Grammas) .80 .40 .25

607	Rich Hinton	.25	.13	.08
608	Vic Correll	.25	.13	.08
609	Fred Norman	.25	.13	.08
610	Greg Luzinski	.50	.25	.15
611	Rich Folkers	.25	.13	.08
612	Joe Lahoud	.25	.13	.08
613	Tim Johnson	.25	.13	.08
614	Fernando Arroyo	.25	.13	.08
615	Mike Cubbage	.25	.13	.08
616	Buck Martinez	.25	.13	.08
617	Darold Knowles	.25	.13	.08
618	Jack Brohamer	.25	.13	.08
619	Bill Butler	.25	.13	.08
620	Al Oliver	.40	.20	.12
621	Tom Hall	.25	.13	.08
622	Rick Auerbach	.25	.13	.08
623	Bob Allietta	.25	.13	.08
624	Tony Taylor	.25	.13	.08
625	J.R. Richard	.25	.13	.08
626	Bob Sheldon	.25	.13	.08
627	Bill Plummer	.25	.13	.08
628	John D'Acquisto	.25	.13	.08
629	Sandy Alomar	.25	.13	.08
630	Chris Speier	.25	.13	.08
631	Braves Team (Dave Bristol)	.80	.40	.25
632	Rogelio Moret	.25	.13	.08
633	*John Stearns*	.25	.13	.08
634	Larry Christenson	.25	.13	.08
635	Jim Fregosi	.25	.13	.08
636	Joe Decker	.25	.13	.08
637	Bruce Bochte	.25	.13	.08
638	Doyle Alexander	.25	.13	.08
639	Fred Kendall	.25	.13	.08
640	Bill Madlock	.50	.25	.15
641	Tom Paciorek	.25	.13	.08
642	Dennis Blair	.25	.13	.08
643	Checklist 529-660	1.50	.70	.45
644	Tom Bradley	.25	.13	.08
645	Darrell Porter	.25	.13	.08
646	John Lowenstein	.25	.13	.08
648	Al Cowens	.25	.13	.08
649	Dave Roberts	.25	.13	.08
650	Thurman Munson	6.00	3.00	1.75
651	John Odom	.25	.13	.08
652	Ed Armbrister	.25	.13	.08
653	*Mike Norris*	.25	.13	.08
654	Doug Griffin	.25	.13	.08
655	Mike Vail	.25	.13	.08
656	White Sox Team (Chuck Tanner)	.80	.40	.25
657	*Roy Smalley*	.25	.13	.08
658	Jerry Johnson	.25	.13	.08
659	Ben Oglivie	.25	.13	.08
660	Dave Lopes	.25	.13	.08

1976 Topps Traded

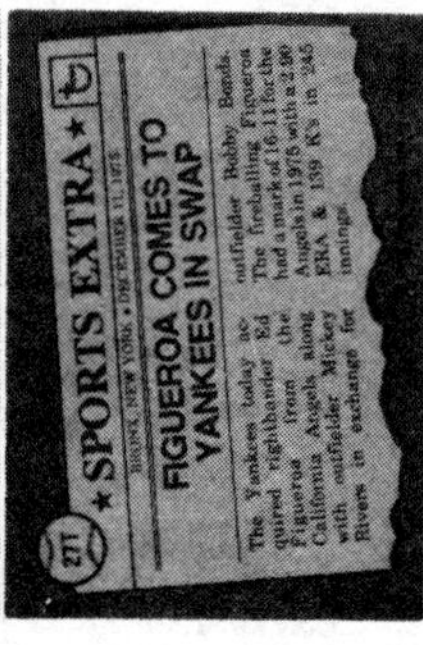

Similar to the Topps Traded set of 1974, the 2-1/2" by 3-1/2" cards feature photos of players traded after the printing deadline. The style of the cards is essentially the same as the regular issue but with a large "Sports Extra" headline announcing the trade and its date. The backs continue in newspaper style to detail the specifics of the trade. There are 43 player cards and one checklist in the set. Numbers remain the same as the player's regular card, with the addition of a "T" suffix.

	NR MT	EX	VG
Complete Set (44):	12.00	6.00	3.50
Common Player:	.25	.13	.08

27T	Ed Figueroa	.25	.13	.08
28T	Dusty Baker	1.25	.60	.40
44T	Doug Rader	.25	.13	.08
58T	Ron Reed	.25	.13	.08
74T	Oscar Gamble	.25	.13	.08
80T	Jim Kaat	1.00	.50	.30
83T	Jim Spencer	.25	.13	.08
85T	Mickey Rivers	.25	.13	.08
99T	Lee Lacy	.25	.13	.08
120T	Rusty Staub	.40	.20	.12
127T	Larvell Blanks	.25	.13	.08
146T	George Medich	.25	.13	.08
158T	Ken Reitz	.25	.13	.08
208T	Mike Lum	.25	.13	.08
211T	Clay Carroll	.25	.13	.08
231T	Tom House	.25	.13	.08
250T	Fergie Jenkins	3.00	1.50	.90
259T	Darrel Chaney	.25	.13	.08
292T	Leon Roberts	.25	.13	.08
296T	Pat Dobson	.25	.13	.08
309T	Bill Melton	.25	.13	.08
338T	Bob Bailey	.25	.13	.08
380T	Bobby Bonds	.90	.45	.25
383T	John Ellis	.25	.13	.08
385T	Mickey Lolich	.90	.45	.25
401T	Ken Brett	.25	.13	.08
410T	Ralph Garr	.25	.13	.08
411T	Bill Singer	.25	.13	.08
428T	Jim Crawford	.25	.13	.08
434T	Morris Nettles	.25	.13	.08
464T	Ken Henderson	.25	.13	.08
497T	Joe McIntosh	.25	.13	.08
524T	Pete Falcone	.25	.13	.08
527T	Mike Anderson	.25	.13	.08
528T	Dock Ellis	.25	.13	.08
532T	Milt May	.25	.13	.08
554T	Ray Fosse	.25	.13	.08
579T	Clay Kirby	.25	.13	.08
583T	Tommy Helms	.25	.13	.08
592T	Willie Randolph	2.00	1.00	.60
618T	Jack Brohamer	.25	.13	.08
632T	Rogelio Moret	.25	.13	.08
649T	Dave Roberts	.25	.13	.08
----	Traded Checklist	.80	.40	.25

1977 Topps

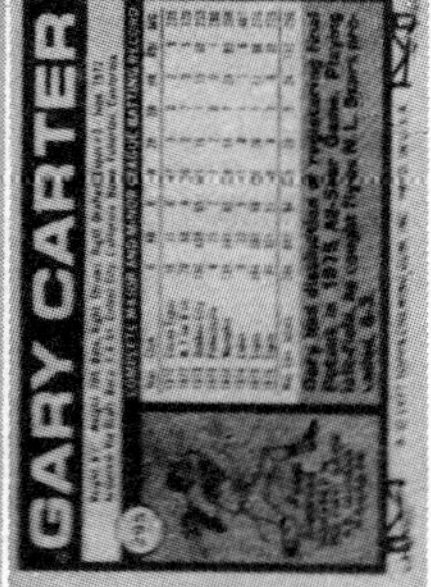

The 1977 Topps Set is a 660-card effort featuring front designs dominated by a color photograph on which there is a facsimile autograph. Above the picture are the player's name, team and position. The backs of the 2-1/2" by 3-1/2" cards include personal and career statistics along with newspaper-style highlights and a cartoon. Specialty cards include statistical leaders, record performances, a new "Turn Back The Clock" feature which highlighted great past moments and a "Big League Brothers" feature.

	NR MT	EX	VG
Complete Set (660):	400.00	200.00	120.00
Common Player:	.20	.10	.06

1	Batting Leaders (George Brett, Bill Madlock)	5.00	2.50	1.50
2	Home Run Leaders (Graig Nettles, Mike Schmidt,	1.50	.70	.45
3	RBI Leaders (George Foster, Lee May)	.20	.10	.06
4	Stolen Base Leaders (Dave Lopes, Bill North)	.20	.10	.06
5	Victory Leaders (Randy Jones, Jim Palmer,	.80	.40	.25
6	Strikeout Leaders (Nolan Ryan, Tom Seaver, Strikeout Leaders)	9.00	4.50	2.75
7	ERA Leaders (John Denny, Mark Fidrych)	.20	.10	.06
8	Leading Firemen (Bill Campbell, Rawly Eastwick)	.20	.10	.06
9	Doug Rader	.20	.10	.06
10	Reggie Jackson	20.00	10.00	6.00
11	Rob Dressler	.20	.10	.06
12	Larry Haney	.20	.10	.06
13	Luis Gomez	.20	.10	.06
14	Tommy Smith	.20	.10	.06
15	Don Gullett	.20	.10	.06
16	Bob Jones	.20	.10	.06
17	Steve Stone	.25	.13	.08
18	Indians Team (Frank Robinson)	2.00	1.00	.60
19	John D'Acquisto	.20	.10	.06
20	Graig Nettles	.45	.25	.14
21	Ken Forsch	.20	.10	.06
22	Bill Freehan	.25	.13	.08
23	Dan Driessen	.20	.10	.06
24	Carl Morton	.20	.10	.06
25	Dwight Evans	1.50	.70	.45
26	Ray Sadecki	.20	.10	.06
27	Bill Buckner	.30	.15	.09
28	Woodie Fryman	.20	.10	.06
29	Bucky Dent	.25	.13	.08
30	Greg Luzinski	.40	.20	.12
31	Jim Todd	.20	.10	.06
32	Checklist 1-132	1.25	.60	.40
33	Wayne Garland	.20	.10	.06
34	Angels Team (Norm Sherry)	.70	.35	.20
35	Rennie Stennett	.20	.10	.06
36	John Ellis	.20	.10	.06
37	Steve Hargan	.20	.10	.06
38	Craig Kusick	.20	.10	.06
39	Tom Griffin	.20	.10	.06
40	Bobby Murcer	.30	.15	.09
41	Jim Kern	.20	.10	.06
42	Jose Cruz	.30	.15	.09
43	Ray Bare	.20	.10	.06
44	Bud Harrelson	.20	.10	.06
45	Rawly Eastwick	.20	.10	.06
46	Buck Martinez	.20	.10	.06
47	Lynn McGlothen	.20	.10	.06
48	Tom Paciorek	.20	.10	.06
49	Grant Jackson	.20	.10	.06
50	Ron Cey	.35	.20	.11
51	Brewers Team (Alex Grammas)	1.25	.60	.40
52	Ellis Valentine	.20	.10	.06
53	Paul Mitchell	.20	.10	.06
54	Sandy Alomar	.20	.10	.06
55	Jeff Burroughs	.20	.10	.06
56	Rudy May	.20	.10	.06
57	Marc Hill	.20	.10	.06
58	Chet Lemon	.20	.10	.06
59	Larry Christenson	.20	.10	.06
60	Jim Rice	4.00	2.00	1.25
61	Manny Sanguillen	.20	.10	.06
62	Eric Raich	.20	.10	.06
63	Tito Fuentes	.20	.10	.06
64	Larry Biittner	.20	.10	.06
65	Skip Lockwood	.20	.10	.06
66	Roy Smalley	.20	.10	.06
67	*Joaquin Andujar*	.20	.10	.06
68	Bruce Bochte	.20	.10	.06
69	Jim Crawford	.20	.10	.06
70	Johnny Bench	10.00	5.00	3.00
71	Dock Ellis	.20	.10	.06
72	Mike Anderson	.20	.10	.06
73	Charlie Williams	.20	.10	.06
74	A's Team (Jack McKeon)	1.25	.60	.40
75	Dennis Leonard	.20	.10	.06
76	Tim Foli	.20	.10	.06
77	Dyar Miller	.20	.10	.06
78	Bob Davis	.20	.10	.06
79	Don Money	.20	.10	.06
80	Andy Messersmith	.20	.10	.06
81	Juan Beniquez	.20	.10	.06
82	Jim Rooker	.20	.10	.06
83	Kevin Bell	.20	.10	.06
84	Ollie Brown	.20	.10	.06
85	Duane Kuiper	.20	.10	.06
86	Pat Zachry	.20	.10	.06
87	Glenn Borgmann	.20	.10	.06
88	Stan Wall	.20	.10	.06
89	*Butch Hobson*	.20	.10	.06
90	Cesar Cedeno	.20	.10	.06
91	John Verhoeven	.20	.10	.06
92	Dave Rosello	.20	.10	.06
93	Tom Poquette	.20	.10	.06
94	Craig Swan	.20	.10	.06
95	Keith Hernandez	1.00	.50	.30
96	Lou Piniella	.30	.15	.09
97	Dave Heaverlo	.20	.10	.06
98	Milt May	.20	.10	.06
99	Tom Hausman	.20	.10	.06
100	Joe Morgan	6.00	3.00	1.75
101	Dick Bosman	.20	.10	.06
102	Jose Morales	.20	.10	.06
103	Mike Bacsik	.20	.10	.06
104	*Omar Moreno*	.20	.10	.06
105	Steve Yeager	.20	.10	.06
106	Mike Flanagan	.20	.10	.06
107	Bill Melton	.20	.10	.06
108	Alan Foster	.20	.10	.06
109	Jorge Orta	.20	.10	.06
110	Steve Carlton	8.00	4.00	2.50
111	Rico Petrocelli	.20	.10	.06
112	Bill Greif	.20	.10	.06
113	Blue Jays Mgr./Coaches (Roy Hartsfield, Don Leppert, Bob Miller, Jackie Moore, Harry Warner)	1.25	.60	.40
114	Bruce Dal Canton	.20	.10	.06
115	Rick Manning	.20	.10	.06
116	Joe Niekro	.30	.15	.09
117	Frank White	.25	.13	.08
118	Rick Jones	.20	.10	.06
119	John Stearns	.20	.10	.06
120	Rod Carew	8.00	4.00	2.50
121	Gary Nolan	.20	.10	.06
122	Ben Oglivie	.20	.10	.06
123	Fred Stanley	.20	.10	.06
124	George Mitterwald	.20	.10	.06
125	Bill Travers	.20	.10	.06
126	Rod Gilbreath	.20	.10	.06
127	Ron Fairly	.20	.10	.06
128	Tommy John	1.25	.60	.40
129	Mike Sadek	.20	.10	.06
130	Al Oliver	.60	.30	.20
131	Orlando Ramirez	.20	.10	.06
132	Chip Lang	.20	.10	.06
133	Ralph Garr	.20	.10	.06
134	Padres Team (John McNamara)	1.25	.60	.40
135	Mark Belanger	.20	.10	.06
136	*Jerry Mumphrey*	.20	.10	.06
137	Jeff Terpko	.20	.10	.06
138	Bob Stinson	.20	.10	.06
139	Fred Norman	.20	.10	.06
140	Mike Schmidt	15.00	7.50	4.50
141	Mark Littell	.20	.10	.06
142	Steve Dillard	.20	.10	.06
143	Ed Herrmann	.20	.10	.06
144	*Bruce Sutter*	3.00	1.50	.90
145	Tom Veryzer	.20	.10	.06
146	Dusty Baker	.25	.13	.08
147	Jackie Brown	.20	.10	.06
148	Fran Healy	.20	.10	.06
149	Mike Cubbage	.20	.10	.06
150	Tom Seaver	9.00	4.50	2.75
151	Johnnie LeMaster	.20	.10	.06
152	Gaylord Perry	3.00	1.50	.90
153	Ron Jackson	.20	.10	.06
154	Dave Giusti	.20	.10	.06
155	Joe Rudi	.25	.13	.08
156	Pete Mackanin	.20	.10	.06
157	Ken Brett	.20	.10	.06
158	Ted Kubiak	.20	.10	.06
159	Bernie Carbo	.20	.10	.06
160	Will McEnaney	.20	.10	.06

161	*Garry Templeton*	.90	.45	.25
162	Mike Cuellar	.20	.10	.06
163	Dave Hilton	.20	.10	.06
164	Tug McGraw	.20	.10	.06
165	Jim Wynn	.20	.10	.06
166	Bill Campbell	.20	.10	.06
167	Rich Hebner	.20	.10	.06
168	Charlie Spikes	.20	.10	.06
169	Darold Knowles	.20	.10	.06
170	Thurman Munson	5.00	2.50	1.50
171	Ken Sanders	.20	.10	.06
172	John Milner	.20	.10	.06
173	Chuck Scrivener	.20	.10	.06
174	Nelson Briles	.20	.10	.06
175	*Butch Wynegar*	.20	.10	.06
176	Bob Robertson	.20	.10	.06
177	Bart Johnson	.20	.10	.06
178	Bombo Rivera	.20	.10	.06
179	Paul Hartzell	.20	.10	.06
180	Dave Lopes	.25	.13	.08
181	Ken McMullen	.20	.10	.06
182	Dan Spillner	.20	.10	.06
183	Cardinals Team (Vern Rapp)	1.25	.60	.40
184	Bo McLaughlin	.20	.10	.06
185	Sixto Lezcano	.20	.10	.06
186	Doug Flynn	.20	.10	.06
187	Dick Pole	.20	.10	.06
188	Bob Tolan	.20	.10	.06
189	Rick Dempsey	.20	.10	.06
190	Ray Burris	.20	.10	.06
191	Doug Griffin	.20	.10	.06
192	Clarence Gaston	.20	.10	.06
193	Larry Gura	.20	.10	.06
194	Gary Matthews	.20	.10	.06
195	Ed Figueroa	.20	.10	.06
196	Len Randle	.20	.10	.06
197	Ed Ott	.20	.10	.06
198	Wilbur Wood	.20	.10	.06
199	Pepe Frias	.20	.10	.06
200	Frank Tanana	.30	.15	.09
201	Ed Kranepool	.20	.10	.06
202	Tom Johnson	.20	.10	.06
203	Ed Armbrister	.20	.10	.06
204	Jeff Newman	.20	.10	.06
205	Pete Falcone	.20	.10	.06
206	Boog Powell	.50	.25	.15
207	Glenn Abbott	.20	.10	.06
208	Checklist 133-264	1.25	.60	.40
209	Rob Andrews	.20	.10	.06
210	Fred Lynn	1.50	.70	.45
211	Giants Team (Joe Altobelli)	1.25	.60	.40
212	Jim Mason	.20	.10	.06
213	Maximino Leon	.20	.10	.06
214	Darrell Porter	.20	.10	.06
215	Butch Metzger	.20	.10	.06
216	Doug DeCinces	.25	.13	.08
217	Tom Underwood	.20	.10	.06
218	*John Wathan*	.60	.30	.20
219	Joe Coleman	.20	.10	.06
220	Chris Chambliss	.20	.10	.06
221	Bob Bailey	.20	.10	.06
222	Francisco Barrios	.20	.10	.06
223	Earl Williams	.20	.10	.06
224	Rusty Torres	.20	.10	.06
225	Bob Apodaca	.20	.10	.06
226	Leroy Stanton	.20	.10	.06
227	*Joe Sambito*	.25	.13	.08
228	Twins Team (Gene Mauch)	1.25	.60	.40
229	Don Kessinger	.20	.10	.06
230	Vida Blue	.40	.20	.12
231	George Brett (RB)	6.00	3.00	1.75
232	Minnie Minoso (RB)	.35	.20	.11
233	Jose Morales (RB)	.20	.10	.06
234	Nolan Ryan (RB)	12.00	6.00	3.50
235	Cecil Cooper	.20	.10	.06
236	Tom Buskey	.20	.10	.06
237	Gene Clines	.20	.10	.06
238	Tippy Martinez	.20	.10	.06
239	Bill Plummer	.20	.10	.06
240	Ron LeFlore	.20	.10	.06
241	Dave Tomlin	.20	.10	.06
242	Ken Henderson	.20	.10	.06
243	Ron Reed	.20	.10	.06
244	John Mayberry	.20	.10	.06
245	Rick Rhoden	.20	.10	.06
246	Mike Vail	.20	.10	.06
247	Chris Knapp	.20	.10	.06
248	Wilbur Howard	.20	.10	.06
249	Pete Redfern	.20	.10	.06
250	Bill Madlock	.40	.20	.12
251	Tony Muser	.20	.10	.06
252	Dale Murray	.20	.10	.06
253	John Hale	.20	.10	.06
254	Doyle Alexander	.20	.10	.06
255	George Scott	.20	.10	.06
256	Joe Hoerner	.20	.10	.06
257	Mike Miley	.20	.10	.06
258	Luis Tiant	.35	.20	.11
259	Mets Team (Joe Frazier)	1.25	.60	.40
260	J.R. Richard	.25	.13	.08
261	Phil Garner	.20	.10	.06
262	Al Cowens	.20	.10	.06
263	Mike Marshall	.20	.10	.06
264	Tom Hutton	.20	.10	.06
265	*Mark Fidrych*	.70	.35	.20
266	Derrel Thomas	.20	.10	.06
267	Ray Fosse	.20	.10	.06
268	Rick Sawyer	.20	.10	.06
269	Joe Lis	.20	.10	.06
270	Dave Parker	4.00	2.00	1.25
271	Terry Forster	.20	.10	.06
272	Lee Lacy	.20	.10	.06
273	Eric Soderholm	.20	.10	.06
274	Don Stanhouse	.20	.10	.06
275	Mike Hargrove	.20	.10	.06
276	A.L. Championship (Chambliss' Dramatic Homer Decides It)	.70	.35	.20
277	N.L. Championship (Reds Sweep Phillies 3 In Row)	.70	.35	.20
278	Danny Frisella	.20	.10	.06
279	Joe Wallis	.20	.10	.06
280	Catfish Hunter	2.00	1.00	.60
281	Roy Staiger	.20	.10	.06
282	Sid Monge	.20	.10	.06
283	Jerry DaVanon	.20	.10	.06
284	Mike Norris	.20	.10	.06
285	Brooks Robinson	6.00	3.00	1.75
286	Johnny Grubb	.20	.10	.06
287	Reds Team (Sparky Anderson)	2.00	1.00	.60
288	Bob Montgomery	.20	.10	.06
289	Gene Garber	.20	.10	.06
290	Amos Otis	.20	.10	.06
291	*Jason Thompson*	.20	.10	.06
292	Rogelio Moret	.20	.10	.06
293	Jack Brohamer	.20	.10	.06
294	George Medich	.20	.10	.06
295	Gary Carter	4.00	2.00	1.25
296	Don Hood	.20	.10	.06
297	Ken Reitz	.20	.10	.06
298	Charlie Hough	.25	.13	.08
299	Otto Velez	.20	.10	.06
300	Jerry Koosman	.20	.10	.06
301	Toby Harrah	.20	.10	.06
302	Mike Garman	.20	.10	.06
303	Gene Tenace	.20	.10	.06
304	Jim Hughes	.20	.10	.06
305	Mickey Rivers	.20	.10	.06
306	Rick Waits	.20	.10	.06
307	Gary Sutherland	.20	.10	.06
308	Gene Pentz	.20	.10	.06
309	Red Sox Team (Don Zimmer)	1.25	.60	.40
310	Larry Bowa	.30	.15	.09
311	Vern Ruhle	.20	.10	.06
312	Rob Belloir	.20	.10	.06
313	Paul Blair	.20	.10	.06
314	Steve Mingori	.20	.10	.06
315	Dave Chalk	.20	.10	.06
316	Steve Rogers	.20	.10	.06
317	Kurt Bevacqua	.20	.10	.06
318	Duffy Dyer	.20	.10	.06
319	Rich Gossage	.60	.30	.20
320	Ken Griffey	.30	.15	.09
321	Dave Goltz	.20	.10	.06
322	Bill Russell	.20	.10	.06
323	Larry Lintz	.20	.10	.06
324	John Curtis	.20	.10	.06
325	Mike Ivie	.20	.10	.06
326	Jesse Jefferson	.20	.10	.06
327	Astros Team (Bill Virdon)	1.25	.60	.40
328	Tommy Boggs	.20	.10	.06
329	Ron Hodges	.20	.10	.06
330	George Hendrick	.20	.10	.06
331	Jim Colborn	.20	.10	.06
332	Elliott Maddox	.20	.10	.06
333	Paul Reuschel	.20	.10	.06
334	Bill Stein	.20	.10	.06
335	Bill Robinson	.20	.10	.06
336	Denny Doyle	.20	.10	.06
337	Ron Schueler	.20	.10	.06
338	Dave Duncan	.20	.10	.06
339	Adrian Devine	.20	.10	.06
340	Hal McRae	.40	.20	.12
341	Joe Kerrigan	.20	.10	.06
342	Jerry Remy	.20	.10	.06
343	Ed Halicki	.20	.10	.06
344	Brian Downing	.25	.13	.08
345	Reggie Smith	.25	.13	.08
346	Bill Singer	.20	.10	.06
347	George Foster	.60	.30	.20
348	Brent Strom	.20	.10	.06
349	Jim Holt	.20	.10	.06
350	Larry Dierker	.20	.10	.06
351	Jim Sundberg	.20	.10	.06
352	Mike Phillips	.20	.10	.06
353	Stan Thomas	.20	.10	.06
354	Pirates Team (Chuck Tanner)	1.25	.60	.40
355	Lou Brock	4.00	2.00	1.25
356	Checklist 265-396	1.25	.60	.40
357	Tim McCarver	.40	.20	.12
358	Tom House	.20	.10	.06
359	Willie Randolph	.60	.30	.20
360	Rick Monday	.25	.13	.08
361	Eduardo Rodriguez	.20	.10	.06
362	Tommy Davis	.30	.15	.09
363	Dave Roberts	.20	.10	.06
364	Vic Correll	.20	.10	.06
365	Mike Torrez	.20	.10	.06
366	Ted Sizemore	.20	.10	.06
367	Dave Hamilton	.20	.10	.06
368	Mike Jorgensen	.20	.10	.06
369	Terry Humphrey	.20	.10	.06
370	John Montefusco	.20	.10	.06
371	Royals Team (Whitey Herzog)	2.00	1.00	.60
372	Rich Folkers	.20	.10	.06
373	Bert Campaneris	.30	.15	.09
374	Kent Tekulve	.70	.35	.20
375	Larry Hisle	.20	.10	.06
376	Nino Espinosa	.20	.10	.06
377	Dave McKay	.20	.10	.06
378	Jim Umbarger	.20	.10	.06
379	Larry Cox	.20	.10	.06
380	Lee May	.20	.10	.06
381	Bob Forsch	.20	.10	.06
382	Charlie Moore	.20	.10	.06
383	Stan Bahnsen	.20	.10	.06
384	Darrel Chaney	.20	.10	.06
385	Dave LaRoche	.20	.10	.06
386	Manny Mota	.20	.10	.06
387	Yankees Team (Billy Martin)	2.00	1.00	.60
388	Terry Harmon	.20	.10	.06
389	Ken Kravec	.20	.10	.06
390	Dave Winfield	28.00	21.00	11.00
391	Dan Warthen	.20	.10	.06
392	Phil Roof	.20	.10	.06
393	John Lowenstein	.20	.10	.06
394	Bill Laxton	.20	.10	.06
395	Manny Trillo	.20	.10	.06
396	Tom Murphy	.20	.10	.06
397	*Larry Herndon*	.40	.20	.12
398	Tom Burgmeier	.20	.10	.06
399	Bruce Boisclair	.20	.10	.06
400	Steve Garvey	3.50	1.75	1.00
401	Mickey Scott	.20	.10	.06
402	Tommy Helms	.20	.10	.06
403	Tom Grieve	.20	.10	.06
404	Eric Rasmussen	.20	.10	.06
405	Claudell Washington	.20	.10	.06
406	Tim Johnson	.20	.10	.06
407	Dave Freisleben	.20	.10	.06
408	Cesar Tovar	.20	.10	.06
409	Pete Broberg	.20	.10	.06
410	Willie Montanez	.20	.10	.06
411	World Series Games 1 & 2 (Joe Morgan/Johnny Bench)	1.50	.70	.45
412	World Series Games 3 & 4 (Johnny Bench)	1.50	.70	.45
413	World Series Summary	.90	.45	.25
414	Tommy Harper	.20	.10	.06
415	Jay Johnstone	.20	.10	.06
416	Chuck Hartenstein	.20	.10	.06
417	Wayne Garrett	.20	.10	.06
418	White Sox Team (Bob Lemon)	1.25	.60	.40
419	Steve Swisher	.20	.10	.06
420	Rusty Staub	.35	.20	.11
421	Doug Rau	.20	.10	.06
422	Freddie Patek	.20	.10	.06
423	Gary Lavelle	.20	.10	.06
424	Steve Brye	.20	.10	.06
425	Joe Torre	.20	.10	.06
426	Dick Drago	.20	.10	.06
427	Dave Rader	.20	.10	.06
428	Rangers Team (Frank Lucchesi)	1.25	.60	.40
429	Ken Boswell	.20	.10	.06
430	Fergie Jenkins	3.00	1.50	.90
431	Dave Collins	.25	.13	.08
432	Buzz Capra	.20	.10	.06
433	Nate Colbert (Turn Back The Clock)	.20	.10	.06
434	Carl Yastrzemski (Turn Back The Clock)	1.50	.70	.45
435	Maury Wills (Turn Back The Clock)	.35	.20	.11
436	Bob Keegan (Turn Back The Clock)	.20	.10	.06
437	Ralph Kiner (Turn Back The Clock)	.35	.20	.11
438	Marty Perez	.20	.10	.06
439	Gorman Thomas	.20	.10	.06
440	Jon Matlack	.20	.10	.06
441	Larvell Blanks	.20	.10	.06
442	Braves Team (Dave Bristol)	1.25	.60	.40
443	Lamar Johnson	.20	.10	.06
444	Wayne Twitchell	.20	.10	.06
445	Ken Singleton	.25	.13	.08
446	Bill Bonham	.20	.10	.06
447	Jerry Turner	.20	.10	.06
448	Ellie Rodriguez	.20	.10	.06
449	Al Fitzmorris	.20	.10	.06
450	Pete Rose	9.00	4.50	2.75
451	Checklist 397-528	1.25	.60	.40
452	Mike Caldwell	.20	.10	.06
453	Pedro Garcia	.20	.10	.06
454	Andy Etchebarren	.20	.10	.06
455	Rick Wise	.20	.10	.06
456	Leon Roberts	.20	.10	.06
457	Steve Luebber	.20	.10	.06
458	Leo Foster	.20	.10	.06
459	Steve Foucault	.20	.10	.06
460	Willie Stargell	4.00	2.00	1.25
461	Dick Tidrow	.20	.10	.06
462	Don Baylor	.35	.20	.11
463	Jamie Quirk	.20	.10	.06
464	Randy Moffitt	.20	.10	.06
465	Rico Carty	.20	.10	.06
466	Fred Holdsworth	.20	.10	.06
467	Phillies Team (Danny Ozark)	1.25	.60	.40
468	Ramon Hernandez	.20	.10	.06
469	Pat Kelly	.20	.10	.06
470	Ted Simmons	.35	.20	.11
471	Del Unser	.20	.10	.06
472	Rookie Pitchers (Don Aase, Bob McClure, Gil Patterson, Dave Wehrmeister)	.20	.10	.06
473	*Andre Dawson*, Gene Richards, John Scott, Denny Walling)	70.00	35.00	21.00
474	Rookie Shortstops (Bob Bailor, Kiko Garcia, Craig Reynolds, Alex Taveras)	.20	.10	.06
475	Rookie Pitchers (Chris Batton, Rick Camp, Scott McGregor, Manny Sarmiento)	.20	.10	.06
476	Rookie Catchers (Gary Alexander, Rick Cerone, Dale Murphy, Kevin Pasley)	22.00	11.00	6.50
477	Rookie Infielders (Doug Ault, Rich Dauer, Orlando Gonzalez, Phil Mankowski)	.20	.10	.06
478	Rookie Pitchers (Jim Gideon, Leon Hooten, Dave Johnson, Mark Lemongello)	.20	.10	.06
479	Rookie Outfielders (Brian Asselstine, Wayne Gross, Sam Mejias, Alvis Woods)	.20	.10	.06
480	Carl Yastrzemski	6.00	3.00	1.75
481	Roger Metzger	.20	.10	.06
482	Tony Solaita	.20	.10	.06
483	Richie Zisk	.20	.10	.06
484	Burt Hooton	.20	.10	.06
485	Roy White	.30	.15	.09
486	Ed Bane	.20	.10	.06
487	Rookie Pitchers (Larry Anderson, Ed Glynn, Joe Henderson, Greg Terlecky)	.20	.10	.06
488	*Jack Clark*, Ruppert Jones, Lee Mazzilli, Dan Thomas)	4.50	2.25	1.25
489	Rookie Pitchers (*Len Barker*, Randy Lerch, Greg Minton, Mike Overy)	.40	.20	.12
490	Rookie Shortstops (*Billy Almon*, Mickey Klutts, Tommy McMillan, Mark Wagner)	.20	.10	.06
491	Rookie Pitchers (Mike Dupree, Denny Martinez, Craig Mitchell, Bob Sykes)	6.00	3.00	1.75

492	Rookie Outfielders (*Tony Armas*, Steve Kemp, Carlos Lopez, Gary Woods)	.80	.40	.25
493	Rookie Pitchers (*Mike Krukow*, Jim Otten, Gary Wheelock, Mike Willis)	.35	.20	.11
494	Rookie Infielders (Juan Bernhardt, Mike Champion, Jim Gantner, Bump Wills)	.35	.20	.11
495	Al Hrabosky	.20	.10	.06
496	Gary Thomasson	.20	.10	.06
497	Clay Carroll	.20	.10	.06
498	Sal Bando	.20	.10	.06
499	Pablo Torrealba	.20	.10	.06
500	Dave Kingman	.30	.15	.09
501	Jim Bibby	.20	.10	.06
502	Randy Hundley	.20	.10	.06
503	Bill Lee	.20	.10	.06
504	Dodgers Team (Tom Lasorda)	2.00	1.00	.60
505	Oscar Gamble	.20	.10	.06
506	Steve Grilli	.20	.10	.06
507	Mike Hegan	.20	.10	.06
508	Dave Pagan	.20	.10	.06
509	Cookie Rojas	.20	.10	.06
510	John Candelaria	.35	.20	.11
511	Bill Fahey	.20	.10	.06
512	Jack Billingham	.20	.10	.06
513	Jerry Terrell	.20	.10	.06
514	Cliff Johnson	.20	.10	.06
515	Chris Speier	.20	.10	.06
516	Bake McBride	.20	.10	.06
517	*Pete Vuckovich*	.50	.25	.15
518	Cubs Team (Herman Franks)	1.25	.60	.40
519	Don Kirkwood	.20	.10	.06
520	Garry Maddox	.20	.10	.06
521	Bob Grich	.25	.13	.08
522	Enzo Hernandez	.20	.10	.06
523	Rollie Fingers	3.00	1.50	.90
524	Rowland Office	.20	.10	.06
525	Dennis Eckersley	9.00	4.50	2.75
526	Larry Parrish	.20	.10	.06
527	Dan Meyer	.20	.10	.06
528	Bill Castro	.20	.10	.06
529	Jim Essian	.20	.10	.06
530	Rick Reuschel	.20	.10	.06
531	Lyman Bostock	.20	.10	.06
532	Jim Willoughby	.20	.10	.06
533	Mickey Stanley	.20	.10	.06
534	Paul Splittorff	.20	.10	.06
535	Cesar Geronimo	.20	.10	.06
536	Vic Albury	.20	.10	.06
537	Dave Roberts	.20	.10	.06
538	Frank Taveras	.20	.10	.06
539	Mike Wallace	.20	.10	.06
540	Bob Watson	.20	.10	.06
541	John Denny	.20	.10	.06
542	Frank Duffy	.20	.10	.06
543	Ron Blomberg	.20	.10	.06
544	Gary Ross	.20	.10	.06
545	Bob Boone	.35	.20	.11
546	Orioles Team (Earl Weaver)	2.00	1.00	.60
547	Willie McCovey	3.00	1.50	.90
548	*Joel Youngblood*	.20	.10	.06
549	Jerry Royster	.20	.10	.06
550	Randy Jones	.20	.10	.06
551	Bill North	.20	.10	.06
552	Pepe Mangual	.20	.10	.06
553	Jack Heidemann	.20	.10	.06
554	Bruce Kimm	.20	.10	.06
555	Dan Ford	.20	.10	.06
556	Doug Bird	.20	.10	.06
557	Jerry White	.20	.10	.06
558	Elias Sosa	.20	.10	.06
559	Alan Bannister	.20	.10	.06
560	Dave Concepcion	.35	.20	.11
561	Pete LaCock	.20	.10	.06
562	Checklist 529-660	1.25	.60	.40
563	Bruce Kison	.20	.10	.06
564	Alan Ashby	.20	.10	.06
565	Mickey Lolich	.35	.20	.11
566	Rick Miller	.20	.10	.06
567	Enos Cabell	.20	.10	.06
568	Carlos May	.20	.10	.06
569	Jim Lonborg	.20	.10	.06
570	Bobby Bonds	.35	.20	.11
571	Darrell Evans	.35	.20	.11
572	Ross Grimsley	.20	.10	.06
573	Joe Ferguson	.20	.10	.06
574	Aurelio Rodriguez	.20	.10	.06
575	Dick Ruthven	.20	.10	.06
576	Fred Kendall	.20	.10	.06
577	Jerry Augustine	.20	.10	.06
578	Bob Randall	.20	.10	.06
579	Don Carrithers	.20	.10	.06
580	George Brett	30.00	15.00	9.00
581	Pedro Borbon	.20	.10	.06
582	Ed Kirkpatrick	.20	.10	.06
583	Paul Lindblad	.20	.10	.06
584	Ed Goodson	.20	.10	.06
585	Rick Burleson	.20	.10	.06
586	Steve Renko	.20	.10	.06
587	Rick Baldwin	.20	.10	.06
588	Dave Moates	.20	.10	.06
589	Mike Cosgrove	.20	.10	.06
590	Buddy Bell	.20	.10	.06
591	Chris Arnold	.20	.10	.06
592	Dan Briggs	.20	.10	.06
593	Dennis Blair	.20	.10	.06
594	Biff Pocoroba	.20	.10	.06
595	John Hiller	.20	.10	.06
596	*Jerry Martin*	.20	.10	.06
597	Mariners Mgr./Coaches (Don Bryant, Jim Busby, Darrell Johnson, Vada Pinson, Wes Stock)	1.25	.60	.40
598	Sparky Lyle	.35	.20	.11
599	Mike Tyson	.20	.10	.06
600	Jim Palmer	4.00	2.00	1.25
601	Mike Lum	.20	.10	.06
602	Andy Hassler	.20	.10	.06
603	Willie Davis	.25	.13	.08
604	Jim Slaton	.20	.10	.06
605	Felix Millan	.20	.10	.06
606	Steve Braun	.20	.10	.06
607	Larry Demery	.20	.10	.06
608	Roy Howell	.20	.10	.06
609	Jim Barr	.20	.10	.06
610	Jose Cardenal	.20	.10	.06
611	Dave Lemanczyk	.20	.10	.06
612	Barry Foote	.20	.10	.06
613	Reggie Cleveland	.20	.10	.06
614	Greg Gross	.20	.10	.06
615	Phil Niekro	1.50	.70	.45
616	Tommy Sandt	.20	.10	.06
617	Bobby Darwin	.20	.10	.06
618	Pat Dobson	.20	.10	.06
619	Johnny Oates	.20	.10	.06
620	Don Sutton	1.50	.70	.45
621	Tigers Team (Ralph Houk)	1.50	.70	.45
622	Jim Wohlford	.20	.10	.06
623	Jack Kucek	.20	.10	.06
624	Hector Cruz	.20	.10	.06
625	Ken Holtzman	.20	.10	.06
626	Al Bumbry	.20	.10	.06
627	Bob Myrick	.20	.10	.06
628	Mario Guerrero	.20	.10	.06
629	Bobby Valentine	.25	.13	.08
630	Bert Blyleven	.90	.45	.25
631	Big League Brothers (George Brett, Ken Brett)	5.00	2.50	1.50
632	Big League Brothers (Bob Forsch, Ken Forsch)	.30	.15	.09
633	Big League Brothers (Carlos May, Lee May)	.30	.15	.09
634	Big League Brothers (Paul Reuschel) (names switched, Rick Reuschel)	.30	.15	.09
635	Robin Yount	30.00	15.00	9.00
636	Santo Alcala	.20	.10	.06
637	Alex Johnson	.20	.10	.06
638	Jim Kaat	.80	.40	.25
639	Jerry Morales	.20	.10	.06
640	Carlton Fisk	4.00	2.00	1.25
641	Dan Larson	.20	.10	.06
642	Willie Crawford	.20	.10	.06
643	Mike Pazik	.20	.10	.06
644	Matt Alexander	.20	.10	.06
645	Jerry Reuss	.25	.13	.08
646	Andres Mora	.20	.10	.06
647	Expos Team (Dick Williams)	1.25	.60	.40
648	Jim Spencer	.20	.10	.06
649	Dave Cash	.20	.10	.06
650	Nolan Ryan	40.00	20.00	12.00
651	Von Joshua	.20	.10	.06
652	Tom Walker	.20	.10	.06
653	Diego Segui	.20	.10	.06
654	Ron Pruitt	.20	.10	.06
655	Tony Perez	1.50	.70	.45
656	Ron Guidry	.90	.45	.25
657	Mick Kelleher	.20	.10	.06
658	Marty Pattin	.20	.10	.06
659	Merv Rettenmund	.20	.10	.06
660	Willie Horton	.20	.10	.06

1977 Topps Cloth Stickers

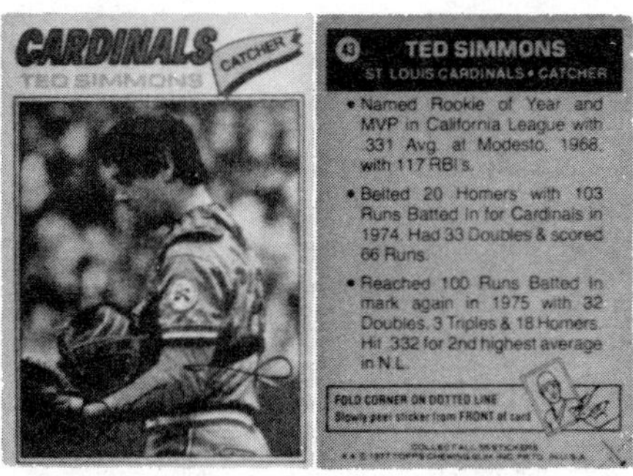

One of the few Topps specialty issues of the late 1970s, the 73-piece set of cloth stickers issued in 1977 includes 55 player stickers and 18 puzzle cards which could be joined to form a photo of the American League or National League All-Star teams. Issued as a separate issue, the 2-1/2" by 3-1/2" stickers have a paper backing which could be removed to allow the cloth to be adhered to a jacket, notebook, etc.

		NR MT	EX	VG
	Complete Set:	300.00	150.00	90.00
	Common Player:	1.00	.50	.30
1	Alan Ashby	1.00	.50	.30
2	Buddy Bell	1.00	.50	.30
3	Johnny Bench	10.00	5.00	3.00
4	Vida Blue	1.50	.70	.45
5	Bert Blyleven	1.50	.70	.45
6	Steve Braun	1.00	.50	.30
7	George Brett	15.00	7.50	4.50
8	Lou Brock	6.00	3.00	1.75
9	Jose Cardenal	1.00	.50	.30
10	Rod Carew	9.00	4.50	2.75
11	Steve Carlton	9.00	4.50	2.75
12	Dave Cash	1.00	.50	.30
13	Cesar Cedeno	1.00	.50	.30
14	Ron Cey	1.50	.70	.45
15	Mark Fidrych	1.50	.70	.45
16	Dan Ford	1.00	.50	.30
17	Wayne Garland	1.00	.50	.30
18	Ralph Garr	1.00	.50	.30
19	Steve Garvey	4.00	2.00	1.25
20	Mike Hargrove	1.00	.50	.30
21	Catfish Hunter	6.00	3.00	1.75
22	Reggie Jackson	12.00	6.00	3.50
23	Randy Jones	1.00	.50	.30
24	Dave Kingman	1.00	.50	.30
25	Bill Madlock	1.50	.70	.45
26	Lee May	1.00	.50	.30
27	John Mayberry	1.00	.50	.30
28	Andy Messersmith	1.00	.50	.30
29	Willie Montanez	1.00	.50	.30
30	John Montefusco	1.00	.50	.30
31	Joe Morgan	6.00	3.00	1.75
32	Thurman Munson	6.00	3.00	1.75
33	Bobby Murcer	1.50	.70	.45
34	Al Oliver	1.50	.70	.45
35	Dave Pagan	1.00	.50	.30
36	Jim Palmer	9.00	4.50	2.75
37	Tony Perez	3.00	1.50	.90
38	Pete Rose	15.00	7.50	4.50
39	Joe Rudi	1.50	.70	.45
40	Nolan Ryan	40.00	20.00	12.00
41	Mike Schmidt	30.00	15.00	9.00
42	Tom Seaver	20.00	10.00	6.00
43	Ted Simmons	1.50	.70	.45
44	Bill Singer	1.00	.50	.30
45	Willie Stargell	6.00	3.00	1.75
46	Rusty Staub	2.00	1.00	.60
47	Don Sutton	2.00	1.00	.60
48	Luis Tiant	1.50	.70	.45
49	Bill Travers	1.00	.50	.30
50	Claudell Washington	1.00	.50	.30
51	Bob Watson	1.00	.50	.30
52	Dave Winfield	20.00	10.00	6.00
53	Carl Yastrzemski	9.00	4.50	2.75
54	Robin Yount	15.00	7.50	4.50
55	Richie Zisk	1.00	.50	.30
----	American League 9-piece puzzle	15.00	7.50	4.50
----	National League 9-piece puzzle	15.00	7.50	4.50

1978 Topps

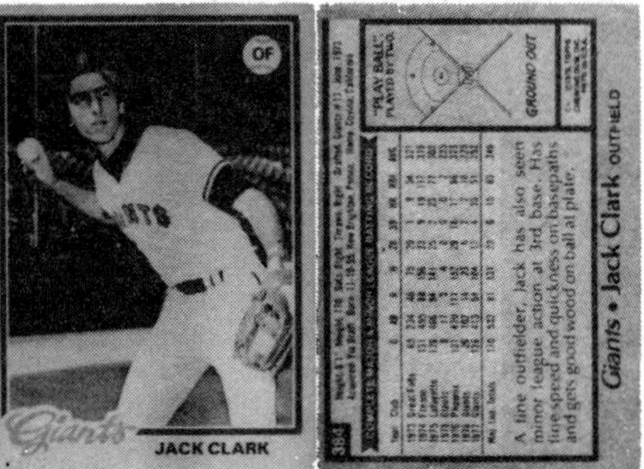

At 726 cards, this was the largest issue from Topps since 1972. In design, the color player photo is slightly larger than usual, with the player's name and team at the bottom. In the upper right-hand corner of the 2-1/2" by 3-1/2" cards there is a small white baseball with the player's position. Most of the starting All-Stars from the previous year had a red, white and blue shield instead of the baseball. Backs feature statistics and a baseball situation which made a card game of baseball possible. Specialty cards include baseball records, statistical leaders and the World Series and playoffs. As one row of cards per sheet had to be double-printed to accommodate the 726-card set size, some cards are more common, yet that seems to have no serious impact on their prices.

		NR MT	EX	VG
	Complete Set (726):	350.00	175.00	105.00
	Common Player:	.20	.10	.06
1	Lou Brock (Record Breaker)	2.00	1.00	.60
2	Sparky Lyle (Record Breaker)	.25	.13	.08
3	Willie McCovey (Record Breaker)	.70	.35	.20
4	Brooks Robinson (Record Breaker)	.90	.45	.25
5	Pete Rose (Record Breaker)	3.00	1.50	.90
6	Nolan Ryan (Record Breaker)	12.00	6.00	3.50
7	Reggie Jackson (Record Breaker)	6.00	3.00	1.75
8	Mike Sadek	.20	.10	.06
9	Doug DeCinces	.25	.13	.08
10	Phil Niekro	1.25	.60	.40
11	Rick Manning	.20	.10	.06
12	Don Aase	.20	.10	.06
13	Art Howe	.20	.10	.06
14	Lerrin LaGrow	.20	.10	.06
15	Tony Perez	.25	.13	.08
16	Roy White	.20	.10	.06
17	Mike Krukow	.20	.10	.06
18	Bob Grich	.25	.13	.08
19	Darrell Porter	.20	.10	.06
20	Pete Rose	.20	.10	.06
21	Steve Kemp	.30	.15	.09
22	Charlie Hough	.20	.10	.06

23	Bump Wills	.20	.10	.06
24	Don Money	.20	.10	.06
25	Jon Matlack	.20	.10	.06
26	Rich Hebner	.20	.10	.06
27	Geoff Zahn	.20	.10	.06
28	Ed Ott	.20	.10	.06
29	Bob Lacey	.20	.10	.06
30	George Hendrick	.20	.10	.06
31	Glenn Abbott	.20	.10	.06
32	Garry Templeton	.20	.10	.06
33	Dave Lemanczyk	.20	.10	.06
34	Willie McCovey	3.00	1.50	.90
35	Sparky Lyle	.30	.15	.09
36	*Eddie Murray*	80.00	40.00	24.00
37	Rick Waits	.20	.10	.06
38	Willie Montanez	.20	.10	.06
39	*Floyd Bannister*	.70	.35	.20
40	Carl Yastrzemski	5.00	2.50	1.50
41	Burt Hooton	.20	.10	.06
42	Jorge Orta	.20	.10	.06
43	Bill Atkinson	.20	.10	.06
44	Toby Harrah	.20	.10	.06
45	Mark Fidrych	.25	.13	.08
46	Al Cowens	.20	.10	.06
47	Jack Billingham	.20	.10	.06
48	Don Baylor	.35	.20	.11
49	Ed Kranepool	.20	.10	.06
50	Rick Reuschel	.20	.10	.06
51	Charlie Moore	.20	.10	.06
52	Jim Lonborg	.20	.10	.06
53	Phil Garner	.20	.10	.06
54	Tom Johnson	.20	.10	.06
55	Mitchell Page	.20	.10	.06
56	Randy Jones	.20	.10	.06
57	Dan Meyer	.20	.10	.06
58	Bob Forsch	.20	.10	.06
59	Otto Velez	.20	.10	.06
60	Thurman Munson	5.00	2.50	1.50
61	Larvell Blanks	.20	.10	.06
62	Jim Barr	.20	.10	.06
63	Don Zimmer	.20	.10	.06
64	Gene Pentz	.20	.10	.06
65	Ken Singleton	.20	.10	.06
66	White Sox Team	.50	.25	.15
67	Claudell Washington	.20	.10	.06
68	Steve Foucault	.20	.10	.06
69	Mike Vail	.20	.10	.06
70	Rich Gossage	.40	.20	.12
71	Terry Humphrey	.20	.10	.06
72	Andre Dawson	22.00	11.00	6.50
73	Andy Hassler	.20	.10	.06
74	Checklist 1-121	.90	.45	.25
75	Dick Ruthven	.20	.10	.06
76	Steve Ontiveros	.20	.10	.06
77	Ed Kirkpatrick	.20	.10	.06
78	Pablo Torrealba	.20	.10	.06
79	Darrell Johnson	.20	.10	.06
80	Ken Griffey	.25	.13	.08
81	Pete Redfern	.20	.10	.06
82	Giants Team	.50	.25	.15
83	Bob Montgomery	.20	.10	.06
84	Kent Tekulve	.20	.10	.06
85	Ron Fairly	.20	.10	.06
86	Dave Tomlin	.20	.10	.06
87	John Lowenstein	.20	.10	.06
88	Mike Phillips	.20	.10	.06
89	Ken Clay	.20	.10	.06
90	Larry Bowa	.30	.15	.09
91	Oscar Zamora	.20	.10	.06
92	Adrian Devine	.20	.10	.06
93	Bobby Cox	.20	.10	.06
94	Chuck Scrivener	.20	.10	.06
95	Jamie Quirk	.20	.10	.06
96	Orioles Team	.50	.25	.15
97	Stan Bahnsen	.20	.10	.06
98	Jim Essian	.20	.10	.06
99	*Willie Hernandez*	.30	.15	.09
100	George Brett	25.00	12.50	7.50
101	Sid Monge	.20	.10	.06
102	Matt Alexander	.20	.10	.06
103	Tom Murphy	.20	.10	.06
104	Lee Lacy	.20	.10	.06
105	Reggie Cleveland	.20	.10	.06
106	Bill Plummer	.20	.10	.06
107	Ed Halicki	.20	.10	.06
108	Von Joshua	.20	.10	.06
109	Joe Torre	.20	.10	.06
110	Richie Zisk	.20	.10	.06
111	Mike Tyson	.20	.10	.06
112	Astros Team	.50	.25	.15
113	Don Carrithers	.20	.10	.06
114	Paul Blair	.20	.10	.06
115	Gary Nolan	.20	.10	.06
116	Tucker Ashford	.20	.10	.06
117	John Montague	.20	.10	.06
118	Terry Harmon	.20	.10	.06
119	Denny Martinez	.25	.13	.08
120	Gary Carter	3.00	1.50	.90
121	Alvis Woods	.20	.10	.06
122	Dennis Eckersley	8.00	4.00	2.50
123	Manny Trillo	.20	.10	.06
124	*Dave Rozema*	.20	.10	.06
125	George Scott	.20	.10	.06
126	Paul Moskau	.20	.10	.06
127	Chet Lemon	.20	.10	.06
128	Bill Russell	.20	.10	.06
129	Jim Colborn	.20	.10	.06
130	Jeff Burroughs	.20	.10	.06
131	Bert Blyleven	.60	.30	.20
132	Enos Cabell	.20	.10	.06
133	Jerry Augustine	.20	.10	.06
134	*Steve Henderson*	.20	.10	.06
135	Ron Guidry	.30	.15	.09
136	Ted Sizemore	.20	.10	.06
137	Craig Kusick	.20	.10	.06
138	Larry Demery	.20	.10	.06
139	Wayne Gross	.20	.10	.06
140	Rollie Fingers	3.00	1.50	.90
141	Ruppert Jones	.20	.10	.06
142	John Montefusco	.20	.10	.06
143	Keith Hernandez	1.00	.50	.30
144	Jesse Jefferson	.20	.10	.06
145	Rick Monday	.20	.10	.06
146	Doyle Alexander	.20	.10	.06
147	Lee Mazzilli	.20	.10	.06
148	Andre Thornton	.25	.13	.08
149	Dale Murray	.20	.10	.06
150	Bobby Bonds	.20	.10	.06
151	Milt Wilcox	.20	.10	.06
152	*Ivan DeJesus*	.20	.10	.06
153	Steve Stone	.20	.10	.06
154	Cecil Cooper	.20	.10	.06
155	Butch Hobson	.20	.10	.06
156	Andy Messersmith	.20	.10	.06
157	Pete LaCock	.20	.10	.06
158	Joaquin Andujar	.20	.10	.06
159	Lou Piniella	.35	.20	.11
160	Jim Palmer	4.00	2.00	1.25
161	Bob Boone	.25	.13	.08
162	Paul Thormodsgard	.20	.10	.06
163	Bill North	.20	.10	.06
164	Bob Owchinko	.20	.10	.06
165	Rennie Stennett	.20	.10	.06
166	Carlos Lopez	.20	.10	.06
167	Tim Foli	.20	.10	.06
168	Reggie Smith	.25	.13	.08
169	Jerry Johnson	.20	.10	.06
170	Lou Brock	3.00	1.50	.90
171	Pat Zachry	.20	.10	.06
172	Mike Hargrove	.20	.10	.06
173	Robin Yount	25.00	12.50	7.50
174	Wayne Garland	.20	.10	.06
175	Jerry Morales	.20	.10	.06
176	Milt May	.20	.10	.06
177	Gene Garber	.20	.10	.06
178	Dave Chalk	.20	.10	.06
179	Dick Tidrow	.20	.10	.06
180	Dave Concepcion	.35	.20	.11
181	Ken Forsch	.20	.10	.06
182	Jim Spencer	.20	.10	.06
183	Doug Bird	.20	.10	.06
184	Checklist 122-242	.90	.45	.25
185	Ellis Valentine	.20	.10	.06
186	*Bob Stanley*	.20	.10	.06
187	Jerry Royster	.20	.10	.06
188	Al Bumbry	.20	.10	.06
189	Tom Lasorda	.50	.25	.15
190	John Candelaria	.25	.13	.08
191	Rodney Scott	.20	.10	.06
192	Padres Team	.50	.25	.15
193	Rich Chiles	.20	.10	.06
194	Derrel Thomas	.20	.10	.06
195	Larry Dierker	.20	.10	.06
196	Bob Bailor	.20	.10	.06
197	Nino Espinosa	.20	.10	.06
198	Ron Pruitt	.20	.10	.06
199	Craig Reynolds	.20	.10	.06
200	Reggie Jackson	15.00	7.50	4.50
201	Batting Leaders (Rod Carew, Dave Parker)	1.00	.50	.30
202	Home Run Leaders (George Foster, Jim Rice)	.25	.13	.08
203	RBI Leaders (George Foster, Larry Hisle)	.25	.13	.08
204	Stolen Base Leaders (Freddie Patek, Frank Taveras)	.20	.10	.06
205	Victory Leaders (Steve Carlton, Dave Goltz, Dennis Leonard, Jim Palmer)	1.50	.70	.45
206	Strikeout Leaders (Phil Niekro, Nolan Ryan)	2.50	1.25	.70
207	ERA Leaders (John Candelaria, Frank Tanana)	.20	.10	.06
208	Leading Firemen (Bill Campbell, Rollie Fingers)	.50	.25	.15
209	Dock Ellis	.20	.10	.06
210	Jose Cardenal	.20	.10	.06
211	Earl Weaver	.50	.25	.15
212	Mike Caldwell	.20	.10	.06
213	Alan Bannister	.20	.10	.06
214	Angels Team	.50	.25	.15
215	Darrell Evans	.35	.20	.11
216	Mike Paxton	.20	.10	.06
217	Rod Gilbreath	.20	.10	.06
218	Marty Pattin	.20	.10	.06
219	Mike Cubbage	.20	.10	.06
220	Pedro Borbon	.20	.10	.06
221	Chris Speier	.20	.10	.06
222	Jerry Martin	.20	.10	.06
223	Bruce Kison	.20	.10	.06
224	Jerry Tabb	.20	.10	.06
225	Don Gullett	.20	.10	.06
226	Joe Ferguson	.20	.10	.06
227	Al Fitzmorris	.20	.10	.06
228	Manny Mota	.20	.10	.06
229	Leo Foster	.20	.10	.06
230	Al Hrabosky	.20	.10	.06
231	Wayne Nordhagen	.20	.10	.06
232	Mickey Stanley	.20	.10	.06
233	Dick Pole	.20	.10	.06
234	Herman Franks	.20	.10	.06
235	Tim McCarver	.30	.15	.09
236	Terry Whitfield	.20	.10	.06
237	Rich Dauer	.20	.10	.06
238	Juan Beniquez	.20	.10	.06
239	Dyar Miller	.20	.10	.06
240	Gene Tenace	.20	.10	.06
241	Pete Vuckovich	.20	.10	.06
242	Barry Bonnell	.20	.10	.06
243	Bob McClure	.20	.10	.06
244	Expos Team	.20	.10	.06
245	Rick Burleson	.20	.10	.06
246	Dan Driessen	.20	.10	.06
247	Larry Christenson	.20	.10	.06
248	Frank White	.20	.10	.06
249	Dave Goltz	.20	.10	.06
250	Graig Nettles	.30	.15	.09
251	Don Kirkwood	.20	.10	.06
252	Steve Swisher	.20	.10	.06
253	Jim Kern	.20	.10	.06
254	Dave Collins	.20	.10	.06
255	Jerry Reuss	.20	.10	.06
256	Joe Altobelli	.20	.10	.06
257	Hector Cruz	.20	.10	.06
258	John Hiller	.20	.10	.06
259	Dodgers Team	.80	.40	.25
260	Bert Campaneris	.25	.13	.08
261	Tim Hosley	.20	.10	.06
262	Rudy May	.20	.10	.06
263	Danny Walton	.20	.10	.06
264	Jamie Easterly	.20	.10	.06
265	Sal Bando	.20	.10	.06
266	*Bob Shirley*	.20	.10	.06
267	Doug Ault	.20	.10	.06
268	Gil Flores	.20	.10	.06
269	Wayne Twitchell	.20	.10	.06
270	Carlton Fisk	5.00	2.50	1.50
271	Randy Lerch	.20	.10	.06
272	Royle Stillman	.20	.10	.06
273	Fred Norman	.20	.10	.06
274	Freddie Patek	.20	.10	.06
275	Dan Ford	.20	.10	.06
276	Bill Bonham	.20	.10	.06
277	Bruce Boisclair	.20	.10	.06
278	Enrique Romo	.20	.10	.06
279	Bill Virdon	.20	.10	.06
280	Buddy Bell	.20	.10	.06
281	Eric Rasmussen	.20	.10	.06
282	Yankees Team	1.00	.50	.30
283	Omar Moreno	.20	.10	.06
284	Randy Moffitt	.20	.10	.06
285	Steve Yeager	.20	.10	.06
286	Ben Oglivie	.20	.10	.06
287	Kiko Garcia	.20	.10	.06
288	Dave Hamilton	.20	.10	.06
289	Checklist 243-363	.90	.45	.25
290	Willie Horton	.20	.10	.06
291	Gary Ross	.20	.10	.06
292	Gene Richard	.20	.10	.06
293	Mike Willis	.20	.10	.06
294	Larry Parrish	.25	.13	.08
295	Bill Lee	.20	.10	.06
296	Biff Pocoroba	.20	.10	.06
297	Warren Brusstar	.20	.10	.06
298	Tony Armas	.20	.10	.06
299	Whitey Herzog	.30	.15	.09
300	Joe Morgan	3.00	1.50	.90
301	Buddy Schultz	.20	.10	.06
302	Cubs Team	.50	.25	.15
303	Sam Hinds	.20	.10	.06
304	John Milner	.20	.10	.06
305	Rico Carty	.20	.10	.06
306	Joe Niekro	.20	.10	.06
307	Glenn Borgmann	.20	.10	.06
308	Jim Rooker	.20	.10	.06
309	Cliff Johnson	.20	.10	.06
310	Don Sutton	2.00	1.00	.60
311	Jose Baez	.20	.10	.06
312	Greg Minton	.20	.10	.06
313	Andy Etchebarren	.20	.10	.06
314	Paul Lindblad	.20	.10	.06
315	Mark Belanger	.20	.10	.06
316	Henry Cruz	.20	.10	.06
317	Dave Johnson	.30	.15	.09
318	Tom Griffin	.20	.10	.06
319	Alan Ashby	.20	.10	.06
320	Fred Lynn	.90	.45	.25
321	Santo Alcala	.20	.10	.06
322	Tom Paciorek	.20	.10	.06
323	Jim Fregosi	.20	.10	.06
324	Vern Rapp	.20	.10	.06
325	Bruce Sutter	.50	.25	.15
326	Mike Lum	.20	.10	.06
327	Rick Langford	.20	.10	.06
328	Brewers Team	.50	.25	.15
329	John Verhoeven	.20	.10	.06
330	Bob Watson	.20	.10	.06
331	Mark Littell	.20	.10	.06
332	Duane Kuiper	.20	.10	.06
333	Jim Todd	.20	.10	.06
334	John Stearns	.20	.10	.06
335	Bucky Dent	.30	.15	.09
336	Steve Busby	.20	.10	.06
337	Tom Grieve	.20	.10	.06
338	Dave Heaverlo	.20	.10	.06
339	Mario Guerrero	.20	.10	.06
340	Bake McBride	.20	.10	.06
341	Mike Flanagan	.20	.10	.06
342	Aurelio Rodriguez	.20	.10	.06
343	John Wathan	.20	.10	.06
344	Sam Ewing	.20	.10	.06
345	Luis Tiant	.35	.20	.11
346	Larry Biittner	.20	.10	.06
347	Terry Forster	.20	.10	.06
348	Del Unser	.20	.10	.06
349	Rick Camp	.20	.10	.06
350	Steve Garvey	4.00	2.00	1.25
351	Jeff Torborg	.20	.10	.06
352	Tony Scott	.20	.10	.06
353	Doug Bair	.20	.10	.06
354	Cesar Geronimo	.20	.10	.06
355	Bill Travers	.20	.10	.06
356	Mets Team	.70	.35	.20
357	Tom Poquette	.20	.10	.06
358	Mark Lemongello	.20	.10	.06
359	Marc Hill	.20	.10	.06
360	Mike Schmidt	15.00	7.50	4.50
361	Chris Knapp	.20	.10	.06
362	Dave May	.20	.10	.06
363	Bob Randall	.20	.10	.06
364	Jerry Turner	.20	.10	.06
365	Ed Figueroa	.20	.10	.06
366	Larry Milbourne	.20	.10	.06
367	Rick Dempsey	.20	.10	.06
368	Balor Moore	.20	.10	.06

369 Tim Nordbrook .20 .10 .06
370 Rusty Staub .30 .15 .09
371 Ray Burris .20 .10 .06
372 Brian Asselstine .20 .10 .06
373 Jim Willoughby .20 .10 .06
374 Jose Morales .20 .10 .06
375 Tommy John .90 .45 .25
376 Jim Wohlford .20 .10 .06
377 Manny Sarmiento .20 .10 .06
378 Bobby Winkles .20 .10 .06
379 Skip Lockwood .20 .10 .06
380 Ted Simmons .40 .20 .12
381 Phillies Team .70 .35 .20
382 Joe Lahoud .20 .10 .06
383 Mario Mendoza .20 .10 .06
384 Jack Clark 2.00 1.00 .60
385 Tito Fuentes .20 .10 .06
386 Bob Gorinski .20 .10 .06
387 Ken Holtzman .20 .10 .06
388 Bill Fahey .20 .10 .06
389 Julio Gonzalez .20 .10 .06
390 Oscar Gamble .20 .10 .06
391 Larry Haney .20 .10 .06
392 Billy Almon .20 .10 .06
393 Tippy Martinez .20 .10 .06
394 Roy Howell .20 .10 .06
395 Jim Hughes .20 .10 .06
396 Bob Stinson .20 .10 .06
397 Greg Gross .20 .10 .06
398 Don Hood .20 .10 .06
399 Pete Mackanin .20 .10 .06
400 Nolan Ryan 40.00 20.00 12.00
401 Sparky Anderson .50 .25 .15
402 Dave Campbell .20 .10 .06
403 Bud Harrelson .20 .10 .06
404 Tigers Team .60 .30 .20
405 Rawly Eastwick .20 .10 .06
406 Mike Jorgensen .20 .10 .06
407 Odell Jones .20 .10 .06
408 Joe Zdeb .20 .10 .06
409 Ron Schueler .20 .10 .06
410 Bill Madlock .50 .25 .15
411 A.L. Championships (Yankees Rally To Defeat Royals) .70 .35 .20
412 N.L. Championships (Dodgers Overpower Phillies In Four) .50 .25 .15
413 Reggie Jackson (WS) 3.00 1.50 .90
414 Darold Knowles .20 .10 .06
415 Ray Fosse .20 .10 .06
416 Jack Brohamer .20 .10 .06
417 Mike Garman .20 .10 .06
418 Tony Muser .20 .10 .06
419 Jerry Garvin .20 .10 .06
420 Greg Luzinski .35 .20 .11
421 Junior Moore .20 .10 .06
422 Steve Braun .20 .10 .06
423 Dave Rosello .20 .10 .06
424 Red Sox Team .70 .35 .20
425 Steve Rogers .20 .10 .06
426 Fred Kendall .20 .10 .06
427 *Mario Soto* .40 .20 .12
428 Joel Youngblood .20 .10 .06
429 Mike Barlow .20 .10 .06
430 Al Oliver .40 .20 .12
431 Butch Metzger .20 .10 .06
432 Terry Bulling .20 .10 .06
433 Fernando Gonzalez .20 .10 .06
434 Mike Norris .20 .10 .06
435 Checklist 364-484 .90 .45 .25
436 Vic Harris .20 .10 .06
437 Bo McLaughlin .20 .10 .06
438 John Ellis .20 .10 .06
439 Ken Kravec .20 .10 .06
440 Dave Lopes .25 .13 .08
441 Larry Gura .20 .10 .06
442 Elliott Maddox .20 .10 .06
443 Darrel Chaney .20 .10 .06
444 Roy Hartsfield .20 .10 .06
445 Mike Ivie .20 .10 .06
446 Tug McGraw .20 .10 .06
447 Leroy Stanton .20 .10 .06
448 Bill Castro .20 .10 .06
449 Tim Blackwell .20 .10 .06
450 Tom Seaver 8.00 4.00 2.50
451 Twins Team .50 .25 .15
452 Jerry Mumphrey .20 .10 .06
453 Doug Flynn .20 .10 .06
454 Dave LaRoche .20 .10 .06
455 Bill Robinson .20 .10 .06
456 Vern Ruhle .20 .10 .06
457 Bob Bailey .20 .10 .06
458 Jeff Newman .20 .10 .06
459 Charlie Spikes .20 .10 .06
460 Catfish Hunter 2.00 1.00 .60
461 Rob Andrews .20 .10 .06
462 Rogelio Moret .20 .10 .06
463 Kevin Bell .20 .10 .06
464 Jerry Grote .20 .10 .06
465 Hal McRae .30 .15 .09
466 Dennis Blair .20 .10 .06
467 Alvin Dark .20 .10 .06
468 *Warren Cromartie* .20 .10 .06
469 Rick Cerone .20 .10 .06
470 J.R. Richard .25 .13 .08
471 Roy Smalley .20 .10 .06
472 Ron Reed .20 .10 .06
473 Bill Buckner .30 .15 .09
474 Jim Slaton .20 .10 .06
475 Gary Matthews .20 .10 .06
476 Bill Stein .20 .10 .06
477 Doug Capilla .20 .10 .06
478 Jerry Remy .20 .10 .06
479 Cardinals Team .50 .25 .15
480 Ron LeFlore .20 .10 .06
481 Jackson Todd .20 .10 .06
482 Rick Miller .20 .10 .06
483 Ken Macha .20 .10 .06
484 Jim Norris .20 .10 .06
485 Chris Chambliss .20 .10 .06
486 John Curtis .20 .10 .06
487 Jim Tyrone .20 .10 .06
488 Dan Spillner .20 .10 .06
489 Rudy Meoli .20 .10 .06
490 Amos Otis .20 .10 .06
491 Scott McGregor .20 .10 .06
492 Jim Sundberg .20 .10 .06
493 Steve Renko .20 .10 .06
494 Chuck Tanner .20 .10 .06
495 Dave Cash .20 .10 .06
496 *Jim Clancy* .20 .10 .06
497 Glenn Adams .20 .10 .06
498 Joe Sambito .20 .10 .06
499 Mariners Team .50 .25 .15
500 George Foster .50 .25 .15
501 Dave Roberts .20 .10 .06
502 Pat Rockett .20 .10 .06
503 Ike Hampton .20 .10 .06
504 Roger Freed .20 .10 .06
505 Felix Millan .20 .10 .06
506 Ron Blomberg .20 .10 .06
507 Willie Crawford .20 .10 .06
508 Johnny Oates .20 .10 .06
509 Brent Strom .20 .10 .06
510 Willie Stargell 3.00 1.50 .90
511 Frank Duffy .20 .10 .06
512 Larry Herndon .20 .10 .06
513 Barry Foote .20 .10 .06
514 Rob Sperring .20 .10 .06
515 Tim Corcoran .20 .10 .06
516 Gary Beare .20 .10 .06
517 Andres Mora .20 .10 .06
518 Tommy Boggs .20 .10 .06
519 Brian Downing .25 .13 .08
520 Larry Hisle .20 .10 .06
521 Steve Staggs .20 .10 .06
522 Dick Williams .20 .10 .06
523 *Donnie Moore* .20 .10 .06
524 Bernie Carbo .20 .10 .06
525 Jerry Terrell .20 .10 .06
526 Reds Team .60 .30 .20
527 Vic Correll .20 .10 .06
528 Rob Picciolo .20 .10 .06
529 Paul Hartzell .20 .10 .06
530 Dave Winfield 24.00 12.00 7.25
531 Tom Underwood .20 .10 .06
532 Skip Jutze .20 .10 .06
533 Sandy Alomar .20 .10 .06
534 Wilbur Howard .20 .10 .06
535 Checklist 485-605 .90 .45 .25
536 Roric Harrison .20 .10 .06
537 Bruce Bochte .20 .10 .06
538 Johnnie LeMaster .20 .10 .06
539 Vic Davalillo .20 .10 .06
540 Steve Carlton 5.00 2.50 1.50
541 Larry Cox .20 .10 .06
542 Tim Johnson .20 .10 .06
543 Larry Harlow .20 .10 .06
544 Len Randle .20 .10 .06
545 Bill Campbell .20 .10 .06
546 Ted Martinez .20 .10 .06
547 John Scott .20 .10 .06
548 Billy Hunter .20 .10 .06
549 Joe Kerrigan .20 .10 .06
550 John Mayberry .20 .10 .06
551 Braves Team .50 .25 .15
552 Francisco Barrios .20 .10 .06
553 *Terry Puhl* .35 .20 .11
554 Joe Coleman .20 .10 .06
555 Butch Wynegar .20 .10 .06
556 Ed Armbrister .20 .10 .06
557 Tony Solaita .20 .10 .06
558 Paul Mitchell .20 .10 .06
559 Phil Mankowski .20 .10 .06
560 Dave Parker 3.00 1.50 .90
561 Charlie Williams .20 .10 .06
562 Glenn Burke .20 .10 .06
563 Dave Rader .20 .10 .06
564 Mick Kelleher .20 .10 .06
565 Jerry Koosman .20 .10 .06
566 Merv Rettenmund .20 .10 .06
567 Dick Drago .20 .10 .06
568 Tom Hutton .20 .10 .06
569 *Lary Sorensen* .20 .10 .06
570 Dave Kingman .30 .15 .09
571 Buck Martinez .20 .10 .06
572 Rick Wise .20 .10 .06
573 Luis Gomez .20 .10 .06
574 Bob Lemon .30 .15 .09
575 Pat Dobson .20 .10 .06
576 Sam Mejias .20 .10 .06
577 A's Team .50 .25 .15
578 Buzz Capra .20 .10 .06
579 *Rance Mulliniks* .35 .20 .11
580 Rod Carew 6.00 3.00 1.75
581 Lynn McGlothen .20 .10 .06
582 Fran Healy .20 .10 .06
583 George Medich .20 .10 .06
584 John Hale .20 .10 .06
585 Woodie Fryman .20 .10 .06
586 Ed Goodson .20 .10 .06
587 John Urrea .20 .10 .06
588 Jim Mason .20 .10 .06
589 *Bob Knepper* .40 .20 .12
590 Bobby Murcer .20 .10 .06
591 George Zeber .20 .10 .06
592 Bob Apodaca .20 .10 .06
593 Dave Skaggs .20 .10 .06
594 Dave Freisleben .20 .10 .06
595 Sixto Lezcano .20 .10 .06
596 Gary Wheelock .20 .10 .06
597 Steve Dillard .20 .10 .06
598 Eddie Solomon .20 .10 .06
599 Gary Woods .20 .10 .06
600 Frank Tanana .25 .13 .08
601 Gene Mauch .20 .10 .06
602 Eric Soderholm .20 .10 .06
603 Will McEnaney .20 .10 .06
604 Earl Williams .20 .10 .06
605 Rick Rhoden .20 .10 .06
606 Pirates Team .50 .25 .15
607 Fernando Arroyo .20 .10 .06
608 Johnny Grubb .20 .10 .06
609 John Denny .20 .10 .06
610 Garry Maddox .20 .10 .06
611 Pat Scanlon .20 .10 .06
612 Ken Henderson .20 .10 .06
613 Marty Perez .20 .10 .06
614 Joe Wallis .20 .10 .06
615 Clay Carroll .20 .10 .06
616 Pat Kelly .20 .10 .06
617 Joe Nolan .20 .10 .06
618 Tommy Helms .20 .10 .06
619 *Thad Bosley* .20 .10 .06
620 Willie Randolph .30 .15 .09
621 Craig Swan .20 .10 .06
622 Champ Summers .20 .10 .06
623 Eduardo Rodriguez .20 .10 .06
624 Gary Alexander .20 .10 .06
625 Jose Cruz .25 .13 .08
626 Blue Jays Team .25 .13 .08
627 Dave Johnson .20 .10 .06
628 Ralph Garr .20 .10 .06
629 Don Stanhouse .20 .10 .06
630 Ron Cey .25 .13 .08
631 Danny Ozark .20 .10 .06
632 Rowland Office .20 .10 .06
633 Tom Veryzer .20 .10 .06
634 Len Barker .20 .10 .06
635 Joe Rudi .20 .10 .06
636 Jim Bibby .20 .10 .06
637 Duffy Dyer .20 .10 .06
638 Paul Splittorff .20 .10 .06
639 Gene Clines .20 .10 .06
640 Lee May .20 .10 .06
641 Doug Rau .20 .10 .06
642 Denny Doyle .20 .10 .06
643 Tom House .20 .10 .06
644 Jim Dwyer .20 .10 .06
645 Mike Torrez .20 .10 .06
646 Rick Auerbach .20 .10 .06
647 Steve Dunning .20 .10 .06
648 Gary Thomasson .20 .10 .06
649 *Moose Haas* .20 .10 .06
650 Cesar Cedeno .25 .13 .08
651 Doug Rader .20 .10 .06
652 Checklist 606-726 .90 .45 .25
653 Ron Hodges .20 .10 .06
654 Pepe Frias .20 .10 .06
655 Lyman Bostock .20 .10 .06
656 Dave Garcia .20 .10 .06
657 Bombo Rivera .20 .10 .06
658 Manny Sanguillen .20 .10 .06
659 Rangers Team .50 .25 .15
660 Jason Thompson .20 .10 .06
661 Grant Jackson .20 .10 .06
662 Paul Dade .20 .10 .06
663 Paul Reuschel .20 .10 .06
664 Fred Stanley .20 .10 .06
665 Dennis Leonard .20 .10 .06
666 Billy Smith .20 .10 .06
667 Jeff Byrd .20 .10 .06
668 Dusty Baker .25 .13 .08
669 Pete Falcone .20 .10 .06
670 Jim Rice 2.50 1.25 .70
671 Gary Lavelle .20 .10 .06
672 Don Kessinger .20 .10 .06
673 Steve Brye .20 .10 .06
674 *Ray Knight* 1.50 .70 .45
675 Jay Johnstone .20 .10 .06
676 Bob Myrick .20 .10 .06
677 Ed Herrmann .20 .10 .06
678 Tom Burgmeier .20 .10 .06
679 Wayne Garrett .20 .10 .06
680 Vida Blue .30 .15 .09
681 Rob Belloir .20 .10 .06
682 Ken Brett .20 .10 .06
683 Mike Champion .20 .10 .06
684 Ralph Houk .20 .10 .06
685 Frank Taveras .20 .10 .06
686 Gaylord Perry 2.00 1.00 .60
687 *Julio Cruz* .25 .13 .08
688 George Mitterwald .20 .10 .06
689 Indians Team .50 .25 .15
690 Mickey Rivers .25 .13 .08
691 Ross Grimsley .20 .10 .06
692 Ken Reitz .20 .10 .06
693 Lamar Johnson .20 .10 .06
694 Elias Sosa .20 .10 .06
695 Dwight Evans 1.00 .50 .30
696 Steve Mingori .20 .10 .06
697 Roger Metzger .20 .10 .06
698 Juan Bernhardt .20 .10 .06
699 Jackie Brown .20 .10 .06
700 Johnny Bench 5.00 2.50 1.50
701 Rookie Pitchers (*Tom Hume*, Larry Landreth, Steve McCatty, Bruce Taylor) .20 .10 .06
702 Rookie Catchers (Bill Nahorodny, Kevin Pasley, Rick Sweet, Don Werner) .20 .10 .06
703 Rookie Pitchers (Larry Andersen, Tim Jones, Mickey Mahler, Jack Morris) 6.00 3.00 1.75
704 Rookie 2nd Basemen (*Garth Iorg*, Dave Oliver, Sam Perlozzo, Lou Whitaker) 20.00 10.00 6.00
705 Rookie Outfielders (*Dave Bergman*, Miguel Dilone, Clint Hurdle, Willie Norwood) .20 .10 .06
706 Rookie 1st Basemen (Wayne Cage, Ted Cox, Pat Putnam, Dave Revering) .20 .10 .06
707 Rookie Shortstops (Mickey Klutts, Paul Molitor, Alan Trammell, U.L. Washington) 100.00 50.00 30.00
708 Rookie Catchers (*Bo Diaz*, Dale Murphy, Lance Parrish, Ernie Whitt) 12.00 6.00 3.50
709 Rookie Pitchers (Steve Burke, Matt Keough, Lance Rautzhan, Dan Schatzeder) .20 .10 .06

710	Rookie Outfielders (Dell Alston, Rick Bosetti, Mike Easler, Keith Smith)	.20	.10	.06
711	Rookie Pitchers (Cardell Camper, Dennis Lamp, Craig Mitchell, Roy Thomas)	.20	.10	.06
712	Bobby Valentine	.25	.13	.08
713	Bob Davis	.20	.10	.06
714	Mike Anderson	.20	.10	.06
715	Jim Kaat	.60	.30	.20
716	Cito Gaston	.35	.20	.11
717	Nelson Briles	.20	.10	.06
718	Ron Jackson	.20	.10	.06
719	Randy Elliott	.20	.10	.06
720	Fergie Jenkins	2.00	1.00	.60
721	Billy Martin	.50	.25	.15
722	Pete Broberg	.20	.10	.06
723	Johnny Wockenfuss	.20	.10	.06
724	Royals Team	.70	.35	.20
725	Kurt Bevacqua	.20	.10	.06
726	Wilbur Wood	.20	.10	.06

1979 Topps

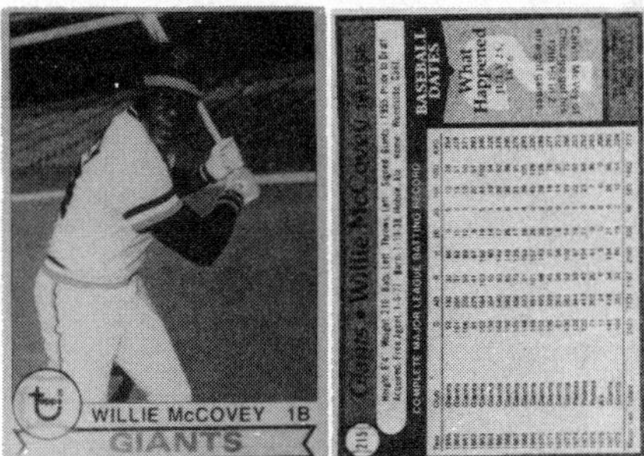

The size of this issue remained the same as in 1978 with 726 cards making their appearance. Actually, the 2-1/2" by 3-1/2" cards have a relatively minor design change from the previous year. The large color photo still dominates the front, with the player's name, team and position below it. The baseball with the player's position was moved to the lower left and the position replaced by a Topps logo. On the back, the printing color was changed and the game situation was replaced by a quiz called "Baseball Dates". Specialty cards include statistical leaders, major league records set during the season and eight cards devoted to career records. For the first time, rookies were arranged by teams under the heading of "Prospects."

		NR MT	EX	VG
	Complete Set (726):	250.00	125.00	75.00
	Common Player:	.15	.08	.05
1	Batting Leaders (Rod Carew, Dave Parker)	3.00	1.50	.90
2	Home Run Leaders (George Foster, Jim Rice)	.30	.15	.09
3	RBI Leaders (George Foster, Jim Rice)	.30	.15	.09
4	Stolen Base Leaders (Ron LeFlore, Omar Moreno)	.15	.08	.05
5	Victory Leaders (Ron Guidry, Gaylord Perry)	.30	.15	.09
6	Strikeout Leaders (J.R. Richard, Nolan Ryan)	4.00	2.00	1.25
7	ERA Leaders (Ron Guidry, Craig Swan)	.25	.13	.08
8	Leading Firemen (Rollie Fingers, Rich Gossage)	.40	.20	.12
9	Dave Campbell	.15	.08	.05
10	Lee May	.20	.10	.06
11	Marc Hill	.15	.08	.05
12	Dick Drago	.15	.08	.05
13	Paul Dade	.15	.08	.05
14	Rafael Landestoy	.15	.08	.05
15	Ross Grimsley	.20	.10	.06
16	Fred Stanley	.20	.10	.06
17	Donnie Moore	.20	.10	.06
18	Tony Solaita	.15	.08	.05
19	Larry Gura	.15	.08	.05
20	Joe Morgan	.40	.20	.12
21	Kevin Kobel	.15	.08	.05
22	Mike Jorgensen	.15	.08	.05
23	Terry Forster	.20	.10	.06
24	Paul Molitor	32.00	16.00	9.75
25	Steve Carlton	4.50	3.50	1.75
26	Jamie Quirk	.15	.08	.05
27	Dave Goltz	.20	.10	.06
28	Steve Brye	.15	.08	.05
29	Rick Langford	.15	.08	.05
30	Dave Winfield	15.00	7.50	4.50
31	Tom House	.15	.08	.05
32	Jerry Mumphrey	.15	.08	.05
33	Dave Rozema	.15	.08	.05
34	Rob Andrews	.15	.08	.05
35	Ed Figueroa	.20	.10	.06
36	Alan Ashby	.15	.08	.05
37	Joe Kerrigan	.15	.08	.05
38	Bernie Carbo	.15	.08	.05
39	Dale Murphy	6.00	3.00	1.75
40	Dennis Eckersley	7.00	3.50	2.00
41	Twins Team (Gene Mauch)	.50	.25	.15
42	Ron Blomberg	.15	.08	.05
43	Wayne Twitchell	.15	.08	.05
44	Kurt Bevacqua	.15	.08	.05
45	Al Hrabosky	.20	.10	.06
46	Ron Hodges	.15	.08	.05
47	Fred Norman	.15	.08	.05
48	Merv Rettenmund	.15	.08	.05
49	Vern Ruhle	.15	.08	.05
50	Steve Garvey	.90	.45	.25
51	Ray Fosse	.15	.08	.05
52	Randy Lerch	.15	.08	.05
53	Mick Kelleher	.15	.08	.05
54	Dell Alston	.15	.08	.05
55	Willie Stargell	2.00	1.00	.60
56	John Hale	.15	.08	.05
57	Eric Rasmussen	.15	.08	.05
58	Bob Randall	.15	.08	.05
59	John Denny	.15	.08	.05
60	Mickey Rivers	.20	.10	.06
61	Bo Diaz	.20	.10	.06
62	Randy Moffitt	.15	.08	.05
63	Jack Brohamer	.15	.08	.05
64	Tom Underwood	.15	.08	.05
65	Mark Belanger	.20	.10	.06
66	Tigers Team (Les Moss)	.60	.30	.20
67	Jim Mason	.15	.08	.05
68	Joe Niekro	.15	.08	.05
69	Elliott Maddox	.15	.08	.05
70	John Candelaria	.25	.13	.08
71	Brian Downing	.20	.10	.06
72	Steve Mingori	.15	.08	.05
73	Ken Henderson	.15	.08	.05
74	*Shane Rawley*	.15	.08	.05
75	Steve Yeager	.15	.08	.05
76	Warren Cromartie	.15	.08	.05
77	Dan Briggs	.15	.08	.05
78	Elias Sosa	.15	.08	.05
79	Ted Cox	.15	.08	.05
80	Jason Thompson	.20	.10	.06
81	Roger Erickson	.15	.08	.05
82	Mets Team (Joe Torre)	.60	.30	.20
83	Fred Kendall	.15	.08	.05
84	Greg Minton	.15	.08	.05
85	Gary Matthews	.20	.10	.06
86	Rodney Scott	.15	.08	.05
87	Pete Falcone	.15	.08	.05
88	Bob Molinaro	.15	.08	.05
89	Dick Tidrow	.20	.10	.06
90	Bob Boone	.25	.13	.08
91	Terry Crowley	.15	.08	.05
92	Jim Bibby	.15	.08	.05
93	Phil Mankowski	.15	.08	.05
94	Len Barker	.15	.08	.05
95	Robin Yount	15.00	7.50	4.50
96	Indians Team (Jeff Torborg)	.50	.25	.15
97	Sam Mejias	.15	.08	.05
98	Ray Burris	.15	.08	.05
99	John Wathan	.20	.10	.06
100	Tom Seaver	4.00	2.00	1.25
101	Roy Howell	.15	.08	.05
102	Mike Anderson	.15	.08	.05
103	Jim Todd	.15	.08	.05
104	Johnny Oates	.15	.08	.05
105	Rick Camp	.15	.08	.05
106	Frank Duffy	.15	.08	.05
107	Jesus Alou	.20	.10	.06
108	Eduardo Rodriguez	.15	.08	.05
109	Joel Youngblood	.15	.08	.05
110	Vida Blue	.30	.15	.09
111	Roger Freed	.15	.08	.05
112	Phillies Team (Danny Ozark)	.50	.25	.15
113	Pete Redfern	.15	.08	.05
114	Cliff Johnson	.20	.10	.06
115	Nolan Ryan	32.00	16.00	9.50
116	*Ozzie Smith*	90.00	45.00	27.00
117	Grant Jackson	.15	.08	.05
118	Bud Harrelson	.20	.10	.06
119	Don Stanhouse	.15	.08	.05
120	Jim Sundberg	.20	.10	.06
121	Checklist 1-121	.25	.13	.08
122	Mike Paxton	.15	.08	.05
123	Lou Whitaker	7.50	3.75	2.25
124	Dan Schatzeder	.15	.08	.05
125	Rick Burleson	.20	.10	.06
126	Doug Bair	.15	.08	.05
127	Thad Bosley	.15	.08	.05
128	Ted Martinez	.15	.08	.05
129	Marty Pattin	.15	.08	.05
130	Bob Watson	.15	.08	.05
131	Jim Clancy	.25	.13	.08
132	Rowland Office	.15	.08	.05
133	Bill Castro	.15	.08	.05
134	Alan Bannister	.15	.08	.05
135	Bobby Murcer	.25	.13	.08
136	Jim Kaat	.60	.30	.20
137	Larry Wolfe	.15	.08	.05
138	Mark Lee	.15	.08	.05
139	Luis Pujols	.15	.08	.05
140	Don Gullett	.20	.10	.06
141	Tom Paciorek	.15	.08	.05
142	Charlie Williams	.15	.08	.05
143	Tony Scott	.15	.08	.05
144	Sandy Alomar	.15	.08	.05
145	Rick Rhoden	.25	.13	.08
146	Duane Kuiper	.15	.08	.05
147	Dave Hamilton	.15	.08	.05
148	Bruce Boisclair	.15	.08	.05
149	Manny Sarmiento	.15	.08	.05
150	Wayne Cage	.15	.08	.05
151	John Hiller	.20	.10	.06
152	Rick Cerone	.20	.10	.06
153	Dennis Lamp	.15	.08	.05
154	Jim Gantner	.15	.08	.05
155	Dwight Evans	.75	.40	.25
156	Buddy Solomon	.15	.08	.05
157	U.L. Washington	.15	.08	.05
158	Joe Sambito	.15	.08	.05
159	Roy White	.25	.13	.08
160	Mike Flanagan	.30	.15	.09
161	Barry Foote	.15	.08	.05
162	Tom Johnson	.15	.08	.05
163	Glenn Burke	.15	.08	.05
164	Mickey Lolich	.30	.15	.09
165	Frank Taveras	.15	.08	.05
166	Leon Roberts	.15	.08	.05
167	Roger Metzger	.15	.08	.05
168	Dave Freisleben	.15	.08	.05
169	Bill Nahorodny	.15	.08	.05
170	Don Sutton	1.25	.60	.40
171	Gene Clines	.15	.08	.05
172	Mike Bruhert	.15	.08	.05
173	John Lowenstein	.15	.08	.05
174	Rick Auerbach	.15	.08	.05
175	George Hendrick	.20	.10	.06
176	Aurelio Rodriguez	.20	.10	.06
177	Ron Reed	.20	.10	.06
178	Alvis Woods	.15	.08	.05
179	Jim Beattie	.15	.08	.05
180	Larry Hisle	.20	.10	.06
181	Mike Garman	.15	.08	.05
182	Tim Johnson	.15	.08	.05
183	Paul Splittorff	.20	.10	.06
184	Darrel Chaney	.15	.08	.05
185	Mike Torrez	.20	.10	.06
186	Eric Soderholm	.15	.08	.05
187	Mark Lemongello	.15	.08	.05
188	Pat Kelly	.15	.08	.05
189	*Eddie Whitson*	.25	.13	.08
190	Ron Cey	.25	.13	.08
191	Mike Norris	.15	.08	.05
192	Cardinals Team (Ken Boyer)	.50	.25	.15
193	Glenn Adams	.15	.08	.05
194	Randy Jones	.20	.10	.06
195	Bill Madlock	.40	.20	.12
196	Steve Kemp	.15	.08	.05
197	Bob Apodaca	.15	.08	.05
198	Johnny Grubb	.15	.08	.05
199	Larry Milbourne	.15	.08	.05
200	Johnny Bench	2.00	1.00	.60
201	Mike Edwards (Record Breaker)	.15	.08	.05
202	Ron Guidry (Record Breaker)	.35	.20	.11
203	J.R. Richard (Record Breaker)	.20	.10	.06
204	Pete Rose (Record Breaker)	1.50	.70	.45
205	John Stearns (Record Breaker)	.15	.08	.05
206	Sammy Stewart (Record Breaker)	.15	.08	.05
207	Dave Lemanczyk	.15	.08	.05
208	Citoence Gaston	.30	.15	.09
209	Reggie Cleveland	.15	.08	.05
210	Larry Bowa	.30	.15	.09
211	Denny Martinez	.20	.10	.06
212	*Carney Lansford*	2.00	1.00	.60
213	Bill Travers	.15	.08	.05
214	Red Sox Team (Don Zimmer)	.60	.30	.20
215	Willie McCovey	2.00	1.00	.60
216	Wilbur Wood	.20	.10	.06
217	Steve Dillard	.15	.08	.05
218	Dennis Leonard	.20	.10	.06
219	Roy Smalley	.20	.10	.06
220	Cesar Geronimo	.20	.10	.06
221	Jesse Jefferson	.15	.08	.05
222	Bob Beall	.15	.08	.05
223	Kent Tekulve	.25	.13	.08
224	Dave Revering	.15	.08	.05
225	Rich Gossage	.40	.20	.12
226	Ron Pruitt	.15	.08	.05
227	Steve Stone	.20	.10	.06
228	Vic Davalillo	.15	.08	.05
229	Doug Flynn	.15	.08	.05
230	Bob Forsch	.20	.10	.06
231	Johnny Wockenfuss	.15	.08	.05
232	Jimmy Sexton	.15	.08	.05
233	Paul Mitchell	.15	.08	.05
234	Toby Harrah	.20	.10	.06
235	Steve Rogers	.20	.10	.06
236	Jim Dwyer	.15	.08	.05
237	Billy Smith	.15	.08	.05
238	Balor Moore	.15	.08	.05
239	Willie Horton	.20	.10	.06
240	Rick Reuschel	.25	.13	.08
241	Checklist 122-242	.25	.13	.08
242	Pablo Torrealba	.15	.08	.05
243	Buck Martinez	.15	.08	.05
244	Pirates Team (Chuck Tanner)	.80	.40	.25
245	Jeff Burroughs	.20	.10	.06
246	Darrell Jackson	.15	.08	.05
247	Tucker Ashford	.15	.08	.05
248	Pete LaCock	.15	.08	.05
249	Paul Thormodsgard	.15	.08	.05
250	Willie Randolph	.30	.15	.09
251	Jack Morris	3.00	1.50	.90
252	Bob Stinson	.15	.08	.05
253	Rick Wise	.20	.10	.06
254	Luis Gomez	.15	.08	.05
255	Tommy John	.80	.40	.25
256	Mike Sadek	.15	.08	.05
257	Adrian Devine	.15	.08	.05
258	Mike Phillips	.15	.08	.05
259	Reds Team (Sparky Anderson)	.60	.30	.20
260	Richie Zisk	.20	.10	.06
261	Mario Guerrero	.15	.08	.05
262	Nelson Briles	.15	.08	.05
263	Oscar Gamble	.20	.10	.06
264	*Don Robinson*	.15	.08	.05
265	Don Money	.15	.08	.05
266	Jim Willoughby	.15	.08	.05
267	Joe Rudi	.20	.10	.06
268	Julio Gonzalez	.15	.08	.05
269	Woodie Fryman	.20	.10	.06
270	Butch Hobson	.15	.08	.05
271	Rawly Eastwick	.15	.08	.05
272	Tim Corcoran	.15	.08	.05
273	Jerry Terrell	.15	.08	.05
274	Willie Norwood	.15	.08	.05
275	Junior Moore	.15	.08	.05
276	Jim Colborn	.15	.08	.05
277	Tom Grieve	.15	.08	.05
278	Andy Messersmith	.25	.13	.08
279	Jerry Grote	.15	.08	.05
280	Andre Thornton	.25	.13	.08
281	Vic Correll	.15	.08	.05
282	Blue Jays Team (Roy Hartsfield)	.50	.25	.15
283	Ken Kravec	.15	.08	.05
284	Johnnie LeMaster	.15	.08	.05
285	Bobby Bonds	.30	.15	.09
286	Duffy Dyer	.15	.08	.05
287	Andres Mora	.15	.08	.05
288	Milt Wilcox	.20	.10	.06

289 Jose Cruz .25 .13 .08
290 Dave Lopes .25 .13 .08
291 Tom Griffin .15 .08 .05
292 Don Reynolds .15 .08 .05
293 Jerry Garvin .15 .08 .05
294 Pepe Frias .15 .08 .05
295 Mitchell Page .15 .08 .05
296 Preston Hanna .15 .08 .05
297 Ted Sizemore .15 .08 .05
298 Rich Gale .15 .08 .05
299 Steve Ontiveros .15 .08 .05
300 Rod Carew 4.00 2.00 1.25
301 Tom Hume .15 .08 .05
302 Braves Team (Bobby Cox) .50 .25 .15
303 Lary Sorensen .15 .08 .05
304 Steve Swisher .15 .08 .05
305 Willie Montanez .15 .08 .05
306 Floyd Bannister .15 .08 .05
307 Larvell Blanks .15 .08 .05
308 Bert Blyleven .30 .15 .09
309 Ralph Garr .20 .10 .06
310 Thurman Munson 4.00 2.00 1.25
311 Gary Lavelle .15 .08 .05
312 Bob Robertson .15 .08 .05
313 Dyar Miller .15 .08 .05
314 Larry Harlow .15 .08 .05
315 Jon Matlack .20 .10 .06
316 Milt May .15 .08 .05
317 Jose Cardenal .15 .08 .05
318 *Bob Welch* 2.50 1.25 .70
319 Wayne Garrett .15 .08 .05
320 Carl Yastrzemski 4.00 2.00 1.25
321 Gaylord Perry 2.00 1.00 .60
322 Danny Goodwin .15 .08 .05
323 Lynn McGlothen .15 .08 .05
324 Mike Tyson .15 .08 .05
325 Cecil Cooper .20 .10 .06
326 Pedro Borbon .15 .08 .05
327 Art Howe .15 .08 .05
328 A's Team (Jack McKeon) .50 .25 .15
329 Joe Coleman .20 .10 .06
330 George Brett 18.00 9.00 5.50
331 Mickey Mahler .15 .08 .05
332 Gary Alexander .15 .08 .05
333 Chet Lemon .20 .10 .06
334 Craig Swan .15 .08 .05
335 Chris Chambliss .25 .13 .08
336 Bobby Thompson .15 .08 .05
337 John Montague .15 .08 .05
338 Vic Harris .15 .08 .05
339 Ron Jackson .15 .08 .05
340 Jim Palmer 4.00 2.00 1.25
341 *Willie Upshaw* .20 .10 .06
342 Dave Roberts .15 .08 .05
343 Ed Glynn .15 .08 .05
344 Jerry Royster .15 .08 .05
345 Tug McGraw .30 .15 .09
346 Bill Buckner .30 .15 .09
347 Doug Rau .15 .08 .05
348 Andre Dawson 10.00 5.00 3.00
349 Jim Wright .15 .08 .05
350 Garry Templeton .20 .10 .06
351 Wayne Nordhagen .15 .08 .05
352 Steve Renko .15 .08 .05
353 Checklist 243-363 .60 .30 .20
354 Bill Bonham .15 .08 .05
355 Lee Mazzilli .20 .10 .06
356 Giants Team (Joe Altobelli) .50 .25 .15
357 Jerry Augustine .15 .08 .05
358 Alan Trammell 10.00 5.00 3.00
359 Dan Spillner .15 .08 .05
360 Amos Otis .20 .10 .06
361 Tom Dixon .15 .08 .05
362 Mike Cubbage .15 .08 .05
363 Craig Skok .15 .08 .05
364 Gene Richards .15 .08 .05
365 Sparky Lyle .30 .15 .09
366 Juan Bernhardt .15 .08 .05
367 Dave Skaggs .15 .08 .05
368 Don Aase .20 .10 .06
369a Bump Wills (Blue Jays) 2.00 1.00 .60
369b Bump Wills (Rangers) 2.50 1.25 .70
370 Dave Kingman .35 .20 .11
371 Jeff Holly .15 .08 .05
372 Lamar Johnson .15 .08 .05
373 Lance Rautzhan .15 .08 .05
374 Ed Herrmann .15 .08 .05
375 Bill Campbell .15 .08 .05
376 Gorman Thomas .25 .13 .08
377 Paul Moskau .15 .08 .05
378 Rob Picciolo .15 .08 .05
379 Dale Murray .15 .08 .05
380 John Mayberry .20 .10 .06
381 Astros Team (Bill Virdon) .50 .25 .15
382 Jerry Martin .15 .08 .05
383 Phil Garner .20 .10 .06
384 Tommy Boggs .15 .08 .05
385 Dan Ford .15 .08 .05
386 Francisco Barrios .15 .08 .05
387 Gary Thomasson .15 .08 .05
388 Jack Billingham .15 .08 .05
389 Joe Zdeb .15 .08 .05
390 Rollie Fingers 2.50 1.25 .70
391 Al Oliver .40 .20 .12
392 Doug Ault .15 .08 .05
393 Scott McGregor .20 .10 .06
394 Randy Stein .15 .08 .05
395 Dave Cash .15 .08 .05
396 Bill Plummer .15 .08 .05
397 Sergio Ferrer .15 .08 .05
398 Ivan DeJesus .15 .08 .05
399 David Clyde .15 .08 .05
400 Jim Rice 1.00 .50 .30
401 Ray Knight .25 .13 .08
402 Paul Hartzell .15 .08 .05
403 Tim Foli .15 .08 .05
404 White Sox Team (Don Kessinger) .50 .25 .15
405 Butch Wynegar .20 .10 .06
406 Joe Wallis .15 .08 .05
407 Pete Vuckovich .20 .10 .06
408 Charlie Moore .15 .08 .05
409 *Willie Wilson* 2.00 1.00 .60
410 Darrell Evans .30 .15 .09
411 All-Time Hits Leaders (Ty Cobb) (career), George Sisler) .70 .35 .20
412 All-Time RBI Leaders (Hank Aaron) (career, Hack Wilson) .70 .35 .20
413 All-Time Home Run Leaders (Hank Aaron) (career, Roger Maris) 1.00 .50 .30
414 All-Time Batting Average Leaders (Ty Cobb) (career, Roger Hornsby) .70 .35 .20
415 All-Time Stolen Bases Leader (Lou Brock) .50 .25 .15
416 All-Time Wins Leaders (Jack Chesbro) (season, Cy Young) .35 .20 .11
417 All-Time Strikeout Leaders (Walter Johnson) (career, Nolan Ryan) 2.00 1.00 .60
418 All-Time ERA Leaders (Walter Johnson) (career, Dutch Leonard) .20 .10 .06
419 Dick Ruthven .15 .08 .05
420 Ken Griffey .25 .13 .08
421 Doug DeCinces .25 .13 .08
422 Ruppert Jones .15 .08 .05
423 Bob Montgomery .15 .08 .05
424 Angels Team (Jim Fregosi) .60 .30 .20
425 Rick Manning .15 .08 .05
426 Chris Speier .20 .10 .06
427 Andy Replogle .15 .08 .05
428 Bobby Valentine .25 .13 .08
429 John Urrea .15 .08 .05
430 Dave Parker 2.00 1.00 .60
431 Glenn Borgmann .15 .08 .05
432 Dave Heaverlo .15 .08 .05
433 Larry Biittner .15 .08 .05
434 Ken Clay .20 .10 .06
435 Gene Tenace .20 .10 .06
436 Hector Cruz .15 .08 .05
437 Rick Williams .15 .08 .05
438 Horace Speed .15 .08 .05
439 Frank White .25 .13 .08
440 Rusty Staub .30 .15 .09
441 Lee Lacy .15 .08 .05
442 Doyle Alexander .25 .13 .08
443 Bruce Bochte .15 .08 .05
444 *Aurelio Lopez* .20 .10 .06
445 Steve Henderson .15 .08 .05
446 Jim Lonborg .20 .10 .06
447 Manny Sanguillen .15 .08 .05
448 Moose Haas .15 .08 .05
449 Bombo Rivera .15 .08 .05
450 Dave Concepcion .30 .15 .09
451 Royals Team (Whitey Herzog) .50 .25 .15
452 Jerry Morales .15 .08 .05
453 Chris Knapp .15 .08 .05
454 Len Randle .15 .08 .05
455 Bill Lee .15 .08 .05
456 Chuck Baker .15 .08 .05
457 Bruce Sutter .40 .20 .12
458 Jim Essian .15 .08 .05
459 Sid Monge .15 .08 .05
460 Graig Nettles .25 .13 .08
461 Jim Barr .15 .08 .05
462 Otto Velez .15 .08 .05
463 Steve Comer .15 .08 .05
464 Joe Nolan .15 .08 .05
465 Reggie Smith .25 .13 .08
466 Mark Littell .15 .08 .05
467 Don Kessinger .15 .08 .05
468 Stan Bahnsen .15 .08 .05
469 Lance Parrish 2.00 1.00 .60
470 Garry Maddox .15 .08 .05
471 Joaquin Andujar .20 .10 .06
472 Craig Kusick .15 .08 .05
473 Dave Roberts .15 .08 .05
474 Dick Davis .15 .08 .05
475 Dan Driessen .20 .10 .06
476 Tom Poquette .15 .08 .05
477 Bob Grich .25 .13 .08
478 Juan Beniquez .15 .08 .05
479 Padres Team (Roger Craig) .50 .25 .15
480 Fred Lynn .70 .35 .20
481 Skip Lockwood .15 .08 .05
482 Craig Reynolds .15 .08 .05
483 Checklist 364-484 .25 .13 .08
484 Rick Waits .15 .08 .05
485 Bucky Dent .25 .13 .08
486 Bob Knepper .25 .13 .08
487 Miguel Dilone .15 .08 .05
488 Bob Owchinko .15 .08 .05
489 Larry Cox (photo actually Dave Rader) .15 .08 .05
490 Al Cowens .15 .08 .05
491 Tippy Martinez .15 .08 .05
492 Bob Bailor .15 .08 .05
493 Larry Christenson .15 .08 .05
494 Jerry White .15 .08 .05
495 Tony Perez .40 .20 .12
496 Barry Bonnell .15 .08 .05
497 Glenn Abbott .15 .08 .05
498 Rich Chiles .15 .08 .05
499 Rangers Team (Pat Corrales) .50 .25 .15
500 Ron Guidry .30 .15 .09
501 Junior Kennedy .15 .08 .05
502 Steve Braun .15 .08 .05
503 Terry Humphrey .15 .08 .05
504 *Larry McWilliams* .20 .10 .06
505 Ed Kranepool .20 .10 .06
506 John D'Acquisto .15 .08 .05
507 Tony Armas .20 .10 .06
508 Charlie Hough .20 .10 .06
509 Mario Mendoza .15 .08 .05
510 Ted Simmons .20 .10 .06
511 Paul Reuschel .15 .08 .05
512 Jack Clark .60 .30 .20
513 Dave Johnson .30 .15 .09
514 Mike Proly .15 .08 .05
515 Enos Cabell .15 .08 .05
516 Champ Summers .15 .08 .05
517 Al Bumbry .20 .10 .06
518 Jim Umbarger .15 .08 .05
519 Ben Oglivie .20 .10 .06
520 Gary Carter 2.00 1.00 .60
521 Sam Ewing .15 .08 .05
522 Ken Holtzman .20 .10 .06
523 John Milner .15 .08 .05
524 Tom Burgmeier .15 .08 .05
525 Freddie Patek .15 .08 .05
526 Dodgers Team (Tom Lasorda) .60 .30 .20
527 Lerrin LaGrow .15 .08 .05
528 Wayne Gross .15 .08 .05
529 Brian Asselstine .15 .08 .05
530 Frank Tanana .25 .13 .08
531 Fernando Gonzalez .15 .08 .05
532 Buddy Schultz .15 .08 .05
533 Leroy Stanton .15 .08 .05
534 Ken Forsch .15 .08 .05
535 Ellis Valentine .15 .08 .05
536 Jerry Reuss .20 .10 .06
537 Tom Veryzer .15 .08 .05
538 Mike Ivie .15 .08 .05
539 John Ellis .15 .08 .05
540 Greg Luzinski .30 .15 .09
541 Jim Slaton .15 .08 .05
542 Rick Bosetti .15 .08 .05
543 Kiko Garcia .15 .08 .05
544 Fergie Jenkins 1.50 .70 .45
545 John Stearns .15 .08 .05
546 Bill Russell .20 .10 .06
547 Clint Hurdle .15 .08 .05
548 Enrique Romo .15 .08 .05
549 Bob Bailey .15 .08 .05
550 Sal Bando .20 .10 .06
551 Cubs Team (Herman Franks) .50 .25 .15
552 Jose Morales .15 .08 .05
553 Denny Walling .15 .08 .05
554 Matt Keough .15 .08 .05
555 Biff Pocoroba .15 .08 .05
556 Mike Lum .15 .08 .05
557 Ken Brett .20 .10 .06
558 Jay Johnstone .20 .10 .06
559 Greg Pryor .15 .08 .05
560 John Montefusco .15 .08 .05
561 Ed Ott .15 .08 .05
562 Dusty Baker .25 .13 .08
563 Roy Thomas .15 .08 .05
564 Jerry Turner .15 .08 .05
565 Rico Carty .25 .13 .08
566 Nino Espinosa .15 .08 .05
567 Rich Hebner .15 .08 .05
568 Carlos Lopez .15 .08 .05
569 Bob Sykes .15 .08 .05
570 Cesar Cedeno .25 .13 .08
571 Darrell Porter .20 .10 .06
572 Rod Gilbreath .15 .08 .05
573 Jim Kern .15 .08 .05
574 Claudell Washington .20 .10 .06
575 Luis Tiant .20 .10 .06
576 Mike Parrott .15 .08 .05
577 Brewers Team (George Bamberger) .50 .25 .15
578 Pete Broberg .15 .08 .05
579 Greg Gross .15 .08 .05
580 Ron Fairly .20 .10 .06
581 Darold Knowles .15 .08 .05
582 Paul Blair .20 .10 .06
583 Julio Cruz .15 .08 .05
584 Jim Rooker .15 .08 .05
585 Hal McRae .25 .13 .08
586 *Bob Horner* .90 .45 .25
587 Ken Reitz .15 .08 .05
588 Tom Murphy .15 .08 .05
589 Terry Whitfield .15 .08 .05
590 J.R. Richard .20 .10 .06
591 Mike Hargrove .20 .10 .06
592 Mike Krukow .20 .10 .06
593 Rick Dempsey .20 .10 .06
594 Bob Shirley .15 .08 .05
595 Phil Niekro 1.25 .60 .40
596 Jim Wohlford .15 .08 .05
597 Bob Stanley .20 .10 .06
598 Mark Wagner .15 .08 .05
599 Jim Spencer .20 .10 .06
600 George Foster .30 .15 .09
601 Dave LaRoche .15 .08 .05
602 Checklist 485-605 .60 .30 .20
603 Rudy May .15 .08 .05
604 Jeff Newman .15 .08 .05
605 Rick Monday .15 .08 .05
606 Expos Team (Dick Williams) .50 .25 .15
607 Omar Moreno .15 .08 .05
608 Dave McKay .15 .08 .05
609 Silvio Martinez .15 .08 .05
610 Mike Schmidt 10.00 5.00 3.00
611 Jim Norris .15 .08 .05
612 *Rick Honeycutt* .15 .08 .05
613 Mike Edwards .15 .08 .05
614 Willie Hernandez .20 .10 .06
615 Ken Singleton .20 .10 .06
616 Billy Almon .15 .08 .05
617 Terry Puhl .15 .08 .05
618 Jerry Remy .15 .08 .05
619 *Ken Landreaux* .15 .08 .05
620 Bert Campaneris .25 .13 .08
621 Pat Zachry .15 .08 .05
622 Dave Collins .20 .10 .06
623 Bob McClure .15 .08 .05
624 Larry Herndon .20 .10 .06
625 Mark Fidrych .25 .13 .08
626 Yankees Team (Bob Lemon) .80 .40 .25
627 Gary Serum .15 .08 .05
628 Del Unser .15 .08 .05
629 Gene Garber .15 .08 .05
630 Bake McBride .15 .08 .05
631 Jorge Orta .15 .08 .05
632 Don Kirkwood .15 .08 .05
633 Rob Wilfong .15 .08 .05
634 Paul Lindblad .20 .10 .06
635 Don Baylor .40 .20 .12
636 Wayne Garland .15 .08 .05
637 Bill Robinson .15 .08 .05
638 Al Fitzmorris .15 .08 .05
639 Manny Trillo .20 .10 .06
640 Eddie Murray 21.00 10.50 6.25
641 *Bobby Castillo* .15 .08 .05
642 Wilbur Howard .15 .08 .05
643 Tom Hausman .15 .08 .05

644	Manny Mota	.20	.10	.06
645	George Scott	.15	.08	.05
646	Rick Sweet	.15	.08	.05
647	Bob Lacey	.15	.08	.05
648	Lou Piniella	.35	.20	.11
649	John Curtis	.15	.08	.05
650	Pete Rose	5.00	2.50	1.50
651	Mike Caldwell	.15	.08	.05
652	Stan Papi	.15	.08	.05
653	Warren Brusstar	.15	.08	.05
654	Rick Miller	.15	.08	.05
655	Jerry Koosman	.15	.08	.05
656	Hosken Powell	.15	.08	.05
657	George Medich	.15	.08	.05
658	Taylor Duncan	.15	.08	.05
659	Mariners Team (Darrell Johnson)	.50	.25	.15
660	Ron LeFlore	.15	.08	.05
661	Bruce Kison	.15	.08	.05
662	Kevin Bell	.15	.08	.05
663	Mike Vail	.15	.08	.05
664	Doug Bird	.15	.08	.05
665	Lou Brock	2.00	1.00	.60
666	Rich Dauer	.15	.08	.05
667	Don Hood	.15	.08	.05
668	Bill North	.15	.08	.05
669	Checklist 606-726	.60	.30	.20
670	Catfish Hunter	1.25	.60	.40
671	Joe Ferguson	.15	.08	.05
672	Ed Halicki	.15	.08	.05
673	Tom Hutton	.15	.08	.05
674	Dave Tomlin	.15	.08	.05
675	Tim McCarver	.30	.15	.09
676	Johnny Sutton	.15	.08	.05
677	Larry Parrish	.15	.08	.05
678	Geoff Zahn	.15	.08	.05
679	Derrel Thomas	.15	.08	.05
680	Carlton Fisk	3.00	1.50	.90
681	*John Henry Johnson*	.15	.08	.05
682	Dave Chalk	.15	.08	.05
683	Dan Meyer	.15	.08	.05
684	Jamie Easterly	.15	.08	.05
685	Sixto Lezcano	.15	.08	.05
686	Ron Schueler	.15	.08	.05
687	Rennie Stennett	.15	.08	.05
688	Mike Willis	.15	.08	.05
689	Orioles Team (Earl Weaver)	.70	.35	.20
690	Buddy Bell	.15	.08	.05
691	Dock Ellis	.15	.08	.05
692	Mickey Stanley	.20	.10	.06
693	Dave Rader	.15	.08	.05
694	Burt Hooton	.20	.10	.06
695	Keith Hernandez	1.00	.50	.30
696	Andy Hassler	.15	.08	.05
697	Dave Bergman	.15	.08	.05
698	Bill Stein	.15	.08	.05
699	Hal Dues	.15	.08	.05
700	Reggie Jackson	5.00	2.50	1.50
701	Orioles Prospects (Mark Corey, John Flinn, Sammy Stewart)	.15	.08	.05
702	Red Sox Prospects (Joel Finch, Garry Hancock, Allen Ripley)	.15	.08	.05
703	Angels Prospects (Jim Anderson, Dave Frost, Bob Slater)	.15	.08	.05
704	White Sox Prospects (Ross Baumgarten, Mike Colbern, Mike Squires)	.15	.08	.05
705	Blue Jays Prospects (*Alfredo Griffin*, Tim Norrid, Dave Oliver)	.70	.35	.20
706	Tigers Prospects (Dave Stegman, Dave Tobik, Kip Young)	.15	.08	.05
707	Royals Prospects (Randy Bass, Jim Gaudet, Randy McGilberry)	.15	.08	.05
708	Brewers Prospects (*Kevin Bass*, Eddie Romero, Ned Yost)	.50	.25	.15
709	Twins Prospects (Sam Perlozzo, Rick Sofield, Kevin Stanfield)	.15	.08	.05
710	Yankees Prospects (Brian Doyle, Mike Heath, Dave Rajsich)	.30	.15	.09
711	A's Prospects (*Dwayne Murphy*, Bruce Robinson, Alan Wirth)	.30	.15	.09
712	Mariners Prospects (Bud Anderson, Greg Biercevicz, Byron McLaughlin)	.15	.08	.05
713	Rangers Prospects (*Danny Darwin*, Pat Putnam, Billy Sample)	.35	.20	.11
714	Blue Jays Prospects (Victor Cruz, Pat Kelly, Ernie Whitt)	.20	.10	.06
715	Braves Prospects (*Bruce Benedict*, Glenn Hubbard, Larry Whisenton)	.40	.20	.12
716	Cubs Prospects (Dave Geisel, Karl Pagel, Scot Thompson)	.15	.08	.05
717	Reds Prospects (*Mike LaCoss*, Ron Oester, Harry Spilman)	.15	.08	.05
718	Astros Prospects (Bruce Bochy, Mike Fischlin, Don Pisker)	.15	.08	.05
719	Dodger Prospects (*Pedro Guerrero*, Rudy Law, Joe Simpson)	2.50	1.25	.70
720	Expos Prospects (*Jerry Fry*, Jerry Pirtle, Scott Sanderson)	.90	.45	.25
721	Mets Prospects (*Juan Berenguer*, Dwight Bernard, Dan Norman)	.15	.08	.05
722	Phillies Prospects (*Jim Morrison*, Lonnie Smith, Jim Wright)	.75	.40	.25
723	Pirates Prospects (*Dale Berra*, Eugenio Cotes, Ben Wiltbank)	.15	.08	.05
724	Cardinals Prospects (Tom Bruno, George Frazier, Terry Kennedy)	.20	.10	.06
725	Padres Prospects (Jim Beswick, Steve Mura, Broderick Perkins)	.15	.08	.05
726	Giants Prospects (Greg Johnston, Joe Strain, John Tamargo)	.15	.08	.05

1979 Topps Comics

Issued as the 3" by 3-3/4" wax wrapper for a piece of bubblegum, this "test" issue was bought up in great quantities by speculators and remains rather common. It is also inexpensive, because the comic-style player representations were not popular with collectors. The set is complete at 33 pieces.

		NR MT	EX	VG
Complete Set:		12.00	6.00	3.50
Common Player:		.10	.05	.03
1	Eddie Murray	.40	.20	.12
2	Jim Rice	.30	.15	.09
3	Carl Yastrzemski	.60	.30	.20
4	Nolan Ryan	2.00	1.00	.60
5	Chet Lemon	.10	.05	.03
6	Andre Thornton	.10	.05	.03
7	Rusty Staub	.15	.08	.05
8	Ron LeFlore	.10	.05	.03
9	George Brett	.90	.45	.25
10	Larry Hisle	.10	.05	.03
11	Rod Carew	.35	.20	.11
12	Reggie Jackson	.50	.25	.15
13	Ron Guidry	.20	.10	.06
14	Mitchell Page	.10	.05	.03
15	Leon Roberts	.10	.05	.03
16	Al Oliver	.15	.08	.05
17	John Mayberry	.10	.05	.03
18	Bob Horner	.20	.10	.06
19	Phil Niekro	.25	.13	.08
20	Dave Kingman	.15	.08	.05
21	John Bench	.40	.20	.12
22	Tom Seaver	.40	.20	.12
23	J.R. Richard	.10	.05	.03
24	Steve Garvey	.35	.20	.11
25	Reggie Smith	.15	.08	.05
26	Ross Grimsley	.10	.05	.03
27	Craig Swan	.10	.05	.03
28	Pete Rose	.90	.45	.25
29	Dave Parker	.40	.20	.12
30	Ted Simmons	.15	.08	.05
31	Dave Winfield	.60	.30	.20
32	Jack Clark	.20	.10	.06
33	Vida Blue	.15	.08	.05

1980 Topps

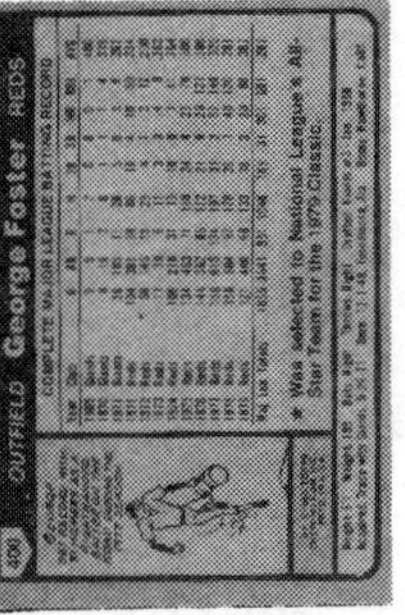

Again numbering 726 cards measuring 2-1/2" by 3-1/2", Topps did make some design changes in 1980. Fronts have the usual color picture with a facsimile autograph. The player's name appears above the picture, while his position is on a pennant at the upper left and his team on another pennant in the lower right. Backs no longer feature games, returning instead to statistics, personal information, a few headlines and a cartoon about the player. Specialty cards include statistical leaders, and previous season highlights. Many rookies again appear in team threesomes.

		NR MT	EX	VG
Complete Set (726):		275.00	137.00	82.00
Common Player:		.12	.06	.04
1	Lou Brock (Highlights, Carl Yastrzemski)	1.00	.50	.30
2	Willie McCovey (Highlights)	.50	.25	.15
3	Manny Mota (Highlights)	.15	.08	.05
4	Highlights (Pete Rose)	2.00	1.00	.60
5	Highlights (Garry Templeton)	.15	.08	.05
6	Highlights (Del Unser)	.12	.06	.04
7	Mike Lum	.12	.06	.04
8	Craig Swan	.12	.06	.04
9	Steve Braun	.12	.06	.04
10	Denny Martinez	.20	.10	.06
11	Jimmy Sexton	.12	.06	.04
12	John Curtis	.12	.06	.04
13	Ron Pruitt	.12	.06	.04
14	Dave Cash	.12	.06	.04
15	Bill Campbell	.12	.06	.04
16	Jerry Narron	.20	.10	.06
17	Bruce Sutter	.20	.10	.06
18	Ron Jackson	.12	.06	.04
19	Balor Moore	.12	.06	.04
20	Dan Ford	.12	.06	.04
21	Manny Sarmiento	.12	.06	.04
22	Pat Putnam	.12	.06	.04
23	Derrel Thomas	.12	.06	.04
24	Jim Slaton	.12	.06	.04
25	Lee Mazzilli	.20	.10	.06
26	Marty Pattin	.12	.06	.04
27	Del Unser	.12	.06	.04
28	Bruce Kison	.12	.06	.04
29	Mark Wagner	.12	.06	.04
30	Vida Blue	.15	.08	.05
31	Jay Johnstone	.20	.10	.06
32	Julio Cruz	.12	.06	.04
33	Tony Scott	.12	.06	.04
34	Jeff Newman	.12	.06	.04
35	Luis Tiant	.15	.08	.05
36	Rusty Torres	.12	.06	.04
37	Kiko Garcia	.12	.06	.04
38	Dan Spillner	.12	.06	.04
39	Rowland Office	.12	.06	.04
40	Carlton Fisk	3.00	1.50	.90
41	Rangers Team (Pat Corrales)	.50	.25	.15
42	*Dave Palmer*	.20	.10	.06
43	Bombo Rivera	.12	.06	.04
44	Bill Fahey	.12	.06	.04
45	Frank White	.15	.08	.05
46	Rico Carty	.12	.06	.04
47	Bill Bonham	.12	.06	.04
48	Rick Miller	.12	.06	.04
49	Mario Guerrero	.12	.06	.04
50	J.R. Richard	.20	.10	.06
51	Joe Ferguson	.12	.06	.04
52	Warren Brusstar	.12	.06	.04
53	Ben Oglivie	.20	.10	.06
54	Dennis Lamp	.12	.06	.04
55	Bill Madlock	.20	.10	.06
56	Bobby Valentine	.20	.10	.06
57	Pete Vuckovich	.12	.06	.04
58	Doug Flynn	.12	.06	.04
59	Eddy Putman	.12	.06	.04
60	Bucky Dent	.15	.08	.05
61	Gary Serum	.12	.06	.04
62	Mike Ivie	.12	.06	.04
63	Bob Stanley	.20	.10	.06
64	Joe Nolan	.12	.06	.04
65	Al Bumbry	.20	.10	.06
66	Royals Team (Jim Frey)	.60	.30	.20
67	Doyle Alexander	.25	.13	.08
68	Larry Harlow	.12	.06	.04
69	Rick Williams	.12	.06	.04
70	Gary Carter	1.25	.60	.40
71	John Milner	.12	.06	.04
72	Fred Howard	.12	.06	.04
73	Dave Collins	.20	.10	.06
74	Sid Monge	.12	.06	.04
75	Bill Russell	.20	.10	.06
76	John Stearns	.12	.06	.04
77	*Dave Stieb*	1.00	.50	.30
78	Ruppert Jones	.12	.06	.04
79	Bob Owchinko	.12	.06	.04
80	Ron LeFlore	.20	.10	.06
81	Ted Sizemore	.12	.06	.04
82	Astros Team (Bill Virdon)	.50	.25	.15
83	*Steve Trout*	.30	.15	.09
84	Gary Lavelle	.12	.06	.04
85	Ted Simmons	.15	.08	.05
86	Dave Hamilton	.12	.06	.04
87	Pepe Frias	.12	.06	.04
88	Ken Landreaux	.20	.10	.06
89	Don Hood	.20	.10	.06
90	Manny Trillo	.20	.10	.06
91	Rick Dempsey	.20	.10	.06
92	Rick Rhoden	.12	.06	.04
93	Dave Roberts	.12	.06	.04
94	*Neil Allen*	.12	.06	.04
95	Cecil Cooper	.35	.20	.11
96	A's Team (Jim Marshall)	.50	.25	.15
97	Bill Lee	.15	.08	.05
98	Jerry Terrell	.12	.06	.04
99	Victor Cruz	.12	.06	.04
100	Johnny Bench	4.00	2.00	1.25
101	Aurelio Lopez	.12	.06	.04
102	Rich Dauer	.12	.06	.04
103	*Bill Caudill*	.20	.10	.06
104	Manny Mota	.20	.10	.06
105	Frank Tanana	.20	.10	.06
106	*Jeff Leonard*	.40	.20	.12
107	Francisco Barrios	.12	.06	.04
108	Bob Horner	.15	.08	.05
109	Bill Travers	.12	.06	.04
110	Fred Lynn	.35	.20	.11
111	Bob Knepper	.20	.10	.06
112	White Sox Team (Tony LaRussa)	.50	.25	.15
113	Geoff Zahn	.12	.06	.04
114	Juan Beniquez	.12	.06	.04
115	Sparky Lyle	.15	.08	.05
116	Larry Cox	.12	.06	.04
117	Dock Ellis	.12	.06	.04
118	Phil Garner	.20	.10	.06
119	Sammy Stewart	.12	.06	.04
120	Greg Luzinski	.20	.10	.06
121	Checklist 1-121	.50	.25	.15
122	Dave Rosello	.12	.06	.04
123	Lynn Jones	.12	.06	.04
124	Dave Lemanczyk	.12	.06	.04
125	Tony Perez	.30	.15	.09

126	Dave Tomlin	.12	.06	.04
127	Gary Thomasson	.12	.06	.04
128	Tom Burgmeier	.12	.06	.04
129	Craig Reynolds	.12	.06	.04
130	Amos Otis	.20	.10	.06
131	Paul Mitchell	.12	.06	.04
132	Biff Pocoroba	.12	.06	.04
133	Jerry Turner	.12	.06	.04
134	Matt Keough	.12	.06	.04
135	Bill Buckner	.15	.08	.05
136	Dick Ruthven	.12	.06	.04
137	*John Castino*	.20	.10	.06
138	Ross Baumgarten	.12	.06	.04
139	*Dane Iorg*	.20	.10	.06
140	Rich Gossage	.30	.15	.09
141	Gary Alexander	.12	.06	.04
142	Phil Huffman	.12	.06	.04
143	Bruce Bochte	.12	.06	.04
144	Steve Comer	.12	.06	.04
145	Darrell Evans	.30	.15	.09
146	Bob Welch	1.00	.50	.30
147	Terry Puhl	.12	.06	.04
148	Manny Sanguillen	.12	.06	.04
149	Tom Hume	.12	.06	.04
150	Jason Thompson	.20	.10	.06
151	Tom Hausman	.12	.06	.04
152	John Fulgham	.12	.06	.04
153	Tim Blackwell	.12	.06	.04
154	Lary Sorensen	.12	.06	.04
155	Jerry Remy	.12	.06	.04
156	Tony Brizzolara	.12	.06	.04
157	Willie Wilson	.20	.10	.06
158	Rob Picciolo	.12	.06	.04
159	Ken Clay	.20	.10	.06
160	Eddie Murray	10.00	5.00	3.00
161	Larry Christenson	.12	.06	.04
162	Bob Randall	.12	.06	.04
163	Steve Swisher	.12	.06	.04
164	Greg Pryor	.12	.06	.04
165	Omar Moreno	.12	.06	.04
166	Glenn Abbott	.12	.06	.04
167	Jack Clark	.50	.25	.15
168	Rick Waits	.12	.06	.04
169	Luis Gomez	.12	.06	.04
170	Burt Hooton	.20	.10	.06
171	Fernando Gonzalez	.12	.06	.04
172	Ron Hodges	.12	.06	.04
173	John Henry Johnson	.12	.06	.04
174	Ray Knight	.15	.08	.05
175	Rick Reuschel	.12	.06	.04
176	Champ Summers	.12	.06	.04
177	Dave Heaverlo	.12	.06	.04
178	Tim McCarver	.15	.08	.05
179	*Ron Davis*	.20	.10	.06
180	Warren Cromartie	.12	.06	.04
181	Moose Haas	.12	.06	.04
182	Ken Reitz	.12	.06	.04
183	Jim Anderson	.12	.06	.04
184	Steve Renko	.12	.06	.04
185	Hal McRae	.25	.13	.08
186	Junior Moore	.12	.06	.04
187	Alan Ashby	.12	.06	.04
188	Terry Crowley	.12	.06	.04
189	Kevin Kobel	.12	.06	.04
190	Buddy Bell	.25	.13	.08
191	Ted Martinez	.12	.06	.04
192	Braves Team (Bobby Cox)	.50	.25	.15
193	Dave Goltz	.20	.10	.06
194	Mike Easler	.20	.10	.06
195	John Montefusco	.20	.10	.06
196	Lance Parrish	.40	.20	.12
197	Byron McLaughlin	.12	.06	.04
198	Dell Alston	.12	.06	.04
199	Mike LaCoss	.20	.10	.06
200	Jim Rice	1.00	.50	.30
201	Batting Leaders (Keith Hernandez, Fred Lynn)	.50	.25	.15
202	Home Run Leaders (Dave Kingman, Gorman Thomas)	.25	.13	.08
203	Runs Batted In Leaders (Don Baylor, Dave Winfield)	.50	.25	.15
204	Stolen Base Leaders (Omar Moreno, Willie Wilson)	.20	.10	.06
205	Victory Leaders (Mike Flanagan, Joe Niekro, Phil Niekro)	.40	.20	.12
206	Strikeout Leaders (J.R. Richard, Nolan Ryan)	2.00	1.00	.60
207	ERA Leaders (Ron Guidry, J.R. Richard)	.25	.13	.08
208	Wayne Cage	.12	.06	.04
209	Von Joshua	.12	.06	.04
210	Steve Carlton	4.00	2.00	1.25
211	Dave Skaggs	.12	.06	.04
212	Dave Roberts	.12	.06	.04
213	Mike Jorgensen	.12	.06	.04
214	Angels Team (Jim Fregosi)	.50	.25	.15
215	Sixto Lezcano	.12	.06	.04
216	Phil Mankowski	.12	.06	.04
217	Ed Halicki	.12	.06	.04
218	Jose Morales	.12	.06	.04
219	Steve Mingori	.12	.06	.04
220	Dave Concepcion	.30	.15	.09
221	Joe Cannon	.12	.06	.04
222	*Ron Hassey*	.25	.13	.08
223	Bob Sykes	.12	.06	.04
224	Willie Montanez	.12	.06	.04
225	Lou Piniella	.15	.08	.05
226	Bill Stein	.12	.06	.04
227	Len Barker	.12	.06	.04
228	Johnny Oates	.12	.06	.04
229	Jim Bibby	.12	.06	.04
230	Dave Winfield	10.00	5.00	3.00
231	Steve McCatty	.12	.06	.04
232	Alan Trammell	4.00	2.00	1.25
233	LaRue Washington	.12	.06	.04
234	Vern Ruhle	.12	.06	.04
235	Andre Dawson	9.00	4.50	2.75
236	Marc Hill	.12	.06	.04
237	Scott McGregor	.20	.10	.06

238	Rob Wilfong	.12	.06	.04
239	Don Aase	.12	.06	.04
240	Dave Kingman	.15	.08	.05
241	Checklist 122-242	.50	.25	.15
242	Lamar Johnson	.12	.06	.04
243	Jerry Augustine	.12	.06	.04
244	Cardinals Team (Ken Boyer)	.50	.25	.15
245	Phil Niekro	.80	.40	.25
246	Tim Foli	.12	.06	.04
247	Frank Riccelli	.12	.06	.04
248	Jamie Quirk	.12	.06	.04
249	Jim Clancy	.20	.10	.06
250	Jim Kaat	.50	.25	.15
251	Kip Young	.12	.06	.04
252	Ted Cox	.12	.06	.04
253	John Montague	.12	.06	.04
254	Paul Dade	.12	.06	.04
255	Dusty Baker	.12	.06	.04
256	Roger Erickson	.12	.06	.04
257	Larry Herndon	.20	.10	.06
258	Paul Moskau	.12	.06	.04
259	Mets Team (Joe Torre)	.60	.30	.20
260	Al Oliver	.20	.10	.06
261	Dave Chalk	.12	.06	.04
262	Benny Ayala	.12	.06	.04
263	Dave LaRoche	.12	.06	.04
264	Bill Robinson	.12	.06	.04
265	Robin Yount	12.00	6.00	3.50
266	Bernie Carbo	.12	.06	.04
267	Dan Schatzeder	.12	.06	.04
268	Rafael Landestoy	.12	.06	.04
269	Dave Tobik	.12	.06	.04
270	Mike Schmidt	6.00	3.00	1.75
271	Dick Drago	.12	.06	.04
272	Ralph Garr	.20	.10	.06
273	Eduardo Rodriguez	.12	.06	.04
274	Dale Murphy	4.00	2.00	1.25
275	Jerry Koosman	.25	.13	.08
276	Tom Veryzer	.12	.06	.04
277	Rick Bosetti	.12	.06	.04
278	Jim Spencer	.20	.10	.06
279	Rob Andrews	.12	.06	.04
280	Gaylord Perry	1.50	.70	.45
281	Paul Blair	.20	.10	.06
282	Mariners Team (Darrell Johnson)	.50	.25	.15
283	John Ellis	.12	.06	.04
284	Larry Murray	.12	.06	.04
285	Don Baylor	.35	.20	.11
286	Darold Knowles	.12	.06	.04
287	John Lowenstein	.12	.06	.04
288	Dave Rozema	.12	.06	.04
289	Bruce Bochy	.12	.06	.04
290	Steve Garvey	1.25	.60	.40
291	Randy Scarbery	.12	.06	.04
292	Dale Berra	.12	.06	.04
293	Elias Sosa	.12	.06	.04
294	Charlie Spikes	.12	.06	.04
295	Larry Gura	.12	.06	.04
296	Dave Rader	.12	.06	.04
297	Tim Johnson	.12	.06	.04
298	Ken Holtzman	.20	.10	.06
299	Steve Henderson	.12	.06	.04
300	Ron Guidry	.30	.15	.09
301	Mike Edwards	.12	.06	.04
302	Dodgers Team (Tom Lasorda)	.60	.30	.20
303	Bill Castro	.12	.06	.04
304	Butch Wynegar	.20	.10	.06
305	Randy Jones	.20	.10	.06
306	Denny Walling	.12	.06	.04
307	Rick Honeycutt	.20	.10	.06
308	Mike Hargrove	.20	.10	.06
309	Larry McWilliams	.12	.06	.04
310	Dave Parker	2.00	1.00	.60
311	Roger Metzger	.12	.06	.04
312	Mike Barlow	.12	.06	.04
313	Johnny Grubb	.12	.06	.04
314	*Tim Stoddard*	.12	.06	.04
315	Steve Kemp	.15	.08	.05
316	Bob Lacey	.12	.06	.04
317	Mike Anderson	.12	.06	.04
318	Jerry Reuss	.20	.10	.06
319	Chris Speier	.12	.06	.04
320	Dennis Eckersley	2.00	1.00	.60
321	Keith Hernandez	.90	.45	.25
322	Claudell Washington	.20	.10	.06
323	Mick Kelleher	.12	.06	.04
324	Tom Underwood	.12	.06	.04
325	Dan Driessen	.20	.10	.06
326	Bo McLaughlin	.12	.06	.04
327	Ray Fosse	.12	.06	.04
328	Twins Team (Gene Mauch)	.50	.25	.15
329	Bert Roberge	.12	.06	.04
330	Al Cowens	.12	.06	.04
331	Rich Hebner	.12	.06	.04
332	Enrique Romo	.12	.06	.04
333	Jim Norris	.12	.06	.04
334	Jim Beattie	.20	.10	.06
335	Willie McCovey	1.50	.70	.45
336	George Medich	.12	.06	.04
337	Carney Lansford	.30	.15	.09
338	Johnny Wockenfuss	.12	.06	.04
339	John D'Acquisto	.12	.06	.04
340	Ken Singleton	.20	.10	.06
341	Jim Essian	.12	.06	.04
342	Odell Jones	.12	.06	.04
343	Mike Vail	.12	.06	.04
344	Randy Lerch	.12	.06	.04
345	Larry Parrish	.20	.10	.06
346	Buddy Solomon	.12	.06	.04
347	*Harry Chappas*	.20	.10	.06
348	Checklist 243-363	.50	.25	.15
349	Jack Brohamer	.12	.06	.04
350	George Hendrick	.20	.10	.06
351	Bob Davis	.12	.06	.04
352	Dan Briggs	.12	.06	.04
353	Andy Hassler	.12	.06	.04
354	Rick Auerbach	.12	.06	.04
355	Gary Matthews	.15	.08	.05
356	Padres Team (Jerry Coleman)	.50	.25	.15

357	Bob McClure	.12	.06	.04
358	Lou Whitaker	1.25	.60	.40
359	Randy Moffitt	.12	.06	.04
360	Darrell Porter	.12	.06	.04
361	Wayne Garland	.12	.06	.04
362	Danny Goodwin	.12	.06	.04
363	Wayne Gross	.12	.06	.04
364	Ray Burris	.12	.06	.04
365	Bobby Murcer	.25	.13	.08
366	Rob Dressler	.12	.06	.04
367	Billy Smith	.12	.06	.04
368	*Willie Aikens*	.20	.10	.06
369	Jim Kern	.12	.06	.04
370	Cesar Cedeno	.25	.13	.08
371	Jack Morris	1.50	.70	.45
372	Joel Youngblood	.12	.06	.04
373	*Dan Petry*	.30	.15	.09
374	Jim Gantner	.20	.10	.06
375	Ross Grimsley	.12	.06	.04
376	Gary Allenson	.12	.06	.04
377	Junior Kennedy	.12	.06	.04
378	Jerry Mumphrey	.12	.06	.04
379	Kevin Bell	.12	.06	.04
380	Garry Maddox	.20	.10	.06
381	Cubs Team (Preston Gomez)	.50	.25	.15
382	Dave Freisleben	.12	.06	.04
383	Ed Ott	.12	.06	.04
384	Joey McLaughlin	.12	.06	.04
385	Enos Cabell	.12	.06	.04
386	Darrell Jackson	.12	.06	.04
387a	Fred Stanley (name in red)	.20	.10	.06
387b	Fred Stanley (name in yellow)	3.00	1.50	.90
388	Mike Paxton	.12	.06	.04
389	Pete LaCock	.12	.06	.04
390	Fergie Jenkins	.40	.20	.12
391	Tony Armas	.12	.06	.04
392	Milt Wilcox	.12	.06	.04
393	Ozzie Smith	20.00	10.00	6.00
394	Reggie Cleveland	.12	.06	.04
395	Ellis Valentine	.12	.06	.04
396	Dan Meyer	.12	.06	.04
397	Roy Thomas	.12	.06	.04
398	Barry Foote	.12	.06	.04
399	Mike Proly	.12	.06	.04
400	George Foster	.25	.13	.08
401	Pete Falcone	.12	.06	.04
402	Merv Rettenmund	.12	.06	.04
403	Pete Redfern	.12	.06	.04
404	Orioles Team (Earl Weaver)	.60	.30	.20
405	Dwight Evans	.90	.45	.25
406	Paul Molitor	15.00	7.50	4.50
407	Tony Solaita	.12	.06	.04
408	Bill North	.12	.06	.04
409	Paul Splittorff	.12	.06	.04
410	Bobby Bonds	.25	.13	.08
411	Frank LaCorte	.12	.06	.04
412	Thad Bosley	.12	.06	.04
413	Allen Ripley	.12	.06	.04
414	George Scott	.12	.06	.04
415	Bill Atkinson	.12	.06	.04
416	*Tom Brookens*	.15	.08	.05
417	Craig Chamberlain	.12	.06	.04
418	Roger Freed	.12	.06	.04
419	Vic Correll	.12	.06	.04
420	Butch Hobson	.12	.06	.04
421	Doug Bird	.12	.06	.04
422	Larry Milbourne	.12	.06	.04
423	Dave Frost	.12	.06	.04
424	Yankees Team (Dick Howser)	.70	.35	.20
425	Mark Belanger	.20	.10	.06
426	Grant Jackson	.12	.06	.04
427	Tom Hutton	.12	.06	.04
428	Pat Zachry	.12	.06	.04
429	Duane Kuiper	.12	.06	.04
430	Larry Hisle	.12	.06	.04
431	Mike Krukow	.20	.10	.06
432	Willie Norwood	.12	.06	.04
433	Rich Gale	.12	.06	.04
434	Johnnie LeMaster	.12	.06	.04
435	Don Gullett	.20	.10	.06
436	Billy Almon	.12	.06	.04
437	Joe Niekro	.20	.10	.06
438	Dave Revering	.12	.06	.04
439	Mike Phillips	.12	.06	.04
440	Don Sutton	1.00	.50	.30
441	Eric Soderholm	.12	.06	.04
442	Jorge Orta	.12	.06	.04
443	Mike Parrott	.12	.06	.04
444	Alvis Woods	.12	.06	.04
445	Mark Fidrych	.20	.10	.06
446	Duffy Dyer	.12	.06	.04
447	Nino Espinosa	.12	.06	.04
448	Jim Wohlford	.12	.06	.04
449	Doug Bair	.12	.06	.04
450	George Brett	12.00	6.00	3.50
451	Indians Team (Dave Garcia)	.50	.25	.15
452	Steve Dillard	.12	.06	.04
453	Mike Bacsik	.12	.06	.04
454	Tom Donohue	.12	.06	.04
455	Mike Torrez	.20	.10	.06
456	Frank Taveras	.12	.06	.04
457	Bert Blyleven	.50	.25	.15
458	Billy Sample	.12	.06	.04
459	Mickey Lolich	.12	.06	.04
460	Willie Randolph	.15	.08	.05
461	Dwayne Murphy	.20	.10	.06
462	Mike Sadek	.12	.06	.04
463	Jerry Royster	.12	.06	.04
464	John Denny	.12	.06	.04
465	Rick Monday	.20	.10	.06
466	Mike Squires	.12	.06	.04
467	Jesse Jefferson	.12	.06	.04
468	Aurelio Rodriguez	.20	.10	.06
469	Randy Niemann	.12	.06	.04
470	Bob Boone	.20	.10	.06
471	Hosken Powell	.12	.06	.04
472	Willie Hernandez	.20	.10	.06
473	Bump Wills	.12	.06	.04
474	Steve Busby	.12	.06	.04

475	Cesar Geronimo	.12	.06	.04
476	Bob Shirley	.12	.06	.04
477	Buck Martinez	.12	.06	.04
478	Gil Flores	.12	.06	.04
479	Expos Team (Dick Williams)	.50	.25	.15
480	Bob Watson	.20	.10	.06
481	Tom Paciorek	.12	.06	.04
482	*Rickey Henderson*	80.00	40.00	24.00
483	Bo Diaz	.20	.10	.06
484	Checklist 364-484	.50	.25	.15
485	Mickey Rivers	.20	.10	.06
486	Mike Tyson	.12	.06	.04
487	Wayne Nordhagen	.12	.06	.04
488	Roy Howell	.12	.06	.04
489	Preston Hanna	.12	.06	.04
490	Lee May	.20	.10	.06
491	Steve Mura	.12	.06	.04
492	Todd Cruz	.12	.06	.04
493	Jerry Martin	.12	.06	.04
494	Craig Minetto	.12	.06	.04
495	Bake McBride	.12	.06	.04
496	Silvio Martinez	.12	.06	.04
497	Jim Mason	.12	.06	.04
498	Danny Darwin	.20	.10	.06
499	Giants Team (Dave Bristol)	.50	.25	.15
500	Tom Seaver	3.00	1.50	.90
501	Rennie Stennett	.12	.06	.04
502	Rich Wortham	.12	.06	.04
503	Mike Cubbage	.12	.06	.04
504	Gene Garber	.12	.06	.04
505	Bert Campaneris	.20	.10	.06
506	Tom Buskey	.12	.06	.04
507	Leon Roberts	.12	.06	.04
508	U.L. Washington	.12	.06	.04
509	Ed Glynn	.12	.06	.04
510	Ron Cey	.25	.13	.08
511	Eric Wilkins	.12	.06	.04
512	Jose Cardenal	.12	.06	.04
513	Tom Dixon	.12	.06	.04
514	Steve Ontiveros	.12	.06	.04
515	Mike Caldwell	.12	.06	.04
516	Hector Cruz	.12	.06	.04
517	Don Stanhouse	.12	.06	.04
518	Nelson Norman	.12	.06	.04
519	Steve Nicosia	.12	.06	.04
520	Steve Rogers	.20	.10	.06
521	Ken Brett	.12	.06	.04
522	Jim Morrison	.12	.06	.04
523	Ken Henderson	.12	.06	.04
524	Jim Wright	.12	.06	.04
525	Clint Hurdle	.12	.06	.04
526	Phillies Team (Dallas Green)	.70	.35	.20
527	Doug Rau	.12	.06	.04
528	Adrian Devine	.12	.06	.04
529	Jim Barr	.12	.06	.04
530	Jim Sundberg	.12	.06	.04
531	Eric Rasmussen	.12	.06	.04
532	Willie Horton	.20	.10	.06
533	Checklist 485-605	.50	.25	.15
534	Andre Thornton	.25	.13	.08
535	Bob Forsch	.20	.10	.06
536	Lee Lacy	.12	.06	.04
537	*Alex Trevino*	.20	.10	.06
538	Joe Strain	.12	.06	.04
539	Rudy May	.12	.06	.04
540	Pete Rose	4.00	2.00	1.25
541	Miguel Dilone	.12	.06	.04
542	Joe Coleman	.12	.06	.04
543	Pat Kelly	.12	.06	.04
544	*Rick Sutcliffe*	2.00	1.00	.60
545	Jeff Burroughs	.20	.10	.06
546	Rick Langford	.12	.06	.04
547	John Wathan	.20	.10	.06
548	Dave Rajsich	.12	.06	.04
549	Larry Wolfe	.12	.06	.04
550	Ken Griffey	.25	.13	.08
551	Pirates Team (Chuck Tanner)	.50	.25	.15
552	Bill Nahorodny	.12	.06	.04
553	Dick Davis	.12	.06	.04
554	Art Howe	.12	.06	.04
555	Ed Figueroa	.20	.10	.06
556	Joe Rudi	.20	.10	.06
557	Mark Lee	.12	.06	.04
558	Alfredo Griffin	.15	.08	.05
559	Dale Murray	.12	.06	.04
560	Dave Lopes	.25	.13	.08
561	Eddie Whitson	.20	.10	.06
562	Joe Wallis	.12	.06	.04
563	Will McEnaney	.12	.06	.04
564	Rick Manning	.12	.06	.04
565	Dennis Leonard	.20	.10	.06
566	Bud Harrelson	.20	.10	.06
567	Skip Lockwood	.12	.06	.04
568	*Gary Roenicke*	.12	.06	.04
569	Terry Kennedy	.12	.06	.04
570	Roy Smalley	.12	.06	.04
571	Joe Sambito	.12	.06	.04
572	Jerry Morales	.12	.06	.04
573	Kent Tekulve	.12	.06	.04
574	Scot Thompson	.12	.06	.04
575	Ken Kravec	.12	.06	.04
576	Jim Dwyer	.12	.06	.04
577	Blue Jays Team (Bobby Mattick)	.50	.25	.15
578	Scott Sanderson	.20	.10	.06
579	Charlie Moore	.12	.06	.04
580	Nolan Ryan	25.00	12.50	7.50
581	Bob Bailor	.12	.06	.04
582	Brian Doyle	.20	.10	.06
583	Bob Stinson	.12	.06	.04
584	Kurt Bevacqua	.12	.06	.04
585	Al Hrabosky	.20	.10	.06
586	Mitchell Page	.12	.06	.04
587	Garry Templeton	.20	.10	.06
588	Greg Minton	.12	.06	.04
589	Chet Lemon	.20	.10	.06
590	Jim Palmer	3.00	1.50	.90
591	Rick Cerone	.12	.06	.04
592	Jon Matlack	.20	.10	.06
593	Jesus Alou	.12	.06	.04
594	Dick Tidrow	.12	.06	.04
595	Don Money	.12	.06	.04
596	Rick Matula	.12	.06	.04
597	Tom Poquette	.12	.06	.04
598	Fred Kendall	.12	.06	.04
599	Mike Norris	.12	.06	.04
600	Reggie Jackson	8.00	4.00	2.50
601	Buddy Schultz	.12	.06	.04
602	Brian Downing	.20	.10	.06
603	Jack Billingham	.12	.06	.04
604	Glenn Adams	.12	.06	.04
605	Terry Forster	.20	.10	.06
606	Reds Team (John McNamara)	.50	.25	.15
607	Woodie Fryman	.20	.10	.06
608	Alan Bannister	.12	.06	.04
609	Ron Reed	.20	.10	.06
610	Willie Stargell	1.50	.70	.45
611	Jerry Garvin	.12	.06	.04
612	Cliff Johnson	.12	.06	.04
613	Randy Stein	.12	.06	.04
614	John Hiller	.20	.10	.06
615	Doug DeCinces	.20	.10	.06
616	Gene Richards	.12	.06	.04
617	Joaquin Andujar	.20	.10	.06
618	Bob Montgomery	.12	.06	.04
619	Sergio Ferrer	.12	.06	.04
620	Richie Zisk	.20	.10	.06
621	Bob Grich	.20	.10	.06
622	Mario Soto	.12	.06	.04
623	Gorman Thomas	.12	.06	.04
624	Lerrin LaGrow	.12	.06	.04
625	Chris Chambliss	.12	.06	.04
626	Tigers Team (Sparky Anderson)	.60	.30	.20
627	Pedro Borbon	.12	.06	.04
628	Doug Capilla	.12	.06	.04
629	Jim Todd	.12	.06	.04
630	Larry Bowa	.25	.13	.08
631	Mark Littell	.12	.06	.04
632	Barry Bonnell	.12	.06	.04
633	Bob Apodaca	.12	.06	.04
634	Glenn Borgmann	.12	.06	.04
635	John Candelaria	.20	.10	.06
636	Toby Harrah	.20	.10	.06
637	Joe Simpson	.12	.06	.04
638	*Mark Clear*	.20	.10	.06
639	Larry Biittner	.12	.06	.04
640	Mike Flanagan	.15	.08	.05
641	Ed Kranepool	.20	.10	.06
642	Ken Forsch	.12	.06	.04
643	John Mayberry	.20	.10	.06
644	Charlie Hough	.20	.10	.06
645	Rick Burleson	.20	.10	.06
646	Checklist 606-726	.50	.25	.15
647	Milt May	.12	.06	.04
648	Roy White	.20	.10	.06
649	Tom Griffin	.12	.06	.04
650	Joe Morgan	2.00	1.00	.60
651	Rollie Fingers	1.00	.50	.30
652	Mario Mendoza	.12	.06	.04
653	Stan Bahnsen	.12	.06	.04
654	Bruce Boisclair	.12	.06	.04
655	Tug McGraw	.15	.08	.05
656	Larvell Blanks	.12	.06	.04
657	Dave Edwards	.12	.06	.04
658	Chris Knapp	.12	.06	.04
659	Brewers Team (George Bamberger)	.50	.25	.15
660	Rusty Staub	.20	.10	.06
661	Orioles Future Stars (Mark Corey, Dave Ford, Wayne Krenchicki)	.12	.06	.04
662	Red Sox Future Stars (Joel Finch, Mike O'Berry, Chuck Rainey)	.12	.06	.04
663	Angels Future Stars (Ralph Botting, Bob Clark, Dickie Thon)	.30	.15	.09
664	White Sox Future Stars (Mike Colbern, Guy Hoffman, Dewey Robinson)	.12	.06	.04
665	Indians Future Stars (Larry Andersen, Bobby Cuellar, Sandy Wihtol)	.12	.06	.04
666	Tigers Future Stars (Mike Chris, Al Greene, Bruce Robbins)	.12	.06	.04
667	Royals Future Stars (Renie Martin, Bill Paschall, Dan Quisenberry)	1.50	.70	.45
668	Brewers Future Stars (Danny Boitano, Willie Mueller, Lenn Sakata)	.12	.06	.04
669	Twins Future Stars (Dan Graham, Rick Sofield, Gary Ward)	.35	.20	.11
670	Yankees Future Stars (Bobby Brown, Brad Gulden, Darryl Jones)	.12	.06	.04
671	A's Future Stars (Derek Bryant, Brian Kingman, Mike Morgan)	1.00	.50	.30
672	Mariners Future Stars (Charlie Beamon, Rodney Craig, Rafael Vasquez)	.20	.10	.06
673	Rangers Future Stars (Brian Allard, Jerry Don Gleaton, Greg Mahlberg)	.12	.06	.04
674	Blue Jays Future Stars (Butch Edge, Pat Kelly, Ted Wilborn)	.12	.06	.04
675	Braves Future Stars (Bruce Benedict, Larry Bradford, Eddie Miller)	.12	.06	.04
676	Cubs Future Stars (Dave Geisel, Steve Macko, Karl Pagel)	.12	.06	.04
677	Reds Future Stars (Art DeFreites, Frank Pastore, Harry Spilman)	.12	.06	.04
678	Astros Future Stars (Reggie Baldwin, Alan Knicely, Pete Ladd)	.12	.06	.04
679	Dodgers Future Stars (Joe Beckwith, Mickey Hatcher, Dave Patterson)	.25	.13	.08
680	Expos Future Stars (*Tony Bernazard*, Randy Miller, John Tamargo)	.20	.10	.06
681	Mets Future Stars (Dan Norman, Jesse Orosco, Mike Scott)	1.50	.70	.45
682	Phillies Future Stars (Ramon Aviles, Dickie Noles, Kevin Saucier)	.12	.06	.04
683	Pirates Future Stars (Dorian Boyland, Alberto Lois, Harry Saferight)	.12	.06	.04
684	Cardinals Future Stars (George Frazier, Tom Herr, Dan O'Brien)	.30	.15	.09
685	Padres Future Stars (Tim Flannery, Brian Greer, Jim Wilhelm)	.12	.06	.04
686	Giants Future Stars (Greg Johnston, Dennis Littlejohn, Phil Nastu)	.12	.06	.04
687	Mike Heath	.12	.06	.04
688	Steve Stone	.20	.10	.06
689	Red Sox Team (Don Zimmer)	.60	.30	.20
690	Tommy John	.60	.30	.20
691	Ivan DeJesus	.12	.06	.04
692	Rawly Eastwick	.12	.06	.04
693	Craig Kusick	.12	.06	.04
694	Jim Rooker	.12	.06	.04
695	Reggie Smith	.20	.10	.06
696	Julio Gonzalez	.12	.06	.04
697	David Clyde	.12	.06	.04
698	Oscar Gamble	.20	.10	.06
699	Floyd Bannister	.20	.10	.06
700	Rod Carew	1.50	.70	.45
701	*Ken Oberkfell*	.12	.06	.04
702	Ed Farmer	.12	.06	.04
703	Otto Velez	.12	.06	.04
704	Gene Tenace	.20	.10	.06
705	Freddie Patek	.12	.06	.04
706	Tippy Martinez	.12	.06	.04
707	Elliott Maddox	.12	.06	.04
708	Bob Tolan	.12	.06	.04
709	Pat Underwood	.12	.06	.04
710	Graig Nettles	.15	.08	.05
711	Bob Galasso	.12	.06	.04
712	Rodney Scott	.12	.06	.04
713	Terry Whitfield	.12	.06	.04
714	Fred Norman	.12	.06	.04
715	Sal Bando	.20	.10	.06
716	Lynn McGlothen	.12	.06	.04
717	Mickey Klutts	.12	.06	.04
718	Greg Gross	.12	.06	.04
719	Don Robinson	.20	.10	.06
720	Carl Yastrzemski	1.50	.70	.45
721	Paul Hartzell	.12	.06	.04
722	Jose Cruz	.20	.10	.06
723	Shane Rawley	.20	.10	.06
724	Jerry White	.12	.06	.04
725	Rick Wise	.20	.10	.06
726	Steve Yeager	.20	.10	.06

1980 Topps Superstar 5x7 Photos

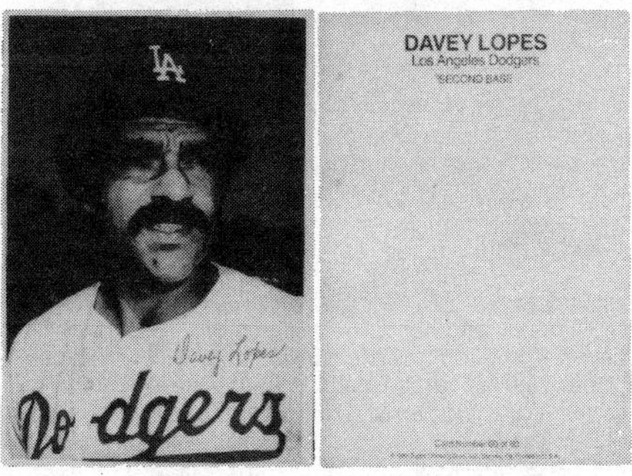

DAVEY LOPES
Los Angeles Dodgers
SECOND BASE
Dodgers

In actuality, these cards measure 4-7/8" by 6-7/8". These were another Topps "test" issue that was bought out almost entirely by investors. The 60 cards have a color photo on the front and a blue ink facsimile autograph. Backs have the player's name, team position and card number. The issue was printed on different cardboard stocks, with the first on thick cardboard with a white back and the second on thinner cardboard with a gray back. Prices below are for the more common gray backs; white backs are valued about three times the figures shown. The issue was distributed in selected geographical areas, but they were hoarded quickly. Those who hoarded them still probably have much of their supply as the set has never taken off, despite the presence of many big-name stars.

		NR MT	EX	VG
Complete Set:		9.00	4.50	2.75
Common Player:		.50	.25	.15
1	Willie Stargell	2.00	1.00	.60
2	Mike Schmidt	4.00	2.00	1.25
3	Johnny Bench	3.00	1.50	.90
4	Jim Palmer	2.00	1.00	.60
5	Jim Rice	1.00	.50	.30
6	Reggie Jackson	4.00	2.00	1.25
7	Ron Guidry	.75	.40	.25
8	Lee Mazzilli	.50	.25	.15
9	Don Baylor	.75	.40	.25
10	Fred Lynn	.75	.40	.25
11	Ken Singleton	.50	.25	.15
12	Rod Carew	2.00	1.00	.60
13	Steve Garvey	1.50	.70	.45
14	George Brett	4.00	2.00	1.25
15	Tom Seaver	3.00	1.50	.90
16	Dave Kingman	.50	.25	.15
17	Dave Parker	2.00	1.00	.60
18	Dave Winfield	3.00	1.50	.90
19	Pete Rose	4.00	2.00	1.25
20	Nolan Ryan	4.00	2.00	1.25
21	Graig Nettles	.50	.25	.15
22	Carl Yastrzemski	3.00	1.50	.90
23	Tommy John	1.00	.50	.30
24	George Foster	.50	.25	.15
25	J.R. Richard	.50	.25	.15
26	Keith Hernandez	.50	.25	.15
27	Bob Horner	.50	.25	.15

28	Eddie Murray	2.00	1.00	.60
29	Steve Kemp	.50	.25	.15
30	Gorman Thomas	.50	.25	.15
31	Sixto Lezcano	.50	.25	.15
32	Bruce Sutter	.50	.25	.15
33	Cecil Cooper	.50	.25	.15
34	Larry Bowa	.50	.25	.15
35	Al Oliver	1.00	.50	.30
36	Ted Simmons	.50	.25	.15
37	Garry Templeton	.50	.25	.15
38	Jerry Koosman	.50	.25	.15
39	Darrell Porter	.50	.25	.15
40	Roy Smalley	.50	.25	.15
41	Craig Swan	.50	.25	.15
42	Jason Thompson	.50	.25	.15
43	Andre Thornton	.50	.25	.15
44	Rick Manning	.50	.25	.15
45	Kent Tekulve	.50	.25	.15
46	Phil Niekro	1.50	.70	.45
47	Buddy Bell	.50	.25	.15
48	Randy Jones	.50	.25	.15
49	Brian Downing	.50	.25	.15
50	Amos Otis	.50	.25	.15
51	Rick Bosetti	.50	.25	.15
52	Gary Carter	1.50	.70	.45
53	Larry Parrish	.50	.25	.15
54	Jack Clark	.50	.25	.15
55	Bruce Bochte	.50	.25	.15
56	Cesar Cedeno	.50	.25	.15
57	Chet Lemon	.50	.25	.15
58	Dave Revering	.50	.25	.15
59	Vida Blue	.50	.25	.15
60	Davey Lopes	.50	.25	.15

1981 Topps

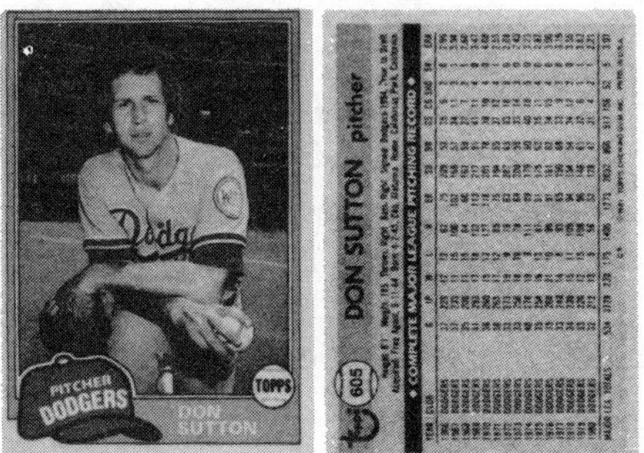

This is another 726-card set of 2-1/2" by 3-1/2" cards from Topps. The cards have the usual color photo with all cards from the same team sharing the same color borders. The player's name appears under the photo with his team and position appearing on a baseball cap at the lower left. The Topps logo returned in a small baseball in the lower right corner. Card backs include the usual stats along with a headline and a cartoon if there was room. Specialty cards include previous season record-breakers, highlights of the playoffs and World Series, along with the final appearance of team cards.

		MT	NR MT	EX
Complete Set (726):		75.00	56.00	30.00
Common Player:		.08	.06	.03
1	Batting Leaders (George Brett, Bill Buckner)	1.00	.70	.40
2	Home Run Leaders (Reggie Jackson, Ben Oglivie, Mike Schmidt)	.80	.60	.30
3	RBI Leaders (Cecil Cooper, Mike Schmidt)	.30	.25	.12
4	Stolen Base Leaders (Rickey Henderson, Ron LeFlore)	.50	.40	.20
5	Victory Leaders (Steve Carlton, Steve Stone)	.20	.15	.08
6	Strikeout Leaders (Len Barker, Steve Carlton)	.20	.15	.08
7	ERA Leaders (Rudy May, Don Sutton)	.15	.11	.06
8	Leading Firemen (Rollie Fingers, Tom Hume, Dan Quisenberry)	.10	.08	.04
9	Pete LaCock	.08	.06	.03
10	Mike Flanagan	.12	.09	.05
11	Jim Wohlford	.08	.06	.03
12	Mark Clear	.08	.06	.03
13	*Joe Charboneau*	.15	.11	.06
14	*John Tudor*	.20	.15	.08
15	Larry Parrish	.15	.11	.06
16	Ron Davis	.10	.08	.04
17	Cliff Johnson	.08	.06	.03
18	Glenn Adams	.08	.06	.03
19	Jim Clancy	.12	.09	.05
20	Jeff Burroughs	.10	.08	.04
21	Ron Oester	.08	.06	.03
22	Danny Darwin	.08	.06	.03
23	Alex Trevino	.08	.06	.03
24	Don Stanhouse	.08	.06	.03
25	Sixto Lezcano	.08	.06	.03
26	U.L. Washington	.08	.06	.03
27	Champ Summers	.08	.06	.03
28	Enrique Romo	.08	.06	.03
29	Gene Tenace	.10	.08	.04
30	Jack Clark	.20	.15	.08
31	Checklist 1-121	.08	.06	.03
32	Ken Oberkfell	.08	.06	.03
33	Rick Honeycutt	.08	.06	.03
34	Aurelio Rodriguez	.10	.08	.04
35	Mitchell Page	.08	.06	.03
36	Ed Farmer	.08	.06	.03
37	Gary Roenicke	.08	.06	.03
38	Win Remmerswaal	.08	.06	.03
39	Tom Veryzer	.08	.06	.03
40	Tug McGraw	.10	.08	.04
41	Rangers Future Stars (Bob Babcock, John Butcher, Jerry Don Gleaton)	.10	.08	.04
42	Jerry White	.08	.06	.03
43	Jose Morales	.08	.06	.03
44	Larry McWilliams	.08	.06	.03
45	Enos Cabell	.08	.06	.03
46	Rick Bosetti	.08	.06	.03
47	Ken Brett	.10	.08	.04
48	Dave Skaggs	.08	.06	.03
49	Bob Shirley	.08	.06	.03
50	Dave Lopes	.12	.09	.05
51	Bill Robinson	.08	.06	.03
52	Hector Cruz	.08	.06	.03
53	Kevin Saucier	.08	.06	.03
54	Ivan DeJesus	.08	.06	.03
55	Mike Norris	.08	.06	.03
56	Buck Martinez	.08	.06	.03
57	Dave Roberts	.08	.06	.03
58	Joel Youngblood	.08	.06	.03
59	Dan Petry	.12	.09	.05
60	Willie Randolph	.15	.11	.06
61	Butch Wynegar	.08	.06	.03
62	Joe Pettini	.08	.06	.03
63	Steve Renko	.08	.06	.03
64	Brian Asselstine	.08	.06	.03
65	Scott McGregor	.10	.08	.04
66	Royals Future Stars (Manny Castillo, Tim Ireland, Mike Jones)	.08	.06	.03
67	Ken Kravec	.08	.06	.03
68	Matt Alexander	.08	.06	.03
69	Ed Halicki	.08	.06	.03
70	Al Oliver	.15	.11	.06
71	Hal Dues	.08	.06	.03
72	Barry Evans	.08	.06	.03
73	Doug Bair	.08	.06	.03
74	Mike Hargrove	.08	.06	.03
75	Reggie Smith	.15	.11	.06
76	Mario Mendoza	.08	.06	.03
77	Mike Barlow	.08	.06	.03
78	Steve Dillard	.08	.06	.03
79	Bruce Robbins	.08	.06	.03
80	Rusty Staub	.15	.11	.06
81	Dave Stapleton	.08	.06	.03
82	Astros Future Stars (Danny Heep, Alan Knicely, Bobby Sprowl)	.08	.06	.03
83	Mike Proly	.08	.06	.03
84	Johnnie LeMaster	.08	.06	.03
85	Mike Caldwell	.08	.06	.03
86	Wayne Gross	.08	.06	.03
87	Rick Camp	.08	.06	.03
88	Joe Lefebvre	.08	.06	.03
89	Darrell Jackson	.08	.06	.03
90	Bake McBride	.08	.06	.03
91	Tim Stoddard	.08	.06	.03
92	Mike Easler	.10	.08	.04
93	Ed Glynn	.08	.06	.03
94	Harry Spilman	.08	.06	.03
95	Jim Sundberg	.10	.08	.04
96	A's Future Stars (Dave Beard, Ernie Camacho, Pat Dempsey)	.12	.09	.05
97	Chris Speier	.08	.06	.03
98	Clint Hurdle	.08	.06	.03
99	Eric Wilkins	.08	.06	.03
100	Rod Carew	2.00	1.50	.80
101	Benny Ayala	.08	.06	.03
102	Dave Tobik	.08	.06	.03
103	Jerry Martin	.08	.06	.03
104	Terry Forster	.10	.08	.04
105	Jose Cruz	.15	.11	.06
106	Don Money	.08	.06	.03
107	Rich Wortham	.08	.06	.03
108	Bruce Benedict	.08	.06	.03
109	Mike Scott	.80	.60	.30
110	Carl Yastrzemski	2.00	1.50	.80
111	Greg Minton	.08	.06	.03
112	White Sox Future Stars (Rusty Kuntz, Fran Mullins, Leo Sutherland)	.08	.06	.03
113	Mike Phillips	.08	.06	.03
114	Tom Underwood	.08	.06	.03
115	Roy Smalley	.08	.06	.03
116	Joe Simpson	.08	.06	.03
117	Pete Falcone	.08	.06	.03
118	Kurt Bevacqua	.08	.06	.03
119	Tippy Martinez	.08	.06	.03
120	Larry Bowa	.20	.15	.08
121	Larry Harlow	.08	.06	.03
122	John Denny	.08	.06	.03
123	Al Cowens	.08	.06	.03
124	Jerry Garvin	.08	.06	.03
125	Andre Dawson	2.00	1.50	.80
126	*Charlie Leibrandt*	.50	.40	.20
127	Rudy Law	.08	.06	.03
128	Gary Allenson	.08	.06	.03
129	Art Howe	.08	.06	.03
130	Larry Gura	.08	.06	.03
131	*Keith Moreland*	.35	.25	.14
132	Tommy Boggs	.08	.06	.03
133	Jeff Cox	.08	.06	.03
134	Steve Mura	.08	.06	.03
135	Gorman Thomas	.12	.09	.05
136	Doug Capilla	.08	.06	.03
137	Hosken Powell	.08	.06	.03
138	*Rich Dotson*	.20	.15	.08
139	Oscar Gamble	.10	.08	.04
140	Bob Forsch	.10	.08	.04
141	Miguel Dilone	.08	.06	.03
142	Jackson Todd	.08	.06	.03
143	Dan Meyer	.08	.06	.03
144	Allen Ripley	.08	.06	.03
145	Mickey Rivers	.10	.08	.04
146	Bobby Castillo	.08	.06	.03
147	Dale Berra	.08	.06	.03
148	Randy Niemann	.08	.06	.03
149	Joe Nolan	.08	.06	.03
150	Mark Fidrych	.12	.09	.05
151	Claudell Washington	.12	.09	.05
152	John Urrea	.08	.06	.03
153	Tom Poquette	.08	.06	.03
154	Rick Langford	.08	.06	.03
155	Chris Chambliss	.12	.09	.05
156	Bob McClure	.08	.06	.03
157	John Wathan	.12	.09	.05
158	Fergie Jenkins	.90	.70	.35
159	Brian Doyle	.08	.06	.03
160	Garry Maddox	.12	.09	.05
161	Dan Graham	.08	.06	.03
162	Doug Corbett	.08	.06	.03
163	Billy Almon	.08	.06	.03
164	*Lamarr Hoyt (LaMarr)*	.20	.15	.08
165	Tony Scott	.08	.06	.03
166	Floyd Bannister	.12	.09	.05
167	Terry Whitfield	.08	.06	.03
168	Don Robinson	.08	.06	.03
169	John Mayberry	.10	.08	.04
170	Ross Grimsley	.08	.06	.03
171	Gene Richards	.08	.06	.03
172	Gary Woods	.08	.06	.03
173	Bump Wills	.08	.06	.03
174	Doug Rau	.08	.06	.03
175	Dave Collins	.10	.08	.04
176	Mike Krukow	.10	.08	.04
177	Rick Peters	.08	.06	.03
178	Jim Essian	.08	.06	.03
179	Rudy May	.08	.06	.03
180	Pete Rose	3.00	2.25	1.25
181	Elias Sosa	.08	.06	.03
182	Bob Grich	.15	.11	.06
183	Dick Davis	.08	.06	.03
184	Jim Dwyer	.08	.06	.03
185	Dennis Leonard	.10	.08	.04
186	Wayne Nordhagen	.08	.06	.03
187	Mike Parrott	.08	.06	.03
188	Doug DeCinces	.15	.11	.06
189	Craig Swan	.08	.06	.03
190	Cesar Cedeno	.15	.11	.06
191	Rick Sutcliffe	.20	.15	.08
192	Braves Future Stars (*Terry Harper*, Ed Miller, Rafael Ramirez)	.10	.08	.04
193	Pete Vuckovich	.10	.08	.04
194	*Rod Scurry*	.10	.08	.04
195	Rich Murray	.08	.06	.03
196	Duffy Dyer	.08	.06	.03
197	Jim Kern	.08	.06	.03
198	Jerry Dybzinski	.08	.06	.03
199	Chuck Rainey	.08	.06	.03
200	George Foster	.25	.20	.10
201	Johnny Bench (Record Breaker)	.40	.30	.15
202	Steve Carlton (Record Breaker)	.40	.30	.15
203	Bill Gullickson (Record Breaker)	.08	.06	.03
204	Ron LeFlore (Record Breaker, Rodney Scott)	.10	.08	.04
205	Pete Rose (Record Breaker)	.70	.50	.30
206	Mike Schmidt (Record Breaker)	.60	.45	.25
207	Ozzie Smith (Record Breaker)	.20	.15	.08
208	Willie Wilson (Record Breaker)	.20	.15	.08
209	Dickie Thon	.10	.08	.04
210	Jim Palmer	2.00	1.50	.80
211	Derrel Thomas	.08	.06	.03
212	Steve Nicosia	.08	.06	.03
213	*Al Holland*	.10	.08	.04
214	Angels Future Stars (Ralph Botting, Jim Dorsey, John Harris)	.08	.06	.03
215	Larry Hisle	.10	.08	.04
216	John Henry Johnson	.08	.06	.03
217	Rich Hebner	.08	.06	.03
218	Paul Splittorff	.08	.06	.03
219	Ken Landreaux	.08	.06	.03
220	Tom Seaver	3.00	2.25	1.25
221	Bob Davis	.08	.06	.03
222	Jorge Orta	.08	.06	.03
223	Roy Lee Jackson	.08	.06	.03
224	Pat Zachry	.08	.06	.03
225	Ruppert Jones	.08	.06	.03
226	Manny Sanguillen	.08	.06	.03
227	Fred Martinez	.08	.06	.03
228	Tom Paciorek	.08	.06	.03
229	Rollie Fingers	.90	.70	.35
230	George Hendrick	.10	.08	.04
231	Joe Beckwith	.08	.06	.03
232	Mickey Klutts	.08	.06	.03
233	Skip Lockwood	.08	.06	.03
234	Lou Whitaker	.60	.45	.25
235	Scott Sanderson	.08	.06	.03
236	Mike Ivie	.08	.06	.03
237	Charlie Moore	.08	.06	.03
238	Willie Hernandez	.12	.09	.05
239	Rick Miller	.08	.06	.03
240	Nolan Ryan	12.00	9.00	4.75
241	Checklist 122-242	.08	.06	.03
242	Chet Lemon	.10	.08	.04
243	Sal Butera	.08	.06	.03
244	Cardinals Future Stars (*Tito Landrum*, Al Olmsted, Andy Rincon)	.15	.11	.06
245	Ed Figueroa	.08	.06	.03
246	Ed Ott	.08	.06	.03
247	Glenn Hubbard	.10	.08	.04
248	Joey McLaughlin	.08	.06	.03
249	Larry Cox	.08	.06	.03
250	Ron Guidry	.20	.15	.08
251	Tom Brookens	.10	.08	.04
252	Victor Cruz	.08	.06	.03
253	Dave Bergman	.08	.06	.03
254	Ozzie Smith	4.00	3.00	1.50
255	Mark Littell	.08	.06	.03
256	Bombo Rivera	.08	.06	.03
257	Rennie Stennett	.08	.06	.03
258	*Joe Price*	.12	.09	.05
259	Mets Future Stars (Juan Berenguer, Hubie Brooks, Mookie Wilson)	1.50	1.25	.60

260 Ron Cey .15 .11 .06
261 Rickey Henderson 9.00 6.75 3.50
262 Sammy Stewart .08 .06 .03
263 Brian Downing .12 .09 .05
264 Jim Norris .08 .06 .03
265 John Candelaria .12 .09 .05
266 Tom Herr .15 .11 .06
267 Stan Bahnsen .08 .06 .03
268 Jerry Royster .08 .06 .03
269 Ken Forsch .08 .06 .03
270 Greg Luzinski .20 .15 .08
271 Bill Castro .08 .06 .03
272 Bruce Kimm .08 .06 .03
273 Stan Papi .08 .06 .03
274 Craig Chamberlain .08 .06 .03
275 Dwight Evans .15 .11 .06
276 Dan Spillner .08 .06 .03
277 Alfredo Griffin .12 .09 .05
278 Rick Sofield .08 .06 .03
279 Bob Knepper .12 .09 .05
280 Ken Griffey .15 .11 .06
281 Fred Stanley .08 .06 .03
282 Mariners Future Stars (Rick Anderson, Greg Biercevicz, Rodney Craig) .08 .06 .03
283 Billy Sample .08 .06 .03
284 Brian Kingman .08 .06 .03
285 Jerry Turner .08 .06 .03
286 Dave Frost .08 .06 .03
287 Lenn Sakata .08 .06 .03
288 Bob Clark .08 .06 .03
289 Mickey Hatcher .10 .08 .04
290 Bob Boone .08 .06 .03
291 Aurelio Lopez .08 .06 .03
292 Mike Squires .08 .06 .03
293 *Charlie Lea* .15 .11 .06
294 Mike Tyson .08 .06 .03
295 Hal McRae .15 .11 .06
296 Bill Nahorodny .08 .06 .03
297 Bob Bailor .08 .06 .03
298 Buddy Solomon .08 .06 .03
299 Elliott Maddox .08 .06 .03
300 Paul Molitor 5.00 3.75 2.00
301 Matt Keough .08 .06 .03
302 Dodgers Future Stars (Jack Perconte, Mike Scioscia, Fernando Valenzuela) 2.50 2.00 1.00
303 Johnny Oates .08 .06 .03
304 John Castino .08 .06 .03
305 Ken Clay .08 .06 .03
306 Juan Beniquez .08 .06 .03
307 Gene Garber .08 .06 .03
308 Rick Manning .08 .06 .03
309 *Luis Salazar* .08 .06 .03
310 Vida Blue .08 .06 .03
311 Freddie Patek .08 .06 .03
312 Rick Rhoden .12 .09 .05
313 Luis Pujols .08 .06 .03
314 Rich Dauer .08 .06 .03
315 *Kirk Gibson* 3.00 2.25 1.25
316 Craig Minetto .08 .06 .03
317 Lonnie Smith .10 .08 .04
318 Steve Yeager .08 .06 .03
319 Rowland Office .08 .06 .03
320 Tom Burgmeier .08 .06 .03
321 *Leon Durham* .25 .20 .10
322 Neil Allen .10 .08 .04
323 Jim Morrison .08 .06 .03
324 Mike Willis .08 .06 .03
325 Ray Knight .12 .09 .05
326 Biff Pocoroba .08 .06 .03
327 Moose Haas .08 .06 .03
328 Twins Future Stars (*Dave Engle*, Greg Johnston, Gary Ward) .12 .09 .05
329 Joaquin Andujar .12 .09 .05
330 Frank White .12 .09 .05
331 Dennis Lamp .08 .06 .03
332 Lee Lacy .08 .06 .03
333 Sid Monge .08 .06 .03
334 Dane Iorg .08 .06 .03
335 Rick Cerone .08 .06 .03
336 Eddie Whitson .08 .06 .03
337 Lynn Jones .08 .06 .03
338 Checklist 243-363 .25 .20 .10
339 John Ellis .08 .06 .03
340 Bruce Kison .08 .06 .03
341 Dwayne Murphy .10 .08 .04
342 Eric Rasmussen .08 .06 .03
343 Frank Taveras .08 .06 .03
344 Byron McLaughlin .08 .06 .03
345 Warren Cromartie .08 .06 .03
346 Larry Christenson .08 .06 .03
347 *Harold Baines* 2.50 2.00 1.00
348 Bob Sykes .08 .06 .03
349 Glenn Hoffman .08 .06 .03
350 J.R. Richard .12 .09 .05
351 Otto Velez .08 .06 .03
352 Dick Tidrow .08 .06 .03
353 Terry Kennedy .12 .09 .05
354 Mario Soto .10 .08 .04
355 Bob Horner .25 .20 .10
356 Padres Future Stars (George Stablein, Craig Stimac, Tom Tellmann) .08 .06 .03
357 Jim Slaton .08 .06 .03
358 Mark Wagner .08 .06 .03
359 Tom Hausman .08 .06 .03
360 Willie Wilson .15 .11 .06
361 Joe Strain .08 .06 .03
362 Bo Diaz .10 .08 .04
363 Geoff Zahn .08 .06 .03
364 *Mike Davis* .25 .20 .10
365 Graig Nettles .12 .09 .05
366 Mike Ramsey .08 .06 .03
367 Denny Martinez .10 .08 .04
368 Leon Roberts .08 .06 .03
369 Frank Tanana .12 .09 .05
370 Dave Winfield 5.00 3.75 2.00
371 Charlie Hough .15 .11 .06
372 Jay Johnstone .10 .08 .04
373 Pat Underwood .08 .06 .03
374 Tom Hutton .08 .06 .03
375 Dave Concepcion .20 .15 .08
376 Ron Reed .08 .06 .03
377 Jerry Morales .08 .06 .03
378 Dave Rader .08 .06 .03
379 Lary Sorensen .08 .06 .03
380 Willie Stargell 1.00 .70 .40
381 Cubs Future Stars (Carlos Lezcano, Steve Macko, Randy Martz) .08 .06 .03
382 *Paul Mirabella* (FC) .12 .09 .05
383 Eric Soderholm .08 .06 .03
384 Mike Sadek .08 .06 .03
385 Joe Sambito .08 .06 .03
386 Dave Edwards .08 .06 .03
387 Phil Niekro .80 .60 .30
388 Andre Thornton .12 .09 .05
389 Marty Pattin .08 .06 .03
390 Cesar Geronimo .08 .06 .03
391 Dave Lemanczyk .08 .06 .03
392 Lance Parrish .15 .11 .06
393 Broderick Perkins .08 .06 .03
394 Woodie Fryman .10 .08 .04
395 Scot Thompson .08 .06 .03
396 Bill Campbell .08 .06 .03
397 Julio Cruz .08 .06 .03
398 Ross Baumgarten .08 .06 .03
399 Orioles Future Stars (*Mike Boddicker*, Mark Corey, Floyd Rayford) .50 .40 .20
400 Reggie Jackson 3.25 2.50 1.25
401 A.L. Championships (Royals Sweep Yankees) .50 .40 .20
402 N.L. Championships (Phillies Squeak Past Astros) .40 .30 .15
403 World Series (Phillies Beat Royals In 6) .25 .20 .10
404 World Series Summary (Phillies Win First World Series) .25 .20 .10
405 Nino Espinosa .08 .06 .03
406 Dickie Noles .08 .06 .03
407 Ernie Whitt .10 .08 .04
408 Fernando Arroyo .08 .06 .03
409 Larry Herndon .10 .08 .04
410 Bert Campaneris .12 .09 .05
411 Terry Puhl .08 .06 .03
412 *Britt Burns* .12 .09 .05
413 Tony Bernazard .08 .06 .03
414 John Pacella .08 .06 .03
415 Ben Oglivie .10 .08 .04
416 Gary Alexander .08 .06 .03
417 Dan Schatzeder .08 .06 .03
418 Bobby Brown .08 .06 .03
419 Tom Hume .08 .06 .03
420 Keith Hernandez .25 .20 .10
421 Bob Stanley .08 .06 .03
422 Dan Ford .08 .06 .03
423 Shane Rawley .15 .11 .06
424 Yankees Future Stars (Tim Lollar, Bruce Robinson, Dennis Werth) .08 .06 .03
425 Al Bumbry .10 .08 .04
426 Warren Brusstar .08 .06 .03
427 John D'Acquisto .08 .06 .03
428 John Stearns .08 .06 .03
429 Mick Kelleher .08 .06 .03
430 Jim Bibby .08 .06 .03
431 Dave Roberts .08 .06 .03
432 Len Barker .10 .08 .04
433 Rance Mulliniks .08 .06 .03
434 Roger Erickson .08 .06 .03
435 Jim Spencer .08 .06 .03
436 Gary Lucas .08 .06 .03
437 Mike Heath .08 .06 .03
438 John Montefusco .10 .08 .04
439 Denny Walling .08 .06 .03
440 Jerry Reuss .12 .09 .05
441 Ken Reitz .08 .06 .03
442 Ron Pruitt .08 .06 .03
443 Jim Beattie .08 .06 .03
444 Garth Iorg .08 .06 .03
445 Ellis Valentine .08 .06 .03
446 Checklist 364-484 .25 .20 .10
447 Junior Kennedy .08 .06 .03
448 Tim Corcoran .08 .06 .03
449 Paul Mitchell .08 .06 .03
450 Dave Kingman .10 .08 .04
451 Indians Future Stars (Chris Bando, Tom Brennan, Sandy Wihtol) .12 .09 .05
452 Renie Martin .08 .06 .03
453 Rob Wilfong .08 .06 .03
454 Andy Hassler .08 .06 .03
455 Rick Burleson .10 .08 .04
456 *Jeff Reardon* 3.00 2.25 1.25
457 Mike Lum .08 .06 .03
458 Randy Jones .10 .08 .04
459 Greg Gross .08 .06 .03
460 Rich Gossage .20 .15 .08
461 Dave McKay .08 .06 .03
462 Jack Brohamer .08 .06 .03
463 Milt May .08 .06 .03
464 Adrian Devine .08 .06 .03
465 Bill Russell .12 .09 .05
466 Bob Molinaro .08 .06 .03
467 Dave Stieb .35 .25 .14
468 Johnny Wockenfuss .08 .06 .03
469 Jeff Leonard .20 .15 .08
470 Manny Trillo .10 .08 .04
471 Mike Vail .08 .06 .03
472 Dyar Miller .08 .06 .03
473 Jose Cardenal .08 .06 .03
474 Mike LaCoss .08 .06 .03
475 Buddy Bell .15 .11 .06
476 Jerry Koosman .15 .11 .06
477 Luis Gomez .08 .06 .03
478 Juan Eichelberger .08 .06 .03
479 Expos Future Stars (Bobby Pate, Tim Raines, Roberto Ramos) 10.00 7.50 4.00
480 Carlton Fisk 1.50 1.25 .60
481 Bob Lacey .08 .06 .03
482 Jim Gantner .10 .08 .04
483 Mike Griffin .08 .06 .03
484 Max Venable .08 .06 .03
485 Garry Templeton .12 .09 .05
486 Marc Hill .08 .06 .03
487 Dewey Robinson .08 .06 .03
488 *Damaso Garcia* .12 .09 .05
489 John Littlefield (photo actually Mark Riggins) .08 .06 .03
490 Eddie Murray 2.00 1.50 .80
491 Gordy Pladson .08 .06 .03
492 Barry Foote .08 .06 .03
493 Dan Quisenberry .20 .15 .08
494 *Bob Walk* .20 .15 .08
495 Dusty Baker .12 .09 .05
496 Paul Dade .08 .06 .03
497 Fred Norman .08 .06 .03
498 Pat Putnam .08 .06 .03
499 Frank Pastore .08 .06 .03
500 Jim Rice .35 .25 .14
501 Tim Foli .08 .06 .03
502 Giants Future Stars (Chris Bourjos, Al Hargesheimer, Mike Rowland) .08 .06 .03
503 Steve McCatty .08 .06 .03
504 Dale Murphy .90 .70 .35
505 Jason Thompson .08 .06 .03
506 Phil Huffman .08 .06 .03
507 Jamie Quirk .08 .06 .03
508 Rob Dressler .08 .06 .03
509 Pete Mackanin .08 .06 .03
510 Lee Mazzilli .10 .08 .04
511 Wayne Garland .08 .06 .03
512 Gary Thomasson .08 .06 .03
513 Frank LaCorte .08 .06 .03
514 George Riley .08 .06 .03
515 Robin Yount 6.00 4.50 2.50
516 Doug Bird .08 .06 .03
517 Richie Zisk .10 .08 .04
518 Grant Jackson .08 .06 .03
519 John Tamargo .08 .06 .03
520 Steve Stone .12 .09 .05
521 Sam Mejias .08 .06 .03
522 Mike Colbern .08 .06 .03
523 John Fulgham .08 .06 .03
524 Willie Aikens .08 .06 .03
525 Mike Torrez .10 .08 .04
526 Phillies Future Stars (Marty Bystrom, Jay Loviglio, Jim Wright) .08 .06 .03
527 Danny Goodwin .08 .06 .03
528 Gary Matthews .12 .09 .05
529 Dave LaRoche .08 .06 .03
530 Steve Garvey .90 .70 .35
531 John Curtis .08 .06 .03
532 Bill Stein .08 .06 .03
533 Jesus Figueroa .08 .06 .03
534 *Dave Smith* .60 .45 .25
535 Omar Moreno .08 .06 .03
536 Bob Owchinko .08 .06 .03
537 Ron Hodges .08 .06 .03
538 Tom Griffin .08 .06 .03
539 Rodney Scott .08 .06 .03
540 Mike Schmidt 4.00 3.00 1.50
541 Steve Swisher .08 .06 .03
542 Larry Bradford .08 .06 .03
543 Terry Crowley .08 .06 .03
544 Rich Gale .08 .06 .03
545 Johnny Grubb .08 .06 .03
546 Paul Moskau .08 .06 .03
547 Mario Guerrero .08 .06 .03
548 Dave Goltz .10 .08 .04
549 Jerry Remy .08 .06 .03
550 Tommy John .50 .40 .20
551 Pirates Future Stars (*Vance Law*, Tony Pena, Pascual Perez) .75 .60 .30
552 Steve Trout .08 .06 .03
553 Tim Blackwell .08 .06 .03
554 Bert Blyleven .15 .11 .06
555 Cecil Cooper .10 .08 .04
556 Jerry Mumphrey .08 .06 .03
557 Chris Knapp .08 .06 .03
558 Barry Bonnell .08 .06 .03
559 Willie Montanez .08 .06 .03
560 Joe Morgan .90 .70 .35
561 Dennis Littlejohn .08 .06 .03
562 Checklist 485-605 .25 .20 .10
563 Jim Kaat .30 .25 .12
564 Ron Hassey .08 .06 .03
565 Burt Hooton .10 .08 .04
566 Del Unser .08 .06 .03
567 Mark Bomback .08 .06 .03
568 Dave Revering .08 .06 .03
569 Al Williams .08 .06 .03
570 Ken Singleton .12 .09 .05
571 Todd Cruz .08 .06 .03
572 Jack Morris .75 .60 .30
573 Phil Garner .10 .08 .04
574 Bill Caudill .08 .06 .03
575 Tony Perez .35 .25 .14
576 Reggie Cleveland .08 .06 .03
577 Blue Jays Future Stars (Luis Leal, Brian Milner, Ken Schrom) .10 .08 .04
578 *Bill Gullickson* .20 .15 .08
579 Tim Flannery .08 .06 .03
580 Don Baylor .15 .11 .06
581 Roy Howell .08 .06 .03
582 Gaylord Perry .70 .50 .30
583 Larry Milbourne .08 .06 .03
584 Randy Lerch .08 .06 .03
585 Amos Otis .10 .08 .04
586 Silvio Martinez .08 .06 .03
587 Jeff Newman .08 .06 .03
588 Gary Lavelle .08 .06 .03
589 Lamar Johnson .08 .06 .03
590 Bruce Sutter .15 .11 .06
591 John Lowenstein .08 .06 .03
592 Steve Comer .08 .06 .03
593 Steve Kemp .12 .09 .05
594 Preston Hanna .08 .06 .03
595 Butch Hobson .08 .06 .03
596 Jerry Augustine .08 .06 .03
597 Rafael Landestoy .08 .06 .03
598 George Vukovich .08 .06 .03

#	Player	MT	NR MT	EX
599	Dennis Kinney	.08	.06	.03
600	Johnny Bench	2.00	1.50	.80
601	Don Aase	.08	.06	.03
602	Bobby Murcer	.15	.11	.06
603	John Verhoeven	.08	.06	.03
604	Rob Picciolo	.08	.06	.03
605	Don Sutton	.70	.50	.30
606	Reds Future Stars (Bruce Berenyi, Geoff Combe, Paul Householder)	.08	.06	.03
607	Dave Palmer	.08	.06	.03
608	Greg Pryor	.08	.06	.03
609	Lynn McGlothen	.08	.06	.03
610	Darrell Porter	.10	.08	.04
611	Rick Matula	.08	.06	.03
612	Duane Kuiper	.08	.06	.03
613	Jim Anderson	.08	.06	.03
614	Dave Rozema	.08	.06	.03
615	Rick Dempsey	.12	.09	.05
616	Rick Wise	.10	.08	.04
617	Craig Reynolds	.08	.06	.03
618	John Milner	.08	.06	.03
619	Steve Henderson	.08	.06	.03
620	Dennis Eckersley	1.50	1.25	.60
621	Tom Donohue	.08	.06	.03
622	Randy Moffitt	.08	.06	.03
623	Sal Bando	.12	.09	.05
624	Bob Welch	.30	.25	.12
625	Bill Buckner	.15	.11	.06
626	Tigers Future Stars (Dave Steffen, Jerry Ujdur, Roger Weaver)	.08	.06	.03
627	Luis Tiant	.10	.08	.04
628	Vic Correll	.08	.06	.03
629	Tony Armas	.12	.09	.05
630	Steve Carlton	3.25	2.50	1.50
631	Ron Jackson	.08	.06	.03
632	Alan Bannister	.08	.06	.03
633	Bill Lee	.10	.08	.04
634	Doug Flynn	.08	.06	.03
635	Bobby Bonds	.15	.11	.06
636	Al Hrabosky	.10	.08	.04
637	Jerry Narron	.08	.06	.03
638	Checklist 606	.25	.20	.10
639	Carney Lansford	.15	.11	.06
640	Dave Parker	.60	.45	.25
641	Mark Belanger	.10	.08	.04
642	Vern Ruhle	.08	.06	.03
643	*Lloyd Moseby*	.40	.30	.15
644	Ramon Aviles	.08	.06	.03
645	Rick Reuschel	.15	.11	.06
646	Marvis Foley	.08	.06	.03
647	Dick Drago	.08	.06	.03
648	Darrell Evans	.15	.11	.06
649	Manny Sarmiento	.08	.06	.03
650	Bucky Dent	.12	.09	.05
651	Pedro Guerrero	.20	.15	.08
652	John Montague	.08	.06	.03
653	Bill Fahey	.08	.06	.03
654	Ray Burris	.08	.06	.03
655	Dan Driessen	.12	.09	.05
656	Jon Matlack	.10	.08	.04
657	Mike Cubbage	.08	.06	.03
658	Milt Wilcox	.08	.06	.03
659	Brewers Future Stars (John Flinn, Ed Romero, Ned Yost)	.08	.06	.03
660	Gary Carter	.80	.60	.30
661	Orioles Team (Earl Weaver)	.30	.25	.12
662	Red Sox Team (Ralph Houk)	.30	.25	.12
663	Angels Team (Jim Fregosi)	.25	.20	.10
664	White Sox Team (Tony LaRussa)	.25	.20	.10
665	Indians Team (Dave Garcia)	.25	.20	.10
666	Tigers Team (Sparky Anderson)	.30	.25	.12
667	Royals Team (Jim Frey)	.25	.20	.10
668	Brewers Team (Bob Rodgers)	.25	.20	.10
669	Twins Team (John Goryl)	.25	.20	.10
670	Yankees Team (Gene Michael)	.35	.25	.14
671	A's Team (Billy Martin)	.30	.25	.12
672	Mariners Team (Maury Wills)	.25	.20	.10
673	Rangers Team (Don Zimmer)	.25	.20	.10
674	Blue Jays Team (Bobby Mattick)	.25	.20	.10
675	Braves Team (Bobby Cox)	.25	.20	.10
676	Cubs Team (Joe Amalfitano)	.25	.20	.10
677	Reds Team (John McNamara)	.25	.20	.10
678	Astros Team (Bill Virdon)	.25	.20	.10
679	Dodgers Team (Tom Lasorda)	.35	.25	.14
680	Expos Team (Dick Williams)	.25	.20	.10
681	Mets Team (Joe Torre)	.30	.25	.12
682	Phillies Team (Dallas Green)	.25	.20	.10
683	Pirates Team (Chuck Tanner)	.25	.20	.10
684	Cardinals Team (Whitey Herzog)	.30	.25	.12
685	Padres Team (Frank Howard)	.25	.20	.10
686	Giants Team (Dave Bristol)	.25	.20	.10
687	Jeff Jones	.08	.06	.03
688	Kiko Garcia	.08	.06	.03
689	Red Sox Future Stars (*Bruce Hurst*, Keith MacWhorter, Reid Nichols)	1.50	1.25	.60
690	Bob Watson	.10	.08	.04
691	Dick Ruthven	.08	.06	.03
692	Lenny Randle	.08	.06	.03
693	*Steve Howe*	.20	.15	.08
694	Bud Harrelson	.08	.06	.03
695	Kent Tekulve	.10	.08	.04
696	Alan Ashby	.08	.06	.03
697	Rick Waits	.08	.06	.03
698	Mike Jorgensen	.08	.06	.03
699	Glenn Abbott	.08	.06	.03
700	George Brett	6.00	4.50	2.50
701	Joe Rudi	.12	.09	.05
702	George Medich	.08	.06	.03
703	Alvis Woods	.08	.06	.03
704	Bill Travers	.08	.06	.03
705	Ted Simmons	.25	.20	.10
706	Dave Ford	.08	.06	.03
707	Dave Cash	.08	.06	.03
708	Doyle Alexander	.12	.09	.05
709	Alan Trammell	.70	.50	.30
710	Ron LeFlore	.08	.06	.03
711	Joe Ferguson	.08	.06	.03
712	Bill Bonham	.08	.06	.03
713	Bill North	.08	.06	.03
714	Pete Redfern	.08	.06	.03
715	Bill Madlock	.15	.11	.06
716	Glenn Borgmann	.08	.06	.03
717	Jim Barr	.08	.06	.03
718	Larry Biittner	.08	.06	.03
719	Sparky Lyle	.12	.09	.05
720	Fred Lynn	.35	.25	.14
721	Toby Harrah	.10	.08	.04
722	Joe Niekro	.20	.15	.08
723	Bruce Bochte	.08	.06	.03
724	Lou Piniella	.20	.15	.08
725	Steve Rogers	.10	.08	.04
726	Rick Monday	.15	.11	.06

1981 Topps Traded

The 132 cards in this extension set are numbered from 727 to 858, technically making them a high-numbered series of the regular Topps set. The set was not packaged in gum packs, but rather placed in a specially designed red box and sold through baseball card dealers only. While many complained about the method, the fact remains, even at higher prices, the set has done well for its owners as it features not only mid-season trades, but also single-player rookie cards of some of the hottest prospects. The cards measure 2-1/2" by 3-1/2".

		MT	NR MT	EX
	Complete Set (132):	45.00	35.00	18.00
	Common Player:	.20	.15	.08
727	Danny Ainge (FC)	6.00	4.50	2.50
728	Doyle Alexander	.20	.15	.08
729	Gary Alexander	.20	.15	.08
730	Billy Almon	.20	.15	.08
731	Joaquin Andujar	.20	.15	.08
732	Bob Bailor	.20	.15	.08
733	Juan Beniquez	.20	.15	.08
734	Dave Bergman	.20	.15	.08
735	Tony Bernazard	.20	.15	.08
736	Larry Biittner	.20	.15	.08
737	Doug Bird	.20	.15	.08
738	Bert Blyleven	1.00	.70	.40
739	Mark Bomback	.20	.15	.08
740	Bobby Bonds	.20	.15	.08
741	Rick Bosetti	.20	.15	.08
742	Hubie Brooks	1.00	.70	.40
743	Rick Burleson	.20	.15	.08
744	Ray Burris	.20	.15	.08
745	Jeff Burroughs	.20	.15	.08
746	Enos Cabell	.20	.15	.08
747	Ken Clay	.20	.15	.08
748	Mark Clear	.20	.15	.08
749	Larry Cox	.20	.15	.08
750	Hector Cruz	.20	.15	.08
751	Victor Cruz	.20	.15	.08
752	Mike Cubbage	.20	.15	.08
753	Dick Davis	.20	.15	.08
754	Brian Doyle	.20	.15	.08
755	Dick Drago	.20	.15	.08
756	Leon Durham	.20	.15	.08
757	Jim Dwyer	.20	.15	.08
758	Dave Edwards	.20	.15	.08
759	Jim Essian	.20	.15	.08
760	Bill Fahey	.20	.15	.08
761	Rollie Fingers	5.00	3.75	2.00
762	Carlton Fisk	5.00	3.75	2.00
763	Barry Foote	.20	.15	.08
764	Ken Forsch	.20	.15	.08
765	Kiko Garcia	.20	.15	.08
766	Cesar Geronimo	.20	.15	.08
767	Gary Gray	.20	.15	.08
768	Mickey Hatcher	.20	.15	.08
769	Steve Henderson	.20	.15	.08
770	Marc Hill	.20	.15	.08
771	Butch Hobson	.20	.15	.08
772	Rick Honeycutt	.20	.15	.08
773	Roy Howell	.20	.15	.08
774	Mike Ivie	.20	.15	.08
775	Roy Lee Jackson	.20	.15	.08
776	Cliff Johnson	.20	.15	.08
777	Randy Jones	.20	.15	.08
778	Ruppert Jones	.20	.15	.08
779	Mick Kelleher	.20	.15	.08
780	Terry Kennedy	.20	.15	.08
781	Dave Kingman	.20	.15	.08
782	Bob Knepper	.20	.15	.08
783	Ken Kravec	.20	.15	.08
784	Bob Lacey	.20	.15	.08
785	Dennis Lamp	.20	.15	.08
786	Rafael Landestoy	.20	.15	.08
787	Ken Landreaux	.20	.15	.08
788	Carney Lansford	.20	.15	.08
789	Dave LaRoche	.20	.15	.08
790	Joe Lefebvre	.20	.15	.08
791	Ron LeFlore	.20	.15	.08
792	Randy Lerch	.20	.15	.08
793	Sixto Lezcano	.20	.15	.08
794	John Littlefield	.20	.15	.08
795	Mike Lum	.20	.15	.08
796	Greg Luzinski	.50	.40	.20
797	Fred Lynn	.50	.40	.20
798	Jerry Martin	.20	.15	.08
799	Buck Martinez	.20	.15	.08
800	Gary Matthews	.20	.15	.08
801	Mario Mendoza	.20	.15	.08
802	Larry Milbourne	.20	.15	.08
803	Rick Miller	.20	.15	.08
804	John Montefusco	.20	.15	.08
805	Jerry Morales	.20	.15	.08
806	Jose Morales	.20	.15	.08
807	Joe Morgan	3.00	2.25	1.25
808	Jerry Mumphrey	.20	.15	.08
809	Gene Nelson (FC)	.20	.15	.08
810	Ed Ott	.20	.15	.08
811	Bob Owchinko	.20	.15	.08
812	Gaylord Perry	2.50	2.00	1.00
813	Mike Phillips	.20	.15	.08
814	Darrell Porter	.20	.15	.08
815	Mike Proly	.20	.15	.08
816	Tim Raines	12.00	9.00	4.75
817	Lenny Randle	.20	.15	.08
818	Doug Rau	.20	.15	.00
819	Jeff Reardon	6.00	4.50	2.50
820	Ken Reitz	.20	.15	.08
821	Steve Renko	.20	.15	.08
822	Rick Reuschel	.20	.15	.08
823	Dave Revering	.20	.15	.08
824	Dave Roberts	.20	.15	.08
825	Leon Roberts	.20	.15	.08
826	Joe Rudi	.20	.15	.08
827	Kevin Saucier	.20	.15	.08
828	Tony Scott	.20	.15	.08
829	Bob Shirley	.20	.15	.08
830	Ted Simmons	.20	.15	.08
831	Lary Sorensen	.20	.15	.08
832	Jim Spencer	.20	.15	.08
833	Harry Spilman	.20	.15	.08
834	Fred Stanley	.20	.15	.08
835	Rusty Staub	.30	.25	.12
836	Bill Stein	.20	.15	.08
837	Joe Strain	.20	.15	.08
838	Bruce Sutter	.50	.40	.20
839	Don Sutton	1.50	1.25	.60
840	Steve Swisher	.20	.15	.08
841	Frank Tanana	.20	.15	.08
842	Gene Tenace	.20	.15	.08
843	Jason Thompson	.20	.15	.08
844	Dickie Thon	.20	.15	.08
845	Bill Travers	.20	.15	.08
846	Tom Underwood	.20	.15	.08
847	John Urrea	.20	.15	.08
848	Mike Vail	.20	.15	.08
849	Ellis Valentine	.20	.15	.08
850	Fernando Valenzuela	2.00	1.50	.80
851	Pete Vuckovich	.20	.15	.08
852	Mark Wagner	.20	.15	.08
853	Bob Walk	.20	.15	.08
854	Claudell Washington	.20	.15	.08
855	Dave Winfield	15.00	11.00	6.00
856	Geoff Zahn	.20	.15	.08
857	Richie Zisk	.20	.15	.08
858	Checklist 727-858	.20	.15	.08

1981 Topps Home Team 5x7 Photos

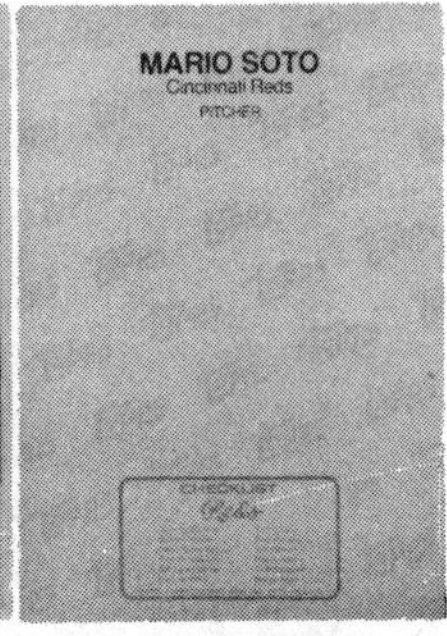

Once again testing the popularity of large cards, Topps issued 4-7/8" by 6-7/8" cards in two different sets. The Home Team cards feature a large color photo, facsimile autograph and white border on the front. Backs have the player's name, team, position and a checklist at the bottom. The 102 cards were sold in limited areas corresponding to the teams' geographic home. It was also possible to order the whole set by mail. Eleven teams are involved in the issue, with the number of players from each team ranging from 6 to 12. Although it is an attractive set featuring many stars, ready availability and many collectors' aversion to large cards keep prices relatively low today.

		MT	NR MT	EX
Complete Set:		40.00	30.00	16.00
Common Player:		.20	.15	.08
(1)	Dusty Baker	.25	.20	.10
(2)	Don Baylor	.40	.30	.15
(3)	Rick Burleson	.20	.15	.08
(4)	Rod Carew	.90	.70	.35
(5)	Ron Cey	.30	.25	.12
(6)	Steve Garvey	.40	.30	.15
(7)	Bobby Grich	.30	.25	.12
(8)	Butch Hobson	.20	.15	.08
(9)	Burt Hooton	.20	.15	.08
(10)	Steve Howe	.20	.15	.08
(11)	Dave Lopes	.25	.20	.10
(12)	Fred Lynn	.50	.40	.20
(13)	Rick Monday	.25	.20	.10
(14)	Jerry Reuss	.25	.20	.10
(15)	Bill Russell	.25	.20	.10
(16)	Reggie Smith	.30	.25	.12
(17)	Bob Welch	.40	.30	.15
(18)	Steve Yeager	.20	.15	.08
(19)	Buddy Bell	.30	.25	.12
(20)	Cesar Cedeno	.30	.25	.12
(21)	Jose Cruz	.30	.25	.12
(22)	Art Howe	.20	.15	.08
(23)	Jon Matlack	.20	.15	.08
(24)	Al Oliver	.40	.30	.15
(25)	Terry Puhl	.20	.15	.08
(26)	Mickey Rivers	.25	.20	.10
(27)	Nolan Ryan	2.00	1.50	.80
(28)	Jim Sundberg	.25	.20	.10
(29)	Don Sutton	.60	.45	.25
(30)	Bump Wills	.20	.15	.08
(31)	Tim Blackwell	.20	.15	.08
(32)	Bill Buckner	.40	.30	.15
(33)	Britt Burns	.20	.15	.08
(34)	Ivan DeJesus	.20	.15	.08
(35)	Rich Dotson	.25	.20	.10
(36)	Leon Durham	.25	.20	.10
(37)	Ed Farmer	.20	.15	.08
(38)	Lamar Johnson	.20	.15	.08
(39)	Dave Kingman	.40	.30	.15
(40)	Mike Krukow	.25	.20	.10
(41)	Ron LeFlore	.25	.20	.10
(42)	Chet Lemon	.25	.20	.10
(43)	Bob Molinaro	.20	.15	.08
(44)	Jim Morrison	.20	.15	.08
(45)	Wayne Nordhagen	.20	.15	.08
(46)	Ken Reitz	.20	.15	.08
(47)	Rick Reuschel	.30	.25	.12
(48)	Mike Tyson	.20	.15	.08
(49)	Neil Allen	.20	.15	.08
(50)	Rick Cerone	.20	.15	.08
(51)	Bucky Dent	.25	.20	.10
(52)	Doug Flynn	.20	.15	.08
(53)	Rich Gossage	.60	.45	.25
(54)	Ron Guidry	.60	.45	.25
(55)	Reggie Jackson	.90	.70	.35
(56)	Tommy John	.50	.40	.20
(57)	Ruppert Jones	.20	.15	.08
(58)	Rudy May	.20	.15	.08
(59)	Lee Mazzilli	.25	.20	.10
(60)	Graig Nettles	.40	.30	.15
(61)	Willie Randolph	.30	.25	.12
(62)	Rusty Staub	.40	.30	.15
(63)	Frank Taveras	.20	.15	.08
(64)	Alex Trevino	.20	.15	.08
(65)	Bob Watson	.25	.20	.10
(66)	Dave Winfield	.90	.70	.35
(67)	Bob Boone	.40	.30	.15
(68)	Larry Bowa	.40	.30	.15
(69)	Steve Carlton	.70	.50	.30
(70)	Greg Luzinski	.40	.30	.15
(71)	Garry Maddox	.25	.20	.10
(72)	Bake McBride	.20	.15	.08
(73)	Tug McGraw	.40	.30	.15
(74)	Pete Rose	1.50	1.25	.60
(75)	Dick Ruthven	.20	.15	.08
(76)	Mike Schmidt	.90	.70	.35
(77)	Manny Trillo	.25	.20	.10
(78)	Del Unser	.20	.15	.08
(79)	Tom Burgmeier	.20	.15	.08
(80)	Dennis Eckersley	.40	.30	.15
(81)	Dwight Evans	.25	.20	.10
(82)	Carlton Fisk	.60	.45	.25
(83)	Glenn Hoffman	.20	.15	.08
(84)	Carney Lansford	.30	.25	.12
(85)	Tony Perez	.50	.40	.20
(86)	Jim Rice	.50	.40	.20
(87)	Bob Stanley	.20	.15	.08
(88)	Dave Stapleton	.20	.15	.08
(89)	Frank Tanana	.25	.20	.10
(90)	Carl Yastrzemski	.90	.70	.35
(91)	Johnny Bench	.90	.70	.35
(92)	Dave Collins	.25	.20	.10
(93)	Dave Concepcion	.40	.30	.15
(94)	Dan Driessen	.25	.20	.10
(95)	George Foster	.40	.30	.15
(96)	Ken Griffey	.40	.30	.15
(97)	Tom Hume	.20	.15	.08
(98)	Ray Knight	.25	.20	.10
(99)	Joe Nolan	.20	.15	.08
(100)	Ron Oester	.20	.15	.08
(101)	Tom Seaver	.90	.70	.35
(102)	Mario Soto	.25	.20	.10

1981 Topps National 5x7 Photos

This set is the other half of Topps' efforts with large cards in 1981. Measuring 4-7/8" by 6-7/8", the National photo issue was limited to 15 cards. They were sold in areas not covered by the Home Team sets and feature ten cards which carry the same photos as found in the Home Team set, but with no checklist on the backs. Five cards are unique to the National set: George Brett, Cecil Cooper, Jim Palmer, Dave Parker and Ted Simmons. With their wide distribution and a limited demand, there are currently plenty of these cards to meet the demand, thus keeping prices fairly low.

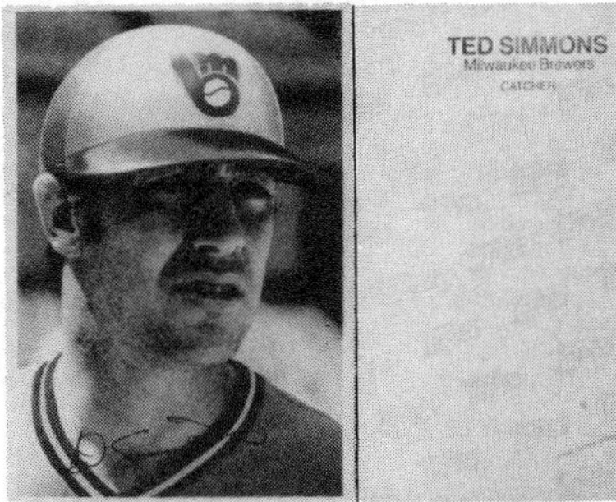

		MT	NR MT	EX
Complete Set:		8.00	6.00	3.25
Common Player:		.30	.25	.12
(1)	Buddy Bell	.30	.25	.12
(2)	Johnny Bench	.60	.45	.25
(3)	George Brett	.90	.70	.35
(4)	Rod Carew	.60	.45	.25
(5)	Cecil Cooper	.40	.30	.15
(6)	Steve Garvey	.60	.45	.25
(7)	Rich Gossage	.40	.30	.15
(8)	Reggie Jackson	.70	.50	.30
(9)	Jim Palmer	.60	.45	.25
(10)	Dave Parker	.60	.45	.25
(11)	Jim Rice	.40	.30	.15
(12)	Pete Rose	.90	.70	.35
(13)	Mike Schmidt	.70	.50	.30
(14)	Tom Seaver	.60	.45	.25
(15)	Ted Simmons	.40	.30	.15

1981 Topps Scratchoffs

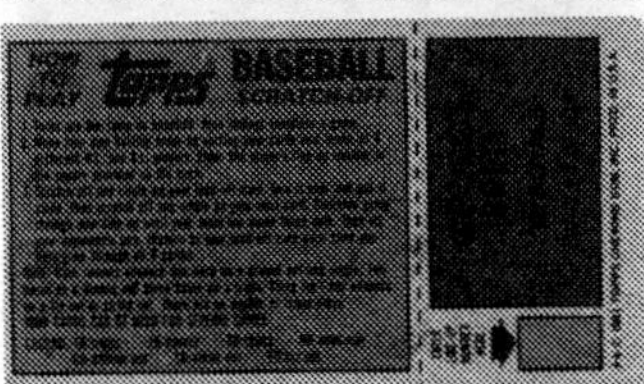

Sold as a separate issue with bubble gum, this 108-card set was issued in three-card panels that measure 3-1/4" by 5-1/4". Each individual card measures 1-13/16" by 3-1/4" and contains a small player photo alongside a series of black dots designed to be scratched off as part of a baseball game. Cards of National League players have a green backgrounds, while American League players have a red background. While there are 108 different players in the set, there are 144 possible panel combinations. An intact panel of three cards is valued approximately 20-25 percent more the sum of the individual cards.

		MT	NR MT	EX
Complete Set:		4.00	3.00	1.50
Common Player:		.05	.04	.02
1	George Brett	.15	.11	.06
2	Cecil Cooper	.06	.05	.02
3	Reggie Jackson	.15	.11	.06
4	Al Oliver	.06	.05	.02
5	Fred Lynn	.08	.06	.03
6	Tony Armas	.05	.04	.02
7	Ben Oglivie	.05	.04	.02
8	Tony Perez	.08	.06	.03
9	Eddie Murray	.15	.11	.06
10	Robin Yount	.10	.08	.04
11	Steve Kemp	.06	.05	.02
12	Joe Charboneau	.06	.05	.02
13	Jim Rice	.15	.11	.06
14	Lance Parrish	.10	.08	.04
15	John Mayberry	.05	.04	.02
16	Richie Zisk	.05	.04	.02
17	Ken Singleton	.06	.05	.02
18	Rod Carew	.15	.11	.06
19	Rick Manning	.05	.04	.02
20	Willie Wilson	.06	.05	.02
21	Buddy Bell	.06	.05	.02
22	Dave Revering	.05	.04	.02
23	Tom Paciorek	.05	.04	.02
24	Champ Summers	.05	.04	.02
25	Carney Lansford	.06	.05	.02
26	Lamar Johnson	.05	.04	.02
27	Willie Aikens	.05	.04	.02
28	Rick Cerone	.05	.04	.02
29	Al Bumbry	.05	.04	.02
30	Bruce Bochte	.05	.04	.02
31	Mickey Rivers	.05	.04	.02
32	Mike Hargrove	.05	.04	.02
33	John Castino	.05	.04	.02
34	Chet Lemon	.06	.05	.02
35	Paul Molitor	.08	.06	.03
36	Willie Randolph	.06	.05	.02
37	Rick Burleson	.05	.04	.02
38	Alan Trammell	.10	.08	.04
39	Rickey Henderson	.15	.11	.06
40	Dan Meyer	.05	.04	.02
41	Ken Landreaux	.05	.04	.02
42	Damaso Garcia	.05	.04	.02
43	Roy Smalley	.05	.04	.02
44	Otto Velez	.05	.04	.02
45	Sixto Lezcano	.05	.04	.02
46	Toby Harrah	.05	.04	.02
47	Frank White	.06	.05	.02
48	Dave Stapleton	.05	.04	.02
49	Steve Stone	.06	.05	.02
50	Jim Palmer	.10	.08	.04
51	Larry Gura	.05	.04	.02
52	Tommy John	.08	.06	.03
53	Mike Norris	.05	.04	.02
54	Ed Farmer	.05	.04	.02
55	Bill Buckner	.06	.05	.02
56	Steve Garvey	.15	.11	.06
57	Reggie Smith	.06	.05	.02
58	Bake McBride	.05	.04	.02
59	Dave Parker	.08	.06	.03
60	Mike Schmidt	.15	.11	.06
61	Bob Horner	.06	.05	.02
62	Pete Rose	.20	.15	.08
63	Ted Simmons	.08	.06	.03
64	Johnny Bench	.15	.11	.06
65	George Foster	.08	.06	.03
66	Gary Carter	.15	.11	.06
67	Keith Hernandez	.10	.08	.04
68	Ozzie Smith	.08	.06	.03
69	Dave Kingman	.08	.06	.03
70	Jack Clark	.08	.06	.03
71	Dusty Baker	.06	.05	.02
72	Dale Murphy	.15	.11	.06
73	Ron Cey	.06	.05	.02
74	Greg Luzinski	.06	.05	.02
75	Lee Mazzilli	.05	.04	.02
76	Gary Matthews	.06	.05	.02
77	Cesar Cedeno	.06	.05	.02
78	Warren Cromartie	.05	.04	.02
79	Steve Henderson	.05	.04	.02
80	Ellis Valentine	.05	.04	.02
81	Mike Easler	.05	.04	.02
82	Garry Templeton	.06	.05	.02
83	Jose Cruz	.06	.05	.02
84	Dave Collins	.05	.04	.02
85	George Hendrick	.05	.04	.02
86	Gene Richards	.05	.04	.02
87	Terry Whitfield	.05	.04	.02
88	Terry Puhl	.05	.04	.02
89	Larry Parrish	.06	.05	.02
90	Andre Dawson	.10	.08	.04
91	Ken Griffey	.06	.05	.02
92	Dave Lopes	.05	.04	.02
93	Doug Flynn	.05	.04	.02
94	Ivan DeJesus	.05	.04	.02
95	Dave Concepcion	.06	.05	.02
96	John Stearns	.05	.04	.02
97	Jerry Mumphrey	.05	.04	.02
98	Jerry Martin	.05	.04	.02
99	Art Howe	.05	.04	.02
100	Omar Moreno	.05	.04	.02
101	Ken Reitz	.05	.04	.02
102	Phil Garner	.05	.04	.02
103	Jerry Reuss	.06	.05	.02
104	Steve Carlton	.15	.11	.06
105	Jim Bibby	.05	.04	.02
106	Steve Rogers	.05	.04	.02
107	Tom Seaver	.15	.11	.06
108	Vida Blue	.06	.05	.02

Values for recent cards and sets are listed in Mint (MT), Near Mint (NM), reflecting the fact that many cards from recent years have been preserved in top condition. Recent cards and sets in less than Excellent condition have little collector interest.

1981 Topps Stickers

The 262 stickers in this full-color set measure 1-15/16" by 2-9/16" and are numbered on both the front and back. They were produced for Topps by the Panini Company of Italy. The set includes a

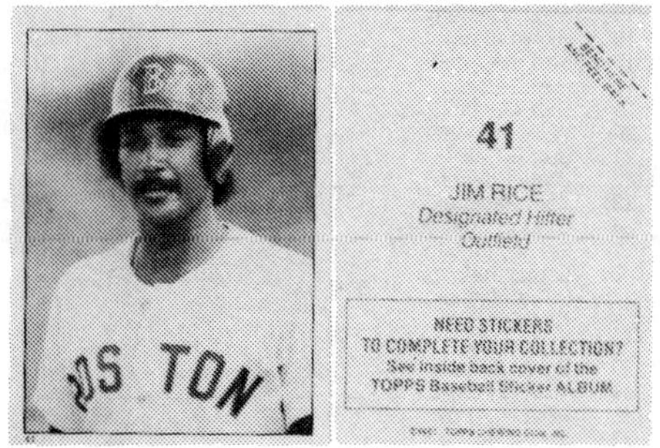

series of "All-Star" stickers printed on silver or gold "foil". An album to house the stickers was also available.

		MT	NR MT	EX
Complete Set:		17.00	12.50	6.75
Common Player:		.03	.02	.01
Sticker Album:		.80	.60	.30
1	Steve Stone	.06	.05	.02
2	Tommy John, Mike Norris	.06	.05	.02
3	Rudy May	.03	.02	.01
4	Mike Norris	.03	.02	.01
5	Len Barker	.03	.02	.01
6	Mike Norris	.03	.02	.01
7	Dan Quisenberry	.06	.05	.02
8	Rich Gossage	.10	.08	.04
9	George Brett	.25	.20	.10
10	Cecil Cooper	.08	.06	.03
11	Reggie Jackson, Ben Oglivie	.06	.05	.02
12	Gorman Thomas	.06	.05	.02
13	Cecil Cooper	.08	.06	.03
14	George Brett, Ben Oglivie	.20	.15	.08
15	Rickey Henderson	.25	.20	.10
16	Willie Wilson	.08	.06	.03
17	Bill Buckner	.06	.05	.02
18	Keith Hernandez	.12	.09	.05
19	Mike Schmidt	.25	.20	.10
20	Bob Horner	.10	.08	.04
21	Mike Schmidt	.25	.20	.10
22	George Hendrick	.06	.05	.02
23	Ron LeFlore	.04	.03	.02
24	Omar Moreno	.03	.02	.01
25	Steve Carlton	.20	.15	.08
26	Joe Niekro	.06	.05	.02
27	Don Sutton	.10	.08	.04
28	Steve Carlton	.20	.15	.08
29	Steve Carlton	.20	.15	.08
30	Nolan Ryan	.20	.15	.08
31	Rollie Fingers, Tom Hume	.08	.06	.03
32	Bruce Sutter	.08	.06	.03
33	Ken Singleton	.06	.05	.02
34	Eddie Murray	.20	.15	.08
35	Al Bumbry	.03	.02	.01
36	Rich Dauer	.03	.02	.01
37	Scott McGregor	.04	.03	.02
38	Rick Dempsey	.04	.03	.02
39	Jim Palmer	.15	.11	.06
40	Steve Stone	.06	.05	.02
41	Jim Rice	.20	.15	.08
42	Fred Lynn	.10	.08	.04
43	Carney Lansford	.06	.05	.02
44	Tony Perez	.10	.08	.04
45	Carl Yastrzemski	.30	.25	.12
46	Carlton Fisk	.12	.09	.05
47	Dave Stapleton	.03	.02	.01
48	Dennis Eckersley	.06	.05	.02
49	Rod Carew	.20	.15	.08
50	Brian Downing	.04	.03	.02
51	Don Baylor	.08	.06	.03
52	Rick Burleson	.04	.03	.02
53	Bobby Grich	.06	.05	.02
54	Butch Hobson	.03	.02	.01
55	Andy Hassler	.03	.02	.01
56	Frank Tanana	.04	.03	.02
57	Chet Lemon	.04	.03	.02
58	Lamar Johnson	.03	.02	.01
59	Wayne Nordhagen	.03	.02	.01
60	Jim Morrison	.03	.02	.01
61	Bob Molinaro	.03	.02	.01
62	Rich Dotson	.04	.03	.02
63	Britt Burns	.03	.02	.01
64	Ed Farmer	.03	.02	.01
65	Toby Harrah	.04	.03	.02
66	Joe Charboneau	.04	.03	.02
67	Miguel Dilone	.03	.02	.01
68	Mike Hargrove	.04	.03	.02
69	Rick Manning	.03	.02	.01
70	Andre Thornton	.06	.05	.02
71	Ron Hassey	.03	.02	.01
72	Len Barker	.03	.02	.01
73	Lance Parrish	.12	.09	.05
74	Steve Kemp	.04	.03	.02
75	Alan Trammell	.15	.11	.06
76	Champ Summers	.03	.02	.01
77	Rick Peters	.03	.02	.01
78	Kirk Gibson	.15	.11	.06
79	Johnny Wockenfuss	.03	.02	.01
80	Jack Morris	.12	.09	.05
81	Willie Wilson	.08	.06	.03
82	George Brett	.25	.20	.10
83	Frank White	.06	.05	.02
84	Willie Aikens	.03	.02	.01
85	Clint Hurdle	.03	.02	.01
86	Hal McRae	.06	.05	.02
87	Dennis Leonard	.04	.03	.02
88	Larry Gura	.03	.02	.01
89	American League Pennant Winner (Kansas City Royals Team)	.04	.03	.02
90	American League Pennant Winner (Kansas City Royals Team)	.04	.03	.02
91	Paul Molitor	.10	.08	.04
92	Ben Oglivie	.04	.03	.02
93	Cecil Cooper	.08	.06	.03
94	Ted Simmons	.08	.06	.03
95	Robin Yount	.15	.11	.06
96	Gorman Thomas	.06	.05	.02
97	Mike Caldwell	.03	.02	.01
98	Moose Haas	.03	.02	.01
99	John Castino	.03	.02	.01
100	Roy Smalley	.03	.02	.01
101	Ken Landreaux	.03	.02	.01
102	Butch Wynegar	.04	.03	.02
103	Ron Jackson	.03	.02	.01
104	Jerry Koosman	.04	.03	.02
105	Roger Erickson	.03	.02	.01
106	Doug Corbett	.03	.02	.01
107	Reggie Jackson	.25	.20	.10
108	Willie Randolph	.04	.03	.02
109	Rick Cerone	.03	.02	.01
110	Bucky Dent	.04	.03	.02
111	Dave Winfield	.20	.15	.08
112	Ron Guidry	.12	.09	.05
113	Rich Gossage	.10	.08	.04
114	Tommy John	.10	.08	.04
115	Rickey Henderson	.25	.20	.10
116	Tony Armas	.04	.03	.02
117	Dave Revering	.03	.02	.01
118	Wayne Gross	.03	.02	.01
119	Dwayne Murphy	.04	.03	.02
120	Jeff Newman	.03	.02	.01
121	Rick Langford	.03	.02	.01
122	Mike Norris	.03	.02	.01
123	Bruce Bochte	.03	.02	.01
124	Tom Paciorek	.03	.02	.01
125	Dan Meyer	.03	.02	.01
126	Julio Cruz	.03	.02	.01
127	Richie Zisk	.04	.03	.02
128	Floyd Bannister	.04	.03	.02
129	Shane Rawley	.04	.03	.02
130	Buddy Bell	.06	.05	.02
131	Al Oliver	.06	.05	.02
132	Mickey Rivers	.04	.03	.02
133	Jim Sundberg	.03	.02	.01
134	Bump Wills	.03	.02	.01
135	Jon Matlack	.04	.03	.02
136	Danny Darwin	.03	.02	.01
137	Damaso Garcia	.04	.03	.02
138	Otto Velez	.03	.02	.01
139	John Mayberry	.04	.03	.02
140	Alfredo Griffin	.04	.03	.02
141	Alvis Woods	.03	.02	.01
142	Dave Stieb	.06	.05	.02
143	Jim Clancy	.04	.03	.02
144	Gary Matthews	.06	.05	.02
145	Bob Horner	.08	.06	.03
146	Dale Murphy	.25	.20	.10
147	Chris Chambliss	.04	.03	.02
148	Phil Niekro	.12	.09	.05
149	Glenn Hubbard	.03	.02	.01
150	Rick Camp	.03	.02	.01
151	Dave Kingman	.08	.06	.03
152	Bill Caudill	.03	.02	.01
153	Bill Buckner	.06	.05	.02
154	Barry Foote	.03	.02	.01
155	Mike Tyson	.03	.02	.01
156	Ivan DeJesus	.03	.02	.01
157	Rick Reuschel	.06	.05	.02
158	Ken Reitz	.03	.02	.01
159	George Foster	.08	.06	.03
160	Johnny Bench	.25	.20	.10
161	Dave Concepcion	.06	.05	.02
162	Dave Collins	.04	.03	.02
163	Ken Griffey	.06	.05	.02
164	Dan Driessen	.04	.03	.02
165	Tom Seaver	.20	.15	.08
166	Tom Hume	.03	.02	.01
167	Cesar Cedeno	.06	.05	.02
168	Rafael Landestoy	.03	.02	.01
169	Jose Cruz	.06	.05	.02
170	Art Howe	.03	.02	.01
171	Terry Puhl	.03	.02	.01
172	Joe Sambito	.03	.02	.01
173	Nolan Ryan	.20	.15	.08
174	Joe Niekro	.06	.05	.02
175	Dave Lopes	.04	.03	.02
176	Steve Garvey	.20	.15	.08
177	Ron Cey	.06	.05	.02
178	Reggie Smith	.06	.05	.02
179	Bill Russell	.04	.03	.02
180	Burt Hooton	.03	.02	.01
181	Jerry Reuss	.06	.05	.02
182	Dusty Baker	.04	.03	.02
183	Larry Parrish	.04	.03	.02
184	Gary Carter	.20	.15	.08
185	Rodney Scott	.03	.02	.01
186	Ellis Valentine	.03	.02	.01
187	Andre Dawson	.12	.09	.05
188	Warren Cromartie	.03	.02	.01
189	Chris Speier	.03	.02	.01
190	Steve Rogers	.03	.02	.01
191	Lee Mazzilli	.04	.03	.02
192	Doug Flynn	.03	.02	.01
193	Steve Henderson	.03	.02	.01
194	John Stearns	.03	.02	.01
195	Joel Youngblood	.03	.02	.01
196	Frank Taveras	.03	.02	.01
197	Pat Zachry	.03	.02	.01
198	Neil Allen	.03	.02	.01
199	Mike Schmidt	.25	.20	.10
200	Pete Rose	.40	.30	.15
201	Larry Bowa	.06	.05	.02
202	Bake McBride	.03	.02	.01
203	Bob Boone	.04	.03	.02
204	Garry Maddox	.04	.03	.02
205	Tug McGraw	.06	.05	.02
206	Steve Carlton	.20	.15	.08
207	National League Pennant Winner (Philadelphia Phillies Team)	.04	.03	.02
208	National League Pennant Winner (Philadelphia Phillies Team)	.04	.03	.02
209	Phil Garner	.04	.03	.02
210	Dave Parker	.12	.09	.05
211	Omar Moreno	.03	.02	.01
212	Mike Easler	.04	.03	.02
213	Bill Madlock	.06	.05	.02
214	Ed Ott	.03	.02	.01
215	Willie Stargell	.20	.15	.08
216	Jim Bibby	.03	.02	.01
217	Garry Templeton	.06	.05	.02
218	Sixto Lezcano	.03	.02	.01
219	Keith Hernandez	.12	.09	.05
220	George Hendrick	.04	.03	.02
221	Bruce Sutter	.08	.06	.03
222	Ken Oberkfell	.03	.02	.01
223	Tony Scott	.03	.02	.01
224	Darrell Porter	.04	.03	.02
225	Gene Richards	.03	.02	.01
226	Broderick Perkins	.03	.02	.01
227	Jerry Mumphrey	.03	.02	.01
228	Luis Salazar	.03	.02	.01
229	Jerry Turner	.03	.02	.01
230	Ozzie Smith	.10	.08	.04
231	John Curtis	.03	.02	.01
232	Rick Wise	.03	.02	.01
233	Terry Whitfield	.03	.02	.01
234	Jack Clark	.10	.08	.04
235	Darrell Evans	.08	.06	.03
236	Larry Herndon	.03	.02	.01
237	Milt May	.03	.02	.01
238	Greg Minton	.03	.02	.01
239	Vida Blue	.06	.05	.02
240	Eddie Whitson	.03	.02	.01
241	Cecil Cooper	.20	.15	.08
242	Willie Randolph	.20	.15	.08
243	George Brett	.40	.30	.15
244	Robin Yount	.30	.25	.12
245	Reggie Jackson	.40	.30	.15
246	Al Oliver	.20	.15	.08
247	Willie Wilson	.20	.15	.08
248	Rick Cerone	.15	.11	.06
249	Steve Stone	.15	.11	.06
250	Tommy John	.25	.20	.10
251	Rich Gossage	.25	.20	.10
252	Steve Garvey	.30	.25	.12
253	Phil Garner	.15	.11	.06
254	Mike Schmidt	.40	.30	.15
255	Garry Templeton	.20	.15	.08
256	George Hendrick	.15	.11	.06
257	Dave Parker	.25	.20	.10
258	Cesar Cedeno	.20	.15	.08
259	Gary Carter	.30	.25	.12
260	Jim Bibby	.15	.11	.06
261	Steve Carlton	.30	.25	.12
262	Tug McGraw	.20	.15	.0

1982 Topps

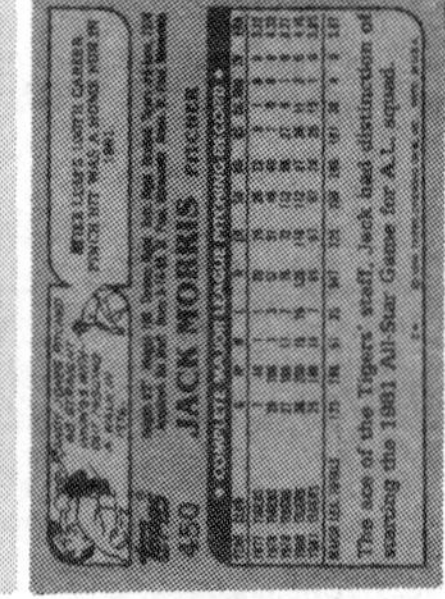

At 792 cards, this was the largest issue produced up to that time, eliminating the need for double-printed cards. The 2-1/2" by 3-1/2" cards feature a front color photo with a pair of stripes down the left side. Under the player's photo are found his name, team and position. A facsimile autograph runs across the front of the picture. Specialty cards include great performances of the previous season, All-Stars, statistical leaders and "In Action" cards (indicated by "IA" in listings below). Managers and hitting/pitching leaders have cards, while rookies are shown as "Future Stars" on group cards.

		MT	NR MT	EX
Complete Set (792):		150.00	112.00	60.00
Common Player:		.08	.06	.03
1	Steve Carlton (1981 Highlight)	.50	.40	.20
2	Ron Davis (1981 Highlight)	.08	.06	.03
3	Tim Raines (1981 Highlight)	.30	.25	.12
4	Pete Rose (1981 Highlight)	.70	.50	.30
5	Nolan Ryan (1981 Highlight)	3.00	2.25	1.25
6	Fernando Valenzuela (1981 Highlight)	.30	.25	.12
7	Scott Sanderson	.08	.06	.03
8	Rich Dauer	.08	.06	.03
9	Ron Guidry	.15	.11	.06
10	Ron Guidry (In Action)	.15	.11	.06

11 Gary Alexander .08 .06 .03
12 Moose Haas .08 .06 .03
13 Lamar Johnson .08 .06 .03
14 Steve Howe .10 .08 .04
15 Ellis Valentine .08 .06 .03
16 Steve Comer .08 .06 .03
17 Darrell Evans .15 .11 .06
18 Fernando Arroyo .08 .06 .03
19 Ernie Whitt .10 .08 .04
20 Garry Maddox .12 .09 .05
21 Orioles Future Stars (*Bob Bonner*, Cal Ripken, Jr., Jeff Schneider) 70.00 52.00 28.00
22 Jim Beattie .08 .06 .03
23 Willie Hernandez .10 .08 .04
24 Dave Frost .08 .06 .03
25 Jerry Remy .08 .06 .03
26 Jorge Orta .08 .06 .03
27 Tom Herr .12 .09 .05
28 John Urrea .08 .06 .03
29 Dwayne Murphy .10 .08 .04
30 Tom Seaver 2.00 1.50 .80
31 Tom Seaver (In Action) 1.00 .70 .40
32 Gene Garber .08 .06 .03
33 Jerry Morales .08 .06 .03
34 Joe Sambito .08 .06 .03
35 Willie Aikens .08 .06 .03
36 Rangers Batting/Pitching Leaders (George Medich, Al Oliver) .12 .09 .05
37 Dan Graham .08 .06 .03
38 Charlie Lea .08 .06 .03
39 Lou Whitaker .40 .30 .15
40 Dave Parker .35 .25 .14
41 Dave Parker (In Action) .15 .11 .06
42 Rick Sofield .08 .06 .03
43 Mike Cubbage .08 .06 .03
44 Britt Burns .08 .06 .03
45 Rick Cerone .08 .06 .03
46 Jerry Augustine .08 .06 .03
47 Jeff Leonard .08 .06 .03
48 Bobby Castillo .08 .06 .03
49 Alvis Woods .08 .06 .03
50 Buddy Bell .08 .06 .03
51 Cubs Future Stars (*Jay Howell*, Carlos Lezcano, Ty Waller) .40 .30 .15
52 Larry Andersen .08 .06 .03
53 Greg Gross .08 .06 .03
54 Ron Hassey .08 .06 .03
55 Rick Burleson .10 .08 .04
56 Mark Littell .08 .06 .03
57 Craig Reynolds .08 .06 .03
58 John D'Acquisto .08 .06 .03
59 *Rich Gedman* (FC) .15 .11 .06
60 Tony Armas .12 .09 .05
61 Tommy Boggs .08 .06 .03
62 Mike Tyson .08 .06 .03
63 Mario Soto .10 .08 .04
64 Lynn Jones .08 .06 .03
65 Terry Kennedy .12 .09 .05
66 Astros Batting/Pitching Leaders (Art Howe, Nolan Ryan) .50 .40 .20
67 Rich Gale .08 .06 .03
68 Roy Howell .08 .06 .03
69 Al Williams .08 .06 .03
70 Tim Raines 1.00 .70 .40
71 Roy Lee Jackson .08 .06 .03
72 Rick Auerbach .08 .06 .03
73 Buddy Solomon .08 .06 .03
74 Bob Clark .08 .06 .03
75 Tommy John .30 .25 .12
76 Greg Pryor .08 .06 .03
77 Miguel Dilone .08 .06 .03
78 George Medich .08 .06 .03
79 Bob Bailor .08 .06 .03
80 Jim Palmer 1.00 .70 .40
81 Jim Palmer (In Action) .30 .25 .12
82 Bob Welch .25 .20 .10
83 Yankees Future Stars (*Steve Balboni* (FC), Andy McGaffigan, Andre Robertson) .15 .11 .06
84 Rennie Stennett .08 .06 .03
85 Lynn McGlothen .08 .06 .03
86 Dane Iorg .08 .06 .03
87 Matt Keough .08 .06 .03
88 Biff Pocoroba .08 .06 .03
89 Steve Henderson .08 .06 .03
90 Nolan Ryan 12.00 9.00 4.75
91 Carney Lansford .12 .09 .05
92 Brad Havens .08 .06 .03
93 Larry Hisle .10 .08 .04
94 Andy Hassler .08 .06 .03
95 Ozzie Smith 2.50 2.00 1.00
96 Royals Batting/Pitching Leaders (George Brett, Larry Gura) .35 .25 .14
97 Paul Moskau .08 .06 .03
98 Terry Bulling .08 .06 .03
99 Barry Bonnell .08 .06 .03
100 Mike Schmidt 3.00 2.25 1.25
101 Mike Schmidt (In Action) 1.25 .90 .50
102 Dan Briggs .08 .06 .03
103 Bob Lacey .08 .06 .03
104 Rance Mulliniks .08 .06 .03
105 Kirk Gibson .50 .40 .20
106 Enrique Romo .08 .06 .03
107 Wayne Krenchicki .08 .06 .03
108 Bob Sykes .08 .06 .03
109 Dave Revering .08 .06 .03
110 Carlton Fisk 1.00 .70 .40
111 Carlton Fisk (In Action) .65 .50 .25
112 Billy Sample .08 .06 .03
113 Steve McCatty .08 .06 .03
114 Ken Landreaux .08 .06 .03
115 Gaylord Perry .50 .40 .20
116 Jim Wohlford .08 .06 .03
117 Rawly Eastwick .08 .06 .03
118 Expos Future Stars (*Terry Francona*, Brad Mills, Bryn Smith) .20 .15 .08
119 Joe Pittman .08 .06 .03
120 Gary Lucas .08 .06 .03
121 Ed Lynch .08 .06 .03
122 Jamie Easterly .08 .06 .03
123 Danny Goodwin .08 .06 .03
124 Reid Nichols .08 .06 .03
125 Danny Ainge 2.00 1.50 .80
126 Braves Batting/Pitching Leaders (Rick Mahler, Claudell Washington) .10 .08 .04
127 Lonnie Smith .10 .08 .04
128 Frank Pastore .08 .06 .03
129 Checklist 1-132 .12 .09 .05
130 Julio Cruz .08 .06 .03
131 Stan Bahnsen .08 .06 .03
132 Lee May .10 .08 .04
133 Pat Underwood .08 .06 .03
134 Dan Ford .08 .06 .03
135 Andy Rincon .08 .06 .03
136 Lenn Sakata .08 .06 .03
137 George Cappuzzello .08 .06 .03
138 Tony Pena .10 .08 .04
139 Jeff Jones .08 .06 .03
140 Ron LeFlore .10 .08 .04
141 Indians Future Stars (Chris Bando, Tom Brennan, Von Hayes) .20 .15 .08
142 Dave LaRoche .08 .06 .03
143 Mookie Wilson .12 .09 .05
144 Fred Breining .08 .06 .03
145 Bob Horner .10 .08 .04
146 Mike Griffin .08 .06 .03
147 Denny Walling .08 .06 .03
148 Mickey Klutts .08 .06 .03
149 Pat Putnam .08 .06 .03
150 Ted Simmons .10 .08 .04
151 Dave Edwards .08 .06 .03
152 Ramon Aviles .08 .06 .03
153 Roger Erickson .08 .06 .03
154 Dennis Werth .08 .06 .03
155 Otto Velez .08 .06 .03
156 A's Batting/Pitching Leaders (Rickey Henderson, Steve McCatty) .25 .20 .10
157 Steve Crawford .08 .06 .03
158 Brian Downing .12 .09 .05
159 Larry Biittner .08 .06 .03
160 Luis Tiant .10 .08 .04
161 Batting Leaders (Carney Lansford, Bill Madlock) .10 .08 .04
162 Home Run Leaders (Tony Armas, Dwight Evans, Bobby Grich, Eddie Murray, Mike Schmidt) .25 .20 .10
163 RBI Leaders (Eddie Murray, Mike Schmidt) .50 .40 .20
164 Stolen Base Leaders (Rickey Henderson, Tim Raines) .90 .70 .35
165 Victory Leaders (Denny Martinez, Steve McCatty, Jack Morris, Tom Seaver, Pete Vuckovich) .20 .15 .08
166 Strikeout Leaders (Len Barker, Fernando Valenzuela) .20 .15 .08
167 ERA Leaders (Steve McCatty, Nolan Ryan) .20 .15 .08
168 Leading Relievers (Rollie Fingers, Bruce Sutter) .20 .15 .08
169 Charlie Leibrandt .12 .09 .05
170 Jim Bibby .08 .06 .03
171 Giants Future Stars (*Bob Brenly* (FC), Chili Davis, Bob Tufts) 2.00 1.50 .80
172 Bill Gullickson .10 .08 .04
173 Jamie Quirk .08 .06 .03
174 Dave Ford .08 .06 .03
175 Jerry Mumphrey .08 .06 .03
176 Dewey Robinson .08 .06 .03
177 John Ellis .08 .06 .03
178 Dyar Miller .08 .06 .03
179 Steve Garvey .80 .60 .30
180 Steve Garvey (In Action) .40 .30 .15
181 Silvio Martinez .08 .06 .03
182 Larry Herndon .10 .08 .04
183 Mike Proly .08 .06 .03
184 Mick Kelleher .08 .06 .03
185 Phil Niekro .50 .40 .20
186 Cardinals Batting/Pitching Leaders (Bob Forsch, Keith Hernandez) .15 .11 .06
187 Jeff Newman .08 .06 .03
188 Randy Martz .08 .06 .03
189 Glenn Hoffman .08 .06 .03
190 J.R. Richard .12 .09 .05
191 *Tim Wallach* 2.50 2.00 1.00
192 Broderick Perkins .08 .06 .03
193 Darrell Jackson .08 .06 .03
194 Mike Vail .08 .06 .03
195 Paul Molitor 4.00 3.00 1.50
196 Willie Upshaw .12 .09 .05
197 Shane Rawley .15 .11 .06
198 Chris Speier .08 .06 .03
199 Don Aase .08 .06 .03
200 George Brett 3.00 2.25 1.25
201 George Brett (In Action) 1.50 1.25 .60
202 Rick Manning .08 .06 .03
203 Blue Jays Future Stars *Jesse Barfield*, Brian Milner, Boomer Wells .50 .40 .20
204 Gary Roenicke .08 .06 .03
205 Neil Allen .08 .06 .03
206 Tony Bernazard .08 .06 .03
207 Rod Scurry .08 .06 .03
208 Bobby Murcer .10 .08 .04
209 Gary Lavelle .08 .06 .03
210 Keith Hernandez .15 .11 .06
211 Dan Petry .10 .08 .04
212 Mario Mendoza .08 .06 .03
213 *Dave Stewart* (FC) 4.00 3.00 1.50
214 Brian Asselstine .08 .06 .03
215 Mike Krukow .10 .08 .04
216 White Sox Batting/Pitching Leaders (Dennis Lamp, Chet Lemon) .10 .08 .04
217 Bo McLaughlin .08 .06 .03
218 Dave Roberts .08 .06 .03
219 John Curtis .08 .06 .03
220 Manny Trillo .10 .08 .04
221 Jim Slaton .08 .06 .03
222 Butch Wynegar .08 .06 .03
223 Lloyd Moseby .10 .08 .04
224 Bruce Bochte .08 .06 .03
225 Mike Torrez .10 .08 .04
226 Checklist 133-264 .12 .09 .05
227 Ray Burris .08 .06 .03
228 Sam Mejias .08 .06 .03
229 Geoff Zahn .08 .06 .03
230 Willie Wilson .20 .15 .08
231 Phillies Future Stars (*Mark Davis*, Bob Dernier, Ozzie Virgil) .20 .15 .08
232 Terry Crowley .08 .06 .03
233 Duane Kuiper .08 .06 .03
234 Ron Hodges .08 .06 .03
235 Mike Easler .10 .08 .04
236 John Martin .08 .06 .03
237 Rusty Kuntz .08 .06 .03
238 Kevin Saucier .08 .06 .03
239 Jon Matlack .10 .08 .04
240 Bucky Dent .12 .09 .05
241 Bucky Dent (In Action) .10 .08 .04
242 Milt May .08 .06 .03
243 Bob Owchinko .08 .06 .03
244 Rufino Linares .08 .06 .03
245 Ken Reitz .08 .06 .03
246 Mets Batting/Pitching Leaders (Hubie Brooks, Mike Scott) .20 .15 .08
247 Pedro Guerrero .20 .15 .08
248 Frank LaCorte .08 .06 .03
249 Tim Flannery .08 .06 .03
250 Tug McGraw .15 .11 .06
251 Fred Lynn .30 .25 .12
252 Fred Lynn (In Action) .15 .11 .06
253 Chuck Baker .08 .06 .03
254 *Jorge Bell* (FC) 3.00 2.25 1.25
255 Tony Perez .30 .25 .12
256 Tony Perez (In Action) .15 .11 .06
257 Larry Harlow .08 .06 .03
258 Bo Diaz .10 .08 .04
259 Rodney Scott .08 .06 .03
260 Bruce Sutter .10 .08 .04
261 Tigers Future Stars (Howard Bailey, Marty Castillo, Dave Rucker) .08 .06 .03
262 Doug Bair .08 .06 .03
263 Victor Cruz .08 .06 .03
264 Dan Quisenberry .10 .08 .04
265 Al Bumbry .10 .08 .04
266 Rick Leach .10 .08 .04
267 Kurt Bevacqua .08 .06 .03
268 Rickey Keeton .08 .06 .03
269 Jim Essian .08 .06 .03
270 Rusty Staub .15 .11 .06
271 Larry Bradford .08 .06 .03
272 Bump Wills .08 .06 .03
273 Doug Bird .08 .06 .03
274 *Bob Ojeda* (FC) .70 .50 .30
275 Bob Watson .10 .08 .04
276 Angels Batting/Pitching Leaders (Rod Carew, Ken Forsch) .25 .20 .10
277 Terry Puhl .08 .06 .03
278 John Littlefield .08 .06 .03
279 Bill Russell .10 .08 .04
280 Ben Oglivie .10 .08 .04
281 John Verhoeven .08 .06 .03
282 Ken Macha .08 .06 .03
283 Brian Allard .08 .06 .03
284 Bob Grich .15 .11 .06
285 Sparky Lyle .12 .09 .05
286 Bill Fahey .08 .06 .03
287 Alan Bannister .08 .06 .03
288 Garry Templeton .12 .09 .05
289 Bob Stanley .08 .06 .03
290 Ken Singleton .12 .09 .05
291 Pirates Future Stars (Vance Law, Bob Long, Johnny Ray) .25 .20 .10
292 Dave Palmer .08 .06 .03
293 Rob Picciolo .08 .06 .03
294 Mike LaCoss .08 .06 .03
295 Jason Thompson .08 .06 .03
296 Bob Walk .12 .09 .05
297 Clint Hurdle .08 .06 .03
298 Danny Darwin .08 .06 .03
299 Steve Trout .08 .06 .03
300 Reggie Jackson 3.50 2.75 1.50
301 Reggie Jackson (In Action) 2.50 2.00 1.00
302 Doug Flynn .08 .06 .03
303 Bill Caudill .08 .06 .03
304 Johnnie LeMaster .08 .06 .03
305 Don Sutton .50 .40 .20
306 Don Sutton (In Action) .25 .20 .10
307 Randy Bass .08 .06 .03
308 Charlie Moore .08 .06 .03
309 Pete Redfern .08 .06 .03
310 Mike Hargrove .08 .06 .03
311 Dodgers Batting/Pitching Leaders (Dusty Baker, Burt Hooton) .12 .09 .05
312 Lenny Randle .08 .06 .03
313 John Harris .08 .06 .03
314 Buck Martinez .08 .06 .03
315 Burt Hooton .10 .08 .04
316 Steve Braun .08 .06 .03
317 Dick Ruthven .08 .06 .03
318 Mike Heath .08 .06 .03
319 Dave Rozema .08 .06 .03
320 Chris Chambliss .10 .08 .04
321 Chris Chambliss (In Action) .10 .08 .04
322 Garry Hancock .08 .06 .03
323 Bill Lee .10 .08 .04
324 Steve Dillard .08 .06 .03
325 Jose Cruz .15 .11 .06
326 Pete Falcone .08 .06 .03
327 Joe Nolan .08 .06 .03
328 Ed Farmer .08 .06 .03
329 U.L. Washington .08 .06 .03
330 Rick Wise .10 .08 .04
331 Benny Ayala .08 .06 .03
332 Don Robinson .10 .08 .04
333 Brewers Future Stars (*Frank DiPino* (FC), Marshall Edwards, Chuck Porter) .12 .09 .05

334 Aurelio Rodriguez .10 .08 .04
335 Jim Sundberg .10 .08 .04
336 Mariners Batting/Pitching Leaders (Glenn Abbott, Tom Paciorek) .10 .08 .04
337 Pete Rose (All-Star) 1.00 .70 .40
338 Dave Lopes (All-Star) .12 .09 .05
339 Mike Schmidt (All-Star) .75 .60 .30
340 Dave Concepcion (All-Star) .12 .09 .05
341 Andre Dawson (All-Star) .45 .35 .20
342a George Foster (All-Star no autograph) 2.25 1.75 .90
342b George Foster (All-Star autograph on front) .20 .15 .08
343 Dave Parker (All-Star) .20 .15 .08
344 Gary Carter (All-Star) .20 .15 .08
345 Fernando Valenzuela (All-Star) .20 .15 .08
346 Tom Seaver (All-Star) .75 .60 .30
347 Bruce Sutter (All-Star) .12 .09 .05
348 Derrel Thomas .08 .06 .03
349 George Frazier .08 .06 .03
350 Thad Bosley .08 .06 .03
351 Reds Future Stars (Scott Brown, Geoff Combe, Paul Householder) .08 .06 .03
352 Dick Davis .08 .06 .03
353 Jack O'Connor .08 .06 .03
354 Roberto Ramos .08 .06 .03
355 Dwight Evans .15 .11 .06
356 Denny Lewallyn .08 .06 .03
357 Butch Hobson .08 .06 .03
358 Mike Parrott .08 .06 .03
359 Jim Dwyer .08 .06 .03
360 Len Barker .10 .08 .04
361 Rafael Landestoy .08 .06 .03
362 Jim Wright .08 .06 .03
363 Bob Molinaro .08 .06 .03
364 Doyle Alexander .12 .09 .05
365 Bill Madlock .10 .08 .04
366 Padres Batting/Pitching Leaders (Juan Eichelberger, Luis Salazar) .10 .08 .04
367 Jim Kaat .25 .20 .10
368 Alex Trevino .08 .06 .03
369 Champ Summers .08 .06 .03
370 Mike Norris .08 .06 .03
371 Jerry Don Gleaton .08 .06 .03
372 Luis Gomez .08 .06 .03
373 *Gene Nelson* .10 .08 .04
374 Tim Blackwell .08 .06 .03
375 Dusty Baker .12 .09 .05
376 Chris Welsh .08 .06 .03
377 Kiko Garcia .08 .06 .03
378 Mike Caldwell .08 .06 .03
379 Rob Wilfong .08 .06 .03
380 Dave Stieb .25 .20 .10
381 Red Sox Future Stars (Bruce Hurst, Dave Schmidt, Julio Valdez) .25 .20 .10
382 Joe Simpson .08 .06 .03
383a Pascual Perez (no position on front) 18.00 13.50 7.25
383b Pascual Perez ("Pitcher" on front) .12 .09 .05
384 Keith Moreland .12 .09 .05
385 Ken Forsch .08 .06 .03
386 Jerry White .08 .06 .03
387 Tom Veryzer .08 .06 .03
388 Joe Rudi .12 .09 .05
389 George Vukovich .08 .06 .03
390 Eddie Murray 1.25 .90 .50
391 Dave Tobik .08 .06 .03
392 Rick Bosetti .08 .06 .03
393 Al Hrabosky .10 .08 .04
394 Checklist 265-396 .12 .09 .05
395 Omar Moreno .08 .06 .03
396 Twins Batting/Pitching Leaders (Fernando Arroyo, John Castino) .10 .08 .04
397 Ken Brett .10 .08 .04
398 Mike Squires .08 .06 .03
399 Pat Zachry .08 .06 .03
400 Johnny Bench 1.50 1.25 .60
401 Johnny Bench (In Action) .40 .30 .15
402 Bill Stein .08 .06 .03
403 Jim Tracy .08 .06 .03
404 Dickie Thon .10 .08 .04
405 Rick Reuschel .15 .11 .06
406 Al Holland .08 .06 .03
407 Danny Boone .08 .06 .03
408 Ed Romero .08 .06 .03
409 Don Cooper .08 .06 .03
410 Ron Cey .15 .11 .06
411 Ron Cey (In Action) .10 .08 .04
412 Luis Leal .08 .06 .03
413 Dan Meyer .08 .06 .03
414 Elias Sosa .08 .06 .03
415 Don Baylor .15 .11 .06
416 Marty Bystrom .08 .06 .03
417 Pat Kelly .08 .06 .03
418 Rangers Future Stars (John Butcher, Bobby Johnson, Dave Schmidt) .08 .06 .03
419 Steve Stone .12 .09 .05
420 George Hendrick .10 .08 .04
421 Mark Clear .08 .06 .03
422 Cliff Johnson .08 .06 .03
423 Stan Papi .08 .06 .03
424 Bruce Benedict .08 .06 .03
425 John Candelaria .12 .09 .05
426 Orioles Batting/Pitching Leaders (Eddie Murray, Sammy Stewart) .25 .20 .10
427 Ron Oester .08 .06 .03
428 Lamarr Hoyt (LaMarr) .08 .06 .03
429 John Wathan .10 .08 .04
430 Vida Blue .15 .11 .06
431 Vida Blue (In Action) .10 .08 .04
432 Mike Scott .25 .20 .10
433 Alan Ashby .08 .06 .03
434 Joe Lefebvre .08 .06 .03
435 Robin Yount 4.00 3.00 1.50
436 Joe Strain .08 .06 .03
437 Juan Berenguer .08 .06 .03
438 Pete Mackanin .08 .06 .03
439 *Dave Righetti* (FC) 1.00 .70 .40
440 Jeff Burroughs .10 .08 .04
441 Astros Future Stars (Danny Heep, Billy Smith, Bobby Sprowl) .08 .06 .03
442 Bruce Kison .08 .06 .03
443 Mark Wagner .08 .06 .03
444 Terry Forster .10 .08 .04
445 Larry Parrish .12 .09 .05
446 Wayne Garland .08 .06 .03
447 Darrell Porter .10 .08 .04
448 Darrell Porter (In Action) .10 .08 .04
449 *Luis Aguayo* (FC) .12 .09 .05
450 Jack Morris .60 .45 .25
451 Ed Miller .08 .06 .03
452 *Lee Smith* 10.00 7.50 4.00
453 Art Howe .08 .06 .03
454 Rick Langford .08 .06 .03
455 Tom Burgmeier .08 .06 .03
456 Cubs Batting & Pitching Ldrs. (Bill Buckner, Randy Martz) .08 .06 .03
457 Tim Stoddard .08 .06 .03
458 Willie Montanez .08 .06 .03
459 Bruce Berenyi .08 .06 .03
460 Jack Clark .10 .08 .04
461 Rich Dotson .10 .08 .04
462 Dave Chalk .08 .06 .03
463 Jim Kern .08 .06 .03
464 Juan Bonilla .08 .06 .03
465 Lee Mazzilli .10 .08 .04
466 Randy Lerch .08 .06 .03
467 Mickey Hatcher .10 .08 .04
468 Floyd Bannister .12 .09 .05
469 Ed Ott .08 .06 .03
470 John Mayberry .10 .08 .04
471 Royals Future Stars (*Atlee Hammaker* (FC), Mike Jones, Darryl Motley) .25 .20 .10
472 Oscar Gamble .10 .08 .04
473 Mike Stanton .08 .06 .03
474 Ken Oberkfell .08 .06 .03
475 Alan Trammell .60 .45 .25
476 Brian Kingman .08 .06 .03
477 Steve Yeager .08 .06 .03
478 Ray Searage .08 .06 .03
479 Rowland Office .08 .06 .03
480 Steve Carlton 1.00 .70 .40
481 Steve Carlton (In Action) .40 .30 .15
482 Glenn Hubbard .10 .08 .04
483 Gary Woods .08 .06 .03
484 Ivan DeJesus .08 .06 .03
485 Kent Tekulve .10 .08 .04
486 Yankees Batting & Pitching Ldrs. (Tommy John, Jerry Mumphrey) .20 .15 .08
487 Bob McClure .08 .06 .03
488 Ron Jackson .08 .06 .03
489 Rick Dempsey .10 .08 .04
490 Dennis Eckersley .20 .15 .08
491 Checklist 397-528 .12 .09 .05
492 Joe Price .08 .06 .03
493 Chet Lemon .10 .08 .04
494 Hubie Brooks .20 .15 .08
495 Dennis Leonard .10 .08 .04
496 Johnny Grubb .08 .06 .03
497 Jim Anderson .08 .06 .03
498 Dave Bergman .08 .06 .03
499 Paul Mirabella .08 .06 .03
500 Rod Carew 1.00 .70 .40
501 Rod Carew (In Action) .40 .30 .15
502 Braves Future Stars (*Steve Bedrosian* (FC), Brett Butler, Larry Owen) 2.00 1.50 .80
503 Julio Gonzalez .08 .06 .03
504 Rick Peters .08 .06 .03
505 Graig Nettles .15 .11 .06
506 Graig Nettles (In Action) .12 .09 .05
507 Terry Harper .08 .06 .03
508 *Jody Davis* (FC) .15 .11 .06
509 Harry Spilman .08 .06 .03
510 Fernando Valenzuela .40 .30 .15
511 Ruppert Jones .08 .06 .03
512 Jerry Dybzinski .08 .06 .03
513 Rick Rhoden .12 .09 .05
514 Joe Ferguson .08 .06 .03
515 Larry Bowa .20 .15 .08
516 Larry Bowa (In Action) .12 .09 .05
517 Mark Brouhard .08 .06 .03
518 Garth Iorg .08 .06 .03
519 Glenn Adams .08 .06 .03
520 Mike Flanagan .12 .09 .05
521 Billy Almon .08 .06 .03
522 Chuck Rainey .08 .06 .03
523 Gary Gray .08 .06 .03
524 Tom Hausman .08 .06 .03
525 Ray Knight .12 .09 .05
526 Expos Batting & Pitching Ldrs. (Warren Cromartie, Bill Gullickson) .10 .08 .04
527 John Henry Johnson .08 .06 .03
528 Matt Alexander .08 .06 .03
529 Allen Ripley .08 .06 .03
530 Dickie Noles .08 .06 .03
531 A's Future Stars (Rich Bordi, Mark Budaska, Kelvin Moore) .08 .06 .03
532 Toby Harrah .10 .08 .04
533 Joaquin Andujar .10 .08 .04
534 Dave McKay .08 .06 .03
535 Lance Parrish .15 .11 .06
536 Rafael Ramirez .10 .08 .04
537 Doug Capilla .08 .06 .03
538 Lou Piniella .15 .11 .06
539 Vern Ruhle .08 .06 .03
540 Andre Dawson .80 .60 .30
541 Barry Evans .08 .06 .03
542 Ned Yost .08 .06 .03
543 Bill Robinson .08 .06 .03
544 Larry Christenson .08 .06 .03
545 Reggie Smith .15 .11 .06
546 Reggie Smith (In Action) .10 .08 .04
547 Rod Carew (All-Star) .35 .25 .14
548 Willie Randolph (All-Star) .12 .09 .05
549 George Brett (All-Star) 1.00 .70 .40
550 Bucky Dent (All-Star) .12 .09 .05
551 Reggie Jackson (All-Star) 1.00 .70 .40
552 Ken Singleton (All-Star) .12 .09 .05
553 Dave Winfield (All-Star) .90 .70 .35
554 Carlton Fisk (All-Star) .20 .15 .08
555 Scott McGregor (All-Star) .12 .09 .05
556 Jack Morris (All-Star) .20 .15 .08
557 Rich Gossage (All-Star) .20 .15 .08
558 John Tudor .15 .11 .06
559 Indians Batting & Pitching Ldrs. (Bert Blyleven, Mike Hargrove) .15 .11 .06
560 Doug Corbett .08 .06 .03
561 Cardinals Future Stars (Glenn Brummer, Luis DeLeon, Gene Roof) .08 .06 .03
562 Mike O'Berry .08 .06 .03
563 Ross Baumgarten .08 .06 .03
564 Doug DeCinces .15 .11 .06
565 Jackson Todd .08 .06 .03
566 Mike Jorgensen .08 .06 .03
567 Bob Babcock .08 .06 .03
568 Joe Pettini .08 .06 .03
569 Willie Randolph .15 .11 .06
570 Willie Randolph (In Action) .10 .08 .04
571 Glenn Abbott .08 .06 .03
572 Juan Beniquez .08 .06 .03
573 Rick Waits .08 .06 .03
574 Mike Ramsey .08 .06 .03
575 Al Cowens .08 .06 .03
576 Giants Batting & Pitching Ldrs. (Vida Blue, Milt May) .15 .11 .06
577 Rick Monday .12 .09 .05
578 Shooty Babitt .08 .06 .03
579 *Rick Mahler* (FC) .08 .06 .03
580 Bobby Bonds .15 .11 .06
581 Ron Reed .08 .06 .03
582 Luis Pujols .08 .06 .03
583 Tippy Martinez .08 .06 .03
584 Hosken Powell .08 .06 .03
585 Rollie Fingers .30 .25 .12
586 Rollie Fingers (In Action) .15 .11 .06
587 Tim Lollar .08 .06 .03
588 Dale Berra .08 .06 .03
589 Dave Stapleton .08 .06 .03
590 Al Oliver .20 .15 .08
591 Al Oliver (In Action) .10 .08 .04
592 Craig Swan .08 .06 .03
593 Billy Smith .08 .06 .03
594 Renie Martin .08 .06 .03
595 Dave Collins .10 .08 .04
596 Damaso Garcia .08 .06 .03
597 Wayne Nordhagen .08 .06 .03
598 Bob Galasso .08 .06 .03
599 White Sox Future Stars (Jay Loviglio, Reggie Patterson, Leo Sutherland) .08 .06 .03
600 Dave Winfield 4.00 3.00 1.50
601 Sid Monge .08 .06 .03
602 Freddie Patek .08 .06 .03
603 Rich Hebner .08 .06 .03
604 Orlando Sanchez .08 .06 .03
605 Steve Rogers .10 .08 .04
606 Blue Jays Batting & Pitching Ldrs. (John Mayberry, Dave Stieb) .15 .11 .06
607 Leon Durham .10 .08 .04
608 Jerry Royster .08 .06 .03
609 Rick Sutcliffe .25 .20 .10
610 Rickey Henderson 4.00 3.00 1.50
611 Joe Niekro .08 .06 .03
612 Gary Ward .10 .08 .04
613 Jim Gantner .10 .08 .04
614 Juan Eichelberger .08 .06 .03
615 Bob Boone .12 .09 .05
616 Bob Boone (In Action) .10 .08 .04
617 Scott McGregor .10 .08 .04
618 Tim Foli .08 .06 .03
619 Bill Campbell .08 .06 .03
620 Ken Griffey .15 .11 .06
621 Ken Griffey (In Action) .10 .08 .04
622 Dennis Lamp .08 .06 .03
623 Mets Future Stars (Ron Gardenhire, Terry Leach, Tim Leary) .25 .20 .10
624 Fergie Jenkins .60 .45 .25
625 Hal McRae .15 .11 .06
626 Randy Jones .10 .08 .04
627 Enos Cabell .08 .06 .03
628 Bill Travers .08 .06 .03
629 Johnny Wockenfuss .08 .06 .03
630 Joe Charboneau .10 .08 .04
631 Gene Tenace .10 .08 .04
632 Bryan Clark .08 .06 .03
633 Mitchell Page .08 .06 .03
634 Checklist 529-660 .12 .09 .05
635 Ron Davis .10 .08 .04
636 Phillies Batting & Pitching Ldrs. (Steve Carlton, Pete Rose) .50 .40 .20
637 Rick Camp .08 .06 .03
638 John Milner .08 .06 .03
639 Ken Kravec .08 .06 .03
640 Cesar Cedeno .15 .11 .06
641 Steve Mura .08 .06 .03
642 Mike Scioscia .10 .08 .04
643 Pete Vuckovich .10 .08 .04
644 John Castino .08 .06 .03
645 Frank White .12 .09 .05
646 Frank White (In Action) .10 .08 .04
647 Warren Brusstar .08 .06 .03
648 Jose Morales .08 .06 .03
649 Ken Clay .08 .06 .03
650 Carl Yastrzemski 1.50 1.25 .60
651 Carl Yastrzemski (In Action) .60 .45 .25
652 Steve Nicosia .08 .06 .03
653 Angels Future Stars *Tom Brunansky*, Luis Sanchez, Daryl Sconiers) .40 .30 .15
654 Jim Morrison .08 .06 .03
655 Joel Youngblood .08 .06 .03
656 Eddie Whitson .08 .06 .03
657 Tom Poquette .08 .06 .03
658 Tito Landrum .08 .06 .03
659 Fred Martinez .08 .06 .03
660 Dave Concepcion .15 .11 .06

#	Player	MT	NR MT	EX
661	Dave Concepcion (In Action)	.10	.08	.04
662	Luis Salazar	.08	.06	.03
663	Hector Cruz	.08	.06	.03
664	Dan Spillner	.08	.06	.03
665	Jim Clancy	.12	.09	.05
666	Tigers Batting & Pitching Ldrs. (Steve Kemp, Dan Petry)	.15	.11	.06
667	Jeff Reardon	1.00	.70	.40
668	Dale Murphy	1.25	.90	.50
669	Larry Milbourne	.08	.06	.03
670	Steve Kemp	.12	.09	.05
671	Mike Davis	.10	.08	.04
672	Bob Knepper	.12	.09	.05
673	Keith Drumright	.08	.06	.03
674	Dave Goltz	.10	.08	.04
675	Cecil Cooper	.08	.06	.03
676	Sal Butera	.08	.06	.03
677	Alfredo Griffin	.12	.09	.05
678	Tom Paciorek	.08	.06	.03
679	Sammy Stewart	.08	.06	.03
680	Gary Matthews	.12	.09	.05
681	Dodgers Future Stars (*Mike Marshall*, Ron Roenicke, Steve Sax)	.75	.60	.30
682	Jesse Jefferson	.08	.06	.03
683	Phil Garner	.10	.08	.04
684	Harold Baines	.25	.20	.10
685	Bert Blyleven	.20	.15	.08
686	Gary Allenson	.08	.06	.03
687	Greg Minton	.08	.06	.03
688	Leon Roberts	.08	.06	.03
689	Lary Sorensen	.08	.06	.03
690	Dave Kingman	.10	.08	.04
691	Dan Schatzeder	.08	.06	.03
692	Wayne Gross	.08	.06	.03
693	Cesar Geronimo	.08	.06	.03
694	Dave Wehrmeister	.08	.06	.03
695	Warren Cromartie	.08	.06	.03
696	Pirates Batting & Pitching Ldrs. (Bill Madlock, Buddy Solomon)	.15	.11	.06
697	John Montefusco	.08	.06	.03
698	Tony Scott	.08	.06	.03
699	Dick Tidrow	.08	.06	.03
700	George Foster	.25	.20	.10
701	George Foster (In Action)	.12	.09	.05
702	Steve Renko	.08	.06	.03
703	Brewers Batting & Pitching Ldrs. (Cecil Cooper, Pete Vuckovich)	.15	.11	.06
704	Mickey Rivers	.10	.08	.04
705	Mickey Rivers (In Action)	.10	.08	.04
706	Barry Foote	.08	.06	.03
707	Mark Bomback	.08	.06	.03
708	Gene Richards	.08	.06	.03
709	Don Money	.08	.06	.03
710	Jerry Reuss	.12	.09	.05
711	Mariners Future Stars (*Dave Edler*, Dave Henderson, Reggie Walton)	1.00	.70	.40
712	Denny Martinez	.10	.08	.04
713	Del Unser	.08	.06	.03
714	Jerry Koosman	.12	.09	.05
715	Willie Stargell	.80	.60	.30
716	Willie Stargell (In Action)	.30	.25	.12
717	Rick Miller	.08	.06	.03
718	Charlie Hough	.12	.09	.05
719	Jerry Narron	.08	.06	.03
720	Greg Luzinski	.20	.15	.08
721	Greg Luzinski (In Action)	.12	.09	.05
722	Jerry Martin	.08	.06	.03
723	Junior Kennedy	.08	.06	.03
724	Dave Rosello	.08	.06	.03
725	Amos Otis	.10	.08	.04
726	Amos Otis (In Action)	.10	.08	.04
727	Sixto Lezcano	.08	.06	.03
728	Aurelio Lopez	.08	.06	.03
729	Jim Spencer	.08	.06	.03
730	Gary Carter	.80	.60	.30
731	Padres Future Stars (Mike Armstrong, Doug Gwosdz, Fred Kuhaulua)	.08	.06	.03
732	Mike Lum	.08	.06	.03
733	Larry McWilliams	.08	.06	.03
734	Mike Ivie	.08	.06	.03
735	Rudy May	.08	.06	.03
736	Jerry Turner	.08	.06	.03
737	Reggie Cleveland	.08	.06	.03
738	Dave Engle	.08	.06	.03
739	Joey McLaughlin	.08	.06	.03
740	Dave Lopes	.12	.09	.05
741	Dave Lopes (In Action)	.10	.08	.04
742	Dick Drago	.08	.06	.03
743	John Stearns	.08	.06	.03
744	*Mike Witt* (FC)	.50	.40	.20
745	Bake McBride	.08	.06	.03
746	Andre Thornton	.12	.09	.05
747	John Lowenstein	.08	.06	.03
748	Marc Hill	.08	.06	.03
749	Bob Shirley	.08	.06	.03
750	Jim Rice	.35	.25	.14
751	Rick Honeycutt	.08	.06	.03
752	Lee Lacy	.08	.06	.03
753	Tom Brookens	.08	.06	.03
754	Joe Morgan	.70	.50	.30
755	Joe Morgan (In Action)	.20	.15	.08
756	Reds Batting & Pitching Ldrs. (Ken Griffey, Tom Seaver)	.30	.25	.12
757	Tom Underwood	.08	.06	.03
758	Claudell Washington	.12	.09	.05
759	Paul Splittorff	.08	.06	.03
760	Bill Buckner	.15	.11	.06
761	Dave Smith	.12	.09	.05
762	Mike Phillips	.08	.06	.03
763	Tom Hume	.08	.06	.03
764	Steve Swisher	.08	.06	.03
765	Gorman Thomas	.12	.09	.05
766	Twins Future Stars (*Lenny Faedo*, Kent Hrbek, Tim Laudner)	2.50	2.00	1.00
767	Roy Smalley	.08	.06	.03
768	Jerry Garvin	.08	.06	.03
769	Richie Zisk	.10	.08	.04
770	Rich Gossage	.15	.11	.06
771	Rich Gossage (In Action)	.08	.06	.03
772	Bert Campaneris	.12	.09	.05
773	John Denny	.08	.06	.03
774	Jay Johnstone	.10	.08	.04
775	Bob Forsch	.10	.08	.04
776	Mark Belanger	.10	.08	.04
777	Tom Griffin	.08	.06	.03
778	Kevin Hickey	.08	.06	.03
779	Grant Jackson	.08	.06	.03
780	Pete Rose	2.25	1.75	.90
781	Pete Rose (In Action)	1.00	.70	.40
782	Frank Taveras	.08	.06	.03
783	*Greg Harris* (FC)	.15	.11	.06
784	Milt Wilcox	.08	.06	.03
785	Dan Driessen	.10	.08	.04
786	Red Sox Batting & Pitching Ldrs. (Carney Lansford, Mike Torrez)	.12	.09	.05
787	Fred Stanley	.08	.06	.03
788	Woodie Fryman	.10	.08	.04
789	Checklist 661-792	.12	.09	.05
790	Larry Gura	.08	.06	.03
791	Bobby Brown	.08	.06	.03
792	Frank Tanana	.12	.09	.05

1982 Topps Traded

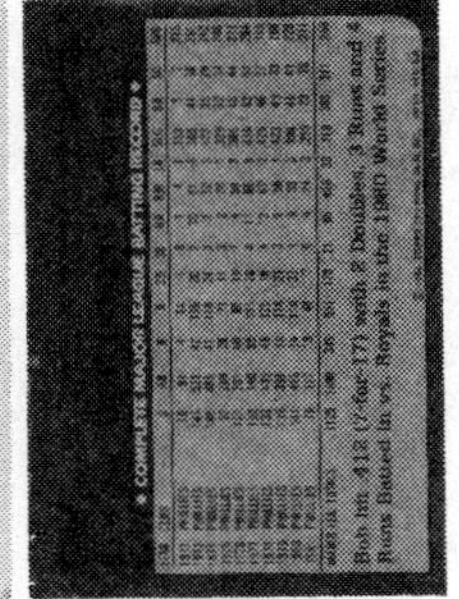

Topps released its second straight 132-card Traded set in September of 1982. Again, the 2-1/2" by 3-1/2" cards feature not only players who had been traded during the season, but also promising rookies who were given their first individual cards. The cards follow the basic design of the regular issues, but have their backs printed in red rather than the regular-issue green. As in 1981, the cards were not available in normal retail outlets and could only be purchased through regular baseball card dealers. Unlike the previous year, the cards are numbered 1-132 with the letter "T" following the number.

		MT	NR MT	EX
Complete Set (132):		275.00	206.00	110.00
Common Player:		.20	.15	.08
1T	Doyle Alexander	.20	.15	.08
2T	Jesse Barfield	.20	.15	.08
3T	Ross Baumgarten	.20	.15	.08
4T	Steve Bedrosian	.20	.15	.08
5T	Mark Belanger	.20	.15	.08
6T	Kurt Bevacqua	.20	.15	.08
7T	Tim Blackwell	.20	.15	.08
8T	Vida Blue	.25	.20	.10
9T	Bob Boone	.30	.25	.12
10T	Larry Bowa	.25	.20	.10
11T	Dan Briggs	.20	.15	.08
12T	Bobby Brown	.20	.15	.08
13T	Tom Brunansky	.50	.40	.20
14T	Jeff Burroughs	.20	.15	.08
15T	Enos Cabell	.20	.15	.08
16T	Bill Campbell	.20	.15	.08
17T	Bobby Castillo	.20	.15	.08
18T	Bill Caudill	.20	.15	.08
19T	Cesar Cedeno	.20	.15	.08
20T	Dave Collins	.20	.15	.08
21T	Doug Corbett	.20	.15	.08
22T	Al Cowens	.20	.15	.08
23T	Chili Davis	2.00	1.50	.80
24T	Dick Davis	.20	.15	.08
25T	Ron Davis	.20	.15	.08
26T	Doug DeCinces	.20	.15	.08
27T	Ivan DeJesus	.20	.15	.08
28T	Bob Dernier	.20	.15	.08
29T	Bo Diaz	.20	.15	.08
30T	Roger Erickson	.20	.15	.08
31T	Jim Essian	.20	.15	.08
32T	Ed Farmer	.20	.15	.08
33T	Doug Flynn	.20	.15	.08
34T	Tim Foli	.20	.15	.08
35T	Dan Ford	.20	.15	.08
36T	George Foster	.40	.30	.15
37T	Dave Frost	.20	.15	.08
38T	Rich Gale	.20	.15	.08
39T	Ron Gardenhire	.20	.15	.08
40T	Ken Griffey	.25	.20	.10
41T	Greg Harris	.20	.15	.08
42T	Von Hayes	.20	.15	.08
43T	Larry Herndon	.20	.15	.08
44T	Kent Hrbek	5.00	3.75	2.00
45T	Mike Ivie	.20	.15	.08
46T	Grant Jackson	.20	.15	.08
47T	Reggie Jackson	15.00	11.00	6.00
48T	Ron Jackson	.20	.15	.08
49T	Fergie Jenkins	2.00	1.50	.80
50T	Lamar Johnson	.20	.15	.08
51T	Randy S. Johnson	.20	.15	.08
52T	Jay Johnstone	.20	.15	.08
53T	Mick Kelleher	.20	.15	.08
54T	Steve Kemp	.20	.15	.08
55T	Junior Kennedy	.20	.15	.08
56T	Jim Kern	.20	.15	.08
57T	Ray Knight	.20	.15	.08
58T	Wayne Krenchicki	.20	.15	.08
59T	Mike Krukow	.20	.15	.08
60T	Duane Kuiper	.20	.15	.08
61T	Mike LaCoss	.20	.15	.08
62T	Chet Lemon	.20	.15	.08
63T	Sixto Lezcano	.20	.15	.08
64T	Dave Lopes	.20	.15	.08
65T	Jerry Martin	.20	.15	.08
66T	Renie Martin	.20	.15	.08
67T	John Mayberry	.20	.15	.08
68T	Lee Mazzilli	.20	.15	.08
69T	Bake McBride	.20	.15	.08
70T	Dan Meyer	.20	.15	.08
71T	Larry Milbourne	.20	.15	.08
72T	Eddie Milner (FC)	.20	.15	.08
73T	Sid Monge	.20	.15	.08
74T	Jose Morales	.20	.15	.08
75T	Keith Moreland	.20	.15	.08
76T	John Montefusco	.20	.15	.08
77T	Jim Morrison	.20	.15	.08
78T	Rance Mulliniks	.20	.15	.08
79T	Steve Mura	.20	.15	.08
80T	Gene Nelson	.20	.15	.08
81T	Joe Nolan	.20	.15	.08
82T	Dickie Noles	.20	.15	.08
83T	Al Oliver	.30	.25	.12
84T	Jorge Orta	.20	.15	.08
85T	Tom Paciorek	.20	.15	.08
86T	Larry Parrish	.20	.15	.08
87T	Jack Perconte	.20	.15	.08
88T	Gaylord Perry	2.00	1.50	.80
89T	Rob Picciolo	.20	.15	.08
90T	Joe Pittman	.20	.15	.08
91T	Hosken Powell	.20	.15	.08
92T	Mike Proly	.20	.15	.08
93T	Greg Pryor	.20	.15	.08
94T	Charlie Puleo (FC)	.20	.15	.08
95T	Shane Rawley	.20	.15	.08
96T	Johnny Ray	.20	.15	.08
97T	Dave Revering	.20	.15	.08
98T	Cal Ripken, Jr.	235.00	176.00	94.00
99T	Allen Ripley	.20	.15	.08
100T	Bill Robinson	.20	.15	.08
101T	Aurelio Rodriguez	.20	.15	.08
102T	Joe Rudi	.20	.15	.08
103T	Steve Sax	1.50	1.25	.60
104T	Dan Schatzeder	.20	.15	.08
105T	Bob Shirley	.20	.15	.08
106T	Eric Show (FC)	.20	.15	.08
107T	Roy Smalley	.20	.15	.08
108T	Lonnie Smith	.20	.15	.08
109T	Ozzie Smith	40.00	30.00	16.00
110T	Reggie Smith	.20	.15	.08
111T	Lary Sorensen	.20	.15	.08
112T	Elias Sosa	.20	.15	.08
113T	Mike Stanton	.20	.15	.08
114T	Steve Stroughter	.20	.15	.08
115T	Champ Summers	.20	.15	.08
116T	Rick Sutcliffe	.50	.40	.20
117T	Frank Tanana	.20	.15	.08
118T	Frank Taveras	.20	.15	.08
119T	Garry Templeton	.20	.15	.08
120T	Alex Trevino	.20	.15	.08
121T	Jerry Turner	.20	.15	.08
122T	Ed Vande Berg (FC)	.20	.15	.08
123T	Tom Veryzer	.20	.15	.08
124T	Ron Washington	.20	.15	.08
125T	Bob Watson	.20	.15	.08
126T	Dennis Werth	.20	.15	.08
127T	Eddie Whitson	.20	.15	.08
128T	Rob Wilfong	.20	.15	.08
129T	Bump Wills	.20	.15	.08
130T	Gary Woods	.20	.15	.08
131T	Butch Wynegar	.20	.15	.08
132T	Checklist 1-132	.20	.15	.08

1982 Topps Insert Stickers

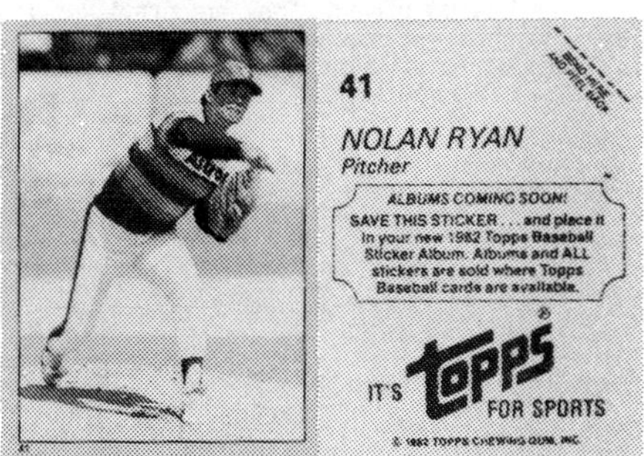

This 48-player set is actually an abbreviated version of the regular 1982 Topps sticker set with different backs. Used to promote the 1982 sticker set, Topps inserted these stickers in its baseball card wax packs. They are identical to the regular 1982 stickers, except for the backs, which advertise that the Topps sticker album will be "Coming Soon." The 48 stickers retain the same numbers used in the regular sticker set, resulting in the smaller set being skip-numbered.

		MT	NR MT	EX
Complete Set:		2.00	1.50	.80
Common Player:		.03	.02	.01
17	Chris Chambliss	.04	.03	.02
21	Bruce Benedict	.03	.02	.01
25	Leon Durham	.06	.05	.02
29	Bill Buckner	.06	.05	.02
33	Dave Collins	.04	.03	.02
37	Dave Concepcion	.06	.05	.02
41	Nolan Ryan	.50	.40	.20
45	Bob Knepper	.04	.03	.02
49	Ken Landreaux	.03	.02	.01
53	Burt Hooton	.03	.02	.01
57	Andre Dawson	.12	.09	.05
61	Gary Carter	.20	.15	.08
65	Joel Youngblood	.03	.02	.01
69	Ellis Valentine	.03	.02	.01
73	Garry Maddox	.04	.03	.02
77	Bob Boone	.04	.03	.02
81	Omar Moreno	.03	.02	.01
85	Willie Stargell	.20	.15	.08
89	Ken Oberkfell	.03	.02	.01
93	Darrell Porter	.04	.03	.02
97	Juan Eichelberger	.03	.02	.01
101	Luis Salazar	.03	.02	.01
105	Enos Cabell	.03	.02	.01
109	Larry Herndon	.03	.02	.01
143	Scott McGregor	.04	.03	.02
148	Mike Flanagan	.06	.05	.02
151	Mike Torrez	.04	.03	.02
156	Carney Lansford	.06	.05	.02
161	Fred Lynn	.10	.08	.04
166	Rich Dotson	.04	.03	.02
171	Tony Bernazard	.03	.02	.01
176	Bo Diaz	.04	.03	.02
181	Alan Trammell	.15	.11	.06
186	Milt Wilcox	.03	.02	.01
191	Dennis Leonard	.04	.03	.02
196	Willie Aikens	.03	.02	.01
201	Ted Simmons	.08	.06	.03
206	Hosken Powell	.03	.02	.01
211	Roger Erickson	.03	.02	.01
215	Graig Nettles	.06	.05	.02
216	Reggie Jackson	.25	.20	.10
221	Rickey Henderson	.25	.20	.10
226	Cliff Johnson	.03	.02	.01
231	Jeff Burroughs	.04	.03	.02
236	Tom Paciorek	.03	.02	.01
241	Pat Putnam	.03	.02	.01
246	Lloyd Moseby	.06	.05	.02
251	Barry Bonnell	.03	.02	.01

1982 Topps Stickers

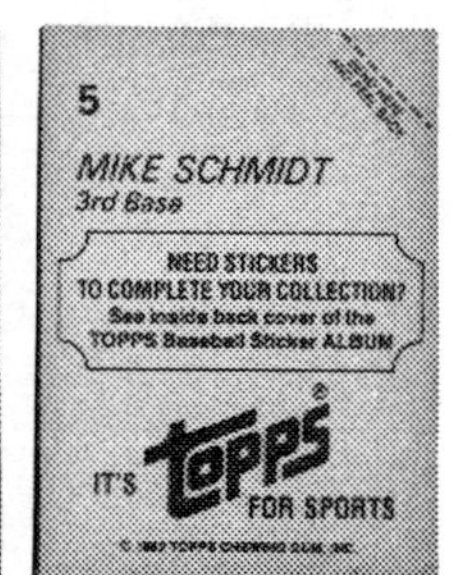

The 1982 Topps sticker set is complete at 260 stickers and includes another series of "foil" All-Stars. The stickers measure 1-15/16" by 2-9/16" and feature full-color photos surrounded by a red border for American League players or a blue border for National League players. They are numbered on both the front and back and were designed to be mounted in a special album.

		MT	NR MT	EX
Complete Set:		15.00	11.00	6.00
Common Player:		.03	.02	.01
Sticker Album:		.80	.60	.30
1	Bill Madlock	.06	.05	.02
2	Carney Lansford	.06	.05	.02
3	Mike Schmidt	.25	.20	.10
4	Tony Armas, Dwight Evans, Bobby Grich, Eddie Murray	.12	.09	.05
5	Mike Schmidt	.25	.20	.10
6	Eddie Murray	.20	.15	.08
7	Tim Raines	.03	.02	.01
8	Rickey Henderson	.25	.20	.10
9	Tom Seaver	.20	.15	.08
10	Denny Martinez, Steve McCatty, Jack Morris, Pete Vuckovich	.06	.05	.02
11	Fernando Valenzuela	.15	.11	.06
12	Len Barker	.03	.02	.01
13	Nolan Ryan	.50	.40	.20
14	Steve McCatty	.03	.02	.01
15	Bruce Sutter	.08	.06	.03
16	Rollie Fingers	.10	.08	.04
17	Chris Chambliss	.04	.03	.02
18	Bob Horner	.08	.06	.03
19	Dale Murphy	.25	.20	.10
20	Phil Niekro	.12	.09	.05
21	Bruce Benedict	.03	.02	.01
22	Claudell Washington	.04	.03	.02
23	Glenn Hubbard	.03	.02	.01
24	Rick Camp	.03	.02	.01
25	Leon Durham	.06	.05	.02
26	Ken Reitz	.03	.02	.01
27	Dick Tidrow	.03	.02	.01
28	Tim Blackwell	.03	.02	.01
29	Bill Buckner	.06	.05	.02
30	Steve Henderson	.03	.02	.01
31	Mike Krukow	.04	.03	.02
32	Ivan DeJesus	.03	.02	.01
33	Dave Collins	.04	.03	.02
34	Ron Oester	.03	.02	.01
35	Johnny Bench	.25	.20	.10
36	Tom Seaver	.20	.15	.08
37	Dave Concepcion	.06	.05	.02
38	Ken Griffey	.06	.05	.02
39	Ray Knight	.06	.05	.02
40	George Foster	.08	.06	.03
41	Nolan Ryan	.50	.40	.20
42	Terry Puhl	.03	.02	.01
43	Art Howe	.03	.02	.01
44	Jose Cruz	.06	.05	.02
45	Bob Knepper	.06	.05	.02
46	Craig Reynolds	.03	.02	.01
47	Cesar Cedeno	.06	.05	.02
48	Alan Ashby	.03	.02	.01
49	Ken Landreaux	.03	.02	.01
50	Fernando Valenzuela	.15	.11	.06
51	Ron Cey	.06	.05	.02
52	Dusty Baker	.04	.03	.02
53	Burt Hooton	.04	.03	.02
54	Steve Garvey	.20	.15	.08
55	Pedro Guerrero	.12	.09	.05
56	Jerry Reuss	.06	.05	.02
57	Andre Dawson	.12	.09	.05
58	Chris Speier	.03	.02	.01
59	Steve Rogers	.03	.02	.01
60	Warren Cromartie	.03	.02	.01
61	Gary Carter	.20	.15	.08
62	Tim Raines	.20	.15	.08
63	Scott Sanderson	.03	.02	.01
64	Larry Parrish	.06	.05	.02
65	Joel Youngblood	.03	.02	.01
66	Neil Allen	.03	.02	.01
67	Lee Mazzilli	.04	.03	.02
68	Hubie Brooks	.06	.05	.02
69	Ellis Valentine	.03	.02	.01
70	Doug Flynn	.03	.02	.01
71	Pat Zachry	.03	.02	.01
72	Dave Kingman	.08	.06	.03
73	Garry Maddox	.04	.03	.02
74	Mike Schmidt	.25	.20	.10
75	Steve Carlton	.20	.15	.08
76	Manny Trillo	.04	.03	.02
77	Bob Boone	.04	.03	.02
78	Pete Rose	.40	.30	.15
79	Gary Matthews	.04	.03	.02
80	Larry Bowa	.06	.05	.02
81	Omar Moreno	.03	.02	.01
82	Rick Rhoden	.04	.03	.02
83	Bill Madlock	.06	.05	.02
84	Mike Easler	.04	.03	.02
85	Willie Stargell	.20	.15	.08
86	Jim Bibby	.03	.02	.01
87	Dave Parker	.12	.09	.05
88	Tim Foli	.03	.02	.01
89	Ken Oberkfell	.03	.02	.01
90	Bob Forsch	.04	.03	.02
91	George Hendrick	.04	.03	.02
92	Keith Hernandez	.12	.09	.05
93	Darrell Porter	.04	.03	.02
94	Bruce Sutter	.08	.06	.03
95	Sixto Lezcano	.03	.02	.01
96	Garry Templeton	.04	.03	.02
97	Juan Eichelberger	.03	.02	.01
98	Broderick Perkins	.03	.02	.01
99	Ruppert Jones	.03	.02	.01
100	Terry Kennedy	.04	.03	.02
101	Luis Salazar	.03	.02	.01
102	Gary Lucas	.03	.02	.01
103	Gene Richards	.03	.02	.01
104	Ozzie Smith	.25	.20	.10
105	Enos Cabell	.03	.02	.01
106	Jack Clark	.10	.08	.04
107	Greg Minton	.03	.02	.01
108	Johnnie LeMaster	.03	.02	.01
109	Larry Herndon	.03	.02	.01
110	Milt May	.03	.02	.01
111	Vida Blue	.06	.05	.02
112	Darrell Evans	.08	.06	.03
113	Len Barker	.03	.02	.01
114	Julio Cruz	.03	.02	.01
115	Billy Martin	.08	.06	.03
116	Tim Raines	.20	.15	.08
117	Pete Rose	.40	.30	.15
118	Bill Stein	.03	.02	.01
119	Fernando Valenzuela	.15	.11	.06
120	Carl Yastrzemski	.25	.20	.10
121	Pete Rose	.40	.30	.15
122	Manny Trillo	.15	.11	.06
123	Mike Schmidt	.40	.30	.15
124	Dave Concepcion	.20	.15	.08
125	Andre Dawson	.25	.20	.10
126	George Foster	.20	.15	.08
127	Dave Parker	.25	.20	.10
128	Gary Carter	.30	.25	.12
129	Steve Carlton	.30	.25	.12
130	Bruce Sutter	.25	.20	.10
131	Rod Carew	.40	.30	.15
132	Jerry Remy	.15	.11	.06
133	George Brett	.40	.30	.15
134	Rick Burleson	.15	.11	.06
135	Dwight Evans	.25	.20	.10
136	Ken Singleton	.20	.15	.08
137	Dave Winfield	.30	.25	.12
138	Carlton Fisk	.25	.20	.10
139	Jack Morris	.25	.20	.10
140	Rich Gossage	.25	.20	.10
141	Al Bumbry	.04	.03	.02
142	Doug DeCinces	.06	.05	.02
143	Scott McGregor	.04	.03	.02
144	Ken Singleton	.06	.05	.02
145	Eddie Murray	.20	.15	.08
146	Jim Palmer	.15	.11	.06
147	Rich Dauer	.03	.02	.01
148	Mike Flanagan	.04	.03	.02
149	Jerry Remy	.03	.02	.01
150	Jim Rice	.20	.15	.08
151	Mike Torrez	.04	.03	.02
152	Tony Perez	.10	.08	.04
153	Dwight Evans	.10	.08	.04
154	Mark Clear	.03	.02	.01
155	Carl Yastrzemski	.25	.20	.10
156	Carney Lansford	.06	.05	.02
157	Rick Burleson	.04	.03	.02
158	Don Baylor	.08	.06	.03
159	Ken Forsch	.03	.02	.01
160	Rod Carew	.20	.15	.08
161	Fred Lynn	.10	.08	.04
162	Bob Grich	.06	.05	.02
163	Dan Ford	.03	.02	.01
164	Butch Hobson	.03	.02	.01
165	Greg Luzinski	.08	.06	.03
166	Rich Dotson	.04	.03	.02
167	Billy Almon	.03	.02	.01
168	Chet Lemon	.04	.03	.02
169	Steve Trout	.03	.02	.01
170	Carlton Fisk	.12	.09	.05
171	Tony Bernazard	.03	.02	.01
172	Ron LeFlore	.04	.03	.02
173	Bert Blyleven	.08	.06	.03
174	Andre Thornton	.06	.05	.02
175	Jorge Orta	.03	.02	.01
176	Bo Diaz	.04	.03	.02
177	Toby Harrah	.04	.03	.02
178	Len Barker	.03	.02	.01
179	Rick Manning	.03	.02	.01
180	Mike Hargrove	.04	.03	.02
181	Alan Trammell	.15	.11	.06
182	Al Cowens	.03	.02	.01
183	Jack Morris	.12	.09	.05
184	Kirk Gibson	.15	.11	.06
185	Steve Kemp	.04	.03	.02
186	Milt Wilcox	.03	.02	.01
187	Lou Whitaker	.12	.09	.05
188	Lance Parrish	.12	.09	.05
189	Willie Wilson	.08	.06	.03
190	George Brett	.25	.20	.10
191	Dennis Leonard	.04	.03	.02
192	John Wathan	.04	.03	.02
193	Frank White	.06	.05	.02
194	Amos Otis	.04	.03	.02
195	Larry Gura	.03	.02	.01
196	Willie Aikens	.03	.02	.01
197	Ben Oglivie	.06	.05	.02
198	Rollie Fingers	.10	.08	.04
199	Cecil Cooper	.08	.06	.03
200	Paul Molitor	.20	.15	.08
201	Ted Simmons	.08	.06	.03
202	Pete Vuckovich	.04	.03	.02
203	Robin Yount	.30	.25	.12
204	Gorman Thomas	.04	.03	.02
205	Rob Wilfong	.03	.02	.01
206	Hosken Powell	.03	.02	.01
207	Roy Smalley	.03	.02	.01
208	Butch Wynegar	.04	.03	.02
209	John Castino	.03	.02	.01
210	Doug Corbett	.03	.02	.01
211	Roger Erickson	.03	.02	.01
212	Mickey Hatcher	.03	.02	.01
213	Dave Winfield	.30	.25	.12
214	Tommy John	.10	.08	.04
215	Graig Nettles	.06	.05	.02
216	Reggie Jackson	.25	.20	.10
217	Rich Gossage	.10	.08	.04
218	Rick Cerone	.03	.02	.01
219	Willie Randolph	.06	.05	.02
220	Jerry Mumphrey	.03	.02	.01
221	Rickey Henderson	.30	.25	.12
222	Mike Norris	.03	.02	.01
223	Jim Spencer	.03	.02	.01
224	Tony Armas	.04	.03	.02
225	Matt Keough	.03	.02	.01
226	Cliff Johnson	.03	.02	.01
227	Dwayne Murphy	.04	.03	.02
228	Steve McCatty	.03	.02	.01
229	Richie Zisk	.04	.03	.02
230	Lenny Randle	.03	.02	.01
231	Jeff Burroughs	.04	.03	.02
232	Bruce Bochte	.03	.02	.01
233	Gary Gray	.03	.02	.01
234	Floyd Bannister	.04	.03	.02
235	Julio Cruz	.03	.02	.01
236	Tom Paciorek	.03	.02	.01
237	Danny Darwin	.03	.02	.01
238	Buddy Bell	.06	.05	.02
239	Al Oliver	.06	.05	.02
240	Jim Sundberg	.04	.03	.02
241	Pat Putnam	.03	.02	.01
242	Steve Comer	.03	.02	.01
243	Mickey Rivers	.04	.03	.02
244	Bump Wills	.03	.02	.01
245	Damaso Garcia	.04	.03	.02
246	Lloyd Moseby	.06	.05	.02
247	Ernie Whitt	.03	.02	.01
248	John Mayberry	.03	.02	.01
249	Otto Velez	.03	.02	.01
250	Dave Stieb	.06	.05	.02
251	Barry Bonnell	.03	.02	.01
252	Alfredo Griffin	.04	.03	.02
253	1981 N.L. Championship (Gary Carter)	.10	.08	.04

254	1981 A.L. Championship (Mike Heath, Larry Milbourne)	.03	.02	.01
255	1981 World Champions (Los Angeles Dodgers Team)	.04	.03	.02
256	1981 World Champions (Los Angeles Dodgers Team)	.04	.03	.02
257	1981 World Series - Game 3 (Fernando Valenzuela)	.10	.08	.04
258	1981 World Series - Game 4 (Steve Garvey)	.10	.08	.04
259	1981 World Series - Game 5 (Jerry Reuss, Steve Yeager)	.03	.02	.01
260	1981 World Series - Game 6 (Pedro Guerrero)	.08	.06	.03

1983 Topps

The 1983 Topps set totals 792 cards. Missing among the regular 2-1/2" by 3-1/2" cards are some form of future stars cards, as Topps was saving them for the now-established late season "Traded" set. The 1983 cards carry a large color photo as well as a smaller color photo on the front, quite similar in design to the 1963 set. Team colors frame the card, which, at the bottom, have the player's name, position and team. At the upper right-hand corner is a Topps Logo. The backs are horizontal and include statistics, personal information and 1982 highlights. Specialty cards include record-breaking performances, league leaders, All-Stars, numbered checklists "Team Leaders" and "Super Veteran" cards which are horizontal with a current and first-season picture of the honored player.

		MT	NR MT	EX
	Complete Set (792):	175.00	125.00	75.00
	Common Player:	.08	.06	.03
1	Tony Armas (Record Breaker)	.12	.09	.05
2	Rickey Henderson (Record Breaker)	.50	.40	.20
3	Greg Minton (Record Breaker)	.08	.06	.03
4	Lance Parrish (Record Breaker)	.08	.06	.03
5	Manny Trillo (Record Breaker)	.08	.06	.03
6	John Wathan (Record Breaker)	.08	.06	.03
7	Gene Richards	.08	.06	.03
8	Steve Balboni	.10	.08	.04
9	Joey McLaughlin	.08	.06	.03
10	Gorman Thomas	.12	.09	.05
11	Billy Gardner	.08	.06	.03
12	Paul Mirabella	.08	.06	.03
13	Larry Herndon	.10	.08	.04
14	Frank LaCorte	.08	.06	.03
15	Ron Cey	.15	.11	.06
16	George Vukovich	.08	.06	.03
17	Kent Tekulve	.10	.08	.04
18	Kent Tekulve (Super Veteran)	.10	.08	.04
19	Oscar Gamble	.10	.08	.04
20	Carlton Fisk	1.00	.70	.40
21	Orioles Batting & Pitching Ldrs. (Eddie Murray, Jim Palmer)	.25	.20	.10
22	Randy Martz	.08	.06	.03
23	Mike Heath	.08	.06	.03
24	Steve Mura	.08	.06	.03
25	Hal McRae	.15	.11	.06
26	Jerry Royster	.08	.06	.03
27	Doug Corbett	.08	.06	.03
28	Bruce Bochte	.08	.06	.03
29	Randy Jones	.10	.08	.04
30	Jim Rice	.35	.25	.14
31	Bill Gullickson	.08	.06	.03
32	Dave Bergman	.08	.06	.03
33	Jack O'Connor	.08	.06	.03
34	Paul Householder	.08	.06	.03
35	Rollie Fingers	.60	.45	.25
36	Rollie Fingers (Super Veteran)	.15	.11	.06
37	Darrell Johnson	.08	.06	.03
38	Tim Flannery	.08	.06	.03
39	Terry Puhl	.08	.06	.03
40	Fernando Valenzuela	.25	.20	.10
41	Jerry Turner	.08	.06	.03
42	Dale Murray	.08	.06	.03
43	Bob Dernier	.08	.06	.03
44	Don Robinson	.10	.08	.04
45	John Mayberry	.10	.08	.04
46	Richard Dotson	.12	.09	.05
47	Dave McKay	.08	.06	.03
48	Lary Sorensen	.08	.06	.03
49	*Willie McGee* (FC)	2.00	1.50	.80
50	Bob Horner	.20	.15	.08
51	Cubs Batting & Pitching Ldrs. (Leon Durham, Fergie Jenkins)	.15	.11	.06
52	*Onix Concepcion* (FC)	.08	.06	.03
53	Mike Witt	.15	.11	.06
54	Jim Maler	.08	.06	.03
55	Mookie Wilson	.12	.09	.05
56	Chuck Rainey	.08	.06	.03
57	Tim Blackwell	.08	.06	.03
58	Al Holland	.08	.06	.03
59	Benny Ayala	.08	.06	.03
60	Johnny Bench	1.50	1.25	.60
61	Johnny Bench (Super Veteran)	.30	.25	.12
62	Bob McClure	.08	.06	.03
63	Rick Monday	.12	.09	.05
64	Bill Stein	.08	.06	.03
65	Jack Morris	.50	.40	.20
66	Bob Lillis	.08	.06	.03
67	Sal Butera	.08	.06	.03
68	*Eric Show*	.15	.11	.06
69	Lee Lacy	.08	.06	.03
70	Steve Carlton	1.25	.90	.50
71	Steve Carlton (Super Veteran)	.30	.25	.12
72	Tom Paciorek	.08	.06	.03
73	Allen Ripley	.08	.06	.03
74	Julio Gonzalez	.08	.06	.03
75	Amos Otis	.10	.08	.04
76	Rick Mahler	.12	.09	.05
77	Hosken Powell	.08	.06	.03
78	Bill Caudill	.08	.06	.03
79	Mick Kelleher	.08	.06	.03
80	George Foster	.12	.09	.05
81	Yankees Batting & Pitching Ldrs. (Jerry Mumphrey, Dave Righetti)	.15	.11	.06
82	Bruce Hurst	.15	.11	.06
83	*Ryne Sandberg* (FC)	45.00	34.00	18.00
84	Milt May	.08	.06	.03
85	Ken Singleton	.12	.09	.05
86	Tom Hume	.08	.06	.03
87	Joe Rudi	.12	.09	.05
88	Jim Gantner	.10	.08	.04
89	Leon Roberts	.08	.06	.03
90	Jerry Reuss	.12	.09	.05
91	Larry Milbourne	.08	.06	.03
92	Mike LaCoss	.08	.06	.03
93	John Castino	.08	.06	.03
94	Dave Edwards	.08	.06	.03
95	Alan Trammell	.50	.40	.20
96	Dick Howser	.08	.06	.03
97	Ross Baumgarten	.08	.06	.03
98	Vance Law	.10	.08	.04
99	Dickie Noles	.08	.06	.03
100	Pete Rose	1.75	1.25	.70
101	Pete Rose (Super Veteran)	.80	.60	.30
102	Dave Beard	.08	.06	.03
103	Darrell Porter	.10	.08	.04
104	Bob Walk	.08	.06	.03
105	Don Baylor	.15	.11	.06
106	Gene Nelson	.08	.06	.03
107	Mike Jorgensen	.08	.06	.03
108	Glenn Hoffman	.08	.06	.03
109	Luis Leal	.08	.06	.03
110	Ken Griffey	.15	.11	.06
111	Expos Batting & Pitching Ldrs. (Al Oliver, Steve Rogers)	.15	.11	.06
112	Bob Shirley	.08	.06	.03
113	Ron Roenicke	.08	.06	.03
114	Jim Slaton	.08	.06	.03
115	Chili Davis	.20	.15	.08
116	Dave Schmidt	.10	.08	.04
117	Alan Knicely	.08	.06	.03
118	Chris Welsh	.08	.06	.03
119	Tom Brookens	.08	.06	.03
120	Len Barker	.10	.08	.04
121	Mickey Hatcher	.10	.08	.04
122	Jimmy Smith	.08	.06	.03
123	George Frazier	.08	.06	.03
124	Marc Hill	.08	.06	.03
125	Leon Durham	.10	.08	.04
126	Joe Torre	.10	.08	.04
127	Preston Hanna	.08	.06	.03
128	Mike Ramsey	.08	.06	.03
129	Checklist 1-132	.12	.09	.05
130	Dave Stieb	.20	.15	.08
131	Ed Ott	.08	.06	.03
132	Todd Cruz	.08	.06	.03
133	Jim Barr	.08	.06	.03
134	Hubie Brooks	.15	.11	.06
135	Dwight Evans	.15	.11	.06
136	Willie Aikens	.08	.06	.03
137	Woodie Fryman	.10	.08	.04
138	Rick Dempsey	.10	.08	.04
139	Bruce Berenyi	.08	.06	.03
140	Willie Randolph	.12	.09	.05
141	Indians Batting & Pitching Ldrs. (Toby Harrah, Rick Sutcliffe)	.12	.09	.05
142	Mike Caldwell	.08	.06	.03
143	Joe Pettini	.08	.06	.03
144	Mark Wagner	.08	.06	.03
145	Don Sutton	.40	.30	.15
146	Don Sutton (Super Veteran)	.20	.15	.08
147	Rick Leach	.08	.06	.03
148	Dave Roberts	.08	.06	.03
149	Johnny Ray	.15	.11	.06
150	Bruce Sutter	.20	.15	.08
151	Bruce Sutter (Super Veteran)	.12	.09	.05
152	Jay Johnstone	.10	.08	.04
153	Jerry Koosman	.12	.09	.05
154	Johnnie LeMaster	.08	.06	.03
155	Dan Quisenberry	.20	.15	.08
156	Billy Martin	.12	.09	.05
157	Steve Bedrosian	.12	.09	.05
158	Rob Wilfong	.08	.06	.03
159	Mike Stanton	.08	.06	.03
160	Dave Kingman	.10	.08	.04
161	Dave Kingman (Super Veteran)	.10	.08	.04
162	Mark Clear	.08	.06	.03
163	Cal Ripken, Jr.	20.00	15.00	8.00
164	Dave Palmer	.08	.06	.03
165	Dan Driessen	.10	.08	.04
166	John Pacella	.08	.06	.03
167	Mark Brouhard	.08	.06	.03
168	Juan Eichelberger	.08	.06	.03
169	Doug Flynn	.08	.06	.03
170	Steve Howe	.10	.08	.04
171	Giants Batting & Pitching Ldrs. (Bill Laskey, Joe Morgan)	.15	.11	.06
172	Vern Ruhle	.08	.06	.03
173	Jim Morrison	.08	.06	.03
174	Jerry Ujdur	.08	.06	.03
175	Bo Diaz	.10	.08	.04
176	Dave Righetti	.15	.11	.06
177	Harold Baines	.25	.20	.10
178	Luis Tiant	.15	.11	.06
179	Luis Tiant (Super Veteran)	.10	.08	.04
180	Rickey Henderson	3.00	2.25	1.25
181	Terry Felton	.08	.06	.03
182	Mike Fischlin	.08	.06	.03
183	*Ed Vande Berg*	.12	.09	.05
184	Bob Clark	.08	.06	.03
185	Tim Lollar	.08	.06	.03
186	Whitey Herzog	.10	.08	.04
187	Terry Leach	.12	.09	.05
188	Rick Miller	.08	.06	.03
189	Dan Schatzeder	.08	.06	.03
190	Cecil Cooper	.10	.08	.04
191	Joe Price	.08	.06	.03
192	Floyd Rayford	.08	.06	.03
193	Harry Spilman	.08	.06	.03
194	Cesar Geronimo	.08	.06	.03
195	Bob Stoddard	.08	.06	.03
196	Bill Fahey	.08	.06	.03
197	*Jim Eisenreich* (FC)	.50	.40	.20
198	Kiko Garcia	.08	.06	.03
199	Marty Bystrom	.08	.06	.03
200	Rod Carew	.70	.50	.30
201	Rod Carew (Super Veteran)	.35	.25	.14
202	Blue Jays Batting & Pitching Ldrs. (Damaso Garcia, Dave Stieb)	.12	.09	.05
203	Mike Morgan	.15	.11	.06
204	Junior Kennedy	.08	.06	.03
205	Dave Parker	.40	.30	.15
206	Ken Oberkfell	.08	.06	.03
207	Rick Camp	.08	.06	.03
208	Dan Meyer	.08	.06	.03
209	*Mike Moore* (FC)	.70	.50	.30
210	Jack Clark	.15	.11	.06
211	John Denny	.08	.06	.03
212	John Stearns	.08	.06	.03
213	Tom Burgmeier	.08	.06	.03
214	Jerry White	.08	.06	.03
215	Mario Soto	.10	.08	.04
216	Tony LaRussa	.10	.08	.04
217	Tim Stoddard	.08	.06	.03
218	Roy Howell	.08	.06	.03
219	Mike Armstrong	.08	.06	.03
220	Dusty Baker	.12	.09	.05
221	Joe Niekro	.15	.11	.06
222	Damaso Garcia	.08	.06	.03
223	John Montefusco	.08	.06	.03
224	Mickey Rivers	.10	.08	.04
225	Enos Cabell	.08	.06	.03
226	Enrique Romo	.08	.06	.03
227	Chris Bando	.08	.06	.03
228	Joaquin Andujar	.10	.08	.04
229	Phillies Batting/Pitching Leaders (Steve Carlton, Bo Diaz)	.20	.15	.08
230	Fergie Jenkins	.60	.45	.25
231	Fergie Jenkins (Super Veteran)	.12	.09	.05
232	Tom Brunansky	.12	.09	.05
233	Wayne Gross	.08	.06	.03
234	Larry Andersen	.08	.06	.03
235	Claudell Washington	.10	.08	.04
236	Steve Renko	.08	.06	.03
237	Dan Norman	.08	.06	.03
238	*Bud Black* (FC)	.70	.50	.30
239	Dave Stapleton	.08	.06	.03
240	Rich Gossage	.20	.15	.08
241	Rich Gossage (Super Veteran)	.15	.11	.06
242	Joe Nolan	.08	.06	.03
243	Duane Walker	.08	.06	.03
244	Dwight Bernard	.08	.06	.03
245	Steve Sax	.15	.11	.06
246	George Bamberger	.08	.06	.03
247	Dave Smith	.12	.09	.05
248	Bake McBride	.08	.06	.03
249	Checklist 133-264	.12	.09	.05
250	Bill Buckner	.15	.11	.06
251	*Alan Wiggins* (FC)	.08	.06	.03
252	Luis Aguayo	.08	.06	.03
253	Larry McWilliams	.08	.06	.03
254	Rick Cerone	.08	.06	.03
255	Gene Garber	.08	.06	.03
256	Gene Garber (Super Veteran)	.08	.06	.03
257	Jesse Barfield	.20	.15	.08
258	Manny Castillo	.08	.06	.03
259	Jeff Jones	.08	.06	.03
260	Steve Kemp	.12	.09	.05
261	Tigers Batting & Pitching Ldrs. (Larry Herndon, Dan Petry)	.10	.08	.04
262	Ron Jackson	.08	.06	.03
263	Renie Martin	.08	.06	.03
264	Jamie Quirk	.08	.06	.03
265	Joel Youngblood	.08	.06	.03
266	Paul Boris	.08	.06	.03
267	Terry Francona	.08	.06	.03
268	*Storm Davis* (FC)	.30	.25	.12
269	Ron Oester	.08	.06	.03
270	Dennis Eckersley	1.50	1.25	.60
271	Ed Romero	.08	.06	.03
272	Frank Tanana	.12	.09	.05
273	Mark Belanger	.10	.08	.04
274	Terry Kennedy	.12	.09	.05
275	Ray Knight	.12	.09	.05
276	Gene Mauch	.10	.08	.04
277	Rance Mulliniks	.08	.06	.03
278	Kevin Hickey	.08	.06	.03
279	Greg Gross	.08	.06	.03
280	Bert Blyleven	.20	.15	.08
281	Andre Robertson	.08	.06	.03
282	Reggie Smith	.12	.09	.05

283 Reggie Smith (Super Veteran) .10 .08 .04
284 Jeff Lahti .08 .06 .03
285 Lance Parrish .12 .09 .05
286 Rick Langford .08 .06 .03
287 Bobby Brown .08 .06 .03
288 *Joe Cowley* (FC) .08 .06 .03
289 Jerry Dybzinski .08 .06 .03
290 Jeff Reardon .60 .45 .25
291 Pirates Batting & Pitching Ldrs. (John Candelaria, Bill Madlock) .15 .11 .06
292 Craig Swan .08 .06 .03
293 Glenn Gulliver .08 .06 .03
294 Dave Engle .08 .06 .03
295 Jerry Remy .08 .06 .03
296 Greg Harris .08 .06 .03
297 Ned Yost .08 .06 .03
298 Floyd Chiffer .08 .06 .03
299 George Wright .08 .06 .03
300 Mike Schmidt 3.00 2.25 1.25
301 Mike Schmidt (Super Veteran) 1.00 .70 .40
302 Ernie Whitt .10 .08 .04
303 Miguel Dilone .08 .06 .03
304 Dave Rucker .08 .06 .03
305 Larry Bowa .15 .11 .06
306 Tom Lasorda .12 .09 .05
307 Lou Piniella .15 .11 .06
308 Jesus Vega .08 .06 .03
309 Jeff Leonard .12 .09 .05
310 Greg Luzinski .15 .11 .06
311 Glenn Brummer .08 .06 .03
312 Brian Kingman .08 .06 .03
313 Gary Gray .08 .06 .03
314 Ken Dayley (FC) .15 .11 .06
315 Rick Burleson .10 .08 .04
316 Paul Splittorff .08 .06 .03
317 Gary Rajsich .08 .06 .03
318 John Tudor .15 .11 .06
319 Lenn Sakata .08 .06 .03
320 Steve Rogers .10 .08 .04
321 Brewers Batting & Pitching Ldrs. (Pete Vuckovich, Robin Yount) .20 .15 .08
322 Dave Van Gorder .08 .06 .03
323 Luis DeLeon .08 .06 .03
324 Mike Marshall .12 .09 .05
325 Von Hayes .20 .15 .08
326 Garth Iorg .08 .06 .03
327 Bobby Castillo .08 .06 .03
328 Craig Reynolds .08 .06 .03
329 Randy Niemann .08 .06 .03
330 Buddy Bell .15 .11 .06
331 Mike Krukow .10 .08 .04
332 *Glenn Wilson* (FC) .12 .09 .05
333 Dave LaRoche .08 .06 .03
334 Dave LaRoche (Super Veteran) .08 .06 .03
335 Steve Henderson .08 .06 .03
336 Rene Lachemann .08 .06 .03
337 Tito Landrum .08 .06 .03
338 Bob Owchinko .08 .06 .03
339 Terry Harper .08 .06 .03
340 Larry Gura .08 .06 .03
341 Doug DeCinces .15 .11 .06
342 Atlee Hammaker .10 .08 .04
343 Bob Bailor .08 .06 .03
344 Roger LaFrancois .08 .06 .03
345 Jim Clancy .10 .08 .04
346 Joe Pittman .08 .06 .03
347 Sammy Stewart .08 .06 .03
348 Alan Bannister .08 .06 .03
349 Checklist 265-396 .12 .09 .05
350 Robin Yount 4.00 3.00 1.50
351 Reds Batting & Pitching Ldrs. (Cesar Cedeno, Mario Soto) .12 .09 .05
352 Mike Scioscia .10 .08 .04
353 Steve Comer .08 .06 .03
354 Randy S. Johnson .08 .06 .03
355 Jim Bibby .08 .06 .03
356 Gary Woods .08 .06 .03
357 *Len Matuszek* (FC) .08 .06 .03
358 Jerry Garvin .08 .06 .03
359 Dave Collins .10 .08 .04
360 Nolan Ryan 14.00 10.50 5.50
361 Nolan Ryan (Super Veteran) 5.00 3.75 2.00
362 Bill Almon .08 .06 .03
363 *John Stuper* (FC) .08 .06 .03
364 Brett Butler .20 .15 .08
365 Dave Lopes .12 .09 .05
366 Dick Williams .08 .06 .03
367 Bud Anderson .08 .06 .03
368 Richie Zisk .10 .08 .04
369 Jesse Orosco .15 .11 .06
370 Gary Carter .25 .20 .10
371 Mike Richardt .08 .06 .03
372 Terry Crowley .08 .06 .03
373 Kevin Saucier .08 .06 .03
374 Wayne Krenchicki .08 .06 .03
375 Pete Vuckovich .10 .08 .04
376 Ken Landreaux .08 .06 .03
377 Lee May .10 .08 .04
378 Lee May (Super Veteran) .10 .08 .04
379 Guy Sularz .08 .06 .03
380 Ron Davis .08 .06 .03
381 Red Sox Batting & Pitching Ldrs. (Jim Rice, Bob Stanley) .15 .11 .06
382 Bob Knepper .12 .09 .05
383 Ozzie Virgil .10 .08 .04
384 *Dave Dravecky* (FC) .50 .40 .20
385 Mike Easler .10 .08 .04
386 Rod Carew (All-Star) .50 .40 .20
387 Bob Grich (All-Star) .10 .08 .04
388 George Brett (All-Star) .75 .60 .30
389 Robin Yount (All-Star) .75 .60 .30
390 Reggie Jackson (All-Star) .75 .60 .30
391 Rickey Henderson (All-Star) .50 .40 .20
392 Fred Lynn (All-Star) .15 .11 .06
393 Carlton Fisk (All-Star) .15 .11 .06
394 Pete Vuckovich (All-Star) .10 .08 .04
395 Larry Gura (All-Star) .08 .06 .03
396 Dan Quisenberry (All-Star) .12 .09 .05
397 Pete Rose (All-Star) .75 .60 .30
398 Manny Trillo (All-Star) .10 .08 .04
399 Mike Schmidt (All-Star) .75 .60 .30
400 Dave Concepcion (All-Star) .12 .09 .05
401 Dale Murphy (All-Star) .40 .30 .15
402 Andre Dawson (All-Star) .30 .25 .12
403 Tim Raines (All-Star) .25 .20 .10
404 Gary Carter (All-Star) .20 .15 .08
405 Steve Rogers (All-Star) .10 .08 .04
406 Steve Carlton (All-Star) .35 .25 .14
407 Bruce Sutter (All-Star) .12 .09 .05
408 Rudy May .08 .06 .03
409 Marvis Foley .08 .06 .03
410 Phil Niekro .40 .30 .15
411 Phil Niekro (Super Veteran) .20 .15 .08
412 Rangers Batting & Pitching Ldrs. (Buddy Bell, Charlie Hough) .12 .09 .05
413 Matt Keough .08 .06 .03
414 Julio Cruz .08 .06 .03
415 Bob Forsch .10 .08 .04
416 Joe Ferguson .08 .06 .03
417 Tom Hausman .08 .06 .03
418 Greg Pryor .08 .06 .03
419 Steve Crawford .08 .06 .03
420 Al Oliver .20 .15 .08
421 Al Oliver (Super Veteran) .12 .09 .05
422 George Cappuzzello .08 .06 .03
423 *Tom Lawless* (FC) .10 .08 .04
424 Jerry Augustine .08 .06 .03
425 Pedro Guerrero .15 .11 .06
426 Earl Weaver .10 .08 .04
427 Roy Lee Jackson .08 .06 .03
428 Champ Summers .08 .06 .03
429 Eddie Whitson .08 .06 .03
430 Kirk Gibson .25 .20 .10
431 *Gary Gaetti* (FC) .70 .50 .30
432 Porfirio Altamirano .08 .06 .03
433 Dale Berra .08 .06 .03
434 Dennis Lamp .08 .06 .03
435 Tony Armas .12 .09 .05
436 Bill Campbell .08 .06 .03
437 Rick Sweet .08 .06 .03
438 *Dave LaPoint* (FC) .10 .08 .04
439 Rafael Ramirez .08 .06 .03
440 Ron Guidry .30 .25 .12
441 Astros Batting & Pitching Ldrs. (Ray Knight, Joe Niekro) .12 .09 .05
442 Brian Downing .12 .09 .05
443 Don Hood .08 .06 .03
444 Wally Backman (FC) .25 .20 .10
445 Mike Flanagan .12 .09 .05
446 Reid Nichols .08 .06 .03
447 Bryn Smith .10 .08 .04
448 Darrell Evans .20 .15 .08
449 *Eddie Milner* .12 .09 .05
450 Ted Simmons .15 .11 .06
451 Ted Simmons (Super Veteran) .08 .06 .03
452 Lloyd Moseby .15 .11 .06
453 Lamar Johnson .08 .06 .03
454 Bob Welch .15 .11 .06
455 Sixto Lezcano .08 .06 .03
456 Lee Elia .08 .06 .03
457 Milt Wilcox .08 .06 .03
458 Ron Washington .08 .06 .03
459 Ed Farmer .08 .06 .03
460 Roy Smalley .08 .06 .03
461 Steve Trout .08 .06 .03
462 Steve Nicosia .08 .06 .03
463 Gaylord Perry .40 .30 .15
464 Gaylord Perry (Super Veteran) .20 .15 .08
465 Lonnie Smith .10 .08 .04
466 Tom Underwood .08 .06 .03
467 Rufino Linares .08 .06 .03
468 Dave Goltz .10 .08 .04
469 Ron Gardenhire .08 .06 .03
470 Greg Minton .08 .06 .03
471 Royals Batting & Pitching Ldrs. (Vida Blue, Willie Wilson) .15 .11 .06
472 Gary Allenson .08 .06 .03
473 John Lowenstein .08 .06 .03
474 Ray Burris .08 .06 .03
475 Cesar Cedeno .12 .09 .05
476 Rob Picciolo .08 .06 .03
477 Tom Niedenfuer (FC) .15 .11 .06
478 Phil Garner .10 .08 .04
479 Charlie Hough .12 .09 .05
480 Toby Harrah .10 .08 .04
481 Scot Thompson .08 .06 .03
482 *Tony Gwynn* (FC) 30.00 22.00 12.00
483 Lynn Jones .08 .06 .03
484 Dick Ruthven .08 .06 .03
485 Omar Moreno .08 .06 .03
486 Clyde King .08 .06 .03
487 Jerry Hairston .08 .06 .03
488 Alfredo Griffin .10 .08 .04
489 Tom Herr .12 .09 .05
490 Jim Palmer 1.00 .70 .40
491 Jim Palmer (Super Veteran) .20 .15 .08
492 Paul Serna .08 .06 .03
493 Steve McCatty .08 .06 .03
494 Bob Brenly .10 .08 .04
495 Warren Cromartie .08 .06 .03
496 Tom Veryzer .08 .06 .03
497 Rick Sutcliffe .20 .15 .08
498 *Wade Boggs* (FC) 35.00 26.00 14.00
499 Jeff Little .10 .08 .04
500 Reggie Jackson 2.50 2.00 1.00
501 Reggie Jackson (Super Veteran) .50 .40 .20
502 Braves Batting & Pitching Ldrs. (Dale Murphy, Phil Niekro) .25 .20 .10
503 Moose Haas .08 .06 .03
504 Don Werner .08 .06 .03
505 Garry Templeton .12 .09 .05
506 *Jim Gott* (FC) .25 .20 .10
507 Tony Scott .08 .06 .03
508 Tom Filer .15 .11 .06
509 Lou Whitaker .40 .30 .15
510 Tug McGraw .15 .11 .06
511 Tug McGraw (Super Veteran) .10 .08 .04
512 Doyle Alexander .12 .09 .05
513 Fred Stanley .08 .06 .03
514 Rudy Law .08 .06 .03
515 Gene Tenace .10 .08 .04
516 Bill Virdon .08 .06 .03
517 Gary Ward .10 .08 .04
518 Bill Laskey .08 .06 .03
519 Terry Bulling .08 .06 .03
520 Fred Lynn .25 .20 .10
521 Bruce Benedict .08 .06 .03
522 Pat Zachry .08 .06 .03
523 Carney Lansford .12 .09 .05
524 Tom Brennan .08 .06 .03
525 Frank White .12 .09 .05
526 Checklist 397-528 .12 .09 .05
527 Larry Biittner .08 .06 .03
528 Jamie Easterly .08 .06 .03
529 Tim Laudner .10 .08 .04
530 Eddie Murray .80 .60 .30
531 Athletics Batting & Pitching Ldrs. (Rickey Henderson, Rick Langford) .30 .25 .12
532 Dave Stewart .75 .60 .30
533 Luis Salazar .08 .06 .03
534 John Butcher .08 .06 .03
535 Manny Trillo .10 .08 .04
536 Johnny Wockenfuss .08 .06 .03
537 Rod Scurry .08 .06 .03
538 Danny Heep .08 .06 .03
539 Roger Erickson .08 .06 .03
540 Ozzie Smith 2.00 1.50 .80
541 Britt Burns .08 .06 .03
542 Jody Davis .12 .09 .05
543 Alan Fowlkes .08 .06 .03
544 Larry Whisenton .08 .06 .03
545 Floyd Bannister .12 .09 .05
546 Dave Garcia .08 .06 .03
547 Geoff Zahn .08 .06 .03
548 Brian Giles .08 .06 .03
549 *Charlie Puleo* .15 .11 .06
550 Carl Yastrzemski 1.00 .70 .40
551 Carl Yastrzemski (Super Veteran) .40 .30 .15
552 Tim Wallach .30 .25 .12
553 Denny Martinez .10 .08 .04
554 Mike Vail .08 .06 .03
555 Steve Yeager .08 .06 .03
556 Willie Upshaw .10 .08 .04
557 Rick Honeycutt .08 .06 .03
558 Dickie Thon .10 .08 .04
559 Pete Redfern .08 .06 .03
560 Ron LeFlore .10 .08 .04
561 Cardinals Batting & Pitching Ldrs. (Joaquin Andujar, Lonnie Smith) .12 .09 .05
562 Dave Rozema .08 .06 .03
563 Juan Bonilla .08 .06 .03
564 Sid Monge .08 .06 .03
565 Bucky Dent .12 .09 .05
566 Manny Sarmiento .08 .06 .03
567 Joe Simpson .08 .06 .03
568 Willie Hernandez .12 .09 .05
569 Jack Perconte .08 .06 .03
570 Vida Blue .15 .11 .06
571 Mickey Klutts .08 .06 .03
572 Bob Watson .10 .08 .04
573 Andy Hassler .08 .06 .03
574 Glenn Adams .08 .06 .03
575 Neil Allen .08 .06 .03
576 Frank Robinson .12 .09 .05
577 Luis Aponte .08 .06 .03
578 David Green .08 .06 .03
579 Rich Dauer .08 .06 .03
580 Tom Seaver 2.00 1.50 .80
581 Tom Seaver (Super Veteran) .50 .40 .20
582 Marshall Edwards .08 .06 .03
583 Terry Forster .10 .08 .04
584 Dave Hostetler .08 .06 .03
585 Jose Cruz .15 .11 .06
586 *Frank Viola* (FC) 3.00 2.25 1.25
587 Ivan DeJesus .08 .06 .03
588 Pat Underwood .08 .06 .03
589 Alvis Woods .08 .06 .03
590 Tony Pena .12 .09 .05
591 White Sox Batting & Pitching Ldrs. (LaMarr Hoyt, Greg Luzinski) .15 .11 .06
592 Shane Rawley .12 .09 .05
593 Broderick Perkins .08 .06 .03
594 Eric Rasmussen .08 .06 .03
595 Tim Raines .60 .45 .25
596 Randy S. Johnson .08 .06 .03
597 Mike Proly .08 .06 .03
598 Dwayne Murphy .10 .08 .04
599 Don Aase .08 .06 .03
600 George Brett 4.00 3.00 1.50
601 Ed Lynch .08 .06 .03
602 Rich Gedman .12 .09 .05
603 Joe Morgan .60 .45 .25
604 Joe Morgan (Super Veteran) .15 .11 .06
605 Gary Roenicke .08 .06 .03
606 Bobby Cox .08 .06 .03
607 Charlie Leibrandt .10 .08 .04
608 Don Money .08 .06 .03
609 Danny Darwin .08 .06 .03
610 Steve Garvey .50 .40 .20
611 Bert Roberge .08 .06 .03
612 Steve Swisher .08 .06 .03
613 Mike Ivie .08 .06 .03
614 Ed Glynn .08 .06 .03
615 Garry Maddox .12 .09 .05
616 Bill Nahorodny .08 .06 .03
617 Butch Wynegar .08 .06 .03
618 LaMarr Hoyt .08 .06 .03
619 Keith Moreland .10 .08 .04
620 Mike Norris .08 .06 .03
621 Mets Batting & Pitching Ldrs. (Craig Swan, Mookie Wilson) .12 .09 .05
622 Dave Edler .08 .06 .03
623 Luis Sanchez .08 .06 .03
624 Glenn Hubbard .10 .08 .04
625 Ken Forsch .08 .06 .03
626 Jerry Martin .08 .06 .03
627 Doug Bair .08 .06 .03

628	Julio Valdez	.08	.06	.03
629	Charlie Lea	.08	.06	.03
630	Paul Molitor	3.00	2.25	1.25
631	Tippy Martinez	.08	.06	.03
632	Alex Trevino	.08	.06	.03
633	Vicente Romo	.08	.06	.03
634	Max Venable	.08	.06	.03
635	Graig Nettles	.20	.15	.08
636	Graig Nettles (Super Veteran)	.12	.09	.05
637	Pat Corrales	.08	.06	.03
638	Dan Petry	.10	.08	.04
639	Art Howe	.08	.06	.03
640	Andre Thornton	.12	.09	.05
641	Billy Sample	.08	.06	.03
642	Checklist 529-660	.12	.09	.05
643	Bump Wills	.08	.06	.03
644	Joe Lefebvre	.08	.06	.03
645	Bill Madlock	.15	.11	.06
646	Jim Essian	.08	.06	.03
647	Bobby Mitchell	.08	.06	.03
648	Jeff Burroughs	.10	.08	.04
649	Tommy Boggs	.08	.06	.03
650	George Hendrick	.10	.08	.04
651	Angels Batting & Pitching Ldrs. (Rod Carew, Mike Witt)	.30	.25	.12
652	Butch Hobson	.08	.06	.03
653	Ellis Valentine	.08	.06	.03
654	Bob Ojeda	.15	.11	.06
655	Al Bumbry	.10	.08	.04
656	Dave Frost	.08	.06	.03
657	Mike Gates	.08	.06	.03
658	Frank Pastore	.08	.06	.03
659	Charlie Moore	.08	.06	.03
660	Mike Hargrove	.08	.06	.03
661	Bill Russell	.10	.08	.04
662	Joe Sambito	.08	.06	.03
663	Tom O'Malley	.08	.06	.03
664	Bob Molinaro	.08	.06	.03
665	Jim Sundberg	.10	.08	.04
666	Sparky Anderson	.12	.09	.05
667	Dick Davis	.08	.06	.03
668	Larry Christenson	.08	.06	.03
669	Mike Squires	.08	.06	.03
670	Jerry Mumphrey	.08	.06	.03
671	Lenny Faedo	.08	.06	.03
672	Jim Kaat	.20	.15	.08
673	Jim Kaat (Super Veteran)	.12	.09	.05
674	Kurt Bevacqua	.08	.06	.03
675	Jim Beattie	.08	.06	.03
676	Biff Pocoroba	.08	.06	.03
677	Dave Revering	.08	.06	.03
678	Juan Beniquez	.08	.06	.03
679	Mike Scott	.20	.15	.08
680	Andre Dawson	1.75	1.25	.70
681	Dodgers Batting & Pitching Ldrs. (Pedro Guerrero, Fernando Valenzuela)	.25	.20	.10
682	Bob Stanley	.08	.06	.03
683	Dan Ford	.08	.06	.03
684	Rafael Landestoy	.08	.06	.03
685	Lee Mazzilli	.10	.08	.04
686	Randy Lerch	.08	.06	.03
687	U.L. Washington	.08	.06	.03
688	Jim Wohlford	.08	.06	.03
689	Ron Hassey	.08	.06	.03
690	Kent Hrbek	.70	.50	.30
691	Dave Tobik	.08	.06	.03
692	Denny Walling	.08	.06	.03
693	Sparky Lyle	.12	.09	.05
694	Sparky Lyle (Super Veteran)	.10	.08	.04
695	Ruppert Jones	.08	.06	.03
696	Chuck Tanner	.08	.06	.03
697	Barry Foote	.08	.06	.03
698	Tony Bernazard	.08	.06	.03
699	Lee Smith	2.50	2.00	1.00
700	Keith Hernandez	.50	.40	.20
701	Batting Leaders (Al Oliver, Willie Wilson)	.15	.11	.06
702	Home Run Leaders (Reggie Jackson, Dave Kingman, Gorman Thomas)	.25	.20	.10
703	Runs Batted In Leaders (Hal McRae, Dale Murphy, Al Oliver)	.35	.25	.14
704	Stolen Base Leaders (Rickey Henderson, Tim Raines)	.35	.25	.14
705	Victory Leaders (Steve Carlton, LaMarr Hoyt)	.20	.15	.08
706	Strikeout Leaders (Floyd Bannister, Steve Carlton)	.20	.15	.08
707	Earned Run Average Leaders (Steve Rogers, Rick Sutcliffe)	.12	.09	.05
708	Leading Firemen (Dan Quisenberry, Bruce Sutter)	.15	.11	.06
709	Jimmy Sexton	.08	.06	.03
710	Willie Wilson	.20	.15	.08
711	Mariners Batting & Pitching Ldrs. (Jim Beattie, Bruce Bochte)	.12	.09	.05
712	Bruce Kison	.08	.06	.03
713	Ron Hodges	.08	.06	.03
714	Wayne Nordhagen	.08	.06	.03
715	Tony Perez	.25	.20	.10
716	Tony Perez (Super Veteran)	.12	.09	.05
717	Scott Sanderson	.08	.06	.03
718	Jim Dwyer	.08	.06	.03
719	Rich Gale	.08	.06	.03
720	Dave Concepcion	.15	.11	.06
721	John Martin	.08	.06	.03
722	Jorge Orta	.08	.06	.03
723	Randy Moffitt	.08	.06	.03
724	Johnny Grubb	.08	.06	.03
725	Dan Spillner	.08	.06	.03
726	Harvey Kuenn	.10	.08	.04
727	Chet Lemon	.10	.08	.04
728	Ron Reed	.08	.06	.03
729	Jerry Morales	.08	.06	.03
730	Jason Thompson	.08	.06	.03
731	Al Williams	.08	.06	.03
732	Dave Henderson	.15	.11	.06
733	Buck Martinez	.08	.06	.03
734	Steve Braun	.08	.06	.03
735	Tommy John	.25	.20	.10
736	Tommy John (Super Veteran)	.12	.09	.05
737	Mitchell Page	.08	.06	.03
738	Tim Foli	.08	.06	.03
739	Rick Ownbey	.08	.06	.03
740	Rusty Staub	.15	.11	.06
741	Rusty Staub (Super Veteran)	.10	.08	.04
742	Padres Batting & Pitching Ldrs. (Terry Kennedy, Tim Lollar)	.12	.09	.05
743	Mike Torrez	.10	.08	.04
744	Brad Mills	.08	.06	.03
745	Scott McGregor	.10	.08	.04
746	John Wathan	.10	.08	.04
747	Fred Breining	.08	.06	.03
748	Derrel Thomas	.08	.06	.03
749	Jon Matlack	.10	.08	.04
750	Ben Oglivie	.10	.08	.04
751	Brad Havens	.08	.06	.03
752	Luis Pujols	.08	.06	.03
753	Elias Sosa	.08	.06	.03
754	Bill Robinson	.08	.06	.03
755	John Candelaria	.12	.09	.05
756	Russ Nixon	.08	.06	.03
757	Rick Manning	.08	.06	.03
758	Aurelio Rodriguez	.10	.08	.04
759	Doug Bird	.08	.06	.03
760	Dale Murphy	.75	.60	.30
761	Gary Lucas	.08	.06	.03
762	Cliff Johnson	.08	.06	.03
763	Al Cowens	.08	.06	.03
764	Pete Falcone	.08	.06	.03
765	Bob Boone	.12	.09	.05
766	Barry Bonnell	.08	.06	.03
767	Duane Kuiper	.08	.06	.03
768	Chris Speier	.08	.06	.03
769	Checklist 661-792	.12	.09	.05
770	Dave Winfield	3.00	2.25	1.25
771	Twins Batting & Pitching Ldrs. (Bobby Castillo, Kent Hrbek)	.20	.15	.08
772	Jim Kern	.08	.06	.03
773	Larry Hisle	.10	.08	.04
774	Alan Ashby	.08	.06	.03
775	Burt Hooton	.10	.08	.04
776	Larry Parrish	.12	.09	.05
777	John Curtis	.08	.06	.03
778	Rich Hebner	.08	.06	.03
779	Rick Waits	.08	.06	.03
780	Gary Matthews	.12	.09	.05
781	Rick Rhoden	.12	.09	.05
782	Bobby Murcer	.12	.09	.05
783	Bobby Murcer (Super Veteran)	.10	.08	.04
784	Jeff Newman	.08	.06	.03
785	Dennis Leonard	.10	.08	.04
786	Ralph Houk	.10	.08	.04
787	Dick Tidrow	.08	.06	.03
788	Dane Iorg	.08	.06	.03
789	Bryan Clark	.08	.06	.03
790	Bob Grich	.12	.09	.05
791	Gary Lavelle	.08	.06	.03
792	Chris Chambliss	.10	.08	.04

1983 Topps All-Star Glossy Set of 40

This set was a "consolation prize" in a scratch-off contest in regular packs of 1983 cards. The 2-1/2" by 3-1/2" cards have a large color photo surrounded by a yellow frame on the front. In very small type on a white border is printed the player's name. Backs carry the player's name, team, position and the card number along with a Topps identification. A major feature is that the surface of the front is glossy, which most collectors find very attractive. With many top stars, the set is a popular one, but the price has not moved too far above the issue price.

		MT	NR MT	EX
Complete Set:		13.00	9.75	5.25
Common Player:		.15	.11	.06
1	Carl Yastrzemski	.75	.60	.30
2	Mookie Wilson	.15	.11	.06
3	Andre Thornton	.15	.11	.06
4	Keith Hernandez	.20	.15	.08
5	Robin Yount	.50	.40	.20
6	Terry Kennedy	.15	.11	.06
7	Dave Winfield	.60	.45	.25
8	Mike Schmidt	.80	.60	.30
9	Buddy Bell	.20	.15	.08
10	Fernando Valenzuela	.25	.20	.10
11	Rich Gossage	.25	.20	.10
12	Bob Horner	.20	.15	.08
13	Toby Harrah	.15	.11	.06
14	Pete Rose	.90	.70	.35
15	Cecil Cooper	.20	.15	.08
16	Dale Murphy	.60	.45	.25
17	Carlton Fisk	.30	.25	.12
18	Ray Knight	.15	.11	.06
19	Jim Palmer	.40	.30	.15
20	Gary Carter	.30	.25	.12
21	Richard Zisk	.15	.11	.06
22	Dusty Baker	.15	.11	.06
23	Willie Wilson	.20	.15	.08
24	Bill Buckner	.15	.11	.06
25	Dave Stieb	.20	.15	.08
26	Bill Madlock	.20	.15	.08
27	Lance Parrish	.30	.25	.12
28	Nolan Ryan	1.00	.70	.40
29	Rod Carew	.60	.45	.25
30	Al Oliver	.20	.15	.08
31	George Brett	.80	.60	.30
32	Jack Clark	.25	.20	.10
33	Rickey Henderson	.70	.50	.30
34	Dave Concepcion	.20	.15	.08
35	Kent Hrbek	.30	.25	.12
36	Steve Carlton	.50	.40	.20
37	Eddie Murray	.60	.45	.25
38	Ruppert Jones	.15	.11	.06
39	Reggie Jackson	.70	.50	.30
40	Bruce Sutter	.20	.15	.08

1983 Topps Traded

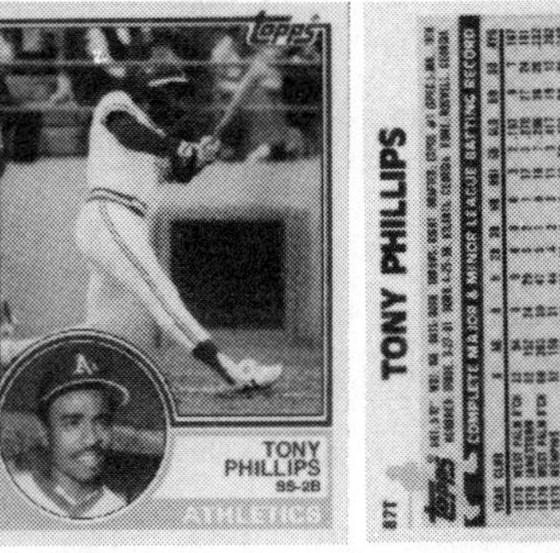

These 2-1/2" by 3-1/2" cards mark a continuation of the traded set introduced in 1981. The 132 cards retain the basic design of the year's regular issue, with their numbering being 1-132 with the "T" suffix. Cards in the set include traded players, new managers and promising rookies. Sold only through dealers, the set was in heavy demand as it contained the first cards of Darryl Strawberry, Ron Kittle, Julio Franco and Mel Hall. While some of those cards were very hot in 1983, it seems likely that some of the rookies may not live up to their initial promise.

		MT	NR MT	EX
Complete Set (132):		60.00	45.00	24.00
Common Player:		.10	.08	.04
1T	Neil Allen	.10	.08	.04
2T	Bill Almon	.10	.08	.04
3T	Joe Altobelli	.10	.08	.04
4T	Tony Armas	.10	.08	.04
5T	Doug Bair	.10	.08	.04
6T	Steve Baker	.10	.08	.04
7T	Floyd Bannister	.10	.08	.04
8T	Don Baylor	.30	.25	.12
9T	Tony Bernazard	.10	.08	.04
10T	Larry Biittner	.10	.08	.04
11T	Dann Bilardello	.10	.08	.04
12T	Doug Bird	.10	.08	.04
13T	Steve Boros	.10	.08	.04
14T	Greg Brock (FC)	.10	.08	.04
15T	Mike Brown	.10	.08	.04
16T	Tom Burgmeier	.10	.08	.04
17T	Randy Bush (FC)	.10	.08	.04
18T	Bert Campaneris	.20	.15	.08
19T	Ron Cey	.25	.20	.10
20T	Chris Codiroli (FC)	.10	.08	.04
21T	Dave Collins	.10	.08	.04
22T	Terry Crowley	.10	.08	.04
23T	Julio Cruz	.10	.08	.04
24T	Mike Davis	.10	.08	.04
25T	Frank DiPino	.10	.08	.04
26T	Bill Doran (FC)	.50	.40	.20
27T	Jerry Dybzinski	.10	.08	.04
28T	Jamie Easterly	.10	.08	.04
29T	Juan Eichelberger	.10	.08	.04
30T	Jim Essian	.10	.08	.04
31T	Pete Falcone	.10	.08	.04
32T	Mike Ferraro	.10	.08	.04
33T	Terry Forster	.10	.08	.04
34T	Julio Franco (FC)	5.00	3.75	2.00
35T	Rich Gale	.10	.08	.04
36T	Kiko Garcia	.10	.08	.04
37T	Steve Garvey	1.50	1.25	.60
38T	Johnny Grubb	.10	.08	.04
39T	Mel Hall (FC)	.25	.20	.10
40T	Von Hayes	.25	.20	.10
41T	Danny Heep	.10	.08	.04
42T	Steve Henderson	.10	.08	.04
43T	Keith Hernandez	.30	.25	.12
44T	Leo Hernandez	.10	.08	.04
45T	Willie Hernandez	.10	.08	.04
46T	Al Holland	.10	.08	.04
47T	Frank Howard	.15	.11	.06
48T	Bobby Johnson	.10	.08	.04

49T	Cliff Johnson	.10	.08	.04
50T	Odell Jones	.10	.08	.04
51T	Mike Jorgensen	.10	.08	.04
52T	Bob Kearney	.10	.08	.04
53T	Steve Kemp	.10	.08	.04
54T	Matt Keough	.10	.08	.04
55T	Ron Kittle (FC)	.10	.08	.04
56T	Mickey Klutts	.10	.08	.04
57T	Alan Knicely	.10	.08	.04
58T	Mike Krukow	.10	.08	.04
59T	Rafael Landestoy	.10	.08	.04
60T	Carney Lansford	.10	.08	.04
61T	Joe Lefebvre	.10	.08	.04
62T	Bryan Little	.10	.08	.04
63T	Aurelio Lopez	.10	.08	.04
64T	Mike Madden	.10	.08	.04
65T	Rick Manning	.10	.08	.04
66T	Billy Martin	.20	.15	.08
67T	Lee Mazzilli	.10	.08	.04
68T	Andy McGaffigan	.10	.08	.04
69T	Craig McMurtry (FC)	.10	.08	.04
70T	John McNamara	.10	.08	.04
71T	Orlando Mercado	.10	.08	.04
72T	Larry Milbourne	.10	.08	.04
73T	Randy Moffitt	.10	.08	.04
74T	Sid Monge	.10	.08	.04
75T	Jose Morales	.10	.08	.04
76T	Omar Moreno	.10	.08	.04
77T	Joe Morgan	3.00	2.25	1.25
78T	Mike Morgan	.10	.08	.04
79T	Dale Murray	.10	.08	.04
80T	Jeff Newman	.10	.08	.04
81T	Pete O'Brien (FC)	.50	.40	.20
82T	Jorge Orta	.10	.08	.04
83T	Alejandro Pena (FC)	.50	.40	.20
84T	Pascual Perez	.20	.15	.08
85T	Tony Perez	1.50	1.25	.60
86T	Broderick Perkins	.10	.08	.04
87T	Tony Phillips (FC)	7.00	5.25	2.75
88T	Charlie Puleo	.10	.08	.04
89T	Pat Putnam	.10	.08	.04
90T	Jamie Quirk	.10	.08	.04
91T	Doug Rader	.10	.08	.04
92T	Chuck Rainey	.10	.08	.04
93T	Bobby Ramos	.10	.08	.04
94T	Gary Redus (FC)	.30	.25	.12
95T	Steve Renko	.10	.08	.04
96T	Leon Roberts	.10	.08	.04
97T	Aurelio Rodriguez	.10	.08	.04
98T	Dick Ruthven	.10	.08	.04
99T	Daryl Sconiers	.10	.08	.04
100T	Mike Scott	.25	.20	.10
101T	Tom Seaver	8.50	6.50	3.50
102T	John Shelby (FC)	.10	.08	.04
103T	Bob Shirley	.10	.08	.04
104T	Joe Simpson	.10	.08	.04
105T	Doug Sisk (FC)	.10	.08	.04
106T	Mike Smithson (FC)	.10	.08	.04
107T	Elias Sosa	.10	.08	.04
108T	Darryl Strawberry	24.00	18.00	9.50
109T	Tom Tellmann	.10	.08	.04
110T	Gene Tenace	.10	.08	.04
111T	Gorman Thomas	.10	.08	.04
112T	Dick Tidrow	.10	.08	.04
113T	Dave Tobik	.10	.08	.04
114T	Wayne Tolleson (FC)	.10	.08	.04
115T	Mike Torrez	.10	.08	.04
116T	Manny Trillo	.10	.08	.04
117T	Steve Trout	.10	.08	.04
118T	Lee Tunnell (FC)	.10	.08	.04
119T	Mike Vail	.10	.08	.04
120T	Ellis Valentine	.10	.08	.04
121T	Tom Veryzer	.10	.08	.04
122T	George Vukovich	.10	.08	.04
123T	Rick Waits	.10	.08	.04
124T	Greg Walker (FC)	.10	.08	.04
125T	Chris Welsh	.10	.08	.04
126T	Len Whitehouse	.10	.08	.04
127T	Eddie Whitson	.10	.08	.04
128T	Jim Wohlford	.10	.08	.04
129T	Matt Young (FC)	.10	.08	.04
130T	Joel Youngblood	.10	.08	.04
131T	Pat Zachry	.10	.08	.04
132T	Checklist 1-132	.10	.08	.04

1983 Topps Foldouts

Another Topps test issue, these 3-1/2" by 5-5/16" cards were printed in booklets like souvenier postcards. Each of the booklets have a theme of currently playing statistical leaders in a specific category such as home runs. The cards feature a color player photo on each side. A black strip at the bottom gives the player's name, position and team along with statistics in the particular category. A facsimile autograph crosses the photograph. Booklets carry nine cards, with eight having players on both sides and one doubling as the back cover, for a total of 17 cards per booklet. There are 85 cards in the set, although some players appear in more than one category. Naturally, most of the players pictured are stars. Even so, the set is a problem as it seems to be most valuable when complete and unseparated, so the cards are difficult to display.

	MT	NR MT	EX
Complete Set:	10.00	7.50	4.00
Common Folder:	1.25	.90	.50

		MT	NR MT	EX
1	Pitching Leaders (Vida Blue, Bert Blyleven, Steve Carlton, Fergie Jenkins, Tommy John, Jim Kaat, Jerry Koosman, Joe Niekro, Phil Niekro, Jim Palmer, Gaylord Perry, Jerry Reuss, Nolan Ryan, Tom Seaver, Paul Splittorff, Don Sutton, Mike Torrez)	1.75	1.25	.70
2	Home Run Leaders (Johnny Bench, Ron Cey, Darrell Evans, George Foster, Reggie Jackson, Dave Kingman, Greg Luzinski, John Mayberry, Rick Monday, Joe Morgan, Bobby Murcer, Graig Nettles, Tony Perez, Jim Rice, Mike Schmidt, Rusty Staub, Carl Yastrzemski)	2.50	2.00	1.00
3	Batting Leaders (George Brett, Rod Carew, Cecil Cooper, Steve Garvey, Ken Griffey, Pedro Guerrero, Keith Hernandez, Dane Iorg, Fred Lynn, Bill Madlock, Bake McBride, Al Oliver, Dave Parker, Jim Rice, Pete Rose, Lonnie Smith, Willie Wilson)	2.50	2.00	1.00
4	Relief Aces (Tom Burgmeier, Bill Campbell, Ed Farmer, Rollie Fingers, Terry Forster, Gene Garber, Rich Gossage, Jim Kern, Gary Lavelle, Tug McGraw, Greg Minton, Randy Moffitt, Dan Quisenberry, Ron Reed, Elias Sosa, Bruce Sutter, Kent Tekulve)	1.25	.90	.50
5	Stolen Base Leaders (Don Baylor, Larry Bowa, Al Bumbry, Rod Carew, Cesar Cedeno, Dave Concepcion, Jose Cruz, Julio Cruz, Rickey Henderson, Ron LeFlore, Davey Lopes, Garry Maddox, Omar Moreno, Joe Morgan, Amos Otis, Mickey Rivers, Willie Wilson)	1.25	.90	.50

1983 Topps Stickers

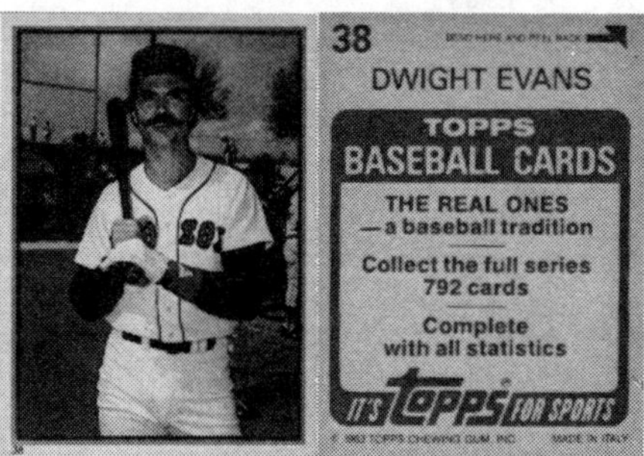

Topps increased the number of stickers in its set to 220 in 1983, but retained the same 1-15/16" by 2-9/16" size. The stickers are again numbered on both the front and back. Similar in style to previous sticker issues, the set includes 28 "foil" stickers, and various special stickers highlighting the 1982 season, playoffs and World Series. An album was also available.

	MT	NR MT	EX
Complete Set (330):	15.00	11.00	6.00
Common Player:	.03	.02	.01
Sticker Album:	.80	.60	.30

		MT	NR MT	EX
1	Hank Aaron	.40	.30	.15
2	Babe Ruth	.60	.45	.25
3	Willie Mays	.40	.30	.15
4	Frank Robinson	.30	.25	.12
5	Reggie Jackson	.20	.15	.08
6	Carl Yastrzemski	.25	.20	.10
7	Johnny Bench	.20	.15	.08
8	Tony Perez	.10	.08	.04
9	Lee May	.06	.05	.02
10	Mike Schmidt	.25	.20	.10
11	Dave Kingman	.08	.06	.03
12	Reggie Smith	.06	.05	.02
13	Graig Nettles	.06	.05	.02
14	Rusty Staub	.06	.05	.02
15	Willie Wilson	.06	.05	.02
16	LaMarr Hoyt	.03	.02	.01
17	Reggie Jackson, Gorman Thomas	.15	.11	.06
18	Floyd Bannister	.04	.03	.02
19	Hal McRae	.06	.05	.02
20	Rick Sutcliffe	.08	.06	.03
21	Rickey Henderson	.25	.20	.10
22	Dan Quisenberry	.06	.05	.02
23	Jim Palmer	.30	.25	.12
24	John Lowenstein	.03	.02	.01
25	Mike Flanagan	.04	.03	.02
26	Cal Ripken, Jr.	.20	.15	.08
27	Rich Dauer	.03	.02	.01
28	Ken Singleton	.06	.05	.02
29	Eddie Murray	.20	.15	.08
30	Rick Dempsey	.04	.03	.02
31	Carl Yastrzemski	.40	.30	.15
32	Carney Lansford	.06	.05	.02
33	Jerry Remy	.03	.02	.01
34	Dennis Eckersley	.06	.05	.02
35	Dave Stapleton	.03	.02	.01
36	Mark Clear	.03	.02	.01
37	Jim Rice	.10	.08	.04
38	Dwight Evans	.08	.06	.03
39	Rod Carew	.20	.15	.08
40	Don Baylor	.08	.06	.03
41	Reggie Jackson	.40	.30	.15
42	Geoff Zahn	.03	.02	.01
43	Bobby Grich	.06	.05	.02
44	Fred Lynn	.10	.08	.04
45	Bob Boone	.04	.03	.02
46	Doug DeCinces	.06	.05	.02
47	Tom Paciorek	.03	.02	.01
48	Britt Burns	.03	.02	.01
49	Tony Bernazard	.03	.02	.01
50	Steve Kemp	.04	.03	.02
51	Greg Luzinski	.20	.15	.08
52	Harold Baines	.10	.08	.04
53	LaMarr Hoyt	.03	.02	.01
54	Carlton Fisk	.12	.09	.05
55	Andre Thornton	.15	.11	.06
56	Mike Hargrove	.04	.03	.02
57	Len Barker	.03	.02	.01
58	Toby Harrah	.04	.03	.02
59	Dan Spillner	.03	.02	.01
60	Rick Manning	.03	.02	.01
61	Rick Sutcliffe	.08	.06	.03
62	Ron Hassey	.03	.02	.01
63	Lance Parrish	.30	.25	.12
64	John Wockenfuss	.03	.02	.01
65	Lou Whitaker	.12	.09	.05
66	Alan Trammell	.15	.11	.06
67	Kirk Gibson	.15	.11	.06
68	Larry Herndon	.03	.02	.01
69	Jack Morris	.12	.09	.05
70	Dan Petry	.04	.03	.02
71	Frank White	.06	.05	.02
72	Amos Otis	.04	.03	.02
73	Willie Wilson	.25	.20	.10
74	Dan Quisenberry	.06	.05	.02
75	Hal McRae	.06	.05	.02
76	George Brett	.25	.20	.10
77	Larry Gura	.03	.02	.01
78	John Wathan	.04	.03	.02
79	Rollie Fingers	.10	.08	.04
80	Cecil Cooper	.08	.06	.03
81	Robin Yount	.30	.25	.12
82	Ben Oglivie	.06	.05	.02
83	Paul Molitor	.10	.08	.04
84	Gorman Thomas	.06	.05	.02
85	Ted Simmons	.06	.05	.02
86	Pete Vuckovich	.04	.03	.02
87	Gary Gaetti	.08	.06	.03
88	Kent Hrbek	.15	.11	.06
89	John Castino	.03	.02	.01
90	Tom Brunansky	.06	.05	.02
91	Bobby Mitchell	.03	.02	.01
92	Gary Ward	.04	.03	.02
93	Tim Laudner	.03	.02	.01
94	Ron Davis	.03	.02	.01
95	Willie Randolph	.06	.05	.02
96	Roy Smalley	.03	.02	.01
97	Jerry Mumphrey	.03	.02	.01
98	Ken Griffey	.06	.05	.02
99	Dave Winfield	.30	.25	.12
100	Rich Gossage	.10	.08	.04
101	Butch Wynegar	.04	.03	.02
102	Ron Guidry	.12	.09	.05
103	Rickey Henderson	.40	.30	.15
104	Mike Heath	.03	.02	.01
105	Dave Lopes	.06	.05	.02
106	Rick Langford	.03	.02	.01
107	Dwayne Murphy	.04	.03	.02
108	Tony Armas	.06	.05	.02
109	Matt Keough	.03	.02	.01
110	Dan Meyer	.03	.02	.01
111	Bruce Bochte	.03	.02	.01
112	Julio Cruz	.03	.02	.01
113	Floyd Bannister	.04	.03	.02
114	Gaylord Perry	.15	.11	.06
115	Al Cowens	.03	.02	.01
116	Richie Zisk	.04	.03	.02
117	Jim Essian	.03	.02	.01
118	Bill Caudill	.03	.02	.01
119	Buddy Bell	.10	.08	.04
120	Larry Parrish	.06	.05	.02
121	Danny Darwin	.03	.02	.01
122	Bucky Dent	.04	.03	.02
123	Johnny Grubb	.03	.02	.01
124	George Wright	.03	.02	.01
125	Charlie Hough	.06	.05	.02
126	Jim Sundberg	.04	.03	.02
127	Dave Stieb	.10	.08	.04
128	Willie Upshaw	.06	.05	.02
129	Alfredo Griffin	.04	.03	.02
130	Lloyd Moseby	.06	.05	.02
131	Ernie Whitt	.03	.02	.01
132	Jim Clancy	.04	.03	.02
133	Barry Bonnell	.03	.02	.01
134	Damaso Garcia	.04	.03	.02
135	Jim Kaat	.08	.06	.03
136	Jim Kaat	.06	.05	.02
137	Greg Minton	.03	.02	.01
138	Greg Minton	.03	.02	.01
139	Paul Molitor	.25	.20	.10
140	Paul Molitor	.25	.20	.10
141	Manny Trillo	.04	.03	.02
142	Manny Trillo	.04	.03	.02
143	Joel Youngblood	.03	.02	.01
144	Joel Youngblood	.03	.02	.01
145	Robin Yount	.35	.25	.14
146	Robin Yount	.35	.25	.14
147	Willie McGee	.08	.06	.03
148	Darrell Porter	.04	.03	.02
149	Darrell Porter	.04	.03	.02
150	Robin Yount	.35	.25	.14
151	Bruce Benedict	.03	.02	.01
152	Bruce Benedict	.03	.02	.01

153	George Hendrick	.04	.03	.02
154	Bruce Benedict	.03	.02	.01
155	Doug DeCinces	.06	.05	.02
156	Paul Molitor	.25	.20	.10
157	Charlie Moore	.03	.02	.01
158	Fred Lynn	.10	.08	.04
159	Rickey Henderson	.35	.25	.14
160	Dale Murphy	.25	.20	.10
161	Willie Wilson	.08	.06	.03
162	Jack Clark	.10	.08	.04
163	Reggie Jackson	.20	.15	.08
164	Andre Dawson	.15	.11	.06
165	Dan Quisenberry	.06	.05	.02
166	Bruce Sutter	.08	.06	.03
167	Robin Yount	.15	.11	.06
168	Ozzie Smith	.10	.08	.04
169	Frank White	.06	.05	.02
170	Phil Garner	.04	.03	.02
171	Doug DeCinces	.06	.05	.02
172	Mike Schmidt	.25	.20	.10
173	Cecil Cooper	.06	.05	.02
174	Al Oliver	.06	.05	.02
175	Jim Palmer	.15	.11	.06
176	Steve Carlton	.15	.11	.06
177	Carlton Fisk	.12	.09	.05
178	Gary Carter	.20	.15	.08
179	Joaquin Andujar	.04	.03	.02
180	Ozzie Smith	.10	.08	.04
181	Cecil Cooper	.06	.05	.02
182	Darrell Porter	.04	.03	.02
183	Darrell Porter	.04	.03	.02
184	Mike Caldwell	.03	.02	.01
185	Mike Caldwell	.03	.02	.01
186	Ozzie Smith	.10	.08	.04
187	Bruce Sutter	.08	.06	.03
188	Keith Hernandez	.12	.09	.05
189	Dane Iorg	.03	.02	.01
190	Dane Iorg	.03	.02	.01
191	Tony Armas	.04	.03	.02
192	Tony Armas	.04	.03	.02
193	Lance Parrish	.12	.09	.05
194	Lance Parrish	.12	.09	.05
195	John Wathan	.04	.03	.02
196	John Wathan	.04	.03	.02
197	Rickey Henderson	.12	.09	.05
198	Rickey Henderson	.12	.09	.05
199	Rickey Henderson	.12	.09	.05
200	Rickey Henderson	.12	.09	.05
201	Rickey Henderson	.12	.09	.05
202	Rickey Henderson	.12	.09	.05
203	Steve Carlton	.15	.11	.06
204	Steve Carlton	.12	.09	.05
205	Al Oliver	.06	.05	.02
206	Dale Murphy, Al Oliver	.20	.15	.08
207	Dave Kingman	.08	.06	.03
208	Steve Rogers	.04	.03	.02
209	Bruce Sutter	.08	.06	.03
210	Tim Raines	.20	.15	.08
211	Dale Murphy	.40	.30	.15
212	Chris Chambliss	.04	.03	.02
213	Gene Garber	.03	.02	.01
214	Bob Horner	.08	.06	.03
215	Glenn Hubbard	.03	.02	.01
216	Claudell Washington	.04	.03	.02
217	Bruce Benedict	.03	.02	.01
218	Phil Niekro	.12	.09	.05
219	Leon Durham	.20	.15	.08
220	Jay Johnstone	.04	.03	.02
221	Larry Bowa	.06	.05	.02
222	Keith Moreland	.06	.05	.02
223	Bill Buckner	.06	.05	.02
224	Fergie Jenkins	.08	.06	.03
225	Dick Tidrow	.03	.02	.01
226	Jody Davis	.06	.05	.02
227	Dave Concepcion	.06	.05	.02
228	Dan Driessen	.04	.03	.02
229	Johnny Bench	.20	.15	.08
230	Ron Oester	.03	.02	.01
231	Cesar Cedeno	.06	.05	.02
232	Alex Trevino	.03	.02	.01
233	Tom Seaver	.20	.15	.08
234	Mario Soto	.20	.15	.08
235	Nolan Ryan	.50	.40	.20
236	Art Howe	.03	.02	.01
237	Phil Garner	.04	.03	.02
238	Ray Knight	.06	.05	.02
239	Terry Puhl	.03	.02	.01
240	Joe Niekro	.06	.05	.02
241	Alan Ashby	.03	.02	.01
242	Jose Cruz	.06	.05	.02
243	Steve Garvey	.20	.15	.08
244	Ron Cey	.06	.05	.02
245	Dusty Baker	.04	.03	.02
246	Ken Landreaux	.03	.02	.01
247	Jerry Reuss	.06	.05	.02
248	Pedro Guerrero	.12	.09	.05
249	Bill Russell	.04	.03	.02
250	Fernando Valenzuela	.15	.11	.06
251	Al Oliver	.25	.20	.10
252	Andre Dawson	.20	.15	.08
253	Tim Raines	.20	.15	.08
254	Jeff Reardon	.08	.06	.03
255	Gary Carter	.20	.15	.08
256	Steve Rogers	.03	.02	.01
257	Tim Wallach	.08	.06	.03
258	Chris Speier	.03	.02	.01
259	Dave Kingman	.08	.06	.03
260	Bob Bailor	.03	.02	.01
261	Hubie Brooks	.06	.05	.02
262	Craig Swan	.03	.02	.01
263	George Foster	.08	.06	.03
264	John Stearns	.03	.02	.01
265	Neil Allen	.03	.02	.01
266	Mookie Wilson	.20	.15	.08
267	Steve Carlton	.30	.25	.12
268	Manny Trillo	.04	.03	.02
269	Gary Matthews	.06	.05	.02
270	Mike Schmidt	.25	.20	.10
271	Ivan DeJesus	.03	.02	.01
272	Pete Rose	.40	.30	.15
273	Bo Diaz	.04	.03	.02
274	Sid Monge	.03	.02	.01
275	Bill Madlock	.25	.20	.10
276	Jason Thompson	.03	.02	.01
277	Don Robinson	.03	.02	.01
278	Omar Moreno	.03	.02	.01
279	Dale Berra	.03	.02	.01
280	Dave Parker	.10	.08	.04
281	Tony Pena	.06	.05	.02
282	John Candelaria	.06	.05	.02
283	Lonnie Smith	.04	.03	.02
284	Bruce Sutter	.10	.08	.04
285	George Hendrick	.04	.03	.02
286	Tom Herr	.06	.05	.02
287	Ken Oberkfell	.03	.02	.01
288	Ozzie Smith	.10	.08	.04
289	Bob Forsch	.04	.03	.02
290	Keith Hernandez	.15	.11	.06
291	Garry Templeton	.06	.05	.02
292	Broderick Perkins	.03	.02	.01
293	Terry Kennedy	.20	.15	.08
294	Gene Richards	.03	.02	.01
295	Ruppert Jones	.03	.02	.01
296	Tim Lollar	.03	.02	.01
297	John Montefusco	.03	.02	.01
298	Sixto Lezcano	.03	.02	.01
299	Greg Minton	.03	.02	.01
300	Jack Clark	.25	.20	.10
301	Milt May	.03	.02	.01
302	Reggie Smith	.06	.05	.02
303	Joe Morgan	.10	.08	.04
304	John LeMaster	.03	.02	.01
305	Darrell Evans	.08	.06	.03
306	Al Holland	.03	.02	.01
307	Jesse Barfield	.08	.06	.03
308	Wade Boggs	.60	.45	.25
309	Tom Brunansky	.06	.05	.02
310	Storm Davis	.04	.03	.02
311	Von Hayes	.06	.05	.02
312	Dave Hostetler	.03	.02	.01
313	Kent Hrbek	.12	.09	.05
314	Tim Laudner	.03	.02	.01
315	Cal Ripken, Jr.	.40	.30	.15
316	Andre Robertson	.03	.02	.01
317	Ed Vande Berg	.03	.02	.01
318	Glenn Wilson	.04	.03	.02
319	Chili Davis	.06	.05	.02
320	Bob Dernier	.03	.02	.01
321	Terry Francona	.03	.02	.01
322	Brian Giles	.03	.02	.01
323	David Green	.03	.02	.01
324	Atlee Hammaker	.03	.02	.01
325	Bill Laskey	.03	.02	.01
326	Willie McGee	.12	.09	.05
327	Johnny Ray	.06	.05	.02
328	Ryne Sandberg	.35	.25	.14
329	Steve Sax	.10	.08	.04
330	Eric Show	.04	.03	.02

1983 Topps Stickers Boxes

These eight cards were printed on the back panels of 1983 Topps sticker boxes, on card per box. The blank-backed cards measure the standard 2-1/2" by 3-1/2" and feature a full-color photo with the player's name at the top. The rest of the back panel advertises the sticker album, while the front of the box has an action photo of Reggie Jackson. The boxes are numbered on the front. Prices in the checklist that follows are for complete boxes.

		MT	NR MT	EX
Complete Set:		6.50	5.00	2.50
Common Player:		.75	.60	.30
1	Fernando Valenzuela	.75	.60	.30
2	Gary Carter	.75	.60	.30
3	Mike Schmidt	1.25	.90	.50
4	Reggie Jackson	1.25	.90	.50
5	Jim Palmer	1.00	.70	.40
6	Rollie Fingers	.75	.60	.30
7	Pete Rose	1.50	1.25	.60
8	Rickey Henderson	1.25	.90	.50

1984 Topps

Another 792-card regular set from Topps. For the second straight year, the 2-1/2" by 3-1/2" cards featured a color action photo on the front along with a small portrait photo in the lower left. The team name runs in big letters down the left side, while the player's name and position runs under the large action photo. In the upper right-hand corner is the Topps logo. Backs have a team logo in the upper

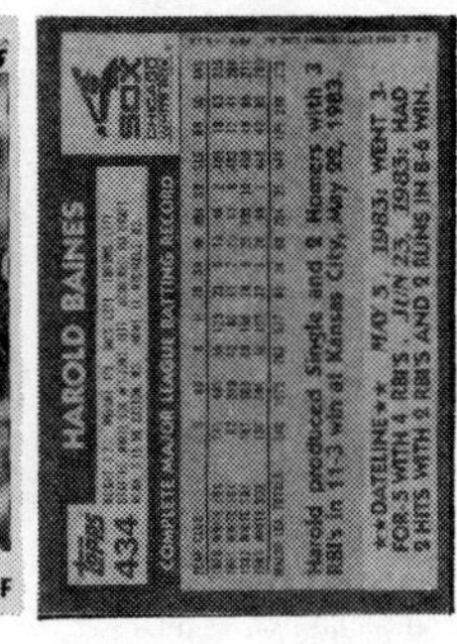

right corner, along with statistics, personal information and a few highlights. The backs have an unusual and hard-to-read red and purple coloring. Specialty cards include past season highlights, team leaders, major league statistical leaders, All-Stars, active career leaders and numbered checklists. Again, promising rookies were saved for the traded set. Late in 1984, Topps introduced a specially boxed "Tiffany" edition of the 1984 set, with the cards printed on white cardboard with a glossy finish. A total of 10,000 sets were produced. Prices for Tiffany edition superstars can run from six to eight times the value of the "regular" edition, while common cards sell in the 40¢ range.

		MT	NR MT	EX
Complete Set (792):		75.00	56.00	30.00
Common Player:		.08	.06	.03
1	Steve Carlton (1983 Highlight)	.30	.25	.12
2	Rickey Henderson (1983 Highlight)	.50	.40	.20
3	Dan Quisenberry (1983 Highlight)	.10	.08	.04
4	Steve Carlton (1983 Highlight, Gaylord Perry, Nolan Ryan)	.30	.25	.12
5	Bob Forsch (1983 Highlight, Dave Righetti, Mike Warren)	.15	.11	.06
6	Johnny Bench (1983 Highlight, Gaylord Perry, Carl Yastrzemski)	.40	.30	.15
7	Gary Lucas	.08	.06	.03
8	*Don Mattingly* (FC)	14.00	10.50	5.50
9	Jim Gott	.10	.08	.04
10	Robin Yount	2.50	2.00	1.00
11	Twins Batting & Pitching Leaders (Kent Hrbek, Ken Schrom)	.20	.15	.08
12	Billy Sample	.08	.06	.03
13	Scott Holman	.08	.06	.03
14	Tom Brookens	.08	.06	.03
15	Burt Hooton	.10	.08	.04
16	Omar Moreno	.08	.06	.03
17	John Denny	.08	.06	.03
18	Dale Berra	.08	.06	.03
19	*Ray Fontenot* (FC)	.10	.08	.04
20	Greg Luzinski	.12	.09	.05
21	Joe Altobelli	.08	.06	.03
22	Bryan Clark	.08	.06	.03
23	Keith Moreland	.10	.08	.04
24	John Martin	.08	.06	.03
25	Glenn Hubbard	.10	.08	.04
26	Bud Black	.10	.08	.04
27	Daryl Sconiers	.08	.06	.03
28	Frank Viola	.40	.30	.15
29	Danny Heep	.08	.06	.03
30	Wade Boggs	4.00	3.00	1.50
31	Andy McGaffigan	.08	.06	.03
32	Bobby Ramos	.08	.06	.03
33	Tom Burgmeier	.08	.06	.03
34	Eddie Milner	.08	.06	.03
35	Don Sutton	.20	.15	.08
36	Denny Walling	.08	.06	.03
37	Rangers Batting & Pitching Leaders (Buddy Bell, Rick Honeycutt)	.12	.09	.05
38	Luis DeLeon	.08	.06	.03
39	Garth Iorg	.08	.06	.03
40	Dusty Baker	.12	.09	.05
41	Tony Bernazard	.08	.06	.03
42	Johnny Grubb	.08	.06	.03
43	Ron Reed	.10	.08	.04
44	Jim Morrison	.08	.06	.03
45	Jerry Mumphrey	.08	.06	.03
46	Ray Smith	.08	.06	.03
47	Rudy Law	.08	.06	.03
48	Julio Franco (FC)	.60	.45	.25
49	John Stuper	.08	.06	.03
50	Chris Chambliss	.10	.08	.04
51	Jim Frey	.08	.06	.03
52	Paul Splittorff	.08	.06	.03
53	Juan Beniquez	.08	.06	.03
54	Jesse Orosco	.10	.08	.04
55	Dave Concepcion	.15	.11	.06
56	Gary Allenson	.08	.06	.03
57	Dan Schatzeder	.08	.06	.03
58	Max Venable	.08	.06	.03
59	Sammy Stewart	.08	.06	.03
60	Paul Molitor	1.75	1.25	.70
61	*Chris Codiroli*	.10	.08	.04
62	Dave Hostetler	.08	.06	.03
63	Ed Vande Berg	.08	.06	.03
64	Mike Scioscia	.08	.06	.03
65	Kirk Gibson	.40	.30	.15
66	Astros Batting & Pitching Leaders (Jose Cruz, Nolan Ryan)	.25	.20	.10

67	Gary Ward	.10	.08	.04
68	Luis Salazar	.08	.06	.03
69	Rod Scurry	.08	.06	.03
70	Gary Matthews	.12	.09	.05
71	Leo Hernandez	.08	.06	.03
72	Mike Squires	.08	.06	.03
73	Jody Davis	.10	.08	.04
74	Jerry Martin	.08	.06	.03
75	Bob Forsch	.10	.08	.04
76	Alfredo Griffin	.10	.08	.04
77	Brett Butler	.10	.08	.04
78	Mike Torrez	.10	.08	.04
79	Rob Wilfong	.08	.06	.03
80	Steve Rogers	.10	.08	.04
81	Billy Martin	.12	.09	.05
82	Doug Bird	.08	.06	.03
83	Richie Zisk	.10	.08	.04
84	Lenny Faedo	.08	.06	.03
85	Atlee Hammaker	.08	.06	.03
86	*John Shelby* (FC)	.10	.08	.04
87	Frank Pastore	.08	.06	.03
88	Rob Picciolo	.08	.06	.03
89	*Mike Smithson* (FC)	.15	.11	.06
90	Pedro Guerrero	.10	.08	.04
91	Dan Spillner	.08	.06	.03
92	Lloyd Moseby	.12	.09	.05
93	Bob Knepper	.10	.08	.04
94	Mario Ramirez	.08	.06	.03
95	Aurelio Lopez	.08	.06	.03
96	Royals Batting & Pitching Leaders (Larry Gura, Hal McRae)	.10	.08	.04
97	LaMarr Hoyt	.08	.06	.03
98	Steve Nicosia	.08	.06	.03
99	*Craig Lefferts*	.30	.25	.12
100	Reggie Jackson	1.50	1.25	.60
101	Porfirio Altamirano	.08	.06	.03
102	Ken Oberkfell	.08	.06	.03
103	Dwayne Murphy	.10	.08	.04
104	Ken Dayley	.08	.06	.03
105	Tony Armas	.12	.09	.05
106	Tim Stoddard	.08	.06	.03
107	Ned Yost	.08	.06	.03
108	Randy Moffitt	.08	.06	.03
109	Brad Wellman	.08	.06	.03
110	Ron Guidry	.10	.08	.04
111	Bill Virdon	.08	.06	.03
112	Tom Niedenfuer	.10	.08	.04
113	Kelly Paris	.08	.06	.03
114	Checklist 1-132	.08	.06	.03
115	Andre Thornton	.12	.09	.05
116	George Bjorkman	.08	.06	.03
117	Tom Veryzer	.08	.06	.03
118	Charlie Hough	.12	.09	.05
119	Johnny Wockenfuss	.08	.06	.03
120	Keith Hernandez	.15	.11	.06
121	*Pat Sheridan* (FC)	.10	.08	.04
122	Cecilio Guante (FC)	.10	.08	.04
123	Butch Wynegar	.08	.06	.03
124	Damaso Garcia	.08	.06	.03
125	Britt Burns	.08	.06	.03
126	Braves Batting & Pitching Leaders (Craig McMurtry, Dale Murphy)	.25	.20	.10
127	Mike Madden	.08	.06	.03
128	Rick Manning	.08	.06	.03
129	Bill Laskey	.08	.06	.03
130	Ozzie Smith	.70	.50	.30
131	Batting Leaders (Wade Boggs, Bill Madlock)	.50	.40	.20
132	Home Run Leaders (Jim Rice, Mike Schmidt)	.50	.40	.20
133	RBI Leaders (Cecil Cooper, Dale Murphy, Jim Rice)	.40	.30	.15
134	Stolen Base Leaders (Rickey Henderson, Tim Raines)	.30	.25	.12
135	Victory Leaders (John Denny, LaMarr Hoyt)	.10	.08	.04
136	Strikeout Leaders (Steve Carlton, Jack Morris)	.25	.20	.10
137	Earned Run Average Leaders (Atlee Hammaker, Rick Honeycutt)	.10	.08	.04
138	Leading Firemen (Al Holland, Dan Quisenberry)	.12	.09	.05
139	Bert Campaneris	.12	.09	.05
140	Storm Davis	.12	.09	.05
141	Pat Corrales	.08	.06	.03
142	Rich Gale	.08	.06	.03
143	Jose Morales	.08	.06	.03
144	*Brian Harper*	1.00	.70	.40
145	Gary Lavelle	.08	.06	.03
146	Ed Romero	.08	.06	.03
147	Dan Petry	.10	.08	.04
148	Joe Lefebvre	.08	.06	.03
149	Jon Matlack	.10	.08	.04
150	Dale Murphy	.70	.50	.30
151	Steve Trout	.08	.06	.03
152	Glenn Brummer	.08	.06	.03
153	Dick Tidrow	.08	.06	.03
154	Dave Henderson	.12	.09	.05
155	Frank White	.12	.09	.05
156	Athletics Batting & Pitching Leaders (Tim Conroy, Rickey Henderson)	.25	.20	.10
157	Gary Gaetti	.50	.40	.20
158	John Curtis	.08	.06	.03
159	Darryl Cias	.08	.06	.03
160	Mario Soto	.10	.08	.04
161	*Junior Ortiz* (FC)	.10	.08	.04
162	Bob Ojeda	.12	.09	.05
163	Lorenzo Gray	.08	.06	.03
164	Scott Sanderson	.08	.06	.03
165	Ken Singleton	.12	.09	.05
166	Jamie Nelson	.08	.06	.03
167	Marshall Edwards	.08	.06	.03
168	Juan Bonilla	.08	.06	.03
169	Larry Parrish	.12	.09	.05
170	Jerry Reuss	.12	.09	.05
171	Frank Robinson	.12	.09	.05
172	Frank DiPino	.08	.06	.03
173	*Marvell Wynne* (FC)	.08	.06	.03
174	Juan Berenguer	.08	.06	.03
175	Graig Nettles	.20	.15	.08
176	Lee Smith	.15	.11	.06
177	Jerry Hairston	.08	.06	.03
178	Bill Krueger	.08	.06	.03
179	Buck Martinez	.08	.06	.03
180	Manny Trillo	.10	.08	.04
181	Roy Thomas	.08	.06	.03
182	*Darryl Strawberry*	3.00	2.25	1.25
183	Al Williams	.08	.06	.03
184	Mike O'Berry	.08	.06	.03
185	Sixto Lezcano	.08	.06	.03
186	Cardinals Batting & Pitching Leaders (Lonnie Smith, John Stuper)	.10	.08	.04
187	Luis Aponte	.08	.06	.03
188	Bryan Little	.08	.06	.03
189	*Tim Conroy* (FC)	.12	.09	.05
190	Ben Oglivie	.10	.08	.04
191	Mike Boddicker	.12	.09	.05
192	*Nick Esasky* (FC)	.15	.11	.06
193	Darrell Brown	.08	.06	.03
194	Domingo Ramos	.08	.06	.03
195	Jack Morris	.30	.25	.12
196	Don Slaught (FC)	.12	.09	.05
197	Garry Hancock	.08	.06	.03
198	*Bill Doran*	.30	.25	.12
199	Willie Hernandez	.12	.09	.05
200	Andre Dawson	.75	.60	.30
201	Bruce Kison	.08	.06	.03
202	Bobby Cox	.08	.06	.03
203	Matt Keough	.08	.06	.03
204	*Bobby Meacham* (FC)	.15	.11	.06
205	Greg Minton	.08	.06	.03
206	*Andy Van Slyke*	2.50	2.00	1.00
207	Donnie Moore	.08	.06	.03
208	*Jose Oquendo* (FC)	.15	.11	.06
209	Manny Sarmiento	.08	.06	.03
210	Joe Morgan	.30	.25	.12
211	Rick Sweet	.08	.06	.03
212	Broderick Perkins	.08	.06	.03
213	Bruce Hurst	.15	.11	.06
214	Paul Householder	.08	.06	.03
215	Tippy Martinez	.08	.06	.03
216	White Sox Batting & Pitching Leaders (Richard Dotson, Carlton Fisk)	.15	.11	.06
217	Alan Ashby	.08	.06	.03
218	Rick Waits	.08	.06	.03
219	Joe Simpson	.08	.06	.03
220	Fernando Valenzuela	.20	.15	.08
221	Cliff Johnson	.08	.06	.03
222	Rick Honeycutt	.08	.06	.03
223	Wayne Krenchicki	.08	.06	.03
224	Sid Monge	.08	.06	.03
225	Lee Mazzilli	.10	.08	.04
226	Juan Eichelberger	.08	.06	.03
227	Steve Braun	.08	.06	.03
228	John Rabb	.08	.06	.03
229	Paul Owens	.08	.06	.03
230	Rickey Henderson	3.00	2.25	1.25
231	Gary Woods	.08	.06	.03
232	Tim Wallach	.15	.11	.06
233	Checklist 133-264	.08	.06	.03
234	Rafael Ramirez	.08	.06	.03
235	*Matt Young*	.15	.11	.06
236	Ellis Valentine	.08	.06	.03
237	John Castino	.08	.06	.03
238	Reid Nichols	.08	.06	.03
239	Jay Howell	.10	.08	.04
240	Eddie Murray	1.00	.75	.40
241	Billy Almon	.08	.06	.03
242	Alex Trevino	.08	.06	.03
243	Pete Ladd	.08	.06	.03
244	Candy Maldonado (FC)	.15	.11	.06
245	Rick Sutcliffe	.15	.11	.06
246	Mets Batting & Pitching Leaders (Tom Seaver, Mookie Wilson)	.25	.20	.10
247	Onix Concepcion	.08	.06	.03
248	*Bill Dawley* (FC)	.10	.08	.04
249	Jay Johnstone	.10	.08	.04
250	Bill Madlock	.12	.09	.05
251	Tony Gwynn	3.00	2.25	1.25
252	Larry Christenson	.08	.06	.03
253	Jim Wohlford	.08	.06	.03
254	Shane Rawley	.12	.09	.05
255	Bruce Benedict	.08	.06	.03
256	Dave Geisel	.08	.06	.03
257	Julio Cruz	.08	.06	.03
258	Luis Sanchez	.08	.06	.03
259	Sparky Anderson	.12	.09	.05
260	Scott McGregor	.10	.08	.04
261	Bobby Brown	.08	.06	.03
262	*Tom Candiotti* (FC)	.25	.20	.10
263	Jack Fimple	.08	.06	.03
264	Doug Frobel	.08	.06	.03
265	*Donnie Hill* (FC)	.15	.11	.06
266	Steve Lubratich	.08	.06	.03
267	*Carmelo Martinez* (FC)	.25	.20	.10
268	Jack O'Connor	.08	.06	.03
269	Aurelio Rodriguez	.10	.08	.04
270	*Jeff Russell* (FC)	.20	.15	.08
271	Moose Haas	.08	.06	.03
272	Rick Dempsey	.10	.08	.04
273	Charlie Puleo	.08	.06	.03
274	Rick Monday	.10	.08	.04
275	Len Matuszek	.08	.06	.03
276	Angels Batting & Pitching Leaders (Rod Carew, Geoff Zahn)	.20	.15	.08
277	Eddie Whitson	.08	.06	.03
278	Jorge Bell	.25	.20	.10
279	Ivan DeJesus	.08	.06	.03
280	Floyd Bannister	.12	.09	.05
281	Larry Milbourne	.08	.06	.03
282	Jim Barr	.08	.06	.03
283	Larry Biittner	.08	.06	.03
284	Howard Bailey	.08	.06	.03
285	Darrell Porter	.10	.08	.04
286	Lary Sorensen	.08	.06	.03
287	Warren Cromartie	.08	.06	.03
288	Jim Beattie	.08	.06	.03
289	Randy S. Johnson	.08	.06	.03
290	Dave Dravecky	.10	.08	.04
291	Chuck Tanner	.08	.06	.03
292	Tony Scott	.08	.06	.03
293	Ed Lynch	.08	.06	.03
294	U.L. Washington	.08	.06	.03
295	Mike Flanagan	.12	.09	.05
296	Jeff Newman	.08	.06	.03
297	Bruce Berenyi	.08	.06	.03
298	Jim Gantner	.10	.08	.04
299	John Butcher	.08	.06	.03
300	Pete Rose	1.00	.70	.40
301	Frank LaCorte	.08	.06	.03
302	Barry Bonnell	.08	.06	.03
303	Marty Castillo	.08	.06	.03
304	Warren Brusstar	.08	.06	.03
305	Roy Smalley	.08	.06	.03
306	Dodgers Batting & Pitching Leaders (Pedro Guerrero, Bob Welch)	.15	.11	.06
307	Bobby Mitchell	.08	.06	.03
308	Ron Hassey	.08	.06	.03
309	*Tony Phillips*	1.00	.70	.40
310	Willie McGee	.20	.15	.08
311	Jerry Koosman	.12	.09	.05
312	Jorge Orta	.08	.06	.03
313	Mike Jorgensen	.08	.06	.03
314	Orlando Mercado	.08	.06	.03
315	Bob Grich	.12	.09	.05
316	Mark Bradley	.08	.06	.03
317	Greg Pryor	.08	.06	.03
318	Bill Gullickson	.08	.06	.03
319	Al Bumbry	.10	.08	.04
320	Bob Stanley	.08	.06	.03
321	Harvey Kuenn	.10	.08	.04
322	Ken Schrom	.08	.06	.03
323	Alan Knicely	.08	.06	.03
324	*Alejandro Pena*	.15	.11	.06
325	Darrell Evans	.15	.11	.06
326	Bob Kearney	.08	.06	.03
327	Ruppert Jones	.08	.06	.03
328	Vern Ruhle	.08	.06	.03
329	Pat Tabler (FC)	.12	.09	.05
330	John Candelaria	.12	.09	.05
331	Bucky Dent	.12	.09	.05
332	*Kevin Gross* (FC)	.15	.11	.06
333	Larry Herndon	.10	.08	.04
334	Chuck Rainey	.08	.06	.03
335	Don Baylor	.15	.11	.06
336	Mariners Batting & Pitching Leaders (Pat Putnam, Matt Young)	.10	.08	.04
337	Kevin Hagen	.08	.06	.03
338	Mike Warren	.08	.06	.03
339	Roy Lee Jackson	.08	.06	.03
340	Hal McRae	.12	.09	.05
341	Dave Tobik	.08	.06	.03
342	Tim Foli	.08	.06	.03
343	Mark Davis	.08	.06	.03
344	Rick Miller	.08	.06	.03
345	Kent Hrbek	.40	.30	.15
346	Kurt Bevacqua	.08	.06	.03
347	Allan Ramirez	.08	.06	.03
348	Toby Harrah	.10	.08	.04
349	Bob L. Gibson	.08	.06	.03
350	George Foster	.10	.08	.04
351	Russ Nixon	.08	.06	.03
352	Dave Stewart	.35	.25	.14
353	Jim Anderson	.08	.06	.03
354	Jeff Burroughs	.10	.08	.04
355	Jason Thompson	.08	.06	.03
356	Glenn Abbott	.08	.06	.03
357	Ron Cey	.12	.09	.05
358	Bob Dernier	.08	.06	.03
359	*Jim Acker* (FC)	.12	.09	.05
360	Willie Randolph	.12	.09	.05
361	Dave Smith	.10	.08	.04
362	David Green	.08	.06	.03
363	Tim Laudner	.08	.06	.03
364	Scott Fletcher (FC)	.15	.11	.06
365	Steve Bedrosian	.12	.09	.05
366	Padres Batting & Pitching Leaders (Dave Dravecky, Terry Kennedy)	.12	.09	.05
367	Jamie Easterly	.08	.06	.03
368	Hubie Brooks	.15	.11	.06
369	Steve McCatty	.08	.06	.03
370	Tim Raines	.50	.40	.20
371	Dave Gumpert	.08	.06	.03
372	Gary Roenicke	.08	.06	.03
373	Bill Scherrer	.08	.06	.03
374	Don Money	.08	.06	.03
375	Dennis Leonard	.10	.08	.04
376	*Dave Anderson* (FC)	.15	.11	.06
377	Danny Darwin	.08	.06	.03
378	Bob Brenly	.08	.06	.03
379	Checklist 265-396	.08	.06	.03
380	Steve Garvey	.35	.25	.14
381	Ralph Houk	.10	.08	.04
382	Chris Nyman	.08	.06	.03
383	Terry Puhl	.08	.06	.03
384	*Lee Tunnell*	.10	.08	.04
385	Tony Perez	.20	.15	.08
386	George Hendrick (All-Star)	.10	.08	.04
387	Johnny Ray (All-Star)	.12	.09	.05
388	Mike Schmidt (All-Star)	.50	.40	.20
389	Ozzie Smith (All-Star)	.15	.11	.06
390	Tim Raines (All-Star)	.25	.20	.10
391	Dale Murphy (All-Star)	.40	.30	.15
392	Andre Dawson (All-Star)	.20	.15	.08
393	Gary Carter (All-Star)	.30	.25	.12
394	Steve Rogers (All-Star)	.10	.08	.04
395	Steve Carlton (All-Star)	.25	.20	.10
396	Jesse Orosco (All-Star)	.10	.08	.04
397	Eddie Murray (All-Star)	.35	.25	.14
398	Lou Whitaker (All-Star)	.20	.15	.08
399	George Brett (All-Star)	.50	.40	.20
400	Cal Ripken, Jr. (All-Star)	1.00	.70	.40
401	Jim Rice (All-Star)	.30	.25	.12
402	Dave Winfield (All-Star)	.30	.25	.12

403	Lloyd Moseby (All-Star)	.12	.09	.05
404	Ted Simmons (All-Star)	.15	.11	.06
405	LaMarr Hoyt (All-Star)	.10	.08	.04
406	Ron Guidry (All-Star)	.20	.15	.08
407	Dan Quisenberry (All-Star)	.12	.09	.05
408	Lou Piniella	.15	.11	.06
409	*Juan Agosto* (FC)	.15	.11	.06
410	Claudell Washington	.10	.08	.04
411	Houston Jimenez	.08	.06	.03
412	Doug Rader	.08	.06	.03
413	*Spike Owen* (FC)	.20	.15	.08
414	Mitchell Page	.08	.06	.03
415	Tommy John	.25	.20	.10
416	Dane Iorg	.08	.06	.03
417	Mike Armstrong	.08	.06	.03
418	Ron Hodges	.08	.06	.03
419	John Henry Johnson	.08	.06	.03
420	Cecil Cooper	.15	.11	.06
421	Charlie Lea	.08	.06	.03
422	Jose Cruz	.12	.09	.05
423	Mike Morgan	.08	.06	.03
424	Dann Bilardello	.08	.06	.03
425	Steve Howe	.10	.08	.04
426	Orioles Leaders (Mike Boddicker, Cal Ripken, Jr.)	.75	.60	.30
427	Rick Leach	.08	.06	.03
428	Fred Breining	.08	.06	.03
429	*Randy Bush*	.15	.11	.06
430	Rusty Staub	.12	.09	.05
431	Chris Bando	.08	.06	.03
432	*Charlie Hudson* (FC)	.10	.08	.04
433	Rich Hebner	.08	.06	.03
434	Harold Baines	.25	.20	.10
435	Neil Allen	.08	.06	.03
436	Rick Peters	.08	.06	.03
437	Mike Proly	.08	.06	.03
438	Biff Pocoroba	.08	.06	.03
439	Bob Stoddard	.08	.06	.03
440	Steve Kemp	.10	.08	.04
441	Bob Lillis	.08	.06	.03
442	Byron McLaughlin	.08	.06	.03
443	Benny Ayala	.08	.06	.03
444	Steve Renko	.08	.06	.03
445	Jerry Remy	.08	.06	.03
446	Luis Pujols	.08	.06	.03
447	Tom Brunansky	.10	.08	.04
448	Ben Hayes	.08	.06	.03
449	Joe Pettini	.08	.06	.03
450	Gary Carter	.40	.30	.15
451	Bob Jones	.08	.06	.03
452	Chuck Porter	.08	.06	.03
453	Willie Upshaw	.10	.08	.04
454	Joe Beckwith	.08	.06	.03
455	Terry Kennedy	.10	.08	.04
456	Cubs Batting & Pitching Leaders (Fergie Jenkins, Keith Moreland)	.15	.11	.06
457	Dave Rozema	.08	.06	.03
458	Kiko Garcia	.08	.06	.03
459	Kevin Hickey	.08	.06	.03
460	Dave Winfield	2.00	1.50	.80
461	Jim Maler	.08	.06	.03
462	Lee Lacy	.08	.06	.03
463	Dave Engle	.08	.06	.03
464	Jeff Jones	.08	.06	.03
465	Mookie Wilson	.12	.09	.05
466	Gene Garber	.08	.06	.03
467	Mike Ramsey	.08	.06	.03
468	Geoff Zahn	.08	.06	.03
469	Tom O'Malley	.08	.06	.03
470	Nolan Ryan	7.00	5.25	2.75
471	Dick Howser	.08	.06	.03
472	Mike Brown	.08	.06	.03
473	Jim Dwyer	.08	.06	.03
474	Greg Bargar	.08	.06	.03
475	*Gary Redus*	.15	.11	.06
476	Tom Tellmann	.08	.06	.03
477	Rafael Landestoy	.08	.06	.03
478	Alan Bannister	.08	.06	.03
479	Frank Tanana	.12	.09	.05
480	Ron Kittle (FC)	.20	.15	.08
481	*Mark Thurmond* (FC)	.10	.08	.04
482	Enos Cabell	.08	.06	.03
483	Fergie Jenkins	.20	.15	.08
484	Ozzie Virgil	.08	.06	.03
485	Rick Rhoden	.12	.09	.05
486	Yankees Batting & Pitching Leaders (Don Baylor, Ron Guidry)	.15	.11	.06
487	Ricky Adams	.08	.06	.03
488	Jesse Barfield	.10	.08	.04
489	Dave Von Ohlen	.08	.06	.03
490	Cal Ripken, Jr.	6.00	4.50	2.50
491	Bobby Castillo	.08	.06	.03
492	Tucker Ashford	.08	.06	.03
493	Mike Norris	.08	.06	.03
494	Chili Davis	.12	.09	.05
495	Rollie Fingers	.20	.15	.08
496	Terry Francona	.08	.06	.03
497	Bud Anderson	.08	.06	.03
498	Rich Gedman	.10	.08	.04
499	Mike Witt	.15	.11	.06
500	George Brett	2.00	1.50	.80
501	Steve Henderson	.08	.06	.03
502	Joe Torre	.08	.06	.03
503	Elias Sosa	.08	.06	.03
504	Mickey Rivers	.10	.08	.04
505	Pete Vuckovich	.10	.08	.04
506	Ernie Whitt	.10	.08	.04
507	Mike LaCoss	.08	.06	.03
508	Mel Hall	.10	.08	.04
509	Brad Havens	.08	.06	.03
510	Alan Trammell	.40	.30	.15
511	Marty Bystrom	.08	.06	.03
512	Oscar Gamble	.10	.08	.04
513	Dave Beard	.08	.06	.03
514	Floyd Rayford	.08	.06	.03
515	Gorman Thomas	.10	.08	.04
516	Expos Batting & Pitching Leaders (Charlie Lea, Al Oliver)	.12	.09	.05
517	John Moses	.12	.09	.05
518	*Greg Walker*	.10	.08	.04
519	Ron Davis	.08	.06	.03
520	Bob Boone	.10	.08	.04
521	Pete Falcone	.08	.06	.03
522	Dave Bergman	.08	.06	.03
523	Glenn Hoffman	.08	.06	.03
524	Carlos Diaz	.08	.06	.03
525	Willie Wilson	.15	.11	.06
526	Ron Oester	.08	.06	.03
527	Checklist 397-528	.08	.06	.03
528	Mark Brouhard	.08	.06	.03
529	*Keith Atherton* (FC)	.20	.15	.08
530	Dan Ford	.08	.06	.03
531	Steve Boros	.08	.06	.03
532	Eric Show	.12	.09	.05
533	Ken Landreaux	.08	.06	.03
534	*Pete O'Brien*	.35	.25	.14
535	Bo Diaz	.10	.08	.04
536	Doug Bair	.08	.06	.03
537	Johnny Ray	.12	.09	.05
538	Kevin Bass	.15	.11	.06
539	George Frazier	.08	.06	.03
540	George Hendrick	.10	.08	.04
541	Dennis Lamp	.08	.06	.03
542	Duane Kuiper	.08	.06	.03
543	*Craig McMurtry*	.12	.09	.05
544	Cesar Geronimo	.08	.06	.03
545	Bill Buckner	.15	.11	.06
546	Indians Batting & Pitching Leaders (Mike Hargrove, Lary Sorensen)	.10	.08	.04
547	Mike Moore	.10	.08	.04
548	Ron Jackson	.08	.06	.03
549	*Walt Terrell*	.20	.15	.08
550	Jim Rice	.30	.25	.12
551	Scott Ullger	.08	.06	.03
552	Ray Burris	.08	.06	.03
553	Joe Nolan	.08	.06	.03
554	Ted Power (FC)	.12	.09	.05
555	Greg Brock	.15	.11	.06
556	Joey McLaughlin	.08	.06	.03
557	Wayne Tolleson	.10	.08	.04
558	Mike Davis	.10	.08	.04
559	Mike Scott	.20	.15	.08
560	Carlton Fisk	.70	.50	.30
561	Whitey Herzog	.10	.08	.04
562	Manny Castillo	.08	.06	.03
563	Glenn Wilson	.10	.08	.04
564	Al Holland	.08	.06	.03
565	Leon Durham	.10	.08	.04
566	Jim Bibby	.08	.06	.03
567	Mike Heath	.08	.06	.03
568	Pete Filson	.08	.06	.03
569	Bake McBride	.08	.06	.03
570	Dan Quisenberry	.12	.09	.05
571	Bruce Bochy	.08	.06	.03
572	Jerry Royster	.08	.06	.03
573	Dave Kingman	.15	.11	.06
574	Brian Downing	.12	.09	.05
575	Jim Clancy	.10	.08	.04
576	Giants Batting & Pitching Leaders (Atlee Hammaker, Jeff Leonard)	.10	.08	.04
577	Mark Clear	.08	.06	.03
578	Lenn Sakata	.08	.06	.03
579	Bob James	.08	.06	.03
580	Lonnie Smith	.10	.08	.04
581	*Jose DeLeon* (FC)	.15	.11	.06
582	Bob McClure	.08	.06	.03
583	Derrel Thomas	.08	.06	.03
584	Dave Schmidt	.08	.06	.03
585	Dan Driessen	.10	.08	.04
586	Joe Niekro	.15	.11	.06
587	Von Hayes	.15	.11	.06
588	Milt Wilcox	.08	.06	.03
589	Mike Easler	.10	.08	.04
590	Dave Stieb	.15	.11	.06
591	Tony LaRussa	.10	.08	.04
592	Andre Robertson	.08	.06	.03
593	Jeff Lahti	.08	.06	.03
594	Gene Richards	.08	.06	.03
595	Jeff Reardon	.60	.45	.25
596	Ryne Sandberg	8.00	6.00	3.25
597	Rick Camp	.08	.06	.03
598	Rusty Kuntz	.08	.06	.03
599	*Doug Sisk*	.10	.08	.04
600	Rod Carew	.50	.40	.20
601	John Tudor	.12	.09	.05
602	John Wathan	.10	.08	.04
603	Renie Martin	.08	.06	.03
604	John Lowenstein	.08	.06	.03
605	Mike Caldwell	.08	.06	.03
606	Blue Jays Batting & Pitching Leaders (Lloyd Moseby, Dave Stieb)	.08	.06	.03
607	Tom Hume	.08	.06	.03
608	Bobby Johnson	.08	.06	.03
609	Dan Meyer	.08	.06	.03
610	Steve Sax	.10	.08	.04
611	Chet Lemon	.10	.08	.04
612	Harry Spilman	.08	.06	.03
613	Greg Gross	.08	.06	.03
614	Len Barker	.10	.08	.04
615	Garry Templeton	.12	.09	.05
616	Don Robinson	.10	.08	.04
617	Rick Cerone	.08	.06	.03
618	Dickie Noles	.08	.06	.03
619	Jerry Dybzinski	.08	.06	.03
620	Al Oliver	.20	.15	.08
621	Frank Howard	.10	.08	.04
622	Al Cowens	.08	.06	.03
623	Ron Washington	.08	.06	.03
624	Terry Harper	.08	.06	.03
625	Larry Gura	.10	.08	.04
626	Bob Clark	.08	.06	.03
627	Dave LaPoint	.10	.08	.04
628	Ed Jurak	.08	.06	.03
629	Rick Langford	.08	.06	.03
630	Ted Simmons	.15	.11	.06
631	Denny Martinez	.10	.08	.04
632	Tom Foley	.08	.06	.03
633	Mike Krukow	.10	.08	.04
634	Mike Marshall	.15	.11	.06
635	Dave Righetti	.10	.08	.04
636	Pat Putnam	.08	.06	.03
637	Phillies Batting & Pitching Leaders (John Denny, Gary Matthews)	.10	.08	.04
638	George Vukovich	.08	.06	.03
639	Rick Lysander	.08	.06	.03
640	Lance Parrish	.10	.08	.04
641	Mike Richardt	.08	.06	.03
642	Tom Underwood	.08	.06	.03
643	Mike Brown	.08	.06	.03
644	Tim Lollar	.08	.06	.03
645	Tony Pena	.12	.09	.05
646	Checklist 529-660	.08	.06	.03
647	Ron Roenicke	.08	.06	.03
648	Len Whitehouse	.08	.06	.03
649	Tom Herr	.12	.09	.05
650	Phil Niekro	.30	.25	.12
651	John McNamara	.08	.06	.03
652	Rudy May	.08	.06	.03
653	Dave Stapleton	.08	.06	.03
654	Bob Bailor	.08	.06	.03
655	Amos Otis	.10	.08	.04
656	Bryn Smith	.08	.06	.03
657	Thad Bosley	.08	.06	.03
658	Jerry Augustine	.08	.06	.03
659	Duane Walker	.08	.06	.03
660	Ray Knight	.12	.09	.05
661	Steve Yeager	.08	.06	.03
662	Tom Brennan	.08	.06	.03
663	Johnnie LeMaster	.08	.06	.03
664	Dave Stegman	.08	.06	.03
665	Buddy Bell	.08	.06	.03
666	Tigers Batting & Pitching Leaders (Jack Morris, Lou Whitaker)	.15	.11	.06
667	Vance Law	.10	.08	.04
668	Larry McWilliams	.08	.06	.03
669	Dave Lopes	.10	.08	.04
670	Rich Gossage	.10	.08	.04
671	Jamie Quirk	.08	.06	.03
672	Ricky Nelson	.08	.06	.03
673	Mike Walters	.08	.06	.03
674	Tim Flannery	.08	.06	.03
675	Pascual Perez	.10	.08	.04
676	Brian Giles	.08	.06	.03
677	Doyle Alexander	.12	.09	.05
678	Chris Speier	.08	.06	.03
679	Art Howe	.08	.06	.03
680	Fred Lynn	.25	.20	.10
681	Tom Lasorda	.12	.09	.05
682	Dan Morogiello	.08	.06	.03
683	*Marty Barrett* (FC)	.15	.11	.06
684	Bob Shirley	.08	.06	.03
685	Willie Aikens	.08	.06	.03
686	Joe Price	.08	.06	.03
687	Roy Howell	.08	.06	.03
688	George Wright	.08	.06	.03
689	Mike Fischlin	.08	.06	.03
690	Jack Clark	.10	.08	.04
691	*Steve Lake* (FC)	.10	.08	.04
692	Dickie Thon	.10	.08	.04
693	Alan Wiggins	.08	.06	.03
694	Mike Stanton	.08	.06	.03
695	Lou Whitaker	.40	.30	.15
696	Pirates Batting & Pitching Leaders (Bill Madlock, Rick Rhoden)	.15	.11	.06
697	Dale Murray	.08	.06	.03
698	Marc Hill	.08	.06	.03
699	Dave Rucker	.08	.06	.03
700	Mike Schmidt	2.50	2.00	1.00
701	NL Active Career Batting Leaders (Bill Madlock, Dave Parker, Pete Rose)	.35	.25	.14
702	NL Active Career Hit Leaders (Tony Perez, Pete Rose, Rusty Staub)	.35	.25	.14
703	NL Active Career Home Run Leaders (Dave Kingman, Tony Perez, Mike Schmidt)	.30	.25	.12
704	NL Active Career RBI Leaders (Al Oliver, Tony Perez, Rusty Staub)	.15	.11	.06
705	NL Active Career Stolen Bases Leaders (Larry Bowa, Cesar Cedeno, Joe Morgan)	.12	.09	.05
706	NL Active Career Victory Leaders (Steve Carlton, Fergie Jenkins, Tom Seaver)	.30	.25	.12
707	NL Active Career Strikeout Leaders (Steve Carlton, Nolan Ryan, Tom Seaver)	.35	.25	.14
708	NL Active Career ERA Leaders (Steve Carlton, Steve Rogers, Tom Seaver)	.25	.20	.10
709	NL Active Career Save Leaders (Gene Garber, Tug McGraw, Bruce Sutter)	.12	.09	.05
710	AL Active Career Batting Leaders (George Brett, Rod Carew, Cecil Cooper)	.30	.25	.12
711	AL Active Career Hit Leaders (Bert Campaneris, Rod Carew, Reggie Jackson)	.30	.25	.12
712	AL Active Career Home Run Leaders (Reggie Jackson, Greg Luzinski, Graig Nettles)	.20	.15	.08
713	AL Active Career RBI Leaders (Reggie Jackson, Graig Nettles, Ted Simmons)	.20	.15	.08
714	AL Active Career Stolen Bases Leaders (Bert Campaneris, Dave Lopes, Omar Moreno)	.10	.08	.04
715	AL Active Career Victory Leaders (Tommy John, Jim Palmer, Don Sutton)	.25	.20	.10
716	AL Active Strikeout Leaders (Bert Blyleven, Jerry Koosman, Don Sutton)	.15	.11	.06
717	AL Active Career ERA Leaders (Rollie Fingers, Ron Guidry, Jim Palmer)	.15	.11	.06
718	AL Active Career Save Leaders (Rollie Fingers, Rich Gossage, Dan Quisenberry)	.15	.11	.06
719	Andy Hassler	.08	.06	.03
720	Dwight Evans	.20	.15	.08
721	Del Crandall	.08	.06	.03
722	Bob Welch	.15	.11	.06
723	Rich Dauer	.08	.06	.03
724	Eric Rasmussen	.08	.06	.03
725	Cesar Cedeno	.12	.09	.05

		MT	NR MT	EX
726	Brewers Batting & Pitching Leaders (Moose Haas, Ted Simmons)	.12	.09	.05
727	Joel Youngblood	.08	.06	.03
728	Tug McGraw	.12	.09	.05
729	Gene Tenace	.10	.08	.04
730	Bruce Sutter	.20	.15	.08
731	Lynn Jones	.08	.06	.03
732	Terry Crowley	.08	.06	.03
733	Dave Collins	.10	.08	.04
734	Odell Jones	.08	.06	.03
735	Rick Burleson	.10	.08	.04
736	Dick Ruthven	.08	.06	.03
737	Jim Essian	.08	.06	.03
738	*Bill Schroeder* (FC)	.20	.15	.08
739	Bob Watson	.10	.08	.04
740	Tom Seaver	1.75	1.25	.70
741	Wayne Gross	.08	.06	.03
742	Dick Williams	.08	.06	.03
743	Don Hood	.08	.06	.03
744	Jamie Allen	.08	.06	.03
745	Dennis Eckersley	.15	.11	.06
746	Mickey Hatcher	.10	.08	.04
747	Pat Zachry	.08	.06	.03
748	Jeff Leonard	.12	.09	.05
749	Doug Flynn	.08	.06	.03
750	Jim Palmer	1.00	.70	.40
751	Charlie Moore	.08	.06	.03
752	Phil Garner	.10	.08	.04
753	Doug Gwosdz	.08	.06	.03
754	Kent Tekulve	.10	.08	.04
755	Garry Maddox	.10	.08	.04
756	Reds Batting & Pitching Leaders (Ron Oester, Mario Soto)	.10	.08	.04
757	Larry Bowa	.15	.11	.06
758	Bill Stein	.08	.06	.03
759	Richard Dotson	.12	.09	.05
760	Bob Horner	.15	.11	.06
761	John Montefusco	.08	.06	.03
762	Rance Mulliniks	.08	.06	.03
763	Craig Swan	.08	.06	.03
764	Mike Hargrove	.08	.06	.03
765	Ken Forsch	.08	.06	.03
766	Mike Vail	.08	.06	.03
767	Carney Lansford	.12	.09	.05
768	Champ Summers	.08	.06	.03
769	Bill Caudill	.08	.06	.03
770	Ken Griffey	.12	.09	.05
771	Billy Gardner	.08	.06	.03
772	Jim Slaton	.08	.06	.03
773	Todd Cruz	.08	.06	.03
774	Tom Gorman	.08	.06	.03
775	Dave Parker	.30	.25	.12
776	Craig Reynolds	.08	.06	.03
777	Tom Paciorek	.08	.06	.03
778	*Andy Hawkins* (FC)	.25	.20	.10
779	Jim Sundberg	.10	.08	.04
780	Steve Carlton	1.00	.70	.40
781	Checklist 661-792	.08	.06	.03
782	Steve Balboni	.10	.08	.04
783	Luis Leal	.08	.06	.03
784	Leon Roberts	.08	.06	.03
785	Joaquin Andujar	.10	.08	.04
786	Red Sox Batting & Pitching Leaders (Wade Boggs, Bob Ojeda)	.40	.30	.15
787	Bill Campbell	.08	.06	.03
788	Milt May	.08	.06	.03
789	Bert Blyleven	.20	.15	.08
790	Doug DeCinces	.12	.09	.05
791	Terry Forster	.10	.08	.04
792	Bill Russell	.10	.08	.04

1984 Topps All-Star Glossy Set of 22

These 2-1/2" by 3-1/2" cards were a result of the success of Topps' efforts the previous year with glossy cards on a mail-in basis. A 22-card set, the cards are divided evenly between the two leagues. Each All-Star Game starter for both leagues, the managers and the honorary team captains have an All-Star Glossy card. The cards feature a large color photo on the front with an All-Star banner across the top and the league emblem in the lower left. The player's name and position appear below the photo. Backs have a name, team, position and card number along with the phrase "1983 All-Star Game Commemorative Set". The '84 Glossy All-Stars were distributed one card per pack in Topps rack packs that year.

		MT	NR MT	EX
Complete Set:		6.00	4.50	2.50
Common Player:		.20	.15	.08
1	Harvey Kuenn	.20	.15	.08
2	Rod Carew	.50	.40	.20
3	Manny Trillo	.20	.15	.08
4	George Brett	.80	.60	.30
5	Robin Yount	.75	.60	.30
6	Jim Rice	.25	.20	.10
7	Fred Lynn	.25	.20	.10
8	Dave Winfield	.50	.40	.20
9	Ted Simmons	.25	.20	.10
10	Dave Stieb	.25	.20	.10
11	Carl Yastrzemski	.80	.60	.30
12	Whitey Herzog	.20	.15	.08
13	Al Oliver	.25	.20	.10
14	Steve Sax	.30	.25	.12
15	Mike Schmidt	.80	.60	.30
16	Ozzie Smith	.50	.40	.20
17	Tim Raines	.35	.25	.14
18	Andre Dawson	.35	.25	.14
19	Dale Murphy	.80	.60	.30
20	Gary Carter	.35	.25	.14
21	Mario Soto	.20	.15	.08
22	Johnny Bench	.60	.45	.25

1984 Topps All-Star Glossy Set of 40

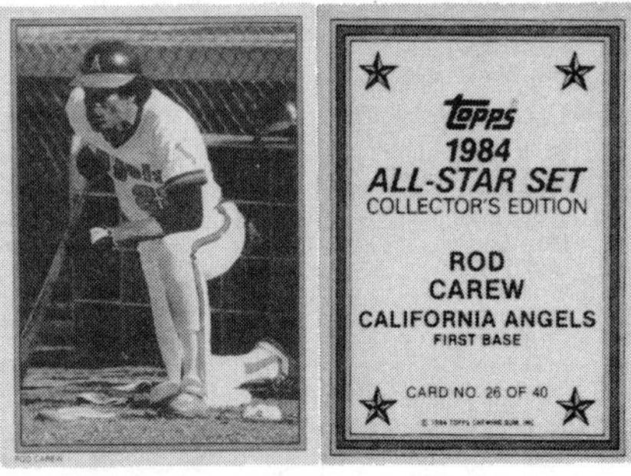

For the second straight year in 1984, Topps produced a 40-card All-Star "Collector's Edition" set as a "consolation prize" for its sweepstakes game. By collecting game cards and sending them in with a bit of cash, the collector could receive one of eight different five-card series. As the previous year, the 2-1/2" by 3-1/2" cards feature a nearly full-frame color photo on its glossy finish front. Backs are printed in red and blue.

		MT	NR MT	EX
Complete Set:		16.00	12.00	6.50
Common Player:		.15	.11	.06
1	Pete Rose	1.25	.90	.50
2	Lance Parrish	.30	.25	.12
3	Steve Rogers	.15	.11	.06
4	Eddie Murray	.60	.45	.25
5	Johnny Ray	.20	.15	.08
6	Rickey Henderson	.70	.50	.30
7	Atlee Hammaker	.15	.11	.06
8	Wade Boggs	3.00	2.25	1.25
9	Gary Carter	.50	.40	.20
10	Jack Morris	.30	.25	.12
11	Darrell Evans	.20	.15	.08
12	George Brett	1.00	.70	.40
13	Bob Horner	.20	.15	.08
14	Ron Guidry	.30	.25	.12
15	Nolan Ryan	1.50	1.25	.60
16	Dave Winfield	.60	.45	.25
17	Ozzie Smith	.45	.35	.20
18	Ted Simmons	.20	.15	.08
19	Bill Madlock	.20	.15	.08
20	Tony Armas	.15	.11	.06
21	Al Oliver	.20	.15	.08
22	Jim Rice	.25	.20	.10
23	George Hendrick	.15	.11	.06
24	Dave Stieb	.20	.15	.08
25	Pedro Guerrero	.25	.20	.10
26	Rod Carew	.60	.45	.25
27	Steve Carlton	.50	.40	.20
28	Dave Righetti	.30	.25	.12
29	Darryl Strawberry	.75	.60	.30
30	Lou Whitaker	.30	.25	.12
31	Dale Murphy	.50	.40	.20
32	LaMarr Hoyt	.15	.11	.06
33	Jesse Orosco	.15	.11	.06
34	Cecil Cooper	.20	.15	.08
35	Andre Dawson	.35	.25	.14
36	Robin Yount	.50	.40	.20
37	Tim Raines	.35	.25	.14
38	Dan Quisenberry	.15	.11	.06
39	Mike Schmidt	1.00	.70	.40
40	Carlton Fisk	.30	.25	.12

1984 Topps Traded

The popular Topps Traded set returned for its fourth year in 1984 with another 132-card set. The 2-1/2" by 3-1/2" cards have an identical design to the

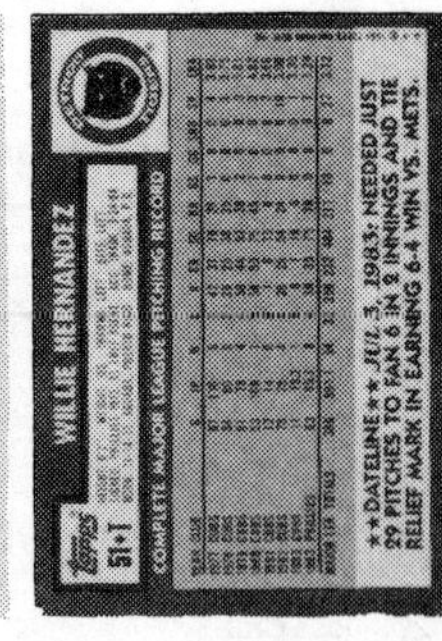

regular Topps cards except that the back cardboard is white and the card numbers carry a "T" suffix. As before, the set was sold only through hobby dealers. Also as before, players who changed teams, new managers and promising rookies are included in the set. The presence of several promising young rookies in especially high demand from investors and speculators had made this one of the most expensive Topps issues of recent years. A glossy-finish "Tiffany" version of the set was also issued, valued at four to five times the price of the normal Traded cards.

		MT	NR MT	EX
Complete Set (132):		60.00	45.00	24.00
Common Player:		.25	.20	.10
1T	Willie Aikens	.25	.20	.10
2T	Luis Aponte	.25	.20	.10
3T	Mike Armstrong	.25	.20	.10
4T	Bob Bailor	.25	.20	.10
5T	Dusty Baker	.50	.40	.20
6T	Steve Balboni	.25	.20	.10
7T	Alan Bannister	.25	.20	.10
8T	Dave Beard	.25	.20	.10
9T	Joe Beckwith	.25	.20	.10
10T	Bruce Berenyi	.25	.20	.10
11T	Dave Bergman	.25	.20	.10
12T	Tony Bernazard	.25	.20	.10
13T	Yogi Berra	.60	.45	.25
14T	Barry Bonnell	.25	.20	.10
15T	Phil Bradley (FC)	.25	.20	.10
16T	Fred Breining	.25	.20	.10
17T	Bill Buckner	.25	.20	.10
18T	Ray Burris	.25	.20	.10
19T	John Butcher	.25	.20	.10
20T	Brett Butler	.25	.20	.10
21T	Enos Cabell	.25	.20	.10
22T	Bill Campbell	.25	.20	.10
23T	Bill Caudill	.25	.20	.10
24T	Bob Clark	.25	.20	.10
25T	Bryan Clark	.25	.20	.10
26T	Jaime Cocanower	.25	.20	.10
27T	Ron Darling (FC)	1.00	.70	.40
28T	Alvin Davis (FC)	.25	.20	.10
29T	Ken Dayley	.25	.20	.10
30T	Jeff Dedmon (FC)	.25	.20	.10
31T	Bob Dernier	.25	.20	.10
32T	Carlos Diaz	.25	.20	.10
33T	Mike Easler	.25	.20	.10
34T	Dennis Eckersley	4.00	3.00	1.50
35T	Jim Essian	.25	.20	.10
36T	Darrell Evans	.25	.20	.10
37T	Mike Fitzgerald (FC)	.25	.20	.10
38T	Tim Foli	.25	.20	.10
39T	George Frazier	.25	.20	.10
40T	Rich Gale	.25	.20	.10
41T	Barbaro Garbey	.25	.20	.10
42T	Dwight Gooden (FC)	18.00	13.50	7.25
43T	Rich Gossage	.40	.30	.15
44T	Wayne Gross	.25	.20	.10
45T	Mark Gubicza (FC)	.90	.70	.35
46T	Jackie Gutierrez	.25	.20	.10
47T	Mel Hall	.30	.25	.12
48T	Toby Harrah	.25	.20	.10
49T	Ron Hassey	.25	.20	.10
50T	Rich Hebner	.25	.20	.10
51T	Willie Hernandez	.25	.20	.10
52T	Ricky Horton (FC)	.25	.20	.10
53T	Art Howe	.25	.20	.10
54T	Dane Iorg	.25	.20	.10
55T	Brook Jacoby (FC)	.25	.20	.10
56T	Mike Jeffcoat (FC)	.25	.20	.10
57T	Dave Johnson	.25	.20	.10
58T	Lynn Jones	.25	.20	.10
59T	Ruppert Jones	.25	.20	.10
60T	Mike Jorgensen	.25	.20	.10
61T	Bob Kearney	.25	.20	.10
62T	Jimmy Key	10.00	7.50	4.00
63T	Dave Kingman	.25	.20	.10
64T	Jerry Koosman	.25	.20	.10
65T	Wayne Krenchicki	.25	.20	.10
66T	Rusty Kuntz	.25	.20	.10
67T	Rene Lachemann	.25	.20	.10
68T	Frank LaCorte	.25	.20	.10
69T	Dennis Lamp	.25	.20	.10
70T	Mark Langston (FC)	10.00	7.50	4.00
71T	Rick Leach	.25	.20	.10
72T	Craig Lefferts	.25	.20	.10
73T	Gary Lucas	.25	.20	.10
74T	Jerry Martin	.25	.20	.10
75T	Carmelo Martinez	.25	.20	.10
76T	Mike Mason (FC)	.25	.20	.10

77T	Gary Matthews	.25	.20	.10
78T	Andy McGaffigan	.25	.20	.10
79T	Larry Milbourne	.25	.20	.10
80T	Sid Monge	.25	.20	.10
81T	Jackie Moore	.25	.20	.10
82T	Joe Morgan	3.00	2.25	1.25
83T	Graig Nettles	.25	.20	.10
84T	Phil Niekro	2.00	1.50	.80
85T	Ken Oberkfell	.25	.20	.10
86T	Mike O'Berry	.25	.20	.10
87T	Al Oliver	.30	.25	.12
88T	Jorge Orta	.25	.20	.10
89T	Amos Otis	.25	.20	.10
90T	Dave Parker	3.00	2.25	1.25
91T	Tony Perez	1.50	1.25	.60
92T	Gerald Perry (FC)	1.50	1.25	.60
93T	Gary Pettis (FC)	.25	.20	.10
94T	Rob Picciolo	.25	.20	.10
95T	Vern Rapp	.25	.20	.10
96T	Floyd Rayford	.25	.20	.10
97T	Randy Ready (FC)	.25	.20	.10
98T	Ron Reed	.25	.20	.10
99T	Gene Richards	.25	.20	.10
100T	Jose Rijo	10.00	7.50	4.00
101T	Jeff Robinson (FC)	.25	.20	.10
102T	Ron Romanick (FC)	.25	.20	.10
103T	Pete Rose	8.00	6.00	3.25
104T	Bret Saberhagen	7.50	5.50	3.00
105T	Juan Samuel (FC)	.50	.40	.20
106T	Scott Sanderson	.25	.20	.10
107T	Dick Schofield (FC)	.25	.20	.10
108T	Tom Seaver	6.00	4.50	2.50
109T	Jim Slaton	.25	.20	.10
110T	Mike Smithson	.25	.20	.10
111T	Lary Sorensen	.25	.20	.10
112T	Tim Stoddard	.25	.20	.10
113T	Champ Summers	.25	.20	.10
114T	Jim Sundberg	.25	.20	.10
115T	Rick Sutcliffe	.50	.40	.20
116T	Craig Swan	.25	.20	.10
117T	Tim Teufel (FC)	.50	.40	.20
118T	Derrel Thomas	.25	.20	.10
119T	Gorman Thomas	.25	.20	.10
120T	Alex Trevino	.25	.20	.10
121T	Manny Trillo	.25	.20	.10
122T	John Tudor	.25	.20	.10
123T	Tom Underwood	.25	.20	.10
124T	Mike Vail	.25	.20	.10
125T	Tom Waddell	.25	.20	.10
126T	Gary Ward	.25	.20	.10
127T	Curt Wilkerson	.25	.20	.10
128T	Frank Williams (FC)	.25	.20	.10
129T	Glenn Wilson	.25	.20	.10
130T	Johnny Wockenfuss	.25	.20	.10
131T	Ned Yost	.25	.20	.10
132T	Checklist 1-132	.25	.20	.10

1984 Topps Cereal Series

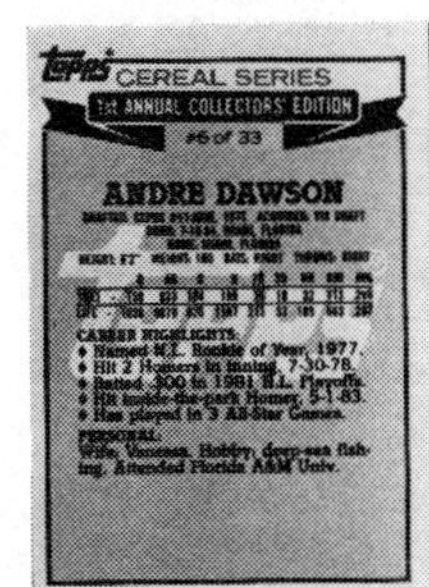

The Topps-produced 1984 Cereal Series set is identical to the Ralston Purina set from the same year in nearly all aspects. On the card fronts the words "Ralston Purina Company" were replaced by "Cereal Series" and Topps logos were substituted for Ralston checkerboard logos. The set is comprised of 33 cards, each measuring 2-1/2" by 3-1/2." The cards were inserted in unmarked boxes of Chex brand cereals.

		MT	NR MT	EX
Complete Set:		13.00	9.75	5.25
Common Player:		.20	.15	.08
1	Eddie Murray	.50	.40	.20
2	Ozzie Smith	.40	.30	.15
3	Ted Simmons	.20	.15	.08
4	Pete Rose	.60	.45	.25
5	Greg Luzinski	.20	.15	.08
6	Andre Dawson	.40	.30	.15
7	Dave Winfield	.50	.40	.20
8	Tom Seaver	.50	.40	.20
9	Jim Rice	.35	.25	.14
10	Fernando Valenzuela	.25	.20	.10
11	Wade Boggs	1.00	.70	.40
12	Dale Murphy	.70	.50	.30
13	George Brett	1.00	.70	.40
14	Nolan Ryan	2.00	1.50	.80
15	Rickey Henderson	.80	.60	.30
16	Steve Carlton	.50	.40	.20
17	Rod Carew	.50	.40	.20
18	Steve Garvey	.40	.30	.15
19	Reggie Jackson	1.00	.70	.40
20	Dave Concepcion	.20	.15	.08
21	Robin Yount	.60	.45	.25
22	Mike Schmidt	1.00	.70	.40
23	Jim Palmer	.60	.45	.25
24	Bruce Sutter	.20	.15	.08
25	Dan Quisenberry	.20	.15	.08
26	Bill Madlock	.20	.15	.08
27	Cecil Cooper	.20	.15	.08
28	Gary Carter	.30	.25	.12
29	Fred Lynn	.30	.25	.12
30	Pedro Guerrero	.20	.15	.08
31	Ron Guidry	.20	.15	.08
32	Keith Hernandez	.20	.15	.08
33	Carlton Fisk	.30	.25	.12

1984 Topps Gallery of Immortals

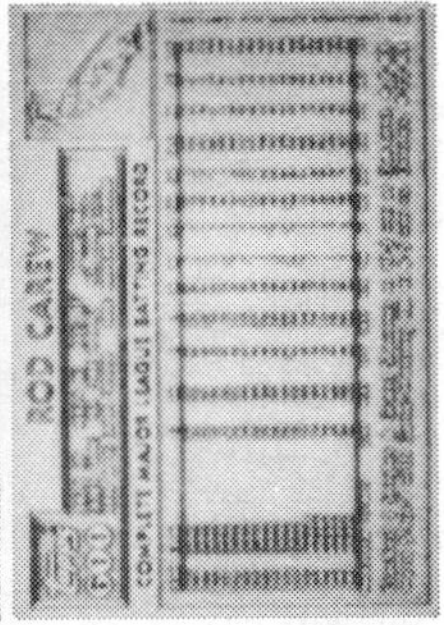

The Gallery of Immortals set of aluminum, bronze and silver replicas was the first miniature set of 12 from Topps and the start of an annual tradition (in 1985, the name was changed to Gallery of Champions). Each mini is an exact replica (one-quarter scale) of the featured player's official Topps baseball card card, both front and back, in minute detail. The bronze and silver sets include a dozen three-dimensional raised metal cards packaged in a velvet-lined case that bears the title of the set in gold-embossed letters. A certificate of authenticity is included with each set. A Tom Seaver pewter metal mini-card was given as a premium to dealers who purchsed bronze and silver sets (value $75). A Darryl Strawberry bronze was given as a premium to dealers who purchased cases of the 1984 Topps Traded sets (value $12). Additionally, a Steve Carlton bronze was issued as a premium in 1983 to dealers who purchased 1983 Topps Traded sets (value $50).

		MT	NR MT	EX
Complete Aluminum Set:		30.00	22.00	12.00
Complete Bronze Set:		175.00	131.00	70.00
Complete Silver Set:		600.00	450.00	240.00
(1a)	George Brett (aluminum)	1.50	1.25	.60
(1b)	George Brett (bronze)	15.00	11.00	6.00
(1c)	George Brett (silver)	80.00	60.00	32.00
(2a)	Rod Carew (aluminum)	1.50	1.25	.60
(2b)	Rod Carew (bronze)	12.50	9.50	5.00
(2c)	Rod Carew (silver)	50.00	37.00	20.00
(3a)	Steve Carlton (aluminum)	1.50	1.25	.60
(3b)	Steve Carlton (bronze)	12.50	9.50	5.00
(3c)	Steve Carlton (silver)	50.00	37.00	20.00
(4a)	Rollie Fingers (aluminum)	1.25	.90	.50
(4b)	Rollie Fingers (bronze)	10.00	7.50	4.00
(4c)	Rollie Fingers (silver)	20.00	15.00	8.00
(5a)	Steve Garvey (aluminum)	1.50	1.25	.60
(5b)	Steve Garvey (bronze)	12.50	9.50	5.00
(5c)	Steve Garvey (silver)	50.00	37.00	20.00
(6a)	Reggie Jackson (aluminum)	1.50	1.25	.60
(6b)	Reggie Jackson (bronze)	15.00	11.00	6.00
(6c)	Reggie Jackson (silver)	80.00	60.00	32.00
(7a)	Joe Morgan (aluminum)	1.25	.90	.50
(7b)	Joe Morgan (bronze)	10.00	7.50	4.00
(7c)	Joe Morgan (silver)	20.00	15.00	8.00
(8a)	Jim Palmer (aluminum)	1.25	.90	.50
(8b)	Jim Palmer (bronze)	10.00	7.50	4.00
(8c)	Jim Palmer (silver)	20.00	15.00	8.00
(9a)	Pete Rose (aluminum)	2.50	2.00	1.00
(9b)	Pete Rose (bronze)	25.00	18.50	10.00
(9c)	Pete Rose (silver)	110.00	82.00	44.00
(10a)	Nolan Ryan (aluminum)	2.50	2.00	1.00
(10b)	Nolan Ryan (bronze)	22.00	16.50	8.75
(10c)	Nolan Ryan (silver)	95.00	71.00	38.00
(11a)	Mike Schmidt (aluminum)	2.00	1.50	.80
(11b)	Mike Schmidt (bronze)	15.00	11.00	6.00
(11c)	Mike Schmidt (silver)	80.00	60.00	32.00
(12a)	Tom Seaver (aluminum)	1.50	1.25	.60
(12b)	Tom Seaver (bronze)	12.50	9.50	5.00
(12c)	Tom Seaver (silver)	50.00	37.00	20.00

1984 Topps Rub Downs

This set, produced by Topps in 1984, consists of 32 "Rub Down" sheets featuring 112 different players. Each sheet measures 2-3/8" by 3-15/16" and includes small, color baseball player figures along with bats, balls and gloves. The pictures can be

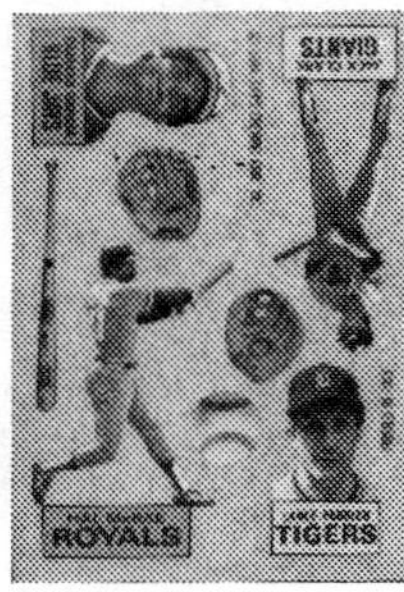

transferred to another surface by rubbing the paper backing. The sheets, which were sold as a separate issue, are somewhat reminiscent of earlier tattoo sets issued by Topps. The sheets are not numbered.

		MT	NR MT	EX
Complete Set:		9.00	6.75	3.50
Common Player:		.10	.08	.04
(1)	Tony Armas, Harold Baines, Lonnie Smith	.10	.08	.04
(2)	Don Baylor, George Hendrick, Ron Kittle, Johnnie LeMaster	.10	.08	.04
(3)	Buddy Bell, Ray Knight, Lloyd Moseby	.10	.08	.04
(4)	Bruce Benedict, Atlee Hammaker, Frank White	.10	.08	.04
(5)	Wade Boggs, Rick Dempsey, Keith Hernandez	.60	.45	.25
(6)	George Brett, Andre Dawson, Paul Molitor, Alan Wiggins	.30	.25	.12
(7)	Tom Brunansky, Pedro Guerrero, Darryl Strawberry	.40	.30	.15
(8)	Bill Buckner, Rich Gossage, Dave Stieb, Rick Sutcliffe	.15	.11	.06
(9)	Rod Carew, Carlton Fisk, Johnny Ray, Matt Young	.25	.20	.10
(10)	Steve Carlton, Bob Horner, Dan Quisenberry	.25	.20	.10
(11)	Gary Carter, Phil Garner, Ron Guidry	.25	.20	.10
(12)	Ron Cey, Steve Kemp, Greg Luzinski, Kent Tekulve	.10	.08	.04
(13)	Chris Chambliss, Dwight Evans, Julio Franco	.15	.11	.06
(14)	Jack Clark, Damaso Garcia, Hal McRae, Lance Parrish	.20	.15	.08
(15)	Dave Concepcion, Cecil Cooper, Fred Lynn, Jesse Orosco	.15	.11	.06
(16)	Jose Cruz, Gary Matthews, Jack Morris, Jim Rice	.20	.15	.08
(17)	Ron Davis, Kent Hrbek, Tom Seaver	.25	.20	.10
(18)	John Denny, Carney Lansford, Mario Soto, Lou Whitaker	.10	.08	.04
(19)	Leon Durham, Dave Lopes, Steve Sax	.15	.11	.06
(20)	George Foster, Gary Gaetti, Bobby Grich, Gary Redus	.15	.11	.06
(21)	Steve Garvey, Bill Russell, Jerry REmy, George Wright	.20	.15	.08
(22)	Moose Haas, Bruce Sutter, Dickie Thon, Andre Thornton	.10	.08	.04
(23)	Toby Harrah, Pat Putnam, Tim Raines, Mike Schmidt	.30	.25	.12
(24)	Rickey Henderson, Dave Righetti, Pete Rose	.70	.50	.30
(25)	Steve Henderson, Bill Madlock, Alan Trammell	.20	.15	.08
(26)	LaMarr Hoyt, Larry Parrish, Nolan Ryan	.45	.35	.20
(27)	Reggie Jackson, Eric Show, Jason Thompson	.30	.25	.12
(28)	Tommy John, Terry Kennedy, Eddie Murray, Ozzie Smith	.25	.20	.10
(29)	Jeff Leonard, Dale Murphy, Ken Singleton, Dave Winfield	.30	.25	.12
(30)	Craig McMurtry, Cal Ripken, Steve Rogers, Willie Upshaw	.25	.20	.10
(31)	Ben Oglivie, Jim Palmer, Darrell Porter	.20	.15	.08
(32)	Tony Pena, Fernando Valenzuela, Robin Yount	.35	.25	.14

Values quoted in this guide reflect the retail price of a card – the price a collector can expect to pay when buying a card from a dealer. The wholesale price – that which a collector can expect to receive from a dealer when selling cards – will be significantly lower, depending on desirability and condition.

1984 Topps Stickers

The largest sticker set issued by Topps, the 1984 set consists of 386 stickers, each measuring 1-15/16" by 2-9/16". The full color photos have stars in each of the corners and are numbered on both the

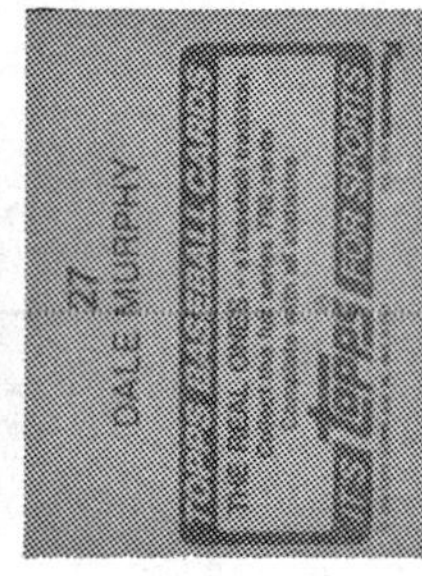

front and the back. The back includes information about the sticker album and a promotion to order stickers through the mail.

		MT	NR MT	EX
Complete Set:		15.00	11.00	6.00
Common Player:		.03	.02	.01
Sticker Album:		.80	.60	.30
1	Steve Carlton	.15	.11	.06
2	Steve Carlton	.12	.09	.05
3	Rickey Henderson	.20	.15	.08
4	Rickey Henderson	.15	.11	.06
5	Fred Lynn	.12	.09	.05
6	Fred Lynn	.10	.08	.04
7	Greg Luzinski	.08	.06	.03
8	Greg Luzinski	.06	.05	.02
9	Dan Quisenberry	.08	.06	.03
10	Dan Quisenberry	.06	.05	.02
11	1983 Championship (LaMarr Hoyt)	.03	.02	.01
12	1983 Championship (Mike Flanagan)	.04	.03	.02
13	1983 Championship (Mike Boddicker)	.04	.03	.02
14	1983 Championship (Tito Landrum)	.03	.02	.01
15	1983 Championship (Steve Carlton)	.12	.09	.05
16	1983 Championship (Fernando Valenzuela)	.12	.09	.05
17	1983 Championship (Charlie Hudson)	.03	.02	.01
18	1983 Championship (Gary Matthews)	.04	.03	.02
19	1983 World Series (John Denny)	.03	.02	.01
20	1983 World Series (John Lowenstein)	.03	.02	.01
21	1983 World Series (Jim Palmer)	.10	.08	.04
22	1983 World Series (Benny Ayala)	.03	.02	.01
23	1983 World Series (Rick Dempsey)	.03	.02	.01
24	1983 World Series (Cal Ripken)	.15	.11	.06
25	1983 World Series (Sammy Stewart)	.03	.02	.01
26	1983 World Series (Eddie Murray)	.15	.11	.06
27	Dale Murphy	.25	.20	.10
28	Chris Chambliss	.04	.03	.02
29	Glenn Hubbard	.04	.03	.02
30	Bob Horner	.08	.06	.03
31	Phil Niekro	.12	.09	.05
32	Claudell Washington	.04	.03	.02
33	Rafael Ramirez	.03	.02	.01
34	Bruce Benedict	.04	.03	.02
35	Gene Garber	.03	.02	.01
36	Pascual Perez	.04	.03	.02
37	Jerry Royster	.03	.02	.01
38	Steve Bedrosian	.06	.05	.02
39	Keith Moreland	.06	.05	.02
40	Leon Durham	.06	.05	.02
41	Ron Cey	.06	.05	.02
42	Bill Buckner	.06	.05	.02
43	Jody Davis	.06	.05	.02
44	Lee Smith	.06	.05	.02
45	Ryne Sandberg	.20	.15	.08
46	Larry Bowa	.04	.03	.02
47	Chuck Rainey	.04	.03	.02
48	Fergie Jenkins	.06	.05	.02
49	Dick Ruthven	.03	.02	.01
50	Jay Johnstone	.04	.03	.02
51	Mario Soto	.06	.05	.02
52	Gary Redus	.04	.03	.02
53	Ron Oester	.04	.03	.02
54	Cesar Cedeno	.06	.05	.02
55	Dan Driessen	.04	.03	.02
56	Dave Concepcion	.06	.05	.02
57	Dann Bilardello	.03	.02	.01
58	Joe Price	.03	.02	.01
59	Tom Hume	.03	.02	.01
60	Eddie Milner	.03	.02	.01
61	Paul Householder	.04	.03	.02
62	Bill Scherrer	.04	.03	.02
63	Phil Garner	.04	.03	.02
64	Dickie Thon	.04	.03	.02
65	Jose Cruz	.06	.05	.02
66	Nolan Ryan	.40	.30	.15
67	Terry Puhl	.03	.02	.01
68	Ray Knight	.06	.05	.02
69	Joe Niekro	.06	.05	.02
70	Jerry Mumphrey	.10	.08	.04
71	Bill Dawley	.03	.02	.01
72	Alan Ashby	.04	.03	.02
73	Denny Walling	.04	.03	.02
74	Frank DiPino	.04	.03	.02
75	Pedro Guerrero	.12	.09	.05
76	Ken Landreaux	.03	.02	.01
77	Bill Russell	.04	.03	.02
78	Steve Sax	.10	.08	.04
79	Fernando Valenzuela	.15	.11	.06
80	Dusty Baker	.04	.03	.02
81	Jerry Reuss	.04	.03	.02
82	Alejandro Pena	.04	.03	.02
83	Rick Monday	.06	.05	.02
84	Rick Honeycutt	.03	.02	.01
85	Mike Marshall	.06	.05	.02
86	Steve Yeager	.04	.03	.02
87	Al Oliver	.06	.05	.02
88	Steve Rogers	.03	.02	.01
89	Jeff Reardon	.08	.06	.03
90	Gary Carter	.20	.15	.08
91	Tim Raines	.15	.11	.06
92	Andre Dawson	.12	.09	.05
93	Manny Trillo	.04	.03	.02
94	Tim Wallach	.06	.05	.02
95	Chris Speier	.03	.02	.01
96	Bill Gullickson	.04	.03	.02
97	Doug Flynn	.04	.03	.02
98	Charlie Lea	.03	.02	.01
99	Bill Madlock	.06	.05	.02
100	Wade Boggs	.25	.20	.10
101	Mike Schmidt	.25	.20	.10
102a	Jim Rice	.06	.05	.02
102b	Reggie Jackson	.15	.11	.06
103	Hubie Brooks	.06	.05	.02
104	Jesse Orosco	.04	.03	.02
105	George Foster	.08	.06	.03
106	Tom Seaver	.20	.15	.08
107	Keith Hernandez	.08	.06	.03
108	Mookie Wilson	.06	.05	.02
109	Bob Bailor	.03	.02	.01
110	Walt Terrell	.04	.03	.02
111	Brian Giles	.06	.05	.02
112	Jose Oquendo	.06	.05	.02
113	Mike Torrez	.03	.02	.01
114	Junior Ortiz	.03	.02	.01
115	Pete Rose	.30	.25	.12
116	Joe Morgan	.12	.09	.05
117	Mike Schmidt	.25	.20	.10
118	Gary Matthews	.06	.05	.02
119	Steve Carlton	.15	.11	.06
120	Bo Diaz	.04	.03	.02
121	Ivan DeJesus	.04	.03	.02
122	John Denny	.03	.02	.01
123	Garry Maddox	.03	.02	.01
124	Von Hayes	.08	.06	.03
125	Al Holland	.03	.02	.01
126	Tony Perez	.06	.05	.02
127	John Candelaria	.06	.05	.02
128	Jason Thompson	.03	.02	.01
129	Tony Pena	.06	.05	.02
130	Dave Parker	.12	.09	.05
131	Bill Madlock	.08	.06	.03
132	Kent Tekulve	.04	.03	.02
133	larry McWilliams	.03	.02	.01
134	Johnny Ray	.04	.03	.02
135	Marvell Wynne	.03	.02	.01
136	Dale Berra	.03	.02	.01
137	Mike Easler	.03	.02	.01
138	Lee Lacy	.03	.02	.01
139	George Hendrick	.04	.03	.02
140	Lonnie Smith	.04	.03	.02
141	Willie McGee	.08	.06	.03
142	Tom Herr	.06	.05	.02
143	Darrell Porter	.04	.03	.02
144	Ozzie Smith	.25	.20	.10
145	Bruce Sutter	.06	.05	.02
146	Dave LaPoint	.03	.02	.01
147	Neil Allen	.03	.02	.01
148	Ken Oberkfell	.04	.03	.02
149	David Green	.03	.02	.01
150	Andy Van Slyke	.04	.03	.02
151	Garry Templeton	.06	.05	.02
152	Juan Bonilla	.03	.02	.01
153	Alan Wiggins	.03	.02	.01
154	Terry Kennedy	.04	.03	.02
155	Dave Dravecky	.04	.03	.02
156	Steve Garvey	.15	.11	.06
157	Bobby Brown	.04	.03	.02
158	Ruppert Jones	.03	.02	.01
159	Luis Salazar	.03	.02	.01
160	Tony Gwynn	.12	.09	.05
161	Gary Lucas	.10	.08	.04
162	Eric Show	.04	.03	.02
163	Darrell Evans	.08	.06	.03
164	Gary Lavelle	.03	.02	.01
165	Atlee Hammaker	.03	.02	.01
166	Jeff Leonard	.06	.05	.02
167	Jack Clark	.10	.08	.04
168	Johnny LeMaster	.03	.02	.01
169	Duane Kuiper	.03	.02	.01
170	Tom O'Malley	.06	.05	.02
171	Chili Davis	.10	.08	.04
172	Bill Laskey	.03	.02	.01
173	Joel Youngblood	.06	.05	.02
174	Bob Brenly	.06	.05	.02
175	Atlee Hammaker	.15	.11	.06
176	Rick Honeycutt	.15	.11	.06
177	John Denny	.06	.05	.02
178	LaMarr Hoyt	.03	.02	.01
179	Tim Raines	.30	.25	.12
180	Dale Murphy	.40	.30	.15
181	Andre Dawson	.25	.20	.10
182	Steve Rogers	.15	.11	.06
183	Gary Carter	.30	.25	.12
184	Steve Carlton	.25	.20	.10
185	George Hendrick	.15	.11	.06
186	Johnny Ray	.15	.11	.06
187	Ozzie Smith	.20	.15	.08
188	Mike Schmidt	.40	.30	.15
189	Jim Rice	.30	.25	.12
190	Dave Winfield	.30	.25	.12
191	Lloyd Moseby	.15	.11	.06
192	LaMarr Hoyt	.15	.11	.06
193	Ted Simmons	.15	.11	.06
194	Ron Guidry	.20	.15	.08
195	Eddie Murray	.40	.30	.15
196	Lou Whitaker	.25	.20	.10
197	Cal Ripken, Jr.	.40	.30	.15
198	George Brett	.40	.30	.15
199	Dale Murphy	.15	.11	.06
200a	Cecil Cooper	.03	.02	.01
200b	Jim Rice	.10	.08	.04
201	Tim Raines	.10	.08	.04
202	Rickey Henderson	.15	.11	.06
203	Eddie Murray	.20	.15	.08
204	Cal Ripken	.20	.15	.08
205	Gary Roenicke	.03	.02	.01
206	Ken Singleton	.06	.05	.02
207	Scott McGregor	.04	.03	.02
208	Tippy Martinez	.03	.02	.01
209	John Lowenstein	.04	.03	.02
210	Mike Flanagan	.04	.03	.02
211	Jim Palmer	.10	.08	.04
212	Dan Ford	.12	.09	.05
213	Rick Dempsey	.04	.03	.02
214	Rich Dauer	.03	.02	.01
215	Jerry Remy	.03	.02	.01
216	Wade Boggs	.50	.40	.20
217	Jim Rice	.20	.15	.08
218	Tony Armas	.06	.05	.02
219	Dwight Evans	.08	.06	.03
220	Bob Stanley	.04	.03	.02
221	Dave Stapleton	.06	.05	.02
222	Rich Gedman	.04	.03	.02
223	Glenn Hoffman	.06	.05	.02
224	Dennis Eckersley	.15	.11	.06
225	John Tudor	.06	.05	.02
226	Bruce Hurst	.04	.03	.02
227	Rod Carew	.20	.15	.08
228	Bobby Grich	.06	.05	.02
229	Doug DeCinces	.06	.05	.02
230	Fred Lynn	.10	.08	.04
231	Reggie Jackson	.20	.15	.08
232	Tommy John	.10	.08	.04
233	Luis Sanchez	.03	.02	.01
234	Bob Boone	.08	.06	.03
235	Bruce Kison	.04	.03	.02
236	Brian Downing	.04	.03	.02
237	Ken Forsch	.03	.02	.01
238	Rick Burleson	.04	.03	.02
239	Dennis Lamp	.03	.02	.01
240	LaMarr Hoyt	.03	.02	.01
241	Richard Dotson	.04	.03	.02
242	Harold Baines	.10	.08	.04
243	Carlton Fisk	.12	.09	.05
244	Greg Luzinski	.08	.06	.03
245	Rudy Law	.06	.05	.02
246	Tom Paciorek	.03	.02	.01
247	Floyd Bannister	.04	.03	.02
248	Julio Cruz	.04	.03	.02
249	Vance Law	.03	.02	.01
250	Scott Fletcher	.04	.03	.02
251	Toby Harrah	.04	.03	.02
252	Pat Tabler	.04	.03	.02
253	Gorman Thomas	.06	.05	.02
254	Rick Sutcliffe	.08	.06	.03
255	Andre Thornton	.06	.05	.02
256	Bake McBride	.03	.02	.01
257	Alan Bannister	.03	.02	.01
258	Jamie Easterly	.03	.02	.01
259	Lary Sorenson	.03	.02	.01
260	Mike Hargrove	.03	.02	.01
261	Bert Blyleven	.06	.05	.02
262	Ron Hassey	.04	.03	.02
263	Jack Morris	.12	.09	.05
264	Larry Herndon	.03	.02	.01
265	Lance Parrish	.12	.09	.05
266	Alan Trammell	.15	.11	.06
267	Lou Whitaker	.12	.09	.05
268	Aurelio Lopez	.03	.02	.01
269	Dan Petry	.04	.03	.02
270	Glenn Wilson	.04	.03	.02
271	Chet Lemon	.04	.03	.02
272	Kirk Gibson	.06	.05	.02
273	Enos Cabell	.04	.03	.02
274	Johnny Wockenfuss	.03	.02	.01
275	George Brett	.25	.20	.10
276	Willie Aikens	.03	.02	.01
277	Frank White	.04	.03	.02
278	Hal McRae	.06	.05	.02
279	Dan Quisenberry	.06	.05	.02
280	Willie Wilson	.08	.06	.03
281	Paul Splitorff	.03	.02	.01
282	U.L. Washington	.03	.02	.01
283	Bud Black	.06	.05	.02
284	John Wathan	.04	.03	.02
285	Larry Gura	.03	.02	.01
286	Pat Sheridan	.03	.02	.01
287a	Rusty Staub	.06	.05	.02
287b	Dave Righetti	.25	.20	.10
288a	Bob Forsch	.03	.02	.01
288b	Mike Warren	.06	.05	.02
289	Al Holland	.10	.08	.04
290	Dan Quisenberry	.15	.11	.06
291	Cecil Cooper	.06	.05	.02
292	Moose Haas	.03	.02	.01
293	Ted Simmons	.08	.06	.03
294	Paul Molitor	.20	.15	.08
295	Robin Yount	.35	.25	.14
296	Ben Oglivie	.04	.03	.02
297	Tom Tellmann	.50	.40	.20
298	Jim Gantner	.04	.03	.02
299	Rick Manning	.03	.02	.01
300	Don Sutton	.06	.05	.02
301	Charlie Moore	.04	.03	.02
302	Jim Slaton	.03	.02	.01
303	Gary Ward	.04	.03	.02
304	Tom Brunansky	.08	.06	.03
305	Kent Hrbek	.12	.09	.05
306	Gary Gaetti	.10	.08	.04

307	John Castino	.03	.02	.01
308	Ken Schrom	.03	.02	.01
309	Ron Davis	.03	.02	.01
310	Lenny Faedo	.03	.02	.01
311	Darrell Brown	.06	.05	.02
312	Frank Viola	.06	.05	.02
313	Dave Engle	.03	.02	.01
314	Randy Bush	.03	.02	.01
315	Dave Righetti	.12	.09	.05
316	Rich Gossage	.12	.09	.05
317	Ken Griffey	.06	.05	.02
318	Ron Guidry	.12	.09	.05
319	Dave Winfield	.30	.25	.12
320	Don Baylor	.08	.06	.03
321	Butch Wynegar	.03	.02	.01
322	Omar Moreno	.03	.02	.01
323	Andre Robertson	.03	.02	.01
324	Willie Randolph	.04	.03	.02
325	Don Mattingly	.50	.40	.20
326	Graig Nettles	.06	.05	.02
327	Rickey Henderson	.25	.20	.10
328	Carney Lansford	.08	.06	.03
329	Jeff Burroughs	.04	.03	.02
330	Chris Codiroli	.03	.02	.01
331	Dave Lopes	.06	.05	.02
332	Dwayne Murphy	.04	.03	.02
333	Wayne Gross	.03	.02	.01
334	Bill Almon	.03	.02	.01
335	Tom Underwood	.04	.03	.02
336	Dave Beard	.03	.02	.01
337	Mike Heath	.03	.02	.01
338	Mike Davis	.04	.03	.02
339	Pat Putnam	.03	.02	.01
340	Tony Bernazard	.03	.02	.01
341	Steve Henderson	.03	.02	.01
342	Richie Zisk	.04	.03	.02
343	Dave Henderson	.06	.05	.02
344	Al Cowens	.03	.02	.01
345	Bill Caudill	.03	.02	.01
346	Jim Beattie	.06	.05	.02
347	Ricky Nelson	.04	.03	.02
348	Roy Thomas	.06	.05	.02
349	Spike Owen	.04	.03	.02
350	Jamie Allen	.03	.02	.01
351	Buddy Bell	.06	.05	.02
352	Billy Sample	.03	.02	.01
353	George Wright	.03	.02	.01
354	Larry Parrish	.06	.05	.02
355	Jim Sundberg	.04	.03	.02
356	Charlie Hough	.06	.05	.02
357	Pete O'Brien	.06	.05	.02
358	Wayne Tolleson	.03	.02	.01
359	Danny Darwin	.03	.02	.01
360	Dave Stewart	.10	.08	.04
361	Mickey Rivers	.04	.03	.02
362	Bucky Dent	.04	.03	.02
363	Willie Upshaw	.06	.05	.02
364	Damaso Garcia	.04	.03	.02
365	Lloyd Moseby	.06	.05	.02
366	Cliff Johnson	.03	.02	.01
367	Jim Clancy	.04	.03	.02
368	Dave Stieb	.06	.05	.02
369	Alfredo Griffin	.04	.03	.02
370	Barry Bonnell	.04	.03	.02
371	Luis Leal	.03	.02	.01
372	Jesse Barfield	.06	.05	.02
373	Ernie Whitt	.03	.02	.01
374	Rance Mulliniks	.06	.05	.02
375	Mike Boddicker	.06	.05	.02
376	Greg Brock	.06	.05	.02
377	Bill Doran	.06	.05	.02
378	Nick Esasky	.06	.05	.02
379	Julio Franco	.08	.06	.03
380	Mel Hall	.06	.05	.02
381	Bob Kearney	.03	.02	.01
382	Ron Kittle	.06	.05	.02
383	Carmelo Martinez	.06	.05	.02
384	Craig McMurtry	.03	.02	.01
385	Darryl Strawberry	.15	.11	.06
386	Matt Young	.04	.03	.02

1984 Topps Stickers Boxes

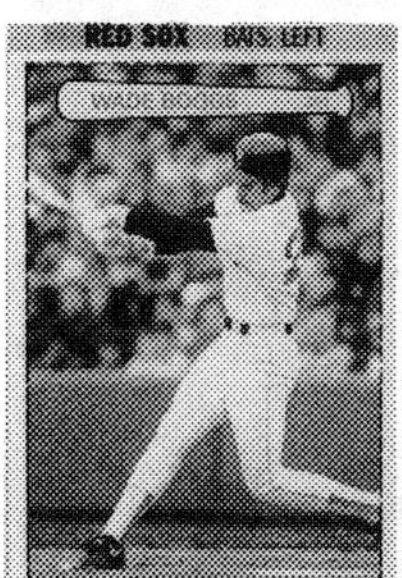

For the second straight year, Topps printed baseball cards on the back of its sticker boxes. The 1984 set, titled "The Super Bats" features 24 hitting leaders. The cards are blank-backed and measure 2-1/2" by 3-1/2". Two cards were printed on each of 12 different boxes. The player's name appears inside a bat above his photo. Prices listed are for complete boxes.

		MT	NR MT	EX
Complete Set:		8.50	6.50	3.50
Common Player:		.75	.60	.30
1	Al Oliver, Lou Whitaker	1.00	.70	.40
2	Ken Oberkfell, Ted Simmons	.75	.60	.30
3	Hal McRae, Alan Wiggins	.75	.60	.30
4	Lloyd Moseby, Tim Raines	1.00	.70	.40
5	Lonnie Smith, Willie Wilson	.75	.60	.30
6	Keith Hernandez, Robin Yount	.75	.60	.30
7	Wade Boggs, Johnny Ray	1.50	1.25	.60
8	Willie McGee, Ken Singleton	.75	.60	.30
9	Ray Knight, Alan Trammell	1.00	.70	.40
11	Rod Carew, George Hendrick	1.25	.90	.50
12	Bill Madlock, Eddie Murray	1.25	.90	.50
13	Jose Cruz, Cal Ripken, Jr.	1.75	1.25	.70

1984 Topps Super

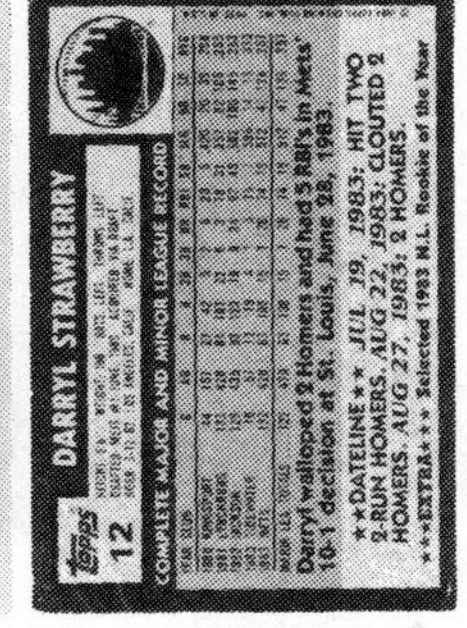

The next installment in Topps' continuing production of large-format cards, these 4-7/8" by 6-7/8" cards were sold in cellophane packs with a complete set being 30 cards. Other than their size and the change in card number on the back, there is nothing to distinguish the Supers from the regular 1984 Topps cards of the same players. One plus is that the players are all big name stars, and are likely to remain in demand.

		MT	NR MT	EX
Complete Set:		12.00	9.00	4.75
Common Player:		.25	.20	.10
1	Cal Ripken, Jr.	2.00	1.50	.80
2	Dale Murphy	.90	.70	.35
3	LaMarr Hoyt	.25	.20	.10
4	John Denny	.25	.20	.10
5	Jim Rice	.50	.40	.20
6	Mike Schmidt	.90	.70	.35
7	Wade Boggs	.75	.60	.30
8	Bill Madlock	.25	.20	.10
9	Dan Quisenberry	.25	.20	.10
10	Al Holland	.25	.20	.10
11	Ron Kittle	.25	.20	.10
12	Darryl Strawberry	.75	.60	.30
13	George Brett	.90	.70	.35
14	Bill Buckner	.25	.20	.10
15	Carlton Fisk	.30	.25	.12
16	Steve Carlton	.50	.40	.20
17	Ron Guidry	.35	.25	.14
18	Gary Carter	.50	.40	.20
19	Rickey Henderson	.90	.70	.35
20	Andre Dawson	.35	.25	.14
21	Reggie Jackson	.90	.70	.35
22	Steve Garvey	.50	.40	.20
23	Fred Lynn	.50	.40	.20
24	Pedro Guerrero	.25	.20	.10
25	Eddie Murray	.60	.45	.25
26	Keith Hernandez	.35	.25	.14
27	Dave Winfield	.50	.40	.20
28	Nolan Ryan	2.00	1.50	.80
29	Robin Yount	.90	.70	.35
30	Fernando Valenzuela	.40	.30	.15

1985 Topps

Holding the line at 792 cards, Topps did initiate some major design changes in its 2-1/2" by 3-1/2" cards in 1985. The use of two photos on the front was discontinued in favor of one large color photo. The Topps logo appears in the upper left-hand corner. At the bottom runs a diagonal rectangular box with the team name. It joins a team logo, and below that point runs the player's position and name. The backs feature statistics, biographical information and a trivia question. Some interesting specialty sets were introduced in 1985, including the revival of the father/son theme from 1976, a subset of the 1984 U.S. Olympic Baseball Team members and a set featuring #1 draft choices since the inception of the baseball draft in 1965. Again in 1985, a glossy-finish "Tiffany" edition of the regular set was produced, though the number was cut back to 5,000 sets. Values range from four times regular value for common cards to five-six times for high-demand stars and rookie cards.

		MT	NR MT	EX
Complete Set (792):		80.00	60.00	32.00
Common Player:		.06	.05	.02
1	Carlton Fisk (Record Breaker)	.25	.20	.10
2	Steve Garvey (Record Breaker)	.20	.15	.08
3	Dwight Gooden (Record Breaker)	.25	.20	.10
4	Cliff Johnson (Record Breaker)	.08	.06	.03
5	Joe Morgan (Record Breaker)	.15	.11	.06
6	Pete Rose (Record Breaker)	.60	.45	.25
7	Nolan Ryan (Record Breaker)	1.50	1.25	.60
8	Juan Samuel (FC) (Record Breaker)	.12	.09	.05
9	Bruce Sutter (Record Breaker)	.12	.09	.05
10	Don Sutton (Record Breaker)	.20	.15	.08
11	Ralph Houk	.08	.06	.03
12	Dave Lopes	.08	.06	.03
13	Tim Lollar	.06	.05	.02
14	Chris Bando	.06	.05	.02
15	Jerry Koosman	.10	.08	.04
16	Bobby Meacham	.06	.05	.02
17	Mike Scott	.15	.11	.06
18	Mickey Hatcher	.06	.05	.02
19	George Frazier	.06	.05	.02
20	Chet Lemon	.08	.06	.03
21	Lee Tunnell	.06	.05	.02
22	Duane Kuiper	.06	.05	.02
23	*Bret Saberhagen*	1.25	.90	.50
24	Jesse Barfield	.15	.11	.06
25	Steve Bedrosian	.12	.09	.05
26	Roy Smalley	.06	.05	.02
27	Bruce Berenyi	.06	.05	.02
28	Dann Bilardello	.06	.05	.02
29	Odell Jones	.06	.05	.02
30	Cal Ripken, Jr.	4.00	3.00	1.50
31	Terry Whitfield	.06	.05	.02
32	Chuck Porter	.06	.05	.02
33	Tito Landrum	.06	.05	.02
34	Ed Nunez (FC)	.08	.06	.03
35	Graig Nettles	.15	.11	.06
36	Fred Breining	.06	.05	.02
37	Reid Nichols	.06	.05	.02
38	Jackie Moore	.06	.05	.02
39	Johnny Wockenfuss	.06	.05	.02
40	Phil Niekro	.25	.20	.10
41	Mike Fischlin	.06	.05	.02
42	Luis Sanchez	.06	.05	.02
43	Andre David	.06	.05	.02
44	Dickie Thon	.08	.06	.03
45	Greg Minton	.06	.05	.02
46	Gary Woods	.06	.05	.02
47	Dave Rozema	.06	.05	.02
48	Tony Fernandez (FC)	.25	.20	.10
49	Butch Davis	.06	.05	.02
50	John Candelaria	.10	.08	.04
51	Bob Watson	.08	.06	.03
52	Jerry Dybzinski	.06	.05	.02
53	Tom Gorman	.06	.05	.02
54	Cesar Cedeno	.10	.08	.04
55	Frank Tanana	.10	.08	.04
56	Jim Dwyer	.06	.05	.02
57	Pat Zachry	.06	.05	.02
58	Orlando Mercado	.06	.05	.02
59	Rick Waits	.06	.05	.02
60	George Hendrick	.08	.06	.03
61	Curt Kaufman	.06	.05	.02
62	Mike Ramsey	.06	.05	.02
63	Steve McCatty	.06	.05	.02
64	*Mark Bailey* (FC)	.10	.08	.04
65	Bill Buckner	.12	.09	.05
66	Dick Williams	.06	.05	.02
67	*Rafael Santana* (FC)	.06	.05	.02
68	Von Hayes	.10	.08	.04
69	*Jim Winn* (FC)	.10	.08	.04
70	Don Baylor	.12	.09	.05
71	Tim Laudner	.06	.05	.02
72	Rick Sutcliffe	.12	.09	.05
73	Rusty Kuntz	.06	.05	.02
74	Mike Krukow	.08	.06	.03
75	Willie Upshaw	.08	.06	.03
76	Alan Bannister	.06	.05	.02
77	Joe Beckwith	.06	.05	.02
78	Scott Fletcher	.08	.06	.03
79	Rick Mahler	.06	.05	.02
80	Keith Hernandez	.12	.09	.05
81	Lenn Sakata	.06	.05	.02
82	Joe Price	.06	.05	.02
83	Charlie Moore	.06	.05	.02
84	Spike Owen	.08	.06	.03
85	Mike Marshall	.08	.06	.03
86	Don Aase	.06	.05	.02
87	David Green	.06	.05	.02
88	Bryn Smith	.06	.05	.02
89	Jackie Gutierrez	.06	.05	.02
90	Rich Gossage	.10	.08	.04
91	Jeff Burroughs	.08	.06	.03
92	Paul Owens	.06	.05	.02
93	*Don Schulze* (FC)	.06	.05	.02
94	Toby Harrah	.08	.06	.03

95 Jose Cruz .10 .08 .04
96 Johnny Ray .06 .05 .02
97 Pete Filson .06 .05 .02
98 Steve Lake .06 .05 .02
99 Milt Wilcox .06 .05 .02
100 George Brett 2.00 1.50 .80
101 Jim Acker .06 .05 .02
102 Tommy Dunbar .06 .05 .02
103 Randy Lerch .06 .05 .02
104 Mike Fitzgerald .08 .06 .03
105 Ron Kittle .06 .05 .02
106 Pascual Perez .08 .06 .03
107 Tom Foley .06 .05 .02
108 Darnell Coles (FC) .06 .05 .02
109 Gary Roenicke .06 .05 .02
110 Alejandro Pena .08 .06 .03
111 Doug DeCinces .10 .08 .04
112 Tom Tellmann .06 .05 .02
113 Tom Herr .10 .08 .04
114 Bob James .06 .05 .02
115 Rickey Henderson 1.25 .90 .50
116 Dennis Boyd (FC) .15 .11 .06
117 Greg Gross .06 .05 .02
118 Eric Show .08 .06 .03
119 Pat Corrales .06 .05 .02
120 Steve Kemp .08 .06 .03
121 Checklist 1-132 .06 .05 .02
122 Tom Brunansky .12 .09 .05
123 Dave Smith .08 .06 .03
124 Rich Hebner .06 .05 .02
125 Kent Tekulve .08 .06 .03
126 Ruppert Jones .06 .05 .02
127 *Mark Gubicza* .25 .20 .10
128 Ernie Whitt .08 .06 .03
129 Gene Garber .06 .05 .02
130 Al Oliver .12 .09 .05
131 Father - Son (Buddy Bell, Gus Bell) .12 .09 .05
132 Father - Son (Dale Berra, Yogi Berra) .20 .15 .08
133 Father - Son (Bob Boone, Ray Boone) .12 .09 .05
134 Father - Son (Terry Francona, Tito Francona) .08 .06 .03
135 Father - Son (Bob Kennedy, Terry Kennedy) .08 .06 .03
136 Father - Son (Bill Kunkel, Jeff Kunkel) .08 .06 .03
137 Father - Son (Vance Law, Vern Law) .10 .08 .04
138 Father - Son (Dick Schofield, Dick Schofield) .08 .06 .03
139 Father - Son (Bob Skinner, Joel Skinner) .08 .06 .03
140 Father - Son (Roy Smalley, Roy Smalley) .08 .06 .03
141 Father - Son (Dave Stenhouse, Mike Stenhouse) .08 .06 .03
142 Father - Son (Dizzy Trout, Steve Trout) .08 .06 .03
143 Father - Son (Ossie Virgil, Ozzie Virgil) .08 .06 .03
144 Ron Gardenhire .06 .05 .02
145 *Alvin Davis* .08 .06 .03
146 Gary Redus .08 .06 .03
147 Bill Swaggerty .06 .05 .02
148 Steve Yeager .06 .05 .02
149 Dickie Noles .06 .05 .02
150 Jim Rice .15 .11 .06
151 Moose Haas .06 .05 .02
152 Steve Braun .06 .05 .02
153 Frank LaCorte .06 .05 .02
154 Argenis Salazar (FC) .06 .05 .02
155 Yogi Berra .12 .09 .05
156 Craig Reynolds .06 .05 .02
157 Tug McGraw .10 .08 .04
158 Pat Tabler .08 .06 .03
159 Carlos Diaz .06 .05 .02
160 Lance Parrish .25 .20 .10
161 Ken Schrom .06 .05 .02
162 *Benny Distefano* (FC) .10 .08 .04
163 Dennis Eckersley .25 .20 .10
164 Jorge Orta .06 .05 .02
165 Dusty Baker .08 .06 .03
166 Keith Atherton .06 .05 .02
167 Rufino Linares .06 .05 .02
168 Garth Iorg .06 .05 .02
169 Dan Spillner .06 .05 .02
170 George Foster .15 .11 .06
171 Bill Stein .06 .05 .02
172 Jack Perconte .06 .05 .02
173 Mike Young (FC) .12 .09 .05
174 Rick Honeycutt .06 .05 .02
175 Dave Parker .25 .20 .10
176 Bill Schroeder .06 .05 .02
177 Dave Von Ohlen .06 .05 .02
178 Miguel Dilone .06 .05 .02
179 Tommy John .20 .15 .08
180 Dave Winfield 1.25 .90 .50
181 *Roger Clemens* (FC) 15.00 11.00 6.00
182 Tim Flannery .06 .05 .02
183 Larry McWilliams .06 .05 .02
184 Carmen Castillo (FC) .10 .08 .04
185 Al Holland .06 .05 .02
186 Bob Lillis .06 .05 .02
187 Mike Walters .06 .05 .02
188 Greg Pryor .06 .05 .02
189 Warren Brusstar .06 .05 .02
190 Rusty Staub .12 .09 .05
191 Steve Nicosia .08 .06 .03
192 Howard Johnson .25 .20 .10
193 *Jimmy Key* 1.25 .90 .50
194 Dave Stegman .06 .05 .02
195 Glenn Hubbard .06 .05 .02
196 Pete O'Brien .12 .09 .05
197 Mike Warren .06 .05 .02
198 Eddie Milner .06 .05 .02
199 Denny Martinez .08 .06 .03
200 Reggie Jackson .80 .60 .30
201 Burt Hooton .08 .06 .03
202 Gorman Thomas .10 .08 .04
203 Bob McClure .06 .05 .02
204 Art Howe .06 .05 .02
205 Steve Rogers .08 .06 .03
206 Phil Garner .08 .06 .03
207 Mark Clear .06 .05 .02
208 Champ Summers .06 .05 .02
209 Bill Campbell .06 .05 .02
210 Gary Matthews .10 .08 .04
211 Clay Christiansen .06 .05 .02
212 George Vukovich .06 .05 .02
213 Billy Gardner .06 .05 .02
214 John Tudor .10 .08 .04
215 Bob Brenly .06 .05 .02
216 Jerry Don Gleaton .06 .05 .02
217 Leon Roberts .06 .05 .02
218 Doyle Alexander .10 .08 .04
219 Gerald Perry .08 .06 .03
220 Fred Lynn .20 .15 .08
221 Ron Reed .06 .05 .02
222 Hubie Brooks .10 .08 .04
223 Tom Hume .06 .05 .02
224 Al Cowens .06 .05 .02
225 Mike Boddicker .10 .08 .04
226 Juan Beniquez .06 .05 .02
227 Danny Darwin .06 .05 .02
228 Dion James (FC) .20 .15 .08
229 Dave LaPoint .08 .06 .03
230 Gary Carter .35 .25 .14
231 Dwayne Murphy .08 .06 .03
232 Dave Beard .06 .05 .02
233 Ed Jurak .06 .05 .02
234 Jerry Narron .06 .05 .02
235 Garry Maddox .10 .08 .04
236 Mark Thurmond .06 .05 .02
237 Julio Franco .50 .40 .20
238 *Jose Rijo* 2.00 1.50 .80
239 Tim Teufel .12 .09 .05
240 Dave Stieb .12 .09 .05
241 Jim Frey .06 .05 .02
242 Greg Harris .06 .05 .02
243 Barbaro Garbey .10 .08 .04
244 Mike Jones .06 .05 .02
245 Chili Davis .10 .08 .04
246 Mike Norris .06 .05 .02
247 Wayne Tolleson .06 .05 .02
248 Terry Forster .08 .06 .03
249 Harold Baines .15 .11 .06
250 Jesse Orosco .08 .06 .03
251 Brad Gulden .06 .05 .02
252 Dan Ford .06 .05 .02
253 *Sid Bream* (FC) .20 .15 .08
254 Pete Vuckovich .08 .06 .03
255 Lonnie Smith .08 .06 .03
256 Mike Stanton .06 .05 .02
257 Brian Little (Bryan) .06 .05 .02
258 Mike Brown .06 .05 .02
259 Gary Allenson .06 .05 .02
260 Dave Righetti .10 .08 .04
261 Checklist 133-264 .06 .05 .02
262 *Greg Booker* (FC) .12 .09 .05
263 Mel Hall .08 .06 .03
264 Joe Sambito .06 .05 .02
265 Juan Samuel (FC) .12 .09 .05
266 Frank Viola .10 .08 .04
267 *Henry Cotto* (FC) .08 .06 .03
268 Chuck Tanner .06 .05 .02
269 *Doug Baker* (FC) .10 .08 .04
270 Dan Quisenberry .10 .08 .04
271 Tim Foli (#1 Draft Pick) .08 .06 .03
272 Jeff Burroughs (#1 Draft Pick) .08 .06 .03
273 Bill Almon (#1 Draft Pick) .08 .06 .03
274 Floyd Bannister (#1 Draft Pick) .10 .08 .04
275 Harold Baines (#1 Draft Pick) .15 .11 .06
276 Bob Horner (#1 Draft Pick) .15 .11 .06
277 Al Chambers (#1 Draft Pick) .08 .06 .03
278 Darryl Strawberry (#1 Draft Pick) .30 .25 .12
279 Mike Moore (FC) (#1 Draft Pick) .20 .15 .08
280 *Shawon Dunston* (#1 Draft Pick) .40 .30 .15
281 *Tim Belcher* (#1 Draft Pick) .60 .45 .25
282 *Shawn Abner* (FC) (#1 Draft Pick) .10 .08 .04
283 Fran Mullins .06 .05 .02
284 Marty Bystrom .06 .05 .02
285 Dan Driessen .08 .06 .03
286 Rudy Law .06 .05 .02
287 Walt Terrell .08 .06 .03
288 *Jeff Kunkel* (FC) .10 .08 .04
289 Tom Underwood .06 .05 .02
290 Cecil Cooper .12 .09 .05
291 Bob Welch .12 .09 .05
292 Brad Komminsk (FC) .08 .06 .03
293 *Curt Young* (FC) .08 .06 .03
294 *Tom Nieto* (FC) .10 .08 .04
295 Joe Niekro .10 .08 .04
296 Ricky Nelson .06 .05 .02
297 Gary Lucas .06 .05 .02
298 Marty Barrett .08 .06 .03
299 Andy Hawkins .08 .06 .03
300 Rod Carew .50 .40 .20
301 John Montefusco .06 .05 .02
302 Tim Corcoran .06 .05 .02
303 *Mike Jeffcoat* .08 .06 .03
304 Gary Gaetti .12 .09 .05
305 Dale Berra .06 .05 .02
306 Rick Reuschel .10 .08 .04
307 Sparky Anderson .08 .06 .03
308 John Wathan .08 .06 .03
309 Mike Witt .12 .09 .05
310 Manny Trillo .08 .06 .03
311 Jim Gott .06 .05 .02
312 Marc Hill .06 .05 .02
313 Dave Schmidt .06 .05 .02
314 Ron Oester .06 .05 .02
315 Doug Sisk .06 .05 .02
316 John Lowenstein .06 .05 .02
317 *Jack Lazorko* (FC) .06 .05 .02
318 Ted Simmons .12 .09 .05
319 Jeff Jones .06 .05 .02
320 Dale Murphy .20 .15 .08
321 *Ricky Horton* .08 .06 .03
322 Dave Stapleton .06 .05 .02
323 Andy McGaffigan .06 .05 .02
324 Bruce Bochy .06 .05 .02
325 John Denny .06 .05 .02
326 Kevin Bass .10 .08 .04
327 Brook Jacoby .08 .06 .03
328 Bob Shirley .06 .05 .02
329 Ron Washington .06 .05 .02
330 Leon Durham .08 .06 .03
331 Bill Laskey .06 .05 .02
332 Brian Harper .06 .05 .02
333 Willie Hernandez .08 .06 .03
334 Dick Howser .06 .05 .02
335 Bruce Benedict .06 .05 .02
336 Rance Mulliniks .06 .05 .02
337 Billy Sample .06 .05 .02
338 Britt Burns .06 .05 .02
339 Danny Heep .06 .05 .02
340 Robin Yount 1.00 .70 .40
341 Floyd Rayford .06 .05 .02
342 Ted Power .06 .05 .02
343 Bill Russell .08 .06 .03
344 Dave Henderson .10 .08 .04
345 Charlie Lea .06 .05 .02
346 *Terry Pendleton* (FC) 2.50 2.00 1.00
347 Rick Langford .06 .05 .02
348 Bob Boone .08 .06 .03
349 Domingo Ramos .06 .05 .02
350 Wade Boggs 1.75 1.25 .70
351 Juan Agosto .06 .05 .02
352 Joe Morgan .30 .25 .12
353 Julio Solano .06 .05 .02
354 Andre Robertson .06 .05 .02
355 Bert Blyleven .12 .09 .05
356 Dave Meier .06 .05 .02
357 Rich Bordi .06 .05 .02
358 Tony Pena .10 .08 .04
359 Pat Sheridan .06 .05 .02
360 Steve Carlton .60 .45 .25
361 Alfredo Griffin .08 .06 .03
362 Craig McMurtry .06 .05 .02
363 Ron Hodges .06 .05 .02
364 Richard Dotson .10 .08 .04
365 Danny Ozark .06 .05 .02
366 Todd Cruz .06 .05 .02
367 Keefe Cato .06 .05 .02
368 Dave Bergman .06 .05 .02
369 *R.J. Reynolds* (FC) .10 .08 .04
370 Bruce Sutter .12 .09 .05
371 Mickey Rivers .08 .06 .03
372 Roy Howell .06 .05 .02
373 Mike Moore .06 .05 .02
374 Brian Downing .10 .08 .04
375 Jeff Reardon .12 .09 .05
376 Jeff Newman .06 .05 .02
377 Checklist 265-396 .06 .05 .02
378 Alan Wiggins .06 .05 .02
379 Charles Hudson .08 .06 .03
380 Ken Griffey .10 .08 .04
381 Roy Smith .06 .05 .02
382 Denny Walling .06 .05 .02
383 Rick Lysander .06 .05 .02
384 Jody Davis .10 .08 .04
385 Jose DeLeon .08 .06 .03
386 *Dan Gladden* .30 .25 .12
387 *Buddy Biancalana* (FC) .12 .09 .05
388 Bert Roberge .06 .05 .02
389 Rod Dedeaux (Team USA) .06 .05 .02
390 Sid Akins (FC) (Team USA) .10 .08 .04
391 Flavio Alfaro (Team USA) .06 .05 .02
392 Don August (FC) (Team USA) .08 .06 .03
393 *Scott Bankhead* (Team USA) .25 .20 .10
394 Bob Caffrey (FC) (Team USA) .08 .06 .03
395 Mike Dunne (FC) (Team USA) .20 .15 .08
396 Gary Green (FC) (Team USA) .08 .06 .03
397 John Hoover (Team USA) .06 .05 .02
398 *Shane Mack* (Team USA) 2.00 1.50 .80
399 John Marzano (FC) (Team USA) .10 .08 .04
400 Oddibe McDowell (FC) (Team USA) .20 .15 .08
401 *Mark McGwire* (Team USA) 15.00 11.00 6.00
402 Pat Pacillo (FC) (Team USA) .10 .08 .04
403 *Cory Snyder* (Team USA) .75 .60 .30
404 *Billy Swift* (Team USA) 2.50 2.00 1.00
405 Tom Veryzer .06 .05 .02
406 Len Whitehouse .06 .05 .02
407 Bobby Ramos .06 .05 .02
408 Sid Monge .06 .05 .02
409 Brad Wellman .06 .05 .02
410 Bob Horner .08 .06 .03
411 Bobby Cox .06 .05 .02
412 Bud Black .06 .05 .02
413 Vance Law .08 .06 .03
414 Gary Ward .08 .06 .03
415 Ron Darling .12 .09 .05
416 Wayne Gross .06 .05 .02
417 *John Franco* (FC) .30 .25 .12
418 Ken Landreaux .06 .05 .02
419 Mike Caldwell .06 .05 .02
420 Andre Dawson .75 .60 .30
421 Dave Rucker .06 .05 .02
422 Carney Lansford .10 .08 .04
423 Barry Bonnell .06 .05 .02
424 *Al Nipper* (FC) .08 .06 .03
425 Mike Hargrove .06 .05 .02
426 Verne Ruhle .06 .05 .02
427 Mario Ramirez .06 .05 .02
428 Larry Andersen .06 .05 .02
429 Rick Cerone .06 .05 .02
430 Ron Davis .06 .05 .02
431 U.L. Washington .06 .05 .02
432 Thad Bosley .06 .05 .02
433 Jim Morrison .06 .05 .02
434 Gene Richards .06 .05 .02
435 Dan Petry .08 .06 .03
436 Willie Aikens .06 .05 .02
437 Al Jones .06 .05 .02

438	Joe Torre	.08	.06	.03
439	Junior Ortiz	.06	.05	.02
440	Fernando Valenzuela	.08	.06	.03
441	Duane Walker	.06	.05	.02
442	Ken Forsch	.06	.05	.02
443	George Wright	.06	.05	.02
444	Tony Phillips	.15	.11	.06
445	Tippy Martinez	.06	.05	.02
446	Jim Sundberg	.08	.06	.03
447	Jeff Lahti	.06	.05	.02
448	Derrel Thomas	.06	.05	.02
449	*Phil Bradley*	.10	.08	.04
450	Steve Garvey	.25	.20	.10
451	Bruce Hurst	.12	.09	.05
452	John Castino	.06	.05	.02
453	Tom Waddell	.06	.05	.02
454	Glenn Wilson	.08	.06	.03
455	Bob Knepper	.08	.06	.03
456	Tim Foli	.06	.05	.02
457	Cecilio Guante	.06	.05	.02
458	Randy S. Johnson	.06	.05	.02
459	Charlie Leibrandt	.08	.06	.03
460	Ryne Sandberg	3.00	2.25	1.25
461	Marty Castillo	.06	.05	.02
462	Gary Lavelle	.06	.05	.02
463	Dave Collins	.08	.06	.03
464	*Mike Mason* (FC)	.06	.05	.02
465	Bob Grich	.10	.08	.04
466	Tony LaRussa	.08	.06	.03
467	Ed Lynch	.06	.05	.02
468	Wayne Krenchicki	.06	.05	.02
469	Sammy Stewart	.06	.05	.02
470	Steve Sax	.10	.08	.04
471	Pete Ladd	.06	.05	.02
472	Jim Essian	.06	.05	.02
473	Tim Wallach	.12	.09	.05
474	Kurt Kepshire	.06	.05	.02
475	Andre Thornton	.10	.08	.04
476	*Jeff Stone* (FC)	.12	.09	.05
477	Bob Ojeda	.10	.08	.04
478	Kurt Bevacqua	.06	.05	.02
479	Mike Madden	.06	.05	.02
480	Lou Whitaker	.25	.20	.10
481	Dale Murray	.06	.05	.02
482	Harry Spilman	.06	.05	.02
483	Mike Smithson	.06	.05	.02
484	Larry Bowa	.10	.08	.04
485	Matt Young	.06	.05	.02
486	Steve Balboni	.08	.06	.03
487	*Frank Williams*	.15	.11	.06
488	Joel Skinner (FC)	.08	.06	.03
489	Bryan Clark	.06	.05	.02
490	Jason Thompson	.06	.05	.02
491	Rick Camp	.06	.05	.02
492	Dave Johnson	.08	.06	.03
493	*Orel Hershiser* (FC)	1.25	.90	.50
494	Rich Dauer	.06	.05	.02
495	Mario Soto	.08	.06	.03
496	Donnie Scott	.06	.05	.02
497	Gary Pettis	.15	.11	.06
498	Ed Romero	.06	.05	.02
499	Danny Cox (FC)	.08	.06	.03
500	Mike Schmidt	1.50	1.25	.60
501	Dan Schatzeder	.06	.05	.02
502	Rick Miller	.06	.05	.02
503	Tim Conroy	.06	.05	.02
504	Jerry Willard	.06	.05	.02
505	Jim Beattie	.06	.05	.02
506	*Franklin Stubbs* (FC)	.10	.08	.04
507	Ray Fontenot	.06	.05	.02
508	John Shelby	.08	.06	.03
509	Milt May	.06	.05	.02
510	Kent Hrbek	.15	.11	.06
511	Lee Smith	.10	.08	.04
512	Tom Brookens	.06	.05	.02
513	Lynn Jones	.06	.05	.02
514	Jeff Cornell	.06	.05	.02
515	Dave Concepcion	.12	.09	.05
516	Roy Lee Jackson	.06	.05	.02
517	Jerry Martin	.06	.05	.02
518	Chris Chambliss	.08	.06	.03
519	Doug Rader	.06	.05	.02
520	LaMarr Hoyt	.06	.05	.02
521	Rick Dempsey	.08	.06	.03
522	Paul Molitor	1.00	.75	.40
523	Candy Maldonado	.10	.08	.04
524	Rob Wilfong	.06	.05	.02
525	Darrell Porter	.08	.06	.03
526	Dave Palmer	.06	.05	.02
527	Checklist 397-528	.06	.05	.02
528	Bill Krueger	.06	.05	.02
529	Rich Gedman	.10	.08	.04
530	Dave Dravecky	.08	.06	.03
531	Joe Lefebvre	.06	.05	.02
532	Frank DiPino	.06	.05	.02
533	Tony Bernazard	.06	.05	.02
534	Brian Dayett (FC)	.06	.05	.02
535	Pat Putnam	.06	.05	.02
536	*Kirby Puckett* (FC)	21.00	15.50	8.50
537	Don Robinson	.08	.06	.03
538	Keith Moreland	.08	.06	.03
539	Aurelio Lopez	.06	.05	.02
540	Claudell Washington	.08	.06	.03
541	Mark Davis	.06	.05	.02
542	Don Slaught	.06	.05	.02
543	Mike Squires	.06	.05	.02
544	Bruce Kison	.06	.05	.02
545	Lloyd Moseby	.10	.08	.04
546	Brent Gaff	.06	.05	.02
547	Pete Rose	.60	.45	.25
548	Larry Parrish	.10	.08	.04
549	Mike Scioscia	.08	.06	.03
550	Scott McGregor	.08	.06	.03
551	Andy Van Slyke	.25	.20	.10
552	Chris Codiroli	.06	.05	.02
553	Bob Clark	.06	.05	.02
554	Doug Flynn	.06	.05	.02
555	Bob Stanley	.06	.05	.02
556	Sixto Lezcano	.06	.05	.02
557	Len Barker	.08	.06	.03
558	Carmelo Martinez	.08	.06	.03
559	Jay Howell	.08	.06	.03
560	Bill Madlock	.12	.09	.05
561	Darryl Motley	.06	.05	.02
562	Houston Jimenez	.06	.05	.02
563	Dick Ruthven	.06	.05	.02
564	Alan Ashby	.06	.05	.02
565	Kirk Gibson	.20	.15	.08
566	Ed Vande Berg	.06	.05	.02
567	Joel Youngblood	.06	.05	.02
568	Cliff Johnson	.06	.05	.02
569	Ken Oberkfell	.06	.05	.02
570	Darryl Strawberry	.40	.30	.15
571	Charlie Hough	.08	.06	.03
572	Tom Paciorek	.06	.05	.02
573	*Jay Tibbs* (FC)	.08	.06	.03
574	Joe Altobelli	.06	.05	.02
575	Pedro Guerrero	.10	.08	.04
576	Jaime Cocanower	.06	.05	.02
577	Chris Speier	.06	.05	.02
578	Terry Francona	.06	.05	.02
579	*Ron Romanick*	.10	.08	.04
580	Dwight Evans	.12	.09	.05
581	Mark Wagner	.06	.05	.02
582	Ken Phelps (FC)	.10	.08	.04
583	Bobby Brown	.06	.05	.02
584	Kevin Gross	.10	.08	.04
585	Butch Wynegar	.06	.05	.02
586	Bill Scherrer	.06	.05	.02
587	Doug Frobel	.06	.05	.02
588	Bobby Castillo	.06	.05	.02
589	Bob Dernier	.06	.05	.02
590	Ray Knight	.10	.08	.04
591	Larry Herndon	.08	.06	.03
592	*Jeff Robinson*	.10	.08	.04
593	Rick Leach	.06	.05	.02
594	Curt Wilkerson (FC)	.08	.06	.03
595	Larry Gura	.06	.05	.02
596	Jerry Hairston	.06	.05	.02
597	Brad Lesley	.06	.05	.02
598	Jose Oquendo	.06	.05	.02
599	Storm Davis	.10	.08	.04
600	Pete Rose	.60	.45	.25
601	Tom Lasorda	.10	.08	.04
602	*Jeff Dedmon*	.12	.09	.05
603	Rick Manning	.06	.05	.02
604	Daryl Sconiers	.06	.05	.02
605	Ozzie Smith	.75	.60	.30
606	Rich Gale	.06	.05	.02
607	Bill Almon	.06	.05	.02
608	Craig Lefferts	.08	.06	.03
609	Broderick Perkins	.06	.05	.02
610	Jack Morris	.12	.09	.05
611	Ozzie Virgil	.06	.05	.02
612	Mike Armstrong	.06	.05	.02
613	Terry Puhl	.06	.05	.02
614	Al Williams	.06	.05	.02
615	Marvell Wynne	.06	.05	.02
616	Scott Sanderson	.06	.05	.02
617	Willie Wilson	.12	.09	.05
618	Pete Falcone	.06	.05	.02
619	Jeff Leonard	.10	.08	.04
620	*Dwight Gooden*	3.00	2.25	1.25
621	Marvis Foley	.06	.05	.02
622	Luis Leal	.06	.05	.02
623	Greg Walker	.12	.09	.05
624	Benny Ayala	.06	.05	.02
625	*Mark Langston*	1.50	1.25	.60
626	German Rivera	.06	.05	.02
627	*Eric Davis* (FC)	2.50	2.00	1.00
628	Rene Lachemann	.06	.05	.02
629	Dick Schofield	.12	.09	.05
630	Tim Raines	.20	.15	.08
631	Bob Forsch	.08	.06	.03
632	Bruce Bochte	.06	.05	.02
633	Glenn Hoffman	.06	.05	.02
634	Bill Dawley	.06	.05	.02
635	Terry Kennedy	.08	.06	.03
636	Shane Rawley	.10	.08	.04
637	Brett Butler	.08	.06	.03
638	*Mike Pagliarulo* (FC)	.12	.09	.05
639	Ed Hodge	.06	.05	.02
640	Steve Henderson	.06	.05	.02
641	Rod Scurry	.06	.05	.02
642	Dave Owen	.06	.05	.02
643	Johnny Grubb	.06	.05	.02
644	Mark Huismann (FC)	.06	.05	.02
645	Damaso Garcia	.06	.05	.02
646	Scot Thompson	.06	.05	.02
647	Rafael Ramirez	.06	.05	.02
648	Bob Jones	.06	.05	.02
649	Sid Fernandez (FC)	.10	.08	.04
650	Greg Luzinski	.10	.08	.04
651	Jeff Russell	.08	.06	.03
652	Joe Nolan	.06	.05	.02
653	Mark Brouhard	.06	.05	.02
654	Dave Anderson	.06	.05	.02
655	Joaquin Andujar	.08	.06	.03
656	Chuck Cottier	.06	.05	.02
657	Jim Slaton	.06	.05	.02
658	Mike Stenhouse	.06	.05	.02
659	Checklist 529-660	.06	.05	.02
660	Tony Gwynn	2.00	1.50	.80
661	Steve Crawford	.06	.05	.02
662	Mike Heath	.06	.05	.02
663	Luis Aguayo	.06	.05	.02
664	*Steve Farr* (FC)	.30	.25	.12
665	Don Mattingly	3.00	2.25	1.25
666	Mike LaCoss	.06	.05	.02
667	Dave Engle	.06	.05	.02
668	Steve Trout	.06	.05	.02
669	Lee Lacy	.06	.05	.02
670	Tom Seaver	.40	.30	.15
671	Dane Iorg	.06	.05	.02
672	Juan Berenguer	.06	.05	.02
673	Buck Martinez	.06	.05	.02
674	Atlee Hammaker	.06	.05	.02
675	Tony Perez	.15	.11	.06
676	*Albert Hall* (FC)	.15	.11	.06
677	Wally Backman	.08	.06	.03
678	Joey McLaughlin	.06	.05	.02
679	Bob Kearney	.06	.05	.02
680	Jerry Reuss	.08	.06	.03
681	Ben Oglivie	.08	.06	.03
682	Doug Corbett	.06	.05	.02
683	Whitey Herzog	.08	.06	.03
684	Bill Doran	.12	.09	.05
685	Bill Caudill	.06	.05	.02
686	Mike Easler	.08	.06	.03
687	Bill Gullickson	.06	.05	.02
688	Len Matuszek	.06	.05	.02
689	Luis DeLeon	.06	.05	.02
690	Alan Trammell	.25	.20	.10
691	Dennis Rasmussen (FC)	.10	.08	.04
692	Randy Bush	.06	.05	.02
693	Tim Stoddard	.06	.05	.02
694	Joe Carter (FC)	5.00	3.75	2.00
695	Rick Rhoden	.10	.08	.04
696	John Rabb	.06	.05	.02
697	Onix Concepcion	.06	.05	.02
698	Jorge Bell	.20	.15	.08
699	Donnie Moore	.06	.05	.02
700	Eddie Murray	.75	.60	.30
701	Eddie Murray (All-Star)	.30	.25	.12
702	Damaso Garcia (All-Star)	.08	.06	.03
703	George Brett (All-Star)	.50	.40	.20
704	Cal Ripken, Jr. (All-Star)	1.00	.70	.40
705	Dave Winfield (All-Star)	.50	.40	.20
706	Rickey Henderson (All-Star)	.25	.20	.10
707	Tony Armas (All-Star)	.08	.06	.03
708	Lance Parrish (All-Star)	.15	.11	.06
709	Mike Boddicker (All-Star)	.08	.06	.03
710	Frank Viola (All-Star)	.10	.07	.04
711	Dan Quisenberry (All-Star)	.10	.08	.04
712	Keith Hernandez (All-Star)	.10	.08	.04
713	Ryne Sandberg (All-Star)	1.00	.70	.40
714	Mike Schmidt (All-Star)	.50	.40	.20
715	Ozzie Smith (All-Star)	.20	.15	.08
716	Dale Murphy (All-Star)	.15	.11	.06
717	Tony Gwynn (All-Star)	.50	.40	.20
718	Jeff Leonard (All-Star)	.06	.05	.02
719	Gary Carter (All-Star)	.15	.11	.06
720	Rick Sutcliffe (All-Star)	.12	.09	.05
721	Bob Knepper (All-Star)	.08	.06	.03
722	Bruce Sutter (All-Star)	.10	.08	.04
723	Dave Stewart	.12	.09	.05
724	Oscar Gamble	.08	.06	.03
725	Floyd Bannister	.10	.08	.04
726	Al Bumbry	.08	.06	.03
727	Frank Pastore	.06	.05	.02
728	Bob Bailor	.06	.05	.02
729	Don Sutton	.20	.15	.08
730	Dave Kingman	.15	.11	.06
731	Neil Allen	.06	.05	.02
732	John McNamara	.06	.05	.02
733	Tony Scott	.06	.05	.02
734	John Henry Johnson	.06	.05	.02
735	Garry Templeton	.08	.06	.03
736	Jerry Mumphrey	.06	.05	.02
737	Bo Diaz	.08	.06	.03
738	Omar Moreno	.06	.05	.02
739	Ernie Camacho	.06	.05	.02
740	Jack Clark	.08	.06	.03
741	John Butcher	.06	.05	.02
742	Ron Hassey	.06	.05	.02
743	Frank White	.10	.08	.04
744	Doug Bair	.06	.05	.02
745	Buddy Bell	.12	.09	.05
746	Jim Clancy	.08	.06	.03
747	Alex Trevino	.06	.05	.02
748	Lee Mazzilli	.08	.06	.03
749	Julio Cruz	.06	.05	.02
750	Rollie Fingers	.20	.15	.08
751	Kelvin Chapman	.06	.05	.02
752	Bob Owchinko	.06	.05	.02
753	Greg Brock	.08	.06	.03
754	Larry Milbourne	.06	.05	.02
755	Ken Singleton	.08	.06	.03
756	Rob Picciolo	.06	.05	.02
757	Willie McGee	.15	.11	.06
758	Ray Burris	.06	.05	.02
759	Jim Fanning	.06	.05	.02
760	Nolan Ryan	5.00	3.75	2.00
761	Jerry Remy	.06	.05	.02
762	Eddie Whitson	.06	.05	.02
763	Kiko Garcia	.06	.05	.02
764	Jamie Easterly	.06	.05	.02
765	Willie Randolph	.10	.08	.04
766	Paul Mirabella	.06	.05	.02
767	Darrell Brown	.06	.05	.02
768	Ron Cey	.10	.08	.04
769	Joe Cowley	.06	.05	.02
770	Carlton Fisk	.30	.25	.12
771	Geoff Zahn	.06	.05	.02
772	Johnnie LeMaster	.06	.05	.02
773	Hal McRae	.10	.08	.04
774	Dennis Lamp	.06	.05	.02
775	Mookie Wilson	.10	.08	.04
776	Jerry Royster	.06	.05	.02
777	Ned Yost	.06	.05	.02
778	Mike Davis	.08	.06	.03
779	Nick Esasky	.08	.06	.03
780	Mike Flanagan	.10	.08	.04
781	Jim Gantner	.08	.06	.03
782	Tom Niedenfuer	.08	.06	.03
783	Mike Jorgensen	.06	.05	.02
784	Checklist 661-792	.06	.05	.02
785	Tony Armas	.10	.08	.04
786	Enos Cabell	.06	.05	.02
787	Jim Wohlford	.06	.05	.02
788	Steve Comer	.06	.05	.02
789	Luis Salazar	.06	.05	.02
790	Ron Guidry	.10	.08	.04
791	Ivan DeJesus	.06	.05	.02
792	Darrell Evans	.12	.09	.05

1985 Topps All-Star Glossy Set of 22

This was the second straight year for this set of 22 cards featuring the starting players, the honorary captains and the managers in the All-Star Game. The set is virtually identical to that of the previous year in design with a color photo, All-Star banner, league emblem, and player's name and position on the front. What makes the cards special is their high gloss finish. The cards were available as inserts in Topps rack packs. With their combination of attractive appearance and big-name stars, these 2-1/2" by 3-1/2" cards will probably continue to enjoy a great deal of popularity.

		MT	NR MT	EX
Complete Set:		7.00	5.25	2.75
Common Player:		.20	.15	.08
1	Paul Owens	.20	.15	.08
2	Steve Garvey	.30	.25	.12
3	Ryne Sandberg	.50	.40	.20
4	Mike Schmidt	.60	.45	.25
5	Ozzie Smith	.30	.25	.12
6	Tony Gwynn	.40	.30	.15
7	Dale Murphy	.40	.30	.15
8	Darryl Strawberry	.40	.30	.15
9	Gary Carter	.30	.25	.12
10	Charlie Lea	.20	.15	.08
11	Willie McCovey	.40	.30	.15
12	Joe Altobelli	.20	.15	.08
13	Rod Carew	.50	.40	.20
14	Lou Whitaker	.30	.25	.12
15	George Brett	.80	.60	.30
16	Cal Ripken, Jr.	.60	.45	.25
17	Dave Winfield	.50	.40	.20
18	Chet Lemon	.20	.15	.08
19	Reggie Jackson	.60	.45	.25
20	Lance Parrish	.30	.25	.12
21	Dave Stieb	.20	.15	.08
22	Hank Greenberg	.25	.20	.10

1985 Topps All-Star Glossy Set of 40

Similar to previous years' glossy sets, the 1985 All-Star "Collector's Edition" glossy set of 40 could be obtained through the mail in eight five-card subsets. To obtain the 2-1/2" by 3-1/2" cards, collectors had to accumulate sweepstakes insert cards from Topps packs, and pay 75¢ postage and handling. Under the circumstances, the complete set of 40 cards was not inexpensive. They are however, rather attractive and popular cards, and the set size enabled Topps to include some players who didn't make their 22-card set.

		MT	NR MT	EX
Complete Set:		18.00	13.50	7.25
Common Player:		.15	.11	.06
1	Dale Murphy	1.00	.70	.40
2	Jesse Orosco	.15	.11	.06
3	Bob Brenly	.15	.11	.06
4	Mike Boddicker	.15	.11	.06
5	Dave Kingman	.25	.20	.10
6	Jim Rice	.35	.25	.14
7	Frank Viola	.30	.25	.12
8	Alvin Davis	.15	.11	.06
9	Rick Sutcliffe	.20	.15	.08
10	Pete Rose	1.25	.90	.50
11	Leon Durham	.15	.11	.06
12	Joaquin Andujar	.15	.11	.06
13	Keith Hernandez	.20	.15	.08
14	Dave Winfield	.60	.45	.25
15	Reggie Jackson	.70	.50	.30
16	Alan Trammell	.35	.25	.14
17	Bert Blyleven	.20	.15	.08
18	Tony Armas	.15	.11	.06
19	Rich Gossage	.25	.20	.10
20	Jose Cruz	.15	.11	.06
21	Ryne Sandberg	.75	.60	.30
22	Bruce Sutter	.20	.15	.08
23	Mike Schmidt	1.00	.70	.40
24	Cal Ripken, Jr.	.75	.60	.30
25	Dan Petry	.15	.11	.06
26	Jack Morris	.30	.25	.12
27	Don Mattingly	2.00	1.50	.80
28	Eddie Murray	.60	.45	.25
29	Tony Gwynn	.60	.45	.25
30	Charlie Lea	.15	.11	.06
31	Juan Samuel	.30	.25	.12
32	Phil Niekro	.35	.25	.14
33	Alejandro Pena	.15	.11	.06
34	Harold Baines	.25	.20	.10
35	Dan Quisenberry	.15	.11	.06
36	Gary Carter	.35	.25	.14
37	Mario Soto	.15	.11	.06
38	Dwight Gooden	.80	.60	.30
39	Tom Brunansky	.20	.15	.08
40	Dave Stieb	.20	.15	.08

1985 Topps Traded

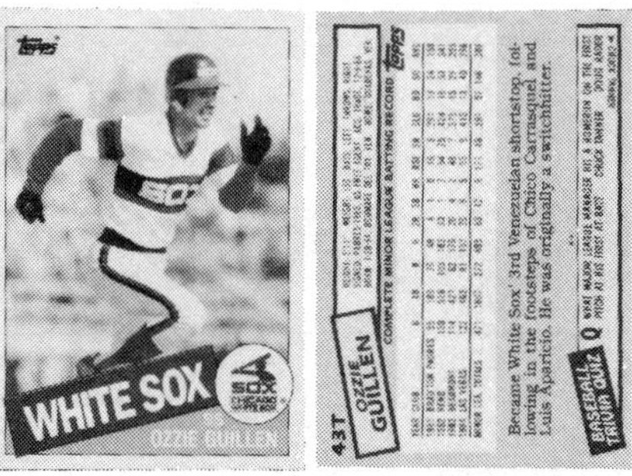

By 1985, the Topps Traded set had become a yearly feature, and Topps continued the tradition with another 132-card set. The 2-1/2" by 3-1/2" cards followed the pattern of being virtually identical in design to the regular cards issued by Topps. Sold only through established hobby dealers, the set features traded veterans and promising rookies. A glossy-finish "Tiffany" edition of the set is valued at four times normal Traded card value for commons, up to five or six times normal value for superstars and hot rookies.

		MT	NR MT	EX
Complete Set (132):		25.00	18.50	10.00
Common Player:		.10	.08	.04
1T	Don Aase	.10	.08	.04
2T	Bill Almon	.10	.08	.04
3T	Benny Ayala	.10	.08	.04
4T	Dusty Baker	.15	.11	.06
5T	George Bamberger	.10	.08	.04
6T	Dale Berra	.10	.08	.04
7T	Rich Bordi	.10	.08	.04
8T	Daryl Boston (FC)	.20	.15	.08
9T	Hubie Brooks	.25	.20	.10
10T	Chris Brown (FC)	.10	.08	.04
11T	Tom Browning (FC)	.60	.45	.25
12T	Al Bumbry	.10	.08	.04
13T	Ray Burris	.10	.08	.04
14T	Jeff Burroughs	.15	.11	.06
15T	Bill Campbell	.10	.08	.04
16T	Don Carman (FC)	.15	.11	.06
17T	Gary Carter	.60	.45	.25
18T	Bobby Castillo	.10	.08	.04
19T	Bill Caudill	.10	.08	.04
20T	Rick Cerone	.10	.08	.04
21T	Bryan Clark	.10	.08	.04
22T	Jack Clark	.12	.09	.05
23T	Pat Clements (FC)	.20	.15	.08
24T	Vince Coleman (FC)	.60	.45	.25
25T	Dave Collins	.15	.11	.06
26T	Danny Darwin	.15	.11	.06
27T	Jim Davenport	.10	.08	.04
28T	Jerry Davis	.10	.08	.04
29T	Brian Dayett	.10	.08	.04
30T	Ivan DeJesus	.10	.08	.04
31T	Ken Dixon	.10	.08	.04
32T	Mariano Duncan (FC)	.50	.40	.20
33T	John Felske	.10	.08	.04
34T	Mike Fitzgerald	.10	.08	.04
35T	Ray Fontenot	.10	.08	.04
36T	Greg Gagne (FC)	.35	.25	.14
37T	Oscar Gamble	.15	.11	.06
38T	Scott Garrelts (FC)	.15	.11	.06
39T	Bob L. Gibson	.10	.08	.04
40T	Jim Gott	.10	.08	.04
41T	David Green	.10	.08	.04
42T	Alfredo Griffin	.15	.11	.06
43T	Ozzie Guillen (FC)	1.50	1.25	.60
44T	Eddie Haas	.10	.08	.04
45T	Terry Harper	.10	.08	.04
46T	Toby Harrah	.15	.11	.06
47T	Greg Harris	.10	.08	.04
48T	Ron Hassey	.10	.08	.04
49T	Rickey Henderson	3.50	2.75	1.50
50T	Steve Henderson	.10	.08	.04
51T	George Hendrick	.15	.11	.06
52T	Joe Hesketh (FC)	.20	.15	.08
53T	Teddy Higuera (FC)	.25	.20	.10
54T	Donnie Hill	.10	.08	.04
55T	Al Holland	.10	.08	.04
56T	Burt Hooton	.15	.11	.06
57T	Jay Howell	.15	.11	.06
58T	Ken Howell (FC)	.15	.11	.06
59T	LaMarr Hoyt	.10	.08	.04
60T	Tim Hulett (FC)	.15	.11	.06
61T	Bob James	.10	.08	.04
62T	Steve Jeltz (FC)	.15	.11	.06
63T	Cliff Johnson	.10	.08	.04
64T	Howard Johnson	.60	.45	.25
65T	Ruppert Jones	.10	.08	.04
66T	Steve Kemp	.15	.11	.06
67T	Bruce Kison	.10	.08	.04
68T	Alan Knicely	.10	.08	.04
69T	Mike LaCoss	.10	.08	.04
70T	Lee Lacy	.10	.08	.04
71T	Dave LaPoint	.10	.08	.04
72T	Gary Lavelle	.10	.08	.04
73T	Vance Law	.15	.11	.06
74T	Johnnie LeMaster	.10	.08	.04
75T	Sixto Lezcano	.10	.08	.04
76T	Tim Lollar	.10	.08	.04
77T	Fred Lynn	.30	.25	.12
78T	Billy Martin	.20	.15	.08
79T	Ron Mathis	.10	.08	.04
80T	Len Matuszek	.10	.08	.04
81T	Gene Mauch	.15	.11	.06
82T	Oddibe McDowell	.25	.20	.10
83T	Roger McDowell (FC)	.50	.40	.20
84T	John McNamara	.10	.08	.04
85T	Donnie Moore	.10	.08	.04
86T	Gene Nelson	.10	.08	.04
87T	Steve Nicosia	.10	.08	.04
88T	Al Oliver	.15	.11	.06
89T	Joe Orsulak (FC)	.20	.15	.08
90T	Rob Picciolo	.10	.08	.04
91T	Chris Pittaro	.10	.08	.04
92T	Jim Presley (FC)	.10	.08	.04
93T	Rick Reuschel	.10	.08	.04
94T	Bert Roberge	.10	.08	.04
95T	Bob Rodgers	.10	.08	.04
96T	Jerry Royster	.10	.08	.04
97T	Dave Rozema	.10	.08	.04
98T	Dave Rucker	.10	.08	.04
99T	Vern Ruhle	.10	.08	.04
100T	Paul Runge (FC)	.10	.08	.04
101T	Mark Salas (FC)	.10	.08	.04
102T	Luis Salazar	.10	.08	.04
103T	Joe Sambito	.10	.08	.04
104T	Rick Schu (FC)	.10	.08	.04
105T	Donnie Scott	.10	.08	.04
106T	Larry Sheets (FC)	.10	.08	.04
107T	Don Slaught	.10	.08	.04
108T	Roy Smalley	.10	.08	.04
109T	Lonnie Smith	.15	.11	.06
110T	Nate Snell	.10	.08	.04
111T	Chris Speier	.10	.08	.04
112T	Mike Stenhouse	.10	.08	.04
113T	Tim Stoddard	.10	.08	.04
114T	Jim Sundberg	.10	.08	.04
115T	Bruce Sutter	.25	.20	.10
116T	Don Sutton	.60	.45	.25
117T	Kent Tekulve	.15	.11	.06
118T	Tom Tellmann	.10	.08	.04
119T	Walt Terrell	.15	.11	.06
120T	Mickey Tettleton (FC)	8.00	6.00	3.25
121T	Derrel Thomas	.10	.08	.04
122T	Rich Thompson	.10	.08	.04
123T	Alex Trevino	.10	.08	.04
124T	John Tudor	.10	.08	.04
125T	Jose Uribe (FC)	.10	.08	.04
126T	Bobby Valentine	.10	.08	.04
127T	Dave Von Ohlen	.10	.08	.04
128T	U.L. Washington	.10	.08	.04
129T	Earl Weaver	.15	.11	.06
130T	Eddie Whitson	.10	.08	.04
131T	Herm Winningham (FC)	.10	.08	.04
132T	Checklist 1-132	.10	.08	.04

A card number in parentheses () indicates the set is unnumbered.

1985 Topps All-Time Record Holders

This 44-card boxed set was produced by Topps for the Woolworth's chain stores. Many hobbyists refer to this as the "Woolworth's" set, but that name does not appear anywhere on the cards. Featuring a combination of black and white and color photos of baseball record holders from all eras, the set is in the standard 2-1/2" by 3-1/2" format. Backs, printed in blue and orange, give career details and personal

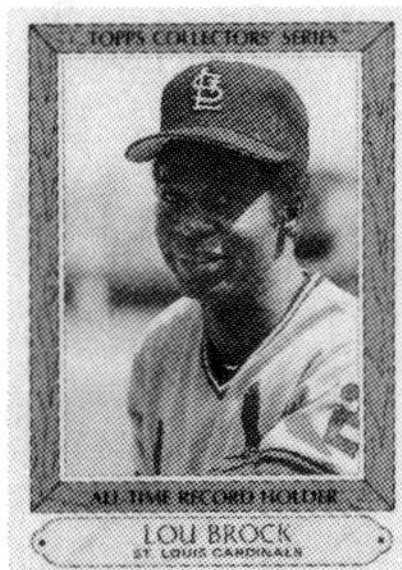

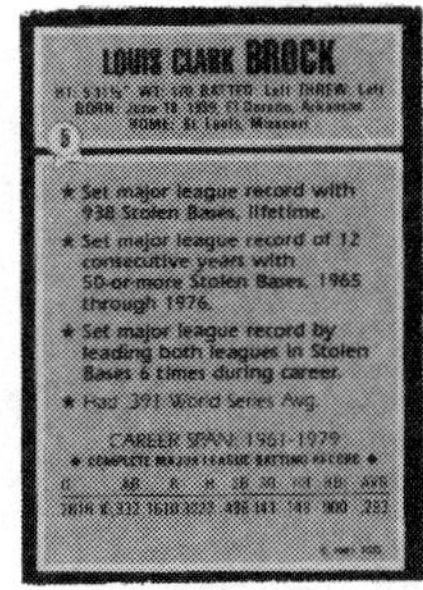

data. Because it combined old-timers with current players, the set did not achieve a great deal of collector popularity.

		MT	NR MT	EX
Complete Set:		5.00	3.75	2.00
Common Player:		.05	.04	.02
1	Hank Aaron	.25	.20	.10
2	Grover Alexander	.10	.08	.04
3	Ernie Banks	.12	.09	.05
4	Yogi Berra	.15	.11	.06
5	Lou Brock	.12	.09	.05
6	Steve Carlton	.12	.09	.05
7	Jack Chesbro	.07	.05	.03
8	Ty Cobb	.30	.25	.12
9	Sam Crawford	.07	.05	.03
10	Rollie Fingers	.07	.05	.03
11	Whitey Ford	.12	.09	.05
12	Johnny Frederick	.05	.04	.02
13	Frankie Frisch	.07	.05	.03
14	Lou Gehrig	.30	.25	.12
15	Jim Gentile	.05	.04	.02
16	Dwight Gooden	.60	.45	.25
17	Rickey Henderson	.15	.11	.06
18	Rogers Hornsby	.12	.09	.05
19	Frank Howard	.07	.05	.03
20	Cliff Johnson	.05	.04	.02
21	Walter Johnson	.15	.11	.06
22	Hub Leonard	.05	.04	.02
23	Mickey Mantle	1.00	.70	.40
24	Roger Maris	.12	.09	.05
25	Christy Mathewson	.12	.09	.05
26	Willie Mays	.20	.15	.08
27	Stan Musial	.20	.15	.08
28	Dan Quisenberry	.05	.04	.02
29	Frank Robinson	.12	.09	.05
30	Pete Rose	.40	.30	.15
31	Babe Ruth	.60	.45	.25
32	Nolan Ryan	.12	.09	.05
33	George Sisler	.10	.08	.04
34	Tris Speaker	.10	.08	.04
35	Ed Walsh	.07	.05	.03
36	Lloyd Waner	.07	.05	.03
37	Earl Webb	.05	.04	.02
38	Ted Williams	.30	.25	.12
39	Maury Wills	.07	.05	.03
40	Hack Wilson	.07	.05	.03
41	Owen Wilson	.05	.04	.02
42	Willie Wilson	.07	.05	.03
43	Rudy York	.05	.04	.02
44	Cy Young	.12	.09	.05

1985 Topps Gallery of Champions

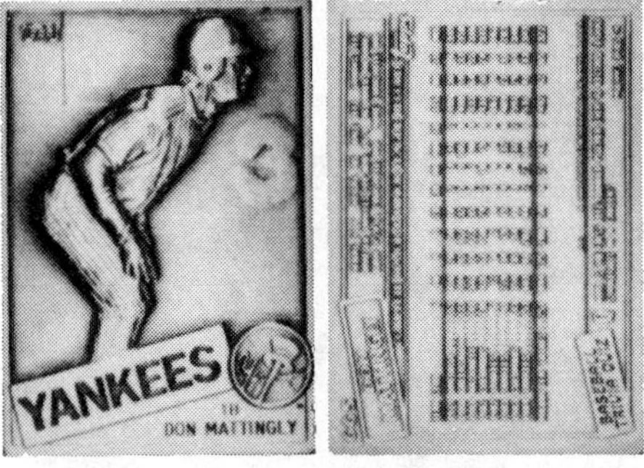

This second annual aluminum, bronze, and silver miniature issues honors 12 award winners from the previous season (MVP, Cy Young, Rookie of Year, Fireman, etc.). Each mini is an exact reproduction, at one-quarter scale of the player's official Topps baseball card, both front and back. The bronze and silver sets were issued in a specially-designed velvet-like case. Aluminum sets came cello-wrapped. A Dwight Gooden pewter replica was given as a premium to dealers who bought bronze and silver sets (value $75). A Pete Rose bronze was issued as a premium to dealers purchasing cases of 1985 Topps Traded sets (value $12).

		MT	NR MT	EX
Complete Aluminum Set:		30.00	22.00	12.00
Complete Bronze Set:		175.00	131.00	70.00
Complete Silver Set:		600.00	450.00	240.00
(1a)	Tony Armas (aluminum)	.70	.50	.30
(1b)	Tony Armas (bronze)	7.50	5.75	3.00
(1c)	Tony Armas (silver)	20.00	15.00	8.00
(2a)	Alvin Davis (aluminum)	.70	.50	.30
(2b)	Alvin Davis (bronze)	7.50	5.50	3.00
(2c)	Alvin Davis (silver)	20.00	15.00	8.00
(3a)	Dwight Gooden (aluminum)	1.50	1.25	.60
(3b)	Dwight Gooden (bronze)	12.50	9.50	5.00
(3c)	Dwight Gooden (silver)	65.00	49.00	26.00
(4a)	Tony Gwynn (aluminum)	1.25	.90	.50
(4b)	Tony Gwynn (bronze)	12.00	9.00	4.75
(4c)	Tony Gwynn (silver)	50.00	37.00	20.00
(5a)	Willie Hernandez (aluminum)	.70	.50	.30
(5b)	Willie Hernandez (bronze)	7.50	5.75	3.00
(5c)	Willie Hernandez (silver)	20.00	15.00	8.00
(6a)	Don Mattingly (aluminum)	8.00	6.00	3.25
(6b)	Don Mattingly (bronze)	50.00	37.00	20.00
(6c)	Don Mattingly (silver)	200.00	150.00	80.00
(7a)	Dale Murphy (aluminum)	1.50	1.25	.60
(7b)	Dale Murphy (bronze)	15.00	11.00	6.00
(7c)	Dale Murphy (silver)	80.00	60.00	32.00
(8a)	Dan Quisenberry (aluminum)	.70	.50	.30
(8b)	Dan Quisenberry (bronze)	7.50	5.75	3.00
(8c)	Dan Quisenberry (silver)	20.00	15.00	8.00
(9a)	Ryne Sandberg (aluminum)	2.00	1.50	.80
(9b)	Ryne Sandberg (bronze)	15.00	11.00	6.00
(9c)	Ryne Sandberg (silver)	95.00	71.00	38.00
(10a)	Mike Schmidt (aluminum)	1.50	1.25	.60
(10b)	Mike Schmidt (bronze)	15.00	11.00	6.00
(10c)	Mike Schmidt (silver)	80.00	60.00	32.00
(11a)	Rick Sutcliffe (aluminum)	.70	.50	.30
(11b)	Rick Sutcliffe (bronze)	7.50	5.75	3.00
(11c)	Rick Sutcliffe (silver)	20.00	15.00	8.00
(12a)	Bruce Sutter (aluminum)	.70	.50	.30
(12b)	Bruce Sutter (bronze)	7.50	5.75	3.00
(12c)	Bruce Sutter (silver)	20.00	15.00	8.00

1985 Topps Rub Downs

Similar in size and design to the Rub Downs of the previous year, the 1985 set again consisted of 32 unnumbered sheets featuring 112 different players. The set was sold by Topps as a separate issue.

		MT	NR MT	EX
Complete Set:		6.00	4.50	2.50
Common Player:		.10	.08	.04
(1)	Tony Armas, Harold Baines, Lonnie Smith	.10	.08	.04
(2)	Don Baylor, George Hendrick, Ron Kittle, Johnnie LeMaster	.10	.08	.04
(3)	Buddy Bell, Tony Gwynn, Lloyd Moseby	.25	.20	.10
(4)	Bruce Benedict, Atlee Hammaker, Frank White	.10	.08	.04
(5)	Mike Boddicker, Rod Carew, Carlton Fisk, Johnny Ray	.25	.20	.10
(6)	Wade Boggs, Rick Dempsey, Keith Hernandez	.60	.45	.25
(7)	George Brett, Andre Dawson, Paul Molitor, Alan Wiggins	.30	.25	.12
(8)	Tom Brunansky, Pedro Guerrero, Darryl Strawberry	.40	.30	.15
(9)	Bill Buckner, Tim Raines, Ryne Sandberg, Mike Schmidt	.50	.40	.20
(10)	Steve Carlton, Bob Horner, Dan Quisenberry	.25	.20	.10
(11)	Gary Carter, Phil Garner, Ron Guidry	.25	.20	.10
(12)	Jack Clark, Damaso Garcia, Hal McRae, Lance Parrish	.20	.15	.08
(13)	Dave Concepcion, Cecil Cooper, Fred Lynn, Jesse Orosco	.15	.11	.06
(14)	Jose Cruz, Jack Morris, Jim Rice, Rick Sutcliffe	.20	.15	.08
(15)	Alvin Davis, Steve Kemp, Greg Luzinski, Kent Tekulve	.20	.15	.08
(16)	Ron Davis, Kent Hrbek, Juan Samuel	.20	.15	.08
(17)	John Denny, Carney Lansford, Mario Soto, Lou Whitaker	.15	.11	.06
(18)	Leon Durham, Willie Hernandez, Steve Sax	.15	.11	.06
(19)	Dwight Evans, Julio Franco, Dwight Gooden	.40	.30	.15
(20)	George Foster, Gary Gaetti, Bobby Grich, Gary Redus	.15	.11	.06
(21)	Steve Garvey, Jerry Remy, Bill Russell, George Wright	.20	.15	.08
(22)	Kirk Gibson, Rich Gossage, Don Mattingly, Dave Stieb	.90	.70	.35
(23)	Moose Haas, Bruce Sutter, Dickie Thon, Andre Thornton	.10	.08	.04
(24)	Rickey Henderson, Dave Righetti, Pete Rose	.70	.50	.30
(25)	Steve Henderson, Bill Madlock, Alan Trammell	.15	.11	.06
(26)	LaMarr Hoyt, Larry Parrish, Nolan Ryan	.45	.35	.20
(27)	Reggie Jackson, Eric Show, Jason Thompson	.30	.25	.12
(28)	Terry Kennedy, Eddie Murray, Tom Seaver, Ozzie Smith	.40	.30	.15
(29)	Mark Langston, Ben Oglivie, Darrell Porter	.15	.11	.06
(30)	Jeff Leonard, Gary Matthews, Dale Murphy, Dave Winfield	.30	.25	.12
(31)	Craig McMurtry, Cal Ripken, Jr., Steve Rogers, Willie Upshaw	.40	.30	.15
(32)	Tony Pena, Fernando Valenzuela, Robin Yount	.20	.15	.08

1985 Topps Stickers

Topps went to a larger size for its stickers in 1985. Each of the 376 stickers measures 2-1/8" by 3" and is numbered on both the front and the back. The backs contain either an offer to obtain an autographed team ball or a poster. An album was also available.

		MT	NR MT	EX
Complete Set:		16.00	12.00	6.50
Common Player:		.03	.02	.01
Sticker Album:		.80	.60	.30
1	Steve Garvey	.15	.11	.06
2	Steve Garvey	.15	.11	.06
3	Dwight Gooden	.15	.11	.06
4	Dwight Gooden	.15	.11	.06
5	Joe Morgan	.10	.08	.04
6	Joe Morgan	.10	.08	.04
7	Don Sutton	.10	.08	.04
8	Don Sutton	.10	.08	.04
9	1984 A.L. Championships (Jack Morris)	.06	.05	.02
10	1984 A.L. Championships (Milt Wilcox)	.03	.02	.01
11	1984 A.L. Championships (Kirk Gibson)	.08	.06	.03
12	1984 N.L. Championships (Gary Matthews)	.04	.03	.02
13	1984 N.L. Championships (Steve Garvey)	.10	.08	.04
14	1984 N.L. Championships (Steve Garvey)	.15	.11	.06
15	1984 World Series (Jack Morris)	.06	.05	.02
16	1984 World Series (Kurt Bevacqua)	.03	.02	.01
17	1984 World Series (Milt Wilcox)	.03	.02	.01
18	1984 World Series (Alan Trammell)	.08	.06	.03
19	1984 World Series (Kirk Gibson)	.08	.06	.03
20	1984 World Series (Alan Trammell)	.12	.09	.05
21	1984 World Series (Chet Lemon)	.03	.02	.01
22	Dale Murphy	.25	.20	.10
23	Steve Bedrosian	.10	.08	.04
24	Bob Horner	.10	.08	.04
25	Claudell Washington	.06	.05	.02
26	Rick Mahler	.06	.05	.02
27	Rafael Ramirez	.04	.03	.02
28	Craig McMurtry	.04	.03	.02
29	Chris Chambliss	.04	.03	.02
30	Alex Trevino	.03	.02	.01
31	Bruce Benedict	.04	.03	.02
32	Ken Oberkfell	.03	.02	.01
33	Glenn Hubbard	.04	.03	.02
34	Ryne Sandberg	.30	.25	.12
35	Rick Sutcliffe	.08	.06	.03
36	Leon Durham	.06	.05	.02
37	Jody Davis	.06	.05	.02
38	Bob Dernier	.04	.03	.02
39	Keith Moreland	.06	.05	.02
40	Scott Sanderson	.04	.03	.02
41	Lee Smith	.10	.08	.04
42	Ron Cey	.06	.05	.02
43	Steve Trout	.06	.05	.02
44	Gary Matthews	.06	.05	.02
45	Larry Bowa	.04	.03	.02
46	Mario Soto	.06	.05	.02
47	Dave Parker	.12	.09	.05
48	Dave Concepcion	.06	.05	.02
49	Gary Redus	.06	.05	.02

50 Ted Power .06 .05 .02
51 Nick Esasky .04 .03 .02
52 Duane Walker .06 .05 .02
53 Eddie Milner .03 .02 .01
54 Ron Oester .03 .02 .01
55 Cesar Cedeno .04 .03 .02
56 Joe Price .03 .02 .01
57 Pete Rose .20 .15 .08
58 Nolan Ryan .40 .30 .15
59 Jose Cruz .06 .05 .02
60 Jerry Mumphrey .04 .03 .02
61 Enos Cabell .03 .02 .01
62 Bob Knepper .04 .03 .02
63 Dickie Thon .04 .03 .02
64 Phil Garner .04 .03 .02
65 Craig Reynolds .06 .05 .02
66 Frank DiPino .03 .02 .01
67 Terry Puhl .03 .02 .01
68 Bill Doran .06 .05 .02
69 Joe Niekro .04 .03 .02
70 Pedro Guerrero .12 .09 .05
71 Fernando Valenzuela .15 .11 .06
72 Mike Marshall .08 .06 .03
73 Alejandro Pena .04 .03 .02
74 Orel Hershiser .10 .08 .04
75 Ken Landreaux .06 .05 .02
76 Bill Russell .06 .05 .02
77 Steve Sax .06 .05 .02
78 Rick Honeycutt .03 .02 .01
79 Mike Scioscia .03 .02 .01
80 Tom Niedenfuer .06 .05 .02
81 Candy Maldonado .03 .02 .01
82 Tim Raines .15 .11 .06
83 Gary Carter .15 .11 .06
84 Charlie Lea .03 .02 .01
85 Jeff Reardon .08 .06 .03
86 Andre Dawson .06 .05 .02
87 Tim Wallach .04 .03 .02
88 Terry Francona .04 .03 .02
89 Steve Rogers .03 .02 .01
90 Bryn Smith .03 .02 .01
91 Bill Gullickson .04 .03 .02
92 Dan Driessen .03 .02 .01
93 Doug Flynn .03 .02 .01
94 Mike Schmidt .20 .15 .08
95 Tony Armas .20 .15 .08
96 Dale Murphy .15 .11 .06
97 Rick Sutcliffe .10 .08 .04
98 Keith Hernandez .12 .09 .05
99 George Foster .08 .06 .03
100 Darryl Strawberry .30 .25 .12
101 Jesse Orosco .04 .03 .02
102 Mookie Wilson .04 .03 .02
103 Doug Sisk .03 .02 .01
104 Hubie Brooks .06 .05 .02
105 Ron Darling .04 .03 .02
106 Wally Backman .04 .03 .02
107 Dwight Gooden .15 .11 .06
108 Mike Fitzgerald .04 .03 .02
109 Walt Terrell .03 .02 .01
110 Ozzie Virgil .04 .03 .02
111 Mike Schmidt .25 .20 .10
112 Steve Carlton .15 .11 .06
113 Al Holland .03 .02 .01
114 Juan Samuel .06 .05 .02
115 Von Hayes .04 .03 .02
116 Jeff Stone .06 .05 .02
117 Jerry Koosman .04 .03 .02
118 Al Oliver .04 .03 .02
119 John Denny .03 .02 .01
120 Charles Hudson .03 .02 .01
121 Garry Maddox .06 .05 .02
122 Bill Madlock .06 .05 .02
123 John Candelaria .06 .05 .02
124 Tony Pena .06 .05 .02
125 Jason Thompson .03 .02 .01
126 Lee Lacy .04 .03 .02
127 Rick Rhoden .06 .05 .02
128 Doug Frobel .06 .05 .02
129 Kent Tekulve .04 .03 .02
130 Johnny Ray .04 .03 .02
131 Marvell Wynne .08 .06 .03
132 Larry McWilliams .03 .02 .01
133 Dale Berra .03 .02 .01
134 George Hendrick .06 .05 .02
135 Bruce Sutter .08 .06 .03
136 Joaquin Andujar .04 .03 .02
137 Ozzie Smith .20 .15 .08
138 Andy Van Slyke .04 .03 .02
139 Lonnie Smith .06 .05 .02
140 Darrell Porter .03 .02 .01
141 Willie McGee .06 .05 .02
142 Tom Herr .04 .03 .02
143 Dave LaPoint .03 .02 .01
144 Neil Allen .04 .03 .02
145 David Green .03 .02 .01
146 Tony Gwynn .20 .15 .08
147 Rich Gossage .12 .09 .05
148 Terry Kennedy .04 .03 .02
149 Steve Garvey .15 .11 .06
150 Alan Wiggins .03 .02 .01
151 Garry Templeton .08 .06 .03
152 Ed Whitson .04 .03 .02
153 Tim Lollar .03 .02 .01
154 Dave Dravecky .04 .03 .02
155 Graig Nettles .04 .03 .02
156 Eric Show .03 .02 .01
157 Carmelo Martinez .03 .02 .01
158 Bob Brenly .03 .02 .01
159 Gary Lavelle .03 .02 .01
160 Jack Clark .10 .08 .04
161 Jeff Leonard .04 .03 .02
162 Chili Davis .06 .05 .02
163 Mike Krukow .03 .02 .01
164 Johnnie LeMaster .03 .02 .01
165 Atlee Hammaker .03 .02 .01
166 Dan Gladden .06 .05 .02
167 Greg Minton .03 .02 .01
168 Joel Youngblood .03 .02 .01
169 Frank Williams .04 .03 .02
170 Tony Gwynn .20 .15 .08
171 Don Mattingly .30 .25 .12
172 Bruce Sutter .15 .11 .06
173 Dan Quisenberry .10 .08 .04
174 Tony Gwynn .40 .30 .15
175 Ryne Sandberg .40 .30 .15
176 Steve Garvey .30 .25 .12
177 Dale Murphy .40 .30 .15
178 Mike Schmidt .40 .30 .15
179 Darryl Strawberry .25 .20 .10
180 Gary Carter .20 .15 .08
181 Ozzie Smith .30 .25 .12
182 Charlie Lea .15 .11 .06
183 Lou Whitaker .25 .20 .10
184 Rod Carew .30 .25 .12
185 Cal Ripken, Jr. .45 .35 .20
186 Dave Winfield .40 .30 .15
187 Reggie Jackson .40 .30 .15
188 George Brett .50 .40 .20
189 Lance Parrish .15 .11 .06
190 Chet Lemon .15 .11 .06
191 Dave Stieb .15 .11 .06
192 Gary Carter .20 .15 .08
193 Mike Schmidt .40 .30 .15
194 Tony Armas .15 .11 .06
195 Mike Witt .10 .08 .04
196 Eddie Murray .20 .15 .08
197 Cal Ripken, Jr. .40 .30 .15
198 Scott McGregor .04 .03 .02
199 Rick Dempsey .04 .03 .02
200 Tippy Martinez .08 .06 .03
201 Ken Singleton .04 .03 .02
202 Mike Boddicker .06 .05 .02
203 Rich Dauer .03 .02 .01
204 John Shelby .04 .03 .02
205 Al Bumbry .04 .03 .02
206 John Lowenstein .04 .03 .02
207 Mike Flanagan .04 .03 .02
209 Tony Armas .04 .03 .02
210 Wade Boggs .60 .45 .25
211 Bruce Hurst .06 .05 .02
212 Dwight Evans .06 .05 .02
213 Mike Easler .04 .03 .02
214 Bill Buckner .04 .03 .02
215 Bob Stanley .04 .03 .02
216 Jackie Gutierrez .03 .02 .01
217 Rich Gedman .04 .03 .02
218 Jerry Remy .03 .02 .01
219 Marty Barrett .04 .03 .02
220 Reggie Jackson .35 .25 .14
221 Geoff Zahn .03 .02 .01
222 Doug DeCinces .06 .05 .02
223 Rod Carew .20 .15 .08
224 Brian Downing .04 .03 .02
225 Fred Lynn .06 .05 .02
226 Gary Pettis .04 .03 .02
227 Mike Witt .06 .05 .02
228 Bob Boone .06 .05 .02
229 Tommy John .06 .05 .02
230 Bobby Grich .06 .05 .02
231 Ron Romanick .04 .03 .02
232 Ron Kittle .06 .05 .02
233 Richard Dotson .06 .05 .02
234 Harold Baines .08 .06 .03
235 Tom Seaver .30 .25 .12
236 Greg Walker .06 .05 .02
237 Roy Smalley .04 .03 .02
238 Greg Luzinski .06 .05 .02
239 Julio Cruz .03 .02 .01
240 Scott Fletcher .03 .02 .01
241 Rudy Law .04 .03 .02
242 Vance Law .03 .02 .01
243 Carlton Fisk .20 .15 .08
244 Andre Thornton .06 .05 .02
245 Julio Franco .15 .11 .06
246 Brett Butler .06 .05 .02
247 Bert Blyleven .08 .06 .03
248 Mike Hargrove .04 .03 .02
249 George Vukovich .04 .03 .02
250 Pat Tabler .04 .03 .02
251 Brook Jacoby .06 .05 .02
252 Tony Bernazard .03 .02 .01
253 Ernie Camacho .03 .02 .01
254 Mel Hall .06 .05 .02
255 Carmen Castillo .04 .03 .02
256 Jack Morris .12 .09 .05
257 Willie Hernandez .06 .05 .02
258 Alan Trammell .15 .11 .06
259 Lance Parrish .12 .09 .05
260 Chet Lemon .10 .08 .04
261 Lou Whitaker .06 .05 .02
262 Howard Johnson .06 .05 .02
263 Barbaro Garbey .06 .05 .02
264 Dan Petry .03 .02 .01
265 Aurelio Lopez .03 .02 .01
266 Larry Herndon .03 .02 .01
267 Kirk Gibson .06 .05 .02
268 George Brett .25 .20 .10
269 Dan Quisenberry .06 .05 .02
270 Hal McRae .06 .05 .02
271 Steve Balboni .06 .05 .02
272 Pat Sheridan .06 .05 .02
273 Jorge Orta .04 .03 .02
274 Frank White .04 .03 .02
275 Bud Black .03 .02 .01
276 Darryl Motley .03 .02 .01
277 Willie Wilson .04 .03 .02
278 Larry Gura .03 .02 .01
279 Don Slaught .03 .02 .01
280 Dwight Gooden .20 .15 .08
281 Mark Langston .30 .25 .12
282 Tim Raines .15 .11 .06
283 Rickey Henderson .30 .25 .12
284 Robin Yount .30 .25 .12
285 Rollie Fingers .10 .08 .04
286 Jim Sundberg .03 .02 .01
287 Cecil Cooper .06 .05 .02
288 Jaime Cocanower .04 .03 .02
289 Mike Caldwell .03 .02 .01
290 Don Sutton .06 .05 .02
291 Rick Manning .04 .03 .02
292 Ben Oglivie .04 .03 .02
293 Moose Haas .15 .11 .06
294 Ted Simmons .04 .03 .02
295 Jim Gantner .03 .02 .01
296 Kent Hrbek .12 .09 .05
297 Ron Davis .03 .02 .01
298 Dave Engle .03 .02 .01
299 Tom Brunansky .06 .05 .02
300 Frank Viola .06 .05 .02
301 Mike Smithson .04 .03 .02
302 Gary Gaetti .06 .05 .02
303 Tim Teufel .04 .03 .02
304 Mickey Hatcher .04 .03 .02
305 John Butcher .03 .02 .01
306 Darrell Brown .03 .02 .01
307 Kirby Puckett .30 .25 .12
308 Dave Winfield .30 .25 .12
309 Phil Niekro .12 .09 .05
310 Don Mattingly .70 .50 .30
311 Don Baylor .08 .06 .03
312 Willie Randolph .04 .03 .02
313 Ron Guidry .06 .05 .02
314 Dave Righetti .06 .05 .02
315 Bobby Meacham .04 .03 .02
316 Butch Wynegar .04 .03 .02
317 Mike Pagliarulo .08 .06 .03
318 Joe Cowley .03 .02 .01
319 John Montefusco .03 .02 .01
320 Dave Kingman .08 .06 .03
321 Rickey Henderson .30 .25 .12
322 Bill Caudill .03 .02 .01
323 Dwayne Murphy .04 .03 .02
324 Steve McCatty .04 .03 .02
325 Joe Morgan .10 .08 .04
326 Mike Heath .03 .02 .01
327 Chris Codiroli .06 .05 .02
328 Ray Burris .04 .03 .02
329 Tony Phillips .10 .08 .04
330 Carney Lansford .04 .03 .02
331 Bruce Bochte .03 .02 .01
332 Alvin Davis .08 .06 .03
333 Al Cowens .03 .02 .01
334 Jim Beattie .03 .02 .01
335 Bob Kearney .03 .02 .01
336 Ed Vande Berg .03 .02 .01
337 Mark Langston .25 .20 .10
338 Dave Henderson .04 .03 .02
339 Spike Owen .03 .02 .01
340 Matt Young .04 .03 .02
341 Jack Perconte .04 .03 .02
342 Barry Bonnell .03 .02 .01
343 Mike Stanton .03 .02 .01
344 Pete O'Brien .08 .06 .03
345 Charlie Hough .06 .05 .02
346 Larry Parrish .06 .05 .02
347 Buddy Bell .08 .06 .03
348 Frank Tanana .06 .05 .02
349 Curt Wilkerson .03 .02 .01
350 Jeff Kunkel .03 .02 .01
351 Billy Sample .03 .02 .01
352 Danny Darwin .03 .02 .01
353 Gary Ward .03 .02 .01
354 Mike Mason .03 .02 .01
355 Mickey Rivers .04 .03 .02
356 Dave Stieb .08 .06 .03
357 Damaso Garcia .04 .03 .02
358 Willie Upshaw .06 .05 .02
359 Lloyd Moseby .08 .06 .03
360 George Bell .08 .06 .03
361 Luis Leal .04 .03 .02
362 Jesse Barfield .06 .05 .02
363 Dave Collins .03 .02 .01
364 Roy Lee Jackson .04 .03 .02
365 Doyle Alexander .04 .03 .02
366 Alfredo Griffin .04 .03 .02
367 Cliff Johnson .04 .03 .02
368 Alvin Davis .08 .06 .03
369 Juan Samuel .10 .08 .04
370 Brook Jacoby .08 .06 .03
371 Dwight Gooden, Mark Langston .30 .25 .12
372 Mike Fitzgerald .04 .03 .02
373 Jackie Gutierrez .03 .02 .01
374 Dan Gladden .08 .06 .03
375 Carmelo Martinez .06 .05 .02
376 Kirby Puckett .30 .25 .12

1985 Topps Super

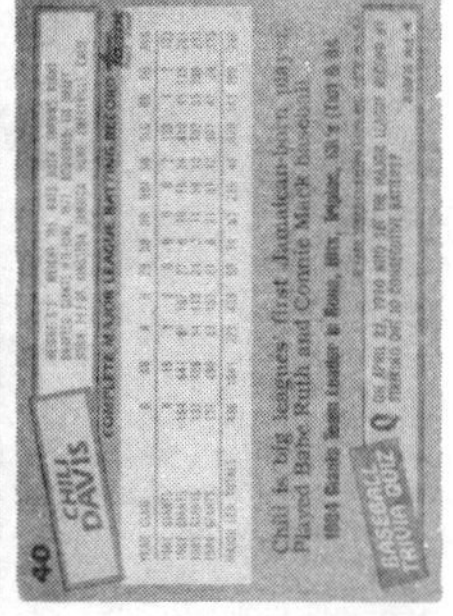

Still trying to sell collectors on the idea of jumbo-sized cards, Topps returned for a second year with its 4-7/8" by 6-7/8" "Super" set. In fact, the set size was doubled from the previous year, to 60 cards.

The Supers are identical to the regular-issue 1985 cards of the same players, only the card numbers on back were changed. The cards were again sold three per pack for 50¢.

		MT	NR MT	EX
Complete Set:		17.50	13.00	7.00
Common Player:		.25	.20	.10
1	Ryne Sandberg	2.00	1.50	.80
2	Willie Hernandez	.25	.20	.10
3	Rick Sutcliffe	.25	.20	.10
4	Don Mattingly	.90	.70	.35
5	Tony Gwynn	.70	.50	.30
6	Alvin Davis	.25	.20	.10
7	Dwight Gooden	1.00	.70	.40
8	Dan Quisenberry	.25	.20	.10
9	Bruce Sutter	.25	.20	.10
10	Tony Armas	.25	.20	.10
11	Dale Murphy	.90	.70	.35
12	Mike Schmidt	.90	.70	.35
13	Gary Carter	.50	.40	.20
14	Rickey Henderson	.70	.50	.30
15	Tim Raines	.50	.40	.20
16	Mike Boddicker	.25	.20	.10
17	Alejandro Pena	.25	.20	.10
18	Eddie Murray	.60	.45	.25
19	Gary Matthews	.25	.20	.10
20	Mark Langston	.30	.25	.12
21	Mario Soto	.25	.20	.10
22	Dave Stieb	.25	.20	.10
23	Nolan Ryan	2.00	1.50	.80
24	Steve Carlton	.90	.70	.35
25	Alan Trammell	.50	.40	.20
26	Steve Garvey	.50	.40	.20
27	Kirk Gibson	.35	.25	.14
28	Juan Samuel	.35	.25	.14
29	Reggie Jackson	.90	.70	.35
30	Darryl Strawberry	.90	.70	.35
31	Tom Seaver	.90	.70	.35
32	Pete Rose	1.25	.90	.50
33	Dwight Evans	.30	.25	.12
34	Jose Cruz	.25	.20	.10
35	Bert Blyleven	.35	.25	.14
36	Keith Hernandez	.35	.25	.14
37	Robin Yount	.75	.60	.30
38	Joaquin Andujar	.25	.20	.10
39	Lloyd Moseby	.25	.20	.10
40	Chili Davis	.35	.25	.14
41	Kent Hrbek	.35	.25	.14
42	Dave Parker	.50	.40	.20
43	Jack Morris	.35	.25	.14
44	Pedro Guerrero	.30	.25	.12
45	Mike Witt	.25	.20	.10
46	George Brett	.90	.70	.35
47	Ozzie Smith	.75	.60	.30
48	Cal Ripken, Jr.	2.00	1.50	.80
49	Rich Gossage	.25	.20	.10
50	Jim Rice	.35	.25	.14
51	Harold Baines	.25	.20	.10
52	Fernando Valenzuela	.35	.25	.14
53	Buddy Bell	.25	.20	.10
54	Jesse Orosco	.25	.20	.10
55	Lance Parrish	.35	.25	.14
56	Jason Thompson	.25	.20	.10
57	Tom Brunansky	.25	.20	.10
58	Dave Righetti	.30	.25	.12
59	Dave Kingman	.25	.20	.10
60	Dave Winfield	.90	.70	.35

1985 Topps 3-D

These 4-1/4" by 6" cards were something new. Printed on plastic, rather than paper, the player picture on the card is actually raised above the surface much like might be found on a relief map; a true 3-D baseball card. The plastic cards include the player's name, a Topps logo and card number across the top, and a team logo on the side. The backs are blank but have two peel-off adhesive strips so that the card may be attached to a flat surface. There are 30 cards in the set, the bulk of whom are stars.

		MT	NR MT	EX
Complete Set:		20.00	15.00	8.00
Common Player:		.25	.20	.10
1	Mike Schmidt	.90	.70	.35
2	Eddie Murray	.50	.40	.20
3	Dale Murphy	.90	.70	.35
4	George Brett	.90	.70	.35
5	Pete Rose	1.25	.90	.50
6	Jim Rice	.40	.30	.15
7	Ryne Sandberg	2.00	1.50	.80
8	Don Mattingly	.80	.60	.30
9	Darryl Strawberry	.30	.25	.12
10	Rickey Henderson	.80	.60	.30
11	Keith Hernandez	.35	.25	.14
12	Dave Kingman	.25	.20	.10
13	Tony Gwynn	.60	.45	.25
14	Reggie Jackson	.90	.70	.35
15	Gary Carter	.40	.30	.15
16	Cal Ripken, Jr.	2.00	1.50	.80
17	Tim Raines	.50	.40	.20
18	Dave Winfield	.90	.70	.35
19	Dwight Gooden	.35	.25	.14
20	Dave Stieb	.25	.20	.10
21	Fernando Valenzuela	.30	.25	.12
22	Mark Langston	.30	.25	.12
23	Bruce Sutter	.25	.20	.10
24	Dan Quisenberry	.25	.20	.10
25	Steve Carlton	.75	.60	.30
26	Mike Boddicker	.25	.20	.10
27	Goose Gossage	.30	.25	.12
28	Jack Morris	.30	.25	.12
29	Rick Sutcliffe	.25	.20	.10
30	Tom Seaver	.60	.45	.25

1986 Topps

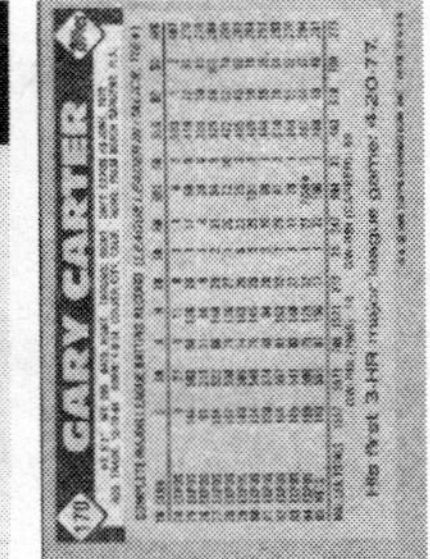

The 1986 Topps set consists of 792 cards. Fronts of the 2-1/2" by 3-1/2" cards feature color photos with the Topps logo in the upper right-hand corner while the player's position is in the lower left-hand corner. Above the picture is the team name, while below it is the player's name. The borders are a departure from previous practice, as the top 7/8" is black, while the remainder was white. There are no card numbers 51 and 171 in the set; the card that should have been #51, Bobby Wine, shares #57 with Bill Doran, while #171, Bob Rodgers, shares #141 with Chuck Cottier. Once again, a 5,000-set glossy-finish "Tiffany" edition was produced. Values are four to six times higher than the same card in the regular issue.

		MT	NR MT	EX
Complete Set (792):		35.00	26.00	14.00
Common Player:		.05	.04	.02
1	Pete Rose	.90	.70	.35
2	Pete Rose (Special 1963-66)	.30	.25	.12
3	Pete Rose (Special 1967-70)	.30	.25	.12
4	Pete Rose (Special 1971-74)	.30	.25	.12
5	Pete Rose (Special 1975-78)	.30	.25	.12
6	Pete Rose (Special 1972-82)	.30	.25	.12
7	Pete Rose (Special 1983-85)	.30	.25	.12
8	Dwayne Murphy	.07	.05	.03
9	Roy Smith	.05	.04	.02
10	Tony Gwynn	1.00	.70	.40
11	Bob Ojeda	.07	.05	.03
12	*Jose Uribe* (FC)	.05	.04	.02
13	Bob Kearney	.05	.04	.02
14	Julio Cruz	.05	.04	.02
15	Eddie Whitson	.05	.04	.02
16	Rick Schu (FC)	.07	.05	.03
17	Mike Stenhouse	.05	.04	.02
18	Brent Gaff	.05	.04	.02
19	Rich Hebner	.05	.04	.02
20	Lou Whitaker	.12	.09	.05
21	George Bamberger	.05	.04	.02
22	Duane Walker	.05	.04	.02
23	*Manny Lee* (FC)	.15	.11	.06
24	Len Barker	.07	.05	.03
25	Willie Wilson	.12	.09	.05
26	Frank DiPino	.05	.04	.02
27	Ray Knight	.07	.05	.03
28	Eric Davis	.35	.25	.14
29	Tony Phillips	.05	.04	.02
30	Eddie Murray	.40	.30	.15
31	Jamie Easterly	.05	.04	.02
32	Steve Yeager	.05	.04	.02
33	Jeff Lahti	.05	.04	.02
34	Ken Phelps (FC)	.07	.05	.03
35	Jeff Reardon	.12	.09	.05
36	Tigers Leaders (Lance Parrish)	.12	.09	.05
37	Mark Thurmond	.05	.04	.02
38	Glenn Hoffman	.05	.04	.02
39	Dave Rucker	.05	.04	.02
40	Ken Griffey	.10	.08	.04
41	Brad Wellman	.05	.04	.02
42	Geoff Zahn	.05	.04	.02
43	Dave Engle	.05	.04	.02
44	*Lance McCullers* (FC)	.10	.08	.04
45	Damaso Garcia	.05	.04	.02
46	Billy Hatcher (FC)	.20	.15	.08
47	Juan Berenguer	.05	.04	.02
48	Bill Almon	.05	.04	.02
49	Rick Manning	.05	.04	.02
50	Dan Quisenberry	.07	.05	.03
51	Not issued, see #57			
52	Chris Welsh	.05	.04	.02
53	*Len Dykstra* (FC)	3.00	2.25	1.25
54	John Franco	.12	.09	.05
55	Fred Lynn	.15	.11	.06
56	Tom Niedenfuer	.07	.05	.03
57a	Bill Doran	.10	.08	.04
57b	Bobby Wine (supposed to be #51)	.05	.04	.02
58	Bill Krueger	.05	.04	.02
59	Andre Thornton	.07	.05	.03
60	Dwight Evans	.12	.09	.05
61	Karl Best	.05	.04	.02
62	Bob Boone	.07	.05	.03
63	Ron Roenicke	.05	.04	.02
64	Floyd Bannister	.10	.08	.04
65	Dan Driessen	.07	.05	.03
66	Cardinals Leaders (Bob Forsch)	.07	.05	.03
67	Carmelo Martinez	.07	.05	.03
68	Ed Lynch	.05	.04	.02
69	Luis Aguayo	.05	.04	.02
70	Dave Winfield	.60	.45	.25
71	Ken Schrom	.05	.04	.02
72	Shawon Dunston	.15	.11	.06
73	Randy O'Neal (FC)	.07	.05	.03
74	Rance Mulliniks	.05	.04	.02
75	Jose DeLeon	.07	.05	.03
76	Dion James	.07	.05	.03
77	Charlie Leibrandt	.07	.05	.03
78	Bruce Benedict	.05	.04	.02
79	Dave Schmidt	.07	.05	.03
80	Darryl Strawberry	.30	.25	.12
81	Gene Mauch	.07	.05	.03
82	Tippy Martinez	.05	.04	.02
83	Phil Garner	.07	.05	.03
84	Curt Young	.07	.05	.03
85	Tony Perez	.15	.11	.06
86	Tom Waddell	.05	.04	.02
87	Candy Maldonado	.10	.08	.04
88	Tom Nieto	.05	.04	.02
89	Randy St. Claire (FC)	.07	.05	.03
90	Garry Templeton	.07	.05	.03
91	Steve Crawford	.05	.04	.02
92	Al Cowens	.05	.04	.02
93	Scot Thompson	.05	.04	.02
94	Rick Bordi	.05	.04	.02
95	Ozzie Virgil	.05	.04	.02
96	Blue Jay Leaders (Jim Clancy)	.07	.05	.03
97	Gary Gaetti	.20	.15	.08
98	Dick Ruthven	.05	.04	.02
99	Buddy Biancalana	.05	.04	.02
100	Nolan Ryan	3.00	2.25	1.25
101	Dave Bergman	.05	.04	.02
102	*Joe Orsulak*	.15	.11	.06
103	Luis Salazar	.05	.04	.02
104	Sid Fernandez	.12	.09	.05
105	Gary Ward	.07	.05	.03
106	Ray Burris	.05	.04	.02
107	Rafael Ramirez	.05	.04	.02
108	Ted Power	.05	.04	.02
109	Len Matuszek	.05	.04	.02
110	Scott McGregor	.07	.05	.03
111	Roger Craig	.07	.05	.03
112	Bill Campbell	.05	.04	.02
113	U.L. Washington	.05	.04	.02
114	Mike Brown	.05	.04	.02
115	Jay Howell	.07	.05	.03
116	Brook Jacoby	.10	.08	.04
117	Bruce Kison	.05	.04	.02
118	Jerry Royster	.05	.04	.02
119	Barry Bonnell	.05	.04	.02
120	Steve Carlton	.40	.30	.15
121	Nelson Simmons	.05	.04	.02
122	Pete Filson	.05	.04	.02
123	Greg Walker	.10	.08	.04
124	Luis Sanchez	.05	.04	.02
125	Dave Lopes	.07	.05	.03
126	Mets Leaders (Mookie Wilson)	.07	.05	.03
127	*Jack Howell* (FC)	.05	.04	.02
128	John Wathan	.07	.05	.03
129	Jeff Dedmon (FC)	.05	.04	.02
130	Alan Trammell	.15	.11	.06
131	Checklist 1-132	.05	.04	.02
132	Razor Shines	.05	.04	.02
133	Andy McGaffigan	.05	.04	.02
134	Carney Lansford	.10	.08	.04
135	Joe Niekro	.10	.08	.04
136	Mike Hargrove	.05	.04	.02
137	Charlie Moore	.05	.04	.02
138	Mark Davis	.05	.04	.02
139	Daryl Boston	.10	.08	.04
140	John Candelaria	.10	.08	.04
141a	Chuck Cottier	.05	.04	.02
141b	Bob Rodgers (supposed to be #171)	.05	.04	.02
142	Bob Jones	.05	.04	.02
143	Dave Van Gorder	.05	.04	.02
144	Doug Sisk	.05	.04	.02
145	Pedro Guerrero	.06	.05	.02
146	Jack Perconte	.05	.04	.02
147	Larry Sheets	.05	.04	.02
148	Mike Heath	.05	.04	.02
149	Brett Butler	.07	.05	.03
150	Joaquin Andujar	.07	.05	.03
151	Dave Stapleton	.05	.04	.02
152	Mike Morgan	.05	.04	.02
153	Ricky Adams	.05	.04	.02
154	Bert Roberge	.05	.04	.02
155	Bob Grich	.10	.08	.04
156	White Sox Leaders (Richard Dotson)	.07	.05	.03
157	Ron Hassey	.05	.04	.02
158	Derrel Thomas	.05	.04	.02

159	Orel Hershiser	.15	.11	.06
160	Chet Lemon	.07	.05	.03
161	Lee Tunnell	.05	.04	.02
162	Greg Gagne	.10	.08	.04
163	Pete Ladd	.05	.04	.02
164	Steve Balboni	.07	.05	.03
165	Mike Davis	.07	.05	.03
166	Dickie Thon	.07	.05	.03
167	Zane Smith (FC)	.15	.11	.06
168	Jeff Burroughs	.07	.05	.03
169	George Wright	.05	.04	.02
170	Gary Carter	.20	.15	.08
171	Not issued, see #141			
172	Jerry Reed	.05	.04	.02
173	Wayne Gross	.05	.04	.02
174	Brian Snyder	.05	.04	.02
175	Steve Sax	.15	.11	.06
176	Jay Tibbs	.05	.04	.02
177	Joel Youngblood	.05	.04	.02
178	Ivan DeJesus	.05	.04	.02
179	*Stu Cliburn* (FC)	.10	.08	.04
180	Don Mattingly	1.00	.75	.40
181	Al Nipper	.05	.04	.02
182	Bobby Brown	.05	.04	.02
183	Larry Andersen	.05	.04	.02
184	Tim Laudner	.05	.04	.02
185	Rollie Fingers	.20	.15	.08
186	Astros Leaders (Jose Cruz)	.07	.05	.03
187	Scott Fletcher	.07	.05	.03
188	Bob Dernier	.05	.04	.02
189	Mike Mason	.05	.04	.02
190	George Hendrick	.07	.05	.03
191	Wally Backman	.07	.05	.03
192	Milt Wilcox	.05	.04	.02
193	Daryl Sconiers	.05	.04	.02
194	Craig McMurtry	.05	.04	.02
195	Dave Concepcion	.12	.09	.05
196	Doyle Alexander	.10	.08	.04
197	Enos Cabell	.05	.04	.02
198	Ken Dixon	.05	.04	.02
199	Dick Howser	.05	.04	.02
200	Mike Schmidt	1.00	.70	.40
201	Vince Coleman (FC) (Record Breaker)	.12	.09	.05
202	Dwight Gooden (Record Breaker)	.20	.15	.08
203	Keith Hernandez (Record Breaker)	.08	.06	.03
204	Phil Niekro (Record Breaker)	.08	.06	.03
205	Tony Perez (Record Breaker)	.10	.08	.04
206	Pete Rose (Record Breaker)	.50	.40	.20
207	Fernando Valenzuela (Recored Breaker)	.08	.06	.03
208	Ramon Romero	.05	.04	.02
209	Randy Ready	.10	.08	.04
210	Calvin Schiraldi (FC)	.10	.08	.04
211	Ed Wojna	.05	.04	.02
212	Chris Speier	.05	.04	.02
213	Bob Shirley	.05	.04	.02
214	Randy Bush	.05	.04	.02
215	Frank White	.10	.08	.04
216	A's Leaders (Dwayne Murphy)	.07	.05	.03
217	Bill Scherrer	.05	.04	.02
218	Randy Hunt	.05	.04	.02
219	Dennis Lamp	.05	.04	.02
220	Bob Horner	.10	.08	.04
221	Dave Henderson	.10	.08	.04
222	Craig Gerber	.05	.04	.02
223	Atlee Hammaker	.05	.04	.02
224	Cesar Cedeno	.10	.08	.04
225	Ron Darling	.15	.11	.06
226	Lee Lacy	.05	.04	.02
227	Al Jones	.05	.04	.02
228	Tom Lawless	.05	.04	.02
229	Bill Gullickson	.05	.04	.02
230	Terry Kennedy	.07	.05	.03
231	Jim Frey	.05	.04	.02
232	Rick Rhoden	.10	.08	.04
233	Steve Lyons (FC)	.07	.05	.03
234	Doug Corbett	.05	.04	.02
235	Butch Wynegar	.05	.04	.02
236	Frank Eufemia	.05	.04	.02
237	Ted Simmons	.12	.09	.05
238	Larry Parrish	.10	.08	.04
239	Joel Skinner	.05	.04	.02
240	Tommy John	.20	.15	.08
241	Tony Fernandez	.20	.15	.08
242	Rich Thompson	.05	.04	.02
243	Johnny Grubb	.05	.04	.02
244	Craig Lefferts	.05	.04	.02
245	Jim Sundberg	.07	.05	.03
246	Phillies Leaders (Steve Carlton)	.15	.11	.06
247	Terry Harper	.05	.04	.02
248	Spike Owen	.05	.04	.02
249	Rob Deer (FC)	.10	.08	.04
250	Dwight Gooden	.50	.40	.20
251	Rich Dauer	.05	.04	.02
252	Bobby Castillo	.05	.04	.02
253	Dann Bilardello	.05	.04	.02
254	*Ozzie Guillen*	.30	.25	.12
255	Tony Armas	.07	.05	.03
256	Kurt Kepshire	.05	.04	.02
257	Doug DeCinces	.10	.08	.04
258	*Tim Burke* (FC)	.10	.08	.04
259	Dan Pasqua (FC)	.06	.05	.02
260	Tony Pena	.10	.08	.04
261	Bobby Valentine	.05	.04	.02
262	Mario Ramirez	.05	.04	.02
263	Checklist 133-264	.05	.04	.02
264	*Darren Daulton* (FC)	2.00	1.50	.80
265	Ron Davis	.05	.04	.02
266	Keith Moreland	.07	.05	.03
267	Paul Molitor	.60	.45	.25
268	Mike Scott	.15	.11	.06
269	Dane Iorg	.05	.04	.02
270	Jack Morris	.10	.07	.04
271	Dave Collins	.07	.05	.03
272	Tim Tolman	.05	.04	.02
273	Jerry Willard	.05	.04	.02
274	Ron Gardenhire	.05	.04	.02
275	Charlie Hough	.08	.06	.03
276	Yankees Leaders (Willie Randolph)	.07	.05	.03
277	Jaime Cocanower	.05	.04	.02
278	Sixto Lezcano	.05	.04	.02
279	Al Pardo	.05	.04	.02
280	Tim Raines	.12	.09	.05
281	Steve Mura	.05	.04	.02
282	Jerry Mumphrey	.05	.04	.02
283	Mike Fischlin	.05	.04	.02
284	Brian Dayett	.05	.04	.02
285	Buddy Bell	.10	.08	.04
286	Luis DeLeon	.05	.04	.02
287	*John Christensen* (FC)	.10	.08	.04
288	Don Aase	.05	.04	.02
289	Johnnie LeMaster	.05	.04	.02
290	Carlton Fisk	.30	.25	.12
291	Tom Lasorda	.07	.05	.03
292	Chuck Porter	.05	.04	.02
293	Chris Chambliss	.07	.05	.03
294	Danny Cox	.10	.08	.04
295	Kirk Gibson	.10	.08	.04
296	Geno Petralli (FC)	.07	.05	.03
297	Tim Lollar	.05	.04	.02
298	Craig Reynolds	.05	.04	.02
299	Bryn Smith	.05	.04	.02
300	George Brett	.75	.60	.30
301	Dennis Rasmussen	.12	.09	.05
302	Greg Gross	.05	.04	.02
303	Curt Wardle	.05	.04	.02
304	*Mike Gallego* (FC)	.12	.09	.05
305	Phil Bradley	.06	.05	.02
306	Padres Leaders (Terry Kennedy)	.07	.05	.03
307	Dave Sax	.05	.04	.02
308	Ray Fontenot	.05	.04	.02
309	John Shelby	.05	.04	.02
310	Greg Minton	.05	.04	.02
311	Dick Schofield	.05	.04	.02
312	Tom Filer	.05	.04	.02
313	Joe DeSa	.05	.04	.02
314	Frank Pastore	.05	.04	.02
315	Mookie Wilson	.10	.08	.04
316	Sammy Khalifa	.05	.04	.02
317	Ed Romero	.05	.04	.02
318	Terry Whitfield	.05	.04	.02
319	Rick Camp	.05	.04	.02
320	Jim Rice	.08	.06	.03
321	Earl Weaver	.07	.05	.03
322	Bob Forsch	.07	.05	.03
323	Jerry Davis	.05	.04	.02
324	Dan Schatzeder	.05	.04	.02
325	Juan Beniquez	.05	.04	.02
326	Kent Tekulve	.07	.05	.03
327	Mike Pagliarulo	.06	.05	.02
328	Pete O'Brien	.10	.08	.04
329	Kirby Puckett	4.00	3.00	1.50
330	Rick Sutcliffe	.12	.09	.05
331	Alan Ashby	.05	.04	.02
332	Darryl Motley	.05	.04	.02
333	Tom Henke (FC)	.20	.15	.08
334	Ken Oberkfell	.05	.04	.02
335	Don Sutton	.20	.15	.08
336	Indians Leaders (Andre Thornton)	.07	.05	.03
337	Darnell Coles	.07	.05	.03
338	Jorge Bell	.15	.11	.06
339	Bruce Berenyi	.05	.04	.02
340	Cal Ripken, Jr.	2.00	1.50	.80
341	Frank Williams	.05	.04	.02
342	Gary Redus	.05	.04	.02
343	Carlos Diaz	.05	.04	.02
344	Jim Wohlford	.05	.04	.02
345	Donnie Moore	.05	.04	.02
346	Bryan Little	.05	.04	.02
347	*Teddy Higuera*	.08	.06	.03
348	Cliff Johnson	.05	.04	.02
349	Mark Clear	.05	.04	.02
350	Jack Clark	.10	.08	.04
351	Chuck Tanner	.05	.04	.02
352	Harry Spilman	.05	.04	.02
353	Keith Atherton	.05	.04	.02
354	Tony Bernazard	.05	.04	.02
355	Lee Smith	.10	.08	.04
356	Mickey Hatcher	.05	.04	.02
357	Ed Vande Berg	.05	.04	.02
358	Rick Dempsey	.07	.05	.03
359	Mike LaCoss	.05	.04	.02
360	Lloyd Moseby	.10	.08	.04
361	Shane Rawley	.10	.08	.04
362	Tom Paciorek	.05	.04	.02
363	Terry Forster	.07	.05	.03
364	Reid Nichols	.05	.04	.02
365	Mike Flanagan	.10	.08	.04
366	Reds Leaders (Dave Concepcion)	.07	.05	.03
367	Aurelio Lopez	.05	.04	.02
368	Greg Brock	.07	.05	.03
369	Al Holland	.05	.04	.02
370	*Vince Coleman*	.25	.20	.10
371	Bill Stein	.05	.04	.02
372	Ben Oglivie	.07	.05	.03
373	*Urbano Lugo* (FC)	.07	.05	.03
374	Terry Francona	.05	.04	.02
375	Rich Gedman	.10	.08	.04
376	Bill Dawley	.05	.04	.02
377	Joe Carter	1.50	1.25	.60
378	Bruce Bochte	.05	.04	.02
379	Bobby Meacham	.05	.04	.02
380	LaMarr Hoyt	.05	.04	.02
381	Ray Miller	.05	.04	.02
382	*Ivan Calderon*	.25	.20	.10
383	*Chris Brown*	.15	.11	.06
384	Steve Trout	.05	.04	.02
385	Cecil Cooper	.10	.08	.04
386	*Cecil Fielder*	5.00	3.75	2.00
387	Steve Kemp	.07	.05	.03
388	Dickie Noles	.05	.04	.02
389	Glenn Davis (FC)	.12	.09	.05
390	Tom Seaver	.40	.30	.15
391	Julio Franco	.10	.08	.04
392	John Russell (FC)	.10	.08	.04
393	Chris Pittaro	.05	.04	.02
394	Checklist 265-396	.05	.04	.02
395	Scott Garrelts	.07	.05	.03
396	Red Sox Leaders (Dwight Evans)	.07	.05	.03
397	*Steve Buechele* (FC)	.20	.15	.08
398	*Earnie Riles* (FC)	.15	.11	.06
399	Bill Swift	.25	.20	.10
400	Rod Carew	.30	.25	.12
401	Turn Back The Clock (Fernando Valenzuela)	.15	.11	.06
402	Turn Back The Clock (Tom Seaver)	.15	.11	.06
403	Turn Back The Clock (Willie Mays)	.20	.15	.08
404	Turn Back The Clock (Frank Robinson)	.15	.11	.06
405	Turn Back The Clock (Roger Maris)	.20	.15	.08
406	Scott Sanderson	.05	.04	.02
407	Sal Butera	.05	.04	.02
408	Dave Smith	.07	.05	.03
409	*Paul Runge*	.07	.05	.03
410	Dave Kingman	.15	.11	.06
411	Sparky Anderson	.07	.05	.03
412	Jim Clancy	.07	.05	.03
413	Tim Flannery	.05	.04	.02
414	Tom Gorman	.05	.04	.02
415	Hal McRae	.10	.08	.04
416	Denny Martinez	.07	.05	.03
417	R.J. Reynolds	.07	.05	.03
418	Alan Knicely	.05	.04	.02
419	Frank Wills	.05	.04	.02
420	Von Hayes	.10	.08	.04
421	Dave Palmer	.05	.04	.02
422	Mike Jorgensen	.05	.04	.02
423	Dan Spillner	.05	.04	.02
424	Rick Miller	.05	.04	.02
425	Larry McWilliams	.05	.04	.02
426	Brewers Leaders (Charlie Moore)	.07	.05	.03
427	Joe Cowley	.05	.04	.02
428	Max Venable	.05	.04	.02
429	Greg Booker	.05	.04	.02
430	Kent Hrbek	.10	.08	.04
431	George Frazier	.05	.04	.02
432	Mark Bailey	.05	.04	.02
433	Chris Codiroli	.05	.04	.02
434	Curt Wilkerson	.05	.04	.02
435	Bill Caudill	.05	.04	.02
436	Doug Flynn	.05	.04	.02
437	Rick Mahler	.05	.04	.02
438	Clint Hurdle	.05	.04	.02
439	Rick Honeycutt	.05	.04	.02
440	Alvin Davis	.06	.05	.02
441	Whitey Herzog	.07	.05	.03
442	Ron Robinson (FC)	.12	.09	.05
443	Bill Buckner	.10	.08	.04
444	Alex Trevino	.05	.04	.02
445	Bert Blyleven	.12	.09	.05
446	Lenn Sakata	.05	.04	.02
447	Jerry Don Gleaton	.05	.04	.02
448	*Herm Winningham*	.15	.11	.06
449	Rod Scurry	.05	.04	.02
450	Graig Nettles	.15	.11	.06
451	Mark Brown	.05	.04	.02
452	Bob Clark	.05	.04	.02
453	Steve Jeltz	.07	.05	.03
454	Burt Hooton	.07	.05	.03
455	Willie Randolph	.10	.08	.04
456	Braves Leaders (Dale Murphy)	.15	.11	.06
457	*Mickey Tettleton*	1.00	.70	.40
458	Kevin Bass	.10	.08	.04
459	Luis Leal	.05	.04	.02
460	Leon Durham	.07	.05	.03
461	Walt Terrell	.07	.05	.03
462	Domingo Ramos	.05	.04	.02
463	Jim Gott	.05	.04	.02
464	Ruppert Jones	.05	.04	.02
465	Jesse Orosco	.07	.05	.03
466	Tom Foley	.05	.04	.02
467	Bob James	.05	.04	.02
468	Mike Scioscia	.07	.05	.03
469	Storm Davis	.10	.08	.04
470	Bill Madlock	.12	.09	.05
471	Bobby Cox	.05	.04	.02
472	Joe Hesketh	.07	.05	.03
473	Mark Brouhard	.05	.04	.02
474	John Tudor	.10	.08	.04
475	Juan Samuel	.12	.09	.05
476	Ron Mathis	.05	.04	.02
477	Mike Easler	.07	.05	.03
478	Andy Hawkins	.05	.04	.02
479	*Bob Melvin* (FC)	.05	.04	.02
480	*Oddibe McDowell*	.06	.05	.02
481	Scott Bradley (FC)	.10	.08	.04
482	Rick Lysander	.05	.04	.02
483	George Vukovich	.05	.04	.02
484	Donnie Hill	.05	.04	.02
485	Gary Matthews	.10	.08	.04
486	Angels Leaders (Bob Grich)	.07	.05	.03
487	Bret Saberhagen	.25	.20	.10
488	Lou Thornton	.05	.04	.02
489	Jim Winn	.05	.04	.02
490	Jeff Leonard	.07	.05	.03
491	Pascual Perez	.07	.05	.03
492	Kelvin Chapman	.05	.04	.02
493	Gene Nelson	.05	.04	.02
494	Gary Roenicke	.05	.04	.02
495	Mark Langston	.20	.15	.08
496	Jay Johnstone	.07	.05	.03
497	John Stuper	.05	.04	.02
498	Tito Landrum	.05	.04	.02
499	Bob L. Gibson	.05	.04	.02
500	Rickey Henderson	.60	.45	.25
501	Dave Johnson	.07	.05	.03
502	Glen Cook	.05	.04	.02

503	Mike Fitzgerald	.05	.04	.02
504	Denny Walling	.05	.04	.02
505	Jerry Koosman	.10	.08	.04
506	Bill Russell	.07	.05	.03
507	*Steve Ontiveros* (FC)	.12	.09	.05
508	Alan Wiggins	.05	.04	.02
509	Ernie Camacho	.05	.04	.02
510	Wade Boggs	.90	.70	.35
511	Ed Nunez	.05	.04	.02
512	Thad Bosley	.05	.04	.02
513	Ron Washington	.05	.04	.02
514	Mike Jones	.05	.04	.02
515	Darrell Evans	.12	.09	.05
516	Giants Leaders (Greg Minton)	.07	.05	.03
517	*Milt Thompson* (FC)	.06	.05	.02
518	Buck Martinez	.05	.04	.02
519	Danny Darwin	.05	.04	.02
520	Keith Hernandez	.12	.09	.05
521	Nate Snell	.05	.04	.02
522	Bob Bailor	.05	.04	.02
523	Joe Price	.05	.04	.02
524	Darrell Miller (FC)	.07	.05	.03
525	Marvell Wynne	.05	.04	.02
526	Charlie Lea	.05	.04	.02
527	Checklist 397-528	.05	.04	.02
528	Terry Pendleton	.20	.15	.08
529	Marc Sullivan	.05	.04	.02
530	Rich Gossage	.10	.08	.04
531	Tony LaRussa	.07	.05	.03
532	*Don Carman*	.08	.06	.03
533	Billy Sample	.05	.04	.02
534	Jeff Calhoun	.05	.04	.02
535	Toby Harrah	.07	.05	.03
536	Jose Rijo	.10	.08	.04
537	Mark Salas	.07	.05	.03
538	Dennis Eckersley	.20	.15	.08
539	Glenn Hubbard	.05	.04	.02
540	Dan Petry	.07	.05	.03
541	Jorge Orta	.05	.04	.02
542	Don Schulze	.05	.04	.02
543	Jerry Narron	.05	.04	.02
544	Eddie Milner	.05	.04	.02
545	Jimmy Key	.15	.11	.06
546	Mariners Leaders (Dave Henderson)	.07	.05	.03
547	*Roger McDowell*	.12	.09	.05
548	Mike Young	.05	.04	.02
549	Bob Welch	.12	.09	.05
550	Tom Herr	.10	.08	.04
551	Dave LaPoint	.07	.05	.03
552	Marc Hill	.05	.04	.02
553	Jim Morrison	.05	.04	.02
554	Paul Householder	.05	.04	.02
555	Hubie Brooks	.10	.08	.04
556	John Denny	.05	.04	.02
557	Gerald Perry	.12	.09	.05
558	Tim Stoddard	.05	.04	.02
559	Tommy Dunbar	.05	.04	.02
560	Dave Righetti	.08	.06	.03
561	Bob Lillis	.05	.04	.02
562	Joe Beckwith	.05	.04	.02
563	Alejandro Sanchez	.05	.04	.02
564	Warren Brusstar	.05	.04	.02
565	Tom Brunansky	.12	.09	.05
566	Alfredo Griffin	.07	.05	.03
567	Jeff Barkley	.05	.04	.02
568	Donnie Scott	.05	.04	.02
569	Jim Acker	.05	.04	.02
570	Rusty Staub	.10	.08	.04
571	Mike Jeffcoat	.05	.04	.02
572	Paul Zuvella	.05	.04	.02
573	Tom Hume	.05	.04	.02
574	Ron Kittle	.10	.08	.04
575	Mike Boddicker	.07	.05	.03
576	Expos Leaders (Andre Dawson)	.12	.09	.05
577	Jerry Reuss	.07	.05	.03
578	Lee Mazzilli	.07	.05	.03
579	Jim Slaton	.05	.04	.02
580	Willie McGee	.15	.11	.06
581	Bruce Hurst	.12	.09	.05
582	Jim Gantner	.07	.05	.03
583	Al Bumbry	.05	.04	.02
584	*Brian Fisher* (FC)	.06	.05	.02
585	Garry Maddox	.07	.05	.03
586	Greg Harris	.05	.04	.02
587	Rafael Santana	.05	.04	.02
588	Steve Lake	.05	.04	.02
589	Sid Bream	.10	.08	.04
590	Bob Knepper	.07	.05	.03
591	Jackie Moore	.05	.04	.02
592	Frank Tanana	.10	.08	.04
593	Jesse Barfield	.08	.06	.03
594	Chris Bando	.05	.04	.02
595	Dave Parker	.15	.11	.06
596	Onix Concepcion	.05	.04	.02
597	Sammy Stewart	.05	.04	.02
598	Jim Presley	.06	.05	.02
599	*Rick Aguilera*	.50	.40	.20
600	Dale Murphy	.12	.09	.05
601	Gary Lucas	.05	.04	.02
602	*Mariano Duncan*	.25	.20	.10
603	Bill Laskey	.05	.04	.02
604	Gary Pettis	.05	.04	.02
605	Dennis Boyd	.07	.05	.03
606	Royals Leaders (Hal McRae)	.07	.05	.03
607	Ken Dayley	.05	.04	.02
608	Bruce Bochy	.05	.04	.02
609	Barbaro Garbey	.05	.04	.02
610	Ron Guidry	.08	.06	.03
611	Gary Woods	.05	.04	.02
612	Richard Dotson	.05	.04	.02
613	Roy Smalley	.05	.04	.02
614	Rick Waits	.05	.04	.02
615	Johnny Ray	.05	.04	.02
616	Glenn Brummer	.05	.04	.02
617	Lonnie Smith	.07	.05	.03
618	Jim Pankovits	.05	.04	.02
619	Danny Heep	.05	.04	.02
620	Bruce Sutter	.12	.09	.05
621	John Felske	.05	.04	.02
622	Gary Lavelle	.05	.04	.02
623	Floyd Rayford	.05	.04	.02
624	Steve McCatty	.05	.04	.02
625	Bob Brenly	.05	.04	.02
626	Roy Thomas	.05	.04	.02
627	Ron Oester	.05	.04	.02
628	*Kirk McCaskill* (FC)	.15	.11	.06
629	*Mitch Webster* (FC)	.06	.05	.02
630	Fernando Valenzuela	.08	.06	.03
631	Steve Braun	.05	.04	.02
632	Dave Von Ohlen	.05	.04	.02
633	Jackie Gutierrez	.05	.04	.02
634	Roy Lee Jackson	.05	.04	.02
635	Jason Thompson	.05	.04	.02
636	Cubs Leaders (Lee Smith)	.07	.05	.03
637	Rudy Law	.05	.04	.02
638	John Butcher	.05	.04	.02
639	Bo Diaz	.07	.05	.03
640	Jose Cruz	.10	.08	.04
641	Wayne Tolleson	.05	.04	.02
642	Ray Searage	.05	.04	.02
643	Tom Brookens	.05	.04	.02
644	Mark Gubicza	.12	.09	.05
645	Dusty Baker	.07	.05	.03
646	Mike Moore	.05	.04	.02
647	Mel Hall	.07	.05	.03
648	Steve Bedrosian	.10	.08	.04
649	Ronn Reynolds	.05	.04	.02
650	Dave Stieb	.12	.09	.05
651	Billy Martin	.12	.09	.05
652	Tom Browning	.08	.06	.03
653	Jim Dwyer	.05	.04	.02
654	Ken Howell	.07	.05	.03
655	Manny Trillo	.07	.05	.03
656	Brian Harper	.05	.04	.02
657	Juan Agosto	.05	.04	.02
658	Rob Wilfong	.05	.04	.02
659	Checklist 529-660	.05	.04	.02
660	Steve Garvey	.15	.11	.06
661	Roger Clemens	3.50	2.75	1.50
662	Bill Schroeder	.05	.04	.02
663	Neil Allen	.05	.04	.02
664	Tim Corcoran	.05	.04	.02
665	Alejandro Pena	.07	.05	.03
666	Rangers Leaders (Charlie Hough)	.07	.05	.03
667	Tim Teufel	.05	.04	.02
668	Cecilio Guante	.05	.04	.02
669	Ron Cey	.10	.08	.04
670	Willie Hernandez	.07	.05	.03
671	Lynn Jones	.05	.04	.02
672	Rob Picciolo	.05	.04	.02
673	Ernie Whitt	.07	.05	.03
674	Pat Tabler	.07	.05	.03
675	Claudell Washington	.07	.05	.03
676	Matt Young	.05	.04	.02
677	Nick Esasky	.07	.05	.03
678	Dan Gladden	.07	.05	.03
679	Britt Burns	.05	.04	.02
680	George Foster	.15	.11	.06
681	Dick Williams	.05	.04	.02
682	Junior Ortiz	.05	.04	.02
683	Andy Van Slyke	.10	.08	.04
684	Bob McClure	.05	.04	.02
685	Tim Wallach	.12	.09	.05
686	Jeff Stone	.05	.04	.02
687	Mike Trujillo	.05	.04	.02
688	Larry Herndon	.07	.05	.03
689	Dave Stewart	.12	.09	.05
690	Ryne Sandberg	2.00	1.50	.80
691	Mike Madden	.05	.04	.02
692	Dale Berra	.05	.04	.02
693	Tom Tellmann	.05	.04	.02
694	Garth Iorg	.05	.04	.02
695	Mike Smithson	.05	.04	.02
696	Dodgers Leaders (Bill Russell)	.07	.05	.03
697	Bud Black	.05	.04	.02
698	Brad Komminsk	.05	.04	.02
699	Pat Corrales	.05	.04	.02
700	Reggie Jackson	.35	.25	.14
701	Keith Hernandez (All-Star)	.10	.08	.04
702	Tom Herr (All-Star)	.07	.05	.03
703	Tim Wallach (All-Star)	.07	.05	.03
704	Ozzie Smith (All-Star)	.15	.11	.06
705	Dale Murphy (All-Star)	.10	.08	.04
706	Pedro Guerrero (All-Star)	.12	.09	.05
707	Willie McGee (All-Star)	.12	.09	.05
708	Gary Carter (All-Star)	.10	.07	.04
709	Dwight Gooden (All-Star)	.10	.07	.04
710	John Tudor (All-Star)	.07	.05	.03
711	Jeff Reardon (All-Star)	.07	.05	.03
712	Don Mattingly (All-Star)	.40	.30	.15
713	Damasco Garcia (All-Star)	.05	.04	.02
714	George Brett (All-Star)	.35	.25	.14
715	Cal Ripken, Jr. (All-Star)	.80	.60	.30
716	Rickey Henderson (All-Star)	.25	.20	.10
717	Dave Winfield (All-Star)	.20	.15	.08
718	George Bell (All-Star)	.10	.08	.04
719	Carlton Fisk (All-Star)	.12	.09	.05
720	Bret Saberhagen (All-Star)	.15	.11	.06
721	Ron Guidry (All-Star)	.10	.08	.04
722	Dan Quisenberry (All-Star)	.07	.05	.03
723	Marty Bystrom	.05	.04	.02
724	Tim Hulett	.07	.05	.03
725	Mario Soto	.07	.05	.03
726	Orioles Leaders (Rick Dempsey)	.07	.05	.03
727	David Green	.05	.04	.02
728	Mike Marshall	.12	.09	.05
729	Jim Beattie	.05	.04	.02
730	Ozzie Smith	.40	.30	.15
731	Don Robinson	.07	.05	.03
732	*Floyd Youmans* (FC)	.12	.09	.05
733	Ron Romanick	.05	.04	.02
734	Marty Barrett	.10	.08	.04
735	Dave Dravecky	.07	.05	.03
736	Glenn Wilson	.07	.05	.03
737	Pete Vuckovich	.07	.05	.03
738	Andre Robertson	.05	.04	.02
739	Dave Rozema	.05	.04	.02
740	Lance Parrish	.08	.06	.03
741	Pete Rose	.40	.30	.15
742	Frank Viola	.15	.11	.06
743	Pat Sheridan	.05	.04	.02
744	Lary Sorensen	.05	.04	.02
745	Willie Upshaw	.07	.05	.03
746	Denny Gonzalez	.05	.04	.02
747	Rick Cerone	.05	.04	.02
748	Steve Henderson	.05	.04	.02
749	Ed Jurak	.05	.04	.02
750	Gorman Thomas	.10	.08	.04
751	Howard Johnson	.15	.11	.06
752	Mike Krukow	.07	.05	.03
753	Dan Ford	.05	.04	.02
754	*Pat Clements*	.12	.09	.05
755	Harold Baines	.15	.11	.06
756	Pirates Leaders (Rick Rhoden)	.07	.05	.03
757	Darrell Porter	.07	.05	.03
758	Dave Anderson	.05	.04	.02
759	Moose Haas	.05	.04	.02
760	Andre Dawson	.40	.30	.15
761	Don Slaught	.05	.04	.02
762	Eric Show	.07	.05	.03
763	Terry Puhl	.05	.04	.02
764	Kevin Gross	.07	.05	.03
765	Don Baylor	.12	.09	.05
766	Rick Langford	.05	.04	.02
767	Jody Davis	.10	.08	.04
768	Vern Ruhle	.05	.04	.02
769	*Harold Reynolds* (FC)	.30	.25	.12
770	Vida Blue	.10	.08	.04
771	John McNamara	.05	.04	.02
772	Brian Downing	.07	.05	.03
773	Greg Pryor	.05	.04	.02
774	Terry Leach	.05	.04	.02
775	Al Oliver	.10	.08	.04
776	Gene Garber	.05	.04	.02
777	Wayne Krenchicki	.05	.04	.02
778	Jerry Hairston	.05	.04	.02
779	Rick Reuschel	.10	.08	.04
780	Robin Yount	.60	.45	.25
781	Joe Nolan	.05	.04	.02
782	Ken Landreaux	.05	.04	.02
783	Ricky Horton	.07	.05	.03
784	Alan Bannister	.05	.04	.02
785	Bob Stanley	.05	.04	.02
786	Twins Leaders (Mickey Hatcher)	.07	.05	.03
787	Vance Law	.07	.05	.03
788	Marty Castillo	.05	.04	.02
789	Kurt Bevacqua	.05	.04	.02
790	Phil Niekro	.12	.09	.05
791	Checklist 661-792	.05	.04	.02
792	Charles Hudson	.06	.05	.02

1986 Topps All-Star Glossy Set of 22

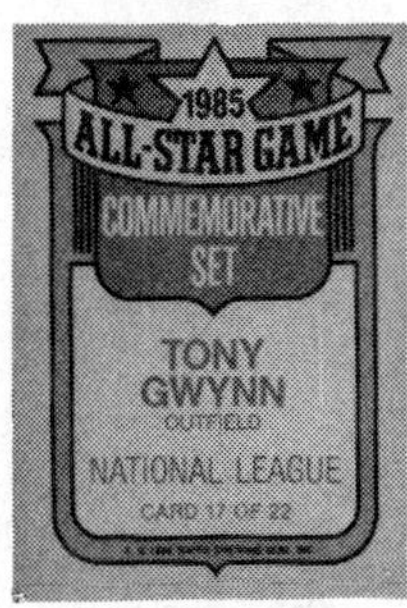

As in previous years, Topps continued to make the popular glossy-surfaced cards as an insert in rack packs. The All-Star Glossy set of 22 2-1/2" by 3-1/2" cards shows little design change from previous years. Cards feature a front color photo and All-Star banner at the top. The bottom has the player's name and position. The set includes the All-Star starting teams as well as the managers and honorary captains.

		MT	NR MT	EX
Complete Set:		6.00	4.50	2.50
Common Player:		.20	.15	.08
1	Sparky Anderson	.20	.15	.08
2	Eddie Murray	.50	.40	.20
3	Lou Whitaker	.30	.25	.12
4	George Brett	.80	.60	.30
5	Cal Ripken, Jr.	.60	.45	.25
6	Jim Rice	.30	.25	.12
7	Rickey Henderson	.60	.45	.25
8	Dave Winfield	.50	.40	.20
9	Carlton Fisk	.30	.25	.12
10	Jack Morris	.30	.25	.12
11	A.L. All-Star Team	.20	.15	.08
12	Dick Williams	.20	.15	.08
13	Steve Garvey	.30	.25	.12
14	Tom Herr	.20	.15	.08
15	Graig Nettles	.20	.15	.08
16	Ozzie Smith	.30	.25	.12
17	Tony Gwynn	.60	.45	.25
18	Dale Murphy	.80	.60	.30
19	Darryl Strawberry	.35	.25	.14
20	Terry Kennedy	.20	.15	.08
21	LaMarr Hoyt	.20	.15	.08
22	N.L. All-Star Team	.20	.15	.08

1986 Topps All-Star Glossy Set of 60

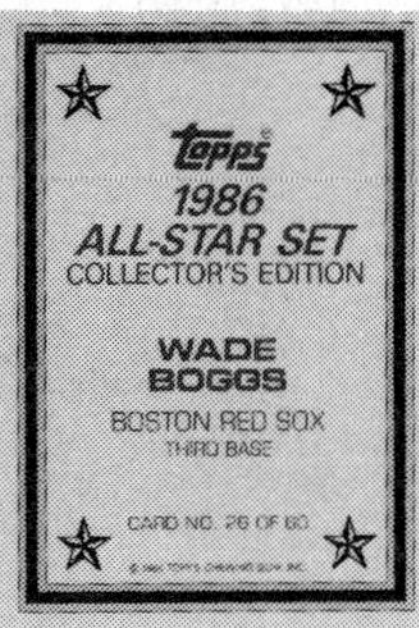

The Topps All-Star & Hot Prospects Glossy Set of 60 cards represents an expansion of a good idea. The 2-1/2" by 3-1/2" cards had a good following when they were limited to stars, but Topps realized that the addition of top young players would spice up the set even further, so in 1986 it was expanded from 40 to 60 cards. The cards themselves are basically all color glossy pictures with the player's name in very small print in the lower left-hand corner. To obtain the set, it was necessary to send $1 plus six special offer cards from wax packs to Topps for each series. At 60 cards, that meant the process had to be repeated six times as there were 10 cards in each series, making the set quite expensive from the outset.

		MT	NR MT	EX
Complete Set:		15.00	11.00	6.00
Common Player:		.15	.11	.06
1	Oddibe McDowell	.25	.20	.10
2	Reggie Jackson	.70	.50	.30
3	Fernando Valenzuela	.35	.25	.14
4	Jack Clark	.25	.20	.10
5	Rickey Henderson	.70	.50	.30
6	Steve Balboni	.15	.11	.06
7	Keith Hernandez	.40	.30	.15
8	Lance Parrish	.30	.25	.12
9	Willie McGee	.25	.20	.10
10	Chris Brown	.40	.30	.15
11	Darryl Strawberry	.90	.70	.35
12	Ron Guidry	.30	.25	.12
13	Dave Parker	.25	.20	.10
14	Cal Ripken	.70	.50	.30
15	Tim Raines	.50	.40	.20
16	Rod Carew	.60	.45	.25
17	Mike Schmidt	.90	.70	.35
18	George Brett	.90	.70	.35
19	Joe Hesketh	.15	.11	.06
20	Dan Pasqua	.20	.15	.08
21	Vince Coleman	1.00	.70	.40
22	Tom Seaver	.50	.40	.20
23	Gary Carter	.50	.40	.20
24	Orel Hershiser	.40	.30	.15
25	Pedro Guerrero	.30	.25	.12
26	Wade Boggs	1.25	.90	.50
27	Bret Saberhagen	.30	.25	.12
28	Carlton Fisk	.25	.20	.10
29	Kirk Gibson	.35	.25	.14
30	Brian Fisher	.20	.15	.08
31	Don Mattingly	3.00	2.25	1.25
32	Tom Herr	.15	.11	.06
33	Eddie Murray	.60	.45	.25
34	Ryne Sandberg	.40	.30	.15
35	Dan Quisenberry	.15	.11	.06
36	Jim Rice	.50	.40	.20
37	Dale Murphy	.90	.70	.35
38	Steve Garvey	.50	.40	.20
39	Roger McDowell	.25	.20	.10
40	Earnie Riles	.15	.11	.06
41	Dwight Gooden	.75	.60	.30
42	Dave Winfield	.50	.40	.20
43	Dave Stieb	.20	.15	.08
44	Bob Horner	.20	.15	.08
45	Nolan Ryan	.50	.40	.20
46	Ozzie Smith	.25	.20	.10
47	Jorge Bell	.50	.40	.20
48	Gorman Thomas	.15	.11	.06
49	Tom Browning	.25	.20	.10
50	Larry Sheets	.20	.15	.08
51	Pete Rose	1.25	.90	.50
52	Brett Butler	.15	.11	.06
53	John Tudor	.20	.15	.08
54	Phil Bradley	.20	.15	.08
55	Jeff Reardon	.20	.15	.08
56	Rich Gossage	.25	.20	.10
57	Tony Gwynn	.60	.45	.25
58	Ozzie Guillen	.25	.20	.10
59	Glenn Davis	.35	.25	.14
60	Darrell Evans	.15	.11	.06

1986 Topps Traded

This 132-card set of 2-1/2" by 3-1/2" cards is one of the most popular sets of recent times. As always, the set features traded veterans, including such players as Phil Niekro and Tom Seaver. They are

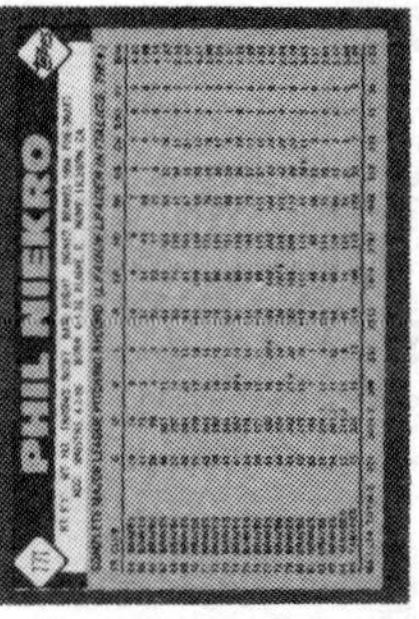

not, however, the reason for the excitement. The demand is there because of a better than usual crop of rookies who also appear in the sets. Among those are Jose Canseco, Wally Joyner, Pete Incaviglia, Todd Worrell and the first card of Bo Jackson. As in the previous two years, a glossy-finish "Tiffany" edition of 5,000 Traded sets was produced. The "Tiffany" cards are worth four to six times the value of the regular Traded cards.

		MT	NR MT	EX
Complete Set (132):		20.00	15.00	8.00
Common Player:		.08	.06	.03
1T	Andy Allanson (FC)	.10	.08	.04
2T	Neil Allen	.08	.06	.03
3T	Joaquin Andujar	.10	.08	.04
4T	Paul Assenmacher (FC)	.10	.08	.04
5T	Scott Bailes (FC)	.10	.08	.04
6T	Don Baylor	.15	.11	.06
7T	Steve Bedrosian	.15	.11	.06
8T	Juan Beniquez	.08	.06	.03
9T	Juan Berenguer	.08	.06	.03
10T	Mike Bielecki (FC)	.08	.06	.03
11T	Barry Bonds (FC)	8.00	6.00	3.25
12T	Bobby Bonilla (FC)	2.00	1.50	.80
13T	Juan Bonilla	.08	.06	.03
14T	Rich Bordi	.08	.06	.03
15T	Steve Boros	.08	.06	.03
16T	Rick Burleson	.08	.06	.03
17T	Bill Campbell	.08	.06	.03
18T	Tom Candiotti	.08	.06	.03
19T	John Cangelosi (FC)	.08	.06	.03
20T	Jose Canseco (FC)	4.00	3.00	1.50
21T	Carmen Castillo	.08	.06	.03
22T	Rick Cerone	.08	.06	.03
23T	John Cerutti (FC)	.08	.06	.03
24T	Will Clark (FC)	4.75	3.50	2.00
25T	Mark Clear	.08	.06	.03
26T	Darnell Coles	.12	.09	.05
27T	Dave Collins	.10	.08	.04
28T	Tim Conroy	.08	.06	.03
29T	Joe Cowley	.08	.06	.03
30T	Joel Davis (FC)	.12	.09	.05
31T	Rob Deer	.08	.06	.03
32T	John Denny	.08	.06	.03
33T	Mike Easler	.10	.08	.04
34T	Mark Eichhorn (FC)	.20	.15	.08
35T	Steve Farr	.08	.06	.03
36T	Scott Fletcher	.15	.11	.06
37T	Terry Forster	.10	.08	.04
38T	Terry Francona	.08	.06	.03
39T	Jim Fregosi	.08	.06	.03
40T	Andres Galarraga (FC)	2.00	1.50	.80
41T	Ken Griffey	.12	.09	.05
42T	Bill Gullickson	.08	.06	.03
43T	Jose Guzman (FC)	.35	.25	.14
44T	Moose Haas	.08	.06	.03
45T	Billy Hatcher	.20	.15	.08
46T	Mike Heath	.08	.06	.03
47T	Tom Hume	.08	.06	.03
48T	Pete Incaviglia (FC)	.75	.60	.30
49T	Dane Iorg	.08	.06	.03
50T	Bo Jackson (FC)	2.00	1.50	.80
51T	Wally Joyner (FC)	.75	.60	.30
52T	Charlie Kerfeld (FC)	.15	.11	.06
53T	Eric King (FC)	.20	.15	.08
54T	Bob Kipper (FC)	.12	.09	.05
55T	Wayne Krenchicki	.08	.06	.03
56T	John Kruk (FC)	2.00	1.50	.80
57T	Mike LaCoss	.08	.06	.03
58T	Pete Ladd	.08	.06	.03
59T	Mike Laga	.08	.06	.03
60T	Hal Lanier	.08	.06	.03
61T	Dave LaPoint	.12	.09	.05
62T	Rudy Law	.08	.06	.03
63T	Rick Leach	.08	.06	.03
64T	Tim Leary	.08	.06	.03
65T	Dennis Leonard	.10	.08	.04
66T	Jim Leyland	.08	.06	.03
67T	Steve Lyons	.12	.09	.05
68T	Mickey Mahler	.08	.06	.03
69T	Candy Maldonado	.15	.11	.06
70T	Roger Mason (FC)	.10	.08	.04
71T	Bob McClure	.08	.06	.03
72T	Andy McGaffigan	.08	.06	.03
73T	Gene Michael	.08	.06	.03
74T	Kevin Mitchell (FC)	.60	.45	.25
75T	Omar Moreno	.08	.06	.03
76T	Jerry Mumphrey	.08	.06	.03
77T	Phil Niekro	.20	.15	.08
78T	Randy Niemann	.08	.06	.03
79T	Juan Nieves (FC)	.06	.05	.02
80T	Otis Nixon (FC)	.25	.20	.10
81T	Bob Ojeda	.12	.09	.05
82T	Jose Oquendo	.08	.06	.03
83T	Tom Paciorek	.08	.06	.03
84T	Dave Palmer	.08	.06	.03
85T	Frank Pastore	.08	.06	.03
86T	Lou Piniella	.12	.09	.05
87T	Dan Plesac (FC)	.12	.09	.05
88T	Darrell Porter	.10	.08	.04
89T	Rey Quinones (FC)	.20	.15	.08
90T	Gary Redus	.10	.08	.04
91T	Bip Roberts	.40	.30	.15
92T	Billy Jo Robidoux (FC)	.15	.11	.06
93T	Jeff Robinson	.12	.09	.05
94T	Gary Roenicke	.08	.06	.03
95T	Ed Romero	.08	.06	.03
96T	Argenis Salazar	.08	.06	.03
97T	Joe Sambito	.08	.06	.03
98T	Billy Sample	.08	.06	.03
99T	Dave Schmidt	.08	.06	.03
100T	Ken Schrom	.08	.06	.03
101T	Tom Seaver	.60	.45	.25
102T	Ted Simmons	.20	.15	.08
103T	Sammy Stewart	.08	.06	.03
104T	Kurt Stillwell (FC)	.08	.06	.03
105T	Franklin Stubbs	.12	.09	.05
106T	Dale Sveum (FC)	.08	.06	.03
107T	Chuck Tanner	.08	.06	.03
108T	Danny Tartabull (FC)	.75	.60	.30
109T	Tim Teufel	.08	.06	.03
110T	Bob Tewksbury (FC)	.60	.45	.25
111T	Andres Thomas (FC)	.12	.09	.05
112T	Milt Thompson	.12	.09	.05
113T	Robby Thompson (FC)	1.00	.70	.40
114T	Jay Tibbs	.08	.06	.03
115T	Wayne Tolleson	.08	.06	.03
116T	Alex Trevino	.08	.06	.03
117T	Manny Trillo	.10	.08	.04
118T	Ed Vande Berg	.08	.06	.03
119T	Ozzie Virgil	.08	.06	.03
120T	Bob Walk	.08	.06	.03
121T	Gene Walter (FC)	.12	.09	.05
122T	Claudell Washington	.12	.09	.05
123T	Bill Wegman (FC)	.20	.15	.08
124T	Dick Williams	.08	.06	.03
125T	Mitch Williams (FC)	.25	.20	.10
126T	Bobby Witt (FC)	.20	.15	.08
127T	Todd Worrell (FC)	.20	.15	.08
128T	George Wright	.08	.06	.03
129T	Ricky Wright	.08	.06	.03
130T	Steve Yeager	.08	.06	.03
131T	Paul Zuvella	.08	.06	.03
132T	Checklist	.08	.06	.03

1986 Topps Box Panels

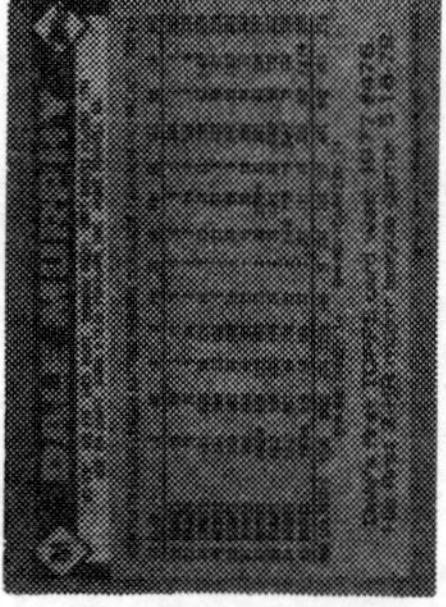

Following the lead of Donruss, which introduced the concept in 1985, Topps produced special cards on the bottom panels of wax boxes. Individual cards measure 2-1/2" by 3-1/2", the same as regular cards. Design of the cards is virtually identical with regular '86 Topps, though the top border is in red, rather than black. The cards are lettered "A" through "P", rather than numbered on the back.

		MT	NR MT	EX
Complete Panel Set:		10.00	7.50	4.00
Complete Singles Set:		5.00	3.75	2.00
Common Panel:		2.00	1.50	.80
Common Single Player:		.15	.11	.06
	Panel	3.50	2.75	1.50
A	Jorge Bell	.20	.15	.08
B	Wade Boggs	.60	.45	.25
C	George Brett	.50	.40	.20
D	Vince Coleman	.35	.25	.14
	Panel	1.50	1.25	.60
E	Carlton Fisk	.15	.11	.06
F	Dwight Gooden	.25	.20	.10
G	Pedro Guerrero	.15	.11	.06
H	Ron Guidry	.15	.11	.06
	Panel	3.50	2.75	1.50
I	Reggie Jackson	.30	.25	.12
J	Don Mattingly	.90	.70	.35
K	Oddibe McDowell	.15	.11	.06
L	Willie McGee	.15	.11	.06
	Panel	3.00	2.25	1.25
M	Dale Murphy	.35	.25	.14
N	Pete Rose	.50	.40	.20
O	Bret Saberhagen	.15	.11	.06
P	Fernando Valenzuela	.20	.15	.08

1986 Topps Gallery of Champions

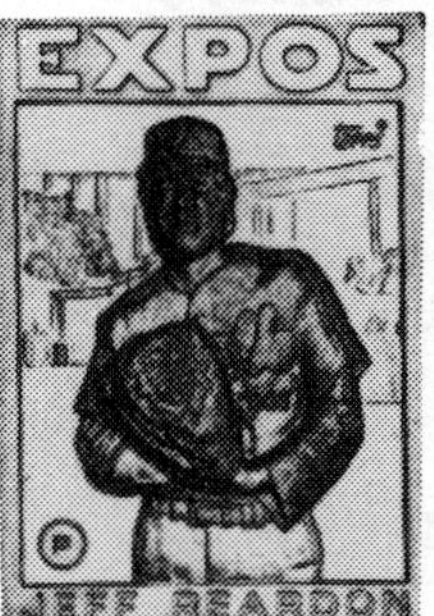

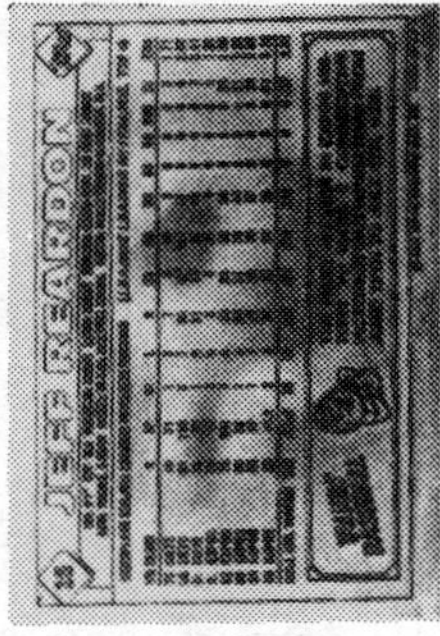

For the third consecutive year Topps issued 12 "metal mini-cards" as a dealer-ordering incentive. The metal replicas were minted 1/4-size (approximately 1-1/4" by 1-3/4") of the regular cards and come in silver, aluminum and bronze. The bronze and silver sets were issued in leather-like velvet-lined display cases. A bronze 1952 Topps Mickey Mantle was given as a premium for dealers purchasing 1986 Traded sets, while a pewter Don Mattingly was issued as a premium to those ordering the aluminum, bronze and silver sets. The Mantle bronze is valued at $12 and the Mattingly pewter at $100.

		MT	NR MT	EX
Complete Aluminum Set:		30.00	22.00	12.00
Complete Bronze Set:		175.00	131.00	70.00
Complete Silver Set:		650.00	487.00	260.00
(1a)	Wade Boggs (aluminum)	3.00	2.25	1.25
(1b)	Wade Boggs (bronze)	25.00	18.50	10.00
(1c)	Wade Boggs (silver)	125.00	94.00	50.00
(2a)	Vince Coleman (aluminum)	1.25	.90	.50
(2b)	Vince Coleman (bronze)	12.00	9.00	4.75
(2c)	Vince Coleman (silver)	50.00	37.00	20.00
(3a)	Darrell Evans (aluminum)	.70	.50	.30
(3b)	Darrell Evans (bronze)	7.50	5.75	3.00
(3c)	Darrell Evans (silver)	20.00	15.00	8.00
(4a)	Dwight Gooden (aluminum)	2.00	1.50	.80
(4b)	Dwight Gooden (bronze)	20.00	15.00	8.00
(4c)	Dwight Gooden (silver)	100.00	75.00	40.00
(5a)	Ozzie Guillen (aluminum)	.70	.50	.30
(5b)	Ozzie Guillen (bronze)	7.50	5.75	3.00
(5c)	Ozzie Guillen (silver)	20.00	15.00	8.00
(6a)	Don Mattingly (aluminum)	8.00	6.00	3.25
(6b)	Don Mattingly (bronze)	50.00	37.00	20.00
(6c)	Don Mattingly (silver)	200.00	150.00	80.00
(7a)	Willie McGee (aluminum)	1.00	.70	.40
(7b)	Willie McGee (bronze)	10.00	7.50	4.00
(7c)	Willie McGee (silver)	30.00	22.00	12.00
(8a)	Dale Murphy (aluminum)	1.50	1.25	.60
(8b)	Dale Murphy (bronze)	15.00	11.00	6.00
(8c)	Dale Murphy (silver)	80.00	60.00	32.00
(9a)	Dan Quisenberry (aluminum)	.70	.50	.30
(9b)	Dan Quisenberry (bronze)	7.50	5.75	3.00
(9c)	Dan Quisenberry (silver)	20.00	15.00	8.00
(10a)	Jeff Reardon (aluminum)	.70	.50	.30
(10b)	Jeff Reardon (bronze)	7.50	5.75	3.00
(10c)	Jeff Reardon (silver)	20.00	15.00	8.00
(11a)	Pete Rose (aluminum)	2.50	2.00	1.00
(11b)	Pete Rose (bronze)	25.00	18.50	10.00
(11c)	Pete Rose (silver)	110.00	82.00	44.00
(12a)	Bret Saberhagen (aluminum)	1.00	.70	.40
(12b)	Bret Saberhagen (bronze)	10.00	7.50	4.00
(12c)	Bret Saberhagen (silver)	30.00	22.00	12.00

1986 Topps Mini League Leaders

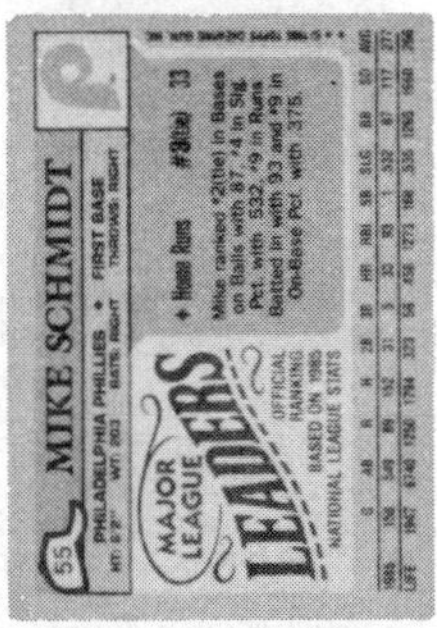

Topps had long experimented with bigger cards, but in 1986, they also decided to try smaller ones. These 2-1/8" by 2-15/16" cards feature top players in a number of categories. Sold in plastic packs as a regular Topps issue, the 66-card set is attractive as well as innovative. The cards feature color photos and a minimum of added information on the fronts where only the player's name and Topps logo appear. Backs limited information as well, but do feature whatever information was required to justify the player's inclusion in a set of league leaders.

		MT	NR MT	EX
Complete Set:		8.00	6.00	3.25
Common Player:		.09	.07	.04
1	Eddie Murray	.40	.30	.15
2	Cal Ripken, Jr.	.50	.40	.20
3	Wade Boggs	.80	.60	.30
4	Dennis Boyd	.09	.07	.04
5	Dwight Evans	.15	.11	.06
6	Bruce Hurst	.15	.11	.06
7	Gary Pettis	.09	.07	.04
8	Harold Baines	.15	.11	.06
9	Floyd Bannister	.09	.07	.04
10	Britt Burns	.09	.07	.04
11	Carlton Fisk	.20	.15	.08
12	Brett Butler	.15	.11	.06
13	Darrell Evans	.15	.11	.06
14	Jack Morris	.25	.20	.10
15	Lance Parrish	.25	.20	.10
16	Walt Terrell	.09	.07	.04
17	Steve Balboni	.09	.07	.04
18	George Brett	.50	.40	.20
19	Charlie Leibrandt	.09	.07	.04
20	Bret Saberhagen	.20	.15	.08
21	Lonnie Smith	.09	.07	.04
22	Willie Wilson	.15	.11	.06
23	Bert Blyleven	.15	.11	.06
24	Mike Smithson	.09	.07	.04
25	Frank Viola	.20	.15	.08
26	Ron Guidry	.20	.15	.08
27	Rickey Henderson	.40	.30	.15
28	Don Mattingly	1.25	.90	.50
29	Dave Winfield	.30	.25	.12
30	Mike Moore	.09	.07	.04
31	Gorman Thomas	.09	.07	.04
32	Toby Harrah	.09	.07	.04
33	Charlie Hough	.09	.07	.04
34	Doyle Alexander	.09	.07	.04
35	Jimmy Key	.15	.11	.06
36	Dave Stieb	.15	.11	.06
37	Dale Murphy	.50	.40	.20
38	Keith Moreland	.09	.07	.04
39	Ryne Sandberg	.45	.35	.20
40	Tom Browning	.15	.11	.06
41	Dave Parker	.20	.15	.08
42	Mario Soto	.09	.07	.04
43	Nolan Ryan	.75	.60	.30
44	Pedro Guerrero	.20	.15	.08
45	Orel Hershiser	.20	.15	.08
46	Mike Scioscia	.09	.07	.04
47	Fernando Valenzuela	.20	.15	.08
48	Bob Welch	.15	.11	.06
49	Tim Raines	.20	.15	.08
50	Gary Carter	.20	.15	.08
51	Sid Fernandez	.15	.11	.06
52	Dwight Gooden	.35	.25	.14
53	Keith Hernandez	.25	.20	.10
54	Juan Samuel	.20	.15	.08
55	Mike Schmidt	.50	.40	.20
56	Glenn Wilson	.09	.07	.04
57	Rick Reuschel	.15	.11	.06
58	Joaquin Andujar	.09	.07	.04
59	Jack Clark	.20	.15	.08
60	Vince Coleman	.30	.25	.12
61	Danny Cox	.09	.07	.04
62	Tom Herr	.09	.07	.04
63	Willie McGee	.15	.11	.06
64	John Tudor	.15	.11	.06
65	Tony Gwynn	.30	.25	.12
66	Checklist	.09	.07	.04

1986 Topps Stickers

The 1986 Topps stickers are 2-1/8" by 3". The 200-piece set features 316 different subjects, with some stickers including two or three players. Numbers run only to 315, however. The set includes some specialty stickers such as League Championships and World Series themes. Stickers are numbered both front and back and included a chance to win a trip to spring training as well as an offer to buy a complete 1986 Topps regular set. An album for the stickers was available in stores.

		MT	NR MT	EX
Complete Set:		15.00	11.00	6.00
Common Player:		.03	.02	.01
Sticker Album:		.70	.50	.30
1	Pete Rose	.25	.20	.10
2	Pete Rose	.25	.20	.10
3	George Brett	.12	.09	.05
4	Rod Carew	.10	.08	.04
5	Vince Coleman	.12	.09	.05
6	Dwight Gooden	.15	.11	.06
7	Phil Niekro	.08	.06	.03
8	Tony Perez	.06	.05	.02
9	Nolan Ryan	.10	.08	.04
10	Tom Seaver	.10	.08	.04
11	N.L. Championship Series (Ozzie Smith)	.06	.05	.02
12	N.L. Championship Series (Bill Madlock)	.04	.03	.02
13	N.L. Championship Series (Cardinals Celebrate)	.03	.02	.01
14	A.L. Championship Series (Al Oliver)	.04	.03	.02
15	A.L. Championship Series (Jim Sundberg)	.03	.02	.01
16	A.L. Championship Series (George Brett)	.10	.08	.04
17	World Series (Bret Saberhagen)	.06	.05	.02
18	World Series (Dane Iorg)	.03	.02	.01
19	World Series (Tito Landrum)	.03	.02	.01
20	World Series (John Tudor)	.04	.03	.02
21	World Series (Buddy Biancalana)	.03	.02	.01
22	World Series (Darryl Motley, Darrell Porter)	.03	.02	.01
23	World Series (George Brett, Frank White)	.10	.08	.04
24	Nolan Ryan	.15	.11	.06
25	Bill Doran	.08	.06	.03
26	Jose Cruz	.04	.03	.02
27	Mike Scott	.08	.06	.03
28	Kevin Bass	.04	.03	.02
29	Glenn Davis	.10	.08	.04
30	Mark Bailey	.06	.05	.02
31	Dave Smith	.10	.08	.04
32	Phil Garner	.03	.02	.01
33	Dickie Thon	.06	.05	.02
34	Bob Horner	.12	.09	.05
35	Dale Murphy	.25	.20	.10
36	Glenn Hubbard	.04	.03	.02
37	Bruce Sutter	.08	.06	.03
38	Ken Oberkfell	.04	.03	.02
39	Claudell Washington	.04	.03	.02
40	Steve Bedrosian	.04	.03	.02
41	Terry Harper	.03	.02	.01
42	Rafael Ramirez	.06	.05	.02
43	Rick Mahler	.03	.02	.01
44	Joaquin Andujar	.06	.05	.02
45	Willie McGee	.10	.08	.04
46	Ozzie Smith	.06	.05	.02
47	Vince Coleman	.12	.09	.05
48	Danny Cox	.04	.03	.02
49	Tom Herr	.04	.03	.02
50	Jack Clark	.08	.06	.03
51	Andy Van Slyke	.04	.03	.02
52	John Tudor	.08	.06	.03
53	Terry Pendleton	.03	.02	.01
54	Keith Moreland	.06	.05	.02
55	Ryne Sandberg	.15	.11	.06
56	Lee Smith	.04	.03	.02
57	Steve Trout	.06	.05	.02
58	Jody Davis	.08	.06	.03
59	Gary Matthews	.04	.03	.02
60	Leon Durham	.04	.03	.02
61	Rick Sutcliffe	.06	.05	.02
62	Dennis Eckersley	.04	.03	.02
63	Bob Dernier	.03	.02	.01
64	Fernando Valenzuela	.15	.11	.06
65	Pedro Guerrero	.12	.09	.05
66	Jerry Reuss	.06	.05	.02
67	Greg Brock	.06	.05	.02
68	Mike Scioscia	.03	.02	.01
69	Ken Howell	.04	.03	.02
70	Bill Madlock	.04	.03	.02
71	Mike Marshall	.06	.05	.02
72	Steve Sax	.06	.05	.02
73	Orel Hershiser	.06	.05	.02
74	Andre Dawson	.12	.09	.05
75	Tim Raines	.12	.09	.05
76	Jeff Reardon	.06	.05	.02
77	Hubie Brooks	.04	.03	.02
78	Bill Gullickson	.04	.03	.02
79	Bryn Smith	.04	.03	.02
80	Terry Francona	.04	.03	.02
81	Vance Law	.03	.02	.01
82	Tim Wallach	.04	.03	.02
83	Herm Winningham	.04	.03	.02
84	Jeff Leonard	.06	.05	.02
85	Chris Brown	.20	.15	.08
86	Scott Garrelts	.03	.02	.01
87	Jose Uribe	.04	.03	.02
88	Manny Trillo	.04	.03	.02
89	Dan Driessen	.04	.03	.02
90	Dan Gladden	.06	.05	.02
91	Mark Davis	.04	.03	.02
92	Bob Brenly	.03	.02	.01
93	Mike Krukow	.04	.03	.02
94	Dwight Gooden	.35	.25	.14
95	Darryl Strawberry	.25	.20	.10
96	Gary Carter	.10	.08	.04
97	Wally Backman	.06	.05	.02
98	Ron Darling	.06	.05	.02
99	Keith Hernandez	.12	.09	.05
100	George Foster	.06	.05	.02
101	Howard Johnson	.06	.05	.02
102	Rafael Santana	.04	.03	.02
103	Roger McDowell	.06	.05	.02
104	Steve Garvey	.15	.11	.06

105	Tony Gwynn	.20	.15	.08
106	Graig Nettles	.06	.05	.02
107	Rich Gossage	.10	.08	.04
108	Andy Hawkins	.04	.03	.02
109	Carmelo Martinez	.04	.03	.02
110	Garry Templeton	.04	.03	.02
111	Terry Kennedy	.06	.05	.02
112	Tim Flannery	.08	.06	.03
113	LaMarr Hoyt	.03	.02	.01
114	Mike Schmidt	.25	.20	.10
115	Ozzie Virgil	.06	.05	.02
116	Steve Carlton	.10	.08	.04
117	Garry Maddox	.03	.02	.01
118	Glenn Wilson	.06	.05	.02
119	Kevin Gross	.03	.02	.01
120	Von Hayes	.04	.03	.02
121	Juan Samuel	.06	.05	.02
122	Rick Schu	.08	.06	.03
123	Shane Rawley	.06	.05	.02
124	Johnny Ray	.06	.05	.02
125	Tony Pena	.06	.05	.02
126	Rick Reuschel	.12	.09	.05
127	Sammy Khalifa	.06	.05	.02
128	Marvell Wynne	.04	.03	.02
129	Jason Thompson	.03	.02	.01
130	Rick Rhoden	.04	.03	.02
131	Bill Almon	.03	.02	.01
132	Joe Orsulak	.06	.05	.02
133	Jim Morrison	.06	.05	.02
134	Pete Rose	.40	.30	.15
135	Dave Parker	.12	.09	.05
136	Mario Soto	.03	.02	.01
137	Dave Concepcion	.10	.08	.04
138	Ron Oester	.03	.02	.01
139	Buddy Bell	.06	.05	.02
140	Ted Power	.03	.02	.01
141	Tom Browning	.06	.05	.02
142	John Franco	.08	.06	.03
143	Tony Perez	.06	.05	.02
144	Willie McGee	.08	.06	.03
145	Dale Murphy	.15	.11	.06
146	Tony Gwynn	.40	.30	.15
147	Tom Herr	.15	.11	.06
148	Steve Garvey	.30	.25	.12
149	Dale Murphy	.40	.30	.15
150	Darryl Strawberry	.40	.30	.15
151	Graig Nettles	.15	.11	.06
152	Terry Kennedy	.15	.11	.06
153	Ozzie Smith	.20	.15	.08
154	LaMarr Hoyt	.15	.11	.06
155	Rickey Henderson	.40	.30	.15
156	Lou Whitaker	.25	.20	.10
157	George Brett	.40	.30	.15
158	Eddie Murray	.40	.30	.15
159	Cal Ripken	.40	.30	.15
160	Dave Winfield	.30	.25	.12
161	Jim Rice	.30	.25	.12
162	Carlton Fisk	.25	.20	.10
163	Jack Morris	.25	.20	.10
164	Wade Boggs	.15	.11	.06
165	Darrell Evans	.06	.05	.02
166	Mike Davis	.06	.05	.02
167	Dave Kingman	.08	.06	.03
168	Alfredo Griffin	.04	.03	.02
169	Carney Lansford	.04	.03	.02
170	Bruce Bochte	.10	.08	.04
171	Dwayne Murphy	.08	.06	.03
172	Dave Collins	.04	.03	.02
173	Chris Codiroli	.10	.08	.04
174	Mike Heath	.03	.02	.01
175	Jay Howell	.12	.09	.05
176	Rod Carew	.20	.15	.08
177	Reggie Jackson	.20	.15	.08
178	Doug DeCinces	.10	.08	.04
179	Bob Boone	.12	.09	.05
180	Ron Romanick	.15	.11	.06
181	Bob Grich	.08	.06	.03
182	Donnie Moore	.06	.05	.02
183	Brian Downing	.10	.08	.04
184	Ruppert Jones	.10	.08	.04
185	Juan Beniquez	.04	.03	.02
186	Dave Stieb	.06	.05	.02
187	Jorge Bell	.20	.15	.08
188	Willie Upshaw	.08	.06	.03
189	Tom Henke	.04	.03	.02
190	Damaso Garcia	.10	.08	.04
191	Jimmy Key	.06	.05	.02
192	Jesse Barfield	.10	.08	.04
193	Dennis Lamp	.03	.02	.01
194	Tony Fernandez	.06	.05	.02
195	Lloyd Moseby	.04	.03	.02
196	Cecil Cooper	.08	.06	.03
197	Robin Yount	.15	.11	.06
198	Rollie Fingers	.08	.06	.03
199	Ted Simmons	.04	.03	.02
200	Ben Oglivie	.04	.03	.02
201	Moose Haas	.04	.03	.02
202	Jim Gantner	.03	.02	.01
203	Paul Molitor	.12	.09	.05
204	Charlie Moore	.03	.02	.01
205	Danny Darwin	.06	.05	.02
206	Brett Butler	.06	.05	.02
207	Brook Jacoby	.08	.06	.03
208	Andre Thornton	.12	.09	.05
209	Tom Waddell	.04	.03	.02
210	Tony Bernazard	.04	.03	.02
211	Julio Franco	.08	.06	.03
212	Pat Tabler	.04	.03	.02
213	Joe Carter	.08	.06	.03
214	George Vukovich	.03	.02	.01
215	Rich Thompson	.04	.03	.02
216	Gorman Thomas	.06	.05	.02
217	Phil Bradley	.10	.08	.04
218	Alvin Davis	.06	.05	.02
219	Jim Presley	.08	.06	.03
220	Matt Young	.04	.03	.02
221	Mike Moore	.04	.03	.02
222	Dave Henderson	.06	.05	.02
223	Ed Nunez	.04	.03	.02
224	Spike Owen	.03	.02	.01
225	Mark Langston	.06	.05	.02
226	Cal Ripken, Jr.	.25	.20	.10
227	Eddie Murray	.20	.15	.08
228	Fred Lynn	.06	.05	.02
229	Lee Lacy	.03	.02	.01
230	Scott McGregor	.04	.03	.02
231	Storm Davis	.04	.03	.02
232	Rick Dempsey	.06	.05	.02
233	Mike Boddicker	.06	.05	.02
234	Mike Young	.06	.05	.02
235	Sammy Stewart	.06	.05	.02
236	Pete O'Brien	.08	.06	.03
237	Oddibe McDowell	.15	.11	.06
238	Toby Harrah	.04	.03	.02
239	Gary Ward	.04	.03	.02
240	Larry Parrish	.04	.03	.02
241	Charlie Hough	.04	.03	.02
242	Burt Hooton	.03	.02	.01
243	Don Slaught	.04	.03	.02
244	Curt Wilkerson	.04	.03	.02
245	Greg Harris	.03	.02	.01
246	Jim Rice	.08	.06	.03
247	Wade Boggs	.60	.45	.25
248	Rich Gedman	.04	.03	.02
249	Dennis Boyd	.04	.03	.02
250	Marty Barrett	.04	.03	.02
251	Dwight Evans	.06	.05	.02
252	Bill Buckner	.04	.03	.02
253	Bob Stanley	.03	.02	.01
254	Tony Armas	.04	.03	.02
255	Mike Easler	.10	.08	.04
256	George Brett	.35	.25	.14
257	Dan Quisenberry	.06	.05	.02
258	Willie Wilson	.06	.05	.02
259	Jim Sundberg	.06	.05	.02
260	Bret Saberhagen	.12	.09	.05
261	Bud Black	.06	.05	.02
262	Charlie Leibrandt	.06	.05	.02
263	Frank White	.04	.03	.02
264	Lonnie Smith	.06	.05	.02
265	Steve Balboni	.06	.05	.02
266	Kirk Gibson	.15	.11	.06
267	Alan Trammell	.15	.11	.06
268	Jack Morris	.10	.08	.04
269	Darrell Evans	.04	.03	.02
270	Dan Petry	.04	.03	.02
271	Larry Herndon	.04	.03	.02
272	Lou Whitaker	.06	.05	.02
273	Lance Parrish	.08	.06	.03
274	Chet Lemon	.03	.02	.01
275	Willie Hernandez	.10	.08	.04
276	Tom Brunansky	.08	.06	.03
277	Kent Hrbek	.12	.09	.05
278	Mark Salas	.03	.02	.01
279	Bert Blyleven	.06	.05	.02
280	Tim Teufel	.03	.02	.01
281	Ron Davis	.04	.03	.02
282	Mike Smithson	.06	.05	.02
283	Gary Gaetti	.08	.06	.03
284	Frank Viola	.06	.05	.02
285	Kirby Puckett	.30	.25	.12
286	Carlton Fisk	.12	.09	.05
287	Tom Seaver	.15	.11	.06
288	Harold Baines	.06	.05	.02
289	Ron Kittle	.04	.03	.02
290	Bob James	.03	.02	.01
291	Rudy Law	.04	.03	.02
292	Britt Burns	.03	.02	.01
293	Greg Walker	.06	.05	.02
294	Ozzie Guillen	.06	.05	.02
295	Tim Hulett	.03	.02	.01
296	Don Mattingly	.70	.50	.30
297	Rickey Henderson	.20	.15	.08
298	Dave Winfield	.30	.25	.12
299	Butch Wynegar	.03	.02	.01
300	Don Baylor	.06	.05	.02
301	Eddie Whitson	.03	.02	.01
302	Ron Guidry	.06	.05	.02
303	Dave Righetti	.08	.06	.03
304	Bobby Meacham	.06	.05	.02
305	Willie Randolph	.08	.06	.03
306	Vince Coleman	.15	.11	.06
307	Oddibe McDowell	.15	.11	.06
308	Larry Sheets	.06	.05	.02
309	Ozzie Guillen	.06	.05	.02
310	Earnie Riles	.04	.03	.02
311	Chris Brown	.10	.08	.04
312	Brian Fisher, Roger McDowell	.08	.06	.03
313	Tom Browning	.04	.03	.02
314	Glenn Davis	.06	.05	.02
315	Mark Salas	.03	.02	.01

1986 Topps Super

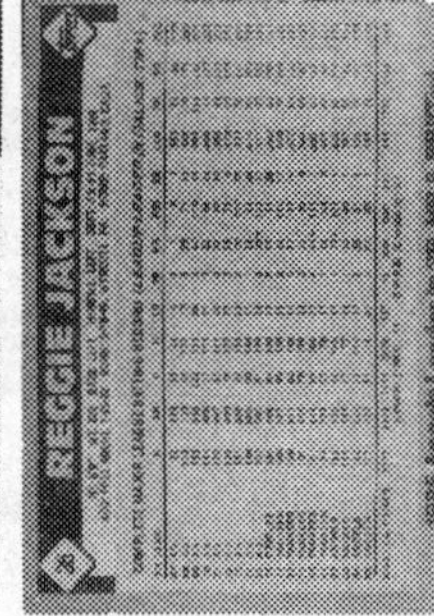

A third year of oversize, 4-7/8" by 6-7/8", versions of Topps' regular issue cards saw the set once again hit the 60-card mark. Besides being four times the size of a normal card, the Supers differ only in the number on the back of the card.

		MT	NR MT	EX
Complete Set:		16.00	12.00	6.50
Common Player:		.25	.20	.10
1	Don Mattingly	.75	.60	.30
2	Willie McGee	.35	.25	.14
3	Bret Saberhagen	.35	.25	.14
4	Dwight Gooden	.45	.35	.20
5	Dan Quisenberry	.25	.20	.10
6	Jeff Reardon	.25	.20	.10
7	Ozzie Guillen	.25	.20	.10
8	Vince Coleman	.35	.25	.14
9	Harold Baines	.25	.20	.10
10	Jorge Bell	.50	.40	.20
11	Bert Blyleven	.25	.20	.10
12	Wade Boggs	.75	.60	.30
13	Phil Bradley	.25	.20	.10
14	George Brett	.90	.70	.35
15	Hubie Brooks	.25	.20	.10
16	Tom Browning	.25	.20	.10
17	Bill Buckner	.25	.20	.10
18	Brett Butler	.25	.20	.10
19	Gary Carter	.50	.40	.20
20	Cecil Cooper	.25	.20	.10
21	Darrell Evans	.25	.20	.10
22	Dwight Evans	.25	.20	.10
23	Carlton Fisk	.30	.25	.12
24	Steve Garvey	.50	.40	.20
25	Kirk Gibson	.35	.25	.14
26	Rich Gossage	.25	.20	.10
27	Pedro Guerrero	.30	.25	.12
28	Ron Guidry	.30	.25	.12
29	Tony Gwynn	.60	.45	.25
30	Rickey Henderson	.70	.50	.30
31	Keith Hernandez	.30	.25	.12
32	Tom Herr	.25	.20	.10
33	Orel Hershiser	.50	.40	.20
34	Jay Howell	.25	.20	.10
35	Reggie Jackson	.90	.70	.35
36	Bob James	.25	.20	.10
37	Charlie Leibrandt	.25	.20	.10
38	Jack Morris	.35	.25	.14
39	Dale Murphy	.80	.60	.30
40	Eddie Murray	.60	.45	.25
41	Dave Parker	.75	.60	.30
42	Tim Raines	.50	.40	.20
43	Jim Rice	.35	.25	.14
44	Dave Righetti	.30	.25	.12
45	Cal Ripken, Jr.	2.00	1.50	.80
46	Pete Rose	1.00	.70	.40
47	Nolan Ryan	2.00	1.50	.80
48	Ryne Sandberg	2.00	1.50	.80
49	Mike Schmidt	.90	.70	.35
50	Tom Seaver	.80	.60	.30
51	Bryn Smith	.25	.20	.10
52	Lee Smith	.35	.25	.14
53	Ozzie Smith	.75	.60	.30
54	Dave Stieb	.25	.20	.10
55	Darryl Strawberry	.50	.40	.20
56	Gorman Thomas	.25	.20	.10
57	John Tudor	.25	.20	.10
58	Fernando Valenzuela	.30	.25	.12
59	Willie Wilson	.25	.20	.10
60	Dave Winfield	.75	.60	.30

1986 Topps Super Star

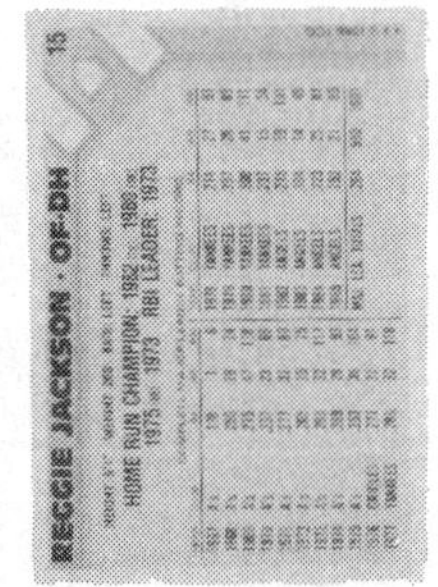

Labeled "Topps' Collector Series" in a red band at the top of the front, this set marked the second year of Topps' production of a special boxed set for the Woolworth chain of stores, though Woolworth's name does not appear anywhere on the card. The cards, which measure 2-1/2" by 3-1/2", feature a color photo with its lower right corner rolled up to reveal the words "Super Star" on a bright yellow border. The player's name appears in the lower left corner. The 66-card set features stars and retains a certain measure of popularity on that basis.

		MT	NR MT	EX
Complete Set:		5.00	3.75	2.00
Common Player:		.09	.07	.04
1	Tony Armas	.09	.07	.04
2	Don Baylor	.12	.09	.05
3	Wade Boggs	.80	.60	.30

4	George Brett	.40	.30	.15
5	Bill Buckner	.09	.07	.04
6	Rod Carew	.30	.25	.12
7	Gary Carter	.30	.25	.12
8	Cecil Cooper	.12	.09	.05
9	Darrell Evans	.12	.09	.05
10	Dwight Evans	.15	.11	.06
11	George Foster	.12	.09	.05
12	Bobby Grich	.09	.07	.04
13	Tony Gwynn	.35	.25	.14
14	Keith Hernandez	.25	.20	.10
15	Reggie Jackson	.30	.25	.12
16	Dave Kingman	.12	.09	.05
17	Carney Lansford	.09	.07	.04
18	Fred Lynn	.12	.09	.05
19	Bill Madlock	.12	.09	.05
20	Don Mattingly	1.50	1.25	.60
21	Willie McGee	.20	.15	.08
22	Hal McRae	.09	.07	.04
23	Dale Murphy	.40	.30	.15
24	Eddie Murray	.35	.25	.14
25	Ben Oglivie	.09	.07	.04
26	Al Oliver	.12	.09	.05
27	Dave Parker	.20	.15	.08
28	Jim Rice	.30	.25	.12
29	Pete Rose	.90	.70	.35
30	Mike Schmidt	.40	.30	.15
31	Gorman Thomas	.09	.07	.04
32	Willie Wilson	.12	.09	.05
33	Dave Winfield	.30	.25	.12

1986 Topps Tattoos

Topps returned to tattoos in 1986, marketing a set of 24 different tattoo sheets. Each sheet of tattoos measures 3-7/16" by 14" and includes both player and smaller action tattoos. As the action tattoos were uniform and not of any particular player, they add little value to the sheet. The player tattoos measure 1-3/16" by 2-3/8". With 24 sheets, eight players per sheet, there are 192 players represented in the set. The sheets are numbered.

		MT	NR MT	EX
Complete Set:		5.00	3.75	2.00
Common Player:		.20	.15	.08
1	Julio Franco, Rich Gossage, Keith Hernandez, Charlie Leibrandt, Jack Perconte, Lee Smith, Dickie Thon, Dave Winfield	.25	.20	.10
2	Jesse Barfield, Shawon Dunston, Dennis Eckersley, Brian Fisher, Moose Haas, Mike Moore, Dale Murphy, Bret Saberhagen	.30	.25	.12
3	George Bell, Bob Brenly, Steve Carlton, Jose DeLeon, Bob Horner, Bob James, Dan Quisenberry, Andre Thornton	.25	.20	.10
4	Mike Davis, Leon Durham, Darrell Evans, Glenn Hubbard, Johnny Ray, Cal Ripken, Ted Simmons	.25	.20	.10
5	John Candelaria, Rick Dempsey, Steve Garvey, Ozzie Guillen, Gary Matthews, Jesse Orosco, Tony Pena	.25	.20	.10
6	Bruce Bochte, George Brett, Cecil Cooper, Sammy Khalifa, Ron Kittle, Scott McGregor, Pete Rose, Mookie Wilson	.45	.35	.20
7	John Franco, Carney Lansford, Don Mattingly, Graig Nettles, Rick Reuschel, Mike Schmidt, Larry Sheets, Don Sutton	.45	.35	.20
8	Cecilio Guante, Willie Hernandez, Mike Krukow, Fred Lynn, Phil Niekro, Ed Nunez, Ryne Sandberg, Pat Tabler	.25	.20	.10
9	Brett Butler, Chris Codiroli, Jim Gantner, Charlie Hough, Dave Parker, Rick Rhoden, Glenn Wilson, Robin Yount	.20	.15	.08
10	Tom Browning, Ron Darling, Von Hayes, Chet Lemon, Tom Seaver, Mike Smithson, Bruce Sutter, Alan Trammell	.25	.20	.10
11	Tony Armas, Jose Cruz, Jay Howell, Rick Mahler, Jack Morris, Rafael Ramirez, Dave Righetti, Mike Young	.20	.15	.08
12	Alvin Davis, Doug DeCinces, Andy Hawkins, Dennis Lamp, Keith Moreland, Jim Presley, Mario Soto, John Tudor	.20	.15	.08
13	Hubie Brooks, Jody Davis, Dwight Evans, Ron Hassey, Charles Hudson, Kirby Puckett, Jose Uribe	.20	.15	.08
14	Tony Bernazard, Phil Bradley, Bill Buckner, Brian Downing, Dan Driessen, Ron Guidry, LaMarr Hoyt, Garry Maddox	.20	.15	.08
15	Buddy Bell, Joe Carter, Tony Fernandez, Tito Landrum, Jeff Leonard, Hal McRae, Willie Randolph, Juan Samuel	.20	.15	.08
16	Dennis Boyd, Vince Coleman, Scott Garrelts, Alfredo Griffin, Donnie Moore, Tony Perez, Ozzie Smith, Frank White	.25	.20	.10
17	Rich Gedman, Kent Hrbek, Reggie Jackson, Mike Marshall, Terry Pendleton, Tim Raines, Mark Salas, Claudell Washington	.25	.20	.10
18	Chris Brown, Tom Brunansky, Glenn Davis, Ron Davis, Burt Hooton, Darryl Strawberry, Frank Viola, Tim Wallach	.30	.25	.12
19	Jack Clark, Bill Doran, Toby Harrah, Bill Madlock, Pete O'Brien, Larry Parrish, Mike Scioscia, Garry Templeton	.20	.15	.08
20	Gary Carter, Andre Dawson, Dwight Gooden, Orel Hershiser, Oddibe McDowell, Roger McDowell, Dwayne Murphy, Jim Rice	.40	.30	.15
21	Steve Balboni, Mike Easler, Charlie Lea, Lloyd Moseby, Steve Sax, Rick Sutcliffe, Gary Ward, Willie Wilson	.20	.15	.08
22	Wade Boggs, Dave Concepcion, Kirk Gibson, Tom Herr, Lance Parrish, Jeff Reardon, Bryn Smith, Gorman Thomas	.30	.25	.12
23	Carlton Fisk, Bob Grich, Pedro Guerrero, Willie McGee, Paul Molitor, Mike Scott, Dave Stieb, Lou Whitaker	.20	.15	.08
24	Bert Blyleven, Damaso Garcia, Phil Garner, Tony Gwynn, Rickey Henderson, Ben Oglivie, Nolan Ryan, Fernando Valenzuela	.30	.25	.12

1986 Topps 3-D

This set is a second effort in the production of over-size (4-1/2" by 6") plastic cards on which the player figure is embossed. Cards were sold one per pack for approximately 50¢. The 30 players in the set are among the game's top stars. The embossed color photo is bordered at bottom by a strip of contrasting color on which the player name appears. At the top, a row of white baseballs each contain a letter of the team nickname. Backs have no printing, and contain two self-adhesive strips with which the cards can be attached to a hard surface.

		MT	NR MT	EX
Complete Set:		15.00	11.00	6.00
Common Player:		.25	.20	.10
1	Bert Blyleven	.30	.25	.12
2	Gary Carter	.50	.40	.20
3	Wade Boggs	.75	.60	.30
4	Dwight Gooden	.40	.30	.15
5	George Brett	.90	.70	.35
6	Rich Gossage	.30	.25	.12
7	Darrell Evans	.25	.20	.10
8	Pedro Guerrero	.30	.25	.12
9	Ron Guidry	.30	.25	.12
10	Keith Hernandez	.30	.25	.12
11	Rickey Henderson	.70	.50	.30
12	Orel Hershiser	.25	.20	.10
13	Reggie Jackson	.90	.70	.35
14	Willie McGee	.30	.25	.12
15	Don Mattingly	.75	.60	.30
16	Dale Murphy	.60	.45	.25
17	Jack Morris	.30	.25	.12
18	Dave Parker	.60	.45	.25
19	Eddie Murray	.60	.45	.25
20	Jeff Reardon	.30	.25	.12
21	Dan Quisenberry	.25	.20	.10
22	Pete Rose	.90	.70	.35
23	Jim Rice	.35	.25	.14
24	Mike Schmidt	.90	.70	.35
25	Bret Saberhagen	.30	.25	.12
26	Darryl Strawberry	.40	.30	.15
27	Dave Stieb	.25	.20	.10
28	John Tudor	.25	.20	.10
29	Dave Winfield	.75	.60	.30
30	Fernando Valenzuela	.30	.25	.12

1987 Topps

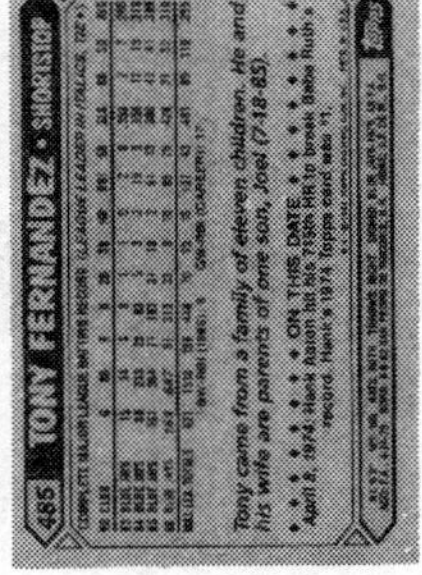

Many collectors feel that Topps' 1987 set of 792 card is a future classic. The 2-1/2" by 3-1/2" design is closely akin to the 1962 set in that the player photo is set against a woodgrain border. Instead of a rolling corner, as in 1962, the player photos in '87 feature a couple of clipped corners at top left and bottom right, where the team logo and player name appear. The player's position is not given on the front of the card. For the first time in several years, the trophy which designates members of Topps All-Star Rookie Team returned to the card design. As in the previous three years, Topps issued a glossy-finish "Tiffany" edition of their 792-card set. However, it was speculated that as many as 50,000 sets were produced as opposed to the 5,000 sets printed in 1985 and 1986. Because of the large print run, the values for the Tiffany cards are only 3-4 times higher than the same card in the regular issue.

		MT	NR MT	EX
Complete Set (792):		15.00	11.00	6.00
Common Player:		.05	.04	.02
1	Roger Clemens (Record Breaker)	.15	.11	.06
2	Jim Deshaies (Record Breaker)	.07	.05	.03
3	Dwight Evans (Record Breaker)	.07	.05	.03
4	Dave Lopes (Record Breaker)	.07	.05	.03
5	Dave Righetti (Record Breaker)	.07	.05	.03
6	Ruben Sierra (Record Breaker)	.25	.20	.10
7	Todd Worrell (Record Breaker)	.07	.05	.03
8	Terry Pendleton	.10	.08	.04
9	Jay Tibbs	.05	.04	.02
10	Cecil Cooper	.10	.08	.04
11	Indians Leaders (Jack Aker, Chris Bando, Phil Niekro)	.07	.05	.03
12	*Jeff Sellers* (FC)	.05	.04	.02
13	Nick Esasky	.07	.05	.03
14	Dave Stewart	.12	.09	.05
15	Claudell Washington	.07	.05	.03
16	Pat Clements	.05	.04	.02
17	Pete O'Brien	.10	.08	.04
18	Dick Howser	.05	.04	.02
19	Matt Young	.05	.04	.02
20	Gary Carter	.10	.08	.04
21	Mark Davis	.05	.04	.02
22	Doug DeCinces	.07	.05	.03
23	Lee Smith	.10	.08	.04
24	Tony Walker	.05	.04	.02
25	Bert Blyleven	.12	.09	.05
26	Greg Brock	.07	.05	.03
27	Joe Cowley	.05	.04	.02
28	Rick Dempsey	.07	.05	.03
29	Jimmy Key	.15	.11	.06
30	Tim Raines	.12	.09	.05
31	Braves Leaders (Glenn Hubbard, Rafael Ramirez)	.07	.05	.03
32	Tim Leary	.07	.05	.03
33	Andy Van Slyke	.12	.09	.05
34	Jose Rijo	.07	.05	.03
35	Sid Bream	.07	.05	.03
36	*Eric King*	.08	.06	.03
37	Marvell Wynne	.05	.04	.02
38	Dennis Leonard	.07	.05	.03
39	Marty Barrett	.07	.05	.03
40	Dave Righetti	.12	.09	.05
41	Bo Diaz	.07	.05	.03
42	Gary Redus	.05	.04	.02
43	Gene Michael	.05	.04	.02
44	Greg Harris	.05	.04	.02
45	Jim Presley	.10	.08	.04
46	Danny Gladden	.05	.04	.02
47	Dennis Powell	.07	.05	.03
48	Wally Backman	.07	.05	.03
49	Terry Harper	.05	.04	.02
50	Dave Smith	.07	.05	.03
51	Mel Hall	.07	.05	.03
52	Keith Atherton	.05	.04	.02
53	Ruppert Jones	.05	.04	.02
54	Bill Dawley	.05	.04	.02
55	Tim Wallach	.10	.08	.04
56	Brewers Leaders (Jamie Cocanower, Paul Molitor, Charlie Moore, Herm Starrette)	.07	.05	.03
57	*Scott Nielsen* (FC)	.10	.08	.04
58	Thad Bosley	.05	.04	.02
59	Ken Dayley	.05	.04	.02
60	Tony Pena	.07	.05	.03
61	*Bobby Thigpen* (FC)	.12	.09	.05
62	Bobby Meacham	.05	.04	.02
63	Fred Toliver (FC)	.07	.05	.03
64	Harry Spilman	.05	.04	.02
65	Tom Browning	.10	.08	.04
66	Marc Sullivan	.05	.04	.02
67	Bill Swift	.05	.04	.02
68	Tony LaRussa	.07	.05	.03
69	Lonnie Smith	.07	.05	.03
70	Charlie Hough	.07	.05	.03
71	*Mike Aldrete* (FC)	.15	.11	.06
72	Walt Terrell	.07	.05	.03
73	Dave Anderson	.05	.04	.02
74	Dan Pasqua	.10	.08	.04
75	Ron Darling	.12	.09	.05
76	Rafael Ramirez	.05	.04	.02
77	Bryan Oelkers	.05	.04	.02
78	Tom Foley	.05	.04	.02
79	Juan Nieves	.05	.04	.02
80	*Wally Joyner*	.40	.30	.15
81	Padres Leaders (Andy Hawkins, Terry Kennedy)	.07	.05	.03
82	*Rob Murphy* (FC)	.15	.11	.06
83	Mike Davis	.07	.05	.03
84	Steve Lake	.05	.04	.02
85	Kevin Bass	.07	.05	.03
86	Nate Snell	.05	.04	.02
87	Mark Salas	.05	.04	.02
88	Ed Wojna	.05	.04	.02

89 Ozzie Guillen .08 .06 .03
90 Dave Stieb .10 .08 .04
91 Harold Reynolds .10 .08 .04
92a Urbano Lugo (no trademark on front) .30 .25 .12
92b Urbano Lugo (trademark on front) .07 .05 .03
93 Jim Leyland .05 .04 .02
94 Calvin Schiraldi .05 .04 .02
95 Oddibe McDowell .07 .05 .03
96 Frank Williams .05 .04 .02
97 Glenn Wilson .07 .05 .03
98 Bill Scherrer .05 .04 .02
99 Darryl Motley .05 .04 .02
100 Steve Garvey .12 .09 .05
101 *Carl Willis* (FC) .10 .08 .04
102 Paul Zuvella .05 .04 .02
103 Rick Aguilera .06 .05 .02
104 Billy Sample .05 .04 .02
105 Floyd Youmans .07 .05 .03
106 Blue Jays Leaders (George Bell, Willie Upshaw) .07 .05 .03
107 John Butcher .05 .04 .02
108 Jim Gantner (photo reversed) .07 .05 .03
109 R.J. Reynolds .05 .04 .02
110 John Tudor .10 .08 .04
111 Alfredo Griffin .07 .05 .03
112 Alan Ashby .05 .04 .02
113 Neil Allen .05 .04 .02
114 Billy Beane .05 .04 .02
115 Donnie Moore .05 .04 .02
116 *Mike Stanley* .10 .08 .04
117 Jim Beattie .05 .04 .02
118 Bobby Valentine .05 .04 .02
119 Ron Robinson .05 .04 .02
120 Eddie Murray .30 .25 .12
121 *Kevin Romine* (FC) .12 .09 .05
122 Jim Clancy .07 .05 .03
123 *John Kruk* .60 .45 .25
124 Ray Fontenot .05 .04 .02
125 Bob Brenly .05 .04 .02
126 *Mike Loynd* (FC) .15 .11 .06
127 Vance Law .07 .05 .03
128 Checklist 1-132 .05 .04 .02
129 Rick Cerone .05 .04 .02
130 Dwight Gooden .15 .11 .06
131 Pirates Leaders (Sid Bream, Tony Pena) .07 .05 .03
132 *Paul Assenmacher* .15 .11 .06
133 Jose Oquendo .05 .04 .02
134 *Rich Yett* (FC) .12 .09 .05
135 Mike Easler .07 .05 .03
136 Ron Romanick .05 .04 .02
137 Jerry Willard .05 .04 .02
138 Roy Lee Jackson .05 .04 .02
139 *Devon White* (FC) .60 .45 .25
140 Bret Saberhagen .15 .11 .06
141 Herm Winningham .05 .04 .02
142 Rick Sutcliffe .10 .08 .04
143 Steve Boros .05 .04 .02
144 Mike Scioscia .07 .05 .03
145 Charlie Kerfeld .07 .05 .03
146 *Tracy Jones* (FC) .08 .06 .03
147 Randy Niemann .05 .04 .02
148 Dave Collins .07 .05 .03
149 Ray Searage .05 .04 .02
150 Wade Boggs .40 .30 .15
151 Mike LaCoss .05 .04 .02
152 Toby Harrah .07 .05 .03
153 *Duane Ward* (FC) .40 .30 .15
154 Tom O'Malley .05 .04 .02
155 Eddie Whitson .05 .04 .02
156 Mariners Leaders (Bob Kearney, Phil Regan, Matt Young) .07 .05 .03
157 Danny Darwin .05 .04 .02
158 Tim Teufel .05 .04 .02
159 Ed Olwine .05 .04 .02
160 Julio Franco .10 .08 .04
161 Steve Ontiveros .05 .04 .02
162 *Mike LaValliere* .10 .07 .04
163 Kevin Gross .07 .05 .03
164 Sammy Khalifa .05 .04 .02
165 Jeff Reardon .10 .08 .04
166 Bob Boone .07 .05 .03
167 *Jim Deshaies* .12 .09 .05
168 Lou Piniella .07 .05 .03
169 Ron Washington .05 .04 .02
170 *Bo Jackson* (Future Stars) 1.00 .70 .40
171 *Chuck Cary* (FC) .10 .08 .04
172 Ron Oester .05 .04 .02
173 Alex Trevino .05 .04 .02
174 Henry Cotto .05 .04 .02
175 Bob Stanley .05 .04 .02
176 Steve Buechele .07 .05 .03
177 Keith Moreland .07 .05 .03
178 Cecil Fielder .75 .60 .30
179 Bill Wegman .10 .08 .04
180 Chris Brown .07 .05 .03
181 Cardinals Leaders (Mike LaValliere, Ozzie Smith, Ray Soff) .07 .05 .03
182 Lee Lacy .05 .04 .02
183 Andy Hawkins .05 .04 .02
184 *Bobby Bonilla* .60 .45 .25
185 Roger McDowell .10 .08 .04
186 Bruce Benedict .05 .04 .02
187 Mark Huismann .05 .04 .02
188 Tony Phillips .05 .04 .02
189 Joe Hesketh .05 .04 .02
190 Jim Sundberg .07 .05 .03
191 Charles Hudson .05 .04 .02
192 Cory Snyder (FC) .10 .08 .04
193 Roger Craig .07 .05 .03
194 Kirk McCaskill .07 .05 .03
195 Mike Pagliarulo .10 .08 .04
196 Randy O'Neal .05 .04 .02
197 Mark Bailey .05 .04 .02
198 Lee Mazzilli .07 .05 .03
199 Mariano Duncan .05 .04 .02
200 Pete Rose .40 .30 .15
201 *John Cangelosi* .12 .09 .05
202 Ricky Wright .05 .04 .02
203 *Mike Kingery* (FC) .15 .11 .06
204 Sammy Stewart .05 .04 .02
205 Graig Nettles .10 .08 .04
206 Twins Leaders (Tim Laudner, Frank Viola) .07 .05 .03
207 George Frazier .05 .04 .02
208 John Shelby .05 .04 .02
209 Rick Schu .05 .04 .02
210 Lloyd Moseby .07 .05 .03
211 John Morris (FC) .07 .05 .03
212 Mike Fitzgerald .05 .04 .02
213 *Randy Myers* (FC) .30 .25 .12
214 Omar Moreno .05 .04 .02
215 Mark Langston .12 .09 .05
216 *B.J. Surhoff* (Future Stars) .15 .11 .06
217 Chris Codiroli .05 .04 .02
218 Sparky Anderson .07 .05 .03
219 Cecilio Guante .05 .04 .02
220 Joe Carter .40 .30 .15
221 Vern Ruhle .05 .04 .02
222 Denny Walling .05 .04 .02
223 Charlie Leibrandt .07 .05 .03
224 Wayne Tolleson .05 .04 .02
225 Mike Smithson .05 .04 .02
226 Max Venable .05 .04 .02
227 *Jamie Moyer* (FC) .10 .08 .04
228 Curt Wilkerson .05 .04 .02
229 *Mike Birkbeck* (FC) .15 .11 .06
230 Don Baylor .10 .08 .04
231 Giants Leaders (Bob Brenly, Mike Krukow) .07 .05 .03
232 *Reggie Williams* .10 .08 .04
233 *Russ Morman* (FC) .10 .08 .04
234 Pat Sheridan .05 .04 .02
235 Alvin Davis .10 .08 .04
236 Tommy John .15 .11 .06
237 Jim Morrison .05 .04 .02
238 Bill Krueger .05 .04 .02
239 Juan Espino .05 .04 .02
240 Steve Balboni .07 .05 .03
241 Danny Heep .05 .04 .02
242 Rick Mahler .05 .04 .02
243 Whitey Herzog .07 .05 .03
244 Dickie Noles .05 .04 .02
245 Willie Upshaw .07 .05 .03
246 Jim Dwyer .05 .04 .02
247 Jeff Reed (FC) .07 .05 .03
248 Gene Walter .07 .05 .03
249 Jim Pankovits .05 .04 .02
250 Teddy Higuera .15 .11 .06
251 Rob Wilfong .05 .04 .02
252 Denny Martinez .05 .04 .02
253 Eddie Milner .05 .04 .02
254 *Bob Tewksbury* .20 .15 .08
255 Juan Samuel .10 .08 .04
256 Royals Leaders (George Brett, Frank White) .12 .09 .05
257 Bob Forsch .07 .05 .03
258 Steve Yeager .05 .04 .02
259 *Mike Greenwell* (FC) .50 .40 .20
260 Vida Blue .07 .05 .03
261 *Ruben Sierra* .75 .60 .30
262 Jim Winn .05 .04 .02
263 Stan Javier (FC) .07 .05 .03
264 Checklist 133-264 .05 .04 .02
265 Darrell Evans .10 .08 .04
266 *Jeff Hamilton* (FC) .08 .06 .03
267 Howard Johnson .10 .08 .04
268 Pat Corrales .05 .04 .02
269 Cliff Speck .05 .04 .02
270 Jody Davis .07 .05 .03
271 Mike Brown .05 .04 .02
272 Andres Galarraga .50 .40 .20
273 Gene Nelson .05 .04 .02
274 *Jeff Hearron* (FC) .05 .04 .02
275 LaMarr Hoyt .05 .04 .02
276 Jackie Gutierrez .05 .04 .02
277 Juan Agosto .05 .04 .02
278 Gary Pettis .05 .04 .02
279 *Dan Plesac* .10 .08 .04
280 Jeffrey Leonard .07 .05 .03
281 Reds Leaders (Bo Diaz, Bill Gullickson, Pete Rose) .10 .08 .04
282 Jeff Calhoun .05 .04 .02
283 *Doug Drabek* (FC) .40 .30 .15
284 John Moses .05 .04 .02
285 Dennis Boyd .07 .05 .03
286 Mike Woodard (FC) .07 .05 .03
287 Dave Von Ohlen .05 .04 .02
288 Tito Landrum .05 .04 .02
289 Bob Kipper .07 .05 .03
290 Leon Durham .07 .05 .03
291 *Mitch Williams* .25 .20 .10
292 Franklin Stubbs .07 .05 .03
293 Bob Rodgers .05 .04 .02
294 Steve Jeltz .05 .04 .02
295 Len Dykstra .15 .11 .06
296 *Andres Thomas* .15 .11 .06
297 Don Schulze .05 .04 .02
298 Larry Herndon .05 .04 .02
299 Joel Davis .07 .05 .03
300 Reggie Jackson .30 .25 .12
301 *Luis Aquino* (FC) .10 .08 .04
302 Bill Schroeder .05 .04 .02
303 Juan Berenguer .05 .04 .02
304 Phil Garner .05 .04 .02
305 John Franco .10 .08 .04
306 Red Sox Leaders (Rich Gedman, John McNamara, Tom Seaver) .07 .05 .03
307 *Lee Guetterman* (FC) .15 .11 .06
308 Don Slaught .05 .04 .02
309 Mike Young .05 .04 .02
310 Frank Viola .15 .11 .06
311 Turn Back The Clock (Rickey Henderson) .12 .09 .05
312 Turn Back The Clock (Reggie Jackson) .10 .08 .04
313 Turn Back The Clock (Roberto Clemente) .10 .08 .04
314 Turn Back The Clock (Carl Yastrzemski) .10 .08 .04
315 Turn Back The Clock (Maury Wills) .07 .05 .03
316 Brian Fisher .07 .05 .03
317 Clint Hurdle .05 .04 .02
318 Jim Fregosi .05 .04 .02
319 *Greg Swindell* (FC) .30 .25 .12
320 *Barry Bonds* 2.75 2.00 1.00
321 Mike Laga .05 .04 .02
322 Chris Bando .05 .04 .02
323 *Al Newman* .07 .05 .03
324 Dave Palmer .05 .04 .02
325 Garry Templeton .07 .05 .03
326 Mark Gubicza .10 .08 .04
327 *Dale Sveum* .08 .06 .03
328 Bob Welch .10 .08 .04
329 Ron Roenicke .05 .04 .02
330 Mike Scott .12 .09 .05
331 Mets Leaders (Gary Carter, Keith Hernandez, Dave Johnson, Darryl Strawberry) .10 .08 .04
332 Joe Price .05 .04 .02
333 Ken Phelps .07 .05 .03
334 *Ed Correa* .05 .04 .02
335 Candy Maldonado .07 .05 .03
336 *Allan Anderson* (FC) .06 .05 .02
337 Darrell Miller .05 .04 .02
338 Tim Conroy .05 .04 .02
339 Donnie Hill .05 .04 .02
340 Roger Clemens .75 .60 .30
341 Mike Brown .05 .04 .02
342 Bob James .05 .04 .02
343 Hal Lanier .05 .04 .02
344a Joe Niekro (copyright outside yellow on back) .30 .25 .12
344b Joe Niekro (copyright inside yellow on back) .07 .05 .03
345 Andre Dawson .20 .15 .08
346 Shawon Dunston .07 .05 .03
347 Mickey Brantley (FC) .07 .05 .03
348 Carmelo Martinez .07 .05 .03
349 Storm Davis .10 .08 .04
350 Keith Hernandez .10 .08 .04
351 Gene Garber .05 .04 .02
352 Mike Felder (FC) .07 .05 .03
353 Ernie Camacho .05 .04 .02
354 Jamie Quirk .05 .04 .02
355 Don Carman .07 .05 .03
356 White Sox Leaders (Ed Brinkman, Julio Cruz) .07 .05 .03
357 *Steve Fireovid* (FC) .07 .05 .03
358 Sal Butera .05 .04 .02
359 Doug Corbett .05 .04 .02
360 Pedro Guerrero .08 .06 .03
361 Mark Thurmond .05 .04 .02
362 *Luis Quinones* (FC) .12 .09 .05
363 Jose Guzman .12 .09 .05
364 Randy Bush .05 .04 .02
365 Rick Rhoden .07 .05 .03
366 *Mark McGwire* .90 .70 .35
367 Jeff Lahti .05 .04 .02
368 John McNamara .05 .04 .02
369 Brian Dayett .05 .04 .02
370 Fred Lynn .15 .11 .06
371 *Mark Eichhorn* .15 .11 .06
372 Jerry Mumphrey .05 .04 .02
373 Jeff Dedmon .05 .04 .02
374 Glenn Hoffman .05 .04 .02
375 Ron Guidry .12 .09 .05
376 Scott Bradley .05 .04 .02
377 John Henry Johnson .05 .04 .02
378 Rafael Santana .05 .04 .02
379 John Russell .05 .04 .02
380 Rich Gossage .15 .11 .06
381 Expos Leaders (Mike Fitzgerald, Bob Rodgers) .07 .05 .03
382 Rudy Law .05 .04 .02
383 Ron Davis .05 .04 .02
384 Johnny Grubb .05 .04 .02
385 Orel Hershiser .12 .09 .05
386 Dickie Thon .07 .05 .03
387 *T.R. Bryden* (FC) .10 .08 .04
388 Geno Petralli .05 .04 .02
389 Jeff Robinson .07 .05 .03
390 Gary Matthews .07 .05 .03
391 Jay Howell .07 .05 .03
392 Checklist 265-396 .05 .04 .02
393 Pete Rose .20 .15 .08
394 Mike Bielecki .07 .05 .03
395 Damaso Garcia .05 .04 .02
396 Tim Lollar .05 .04 .02
397 Greg Walker .07 .05 .03
398 Brad Havens .05 .04 .02
399 Curt Ford (FC) .07 .05 .03
400 George Brett .40 .30 .15
401 Billy Jo Robidoux .07 .05 .03
402 Mike Trujillo .05 .04 .02
403 Jerry Royster .05 .04 .02
404 Doug Sisk .05 .04 .02
405 Brook Jacoby .10 .08 .04
406 Yankees Leaders (Rickey Henderson, Don Mattingly) .25 .20 .10
407 Jim Acker .05 .04 .02
408 John Mizerock .05 .04 .02
409 Milt Thompson .07 .05 .03
410 Fernando Valenzuela .08 .06 .03
411 Darnell Coles .07 .05 .03
412 Eric Davis .20 .15 .08
413 Moose Haas .05 .04 .02
414 Joe Orsulak .05 .04 .02
415 *Bobby Witt* .12 .09 .05
416 Tom Nieto .05 .04 .02
417 Pat Perry (FC) .07 .05 .03
418 Dick Williams .05 .04 .02

No.	Player			
419	*Mark Portugal* (FC)	.12	.09	.05
420	*Will Clark*	1.75	1.25	.70
421	Jose DeLeon	.07	.05	.03
422	Jack Howell	.07	.05	.03
423	Jaime Cocanower	.05	.04	.02
424	Chris Speier	.05	.04	.02
425	Tom Seaver	.30	.25	.12
426	Floyd Rayford	.05	.04	.02
427	Ed Nunez	.05	.04	.02
428	Bruce Bochy	.05	.04	.02
429	*Tim Pyznarski* (FC) (Future Stars)	.10	.08	.04
430	Mike Schmidt	.40	.30	.15
431	Dodgers Leaders (Tom Niedenfuer, Ron Perranoski, Alex Trevino)	.07	.05	.03
432	Jim Slaton	.05	.04	.02
433	*Ed Hearn* (FC)	.10	.08	.04
434	Mike Fischlin	.05	.04	.02
435	Bruce Sutter	.12	.09	.05
436	*Andy Allanson*	.15	.11	.06
437	Ted Power	.05	.04	.02
438	*Kelly Downs* (FC)	.10	.08	.04
439	Karl Best	.05	.04	.02
440	Willie McGee	.10	.08	.04
441	*Dave Leiper* (FC)	.10	.08	.04
442	Mitch Webster	.07	.05	.03
443	John Felske	.05	.04	.02
444	Jeff Russell	.05	.04	.02
445	Dave Lopes	.07	.05	.03
446	*Chuck Finley* (FC)	.25	.20	.10
447	Bill Almon	.05	.04	.02
448	*Chris Bosio* (FC)	.20	.15	.08
449	*Pat Dodson* (FC) (Future Stars)	.10	.08	.04
450	Kirby Puckett	1.00	.70	.40
451	Joe Sambito	.05	.04	.02
452	Dave Henderson	.10	.08	.04
453	*Scott Terry* (FC)	.12	.09	.05
454	Luis Salazar	.05	.04	.02
455	Mike Boddicker	.07	.05	.03
456	A's Leaders (Carney Lansford, Tony LaRussa, Mickey Tettleton, Dave Von Ohlen)	.07	.05	.03
457	Len Matuszek	.05	.04	.02
458	Kelly Gruber (FC)	.15	.11	.06
459	Dennis Eckersley	.10	.08	.04
460	Darryl Strawberry	.15	.11	.06
461	Craig McMurtry	.05	.04	.02
462	Scott Fletcher	.07	.05	.03
463	Tom Candiotti	.05	.04	.02
464	Butch Wynegar	.05	.04	.02
465	Todd Worrell	.08	.06	.03
466	Kal Daniels (FC)	.10	.08	.04
467	Randy St. Claire	.05	.04	.02
468	George Bamberger	.05	.04	.02
469	*Mike Diaz* (FC)	.10	.08	.04
470	Dave Dravecky	.07	.05	.03
471	Ronn Reynolds	.05	.04	.02
472	Bill Doran	.07	.05	.03
473	Steve Farr	.05	.04	.02
474	Jerry Narron	.05	.04	.02
475	Scott Garrelts	.05	.04	.02
476	Danny Tartabull	.30	.25	.12
477	Ken Howell	.05	.04	.02
478	Tim Laudner	.05	.04	.02
479	*Bob Sebra* (FC)	.10	.08	.04
480	Jim Rice	.12	.09	.05
481	Phillies Leaders (Von Hayes, Juan Samuel, Glenn Wilson)	.07	.05	.03
482	Daryl Boston	.05	.04	.02
483	Dwight Lowry	.05	.04	.02
484	Jim Traber (FC)	.15	.11	.06
485	Tony Fernandez	.10	.08	.04
486	Otis Nixon	.10	.08	.04
487	Dave Gumpert	.05	.04	.02
488	Ray Knight	.07	.05	.03
489	Bill Gullickson	.05	.04	.02
490	Dale Murphy	.12	.09	.05
491	*Ron Karkovice* (FC)	.10	.08	.04
492	Mike Heath	.05	.04	.02
493	Tom Lasorda	.07	.05	.03
494	*Barry Jones* (FC)	.12	.09	.05
495	Gorman Thomas	.10	.08	.04
496	Bruce Bochte	.05	.04	.02
497	*Dale Mohorcic* (FC)	.15	.11	.06
498	Bob Kearney	.05	.04	.02
499	*Bruce Ruffin* (FC)	.08	.06	.03
500	Don Mattingly	.40	.30	.15
501	Craig Lefferts	.05	.04	.02
502	Dick Schofield	.05	.04	.02
503	Larry Andersen	.05	.04	.02
504	Mickey Hatcher	.05	.04	.02
505	Bryn Smith	.05	.04	.02
506	Orioles Leaders (Rich Bordi, Rick Dempsey, Earl Weaver)	.07	.05	.03
507	Dave Stapleton	.05	.04	.02
508	*Scott Bankhead*	.10	.08	.04
509	Enos Cabell	.05	.04	.02
510	Tom Henke	.07	.05	.03
511	Steve Lyons	.05	.04	.02
512	*Dave Magadan* (FC) (Future Stars)	.20	.15	.08
513	Carmen Castillo	.05	.04	.02
514	Orlando Mercado	.05	.04	.02
515	Willie Hernandez	.07	.05	.03
516	Ted Simmons	.10	.08	.04
517	Mario Soto	.07	.05	.03
518	Gene Mauch	.07	.05	.03
519	Curt Young	.07	.05	.03
520	Jack Clark	.15	.11	.06
521	Rick Reuschel	.10	.08	.04
522	Checklist 397-528	.05	.04	.02
523	Earnie Riles	.05	.04	.02
524	Bob Shirley	.05	.04	.02
525	Phil Bradley	.10	.08	.04
526	Roger Mason	.05	.04	.02
527	Jim Wohlford	.05	.04	.02
528	Ken Dixon	.05	.04	.02
529	*Alvaro Espinoza* (FC)	.07	.05	.03
530	Tony Gwynn	.30	.25	.12
531	Astros Leaders (Yogi Berra, Hal Lanier, Denis Menke, Gene Tenace)	.07	.05	.03
532	Jeff Stone	.05	.04	.02
533	Argenis Salazar	.05	.04	.02
534	Scott Sanderson	.05	.04	.02
535	Tony Armas	.07	.05	.03
536	*Terry Mulholland* (FC)	.35	.25	.14
537	Rance Mulliniks	.05	.04	.02
538	Tom Niedenfuer	.07	.05	.03
539	Reid Nichols	.05	.04	.02
540	Terry Kennedy	.07	.05	.03
541	*Rafael Belliard* (FC)	.10	.08	.04
542	Ricky Horton	.07	.05	.03
543	Dave Johnson	.07	.05	.03
544	Zane Smith	.07	.05	.03
545	Buddy Bell	.07	.05	.03
546	Mike Morgan	.05	.04	.02
547	Rob Deer	.10	.08	.04
548	*Bill Mooneyham* (FC)	.10	.08	.04
549	Bob Melvin	.05	.04	.02
550	*Pete Incaviglia*	.25	.20	.10
551	Frank Wills	.05	.04	.02
552	Larry Sheets	.07	.05	.03
553	*Mike Maddux* (FC)	.15	.11	.06
554	Buddy Biancalana	.05	.04	.02
555	Dennis Rasmussen	.10	.08	.04
556	Angels Leaders (Bob Boone, Marcel Lachemann, Mike Witt)	.07	.05	.03
557	*John Cerutti*	.15	.11	.06
558	Greg Gagne	.05	.04	.02
559	Lance McCullers	.07	.05	.03
560	Glenn Davis	.06	.05	.02
561	*Rey Quinones*	.15	.11	.06
562	*Bryan Clutterbuck* (FC)	.10	.08	.04
563	John Stefero	.05	.04	.02
564	Larry McWilliams	.05	.04	.02
565	Dusty Baker	.07	.05	.03
566	Tim Hulett	.05	.04	.02
567	*Greg Mathews* (FC)	.08	.06	.03
568	Earl Weaver	.07	.05	.03
569	Wade Rowdon (FC)	.07	.05	.03
570	Sid Fernandez	.10	.08	.04
571	Ozzie Virgil	.05	.04	.02
572	Pete Ladd	.05	.04	.02
573	Hal McRae	.07	.05	.03
574	Manny Lee	.05	.04	.02
575	Pat Tabler	.07	.05	.03
576	Frank Pastore	.05	.04	.02
577	Dann Bilardello	.05	.04	.02
578	Billy Hatcher	.07	.05	.03
579	Rick Burleson	.07	.05	.03
580	Mike Krukow	.07	.05	.03
581	Cubs Leaders (Ron Cey, Steve Trout)	.07	.05	.03
582	Bruce Berenyi	.05	.04	.02
583	Junior Ortiz	.05	.04	.02
584	Ron Kittle	.07	.05	.03
585	*Scott Bailes*	.15	.11	.06
586	Ben Oglivie	.07	.05	.03
587	Eric Plunk (FC)	.10	.08	.04
588	Wallace Johnson	.05	.04	.02
589	Steve Crawford	.05	.04	.02
590	Vince Coleman	.10	.08	.04
591	Spike Owen	.05	.04	.02
592	Chris Welsh	.05	.04	.02
593	Chuck Tanner	.05	.04	.02
594	Rick Anderson	.05	.04	.02
595	Keith Hernandez (All-Star)	.12	.09	.05
596	Steve Sax (All-Star)	.07	.05	.03
597	Mike Schmidt (All-Star)	.20	.15	.08
598	Ozzie Smith (All-Star)	.07	.05	.03
599	Tony Gwynn (All-Star)	.20	.15	.08
600	Dave Parker (All-Star)	.10	.08	.04
601	Darryl Strawberry (All-Star)	.10	.08	.04
602	Gary Carter (All-Star)	.15	.11	.06
603a	Dwight Gooden (All-Star, no trademark on front)	.80	.60	.30
603b	Dwight Gooden (All-Star, trademark on front)	.10	.08	.04
604	Fernando Valenzuela (All-Star)	.12	.09	.05
605	Todd Worrell (All-Star)	.10	.08	.04
606a	Don Mattingly (All-Star, no trademark on front)	1.25	.90	.50
606b	Don Mattingly (All-Star, trademark on front)	.25	.20	.10
607	Tony Bernazard (All-Star)	.05	.04	.02
608	Wade Boggs (All-Star)	.20	.15	.08
609	Cal Ripken, Jr. (All-Star)	.40	.30	.15
610	Jim Rice (All-Star)	.15	.11	.06
611	Kirby Puckett (All-Star)	.30	.25	.12
612	George Bell (All-Star)	.12	.09	.05
613	Lance Parrish (All-Star)	.10	.08	.04
614	Roger Clemens (All-Star)	.20	.15	.08
615	Teddy Higuera (All-Star)	.10	.08	.04
616	Dave Righetti (All-Star)	.10	.08	.04
617	Al Nipper	.05	.04	.02
618	Tom Kelly	.05	.04	.02
619	Jerry Reed	.05	.04	.02
620	Jose Canseco	1.00	.75	.40
621	Danny Cox	.07	.05	.03
622	*Glenn Braggs* (FC)	.10	.08	.04
623	*Kurt Stillwell* (FC)	.12	.09	.05
624	Tim Burke	.05	.04	.02
625	Mookie Wilson	.07	.05	.03
626	Joel Skinner	.05	.04	.02
627	Ken Oberkfell	.05	.04	.02
628	Bob Walk	.05	.04	.02
629	Larry Parrish	.07	.05	.03
630	John Candelaria	.07	.05	.03
631	Tigers Leaders Sparky Anderson, Mike Heath, Willie Hernandez)	.07	.05	.03
632	Rob Woodward (FC)	.07	.05	.03
633	Jose Uribe	.07	.05	.03
634	*Rafael Palmeiro*	1.75	1.25	.70
635	Ken Schrom	.05	.04	.02
636	Darren Daulton	.40	.30	.15
637	*Bip Roberts*	.10	.08	.04
638	Rich Bordi	.05	.04	.02
639	Gerald Perry	.10	.08	.04
640	Mark Clear	.05	.04	.02
641	Domingo Ramos	.05	.04	.02
642	Al Pulido	.05	.04	.02
643	Ron Shepherd	.05	.04	.02
644	John Denny	.05	.04	.02
645	Dwight Evans	.12	.09	.05
646	Mike Mason	.05	.04	.02
647	Tom Lawless	.05	.04	.02
648	*Barry Larkin*	.90	.70	.35
649	Mickey Tettleton	.20	.15	.08
650	Hubie Brooks	.07	.05	.03
651	Benny Distefano	.05	.04	.02
652	Terry Forster	.07	.05	.03
653	*Kevin Mitchell*	.35	.25	.14
654	Checklist 529-660	.05	.04	.02
655	Jesse Barfield	.15	.11	.06
656	Rangers Leaders (Bobby Valentine, Rickey Wright)	.07	.05	.03
657	Tom Waddell	.05	.04	.02
658	*Robby Thompson*	.30	.25	.12
659	Aurelio Lopez	.05	.04	.02
660	Bob Horner	.10	.08	.04
661	Lou Whitaker	.15	.11	.06
662	Frank DiPino	.05	.04	.02
663	Cliff Johnson	.05	.04	.02
664	Mike Marshall	.10	.08	.04
665	Rod Scurry	.05	.04	.02
666	Von Hayes	.07	.05	.03
667	Ron Hassey	.05	.04	.02
668	Juan Bonilla	.05	.04	.02
669	Bud Black	.05	.04	.02
670	Jose Cruz	.07	.05	.03
671a	Ray Soff (no "D*" before copyright line)	.20	.15	.08
671b	Ray Soff ("D*" before copyright line)	.05	.04	.02
672	Chili Davis	.07	.05	.03
673	Don Sutton	.10	.07	.04
674	Bill Campbell	.05	.04	.02
675	Ed Romero	.05	.04	.02
676	Charlie Moore	.05	.04	.02
677	Bob Grich	.07	.05	.03
678	Carney Lansford	.07	.05	.03
679	Kent Hrbek	.10	.08	.04
680	Ryne Sandberg	1.00	.70	.40
681	George Bell	.10	.07	.04
682	Jerry Reuss	.07	.05	.03
683	Gary Roenicke	.05	.04	.02
684	Kent Tekulve	.07	.05	.03
685	Jerry Hairston	.05	.04	.02
686	Doyle Alexander	.07	.05	.03
687	Alan Trammell	.12	.09	.05
688	Juan Beniquez	.05	.04	.02
689	Darrell Porter	.07	.05	.03
690	Dane Iorg	.05	.04	.02
691	Dave Parker	.10	.08	.04
692	Frank White	.07	.05	.03
693	Terry Puhl	.05	.04	.02
694	Phil Niekro	.10	.08	.04
695	Chico Walker	.05	.04	.02
696	Gary Lucas	.05	.04	.02
697	Ed Lynch	.05	.04	.02
698	Ernie Whitt	.07	.05	.03
699	Ken Landreaux	.05	.04	.02
700	Dave Bergman	.05	.04	.02
701	Willie Randolph	.07	.05	.03
702	Greg Gross	.05	.04	.02
703	Dave Schmidt	.05	.04	.02
704	Jesse Orosco	.07	.05	.03
705	Bruce Hurst	.10	.08	.04
706	Rick Manning	.05	.04	.02
707	Bob McClure	.05	.04	.02
708	Scott McGregor	.07	.05	.03
709	Dave Kingman	.10	.08	.04
710	Gary Gaetti	.15	.11	.06
711	Ken Griffey	.07	.05	.03
712	Don Robinson	.07	.05	.03
713	Tom Brookens	.05	.04	.02
714	Dan Quisenberry	.07	.05	.03
715	Bob Dernier	.05	.04	.02
716	Rick Leach	.05	.04	.02
717	Ed Vande Berg	.05	.04	.02
718	Steve Carlton	.20	.15	.08
719	Tom Hume	.05	.04	.02
720	Richard Dotson	.07	.05	.03
721	Tom Herr	.07	.05	.03
722	Bob Knepper	.07	.05	.03
723	Brett Butler	.07	.05	.03
724	Greg Minton	.05	.04	.02
725	George Hendrick	.07	.05	.03
726	Frank Tanana	.07	.05	.03
727	Mike Moore	.05	.04	.02
728	Tippy Martinez	.05	.04	.02
729	Tom Paciorek	.05	.04	.02
730	Eric Show	.07	.05	.03
731	Dave Concepcion	.10	.08	.04
732	Manny Trillo	.07	.05	.03
733	Bill Caudill	.05	.04	.02
734	Bill Madlock	.10	.08	.04
735	Rickey Henderson	.25	.20	.10
736	Steve Bedrosian	.10	.08	.04
737	Floyd Bannister	.07	.05	.03
738	Jorge Orta	.05	.04	.02
739	Chet Lemon	.07	.05	.03
740	Rich Gedman	.07	.05	.03
741	Paul Molitor	.25	.20	.10
742	Andy McGaffigan	.05	.04	.02
743	Dwayne Murphy	.07	.05	.03
744	Roy Smalley	.05	.04	.02
745	Glenn Hubbard	.05	.04	.02
746	Bob Ojeda	.07	.05	.03
747	Johnny Ray	.07	.05	.03
748	Mike Flanagan	.07	.05	.03
749	Ozzie Smith	.25	.20	.10
750	Steve Trout	.07	.05	.03
751	Garth Iorg	.05	.04	.02

752	Dan Petry	.07	.05	.03
753	Rick Honeycutt	.05	.04	.02
754	Dave LaPoint	.07	.05	.03
755	Luis Aguayo	.05	.04	.02
756	Carlton Fisk	.20	.15	.08
757	Nolan Ryan	1.25	.90	.50
758	Tony Bernazard	.05	.04	.02
759	Joel Youngblood	.05	.04	.02
760	Mike Witt	.07	.05	.03
761	Greg Pryor	.05	.04	.02
762	Gary Ward	.07	.05	.03
763	Tim Flannery	.05	.04	.02
764	Bill Buckner	.07	.05	.03
765	Kirk Gibson	.10	.08	.04
766	Don Aase	.05	.04	.02
767	Ron Cey	.07	.05	.03
768	Dennis Lamp	.05	.04	.02
769	Steve Sax	.15	.11	.06
770	Dave Winfield	.35	.25	.14
771	Shane Rawley	.07	.05	.03
772	Harold Baines	.12	.09	.05
773	Robin Yount	.40	.30	.15
774	Wayne Krenchicki	.05	.04	.02
775	Joaquin Andujar	.07	.05	.03
776	Tom Brunansky	.10	.08	.04
777	Chris Chambliss	.07	.05	.03
778	Jack Morris	.10	.07	.04
779	Craig Reynolds	.05	.04	.02
780	Andre Thornton	.07	.05	.03
781	Atlee Hammaker	.05	.04	.02
782	Brian Downing	.07	.05	.03
783	Willie Wilson	.10	.08	.04
784	Cal Ripken, Jr.	.90	.70	.35
785	Terry Francona	.05	.04	.02
786	Jimy Williams	.05	.04	.02
787	Alejandro Pena	.07	.05	.03
788	Tim Stoddard	.05	.04	.02
789	Dan Schatzeder	.05	.04	.02
790	Julio Cruz	.05	.04	.02
791	Lance Parrish	.15	.11	.06
792	Checklist 661-792	.05	.04	.02

1987 Topps All-Star Glossy Set of 22

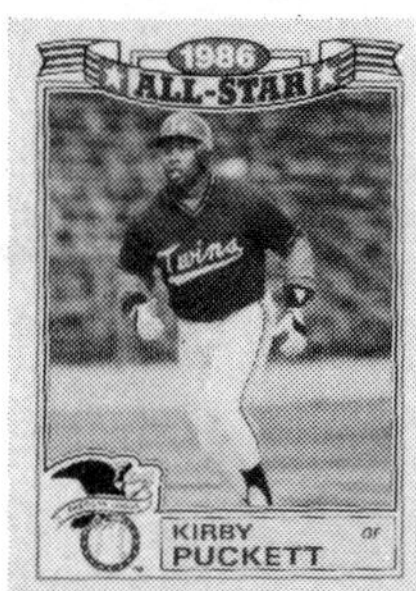

For the fourth consecutive year, Topps produced an All-Star Game commemorative set of 22 cards. The glossy cards, which measure 2-1/2" by 3-1/2", were included in rack packs. Using the same basic card design as in previous efforts with a few minor changes, the 1987 edition features American and National League logos on the card fronts. Card #'s 1-12 feature representatives from the American League, while #'s 13-22 are National Leaguers.

		MT	NR MT	EX
	Complete Set:	5.00	3.75	2.00
	Common Player:	.15	.11	.06
1	Whitey Herzog	.15	.11	.06
2	Keith Hernandez	.20	.15	.08
3	Ryne Sandberg	.50	.40	.20
4	Mike Schmidt	.70	.50	.30
5	Ozzie Smith	.30	.25	.12
6	Tony Gwynn	.30	.25	.12
7	Dale Murphy	.30	.25	.12
8	Darryl Strawberry	.30	.25	.12
9	Gary Carter	.30	.25	.12
10	Dwight Gooden	.30	.25	.12
11	Fernando Valenzuela	.30	.25	.12
12	Dick Howser	.15	.11	.06
13	Wally Joyner	.30	.25	.12
14	Lou Whitaker	.25	.20	.10
15	Wade Boggs	.50	.40	.20
16	Cal Ripken, Jr.	.50	.40	.20
17	Dave Winfield	.40	.30	.15
18	Rickey Henderson	.50	.40	.20
19	Kirby Puckett	.40	.30	.15
20	Lance Parrish	.20	.15	.08
21	Roger Clemens	.30	.25	.12
22	Teddy Higuera	.20	.15	.08

1987 Topps All-Star Glossy Set of 60

Using the same design as the previous year, the 1987 Topps All-Star Glossy set includes 48 All-Star performers plus 12 potential superstars branded as "Hot Prospects". The card fronts are uncluttered,

save the player's name found in very small print at the bottom. The set was available via a mail-in offer. Six subsets make up the 60-card set, with each subset being available for $1.00 plus six special offer cards that were found in wax packs.

		MT	NR MT	EX
	Complete Set:	12.00	9.00	4.75
	Common Player:	.15	.11	.06
1	Don Mattingly	2.00	1.50	.80
2	Tony Gwynn	.60	.45	.25
3	Gary Gaetti	.25	.20	.10
4	Glenn Davis	.20	.15	.08
5	Roger Clemens	.45	.35	.20
6	Dale Murphy	.60	.45	.25
7	Lou Whitaker	.30	.25	.12
8	Roger McDowell	.15	.11	.06
9	Cory Snyder	.15	.11	.06
10	Todd Worrell	.20	.15	.08
11	Gary Carter	.30	.25	.12
12	Eddie Murray	.60	.45	.25
13	Bob Knepper	.15	.11	.06
14	Harold Baines	.20	.15	.08
15	Jeff Reardon	.20	.15	.08
16	Joe Carter	.40	.30	.15
17	Dave Parker	.40	.30	.15
18	Wade Boggs	1.25	.90	.50
19	Danny Tartabull	.35	.25	.14
20	Jim Deshaies	.20	.15	.08
21	Rickey Henderson	.70	.50	.30
22	Rob Deer	.15	.11	.06
23	Ozzie Smith	.40	.30	.15
24	Dave Righetti	.15	.11	.06
25	Kent Hrbek	.30	.25	.12
26	Keith Hernandez	.20	.15	.08
27	Don Baylor	.25	.20	.10
28	Mike Schmidt	.90	.70	.35
29	Pete Incaviglia	.25	.20	.10
30	Barry Bonds	.80	.60	.30
31	George Brett	.90	.70	.35
32	Darryl Strawberry	.35	.25	.14
33	Mike Witt	.15	.11	.06
34	Kevin Bass	.15	.11	.06
35	Jesse Barfield	.15	.11	.06
36	Bob Ojeda	.15	.11	.06
37	Cal Ripken, Jr.	1.50	1.25	.60
38	Vince Coleman	.25	.20	.10
39	Wally Joyner	.60	.45	.25
40	Robby Thompson	.35	.25	.14
41	Pete Rose	.80	.60	.30
42	Jim Rice	.25	.20	.10
43	Tony Bernazard	.15	.11	.06
44	Eric Davis	.35	.25	.14
45	George Bell	.30	.25	.12
46	Hubie Brooks	.15	.11	.06
47	Jack Morris	.25	.20	.10
48	Tim Raines	.30	.25	.12
49	Mark Eichhorn	.20	.15	.08
50	Kevin Mitchell	.25	.20	.10
51	Dwight Gooden	.40	.30	.15
52	Doug DeCinces	.15	.11	.06
53	Fernando Valenzuela	.25	.20	.10
54	Reggie Jackson	.70	.50	.30
55	Johnny Ray	.15	.11	.06
56	Mike Pagliarulo	.20	.15	.08
57	Kirby Puckett	.60	.45	.25
58	Lance Parrish	.20	.15	.08
59	Jose Canseco	2.00	1.50	.80
60	Greg Mathews	.15	.11	.06

Values for recent cards and sets are listed in Mint (MT), Near Mint (NM), reflecting the fact that many cards from recent years have been preserved in top condition. Recent cards and sets in less than Excellent condition have little collector interest.

1987 Topps Traded

The Topps Traded set consists of 132 cards as have all Traded sets issued by Topps since 1981. The cards measure the standard 2-1/2" by 3-1/2" and are identical in design to the regular edition set. The purpose of the set is to update player trades and feature rookies not included in the regular issue. As they had done the previous three years, Topps produced a glossy-coated "Tiffany" edition of the

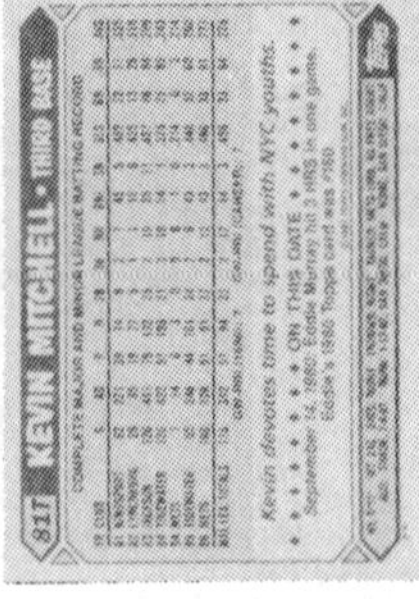

Traded set. The Tiffany edition cards are valued at two to three times greater than the regular Traded cards.

		MT	NR MT	EX
	Complete Set (132):	8.00	6.00	3.25
	Common Player:	.06	.05	.02
1T	Bill Almon	.06	.05	.02
2T	Scott Bankhead	.08	.06	.03
3T	Eric Bell (FC)	.08	.06	.03
4T	Juan Beniquez	.06	.05	.02
5T	Juan Berenguer	.06	.05	.02
6T	Greg Booker	.06	.05	.02
7T	Thad Bosley	.06	.05	.02
8T	Larry Bowa	.10	.08	.04
9T	Greg Brock	.06	.05	.02
10T	Bob Brower (FC)	.06	.05	.02
11T	Jerry Browne (FC)	.10	.08	.04
12T	Ralph Bryant (FC)	.06	.05	.02
13T	DeWayne Buice (FC)	.06	.05	.02
14T	Ellis Burks (FC)	.80	.60	.30
15T	Ivan Calderon	.12	.09	.05
16T	Jeff Calhoun	.06	.05	.02
17T	Casey Candaele (FC)	.10	.08	.04
18T	John Cangelosi	.06	.05	.02
19T	Steve Carlton	.30	.25	.12
20T	Juan Castillo (FC)	.06	.05	.02
21T	Rick Cerone	.06	.05	.02
22T	Ron Cey	.10	.08	.04
23T	John Christensen	.06	.05	.02
24T	Dave Cone (FC)	.75	.60	.30
25T	Chuck Crim (FC)	.15	.11	.06
26T	Storm Davis	.06	.05	.02
27T	Andre Dawson	.40	.30	.15
28T	Rick Dempsey	.08	.06	.03
29T	Doug Drabek	.30	.25	.12
30T	Mike Dunne	.10	.08	.04
31T	Dennis Eckersley	.30	.25	.12
32T	Lee Elia	.06	.05	.02
33T	Brian Fisher	.10	.08	.04
34T	Terry Francona	.06	.05	.02
35T	Willie Fraser (FC)	.10	.08	.04
36T	Billy Gardner	.06	.05	.02
37T	Ken Gerhart (FC)	.10	.08	.04
38T	Danny Gladden	.06	.05	.02
39T	Jim Gott	.06	.05	.02
40T	Cecilio Guante	.06	.05	.02
41T	Albert Hall	.06	.05	.02
42T	Terry Harper	.06	.05	.02
43T	Mickey Hatcher	.06	.05	.02
44T	Brad Havens	.06	.05	.02
45T	Neal Heaton	.06	.05	.02
46T	Mike Henneman (FC)	.30	.25	.12
47T	Donnie Hill	.06	.05	.02
48T	Guy Hoffman	.06	.05	.02
49T	Brian Holton (FC)	.15	.11	.06
50T	Charles Hudson	.06	.05	.02
51T	Danny Jackson (FC)	.08	.06	.03
52T	Reggie Jackson	.50	.40	.20
53T	Chris James (FC)	.10	.08	.04
54T	Dion James	.10	.08	.04
55T	Stan Jefferson (FC)	.08	.06	.03
56T	Joe Johnson (FC)	.08	.06	.03
57T	Terry Kennedy	.08	.06	.03
58T	Mike Kingery	.08	.06	.03
59T	Ray Knight	.10	.08	.04
60T	Gene Larkin (FC)	.15	.11	.06
61T	Mike LaValliere	.10	.08	.04
62T	Jack Lazorko	.06	.05	.02
63T	Terry Leach	.06	.05	.02
64T	Tim Leary	.06	.05	.02
65T	Jim Lindeman (FC)	.08	.06	.03
66T	Steve Lombardozzi (FC)	.06	.05	.02
67T	Bill Long (FC)	.06	.05	.02
68T	Barry Lyons (FC)	.08	.06	.03
69T	Shane Mack	.40	.30	.15
70T	Greg Maddux (FC)	4.00	3.00	1.50
71T	Bill Madlock	.15	.11	.06
72T	Joe Magrane (FC)	.12	.09	.05
73T	Dave Martinez (FC)	.08	.06	.03
74T	Fred McGriff (FC)	3.00	2.25	1.25
75T	Mark McLemore (FC)	.10	.08	.04
76T	Kevin McReynolds (FC)	.10	.08	.04
77T	Dave Meads (FC)	.08	.06	.03
78T	Eddie Milner	.06	.05	.02
79T	Greg Minton	.06	.05	.02
80T	John Mitchell (FC)	.08	.06	.03
81T	Kevin Mitchell	.15	.11	.06
82T	Charlie Moore	.06	.05	.02
83T	Jeff Musselman (FC)	.12	.09	.05
84T	Gene Nelson	.06	.05	.02
85T	Graig Nettles	.12	.09	.05
86T	Al Newman	.06	.05	.02

87T	Reid Nichols	.06	.05	.02
88T	Tom Niedenfuer	.08	.06	.03
89T	Joe Niekro	.10	.08	.04
90T	Tom Nieto	.06	.05	.02
91T	Matt Nokes (FC)	.20	.15	.08
92T	Dickie Noles	.06	.05	.02
93T	Pat Pacillo	.08	.06	.03
94T	Lance Parrish	.10	.08	.04
95T	Tony Pena	.10	.08	.04
96T	Luis Polonia (FC)	.40	.30	.15
97T	Randy Ready	.06	.05	.02
98T	Jeff Reardon	.12	.09	.05
99T	Gary Redus	.08	.06	.03
100T	Jeff Reed	.06	.05	.02
101T	Rick Rhoden	.10	.08	.04
102T	Cal Ripken, Sr.	.06	.05	.02
103T	Wally Ritchie (FC)	.10	.08	.04
104T	Jeff Robinson (FC)	.10	.08	.04
105T	Gary Roenicke	.06	.05	.02
106T	Jerry Royster	.06	.05	.02
107T	Mark Salas	.06	.05	.02
108T	Luis Salazar	.06	.05	.02
109T	Benny Santiago (FC)	.35	.25	.14
110T	Dave Schmidt	.08	.06	.03
111T	Kevin Seitzer (FC)	.12	.09	.05
112T	John Shelby	.06	.05	.02
113T	Steve Shields (FC)	.08	.06	.03
114T	John Smiley (FC)	.25	.20	.10
115T	Chris Speier	.06	.05	.02
116T	Mike Stanley (FC)	.06	.05	.02
117T	Terry Steinbach (FC)	.20	.15	.08
118T	Les Straker (FC)	.08	.06	.03
119T	Jim Sundberg	.08	.06	.03
120T	Danny Tartabull	.25	.20	.10
121T	Tom Trebelhorn	.08	.06	.03
122T	Dave Valle (FC)	.12	.09	.05
123T	Ed Vande Berg	.06	.05	.02
124T	Andy Van Slyke	.20	.15	.08
125T	Gary Ward	.06	.05	.02
126T	Alan Wiggins	.06	.05	.02
127T	Bill Wilkinson (FC)	.15	.11	.06
128T	Frank Williams	.08	.06	.03
129T	Matt Williams (FC)	3.00	2.25	1.25
130T	Jim Winn	.06	.05	.02
131T	Matt Young	.06	.05	.02
132T	Checklist 1T-132T	.06	.05	.02

1987 Topps Box Panels

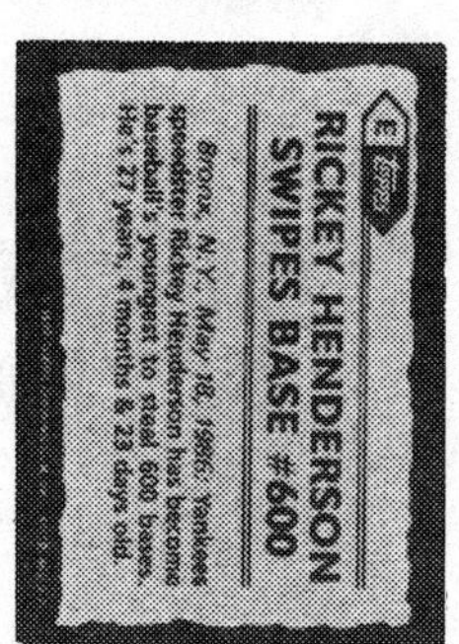

Offering baseball cards on retail boxes for a second straight year, Topps reduced the size of the cards to 2-1/8" by 3". Four different wax pack boxes were available, each featuring two cards that were placed on the sides of the boxes. The card fronts are identical in design to the regular issue cards. The backs are printed in blue and yellow and carry a commentary imitating a newspaper format. The cards are numbered A through H.

		MT	NR MT	EX
Complete Panel Set:		5.00	3.75	2.00
Complete Singles Set:		2.00	1.50	.80
Common Panel:		.75	.60	.30
Common Single Player:		.15	.11	.06
	Panel	1.25	.90	.50
A	Don Baylor	.15	.11	.06
B	Steve Carlton	.30	.25	.12
	Panel	.75	.60	.30
C	Ron Cey	.15	.11	.06
D	Cecil Cooper	.15	.11	.06
	Panel	1.75	1.25	.70
E	Rickey Henderson	.40	.30	.15
F	Jim Rice	.25	.20	.10
	Panel	1.25	.90	.50
G	Don Sutton	.15	.11	.06
H	Dave Winfield	.35	.25	.15

Definitions for grading conditions are located in the Introduction of this price guide.

1987 Topps Baseball Highlights

The "Baseball Highlights" boxed set of 33 cards was prepared by Topps for distribution at stores in the Woolworth's chain. Each card measures 2-1/2"

by 3-1/2" in size and features a memorable baseball event that occurred during the 1986 season. The glossy set sold for $1.99 in Woolworth's stores.

		MT	NR MT	EX
Complete Set:		5.00	3.75	2.00
Common Player:		.09	.07	.04
1	Steve Carlton	.30	.25	.12
2	Cecil Cooper	.12	.09	.05
3	Rickey Henderson	.50	.40	.20
4	Reggie Jackson	.30	.25	.12
5	Jim Rice	.15	.11	.06
6	Don Sutton	.20	.15	.08
7	Roger Clemens	.50	.40	.20
8	Mike Schmidt	.35	.25	.14
9	Jesse Barfield	.15	.11	.06
10	Wade Boggs	.70	.50	.30
11	Tim Raines	.30	.25	.12
12	Jose Canseco	1.00	.70	.40
13	Todd Worrell	.15	.11	.06
14	Dave Righetti	.15	.11	.06
15	Don Mattingly	1.25	.90	.50
16	Tony Gwynn	.35	.25	.14
17	Marty Barrett	.09	.07	.04
18	Mike Scott	.12	.09	.05
19	World Series Game #1 (Bruce Hurst)	.12	.09	.05
20	World Series Game #1 (Calvin Schiraldi)	.09	.07	.04
21	World Series Game #2 (Dwight Evans)	.12	.09	.05
22	World Series Game #2 (Dave Henderson)	.09	.07	.04
23	World Series Game #3 (Len Dykstra)	.20	.15	.08
24	World Series Game #3 (Bob Ojeda)	.09	.07	.04
25	World Series Game #4 (Gary Carter)	.20	.15	.08
26	World Series Game #4 (Ron Darling)	.15	.11	.06
27	Jim Rice	.15	.11	.06
28	Bruce Hurst	.09	.07	.04
29	World Series Game #6 (Darryl Strawberry)	.25	.20	.10
30	World Series Game #6 (Ray Knight)	.09	.07	.04
31	World Series Game #6 (Keith Hernandez)	.25	.20	.10
32	World Series Games #7 (Mets Celebrate)	.12	.09	.05
33	Ray Knight	.09	.07	.04

1987 Topps Coins

For the first time since 1971, Topps issued a set of baseball "coins." Similar in design to the 1964 edition of Topps coins, the metal discs measure 1-1/2" in diameter. The aluminum coins were sold on a limited basis in retail outlets. Three coins and three sticks of gum were found in a pack. The coin fronts feature a full-color photo along with the player's name, team and position in a white band at the bottom of the coin. Gold-colored rims are found for American League players; National League players have silver-colored rims. Backs are silver in color and carry the coin number, player's name and personal and statistical information.

		MT	NR MT	EX
Complete Set:		10.00	7.50	4.00
Common Player:		.15	.11	.06
1	Harold Baines	.15	.11	.06
2	Jesse Barfield	.15	.11	.06
3	George Bell	.15	.11	.06
4	Wade Boggs	.70	.50	.30
5	George Brett	.75	.60	.30
6	Jose Canseco	.60	.45	.25
7	Joe Carter	.25	.20	.10
8	Roger Clemens	.40	.30	.15
9	Alvin Davis	.15	.11	.06
10	Rob Deer	.15	.11	.06
11	Kirk Gibson	.20	.15	.08
12	Rickey Henderson	.60	.45	.25
13	Kent Hrbek	.20	.15	.08
14	Pete Incaviglia	.15	.11	.06
15	Reggie Jackson	.50	.40	.20
16	Wally Joyner	.25	.20	.10
17	Don Mattingly	.75	.60	.30
18	Jack Morris	.15	.11	.06
19	Eddie Murray	.25	.20	.10
20	Kirby Puckett	.45	.35	.20
21	Jim Rice	.25	.20	.10
22	Dave Righetti	.15	.11	.06
23	Cal Ripken, Jr.	1.50	1.25	.60
24	Cory Snyder	.15	.11	.06
25	Danny Tartabull	.20	.15	.08
26	Dave Winfield	.45	.35	.20
27	Hubie Brooks	.15	.11	.06
28	Gary Carter	.25	.20	.10
29	Vince Coleman	.20	.15	.08
30	Eric Davis	.50	.40	.20
31	Glenn Davis	.15	.11	.06
32	Steve Garvey	.25	.20	.10
33	Dwight Gooden	.40	.30	.15
34	Tony Gwynn	.30	.25	.12
35	Von Hayes	.15	.11	.06
36	Keith Hernandez	.15	.11	.06
37	Dale Murphy	.30	.25	.12
38	Dave Parker	.30	.25	.12
39	Tony Pena	.15	.11	.06
40	Nolan Ryan	2.00	1.50	.80
41	Ryne Sandberg	1.50	1.25	.60
42	Steve Sax	.15	.11	.06
43	Mike Schmidt	.60	.45	.25
44	Mike Scott	.15	.11	.06
45	Ozzie Smith	.25	.20	.10
46	Darryl Strawberry	.20	.15	.08
47	Fernando Valenzuela	.15	.11	.06
48	Todd Worrell	.15	.11	.06

1987 Topps Gallery of Champions

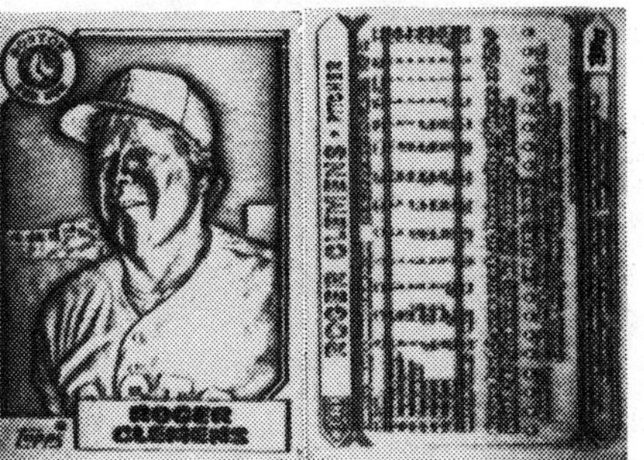

Designed as a tribute to the 1986 season's winners of baseball's most prestigious awards, the Gallery of Champions are metal "cards" that are one-quarter size replicas of the regular issue Topps cards. The bronze and silver sets were issued in leather-like velvet-lined display cases; the aluminum sets came cello-wrapped. Hobby dealers who purchased one bronze set or a 16-set case of aluminum "cards" received one free Jose Canseco pewter metal mini-card (value $60). The purchase of a silver set included five Canseco pewters. A 1953 Willie Mays bronze was given to dealers who brought cases of 1987 Topps Traded sets (value $10).

		MT	NR MT	EX
Complete Aluminum Set:		30.00	22.00	12.00
Complete Bronze Set:		175.00	131.00	70.00
Complete Silver Set:		700.00	525.00	280.00
(1a)	Jesse Barfield (aluminum)	.70	.50	.30
(1b)	Jesse Barfield (bronze)	7.50	5.75	3.00
(1c)	Jesse Barfield (silver)	20.00	15.00	8.00
(2a)	Wade Boggs (aluminum)	3.00	2.25	1.25
(2b)	Wade Boggs (bronze)	25.00	18.50	10.00
(2c)	Wade Boggs (silver)	125.00	94.00	50.00
(3a)	Jose Canseco (aluminum)	3.00	2.25	1.25
(3b)	Jose Canseco (bronze)	25.00	18.50	10.00
(3c)	Jose Canseco (silver)	125.00	94.00	50.00
(4a)	Joe Carter (aluminum)	1.50	1.25	.60
(4b)	Joe Carter (bronze)	12.00	9.00	4.75
(4c)	Joe Carter (silver)	50.00	37.00	20.00

(5a)	Roger Clemens (aluminum)	2.00	1.50	.80
(5b)	Roger Clemens (bronze)	20.00	15.00	8.00
(5c)	Roger Clemens (silver)	90.00	67.00	36.00
(6a)	Tony Gwynn (aluminum)	1.25	.90	.50
(6b)	Tony Gwynn (bronze)	12.00	9.00	4.75
(6c)	Tony Gwynn (silver)	50.00	37.00	20.00
(7a)	Don Mattingly (aluminum)	6.00	4.50	2.50
(7b)	Don Mattingly (bronze)	35.00	26.00	14.00
(7c)	Don Mattingly (silver)	150.00	112.00	60.00
(8a)	Tim Raines (aluminum)	1.00	.70	.40
(8b)	Tim Raines (bronze)	10.00	7.50	4.00
(8c)	Tim Raines (silver)	30.00	22.00	12.00
(9a)	Dave Righetti (aluminum)	1.00	.70	.40
(9b)	Dave Righetti (bronze)	10.00	7.50	4.00
(9c)	Dave Righetti (silver)	30.00	22.00	12.00
(10a)	Mike Schmidt (aluminum)	3.00	2.25	1.25
(10b)	Mike Schmidt (bronze)	25.00	18.50	10.00
(10c)	Mike Schmidt (silver)	125.00	94.00	50.00
(11a)	Mike Scott (aluminum)	.70	.50	.30
(11b)	Mike Scott (bronze)	7.50	5.75	3.00
(11c)	Mike Scott (silver)	20.00	15.00	8.00
(12a)	Todd Worrell (aluminum)	.70	.50	.30
(12b)	Todd Worrell (bronze)	7.50	5.75	3.00
(12c)	Todd Worrell (silver)	20.00	15.00	8.00

1987 Topps Glossy Rookies

The 1987 Topps Glossy Rookies set of 22 cards was introduced with Topps' new 100-card "Jumbo Packs". Intended for sale in supermarkets, the jumbo packs contained one glossy card. Measuring the standard 2-1/2" by 3-1/2" size, the special insert cards feature the top rookies from the previous season.

		MT	NR MT	EX
Complete Set:		12.00	9.00	4.75
Common Player:		.20	.15	.08
1	Andy Allanson	.20	.15	.08
2	John Cangelosi	.20	.15	.08
3	Jose Canseco	3.00	2.25	1.25
4	Will Clark	3.00	2.25	1.25
5	Mark Eichhorn	.40	.30	.15
6	Pete Incaviglia	.70	.50	.30
7	Wally Joyner	.90	.70	.35
8	Eric King	.30	.25	.12
9	Dave Magadan	.60	.45	.25
10	John Morris	.20	.15	.08
11	Juan Nieves	.40	.30	.15
12	Rafael Palmeiro	1.00	.70	.40
13	Billy Jo Robidoux	.20	.15	.08
14	Bruce Ruffin	.40	.30	.15
15	Ruben Sierra	.90	.70	.35
16	Cory Snyder	.40	.30	.15
17	Kurt Stillwell	.40	.30	.15
18	Dale Sveum	.40	.30	.15
19	Danny Tartabull	.80	.60	.30
20	Andres Thomas	.20	.15	.08
21	Robby Thompson	.40	.30	.15
22	Todd Worrell	.30	.25	.12

1987 Topps Mini League Leaders

Returning for 1987, the Topps "Major League Leaders" set was increased in size from 66 to 76 cards. The 2-1/8" by 3" cards feature wood grain borders that encompass a white-bordered full-color photo. The card backs are printed in yellow, orange and brown and list the player's official ranking based on his 1986 American or National League statistics. The players featured are those who finished the top five in their leagues' various batting and pitching statistics. The cards were sold in plastic-wrapped packs, seven cards plus a game card per pack.

		MT	NR MT	EX
Complete Set:		8.00	6.00	3.25
Common Player:		.09	.07	.04
1	Bob Horner	.20	.15	.08
2	Dale Murphy	.50	.40	.20
3	Lee Smith	.20	.15	.08
4	Eric Davis	.15	.11	.06
5	John Franco	.15	.11	.06
6	Dave Parker	.20	.15	.08
7	Kevin Bass	.09	.07	.04
8	Glenn Davis	.09	.07	.04
9	Bill Doran	.09	.07	.04
10	Bob Knepper	.09	.07	.04
11	Mike Scott	.12	.09	.05
12	Dave Smith	.09	.07	.04
13	Mariano Duncan	.20	.15	.08
14	Orel Hershiser	.30	.25	.12
15	Steve Sax	.12	.09	.05
16	Fernando Valenzuela	.12	.09	.05
17	Tim Raines	.15	.11	.06
18	Jeff Reardon	.15	.11	.06
19	Floyd Youmans	.09	.07	.04
20	Gary Carter	.15	.11	.06
21	Ron Darling	.15	.11	.06
22	Sid Fernandez	.12	.09	.05
23	Dwight Gooden	.25	.20	.10
24	Keith Hernandez	.15	.11	.06
25	Bob Ojeda	.09	.07	.04
26	Darryl Strawberry	.25	.20	.10
27	Steve Bedrosian	.15	.11	.06
28	Von Hayes	.15	.11	.06
29	Juan Samuel	.12	.09	.05
30	Mike Schmidt	.50	.40	.20
31	Rick Rhoden	.09	.07	.04
32	Vince Coleman	.20	.15	.08
33	Danny Cox	.09	.07	.04
34	Todd Worrell	.15	.11	.06
35	Tony Gwynn	.40	.30	.15
36	Mike Krukow	.09	.07	.04
37	Candy Maldonado	.09	.07	.04
38	Don Aase	.09	.07	.04
39	Eddie Murray	.40	.30	.15
40	Cal Ripken, Jr.	.60	.45	.25
41	Wade Boggs	.80	.60	.30
42	Roger Clemens	.45	.35	.20
43	Bruce Hurst	.12	.09	.05
44	Jim Rice	.15	.11	.06
45	Wally Joyner	.30	.25	.12
46	Donnie Moore	.09	.07	.04
47	Gary Pettis	.09	.07	.04
48	Mike Witt	.09	.07	.04
49	John Cangelosi	.09	.07	.04
50	Tom Candiotti	.09	.07	.04
51	Joe Carter	.30	.25	.12
52	Pat Tabler	.09	.07	.04
53	Kirk Gibson	.25	.20	.10
54	Willie Hernandez	.09	.07	.04
55	Jack Morris	.15	.11	.06
56	Alan Trammell	.30	.25	.12
57	George Brett	.75	.60	.30
58	Willie Wilson	.15	.11	.06
59	Rob Deer	.09	.07	.04
60	Teddy Higuera	.12	.09	.05
61	Bert Blyleven	.15	.11	.06
62	Gary Gaetti	.20	.15	.08
63	Kirby Puckett	.45	.35	.20
64	Rickey Henderson	.60	.45	.25
65	Don Mattingly	.90	.70	.35
66	Dennis Rasmussen	.15	.11	.06
67	Dave Righetti	.20	.15	.08
68	Jose Canseco	1.00	.70	.40
69	Dave Kingman	.15	.11	.06
70	Phil Bradley	.15	.11	.06
71	Mark Langston	.15	.11	.06
72	Pete O'Brien	.09	.07	.04
73	Jesse Barfield	.15	.11	.06
74	George Bell	.15	.11	.06
75	Tony Fernandez	.15	.11	.06
76	Tom Henke	.09	.07	.04
77	Checklist	.09	.07	.04

1987 Topps Stickers

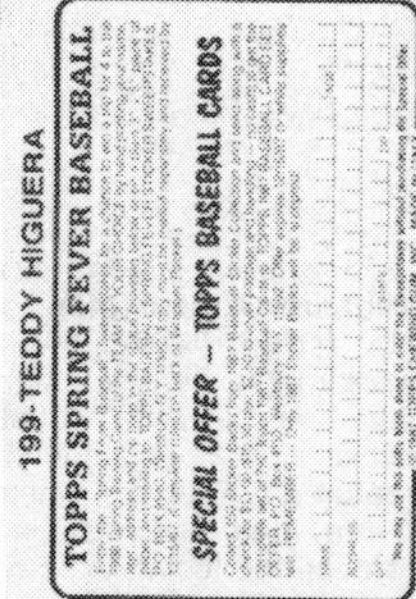

For the seventh consecutive year, Topps issued stickers to be housed in a specially designed yearbook. The stickers, which measure 2-1/8" by 3", offer a full-color front with a peel-off back printed in blue ink on white stock. The sticker fronts feature either one full-size player picture or two half-size individual stickers. The sticker yearbook measures 9" by 10-3/4" and contains 36 glossy, magazine-style pages, all printed in full color. Mike Schmidt, 1986 National League MVP, is featured on the cover. The yearbook sold in retail outlets for 35¢, while stickers were sold five in a pack for 25¢. The number in parentheses in the following checklist is the sticker number the player shares the sticker with.

		MT	NR MT	EX
Complete Set:		18.00	13.50	7.25
Common Player:		.03	.02	.01
Sticker Album:		.70	.50	.30
1	1986 Highlights (Jim Deshaies) (172)	.04	.03	.02
2	1986 Highlights (Roger Clemens) (175)	.15	.11	.06
3	1986 Highlights (Roger Clemens) (176)	.15	.11	.06
4	1986 Highlights (Dwight Evans) (177)	.06	.05	.02
5	1986 Highlights (Dwight Gooden) (178)	.08	.06	.03
6	1986 Highlights (Dwight Gooden) (180)	.08	.06	.03
7	1986 Highlights (Dave Lopes) (181)	.03	.02	.01
8	1986 Highlights (Dave Righetti) (182)	.06	.05	.02
9	1986 Highlights (Dave Righetti) (183)	.06	.05	.02
10	1986 Highlights (Ruben Sierra) (185)	.15	.11	.06
11	1986 Highlights (Todd Worrell) (186)	.06	.05	.02
12	1986 Highlights (Todd Worrell) (187)	.06	.05	.02
13	N.L. Championship Series (Lenny Dykstra)	.06	.05	.02
14	N.L. Championship Series (Gary Carter)	.08	.06	.03
15	N.L. Championship Series (Mike Scott)	.06	.05	.02
16	A.L. Championship Series (Gary Pettis)	.03	.02	.01
17	A.L. Championship Series (Jim Rice)	.05	.04	.02
18	A.L. Championship Series (Bruce Hurst)	.04	.03	.02
19	1986 World Series (Bruce Hurst)	.04	.03	.02
20	1986 World Series (Wade Boggs)	.15	.11	.06
21	1986 World Series (Lenny Dykstra)	.06	.05	.02
22	1986 World Series (Gary Carter)	.08	.06	.03
23	1986 World Series (Dave Henderson)	.04	.03	.02
24	1986 World Series (Howard Johnson)	.04	.03	.02
25	1986 World Series (Mets Celebrate)	.08	.06	.03
26	Glenn Davis	.08	.06	.03
27	Nolan Ryan (188)	.25	.20	.10
28	Charlie Kerfeld (189)	.03	.02	.01
29	Jose Cruz (190)	.04	.03	.02
30	Phil Garner (191)	.06	.05	.02
31	Bill Doran (192)	.06	.05	.02
32	Bob Knepper (195)	.03	.02	.01
33	Denny Walling (196)	.06	.05	.02
34	Kevin Bass (197)	.04	.03	.02
35	Mike Scott	.06	.05	.02
36	Dale Murphy	.25	.20	.10
37	Paul Assenmacher (198)	.06	.05	.02
38	Ken Oberkfell (200)	.06	.05	.02
39	Andres Thomas (201)	.08	.06	.03
40	Gene Garber (202)	.03	.02	.01
41	Bob Horner	.08	.06	.03
42	Rafael Ramirez (203)	.03	.02	.01
43	Rick Mahler (204)	.03	.02	.01
44	Omar Moreno (205)	.03	.02	.01
45	Dave Palmer (206)	.03	.02	.01
46	Ozzie Smith	.15	.11	.06
47	Bob Forsch (207)	.03	.02	.01
48	Willie McGee (209)	.06	.05	.02
49	Tom Herr (210)	.06	.05	.02
50	Vince Coleman (211)	.08	.06	.03
51	Andy Van Slyke (212)	.06	.05	.02
52	Jack Clark (215)	.08	.06	.03
53	John Tudor (216)	.04	.03	.02
54	Terry Pendleton (217)	.03	.02	.01
55	Todd Worrell	.10	.08	.04
56	Lee Smith	.06	.05	.02
57	Leon Durham (218)	.03	.02	.01
58	Jerry Mumphrey (219)	.06	.05	.02
59	Shawon Dunston (220)	.06	.05	.02
60	Scott Sanderson (221)	.06	.05	.02
61	Ryne Sandberg	.25	.20	.10
62	Gary Matthews (222)	.04	.03	.02
63	Dennis Eckersley (225)	.06	.05	.02
64	Jody Davis (226)	.06	.05	.02
65	Keith Moreland (227)	.04	.03	.02
66	Mike Marshall (228)	.06	.05	.02
67	Bill Madlock (229)	.06	.05	.02
68	Greg Brock (230)	.04	.03	.02
69	Pedro Guerrero (231)	.08	.06	.03
70	Steve Sax	.12	.09	.05
71	Rick Honeycutt (232)	.03	.02	.01
72	Franklin Stubbs (235)	.03	.02	.01
73	Mike Scioscia (236)	.10	.08	.04
74	Mariano Duncan (237)	.03	.02	.01
75	Fernando Valenzuela	.08	.06	.03

76	Hubie Brooks	.06	.05	.02
77	Andre Dawson (238)	.08	.06	.03
78	Tim Burke (240)	.04	.03	.02
79	Floyd Youmans (241)	.03	.02	.01
80	Tim Wallach (242)	.04	.03	.02
81	Jeff Reardon (243)	.06	.05	.02
82	Mitch Webster (244)	.08	.06	.03
83	Bryn Smith (245)	.03	.02	.01
84	Andres Galarraga (246)	.12	.09	.05
85	Tim Raines	.15	.11	.06
86	Chris Brown	.08	.06	.03
87	Bob Brenly (247)	.03	.02	.01
88	Will Clark (249)	.25	.20	.10
89	Scott Garrelts (250)	.04	.03	.02
90	Jeffrey Leonard (251)	.06	.05	.02
91	Robby Thompson (252)	.06	.05	.02
92	Mike Krukow (255)	.03	.02	.01
93	Danny Gladden (256)	.03	.02	.01
94	Candy Maldonado (257)	.04	.03	.02
95	Chili Davis	.04	.03	.02
96	Dwight Gooden	.15	.11	.06
97	Sid Fernandez (258)	.04	.03	.02
98	Len Dykstra (259)	.06	.05	.02
99	Bob Ojeda (260)	.04	.03	.02
100	Wally Backman (261)	.04	.03	.02
101	Gary Carter	.15	.11	.06
102	Keith Hernandez (262)	.10	.08	.04
103	Darryl Strawberry (265)	.10	.08	.04
104	Roger McDowell (266)	.08	.06	.03
105	Ron Darling (267)	.08	.06	.03
106	Tony Gwynn	.20	.15	.08
107	Dave Dravecky (268)	.04	.03	.02
108	Terry Kennedy (269)	.08	.06	.03
109	Rich Gossage (270)	.10	.08	.04
110	Garry Templeton (271)	.04	.03	.02
111	Lance McCullers (272)	.04	.03	.02
112	Eric Show (275)	.04	.03	.02
113	John Kruk (276)	.15	.11	.06
114	Tim Flannery (277)	.06	.05	.02
115	Steve Garvey	.15	.11	.06
116	Mike Schmidt	.25	.20	.10
117	Glenn Wilson (278)	.06	.05	.02
118	Kent Tekulve (280)	.06	.05	.02
119	Gary Redus (281)	.08	.06	.03
120	Shane Rawley (282)	.03	.02	.01
121	Von Hayes	.06	.05	.02
122	Don Carman (283)	.04	.03	.02
123	Bruce Ruffin (285)	.04	.03	.02
124	Steve Bedrosian (286)	.06	.05	.02
125	Juan Samuel (287)	.06	.05	.02
126	Sid Bream (288)	.06	.05	.02
127	Cecilio Guante (289)	.03	.02	.01
128	Rick Reuschel (290)	.04	.03	.02
129	Tony Pena (291)	.04	.03	.02
130	Rick Rhoden	.06	.05	.02
131	Barry Bonds (292)	.10	.08	.04
132	Joe Orsulak (295)	.03	.02	.01
133	Jim Morrison (296)	.12	.09	.05
134	R.J. Reynolds (297)	.04	.03	.02
135	Johnny Ray	.06	.05	.02
136	Eric Davis	.30	.25	.12
137	Tom Browning (298)	.10	.08	.04
138	John Franco (300)	.06	.05	.02
139	Pete Rose (301)	.20	.15	.08
140	Bill Gullickson (302)	.04	.03	.02
141	Ron Oester (303)	.04	.03	.02
142	Bo Diaz (304)	.12	.09	.05
143	Buddy Bell (305)	.04	.03	.02
144	Eddie Milner (306)	.08	.06	.03
145	Dave Parker	.10	.08	.04
146	Kirby Puckett	.35	.25	.14
147	Rickey Henderson	.40	.30	.15
148	Wade Boggs	.60	.45	.25
149	Lance Parrish	.15	.11	.06
150	Wally Joyner	.25	.20	.10
151	Cal Ripken, Jr.	.40	.30	.15
152	Dave Winfield	.30	.25	.12
153	Lou Whitaker	.25	.20	.10
154	Roger Clemens	.25	.20	.10
155	Tony Gwynn	.30	.25	.12
156	Ryne Sandberg	.50	.40	.20
157	Keith Hernandez	.15	.11	.06
158	Gary Carter	.20	.15	.08
159	Darryl Strawberry	.20	.15	.08
160	Mike Schmidt	.40	.30	.15
161	Dale Murphy	.35	.25	.14
162	Ozzie Smith	.25	.20	.10
163	Dwight Gooden	.25	.20	.10
164	Jose Canseco	.80	.60	.30
165	Curt Young (307)	.04	.03	.02
166	Alfredo Griffin (308)	.08	.06	.03
167	Dave Stewart (309)	.06	.05	.02
168	Mike Davis (310)	.06	.05	.02
169	Bruce Bochte (311)	.03	.02	.01
170	Dwayne Murphy (312)	.04	.03	.02
171	Carney Lansford (313)	.08	.06	.03
172	Joaquin Andujar (1)	.04	.03	.02
173	Dave Kingman	.08	.06	.03
174	Wally Joyner	.20	.15	.08
175	Gary Pettis (2)	.15	.11	.06
176	Dick Schofield (3)	.15	.11	.06
177	Donnie Moore (4)	.06	.05	.02
178	Brian Downing (5)	.15	.11	.06
179	Mike Witt	.06	.05	.02
180	Bob Boone (6)	.15	.11	.06
181	Kirk McCaskill (7)	.03	.02	.01
182	Doug DeCinces (8)	.06	.05	.02
183	Don Sutton (9)	.10	.08	.04
184	Jessie Barfield	.10	.08	.04
185	Tom Henke (10)	.08	.06	.03
186	Willie Upshaw (11)	.06	.05	.02
187	Mark Eichhorn (12)	.06	.05	.02
188	Damaso Garcia (27)	.10	.08	.04
189	Jim Clancy (28)	.03	.02	.01
190	Lloyd Moseby (29)	.04	.03	.02
191	Tony Fernandez (30)	.06	.05	.02
192	Jimmy Key (31)	.06	.05	.02
193	George Bell	.20	.15	.08
194	Rob Deer	.06	.05	.02
195	Mark Clear (32)	.03	.02	.01
196	Robin Yount (33)	.25	.20	.10
197	Jim Gantner (34)	.04	.03	.02
198	Cecil Cooper (37)	.06	.05	.02
199	Teddy Higuera	.08	.06	.03
200	Paul Molitor (38)	.20	.15	.08
201	Dan Plesac (39)	.08	.06	.03
202	Billy Jo Robidoux (40)	.03	.02	.01
203	Earnie Riles (42)	.03	.02	.01
204	Ken Schrom (43)	.03	.02	.01
205	Pat Tabler (44)	.03	.02	.01
206	Mel Hall (45)	.03	.02	.01
207	Tony Bernazard (47)	.03	.02	.01
208	Joe Carter	.20	.15	.08
209	Ernie Camacho (48)	.06	.05	.02
210	Julio Franco (49)	.06	.05	.02
211	Tom Candiotti (50)	.08	.06	.03
212	Brook Jacoby (51)	.06	.05	.02
213	Cory Snyder	.12	.09	.05
214	Jim Presley	.08	.06	.03
215	Mike Moore (52)	.08	.06	.03
216	Harold Reynolds (53)	.04	.03	.02
217	Scott Bradley (54)	.03	.02	.01
218	Matt Young (57)	.03	.02	.01
219	Mark Langston (58)	.06	.05	.02
220	Alvin Davis (59)	.06	.05	.02
221	Phil Bradley (60)	.06	.05	.02
222	Ken Phelps (62)	.04	.03	.02
223	Danny Tartabull	.20	.15	.08
224	Eddie Murray	.30	.25	.12
225	Rick Dempsey (63)	.06	.05	.02
226	Fred Lynn (64)	.06	.05	.02
227	Mike Boddicker (65)	.04	.03	.02
228	Don Aase (66)	.06	.05	.02
229	Larry Sheets (67)	.06	.05	.02
230	Storm Davis (68)	.04	.03	.02
231	Lee Lacy (69)	.08	.06	.03
232	Jim Traber (71)	.03	.02	.01
233	Cal Ripken, Jr.	.25	.20	.10
234	Larry Parrish	.06	.05	.02
235	Gary Ward (72)	.03	.02	.01
236	Pete Incaviglia (73)	.10	.08	.04
237	Scott Fletcher (74)	.03	.02	.01
238	Greg Harris (77)	.08	.06	.03
239	Pete O'Brien	.06	.05	.02
240	Charlie Hough (78)	.04	.03	.02
241	Don Slaught (79)	.03	.02	.01
242	Steve Buechele (80)	.04	.03	.02
243	Oddibe McDowell (81)	.06	.05	.02
244	Roger Clemens (82)	.15	.11	.06
245	Bob Stanley (83)	.03	.02	.01
246	Tom Seaver (84)	.12	.09	.05
247	Rich Gedman (87)	.03	.02	.01
248	Jim Rice	.15	.11	.06
249	Dennis Boyd (88)	.10	.08	.04
250	Bill Buckner (89)	.04	.03	.02
251	Dwight Evans (90)	.06	.05	.02
252	Don Baylor (91)	.06	.05	.02
253	Wade Boggs	.40	.30	.15
254	George Brett	.25	.20	.10
255	Steve Farr (92)	.03	.02	.01
256	Jim Sundberg (93)	.03	.02	.01
257	Dan Quisenberry (94)	.04	.03	.02
258	Charlie Leibrandt (97)	.04	.03	.02
259	Argenis Salazar (98)	.06	.05	.02
260	Frank White (99)	.04	.03	.02
261	Willie Wilson (100)	.04	.03	.02
262	Lonnie Smith (102)	.10	.08	.04
263	Steve Balboni	.04	.03	.02
264	Darrell Evans	.06	.05	.02
265	Johnny Grubb (103)	.08	.06	.03
266	Jack Morris (104)	.08	.06	.03
267	Lou Whitaker (105)	.08	.06	.03
268	Chet Lemon (107)	.04	.03	.02
269	Lance Parrish (108)	.08	.06	.03
270	Alan Trammell (109)	.10	.08	.04
271	Darnell Coles (110)	.04	.03	.02
272	Willie Hernandez (111)	.04	.03	.02
273	Kirk Gibson	.15	.11	.06
274	Kirby Puckett	.35	.25	.14
275	Mike Smithson (112)	.04	.03	.02
276	Mickey Hatcher (113)	.06	.05	.02
277	Frank Viola (114)	.06	.05	.02
278	Bert Blyleven (117)	.06	.05	.02
279	Gary Gaetti	.10	.08	.04
280	Tom Brunansky (118)	.06	.05	.02
281	Kent Hrbek (119)	.08	.06	.03
282	Roy Smalley (120)	.03	.02	.01
283	Greg Gagne (122)	.04	.03	.02
284	Harold Baines	.10	.08	.04
285	Ron Hassey (123)	.04	.03	.02
286	Floyd Bannister (124)	.06	.05	.02
287	Ozzie Guillen (125)	.06	.05	.02
288	Carlton Fisk (126)	.06	.05	.02
289	Tim Hulett (127)	.03	.02	.01
290	Joe Cowley (128)	.04	.03	.02
291	Greg Walker (129)	.04	.03	.02
292	Neil Allen (131)	.10	.08	.04
293	John Cangelosi	.04	.03	.02
294	Don Mattingly	.90	.70	.35
295	Mike Easler (132)	.03	.02	.01
296	Rickey Henderson (133)	.20	.15	.08
297	Dan Pasqua (134)	.04	.03	.02
298	Dave Winfield (137)	.10	.08	.04
299	Dave Righetti	.12	.09	.05
300	Mike Pagliarulo (138)	.06	.05	.02
301	Ron Guidry (139)	.12	.09	.05
302	Willie Randolph (140)	.04	.03	.02
303	Dennis Rasmussen (141)	.04	.03	.02
304	Jose Canseco (142)	.40	.30	.15
305	Andres Thomas (143)	.04	.03	.02
306	Danny Tartabull (144)	.08	.06	.03
307	Robby Thompson (165)	.04	.03	.02
308	Pete Incaviglia, Cory Snyder	.12	.09	.05
309	Dale Sveum (167)	.06	.05	.02
310	Todd Worrell (168)	.06	.05	.02
311	Andy Allanson (169)	.03	.02	.01
312	Bruce Ruffin (170)	.04	.03	.02
313	Wally Joyner (171)	.20	.15	.08

1988 Topps

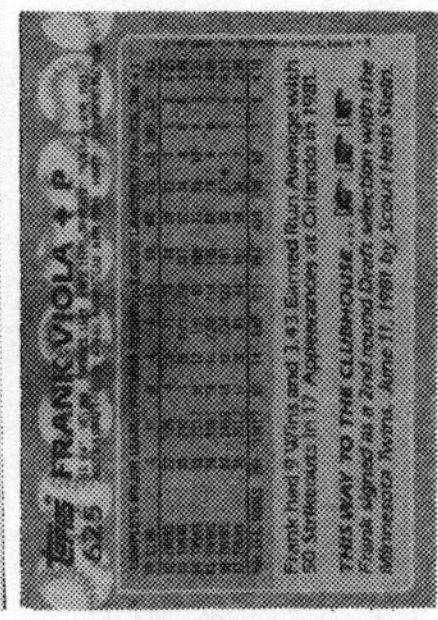

The 1988 Topps set features a clean, attractive design that should prove to be very popular with collectors for many years to come. The full-color player photo is surrounded by a thin yellow frame which is encompassed by a white border. The player's name appears in the lower right corner in a colored band which appears to wrap around the player photo. The player's team nickname is located in large letters at the top of the card. The Topps logo is placed in the lower left corner of the card. The card backs feature black print on orange and gray stock and includes the usual player personal and career statistics. Many of the cards contain a new feature entitled "This Way To The Clubhouse", which explains how the player joined his current team, be it by trade, free agency, etc. The 792-card set includes a number of special subsets including "Future Stars", "Turn Back The Clock", All-Star teams, All-Star rookie selections, and Record Breakers. All cards measure 2-1/2" by 3-1/2". For the fifth consecutive year, Topps issued a glossy "Tiffany" edition of its 792-card regular-issue set. The Tiffany cards have a value of 3-4 times greater than the same card in the regular issue. The Tiffany edition could be purchased by collectors directly from Topps for $99. The company placed ads for the Tiffany set in publications such as USA Today and The Sporting News.

		MT	NR MT	EX
	Complete Set (792):	15.00	11.00	6.00
	Common Player:	.04	.03	.02
1	Vince Coleman (Record Breakers)	.08	.06	.03
2	Don Mattingly (Record Breakers)	.15	.11	.06
3a	Mark Mcgwire (Record Breakers, white triangle by left foot)	.40	.30	.15
3b	Mark McGwire (Record Breakers)	.15	.11	.06
4a	Eddie murray (Record Breakers, no mention of record on front)	.25	.20	.10
4b	Eddie Murray (Record Breakers)	.10	.08	.04
5	Joe Niekro (Record Breakers, Phil Niekro)	.10	.08	.04
6	Nolan Ryan (Record Breakers)	.40	.30	.15
7	Benito Santiago (Record Breakers)	.15	.11	.06
8	Kevin Elster (FC) (Future Stars)	.06	.05	.02
9	Andy Hawkins	.04	.03	.02
10	Ryne Sandberg	.50	.40	.20
11	Mike Young	.04	.03	.02
12	Bill Schroeder	.04	.03	.02
13	Andres Thomas	.06	.05	.02
14	Sparky Anderson	.06	.05	.02
15	Chili Davis	.06	.05	.02
16	Kirk McCaskill	.06	.05	.02
17	Ron Oester	.04	.03	.02
18a	*Al Leiter* (FC) (Future Stars, no "NY" on shirt, photo actually Steve George)	.40	.30	.15
18b	*Al Leiter* (FC) (Future Stars, "NY" on shirt, correct photo)	.10	.08	.04
19	*Mark Davidson* (FC)	.06	.05	.02
20	Kevin Gross	.06	.05	.02
21	Red Sox Leaders (Wade Boggs, Spike Owen)	.15	.11	.06
22	Greg Swindell	.15	.11	.06
23	Ken Landreaux	.04	.03	.02
24	Jim Deshaies	.06	.05	.02
25	Andres Galarraga	.15	.11	.06
26	Mitch Williams	.06	.05	.02
27	R.J. Reynolds	.04	.03	.02
28	*Jose Nunez* (FC)	.10	.08	.04
29	Argenis Salazar	.04	.03	.02
30	Sid Fernandez	.08	.06	.03
31	Bruce Bochy	.04	.03	.02
32	Mike Morgan	.04	.03	.02
33	Rob Deer	.06	.05	.02
34	Ricky Horton	.06	.05	.02
35	Harold Baines	.10	.08	.04
36	Jamie Moyer	.06	.05	.02
37	Ed Romero	.04	.03	.02
38	Jeff Calhoun	.04	.03	.02
39	Gerald Perry	.08	.06	.03
40	Orel Hershiser	.08	.06	.03
41	Bob Melvin	.04	.03	.02
42	*Bill Landrum* (FC)	.04	.03	.02
43	Dick Schofield	.04	.03	.02
44	Lou Piniella	.06	.05	.02
45	Kent Hrbek	.12	.09	.05
46	Darnell Coles	.06	.05	.02
47	Joaquin Andujar	.06	.05	.02
48	Alan Ashby	.04	.03	.02

49 Dave Clark (FC) .10 .08 .04
50 Hubie Brooks .08 .06 .03
51 Orioles Leaders (Eddie Murray, Cal Ripken, Jr.) .12 .09 .05
52 Don Robinson .06 .05 .02
53 Curt Wilkerson .04 .03 .02
54 Jim Clancy .06 .05 .02
55 Phil Bradley .08 .06 .03
56 Ed Hearn .04 .03 .02
57 *Tim Crews* (FC) .15 .11 .06
58 Dave Magadan .10 .08 .04
59 Danny Cox .06 .05 .02
60 Rickey Henderson .35 .25 .14
61 *Mark Knudson* (FC) .10 .08 .04
62 Jeff Hamilton .08 .06 .03
63 Jimmy Jones (FC) .10 .08 .04
64 *Ken Caminiti* (FC) .40 .30 .15
65 Leon Durham .06 .05 .02
66 Shane Rawley .06 .05 .02
67 Ken Oberkfell .04 .03 .02
68 Dave Dravecky .06 .05 .02
69 *Mike Hart* (FC) .04 .03 .02
70 Roger Clemens .50 .40 .20
71 Gary Pettis .04 .03 .02
72 Dennis Eckersley .10 .08 .04
73 Randy Bush .04 .03 .02
74 Tom Lasorda .06 .05 .02
75 Joe Carter .25 .20 .10
76 Denny Martinez .04 .03 .02
77 Tom O'Malley .04 .03 .02
78 Dan Petry .06 .05 .02
79 Ernie Whitt .06 .05 .02
80 Mark Langston .10 .08 .04
81 Reds Leaders (John Franco, Ron Robinson) .06 .05 .02
82 *Darrel Akerfelds* (FC) .04 .03 .02
83 Jose Oquendo .04 .03 .02
84 Cecilio Guante .04 .03 .02
85 Howard Johnson .08 .06 .03
86 Ron Karkovice .04 .03 .02
87 Mike Mason .04 .03 .02
88 Earnie Riles .04 .03 .02
89 *Gary Thurman* (FC) .08 .06 .03
90 Dale Murphy .10 .08 .04
91 *Joey Cora* (FC) .12 .09 .05
92 Len Matuszek .04 .03 .02
93 Bob Sebra .04 .03 .02
94 *Chuck Jackson* (FC) .04 .03 .02
95 Lance Parrish .12 .09 .05
96 *Todd Benzinger* (FC) .10 .08 .04
97 Scott Garrelts .04 .03 .02
98 *Rene Gonzales* (FC) .06 .05 .02
99 Chuck Finley .06 .05 .02
100 Jack Clark .06 .05 .02
101 Allan Anderson .06 .05 .02
102 Barry Larkin .12 .09 .05
103 Curt Young .06 .05 .02
104 Dick Williams .04 .03 .02
105 Jesse Orosco .06 .05 .02
106 *Jim Walewander* (FC) .04 .03 .02
107 Scott Bailes .06 .05 .02
108 Steve Lyons .04 .03 .02
109 Joel Skinner .04 .03 .02
110 Teddy Higuera .08 .06 .03
111 Expos Leaders (Hubie Brooks, Vance Law) .06 .05 .02
112 *Les Lancaster* (FC) .15 .11 .06
113 Kelly Gruber .04 .03 .02
114 Jeff Russell .04 .03 .02
115 Johnny Ray .06 .05 .02
116 Jerry Don Gleaton .04 .03 .02
117 *James Steels* (FC) .04 .03 .02
118 Bob Welch .08 .06 .03
119 *Robbie Wine* (FC) .04 .03 .02
120 Kirby Puckett .40 .30 .15
121 Checklist 1-132 .04 .03 .02
122 Tony Bernazard .04 .03 .02
123 Tom Candiotti .04 .03 .02
124 Ray Knight .06 .05 .02
125 Bruce Hurst .08 .06 .03
126 Steve Jeltz .04 .03 .02
127 Jim Gott .04 .03 .02
128 Johnny Grubb .04 .03 .02
129 Greg Minton .04 .03 .02
130 Buddy Bell .08 .06 .03
131 Don Schulze .04 .03 .02
132 Donnie Hill .04 .03 .02
133 Greg Mathews .06 .05 .02
134 Chuck Tanner .04 .03 .02
135 Dennis Rasmussen .08 .06 .03
136 Brian Dayett .04 .03 .02
137 Chris Bosio .06 .05 .02
138 Mitch Webster .06 .05 .02
139 Jerry Browne .06 .05 .02
140 Jesse Barfield .10 .08 .04
141 Royals Leaders (George Brett, Bret Saberhagen) .12 .09 .05
142 Andy Van Slyke .10 .08 .04
143 Mickey Tettleton .12 .09 .05
144 *Don Gordon* (FC) .08 .06 .03
145 Bill Madlock .08 .06 .03
146 *Donell Nixon* (FC) .06 .05 .02
147 Bill Buckner .08 .06 .03
148 Carmelo Martinez .06 .05 .02
149 Ken Howell .04 .03 .02
150 Eric Davis .12 .09 .05
151 Bob Knepper .06 .05 .02
152 *Jody Reed* (FC) .15 .11 .06
153 John Habyan .04 .03 .02
154 Jeff Stone .04 .03 .02
155 Bruce Sutter .10 .08 .04
156 Gary Matthews .06 .05 .02
157 Atlee Hammaker .04 .03 .02
158 Tim Hulett .04 .03 .02
159 *Brad Arnsberg* (FC) .12 .09 .05
160 Willie McGee .10 .08 .04
161 Bryn Smith .06 .05 .02
162 Mark McLemore .06 .05 .02
163 Dale Mohorcic .04 .03 .02
164 Dave Johnson .06 .05 .02
165 Robin Yount .20 .15 .08
166 *Rick Rodriguez* (FC) .06 .05 .02
167 Rance Mulliniks .04 .03 .02
168 Barry Jones .04 .03 .02
169 *Ross Jones* (FC) .04 .03 .02
170 Rich Gossage .06 .05 .02
171 Cubs Leaders (Shawon Dunston, Manny Trillo) .06 .05 .02
172 *Lloyd McClendon* (FC) .10 .08 .04
173 Eric Plunk .04 .03 .02
174 Phil Garner .04 .03 .02
175 Kevin Bass .06 .05 .02
176 Jeff Reed .04 .03 .02
177 Frank Tanana .06 .05 .02
178 Dwayne Henry (FC) .06 .05 .02
179 Charlie Puleo .04 .03 .02
180 Terry Kennedy .06 .05 .02
181 Dave Cone (FC) .10 .08 .04
182 Ken Phelps .06 .05 .02
183 Tom Lawless .04 .03 .02
184 Ivan Calderon .08 .06 .03
185 Rick Rhoden .06 .05 .02
186 Rafael Palmeiro .20 .15 .08
187 Steve Kiefer (FC) .06 .05 .02
188 John Russell .04 .03 .02
189 *Wes Gardner* (FC) .06 .05 .02
190 Candy Maldonado .06 .05 .02
191 John Cerutti .06 .05 .02
192 Devon White .08 .06 .03
193 Brian Fisher .06 .05 .02
194 Tom Kelly .04 .03 .02
195 Dan Quisenberry .06 .05 .02
196 Dave Engle .04 .03 .02
197 Lance McCullers .06 .05 .02
198 Franklin Stubbs .06 .05 .02
199 *Dave Meads* .06 .05 .02
200 Wade Boggs .30 .25 .12
201 Rangers Leaders (Steve Buechele, Pete Incaviglia, Pete O'Brien, Bobby Valentine) .06 .05 .02
202 Glenn Hoffman .04 .03 .02
203 Fred Toliver .04 .03 .02
204 Paul O'Neill (FC) .12 .09 .05
205 *Nelson Liriano* (FC) .08 .06 .03
206 Domingo Ramos .04 .03 .02
207 *John Mitchell* (FC) .06 .05 .02
208 Steve Lake .04 .03 .02
209 Richard Dotson .06 .05 .02
210 Willie Randolph .06 .05 .02
211 Frank DiPino .04 .03 .02
212 Greg Brock .06 .05 .02
213 Albert Hall .04 .03 .02
214 Dave Schmidt .04 .03 .02
215 Von Hayes .06 .05 .02
216 Jerry Reuss .06 .05 .02
217 Harry Spilman .04 .03 .02
218 Dan Schatzeder .04 .03 .02
219 Mike Stanley .08 .06 .03
220 Tom Henke .06 .05 .02
221 Rafael Belliard .04 .03 .02
222 Steve Farr .04 .03 .02
223 Stan Jefferson .08 .06 .03
224 Tom Trebelhorn .04 .03 .02
225 Mike Scioscia .06 .05 .02
226 Dave Lopes .06 .05 .02
227 Ed Correa .04 .03 .02
228 Wallace Johnson .04 .03 .02
229 Jeff Musselman .08 .06 .03
230 Pat Tabler .06 .05 .02
231 Pirates Leaders (Barry Bonds, Bobby Bonilla) .15 .11 .06
232 Bob James .04 .03 .02
233 Rafael Santana .04 .03 .02
234 Ken Dayley .04 .03 .02
235 Gary Ward .06 .05 .02
236 Ted Power .04 .03 .02
237 Mike Heath .04 .03 .02
238 *Luis Polonia* .30 .25 .12
239 Roy Smalley .04 .03 .02
240 Lee Smith .08 .06 .03
241 Damaso Garcia .04 .03 .02
242 Tom Niedenfuer .06 .05 .02
243 Mark Ryal (FC) .04 .03 .02
244 Jeff Robinson .04 .03 .02
245 Rich Gedman .06 .05 .02
246 *Mike Campbell* (FC) (Future Stars) .06 .05 .02
247 Thad Bosley .04 .03 .02
248 Storm Davis .08 .06 .03
249 Mike Marshall .06 .05 .02
250 Nolan Ryan .70 .50 .30
251 Tom Foley .04 .03 .02
252 Bob Brower .06 .05 .02
253 Checklist 133-264 .04 .03 .02
254 Lee Elia .04 .03 .02
255 Mookie Wilson .06 .05 .02
256 Ken Schrom .04 .03 .02
257 Jerry Royster .04 .03 .02
258 Ed Nunez .04 .03 .02
259 Ron Kittle .06 .05 .02
260 Vince Coleman .08 .06 .03
261 Giants Leaders (Will Clark, Candy Maldonado, Kevin Mitchell, Robby Thompson, Jose Uribe) .10 .08 .04
262 Drew Hall (FC) .04 .03 .02
263 Glenn Braggs .08 .06 .03
264 *Les Straker* .04 .03 .02
265 Bo Diaz .06 .05 .02
266 Paul Assenmacher .04 .03 .02
267 *Billy Bean* (FC) .04 .03 .02
268 Bruce Ruffin .06 .05 .02
269 *Ellis Burks* .40 .30 .15
270 Mike Witt .06 .05 .02
271 Ken Gerhart .06 .05 .02
272 Steve Ontiveros .04 .03 .02
273 Garth Iorg .04 .03 .02
274 Junior Ortiz .04 .03 .02
275 Kevin Seitzer .08 .06 .03
276 Luis Salazar .04 .03 .02
277 Alejandro Pena .06 .05 .02
278 Jose Cruz .06 .05 .02
279 Randy St. Claire .04 .03 .02
280 Pete Incaviglia .08 .06 .03
281 Jerry Hairston .04 .03 .02
282 Pat Perry .04 .03 .02
283 Phil Lombardi (FC) .06 .05 .02
284 Larry Bowa .06 .05 .02
285 Jim Presley .08 .06 .03
286 *Chuck Crim* .12 .09 .05
287 Manny Trillo .06 .05 .02
288 *Pat Pacillo* .06 .05 .02
289 Dave Bergman .04 .03 .02
290 Tony Fernandez .10 .08 .04
291 Astros Leaders (Kevin Bass, Billy Hatcher) .06 .05 .02
292 Carney Lansford .08 .06 .03
293 *Doug Jones* (FC) .25 .20 .10
294 *Al Pedrique* (FC) .06 .05 .02
295 Bert Blyleven .10 .08 .04
296 Floyd Rayford .04 .03 .02
297 Zane Smith .06 .05 .02
298 Milt Thompson .04 .03 .02
299 Steve Crawford .04 .03 .02
300 Don Mattingly .30 .25 .12
301 Bud Black .04 .03 .02
302 Jose Uribe .04 .03 .02
303 Eric Show .06 .05 .02
304 George Hendrick .06 .05 .02
305 Steve Sax .08 .06 .03
306 Billy Hatcher .06 .05 .02
307 Mike Trujillo .04 .03 .02
308 Lee Mazzilli .06 .05 .02
309 *Bill Long* .08 .06 .03
310 Tom Herr .06 .05 .02
311 Scott Sanderson .04 .03 .02
312 Joey Meyer (FC) (Future Stars) .08 .06 .03
313 Bob McClure .04 .03 .02
314 Jimy Williams .04 .03 .02
315 Dave Parker .12 .09 .05
316 Jose Rijo .06 .05 .02
317 Tom Nieto .04 .03 .02
318 Mel Hall .06 .05 .02
319 Mike Loynd .04 .03 .02
320 Alan Trammell .10 .08 .04
321 White Sox Leaders (Harold Baines, Carlton Fisk) .08 .06 .03
322 *Vicente Palacios* (FC) .10 .08 .04
323 Rick Leach .04 .03 .02
324 Danny Jackson .10 .08 .04
325 Glenn Hubbard .04 .03 .02
326 Al Nipper .04 .03 .02
327 Larry Sheets .06 .05 .02
328 *Greg Cadaret* (FC) .06 .05 .02
329 Chris Speier .04 .03 .02
330 Eddie Whitson .04 .03 .02
331 Brian Downing .06 .05 .02
332 Jerry Reed .04 .03 .02
333 Wally Backman .06 .05 .02
334 Dave LaPoint .06 .05 .02
335 Claudell Washington .06 .05 .02
336 Ed Lynch .04 .03 .02
337 Jim Gantner .04 .03 .02
338 Brian Holton .08 .06 .03
339 Kurt Stillwell .08 .06 .03
340 Jack Morris .10 .08 .04
341 Carmen Castillo .04 .03 .02
342 Larry Andersen .04 .03 .02
343 Greg Gagne .04 .03 .02
344 Tony LaRussa .04 .03 .02
345 Scott Fletcher .06 .05 .02
346 Vance Law .06 .05 .02
347 Joe Johnson .04 .03 .02
348 Jim Eisenreich .04 .03 .02
349 Bob Walk .04 .03 .02
350 Will Clark .40 .30 .15
351 Cardinals Leaders (Tony Pena, Red Schoendienst) .06 .05 .02
352 *Billy Ripken* (FC) .06 .05 .02
353 Ed Olwine .04 .03 .02
354 Marc Sullivan .04 .03 .02
355 Roger McDowell .08 .06 .03
356 Luis Aguayo .04 .03 .02
357 Floyd Bannister .06 .05 .02
358 Rey Quinones .04 .03 .02
359 Tim Stoddard .04 .03 .02
360 Tony Gwynn .25 .20 .10
361 Greg Maddux .70 .50 .30
362 Juan Castillo .04 .03 .02
363 Willie Fraser .06 .05 .02
364 Nick Esasky .06 .05 .02
365 Floyd Youmans .04 .03 .02
366 Chet Lemon .06 .05 .02
367 Tim Leary .06 .05 .02
368 *Gerald Young* (FC) .08 .06 .03
369 Greg Harris .04 .03 .02
370 Jose Canseco .40 .30 .15
371 Joe Hesketh .04 .03 .02
372 *Matt Williams* 1.50 1.25 .60
373 Checklist 265-396 .04 .03 .02
374 Doc Edwards .04 .03 .02
375 Tom Brunansky .08 .06 .03
376 *Bill Wilkinson* .04 .03 .02
377 *Sam Horn* (FC) .04 .03 .02
378 *Todd Frohwirth* (FC) .08 .06 .03
379 Rafael Ramirez .04 .03 .02
380 *Joe Magrane* .10 .08 .04
381 Angels Leaders (Jack Howell, Wally Joyner) .12 .09 .05
382 *Keith Miller* (FC) .08 .06 .03
383 Eric Bell .06 .05 .02
384 Neil Allen .04 .03 .02
385 Carlton Fisk .20 .15 .08
386 Don Mattingly (All-Star) .15 .11 .06
387 Willie Randolph (All-Star) .06 .05 .02
388 Wade Boggs (All-Star) .12 .09 .05
389 Alan Trammell (All-Star) .08 .06 .03
390 George Bell (All-Star) .10 .08 .04
391 Kirby Puckett (All-Star) .20 .15 .08

392	Dave Winfield (All-Star)	.15	.11	.06
393	Matt Nokes (All-Star)	.15	.11	.06
394	Roger Clemens (All-Star)	.15	.11	.06
395	Jimmy Key (All-Star)	.06	.05	.02
396	Tom Henke (All-Star)	.06	.05	.02
397	Jack Clark (All-Star)	.06	.05	.02
398	Juan Samuel (All-Star)	.06	.05	.02
399	Tim Wallach (All-Star)	.06	.05	.02
400	Ozzie Smith (All-Star)	.10	.08	.04
401	Andre Dawson (All-Star)	.10	.08	.04
402	Tony Gwynn (All-Star)	.15	.11	.06
403	Tim Raines (All-Star)	.12	.09	.05
404	Benny Santiago (All-Star)	.10	.08	.04
405	Dwight Gooden (All-Star)	.10	.08	.04
406	Shane Rawley (All-Star)	.06	.05	.02
407	Steve Bedrosian (All-Star)	.08	.06	.03
408	Dion James	.06	.05	.02
409	Joel McKeon (FC)	.04	.03	.02
410	Tony Pena	.06	.05	.02
411	Wayne Tolleson	.04	.03	.02
412	Randy Myers	.10	.08	.04
413	John Christensen	.04	.03	.02
414	John McNamara	.04	.03	.02
415	Don Carman	.06	.05	.02
416	Keith Moreland	.06	.05	.02
417	*Mark Ciardi* (FC)	.04	.03	.02
418	Joel Youngblood	.04	.03	.02
419	Scott McGregor	.06	.05	.02
420	Wally Joyner	.12	.09	.05
421	Ed Vande Berg	.04	.03	.02
422	Dave Concepcion	.06	.05	.02
423	*John Smiley*	.20	.15	.08
424	Dwayne Murphy	.06	.05	.02
425	Jeff Reardon	.08	.06	.03
426	Randy Ready	.04	.03	.02
427	*Paul Kilgus* (FC)	.08	.06	.03
428	John Shelby	.04	.03	.02
429	Tigers Leaders (Kirk Gibson, Alan Trammell)	.08	.06	.03
430	Glenn Davis	.06	.05	.02
431	Casey Candaele	.04	.03	.02
432	Mike Moore	.04	.03	.02
433	*Bill Pecota* (FC)	.08	.06	.03
434	Rick Aguilera	.04	.03	.02
435	Mike Pagliarulo	.08	.06	.03
436	Mike Bielecki	.04	.03	.02
437	*Fred Manrique* (FC)	.06	.05	.02
438	*Rob Ducey* (FC)	.06	.05	.02
439	Dave Martinez	.08	.06	.03
440	Steve Bedrosian	.10	.08	.04
441	Rick Manning	.04	.03	.02
442	*Tom Bolton* (FC)	.08	.06	.03
443	Ken Griffey	.06	.05	.02
444	Cal Ripken, Sr.	.04	.03	.02
445	Mike Krukow	.06	.05	.02
446	Doug DeCinces	.06	.05	.02
447	*Jeff Montgomery* (FC)	.50	.40	.20
448	Mike Davis	.06	.05	.02
449	*Jeff Robinson*	.06	.05	.02
450	Barry Bonds	.60	.45	.25
451	Keith Atherton	.04	.03	.02
452	Willie Wilson	.08	.06	.03
453	Dennis Powell	.04	.03	.02
454	Marvell Wynne	.04	.03	.02
455	*Shawn Hillegas* (FC)	.06	.05	.02
456	Dave Anderson	.04	.03	.02
457	Terry Leach	.04	.03	.02
458	Ron Hassey	.04	.03	.02
459	Yankees Leaders (Willie Randolph, Dave Winfield)	.08	.06	.03
460	Ozzie Smith	.12	.09	.05
461	Danny Darwin	.04	.03	.02
462	Don Slaught	.04	.03	.02
463	*Fred McGriff*	.20	.15	.08
464	Jay Tibbs	.04	.03	.02
465	Paul Molitor	.15	.11	.06
466	Jerry Mumphrey	.04	.03	.02
467	Don Aase	.04	.03	.02
468	Darren Daulton	.04	.03	.02
469	Jeff Dedmon	.04	.03	.02
470	Dwight Evans	.10	.08	.04
471	Donnie Moore	.04	.03	.02
472	Robby Thompson	.06	.05	.02
473	Joe Niekro	.06	.05	.02
474	Tom Brookens	.04	.03	.02
475	Pete Rose	.20	.15	.08
476	Dave Stewart	.08	.06	.03
477	Jamie Quirk	.04	.03	.02
478	Sid Bream	.06	.05	.02
479	Brett Butler	.06	.05	.02
480	Dwight Gooden	.10	.08	.04
481	Mariano Duncan	.04	.03	.02
482	Mark Davis	.04	.03	.02
483	*Rod Booker* (FC)	.04	.03	.02
484	Pat Clements	.04	.03	.02
485	Harold Reynolds	.06	.05	.02
486	*Pat Keedy* (FC)	.10	.08	.04
487	Jim Pankovits	.04	.03	.02
488	Andy McGaffigan	.04	.03	.02
489	Dodgers Leaders (Pedro Guerrero, Fernando Valenzuela)	.08	.06	.03
490	Larry Parrish	.06	.05	.02
491	B.J. Surhoff	.10	.08	.04
492	Doyle Alexander	.06	.05	.02
493	Mike Greenwell	.12	.09	.05
494	*Wally Ritchie*	.06	.05	.02
495	Eddie Murray	.25	.20	.10
496	Guy Hoffman	.04	.03	.02
497	Kevin Mitchell	.12	.09	.05
498	Bob Boone	.06	.05	.02
499	Eric King	.06	.05	.02
500	Andre Dawson	.15	.11	.06
501	Tim Birtsas (FC)	.06	.05	.02
502	Danny Gladden	.04	.03	.02
503	*Junior Noboa* (FC)	.04	.03	.02
504	Bob Rodgers	.04	.03	.02
505	Willie Upshaw	.06	.05	.02
506	John Cangelosi	.04	.03	.02
507	Mark Gubicza	.10	.08	.04
508	Tim Teufel	.04	.03	.02
509	Bill Dawley	.04	.03	.02
510	Dave Winfield	.20	.15	.08
511	Joel Davis	.04	.03	.02
512	Alex Trevino	.04	.03	.02
513	Tim Flannery	.04	.03	.02
514	Pat Sheridan	.04	.03	.02
515	Juan Nieves	.06	.05	.02
516	Jim Sundberg	.06	.05	.02
517	Ron Robinson	.04	.03	.02
518	Greg Gross	.04	.03	.02
519	Mariners Leaders (Phil Bradley, Harold Reynolds)	.06	.05	.02
520	Dave Smith	.06	.05	.02
521	Jim Dwyer	.04	.03	.02
522	*Bob Patterson* (FC)	.12	.09	.05
523	Gary Roenicke	.04	.03	.02
524	Gary Lucas	.04	.03	.02
525	Marty Barrett	.06	.05	.02
526	Juan Berenguer	.04	.03	.02
527	Steve Henderson	.04	.03	.02
528	Checklist 397-528	.04	.03	.02
529	Tim Burke	.04	.03	.02
530	Gary Carter	.15	.11	.06
531	Rich Yett	.04	.03	.02
532	Mike Kingery	.04	.03	.02
533	*John Farrell* (FC)	.08	.06	.03
534	John Wathan	.06	.05	.02
535	Ron Guidry	.12	.09	.05
536	John Morris	.04	.03	.02
537	Steve Buechele	.04	.03	.02
538	Bill Wegman	.04	.03	.02
539	Mike LaValliere	.06	.05	.02
540	Bret Saberhagen	.10	.08	.04
541	Juan Beniquez	.04	.03	.02
542	*Paul Noce* (FC)	.04	.03	.02
543	Kent Tekulve	.06	.05	.02
544	Jim Traber	.06	.05	.02
545	Don Baylor	.08	.06	.03
546	John Candelaria	.06	.05	.02
547	*Felix Fermin* (FC)	.12	.09	.05
548	*Shane Mack*	.15	.11	.06
549	Braves Leaders (Ken Griffey, Dion James, Dale Murphy, Gerald Perry)	.08	.06	.03
550	Pedro Guerrero	.15	.11	.06
551	Terry Steinbach	.15	.11	.06
552	Mark Thurmond	.04	.03	.02
553	Tracy Jones	.06	.05	.02
554	Mike Smithson	.04	.03	.02
555	Brook Jacoby	.08	.06	.03
556	*Stan Clarke* (FC)	.04	.03	.02
557	Craig Reynolds	.04	.03	.02
558	Bob Ojeda	.06	.05	.02
559	*Ken Williams* (FC)	.08	.06	.03
560	Tim Wallach	.08	.06	.03
561	Rick Cerone	.04	.03	.02
562	Jim Lindeman	.04	.03	.02
563	Jose Guzman	.06	.05	.02
564	Frank Lucchesi	.04	.03	.02
565	Lloyd Moseby	.06	.05	.02
566	*Charlie O'Brien* (FC)	.04	.03	.02
567	Mike Diaz	.06	.05	.02
568	Chris Brown	.06	.05	.02
569	Charlie Leibrandt	.06	.05	.02
570	Jeffrey Leonard	.06	.05	.02
571	*Mark Williamson* (FC)	.06	.05	.02
572	Chris James	.06	.05	.02
573	Bob Stanley	.04	.03	.02
574	Graig Nettles	.08	.06	.03
575	Don Sutton	.12	.09	.05
576	*Tommy Hinzo* (FC)	.04	.03	.02
577	Tom Browning	.08	.06	.03
578	Gary Gaetti	.10	.08	.04
579	Mets Leaders (Gary Carter, Kevin McReynolds)	.08	.06	.03
580	Mark McGwire	.35	.25	.14
581	Tito Landrum	.04	.03	.02
582	*Mike Henneman*	.25	.20	.10
583	Dave Valle (FC)	.06	.05	.02
584	Steve Trout	.04	.03	.02
585	Ozzie Guillen	.06	.05	.02
586	Bob Forsch	.06	.05	.02
587	Terry Puhl	.04	.03	.02
588	*Jeff Parrett* (FC)	.06	.05	.02
589	Geno Petralli	.04	.03	.02
590	George Bell	.12	.09	.05
591	Doug Drabek	.06	.05	.02
592	Dale Sveum	.06	.05	.02
593	Bob Tewksbury	.04	.03	.02
594	Bobby Valentine	.04	.03	.02
595	Frank White	.06	.05	.02
596	John Kruk	.12	.09	.05
597	Gene Garber	.04	.03	.02
598	Lee Lacy	.04	.03	.02
599	Calvin Schiraldi	.04	.03	.02
600	Mike Schmidt	.40	.30	.15
601	Jack Lazorko	.04	.03	.02
602	Mike Aldrete	.06	.05	.02
603	Rob Murphy	.06	.05	.02
604	Chris Bando	.04	.03	.02
605	Kirk Gibson	.15	.11	.06
606	Moose Haas	.04	.03	.02
607	Mickey Hatcher	.04	.03	.02
608	Charlie Kerfeld	.04	.03	.02
609	Twins Leaders (Gary Gaetti, Kent Hrbek)	.08	.06	.03
610	Keith Hernandez	.06	.05	.02
611	Tommy John	.12	.09	.05
612	Curt Ford	.04	.03	.02
613	Bobby Thigpen	.08	.06	.03
614	Herm Winningham	.04	.03	.02
615	Jody Davis	.06	.05	.02
616	*Jay Aldrich* (FC)	.04	.03	.02
617	Oddibe McDowell	.06	.05	.02
618	Cecil Fielder	.35	.25	.14
619	*Mike Dunne*	.06	.05	.02
620	Cory Snyder	.08	.06	.03
621	Gene Nelson	.04	.03	.02
622	Kal Daniels	.06	.05	.02
623	Mike Flanagan	.06	.05	.02
624	Jim Leyland	.04	.03	.02
625	Frank Viola	.12	.09	.05
626	Glenn Wilson	.06	.05	.02
627	*Joe Boever* (FC)	.04	.03	.02
628	Dave Henderson	.08	.06	.03
629	Kelly Downs	.08	.06	.03
630	Darrell Evans	.08	.06	.03
631	Jack Howell	.06	.05	.02
632	*Steve Shields*	.04	.03	.02
633	*Barry Lyons*	.04	.03	.02
634	Jose DeLeon	.06	.05	.02
635	Terry Pendleton	.12	.09	.05
636	Charles Hudson	.04	.03	.02
637	*Jay Bell* (FC)	.50	.40	.20
638	Steve Balboni	.06	.05	.02
639	Brewers Leaders (Glenn Braggs, Tony Muser)	.06	.05	.02
640	Garry Templeton	.06	.05	.02
641	Rick Honeycutt	.04	.03	.02
642	Bob Dernier	.04	.03	.02
643	*Rocky Childress* (FC)	.04	.03	.02
644	Terry McGriff (FC)	.06	.05	.02
645	*Matt Nokes*	.10	.08	.04
646	Checklist 529-660	.04	.03	.02
647	Pascual Perez	.06	.05	.02
648	Al Newman	.04	.03	.02
649	*DeWayne Buice*	.04	.03	.02
650	Cal Ripken, Jr.	.40	.30	.15
651	*Mike Jackson* (FC)	.15	.11	.06
652	Bruce Benedict	.04	.03	.02
653	Jeff Sellers	.06	.05	.02
654	Roger Craig	.06	.05	.02
655	Len Dykstra	.12	.09	.05
656	Lee Guetterman	.04	.03	.02
657	Gary Redus	.04	.03	.02
658	Tim Conroy	.04	.03	.02
659	Bobby Meacham	.04	.03	.02
660	Rick Reuschel	.08	.06	.03
661	Turn Back The Clock (Nolan Ryan)	.25	.20	.10
662	Turn Back The Clock (Jim Rice)	.08	.06	.03
663	Turn Back The Clock (Ron Blomberg)	.04	.03	.02
664	Turn Back The Clock (Bob Gibson)	.08	.06	.03
665	Turn Back The Clock (Stan Musial)	.12	.09	.05
666	Mario Soto	.06	.05	.02
667	Luis Quinones	.04	.03	.02
668	Walt Terrell	.06	.05	.02
669	Phillies Leaders (Lance Parrish, Mike Ryan)	.06	.05	.02
670	Dan Plesac	.08	.06	.03
671	Tim Laudner	.04	.03	.02
672	*John Davis* (FC)	.04	.03	.02
673	Tony Phillips	.04	.03	.02
674	Mike Fitzgerald	.04	.03	.02
675	Jim Rice	.08	.06	.03
676	Ken Dixon	.04	.03	.02
677	Eddie Milner	.04	.03	.02
678	Jim Acker	.04	.03	.02
679	Darrell Miller	.04	.03	.02
680	Charlie Hough	.06	.05	.02
681	Bobby Bonilla	.15	.11	.06
682	Jimmy Key	.10	.08	.04
683	Julio Franco	.08	.06	.03
684	Hal Lanier	.04	.03	.02
685	Ron Darling	.04	.03	.02
686	Terry Francona	.04	.03	.02
687	Mickey Brantley	.04	.03	.02
688	Jim Winn	.04	.03	.02
689	*Tom Pagnozzi* (FC)	.10	.08	.04
690	Jay Howell	.06	.05	.02
691	Dan Pasqua	.08	.06	.03
692	Mike Birkbeck	.06	.05	.02
693	Benny Santiago	.12	.09	.05
694	*Eric Nolte* (FC)	.06	.05	.02
695	Shawon Dunston	.08	.06	.03
696	Duane Ward	.04	.03	.02
697	Steve Lombardozzi	.08	.06	.03
698	Brad Havens	.04	.03	.02
699	Padres Leaders (Tony Gwynn, Benny Santiago)	.12	.09	.05
700	George Brett	.20	.15	.08
701	Sammy Stewart	.04	.03	.02
702	Mike Gallego	.04	.03	.02
703	Bob Brenly	.04	.03	.02
704	Dennis Boyd	.06	.05	.02
705	Juan Samuel	.10	.08	.04
706	Rick Mahler	.04	.03	.02
707	Fred Lynn	.10	.08	.04
708	Gus Polidor (FC)	.06	.05	.02
709	George Frazier	.04	.03	.02
710	Darryl Strawberry	.15	.11	.06
711	Bill Gullickson	.04	.03	.02
712	John Moses	.04	.03	.02
713	Willie Hernandez	.06	.05	.02
714	Jim Fregosi	.04	.03	.02
715	Todd Worrell	.08	.06	.03
716	Lenn Sakata	.04	.03	.02
717	Jay Baller (FC)	.06	.05	.02
718	Mike Felder	.04	.03	.02
719	Denny Walling	.04	.03	.02
720	Tim Raines	.10	.08	.04
721	Pete O'Brien	.06	.05	.02
722	Manny Lee	.04	.03	.02
723	Bob Kipper	.04	.03	.02
724	Danny Tartabull	.10	.08	.04
725	Mike Boddicker	.06	.05	.02
726	Alfredo Griffin	.06	.05	.02
727	Greg Booker	.04	.03	.02
728	Andy Allanson	.06	.05	.02
729	Blue Jays Leaders (George Bell, Fred McGriff)	.10	.08	.04
730	John Franco	.08	.06	.03
731	Rick Schu	.04	.03	.02
732	Dave Palmer	.04	.03	.02
733	Spike Owen	.04	.03	.02

No.	Player	MT	NR MT	EX
734	Craig Lefferts	.04	.03	.02
735	Kevin McReynolds	.10	.08	.04
736	Matt Young	.04	.03	.02
737	Butch Wynegar	.04	.03	.02
738	Scott Bankhead	.04	.03	.02
739	Daryl Boston	.04	.03	.02
740	Rick Sutcliffe	.08	.06	.03
741	Mike Easler	.06	.05	.02
742	Mark Clear	.04	.03	.02
743	Larry Herndon	.04	.03	.02
744	Whitey Herzog	.06	.05	.02
745	Bill Doran	.06	.05	.02
746	*Gene Larkin*	.10	.08	.04
747	Bobby Witt	.08	.06	.03
748	Reid Nichols	.04	.03	.02
749	Mark Eichhorn	.06	.05	.02
750	Bo Jackson	.40	.30	.15
751	Jim Morrison	.04	.03	.02
752	Mark Grant	.04	.03	.02
753	Danny Heep	.04	.03	.02
754	Mike LaCoss	.04	.03	.02
755	Ozzie Virgil	.04	.03	.02
756	Mike Maddux	.06	.05	.02
757	*John Marzano*	.06	.05	.02
758	*Eddie Williams* (FC)	.08	.06	.03
759	Jose Canseco, Mark McGwire)	.25	.20	.10
760	Mike Scott	.10	.08	.04
761	Tony Armas	.06	.05	.02
762	Scott Bradley	.04	.03	.02
763	Doug Sisk	.04	.03	.02
764	Greg Walker	.06	.05	.02
765	Neal Heaton	.06	.05	.02
766	Honry Cotto	.04	.03	.02
767	*Jose Lind* (FC) (Future Stars)	.25	.20	.10
768	Dickie Noles	.04	.03	.02
769	Cecil Cooper	.08	.06	.03
770	Lou Whitaker	.10	.08	.04
771	Ruben Sierra	.15	.11	.06
772	Sal Butera	.04	.03	.02
773	Frank Williams	.04	.03	.02
774	Gene Mauch	.06	.05	.02
775	Dave Stieb	.08	.06	.03
776	Checklist 661-792	.04	.03	.02
777	Lonnie Smith	.06	.05	.02
778a	*Keith Comstock* (FC) (white team letters)	.60	.45	.25
778b	*Keith Comstock* (FC) (blue team letters)	.25	.20	.10
779	*Tom Glavine* (FC)	1.50	1.25	.60
780	Fernando Valenzuela	.15	.11	.06
781	*Keith Hughes* (FC)	.06	.05	.02
782	*Jeff Ballard* (FC)	.08	.06	.03
783	Ron Roenicke	.04	.03	.02
784	Joe Sambito	.04	.03	.02
785	Alvin Davis	.04	.03	.02
786	Joe Price	.04	.03	.02
787	Bill Almon	.04	.03	.02
788	Ray Searage	.04	.03	.02
789	Indians Leaders (Joe Carter, Cory Snyder)	.10	.07	.04
790	Dave Righetti	.06	.05	.02
791	Ted Simmons	.08	.06	.03
792	John Tudor	.08	.06	.03

1988 Topps All-Star Glossy Set of 22

The fifth edition of Topps' special All-Star inserts (22 cards) was included in the company's 1988 rack packs. The 1987 American and National League All-Star lineup, plus honorary captains Jim Hunter and Billy Williams, are featured on the standard-size All-Star inserts. The glossy full-color card fronts contain player photos centered between a red and yellow "1987 All-Star" logo printed across the card top and the player name (also red and yellow) which is printed across the bottom margin. A National or American League logo appears in the lower left corner. Card backs are printed in red and blue on a white background, with the title and All-Star logo emblem printed above the player name and card number.

		MT	NR MT	EX
	Complete Set:	4.00	3.00	1.50
	Common Player:	.15	.11	.06
1	John McNamara	.15	.11	.06
2	Don Mattingly	1.00	.70	.40
3	Willie Randolph	.15	.11	.06
4	Wade Boggs	.80	.60	.30
5	Cal Ripken, Jr.	.75	.60	.30
6	George Bell	.30	.25	.12
7	Rickey Henderson	.50	.40	.20
8	Dave Winfield	.40	.30	.15
9	Terry Kennedy	.15	.11	.06
10	Bret Saberhagen	.25	.20	.10
11	Catfish Hunter	.25	.20	.10
12	Davey Johnson	.15	.11	.06
13	Jack Clark	.15	.11	.06
14	Ryne Sandberg	.75	.60	.30
15	Mike Schmidt	.60	.45	.25
16	Ozzie Smith	.35	.25	.14
17	Eric Davis	.25	.20	.10
18	Andre Dawson	.25	.20	.10
19	Darryl Strawberry	.25	.20	.10
20	Gary Carter	.25	.20	.10
21	Mike Scott	.15	.11	.06
22	Billy Williams	.25	.20	.10

1988 Topps All-Star Glossy Set of 60

This standard-size collectors set includes 60 full-color glossy cards featuring All-Stars and Prospects in six separate 10-card sets. In 1986, Topps issued a similar set that included only All-Stars. Card fronts have a white border and a thin red line framing the player photo, with the player's name in the lower left corner. Card backs, in red and blue, include very basic player information (name, team and position), along with the card set logo and card number. Topps glossy collector sets were marketed via a special offer printed on a card packaged in all Topps wax packs. For six special offer cards and $1.25, collectors received one of the six 10-card sets; 18 special offer cards and $7.50 earned the entire 60-card collection.

		MT	NR MT	EX
	Complete Set:	14.00	10.50	5.50
	Common Player:	.15	.11	.06
1	Andre Dawson	.30	.25	.12
2	Jesse Barfield	.20	.15	.08
3	Mike Schmidt	.70	.50	.30
4	Ruben Sierra	.40	.30	.15
5	Mike Scott	.20	.15	.08
6	Cal Ripken, Jr.	.70	.50	.30
7	Gary Carter	.30	.25	.12
8	Kent Hrbek	.30	.25	.12
9	Kevin Seitzer	.25	.20	.10
10	Mike Henneman	.35	.25	.14
11	Don Mattingly	2.00	1.50	.80
12	Tim Raines	.25	.20	.10
13	Roger Clemens	.60	.45	.25
14	Ryne Sandberg	.70	.50	.30
15	Tony Fernandez	.20	.15	.08
16	Eric Davis	.25	.20	.10
17	Jack Morris	.20	.15	.08
18	Tim Wallach	.20	.15	.08
19	Mike Dunne	.25	.20	.10
20	Mike Greenwell	.60	.45	.25
21	Dwight Evans	.20	.15	.08
22	Darryl Strawberry	.40	.30	.15
23	Cory Snyder	.20	.15	.08
24	Pedro Guerrero	.20	.15	.08
25	Rickey Henderson	.60	.45	.25
26	Dale Murphy	.60	.45	.25
27	Kirby Puckett	.50	.40	.20
28	Steve Bedrosian	.20	.15	.08
29	Devon White	.25	.20	.10
30	Benny Santiago	.25	.20	.10
31	George Bell	.25	.20	.10
32	Keith Hernandez	.25	.20	.10
33	Dave Stewart	.25	.20	.10
34	Dave Parker	.25	.20	.10
35	Tom Henke	.15	.11	.06
36	Willie McGee	.20	.15	.08
37	Alan Trammell	.30	.25	.12
38	Tony Gwynn	.50	.40	.20
39	Mark McGwire	.50	.40	.20
40	Joe Magrane	.25	.20	.10
41	Jack Clark	.25	.20	.10
42	Willie Randolph	.15	.11	.06
43	Juan Samuel	.25	.20	.10
44	Joe Carter	.35	.25	.14
45	Shane Rawley	.15	.11	.06
46	Dave Winfield	.50	.40	.20
47	Ozzie Smith	.35	.25	.14
48	Wally Joyner	.35	.25	.14
49	B.J. Surhoff	.20	.15	.08
50	Ellis Burks	.35	.25	.14
51	Wade Boggs	.80	.60	.30
52	Howard Johnson	.20	.15	.08
53	George Brett	.70	.50	.30
54	Dwight Gooden	.35	.25	.14
55	Jose Canseco	2.00	1.50	.80
56	Lee Smith	.25	.20	.10
57	Paul Molitor	.40	.30	.15
58	Andres Galarraga	.30	.25	.12
59	Matt Nokes	.20	.15	.08
60	Casey Candaele	.15	.11	.06

1988 Topps Traded

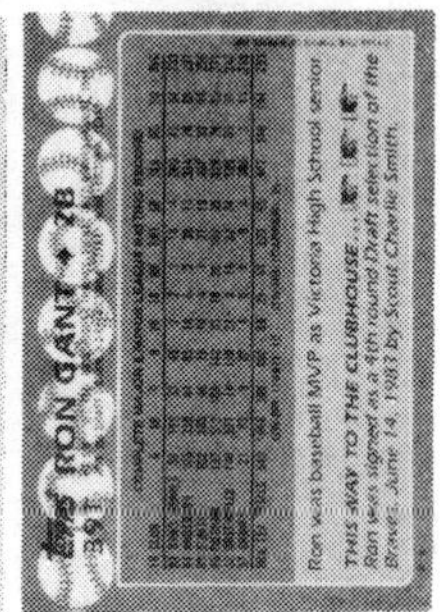

In addition to new players and traded veterans, 21 members of the U.S.A. Olympic Baseball team are showcased in this 132-card set, numbered 1T-132T. The standard-size (2-1/2" by 3-1/2") set follows the same design as the basic Topps issue - white borders, large full-color photos, team name (or U.S.A.) in large bold letters at the top of the card face, player name on a diagonal stripe across the lower right corner. Topps has issued its traded series each year since 1981 in boxed complete sets available through hobby dealers.

		MT	NR MT	EX
	Complete Set (132):	30.00	22.00	12.00
	Common Player:	.06	.05	.02
1T	Jim Abbott (USA)	6.00	4.50	2.50
2T	Juan Agosto	.06	.05	.02
3T	Luis Alicea (FC)	.15	.11	.06
4T	Roberto Alomar (FC)	8.00	6.00	3.25
5T	Brady Anderson (FC)	1.00	.70	.40
6T	Jack Armstrong	.25	.20	.10
7T	Don August	.08	.06	.03
8T	Floyd Bannister	.08	.06	.03
9T	Bret Barberie (FC) (USA)	.50	.40	.20
10T	Jose Bautista (FC)	.15	.11	.06
11T	Don Baylor	.10	.08	.04
12T	Tim Belcher	.20	.15	.08
13T	Buddy Bell	.10	.08	.04
14T	Andy Benes (FC) (USA)	2.50	2.00	1.00
15T	Damon Berryhill	.10	.08	.04
16T	Bud Black	.06	.05	.02
17T	Pat Borders	.20	.15	.08
18T	Phil Bradley	.10	.08	.04
19T	Jeff Branson (FC) (USA)	.06	.05	.02
20T	Tom Brunansky	.06	.05	.02
21T	Jay Buhner	1.25	.90	.50
22T	Brett Butler	.10	.08	.04
23T	Jim Campanis (FC) (USA)	.20	.15	.08
24T	Sil Campusano (FC)	.10	.08	.04
25T	John Candelaria	.08	.06	.03
26T	Jose Cecena (FC)	.06	.05	.02
27T	Rick Cerone	.06	.05	.02
28T	Jack Clark	.08	.06	.03
29T	Kevin Coffman (FC)	.10	.08	.04
30T	Pat Combs (USA)	.10	.08	.04
31T	Henry Cotto	.06	.05	.02
32T	Chili Davis	.12	.09	.05
33T	Mike Davis	.08	.06	.03
34T	Jose DeLeon	.08	.06	.03
35T	Richard Dotson	.10	.08	.04
36T	Cecil Espy	.06	.05	.02
37T	Tom Filer	.06	.05	.02
38T	Mike Fiore (FC) (USA)	.10	.08	.04
39T	Ron Gant	1.50	1.25	.60
40T	Kirk Gibson	.10	.08	.04
41T	Rich Gossage	.15	.11	.06
42T	Mark Grace (FC)	2.00	1.50	.80
43T	Alfredo Griffin	.08	.06	.03
44T	Ty Griffin (FC) (USA)	.10	.08	.04
45T	Bryan Harvey	1.50	1.25	.60
46T	Ron Hassey	.06	.05	.02
47T	Ray Hayward (FC)	.08	.06	.03
48T	Dave Henderson	.20	.15	.08
49T	Tom Herr	.10	.08	.04
50T	Bob Horner	.10	.08	.04
51T	Ricky Horton	.08	.06	.03
52T	Jay Howell	.08	.06	.03
53T	Glenn Hubbard	.06	.05	.02
54T	Jeff Innis (FC)	.10	.08	.04
55T	Danny Jackson	.15	.11	.06
56T	Darrin Jackson	.30	.25	.12
57T	Roberto Kelly	.75	.60	.30
58T	Ron Kittle	.10	.08	.04
59T	Ray Knight	.08	.06	.03
60T	Vance Law	.08	.06	.03
61T	Jeffrey Leonard	.08	.06	.03
62T	Mike Macfarlane	.40	.30	.15
63T	Scotti Madison (FC)	.08	.06	.03
64T	Kirt Manwaring (FC)	.20	.15	.08

65T	Mark Marquess (USA)	.06	.05	.02
66T	Tino Martinez (USA)	.75	.60	.30
67T	Billy Masse (FC) (USA)	.12	.09	.05
68T	Jack McDowell	1.50	1.25	.60
69T	Jack McKeon	.06	.05	.02
70T	Larry McWilliams	.06	.05	.02
71T	Mickey Morandini (USA)	.50	.40	.20
72T	Keith Moreland	.08	.06	.03
73T	Mike Morgan	.06	.05	.02
74T	Charles Nagy (USA)	.75	.60	.30
75T	Al Nipper	.06	.05	.02
76T	Russ Nixon	.06	.05	.02
77T	Jesse Orosco	.08	.06	.03
78T	Joe Orsulak	.06	.05	.02
79T	Dave Palmer	.06	.05	.02
80T	Mark Parent (FC)	.10	.08	.04
81T	Dave Parker	.12	.09	.05
82T	Dan Pasqua	.10	.08	.04
83T	Melido Perez	.20	.15	.08
84T	Steve Peters (FC)	.08	.06	.03
85T	Dan Petry	.08	.06	.03
86T	Gary Pettis	.08	.06	.03
87T	Jeff Pico (FC)	.08	.06	.03
88T	Jim Poole (USA)	.10	.08	.04
89T	Ted Power	.06	.05	.02
90T	Rafael Ramirez	.06	.05	.02
91T	Dennis Rasmussen	.10	.08	.04
92T	Jose Rijo	.15	.11	.06
93T	Earnie Riles	.06	.05	.02
94T	Luis Rivera (FC)	.08	.06	.03
95T	Doug Robbins (FC) (USA)	.10	.08	.04
96T	Frank Robinson	.15	.11	.06
97T	Cookie Rojas	.06	.05	.02
98T	Chris Sabo (FC)	.40	.30	.15
99T	Mark Salas	.06	.05	.02
100T	Luis Salazar	.06	.05	.02
101T	Rafael Santana	.06	.05	.02
102T	Nelson Santovenia (FC)	.10	.08	.04
103T	Mackey Sasser (FC)	.10	.08	.04
104T	Calvin Schiraldi	.06	.05	.02
105T	Mike Schooler (FC)	.15	.11	.06
106T	Scott Servais (FC) (USA)	.10	.08	.04
107T	Dave Silvestri (USA)	.10	.08	.04
108T	Don Slaught	.06	.05	.02
109T	Joe Slusarski (FC) (USA)	.12	.09	.05
110T	Lee Smith	.12	.09	.05
111T	Pete Smith (FC)	.40	.30	.15
112T	Jim Snyder	.06	.05	.02
113T	Ed Sprague (FC) (USA)	.60	.45	.25
114T	Pete Stanicek (FC)	.15	.11	.06
115T	Kurt Stillwell	.10	.08	.04
116T	Todd Stottlemyre	.25	.20	.10
117T	Bill Swift	.20	.15	.08
118T	Pat Tabler	.08	.06	.03
119T	Scott Terry (FC)	.10	.08	.04
120T	Mickey Tettleton	.20	.15	.08
121T	Dickie Thon	.08	.06	.03
122T	Jeff Treadway	.10	.08	.04
123T	Willie Upshaw	.08	.06	.03
124T	Robin Ventura (FC)	6.00	4.50	2.50
125T	Ron Washington	.06	.05	.02
126T	Walt Weiss (FC)	.30	.25	.12
127T	Bob Welch	.10	.08	.04
128T	David Wells (FC)	.25	.20	.10
129T	Glenn Wilson	.08	.06	.03
130T	Ted Wood (FC) (USA)	.15	.11	.06
131T	Don Zimmer	.06	.05	.02
132T	Checklist 1T-132T	.06	.05	.02

1988 Topps Box Panels

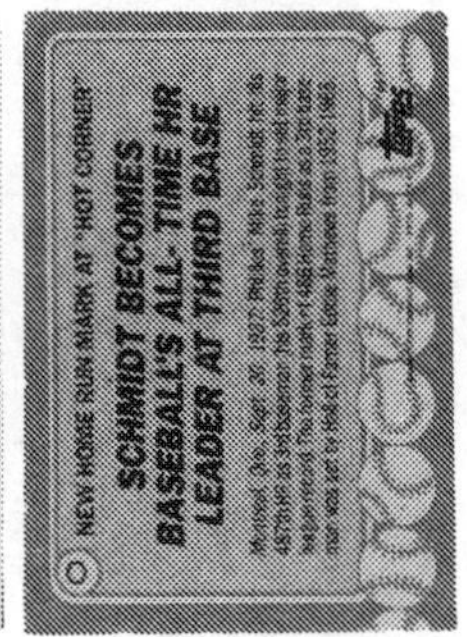

After a one-year hiatus during which they appeared on the sides of Topps wax pack display boxes, Topps retail box cards returned to box bottoms in 1988. Topps first issued box-bottom cards in 1986, following the introduction of the concept by Donruss in 1985. Topps 1988 box-bottom series includes 16 standard-size baseball cards, four cards per each of four different display boxes. Card fronts follow the same design as the 1988 Topps basic issue; full-color player photos, framed in yellow, surrounded by a white border; diagonal player name lower right; team name in large letters at the top of the card front. Card backs are "numbered" A through P and are printed in black and orange.

		MT	NR MT	EX
Complete Panel Set:		7.00	5.25	2.75
Complete Singles Set:		3.00	2.25	1.25
Common Panel:		1.00	.70	.40
Common Single Player:		.08	.06	.03
	Panel	1.00	.70	.40
A	Don Baylor	.15	.11	.06
B	Steve Bedrosian	.12	.09	.05
C	Juan Beniquez	.08	.06	.03
D	Bob Boone	.12	.09	.05
	Panel	1.75	1.25	.70
E	Darrell Evans	.12	.09	.05
F	Tony Gwynn	.30	.25	.12
G	John Kruk	.25	.20	.10
H	Marvell Wynne	.08	.06	.03
	Panel	2.25	1.75	.90
I	Joe Carter	.25	.20	.10
J	Eric Davis	.25	.20	.10
K	Howard Johnson	.12	.09	.05
L	Darryl Strawberry	.20	.15	.08
	Panel	3.00	2.25	1.25
M	Rickey Henderson	.50	.40	.20
N	Nolan Ryan	.75	.60	.30
O	Mike Schmidt	.35	.25	.15
P	Kent Tekulve	.08	.06	.03

1988 Topps American Baseball

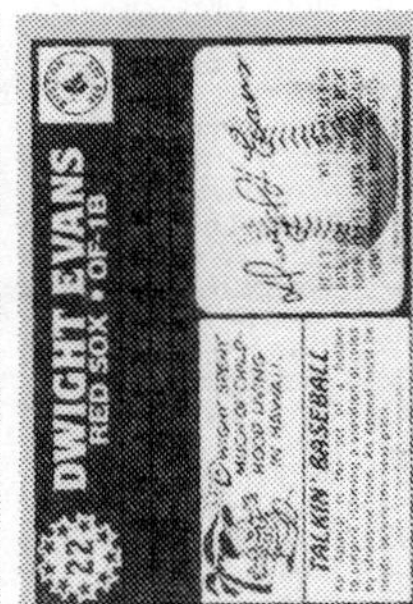

This 88-card set, unlike Topps' United Kingdom football cards, was made available for distribution by U.S. hobby dealers. The cards were packaged in checklist-backed boxes with an American flag on the top flap. The 2-1/4" by 3" cards feature full-color player photos printed on white stock with a red line framing the photo. The team name, printed in individual team colors, intersects the red frame at the top of the card. A bright yellow name banner appears below the photo. Card backs have bright blue borders and cartoon-style horizontal layouts. The card number appears within a circle of red stars upper left, beside the player's name and team logo. A red banner containing the player career stats runs the length of the card back. The lower half of the flip side features a caricature of the player and a one-line caption. Below the cartoon, a short "Talkin' Baseball" paragraph provides elementary baseball information, obviously designed to acquaint soccer-playing European collectors with American baseball rules and terminology. A glossy edition of the set was issued and is valued at 2-3 times greater than the regular issue.

		MT	NR MT	EX
Complete Set:		10.00	7.50	4.00
Common Player:		.08	.06	.03
1	Harold Baines	.15	.11	.06
2	Steve Bedrosian	.10	.08	.04
3	George Bell	.12	.09	.05
4	Wade Boggs	.70	.50	.30
5	Barry Bonds	.60	.45	.25
6	Bob Boone	.15	.11	.06
7	George Brett	.60	.45	.25
8	Hubie Brooks	.08	.06	.03
9	Ivan Calderon	.08	.06	.03
10	Jose Canseco	1.25	.90	.50
11	Gary Carter	.30	.25	.12
12	Joe Carter	.25	.20	.10
13	Jack Clark	.20	.15	.08
14	Will Clark	.60	.45	.25
15	Roger Clemens	.45	.35	.20
16	Vince Coleman	.20	.15	.08
17	Alvin Davis	.08	.06	.03
18	Eric Davis	.30	.25	.12
19	Glenn Davis	.08	.06	.03
20	Andre Dawson	.25	.20	.10
21	Mike Dunne	.15	.11	.06
22	Dwight Evans	.10	.08	.04
23	Tony Fernandez	.15	.11	.06
24	John Franco	.10	.08	.04
25	Gary Gaetti	.20	.15	.08
26	Kirk Gibson	.15	.11	.06
27	Dwight Gooden	.25	.20	.10
28	Pedro Guerrero	.12	.09	.05
29	Tony Gwynn	.35	.25	.14
30	Billy Hatcher	.15	.11	.06
31	Rickey Henderson	.35	.25	.14
32	Tom Henke	.08	.06	.03
33	Keith Hernandez	.15	.11	.06
34	Orel Hershiser	.20	.15	.08
35	Teddy Higuera	.10	.08	.04
36	Charlie Hough	.08	.06	.03
37	Kent Hrbek	.25	.20	.10
38	Brook Jacoby	.10	.08	.04
39	Dion James	.08	.06	.03
40	Wally Joyner	.25	.20	.10
41	John Kruk	.20	.15	.08
42	Mark Langston	.15	.11	.06
43	Jeffrey Leonard	.08	.06	.03
44	Candy Maldonaldo	.08	.06	.03
45	Don Mattingly	.90	.70	.35
46	Willie McGee	.15	.11	.06
47	Mark McGwire	.45	.35	.20
48	Kevin Mitchell	.12	.09	.05
49	Paul Molitor	.35	.25	.14
50	Jack Morris	.15	.11	.06
51	Lloyd Moseby	.10	.08	.04
52	Dale Murphy	.40	.30	.15
53	Eddie Murray	.40	.30	.15
54	Matt Nokes	.20	.15	.08
55	Dave Parker	.25	.20	.10
56	Larry Parrish	.08	.06	.03
57	Kirby Puckett	.40	.30	.15
58	Tim Raines	.20	.15	.08
59	Willie Randolph	.08	.06	.03
60	Harold Reynolds	.08	.06	.03
61	Cal Ripken, Jr.	.75	.60	.30
62	Nolan Ryan	.90	.70	.35
63	Bret Saberhagen	.20	.15	.08
64	Juan Samuel	.15	.11	.06
65	Ryne Sandberg	.60	.45	.25
66	Benny Santiago	.15	.11	.06
67	Mike Schmidt	.60	.45	.25
68	Mike Scott	.10	.08	.04
69	Kevin Seitzer	.10	.08	.04
70	Larry Sheets	.08	.06	.03
71	Ruben Sierra	.25	.20	.10
72	Ozzie Smith	.40	.30	.15
73	Zane Smith	.08	.06	.03
74	Cory Snyder	.08	.06	.03
75	Dave Stewart	.15	.11	.06
76	Darryl Strawberry	.20	.15	.08
77	Rick Sutcliffe	.15	.11	.06
78	Danny Tartabull	.20	.15	.08
79	Alan Trammell	.25	.20	.10
80	Fernando Valenzuela	.12	.09	.05
81	Andy Van Slyke	.15	.11	.06
82	Frank Viola	.15	.11	.06
83	Greg Walker	.10	.08	.04
84	Tim Wallach	.10	.08	.04
85	Dave Winfield	.40	.30	.15
86	Mike Witt	.08	.06	.03
87	Robin Yount	.35	.25	.14
88	Checklist	.08	.06	.03

1988 Topps Big Baseball

1988 Topps Big Baseball cards (2-5/8" by 3-3/4") were issued in three series, 88 cards per series (a total set of 264 cards). Each series features current star players, sold in 7-card packages. The glossy cards are similar in format, both front and back, to the 1956 Topps 340-card set. Each card features a posed head shot and a close-up action photo on the front, framed by a wide white border and a dark blue inner border. A white outlines highlights the player closeup. The player's name appears below his head shot, in reversed type on a splash of color that fades from yellow to orange to red to pink. On the card back, the player's name is printed in large red letters across the top, followed by his team name and position in black. Personal info is printed in a red rectangle beside a Topps baseball logo bearing the card number. A triple cartoon strip, in full-color, illustrates career highlights, performance, personal background, etc. A red, white and blue statistics box (pitching, batting, fielding) is printed across the bottom.

		MT	NR MT	EX
Complete Set:		20.00	15.00	8.00
Common Player:		.05	.04	.02
1	Paul Molitor	.20	.15	.08
2	Milt Thompson	.05	.04	.02
3	Billy Hatcher	.05	.04	.02
4	Mike Witt	.05	.04	.02
5	Vince Coleman	.12	.09	.05
6	Dwight Evans	.10	.08	.04

7	Tim Wallach	.10	.08	.04
8	Alan Trammell	.15	.11	.06
9	Will Clark	.80	.60	.30
10	Jeff Reardon	.08	.06	.03
11	Dwight Gooden	.25	.20	.10
12	Benny Santiago	.12	.09	.05
13	Jose Canseco	1.25	.90	.50
14	Dale Murphy	.30	.25	.12
15	George Bell	.20	.15	.08
16	Ryne Sandberg	.45	.35	.20
17	Brook Jacoby	.08	.06	.03
18	Fernando Valenzuela	.15	.11	.06
19	Scott Fletcher	.05	.04	.02
20	Eric Davis	.25	.20	.10
21	Willie Wilson	.10	.08	.04
22	B.J. Surhoff	.10	.08	.04
23	Steve Bedrosian	.08	.06	.03
24	Dave Winfield	.45	.35	.20
25	Bobby Bonilla	.15	.11	.06
26	Larry Sheets	.08	.06	.03
27	Ozzie Guillen	.08	.06	.03
28	Checklist 1-88	.05	.04	.02
29	Nolan Ryan	1.25	.90	.50
30	Bob Boone	.05	.04	.02
31	Tom Herr	.08	.06	.03
32	Wade Boggs	.90	.70	.35
33	Neal Heaton	.05	.04	.02
34	Doyle Alexander	.05	.04	.02
35	Candy Maldonado	.08	.06	.03
36	Kirby Puckett	.40	.30	.15
37	Gary Carter	.20	.15	.08
38	Lance McCullers	.08	.06	.03
39a	Terry Steinbach (black Topps logo on front)	.12	.09	.05
39b	Terry Steinbach (white Topps logo on front)	.12	.09	.05
40	Gerald Perry	.10	.08	.04
41	Tom Henke	.05	.04	.02
42	Leon Durham	.05	.04	.02
43	Cory Snyder	.12	.09	.05
44	Dale Sveum	.05	.04	.02
45	Lance Parrish	.12	.09	.05
46	Steve Sax	.12	.09	.05
47	Charlie Hough	.05	.04	.02
48	Kal Daniels	.15	.11	.06
49	Bo Jackson	.60	.45	.25
50	Ron Guidry	.10	.08	.04
51	Bill Doran	.08	.06	.03
52	Wally Joyner	.40	.30	.15
53	Terry Pendleton	.15	.11	.06
54	Marty Barrett	.08	.06	.03
55	Andres Galarraga	.25	.20	.10
56	Larry Herndon	.05	.04	.02
57	Kevin Mitchell	.08	.06	.03
58	Greg Gagne	.05	.04	.02
59	Keith Hernandez	.10	.08	.04
60	John Kruk	.15	.11	.06
61	Mike LaValliere	.08	.06	.03
62	Cal Ripken, jr.	.45	.35	.20
63	Ivan Calderon	.08	.06	.03
64	Alvin Davis	.10	.08	.04
65	Luis Polonia	.08	.06	.03
66	Robin Yount	.30	.25	.12
67	Juan Samuel	.12	.09	.05
68	Andres Thomas	.05	.04	.02
69	Jeff Musselman	.05	.04	.02
70	Jerry Mumphrey	.05	.04	.02
71	Joe Carter	.20	.15	.08
72	Mike Scioscia	.05	.04	.02
73	Pete Incaviglia	.10	.08	.04
74	Barry Larkin	.15	.11	.06
75	Frank White	.08	.06	.03
76	Willie Randolph	.08	.06	.03
77	Kevin Bass	.05	.04	.02
78	Brian Downing	.08	.06	.03
79	Willie McGee	.10	.08	.04
80	Ellis Burks	.20	.15	.08
81	Hubie Brooks	.08	.06	.03
82	Darrell Evans	.08	.06	.03
83	Robby Thompson	.05	.04	.02
84	Kent Hrbek	.15	.11	.06
85	Ron Darling	.12	.09	.05
86	Stan Jefferson	.05	.04	.02
87	Teddy Higuera	.10	.08	.04
88	Mike Schmidt	.60	.45	.25
89	Barry Bonds	.75	.60	.30
90	Jim Presley	.08	.06	.03
91	Orel Hershiser	.25	.20	.10
92	Jesse Barfield	.10	.08	.04
93	Tom Candiotti	.05	.04	.02
94	Bret Saberhagen	.12	.09	.05
95	Jose Uribe	.05	.04	.02
96	Tom Browning	.10	.08	.04
97	Johnny Ray	.08	.06	.03
98	Mike Morgan	.05	.04	.02
100	Jim Sundberg	.05	.04	.02
101	Roger McDowell	.08	.06	.03
102	Randy Ready	.05	.04	.02
103	Mike Gallego	.05	.04	.02
104	Steve Buechele	.05	.04	.02
105	Greg Walker	.08	.06	.03
106	Jose Lind	.12	.09	.05
107	Steve Trout	.05	.04	.02
108	Rick Rhoden	.08	.06	.03
109	Jim Pankovits	.05	.04	.02
110	Ken Griffey	.08	.06	.03
111	Danny Cox	.08	.06	.03
112	Franklin Stubbs	.05	.04	.02
113	Lloyd Moseby	.08	.06	.03
114	Mel Hall	.08	.06	.03
115	Kevin Seitzer	.05	.04	.02
116	Tim Raines	.25	.20	.10
117	Juan Castillo	.05	.04	.02
118	Roger Clemens	.50	.40	.20
119	Mike Aldrete	.08	.06	.03
120	Mario Soto	.05	.04	.02
121	Jack Howell	.05	.04	.02
122	Rick Schu	.05	.04	.02
123	Jeff Robinson	.10	.08	.04
124	Doug Drabek	.08	.06	.03
125	Henry Cotto	.05	.04	.02
126	Checklist 89-176	.05	.04	.02
127	Gary Gaetti	.12	.09	.05
128	Rick Sutcliffe	.10	.08	.04
129	Howard Johnson	.08	.06	.03
130	Chris Brown	.08	.06	.03
131	Dave Henderson	.08	.06	.03
132	Curt Wilkerson	.05	.04	.02
133	Mike Marshall	.10	.08	.04
134	Kelly Gruber	.05	.04	.02
135	Julio Franco	.10	.08	.04
136	Kurt Stillwell	.08	.06	.03
137	Donnie Hill	.05	.04	.02
138	Mike Pagliarulo	.10	.08	.04
139	Von Hayes	.08	.06	.03
140	Mike Scott	.10	.08	.04
141	Bob Kipper	.05	.04	.02
142	Harold Reynolds	.08	.06	.03
143	Bob Brenly	.05	.04	.02
144	Dave Concepcion	.08	.06	.03
145	Devon White	.20	.15	.08
146	Jeff Stone	.05	.04	.02
147	Chet Lemon	.05	.04	.02
148	Ozzie Virgil	.05	.04	.02
149	Todd Worrell	.10	.08	.04
150	Mitch Webster	.05	.04	.02
151	Rob Deer	.08	.06	.03
152	Rich Gedman	.08	.06	.03
153	Andre Dawson	.15	.11	.06
154	Mike Davis	.05	.04	.02
155	Nelson Liriano	.08	.06	.03
156	Greg Swindell	.10	.08	.04
157	George Brett	.45	.35	.20
158	Kevin McReynolds	.15	.11	.06
159	Brian Fisher	.08	.06	.03
160	Mike Kingery	.05	.04	.02
161	Tony Gwynn	.25	.20	.10
162	Don Baylor	.10	.08	.04
163	Jerry Browne	.05	.04	.02
164	Dan Pasqua	.08	.06	.03
165	Rickey Henderson	.25	.20	.10
166	Brett Butler	.08	.06	.03
167	Nick Esasky	.05	.04	.02
168	Kirk McCaskill	.05	.04	.02
169	Fred Lynn	.10	.08	.04
170	Jack Morris	.12	.09	.05
171	Pedro Guerrero	.12	.09	.05
172	Dave Stieb	.10	.08	.04
173	Pat Tabler	.08	.06	.03
174	Floyd Bannister	.05	.04	.02
175	Rafael Belliard	.05	.04	.02
176	Mark Langston	.10	.08	.04
177	Greg Mathews	.08	.06	.03
178	Claudell Washington	.05	.04	.02
179	Mark McGwire	.40	.30	.15
180	Bert Blyleven	.10	.08	.04
181	Jim Rice	.10	.08	.04
182	Mookie Wilson	.08	.06	.03
183	Willie Fraser	.05	.04	.02
184	Andy Van Slyke	.10	.08	.04
185	Matt Nokes	.10	.08	.04
186	Eddie Whitson	.05	.04	.02
187	Tony Fernandez	.10	.08	.04
188	Rick Reuschel	.08	.06	.03
189	Ken Phelps	.05	.04	.02
190	Juan Nieves	.08	.06	.03
191	Kirk Gibson	.10	.08	.04
192	Glenn Davis	.10	.08	.04
193	Zane Smith	.05	.04	.02
194	Jose DeLeon	.08	.06	.03
195	Gary Ward	.05	.04	.02
196	Pascual Perez	.05	.04	.02
197	Carlton Fisk	.12	.09	.05
198	Oddibe McDowell	.08	.06	.03
199	Mark Gubicza	.10	.08	.04
200	Glenn Hubbard	.05	.04	.02
201	Frank Viola	.15	.11	.06
202	Jody Reed	.12	.09	.05
203	Len Dykstra	.15	.11	.06
204	Dick Schofield	.05	.04	.02
205	Sid Bream	.05	.04	.02
206	Guillermo Hernandez	.05	.04	.02
207	Keith Moreland	.05	.04	.02
208	Mark Eichhorn	.05	.04	.02
209	Rene Gonzales	.08	.06	.03
210	Dave Valle	.05	.04	.02
211	Tom Brunansky	.10	.08	.04
212	Charles Hudson	.05	.04	.02
213	John Farrell	.10	.08	.04
214	Jeff Treadway	.08	.06	.03
215	Eddie Murray	.25	.20	.10
216	Checklist 177-264	.05	.04	.02
217	Greg Brock	.08	.06	.03
218	John Shelby	.05	.04	.02
219	Craig Reynolds	.05	.04	.02
220	Dion James	.05	.04	.02
221	Carney Lansford	.08	.06	.03
222	Juan Berenguer	.05	.04	.02
223	Luis Rivera	.08	.06	.03
224	Harold Baines	.12	.09	.05
225	Shawon Dunston	.08	.06	.03
226	Luis Aguayo	.05	.04	.02
227	Pete O'Brien	.08	.06	.03
228	Ozzie Smith	.20	.15	.08
229	Don Mattingly	1.00	.70	.40
230	Danny Tartabull	.15	.11	.06
231	Andy Allanson	.05	.04	.02
232	John Franco	.08	.06	.03
233	Mike Greenwell	.40	.30	.15
234	Bob Ojeda	.08	.06	.03
235	Chili Davis	.08	.06	.03
236	Mike Dunne	.12	.09	.05
237	Jim Morrison	.05	.04	.02
238	Carmelo Martinez	.05	.04	.02
239	Ernie Whitt	.05	.04	.02
240	Scott Garrelts	.05	.04	.02
241	Mike Moore	.05	.04	.02
242	Dave Parker	.20	.15	.08
243	Tim Laudner	.05	.04	.02
244	Bill Wegman	.05	.04	.02
245	Bob Horner	.08	.06	.03
246	Rafael Santana	.05	.04	.02
247	Alfredo Griffin	.05	.04	.02
248	Mark Bailey	.05	.04	.02
249	Ron Gant	.20	.15	.08
250	Bryn Smith	.05	.04	.02
251	Lance Johnson	.10	.08	.04
252	Sam Horn	.10	.08	.04
253	Darryl Strawberry	.20	.15	.08
254	Chuck Finley	.05	.04	.02
255	Darnell Coles	.08	.06	.03
256	Mike Henneman	.10	.08	.04
257	Andy Hawkins	.08	.06	.03
258	Jim Clancy	.08	.06	.03
259	Atlee Hammaker	.05	.04	.02
260	Glenn Wilson	.05	.04	.02
261	Larry McWilliams	.05	.04	.02
262	Jack Clark	.12	.09	.05
263	Walt Weiss	.40	.30	.15
264	Gene Larkin	.08	.06	.03

1988 Topps Coins

This edition of 60 lightweight metal coins is similar in design to Topps' 1964 set. The 1988 coins are 1-1/2" in diameter and feature full-color player close-ups under crimped edges in silver, gold and pink. Curved under the photo is a red and white player name banner pinned by two gold stars. Coin backs list the coin number, player name, personal information and career summary in black letters on a silver background.

		MT	NR MT	EX
Complete Set:		10.00	7.50	4.50
Common Player:		.10	.08	.04
1	George Bell	.10	.08	.04
2	Roger Clemens	.40	.30	.15
3	Mark McGwire	.40	.30	.15
4	Wade Boggs	.70	.50	.30
5	Harold Baines	.10	.08	.04
6	Ivan Calderon	.10	.08	.04
7	Jose Canseco	.50	.40	.20
8	Joe Carter	.20	.15	.08
9	Jack Clark	.10	.08	.04
10	Alvin Davis	.10	.08	.04
11	Dwight Evans	.10	.08	.04
12	Tony Fernandez	.10	.08	.04
13	Gary Gaetti	.10	.08	.04
14	Mike Greenwell	.20	.15	.08
15	Charlie Hough	.10	.08	.04
16	Wally Joyner	.20	.15	.08
17	Jimmy Key	.10	.08	.04
18	Mark Langston	.10	.08	.04
19	Don Mattingly	1.00	.70	.40
20	Paul Molitor	.25	.20	.10
21	Jack Morris	.10	.08	.04
22	Eddie Murray	.20	.15	.08
23	Kirby Puckett	.35	.25	.14
24	Cal Ripken, Jr.	1.25	.90	.50
25	Bret Saberhagen	.10	.08	.04
26	Ruben Sierra	.15	.11	.06
27	Cory Snyder	.10	.08	.04
28	Terry Steinbach	.10	.08	.04
29	Danny Tartabull	.15	.11	.06
30	Alan Trammell	.20	.15	.08
31	Devon White	.15	.11	.06
32	Robin Yount	.50	.40	.20
33	Andre Dawson	.15	.11	.06
34	Steve Bedrosian	.10	.08	.04
35	Benny Santiago	.10	.08	.04
36	Tony Gwynn	.25	.20	.10
37	Bobby Bonilla	.15	.11	.06
38	Will Clark	.30	.25	.12
39	Eric Davis	.25	.20	.10
40	Mike Dunne	.10	.08	.04
41	John Franco	.10	.08	.04
42	Dwight Gooden	.30	.25	.12
43	Pedro Guerrero	.10	.08	.04
44	Dion James	.10	.08	.04
45	John Kruk	.15	.11	.06
46	Jeffrey Leonard	.10	.08	.04
47	Carmelo Martinez	.10	.08	.04
48	Dale Murphy	.30	.25	.12
49	Tim Raines	.20	.15	.08
50	Nolan Ryan	1.50	1.25	.60
51	Juan Samuel	.10	.08	.04
52	Ryne Sandberg	1.25	.90	.50
53	Mike Schmidt	.60	.45	.25
54	Mike Scott	.10	.08	.04
55	Ozzie Smith	.25	.20	.10

56	Darryl Strawberry	.20	.15	.08
57	Rick Sutcliffe	.10	.08	.04
58	Fernando Valenzuela	.10	.08	.04
59	Tim Wallach	.10	.08	.04
60	Todd Worrell	.10	.08	.04

1988 Topps Gallery of Champions

These bronze replicas are exact reproductions at one-quarter scale of Topps official 1988 cards, both front and back. The set includes 12 three-dimensional raised metal cards packaged in a velvet-lined case that bears the title of the set in gold embossed letters. A deluxe limited edition of the set (1,000) was produced in sterling silver and an economy version in aluminum. Topps first issued the metal mini-cards in 1984 (the initial set was called Gallery of Immortals). Since 1985, the metal cards have honored award-winning players from the previous season. A Mark McGwire pewter replica was given as a premium to dealers ordering the aluminum, bronze and silver sets ($50 value). The special pewter card is distinguished from the regular issue by a diagonal name banner in the lower right corner (regular) replicas have a rectangular name banner printer parallel to the lower edge of the card). A 1955 Topps Duke Snider bronze (value $10) was available to dealers purchasing cases of the 1988 Topps Traded sets.

		MT	NR MT	EX
Complete Aluminum Set:		20.00	15.00	8.00
Complete Bronze Set:		125.00	94.00	50.00
Complete Silver Set:		500.00	375.00	200.00
(1a)	Steve Bedrosian (aluminum)	.70	.50	.30
(1b)	Steve Bedrosian (bronze)	7.50	5.75	3.00
(1c)	Steve Bedrosian (silver)	20.00	15.00	8.00
(2a)	George Bell (aluminum)	.80	.60	.30
(2b)	George Bell (bronze)	10.00	7.50	4.00
(2c)	George Bell (silver)	20.00	15.00	8.00
(3a)	Wade Boggs (aluminum)	3.00	2.25	1.25
(3b)	Wade Boggs (bronze)	25.00	18.50	10.00
(3c)	Wade Boggs (silver)	125.00	94.00	50.00
(4a)	Jack Clark (aluminum)	.70	.50	.30
(4b)	Jack Clark (bronze)	7.50	5.75	3.00
(4c)	Jack Clark (silver)	20.00	15.00	8.00
(5a)	Roger Clemens (aluminum)	2.00	1.50	.80
(5b)	Roger Clemens (bronze)	20.00	15.00	8.00
(5c)	Roger Clemens (silver)	90.00	67.00	36.00
(6a)	Andre Dawson (aluminum)	1.00	.70	.40
(6b)	Andre Dawson (bronze)	10.00	7.50	4.00
(6c)	Andre Dawson (silver)	20.00	15.00	8.00
(7a)	Tony Gwynn (aluminum)	1.25	.90	.50
(7b)	Tony Gwynn (bronze)	12.00	9.00	4.75
(7c)	Tony Gwynn (silver)	50.00	37.00	20.00
(8a)	Mark Langston (aluminum)	.70	.50	.30
(8b)	Mark Langston (bronze)	7.50	5.75	3.00
(8c)	Mark Langston (silver)	20.00	15.00	8.00
(9a)	Mark McGwire (aluminum)	3.00	2.25	1.25
(9b)	Mark McGwire (bronze)	25.00	18.50	10.00
(9c)	Mark McGwire (silver)	125.00	94.00	50.00
(10a)	Dave Righetti (aluminum)	1.00	.70	.40
(10b)	Dave Righetti (bronze)	10.00	7.50	4.00
(10c)	Dave Righetti (silver)	20.00	15.00	8.00
(11a)	Nolan Ryan (aluminum)	3.00	2.25	1.25
(11b)	Nolan Ryan (bronze)	25.00	18.50	10.00
(11c)	Nolan Ryan (silver)	125.00	94.00	50.00
(12a)	Benny Santiago (aluminum)	1.00	.70	.40
(12b)	Benny Santiago (bronze)	10.00	7.50	4.00
(12c)	Benny Santiago (silver)	20.00	15.00	8.00

Regional interest may affect the value of a card.

1988 Topps Glossy Rookies

The Topps 1988 Rookies special insert cards follow the same basic design as the All-Star inserts. The set consists of 22 standard-size cards. Large, glossy color player photos are printed on a white background below a red, yellow and blue "1987 Rookies" banner. A red and yellow player name appears beneath the photo. Red, white and blue

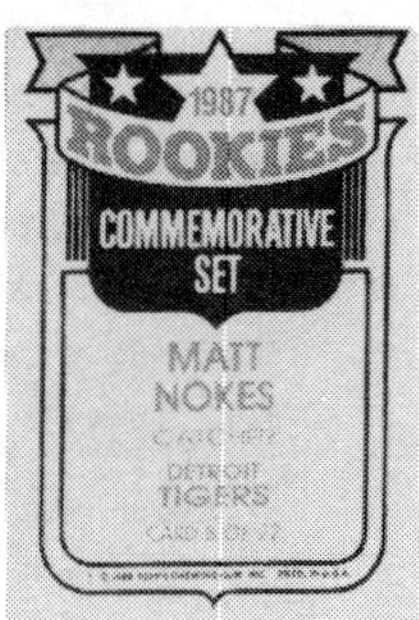

card backs bear the title of the special insert set, the Rookies logo emblem, player name and card number.

		MT	NR MT	EX
Complete Set:		10.00	7.50	4.00
Common Player:		.20	.15	.08
1	Billy Ripken	.20	.15	.08
2	Ellis Burks	.75	.60	.30
3	Mike Greenwell	1.00	.70	.40
4	DeWayne Buice	.20	.15	.08
5	Devon White	.40	.30	.15
6	Fred Manrique	.20	.15	.08
7	Mike Henneman	.40	.30	.15
8	Matt Nokes	.80	.60	.30
9	Kevin Seitzer	.40	.30	.15
10	B.J. Surhoff	.40	.30	.15
11	Casey Candaele	.20	.15	.08
12	Randy Myers	.60	.45	.25
13	Mark McGwire	.80	.60	.30
14	Luis Polonia	.25	.20	.10
15	Terry Steinbach	.40	.30	.15
16	Mike Dunne	.20	.15	.08
17	Al Pedrique	.20	.15	.08
18	Benny Santiago	.70	.50	.30
19	Kelly Downs	.20	.15	.08
20	Joe Magrane	.40	.30	.15
21	Jerry Browne	.40	.30	.15
22	Jeff Musselman	.20	.15	.08

1988 Topps Mini League Leaders

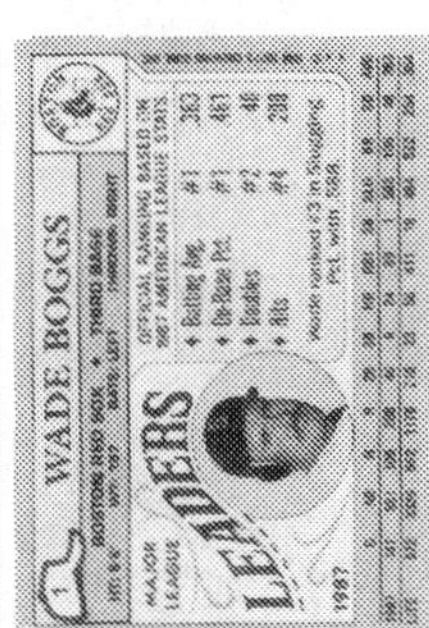

The third consecutive issue of Topps mini-cards (2-1/8" by 3") includes 77 cards spotlighting the top five ranked pitchers and batters. This set is unique in that it was the first time Topps included full-color player photos on both the front and back. Glossy action shots on the card fronts fade into a white border with a Topps logo in an upper corner. The player's name is printed in bold black letters beneath the photo. Horizontal reverses feature circular player photos on a blue and white background with the card number, player name, personal information, 1987 ranking and lifetime/1987 stats printed in red, black and yellow lettering.

		MT	NR MT	EX
Complete Set:		6.00	4.50	2.50
Common Player:		.09	.07	.04
1	Wade Boggs	.80	.60	.30
2	Roger Clemens	.60	.45	.25
3	Dwight Evans	.15	.11	.06
4	DeWayne Buice	.09	.07	.04
5	Brian Downing	.09	.07	.04
6	Wally Joyner	.60	.45	.25
7	Ivan Calderon	.15	.11	.06
8	Carlton Fisk	.20	.15	.08
9	Gary Redus	.09	.07	.04
10	Darrell Evans	.15	.11	.06
11	Jack Morris	.20	.15	.08
12	Alan Trammell	.35	.25	.14
13	Lou Whitaker	.20	.15	.08
14	Bret Saberhagen	.30	.25	.12
15	Kevin Seitzer	.20	.15	.08
16	Danny Tartabull	.25	.20	.10
17	Willie Wilson	.15	.11	.06
18	Teddy Higuera	.15	.11	.06
19	Paul Molitor	.35	.25	.14
20	Dan Plesac	.15	.11	.06
21	Robin Yount	.45	.35	.20
22	Kent Hrbek	.25	.20	.10
23	Kirby Puckett	.45	.35	.20
24	Jeff Reardon	.15	.11	.06
25	Frank Viola	.20	.15	.08
26	Rickey Henderson	.60	.45	.25
27	Don Mattingly	.90	.70	.35
28	Willie Randolph	.15	.11	.06
29	Dave Righetti	.20	.15	.08
30	Jose Canseco	1.00	.70	.40
31	Mark McGwire	.45	.35	.20
32	Dave Stewart	.20	.15	.08
33	Phil Bradley	.15	.11	.06
34	Mark Langston	.15	.11	.06
35	Harold Reynolds	.09	.07	.04
36	Charlie Hough	.15	.11	.06
37	George Bell	.20	.15	.08
38	Tom Henke	.09	.07	.04
39	Jimmy Key	.15	.11	.06
40	Dion James	.09	.07	.04
41	Dale Murphy	.50	.40	.20
42	Zane Smith	.09	.07	.04
43	Andre Dawson	.35	.25	.14
44	Lee Smith	.25	.20	.10
45	Rick Sutcliffe	.15	.11	.06
46	Eric Davis	.30	.25	.12
47	John Franco	.15	.11	.06
48	Dave Parker	.25	.20	.10
49	Billy Hatcher	.15	.11	.06
50	Nolan Ryan	1.50	1.25	.60
51	Mike Scott	.20	.15	.08
52	Pedro Guerrero	.20	.15	.08
53	Orel Hershiser	.30	.25	.12
54	Fernando Valenzuela	.25	.20	.10
55	Bob Welch	.15	.11	.06
56	Andres Galarraga	.30	.25	.12
57	Tim Raines	.20	.15	.08
58	Tim Wallach	.15	.11	.06
59	Len Dykstra	.25	.20	.10
60	Dwight Gooden	.25	.20	.10
61	Howard Johnson	.15	.11	.06
62	Roger McDowell	.15	.11	.06
63	Darryl Strawberry	.25	.20	.10
64	Steve Bedrosian	.15	.11	.06
65	Shane Rawley	.09	.07	.04
66	Juan Samuel	.10	.08	.04
67	Mike Schmidt	.50	.40	.20
68	Mike Dunne	.15	.11	.06
69	Jack Clark	.10	.08	.04
70	Vince Coleman	.20	.15	.08
71	Willie McGee	.15	.11	.06
72	Ozzie Smith	.30	.25	.12
73	Todd Worrell	.15	.11	.06
74	Tony Gwynn	.40	.30	.15
75	John Kruk	.25	.20	.10
76	Rick Rueschel	.15	.11	.06
77	Checklist	.09	.07	.04

1988 Topps Stickercards

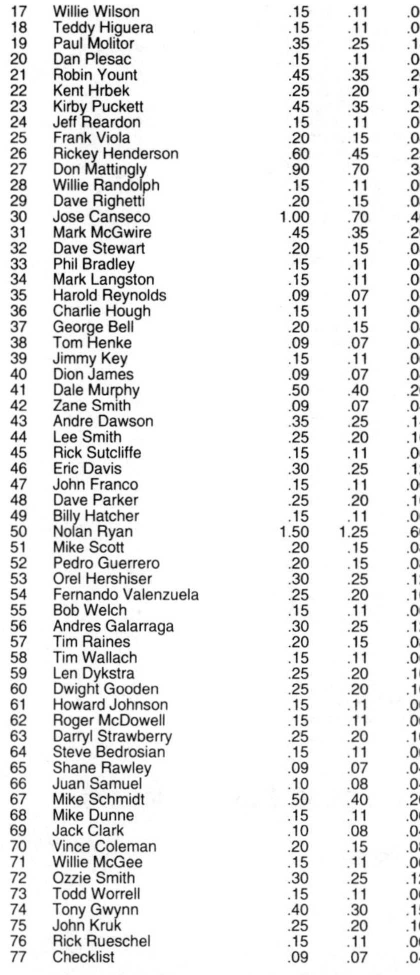

Actually a part of the 1988 Topps Stickers issue, this set consists of 67 cards. The cards are the backs of the peel-off stickers and measure 2-1/8" by 3". To determine total value, combine the prices of the stickers (found in the 1988 Topps Stickers checklist) on the stickercard front with the value assigned to the stickercard in the following checklist.

		MT	NR MT	EX
Complete Set:		2.00	1.50	.80
Common Player:		.05	.02	.01
1	Jack Clark	.05	.04	.02
2	Andres Galarraga	.10	.08	.04
3	Keith Hernandez	.05	.04	.02
4	Tom Herr	.05	.04	.02
5	Juan Samuel	.05	.04	.02
6	Ryne Sandberg	.25	.20	.10
7	Terry Pendleton	.05	.04	.02
8	Mike Schmidt	.10	.08	.04
9	Tim Wallach	.05	.04	.02
10	Hubie Brooks	.05	.04	.02
11	Shawon Dunston	.05	.04	.02
12	Ozzie Smith	.08	.06	.03
13	Andre Dawson	.05	.04	.02
14	Eric Davis	.06	.05	.02
15	Pedro Guerrero	.05	.04	.02
16	Tony Gwynn	.08	.06	.03
17	Jeffrey Leonard	.05	.04	.02
18	Dale Murphy	.06	.05	.02
19	Dave Parker	.08	.06	.03

20	Tim Raines	.05	.04	.02
21	Darryl Strawberry	.06	.05	.02
22	Gary Carter	.05	.04	.02
23	Jody Davis	.05	.04	.02
24	Ozzie Virgil	.05	.04	.02
25	Dwight Gooden	.08	.06	.03
26	Mike Scott	.05	.04	.02
27	Rick Sutcliffe	.05	.04	.02
28	Sid Fernandez	.05	.04	.02
29	Neal Heaton	.05	.04	.02
30	Fernando Valenzuela	.05	.04	.02
31	Steve Bedrosian	.05	.04	.02
32	John Franco	.05	.04	.02
33	Lee Smith	.08	.06	.03
34	Wally Joyner	.06	.05	.02
35	Don Mattingly	.20	.15	.08
36	Mark McGwire	.08	.06	.03
37	Willie Randolph	.05	.04	.02
38	Lou Whitaker	.05	.04	.02
39	Frank White	.05	.04	.02
40	Wade Boggs	.10	.08	.04
41	George Brett	.10	.08	.04
42	Paul Molitor	.10	.08	.04
43	Tony Fernandez	.05	.04	.02
44	Cal Ripken, Jr.	.25	.20	.10
45	Alan Trammell	.08	.06	.03
46	Jesse Barfield	.05	.04	.02
47	George Bell	.05	.04	.02
48	Jose Canseco	.20	.15	.08
49	Joe Carter	.10	.08	.04
50	Dwight Evans	.05	.04	.02
51	Rickey Henderson	.15	.11	.06
52	Kirby Puckett	.15	.11	.06
53	Cory Snyder	.05	.04	.02
54	Dave Winfield	.15	.11	.06
55	Terry Kennedy	.05	.04	.02
56	Matt Nokes	.05	.04	.02
57	B.J. Surhoff	.05	.04	.02
58	Roger Clemens	.15	.11	.06
59	Jack Morris	.05	.04	.02
60	Bret Saberhagen	.05	.04	.02
61	Ron Guidry	.05	.04	.02
62	Bruce Hurst	.05	.04	.02
63	Mark Langston	.05	.04	.02
64	Tom Henke	.05	.04	.02
65	Dan Plesac	.05	.04	.02
66	Dave Righetti	.05	.04	.02
67	Checklist	.05	.04	.02

1988 Topps Stickers

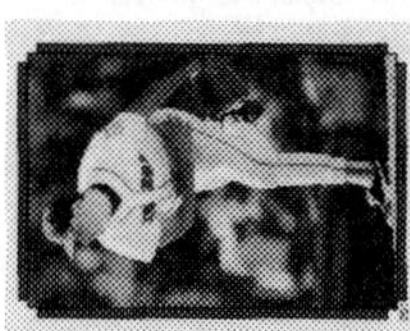

This set of 313 stickers (on 198 cards) offers a new addition for 1988 - 66 different players are pictured on the reverse of the sticker cards. The stickers come in two sizes (2-1/8" by 3" or 1-1/2" by 2-1/8"). Larger stickers fill an entire card, smaller ones are attached in pairs. A 36-page sticker yearbook produced by Topps has a designated space inside for each sticker,with one page per team and special pages of 1987 Highlights, World Series, All-Stars and Future Stars. No printing appears on the full-color action shot stickers except for a small black number in the lower left corner. Sticker card backs carry a Super Star header, player close-up and stats. Stickers were sold in packages of five (with gum) for 25 cents per pack. Unlike the 1987 Topps Stickers set, different pairings can be found, rather than the same two players/numbers always sharing the same sticker. To determine total value, combine the value of the stickercard (found in the 1988 Topps Stickercard checklist) with the values assigned the stickers in the following checklist.

		MT	NR MT	EX
Complete Set:		15.00	11.00	6.00
Common Player:		.02	.02	.01
Sticker Album:		.60	.45	.25
1	1987 Highlights (Mark McGwire)	.20	.15	.08
2	1987 Highlights (Benny Santiago)	.04	.03	.02
3	1987 Highlights (Don Mattingly)	.25	.20	.10
4	1987 Highlights (Vince Coleman)	.04	.03	.02
5	1987 Highlights (Bob Boone)	.02	.02	.01
6	1987 Highlights (Steve Bedrosian)	.02	.02	.01
7	1987 Highlights (Nolan Ryan)	.20	.15	.08
8	1987 Highlights (Darrell Evans)	.02	.02	.01
9	1987 Highlights (Mike Schmidt)	.10	.08	.04
10	1987 Highlights (Don Baylor)	.04	.03	.02
11	1987 Highlights (Eddie Murray)	.08	.06	.03
12	1987 Highlights (Juan Beniquez)	.02	.02	.01
13	1987 Championship Series (John Tudor)	.04	.03	.02
14	1987 Championship Series (Jeff Reardon)	.04	.03	.02
15	1987 Championship Series (Tom Brunansky)	.06	.05	.02
16	1987 Championship Series (Jeffrey Leonard)	.04	.03	.02
17	1987 Championship Series (Gary Gaetti)	.10	.08	.04
18	1987 Championship Series (Cardinals Celebrate)	.04	.03	.02
19	1987 World Series (Danny Gladden)	.04	.03	.02
20	1987 World Series (Bert Blyleven)	.08	.06	.03
21	1987 World Series (John Tudor)	.06	.05	.02
22	1987 World Series (Tom Lawless)	.04	.03	.02
23	1987 World Series (Curt Ford)	.04	.03	.02
24	1987 World Series (Kent Hrbek)	.12	.09	.05
25	1987 World Series (Frank Viola)	.10	.08	.04
26	Dave Smith	.02	.02	.01
27	Jim Deshaies	.02	.02	.01
28	Billy Hatcher	.05	.04	.02
29	Kevin Bass	.02	.02	.01
30	Mike Scott	.04	.03	.02
31	Danny Walling	.02	.02	.01
32	Alan Ashby	.02	.02	.01
33	Ken Caminiti	.05	.04	.02
34	Bill Doran	.02	.02	.01
35	Glenn Davis	.04	.03	.02
36	Ozzie Virgil	.02	.02	.01
37	Ken Oberkfell	.02	.02	.01
38	Ken Griffey	.02	.02	.01
39	Albert Hall	.02	.02	.01
40	Zane Smith	.02	.02	.01
41	Andres Thomas	.02	.02	.01
42	Dion James	.02	.02	.01
43	Jim Acker	.02	.02	.01
44	Tom Glavine	.20	.15	.08
45	Dale Murphy	.25	.20	.10
46	Jack Clark	.05	.04	.02
47	Vince Coleman	.04	.03	.02
48	Ricky Horton	.02	.02	.01
49	Terry Pendleton	.05	.04	.02
50	Tom Herr	.02	.02	.01
51	Joe Magrane	.04	.03	.02
52	Tony Pena	.02	.02	.01
53	Ozzie Smith	.10	.08	.04
54	Todd Worrell	.04	.03	.02
55	Willie McGee	.06	.05	.02
56	Andre Dawson	.15	.11	.06
57	Ryne Sandberg	.25	.20	.10
58	Keith Moreland	.02	.02	.01
59	Greg Maddux	.15	.11	.06
60	Jody Davis	.02	.02	.01
61	Rick Sutcliffe	.08	.06	.03
62	Jamie Moyer	.02	.02	.01
63	Leon Durham	.02	.02	.01
64	Lee Smith	.05	.04	.02
65	Shawon Dunston	.02	.02	.01
66	Franklin Stubbs	.02	.02	.01
67	Mike Scioscia	.02	.02	.01
68	Orel Hershiser	.06	.05	.02
69	Mike Marshall	.04	.03	.02
70	Fernando Valenzuela	.08	.06	.03
71	Mickey Hatcher	.02	.02	.01
72	Matt Young	.02	.02	.01
73	Bob Welch	.04	.03	.02
74	Steve Sax	.04	.03	.02
75	Pedro Guerrero	.12	.09	.05
76	Tim Raines	.10	.08	.04
77	Casey Candaele	.02	.02	.01
78	Mike Fitzgerald	.02	.02	.01
79	Andres Galarraga	.10	.08	.04
80	Neal Heaton	.02	.02	.01
81	Hubie Brooks	.02	.02	.01
82	Floyd Youmans	.02	.02	.01
83	Herm Winningham	.02	.02	.01
84	Denny Martinez	.02	.02	.01
85	Tim Wallach	.08	.06	.03
86	Jeffrey Leonard	.04	.03	.02
87	Will Clark	.15	.11	.06
88	Kevin Mitchell	.04	.03	.02
89	Mike Aldrete	.02	.02	.01
90	Scott Garrelts	.02	.02	.01
91	Jose Uribe	.02	.02	.01
92	Bob Brenly	.02	.02	.01
93	Robby Thompson	.05	.04	.02
94	Don Robinson	.02	.02	.01
95	Candy Maldonado	.04	.03	.02
96	Darryl Strawberry	.10	.08	.04
97	Keith Hernandez	.06	.05	.02
98	Ron Darling	.04	.03	.02
99	Howard Johnson	.04	.03	.02
100	Roger McDowell	.02	.02	.01
101	Dwight Gooden	.10	.08	.04
102	Kevin McReynolds	.04	.03	.02
103	Sid Fernandez	.02	.02	.01
104	Dave Magadan	.04	.03	.02
105	Gary Carter	.08	.06	.03
106	Carmelo Martinez	.02	.02	.01
107	Eddie Whitson	.02	.02	.01
108	Tim Flannery	.02	.02	.01
109	Stan Jefferson	.02	.02	.01
110	John Kruk	.10	.08	.04
111	Chris Brown	.04	.03	.02
112	Benny Santiago	.06	.05	.02
113	Garry Templeton	.02	.02	.01
114	Lance McCullers	.02	.02	.01
115	Tony Gwynn	.20	.15	.08
116	Steve Bedrosian	.06	.05	.02
117	Von Hayes	.02	.02	.01
118	Kevin Gross	.02	.02	.01
119	Bruce Ruffin	.02	.02	.01
120	Juan Samuel	.04	.03	.02
121	Shane Rawley	.02	.02	.01
122	Chris James	.04	.03	.02
123	Lance Parrish	.04	.03	.02
124	Glenn Wilson	.02	.02	.01
125	Mike Schmidt	.25	.20	.10
126	Andy Van Slyke	.08	.06	.03
127	Jose Lind	.04	.03	.02
128	Al Pedrique	.02	.02	.01
129	Bobby Bonilla	.04	.03	.02
130	Sed Bream	.02	.02	.01
131	Mike LaValliere	.02	.02	.01
132	Mike Dunne	.04	.03	.02
133	Jeff Robinson	.02	.02	.01
134	Doug Drabek	.02	.02	.01
135	Barry Bonds	.15	.11	.06
136	Dave Parker	.08	.06	.03
137	Nick Esasky	.02	.02	.01
138	Buddy Bell	.02	.02	.01
139	Kal Daniels	.04	.03	.02
140	Barry Larkin	.04	.03	.02
141	Eric Davis	.10	.08	.04
142	John Franco	.02	.02	.01
143	Bo Diaz	.02	.02	.01
144	Ron Oester	.02	.02	.01
145	Dennis Rasmussen	.02	.02	.01
146	Eric Davis	.10	.08	.04
147	Ryne Sandberg	.30	.25	.12
148	Andre Dawson	.20	.15	.08
149	Mike Schmidt	.40	.30	.15
150	Jack Clark	.10	.08	.04
151	Darryl Strawberry	.15	.11	.06
152	Gary Carter	.20	.15	.08
153	Ozzie Smith	.20	.15	.08
154	Mike Scott	.08	.06	.03
155	Rickey Henderson	.20	.15	.08
156	Don Mattingly	.40	.30	.15
157	Wade Boggs	.40	.30	.15
158	George Bell	.10	.08	.04
159	Dave Winfield	.30	.25	.12
160	Cal Ripken, Jr.	.40	.30	.15
161	Terry Kennedy	.08	.06	.03
162	Willie Randolph	.08	.06	.03
163	Bret Saberhagen	.15	.11	.06
164	Mark McGwire	.20	.15	.08
165	Tony Phillips	.05	.04	.02
166	Jay Howell	.02	.02	.01
167	Carney Lansford	.02	.02	.01
168	Dave Stewart	.05	.04	.02
169	Alfredo Griffin	.02	.02	.01
170	Dennis Eckersley	.08	.06	.03
171	Mike Davis	.02	.02	.01
172	Luis Polonia	.05	.04	.02
173	Jose Canseco	.60	.45	.25
174	Mike Witt	.06	.05	.02
175	Jack Howell	.02	.02	.01
176	Greg Minton	.02	.02	.01
177	Dick Schofield	.02	.02	.01
178	Gary Pettis	.02	.02	.01
179	Wally Joyner	.15	.11	.06
180	DeWayne Buice	.02	.02	.01
181	Brian Downing	.02	.02	.01
182	Bob Boone	.02	.02	.01
183	Devon White	.10	.08	.04
184	Jim Clancy	.02	.02	.01
185	Willie Upshaw	.02	.02	.01
186	Tom Henke	.02	.02	.01
187	Ernie Whitt	.02	.02	.01
188	George Bell	.10	.08	.04
189	Lloyd Moseby	.02	.02	.01
190	Jimmy Key	.02	.02	.01
191	Dave Stieb	.02	.02	.01
192	Jesse Barfield	.04	.03	.02
193	Tony Fernandez	.10	.08	.04
194	Paul Molitor	.15	.11	.06
195	Jim Gantner	.02	.02	.01
196	Teddy Higuera	.04	.03	.02
197	Glenn Braggs	.02	.02	.01
198	Rob Deer	.02	.02	.01
199	Dale Sveum	.02	.02	.01
200	Bill Wegman	.02	.02	.01
201	Robin Yount	.20	.15	.08
202	B.J. Surhoff	.04	.03	.02
203	Dan Plesac	.06	.05	.02
204	Pat Tabler	.04	.03	.02
205	Mel Hall	.02	.02	.01
206	Scott Bailes	.02	.02	.01
207	Julio Franco	.15	.11	.06
208	Cory Snyder	.06	.05	.02
209	Chris Bando	.02	.02	.01
210	Greg Swindell	.04	.03	.02
211	Brook Jacoby	.02	.02	.01
212	Brett Butler	.02	.02	.01
213	Joe Carter	.15	.11	.06
214	Mark Langston	.08	.06	.03
215	Rey Quinones	.02	.02	.01
216	Ed Nunez	.02	.02	.01
217	Jim Presley	.02	.02	.01
218	Phil Bradley	.04	.03	.02
219	Alvin Davis	.04	.03	.02
220	Dave Valle	.02	.02	.01
221	Harold Reynolds	.02	.02	.01
222	Scott Bradley	.02	.02	.01
223	Gary Matthews	.02	.02	.01
224	Eric Bell	.02	.02	.01
225	Terry Kennedy	.02	.02	.01
226	Dave Schmidt	.02	.02	.01
227	Billy Ripken	.04	.03	.02
228	Cal Ripken, Jr.	.40	.30	.15
229	Ray Knight	.02	.02	.01
230	Larry Sheets	.02	.02	.01
231	Mike Boddicker	.02	.02	.01
232	Tom Niedenfuer	.02	.02	.01
233	Eddie Murray	.20	.15	.08
234	Ruben Sierra	.12	.09	.05
235	Steve Buechele	.02	.02	.01
236	Charlie Hough	.02	.02	.01
237	Oddibe McDowell	.02	.02	.01
238	Mike Stanley	.02	.02	.01
239	Pete Incaviglia	.04	.03	.02
240	Pete O'Brien	.02	.02	.01
241	Scott Fletcher	.02	.02	.01
242	Dale Mohorcic	.02	.02	.01
243	Larry Parrish	.04	.03	.02
244	Wade Boggs	.35	.25	.14
245	Dwight Evans	.04	.03	.02

246	Sam Horn	.04	.03	.02
247	Jim Rice	.06	.05	.02
248	Marty Barrett	.02	.02	.01
249	Mike Greenwell	.10	.08	.04
250	Ellis Burks	.10	.08	.04
251	Roger Clemens	.15	.11	.06
252	Rich Gedman	.02	.02	.01
253	Bruce Hurst	.06	.05	.02
254	Bret Saberhagen	.15	.11	.06
255	Frank White	.02	.02	.01
256	Dan Quisenberry	.02	.02	.01
257	Danny Tartabull	.06	.05	.02
258	Bo Jackson	.08	.06	.03
259	George Brett	.25	.20	.10
260	Charlie Leibrandt	.02	.02	.01
261	Kevin Seitzer	.04	.03	.02
262	Mark Gubicza	.04	.03	.02
263	Willie Wilson	.04	.03	.02
264	Frank Tanana	.02	.02	.01
265	Darrell Evans	.02	.02	.01
266	Bill Madlock	.04	.03	.02
267	Kirk Gibson	.06	.05	.02
268	Jack Morris	.08	.06	.03
269	Matt Nokes	.06	.05	.02
270	Lou Whitaker	.04	.03	.02
271	Eric King	.02	.02	.01
272	Jim Morrison	.02	.02	.01
273	Alan Trammell	.20	.15	.08
274	Kent Hrbek	.12	.09	.05
275	Tom Brunansky	.04	.03	.02
276	Bert Blyleven	.04	.03	.02
277	Gary Gaetti	.04	.03	.02
278	Tim Laudner	.04	.03	.02
279	Gene Larkin	.02	.02	.01
280	Jeff Reardon	.02	.02	.01
281	Danny Gladden	.02	.02	.01
282	Frank Viola	.04	.03	.02
283	Kirby Puckett	.30	.25	.12
284	Ozzie Guillen	.15	.11	.06
285	Ivan Calderon	.02	.02	.01
286	Donnie Hill	.02	.02	.01
287	Ken Williams	.04	.03	.02
288	Jim Winn	.02	.02	.01
289	Bob James	.02	.02	.01
290	Carlton Fisk	.10	.08	.04
291	Richard Dotson	.02	.02	.01
292	Greg Walker	.02	.02	.01
293	Harold Baines	.10	.08	.04
294	Willie Randolph	.06	.05	.02
295	Mike Pagliarulo	.04	.03	.02
296	Ron Guidry	.04	.03	.02
297	Rickey Henderson	.15	.11	.06
298	Rick Rhoden	.02	.02	.01
299	Don Mattingly	.70	.50	.30
300	Dave Righetti	.04	.03	.02
301	Claudell Washington	.02	.02	.01
302	Dave Winfield	.15	.11	.06
303	Gary Ward	.02	.02	.01
304	Al Pedrique	.02	.02	.01
305	Casey Candaele	.02	.02	.01
306	Kevin Seitzer	.05	.04	.02
307	Mike Dunne	.04	.03	.02
308	Jeff Musselman	.02	.02	.01
309	Mark McGwire	.20	.15	.08
310	Ellis Burks	.10	.08	.04
311	Matt Nokes	.06	.05	.02
312	Mike Greenwell	.10	.08	.04
313	Devon White	.04	.03	.02

1989 Topps

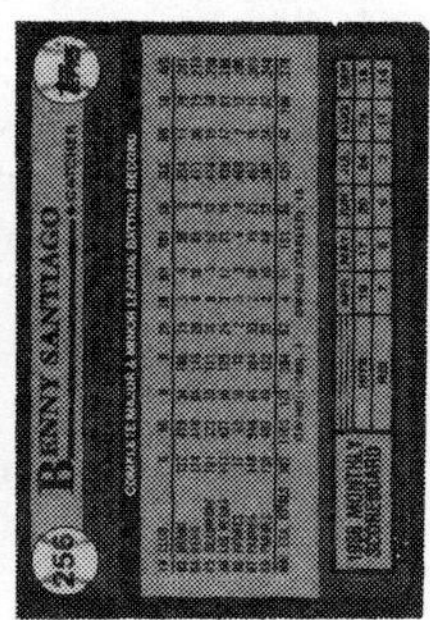

Ten top young players who led the June 1988 draft picks are featured on "#1 Draft Pick" cards in this full-color basic set of 792 standard-size baseball cards. An additional five cards salute 1989 Future Stars, 22 cards highlight All-Stars, seven contain Record Breakers, five are designated Turn Back The Clock, and six contain checklists. This set features the familiar white borders, but two inner photo corners (upper left and lower right) have been rounded off and the rectangular player name was replaced by a curved name banner in bright red or blue that leads to the team name in large script in the lower right corner. The card backs are printed in black on a red background and include personal information and complete minor and major league stats. Another new addition in this set is the special Monthly Scoreboard chart that lists monthly stats (April through September) in two of several categories (hits, run, home runs, stolen bases, RBIs, wins, strikeouts, games or saves).

		MT	NR MT	EX
	Complete Set (792):	15.00	11.00	6.00
	Common Player:	.03	.02	.01
1	George Bell (Record Breaker)	.08	.06	.03
2	Wade Boggs (Record Breaker)	.12	.09	.05
3	Gary Carter (Record Breaker)	.10	.08	.04
4	Andre Dawson (Record Breaker)	.08	.06	.03
5	Orel Hershiser (Record Breaker)	.10	.08	.04
6	Doug Jones (Record Breaker)	.06	.05	.02
7	Kevin McReynolds (Record Breaker)	.08	.06	.03
8	*Dave Eiland* (FC)	.03	.02	.01
9	Tim Teufel	.03	.02	.01
10	Andre Dawson	.15	.11	.06
11	Bruce Sutter	.08	.06	.03
12	Dale Sveum	.06	.05	.02
13	Doug Sisk	.03	.02	.01
14	Tom Kelly	.03	.02	.01
15	Robby Thompson	.06	.05	.02
16	Ron Robinson	.03	.02	.01
17	Brian Downing	.06	.05	.02
18	Rick Rhoden	.06	.05	.02
19	Greg Gagne	.03	.02	.01
20	Steve Bedrosian	.08	.06	.03
21	White Sox Leaders (Greg Walker)	.06	.05	.02
22	Tim Crews	.06	.05	.02
23	Mike Fitzgerald	.03	.02	.01
24	Larry Andersen	.03	.02	.01
25	Frank White	.06	.05	.02
26	Dale Mohorcic	.03	.02	.01
27	*Orestes Destrade*	.15	.11	.06
28	Mike Moore	.03	.02	.01
29	Kelly Gruber	.03	.02	.01
30	Doc Gooden	.08	.06	.03
31	Terry Francona	.03	.02	.01
32	Dennis Rasmussen	.08	.06	.03
33	B.J. Surhoff	.08	.06	.03
34	Ken Williams	.06	.05	.02
35	John Tudor	.08	.06	.03
36	Mitch Webster	.06	.05	.02
37	Bob Stanley	.03	.02	.01
38	Paul Runge	.03	.02	.01
39	Mike Maddux	.03	.02	.01
40	Steve Sax	.06	.05	.02
41	Terry Mulholland	.03	.02	.01
42	Jim Eppard (FC)	.08	.06	.03
43	Guillermo Hernandez	.06	.05	.02
44	Jim Snyder	.03	.02	.01
45	Kal Daniels	.03	.02	.01
46	Mark Portugal	.03	.02	.01
47	Carney Lansford	.06	.05	.02
48	Tim Burke	.03	.02	.01
49	*Craig Biggio* (FC)	.40	.30	.15
50	George Bell	.05	.04	.02
51	Angels Leaders (Mark McLemore)	.06	.05	.02
52	Bob Brenly	.03	.02	.01
53	Ruben Sierra	.15	.11	.06
54	Steve Trout	.03	.02	.01
55	Julio Franco	.08	.06	.03
56	Pat Tabler	.06	.05	.02
57	Alejandro Pena	.06	.05	.02
58	Lee Mazzilli	.06	.05	.02
59	Mark Davis	.03	.02	.01
60	Tom Brunansky	.06	.05	.02
61	Neil Allen	.03	.02	.01
62	Alfredo Griffin	.06	.05	.02
63	Mark Clear	.03	.02	.01
64	Alex Trevino	.03	.02	.01
65	Rick Reuschel	.08	.06	.03
66	Manny Trillo	.03	.02	.01
67	Dave Palmer	.03	.02	.01
68	Darrell Miller	.03	.02	.01
69	Jeff Ballard	.06	.05	.02
70	Mark McGwire	.25	.20	.10
71	Mike Boddicker	.06	.05	.02
72	John Moses	.03	.02	.01
73	Pascual Perez	.06	.05	.02
74	Nick Leyva	.03	.02	.01
75	Tom Henke	.06	.05	.02
76	*Terry Blocker* (FC)	.06	.05	.02
77	Doyle Alexander	.06	.05	.02
78	Jim Sundberg	.06	.05	.02
79	Scott Bankhead	.03	.02	.01
80	Cory Snyder	.15	.11	.06
81	Expos Leaders (Tim Raines)	.08	.06	.03
82	Dave Leiper	.03	.02	.01
83	Jeff Blauser (FC)	.15	.11	.06
84	*Bill Bene* (FC) (#1 Draft Pick)	.15	.11	.06
85	Kevin McReynolds	.12	.09	.05
86	Al Nipper	.03	.02	.01
87	Larry Owen	.03	.02	.01
88	*Darryl Hamilton*	.25	.20	.10
89	Dave LaPoint	.06	.05	.02
90	Vince Coleman	.12	.09	.05
91	Floyd Youmans	.03	.02	.01
92	Jeff Kunkel	.03	.02	.01
93	Ken Howell	.03	.02	.01
94	Chris Speier	.03	.02	.01
95	Gerald Young	.10	.08	.04
96	Rick Cerone	.03	.02	.01
97	Greg Mathews	.06	.05	.02
98	Larry Sheets	.06	.05	.02
99	*Sherman Corbett* (FC)	.12	.09	.05
100	Mike Schmidt	.35	.25	.14
101	Les Straker	.06	.05	.02
102	Mike Gallego	.03	.02	.01
103	Tim Birtsas	.03	.02	.01
104	Dallas Green	.03	.02	.01
105	Ron Darling	.10	.08	.04
106	Willie Upshaw	.06	.05	.02
107	Jose DeLeon	.06	.05	.02
108	Fred Manrique	.06	.05	.02
109	*Hipolito Pena* (FC)	.12	.09	.05
110	Paul Molitor	.20	.15	.08
111	Reds Leaders (Eric Davis)	.10	.08	.04
112	Jim Presley	.06	.05	.02
113	Lloyd Moseby	.06	.05	.02
114	Bob Kipper	.03	.02	.01
115	Jody Davis	.06	.05	.02
116	Jeff Montgomery	.06	.05	.02
117	Dave Anderson	.03	.02	.01
118	Checklist 1-132	.03	.02	.01
119	Terry Puhl	.03	.02	.01
120	Frank Viola	.12	.09	.05
121	Garry Templeton	.06	.05	.02
122	Lance Johnson (FC)	.10	.08	.04
123	Spike Owen	.03	.02	.01
124	Jim Traber	.06	.05	.02
125	Mike Krukow	.06	.05	.02
126	Sid Bream	.06	.05	.02
127	Walt Terrell	.06	.05	.02
128	Milt Thompson	.03	.02	.01
129	*Terry Clark* (FC)	.12	.09	.05
130	Gerald Perry	.08	.06	.03
131	Dave Otto (FC)	.08	.06	.03
132	Curt Ford	.03	.02	.01
133	Bill Long	.06	.05	.02
134	Don Zimmer	.03	.02	.01
135	Jose Rijo	.06	.05	.02
136	Joey Meyer	.08	.06	.03
137	Geno Petralli	.03	.02	.01
138	Wallace Johnson	.03	.02	.01
139	Mike Flanagan	.06	.05	.02
140	Shawon Dunston	.08	.06	.03
141	Indians Leaders (Brook Jacoby)	.06	.05	.02
142	Mike Diaz	.06	.05	.02
143	Mike Campbell	.08	.06	.03
144	Jay Bell	.06	.05	.02
145	Dave Stewart	.08	.06	.03
146	Gary Pettis	.03	.02	.01
147	DeWayne Buice	.03	.02	.01
148	Bill Pecota	.06	.05	.02
149	*Doug Dascenzo* (FC)	.08	.06	.03
150	Fernando Valenzuela	.06	.05	.02
151	Terry McGriff	.03	.02	.01
152	Mark Thurmond	.03	.02	.01
153	Jim Pankovits	.03	.02	.01
154	Don Carman	.06	.05	.02
155	Marty Barrett	.06	.05	.02
156	*Dave Gallagher* (FC)	.06	.05	.02
157	Tom Glavine	.50	.40	.20
158	Mike Aldrete	.06	.05	.02
159	Pat Clements	.03	.02	.01
160	Jeffrey Leonard	.06	.05	.02
161	*Gregg Olson* (#1 Draft Pick)	.25	.20	.10
162	John Davis	.03	.02	.01
163	Bob Forsch	.06	.05	.02
164	Hal Lanier	.03	.02	.01
165	Mike Dunne	.08	.06	.03
166	*Doug Jennings* (FC)	.12	.09	.05
167	Future Star (*Steve Searcy* (FC))	.12	.09	.05
168	Willie Wilson	.08	.06	.03
169	Mike Jackson	.06	.05	.02
170	Tony Fernandez	.10	.08	.04
171	Braves Leaders (Andres Thomas)	.06	.05	.02
172	Frank Williams	.03	.02	.01
173	Mel Hall	.06	.05	.02
174	*Todd Burns* (FC)	.12	.09	.05
175	John Shelby	.03	.02	.01
176	Jeff Parrett	.08	.06	.03
177	*Monty Fariss* (#1 Draft Pick)	.12	.09	.05
178	Mark Grant	.03	.02	.01
179	Ozzie Virgil	.03	.02	.01
180	Mike Scott	.10	.08	.04
181	*Craig Worthington* (FC)	.12	.09	.05
182	Bob McClure	.03	.02	.01
183	Oddibe McDowell	.06	.05	.02
184	*John Costello*	.10	.08	.04
185	Claudell Washington	.06	.05	.02
186	Pat Perry	.03	.02	.01
187	Darren Daulton	.15	.11	.06
188	Dennis Lamp	.03	.02	.01
189	Kevin Mitchell	.10	.08	.04
190	Mike Witt	.06	.05	.02
191	*Sil Campusano*	.20	.15	.08
192	Paul Mirabella	.03	.02	.01
193	Sparky Anderson	.06	.05	.02
194	*Greg Harris* (FC)	.10	.08	.04
195	Ozzie Guillen	.06	.05	.02
196	Denny Walling	.03	.02	.01
197	Neal Heaton	.03	.02	.01
198	Danny Heep	.03	.02	.01
199	*Mike Schooler*	.10	.08	.04
200	George Brett	.30	.25	.12
201	Blue Jays Leaders (Kelly Gruber)	.06	.05	.02
202	*Brad Moore* (FC)	.12	.09	.05
203	Rob Ducey	.03	.02	.01
204	Brad Havens	.03	.02	.01
205	Dwight Evans	.10	.08	.04
206	Roberto Alomar	.75	.60	.30
207	Terry Leach	.03	.02	.01
208	Tom Pagnozzi	.06	.05	.02
209	*Jeff Bittiger* (FC)	.12	.09	.05
210	Dale Murphy	.10	.08	.04
211	Mike Pagliarulo	.08	.06	.03
212	Scott Sanderson	.03	.02	.01
213	Rene Gonzales	.06	.05	.02
214	Charlie O'Brien	.03	.02	.01
215	Kevin Gross	.06	.05	.02
216	Jack Howell	.06	.05	.02
217	Joe Price	.03	.02	.01
218	Mike LaValliere	.06	.05	.02
219	Jim Clancy	.06	.05	.02
220	Gary Gaetti	.12	.09	.05
221	Cecil Espy	.08	.06	.03
222	*Mark Lewis* (#1 Draft Pick)	.15	.11	.06
223	Jay Buhner	.15	.11	.06
224	Tony LaRussa	.06	.05	.02
225	*Ramon Martinez*	.60	.45	.25
226	Bill Doran	.06	.05	.02
227	John Farrell	.08	.06	.03
228	*Nelson Santovenia*	.15	.11	.06
229	Jimmy Key	.08	.06	.03
230	Ozzie Smith	.12	.09	.05
231	Padres Leaders (Roberto Alomar)	.12	.09	.05
232	Ricky Horton	.06	.05	.02
233	Gregg Jefferies (Future Star)	.30	.25	.12

234 Tom Browning .08 .06 .03
235 John Kruk .06 .05 .02
236 Charles Hudson .03 .02 .01
237 Glenn Hubbard .03 .02 .01
238 Eric King .03 .02 .01
239 Tim Laudner .03 .02 .01
240 Greg Maddux .30 .25 .12
241 Brett Butler .06 .05 .02
242 Ed Vande Berg .03 .02 .01
243 Bob Boone .06 .05 .02
244 Jim Acker .03 .02 .01
245 Jim Rice .10 .08 .04
246 Rey Quinones .03 .02 .01
247 Shawn Hillegas .06 .05 .02
248 Tony Phillips .03 .02 .01
249 Tim Leary .06 .05 .02
250 Cal Ripken, Jr. .40 .30 .15
251 *John Dopson* (FC) .10 .08 .04
252 Billy Hatcher .06 .05 .02
253 *Jose Alvarez* (FC) .08 .06 .03
254 Tom LaSorda .06 .05 .02
255 Ron Guidry .12 .09 .05
256 Benny Santiago .12 .09 .05
257 Rick Aguilera .03 .02 .01
258 Checklist 133-264 .03 .02 .01
259 Larry McWilliams .03 .02 .01
260 Dave Winfield .25 .20 .10
261 Cardinals Leaders (Tom Brunansky) .06 .05 .02
262 *Jeff Pico* .06 .05 .02
263 Mike Felder .03 .02 .01
264 *Rob Dibble* .15 .11 .06
265 Kent Hrbek .15 .11 .06
266 Luis Aquino .03 .02 .01
267 Jeff Robinson .06 .05 .02
268 Keith Miller .06 .05 .02
269 Tom Bolton .06 .05 .02
270 Wally Joyner .06 .05 .02
271 Jay Tibbs .03 .02 .01
272 Ron Hassey .03 .02 .01
273 Jose Lind .08 .06 .03
274 Mark Eichhorn .06 .05 .02
275 Danny Tartabull .15 .11 .06
276 Paul Kilgus .08 .06 .03
277 Mike Davis .06 .05 .02
278 Andy McGaffigan .03 .02 .01
279 Scott Bradley .03 .02 .01
280 Bob Knepper .06 .05 .02
281 Gary Redus .03 .02 .01
282 *Cris Carpenter* (FC) .15 .11 .06
283 Andy Allanson .03 .02 .01
284 Jim Leyland .03 .02 .01
285 John Candelaria .06 .05 .02
286 Darrin Jackson .08 .06 .03
287 Juan Nieves .06 .05 .02
288 Pat Sheridan .03 .02 .01
289 Ernie Whitt .06 .05 .02
290 John Franco .08 .06 .03
291 Mets Leaders (Darryl Strawberry) .12 .09 .05
292 *Jim Corsi* (FC) .08 .06 .03
293 Glenn Wilson .06 .05 .02
294 Juan Berenguer .03 .02 .01
295 Scott Fletcher .06 .05 .02
296 Ron Gant .20 .15 .08
297 *Oswald Peraza* (FC) .08 .06 .03
298 Chris James .08 .06 .03
299 *Steve Ellsworth* (FC) .12 .09 .05
300 Darryl Strawberry .15 .11 .06
301 Charlie Leibrandt .06 .05 .02
302 Gary Ward .06 .05 .02
303 Felix Fermin .06 .05 .02
304 Joel Youngblood .03 .02 .01
305 Dave Smith .06 .05 .02
306 Tracy Woodson (FC) .10 .08 .04
307 Lance McCullers .06 .05 .02
308 Ron Karkovice .03 .02 .01
309 Mario Diaz (FC) .10 .08 .04
310 Rafael Palmeiro .20 .15 .08
311 Chris Bosio .03 .02 .01
312 Tom Lawless .03 .02 .01
313 Denny Martinez .06 .05 .02
314 Bobby Valentine .03 .02 .01
315 Greg Swindell .10 .08 .04
316 Walt Weiss .20 .15 .08
317 *Jack Armstrong* .12 .09 .05
318 Gene Larkin .08 .06 .03
319 Greg Booker .03 .02 .01
320 Lou Whitaker .15 .11 .06
321 Red Sox Leaders (Jody Reed) .06 .05 .02
322 John Smiley .10 .08 .04
323 Gary Thurman .10 .08 .04
324 *Bob Milacki* (FC) .10 .08 .04
325 Jesse Barfield .08 .06 .03
326 Dennis Boyd .06 .05 .02
327 *Mark Lemke* .12 .09 .05
328 Rick Honeycutt .03 .02 .01
329 Bob Melvin .03 .02 .01
330 Eric Davis .08 .06 .03
331 Curt Wilkerson .03 .02 .01
332 Tony Armas .06 .05 .02
333 Bob Ojeda .06 .05 .02
334 Steve Lyons .03 .02 .01
335 Dave Righetti .10 .08 .04
336 Steve Balboni .06 .05 .02
337 Calvin Schiraldi .03 .02 .01
338 Jim Adduci (FC) .06 .05 .02
339 Scott Bailes .03 .02 .01
340 Kirk Gibson .15 .11 .06
341 Jim Deshaies .03 .02 .01
342 Tom Brookens .03 .02 .01
343 *Gary Sheffield* (FC) (Future Star) 1.25 .90 .50
344 Tom Trebelhorn .03 .02 .01
345 Charlie Hough .06 .05 .02
346 Rex Hudler (FC) .06 .05 .02
347 John Cerutti .06 .05 .02
348 Ed Hearn .03 .02 .01
349 *Ron Jones* (FC) .15 .11 .06
350 Andy Van Slyke .12 .09 .05
351 Giants Leaders (Bob Melvin) .06 .05 .02
352 Rick Schu .03 .02 .01
353 Marvell Wynne .03 .02 .01
354 Larry Parrish .06 .05 .02
355 Mark Langston .08 .06 .03
356 Kevin Elster .08 .06 .03
357 Jerry Reuss .06 .05 .02
358 *Ricky Jordan* .10 .07 .04
359 Tommy John .10 .08 .04
360 Ryne Sandberg .30 .25 .12
361 Kelly Downs .08 .06 .03
362 Jack Lazorko .03 .02 .01
363 Rich Yett .03 .02 .01
364 Rob Deer .06 .05 .02
365 Mike Henneman .08 .06 .03
366 Herm Winningham .03 .02 .01
367 *Johnny Paredes* (FC) .15 .11 .06
368 Brian Holton .06 .05 .02
369 Ken Caminiti .06 .05 .02
370 Dennis Eckersley .10 .08 .04
371 Manny Lee .03 .02 .01
372 Craig Lefferts .03 .02 .01
373 Tracy Jones .08 .06 .03
374 John Wathan .06 .05 .02
375 Terry Pendleton .08 .06 .03
376 Steve Lombardozzi .03 .02 .01
377 Mike Smithson .03 .02 .01
378 Checklist 265-396 .03 .02 .01
379 Tim Flannery .03 .02 .01
380 Rickey Henderson .30 .25 .12
381 Orioles Leaders (Larry Sheets) .06 .05 .02
382 *John Smoltz* .50 .40 .20
383 Howard Johnson .07 .05 .03
384 Mark Salas .03 .02 .01
385 Von Hayes .08 .06 .03
386 Andres Galarraga (All-Star) .08 .06 .03
387 Ryne Sandberg (All-Star) .15 .11 .06
388 Bobby Bonilla (All-Star) .08 .06 .03
389 Ozzie Smith (All-Star) .12 .09 .05
390 Darryl Strawberry (All-Star) .15 .11 .06
391 Andre Dawson (All-Star) .10 .08 .04
392 Andy Van Slyke (All-Star) .08 .06 .03
393 Gary Carter (All-Star) .10 .08 .04
394 Orel Hershiser (All-Star) .12 .09 .05
395 Danny Jackson (All-Star) .08 .06 .03
396 Kirk Gibson (All-Star) .08 .06 .03
397 Don Mattingly (All-Star) .20 .15 .08
398 Julio Franco (All-Star) .06 .05 .02
399 Wade Boggs (All-Star) .15 .11 .06
400 Alan Trammell (All-Star) .08 .06 .03
401 Jose Canseco (All-Star) .20 .15 .08
402 Mike Greenwell (All-Star) .15 .11 .06
403 Kirby Puckett (All-Star) .20 .15 .08
404 Bob Boone (All-Star) .06 .05 .02
405 Roger Clemens (All-Star) .15 .11 .06
406 Frank Viola (All-Star) .08 .06 .03
407 Dave Winfield (All-Star) .12 .09 .05
408 Greg Walker .06 .05 .02
409 Ken Dayley .03 .02 .01
410 Jack Clark .12 .09 .05
411 Mitch Williams .06 .05 .02
412 Barry Lyons .03 .02 .01
413 Mike Kingery .03 .02 .01
414 Jim Fregosi .03 .02 .01
415 Rich Gossage .10 .08 .04
416 Fred Lynn .10 .08 .04
417 Mike LaCoss .03 .02 .01
418 Bob Dernier .03 .02 .01
419 Tom Filer .03 .02 .01
420 Joe Carter .10 .08 .04
421 Kirk McCaskill .06 .05 .02
422 Bo Diaz .06 .05 .02
423 Brian Fisher .06 .05 .02
424 Luis Polonia .06 .05 .02
425 Jay Howell .06 .05 .02
426 Danny Gladden .03 .02 .01
427 Eric Show .06 .05 .02
428 Craig Reynolds .03 .02 .01
429 Twins Leaders (Greg Gagne) .06 .05 .02
430 Mark Gubicza .08 .06 .03
431 Luis Rivera .06 .05 .02
432 *Chad Kreuter* (FC) .15 .11 .06
433 Albert Hall .03 .02 .01
434 *Ken Patterson* (FC) .15 .11 .06
435 Len Dykstra .10 .08 .04
436 Bobby Meacham .03 .02 .01
437 *Andy Benes* (#1 Draft Pick) .50 .40 .20
438 Greg Gross .03 .02 .01
439 Frank DiPino .03 .02 .01
440 Bobby Bonilla .15 .11 .06
441 Jerry Reed .03 .02 .01
442 Jose Oquendo .03 .02 .01
443 *Rod Nichols* (FC) .06 .05 .02
444 Moose Stubing .03 .02 .01
445 Matt Nokes .15 .11 .06
446 Rob Murphy .03 .02 .01
447 Donell Nixon .03 .02 .01
448 Eric Plunk .03 .02 .01
449 Carmelo Martinez .03 .02 .01
450 Roger Clemens .40 .30 .15
451 Mark Davidson .06 .05 .02
452 *Israel Sanchez* .12 .09 .05
453 Tom Prince (FC) .08 .06 .03
454 Paul Assenmacher .03 .02 .01
455 Johnny Ray .06 .05 .02
456 Tim Belcher .08 .06 .03
457 Mackey Sasser .06 .05 .02
458 *Donn Pall* (FC) .12 .09 .05
459 Mariners Leaders (Dave Valle) .06 .05 .02
460 Dave Stieb .08 .06 .03
461 Buddy Bell .06 .05 .02
462 Jose Guzman .08 .06 .03
463 Steve Lake .03 .02 .01
464 Bryn Smith .03 .02 .01
465 Mark Grace .20 .15 .08
466 Chuck Crim .03 .02 .01
467 Jim Walewander .03 .02 .01
468 Henry Cotto .03 .02 .01
469 *Jose Bautista* .06 .05 .02
470 Lance Parrish .12 .09 .05
471 *Steve Curry* (FC) .15 .11 .06
472 Brian Harper .03 .02 .01
473 Don Robinson .03 .02 .01
474 Bob Rodgers .03 .02 .01
475 Dave Parker .10 .08 .04
476 Jon Perlman (FC) .06 .05 .02
477 Dick Schofield .03 .02 .01
478 Doug Drabek .06 .05 .02
479 *Mike Macfarlane* .15 .11 .06
480 Keith Hernandez .15 .11 .06
481 Chris Brown .06 .05 .02
482 *Steve Peters* .12 .09 .05
483 Mickey Hatcher .03 .02 .01
484 Steve Shields .03 .02 .01
485 Hubie Brooks .08 .06 .03
486 Jack McDowell .30 .25 .12
487 Scott Lusader (FC) .08 .06 .03
488 Kevin Coffman .06 .05 .02
489 Phillies Leaders (Mike Schmidt) .12 .09 .05
490 *Chris Sabo* .20 .15 .08
491 Mike Birkbeck .03 .02 .01
492 Alan Ashby .03 .02 .01
493 Todd Benzinger .10 .08 .04
494 Shane Rawley .06 .05 .02
495 Candy Maldonado .06 .05 .02
496 Dwayne Henry .03 .02 .01
497 Pete Stanicek .12 .09 .05
498 Dave Valle .03 .02 .01
499 *Don Heinkel* (FC) .15 .11 .06
500 Jose Canseco .25 .20 .10
501 Vance Law .06 .05 .02
502 Duane Ward .03 .02 .01
503 Al Newman .03 .02 .01
504 Bob Walk .03 .02 .01
505 Pete Rose .20 .15 .08
506 Kirt Manwaring .10 .08 .04
507 Steve Farr .03 .02 .01
508 Wally Backman .06 .05 .02
509 Bud Black .03 .02 .01
510 Bob Horner .08 .06 .03
511 Richard Dotson .06 .05 .02
512 Donnie Hill .03 .02 .01
513 Jesse Orosco .06 .05 .02
514 Chet Lemon .06 .05 .02
515 Barry Larkin .10 .08 .04
516 Eddie Whitson .03 .02 .01
517 Greg Brock .06 .05 .02
518 Bruce Ruffin .03 .02 .01
519 Yankees Leaders (Willie Randolph) .03 .02 .01
520 Rick Sutcliffe .08 .06 .03
521 Mickey Tettleton .03 .02 .01
522 *Randy Kramer* (FC) .06 .05 .02
523 Andres Thomas .06 .05 .02
524 Checklist 397-528 .03 .02 .01
525 Chili Davis .06 .05 .02
526 Wes Gardner .06 .05 .02
527 Dave Henderson .08 .06 .03
528 *Luis Medina* (FC) .03 .02 .01
529 Tom Foley .03 .02 .01
530 Nolan Ryan .50 .40 .20
531 Dave Hengel (FC) .08 .06 .03
532 Jerry Browne .03 .02 .01
533 Andy Hawkins .03 .02 .01
534 Doc Edwards .03 .02 .01
535 Todd Worrell .08 .06 .03
536 Joel Skinner .03 .02 .01
537 Pete Smith .08 .06 .03
538 Juan Castillo .03 .02 .01
539 Barry Jones .03 .02 .01
540 Bo Jackson .30 .25 .12
541 Cecil Fielder .30 .25 .12
542 Todd Frohwirth .06 .05 .02
543 Damon Berryhill .06 .05 .02
544 Jeff Sellers .03 .02 .01
545 Mookie Wilson .06 .05 .02
546 Mark Williamson .06 .05 .02
547 Mark McLemore .03 .02 .01
548 Bobby Witt .08 .06 .03
549 Cubs Leaders (Jamie Moyer) .03 .02 .01
550 Orel Hershiser .08 .06 .03
551 Randy Ready .03 .02 .01
552 Greg Cadaret .06 .05 .02
553 Luis Salazar .03 .02 .01
554 Nick Esasky .06 .05 .02
555 Bert Blyleven .10 .08 .04
556 Bruce Fields (FC) .06 .05 .02
557 *Keith Miller* (FC) .06 .05 .02
558 Dan Pasqua .08 .06 .03
559 Juan Agosto .03 .02 .01
560 Tim Raines .08 .06 .03
561 Luis Aguayo .03 .02 .01
562 Danny Cox .06 .05 .02
563 Bill Schroeder .03 .02 .01
564 Russ Nixon .03 .02 .01
565 Jeff Russell .03 .02 .01
566 Al Pedrique .03 .02 .01
567 David Wells .08 .06 .03
568 Mickey Brantley .03 .02 .01
569 *German Jimenez* (FC) .08 .06 .03
570 Tony Gwynn .30 .25 .12
571 Billy Ripken .06 .05 .02
572 Atlee Hammaker .03 .02 .01
573 *Jim Abbott* (#1 Draft Pick) .90 .70 .35
574 Dave Clark .06 .05 .02
575 Juan Samuel .10 .08 .04
576 Greg Minton .03 .02 .01
577 Randy Bush .03 .02 .01
578 John Morris .03 .02 .01
579 Astros Leaders (Glenn Davis) .08 .06 .03
580 Harold Reynolds .06 .05 .02
581 Gene Nelson .03 .02 .01
582 Mike Marshall .10 .08 .04
583 *Paul Gibson* (FC) .06 .05 .02
584 Randy Velarde (FC) .10 .08 .04
585 Harold Baines .10 .08 .04
586 Joe Boever .03 .02 .01
587 Mike Stanley .03 .02 .01
588 *Luis Alicea* .15 .11 .06

589	Dave Meads	.03	.02	.01
590	Andres Galarraga	.12	.09	.05
591	Jeff Musselman	.06	.05	.02
592	John Cangelosi	.03	.02	.01
593	Drew Hall	.10	.08	.04
594	Jimy Williams	.03	.02	.01
595	Teddy Higuera	.08	.06	.03
596	Kurt Stillwell	.06	.05	.02
597	*Terry Taylor* (FC)	.12	.09	.05
598	Ken Gerhart	.06	.05	.02
599	Tom Candiotti	.03	.02	.01
600	Wade Boggs	.25	.20	.10
601	Dave Dravecky	.06	.05	.02
602	Devon White	.10	.08	.04
603	Frank Tanana	.06	.05	.02
604	Paul O'Neill	.03	.02	.01
605a	Bob Welch (missing Complete Major League Pitching Record line)	3.00	2.25	1.25
605b	Bob Welch (contains Complete Major League Pitching Record line)	.08	.06	.03
606	Rick Dempsey	.06	.05	.02
607	*Willie Ansley* (#1 Draft Pick)	.15	.11	.06
608	Phil Bradley	.08	.06	.03
609	Tigers Leaders (Frank Tanana)	.06	.05	.02
610	Randy Myers	.08	.06	.03
611	Don Slaught	.03	.02	.01
612	Dan Quisenberry	.06	.05	.02
613	*Gary Varsho* (FC)	.15	.11	.06
614	Joe Hesketh	.03	.02	.01
615	Robin Yount	.25	.20	.10
616	*Steve Rosenberg* (FC)	.06	.05	.02
617	*Mark Parent*	.06	.05	.02
618	Rance Mulliniks	.03	.02	.01
619	Checklist 529-660	.03	.02	.01
620	Barry Bonds	.40	.30	.15
621	Rick Mahler	.03	.02	.01
622	Stan Javier	.03	.02	.01
623	Fred Toliver	.03	.02	.01
624	Jack McKeon	.03	.02	.01
625	Eddie Murray	.15	.11	.06
626	Jeff Reed	.03	.02	.01
627	Greg Harris	.03	.02	.01
628	Matt Williams	.20	.15	.08
629	Pete O'Brien	.06	.05	.02
630	Mike Greenwell	.08	.06	.03
631	Dave Bergman	.03	.02	.01
632	*Bryan Harvey*	.25	.20	.10
633	Daryl Boston	.03	.02	.01
634	Marvin Freeman (FC)	.08	.06	.03
635	Willie Randolph	.06	.05	.02
636	Bill Wilkinson	.06	.05	.02
637	Carmen Castillo	.03	.02	.01
638	Floyd Bannister	.06	.05	.02
639	Athletics Leaders (Walt Weiss)	.15	.11	.06
640	Willie McGee	.10	.08	.04
641	Curt Young	.06	.05	.02
642	Argenis Salazar	.03	.02	.01
643	*Louie Meadows* (FC)	.12	.09	.05
644	Lloyd McClendon	.03	.02	.01
645	Jack Morris	.12	.09	.05
646	Kevin Bass	.06	.05	.02
647	*Randy Johnson* (FC)	.75	.60	.30
648	*Sandy Alomar* (Future Star)	.40	.30	.15
649	Stewart Cliburn	.03	.02	.01
650	Kirby Puckett	.25	.20	.10
651	Tom Niedenfuer	.06	.05	.02
652	Rich Gedman	.06	.05	.02
653	*Tommy Barrett* (FC)	.06	.05	.02
654	Whitey Herzog	.06	.05	.02
655	Dave Magadan	.08	.06	.03
656	Ivan Calderon	.06	.05	.02
657	Joe Magrane	.08	.06	.03
658	R.J. Reynolds	.03	.02	.01
659	Al Leiter	.06	.05	.02
660	Will Clark	.50	.40	.20
661	Turn Back The Clock (Dwight Gooden)	.10	.08	.04
662	Turn Back The Clock (Lou Brock)	.08	.06	.03
663	Turn Back The Clock (Hank Aaron)	.15	.11	.06
664	Turn Back The Clock (Gil Hodges)	.06	.05	.02
665	Turn Back The Clock (Tony Oliva)	.06	.05	.02
666	Randy St. Claire	.03	.02	.01
667	Dwayne Murphy	.06	.05	.02
668	Mike Bielecki	.03	.02	.01
669	Dodgers Leaders (Orel Hershiser)	.12	.09	.05
670	Kevin Seitzer	.12	.09	.05
671	Jim Gantner	.03	.02	.01
672	Allan Anderson	.06	.05	.02
673	Don Baylor	.08	.06	.03
674	Otis Nixon	.03	.02	.01
675	Bruce Hurst	.08	.06	.03
676	Ernie Riles	.03	.02	.01
677	Dave Schmidt	.03	.02	.01
678	Dion James	.03	.02	.01
679	Willie Fraser	.03	.02	.01
680	Gary Carter	.15	.11	.06
681	Jeff Robinson	.10	.08	.04
682	Rick Leach	.03	.02	.01
683	*Jose Cecena*	.15	.11	.06
684	Dave Johnson	.06	.05	.02
685	Jeff Treadway	.10	.08	.04
686	Scott Terry	.08	.06	.03
687	Alvin Davis	.10	.08	.04
688	Zane Smith	.06	.05	.02
689	Stan Jefferson	.03	.02	.01
690	Doug Jones	.10	.08	.04
691	Roberto Kelly	.25	.20	.10
692	Steve Ontiveros	.03	.02	.01
693	*Pat Borders*	.30	.25	.12
694	Les Lancaster	.06	.05	.02
695	Carlton Fisk	.20	.15	.08
696	Don August	.08	.06	.03
697	Franklin Stubbs	.03	.02	.01
698	Keith Atherton	.03	.02	.01
699	Pirates Leaders (Al Pedrique)	.06	.05	.02
700	Don Mattingly	.25	.20	.10
701	Storm Davis	.08	.06	.03
702	Jamie Quirk	.03	.02	.01
703	Scott Garrelts	.03	.02	.01
704	*Carlos Quintana*	.10	.07	.04
705	Terry Kennedy	.06	.05	.02
706	Pete Incaviglia	.08	.06	.03
707	Steve Jeltz	.03	.02	.01
708	Chuck Finley	.03	.02	.01
709	Tom Herr	.06	.05	.02
710	Dave Cone	.15	.11	.06
711	*Candy Sierra* (FC)	.03	.02	.01
712	Bill Swift	.03	.02	.01
713	*Ty Griffin* (#1 Draft Pick)	.10	.08	.04
714	Joe M. Morgan	.03	.02	.01
715	Tony Pena	.06	.05	.02
716	Wayne Tolleson	.03	.02	.01
717	Jamie Moyer	.03	.02	.01
718	Glenn Braggs	.06	.05	.02
719	Danny Darwin	.03	.02	.01
720	Tim Wallach	.08	.06	.03
721	*Ron Tingley* (FC)	.03	.02	.01
722	Todd Stottlemyre	.15	.11	.06
723	Rafael Belliard	.03	.02	.01
724	Jerry Don Gleaton	.03	.02	.01
725	Terry Steinbach	.08	.06	.03
726	Dickie Thon	.03	.02	.01
727	Joe Orsulak	.03	.02	.01
728	Charlie Puleo	.03	.02	.01
729	Rangers Leaders (Steve Buechele)	.06	.05	.02
730	Danny Jackson	.12	.09	.05
731	Mike Young	.03	.02	.01
732	Steve Buechele	.03	.02	.01
733	*Randy Bockus* (FC)	.06	.05	.02
734	Jody Reed	.10	.08	.04
735	Roger McDowell	.08	.06	.03
736	Jeff Hamilton	.06	.05	.02
737	*Norm Charlton*	.20	.15	.08
738	Darnell Coles	.06	.05	.02
739	Brook Jacoby	.08	.06	.03
740	Dan Plesac	.08	.06	.03
741	Ken Phelps	.06	.05	.02
742	*Mike Harkey* (FC) (Future Star)	.15	.11	.06
743	Mike Heath	.03	.02	.01
744	Roger Craig	.06	.05	.02
745	Fred McGriff	.15	.11	.06
746	*German Gonzalez* (FC)	.06	.05	.02
747	Wil Tejada (FC)	.06	.05	.02
748	Jimmy Jones	.03	.02	.01
749	Rafael Ramirez	.03	.02	.01
750	Bret Saberhagen	.12	.09	.05
751	Ken Oberkfell	.03	.02	.01
752	Jim Gott	.03	.02	.01
753	Jose Uribe	.03	.02	.01
754	Bob Brower	.03	.02	.01
755	Mike Scioscia	.06	.05	.02
756	*Scott Medvin* (FC)	.06	.05	.02
757	*Brady Anderson*	.35	.25	.14
758	Gene Walter	.03	.02	.01
759	Brewers Leaders (Rob Deer)	.06	.05	.02
760	Lee Smith	.08	.06	.03
761	*Dante Bichette*	.75	.60	.30
762	Bobby Thigpen	.08	.06	.03
763	Dave Martinez	.06	.05	.02
764	*Robin Ventura* (#1 Draft Pick)	1.00	.70	.40
765	Glenn Davis	.06	.05	.02
766	Cecilio Guante	.03	.02	.01
767	*Mike Capel* (FC)	.03	.02	.01
768	Bill Wegman	.03	.02	.01
769	Junior Ortiz	.03	.02	.01
770	Alan Trammell	.08	.06	.03
771	Ron Kittle	.06	.05	.02
772	Ron Oester	.03	.02	.01
773	Keith Moreland	.06	.05	.02
774	Frank Robinson	.08	.06	.03
775	Jeff Reardon	.08	.06	.03
776	Nelson Liriano	.06	.05	.02
777	Ted Power	.03	.02	.01
778	Bruce Benedict	.03	.02	.01
779	Craig McMurtry	.03	.02	.01
780	Pedro Guerrero	.06	.05	.02
781	*Greg Briley* (FC)	.08	.06	.03
782	Checklist 661-792	.03	.02	.01
783	*Trevor Wilson* (FC)	.15	.11	.06
784	*Steve Avery* (#1 Draft Pick)	1.00	.75	.40
785	Ellis Burks	.10	.08	.04
786	Melido Perez	.08	.06	.03
787	*Dave West*	.15	.11	.06
788	Mike Morgan	.03	.02	.01
789	Royals Leaders (Bo Jackson)	.12	.09	.05
790	Sid Fernandez	.08	.06	.03
791	Jim Lindeman	.03	.02	.01
792	Rafael Santana	.03	.02	.01

1989 Topps All-Star Glossy Set of 22

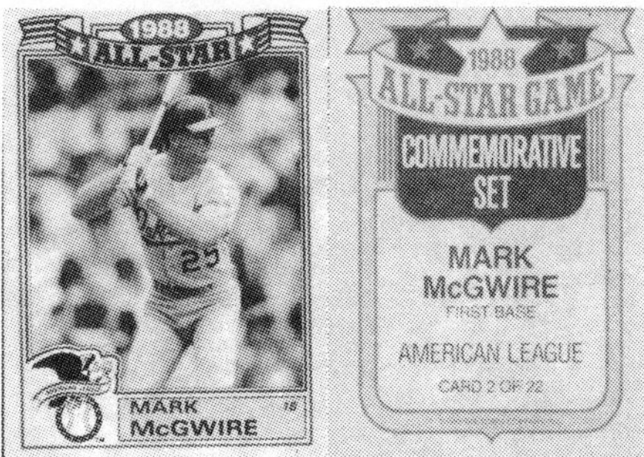

The glossy All-Stars were included in the Topps 1989 rack packs. Format was very similar to the sets produced since 1984. Besides the starting lineups of the 1988 All-Star Game, the set included the managers and honorary team captains, Bobby Doerr and Willie Stargell.

		MT	NR MT	EX
Complete Set (22):		2.00	1.50	.80
Common Player:		.05	.04	.02
1	Tom Kelly	.05	.04	.02
2	Mark McGwire	.15	.11	.06
3	Paul Molitor	.15	.11	.06
4	Wade Boggs	.15	.11	.06
5	Cal Ripken, Jr.	.25	.20	.10
6	Jose Canseco	.20	.15	.08
7	Rickey Henderson	.15	.11	.06
8	Dave Winfield	.15	.11	.06
9	Terry Steinbach	.05	.04	.02
10	Frank Viola	.05	.04	.02
11	Bobby Doerr	.05	.04	.02
12	Whitey Herzog	.05	.04	.02
13	Will Clark	.20	.15	.08
14	Ryne Sandberg	.25	.20	.10
15	Bobby Bonilla	.10	.08	.04
16	Ozzie Smith	.10	.08	.04
17	Vince Coleman	.05	.04	.02
18	Andre Dawson	.10	.08	.04
19	Darryl Strawberry	.10	.08	.04
20	Gary Carter	.05	.04	.02
21	Dwight Gooden	.10	.08	.04
22	Willie Stargell	.10	.08	.04

1989 Topps Glossy Rookies Set Of 22

Bearing the same design and style of the past two years, Topps featured the top first-year players from the 1988 season in this glossy set. The full-color player photos appears beneath the "1988 Rookies" banner. The player's name is displayed beneath the photo. The flip side features the "1988 Rookies Commemorative Set" logo followed by the player's name, position, team, and card number.

		MT	NR MT	EX
Complete Set:		3.50	2.75	1.50
Common Player:		.15	.11	.06
1	Roberto Alomar	.25	.20	.10
2	Brady Anderson	.20	.15	.08
3	Tim Belcher	.15	.11	.06
4	Damon Berryhill	.15	.11	.06
5	Jay Buhner	.20	.15	.08
6	Kevin Elster	.15	.11	.06
7	Cecil Espy	.15	.11	.06
8	Dave Gallagher	.15	.11	.06
9	Ron Gant	.25	.20	.10
10	Paul Gibson	.15	.11	.06
11	Mark Grace	.45	.35	.20
12	Darrin Jackson	.15	.11	.06
13	Gregg Jefferies	.60	.45	.25
14	Ricky Jordan	.15	.11	.06
15	Al Leiter	.15	.11	.06
16	Melido Perez	.15	.11	.06
17	Chris Sabo	.35	.25	.14
18	Nelson Santovenia	.15	.11	.06
19	Mackey Sasser	.15	.11	.06
20	Gary Sheffield	.30	.25	.12
21	Walt Weiss	.15	.11	.06
22	David Wells	.15	.11	.06

1989 Topps All-Star Glossy Set of 60

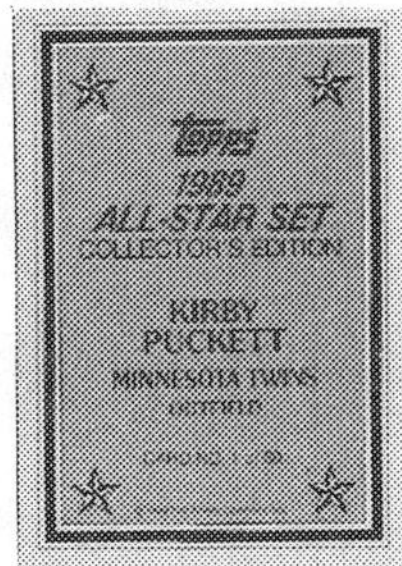

For the seventh straight year Topps issued this "send-away" glossy set. Divided into six 10-card sets, it was available only by sending in special offer cards from the 1989 Topps wax packs. The 2-1/2" by 3-1/2" cards feature full-color photos bordered in white with a thin yellow frame. The player's name appears in small print in the lower right corner. Red-and-blue-printed flip sides provide basic information including player's name, team, and position. Any of the six 10-card sets were available for $1.25 and six special offer cards. The set was also made available in its complete 60-card set form for $7.50 and 18 special offer cards.

		MT	NR MT	EX
Complete Set:		10.00	7.50	4.00
Common Player:		.15	.11	.06
1	Kirby Puckett	.50	.40	.20
2	Eric Davis	.20	.15	.08
3	Joe Carter	.30	.25	.12
4	Andy Van Slyke	.20	.15	.08
5	Wade Boggs	.70	.50	.30
6	Dave Cone	.25	.20	.10
7	Kent Hrbek	.15	.11	.06
8	Darryl Strawberry	.25	.20	.10
9	Jay Buhner	.20	.15	.08
10	Ron Gant	.30	.25	.12
11	Will Clark	1.00	.70	.40
12	Jose Canseco	1.25	.90	.50
13	Juan Samuel	.15	.11	.06
14	George Brett	.40	.30	.15
15	Benny Santiago	.20	.15	.08
16	Dennis Eckersley	.20	.15	.08
17	Gary Carter	.15	.11	.06
18	Frank Viola	.20	.15	.08
19	Roberto Alomar	.35	.25	.14
20	Paul Gibson	.15	.11	.06
21	Dave Winfield	.40	.30	.15
22	Howard Johnson	.20	.15	.08
23	Roger Clemens	.40	.30	.15
24	Bobby Bonilla	.25	.20	.10
25	Alan Trammell	.20	.15	.08
26	Kevin McReynolds	.20	.15	.08
27	George Bell	.20	.15	.08
28	Bruce Hurst	.15	.11	.06
29	Mark Grace	.35	.25	.14
30	Tim Belcher	.20	.15	.08
31	Mike Greenwell	.35	.25	.14
32.	Glenn Davis	.15	.11	.06
33	Gary Gaetti	.15	.11	.06
34	Ryne Sandberg	.75	.60	.30
35	Rickey Henderson	.70	.50	.30
36	Dwight Evans	.15	.11	.06
37	Doc Gooden	.25	.20	.10
38	Robin Yount	.40	.30	.15
39	Damon Berryhill	.15	.11	.06
40	Chris Sabo	.20	.15	.08
41	Mark McGwire	.35	.25	.14
42	Ozzie Smith	.25	.20	.10
43	Paul Molitor	.30	.25	.12
44	Andres Galarraga	.30	.25	.12
45	Dave Stewart	.15	.11	.06
46	Tom Browning	.15	.11	.06
47	Cal Ripken, Jr.	.50	.40	.20
48	Orel Hershiser	.20	.15	.08
49	Dave Gallagher	.15	.11	.06
50	Walt Weiss	.20	.15	.08
51	Don Mattingly	.90	.70	.35
52	Tony Fernandez	.20	.15	.08
53	Tim Raines	.20	.15	.08
54	Jeff Reardon	.15	.11	.06
55	Kirk Gibson	.20	.15	.08
56	Jack Clark	.20	.15	.08
57	Danny Jackson	.15	.11	.06
58	Tony Gwynn	.40	.30	.15
59	Cecil Espy	.15	.11	.06
60	Jody Reed	.15	.11	.06

1989 Topps Traded

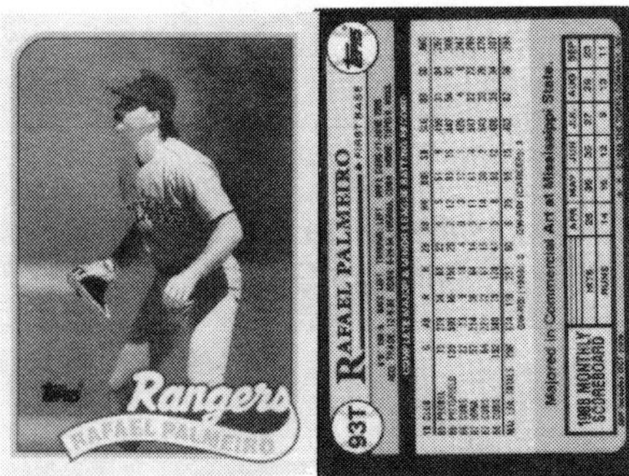

For the ninth straight year, Topps issued its annual 132-card "Traded" set at the end of the 1989 baseball season. The set, which was packaged in a special box and sold by hobby dealers, includes traded players and rookies who were not in the regular 1989 Topps set.

		MT	NR MT	EX
Complete Set (132):		6.00	4.50	2.50
Common Player:		.05	.04	.02
1T	Don Aase	.05	.04	.02
2T	Jim Abbott	.75	.60	.30
3T	Kent Anderson (FC)	.05	.04	.02
4T	Keith Atherton	.05	.04	.02
5T	Wally Backman	.05	.04	.02
6T	Steve Balboni	.05	.04	.02
7T	Jesse Barfield	.05	.04	.02
8T	Steve Bedrosian	.05	.04	.02
9T	Todd Benzinger	.05	.04	.02
10T	Geronimo Berroa	.12	.09	.05
11T	Bert Blyleven	.05	.04	.02
12T	Bob Boone	.05	.04	.02
13T	Phil Bradley	.05	.04	.02
14T	Jeff Brantley (FC)	.05	.04	.02
15T	Kevin Brown (FC)	.05	.04	.02
16T	Jerry Browne	.05	.04	.02
17T	Chuck Cary	.05	.04	.02
18T	Carmen Castillo	.05	.04	.02
19T	Jim Clancy	.05	.04	.02
20T	Jack Clark	.05	.04	.02
21T	Bryan Clutterbuck	.05	.04	.02
22T	Jody Davis	.05	.04	.02
23T	Mike Devereaux	.15	.11	.06
24T	Frank DiPino	.05	.04	.02
25T	Benny Distefano	.05	.04	.02
26T	John Dopson	.05	.04	.02
27T	Len Dykstra	.15	.11	.06
28T	Jim Eisenreich	.05	.04	.02
29T	Nick Esasky	.05	.04	.02
30T	Alvaro Espinoza	.05	.04	.02
31T	Darrell Evans	.05	.04	.02
32T	Junior Felix	.12	.09	.05
33T	Felix Fermin	.05	.04	.02
34T	Julio Franco	.05	.04	.02
35T	Terry Francona	.05	.04	.02
36T	Cito Gaston	.05	.04	.02
37T	Bob Geren (FC) (photo actually Mike Fennell)	.05	.04	.02
38T	*Tom Gordon*	.10	.07	.04
39T	Tommy Gregg (FC)	.05	.04	.02
40T	Ken Griffey	.15	.11	.06
41T	Ken Griffey, Jr. (FC)	4.00	3.00	1.50
42T	Kevin Gross	.05	.04	.02
43T	Lee Guetterman	.05	.04	.02
44T	Mel Hall	.05	.04	.02
45T	Erik Hanson (FC)	.30	.25	.12
46T	Gene Harris (FC)	.05	.04	.02
47T	Andy Hawkins	.05	.04	.02
48T	Rickey Henderson	.20	.15	.08
49T	Tom Herr	.05	.04	.02
50T	*Ken Hill*	.40	.30	.15
51T	Brian Holman (FC)	.05	.04	.02
52T	Brian Holton	.05	.04	.02
53T	Art Howe	.05	.04	.02
54T	Ken Howell	.05	.04	.02
55T	Bruce Hurst	.05	.04	.02
56T	Chris James	.05	.04	.02
57T	Randy Johnson	.75	.60	.30
58T	Jimmy Jones	.05	.04	.02
59T	Terry Kennedy	.05	.04	.02
60T	Paul Kilgus	.05	.04	.02
61T	Eric King	.05	.04	.02
62T	Ron Kittle	.05	.04	.02
63T	John Kruk	.25	.20	.10
64T	Randy Kutcher (FC)	.05	.04	.02
65T	Steve Lake	.05	.04	.02
66T	Mark Langston	.25	.20	.10
67T	Dave LaPoint	.05	.04	.02
68T	Rick Leach	.05	.04	.02
69T	Terry Leach	.05	.04	.02
70T	Jim Levebvre	.05	.04	.02
71T	Al Leiter	.05	.04	.02
72T	Jeffrey Leonard	.05	.04	.02
73T	Derek Lilliquist (FC)	.05	.04	.02
74T	Rick Mahler	.05	.04	.02
75T	Tom McCarthy (FC)	.05	.04	.02
76T	Lloyd McClendon	.05	.04	.02
77T	Lance McCullers	.05	.04	.02
78T	Oddibe McDowell	.05	.04	.02
79T	Roger McDowell	.05	.04	.02
80T	Larry McWilliams	.05	.04	.02
81T	Randy Milligan	.10	.08	.04
82T	Mike Moore	.15	.11	.06
83T	Keith Moreland	.05	.04	.02
84T	Mike Morgan	.05	.04	.02
85T	Jamie Moyer	.05	.04	.02
86T	Rob Murphy	.05	.04	.02
87T	Eddie Murray	.30	.25	.12
88T	Pete O'Brien	.05	.04	.02
89T	Gregg Olson	.25	.20	.10
90T	Steve Ontiveros	.05	.04	.02
91T	Jesse Orosco	.05	.04	.02
92T	Spike Owen	.05	.04	.02
93T	Rafael Palmeiro	.40	.30	.15
94T	Clay Parker (FC)	.05	.04	.02
95T	Jeff Parrett	.05	.04	.02
96T	Lance Parrish	.05	.04	.02
97T	Dennis Powell	.05	.04	.02
98T	Rey Quinones	.05	.04	.02
99T	Doug Rader	.05	.04	.02
100T	Willie Randolph	.10	.08	.04
101T	Shane Rawley	.05	.04	.02
102T	Randy Ready	.05	.04	.02
103T	Bip Roberts	.05	.04	.02
104T	Kenny Rogers (FC)	.25	.20	.10
105T	Ed Romero	.05	.04	.02
106T	Nolan Ryan	1.50	1.25	.60
107T	Luis Salazar	.05	.04	.02
108T	Juan Samuel	.05	.04	.02
109T	Alex Sanchez (FC)	.05	.04	.02
110T	Deion Sanders (FC)	1.75	1.25	.70
111T	Steve Sax	.10	.08	.04
112T	Rick Schu	.05	.04	.02
113T	Dwight Smith (FC)	.15	.11	.06
114T	Lonnie Smith	.05	.04	.02
115T	Billy Spiers (FC)	.15	.11	.06
116T	Kent Tekulve	.05	.04	.02
117T	Walt Terrell	.05	.04	.02
118T	Milt Thompson	.05	.04	.02
119T	Dickie Thon	.05	.04	.02
120T	Jeff Torborg	.05	.04	.02
121T	Jeff Treadway	.05	.04	.02
122T	Omar Vizquel (FC)	.30	.25	.12
123T	Jerome Walton (FC)	.10	.08	.04
124T	Gary Ward	.05	.04	.02
125T	Claudell Washington	.05	.04	.02
126T	Curt Wilkerson	.05	.04	.02
127T	Eddie Williams	.05	.04	.02
128T	Frank Williams	.05	.04	.02
129T	Ken Williams	.05	.04	.02
130T	Mitch Williams	.20	.15	.08
131T	Steve Wilson (FC)	.10	.08	.04
132T	Checklist	.05	.04	.02

1989 Topps Box Panels

Continuing its practice of printing baseball cards on the bottom panels of its wax pack boxes, Topps in 1989 issued a special 16-card set, printing four cards on each of four different box-bottom panels. The cards are identical in design to the regular 1989 Topps cards. They are designated by letter (from A through P) rather than by number.

		MT	NR MT	EX
Complete Panel Set:		5.00	3.75	2.00
Complete Singles Set:		2.00	1.50	.80
Common Panel:		.75	.60	.30
Common Single Player:		.08	.06	.03
	Panel	.75	.60	.30
A	George Brett	.25	.20	.10
B	Bill Buckner	.08	.06	.03
C	Darrell Evans	.08	.06	.03
D	Rich Gossage	.10	.07	.04
	Panel	1.00	.70	.40
E	Greg Gross	.08	.06	.03
F	Rickey Henderson	.30	.25	.12
G	Keith Hernandez	.08	.06	.03
H	Tom Lasorda	.08	.06	.03
	Panel	2.50	2.00	1.00
I	Jim Rice	.15	.11	.06
J	Cal Ripken, Jr.	.35	.25	.14
K	Nolan Ryan	.50	.40	.20
L	Mike Schmidt	.25	.20	.10
	Panel	1.00	.70	.40
M	Bruce Sutter	.15	.11	.06
N	Don Sutton	.10	.08	.04
O	Kent Tekulve	.08	.06	.03
P	Dave Winfield	.25	.20	.10

1989 Topps Batting Leaders

The active career batting leaders are showcased in this 22-card set. The standard-size cards are printed on super glossy stock with full-color photos. A unique left-handed or right-handed batter creates one of the vertical borders. The Topps logo appears in the upper left portion of the photo, while a "Top Active Career Batting Leaders" cup is displayed in the lower left. The player's name appears above the photo. This set is specially numbered in accordance to career batting average. Wade Boggs is featured on card number one as the top active career batting leader. The flip sides present batting statistics. One batting leader card was included in each K-Mart blister pack, which also includes 100 cards from the 1989 regular Topps set.

		MT	NR MT	EX
Complete Set:		19.00	14.00	7.50
Common Player:		.50	.40	.20
1	Wade Boggs	2.00	1.50	.80
2	Tony Gwynn	1.50	1.25	.60
3	Don Mattingly	2.00	1.50	.80
4	Kirby Puckett	2.00	1.50	.80
5	George Brett	2.00	1.50	.80
6	Pedro Guerrero	.50	.40	.20
7	Tim Raines	.60	.45	.25
8	Keith Hernandez	.50	.40	.20
9	Jim Rice	.60	.45	.25
10	Paul Molitor	1.50	1.25	.60
11	Eddie Murray	1.00	.70	.40
12	Willie McGee	.60	.45	.25

13	Dave Parker	.75	.60	.30
14	Julio Franco	.75	.60	.30
15	Rickey Henderson	1.50	1.25	.60
16	Kent Hrbek	.60	.45	.25
17	Willie Wilson	.50	.40	.20
18	Johnny Ray	.50	.40	.20
19	Pat Tabler	.50	.40	.20
20	Carney Lansford	.50	.40	.20
21	Robin Yount	2.00	1.50	.80
22	Alan Trammell	1.00	.70	.40

1989 Topps Big Baseball

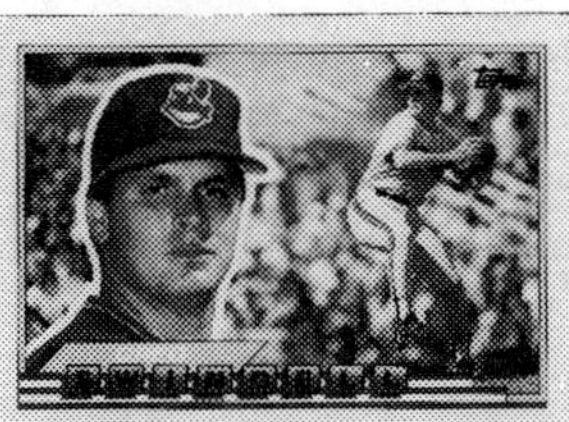

Known by collectors as Topps "Big Baseball," the cards in this 330-card set measure 2-5/8" by 3-3/4" and are patterned after the 1956 Topps cards. The glossy card fronts are horizontally-designed and include two photos of each player, a posed head shot alongside an action photo. The backs include 1988 and career stats, but are dominated by a color cartoon featuring the player. The set was issued in three series of 110 cards each.

		MT	NR MT	EX
	Complete Set:	20.00	15.00	8.00
	Common Player:	.05	.04	.02
1	Orel Hershiser	.15	.11	.06
2	Harold Reynolds	.08	.06	.03
3	Jody Davis	.05	.04	.02
4	Greg Walker	.05	.04	.02
5	Barry Bonds	.08	.06	.03
6	Bret Saberhagen	.12	.09	.05
7	Johnny Ray	.05	.04	.02
8	Mike Fiore	.20	.15	.08
9	Juan Castillo	.05	.04	.02
10	Todd Burns	.05	.04	.02
11	Carmelo Martinez	.05	.04	.02
12	Geno Petralli	.05	.04	.02
13	Mel Hall	.05	.04	.02
14	Tom Browning	.08	.06	.03
15	Fred McGriff	.15	.11	.06
16	Kevin Elster	.05	.04	.02
17	Tim Leary	.05	.04	.02
18	Jim Rice	.05	.04	.02
19	Bret Barberie	.15	.11	.06
20	Jay Buhner	.05	.04	.02
21	Atlee Hammaker	.05	.04	.02
22	Lou Whitaker	.05	.04	.02
23	Paul Runge	.05	.04	.02
24	Carlton Fisk	.08	.06	.03
25	Jose Lind	.05	.04	.02
26	Mark Gubicza	.08	.06	.03
27	Billy Ripken	.05	.04	.02
28	Mike Pagliarulo	.05	.04	.02
29	Jim Deshaies	.05	.04	.02
30	Mark McLemore	.05	.04	.02
31	Scott Terry	.05	.04	.02
32	Franklin Stubbs	.05	.04	.02
33	Don August	.05	.04	.02
34	Mark McGwire	1.00	.70	.40
35	Eric Show	.05	.04	.02
36	Cecil Espy	.05	.04	.02
37	Ron Tingley	.05	.04	.02
38	Mickey Brantley	.05	.04	.02
39	Paul O'Neill	.05	.04	.02
40	Ed Sprague	.35	.25	.14
41	Len Dykstra	.05	.04	.02
42	Roger Clemens	.25	.20	.10
43	Ron Gant	.15	.11	.06
44	Dan Pasqua	.05	.04	.02
45	Jeff Robinson	.05	.04	.02
46	George Brett	.15	.11	.06
47	Bryn Smith	.05	.04	.02
48	Mike Marshall	.05	.04	.02
49	Doug Robbins	.15	.11	.06
50	Don Mattingly	1.50	1.25	.60
51	Mike Scott	.08	.06	.03
52	Steve Jeltz	.05	.04	.02
53	Dick Schofield	.05	.04	.02
54	Tom Brunansky	.08	.06	.03
55	Gary Sheffield	.75	.60	.30
56	Dave Valle	.05	.04	.02
57	Carney Lansford	.08	.06	.03
58	Tony Gwynn	.15	.11	.06
59	Checklist	.05	.04	.02
60	Damon Berryhill	.05	.04	.02
61	Jack Morris	.05	.04	.02
62	Brett Butler	.05	.04	.02
63	Mickey Hatcher	.05	.04	.02
64	Bruce Sutter	.05	.04	.02
65	Robin Ventura	.80	.60	.30
66	Junior Oritiz	.05	.04	.02
67	Pat Tabler	.05	.04	.02
68	Greg Swindell	.08	.06	.03
69	Jeff Branson	.20	.15	.08
70	Manny Lee	.05	.04	.02
71	Dave Magadan	.05	.04	.02
72	Rich Gedman	.05	.04	.02
73	Tim Raines	.08	.06	.03
74	Mike Maddux	.05	.04	.02
75	Jim Presley	.05	.04	.02
76	Chuck Finley	.05	.04	.02
77	Jose Oquendo	.05	.04	.02
78	Rob Deer	.05	.04	.02
79	Jay Howell	.05	.04	.02
80	Terry Steinbach	.08	.06	.03
81	Eddie Whitson	.05	.04	.02
82	Ruben Sierra	.20	.15	.08
83	Bruce Benedict	.05	.04	.02
84	Fred Manrique	.05	.04	.02
85	John Smiley	.05	.04	.02
86	Mike Macfarlane	.05	.04	.02
87	Rene Gonzales	.05	.04	.02
88	Charles Hudson	.05	.04	.02
90	Les Straker	.05	.04	.02
91	Carmen Castillo	.05	.04	.02
92	Tracy Woodson	.05	.04	.02
93	Tino Martinez	.70	.50	.30
94	Herm Winningham	.05	.04	.02
95	Kelly Gruber	.05	.04	.02
96	Terry Leach	.05	.04	.02
97	Jody Reed	.05	.04	.02
98	Nelson Santovenia	.05	.04	.02
99	Tony Armas	.05	.04	.02
100	Greg Brock	.05	.04	.02
101	Dave Stewart	.10	.08	.04
102	Roberto Alomar	.15	.11	.06
103	Jim Sundberg	.05	.04	.02
104	Albert Hall	.05	.04	.02
105	Steve Lyons	.05	.04	.02
106	Sid Bream	.05	.04	.02
107	Danny Tartabull	.08	.06	.03
108	Rick Dempsey	.05	.04	.02
109	Rich Renteria	.15	.11	.06
110	Ozzie Smith	.08	.06	.03
111	Steve Sax	.08	.06	.03
112	Kelly Downs	.05	.04	.02
113	Larry Sheets	.05	.04	.02
114	Andy Benes	.50	.40	.20
115	Pete O'Brien	.05	.04	.02
116	Kevin McReynolds	.08	.06	.03
117	Juan Berenguer	.05	.04	.02
118	Billy Hatcher	.05	.04	.02
119	Rick Cerone	.05	.04	.02
120	Andre Dawson	.08	.06	.03
121	Storm Davis	.05	.04	.02
122	Devon White	.08	.06	.03
123	Alan Trammell	.15	.11	.06
124	Vince Coleman	.08	.06	.03
125	Al Leiter	.05	.04	.02
126	Dale Sveum	.05	.04	.02
127	Pete Incaviglia	.05	.04	.02
128	Dave Stieb	.08	.06	.03
129	Kevin Mitchell	.15	.11	.06
130	Dave Schmidt	.05	.04	.02
131	Gary Redus	.05	.04	.02
132	Ron Robinson	.05	.04	.02
133	Darnell Coles	.05	.04	.02
134	Benny Santiago	.08	.06	.03
135	John Farrell	.05	.04	.02
136	Willie Wilson	.05	.04	.02
137	Steve Bedrosian	.05	.04	.02
138	Don Slaught	.05	.04	.02
139	Darryl Strawberry	.15	.11	.06
140	Frank Viola	.10	.08	.04
141	Dave Silvestri	.20	.15	.08
142	Carlos Quintana	.05	.04	.02
143	Vance Law	.05	.04	.02
144	Dave Parker	.05	.04	.02
145	Tim Belcher	.05	.04	.02
146	Will Clark	.90	.70	.35
147	Mark Williamson	.05	.04	.02
148	Ozzie Guillen	.05	.04	.02
149	Kirk McCaskill	.05	.04	.02
150	Pat Sheridan	.05	.04	.02
151	Terry Pendleton	.10	.08	.04
152	Roberto Kelly	.08	.06	.03
153	Joey Meyer	.05	.04	.02
154	Mark Grant	.05	.04	.02
155	Joe Carter	.08	.06	.03
156	Steve Buechele	.05	.04	.02
157	Tony Fernandez	.08	.06	.03
158	Jeff Reed	.05	.04	.02
159	Bobby Bonilla	.08	.06	.03
160	Henry Cotto	.05	.04	.02
161	Kurt Stillwell	.05	.04	.02
162	Mickey Morandini	.25	.20	.10
163	Robby Thompson	.05	.04	.02
164	Rick Schu	.05	.04	.02
165	Stan Jefferson	.05	.04	.02
166	Ron Darling	.05	.04	.02
167	Kirby Puckett	.25	.20	.10
168	Bill Doran	.05	.04	.02
169	Dennis Lamp	.05	.04	.02
170	Ty Griffin	.30	.25	.12
171	Ron Hassey	.05	.04	.02
172	Dale Murphy	.08	.06	.03
173	Andres Galarraga	.08	.06	.03
174	Tim Flannery	.05	.04	.02
175	Cory Snyder	.05	.04	.02
176	Checklist	.05	.04	.02
177	Tommy Barrett	.05	.04	.02
178	Dan Petry	.05	.04	.02
179	Billy Masse	.10	.08	.04
180	Terry Kennedy	.05	.04	.02
181	Joe Orsulak	.05	.04	.02
182	Doyle Alexander	.05	.04	.02
183	Willie McGee	.05	.04	.02
184	Jim Gantner	.05	.04	.02
185	Keith Hernandez	.05	.04	.02
186	Greg Gagne	.05	.04	.02
187	Kevin Bass	.05	.04	.02
188	Mark Eichhorn	.05	.04	.02
189	Mark Grace	.15	.11	.06
190	Jose Canseco	1.00	.70	.40
191	Bobby Witt	.05	.04	.02
192	Rafael Santana	.05	.04	.02
193	Dwight Evans	.05	.04	.02
194	Greg Booker	.05	.04	.02
195	Brook Jacoby	.05	.04	.02
196	Rafael Belliard	.05	.04	.02
197	Candy Maldonado	.05	.04	.02
198	Mickey Tettleton	.08	.06	.03
199	Barry Larkin	.08	.06	.03
200	Frank White	.05	.04	.02
201	Wally Joyner	.15	.11	.06
202	Chet Lemon	.05	.04	.02
203	Joe Magrane	.05	.04	.02
204	Glenn Braggs	.05	.04	.02
205	Scott Fletcher	.05	.04	.02
206	Gary Ward	.05	.04	.02
207	Nelson Liriano	.05	.04	.02
208	Howard Johnson	.15	.11	.06
209	Kent Hrbek	.08	.06	.03
210	Ken Caminiti	.05	.04	.02
211	Mike Greenwell	.50	.40	.20
212	Ryne Sandberg	.35	.25	.14
213	Joe Slusarski	.10	.08	.04
214	Donnell Nixon	.05	.04	.02
215	Tim Wallach	.05	.04	.02
216	John Kruk	.05	.04	.02
217	Charles Nagy	.25	.20	.10
218	Alvin Davis	.08	.06	.03
219	Oswald Peraza	.05	.04	.02
220	Mike Schmidt	.30	.25	.12
221	Spike Owen	.05	.04	.02
222	Mike Smithson	.05	.04	.02
223	Dion James	.05	.04	.02
224	Ernie Whitt	.05	.04	.02
225	Mike Davis	.05	.04	.02
226	Gene Larkin	.05	.04	.02
227	Pat Combs	.25	.20	.10
228	Jack Howell	.05	.04	.02
229	Ron Oester	.05	.04	.02
230	Paul Gibson	.05	.04	.02
231	Mookie Wilson	.05	.04	.02
232	Glenn Hubbard	.05	.04	.02
233	Shawon Dunston	.05	.04	.02
234	Otis Nixon	.05	.04	.02
235	Melido Perez	.05	.04	.02
236	Jerry Browne	.05	.04	.02
237	Rick Rhoden	.05	.04	.02
238	Bo Jackson	.25	.20	.10
239	Randy Velarde	.05	.04	.02
240	Jack Clark	.05	.04	.02
241	Wade Boggs	.80	.60	.30
242	Lonnie Smith	.05	.04	.02
243	Mike Flanagan	.05	.04	.02
244	Willie Randolph	.05	.04	.02
245	Oddibe McDowell	.05	.04	.02
246	Ricky Jordan	.10	.08	.04
247	Greg Briley	.20	.15	.08
248	Rex Hudler	.05	.04	.02
249	Robin Yount	.25	.20	.10
250	Lance Parrish	.05	.04	.02
251	Chris Sabo	.20	.15	.08
252	Mike Henneman	.05	.04	.02
253	Gregg Jefferies	.60	.45	.25
254	Curt Young	.05	.04	.02
255	Andy Van Slyke	.08	.06	.03
256	Rod Booker	.05	.04	.02
257	Rafael Palmeiro	.05	.04	.02
258	Jose Uribe	.05	.04	.02
259	Ellis Burks	.10	.08	.04
260	John Smoltz	.10	.08	.04
261	Tom Foley	.05	.04	.02
262	Lloyd Moseby	.05	.04	.02
263	Jim Poole	.10	.08	.04
264	Gary Gaetti	.08	.06	.03
265	Bob Dernier	.05	.04	.02
266	Harold Baines	.08	.06	.03
267	Tom Candiotti	.05	.04	.02
268	Rafael Ramirez	.05	.04	.02
269	Bob Boone	.05	.04	.02
270	Buddy Bell	.05	.04	.02
271	Rickey Henderson	.15	.11	.06
272	Willie Fraser	.05	.04	.02
273	Eric Davis	.15	.11	.06
274	Jeff Robinson	.05	.04	.02
275	Damaso Garcia	.05	.04	.02
276	Sid Fernandez	.05	.04	.02
277	Stan Javier	.05	.04	.02
278	Marty Barrett	.05	.04	.02
279	Gerald Perry	.05	.04	.02
280	Rob Ducey	.05	.04	.02
281	Mike Scioscia	.05	.04	.02
282	Randy Bush	.05	.04	.02
283	Tom Herr	.05	.04	.02
284	Glenn Wilson	.05	.04	.02
285	Pedro Guerrero	.10	.08	.04
286	Cal Ripken, Jr.	.30	.25	.12
287	Randy Johnson	.15	.11	.06
288	Julio Franco	.08	.06	.03
289	Ivan Calderon	.05	.04	.02
290	Rich Yett	.05	.04	.02
291	Scott Servais	.10	.08	.04
292	Bill Pecota	.05	.04	.02
293	Ken Phelps	.05	.04	.02
294	Chili Davis	.05	.04	.02
295	Manny Trillo	.05	.04	.02
296	Mike Boddicker	.05	.04	.02
297	Geronimo Berroa	.05	.04	.02
298	Todd Stottlemyre	.05	.04	.02
299	Kirk Gibson	.05	.04	.02
300	Wally Backman	.05	.04	.02
301	Hubie Brooks	.05	.04	.02
302	Von Hayes	.05	.04	.02
303	Matt Nokes	.05	.04	.02

304	Dwight Gooden	.10	.08	.04
305	Walt Weiss	.10	.08	.04
306	Mike LaValliere	.05	.04	.02
307	Cris Carpenter	.10	.08	.04
308	Ted Wood	.10	.08	.04
309	Jeff Russell	.05	.04	.02
310	Dave Gallagher	.05	.04	.02
311	Andy Allanson	.05	.04	.02
312	Craig Reynolds	.05	.04	.02
313	Kevin Seitzer	.08	.06	.03
314	Dave Winfield	.20	.15	.08
315	Andy McGaffigan	.05	.04	.02
316	Nick Esasky	.05	.04	.02
317	Jeff Blauser	.05	.04	.02
318	George Bell	.10	.08	.04
319	Eddie Murray	.10	.08	.04
320	Mark Davidson	.05	.04	.02
321	Juan Samuel	.05	.04	.02
322	Jim Abbott	.50	.40	.20
323	Kal Daniels	.05	.04	.02
324	Mike Brumley	.05	.04	.02
325	Gary Carter	.05	.04	.02
326	Dave Henderson	.05	.04	.02
327	Checklist	.05	.04	.02
328	Garry Templeton	.05	.04	.02
329	Pat Perry	.05	.04	.02
330	Paul Molitor	.15	.11	.06

1989 Topps Coins

Similar in format to previous Topps coins, this 60-piece set features 1-1/2" diameter coins with rolled colored edges. A shooting star device printed over the player photo gives his name, team and position. Backs have a few biographical details and a summary of the player's previous season performance printed in black on silver. The coins were sold three per pack, with each pack including an offer card for an album to house the pieces.

		MT	NR MT	EX
	Complete Set (60):	9.00	6.75	3.50
	Common Player:	.10	.08	.04
1	Kirk Gibson	.15	.11	.06
2	Orel Herhiser	.15	.11	.06
3	Chris Sabo	.10	.08	.04
4	Tony Gwynn	.20	.15	.08
5	Brett Butler, Bobby Bonilla	.10	.08	.04
7	Jack Clark, Will Clark	.10	.08	.04
9	Eric Davis	.15	.11	.06
10	Glenn Davis	.10	.08	.04
11	Andre Dawson	.20	.15	.08
12	John Franco	.10	.08	.04
13	Andres Galarraga	.15	.11	.06
14	Dwight Gooden	.20	.15	.08
15	Mark Grace	.15	.11	.06
16	Pedro Guerrero	.10	.08	.04
17	Ricky Jordan	.10	.08	.04
18	Mike Marshall	.10	.08	.04
19	Dale Murphy	.25	.20	.10
20	Eddie Murray	.20	.15	.08
21	Gerald Perry	.10	.08	.04
22	Tim Raines	.15	.11	.06
23	Juan Samuel	.10	.08	.04
24	Benito Santiago	.15	.11	.06
25	Ozzie Smith	.20	.15	.08
26	Darryl Strawberry	.15	.11	.06
27	Andy Van Slyke	.15	.11	.06
28	Gerald Young	.10	.08	.04
29	Jose Canseco	.25	.20	.10
30	Frank Viola	.10	.08	.04
31	Walt Weiss	.15	.11	.06
32	Wade Boggs	.35	.25	.14
33	Harold Baines	.10	.08	.04
34	George Brett	.45	.35	.20
35	Jay Buhner	.15	.11	.06
36	Joe Carter	.20	.15	.08
37	Roger Clemens	.35	.25	.14
38	Alvin Davis	.10	.08	.04
39	Tony Fernandez	.10	.08	.04
40	Carlton Fisk	.20	.15	.08
41	Mike Greenwell	.15	.11	.06
42	Kent Hrbek	.15	.11	.06
43	Don Mattingly	.50	.40	.20
44	Fred McGriff	.25	.20	.10
45	Mark McGwire	.25	.20	.10
46	Paul Molitor	.25	.20	.10
47	Rafael Palmeiro	.20	.15	.08
48	Kirby Puckett	.25	.20	.10
49	Johnny Ray	.10	.08	.04
50	Cal Ripken, Jr.	.50	.40	.20
51	Ruben Sierra	.15	.11	.06
52	Pete Stanicek	.10	.08	.04
53	Dave Stewart	.15	.11	.06
54	Greg Swindell	.10	.08	.04
55	Danny Tartabull	.15	.11	.06
56	Alan Trammell	.20	.15	.08
57	Lou Whitaker	.15	.11	.06
58	Dave Winfield	.45	.35	.20
59	Mike Witt	.10	.08	.04
60	Robin Yount	.45	.35	.20

1989 Topps Double Headers All-Stars

This scarce test issue was produced in two versions, an All-Stars set and a set of exclusively Mets and Yankees players. The "cards" are two-sided miniature (1-5/8" x 2-1/4") reproductions of the player's 1989 Topps card and his Topps rookie card, encased in a clear plastic stand.

		MT	NR MT	EX
	Complete Set (24):	65.00	49.00	26.00
	Common Player:	2.00	1.50	.80
(1)	Alan Ashby	2.00	1.50	.80
(2)	Wade Boggs	6.00	4.50	2.50
(3)	Bobby Bonilla	3.00	2.25	1.25
(4)	Jose Canseco	6.00	4.50	2.50
(5)	Will Clark	5.00	3.75	2.00
(6)	Roger Clemens	3.00	2.25	1.25
(7)	Andre Dawson	2.50	2.00	1.00
(9)	Carlton Fisk	2.50	2.00	1.00
(10)	John Franco	2.00	1.50	.80
(11)	Julio Franco	2.50	2.00	1.00
(12)	Kirk Gibson	2.50	2.00	1.00
(13)	Mike Greenwell	2.50	2.00	1.00
(14)	Orel Hershiser	2.50	2.00	1.00
(15)	Danny Jackson	2.00	1.50	.80
(16)	Don Mattingly	6.00	4.50	2.50
(17)	Mark McGwire	4.00	3.00	1.50
(18)	Kirby Puckett	6.00	4.50	2.50
(19)	Ryne Sandberg	8.00	6.00	3.25
(20)	Ozzie Smith	3.00	2.25	1.25
(21)	Darryl Strawberry	2.50	2.00	1.00
(22)	Alan Trammell	3.00	2.25	1.25
(23)	Andy Van Slyke	2.50	2.00	1.00
(24)	Frank Viola	2.00	1.50	.80

1989 Topps Major League Debut

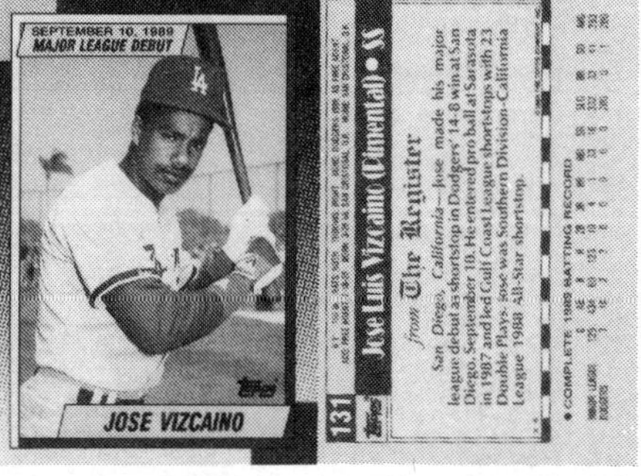

This 150-card set highlights the debut date of 1989 Major League rookies. Two checklist cards are also included in this boxed set. The checklist cards list the players in order of debut date, but the cards are numbered alphabetically. The card fronts resemble the 1990 Topps cards in style. A debut banner appears in an upper corner of the card. The flip sides are horizontal and are printed in black on yellow stock. An overview of the player's first game is provided on the card back. The set is packaged in an attractive red, blue, green and yellow collectors box. The set was available through select hobby dealers.

		MT	NR MT	EX
	Complete Set:	18.00	13.50	7.25
	Common Player:	.08	.06	.03
1	Jim Abbott	.30	.25	.12
2	Beau Allred	.08	.06	.03
3	Wilson Alvarez	.25	.20	.10
4	Kent Anderson	.08	.06	.03
5	Eric Anthony	.20	.15	.08
6	Kevin Appier	.15	.11	.06
7	Larry Arndt	.08	.06	.03
8	John Barfield	.08	.06	.03
9	Billy Bates	.08	.06	.03
10	Kevin Batiste	.10	.08	.04
11	Blaine Beatty	.10	.08	.04
12	Stan Belinda	.15	.11	.06
13	Juan Bell	.15	.11	.06
14	Joey Belle	.35	.25	.14
15	Andy Benes	.30	.25	.12
16	Mike Benjamin	.10	.08	.04
17	Geronimo Berroa	.08	.06	.03
18	Mike Blowers	.10	.08	.04
19	Brian Brady	.08	.06	.03
20	Francisco Cabrera	.10	.08	.04
21	George Canale	.08	.06	.03
22	Jose Cano	.08	.06	.03
23	Steve Carter	.10	.08	.04
24	Pat Combs	.15	.11	.06
25	Scott Coolbaugh	.15	.11	.06
26	Steve Cummings	.10	.08	.04
27	Pete Dalena	.08	.06	.03
28	Jeff Datz	.08	.06	.03
29	Bobby Davidson	.08	.06	.03
30	Drew Denson	.08	.06	.03
31	Gary DiSarcina	.20	.15	.08
32	Brian DuBois	.15	.11	.06
33	Mike Dyer	.10	.08	.04
34	Wayne Edwards	.10	.08	.04
35	Junior Felix	.30	.25	.12
36	Mike Fetters	.15	.11	.06
37	Steve Finley	.20	.15	.08
38	Darren Fletcher	.20	.15	.08
39	LaVel Freeman	.08	.06	.03
40	Steve Frey	.10	.08	.04
41	Mark Gardner	.20	.15	.08
42	Joe Girardi	.20	.15	.08
43	Juan Gonzalez	2.00	1.50	.80
44	Goose Gozzo	.08	.06	.03
45	Tommy Greene	.15	.11	.06
46	Ken Griffey, Jr.	3.50	2.75	1.50
47	Jason Grimsley	.20	.15	.08
48	Marquis Grissom	.40	.30	.15
49	Mark Guthrie	.10	.08	.04
50	Chip Hale	.08	.06	.03
51	John Hardy	.08	.06	.03
52	Gene Harris	.10	.08	.04
53	Mike Hartley	.10	.08	.04
54	Scott Hemond	.10	.08	.04
55	Xavier Hernandez	.10	.08	.04
56	Eric Hetzel	.08	.06	.03
57	Greg Hibbard	.10	.08	.04
58	Mark Higgins	.08	.06	.03
59	Glenallen Hill	.20	.15	.08
60	Chris Hoiles	.30	.25	.12
61	Shawn Holman	.10	.08	.04
62	Dann Howitt	.10	.08	.04
63	Mike Huff	.10	.08	.04
64	Terry Jorgenson	.10	.08	.04
65	Dave Justice	2.00	1.50	.80
66	Jeff King	.20	.15	.08
67	Matt Kinzer	.08	.06	.03
68	Joe Kraemer	.08	.06	.03
69	Marcus Lawton	.08	.06	.03
70	Derek Lilliquist	.15	.11	.06
71	Scott Little	.08	.06	.03
72	Greg Litton	.15	.11	.06
73	Rick Lueken	.10	.08	.04
74	Julio Machado	.08	.06	.03
75	Tom Magrann	.08	.06	.03
76	Kelly Mann	.10	.08	.04
77	Randy McCament	.08	.06	.03
78	Ben McDonald	.50	.40	.20
79	Chuck McElroy	.20	.15	.08
80	Jeff McKnight	.10	.08	.04
81	Kent Mercker	.25	.20	.10
82	Matt Merullo	.08	.06	.03
83	Hensley Meulens	.15	.11	.06
84	Kevin Mmahat	.08	.06	.03
85	Mike Munoz	.08	.06	.03
86	Dan Murphy	.08	.06	.03
87	Jaime Navarro	.20	.15	.08
88	Randy Nosek	.10	.08	.04
89	John Olerud	.50	.40	.20
90	Steve Olin	.10	.08	.04
91	Joe Oliver	.20	.15	.08
92	Francisco Oliveras	.10	.08	.04
93	Greg Olson	.15	.11	.06
94	John Orton	.10	.08	.04
95	Dean Palmer	.20	.15	.08
96	Ramon Pena	.08	.06	.03
97	Jeff Peterek	.08	.06	.03
98	Marty Pevey	.08	.06	.03
99	Rusty Richards	.08	.06	.03
100	Jeff Richardson	.08	.06	.03
101	Rob Richie	.08	.06	.03
102	Kevin Ritz	.10	.08	.04
103	Rosario Rodriguez	.10	.08	.04
104	Mike Roesler	.10	.08	.04
105	Kenny Rogers	.15	.11	.06
106	Bobby Rose	.10	.08	.04
107	Alex Sanchez	.15	.11	.06
108	Deion Sanders	.25	.20	.10
109	Jeff Schaefer	.08	.06	.03
110	Jeff Schulz	.10	.08	.04
111	Mike Schwabe	.10	.08	.04
112	Dick Scott	.08	.06	.03
113	Scott Scudder	.15	.11	.06
114	Rudy Seanez	.15	.11	.06

		MT	NR MT	EX
115	Joe Skalski	.08	.06	.03
116	Dwight Smith	.10	.08	.04
117	Greg Smith	.15	.11	.06
118	Mike Smith	.10	.08	.04
119	Paul Sorrento	.15	.11	.06
120	Sammy Sosa	.50	.40	.20
121	Billy Spiers	.15	.11	.06
122	Mike Stanton	.20	.15	.08
123	Phil Stephenson	.08	.06	.03
124	Doug Strange	.08	.06	.03
125	Russ Swan	.10	.08	.04
126	Kevin Tapani	.35	.25	.14
127	Stu Tate	.08	.06	.03
128	Greg Vaughn	.40	.30	.15
129	Robin Ventura	.25	.20	.10
130	Randy Veres	.08	.06	.03
131	Jose Vizcaino	.15	.11	.06
132	Omar Vizquel	.10	.08	.04
133	Larry Walker	.40	.30	.15
134	Jerome Walton	.15	.11	.06
135	Gary Wayne	.10	.08	.04
136	Lenny Webster	.10	.08	.04
137	Mickey Weston	.10	.08	.04
138	Jeff Wetherby	.08	.06	.03
139	John Wetteland	.25	.20	.10
140	Ed Whited	.08	.06	.03
141	Wally Whitehurst	.10	.08	.04
142	Kevin Wickander	.15	.11	.06
143	Dean Wilkins	.10	.08	.04
144	Dana Williams	.10	.08	.04
145	Paul Wilmet	.08	.06	.03
146	Craig Wilson	.15	.11	.06
147	Matt Winters	.08	.06	.03
148	Eric Yelding	.25	.20	.10
149	Clint Zavaras	.15	.11	.06
150	Todd Zeile	.30	.25	.12
----	Checklist (1 of 2)	.08	.06	.03
----	Checklist (2 of 2)	.08	.06	.03

1989 Topps Mini League Leaders

This 77-card set from Topps features baseball's statistical leaders from the 1988 season, and is referred to as a "mini" set because of the cards' small (2-1/8" by 3") size. The glossy cards feature action photos that have a soft focus on all edges. The player's team and name appear along the bottom of the card. The back features a head-shot of the player along with his 1988 season ranking and stats.

		MT	NR MT	EX
Complete Set:		6.00	4.50	2.50
Common Player:		.09	.07	.04
1	Dale Murphy	.35	.25	.14
2	Gerald Perry	.09	.07	.04
3	Andre Dawson	.20	.15	.08
4	Greg Maddux	.25	.20	.10
5	Rafael Palmeiro	.25	.20	.10
6	Tom Browning	.12	.09	.05
7	Kal Daniels	.10	.08	.04
8	Eric Davis	.20	.15	.08
9	John Franco	.09	.07	.04
10	Danny Jackson	.09	.07	.04
11	Barry Larkin	.15	.11	.06
12	Jose Rijo	.15	.11	.06
13	Chris Sabo	.20	.15	.08
14	Nolan Ryan	.50	.40	.20
15	Mike Scott	.09	.07	.04
16	Gerald Young	.09	.07	.04
17	Kirk Gibson	.12	.09	.05
18	Orel Hershiser	.25	.20	.10
19	Steve Sax	.12	.09	.05
20	John Tudor	.09	.07	.04
21	Hubie Brooks	.09	.07	.04
22	Andres Galarraga	.15	.11	.06
23	Otis Nixon	.09	.07	.04
24	Dave Cone	.15	.11	.06
25	Sid Fernandez	.12	.09	.05
26	Dwight Gooden	.15	.11	.06
27	Kevin McReynolds	.20	.15	.08
28	Darryl Strawberry	.15	.11	.06
29	Juan Samuel	.09	.07	.04
30	Bobby Bonilla	.12	.09	.05
31	Sid Bream	.09	.07	.04
32	Jim Gott	.09	.07	.04
33	Andy Van Slyke	.12	.09	.05
34	Vince Coleman	.12	.09	.05
35	Jose DeLeon	.09	.07	.04
36	Joe Magrane	.12	.09	.05
37	Ozzie Smith	.20	.15	.08
38	Todd Worrell	.09	.07	.04
39	Tony Gwynn	.30	.25	.12
40	Brett Butler	.12	.09	.05
41	Will Clark	.80	.60	.30
42	Rick Reuschel	.12	.09	.05
43	Checklist	.09	.07	.04
44	Eddie Murray	.20	.15	.08
45	Wade Boggs	.80	.60	.30
46	Roger Clemens	.30	.25	.12
47	Dwight Evans	.12	.09	.05
48	Mike Greenwell	.50	.40	.20
49	Bruce Hurst	.12	.09	.05
50	Johnny Ray	.09	.07	.04
51	Doug Jones	.09	.07	.04
52	Greg Swindell	.15	.11	.06
53	Gary Pettis	.09	.07	.04
54	George Brett	.35	.25	.14
55	Mark Gubicza	.15	.11	.06
56	Willie Wilson	.09	.07	.04
57	Teddy Higuera	.12	.09	.05
58	Paul Molitor	.25	.20	.10
59	Robin Yount	.35	.25	.14
60	Allan Anderson	.09	.07	.04
61	Gary Gaetti	.12	.09	.05
62	Kirby Puckett	.35	.25	.14
63	Jeff Reardon	.09	.07	.04
64	Frank Viola	.12	.09	.05
65	Jack Clark	.12	.09	.05
66	Rickey Henderson	.25	.20	.10
67	Dave Winfield	.30	.25	.12
68	Jose Canseco	.80	.60	.30
69	Dennis Eckersley	.15	.11	.06
70	Mark McGwire	.60	.45	.25
71	Dave Stewart	.15	.11	.06
72	Alvin Davis	.12	.09	.05
73	Mark Langston	.12	.09	.05
74	Harold Reynolds	.12	.09	.05
75	George Bell	.15	.11	.06
76	Tony Fernandez	.15	.11	.06
77	Fred McGriff	.25	.20	.10

1989 Topps American Baseball

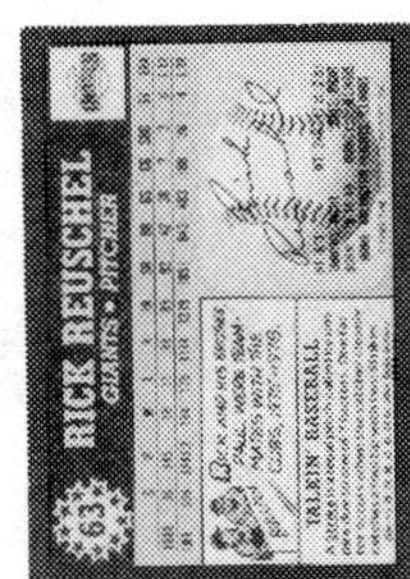

For the second consecutive year Topps released an 88-card set of baseball cards available in both the United States and the United Kingdom. The mini-sized cards (2-1/4" by 3") feature full-color photos on the card fronts. The cards are printed on white stock with a low gloss finish. The player action photo is outlined in red, white, and blue and framed in white. The card backs are printed horizontally and include a characterization cartoon along with biographical information and statistics. The cards are sold in packs of five cards with a stick of bubble gum.

		MT	NR MT	EX
Complete Set:		8.00	6.00	3.25
Common Player:		.08	.06	.03
1	Brady Anderson	.08	.06	.03
2	Harold Baines	.15	.11	.06
3	George Bell	.15	.11	.06
4	Wade Boggs	1.00	.70	.40
5	Barry Bonds	.80	.60	.30
6	Bobby Bonilla	.20	.15	.08
7	George Brett	.15	.11	.06
8	Hubie Brooks	.08	.06	.03
9	Tom Brunansky	.08	.06	.03
10	Jay Buhner	.15	.11	.06
11	Brett Butler	.08	.06	.03
12	Jose Canseco	1.25	.90	.50
13	Joe Carter	.15	.11	.06
14	Jack Clark	.08	.06	.03
15	Will Clark	.80	.60	.30
16	Roger Clemens	.30	.25	.12
17	Dave Cone	.08	.06	.03
18	Alvin Davis	.08	.06	.03
19	Eric Davis	.15	.11	.06
20	Glenn Davis	.08	.06	.03
21	Andre Dawson	.15	.11	.06
22	Bill Doran	.08	.06	.03
23	Dennis Eckersley	.12	.09	.05
24	Dwight Evans	.08	.06	.03
25	Tony Fernandez	.08	.06	.03
26	Carlton Fisk	.12	.09	.05
27	John Franco	.08	.06	.03
28	Andres Galarraga	.15	.11	.06
29	Ron Gant	.10	.08	.04
30	Kirk Gibson	.08	.06	.03
31	Dwight Gooden	.15	.11	.06
32	Mike Greenwell	.20	.15	.08
33	Mark Gubicza	.08	.06	.03
34	Pedro Gurrero	.12	.09	.05
35	Ozzie Guillen	.08	.06	.03
36	Tony Gwynn	.15	.11	.06
37	Rickey Henderson	.25	.20	.10
38	Orel Hershiser	.15	.11	.06
39	Teddy Higuera	.08	.06	.03
40	Charlie Hough	.08	.06	.03
41	Kent Hrbek	.12	.09	.05
42	Bruce Hurst	.08	.06	.03
43	Bo Jackson	.25	.20	.10
44	Gregg Jefferies	.30	.25	.12
45	Ricky Jordan	.10	.08	.04
46	Wally Joyner	.15	.11	.06
47	Mark Langston	.12	.09	.05
48	Mike Marshall	.08	.06	.03
49	Don Mattingly	2.00	1.50	.80
50	Fred McGriff	.35	.25	.14
51	Mark McGwire	.80	.60	.30
52	Kevin McReynolds	.15	.11	.06
53	Paul Molitor	.35	.25	.14
54	Jack Morris	.08	.06	.03
55	Dale Murphy	.25	.20	.10
56	Eddie Murray	.25	.20	.10
57	Pete O'Brien	.08	.06	.03
58	Rafael Palmeiro	.25	.20	.10
59	Gerald Perry	.08	.06	.03
60	Kirby Puckett	.35	.25	.14
61	Tim Raines	.15	.11	.06
62	Johnny Ray	.08	.06	.03
63	Rick Reuschel	.08	.06	.03
64	Cal Ripken	.80	.60	.30
65	Chris Sabo	.15	.11	.06
66	Juan Samuel	.08	.06	.03
67	Ryne Sandberg	.80	.60	.30
68	Benny Santiago	.15	.11	.06
69	Steve Sax	.08	.06	.03
70	Mike Schmidt	.75	.60	.30
71	Ruben Sierra	.20	.15	.08
72	Ozzie Smith	.25	.20	.10
73	Cory Snyder	.08	.06	.03
74	Dave Stewart	.12	.09	.05
75	Darryl Strawberry	.15	.11	.06
76	Greg Swindell	.08	.06	.03
77	Alan Trammell	.15	.11	.06
78	Fernando Valenzuela	.08	.06	.03
79	Andy Van Slyke	.20	.15	.08
80	Frank Viola	.20	.15	.08
81	Claudell Washington	.08	.06	.03
82	Walt Weiss	.08	.06	.03
83	Lou Whitaker	.15	.11	.06
84	Dave Winfield	.35	.25	.14
85	Mike Witt	.08	.06	.03
86	Gerald Young	.08	.06	.03
87	Robin Yount	.45	.35	.20
88	Checklist	.08	.06	.03

1990 Topps

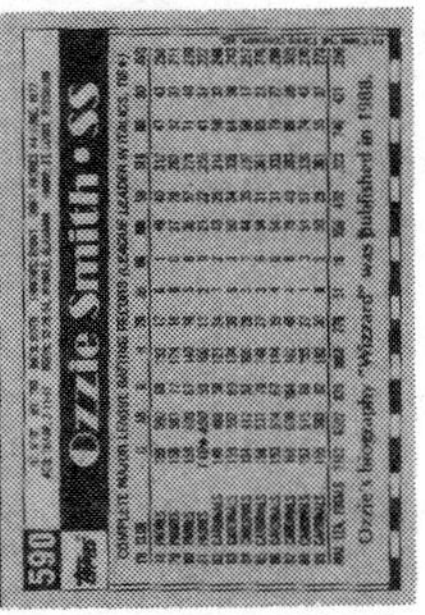

The 1990 Topps set again included 792 cards, and sported a newly-designed front that featured six different color schemes. The set led off with a special four-card salute to Nolan Ryan, and featured various other specials, including All-Stars, Number 1 Draft Picks, Record Breakers, manager cards, rookies, and "Turn Back the Clock" cards. The set also includes a special card commemorating A. Bartlett Giamatti, the late Baseball Commissioner. The backs are printed in black on a chartreuse background with the card number in the upper left corner. The set features 725 different individual player cards, the most ever, including 138 players making their first appearance in a regular Topps set.

		MT	NR MT	EX
Complete Set (792):		15.00	11.00	6.00
Common Player:		.03	.02	.01
1	Nolan Ryan	.50	.40	.20
2	Nolan Ryan (Mets)	.20	.15	.08
3	Nolan Ryan (Angels)	.20	.15	.08
4	Nolan Ryan (Astros)	.20	.15	.08
5	Nolan Ryan (Rangers)	.20	.15	.08
6	Vince Coleman (Record Breaker)	.10	.08	.04
7	Rickey Henderson (Record Breaker)	.20	.15	.08
8	Cal Ripken, Jr. (Record Breaker)	.15	.11	.06
9	Eric Plunk	.03	.02	.01
10	Barry Larkin	.10	.07	.04

11	Paul Gibson	.04	.03	.02
12	Joe Girardi (FC)	.10	.07	.04
13	Mark Williamson	.03	.02	.01
14	*Mike Fetters*	.10	.07	.04
15	Teddy Higuera	.06	.05	.02
16	*Kent Anderson*	.10	.08	.04
17	Kelly Downs	.05	.04	.02
18	Carlos Quintana	.09	.07	.04
19	Al Newman	.03	.02	.01
20	Mark Gubicza	.12	.09	.05
21	Jeff Torborg	.03	.02	.01
22	Bruce Ruffin	.03	.02	.01
23	Randy Velarde	.07	.05	.03
24	Joe Hesketh	.03	.02	.01
25	Willie Randolph	.08	.06	.03
26	Don Slaught	.03	.02	.01
27	Rick Leach	.03	.02	.01
28	Duane Ward	.04	.03	.02
29	John Cangelosi	.03	.02	.01
30	David Cone	.10	.08	.04
31	Henry Cotto	.03	.02	.01
32	John Farrell	.05	.04	.02
33	Greg Walker	.05	.04	.02
34	*Tony Fossas* (FC)	.07	.05	.03
35	Benito Santiago	.12	.09	.05
36	John Costello	.04	.03	.02
37	Domingo Ramos	.03	.02	.01
38	Wes Gardner	.04	.03	.02
39	Curt Ford	.04	.03	.02
40	Jay Howell	.06	.05	.02
41	Matt Williams	.20	.15	.08
42	Jeff Robinson	.05	.04	.02
43	Dante Bichette	.15	.11	.06
44	*Roger Salkeld* (#1 Draft Pick)	.25	.20	.10
45	Dave Parker	.09	.07	.04
46	Rob Dibble	.07	.05	.03
47	Brian Harper	.04	.03	.02
48	Zane Smith	.03	.02	.01
49	Tom Lawless	.03	.02	.01
50	Glenn Davis	.08	.06	.03
51	Doug Rader	.03	.02	.01
52	*Jack Daugherty* (FC)	.20	.15	.08
53	Mike LaCoss	.04	.03	.02
54	Joel Skinner	.04	.03	.02
55	Darrell Evans	.05	.04	.02
56	Franklin Stubbs	.04	.03	.02
57	*Greg Vaughn*	.35	.25	.14
58	Keith Miller	.10	.08	.04
59	Ted Power	.03	.02	.01
60	George Brett	.25	.20	.10
61	*Deion Sanders*	.35	.25	.14
62	Ramon Martinez	.25	.20	.10
63	Mike Pagliarulo	.04	.03	.02
64	Danny Darwin	.03	.02	.01
65	Devon White	.07	.05	.03
66	*Greg Litton*	.15	.11	.06
67	Scott Sanderson	.04	.03	.02
68	Dave Henderson	.06	.05	.02
69	Todd Frohwirth	.03	.02	.01
70	Mike Greenwell	.10	.07	.04
71	Allan Anderson	.05	.04	.02
72	*Jeff Huson*	.10	.07	.04
73	Bob Milacki	.05	.04	.02
74	*Jeff Jackson* (#1 Draft Pick)	.20	.15	.08
75	Doug Jones	.05	.04	.02
76	Dave Valle	.03	.02	.01
77	Dave Bergman	.03	.02	.01
78	Mike Flanagan	.04	.03	.02
79	Ron Kittle	.05	.04	.02
80	Jeff Russell	.05	.04	.02
81	Bob Rodgers	.03	.02	.01
82	Scott Terry	.04	.03	.02
83	Hensley Meulens	.10	.07	.04
84	Ray Searage	.03	.02	.01
85	Juan Samuel	.05	.04	.02
86	Paul Kilgus	.03	.02	.01
87	*Rick Luecken* (FC)	.15	.11	.06
88	Glenn Braggs	.05	.04	.02
89	*Clint Zavaras*	.10	.07	.04
90	Jack Clark	.06	.05	.02
91	*Steve Frey*	.10	.07	.04
92	Mike Stanley	.03	.02	.01
93	Shawn Hillegas	.03	.02	.01
94	Herm Winningham	.03	.02	.01
95	Todd Worrell	.05	.04	.02
96	Jody Reed	.04	.03	.02
97	Curt Schilling (FC)	.20	.15	.08
98	Jose Gonzalez (FC)	.10	.08	.04
99	*Rich Monteleone*	.10	.07	.04
100	Will Clark	.30	.25	.12
101	Shane Rawley	.04	.03	.02
102	Stan Javier	.04	.03	.02
103	Marvin Freeman	.09	.07	.04
104	Bob Knepper	.03	.02	.01
105	Randy Myers	.05	.04	.02
106	Charlie O'Brien	.03	.02	.01
107	Fred Lynn	.05	.04	.02
108	Rod Nichols	.04	.03	.02
109	Roberto Kelly	.08	.06	.03
110	Tommy Helms	.03	.02	.01
111	Ed Whited	.20	.15	.08
112	Glenn Wilson	.03	.02	.01
113	Manny Lee	.03	.02	.01
114	Mike Bielecki	.05	.04	.02
115	Tony Pena	.06	.05	.02
116	Floyd Bannister	.04	.03	.02
117	Mike Sharperson (FC)	.09	.07	.04
118	Erik Hanson	.10	.08	.04
119	Billy Hatcher	.04	.03	.02
120	John Franco	.05	.04	.02
121	Robin Ventura	.60	.45	.25
122	Shawn Abner	.03	.02	.01
123	Rich Gedman	.04	.03	.02
124	Dave Dravecky	.04	.03	.02
125	Kent Hrbek	.07	.05	.03
126	Randy Kramer	.03	.02	.01
127	Mike Devereaux	.06	.05	.02
128	Checklist 1-132	.03	.02	.01

129	Ron Jones	.10	.08	.04
130	Bert Blyleven	.05	.04	.02
131	Matt Nokes	.06	.05	.02
132	Lance Blankenship (FC)	.10	.08	.04
133	Ricky Horton	.03	.02	.01
134	*Earl Cunningham* (#1 Draft Pick)	.15	.11	.06
135	Dave Magadan	.05	.04	.02
136	Kevin Brown	.06	.05	.02
137	*Marty Pevey* (FC)	.15	.11	.06
138	Al Leiter	.04	.03	.02
139	Greg Brock	.04	.03	.02
140	Andre Dawson	.12	.09	.05
141	John Hart	.05	.04	.02
142	*Jeff Wetherby* (FC)	.15	.11	.06
143	Rafael Belliard	.03	.02	.01
144	Bud Black	.03	.02	.01
145	Terry Steinbach	.07	.05	.03
146	*Rob Richie* (FC)	.15	.11	.06
147	Chuck Finley	.04	.03	.02
148	Edgar Martinez (FC)	.09	.07	.04
149	Steve Farr	.04	.03	.02
150	Kirk Gibson	.09	.07	.04
151	Rick Mahler	.03	.02	.01
152	Lonnie Smith	.05	.04	.02
153	Randy Milligan	.05	.04	.02
154	Mike Maddux	.05	.04	.02
155	Ellis Burks	.12	.09	.05
156	Ken Patterson	.04	.03	.02
157	Craig Biggio	.10	.07	.04
158	Craig Lefferts	.04	.03	.02
159	Mike Felder	.03	.02	.01
160	Dave Righetti	.06	.05	.02
161	Harold Reynolds	.06	.05	.02
162	*Todd Zeile*	.25	.20	.10
163	Phil Bradley	.05	.04	.02
164	*Jeff Juden* (FC) (#1 Draft Pick)	.30	.25	.12
165	Walt Weiss	.08	.06	.03
166	Bobby Witt	.04	.03	.02
167	*Kevin Appier* (FC)	.35	.25	.14
168	Jose Lind	.04	.03	.02
169	Richard Dotson	.03	.02	.01
170	George Bell	.12	.09	.05
171	Russ Nixon	.03	.02	.01
172	Tom Lampkin (FC)	.10	.08	.04
173	Tim Belcher	.12	.09	.05
174	Jeff Kunkel	.03	.02	.01
175	Mike Moore	.07	.05	.02
176	Luis Quinones	.03	.02	.01
177	Mike Henneman	.05	.04	.02
178	Chris James	.06	.05	.02
179	Brian Holton	.04	.03	.02
180	Rock Raines	.10	.08	.04
181	Juan Agosto	.03	.02	.01
182	Mookie Wilson	.05	.04	.02
183	Steve Lake	.03	.02	.01
184	Danny Cox	.04	.03	.02
185	Ruben Sierra	.20	.15	.08
186	Dave LaPoint	.03	.02	.01
187	*Rick Wrona* (FC)	.12	.09	.05
188	Mike Smithson	.03	.02	.01
189	Dick Schofield	.04	.03	.02
190	Rick Reuschel	.06	.05	.02
191	Pat Borders	.08	.06	.03
192	Don August	.04	.03	.02
193	Andy Benes	.25	.20	.10
194	Glenallen Hill (FC)	.10	.07	.04
195	Tim Burke	.05	.04	.02
196	Gerald Young	.04	.03	.02
197	Doug Drabek	.07	.05	.03
198	Mike Marshall	.06	.05	.02
199	*Sergio Valdez*	.10	.07	.04
200	Don Mattingly	.40	.30	.15
201	Cito Gaston	.03	.02	.01
202	Mike Macfarlane	.03	.02	.01
203	*Mike Roesler*	.10	.07	.04
204	Bob Dernier	.03	.02	.01
205	Mark Davis	.09	.07	.04
206	Nick Esasky	.07	.05	.02
207	Bob Ojeda	.04	.03	.02
208	Brook Jacoby	.04	.03	.02
209	Greg Mathews	.04	.03	.02
210	Ryne Sandberg	.30	.25	.12
211	John Cerutti	.04	.03	.02
212	Joe Orsulak	.03	.02	.01
213	Scott Bankhead	.05	.04	.02
214	Terry Francona	.03	.02	.01
215	Kirk McCaskill	.04	.03	.02
216	Ricky Jordan	.08	.06	.03
217	Don Robinson	.04	.03	.02
218	Wally Backman	.04	.03	.02
219	Donn Pall	.03	.02	.01
220	Barry Bonds	.50	.40	.20
221	*Gary Mielke*	.10	.07	.04
222	Kurt Stillwell	.05	.04	.02
223	Tommy Gregg	.06	.05	.02
224	*Delino DeShields* (FC)	.60	.45	.25
225	Jim Deshaies	.05	.04	.02
226	Mickey Hatcher	.03	.02	.01
227	*Kevin Tapani* (FC)	.40	.30	.15
228	Dave Martinez	.03	.02	.01
229	David Wells	.03	.02	.01
230	Keith Hernandez	.07	.05	.03
231	Jack McKeon	.03	.02	.01
232	Darnell Coles	.04	.03	.02
233	Ken Hill (FC)	.20	.15	.08
234	Mariano Duncan	.05	.04	.02
235	Jeff Reardon	.04	.03	.02
236	Hal Morris (FC)	.25	.20	.10
237	*Kevin Ritz* (FC)	.15	.11	.06
238	Felix Jose (FC)	.10	.08	.04
239	Eric Show	.04	.03	.02
240	Mark Grace	.25	.20	.10
241	Mike Krukow	.04	.03	.02
242	Fred Manrique	.03	.02	.01
243	Barry Jones	.03	.02	.01
244	Bill Schroeder	.03	.02	.01
245	Roger Clemens	.25	.20	.10
246	Jim Eisenreich	.03	.02	.01

247	Jerry Reed	.03	.02	.01
248	Dave Anderson	.03	.02	.01
249	*Mike Smith*	.10	.07	.04
250	Jose Canseco	.30	.25	.12
251	Jeff Blauser	.05	.04	.02
252	Otis Nixon	.03	.02	.01
253	Mark Portugal	.03	.02	.01
254	Francisco Cabrera	.10	.07	.04
255	Bobby Thigpen	.07	.05	.03
256	Marvell Wynne	.03	.02	.01
257	Jose DeLeon	.07	.05	.03
258	Barry Lyons	.03	.02	.01
259	Lance McCullers	.05	.04	.02
260	Eric Davis	.10	.07	.04
261	Whitey Herzog	.03	.02	.01
262	Checklist 133-264	.03	.02	.01
263	*Mel Stottlemyre, Jr.* (FC)	.12	.09	.05
264	Bryan Clutterbuck	.03	.02	.01
265	Pete O'Brien	.06	.05	.02
266	German Gonzalez	.04	.03	.02
267	Mark Davidson	.03	.02	.01
268	Rob Murphy	.03	.02	.01
269	Dickie Thon	.03	.02	.01
270	Dave Stewart	.08	.06	.03
271	Chet Lemon	.05	.04	.02
272	Bryan Harvey	.04	.03	.02
273	Bobby Bonilla	.15	.11	.06
274	*Goose Gozzo*	.15	.11	.06
275	Mickey Tettleton	.07	.05	.03
276	Gary Thurman	.03	.02	.01
277	Lenny Harris (FC)	.12	.09	.05
278	Pascual Perez	.04	.03	.02
279	Steve Buechele	.04	.03	.02
280	Lou Whitaker	.07	.05	.03
281	Kevin Bass	.05	.04	.02
282	Derek Lilliquist	.10	.08	.04
283	*Albert Belle*	1.25	.90	.50
284	*Mark Gardner*	.12	.09	.05
285	Willie McGee	.06	.05	.02
286	Lee Guetterman	.03	.02	.01
287	Vance Law	.03	.02	.01
288	Greg Briley	.10	.07	.04
289	Norm Charlton	.10	.08	.04
290	Robin Yount	.25	.20	.10
291	Dave Johnson	.03	.02	.01
292	Jim Gott	.04	.03	.02
293	Mike Gallego	.04	.03	.02
294	Craig McMurtry	.03	.02	.01
295	Fred McGriff	.25	.20	.10
296	Jeff Ballard	.07	.05	.03
297	Tom Herr	.06	.05	.02
298	Danny Gladden	.05	.04	.02
299	Adam Peterson (FC)	.09	.07	.04
300	Bo Jackson	.20	.15	.08
301	Don Aase	.03	.02	.01
302	*Marcus Lawton* (FC)	.08	.06	.03
303	Rick Cerone	.03	.02	.01
304	Marty Clary (FC)	.08	.06	.03
305	Eddie Murray	.15	.11	.06
306	Tom Niedenfuer	.03	.02	.01
307	Bip Roberts	.08	.06	.03
308	Jose Guzman	.05	.04	.02
309	*Eric Yelding*	.10	.07	.04
310	Steve Bedrosian	.05	.04	.02
311	Dwight Smith	.10	.07	.04
312	Dan Quisenberry	.05	.04	.02
313	Gus Polidor	.03	.02	.01
314	*Donald Harris* (#1 Draft Pick)	.10	.07	.04
315	Bruce Hurst	.06	.05	.02
316	Carney Lansford	.06	.05	.02
317	*Mark Guthrie*	.10	.07	.04
318	Wallace Johnson	.03	.02	.01
319	Dion James	.04	.03	.02
320	Dave Steib	.07	.05	.03
321	Joe M. Morgan	.03	.02	.01
322	Junior Ortiz	.03	.02	.01
323	Willie Wilson	.04	.03	.02
324	Pete Harnisch (FC)	.10	.08	.04
325	Robby Thompson	.06	.05	.02
326	*Tom McCarthy*	.10	.08	.04
327	Ken Williams	.03	.02	.01
328	Curt Young	.03	.02	.01
329	Oddibe McDowell	.06	.05	.02
330	Ron Darling	.09	.07	.04
331	*Juan Gonzalez* (FC)	2.00	1.50	.80
332	Paul O'Neill	.07	.05	.03
333	Bill Wegman	.03	.02	.01
334	Johnny Ray	.05	.04	.02
335	Andy Hawkins	.05	.04	.02
336	Ken Griffey, Jr.	1.75	1.25	.70
337	Lloyd McClendon	.06	.05	.02
338	Dennis Lamp	.03	.02	.01
339	Dave Clark	.04	.03	.02
340	Fernando Valenzuela	.06	.05	.02
341	Tom Foley	.03	.02	.01
342	Alex Trevino	.03	.02	.01
343	Frank Tanana	.04	.03	.02
344	*George Canale* (FC)	.10	.07	.04
345	Harold Baines	.09	.07	.04
346	Jim Presley	.04	.03	.02
347	*Junior Felix*	.10	.07	.04
348	*Gary Wayne* (FC)	.12	.09	.05
349	*Steve Finley* (FC)	.10	.07	.04
350	Bret Saberhagen	.10	.08	.04
351	Roger Craig	.03	.02	.01
352	Bryn Smith	.05	.04	.02
353	Sandy Alomar	.12	.09	.05
354	*Stan Belinda* (FC)	.20	.15	.08
355	Marty Barrett	.05	.04	.02
356	Randy Ready	.03	.02	.01
357	Dave West	.10	.07	.04
358	Andres Thomas	.04	.03	.02
359	Jimmy Jones	.03	.02	.01
360	Paul Molitor	.15	.11	.06
361	*Randy McCament* (FC)	.10	.07	.04
362	Damon Berryhill	.06	.05	.02
363	Dan Petry	.03	.02	.01
364	Rolando Roomes (FC)	.10	.07	.04

365	Ozzie Guillen	.05	.04	.02
366	Mike Heath	.03	.02	.01
367	Mike Morgan	.03	.02	.01
368	Bill Doran	.06	.05	.02
369	Todd Burns	.04	.03	.02
370	Tim Wallach	.07	.05	.03
371	Jimmy Key	.08	.06	.03
372	Terry Kennedy	.03	.02	.01
373	Alvin Davis	.08	.06	.03
374	*Steve Cummings*	.10	.07	.04
375	Dwight Evans	.08	.06	.03
376	Checklist 265-396	.03	.02	.01
377	*Mickey Weston*	.10	.07	.04
378	Luis Salazar	.03	.02	.01
379	Steve Rosenberg	.03	.02	.01
380	Dave Winfield	.15	.11	.06
381	Frank Robinson	.03	.02	.01
382	Jeff Musselman	.03	.02	.01
383	John Morris	.04	.03	.02
384	*Pat Combs*	.10	.07	.04
385	Fred McGriff (All-Star)	.20	.15	.08
386	Julio Franco (All-Star)	.10	.08	.04
387	Wade Boggs (All-Star)	.20	.15	.08
388	Cal Ripken, Jr. (All-Star)	.25	.20	.10
389	Robin Yount (All-Star)	.15	.11	.06
390	Ruben Sierra (All-Star)	.10	.07	.04
391	Kirby Puckett (All-Star)	.20	.15	.08
392	Carlton Fisk (All-Star)	.08	.06	.03
393	Bret Saberhagen (All-Star)	.10	.08	.04
394	Jeff Ballard (All-Star)	.08	.06	.03
395	Jeff Russell (All-Star)	.08	.06	.03
396	A. Bartlett Giamatti	.30	.25	.12
397	Will Clark (All-Star)	.25	.20	.10
398	Ryne Sandberg (All-Star)	.20	.15	.08
399	Howard Johnson (All-Star)	.08	.06	.03
400	Ozzie Smith (All-Star)	.15	.11	.06
401	Kevin Mitchell (All-Star)	.10	.08	.04
402	Eric Davis (All-Star)	.10	.08	.04
403	Tony Gwynn (All-Star)	.15	.11	.06
404	Craig Biggio (All-Star)	.10	.07	.04
405	Mike Scott (All-Star)	.08	.06	.03
406	Joe Magrane (All-Star)	.08	.06	.03
407	Mark Davis (All-Star)	.08	.06	.03
408	Trevor Wilson	.06	.05	.02
409	Tom Brunansky	.09	.07	.04
410	Joe Boever	.06	.05	.02
411	Ken Phelps	.03	.02	.01
412	Jamie Moyer	.04	.03	.02
413	*Brian DuBois*	.10	.07	.04
414a	*Frank Thomas* (#1 Draft Pick, no name on front)	80.00	60.00	32.00
414b	*Frank Thomas* (#1 Draft Pick, name on front)	4.00	3.00	1.50
415	Shawon Dunston	.06	.05	.02
416	*Dave Johnson* (FC)	.12	.09	.05
417	Jim Gantner	.06	.05	.02
418	Tom Browning	.08	.06	.03
419	*Beau Allred*	.10	.07	.04
420	Carlton Fisk	.08	.06	.03
421	Greg Minton	.03	.02	.01
422	Pat Sheridan	.03	.02	.01
423	Fred Toliver	.03	.02	.01
424	Jerry Reuss	.05	.04	.02
425	Bill Landrum	.05	.04	.02
426	Jeff Hamilton	.05	.04	.02
427	Carmem Castillo	.03	.02	.01
428	*Steve Davis* (FC)	.12	.09	.05
429	Tom Kelly	.03	.02	.01
430	Pete Incaviglia	.06	.05	.02
431	Randy Johnson	.10	.08	.04
432	Damaso Garcia	.03	.02	.01
433	*Steve Olin* (FC)	.12	.08	.04
434	Mark Carreon (FC)	.09	.07	.04
435	Kevin Seitzer	.09	.07	.04
436	Mel Hall	.05	.04	.02
437	Les Lancaster	.05	.04	.02
438	Greg Myers (FC)	.10	.08	.04
439	Jeff Parrett	.06	.05	.02
440	Alan Trammell	.09	.07	.04
441	Bob Kipper	.03	.02	.01
442	Jerry Browne	.07	.05	.02
443	Cris Carpenter	.09	.07	.04
444	*Kyle Abbott* (FDP)	.10	.07	.04
445	Danny Jackson	.05	.04	.02
446	Dan Pasqua	.05	.04	.02
447	Atlee Hammaker	.03	.02	.01
448	Greg Gagne	.04	.03	.02
449	Dennis Rasmussen	.04	.03	.02
450	Rickey Henderson	.25	.20	.10
451	Mark Lemke (FC)	.10	.08	.04
452	Luis de los Santos (FC)	.10	.08	.04
453	Jody Davis	.03	.02	.01
454	Jeff King (FC)	.10	.08	.04
455	Jeffrey Leonard	.06	.05	.02
456	Chris Gwynn (FC)	.09	.07	.03
457	Gregg Jefferies	.30	.25	.12
458	Bob McClure	.03	.02	.01
459	Jim Lefebvre	.03	.02	.01
460	Mike Scott	.09	.07	.03
461	*Carlos Martinez* (FC)	.10	.08	.04
462	Denny Walling	.03	.02	.01
463	Drew Hall	.03	.02	.01
464	*Jerome Walton*	.25	.20	.10
465	Kevin Gross	.06	.05	.02
466	Rance Mulliniks	.03	.02	.01
467	Juan Nieves	.04	.03	.02
468	Billy Ripken	.04	.03	.02
469	John Kruk	.07	.05	.02
470	Frank Viola	.09	.07	.04
471	Mike Brumley	.03	.02	.01
472	Jose Uribe	.04	.03	.02
473	Joe Price	.03	.02	.01
474	Rich Thompson	.04	.03	.02
475	Bob Welch	.06	.05	.02
476	Brad Komminsk	.03	.02	.02
477	Willie Fraser	.03	.02	.02
478	Mike LaValliere	.04	.03	.02
479	Frank White	.06	.05	.02
480	Sid Fernandez	.09	.07	.04
481	Garry Templeton	.05	.04	.02
482	*Steve Carter*	.10	.07	.04
483	Alejandro Pena	.04	.03	.02
484	Mike Fitzgerald	.03	.02	.01
485	John Candelaria	.05	.04	.02
486	Jeff Treadway	.05	.04	.02
487	Steve Searcy	.05	.04	.02
488	Ken Oberkfell	.03	.02	.01
489	Nick Leyva	.03	.02	.01
490	Dan Plesac	.07	.05	.03
491	*Dave Cochrane*	.10	.07	.04
492	Ron Oester	.04	.03	.02
493	*Jason Grimsley*	.10	.07	.04
494	Terry Puhl	.03	.02	.01
495	Lee Smith	.06	.05	.02
496	Cecil Espy	.06	.05	.02
497	Dave Schmidt	.03	.02	.01
498	Rick Schu	.03	.02	.01
499	Bill Long	.04	.03	.02
500	Kevin Mitchell	.15	.11	.06
501	Matt Young	.03	.02	.01
502	Mitch Webster	.04	.03	.02
503	Randy St. Claire	.03	.02	.01
504	Tom O'Malley	.03	.02	.01
505	Kelly Gruber	.08	.06	.03
506	Tom Glavine	.20	.15	.08
507	Gary Redus	.04	.03	.02
508	Terry Leach	.03	.02	.01
509	Tom Pagnozzi	.03	.02	.01
510	Dwight Gooden	.10	.07	.04
511	Clay Parker	.07	.05	.03
512	Gary Pettis	.03	.02	.01
513	Mark Eichhorn	.03	.02	.01
514	Andy Allanson	.03	.02	.01
515	Len Dykstra	.06	.05	.02
516	Tim Leary	.05	.04	.02
517	Roberto Alomar	.25	.20	.10
518	Bill Krueger	.03	.02	.01
519	Bucky Dent	.03	.02	.01
520	Mitch Williams	.09	.07	.03
521	Craig Worthington	.15	.11	.06
522	Mike Dunne	.04	.03	.02
523	Jay Bell	.03	.02	.01
524	Daryl Boston	.03	.02	.01
525	Wally Joyner	.10	.07	.04
526	Checklist 397-528	.03	.02	.01
527	Ron Hassey	.03	.02	.01
528	*Kevin Wickander*	.10	.07	.04
529	Greg Harris	.03	.02	.01
530	Mark Langston	.10	.08	.04
531	Ken Caminiti	.06	.05	.02
532	Cecilio Guante	.03	.02	.01
533	Tim Jones (FC)	.07	.05	.03
534	Louie Meadows	.07	.05	.03
535	John Smoltz	.15	.11	.06
536	*Bob Geren*	.10	.07	.04
537	Mark Grant	.03	.02	.01
538	*Billy Spiers*	.10	.07	.04
539	Neal Heaton	.03	.02	.01
540	Danny Tartabull	.09	.07	.03
541	Pat Perry	.03	.02	.01
542	Darren Daulton	.03	.02	.01
543	Nelson Liriano	.03	.02	.01
544	Dennis Boyd	.05	.04	.02
545	Kevin McReynolds	.09	.07	.04
546	Kevin Hickey	.05	.04	.02
547	Jack Howell	.05	.04	.02
548	Pat Clements	.03	.02	.01
549	Don Zimmer	.03	.02	.01
550	Julio Franco	.09	.07	.04
551	Tim Crews	.03	.02	.01
552	*Mike Smith* (FC)	.12	.09	.05
553	*Scott Scudder*	.10	.07	.04
554	Jay Buhner	.08	.06	.03
555	Jack Morris	.07	.05	.03
556	Gene Larkin	.03	.02	.01
557	*Jeff Innis*	.10	.07	.04
558	Rafael Ramirez	.04	.03	.02
559	Andy McGaffigan	.04	.03	.02
560	Steve Sax	.08	.06	.03
561	Ken Dayley	.03	.02	.01
562	Chad Kreuter	.10	.08	.04
563	Alex Sanchez	.10	.08	.04
564	*Tyler Houston* (#1 Draft Pick)	.10	.07	.04
565	Scott Fletcher	.05	.04	.02
566	Mark Knudson	.06	.05	.02
567	Ron Gant	.15	.11	.06
568	John Smiley	.07	.05	.03
569	Ivan Calderon	.05	.04	.02
570	Cal Ripken, Jr.	.35	.25	.14
571	Brett Butler	.06	.05	.02
572	Greg Harris	.09	.07	.04
573	Danny Heep	.03	.02	.01
574	Bill Swift	.04	.03	.02
575	Lance Parrish	.07	.05	.03
576	*Mike Dyer*	.10	.07	.04
577	Charlie Hayes (FC)	.10	.08	.04
578	Joe Magrane	.09	.07	.04
579	Art Howe	.03	.02	.01
580	Joe Carter	.15	.11	.06
581	Ken Griffey	.05	.04	.02
582	Rick Honeycutt	.03	.02	.01
583	Bruce Benedict	.03	.02	.01
584	*Phil Stephenson* (FC)	.09	.07	.04
585	Kal Daniels	.10	.08	.04
586	Ed Nunez	.03	.02	.01
587	Lance Johnson	.08	.06	.03
588	Rick Rhoden	.03	.02	.01
589	Mike Aldrete	.03	.02	.01
590	Ozzie Smith	.10	.08	.04
591	Todd Stottlemyre	.08	.06	.03
592	R.J. Reynolds	.03	.02	.01
593	Scott Bradley	.03	.02	.01
594	*Luis Sojo*	.10	.07	.04
595	Greg Swindell	.10	.08	.04
596	Jose DeJesus (FC)	.10	.08	.04
597	Chris Bosio	.07	.05	.03
598	Brady Anderson	.05	.04	.02
599	Frank Williams	.03	.02	.01
600	Darryl Strawberry	.15	.11	.06
601	Luis Rivera	.04	.03	.02
602	Scott Garrelts	.07	.05	.03
603	Tony Armas	.03	.02	.01
604	Ron Robinson	.03	.02	.01
605	Mike Scioscia	.07	.05	.03
606	Storm Davis	.07	.05	.03
607	Steve Jeltz	.03	.02	.01
608	*Eric Anthony* (FC)	.30	.25	.12
609	Sparky Anderson	.03	.02	.01
610	Pedro Guererro	.12	.09	.05
611	Walt Terrell	.05	.04	.02
612	Dave Gallagher	.07	.05	.02
613	Jeff Pico	.04	.03	.02
614	Nelson Santovenia	.09	.07	.04
615	Rob Deer	.07	.05	.03
616	Brian Holman	.10	.08	.04
617	Geronimo Berroa	.08	.06	.03
618	Eddie Whitson	.05	.04	.02
619	Rob Ducey	.08	.06	.03
620	*Tony Castillo*	.10	.07	.04
621	Melido Perez	.07	.05	.03
622	Sid Bream	.05	.04	.02
623	Jim Corsi	.05	.04	.02
624	Darrin Jackson	.04	.03	.02
625	Roger McDowell	.07	.05	.03
626	Bob Melvin	.03	.02	.01
627	Jose Rijo	.07	.05	.03
628	Candy Maldonado	.04	.03	.02
629	Eric Hetzel (FC)	.10	.08	.04
630	Gary Gaetti	.10	.08	.04
631	*John Wetteland* (FC)	.25	.20	.10
632	Scott Lusader	.06	.05	.02
633	Dennis Cook (FC)	.10	.07	.04
634	Luis Polonia	.06	.05	.02
635	Brian Downing	.06	.05	.02
636	Jesse Orosco	.03	.02	.01
637	Craig Reynolds	.03	.02	.01
638	Jeff Montgomery	.07	.05	.03
639	Tony LaRussa	.03	.02	.01
640	Rick Sutcliffe	.06	.05	.02
641	*Doug Strange* (FC)	.10	.07	.04
642	Jack Armstrong	.04	.03	.02
643	Alfredo Griffin	.04	.03	.02
644	Paul Assenmacher	.04	.03	.02
645	Jose Oquendo	.06	.05	.02
646	Checklist 529-660	.03	.02	.01
647	Rex Hudler	.03	.02	.01
648	Jim Clancy	.03	.02	.01
649	*Dan Murphy*	.10	.07	.04
650	Mike Witt	.06	.05	.02
651	Rafael Santana	.06	.05	.02
652	Mike Boddicker	.06	.05	.02
653	John Moses	.03	.02	.01
654	*Paul Coleman* (#1 Draft Pick)	.10	.07	.04
655	Gregg Olson	.10	.07	.04
656	Mackey Sasser	.05	.04	.02
657	Terry Mulholland	.06	.05	.02
658	Donell Nixon	.03	.02	.01
659	Greg Cadaret	.03	.02	.01
660	Vince Coleman	.10	.08	.04
661	Turn Back The Clock - 1985 (Dick Howser)	.07	.05	.03
662	Turn Back The Clock - 1980 (Mike Schmidt)	.07	.05	.03
663	Turn Back The Clock - 1975 (Fred Lynn)	.07	.05	.03
664	Turn Back The Clock - 1970 (Johnny Bench)	.07	.05	.03
665	Turn Back The Clock - 1965 (Sandy Koufax)	.07	.05	.03
666	Brian Fisher	.05	.04	.02
667	Curt Wilkerson	.03	.02	.01
668	*Joe Oliver*	.10	.07	.04
669	Tom Lasorda	.03	.02	.01
670	Dennis Eckersley	.09	.07	.04
671	Bob Boone	.09	.07	.04
672	Roy Smith	.03	.02	.01
673	Joey Meyer	.03	.02	.01
674	Spike Owen	.05	.04	.02
675	Jim Abbott	.20	.15	.08
676	Randy Kutcher (FC)	.07	.05	.03
677	Jay Tibbs	.03	.02	.01
678	Kirt Manwaring	.10	.08	.04
679	Gary Ward	.04	.03	.02
680	Howard Johnson	.08	.06	.03
681	Mike Schooler	.07	.05	.03
682	Dann Bilardello	.03	.02	.01
683	*Kenny Rogers*	.10	.08	.04
684	*Julio Machado*	.08	.06	.03
685	Tony Fernandez	.09	.07	.04
686	Carmelo Martinez	.06	.05	.02
687	Tim Birtsas	.03	.02	.01
688	Milt Thompson	.06	.05	.02
689	Rich Yett	.03	.02	.01
690	Mark McGwire	.30	.25	.12
691	Chuck Cary	.03	.02	.01
692	*Sammy Sosa*	.50	.40	.20
693	Calvin Schiraldi	.03	.02	.01
694	*Mike Stanton*	.15	.11	.06
695	Tom Henke	.06	.05	.02
696	B.J. Surhoff	.07	.05	.03
697	Mike Davis	.03	.02	.01
698	*Omar Vizquel*	.10	.08	.04
699	Jim Leyland	.03	.02	.01
700	Kirby Puckett	.25	.20	.10
701	*Bernie Williams*	.30	.25	.12
702	Tony Phillips	.04	.03	.02
703	*Jeff Brantley*	.12	.09	.05
704	*Chip Hale*	.10	.07	.04
705	Claudell Washington	.07	.05	.03
706	Geno Petralli	.03	.02	.01
707	Luis Aquino	.03	.02	.01
708	Larry Sheets	.03	.02	.01
709	Juan Berneguer	.03	.02	.01
710	Von Hayes	.09	.07	.04

711	Rick Aguilera	.05	.04	.02
712	Todd Benzinger	.09	.07	.04
713	*Tim Drummond*	.10	.07	.04
714	*Marquis Grissom* (FC)	.50	.40	.20
715	Greg Maddux	.15	.11	.06
716	Steve Balboni	.03	.02	.01
717	Ron Kakovice	.03	.02	.01
718	Gary Sheffield	.25	.20	.10
719	*Wally Whitehurst*	.10	.07	.04
720	Andres Galarraga	.25	.20	.10
721	Lee Mazzilli	.03	.02	.01
722	Felix Fermin	.03	.02	.01
723	Jeff Robinson	.05	.04	.02
724	Juan Bell (FC)	.10	.08	.04
725	Terry Pendleton	.06	.05	.02
726	Gene Nelson	.03	.02	.01
727	Pat Tabler	.05	.04	.02
728	Jim Acker	.03	.02	.01
729	Bobby Valentine	.03	.02	.01
730	Tony Gwynn	.20	.15	.08
731	Don Carman	.05	.04	.02
732	Ernie Riles	.03	.02	.01
733	John Dopson	.09	.07	.04
734	Kevin Elster	.06	.05	.02
735	Charlie Hough	.06	.05	.02
736	Rick Dempsey	.03	.02	.01
737	Chris Sabo	.15	.11	.06
738	*Gene Harris*	.10	.08	.04
739	Dale Sveum	.04	.03	.02
740	Jesse Barfield	.08	.06	.03
741	Steve Wilson	.10	.08	.04
742	Ernie Whitt	.05	.04	.02
743	Tom Candiotti	.05	.04	.02
744	*Kelly Mann*	.10	.07	.04
745	Hubie Brooks	.06	.05	.02
746	Dave Smith	.06	.05	.02
747	Randy Bush	.03	.02	.01
748	Doyle Alexander	.06	.05	.02
749	Mark Parent	.04	.03	.02
750	Dale Murphy	.10	.08	.04
751	Steve Lyons	.04	.03	.02
752	Tom Gordon	.15	.11	.06
753	Chris Speier	.03	.02	.01
754	Bob Walk	.05	.04	.02
755	Rafael Palmeiro	.10	.07	.04
756	Ken Howell	.03	.02	.01
757	*Larry Walker*	.50	.40	.20
758	Mark Thurmond	.03	.02	.01
759	Tom Trebelhorn	.03	.02	.01
760	Wade Boggs	.30	.25	.12
761	Mike Jackson	.05	.04	.02
762	Doug Dascenzo	.07	.05	.03
763	Denny Martinez	.07	.05	.03
764	Tim Teufel	.05	.04	.02
765	Chili Davis	.07	.05	.03
766	Brian Meyer (FC)	.10	.08	.04
767	Tracy Jones	.06	.05	.02
768	Chuck Crim	.04	.03	.02
769	*Greg Hibbard*	.15	.11	.06
770	Cory Snyder	.09	.07	.04
771	Pete Smith	.06	.05	.02
772	Jeff Reed	.03	.02	.01
773	Dave Leiper	.03	.02	.01
774	*Ben McDonald*	.40	.30	.15
775	Andy Van Slyke	.08	.06	.03
776	Charlie Leibrandt	.04	.03	.02
777	Tim Laudner	.03	.02	.01
778	Mike Jeffcoat	.03	.02	.01
779	Lloyd Moseby	.06	.05	.02
780	Orel Hershiser	.08	.06	.03
781	Mario Diaz	.03	.02	.01
782	Jose Alvarez	.03	.02	.01
783	Checklist 661-792	.03	.02	.01
784	Scott Bailes	.03	.02	.01
785	Jim Rice	.07	.05	.03
786	Eric King	.04	.03	.02
787	Rene Gonzales	.03	.02	.01
788	Frank DiPino	.03	.02	.01
789	John Wathan	.03	.02	.01
790	Gary Carter	.06	.05	.02
791	Alvaro Espinoza	.15	.11	.06
792	Gerald Perry	.06	.05	.02

1990 Topps Glossy Rookies

While the size of the annual glossy rookies set increased to 33 cards from previous years' issues of 22, the format remained identical in 1990. Above the player photo is a red, white, blue and yellow banner with "1989 Rookies." The player's name appears in red in a yellow bar beneath the photo. Backs are printed in red and blue and contain a shield design with the notation, "1989 Rookies Commemorative Set". The player's name, position and team are listed below, along with a card number. Cards are numbered alphabetically in the set. The glossy rookies were found one per pack in Topps jumbo (100-card) cello packs.

		MT	NR MT	EX
	Complete Set (33):	10.00	7.50	4.00
	Common Player:	.25	.20	.10
1	Jim Abbott	.50	.40	.20
2	Joey Belle	.75	.60	.30
3	Andy Benes	.35	.25	.14
4	Greg Briley	.25	.20	.10
5	Kevin Brown	.25	.20	.10
6	Mark Carreon	.25	.20	.10
7	Mike Devereaux	.35	.25	.14
8	Junior Felix	.30	.25	.12
9	Bob Geren	.30	.25	.12
10	Tom Gordon	.25	.20	.10
11	Ken Griffey, Jr.	3.00	2.25	1.25
12	Pete Harnisch	.30	.25	.12
13	Greg W. Harris	.25	.20	.10
14	Greg Hibbard	.25	.20	.10
15	Ken Hill	.25	.20	.10
16	Gregg Jefferies	.45	.35	.20
17	Jeff King	.35	.25	.14
18	Derek Lilliquist	.25	.20	.10
19	Carlos Martinez	.25	.20	.10
20	Ramon Martinez	.25	.20	.10
21	Bob Milacki	.25	.20	.10
22	Gregg Olson	.25	.20	.10
23	Donn Pall	.25	.20	.10
24	Kenny Rogers	.25	.20	.10
25	Gary Sheffield	.35	.25	.14
26	Dwight Smith	.25	.20	.10
27	Billy Spiers	.25	.20	.10
28	Omar Vizquel	.30	.25	.12
29	Jerome Walton	.25	.20	.10
30	Dave West	.25	.20	.10
31	John Wetteland	.25	.20	.10
32	Steve Wilson	.25	.20	.10
33	Craig Worthington	.25	.20	.10

1990 Topps All-Star Glossy Set of 22

One glossy All-Star card was included in each 1990 Topps rack pack. The cards measure 2-1/2" by 3-1/2" and feature a similar style to past glossy All-Star cards. Special cards of All-Star team captains Carl Yastrzemski and Don Drysdale are included in the set.

		MT	NR MT	EX
	Complete Set:	3.50	2.75	1.50
	Common Player:	.12	.09	.05
1	Tom Lasorda	.12	.09	.05
2	Will Clark	.35	.25	.14
3	Ryne Sandberg	.40	.30	.15
4	Howard Johnson	.15	.11	.06
5	Ozzie Smith	.20	.15	.08
6	Kevin Mitchell	.20	.15	.08
7	Eric Davis	.15	.11	.06
8	Tony Gwynn	.20	.15	.08
9	Benny Santiago	.15	.11	.06
10	Rick Rueschel	.12	.09	.05
11	Don Drysdale	.20	.15	.08
12	Tony LaRussa	.12	.09	.05
13	Mark McGwire	.30	.25	.12
14	Julio Franco	.15	.11	.06
15	Wade Boggs	.25	.20	.10
16	Cal Ripken, Jr.	.40	.30	.15
17	Bo Jackson	.30	.25	.12
18	Kirby Puckett	.35	.25	.14
19	Ruben Sierra	.25	.20	.10
20	Terry Steinbach	.12	.09	.05
21	Dave Stewart	.15	.11	.06
22	Carl Yastrzemski	.20	.15	.08

1990 Topps All-Star Glossy Set of 60

Sharp color photographs and a clutter-free design are features of the cards in this 60-card send away set. Topps initiated the redemption series in 1983 and increased the size of the set to 60 in 1986.

Six special offer cards, which were included in Topps baseball wax packs, are necessary to obtain each of the six 10-card sets in the series.

		MT	NR MT	EX
	Complete Set:	9.00	6.75	3.50
	Common Player:	.10	.08	.04
1	Ryne Sandberg	.70	.50	.30
2	Nolan Ryan	.90	.70	.35
3	Glenn Davis	.10	.08	.04
4	Dave Stewart	.15	.11	.06
5	Barry Larkin	.15	.11	.06
6	Carney Lansford	.10	.08	.04
7	Darryl Strawberry	.30	.25	.12
8	Steve Sax	.10	.08	.04
9	Carlos Martinez	.10	.08	.04
10	Gary Sheffield	.40	.30	.15
11	Don Mattingly	.80	.60	.30
12	Mark Grace	.40	.30	.15
13	Bret Saberhagen	.20	.15	.08
14	Mike Scott	.10	.08	.04
15	Robin Yount	.40	.30	.15
16	Ozzie Smith	.25	.20	.10
17	Jeff Ballard	.10	.08	.04
18	Rick Reuschel	.10	.08	.04
19	Greg Briley	.10	.08	.04
20	Ken Griffey, Jr.	1.75	1.25	.70
21	Kevin Mitchell	.30	.25	.12
22	Wade Boggs	.60	.45	.25
23	Dwight Gooden	.25	.20	.10
24	George Bell	.15	.11	.06
25	Eric Davis	.20	.15	.08
26	Ruben Sierra	.25	.20	.10
27	Roberto Alomar	.30	.25	.12
28	Gary Gaetti	.15	.11	.06
29	Gregg Olson	.20	.15	.08
30	Tom Gordon	.10	.08	.04
31	Jose Canseco	.80	.60	.30
32	Pedro Guerrero	.10	.08	.04
33	Joe Carter	.25	.20	.10
34	Mike Scioscia	.10	.08	.04
35	Julio Franco	.15	.11	.06
36	Joe Magrane	.10	.08	.04
37	Rickey Henderson	.40	.30	.15
38	Tim Raines	.15	.11	.06
39	Jerome Walton	.10	.08	.04
40	Bob Geren	.10	.08	.04
41	Andre Dawson	.25	.20	.10
42	Mark McGwire	.35	.25	.14
43	Howard Johnson	.20	.15	.08
44	Bo Jackson	.40	.30	.15
45	Shawon Dunston	.20	.15	.08
46	Carlton Fisk	.20	.15	.08
47	Mitch Williams	.10	.08	.04
48	Kirby Puckett	.35	.25	.14
49	Craig Worthington	.10	.08	.04
50	Jim Abbott	.20	.15	.08
51	Cal Ripken, Jr.	.70	.50	.30
52	Will Clark	.50	.40	.20
53	Dennis Eckersley	.20	.15	.08
54	Craig Biggio	.15	.11	.06
55	Fred McGriff	.20	.15	.08
56	Tony Gwynn	.20	.15	.08
57	Mickey Tettleton	.15	.11	.06
58	Mark Davis	.10	.08	.04
59	Omar Vizquel	.10	.08	.04
60	Gregg Jefferies	.20	.15	.08

1990 Topps Traded

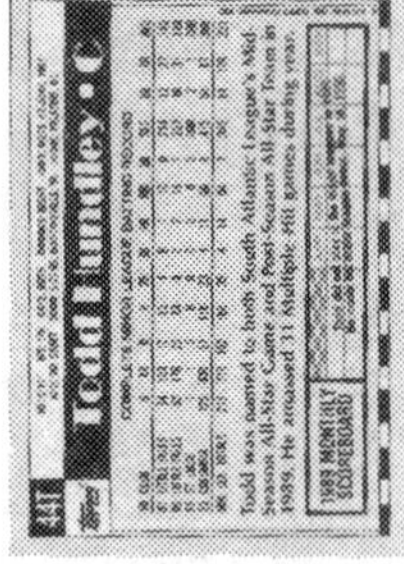

For the first time, Topps "Traded" series cards were made available nationwide in retail wax packs. The 132-card set was also sold in complete boxed form as it has been in recent years. The wax pack traded cards feature gray backs, while the boxed set cards feature white backs. The cards are numbered 1T-132T and showcase rookies, players who changed teams and new managers.

		MT	NR MT	EX
	Complete Set (132):	8.00	6.00	3.25
	Common Player:	.05	.04	.02
1T	Darrel Akerfelds	.05	.04	.02
2T	Sandy Alomar, Jr.	.10	.08	.04
3T	Brad Arnsberg	.05	.04	.02
4T	Steve Avery	.80	.60	.30
5T	Wally Backman	.05	.04	.02
6T	Carlos Baerga (FC)	1.50	1.25	.60
7T	Kevin Bass	.06	.05	.02
8T	Willie Blair (FC)	.10	.08	.04
9T	Mike Blowers (FC)	.10	.07	.04

10T	Shawn Boskie (FC)	.10	.07	.04
11T	Daryl Boston	.05	.04	.02
12T	Dennis Boyd	.06	.05	.02
13T	Glenn Braggs	.06	.05	.02
14T	Hubie Brooks	.08	.06	.03
15T	Tom Brunansky	.08	.06	.03
16T	John Burkett (FC)	.40	.30	.15
17T	Casey Candaele	.05	.04	.02
18T	John Candelaria	.06	.05	.02
19T	Gary Carter	.10	.08	.04
20T	Joe Carter	.25	.20	.10
21T	Rick Cerone	.05	.04	.02
22T	Scott Coolbaugh (FC)	.10	.07	.04
23T	Bobby Cox	.05	.04	.02
24T	Mark Davis	.06	.05	.02
25T	Storm Davis	.06	.05	.02
26T	Edgar Diaz (FC)	.10	.08	.04
27T	Wayne Edwards (FC)	.10	.07	.04
28T	Mark Eichhorn	.05	.04	.02
29T	Scott Erickson (FC)	.20	.15	.08
30T	Nick Esasky	.06	.05	.02
31T	Cecil Fielder	.25	.20	.10
32T	John Franco	.08	.06	.03
33T	Travis Fryman (FC)	1.50	1.25	.60
34T	Bill Gullickson	.05	.04	.02
35T	Darryl Hamilton	.15	.11	.06
36T	Mike Harkey	.10	.07	.04
37T	Bud Harrelson	.05	.04	.02
38T	Billy Hatcher	.06	.05	.02
39T	Keith Hernandez	.08	.06	.03
40T	Joe Hesketh	.05	.04	.02
41T	Dave Hollins (FC)	.40	.30	.15
42T	Sam Horn	.08	.06	.03
43T	Steve Howard (FC)	.10	.07	.04
44T	Todd Hundley (FC)	.25	.20	.10
45T	Jeff Huson	.10	.08	.04
46T	Chris James	.05	.04	.02
47T	Stan Javier	.05	.04	.02
48T	Dave Justice (FC)	1.25	.90	.50
49T	Jeff Kaiser (FC)	.12	.09	.05
50T	Dana Kiecker (FC)	.10	.07	.04
51T	Joe Klink (FC)	.10	.08	.04
52T	Brent Knackert (FC)	.12	.09	.05
53T	Brad Komminsk	.05	.04	.02
54T	Mark Langston	.10	.08	.04
55T	Tim Layana (FC)	.10	.07	.04
56T	Rick Leach	.05	.04	.02
57T	Terry Leach	.05	.04	.02
58T	Tim Leary	.05	.04	.02
59T	Craig Lefferts	.05	.04	.02
60T	Charlie Leibrandt	.05	.04	.02
61T	Jim Leyritz (FC)	.20	.15	.08
62T	Fred Lynn	.06	.05	.02
63T	Kevin Maas (FC)	.15	.11	.06
64T	Shane Mack	.08	.06	.03
65T	Candy Maldonado	.06	.05	.02
66T	Fred Manrique	.05	.04	.02
67T	Mike Marshall	.05	.04	.02
68T	Carmelo Martinez	.05	.04	.02
69T	John Marzano	.06	.05	.02
70T	Ben McDonald	.60	.45	.25
71T	Jack McDowell	.20	.15	.08
72T	John McNamara	.05	.04	.02
73T	Orlando Mercado	.05	.04	.02
74T	Stump Merrill	.05	.04	.02
75T	Alan Mills (FC)	.10	.07	.04
76T	Hal Morris	.20	.15	.08
77T	Lloyd Moseby	.06	.05	.02
78T	Randy Myers	.08	.06	.03
79T	Tim Naehring (FC)	.35	.25	.14
80T	Junior Noboa	.06	.05	.02
81T	Matt Nokes	.06	.05	.02
82T	Pete O'Brien	.05	.04	.02
83T	John Olerud (FC)	1.25	.90	.50
84T	Greg Olson (FC)	.15	.11	.06
85T	Junior Ortiz	.05	.04	.02
86T	Dave Parker	.15	.11	.06
87T	Rick Parker (FC)	.15	.11	.06
88T	Bob Patterson	.05	.04	.02
89T	Alejandro Pena	.05	.04	.02
90T	Tony Pena	.08	.06	.03
91T	Pascual Perez	.05	.04	.02
92T	Gerald Perry	.05	.04	.02
93T	Dan Petry	.05	.04	.02
94T	Gary Pettis	.06	.05	.02
95T	Tony Phillips	.05	.04	.02
96T	Lou Pinella	.05	.04	.02
97T	Luis Polonia	.05	.04	.02
98T	Jim Presley	.06	.05	.02
99T	Scott Radinsky (FC)	.25	.20	.10
100T	Willie Randolph	.08	.06	.03
101T	Jeff Reardon	.08	.06	.03
102T	Greg Riddoch	.05	.04	.02
103T	Jeff Robinson	.05	.04	.02
104T	Ron Robinson	.05	.04	.02
105T	Kevin Romine	.05	.04	.02
106T	Scott Ruskin (FC)	.10	.07	.04
107T	John Russell	.05	.04	.02
108T	Bill Sampen (FC)	.10	.07	.04
109T	Juan Samuel	.08	.06	.03
110T	Scott Sanderson	.06	.05	.02
111T	Jack Savage (FC)	.10	.08	.04
112T	Dave Schmidt	.05	.04	.02
113T	Red Schoendienst	.05	.04	.02
114T	Terry Shumpert (FC)	.10	.07	.04
115T	Matt Sinatro	.05	.04	.02
116T	Don Slaught	.05	.04	.02
117T	Bryn Smith	.05	.04	.02
118T	Lee Smith	.08	.06	.03
119T	Paul Sorrento (FC)	.30	.25	.12
120T	Franklin Stubbs	.05	.04	.02
121T	Russ Swan (FC)	.10	.07	.04
122T	Bob Tewksbury	.05	.04	.02
123T	Wayne Tolleson	.05	.04	.02
124T	John Tudor	.06	.05	.02
125T	Randy Veres (FC)	.10	.08	.04
126T	Hector Villanueva (FC)	.10	.07	.04
127T	Mitch Webster	.05	.04	.02
128T	Ernie Whitt	.06	.05	.02
129T	Frank Wills	.06	.05	.02
130T	Dave Winfield	.20	.15	.08
131T	Matt Young	.05	.04	.02
132T	Checklist	.05	.04	.02

1990 Topps Box Panels

This special 16-card set features four cards on four different box-bottom panels. The cards are identical in design to the regular 1990 Topps cards. The cards are designated by letter.

		MT	NR MT	EX
Complete Panel Set:		3.00	2.25	1.25
Complete Singles Set:		1.50	1.25	.60
Common Panel:		.75	.60	.30
Common Single Player:		.06	.05	.02
	Panel	.75	.60	.30
A	Wade Boggs	.25	.20	.10
B	George Brett	.30	.25	.12
C	Andre Dawson	.15	.11	.06
D	Darrell Evans, Panel	.06	.05	.02
	Panel	.75	.60	.30
E	Dwight Gooden	.25	.20	.10
F	Rickey Henderson	.25	.20	.10
G	Tom Lasorda	.06	.05	.02
H	Fred Lynn, Panel	.06	.05	.02
	Panel	.90	.70	.35
I	Mark McGwire	.25	.20	.10
J	Dave Parker	.10	.08	.04
K	Jeff Reardon	.06	.05	.02
L	Rick Reuschel, Panel	.06	.05	.02
	Panel	1.50	1.25	.60
M	Jim Rice	.06	.05	.02
N	Cal Ripken, Jr.	.25	.20	.10
O	Nolan Ryan	.35	.25	.14
P	Ryne Sandberg	.25	.20	.10

1990 Topps Batting Leaders

Once again produced as an exclusive insert in jumbo blister packs for K-Mart stores, the 1990 career batting leaders cards are similar in concept and design to the previous year's issue; in fact, some of the same player photos were used. The 22 cards in the set are arranged roughly in order of the players' standings in lifetime batting average. Cards fronts are bordered in bright green and backs are printed in red, white and dark green.

		MT	NR MT	EX
Complete Set:		15.00	11.00	6.00
Common Player:		.50	.40	.20
1	Wade Boggs	1.50	1.25	.60
2	Tony Gwynn	.75	.60	.30
3	Kirby Puckett	1.50	1.25	.60
4	Don Mattingly	1.50	1.25	.60
5	George Brett	1.50	1.25	.60
6	Pedro Guerrero	.50	.40	.20
7	Tim Raines	.60	.45	.25
8	Paul Molitor	1.00	.70	.40
9	Jim Rice	.60	.45	.25
10	Keith Hernandez	.50	.40	.20
11	Julio Franco	.50	.40	.20
12	Carney Lansford	.50	.40	.20
13	Dave Parker	.75	.60	.30
14	Willie McGee	.60	.45	.25
15	Robin Yount	1.50	1.25	.60
16	Tony Fernandez	.50	.40	.20
17	Eddie Murray	.75	.60	.30
18	Johnny Ray	.50	.40	.20
19	Lonnie Smith	.50	.40	.20
20	Phil Bradley	.50	.40	.20
21	Rickey Henderson	1.50	1.25	.60
22	Kent Hrbek	.60	.45	.25

1990 Topps Big Baseball

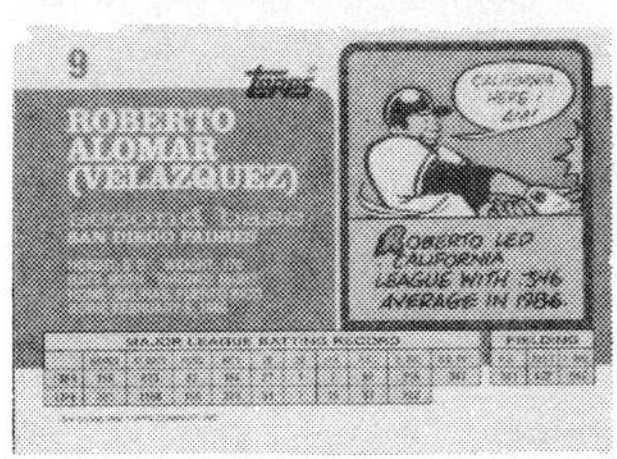

For the third consecutive year, Topps issued a 330-card set of the oversized cards (2-5/8" by 3-3/4"). The cards were issued in three 110-card series. The cards are reminiscent of Topps cards from the mid-1950s in that they feature players in portrait and action shots. The 1990 set has action photos in freeze frames. As in previous years, the cards are printed on white card stock with a glossy finish on the front. The card backs include 1989 and career hitting, fielding and pitching stats and a player cartoon.

		MT	NR MT	EX
Complete Set:		18.00	13.50	7.25
Common Player:		.05	.04	.02
1	Dwight Evans	.08	.06	.03
2	Kirby Puckett	.25	.20	.10
3	Kevin Gross	.06	.05	.02
4	Ron Hassey	.05	.04	.02
5	Lloyd McClendon	.05	.04	.02
6	Bo Jackson	.50	.40	.20
7	Lonnie Smith	.06	.05	.02
8	Alvaro Espinoza	.06	.05	.02
9	Roberto Alomar	.15	.11	.06
10	Glenn Braggs	.06	.05	.02
11	David Cone	.10	.08	.04
12	Clauudell Washington	.05	.04	.02
13	Pedro Guerrero	.10	.08	.04
14	Todd Benzinger	.06	.05	.02
15	Jeff Russell	.06	.05	.02
16	Terry Kennedy	.05	.04	.02
17	Kelly Gruber	.15	.11	.06
18	Alfredo Griffin	.05	.04	.02
19	Mark Grace	.20	.15	.08
20	Dave Winfield	.12	.09	.05
21	Bret Saberhagen	.15	.11	.06
22	Roger Clemens	.30	.25	.12
23	Bob Walk	.05	.04	.02
24	Dave Magadan	.15	.11	.06
25	Spike Owen	.06	.05	.02
26	Jody Davis	.05	.04	.02
27	Kent Hrbek	.12	.09	.05
28	Mark McGwire	.50	.40	.20
29	Eddie Murray	.15	.11	.06
30	Paul O'Neill	.06	.05	.02
31	Jose DeLeon	.06	.05	.02
32	Steve Lyons	.05	.04	.02
33	Dan Plesac	.06	.05	.02
34	Jack Howell	.05	.04	.02
35	Greg Briley	.06	.05	.02
36	Andy Hawkins	.06	.05	.02
37	Cecil Espy	.05	.04	.02
38	Rick Sutcliffe	.08	.06	.03
39	Jack Clark	.12	.09	.05
40	Dale Murphy	.12	.09	.05
41	Mike Henneman	.06	.05	.02
42	Rick Honeycutt	.05	.04	.02
43	Willie Randolph	.06	.05	.02
44	Marty Barrett	.06	.05	.02
45	Willie Wilson	.06	.05	.02
46	Wallace Johnson	.05	.04	.02
47	Greg Brock	.06	.05	.02
48	Tom Browning	.06	.05	.02
49	Gerald Young	.05	.04	.02
50	Dennis Eckersley	.15	.11	.06
51	Scott Garrelts	.06	.05	.02
52	Gary Redus	.05	.04	.02
53	Al Newman	.05	.04	.02
54	Darryl Boston	.05	.04	.02
55	Ron Oester	.05	.04	.02
56	Danny Tartabull	.08	.06	.03
57	Gregg Jefferies	.15	.11	.06

58	Tom Foley	.05	.04	.02
59	Robin Yount	.20	.15	.08
60	Pat Borders	.06	.05	.02
61	Mike Greenwell	.30	.25	.12
62	Shawon Dunston	.10	.08	.04
63	Steve Buechele	.05	.04	.02
64	Dave Stewart	.12	.09	.05
65	Jose Oquendo	.05	.04	.02
66	Ron Gant	.20	.15	.08
67	Mike Scioscia	.06	.05	.02
68	Randy Velarde	.05	.04	.02
69	Charlie Hayes	.06	.05	.02
70	Tim Wallach	.08	.06	.03
71	Eric Show	.06	.05	.02
72	Eric Davis	.25	.20	.10
73	Mike Gallego	.05	.04	.02
74	Rob Deer	.06	.05	.02
75	Ryne Sandberg	.40	.30	.15
76	Kevin Seitzer	.08	.06	.03
77	Wade Boggs	.50	.40	.20
78	Greg Gagne	.06	.05	.02
79	John Smiley	.06	.05	.02
80	Ivan Calderon	.08	.06	.03
81	Pete Incaviglia	.06	.05	.02
82	Orel Hershiser	.12	.09	.05
83	Carney Lansford	.08	.06	.03
84	Mike Fitzgerald	.05	.04	.02
85	Don Mattingly	.60	.45	.25
86	Chet Lemon	.06	.05	.02
87	Rolando Roomes	.05	.04	.02
88	Bill Spiers	.06	.05	.02
89	Pat Tabler	.06	.05	.02
90	Danny Heep	.05	.04	.02
91	Andre Dawson	.15	.11	.06
92	Randy Bush	.05	.04	.02
93	Tony Gwynn	.15	.11	.06
94	Tom Brunansky	.08	.06	.03
95	Johnny Ray	.06	.05	.02
96	Matt Williams	.15	.11	.06
97	Barry Lyons	.05	.04	.02
98	Jeff Hamilton	.05	.04	.02
99	Tom Glavine	.06	.05	.02
100	Ken Griffey,Sr.	.06	.05	.02
101	Tom Henke	.06	.05	.02
102	Dave Righetti	.08	.06	.03
103	Paul Molitor	.12	.09	.05
104	Mike LaValliere	.06	.05	.02
105	Frank White	.06	.05	.02
106	Bob Welch	.08	.06	.03
107	Ellis Burks	.25	.20	.10
108	Andres Galarraga	.08	.06	.03
109	Mitch Williams	.08	.06	.03
110	Checklist	.05	.04	.02
111	Craig Biggio	.08	.06	.03
112	Dave Steib	.08	.06	.03
113	Ron Darling	.06	.05	.02
114	Bert Blyleven	.10	.08	.04
115	Dickie Thon	.05	.04	.02
116	Carlos Martinez	.06	.05	.02
117	Jeff King	.06	.05	.02
118	Terry Steinbach	.06	.05	.02
119	Frank Tanana	.06	.05	.02
120	Mark Lemke	.06	.05	.02
121	Chris Sabo	.10	.08	.04
122	Glenn Davis	.15	.11	.06
123	Mel Hall	.06	.05	.02
124	Jim Gantner	.06	.05	.02
125	Benito Santiago	.10	.08	.04
126	Milt Thompson	.06	.05	.02
127	Rafael Palmeiro	.12	.09	.05
128	Barry Bonds	.40	.30	.15
129	Mike Bielecki	.06	.05	.02
130	Lou Whitaker	.10	.08	.04
131	Bob Ojeda	.05	.04	.02
132	Dion James	.05	.04	.02
133	Denny Martinez	.06	.05	.02
134	Fred McGriff	.20	.15	.08
135	Terry Pendleton	.06	.05	.02
136	Pat Combs	.10	.08	.04
137	Kevin Mitchell	.30	.25	.12
138	Marquis Grissom	.50	.40	.20
139	Chris Bosio	.06	.05	.02
140	Omar Vizquel	.05	.04	.02
141	Steve Sax	.10	.08	.04
142	Nelson Liriano	.05	.04	.02
143	Kevin Elster	.06	.05	.02
144	Dan Pasqua	.06	.05	.02
145	Dave Smith	.06	.05	.02
146	Craig Worthington	.06	.05	.02
147	Dan Gladden	.06	.05	.02
148	Oddibe McDowell	.05	.04	.02
149	Bip Roberts	.06	.05	.02
150	Randy Ready	.05	.04	.02
151	Dwight Smith	.10	.08	.04
152	Ed Whitson	.06	.05	.02
153	George Bell	.12	.09	.05
154	Tim Raines	.15	.11	.06
155	Sid Fernandez	.08	.06	.03
156	Henry Cotto	.05	.04	.02
157	Harold Baines	.12	.09	.05
158	Willie McGee	.10	.08	.04
159	Bill Doran	.06	.05	.02
160	Steve Balboni	.05	.04	.02
161	Pete Smith	.06	.05	.02
162	Frank Viola	.12	.09	.05
163	Gary Sheffield	.25	.20	.10
164	Bill Landrum	.06	.05	.02
165	Tony Fernandez	.08	.06	.03
166	Mike Heath	.05	.04	.02
167	Jody Reed	.08	.06	.03
168	Wally Joyner	.08	.06	.03
169	Robby Thompson	.06	.05	.02
170	Ken Caminiti	.06	.05	.02
171	Nolan Ryan	.50	.40	.20
172	Ricky Jordan	.08	.06	.03
173	Lance Blankenship	.05	.04	.02
174	Dwight Gooden	.20	.15	.08
175	Ruben Sierra	.20	.15	.08
176	Carlton Fisk	.15	.11	.06
177	Garry Templeton	.06	.05	.02
178	Mike Devereaux	.06	.05	.02
179	Mookie Wilson	.06	.05	.02
180	Jeff Blauser	.06	.05	.02
181	Scott Bradley	.05	.04	.02
182	Luis Salazar	.05	.04	.02
183	Rafael Ramirez	.06	.05	.02
184	Vince Coleman	.08	.06	.03
185	Doug Drabek	.10	.08	.04
186	Darryl Strawberry	.30	.25	.12
187	Tim Burke	.06	.05	.02
188	Jesse Barfield	.08	.06	.03
189	Barry Larkin	.15	.11	.06
190	Alan Trammell	.10	.08	.04
191	Steve Lake	.05	.04	.02
192	Derek Lilliquist	.06	.05	.02
193	Don Robinson	.06	.05	.02
194	Kevin McReynolds	.08	.06	.03
195	Melido Perez	.06	.05	.02
196	Jose Lind	.06	.05	.02
197	Eric Anthony	.25	.20	.10
198	B.J. Surhoff	.06	.05	.02
199	John Olerud	.50	.40	.20
200	Mike Moore	.06	.05	.02
201	Mark Gubicza	.08	.06	.03
202	Phil Bradley	.06	.05	.02
203	Ozzie Smith	.12	.09	.05
204	Greg Maddux	.08	.06	.03
205	Julio Franco	.12	.09	.05
206	Tom Herr	.06	.05	.02
207	Scott Fletcher	.05	.04	.02
208	Bobby Bonilla	.15	.11	.06
209	Bob Geren	.06	.05	.02
210	Junior Felix	.20	.15	.08
211	Dick Schofield	.05	.04	.02
212	Jim Deshaies	.06	.05	.02
213	Jose Uribe	.06	.05	.02
214	John Kruk	.15	.11	.06
215	Ozzie Guillen	.08	.06	.03
216	Howard Johnson	.10	.08	.04
217	Andy Van Slyke	.08	.06	.03
218	Tim Laudner	.05	.04	.02
219	Manny Lee	.06	.05	.02
220	Checklist	.05	.04	.02
221	Cory Snyder	.08	.06	.03
222	Billy Hatcher	.06	.05	.02
223	Bud Black	.05	.04	.02
224	Will Clark	.40	.30	.15
225	Kevin Tapani	.20	.15	.08
226	Mike Pagliarulo	.06	.05	.02
227	Dave Parker	.12	.09	.05
228	Ben McDonald	.50	.40	.20
229	Carlos Baerga	.50	.40	.20
230	Roger McDowell	.06	.05	.02
231	Delino DeShields	.50	.40	.20
232	Mark Langston	.10	.08	.04
233	Wally Backman	.06	.05	.02
234	Jim Eisenreich	.06	.05	.02
235	Mike Schooler	.06	.05	.02
236	Kevin Bass	.06	.05	.02
237	John Farrell	.05	.04	.02
238	Kal Daniels	.10	.08	.04
239	Tony Phillips	.06	.05	.02
240	Todd Stottlemyre	.06	.05	.02
241	Greg Olson	.15	.11	.06
242	Charlie Hough	.06	.05	.02
243	Mariano Duncan	.06	.05	.02
244	Billy Ripken	.05	.04	.02
245	Joe Carter	.12	.09	.05
246	Tim Belcher	.08	.06	.03
247	Roberto Kelly	.08	.06	.03
248	Candy Maldonado	.08	.06	.03
249	Mike Scott	.08	.06	.03
250	Ken Griffey, Jr.	1.25	.90	.50
251	Nick Esasky	.06	.05	.02
252	Tom Gordon	.15	.11	.06
253	John Tudor	.06	.05	.02
254	Gary Gaetti	.10	.08	.04
255	Neal Heaton	.06	.05	.02
256	Jerry Browne	.06	.05	.02
257	Joe Rijo	.06	.05	.02
258	Mike Boddicker	.06	.05	.02
259	Brett Butler	.06	.05	.02
260	Andy Benes	.10	.08	.04
261	Kevin Brown	.08	.06	.03
262	Hubie Brooks	.08	.06	.03
263	Randy Milligan	.06	.05	.02
264	John Franco	.10	.08	.04
265	Sandy Alomar	.10	.08	.04
266	Dave Valle	.06	.05	.02
267	Jerome Walton	.10	.08	.04
268	Bob Boone	.08	.06	.03
269	Ken Howell	.06	.05	.02
270	Jose Canseco	.50	.40	.20
271	Joe Magrane	.08	.06	.03
272	Brian DuBois	.08	.06	.03
273	Carlos Quintana	.08	.06	.03
274	Lance Johnson	.06	.05	.02
275	Steve Bedrosian	.06	.05	.02
276	Brook Jacoby	.08	.06	.03
277	Fred Lynn	.06	.05	.02
278	Jeff Ballard	.06	.05	.02
279	Otis Nixon	.05	.04	.02
280	Chili Davis	.06	.05	.02
281	Joe Oliver	.12	.09	.05
282	Brian Holman	.08	.06	.03
283	Juan Samuel	.08	.06	.03
284	Rick Aguilera	.06	.05	.02
285	Jeff Reardon	.08	.06	.03
286	Sammy Sosa	.30	.25	.12
287	Carmelo Martinez	.06	.05	.02
288	Greg Swindell	.08	.06	.03
289	Erik Hanson	.15	.11	.06
290	Tony Pena	.08	.06	.03
291	Pascual Perez	.06	.05	.02
292	Rickey Henderson	.35	.25	.14
293	Kurt Stillwell	.06	.05	.02
294	Todd Zeile	.50	.40	.20
295	Bobby Thigpen	.10	.08	.04
296	Larry Walker	.30	.25	.12
297	Rob Murphy	.05	.04	.02
298	Mitch Webster	.05	.04	.02
299	Devon White	.12	.09	.05
300	Len Dykstra	.15	.11	.06
301	Keith Hernandez	.06	.05	.02
302	Gene Larkin	.06	.05	.02
303	Jeffrey Leonard	.06	.05	.02
304	Jim Presley	.06	.05	.02
305	Lloyd Moseby	.08	.06	.03
306	John Smoltz	.08	.06	.03
307	Sam Horn	.06	.05	.02
308	Greg Litton	.06	.05	.02
309	Dave Henderson	.08	.06	.03
310	Mark McLemore	.05	.04	.02
311	Gary Pettis	.06	.05	.02
312	Mark Davis	.05	.04	.02
313	Cecil Fielder	.50	.40	.20
314	Jack Armstrong	.08	.06	.03
315	Alvin Davis	.08	.06	.03
316	Doug Jones	.08	.06	.03
317	Eric Yelding	.08	.06	.03
318	Joe Orsulak	.06	.05	.02
319	Chuck Finley	.08	.06	.03
320	Glenn Wilson	.06	.05	.02
321	Harold Reynolds	.08	.06	.03
322	Teddy Higuera	.08	.06	.03
323	Lance Parrish	.08	.06	.03
324	Bruce Hurst	.06	.05	.02
325	Dave West	.06	.05	.02
326	Kirk Gibson	.10	.08	.04
327	Cal Ripken, Jr.	.35	.25	.14
328	Rick Reuschel	.06	.05	.02
329	Jim Abbott	.15	.11	.06
330	Checklist	.05	.04	.02

1990 Topps Major League Debut Promo

This one-card "set" was given out at the United States Baseball Federation awards luncheon in New York City on Nov. 14, 1990. The Alex Fernandez promo card introduced Topps' second annual boxed set of all players who made their major league debuts during the 1990 season. The rough borders found on many of these cards indicates they were cut from the press sheet by hand.

----	Alex Fernandez	40.00	30.00	15.00

1990 Topps Major League Debut

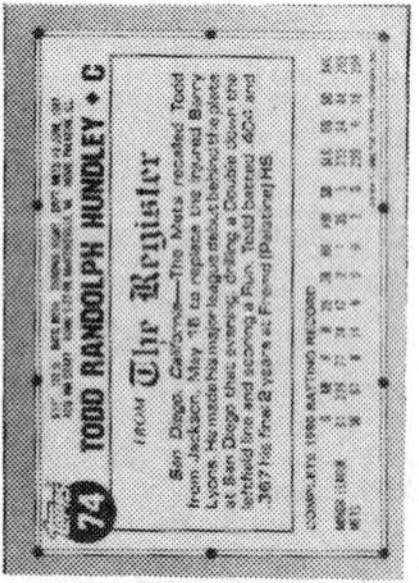

This 171-card set features the players who made their Major League debut in 1990. The cards are styled like the 1991 Topps cards and are numbered in alphabetical order. The card backs are printed horizontally and feature information about the player's debut and statistics.

		MT	NR MT	EX
Complete Set:		20.00	11.00	6.00
Common Player:		.05	.04	.02
1	Paul Abbott	.06	.05	.02
2	Steve Adkins	.05	.04	.02

3	Scott Aldred	.08	.06	.03
4	Gerald Alexander	.06	.05	.02
5	Moises Alou	.25	.20	.10
6	Steve Avery	.80	.60	.30
7	Oscar Azocar	.05	.04	.02
8	Carlos Baerga	.30	.25	.12
9	Kevin Baez	.05	.04	.02
10	Jeff Baldwin	.05	.04	.02
11	Brian Barnes	.12	.09	.05
12	Kevin Bearse	.06	.05	.02
13	Kevin Belcher	.10	.08	.04
14	Mike Bell	.10	.08	.04
15	Sean Berry	.08	.06	.03
16	Joe Bitker	.08	.06	.03
17	Willie Blair	.06	.05	.02
18	Brian Bohanon	.06	.05	.02
19	Mike Bordick	.20	.15	.08
20	Shawn Boskie	.10	.08	.04
21	Rod Brewer	.06	.05	.02
22	Kevin Brown	.05	.04	.02
23	Dave Burba	.06	.05	.02
24	Jim Campbell	.05	.04	.02
25	Ozzie Canseco	.10	.08	.04
26	Chuck Carr	.08	.06	.03
27	Larry Casian	.06	.05	.02
28	Andujar Cedeno	.30	.25	.12
29	Wes Chamberlain	.30	.25	.12
30	Scott Chiamparino	.08	.06	.03
31	Steve Chitren	.08	.06	.03
32	Pete Coachman	.05	.04	.02
33	Alex Cole	.15	.11	.06
34	Jeff Conine	.15	.11	.06
35	Scott Cooper	.15	.11	.06
36	Milt Cuyler	.20	.15	.08
37	Steve Decker	.15	.11	.06
38	Rich DeLucia	.08	.06	.03
39	Delino DeShields	.35	.25	.14
40	Mark Dewey	.05	.04	.02
41	Carlos Diaz	.05	.04	.02
42	Lance Dickson	.10	.08	.04
43	Narciso Elvira	.06	.05	.02
44	Luis Encarnacion	.05	.04	.02
45	Scott Erickson	.40	.30	.15
46	Paul Faries	.06	.05	.02
47	Howard Farmer	.06	.05	.02
48	Alex Fernandez	.30	.25	.12
49	Travis Fryman	.80	.60	.30
50	Rich Garces	.06	.05	.02
51	Carlos Garcia	.05	.04	.02
52	Mike Gardiner	.08	.06	.03
53	Bernard Gilkey	.25	.20	.10
54	Tom Gilles	.05	.04	.02
55	Jerry Goff	.06	.05	.02
56	Leo Gomez	.30	.25	.12
57	Luis Gonzalez	.30	.25	.12
58	Joe Grahe	.15	.11	.06
59	Craig Grebeck	.10	.08	.04
60	Kip Gross	.08	.06	.03
61	Eric Gunderson	.06	.05	.02
62	Chris Hammond	.10	.08	.04
63	Dave Hansen	.10	.08	.04
64	Reggie Harris	.06	.05	.02
65	Bill Haselman	.05	.04	.02
66	Randy Hennis	.05	.04	.02
67	Carlos Hernandez	.10	.08	.04
68	Howard Hilton	.05	.04	.02
69	Dave Hollins	.25	.20	.10
70	Darren Holmes	.06	.05	.02
71	John Hoover	.05	.04	.02
72	Steve Howard	.06	.05	.02
73	Thomas Howard	.10	.08	.04
74	Todd Hundley	.20	.15	.08
75	Daryl Irvine	.10	.08	.04
76	Chris Jelic	.06	.05	.02
77	Dana Kiecker	.06	.05	.02
78	Brent Knackert	.05	.04	.02
79	Jimmy Kremers	.05	.04	.02
80	Jerry Kutzler	.05	.04	.02
81	Ray Lankford	.70	.50	.30
82	Tim Layana	.06	.05	.02
83	Terry Lee	.06	.05	.02
84	Mark Leiter	.08	.06	.03
85	Scott Leius	.15	.11	.06
86	Mark Leonard	.10	.08	.04
87	Darren Lewis	.20	.15	.08
88	Scott Lewis	.08	.06	.03
89	Jim Leyritz	.08	.06	.03
90	Dave Liddell	.05	.04	.02
91	Luis Lopez	.05	.04	.02
92	Kevin Maas	.35	.25	.14
93	Bob MacDonald	.06	.05	.02
94	Carlos Maldonado	.05	.04	.02
95	Chuck Malone	.05	.04	.02
96	Ramon Manon	.05	.04	.02
97	Jeff Manto	.08	.06	.03
98	Paul Marak	.06	.05	.02
99	Tino Martinez	.25	.20	.10
100	Derrick May	.25	.20	.10
101	Brent Mayne	.12	.09	.05
102	Paul McClellan	.08	.06	.03
103	Rodney McCray	.08	.06	.03
104	Tim McIntosh	.08	.06	.03
105	Brian McRae	.30	.25	.12
106	Jose Melendez	.06	.05	.02
107	Orlando Merced	.30	.25	.12
108	Alan Mills	.06	.05	.02
109	Gino Minutelli	.15	.11	.06
110	Mickey Morandini	.20	.15	.08
111	Pedro Munoz	.40	.30	.15
112	Chris Nabholz	.15	.11	.06
113	Tim Naehring	.10	.08	.04
114	Charles Nagy	.30	.25	.12
115	Jim Neidlinger	.08	.06	.03
116	Rafael Novoa	.08	.06	.03
117	Jose Offerman	.20	.15	.08
118	Omar Olivares	.10	.08	.04
119	Javier Ortiz	.08	.06	.03
120	Al Osuna	.08	.06	.03
121	Rick Parker	.06	.05	.02
122	Dave Pavlas	.05	.04	.02
123	Geronimo Pena	.20	.15	.08
124	Mike Perez	.08	.06	.03
125	Phil Plantier	.70	.50	.30
126	Jim Poole	.06	.05	.02
127	Tom Quinlan	.05	.04	.02
128	Scott Radinsky	.10	.08	.04
129	Darren Reed	.12	.09	.05
130	Karl Rhodes	.10	.08	.04
131	Jeff Richardson	.05	.04	.02
132	Rich Rodriguez	.06	.05	.02
133	Dave Rohde	.05	.04	.02
134	Mel Rojas	.08	.06	.03
135	Vic Rosario	.06	.05	.02
136	Rich Rowland	.06	.05	.02
137	Scott Ruskin	.08	.06	.03
138	Bill Sampen	.08	.06	.03
139	Andres Santana	.08	.06	.03
140	David Segui	.08	.06	.03
141	Jeff Shaw	.05	.04	.02
142	Tim Sherrill	.05	.04	.02
143	Terry Shumpert	.08	.06	.03
144	Mike Simms	.08	.06	.03
145	Daryl Smith	.05	.04	.02
146	Luis Sojo	.15	.11	.06
147	Steve Springer	.05	.04	.02
148	Ray Stephens	.05	.04	.02
149	Lee Stevens	.15	.11	.06
150	Mel Stottlemyre, Jr.	.05	.04	.02
151	Glenn Sutko	.05	.04	.02
152	Anthony Telford	.08	.06	.03
153	Frank Thomas	1.50	1.25	.60
154	Randy Tomlin	.20	.15	.08
155	Brian Traxler	.05	.04	.02
156	Efrain Valdez	.06	.05	.02
157	Rafael Valdez	.06	.05	.02
158	Julio Valera	.15	.11	.06
159	Jim Vatcher	.08	.06	.03
160	Hector Villanueva	.12	.09	.05
161	Hector Wagner	.05	.04	.02
162	Dave Walsh	.05	.04	.02
163	Steve Wapnick	.08	.06	.03
164	Colby Ward	.06	.05	.02
165	Turner Ward	.15	.11	.06
166	Terry Wells	.05	.04	.02
167	Mark Whiten	.20	.15	.08
168	Mike York	.05	.04	.02
169	Cliff Young	.08	.06	.03
170	Checklist	.05	.04	.02
171	Checklist	.05	.04	.02

1990 Topps TV All-Stars

This 66-card boxed set was sold only through a television offer in limited markets. Consequently, production numbers are relatively low and single cards are seldom offered in the hobby market. Most of the game's top stars are included in the issue. Fronts feature a high-gloss surface. On the red-bordered backs there are several lines of biographical data plus each player's "Career Bests" in various statistical categories, set against a pastel background shield.

		MT	NR MT	EX
Complete Set:		50.00	37.00	20.00
Common Player:		1.00	.70	.40
1	Mark McGwire	3.00	2.25	1.25
2	Julio Franco	1.00	.70	.40
3	Ozzie Guillen	1.00	.70	.40
4	Carney Lansford	1.00	.70	.40
5	Bo Jackson	4.00	3.00	1.50
6	Kirby Puckett	5.00	3.75	2.00
7	Ruben Sierra	3.00	2.25	1.25
8	Carlton Fisk	2.50	2.00	1.00
9	Nolan Ryan	6.00	4.50	2.50
10	Rickey Henderson	4.00	3.00	1.50
11	Jose Canseco	2.50	2.00	1.00
12	Mark Davis	1.00	.70	.40
13	Dennis Eckersley	1.50	1.25	.60
14	Chuck Finley	1.00	.70	.40
15	Bret Saberhagen	1.00	.70	.40
16	Dave Stewart	1.00	.70	.40
17	Don Mattingly	3.00	2.25	1.25
18	Steve Sax	1.00	.70	.40
19	Cal Ripken, Jr.	5.00	3.75	2.00
20	Wade Boggs	3.00	2.25	1.25
21	George Bell	1.00	.70	.40
22	Mike Greenwell	1.00	.70	.40
23	Robin Yount	4.00	3.00	1.50
24	Mickey Tettleton	1.00	.70	.40
25	Roger Clemens	2.00	1.50	.80
26	Fred McGriff	2.50	2.00	1.00
27	Jeff Ballard	1.00	.70	.40
28	Dwight Evans	1.00	.70	.40
29	Paul Molitor	3.00	2.25	1.25
30	Gregg Olson	1.00	.70	.40
31	Dan Plesac	1.00	.70	.40
32	Greg Swindell	1.00	.70	.40
33	Cito Gaston, Tony LaRussa	1.00	.70	.40
34	Will Clark	3.50	2.75	1.50
35	Roberto Alomar	3.00	2.25	1.25
36	Barry Larkin	1.00	.70	.40
37	Ken Caminiti	1.00	.70	.40
38	Eric Davis	1.25	.90	.50
39	Tony Gwynn	1.50	1.25	.60
40	Kevin Mitchell	1.00	.70	.40
41	Craig Biggio	1.00	.70	.40
42	Mike Scott	1.00	.70	.40
43	Joe Carter	2.00	1.50	.80
44	Jack Clark	1.00	.70	.40
45	Glenn Davis	1.00	.70	.40
46	Orel Hershiser	1.50	1.25	.60
47	Jay Howell	1.00	.70	.40
48	Bruce Hurst	1.00	.70	.40
49	Dave Smith	1.00	.70	.40
50	Pedro Guerrero	1.00	.70	.40
51	Ryne Sandberg	5.00	3.75	2.00
52	Ozzie Smith	4.00	3.00	1.50
53	Howard Johnson	1.50	1.25	.60
54	Von Hayes	1.00	.70	.40
55	Tim Raines	1.75	1.25	.70
56	Darryl Strawberry	1.50	1.25	.60
57	Mike LaValliere	1.00	.70	.40
58	Dwight Gooden	1.50	1.25	.60
59	Bobby Bonilla	2.00	1.50	.80
60	Tim Burke	1.00	.70	.40
61	Sid Fernandez	1.00	.70	.40
62	Andres Galarraga	1.75	1.25	.70
63	Mark Grace	2.00	1.50	.80
64	Joe Magrane	1.00	.70	.40
65	Mitch Williams	1.00	.70	.40
66	Roger Craig, Don Zimmer	1.00	.70	.40

1990 Topps TV Cardinals Team Set

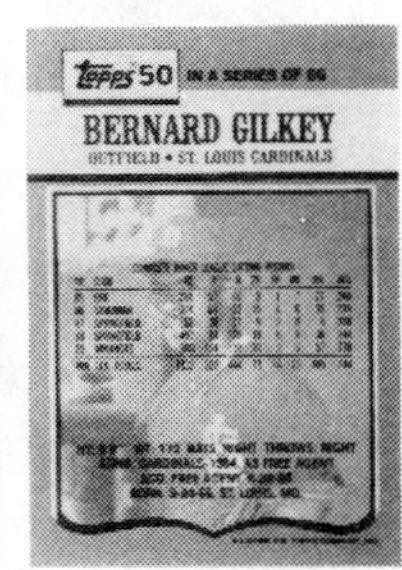

Available only as a boxed set via a limited television offer, this team set includes cards of all players on the opening day roster plus the manager, selected coaches and many of the organization's top prospects. In many cases this is the first card of a player in major league uniform, and in some cases represents the only card which will ever be issued of the player as a major leaguer. Cards feature a high-gloss front surface. Backs have a red border and feature a "ghost image" of the photo on the front as a background to the statistical and biographical data. Because of the relatively limited production and the fact it was sold as a boxed set only, single cards are seldom available.

		MT	NR MT	EX
Complete Set:		60.00	45.00	24.00
Common Player:		1.00	.70	.40
1	Whitey Herzog	2.00	1.50	.80
2	Steve Braun	1.00	.70	.40
3	Rich Hacker	1.00	.70	.40
4	Dave Ricketts	1.00	.70	.40
5	Jim Riggleman	1.00	.70	.40
6	Mike Roarke	1.00	.70	.40
7	Cris Carpenter	1.00	.70	.40
8	John Costello	1.00	.70	.40
9	Danny Cox	1.00	.70	.40
10	Ken Dayley	1.00	.70	.40
11	Jose DeLeon	1.00	.70	.40
12	Frank DiPino	1.00	.70	.40
13	Ken Hill	1.00	.70	.40
14	Howard Hilton	1.00	.70	.40
15	Ricky Horton	1.00	.70	.40
16	Joe Magrane	1.00	.70	.40
17	Greg Mathews	1.00	.70	.40
18	Bryn Smith	1.00	.70	.40
19	Scott Terry	1.00	.70	.40
20	Bob Tewksbury	2.50	2.00	1.00
21	John Tudor	1.00	.70	.40
22	Todd Worrell	1.50	1.25	.60
23	Tom Pagnozzi	1.00	.70	.40
24	Todd Zeile	2.00	1.50	.80
25	Pedro Guerrero	1.50	1.25	.60
26	Tim Jones	1.00	.70	.40

27	Jose Oquendo	1.50	1.25	.60
28	Terry Pendleton	3.00	2.25	1.25
29	Ozzie Smith	5.00	3.75	2.00
30	Denny Walling	1.00	.70	.40
31	Tom Brunansky	1.00	.70	.40
32	Vince Colemen	2.00	1.50	.80
33	Dave Collins	1.00	.70	.40
34	Willie McGee	2.50	2.00	1.00
35	John Morris	1.00	.70	.40
36	Milt Thompson	1.00	.70	.40
37	Gibson Alba	1.00	.70	.40
38	Scott Arnold	1.00	.70	.40
39	Rod Brewer	1.00	.70	.40
40	Greg Carmona	1.00	.70	.40
41	Mark Clark	1.50	1.25	.60
42	Stan Clarke	1.00	.70	.40
43	Paul Coleman	1.00	.70	.40
44	Todd Crosby	1.00	.70	.40
45	Brad DuVall	1.00	.70	.40
46	John Ericks	1.00	.70	.40
47	Bien Figueroa	1.00	.70	.40
48	Terry Francona	1.00	.70	.40
49	Ed Fulton	1.00	.70	.40
50	Bernard Gilkey	3.00	2.25	1.25
51	Ernie Camacho	1.00	.70	.40
52	Mike Hinkle	1.00	.70	.40
53	Ray Lankford	3.00	2.25	1.25
54	Julian Martinez	1.00	.70	.40
55	Jesus Mendez	1.00	.70	.40
56	Mike Milchin	1.00	.70	.40
57	Mauricio Nunez	1.00	.70	.40
58	Omar Olivares	2.00	1.50	.80
59	Geronimo Pena	2.00	1.50	.80
60	Mike Perez	2.00	1.50	.80
61	Gaylen Pitts	1.00	.70	.40
62	Mark Riggins	1.00	.70	.40
63	Tim Sherrill	1.00	.70	.40
64	Roy Silver	1.00	.70	.40
65	Ray Stephens	1.00	.70	.40
66	Craig Wilson	1.00	.70	.40

1990 Topps TV Cubs Team Set

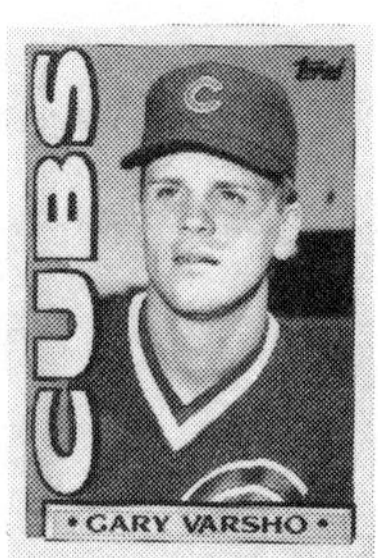

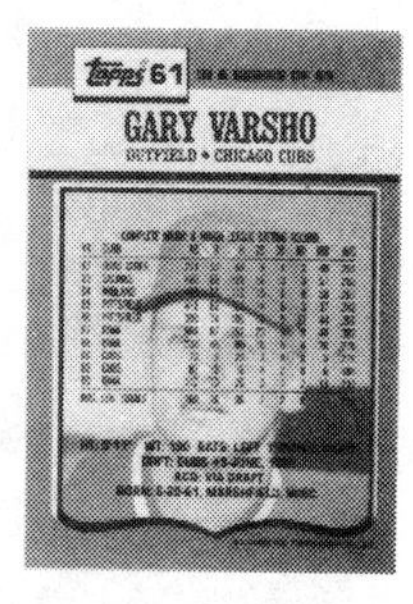

Sold only in boxed set form via a limited television offer, this 66-card issue includes all players on the team's 1990 opening day roster as well as the manager, selected coaches and some of the organization's top minor league prospects. For the latter group, this sets offers the first - and in many cases the only - card of the player in a major league uniform. The cards have a high-gloss front surface. Card backs feature a "ghost image" of the color photo used on the front as a background to the stats and biographical information. A red border completes the back design. Because the set was sold only in boxed form, and production was relatively low, single cards are seldom seen in the market.

		MT	NR MT	EX
	Complete Set:	60.00	45.00	24.00
	Common Player:	1.00	.70	.40
1	Don Zimmer	1.50	1.25	.60
2	Joe Altobelli	1.00	.70	.40
3	Chuck Cottier	1.00	.70	.40
4	Jose Martinez	1.00	.70	.40
5	Dick Pole	1.00	.70	.40
6	Phil Roof	1.00	.70	.40
7	Paul Assenmacher	1.00	.70	.40
8	Mike Bielecki	1.00	.70	.40
9	Mike Harkey	1.50	1.25	.60
10	Joe Kraemer	1.00	.70	.40
11	Les Lancaster	1.00	.70	.40
12	Greg Maddux	3.00	2.25	1.25
13	Jose Nunez	1.00	.70	.40
14	Jeff Pico	1.00	.70	.40
15	Rick Sutcliffe	1.50	1.25	.60
16	Dean Wilkins	1.00	.70	.40
17	Mitch Williams	1.50	1.25	.60
18	Steve Wilson	1.00	.70	.40
19	Damon Berryhill	1.00	.70	.40
20	Joe Girardi	1.50	1.25	.60
21	Rick Wrona	1.00	.70	.40
22	Shawon Dunston	2.00	1.50	.80
23	Mark Grace	3.00	2.25	1.25
24	Domingo Ramos	1.00	.70	.40
25	Luis Salazar	1.00	.70	.40
26	Ryne Sandberg	7.50	5.75	3.00
27	Greg Smith	1.00	.70	.40
28	Curtis Wilkerson	1.00	.70	.40
29	Dave Clark	1.00	.70	.40
30	Doug Dascenzo	1.00	.70	.40
31	Andre Dawson	4.00	3.00	1.50
32	Lloyd McClendon	1.00	.70	.40
33	Dwight Smith	1.50	1.25	.60
34	Jerome Walton	1.50	1.25	.60
35	Marvell Wynne	1.00	.70	.40
36	Alex Arias	2.00	1.50	.80
37	Bob Bafia	1.00	.70	.40
38	Brad Bierley	1.00	.70	.40
39	Shawn Boskie	2.50	2.00	1.00
40	Danny Clay	1.00	.70	.40
41	Rusty Crockett	1.00	.70	.40
42	Earl Cunningham	1.50	1.25	.60
43	Len Damian	1.00	.70	.40
44	Darrin Duffy	1.00	.70	.40
45	Ty Griffin	1.00	.70	.40
46	Brian Guinn	1.00	.70	.40
47	Phil Hannon	1.00	.70	.40
48	Phil Harrison	1.00	.70	.40
49	Jeff Hearron	1.00	.70	.40
50	Greg Kallevig	1.00	.70	.40
51	Cedric Landrum	1.00	.70	.40
52	Bill Long	1.00	.70	.40
53	Derrick May	3.00	2.25	1.25
54	Ray Mullino	1.00	.70	.40
55	Erik Pappas	1.50	1.25	.60
56	Steve Parker	1.00	.70	.40
57	Dave Pavlas	1.00	.70	.40
58	Laddie Renfroe	1.00	.70	.40
59	Jeff Small	1.00	.70	.40
60	Doug Strange	1.00	.70	.40
61	Gary Varsho	1.00	.70	.40
62	Hector Villanueva	1.50	1.25	.60
63	Rick Wilkins	3.00	2.25	1.25
64	Dana Williams	1.00	.70	.40
65	Bill Wrona	1.00	.70	.40
66	Fernando Zarranz	1.00	.70	.40

1990 Topps TV Mets Team Set

This late-season issue, sold only as a boxed set via a television offer in limited areas, features all of the players on the 1990 opening day roster, plus the manager, selected coaches and many of the organization's top minor league prospects. For many of the prospects, this is the first, if not the only, card on which they appear in major league uniform. A highlight of the back design is a "ghost image" full-color reproduction of the front photo, used as a background to the statistical and biographical information. A red border dominates the remainder of the back design. Because it was sold only as a boxed set, and production was relatively limited, single cards are seldom available.

		MT	NR MT	EX
	Complete Set:	60.00	45.00	24.00
	Common Player:	1.00	.70	.40
1	Dave Johnson	1.00	.70	.40
2	Mike Cubbage	1.00	.70	.40
3	Doc Edwards	1.00	.70	.40
4	Bud Harrelson	1.00	.70	.40
5	Greg Pavlick	1.00	.70	.40
6	Mel Stottlemyre, Sr.	1.50	1.25	.60
7	Blaine Beatty	1.00	.70	.40
8	David Cone	2.00	1.50	.80
9	Ron Darling	2.00	1.50	.80
10	Sid Fernandez	2.00	1.50	.80
11	John Franco	2.00	1.50	.80
12	Dwight Gooden	3.00	2.25	1.25
13	Jeff Innis	1.00	.70	.40
14	Julio Machado	1.00	.70	.40
15	Jeff Musselman	1.00	.70	.40
16	Bob Ojeda	1.50	1.25	.60
17	Alejandro Pena	1.00	.70	.40
18	Frank Viola	2.50	2.00	1.00
19	Wally Whitehurst	1.00	.70	.40
20	Barry Lyons	1.00	.70	.40
21	Orlando Mercado	2.50	2.00	1.00
22	Mackey Sasser	1.00	.70	.40
23	Kevin Elster	1.00	.70	.40
24	Gregg Jefferies	3.00	2.25	1.25
25	Howard Johnson	2.50	2.00	1.00
26	Dave Magadan	2.00	1.50	.80
27	Mike Marshall	1.00	.70	.40
28	Tom O'Malley	1.00	.70	.40
29	Tim Teufel	1.00	.70	.40
30	Mark Carreon	1.50	1.25	.60
31	Kevin McReynolds	1.50	1.25	.60
32	Keith Miller	1.00	.70	.40
33	Darryl Strawberry	4.00	3.00	1.50
34	Lou Thornton	1.00	.70	.40
35	Shawn Barton	1.00	.70	.40
36	Tim Bogar	1.00	.70	.40
37	Terry Bross	1.00	.70	.40
38	Kevin Brown	1.00	.70	.40
39	Mike DeButch	1.00	.70	.40
40	Alex Diaz	1.00	.70	.40
41	Chris Donnels	1.00	.70	.40
42	Jeff Gardner	1.00	.70	.40
43	Denny Gonzalez	1.00	.70	.40
44	Kenny Graves	1.00	.70	.40
45	Manny Hernandez	1.00	.70	.40
46	Keith Hughes	1.00	.70	.40
47	Todd Hundley	2.00	1.50	.80
48	Chris Jelic	1.00	.70	.40
49	Dave Liddell	1.00	.70	.40
50	Terry McDaniel	1.00	.70	.40
51	Cesar Mejia	1.00	.70	.40
52	Scott Nielsen	1.00	.70	.40
53	Dale Plummer	1.00	.70	.40
54	Darren Reed	1.00	.70	.40
55	Gil Roca	1.00	.70	.40
56	Jaime Roseboro	1.00	.70	.40
57	Roger Samuels	1.00	.70	.40
58	Zoilo Sanchez	1.00	.70	.40
59	Pete Schourek	1.50	1.25	.60
60	Craig Shipley	1.00	.70	.40
61	Ray Soff	1.00	.70	.40
62	Steve Swisher	1.00	.70	.40
63	Kelvin Torve	1.00	.70	.40
64	Dave Trautwein	1.00	.70	.40
65	Julio Valera	1.00	.70	.40
66	Alan Zinter	1.00	.70	.40

1990 Topps TV Red Sox Team Set

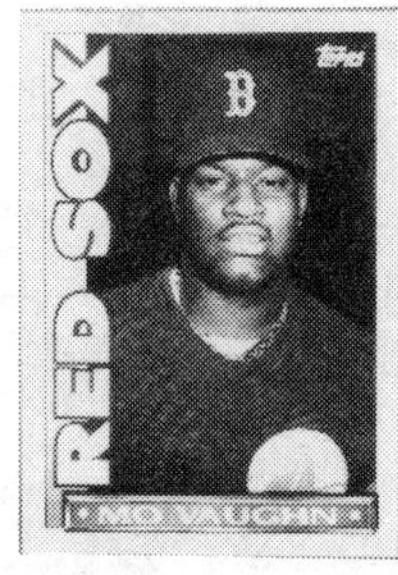

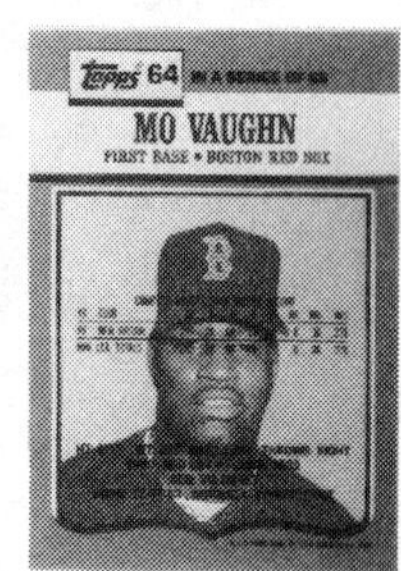

This 66-card set was available only via a television offer in certain limited areas. Production was relatively low and single cards are hard to find. Player selection includes all those on the team's opening day roster in 1990, plus the manager, selected coaches and the team's top minor league prospects. In many cases this represents the first, or even the only, appearance of these prospects on major league baseball cards. Fronts have a high-gloss surface. Card backs, bordered in red, feature a "ghost image" reproduction of the front photo as a background to the statistics and biographical data.

		MT	NR MT	EX
	Complete Set:	60.00	45.00	24.00
	Common Player:	1.00	.70	.40
1	Joe Morgan	1.00	.70	.40
2	Dick Berardino	1.00	.70	.40
3	Al Bumbry	1.00	.70	.40
4	Bill Fischer	1.00	.70	.40
5	Richie Hebner	1.00	.70	.40
6	Rac Slider	1.00	.70	.40
7	Mike Boddicker	1.00	.70	.40
8	Roger Clemens	5.00	3.75	2.00
9	John Dopson	1.00	.70	.40
10	Wes Gardner	1.00	.70	.40
11	Greg Harris	1.00	.70	.40
12	Dana Kiecker	1.00	.70	.40
13	Dennis Lamp	1.00	.70	.40
14	Rob Murphy	1.00	.70	.40
15	Jeff Reardon	1.50	1.25	.60
16	Mike Rochford	1.00	.70	.40
17	Lee Smith	3.00	2.25	1.25
18	Rich Gedman	1.00	.70	.40
19	John Marzano	1.00	.70	.40
20	Tony Pena	1.50	1.25	.60
21	Marty Barrett	1.00	.70	.40
22	Wade Boggs	5.00	3.75	2.00
23	Bill Buckner	1.00	.70	.40
24	Danny Heep	1.00	.70	.40
25	Jody Reed	1.50	1.25	.60
26	Luis Rivera	1.00	.70	.40
27	Billy Jo Robidoux	1.00	.70	.40
28	Ellis Burks	1.50	1.25	.60
29	Dwight Evans	1.50	1.25	.60
30	Mike Greenwell	2.00	1.50	.80
31	Randy Kutcher	1.00	.70	.40
32	Carlos Quintana	1.00	.70	.40
33	Kevin Romine	1.00	.70	.40
34	Ed Nottle	1.00	.70	.40
35	Mark Meleski	1.00	.70	.40

#	Player	MT	NR MT	EX
36	Steve Bast	1.00	.70	.40
37	Greg Blosser	1.00	.70	.40
38	Tom Bolton	1.00	.70	.40
39	Scott Cooper	2.00	1.50	.80
40	Zach Crouch	1.00	.70	.40
41	Steve Curry	1.00	.70	.40
42	Mike Dalton	1.00	.70	.40
43	John Flaherty	1.00	.70	.40
44	Angel Gonzalez	1.00	.70	.40
45	Eric Hetzel	1.00	.70	.40
46	Daryl Irvine	1.00	.70	.40
47	Joe Johnson	1.00	.70	.40
48	Rick Lancellotti	1.00	.70	.40
49	John Leister	1.00	.70	.40
50	Derek Livernois	1.00	.70	.40
51	Josias Manzanillo	1.00	.70	.40
52	Kevin Morton	1.00	.70	.40
53	Julius McDougal	1.00	.70	.40
54	Tim Naehring	1.50	1.25	.60
55	Jim Pankovits	1.00	.70	.40
56	Mickey Pina	1.00	.70	.40
57	Phil Plantier	3.00	2.25	1.25
58	Jerry Reed	1.00	.70	.40
59	Larry Shikles	1.00	.70	.40
60	Tito Stewart	1.00	.70	.40
61	Jeff Stone	1.00	.70	.40
62	John Trautwein	1.00	.70	.40
63	Gary Tremblay	1.00	.70	.40
64	Mo Vaughn	4.00	3.00	1.50
65	Scott Wade	1.00	.70	.40
66	Eric Wedge	1.00	.70	.40

1990 Topps TV Yankees Team Set

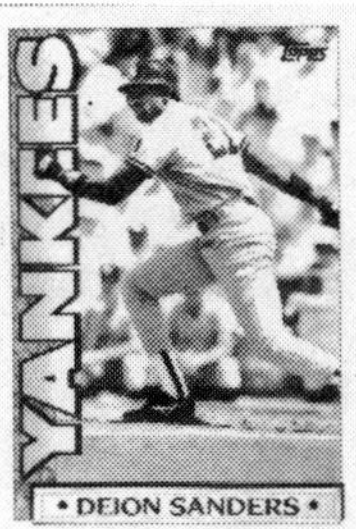

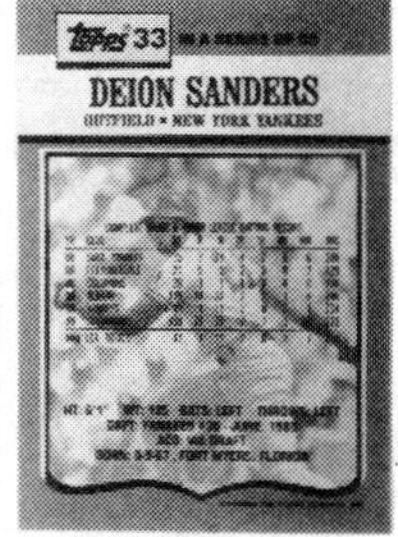

The first - and in many cases the only - baseball card appearance of top minor league prospects occurs in this special 66-card boxed set which was sold only via a special television offer in limited markets. The set also includes all players on the team's opening day roster, plus the manager and selected coaches. Card fronts have a high-gloss surface. On back, framed by a red border, the design features a "ghost image" of the color front photo, used as a background to the statistical and biographical information. Because the cards were sold only as a complete set, single cards are seldom available.

		MT	NR MT	EX
Complete Set:		60.00	45.00	24.00
Common Player:		1.00	.70	.40
1	Bucky Dent	1.50	1.25	.60
2	Mark Connor	1.00	.70	.40
3	Billy Connors	1.00	.70	.40
4	Mike Ferraro	1.00	.70	.40
5	Joe Sparks	1.00	.70	.40
6	Champ Summers	1.00	.70	.40
7	Greg Cadaret	1.00	.70	.40
8	Chuck Cary	1.00	.70	.40
9	Lee Guetterman	1.00	.70	.40
10	Andy Hawkins	1.00	.70	.40
11	Dave LaPoint	1.00	.70	.40
12	Tim Leary	1.00	.70	.40
13	Lance McCullers	1.00	.70	.40
14	Alan Mills	1.00	.70	.40
15	Clay Parker	1.00	.70	.40
16	Pascual Perez	1.00	.70	.40
17	Eric Plunk	1.00	.70	.40
18	Dave Righetti	1.50	1.25	.60
19	Jeff Robinson	1.00	.70	.40
20	Rick Cerone	1.00	.70	.40
21	Bob Geren	1.00	.70	.40
22	Steve Balboni	1.00	.70	.40
23	Mike Blowers	1.00	.70	.40
24	Alvaro Espinoza	1.00	.70	.40
25	Don Mattingly	5.00	3.75	2.00
26	Steve Sax	1.50	1.25	.60
27	Wayne Tolleson	1.00	.70	.40
28	Randy Velarde	1.00	.70	.40
29	Jesse Barfield	1.50	1.25	.60
30	Mel Hall	1.00	.70	.40
31	Roberto Kelly	2.00	1.50	.80
32	Luis Polonia	2.00	1.50	.80
33	Deion Sanders	4.00	3.00	1.50
34	Dave Winfield	5.00	3.75	2.00
35	Steve Adkins	1.00	.70	.40
36	Oscar Azocar	1.00	.70	.40
37	Bob Brower	1.00	.70	.40
38	Britt Burns	1.00	.70	.40
39	Bob Davidson	1.00	.70	.40
40	Brian Dorsett	1.00	.70	.40
41	Dave Eiland	1.00	.70	.40
42	John Fishel	1.00	.70	.40
43	Andy Fox	1.00	.70	.40
44	John Habyan	1.00	.70	.40
45	Cullen Hartzog	1.00	.70	.40
46	Sterling Hitchcock	2.00	1.50	.80
47	Brian Johnson	1.00	.70	.40
48	Jimmy Jones	1.00	.70	.40
49	Scott Kamieniecki	1.00	.70	.40
50	Mark Leiter	1.00	.70	.40
51	Jim Leyritz	2.00	1.50	.80
52	Jason Maas	1.00	.70	.40
53	Kevin Maas	1.50	1.25	.60
54	Hensley Meulens	1.50	1.25	.60
55	Kevin Mmahat	1.50	1.25	.60
56	Rich Monteleone	1.00	.70	.40
57	Vince Phillips	1.00	.70	.40
58	Carlos Rodriguez	1.00	.70	.40
59	Dave Sax	1.00	.70	.40
60	Willie Smith	1.00	.70	.40
61	Van Snider	1.00	.70	.40
62	Andy Stankiewicz	1.50	1.25	.60
63	Wade Taylor	1.00	.70	.40
64	Ricky Torres	1.00	.70	.40
65	Jim Walewander	1.00	.70	.40
66	Bernie Williams	2.00	1.50	.80

1990 Topps Heads Up!

Following up a much rarer test issue of the previous year, the Heads Up! Baseball Stars of 1990 was a 24-piece set which received rather wider distribution, but proved unpopular with collectors. On heavy cardboard, die-cut to approximately 5" x 6", these novelties featured only a head-and-cap photo of the player. Backs have the player's name and team, along with an adhesive strip and plastic suction cup which could be used to "hang" the player.

		MT	NR MT	EX
Complete Set (24):		7.50	5.50	3.00
Common Player:		.25	.20	.10
1	Tony Gwynn	.35	.25	.14
2	Will Clark	.50	.40	.20
3	Dwight Gooden	.25	.20	.10
4	Dennis Eckersley	.25	.20	.10
5	Ken Griffey, Jr.	2.00	1.50	.80
6	Craig Biggio	.25	.20	.10
7	Bret Saberhagen	.25	.20	.10
8	Bo Jackson	.40	.30	.15
9	Ryne Sandberg	1.00	.70	.40
10	Gregg Olson	.25	.20	.10
11	John Franco	.25	.20	.10
12	Rafael Palmeiro	.35	.25	.14
13	Gary Sheffield	.25	.20	.10
14	Mark McGwire	.35	.25	.14
15	Kevin Mitchell	.25	.20	.10
16	Jim Abbott	.35	.25	.14
17	Harold Reynolds	.25	.20	.10
18	Jose Canseco	.35	.25	.14
19	Don Mattingly	.60	.45	.25
20	Kirby Puckett	.35	.25	.14
21	Tom Gordon	.25	.20	.10
22	Craig Worthington	.25	.20	.10
23	Dwight Smith	.25	.20	.10
24	Jerome Walton	.25	.20	.10

1990 Topps Coins

Sixty of the game's top stars and promising rookies are featured in this fourth annual coin set. Fronts of the 1-1/2" diameter coins feature a player photo with a symbolic infield in front of and behind the photo. The player's name and team appear below. Most coins feature natural aluminum coloring on the rolled edges and on the back. Special coins of major award winners have different colors in the background and edges. Backs feature a coin number, minimal biographical data and a previous season career summary. Coins were sold three per pack which included an offer card for a coin holder and Topps magazine subscription offer.

		MT	NR MT	EX
Complete Set (60):		8.00	6.00	3.25
Common Player:		.10	.08	.04
1	Robin Yount	.40	.30	.15
2	Bret Saberhagen	.10	.08	.04
3	Gregg Olson	.10	.08	.04
4	Kirby Puckett	.20	.15	.08
5	George Bell	.10	.08	.04
6	Wade Boggs	.35	.25	.14
7	Jerry Browne	.10	.08	.04
8	Ellis Burks	.10	.08	.04
9	Ivan Calderon	.10	.08	.04
10	Tom Candiotti	.10	.08	.04
11	Alvin Davis	.10	.08	.04
12	Chil Davis	.15	.11	.06
13	Chuck Finley	.10	.08	.04
14	Gary Gaetti	.10	.08	.04
15	Tom Gordon	.10	.08	.04
16	Ken Griffey, Jr.	.60	.45	.25
17	Rickey Henderson	.20	.15	.08
18	Kent Hrbek	.15	.11	.06
19	Bo Jackson	.25	.20	.10
20	Carlos Martinez	.10	.08	.04
21	Don Mattingly	.35	.25	.14
22	Fred McGriff	.20	.15	.08
23	Paul Molitor	.20	.15	.08
24	Cal Ripken, Jr.	.35	.25	.14
25	Nolan Ryan	.60	.45	.25
26	Steve Sax	.10	.08	.04
27	Gary Sheffield	.15	.11	.06
28	Ruben Sierra	.15	.11	.06
29	Dave Stewart	.10	.08	.04
30	Mickey Tettleton	.10	.08	.04
31	Alan Trammell	.20	.15	.08
32	Lou Whitaker	.15	.11	.06
33	Kevin Mitchell	.10	.08	.04
34	Mark Davis	.10	.08	.04
35	Jerome Walton	.10	.08	.04
36	Tony Gwynn	.20	.15	.08
37	Roberto Alomar	.20	.15	.08
38	Tim Belcher	.10	.08	.04
39	Craig Biggio	.10	.08	.04
40	Barry Bonds	.25	.20	.10
41	Bobby Bonilla	.15	.11	.06
42	Joe Carter	.15	.11	.06
43	Will Clark	.25	.20	.10
44	Eric Davis	.15	.11	.06
45	Glenn Davis	.10	.08	.04
46	Sid Fernandez	.10	.08	.04
47	Pedro Guerrero	.10	.08	.04
48	Von Hayes	.10	.08	.04
49	Tom Herr	.10	.08	.04
50	Howard Johnson	.15	.11	.06
51	Barry Larkin	.15	.11	.06
52	Joe Magrane	.10	.08	.04
53	Dale Murphy	.20	.15	.08
54	Tim Raines	.15	.11	.06
55	Willie Randolph	.10	.08	.04
56	Ryne Sandberg	.35	.25	.14
57	Dwight Smith	.10	.08	.04
58	Lonnie Smith	.10	.08	.04
59	Robby Thompson	.15	.11	.06
60	Tim Wallach	.10	.08	.04

1990 Topps Senior League

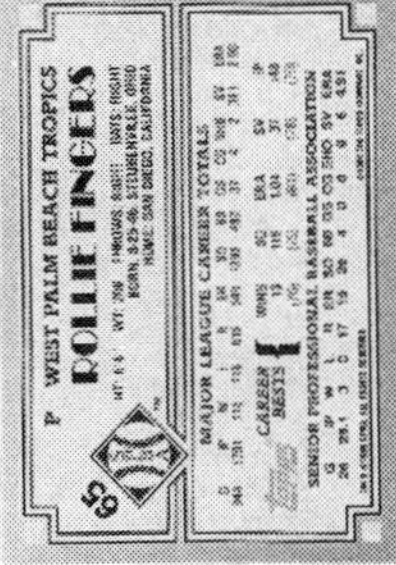

Topps was among several companies to produce a Senior League set in 1990. The set includes 132 cards and was sold as a boxed set. The card fronts have the Senior Baseball and Topps logo on top and the player's name and team logo on the bottom, with a woodgrain-like border surrounding the front photo. The backs of the card include traditional biographical information, plus career major league statistics, career ML bests and stats from any Senior League experience.

	MT	NR MT	EX
Complete Set:	9.00	6.75	3.50
Common Player:	.10	.08	.04

1	George Foster	.15	.11	.06
2	Dwight Lowry	.10	.08	.04
3	Bob Jones	.10	.08	.04
4	Clete Boyer	.10	.08	.04
5	Rafael Landestoy	.10	.08	.04
6	Bob Shirley	.10	.08	.04
7	Ivan Murrell	.10	.08	.04
8	Jerry White	.10	.08	.04
9	Steve Henderson	.10	.08	.04
10	Marty Castillo	.10	.08	.04
11	Bruce Kison	.10	.08	.04
12	George Hendrick	.10	.08	.04
13	Bernie Carbo	.10	.08	.04
14	Jerry Martin	.10	.08	.04
15	Al Hrabosky	.10	.08	.04
16	Luis Gomez	.10	.08	.04
17	Dick Drago	.10	.08	.04
18	Bobby Ramos	.10	.08	.04
19	Joe Pittman	.10	.08	.04
20	Ike Blessitt	.10	.08	.04
21	Bill Travers	.10	.08	.04
22	Dick Williams	.15	.11	.06
23	Randy Lerch	.10	.08	.04
24	Tom Spencer	.10	.08	.04
25	Graig Nettles	.15	.11	.06
26	Jim Gideon	.10	.08	.04
27	Al Bumbry	.10	.08	.04
28	Tom Murphy	.10	.08	.04
29	Rodney Scott	.10	.08	.04
30	Alan Bannister	.10	.08	.04
31	John D'Acquisto	.10	.08	.04
32	Bert Campaneris	.15	.11	.06
33	Bill Lee	.10	.08	.04
34	Jerry Grote	.10	.08	.04
35	Ken Reitz	.10	.08	.04
36	Al Oliver	.15	.11	.06
37	Tim Stoddard	.10	.08	.04
38	Lenny Randle	.10	.08	.04
39	Rick Manning	.10	.08	.04
40	Bobby Bonds	.15	.11	.06
41	Rick Wise	.10	.08	.04
42	Sal Butera	.10	.08	.04
43	Ed Figueroa	.10	.08	.04
44	Ron Washington	.10	.08	.04
45	Elias Sosa	.10	.08	.04
46	Dan Driessen	.10	.08	.04
47	Wayne Nordhagen	.10	.08	.04
48	Vida Blue	.15	.11	.06
49	Butch Hobson	.10	.08	.04
50	Randy Bass	.10	.08	.04
51	Paul Mirabella	.10	.08	.04
52	Steve Kemp	.10	.08	.04
53	Kim Allen	.10	.08	.04
54	Stan Cliburn	.10	.08	.04
55	Derrel Thomas	.10	.08	.04
56	Pete Falcone	.10	.08	.04
57	Willie Aikens	.10	.08	.04
58	Toby Harrah	.10	.08	.04
59	Bob Tolan	.10	.08	.04
60	Rick Waits	.10	.08	.04
61	Jim Morrison	.10	.08	.04
62	Stan Bahnsen	.10	.08	.04
63	Gene Richards	.10	.08	.04
64	Dave Cash	.10	.08	.04
65	Rollie Fingers	.50	.40	.20
66	Butch Benton	.10	.08	.04
67	Tim Ireland	.10	.08	.04
68	Rick Lysander	.10	.08	.04
69	Cesar Cedeno	.10	.08	.04
70	Jim Willoughby	.10	.08	.04
71	Bill Madlock	.15	.11	.06
72	Lee Lacy	.10	.08	.04
73	Milt Wilcox	.10	.08	.04
74	Ron Pruitt	.10	.08	.04
75	Wayne Krenchicki	.10	.08	.04
76	Earl Weaver	.25	.20	.10
77	Pedro Borbon	.10	.08	.04
78	Jose Cruz	.15	.11	.06
79	Steve Ontiveros	.10	.08	.04
80	Mike Easler	.10	.08	.04
81	Amos Otis	.10	.08	.04
82	Mickey Mahler	.10	.08	.04
83	Orlando Gonzalez	.10	.08	.04
84	Doug Simunic	.10	.08	.04
85	Felix Millan	.10	.08	.04
86	Garth Iorg	.10	.08	.04
87	Pete Broberg	.10	.08	.04
88	Roy Howell	.10	.08	.04
89	Dave LaRoche	.10	.08	.04
90	Jerry Manuel	.10	.08	.04
91	Tony Scott	.10	.08	.04
92	Larvell Blanks	.10	.08	.04
93	Joaquin Andujar	.10	.08	.04
94	Tito Landrum	.10	.08	.04
95	Joe Sambito	.10	.08	.04
96	Pat Dobson	.10	.08	.04
97	Dan Meyer	.10	.08	.04
98	Clint Hurdle	.10	.08	.04
99	Pete LaCock	.10	.08	.04
100	Bob Galasso	.10	.08	.04
101	Dave Kingman	.15	.11	.06
102	Jon Matlack	.10	.08	.04
103	Larry Harlow	.10	.08	.04
104	Rick Peterson	.10	.08	.04
105	Joe Hicks	.10	.08	.04
106	Bill Campbell	.10	.08	.04
107	Tom Paciorek	.10	.08	.04
108	Ray Burris	.10	.08	.04
109	Ken Landreaux	.10	.08	.04
110	Steve McCatty	.10	.08	.04
111	Ron LeFlore	.10	.08	.04
112	Joe Decker	.10	.08	.04
113	Leon Roberts	.10	.08	.04
114	Doug Corbett	.10	.08	.04
115	Mickey Rivers	.10	.08	.04
116	Dock Ellis	.10	.08	.04
117	Ron Jackson	.10	.08	.04
118	Bob Molinaro	.10	.08	.04
119	Fergie Jenkins	.50	.40	.20
120	U.L. Washington	.10	.08	.04
121	Roy Thomas	.10	.08	.04
122	Hal McRae	.20	.15	.08
123	Juan Eichelberger	.10	.08	.04
124	Gary Rajsich	.10	.08	.04
125	Dennis Leonard	.10	.08	.04
126	Walt Williams	.10	.08	.04
127	Rennie Stennett	.10	.08	.04
128	Jim Bibby	.10	.08	.04
129	Dyar Miller	.10	.08	.04
130	Luis Pujols	.10	.08	.04
131	Juan Beniquez	.10	.08	.04
132	Checklist	.10	.08	.04

1991 Topps

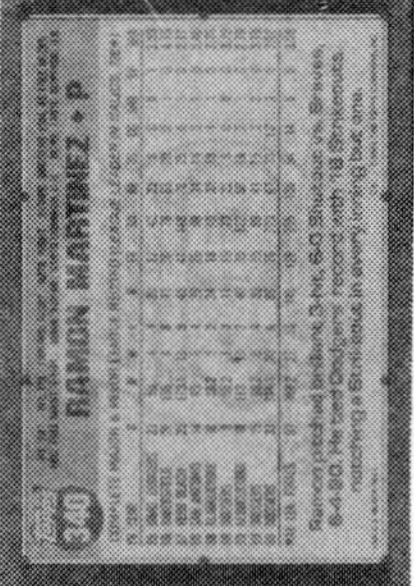

Topps celebrated its 40th anniversary in 1991 with the biggest promotional campaign in baseball card history. More than 300,000 vintage Topps cards (or certificates which can be redeemed for valuable older cards) produced from 1952 to present were randomly inserted in packs. Also a grand prize winner will receive one complete set from each year, and others will receive a single set from 1952-present. The 1991 Topps card fronts feature the "Topps 40 Years of Baseball" logo in the upper left corner. Card borders frame the player photos. All players of the same team have cards with the same frame/border colors. Both action and posed shots appear in full-color on the card fronts. The flip sides are printed horizontally and feature complete statistics. Record Breakers and other special cards were once again included in the set. The cards measure 2-1/2" by 3-1/2". Several cards feature horizontal fronts. 6,313 forms of this set were released with gold "Operation Desert Shield" stamps on the fronts of the cards. The cards were released to U.S. troops serving in the Persian Gulf. Due to scarcity, these cards are quite valuable. Complete "Desert Shield" sets list for around $2,000.

	MT	NR MT	EX
Complete Set (792):	18.00	13.50	7.25
Common Player:	.03	.02	.01

1	Nolan Ryan	.30	.25	.12
2	George Brett (Record Breaker)	.12	.09	.05
3	Carlton Fisk (Record Breaker)	.08	.06	.03
4	Kevin Maas (Record Breaker)	.10	.08	.04
5	Cal Ripken, Jr. (Record Breaker)	.10	.08	.04
6	Nolan Ryan (Record Breaker)	.25	.20	.10
7	Ryne Sandberg (Record Breaker)	.15	.11	.06
8	Bobby Thigpen (Record Breaker)	.08	.06	.03
9	Darrin Fletcher (FC)	.10	.08	.04
10	Gregg Olson	.08	.06	.03
11	Roberto Kelly	.08	.06	.03
12	Paul Assenmacher	.04	.03	.02
13	Mariano Duncan	.06	.05	.02
14	Dennis Lamp	.03	.02	.01
15	Von Hayes	.08	.06	.03
16	Mike Heath	.04	.03	.02
17	Jeff Brantley	.06	.05	.02
18	Nelson Liriano	.03	.02	.01
19	Jeff Robinson	.04	.03	.02
20	Pedro Guerrero	.08	.06	.03
21	Joe M. Morgan	.03	.02	.01
22	Storm Davis	.06	.05	.02
23	Jim Gantner	.04	.03	.02
24	Dave Martinez	.05	.04	.02
25	Tim Belcher	.08	.06	.03
26	Luis Sojo	.06	.05	.02
27	Bobby Witt	.08	.06	.03
28	Alvaro Espinoza	.05	.04	.02
29	Bob Walk	.03	.02	.01
30	Gregg Jefferies	.15	.11	.06
31	*Colby Ward* (FC)	.15	.11	.06
32	*Mike Simms* (FC)	.20	.15	.08
33	Barry Jones	.05	.04	.02
34	Atlee Hammaker	.03	.02	.01
35	Greg Maddux	.08	.06	.03
36	Donnie Hill	.03	.02	.01
37	Tom Bolton	.05	.04	.02
38	Scott Bradley	.03	.02	.01
39	*Jim Neidlinger* (FC)	.15	.11	.06
40	Kevin Mitchell	.20	.15	.08
41	Ken Dayley	.04	.03	.02
42	*Chris Hoiles* (FC)	.20	.15	.08
43	Roger McDowell	.06	.05	.02
44	Mike Felder	.04	.03	.02
45	Chris Sabo	.10	.08	.04
46	Tim Drummond	.06	.05	.02
47	Brook Jacoby	.06	.05	.02
48	Dennis Boyd	.05	.04	.02
49a	Pat Borders (40 stolen bases in Kinston 1986)	.20	.15	.08
49b	Pat Borders (0 stolen bases in Kinston 1986)	.15	.11	.06
50	Bob Welch	.08	.06	.03
51	Art Howe	.03	.02	.01
52	*Francisco Oliveras* (FC)	.10	.08	.04
53	Mike Sharperson	.06	.05	.02
54	Gary Mielke	.05	.04	.02
55	Jeffrey Leonard	.05	.04	.02
56	Jeff Parrett	.04	.03	.02
57	Jack Howell	.04	.03	.02
58	Mel Stottlemyre	.08	.06	.03
59	Eric Yelding	.06	.05	.02
60	Frank Viola	.12	.09	.05
61	Stan Javier	.04	.03	.02
62	Lee Guetterman	.03	.02	.01
63	Milt Thompson	.04	.03	.02
64	Tom Herr	.05	.04	.02
65	Bruce Hurst	.06	.05	.02
66	Terry Kennedy	.03	.02	.01
67	Rick Honeycutt	.03	.02	.01
68	Gary Sheffield	.15	.11	.06
69	Steve Wilson	.06	.05	.02
70	Ellis Burks	.15	.11	.06
71	Jim Acker	.03	.02	.01
72	Junior Ortiz	.03	.02	.01
73	Craig Worthington	.06	.05	.02
74	*Shane Andrews* (#1 Draft Pick)	.20	.15	.08
75	Jack Morris	.08	.06	.03
76	Jerry Browne	.05	.04	.02
77	Drew Hall	.03	.02	.01
78	Geno Petralli	.03	.02	.01
79	Frank Thomas	1.00	.70	.40
80a	Fernando Valenzuela (no diamond after 104 ER in 1990)	.25	.20	.10
80b	Fernando Valenzuela (diamond after 104 ER in 1990)	.12	.09	.05
81	Cito Gaston	.03	.02	.01
82	Tom Glavine	.05	.04	.02
83	Daryl Boston	.03	.02	.01
84	Bob McClure	.03	.02	.01
85	Jesse Barfield	.08	.06	.03
86	Les Lancaster	.04	.03	.02
87	Tracy Jones	.03	.02	.01
88	Bob Tewksbury	.04	.03	.02
89	Darren Daulton	.06	.05	.02
90	Danny Tartabull	.08	.06	.03
91	*Greg Colbrunn* (FC) (Future Star)	.10	.08	.04
92	Danny Jackson	.06	.05	.02
93	Ivan Calderon	.08	.06	.03
94	John Dopson	.05	.04	.02
95	Paul Molitor	.10	.08	.04
96	Trevor Wilson	.04	.03	.02
97a	Brady Anderson (3H, 2RBI in Sept. scoreboard)	.04	.03	.02
97b	Brady Anderson (14H, 3 RBI in Sept. scoreboard)	.08	.06	.03
98	Sergio Valdez	.05	.04	.02
99	Chris Gwynn	.05	.04	.02
100a	Don Mattingly (10 hits 1990)	.60	.45	.25
100b	Don Mattingly (101 hits in 1990)	.10	.08	.04
101	Rob Ducey	.04	.03	.02
102	Gene Larkin	.06	.05	.02
103	*Tim Costo* (#1 Draft Pick)	.15	.11	.06
104	Don Robinson	.04	.03	.02
105	Kevin McReynolds	.05	.04	.02
106	Ed Nunez	.03	.02	.01
107	Luis Polonia	.04	.03	.02
108	Matt Young	.04	.03	.02
109	Greg Riddoch	.03	.02	.01
110	Tom Henke	.06	.05	.02
111	Andres Thomas	.03	.02	.01
112	Frank DiPino	.03	.02	.01
113	*Carl Everett* (#1 Draft Pick)	.20	.15	.08
114	*Lance Dickson* (FC) (Future Star)	.10	.08	.04
115	Hubie Brooks	.08	.06	.03
116	Mark Davis	.05	.04	.02
117	Dion James	.03	.02	.01
118	*Tom Edens* (FC)	.10	.08	.04
119	Carl Nichols (FC)	.05	.04	.02
120	Joe Carter	.08	.06	.03
121	Eric King	.05	.04	.02
122	Paul O'Neill	.06	.05	.02
123	Greg Harris	.05	.04	.02
124	Randy Bush	.04	.03	.02
125	Steve Bedrosian	.06	.05	.02
126	*Bernard Gilkey* (FC)	.20	.15	.08
127	Joe Price	.03	.02	.01
128	*Travis Fryman*	.60	.45	.25
129	Mark Eichhorn	.03	.02	.01
130	Ozzie Smith	.08	.06	.03
131a	Checklist 1 (Phil Bradley #727)	.03	.02	.01
131b	Checklist 1 (Phil Bradley #717)	.03	.02	.01
132	Jamie Quirk	.03	.02	.01
133	Greg Briley	.08	.06	.03
134	Kevin Elster	.04	.03	.02
135	Jerome Walton	.08	.06	.03
136	Dave Schmidt	.03	.02	.01
137	Randy Ready	.03	.02	.01
138	Jamie Moyer	.04	.03	.02
139	Jeff Treadway	.05	.04	.02
140	Fred McGriff	.10	.08	.04
141	Nick Leyva	.03	.02	.01

142 Curtis Wilkerson .04 .03 .02
143 John Smiley .04 .03 .02
144 Dave Henderson .06 .05 .02
145 Lou Whitaker .08 .06 .03
146 Dan Plesac .06 .05 .02
147 *Carlos Baerga* .20 .15 .08
148 Rey Palacios .04 .03 .02
149 *Al Osuna* (FC) .15 .11 .06
150 Cal Ripken, Jr. .15 .11 .06
151 Tom Browning .06 .05 .02
152 Mickey Hatcher .04 .03 .02
153 Bryan Harvey .06 .05 .02
154 Jay Buhner .06 .05 .02
155a Dwight Evans (diamond after 162 game 1982)
.08 .06 .03
155b Dwight Evans (no diamond after 162 G 1982)
.12 .09 .05
156 Carlos Martinez .06 .05 .02
157 John Smoltz .08 .06 .03
158 Jose Uribe .04 .03 .02
159 Joe Boever .03 .02 .01
160 Vince Coleman .08 .06 .03
161 Tim Leary .04 .03 .02
162 *Ozzie Canseco* (FC) .15 .11 .06
163 Dave Johnson .04 .03 .02
164 Edgar Diaz .05 .04 .02
165 Sandy Alomar .15 .11 .06
166 Harold Baines .08 .06 .03
167a *Randy Tomlin* (FC) ("Harriburg" 1989-90)
.08 .06 .03
167b Randy Tomlin ("Harrisburg" 1989-90)
.15 .11 .06
168 John Olerud .40 .30 .15
169 Luis Aquino .04 .03 .02
170 Carlton Fisk .10 .08 .04
171 Tony LaRussa .04 .03 .02
172 Pete Incaviglia .06 .05 .02
173 Jason Grimsley .06 .05 .02
174 Ken Caminiti .05 .04 .02
175 Jack Armstrong .08 .06 .03
176 John Orton (FC) .06 .05 .02
177 *Reggie Harris* (FC) .15 .11 .06
178 Dave Valle .04 .03 .02
179 Pete Harnisch .06 .05 .02
180 Tony Gwynn .12 .09 .05
181 Duane Ward .04 .03 .02
182 Junior Noboa .04 .03 .02
183 Clay Parker .04 .03 .02
184 Gary Green .10 .08 .04
185 Joe Magrane .06 .05 .02
186 Rod Booker .03 .02 .01
187 Greg Cadaret .03 .02 .01
188 Damon Berryhill .06 .05 .02
189 *Daryl Irvine* (FC) .15 .11 .06
190 Matt Williams .15 .11 .06
191 *Willie Blair* .10 .08 .04
192 Rob Deer .06 .05 .02
193 Felix Fermin .03 .02 .01
194 Xavier Hernandez (FC) .08 .06 .03
195 Wally Joyner .10 .08 .04
196 *Jim Vatcher* (FC) .12 .09 .05
197 *Chris Nabholz* (FC) .20 .15 .08
198 R.J. Reynolds .04 .03 .02
199 Mike Hartley (FC) .15 .11 .06
200 Darryl Strawberry .15 .11 .06
201 Tom Kelly .03 .02 .01
202 *Jim Leyritz* .12 .09 .05
203 Gene Harris .05 .04 .02
204 Herm Winningham .04 .03 .02
205 *Mike Perez* (FC) .15 .11 .06
206 Carlos Quintana .08 .06 .03
207 Gary Wayne .05 .04 .02
208 Willie Wilson .06 .05 .02
209 Ken Howell .05 .04 .02
210 Lance Parrish .08 .06 .03
211 *Brian Barnes* (FC) (Future Star) .15 .11 .06
212 Steve Finley .06 .05 .02
213 Frank Wills .06 .05 .02
214 Joe Girardi .06 .05 .02
215 Dave Smith .06 .05 .02
216 Greg Gagne .04 .03 .02
217 Chris Bosio .05 .04 .02
218 *Rick Parker* .03 .02 .01
219 Jack McDowell .06 .05 .02
220 Tim Wallach .08 .06 .03
221 Don Slaught .04 .03 .02
222 *Brian McRae* (FC) .25 .20 .10
223 Allan Anderson .04 .03 .02
224 Juan Gonzalez .60 .45 .25
225 Randy Johnson .06 .05 .02
226 Alfredo Griffin .04 .03 .02
227 Steve Avery .15 .11 .06
228 Rex Hudler .04 .03 .02
229 Rance Mulliniks .03 .02 .01
230 Sid Fernandez .08 .06 .03
231 Doug Rader .03 .02 .01
232 Jose DeJesus .08 .06 .03
233 Al Leiter .03 .02 .01
234 *Scott Erickson* .12 .09 .05
235 Dave Parker .10 .08 .04
236a Frank Tanana (no diamond after 269 SO 1975)
.06 .05 .02
236b Frank Tanana (diamond after 269 SO 1975)
.12 .09 .05
237 Rick Cerone .03 .02 .01
238 Mike Dunne .03 .02 .01
239 *Darren Lewis* (FC) .25 .20 .10
240 Mike Scott .08 .06 .03
241 Dave Clark .04 .03 .02
242 Mike LaCoss .03 .02 .01
243 Lance Johnson .06 .05 .02
244 Mike Jeffcoat .03 .02 .01
245 Kal Daniels .08 .06 .03
246 Kevin Wickander .05 .04 .02
247 Jody Reed .08 .06 .03
248 Tom Gordon .08 .06 .03
249 Bob Melvin .03 .02 .01
250 Dennis Eckersley .10 .08 .04

251 Mark Lemke .05 .04 .02
252 *Mel Rojas* (FC) .10 .08 .04
253 Garry Templeton .04 .03 .02
254 *Shawn Boskie* .15 .11 .06
255 Brian Downing .05 .04 .02
256 Greg Hibbard .08 .06 .03
257 Tom O'Malley .03 .02 .01
258 Chris Hammond (FC) .15 .11 .06
259 Hensley Meulens .08 .06 .03
260 Harold Reynolds .06 .05 .02
261 Bud Harrelson .03 .02 .01
262 Tim Jones .04 .03 .02
263 Checklist 2 .03 .02 .01
264 *Dave Hollins* .25 .20 .10
265 Mark Gubicza .06 .05 .02
266 Carmen Castillo .03 .02 .01
267 Mark Knudson .03 .02 .01
268 Tom Brookens .04 .03 .02
269 Joe Hesketh .03 .02 .01
270a Mark McGwire (1987 SLG .618) .20 .15 .08
270b Mark McGwire (1987 SLG 618) .20 .15 .08
271 *Omar Olivares* (FC) .15 .11 .06
272 Jeff King .06 .05 .02
273 Johnny Ray .05 .04 .02
274 Ken Williams .03 .02 .01
275 Alan Trammell .10 .08 .04
276 Bill Swift .05 .04 .02
277 Scott Coolbaugh .06 .05 .02
278 *Alex Fernandez* (FC) (#1 Draft Pick)
.60 .45 .25
279a Jose Gonzalez (photo of Billy Bean, left-handed batter) .20 .15 .08
279b Jose Gonzalez (correct photo, right-handed batter)
.12 .09 .05
280 Bret Saberhagen .08 .06 .03
281 Larry Sheets .04 .03 .02
282 Don Carman .04 .03 .02
283 Marquis Grissom .10 .08 .04
284 Bill Spiers .06 .05 .02
285 Jim Abbott .10 .08 .04
286 Ken Oberkfell .04 .03 .02
287 Mark Grant .03 .02 .01
288 Derrick May (FC) .25 .20 .10
289 Tim Birtsas .03 .02 .01
290 Steve Sax .08 .06 .03
291 John Wathan .03 .02 .01
292 Bud Black .04 .03 .02
293 Jay Bell .06 .05 .02
294 Mike Moore .06 .05 .02
295 Rafael Palmeiro .08 .06 .03
296 Mark Williamson .04 .03 .02
297 Manny Lee .04 .03 .02
298 Omar Vizquel .04 .03 .02
299 *Scott Radinsky* .15 .11 .06
300 Kirby Puckett .20 .15 .08
301 Steve Farr .04 .03 .02
302 Tim Teufel .03 .02 .01
303 Mike Boddicker .06 .05 .02
304 Kevin Reimer (FC) .10 .08 .04
305 Mike Scioscia .06 .05 .02
306a Lonnie Smith (136 G 1990) .06 .05 .02
306b Lonnie Smith (135 G 1990) .08 .06 .03
307 Andy Benes .08 .06 .03
308 Tom Pagnozzi .04 .03 .02
309 Norm Charlton .08 .06 .03
310 Gary Carter .08 .06 .03
311 Jeff Pico .03 .02 .01
312 Charlie Hayes .06 .05 .02
313 Ron Robinson .06 .05 .02
314 Gary Pettis .04 .03 .02
315 Roberto Alomar .25 .20 .10
316 Gene Nelson .03 .02 .01
317 Mike Fitzgerald .03 .02 .01
318 Rick Aguilera .06 .05 .02
319 Jeff McKnight (FC) .06 .05 .02
320 Tony Fernandez .08 .06 .03
321 Bob Rodgers .03 .02 .01
322 *Terry Shumpert* .15 .11 .06
323 Cory Snyder .08 .06 .03
324a Ron Kittle ("6 Home Runs" in career summary)
.08 .06 .03
324b Ron Kittle ("7 Home Runs" in career summary)
.08 .06 .03
325 Brett Butler .06 .05 .02
326 Ken Patterson .04 .03 .02
327 Ron Hassey .03 .02 .01
328 Walt Terrell .04 .03 .02
329 Dave Justice .30 .25 .12
330 Dwight Gooden .15 .11 .06
331 Eric Anthony .10 .08 .04
332 Kenny Rogers .06 .05 .02
333 *Chipper Jones* (#1 Draft Pick) 1.00 .70 .40
334 Todd Benzinger .05 .04 .02
335 Mitch Williams .08 .06 .03
336 Matt Nokes .06 .05 .02
337a Keith Comstock (Mariners logo) .03 .02 .01
337b Keith Comstock (Cubs logo) .10 .08 .04
338 Luis Rivera .04 .03 .02
339 Larry Walker .15 .11 .06
340 Ramon Martinez .08 .06 .03
341 John Moses .03 .02 .01
342 *Mickey Morandini* .10 .08 .04
343 Jose Oquendo .04 .03 .02
344 Jeff Russell .06 .05 .02
345 Len Dykstra .10 .07 .04
346 Jesse Orosco .04 .03 .02
347 Greg Vaughn .10 .08 .04
348 Todd Stottlemyre .06 .05 .02
349 Dave Gallagher .04 .03 .02
350 Glenn Davis .12 .09 .05
351 Joe Torre .03 .02 .01
352 Frank White .06 .05 .02
353 Tony Castillo .05 .04 .02
354 Sid Bream .05 .04 .02
355 Chili Davis .06 .05 .02
356 Mike Marshall .06 .05 .02
357 Jack Savage .10 .08 .04
358 Mark Parent .03 .02 .01

359 Chuck Cary .04 .03 .02
360 Tim Raines .15 .11 .06
361 Scott Garrelts .05 .04 .02
362 *Hector Villanueva* .15 .11 .06
363 Rick Mahler .04 .03 .02
364 Dan Pasqua .06 .05 .02
365 Mike Schooler .06 .05 .02
366a Checklist 3 (Carl Nichols #19) .03 .02 .01
366b Checklist 3 (Carl Nichols #119) .03 .02 .01
367 *Dave Walsh* (FC) .10 .08 .04
368 Felix Jose .06 .05 .02
369 Steve Searcy .06 .05 .02
370 Kelly Gruber .10 .08 .04
371 Jeff Montgomery .06 .05 .02
372 Spike Owen .05 .04 .02
373 Darrin Jackson .04 .03 .02
374 *Larry Casian* .15 .11 .06
375 Tony Pena .06 .05 .02
376 Mike Harkey .08 .06 .03
377 Rene Gonzales .03 .02 .01
378a *Wilson Alvarez* (FC) (no 1989 Port Charlotte stats) .20 .15 .08
378b *Wilson Alvarez* (FC) (1989 Port Charlotte stats)
.20 .15 .08
379 Randy Velarde .04 .03 .02
380 Willie McGee .08 .06 .03
381 Jim Leyland .03 .02 .01
382 Mackey Sasser .05 .04 .02
383 Pete Smith .06 .05 .02
384 Gerald Perry .05 .04 .02
385 Mickey Tettleton .05 .04 .02
386 Cecil Fielder (All-Star) .10 .08 .04
387 Julio Franco (All-Star) .08 .06 .03
388 Kelly Gruber (All-Star) .08 .06 .03
389 Alan Trammell (All-Star) .06 .05 .02
390 Jose Canseco (All-Star) .10 .08 .04
391 Rickey Henderson (All-Star) .10 .08 .04
392 Ken Griffey, Jr. (All-Star) .30 .25 .12
393 Carlton Fisk (All-Star) .08 .06 .03
394 Bob Welch (All-Star) .06 .05 .02
395 Chuck Finley (All-Star) .06 .05 .02
396 Bobby Thigpen (All-Star) .08 .06 .03
397 Eddie Murray (All-Star) .08 .06 .03
398 Ryne Sandberg (All-Star) .10 .08 .04
399 Matt Williams (All-Star) .08 .06 .03
400 Barry Larkin (All-Star) .08 .06 .03
401 Barry Bonds (All-Star) .15 .11 .06
402 Darryl Strawberry (All-Star) .10 .08 .04
403 Bobby Bonilla (All-Star) .10 .08 .04
404 Mike Scoscia (All-Star) .06 .05 .02
405 Doug Drabek (All-Star) .08 .06 .03
406 Frank Viola (All-Star) .08 .06 .03
407 John Franco (All-Star) .06 .05 .02
408 Ernie Riles .04 .03 .02
409 Mike Stanley .03 .02 .01
410 Dave Righetti .08 .06 .03
411 Lance Blankenship .04 .03 .02
412 Dave Bergman .03 .02 .01
413 Terry Mulholland .06 .05 .02
414 Sammy Sosa .15 .11 .06
415 Rick Sutcliffe .08 .06 .03
416 Randy Milligan .06 .05 .02
417 Bill Krueger .03 .02 .01
418 Nick Esasky .06 .05 .02
419 Jeff Reed .03 .02 .01
420 Bobby Thigpen .08 .06 .03
421 Alex Cole (FC) .20 .15 .08
422 Rick Rueschel .06 .05 .02
423 Rafael Ramirez .04 .03 .02
424 Calvin Schiraldi .03 .02 .01
425 Andy Van Slyke .08 .06 .03
426 *Joe Grahe* (FC) .15 .11 .06
427 Rick Dempsey .03 .02 .01
428 *John Barfield* (FC) .10 .08 .04
429 Stump Merrill .03 .02 .01
430 Gary Gaetti .08 .06 .03
431 Paul Gibson .03 .02 .01
432 Delino DeShields .15 .11 .06
433 Pat Tabler .04 .03 .02
434 Julio Machado (FC) .10 .08 .04
435 Kevin Maas .08 .06 .03
436 Scott Bankhead .05 .04 .02
437 Doug Dascenzo .04 .03 .02
438 Vicente Palacios .05 .04 .02
439 Dickie Thon .03 .02 .01
440 George Bell .08 .06 .03
441 Zane Smith .04 .03 .02
442 Charlie O'Brien .04 .03 .02
443 Jeff Innis .05 .04 .02
444 Glenn Braggs .05 .04 .02
445 Greg Swindell .06 .05 .02
446 *Craig Grebeck* (FC) .08 .06 .03
447 John Burkett .12 .09 .05
448 Craig Lefferts .05 .04 .02
449 Juan Berenguer .03 .02 .01
450 Wade Boggs .12 .09 .05
451 Neal Heaton .05 .04 .02
452 Bill Schroeder .03 .02 .01
453 Lenny Harris .05 .04 .02
454a Kevin Appier (no 1990 Omaha stats)
.08 .06 .03
454b Kevin Appier (1990 Omaha stats) .08 .06 .03
455 Walt Weiss .06 .05 .02
456 Charlie Leibrandt .05 .04 .02
457 *Todd Hundley* .10 .08 .04
458 Brian Holman .06 .05 .02
459 Tom Trebelhorn .03 .02 .01
460 Dave Steib .08 .06 .03
461 Robin Ventura .15 .11 .06
462 Steve Frey .06 .05 .02
463 Dwight Smith .06 .05 .02
464 Steve Buechele .04 .03 .02
465 Ken Griffey .05 .04 .02
466 Charles Nagy (FC) .10 .08 .04
467 Dennis Cook .06 .05 .02
468 Tim Hulett .04 .03 .02
469 Chet Lemon .05 .04 .02
470 Howard Johnson .07 .05 .03

471	*Mike Lieberthal* (#1 Draft Pick)	.20	.15	.08
472	Kirt Manwaring	.05	.04	.02
473	Curt Young	.04	.03	.02
474	*Phil Plantier* (FC)	.50	.40	.20
475	Teddy Higuera	.08	.06	.03
476	Glenn Wilson	.05	.04	.02
477	Mike Fetters	.06	.05	.02
478	Kurt Stillwell	.05	.04	.02
479	Bob Patterson	.03	.02	.01
480	Dave Magadan	.10	.08	.04
481	Eddie Whitson	.05	.04	.02
482	Tino Martinez	.10	.08	.04
483	Mike Aldrete	.04	.03	.02
484	Dave LaPoint	.04	.03	.02
485	Terry Pendleton	.06	.05	.02
486	Tommy Greene (FC)	.10	.08	.04
487	Rafael Belliard	.03	.02	.01
488	Jeff Manto (FC)	.15	.11	.06
489	Bobby Valentine	.03	.02	.01
490	Kirk Gibson	.08	.06	.03
491	*Kurt Miller* (#1 Draft Pick)	.30	.25	.12
492	Ernie Whitt	.05	.04	.02
493	Jose Rijo	.08	.06	.03
494	Chris James	.06	.05	.02
495	Charlie Hough	.04	.03	.02
496	Marty Barrett	.05	.04	.02
497	Ben McDonald	.12	.09	.05
498	Mark Salas	.03	.02	.01
499	Melido Perez	.06	.05	.02
500	Will Clark	.20	.15	.08
501	Mike Bielecki	.05	.04	.02
502	Carney Lansford	.06	.05	.02
503	Roy Smith	.04	.03	.02
504	*Julio Valera* (FC)	.10	.08	.04
505	Chuck Finley	.08	.06	.03
506	Darnell Coles	.04	.03	.02
507	Steve Jeltz	.03	.02	.01
508	*Mike York* (FC)	.15	.11	.06
509	Glenallen Hill	.06	.05	.02
510	John Franco	.08	.06	.03
511	Steve Balboni	.03	.02	.01
512	Jose Mesa (FC)	.05	.04	.02
513	Jerald Clark	.05	.04	.02
514	Mike Stanton	.08	.06	.03
515	Alvin Davis	.08	.06	.03
516	*Karl Rhodes* (FC)	.10	.08	.04
517	Joe Oliver	.06	.05	.02
518	Cris Carpenter	.05	.04	.02
519	Sparky Anderson	.04	.03	.02
520	Mark Grace	.10	.08	.04
521	Joe Orsulak	.05	.04	.02
522	Stan Belinda	.06	.05	.02
523	*Rodney McCray* (FC)	.08	.06	.03
524	Darrel Akerfelds	.04	.03	.02
525	Willie Randolph	.06	.05	.02
526a	Moises Alou (FC) (37 R 1990 Pirates)	.30	.25	.12
526b	Moises Alou (FC) (0 R 1990 Pirates)	.30	.25	.12
527a	Checklist 4 (Kevin McReynolds #719)	.03	.02	.01
527b	Checklist 4 (Kevin McReynolds #105)	.03	.02	.01
528	Denny Martinez	.06	.05	.02
529	*Mark Newfield* (#1 Draft Pick)	.40	.30	.15
530	Roger Clemens	.20	.15	.08
531	*Dave Rhode* (FC)	.15	.11	.06
532	Kirk McCaskill	.06	.05	.02
533	Oddibe McDowell	.05	.04	.02
534	Mike Jackson	.04	.03	.02
535	Ruben Sierra	.15	.11	.06
536	Mike Witt	.04	.03	.02
537	Jose Lind	.05	.04	.02
538	Bip Roberts	.05	.04	.02
539	Scott Terry	.03	.02	.01
540	George Brett	.15	.11	.06
541	Domingo Ramos	.03	.02	.01
542	Rob Murphy	.03	.02	.01
543	Junior Felix	.08	.06	.03
544	Alejandro Pena	.03	.02	.01
545	Dale Murphy	.10	.08	.04
546	Jeff Ballard	.05	.04	.02
547	Mike Pagliarulo	.04	.03	.02
548	Jaime Navarro	.10	.08	.04
549	John McNamara	.03	.02	.01
550	Eric Davis	.15	.11	.06
551	Bob Kipper	.03	.02	.01
552	Jeff Hamilton	.04	.03	.02
553	*Joe Klink*	.10	.08	.04
554	Brian Harper	.06	.05	.02
555	*Turner Ward* (FC)	.10	.08	.04
556	Gary Ward	.04	.03	.02
557	Wally Whitehurst	.06	.05	.02
558	Otis Nixon	.03	.02	.01
559	Adam Peterson	.06	.05	.02
560	Greg Smith (FC)	.15	.11	.06
561	Tim McIntosh (FC) (Future Star)	.15	.11	.06
562	Jeff Kunkel	.03	.02	.01
563	*Brent Knackert*	.10	.08	.04
564	Dante Bichette	.08	.06	.03
565	Craig Biggio	.08	.06	.03
566	*Craig Wilson* (FC)	.15	.11	.06
567	Dwayne Henry	.03	.02	.01
568	Ron Karkovice	.04	.03	.02
569	Curt Schilling	.05	.04	.02
570	Barry Bonds	.30	.25	.12
571	Pat Combs	.08	.06	.03
572	Dave Anderson	.03	.02	.01
573	*Rich Rodriguez* (FC)	.15	.11	.06
574	John Marzano	.04	.03	.02
575	Robin Yount	.15	.11	.06
576	Jeff Kaiser (FC)	.10	.08	.04
577	Bill Doran	.06	.05	.02
578	Dave West	.06	.05	.02
579	Roger Craig	.03	.02	.01
580	Dave Stewart	.12	.09	.05
581	Luis Quinones	.03	.02	.01
582	Marty Clary	.03	.02	.01
583	Tony Phillips	.04	.03	.02
584	Kevin Brown	.06	.05	.02
585	Pete O'Brien	.04	.03	.02
586	Fred Lynn	.05	.04	.02
587	Jose Offerman (FC) (Future Star)	.10	.08	.04
588a	*Mark Whiten* (FC) (hand inside left border)	.30	.25	.12
588b	*Mark Whiten* (FC) (hand over left border)	.30	.25	.12
589	*Scott Ruskin*	.10	.08	.04
590	Eddie Murray	.12	.09	.05
591	Ken Hill	.05	.04	.02
592	B.J. Surhoff	.06	.05	.02
593a	*Mike Walker* (FC) (No 1990 Canton-Akron stats)	.15	.11	.06
593b	*Mike Walker* (FC) (1990 Canton-Akron stats)	.15	.11	.06
594	*Rich Garces* (FC) (Future Star)	.15	.11	.06
595	Bill Landrum	.05	.04	.02
596	*Ronnie Walden* (FC) (#1 Draft Pick)	.10	.08	.04
597	Jerry Don Gleaton	.03	.02	.01
598	Sam Horn	.05	.04	.02
599a	Greg Myers (no 1990 Syracuse stats)	.04	.03	.02
599b	Greg Myers (1990 Syracuse stats)	.04	.03	.02
600	Bo Jackson	.20	.15	.08
601	Bob Ojeda	.04	.03	.02
602	Casey Candaele	.04	.03	.02
603a	*Wes Chamberlain* (FC) (photo of Louie Meadows, no bat)	.50	.40	.20
603b	*Wes Chamberlain* (FC) (correct photo, holding bat)	.15	.11	.06
604	Billy Hatcher	.05	.04	.02
605	Jeff Reardon	.08	.06	.03
606	Jim Gott	.04	.03	.02
607	Edgar Martinez	.06	.05	.02
608	Todd Burns	.03	.02	.01
609	Jeff Torborg	.03	.02	.01
610	Andres Galarraga	.08	.06	.03
611	Dave Eiland	.04	.03	.02
612	Steve Lyons	.04	.03	.02
613	Eric Show	.04	.03	.02
614	Luis Salazar	.04	.03	.02
615	Bert Blyleven	.08	.06	.03
616	Todd Zeile	.15	.11	.06
617	Bill Wegman	.04	.03	.02
618	Sil Campusano	.04	.03	.02
619	David Wells	.04	.03	.02
620	Ozzie Guillen	.08	.06	.03
621	Ted Power	.03	.02	.01
622	Jack Daugherty	.05	.04	.02
623	Jeff Blauser	.04	.03	.02
624	Tom Candiotti	.04	.03	.02
625	Terry Steinbach	.06	.05	.02
626	Gerald Young	.03	.02	.01
627	*Tim Layana*	.15	.11	.06
628	Greg Litton	.05	.04	.02
629	Wes Gardner	.04	.03	.02
630	Dave Winfield	.10	.08	.04
631	Mike Morgan	.04	.03	.02
632	Lloyd Moseby	.06	.05	.02
633	Kevin Tapani	.10	.08	.04
634	Henry Cotto	.03	.02	.01
635	Andy Hawkins	.04	.03	.02
636	*Geronimo Pena* (FC)	.10	.08	.04
637	Bruce Ruffin	.04	.03	.02
638	Mike Macfarlane	.04	.03	.02
639	Frank Robinson	.05	.04	.02
640	Andre Dawson	.10	.08	.04
641	Mike Henneman	.06	.05	.02
642	Hal Morris	.15	.11	.06
643	Jim Presley	.06	.05	.02
644	Chuck Crim	.04	.03	.02
645	Juan Samuel	.06	.05	.02
646	*Andujar Cedeno* (FC)	.20	.15	.08
647	Mark Portugal	.04	.03	.02
648	Lee Stevens (FC)	.15	.11	.06
649	*Bill Sampen*	.15	.11	.06
650	Jack Clark	.08	.06	.03
651	*Alan Mills*	.12	.09	.05
652	Kevin Romine	.03	.02	.01
653	*Anthony Telford* (FC)	.20	.15	.08
654	Paul Sorrento (FC)	.15	.11	.06
655	Erik Hanson	.08	.06	.03
656a	Checklist 5 (Vincente Palacios #348)	.03	.02	.01
656b	Checklist 5 (Vincente Palacios #438)	.03	.02	.01
657	Mike Kingery	.03	.02	.01
658	*Scott Aldred* (FC)	.12	.09	.05
659	*Oscar Azocar* (FC)	.15	.11	.06
660	Lee Smith	.06	.05	.02
661	Steve Lake	.03	.02	.01
662	Rob Dibble	.08	.06	.03
663	Greg Brock	.05	.04	.02
664	John Farrell	.04	.03	.02
665	Mike LaValliere	.03	.02	.01
666	Danny Darwin	.06	.05	.02
667	Kent Anderson	.04	.03	.02
668	Bill Long	.04	.03	.02
669	Lou Pinella	.04	.03	.02
670	Rickey Henderson	.12	.09	.05
671	Andy McGaffigan	.03	.02	.01
672	Shane Mack	.06	.05	.02
673	*Greg Olson*	.20	.15	.08
674a	Kevin Gross (no diamond after 89 BB 1988)	.06	.05	.02
674b	Kevin Gross (diamond after 89 BB 1988)	.06	.05	.02
675	Tom Brunansky	.08	.06	.03
676	*Scott Chiamparino* (FC)	.20	.15	.08
677	Billy Ripken	.04	.03	.02
678	Mark Davidson	.03	.02	.01
679	Bill Bathe (FC)	.04	.03	.02
680	David Cone	.06	.05	.02
681	*Jeff Schaefer* (FC)	.10	.08	.04
682	*Ray Lankford* (FC)	.40	.30	.15
683	Derek Lilliquist	.05	.04	.02
684	Milt Cuyler (FC)	.10	.08	.04
685	Doug Drabek	.08	.06	.03
686	Mike Gallego	.03	.02	.01
687a	John Cerutti (4.46 ERA 1990)	.03	.02	.01
687b	John Cerutti (4.76 ERA 1990)	.03	.02	.01
688	*Rosario Rodriguez* (FC)	.10	.08	.04
689	John Kruk	.06	.05	.02
690	Orel Hershiser	.10	.08	.04
691	Mike Blowers	.10	.08	.04
692a	*Efrain Valdez* (FC) (no text below stats)	.15	.11	.06
692b	*Efrain Valdez* (FC) (two lines of text below stats)	.15	.11	.06
693	Francisco Cabrera	.08	.06	.03
694	Randy Veres	.03	.02	.01
695	Kevin Seitzer	.08	.06	.03
696	Steve Olin	.05	.04	.02
697	Shawn Abner	.04	.03	.02
698	Mark Guthrie	.05	.04	.02
699	Jim Lefebvre	.03	.02	.01
700	Jose Canseco	.15	.11	.06
701	Pascual Perez	.05	.04	.02
702	*Tim Naehring*	.20	.15	.08
703	Juan Agosto	.03	.02	.01
704	Devon White	.06	.05	.02
705	Robby Thompson	.05	.04	.02
706a	Brad Arnsberg (68.2 IP Rangers 1990)	.04	.03	.02
706b	Brad Arnsberg (62.2 IP Rangers 1990)	.04	.03	.02
707	Jim Eisenreich	.04	.03	.02
708	John Mitchell (FC)	.12	.09	.05
709	Matt Sinatro	.03	.02	.01
710	Kent Hrbek	.08	.06	.03
711	Jose DeLeon	.05	.04	.02
712	Ricky Jordan	.06	.05	.02
713	Scott Scudder	.08	.06	.03
714	Marvell Wynne	.04	.03	.02
715	Tim Burke	.06	.05	.02
716	Bob Geren	.06	.05	.02
717	Phil Bradley	.06	.05	.02
718	Steve Crawford	.03	.02	.01
719	Keith Miller	.06	.05	.02
720	Cecil Fielder	.15	.11	.06
721	*Mark Lee* (FC)	.10	.08	.04
722	Wally Backman	.04	.03	.02
723	Candy Maldonado	.08	.06	.03
724	*David Segui* (FC)	.10	.08	.04
725	Ron Gant	.15	.11	.06
726	Phil Stephenson	.04	.03	.02
727	Mookie Wilson	.06	.05	.02
728	Scott Sanderson	.04	.03	.02
729	Don Zimmer	.04	.03	.02
730	Barry Larkin	.12	.09	.05
731	*Jeff Gray* (FC)	.15	.11	.06
732	Franklin Stubbs	.05	.04	.02
733	Kelly Downs	.04	.03	.02
734	John Russell	.03	.02	.01
735	Ron Darling	.06	.05	.02
736	Dick Schofield	.04	.03	.02
737	Tim Crews	.03	.02	.01
738	Mel Hall	.04	.03	.02
739	*Russ Swan*	.10	.08	.04
740	Ryne Sandberg	.20	.15	.08
741	Jimmy Key	.06	.05	.02
742	Tommy Gregg	.04	.03	.02
743	Bryn Smith	.04	.03	.02
744	Nelson Santovenia	.05	.04	.02
745	Doug Jones	.08	.06	.03
746	John Shelby	.03	.02	.01
747	Tony Fossas	.03	.02	.01
748	Al Newman	.03	.02	.01
749	Greg Harris	.04	.03	.02
750	Bobby Bonilla	.12	.09	.05
751	*Wayne Edwards*	.10	.08	.04
752	Kevin Bass	.05	.04	.02
753	*Paul Marak* (FC)	.15	.11	.06
754	Bill Pecota	.04	.03	.02
755	Mark Langston	.10	.08	.04
756	Jeff Huson	.05	.04	.02
757	Mark Gardner	.06	.05	.02
758	Mike Devereaux	.06	.05	.02
759	Bobby Cox	.03	.02	.01
760	Benny Santiago	.08	.06	.03
761	Larry Andersen	.04	.03	.02
762	Mitch Webster	.04	.03	.02
763	*Dana Kiecker*	.10	.08	.04
764	Mark Carreon	.05	.04	.02
765	Shawon Dunston	.08	.06	.03
766	Jeff Robinson	.05	.04	.02
767	*Dan Wilson* (FC) (#1 Draft Pick)	.30	.25	.12
768	Donn Pall	.04	.03	.02
769	*Tim Sherrill* (FC)	.10	.08	.04
770	Jay Howell	.06	.05	.02
771	Gary Redus	.03	.02	.01
772	Kent Mercker (FC)	.10	.08	.04
773	Tom Foley	.03	.02	.01
774	Dennis Rasmussen	.04	.03	.02
775	Julio Franco	.08	.06	.03
776	Brent Mayne (FC)	.15	.11	.06
777	John Candelaria	.05	.04	.02
778	Danny Gladden	.05	.04	.02
779	Carmelo Martinez	.04	.03	.02
780a	Randy Myers (Career losses 15)	.08	.06	.03
780b	Randy Myers (Career losses 19)	.08	.06	.03
781	Darryl Hamilton	.05	.04	.02
782	Jim Deshaies	.05	.04	.02
783	Joel Skinner	.03	.02	.01
784	Willie Fraser	.04	.03	.02
785	Scott Fletcher	.04	.03	.02
786	Eric Plunk	.03	.02	.01
787	Checklist 6	.03	.02	.01
788	Bob Milacki	.06	.05	.02
789	Tom Lasorda	.04	.03	.02
790	Ken Griffey, Jr.	.60	.45	.25
791	Mike Benjamin (FC)	.15	.11	.06
792	Mike Greenwell	.15	.11	.06

1991 Topps Wax Box Cards

Styled like the standard 1991 Topps cards, this 16-card set honors milestones of the featured players. The cards were found on the bottom of wax pack boxes. The cards are designated in alphabetical order by (A-P) and are not numbered.

		MT	NR MT	EX
Complete Set:		2.50	2.00	1.00
Common Player:		.08	.06	.03
(1)	Bert Blyleven	.08	.06	.03
(2)	George Brett	.20	.15	.08
(3)	Brett Butler	.10	.08	.04
(4)	Andre Dawson	.15	.11	.06
(5)	Dwight Evans	.10	.08	.04
(6)	Carlton Fisk	.20	.15	.08
(7)	Alfredo Griffin	.08	.06	.03
(8)	Rickey Henderson	.30	.25	.12
(9)	Willie McGee	.15	.11	.06
(10)	Dale Murphy	.20	.15	.08
(11)	Eddie Murray	.20	.15	.08
(12)	Dave Parker	.15	.11	.06
(13)	Jeff Reardon	.15	.11	.06
(14)	Nolan Ryan	.60	.45	.25
(15)	Juan Samuel	.08	.06	.03
(16)	Robin Yount	.20	.15	.08

1991 Topps All-Star Glossy Set of 22

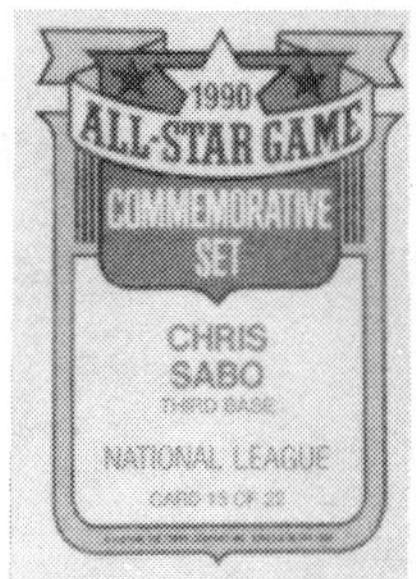

Continuing the same basic format used since 1984, these glossy-front rak-pak inserts honor the players, manager and honorary captains of the previous year's All-Star Game. Fronts have a league logo in the lower-left corner, a 1990 All-Star banner above the photo. and a Topps 40th anniversary logo superimposed over the photo. Backs have a shield and star design and the legend "1990 All-Star Commemorative Set" above the player's name, position and card number. Backs are printed in red and blue.

		MT	NR MT	EX
Complete Set (22):		4.00	3.00	1.50
Common Player:		.10	.08	.04
1	Tony LaRussa	.10	.08	.04
2	Mark McGwire	.30	.25	.12
3	Steve Sax	.10	.08	.04
4	Wade Boggs	.40	.30	.15
5	Cal Ripken, Jr.	.50	.40	.20
6	Rickey Henderson	.40	.30	.15
7	Ken Griffey, Jr.	.70	.50	.30
8	Jose Canseco	.30	.25	.12
9	Sandy Alomar, Jr.	.10	.08	.04
10	Bob Welch	.10	.08	.04
11	Al Lopez	.10	.08	.04
12	Roger Craig	.10	.08	.04
13	Will Clark	.30	.25	.12
14	Ryne Sandberg	.50	.40	.20
15	Chris Sabo	.10	.08	.04
16	Ozzie Smith	.30	.25	.12
17	Kevin Mitchell	.10	.08	.04
18	Len Dykstra	.20	.15	.08
19	Andre Dawson	.30	.25	.12
20	Mike Scoscia	.10	.08	.04
21	Jack Armstrong	.10	.08	.04
22	Juan Marichal	.20	.15	.08

1991 Topps Glossy Rookies

Similar in format to previous years' glossy rookies sets, this 33-card issue was available one per pack in 100-card jumbo cello packs of 1991 Topps cards. Card fronts have a red, white, blue and yellow "1990 Rookies" banner above the player photo, with the player's name in red in a yellow bar beneath. The Topps 40th anniversary logo appears in one of the upper corners of the photo. Backs are printed in red and blue and feature a "1990 Rookies Commemorative Set" shield logo. The player's name, position, team and card number are printed beneath. Cards are numbered alphabetically.

		MT	NR MT	EX
Complete Set (33):		12.00	9.00	4.75
Common Player:		.25	.20	.10
1	Sandy Alomar, Jr.	.25	.20	.10
2	Kevin Appier	.25	.20	.10
3	Steve Avery	.35	.25	.14
4	Carlos Baerga	.75	.60	.30
5	John Burkett	.35	.25	.14
6	Alex Cole	.25	.20	.10
7	Pat Combs	.25	.20	.10
8	Delino DeShields	.35	.25	.14
9	Travis Fryman	.35	.25	.14
10	Marquis Grissom	.35	.25	.14
11	Mike Harkey	.25	.20	.10
12	Glenallen Hill	.25	.20	.10
13	Jeff Huson	.25	.20	.10
14	Felix Jose	.30	.25	.12
15	Dave Justice	.75	.60	.30
16	Jim Leyritz	.30	.25	.12
17	Kevin Maas	.25	.20	.10
18	Ben McDonald	.30	.25	.12
19	Kent Mercker	.25	.20	.10
20	Hal Morris	.35	.25	.14
21	Chris Nabholz	.25	.20	.10
22	Tim Naehring	.25	.20	.10
23	Jose Offerman	.30	.25	.12
24	John Olerud	.50	.40	.20
25	Scott Radinsky	.25	.20	.10
26	Scott Ruskin	.25	.20	.10
27	Kevin Tapani	.25	.20	.10
28	Frank Thomas	3.00	2.25	1.25
29	Randy Tomlin	.25	.20	.10
30	Greg Vaughn	.30	.25	.12
31	Robin Ventura	.45	.35	.20
32	Larry Walker	.35	.25	.14
33	Todd Zeile	.35	.25	.14

1991 Topps Traded

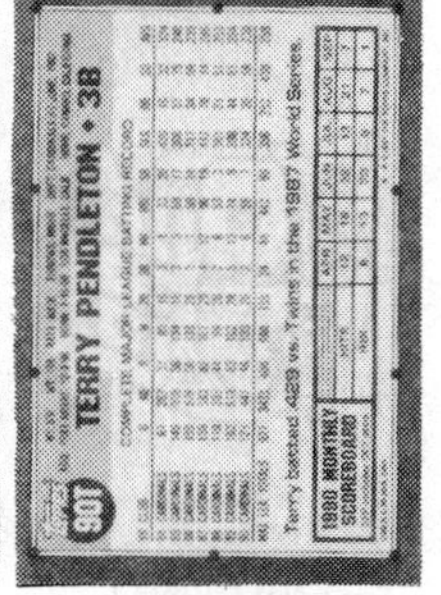

"Team USA" is featured in the 1991 Topps Traded set. The cards feature the same style as the regular 1991 issue, including the 40th anniversary logo. The set includes 132 cards and showcases rookies and traded players along with "Team USA." The cards are numbered with a "T" designation in alphabetical order.

		MT	NR MT	EX
Complete Set (132):		15.00	11.00	6.00
Common Player:		.05	.04	.02
1	Juan Agosto	.05	.04	.02
2	Roberto Alomar	.25	.20	.10
3	Wally Backman	.05	.04	.02
4	Jeff Bagwell (FC)	2.00	1.50	.80
5	Skeeter Barnes (FC)	.15	.11	.06
6	Steve Bedrosian	.06	.05	.02
7	Derek Bell (FC)	.35	.25	.14
8	George Bell	.10	.08	.04
9	Rafael Belliard	.05	.04	.02
10	Dante Bichette	.06	.05	.02
11	Bud Black	.05	.04	.02
12	Mike Boddicker	.06	.05	.02
13	Sid Bream	.06	.05	.02
14	Hubie Brooks	.06	.05	.02
15	Brett Butler	.08	.06	.03
16	Ivan Calderon	.08	.06	.03
17	John Candelaria	.05	.04	.02
18	Tom Candiotti	.06	.05	.02
19	Gary Carter	.08	.06	.03
20	Joe Carter	.12	.09	.05
21	Rick Cerone	.05	.04	.02
22	Jack Clark	.08	.06	.03
23	Vince Coleman	.15	.11	.06
24	Scott Coolbaugh	.10	.08	.04
25	Danny Cox	.05	.04	.02
26	Danny Darwin	.05	.04	.02
27	Chili Davis	.08	.06	.03
28	Glenn Davis	.08	.06	.03
29	Steve Decker (FC)	.25	.20	.10
30	Rob Deer	.06	.05	.02
31	Rich DeLucia (FC)	.15	.11	.06
32	*John Dettmer* (USA)	.20	.15	.08
33	Brian Downing	.05	.04	.02
34	*Darren Dreifort* (USA)	1.00	.70	.40
35	Kirk Dressendorfer	.40	.30	.15
36	Jim Essian	.05	.04	.02
37	Dwight Evans	.08	.06	.03
38	Steve Farr	.06	.05	.02
39	Jeff Fassero	.20	.15	.08
40	Junior Felix	.08	.06	.03
41	Tony Fernandez	.08	.06	.03
42	Steve Finley	.08	.06	.03
43	Jim Fregosi	.05	.04	.02
44	Gary Gaetti	.06	.05	.02
45	*Jason Giambi* (USA)	.30	.25	.12
46	Kirk Gibson	.08	.06	.03
47	Leo Gomez (FC)	.30	.25	.12
48	Luis Gonzalez	.30	.25	.12
49	*Jeff Granger* (USA)	.80	.60	.30
50	*Todd Greene* (USA)	.20	.15	.08
51	*Jeffrey Hammonds* (USA)	2.00	1.50	.80
52	Mike Hargrove	.05	.04	.02
53	Pete Harnisch	.08	.06	.03
54	*Rick Helling* (USA)	.20	.15	.08
55	Glenallen Hill	.08	.06	.03
56	Charlie Hough	.06	.05	.02
57	Pete Incaviglia	.08	.06	.03
58	Bo Jackson	.50	.40	.20
59	Danny Jackson	.06	.05	.02
60	Reggie Jefferson (FC)	.30	.25	.12
61	*Charles Johnson* (USA)	1.25	.90	.50
62	Jeff Johnson (FC)	.20	.15	.08
63	*Todd Johnson* (USA)	.20	.15	.08
64	Barry Jones	.05	.04	.02
65	Chris Jones	.20	.15	.08
66	Scott Kamieniecki	.20	.15	.08
67	*Pat Kelly*	.25	.15	.08
68	Darryl Kile (FC)	.20	.15	.08
69	Chuck Knoblauch (FC)	.40	.30	.15
70	Bill Krueger	.05	.04	.02
71	Scott Leius (FC)	.15	.11	.06
72	*Donnie Leshnock* (USA)	.20	.15	.08
73	Mark Lewis	.30	.25	.12
74	Candy Maldonado	.06	.05	.02
75	*Jason McDonald* (USA)	.25	.20	.10
76	Willie McGee	.08	.06	.03
77	Fred McGriff	.10	.08	.04
78	*Billy McMillon* (USA)	.20	.15	.08
79	Hal McRae	.06	.05	.02
80	*Dan Melendez* (USA)	.30	.25	.12
81	Orlando Merced (FC)	.40	.30	.15
82	Jack Morris	.08	.06	.03
83	*Phil Nevin* (USA)	2.00	1.50	.80
84	Otis Nixon	.06	.05	.02
85	Johnny Oates	.05	.04	.02
86	Bob Ojeda	.05	.04	.02
87	Mike Pagliarulo	.05	.04	.02
88	Dean Palmer (FC)	.35	.25	.14
89	Dave Parker	.08	.06	.03
90	Terry Pendleton	.08	.06	.03
91	*Tony Phillips* (USA)	.20	.15	.08
92	Doug Piatt (FC)	.20	.15	.08
93	Ron Polk (U.S.A.)	.06	.05	.02
94	Rock Raines	.12	.09	.05
95	Willie Randolph	.06	.05	.02
96	Dave Righetti	.06	.05	.02
97	Ernie Riles	.05	.04	.02
98	*Chris Roberts* (USA)	.30	.25	.12
99	Jeff Robinson (Angels)	.05	.04	.02
100	Jeff Robinson (Orioles)	.05	.04	.02
101	*Ivan Rodriguez*	1.00	.70	.40
102	*Steve Rodriguez* (USA)	.20	.15	.08
103	Tom Runnells	.05	.04	.02
104	Scott Sanderson	.06	.05	.02
105	Bob Scanlan (FC)	.15	.11	.06
106	Pete Schourek (FC)	.15	.11	.06
107	Gary Scott (FC)	.35	.25	.14
108	*Paul Shuey* (USA)	.40	.30	.15
109	*Doug Simons*	.20	.15	.08
110	Dave Smith	.06	.05	.02
111	Cory Snyder	.05	.04	.02
112	Luis Sojo	.06	.05	.02
113	*Kennie Steenstra* (USA)	.20	.15	.08
114	Darryl Strawberry	.30	.25	.12
115	Franklin Stubbs	.05	.04	.02
116	*Todd Taylor* (USA)	.20	.15	.08
117	Wade Taylor (FC)	.20	.15	.08
118	Garry Templeton	.06	.05	.02
119	Mickey Tettleton	.06	.05	.02
120	Tim Teufel	.05	.04	.02
121	Mike Timlin	.20	.15	.08

122	*David Tuttle* (USA)	.20	.15	.08
123	Mo Vaughn (FC)	.50	.40	.20
124	Jeff Ware (FC) (USA)	.20	.15	.08
125	Devon White	.08	.06	.03
126	Mark Whiten	.20	.15	.08
127	Mitch Williams	.08	.06	.03
128	*Craig Wilson* (USA)	.20	.15	.08
129	Willie Wilson	.06	.05	.02
130	*Chris Wimmer* (USA)	.30	.25	.12
131	*Ivan Zweig* (USA)	.20	.15	.08
132	Checklist	.05	.04	.02

1991 Topps Babe Ruth

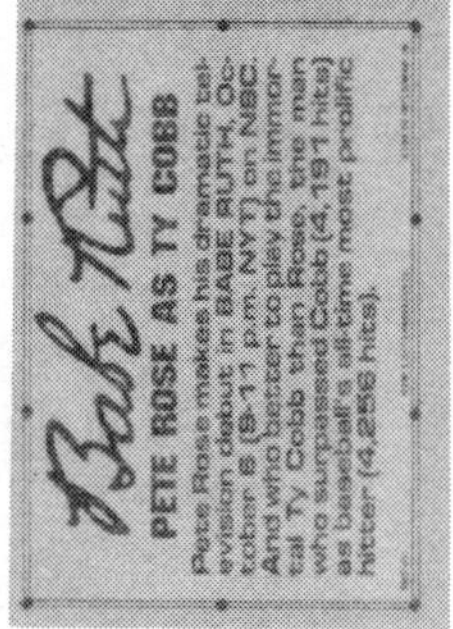

This 11-card set by Topps was released in honor of the NBC movie about Babe Ruth. The cards were released on a limited basis. The card fronts feature full-color photos from the movie, while the flip sides are printed horizontally and describe the front photo. The cards are numbered on the back.

		MT	NR MT	EX
Complete Set:		30.00	22.00	12.00
Common Player:		2.00	1.50	.80
1	Sunday October 6th NBC	2.00	1.50	.80
2	Stephen Lang as Babe Ruth	2.00	1.50	.80
3	Bruce Weitz as Miller Huggins	2.00	1.50	.80
4	Lisa Zane as Claire Ruth	2.00	1.50	.80
5	Donald Moffat as Jacob Ruppert	2.00	1.50	.80
6	Neil McDonough as Lou Gehrig	2.00	1.50	.80
7	Pete Rose as Ty Cobb	10.00	7.50	4.00
8	Rod Carew Baseball Consultant	6.00	4.50	2.50
9	Ruth and Manager Huggins	2.00	1.50	.80
10	Ruth In Action	2.00	1.50	.80
11	Babe Calls His Shot	2.00	1.50	.80

1991 Topps Major League Debut

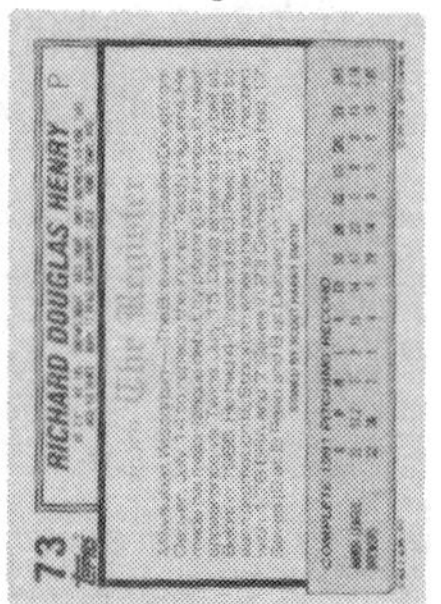

This 194-card set highlights the debut date of 1991 Major League rookies. Two checklist cards are also included in this boxed set. The card fronts resemble the 1992 Topps cards. A debut banner appears in the lower right hand corner of the card front. The set is packaged in an attractive collector box and the cards are numbered alphabetically. This set was available through select hobby dealers.

		MT	NR MT	EX
Complete Set:		24.00	18.00	9.50
Common Player:		.08	.06	.03
1	Kyle Abbott	.20	.15	.08
2	Dana Allison	.15	.11	.06
3	Rich Amaral	.08	.06	.03
4	Ruben Amaro	.10	.08	.04
5	Andy Ashby	.15	.11	.06
6	Jim Austin	.08	.06	.03
7	Jeff Bagwell	1.50	1.25	.60
8	Jeff Banister	.10	.08	.04
9	Willie Banks	.25	.20	.10
10	Bret Barberie	.20	.15	.08
11	Kim Batiste	.10	.08	.04
12	Chris Beasley	.10	.08	.04
13	Rodd Beck	.08	.06	.03
14	Derek Bell	.50	.40	.20
15	Esteban Beltre	.08	.06	.03
16	Freddie Benavides	.10	.08	.04
17	Rickey Bones	.10	.08	.04
18	Denis Boucher	.15	.11	.06
19	Ryan Bowen	.20	.15	.08
20	Cliff Brantley	.10	.08	.04
21	John Briscoe	.10	.08	.04
22	Scott Brosius	.10	.08	.04
23	Terry Bross	.08	.06	.03
24	Jarvis Brown	.10	.08	.04
25	Scott Bullett	.10	.08	.04
26	Kevin Campbell	.08	.06	.03
27	Amalio Carreno	.08	.06	.03
28	Matias Carrillo	.10	.08	.04
29	Jeff Carter	.08	.06	.03
30	Vinny Castilla	.10	.08	.04
31	Braulio Castillo	.10	.08	.04
32	Frank Castillo	.25	.20	.10
33	Darrin Chapin	.10	.08	.04
34	Mike Christopher	.08	.06	.03
35	Mark Clark	.15	.11	.06
36	Royce Clayton	.25	.20	.10
37	Stu Cole	.10	.08	.04
38	Gary Cooper	.08	.06	.03
39	Archie Corbin	.10	.08	.04
40	Rheal Cormier	.20	.15	.08
41	Chris Cron	.08	.06	.03
42	Mike Dalton	.08	.06	.03
43	Mark Davis	.08	.06	.03
44	Francisco de la Rosa	.08	.06	.03
45	Chris Donnels	.15	.11	.06
46	Brian Drahman	.15	.11	.06
47	Tom Drees	.15	.11	.06
48	Kirk Dressendorfer	.40	.30	.15
49	Bruce Egloff	.10	.08	.04
50	Cal Eldred	.30	.25	.12
51	Jose Escobar	.10	.08	.04
52	Tony Eusebio	.08	.06	.03
53	Hector Fajardo	.10	.08	.04
54	Monty Farriss	.10	.08	.04
55	Jeff Fassero	.15	.11	.06
56	Dave Fleming	.10	.08	.04
57	Kevin Flora	.10	.08	.04
58	Steve Foster	.10	.08	.04
59	Dan Gakeler	.08	.06	.03
60	Ramon Garcia	.15	.11	.06
61	Chris Gardner	.10	.08	.04
62	Jeff Gardner	.15	.11	.06
63	Chris George	.15	.11	.06
64	Ray Giannelli	.08	.06	.03
65	Tom Goodwin	.20	.15	.08
66	Mark Grater	.08	.06	.03
67	Johnny Guzman	.15	.11	.06
68	Juan Guzman	.60	.45	.25
69	Dave Haas	.08	.06	.03
70	Chris Haney	.25	.20	.10
71	Shawn Hare	.08	.06	.03
72	Donald Harris	.20	.15	.08
73	Doug Henry	.20	.15	.08
74	Pat Hentgen	.10	.08	.04
75	Gil Heredia	.20	.15	.08
76	Jeremy Hernandez	.20	.15	.08
77	Jose Hernandez	.08	.06	.03
78	Roberto Hernandez	.10	.08	.04
79	Bryan Hickerson	.15	.11	.06
80	Milt Hill	.08	.06	.03
81	Vince Horsman	.08	.06	.03
82	Wayne Housie	.08	.06	.03
83	Chris Howard	.15	.11	.06
84	David Howard	.20	.15	.08
85	Mike Humphreys	.15	.11	.06
86	Brian Hunter	.30	.25	.12
87	Jim Hunter	.08	.06	.03
88	Mike Ignasiak	.08	.06	.03
89	Reggie Jefferson	.35	.25	.14
90	Jeff Johnson	.20	.15	.08
91	Joel Johnson	.10	.08	.04
92	Calvin Jones	.15	.11	.06
93	Chris Jones	.25	.20	.10
94	Stacy Jones	.08	.06	.03
95	Jeff Juden	.25	.20	.10
96	Scott Kamieniecki	.20	.15	.08
97	Eric Karros	.60	.45	.25
98	Pat Kelly	.25	.20	.10
99	John Kiely	.08	.06	.03
100	Darryl Kile	.20	.15	.08
101	Wayne Kirby	.08	.06	.03
102	Garland Kiser	.10	.08	.04
103	Chuck Knoblauch	.60	.45	.25
104	Randy Knorr	.08	.06	.03
105	Tom Kramer	.08	.06	.03
106	Ced Landrum	.20	.15	.08
107	Patrick Lennon	.20	.15	.08
108	Jim Lewis	.08	.06	.03
109	Mark Lewis	.20	.15	.08
110	Doug Lindsey	.08	.06	.03
111	Scott Livingstone	.30	.25	.12
112	Kenny Lofton	.60	.45	.25
113	Ever Magallanes	.10	.08	.04
114	Mike Magnante	.10	.08	.04
115	Barry Manuel	.10	.08	.04
116	Josias Manzanillo	.10	.08	.04
117	Chito Martinez	.30	.25	.12
118	Terry Mathews	.08	.06	.03
119	Rob Mauer	.10	.08	.04
120	Tim Mauser	.08	.06	.03
121	Terry McDaniel	.20	.15	.08
122	Rusty Meacham	.15	.11	.06
123	Luis Mercedes	.25	.20	.10
124	Paul Miller	.15	.11	.06
125	Keith Mitchell	.25	.20	.10
126	Bobby Moore	.08	.06	.03
127	Kevin Morton	.15	.11	.06
128	Andy Mota	.15	.11	.06
129	Jose Mota	.15	.11	.06
130	Mike Mussina	.25	.20	.10
131	Jeff Mutis	.08	.06	.03
132	Denny Neagle	.40	.30	.15
133	Warren Newson	.15	.11	.06
134	Jim Olander	.08	.06	.03
135	Erik Pappas	.15	.11	.06
136	Jorge Pedre	.10	.08	.04
137	Yorkis Perez	.15	.11	.06
138	Mark Petkovsek	.15	.11	.06
139	Doug Piatt	.15	.11	.06
140	Jeff Plympton	.15	.11	.06
141	Harvey Pulliam	.15	.11	.06
142	John Ramos	.15	.11	.06
143	Mike Remlinger	.10	.08	.04
144	Laddie Renfroe	.10	.08	.04
145	Armando Reynoso	.10	.08	.04
146	Arthur Rhodes	.20	.15	.08
147	Pat Rice	.15	.11	.06
148	Nikco Riesgo	.10	.08	.04
149	Carlos Rodriguez	.10	.08	.04
150	Ivan Rodriguez	1.50	1.25	.60
151	Wayne Rosenthal	.10	.08	.04
152	Rico Rossy	.08	.06	.03
153	Stan Royer	.15	.11	.06
154	Rey Sanchez	.08	.06	.03
155	Reggie Sanders	.40	.30	.15
156	Mo Sanford	.35	.25	.14
157	Bob Scanlan	.15	.11	.06
158	Pete Schourek	.15	.11	.06
159	Gary Scott	.25	.20	.10
160	Tim Scott	.08	.06	.03
161	Tony Scruggs	.10	.08	.04
162	Scott Servais	.10	.08	.04
163	Doug Simons	.15	.11	.06
164	Heathcliff Slocumb	.10	.08	.04
165	Joe Slusarski	.10	.08	.04
166	Tim Spehr	.15	.11	.06
167	Ed Sprague	.10	.08	.04
168	Jeff Tackett	.08	.06	.03
169	Eddie Taubensee	.15	.11	.06
170	Wade Taylor	.15	.11	.06
171	Jim Thome	.60	.45	.25
172	Mike Timlin	.25	.20	.10
173	Jose Tolentino	.10	.08	.04
174	John Vander Wal	.08	.06	.03
175	Todd Van Poppel	.45	.35	.20
176	Mo Vaughn	.50	.40	.20
177	Dave Wainhouse	.15	.11	.06
178	Don Wakamatsu	.10	.08	.04
179	Bruce Walton	.08	.06	.03
180	Kevin Ward	.08	.06	.03
181	Dave Weathers	.08	.06	.03
182	Eric Wedge	.08	.06	.03
183	John Wehner	.25	.20	.10
184	Rick Wilkins	.30	.25	.12
185	Bernie Williams	.35	.25	.14
186	Brian Williams	.15	.11	.06
187	Ron Witmeyer	.08	.06	.03
188	Mark Wohlers	.25	.20	.10
189	Ted Wood	.20	.15	.08
190	Anthony Young	.50	.40	.20
191	Eddie Zosky	.20	.15	.08
192	Bob Zupcic	.15	.11	.06
193	Checklist	.08	.06	.03
194	Checklist	.08	.06	.03

1991 Topps Stadium Club

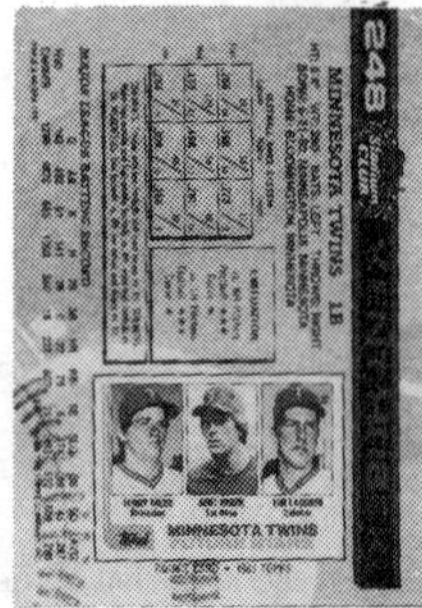

One of the most popular sets of 1991, this 600-card issue was released in two 300-card series. The cards were available in foil packs only. No factory sets were available. The cards feature borderless high gloss photos on the front and a player evaluation and card photo on the back. Stadium Club cards were considered scarce in many areas, thus driving up the price per pack. A special Stadium Club membership package was made available for $29.95 with 10 proof of purchase seals from wrappers.

		MT	NR MT	EX
Complete Set (600):		150.00	125.00	60.00
Complete Series 1 (300):		90.00	67.00	36.00
Complete Series 2 (300):		60.00	45.00	24.00
Common Player:		.20	.15	.08
1	Dave Stewart	.50	.40	.20
2	Wally Joyner	.30	.25	.12
3	Shawon Dunston	.25	.20	.10
4	Darren Daulton	.60	.45	.25
5	Will Clark	2.00	1.50	.80
6	Sammy Sosa	2.00	1.50	.80
7	Dan Plesac	.20	.15	.08
8	Marquis Grissom	2.00	1.50	.80
9	Erik Hanson	.30	.25	.12
10	Geno Petralli	.20	.15	.08
11	Jose Rijo	.25	.20	.10
12	Carlos Quintana	.20	.15	.08

13	Junior Ortiz	.20	.15	.08
14	Bob Walk	.20	.15	.08
15	Mike Macfarlane	.20	.15	.08
16	Eric Yelding	.20	.15	.08
17	Bryn Smith	.20	.15	.08
18	Bip Roberts	.20	.15	.08
19	Mike Scioscia	.20	.15	.08
20	Mark Williamson	.20	.15	.08
21	Don Mattingly	1.50	1.25	.60
22	John Franco	.20	.15	.08
23	Chet Lemon	.20	.15	.08
24	Tom Henke	.20	.15	.08
25	Jerry Browne	.20	.15	.08
26	Dave Justice	5.00	3.75	2.00
27	Mark Langston	.30	.25	.12
28	Damon Berryhill	.20	.15	.08
29	Kevin Bass	.20	.15	.08
30	Scott Fletcher	.20	.15	.08
31	Moises Alou	2.00	1.50	.80
32	Dave Valle	.20	.15	.08
33	Jody Reed	.20	.15	.08
34	Dave West	.20	.15	.08
35	Kevin McReynolds	.25	.20	.10
36	Pat Combs	.20	.15	.08
37	Eric Davis	.50	.40	.20
38	Bret Saberhagen	.30	.25	.12
39	Stan Javier	.20	.15	.08
40	Chuck Cary	.20	.15	.08
41	Tony Phillips	.20	.15	.08
42	Lee Smith	.25	.20	.10
43	Tim Teufel	.20	.15	.08
44	Lance Dickson	.30	.25	.12
45	Greg Litton	.20	.15	.08
46	Teddy Higuera	.25	.20	.10
47	Edgar Martinez	.30	.25	.12
48	Steve Avery	4.50	3.50	1.75
49	Walt Weiss	.20	.15	.08
50	David Segui	.30	.25	.12
51	Andy Benes	.60	.45	.25
52	Karl Rhodes	.75	.60	.30
53	Neal Heaton	.20	.15	.08
54	Dan Gladden	.20	.15	.08
55	Luis Rivera	.20	.15	.08
56	Kevin Brown	.20	.15	.08
57	Frank Thomas	24.00	18.00	9.50
58	Terry Mulholland	.25	.20	.10
59	Dick Schofield	.20	.15	.08
60	Ron Darling	.20	.15	.08
61	Sandy Alomar, Jr.	.35	.25	.14
62	Dave Stieb	.20	.15	.08
63	Alan Trammell	.40	.30	.15
64	Matt Nokes	.20	.15	.08
65	Lenny Harris	.20	.15	.08
66	Milt Thompson	.20	.15	.08
67	Storm Davis	.20	.15	.08
68	Joe Oliver	.20	.15	.08
69	Andres Galarraga	.75	.60	.30
70	Ozzie Guillen	.25	.20	.10
71	Ken Howell	.20	.15	.08
72	Garry Templeton	.20	.15	.08
73	Derrick May	2.00	1.50	.80
74	Xavier Hernandez	.20	.15	.08
75	Dave Parker	.25	.20	.10
76	Rick Aguilera	.20	.15	.08
77	Robby Thompson	.20	.15	.08
78	Pete Incaviglia	.20	.15	.08
79	Bob Welch	.25	.20	.10
80	Randy Milligan	.25	.20	.10
81	Chuck Finley	.35	.25	.14
82	Alvin Davis	.20	.15	.08
83	Tim Naehring	.35	.25	.14
84	Jay Bell	.25	.20	.10
85	Joe Magrane	.25	.20	.10
86	Howard Johnson	.30	.25	.12
87	Jack McDowell	1.00	.75	.40
88	Kevin Seitzer	.20	.15	.08
89	Bruce Ruffin	.20	.15	.08
90	Fernando Valenzuela	.30	.25	.12
91	Terry Kennedy	.20	.15	.08
92	Barry Larkin	.60	.45	.25
93	Larry Walker	2.50	2.00	1.00
94	Luis Salazar	.20	.15	.08
95	Gary Sheffield	3.00	2.25	1.25
96	Bobby Witt	.20	.15	.08
97	Lonnie Smith	.20	.15	.08
98	Bryan Harvey	.25	.20	.10
99	Mookie Wilson	.25	.20	.10
100	Dwight Gooden	.40	.30	.15
101	Lou Whitaker	.25	.20	.10
102	Ron Karkovice	.20	.15	.08
103	Jesse Barfield	.25	.20	.10
104	Jose DeJesus	.25	.20	.10
105	Benito Santiago	.25	.20	.10
106	Brian Holman	.20	.15	.08
107	Rafael Ramirez	.20	.15	.08
108	Ellis Burks	.50	.40	.20
109	Mike Bielecki	.20	.15	.08
110	Kirby Puckett	3.00	2.25	1.25
111	Terry Shumpert	.25	.20	.10
112	Chuck Crim	.20	.15	.08
113	Todd Benzinger	.20	.15	.08
114	Brian Barnes	.40	.30	.15
115	Carlos Baerga	5.00	3.75	2.00
116	Kal Daniels	.25	.20	.10
117	Dave Johnson	.20	.15	.08
118	Andy Van Slyke	.30	.25	.12
119	John Burkett	1.00	.70	.40
120	Rickey Henderson	1.25	.90	.50
121	Tim Jones	.20	.15	.08
122	Daryl Irvine	.30	.25	.12
123	Ruben Sierra	1.25	.90	.50
124	Jim Abbott	.75	.60	.30
125	Daryl Boston	.20	.15	.08
126	Greg Maddux	1.25	.90	.50
127	Von Hayes	.20	.15	.08
128	Mike Fitzgerald	.20	.15	.08
129	Wayne Edwards	.20	.15	.08
130	Greg Briley	.20	.15	.08
131	Rob Dibble	.30	.25	.12
132	Gene Larkin	.20	.15	.08
133	David Wells	.20	.15	.08
134	Steve Balboni	.20	.15	.08
135	Greg Vaughn	1.25	.90	.50
136	Mark Davis	.20	.15	.08
137	Dave Rohde	.20	.15	.08
138	Eric Show	.20	.15	.08
139	Bobby Bonilla	1.00	.70	.40
140	Dana Kiecker	.25	.20	.10
141	Gary Pettis	.20	.15	.08
142	Dennis Boyd	.20	.15	.08
143	Mike Benjamin	.20	.15	.08
144	Luis Polonia	.20	.15	.08
145	Doug Jones	.20	.15	.08
146	Al Newman	.20	.15	.08
147	Alex Fernandez	3.00	2.25	1.25
148	Bill Doran	.20	.15	.08
149	Kevin Elster	.20	.15	.08
150	Len Dykstra	.30	.25	.12
151	Mike Gallego	.20	.15	.08
152	Tim Belcher	.20	.15	.08
153	Jay Buhner	.20	.15	.08
154	Ozzie Smith	.70	.50	.30
155	Jose Canseco	1.50	1.25	.60
156	Gregg Olson	.30	.25	.12
157	Charlie O'Brien	.20	.15	.08
158	Frank Tanana	.20	.15	.08
159	George Brett	1.50	1.25	.60
160	Jeff Huson	.20	.15	.08
161	Kevin Tapani	.35	.25	.14
162	Jerome Walton	.25	.20	.10
163	Charlie Hayes	.20	.15	.08
164	Chris Bosio	.20	.15	.08
165	Chris Sabo	.40	.30	.15
166	Lance Parrish	.20	.15	.08
167	Don Robinson	.20	.15	.08
168	Manuel Lee	.20	.15	.08
169	Dennis Rasmussen	.20	.15	.08
170	Wade Boggs	1.00	.75	.40
171	Bob Geren	.20	.15	.08
172	Mackey Sasser	.20	.15	.08
173	Julio Franco	.30	.25	.12
174	Otis Nixon	.20	.15	.08
175	Bert Blyleven	.20	.15	.08
176	Craig Biggio	.40	.30	.15
177	Eddie Murray	.60	.45	.25
178	Randy Tomlin	.30	.25	.12
179	Tino Martinez	.50	.40	.20
180	Carlton Fisk	.80	.60	.30
181	Dwight Smith	.20	.15	.08
182	Scott Garrelts	.20	.15	.08
183	Jim Gantner	.20	.15	.08
184	Dickie Thon	.20	.15	.08
185	John Farrell	.20	.15	.08
186	Cecil Fielder	2.00	1.50	.80
187	Glenn Braggs	.20	.15	.08
188	Allan Anderson	.20	.15	.08
189	Kurt Stillwell	.20	.15	.08
190	Jose Oquendo	.20	.15	.08
191	Joe Orsulak	.20	.15	.08
192	Ricky Jordan	.20	.15	.08
193	Kelly Downs	.20	.15	.08
194	Delino DeShields	1.50	1.25	.60
195	Omar Vizquel	.20	.15	.08
196	Mark Carreon	.20	.15	.08
197	Mike Harkey	.20	.15	.08
198	Jack Howell	.20	.15	.08
199	Lance Johnson	.20	.15	.08
200	Nolan Ryan	15.00	11.00	6.00
201	John Marzano	.20	.15	.08
202	Doug Drabek	.30	.25	.12
203	Mark Lemke	.30	.25	.12
204	Steve Sax	.30	.25	.12
205	Greg Harris	.20	.15	.08
206	B.J. Surhoff	.20	.15	.08
207	Todd Burns	.20	.15	.08
208	Jose Gonzalez	.20	.15	.08
209	Mike Scott	.20	.15	.08
210	Dave Magadan	.30	.25	.12
211	Dante Bichette	1.00	.75	.40
212	Trevor Wilson	.20	.15	.08
213	Hector Villanueva	.20	.15	.08
214	Dan Pasqua	.20	.15	.08
215	Greg Colbrunn	.30	.25	.12
216	Mike Jeffcoat	.20	.15	.08
217	Harold Reynolds	.25	.20	.10
218	Paul O'Neill	.25	.20	.10
219	Mark Guthrie	.25	.20	.10
220	Barry Bonds	5.00	3.75	2.00
221	Jimmy Key	.25	.20	.10
222	Billy Ripken	.20	.15	.08
223	Tom Pagnozzi	.20	.15	.08
224	Bo Jackson	2.00	1.50	.80
225	Sid Fernandez	.20	.15	.08
226	Mike Marshall	.20	.15	.08
227	John Kruk	.25	.20	.10
228	Mike Fetters	.20	.15	.08
229	Eric Anthony	.20	.15	.08
230	Ryne Sandberg	3.00	2.25	1.25
231	Carney Lansford	.20	.15	.08
232	Melido Perez	.20	.15	.08
233	Jose Lind	.20	.15	.08
234	Darryl Hamilton	.20	.15	.08
235	Tom Browning	.20	.15	.08
236	Spike Owen	.20	.15	.08
237	Juan Gonzalez	22.00	16.50	8.75
238	Felix Fermin	.20	.15	.08
239	Keith Miller	.20	.15	.08
240	Mark Gubicza	.20	.15	.08
241	Kent Anderson	.20	.15	.08
242	Alvaro Espinoza	.20	.15	.08
243	Dale Murphy	.25	.20	.10
244	Orel Hershiser	.30	.25	.12
245	Paul Molitor	1.50	1.25	.60
246	Eddie Whitson	.20	.15	.08
247	Joe Girardi	.20	.15	.08
248	Kent Hrbek	.25	.20	.10
249	Bill Sampen	.20	.15	.08
250	Kevin Mitchell	.45	.35	.20
251	Mariano Duncan	.20	.15	.08
252	Scott Bradley	.20	.15	.08
253	Mike Greenwell	.30	.25	.12
254	Tom Gordon	.25	.20	.10
255	Todd Zeile	.60	.45	.25
256	Bobby Thigpen	.25	.20	.10
257	Gregg Jefferies	1.25	.90	.50
258	Kenny Rogers	.20	.15	.08
259	Shane Mack	.30	.25	.12
260	Zane Smith	.20	.15	.08
261	Mitch Williams	.25	.20	.10
262	Jim DeShaies	.20	.15	.08
263	Dave Winfield	1.00	.70	.40
264	Ben McDonald	1.00	.70	.40
265	Randy Ready	.20	.15	.08
266	Pat Borders	.20	.15	.08
267	Jose Uribe	.20	.15	.08
268	Derek Lilliquist	.20	.15	.08
269	Greg Brock	.20	.15	.08
270	Ken Griffey, Jr.	20.00	15.00	8.00
271	Jeff Gray	.25	.20	.10
272	Danny Tartabull	.40	.30	.15
273	Dennis Martinez	.20	.15	.08
274	Robin Ventura	3.00	2.25	1.25
275	Randy Myers	.20	.15	.08
276	Jack Daugherty	.20	.15	.08
277	Greg Gagne	.20	.15	.08
278	Jay Howell	.20	.15	.08
279	Mike LaValliere	.20	.15	.08
280	Rex Hudler	.20	.15	.08
281	Mike Simms	.35	.25	.14
282	Kevin Maas	.30	.25	.12
283	Jeff Ballard	.20	.15	.08
284	Dave Henderson	.30	.25	.12
285	Pete O'Brien	.20	.15	.08
286	Brook Jacoby	.20	.15	.08
287	Mike Henneman	.20	.15	.08
288	Greg Olson	.20	.15	.08
289	Greg Myers	.20	.15	.08
290	Mark Grace	1.25	.90	.50
291	Shawn Abner	.20	.15	.08
292	Frank Viola	.30	.25	.12
293	Lee Stevens	.30	.25	.12
294	Jason Grimsley	.20	.15	.08
295	Matt Williams	1.50	1.25	.60
296	Ron Robinson	.20	.15	.08
297	Tom Brunansky	.20	.15	.08
298	Checklist	.20	.15	.08
299	Checklist	.20	.15	.08
300	Checklist	.20	.15	.08
301	Darryl Strawberry	.50	.40	.20
302	Bud Black	.20	.15	.08
303	Harold Baines	.30	.25	.12
304	Roberto Alomar	5.00	3.75	2.00
305	Norm Charlton	.20	.15	.08
306	Gary Thurman	.20	.15	.08
307	Mike Felder	.20	.15	.08
308	Tony Gwynn	1.50	1.25	.60
309	Roger Clemens	2.00	1.50	.80
310	Andre Dawson	.50	.40	.20
311	Scott Radinsky	.20	.15	.08
312	Bob Melvin	.20	.15	.08
313	Kirk McCaskill	.20	.15	.08
314	Pedro Guerrero	.35	.25	.14
315	Walt Terrell	.20	.15	.08
316	Sam Horn	.20	.15	.08
317	*Wes Chamberlain*	.75	.60	.30
318	*Pedro Munoz*	.50	.40	.20
319	Roberto Kelly	.35	.25	.14
320	Mark Portugal	.20	.15	.08
321	Tim McIntosh	.20	.15	.08
322	Jesse Orosco	.20	.15	.08
323	Gary Green	.20	.15	.08
324	Greg Harris	.20	.15	.08
325	Hubie Brooks	.20	.15	.08
326	Chris Nabholz	.20	.15	.08
327	Terry Pendleton	.35	.25	.14
328	Eric King	.20	.15	.08
329	Chili Davis	.20	.15	.08
330	Anthony Telford	.20	.15	.08
331	Kelly Gruber	.35	.25	.14
332	Dennis Eckersley	.35	.25	.14
333	Mel Hall	.20	.15	.08
334	Bob Kipper	.20	.15	.08
335	Willie McGee	.30	.25	.12
336	Steve Olin	.20	.15	.08
337	Steve Buechele	.20	.15	.08
338	Scott Leius	.35	.25	.14
339	Hal Morris	.40	.30	.15
340	Jose Offerman	.40	.30	.15
341	Kent Mercker	.30	.25	.12
342	Ken Griffey	.20	.15	.08
343	Pete Harnisch	.20	.15	.08
344	Kirk Gibson	.30	.25	.12
345	Dave Smith	.20	.15	.08
346	Dave Martinez	.20	.15	.08
347	Atlee Hammaker	.20	.15	.08
348	Brian Downing	.20	.15	.08
349	Todd Hundley	.35	.25	.14
350	Candy Maldonado	.20	.15	.08
351	Dwight Evans	.30	.25	.12
352	Steve Searcy	.20	.15	.08
353	Gary Gaetti	.25	.20	.10
354	Jeff Reardon	.25	.20	.10
355	Travis Fryman	9.00	6.75	3.50
356	Dave Righetti	.20	.15	.08
357	Fred McGriff	1.50	1.25	.60
358	Don Slaught	.20	.15	.08
359	Gene Nelson	.20	.15	.08
360	Billy Spiers	.20	.15	.08
361	Lee Guetterman	.20	.15	.08
362	Darren Lewis	1.00	.70	.40
363	Duane Ward	.20	.15	.08
364	Lloyd Moseby	.20	.15	.08
365	John Smoltz	1.00	.75	.40
366	Felix Jose	.50	.40	.20

367	David Cone	.30	.25	.12
368	Wally Backman	.20	.15	.08
369	Jeff Montgomery	.20	.15	.08
370	Rich Garces	.35	.25	.14
371	Billy Hatcher	.20	.15	.08
372	Bill Swift	.20	.15	.08
373	Jim Eisenreich	.20	.15	.08
374	Rob Ducey	.20	.15	.08
375	Tim Crews	.20	.15	.08
376	Steve Finley	.20	.15	.08
377	Jeff Blauser	.20	.15	.08
378	Willie Wilson	.20	.15	.08
379	Gerald Perry	.20	.15	.08
380	Jose Mesa	.20	.15	.08
381	Pat Kelly	1.25	.90	.50
382	Matt Merullo	.20	.15	.08
383	Ivan Calderon	.30	.25	.12
384	Scott Chiamparino	.20	.15	.08
385	Lloyd McClendon	.20	.15	.08
386	Dave Bergman	.20	.15	.08
387	Ed Sprague	.40	.30	.15
388	Jeff Bagwell	11.00	8.25	4.50
389	Brett Butler	.25	.20	.10
390	Larry Andersen	.20	.15	.08
391	Glenn Davis	.30	.25	.12
392	Alex Cole (photo of Otis Nixon)	.30	.25	.12
393	Mike Heath	.20	.15	.08
394	Danny Darwin	.20	.15	.08
395	Steve Lake	.20	.15	.08
396	Tim Layana	.20	.15	.08
397	Terry Leach	.20	.15	.08
398	Bill Wegman	.20	.15	.08
399	Mark McGwire	.50	.40	.20
400	Mike Boddicker	.20	.15	.08
401	Steve Howe	.20	.15	.08
402	Bernard Gilkey	.40	.30	.15
403	Thomas Howard	.20	.15	.08
404	Rafael Belliard	.20	.15	.08
405	Tom Candiotti	.20	.15	.08
406	Rene Gonzalez	.25	.20	.10
407	Chuck McElroy	.25	.20	.10
408	Paul Sorrento	.25	.20	.10
409	Randy Johnson	1.50	1.25	.60
410	Brady Anderson	.20	.15	.08
411	Dennis Cook	.20	.15	.08
412	Mickey Tettleton	.25	.20	.10
413	Mike Stanton	.20	.15	.08
414	Ken Oberkfell	.20	.15	.08
415	Rick Honeycutt	.20	.15	.08
416	Nelson Santovenia	.20	.15	.08
417	Bob Tewksbury	.20	.15	.08
418	Brent Mayne	.20	.15	.08
419	Steve Farr	.20	.15	.08
420	Phil Stephenson	.20	.15	.08
421	Jeff Russell	.20	.15	.08
422	Chris James	.20	.15	.08
423	Tim Leary	.20	.15	.08
424	Gary Carter	.30	.25	.12
425	Glenallen Hill	.30	.25	.12
426	Matt Young	.20	.15	.08
427	Sid Bream	.20	.15	.08
428	Greg Swindell	.30	.25	.12
429	Scott Aldred	.30	.25	.12
430	Cal Ripken, Jr.	2.50	2.00	1.00
431	Bill Landrum	.20	.15	.08
432	Ernie Riles	.20	.15	.08
433	Danny Jackson	.20	.15	.08
434	Casey Candaele	.20	.15	.08
435	Ken Hill	.20	.15	.08
436	Jaime Navarro	.20	.15	.08
437	Lance Blankenship	.20	.15	.08
438	Randy Velarde	.20	.15	.08
439	Frank DiPino	.20	.15	.08
440	Carl Nichols	.20	.15	.08
441	Jeff Robinson	.20	.15	.08
442	Deion Sanders	.35	.25	.14
443	Vincente Palacios	.20	.15	.08
444	Devon White	.30	.25	.12
445	John Cerutti	.20	.15	.08
446	Tracy Jones	.20	.15	.08
447	Jack Morris	.30	.25	.12
448	Mitch Webster	.20	.15	.08
449	Bob Ojeda	.20	.15	.08
450	Oscar Azocar	.20	.15	.08
451	Luis Aquino	.20	.15	.08
452	Mark Whiten	.75	.60	.30
453	Stan Belinda	.20	.15	.08
454	Ron Gant	1.00	.75	.40
455	Jose DeLeon	.20	.15	.08
456	Mark Salas	.20	.15	.08
457	Junior Felix	.20	.15	.08
458	Wally Whitehurst	.20	.15	.08
459	Phil Plantier	4.00	3.00	1.50
460	Juan Berenguer	.20	.15	.08
461	Franklin Stubbs	.20	.15	.08
462	Joe Boever	.20	.15	.08
463	Tim Wallach	.30	.25	.12
464	Mike Moore	.20	.15	.08
465	Albert Belle	6.00	4.50	2.50
466	Mike Witt	.20	.15	.08
467	Craig Worthington	.20	.15	.08
468	Jerald Clark	.20	.15	.08
469	Scott Terry	.20	.15	.08
470	Milt Cuyler	.60	.45	.25
471	John Smiley	.25	.20	.10
472	Charles Nagy	.25	.20	.10
473	Alan Mills	.20	.15	.08
474	John Russell	.20	.15	.08
475	Bruce Hurst	.20	.15	.08
476	Andujar Cedeno	2.00	1.50	.80
477	Dave Eiland	.20	.15	.08
478	Brian McRae	2.00	1.50	.80
479	Mike LaCoss	.20	.15	.08
480	Chris Gwynn	.20	.15	.08
481	Jamie Moyer	.20	.15	.08
482	John Olerud	5.00	3.75	2.00
483	Efrain Valdez	.20	.15	.08
484	Sil Campusano	.20	.15	.08
485	Pascual Perez	.20	.15	.08
486	Gary Redus	.20	.15	.08
487	Andy Hawkins	.20	.15	.08
488	Cory Snyder	.20	.15	.08
489	Chris Hoiles	.25	.20	.10
490	Ron Hassey	.20	.15	.08
491	Gary Wayne	.20	.15	.08
492	Mark Lewis	.80	.60	.30
493	Scott Coolbaugh	.20	.15	.08
494	Gerald Young	.20	.15	.08
495	Juan Samuel	.20	.15	.08
496	Willie Fraser	.20	.15	.08
497	Jeff Treadway	.20	.15	.08
498	Vince Coleman	.30	.25	.12
499	Cris Carpenter	.20	.15	.08
500	Jack Clark	.30	.25	.12
501	Kevin Appier	2.00	1.50	.80
502	Rafael Palmeiro	1.00	.70	.40
503	Hensley Meulens	.30	.25	.12
504	George Bell	.30	.25	.12
505	Tony Pena	.30	.25	.12
506	Roger McDowell	.20	.15	.08
507	Luis Sojo	.20	.15	.08
508	Mike Schooler	.20	.15	.08
509	Robin Yount	1.50	1.25	.60
510	Jack Armstrong	.20	.15	.08
511	Rick Cerone	.20	.15	.08
512	Curt Wilkerson	.20	.15	.08
513	Joe Carter	1.50	1.25	.60
514	Tim Burke	.20	.15	.08
515	Tony Fernandez	.25	.20	.10
516	Ramon Martinez	.40	.30	.15
517	Tim Hulett	.20	.15	.08
518	Terry Steinbach	.20	.15	.08
519	Pete Smith	.20	.15	.08
520	Ken Caminiti	.20	.15	.08
521	Shawn Boskie	.20	.15	.08
522	Mike Pagliarulo	.20	.15	.08
523	Tim Raines	.35	.25	.14
524	Alfredo Griffin	.20	.15	.08
525	Henry Cotto	.20	.15	.08
526	Mike Stanley	.20	.15	.08
527	Charlie Leibrandt	.20	.15	.08
528	Jeff King	.20	.15	.08
529	Eric Plunk	.20	.15	.08
530	Tom Lampkin	.20	.15	.08
531	Steve Bedrosian	.20	.15	.08
532	Tom Herr	.20	.15	.08
533	Craig Lefferts	.20	.15	.08
534	Jeff Reed	.20	.15	.08
535	Mickey Morandini	.35	.25	.14
536	Greg Cadaret	.20	.15	.08
537	Ray Lankford	2.00	1.50	.80
538	John Candelaria	.20	.15	.08
539	Rob Deer	.20	.15	.08
540	Brad Arnsberg	.20	.15	.08
541	Mike Sharperson	.20	.15	.08
542	Jeff Robinson	.20	.15	.08
543	Mo Vaughn	3.50	2.75	1.50
544	Jeff Parrett	.20	.15	.08
545	Willie Randolph	.20	.15	.08
546	Herm Winningham	.20	.15	.08
547	Jeff Innis	.20	.15	.08
548	Chuck Knoblauch	1.25	.90	.50
549	Tommy Greene	.25	.20	.10
550	Jeff Hamilton	.20	.15	.08
551	Barry Jones	.20	.15	.08
552	Ken Dayley	.20	.15	.08
553	Rick Dempsey	.20	.15	.08
554	Greg Smith	.20	.15	.08
555	Mike Devereaux	.20	.15	.08
556	Keith Comstock	.20	.15	.08
557	Paul Faries	.20	.15	.08
558	Tom Glavine	2.00	1.50	.80
559	Craig Grebeck	.20	.15	.08
560	Scott Erickson	.40	.30	.15
561	Joel Skinner	.20	.15	.08
562	Mike Morgan	.20	.15	.08
563	Dave Gallagher	.20	.15	.08
564	Todd Stottlemyre	.25	.20	.10
565	Rich Rodriguez	.25	.20	.10
566	Craig Wilson	.25	.20	.10
567	Jeff Brantley	.25	.20	.10
568	Scott Kamieniecki	.30	.25	.12
569	Steve Decker	.80	.60	.30
570	Juan Agosto	.20	.15	.08
571	Tommy Gregg	.20	.15	.08
572	Kevin Wickander	.20	.15	.08
573	Jamie Quirk	.20	.15	.08
574	Jerry Don Gleaton	.20	.15	.08
575	Chris Hammond	.20	.15	.08
576	Luis Gonzalez	1.50	1.25	.60
577	Russ Swan	.20	.15	.08
578	Jeff Conine	2.50	2.00	1.00
579	Charlie Hough	.20	.15	.08
580	Jeff Kunkel	.20	.15	.08
581	Darrel Akerfelds	.20	.15	.08
582	Jeff Manto	.25	.20	.10
583	Alejandro Pena	.20	.15	.08
584	Mark Davidson	.20	.15	.08
585	Bob MacDonald	.25	.20	.10
586	Paul Assenmacher	.20	.15	.08
587	Dan Wilson	.60	.45	.25
588	Tom Bolton	.20	.15	.08
589	Brian Harper	.20	.15	.08
590	John Habyan	.20	.15	.08
591	John Orton	.20	.15	.08
592	Mark Gardner	.20	.15	.08
593	Turner Ward	.40	.30	.15
594	Bob Patterson	.20	.15	.08
595	Edwin Nunez	.20	.15	.08
596	Gary Scott	.40	.30	.15
597	Scott Bankhead	.20	.15	.08
598	Checklist	.20	.15	.08
599	Checklist	.20	.15	.08
600	Checklist	.20	.15	.08

1991 Topps Stadium Club Charter Members

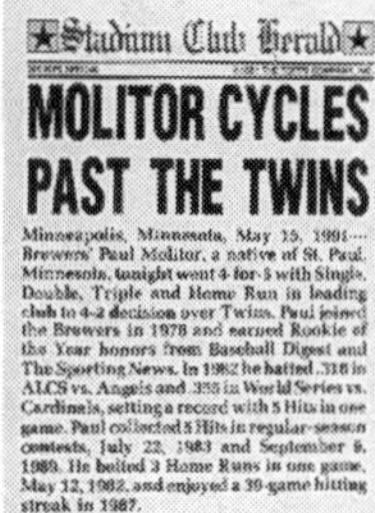

★Stadium Club Herald★

MOLITOR CYCLES PAST THE TWINS

Minneapolis, Minnesota, May 15, 1991—Brewers' Paul Molitor, a native of St. Paul, Minnesota, tonight went 4-for-5 with Single, Double, Triple and Home Run in leading club to 4-2 decision over Twins. Paul joined the Brewers in 1978 and earned Rookie of the Year honors from Baseball Digest and The Sporting News. In 1982 he batted .316 in ALCS vs. Angels and .355 in World Series vs. Cardinals, setting a record with 5 Hits in one game. Paul collected 5 Hits in regular-season contests, July 22, 1983 and September 6, 1989. He belted 3 Home Runs in one game, May 12, 1982, and enjoyed a 39-game hitting streak in 1987.

Charter members of Topps Stadium Club received a package which included a 50-card multi-sport set unavailable in any other fashion. Cards were similar in format to S.C. regular issues, with full-bleed photos on front, UV coating and gold-foil highlights. This special edition has a gold foil "Charter Member" notation at the bottom of each card front. Backs have a simulated newspaper page decsribing a career highlight. The cards are unnumbered and the checklist here includes only the baseball cards from the set.

		MT	NR MT	EX
Complete Set (32):		16.50	12.50	6.50
Common Player:		.25	.20	.10
(1)	Sandy Alomar, Jr.	.25	.20	.10
(2)	George Brett	2.00	1.50	.80
(3)	Barry Bonds	1.50	1.25	.60
(4)	Ellis Burks	.25	.20	.10
(5)	Eric Davis	.30	.25	.12
(6)	Delino DeShields	.35	.25	.14
(7)	Doug Drabek	.25	.20	.10
(8)	Cecil Fielder	.60	.45	.25
(9)	Carlton Fisk	.50	.40	.20
(10)	Ken Griffey, Jr., Ken Griffey, Sr.	2.00	1.50	.80
(11)	Billy Hatcher	.25	.20	.10
(12)	Andy Hawkins	.25	.20	.10
(13)	Rickey Henderson (A.L. MVP)	.60	.45	.25
(14)	Rickey Henderson (A.L. base-stealing leader)	.60	.45	.25
(15)	Randy Johnson	.25	.20	.10
(16)	Dave Justice	.60	.45	.25
(17)	Mark Langston, Mike Witt	.25	.20	.10
(18)	Kevin Maas	.25	.20	.10
(19)	Ramon Martinez	.25	.20	.10
(20)	Wille McGee	.25	.20	.10
(21)	Terry Mulholland	.25	.20	.10
(22)	Jose Offerman	.25	.20	.10
(23)	Melido Perez	.25	.20	.10
(24)	Nolan Ryan (no-hitter)	2.50	2.00	1.00
(25)	Nolan Ryan (300th win)	2.50	2.00	1.00
(26)	Ryne Sanberg	1.00	.70	.40
(27)	Dave Stewart	.25	.20	.10
(28)	Dave Stieb	.25	.20	.10
(29)	Bobby Thigpen	.25	.20	.10
(30)	Fernando Valenzuela	.25	.20	.10
(31)	Frank Viola	.25	.20	.10

1991 Topps Stadium Club Members Only

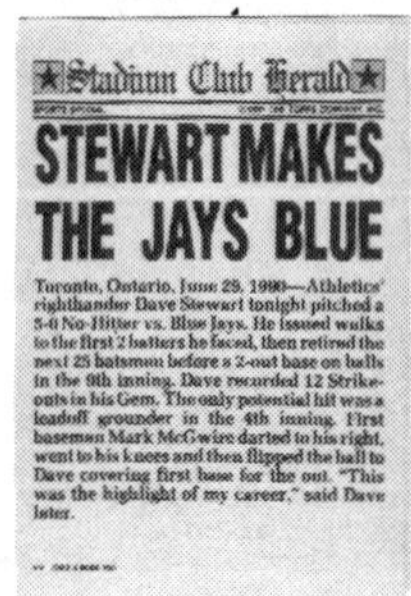

★Stadium Club Herald★

STEWART MAKES THE JAYS BLUE

Toronto, Ontario, June 29, 1990—Athletics' righthander Dave Stewart tonight pitched a 5-0 No-Hitter vs. Blue Jays. He issued walks to the first 2 batters he faced, then retired the next 25 batsmen before a 2-out base on balls in the 9th inning. Dave recorded 12 Strike-outs in his Gem. The only potential hit was a leadoff grounder in the 4th inning. First baseman Mark McGwire darted to his right, went to his knees and then flipped the ball to Dave covering first base for the out. "This was the highlight of my career," said Dave later.

Each member of Topps Stadium Club during 1991 received three packages of multi-sport cards bearing a special design and stamped "Members Only" in gold foil on the front. Cards followed the basic Stadium Club format of full-bleed action photos on front. Backs have a facsimile newspaper page - the "Stadium Club Herald" - which gives details of a career highlight. Cards are unnumbered and the baseball-only checklist here is arranged alphabetically.

	MT	NR MT	EX
Complete Set (30):	12.00	9.00	4.75
Common Player:	.25	.20	.10
(1) A.L. Home Run Leaders (Jose Canseco, Cecil Fielder)	.40	.30	.15
(2) Wilson Alvarez	.25	.20	.10
(3) Andy Ashby	.25	.20	.10
(4) Jeff Bagwell	.60	.45	.25
(5) Braves no-hitter (Kent Mercker, Mark Wohlers, Alejandro Pena)	.25	.20	.10
(6) Roger Clemens	.90	.70	.35
(7) David Cone	.25	.20	.10
(8) Carlton Fisk	.40	.30	.15
(9) Julio Franco	.25	.20	.10
(10) Tom Glavine	.25	.20	.10
(11) Tommy Greene	.25	.20	.10
(12) Pete Harnisch	.25	.20	.10
(13) Rickey Henderson (all-time theft leader)	.50	.40	.20
(14) Rickey Henderson (11th time A.L. theft leader)	.50	.40	.20
(15) Howard Johnson	.25	.20	.10
(16) Chuck Knoblauch	.40	.30	.15
(17) Ray Lankford	.35	.25	.14
(18) Denny Martinez	.25	.20	.10
(19) Paul Molitor	.50	.40	.20
(20) Jack Morris	.25	.20	.10
(21) Orioles no-hitter (Bob Milacki, Mike Flanagan, Mark Williamson, Gregg Olson, Chris Hoiles)	.25	.20	.10
(22) Terry Pendleton (N.L. leading hitter)	.25	.20	.10
(23) Terry Pendleton (MVP)	.25	.20	.10
(24) Jeff Reardon	.25	.20	.10
(25) Cal Ripken, Jr.	1.00	.70	.40
(26) Nolan Ryan (7th no-hitter)	2.00	1.50	.80
(27) Nolan Ryan (22nd 100-K season)	2.00	1.50	.80
(28) Bret Saberhagen	.25	.20	.10
(29) Robby Thompson	.25	.20	.10
(30) Dave Winfield	.50	.40	.20

1991 Topps East Coast National Reprints

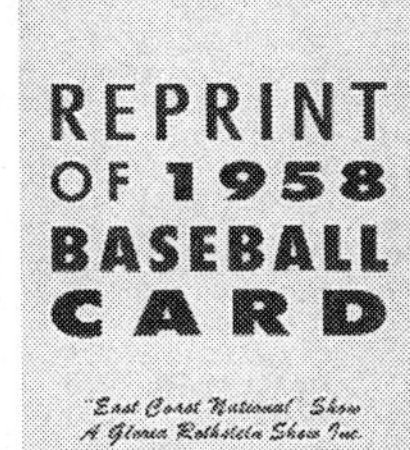

Produced in Topps' 40th anniversay year, this four-card set was issued at the 1991 East Coast National card show, the first card show in which Topps had ever participated. A total of 40,000 sets were reportedly issued in the now-standard 2-1/2" x 3-1/2" format. Fronts reproduce first Topps cards of four baseball greats while backs, printed in blue, carry a reprint notice, ad for the card show and Topps copyright.

	MT	NR MT	EX
Complete Set (4):	12.00	9.00	4.75
Common Card:	2.00	1.50	.80
(1) Mickey Mantle (1952)	6.00	4.50	2.50
(2) Hank Aaron (1954)	4.00	3.00	1.50
(3) Frank Robinson (1957)	2.00	1.50	.80
(4) Stan Musial (1958)	2.00	1.50	.80

1991 "1953" Topps Archives Promos

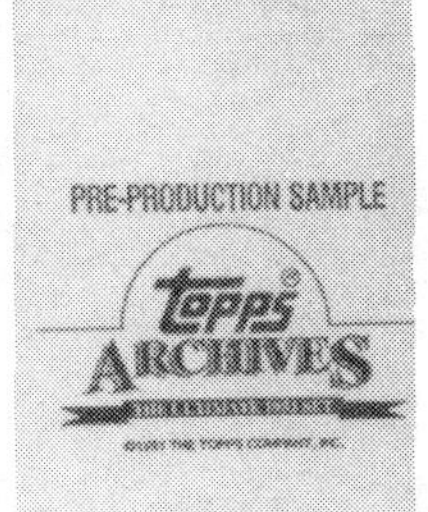

This nine-card set was issued to promote Topps' 1953 Archives set. Besides seven of the cards being reprinted from the '53 set, the promo set included two of the "new" 1953-style cards which were included in the Archives issue - cards of Hank Aaron and Eleanor Engle, the first woman to sign a minor league contract in modern times. Card fronts are identical to the issued Archives cards, while the backs are white with red Archives logo and "Pre-production Sample" notation.

	MT	NR MT	EX
Complete Set (9):	150.00	110.00	60.00
Common Player:	15.00	11.00	6.00
(1) Hank Aaron	24.00	18.00	9.50
(2) Roy Campanella	20.00	15.00	8.00
(3) Eleanor Engle	15.00	11.00	6.00
(4) Bob Feller	15.00	11.00	6.00
(5) Whitey Ford	15.00	11.00	6.00
(6) Mickey Mantle	45.00	34.00	18.00
(7) Willie Mays	24.00	18.00	9.50
(8) Jackie Robinson	24.00	18.00	9.50
(9) Satchell Paige	24.00	18.00	9.50

1991 "1953" Topps Archives

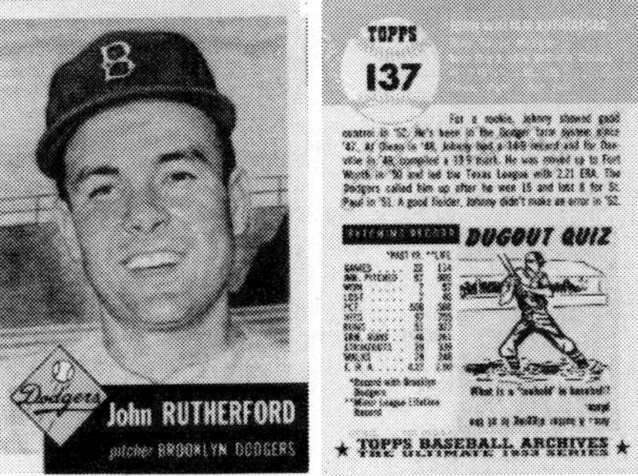

Billed as "The Ultimate 1953 Set," this issue reproduced 273 of the original 274-card 1953 Topps set. (Card #174, Billy Loes, was not reproduced due to lack of permission from the former Dodgers pitcher.) The Archives issue downsized the cards from their original 2-5/8" x 3-3/4" size to the now-standard 2-1/2" x 3-1/2" format. More than 50 cards of players who were not included in the 1953 Topps set were created as part of the Archives issue. Because Topps chose to use black-and-white photos and colorized backgrounds for most of the "extended" cards, rather than paintings as on the originals, collector interest in the Archives issue was diminished. While only 18,000 cases were reported produced, demand has not been strong and prices have remained about as issued.

		MT	NR MT	EX
Complete Set:		60.00	45.00	25.00
Common Player:		.20	.15	.08
1	Jackie Robinson	4.00	3.00	1.50
2	Luke Easter	.20	.15	.08
3	George Crowe	.20	.15	.08
4	Ben Wade	.20	.15	.08
5	Joe Dobson	.20	.15	.08
6	Sam Jones	.20	.15	.08
7	Bob Borkowski	.20	.15	.08
8	Clem Koshorek	.20	.15	.08
9	Joe Collins	.20	.15	.08
10	Smoky Burgess	.20	.15	.08
11	Sal Yvars	.20	.15	.08
12	Howie Judson	.20	.15	.08
13	Conrado Marrero	.20	.15	.08
14	Clem Labine	.20	.15	.08
15	Bobo Newsom	.20	.15	.08
16	Peanuts Lowrey	.20	.15	.08
17	Billy Hitchcock	.20	.15	.08
18	Ted Lepcio	.20	.15	.08
19	Mel Parnell	.20	.15	.08
20	Hank Thompson	.20	.15	.08
21	Billy Johnson	.20	.15	.08
22	Howie Fox	.20	.15	.08
23	Toby Atwell	.20	.15	.08
24	Ferris Fain	.20	.15	.08
25	Ray Boone	.20	.15	.08
26	Dale Mitchell	.25	.20	.10
27	Roy Campanella	2.50	2.00	1.00
28	Eddie Pellagrini	.20	.15	.08
29	Hal Jeffcoat	.20	.15	.08
30	Willard Nixon	.20	.15	.08
31	Ewell Blackwell	.20	.15	.08
32	Clyde Vollmer	.20	.15	.08
33	Bob Kennedy	.20	.15	.08
34	George Shuba	.20	.15	.08
35	Irv Noren	.20	.15	.08
37	Eddie Mathews	1.00	.70	.40
38	Jim Hearn	.20	.15	.08
39	Eddie Miksis	.20	.15	.08
40	John Lipon	.20	.15	.08
41	Enos Slaughter	.50	.40	.20
42	Gus Zernial	.20	.15	.08
43	Gil McDougald	.25	.20	.10
44	Ellis Kinder	.20	.15	.08
45	Grady Hatton	.20	.15	.08
46	Johnny Klippstein	.20	.15	.08
47	Bubba Church	.20	.15	.08
48	Bob Del Greco	.20	.15	.08
49	Faye Throneberry	.20	.15	.08
50	Chuck Dressen	.20	.15	.08
51	Frank Campos	.20	.15	.08
52	Ted Gray	.20	.15	.08
53	Sherman Lollar	.20	.15	.08
54	Bob Feller	1.00	.70	.40
55	Maurice McDermott	.20	.15	.08
56	Gerald Staley	.20	.15	.08
57	Carl Scheib	.20	.15	.08
58	George Metkovich	.20	.15	.08
59	Karl Drews	.20	.15	.08
60	Cloyd Boyer	.20	.15	.08
61	Early Wynn	.50	.40	.20
62	Monte Irvin	.50	.40	.20
63	Gus Niarhos	.20	.15	.08
64	Dave Philley	.20	.15	.08
65	Earl Harrist	.20	.15	.08
66	Orestes Minoso	.35	.25	.14
67	Roy Sievers	.20	.15	.08
68	Del Rice	.20	.15	.08
69	Dick Brodowski	.20	.15	.08
70	Ed Yuhas	.20	.15	.08
71	Tony Bartirome	.20	.15	.08
72	Fred Hutchinson	.20	.15	.08
73	Eddie Robinson	.20	.15	.08
74	Joe Rossi	.20	.15	.08
75	Mike Garcia	.20	.15	.08
76	Pee Wee Reese	2.00	1.50	.80
77	John Mize	.75	.60	.30
78	Al Schoendienst	.50	.40	.20
79	Johnny Wyrostek	.20	.15	.08
80	Jim Hegan	.20	.15	.08
81	Joe Black	.20	.15	.08
82	Mickey Mantle	15.00	11.00	6.00
83	Howie Pollet	.20	.15	.08
84	Bob Hooper	.20	.15	.08
85	Bobby Morgan	.20	.15	.08
86	Billy Martin	.35	.25	.14
87	Ed Lopat	.25	.20	.10
88	Willie Jones	.20	.15	.08
89	Chuck Stobbs	.20	.15	.08
90	Hank Edwards	.20	.15	.08
91	Ebba St. Claire	.20	.15	.08
92	Paul Minner	.20	.15	.08
93	Hal Rice	.20	.15	.08
94	William Kennedy	.20	.15	.08
95	Willard Marshall	.20	.15	.08
96	Virgil Trucks	.20	.15	.08
97	Don Kolloway	.20	.15	.08
98	Cal Abrams	.20	.15	.08
99	Dave Madison	.20	.15	.08
100	Bill Miller	.20	.15	.08
101	Ted Wilks	.20	.15	.08
102	Connie Ryan	.20	.15	.08
103	Joe Astroth	.20	.15	.08
104	Yogi Berra	2.50	2.00	1.00
105	Joe Nuxhall	.20	.15	.08
106	John Antonelli	.20	.15	.08
107	Danny O'Connell	.20	.15	.08
108	Bob Porterfield	.20	.15	.08
109	Alvin Dark	.20	.15	.08
110	Herman Wehmeier	.20	.15	.08
111	Hank Sauer	.20	.15	.08
112	Ned Garver	.20	.15	.08
113	Jerry Priddy	.20	.15	.08
114	Phil Rizzuto	2.00	1.50	.80
115	George Spencer	.20	.15	.08
116	Frank Smith	.20	.15	.08
117	Sid Gordon	.20	.15	.08
118	Gus Bell	.20	.15	.08
119	John Sain	.35	.25	.14
120	Davey Williams	.20	.15	.08
121	Walt Dropo	.20	.15	.08
122	Elmer Valo	.20	.15	.08
123	Tommy Byrne	.20	.15	.08
124	Sibby Sisti	.20	.15	.08
125	Dick Williams	.25	.20	.10
126	Bill Connelly	.20	.15	.08
127	Clint Courtney	.20	.15	.08
128	Wilmer Mizell	.20	.15	.08
129	Keith Thomas	.20	.15	.08
130	Turk Lown	.20	.15	.08
131	Harry Byrd	.20	.15	.08
132	Tom Morgan	.20	.15	.08
133	Gil Coan	.20	.15	.08
134	Rube Walker	.20	.15	.08
135	Al Rosen	.25	.20	.10
136	Ken Heintzelman	.20	.15	.08
137	John Rutherford	.20	.15	.08
138	George Kell	.50	.40	.20
139	Sammy White	.20	.15	.08
140	Tommy Glaviano	.20	.15	.08
141	Allie Reynolds	.35	.25	.14
142	Vic Wertz	.20	.15	.08
143	Billy Pierce	.25	.20	.10
144	Bob Schultz	.20	.15	.08
145	Harry Dorish	.20	.15	.08
146	Granville Hamner	.20	.15	.08
147	Warren Spahn	1.00	.70	.40
148	Mickey Grasso	.20	.15	.08
149	Dom DiMaggio	.25	.20	.10
150	Harry Simpson	.20	.15	.08
151	Hoyt Wilhelm	.75	.60	.30
152	Bob Adams	.20	.15	.08
153	Andy Seminick	.20	.15	.08
154	Dick Groat	.25	.20	.10
155	Dutch Leonard	.20	.15	.08
156	Jim Rivera	.20	.15	.08
157	Bob Addis	.20	.15	.08
158	John Logan	.20	.15	.08
159	Wayne Terwilliger	.20	.15	.08
160	Bob Young	.20	.15	.08
161	Vern Bickford	.20	.15	.08

162	Ted Kluszewski	.35	.25	.14
163	Fred Hatfield	.20	.15	.08
164	Frank Shea	.20	.15	.08
165	Billy Hoeft	.20	.15	.08
166	Bill Hunter	.20	.15	.08
167	Art Schult	.20	.15	.08
168	Willard Schmidt	.20	.15	.08
169	Dizzy Trout	.20	.15	.08
170	Bill Werle	.20	.15	.08
171	Bill Glynn	.20	.15	.08
172	Rip Repulski	.20	.15	.08
173	Preston Ward	.20	.15	.08
175	Ron Kline	.20	.15	.08
176	Don Hoak	.20	.15	.08
177	Jim Dyck	.20	.15	.08
178	Jim Waugh	.20	.15	.08
179	Gene Hermanski	.20	.15	.08
180	Virgil Stallcup	.20	.15	.08
181	Al Zarilla	.20	.15	.08
182	Bob Hofman	.20	.15	.08
183	Stu Miller	.20	.15	.08
184	Hal Brown	.20	.15	.08
185	Jim Pendleton	.20	.15	.08
186	Charlie Bishop	.20	.15	.08
187	Jim Fridley	.20	.15	.08
188	Andy Carey	.20	.15	.08
189	Ray Jablonski	.20	.15	.08
190	Dixie Walker	.20	.15	.08
191	Ralph Kiner	.50	.40	.20
192	Wally Westlake	.20	.15	.08
193	Mike Clark	.20	.15	.08
194	Eddie Kazak	.20	.15	.08
195	Ed McGhee	.20	.15	.08
196	Bob Keegan	.20	.15	.08
197	Del Crandall	.20	.15	.08
198	Forrest Main	.20	.15	.08
199	Marion Fricano	.20	.15	.08
200	Gordon Goldsberry	.20	.15	.08
201	Paul La Palme	.20	.15	.08
202	Carl Sawatski	.20	.15	.08
203	Cliff Fannin	.20	.15	.08
204	Dick Bokelmann	.20	.15	.08
205	Vern Benson	.20	.15	.08
206	Ed Bailey	.20	.15	.08
207	Whitey Ford	2.00	1.50	.80
208	Jim Wilson	.20	.15	.08
209	Jim Greengrass	.20	.15	.08
210	Bob Cerv	.20	.15	.08
211	J.W. Porter	.20	.15	.08
212	Jack Dittmer	.20	.15	.08
213	Ray Scarborough	.20	.15	.08
214	Bill Bruton	.20	.15	.08
215	Gene Conley	.20	.15	.08
216	Jim Hughes	.20	.15	.08
217	Murray Wall	.20	.15	.08
218	Les Fusselman	.20	.15	.08
219	Pete Runnels	.20	.15	.08
220	Satchell Paige	4.00	3.00	1.50
221	Bob Milliken	.20	.15	.08
222	Vic Janowicz	.20	.15	.08
223	John O'Brien	.20	.15	.08
224	Lou Sleater	.20	.15	.08
225	Bobby Shantz	.25	.20	.10
226	Ed Erautt	.20	.15	.08
227	Morris Martin	.20	.15	.08
228	Hal Newhouser	.20	.15	.08
229	Rocky Krshnich	.20	.15	.08
230	Johnny Lindell	.20	.15	.08
231	Solly Hemus	.20	.15	.08
232	Dick Kokos	.20	.15	.08
233	Al Aber	.20	.15	.08
234	Ray Murray	.20	.15	.08
235	John Hetki	.20	.15	.08
236	Harry Perkowski	.20	.15	.08
237	Clarence Podbielan	.20	.15	.08
238	Cal Hogue	.20	.15	.08
239	Jim Delsing	.20	.15	.08
240	Freddie Marsh	.20	.15	.08
241	Al Sima	.20	.15	.08
242	Charlie Silvera	.20	.15	.08
243	Carlos Bernier	.20	.15	.08
244	Willie Mays	.25	.20	.10
245	Bill Norman	.20	.15	.08
246	Roy Face	.20	.15	.08
247	Mike Sandlock	.20	.15	.08
248	Gene Stephens	.20	.15	.08
249	Ed O'Brien	.20	.15	.08
250	Bob Wilson	.20	.15	.08
251	Sid Hudson	.20	.15	.08
252	Henry Foiles	.20	.15	.08
254	Preacher Roe	.20	.15	.08
255	Dixie Howell	.20	.15	.08
256	Les Peden	.20	.15	.08
257	Bob Boyd	.20	.15	.08
258	Jim Gilliam	.35	.25	.14
259	Roy McMillan	.20	.15	.08
260	Sam Calderone	.20	.15	.08
262	Bob Oldis	.20	.15	.08
263	John Podres	.35	.25	.14
264	Gene Woodling	.35	.25	.14
265	Jackie Jensen	.35	.25	.14
266	Bob Cain	.20	.15	.08
269	Duane Pillette	.20	.15	.08
270	Vern Stephens	.20	.15	.08
272	Bill Antonello	.20	.15	.08
273	Harvey Haddix	.20	.15	.08
274	John Riddle	.20	.15	.08
276	Ken Raffensberger	.20	.15	.08
277	Don Lund	.20	.15	.08
278	Willie Miranda	.20	.15	.08
279	Joe Coleman	.20	.15	.08
280	Milt Bolling	.20	.15	.08
281	Jimmie Dykes	.20	.15	.08
282	Ralph Houk	.35	.25	.14
283	Frank J. Thomas	.20	.15	.08
284	Bob Lemon	.50	.40	.20
285	Joe Adcock	.20	.15	.08
286	Jimmy Piersall	.25	.20	.10
287	Mickey Vernon	.20	.15	.08
288	Robin Roberts	.50	.40	.20
289	Rogers Hornsby	.75	.60	.30
290	Hank Bauer	.20	.15	.08
291	Hoot Evers	.20	.15	.08
292	Whitey Lockman	.20	.15	.08
293	Ralph Branca	.25	.20	.10
294	Wally Post	.20	.15	.08
295	Phil Cavarretta	.20	.15	.08
296	Gil Hodges	.35	.25	.14
297	Roy Smalley	.20	.15	.08
298	Bob Friend	.20	.15	.08
299	Dusty Rhodes	.25	.20	.10
300	Eddie Stanky	.20	.15	.08
301	Harvey Kuenn	.25	.20	.10
302	Marty Marion	.20	.15	.08
303	Sal Maglie	.20	.15	.08
304	Lou Boudreau	.50	.40	.20
305	Carl Furillo	.35	.25	.14
306	Bobo Holloman	.20	.15	.08
307	Steve O'Neill	.20	.15	.08
308	Carl Erskine	.25	.20	.10
309	Leo Durocher	.25	.20	.10
310	Lew Burdette	.20	.15	.08
311	Richie Ashburn	.35	.25	.14
312	Hoyt Wilhelm	.60	.45	.25
313	Bucky Harris	.50	.40	.20
314	Joe Garagiola	.75	.60	.30
315	Johnny Pesky	.20	.15	.08
316	Fred Haney	.20	.15	.08
317	Hank Aaron	7.50	5.75	3.00
318	Curt Simmons	.20	.15	.08
319	Ted Williams	6.00	4.50	2.50
320	Don Newcombe	.35	.25	.14
321	Charlie Grimm	.20	.15	.08
322	Paul Richards	.20	.15	.08
323	Wes Westrum	.20	.15	.08
324	Vern Law	.20	.15	.08
325	Casey Stengel	1.00	.70	.40
326	Hall of Fame Inductees (Dizzy Dean, Al Simmons)	1.00	.70	.40
327	Duke Snider	1.50	1.25	.60
328	Bill Rigney	.20	.15	.08
329	Al Lopez	.50	.40	.20
330	Bobby Thomson	.35	.25	.14
331	Nellie Fox	.35	.25	.14
332	Eleanor Engle	.20	.15	.08
333	Larry Doby	.25	.20	.10
334	Billy Goodman	.20	.15	.08
335	Checklist 1-140	.20	.15	.08
336	Checklist 141-280	.20	.15	.08
337	Checklist 281-337	.20	.15	.08

1992 Topps Promo Sheet

To preview its 1992 card set for dealers, Topps distributed a nine-card sheet in the basic format of its 1992 issue. The 8" x 10" sheets are often found cut into standard 2-1/2" x 3-1/2" singles. Card numbers on the backs of these promo cards do not correspond to the same cards in the regular set, and the stats for 1991 are not included. The preview cards have a gray oval on back, with the words, "1992 Pre-Production Sample".

		MT	NR MT	EX
	Complete Set (sheet):	8.00	6.00	3.25
	Complete Set (9):	8.00	6.00	3.25
	Common Player:	1.00	.70	.40
3	Shawon Dunston	1.00	.70	.40
16	Mike Heath	1.00	.70	.40
18	Todd Frowirth	1.00	.70	.40
20	Bip Roberts	1.00	.70	.40
131	Rob Dibble	1.00	.70	.40
174	Otis Nixon	1.00	.70	.40
273	Dennis Martinez	1.00	.70	.40
325	Brett Butler	1.00	.70	.40
798	Tom Lasorda	1.50	1.25	.90

Grading Guide

Mint (MT): A perfect card. Well-centered with all corners sharp and square. No creases, stains, edge nicks, surface marks, yellowing or fading.

Near Mint (NM): A nearly perfect card. At first glance, a NM card appears to be perfect. May be slightly off-center. No surface marks, creases or loss of gloss.

Excellent (EX): Corners are still fairly sharp with only moderate wear. Borders may be off-center. No creases or stains on fronts or backs, but may show slight loss of surface luster.

Very Good (VG): Shows obvious handling. May have rounded corners, minor creases, major gum or wax stains. No major creases, tape marks, writing, etc.

Good (G): A well-worn card, but exhibits no intentional damage. May have major or multiple creases. Corners may be rounded well beyond card border.

1992 Topps

This 792-card set features white stock much like the 1991 issue. The card fronts feature full-color action and posed photos with a gray inner frame and the player name and position on the bottom. The backs feature biographical information, statistics and stadium photos on player cards where space is available. All-Star cards and #1 Draft Pick cards are once again included. Topps brought back four-

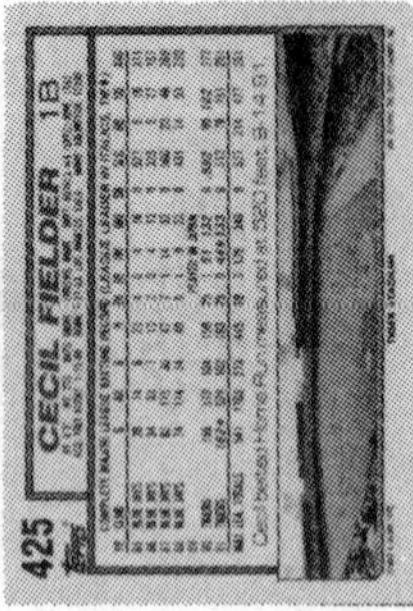

player rookie cards in 1992. Nine Top Prospect cards of this nature can be found within the set. Several cards can once again be found with horizontal fronts. "Match the Stats" game cards were inserted into packs of 1992 Topps cards. Special bonus cards were given away to winners of this insert game. Record Breaker cards are also featured in this set.

		MT	NR MT	EX
	Complete Set (792):	20.00	15.00	8.00
	Common Player:	.03	.02	.01
1	Nolan Ryan	.50	.40	.20
2	Record Breaker (Rickey Henderson)	.10	.08	.04
3	Record Breaker (Jeff Reardon)	.05	.04	.02
4	Record Breaker (Nolan Ryan)	.10	.08	.04
5	Record Breaker (Dave Winfield)	.06	.05	.02
6	*Brien Taylor* (Draft Pick)	1.50	1.25	.60
7	*Jim Olander* (FC)	.10	.08	.04
8	*Bryan Hickerson* (FC)	.10	.08	.04
9	John Farrell (Draft Pick)	.03	.02	.01
10	Wade Boggs	.15	.11	.06
11	Jack McDowell	.08	.06	.03
12	Luis Gonzalez	.08	.06	.03
13	Mike Scioscia	.04	.03	.02
14	Wes Chamberlain	.08	.06	.03
15	Denny Martinez	.04	.03	.02
16	Jeff Montgomery	.04	.03	.02
17	Randy Milligan	.06	.05	.02
18	Greg Cadaret	.03	.02	.01
19	Jamie Quirk	.03	.02	.01
20	Bip Roberts	.05	.04	.02
21	Buck Rodgers	.03	.02	.01
22	Bill Wegman	.04	.03	.02
23	Chuck Knoblauch	.10	.08	.04
24	Randy Myers	.05	.04	.02
25	Ron Gant	.15	.11	.06
26	Mike Bielecki	.03	.02	.01
27	Juan Gonzalez	.75	.60	.30
28	Mike Schooler	.04	.03	.02
29	Mickey Tettleton	.05	.04	.02
30	John Kruk	.06	.05	.02
31	Bryn Smith	.03	.02	.01
32	Chris Nabholz	.06	.05	.02
33	Carlos Baerga	.20	.15	.08
34	Jeff Juden	.15	.11	.06
35	Dave Righetti	.06	.05	.02
36	*Scott Ruffcorn* (Draft Pick)	.30	.25	.12
37	Luis Polonia	.04	.03	.02
38	Tom Candiotti	.04	.03	.02
39	Greg Olson	.04	.03	.02
40	Cal Ripken, Jr.	.20	.15	.08
41	Craig Lefferts	.04	.03	.02
42	Mike Macfarlane	.04	.03	.02
43	Jose Lind	.04	.03	.02
44	Rick Aguilera	.05	.04	.02
45	Gary Carter	.08	.06	.03
46	Steve Farr	.04	.03	.02
47	Rex Hudler	.04	.03	.02
48	Scott Scudder	.05	.04	.02
49	Damon Berryhill	.04	.03	.02
50	Ken Griffey, Jr.	.75	.60	.30
51	Tom Runnells	.03	.02	.01
52	Juan Bell	.05	.04	.02
53	Tommy Gregg	.03	.02	.01
54	David Wells	.04	.03	.02
55	Rafael Palmeiro	.10	.08	.04
56	Charlie O'Brien	.03	.02	.01
57	Donn Pall	.03	.02	.01
58	Top Prospects-Catchers (*Brad Ausmus* (FC), Jim Campanis, Dave Nilsson, Doug Robbins)	.20	.15	.08
59	Mo Vaughn	.25	.20	.10
60	Tony Fernandez	.05	.04	.02
61	Paul O'Neill	.06	.05	.02
62	Gene Nelson	.03	.02	.01
63	Randy Ready	.03	.02	.01
64	Bob Kipper	.03	.02	.01
65	Willie McGee	.08	.06	.03
66	*Scott Stahoviak* (Draft Pick)	.30	.25	.12
67	Luis Salazar	.03	.02	.01
68	Marvin Freeman	.03	.02	.01
69	*Kenny Lofton*	.40	.30	.15
70	Gary Gaetti	.06	.05	.02
71	Erik Hanson	.08	.06	.03
72	Eddie Zosky (FC)	.10	.08	.04
73	Brian Barnes	.10	.08	.04
74	Scott Leius	.10	.08	.04
75	Bret Saberhagen	.08	.06	.03
76	Mike Gallego	.03	.02	.01
77	Jack Armstrong	.05	.04	.02
78	*Ivan Rodriguez*	.30	.25	.12

79 Jesse Orosco .03 .02 .01
80 David Justice .30 .25 .12
81 *Ced Landrum* (FC) .15 .11 .06
82 *Doug Simons* .10 .08 .04
83 Tommy Greene .06 .05 .02
84 Leo Gomez .15 .11 .06
85 Jose DeLeon .04 .03 .02
86 Steve Finley .06 .05 .02
87 *Bob MacDonald* (FC) .15 .11 .06
88 Darrin Jackson .04 .03 .02
89 Neal Heaton .03 .02 .01
90 Robin Yount .12 .09 .05
91 Jeff Reed .03 .02 .01
92 Lenny Harris .04 .03 .02
93 Reggie Jefferson .15 .11 .06
94 Sammy Sosa .08 .06 .03
95 Scott Bailes .03 .02 .01
96 *Tom McKinnon* (Draft Pick) .15 .11 .06
97 Luis Rivera .03 .02 .01
98 Mike Harkey .06 .05 .02
99 Jeff Treadway .04 .03 .02
100 Jose Canseco .10 .08 .04
101 Omar Vizquel .03 .02 .01
102 *Scott Kamieniecki* .12 .09 .05
103 Ricky Jordan .06 .05 .02
104 Jeff Ballard .04 .03 .02
105 Felix Jose .10 .08 .04
106 Mike Boddicker .05 .04 .02
107 Dan Pasqua .04 .03 .02
108 *Mike Timlin* .12 .09 .05
109 Roger Craig .04 .03 .02
110 Ryne Sandberg .20 .15 .08
111 Mark Carreon .03 .02 .01
112 Oscar Azocar .04 .03 .02
113 Mike Greenwell .10 .08 .04
114 Mark Portugal .03 .02 .01
115 Terry Pendleton .08 .06 .03
116 Willie Randolph .05 .04 .02
117 Scott Terry .03 .02 .01
118 Chili Davis .08 .06 .03
119 Mark Gardner .05 .04 .02
120 Alan Trammell .10 .08 .04
121 Derek Bell .15 .11 .06
122 Gary Varsho .03 .02 .01
123 Bob Ojeda .04 .03 .02
124 *Shawn Livsey* (Draft Pick) .15 .11 .06
125 Chris Hoiles .08 .06 .03
126 Top Prospects-1st Baseman (Rico Brogna (FC), John Jaha, Ryan Klesko, Dave Staton) 1.00 .70 .40
127 Carlos Quintana .06 .05 .02
128 Kurt Stillwell .04 .03 .02
129 Melido Perez .04 .03 .02
130 Alvin Davis .06 .05 .02
131 Checklist 1 .03 .02 .01
132 Eric Show .03 .02 .01
133 Rance Mulliniks .03 .02 .01
134 Darryl Kile .08 .06 .03
135 Von Hayes .05 .04 .02
136 Bill Doran .05 .04 .02
137 Jeff Robinson .03 .02 .01
138 Monty Fariss .08 .06 .03
139 Jeff Innis .05 .04 .02
140 Mark Grace .12 .09 .05
141 Jim Leyland .03 .02 .01
142 Todd Van Poppel (FC) .30 .25 .12
143 Paul Gibson .03 .02 .01
144 Bill Swift .04 .03 .02
145 Danny Tartabull .08 .06 .03
146 Al Newman .03 .02 .01
147 Cris Carpenter .04 .03 .02
148 *Anthony Young* (FC) .25 .20 .10
149 *Brian Bohanon* (FC) .15 .11 .06
150 Roger Clemens .15 .11 .06
151 Jeff Hamilton .03 .02 .01
152 Charlie Leibrandt .04 .03 .02
153 Ron Karkovice .04 .03 .02
154 Hensley Meulens .08 .06 .03
155 Scott Bankhead .04 .03 .02
156 *Manny Ramirez* (Draft Pick) 1.25 .90 .50
157 Keith Miller .03 .02 .01
158 Todd Frohwirth .03 .02 .01
159 Darrin Fletcher .05 .04 .02
160 Bobby Bonilla .12 .09 .05
161 Casey Candaele .03 .02 .01
162 Paul Faries (FC) .10 .08 .04
163 Dana Kiecker .03 .02 .01
164 Shane Mack .08 .06 .03
165 Mark Langston .10 .08 .04
166 Geronimo Pena .06 .05 .02
167 Andy Allanson .03 .02 .01
168 Dwight Smith .04 .03 .02
169 Chuck Crim .03 .02 .01
170 Alex Cole .05 .04 .02
171 Bill Plummer .03 .02 .01
172 Juan Berenguer .03 .02 .01
173 Brian Downing .04 .03 .02
174 Steve Frey .03 .02 .01
175 Orel Hershiser .08 .06 .03
176 *Ramon Garcia* (FC) .15 .11 .06
177 Danny Gladden .04 .03 .02
178 Jim Acker .03 .02 .01
179 Top Prospects-2nd Baseman (*Cesar Bernhardt*, Bobby DeJardin, Armando Moreno, Andy Stankiewicz) .25 .20 .10
180 Kevin Mitchell .10 .08 .04
181 Hector Villanueva .06 .05 .02
182 Jeff Reardon .06 .05 .02
183 Brent Mayne .06 .05 .02
184 Jimmy Jones .03 .02 .01
185 Benny Santiago .08 .06 .03
186 *Cliff Floyd* (Draft Pick) 1.75 1.25 .70
187 Ernie Riles .03 .02 .01
188 Jose Guzman .05 .04 .02
189 Junior Felix .06 .05 .02
190 Glenn Davis .08 .06 .03
191 Charlie Hough .04 .03 .02
192 *Dave Fleming* (FC) .20 .15 .08
193 Omar Oliveras (FC) .08 .06 .03
194 Eric Karros (FC) .30 .25 .12
195 David Cone .08 .06 .03
196 *Frank Castillo* (FC) .12 .09 .05
197 Glenn Braggs .04 .03 .02
198 Scott Aldred .06 .05 .02
199 Jeff Blauser .04 .03 .02
200 Len Dykstra .08 .06 .03
201 Buck Showalter .03 .02 .01
202 Rick Honeycutt .03 .02 .01
203 Greg Myers .03 .02 .01
204 Trevor Wilson .05 .04 .02
205 Jay Howell .04 .03 .02
206 Luis Sojo .05 .04 .02
207 Jack Clark .08 .06 .03
208 Julio Machado .03 .02 .01
209 Lloyd McClendon .03 .02 .01
210 Ozzie Guillen .06 .05 .02
211 *Jeremy Hernandez* (FC) .15 .11 .06
212 Randy Velarde .03 .02 .01
213 Les Lancaster .03 .02 .01
214 *Andy Mota* (FC) .15 .11 .06
215 Rich Gossage .05 .04 .02
216 *Brent Gates* (Draft Pick) .40 .30 .15
217 Brian Harper .05 .04 .02
218 Mike Flanagan .03 .02 .01
219 Jerry Browne .04 .03 .02
220 Jose Rijo .08 .06 .03
221 Skeeter Barnes .04 .03 .02
222 Jaime Navarro .04 .03 .02
223 Mel Hall .04 .03 .02
224 *Brett Barberie* .20 .15 .08
225 Roberto Alomar .15 .11 .06
226 Pete Smith .03 .02 .01
227 Daryl Boston .03 .02 .01
228 Eddie Whitson .04 .03 .02
229 Shawn Boskie .04 .03 .02
230 Dick Schofield .03 .02 .01
231 *Brian Drahman* (FC) .10 .08 .04
232 John Smiley .05 .04 .02
233 Mitch Webster .04 .03 .02
234 Terry Steinbach .05 .04 .02
235 Jack Morris .08 .06 .03
236 Bill Pecota .04 .03 .02
237 *Jose Hernandez* (FC) .10 .08 .04
238 Greg Litton .03 .02 .01
239 Brian Holman .05 .04 .02
240 Andres Galarraga .06 .05 .02
241 Gerald Young .03 .02 .01
242 Mike Mussina (FC) .50 .40 .20
243 Alvaro Espinoza .03 .02 .01
244 Darren Daulton .04 .03 .02
245 John Smoltz .08 .06 .03
246 *Jason Pruitt* (Draft Pick) .15 .11 .06
247 Chuck Finley .08 .06 .03
248 Jim Gantner .04 .03 .02
249 Tony Fossas .03 .02 .01
250 Ken Griffey .05 .04 .02
251 Kevin Elster .04 .03 .02
252 Dennis Rasmussen .03 .02 .01
253 Terry Kennedy .03 .02 .01
254 *Ryan Bowen* (FC) .15 .11 .06
255 Robin Ventura .15 .11 .06
256 Mike Aldrete .03 .02 .01
257 Jeff Russell .04 .03 .02
258 Jim Lindeman .03 .02 .01
259 Ron Darling .05 .04 .02
260 Devon White .06 .05 .02
261 Tom Lasorda .04 .03 .02
262 Terry Lee (FC) .10 .08 .04
263 Bob Patterson .03 .02 .01
264 Checklist 2 .03 .02 .01
265 Teddy Higuera .05 .04 .02
266 Roberto Kelly .08 .06 .03
267 Steve Bedrosian .04 .03 .02
268 Brady Anderson .03 .02 .01
269 *Ruben Amaro* (FC) .15 .11 .06
270 Tony Gwynn .12 .09 .05
271 Tracy Jones .03 .02 .01
272 Jerry Don Gleaton .03 .02 .01
273 Craig Grebeck .04 .03 .02
274 *Bob Scanlan* .10 .08 .04
275 Todd Zeile .10 .08 .04
276 *Shawn Green* (Draft Pick) .25 .20 .10
277 Scott Chiamparino .04 .03 .02
278 Darryl Hamilton .04 .03 .02
279 Jim Clancy .03 .02 .01
280 Carlos Martinez .04 .03 .02
281 Kevin Appier .05 .04 .02
282 *John Wehner* (FC) .15 .11 .06
283 Reggie Sanders .20 .15 .08
284 Gene Larkin .04 .03 .02
285 Bob Welch .06 .05 .02
286 Gilberto Reyes (FC) .05 .04 .02
287 *Pete Schourek* .15 .11 .06
288 Andujar Cedeno .15 .11 .06
289 Mike Morgan .04 .03 .02
290 Bo Jackson .20 .15 .08
291 Phil Garner .03 .02 .01
292 Ray Lankford .15 .11 .06
293 Mike Henneman .05 .04 .02
294 Dave Valle .03 .02 .01
295 Alonzo Powell (FC) .08 .06 .03
296 Tom Brunansky .05 .04 .02
297 Kevin Brown .05 .04 .02
298 Kelly Gruber .08 .06 .03
299 Charles Nagy .06 .05 .02
300 Don Mattingly .15 .11 .06
301 Kirk McCaskill .04 .03 .02
302 Joey Cora .04 .03 .02
303 Dan Plesac .04 .03 .02
304 Joe Oliver .04 .03 .02
305 Tom Glavine .08 .06 .03
306 *Al Shirley* (Draft Pick) .15 .11 .06
307 Bruce Ruffin .03 .02 .01
308 *Craig Shipley* (FC) .08 .06 .03
309 Dave Martinez .04 .03 .02
310 Jose Mesa .03 .02 .01
311 Henry Cotto .03 .02 .01
312 Mike LaValliere .04 .03 .02
313 Kevin Tapani .08 .06 .03
314 Jeff Huson .04 .03 .02
315 Juan Samuel .06 .05 .02
316 Curt Schilling .06 .05 .02
317 Mike Bordick (FC) .06 .05 .02
318 Steve Howe .04 .03 .02
319 Tony Phillips .04 .03 .02
320 George Bell .10 .08 .04
321 Lou Pinella .03 .02 .01
322 Tim Burke .04 .03 .02
323 Milt Thompson .04 .03 .02
324 Danny Darwin .04 .03 .02
325 Joe Orsulak .03 .02 .01
326 Eric King .04 .03 .02
327 Jay Buhner .05 .04 .02
328 *Joel Johnston* (FC) .15 .11 .06
329 Franklin Stubbs .03 .02 .01
330 Will Clark .20 .15 .08
331 Steve Lake .03 .02 .01
332 *Chris Jones* .10 .08 .04
333 Pat Tabler .03 .02 .01
334 Kevin Gross .03 .02 .01
335 Dave Henderson .08 .06 .03
336 *Greg Anthony* (Draft Pick) .15 .11 .06
337 Alejandro Pena .04 .03 .02
338 Shawn Abner .03 .02 .01
339 Tom Browning .06 .05 .02
340 Otis Nixon .04 .03 .02
341 Bob Geren .03 .02 .01
342 *Tim Spehr* (FC) .10 .08 .04
343 *Jon Vander Wal* (FC) .20 .15 .08
344 Jack Daugherty .03 .02 .01
345 Zane Smith .04 .03 .02
346 *Rheal Cormier* (FC) .15 .11 .06
347 Kent Hrbek .06 .05 .02
348 *Rick Wilkins* (FC) .15 .11 .06
349 Steve Lyons .03 .02 .01
350 Gregg Olson .08 .06 .03
351 Greg Riddoch .03 .02 .01
352 Ed Nunez .03 .02 .01
353 *Braulio Castillo* (FC) .08 .06 .03
354 Dave Bergman .03 .02 .01
355 *Warren Newson* (FC) .15 .11 .06
356 Luis Quinones .03 .02 .01
357 Mike Witt .04 .03 .02
358 *Ted Wood* .15 .11 .06
359 Mike Moore .04 .03 .02
360 Lance Parrish .06 .05 .02
361 Barry Jones .03 .02 .01
362 *Javier Ortiz* (FC) .10 .08 .04
363 John Candelaria .04 .03 .02
364 Glenallen Hill .06 .05 .02
365 Duane Ward .04 .03 .02
366 Checklist 3 .03 .02 .01
367 Rafael Belliard .03 .02 .01
368 Bill Krueger .03 .02 .01
369 *Steve Whitaker* (Draft Pick) .20 .15 .08
370 Shawon Dunston .06 .05 .02
371 Dante Bichette .04 .03 .02
372 *Kip Gross* (FC) .10 .08 .04
373 Don Robinson .03 .02 .01
374 Bernie Williams .03 .02 .01
375 Bert Blyleven .05 .04 .02
376 *Chris Donnels* (FC) .15 .11 .06
377 *Bob Zupcic* (FC) .30 .25 .12
378 Joel Skinner .03 .02 .01
379 Steve Chitren .06 .05 .02
380 Barry Bonds .40 .30 .15
381 Sparky Anderson .03 .02 .01
382 Sid Fernandez .05 .04 .02
383 Dave Hollins .06 .05 .02
384 Mark Lee .03 .02 .01
385 Tim Wallach .05 .04 .02
386 Will Clark (All-Star) .10 .08 .04
387 Ryne Sandberg (All-Star) .10 .08 .04
388 Howard Johnson (All-Star) .05 .04 .02
389 Barry Larkin (All-Star) .05 .04 .02
390 Barry Bonds (All-Star) .10 .08 .04
391 Ron Gant (All-Star) .08 .06 .03
392 Bobby Bonilla (All-Star) .08 .06 .03
393 Craig Biggio (All-Star) .05 .04 .02
394 Denny Martinez (All-Star) .04 .03 .02
395 Tom Glavine (All-Star) .05 .04 .02
396 Lee Smith (All-Star) .08 .06 .03
397 Cecil Fielder (All-Star) .10 .08 .04
398 Julio Franco (All-Star) .08 .06 .03
399 Wade Boggs (All-Star) .10 .08 .04
400 Cal Ripken, Jr. (All-Star) .15 .11 .06
401 Jose Canseco (All-Star) .10 .08 .04
402 Joe Carter (All-Star) .08 .06 .03
403 Ruben Sierra (All-Star) .10 .08 .04
404 Matt Nokes (All-Star) .04 .03 .02
405 Roger Clemens (All-Star) .12 .09 .05
406 Jim Abbott (All-Star) .08 .06 .03
407 Bryan Harvey (All-Star) .05 .04 .02
408 Bob Milacki .03 .02 .01
409 Geno Petralli .03 .02 .01
410 Dave Stewart .08 .06 .03
411 Mike Jackson .03 .02 .01
412 Luis Aquino .03 .02 .01
413 Tim Teufel .03 .02 .01
414 *Jeff Ware* (Draft Pick) .15 .11 .06
415 Jim Deshaies .04 .03 .02
416 Ellis Burks .10 .08 .04
417 Allan Anderson .03 .02 .01
418 Alfredo Griffin .03 .02 .01
419 Wally Whitehurst .05 .04 .02
420 Sandy Alomar .08 .06 .03
421 Juan Agosto .03 .02 .01
422 Sam Horn .03 .02 .01
423 *Jeff Fassero* .10 .08 .04
424 *Paul McClellan* (FC) .10 .08 .04
425 Cecil Fielder .15 .11 .06
426 Tim Raines .10 .08 .04
427 *Eddie Taubensee* (FC) .20 .15 .08
428 Dennis Boyd .05 .04 .02
429 Tony LaRussa .03 .02 .01
430 Steve Sax .06 .05 .02
431 Tom Gordon .08 .06 .03
432 Billy Hatcher .04 .03 .02
433 Cal Eldred (FC) .25 .20 .10
434 Wally Backman .03 .02 .01
435 Mark Eichhorn .03 .02 .01
436 Mookie Wilson .03 .02 .01
437 *Scott Servais* .10 .08 .04
438 Mike Maddux .03 .02 .01
439 *Chico Walker* (FC) .10 .08 .04
440 Doug Drabek .08 .06 .03

441 Rob Deer .04 .03 .02
442 Dave West .04 .03 .02
443 Spike Owen .03 .02 .01
444 *Tyrone Hill* (Draft Pick) .25 .20 .10
445 Matt Williams .12 .09 .05
446 Mark Lewis .12 .09 .05
447 David Segui .08 .06 .03
448 Tom Pagnozzi .04 .03 .02
449 *Jeff Johnson* .12 .09 .05
450 Mark McGwire .12 .09 .05
451 Tom Henke .05 .04 .02
452 Wilson Alvarez .08 .06 .03
453 Gary Redus .03 .02 .01
454 Darren Holmes .03 .02 .01
455 Pete O'Brien .03 .02 .01
456 Pat Combs .04 .03 .02
457 Hubie Brooks .04 .03 .02
458 Frank Tanana .03 .02 .01
459 Tom Kelly .03 .02 .01
460 Andre Dawson .12 .09 .05
461 Doug Jones .04 .03 .02
462 Rich Rodriguez .04 .03 .02
463 *Mike Simms* .10 .08 .04
464 Mike Jeffcoat .03 .02 .01
465 Barry Larkin .12 .09 .05
466 Stan Belinda .04 .03 .02
467 Lonnie Smith .04 .03 .02
468 Greg Harris .03 .02 .01
469 Jim Eisenreich .03 .02 .01
470 Pedro Guerrero .08 .06 .03
471 Jose DeJesus .04 .03 .02
472 *Rich Rowland* (FC) .15 .11 .06
473 Top Prospects-3rd Baseman (*Frank Bolick* (FC), Craig Paquette, Tom Redington, Paul Russo) .35 .25 .14
474 *Mike Rossiter* (Draft Pick) .25 .20 .10
475 Robby Thompson .04 .03 .02
476 Randy Bush .03 .02 .01
477 Greg Hibbard .04 .03 .02
478 Dale Sveum .03 .02 .01
479 *Chito Martinez* (FC) .10 .08 .04
480 Scott Sanderson .04 .03 .02
481 Tino Martinez .10 .08 .04
482 Jimmy Key .05 .04 .02
483 Terry Shumpert .03 .02 .01
484 Mike Hartley .03 .02 .01
485 Chris Sabo .08 .06 .03
486 Bob Walk .03 .02 .01
487 John Cerutti .03 .02 .01
488 Scott Cooper (FC) .10 .08 .04
489 Bobby Cox .03 .02 .01
490 Julio Franco .10 .08 .04
491 Jeff Brantley .04 .03 .02
492 Mike Devereaux .04 .03 .02
493 Jose Offerman .10 .08 .04
494 Gary Thurman .03 .02 .01
495 Carney Lansford .06 .05 .02
496 Joe Grahe .04 .03 .02
497 *Andy Ashby* (FC) .08 .06 .03
498 Gerald Perry .03 .02 .01
499 Dave Otto .03 .02 .01
500 Vince Coleman .08 .06 .03
501 *Rob Mallicoat* (FC) .06 .05 .02
502 Greg Briley .03 .02 .01
503 Pascual Perez .03 .02 .01
504 *Aaron Sele* (Draft Pick) 1.50 1.25 .60
505 Bobby Thigpen .08 .06 .03
506 Todd Benzinger .04 .03 .02
507 Candy Maldonado .04 .03 .02
508 Bill Gullickson .05 .04 .02
509 Doug Dascenzo .03 .02 .01
510 Frank Viola .08 .06 .03
511 Kenny Rogers .04 .03 .02
512 Mike Heath .03 .02 .01
513 Kevin Bass .04 .03 .02
514 *Kim Batiste* (FC) .10 .08 .04
515 Delino DeShields .08 .06 .03
516 *Ed Sprague* .10 .08 .04
517 Jim Gott .03 .02 .01
518 *Jose Melendez* (FC) .10 .08 .04
519 Hal McRae .03 .02 .01
520 *Jeff Bagwell* .30 .25 .12
521 Joe Hesketh .03 .02 .01
522 Milt Cuyler .12 .09 .05
523 Shawn Hillegas .03 .02 .01
524 Don Slaught .03 .02 .01
525 Randy Johnson .06 .05 .02
526 *Doug Piatt* .10 .08 .04
527 Checklist 4 .03 .02 .01
528 *Steve Foster* (FC) .15 .11 .06
529 Joe Girardi .04 .03 .02
530 Jim Abbott .10 .08 .04
531 Larry Walker .08 .06 .03
532 Mike Huff .04 .03 .02
533 Mackey Sasser .03 .02 .01
534 *Benji Gil* (Draft Pick) .35 .25 .14
535 Dave Stieb .06 .05 .02
536 Willie Wilson .04 .03 .02
537 *Mark Leiter* (FC) .10 .08 .04
538 Jose Uribe .03 .02 .01
539 Thomas Howard .03 .02 .01
540 Ben McDonald .12 .09 .05
541 *Jose Tolentino* (FC) .15 .11 .06
542 *Keith Mitchell* (FC) .10 .08 .04
543 Jerome Walton .08 .06 .03
544 *Cliff Brantley* (FC) .15 .11 .06
545 Andy Van Slyke .08 .06 .03
546 Paul Sorrento .04 .03 .02
547 Herm Winningham .03 .02 .01
548 Mark Guthrie .04 .03 .02
549 Joe Torre .03 .02 .01
550 Darryl Strawberry .12 .09 .05
551 Top Prospects-Shortstops (*Manny Alexander*, Alex Arias, Wil Cordero, Chipper Jones) .60 .45 .25
552 Dave Gallagher .04 .03 .02
553 Edgar Martinez .06 .05 .02
554 Donald Harris .15 .11 .06
555 Frank Thomas 1.00 .70 .40
556 Storm Davis .04 .03 .02
557 Dickie Thon .03 .02 .01
558 Scott Garrelts .03 .02 .01

559 Steve Olin .03 .02 .01
560 Rickey Henderson .15 .11 .06
561 Jose Vizcaino .04 .03 .02
562 *Wade Taylor* .10 .08 .04
563 Pat Borders .04 .03 .02
564 *Jimmy Gonzalez* (Draft Pick) .20 .15 .08
565 Lee Smith .05 .04 .02
566 Bill Sampen .05 .04 .02
567 Dean Palmer .12 .09 .05
568 Bryan Harvey .05 .04 .02
569 Tony Pena .05 .04 .02
570 Lou Whitaker .06 .05 .02
571 Randy Tomlin .06 .05 .02
572 Greg Vaughn .12 .09 .05
573 Kelly Downs .03 .02 .01
574 Steve Avery .20 .15 .08
575 Kirby Puckett .15 .11 .06
576 *Heathcliff Slocumb* (FC) .10 .08 .04
577 Kevin Seitzer .04 .03 .02
578 Lee Guetterman .03 .02 .01
579 Johnny Oates .03 .02 .01
580 Greg Maddux .05 .04 .02
581 Stan Javier .03 .02 .01
582 Vicente Palacios .03 .02 .01
583 Mel Rojas .03 .02 .01
584 *Wayne Rosenthal* (FC) .10 .08 .04
585 Lenny Webster (FC) .10 .08 .04
586 Rod Nichols .03 .02 .01
587 Mickey Morandini .08 .06 .03
588 Russ Swan .03 .02 .01
589 Mariano Duncan .04 .03 .02
590 Howard Johnson .10 .08 .04
591 Top Prospects-Outfielders (*Jacob Brumfield*, Jeremy Burnitz, Alan Cockrell, D.J. Dozier) .50 .40 .20
592 *Denny Neagle* (FC) .15 .11 .06
593 Steve Decker .10 .08 .04
594 *Brian Barber* (Draft Pick) .15 .11 .06
595 Bruce Hurst .04 .03 .02
596 Kent Mercker .04 .03 .02
597 *Mike Magnante* .10 .08 .04
598 Jody Reed .04 .03 .02
599 Steve Searcy .03 .02 .01
600 Paul Molitor .10 .08 .04
601 Dave Smith .05 .04 .02
602 Mike Fetters .04 .03 .02
603 *Luis Mercedes* (FC) .10 .08 .04
604 Chris Gwynn .03 .02 .01
605 Scott Erickson .10 .08 .04
606 Brook Jacoby .04 .03 .02
607 Todd Stottlemyre .05 .04 .02
608 Scott Bradley .03 .02 .01
609 Mike Hargrove .03 .02 .01
610 Eric Davis .12 .09 .05
611 *Brian Hunter* (FC) .10 .08 .04
612 Pat Kelly .10 .08 .04
613 Pedro Munoz (FC) .15 .11 .06
614 Al Osuna .04 .03 .02
615 Matt Merullo .03 .02 .01
616 Larry Andersen .03 .02 .01
617 Junior Ortiz .03 .02 .01
618 Top Prospects-Outfielders (*Cesar Hernandez*, Steve Hosey, Dan Peltier, Jeff McNeely) .50 .40 .20
619 Danny Jackson .04 .03 .02
620 George Brett .12 .09 .05
621 *Dan Gakeler* (FC) .10 .08 .04
622 Steve Buechele .04 .03 .02
623 Bob Tewksbury .03 .02 .01
624 *Shawn Estes* (Draft Pick) .15 .11 .06
625 Kevin McReynolds .08 .06 .03
626 *Chris Haney* (FC) .08 .06 .03
627 Mike Sharperson .03 .02 .01
628 Mark Williamson .03 .02 .01
629 Wally Joyner .10 .08 .04
630 Carlton Fisk .12 .09 .05
631 *Armando Reynoso* (FC) .10 .08 .04
632 Felix Fermin .03 .02 .01
633 Mitch Williams .05 .04 .02
634 Manuel Lee .04 .03 .02
635 Harold Baines .08 .06 .03
636 Greg Harris .05 .04 .02
637 Orlando Merced .12 .09 .05
638 Chris Bosio .04 .03 .02
639 *Wayne Housie* (FC) .10 .08 .04
640 Xavier Hernandez .04 .03 .02
641 *David Howard* (FC) .10 .08 .04
642 Tim Crews .03 .02 .01
643 Rick Cerone .03 .02 .01
644 Terry Leach .03 .02 .01
645 Deion Sanders .12 .09 .05
646 Craig Wilson .04 .03 .02
647 Marquis Grissom .12 .09 .05
648 Scott Fletcher .03 .02 .01
649 Norm Charlton .04 .03 .02
650 Jesse Barfield .06 .05 .02
651 *Joe Slusarski* .10 .08 .04
652 Bobby Rose .04 .03 .02
653 Dennis Lamp .03 .02 .01
654 *Allen Watson* (Draft Pick) .50 .40 .20
655 Brett Butler .06 .05 .02
656 Top Prospects-Outfielders (*Rudy Pemberton* (FC), Henry Rodriguez, Lee Tinsley, Gerald Williams) .50 .40 .20
657 Dave Johnson .03 .02 .01
658 Checklist 5 .03 .02 .01
659 Brian McRae .10 .08 .04
660 Fred McGriff .10 .08 .04
661 Bill Landrum .03 .02 .01
662 *Juan Guzman* (FC) .50 .40 .20
663 Greg Gagne .03 .02 .01
664 Ken Hill .04 .03 .02
665 *Dave Haas* (FC) .10 .08 .04
666 Tom Foley .03 .02 .01
667 *Roberto Hernandez* (FC) .10 .08 .04
668 Dwayne Henry .03 .02 .01
669 Jim Fregosi .03 .02 .01
670 Harold Reynolds .05 .04 .02
671 Mark Whiten .10 .08 .04
672 Eric Plunk .03 .02 .01
673 Todd Hundley .10 .08 .04

674 *Mo Sanford* (FC) .10 .08 .04
675 Bobby Witt .04 .03 .02
676 Top Prospects-Pitchers (*Pat Mahomes* (FC), Sam Militello, Roger Salkeld, Turk Wendell) .30 .25 .12
677 John Marzano .03 .02 .01
678 Joe Klink .03 .02 .01
679 Pete Incaviglia .04 .03 .02
680 Dale Murphy .08 .06 .03
681 Rene Gonzales .03 .02 .01
682 Andy Benes .08 .06 .03
683 Jim Poole (FC) .08 .06 .03
684 *Trever Miller* (Draft Pick) .15 .11 .06
685 *Scott Livingstone* (FC) .12 .09 .05
686 Rich DeLucia .04 .03 .02
687 *Harvey Pulliam* (FC) .10 .08 .04
688 Tim Belcher .04 .03 .02
689 Mark Lemke .05 .04 .02
690 John Franco .06 .05 .02
691 Walt Weiss .06 .05 .02
692 Scott Ruskin .04 .03 .02
693 Jeff King .04 .03 .02
694 Mike Gardiner (FC) .06 .05 .02
695 Gary Sheffield .12 .09 .05
696 Joe Boever .03 .02 .01
697 Mike Felder .03 .02 .01
698 John Habyan .03 .02 .01
699 Cito Gaston .03 .02 .01
700 Ruben Sierra .15 .11 .06
701 Scott Radinsky .03 .02 .01
702 Lee Stevens .06 .05 .02
703 *Mark Wohlers* (FC) .10 .08 .04
704 Curt Young .03 .02 .01
705 Dwight Evans .06 .05 .02
706 Rob Murphy .03 .02 .01
707 Gregg Jefferies .10 .08 .04
708 Tom Bolton .03 .02 .01
709 Chris James .03 .02 .01
710 Kevin Maas .12 .09 .05
711 *Ricky Bones* (FC) .10 .08 .04
712 Curt Wilkerson .03 .02 .01
713 Roger McDowell .04 .03 .02
714 *Calvin Reese* (Draft Pick) .20 .15 .08
715 Craig Biggio .08 .06 .03
716 *Kirk Dressendorfer* .10 .08 .04
717 Ken Dayley .03 .02 .01
718 B.J. Surhoff .05 .04 .02
719 Terry Mulholland .05 .04 .02
720 Kirk Gibson .06 .05 .02
721 Mike Pagliarulo .04 .03 .02
722 Walt Terrell .03 .02 .01
723 Jose Oquendo .03 .02 .01
724 Kevin Morton (FC) .08 .06 .03
725 Dwight Gooden .12 .09 .05
726 Kirt Manwaring .04 .03 .02
727 Chuck McElroy .03 .02 .01
728 Dave Burba (FC) .06 .05 .02
729 Art Howe .03 .02 .01
730 Ramon Martinez .10 .08 .04
731 Donnie Hill .03 .02 .01
732 Nelson Santovenia .03 .02 .01
733 Bob Melvin .03 .02 .01
734 *Scott Hatteberg* (Draft Pick) .15 .11 .06
735 Greg Swindell .05 .04 .02
736 Lance Johnson .03 .02 .01
737 Kevin Reimer .05 .04 .02
738 Dennis Eckersley .08 .06 .03
739 Rob Ducey .03 .02 .01
740 Ken Caminiti .04 .03 .02
741 Mark Gubicza .04 .03 .02
742 Billy Spiers .04 .03 .02
743 Darren Lewis .08 .06 .03
744 Chris Hammond .05 .04 .02
745 Dave Magadan .05 .04 .02
746 Bernard Gilkey .10 .08 .04
747 Willie Banks (FC) .10 .08 .04
748 Matt Nokes .04 .03 .02
749 Jerald Clark .04 .03 .02
750 Travis Fryman .15 .11 .06
751 Steve Wilson .03 .02 .01
752 Billy Ripken .03 .02 .01
753 Paul Assenmacher .03 .02 .01
754 Charlie Hayes .04 .03 .02
755 Alex Fernandez .15 .11 .06
756 Gary Pettis .03 .02 .01
757 Rob Dibble .08 .06 .03
758 Tim Naehring .08 .06 .03
759 Jeff Torborg .03 .02 .01
760 Ozzie Smith .10 .08 .04
761 Mike Fitzgerald .03 .02 .01
762 John Burkett .04 .03 .02
763 Kyle Abbott .06 .05 .02
764 *Tyler Green* (Draft Pick) .30 .25 .12
765 Pete Harnisch .06 .05 .02
766 Mark Davis .03 .02 .01
767 Kal Daniels .06 .05 .02
768 *Jim Thome* (FC) .20 .15 .08
769 Jack Howell .03 .02 .01
770 Sid Bream .05 .04 .02
771 *Arthur Rhodes* (FC) .20 .15 .08
772 Garry Templeton .04 .03 .02
773 Hal Morris .12 .09 .05
774 Bud Black .04 .03 .02
775 Ivan Calderon .06 .05 .02
776 *Doug Henry* (FC) .15 .11 .06
777 John Olerud .12 .09 .05
778 Tim Leary .04 .03 .02
779 Jay Bell .05 .04 .02
780 Eddie Murray .10 .08 .04
781 Paul Abbott (FC) .08 .06 .03
782 Phil Plantier .20 .15 .08
783 Joe Magrane .05 .04 .02
784 Ken Patterson .03 .02 .01
785 Albert Belle .15 .11 .06
786 Royce Clayton (FC) .25 .20 .10
787 Checklist 6 .03 .02 .01
788 Mike Stanton .04 .03 .02
789 Bobby Valentine .03 .02 .01
790 Joe Carter .10 .08 .04
791 Danny Cox .03 .02 .01
792 Dave Winfield .12 .09 .05

1992 Topps Gold Promo Sheet

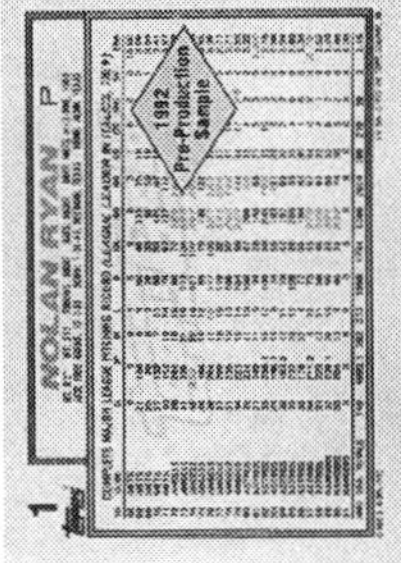

Similar in form and function to the nine-card promo sheet issued for the regular 1992 Topps set, this 8" x 11" sheet previewed the Topps Gold cards for dealers. Fronts are identical to the regular-issue '92 Topps cards. Backs differ in that actual 1991 stats are not printed, and there is a diamond over the stat box which reads, "1992 Pre-Production Sample". Card numbers on the gold preview cards correspond to the regular Topps cards. Single cards in the standard 2-1/2" x 3-1/2" size are frequently offered cut from these sheets.

		MT	NR MT	EX
Complete Set (sheet):		30.00	22.00	12.00
Complete Set (9):		24.00	18.00	9.50
Common Player:		2.00	1.50	.80
1	Nolan Ryan	10.00	7.50	4.00
15	Dennis Martinez	2.00	1.50	.80
20	Bip Roberts	2.00	1.50	.80
40	Cal Ripken, Jr.	8.00	6.00	3.25
261	Tom Lasorda	3.00	2.25	1.25
370	Shawon Dunston	2.00	1.50	.80
512	Mike Heath	2.00	1.50	.80
655	Brett Butler	2.00	1.50	.80
757	Rob Dibble	2.00	1.50	.80

1992 Topps Gold

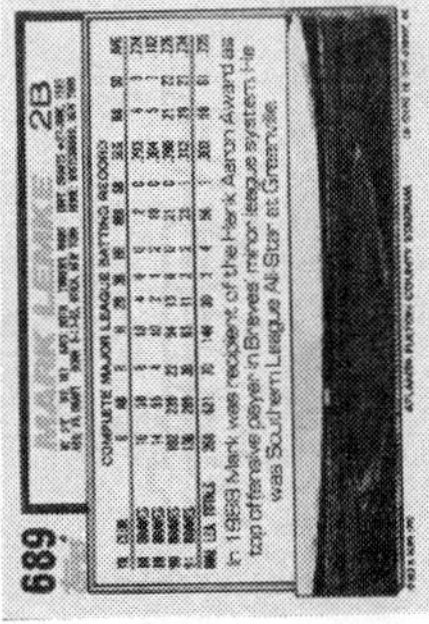

Two versions of each card in the regular Topps set were produced as premium cards with gold-foil enhancements. Topps Gold cards feature the same format as the regular card except the color bars beneath the photo with the player's name and team have been replaced with gold-foil elements. On back, the light blue Topps logo printed under the stats has been replaced with a gold "ToppsGold" logo. Topps Gold cards were random inserts in wax packs. Ten Gold cards were included in each Topps factory set, and complete factory sets of Gold cards were sold.

	MT	NR MT	EX
Complete Set (792):	375.00	225.00	125.00
Brien	50.00	40.00	20.00
Common Player:	.50	.40	.20
Stars: 5X-10X regular Topps			

A player's name in italic type indicates a rookie card. An (FC) indicates a player's first card for that particular card company.

Values for recent cards and sets are listed in Mint (MT), Near Mint (NM), reflecting the fact that many cards from recent years have been preserved in top condition. Recent cards and sets in less than Excellent condition have little collector interest.

1992 Topps Gold Winners

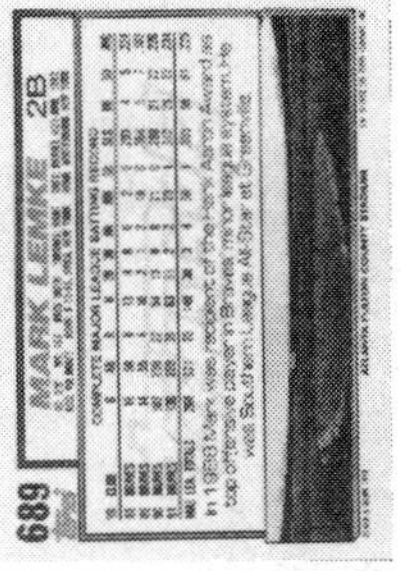

Gold Winner cards were prizes in a scratch-off contest found in each pack. They are identical to the Topps Gold cards except for the addition of a gold-foil "Winner" and star added above the team name.

	MT	NR MT	EX
Complete Set (792):	125.00	90.00	50.00
Common Player:	.25	.20	.10
Stars: 3X-5X regular Topps			

1992 Topps Traded

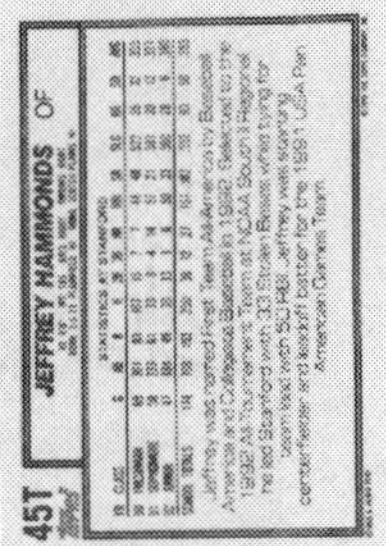

Members of the United States baseball team are featured in this 132-card boxed set released by Topps. The cards are styled after the regular 1992 Topps cards and are numbered alphabetically. Several United States baseball players featured in this set were also featured in the 1991 Topps Traded set.

		MT	NR MT	EX
Complete Set (132):		15.00	11.00	6.00
Common Player:		.05	.04	.02
1	*Willie Adams* (USA)	.20	.15	.08
2	Jeff Alkire (USA)	1.00	.70	.40
3	Felipe Alou	.05	.04	.02
4	Moises Alou	.50	.40	.20
5	Ruben Amaro (FC)	.10	.08	.04
6	Jack Armstrong	.05	.04	.02
7	Scott Bankhead	.05	.04	.02
8	Tim Belcher	.08	.06	.03
9	George Bell	.08	.06	.03
10	Freddie Benavides (FC)	.12	.09	.05
11	Todd Benzinger	.05	.04	.02
12	Joe Boever	.05	.04	.02
13	Ricky Bones	.10	.08	.04
15	Hubie Brooks	.05	.04	.02
16	Jerry Browne	.05	.04	.02
17	Jim Bullinger	.10	.08	.04
18	Dave Burba	.05	.04	.02
19	Kevin Campbell (FC)	.12	.09	.05
20	Tom Candiotti	.05	.04	.02
21	Mark Carreon	.05	.04	.02
23	Archi Cianfrocco	.30	.25	.12
24	Phil Clark	.10	.08	.04
25	Chad Curtis	1.00	.70	.40
26	Eric Davis	.08	.06	.03
27	Tim Davis (USA)	.20	.15	.08
28	Gary DiSarcina	.05	.04	.02
29	Darren Dreifort (USA)	1.00	.70	.40
30	Mariano Duncan	.05	.04	.02
31	Mike Fitzgerald	.05	.04	.02
32	John Flaherty (FC)	.12	.09	.05
33	Darrin Fletcher	.05	.04	.02
34	Scott Fletcher	.05	.04	.02
35	Ron Fraser (USA)	.08	.06	.03
36	Andres Galarraga	.06	.05	.02
37	Dave Gallagher	.05	.04	.02
38	Mike Gallego	.05	.04	.02
39	Nomar Garciaparra (USA)	.20	.15	.08
40	Jason Giambi (USA)	.75	.60	.30
41	Danny Gladden	.05	.04	.02
42	Rene Gonzales	.05	.04	.02
43	Jeff Granger (USA)	.40	.30	.15
44	Rick Greene (USA)	.20	.15	.08
45	Jeffrey Hammonds (USA)	2.50	2.00	1.00
46	Charlie Hayes	.05	.04	.02
47	Von Hayes	.05	.04	.02
48	Rick Helling (USA)	.75	.60	.30
49	Butch Henry (FC)	.12	.09	.05
50	Carlos Hernandez (FC)	.12	.09	.05
51	Ken Hill	.08	.06	.03
52	Butch Hobson	.05	.04	.02
53	Vince Horsman (FC)	.10	.08	.04
54	Pete Incaviglia	.06	.05	.02
55	Gregg Jefferies	.08	.06	.03
56	Charles Johnson (USA)	.75	.60	.30
57	Doug Jones	.05	.04	.02
58	Brian Jordan	.30	.25	.12
59	Wally Joyner	.08	.06	.03
60	*Daron Kirkreit* (USA)	.20	.15	.08
61	Bill Krueger	.06	.05	.02
62	Gene Lamont	.06	.05	.02
63	Jim Lefebvre	.06	.05	.02
64	*Danny Leon*	.20	.15	.08
65	Pat Listach	.50	.40	.20
66	Kenny Lofton	1.00	.70	.40
67	Dave Martinez	.05	.04	.02
68	Derrick May	.10	.08	.04
69	Kirk McCaskill	.06	.05	.02
70	*Chad McConnell* (USA)	.75	.60	.30
71	Kevin McReynolds	.06	.05	.02
72	Rusty Meacham (FC)	.10	.08	.04
73	Keith Miller	.06	.05	.02
74	Kevin Mitchell	.08	.06	.03
75	*Jason Moler* (USA)	.60	.45	.25
76	Mike Morgan	.06	.05	.02
77	Jack Morris	.08	.06	.03
78	*Calvin Murray* (USA)	.50	.40	.20
79	Eddie Murray	.08	.06	.03
80	Randy Myers	.06	.05	.02
81	Denny Neagle (FC)	.10	.08	.04
82	Phil Nevin (USA)	1.25	.90	.50
83	Dave Nilsson	.20	.15	.08
84	Junior Ortiz	.05	.04	.02
85	Donovan Osborne	.20	.15	.08
86	Bill Pecota	.05	.04	.02
87	Melido Perez	.05	.04	.02
88	Mike Perez (FC)	.10	.08	.04
89	Hipolito Pena (FC)	.10	.08	.04
90	Willie Randolph	.06	.05	.02
91	Darren Reed (FC)	.12	.09	.05
92	Bip Roberts	.08	.06	.03
93	Chris Roberts (USA)	.60	.45	.25
94	Steve Rodriguez (USA)	.12	.09	.05
95	Bruce Ruffin	.05	.04	.02
96	Scott Ruskin	.05	.04	.02
97	Bret Saberhagen	.08	.06	.03
98	Rey Sanchez (FC)	.12	.09	.05
99	Steve Sax	.08	.06	.03
100	Curt Schilling	.06	.05	.02
101	Dick Schofield	.05	.04	.02
102	Gary Scott	.10	.08	.04
103	Kevin Seitzer	.06	.05	.02
104	Frank Seminara (FC)	.12	.09	.05
105	Gary Sheffield	.30	.25	.12
106	John Smiley	.06	.05	.02
107	Cory Snyder	.06	.05	.02
108	Paul Sorrento	.06	.05	.02
109	Sammy Sosa	.20	.15	.08
110	Matt Stairs	.12	.09	.05
111	Andy Stankiewicz	.20	.15	.08
112	Kurt Stillwell	.06	.05	.02
113	Rick Sutcliffe	.06	.05	.02
114	Bill Swift	.06	.05	.02
115	Jeff Tackett (FC)	.12	.09	.05
116	Danny Tartabull	.08	.06	.03
117	Eddie Taubensee (FC)	.12	.09	.05
118	Dickie Thon	.05	.04	.02
119	*Michael Tucker* (USA)	1.75	1.25	.70
120	Scooter Tucker (FC)	.12	.09	.05
121	*Marc Valdes* (USA)	.20	.15	.08
122	Julio Valera (FC)	.10	.08	.04
123	*Jason Vilaitek* (USA)	.20	.15	.08
124	*Ron Villone* (USA)	.20	.15	.08
125	Frank Viola	.08	.06	.03
126	*B.J. Wallace* (USA)	1.00	.70	.40
127	Dan Walters (FC)	.12	.09	.05
128	Craig Wilson (USA)	.12	.09	.05
129	Chris Wimmer (USA)	.12	.09	.05
130	Dave Winfield	.15	.11	.06
131	Herm Winningham	.05	.04	.02
132	Checklist	.05	.04	.02

1992 Topps Traded Gold

A reported 6,000 sets of 1992 Topps Traded were produced in a gold edition, with gold foil strips on front containing the player and team name. The cards are in all other respects identical to the regular boxed Traded issue.

	MT	NR MT	EX
Complete Set (132):	90.00	60.00	30.00
Common Player:	.25	.15	.10
Stars: 3-5X Topps Traded			

1992 Topps Kids

In a market which had increasingly become the province of adult collectors, Topps in 1992 offered an issue unashamedly aimed at the youngster. Called "Topps Kids," the 132-card set featured bright colors, garish graphics and the game's top stars. Sold at 35 cents per pack (with bubble gum), the issue was even priced for the young collector. Unfortunately, the concept was a flop and was not repeated in subsequent years. Card fronts featured player photos, sometimes only the player's head on a cartoon body, against a background of wild designs or cartoon ballplayers in action. Player

names at bottom were rendered in superhero comic-book style. Backs featured a few 1991 and career stats, and/or a cartoon or two about the player or baseball trivia.

		MT	NR MT	EX
Complete Set (132):		8.00	6.00	3.25
Common Player:		.05	.04	.02
1	Ryne Sandberg	.25	.20	.10
2	Andre Dawson	.10	.08	.04
3	George Bell	.05	.04	.02
4	Mark Grace	.10	.08	.04
5	Shawon Dunston	.05	.04	.02
6	Tim Wallach	.05	.04	.02
7	Ivan Calderon	.05	.04	.02
8	Marquis Grissom	.05	.04	.02
9	Delino DeShields	.05	.04	.02
10	Denny Martinez	.05	.04	.02
11	Dwight Gooden	.10	.08	.04
12	Howard Johnson	.10	.08	.04
13	John Franco	.05	.04	.02
14	Gregg Jefferies	.15	.11	.06
15	Kevin McReynolds	.05	.04	.02
16	David Cone	.05	.04	.02
17	Len Dykstra	.10	.08	.04
18	John Kruk	.10	.08	.04
19	Von Hayes	.05	.04	.02
20	Mitch Williams	.05	.04	.02
21	Barry Bonds	.20	.15	.08
22	Bobby Bonilla	.10	.08	.04
23	Andy Van Slyke	.10	.08	.04
24	Doug Drabek	.05	.04	.02
25	Ozzie Smith	.20	.15	.08
26	Pedro Guerrero	.05	.04	.02
27	Todd Zelle	.05	.04	.02
28	Lee Smith	.05	.04	.02
29	Felix Jose	.05	.04	.02
30	Jose DeLeon	.05	.04	.02
31	David Justice	.15	.11	.06
32	Ron Gant	.10	.08	.04
33	Terry Pendleton	.05	.04	.02
34	Tom Glavine	.05	.04	.02
35	Otis Nixon	.05	.04	.02
36	Steve Avery	.10	.08	.04
37	Barry Larkin	.10	.08	.04
38	Eric Davis	.15	.11	.06
39	Chris Sabo	.10	.08	.04
40	Rob Dibble	.05	.04	.02
41	Paul O'Neill	.10	.08	.04
42	Jose Rijo	.10	.08	.04
43	Craig Biggio	.05	.04	.02
44	Jeff Bagwell	.10	.08	.04
45	Ken Caminiti	.05	.04	.02
46	Steve Finley	.05	.04	.02
47	Darryl Strawberry	.15	.11	.06
48	Ramon Martinez	.05	.04	.02
49	Brett Butler	.05	.04	.02
50	Eddie Murray	.15	.11	.06
51	Kal Daniels	.05	.04	.02
52	Orel Hershiser	.10	.08	.04
53	Tony Gwynn	.15	.11	.06
54	Benny Santiago	.05	.04	.02
55	Fred McGriff	.10	.08	.04
56	Bip Roberts	.05	.04	.02
57	Tony Fernandez	.05	.04	.02
58	Will Clark	.20	.15	.08
59	Kevin Mitchell	.05	.04	.02
60	Matt Williams	.10	.08	.04
61	Willie McGee	.05	.04	.02
62	Dave Righetti	.05	.04	.02
63	Cal Ripken, Jr.	.25	.20	.10
64	Ben McDonald	.05	.04	.02
65	Glenn Davis	.05	.04	.02
66	Gregg Olson	.05	.04	.02
67	Roger Clemens	.15	.11	.06
68	Wade Boggs	.20	.15	.08
69	Mike Greenwell	.10	.08	.04
70	Ellis Burks	.05	.04	.02
71	Sandy Alomar	.05	.04	.02
72	Greg Swindell	.05	.04	.02
73	Albert Belle	.10	.08	.04
74	Mark Whiten	.05	.04	.02
75	Alan Trammell	.15	.11	.06
76	Cecil Fielder	.20	.15	.08
77	Lou Whitaker	.10	.08	.04
78	Travis Fryman	.10	.08	.04
79	Tony Phillips	.05	.04	.02
80	Robin Yount	.20	.15	.08
81	Paul Molitor	.15	.11	.06
82	B.J. Surhoff	.05	.04	.02
83	Greg Vaughn	.05	.04	.02
84	Don Mattingly	.20	.15	.08
85	Steve Sax	.05	.04	.02
86	Kevin Maas	.05	.04	.02
87	Mel Hall	.05	.04	.02
88	Roberto Kelly	.10	.08	.04
89	Joe Carter	.10	.08	.04
90	Roberto Alomar	.15	.11	.06
91	Dave Stieb	.05	.04	.02
92	Kelly Gruber	.05	.04	.02
93	Tom Henke	.05	.04	.02
94	Chuck Finley	.05	.04	.02
95	Wally Joyner	.10	.08	.04
96	Dave Winfield	.20	.15	.08
97	Jim Abbott	.15	.11	.06
98	Mark Langston	.05	.04	.02
99	Frank Thomas	.35	.25	.14
100	Ozzie Guillen	.05	.04	.02
101	Bobby Thigpen	.05	.04	.02
102	Robin Ventura	.10	.08	.04
103	Bo Jackson	.20	.15	.08
104	Tim Raines	.10	.08	.04
105	George Brett	.20	.15	.08
106	Danny Tartabull	.10	.08	.04
107	Bret Saberhagen	.05	.04	.02
108	Brian McRae	.05	.04	.02
109	Kirby Puckett	.20	.15	.08
110	Scott Erickson	.05	.04	.02
111	Kent Hrbek	.10	.08	.04
112	Chuck Knoblauch	.05	.04	.02
113	Chili Davis	.10	.08	.04
114	Rick Aguilera	.05	.04	.02
115	Jose Canseco	.20	.15	.08
116	Dave Henderson	.05	.04	.02
117	Dave Stewart	.10	.08	.04
118	Rickey Henderson	.15	.11	.06
119	Dennis Eckersley	.10	.08	.04
120	Harold Baines	.05	.04	.02
121	Mark McGwire	.20	.15	.08
122	Ken Griffey, Jr.	.35	.25	.14
123	Harold Reynolds	.05	.04	.02
124	Erik Hanson	.05	.04	.02
125	Edgar Martinez	.10	.08	.04
126	Randy Johnson	.10	.08	.04
127	Nolan Ryan	.35	.25	.14
128	Ruben Sierra	.15	.11	.06
129	Julio Franco	.05	.04	.02
130	Rafael Palmeiro	.10	.08	.04
131	Juan Gonzalez	.20	.15	.08
132	Checklist	.05	.04	.02

1992 Topps Triple Header Photo Balls

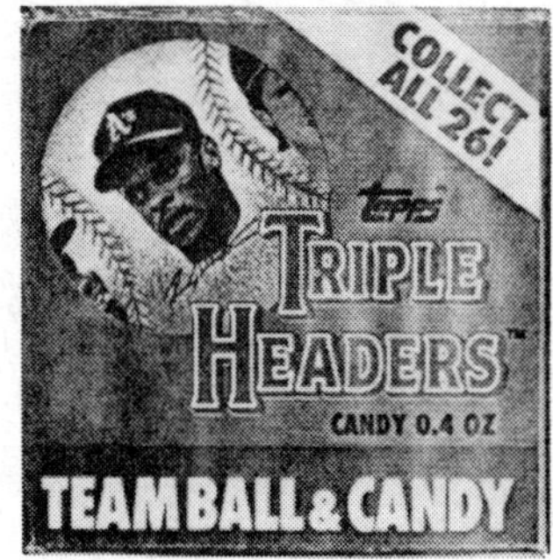

Picture a slightly oversize ping pong ball painted like a baseball with the heads and facsimile autographs of three different players on it and you've got the idea behind the Triple Headers test issue. Very limited in distribution, the team balls were sold in a small box with a package of candy.

		MT	NR MT	EX
Complete Set (26):		150.00	112.00	60.00
Common Ball:		6.00	4.50	2.50
(1)	California Angels (Chuck Finley/Dave Winfield/Wally Joyner)	6.00	4.50	2.50
(2)	Houston Astros (Jeff Bagwell/Craig Biggio/Ken Caminiti)	6.00	4.50	2.50
(3)	Oakland Athletics (Jose Canseco/Dave Henderson/Rickey Henderson)	8.00	6.00	3.25
(4)	Toronto Blue Jays (Roberto Alomar/Kelly Gruber/Joe Carter)	7.00	5.25	2.75
(5)	Atlanta Braves (Ron Gant/Tom Glavine/Dave Justice)	7.00	5.25	2.75
(6)	Milwaukee Brewers (Paul Molitor/Robin Yount/Greg Vaughn)	7.00	5.25	2.75
(7)	St. Louis Cardinals (Pedro Guerrero/Ozzie Smith/Todd Zeile)	6.00	4.50	2.50
(8)	Chicago Cubs (Ryne Sandberg/George Bell/Mark Grace)	10.00	7.50	4.00
(9)	Los Angeles Dodgers (Ramon Martinez/Eddie Murray/Darryl Strawberry)	7.00	5.25	2.75
(10)	Montreal Expos (Delino DeShields/Dennis Martinez/Ivan Calderon)	6.00	4.50	2.50
(11)	San Francisco Giants (Will Clark/Kevin Mitchell/Matt Williams)	7.00	5.25	2.75
(12)	Cleveland Indians (Sandy Alomar, Jr./Alex Cole/Mark Lewis)	6.00	4.50	2.50
(13)	Seattle Mariners (Ken Griffey, Jr./Harold Reynolds/Ken Griffey Sr.)	10.00	7.50	4.00
(14)	New York Mets (Vince Coleman/Dwight Gooden/Howard Johnson)	6.00	4.50	2.50
(15)	Baltimore Orioles (Ben McDonald/Cal Ripken, Jr./Gregg Olson)	10.00	7.50	4.00
(16)	San Diego Padres (Fred McGriff/Tony Gwynn/Benito Santiago)	6.00	4.50	2.50
(17)	Philadelphia Phillies (Len Dykstra/John Kruk/Dale Murphy)	6.00	4.50	2.50
(18)	Pittsburgh Pirates (Barry Bonds/Bobby Bonilla/Andy Van Slyke)	7.50	5.75	3.00
(19)	Cincinnati Reds (Eric Davis/Barry Larkin/Chris Sabo)	6.00	4.50	2.50
(20)	Boston Red Sox (Wade Boggs/Mike Greenwell/Roger Clemens)	7.00	5.25	2.75
(21)	Kansas City Royals (George Brett/Danny Tartabull/Bret Saberhagen)	7.00	5.25	2.75
(22)	Texas Rangers (Julio Franco/Nolan Ryan/Juan Gonzalez)	10.00	7.50	4.00
(23)	Minnesota Twins (Scott Erickson/Kirby Puckett/Kent Hrbek)	7.00	5.25	2.75
(24)	Detroit Tigers (Cecil Fielder/Tony Phillips/Alan Trammell)	6.00	4.50	2.50
(25)	Chicago White Sox (Carlton Fisk/Robin Ventura/Frank Thomas)	10.00	7.50	4.00
(26)	New York Yankees (Don Mattingly/Steve Sax/Willie Randolph)	7.00	5.25	2.75

1992 Topps Stadium Club

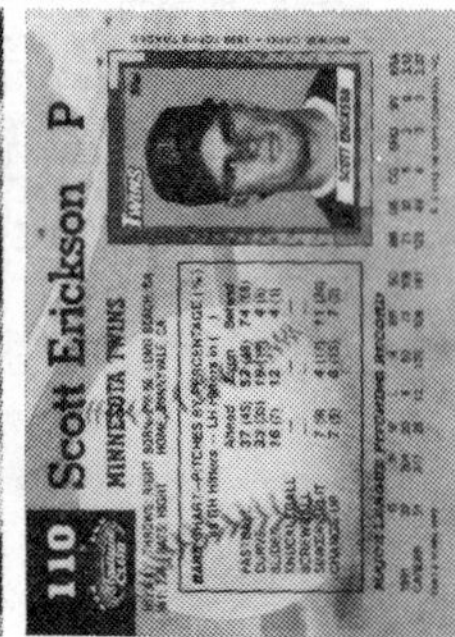

This 900-card set was released in three 300-card series. Like the 1991 issue, the cards feature borderless high gloss photos on the front. The flip sides feature the player's first Topps card and a player evaluation. Topps released updated cards in the third series for traded player and free agents. Several players appear on two cards. Special Members Choice cards are included in the set. Series III featured special inserts of the last three number one picks overall, Phil Nevin, Brien Taylor and Chipper Jones.

		MT	NR MT	EX
Complete Set (900):		70.00	50.00	30.00
Common Player:		.10	.08	.04
1	Cal Ripken, Jr.	1.00	.70	.40
2	Eric Yelding	.10	.08	.04
3	Geno Petralli	.10	.08	.04
4	Wally Backman	.10	.08	.04
5	Milt Cuyler	.10	.08	.04
6	Kevin Bass	.10	.08	.04
7	Dante Bichette	.15	.11	.06
8	Ray Lankford	.20	.15	.08
9	Mel Hall	.15	.11	.06
10	Joe Carter	.40	.30	.15
11	Juan Samuel	.10	.08	.04
12	Jeff Montgomery	.15	.11	.06
13	Glenn Braggs	.15	.11	.06
14	Henry Cotto	.10	.08	.04
15	Deion Sanders	.30	.25	.12
16	Dick Schofield	.10	.08	.04
17	David Cone	.20	.15	.08
18	Chili Davis	.20	.15	.08
19	Tom Foley	.10	.08	.04
20	Ozzie Guillen	.15	.11	.06
21	Luis Salazar	.10	.08	.04
22	Terry Steinbach	.15	.11	.06
23	Chris James	.10	.08	.04
24	Jeff King	.10	.08	.04
25	Carlos Quintana	.10	.08	.04
26	Mike Maddux	.10	.08	.04
27	Tommy Greene	.15	.11	.06
28	Jeff Russell	.15	.11	.06
29	Steve Finley	.20	.15	.08
30	Mike Flanagan	.10	.08	.04
31	Darren Lewis	.10	.08	.04
32	Mark Lee	.10	.08	.04
33	Willie Fraser	.10	.08	.04
34	Mike Henneman	.15	.11	.06
35	Kevin Maas	.30	.25	.12
36	Dave Hansen	.25	.20	.10
37	Erik Hanson	.10	.08	.04
38	Bill Doran	.10	.08	.04
39	Mike Boddicker	.10	.08	.04
40	Vince Coleman	.15	.11	.06
41	Devon White	.15	.11	.06
42	Mark Gardner	.10	.08	.04
43	Scott Lewis	.10	.08	.04
44	Juan Berenguer	.10	.08	.04
45	Carney Lansford	.10	.08	.04
46	Curt Wilkerson	.10	.08	.04
47	Shane Mack	.15	.11	.06
48	Bip Roberts	.15	.11	.06
49	Greg Harris	.10	.08	.04
50	Ryne Sandberg	1.00	.70	.40
51	Mark Whiten	.15	.11	.06
52	Jack McDowell	.20	.15	.08
53	Jimmy Jones	.10	.08	.04
54	Shane Lake	.10	.08	.04

55	Bud Black	.10	.08	.04
56	Dave Valle	.10	.08	.04
57	Kevin Reimer	.10	.08	.04
58	Rich Gedman	.10	.08	.04
59	Travis Fryman	1.00	.75	.40
60	Steve Avery	.75	.60	.30
61	Francisco de la Rosa	.15	.11	.06
62	Scott Hemond	.10	.08	.04
63	Hal Morris	.10	.08	.04
64	Hensley Meulens	.10	.08	.04
65	Frank Castillo	.15	.11	.06
66	Gene Larkin	.10	.08	.04
67	Jose DeLeon	.10	.08	.04
68	Al Osuna	.10	.08	.04
69	Dave Cochrane	.10	.08	.04
70	Robin Ventura	.50	.40	.20
71	John Cerutti	.10	.08	.04
72	Kevin Gross	.10	.08	.04
73	Ivan Calderon	.15	.11	.06
74	Mike Macfarlane	.10	.08	.04
75	Stan Belinda	.10	.08	.04
76	Shawn Hillegas	.10	.08	.04
77	Pat Borders	.10	.08	.04
78	Jim Vatcher	.10	.08	.04
79	Bobby Rose	.10	.08	.04
80	Roger Clemens	.75	.60	.30
81	Craig Worthington	.10	.08	.04
82	Jeff Treadway	.10	.08	.04
83	Jamie Quirk	.10	.08	.04
84	Randy Bush	.10	.08	.04
85	Anthony Young	.10	.08	.04
86	Trevor Wilson	.10	.08	.04
87	Jaime Navarro	.15	.11	.06
88	Les Lancaster	.10	.08	.04
89	Pat Kelly	.15	.11	.06
90	Alvin Davis	.10	.08	.04
91	Larry Andersen	.10	.08	.04
92	Rob Deer	.10	.08	.04
93	Mike Sharperson	.10	.08	.04
94	Lance Parrish	.10	.08	.04
95	Cecil Espy	.10	.08	.04
96	Tim Spehr	.15	.11	.06
97	Dave Stieb	.15	.11	.06
98	Terry Mulholland	.15	.11	.06
99	Dennis Boyd	.10	.08	.04
100	Barry Larkin	.15	.11	.06
101	Ryan Bowen	.10	.08	.04
102	Felix Fermin	.10	.08	.04
103	Luis Alicea	.10	.08	.04
104	Tim Hulett	.10	.08	.04
105	Rafael Belliard	.10	.08	.04
106	Mike Gallego	.10	.08	.04
107	Dave Righetti	.10	.08	.04
108	Jeff Schaefer	.10	.08	.04
109	Ricky Bones	.10	.08	.04
110	Scott Erickson	.10	.08	.04
111	Matt Nokes	.10	.08	.04
112	Bob Scanlan	.10	.08	.04
113	Tom Candiotti	.15	.11	.06
114	Sean Berry	.15	.11	.06
115	Kevin Morton	.15	.11	.06
116	Scott Fletcher	.10	.08	.04
117	B.J. Surhoff	.10	.08	.04
118	Dave Magadan	.10	.08	.04
119	Bill Gullickson	.10	.08	.04
120	Marquis Grissom	.25	.20	.10
121	Lenny Harris	.10	.08	.04
122	Wally Joyner	.20	.15	.08
123	Kevin Brown	.15	.11	.06
124	Braulio Castillo	.15	.11	.06
125	Eric King	.10	.08	.04
126	Mark Portugal	.10	.08	.04
127	Calvin Jones	.10	.08	.04
128	Mike Heath	.10	.08	.04
129	Todd Van Poppel	.25	.20	.10
130	Benny Santiago	.15	.11	.06
131	Gary Thurman	.10	.08	.04
132	Joe Girardi	.10	.08	.04
133	Dave Eiland	.10	.08	.04
134	Orlando Merced	.15	.11	.06
135	Joe Orsulak	.10	.08	.04
136	John Burkett	.10	.08	.04
137	Ken Dayley	.10	.08	.04
138	Ken Hill	.15	.11	.06
139	Walt Terrell	.10	.08	.04
140	Mike Scioscia	.10	.08	.04
141	Junior Felix	.10	.08	.04
142	Ken Caminiti	.10	.08	.04
143	Carlos Baerga	1.00	.70	.40
144	Tony Fossas	.10	.08	.04
145	Craig Grebeck	.10	.08	.04
146	Scott Bradley	.10	.08	.04
147	Kent Mercker	.10	.08	.04
148	Derrick May	.20	.15	.08
149	Jerald Clark	.15	.11	.06
150	George Brett	.75	.60	.30
151	Luis Quinones	.15	.11	.06
152	Mike Pagliarulo	.15	.11	.06
153	Jose Guzman	.15	.11	.06
154	Charlie O'Brien	.15	.11	.06
155	Darren Holmes	.15	.11	.06
156	Joe Boever	.15	.11	.06
157	Rich Monteleone	.15	.11	.06
158	Reggie Harris	.15	.11	.06
159	Roberto Alomar	.75	.60	.30
160	Robby Thompson	.15	.11	.06
161	Chris Hoiles	.25	.20	.10
162	Tom Pagnozzi	.10	.08	.04
163	Omar Vizquel	.10	.08	.04
164	John Candelaria	.10	.08	.04
165	Terry Shumpert	.10	.08	.04
166	Andy Mota	.15	.11	.06
167	Scott Bailes	.10	.08	.04
168	Jeff Blauser	.10	.08	.04
169	Steve Olin	.10	.08	.04
170	Doug Drabek	.20	.15	.08
171	Dave Bergman	.10	.08	.04
172	Eddie Whitson	.10	.08	.04
173	Gilberto Reyes	.10	.08	.04
174	Mark Grace	.25	.20	.10
175	Paul O'Neill	.15	.11	.06
176	Greg Cadaret	.10	.08	.04
177	Mark Williamson	.10	.08	.04
178	Casey Candaele	.10	.08	.04
179	Candy Maldonado	.10	.08	.04
180	Lee Smith	.15	.11	.06
181	Harold Reynolds	.10	.08	.04
182	Dave Justice	1.25	.90	.50
183	Lenny Webster	.10	.08	.04
184	Donn Pall	.10	.08	.04
185	Gerald Alexander	.10	.08	.04
186	Jack Clark	.10	.08	.04
187	Stan Javier	.10	.08	.04
188	Ricky Jordan	.15	.11	.06
189	Franklin Stubbs	.10	.08	.04
190	Dennis Eckersley	.25	.20	.10
191	Danny Tartabull	.20	.15	.08
192	Pete O'Brien	.10	.08	.04
193	Mark Lewis	.10	.08	.04
194	Mike Felder	.10	.08	.04
195	Mickey Tettleton	.15	.11	.06
196	Dwight Smith	.10	.08	.04
197	Shawn Abner	.10	.08	.04
198	Jim Leyritz	.10	.08	.04
199	Mike Devereaux	.20	.15	.08
200	Craig Biggio	.15	.11	.06
201	Kevin Elster	.10	.08	.04
202	Rance Mulliniks	.10	.08	.04
203	Tony Fernandez	.15	.11	.06
204	Allan Anderson	.10	.08	.04
205	Herm Winningham	.10	.08	.04
206	Tim Jones	.10	.08	.04
207	Ramon Martinez	.10	.08	.04
208	Teddy Higuera	.10	.08	.04
209	John Kruk	.15	.11	.06
210	Jim Abbott	.25	.20	.10
211	Dean Palmer	.35	.25	.14
212	Mark Davis	.10	.08	.04
213	Jay Buhner	.10	.08	.04
214	Jesse Barfield	.10	.08	.04
215	Kevin Mitchell	.15	.11	.06
216	Mike LaValliere	.15	.11	.06
217	Mark Wohlers	.10	.08	.04
218	Dave Henderson	.15	.11	.06
219	Dave Smith	.10	.08	.04
220	Albert Belle	1.00	.75	.40
221	Spike Owen	.10	.08	.04
222	Jeff Gray	.10	.08	.04
223	Paul Gibson	.10	.08	.04
224	Bobby Thigpen	.15	.11	.06
225	Mike Mussina	1.25	.90	.50
226	Darrin Jackson	.10	.08	.04
227	Luis Gonzalez	.10	.08	.04
228	Greg Briley	.10	.08	.04
229	Brent Mayne	.10	.08	.04
230	Paul Molitor	.35	.25	.14
231	Al Leiter	.10	.08	.04
232	Andy Van Slyke	.15	.11	.06
233	Ron Tingley	.10	.08	.04
234	Bernard Gilkey	.15	.11	.06
235	Kent Hrbek	.15	.11	.06
236	Eric Karros	.40	.30	.15
237	Randy Velarde	.10	.08	.04
238	Andy Allanson	.10	.08	.04
239	Willie McGee	.15	.11	.06
240	Juan Gonzalez	4.00	3.00	1.50
241	Karl Rhodes	.12	.09	.05
242	Luis Mercedes	.20	.15	.08
243	Billy Swift	.15	.11	.06
244	Tommy Gregg	.10	.08	.04
245	David Howard	.10	.08	.04
246	Dave Hollins	.50	.40	.20
247	Kip Gross	.10	.08	.04
248	Walt Weiss	.10	.08	.04
249	Mackey Sasser	.10	.08	.04
250	Cecil Fielder	.50	.40	.20
251	Jerry Browne	.10	.08	.04
252	Doug Dascenzo	.10	.08	.04
253	Darryl Hamilton	.10	.08	.04
254	Dann Bilardello	.10	.08	.04
255	Luis Rivera	.10	.08	.04
256	Larry Walker	.30	.25	.12
257	Ron Karkovice	.10	.08	.04
258	Bob Tewksbury	.15	.11	.06
259	Jimmy Key	.15	.11	.06
260	Bernie Williams	.15	.11	.06
261	Gary Wayne	.10	.08	.04
262	Mike Simms	.10	.08	.04
263	John Orton	.10	.08	.04
264	Marvin Freeman	.10	.08	.04
265	Mike Jeffcoat	.10	.08	.04
266	Roger Mason	.10	.08	.04
267	Edgar Martinez	.20	.15	.08
268	Henry Rodriguez	.25	.20	.10
269	Sam Horn	.10	.08	.04
270	Brian McRae	.15	.11	.06
271	Kirt Manwaring	.10	.08	.04
272	Mike Bordick	.15	.11	.06
273	Chris Sabo	.15	.11	.06
274	Jim Olander	.10	.08	.04
275	Greg Harris	.10	.08	.04
276	Dan Gakeler	.10	.08	.04
277	Bill Sampen	.10	.08	.04
278	Joel Skinner	.10	.08	.04
279	Curt Schilling	.10	.08	.04
280	Dale Murphy	.25	.20	.10
281	Lee Stevens	.10	.08	.04
282	Lonnie Smith	.10	.08	.04
283	Manuel Lee	.10	.08	.04
284	Shawn Boskie	.10	.08	.04
285	Kevin Seitzer	.10	.08	.04
286	Stan Royer	.15	.11	.06
287	John Dopson	.10	.08	.04
288	Scott Bullett	.20	.15	.08
289	Ken Patterson	.10	.08	.04
290	Todd Hundley	.15	.11	.06
291	Tim Leary	.10	.08	.04
292	Brett Butler	.10	.08	.04
293	Gregg Olson	.15	.11	.06
294	Jeff Brantley	.10	.08	.04
295	Brian Holman	.10	.08	.04
296	Brian Harper	.15	.11	.06
297	Brian Bohanon	.15	.11	.06
298	Checklist 1-100	.15	.11	.06
299	Checklist 101-200	.15	.11	.06
300	Checklist 201-300	.15	.11	.06
301	Frank Thomas	6.00	4.50	2.50
302	Lloyd McClendon	.15	.11	.06
303	Brady Anderson	.20	.15	.08
304	Julio Valera	.15	.11	.06
305	Mike Aldrete	.15	.11	.06
306	Joe Oliver	.15	.11	.06
307	Todd Stottlemyre	.15	.11	.06
308	Rey Sanchez	.15	.11	.06
309	Gary Sheffield	.40	.30	.15
310	Andujar Cedeno	.30	.25	.12
311	Kenny Rogers	.10	.08	.04
312	Bruce Hurst	.15	.11	.06
313	Mike Schooler	.10	.08	.04
314	Mike Benjamin	.10	.08	.04
315	Chuck Finley	.15	.11	.06
316	Mark Lemke	.10	.08	.04
317	Scott Livingstone	.15	.11	.06
318	Chris Nabholz	.10	.08	.04
319	Mike Humphreys	.15	.11	.06
320	Pedro Guerrero	.15	.11	.06
321	Willie Banks	.15	.11	.06
322	Tom Goodwin	.15	.11	.06
323	Hector Wagner	.10	.08	.04
324	Wally Ritchie	.10	.08	.04
325	Mo Vaughn	1.00	.75	.40
326	Joe Klink	.10	.08	.04
327	Cal Eldred	.30	.25	.12
328	Daryl Boston	.10	.08	.04
329	Mike Huff	.10	.08	.04
330	Jeff Bagwell	.75	.60	.30
331	Bob Milacki	.10	.08	.04
332	Tom Prince	.10	.08	.04
333	Pat Tabler	.10	.08	.04
334	Ced Landrum	.10	.08	.04
335	Reggie Jefferson	.15	.11	.06
336	Mo Sanford	.15	.11	.06
337	Kevin Ritz	.10	.08	.04
338	Gerald Perry	.10	.08	.04
339	Jeff Hamilton	.10	.08	.04
340	Tim Wallach	.15	.11	.06
341	Jeff Huson	.15	.11	.06
342	Jose Melendez	.15	.11	.06
343	Willie Wilson	.15	.11	.06
344	Mike Stanton	.10	.08	.04
345	Joel Johnston	.15	.11	.06
346	Lee Guetterman	.10	.08	.04
347	Francisco Olivares	.10	.08	.04
348	Dave Burba	.10	.08	.04
349	Tim Crews	.10	.08	.04
350	Scott Leius	.15	.11	.06
351	Danny Cox	.10	.08	.04
352	Wayne Housie	.15	.11	.06
353	Chris Donnels	.10	.08	.04
354	Chris George	.10	.08	.04
355	Gerald Young	.10	.08	.04
356	Roberto Hernandez	.15	.11	.06
357	Neal Heaton	.10	.08	.04
358	Todd Frohwirth	.10	.08	.04
359	Jose Vizcaino	.10	.08	.04
360	Jim Thome	1.00	.75	.40
361	Craig Wilson	.10	.08	.04
362	Dave Haas	.10	.08	.04
363	Billy Hatcher	.10	.08	.04
364	John Barfield	.10	.08	.04
365	Luis Aquino	.10	.08	.04
366	Charlie Leibrandt	.10	.08	.04
367	Howard Farmer	.10	.08	.04
368	Bryn Smith	.10	.08	.04
369	Mickey Morandini	.15	.11	.06
370	Jose Canseco (Members Choice, should have been #597)	.50	.40	.20
371	Jose Uribe	.10	.08	.04
372	Bob MacDonald	.10	.08	.04
373	Luis Sojo	.10	.08	.04
374	Craig Shipley	.10	.08	.04
375	Scott Bankhead	.10	.08	.04
376	Greg Gagne	.10	.08	.04
377	Scott Cooper	.25	.20	.10
378	Jose Offerman	.10	.08	.04
379	Billy Spiers	.10	.08	.04
380	John Smiley	.15	.11	.06
381	Jeff Carter	.10	.08	.04
382	Heathcliff Slocumb	.10	.08	.04
383	Jeff Tackett	.10	.08	.04
384	John Kiely	.15	.11	.06
385	John Vander Wal	.15	.11	.06
386	Omar Olivares	.10	.08	.04
387	Ruben Sierra	.25	.20	.10
388	Tom Gordon	.10	.08	.04
389	Charles Nagy	.10	.08	.04
390	Dave Stewart	.15	.11	.06
391	Pete Harnisch	.15	.11	.06
392	Tim Burke	.10	.08	.04
393	Roberto Kelly	.10	.08	.04
394	Freddie Benavides	.10	.08	.04
395	Tom Glavine	.60	.45	.25
396	Wes Chamberlain	.15	.11	.06
397	Eric Gunderson	.10	.08	.04
398	Dave West	.10	.08	.04
399	Ellis Burks	.20	.15	.08
400	Ken Griffey, Jr.	5.00	3.75	2.00
401	Thomas Howard	.10	.08	.04
402	Juan Guzman	.75	.60	.30
403	Mitch Webster	.10	.08	.04
404	Matt Merullo	.10	.08	.04
405	Steve Buechele	.10	.08	.04
406	Danny Jackson	.10	.08	.04
407	Felix Jose	.10	.08	.04

408	Doug Piatt	.10	.08	.04
409	Jim Eisenreich	.10	.08	.04
410	Bryan Harvey	.15	.11	.06
411	Jim Austin	.15	.11	.06
412	Jim Poole	.10	.08	.04
413	Glenallen Hill	.15	.11	.06
414	Gene Nelson	.10	.08	.04
415	Ivan Rodriguez	.50	.40	.20
416	Frank Tanana	.10	.08	.04
417	Steve Decker	.10	.08	.04
418	Jason Grimsley	.10	.08	.04
419	Tim Layana	.10	.08	.04
420	Don Mattingly	.75	.60	.30
421	Jerome Walton	.10	.08	.04
422	Rob Ducey	.10	.08	.04
423	Andy Benes	.15	.11	.06
424	John Marzano	.10	.08	.04
425	Gene Harris	.10	.08	.04
426	Tim Raines	.20	.15	.08
427	Bret Barberie	.10	.08	.04
428	Harvey Pulliam	.12	.09	.05
429	Cris Carpenter	.10	.08	.04
430	Howard Johnson	.10	.08	.04
431	Orel Hershiser	.10	.08	.04
432	Brian Hunter	.10	.08	.04
433	Kevin Tapani	.15	.11	.06
434	Rick Reed	.15	.11	.06
435	Ron Witmeyer	.15	.11	.06
436	Gary Gaetti	.15	.11	.06
437	Alex Cole	.15	.11	.06
438	Chito Martinez	.10	.08	.04
439	Greg Litton	.15	.11	.06
440	Julio Franco	.15	.11	.06
441	Mike Munoz	.15	.11	.06
442	Erik Pappas	.15	.11	.06
443	Pat Combs	.15	.11	.06
444	Lance Johnson	.15	.11	.06
445	Ed Sprague	.15	.11	.06
446	Mike Greenwell	.15	.11	.06
447	Milt Thompson	.15	.11	.06
448	Mike Magnante	.15	.11	.06
449	Chris Haney	.15	.11	.06
450	Robin Yount	.75	.60	.30
451	Rafael Ramirez	.15	.11	.06
452	Gino Minutelli	.15	.11	.06
453	Tom Lampkin	.15	.11	.06
454	Tony Perezchica	.15	.11	.06
455	Dwight Gooden	.15	.11	.06
456	Mark Guthrie	.15	.11	.06
457	Jay Howell	.15	.11	.06
458	Gary DiSarcina	.15	.11	.06
459	John Smoltz	.15	.11	.06
460	Will Clark	.50	.40	.20
461	Dave Otto	.15	.11	.06
462	Rob Maurer	.15	.11	.06
463	Dwight Evans	.15	.11	.06
464	Tom Brunansky	.10	.08	.04
465	*Shawn Hare*	.15	.11	.06
466	Geronimo Pena	.15	.11	.06
467	Alex Fernandez	.60	.45	.25
468	Greg Myers	.10	.08	.04
469	Jeff Fassero	.20	.15	.08
470	Len Dykstra	.25	.20	.10
471	Jeff Johnson	.15	.11	.06
472	Russ Swan	.10	.08	.04
473	Archie Corbin	.15	.11	.06
474	Chuck McElroy	.10	.08	.04
475	Mark McGwire	.50	.40	.20
476	Wally Whitehurst	.10	.08	.04
477	Tim McIntosh	.10	.08	.04
478	Sid Bream	.10	.08	.04
479	Jeff Juden	.15	.11	.06
480	Carlton Fisk	.20	.15	.08
481	Jeff Plympton	.15	.11	.06
482	Carlos Martinez	.10	.08	.04
483	Jim Gott	.10	.08	.04
484	Bob McClure	.10	.08	.04
485	Tim Teufel	.10	.08	.04
486	Vicente Palacios	.10	.08	.04
487	Jeff Reed	.10	.08	.04
488	Tony Phillips	.15	.11	.06
489	Mel Rojas	.10	.08	.04
490	Ben McDonald	.40	.30	.15
491	Andres Santana	.15	.11	.06
492	Chris Beasley	.12	.09	.05
493	Mike Timlin	.15	.11	.06
494	Brian Downing	.10	.08	.04
495	Kirk Gibson	.10	.08	.04
496	Scott Sanderson	.10	.08	.04
497	Nick Esasky	.10	.08	.04
498	*Johnny Guzman*	.30	.25	.12
499	Mitch Williams	.15	.11	.06
500	Kirby Puckett	1.00	.75	.40
501	Mike Harkey	.10	.08	.04
502	Jim Gantner	.10	.08	.04
503	Bruce Egloff	.15	.11	.06
504	Josias Manzanillo	.15	.11	.06
505	Delino DeShields	.20	.15	.08
506	Rheal Cormier	.15	.11	.06
507	Jay Bell	.15	.11	.06
508	Rich Rowland	.15	.11	.06
509	Scott Servais	.15	.11	.06
510	Terry Pendleton	.15	.11	.06
511	Rich DeLucia	.10	.08	.04
512	Warren Newson	.10	.08	.04
513	Paul Faries	.10	.08	.04
514	Kal Daniels	.10	.08	.04
515	Jarvis Brown	.15	.11	.06
516	Rafael Palmeiro	.20	.15	.08
517	Kelly Downs	.10	.08	.04
518	Steve Chitren	.10	.08	.04
519	Moises Alou	.40	.30	.15
520	Wade Boggs	.25	.20	.10
521	Pete Schourek	.10	.08	.04
522	Scott Terry	.10	.08	.04
523	Kevin Appier	.20	.15	.08
524	Gary Redus	.10	.08	.04
525	George Bell	.15	.11	.06
526	Jeff Kaiser	.20	.15	.08
527	Alvaro Espinoza	.10	.08	.04
528	Luis Polonia	.10	.08	.04
529	Darren Daulton	.25	.20	.10
530	Norm Charlton	.20	.15	.08
531	John Olerud	1.25	.90	.50
532	Dan Plesac	.10	.08	.04
533	Billy Ripken	.10	.08	.04
534	Rod Nichols	.10	.08	.04
535	Joey Cora	.10	.08	.04
536	Harold Baines	.10	.08	.04
537	Bob Ojeda	.10	.08	.04
538	Mark Leonard	.10	.08	.04
539	Danny Darwin	.10	.08	.04
540	Shawon Dunston	.15	.11	.06
541	Pedro Munoz	.10	.08	.04
542	Mark Gubicza	.15	.11	.06
543	Kevin Baez	.15	.11	.06
544	Todd Zeile	.15	.11	.06
545	Don Slaught	.10	.08	.04
546	Tony Eusebio	.15	.11	.06
547	Alonzo Powell	.10	.08	.04
548	Gary Pettis	.10	.08	.04
549	Brian Barnes	.15	.11	.06
550	Lou Whitaker	.15	.11	.06
551	Keith Mitchell	.10	.08	.04
552	Oscar Azocar	.10	.08	.04
553	Stu Cole	.15	.11	.06
554	Steve Wapnick	.10	.08	.04
555	Derek Bell	.35	.25	.14
556	Luis Lopez	.15	.11	.06
557	Anthony Telford	.15	.11	.06
558	Tim Mauser	.15	.11	.06
559	Glenn Sutko	.10	.08	.04
560	Darryl Strawberry	.15	.11	.06
561	Tom Bolton	.10	.08	.04
562	Cliff Young	.10	.08	.04
563	Bruce Walton	.10	.08	.04
564	Chico Walker	.10	.08	.04
565	John Franco	.15	.11	.06
566	Paul McClellan	.15	.11	.06
567	Paul Abbott	.15	.11	.06
568	Gary Varsho	.10	.08	.04
569	Carlos Maldonado	.20	.15	.08
570	Kelly Gruber	.10	.08	.04
571	Jose Oquendo	.10	.08	.04
572	Steve Frey	.10	.08	.04
573	Tino Martinez	.20	.15	.08
574	Bill Haselman	.10	.08	.04
575	Eric Anthony	.15	.11	.06
576	John Habyan	.10	.08	.04
577	Jeffrey McNeely	.20	.15	.08
578	Chris Bosio	.15	.11	.06
579	Joe Grahe	.15	.11	.06
580	Fred McGriff	.60	.45	.25
581	Rick Honeycutt	.10	.08	.04
582	Matt Williams	.25	.20	.10
583	Cliff Brantley	.15	.11	.06
584	Rob Dibble	.12	.09	.05
585	Skeeter Barnes	.10	.08	.04
586	Greg Hibbard	.10	.08	.04
587	Randy Milligan	.10	.08	.04
588	Checklist 301-400	.10	.08	.04
589	Checklist 401-500	.10	.08	.04
590	Checklist 501-600	.10	.08	.04
591	Frank Thomas (Members Choice)	2.75	2.00	1.00
592	David Justice (Members Choice)	.50	.40	.20
593	Roger Clemens (Members Choice)	.40	.30	.15
594	Steve Avery (Members Choice)	.30	.25	.12
595	Cal Ripken, Jr. (Members Choice)	.50	.40	.20
596	Barry Larkin (Members Choice)	.15	.11	.06
597	Not issued (See #370)			
598	Will Clark (Members Choice)	.35	.25	.14
599	Cecil Fielder (Members Choice)	.15	.11	.06
600	Ryne Sandberg (Members Choice)	.60	.45	.25
601	Chuck Knoblauch (Members Choice)	.12	.09	.05
602	Dwight Gooden (Members Choice)	.15	.11	.06
603	Ken Griffey, Jr. (Members Choice)	2.50	2.00	1.00
604	Barry Bonds (Members Choice)	.75	.60	.30
605	Nolan Ryan (Members Choice)	1.50	1.25	.60
606	Jeff Bagwell (Members Choice)	.50	.40	.20
607	Robin Yount (Members Choice)	.40	.30	.15
608	Bobby Bonilla (Members Choice)	.15	.11	.06
609	George Brett (Members Choice)	.50	.40	.20
610	Howard Johnson (Members Choice)	.10	.07	.04
611	Esteban Beltre	.10	.08	.04
612	Mike Christopher	.20	.15	.08
613	Troy Afenir	.10	.08	.04
614	Mariano Duncan	.10	.08	.04
615	Doug Henry	.15	.11	.06
616	Doug Jones	.15	.11	.06
617	Alvin Davis	.10	.08	.04
618	Craig Lefferts	.10	.08	.04
619	Kevin McReynolds	.20	.15	.08
620	Barry Bonds	1.50	1.25	.60
621	Turner Ward	.20	.15	.08
622	Joe Magrane	.15	.11	.06
623	Mark Parent	.10	.08	.04
624	Tom Browning	.15	.11	.06
625	John Smiley	.15	.11	.06
626	Steve Wilson	.10	.08	.04
627	Mike Gallego	.10	.08	.04
628	Sammy Sosa	.15	.11	.06
629	Rico Rossy	.15	.11	.06
630	Royce Clayton	.40	.30	.15
631	Clay Parker	.10	.08	.04
632	Pete Smith	.10	.08	.04
633	Jeff McKnight	.10	.08	.04
634	Jack Daugherty	.10	.08	.04
635	Steve Sax	.20	.15	.08
636	Joe Hesketh	.10	.08	.04
637	Vince Horsman	.20	.15	.08
638	Eric King	.10	.08	.04
639	Joe Boever	.10	.08	.04
640	Jack Morris	.10	.08	.04
641	Arthur Rhodes	.20	.15	.08
642	Bob Melvin	.10	.08	.04
643	Rick Wilkins	.20	.15	.08
644	Scott Scudder	.10	.08	.04
645	Bip Roberts	.20	.15	.08
646	Julio Valera	.20	.15	.08
647	Kevin Campbell	.20	.15	.08
648	Steve Searcy	.10	.08	.04
649	Scott Kamieniecki	.10	.08	.04
650	Kurt Stillwell	.10	.08	.04
651	Bob Welch	.15	.11	.06
652	Andres Galarraga	.15	.11	.06
653	Mike Jackson	.10	.08	.04
654	Bo Jackson	.60	.45	.25
655	Sid Fernandez	.15	.11	.06
656	Mike Bielecki	.10	.08	.04
657	Jeff Reardon	.15	.11	.06
658	Wayne Rosenthal	.10	.08	.04
659	Eric Bullock	.10	.08	.04
660	Eric Davis	.25	.20	.10
661	Randy Tomlin	.20	.15	.08
662	Tom Edens	.10	.08	.04
663	Rob Murphy	.10	.08	.04
664	Leo Gomez	.10	.08	.04
665	Greg Maddux	.25	.20	.10
666	Greg Vaughn	.15	.11	.06
667	Wade Taylor	.10	.08	.04
668	Brad Arnsberg	.10	.08	.04
669	Mike Moore	.15	.11	.06
670	Mark Langston	.15	.11	.06
671	Barry Jones	.10	.08	.04
672	Bill Landrum	.10	.08	.04
673	Greg Swindell	.20	.15	.08
674	Wayne Edwards	.10	.08	.04
675	Greg Olson	.10	.08	.04
676	Bill Pulsipher	.20	.15	.08
677	Bobby Witt	.15	.11	.06
678	Mark Carreon	.10	.08	.04
679	Patrick Lennon	.15	.11	.06
680	Ozzie Smith	.40	.30	.15
681	John Briscoe	.20	.15	.08
682	Matt Young	.10	.08	.04
683	Jeff Conine	.20	.15	.08
684	Phil Stephenson	.10	.08	.04
685	Ron Darling	.15	.11	.06
686	Bryan Hickerson	.15	.11	.06
687	Dale Sveum	.10	.08	.04
688	Kirk McCaskill	.10	.08	.04
689	Rich Amaral	.15	.11	.06
690	Danny Tartabull	.15	.11	.06
691	Donald Harris	.15	.11	.06
692	Doug Davis	.20	.15	.08
693	John Farrell	.10	.08	.04
694	Paul Gibson	.10	.08	.04
695	Kenny Lofton	1.25	.90	.50
696	Mike Fetters	.10	.08	.04
697	Rosario Rodriguez	.10	.08	.04
698	Chris Jones	.15	.11	.06
699	Jeff Manto	.10	.08	.04
700	Rick Sutcliffe	.15	.11	.06
701	Scott Bankhead	.10	.08	.04
702	Donnie Hill	.10	.08	.04
703	Todd Worrell	.15	.11	.06
704	Rene Gonzales	.10	.08	.04
705	Rick Cerone	.10	.08	.04
706	Tony Pena	.10	.08	.04
707	Paul Sorrento	.10	.08	.04
708	Gary Scott	.15	.11	.06
709	Junior Noboa	.10	.08	.04
710	Wally Joyner	.20	.15	.08
711	Charlie Hayes	.15	.11	.06
712	Rich Rodriguez	.10	.08	.04
713	Rudy Seanez	.10	.08	.04
714	Jim Bullinger	.12	.09	.05
715	Jeff Robinson	.10	.08	.04
716	Jeff Branson	.25	.20	.10
717	Andy Ashby	.10	.08	.04
718	Dave Burba	.10	.08	.04
719	Rich Gossage	.20	.15	.08
720	Randy Johnson	.20	.15	.08
721	David Wells	.10	.08	.04
722	Paul Kilgus	.10	.08	.04
723	Dave Martinez	.10	.08	.04
724	Denny Neagle	.15	.11	.06
725	Andy Stankiewicz	.10	.08	.04
726	Rick Aguilera	.15	.11	.06
727	Junior Ortiz	.10	.08	.04
728	Storm Davis	.10	.08	.04
729	Don Robinson	.10	.08	.04
730	Ron Gant	.20	.15	.08
731	Paul Assenmacher	.10	.08	.04
732	Mark Gardiner	.10	.08	.04
733	Milt Hill	.10	.08	.04
734	Jeremy Hernandez	.15	.11	.06
735	Ken Hill	.20	.15	.08
736	Xavier Hernandez	.10	.08	.04
737	Gregg Jefferies	.25	.20	.10
738	Dick Schofield	.10	.08	.04
739	Ron Robinson	.10	.08	.04
740	Sandy Alomar	.20	.15	.08
741	Mike Stanley	.10	.08	.04
742	Butch Henry	.10	.08	.04
743	Floyd Bannister	.10	.08	.04
744	Brian Drahman	.15	.11	.06
745	Dave Winfield	.60	.45	.25
746	Bob Walk	.10	.08	.04
747	Chris James	.10	.08	.04
748	Don Prybylinski	.20	.15	.08
749	Dennis Rasmussen	.10	.08	.04
750	Rickey Henderson	.35	.25	.14
751	Chris Hammond	.15	.11	.06
752	Bob Kipper	.10	.08	.04
753	Dave Rohde	.10	.08	.04

754	Hubie Brooks	.10	.08	.04
755	Bret Saberhagen	.15	.11	.06
756	Jeff Robinson	.10	.08	.04
757	*Pat Listach*	.25	.20	.10
758	Bill Wegman	.15	.11	.06
759	John Wetteland	.15	.11	.06
760	Phil Plantier	.60	.45	.25
761	Wilson Alvarez	.10	.08	.04
762	Scott Aldred	.10	.08	.04
763	*Armando Reynoso*	.30	.25	.12
764	Todd Benzinger	.10	.08	.04
765	Kevin Mitchell	.20	.15	.08
766	Gary Sheffield	.50	.40	.20
767	Allan Anderson	.10	.08	.04
768	Rusty Meacham	.15	.11	.06
769	Rick Parker	.10	.08	.04
770	Nolan Ryan	3.00	2.25	1.25
771	Jeff Ballard	.10	.08	.04
772	Cory Snyder	.10	.08	.04
773	Denis Boucher	.15	.11	.06
774	Jose Gonzales	.10	.08	.04
775	Juan Guerrero	.10	.08	.04
776	Ed Nunez	.10	.08	.04
777	Scott Ruskin	.10	.08	.04
778	Terry Leach	.10	.08	.04
779	Carl Willis	.10	.08	.04
780	Bobby Bonilla	.20	.15	.08
781	Duane Ward	.15	.11	.06
782	Joe Slusarski	.15	.11	.06
783	David Segui	.15	.11	.06
784	Kirk Gibson	.10	.08	.04
785	Frank Viola	.20	.15	.08
786	Keith Miller	.10	.08	.04
787	Mike Morgan	.10	.08	.04
788	Kim Batiste	.15	.11	.06
789	Sergio Valdez	.15	.11	.06
790	Eddie Taubensee	.15	.11	.06
791	Jack Armstrong	.10	.08	.04
792	Scott Fletcher	.10	.08	.04
793	Steve Farr	.10	.08	.04
794	Dan Pasqua	.10	.08	.04
795	Eddie Murray	.20	.15	.08
796	John Morris	.10	.08	.04
797	Francisco Cabrera	.10	.08	.04
798	Mike Perez	.20	.15	.08
799	Ted Wood	.20	.15	.08
800	Jose Rijo	.20	.15	.08
801	Danny Gladden	.10	.08	.04
802	Arci Cianfrocco	.15	.11	.06
803	Monty Fariss	.15	.11	.06
804	Roger McDowell	.10	.08	.04
805	Randy Myers	.15	.11	.06
806	Kirk Dressendorfer	.15	.11	.06
807	Zane Smith	.10	.08	.04
808	Glenn Davis	.15	.11	.06
809	Torey Lovullo	.10	.08	.04
810	Andre Dawson	.25	.20	.10
811	Bill Pecota	.10	.08	.04
812	Ted Power	.10	.08	.04
813	Willie Blair	.10	.08	.04
814	Dave Fleming	.25	.20	.10
815	Chris Gwynn	.10	.08	.04
816	Jody Reed	.10	.08	.04
817	Mark Dewey	.10	.08	.04
818	Kyle Abbott	.10	.08	.04
819	Tom Henke	.10	.08	.04
820	Kevin Seitzer	.10	.08	.04
821	Al Newman	.10	.08	.04
822	Tim Sherrill	.20	.15	.08
823	Chuck Crim	.10	.08	.04
824	Darren Reed	.15	.11	.06
825	Tony Gwynn	.40	.30	.15
826	Steve Foster	.20	.15	.08
827	Steve Howe	.10	.08	.04
828	Brook Jacoby	.10	.08	.04
829	Rodney McCray	.10	.08	.04
830	Chuck Knoblauch	.15	.11	.06
831	John Wehner	.15	.11	.06
832	Scott Garrelts	.10	.08	.04
833	Alejandro Pena	.10	.08	.04
834	Jeff Parrett	.10	.08	.04
835	Juan Bell	.10	.08	.04
836	Lance Dickson	.10	.08	.04
837	Darryl Kile	.15	.11	.06
838	Efrain Valdez	.15	.11	.06
839	*Bob Zupcic*	.20	.15	.08
840	George Bell	.15	.11	.06
841	Dave Gallagher	.10	.08	.04
842	Tim Belcher	.15	.11	.06
843	Jeff Shaw	.10	.08	.04
844	Mike Fitgerald	.10	.08	.04
845	Gary Carter	.15	.11	.06
846	John Russell	.10	.08	.04
847	*Eric Hillman*	.30	.25	.12
848	Mike Witt	.10	.08	.04
849	Curt Wilkerson	.10	.08	.04
850	Alan Trammell	.15	.11	.06
851	Rex Hudler	.10	.08	.04
852	*Michael Walkden*	.15	.11	.06
853	Kevin Ward	.15	.11	.06
854	Tim Naehring	.15	.11	.06
855	Bill Swift	.15	.11	.06
856	Damon Berryhill	.10	.08	.04
857	Mark Eichhorn	.10	.08	.04
858	Hector Villanueva	.10	.08	.04
859	Jose Lind	.10	.08	.04
860	Denny Martinez	.15	.11	.06
861	Bill Krueger	.10	.08	.04
862	Mike Kingery	.10	.08	.04
863	Jeff Innis	.10	.08	.04
864	Derek Lilliquist	.10	.08	.04
865	Reggie Sanders	.60	.45	.25
866	Ramon Garcia	.20	.15	.08
867	Bruce Ruffin	.10	.08	.04
868	Dickie Thon	.10	.08	.04
869	Melido Perez	.15	.11	.06
870	Ruben Amaro	.15	.11	.06
871	Alan Mills	.10	.08	.04
872	Matt Sinatro	.10	.08	.04
873	Eddie Zosky	.20	.15	.08
874	Pete Incaviglia	.10	.08	.04
875	Tom Candiotti	.10	.08	.04
876	Bob Patterson	.10	.08	.04
877	Neal Heaton	.10	.08	.04
878	*Terrel Hansen*	.15	.11	.06
879	Dave Eiland	.10	.08	.04
880	Von Hayes	.10	.08	.04
881	Tim Scott	.20	.15	.08
882	Otis Nixon	.15	.11	.06
883	Herm Winningham	.10	.08	.04
884	Dion James	.10	.08	.04
885	Dave Wainhouse	.15	.11	.06
886	Frank DiPino	.10	.08	.04
887	Dennis Cook	.10	.08	.04
888	Jose Mesa	.10	.08	.04
889	Mark Leiter	.10	.08	.04
890	Willie Randolph	.15	.11	.06
891	Craig Colbert	.15	.11	.06
892	Dwayne Henry	.10	.08	.04
893	Jim Lindeman	.10	.08	.04
894	Charlie Hough	.10	.08	.04
895	Gil Heredia	.10	.08	.04
896	Scott Chiamparino	.10	.08	.04
897	Lance Blankenship	.10	.08	.04
898	Checklist 601-700	.10	.08	.04
899	Checklist 701-800	.10	.08	.04
900	Checklist 801-900	.10	.08	.04

1992 Topps Stadium Club Master Photos

Uncropped versions of the photos which appear on regular Stadium Club cards are featured on these large-format (5" x 7") cards. The photos are set against a white background and trimmed with holographic foil. Backs are blank and the cards are unnumbered. Members of Topps' Stadium Club received a Master Photo in their members' packs for 1992. The cards were also available as inserts in special boxes of Stadium Club cards sold at Wal-Mart stores.

		MT	NR MT	EX
Complete Set (15):		60.00	45.00	24.00
Common Player:		2.00	1.50	.80
(1)	Wade Boggs	4.50	3.50	1.75
(2)	Barry Bonds	6.00	4.50	2.50
(3)	Jose Canseco	4.00	3.00	1.50
(4)	Will Clark	4.00	3.00	1.50
(5)	Cecil Fielder	4.00	3.00	1.50
(6)	Dwight Gooden	4.00	3.00	1.50
(7)	Ken Griffey, Jr.	8.00	6.00	3.25
(8)	Rickey Henderson	4.00	3.00	1.50
(9)	Lance Johnson	2.00	1.50	.80
(10)	Cal Ripken, Jr.	7.50	5.75	3.00
(11)	Nolan Ryan	9.00	6.75	3.50
(12)	Deion Sanders	3.50	2.75	1.50
(13)	Darryl Strawberry	4.00	3.00	1.50
(14)	Danny Tartabull	2.00	1.50	.80
(15)	Frank Thomas	8.00	6.00	3.25

1992 Topps Stadium Club Special Edition

This 200-card special Stadium Club set from Topps was uniquely packaged in a plastic replica of the Toronto SkyDome, the home of the 1991 All-Star Game. Featured in the set are members of Team USA, All-Stars, draft picks, top prospects and highlight cards from the World Series between the Twins and Braves. The cards are styled much like the regular Stadium Club cards.

		MT	NR MT	EX
Complete Set (200):		30.00	22.00	12.00
Common Player:		.15	.11	.06
1	Terry Adams	.30	.25	.12
2	Tommy Adams	.20	.15	.08
3	Rick Aguilera	.15	.11	.06
4	Ron Allen	.25	.20	.10
5	Roberto Alomar (AS)	.60	.45	.25
6	Sandy Alomar	.25	.20	.10
7	Greg Anthony	.15	.11	.06
8	James Austin	.25	.20	.10
9	Steve Avery	.40	.30	.15
10	Harold Baines	.15	.11	.06
11	Brian Barber	.60	.45	.25
12	Jon Barnes	.25	.20	.10
13	George Bell	.15	.11	.06
14	Doug Bennett	.25	.20	.10
15	Sean Bergman	.25	.20	.10
16	Bill Bliss	.25	.20	.10
17	Craig Biggio	.15	.11	.06
18	Wade Boggs (AS)	.30	.25	.12
19	Bobby Bonilla (AS)	.25	.20	.10
20	Russell Brock	.30	.25	.12
21	Tarrik Brock	.30	.25	.12
22	Tom Browning	.15	.11	.06
23	Brett Butler	.15	.11	.06
24	Ivan Calderon	.15	.11	.06
25	Joe Carter	.40	.30	.15
26	Joe Caruso	.25	.20	.10
27	Dan Cholowsky	.40	.30	.15
28	Will Clark (AS)	.40	.30	.15
29	Roger Clemens (AS)	.30	.25	.12
30	Shawn Curran	.25	.20	.10
31	Chris Curtis	.15	.11	.06
32	Chili Davis	.15	.11	.06
33	Andre Dawson	.25	.20	.10
34	Joe DeBerry	.25	.20	.10
35	John Dettmer	.40	.30	.15
36	Rob Dibble	.15	.11	.06
37	John Donati	.30	.25	.12
38	Dave Doorneweerd	.25	.20	.10
39	Darren Dreifort	1.50	1.25	.60
40	Mike Durant	.30	.25	.12
41	Chris Durkin	.30	.25	.12
42	Dennis Eckersley	.20	.15	.08
43	Brian Edmondson	.30	.25	.12
44	Vaughn Eshelman	.25	.20	.10
45	Shawn Estes	.35	.25	.14
46	Jorge Fabregas	.40	.30	.15
47	Jon Farrell	.35	.25	.14
48	Cecil Fielder (AS)	.25	.20	.10
49	Carlton Fisk	.20	.15	.08
50	Tim Flannelly	.25	.20	.10
51	Cliff Floyd	7.00	5.25	2.75
52	Julio Franco	.15	.11	.06
53	Greg Gagne	.15	.11	.06
54	Chris Gambs	.30	.25	.12
55	Ron Gant	.25	.20	.10
56	Brent Gates	1.50	1.25	.60
57	Dwayne Gerald	.30	.25	.12
58	Jason Giambi	.75	.60	.30
59	Benji Gil	.75	.60	.30
60	Mark Gipner	.30	.25	.12
61	Danny Gladden	.15	.11	.06
62	Tom Glavine	.25	.20	.10
63	Jimmy Gonzalez	.25	.20	.10
64	Jeff Granger	1.00	.70	.40
65	Dan Grapenthien	.25	.20	.10
66	Dennis Gray	.25	.20	.10
67	Shawn Green	.60	.45	.25
68	Tyler Green	.60	.45	.25
69	Todd Greene	.40	.30	.15
70	Ken Griffey, Jr. (AS)	2.50	2.00	1.00
71	Kelly Gruber	.15	.11	.06
72	Ozzie Guillen	.15	.11	.06
73	Tony Gwynn (AS)	.30	.25	.12
74	Shane Halter	.25	.20	.10
75	Jeffrey Hammonds	5.00	3.75	2.00
76	Larry Hanlon	.25	.20	.10
77	Pete Harnisch	.15	.11	.06
78	Mike Harrison	.25	.20	.10
79	Bryan Harvey	.15	.11	.06
80	Scott Hatteberg	.40	.30	.15
81	Rick Helling	.30	.25	.12
82	Dave Henderson	.15	.11	.06
83	Rickey Henderson (AS)	.35	.25	.14
84	Tyrone Hill	.50	.40	.20
85	Todd Hollandsworth	1.50	1.25	.60
86	Brian Holliday	.25	.20	.10
87	Terry Horn	.25	.20	.10
88	Jeff Hostetler	.30	.25	.12
89	Kent Hrbek	.15	.11	.06
90	Mark Hubbard	.25	.20	.10
91	Charles Johnson	1.50	1.25	.60
92	Howard Johnson	.15	.11	.06
93	Todd Johnson	.40	.30	.15
94	Bobby Jones	.90	.70	.35
95	Dan Jones	.25	.20	.10
96	Felix Jose	.15	.11	.06
97	Dave Justice	.40	.30	.15
98	Jimmy Key	.15	.11	.06
99	Marc Kroom	.25	.20	.10
100	John Kruk	.25	.20	.10
101	Mark Langston	.15	.11	.06
102	Barry Larkin	.25	.20	.10
103	Mike LaValliere	.15	.11	.06

104	Scott Leius	.15	.11	.06
105	Mark Lemke	.15	.11	.06
106	Donnie Leshnock	.25	.20	.10
107	Jimmy Lewis	.25	.20	.10
108	Shawn Livesy	.40	.30	.15
109	Ryan Long	.25	.20	.10
110	Trevor Mallory	.25	.20	.10
111	Denny Martinez	.15	.11	.06
112	Justin Mashore	.25	.20	.10
113	Jason McDonald	.25	.20	.10
114	Jack McDowell	.25	.20	.10
115	Tom McKinnon	.35	.25	.14
116	Billy McKinnon	.25	.20	.10
117	Buck McNabb	.25	.20	.10
118	Jim Mecir	.25	.20	.10
119	Dan Melendez	.25	.20	.10
120	Shawn Miller	.25	.20	.10
121	Trever Miller	.25	.20	.10
122	Paul Molitor	.40	.30	.15
123	Vincent Moore	.25	.20	.10
124	Mike Morgan	.15	.11	.06
125	Jack Morris	.15	.11	.06
126	Jack Morris	.15	.11	.06
127	Sean Mulligan	.25	.20	.10
128	Eddie Murray	.30	.25	.12
129	Mike Neill	.60	.45	.25
130	Phil Nevin	2.50	2.00	1.00
131	Mark O'Brien	.25	.20	.10
132	Alex Ochoa	1.00	.75	.40
133	Chad Ogea	.75	.60	.30
134	Greg Olson	.15	.11	.06
135	Paul O'Neill	.15	.11	.06
136	Jared Osentowski	.30	.25	.12
137	Mike Pagliarulo	.15	.11	.06
138	Rafael Palmeiro	.25	.20	.10
139	Rodney Pedraza	.25	.20	.10
140	Tony Phillips	.15	.11	.06
141	Scott Pisciotta	.30	.25	.12
142	Chris Pritchett	.30	.25	.12
143	Jason Pruitt	.25	.20	.10
144	Kirby Puckett (WS)	.60	.45	.25
145	Kirby Puckett (AS)	.60	.45	.25
146	Manny Ramirez	5.00	3.75	2.00
147	Eddie Ramos	.30	.25	.12
148	Mark Ratekin	.30	.25	.12
149	Jeff Reardon	.15	.11	.06
150	Sean Rees	.25	.20	.10
151	Calvin Reese	.60	.45	.25
152	Desmond Relaford	.25	.20	.10
153	Eric Richardson	.25	.20	.10
154	Cal Ripken, Jr. (AS)	.75	.60	.30
155	Chris Roberts	.40	.30	.15
156	Mike Robertson	.35	.25	.14
157	Steve Rodriguez	.35	.25	.14
158	Mike Rossiter	.20	.15	.08
159	Scott Ruffcorn	1.00	.75	.40
160	Chris Sabo	.15	.11	.06
161	Juan Samuel	.15	.11	.06
162	Ryne Sandberg (AS)	.75	.60	.30
163	Scott Sanderson	.15	.11	.06
164	Benito Santiago	.15	.11	.06
165	Gene Schall	.30	.25	.12
166	Chad Schoenvogel	.30	.25	.12
167	Chris Seelbach	.30	.25	.12
168	Aaron Sele	5.00	3.75	2.00
169	Basil Shabazz	.50	.40	.20
170	Al Shirley	.25	.20	.10
171	Paul Shuey	.25	.20	.10
172	Ruben Sierra	.25	.20	.10
173	John Smiley	.15	.11	.06
174	Lee Smith	.30	.25	.12
175	Ozzie Smith	.35	.25	.14
176	Tim Smith	.25	.20	.10
177	Zane Smith	.15	.11	.06
178	John Smoltz	.15	.11	.06
179	Scott Stahoviak	.40	.30	.15
180	Kennie Steenstra	.50	.40	.20
181	Kevin Stocker	1.50	1.25	.60
182	Chris Stynes	.15	.11	.06
183	Danny Tartabull	.15	.11	.06
184	Brien Taylor	1.00	.75	.40
185	Todd Taylor	.30	.25	.12
186	Larry Thomas	.30	.25	.12
187a	Ozzie Timmons	.30	.25	.12
187b	David Tuttle (should be #188)	.30	.25	.12
188	Not issued			
189	Andy Van Slyke	.15	.11	.06
190	Frank Viola	.15	.11	.06
191	Michael Walkden	.30	.25	.12
192	Jeff Ware	.25	.20	.10
193	Allen Watson	1.50	1.25	.60
194	Steve Whitaker	.40	.30	.15
195	Jerry Willard	.15	.11	.06
196	Craig Wilson	.25	.20	.10
197	Chris Wimmer	.25	.20	.10
198	Steve Wojciechowski	.30	.25	.12
199	Joel Wolfe	.25	.20	.10
200	Ivan Zweig	.15	.11	.06

Regional interest may affect the value of a card.

1992 Topps Stadium Club Members Only

This set of 10 baseball cards was sent to members of Topps' Stadium Club as part of their 1992 benefits package. Cards are similar in format to regular Stadium Club cards, 2-1/2" x 3-1/2", UV coated on front and back. Fronts have a special gold foil "Members Only" logo on front. Backs have a stadium

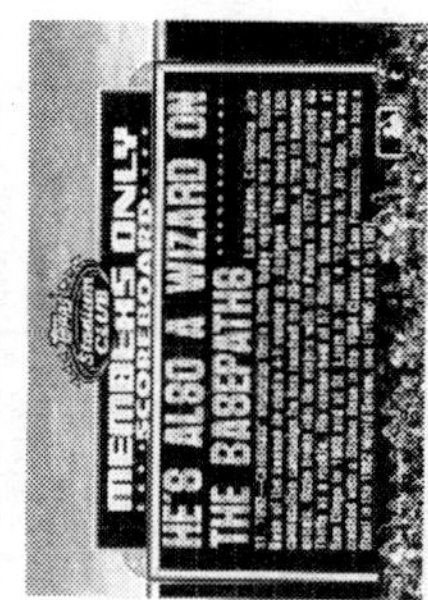

scoreboard design with details of a career highlight. The unnumbered cards are checklisted here alphabetically.

		MT	NR MT	EX
Complete Set (10):		6.00	4.50	2.50
Common Player:		.25	.20	.10
(1)	Wade Boggs	1.00	.70	.40
(2)	George Brett	2.00	1.50	.80
(3)	Gary Carter	.40	.30	.15
(4)	Roger Clemens, Matt Young	.25	.20	.10
(5)	Dave Eiland	.25	.20	.10
(6)	Dwight Gooden, Gary Sheffield	.35	.25	.14
(7)	Jack Morris	.25	.20	.10
(8)	Eddie Murray	.40	.30	.15
(9)	Ozzie Smith (Stolen base record)	.75	.60	.30
(10)	Ozzie Smith (7,000 assists)	.75	.60	.30

1992 Topps Stadium Club First Draft Picks

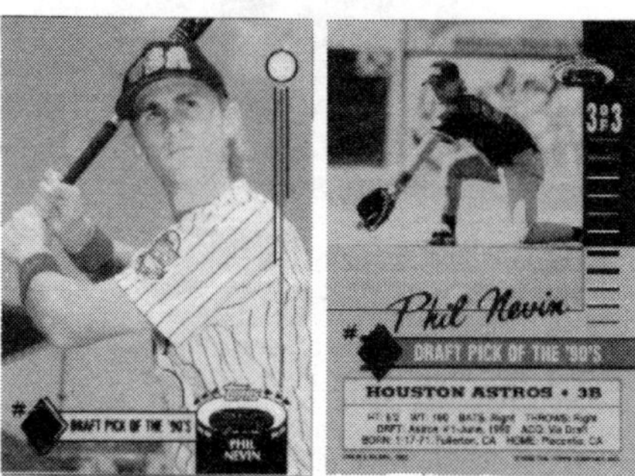

Issued as inserts with Stadium Club Series III, this three-card set features the No. 1 draft picks of 1990-92. Fronts have a full-bleed photo with S.C. logo and player name in the lower-right corner. At bottom-left in a red strip is a gold-foil stamping, "#1 Draft Pick of the '90's. An orange circle at upper-right has the year the player was the No. 1 choice. The basic red-and-black back has a color photo, afew biographical and draft details and a gold facsimile autograph among other gold-foil highlights.

		MT	NR MT	EX
Complete Set (3):		12.00	9.00	4.75
Common Player:		3.00	2.25	1.25
1	Chipper Jones	5.00	3.75	2.00
2	Brien Taylor	3.00	2.25	1.25
3	Phil Nevin	4.00	3.00	1.50

1993 Topps Promo Sheet

Originally produced as an 8" x 11" nine-card sheet, these pre-production sample cards are rarely found as singles. Cards are in the same basic format as the regular-issue 1993 Topps cards. Backs differ in that all cards are numbered "000" with all zeroes for 1992 stats and bogus career highlights. A large gray circle over the stats box reads "1993 Pre-Production Sample For General Look Only".

	MT	NR MT	EX
Complete Set (sheet):	8.00	6.00	3.25
Complete Set (9):	8.00	6.00	3.25
Common Player:	.50	.40	.20

Roberto Alomar, Bobby Bonilla, Gary Carter, Andre Dawson, Dave Fleming, Ken Griffey, Jr., Pete Incaviglia, Spike Owen, Larry Walker

1993 Topps Promos

Specially marked 1992 Topps factory sets included this nine-card preview of the coming year's issue. The preview cards are identical to the regular-issue versions except the backs have a gray oval over the stats box with the notation, "1993 Pre-Production Sample".

		MT	NR MT	EX
Complete Set (9):		8.00	6.00	3.25
Common Player:		.50	.40	.20
1	Robin Yount	1.50	1.25	.60
2	Barry Bonds	1.25	.90	.50
11	Eric Karros	.75	.60	.30
32	Don Mattingly	1.25	.90	.60
100	Mark McGwire	1.00	.70	.40
150	Frank Thomas	2.50	2.00	1.00
179	Ken Griffey, Jr.	2.50	2.00	1.00
230	Carlton Fisk	.50	.40	.20
250	Chuck Knoblauch	.50	.40	.20

1993 Topps

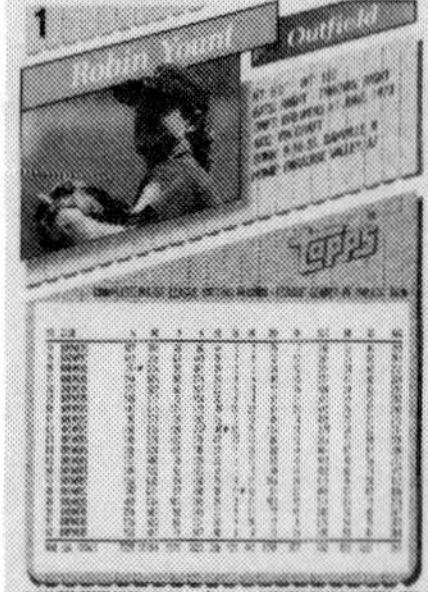

Topps used a two series format in 1993. Series I featured cards 1-396. The card fronts feature full-color photos enclosed by a white border. The player's name and team appear at the bottom. The backs feature an additional player photo and biographical information at the top. The bottom box includes statistics and player information. Like in recent years, several cards are printed horizontally. The cards are numbered in red on the back. The number appears in a yellow flag in the upper left corner of the card.

		MT	NR MT	EX
Complete Set (825):		30.00	22.00	12.00
Common Player:		.03	.02	.01
1	Robin Yount	.15	.11	.06
2	Barry Bonds	.25	.20	.10
3	Ryne Sandberg	.20	.15	.08
4	Roger Clemens	.15	.11	.06
5	Tony Gwynn	.12	.09	.05
6	*Jeff Tackett*	.12	.09	.05
7	Pete Incaviglia	.05	.04	.02
8	Mark Wohlers	.05	.04	.02
9	Kent Hrbek	.06	.05	.02
10	Will Clark	.15	.11	.06
11	Eric Karros	.15	.11	.06
12	Lee Smith	.06	.05	.02
13	Esteban Beltre	.05	.04	.02
14	Greg Briley	.03	.02	.01
15	Marquis Grissom	.08	.06	.03
16	Dan Plesac	.04	.03	.02
17	Dave Hollins	.08	.06	.03
18	Terry Steinbach	.06	.05	.02
19	Ed Nunez	.03	.02	.01
20	*Tim Salmon*	1.50	1.25	.60
21	Luis Salazar	.04	.03	.02
22	Jim Eisenreich	.03	.02	.01
23	Todd Stottlemyre	.05	.04	.02
24	Tim Naehring	.05	.04	.02
25	John Franco	.06	.05	.02
26	Skeeter Barnes	.06	.05	.02
27	*Carlos Garcia*	.25	.20	.10
28	Joe Orsulak	.04	.03	.02
29	Dwayne Henry	.03	.02	.01
30	Fred McGriff	.10	.08	.04
31	Derek Lilliquist	.03	.02	.01
32	Don Mattingly	.12	.09	.05
33	B.J. Wallace (1992 Draft Pick)	.30	.25	.12

34	Juan Gonzalez	.50	.40	.20
35	John Smoltz	.08	.06	.03
36	Scott Servais	.08	.06	.03
37	Lenny Webster	.08	.06	.03
38	Chris James	.04	.03	.02
39	Roger McDowell	.04	.03	.02
40	Ozzie Smith	.10	.08	.04
41	Alex Fernandez	.08	.06	.03
42	Spike Owen	.03	.02	.01
43	Ruben Amaro	.05	.04	.02
44	Kevin Seitzer	.05	.04	.02
45	Dave Fleming	.10	.08	.04
46	*Eric Fox*	.12	.09	.05
47	Bob Scanlan	.03	.02	.01
48	Bert Blyleven	.06	.05	.02
49	Brian McRae	.06	.05	.02
50	Roberto Alomar	.15	.11	.06
51	Mo Vaughn	.05	.04	.02
52	Bobby Bonilla	.10	.08	.04
53	Frank Tanana	.04	.03	.02
54	Mike LaValliere	.04	.03	.02
55	Mark McLemore	.03	.02	.01
56	*Chad Mottola* (1992 Draft Pick)	1.00	.70	.40
57	Norm Charlton	.06	.05	.02
58	Jose Melendez	.08	.06	.03
59	Carlos Martinez	.03	.02	.01
60	Roberto Kelly	.08	.06	.03
61	Gene Larkin	.03	.02	.01
62	Rafael Belliard	.03	.02	.01
63	Al Osuna	.03	.02	.01
64	Scott Chiamparino	.03	.02	.01
65	Brett Butler	.06	.05	.02
66	John Burkett	.04	.03	.02
67	Felix Jose	.08	.06	.03
68	Omar Vizquel	.03	.02	.01
69	*John Vander Wal*	.12	.09	.05
70	Roberto Hernandez	.08	.06	.03
71	Ricky Bones	.05	.04	.02
72	*Jeff Grotewold*	.12	.09	.05
73	Mike Moore	.05	.04	.02
74	Steve Buechele	.05	.04	.02
75	Juan Guzman	.10	.08	.04
76	Kevin Appier	.08	.06	.03
77	Junior Felix	.05	.04	.02
78	Greg Harris	.04	.03	.02
79	Dick Schofield	.04	.03	.02
80	Cecil Fielder	.10	.08	.04
81	Lloyd McClendon	.04	.03	.02
82	David Segui	.05	.04	.02
83	Reggie Sanders	.15	.11	.06
84	Kurt Stillwell	.04	.03	.02
85	Sandy Alomar	.08	.06	.03
86	John Habyan	.03	.02	.01
87	Kevin Reimer	.05	.04	.02
88	Mike Stanton	.05	.04	.02
89	Eric Anthony	.06	.05	.02
90	Scott Erickson	.08	.06	.03
91	Craig Colbert	.06	.05	.02
92	Tom Pagnozzi	.06	.05	.02
93	*Pedro Astacio* (FC)	.15	.11	.06
94	Lance Johnson	.04	.03	.02
95	Larry Walker	.10	.08	.04
96	Russ Swan	.03	.02	.01
97	Scott Fletcher	.03	.02	.01
98	*Derek Jeter* (FC) (1992 Draft Pick)	.30	.25	.12
99	*Mike Williams* (FC)	.15	.11	.06
100	Mark McGwire	.10	.08	.04
101	*Jim Bullinger*	.12	.09	.05
102	Brian Hunter	.08	.06	.03
103	Jody Reed	.04	.03	.02
104	*Mike Butcher* (FC)	.15	.11	.06
105	Gregg Jefferies	.08	.06	.03
106	Howard Johnson	.06	.05	.02
107	*John Kiely*	.12	.09	.05
108	Jose Lind	.04	.03	.02
109	Sam Horn	.03	.02	.01
110	Barry Larkin	.08	.06	.03
111	Bruce Hurst	.05	.04	.02
112	Brian Barnes	.04	.03	.02
113	Thomas Howard	.04	.03	.02
114	Mel Hall	.06	.05	.02
115	Robby Thompson	.04	.03	.02
116	Mark Lemke	.04	.03	.02
117	Eddie Taubensee	.08	.06	.03
118	David Hulse	.10	.08	.04
119	Pedro Munoz	.10	.08	.04
120	Ramon Martinez	.08	.06	.03
121	Todd Worrell	.05	.04	.02
122	Joey Cora	.03	.02	.01
123	Moises Alou	.08	.06	.03
124	Franklin Stubbs	.03	.02	.01
125	Pete O'Brien	.03	.02	.01
126	*Bob Ayrault* (FC)	.12	.09	.05
127	Carney Lansford	.05	.04	.02
128	Kal Daniels	.05	.04	.02
129	Joe Grahe	.05	.04	.02
130	Jeff Montgomery	.05	.04	.02
131	Dave Winfield	.20	.15	.08
132	*Preston Wilson* (1992 Draft Pick)	.50	.40	.20
133	Steve Wilson	.04	.03	.02
134	Lee Guetterman	.03	.02	.01
135	Mickey Tettleton	.08	.06	.03
136	Jeff King	.04	.03	.02
137	Alan Mills	.03	.02	.01
138	Joe Oliver	.04	.03	.02
139	Gary Gaetti	.04	.03	.02
140	Gary Sheffield	.10	.08	.04
141	Dennis Cook	.03	.02	.01
142	Charlie Hayes	.04	.03	.02
143	Jeff Huson	.04	.03	.02
144	Kent Mercker	.04	.03	.02
145	*Eric Young* (FC)	.15	.11	.06
146	Scott Leius	.04	.03	.02
147	Bryan Hickerson	.04	.03	.02
148	Steve Finley	.06	.05	.02
149	Rheal Cormier	.08	.06	.03
150	Frank Thomas	.75	.60	.30
151	*Archi Cianfrocco*	.15	.11	.06
152	Rich DeLucia	.04	.03	.02
153	Greg Vaughn	.06	.05	.02
154	Wes Chamberlain	.05	.04	.02
155	Dennis Eckersley	.08	.06	.03
156	Sammy Sosa	.04	.03	.02
157	Gary DiSarcina	.06	.05	.02
158	*Kevin Koslofski* (FC)	.12	.09	.05
159	*Doug Linton* (FC)	.12	.09	.05
160	Lou Whitaker	.06	.05	.02
161	Chad McDonnell (1992 Draft Pick)	.12	.09	.05
162	Joe Hesketh	.03	.02	.01
163	*Tim Wakefield*	.10	.08	.04
164	Leo Gomez	.05	.04	.02
165	Jose Rijo	.06	.05	.02
166	*Tim Scott* (FC)	.12	.09	.05
167	Steve Olin	.05	.04	.02
168	Kevin Maas	.05	.04	.02
169	Kenny Rogers	.04	.03	.02
170	David Justice	.20	.15	.08
171	Doug Jones	.04	.03	.02
172	*Jeff Reboulet* (FC)	.12	.09	.05
173	Andres Galarraga	.05	.04	.02
174	Randy Velarde	.03	.02	.01
175	Kirk McCaskill	.04	.03	.02
176	Darren Lewis	.04	.03	.02
177	Lenny Harris	.04	.03	.02
178	Jeff Fassero	.04	.03	.02
179	Ken Griffey, Jr.	.50	.40	.20
180	Darren Daulton	.08	.06	.03
181	John Jaha	.12	.09	.05
182	Ron Darling	.05	.04	.02
183	Greg Maddux	.08	.06	.03
184	*Damion Easley* (FC)	.15	.11	.06
185	Jack Morris	.08	.06	.03
186	Mike Magnante	.05	.04	.02
187	John Dopson	.05	.04	.02
188	Sid Fernandez	.08	.06	.03
189	Tony Phillips	.08	.06	.03
190	Doug Drabek	.08	.06	.03
191	*Sean Lowe* (FC) (1992 Draft Pick)	.15	.11	.06
192	Bob Milacki	.03	.02	.01
193	*Steve Foster* (FC)	.15	.11	.06
194	Jerald Clark	.05	.04	.02
195	Pete Harnisch	.06	.05	.02
196	Pat Kelly	.06	.05	.02
197	*Jeff Frye* (FC)	.12	.09	.05
198	Alejandro Pena	.04	.03	.02
199	Junior Ortiz	.03	.02	.01
200	Kirby Puckett	.15	.11	.06
201	Jose Uribe	.03	.02	.01
202	Mike Scioscia	.04	.03	.02
203	Bernard Gilkey	.06	.05	.02
204	Dan Pasqua	.04	.03	.02
205	Gary Carter	.08	.06	.03
206	Henry Cotto	.03	.02	.01
207	Paul Molitor	.08	.06	.03
208	Mike Hartley	.04	.03	.02
209	Jeff Parrett	.03	.02	.01
210	Mark Langston	.08	.06	.03
211	Doug Dascenzo	.03	.02	.01
212	Rick Reed	.03	.02	.01
213	Candy Maldonado	.05	.04	.02
214	Danny Darwin	.03	.02	.01
215	*Pat Howell* (FC)	.12	.09	.05
216	Mark Leiter	.03	.02	.01
217	Kevin Mitchell	.08	.06	.03
218	Ben McDonald	.08	.06	.03
219	Bip Roberts	.08	.06	.03
220	Benny Santiago	.08	.06	.03
221	Carlos Baerga	.10	.08	.04
222	Bernie Williams	.10	.08	.04
223	*Roger Pavlik* (FC)	.12	.09	.05
224	Sid Bream	.04	.03	.02
225	Matt Williams	.08	.06	.03
226	Willie Banks	.08	.06	.03
227	Jeff Bagwell	.12	.09	.05
228	Tom Goodwin	.08	.06	.03
229	Mike Perez	.08	.06	.03
230	Carlton Fisk	.08	.06	.03
231	John Wetteland	.08	.06	.03
232	Tino Martinez	.08	.06	.03
233	*Rick Greene* (FC) (1992 Draft Pick)	.12	.09	.05
234	Tim McIntosh	.04	.03	.02
235	Mitch Williams	.06	.05	.02
236	*Kevin Campbell*	.10	.08	.04
237	Jose Vizcaino	.03	.02	.01
238	Chris Donnels	.05	.04	.02
239	Mike Boddicker	.04	.03	.02
240	John Olerud	.20	.15	.08
241	Mike Gardiner	.04	.03	.02
242	Charlie O'Brien	.03	.02	.01
243	Rob Deer	.04	.03	.02
244	Denny Neagle	.08	.06	.03
245	Chris Sabo	.08	.06	.03
246	Gregg Olson	.08	.06	.03
247	Frank Seminara	.08	.06	.03
248	Scott Scudder	.03	.02	.01
249	Tim Burke	.03	.02	.01
250	Chuck Knoblauch	.08	.06	.03
251	Mike Bielecki	.04	.03	.02
252	Xavier Hernandez	.03	.02	.01
253	Jose Guzman	.04	.03	.02
254	Cory Snyder	.04	.03	.02
255	Orel Hershiser	.08	.06	.03
256	Wil Cordero	.12	.09	.05
257	Luis Alicea	.04	.03	.02
258	Mike Schooler	.04	.03	.02
259	Craig Grebeck	.03	.02	.01
260	Duane Ward	.04	.03	.02
261	Bill Wegman	.04	.03	.02
262	Mickey Morandini	.08	.06	.03
263	*Vince Horsman*	.12	.09	.05
264	Paul Sorrento	.06	.05	.02
265	Andre Dawson	.10	.08	.04
266	Rene Gonzales	.03	.02	.01
267	Keith Miller	.04	.03	.02
268	Derek Bell	.10	.08	.04
269	*Todd Steverson* (FC) (1992 Draft Pick)	.20	.15	.08
270	Frank Viola	.08	.06	.03
271	Wally Whitehurst	.04	.03	.02
272	*Kurt Knudsen*	.12	.09	.05
273	*Dan Walters*	.12	.09	.05
274	Rick Sutcliffe	.06	.05	.02
275	Andy Van Slyke	.08	.06	.03
276	Paul O'Neill	.06	.05	.02
277	Mark Whiten	.10	.08	.04
278	Chris Nabholz	.06	.05	.02
279	Todd Burns	.03	.02	.01
280	Tom Glavine	.10	.08	.04
281	*Butch Henry* (FC)	.12	.09	.05
282	Shane Mack	.08	.06	.03
283	Mike Jackson	.03	.02	.01
284	Henry Rodriguez	.06	.05	.02
285	Bob Tewksbury	.06	.05	.02
286	Ron Karkovice	.04	.03	.02
287	Mike Gallego	.04	.03	.02
288	Dave Cochrane	.03	.02	.01
289	Jesse Orosco	.03	.02	.01
290	Dave Stewart	.08	.06	.03
291	Tommy Greene	.08	.06	.03
292	Rey Sanchez	.08	.06	.03
293	Rob Ducey	.03	.02	.01
294	Brent Mayne	.04	.03	.02
295	Dave Stieb	.05	.04	.02
296	Luis Rivera	.03	.02	.01
297	Jeff Innis	.04	.03	.02
298	Scott Livingstone	.08	.06	.03
299	Bob Patterson	.03	.02	.01
300	Cal Ripken, Jr.	.25	.20	.10
301	Cesar Hernandez	.10	.08	.04
302	Randy Myers	.06	.05	.02
303	Brook Jacoby	.04	.03	.02
304	Melido Perez	.04	.03	.02
305	Rafael Palmeiro	.08	.06	.03
306	Damon Berryhill	.03	.02	.01
307	*Dan Serafini* (FC) (1992 Draft Pick)	.20	.15	.08
308	Darryl Kile	.06	.05	.02
309	*J.T. Bruett*	.15	.11	.06
310	Dave Righetti	.05	.04	.02
311	Jay Howell	.05	.04	.02
312	Geronimo Pena	.05	.04	.02
313	Greg Hibbard	.05	.04	.02
314	Mark Gardner	.05	.04	.02
315	Edgar Martinez	.08	.06	.03
316	Dave Nilsson	.10	.08	.04
317	Kyle Abbott	.08	.06	.03
318	Willie Wilson	.06	.05	.02
319	Paul Assenmacher	.04	.03	.02
320	*Tim Fortugno*	.12	.09	.05
321	Rusty Meacham	.08	.06	.03
322	Pat Borders	.05	.04	.02
323	Mike Greenwell	.06	.05	.02
324	Willie Randolph	.06	.05	.02
325	Bill Gullickson	.05	.04	.02
326	Gary Varsho	.03	.02	.01
327	Tim Hulett	.03	.02	.01
328	Scott Ruskin	.03	.02	.01
329	Mike Maddux	.03	.02	.01
330	Danny Tartabull	.08	.06	.03
331	Kenny Lofton	.25	.20	.10
332	Geno Petralli	.03	.02	.01
333	Otis Nixon	.05	.04	.02
334	*Jason Kendall* (FC) (1992 Draft Pick)	.30	.25	.12
335	Mark Portugal	.03	.02	.01
336	Mike Pagliarulo	.04	.03	.02
337	Kirt Manwaring	.04	.03	.02
338	Bob Ojeda	.04	.03	.02
339	*Mark Clark* (FC)	.12	.09	.05
340	John Kruk	.08	.06	.03
341	Mel Rojas	.04	.03	.02
342	Erik Hanson	.06	.05	.02
343	Doug Henry	.06	.05	.02
344	Jack McDowell	.08	.06	.03
345	Harold Baines	.08	.06	.03
346	Chuck McElroy	.03	.02	.01
347	Luis Sojo	.03	.02	.01
348	Andy Stankiewicz	.10	.08	.04
349	*Hipolito Pichardo*	.10	.08	.04
350	Joe Carter	.08	.06	.03
351	Ellis Burks	.06	.05	.02
352	Pete Schourek	.06	.05	.02
353	*Buddy Groom* (FC)	.20	.15	.08
354	Jay Bell	.06	.05	.02
355	Brady Anderson	.08	.06	.03
356	Freddie Benavides	.06	.05	.02
357	Phil Stephenson	.03	.02	.01
358	Kevin Wickander	.03	.02	.01
359	Mike Stanley	.03	.02	.01
360	Ivan Rodriguez	.12	.09	.05
361	Scott Bankhead	.04	.03	.02
362	Luis Gonzalez	.08	.06	.03
363	John Smiley	.06	.05	.02
364	Trevor Wilson	.04	.03	.02
365	Tom Candiotti	.04	.03	.02
366	Craig Wilson	.04	.03	.02
367	Steve Sax	.06	.05	.02
368	Delino Deshields	.06	.05	.02
369	Jaime Navarro	.06	.05	.02
370	Dave Valle	.03	.02	.01
371	Mariano Duncan	.04	.03	.02
372	Rod Nichols	.03	.02	.01
373	Mike Morgan	.05	.04	.02
374	Julio Valera	.08	.06	.03
375	Wally Joyner	.08	.06	.03
376	Tom Henke	.08	.06	.03
377	Herm Winningham	.03	.02	.01
378	Orlando Merced	.06	.05	.02
379	Mike Munoz	.08	.06	.03
380	Todd Hundley	.08	.06	.03
381	Mike Flanagan	.03	.02	.01
382	Tim Belcher	.06	.05	.02
383	Jerry Browne	.03	.02	.01
384	Mike Benjamin	.03	.02	.01
385	Jim Leyritz	.03	.02	.01
386	Ray Lankford	.12	.09	.05
387	Devon White	.06	.05	.02
388	Jeremy Hernandez	.08	.06	.03
389	Brian Harper	.06	.05	.02
390	Wade Boggs	.12	.09	.05
391	Derrick May	.10	.08	.04
392	Travis Fryman	.15	.11	.06
393	Ron Gant	.08	.06	.03
394	Checklist 1-132	.03	.02	.01
395	Checklist 133-264	.03	.02	.01
396	Checklist 265-396	.03	.02	.01
397	George Brett	.10	.08	.04
398	Bobby Witt	.03	.02	.01

399 Daryl Boston .03 .02 .01
400 Bo Jackson .15 .11 .06
401 Fred McGriff (All-Star, Frank Thomas) .20 .15 .08
402 Ryne Sandberg (All-Star, Carlos Baerga) .15 .11 .06
403 Gary Sheffield (All-Star, Edgar Martinez) .03 .02 .01
404 Barry Larkin (All-Star, Travis Fryman) .03 .02 .01
405 Andy Van Slyke (All-Star, Ken Griffey, Jr.) .25 .20 .10
406 Larry Walker (All-Star, Kirby Puckett) .03 .02 .01
407 Barry Bonds (All-Star, Joe Carter) .15 .11 .06
408 Darren Daulton (All-Star, Brian Harper) .03 .02 .01
409 Greg Maddux (All-Star, Roger Clemens) .03 .02 .01
410 Tom Glavine (All-Star, Dave Fleming) .03 .02 .01
411 Lee Smith (All-Star, Dennis Eckersley) .03 .02 .01
412 Jamie McAndrew .03 .02 .01
413 Pete Smith .03 .02 .01
414 Juan Guerrero .03 .02 .01
415 Todd Frohwirth .03 .02 .01
416 Randy Tomlin .03 .02 .01
417 B.J. Surhoff .03 .02 .01
418 Jim Gott .03 .02 .01
419 Mark Thompson (1992 Draft Pick) .03 .02 .01
420 Kevin Tapani .03 .02 .01
421 Curt Schilling .03 .02 .01
422 *J.T. Snow* (FC) .75 .60 .30
423 Top Prospects 1B (Ryan Klesko, Ivan Cruz, Bubba Smith, Larry Sutton) .60 .45 .25
424 John Valentin .03 .02 .01
425 Joe Girardi .03 .02 .01
426 *Nigel Wilson* (FC) .80 .60 .30
427 Bob MacDonald .03 .02 .01
428 Todd Zeile .03 .02 .01
429 Milt Cuyler .03 .02 .01
430 Eddie Murray .03 .02 .01
431 Rich Amaral .03 .02 .01
432 Pete Young .03 .02 .01
433 Rookies Future Stars (Roger Bailey, Tom Schmidt) .30 .25 .12
434 Jack Armstrong .03 .02 .01
435 Willie McGee .03 .02 .01
436 Greg Harris .03 .02 .01
437 Chris Hammond .03 .02 .01
438 *Ritchie Moody* (FC) (1992 Draft Pick) .15 .11 .06
439 Bryan Harvey .03 .02 .01
440 Ruben Sierra .15 .11 .06
441 Marlins Future Stars (Don Lemon, Todd Pridy) .40 .30 .15
442 Kevin McReynolds .03 .02 .01
443 Terry Leach .03 .02 .01
444 *David Nied* .40 .30 .15
445 Dale Murphy .04 .03 .02
446 Luis Mercedes .03 .02 .01
447 *Keith Shepherd* .15 .11 .06
448 Ken Caminiti .03 .02 .01
449 James Austin .03 .02 .01
450 Darryl Strawberry .10 .08 .04
451 Top Prospects 2B (Ramon Caraballo, Jon Shave, Brent Gates, Quinton McCracken) .25 .20 .10
452 Bob Wickman .20 .15 .08
453 Victor Cole .03 .02 .01
454 *John Johnstone* (FC) .20 .15 .08
455 Chili Davis .03 .02 .01
456 Scott Taylor .03 .02 .01
457 Tracy Woodson .03 .02 .01
458 David Wells .03 .02 .01
459 *Derek Wallace* (FC) (1992 Draft Pick) .20 .15 .08
460 Randy Johnson .03 .02 .01
461 Steve Reed .03 .02 .01
462 Felix Fermin .03 .02 .01
463 Scott Aldred .03 .02 .01
464 Greg Colbrunn .03 .02 .01
465 Tony Fernandez .03 .02 .01
466 Mike Felder .03 .02 .01
467 Lee Stevens .03 .02 .01
468 Matt Whiteside .03 .02 .01
469 Dave Hansen .03 .02 .01
470 Rob Dibble .03 .02 .01
471 Dave Gallagher .03 .02 .01
472 Chris Gwynn .03 .02 .01
473 Dave Henderson .03 .02 .01
474 Ozzie Guillen .03 .02 .01
475 Jeff Reardon .03 .02 .01
476 Rockies Future Stars (Mark Voisard, Will Scalzitti) .25 .20 .10
477 Jimmy Jones .03 .02 .01
478 Greg Cadaret .03 .02 .01
479 Todd Pratt .03 .02 .01
480 Pat Listach .08 .06 .03
481 *Ryan Luzinski* (1992 Draft Pick) .30 .25 .12
482 Darren Reed .03 .02 .01
483 *Brian Griffiths* .15 .11 .06
484 John Wehner .03 .02 .01
485 Glenn Davis .03 .02 .01
486 *Eric Wedge* .25 .20 .10
487 Jesse Hollins .03 .02 .01
488 Manuel Lee .03 .02 .01
489 *Scott Fredrickson* .15 .11 .06
490 Omar Olivares .03 .02 .01
491 Shawn Hare .03 .02 .01
492 Tom Lampkin .03 .02 .01
493 Jeff Nelson .03 .02 .01
494 Top Prospects 3B (Kevin Young, Adell Davenport, Eduardo Perez, Lou Lucca) .35 .25 .14
495 Ken Hill .03 .02 .01
496 Reggie Jefferson .03 .02 .01
497 Marlins Future Stars (Matt Petersen, Willie Brown) .35 .25 .14
498 Bud Black .03 .02 .01
499 Chuck Crim .03 .02 .01
500 Jose Canseco .10 .08 .04
501 Major League Managers (Johnny Oates, Bobby Cox) .03 .02 .01
502 Major League Managers (Butch Hobson, Jim Lefebvre) .03 .02 .01
503 Major League Managers (Buck Rodgers, Tony Perez) .03 .02 .01
504 Major League Managers (Gene Lamont, Don Baylor) .03 .02 .01
505 Major League Managers (Mike Hargrove, Rene Lachmann) .03 .02 .01
506 Major League Managers (Sparky Anderson, Art Howe) .03 .02 .01
507 Major League Managers (Hal McRae, Tom Lasorda) .03 .02 .01
508 Major League Manager (Phil Garner, Felipe Alou) .03 .02 .01
509 Major League Managers (Tom Kelly, Jeff Torborg) .03 .02 .01
510 Major League Managers (Buck Showalter, Jim Fregosi) .03 .02 .01
511 Major League Managers (Tony LaRussa, Jim Leyland) .03 .02 .01
512 Major League Managers (Lou Piniella, Joe Torre) .03 .02 .01
513 Major League Managers (Toby Harrah, Jim Riggleman) .03 .02 .01
514 Major League Managers (Cito Gaston, Dusty Baker) .03 .02 .01
515 Greg Swindell .03 .02 .01
516 Alex Arias .03 .02 .01
517 Bill Pecota .03 .02 .01
518 *Benji Grigsby* (1992 Draft Pick) .20 .15 .08
519 David Howard .03 .02 .01
520 Charlie Hough .03 .02 .01
521 Kevin Flora .03 .02 .01
522 Shane Reynolds .03 .02 .01
523 *Doug Bochtler* .15 .11 .06
524 Chris Hoiles .03 .02 .01
525 Scott Sanderson .03 .02 .01
526 Mike Sharperson .03 .02 .01
527 Mike Fetters .03 .02 .01
528 Paul Quantrill .03 .02 .01
529 Top Propsects SS (Dave Silvestri, Chipper Jones, Benji Gil, Jeff Patzke) .30 .25 .12
530 Sterling Hitchcock .03 .02 .01
531 Joe Millette .03 .02 .01
532 Tom Brunansky .03 .02 .01
533 Frank Castillo .03 .02 .01
534 Randy Knorr .03 .02 .01
535 Jose Oquendo .03 .02 .01
536 Dave Haas .03 .02 .01
537 Rockies Future Stars (Jason Hutchins, Ryan Turner) .20 .15 .08
538 Jimmy Baron (1992 Draft Pick) .03 .02 .01
539 Kerry Woodson .03 .02 .01
540 Ivan Calderon .03 .02 .01
541 Denis Boucher .03 .02 .01
542 Royce Clayton .03 .02 .01
543 Reggie Williams .03 .02 .01
544 Steve Decker .03 .02 .01
545 Dean Palmer .03 .02 .01
546 Hal Morris .03 .02 .01
547 *Ryan Thompson* (FC) .20 .15 .08
548 Lance Blankenship .03 .02 .01
549 Hensley Meulens .03 .02 .01
550 Scott Radinsky .03 .02 .01
551 *Eric Young* (FC) .20 .15 .08
552 Jeff Blauser .03 .02 .01
553 Andujar Cedeno .03 .02 .01
554 Arthur Rhodes .03 .02 .01
555 Terry Mulholland .03 .02 .01
556 Darryl Hamilton .03 .02 .01
557 Pedro Martinez .03 .02 .01
558 Marlins Future Stars (Ryan Whitman, Mark Skeels) .25 .20 .10
559 *Jamie Arnold* (FC) (1992 Draft Pick) .20 .15 .08
560 Zane Smith .03 .02 .01
561 Matt Nokes .03 .02 .01
562 Bob Zupcic .03 .02 .01
563 Shawn Boskie .03 .02 .01
564 Mike Timlin .03 .02 .01
565 Jerald Clark .03 .02 .01
566 Rod Brewer .03 .02 .01
567 Mark Carreon .03 .02 .01
568 Andy Benes .03 .02 .01
569 Shawn Barton .03 .02 .01
570 Tim Wallach .03 .02 .01
571 Dave Mlicki .03 .02 .01
572 Trevor Hoffman .03 .02 .01
573 John Patterson .03 .02 .01
574 DeShawn Warren (1992 Draft Pick) .03 .02 .01
575 Monty Fariss .03 .02 .01
576 Top Prospects OF (Darrell Sherman, Damon Buford, Cliff Floyd, Michael Moore) .60 .45 .25
577 Tim Costo .03 .02 .01
578 Dave Magadan .03 .02 .01
579 Rockies Future Stars (Neil Garret, Jason Bates) .30 .25 .12
580 Walt Weiss .03 .02 .01
581 Chris Haney .03 .02 .01
582 Shawn Abner .03 .02 .01
583 Marvin Freeman .03 .02 .01
584 Casey Candaele .03 .02 .01
585 Ricky Jordan .03 .02 .01
586 Jeff Tabaka .03 .02 .01
587 Manny Alexander .03 .02 .01
588 Mike Trombley .03 .02 .01
589 Carlos Hernandez .03 .02 .01
590 Cal Eldred .03 .02 .01
591 Alex Cole .03 .02 .01
592 Phil Plantier .03 .02 .01
593 Brett Merriman .03 .02 .01
594 Jerry Nielsen .03 .02 .01
595 Shawon Dunston .03 .02 .01
596 Jimmy Key .03 .02 .01
597 Gerald Perry .03 .02 .01
598 Rico Brogna .03 .02 .01
599 Marlins Future Stars (Clemente Nunez, Daniel Robinson) .30 .25 .12
600 Bret Saberhagen .03 .02 .01
601 Craig Shipley .03 .02 .01
602 Henry Mercedes .03 .02 .01
603 Jim Thome .03 .02 .01
604 Rod Beck .03 .02 .01
605 Chuck Finley .03 .02 .01
606 J. Owens .03 .02 .01
607 Dan Smith .03 .02 .01
608 Bill Doran .03 .02 .01
609 Lance Parrish .03 .02 .01
610 Denny Martinez .03 .02 .01
611 Tom Gordon .03 .02 .01
612 Byron Mathews (1992 Draft Pick) .03 .02 .01
613 Joel Adamson .03 .02 .01
614 Brian Williams .03 .02 .01
615 Steve Avery .03 .02 .01
616 Top Prospects OF (Matt Mieske, Tracy Sanders, Midre Cummings, Ryan Freeburg) .30 .25 .12
617 Craig Lefferts .03 .02 .01
618 Tony Pena .03 .02 .01
619 Billy Spiers .03 .02 .01
620 Todd Benzinger .03 .02 .01
621 Rockies Future Stars (Mike Kotarski, Greg Boyd) .30 .25 .12
622 Ben Rivera .03 .02 .01
623 *Al Martin* (FC) .25 .20 .10
624 Sam Militello .03 .02 .01
625 Rick Aguilera .03 .02 .01
626 Danny Gladden .03 .02 .01
627 Andres Berumen .03 .02 .01
628 Kelly Gruber .03 .02 .01
629 Cris Carpenter .03 .02 .01
630 Mark Grace .03 .02 .01
631 Jeff Brantley .03 .02 .01
632 Chris Widger (1992 Draft Pick) .03 .02 .01
633 Russian Angels (Rudy Razjigaev, Yevgeny Puchkov, Ilya Bogatyrev) .25 .20 .10
634 Mo Sanford .03 .02 .01
635 Albert Belle .03 .02 .01
636 Tim Teufel .03 .02 .01
637 Greg Myers .03 .02 .01
638 Brian Bohanon .03 .02 .01
639 Mike Bordick .03 .02 .01
640 Dwight Gooden .03 .02 .01
641 Marlins Future Stars (Pat Leahy, Gavin Baugh) .20 .15 .08
642 Milt Hill .03 .02 .01
643 Luis Aquino .03 .02 .01
644 Dante Bichette .03 .02 .01
645 Bobby Thigpen .03 .02 .01
646 Rich Scheid .03 .02 .01
647 Brian Sackinsky (1992 Draft Pick) .03 .02 .01
648 Ryan Hawblitzel .03 .02 .01
649 Tom Marsh .03 .02 .01
650 Terry Pendleton .03 .02 .01
651 *Rafael Bournigal* (FC) .25 .20 .10
652 Dave West .03 .02 .01
653 Steve Hosey .03 .02 .01
654 Gerald Williams .03 .02 .01
655 Scott Cooper .03 .02 .01
656 Gary Scott .03 .02 .01
657 Mike Harkey .03 .02 .01
658 Top Prospects OF (Jeromy Burnitz, Melvin Nieves, Rich Becker, Shon Walker) .30 .25 .12
659 Ed Sprague .03 .02 .01
660 Alan Trammell .03 .02 .01
661 Rockies Future Stars (Garvin Alston, Michael Case) .25 .20 .10
662 Donovan Osborne .03 .02 .01
663 Jeff Gardner .03 .02 .01
664 Calvin Jones .03 .02 .01
665 Darrin Fletcher .03 .02 .01
666 Glenallen Hill .03 .02 .01
667 Jim Rosenbohm (1992 Draft Pick) .03 .02 .01
668 Scott Lewis .03 .02 .01
669 Kip Yaughn .03 .02 .01
670 Julio Franco .03 .02 .01
671 Dave Martinez .03 .02 .01
672 Kevin Bass .03 .02 .01
673 Todd Van Poppel .03 .02 .01
674 Mark Gubicza .03 .02 .01
675 Tim Raines .03 .02 .01
676 Rudy Seanez .03 .02 .01
677 Charlie Leibrandt .03 .02 .01
678 Randy Milligan .03 .02 .01
679 Kim Batiste .03 .02 .01
680 Craig Biggio .03 .02 .01
681 Darren Holmes .03 .02 .01
682 John Candelaria .03 .02 .01
683 Marlins Future Stars (Jerry Stafford, Eddie Christian) .25 .20 .10
684 Pat Mahomes .03 .02 .01
685 Bob Walk .03 .02 .01
686 Russ Springer .03 .02 .01
687 Tony Sheffield (1992 Draft Picks) .03 .02 .01
688 Dwight Smith .03 .02 .01
689 Eddie Zosky .03 .02 .01
690 Bien Figueroa .03 .02 .01
691 Jim Tatum .03 .02 .01
692 Chad Kreuter .03 .02 .01
693 Rich Rodriguez .03 .02 .01
694 Shane Turner .03 .02 .01
695 Kent Bottenfield .03 .02 .01
696 Jose Mesa .03 .02 .01
697 *Darrell Whitmore* .20 .15 .08
698 Ted Wood .03 .02 .01
699 Chad Curtis .03 .02 .01
700 Nolan Ryan .40 .30 .15
701 Catching Prospects, Mike Piazza, Carlos Delgado, Brook Fordyce, Donnie Leshnock 2.00 1.50 .80
702 *Tim Pugh* (FC) .25 .20 .10
703 Jeff Kent .03 .02 .01
704 Rockies Future Stars (Jon Goodrich, Danny Figueroa) .20 .15 .08
705 Bob Welch .03 .02 .01
706 Sherard Clinkscales (1992 Draft Pick) .03 .02 .01
707 Donn Pall .03 .02 .01
708 Greg Olson .03 .02 .01
709 Jeff Juden .03 .02 .01
710 Mike Mussina .25 .20 .10
711 Scott Chiamparino .03 .02 .01
712 Stan Javier .03 .02 .01
713 John Doherty .03 .02 .01
714 Kevin Gross .03 .02 .01
715 Greg Gagne .03 .02 .01

716	Steve Cooke	.03	.02	.01
717	Steve Farr	.03	.02	.01
718	Jay Buchner	.03	.02	.01
719	Butch Henry	.03	.02	.01
720	David Cone	.03	.02	.01
721	Rick Wilkins	.03	.02	.01
722	Chuck Carr	.03	.02	.01
723	*Kenny Felder* (FC) (1992 Draft Pick)	.30	.25	.12
724	Guillermo Velasquez	.03	.02	.01
725	Billy Hatcher	.03	.02	.01
726	Marlins Future Stars (Mike Veneziale, Ken Kendrena)	.20	.15	.08
727	Jonathan Hurst	.03	.02	.01
728	Steve Frey	.03	.02	.01
729	Mark Leonard	.03	.02	.01
730	Charles Nagy	.03	.02	.01
731	Donald Harris	.03	.02	.01
732	Travis Buckley	.03	.02	.01
733	Tom Browning	.03	.02	.01
734	Anthony Young	.03	.02	.01
735	Steve Shifflett	.03	.02	.01
736	Jeff Russell	.03	.02	.01
737	Wilson Alvarez	.03	.02	.01
738	Lance Painter	.03	.02	.01
739	Dave Weathers	.03	.02	.01
740	Len Dykstra	.03	.02	.01
741	Mike Devereaux	.03	.02	.01
742	Top Prospects SP (Rene Arocha, Alan Embree, Tim Crabtree, Brien Taylor)	.60	.45	.25
743	Dave Landaker (1992 Draft Pick)	.03	.02	.01
744	Chris George	.03	.02	.01
745	Eric Davis	.03	.02	.01
746	Rockies Future Stars (Mark Strittmatter, Lamarr Rogers)	.25	.20	.10
747	Carl Willis	.03	.02	.01
748	Stan Belinda	.03	.02	.01
749	Scott Kamieniecki	.03	.02	.01
750	Rickey Henderson	.15	.11	.06
751	Eric Hillman	.03	.02	.01
752	Pat Hentgen	.03	.02	.01
753	Jim Corsi	.03	.02	.01
754	Brian Jordan	.15	.11	.06
755	Bill Swift	.03	.02	.01
756	Mike Henneman	.03	.02	.01
757	Harold Reynolds	.03	.02	.01
758	Sean Berry	.06	.05	.02
759	Charlie Hayes	.06	.05	.02
760	Luis Polonia	.03	.02	.01
761	Darrin Jackson	.03	.02	.01
762	Mark Lewis	.03	.02	.01
763	Rob Maurer	.03	.02	.01
764	Willie Greene	.03	.02	.01
765	Vince Coleman	.03	.02	.01
766	Todd Revenig	.03	.02	.01
767	Rich Ireland (1992 Draft Pick)	.03	.02	.01
768	Mike MacFarlane	.03	.02	.01
769	Francisco Cabrera	.03	.02	.01
770	Robin Ventura	.03	.02	.01
771	Kevin Ritz	.03	.02	.01
772	Chito Martinez	.03	.02	.01
773	Cliff Brantley	.03	.02	.01
774	Curtis Leskanic	.03	.02	.01
775	Chris Bosio	.03	.02	.01
776	Jose Offerman	.03	.02	.01
777	Mark Guthrie	.03	.02	.01
778	Don Slaught	.03	.02	.01
779	Rich Monteleone	.03	.02	.01
780	Jim Abbott	.03	.02	.01
781	Jack Clark	.03	.02	.01
782	Marlins Future Stars (Rafael Mendoza, Dan Roman)	.20	.15	.08
783	Heathcliff Slocumb	.03	.02	.01
784	Jeff Branson	.03	.02	.01
785	Kevin Brown	.03	.02	.01
786	Top Prospects RP (Mike Christopher, Ken Ryan, Aaaron Taylor, Gus Gandarillas)	.25	.20	.10
787	Mike Matthews (1992 Draft Pick)	.03	.02	.01
788	Mackey Sasser	.03	.02	.01
789	Jeff Conine	.03	.02	.01
790	George Bell	.03	.02	.01
791	Pat Rapp	.03	.02	.01
792	Joe Boever	.03	.02	.01
793	Jim Poole	.03	.02	.01
794	Andy Ashby	.03	.02	.01
795	Deion Sanders	.03	.02	.01
796	Scott Brosius	.03	.02	.01
797	Brad Pennington (Coming Attraction)	.03	.02	.01
798	Greg Blosser (Coming Attraction)	.03	.02	.01
799	Jim Edmonds (Coming Attraction)	.03	.02	.01
800	Shawn Jeter (Coming Attraction)	.03	.02	.01
801	Jesse Levis (Coming Attraction)	.03	.02	.01
802	Phil Clark (Coming Attraction)	.03	.02	.01
803	Ed Pierce (Coming Attraction)	.03	.02	.01
804	Jose Valentin (Coming Attraction)	.03	.02	.01
805	Terry Jorgensen (Coming Attraction)	.03	.02	.01
806	Mark Hutton (Coming Attraction)	.03	.02	.01
807	*Troy Neel* (FC) (Coming Attraction)	.20	.15	.08
808	*Bret Boone* (FC) (Coming Attraction)	.20	.15	.08
809	Chris Colon (Coming Attraction)	.03	.02	.01
810	*Domingo Martinez* (Coming Attraction)	.25	.20	.10
811	*Javier Lopez* (Coming Attraction)	.40	.30	.15
812	Matt Walbeck (Coming Attraction)	.03	.02	.01
813	Dan Wilson (Coming Attraction)	.03	.02	.01
814	Scooter Tucker (Coming Attraction)	.03	.02	.01
815	*Billy Ashley* (FC) (Coming Attraction)	.30	.25	.12
816	*Tim Laker* (FC) (Coming Attraction)	.20	.15	.08
817	*Bobby Jones* (FC) (Coming Attraction)	.30	.25	.12
818	Brad Brink (Coming Attraction)	.03	.02	.01
819	William Pennyfeather (Coming Attraction)	.03	.02	.01
820	Stan Royer (Coming Attraction)	.03	.02	.01
821	Doug Brocail (Coming Attraction)	.03	.02	.01
822	Kevin Rogers (Coming Attraction)	.03	.02	.01
823	Checklist 397-540	.03	.02	.01
824	Checklist 541-691	.03	.02	.01
825	Checklist 692-825	.03	.02	.01

1993 Topps Gold

Expanding on the concept begun in 1992, Topps issued a "Gold" version of each of its regular 1993 cards as a premium insert. One Gold card was found in each wax pack; three per rack pack and five per jumbo. Ten Gold cards were included in each Topps factory set. Identical in format to the 1993 Topps regular-issue cards, the gold version replaces the black or white Topps logo in the card's upper corner with a "Topps Gold" logo in gold foil. The color bars and angled strips below the player photo which contain the player's name and team on a regular card are replaced with a gold-foil version on the inserts. Backs are identical to the regular cards.

	MT	NR MT	EX
Complete Set (825):	140.00	100.00	55.00
Common Gold Card:	.15	.11	.06
Gold Stars:			

1993 Topps Black Gold

Randomly inserted in regular 1993 Topps packs, as well as 10 per factory set, Black Gold cards are found in both single-player versions and "Winner" cards. The single-player cards feature an action photo set against a black background and highlighted at top and bottom with gold foil. Backs have another player photo at left, again on a black background. A career summary is printed in a blue box at right. A "Topps Black Gold" logo appears at top left, and the player's name is printed in gold foil in an art deco device at top right. The Winner cards picture tiny versions of the Black Gold player cards for which they could be redeemed by mail.

	MT	NR MT	EX
Complete Set (44):	22.00	16.50	8.75
Common Player:	.25	.20	.10
Winner A (1-11):	.50	.40	.20
Winner B (12-22):	.50	.40	.20
Winner C (23-33):	.50	.40	.20
Winner D (34-44):	.50	.40	.20
Winner AB (1-22):	1.00	.70	.40
Winner CD (23-44):	1.00	.70	.40
Winner ABCD (1-44):	2.00	1.50	.80

1	Barry Bonds	2.00	1.50	.80
2	Will Clark	.75	.60	.30
3	Darren Daulton	.50	.40	.20
4	Andre Dawson	.50	.40	.20
5	Delino DeShields	.50	.40	.20
6	Tom Glavine	.75	.60	.30
7	Marquis Grissom	.75	.60	.30
8	Tony Gwynn	.60	.45	.25
9	Eric Karros	.60	.45	.25
10	Ray Lankford	.25	.20	.10
11	Barry Larkin	.40	.30	.15
12	Greg Maddux	.60	.45	.25
13	Fred McGriff	.75	.60	.30
14	Joe Oliver	.25	.20	.10
15	Terry Pendleton	.25	.20	.10
16	Bip Roberts	.25	.20	.10
17	Ryne Sandberg	1.50	1.25	.60
18	Gary Sheffield	.50	.40	.20
19	Lee Smith	.25	.20	.10
20	Ozzie Smith	.40	.30	.15
21	Andy Van Slyke	.25	.20	.10
22	Larry Walker	.40	.30	.15
23	Roberto Alomar	1.50	1.25	.60
24	Brady Anderson	.25	.20	.10
25	Carlos Baerga	1.50	1.25	.60
26	Joe Carter	.75	.60	.30
27	Roger Clemens	.75	.60	.30
28	Mike Devereaux	.25	.20	.10
29	Dennis Eckersley	.25	.20	.10
30	Cecil Fielder	.75	.60	.30
31	Travis Fryman	1.50	1.25	.60
32	Juan Gonzalez	3.50	2.75	1.50
33	Ken Griffey Jr.	3.50	2.75	1.50
34	Brian Harper	.25	.20	.10
35	Pat Listach	.25	.20	.10
36	Kenny Lofton	.60	.45	.25
37	Edgar Martinez	.25	.20	.10
38	Jack McDowell	.60	.45	.25
39	Mark McGwire	.50	.40	.20
40	Kirby Puckett	1.50	1.25	.60
41	Mickey Tettleton	.25	.20	.10
42	Frank Thomas	4.50	3.50	1.75
43	Robin Ventura	.60	.45	.25
44	Dave Winfield	.50	.40	.20

1993 Topps Traded

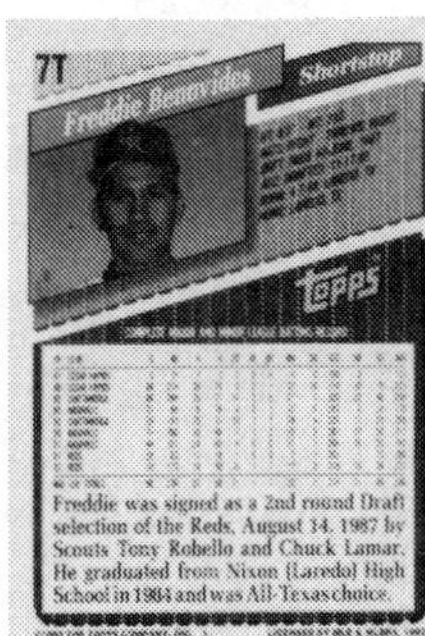

The 1993 Topps Traded baseball set features many players in their new uniforms. National League sluggers Fred McGriff and Gary Sheffield each appear in Atlanta and Florida uniforms, respectively. The set features 35 expansion players from the Colorado Rockies and Florida Marlins, as well as 22 Team USA members exclusive to Topps. The 132-card set is packed in a color deluxe printed box.

	MT	NR MT	EX
Complete Set (132):	14.00	10.50	5.50
Common Player:	.05	.04	.02

1	Barry Bonds	.50	.40	.20
2	Rich Renteria	.05	.04	.02
3	Aaron Sele	.60	.45	.25
4	*Carlton Loewer* (USA)	.30	.25	.12
5	Erik Pappas	.05	.04	.02
6	*Greg McMichael*	.15	.11	.06
7	Freddie Benavides	.05	.04	.02
8	Kirk Gibson	.05	.04	.02
9	Tony Fernandez	.05	.04	.02
10	*Jay Gainer* (USA)	.25	.20	.10
11	Orestes Destrade	.05	.04	.02
12	*A.J. Hinch* (USA)	.30	.25	.12
13	Bobby Munoz	.05	.04	.02
14	Tom Henke	.05	.04	.02
15	Rob Butler	.10	.08	.04
16	Gary Wayne	.05	.04	.02
17	David McCarty	.25	.20	.10
18	Walt Weiss	.05	.04	.02
19	*Todd Helton* (USA)	.50	.40	.20
20	Mark Whiten	.05	.04	.02
21	Ricky Gutierrez	.10	.08	.04
22	*Dustin Hermanson* (USA)	.25	.20	.10
23	*Sherman Obando*	.10	.08	.04
24	Mike Piazza	2.50	2.00	1.00
25	Jeff Russell	.05	.04	.02
26	Jason Bere	1.00	.70	.40
27	*Jack Voight*	.10	.08	.04
28	Chris Bosio	.05	.04	.02
29	Phil Hiatt	.15	.11	.06
30	*Matt Beaumont* (USA)	.25	.20	.10
31	Andres Galarraga	.10	.08	.04
32	Greg Swindell	.05	.04	.02
33	Vinny Castilla	.05	.04	.02
34	*Pat Clougherty* (USA)	.25	.20	.10
35	Greg Briley	.05	.04	.02
36	Dallas Green, Davey Johnson	.05	.04	.02
37	Tyler Green	.10	.08	.04
38	Craig Paquette	.10	.08	.04
39	Danny Sheaffer	.05	.04	.02
40	Jim Converse	.05	.04	.02
41	Terry Harvey	.05	.04	.02
42	Phil Plantier	.10	.08	.04
43	*Doug Saunders*	.10	.08	.04
44	Benny Santiago	.05	.04	.02
45	*Dante Powell* (USA)	.50	.40	.20
46	Jeff Parrett	.05	.04	.02
47	Wade Boggs	.10	.08	.04
48	Paul Molitor	.20	.15	.08
49	Turk Wendell	.05	.04	.02
50	David Wells	.05	.04	.02
51	Gary Sheffield	.10	.08	.04

52	Kevin Young	.15	.11	.06
53	Nelson Liriano	.05	.04	.02
54	Greg Maddux	.15	.11	.06
55	Derek Bell	.05	.04	.02
56	*Matt Turner*	.20	.15	.08
57	*Charlie Nelson* (USA)	.25	.20	.10
58	Mike Hampton	.05	.04	.02
59	*Troy O'Leary*	.15	.11	.06
60	Benji Gil	.15	.11	.06
61	*Mitch Lyden*	.15	.11	.06
62	J.T. Snow	.40	.30	.15
63	Damon Buford	.05	.04	.02
64	Gene Harris	.05	.04	.02
65	Randy Myers	.05	.04	.02
66	Felix Jose	.05	.04	.02
67	*Todd Dunn* (USA)	.25	.20	.10
68	Jimmy Key	.05	.04	.02
69	Pedro Castellano	.10	.08	.04
70	*Mark Merila* (USA)	.25	.20	.10
71	Rich Rodriguez	.05	.04	.02
72	Matt Mieske	.05	.04	.02
73	Pete Incaviglia	.05	.04	.02
74	Carl Everett	.10	.08	.04
75	Jim Abbott	.10	.08	.04
76	Luis Aquino	.05	.04	.02
77	*Rene Arocha*	.25	.20	.10
78	*Jon Shave*	.10	.08	.04
79	*Todd Walker* (USA)	1.25	.90	.50
80	Jack Armstrong	.05	.04	.02
81	Jeff Richardson	.05	.04	.02
82	Blas Minor	.05	.04	.02
83	Dave Winfield	.15	.11	.06
84	Paul O'Neill	.05	.04	.02
85	*Steve Reich* (USA)	.25	.20	.10
86	Chris Hammond	.05	.04	.02
87	*Hilly Hathaway*	.25	.20	.10
88	Fred McGriff	.20	.15	.08
89	*Dave Telgheder*	.10	.08	.04
90	*Richie Lewis*	.15	.11	.06
91	Brent Gates	.20	.15	.08
92	Andre Dawson	.05	.04	.02
93	*Andy Barkett* (USA)	.25	.20	.10
94	Doug Drabek	.05	.04	.02
95	Joe Klink	.05	.04	.02
96	Willie Blair	.05	.04	.02
97	*Danny Graves* (USA)	.25	.20	.10
98	Pat Meares	.10	.08	.04
99	Mike Lansing	.25	.20	.10
100	*Marcos Armas*	.25	.20	.10
101	*Darren Grass* (USA)	.25	.20	.10
102	Chris Jones	.05	.04	.02
103	*Ken Ryan*	.15	.11	.06
104	Ellis Burks	.05	.04	.02
105	Bobby Kelly	.05	.04	.02
106	Dave Magadan	.05	.04	.02
107	*Paul Wilson* (USA)	.40	.30	.15
108	Rob Natal	.05	.04	.02
109	Paul Wagner	.05	.04	.02
110	Jeromy Burnitz	.15	.11	.06
111	Monty Fariss	.05	.04	.02
112	Kevin Mitchell	.05	.04	.02
113	*Scott Pose*	.15	.11	.06
114	Dave Stewart	.05	.04	.02
115	*Russ Johnson* (USA)	.40	.30	.15
116	Armando Reynoso	.05	.04	.02
117	Geronimo Berroa	.05	.04	.02
118	*Woody Williams*	.15	.11	.06
119	*Tim Bogar*	.15	.11	.06
120	*Bob Scafa* (USA)	.30	.25	.12
121	Henry Cotto	.05	.04	.02
122	Gregg Jefferies	.10	.08	.04
123	Norm Charlton	.05	.04	.02
124	*Bret Wagner* (USA)	.25	.20	.10
125	David Cone	.05	.04	.02
126	Daryl Boston	.05	.04	.02
127	Tim Wallach	.05	.04	.02
128	*Mike Martin* (USA)	.25	.20	.10
129	*John Cummings*	.15	.11	.06
130	Ryan Bowen	.05	.04	.02
131	*John Powell* (USA)	.50	.40	.20
132	Checklist 1	.05	.04	.02

Grading Guide

Mint (MT): A perfect card. Well-centered with all corners sharp and square. No creases, stains, edge nicks, surface marks, yellowing or fading.

Near Mint (NM): A nearly perfect card. At first glance, a NM card appears to be perfect. May be slightly off-center. No surface marks, creases or loss of gloss.

Excellent (EX): Corners are still fairly sharp with only moderate wear. Borders may be off-center. No creases or stains on fronts or backs, but may show slight loss of surface luster.

Very Good (VG): Shows obvious handling. May have rounded corners, minor creases, major gum or wax stains. No major creases, tape marks, writing, etc.

Good (G): A well-worn card, but exhibits no intentional damage. May have major or multiple creases. Corners may be rounded well beyond card border.

1993 Topps Colorado Rockies Inaugural Year

To mark the team's inaugural year in the Major Leagues, Topps produced a special run of 10,000 of its 1993 factory sets in which each card was embossed with a special gold seal incorporating the

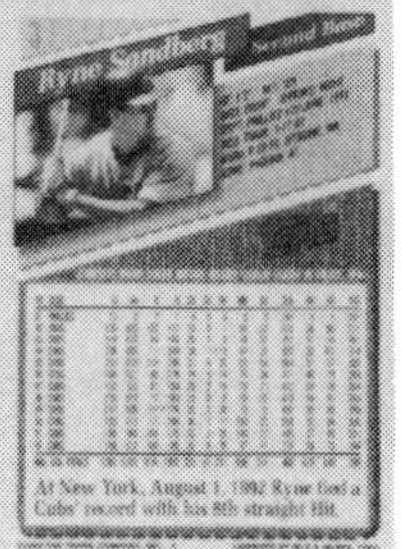

Rockies logo. Sets sold for $100 at the team's normal souvenir outlets. The factory sets were sealed with a sticker featuring the inaugural year logo.

	MT	NR MT	EX
Complete Set (825):	100.00	75.00	40.00
Common Player:	.50	.40	.20

1993 Topps Florida Marlins Inaugural Year

To commemorate the team's inaugural year in the Major Leagues, Topps produced a special edition of 6,000 of its 1993 factory sets in which every card was embossed with a special gold seal incorporating the Marlins logo. The sets were sold for $100 at the team's normal souvenir outlets. Factory sets are sealed with a sticker incorporating the inaugural year logo.

	MT	NR MT	EX
Complete Set (825):	175.00	125.00	67.50
Common Player:	.50	.40	.20

Values for recent cards and sets are listed in Mint (MT), Near Mint (NM), reflecting the fact that many cards from recent years have been preserved in top condition. Recent cards and sets in less than Excellent condition have little collector interest.

1993 Topps Stadium Club

Topps' premium set for 1993 was issued in three series, two 300-card series and a final series of 150. Boxes contained 24 packs this year, compared to 36 in the past. Packs had 14 cards and an insert card. Each box had a 5" by 7" Master Photo card.

	MT	NR MT	EX
Complete Set (750):	60.00	45.00	24.00
Complete Series 1 (300):	20.00	15.00	8.00
Complete Series 2 (300):	30.00	22.00	12.00
Complete Series 3 (150):	10.00	7.50	4.00
Common Player:	.10	.08	.04

1	Pat Borders	.10	.08	.04
2	Greg Maddux	.30	.25	.12
3	Daryl Boston	.10	.08	.04
4	Bob Ayrault	.10	.08	.04
5	Tony Phillips	.10	.08	.04
6	Damion Easley	.15	.11	.06
7	Kip Gross	.10	.08	.04
8	Jim Thome	.60	.45	.25
9	Tim Belcher	.10	.08	.04
10	Gary Wayne	.10	.08	.04
11	Sam Militello	.15	.11	.06
12	Mike Magnante	.10	.08	.04
13	Tim Wakefield	.12	.09	.05
14	Tim Hulett	.10	.08	.04
15	Rheal Cormier	.10	.08	.04
16	Juan Guerrero	.15	.11	.06
17	Rich Gossage	.10	.08	.04
18	Tim Laker	.10	.08	.04
19	Darrin Jackson	.10	.08	.04
20	Jack Clark	.10	.08	.04
21	Roberto Hernandez	.10	.08	.04
22	Dean Palmer	.20	.15	.08
23	Harold Reynolds	.10	.08	.04
24	Dan Plesac	.10	.08	.04
25	Brent Mayne	.10	.08	.04
26	Pat Hentgen	.35	.25	.14
27	Luis Sojo	.10	.08	.04
28	Ron Gant	.20	.15	.08
29	Paul Gibson	.10	.08	.04
30	Bip Roberts	.10	.08	.04
31	Mickey Tettleton	.12	.09	.05
32	Randy Velarde	.10	.08	.04
33	Brian McRae	.10	.08	.04
34	Wes Chamberlain	.10	.08	.04
35	Wayne Kirby	.10	.08	.04
36	Rey Sanchez	.10	.08	.04
37	Jesse Orosco	.10	.08	.04
38	Mike Stanton	.10	.08	.04
39	Royce Clayton	.30	.25	.12
40	Cal Ripken, Jr.	.80	.60	.30
41	John Dopson	.10	.08	.04
42	Gene Larkin	.10	.08	.04
43	Tim Raines	.12	.09	.05
44	Randy Myers	.10	.08	.04
45	Clay Parker	.10	.08	.04
46	Mike Scioscia	.10	.08	.04
47	Pete Incaviglia	.10	.08	.04
48	Todd Van Poppel	.30	.25	.12
49	Ray Lankford	.15	.11	.06
50	Eddie Murray	.25	.20	.10
51	Barry Bonds	1.00	.70	.40
52	Gary Thurman	.10	.08	.04
53	Bob Wickman	.25	.20	.10
54	Joey Cora	.10	.08	.04
55	Kenny Rogers	.10	.08	.04
56	Mike Devereaux	.10	.08	.04
57	Kevin Seitzer	.10	.08	.04
58	Rafael Belliard	.10	.08	.04
59	David Wells	.10	.08	.04
60	Mark Clark	.10	.08	.04
61	Carlos Baerga	.50	.40	.20
62	Scott Brosius	.10	.08	.04
63	Jeff Grotewold	.25	.20	.10
64	Rick Wrona	.10	.08	.04
65	Kurt Knudsen	.10	.08	.04
66	Lloyd McClendon	.10	.08	.04
67	Omar Vizquel	.10	.08	.04
68	Jose Vizcaino	.10	.08	.04
69	Rob Ducey	.10	.08	.04
70	Casey Candaele	.10	.08	.04
71	Ramon Martinez	.25	.20	.10
72	Todd Hundley	.10	.08	.04
73	John Marzano	.10	.08	.04
74	Derek Parks	.10	.08	.04
75	Jack McDowell	.25	.20	.10
76	Tim Scott	.25	.20	.10
77	Mike Mussina	.60	.45	.25
78	Delino DeShields	.20	.15	.08
79	Chris Bosio	.10	.08	.04
80	Mike Bordick	.10	.08	.04

81 Rod Beck .10 .08 .04
82 Ted Power .10 .08 .04
83 John Kruk .12 .09 .05
84 Steve Shifflett .30 .25 .12
85 Danny Tartabull .10 .08 .04
86 Mike Greenwell .10 .08 .04
87 Jose Melendez .10 .08 .04
88 Craig Wilson .30 .25 .12
89 Melvin Nieves .35 .25 .14
90 Ed Sprague .10 .08 .04
91 Willie McGee .10 .08 .04
92 Joe Orsulak .10 .08 .04
93 Jeff King .10 .08 .04
94 Dan Pasqua .10 .08 .04
95 Brian Harper .10 .08 .04
96 Joe Oliver .10 .08 .04
97 Shane Turner .15 .11 .06
98 Lenny Harris .10 .08 .04
99 Jeff Parrett .10 .08 .04
100 Luis Polonia .10 .08 .04
101 Kent Bottenfield .15 .11 .06
102 Albert Belle .50 .40 .20
103 Mike Maddux .10 .08 .04
104 Randy Tomlin .10 .08 .04
105 Andy Stankiewicz .10 .08 .04
106 Rico Rossy .10 .08 .04
107 Joe Hesketh .10 .08 .04
108 Dennis Powell .10 .08 .04
109 Derrick May .10 .08 .04
110 Pete Harnisch .10 .08 .04
111 Kent Mercker .10 .08 .04
112 Scott Fletcher .10 .08 .04
113 Rex Hudler .10 .08 .04
114 Chico Walker .10 .08 .04
115 Rafael Palmeiro .25 .20 .10
116 Mark Leiter .10 .08 .04
117 Pedro Munoz .25 .20 .10
118 Jim Bullinger .10 .08 .04
119 Ivan Calderon .10 .08 .04
120 Mike Timlin .10 .08 .04
121 Rene Gonzales .10 .08 .04
122 Greg Vaughn .25 .20 .10
123 Mike Flanagan .10 .08 .04
124 Mike Hartley .10 .08 .04
125 Jeff Montgomery .10 .08 .04
126 Mike Gallego .10 .08 .04
127 Don Slaught .10 .08 .04
128 Charlie O'Brien .10 .08 .04
129 Jose Offerman .25 .20 .10
130 Mark Wohlers .10 .08 .04
131 Eric Fox .15 .11 .06
132 Doug Strange .10 .08 .04
133 Jeff Frye .10 .08 .04
134 Wade Boggs .30 .25 .12
135 Lou Whitaker .10 .08 .04
136 Craig Grebeck .10 .08 .04
137 Rich Rodriguez .10 .08 .04
138 Jay Bell .10 .08 .04
139 Felix Fermin .10 .08 .04
140 Denny Martinez .10 .08 .04
141 Eric Anthony .10 .08 .04
142 Roberto Alomar .70 .50 .30
143 Darren Lewis .10 .08 .04
144 Mike Blowers .10 .08 .04
145 Scott Bankhead .10 .08 .04
146 Jeff Reboulet .10 .08 .04
147 Frank Viola .10 .08 .04
148 Bill Pecota .10 .08 .04
149 Carlos Hernandez .10 .08 .04
150 Bobby Witt .10 .08 .04
151 Sid Bream .10 .08 .04
152 Todd Zeile .25 .20 .10
153 Dennis Cook .10 .08 .04
154 Brian Bohanon .10 .08 .04
155 Pat Kelly .10 .08 .04
156 Milt Cuyler .10 .08 .04
157 Juan Bell .10 .08 .04
158 Randy Milligan .10 .08 .04
159 Mark Gardner .10 .08 .04
160 Pat Tabler .10 .08 .04
161 Jeff Reardon .10 .08 .04
162 Ken Patterson .10 .08 .04
163 Bobby Bonilla .12 .09 .05
164 Tony Pena .10 .08 .04
165 Greg Swindell .25 .20 .10
166 Kirk McCaskill .10 .08 .04
167 Doug Drabek .25 .20 .10
168 Franklin Stubbs .10 .08 .04
169 Ron Tingley .10 .08 .04
170 Willie Banks .10 .08 .04
171 Sergio Valdez .25 .20 .10
172 Mark Lemke .10 .08 .04
173 Robin Yount .50 .40 .20
174 Storm Davis .10 .08 .04
175 Dan Walters .10 .08 .04
176 Steve Farr .10 .08 .04
177 Curt Wilkerson .10 .08 .04
178 Luis Alicea .10 .08 .04
179 Russ Swan .10 .08 .04
180 Mitch Williams .10 .08 .04
181 Wilson Alvarez .10 .08 .04
182 Carl Willis .10 .08 .04
183 Craig Biggio .10 .08 .04
184 Sean Berry .25 .20 .10
185 Trevor Wilson .10 .08 .04
186 Jeff Tackett .10 .08 .04
187 Ellis Burks .25 .20 .10
188 Jeff Branson .25 .20 .10
189 Matt Nokes .10 .08 .04
190 John Smiley .10 .08 .04
191 Danny Gladden .10 .08 .04
192 Mike Boddicker .10 .08 .04
193 Roger Pavlik .10 .08 .04
194 Paul Sorrento .10 .08 .04
195 Vince Coleman .10 .08 .04
196 Gary DiSarcina .10 .08 .04
197 Rafael Bournigal .15 .11 .06
198 Mike Schooler .10 .08 .04
199 Scott Ruskin .10 .08 .04
200 Frank Thomas 3.50 2.75 1.50
201 Kyle Abbott .10 .08 .04
202 Mike Perez .10 .08 .04
203 Andre Dawson .15 .11 .06
204 Bill Swift .10 .08 .04
205 Alejandro Pena .10 .08 .04
206 Dave Winfield .40 .30 .15
207 Andujar Cedeno .15 .11 .06
208 Terry Steinbach .10 .08 .04
209 Chris Hammond .10 .08 .04
210 Todd Burns .10 .08 .04
211 Hipolito Pichardo .10 .08 .04
212 John Kiely .30 .25 .12
213 Tim Teufel .10 .08 .04
214 Lee Guetterman .10 .08 .04
215 Geronimo Pena .10 .08 .04
216 Brett Butler .10 .08 .04
217 Bryan Hickerson .10 .08 .04
218 Rick Trlicek .30 .25 .12
219 Lee Stevens .10 .08 .04
220 Roger Clemens .50 .40 .20
221 Carlton Fisk .15 .11 .06
222 Chili Davis .10 .08 .04
223 Walt Terrell .10 .08 .04
224 Jim Eisenreich .10 .08 .04
225 Ricky Bones .10 .08 .04
226 Henry Rodriguez .10 .08 .04
227 Ken Hill .15 .11 .06
228 Rick Wilkins .10 .08 .04
229 Ricky Jordan .10 .08 .04
230 Bernard Gilkey .10 .08 .04
231 Tim Fortugno .10 .08 .04
232 Geno Petralli .10 .08 .04
233 Jose Rijo .10 .08 .04
234 Jim Leyritz .10 .08 .04
235 Kevin Campbell .10 .08 .04
236 Al Osuna .10 .08 .04
237 Pete Smith .10 .08 .04
238 Pete Schourek .10 .08 .04
239 Moises Alou .20 .15 .08
240 Donn Pall .10 .08 .04
241 Denny Neagle .10 .08 .04
242 Dan Peltier .10 .08 .04
243 Scott Scudder .10 .08 .04
244 Juan Guzman .40 .30 .15
245 Dave Burba .10 .08 .04
246 Rick Sutcliffe .10 .08 .04
247 Tony Fossas .10 .08 .04
248 Mike Munoz .10 .08 .04
249 Tim Salmon 2.50 2.00 1.00
250 Rob Murphy .10 .08 .04
251 Roger McDowell .10 .08 .04
252 Lance Parrish .10 .08 .04
253 Cliff Brantley .10 .08 .04
254 Scott Leius .10 .08 .04
255 Carlos Martinez .10 .08 .04
256 Vince Horsman .10 .08 .04
257 Oscar Azocar .10 .08 .04
258 Craig Shipley .10 .08 .04
259 Ben McDonald .30 .25 .12
260 Jeff Brantley .10 .08 .04
261 Damon Berryhill .10 .08 .04
262 Joe Grahe .10 .08 .04
263 Dave Hansen .10 .08 .04
264 Rich Amaral .30 .25 .12
265 *Tim Pugh* .35 .25 .14
266 Dion James .10 .08 .04
267 Frank Tanana .10 .08 .04
268 Stan Belinda .10 .08 .04
269 Jeff Kent .10 .08 .04
270 Bruce Ruffin .10 .08 .04
271 Xavier Hernandez .10 .08 .04
272 Darrin Fletcher .10 .08 .04
273 Tino Martinez .10 .08 .04
274 Benny Santiago .15 .11 .06
275 Scott Radinsky .10 .08 .04
276 Mariano Duncan .10 .08 .04
277 Kenny Lofton .50 .40 .20
278 Dwight Smith .10 .08 .04
279 Joe Carter .40 .30 .15
280 Tim Jones .10 .08 .04
281 Jeff Huson .10 .08 .04
282 Phil Plantier .30 .25 .12
283 Kirby Puckett .75 .60 .30
284 Johnny Guzman .10 .08 .04
285 Mike Morgan .10 .08 .04
286 Chris Sabo .10 .08 .04
287 Matt Williams .10 .08 .04
288 Checklist 1-100 .10 .08 .04
289 Checklist 101-200 .10 .08 .04
290 Checklist 201-300 .10 .08 .04
291 Dennis Eckersley (Members Choice) .50 .40 .20
292 Eric Karros (Members Choice) .15 .11 .06
293 Pat Listach (Members Choice) .20 .15 .08
294 Andy Van Slyke (Members Choice) .15 .11 .06
295 Robin Ventura (Members Choice) .20 .15 .08
296 Tom Glavine (Members Choice) .25 .20 .10
297 Juan Gonzalez (Members Choice) 1.00 .70 .40
298 Travis Fryman (Members Choice) .40 .30 .15
299 Larry Walker (Members Choice) .15 .11 .06
300 Gary Sheffield (Members Choice) .20 .15 .08
301 Chuck Finley .10 .08 .04
302 Luis Gonzalez .10 .08 .04
303 Darryl Hamilton .10 .08 .04
304 Bien Figueroa .10 .08 .04
305 Ron Darling .10 .08 .04
306 Jonathan Hurst .10 .08 .04
307 Mike Sharperson .10 .08 .04
308 Mike Christopher .10 .08 .04
309 Marvin Freeman .10 .08 .04
310 Jay Buhner .15 .11 .06
311 Butch Henry .10 .08 .04
312 Greg Harris .10 .08 .04
313 Darren Daulton .15 .11 .06
314 Chuck Knoblauch .15 .11 .06
315 Greg Harris .10 .08 .04
316 John Franco .10 .08 .04
317 John Wehner .10 .08 .04
318 Donald Harris .10 .08 .04
319 Benny Santiago .10 .08 .04
320 Larry Walker .20 .15 .08
321 Randy Knorr .10 .08 .04
322 *Ramon D. Martinez* .15 .11 .06
323 Mike Stanley .10 .08 .04
324 Bill Wegman .10 .08 .04
325 Tom Candiotti .10 .08 .04
326 Glenn Davis .10 .08 .04
327 Chuck Crim .10 .08 .04
328 Scott Livingstone .10 .08 .04
329 Eddie Taubensee .10 .08 .04
330 George Bell .10 .08 .04
331 Edgar Martinez .10 .08 .04
332 Paul Assenmacher .10 .08 .04
333 Steve Hosey .15 .11 .06
334 Mo Vaughn .50 .40 .20
335 Bret Saberhagen .10 .08 .04
336 Mike Trombley .10 .08 .04
337 Mark Lewis .10 .08 .04
338 Terry Pendleton .10 .08 .04
339 Dave Hollins .15 .11 .06
340 Jeff Conine .10 .08 .04
341 Bob Tewksbury .10 .08 .04
342 Billy Ashley .50 .40 .20
343 Zane Smith .10 .08 .04
344 John Wetteland .10 .08 .04
345 Chris Hoiles .15 .11 .06
346 Frank Castillo .10 .08 .04
347 Bruce Hurst .10 .08 .04
348 Kevin McReynolds .10 .08 .04
349 Dave Henderson .10 .08 .04
350 Ryan Bowen .10 .08 .04
351 Sid Fernandez .10 .08 .04
352 Mark Whiten .15 .11 .06
353 Nolan Ryan 2.00 1.50 .80
354 Rick Aguilera .10 .08 .04
355 Mark Langston .10 .08 .04
356 Jack Morris .10 .08 .04
357 Rob Deer .10 .08 .04
358 Dave Fleming .15 .11 .06
359 Lance Johnson .10 .08 .04
360 Joe Millette .10 .08 .04
361 Wil Cordero .15 .11 .06
362 Chito Martinez .10 .08 .04
363 Scott Servais .10 .08 .04
364 Bernie Williams .10 .08 .04
365 Pedro Martinez .25 .20 .10
366 Ryne Sandberg .75 .60 .30
367 Brad Ausmus .10 .08 .04
368 Scott Cooper .10 .08 .04
369 Rob Dibble .10 .08 .04
370 Walt Weiss .10 .08 .04
371 Mark Davis .10 .08 .04
372 Orlando Merced .10 .08 .04
373 Mike Jackson .10 .08 .04
374 Kevin Appier .15 .11 .06
375 Esteban Beltre .10 .08 .04
376 Joe Slusarski .10 .08 .04
377 William Suero .10 .08 .04
378 Pete O'Brien .10 .08 .04
379 Alan Embree .15 .11 .06
380 Lenny Webster .10 .08 .04
381 Eric Davis .10 .08 .04
382 Duane Ward .10 .08 .04
383 John Habyan .10 .08 .04
384 Jeff Bagwell .50 .40 .20
385 Ruben Amaro .10 .08 .04
386 Julio Valera .10 .08 .04
387 Robin Ventura .30 .25 .12
388 Archi Cianfrocco .10 .08 .04
389 Skeeter Barnes .10 .08 .04
390 Tim Costo .15 .11 .06
391 Luis Mercedes .10 .08 .04
392 Jeremy Hernandez .10 .08 .04
393 Shawon Dunston .10 .08 .04
394 Andy Van Slyke .10 .08 .04
395 Kevin Maas .10 .08 .04
396 Kevin Brown .10 .08 .04
397 J.T. Bruett .10 .08 .04
398 Darryl Strawberry .10 .08 .04
399 Tom Pagnozzi .10 .08 .04
400 Sandy Alomar .10 .08 .04
401 Keith Miller .10 .08 .04
402 Rich DeLucia .10 .08 .04
403 Shawn Abner .10 .08 .04
404 Howard Johnson .10 .08 .04
405 Mike Benjamin .10 .08 .04
406 *Roberto Mejia* .60 .45 .25
407 Mike Butcher .10 .08 .04
408 Deion Sanders .30 .25 .12
409 Todd Stottlemyre .10 .08 .04
410 Scott Kamieniecki .10 .08 .04
411 Doug Jones .10 .08 .04
412 John Burkett .10 .08 .04
413 Lance Blankenship .10 .08 .04
414 Jeff Parrett .10 .08 .04
415 Barry Larkin .15 .11 .06
416 Alan Trammell .10 .08 .04
417 Mark Kiefer .10 .08 .04
418 Gregg Olson .10 .08 .04
419 Mark Grace .20 .15 .08
420 Shane Mack .10 .08 .04
421 Bob Walk .10 .08 .04
422 Curt Schilling .10 .08 .04
423 Erik Hanson .10 .08 .04
424 George Brett .60 .45 .25
425 Reggie Jefferson .10 .08 .04
426 Mark Portugal .10 .08 .04
427 Ron Karkovice .10 .08 .04
428 Matt Young .10 .08 .04
429 Troy Neel .35 .25 .14
430 Hector Fajardo .10 .08 .04
431 Dave Righetti .10 .08 .04

432	Pat Listach	.15	.11	.06
433	Jeff Innis	.10	.08	.04
434	Bob MacDonald	.10	.08	.04
435	Brian Jordan	.10	.08	.04
436	Jeff Blauser	.10	.08	.04
437	*Mike Myers*	.25	.20	.10
438	Frank Seminara	.10	.08	.04
439	Rusty Meacham	.10	.08	.04
440	Greg Briley	.10	.08	.04
441	Derek Lilliquist	.10	.08	.04
442	John Vander Wal	.10	.08	.04
443	Scott Erickson	.10	.08	.04
444	Bob Scanlan	.10	.08	.04
445	Todd Frohwirth	.10	.08	.04
446	Tom Goodwin	.10	.08	.04
447	William Pennyfeather	.10	.08	.04
448	Travis Fryman	.50	.40	.20
449	Mickey Morandini	.10	.08	.04
450	Greg Olson	.10	.08	.04
451	Trevor Hoffman	.10	.08	.04
452	Dave Magadan	.10	.08	.04
453	Shawn Jeter	.15	.11	.06
454	Andres Galarraga	.15	.11	.06
455	Ted Wood	.10	.08	.04
456	Freddie Benavides	.10	.08	.04
457	Junior Felix	.10	.08	.04
458	Alex Cole	.10	.08	.04
459	John Orton	.10	.08	.04
460	Eddie Zosky	.10	.08	.04
461	Dennis Eckersley	.10	.08	.04
462	Lee Smith	.10	.08	.04
463	John Smoltz	.15	.11	.06
464	Ken Caminiti	.10	.08	.04
465	Melido Perez	.10	.08	.04
466	Tom Marsh	.10	.08	.04
467	Jeff Nelson	.10	.08	.04
468	Jesse Levis	.10	.08	.04
469	Chris Nabholz	.10	.08	.04
470	Mike Mcfarlane	.10	.08	.04
471	Reggie Sanders	.20	.15	.08
472	Chuck McElroy	.10	.08	.04
473	Kevin Gross	.10	.08	.04
474	*Matt Whiteside*	.20	.15	.08
475	Cal Eldred	.15	.11	.06
476	Dave Gallagher	.10	.08	.04
477	Len Dykstra	.20	.15	.08
478	Mark McGwire	.25	.20	.10
479	David Segui	.10	.08	.04
480	Mike Henneman	.10	.08	.04
481	Bret Barberie	.10	.08	.04
482	Steve Sax	.10	.08	.04
483	Dave Valle	.10	.08	.04
484	Danny Darwin	.10	.08	.04
485	Devon White	.15	.11	.06
486	Eric Plunk	.10	.08	.04
487	Jim Gott	.10	.08	.04
488	Scooter Tucker	.10	.08	.04
489	Omar Oliveres	.10	.08	.04
490	Greg Myers	.10	.08	.04
491	Brian Hunter	.10	.08	.04
492	Kevin Tapani	.10	.08	.04
493	Rich Monteleone	.10	.08	.04
494	Steve Buechele	.10	.08	.04
495	Bo Jackson	.25	.20	.10
496	Mike LaValliere	.10	.08	.04
497	Mark Leonard	.10	.08	.04
498	Daryl Boston	.10	.08	.04
499	Jose Canseco	.25	.20	.10
500	Brian Barnes	.10	.08	.04
501	Randy Johnson	.15	.11	.06
502	Tim McIntosh	.10	.08	.04
503	Cecil Fielder	.40	.30	.15
504	Derek Bell	.15	.11	.06
505	Kevin Koslofski	.10	.08	.04
506	Darren Holmes	.10	.08	.04
507	Brady Anderson	.10	.08	.04
508	John Valentin	.25	.20	.10
509	Jerry Browne	.10	.08	.04
510	Fred McGriff	.60	.45	.25
511	Pedro Astacio	.25	.20	.10
512	Gary Gaetti	.10	.08	.04
513	*John Burke*	.30	.25	.12
514	Dwight Gooden	.10	.08	.04
515	Thomas Howard	.10	.08	.04
516	*Darrell Whitmore*	.75	.60	.30
517	Ozzie Guillen	.10	.08	.04
518	Darryl Kile	.10	.08	.04
519	Rich Rowland	.10	.08	.04
520	Carlos Delgado	2.00	1.50	.80
521	Doug Henry	.10	.08	.04
522	Greg Colbrunn	.10	.08	.04
523	Tom Gordon	.10	.08	.04
524	Ivan Rodriquez	.25	.20	.10
525	Kent Hrbek	.10	.08	.04
526	Eric Young	.25	.20	.10
527	Rod Brewer	.10	.08	.04
528	Eric Karros	.25	.20	.10
529	Marquis Grissom	.20	.15	.08
530	Rico Brogna	.10	.08	.04
531	Sammy Sosa	.15	.11	.06
532	Bret Boone	.15	.11	.06
533	Luis Rivera	.10	.08	.04
534	Hal Morris	.10	.08	.04
535	Monty Fariss	.10	.08	.04
536	Leo Gomez	.10	.08	.04
537	Wally Joyner	.10	.08	.04
538	Tony Gwynn	.25	.20	.10
539	Mike Williams	.10	.08	.04
540	Juan Gonzalez	2.50	2.00	1.00
541	Ryan Klesko	.60	.45	.25
542	Ryan Thompson	.15	.11	.06
543	Chad Curtis	.30	.25	.12
544	Orel Hershiser	.10	.08	.04
545	Carlos Garcia	.15	.11	.06
546	Bob Welch	.10	.08	.04
547	Vinny Castilla	.10	.08	.04
548	Ozzie Smith	.30	.25	.12
549	Luis Salazar	.10	.08	.04
550	Mark Guthrie	.10	.08	.04
551	Charles Nagy	.10	.08	.04
552	Alex Fernandez	.20	.15	.08
553	Mel Rojas	.10	.08	.04
554	Orestes Destrade	.10	.08	.04
555	Mark Gubicza	.10	.08	.04
556	Steve Finley	.10	.08	.04
557	Don Mattingly	.40	.30	.15
558	Rickey Henderson	.25	.20	.10
559	Tommy Greene	.10	.08	.04
560	Arthur Rhodes	.10	.08	.04
561	Alfredo Griffin	.10	.08	.04
562	Will Clark	.30	.25	.12
563	Bob Zupcic	.10	.08	.04
564	Chuck Carr	.10	.08	.04
565	Henry Cotto	.10	.08	.04
566	Billy Spiers	.10	.08	.04
567	Jack Armstrong	.10	.08	.04
568	Kurt Stillwell	.10	.08	.04
569	David McCarty	.40	.30	.15
570	Joe Vitiello	.40	.30	.15
571	Gerald Williams	.10	.08	.04
572	Dale Murphy	.10	.08	.04
573	Scott Aldred	.10	.08	.04
574	Bill Gullickson	.10	.08	.04
575	Bobby Thigpen	.10	.08	.04
576	Glenallen Hill	.10	.08	.04
577	Dwayne Henry	.10	.08	.04
578	Calvin Jones	.10	.08	.04
579	Al Martin	.35	.25	.14
580	Ruben Sierra	.25	.20	.10
581	Andy Benes	.10	.08	.04
582	Anthony Young	.10	.08	.04
583	Shawn Boskie	.10	.08	.04
584	*Scott Pose*	.30	.25	.12
585	Mike Piazza	5.00	3.75	2.00
586	Donovan Osborne	.15	.11	.06
587	James Austin	.10	.08	.04
588	Checklist 301-400	.10	.08	.04
589	Checklist 401-500	.10	.08	.04
590	Checklist 501-600	.10	.08	.04
591	Ken Griffey, Jr. (Members Choice)	1.75	1.25	.70
592	Ivan Rodriguez (Members Choice)	.20	.15	.08
593	Carlos Baerga (Members Choice)	.35	.25	.14
594	Fred McGriff (Members Choice)	.35	.25	.14
595	Mark McGwire (Members Choice)	.15	.11	.06
596	Roberto Alomar (Members Choice)	.35	.25	.14
597	Kirby Puckett (Members Choice)	.40	.30	.15
598	Marquis Grissom (Members Choice)	.15	.11	.06
599	John Smoltz (Members Choice)	.10	.08	.04
600	Ryne Sandberg (Members Choice)	.50	.40	.20
601	Wade Boggs	.20	.15	.08
602	Jeff Reardon	.10	.08	.04
603	Billy Ripken	.10	.08	.04
604	Bryan Harvey	.10	.08	.04
605	Carlos Quintana	.10	.08	.04
606	Greg Hibbard	.10	.08	.04
607	Ellis Burks	.10	.08	.04
608	Greg Swindell	.10	.08	.04
609	Dave Winfield	.40	.30	.15
610	Charlie Hough	.10	.08	.04
611	Chili Davis	.10	.08	.04
612	Jody Reed	.10	.08	.04
613	Mark Williamson	.10	.08	.04
614	Phil Plantier	.20	.15	.08
615	Jim Abbott	.15	.11	.06
616	Dante Bichette	.10	.08	.04
617	Mark Eichhorn	.10	.08	.04
618	Gary Sheffield	.25	.20	.10
619	*Richie Lewis*	.20	.15	.08
620	Joe Girardi	.10	.08	.04
621	Jaime Navarro	.10	.08	.04
622	Willie Wilson	.10	.08	.04
623	Scott Fletcher	.10	.08	.04
624	Bud Black	.10	.08	.04
625	Tom Brunansky	.10	.08	.04
626	Steve Avery	.35	.25	.14
627	Paul Molitor	.35	.25	.14
628	Gregg Jefferies	.10	.08	.04
629	Dave Stewart	.10	.08	.04
630	Javy Lopez	1.50	1.25	.60
631	Greg Gagne	.10	.08	.04
632	Bobby Kelly	.10	.08	.04
633	Mike Fetters	.10	.08	.04
634	Ozzie Canseco	.10	.08	.04
635	Jeff Russell	.10	.08	.04
636	Pete Incaviglia	.10	.08	.04
637	Tom Henke	.10	.08	.04
638	Chipper Jones	1.25	.90	.50
639	Jimmy Key	.10	.08	.04
640	Dave Martinez	.10	.08	.04
641	Dave Stieb	.10	.08	.04
642	Milt Thompson	.10	.08	.04
643	Alan Mills	.10	.08	.04
644	Tony Fernandez	.10	.08	.04
645	Randy Bush	.10	.08	.04
646	Joe Magrane	.10	.08	.04
647	Ivan Calderon	.10	.08	.04
648	Jose Guzman	.10	.08	.04
649	John Olerud	.75	.60	.30
650	Tom Glavine	.30	.25	.12
651	Julio Franco	.10	.08	.04
652	Armando Reynoso	.10	.08	.04
653	Felix Jose	.10	.08	.04
654	Ben Rivera	.10	.08	.04
655	Andre Dawson	.15	.11	.06
656	Mike Harkey	.10	.08	.04
657	Kevin Seitzer	.10	.08	.04
658	Lonnie Smith	.10	.08	.04
659	Norm Charlton	.10	.08	.04
660	Dave Justice	.75	.60	.30
661	Fernando Valezuela	.10	.08	.04
662	Dan Wilson	.15	.11	.06
663	Mark Gardner	.10	.08	.04
664	Doug Dascenzo	.10	.08	.04
665	Greg Maddux	.25	.20	.10
666	Harold Baines	.10	.08	.04
667	Randy Myers	.10	.08	.04
668	Harold Reynolds	.10	.08	.04
669	Candy Maldonado	.10	.08	.04
670	Al Leiter	.10	.08	.04
671	Jerald Clark	.10	.08	.04
672	Doug Drabek	.10	.08	.04
673	Kirk Gibson	.10	.08	.04
674	Steve Reed	.10	.08	.04
675	Mike Felder	.10	.08	.04
676	Ricky Gutierrez	.15	.11	.06
677	Spike Owen	.10	.08	.04
678	Otis Nixon	.10	.08	.04
679	Scott Sanderson	.10	.08	.04
680	Mark Carreon	.10	.08	.04
681	Troy Percival	.15	.11	.06
682	Kevin Stocker	1.50	1.25	.60
683	*Jim Converse*	.20	.15	.08
684	Barry Bonds	1.00	.70	.40
685	Greg Gohr	.10	.08	.04
686	Tim Wallach	.10	.08	.04
687	Matt Mieske	.15	.11	.06
688	Robby Thompson	.10	.08	.04
689	Brien Taylor	.60	.45	.25
690	Kirt Manwaring	.10	.08	.04
691	*Mike Lansing*	.40	.30	.15
692	Steve Decker	.10	.08	.04
693	Mike Moore	.10	.08	.04
694	Kevin Mitchell	.10	.08	.04
695	Phil Hiatt	.40	.30	.15
696	*Tony Tarasco*	.75	.60	.30
697	Benji Gil	.50	.40	.20
698	Jeff Juden	.10	.08	.04
699	Kevin Reimer	.10	.08	.04
700	Andy Ashby	.10	.08	.04
701	John Jaha	.15	.11	.06
702	*Tim Bogar*	.25	.20	.10
703	David Cone	.10	.08	.04
704	Willie Greene	.35	.25	.14
705	*David Hulse*	.25	.20	.10
706	Cris Carpenter	.10	.08	.04
707	Ken Griffey, Jr.	3.50	2.75	1.50
708	Steve Bedrosian	.10	.08	.04
709	Dave Nilsson	.10	.08	.04
710	Paul Wagner	.10	.08	.04
711	B.J. Surhoff	.10	.08	.04
712	*Rene Arocha*	.40	.30	.15
713	Manny Lee	.10	.08	.04
714	Brian Williams	.10	.08	.04
715	*Sherman Obando*	.25	.20	.10
716	Terry Mulholland	.10	.08	.04
717	Paul O'Neill	.10	.08	.04
718	David Nied	.50	.40	.20
719	J.T. Snow	.50	.40	.20
720	Nigel Wilson	.40	.30	.15
721	Mike Bielecki	.10	.08	.04
722	Kevin Young	.35	.25	.14
723	Charlie Leibrandt	.10	.08	.04
724	Frank Bolick	.10	.08	.04
725	*Jon Shave*	.15	.11	.06
726	Steve Cooke	.25	.20	.10
727	*Domingo Martinez*	.25	.20	.10
728	Todd Worrell	.10	.08	.04
729	Jose Lind	.10	.08	.04
730	*Jim Tatum*	.25	.20	.10
731	Mike Hampton	.10	.08	.04
732	Mike Draper	.10	.08	.04
733	Henry Mercedes	.15	.11	.06
734	*John Johnstone*	.25	.20	.10
735	Mitch Webster	.10	.08	.04
736	Russ Springer	.10	.08	.04
737	Rob Natal	.10	.08	.04
738	Steve Howe	.10	.08	.04
739	*Darrell Sherman*	.25	.20	.10
740	Pat Mahomes	.10	.08	.04
741	Alex Arias	.10	.08	.04
742	Damon Buford	.10	.08	.04
743	Charlie Hayes	.10	.08	.04
744	Guillermo Velasquez	.15	.11	.06
745	Checklist 601-750	.10	.08	.04
746	Frank Thomas (Members Choice)	1.75	1.25	.70
747	Barry Bonds (Members Choice)	.50	.40	.20
748	Roger Clemens (Members Choice)	.25	.20	.10
749	Joe Carter (Members Choice)	.20	.15	.08
750	Greg Maddux (Members Choice)	.10	.08	.04

1993 Topps Stadium Club Master Photos

Each box of 1993 Stadium Club packs included one Master Photo premium insert. Prize cards good for three Master Photos in a mail-in offer were also included in each of the three 1993 S.C. series. The 5" x 7" Master Photos feature wide white borders and a large Stadium Club logo at top, highlighted by prismatic foil. The same foil is used as a border for a larger-format version of the player's regular S.C. card at the center of the Master Photo. A "Members Only" version of each of the 1993 Master Photos was available as a premium with the purchase of a Members Only Stadium Club set. The Members Only Master Photos have a goldfoil seal in the upper-right on front.

		MT	NR MT	EX
Complete Set (30):		55.00	41.00	22.00
Common Player:		1.00	.70	.40
	Series I			
(1)	Carlos Baerga	2.50	2.00	1.00
(2)	Delino DeShields	1.50	1.25	.60
(3)	Brian McRae	1.00	.70	.40
(4)	Sam Militello	1.00	.70	.40
(5)	Joe Oliver	1.00	.70	.40
(6)	Kirby Puckett	4.00	3.00	1.50
(7)	Cal Ripken, Jr.	6.00	4.50	2.50
(8)	Bip Roberts	1.00	.70	.40
(9)	Mike Scioscia	1.00	.70	.40
(10)	Rick Sutcliffe	1.00	.70	.40
(11)	Danny Tartabull	1.50	1.25	.60
(12)	Tim Wakefield	1.00	.70	.40
	Series II			
(13)	George Brett	4.00	3.00	1.50
(14)	Jose Canseco	4.00	3.00	1.50
(15)	Will Clark	3.00	2.25	1.25
(16)	Travis Fryman	1.50	1.25	.60
(17)	Dwight Gooden	1.50	1.25	.60
(18)	Mark Grace	1.50	1.25	.60
(19)	Rickey Henderson	2.50	2.00	1.00
(20)	Mark McGwire	2.50	2.00	1.00
(21)	Nolan Ryan	7.00	5.25	2.75
(22)	Ruben Sierra	1.50	1.25	.60
(23)	Darryl Strawberry	1.50	1.25	.60
(24)	Larry Walker	1.00	.70	.40
	Series III			
(25)	Barry Bonds	6.00	4.50	2.50
(26)	Ken Griffey, Jr.	9.00	6.75	3.50
(27)	Greg Maddux	2.00	1.50	.80
(28)	David Nied	2.00	1.50	.80
(29)	J.T. Snow	1.50	1.25	.60
(30)	Brien Taylor	1.50	1.25	.60

1993 Topps Stadium Club First Day Production

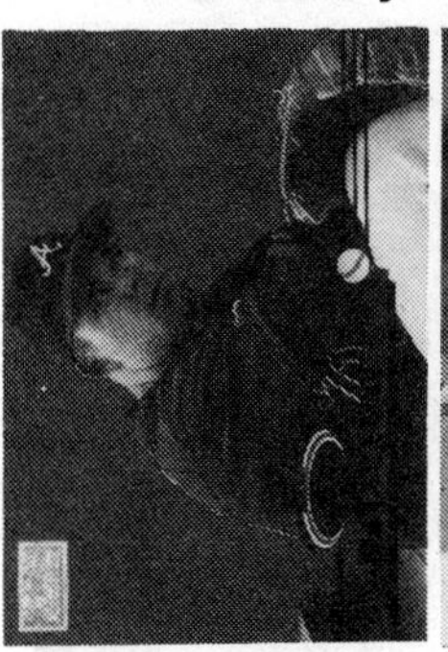

Inserted at the rate of about one per wax box, with an estimated production of about 2,000 apiece, Stadium Club First Day Production cards are regular-issue S.C. cards to which an embossed silver holographic logo has been added in one of the upper corners. Because values for FDP-logo cards are 25 to 50 times greater than regular Stadium Club cards, collectors should be aware of fake FDP star cards made by cutting the logo off a common card and gluing it to a star player's card.

	MT	NR MT	EX
Complete Set (750):	6000.	4500.	2500.
Common FDP card:	5.00	3.75	2.00
Stars: 25X to 50X S.C. price			

A player's name in italic type indicates a rookie card. An (FC) indicates a player's first card for that particular card company.

1993 Topps Stadium Club I Inserts

Four bonus cards were produced as special inserts in Series I Stadium Club packs. Two of the full-bleed, gold-foil enhanced cards honor Robin Yount and George Brett for achieving the 3,000-hit

mark, while the other two commemorate the first picks in the 1993 expansion draft by the Colorado Rockies (David Nied) and Marlins (Nigel Wilson).

		MT	NR MT	EX
Complete Set (4):		12.00	9.00	4.75
Common Player:		3.50	2.75	1.50
1	Robin Yount (3,000 hits)	4.00	3.00	1.50
2	George Brett (3,000 hits)	6.00	4.50	2.50
3	David Nied (#1 pick)	3.50	2.75	1.50
4	Nigel Wilson (#1 pick)	3.50	2.75	1.50

1993 Topps Stadium Club II Inserts

Cross-town and regional rivals were featured in this four-card insert set found, on average, one per 24 packs of Series II Stadium Club. Each of the two-faced cards is typical S.C. quality with gold-foil stamping and UV coating front and back.

		MT	NR MT	EX
Complete Set (4):		20.00	15.00	8.00
Common Card:		4.00	3.00	1.50
1	Pacific Terrific (Will Clark, Mark McGwire)	4.50	3.50	1.75
2	Broadway Stars (Dwight Gooden, Don Mattingly)	4.00	3.00	1.50
3	Second City Sluggers (Ryne Sandberg, Frank Thomas)	10.00	7.50	4.00
4	Pacific Terrific (Ken Griffey, Jr., Darryl Strawberry)	7.00	5.25	2.75

1993 Topps Stadium Club III Inserts

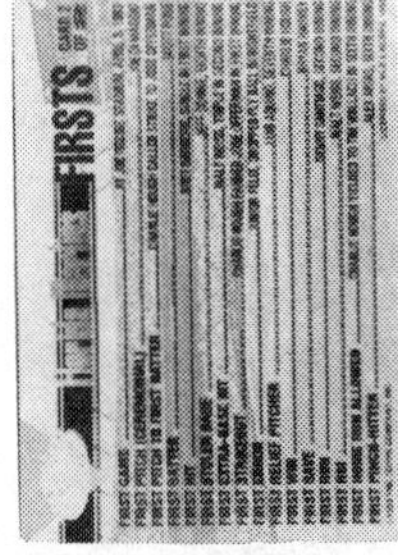

Team "firsts" - first game, first pitch, first batter, etc. - for the 1993 expansion Florida Marlins and Colorado Rockies were featured on this pair of inserts found in Series III Stadium Club packs. Fronts featured game-action photos with the player's name in gold foil. On back is a stadium scene with the team first overprinted in black. At top the team name and Stadium Club logo are in gold foil.

		MT	NR MT	EX
Complete Set (2):		5.00	3.75	2.00
Common Player:		2.00	1.50	.80
1	David Nied	3.50	2.75	1.50
2	Charlie Hough	2.00	1.50	.80

1993 Topps Stadium Club Special

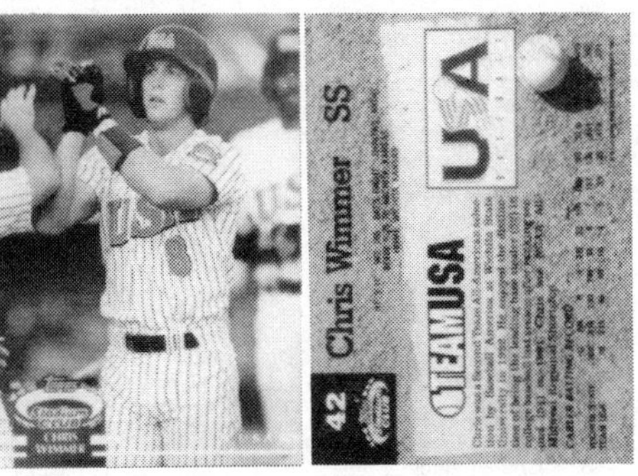

Though the packaging and the cards themselves identify this 200-card set as a 1992 issue, it was not released until 1993 and is thought of by the hobby at large as a 1993 set. The set is sold in a plastic replica of Jack Murphy Stadium in San Diego, venue for the 1992 All-Star Game. Fifty-six of the cards feature players from that contest and are so identified by a line of gold-foil on the card front and an All-Star logo on back. Twenty-five members of the 1992 Team U.S.A. Olympic baseball squad are also included in the set, with appropriate logos and notations front and pack. There are 19 cards depicting action and stars of the 1992 League Championships and World Series. The other 100 cards in the set are 1992 draft picks. All cards have the same basic format as the regular-issue 1992 Topps Stadium Club cards, full-bleed photos on front and back, UV coating on both sides and gold-foil highlights on front. Besides the 200 standard-size cards, the Special Edition set included a dozen "Master Photos," 5" x 7" white-bordered premium cards.

		MT	NR MT	EX
Complete Set (200):		35.00	26.00	14.00
Common Player:		.10	.08	.04
1	Dave Winfield	.15	.11	.06
2	Juan Guzman	.10	.08	.04
3	Tony Gwynn	.20	.15	.08
4	Chris Roberts	.50	.40	.20
5	Benny Santiago	.10	.08	.04
6	Sherard Clinkscales	.20	.15	.08
7	Jonathan Nunnally	.20	.15	.08
8	Chuck Knoblauch	.10	.08	.04
9	Bob Wolcott	.20	.15	.08
10	Steve Rodriguez	.12	.09	.05
11	*Mark Williams*	.12	.09	.05
12	Danny Clyburn	.70	.50	.30
13	Darren Dreifort	1.00	.70	.40
14	Andy Van Slyke	.15	.11	.06
15	Wade Boggs	.25	.20	.10
16	Scott Patton	.10	.08	.04
17	Gary Sheffield	.15	.11	.06
18	Ron Villone	.30	.25	.12
19	Roberto Alomar	.35	.25	.14
20	Marc Valdes	.50	.40	.20
21	Daron Kirkreit	.40	.30	.15
22	Jeff Granger	.25	.20	.10
23	Levon Largusa	.25	.20	.10
24	Jimmy Key	.10	.08	.04
25	Kevin Pearson	.10	.08	.04
26	Michael Moore	.60	.45	.25
27	Preston Wilson	1.00	.70	.40
28	Kirby Puckett	.50	.40	.20
29	Tim Crabtree	.30	.25	.12
30	Bip Roberts	.10	.08	.04
31	Kelly Gruber	.10	.08	.04
32	Tony Fernandez	.10	.08	.04
33	Jason Angel	.30	.25	.12
34	Calvin Murray	.75	.60	.30
35	Chad McConnell	.50	.40	.20
36	Jason Moler	.30	.25	.12
37	Mark Lemke	.10	.08	.04
38	Tom Knauss	.10	.08	.04
39	Larry Mitchell	.30	.25	.12
40	Doug Mirabelli	.10	.08	.04
41	Everett Stull II	.30	.25	.12
42	Chris Wimmer	.10	.08	.04
43	Dan Serafini	.30	.25	.12
44	Ryne Sandberg	.30	.25	.12
45	Steve Lyons	.10	.08	.04
46	Ryan Freeburg	.30	.25	.12
47	Ruben Sierra	.10	.08	.04
48	David Mysel	.10	.08	.04
49	Joe Hamilton	.10	.08	.04
50	Steve Rodriguez	.10	.08	.04

51	Tim Wakefield	.20	.15	.08
52	Scott Gentile	.25	.20	.10
53	Doug Jones	.10	.08	.04
54	Willie Brown	.10	.08	.04
55	Chad Mottola	2.50	2.00	1.00
56	Ken Griffey, Jr	1.25	.90	.50
57	Jon Lieber	.10	.08	.04
58	Denny Martinez	.10	.08	.04
59	Joe Petcka	.10	.08	.04
60	Benji Simonton	.10	.08	.04
61	Brett Backlund	.80	.60	.30
62	Damon Berryhill	.10	.08	.04
63	Juan Guzman	.30	.25	.12
64	Doug Hecker	.30	.25	.12
65	Jamie Arnold	.30	.25	.12
66	Bob Tewksbury	.10	.08	.04
67	Tim Leger	.10	.08	.04
68	Todd Etler	.10	.08	.04
69	Lloyd McClendon	.10	.08	.04
70	Kurt Ehmann	.10	.08	.04
71	Rick Magdaleno	.10	.08	.04
72	Tom Pagnozzi	.10	.08	.04
73	Jeffrey Hammonds	2.00	1.50	.80
74	Joe Carter	.25	.20	.10
75	Chris Holt	.10	.08	.04
76	Charles Johnson	1.00	.70	.40
77	Bob Walk	.10	.08	.04
78	Fred McGriff	.25	.20	.10
79	Tom Evans	.10	.08	.04
80	Scott Klingenbeck	.10	.08	.04
81	Chad McConnell	.40	.30	.15
82	Chris Eddy	.10	.08	.04
83	Phil Nevin	2.00	1.50	.80
84	John Kruk	.10	.08	.04
85	Tony Sheffield	.10	.08	.04
86	John Smoltz	.10	.08	.04
87	Trevor Humphry	.10	.08	.04
88	Charles Nagy	.10	.08	.04
89	Sean Runyan	.10	.08	.04
90	Mike Gulan	.25	.20	.10
91	Darren Daulton	.10	.08	.04
92	Otis Nixon	.10	.08	.04
93	Nomar Garciaparra	.30	.25	.12
94	Larry Walker	.30	.25	.12
95	Hut Smith	.10	.08	.04
96	Rick Helling	.30	.25	.12
97	Roger Clemens	.60	.45	.25
98	Ron Gant	.10	.08	.04
99	Kenny Felder	.60	.45	.25
100	Steve Murphy	.10	.08	.04
101	Mike Smith	.10	.08	.04
102	Terry Pendleton	.10	.08	.04
103	Tim Davis	.10	.08	.04
104	Jeff Patzke	.10	.08	.04
105	Craig Wilson	.10	.08	.04
106	Tom Glavine	.10	.08	.04
107	Mark Langston	.10	.08	.04
108	Mark Thompson	.10	.08	.04
109	Eric Owens	.10	.08	.04
110	Keith Johnson	.10	.08	.04
111	Robin Ventura	.30	.25	.12
112	Ed Sprague	.10	.08	.04
113	Jeff Schmidt	.10	.08	.04
114	Don Wengert	.10	.08	.04
115	Craig Biggio	.10	.08	.04
116	Kenny Carlyle	.10	.08	.04
117	Derek Jeter	1.75	1.25	.70
118	Manuel Lee	.10	.08	.04
119	Jeff Haas	.10	.08	.04
120	Roger Bailey	.10	.08	.04
121	Sean Lowe	.40	.30	.15
122	Rick Aguilera	.10	.08	.04
123	Sandy Alomar	.10	.08	.04
124	Derek Wallace	.40	.30	.15
125	B.J. Wallace	.70	.50	.30
126	Greg Maddux	.10	.08	.04
127	Tim Moore	.10	.08	.04
128	Lee Smith	.10	.08	.04
129	Todd Steverson	.70	.50	.30
130	Chris Widger	.10	.08	.04
131	Paul Molitor	.25	.20	.10
132	Chris Smith	.10	.08	.04
133	Chris Gomez	.10	.08	.04
134	Jimmy Baron	.10	.08	.04
135	John Smoltz	.10	.08	.04
136	Pat Borders	.10	.08	.04
137	Donnie Leshnock	.10	.08	.04
138	Gus Gandarillos	.10	.08	.04
139	Will Clark	.40	.30	.15
140	Ryan Luzinski	.60	.45	.25
141	Cal Ripken, Jr.	.60	.45	.25
142	B.J. Wallace	2.00	1.50	.80
143	Trey Beamon	.80	.60	.30
144	Norm Charlton	.10	.08	.04
145	Mike Mussina	.80	.60	.30
146	Billy Owens	.50	.40	.20
147	Ozzie Smith	.15	.11	.06
148	Jason Kendall	.50	.40	.20
149	Mike Matthews	.50	.40	.20
150	David Spykstra	.10	.08	.04
151	Benji Grigsby	.50	.40	.20
152	Sean Smith	.10	.08	.04
153	Mark McGwire	.20	.15	.08
154	David Cone	.10	.08	.04
155	Shon Walker	.80	.60	.30
156	Jason McDowell	.10	.08	.04
157	Jack McDowell	.10	.08	.04
158	Paxton Briley	.10	.08	.04
159	Edgar Martinez	.10	.08	.04
160	Brian Sackinsky	.10	.08	.04
161	Barry Bonds	.50	.40	.20
162	Roberto Kelly	.10	.08	.04
163	Jeff Alkire	1.00	.70	.40
164	Mike Sharperson	.10	.08	.04
165	Jamie Taylor	.30	.25	.12
166	John Saffer	.30	.25	.12
167	Jerry Browne	.10	.08	.04
168	Travis Fryman	.40	.30	.15
169	Brady Anderson	.10	.08	.04
170	Chris Roberts	.10	.08	.04
171	Lloyd Peever	.10	.08	.04
172	Francisco Cabrera	.10	.08	.04
173	Ramiro Martinez	.10	.08	.04
174	Jeff Alkire	.10	.08	.04
175	Ivan Rodriguez	.15	.11	.06
176	Kevin Brown	.10	.08	.04
177	Chad Roper	.10	.08	.04
178	Rod Henderson	.10	.08	.04
179	Dennis Eckersley	.10	.08	.04
180	Shannon Stewart	.30	.25	.12
181	DeShawn Warren	.10	.08	.04
182	Lonnie Smith	.10	.08	.04
183	Willie Adams	.10	.08	.04
184	Jeff Montgomery	.10	.08	.04
185	Damon Hollins	.10	.08	.04
186	Byron Matthews	.10	.08	.04
187	Harold Baines	.10	.08	.04
188	Rick Greene	.30	.25	.12
189	Carlos Baerga	.30	.25	.12
190	Brandon Cromer	.10	.08	.04
191	Roberto Alomar	.40	.30	.15
192	Rich Ireland	.10	.08	.04
193	Steve Montgomery	.10	.08	.04
194	Brant Brown	.10	.08	.04
195	Ritchie Moody	.10	.08	.04
196	Michael Tucker	1.75	1.25	.70
197	Jason Varitek	1.25	.90	.50
198	David Manning	.10	.08	.04
199	Marquis Riley	.10	.08	.04
200	Jason Giambi	.30	.25	.12

1993 Topps Stadium Club Special Master Photos

Each 1993 Stadium Club Special (Jack Murphy Stadium) set included one of a dozen Master Photos replicating cards from the set. There were nine All-Stars, two '92 rookies and a Team USA player among the Master Photos. Gold-tone prismatic foil highlights the 5" x 7" cards, decorating the large logo at top and separating the card photo from the wide white border. Backs have Stadium Club and MLB logos and copyright information printed in black. The unnumbered cards are checklisted here in alphabetical order.

		MT	NR MT	EX
Complete Set (12):		6.00	4.50	2.50
Common Player:		.25	.20	.10
(1)	Sandy Alomar	.25	.20	.10
(2)	Tom Glavine	.50	[illegible]	.20
(3)	Ken Griffey, Jr.	3.00	[illegible]	1.25
(4)	Tony Gwynn	.75	.60	.30
(5)	Chuck Knoblauch	.75	.60	.30
(6)	Chad Mottola	.75	.60	.30
(7)	Kirby Puckett	1.25	.90	.50
(8)	Chris Roberts	.75	.60	.30
(9)	Ryne Sandberg	2.00	1.50	.80
(10)	Gary Sheffield	.75	.60	.30
(11)	Larry Walker	.50	.40	.20
(12)	Preston Wilson	.75	.60	.30

1993 Topps Stadium Club Members Only

As a benefit of membership in Topps' Stadium Club, each member received a 59-card set in four separate shipments. The cards featured highlights of the 1993 baseball, hockey, football and basketball seasons. Besides the 28 baseball player cards checklisted here there were nine football cards, six hockey cards and 16 basketball cards. Each sport's cards came separately in a heat-sealed cello wrap in a special box. Cards were typical S.C. quality, featuring full-bleed action photos on the front, with the Stadium Club logo and player name enhanced with gold-foil stamping and a gold-foil "Members Only" notice beneath the player's name. Backs feature a parti-color background with a colorized, stylized player figure at right. At left is the story of the player's season or career highlight. The cards are unnumbered and are checklisted here alphabetically.

		MT	NR MT	EX
Complete Set (28):		24.00	18.00	9.50
Common Player:		.50	.40	.20
(1)	Jim Abbott	1.00	.70	.40
(2)	Barry Bonds	2.00	1.50	.80
(3)	Chris Bosio	.50	.40	.20
(4)	George Brett	2.00	1.50	.80
(5)	Jay Buhner	.50	.40	.20
(6)	Joe Carter (3 HR in game 5th time)	.75	.60	.30
(7)	Joe Carter (World Series-winning HR)	.75	.60	.30
(8)	Carlton Fisk	.75	.60	.30
(9)	Travis Fryman	.50	.40	.20
(10)	Mark Grace	.75	.60	.30
(11)	Ken Griffey, Jr.	4.00	3.00	1.50
(12)	Darryl Kile	.50	.40	.20
(13)	Darren Lewis	.50	.40	.20
(14)	Greg Maddux	.75	.60	.30
(15)	Jack McDowell	.50	.40	.20
(16)	Paul Molitor	1.50	1.25	.60
(17)	Eddie Murray	.75	.60	.30
(18)	Mike Piazza (Rookie catcher HR record)	1.00	.70	.40
(19)	Mike Piazza (N.L. Rookie of the Year)	1.00	.70	.40
(20)	Kirby Puckett	2.00	1.50	.80
(21)	Jeff Reardon	.50	.40	.20
(22)	Tim Salmon	1.00	.70	.40
(23)	Curt Schilling	.50	.40	.20
(24)	Lee Smith	.50	.40	.20
(25)	Dave Stewart	.50	.40	.20
(26)	Frank Thomas	4.00	3.00	1.50
(27)	Mark Whiten	.50	.40	.20
(28)	Dave Winfield	1.00	.70	.40

1993 Topps Stadium Club Team Sets

This special edition of Stadium Club cards consists of 16 separate team sets of 30 cards each. Each blister-packed team set was priced around $6 and they sold exclusively at Wal-Mart. Fronts of the UV-coated cards have a player photo that is borderless at the top, bottom and left. At right is a green stripe, at top of which is a partial baseball design and some othher striping in gold foil. Backs are basically green, with a light blue box at lower-right containing personal information and stats, along with the S.C. logo. A player photo is at upper-left, with his name superimposed on a bat. Cards are checklisted here within team set.

		MT	NR MT	EX
Complete Set (480):		95.00	71.00	38.00
Common Player:		.10	.08	.04
	ATLANTA BRAVES			
1	Tom Glavine	.50	.40	.20
2	Bill Pecota	.10	.08	.04
3	David Justice	.50	.40	.20
4	Mark Lemke	.10	.08	.04
5	Jeff Blauser	.10	.08	.04
6	Ron Gant	.50	.40	.20
7	Greg Olson	.10	.08	.04
8	Francisco Cabrera	.10	.08	.04
9	Chipper Jones	.50	.40	.20
10	Steve Avery	.50	.40	.20
11	Kent Mercker	.10	.08	.04

12	John Smoltz	.35	.25	.14
13	Pete Smith	.10	.08	.04
14	Damon Berryhill	.10	.08	.04
15	Sid Bream	.10	.08	.04
16	Otis Nixon	.10	.08	.04
17	Mike Stanton	.10	.08	.04
18	Greg Maddux	.50	.40	.20
19	Jay Howell	.10	.08	.04
20	Rafael Belliard	.10	.08	.04
21	Terry Pendleton	.10	.08	.04
22	Deion Sanders	.50	.40	.20
23	Brian Hunter	.10	.08	.04
24	Marvin Freeman	.10	.08	.04
25	Mark Wohlers	.10	.08	.04
26	Ryan Klesko	.50	.40	.20
27	Javy Lopez	.75	.60	.30
28	Melvin Nieves	.25	.20	.10
29	Tony Tarasco	.25	.20	.10
30	Ramon Caraballo	.25	.20	.10
	CHICAGO CUBS			
1	Ryne Sandberg	1.25	.90	.50
2	Greg Hibbard	.10	.08	.04
4	Candy Maldonado	.10	.08	.04
5	Willie Wilson	.15	.11	.06
6	Dan Plesac	.10	.08	.04
7	Steve Buechele	.10	.08	.04
8	Mark Grace	.25	.20	.10
9	Shawon Dunston	.20	.15	.08
10	Steve Lake	.10	.08	.04
11	Dwight Smith	.10	.08	.04
12	Derrick May	.25	.20	.10
13	Paul Assenmacher	.10	.08	.04
14	Mike Harkey	.10	.08	.04
15	Lance Dickson	.10	.08	.04
16	Randy Myers	.25	.20	.10
17	Mike Morgan	.10	.08	.04
18	Chuck McElroy	.10	.08	.04
19	Jose Guzman	.10	.08	.04
20	Jose Vizcaino	.10	.08	.04
21	Frank Castillo	.10	.08	.04
22	Bob Scanlon	.10	.08	.04
23	Rick Wilkins	.25	.20	.10
24	Rey Sanchez	.10	.08	.04
25	Phil Dauphin	.15	.11	.06
26	Jim Bullinger	.10	.08	.04
27	Jessie Hollins	.15	.11	.06
28	Matt Walbeck	.25	.20	.10
29	Fernando Ramsey	.15	.11	.06
30	Jose Bautista	.15	.11	.06
	CALIFORNIA ANGELS			
1	J.T. Snow	.25	.20	.10
2	Chuck Crim	.10	.08	.04
3	Chili Davis	.25	.20	.10
4	Mark Langston	.25	.20	.10
5	Ron Tingley	.10	.08	.04
6	Eduardo Perez	.15	.11	.06
7	Scott Sanderson	.10	.08	.04
8	Jorge Fabregas	.15	.11	.06
9	Troy Percival	.15	.11	.06
10	Rod Carreia	.10	.08	.04
11	Greg Myers	.10	.08	.04
12	Steve Frey	.10	.08	.04
13	Tim Salmon	1.00	.70	.40
14	Scott Lewis	.10	.08	.04
15	Rene Gonzales	.10	.08	.04
16	Chuck Finley	.25	.20	.10
17	John Orton	.10	.08	.04
18	Joe Grahe	.10	.08	.04
19	Luis Polonia	.25	.20	.10
20	John Farrell	.10	.08	.04
21	Damion Easley	.20	.15	.08
22	Gene Nelson	.10	.08	.04
23	Chad Curtis	.50	.40	.20
24	Russ Springer	.10	.08	.04
25	De Shawn Warren	.15	.11	.06
26	Darryl Scott	.10	.08	.04
27	Gary DiSarcina	.10	.08	.04
28	Jerry Nielson	.15	.11	.06
29	Torey Lovullo	.10	.08	.04
30	Julio Valera	.10	.08	.04
	CHICAGO WHITE SOX			
1	Frank Thomas	1.50	1.25	.60
2	Bo Jackson	.50	.40	.20
3	Rod Bolton	.10	.08	.04
4	Dave Stieb	.20	.15	.08
5	Tim Raines	.25	.20	.10
6	Joey Cora	.10	.08	.04
7	Warren Newson	.10	.08	.04
8	Roberto Hernandez	.20	.15	.08
9	Brandon WIlson	.10	.08	.04
10	Wilson Alvarez	.20	.15	.08
11	Dan Pasqua	.10	.08	.04
12	Ozzie Guillen	.20	.15	.08
13	Robin Ventura	.35	.25	.14
14	Craig Grebeck	.10	.08	.04
15	Lance Johnson	.25	.20	.10
16	Carlton Fisk	.50	.40	.20
17	Ron Karkovice	.10	.08	.04
18	Jack McDowell	.50	.40	.20
19	Scott Radinsky	.20	.15	.08
20	Bobby Thigpen	.10	.08	.04
21	Donn Pall	.10	.08	.04
22	George Bell	.20	.15	.08
23	Alex Fernandez	.25	.20	.10
24	Mike Hiff	.10	.08	.04
25	Jason Bere	.50	.40	.20
26	Johnny Ruffin	.15	.11	.06
27	Ellis Burks	.20	.15	.08
28	Kirk McCaskill	.20	.15	.08
29	Terry Leach	.10	.08	.04
30	Shawn Gilbert	.15	.11	.06
	COLORADO ROCKIES			
1	David Nied	.50	.40	.20
2	Quinton McCracken	.15	.11	.06
3	Charlie Hayes	.20	.15	.08
4	Bryn Smith	.10	.08	.04
5	Dante Bichette	.25	.20	.10
6	Alex Cole	.20	.15	.08
7	Scott Aldred	.15	.11	.06
8	Roberto Mejia	.10	.08	.04
9	Jeff Parrett	.10	.08	.04
10	Joe Girardi	.20	.15	.08
11	Andres Galarraga	.50	.40	.20
12	Daryl Boston	.20	.15	.08
13	Jerald Clark	.10	.08	.04
14	Gerald Young	.10	.08	.04
15	Bruce Ruffin	.10	.08	.04
16	Rudy Seanez	.15	.11	.06
17	Darren Holmes	.15	.11	.06
18	Andy Ashby	.10	.08	.04
19	Chris Jones	.10	.08	.04
20	Mark Thompson	.10	.08	.04
21	Freddie Benavides	.10	.08	.04
22	Eric Wedge	.15	.11	.06
23	Vinny Castilla	.10	.08	.04
24	Butch Henry	.10	.08	.04
25	Jim Tatum	.10	.08	.04
26	Steve Reed	.10	.08	.04
27	Eric Young	.15	.11	.06
28	Danny Sheaffer	.10	.08	.04
29	Roger Bailey	.15	.11	.06
30	Brad Ausmus	.10	.08	.04
	FLORIDA MARLINS			
1	Nigel Wilson	.50	.40	.20
2	Bryan Harvey	.50	.40	.20
3	Bob McClure	.10	.08	.04
4	Alex Arias	.10	.08	.04
5	Walt Weiss	.20	.15	.08
6	Charlie Hough	.20	.15	.08
7	Scott Chiamparino	.20	.15	.08
8	Junior Felix	.10	.08	.04
9	Jack Armstrong	.10	.08	.04
10	Dave Magadan	.25	.20	.10
11	Cris Carpenter	.10	.08	.04
12	Benny Santiago	.35	.25	.14
13	Jeff Conine	.35	.25	.14
14	Jerry Don Gleaton	.10	.08	.04
15	Steve Decker	.10	.08	.04
16	Ryan Bowen	.20	.15	.08
17	Ramon Martinez	.15	.11	.06
18	Bret Barberie	.20	.15	.08
19	Monty Fariss	.20	.15	.08
20	Trevor Hoffman	.20	.15	.08
21	Scott Pose	.10	.08	.04
22	Mike Myers	.10	.08	.04
23	Geronimo Berroa	.10	.08	.04
24	Darrell Whitmore	.10	.08	.04
25	Chuck Carr	.20	.15	.08
26	Dave Weathers	.10	.08	.04
27	Matt Turner	.10	.08	.04
28	Jose Martinez	.10	.08	.04
29	Orestes Destrade	.25	.20	.10
30	Carl Everett	.10	.08	.04
	HOUSTON ASTROS			
1	Doug Drebek	.20	.15	.08
2	Eddie Taubensee	.10	.08	.04
3	James Mouton	.15	.11	.06
4	Ken Caminiti	.20	.15	.08
5	Chris James	.10	.08	.04
6	Jeff Juden	.25	.20	.10
7	Eric Anthony	.25	.20	.10
8	Jeff Bagwell	.50	.40	.20
9	Greg Swindall	.25	.20	.10
10	Steve Finley	.25	.20	.10
11	Al Osunea	.10	.08	.04
12	Gary Mota	.10	.08	.04
13	Scott Servais	.10	.08	.04
14	Craig Biggio	.50	.40	.20
15	Doug James	.10	.08	.04
16	Rob Mallicoat	.10	.08	.04
17	Darryl Kile	.50	.40	.20
18	Kevin Bass	.10	.08	.04
19	Pete Harnisch	.20	.15	.08
20	Andujar Cedeno	.20	.15	.08
21	Brian Hunter	.10	.08	.04
22	Brian Williams	.10	.08	.04
23	Chris Donnels	.10	.08	.04
24	Xavier Hernandez	.15	.11	.06
25	Todd Jones	.10	.08	.04
26	Luis Gonzalez	.10	.08	.04
27	Rick Parker	.15	.11	.06
28	Casey Candaele	.10	.08	.04
29	Tony Eusebio	.15	.11	.06
30	Mark Portugal	.10	.08	.04
	KANSAS CITY ROYALS			
1	George Brett	1.00	.70	.40
2	Mike MacFarlane	.25	.20	.10
3	Tom Gordon	.10	.08	.04
4	Waily Joyner	.50	.40	.20
5	Kevin Appier	.25	.20	.10
6	Phil Hiatt	.25	.20	.10
7	Keith Miller	.10	.08	.04
8	Hipolito Pichardo	.10	.08	.04
9	Chris Gwynn	.10	.08	.04
10	Jose Lind	.25	.20	.10
11	Mark Gubicza	.25	.20	.10
12	Dennis Rasmussen	.25	.20	.10
13	Mike Magnante	.15	.11	.06
14	Joe Vitiello	.15	.11	.06
15	Kevin McReynolds	.15	.11	.06
16	Greg Gagne	.15	.11	.06
17	David Cone	.20	.15	.08
18	Brent Mayne	.20	.15	.08
19	Jeff Montgomery	.25	.20	.10
20	Joe Randa	.10	.08	.04
21	Felix Jose	.25	.20	.10
22	Bill Sampen	.10	.08	.04
23	Curt Wilkerson	.10	.08	.04
24	Mark Gardner	.10	.08	.04
25	Brian McRae	.25	.20	.10
26	Hubie Brooks	.15	.11	.06
27	Chris Eddy	.15	.11	.06
28	Harvey Pulliam	.15	.11	.06
29	Rusty Meacham	.10	.08	.04
30	Danny Miceli	.15	.11	.06
	LOS ANGELES DODGERS			
1	Darryl Strawberry	.50	.40	.20
2	Pedro Martinez	.25	.20	.10
3	Jody Reed	.10	.08	.04
4	Carlos Hernandez	.50	.40	.20
5	Kevin Gross	.10	.08	.04
6	Mike Piazza	1.00	.70	.40
7	Jim Gott	.10	.08	.04
8	Eric Karros	.50	.40	.20
9	Mike Sharperson	.10	.08	.04
10	Ramon Martinez	.25	.20	.10
11	Tim Wallach	.25	.20	.10
12	Pedro Astacio	.15	.11	.06
13	Lenny Harris	.10	.08	.04
14	Brett Butler	.15	.11	.06
15	Raul Mondesi	.15	.11	.06
16	Todd Worrell	.10	.08	.04
17	Jose Offerman	.15	.11	.06
18	Mitch Webster	.10	.08	.04
19	Tom Candiotti	.10	.08	.04
20	Eric Davis	.35	.25	.14
21	Michael Moore	.10	.08	.04
22	Billy Ashley	.15	.11	.06
23	Orel Hershiser	.25	.20	.10
24	Roger Cedeno	.15	.11	.06
25	Roger McDowell	.15	.11	.06
26	Mike James	.15	.11	.06
27	Steve Wilson	.10	.08	.04
28	Todd Hollandsworth	.15	.11	.06
29	Cory Snyder	.10	.08	.04
30	Todd Williams	.15	.11	.06
	NEW YORK YANKEES			
1	Don Mattingly	.75	.60	.30
2	Jim Abbott	.50	.40	.20
3	Matt Nokes	.25	.20	.10
4	Danny Tartabull	.25	.20	.10
5	Wade Boggs	.75	.60	.30
6	Melido Perez	.10	.08	.04
7	Steve Farr	.10	.08	.04
8	Kevin Maas	.10	.08	.04
9	Randy Velarde	.10	.08	.04
10	Mike Humphreys	.10	.08	.04
11	Mike Gallego	.10	.08	.04
12	Mike Stanley	.10	.08	.04
13	Jimmy Key	.10	.08	.04
14	Paul O'Neill	.25	.20	.10
15	Spike Owen	.10	.08	.04
16	Pat Kelly	.25	.20	.10
17	Sterling Hitchcock	.25	.20	.10
18	Mike Witt	.10	.08	.04
19	Scott Kamieniecki	.10	.08	.04
20	John Habyan	.10	.08	.04
21	Bernie Williams	.10	.08	.04
22	Brien Taylor	.22	.15	.09
23	Rich Monteleone	.10	.08	.04
24	Mark Hutton	.10	.08	.04
25	Robert Eenhoorn	.15	.11	.06
26	Gerald Williams	.10	.08	.04
27	Sam Militello	.25	.20	.10
28	Bob Wickman	.25	.20	.10
29	Andy Stankiewicz	.20	.15	.08
30	Domingo Jean	.20	.15	.08
	OAKLAND A'S			
1	Dennis Eckersley	.50	.40	.20
2	Lance Blankenship	.10	.08	.04
3	Mike Mohler	.10	.08	.04
4	Jerry Browne	.10	.08	.04
5	Kevin Seitzer	.10	.08	.04
6	Storm Davis	.10	.08	.04
7	Mark McGwire	.60	.45	.25
8	Rickey Henderson	.75	.60	.30
9	Terry Steinbach	.10	.08	.04
10	Ruben Sierra	.40	.30	.15
11	Dave Henderson	.10	.08	.04
12	Bob Welch	.20	.15	.08
13	Rick Honeycutt	.10	.08	.04
14	Ron Darling	.10	.08	.04
16	Joe Boever	.10	.08	.04
17	Izzy Molina	.15	.11	.06
18	Mike Bordick	.10	.08	.04
19	Brent Gates	.10	.08	.04
20	Shawn Hillegas	.10	.08	.04
21	Scott Hammond	.10	.08	.04
22	Todd Van Poppel	.25	.20	.10
23	Johnny Guzman	.15	.11	.06
24	Scott Lydy	.10	.08	.04
25	Scott Baker	.10	.08	.04
26	Todd Revenig	.10	.08	.04
27	Scott Brosius	.10	.08	.04
28	Troy Neel	.15	.11	.06
29	Dale Sveum	.10	.08	.04
30	Mike Neill	.15	.11	.06
	PHILADELPHIA PHILLIES			
1	Darren Daulton	.25	.20	.10
2	Larry Anderson	.10	.08	.04
3	Kyle Abbott			
4	Chad McConnell	.15	.11	.06
5	Danny Jackson	.10	.08	.04
6	Kevin Stocker	.20	.15	.08
7	Jim Eisenreich	.10	.08	.04
8	Mickey Morandini	.10	.08	.04
9	Bob Ayrault	.10	.08	.04
10	Doug Lindsey	.15	.11	.06
11	Dave Hollins	.25	.20	.10
12	Dave West	.10	.08	.04
13	Wes Chamberlain	.10	.08	.04
14	Curt Schilling	.10	.08	.04
15	Len Dykstra	.50	.40	.20
16	Trevor Humphry	.15	.11	.06
17	Terry Mulholland	.25	.20	.10
18	Gene Schall	.15	.11	.06
19	Mike Lieberthal	.15	.11	.06
20	Ben Rivera	.10	.08	.04
21	Mariano Duncan	.20	.15	.08
22	Pete Incaviglia	.25	.20	.10
23	Ron Blazier	.15	.11	.06
24	Jeff Jackson	.15	.11	.06
25	Jose DeLeon	.10	.08	.04

26	Ron Lockett	.10	.08	.04
27	Tommy Greene	.25	.20	.10
28	Milt Thompson	.10	.08	.04
29	Mitch Williams	.50	.40	.20
30	John Kruk	.50	.40	.20
	ST. LOUIS CARDINALS			
1	Ozzie Smith	.75	.60	.30
2	Rene Arocha	.25	.20	.10
3	Bernard Gilkey	.25	.20	.10
4	Jose Oquendo	.10	.08	.04
5	Mike Perez	.10	.08	.04
6	Tom Pagnozzi	.10	.08	.04
7	Rod Brewer	.10	.08	.04
8	Joe Magrane	.10	.08	.04
9	Todd Zeile	.25	.20	.10
10	Bob Tewksbury	.15	.11	.06
11	Darrel Deak	.15	.11	.06
12	Gregg Jefferies	.50	.40	.20
13	Lee Smith	.25	.20	.10
14	Ozzie Canseco	.10	.08	.04
15	Tom Urbani	.15	.11	.06
16	Donovan Osborne	.10	.08	.04
17	Ray Lankford	.25	.20	.10
18	Rheal Cormier	.25	.20	.10
19	Allen Watson	.25	.20	.10
20	Geronimo Pena	.10	.08	.04
21	Rob Murphy	.10	.08	.04
22	Tracy Woodson	.10	.08	.04
23	Basil Shabazz	.15	.11	.06
24	Omar Olivares	.10	.08	.04
25	Brian Jordan	.15	.11	.06
26	Les Lancaster	.10	.08	.04
27	Sean Lowe	.15	.11	.06
28	Hector Villanueva	.10	.08	.04
29	Brian Barber	.15	.11	.06
30	Aaron Holbert	.15	.11	.06
	SAN FRANCISCO GIANTS			
1	Barry Bonds	.75	.60	.30
2	Dave Righetti	.25	.20	.10
3	Matt Williams	.40	.30	.15
4	Royce Clayton	.10	.08	.04
5	Salomon Torres	.15	.11	.06
6	Kirt Manwaring	.10	.08	.04
7	J.R. Phillips	.15	.11	.06
8	Kevin Rogers	.15	.11	.06
9	Will Clark	.75	.60	.30
10	John Burkett	.25	.20	.10
11	Willie McGee	.25	.20	.10
12	Rod Beck	.10	.08	.04
13	Jeff Reed	.10	.08	.04
14	Jeff Brantley	.10	.08	.04
15	Steve Hosey	.10	.08	.04
16	Chris Hancock	.15	.11	.06
17	Adell Davenport	.15	.11	.06
18	Mike Jackson	.10	.08	.04
19	Dave Martinez	.10	.08	.04
20	Bill Swift	.25	.20	.10
21	Steve Scarsone	.10	.08	.04
22	Trevor Wilson	.15	.11	.06
23	Mark Carreon	.10	.08	.04
24	Bud Black	.15	.11	.06
25	Darren Lewis	.25	.20	.10
26	Dan Carlson	.15	.11	.06
27	Craig Colbert	.15	.11	.06
28	Greg Brummet	.15	.11	.06
29	Bryan Hickerson	.10	.08	.04
30	Robby Thompson	.25	.20	.10
	SEATTLE MARINERS			
1	Ken Griffey Jr.	1.50	1.25	.60
2	Desi Realford	.15	.11	.06
3	Dave Weinhouse	.15	.11	.06
4	Rich Amaral	.10	.08	.04
5	Brian Deak	.10	.08	.04
6	Bret Boone	.25	.20	.10
7	Bill Haselman	.10	.08	.04
8	Dave Fleming	.10	.08	.04
9	Fernando Vina	.15	.11	.06
10	Greg Litton	.10	.08	.04
11	Mackey Sasser	.10	.08	.04
12	Lee Tinsley	.10	.08	.04
13	Norm Charlton	.25	.20	.10
14	Russ Swan	.10	.08	.04
15	Brian Holman	.10	.08	.04
16	Randy Johnson	.35	.25	.14
17	Erik Hanson	.10	.08	.04
18	Tino Martinez	.25	.20	.10
19	Marc Newfield	.25	.20	.10
20	Dave Valle	.10	.08	.04
21	John Cummings	.15	.11	.06
22	Mike Hampton	.15	.11	.06
23	Jay Buhner	.25	.20	.10
24	Edgar Martinez	.35	.25	.14
25	Omar Vizquel	.25	.20	.10
26	Pete O'Brien	.10	.08	.04
27	Brian Turang	.15	.11	.06
28	Chris Bosio	.15	.11	.06
29	Mike Felder	.10	.08	.04
30	Shawn Estes	.10	.08	.04
	TEXAS RANGERS			
1	Nolan Ryan	1.50	1.25	.60
2	Ritchie Moody	.15	.11	.06
3	Matt Whiteside	.10	.08	.04
4	David Hulse	.15	.11	.06
5	Roger Pavlik	.10	.08	.04
6	Dan Smith	.10	.08	.04
7	Donald Harris	.15	.11	.06
8	Butch Davis	.10	.08	.04
9	Benji Gil	.10	.08	.04
10	Ivan Rodriguez	.35	.25	.14
11	Dean Palmer	.25	.20	.10
12	Jeff Huson	.10	.08	.04
13	Rob Mauer	.10	.08	.04
14	Gary Redus	.10	.08	.04
15	Doug Dascenzo	.10	.08	.04
16	Charlie Liebrandt	.10	.08	.04
17	Tom Henke	.10	.08	.04
18	Manuel Lee	.10	.08	.04
19	Kenny Rogers	.10	.08	.04
20	Kevin Brown	.10	.08	.04
21	Juan Gonzalez	.75	.60	.30
22	Geno Petralli	.10	.08	.04
23	John Russell	.10	.08	.04
24	Robb Nen	.10	.08	.04
25	Julio Franco	.10	.08	.04
26	Rafael Palmeiro	.40	.30	.15
27	Todd Burns	.10	.08	.04
28	Jose Canseco	.40	.30	.15
29	Billy Ripken	.15	.11	.06
30	Dan Peltier	.10	.08	.04

1993 Topps Stadium Club Ultra Pro

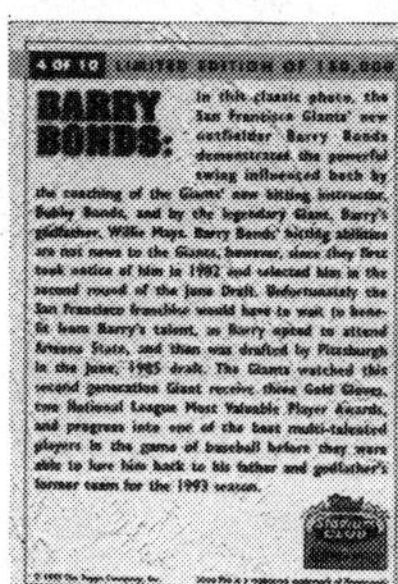

Special packages of plastic sheets and sleeves carrying the "Topps Stadium Club UltraPro" brand name included one of 10 special Stadium Club cards of Barry Bonds, Bobby Bonds and/or Willie Mays. Cards are typical UV-coated, gold-foil quality, but because the cards were not licensed by Major League Baseball, team logos were removed from the photos.

		MT	NR MT	EX
Complete Set (10):		16.00	12.00	6.50
Common Card:		1.00	.70	.40
1	Barry Bonds, Willie Mays, Bobby Bonds			
		1.00	.70	.40
2		3.00	2.25	1.25
3	Bobby Bonds	1.00	.70	.40
4	Barry Bonds	2.00	1.50	.80
5	Barry Bonds, Bobby Bonds	1.00	.70	.40
6	Willie Mays	3.00	2.25	1.25
7	Barry Bonds (business suit)	2.00	1.50	.80
8	Willie Mays, Bobby Bonds	1.50	1.25	.60
9	Willie Mays	3.00	2.25	1.25
10	Barry Bonds (tuxedo)	2.00	1.50	.80

1993 Topps Finest Promos

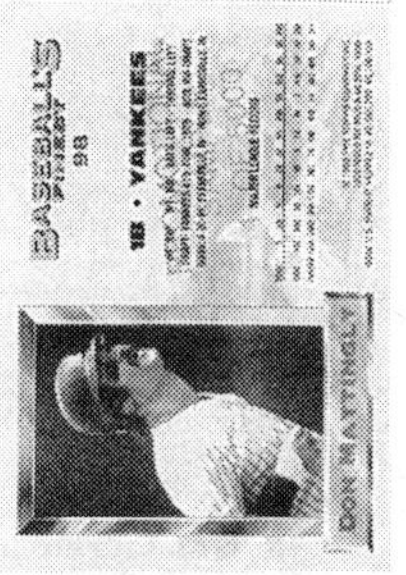

Debuting at the 1993 National Convention in Chicago, this three-card set introduced the hobby to Topps Finest baseball issue. While the promos are identical in high-tech format to the regular Finest cards issued later, including the same card numbers, there are differences in the promos; some subtle, some glaring. For instance, the Ryan and Alomar cards were issued in promo form in the "gray" style of the basic set. In the regularly issued set, those cards were in the green All-Star format. Each of the promos is overprinted in red on the back, "Promotional Sample 1 of 5000".

		MT	NR MT	EX
Complete Set (3):		120.00	90.00	47.50
Common Player:		25.00	18.50	10.00
88	Roberto Alomar	25.00	18.50	10.00
98	Don Mattingly	25.00	18.50	10.00
107	Nolan Ryan	75.00	56.00	30.00

A card number in parentheses () indicates the set is unnumbered.

1993 Topps Finest

This 199-card set uses a process of multi-color metallization; this chromium technology adds depth and dimension to the card. The set has a 33-card subset of All-Stars; these cards (Refractors) were also recreated with refracting foil using the metallization enhancement process. There is one refracting foil card in every nine packs. Packs have five cards. Each 18-count box contains a 5" by 7" version of one of the 199 players in the regular set. Each jumbo card was produced using the metallization process, and one of every six will be enhanced with special refracting foil.

		MT	NR MT	EX
Complete Set (199):		350.00	260.00	140.00
Common Player:		1.00	.70	.40
1	Dave Justice	8.00	6.00	3.25
2	Lou Whitaker	1.00	.70	.40
3	Bryan Harvey	1.00	.70	.40
4	Carlos Garcia	2.50	2.00	1.00
5	Sid Fernandez	1.00	.70	.40
6	Brett Butler	1.00	.70	.40
7	Scott Cooper	1.00	.70	.40
8	B.J. Surhoff	1.00	.70	.40
9	Steve Finley	1.00	.70	.40
10	Curt Schilling	1.00	.70	.40
11	Jeff Bagwell	9.00	6.75	3.50
12	Alex Cole	1.00	.70	.40
13	John Olerud	6.00	4.50	2.50
14	John Smiley	1.00	.70	.40
15	Bip Roberts	1.00	.70	.40
16	Albert Belle	9.00	6.75	3.50
17	Duane Ward	1.00	.70	.40
18	Alan Trammell	1.00	.70	.40
19	Andy Benes	1.50	1.25	.60
20	Reggie Sanders	2.00	1.50	.80
21	Todd Zeile	1.50	1.25	.60
22	Rick Aguilera	1.00	.70	.40
23	Dave Hollins	1.50	1.25	.60
24	Jose Rijo	1.00	.70	.40
25	Matt Williams	2.75	2.00	1.00
26	Sandy Alomar	1.00	.70	.40
27	Alex Fernandez	3.00	2.25	1.25
28	Ozzie Smith	4.50	3.50	1.75
29	Ramon Martinez	1.00	.70	.40
30	Bernie Williams	1.00	.70	.40
31	Gary Sheffield	3.50	2.75	1.50
32	Eric Karros	1.50	1.25	.60
33	Frank Viola	1.00	.70	.40
34	Kevin Young	1.50	1.25	.60
35	Ken Hill	1.00	.70	.40
36	Tony Fernandez	1.00	.70	.40
37	Tim Wakefield	1.00	.70	.40
38	John Kruk	2.00	1.50	.80
39	Chris Sabo	1.00	.70	.40
40	Marquis Grissom	2.00	1.50	.80
41	Glenn Davis	1.00	.70	.40
42	Jeff Montgomery	1.00	.70	.40
43	Kenny Lofton	5.00	3.75	2.00
44	John Burkett	1.00	.70	.40
45	Darryl Hamilton	1.00	.70	.40
46	Jim Abbott	2.00	1.50	.80
47	Ivan Rodriguez	3.00	2.25	1.25
48	Eric Young	1.50	1.25	.60
49	Mitch Williams	1.00	.70	.40
50	Harold Reynolds	1.00	.70	.40
51	Brian Harper	1.00	.70	.40
52	Rafael Palmeiro	3.00	2.25	1.25
53	Bret Saberhagen	1.00	.70	.40
54	Jeff Conine	2.50	2.00	1.00
55	Ivan Calderon	1.00	.70	.40
56	Juan Guzman	1.50	1.25	.60
57	Carlos Baerga	7.00	5.50	3.00
58	Charles Nagy	1.00	.70	.40
59	Wally Joyner	1.00	.70	.40
60	Charlie Hayes	1.00	.70	.40
61	Shane Mack	1.00	.70	.40
62	Pete Harnisch	1.00	.70	.40
63	George Brett	9.00	6.75	3.50
64	Lance Johnson	1.00	.70	.40
65	Ben McDonald	1.00	.70	.40
66	Bobby Bonilla	1.75	1.25	.70
67	Terry Steinbach	1.00	.70	.40
68	Ron Gant	2.00	1.50	.80
69	Doug Jones	1.00	.70	.40
70	Paul Molitor	5.00	3.75	2.00
71	Brady Anderson	1.00	.70	.40
72	Chuck Finley	1.00	.70	.40
73	Mark Grace	3.00	2.25	1.25
74	Mike Devereaux	1.00	.70	.40
75	Tony Phillips	1.00	.70	.40

76	Chuck Knoblauch	1.75	1.25	.70
77	Tony Gwynn	4.00	3.00	1.50
78	Kevin Appier	1.00	.70	.40
79	Sammy Sosa	3.00	2.25	1.25
80	Mickey Tettleton	1.00	.70	.40
81	Felix Jose	1.00	.70	.40
82	Mark Langston	1.00	.70	.40
83	Gregg Jefferies	2.50	2.00	1.00
84	Andre Dawson (AS)	3.50	2.75	1.50
85	Greg Maddux (AS)	6.00	4.50	2.50
86	Rickey Henderson (AS)	3.50	2.75	1.50
87	Tom Glavine (AS)	6.00	4.50	2.50
88	Roberto Alomar (AS)	8.00	6.00	3.25
89	Darryl Strawberry (AS)	1.00	.70	.40
90	Wade Boggs (AS)	3.00	2.25	1.25
91	Bo Jackson (AS)	3.00	2.25	1.25
92	Mark McGwire (AS)	3.00	2.25	1.25
93	Robin Ventura (AS)	4.50	3.50	1.75
94	Joe Carter (AS)	5.00	3.75	2.00
95	Lee Smith (AS)	1.00	.70	.40
96	Cal Ripken, Jr. (AS)	10.00	7.50	4.00
97	Larry Walker (AS)	2.00	1.50	.80
98	Don Mattingly (AS)	8.00	6.00	3.25
99	Jose Canseco (AS)	5.00	3.75	2.00
100	Dennis Eckersley (AS)	1.25	.90	.50
101	Terry Pendleton (AS)	1.50	1.25	.60
102	Frank Thomas (AS)	35.00	26.00	14.00
103	Barry Bonds (AS)	12.00	9.00	4.75
104	Roger Clemens	7.00	5.50	3.00
105	Ryne Sandberg (AS)	8.00	6.00	3.25
106	Fred McGriff (AS)	6.00	4.50	2.50
107	Nolan Ryan (AS)	40.00	30.00	15.00
108	Will Clark (AS)	6.00	4.50	2.50
109	Pat Listach (AS)	1.25	.90	.50
110	Ken Griffey, Jr. (AS)	35.00	26.00	14.00
111	Cecil Fielder (AS)	4.00	3.00	1.50
112	Kirby Puckett (AS)	9.00	6.75	3.50
113	Dwight Gooden (AS)	1.25	.90	.50
114	Barry Larkin (AS)	1.50	1.25	.60
115	David Cone (AS)	1.00	.70	.40
116	Juan Gonzalez (AS)	24.00	18.00	9.50
117	Kent Hrbek	1.00	.70	.40
118	Tim Wallach	1.00	.70	.40
119	Craig Biggio	1.00	.70	.40
120	Bobby Kelly	1.00	.70	.40
121	Greg Olson	1.00	.70	.40
122	Eddie Murray	3.00	2.25	1.25
123	Wil Cordero	2.50	2.00	1.00
124	Jay Buhner	1.00	.70	.40
125	Carlton Fisk	2.00	1.50	.80
126	Eric Davis	2.00	1.50	.80
127	Doug Drabek	1.00	.70	.40
128	Ozzie Guillen	1.00	.70	.40
129	John Wetteland	1.00	.70	.40
130	Andres Galarraga	3.00	2.25	1.25
131	Ken Caminiti	1.00	.70	.40
132	Tom Candiotti	1.00	.70	.40
133	Pat Borders	1.00	.70	.40
134	Kevin Brown	1.00	.70	.40
135	Travis Fryman	6.00	4.50	2.50
136	Kevin Mitchell	1.00	.70	.40
137	Greg Swindell	1.00	.70	.40
138	Benny Santiago	1.00	.70	.40
139	Reggie Jefferson	1.00	.70	.40
140	Chris Bosio	1.00	.70	.40
141	Deion Sanders	5.00	3.75	2.00
142	Scott Erickson	1.00	.70	.40
143	Howard Johnson	1.00	.70	.40
144	Orestes Destrade	1.00	.70	.40
145	Jose Guzman	1.00	.70	.40
146	Chad Curtis	1.50	1.25	.60
147	Cal Eldred	1.50	1.25	.60
148	Willie Greene	1.00	.70	.40
149	Tommy Greene	1.50	1.25	.60
150	Erik Hanson	1.00	.70	.40
151	Bob Welch	1.00	.70	.40
152	John Jaha	1.50	1.25	.60
153	Harold Baines	1.00	.70	.40
154	Randy Johnson	2.50	2.00	1.00
155	Al Martin	2.00	1.50	.80
156	J.T. Snow	2.50	2.00	1.00
157	Mike Mussina	6.00	4.50	2.50
158	Ruben Sierra	2.00	1.50	.80
159	Dean Palmer	2.00	1.50	.80
160	Steve Avery	6.00	4.50	2.50
161	Julio Franco	1.00	.70	.40
162	Dave Winfield	5.00	3.75	2.00
163	Tim Salmon	18.00	13.50	7.25
164	Tom Henke	1.00	.70	.40
165	Mo Vaughn	3.50	2.75	1.50
166	John Smoltz	2.00	1.50	.80
167	Danny Tartabull	1.00	.70	.40
168	Delino DeShields	2.00	1.50	.80
169	Charlie Hough	1.00	.70	.40
170	Paul O'Neill	1.00	.70	.40
171	Darren Daulton	3.00	2.25	1.25
172	Jack McDowell	3.00	2.25	1.25
173	Junior Felix	1.00	.70	.40
174	Jimmy Key	1.00	.70	.40
175	George Bell	1.00	.70	.40
176	Mike Stanton	1.00	.70	.40
177	Len Dykstra	4.00	3.00	1.50
178	Norm Charlton	1.00	.70	.40
179	Eric Anthony	1.00	.70	.40
180	Bob Dibble	1.00	.70	.40
181	Otis Nixon	1.00	.70	.40
182	Randy Myers	1.00	.70	.40
183	Tim Raines	1.00	.70	.40
184	Orel Hershiser	1.00	.70	.40
185	Andy Van Slyke	1.50	1.25	.60
186	*Mike Lansing*	2.50	2.00	1.00
187	Ray Lankford	1.00	.70	.40
188	Mike Morgan	1.00	.70	.40
189	Moises Alou	3.00	2.25	1.25
190	Edgar Martinez	1.00	.70	.40
191	John Franco	1.00	.70	.40
192	Robin Yount	6.00	4.50	2.50
193	Bob Tewksbury	1.00	.70	.40
194	Jay Bell	1.00	.70	.40
195	Luis Gonzalez	1.25	.90	.50
196	Dave Fleming	1.50	1.25	.60
197	Mike Greenwell	1.00	.70	.40
198	David Nied	3.00	2.25	1.25
199	Mike Piazza	35.00	26.00	14.00

1993 Topps Finest Refractors

This insert set features each of the cards from the regular Topps Finest set recreated with refracting foil using the metallization enhancement process. One refracting foil card was inserted in every nine packs, on average.

	MT	NR MT	EX
Complete Set (199):	9000.	6500.	3500.
Common Player:	20.00	15.00	8.00
Stars: 8X to 12X Finest price			

1993 Topps Finest Jumbo All-Stars

These 5" by 7" cards were produced using the metallization process. Each 18-count box contains one of the cards, while one of every six cards is enhanced with special refracting foil.

		MT	NR MT	EX
Complete Set (33):		750.00	560.00	300.00
Common Player (84-116):		12.50	9.50	5.00
84	Andre Dawson	12.50	9.50	5.00
85	Greg Maddux	20.00	15.00	8.00
86	Rickey Henderson	18.00	13.50	7.25
87	Tom Glavine	20.00	15.00	8.00
88	Roberto Alomar	32.00	24.00	13.00
89	Darryl Strawberry	12.50	9.50	5.00
90	Wade Boggs	15.00	11.00	6.00
91	Bo Jackson	20.00	15.00	8.00
92	Mark McGwire	17.50	13.00	7.00
93	Robin Ventura	20.00	15.00	8.00
94	Joe Carter	24.00	18.00	9.50
95	Lee Smith	12.50	9.50	5.00
96	Cal Ripken, Jr.	45.00	34.00	18.00
97	Larry Walker	12.50	9.50	5.00
98	Don Mattingly	32.00	24.00	13.00
99	Jose Canseco	17.50	13.00	7.00
100	Dennis Eckersley	12.50	9.50	5.00
101	Terry Pendleton	12.50	9.50	5.00
102	Frank Thomas	80.00	60.00	45.00
103	Barry Bonds	48.00	36.00	19.00
104	Roger Clemens	30.00	22.00	12.00
105	Ryne Sandberg	45.00	30.00	20.00
106	Fred McGriff	28.00	21.00	11.00
107	Nolan Ryan	85.00	60.00	45.00
108	Will Clark	25.00	15.00	10.00
109	Pat Listach	12.50	9.50	5.00
110	Ken Griffey, Jr.	70.00	50.00	25.00
111	Cecil Fielder	25.00	15.00	10.00
112	Kirby Puckett	40.00	30.00	20.00
113	Dwight Gooden	12.50	9.50	5.00
114	Barry Larkin	12.50	9.50	5.00
115	David Cone	12.50	9.50	5.00
116	Juan Gonzalez	65.00	49.00	26.00

1993 Topps Full Shot Super

Just as rivals Upper Deck and Donruss did, Topps issued a set of 21 oversized cards (3-1/2" by 5") that was available in retail outlets in packages that contained one of the large cards and two packs of regular issue Topps cards from the same year. The Topps Full Shot cards feature many of the top players in the game, and unlike the Upper Deck oversized cards, the Topps cards were not enlarged versions of existing cards but rather photos and a design that appeared only in this format.

		MT	NR MT	EX
Complete Set:		90.00	67.00	36.00
Common Player:		3.00	2.25	1.25
1	Frank Thomas	12.00	9.00	4.75
2	Ken Griffey, Jr.	12.00	9.00	4.75
3	Barry Bonds	8.00	6.00	3.25
4	Juan Gonzalez	9.00	6.75	3.50
5	Roberto Alomar	6.00	4.50	2.50
6	Mike Piazza	6.00	4.50	2.50
7	Tony Gwynn	4.00	3.00	1.50
8	Jeff Bagwell	4.00	3.00	1.50
9	Tim Salmon	6.00	4.50	2.50
10	John Olerud	4.00	3.00	1.50
11	Cal Ripken, Jr.	9.00	6.75	3.50
12	David McCarty	4.00	3.00	1.50
13	Darren Daulton	3.00	2.25	1.25
14	Carlos Baerga	5.00	3.75	2.00
15	Roger Clemens	4.00	3.00	1.50
16	John Kruk	3.00	2.25	1.25
17	Barry Larkin	3.00	2.25	1.25
18	Gary Sheffield	4.00	3.00	1.50
19	Tom Glavine	3.00	2.25	1.25
20	Andres Galarraga	4.00	3.00	1.50
21	Fred McGriff	4.00	3.00	1.50

1994 Topps Preview

Two different versions of this nine-card set exist. A cello-wrapped version, designated (a) in the checklist, was given away to dealers and the hobby press. A second version, designated (b), was included in 1993 Topps factory sets. It is currently unknown which version, if either, will become more valuable due to demand and perceived scarcity. Both versions are similar to the regular-issue '94 Topps cards, except for the sample notation on back.

		MT	NR MT	EX
Complete Set (a)(9):		7.50	5.75	3.00
Complete Set (b) (9):		7.50	5.75	3.00
Common Player (a):		.25	.20	.10
Common Player (b):		.25	.20	.10
2a	Barry Bonds (vertical format)	1.75	1.25	.70
2b	Barry Bonds (horizontal)	1.75	1.25	.70
6a	Jeff Tackett (full bat label visible)	.25	.20	.10
6b	Jeff Tackett (partial bat label)	.25	.20	.10
34a	Juan Gonzalez (green triangle behind "Juan")	1.50	1.25	.60
34b	Juan Gonzalez (brown triangle)	1.50	1.25	.60
225a	Matt Williams (green triangle behind "Matt")	.50	.40	.20

225b	Matt Williams (blue triangle)	.50	.40	.20
294a	Carlos Quintana (team/position yellow)	.25	.20	.10
294b	Carlos Quintana (team/position black)	.25	.20	.10
331a	Ken Lofton (team/position white)	.25	.20	.10
331b	Ken Lofton (team/position black)	.25	.20	.10
390a	Wade Boggs (team/position yellow)	.75	.60	.30
390b	Wade Boggs (team/position black)	.75	.60	.30
397a	George Brett (vertical format)	1.00	.70	.40
397b	George Brett (horizontal)	1.00	.70	.40
700a	Nolan Ryan (vertical format)	2.00	1.50	.80
700b	Nolan Ryan (horizontal)	2.00	1.50	.80

1994 Topps

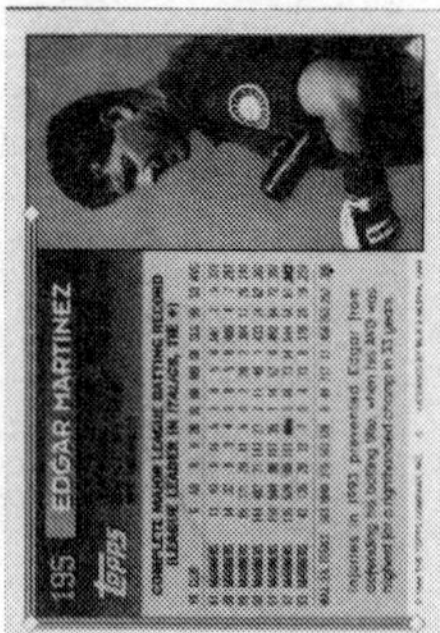

Once again released in two series, Topps basic baseball card for 1994 offers a standard mix of regular player cards, Future Stars, multi-player rookie cards and double-header All-Star cards. On the basic cards, the action player photo on front is framed in a home-plate shaped design. The player's name appears in script beneath the photo and a team color-coded strip at bottom carries the team and position designations. On back there is a player photo at the left or right end. A red box at top has biographical details while a marbled panel carries the stats and a career highlight. Cards are UV coated on each side. Inserts include a gold-enhanced card in every pack, plus random Black Gold cards.

	MT	NR MT	EX
Complete Set (792):	28.00	21.00	11.00
Complete Series 1 (396):	14.00	10.50	5.50
Complete Series 2 (396):	14.00	10.50	5.50
Common Player:	.04	.03	.02

1	Mike Piazza	1.50	1.25	.60
2	Bernie Williams	.04	.03	.02
3	Kevin Rogers	.04	.03	.02
4	Paul Carey	.04	.03	.02
5	Ozzie Guillen	.04	.03	.02
6	Derrick May	.04	.03	.02
7	Jose Mesa	.04	.03	.02
8	Todd Hundley	.04	.03	.02
9	Chris Haney	.04	.03	.02
10	John Olerud	.15	.11	.06
11	Andujar Cedeno	.04	.03	.02
12	John Smiley	.04	.03	.02
13	Phil Plantier	.04	.03	.02
14	Willie Banks	.04	.03	.02
15	Jay Bell	.04	.03	.02
16	Doug Henry	.04	.03	.02
17	Lance Blankenship	.04	.03	.02
18	Greg Harris	.04	.03	.02
19	Scott Livingstone	.04	.03	.02
20	Bryan Harvey	.04	.03	.02
21	Wil Cordero	.04	.03	.02
22	Roger Pavlik	.04	.03	.02
23	Mark Lemke	.04	.03	.02
24	Jeff Nelson	.04	.03	.02
25	Todd Zeile	.04	.03	.02
26	Billy Hatcher	.04	.03	.02
27	Joe Magrane	.04	.03	.02
28	Tony Longmire	.04	.03	.02
29	Omar Daal	.04	.03	.02
30	Kirt Manwaring	.04	.03	.02
31	Melido Perez	.04	.03	.02
32	Tim Hulett	.04	.03	.02
33	Jeff Schwarz	.04	.03	.02
34	Nolan Ryan	.40	.30	.15
35	Jose Guzman	.04	.03	.02
36	Felix Fermin	.04	.03	.02
37	Jeff Innis	.04	.03	.02
38	Brent Mayne	.04	.03	.02
39	Huck Flener	.04	.03	.02
40	Jeff Bagwell	.15	.11	.06
41	Kevin Wickander	.04	.03	.02
42	Ricky Gutierrez	.04	.03	.02
43	Pat Mahomes	.04	.03	.02
44	Jeff King	.04	.03	.02
45	Cal Eldred	.10	.08	.04
46	Craig Paquette	.04	.03	.02
47	Richie Lewis	.04	.03	.02
48	Tony Phillips	.04	.03	.02
49	Armando Reynoso	.04	.03	.02
50	Moises Alou	.08	.06	.03
51	Manuel Lee	.04	.03	.02
52	Otis Nixon	.04	.03	.02
53	*Billy Ashley*	.40	.30	.15
54	Mark Whiten	.04	.03	.02
55	Jeff Russell	.04	.03	.02
56	Chad Curtis	.04	.03	.02
57	*Kevin Stocker*	.50	.40	.20
58	Mike Jackson	.04	.03	.02
59	Matt Nokes	.04	.03	.02
60	Chris Bosio	.04	.03	.02
61	Damon Buford	.04	.03	.02
62	Tim Belcher	.04	.03	.02
63	Glenallen Hill	.04	.03	.02
64	Bill Wertz	.04	.03	.02
65	Eddie Murray	.04	.03	.02
66	Tom Gordon	.04	.03	.02
67	*Alex Gonzalez*	.50	.40	.20
68	Eddie Taubensee	.04	.03	.02
69	Jacob Brumfield	.04	.03	.02
70	Andy Benes	.04	.03	.02
71	Rich Becker	.04	.03	.02
72	Steve Cooke	.04	.03	.02
73	Billy Spiers	.04	.03	.02
74	Scott Brosius	.04	.03	.02
75	Alan Trammell	.04	.03	.02
76	Luis Aquino	.04	.03	.02
77	Jerald Clark	.04	.03	.02
78	Mel Rojas	.04	.03	.02
79	Billy Masse, Stanton Cameron, Tim Clark, Craig McClure	.04	.03	.02
80	Jose Canseco	.10	.08	.04
81	Greg McMichael	.10	.08	.04
82	Brian Turang	.04	.03	.02
83	Tom Urban	.04	.03	.02
84	Garret Anderson	.04	.03	.02
85	Tony Pena	.04	.03	.02
86	Ricky Jordan	.04	.03	.02
87	Jim Gott	.04	.03	.02
88	Pat Kelly	.04	.03	.02
89	Bud Black	.04	.03	.02
90	Robin Ventura	.10	.08	.04
91	Rick Sutcliffe	.04	.03	.02
92	Jose Bautista	.04	.03	.02
93	Bob Ojeda	.04	.03	.02
94	Phil Hiatt	.20	.15	.08
95	Tim Pugh	.04	.03	.02
96	Randy Knorr	.04	.03	.02
97	Todd Jones	.04	.03	.02
98	Ryan Thompson	.04	.03	.02
99	Tim Mauser	.04	.03	.02
100	Kirby Puckett	.20	.15	.08
101	Mark Dewey	.04	.03	.02
102	B.J. Surhoff	.04	.03	.02
103	Sterling Hitchcock	.04	.03	.02
104	Alex Arias	.04	.03	.02
105	David Wells	.04	.03	.02
106	Daryl Boston	.04	.03	.02
107	Mike Stanton	.04	.03	.02
108	Gary Redus	.04	.03	.02
109	Delino DeShields	.04	.03	.02
110	Lee Smith	.04	.03	.02
111	Greg Litton	.04	.03	.02
112	Frank Rodriguez	.10	.08	.04
113	Russ Springer	.04	.03	.02
114	Mitch Williams	.04	.03	.02
115	Eric Karros	.10	.08	.04
116	Jeff Brantley	.04	.03	.02
117	Jack Voight	.04	.03	.02
118	*Jason Bere*	.50	.40	.20
119	Kevin Roberson	.25	.20	.10
120	Jimmy Key	.04	.03	.02
121	Reggie Jefferson	.04	.03	.02
122	Jeremy Burnitz	.10	.08	.04
123	Billy Brewer	.04	.03	.02
124	Willie Canate	.04	.03	.02
125	Greg Swindell	.04	.03	.02
126	Hal Morris	.04	.03	.02
127	Brad Ausmus	.04	.03	.02
128	George Tsamis	.04	.03	.02
129	Denny Neagle	.04	.03	.02
130	Pat Listach	.10	.08	.04
131	Steve Karsay	.04	.03	.02
132	Bret Barberie	.04	.03	.02
133	Mark Leiter	.04	.03	.02
134	Greg Colbrunn	.04	.03	.02
135	David Nied	.10	.08	.04
136	Dean Palmer	.04	.03	.02
137	Steve Avery	.10	.08	.04
138	Bill Haselman	.04	.03	.02
139	Tripp Cromer	.04	.03	.02
140	Frank Viola	.04	.03	.02
141	Rene Gonzales	.04	.03	.02
142	Curt Schilling	.04	.03	.02
143	Tim Wallach	.04	.03	.02
144	Bobby Munoz	.04	.03	.02
145	Brady Anderson	.04	.03	.02
146	Rod Beck	.04	.03	.02
147	Mike LaValliere	.04	.03	.02
148	Greg Hibbard	.04	.03	.02
149	Kenny Lofton	.10	.08	.04
150	Doc Gooden	.04	.03	.02
151	Greg Gagne	.04	.03	.02
152	Ray McDavid	.04	.03	.02
153	Chris Donnels	.04	.03	.02
154	Dan Wilson	.04	.03	.02
155	Todd Stottlemyre	.04	.03	.02
156	David McCarty	.08	.06	.03
157	Paul Wagner	.04	.03	.02
158	Orlando Miller, Brandon Wilson, Derek Jeter, Mike Neal	.04	.03	.02
159	Mike Fetters	.04	.03	.02
160	Scott Lydy	.04	.03	.02
161	Darrell Whitmore	.15	.11	.06
162	Bob MacDonald	.04	.03	.02
163	Vinny Castilla	.04	.03	.02
164	Denis Boucher	.04	.03	.02
165	Ivan Rodriguez	.10	.08	.04
166	Ron Gant	.08	.06	.03
167	Tim Davis	.04	.03	.02
168	Steve Dixon	.04	.03	.02
169	Scott Fletcher	.04	.03	.02
170	Terry Mulholland	.04	.03	.02
171	Greg Myers	.04	.03	.02
172	Brett Butler	.04	.03	.02
173	Bob Wickman	.04	.03	.02
174	Dave Martinez	.04	.03	.02
175	Fernando Valenzuela	.04	.03	.02
176	Craig Grebeck	.04	.03	.02
177	Shawn Boskie	.04	.03	.02
178	Albie Lopez	.04	.03	.02
179	Butch Huskey	.04	.03	.02
180	George Brett	.15	.11	.06
181	Juan Guzman	.10	.08	.04
182	Eric Anthony	.04	.03	.02
183	Bob Dibble	.04	.03	.02
184	Craig Shipley	.04	.03	.02
185	Kevin Tapani	.04	.03	.02
186	Marcus Moore	.04	.03	.02
187	Graeme Lloyd	.10	.08	.04
188	Mike Bordick	.10	.08	.04
189	Chris Hammond	.04	.03	.02
190	Cecil Fielder	.10	.08	.04
191	Curtis Leskanic	.04	.03	.02
192	Lou Frazier	.04	.03	.02
193	Steve Dreyer	.04	.03	.02
194	Javier Lopez	.40	.30	.15
195	Edgar Martinez	.04	.03	.02
196	Allen Watson	.20	.15	.08
197	John Flaherty	.04	.03	.02
198	Kurt Stillwell	.04	.03	.02
199	Danny Jackson	.04	.03	.02
200	Cal Ripken	.25	.20	.10
201	Mike Bell	.04	.03	.02
202	*Alan Benes*	.15	.11	.06
203	Matt Farner	.04	.03	.02
204	*Jeff Granger*	.15	.11	.06
205	Brooks Kieschnick	.04	.03	.02
206	Jeremy Lee	.04	.03	.02
207	Charles Peterson, Andy Rice	.04	.03	.02
209	*Billy Wagner*	.10	.08	.04
210	Kelly Wunsch	.04	.03	.02
211	Tom Candiotti	.04	.03	.02
212	Domingo Jean	.10	.08	.04
213	John Burkett	.04	.03	.02
214	George Bell	.04	.03	.02
215	Dan Plesac	.04	.03	.02
216	Manny Ramirez	.20	.15	.08
217	Mike Maddux	.04	.03	.02
218	Kevin McReynolds	.04	.03	.02
219	Pat Borders	.04	.03	.02
220	Doug Drabek	.04	.03	.02
221	Larry Luebbers	.04	.03	.02
222	Trevor Hoffman	.04	.03	.02
223	Pat Meares	.04	.03	.02
224	Danny Miceli	.04	.03	.02
225	Greg Vaughn	.04	.03	.02
226	Scott Hemond	.04	.03	.02
227	Pat Rapp	.04	.03	.02
228	Kirk Gibson	.04	.03	.02
229	Lance Painter	.04	.03	.02
230	Larry Walker	.08	.06	.03
231	*Benji Gil*	.25	.20	.10
232	Mark Wohlers	.04	.03	.02
233	Rich Amaral	.06	.05	.02
234	Erik Pappas	.04	.03	.02
235	Scott Cooper	.04	.03	.02
236	Mike Butcher	.04	.03	.02
237	*Curtis Pride*, Shawn Green, Mark Sweeney, Eddie Davis	.20	.15	.08
238	Kim Batiste	.04	.03	.02
239	Paul Assenmacher	.04	.03	.02
240	Will Clark	.15	.11	.06
241	Jose Offerman	.04	.03	.02
242	Todd Frohwirth	.04	.03	.02
243	Tim Raines	.04	.03	.02
244	Rick Wilkins	.04	.03	.02
245	Bret Saberhagen	.04	.03	.02
246	Thomas Howard	.04	.03	.02
247	Stan Belinda	.04	.03	.02
248	Rickey Henderson	.10	.08	.04
249	Brian Williams	.04	.03	.02
250	Barry Larkin	.04	.03	.02
251	Jose Valentin	.04	.03	.02
252	Lenny Webster	.04	.03	.02
253	Blas Minor	.10	.08	.04
254	Tim Teufel	.04	.03	.02
255	Bobby Witt	.04	.03	.02
256	Walt Weiss	.04	.03	.02
257	Chad Kreuter	.04	.03	.02
258	Roberto Mejia	.10	.08	.04
259	Cliff Floyd	.50	.40	.20
260	Julio Franco	.04	.03	.02
261	Rafael Belliard	.04	.03	.02
262	Marc Newfield	.10	.08	.04
263	Gerald Perry	.04	.03	.02
264	Ken Ryan	.04	.03	.02
265	Chili Davis	.04	.03	.02
266	Dave West	.04	.03	.02
267	Royce Clayton	.04	.03	.02
268	Pedro Martinez	.10	.08	.04
269	Mark Hutton	.04	.03	.02
270	Frank Thomas	1.00	.70	.40
271	Brad Pennington	.04	.03	.02
272	Mike Harkey	.04	.03	.02
273	Sandy Alomar	.04	.03	.02
274	Dave Gallagher	.04	.03	.02
275	Wally Joyner	.04	.03	.02
276	Ricky Trlicek	.04	.03	.02
277	Al Osuna	.04	.03	.02
278	Calvin Reese	.04	.03	.02
279	Kevin Higgins	.04	.03	.02
280	Rick Aguilera	.04	.03	.02
281	Orlando Merced	.04	.03	.02
282	Mike Mohler	.04	.03	.02
283	John Jaha	.04	.03	.02
284	Robb Nen	.04	.03	.02
285	Travis Fryman	.10	.08	.04
286	Mark Thompson	.04	.03	.02

287	Mike Lansing	.10	.08	.04
288	Craig Lefferts	.04	.03	.02
289	Damon Berryhill	.04	.03	.02
290	Randy Johnson	.08	.06	.03
291	Jeff Reed	.04	.03	.02
292	Danny Darwin	.04	.03	.02
293	J.T. Snow	.40	.30	.15
294	Tyler Green	.04	.03	.02
295	Chris Hoiles	.04	.03	.02
296	Roger McDowell	.04	.03	.02
297	Spike Owen	.04	.03	.02
298	Salomon Torres	.10	.08	.04
299	Wilson Alvarez	.04	.03	.02
300	Ryne Sandberg	.20	.15	.08
301	Derek Lilliquist	.04	.03	.02
302	Howard Johnson	.04	.03	.02
303	Greg Cadaret	.04	.03	.02
304	Pat Hentgen	.04	.03	.02
305	Craig Biggio	.04	.03	.02
306	Scott Service	.04	.03	.02
307	Melvin Nieves	.04	.03	.02
308	Mike Trombley	.04	.03	.02
309	Carlos Garcia	.04	.03	.02
310	Robin Yount	.15	.11	.06
311	Marcos Armas	.04	.03	.02
312	Rich Rodriguez	.04	.03	.02
313	Justin Thompson	.04	.03	.02
314	Danny Sheaffer	.04	.03	.02
315	Ken Hill	.04	.03	.02
316	Chad Ogea, Duff Brumley, Terrell Wade, Chris Michalak	.04	.03	.02
317	Cris Carpenter	.04	.03	.02
318	Jeff Blauser	.04	.03	.02
319	Ted Power	.04	.03	.02
320	Ozzie Smith	.10	.08	.04
321	John Dopson	.04	.03	.02
322	Chris Turner	.04	.03	.02
323	Pete Incaviglia	.04	.03	.02
324	Alan Mills	.04	.03	.02
325	Jody Reed	.04	.03	.02
326	Rich Monteleone	.04	.03	.02
327	Mark Carreon	.04	.03	.02
328	Donn Pall	.04	.03	.02
329	Matt Walbeck	.04	.03	.02
330	Charles Nagy	.04	.03	.02
331	Jeff McKnight	.04	.03	.02
332	Jose Lind	.04	.03	.02
333	Mike Timlin	.04	.03	.02
334	Doug Jones	.04	.03	.02
335	Kevin Mitchell	.04	.03	.02
336	Luis Lopez	.04	.03	.02
337	Shane Mack	.04	.03	.02
338	Randy Tomlin	.04	.03	.02
339	Matt Mieske	.08	.06	.03
340	Mark McGwire	.10	.08	.04
341	Nigel Wilson	.10	.08	.04
342	Danny Gladden	.04	.03	.02
343	Mo Sanford	.04	.03	.02
344	Sean Berry	.04	.03	.02
345	Kevin Brown	.04	.03	.02
346	Greg Olson	.04	.03	.02
347	Dave Magadan	.04	.03	.02
348	Rene Arocha	.10	.08	.04
349	Carlos Quintana	.04	.03	.02
350	Jim Abbott	.04	.03	.02
351	Gary DiSarcina	.04	.03	.02
352	Ben Rivera	.04	.03	.02
353	Carlos Hernandez	.04	.03	.02
354	Darren Lewis	.04	.03	.02
355	Harold Reynolds	.04	.03	.02
356	Scott Ruffcorn	.04	.03	.02
357	Mark Gubicza	.04	.03	.02
358	Paul Sorrento	.04	.03	.02
359	Anthony Young	.04	.03	.02
360	Mark Grace	.08	.06	.03
361	Rob Butler	.04	.03	.02
362	Kevin Bass	.04	.03	.02
363	Eric Helfand	.04	.03	.02
364	Derek Bell	.04	.03	.02
365	Scott Erickson	.04	.03	.02
366	Al Martin	.10	.08	.04
367	Ricky Bones	.04	.03	.02
368	Jeff Branson	.04	.03	.02
369	Luis Ortiz, David Bell, Jason Giambi, George Arias	.04	.03	.02
370a	Benny Santiago	.04	.03	.02
370b	Mark McLemore (originally checklisted as #379)	.04	.03	.02
371	John Doherty	.04	.03	.02
372	Joe Girardi	.04	.03	.02
373	Tim Scott	.04	.03	.02
374	Marvin Freeman	.04	.03	.02
375	Deion Sanders	.10	.08	.04
376	Roger Salkeld	.04	.03	.02
377	Bernard Gilkey	.04	.03	.02
378	Tony Fossas	.04	.03	.02
380	Darren Daulton	.04	.03	.02
381	Chuck Finley	.04	.03	.02
382	Mitch Webster	.04	.03	.02
383	Gerald Williams	.04	.03	.02
384	Frank Thomas, Fred McGriff	1.00	.70	.40
385	Roberto Alomar, Robby Thompson	.25	.20	.10
386	Wade Boggs, Matt Williams	.10	.08	.04
387	Cal Ripken, Jeff Blauser	.20	.15	.08
388	Ken Griffey Jr., Len Dykstra	.60	.45	.25
389	Juan Gonzalez, David Justice	.60	.45	.25
390	Albert Belle, Barry Bonds	.20	.15	.08
391	Mike Stanley, Mike Piazza	.04	.03	.02
392	Jack McDowell, Greg Maddux	.08	.06	.03
393	Jimmy Key, Tom Glavine	.04	.03	.02
394	Jeff Montgomery, Randy Myers	.04	.03	.02
395	Checklist 1	.04	.03	.02
396	Checklist 2	.04	.03	.02
397	Tim Salmon	.75	.60	.30
398	Todd Benzinger	.04	.03	.02
399	Frank Castillo	.04	.03	.02
400	Ken Griffey, Jr.	1.00	.70	.40
401	John Kruk	.05	.04	.02
402	Dave Telgheder	.05	.04	.02
403	Gary Gaetti	.04	.03	.02
404	Jim Edmonds	.04	.03	.02
405	Don Slaught	.04	.03	.02
406	Jose Oquendo	.04	.03	.02
407	Bruce Ruffin	.04	.03	.02
408	Phil Clark	.04	.03	.02
409	Joe Klink	.04	.03	.02
410	Lou Whitaker	.04	.03	.02
411	Kevin Seitzer	.04	.03	.02
412	Darrin Fletcher	.04	.03	.02
413	Kenny Rogers	.04	.03	.02
414	Bill Pecota	.04	.03	.02
415	Dave Fleming	.04	.03	.02
416	Luis Alicea	.06	.05	.02
417	Paul Quantrill	.05	.04	.02
418	Damion Easley	.07	.05	.03
419	Wes Chamberlain	.04	.03	.02
420	Harold Baines	.04	.03	.02
421	Scott Radinsky	.04	.03	.02
422	Rey Sanchez	.04	.03	.02
423	Junior Ortiz	.04	.03	.02
424	Jeff Kent	.05	.04	.02
425	Brian McRae	.04	.03	.02
426	Ed Sprague	.04	.03	.02
427	Tom Edens	.04	.03	.02
428	Willie Greene	.05	.04	.02
429	Bryan Hickerson	.04	.03	.02
430	Dave Winfield	.08	.06	.03
431	Pedro Astacio	.05	.04	.02
432	Mike Gallego	.04	.03	.02
433	Dave Burba	.04	.03	.02
434	Bob Walk	.04	.03	.02
435	Darryl Hamilton	.04	.03	.02
436	Vince Horsman	.05	.04	.02
437	Bob Natal	.04	.03	.02
438	Mike Henneman	.04	.03	.02
439	Willie Blair	.04	.03	.02
440	Denny Martinez	.04	.03	.02
441	Dan Peltier	.06	.05	.02
442	Tony Tarasco	.20	.15	.08
443	John Cummings	.04	.03	.02
444	Geronimo Pena	.04	.03	.02
445	Aaron Sele	.40	.30	.15
446	Stan Javier	.04	.03	.02
447	Mike Williams	.04	.03	.02
448	1994 Prospects-1B	.50	.40	.20
449	Jim Poole	.04	.03	.02
450	Carlos Baerga	.20	.15	.08
451	Bob Scanlan	.05	.04	.02
452	Lance Johnson	.04	.03	.02
453	Eric Hillman	.04	.03	.02
454	Keith Miller	.04	.03	.02
455	Dave Stewart	.05	.04	.02
456	Pete Harnisch	.04	.03	.02
457	Roberto Kelly	.05	.04	.02
458	Tim Worrell	.04	.03	.02
459	Pedro Munoz	.04	.03	.02
460	Orel Hershiser	.05	.04	.02
461	Randy Velarde	.04	.03	.02
462	Trevor Wilson	.04	.03	.02
463	Jerry Goff	.04	.03	.02
464	Bill Wegman	.04	.03	.02
465	Dennis Eckersley	.05	.04	.02
466	Jeff Conine	.05	.04	.02
467	Joe Boever	.04	.03	.02
468	Dante Bichette	.05	.04	.02
469	Jeff Shaw	.04	.03	.02
470	Rafael Palmeiro	.05	.04	.02
471	*Phil Leftwich*	.10	.08	.04
472	Jay Buhner	.04	.03	.02
473	Bob Tewksbury	.04	.03	.02
474	Tim Naehring	.08	.06	.03
475	Tom Glavine	.15	.11	.06
476	Dave Hollins	.06	.05	.02
477	Arthur Rhodes	.05	.04	.02
478	Joey Cora	.04	.03	.02
479	Mike Morgan	.04	.03	.02
480	Albert Belle	.15	.11	.06
481	John Franco	.04	.03	.02
482	Hipolito Pichardo	.04	.03	.02
483	Duane Ward	.04	.03	.02
484	Luis Gonzalez	.04	.03	.02
485	Joe Oliver	.04	.03	.02
486	Wally Whitehurst	.04	.03	.02
487	Mike Benjamin	.04	.03	.02
488	Eric Davis	.05	.04	.02
489	Scott Kamieniecki	.05	.04	.02
490	Kent Hrbek	.04	.03	.02
491	*John Hope*	.15	.11	.06
492	Jesse Orosco	.04	.03	.02
493	Troy Neel	.05	.04	.02
494	Ryan Bowen	.06	.05	.02
495	Mickey Tettleton	.04	.03	.02
496	Chris Jones	.04	.03	.02
497	John Wetteland	.04	.03	.02
498	David Hulse	.05	.04	.02
499	Greg Maddux	.20	.15	.08
500	Bo Jackson	.08	.06	.03
501	Donovan Osborne	.04	.03	.02
502	Mike Greenwell	.04	.03	.02
503	Steve Frey	.04	.03	.02
504	Jim Eisenreich	.04	.03	.02
505	Robby Thompson	.04	.03	.02
506	Leo Gomez	.04	.03	.02
507	Dave Staton	.04	.03	.02
508	Wayne Kirby	.05	.04	.02
509	Tim Bogar	.05	.04	.02
510	David Cone	.04	.03	.02
511	Devon White	.04	.03	.02
512	Xavier Hernandez	.04	.03	.02
513	Tim Costo	.04	.03	.02
514	Gene Harris	.04	.03	.02
515	Jack McDowell	.06	.05	.02
516	Kevin Gross	.04	.03	.02
517	Scott Leius	.04	.03	.02
518	Lloyd McClendon	.04	.03	.02
519	*Alex Diaz*	.08	.06	.03
520	Wade Boggs	.12	.09	.05
521	Bob Welch	.04	.03	.02
522	Henry Cotto	.04	.03	.02
523	Mike Moore	.04	.03	.02
524	Tim Laker	.04	.03	.02
525	Andres Galarraga	.05	.04	.02
526	Jamie Moyer	.04	.03	.02
527	1994 Prospects-2B	.20	.15	.08
528	Sid Bream	.04	.03	.02
529	Erik Hanson	.04	.03	.02
530	Ray Lankford	.05	.04	.02
531	Rob Deer	.04	.03	.02
532	Rod Correia	.04	.03	.02
533	Roger Mason	.04	.03	.02
534	Mike Devereaux	.04	.03	.02
535	Jeff Montgomery	.04	.03	.02
536	Dwight Smith	.04	.03	.02
537	Jeremy Hernandez	.04	.03	.02
538	Ellis Burks	.05	.04	.02
539	Bobby Jones	.15	.11	.06
540	Paul Molitor	.20	.15	.08
541	Jeff Juden	.04	.03	.02
542	Chris Sabo	.04	.03	.02
543	Larry Casian	.04	.03	.02
544	Jeff Gardner	.05	.04	.02
545	Ramon Martinez	.04	.03	.02
546	Paul O'Neill	.04	.03	.02
547	Steve Hosey	.04	.03	.02
548	Dave Nilsson	.04	.03	.02
549	Ron Darling	.04	.03	.02
550	Matt Williams	.05	.04	.02
551	Jack Armstrong	.04	.03	.02
552	Bill Krueger	.04	.03	.02
553	Freddie Benavides	.04	.03	.02
554	Jeff Fassero	.05	.04	.02
555	Chuck Knoblauch	.05	.04	.02
556	Guillermo Velasquez	.04	.03	.02
557	Joel Johnston	.04	.03	.02
558	Tom Lampkin	.04	.03	.02
559	Todd Van Poppel	.05	.04	.02
560	Gary Sheffield	.06	.05	.02
561	Skeeter Barnes	.05	.04	.02
562	Darren Holmes	.04	.03	.02
563	John Vander Wal	.04	.03	.02
564	Mike Ignasiak	.04	.03	.02
565	Fred McGriff	.15	.11	.06
566	Luis Polonia	.04	.03	.02
567	Mike Perez	.04	.03	.02
568	John Valentin	.04	.03	.02
569	Mike Felder	.04	.03	.02
570	Tommy Greene	.04	.03	.02
571	David Segui	.04	.03	.02
572	Roberto Hernandez	.04	.03	.02
573	Steve Wilson	.04	.03	.02
574	Willie McGee	.04	.03	.02
575	Randy Myers	.04	.03	.02
576	Darrin Jackson	.05	.04	.02
577	Eric Plunk	.04	.03	.02
578	Mike MacFarlane	.04	.03	.02
579	Doug Brocail	.04	.03	.02
580	Steve Finley	.04	.03	.02
581	John Roper	.04	.03	.02
582	Danny Cox	.04	.03	.02
583	Chip Hale	.05	.04	.02
584	Scott Bullett	.08	.06	.03
585	Kevin Reimer	.04	.03	.02
586	Brent Gates	.10	.08	.04
587	Matt Turner	.05	.04	.02
588	Rich Rowland	.05	.04	.02
589	Kent Bottenfield	.04	.03	.02
590	Marquis Grissom	.07	.05	.03
591	Doug Strange	.04	.03	.02
592	Jay Howell	.04	.03	.02
593	Omar Vizquel	.04	.03	.02
594	Rheal Cormier	.04	.03	.02
595	Andre Dawson	.06	.05	.02
596	Hilly Hathaway	.05	.04	.02
597	Todd Pratt	.04	.03	.02
598	Mike Mussina	.30	.25	.12
599	Alex Fernandez	.06	.05	.02
600	Don Mattingly	.25	.20	.10
601	Frank Thomas (Stat Twins)	.75	.60	.30
602	Ryne Sandberg (Stat Twins)	.10	.08	.04
603	Wade Boggs (Stat Twins)	.08	.06	.03
604	Cal Ripken, Jr. (Stat Twins)	.30	.25	.12
605	Barry Bonds (Stat Twins)	.30	.25	.12
606	Ken Griffey, Jr. (Stat Twins)	.75	.60	.30
607	Kirby Puckett (Stat Twins)	.25	.20	.10
608	Darren Daulton (Stat Twins)	.06	.05	.02
609	Paul Molitor (Stat Twins)	.10	.08	.04
610	Terry Steinbach	.04	.03	.02
611	Todd Worrell	.04	.03	.02
612	Jim Thome	.20	.15	.08
613	Chuck McElroy	.04	.03	.02
614	John Habyan	.04	.03	.02
615	Sid Fernandez	.04	.03	.02
616	1994 Prospects-Of	.50	.40	.20
617	Steve Bedrosian	.04	.03	.02
618	Rob Ducey	.04	.03	.02
619	Tom Browning	.04	.03	.02
620	Tony Gwynn	.15	.11	.06
621	Carl Willis	.04	.03	.02
622	Kevin Young	.05	.04	.02
623	Rafael Novoa	.05	.04	.02
624	Jerry Browne	.04	.03	.02
625	Charlie Hough	.04	.03	.02
626	Chris Gomez	.04	.03	.02
627	Steve Reed	.04	.03	.02
628	Kirk Rueter	.25	.20	.10
629	Matt Whiteside	.04	.03	.02
630	Dave Justice	.25	.20	.10
631	Brad Holman	.04	.03	.02
632	Brian Jordan	.05	.04	.02
633	Scott Bankhead	.04	.03	.02
634	Torey Lovullo	.04	.03	.02
635	Len Dykstra	.06	.05	.02
636	Ben McDonald	.05	.04	.02

637	Steve Howe	.04	.03	.02
638	Jose Vizcaino	.04	.03	.02
639	Bill Swift	.04	.03	.02
640	Darryl Strawberry	.06	.05	.02
641	Steve Farr	.04	.03	.02
642	Tom Kramer	.04	.03	.02
643	Joe Orsulak	.04	.03	.02
644	Tom Henke	.04	.03	.02
645	Joe Carter	.15	.11	.06
646	Ken Caminiti	.04	.03	.02
647	Reggie Sanders	.06	.05	.02
648	Andy Ashby	.04	.03	.02
649	Derek Parks	.05	.04	.02
650	Andy Van Slyke	.04	.03	.02
651	Juan Bell	.04	.03	.02
652	Roger Smithberg	.04	.03	.02
653	Chuck Carr	.04	.03	.02
654	Bill Gullickson	.04	.03	.02
655	Charlie Hayes	.04	.03	.02
656	Chris Nabholz	.04	.03	.02
657	Karl Rhodes	.05	.04	.02
658	Pete Smith	.04	.03	.02
659	Bret Boone	.05	.04	.02
660	Gregg Jefferies	.06	.05	.02
661	Bob Zupcic	.04	.03	.02
662	Steve Sax	.04	.03	.02
663	Mariano Duncan	.04	.03	.02
664	Jeff Tackett	.04	.03	.02
665	Mark Langston	.04	.03	.02
666	Steve Buechele	.04	.03	.02
667	Candy Maldonado	.04	.03	.02
668	Woody Williams	.04	.03	.02
669	Tim Wakefield	.04	.03	.02
670	Danny Tartabull	.05	.04	.02
671	Charlie O'Brien	.04	.03	.02
672	Felix Jose	.04	.03	.02
673	Bobby Ayala	.04	.03	.02
674	Scott Servais	.04	.03	.02
675	Roberto Alomar	.25	.20	.10
676	Pedro Martinez	.05	.04	.02
677	Eddie Guardado	.04	.03	.02
678	Mark Lewis	.04	.03	.02
679	Jaime Navarro	.04	.03	.02
680	Ruben Sierra	.05	.04	.02
681	Rick Renteria	.04	.03	.02
682	Storm Davis	.04	.03	.02
683	Cory Snyder	.04	.03	.02
684	Ron Karkovice	.04	.03	.02
685	Juan Gonzalez	.75	.60	.30
686	1994 Prospects-C	.75	.60	.30
687	John Smoltz	.05	.04	.02
688	Brian Dorsett	.05	.04	.02
689	Omar Olivares	.04	.03	.02
690	Mo Vaughn	.06	.05	.02
691	Joe Grahe	.04	.03	.02
692	Mickey Morandini	.04	.03	.02
693	Tino Martinez	.04	.03	.02
694	Brian Barnes	.04	.03	.02
695	Mike Stanley	.04	.03	.02
696	Mark Clark	.04	.03	.02
697	Dave Hansen	.04	.03	.02
698	Willie Wilson	.04	.03	.02
699	Pete Schourek	.04	.03	.02
700	Barry Bonds	.40	.30	.15
701	Kevin Appier	.04	.03	.02
702	Tony Fernandez	.04	.03	.02
703	Darryl Kile	.04	.03	.02
704	Archi Cianfrocco	.04	.03	.02
705	Jose Rijo	.04	.03	.02
706	Brian Harper	.04	.03	.02
707	Zane Smith	.04	.03	.02
708	Dave Henderson	.04	.03	.02
709	Angel Miranda	.04	.03	.02
710	Orestes Destrade	.04	.03	.02
711	Greg Gohr	.04	.03	.02
712	Eric Young	.04	.03	.02
713	1994 Prospects-Rel	.15	.11	.06
714	Tim Spehr	.04	.03	.02
715	Hank Aaron	.50	.40	.20
716	Nate Minchey	.04	.03	.02
717	Mike Blowers	.04	.03	.02
718	Kent Mercker	.04	.03	.02
719	Tom Pagnozzi	.04	.03	.02
720	Roger Clemens	.20	.15	.08
721	Eduardo Perez	.15	.11	.06
722	Milt Thompson	.04	.03	.02
723	Gregg Olson	.04	.03	.02
724	Kirk McCaskill	.04	.03	.02
725	Sammy Sosa	.05	.04	.02
726	Alvaro Espinoza	.04	.03	.02
727	Henry Rodriguez	.05	.04	.02
728	Jim Leyritz	.04	.03	.02
729	Steve Scarsone	.04	.03	.02
730	Bobby Bonilla	.06	.05	.02
731	Chris Gwynn	.04	.03	.02
732	Al Leiter	.04	.03	.02
733	Bip Roberts	.04	.03	.02
734	Mark Portugal	.04	.03	.02
735	Terry Pendleton	.05	.04	.02
736	Dave Valle	.04	.03	.02
737	Paul Kilgus	.04	.03	.02
738	Greg Harris	.04	.03	.02
739	*Jon Ratliff*	.20	.15	.08
740	*Kirk Presley*	.60	.45	.25
741	*Josue Estrada*	.15	.11	.06
742	*Wayne Gomes*	.25	.20	.10
743	*Pat Watkins*	.15	.11	.06
744	*Jamey Wright*	.25	.20	.10
745	*Jay Powell*	.15	.11	.06
746	*Ryan McGuire*	.25	.20	.10
747	*Marc Barcelo*	.10	.08	.04
748	*Sloan Smith*	.15	.11	.06
749	*John Wasin*	.15	.11	.06
750	Marc Valdes	.10	.08	.04
751	*Dan Ehler*	.10	.08	.04
752	*Andre King*	.30	.25	.12
753	*Greg Keagle*	.20	.15	.08
754	*Jason Myers*	.10	.08	.04
755	*Dax Winslett*	.10	.08	.04
756	*Casey Whitten*	.15	.11	.06
757	*Tony Fuduric*	.12	.09	.05
758	*Greg Norton*	.10	.08	.04
759	*Jeff D'Amico*	.25	.20	.10
760	*Ryan Hancock*	.15	.11	.06
761	*David Cooper*	.12	.09	.05
762	*Kevin Orie*	.25	.20	.10
763	J. O'Donoghue, M. Oquist	.10	.08	.04
764	C. Bailey, S. Hatteberg	.12	.09	.05
765	M. Holzemer, P. Swingle	.10	.08	.04
766	James Baldwin, R. Bolton	.40	.30	.15
767	*J. DiPoto*, J. Tavarez	.25	.20	.10
768	D. Bautista, S. Bergman	.10	.08	.04
769	Bob Hamelin, J. Vitiello	.20	.15	.08
770	MKiefer, T. O'Leary	.10	.08	.04
771	D. Hocking, O. Munoz	.15	.11	.06
772	Russ Davis, B Taylor	.20	.15	.08
773	K. Abbott, Miguel Jimenez	.20	.15	.08
774	K. King, E. Plantenberg	.15	.11	.06
775	J. Shave, D. Wilson	.15	.11	.06
776	D. Cedeno, P. Spoljaric	.10	.08	.04
777	Chipper Jones, Ryan Klesko	.50	.40	.20
778	Steve Trachsel, Turk Wendell	.30	.25	.12
779	J. Ruffin, J. Spradlin	.08	.06	.03
780	J. Bates, J. Burke	.12	.09	.05
781	C. Everett, D. Weathers	.12	.09	.05
782	Gary Mota, James Mouton	.50	.40	.20
783	Raul Mondesi, B. Van Ryn	.60	.45	.25
784	Gabe White, Rondell White	.35	.25	.14
785	Brook Fordyce, B. Pulsipher	.10	.08	.04
786	K. Foster, G. Schall	.15	.11	.06
787	Rich Aude, Midre Cummings	.50	.40	.20
788	B. Barber, R. Batchelor	.10	.08	.04
789	B. Johnson, S. Sanders	.10	.08	.04
790	R. Faneyte, J.R. Phillips	.25	.20	.10
791	Checklist 3 X	.04	.03	.02
792	Checklist 4 X	.04	.03	.02

1994 Topps Gold

Gold-foil highlighted versions of each of Topps' 1994 baseball cards were produced as pack inserts in both Series I and Series II. The gold cards are identical to the regular-issue Topps cards except for the "Topps Gold" logo at top and the use of gold foil for the player's name at bottom. Gold cards were packaged one per foil pack on average, with every fourth pack containing two gold cards. Topps rack packs have three gold cards.

	MT	NR MT	EX
Complete Set (792):	100.00	75.00	40.00
Common Player:	.25	.20	.10

Star cards are valued at 5-10X

1994 Topps Black Gold

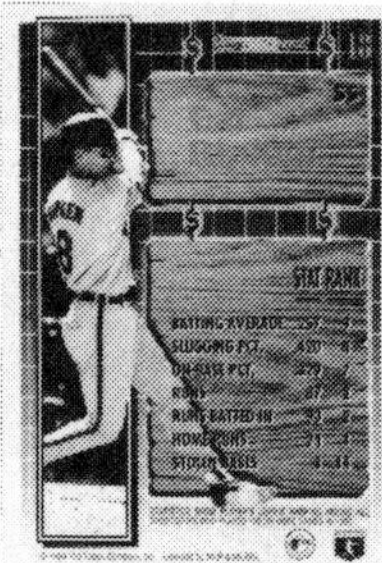

The popular Black Gold insert set returned for 1994 randomly included in all types of Topps packaging. Single Black Gold cards, as well as cards redeemable by mail for 11, 22 or 44 Black Gold cards, were produced. The basic single-player card features an action photo, the background of which has been almost completely blacked out. At top is the team name in black letters against a gold prismatic foil background. The player name at bottom is in the same gold foil. A black, white and yellow "Topps Black Gold" logo appears under the team-name cartouche, and the same typographical logo appears in black in the background of the gold-foil devices. A white border completes the front design. On back, bordered in white, is a background which fades from black at top to gray at the bottom and is gridded with white lines. To the left is another color player action photo. The Topps Black Gold logo and player name appear in gold foil; the latter printed on a simulated wooden board "hanging" from the top of the card. A second hanging plank has player stats and rankings from the 1993 season. The multi-card redemption cards come in two versions. The type found in packs has all 11, 22 or 44 of the cards pictured on front in miniature and redemption details printed on back. A second version, returned with the single cards won, has on back a checklist and non-redemption notice. Stated odds of winning Black Gold cards were one in 72 packs for single cards; one in 180 packs for 11-card winners and one in 720 packs (one per foil-pack case) for a 22-card winner.

		MT	NR MT	EX
Complete Set (44):		30.00	22.00	12.00
Common Player:		.25	.20	.10
1	Roberto Alomar	1.25	.90	.50
2	Carlos Baerga	1.00	.75	.40
3	Albert Belle	1.25	.90	.50
4	Joe Carter	.75	.60	.30
5	Cecil Fielder	.50	.40	.20
6	Travis Fryman	.60	.45	.25
7	Juan Gonzalez	2.50	2.00	1.00
8	Ken Griffey, Jr.	4.00	3.00	1.50
9	Chris Hoiles	.25	.20	.10
10	Randy Johnson	.25	.20	.10
11	Kenny Lofton	.50	.40	.20
12	Jack McDowell	.35	.25	.14
13	Paul Molitor	.75	.60	.30
14	Jeff Montgomery	.25	.20	.10
15	John Olerud	1.00	.75	.40
16	Rafael Palmeiro	.60	.45	.25
17	Kirby Puckett	1.25	.90	.50
18	Cal Ripken, Jr.	1.25	.90	.50
19	Tim Salmon	2.00	1.50	.80
20	Mike Stanley	.25	.20	.10
21	Frank Thomas	4.00	3.00	1.50
22	Robin Ventura	.75	.60	.30
23	Jeff Bagwell	1.00	.75	.40
24	Jay Bell	.25	.20	.10
25	Craig Biggio	.40	.30	.15
26	Jeff Blauser	.25	.20	.10
27	Barry Bonds	1.50	1.25	.60
28	Darren Daulton	.50	.40	.20
29	Len Dykstra	.60	.45	.25
30	Andres Galarraga	.40	.30	.15
31	Ron Gant	.60	.45	.25
32	Tom Glavine	.75	.60	.30
33	Mark Grace	.60	.45	.25
34	Marquis Grissom	.50	.40	.20
35	Gregg Jefferies	.50	.40	.20
36	Dave Justice	1.25	.90	.50
37	John Kruk	.50	.40	.20
38	Greg Maddux	.75	.60	.30
39	Fred McGriff	.75	.60	.30
40	Randy Myers	.25	.20	.10
41	Mike Piazza	3.00	2.25	1.25
42	Sammy Sosa	.60	.45	.25
43	Robby Thompson	.25	.20	.10
44	Matt Williams	.50	.40	.20
----	Winner A	7.50	5.50	3.00
----	Winner B	7.50	5.50	3.00
----	Winner C	5.00	3.75	2.00
----	Winner D	5.00	3.75	2.00
----	Winner A/B	14.00	10.50	5.50
----	Winner C/D	9.00	6.75	3.50
----	Winner A/B/C/D	18.00	13.50	7.25

1994 Topps Finest Promos

Forty cards premiering the upcoming 1994 Topps Finest set were issued as a random insert in packs of Topps Series II regular-issue cards. The cards are in the same format as the regular-issue Finest cards and share the same card numbers. On back there is a red "Pre-Production" notice printed diagonally over the statistics.

		MT	NR MT	EX
Complete Set (40):		140.00	105.00	55.00
Common Player:		2.50	2.00	1.00
22	Deion Sanders	8.00	6.00	3.25
23	Jose Offerman	2.50	2.00	1.00
26	Alex Fernandez	2.50	2.00	1.00
31	Steve Finley	2.50	2.00	1.00
35	Andre Galarraga	3.00	2.25	1.25
43	Reggie Sanders	3.00	2.25	1.25
47	Dave Hollins	3.00	2.25	1.25
52	David Cone	2.50	2.00	1.00
59	Dante Bichette	3.00	2.25	1.25
61	Orlando Merced	2.50	2.00	1.00
62	Brian McRae	2.50	2.00	1.00
66	Mike Mussina	12.00	9.00	4.75
76	Mike Stanley	2.50	2.00	1.00
78	Mark McGwire	3.00	2.25	1.25
79	Pat Listach	2.50	2.00	1.00
82	Dwight Gooden	2.50	2.00	1.00
84	Phil Plantier	2.50	2.00	1.00
90	Jeff Russell	2.50	2.00	1.00
92	Gregg Jefferies	2.50	2.00	1.00
93	Jose Guzman	2.50	2.00	1.00
100	John Smoltz	2.50	2.00	1.00
102	Jim Thome	5.00	3.75	2.00
121	Moises Alou	3.50	2.75	1.50
125	Devon White	2.50	2.00	1.00
126	Ivan Rodriguez	3.00	2.25	1.25
130	Dave Magadan	2.50	2.00	1.00
136	Ozzie Smith	10.00	7.50	4.00
141	Chris Hoiles	2.50	2.00	1.00
149	Jim Abbott	3.00	2.25	1.25
151	Bill Swift	2.50	2.00	1.00
154	Edgar Martinez	2.50	2.00	1.00
157	J.T. Snow	2.50	2.00	1.00
159	Alan Trammell	2.50	2.00	1.00
163	Roberto Kelly	2.50	2.00	1.00
166	Scott Erickson	2.50	2.00	1.00
168	Scott Cooper	2.50	2.00	1.00
169	Rod Beck	2.50	2.00	1.00
177	Dean Palmer	2.50	2.00	1.00
182	Todd Van Poppel	2.50	2.00	1.00
185	Paul Sorrento	2.50	2.00	1.00

1994 Topps Finest Series I

		MT	NR MT	EX
Complete Set (220):		175.00	130.00	70.00
Common Player:		.75	.60	.30
1	Mike Piazza	15.00	11.00	6.00
2	Kevin Stocker	1.00	.75	.40
3	Greg McMichael	.75	.60	.30
4	Jeff Conine	1.00	.75	.40
5	Rene Arocha	.75	.60	.30
6	Aaron Sele	4.00	3.00	1.50
7	Brent Gates	1.50	1.25	.60
8	Chuck Carr	.75	.60	.30
9	Kirk Rueter	1.50	1.25	.60
10	Mike Lansing	.75	.60	.30
11	Al Martin	.75	.60	.30
12	Jason Bere	5.00	3.75	2.00
13	Troy Neel	.75	.60	.30
14	Armando Reynoso	.75	.60	.30
15	Jeromy Burnitz	.75	.60	.30
16	Rich Amaral	.75	.60	.30
17	David McCarty	1.00	.75	.40
18	Tim Salmon	7.50	5.50	3.00
19	Steve Cooke	.75	.60	.30
20	Wil Cordero	1.00	.75	.40
21	Kevin Tapani	.75	.60	.30
22	Deion Sanders	2.00	1.50	.80
23	Jose Offerman	.75	.60	.30
24	Mark Langston	.75	.60	.30
25	Ken Hill	.75	.60	.30
26	Alex Fernandez	1.00	.75	.40
27	Jeff Blauser	.75	.60	.30
28	Royce Clayton	.75	.60	.30
29	Brad Ausmus	.75	.60	.30
30	Ryan Bowen	.75	.60	.30
31	Steve Finley	.75	.60	.30
32	Charlie Hayes	.75	.60	.30
33	Jeff Kent	1.50	1.25	.60
34	Mike Henneman	.75	.60	.30
35	Andres Galarraga	1.75	1.25	.70
36	Wayne Kirby	.75	.60	.30
37	Joe Oliver	.75	.60	.30
38	Terry Steinbach	.75	.60	.30
39	Ryan Thompson	.75	.60	.30
40	Luis Alicea	.75	.60	.30
41	Randy Velarde	.75	.60	.30
42	Bob Tewksbury	.75	.60	.30
43	Reggie Sanders	1.00	.75	.40
44	Brian Williams	.75	.60	.30
45	Joe Orsulak	.75	.60	.30
46	Jose Lind	.75	.60	.30
47	Dave Hollins	1.00	.75	.40
48	Graeme Lloyd	.75	.60	.30
49	Jim Gott	.75	.60	.30
50	Andre Dawson	1.00	.75	.40
51	Steve Buechele	.75	.60	.30
52	David Cone	.75	.60	.30
53	Ricky Gutierrez	.75	.60	.30
54	Lance Johnson	.75	.60	.30
55	Tino Martinez	.75	.60	.30
56	Phil Hiatt	1.00	.75	.40
57	Carlos Garcia	.75	.60	.30
58	Danny Darwin	.75	.60	.30
59	Dante Bichette	1.00	.75	.40
60	Scott Kamieniecki	.75	.60	.30
61	Orlando Merced	.75	.60	.30
62	Brian McRae	.75	.60	.30
63	Pat Kelly	.75	.60	.30
64	Tom Henke	.75	.60	.30
65	Jeff King	.75	.60	.30
66	Mike Mussina	4.00	3.00	1.50
67	Tim Pugh	.75	.60	.30
68	Robby Thompson	.75	.60	.30
69	Paul O'Neill	.75	.60	.30
70	Hal Morris	.75	.60	.30
71	Ron Karkovice	.75	.60	.30
72	Joe Girardi	.75	.60	.30
73	Eduardo Perez	1.25	.90	.50
74	Raul Mondesi	12.00	9.00	4.75
75	Mike Gallego	.75	.60	.30
76	Mike Stanley	.75	.60	.30
77	Kevin Roberson	1.00	.75	.40
78	Mark McGwire	1.50	1.25	.60
79	Pat Listach	.75	.60	.30
80	Eric Davis	.75	.60	.30
81	Mike Bordick	.75	.60	.30
82	Dwight Gooden	.75	.60	.30
83	Mike Moore	.75	.60	.30
84	Phil Plantier	.75	.60	.30
85	Darren Lewis	.75	.60	.30
86	Rick Wilkins	.75	.60	.30
87	Darryl Strawberry	1.00	.75	.40
88	Rob Dibble	.75	.60	.30
89	Greg Vaughn	.75	.60	.30
90	Jeff Russell	.75	.60	.30
91	Mark Lewis	.75	.60	.30
92	Gregg Jefferies	.75	.60	.30
93	Jose Guzman	.75	.60	.30
94	Kenny Rogers	.75	.60	.30
95	Mark Lemke	.75	.60	.30
96	Mike Morgan	.75	.60	.30
97	Andujar Cedeno	.75	.60	.30
98	Orel Hershiser	.75	.60	.30
99	Greg Swindell	.75	.60	.30
100	John Smoltz	1.00	.75	.40
101	Pedro Martinez	1.00	.75	.40
102	Jim Thome	3.00	2.25	1.25
103	David Segui	.75	.60	.30
104	Charles Nagy	.75	.60	.30
105	Shane Mack	.75	.60	.30
106	John Jaha	.75	.60	.30
107	Tom Candiotti	.75	.60	.30
108	David Wells	.75	.60	.30
109	Bobby Jones	2.50	2.00	1.00
110	Bob Hamelin	1.00	.75	.40
111	Bernard Gilkey	.75	.60	.30
112	Chili Davis	.75	.60	.30
113	Todd Stottlemyre	.75	.60	.30
114	Derek Bell	.75	.60	.30
115	Mark McLemore	.75	.60	.30
116	Mark Whiten	.75	.60	.30
117	Mike Devereaux	.75	.60	.30
118	Terry Pendleton	.75	.60	.30
119	Pat Meares	.75	.60	.30
120	Pete Harnisch	.75	.60	.30
121	Moises Alou	1.00	.75	.40
122	Jay Buhner	.75	.60	.30
123	Wes Chamberlain	.75	.60	.30
124	Mike Perez	.75	.60	.30
125	Devon White	.75	.60	.30
126	Ivan Rodriguez	1.25	.90	.50
127	Don Slaught	.75	.60	.30
128	John Valentin	.75	.60	.30
129	Jaime Navarro	.75	.60	.30
130	Dave Magadan	.75	.60	.30
131	Brady Anderson	.75	.60	.30
132	Juan Guzman	.75	.60	.30
133	John Wetteland	.75	.60	.30
134	Dave Stewart	.75	.60	.30
135	Scott Servais	.75	.60	.30
136	Ozzie Smith	2.00	1.50	.80
137	Darrin Fletcher	.75	.60	.30
138	Jose Mesa	.75	.60	.30
139	Wilson Alvarez	1.25	.90	.50
140	Pete Incaviglia	.75	.60	.30
141	Chris Hoiles	.75	.60	.30
142	Darryl Hamilton	.75	.60	.30
143	Chuck Finley	.75	.60	.30
144	Archi Cianfrocco	.75	.60	.30
145	Bill Wegman	.75	.60	.30
146	Joey Cora	.75	.60	.30
147	Darrell Whitmore	.75	.60	.30
148	David Hulse	.75	.60	.30
149	Jim Abbott	1.00	.75	.40
150	Curt Schilling	.75	.60	.30
151	Bill Swift	.75	.60	.30
152	Tommy Greene	.75	.60	.30
153	Roberto Mejia	.75	.60	.30
154	Edgar Martinez	.75	.60	.30
155	Roger Pavlik	.75	.60	.30
156	Randy Tomlin	.75	.60	.30
157	J.T. Snow	1.50	1.25	.60
158	Bob Welch	.75	.60	.30
159	Alan Trammell	.75	.60	.30
160	Ed Sprague	.75	.60	.30
161	Ben McDonald	1.25	.90	.50
162	Derrick May	.75	.60	.30
163	Roberto Kelly	.75	.60	.30
164	Bryan Harvey	.75	.60	.30
165	Ron Gant	1.25	.90	.50
166	Scott Erickson	.75	.60	.30
167	Anthony Young	.75	.60	.30
168	Scott Cooper	.75	.60	.30
169	Rod Beck	.75	.60	.30
170	John Franco	.75	.60	.30
171	Gary DiSarcina	.75	.60	.30
172	Dave Fleming	.75	.60	.30
173	Wade Boggs	2.00	1.50	.80
174	Kevin Appier	.75	.60	.30
175	Jose Bautista	.75	.60	.30
176	Wally Joyner	.75	.60	.30
177	Dean Palmer	.90	.70	.35
178	Tony Phillips	.75	.60	.30
179	John Smiley	.75	.60	.30
180	Charlie Hough	.75	.60	.30
181	Scott Fletcher	.75	.60	.30
182	Todd Van Poppel	1.00	.75	.40
183	Mike Blowers	.75	.60	.30
184	Willie McGee	.75	.60	.30
185	Paul Sorrento	.75	.60	.30
186	Eric Young	.75	.60	.30
187	Bret Barberie	.75	.60	.30
188	Maneul Lee	.75	.60	.30
189	Jeff Branson	.75	.60	.30
190	Jim Deshaies	.75	.60	.30
191	Ken Caminiti	.75	.60	.30
192	Tim Raines	.75	.60	.30
193	Joe Grahe	.75	.60	.30
194	Hipolito Pichardo	.75	.60	.30
195	Denny Neagle	.75	.60	.30
196	Jeff Gardner	.75	.60	.30
197	Mike Benjamin	.75	.60	.30
198	Milt Thompson	.75	.60	.30
199	Bruce Ruffin	.75	.60	.30
200	Chris Hammond	.75	.60	.30
201	Tony Gwynn	2.50	2.00	1.00
202	Robin Ventura	1.50	1.25	.60
203	Frank Thomas	20.00	15.00	8.00
204	Kirby Puckett	6.00	4.50	2.50
205	Roberto Alomar	4.00	3.00	1.50
206	Dennis Eckersley	.75	.60	.30
207	Joe Carter	3.00	2.25	1.25
208	Albert Belle	4.50	3.50	1.75
209	Greg Maddux	1.75	1.25	.70
210	Ryne Sandberg	5.00	3.75	2.00
211	Juan Gonzalez	10.00	7.50	4.00
212	Jeff Bagwell	2.50	2.00	1.00
213	Randy Johnson	1.00	.75	.40
214	Matt Williams	1.00	.75	.40
215	Dave Winfield	2.00	1.50	.80
216	Larry Walker	1.00	.75	.40
217	Roger Clemens	5.00	3.75	2.00
218	Kenny Lofton	3.00	2.25	1.25
219	Cecil Fielder	1.50	1.25	.60
220	Darren Dauton	.75	.60	.30

1994 Topps Finest Refractors Series I

		MT	NR MT	EX
Complete Set (220):		1750.	1300.	700.00
Common Player:		5.00	3.75	2.00
1	Mike Piazza	110.00	82.50	45.00
2	Kevin Stocker	6.00	4.50	2.50
3	Greg McMichael	5.00	3.75	2.00
4	Jeff Conine	5.00	3.75	2.00
5	Rene Arocha	5.00	3.75	2.00
6	Aaron Sele	25.00	18.00	10.00
7	Brent Gates	8.00	6.00	3.25
8	Chuck Carr	5.00	3.75	2.00
9	Kirk Rueter	8.00	6.00	3.25
10	Mike Lansing	5.00	3.75	2.00
11	Al Martin	5.00	3.75	2.00
12	Jason Bere	30.00	22.00	12.00
13	Troy Neel	5.00	3.75	2.00
14	Armando Reynoso	5.00	3.75	2.00
15	Jeromy Burnitz	5.00	3.75	2.00
16	Rich Amaral	5.00	3.75	2.00
17	David McCarty	5.00	3.75	2.00
18	Tim Salmon	35.00	26.00	14.00
19	Steve Cooke	5.00	3.75	2.00
20	Wil Cordero	7.00	5.25	2.75
21	Kevin Tapani	5.00	3.75	2.00
22	Deion Sanders	15.00	11.00	6.00
23	Jose Offerman	5.00	3.75	2.00
24	Mark Langston	5.00	3.75	2.00
25	Ken Hill	5.00	3.75	2.00
26	Alex Fernandez	6.00	4.50	2.50

27	Jeff Blauser	5.00	3.75	2.00
28	Royce Clayton	5.00	3.75	2.00
29	Brad Ausmus	5.00	3.75	2.00
30	Ryan Bowen	5.00	3.75	2.00
31	Steve Finley	5.00	3.75	2.00
32	Charlie Hayes	5.00	3.75	2.00
33	Jeff Kent	8.00	6.00	3.25
34	Mike Henneman	5.00	3.75	2.00
35	Andres Galarraga	8.00	6.00	3.25
36	Wayne Kirby	5.00	3.75	2.00
37	Joe Oliver	5.00	3.75	2.00
38	Terry Steinbach	5.00	3.75	2.00
39	Ryan Thompson	5.00	3.75	2.00
40	Luis Alicea	5.00	3.75	2.00
41	Randy Velarde	5.00	3.75	2.00
42	Bob Tewksbury	5.00	3.75	2.00
43	Reggie Sanders	6.00	4.50	2.50
44	Brian Williams	5.00	3.75	2.00
45	Joe Orsulak	5.00	3.75	2.00
46	Jose Lind	5.00	3.75	2.00
47	Dave Hollins	7.00	5.25	2.75
48	Graeme Lloyd	5.00	3.75	2.00
49	Jim Gott	5.00	3.75	2.00
50	Andre Dawson	7.00	5.25	2.75
51	Steve Buechele	5.00	3.75	2.00
52	David Cone	5.00	3.75	2.00
53	Ricky Gutierrez	5.00	3.75	2.00
54	Lance Johnson	5.00	3.75	2.00
55	Tino Martinez	5.00	3.75	2.00
56	Phil Hiatt	5.00	3.75	2.00
57	Carlos Garcia	5.00	3.75	2.00
58	Danny Darwin	5.00	3.75	2.00
59	Dante Bichette	5.00	3.75	2.00
60	Scott Kamieniecki	5.00	3.75	2.00
61	Orlando Merced	5.00	3.75	2.00
62	Brian McRae	5.00	3.75	2.00
63	Pat Kelly	5.00	3.75	2.00
64	Tom Henke	5.00	3.75	2.00
65	Jeff King	5.00	3.75	2.00
66	Mike Mussina	25.00	18.00	10.00
67	Tim Pugh	5.00	3.75	2.00
68	Robby Thompson	5.00	3.75	2.00
69	Paul O'Neill	5.00	3.75	2.00
70	Hal Morris	5.00	3.75	2.00
71	Ron Karkovice	5.00	3.75	2.00
72	Joe Girardi	5.00	3.75	2.00
73	Eduardo Perez	7.00	5.25	2.75
74	Raul Mondesi	90.00	67.00	36.00
75	Mike Gallego	5.00	3.75	2.00
76	Mike Stanley	5.00	3.75	2.00
77	Kevin Roberson	5.00	3.75	2.00
78	Mark McGwire	10.00	7.50	4.00
79	Pat Listach	5.00	3.75	2.00
80	Eric Davis	5.00	3.75	2.00
81	Mike Bordick	5.00	3.75	2.00
82	Dwight Gooden	5.00	3.75	2.00
83	Mike Moore	5.00	3.75	2.00
84	Phil Plantier	6.00	4.50	2.50
85	Darren Lewis	5.00	3.75	2.00
86	Rick Wilkens	5.00	3.75	2.00
87	Darryl Strawberry	6.00	4.50	2.50
88	Rob Dibble	5.00	3.75	2.00
89	Greg Vaughn	5.00	3.75	2.00
90	Jeff Russell	5.00	3.75	2.00
91	Mark Lewis	5.00	3.75	2.00
92	Gregg Jefferies	6.00	4.50	2.50
93	Jose Guzman	5.00	3.75	2.00
94	Kenny Rogers	5.00	3.75	2.00
95	Mark Lemke	5.00	3.75	2.00
96	Mike Morgan	5.00	3.75	2.00
97	Andujar Cedeno	5.00	3.75	2.00
98	Orel Hershiser	5.00	3.75	2.00
99	Greg Swindell	5.00	3.75	2.00
100	John Smoltz	6.00	4.50	2.50
101	Pedro Martinez	6.00	4.50	2.50
102	Jim Thome	12.00	9.00	4.75
103	David Segui	5.00	3.75	2.00
104	Charles Nagy	5.00	3.75	2.00
105	Shane Mack	5.00	3.75	2.00
106	John Jaha	5.00	3.75	2.00
107	Tom Candiotti	5.00	3.75	2.00
108	David Wells	5.00	3.75	2.00
109	Bobby Jones	10.00	7.50	4.00
110	Bob Hamelin	7.00	5.25	2.75
111	Bernard Gilkey	5.00	3.75	2.00
112	Chili Davis	5.00	3.75	2.00
113	Todd Stottlemyre	5.00	3.75	2.00
114	Derek Bell	5.00	3.75	2.00
115	Mark McLemore	5.00	3.75	2.00
116	Mark Whiten	5.00	3.75	2.00
117	Mike Devereaux	5.00	3.75	2.00
118	Terry Pendleton	5.00	3.75	2.00
119	Pat Meares	5.00	3.75	2.00
120	Pete Harnisch	5.00	3.75	2.00
121	Moises Alou	7.50	5.50	3.00
122	Jay Buhner	5.00	3.75	2.00
123	Wes Chamberlain	5.00	3.75	2.00
124	Mike Perez	5.00	3.75	2.00
125	Devon White	5.00	3.75	2.00
126	Ivan Rodriguez	6.00	4.50	2.50
127	Don Slaught	5.00	3.75	2.00
128	John Valentin	5.00	3.75	2.00
129	Jaime Navarro	5.00	3.75	2.00
130	Dave Magadan	5.00	3.75	2.00
131	Brady Anderson	5.00	3.75	2.00
132	Juan Guzman	5.00	3.75	2.00
133	John Wetteland	5.00	3.75	2.00
134	Dave Stewart	5.00	3.75	2.00
135	Scott Servais	5.00	3.75	2.00
136	Ozzie Smith	15.00	11.00	6.00
137	Darrin Fletcher	5.00	3.75	2.00
138	Jose Mesa	5.00	3.75	2.00
139	Wilson Alvarez	9.00	6.75	3.50
140	Pete Incaviglia	5.00	3.75	2.00
141	Chris Hoiles	5.00	3.75	2.00
142	Darryl Hamilton	5.00	3.75	2.00
143	Chuck Finley	5.00	3.75	2.00
144	Archi Cianfrocco	5.00	3.75	2.00
145	Bill Wegman	5.00	3.75	2.00
146	Joey Cora	5.00	3.75	2.00
147	Darrell Whitmore	5.00	3.75	2.00
148	David Hulse	5.00	3.75	2.00
149	Jim Abbott	5.00	3.75	2.00
150	Curt Schilling	5.00	3.75	2.00
151	Bill Swift	5.00	3.75	2.00
152	Tommy Greene	5.00	3.75	2.00
153	Roberto Mejia	5.00	3.75	2.00
154	Edgar Martinez	5.00	3.75	2.00
155	Roger Pavlik	5.00	3.75	2.00
156	Randy Tomlin	5.00	3.75	2.00
157	J.T. Snow	5.00	3.75	2.00
158	Bob Welch	5.00	3.75	2.00
159	Alan Trammell	5.00	3.75	2.00
160	Ed Sprague	5.00	3.75	2.00
161	Ben McDonald	5.00	3.75	2.00
162	Derrick May	5.00	3.75	2.00
163	Roberto Kelly	5.00	3.75	2.00
164	Bryan Harvey	5.00	3.75	2.00
165	Ron Gant	5.00	3.75	2.00
166	Scott Erickson	5.00	3.75	2.00
167	Anthony Young	5.00	3.75	2.00
168	Scott Cooper	5.00	3.75	2.00
169	Rod Beck	5.00	3.75	2.00
170	John Franco	5.00	3.75	2.00
171	Gary DiSarcina	5.00	3.75	2.00
172	Dave Fleming	5.00	3.75	2.00
173	Wade Boggs	18.00	13.50	7.25
174	Kevin Appier	5.00	3.75	2.00
175	Jose Bautista	5.00	3.75	2.00
176	Wally Joyner	5.00	3.75	2.00
177	Dean Palmer	5.00	3.75	2.00
178	Tony Phillips	5.00	3.75	2.00
179	John Smiley	5.00	3.75	2.00
180	Charlie Hough	5.00	3.75	2.00
181	Scott Fletcher	5.00	3.75	2.00
182	Todd Van Poppel	7.00	5.25	2.75
183	Mike Blowers	5.00	3.75	2.00
184	Willie McGee	5.00	3.75	2.00
185	Paul Sorrento	5.00	3.75	2.00
186	Eric Young	5.00	3.75	2.00
187	Bret Barberie	5.00	3.75	2.00
188	Manuel Lee	5.00	3.75	2.00
189	Jeff Branson	5.00	3.75	2.00
190	Jim Deshaies	5.00	3.75	2.00
191	Ken Caminiti	5.00	3.75	2.00
192	Tim Raines	5.00	3.75	2.00
193	Joe Grahe	5.00	3.75	2.00
194	Hipolito Pichardo	5.00	3.75	2.00
195	Denny Neagle	5.00	3.75	2.00
196	Jeff Gardner	5.00	3.75	2.00
197	Mike Benjamin	5.00	3.75	2.00
198	Milt Thompson	5.00	3.75	2.00
199	Bruce Ruffin	5.00	3.75	2.00
200	Chris Hammond	5.00	3.75	2.00
201	Tony Gwynn	22.00	16.50	8.75
202	Robin Ventura	10.00	7.50	4.00
203	Frank Thomas	160.00	120.00	65.00
204	Kirby Puckett	45.00	34.00	18.00
205	Roberto Alomar	35.00	26.00	14.00
206	Dennis Eckersley	5.00	3.75	2.00
207	Joe Carter	15.00	11.00	6.00
208	Albert Belle	35.00	26.00	14.00
209	Greg Maddux	15.00	11.00	6.00
210	Ryne Sandberg	40.00	30.00	15.00
211	Juan Gonzalez	90.00	67.00	36.00
212	Jeff Bagwell	20.00	15.00	8.00
213	Randy Johnson	6.00	4.50	2.50
214	Matt Williams	7.50	5.50	3.00
215	Dave Winfield	15.00	11.00	6.00
216	Larry Walker	6.00	4.50	2.50
217	Roger Clemens	30.00	22.00	12.00
218	Kenny Lofton	18.00	13.50	7.25
219	Cecil Fielder	12.00	9.00	4.75
220	Darren Daulton	5.00	3.75	2.00

1994 Topps Finest Superstars

		MT	NR MT	EX
	Complete Set (40):	275.00	210.00	110.00
	Common Player:	5.00	3.75	2.00
1	Mike Piazza	40.00	30.00	15.00
2	Kevin Stocker	5.00	3.75	2.00
3	Greg McMichael	5.00	3.75	2.00
4	Jeff Conine	7.00	5.50	3.00
5	Rene Arocha	5.00	3.75	2.00
6	Aaron Sele	15.00	11.00	6.00
7	Brent Gates	6.00	4.50	2.50
8	Chuck Carr	5.00	3.75	2.00
9	Kirk Rueter	10.00	7.50	4.00
10	Mike Lansing	5.00	3.75	2.00
11	Al Martin	5.00	3.75	2.00
12	Jason Bere	12.00	9.00	4.75
13	Troy Neel	5.00	3.75	2.00
14	Armando Reynoso	5.00	3.75	2.00
15	Jeromy Burnitz	5.00	3.75	2.00
16	Rich Amaral	5.00	3.75	2.00
17	David McCarty	5.00	3.75	2.00
18	Tim Salmon	15.00	11.00	6.00
19	Steve Cooke	5.00	3.75	2.00
20	Wil Cordero	6.00	4.50	2.50
201	Tony Gwynn	8.00	6.00	3.25
202	Robin Ventura	8.00	6.00	3.25
203	Frank Thomas	75.00	60.00	30.00
204	Kirby Puckett	20.00	15.00	8.00
205	Roberto Alomar	15.00	11.00	6.00
206	Dennis Eckersley	5.00	3.75	2.00
207	Joe Carter	12.00	9.00	4.75
208	Albert Belle	15.00	11.00	6.00
209	Greg Maddux	8.00	6.00	3.25
210	Ryne Sandberg	15.00	11.00	6.00
211	Juan Gonzalez	20.00	15.00	8.00
212	Jeff Bagwell	8.00	6.00	3.25
213	Randy Johnson	5.00	3.75	2.00
214	Matt Williams	6.00	4.50	2.50
215	Dave Winfield	7.50	5.50	3.00
216	Larry Walker	5.00	3.75	2.00
217	Roger Clemens	10.00	7.50	4.00
218	Kenny Lofton	15.00	11.00	6.00
219	Cecil Fielder	10.00	7.50	4.00
220	Darren Daulton	5.00	3.75	2.00

1994 Topps Stadium Club

Issued in three series to a total of 720 cards, Topps mid-price brand features a hip look and a wide range of insert specials. The regular cards feature a full-bleed photo with the player's name presented in a unique typewriter/label maker style at bottom. The player's last name and Topps Stadium Club logo at top are in red foil. Backs feature another player photo, some personal data and a headlined career summary. Various stats and skills rankings complete the data. Subsets within the issue include cards annoted with Major League debut dates, 1993 awards won, home run club cards, cards featuring two or three players, and Final Tribute cards for George Brett and Nolan Ryan.

		MT	NR MT	EX
	Complete Set (540):	24.00	18.00	9.50
	Common Player:	.10	.08	.04
1	Robin Yount	.35	.25	.14
2	Rick Wilkins	.10	.08	.04
3	Steve Scarsone	.10	.08	.04
4	Gary Sheffield	.25	.20	.10
5	George Brett	.50	.40	.20
6	Al Martin	.12	.09	.05
7	Joe Oliver	.10	.08	.04
8	Stan Belinda	.10	.08	.04
9	Denny Hocking	.10	.08	.04
10	Roberto Alomar	.50	.40	.20
11	Luis Polonia	.10	.08	.04
12	Scott Hemond	.10	.08	.04
13	Joey Reed	.10	.08	.04
14	Mel Rojas	.10	.08	.04
15	Junior Ortiz	.10	.08	.04
16	Harold Baines	.10	.08	.04
17	Brad Pennington	.10	.08	.04
18	Jay Bell	.10	.08	.04
19	Tom Henke	.10	.08	.04
20	Jeff Branson	.10	.08	.04
21	Roberto Mejia	.15	.11	.06
22	Pedro Munoz	.12	.09	.05
23	Matt Nokes	.10	.08	.04
24	Jack McDowell	.20	.15	.08
25	Cecil Fielder	.30	.25	.12
26	Tony Fossas	.10	.08	.04
27	Jim Eisenreich	.10	.08	.04
28	Anthony Young	.10	.08	.04
29	Chuck Carr	.12	.09	.05
30	Jeff Treadway	.10	.08	.04
31	Chris Nabholz	.10	.08	.04
32	Tom Candiotti	.10	.08	.04
33	Mike Maddix	.10	.08	.04
34	Nolan Ryan	1.75	1.25	.70
35	Luis Gonzalez	.12	.09	.05
36	Tim Salmon	1.25	.90	.50
37	Mark Whiten	.10	.08	.04
38	Roger McDowell	.10	.08	.04
39	Royce Clayton	.12	.09	.05
40	Troy Neel	.20	.15	.08
41	Mike Harkey	.10	.08	.04

No.	Player			
42	Darrin Fletcher	.10	.08	.04
43	Wayne Kirby	.10	.08	.04
44	Rich Amaral	.10	.08	.04
45	Robb Nen	.10	.08	.04
46	Tim Teufel	.10	.08	.04
47	Steve Cooke	.10	.08	.04
48	Jeff McNeely	.20	.15	.08
49	Jeff Montgomery	.10	.08	.04
50	Skeeter Barnes	.15	.11	.06
51	Scott Stahoviak	.10	.08	.04
52	Pat Kelly	.12	.09	.05
53	Brady Anderson	.10	.08	.04
54	Mariano Duncan	.10	.08	.04
55	Brian Bohanon	.10	.08	.04
56	Jerry Spradlin	.10	.08	.04
57	Ron Karkovice	.10	.08	.04
58	Jeff Gardner	.10	.08	.04
59	Bobby Bonilla	.15	.11	.06
60	Tino Martinez	.10	.08	.04
61	Todd Benzinger	.10	.08	.04
62	*Steve Trachsel*	.35	.25	.14
63	Brian Jordan	.12	.09	.05
64	Steve Bedrosian	.10	.08	.04
65	Brent Gates	.25	.20	.10
66	Shawn Green	.20	.15	.08
67	Sean Berry	.10	.08	.04
68	Joe Klink	.10	.08	.04
69	Fernando Valenzuela	.10	.08	.04
70	Andy Tomberlin	.25	.20	.10
71	Tony Pena	.10	.08	.04
72	Eric Young	.10	.08	.04
73	Chris Gomez	.10	.08	.04
74	Paul O'Neill	.10	.08	.04
75	Ricky Gutierrez	.10	.08	.04
76	Brad Holman	.10	.08	.04
77	Lance Painter	.10	.08	.04
78	Mike Butcher	.10	.08	.04
79	Sid Bream	.10	.08	.04
80	Sammy Sosa	.15	.11	.06
81	Felix Fermin	.10	.08	.04
82	Todd Hundley	.10	.08	.04
83	Kevin Higgins	.10	.08	.04
84	Todd Pratt	.10	.08	.04
85	Ken Griffey, Jr.	2.50	2.00	1.00
86	John O'Donoghue	.10	.08	.04
87	Rick Renteria	.10	.08	.04
88	John Burkett	.10	.08	.04
89	Jose Vizcaino	.10	.08	.04
90	Kevin Seitzer	.10	.08	.04
91	Bobby Witt	.10	.08	.04
92	Chris Turner	.10	.08	.04
93	Omar Vizquel	.10	.08	.04
94	Dave Justice	.75	.60	.30
95	David Segui	.10	.08	.04
96	Dave Hollins	.12	.09	.05
97	Doug Strange	.10	.08	.04
98	Jerald Clark	.10	.08	.04
99	Mike Moore	.10	.08	.04
100	Joey Cora	.10	.08	.04
101	Scott Kamieniecki	.10	.08	.04
102	Andy Benes	.15	.11	.06
103	Chris Bosio	.10	.08	.04
104	Rey Sanchez	.10	.08	.04
105	John Jaha	.15	.11	.06
106	Otis Nixon	.10	.08	.04
107	Rickey Henderson	.20	.15	.08
108	Jeff Bagwell	.35	.25	.14
109	Gregg Jefferies	.12	.09	.05
110	Blue Jays	.10	.08	.04
111	Braves	.10	.08	.04
112	Rangers	.10	.08	.04
113	Greg Swindell	.10	.08	.04
114	Bill Hasleman	.10	.08	.04
115	Phil Plantier	.15	.11	.06
116	Ivan Rodriguez	.20	.15	.08
117	Kevin Tapani	.10	.08	.04
118	Mike LaValliere	.10	.08	.04
119	Tim Costo	.12	.09	.05
120	Mickey Morandini	.10	.08	.04
121	Brett Butler	.12	.09	.05
122	Tom Pagnozzi	.10	.08	.04
123	Ron Gant	.20	.15	.08
124	Damion Easley	.15	.11	.06
125	Dennis Eckersley	.12	.09	.05
126	Matt Mieske	.12	.09	.05
127	Cliff Floyd	1.50	1.25	.60
128	*Julian Tavarez*	.40	.30	.15
129	Arthur Rhodes	.12	.09	.05
130	Dave West	.10	.08	.04
131	Tim Naehring	.10	.08	.04
132	Freddie Benavides	.10	.08	.04
133	Paul Assenmacher	.10	.08	.04
134	David McCarty	.15	.11	.06
135	Jose Lind	.10	.08	.04
136	Reggie Sanders	.20	.15	.08
137	Don Slaught	.10	.08	.04
138	Andujar Cedeno	.12	.09	.05
139	Rob Deer	.10	.08	.04
140	Mike Piazza	2.50	2.00	1.00
141	Moises Alou	.15	.11	.06
142	Tom Foley	.20	.15	.08
143	Benny Santiago	.10	.08	.04
144	Sandy Alomar	.10	.08	.04
145	Carlos Hernandez	.20	.15	.08
146	Luis Alicea	.10	.08	.04
147	Tom Lampkin	.10	.08	.04
148	Ryan Klesko	.60	.45	.25
149	Juan Guzman	.35	.25	.14
150	Scott Servais	.10	.08	.04
151	Tony Gwynn	.20	.15	.08
152	Tim Wakefield	.12	.09	.05
153	David Nied	.40	.30	.15
154	Chris Haney	.10	.08	.04
155	Danny Bautista	.10	.08	.04
156	Randy Myers	.10	.08	.04
157	Darrin Jackson	.10	.08	.04
158	*J.R. Phillips*	.50	.40	.20
159	Greg Gagne	.10	.08	.04
160	Luis Aquino	.10	.08	.04
161	John Vander Wal	.10	.08	.04
162	Randy Myers	.10	.08	.04
163	Ted Power	.10	.08	.04
164	Scott Brosius	.10	.08	.04
165	Len Dykstra	.15	.11	.06
166	Jacob Brumfield	.25	.20	.10
167	Bo Jackson	.20	.15	.08
168	Eddie Taubensee	.10	.08	.04
169	Carlos Baerga	.40	.30	.15
170	Tim Bogar	.10	.08	.04
171	Jose Canseco	.30	.25	.12
172	Greg Blosser	.20	.15	.08
173	Chili Davis	.10	.08	.04
174	Randy Knorr	.10	.08	.04
175	Mike Perez	.10	.08	.04
176	Henry Rodriguez	.12	.09	.05
177	*Brian Turang*	.35	.25	.14
178	Roger Pavlik	.10	.08	.04
179	Aaron Sele	1.25	.90	.50
180	Fred McGriff, Gary Sheffield	.15	.11	.06
181	J.T. Snow, Tim Salmon	.75	.60	.30
182	Roberto Hernandez	.10	.08	.04
183	Jeff Reboulet	.10	.08	.04
184	John Doherty	.10	.08	.04
185	Danny Sheaffer	.10	.08	.04
186	Bip Roberts	.10	.08	.04
187	Denny Martinez	.10	.08	.04
188	Darryl Hamilton	.10	.08	.04
189	Eduardo Perez	.50	.40	.20
190	Pete Harnisch	.10	.08	.04
191	Rick Gossage	.10	.08	.04
192	Mickey Tettleton	.10	.08	.04
193	Lenny Webster	.10	.08	.04
194	Lance Johnson	.10	.08	.04
195	Don Mattingly	.30	.25	.12
196	Gregg Olson	.10	.08	.04
197	Mark Gubicza	.10	.08	.04
198	Scott Fletcher	.10	.08	.04
199	Jon Shave	.10	.08	.04
200	Tim Mauser	.10	.08	.04
201	Jeromy Burnitz	.10	.08	.04
202	Rob Dibble	.10	.08	.04
203	Will Clark	.25	.20	.10
204	Steve Buechele	.10	.08	.04
205	Brian Williams	.10	.08	.04
206	Carlos Garcia	.15	.11	.06
207	Mark Clark	.10	.08	.04
208	Rafael Palmeiro	.15	.11	.06
209	Eric Davis	.10	.08	.04
210	Pat Meares	.10	.08	.04
211	Chuck Finley	.10	.08	.04
212	Jason Bere	1.00	.70	.40
213	Gary DiSarcina	.10	.08	.04
214	Tony Fernandez	.10	.08	.04
215	B.J. Surhoff	.10	.08	.04
216	Lee Guetterman	.10	.08	.04
217	Tim Wallach	.10	.08	.04
218	Kirt Manwaring	.10	.08	.04
219	Albert Belle	.40	.30	.15
220	Dwight Gooden	.10	.08	.04
221	Archi Cianfrocco	.10	.08	.04
222	Terry Mulholland	.10	.08	.04
223	Hipolito Pichardo	.10	.08	.04
224	Kent Hrbek	.10	.08	.04
225	Criag Grebeck	.10	.08	.04
226	Todd Jones	.10	.08	.04
227	Mike Bordick	.12	.09	.05
228	John Olerud	.75	.60	.30
229	Jeff Blauser	.10	.08	.04
230	Alex Arias	.15	.11	.06
231	Bernard Gilkey	.10	.08	.04
232	Denny Neagle	.12	.09	.05
233	*Pedro Borbon*	.25	.20	.10
234	Dick Schofield	.10	.08	.04
235	Matias Carrillo	.20	.15	.08
236	Juan Bell	.10	.08	.04
237	Mike Hampton	.10	.08	.04
238	Barry Bonds	.75	.60	.30
239	Cris Carpenter	.10	.08	.04
240	Eric Karros	.20	.15	.08
241	Greg McMichael	.20	.15	.08
242	Pat Hentgen	.25	.20	.10
243	Tim Pugh	.10	.08	.04
244	Vinny Castilla	.10	.08	.04
245	Charlie Hough	.10	.08	.04
246	Bobby Munoz	.10	.08	.04
247	Kevin Baez	.10	.08	.04
248	Todd Frohwirth	.10	.08	.04
249	Charlie Hayes	.10	.08	.04
250	Mike Macfarlane	.10	.08	.04
251	Danny Darwin	.10	.08	.04
252	Ben Rivera	.10	.08	.04
253	Dave Henderson	.10	.08	.04
254	Steve Avery	.35	.25	.14
255	Tim Belcher	.10	.08	.04
256	Dan Plesac	.10	.08	.04
257	Jim Thome	.10	.08	.04
258	Albert Belle (35+ HR Hitter)	.25	.20	.10
259	Barry Bonds (35+ HR Hitter)	.40	.30	.15
260	Ron Gant (35+ HR Hitter)	.15	.11	.06
261	Juan Gonzalez (35+ HR Hitter)	1.00	.70	.40
262	Ken Griffey, Jr. (35+ HR Hitter)	2.00	1.50	.80
263	Dave Justice (35+ HR Hitter)	.35	.25	.14
264	Fred McGriff (35+ HR Hitter)	.20	.15	.08
265	Rafael Palmeiro (35+ HR Hitter)	.12	.09	.05
266	Mike Piazza (35+ HR Hitter)	1.00	.70	.40
267	Frank Thomas (35+ HR Hitter)	2.00	1.50	.80
268	Matt Williams (35+ HR Hitter)	.12	.09	.05
269	Checklist I 1-135	.10	.08	.04
270	Checklist II 136-270	.10	.08	.04
271	Mike Stanley	.10	.08	.04
272	Tony Tarasco	.40	.30	.15
273	Teddy Higuera	.10	.08	.04
274	Ryan Thompson	.10	.08	.04
275	Rick Aguilera	.10	.08	.04
276	Ramon Martinez	.10	.08	.04
277	Orlando Merced	.10	.08	.04
278	Guillermo Velasquez	.10	.08	.04
279	Mark Hutton	.10	.08	.04
280	Larry Walker	.12	.09	.05
281	Kevin Gross	.10	.08	.04
282	Jose Offerman	.10	.08	.04
283	Jim Leyritz	.10	.08	.04
284	Jamie Moyer	.10	.08	.04
285	Frank Thomas	3.00	2.25	1.25
286	Derek Bell	.12	.09	.05
287	Derrick May	.10	.08	.04
288	Dave Winfield	.20	.15	.08
289	Curt Schilling	.10	.08	.04
290	Carlos Quintana	.10	.08	.04
291	Bob Natal	.10	.08	.04
292	David Cone	.10	.08	.04
293	Al Osuna	.10	.08	.04
294	Bob Hamelin	.12	.09	.05
295	Chad Curtis	.15	.11	.06
296	Danny Jackson	.10	.08	.04
297	Bob Welch	.10	.08	.04
298	Felix Jose	.10	.08	.04
299	Jay Buhner	.12	.09	.05
300	Joe Carter	.20	.15	.08
301	Kenny Lofton	.15	.11	.06
302	*Kirk Rueter*	.60	.45	.25
303	Kim Batiste	.10	.08	.04
304	Mike Morgan	.10	.08	.04
305	Pat Borders	.10	.08	.04
306	Rene Arocha	.12	.09	.05
307	Ruben Sierra	.15	.11	.06
308	Steve Finley	.10	.08	.04
309	Travis Fryman	.25	.20	.10
310	Zane Smith	.10	.08	.04
311	Willie Wilson	.10	.08	.04
312	Trevor Hoffman	.10	.08	.04
313	Terry Pendleton	.12	.09	.05
314	Salomon Torres	.30	.25	.12
315	Robin Ventura	.20	.15	.08
316	Randy Tomlin	.10	.08	.04
317	Dave Stewart	.10	.08	.04
318	Mike Benjamin	.10	.08	.04
319	Matt Turner	.10	.08	.04
320	Manny Ramirez	1.50	1.25	.60
321	Kevin Young	.12	.09	.05
322	Ken Caminiti	.10	.08	.04
323	Joe Girardi	.10	.08	.04
324	Jeff McKnight	.10	.08	.04
325	Gene Harris	.10	.08	.04
326	Devon White	.10	.08	.04
327	Darryl Kile	.10	.08	.04
328	Craig Paquette	.10	.08	.04
329	Cal Eldred	.12	.09	.05
330	Bill Swift	.10	.08	.04
331	Alan Trammell	.10	.08	.04
332	Armando Reynoso	.10	.08	.04
333	Brent Mayne	.10	.08	.04
334	Chris Donnels	.10	.08	.04
335	Darryl Strawberry	.12	.09	.05
336	Dean Palmer	.12	.09	.05
337	Frank Castillo	.10	.08	.04
338	Jeff King	.10	.08	.04
339	John Franco	.10	.08	.04
340	Kevin Appier	.10	.08	.04
341	Lance Blankenship	.10	.08	.04
342	Mark McLemore	.10	.08	.04
343	Pedro Astacio	.10	.08	.04
344	Rich Batchelor	.15	.11	.06
345		.10	.08	.04
346	Terry Steinbach	.10	.08	.04
347	Troy O'Leary	.25	.20	.10
348	Willie Blair	.10	.08	.04
349	Wade Boggs	.20	.15	.08
350	Tim Raines	.12	.09	.05
351	Scott Livingstone	.10	.08	.04
352	Rod Carreia	.10	.08	.04
353	Ray Lankford	.12	.09	.05
354	Pat Listach	.12	.09	.05
355	Milt Thompson	.10	.08	.04
356	Miguel Jimenez	.10	.08	.04
357	Marc Newfield	.20	.15	.08
358	Mark McGwire	.20	.15	.08
359	Kirby Puckett	.35	.25	.14
360	Kent Mercker	.12	.09	.05
361	John Kruk	.12	.09	.05
362	Jeff Kent	.12	.09	.05
363	Hal Morris	.10	.08	.04
364	Edgar Martinez	.10	.08	.04
365	Dave Magadan	.10	.08	.04
366	Dante Bichette	.10	.08	.04
367	Chris Hammond	.10	.08	.04
368	Bret Saberhagen	.10	.08	.04
369	Billy Ripken	.10	.08	.04
370	Bill Gullickson	.10	.08	.04
371	Andre Dawson	.12	.09	.05
372	Bobby Kelly	.10	.08	.04
373	Cal Ripken, Jr.	.75	.60	.30
374	Craig Biggio	.10	.08	.04
375	Dan Pasqua	.10	.08	.04
376	Dave Nilsson	.12	.09	.05
377	Duane Ward	.10	.08	.04
378	Greg Vaughn	.12	.09	.05
379	Jeff Fassero	.15	.11	.06
380	Jerry Dipoto	.10	.08	.04
381	John Patterson	.10	.08	.04
382	Kevin Brown	.10	.08	.04
383	Kevin Roberson	.15	.11	.06
384	Joe Orsulak	.10	.08	.04
385	Hilly Hathaway	.10	.08	.04
386	Mike Greenwell	.10	.08	.04
387	Orestes Destrade	.10	.08	.04
388	Mike Gallego	.10	.08	.04
389	Ozzie Guillen	.10	.08	.04
390	Raul Mondesi	1.50	1.25	.60
391	Scott Lydy	.15	.11	.06
392	Tom Urbani	.12	.09	.05
393	Wil Cordero	.12	.09	.05
394	Tony Longmire	.15	.11	.06
395	Todd Zeile	.10	.08	.04

396	Scott Cooper	.10	.08	.04
397	Ryne Sandberg	.40	.30	.15
398	Ricky Bones	.10	.08	.04
399	Phil Clark	.10	.08	.04
400	Orel Hershiser	.10	.08	.04
401	Mike Henneman	.10	.08	.04
402	Mark Lemke	.10	.08	.04
403	Mark Grace	.12	.09	.05
404	Ken Ryan	.10	.08	.04
405	John Smoltz	.10	.08	.04
406	Jeff Conine	.10	.08	.04
407	Greg Harris	.10	.08	.04
408	Doug Drabek	.10	.08	.04
409	Dave Fleming	.10	.08	.04
410	Danny Tartabull	.10	.08	.04
411	Chad Kreuter	.10	.08	.04
412	Brad Ausmus	.10	.08	.04
413	Ben McDonald	.12	.09	.05
414	Barry Larkin	.10	.08	.04
415	Bret Barberie	.10	.08	.04
416	Chuck Knoblauch	.12	.09	.05
417	Ozzie Smith	.20	.15	.08
418	Ed Sprague	.10	.08	.04
419	Matt Williams	.12	.09	.05
420	Jeremy Hernandez	.10	.08	.04
421	Jose Bautista	.10	.08	.04
422	Kevin Mitchell	.10	.08	.04
423	Manuel Lee	.10	.08	.04
424	Mike Devereaux	.10	.08	.04
425	Omar Olivares	.10	.08	.04
426	Rafael Belliard	.10	.08	.04
427	Richie Lewis	.10	.08	.04
428	Ron Darling	.10	.08	.04
429	Shane Mack	.10	.08	.04
430	Tim Hulett	.10	.08	.04
431	Walley Joyner	.10	.08	.04
432	Wes Chamberlain	.10	.08	.04
433	Tom Browning	.10	.08	.04
434	Scott Radinsky	.10	.08	.04
435	Rondell White	.50	.40	.20
436	Rod Beck	.10	.08	.04
437	Rheal Cormier	.10	.08	.04
438	Randy Johnson	.10	.08	.04
439	Pete Schourek	.10	.08	.04
440	Mo Vaughn	.15	.11	.06
441	Mike Timlin	.10	.08	.04
442	Mark Langston	.10	.08	.04
443	Lou Whitaker	.10	.08	.04
444	Kevin Stocker	.20	.15	.08
445	Ken Hill	.12	.09	.05
446	John Wetteland	.10	.08	.04
447	J.T. Snow	.25	.20	.10
448	Erik Pappas	.10	.08	.04
449	David Hulse	.10	.08	.04
450	Darren Daulton	.10	.08	.04
451	Chris Hoiles	.10	.08	.04
452	Bryan Harvey	.10	.08	.04
453	Darren Lewis	.10	.08	.04
454	Andres Galarraga	.10	.08	.04
455	Joe Hesketh	.10	.08	.04
456	Jose Valentin	.10	.08	.04
457	Dan Peltier	.10	.08	.04
458	Joe Boever	.10	.08	.04
459	Kevin Rogers	.10	.08	.04
460	Craig Shipley	.10	.08	.04
461	Alvaro Espinoza	.10	.08	.04
462	Wilson Alvarez	.10	.08	.04
463	Cory Snyder	.10	.08	.04
464	Candy Maldonado	.10	.08	.04
465	Blas Minor	.15	.11	.06
466	Rod Bolton	.10	.08	.04
467	Kenny Rogers	.10	.08	.04
468	Greg Myers	.10	.08	.04
469	Jimmy Key	.10	.08	.04
470	Tony Castillo	.10	.08	.04
471	Mike Stanton	.10	.08	.04
472	Deion Sanders	.20	.15	.08
473	Tito Navarro	.15	.11	.06
474	Mike Gardiner	.12	.09	.05
475	Steve Reed	.12	.09	.05
476	John Roper	.12	.09	.05
477	Mike Trombley	.10	.08	.04
478	Charles Nagy	.10	.08	.04
479	Larry Casian	.10	.08	.04
480	Eric Hillman	.10	.08	.04
481	Bill Wertz	.10	.08	.04
482	Jeff Schwarz	.10	.08	.04
483	John Valentin	.10	.08	.04
484	Carl Willis	.10	.08	.04
485	Gary Gaetti	.10	.08	.04
486	Bill Pecota	.10	.08	.04
487	John Smiley	.10	.08	.04
488	Mike Mussina	.20	.15	.08
489	*Mike Ignasiak*	.20	.15	.08
490	Billy Brewer	.10	.08	.04
491	Jack Voigt	.10	.08	.04
492	Mike Munoz	.10	.08	.04
493	Lee Tinsley	.10	.08	.04
494	Bob Wickman	.10	.08	.04
495	Roger Salkeld	.10	.08	.04
496	Thomas Howard	.10	.08	.04
497	Mark Davis	.10	.08	.04
498	Dave Clark	.10	.08	.04
499	Turk Wendell	.10	.08	.04
500	Rafael Bournigal	.10	.08	.04
501	Chip Hale	.10	.08	.04
502	Matt Whiteside	.10	.08	.04
503	Brian Koelling	.10	.08	.04
504	Jeff Reed	.10	.08	.04
505	Paul Wagner	.10	.08	.04
506	Torey Lovullo	.10	.08	.04
507	Curtis Leskanic	.10	.08	.04
508	Derek Lilliquist	.10	.08	.04
509	Joe Magrane	.10	.08	.04
510	Mackey Sasser	.10	.08	.04
511	Lloyd McClendon	.10	.08	.04
512	*Jayhawk Owens*	.25	.20	.10
513	*Woody Williams*	.20	.15	.08
514	Gary Redus	.10	.08	.04
515	Tim Spehr	.10	.08	.04
516	Jim Abbott	.12	.09	.05
517	Lou Frazier	.10	.08	.04
518	Erik Plantenberg	.10	.08	.04
519	Tim Worrell	.10	.08	.04
520	Brian McRae	.10	.08	.04
521	*Chan Ho Park*	.40	.30	.15
522	Mark Wohlers	.10	.08	.04
523	Geronimo Pena	.10	.08	.04
524	Andy Ashby	.10	.08	.04
525	Tim Raines, Andre Dawson	.10	.08	.04
526	Paul Molitor, Dave Winfield	.25	.20	.10
527	Joe Carter	.20	.15	.08
528	Frank Thomas	1.50	1.25	.60
529	Ken Griffey, Jr.	1.50	1.25	.60
530	Dave Justice	.30	.25	.12
531	Gregg Jefferies	.10	.08	.04
532	Barry Bonds	.40	.30	.15
533	John Kruk	.10	.08	.04
534	Roger Clemens	.20	.15	.08
535	Cecil Fielder	.20	.15	.08
536	Ruben Sierra	.12	.09	.05
537	Tony Gwynn	.20	.15	.08
538	Tom Glavine	.15	.11	.06
539	Checklist I 271-405	.10	.08	.04

1994 Topps Stadium Club Super Teams

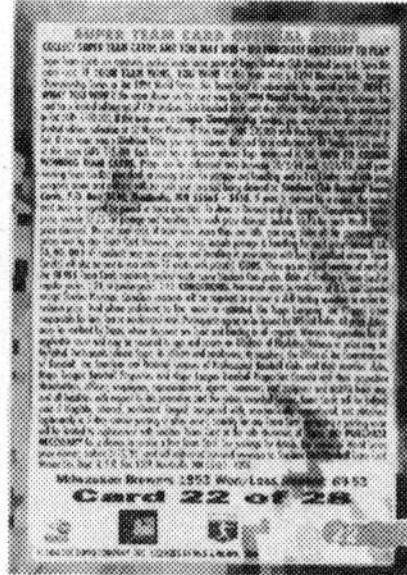

With its football card issue the previous year, Topps Stadium Club debuted the idea of an insert card set whose value rose and fell with the on-field performance of each team. Super Team cards were issued for each of the 28 major league teams and inserted at the rate of one per 24 regular packs and one per 15 jumbo packs. At the end of the season, persons holding Super Team cards of the divisions winners, league champions and World Champions could redeem the cards for prizes. Division winning team cards could be redeemed for a set of 10 S.C. cards of that team with a special division winner embossed logo. League champion cards could be redeemed for a set of 10 Master Photos of the team with a special league logo embossed. Persons with a Super Team card of the eventual World Series champion could trade the card in for a complete set of Stadium Club cards embossed with a World's Champion logo. Each of the Super Team cards featured a small group of players on the front with the Super Team Card and S.C. logos in gold foil, and the team name in prismatic foil. Backs contained redemption rules. Following the close of the 1994 baseball season and the end of the redemption period, the value of the winning teams' cards will drop precipitously.

		MT	NR MT	EX
Complete Set (28):		250.00	185.00	100.00
Common Team:		4.00	3.00	1.50
1	Atlanta Braves	40.00	30.00	15.00
2	Chicago Cubs	6.00	4.50	2.50
3	Cincinnati Reds	15.00	11.00	6.00
4	Colorado Rockies	5.00	3.75	2.00
5	Florida Marlins	5.00	3.75	2.00
6	Houston Astros	12.00	9.00	4.75
7	Los Angeles Dodgers	12.00	9.00	4.75
8	Montreal Expos	15.00	11.00	6.00
9	New York Mets	4.00	3.00	1.50
10	Philadelphia Phillies	20.00	15.00	8.00
11	Pittsburgh Pirates	4.00	3.00	1.50
12	St. Louis Cardinals	6.00	4.50	2.50
13	San Diego Padres	4.00	3.00	1.50
14	San Francisco Giants	20.00	15.00	8.00
15	Baltimore Orioles	20.00	15.00	8.00
16	Boston Red Sox	15.00	11.00	6.00
17	California Angels	4.00	3.00	1.50
18	Chicago White Sox	30.00	22.00	12.00
19	Cleveland Indians	20.00	15.00	8.00
20	Detroit Tigers	4.00	3.00	1.50
21	Kansas City Royals	4.00	3.00	1.50
22	Milwaukee Brewers	4.00	3.00	1.50
23	Minnesota Twins	8.00	6.00	3.25
24	New York Yankees	20.00	15.00	8.00
25	Oakland Athletics	4.00	3.00	1.50
26	Seattle Mariners	12.00	9.00	4.75
27	Texas Rangers	12.00	9.00	4.75
28	Toronto Blue Jays	25.00	18.00	10.00

1994 Topps Stadium Club Dugout Dirt Series I

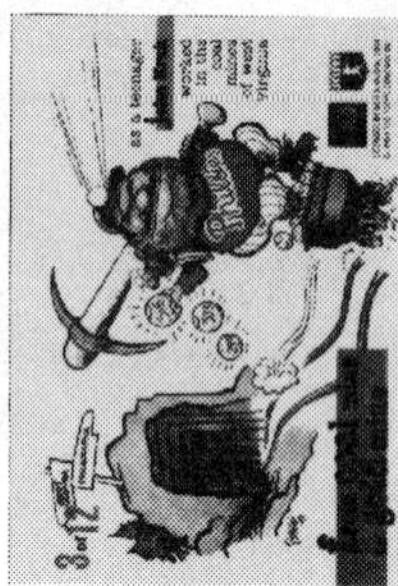

Cartoons of some of baseball's top stars are featured on the backs of this 12-card insert set. Fronts are virtually identical in format to regular S.C. cards, except the logo and box with the player's last name are in gold foil, rather than red.

		MT	NR MT	EX
Complete Set (4):		7.00	5.25	2.75
Common Player:		.50	.40	.20
1	Mike Piazza (The New Wave)	4.00	3.00	1.50
2	Dave Winfield (The Road to 3,000)	1.25	.90	.50
3	John Kruk (From Coal Mine to Gold Mine)	.50	.40	.20
4	Cal Ripken, Jr. (On Track)	2.00	1.50	.80

1994 Topps Stadium Club First Day Production

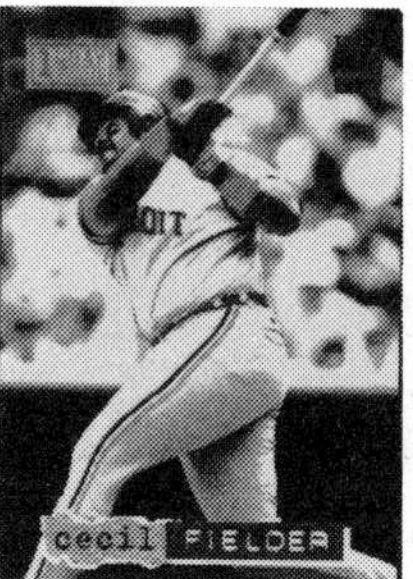

A special silver-foil embossment designating "1st Day Issue" was placed on fewer than 2,000 of each of the 720 regular cards in the '94 Stadium Club set. Inserted at the rate of one per 24 foil packs and one per 15 jumbo packs, the cards are otherwise in every way identical to the regular S.C. cards.

	MT	NR MT	EX
Complete Set:	2750.	2100.	1100.
Common Player:	3.00	2.25	1.25

Stars valued at 30-40X regular

1994 Topps Stadium Club Golden Rainbow

Found at the rate of one per pack, Stadium Club "Golden Rainbow" cards were issued for each of the 720 cards in the regular set. These inserts are distinguished by the use of gold prismatic foil highlights for the S.C. logo and box with the player's last name, instead of the red foil found on regular

	MT	NR MT	EX
Complete Set:	150.00	110.00	60.00
Common Player:	.50	.40	.20

Stars valued at 5X price of regular Topps S.C.

1994 Topps Stadium Club Infocards

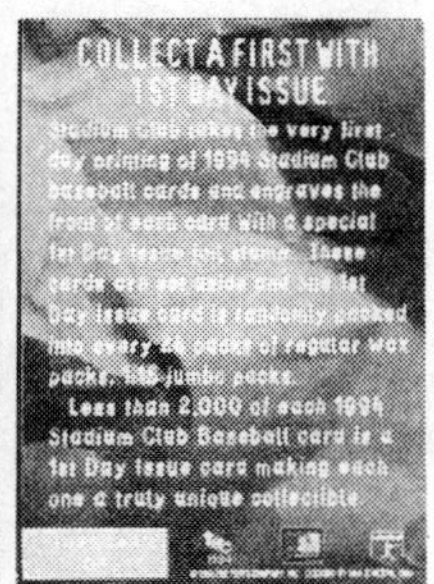

Though they do not picture ballplayers, and thus may never attain significant collector value, the fact that one of these "Infocards" was included in each pack of Series I Stadium Club cards warrants their inclusion in this catalog. The cards feature a baseball with Stadium Club logo on front. Backs have information on some aspect of the Stadium Club set or about baseball in general. Card #7 is missing the "7" in the "7 of 10" card number on back.

		MT	NR MT	EX
Complete Set (10):		.50	.40	.20
Common Card:		.05	.04	.02
1	1st Day Issue	.05	.04	.02
2	Tale of 2 Players	.05	.04	.02
3	Topps Trios	.05	.04	.02
4	Superteam Cards	.05	.04	.02
5	Dugout Dirt	.05	.04	.02
6	Home Run Club	.05	.04	.02
7	1993 Award Winners	.05	.04	.02
8	Major League Debut	.05	.04	.02
9	A Final Tribute	.05	.04	.02
10	New MLB Division Alignments	.05	.04	.02

1994 "1954" Topps Archives

Marketed as "The Ultimate 1954 Series," this Topps Archives set was a virtual reproduction of the popular 1954 baseball card issue. Of the 249 players, managers and coaches in the original set, 248 were included in the Archives release. Ted Williams, who was on cards #1 and 250 in the '54 set, was contractually prohibited by Upper Deck from appearing in the Archives issue. Eight "1954 Prospect" cards featuring future Hall of Famers and star players were appended to the reproduction cards to create a 256-card Archives issue. Cards were sold in 12-card packs, with one Gold card in each pack. There were 1,954 personally autographed cards of Henry Aaron inserted at random, along with cards that could be redeemed for genuine 1954 Topps cards and complete sets of Gold Archives cards. The Archives cards were produced in the now-standard 2-1/2" x 3-1/2" size, instead of the original 1954 dimensions of 2-5/8" x 3-3/4". That format allowed the Archives cards to have a white border at top which the originals lacked. While the card backs identify the Archives issue, they do not specify a 1994 production date anywhere.

		MT	NR MT	EX
Complete Set (256):		40.00	30.00	16.00
Common Player:		.20	.15	.08
2	Gus Zernial	.20	.15	.08
3	Monte Irvin	.30	.25	.12
4	Hank Sauer	.20	.15	.08
5	Ed Lopat	.25	.20	.10
6	Pete Runnels	.20	.15	.08
7	Ted Kluszewski	.25	.20	.10
8	Bobby Young	.20	.15	.08
9	Harvey Haddix	.20	.15	.08
10	Jackie Robinson	1.00	.70	.40
11	Paul Smith	.20	.15	.08
12	Del Crandall	.20	.15	.08
13	Billy Martin	.35	.25	.14
14	Preacher Roe	.25	.20	.10
15	Al Rosen	.20	.15	.08
16	Vic Janowicz	.20	.15	.08
17	Phil Rizzuto	.40	.30	.15
18	Walt Dropo	.20	.15	.08
19	Johnny Lipon	.20	.15	.08
20	Warren Spahn	.30	.25	.12
21	Bobby Shantz	.20	.15	.08
22	Jim Greengrass	.20	.15	.08
23	Luke Easter	.20	.15	.08
24	Granny Hamner	.20	.15	.08
25	Harvey Kuenn	.20	.15	.08
26	Ray Jablonski	.20	.15	.08
27	Ferris Fain	.20	.15	.08
28	Paul Minner	.20	.15	.08
29	Jim Hegan	.20	.15	.08
30	Eddie Mathews	.30	.25	.12
31	Johnny Klippstein	.20	.15	.08
32	Duke Snider	.60	.45	.25
33	Johnny Schmitz	.20	.15	.08
34	Jim Rivera	.20	.15	.08
35	Junior Gilliam	.25	.20	.10
36	Hoyt Wilhelm	.30	.25	.12
37	Whitey Ford	.45	.35	.20
38	Eddie Stanky	.20	.15	.08
39	Sherm Lollar	.20	.15	.08
40	Mel Parnell	.20	.15	.08
41	Willie Jones	.20	.15	.08
42	Don Mueller	.20	.15	.08
43	Dick Groat	.20	.15	.08
44	Ned Garver	.20	.15	.08
45	Richie Ashburn	.35	.25	.14
46	Ken Raffensberger	.20	.15	.08
47	Ellis Kinder	.20	.15	.08
48	Billy Hunter	.20	.15	.08
49	Ray Murray	.20	.15	.08
50	Yogi Berra	.60	.45	.25
51	Johnny Lindell	.20	.15	.08
52	Vic Power	.20	.15	.08
53	Jack Dittmer	.20	.15	.08
54	Vern Stephens	.20	.15	.08
55	Phil Cavarretta	.20	.15	.08
56	Willie Miranda	.25	.20	.10
57	Luis Aloma	.20	.15	.08
58	Bob Wilson	.20	.15	.08
59	Gene Conley	.20	.15	.08
60	Frank Baumholtz	.20	.15	.08
61	Bob Cain	.20	.15	.08
62	Eddie Robinson	.25	.20	.10
63	Johnny Pesky	.20	.15	.08
64	Hank Thompson	.20	.15	.08
65	Bob Swift	.20	.15	.08
66	Ted Lepcio	.20	.15	.08
67	Jim Willis	.20	.15	.08
68	Sam Calderone	.20	.15	.08
69	Bud Podbielan	.20	.15	.08
70	Larry Doby	.25	.20	.10
71	Frank Smith	.20	.15	.08
72	Preston Ward	.20	.15	.08
73	Wayne Terwilliger	.20	.15	.08
74	Bill Taylor	.20	.15	.08
75	Fred Haney	.20	.15	.08
76	Bob Scheffing	.20	.15	.08
77	Ray Boone	.20	.15	.08
78	Ted Kazanski	.20	.15	.08
79	Andy Pafko	.20	.15	.08
80	Jackie Jensen	.25	.20	.10
81	Dave Hoskins	.20	.15	.08
82	Milt Bolling	.20	.15	.08
83	Joe Collins	.25	.20	.10
84	Dick Cole	.20	.15	.08
85	Bob Turley	.30	.25	.12
86	Billy Herman	.25	.20	.10
87	Roy Face	.20	.15	.08
88	Matt Batts	.20	.15	.08
89	Howie Pollet	.20	.15	.08
90	Willie Mays	2.00	1.50	.80
91	Bob Oldis	.20	.15	.08
92	Wally Westlake	.20	.15	.08
93	Sid Hudson	.20	.15	.08
94	Ernie Banks	2.50	2.00	1.00
95	Hal Rice	.20	.15	.08
96	Charlie Silvera	.25	.20	.10
97	Jerry Lane	.20	.15	.08
98	Joe Black	.20	.15	.08
99	Bob Hofman	.20	.15	.08
100	Bob Keegan	.20	.15	.08
101	Gene Woodling	.25	.20	.10
102	Gil Hodges	.30	.25	.12
103	*Jim Lemon*	.20	.15	.08
104	Mike Sandlock	.20	.15	.08
105	Andy Carey	.25	.20	.10
106	Dick Kokos	.20	.15	.08
107	Duane Pillette	.20	.15	.08
108	Thornton Kipper	.20	.15	.08
109	Bill Bruton	.20	.15	.08
110	Harry Dorish	.20	.15	.08
111	Jim Delsing	.20	.15	.08
112	Bill Renna	.20	.15	.08
113	Bob Boyd	.20	.15	.08
114	Dean Stone	.20	.15	.08
115	"Rip" Repulski	.20	.15	.08
116	Steve Bilko	.20	.15	.08
117	Solly Hemus	.20	.15	.08
118	Carl Scheib	.20	.15	.08
119	Johnny Antonelli	.20	.15	.08
120	Roy McMillan	.20	.15	.08
121	Clem Labine	.25	.20	.10
122	Johnny Logan	.20	.15	.08
123	Bobby Adams	.20	.15	.08
124	Marion Fricano	.20	.15	.08
125	Harry Perkowski	.20	.15	.08
126	Ben Wade	.20	.15	.08
127	Steve O'Neill	.20	.15	.08
128	Hank Aaron	3.00	2.25	1.25
129	Forrest Jacobs	.20	.15	.08
130	Hank Bauer	.30	.25	.12
131	Reno Bertoia	.20	.15	.08
132	Tom Lasorda	.75	.60	.30
133	Del Baker	.20	.15	.08
134	Cal Hogue	.20	.15	.08
135	Joe Presko	.20	.15	.08
136	Connie Ryan	.20	.15	.08
137	Wally Moon	.20	.15	.08
138	Bob Borkowski	.20	.15	.08
139	Ed & Johnny O'Brien	.25	.20	.10
140	Tom Wright	.20	.15	.08
141	Joe Jay	.20	.15	.08
142	Tom Poholsky	.20	.15	.08
143	Rollie Hemsley	.20	.15	.08
144	Bill Werle	.20	.15	.08
145	Elmer Valo	.20	.15	.08
146	Don Johnson	.20	.15	.08
147	John Riddle	.20	.15	.08
148	Bob Trice	.20	.15	.08
149	Jim Robertson	.20	.15	.08
150	Dick Kryhoski	.20	.15	.08
151	Alex Grammas	.20	.15	.08
152	Mike Blyzka	.20	.15	.08
153	Rube Walker	.20	.15	.08
154	Mike Fornieles	.20	.15	.08
155	Bob Kennedy	.20	.15	.08
156	Joe Coleman	.20	.15	.08
157	Don Lenhardt	.20	.15	.08
158	Peanuts Lowrey	.20	.15	.08
159	Dave Philley	.20	.15	.08
160	Red Kress	.20	.15	.08
161	John Hetki	.20	.15	.08
162	Herman Wehmeier	.20	.15	.08
163	Frank House	.20	.15	.08
164	Stu Miller	.20	.15	.08
165	Jim Pendleton	.20	.15	.08
166	Johnny Podres	.30	.25	.12
167	Don Lund	.20	.15	.08
168	Morrie Martin	.20	.15	.08
169	Jim Hughes	.20	.15	.08
170	Dusty Rhodes	.20	.15	.08
171	Leo Kiely	.20	.15	.08
172	Hal Brown	.20	.15	.08
173	Jack Harshman	.20	.15	.08
174	Tom Qualters	.20	.15	.08
175	Frank Leja	.25	.20	.10
176	Bob Keely	.20	.15	.08
177	Bob Milliken	.20	.15	.08
178	Bill Glynn	.20	.15	.08
179	Gair Allie	.20	.15	.08
180	Wes Westrum	.20	.15	.08
181	Mel Roach	.20	.15	.08
182	Chuck Harmon	.20	.15	.08
183	Earle Combs	.20	.15	.08
184	Ed Bailey	.20	.15	.08
185	Chuck Stobbs	.20	.15	.08
186	Karl Olson	.20	.15	.08
187	Heinie Manush	.20	.15	.08
188	Dave Jolly	.20	.15	.08
189	Bob Ross	.20	.15	.08
190	Ray Herbert	.20	.15	.08
191	*Dick Schofield*	.20	.15	.08
192	Cot Deal	.20	.15	.08
193	Johnny Hopp	.20	.15	.08
194	Bill Sarni	.20	.15	.08
195	Bill Consolo	.20	.15	.08
196	Stan Jok	.20	.15	.08
197	Schoolboy Rowe	.20	.15	.08
198	Carl Sawatski	.20	.15	.08
199	Rocky Nelson	.20	.15	.08
200	Larry Jansen	.20	.15	.08
201	Al Kaline	2.00	1.50	.80
202	Bob Purkey	.20	.15	.08
203	Harry Brecheen	.20	.15	.08
204	Angel Scull	.20	.15	.08
205	Johnny Sain	.30	.25	.12
206	Ray Crone	.20	.15	.08
207	Tom Oliver	.20	.15	.08
208	Grady Hatton	.20	.15	.08
209	Charlie Thompson	.20	.15	.08
210	Bob Buhl	.20	.15	.08
211	Don Hoak	.25	.20	.10
212	Mickey Micelotta	.20	.15	.08
213	John Fitzpatrick	.20	.15	.08
214	Arnold Portocarrero	.20	.15	.08
215	Ed McGhee	.20	.15	.08
216	Al Sima	.20	.15	.08
217	Paul Schreiber	.20	.15	.08
218	Fred Marsh	.20	.15	.08
219	Charlie Kress	.20	.15	.08
220	Ruben Gomez	.20	.15	.08
221	Dick Brodowski	.20	.15	.08
222	Bill Wilson	.20	.15	.08
223	Joe Haynes	.20	.15	.08
224	Dick Weik	.20	.15	.08
225	Don Liddle	.20	.15	.08
226	Jehosie Heard	.20	.15	.08
227	Buster Mills	.20	.15	.08
228	Gene Hermanski	.20	.15	.08
229	Bob Talbot	.20	.15	.08
230	Bob Kuzava	.25	.20	.10
231	Roy Smalley	.20	.15	.08
232	Lou Limmer	.20	.15	.08
233	Augie Galan	.20	.15	.08

234	Jerry Lynch	.20	.15	.08
235	Vern Law	.20	.15	.08
236	Paul Penson	.20	.15	.08
237	Mike Ryba	.20	.15	.08
238	Al Aber	.20	.15	.08
239	Bill Skowron	.45	.35	.20
240	Sam Mele	.20	.15	.08
241	Bob Miller	.20	.15	.08
242	Curt Roberts	.20	.15	.08
243	Ray Blades	.20	.15	.08
244	Leroy Wheat	.20	.15	.08
245	Roy Sievers	.20	.15	.08
246	Howie Fox	.20	.15	.08
247	Eddie Mayo	.20	.15	.08
248	*Al Smith*	.20	.15	.08
249	Wilmer Mizell	.20	.15	.08
251	Roberto Clemente	3.00	2.25	1.25
252	Bob Grim	.25	.20	.10
253	Elston Howard	.30	.25	.12
254	Harmon Killebrew	1.00	.70	.40
255	Camilo Pascual	.20	.15	.08
256	Herb Score	.20	.15	.08
257	Bill Virdon	.20	.15	.08
258	Don Zimmer	.30	.25	.12

1994 Topps Gold Archives

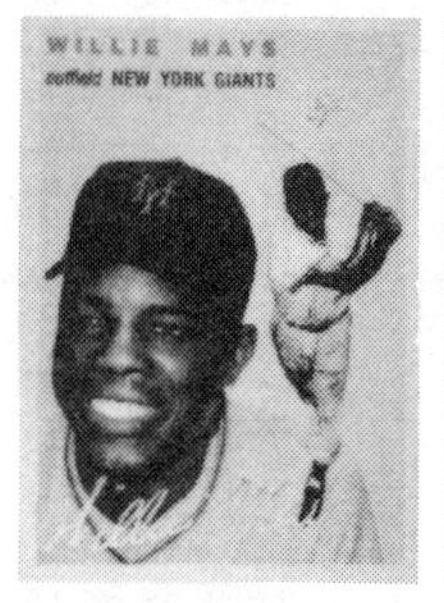

Issued as a premium insert at the rate of one per foil pack, gold versions of each of the cards in the 1954 Archives set differ from the regular cards only in that the team logo at top and player facsimile autograph on bottom are printed in gold foil. Redemption cards for complete Archives gold sets were also randomly inserted into Archives packs.

	MT	NR MT	EX
Complete Set (256):	150.00	110.00	60.00
Common Player:	.50	.40	.20

Star cards: Valued at 5x to 7x regular Topps Archives

1987 Toys "R" Us

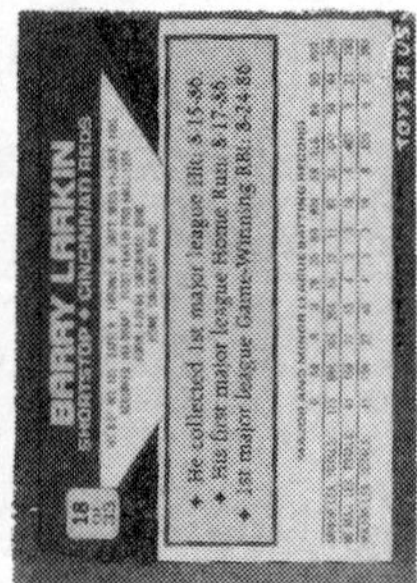

Marked as a collectors' edition set and titled "Baseball Rookies," the 1987 Toys "R" Us issue was produced by Topps for the toy store chain. The set is comprised of 33 glossy-coated cards, each measuring 2-1/2" by 3-1/2". The card fronts are very colorful, employing nine different colors including deep black borders. The backs, printed in blue and orange, contain career highlights and composite minor and major league statistics. The set was distributed in a specially designed box and sold for $1.99 in retail outlets.

	MT	NR MT	EX
Complete Set:	6.00	4.50	2.50
Common Player:	.10	.08	.04

1	Andy Allanson	.10	.08	.04
2	Paul Assenmacher	.12	.09	.05
3	Scott Bailes	.10	.08	.04
4	Barry Bonds	.60	.45	.25
5	Jose Canseco	.90	.70	.35
6	John Cerutti	.10	.08	.04
7	Will Clark	.60	.45	.25
8	Kal Daniels	.15	.11	.06
9	Jim Deshaies	.10	.08	.04
10	Mark Eichhorn	.10	.08	.04
11	Ed Hearn	.10	.08	.04
12	Pete Incaviglia	.12	.09	.05
13	Bo Jackson	.60	.45	.25
14	Wally Joyner	.30	.25	.12
15	Charlie Kerfeld	.10	.08	.04
16	Eric King	.10	.08	.04
17	John Kruk	.40	.30	.15
18	Barry Larkin	.30	.25	.12
19	Mike LaValliere	.10	.08	.04
20	Greg Mathews	.10	.08	.04
21	Kevin Mitchell	.20	.15	.08
22	Dan Plesac	.10	.08	.04
23	Bruce Ruffin	.10	.08	.04
24	Ruben Sierra	.50	.40	.20
25	Cory Snyder	.10	.08	.04
26	Kurt Stillwell	.10	.08	.04
27	Dale Sveum	.10	.08	.04
28	Danny Tartabull	.30	.25	.12
29	Andres Thomas	.10	.08	.04
30	Robby Thompson	.25	.20	.10
31	Jim Traber	.10	.08	.04
32	Mitch Williams	.15	.11	.06
33	Todd Worrell	.15	.11	.06

1988 Toys "R" Us Rookies

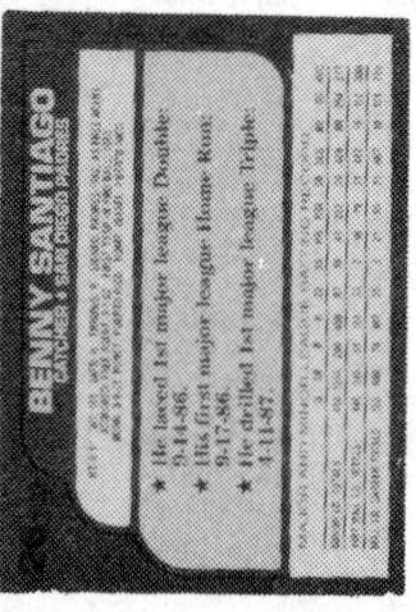

This 33-card boxed edition was produced by Topps for exclusive distribution at Toys "R" Us stores. The glossy standard-size cards spotlight rookies in both closeups and action photos on a bright blue background inlaid with yellow. The Toys "R" Us logo frames the top left corner, above a curving white banner that reads "Topps 1988 Collectors' Edition Rookies". A black Topps logo hugs the upper right-hand edge of the photo. The player name, red-lettered on a tube of yellow, frames the bottom. Card backs are horizontal, blue and pink on a bright pink background and include the player name, personal information and career highlights and stats.

	MT	NR MT	EX
Complete Set:	5.00	3.75	2.00
Common Player:	.10	.08	.04

1	Todd Benzinger	.20	.15	.08
2	Bob Brower	.10	.08	.04
3	Jerry Browne	.10	.08	.04
4	DeWayne Buice	.10	.08	.04
5	Ellis Burks	.30	.25	.12
6	Ken Caminiti	.20	.15	.08
7	Casey Candaele	.10	.08	.04
8	Dave Cone	.35	.25	.14
9	Kelly Downs	.10	.08	.04
10	Mike Dunne	.10	.08	.04
11	Ken Gerhart	.10	.08	.04
12	Mike Greenwell	.35	.25	.14
13	Mike Henneman	.15	.11	.06
14	Sam Horn	.10	.08	.04
15	Joe Magrane	.10	.08	.04
16	Fred Manrique	.10	.08	.04
17	John Marzano	.10	.08	.04
18	Fred McGriff	.40	.30	.15
19	Mark McGwire	.50	.40	.20
20	Jeff Musselman	.10	.08	.04
21	Randy Myers	.20	.15	.08
22	Matt Nokes	.15	.11	.06
23	Al Pedrique	.10	.08	.04
24	Luis Polonia	.15	.11	.06
25	Billy Ripken	.10	.08	.04
26	Benny Santiago	.30	.25	.12
27	Kevin Seitzer	.10	.08	.04
28	John Smiley	.12	.09	.05
29	Mike Stanley	.10	.08	.04
30	Terry Steinbach	.20	.15	.08
31	B.J. Surhoff	.15	.11	.06
32	Bobby Thigpen	.15	.11	.06
33	Devon White	.25	.20	.10

1989 Toys "R" Us Rookies

This glossy set of 33 top rookies was produced by Topps for the Toys "R" Us chain and was sold in a special box. Each player's name and position appear below the full-color photo, while the Toys "R"

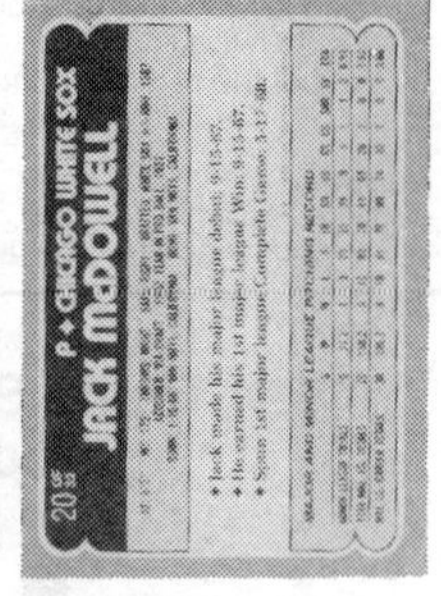

Us logo and "Topps 1989 Collector's Edition" appear along the top. Major and minor league stats are on the back. The set is numbered alphabetically.

	MT	NR MT	EX
Complete Set:	4.00	3.00	1.50
Common Player:	.10	.08	.04

1	Roberto Alomar	.50	.40	.20
2	Brady Anderson	.15	.11	.06
3	Tim Belcher	.15	.11	.06
4	Damon Berryhill	.10	.08	.04
5	Jay Buhner	.12	.09	.05
6	Sherman Corbett	.10	.08	.04
7	Kevin Elster	.10	.08	.04
8	Cecil Espy	.10	.08	.04
9	Dave Gallagher	.12	.09	.05
10	Ron Gant	.35	.25	.14
11	Paul Gibson	.10	.08	.04
12	Mark Grace	.40	.30	.15
13	Bryan Harvey	.20	.15	.08
14	Darrin Jackson	.10	.08	.04
15	Gregg Jefferies	.40	.30	.15
16	Ron Jones	.10	.08	.04
17	Ricky Jordan	.10	.08	.04
18	Roberto Kelly	.30	.25	.12
19	Al Leiter	.10	.08	.04
20	Jack McDowell	.35	.25	.14
21	Melido Perez	.10	.08	.04
22	Jeff Pico	.10	.08	.04
23	Jody Reed	.10	.08	.04
24	Chris Sabo	.25	.20	.10
25	Nelson Santovenia	.10	.08	.04
26	Mackey Sasser	.10	.08	.04
27	Mike Schooler	.12	.09	.05
28	Gary Sheffield	.40	.30	.15
29	Pete Smith	.15	.11	.06
30	Pete Stanicek	.10	.08	.04
31	Jeff Treadway	.10	.08	.04
32	Walt Weiss	.25	.20	.10
33	Dave West	.15	.11	.06

1990 Toys "R" Us Rookies

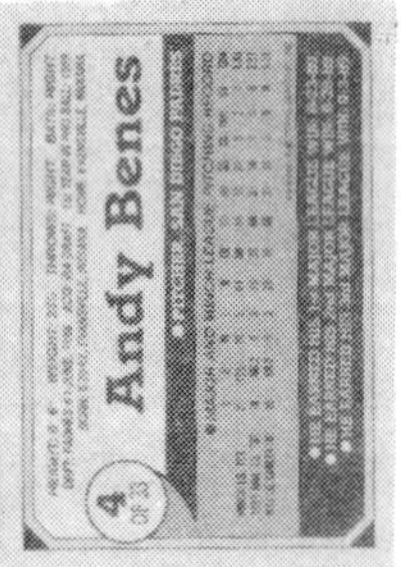

This 33-card set marks the fourth straight year that Topps has produced a set to be sold exclusively at Toys "R" Us stores. The card fronts contain full-color photos of 1989 rookies. The flip sides are horizontal and provide both minor and major league totals. The complete set is packaged in a special box which features a checklist uon the back.

	MT	NR MT	EX
Complete Set:	5.00	3.75	2.00
Common Player:	.10	.08	.04

1	Jim Abbott	.50	.40	.20
2	Eric Anthony	.30	.25	.12
3	Joey Belle	.60	.45	.25
4	Andy Benes	.20	.15	.08
5	Greg Briley	.15	.11	.06
6	Kevin Brown	.10	.08	.04
7	Mark Carreon	.10	.08	.04
8	Mike Devereaux	.15	.11	.06
9	Junior Felix	.25	.20	.10
10	Mark Gardner	.15	.11	.06
11	Bob Geren	.10	.08	.04
12	Tom Gordon	.10	.08	.04

13	Ken Griffey, Jr.	2.00	1.50	.80
14	Pete Harnisch	.10	.08	.04
15	Ken Hill	.10	.08	.04
16	Gregg Jefferies	.30	.25	.12
17	Derek Lilliquist	.10	.08	.04
18	Carlos Martinez	.10	.08	.04
19	Ramon Martinez	.20	.15	.08
20	Bob Milacki	.10	.08	.04
21	Gregg Olson	.15	.11	.06
22	Kenny Rogers	.10	.08	.04
23	Alex Sanchez	.10	.08	.04
24	Gary Sheffield	.30	.25	.12
25	Dwight Smith	.10	.08	.04
26	Billy Spiers	.10	.08	.04
27	Greg Vaughn	.30	.25	.12
28	Robin Ventura	.40	.30	.15
29	Jerome Walton	.10	.08	.04
30	Dave West	.10	.08	.04
31	John Wetteland	.15	.11	.06
32	Craig Worthington	.10	.08	.04
33	Todd Zeile	.20	.15	.08

1991 Toys "R" Us Rookies

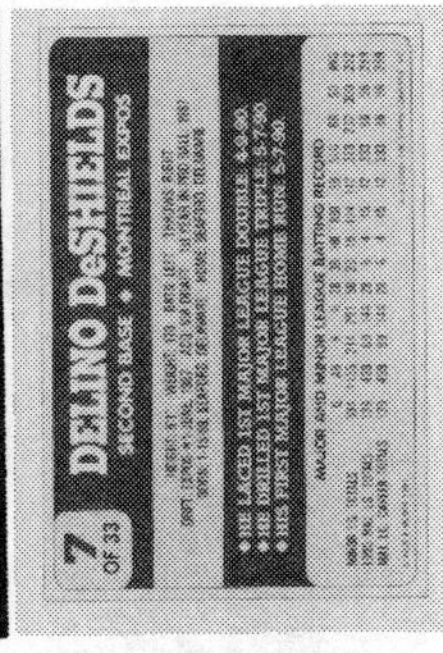

Produced by Topps, this 33-card set features baseball's top young players. The cards are styled much like past Toys "R" Us issues featuring glossy photos. The backs are printed horizontally and include player information and statistics. This set is the fifth of its kind produced by Topps for Toys "R" Us.

		MT	NR MT	EX
	Complete Set:	5.00	3.75	2.00
	Common Player:	.10	.08	.04
1	Sandy Alomar, Jr.	.10	.08	.04
2	Kevin Appier	.15	.11	.06
3	Steve Avery	.40	.30	.15
4	Carlos Baerga	.60	.45	.25
5	Alex Cole	.15	.11	.06
6	Pat Combs	.10	.08	.04
7	Delino DeShields	.30	.25	.12
8	Travis Fryman	.40	.30	.15
9	Marquis Grissom	.30	.25	.12
10	Mike Harkey	.10	.08	.04
11	Glenallen Hill	.10	.08	.04
12	Jeff Huson	.10	.08	.04
13	Felix Jose	.20	.15	.08
14	Dave Justice	.60	.45	.25
15	Dana Kiecker	.10	.08	.04
16	Kevin Maas	.15	.11	.06
17	Ben McDonald	.20	.15	.08
18	Brian McRae	.30	.25	.12
19	Kent Mercker	.10	.08	.04
20	Hal Morris	.20	.15	.08
21	Chris Nabholz	.10	.08	.04
22	Tim Naehring	.10	.08	.04
23	Jose Offerman	.15	.11	.06
24	John Olerud	.35	.25	.14
25	Scott Radinsky	.10	.08	.04
26	Bill Sampen	.10	.08	.04
27	Frank Thomas	2.00	1.50	.80
28	Randy Tomlin	.15	.11	.06
29	Greg Vaughn	.20	.15	.08
30	Robin Ventura	.40	.30	.15
31	Larry Walker	.30	.25	.12
32	Wally Whitehurst	.10	.08	.04
33	Todd Zeile	.20	.15	.08

1993 Toys "R" Us Topps Stadium Club

Featuring subsets labeled "Young Stars," "Future Stars" and "Rookie Stars," this 100-card set was sold in a plastic replica of a Toys "R" Us store, packaged with a dozen "Master Photos." Similar to regular 1993 Topps Stadium Club cards, the Toys "R" Us version features full-bleed photos on front, highlighed with goil-foil and a color Toys "R" Us logo in one of the upper corners. Backs have a background of a cloud-filled blue sky and green grass. A small player photo is at upper-right. Back information offers a few personal details, 1992 and career stats and a few career highlights. At bottom are the logos of all involved parties. The cards are UV-

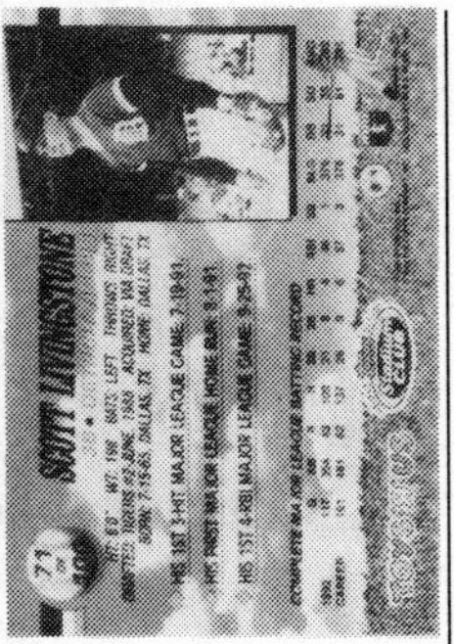

coated front and back. Each card is designated on the front as "Rookie Star," "Young Star" or "Future Star" in gold foil.

		MT	NR MT	EX
	Complete Set:	9.00	6.75	3.50
	Common Player:	.10	.08	.04
1	Ken Griffey, Jr.	1.50	1.25	.60
2	Chad Curtis	.15	.11	.06
3	Mike Bordick	.10	.08	.04
4	Ryan Klesko	.40	.30	.15
5	Pat Listach	.10	.08	.04
6	Jim Bullinger	.10	.08	.04
7	Tim Laker	.10	.08	.04
8	Mike Devereaux	.10	.08	.04
9	Kevin Young	.20	.15	.08
10	John Valentin	.10	.08	.04
11	Pat Mahomes	.15	.11	.06
12	Todd Hundley	.10	.08	.04
13	Roberto Alomar	.30	.25	.12
14	David Justice	.30	.25	.12
15	Mike Perez	.10	.08	.04
16	Royce Clayton	.10	.08	.04
17	Ryan Thompson	.10	.08	.04
18	Dave Hollins	.15	.11	.06
19	Brien Taylor	.20	.15	.08
20	Melvin Nieves	.20	.15	.08
21	Rheal Cormier	.20	.15	.08
22	Mike Piazza	.75	.60	.30
23	Larry Walker	.15	.11	.06
24	Tim Wakefield	.10	.08	.04
25	Tim Costo	.10	.08	.04
26	Pedro Munoz	.10	.08	.04
27	Reggie Sanders	.15	.11	.06
28	Arthur Rhodes	.15	.11	.06
29	Scott Cooper	.10	.08	.04
30	Marquis Grissom	.20	.15	.08
31	Dave Nilsson	.10	.08	.04
32	John Patterson	.10	.08	.04
33	Ivan Rodriguez	.20	.15	.08
34	Andy Stankiewicz	.12	.09	.05
35	Bret Boone	.12	.09	.05
36	Gerald Williams	.12	.09	.05
37	Mike Mussina	.20	.15	.08
38	Henry Rodriguez	.15	.11	.06
39	Chuck Knoblauch	.15	.11	.06
40	Bob Wickman	.10	.08	.04
41	Donovan Osborne	.10	.08	.04
42	Mike Timlin	.10	.08	.04
43	Damion Easley	.15	.11	.06
44	Pedro Astacio	.15	.11	.06
45	David Segui	.10	.08	.04
46	Willie Greene	.15	.11	.06
47	Mike Trombley	.10	.08	.04
48	Bernie Williams	.12	.09	.05
49	Eric Anthony	.15	.11	.06
50	Tim Naehring	.10	.08	.04
51	Carlos Baerga	.30	.25	.12
52	Brady Anderson	.12	.09	.05
53	Mo Vaughn	.15	.11	.06
54	Willie Banks	.12	.09	.05
55	Mark Wohlers	.10	.08	.04
56	Jeff Bagwell	.15	.11	.06
57	Frank Seminara	.10	.08	.04
58	Robin Ventura	.20	.15	.08
59	Alan Embree	.10	.08	.04
60	Rey Sanchez	.10	.08	.04
61	Delino DeShields	.15	.11	.06
62	Todd Van Poppel	.20	.15	.08
63	Eric Karros	.25	.20	.10
64	Gary Sheffield	.20	.15	.08
65	Dan Wilson	.12	.09	.05
66	Frank Thomas	1.50	1.25	.60
67	Tim Salmon	.90	.70	.35
68	Dan Smith	.15	.11	.06
69	Kenny Lofton	.25	.20	.10
70	Carlos Garcia	.15	.11	.06
71	Scott Livingstone	.15	.11	.06
72	Sam Militello	.10	.08	.04
73	Juan Guzman	.12	.09	.05
74	Greg Colbrunn	.10	.08	.04
75	David Hulse	.10	.08	.04
76	Rusty Meacham	.10	.08	.04
77	Dave Fleming	.10	.08	.04
78	Rene Arocha	.15	.11	.06
79	Derrick May	.15	.11	.06
80	Cal Eldred	.10	.08	.04
81	Bernard Gilkey	.15	.11	.06
82	Deion Sanders	.20	.15	.08
83	Reggie Jefferson	.10	.08	.04
84	Jeff Kent	.10	.08	.04
85	Juan Gonzalez	.60	.45	.25
86	Bill Ashley	.10	.08	.04
87	Travis Fryman	.20	.15	.08
88	Roberto Hernandez	.12	.09	.05
89	Hipolito Pichardo	.10	.08	.04
90	Wil Cordero	.20	.15	.08
91	John Jaha	.10	.08	.04
92	Javy Lopez	.30	.25	.12
93	Derek Bell	.15	.11	.06
94	Jeff Juden	.10	.08	.04
95	Steve Avery	.20	.15	.08
96	Moises Alou	.20	.15	.08
97	Brian Jordan	.15	.11	.06
98	Brian Williams	.10	.08	.04
99	Bob Zupcic	.10	.08	.04
100	Ray Lankford	.15	.11	.06

1993 Toys "R" Us Master Photos

Each boxed set of Toys "R" Us Stadium Club cards comes with a set of 12 Master Photos. Similar to the regular 1993 S.C. Master Photos, they feature at center a larger 2-3/4" x 3-3/4"), uncropped version of the photo used on the Toys "R" Us card. A gold holographic box on the photo delineates the dimensions of the regular card, while another separates the photo from the 5" x 7" white background. Topps, Toys "R" Us, and Master Photo logos appear at the top of the card. Blank white backs have a few logos and copyrights printed in black.

		MT	NR MT	EX
	Complete Set:	4.50	3.50	1.75
	Common Player:	.50	.40	.20
(1)	Willie Greene	.50	.40	.20
(2)	Frank Thomas	1.50	1.25	.60
(3)	Chuck Knoblauch	.50	.40	.20
(4)	Marquis Grissom	.50	.40	.20
(5)	Scott Livingstone	.50	.40	.20
(6)	Ken Griffey, Jr.	1.50	1.25	.60
(7)	Carlos Baerga	.60	.45	.25
(8)	Ivan Rodriguez	.50	.40	.20
(9)	Moises Alou	.50	.40	.20
(10)	Sam Militello	.50	.40	.20
(11)	Eric Anthony	.50	.40	.20
(12)	Gary Sheffield	.60	.45	.25

1969 Transogram

Produced by the Transogram toy company, the 2-1/2" by 3-1/2" cards were printed on the bottom of toy baseball player statue boxes. The cards feature a color photo of the player surrounded by a rounded white border. Below the photo is the player's name in red and his team and other personal details all printed in black. The overall background is yellow. The cards were designed to be cut off the box, but collectors prefer to find the box intact and better still, with the statue inside. Although the 60-card set features a lot of stars, and is fairly scarce, it does not enjoy a lot of popularity today.

		NR MT	EX	VG
	Complete Set:	650.00	325.00	195.00
	Common Player:	.80	.40	.25
(1)	Hank Aaron	30.00	15.00	9.00
(2)	Richie Allen	4.00	2.00	1.25

(3)	Felipe Alou	4.00	2.00	1.25
(4)	Matty Alou	3.00	1.50	.90
(5)	Luis Aparicio	15.00	7.50	4.50
(6)	Joe Azcue	2.00	1.00	.60
(7)	Ernie Banks	20.00	10.00	6.00
(8)	Lou Brock	15.00	7.50	4.50
(9)	John Callison	3.00	1.50	.90
(10)	Jose Cardenal	2.00	1.00	.60
(11)	Danny Cater	2.00	1.00	.60
(12)	Roberto Clemente	30.00	15.00	9.00
(13)	Willie Davis	1.00	.50	.30
(14)	Mike Epstein	2.00	1.00	.60
(15)	Jim Fregosi	1.00	.50	.30
(16)	Bob Gibson	15.00	7.50	4.50
(17)	Tom Haller	2.00	1.00	.60
(18)	Ken Harrelson	3.00	1.50	.90
(19)	Willie Horton	3.00	1.50	.90
(20)	Frank Howard	1.50	.70	.45
(21)	Tommy John	8.00	4.00	2.50
(22)	Al Kaline	20.00	10.00	6.00
(23)	Harmon Killebrew	20.00	10.00	6.00
(24)	Bobby Knoop	1.00	.50	.30
(25)	Jerry Koosman	1.50	.70	.45
(26)	Jim Lefebvre	1.50	.70	.45
(27)	Mickey Mantle	125.00	62.00	37.00
(28)	Juan Marichal	15.00	7.50	4.50
(29)	Lee May	1.00	.50	.30
(30)	Willie Mays	30.00	15.00	9.00
(31)	Bill Mazeroski	8.00	4.00	2.50
(32)	Tim McCarver	3.00	1.50	.90
(33)	Willie McCovey	20.00	10.00	6.00
(34)	Denny McLain	1.50	.70	.45
(35)	Dave McNally	1.00	.50	.30
(36)	Rick Monday	1.00	.50	.30
(37)	Blue Moon Odom	.80	.40	.25
(38)	Tony Oliva	1.50	.70	.45
(39)	Camilo Pascual	1.00	.50	.30
(40)	Tony Perez	6.00	3.00	1.75
(41)	Rico Petrocelli	1.00	.50	.30
(42)	Rick Reichardt	.80	.40	.25
(43)	Brooks Robinson	25.00	12.50	7.50
(44)	Frank Robinson	20.00	10.00	6.00
(45)	Cookie Rojas	1.00	.50	.30
(46)	Pete Rose	30.00	15.00	9.00
(47)	Ron Santo	1.50	.70	.45
(48)	Tom Seaver	20.00	10.00	6.00
(49)	Rusty Staub	2.00	1.00	.60
(50)	Mel Stottlemyre	1.00	.50	.30
(51)	Ron Swoboda	.80	.40	.25
(52)	Luis Tiant	3.00	1.50	.90
(53)	Joe Torre	3.00	1.50	.90
(54)	Cesar Tovar	.80	.40	.25
(55)	Pete Ward	.80	.40	.25
(56)	Roy White	1.50	.70	.45
(57)	Billy Williams	15.00	7.50	4.50
(58)	Don Wilson	.80	.40	.25
(59)	Jim Wynn	.80	.40	.25
(60)	Carl Yastrzemski	25.00	12.50	7.50

1970 Transogram

Like the 1969 cards, the 1970 Transogram cards were available on boxes of Transogram baseball statues. The cards are slightly larger at 2-9/16" by 3-1/2". The 30-card set has the same pictures as the 1969 set except for Joe Torre. All players in the '70 set were included in the '69 Transogram issue except for Reggie Jackson, Sam McDowell and Boog Powell. Transogram box in 1970. When available, most collectors prefer to find the cards as uncut panels of three, better yet, as complete boxes.

		NR MT	EX	VG
Complete Set:		325.00	162.00	97.00
Common Player:		.80	.40	.25
(1)	Hank Aaron	30.00	15.00	9.00
(2)	Ernie Banks	18.00	9.00	5.50
(3)	Roberto Clemente	30.00	15.00	9.00
(4)	Willie Davis	1.00	.50	.30
(5)	Jim Fregosi	1.00	.50	.30
(6)	Bob Gibson	15.00	7.50	4.50
(7)	Frank Howard	1.50	.70	.45
(8)	Reggie Jackson	30.00	15.00	9.00
(9)	Cleon Jones	.80	.40	.25
(10)	Al Kaline	18.00	9.00	5.50
(11)	Harmon Killebrew	18.00	9.00	5.50
(12)	Jerry Koosman	.80	.40	.25
(13)	Willie McCovey	18.00	9.00	5.50
(14)	Sam McDowell	3.00	1.50	.90
(15)	Denny McLain	3.00	1.50	.90
(16)	Juan Marichal	12.00	6.00	3.50
(17)	Willie Mays	30.00	15.00	9.00
(18)	Blue Moon Odom	.80	.40	.25
(19)	Tony Oliva	1.50	.70	.45
(20)	Rico Petrocelli	1.00	.50	.30
(21)	Boog Powell	4.00	2.00	1.25
(22)	Rick Reichardt	.80	.40	.25
(23)	Frank Robinson	18.00	9.00	5.50
(24)	Pete Rose	30.00	15.00	9.00
(25)	Ron Santo	1.50	.70	.45
(26)	Tom Seaver	18.00	9.00	5.50
(27)	Mel Stottlemyre	1.00	.50	.30
(28)	Joe Torre	4.00	2.00	1.25
(29)	Jim Wynn	.80	.40	.25
(30)	Carl Yastrzemski	25.00	12.50	7.50

1970 Transogram Mets

The Transogram Mets set is a second set that the company produced in 1970. The cards are 2-9/16" by 3-1/2" and feature members of the World Champions Mets team. There are 15 cards in the set which retains the basic color picture with player's names in red and team, position and biographical details in a black format. As with the other Transogram sets, the cards are most valuable when they are still part of their original box with the statues. Values decrease for them if the cards are removed from the box. While the Mets set does not have the attraction of many Hall of Famers as was the case with the regular set, it does make a very nice item for the Mets team collector.

		NR MT	EX	VG
Complete Set:		200.00	100.00	60.00
Common Player:		1.50	.70	.45
(1)	Tommie Agee	3.00	1.50	.90
(2)	Ken Boswell	1.50	.70	.45
(3)	Donn Clendenon	3.00	1.50	.90
(4)	Gary Gentry	1.50	.70	.45
(5)	Jerry Grote	3.00	1.50	.90
(6)	Bud Harrelson	3.00	1.50	.90
(7)	Cleon Jones	1.50	.70	.45
(8)	Jerry Koosman	1.50	.70	.45
(9)	Ed Kranepool	3.00	1.50	.90
(10)	Tug McGraw	7.00	3.50	2.00
(11)	Nolan Ryan	125.00	62.00	37.00
(12)	Art Shamsky	2.00	1.00	.60
(13)	Tom Seaver	40.00	20.00	12.00
(14)	Ron Swoboda	1.50	.70	.45
(15)	Al Weis	1.50	.70	.45

1983 True Value White Sox

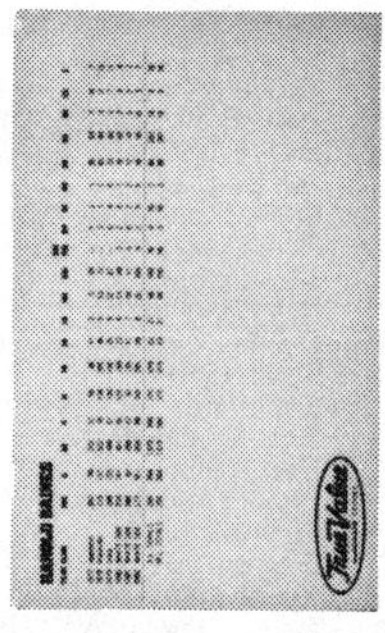

Issued by the Chicago White Sox and True Value hardware stores, these 2-5/8" by 4-1/8" cards are a rather expensive and scarce regional set. The 23-card set was originally scheduled as part of a promotion in which cards were given out at special Tuesday night games. The idea was sound, but rain-outs forced the cancellation of some games so those scheduled cards were never given out. They were, however, smuggled out to hobby channels making it possible, although not easy, to assemble complete sets. The cards feature a large color photo with a wide white border. A red and blue White Sox logo is in the lower left corner, while the player's name, position and team number are in the lower right. Backs feature a True Value ad along with statistics. The three cards which were never given out through the normal channels are considered more scarce than the others. They are Marc Hill, Harold Baines and Salome Barojas.

		MT	NR MT	EX
Complete Set:		30.00	22.00	12.00
Common Player:		.40	.30	.15
1	Scott Fletcher	.60	.45	.25
2	Harold Baines	7.00	5.25	2.75
5	Vance Law	.40	.30	.15
7	Marc Hill	3.25	2.50	1.25
10	Tony LaRussa	.75	.60	.30
11	Rudy Law	.40	.30	.15
14	Tony Bernazard	.40	.30	.15
17	Jerry Hairston	.40	.30	.15
19	Greg Luzinski	1.00	.70	.40
24	Floyd Bannister	.60	.45	.25
25	Mike Squires	.40	.30	.15
30	Salome Barojas	3.25	2.50	1.25
31	LaMarr Hoyt	.50	.40	.20
34	Richard Dotson	.40	.30	.15
36	Jerry Koosman	.70	.50	.30
40	Britt Burns	.40	.30	.15
41	Dick Tidrow	.40	.30	.15
42	Ron Kittle	1.75	1.25	.70
44	Tom Paciorek	.40	.30	.15
45	Kevin Hickey	.40	.30	.15
53	Dennis Lamp	.40	.30	.15
67	Jim Kern	.40	.30	.15
72	Carlton Fisk	3.00	2.25	1.25

1984 True Value White Sox

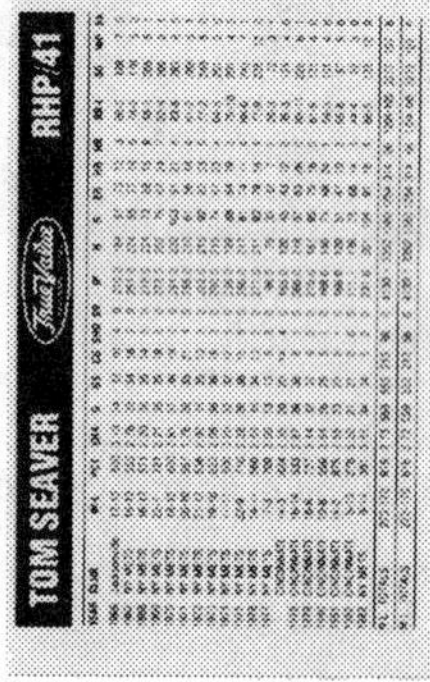

True Value hardware stores and the Chicago White Sox gave their Tuesday night baseball card promotion at Comiskey Park another try in 1984. The cards measure 2-5/8" by 4-1/8" with 30 cards comprising the set. In addition to the players, there are cards for manager Tony LaRussa, the coaching staff, and former Sox greats Luis Aparicio and Minnie Minoso. Cards designs are very similar to the 1983 cards. As the cards were given out two at a time, it was very difficult to acquire a complete set. Additionally, as numbers available vary because of attendance, some cards are scarcer than others.

		MT	NR MT	EX
Complete Set:		25.00	18.50	10.00
Common Player:		.40	.30	.15
1	Scott Fletcher	.60	.45	.25
3	Harold Baines	2.25	1.75	.90
5	Vance Law	.50	.40	.20
7	Marc Hill	.40	.30	.15
8	Dave Stegman	.40	.30	.15
10	Tony LaRussa	.50	.40	.20
11	Rudy Law	.40	.30	.15
16	Julio Cruz	.40	.30	.15
17	Jerry Hairston	.40	.30	.15
19	Greg Luzinski	.90	.70	.35
20	Jerry Dybzinski	.40	.30	.15
24	Floyd Bannister	.60	.45	.25
25	Mike Squires	.40	.30	.15
27	Ron Reed	.40	.30	.15
29	Greg Walker	.50	.40	.20
30	Salome Barojas	.40	.30	.15
31	LaMarr Hoyt	.50	.40	.20
32	Tim Hulett	1.00	.70	.40
34	Richard Dotson	.70	.50	.30
40	Britt Burns	.40	.30	.15
41	Tom Seaver	4.00	3.00	1.50
42	Ron Kittle	1.00	.70	.40
44	Tom Paciorek	.40	.30	.15
50	Juan Agosto	.40	.30	.15
59	Tom Brennan	1.00	.70	.40
72	Carlton Fisk	2.00	1.50	.80
----	Minnie Minoso	2.00	1.50	.80
----	Luis Aparicio	2.00	1.50	.80
----	Nancy Faust (organist)	1.00	.70	.40
----	The Coaching Staff (Ed Brinkman, Dave Duncan, Art Kusnyer, Tony LaRussa, Jim Leyland, Dave Nelson, Joe Nossek)	.40	.30	.15

Regional interest may affect the value of a card.

1986 True Value

A 30-card set of 2-1/2" by 3-1/2" cards was available in three-card packets at True Value hardware stores with a purchase of $5 or more. Cards feature a photo enclosed by stars and a ball and bat at the bottom. The player's name and team are in the lower left while his position and a Major League Baseball logo are in the lower right. The True Value logo is in the upper left. Above the picture runs the phrase "Collector Series." Backs feature some personal information and brief 1985 statistics. Along with the player cards, the folders contained a sweepstakes card offering trips to post-season games and other prizes.

		MT	NR MT	EX
Complete Panel Set:		12.00	9.00	4.75
Complete Singles Set:		6.00	4.50	2.50
Common Panel:		.40	.30	.15
Common Single Player:		.05	.04	.02
	Panel	1.00	.70	.40
1	Pedro Guerrero	.08	.06	.03
2	Steve Garvey	.15	.11	.06
3	Eddie Murray	.20	.15	.08
	Panel	3.25	2.50	1.25
4	Pete Rose	.30	.25	.12
5	Don Mattingly	.80	.60	.30
6	Fernando Valenzuela	.10	.08	.04
	Panel	.75	.60	.30
7	Jim Rice	.10	.08	.04
8	Kirk Gibson	.10	.08	.04
9	Ozzie Smith	.25	.20	.10
	Panel	1.00	.70	.40
10	Dale Murphy	.20	.15	.08
11	Robin Yount	.25	.20	.10
12	Tom Seaver	.15	.11	.06
	Panel	1.25	.90	.50
13	Reggie Jackson	.25	.20	.10
14	Ryne Sandberg	.40	.30	.15
15	Bruce Sutter	.05	.04	.02
	Panel	1.00	.70	.40
16	Gary Carter	.15	.11	.06
17	George Brett	.30	.25	.12
18	Rick Sutcliffe	.05	.04	.02
	Panel	.40	.30	.15
19	Dave Stieb	.05	.04	.02
20	Buddy Bell	.05	.04	.02
21	Alvin Davis	.05	.04	.02
	Panel	1.00	.70	.40
22	Cal Ripken, Jr.	.40	.30	.15
23	Bill Madlock	.05	.04	.02
24	Kent Hrbek	.10	.08	.04
	Panel	1.50	1.25	.60
25	Lou Whitaker	.08	.06	.03
26	Nolan Ryan	.50	.40	.20
27	Dwayne Murphy	.05	.04	.02
	Panel	2.00	1.50	.80
28	Mike Schmidt	.30	.25	.12
29	Andre Dawson	.20	.15	.08
30	Wade Boggs	.40	.30	.15

1932 U.S. Caramel

Produced by the U.S. Caramel Company, Boston, this set is not limited to baseball. Rather, it is a set of 31 "Famous Athletes" of which some 27 are baseball players. The 2-1/2" by 3" cards have a black and white picture on the front with a red background and white border. The player's name appears in white above the picture. The backs feature the player's name, position, team and league as well as a redemption ad and card number. The cards were among the last of the caramel card sets and are very scarce today. The cards could be

redeemed for a baseball and baseball glove. Card #16 was recently discovered and is not included in the complete set price.

		NR MT	EX	VG
Complete Set:		20000.	10000.	6000.
Common Player:		575.00	287.00	172.00
1	Edward T. (Eddie) Collins	850.00	425.00	255.00
2	Paul (Big Poison) Waner	650.00	325.00	195.00
4	William (Bill) Terry	650.00	325.00	195.00
5	Earl B. Combs (Earle)	650.00	325.00	195.00
6	William (Bill) Dickey	850.00	425.00	255.00
7	Joseph (Joe) Cronin	875.00	437.00	262.00
8	Charles (Chick) Hafey	650.00	325.00	195.00
10	Walter (Rabbit) Maranville	650.00	325.00	195.00
11	Rogers (Rajah) Hornsby	1100.	550.00	330.00
12	Gordon (Mickey) Cochrane	650.00	325.00	195.00
13	Lloyd (Little Poison) Waner	650.00	325.00	195.00
14	Tyrus (Ty) Cobb	3250.	1625.	975.00
16	Charles (Lindy) Lindstrom	25000.	12500.	7500.
17	Al. Simmons	650.00	325.00	195.00
18	Anthony (Tony) Lazzeri	650.00	325.00	195.00
19	Walter (Wally) Berger	575.00	287.00	172.00
20	Charles (Large Charlie) Ruffing	650.00	325.00	195.00
21	Charles (Chuck) Klein	650.00	325.00	195.00
23	James (Jimmy) Foxx	850.00	425.00	255.00
24	Frank J. (Lefty) O'Doul	575.00	287.00	172.00
26	Henry (Lou) Gehrig	3250.	1625.	975.00
27	Robert (Lefty) Grove	1000.	500.00	300.00
28	Edward Brant (Brandt)	575.00	287.00	172.00
29	George Earnshaw	575.00	287.00	172.00
30	Frank (Frankie) Frisch	875.00	437.00	262.00
31	Vernon (Lefty) Gomez	875.00	437.00	262.00
32	George (Babe) Ruth	4500.	2250.	1350.

1989 Upper Deck Promos

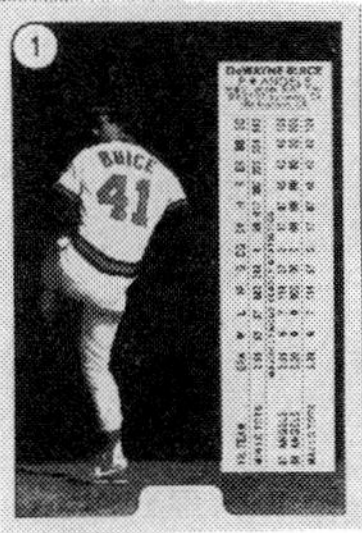

In 1988 Upper Deck produced a two-card test set to be distributed as samples for the 1989 set; 18,000 of each card were produced. The cards were distributed to dealers at the 1988 National Sports Collectors Convention. Two other variations of the promo cards exist. Both variations involve differences in where the hologram was placed. Fewer than 5,000 of one of the hologram variations exist, while less than 1,000 of the third variation exist. Joyner and Buice were selected for the promo cards because of a reported investment interest in Upper Deck; they were later required to sell their interest in the card company due to their active-player status.

		MT	NR MT	EX
Complete Set (2):		150.00	110.00	60.00
Complete Set (2):		300.00	225.00	125.00
Complete Set (2):		500.00	375.00	200.00
1a	DeWayne Buice (1/2" x 3/16" hologram at bottom)	50.00	37.00	20.00
1b	DeWayne Buice (hologram extends to bottom edge)	100.00	75.00	40.00
1c	DeWayne Buice (hologram at top)	150.00	110.00	60.00
700a	Wally Joyner (1/2" x 3/16" hologram at bottom)	75.00	55.00	30.00
700b	Wally Joyner (hologram extends to bottom edge)	200.00	150.00	80.00
700c	Wally Joyner (hologram at top)	350.00	260.00	140.00

1989 Upper Deck

This premiere "Collector's Choice' issue from Upper Deck contains 700 cards (2-1/2" by 3-1/2") with full-color photos on both sides. The first 26 cards feature Star Rookies. The set also includes 26 special portrait cards with team checklist backs and seven numberical checklist cards (one for each 100 numbers). Team checklist cards feature individual player portraits by artist Vernon Wells. Major 1988 award winners (Cy Young, Rookie of Year, MVP) are honored on 10 cards in the set, in addition to their individual player cards. There are also special cards for the Most Valuable Players in both League Championship series and the World Series. The card fronts feature head-and-shoulder poses framed by a white border. A vertical brown and green artist's rendition of the runner's lane that leads from home plate to first base is found along the right margin. The backs carry full-color action poses that fill the card back, except for a compact (yet complete) stats chart. A high-number series, cards 701-800, featuring rookies and traded players, was released in mid-season in foil packs mixed within the complete set, in boxed complete sets and in high number set boxes.

		MT	NR MT	EX
Complete Set (800):		120.00	90.00	47.50
Complete Set (700):		95.00	75.00	40.00
Common Player (1-700):		.08	.06	.03
Common Player (701-800):		.10	.08	.04
1	*Ken Griffey, Jr.*	65.00	49.00	26.00
2	*Luis Medina*	.12	.09	.05
3	*Tony Chance*	.15	.11	.06
4	*Dave Otto*	.08	.06	.03
5	*Sandy Alomar, Jr.*	.50	.40	.20
6	*Rolando Roomes*	.15	.11	.06
7	*David West*	.25	.20	.10
8	*Cris Carpenter*	.30	.25	.12
9	Gregg Jefferies	1.50	1.25	.60
10	*Doug Dascenzo*	.25	.20	.10
11	*Ron Jones*	.20	.15	.08
12	*Luis de los Santos*	.15	.11	.06
13a	*Gary Sheffield* ("SS" upside-down)	7.50	5.50	3.00
13b	*Gary Sheffield* ("SS" correct)	7.50	5.50	3.00
14	*Mike Harkey*	.30	.25	.12
15	*Lance Blankenship*	.25	.20	.10
16	*William Brennan*	.15	.11	.06
17	*John Smoltz*	2.00	1.50	.80
18	*Ramon Martinez*	1.25	.90	.50
19	*Mark Lemke*	.35	.25	.14
20	*Juan Bell*	.20	.15	.08
21	*Rey Palacios*	.15	.11	.06
22	*Felix Jose*	.60	.45	.25
23	*Van Snider*	.25	.20	.10
24	*Dante Bichette*	2.75	2.00	1.00
25	*Randy Johnson*	2.00	1.50	.80
26	*Carlos Quintana*	.25	.20	.10
27	Star Rookie Checklist 1-26	.08	.06	.03
28	*Mike Schooler*	.10	.08	.04
29	Randy St. Claire	.08	.06	.03
30	*Jerald Clark*	.35	.25	.14
31	Kevin Gross	.08	.06	.03
32	*Dan Firova*	.20	.15	.08
33	Jeff Calhoun	.08	.06	.03
34	Tommy Hinzo	.08	.06	.03
35	*Ricky Jordan*	.30	.25	.12
36	Larry Parrish	.08	.06	.03
37	Bret Saberhagen	.15	.11	.06
38	Mike Smithson	.08	.06	.03
39	Dave Dravecky	.08	.06	.03
40	Ed Romero	.08	.06	.03
41	Jeff Musselman	.08	.06	.03
42	Ed Hearn	.08	.06	.03
43	Rance Mulliniks	.08	.06	.03
44	Jim Eisenreich	.08	.06	.03
45	*Sil Campusano*	.20	.15	.08
46	Mike Krukow	.08	.06	.03
47	*Paul Gibson*	.20	.15	.08
48	Mike LaCoss	.08	.06	.03
49	Larry Herndon	.08	.06	.03
50	Scott Garrelts	.08	.06	.03
51	Dwayne Henry	.08	.06	.03
52	Jim Acker	.08	.06	.03
53	Steve Sax	.15	.11	.06
54	Pete O'Brien	.08	.06	.03
55	Paul Runge	.08	.06	.03
56	Rick Rhoden	.08	.06	.03
57	*John Dopson*	.08	.06	.03
58	Casey Candaele	.08	.06	.03

59 Dave Righetti .12 .09 .05
60 Joe Hesketh .08 .06 .03
61 Frank DiPino .08 .06 .03
62 Tim Laudner .08 .06 .03
63 Jamie Moyer .08 .06 .03
64 Fred Toliver .08 .06 .03
65 Mitch Webster .08 .06 .03
66 John Tudor .10 .08 .04
67 John Cangelosi .08 .06 .03
68 Mike Devereaux .25 .20 .10
69 Brian Fisher .08 .06 .03
70 Mike Marshall .12 .09 .05
71 Zane Smith .08 .06 .03
72a Brian Holton (ball not visible on card front, photo actually Shawn Hillegas) 1.50 1.25 .60
72b Brian Holton (ball visible, correct photo) .15 .11 .06
73 Jose Guzman .10 .08 .04
74 Rick Mahler .08 .06 .03
75 John Shelby .08 .06 .03
76 Jim Deshaies .08 .06 .03
77 Bobby Meacham .08 .06 .03
78 Bryn Smith .08 .06 .03
79 Joaquin Andujar .08 .06 .03
80 Richard Dotson .08 .06 .03
81 Charlie Lea .08 .06 .03
82 Calvin Schiraldi .08 .06 .03
83 Les Straker .08 .06 .03
84 Les Lancaster .08 .06 .03
85 Allan Anderson .08 .06 .03
86 Junior Ortiz .08 .06 .03
87 Jesse Orosco .08 .06 .03
88 Felix Fermin .08 .06 .03
89 Dave Anderson .08 .06 .03
90 Rafael Belliard .08 .06 .03
91 Franklin Stubbs .08 .06 .03
92 Cecil Espy .08 .06 .03
93 Albert Hall .08 .06 .03
94 Tim Leary .08 .06 .03
95 Mitch Williams .08 .06 .03
96 Tracy Jones .10 .08 .04
97 Danny Darwin .08 .06 .03
98 Gary Ward .08 .06 .03
99 Neal Heaton .08 .06 .03
100 Jim Pankovits .08 .06 .03
101 Bill Doran .08 .06 .03
102 Tim Wallach .10 .08 .04
103 Joe Magrane .10 .08 .04
104 Ozzie Virgil .08 .06 .03
105 Alvin Davis .12 .09 .05
106 Tom Brookens .08 .06 .03
107 Shawon Dunston .10 .08 .04
108 Tracy Woodson .10 .08 .04
109 Nelson Liriano .08 .06 .03
110 Devon White .12 .09 .05
111 Steve Balboni .08 .06 .03
112 Buddy Bell .08 .06 .03
113 *German Jimenez* .08 .06 .03
114 Ken Dayley .08 .06 .03
115 Andres Galarraga .50 .40 .20
116 Mike Scioscia .08 .06 .03
117 Gary Pettis .08 .06 .03
118 Ernie Whitt .08 .06 .03
119 Bob Boone .08 .06 .03
120 Ryne Sandberg 1.50 1.25 .60
121 Bruce Benedict .08 .06 .03
122 Hubie Brooks .10 .08 .04
123 Mike Moore .08 .06 .03
124 Wallace Johnson .08 .06 .03
125 Bob Horner .10 .08 .04
126 Chili Davis .08 .06 .03
127 Manny Trillo .08 .06 .03
128 Chet Lemon .08 .06 .03
129 John Cerutti .08 .06 .03
130 Orel Hershiser .10 .08 .04
131 Terry Pendleton .30 .25 .12
132 Jeff Blauser .25 .20 .10
133 Mike Fitzgerald .08 .06 .03
134 Henry Cotto .08 .06 .03
135 Gerald Young .12 .09 .05
136 Luis Salazar .08 .06 .03
137 Alejandro Pena .08 .06 .03
138 Jack Howell .08 .06 .03
139 Tony Fernandez .12 .09 .05
140 Mark Grace 1.00 .75 .40
141 Ken Caminiti .08 .06 .03
142 Mike Jackson .08 .06 .03
143 Larry McWilliams .08 .06 .03
144 Andres Thomas .08 .06 .03
145 Nolan Ryan 4.00 3.00 1.50
146 Mike Davis .08 .06 .03
147 DeWayne Buice .08 .06 .03
148 Jody Davis .08 .06 .03
149 Jesse Barfield .10 .08 .04
150 Matt Nokes .15 .11 .06
151 Jerry Reuss .08 .06 .03
152 Rick Cerone .08 .06 .03
153 Storm Davis .10 .08 .04
154 Marvell Wynne .08 .06 .03
155 Will Clark 1.25 .90 .50
156 Luis Aguayo .08 .06 .03
157 Willie Upshaw .08 .06 .03
158 Randy Bush .08 .06 .03
159 Ron Darling .12 .09 .05
160 Kal Daniels .15 .11 .06
161 Spike Owen .08 .06 .03
162 Luis Polonia .08 .06 .03
163 Kevin Mitchell .20 .15 .08
164 *Dave Gallagher* .25 .20 .10
165 Benito Santiago .15 .11 .06
166 Greg Gagne .08 .06 .03
167 Ken Phelps .08 .06 .03
168 Sid Fernandez .10 .08 .04
169 Bo Diaz .08 .06 .03
170 Cory Snyder .15 .11 .06
171 Eric Show .08 .06 .03
172 Robby Thompson .08 .06 .03
173 Marty Barrett .08 .06 .03
174 Dave Henderson .10 .08 .04
175 Ozzie Guillen .08 .06 .03
176 Barry Lyons .08 .06 .03
177 *Kelvin Torve* (FC) .20 .15 .08
178 Don Slaught .08 .06 .03
179 Steve Lombardozzi .08 .06 .03
180 *Chris Sabo* .40 .30 .15
181 Jose Uribe .08 .06 .03
182 Shane Mack .08 .06 .03
183 Ron Karkovice .08 .06 .03
184 Todd Benzinger .12 .09 .05
185 Dave Stewart .10 .08 .04
186 Julio Franco .10 .08 .04
187 Ron Robinson .08 .06 .03
188 Wally Backman .08 .06 .03
189 Randy Velarde .08 .06 .03
190 Joe Carter 1.00 .75 .40
191 Bob Welch .10 .08 .04
192 Kelly Paris .08 .06 .03
193 Chris Brown .08 .06 .03
194 Rick Reuschel .10 .08 .04
195 Roger Clemens .90 .70 .35
196 Dave Concepcion .10 .08 .04
197 Al Newman .08 .06 .03
198 Brook Jacoby .10 .08 .04
199 Mookie Wilson .08 .06 .03
200 Don Mattingly 1.00 .70 .40
201 Dick Schofield .08 .06 .03
202 Mark Gubicza .10 .08 .04
203 Gary Gaetti .15 .11 .06
204 Dan Pasqua .10 .08 .04
205 Andre Dawson .40 .30 .15
206 Chris Speier .08 .06 .03
207 Kent Tekulve .08 .06 .03
208 Rod Scurry .08 .06 .03
209 Scott Bailes .08 .06 .03
210 Rickey Henderson .75 .60 .30
211 Harold Baines .12 .09 .05
212 Tony Armas .08 .06 .03
213 Kent Hrbek .10 .08 .04
214 Darrin Jackson .08 .06 .03
215 George Brett 1.00 .75 .40
216 Rafael Santana .08 .06 .03
217 Andy Allanson .08 .06 .03
218 Brett Butler .08 .06 .03
219 Steve Jeltz .08 .06 .03
220 Jay Buhner .50 .40 .20
221 Bo Jackson .70 .50 .30
222 Angel Salazar .08 .06 .03
223 Kirk McCaskill .08 .06 .03
224 Steve Lyons .08 .06 .03
225 Bert Blyleven .10 .08 .04
226 Scott Bradley .08 .06 .03
227 Bob Melvin .08 .06 .03
228 Ron Kittle .08 .06 .03
229 Phil Bradley .10 .08 .04
230 Tommy John .12 .09 .05
231 Greg Walker .08 .06 .03
232 Juan Berenguer .08 .06 .03
233 Pat Tabler .08 .06 .03
234 *Terry Clark* .20 .15 .08
235 Rafael Palmeiro 1.50 1.25 .60
236 Paul Zuvella .08 .06 .03
237 Willie Randolph .08 .06 .03
238 Bruce Fields .08 .06 .03
239 Mike Aldrete .08 .06 .03
240 Lance Parrish .15 .11 .06
241 Greg Maddux 1.25 .90 .50
242 John Moses .08 .06 .03
243 Melido Perez .10 .08 .04
244 Willie Wilson .10 .08 .04
245 Mark McLemore .08 .06 .03
246 Von Hayes .10 .08 .04
247 Matt Williams 1.50 1.25 .60
248 John Candelaria .08 .06 .03
249 Harold Reynolds .08 .06 .03
250 Greg Swindell .12 .09 .05
251 Juan Agosto .08 .06 .03
252 Mike Felder .08 .06 .03
253 Vince Coleman .15 .11 .06
254 Larry Sheets .08 .06 .03
255 George Bell .12 .09 .05
256 Terry Steinbach .10 .08 .04
257 *Jack Armstrong* .20 .15 .08
258 Dickie Thon .08 .06 .03
259 Ray Knight .08 .06 .03
260 Darryl Strawberry .20 .15 .08
261 Doug Sisk .08 .06 .03
262 Alex Trevino .08 .06 .03
263 Jeff Leonard .08 .06 .03
264 Tom Henke .08 .06 .03
265 Ozzie Smith .40 .30 .15
266 Dave Bergman .08 .06 .03
267 Tony Phillips .08 .06 .03
268 Mark Davis .08 .06 .03
269 Kevin Elster .10 .08 .04
270 Barry Larkin .35 .25 .14
271 Manny Lee .08 .06 .03
272 Tom Brunansky .12 .09 .05
273 *Craig Biggio* 1.75 1.25 .70
274 Jim Gantner .08 .06 .03
275 Eddie Murray .40 .30 .15
276 Jeff Reed .08 .06 .03
277 Tim Teufel .08 .06 .03
278 Rick Honeycutt .08 .06 .03
279 Guillermo Hernandez .08 .06 .03
280 John Kruk .30 .25 .12
281 *Luis Alicea* .20 .15 .08
282 Jim Clancy .08 .06 .03
283 Billy Ripken .08 .06 .03
284 Craig Reynolds .08 .06 .03
285 Robin Yount .80 .60 .30
286 Jimmy Jones .08 .06 .03
287 Ron Oester .08 .06 .03
288 Terry Leach .08 .06 .03
289 Dennis Eckersley .30 .25 .12
290 Alan Trammell .10 .08 .04
291 Jimmy Key .25 .20 .10
292 Chris Bosio .08 .06 .03
293 Jose DeLeon .08 .06 .03
294 Jim Traber .08 .06 .03
295 Mike Scott .12 .09 .05
296 Roger McDowell .10 .08 .04
297 Garry Templeton .08 .06 .03
298 Doyle Alexander .08 .06 .03
299 Nick Esasky .08 .06 .03
300 Mark McGwire .70 .50 .30
301 *Darryl Hamilton* .35 .25 .14
302 Dave Smith .08 .06 .03
303 Rick Sutcliffe .10 .08 .04
304 Dave Stapleton .08 .06 .03
305 Alan Ashby .08 .06 .03
306 Pedro Guerrero .15 .11 .06
307 Ron Guidry .12 .09 .05
308 Steve Farr .08 .06 .03
309 Curt Ford .08 .06 .03
310 Claudell Washington .08 .06 .03
311 Tom Prince .08 .06 .03
312 *Chad Kreuter* .40 .30 .15
313 Ken Oberkfell .08 .06 .03
314 Jerry Browne .08 .06 .03
315 R.J. Reynolds .08 .06 .03
316 Scott Bankhead .08 .06 .03
317 Milt Thompson .08 .06 .03
318 Mario Diaz .10 .08 .04
319 Bruce Ruffin .08 .06 .03
320 Dave Valle .08 .06 .03
321a *Gary Varsho* (batting righty on card back, photo actually Mike Bielecki) 2.00 1.50 .80
321b *Gary Varsho* (batting lefty on card back, correct photo) .30 .25 .12
322 Paul Mirabella .08 .06 .03
323 Chuck Jackson .08 .06 .03
324 Drew Hall .10 .08 .04
325 Don August .10 .08 .04
326 *Israel Sanchez* .15 .11 .06
327 Denny Walling .08 .06 .03
328 Joel Skinner .08 .06 .03
329 Danny Tartabull .30 .25 .12
330 Tony Pena .08 .06 .03
331 Jim Sundberg .08 .06 .03
332 Jeff Robinson .12 .09 .05
333 Odibbe McDowell .08 .06 .03
334 Jose Lind .10 .08 .04
335 Paul Kilgus .10 .08 .04
336 Juan Samuel .12 .09 .05
337 Mike Campbell .10 .08 .04
338 Mike Maddux .08 .06 .03
339 Darnell Coles .08 .06 .03
340 Bob Dernier .08 .06 .03
341 Rafael Ramirez .08 .06 .03
342 Scott Sanderson .08 .06 .03
343 B.J. Surhoff .10 .08 .04
344 Billy Hatcher .08 .06 .03
345 Pat Perry .08 .06 .03
346 Jack Clark .15 .11 .06
347 Gary Thurman .12 .09 .05
348 *Timmy Jones* .20 .15 .08
349 Dave Winfield .75 .60 .30
350 Frank White .08 .06 .03
351 Dave Collins .08 .06 .03
352 Jack Morris .20 .15 .08
353 Eric Plunk .08 .06 .03
354 Leon Durham .08 .06 .03
355 Ivan DeJesus .08 .06 .03
356 *Brian Holman* .20 .15 .08
357a Dale Murphy (reversed negative) 40.00 30.00 16.00
357b Dale Murphy (corrected) .35 .25 .14
358 Mark Portugal .08 .06 .03
359 Andy McGaffigan .08 .06 .03
360 Tom Glavine 2.50 2.00 1.00
361 Keith Moreland .08 .06 .03
362 Todd Stottlemyre .15 .11 .06
363 Dave Leiper .08 .06 .03
364 Cecil Fielder 1.00 .70 .40
365 Carmelo Martinez .08 .06 .03
366 Dwight Evans .10 .08 .04
367 Kevin McReynolds .15 .11 .06
368 Rich Gedman .08 .06 .03
369 Len Dykstra .50 .40 .20
370 Jody Reed .12 .09 .05
371 Jose Canseco .75 .60 .30
372 Rob Murphy .08 .06 .03
373 Mike Henneman .10 .08 .04
374 Walt Weiss .10 .08 .04
375 *Rob Dibble* .25 .20 .10
376 Kirby Puckett 1.50 1.25 .60
377 Denny Martinez .08 .06 .03
378 Ron Gant .75 .60 .30
379 Brian Harper .08 .06 .03
380 *Nelson Santovenia* .08 .06 .03
381 Lloyd Moseby .08 .06 .03
382 Lance McCullers .08 .06 .03
383 Dave Stieb .10 .08 .04
384 Tony Gwynn .80 .60 .30
385 Mike Flanagan .08 .06 .03
386 Bob Ojeda .08 .06 .03
387 Bruce Hurst .10 .08 .04
388 Dave Magadan .10 .08 .04
389 Wade Boggs .60 .45 .25
390 Gary Carter .10 .08 .04
391 Frank Tanana .08 .06 .03
392 Curt Young .08 .06 .03
393 Jeff Treadway .10 .08 .04
394 Darrell Evans .10 .08 .04
395 Glenn Hubbard .08 .06 .03
396 Chuck Cary .08 .06 .03
397 Frank Viola .15 .11 .06
398 Jeff Parrett .10 .08 .04
399 *Terry Blocker* .15 .11 .06
400 Dan Gladden .08 .06 .03
401 *Louie Meadows* .15 .11 .06
402 Tim Raines .25 .20 .10
403 Joey Meyer .10 .08 .04
404 Larry Andersen .08 .06 .03
405 Rex Hudler .08 .06 .03
406 Mike Schmidt 2.00 1.50 .80
407 John Franco .10 .08 .04

408 *Brady Anderson* .75 .60 .30
409 Don Carman .08 .06 .03
410 Eric Davis .25 .20 .10
411 Bob Stanley .08 .06 .03
412 Pete Smith .10 .08 .04
413 Jim Rice .10 .08 .04
414 Bruce Sutter .10 .08 .04
415 Oil Can Boyd .08 .06 .03
416 Ruben Sierra .50 .40 .20
417 Mike LaValliere .08 .06 .03
418 Steve Buechele .08 .06 .03
419 Gary Redus .08 .06 .03
420 Scott Fletcher .08 .06 .03
421 Dale Sveum .08 .06 .03
422 Bob Knepper .08 .06 .03
423 Luis Rivera .08 .06 .03
424 Ted Higuera .10 .08 .04
425 Kevin Bass .08 .06 .03
426 Ken Gerhart .08 .06 .03
427 Shane Rawley .08 .06 .03
428 Paul O'Neill .08 .06 .03
429 Joe Orsulak .08 .06 .03
430 Jackie Gutierrez .08 .06 .03
431 Gerald Perry .10 .08 .04
432 Mike Greenwell .10 .08 .04
433 Jerry Royster .08 .06 .03
434 Ellis Burks .10 .08 .04
435 Ed Olwine .08 .06 .03
436 Dave Rucker .08 .06 .03
437 Charlie Hough .08 .06 .03
438 Bob Walk .08 .06 .03
439 Bob Brower .08 .06 .03
440 Barry Bonds 2.00 1.50 .80
441 Tom Foley .08 .06 .03
442 Rob Deer .08 .06 .03
443 Glenn Davis .08 .06 .03
444 Dave Martinez .08 .06 .03
445 Bill Wegman .08 .06 .03
446 Lloyd McClendon .08 .06 .03
447 Dave Schmidt .08 .06 .03
448 Darren Daulton .40 .30 .15
449 Frank Williams .08 .06 .03
450 Don Aase .08 .06 .03
451 Lou Whitaker .15 .11 .06
452 Goose Gossage .12 .09 .05
453 Ed Whitson .08 .06 .03
454 Jim Walewander .08 .06 .03
455 Damon Berryhill .12 .09 .05
456 Tim Burke .08 .06 .03
457 Barry Jones .08 .06 .03
458 Joel Youngblood .08 .06 .03
459 Floyd Youmans .08 .06 .03
460 Mark Salas .08 .06 .03
461 Jeff Russell .08 .06 .03
462 Darrell Miller .08 .06 .03
463 Jeff Kunkel .08 .06 .03
464 *Sherman Corbett* .20 .15 .08
465 Curtis Wilkerson .08 .06 .03
466 Bud Black .08 .06 .03
467 Cal Ripken, Jr. 1.75 1.25 .70
468 John Farrell .10 .08 .04
469 Terry Kennedy .08 .06 .03
470 Tom Candiotti .08 .06 .03
471 Roberto Alomar 5.00 3.75 2.00
472 Jeff Robinson .12 .09 .05
473 Vance Law .08 .06 .03
474 Randy Ready .08 .06 .03
475 Walt Terrell .08 .06 .03
476 Kelly Downs .10 .08 .04
477 *Johnny Paredes* .15 .11 .06
478 Shawn Hillegas .08 .06 .03
479 Bob Brenly .08 .06 .03
480 Otis Nixon .08 .06 .03
481 Johnny Ray .08 .06 .03
482 Geno Petralli .08 .06 .03
483 Stu Cliburn .08 .06 .03
484 Pete Incaviglia .10 .08 .04
485 Brian Downing .08 .06 .03
486 Jeff Stone .08 .06 .03
487 Carmen Castillo .08 .06 .03
488 Tom Niedenfuer .08 .06 .03
489 Jay Bell .30 .25 .12
490 Rick Schu .08 .06 .03
491 *Jeff Pico* .15 .11 .06
492 *Mark Parent* .20 .15 .08
493 Eric King .08 .06 .03
494 Al Nipper .08 .06 .03
495 Andy Hawkins .08 .06 .03
496 Daryl Boston .08 .06 .03
497 Ernie Riles .08 .06 .03
498 Pascual Perez .08 .06 .03
499 Bill Long .08 .06 .03
500 Kirt Manwaring .10 .08 .04
501 Chuck Crim .08 .06 .03
502 Candy Maldonado .08 .06 .03
503 Dennis Lamp .08 .06 .03
504 Glenn Braggs .08 .06 .03
505 Joe Price .08 .06 .03
506 Ken Williams .08 .06 .03
507 Bill Pecota .08 .06 .03
508 Rey Quinones .08 .06 .03
509 *Jeff Bittiger* .15 .11 .06
510 Kevin Seitzer .08 .06 .03
511 Steve Bedrosian .10 .08 .04
512 Todd Worrell .10 .08 .04
513 Chris James .10 .08 .04
514 Jose Oquendo .08 .06 .03
515 David Palmer .08 .06 .03
516 John Smiley .12 .09 .05
517 Dave Clark .08 .06 .03
518 Mike Dunne .10 .08 .04
519 Ron Washington .08 .06 .03
520 Bob Kipper .08 .06 .03
521 Lee Smith .10 .08 .04
522 Juan Castillo .08 .06 .03
523 Don Robinson .08 .06 .03
524 Kevin Romine .08 .06 .03
525 Paul Molitor .75 .60 .30
526 Mark Langston .15 .11 .06
527 Donnie Hill .08 .06 .03
528 Larry Owen .08 .06 .03
529 Jerry Reed .08 .06 .03
530 Jack McDowell 1.00 .75 .40
531 Greg Mathews .08 .06 .03
532 John Russell .08 .06 .03
533 Don Quisenberry .08 .06 .03
534 Greg Gross .08 .06 .03
535 Danny Cox .08 .06 .03
536 Terry Francona .08 .06 .03
537 Andy Van Slyke .15 .11 .06
538 Mel Hall .08 .06 .03
539 Jim Gott .08 .06 .03
540 Doug Jones .10 .08 .04
541 Criag Lefferts .08 .06 .03
542 Mike Boddicker .08 .06 .03
543 Greg Brock .08 .06 .03
544 Atlee Hammaker .08 .06 .03
545 Tom Bolton .08 .06 .03
546 *Mike Macfarlane* .40 .30 .15
547 *Rich Renteria* .15 .11 .06
548 John Davis .08 .06 .03
549 Floyd Bannister .08 .06 .03
550 Mickey Brantley .08 .06 .03
551 Duane Ward .08 .06 .03
552 Dan Petry .08 .06 .03
553 Mickey Tettleton .15 .11 .06
554 Rick Leach .08 .06 .03
555 Mike Witt .08 .06 .03
556 Sid Bream .08 .06 .03
557 Bobby Witt .10 .08 .04
558 Tommy Herr .08 .06 .03
559 Randy Milligan .08 .06 .03
560 *Jose Cecena* .20 .15 .08
561 Mackey Sasser .08 .06 .03
562 Carney Lansford .08 .06 .03
563 Rick Aguilera .08 .06 .03
564 Ron Hassey .08 .06 .03
565 Dwight Gooden .20 .15 .08
566 Paul Assenmacher .08 .06 .03
567 Neil Allen .08 .06 .03
568 Jim Morrison .08 .06 .03
569 Mike Pagliarulo .10 .08 .04
570 Ted Simmons .10 .08 .04
571 Mark Thurmond .08 .06 .03
572 Fred McGriff 1.25 .90 .50
573 Wally Joyner .10 .08 .04
574 *Jose Bautista* .15 .11 .06
575 Kelly Gruber .08 .06 .03
576 Cecilio Guante .08 .06 .03
577 Mark Davidson .08 .06 .03
578 Bobby Bonilla .25 .20 .10
579 Mike Stanley .12 .09 .05
580 Gene Larkin .10 .08 .04
581 Stan Javier .08 .06 .03
582 Howard Johnson .10 .08 .04
583a Mike Gallego (photo on card back reversed)
1.00 .70 .40
583b Mike Gallego (correct photo) .15 .11 .06
584 David Cone .35 .25 .14
585 *Doug Jennings* .10 .08 .04
586 Charlie Hudson .08 .06 .03
587 Dion James .08 .06 .03
588 Al Leiter .15 .11 .06
589 Charlie Puleo .08 .06 .03
590 Roberto Kelly .25 .20 .10
591 Thad Bosley .08 .06 .03
592 Pete Stanicek .10 .08 .04
593 *Pat Borders* .40 .30 .15
594 *Bryan Harvey* .50 .40 .20
595 Jeff Ballard .10 .08 .04
596 Jeff Reardon .10 .08 .04
597 Doug Drabek .08 .06 .03
598 Edwin Correa .08 .06 .03
599 Keith Atherton .08 .06 .03
600 Dave LaPoint .08 .06 .03
601 Don Baylor .10 .08 .04
602 Tom Pagnozzi .08 .06 .03
603 Tim Flannery .08 .06 .03
604 Gene Walter .08 .06 .03
605 Dave Parker .12 .09 .05
606 Mike Diaz .08 .06 .03
607 Chris Gwynn .10 .08 .04
608 Odell Jones .08 .06 .03
609 Carlton Fisk .60 .45 .25
610 Jay Howell .08 .06 .03
611 Tim Crews .08 .06 .03
612 Keith Hernandez .08 .06 .03
613 Willie Fraser .08 .06 .03
614 Jim Eppard .08 .06 .03
615 Jeff Hamilton .08 .06 .03
616 Kurt Stillwell .08 .06 .03
617 Tom Browning .10 .08 .04
618 Jeff Montgomery .40 .30 .15
619 Jose Rijo .15 .11 .06
620 Jamie Quirk .08 .06 .03
621 Willie McGee .12 .09 .05
622 Mark Grant .08 .06 .03
623 Bill Swift .08 .06 .03
624 Orlando Mercado .08 .06 .03
625 *John Costello* .15 .11 .06
626 Jose Gonzalez .08 .06 .03
627a Bill Schroeder (putting on shin guards on card back,
photo actually Ronn Reynolds) 1.25 .90 .50
627b Bill Schroeder (arms crossed on card back, correct
photo) .15 .11 .06
628a Fred Manrique (throwing on card back, photo
actually Ozzie Guillen) 1.25 .90 .50
628b Fred Manrique (batting on card back, correct
photo) .15 .11 .06
629 Ricky Horton .08 .06 .03
630 Dan Plesac .10 .08 .04
631 Alfredo Griffin .08 .06 .03
632 Chuck Finley .08 .06 .03
633 Kirk Gibson .20 .15 .08
634 Randy Myers .10 .08 .04
635 Greg Minton .08 .06 .03
636 Herm Winningham .08 .06 .03
637 Charlie Leibrandt .08 .06 .03
638 Tim Birtsas .08 .06 .03
639 Bill Buckner .10 .08 .04
640 Danny Jackson .15 .11 .06
641 Greg Booker .08 .06 .03
642 Jim Presley .08 .06 .03
643 Gene Nelson .08 .06 .03
644 Rod Booker .08 .06 .03
645 Dennis Rasmussen .10 .08 .04
646 Juan Nieves .08 .06 .03
647 Bobby Thigpen .10 .08 .04
648 Tim Belcher .10 .08 .04
649 Mike Young .08 .06 .03
650 Ivan Calderon .08 .06 .03
651 *Oswaldo Peraza* .20 .15 .08
652a Pat Sheridan (no position on front)
30.00 22.00 12.00
652b Pat Sheridan (position on front) .08 .06 .03
653 Mike Morgan .08 .06 .03
654 Mike Heath .08 .06 .03
655 Jay Tibbs .08 .06 .03
656 Fernando Valenzuela .08 .06 .03
657 Lee Mazzilli .08 .06 .03
658 Frank Viola .08 .06 .03
659 Jose Canseco .40 .30 .15
660 Walt Weiss .08 .06 .03
661 Orel Hershiser .08 .06 .03
662 Kirk Gibson .08 .06 .03
663 Chris Sabo .15 .11 .06
664 Dennis Eckersley .08 .06 .03
665 Orel Hershiser .08 .06 .03
666 Kirk Gibson .08 .06 .03
667 Orel Hershiser .08 .06 .03
668 Wally Joyner (TC) .08 .06 .03
669 Nolan Ryan (TC) .60 .45 .25
670 Jose Canseco (TC) .25 .20 .10
671 Fred McGriff (TC) .15 .11 .06
672 Dale Murphy (TC) .08 .06 .03
673 Paul Molitor (TC) .20 .15 .08
674 Ozzie Smith (TC) .08 .06 .03
675 Ryne Sandberg (TC) .30 .25 .12
676 Kirk Gibson (TC) .08 .06 .03
677 Andres Galarraga (TC) .08 .06 .03
678 Will Clark (TC) .30 .25 .12
679 Cory Snyder (TC) .08 .06 .03
680 Alvin Davis (TC) .08 .06 .03
681 Darryl Strawberry (TC) .08 .06 .03
682 Cal Ripken, Jr. (TC) .40 .30 .15
683 Tony Gwynn (TC) .25 .20 .10
684 Mike Schmidt (TC) .40 .30 .15
685 Andy Van Slyke (TC) .08 .06 .03
686 Ruben Sierra (TC) .08 .06 .03
687 Wade Boggs (TC) .20 .15 .08
688 Eric Davis (TC) .08 .06 .03
689 George Brett (TC) .25 .20 .10
690 Alan Trammell (TC) .08 .06 .03
691 Frank Viola (TC) .08 .06 .03
692 Harold Baines (TC) .08 .06 .03
693 Don Mattingly (TC) .20 .15 .08
694 Checklist 1-100 .08 .06 .03
695 Checklist 101-200 .08 .06 .03
696 Checklist 201-300 .08 .06 .03
697 Checklist 301-400 .08 .06 .03
698 Checklist 401-500 .08 .06 .03
699 Checklist 501-600 .08 .06 .03
700 Checklist 601-700 .08 .06 .03
701 Checklist 701-800 .20 .15 .08
702 Jessie Barfield .10 .08 .04
703 Walt Terrell .10 .08 .04
704 Dickie Thon .10 .08 .04
705 Al Leiter .10 .08 .04
706 Dave LaPoint .10 .08 .04
707 Charlie Hayes (FC) 1.50 1.25 .60
708 Andy Hawkins .10 .08 .04
709 Mickey Hatcher .10 .08 .04
710 Lance McCullers .10 .08 .04
711 Ron Kittle .10 .08 .04
712 Bert Blyleven .10 .08 .04
713 Rick Dempsey .10 .08 .04
714 Ken Williams .10 .08 .04
715 Steve Rosenberg (FC) .15 .11 .06
716 Joe Skalski (FC) .20 .15 .08
717 Spike Owen .10 .08 .04
718 Todd Burns .10 .08 .04
719 Kevin Gross .10 .08 .04
720 Tommy Herr .10 .08 .04
721 Rob Ducey .10 .08 .04
722 Gary Green (FC) .15 .11 .06
723 Gregg Olson (FC) .40 .30 .15
724 Greg Harris (FC) .15 .11 .06
725 Craig Worthington (FC) .10 .08 .04
726 Tom Howard (FC) .25 .20 .10
727 Dale Mohorcic .10 .08 .04
728 Rich Yett .10 .08 .04
729 Mel Hall .10 .08 .04
730 Floyd Youmans .10 .08 .04
731 Lonnie Smith .15 .11 .06
732 Wally Backman .10 .08 .04
733 Trevor Wilson .10 .08 .04
734 Jose Alvarez .10 .08 .04
735 Bob Milacki (FC) .15 .11 .06
736 Tom Gordon (FC) .30 .25 .12
737 Wally Whitehurst (FC) .25 .20 .10
738 Mike Aldrete .10 .08 .04
739 Keith Miller .10 .08 .04
740 Randy Milligan .10 .08 .04
741 Jeff Parrett .10 .08 .04
742 Steve Finley (FC) .35 .25 .14
743 Junior Felix (FC) .25 .20 .10
744 Pete Harnisch (FC) .50 .40 .20
745 Bill Spiers (FC) .15 .11 .06
746 Hensley Meulens (FC) .20 .15 .08
747 Juan Bell .20 .15 .08
748 Steve Sax .15 .11 .06
749 Phil Bradley .10 .08 .04
750 Rey Quinones .10 .08 .04
751 Tommy Gregg (FC) .15 .11 .06
752 Kevin Brown (FC) .40 .30 .15
753 Derek Lilliquist (FC) .15 .11 .06
754 Todd Zeile (FC) 1.00 .70 .40

755	Jim Abbott (FC)	4.00	3.00	1.50
756	Ozzie Canseco (FC)	.10	.08	.04
757	Nick Esasky	.10	.08	.04
758	Mike Moore	.15	.11	.06
759	Rob Murphy	.10	.08	.04
760	Rick Mahler	.10	.08	.04
761	Fred Lynn	.10	.08	.04
762	Kevin Blankenship (FC)	.10	.08	.04
763	Eddie Murray	.50	.40	.20
764	Steve Searcy (FC)	.10	.08	.04
765	Jerome Walton (FC)	.10	.08	.04
766	Erik Hanson (FC)	.80	.60	.30
767	Bob Boone	.15	.11	.06
768	Edgar Martinez (FC)	.50	.40	.20
769	Jose DeJesus (FC)	.10	.08	.04
770	Greg Briley (FC)	.10	.08	.04
771	Steve Peters (FC)	.10	.08	.04
772	Rafael Palmeiro	1.25	.90	.50
773	Jack Clark	.15	.11	.06
774	Nolan Ryan	4.00	3.00	1.50
775	Lance Parrish	.10	.08	.04
776	Joe Girardi (FC)	.25	.20	.10
777	Willie Randolph	.10	.08	.04
778	Mitch Williams	.15	.11	.06
779	Dennis Cook (FC)	.15	.11	.06
780	Dwight Smith (FC)	.25	.20	.10
781	Lenny Harris (FC)	.25	.20	.10
782	Torey Lovullo (FC)	.15	.11	.06
783	Norm Charlton (FC)	.50	.40	.20
784	Chris Brown	.10	.08	.04
785	Todd Benzinger	.10	.08	.04
786	Shane Rawley	.10	.08	.04
787	Omar Vizquel (FC)	.40	.30	.15
788	LaVel Freeman (FC)	.15	.11	.06
789	Jeffrey Leonard	.10	.08	.04
790	Eddie Williams (FC)	.10	.08	.04
791	Jamie Moyer	.10	.08	.04
792	Bruce Hurst	.10	.08	.04
793	Julio Franco	.30	.25	.12
794	Claudell Washington	.10	.08	.04
795	Jody Davis	.10	.08	.04
796	Odibbe McDowell	.10	.08	.04
797	Paul Kilgus	.10	.08	.04
798	Tracy Jones	.10	.08	.04
799	Steve Wilson (FC)	.20	.15	.08
800	Pete O'Brien	.10	.08	.04

1990 Upper Deck

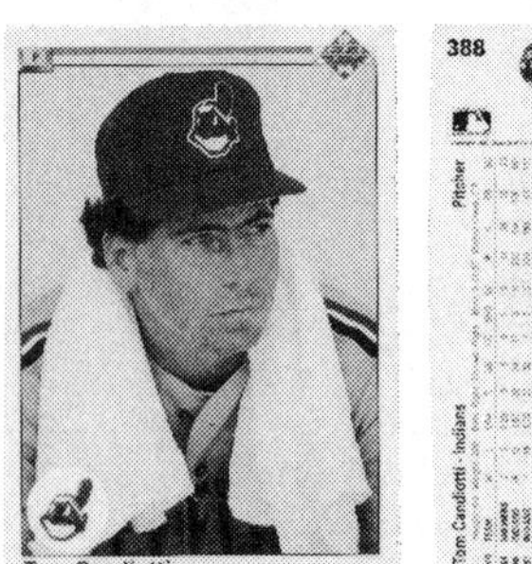
Tom Candiotti

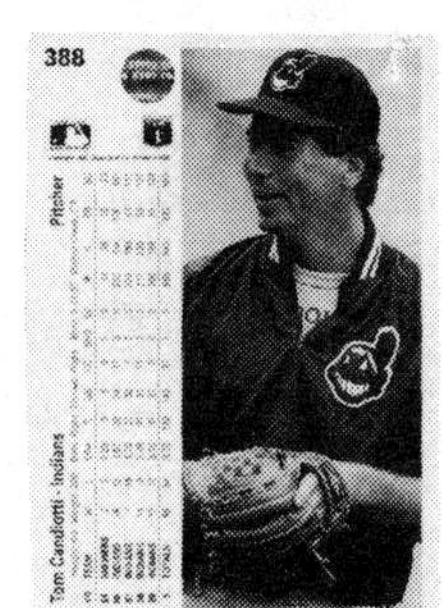

Following the success of its first issue, Upper Deck released another 800-card set in 1990. The cards contain full-color photos on both sides and are 2-1/2" by 3-1/2" in size. The artwork of Vernon Wells is featured on the front of all team checklist cards. The 1990 set also introduces two new Wells illustrations - a tribute to Mike Schmidt upon his retirement and one commemorating Nolan Ryan's 5,000 career strikeouts. The cards are similar in design to the 1989 issue. The Wade Boggs card depicts the Red Sox star in four stages of his batting swing via a quad-action photograph, much like the Jim Abbott card of 1989. The high- number series (701-800) was released as a boxed set, in factory sets and in foil packs at mid-season.

	MT	NR MT	EX
Complete Set (800):	35.00	26.00	14.00
Complete Set (700):	28.00	21.00	11.00
Common Player (1-700):	.06	.05	.02
Common Player (701-800):	.10	.08	.04

1	Star Rookie Checklist	.06	.05	.02
2	*Randy Nosek* (FC)	.06	.05	.02
3	*Tom Dress* (FC)	.08	.06	.03
4	Curt Young	.06	.05	.02
5	Angels Checklist	.06	.05	.02
6	Luis Salazar	.06	.05	.02
7	Phillies Checklist	.06	.05	.02
8	Jose Bautista	.08	.06	.03
9	*Marquis Grissom*	1.50	1.25	.60
10	Dodgers Checklist	.06	.05	.02
11	Rick Aguilera	.08	.06	.03
12	Padres Checklist	.06	.05	.02
13	*Deion Sanders* (FC)	2.00	1.50	.80
14	Marvell Wynne	.06	.05	.02
15	David West	.15	.11	.06
16	Pirates Checklist	.06	.05	.02
17	*Sammy Sosa*	1.25	.90	.50
18	Yankees Checklist	.06	.05	.02
19	Jack Howell	.06	.05	.02
20	Mike Schmidt (SPEC)	.50	.40	.20
21	Robin Ventura	1.50	1.25	.60
22	Brian Meyer (FC)	.20	.15	.08
23	*Blaine Beatty* (FC)	.08	.06	.03
24	Ken Griffey, Jr. (TC)	.40	.30	.15
25	*Greg Vaughn*	1.00	.70	.40
26	*Xavier Hernandez*	.15	.11	.06
27	*Jason Grimsley*	.25	.20	.10
28	*Eric Anthony*	.75	.60	.30
29	Expos Checklist	.06	.05	.02
30	David Wells	.06	.05	.02
31	Hal Morris	.30	.25	.12
32	Bo Jackson (TC)	.25	.20	.10
33	*Kelly Mann* (FC)	.06	.05	.02
34	Nolan Ryan (SPEC)	1.00	.75	.40
35	*Scott Service* (FC)	.08	.06	.03
36	Athletics Checklist	.06	.05	.02
37	*Tino Martinez*	.25	.20	.10
38	Chili Davis	.09	.07	.04
39	Scott Sanderson	.06	.05	.02
40	Giants Checklist	.06	.05	.02
41	Tigers Checklist	.06	.05	.02
42	*Scott Coolbaugh* (FC)	.08	.06	.03
43	*Jose Cano* (FC)	.10	.08	.04
44	*Jose Vizcaino*	.30	.25	.12
45	*Bob Hamelin*	.40	.30	.15
46	*Jose Offerman*	.25	.20	.10
47	Kevin Blankenship	.10	.08	.04
48	Kirby Puckett (TC)	.20	.15	.08
49	*Tommy Greene*	.75	.60	.30
50	Will Clark (SPEC)	.30	.25	.12
51	Rob Nelson (FC)	.09	.07	.04
52	*Chris Hammond*	.30	.25	.12
53	Indians Checklist	.06	.05	.02
54a	*Ben McDonald* (Orioles Logo)	15.00	11.00	6.00
54b	*Ben McDonald* (COR)	1.25	.90	.50
55	Andy Benes (FC)	.70	.50	.30
56	*John Olerud* (FC)	4.00	3.00	1.50
57	Red Sox Checklist	.06	.05	.02
58	Tony Armas	.06	.05	.02
59	*George Canale* (FC)	.06	.05	.02
60a	Orioles Checklist (Jamie Weston)	4.00	3.00	1.50
60b	Orioles Checklist (Mickey Weston)	.08	.06	.03
61	*Mike Stanton* (FC)	.20	.15	.08
62	Mets Checklist	.06	.05	.02
63	*Kent Mercker* (FC)	.35	.25	.14
64	*Francisco Cabrera*	.20	.15	.08
65	*Steve Avery*	1.50	1.25	.60
66	Jose Canseco	.40	.30	.15
67	*Matt Merullo* (FC)	.08	.06	.03
68	Cardinals Checklist	.06	.05	.02
69	Ron Karkovice	.06	.05	.02
70	*Kevin Maas*	.15	.11	.06
71	Dennis Cook	.10	.08	.04
72	*Juan Gonzalez*	9.00	6.75	3.50
73	Cubs Checklist	.06	.05	.02
74	*Dean Palmer*	1.00	.75	.40
75	Bo Jackson (SPEC)	.50	.40	.20
76	*Rob Richie* (FC)	.15	.11	.06
77	*Bobby Rose* (FC)	.08	.06	.03
78	*Brian DuBois* (FC)	.08	.06	.03
79	White Sox Checklist	.06	.05	.02
80	Gene Nelson	.06	.05	.02
81	Bob McClure	.06	.05	.02
82	Rangers Checklist	.06	.05	.02
83	Greg Minton	.06	.05	.02
84	Braves Checklist	.06	.05	.02
85	Willie Fraser	.06	.05	.02
86	Neal Heaton	.06	.05	.02
87	*Kevin Tapani*	.40	.30	.15
88	Astros Checklist	.06	.05	.02
89a	Jim Gott (incorrect photo)	5.00	3.75	2.00
89b	Jim Gott (correct photo)	.10	.08	.04
90	Lance Johnson	.09	.07	.04
91	Brewers Checklist	.06	.05	.02
92	Jeff Parrett	.08	.06	.03
93	*Julio Machado* (FC)	.06	.05	.02
94	Ron Jones	.10	.08	.04
95	Blue Jays Checklist	.06	.05	.02
96	Jerry Reuss	.06	.05	.02
97	Brian Fisher	.06	.05	.02
98	*Kevin Ritz* (FC)	.12	.09	.05
99	Reds Checklist	.06	.05	.02
100	Checklist 1-100	.06	.05	.02
101	Gerald Perry	.06	.05	.02
102	*Kevin Appier*	1.00	.70	.40
103	Julio Franco	.10	.08	.04
104	Craig Biggio	.15	.11	.06
105	Bo Jackson	.40	.30	.15
106	*Junior Felix*	.10	.08	.04
107	Mike Harkey (FC)	.08	.06	.03
108	Fred McGriff	.35	.25	.14
109	Rick Sutcliffe	.08	.06	.03
110	Pete O'Brien	.08	.06	.03
111	Kelly Gruber	.10	.08	.04
112	Pat Borders	.10	.08	.04
113	Dwight Evans	.10	.08	.04
114	Dwight Gooden	.10	.08	.04
115	*Kevin Batiste*	.15	.11	.06
116	Eric Davis	.12	.09	.05
117	Kevin Mitchell	.12	.09	.05
118	Ron Oester	.06	.05	.02
119	Brett Butler	.09	.07	.04
120	Danny Jackson	.06	.05	.02
121	Tommy Gregg	.06	.05	.02
122	Ken Caminiti	.08	.06	.03
123	Kevin Brown	.10	.08	.04
124	George Brett	.50	.40	.20
125	Mike Scott	.10	.08	.04
126	Cory Snyder	.10	.08	.04
127	George Bell	.10	.07	.04
128	Mark Grace	.30	.25	.12
129	Devon White	.10	.08	.04
130	Tony Fernandez	.15	.11	.06
131	Dan Aase	.06	.05	.02
132	Rance Mulliniks	.06	.05	.02
133	Marty Barrett	.08	.06	.03
134	Nelson Liriano	.07	.05	.03
135	Mark Carreon (FC)	.15	.11	.06
136	Candy Maldonado	.06	.05	.02
137	Tim Birtsas	.06	.05	.02
138	Tom Brookens	.06	.05	.02
139	John Franco	.08	.06	.03
140	Mike LaCoss	.06	.05	.02
141	Jeff Treadway	.07	.05	.03
142	Pat Tabler	.07	.05	.03
143	Darrell Evans	.06	.05	.02
144	Rafael Ramirez	.06	.05	.02
145	Oddibe McDowell	.09	.07	.04
146	Brian Downing	.09	.07	.04
147	Curtis Wilkerson	.06	.05	.02
148	Ernie Whitt	.07	.05	.03
149	Bill Schroeder	.06	.05	.02
150	Domingo Ramos	.06	.05	.02
151	Rick Honeycutt	.06	.05	.02
152	Don Slaught	.06	.05	.02
153	Mitch Webster	.06	.05	.02
154	Tony Phillips	.07	.05	.03
155	Paul Kilgus	.06	.05	.02
156	Ken Griffey, Jr.	5.00	3.75	2.00
157	Gary Sheffield	.60	.45	.25
158	Wally Backman	.06	.05	.02
159	B.J. Surhoff	.08	.06	.03
160	Louie Meadows	.08	.06	.03
161	Paul O'Neill	.09	.07	.04
162	*Jeff McKnight* (FC)	.06	.05	.02
163	Alvaro Espinoza (FC)	.06	.05	.02
164	*Scott Scudder* (FC)	.08	.06	.03
165	Jeff Reed	.06	.05	.02
166	Gregg Jefferies	.40	.30	.15
167	Barry Larkin	.12	.09	.05
168	Gary Carter	.10	.08	.04
169	Robby Thompson	.09	.07	.04
170	Rolando Roomes	.15	.11	.06
171	Mark McGwire	.35	.25	.14
172	Steve Sax	.10	.08	.04
173	Mark Williamson	.06	.05	.02
174	Mitch Williams	.15	.11	.06
175	Brian Holton	.06	.05	.02
176	Rob Deer	.08	.06	.03
177	Tim Raines	.12	.09	.05
178	Mike Felder	.06	.05	.02
179	Harold Reynolds	.10	.08	.04
180	Terry Francona	.06	.05	.02
181	Chris Sabo	.12	.09	.05
182	Darryl Strawberry	.12	.09	.05
183	Willie Randolph	.10	.08	.04
184	Billy Ripken	.06	.05	.02
185	Mackey Sasser	.08	.06	.03
186	Todd Benzinger	.08	.06	.03
187	Kevin Elster	.07	.05	.03
188	Jose Uribe	.06	.05	.02
189	Tom Browning	.10	.08	.04
190	Keith Miller	.09	.07	.04
191	Don Mattingly	.40	.30	.15
192	Dave Parker	.12	.09	.05
193	Roberto Kelly	.15	.11	.06
194	Phil Bradley	.09	.07	.04
195	Ron Hassey	.07	.05	.03
196	Gerald Young	.06	.05	.02
197	Hubie Brooks	.08	.06	.03
198	Bill Doran	.09	.07	.04
199	Al Newman	.06	.05	.02
200	Checklist 101-200	.06	.05	.02
201	Terry Puhl	.06	.05	.02
202	Frank DiPino	.06	.05	.02
203	Jim Clancy	.06	.05	.02
204	Bob Ojeda	.07	.05	.03
205	Alex Trevino	.06	.05	.02
206	Dave Henderson	.10	.08	.04
207	Henry Cotto	.06	.05	.02
208	Rafael Belliard	.06	.05	.02
209	Stan Javier	.07	.05	.03
210	Jerry Reed	.06	.05	.02
211	Doug Dascenzo	.08	.06	.03
212	Andres Thomas	.07	.05	.03
213	Greg Maddux	.30	.25	.12
214	Mike Schooler	.09	.07	.04
215	Lonnie Smith	.09	.07	.04
216	Jose Rijo	.10	.08	.04
217	Greg Gagne	.08	.06	.03
218	Jim Gantner	.08	.06	.03
219	Allan Anderson	.09	.07	.04
220	Rick Mahler	.06	.05	.02
221	Jim Deshaies	.09	.07	.04
222	Keith Hernandez	.10	.08	.04
223	Vince Coleman	.12	.09	.05
224	David Cone	.15	.11	.06
225	Ozzie Smith	.20	.15	.08
226	Matt Nokes	.10	.08	.04
227	Barry Bonds	1.00	.75	.40
228	Felix Jose	.10	.07	.04
229	Dennis Powell	.06	.05	.02
230	Mike Gallego	.06	.05	.02
231	Shawon Dunston	.09	.07	.04
232	Ron Gant	.25	.20	.10
233	*Omar Vizquel*	.10	.08	.04
234	Derek Lilliquist	.10	.08	.04
235	Erik Hanson	.10	.08	.04
236	Kirby Puckett	.75	.60	.30
237	*Bill Spiers*	.08	.06	.03
238	Dan Gladden	.07	.05	.03
239	Bryan Clutterbuck (FC)	.07	.05	.03
240	John Moses	.06	.05	.02
241	Ron Darling	.12	.09	.05
242	Joe Magrane	.12	.09	.05
243	Dave Magadan	.09	.07	.04
244	Pedro Guererro	.06	.05	.02
245	Glenn Davis	.10	.08	.04
246	Terry Steinbach	.12	.09	.05
247	Fred Lynn	.09	.07	.04
248	Gary Redus	.06	.05	.02
249	Kenny Williams	.06	.05	.02
250	Sid Bream	.06	.05	.02
251	Bob Welch	.08	.06	.03
252	Bill Buckner	.07	.05	.03
253	Carney Lansford	.09	.07	.04
254	Paul Molitor	.35	.25	.14
255	Jose DeJesus	.10	.07	.04
256	Orel Hershiser	.10	.08	.04
257	Tom Brunansky	.10	.08	.04

258	Mike Davis	.06	.05	.02
259	Jeff Ballard	.12	.09	.05
260	Scott Terry	.09	.07	.04
261	Sid Fernandez	.10	.08	.04
262	Mike Marshall	.08	.06	.03
263	Howard Johnson	.08	.06	.03
264	Kirk Gibson	.09	.07	.04
265	Kevin McReynolds	.06	.05	.02
266	Cal Ripken, Jr.	.60	.45	.25
267	Ozzie Guillen	.07	.05	.03
268	Jim Traber	.06	.05	.02
269	Bobby Thigpen	.09	.07	.04
270	Joe Orsulak	.06	.05	.02
271	Bob Boone	.09	.07	.04
272	Dave Stewart	.09	.07	.04
273	Tim Wallach	.09	.07	.04
274	Luis Aquino	.06	.05	.02
275	Mike Moore	.10	.08	.04
276	Tony Pena	.08	.06	.03
277	Eddie Murray	.15	.11	.06
278	Milt Thompson	.07	.05	.03
279	Alejandro Pena	.06	.05	.02
280	Ken Dayley	.06	.05	.02
281	Carmen Castillo	.06	.05	.02
282	Tom Henke	.08	.06	.03
283	Mickey Hatcher	.06	.05	.02
284	Roy Smith (FC)	.06	.05	.02
285	Manny Lee	.06	.05	.02
286	Dan Pasqua	.07	.05	.03
287	Larry Sheets	.06	.05	.02
288	Garry Templeton	.07	.05	.03
289	Eddie Williams	.07	.05	.03
290	Brady Anderson	.15	.11	.06
291	Spike Owen	.07	.05	.03
292	Storm Davis	.09	.07	.04
293	Chris Bosio	.09	.07	.04
294	Jim Eisenreich	.07	.05	.03
295	Don August	.07	.05	.03
296	Jeff Hamilton	.07	.05	.03
297	Mickey Tettleton	.10	.08	.04
298	Mike Scioscia	.09	.07	.04
299	Kevin Hickey (FC)	.06	.05	.02
300	Checklist 201-300	.06	.05	.02
301	Shawn Abner	.06	.05	.02
302	Kevin Bass	.08	.06	.03
303	Bip Roberts (FC)	.08	.06	.03
304	Joe Girardi	.10	.08	.04
305	Danny Darwin	.06	.05	.02
306	Mike Heath	.06	.05	.02
307	Mike Macfarlane	.06	.05	.02
308	Ed Whitson	.08	.06	.03
309	Tracy Jones	.07	.05	.03
310	Scott Fletcher	.07	.05	.03
311	Darnell Coles	.07	.05	.03
312	Mike Brumley	.06	.05	.02
313	Bill Swift	.06	.05	.02
314	Charlie Hough	.07	.05	.03
315	Jim Presley	.08	.06	.03
316	Luis Polonia	.07	.05	.03
317	Mike Morgan	.06	.05	.02
318	Lee Guetterman	.06	.05	.02
319	Jose Oquendo	.08	.06	.03
320	Wayne Tollenson	.06	.05	.02
321	Jody Reed	.07	.05	.03
322	Damon Berryhill	.09	.07	.04
323	Roger Clemens	.50	.40	.20
324	Ryne Sandberg	.60	.45	.25
325	Benito Santiago	.10	.08	.04
326	Bret Saberhagen	.08	.06	.03
327	Lou Whitaker	.10	.08	.04
328	Dave Gallagher	.10	.08	.04
329	Mike Pagliarulo	.07	.05	.03
330	Doyle Alexander	.07	.05	.03
331	Jeffrey Leonard	.09	.07	.04
332	Torey Lovullo	.15	.11	.06
333	Pete Incaviglia	.09	.07	.04
334	Rickey Henderson	.25	.20	.10
335	Rafael Palmeiro	.20	.15	.08
336	Ken Hill	.40	.30	.15
337	Dave Winfield	.30	.25	.12
338	Alfredo Griffin	.07	.05	.03
339	Andy Hawkins	.07	.05	.03
340	Ted Power	.06	.05	.02
341	Steve Wilson	.10	.08	.04
342	Jack Clark	.10	.08	.04
343	Ellis Burks	.08	.06	.03
344	Tony Gwynn	.25	.20	.10
345	Jerome Walton	.06	.05	.02
346	Roberto Alomar	1.00	.70	.40
347	*Carlos Martinez* (FC)	.08	.06	.03
348	Chet Lemon	.07	.05	.03
349	Willie Wilson	.07	.05	.03
350	Greg Walker	.07	.05	.03
351	Tom Bolton	.06	.05	.02
352	German Gonzalez (FC)	.08	.06	.03
353	Harold Baines	.10	.08	.04
354	Mike Greenwell	.10	.08	.04
355	Ruben Sierra	.20	.15	.08
356	Andres Galarraga	.20	.15	.08
357	Andre Dawson	.15	.11	.06
358	*Jeff Brantley* (FC)	.10	.08	.04
359	Mike Bielecki	.08	.06	.03
360	Ken Oberkfell	.06	.05	.02
361	Kurt Stillwell	.07	.05	.03
362	Brian Holman	.09	.07	.04
363	Kevin Seitzer	.12	.09	.05
364	Alvin Davis	.06	.05	.02
365	Tom Gordon	.06	.05	.02
366	Bobby Bonilla	.12	.09	.05
367	Carlton Fisk	.10	.08	.04
368	*Steve Carter* (FC)	.08	.06	.03
369	Joel Skinner	.06	.05	.02
370	John Cangelosi	.06	.05	.02
371	Cecil Espy	.08	.06	.03
372	*Gary Wayne* (FC)	.08	.06	.03
373	Jim Rice	.08	.06	.03
374	*Mike Dyer* (FC)	.08	.06	.03
375	Joe Carter	.50	.40	.20
376	Dwight Smith	.06	.05	.02
377	*John Wetteland*	.35	.25	.14
378	Ernie Riles	.06	.05	.02
379	Otis Nixon	.06	.05	.02
380	Vance Law	.06	.05	.02
381	Dave Bergman	.06	.05	.02
382	Frank White	.07	.05	.03
383	Scott Bradley	.06	.05	.02
384	Israel Sanchez	.06	.05	.02
385	Gary Pettis	.06	.05	.02
386	Donn Pall (FC)	.06	.05	.02
387	John Smiley	.10	.08	.04
388	Tom Candiotti	.07	.05	.03
389	Junior Ortiz	.06	.05	.02
390	Steve Lyons	.06	.05	.02
391	Brian Harper	.06	.05	.02
392	Fred Manrique	.06	.05	.02
393	Lee Smith	.08	.06	.03
394	Jeff Kunkel	.06	.05	.02
395	Claudell Washington	.08	.06	.03
396	John Tudor	.07	.05	.03
397	Terry Kennedy	.07	.05	.03
398	Lloyd McClendon	.09	.07	.04
399	Craig Lefferts	.06	.05	.02
400	Checklist 301-400	.06	.05	.02
401	Keith Moreland	.06	.05	.02
402	Rich Gedman	.07	.05	.03
403	Jeff Robinson	.07	.05	.03
404	Randy Ready	.06	.05	.02
405	Rick Cerone	.06	.05	.02
406	Jeff Blauser	.07	.05	.03
407	Larry Andersen	.06	.05	.02
408	Joe Boever	.08	.06	.03
409	Felix Fermin	.06	.05	.02
410	Glenn Wilson	.06	.05	.02
411	Rex Hudler	.06	.05	.02
412	Mark Grant	.06	.05	.02
413	Dennis Martinez	.08	.06	.03
414	Darrin Jackson	.06	.05	.02
415	Mike Aldrete	.06	.05	.02
416	Roger McDowell	.09	.07	.04
417	Jeff Reardon	.10	.08	.04
418	Darren Daulton	.20	.15	.08
419	Tim Laudner	.08	.06	.03
420	Don Carman	.07	.05	.03
421	Lloyd Moseby	.09	.07	.04
422	Doug Drabek	.10	.08	.04
423	Lenny Harris	.09	.07	.04
424	Jose Lind	.07	.05	.03
425	*Dave Johnson*	.08	.06	.03
426	Jerry Browne	.09	.07	.04
427	*Eric Yelding* (FC)	.12	.09	.05
428	Brad Komminsk (FC)	.06	.05	.02
429	Jody Davis	.06	.05	.02
430	Mariano Duncan (FC)	.09	.07	.04
431	Mark Davis	.12	.09	.05
432	Nelson Santovenia	.10	.08	.04
433	Bruce Hurst	.10	.08	.04
434	*Jeff Huson* (FC)	.10	.08	.04
435	Chris James	.09	.07	.04
436	*Mark Guthrie* (FC)	.08	.06	.03
437	Charlie Hayes (FC)	.10	.08	.04
438	Shane Rawley	.08	.06	.03
439	Dickie Thon	.06	.05	.02
440	Juan Berenguer	.06	.05	.02
441	Kevin Romine	.06	.05	.02
442	Bill Landrum	.09	.07	.04
443	Todd Frohwirth	.07	.05	.03
444	Craig Worthington	.10	.08	.04
445	Fernando Valenzuela	.09	.07	.04
446	*Albert Belle*	3.00	2.25	1.25
447	*Ed Whited* (FC)	.08	.06	.03
448	Dave Smith	.09	.07	.04
449	Dave Clark	.07	.05	.03
450	Juan Agosto	.06	.05	.02
451	Dave Valle	.06	.05	.02
452	Kent Hrbek	.15	.11	.06
453	Von Hayes	.10	.08	.04
454	Gary Gaetti	.06	.05	.02
455	Greg Briley	.06	.05	.02
456	Glenn Braggs	.08	.06	.03
457	Kirt Manwaring	.10	.08	.04
458	Mel Hall	.07	.05	.03
459	Brook Jacoby	.08	.06	.03
460	Pat Sheridan	.06	.05	.02
461	Rob Murphy	.06	.05	.02
462	Jimmy Key	.10	.08	.04
463	Nick Esasky	.10	.08	.04
464	Rob Ducey	.09	.07	.04
465	Carlos Quintana	.09	.07	.04
466	*Larry Walker*	1.50	1.25	.60
467	Todd Worrell	.10	.08	.04
468	Kevin Gross	.09	.07	.04
469	Terry Pendleton	.09	.07	.04
470	Dave Martinez	.07	.05	.03
471	Gene Larkin	.06	.05	.02
472	Len Dykstra	.20	.15	.08
473	Barry Lyons	.06	.05	.02
474	Terry Mulholland (FC)	.10	.08	.04
475	*Chip Hale* (FC)	.08	.06	.03
476	Jesse Barfield	.08	.06	.03
477	Dan Plesac	.09	.07	.04
478a	Scott Garrelts (Photo actually Bill Bathe)	3.00	2.25	1.25
478b	Scott Garrelts (Correct photo)	.10	.08	.04
479	Dave Righetti	.10	.08	.04
480	Gus Polidor (FC)	.06	.05	.02
481	Mookie Wilson	.09	.07	.04
482	Luis Rivera	.06	.05	.02
483	Mike Flanagan	.07	.05	.03
484	Dennis "Oil Can" Boyd	.07	.05	.03
485	John Cerutti	.07	.05	.03
486	John Costello	.07	.05	.03
487	Pascual Perez	.07	.05	.03
488	Tommy Herr	.09	.07	.04
489	Tom Foley	.06	.05	.02
490	Curt Ford	.06	.05	.02
491	Steve Lake	.06	.05	.02
492	Tim Teufel	.06	.05	.02
493	Randy Bush	.06	.05	.02
494	Mike Jackson	.06	.05	.02
495	Steve Jeltz	.06	.05	.02
496	Paul Gibson	.08	.06	.03
497	Steve Balboni	.06	.05	.02
498	Bud Black	.06	.05	.02
499	Dale Sveum	.06	.05	.02
500	Checklist 401-500	.06	.05	.02
501	Timmy Jones	.06	.05	.02
502	Mark Portugal	.06	.05	.02
503	Ivan Calderon	.07	.05	.03
504	Rick Rhoden	.06	.05	.02
505	Willie McGee	.09	.07	.04
506	Kirk McCaskill	.08	.06	.03
507	Dave LaPoint	.07	.05	.03
508	Jay Howell	.10	.08	.04
509	Johnny Ray	.08	.06	.03
510	Dave Anderson	.06	.05	.02
511	Chuck Crim	.06	.05	.02
512	Joe Hesketh	.06	.05	.02
513	Dennis Eckersley	.10	.08	.04
514	Greg Brock	.08	.06	.03
515	Tim Burke (FC)	.08	.06	.03
516	Frank Tanana	.07	.05	.03
517	Jay Bell	.07	.05	.03
518	Guillermo Hernandez	.07	.05	.03
519	Randy Kramer (FC)	.08	.06	.03
520	Charles Hudson	.06	.05	.02
521	Jim Corsi (FC)	.08	.06	.03
522	Steve Rosenberg	.08	.06	.03
523	Cris Carpenter	.10	.08	.04
524	*Matt Winters* (FC)	.12	.09	.05
525	Melido Perez	.08	.06	.03
526	Chris Gwynn (FC)	.08	.06	.03
527	Bert Blyleven	.09	.07	.04
528	Chuck Cary (FC)	.07	.05	.03
529	Daryl Boston	.06	.05	.02
530	Dale Mohorcic	.06	.05	.02
531	Geronimo Berroa (FC)	.12	.09	.05
532	Edgar Martinez	.09	.07	.04
533	Dale Murphy	.10	.08	.04
534	Jay Buhner	.15	.11	.06
535	John Smoltz (FC)	.15	.11	.06
536	Andy Van Slyke	.15	.11	.06
537	Mike Henneman (FC)	.09	.07	.04
538	Miguel Garcia (FC)	.07	.05	.03
539	Frank Williams (FC)	.06	.05	.02
540	R.J. Reynolds	.06	.05	.02
541	Shawn Hillegas (FC)	.06	.05	.02
542	Walt Weiss	.10	.08	.04
543	*Greg Hibbard* (FC)	.15	.11	.06
544	Nolan Ryan	1.25	.90	.50
545	Todd Zeile	.40	.30	.15
546	Hensley Meulens	.08	.06	.03
547	Tim Belcher (FC)	.10	.08	.04
548	Mike Witt	.08	.06	.03
549	Greg Cadaret (FC)	.06	.05	.02
550	Franklin Stubbs	.06	.05	.02
551	*Tony Castillo* (FC)	.12	.09	.05
552	Jeff Robinson	.08	.06	.03
553	*Steve Olin* (FC)	.12	.09	.05
554	Alan Trammell	.10	.08	.04
555	Wade Boggs	.25	.20	.10
556	Will Clark	.40	.30	.15
557	Jeff King	.10	.08	.04
558	Mike Fitzgerald	.06	.05	.02
559	Ken Howell (FC)	.06	.05	.02
560	Bob Kipper	.06	.05	.02
561	Scott Bankhead (FC)	.09	.07	.04
562a	*Jeff Innis* (FC) (Photo actually David West)	3.00	2.25	1.25
562b	*Jeff Innis* (FC) (Corrected)	.08	.06	.03
563	Randy Johnson	.25	.20	.10
564	*Wally Whitehurst* (FC)	.10	.08	.04
565	*Gene Harris* (FC)	.10	.08	.04
566	Norm Charlton (FC)	.09	.07	.04
567	Robin Yount	.50	.40	.20
568	*Joe Oliver*	.15	.11	.06
569	Mark Parent	.07	.05	.03
570	John Farrell (FC)	.07	.05	.03
571	Tom Glavine	.40	.30	.15
572	Rod Nichols (FC)	.06	.05	.02
573	Jack Morris	.09	.07	.04
574	Greg Swindell (FC)	.12	.09	.05
575	Steve Searcy (FC)	.09	.07	.04
576	Ricky Jordan (FC)	.08	.06	.03
577	Matt Williams	.25	.20	.10
578	Mike LaValliere (FC)	.07	.05	.03
579	Bryn Smith	.08	.06	.03
580	Bruce Ruffin (FC)	.06	.05	.02
581	Randy Myers	.08	.06	.03
582	*Rick Wrona* (FC)	.08	.06	.03
583	Juan Samuel	.09	.07	.04
584	Les Lancaster (FC)	.07	.05	.03
585	Jeff Musselman	.07	.05	.03
586	Rob Dibble (FC)	.09	.07	.04
587	Eric Show	.07	.05	.03
588	Jesse Orosco	.06	.05	.02
589	Herm Winningham	.06	.05	.02
590	Andy Allanson	.06	.05	.02
591	Dion James	.06	.05	.02
592	Carmelo Martinez (FC)	.08	.06	.03
593	Luis Quinones (FC)	.08	.06	.03
594	Dennis Rasmussen (FC)	.08	.06	.03
595	Rich Yett	.06	.05	.02
596	Bob Walk (FC)	.08	.06	.03
597a	Andy McGaffigan (player #48, photo actually Rich Thompson)	.70	.50	.30
597b	Andy McGaffigan (player #27, correct photo)	.07	.05	.03
598	Billy Hatcher (FC)	.07	.05	.03
599	Bob Knepper	.06	.05	.02
600	Checklist 501-600	.06	.05	.02
601	Joey Cora (FC)	.10	.08	.04
602	*Steve Finley*	.20	.15	.08
603	Kal Daniels	.10	.08	.04
604	Gregg Olson	.12	.09	.05
605	Dave Steib	.09	.07	.04
606	*Kenny Rogers* (FC)	.08	.06	.03
607	Zane Smith	.06	.05	.02

608	*Bob Geren* (FC)	.08	.06	.03
609	Chad Kreuter	.10	.08	.04
610	Mike Smithson (FC)	.06	.05	.02
611	*Jeff Wetherby* (FC)	.08	.06	.03
612	*Gary Mielke* (FC)	.08	.06	.03
613	Pete Smith	.08	.06	.03
614	*Jack Daugherty* (FC)	.08	.06	.03
615	Lance McCullers	.08	.06	.03
616	Don Robinson (FC)	.06	.05	.02
617	Jose Guzman	.06	.05	.02
618	Steve Bedrosian (FC)	.08	.06	.03
619	Jamie Moyer	.06	.05	.02
620	Atlee Hammaker (FC)	.06	.05	.02
621	*Rick Luecken* (FC)	.08	.06	.03
622	Greg W. Harris (FC)	.09	.07	.04
623	Pete Harnisch	.10	.08	.04
624	Jerald Clark (FC)	.10	.08	.04
625	Jack McDowell	.30	.25	.12
626	Frank Viola	.12	.09	.05
627	Ted Higuera	.09	.07	.04
628	*Marty Pevey* (FC)	.06	.05	.02
629	Bill Wegman	.06	.05	.02
630	Eric Plunk (FC)	.06	.05	.02
631	Drew Hall	.06	.05	.02
632	Doug Jones (FC)	.08	.06	.03
633	Geno Petralli	.06	.05	.02
634	Jose Alvarez (FC)	.06	.05	.02
635	Bob Milacki	.10	.08	.04
636	Bobby Witt (FC)	.07	.05	.03
637	Trevor Wilson	.08	.06	.03
638	Jeff Russell (FC)	.08	.06	.03
639	Mike Krukow	.07	.05	.03
640	Rick Leach (FC)	.06	.05	.02
641	Dave Schmidt	.06	.05	.02
642	Terry Leach (FC)	.06	.05	.02
643	Calvin Schiraldi	.06	.05	.02
644	Bob Melvin (FC)	.06	.05	.02
645	Jim Abbott	.25	.20	.10
646	*Jaime Navarro*	.20	.15	.08
647	Mark Langston	.10	.08	.04
648	Juan Nieves (FC)	.08	.06	.03
649	Damaso Garcia	.06	.05	.02
650	Charlie O'Brien (FC)	.06	.05	.02
651	Eric King	.06	.05	.02
652	Mike Boddicker	.08	.06	.03
653	Duan Ward	.07	.05	.03
654	Bob Stanley	.06	.05	.02
655	Sandy Alomar, Jr.	.10	.08	.04
656	Danny Tartabull	.15	.11	.06
657	Randy McCament	.06	.05	.02
658	Charlie Leibrandt	.07	.05	.03
659	Dan Quisenberry	.07	.05	.03
660	Paul Assenmacher (FC)	.06	.05	.02
661	Walt Terrell	.07	.05	.03
662	Tim Leary	.07	.05	.03
663	Randy Milligan	.08	.06	.03
664	Bo Diaz (FC)	.06	.05	.02
665	Mark Lemke	.07	.05	.03
666	Jose Gonzalez (FC)	.08	.06	.03
667	Chuck Finley	.07	.05	.03
668	John Kruk	.12	.09	.05
669	Dick Schofield	.07	.05	.03
670	Tim Crews	.06	.05	.02
671	John Dopson	.09	.07	.04
672	*John Orton*	.15	.11	.06
673	Eric Hetzel (FC)	.10	.08	.04
674	Lance Parrish	.08	.06	.03
675	Ramon Martinez	.12	.09	.05
676	Mark Gubicza	.10	.08	.04
677	Greg Litton	.10	.07	.04
678	Greg Mathews	.07	.05	.03
679	Dave Dravecky	.07	.05	.03
680	Steve Farr (FC)	.07	.05	.03
681	Mike Devereaux	.09	.07	.04
682	Ken Griffey, Sr.	.08	.06	.03
683a	*Mickey Weston* (FC) (Jamie)	4.00	3.00	1.50
683b	*Mickey Weston* (FC) (corrected)	.10	.08	.04
684	Jack Armstrong	.07	.05	.03
685	Steve Buechele	.07	.05	.03
686	Bryan Harvey	.07	.05	.03
687	Lance Blankenship	.09	.07	.04
688	Dante Bichette	.20	.15	.08
689	Todd Burns (FC)	.09	.07	.04
690	Dan Petry	.06	.05	.02
691	*Kent Anderson*	.08	.06	.03
692	Todd Stottlemyre	.08	.06	.03
693	Wally Joyner	.05	.04	.02
694	Mike Rochford (FC)	.10	.08	.04
695	Floyd Bannister	.07	.05	.03
696	Rick Reuschel	.09	.07	.04
697	Jose DeLeon (FC)	.09	.07	.04
698	Jeff Montgomery	.08	.06	.03
699	Jeff Montgomery	.08	.06	.03
700a	Checklist 601-700 (Jamie Weston)	.05	.04	.02
700b	Checklist 601-700 (Mickey Weston)	.10	.08	.04
701	Jim Gott	.10	.08	.04
702	"Rookie Threats" (Delino DeShields, Larry Walker, Marquis Grissom)	1.00	.70	.40
703	Alejandro Pena	.10	.08	.04
704	Willie Randolph	.12	.09	.05
705	Tim Leary	.10	.08	.04
706	Chuck McElroy (FC)	.12	.09	.05
707	Gerald Perry (FC)	.10	.08	.04
708	Tom Brunansky	.12	.09	.05
709	John Franco	.15	.11	.06
710	Mark Davis	.10	.08	.04
711	*Dave Justice*	3.00	2.25	1.25
712	Storm Davis	.10	.08	.04
713	Scott Ruskin (FC)	.10	.08	.04
714	Glenn Braggs	.10	.08	.04
715	Kevin Bearse (FC)	.10	.08	.04
716	Jose Nunez (FC)	.15	.11	.06
717	Tim Layana (FC)	.08	.06	.03
718	Greg Myers (FC)	.12	.09	.05
719	Pete O'Brien	.10	.08	.04
720	John Candelaria	.10	.08	.04
721	Craig Grebeck (FC)	.25	.20	.10
722	Shawn Boskie (FC)	.12	.09	.05
723	Jim Leyritz (FC)	.20	.15	.08
724	Bill Sampen (FC)	.10	.08	.04
725	Scott Radinsky (FC)	.20	.15	.08
726	*Todd Hundley*	.30	.25	.12
727	Scott Hemond (FC)	.12	.09	.05
728	Lenny Webster (FC)	.10	.08	.04
729	Jeff Reardon	.12	.09	.05
730	Mitch Webster	.10	.08	.04
731	Brian Bohanon (FC)	.10	.08	.04
732	Rick Parker (FC)	.08	.06	.03
733	Terry Shumpert (FC)	.08	.06	.03
734a	Nolan Ryan (300-win stripe on front)	2.00	1.50	.80
734b	Nolan Ryan (no stripe)	8.00	6.00	3.25
735	John Burkett (FC)	.40	.30	.15
736	Derrick May (FC)	1.00	.70	.40
737	Carlos Baerga (FC)	3.50	2.75	1.50
738	Greg Smith (FC)	.15	.11	.06
739	Joe Kraemer (FC)	.15	.11	.06
740	Scott Sanderson (FC)	.10	.08	.04
741	Hector Villanueva (FC)	.10	.08	.04
742	Mike Fetters (FC)	.12	.09	.05
743	Mark Gardner (FC)	.20	.15	.08
744	Matt Nokes (FC)	.10	.08	.04
745	Dave Winfield	.25	.20	.10
746	*Delino DeShields*	.75	.60	.30
747	Dann Howitt (FC)	.08	.06	.03
748	Tony Pena	.12	.09	.05
749	Oil Can Boyd	.12	.09	.05
750	Mike Benjamin (FC)	.10	.08	.04
751	Alex Cole (FC)	.20	.15	.08
752	Eric Gunderson (FC)	.20	.15	.08
753	Howard Farmer (FC)	.12	.09	.05
754	Joe Carter	.40	.30	.15
755	*Ray Lankford*	1.00	.75	.40
756	Sandy Alomar,Jr.	.10	.08	.04
757	Alex Sanchez (FC)	.15	.11	.06
758	Nick Esasky	.10	.08	.04
759	Stan Belinda (FC)	.20	.15	.08
760	Jim Presley (FC)	.10	.08	.04
761	Gary DiSarcina (FC)	.20	.15	.08
762	Wayne Edwards (FC)	.20	.15	.08
763	Pat Combs (FC)	.20	.15	.08
764	Mickey Pina (FC)	.20	.15	.08
765	*Wilson Alvarez*	1.25	.90	.50
766	Dave Parker	.15	.11	.06
767	Mike Blowers (FC)	.20	.15	.08
768	Tony Phillips	.10	.08	.04
769	Pascual Perez	.10	.08	.04
770	Gary Pettis	.10	.08	.04
771	Fred Lynn	.10	.08	.04
772	*Mel Rojas*	.20	.15	.08
773	David Segui (FC)	.15	.11	.06
774	Gary Carter	.10	.07	.04
775	Rafael Valdez (FC)	.15	.11	.06
776	Glenallen Hill (FC)	.15	.11	.06
777	Keith Hernandez	.12	.09	.05
778	Billy Hatcher	.12	.09	.05
779	Marty Clary (FC)	.10	.08	.04
780	Candy Maldonado (FC)	.12	.09	.05
781	Mike Marshall	.10	.08	.04
782	Billy Jo Robidoux (FC)	.10	.08	.04
783	Mark Langston	.12	.09	.05
784	*Paul Sorrento*	.40	.30	.15
785	*Dave Hollins*	1.00	.75	.40
786	Cecil Fielder	.40	.30	.15
787	Matt Young	.10	.08	.04
788	Jeff Huson	.15	.11	.06
789	Lloyd Moseby	.12	.09	.05
790	Ron Kittle	.12	.09	.05
791	Hubie Brooks	.12	.09	.05
792	Craig Lefferts	.10	.08	.04
793	Kevin Bass	.10	.08	.04
794	Bryn Smith (FC)	.10	.08	.04
795	Juan Samuel	.12	.09	.05
796	Sam Horn	.15	.11	.06
797	Randy Myers	.12	.09	.05
798	Chris James (FC)	.10	.08	.04
799	Bill Gullickson	.10	.08	.04
800	Checklist 701-800	.10	.08	.04

1990 Upper Deck Reggie Jackson Heroes

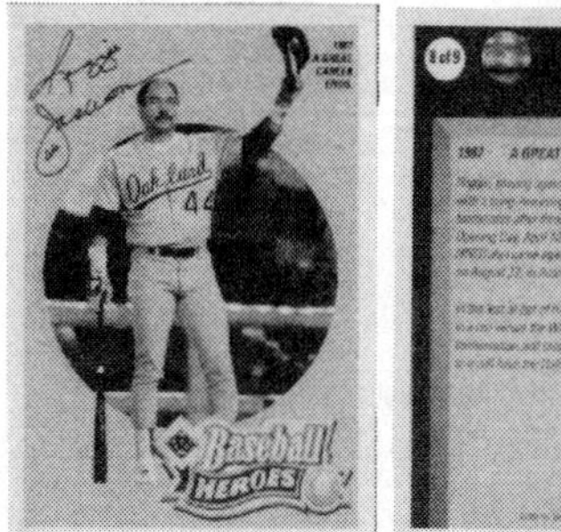

This Baseball Heroes set is devoted to Reggie Jackson. The cards, numbered 1-9, are the first in a continuing series of cards which have been issued in subsequent years. An unnumbered cover card that says "Baseball Heroes" was also issued. The Jackson cards were randomly inserted in high number foil packs only. Jackson also autographed 2,500 numbered cards, which were randomly included in high number packs.

		MT	NR MT	EX
	Complete Set (10):	27.50	21.00	11.00
	Common Reggie:	3.00	2.25	1.25
	Autographed Card:	450.00	337.00	180.00
	Header card	3.00	2.25	1.25
1	1969 Emerging Superstar (Reggie Jackson)	3.00	2.25	1.25
2	1973 An MVP Year (Reggie Jackson)	3.00	2.25	1.25
3	1977 "Mr. October" (Reggie Jackson)	3.00	2.25	1.25
4	1978 Jackson vs. Welch (Reggie Jackson)	3.00	2.25	1.25
5	1982 Under the Halo (Reggie Jackson)	3.00	2.25	1.25
6	1984 500! (Reggie Jackson)	3.00	2.25	1.25
7	1986 Moving Up the List (Reggie Jackson)	3.00	2.25	1.25
8	1987 A Great Career Ends (Reggie Jackson)	3.00	2.25	1.25
9	Heroes Checklist 1-9 (Reggie Jackson)	3.00	2.25	1.25

1991 Upper Deck

More than 110 rookies are included among the first 700 cards in the 1991 Upper Deck set. A 100-card high-number series was once again released in late summer. The 1991 Upper Deck cards feature high quality white stock and color photos on both the front and backs of the cards. A nine-card "Baseball Heroes" bonus set honoring Nolan Ryan, is among the many insert specials in the 1991 Upper Deck set. Others include a card of Chicago Bulls superstar Michael Jordan. Along with the Ryan bonus cards, 2,500 limited-edition cards personally autographed and numbered by Ryan were randomly inserted. Upper Deck cards are packaged in tamper-proof foil packs. Each pack contains 15 cards and a 3-D team logo hologram sticker. The 1991 hologram stickers are full size.

		MT	NR MT	EX
	Complete Set (800):	28.00	20.00	12.00
	Common Player (1-700):	.05	.04	.02
	Common Player (701-800):	.10	.08	.04
1	Star Rookie Checklist	.05	.04	.02
2	*Phil Plantier* (FC)	.70	.50	.30
3	*D.J. Dozier* (FC)	.10	.08	.04
4	Dave Hansen (FC)	.25	.20	.10
5	Mo Vaughn (FC)	1.00	.70	.40
6	*Leo Gomez*	.30	.25	.12
7	*Scott Aldred* (FC)	.15	.11	.06
8	*Scott Chiamparino*	.30	.25	.12
9	*Lance Dickson*	.12	.09	.05
10	*Sean Berry*	.20	.15	.08
11	Bernie Williams (FC)	.40	.30	.15
12	*Brian Barnes*	.15	.11	.06
13	*Narciso Elvira*	.10	.07	.04
14	*Mike Gardiner*	.15	.11	.06
15	*Greg Colbrunn*	.30	.25	.12
16	*Bernard Gilkey*	.50	.40	.20
17	Mark Lewis (FC)	.15	.11	.06
18	*Mickey Morandini*	.15	.11	.06
19	Charles Nagy (FC)	.12	.09	.05
20	*Geronimo Pena*	.20	.15	.08
21	*Henry Rodriguez*	.50	.40	.20
22	Scott Cooper (FC)	.40	.30	.15
23	*Andujar Cedeno*	.50	.40	.20
24	*Eric Karros*	1.00	.70	.40
25	*Steve Decker*	.15	.11	.06
26	*Kevin Belcher*	.20	.15	.08
27	*Jeff Conine*	.60	.45	.25
28	Oakland Athletics Checklist	.10	.08	.04
29	Chicago White Sox Checklist	.08	.06	.03
30	Texas Rangers Checklist	.08	.06	.03
31	California Angels Checklist	.08	.06	.03
32	Seattle Mariners Checklist	.10	.08	.04
33	Kansas City Royals Checklist	.10	.08	.04
34	Minnesota Twins Checklist	.08	.06	.03
35	Scott Leius	.10	.08	.04
36	Neal Heaton	.06	.05	.02
37	*Terry Lee*	.10	.07	.04
38	Gary Redus	.05	.04	.02
39	Barry Jones	.06	.05	.02
40	Chuck Knoblauch (FC)	.75	.60	.30
41	Larry Andersen	.05	.04	.02
43	Darryl Hamilton	.06	.05	.02
44	Toronto Blue Jays Checklist	.08	.06	.03

45	Detroit Tigers Checklist	.10	.08	.04
46	Cleveland Indians Checklist	.08	.06	.03
47	Baltimore Orioles Checklist	.08	.06	.03
48	Milwaukee Brewers Checklist	.08	.06	.03
49	New York Yankees Checklist	.08	.06	.03
50	Top Prospect Checklist	.05	.04	.02
51	*Kyle Abbott*	.12	.09	.05
52	Jeff Juden (FC)	.25	.20	.10
53	*Todd Van Poppel*	.40	.30	.15
54	*Steve Karsay*	.60	.45	.25
55	*Chipper Jones*	1.00	.75	.40
56	*Chris Johnson*	.10	.07	.04
57	*John Ericks*	.10	.07	.04
58	*Gary Scott*	.10	.07	.04
59	Kiki Jones (FC)	.12	.09	.05
60	*Wil Cordero*	.90	.70	.35
61	*Royce Clayton*	.50	.40	.20
62	*Tim Costo*	.30	.25	.12
63	Roger Salkeld (FC)	.40	.30	.15
64	*Brook Fordyce*	.25	.20	.10
65	*Mike Mussina*	2.00	1.50	.80
66	*Dave Staton*	.25	.20	.10
67	*Mike Lieberthal*	.30	.25	.12
68	*Kurt Miller*	.30	.25	.12
69	*Dan Peltier*	.25	.20	.10
70	Greg Blosser (FC)	.25	.20	.10
71	*Reggie Sanders*	1.00	.70	.40
72	Brent Mayne (FC)	.15	.11	.06
73	*Rico Brogna*	.15	.11	.06
74	*Willie Banks*	.40	.30	.15
75	*Len Brutcher*	.10	.08	.04
76	*Pat Kelly*	.25	.20	.10
77	Cincinnati Reds Checklist	.08	.06	.03
78	Los Angeles Dodgers Checklist	.08	.06	.03
79	San Francisco Giants Checklist	.08	.06	.03
80	San Diego Padres Checklist	.08	.06	.03
81	Houston Astros Checklist	.08	.06	.03
82	Atlanta Braves Checklist	.10	.08	.04
83	"Fielder's Feat"	.20	.15	.08
84	*Orlando Merced*	.40	.30	.15
85	Domingo Ramos	.05	.04	.02
86	Tom Bolton	.05	.04	.02
87	*Andres Santana* (FC)	.12	.09	.05
88	John Dopson (FC)	.05	.04	.02
89	Kenny Williams	.05	.04	.02
90	Marty Barrett	.06	.05	.02
91	Tom Pagnozzi	.06	.05	.02
92	Carmelo Martinez	.06	.05	.02
93	"Save Master"	.10	.08	.04
94	Pittsburgh Pirates Checklist	.10	.08	.04
95	New York Mets Checklist	.10	.08	.04
96	Montreal Expos Checklist	.08	.06	.03
97	Philadelphia Phillies Checklist	.08	.06	.03
98	St. Louis Cardinals Checklist	.08	.06	.03
99	Chicago Cubs Checklist	.10	.08	.04
100	Checklist 1-100	.05	.04	.02
101	Kevin Elster	.06	.05	.02
102	Tom Brookens	.05	.04	.02
103	Mackey Sasser	.08	.06	.03
104	Felix Fermin (FC)	.05	.04	.02
105	Kevin McReynolds	.12	.09	.05
106	Dave Steib	.12	.09	.05
107	Jeffrey Leonard	.06	.05	.02
108	Dave Henderson	.08	.06	.03
109	Sid Bream	.06	.05	.02
110	Henry Cotto	.05	.04	.02
111	Shawon Dunston	.12	.09	.05
112	Mariano Duncan (FC)	.08	.06	.03
113	Joe Girardi	.08	.06	.03
114	Billy Hatcher	.08	.06	.03
115	Greg Maddux	.20	.15	.08
116	Jerry Browne (FC)	.08	.06	.03
117	Juan Samuel	.08	.06	.03
118	Steve Olin	.06	.05	.02
119	Alfredo Griffin	.06	.05	.02
120	Mitch Webster (FC)	.06	.05	.02
121	Joel Skinner	.05	.04	.02
122	Frank Viola	.15	.11	.06
123	Cory Snyder	.10	.08	.04
124	Howard Johnson	.12	.09	.05
125	Carlos Baerga	.60	.45	.25
126	Tony Fernandez	.12	.09	.05
127	Dave Stewart	.12	.09	.05
128	Jay Buhner	.08	.06	.03
129	Mike LaValliere	.06	.05	.02
130	Scott Bradley	.05	.04	.02
131	Tony Phillips	.06	.05	.02
132	Ryne Sandberg	.40	.30	.15
133	Paul O'Neill	.08	.06	.03
134	Mark Grace	.15	.11	.06
135	Chris Sabo	.12	.09	.05
136	Ramon Martinez	.10	.08	.04
137	Brook Jacoby	.08	.06	.03
138	Candy Maldonado	.08	.06	.03
139	Mike Scioscia	.08	.06	.03
140	Chris James (FC)	.08	.06	.03
141	Craig Worthington	.08	.06	.03
142	Manny Lee	.06	.05	.02
143	Tim Raines	.12	.09	.05
144	Sandy Alomar, Jr.	.12	.09	.05
145	John Olerud	.75	.60	.30
146	*Ozzie Canseco*	.15	.11	.06
147	Pat Borders	.06	.05	.02
148	Harold Reynolds	.10	.08	.04
149	Tom Henke	.08	.06	.03
150	R.J. Reynolds	.05	.04	.02
151	Mike Gallego	.05	.04	.02
152	Bobby Bonilla	.20	.15	.08
153	Terry Steinbach	.06	.05	.02
154	Barry Bonds	.50	.40	.20
155	Jose Canseco	.25	.20	.10
156	Gregg Jefferies	.15	.11	.06
157	Matt Williams	.20	.15	.08
158	Craig Biggio	.08	.06	.03
159	Daryl Boston	.05	.04	.02
160	Ricky Jordan	.08	.06	.03
161	Stan Belinda	.20	.15	.08
162	Ozzie Smith	.20	.15	.08
163	Tom Brunansky	.08	.06	.03
164	Todd Zeile	.25	.20	.10
165	Mike Greenwell	.15	.11	.06
166	Kal Daniels	.10	.08	.04
167	Kent Hrbek	.12	.09	.05
168	Franklin Stubbs	.06	.05	.02
169	Dick Schofield	.05	.04	.02
170	Junior Ortiz	.05	.04	.02
171	*Hector Villanueva*	.20	.15	.08
172	Dennis Eckersley	.15	.11	.06
173	Mitch Williams	.08	.06	.03
174	Mark McGwire	.35	.25	.14
175	Fernando Valenzuela	.10	.08	.04
176	Gary Carter	.10	.08	.04
177	Dave Magadan	.10	.08	.04
178	Robby Thompson	.08	.06	.03
179	Bob Ojeda	.05	.04	.02
180	Ken Caminiti	.06	.05	.02
181	Don Slaught	.05	.04	.02
182	Luis Rivera	.05	.04	.02
183	Jay Bell	.06	.05	.02
184	Jody Reed	.08	.06	.03
185	Wally Backman	.06	.05	.02
186	Dave Martinez	.06	.05	.02
187	Luis Polonia	.05	.04	.02
188	Shane Mack	.06	.05	.02
189	Spike Owen	.06	.05	.02
190	Scott Bailes	.05	.04	.02
191	John Russell	.05	.04	.02
192	Walt Weiss	.08	.06	.03
193	Jose Oquendo	.06	.05	.02
194	Carney Lansford	.08	.06	.03
195	Jeff Huson	.08	.06	.03
196	Keith Miller	.06	.05	.02
197	Eric Yelding	.10	.08	.04
198	Ron Darling	.06	.05	.02
199	John Kruk	.06	.05	.02
200	Checklist 101-200	.05	.04	.02
201	John Shelby	.05	.04	.02
202	Bob Geren	.06	.05	.02
203	Lance McCullers	.05	.04	.02
204	Alvaro Espinoza	.06	.05	.02
205	Mark Salas	.05	.04	.02
206	Mike Pagliarulo	.06	.05	.02
207	Jose Uribe	.06	.05	.02
208	Jim Deshaies (FC)	.06	.05	.02
209	Ron Karkovice	.05	.04	.02
210	Rafael Ramirez	.06	.05	.02
211	Donnie Hill	.05	.04	.02
212	Brian Harper (FC)	.08	.06	.03
213	Jack Howell	.05	.04	.02
214	Wes Gardner	.05	.04	.02
215	Tim Burke	.08	.06	.03
216	Doug Jones (FC)	.08	.06	.03
217	Hubie Brooks	.10	.08	.04
218	Tom Candiotti	.06	.05	.02
219	Gerald Perry	.06	.05	.02
220	Jose DeLeon (FC)	.06	.05	.02
221	Wally Whitehurst	.08	.06	.03
222	*Alan Mills*	.15	.11	.06
223	Alan Trammell	.12	.09	.05
224	Dwight Gooden	.10	.07	.04
225	*Travis Fryman*	1.50	1.25	.60
226	Joe Carter	.25	.20	.10
227	Julio Franco	.10	.08	.04
228	Craig Lefferts	.06	.05	.02
229	Gary Pettis	.06	.05	.02
230	Dennis Rasmussen	.06	.05	.02
231a	Brian Downing (no position on front)	.60	.45	.25
231b	Brian Downing (DH on front)	.06	.05	.02
232	Carlos Quintana (FC)	.10	.08	.04
233	Gary Gaetti	.12	.09	.05
234	Mark Langston	.15	.11	.06
235	Tim Wallach	.10	.08	.04
236	Greg Swindell	.10	.08	.04
237	Eddie Murray	.20	.15	.08
238	Jeff Manto (FC)	.20	.15	.08
239	Lenny Harris	.08	.06	.03
240	Jesse Orosco	.05	.04	.02
241	Scott Lusader	.05	.04	.02
242	Sid Fernandez	.08	.06	.03
243	*Jim Leyritz*	.08	.06	.03
244	Cecil Fielder	.20	.15	.08
245	Darryl Strawberry	.12	.09	.05
246	Frank Thomas (FC)	4.00	3.00	1.50
247	Kevin Mitchell	.12	.09	.05
248	Lance Johnson (FC)	.06	.05	.02
249	Rick Reuschel	.08	.06	.03
250	Mark Portugal	.05	.04	.02
251	Derek Lilliquist	.06	.05	.02
252	Brian Holman (FC)	.08	.06	.03
253	Rafael Valdez	.08	.06	.03
254	B.J. Surhoff	.06	.05	.02
255	Tony Gwynn	.15	.11	.06
256	Andy Van Slyke	.10	.07	.04
257	Todd Stottlemyre	.08	.06	.03
258	Jose Lind	.06	.05	.02
259	Greg Myers	.06	.05	.02
260	Jeff Ballard (FC)	.06	.05	.02
261	Bobby Thigpen	.10	.08	.04
262	*Jimmy Kremers* (FC)	.15	.11	.06
263	Robin Ventura	.40	.30	.15
264	John Smoltz	.15	.11	.06
265	Sammy Sosa	.20	.15	.08
266	Gary Sheffield	.25	.20	.10
267	Len Dykstra	.15	.11	.06
268	Bill Spiers	.06	.05	.02
269	Charlie Hayes	.08	.06	.03
270	Brett Butler	.08	.06	.03
271	Bip Roberts	.08	.06	.03
272	Rob Deer	.06	.05	.02
273	Fred Lynn	.08	.06	.03
274	Dave Parker	.10	.07	.04
275	Andy Benes	.10	.08	.04
276	Glenallen Hill (FC)	.08	.06	.03
277	*Steve Howard* (FC)	.12	.09	.05
278	Doug Drabek	.10	.08	.04
279	Joe Oliver	.08	.06	.03
280	Todd Benzinger	.06	.05	.02
281	Eric King	.06	.05	.02
282	Jim Presley	.06	.05	.02
283	Ken Patterson (FC)	.06	.05	.02
284	Jack Daugherty (FC)	.08	.06	.03
285	Ivan Calderon	.10	.08	.04
286	*Edgar Diaz* (FC)	.10	.08	.04
287	Kevin Bass	.08	.06	.03
288	Don Carman (FC)	.06	.05	.02
289	Greg Brock	.06	.05	.02
290	John Franco	.10	.08	.04
291	Joey Cora	.06	.05	.02
292	Bill Wegman	.06	.05	.02
293	Eric Show	.06	.05	.02
294	Scott Bankhead	.08	.06	.03
295	Garry Templeton	.06	.05	.02
296	Mickey Tettleton	.06	.05	.02
297	Luis Sojo	.15	.11	.06
298	Jose Rijo	.08	.06	.03
299	Dave Johnson	.06	.05	.02
300	Checklist 201-300	.05	.04	.02
301	Mark Grant	.05	.04	.02
302	Pete Harnisch	.08	.06	.03
303	Greg Olson	.10	.08	.04
304	*Anthony Telford* (FC)	.15	.11	.06
305	Lonnie Smith	.06	.05	.02
306	*Chris Hoiles*	.30	.25	.12
307	Bryn Smith	.06	.05	.02
308	Mike Devereaux	.06	.05	.02
309a	Milt Thompson ("86" in stats obscured by "bull's eye")	.60	.45	.25
309b	Milt Thompson ("86" visible)	.06	.05	.02
310	Bob Melvin	.05	.04	.02
311	Luis Salazar	.05	.04	.02
312	Ed Whitson (FC)	.06	.05	.02
313	Charlie Hough	.06	.05	.02
314	Dave Clark	.05	.04	.02
315	*Eric Gunderson*	.15	.11	.06
316	Dan Petry	.05	.04	.02
317	Dante Bichette	.12	.09	.05
318	Mike Heath	.05	.04	.02
319	Damon Berryhill	.06	.05	.02
320	Walt Terrell	.05	.04	.02
321	Scott Fletcher	.05	.04	.02
322	Dan Plesac	.08	.06	.03
323	Jack McDowell	.12	.09	.05
324	Paul Molitor	.20	.15	.08
325	Ozzie Guillen	.10	.08	.04
326	Gregg Olson	.10	.08	.04
327	Pedro Guererro	.10	.08	.04
328	Bob Milacki (FC)	.06	.05	.02
329	John Tudor	.08	.06	.03
330	Steve Finley	.08	.06	.03
331	Jack Clark	.10	.08	.04
332	Jerome Walton	.08	.06	.03
333	Andy Hawkins	.06	.05	.02
334	Derrick May	.30	.25	.12
335	Roberto Alomar	.40	.30	.15
336	Jack Morris	.08	.06	.03
337	Dave Winfield	.15	.11	.06
338	Steve Searcy	.08	.06	.03
339	Chili Davis	.08	.06	.03
340	Larry Sheets	.06	.05	.02
341	Ted Higuera	.08	.06	.03
342	*David Segui*	.15	.11	.06
343	Greg Cadaret	.05	.04	.02
344	Robin Yount	.20	.15	.08
345	Nolan Ryan	.75	.60	.30
346	Ray Lankford	.40	.30	.15
347	Cal Ripken, Jr.	.40	.30	.15
348	Lee Smith	.08	.06	.03
349	Brady Anderson	.10	.07	.04
350	Frank DiPino	.05	.04	.02
351	Hal Morris	.10	.08	.04
352	Deion Sanders	.30	.25	.12
353	Barry Larkin	.10	.08	.04
354	Don Mattingly	.25	.20	.10
355	Eric Davis	.20	.15	.08
356	Jose Offerman	.12	.09	.05
357	*Mel Rojas*	.12	.09	.05
358	Rudy Seanez (FC)	.10	.08	.04
359	Oil Can Boyd	.06	.05	.02
360	Nelson Liriano	.05	.04	.02
361	Ron Gant	.15	.11	.06
362	*Howard Farmer*	.15	.11	.06
363	Dave Justice	.75	.60	.30
364	Delino DeShields	.30	.25	.12
365	Steve Avery	.25	.20	.10
366	David Cone	.10	.07	.04
367	lou Whitaker	.10	.08	.04
368	Von Hayes	.10	.08	.04
369	Frank Tanana	.06	.05	.02
370	Tim Teufel	.05	.04	.02
371	Randy Myers	.10	.08	.04
372	Roberto Kelly	.10	.08	.04
373	Jack Armstrong	.08	.06	.03
374	Kelly Gruber	.10	.08	.04
375	Kevin Maas	.08	.06	.03
376	Randy Johnson	.10	.08	.04
377	David West	.06	.05	.02
378	*Brent Knackert*	.12	.09	.05
379	Rick Honeycutt	.05	.04	.02
380	Kevin Gross	.08	.06	.03
381	Tom Foley	.05	.04	.02
382	Jeff Blauser	.06	.05	.02
383	*Scott Ruskin*	.15	.11	.06
384	Andres Thomas (FC)	.05	.04	.02
385	Dennis Martinez	.08	.06	.03
386	Mike Henneman	.08	.06	.03
387	Felix Jose	.10	.07	.04
388	Alejandro Pena	.05	.04	.02
389	Chet Lemon	.06	.05	.02
390	*Craig Wilson*	.20	.15	.08
391	Chuck Crim	.05	.04	.02
392	Mel Hall	.06	.05	.02
393	Mark Knudson	.05	.04	.02
394	Norm Charlton	.08	.06	.03

395	Mike Felder	.05	.04	.02
396	*Tim Layana*	.08	.06	.03
397	Steve Frey (FC)	.06	.05	.02
398	Bill Doran	.08	.06	.03
399	Dion James	.05	.04	.02
400	Checklist 301-400	.05	.04	.02
401	Ron Hassey	.05	.04	.02
402	Don Robinson	.06	.05	.02
403	Gene Nelson	.05	.04	.02
404	Terry Kennedy	.05	.04	.02
405	Todd Burns	.05	.04	.02
406	Roger McDowell	.08	.06	.03
407	Bob Kipper	.05	.04	.02
408	Darren Daulton	.08	.06	.03
409	Chuck Cary	.06	.05	.02
410	Bruce Ruffin	.06	.05	.02
411	Juan Berenguer	.05	.04	.02
412	Gary Ward	.05	.04	.02
413	Al Newman	.05	.04	.02
414	Danny Jackson	.08	.06	.03
415	Greg Gagne	.06	.05	.02
416	Tom Herr	.06	.05	.02
417	Jeff Parrett	.06	.05	.02
418	Jeff Reardon	.08	.06	.03
419	Mark Lemke	.06	.05	.02
420	Charlie O'Brien (FC)	.05	.04	.02
421	Willie Randolph	.08	.06	.03
422	Steve Bedrosian	.08	.06	.03
423	Mike Moore	.08	.06	.03
424	Jeff Brantley (FC)	.08	.06	.03
425	Bob Welch	.10	.08	.04
426	Terry Mulholland	.08	.06	.03
427	*Willie Blair* (FC)	.15	.11	.06
428	Darrin Fletcher (FC)	.10	.08	.04
429	Mike Witt	.06	.05	.02
430	Joe Boever	.05	.04	.02
431	Tom Gordon	.12	.09	.05
432	*Pedro Munoz* (FC)	.20	.15	.08
433	Kevin Seitzer	.10	.08	.04
434	Kevin Tapani	.15	.11	.06
435	Bret Saberhagen	.12	.09	.05
436	Ellis Burks	.10	.07	.04
437	Chuck Finley	.10	.08	.04
438	Mike Boddicker	.08	.06	.03
439	Francisco Cabrera	.08	.06	.03
440	*Todd Hundley* (FC)	.15	.11	.06
441	Kelly Downs	.06	.05	.02
442	*Dann Howitt* (FC)	.15	.11	.06
443	Scott Garrelts	.08	.06	.03
444	Rickey Henderson	.20	.15	.08
445	Will Clark	.30	.25	.12
446	Ben McDonald	.15	.11	.06
447	Dale Murphy	.10	.07	.04
448	Dave Righetti	.10	.08	.04
449	Dickie Thon	.05	.04	.02
450	Ted Power	.05	.04	.02
451	Scott Coolbaugh	.08	.06	.03
452	Dwight Smith	.08	.06	.03
453	Pete Incaviglia (FC)	.08	.06	.03
454	Andre Dawson	.15	.11	.06
455	Ruben Sierra	.15	.11	.06
456	Andres Galarraga	.10	.08	.04
457	Alvin Davis	.10	.08	.04
458	Tony Castillo	.06	.05	.02
459	Pete O'Brien	.06	.05	.02
460	Charlie Leibrandt	.06	.05	.02
461	Vince Coleman	.10	.08	.04
462	Steve Sax	.10	.08	.04
463	*Omar Oliveras* (FC)	.15	.11	.06
464	*Oscar Azocar* (FC)	.10	.07	.04
465	Joe Magrane (FC)	.08	.06	.03
466	*Karl Rhodes*	.25	.20	.10
467	Benito Santiago	.10	.08	.04
468	*Joe Klink* (FC)	.10	.08	.04
469	Sil Campusano (FC)	.05	.04	.02
470	Mark Parent	.05	.04	.02
471	*Shawn Boskie*	.20	.15	.08
472	Kevin Brown	.10	.08	.04
473	Rick Sutcliffe	.08	.06	.03
474	Rafael Palmeiro	.12	.09	.05
475	Mike Harkey	.10	.08	.04
476	Jaime Navarro	.15	.11	.06
477	Marquis Grissom	.20	.15	.08
478	Marty Clary	.05	.04	.02
479	Greg Briley (FC)	.10	.08	.04
480	Tom Glavine	.25	.20	.10
481	Lee Guetterman	.05	.04	.02
482	Rex Hudler	.06	.05	.02
483	Dave LaPoint (FC)	.06	.05	.02
484	Terry Pendleton	.08	.06	.03
485	Jesse Barfield	.08	.06	.03
486	Jose DeJesus	.08	.06	.03
487	*Paul Abbott* (FC)	.12	.09	.05
488	Ken Howell	.06	.05	.02
489	Greg W. Harris	.06	.05	.02
490	Roy Smith	.05	.04	.02
491	Paul Assenmacher	.05	.04	.02
492	Geno Petralli	.05	.04	.02
493	Steve Wilson	.08	.06	.03
494	Kevin Reimer (FC)	.08	.06	.03
495	Bill Long	.05	.04	.02
496	Mike Jackson (FC)	.06	.05	.02
497	Oddibe McDowell	.06	.05	.02
498	Bill Swift	.06	.05	.02
499	Jeff Treadway	.06	.05	.02
500	Checklist 401-500	.05	.04	.02
501	Gene Larkin	.06	.05	.02
502	Bob Boone	.08	.06	.03
503	Allan Anderson	.06	.05	.02
504	Luis Aquino (FC)	.06	.05	.02
505	Mark Guthrie	.06	.05	.02
506	Joe Orsulak	.06	.05	.02
507	*Dana Kiecker* (FC)	.15	.11	.06
508	Dave Gallagher (FC)	.05	.04	.02
509	Greg W. Harris	.06	.05	.02
510	Mark Williamson	.05	.04	.02
511	Casey Candaele	.05	.04	.02
512	Mookie Wilson	.06	.05	.02

513	Dave Smith	.08	.06	.03
514	*Chuck Carr*	.20	.15	.08
515	Glenn Wilson	.06	.05	.02
516	Mike Fitzgerald (FC)	.05	.04	.02
517	Devon White	.08	.06	.03
518	Dave Hollins	.25	.20	.10
519	Mark Eichhorn	.05	.04	.02
520	Otis Nixon	.05	.04	.02
521	*Terry Shumpert*	.20	.15	.08
522	*Scott Erickson*	.15	.11	.06
523	Danny Tartabull	.10	.08	.04
524	Orel Hershiser	.10	.07	.04
525	George Brett	.25	.20	.10
526	Greg Vaughn	.20	.15	.08
527	*Tim Naehring* (FC)	.10	.08	.04
528	Curt Schilling (FC)	.06	.05	.02
529	Chris Bosio	.06	.05	.02
530	Sam Horn	.08	.06	.03
531	Mike Scott	.10	.08	.04
532	George Bell	.15	.11	.06
533	Eric Anthony	.15	.11	.06
534	*Julio Valera*	.15	.11	.06
535	Glenn Davis	.08	.06	.03
536	Larry Walker	.25	.20	.10
537	Pat Combs	.15	.11	.06
538	*Chris Nabholz*	.12	.09	.05
539	Kirk McCaskill	.08	.06	.03
540	Randy Ready	.05	.04	.02
541	Mark Gubicza	.10	.08	.04
542	Rick Aguilera	.08	.06	.03
543	*Brian McRae*	.35	.25	.14
544	Kirby Puckett	.30	.25	.12
545	Bo Jackson	.25	.20	.10
546	Wade Boggs	.20	.15	.08
547	Tim McIntosh (FC)	.12	.09	.05
548	Randy Milligan (FC)	.08	.06	.03
549	Dwight Evans	.08	.06	.03
550	Billy Ripken	.05	.04	.02
551	Erik Hanson	.15	.11	.06
552	Lance Parrish	.10	.08	.04
553	Tino Martinez	.10	.08	.04
554	Jim Abbott	.15	.11	.06
555	Ken Griffey, Jr.	2.00	1.50	.80
556	Milt Cuyler (FC)	.10	.08	.04
557	*Mark Leonard* (FC)	.10	.08	.04
558	Jay Howell	.08	.06	.03
559	Lloyd Moseby	.08	.06	.03
560	Chris Gwynn	.06	.05	.02
561	*Mark Whiten* (FC)	.40	.30	.15
562	Harold Baines	.10	.08	.04
563	Junior Felix	.15	.11	.06
564	*Darren Lewis*	.20	.15	.08
565	Fred McGriff	.25	.20	.10
566	Kevin Appier	.15	.11	.06
567	*Luis Gonzalez*	.40	.30	.15
568	Frank White	.08	.06	.03
569	Juan Agosto	.05	.04	.02
570	Mike Macfarlane	.06	.05	.02
571	Bert Blyleven	.10	.08	.04
572	Ken Griffey,Sr.	.10	.08	.04
573	Lee Stevens (FC)	.20	.15	.08
574	Edgar Martinez	.08	.06	.03
575	Wally Joyner	.10	.08	.04
576	Tim Belcher	.08	.06	.03
577	John Burkett	.10	.08	.04
578	Mike Morgan	.06	.05	.02
579	Paul Gibson	.05	.04	.02
580	Jose Vizcaino (FC)	.10	.08	.04
581	Duane Ward	.06	.05	.02
582	Scott Sanderson	.06	.05	.02
583	David Wells	.06	.05	.02
584	Willie McGee	.10	.08	.04
585	John Cerutti	.05	.04	.02
586	Danny Darwin	.08	.06	.03
587	Kurt Stillwell	.08	.06	.03
588	Rich Gedman	.05	.04	.02
589	Mark Davis	.08	.06	.03
590	Bill Gullickson	.06	.05	.02
591	Matt Young	.06	.05	.02
592	Bryan Harvey (FC)	.08	.06	.03
593	Omar Vizquel	.06	.05	.02
594	*Scott Lewis*	.15	.11	.06
595	Dave Valle	.06	.05	.02
596	Tim Crews (FC)	.05	.04	.02
597	Mike Bielecki	.06	.05	.02
598	Mike Sharperson	.06	.05	.02
599	Dave Bergman	.05	.04	.02
600	Checklist 501-600	.05	.04	.02
601	Steve Lyons	.06	.05	.02
602	Bruce Hurst	.08	.06	.03
603	Donn Pall	.05	.04	.02
604	*Jim Vatcher* (FC)	.15	.11	.06
605	Dan Pasqua	.06	.05	.02
606	Kenny Rogers	.08	.06	.03
607	*Jeff Schulz* (FC)	.15	.11	.06
608	Brad Arnsberg (FC)	.10	.08	.04
609	Willie Wilson	.08	.06	.03
610	Jamie Moyer	.06	.05	.02
611	Ron Oester	.05	.04	.02
612	Dennis Cook (FC)	.08	.06	.03
613	Rick Mahler	.05	.04	.02
614	Bill Landrum	.06	.05	.02
615	Scott Scudder	.15	.11	.06
616	*Tom Edens* (FC)	.08	.06	.03
617	"1917 Revisited"	.12	.09	.05
618	Jim Gantner	.06	.05	.02
619	Darrel Akerfelds (FC)	.06	.05	.02
620	Ron Robinson	.06	.05	.02
621	Scott Radinsky	.10	.07	.04
622	Pete Smith	.06	.05	.02
623	Melido Perez	.08	.06	.03
624	Jerald Clark (FC)	.06	.05	.02
625	Carlos Martinez	.08	.06	.03
626	*Wes Chamberlain*	.30	.25	.12
627	Bobby Witt	.08	.06	.03
628	Ken Dayley (FC)	.06	.05	.02
629	*John Barfield* (FC)	.10	.08	.04
630	Bob Tewksbury	.06	.05	.02

631	Glenn Braggs	.06	.05	.02
632	*Jim Neidlinger* (FC)	.20	.15	.08
633	Tom Browning	.08	.06	.03
634	Kirk Gibson	.12	.09	.05
635	Rob Dibble	.12	.09	.05
636	"Stolen Base Leaders"	.30	.25	.12
637	Jeff Montgomery	.08	.06	.03
638	Mike Schooler	.08	.06	.03
639	Storm Davis	.06	.05	.02
640	*Rich Rodriguez* (FC)	.15	.11	.06
641	Phil Bradley	.08	.06	.03
642	Kent Mercker	.15	.11	.06
643	Carlton Fisk	.12	.09	.05
644	*Mike Bell* (FC)	.10	.08	.04
645	*Alex Fernandez* (FC)	.60	.45	.25
646	Juan Gonzalez	1.50	1.25	.80
647	Ken Hill	.06	.05	.02
648	Jeff Russell	.08	.06	.03
649	*Chuck Malone* (FC)	.15	.11	.06
650	Steve Buechele	.06	.05	.02
651	Mike Benjamin	.15	.11	.06
652	Tony Pena	.08	.06	.03
653	Trevor Wilson	.08	.06	.03
654	Alex Cole	.30	.25	.12
655	Roger Clemens	.25	.20	.10
656	"The Bashing Years"	.15	.11	.06
657	*Joe Grahe* (FC)	.15	.11	.06
658	Jim Eisenreich	.06	.05	.02
659	Dan Gladden	.06	.05	.02
660	Steve Farr (FC)	.06	.05	.02
661	*Bill Sampen*	.20	.15	.08
662	*Dave Rohde* (FC)	.15	.11	.06
663	Mark Gardner	.10	.07	.04
664	*Mike Simms*	.10	.08	.04
665	Moises Alou (FC)	.90	.70	.35
666	Mickey Hatcher	.06	.05	.02
667	Jimmy Key	.08	.06	.03
668	John Wetteland	.10	.08	.04
669	John Smiley	.06	.05	.02
670	Jim Acker	.05	.04	.02
671	Pascual Perez	.06	.05	.02
672	*Reggie Harris*	.10	.07	.04
673	Matt Nokes	.08	.06	.03
674	*Rafael Novoa*	.10	.07	.04
675	Hensley Meulens	.10	.08	.04
676	Jeff M. Robinson (FC)	.06	.05	.02
677	"Ground Breaking"	.20	.15	.08
678	Johnny Ray	.06	.05	.02
679	Greg Hibbard	.10	.08	.04
680	Paul Sorrento	.10	.07	.04
681	Mike Marshall	.06	.05	.02
682	Jim Clancy	.05	.04	.02
683	Rob Murphy	.05	.04	.02
684	Dave Schmidt (FC)	.05	.04	.02
685	*Jeff Gray* (FC)	.15	.11	.06
686	Mike Hartley (FC)	.08	.06	.03
687	Jeff King	.08	.06	.03
688	Stan Javier (FC)	.06	.05	.02
689	Bob Walk	.06	.05	.02
690	Jim Gott	.06	.05	.02
691	Mike LaCoss	.05	.04	.02
692	John Farrell	.06	.05	.02
693	Tim Leary	.06	.05	.02
694	*Mike Walker*	.08	.06	.03
695	Eric Plunk	.05	.04	.02
696	Mike Fetters (FC)	.08	.06	.03
697	Wayne Edwards	.10	.08	.04
698	Tim Drummond (FC)	.10	.07	.04
699	Willie Fraser	.05	.04	.02
700	Checklist 601-700	.05	.04	.02
701	Mike Heath	.10	.08	.04
702	"Rookie Threats"	.60	.45	.25
703	Jose Mesa	.10	.08	.04
704	Dave Smith (FC)	.10	.08	.04
705	Danny Darwin	.10	.08	.04
706	Rafael Belliard	.10	.08	.04
707	Rob Murphy	.10	.08	.04
708	Terry Pendleton	.12	.09	.05
709	Mike Pagliarulo	.10	.08	.04
710	Sid Bream	.12	.09	.05
711	Junior Felix	.12	.09	.05
712	Dante Bichette	.12	.09	.05
713	Kevin Gross	.10	.08	.04
714	Luis Sojo	.12	.09	.05
715	Bob Ojeda	.10	.08	.04
716	Julio Machado (FC)	.08	.06	.03
717	Steve Farr	.10	.08	.04
718	Franklin Stubbs	.10	.08	.04
719	Mike Boddicker	.12	.09	.05
720	Willie Randolph	.12	.09	.05
721	Willie McGee	.15	.11	.06
722	Chili Davis	.15	.11	.06
723	Danny Jackson	.12	.09	.05
724	Cory Snyder	.10	.08	.04
725	"MVP Lineup"	.15	.11	.06
726	Rob Deer	.10	.08	.04
727	Rich DeLucia (FC)	.15	.11	.06
728	Mike Perez (FC)	.15	.11	.06
729	Mickey Tettleton	.12	.09	.05
730	Mike Blowers	.10	.08	.04
731	Gary Gaetti	.12	.09	.05
732	Brett Butler	.12	.09	.05
733	Dave Parker	.10	.07	.04
734	Eddie Zosky (FC)	.10	.08	.04
735	Jack Clark	.12	.09	.05
736	Jack Morris	.10	.07	.04
737	Kirk Gibson	.12	.09	.05
738	Steve Bedrosian	.10	.08	.04
739	Candy Maldonado	.10	.08	.04
740	Matt Young	.10	.08	.04
741	Rich Garces (FC)	.12	.09	.05
742	George Bell	.10	.07	.04
743	Deion Sanders	.25	.20	.10
744	Bo Jackson	.50	.40	.20
745	Luis Mercedes (FC)	.25	.20	.10
746	Reggie Jefferson (FC)	.30	.25	.12
747	Pete Incaviglia	.10	.08	.04
748	Chris Hammond	.10	.07	.04

749	Mike Stanton	.12	.09	.05
750	Scott Sanderson	.10	.08	.04
751	Paul Faries (FC)	.10	.07	.04
752	Al Osuna (FC)	.15	.11	.06
753	Steve Chitren (FC)	.10	.08	.04
754	Tony Fernandez	.15	.11	.06
755	Jeff Bagwell (FC)	1.75	1.25	.70
756	Kirk Dressendorfer (FC)	.10	.08	.04
757	Glenn Davis	.15	.11	.06
758	Gary Carter	.12	.09	.05
759	Zane Smith	.10	.08	.04
760	Vance Law	.10	.08	.04
761	Denis Boucher (FC)	.20	.15	.08
762	Turner Ward (FC)	.10	.08	.04
763	Roberto Alomar	.50	.40	.20
764	Albert Belle	.40	.30	.15
765	Joe Carter	.20	.15	.08
766	Pete Schourek (FC)	.15	.11	.06
767	Heathcliff Slocumb (FC)	.15	.11	.06
768	Vince Coleman	.15	.11	.06
769	Mitch Williams	.12	.09	.05
770	Brian Downing	.10	.08	.04
771	Dana Allison (FC)	.15	.11	.06
772	Pete Harnisch	.12	.09	.05
773	Tim Raines	.15	.11	.06
774	Darryl Kile (FC)	.35	.25	.14
775	Fred McGriff	.25	.20	.10
776	Dwight Evans	.12	.09	.05
777	Joe Slusarski	.12	.09	.05
778	Dave Righetti	.12	.09	.05
779	Jeff Hamilton	.10	.08	.04
780	Ernest Riles	.10	.08	.04
781	Ken Dayley	.10	.08	.04
782	Eric King	.10	.08	.04
783	Devon White	.12	.09	.05
784	Beau Allred (FC)	.10	.08	.04
785	Mike Timlin (FC)	.12	.09	.05
786	Ivan Calderon	.15	.11	.06
787	Hubie Brooks	.12	.09	.05
788	Juan Agosto (FC)	.10	.08	.04
789	Barry Jones	.10	.08	.04
790	Wally Backman	.10	.08	.04
791	Jim Presley	.10	.08	.04
792	Charlie Hough	.10	.08	.04
793	Larry Andersen	.10	.08	.04
794	Steve Finley	.12	.09	.05
795	Shawn Abner	.10	.08	.04
796	Jeff M. Robinson	.10	.08	.04
797	Joe Bitker (FC)	.10	.08	.04
798	Eric Show	.10	.08	.04
799	Bud Black	.10	.08	.04
800	Checklist 701-800	.10	.08	.04
----	Michael Jordan (SP1)	15.00	11.00	6.00
----	A Day to Remember (Rickey Henderson/Nolan Ryan) (SP2)	4.00	3.00	1.50
----	Hank Aaron hologram (HH1)	4.00	3.00	1.50

1991 Upper Deck Final Edition

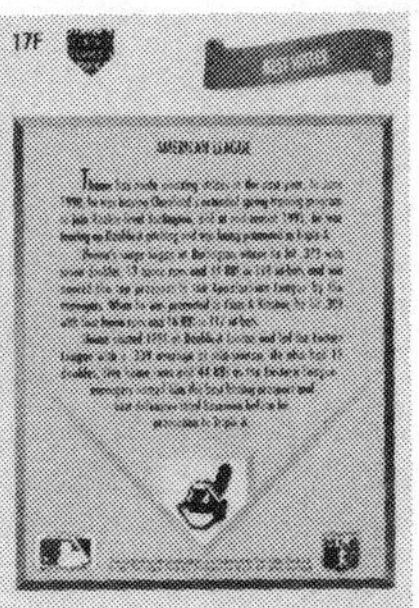

Upper Deck surprised the hobby with the release of this 100-card boxed set. The cards are numbered with an "F" designation. A special "Minor League Diamond Skills" subset (cards #1-21) features several top prospects. An All-Star subset (cards #79-99) is also included in this set. The cards are styled like the regular 1991 Upper Deck issue. Special team hologram cards are also included with the set.

		MT	NR MT	EX
	Complete Set (100):	7.50	5.50	3.00
	Common Player:	.05	.03	.01
1	Ryan Klesko/Reggie Sanders (Minor League Diamond Skills Checklist)	.50	.40	.20
2	Pedro Martinez (FC)	.60	.45	.25
3	Lance Dickson (FC)	.10	.08	.04
4	Royce Clayton	.40	.30	.15
5	Scott Bryant (FC)	.35	.25	.14
6	Dan Wilson (FC)	.30	.25	.12
7	Dmitri Young (FC)	.60	.45	.25
8	Ryan Klesko (FC)	2.00	1.50	.80
9	Tom Goodwin (FC)	.15	.11	.06
10	Rondell White (FC)	1.25	.90	.50
11	Reggie Sanders	.50	.40	.20
12	Todd Van Poppel	.35	.25	.14
13	Arthur Rhodes (FC)	.30	.25	.12
14	Eddie Zosky	.10	.07	.04
15	Gerald Williams (FC)	.40	.30	.15
16	Robert Eenhoorn (FC)	.12	.09	.05
17	Jim Thome (FC)	.75	.60	.30
18	Marc Newfield (FC)	1.00	.70	.40
19	Kerwin Moore (FC)	.25	.20	.10
20	Jeff McNeely (FC)	.20	.15	.08
21	Frankie Rodriguez (FC)	.75	.60	.30
22	Andy Mota (FC)	.25	.20	.10
23	Chris Haney (FC)	.15	.11	.06
24	Kenny Lofton (FC)	1.50	1.25	.60
25	Dave Nilsson (FC)	.25	.20	.10
26	Derek Bell (FC)	.70	.50	.30
27	Frank Castillo (FC)	.35	.25	.14
28	Candy Maldonado	.10	.07	.04
29	Chuck McElroy	.20	.15	.08
30	Chito Martinez (FC)	.10	.07	.04
31	Steve Howe (FC)	.10	.07	.04
32	Freddie Benavides (FC)	.10	.07	.04
33	Scott Kamieniecki (FC)	.25	.20	.10
34	Denny Neagle (FC)	.15	.11	.06
35	Mike Humphreys (FC)	.20	.15	.08
36	Mike Remlinger (FC)	.20	.15	.08
37	Scott Coolbaugh	.20	.15	.08
38	Darren Lewis	.15	.11	.06
39	Thomas Howard (FC)	.20	.15	.08
40	John Candelaria	.20	.15	.08
41	Todd Benzinger	.20	.15	.08
42	Wilson Alvarez	.35	.25	.14
43	Patrick Lennon (FC)	.15	.11	.06
44	Rusty Meacham (FC)	.25	.20	.10
45	*Ryan Bowen*	.20	.15	.08
46	*Rick Wilkins*	.60	.45	.25
47	*Ed Sprague*	.25	.20	.10
48	*Bob Scanlan*	.10	.07	.04
49	Tom Candiotti	.20	.15	.08
50	Dennis Martinez (Perfecto)	.20	.15	.08
51	Oil Can Boyd	.10	.07	.04
52	Glenallen Hill	.10	.07	.04
53	*Scott Livingstone*	.25	.20	.10
54	*Brian Hunter*	.20	.15	.08
55	*Ivan Rodriguez*	1.00	.70	.40
56	*Keith Mitchell*	.12	.09	.05
57	Roger McDowell	.12	.09	.05
58	Otis Nixon	.12	.09	.05
59	*Juan Bell*	.20	.15	.08
60	Bill Krueger	.10	.07	.04
61	*Chris Donnels*	.12	.09	.05
62	Tommy Greene	.25	.20	.10
63	Doug Simons (FC)	.12	.09	.05
64	*Andy Ashby*	.20	.15	.08
65	*Anthony Young*	.15	.11	.06
66	*Kevin Morton*	.15	.11	.06
67	*Bret Barberie*	.15	.11	.06
68	*Scott Servais*	.10	.07	.04
69	Ron Darling	.10	.07	.04
70	Vicente Palacios	.10	.07	.04
71	*Tim Burke*	.20	.15	.08
72	*Gerald Alexander*	.10	.07	.04
73	Reggie Jefferson	.20	.15	.08
74	Dean Palmer	.60	.45	.25
75	Mark Whiten (FC)	.30	.25	.12
76	Randy Tomlin (FC)	.20	.15	.08
77	*Mark Wohlers*	.25	.20	.10
78	Brook Jacoby	.10	.07	.04
79	Ken Griffey, Jr./Ryne Sandberg (All-Star Checklist)	.40	.30	.15
80	Jack Morris (AS)	.10	.07	.04
81	Sandy Alomar, Jr. (AS)	.15	.11	.06
82	Cecil Fielder (AS)	.25	.20	.10
83	Roberto Alomar (AS)	.30	.25	.12
84	Wade Boggs (AS)	.10	.08	.04
85	Cal Ripken, Jr. (AS)	.50	.40	.20
86	Rickey Henderson (AS)	.20	.15	.08
87	Ken Griffey, Jr. (AS)	.75	.60	.30
88	Dave Henderson (AS)	.10	.07	.04
89	Danny Tartabull (AS)	.12	.09	.05
90	Tom Glavine (AS)	.20	.15	.08
91	Benito Santiago (AS)	.10	.07	.04
92	Will Clark (AS)	.20	.15	.08
93	Ryne Sandberg (AS)	.30	.25	.12
94	Chris Sabo (AS)	.10	.07	.04
95	Ozzie Smith (AS)	.10	.08	.04
96	Ivan Calderon (AS)	.10	.08	.04
97	Tony Gwynn (AS)	.15	.11	.06
98	Andre Dawson (AS)	.10	.08	.04
99	Bobby Bonilla (AS)	.12	.09	.05
100	Checklist	.10	.07	.04

Definitions for grading conditions are located in the Introduction of this price guide.

1991 Upper Deck Hank Aaron Heroes

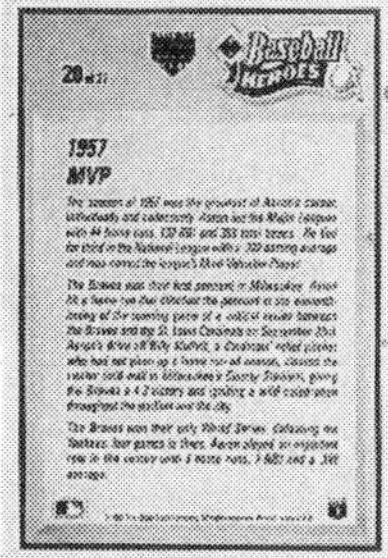

This set devoted to Hank Aaron is numbered 19-27 and includes an unnumbered cover card that says "Baseball Heroes." The cards are found in foil and jumbo packs of Upper Deck high number packs.

		MT	NR MT	EX
	Complete Set (10):	7.00	5.25	2.75
	Common Aaron:	.50	.40	.20
	Autographed Card:	400.00	300.00	160.00
	Aaron Header:	4.00	3.00	1.50
19	1954 Rookie Year	.50	.40	.20
20	1957 MVP	.50	.40	.20
21	1966 Move to Atlanta	.50	.40	.20
22	1970 3,000	.50	.40	.20
23	1974 715	.50	.40	.20
24	1975 Return to Milwaukee	.50	.40	.20
25	1976 755	.50	.40	.20
26	1982 Hall of Fame	.50	.40	.20
27	Checklist - Heroes 19-27	.50	.40	.20

1991 Upper Deck Nolan Ryan Heroes

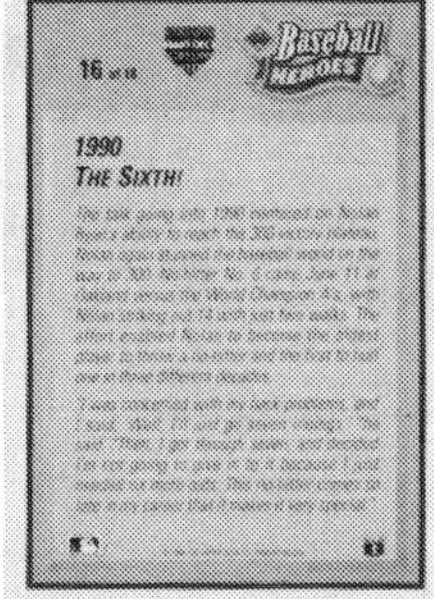

This set devoted to Nolan Ryan is numbered 10-18 and includes an unnumbered cover card that says "Baseball Heroes." The cards are found in foil and jumbo boxes of low number Upper Deck packs.

		MT	NR MT	EX
	Complete Set (10):	7.00	5.25	2.75
	Common Ryan (10-18):	.50	.40	.20
	Ryan Header Card:	4.00	3.00	1.50
	Autographed Card:	600.00	450.00	240.00
10	1968 Victory #1	.50	.40	.20
11	1973 A Career Year	.50	.40	.20
12	1975 Double Milestone	.50	.40	.20
13	1979 Back Home	.50	.40	.20
14	1981 All-Time Leader	.50	.40	.20
15	1989 5,000	.50	.40	.20
16	1990 The Sixth	.50	.40	.20
17	1990 ... and Still Counting	.50	.40	.20
18	Checklist - Heroes 10-18	.50	.40	.20

1991 Upper Deck Heroes of Baseball

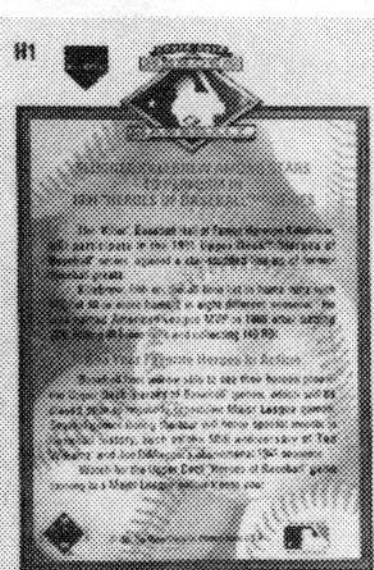

This four-card set features three members of Baseball's Hall of Fame: Harmon Killebrew, Gaylord Perry and Ferguson Jenkins. Each has a card for himself, plus there's a card which features all three players. The cards were found in specially-marked low number foil packs. The cards are numbered H1-H4. Upper Deck also produced 3,000 autographed and numbered cards for each player.

		MT	NR MT	EX
	Complete Set (4):	45.00	30.00	15.00
	Autographed Card:	120.00	80.00	40.00
1	Harmon Killebrew	15.00	10.00	5.00
2	Gaylord Perry	15.00	10.00	5.00
3	Ferguson Jenkins	15.00	10.00	5.00
4	Gaylord Perry, Ferguson Jenkins, Harmon Killebrew	15.00	11.00	6.00

1991 Upper Deck Silver Sluggers

Each year the "Silver Slugger" award is presented to the player at each position with the highest batting average in the American and National Leagues. Upper Deck produced special cards in honor of the players who received this award for the 1990 season. The cards were randomly inserted in jumbo packs of Upper Deck cards. The cards feature a "SS" designation along with the card number. The cards are designed like the regular issue Upper Deck cards from 1991, but feature a Silver Slugger bat along the left border of the card.

		MT	NR MT	EX
Complete Set (18):		18.00	13.50	7.25
Common Player:		.50	.30	.15
1	Julio Franco	.50	.40	.20
2	Alan Trammell	.50	.40	.20
3	Rickey Henderson	1.25	.90	.50
4	Jose Canseco	1.00	.70	.40
5	Barry Bonds	4.00	3.00	1.50
6	Eddie Murray	1.00	.70	.40
7	Kelly Gruber	.50	.40	.20
8	Ryne Sandberg	3.50	2.75	1.50
9	Darryl Strawberry	.75	.60	.30
10	Ellis Burks	.50	.40	.20
11	Lance Parrish	.50	.40	.20
12	Cecil Fielder	2.00	1.50	.80
13	Matt Williams	.75	.60	.30
14	Dave Parker	.50	.40	.20
15	Bobby Bonilla	.75	.60	.30
16	Don Robinson	.50	.40	.20
17	Benito Santiago	.50	.40	.20
18	Barry Larkin	.75	.60	.30

1991 Upper Deck Comic Ball 2

Despite the presence of two popular superstars on dozens of the cards, this 198-piece issue has found little favor with collectors. Most of the cards are arranged in 18-card sequences which tell a baseball-related cartoon tale starring Bugs Bunny, Daffy Duck, Wile E. Coyote and the rest of the Looney Tune characters. Actual-photo "guest appearances" by Nolan Ryan and Reggie Jackson highlight these presentations. There are also "Seventh Inning Stretch" cards featuring the ballplayers in scenes with the cartoon figures. When arranged in nine-pocket plastic sheets (use of the special Comic Ball 2 album was recommended), card backs form a cartoon picture puzzle. Cards are typical Upper Deck quality with semi-gloss front and back surfaces and a circular hologram on the backs in the standard 2-1/2" x 3-1/2" format. Nine hologram stickers featuring Ryan and Jackson along with the cartton characters were produced as random pack inserts. Because the cards are licensed by Major League Baseball, the players and cartoon critters are depicted in Major League uniforms.

	MT	NR MT	EX
Complete Set (198):	9.00	6.75	3.50
Common Card, Cartoon:	.05	.04	.02
Common Card, Ryan/Jackson:	.10	.08	.04
Hologram Sticker:	2.00	1.50	.80

1992 Upper Deck

Upper Deck introduced a new look in 1992. The baseline style was no longer used. The 1992 cards feature full-color action photos on white stock, with the player's name and the Upper Deck logo along the top border. The team name is inserted in the bottom right corner of the photo. Once again a 100-card high number series was released in late summer. Ted Williams autographed 2,500 Baseball Heroes cards which were randomly inserted into Upper Deck packs. Several subsets are also featured in the 1992 issue including Star Rookies and Top Prospects.

		MT	NR MT	EX
Complete Set (800):		35.00	26.00	14.00
Common Player:		.05	.04	.02
1	Star Rookie Checklist (Ryan Klesko/Jim Thome)	.25	.20	.10
2	Royce Clayton (Star Rookie)	.20	.15	.08
3	*Brian Jordan* (Star Rookie)	.30	.25	.12
4	*Dave Fleming* (Star Rookie)	.20	.15	.08
5	Jim Thome (Star Rookie)	.40	.30	.15
6	Jeff Juden (Star Rookie)	.10	.08	.04
7	*Roberto Hernandez* (Star Rookie)	.10	.08	.04
8	Kyle Abbott (FC) (Star Rookie)	.10	.08	.04
9	*Chris George* (Star Rookie)	.20	.15	.08
10	*Rob Maurer* (Star Rookie)	.10	.08	.04
11	*Donald Harris* (FC) (Star Rookie)	.12	.09	.05
12	*Ted Wood* (Star Rookie)	.10	.08	.04
13	*Patrick Lennon* (Star Rookie)	.20	.15	.08
14	Willie Banks (Star Rookie)	.15	.11	.06
15	Roger Salkeld (FC) (Star Rookie)	.20	.15	.08
16	Wil Cordero (Star Rookie)	.25	.20	.10
17	*Arthur Rhodes* (Star Rookie)	.15	.11	.06
18	*Pedro Martinez* (Star Rookie)	.30	.25	.12
19	*Andy Ashby* (Star Rookie)	.10	.08	.04
20	Tom Goodwin (Star Rookie)	.15	.11	.06
21	*Braulio Castillo* (Star Rookie)	.10	.08	.04
22	Todd Van Poppel (Star Rookie)	.15	.11	.06
23	*Brian Williams* (Star Rookie)	.10	.08	.04
24	Ryan Klesko (Star Rookie)	1.00	.75	.40
25	*Kenny Lofton* (Star Rookie)	.50	.40	.20
26	Derek Bell (Star Rookie)	.25	.20	.10
27	Reggie Sanders (Star Rookie)	.20	.15	.08
28	"Winfield's 400th" (Dave Winfield)	.10	.08	.04
29	Atlanta Braves Checklist (Dave Justice)	.08	.06	.03
30	Cincinnati Reds Checklist (Rob Dibble)	.05	.04	.02
31	Houston Astros Checklist (Craig Biggio (FC))	.05	.04	.02
32	Los Angeles Dodgers Checklist (Eddie Murray)	.05	.04	.02
33	San Diego Padres Checklist (Fred McGriff)	.05	.04	.02
34	San Francisco Giants Checklist (Willie McGee)	.05	.04	.02
35	Chicago Cubs Checklist (Shawon Dunston)	.05	.04	.02
36	Montreal Expos Checklist (Delino DeShields)	.05	.04	.02
37	New York Mets Checklist (Howard Johnson)	.05	.04	.02
38	Philadelphia Phillies Checklist (John Kruk)	.05	.04	.02
39	Pittsburgh Pirates Checklist (Doug Drabeck)	.05	.04	.02
40	St. Louis Cardinals Checklist (Todd Zeile)	.05	.04	.02
41	"Playoff Perfection" (Steve Avery)	.10	.08	.04
42	*Jeremy Hernandez*	.20	.15	.08
43	*Doug Henry*	.20	.15	.08
44	*Chris Donnels*	.25	.20	.10
45	*Mo Sanford*	.15	.11	.06
46	*Scott Kamieniecki*	.15	.11	.06
47	Mark Lemke	.06	.05	.02
48	Steve Farr	.05	.04	.02
49	Francisco Oliveras	.05	.04	.02
50	*Ced Landrum*	.10	.08	.04
51	Top Prospect Checklist, Rondell White	.25	.20	.10
52	*Eduardo Perez,*	.60	.45	.25
53	*Tom Nevers* (Top Prospect)	.15	.11	.06
54	*David Zancanaro* (Top Prospect)	.15	.11	.06
55	*Shawn Green,*	.20	.15	.08
56	*Mark Wohlers,*	.20	.15	.08
57	Dave Nilsson,	.30	.25	.12
58	Dmitri Young,	.20	.15	.08
59	*Ryan Hawblitzel* (FC) (Top Prospect)	.15	.11	.06
60	*Raul Mondesi,*	1.75	1.25	.70
61	Rondell White,	.75	.60	.30
62	Steve Hosey (Top Prospect)	.15	.11	.06
63	*Manny Ramirez,*	1.75	1.25	.70
64	Marc Newfield,	.50	.40	.20
65	Jeromy Burnitz,	.40	.30	.15
66	*Mark Smith* (Top Prospect)	.10	.08	.04
67	*Joey Hamilton* (FC) (Top Prospect)	.12	.09	.05
68	*Tyler Green* (Top Prospect)	.15	.11	.06
69	*John Farrell* (Top Prospect)	.15	.11	.06
70	*Kurt Miller,*	.20	.15	.08
71	*Jeff Plympton* (Top Prosepct)	.10	.08	.04
72	Dan Wilson (FC,	.35	.25	.14
73	*Joe Vitiello,*	.40	.30	.15
74	Rico Brogna (FC) (Top Prospect)	.10	.08	.04
75	*David McCarty,*	.75	.60	.30
76	*Bob Wickman,*	.30	.25	.12
77	*Carlos Rodriguez* (Top Prospect)	.15	.11	.06
78	"Stay in School" (Jim Abbott)	.10	.08	.04
79	Bloodlines (Ramon & Pedro Martinez)	.10	.08	.04
80	Bloodlines (Kevin & Keith Mitchell)	.10	.08	.04
81	Bloodlines (Sandy Jr. & Roberto Alomar)	.10	.08	.04
82	Bloodlines (Cal Jr. & Billy Ripken)	.15	.11	.06
83	Bloodlines (Tony & Chris Gwynn)	.10	.08	.04
84	Bloodlines (Dwight Gooden & Gary Sheffield)	.10	.08	.04
85	Bloodlines, Ken Griffey, Jr.	.80	.60	.30
86	California Angels Checklist (Jim Abbott)	.05	.04	.02
87	Chicago White Sox Checklist (Frank Thomas)	.20	.15	.08
88	Kansas City Royals Checklist (Danny Tartabull)	.05	.04	.02
89	Minnesota Twins Checklist (Scott Erickson)	.05	.04	.02
90	Oakland Athletics Checklist (Rickey Henderson)	.05	.04	.02
91	Seattle Mariners Checklist (Edgar Martinez)	.05	.04	.02
92	Texas Rangers Checklist (Nolan Ryan)	.20	.15	.08
93	Baltimore Orioles Checklist (Ben McDonald)	.05	.04	.02
94	Boston Red Sox Checklist (Ellis Burks)	.05	.04	.02
95	Cleveland Indians Checklist (Greg Swindell)	.05	.04	.02
96	Detroit Tigers Checklist (Cecil Fielder)	.10	.08	.04
97	Milwaukee Brewers Checklist (Greg Vaughn)	.05	.04	.02
98	New York Yankees Checklist (Kevin Maas)	.05	.04	.02
99	Toronto Blue Jays Checklist (Dave Steib)	.05	.04	.02
100	Checklist 1-100	.05	.04	.02
101	Joe Oliver	.05	.04	.02
102	Hector Villanueva	.06	.05	.02
103	Ed Whitson	.05	.04	.02
104	Danny Jackson	.05	.04	.02
105	Chris Hammond	.06	.05	.02
106	Ricky Jordan	.06	.05	.02
107	Kevin Bass	.05	.04	.02
108	Darrin Fletcher	.05	.04	.02
109	Junior Ortiz	.05	.04	.02
110	Tom Bolton	.05	.04	.02
111	Jeff King	.06	.05	.02
112	Dave Magadan	.08	.06	.03
113	Mike LaValliere	.06	.05	.02
114	Hubie Brooks	.06	.05	.02
115	Jay Bell	.06	.05	.02
116	David Wells	.05	.04	.02
117	Jim Leyritz	.05	.04	.02
118	Manuel Lee	.05	.04	.02
119	Alvaro Espinoza	.05	.04	.02
120	B.J. Surhoff	.06	.05	.02
121	Hal Morris	.20	.15	.08
122	Shawon Dunston	.08	.06	.03
123	Chris Sabo	.10	.08	.04
124	Andre Dawson	.15	.11	.06
125	Eric Davis	.15	.11	.06
126	Chili Davis	.08	.06	.03
127	Dale Murphy	.10	.08	.04
128	Kirk McCaskill	.06	.05	.02
129	Terry Mulholland	.06	.05	.02
130	Rick Aguilera	.08	.06	.03
131	Vince Coleman	.10	.08	.04
132	Andy Van Slyke	.12	.09	.05
133	Gregg Jefferies	.15	.11	.06
134	Barry Bonds	.30	.25	.12
135	Dwight Gooden	.08	.06	.03
136	Dave Stieb	.08	.06	.03
137	Albert Belle	.25	.20	.10
138	Teddy Higuera	.08	.06	.03
139	Jesse Barfield	.08	.06	.03
140	Pat Borders	.06	.05	.02
141	Bip Roberts	.06	.05	.02
142	Rob Dibble	.10	.08	.04
143	Mark Grace	.15	.11	.06
144	Barry Larkin	.10	.07	.04
145	Ryne Sandberg	.25	.20	.10
146	Scott Erickson	.10	.08	.04
147	Luis Polonia	.06	.05	.02
148	John Burkett	.06	.05	.02
149	Luis Sojo	.06	.05	.02
150	Dickie Thon	.05	.04	.02
151	Walt Weiss	.06	.05	.02
152	Mike Scioscia	.06	.05	.02
153	Mark McGwire	.15	.11	.06
154	Matt Williams	.15	.11	.06
155	Rickey Henderson	.20	.15	.08
156	Sandy Alomar, Jr.	.10	.08	.04
157	Brian McRae	.20	.15	.08
158	Harold Baines	.08	.06	.03
159	Kevin Appier	.06	.05	.02
160	Felix Fermin	.05	.04	.02
161	Leo Gomez	.08	.06	.03

162	Craig Biggio	.10	.08	.04
163	Ben McDonald	.20	.15	.08
164	Randy Johnson	.08	.06	.03
165	Cal Ripken, Jr.	.30	.25	.12
166	Frank Thomas	1.25	.90	.50
167	Delino DeShields	.08	.06	.03
168	Greg Gagne	.05	.04	.02
169	Ron Karkovice	.05	.04	.02
170	Charlie Leibrandt	.05	.04	.02
171	Dave Righetti	.08	.06	.03
172	Dave Henderson	.10	.08	.04
173	Steve Decker	.15	.11	.06
174	Darryl Strawberry	.10	.08	.04
175	Will Clark	.25	.20	.10
176	Ruben Sierra	.15	.11	.06
177	Ozzie Smith	.15	.11	.06
178	Charles Nagy	.08	.06	.03
179	Gary Pettis	.05	.04	.02
180	Kirk Gibson	.08	.06	.03
181	Randy Milligan	.06	.05	.02
182	Dave Valle	.05	.04	.02
183	Chris Hoiles	.10	.08	.04
184	Tony Phillips	.05	.04	.02
185	Brady Anderson	.05	.04	.02
186	Scott Fletcher	.05	.04	.02
187	Gene Larkin	.05	.04	.02
188	Lance Johnson	.05	.04	.02
189	Greg Olson	.05	.04	.02
190	Melido Perez	.05	.04	.02
191	Lenny Harris	.05	.04	.02
192	Terry Kennedy	.05	.04	.02
193	Mike Gallego	.05	.04	.02
194	Willie McGee	.08	.06	.03
195	Juan Samuel	.06	.05	.02
196	Jeff Huson	.05	.04	.02
197	Alex Cole	.06	.05	.02
198	Ron Robinson	.06	.05	.02
199	Joel Skinner	.06	.05	.02
200	Checklist 101-200	.06	.05	.02
201	Kevin Reimer	.06	.05	.02
202	Stan Belinda	.05	.04	.02
203	Pat Tabler	.05	.04	.02
204	Jose Guzman	.05	.04	.02
205	Jose Lind	.05	.04	.02
206	Spike Owen	.05	.04	.02
207	Joe Orsulak	.05	.04	.02
208	Charlie Hayes	.05	.04	.02
209	Mike Devereaux	.06	.05	.02
210	Mike Fitzgerald	.05	.04	.02
211	Willie Randolph	.05	.04	.02
212	Rod Nichols	.05	.04	.02
213	Mike Boddicker	.05	.04	.02
214	Bill Spiers	.05	.04	.02
215	Steve Olin	.05	.04	.02
216	*David Howard* (FC)	.10	.08	.04
217	Gary Varsho	.05	.04	.02
218	Mike Harkey	.06	.05	.02
219	Luis Aquino	.05	.04	.02
220	Chuck McElroy (FC)	.05	.04	.02
221	Doug Drabek	.08	.06	.03
222	Dave Winfield	.15	.11	.06
223	Rafael Palmeiro	.12	.09	.05
224	Joe Carter	.20	.15	.08
225	Bobby Bonilla	.12	.09	.05
226	Ivan Calderon	.10	.08	.04
227	Gregg Olson	.10	.08	.04
228	Tim Wallach	.08	.06	.03
229	Terry Pendleton	.10	.08	.04
230	Gilberto Reyes (FC)	.08	.06	.03
231	Carlos Baerga	.15	.11	.06
232	Greg Vaughn	.10	.08	.04
233	Bret Saberhagen	.06	.05	.02
234	Gary Sheffield	.10	.08	.04
235	Mark Lewis	.06	.05	.02
236	George Bell	.10	.08	.04
237	Danny Tartabull	.10	.08	.04
238	Willie Wilson	.06	.05	.02
239	Doug Dascenzo	.05	.04	.02
240	Bill Pecota	.05	.04	.02
241	Julio Franco	.08	.06	.03
242	Ed Sprague	.10	.08	.04
243	Juan Gonzalez	.80	.60	.30
244	Chuck Finley	.10	.08	.04
245	Ivan Rodriguez	.40	.30	.15
246	Len Dykstra	.10	.08	.04
247	Deion Sanders	.15	.11	.06
248	Dwight Evans	.08	.06	.03
249	Larry Walker	.10	.08	.04
250	Billy Ripken	.05	.04	.02
251	Mickey Tettleton	.06	.05	.02
252	Tony Pena	.06	.05	.02
253	Benito Santiago	.08	.06	.03
254	Kirby Puckett	.20	.15	.08
255	Cecil Fielder	.20	.15	.08
256	Howard Johnson	.06	.05	.02
257	Andujar Cedeno	.06	.05	.02
258	Jose Rijo	.08	.06	.03
259	Al Osuna	.05	.04	.02
260	Todd Hundley	.06	.05	.02
261	Orel Hershiser	.08	.06	.03
262	Ray Lankford	.08	.06	.03
263	Robin Ventura	.15	.11	.06
264	Felix Jose	.10	.08	.04
265	Eddie Murray	.15	.11	.06
266	Kevin Mitchell	.08	.06	.03
267	Gary Carter	.08	.06	.03
268	Mike Benjamin	.05	.04	.02
269	Dick Schofield	.05	.04	.02
270	Jose Uribe	.05	.04	.02
271	Pete Incaviglia	.06	.05	.02
272	Tony Fernandez	.08	.06	.03
273	Alan Trammell	.10	.08	.04
274	Tony Gwynn	.15	.11	.06
275	Mike Greenwell	.10	.08	.04
276	Jeff Bagwell	.35	.25	.14
277	Frank Viola	.10	.08	.04
278	Randy Myers	.06	.05	.02
279	Ken Caminiti	.06	.05	.02
280	Bill Doran	.06	.05	.02
281	Dan Pasqua	.05	.04	.02
282	Alfredo Griffin	.05	.04	.02
283	Jose Oquendo	.05	.04	.02
284	Kal Daniels	.08	.06	.03
285	Bobby Thigpen	.08	.06	.03
286	Robby Thompson	.05	.04	.02
287	Mark Eichhorn	.05	.04	.02
288	Mike Felder	.05	.04	.02
289	Dave Gallagher	.05	.04	.02
290	Dave Anderson	.05	.04	.02
291	Mel Hall	.06	.05	.02
292	Jerald Clark	.06	.05	.02
293	Al Newman	.05	.04	.02
294	Rob Deer	.05	.04	.02
295	Matt Nokes	.06	.05	.02
296	Jack Armstrong	.06	.05	.02
297	Jim Deshaies	.05	.04	.02
298	Jeff Innis	.05	.04	.02
299	Jeff Reed	.05	.04	.02
300	Checklist 201-300	.05	.04	.02
301	Lonnie Smith	.05	.04	.02
302	Jimmy Key	.06	.05	.02
303	Junior Felix	.08	.06	.03
304	Mike Heath	.05	.04	.02
305	Mark Langston	.10	.08	.04
306	Greg W. Harris	.06	.05	.02
307	Brett Butler	.08	.06	.03
308	Luis Rivera (FC)	.05	.04	.02
309	Bruce Ruffin	.05	.04	.02
310	Paul Faries	.08	.06	.03
311	Terry Leach	.05	.04	.02
312	*Scott Brosius*	.15	.11	.06
313	Scott Leius	.08	.06	.03
314	Harold Reynolds	.08	.06	.03
315	Jack Morris	.10	.08	.04
316	David Segui	.10	.08	.04
317	Bill Gullickson	.06	.05	.02
318	Todd Frohwirth	.05	.04	.02
319	*Mark Leiter* (FC)	.10	.08	.04
320	Jeff M. Robinson	.05	.04	.02
321	Gary Gaetti	.08	.06	.03
322	John Smoltz	.10	.08	.04
323	Andy Benes	.10	.08	.04
324	Kelly Gruber	.08	.06	.03
325	Jim Abbott	.15	.11	.06
326	John Kruk	.08	.06	.03
327	Kevin Seitzer	.06	.05	.02
328	Darrin Jackson	.05	.04	.02
329	Kurt Stillwell (FC)	.05	.04	.02
330	Mike Maddux	.05	.04	.02
331	Dennis Eckersley	.08	.06	.03
332	Dan Gladden	.05	.04	.02
333	Jose Canseco	.25	.20	.10
334	Kent Hrbek	.06	.05	.02
335	Ken Griffey, Sr.	.06	.05	.02
336	Greg Swindell	.08	.06	.03
337	Trevor Wilson (FC)	.06	.05	.02
338	Sam Horn	.05	.04	.02
339	Mike Henneman	.06	.05	.02
340	Jerry Browne	.05	.04	.02
341	Glenn Braggs	.05	.04	.02
342	Tom Glavine	.10	.08	.04
343	Wally Joyner	.10	.08	.04
344	Fred McGriff	.15	.11	.06
345	Ron Gant	.15	.11	.06
346	Ramon Martinez	.08	.06	.03
347	Wes Chamberlain	.15	.11	.06
348	Terry Shumpert	.05	.04	.02
349	Tim Teufel	.05	.04	.02
350	Wally Backman	.05	.04	.02
351	Joe Girardi	.05	.04	.02
352	Devon White	.08	.06	.03
353	Greg Maddux	.15	.11	.06
354	*Ryan Bowen*	.15	.11	.06
355	Roberto Alomar	.25	.20	.10
356	Don Mattingly	.25	.20	.10
357	Pedro Guerrero	.06	.05	.02
358	Steve Sax	.06	.05	.02
359	Joey Cora	.05	.04	.02
360	Jim Gantner	.05	.04	.02
361	Brian Barnes (FC)	.10	.08	.04
362	Kevin McReynolds	.10	.08	.04
363	*Bret Barberie*	.15	.11	.06
364	David Cone	.10	.07	.04
365	Dennis Martinez	.08	.06	.03
366	*Brian Hunter*	.12	.09	.05
367	Edgar Martinez	.08	.06	.03
368	Steve Finley	.08	.06	.03
369	Greg Briley	.05	.04	.02
370	Jeff Blauser	.05	.04	.02
371	Todd Stottlemyre	.06	.05	.02
372	Luis Gonzalez	.08	.06	.03
373	Rick Wilkins	.10	.07	.04
374	*Darryl Kile*	.15	.11	.06
375	John Olerud	.25	.20	.10
376	Lee Smith	.08	.06	.03
377	Kevin Maas	.08	.06	.03
378	Dante Bichette	.06	.05	.02
379	Tom Pagnozzi	.06	.05	.02
380	Mike Flanagan	.05	.04	.02
381	Charlie O'Brien	.05	.04	.02
382	Dave Martinez	.05	.04	.02
383	Keith Miller	.05	.04	.02
384	Scott Ruskin	.05	.04	.02
385	Kevin Elster	.05	.04	.02
386	Alvin Davis	.08	.06	.03
387	Casey Candaele	.05	.04	.02
388	Pete O'Brien	.05	.04	.02
389	Jeff Treadway (FC)	.05	.04	.02
390	Scott Bradley	.05	.04	.02
391	Mookie Wilson	.05	.04	.02
392	Jimmy Jones	.05	.04	.02
393	Candy Maldonado	.05	.04	.02
394	Eric Yelding	.05	.04	.02
395	Tom Henke	.06	.05	.02
396	Franklin Stubbs	.05	.04	.02
397	Milt Thompson	.05	.04	.02
398	Mark Carreon	.05	.04	.02
399	Randy Velarde	.05	.04	.02
400	Checklist 301-400	.05	.04	.02
401	Omar Vizquel	.05	.04	.02
402	Joe Boever	.05	.04	.02
403	Bill Krueger	.05	.04	.02
404	Jody Reed	.06	.05	.02
405	Mike Schooler (FC)	.06	.05	.02
406	Jason Grimsley	.06	.05	.02
407	Greg Myers	.05	.04	.02
408	Randy Ready	.05	.04	.02
409	*Mike Timlin*	.08	.06	.03
410	Mitch Williams	.08	.06	.03
411	Garry Templeton	.06	.05	.02
412	Greg Cadaret	.05	.04	.02
413	Donnie Hill	.05	.04	.02
414	Wally Whitehurst	.05	.04	.02
415	Scott Sanderson	.06	.05	.02
416	Thomas Howard	.06	.05	.02
417	Neal Heaton	.05	.04	.02
418	Charlie Hough	.06	.05	.02
419	Jack Howell	.05	.04	.02
420	Greg Hibbard	.06	.05	.02
421	Carlos Quintana	.06	.05	.02
422	*Kim Batiste*	.10	.08	.04
423	Paul Molitor	.15	.11	.06
424	Ken Griffey, Jr.	1.00	.75	.40
425	Phil Plantier	.15	.11	.06
426	Denny Neagle	.08	.06	.03
427	Von Hayes	.06	.05	.02
428	Shane Mack	.08	.06	.03
429	Darren Daulton	.06	.05	.02
430	Dwayne Henry	.05	.04	.02
431	Lance Parrish	.06	.05	.02
432	*Mike Humphreys*	.10	.08	.04
433	Tim Burke	.05	.04	.02
434	Bryan Harvey	.06	.05	.02
435	Pat Kelly	.10	.08	.04
436	Ozzie Guillen	.08	.06	.03
437	Bruce Hurst	.06	.05	.02
438	Sammy Sosa	.08	.06	.03
439	Dennis Rasmussen	.05	.04	.02
440	Ken Patterson	.05	.04	.02
441	Jay Buhner	.08	.06	.03
442	Pat Combs	.06	.05	.02
443	Wade Boggs	.15	.11	.06
444	George Brett	.20	.15	.08
445	Mo Vaughn	.25	.20	.10
446	Chuck Knoblauch	.15	.11	.06
447	Tom Candiotti	.06	.05	.02
448	Mark Portugal	.05	.04	.02
449	Mickey Morandini	.10	.08	.04
450	Duane Ward	.05	.04	.02
451	Otis Nixon	.05	.04	.02
452	Bob Welch	.08	.06	.03
453	Rusty Meacham	.10	.08	.04
454	Keith Mitchell	.10	.08	.04
455	Marquis Grissom	.10	.08	.04
456	Robin Yount	.20	.15	.08
457	*Harvey Pulliam*	.08	.06	.03
458	Jose DeLeon (FC)	.05	.04	.02
459	Mark Gubicza	.06	.05	.02
460	Darryl Hamilton	.06	.05	.02
461	Tom Browning	.08	.06	.03
462	Monty Fariss	.10	.08	.04
463	Jerome Walton	.05	.04	.02
464	Paul O'Neill	.08	.06	.03
465	Dean Palmer	.15	.11	.06
466	Travis Fryman	.20	.15	.08
467	John Smiley	.06	.05	.02
468	Lloyd Moseby	.05	.04	.02
469	*John Wehner*	.08	.06	.03
470	Skeeter Barnes (FC)	.06	.05	.02
471	Steve Chitren	.06	.05	.02
472	Kent Mercker	.06	.05	.02
473	Terry Steinbach	.06	.05	.02
474	Andres Galarraga	.08	.06	.03
475	Steve Avery	.15	.11	.06
476	Tom Gordon	.10	.08	.04
477	Cal Eldred	.15	.11	.06
478	Omar Olivares (FC)	.08	.06	.03
479	Julio Machado	.05	.04	.02
480	Bob Milacki	.05	.04	.02
481	Les Lancaster	.05	.04	.02
482	John Candelaria	.05	.04	.02
483	Brian Downing	.05	.04	.02
484	Roger McDowell	.05	.04	.02
485	Scott Scudder	.05	.04	.02
486	Zane Smith	.06	.05	.02
487	John Cerutti	.05	.04	.02
488	Steve Buechele	.06	.05	.02
489	Paul Gibson	.05	.04	.02
490	Curtis Wilkerson	.05	.04	.02
491	Marvin Freeman	.05	.04	.02
492	Tom Foley	.05	.04	.02
493	Juan Berenguer	.05	.04	.02
494	Ernest Riles	.05	.04	.02
495	Sid Bream	.06	.05	.02
496	Chuck Crim	.05	.04	.02
497	Mike Macfarlane	.05	.04	.02
498	Dale Sveum	.05	.04	.02
499	Storm Davis	.05	.04	.02
500	Checklist 401-500	.05	.04	.02
501	Jeff Reardon	.08	.06	.03
502	Shawn Abner	.05	.04	.02
503	Tony Fossas	.05	.04	.02
504	Cory Snyder	.05	.04	.02
505	Matt Young	.05	.04	.02
506	Allan Anderson (FC)	.05	.04	.02
507	Mark Lee	.05	.04	.02
508	Gene Nelson	.05	.04	.02
509	Mike Pagliarulo	.05	.04	.02
510	Rafael Belliard	.05	.04	.02
511	Jay Howell	.06	.05	.02
512	Bob Tewksbury	.05	.04	.02
513	Mike Morgan	.05	.04	.02
514	John Franco	.06	.05	.02
515	Kevin Gross	.05	.04	.02

516 Lou Whitaker .08 .06 .03
517 Orlando Merced .10 .08 .04
518 Todd Benzinger .05 .04 .02
519 Gary Redus .05 .04 .02
520 Walt Terrell .05 .04 .02
521 Jack Clark .08 .06 .03
522 Dave Parker .10 .08 .04
523 Tim Naehring .10 .08 .04
524 Mark Whiten .15 .11 .06
525 Ellis Burks .10 .08 .04
526 *Frank Castillo* (FC) .10 .08 .04
527 Brian Harper .06 .05 .02
528 Brook Jacoby .06 .05 .02
529 Rick Sutcliffe .06 .05 .02
530 Joe Klink .05 .04 .02
531 Terry Bross .05 .04 .02
532 Jose Offerman .10 .08 .04
533 Todd Zeile .12 .09 .05
534 Eric Karros .20 .15 .08
535 *Anthony Young* .08 .06 .03
536 Milt Cuyler .10 .08 .04
537 Randy Tomlin .08 .06 .03
538 *Scott Livingstone* (FC) .08 .06 .03
539 Jim Eisenreich .05 .04 .02
540 Don Slaught .05 .04 .02
541 Scott Cooper .08 .06 .03
542 Joe Grahe (FC) .06 .05 .02
543 Tom Brunansky .06 .05 .02
544 Eddie Zosky .10 .08 .04
545 Roger Clemens .20 .15 .08
546 Dave Justice .30 .25 .12
547 Dave Stewart .10 .08 .04
548 David West .05 .04 .02
549 Dave Smith .06 .05 .02
550 Dan Plesac .06 .05 .02
551 Alex Fernandez .15 .11 .06
552 Bernard Gilkey .10 .08 .04
553 Jack McDowell .08 .06 .03
554 Tino Martinez .10 .08 .04
555 Bo Jackson .25 .20 .10
556 Bernie Williams .10 .08 .04
557 Mark Gardner .06 .05 .02
558 Glenallen Hill .08 .06 .03
559 Oil Can Boyd .05 .04 .02
560 Chris James .05 .04 .02
561 *Scott Servais* .10 .08 .04
562 *Rey Sanchez* (FC) .20 .15 .08
563 *Paul McClellan* (FC) .08 .06 .03
564 *Andy Mota* .08 .06 .03
565 Darren Lewis .08 .06 .03
566 *Jose Melendez* (FC) .08 .06 .03
567 Tommy Greene .08 .06 .03
568 Rich Rodriguez .06 .05 .02
569 *Heathcliff Slocumb* .10 .08 .04
570 Joe Hesketh (FC) .05 .04 .02
571 Carlton Fisk .08 .06 .03
572 Erik Hanson .10 .08 .04
573 Wilson Alvarez .10 .08 .04
574 *Rheal Cormier* (FC) .15 .11 .06
575 Tim Raines .10 .08 .04
576 Bobby Witt .06 .05 .02
577 Roberto Kelly .10 .08 .04
578 Kevin Brown .06 .05 .02
579 Chris Nabholz .06 .05 .02
580 Jesse Orosco .05 .04 .02
581 Jeff Brantley .06 .05 .02
582 Rafael Ramirez .05 .04 .02
583 Kelly Downs .05 .04 .02
584 Mike Simms .10 .08 .04
585 *Mike Remlinger* .10 .08 .04
586 Dave Hollins .08 .06 .03
587 Larry Andersen .05 .04 .02
588 Mike Gardiner .08 .06 .03
589 Craig Lefferts .05 .04 .02
590 Paul Assenmacher (FC) .05 .04 .02
591 Bryn Smith .05 .04 .02
592 Donn Pall .05 .04 .02
593 Mike Jackson .05 .04 .02
594 Scott Radinsky .05 .04 .02
595 Brian Holman .06 .05 .02
596 Geronimo Pena .08 .06 .03
597 Mike Jeffcoat .05 .04 .02
598 Carlos Martinez (FC) .05 .04 .02
599 Geno Petralli .05 .04 .02
600 Checklist 501-600 .05 .04 .02
601 Jerry Don Gleaton .05 .04 .02
602 Adam Peterson (FC) .05 .04 .02
603 Craig Grebeck .05 .04 .02
604 Mark Guthrie .05 .04 .02
605 Frank Tanana .05 .04 .02
606 Hensley Meulens (FC) .08 .06 .03
607 Mark Davis .05 .04 .02
608 Eric Plunk .05 .04 .02
609 Mark Williamson .05 .04 .02
610 Lee Guetterman (FC) .05 .04 .02
611 Bobby Rose .05 .04 .02
612 Bill Wegman .06 .05 .02
613 Mike Hartley .05 .04 .02
614 *Chris Beasley* (FC) .10 .08 .04
615 Chris Bosio .05 .04 .02
616 Henry Cotto .05 .04 .02
617 *Chico Walker* (FC) .10 .08 .04
618 Russ Swan (FC) .05 .04 .02
619 Bob Walk .05 .04 .02
620 Billy Swift .05 .04 .02
621 *Warren Newson* .15 .11 .06
622 Steve Bedrosian (FC) .05 .04 .02
623 *Ricky Bones* (FC) .08 .06 .03
624 Kevin Tapani .10 .08 .04
625 *Juan Guzman* (FC) .40 .30 .15
626 *Jeff Johnson* (FC) .08 .06 .03
627 Jeff Montgomery .06 .05 .02
628 Ken Hill .06 .05 .02
629 Gary Thurman .05 .04 .02
630 Steve Howe (FC) .06 .05 .02
631 Jose DeJesus .06 .05 .02
632 Bert Blyleven .06 .05 .02
633 Jaime Navarro .06 .05 .02
634 Lee Stevens (FC) .08 .06 .03
635 Pete Harnisch .08 .06 .03
636 Bill Landrum .05 .04 .02
637 Rich DeLucia .06 .05 .02
638 Luis Salazar (FC) .05 .04 .02
639 Rob Murphy .05 .04 .02
640 A.L. Diamond Skills Checklist (Rickey Henderson/Jose Canseco) .05 .04 .02
641 Roger Clemens (Diamond Skills) .10 .08 .04
642 Jim Abbott (Diamond Skills) .08 .06 .03
643 Travis Fryman, .20 .15 .08
644 Jesse Barfield (Diamond Skills) .06 .05 .02
645 Cal Ripken, Jr., .25 .20 .10
646 Wade Boggs (Diamond Skills) .10 .08 .04
647 Cecil Fielder (Diamond Skills) .10 .08 .04
648 Rickey Henderson (Diamond Skills) .10 .08 .04
649 Jose Canseco (Diamond Skills) .10 .08 .04
650 Ken Griffey, Jr., .50 .40 .20
651 Kenny Rogers .05 .04 .02
652 *Luis Mercedes* (FC) .10 .08 .04
653 Mike Stanton .06 .05 .02
654 Glenn Davis .10 .08 .04
655 Nolan Ryan .40 .30 .15
656 Reggie Jefferson .10 .08 .04
657 *Javier Ortiz* (FC) .08 .06 .03
658 Greg A. Harris (FC) .05 .04 .02
659 Mariano Duncan .06 .05 .02
660 Jeff Shaw .05 .04 .02
661 Mike Moore .06 .05 .02
662 *Chris Haney* (FC) .08 .06 .03
663 *Joe Slusarski* .08 .06 .03
664 *Wayne Housie* .20 .15 .08
665 Carlos Garcia .15 .11 .06
666 Bob Ojeda .05 .04 .02
667 *Bryan Hickerson* .20 .15 .08
668 Tim Belcher .06 .05 .02
669 Ron Darling .06 .05 .02
670 Rex Hudler (FC) .05 .04 .02
671 Sid Fernandez .08 .06 .03
672 *Chito Martinez* .08 .06 .03
673 *Pete Schourek* .06 .05 .02
674 *Armando Renoso* .15 .11 .06
675 Mike Mussina .25 .20 .10
676 Kevin Morton (FC) .08 .06 .03
677 Norm Charlton .06 .05 .02
678 Danny Darwin .05 .04 .02
679 Eric King .05 .04 .02
680 Ted Power .05 .04 .02
681 Barry Jones .05 .04 .02
682 Carney Lansford .08 .06 .03
683 Mel Rojas .06 .05 .02
684 Rick Honeycutt .05 .04 .02
685 *Jeff Fassero* (FC) .10 .08 .04
686 Cris Carpenter (FC) .06 .05 .02
687 Tim Crews .05 .04 .02
688 Scott Terry .05 .04 .02
689 Chris Gwynn .05 .04 .02
690 Gerald Perry .05 .04 .02
691 John Barfield .05 .04 .02
692 Bob Melvin .05 .04 .02
693 Juan Agosto .05 .04 .02
694 Alejandro Pena (FC) .06 .05 .02
695 Jeff Russell .06 .05 .02
696 Carmelo Martinez .05 .04 .02
697 Bud Black .05 .04 .02
698 Dave Otto (FC) .05 .04 .02
699 Billy Hatcher .05 .04 .02
700 Checklist 601-700 .05 .04 .02
701 Clemente Nunez (FC) .20 .15 .08
702 "Rookie Threats" (Donovan Osborne/Brian Jordan/Mark Clark) .12 .09 .05
703 Mike Morgan .06 .05 .02
704 Keith Miller .06 .05 .02
705 Kurt Stillwell .06 .05 .02
706 Damon Berryhill .06 .05 .02
707 Von Hayes .06 .05 .02
708 Rick Sutcliffe .08 .06 .03
709 Hubie Brooks .06 .05 .02
710 Ryan Turner (FC) .25 .20 .10
711 N.L. Diamond Skills Checklist (Barry Bonds/Andy Van Slyke) .06 .05 .02
712 Jose Rijo (Diamond Skills) .06 .05 .02
713 Tom Glavine (Diamond Skills) .10 .08 .04
714 Shawon Dunston (Diamond Skills) .08 .06 .03
715 Andy Van Slyke (Diamond Skills) .08 .06 .03
716 Ozzie Smith (Diamond Skills) .15 .11 .06
717 Tony Gwynn (Diamond Skills) .15 .11 .06
718 Will Clark (Diamond Skills) .15 .11 .06
719 Marquis Grissom (Diamond Skills) .08 .06 .03
720 Howard Johnson (Diamond Skills) .08 .06 .03
721 Barry Bonds (Diamond Skills) .20 .15 .08
722 Kirk McCaskill .06 .05 .02
723 Sammy Sosa .06 .05 .02
724 George Bell .08 .06 .03
725 Gregg Jefferies .08 .06 .03
726 Gary DiSarcina (FC) .06 .05 .02
727 Mike Bordick .12 .09 .05
728 "400 Home Run Club" (Eddie Murray) .12 .09 .05
729 Rene Gonzales .06 .05 .02
730 Mike Bielecki .06 .05 .02
731 Calvin Jones (FC) .12 .09 .05
732 Jack Morris .05 .04 .02
733 Frank Viola .05 .04 .02
734 Dave Winfield .15 .11 .06
735 Kevin Mitchell .08 .06 .03
736 Billy Swift .08 .06 .03
737 Dan Gladden .06 .05 .02
738 Mike Jackson .06 .05 .02
739 Mark Carreon .06 .05 .02
740 Kirt Manwaring .06 .05 .02
741 Randy Myers .06 .05 .02
742 Kevin McReynolds .08 .06 .03
743 Steve Sax .08 .06 .03
744 Wally Joyner .08 .06 .03
745 Gary Sheffield .15 .11 .06
746 Danny Tartabull .06 .05 .02
747 Julio Valera .10 .08 .04
748 Denny Neagle .10 .08 .04
749 Lance Blankenship .06 .05 .02
750 Mike Gallego .06 .05 .02
751 Bret Saberhagen .05 .04 .02
752 Ruben Amaro (FC) .15 .11 .06
753 Eddie Murray .08 .06 .03
754 Kyle Abbott (FC) .08 .06 .03
755 Bobby Bonilla .10 .07 .04
756 Eric Davis .10 .07 .04
757 Eddie Taubensee (FC) .15 .11 .06
758 Andres Galarraga .08 .06 .03
759 Pete Incaviglia .08 .06 .03
760 Tom Candiotti .08 .06 .03
761 Tim Belcher .08 .06 .03
762 Ricky Bones .08 .06 .03
763 Bip Roberts .08 .06 .03
764 Pedro Munoz .10 .07 .04
765 Greg Swindell .08 .06 .03
766 *Kenny Lofton* .50 .40 .20
767 Gary Carter .08 .06 .03
768 Charlie Hayes .06 .05 .02
769 Dickie Thon .06 .05 .02
770 Diamond Debuts Checklist (Donovan Osborne) .06 .05 .02
771 *Bret Boone* (Diamond Debuts) .20 .15 .08
772 *Archi Cianfrocco* (Diamond Debuts) .15 .11 .06
773 *Mark Clark* (Diamond Debuts) .15 .11 .06
774 *Chad Curtis* (Diamond Debuts) .35 .25 .14
775 *Pat Listach* (Diamond Debuts) .25 .20 .10
776 *Pat Mahomes* (Diamond Debuts) .15 .11 .06
777 *Donovan Osborne* (Diamond Debuts) .15 .11 .06
778 *John Patterson* (Diamond Debuts) .08 .06 .03
779 *Andy Stankiewicz* (Diamond Debuts) .10 .08 .04
780 *Turk Wendell* (Diamond Debuts) .10 .08 .04
781 Bill Krueger .06 .05 .02
782 "Grand Theft", Rickey Henderson .15 .11 .06
783 Kevin Seitzer .06 .05 .02
784 Dave Martinez .06 .05 .02
785 John Smiley .08 .06 .03
786 Matt Stairs .08 .06 .03
787 Scott Scudder .06 .05 .02
788 John Wetteland .10 .08 .04
789 Jack Armstrong .06 .05 .02
790 Ken Hill (FC) .08 .06 .03
791 Dick Schofield .06 .05 .02
792 Mariano Duncan .06 .05 .02
793 Bill Pecota .06 .05 .02
794 *Mike Kelly* .75 .60 .30
795 Willie Randolph .06 .05 .02
796 *Butch Henry* .08 .06 .03
797 *Carlos Hernandez* .10 .08 .04
798 Doug Jones .06 .05 .02
799 Melido Perez .06 .05 .02
800 Checklist .06 .05 .02
---- "Prime Time's Two" (Deion Sanders) (SP3) 4.00 3.00 1.50
---- "Mr. Baseball" (Tom Selleck/Frank Thomas) (SP4) 5.00 3.75 2.00
---- Ted Williams hologram (HH2) 3.00 2.25 1.25

1992 Upper Deck College POY Holograms

This three-card hologram set features the College Player of the Year winners from 1989-91. Cards were randomly inserted in high number foil packs and have a CP prefix for numbering.

	MT	NR MT	EX
Complete Set (3):	1.00	.75	.40
Common Player:	.25	.20	.10

		MT	NR MT	EX
1	David McCarty	.50	.40	.20
2	Mike Kelly	.75	.60	.30
3	Ben McDonald	.25	.20	.10

Values for recent cards and sets are listed in Mint (MT), Near Mint (NM), reflecting the fact that many cards from recent years have been preserved in top condition. Recent cards and sets in less than Excellent condition have little collector interest.

1992 Upper Deck Ted Williams Heroes

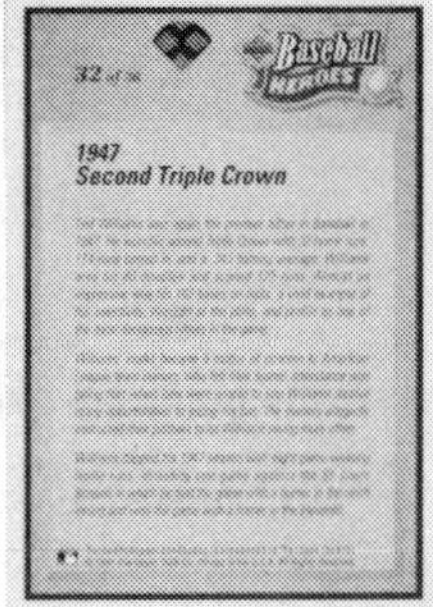

This Baseball Heroes set devoted to Ted Williams continues where previous efforts left off by numbering it from 28-36. An unnumbered cover card is also included that says "Baseball Heroes." Cards were found in low number foil and jumbo packs. Williams also autographed 2,500 cards, which were numbered and randomly inserted in low number packs.

		MT	NR MT	EX
Complete Set (10):		7.50	5.75	3.00
Common Williams:		.50	.40	.20
Autographed Card:		450.00	337.00	180.00
	Williams Header	4.00	3.00	1.50
28	1939 Rookie Year	.50	.40	.20
29	1941 .406!	.50	.40	.20
30	1942 Triple Crown Year	.50	.40	.20
31	1946 & 1949 MVP	.50	.40	.20
32	1947 Second Triple Crown	.50	.40	.20
33	1950s Player of the Decade	.50	.40	.30
34	1960 500 Home Run Club	.50	.40	.20
35	1966 Hall of Fame	.50	.40	.20
36	Checklist - Heroes 28-36	.50	.40	.20

1992 Upper Deck Bench/Morgan Heroes

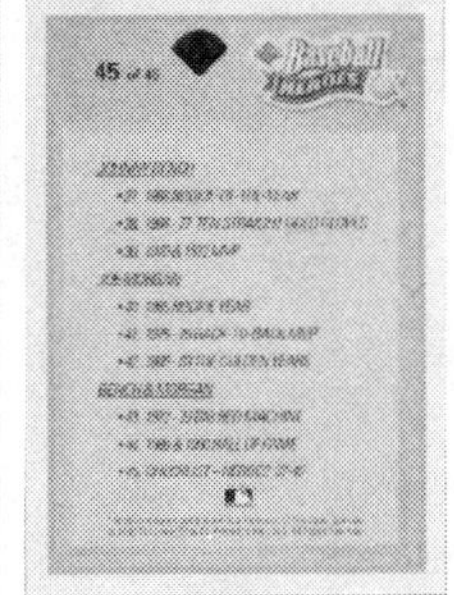

This set is devoted to two of the vital cogs in Cincinnati's Big Red Machine: Hall of Famers Johnny Bench and Joe Morgan. Cards, numbered 37-45, were included in high number packs. An unnumbered cover card was also produced, as were 2,500 cards numbered and signed by both players. They were also randomly inserted in high number packs.

	MT	NR MT	EX
Complete Set (10):	14.00	10.50	5.50
Common Card:	1.00	.70	.40
Header Card:	7.50	5.50	3.00
Autograph:	300.00	225.00	125.00

1992 Upper Deck Hall of Fame Heroes

This set features three top players from the 1970s: Vida Blue, Lou Brock and Rollie Fingers. The cards continue from last year's set by using numbers H5-H8. The three players are each on one card; the fourth card features all three. They were found in low foil packs and specially-marked jumbo packs. Both types of packs could also contain autographed cards; each player signed 3,000 cards.

		MT	NR MT	EX
Complete Set (4):		35.00	26.00	14.00
Common Player:		8.00	6.00	3.25
Vida		75.00	56.00	30.00
Lou		100.00	75.00	40.00
Rollie		90.00	67.00	36.00
5	Vida Blue	8.00	6.00	3.25
6	Lou Brock	10.00	7.50	4.00
7	Rollie Fingers	9.00	6.75	3.50
8	Vida Blue/Lou Brock/Rollie Fingers	10.00	7.50	4.00

1992 Upper Deck Home Run Heroes

This 26-card set features a top home run hitter from each major league team. The cards, numbered HR1-HR26, were found in low number jumbo packs, one per pack.

		MT	NR MT	EX
Complete Set (26):		18.00	13.50	7.25
Common Player:		.40	.30	.15
1	Jose Canseco	1.00	.75	.40
2	Cecil Fielder	.75	.60	.30
3	Howard Johnson	.40	.30	.15
4	Cal Ripken, Jr.	1.50	1.25	.60
5	Matt Williams	.75	.60	.30
6	Joe Carter	1.00	.75	.40
7	Ron Gant	.50	.40	.20
8	Frank Thomas	4.50	3.50	1.75
9	Andre Dawson	.50	.40	.20
10	Fred McGriff	1.00	.75	.40
11	Danny Tartabull	.40	.30	.15
12	Chili Davis	.40	.30	.15
13	Albert Belle	1.50	1.25	.60
14	Jack Clark	.40	.30	.15
15	Paul O'Neill	.40	.30	.15
16	Darryl Strawberry	.50	.40	.20
17	Dave Winfield	.75	.60	.30
18	Jay Buhner	.40	.30	.15
19	Juan Gonzalez	3.00	2.25	1.25
20	Greg Vaughn	.50	.40	.20
21	Barry Bonds	1.50	1.25	.60
22	Matt Nokes	.40	.30	.15
23	John Kruk	.50	.40	.20
24	Ivan Calderon	.40	.30	.15
25	Jeff Bagwell	1.50	1.25	.60
26	Todd Zeile	.40	.30	.15

1992 Upper Deck Scouting Report

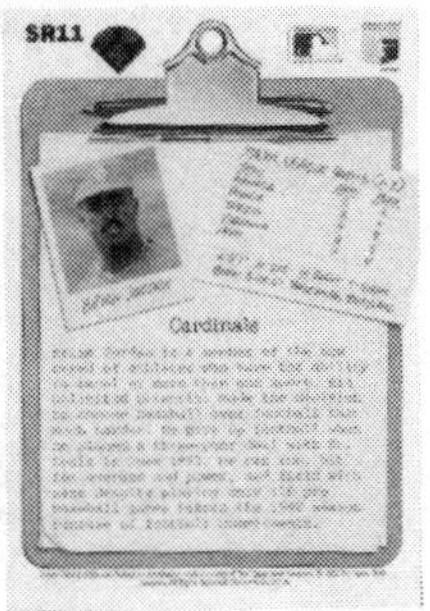

These cards were randomly inserted in Upper Deck high number jumbo packs. The set is numbered SR1-SR25 and features 25 top prospects, including 1992 Rookies of the Year Pat Listach and Eric Karros. "Scouting Report" is written down the side on the front in silver lettering. The back features a clipboard which shows a photo, a player profile and a major league scouting report.

		MT	NR MT	EX
Complete Set (25):		18.00	13.50	7.25
Common Player:		.25	.20	.10
1	Andy Ashby	.50	.40	.20
2	Willie Banks	.35	.25	.14
3	Kim Batiste	.25	.20	.10
4	Derek Bell	1.00	.75	.40
5	Archi Cianfrocco	.25	.20	.10
6	Royce Clayton	1.50	1.25	.60
7	Gary DiSarcina	.25	.20	.10
8	Dave Fleming	.50	.40	.20
9	Butch Henry	.25	.20	.10
10	Todd Hundley	.40	.30	.15
11	Brian Jordan	1.00	.75	.40
12	Eric Karros	1.00	.75	.40
13	Pat Listach	.50	.40	.20
14	Scott Livingstone	.25	.20	.10
15	Kenny Lofton	4.50	3.50	1.75
16	Pat Mahomes	.60	.45	.25
17	Denny Neagle	.30	.25	.12
18	Dave Nilsson	1.00	.75	.40
19	Donovan Osborne	1.00	.75	.40
20	Reggie Sanders	1.50	1.25	.60
21	Andy Stankiewicz	.25	.20	.10
22	Jim Thome	3.00	2.25	1.25
23	Julio Valera	.25	.20	.10
24	Mark Wohlers	.25	.20	.10
25	Anthony Young	.25	.20	.10

1992 Upper Deck Ted Williams' Best

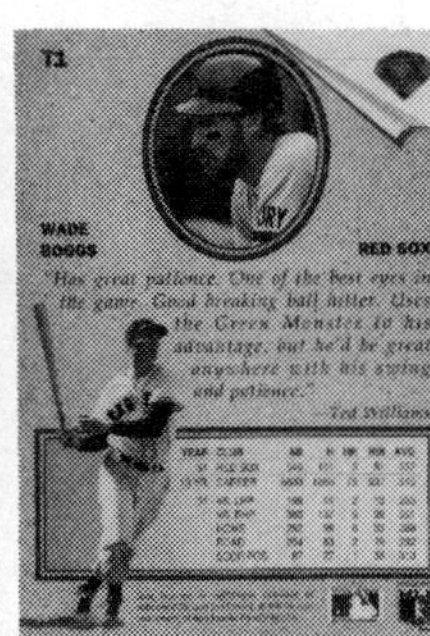

Twenty of the best hitters in baseball according to legend Ted Williams are featured in this special insert set from Upper Deck. The cards are styled much like the 1992 FanFest cards and showcase each chosen player. Each card is numbered with a "T" designation.

		MT	NR MT	EX
Complete Set (20):		22.00	16.50	8.75
Common Player:		.60	.45	.25
1	Wade Boggs	1.00	.70	.40
2	Barry Bonds	2.50	2.00	1.00
3	Jose Canseco	1.50	1.25	.60
4	Will Clark	1.25	.90	.50
5	Cecil Fielder	1.00	.75	.40
6	Tony Gwynn	1.00	.70	.40
7	Rickey Henderson	1.00	.70	.40
8	Fred McGriff	1.50	1.25	.60
9	Kirby Puckett	1.75	1.25	.70
10	Ruben Sierra	.60	.45	.25
11	Roberto Alomar	2.00	1.50	.80
12	Jeff Bagwell	2.00	1.50	.80
13	Albert Belle	2.00	1.50	.80
14	Juan Gonzalez	4.00	3.00	1.50
15	Ken Griffey, Jr.	6.00	4.50	2.50
16	Chris Hoiles	.60	.45	.25
17	Dave Justice	2.00	1.50	.80
18	Phil Plantier	.90	.70	.35
19	Frank Thomas	6.00	4.50	2.50
20	Robin Ventura	1.00	.75	.40

1992 Upper Deck FanFest

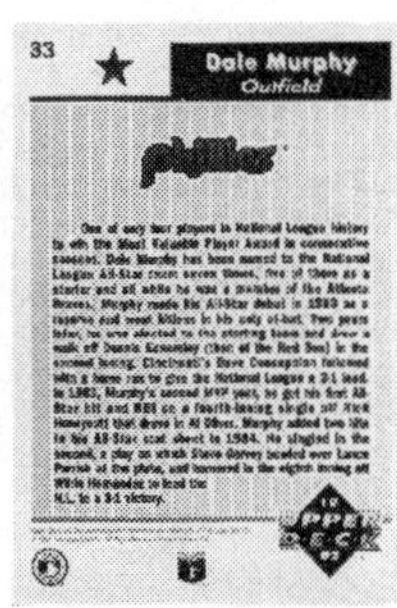

This 54-card boxed set was made available through special offers at the 1992 National Sports Collectors Convention and at the 1992 All-Star FanFest in San Diego. Card fronts feature a glossy UV finish, silver-foil stamping and the All-Star FanFest logo. The card backs include a player profile. Both "Future Heroes" and past and present "All-Star Heroes" are featured. The complete set was packaged in an attractive blue box with white pinstripes.

		MT	NR MT	EX
Complete Set:		16.00	12.00	6.50
Common Player:		.10	.08	.04
1	Steve Avery	.30	.25	.12
2	Ivan Rodriguez	.60	.45	.25

3	Jeff Bagwell	.30	.25	.12
4	Delino DeShields	.15	.11	.06
5	Royce Clayton	.25	.20	.10
6	Robin Ventura	.30	.25	.12
7	Phil Plantier	.25	.20	.10
8	Ray Lankford	.20	.15	.08
9	Juan Gonzalez	.60	.45	.25
10	Frank Thomas	1.25	.90	.50
11	Roberto Alomar	.80	.60	.30
12	Sandy Alomar, Jr.	.10	.08	.04
13	Wade Boggs	.30	.25	.12
14	Barry Bonds	.25	.20	.10
15	Bobby Bonilla	.25	.20	.10
16	George Brett	.30	.25	.12
17	Jose Canseco	.60	.45	.25
18	Will Clark	.60	.45	.25
19	Roger Clemens	.30	.25	.12
20	Eric Davis	.10	.08	.04
21	Rob Dibble	.10	.08	.04
22	Cecil Fielder	.25	.20	.10
23	Dwight Gooden	.20	.15	.08
24	Ken Griffey, Jr.	1.00	.70	.40
25	Tony Gwynn	.60	.45	.25
26	Bryan Harvey	.10	.08	.04
27	Rickey Henderson	.30	.25	.12
28	Howard Johnson	.10	.08	.04
29	Wally Joyner	.10	.08	.04
30	Barry Larkin	.20	.15	.08
31	Don Mattingly	.25	.20	.10
32	Mark McGwire	.35	.25	.14
33	Dale Murphy	.10	.08	.04
34	Rafael Palmeiro	.10	.08	.04
35	Kirby Puckett	.50	.40	.20
36	Cal Ripken, Jr.	1.00	.70	.40
37	Nolan Ryan	.80	.60	.30
38	Chris Sabo	.10	.08	.04
39	Ryne Sandberg	.60	.45	.25
40	Benito Santiago	.10	.08	.04
41	Ruben Sierra	.25	.20	.10
42	Ozzie Smith	.30	.25	.12
43	Darryl Strawberry	.25	.20	.10
44	Robin Yount	.30	.25	.12
45	Rollie Fingers	.30	.25	.12
46	Reggie Jackson	.60	.45	.25
47	Billy Williams	.10	.08	.04
48	Lou Brock	.30	.25	.12
49	Gaylord Perry	.25	.20	.10
50	Ted Williams	.70	.50	.30
51	Brooks Robinson	.50	.40	.20
52	Bob Gibson	.25	.20	.10
53	Bobby Bonds	.10	.08	.04
54	Robin Roberts	.10	.08	.04

1992 Upper Deck MVP Holograms

State of the art holography is presented in this 54-card plastic-cased set featuring a top pitcher and a top position player from each major league team, plus 1991 MVPs Terry Pendleton and Cal Ripken, Jr. The hologram on the front of each card feature a closeup and a field-action photo of the player; his name and position are in a strip at bottom. Full-color backs have a player photo on the right and career summary on the left. A custom album for the set was available via a mail offer for $10. Each set includes a numbered certificate of authenticity, verifying its position among a total issue of 216,000 sets.

		MT	NR MT	EX
Complete Set (54):		18.00	13.50	7.25
Common Player:		.25	.20	.10
1	A.L. Checklist (Cal Ripken, Jr.)	.25	.20	.10
2	N.L. Checkklist (Terry Pendleton)	.25	.20	.10
3	Jim Abbott	.35	.25	.14
4	Roberto Alomar	.60	.45	.25
5	Kevin Appier	.25	.20	.10
6	Steve Avery	.40	.30	.15
7	Jeff Bagwell	.40	.30	.15
8	Albert Belle	.50	.40	.20
9	Andy Benes	.25	.20	.10
10	Wade Boggs	.40	.30	.15
11	Barry Bonds	1.00	.70	.40
12	George Brett	.75	.60	.30
13	Ivan Calderon	.25	.20	.10
14	Jose Canseco	.50	.40	.20
15	Will Clark	.50	.40	.20
16	Roger Clemens	.40	.30	.15
17	David Cone	.25	.20	.10
18	Doug Drabek	.25	.20	.10
19	Dennis Eckersley	.35	.25	.14
20	Scott Erickson	.25	.20	.10
21	Cecil Fielder	.50	.40	.20
22	Ken Griffey, Jr.	2.00	1.50	.80
23	Bill Gullickson	.25	.20	.10
24	Juan Guzman	.25	.20	.10
25	Pete Harnisch	.25	.20	.10
26	Howard Johnson	.25	.20	.10
27	Randy Johnson	.30	.25	.12
28	John Kruk	.35	.25	.14
29	Barry Larkin	.30	.25	.12
30	Greg Maddux	.40	.30	.15
31	Dennis Martinez	.25	.20	.10
32	Ramon Martinez	.25	.20	.10
33	Don Mattingly	.75	.60	.30
34	Jack McDowell	.35	.25	.14
35	Fred McGriff	.50	.40	.20
36	Paul Molitor	.60	.45	.25
37	Charles Nagy	.25	.20	.10
38	Gregg Olson	.25	.20	.10
39	Terry Pendleton	.25	.20	.10
40	Luis Polonia	.25	.20	.10
41	Kirby Puckett	.50	.40	.20
42	Dave Righetti	.25	.20	.10
43	Jose Rijo	.25	.20	.10
44	Cal Ripken, Jr.	1.00	.75	.40
45	Nolan Ryan	2.00	1.50	.80
46	Ryne Sandberg	1.00	.75	.40
47	Scott Sanderson	.25	.20	.10
48	Ruben Sierra	.35	.25	.14
49	Lee Smith	.25	.20	.10
50	Ozzie Smith	.40	.30	.15
51	Darryl Strawberry	.30	.25	.12
52	Frank Thomas	3.00	2.25	1.25
53	Bill Wegman	.25	.20	.10
54	Mitch Williams	.25	.20	.10

1993 Upper Deck

Upper Deck introduced its 1993 set in a two-series format to adjust to expansion. Cards 1-420 make up the first series. Special subsets in series one include rookies, teammates and community heroes. The card fronts feature full-color player photos surrounded by a white border. "Upper Deck" appears at the top of the photo and the player's name, team and position appear at the bottom. The backs feature vertical photos, which is a change from the past, and more complete statistics than what Upper Deck has had in the past. The hologram appears in the lower left corner on the card back.

		MT	NR MT	EX
Complete Set (840):		40.00	30.00	15.00
Common Player:		.05	.04	.02
1	Tim Salmon (Checklist)	.35	.25	.14
2	*Mike Piazza* (Star Rookie)	2.50	2.00	1.00
3	*Rene Arocha* (Star Rookie)	.30	.25	.12
4	*Willie Greene* (Star Rookie)	.12	.09	.05
5	*Manny Alexander* (Star Rookie)	.20	.15	.08
6	Dan Wilson (Star Rookie)	.12	.09	.05
7	*Dan Smith* (Star Rookie)	.10	.07	.04
8	*Kevin Rogers* (Star Rookie)	.10	.07	.04
9	*Nigel Wilson* (Star Rookie)	.20	.15	.08
10	*Joe Vitko* (Star Rookie)	.15	.11	.06
11	Tim Costo (FC) (Star Rookie)	.15	.11	.06
12	Alan Embree (Star Rookie)	.15	.11	.06
13	*Jim Tatum* (Star Rookie)	.15	.11	.06
14	*Cris Colon* (Star Rookie)	.15	.11	.06
15	Steve Hosey (FC) (Star Rookie)	.12	.09	.05
16	*Sterling Hitchcock* (Star Rookie)	.15	.11	.06
17	*Dave Mlicki* (Star Rookie)	.15	.11	.06
18	*Jessie Hollins* (Star Rookie)	.15	.11	.06
19	*Bobby Jones* (Star Rookie)	.40	.30	.15
20	*Kurt Miller* (Star Rookie)	.15	.11	.06
21	*Melvin Nieves* (Star Rookie)	.30	.25	.12
22	*Billy Ashley* (Star Rookie)	.25	.20	.10
23	*J.T. Snow* (Star Rookie)	.25	.20	.10
24	Chipper Jones (Star Rookie)	.40	.30	.15
25	*Tim Salmon* (Star Rookie)	1.25	.90	.50
26	*Tim Pugh* (Star Rookie)	.15	.11	.06
27	David Nied (Star Rookie)	.20	.15	.08
28	*Mike Trombley* (Star Rookie)	.12	.09	.05
29	*Javier Lopez* (Star Rookie)	.75	.60	.30
30	Community Heroes Checklist (Jim Abbott)	.05	.04	.02
31	Jim Abbott (Community Heroes)	.10	.08	.04
32	Dale Murphy (Community Heroes)	.10	.08	.04
33	Tony Pena (Community Heroes)	.10	.08	.04
34	Kirby Puckett (Community Heroes)	.15	.11	.06
35	Harold Reynolds (Community Heroes)	.10	.08	.04
36	Cal Ripken, Jr. (Community Heroes)	.20	.15	.08
37	Nolan Ryan (Community Heroes)	.50	.40	.20
38	Ryne Sandberg (Community Heroes)	.25	.20	.10
39	Dave Stewart (Community Heroes)	.10	.08	.04
40	Dave Winfield (Community Heroes)	.10	.07	.04
41	Teammates Checklist (Joe Carter/Mark McGwire)	.05	.04	.02
42	Blockbuster Trade (Joe Carter/Roberto Alomar)	.12	.09	.05
43	Brew Crew (Pat Listach, Robin Yount, Paul Molitor)	.15	.11	.06
44	Iron and Steal (Brady Anderson, Cal Ripken, Jr.)	.20	.15	.08
45	Youthful Tribe (Albert Belle/Sandy Alomar, Jr./ Jim Thome/Carlos Baerga/Kenny Lofton)	.12	.09	.05
46	Motown Mashers (Cecil Fielder/Mickey Tettleton)	.12	.09	.05
47	Yankee Pride (Roberto Kelly/Don Mattingly)	.12	.09	.05
48	Boston Cy Sox (Frank Viola/Roger Clemens)	.12	.09	.05
49	Bash Brothers (Ruben Sierra/Mark McGwire)	.12	.09	.05
50	Twin Titles (Kent Hrbek/Kirby Puckett)	.12	.09	.05
51	Southside Sluggers (Robin Ventura, Frank Thomas)	.60	.45	.25
52	Latin Stars (Jose Canseco, Ivan Rodriguez, Rafael Palmeiro, Juan Gonzalez)	.25	.20	.10
53	Lethal Lefties (Mark Langston/Jim Abbott/Chuck Finley)	.12	.09	.05
54	Royal Family (Wally Joyner/George Brett/Gregg Jefferies)	.12	.09	.05
55	Pacific Sox Exchange (Kevin Mitchell, Jay Buhner, Ken Griffey, Jr.)	.50	.40	.20
56	George Brett	.20	.15	.08
57	Scott Cooper	.08	.06	.03
58	Mike Maddux	.05	.04	.02
59	*Rusty Meacham* (FC)	.12	.09	.05
60	Wil Cordero	.15	.11	.06
61	Tim Teufel	.05	.04	.02
62	Jeff Montgomery	.06	.05	.02
63	Scott Livingstone (FC)	.08	.06	.03
64	Doug Dascenzo	.05	.04	.02
65	Bret Boone	.15	.11	.06
66	*Tim Wakefield*	.10	.07	.04
67	Curt Schilling	.08	.06	.03
68	Frank Tanana	.05	.04	.02
69	Len Dykstra	.10	.07	.04
70	Derek Lilliquist	.05	.04	.02
71	Anthony Young (FC)	.08	.06	.03
72	*Hipolito Pichardo*	.12	.09	.05
73	Rob Beck (FC)	.06	.05	.02
74	Kent Hrbek	.08	.06	.03
75	Tom Glavine	.15	.11	.06
76	Kevin Brown	.08	.06	.03
77	Chuck Finley	.08	.06	.03
78	Bob Walk	.05	.04	.02
79	Rheal Cormier	.10	.08	.04
80	Rick Sutcliffe	.08	.06	.03
81	Harold Baines	.08	.06	.03
82	Lee Smith	.08	.06	.03
83	Geno Petralli	.05	.04	.02
84	Jose Oquendo	.05	.04	.02
85	Mark Gubicza	.06	.05	.02
86	Mickey Tettleton	.08	.06	.03
87	Bobby Witt	.06	.05	.02
88	Mark Lewis	.06	.05	.02
89	Kevin Appier	.08	.06	.03
90	Mike Stanton	.05	.04	.02
91	Rafael Belliard	.05	.04	.02
92	Kenny Rogers	.05	.04	.02
93	Randy Velarde	.05	.04	.02
94	Luis Sojo	.05	.04	.02
95	Mark Leiter	.05	.04	.02
96	Jody Reed	.06	.05	.02
97	Pete Harnisch	.06	.05	.02
98	Tom Candiotti	.06	.05	.02
99	Mark Portugal	.05	.04	.02
100	Dave Valle	.05	.04	.02
101	Shawon Dunston	.08	.06	.03
102	B.J. Surhoff	.08	.06	.03
103	Jay Bell	.08	.06	.03
104	Sid Bream	.05	.04	.02
105	Checklist 1-105 (Frank Thomas)	.10	.07	.04
106	Mike Morgan	.05	.04	.02
107	Bill Doran	.05	.04	.02
108	Lance Blankenship	.05	.04	.02
109	Mark Lemke	.05	.04	.02
110	Brian Harper	.06	.05	.02
111	Brady Anderson	.08	.06	.03
112	Bip Roberts	.08	.06	.03
113	Mitch Williams	.08	.06	.03
114	Craig Biggio	.08	.06	.03
115	Eddie Murray	.08	.06	.03
116	Matt Nokes	.06	.05	.02
117	Lance Parrish	.06	.05	.02
118	Bill Swift	.06	.05	.02
119	Jeff Innis	.05	.04	.02
120	Mike LaValliere	.05	.04	.02
121	Hal Morris	.08	.06	.03
122	Walt Weiss	.06	.05	.02
123	Ivan Rodriguez	.15	.11	.06
124	Andy Van Slyke	.08	.06	.03
125	Roberto Alomar	.25	.20	.10
126	Robby Thompson	.06	.05	.02
127	Sammy Sosa	.07	.05	.03
128	Mark Langston	.06	.05	.02
129	Jerry Browne	.05	.04	.02
130	Chuck McElroy	.05	.04	.02
131	Frank Viola	.08	.06	.03

132	Leo Gomez	.08	.06	.03
133	Ramon Martinez	.08	.06	.03
134	Don Mattingly	.30	.25	.12
135	Roger Clemens	.20	.15	.08
136	Rickey Henderson	.15	.11	.06
137	Darren Daulton	.10	.07	.04
138	Ken Hill	.08	.06	.03
139	Ozzie Guillen	.08	.06	.03
140	Jerald Clark	.08	.06	.03
141	Dave Fleming	.15	.11	.06
142	Delino DeShields	.12	.09	.05
143	Matt Williams	.10	.07	.04
144	Larry Walker	.10	.07	.04
145	Ruben Sierra	.10	.07	.04
146	Ozzie Smith	.10	.07	.04
147	Chris Sabo	.08	.06	.03
148	*Carlos Hernandez*	.08	.06	.03
149	Pat Borders	.08	.06	.03
150	Orlando Merced	.08	.06	.03
151	Royce Clayton	.08	.06	.03
152	Kurt Stillwell	.06	.05	.02
153	Dave Hollins	.10	.08	.04
154	Mike Greenwell	.08	.06	.03
155	Nolan Ryan	1.00	.75	.40
156	Felix Jose	.08	.06	.03
157	Junior Felix	.06	.05	.02
158	Derek Bell	.10	.08	.04
159	Steve Buechele	.06	.05	.02
160	John Burkett	.06	.05	.02
161	*Pat Howell*	.15	.11	.06
162	Milt Cuyler	.06	.05	.02
163	Terry Pendleton	.10	.08	.04
164	Jack Morris	.10	.08	.04
165	Tony Gwynn	.15	.11	.06
166	Deion Sanders	.15	.11	.06
167	Mike Devereaux	.08	.06	.03
168	Ron Darling	.08	.06	.03
169	Orel Hershiser	.08	.06	.03
170	Mike Jackson	.05	.04	.02
171	Doug Jones	.06	.05	.02
172	*Dan Walters* (FC)	.12	.09	.05
173	Darren Lewis	.08	.06	.03
174	Carlos Baerga	.20	.15	.08
175	Ryne Sandberg	.25	.20	.10
176	Gregg Jefferies	.12	.09	.05
177	John Jaha	.10	.07	.04
178	Luis Polonia	.05	.04	.02
179	Kirt Manwaring	.05	.04	.02
180	Mike Magnante	.08	.06	.03
181	Billy Ripken	.05	.04	.02
182	Mike Moore	.06	.05	.02
183	Eric Anthony	.06	.05	.02
184	Lenny Harris	.05	.04	.02
185	Tony Pena	.06	.05	.02
186	Mike Felder	.05	.04	.02
187	Greg Olson	.05	.04	.02
188	Rene Gonzales	.05	.04	.02
189	Mike Bordick	.08	.06	.03
190	Mel Rojas	.05	.04	.02
191	Todd Frohwirth	.05	.04	.02
192	Darryl Hamilton	.08	.06	.03
193	Mike Fetters	.05	.04	.02
194	Omar Olivares (FC)	.05	.04	.02
195	Tony Phillips	.08	.06	.03
196	Paul Sorrento	.08	.06	.03
197	Trevor Wilson	.06	.05	.02
198	Kevin Gross	.05	.04	.02
199	Ron Karkovice	.05	.04	.02
200	Brook Jacoby	.05	.04	.02
201	Mariano Duncan	.05	.04	.02
202	Dennis Cook	.05	.04	.02
203	Daryl Boston	.05	.04	.02
204	Mike Perez	.08	.06	.03
205	Manuel Lee	.05	.04	.02
206	Steve Olin	.05	.04	.02
207	Charlie Hough	.05	.04	.02
208	Scott Scudder	.05	.04	.02
209	Charlie O'Brien	.05	.04	.02
210	Checklist 106-210 (Barry Bonds)	.10	.07	.04
211	Jose Vizcaino	.05	.04	.02
212	Scott Leius	.05	.04	.02
213	Kevin Mitchell	.08	.06	.03
214	Brian Barnes	.08	.06	.03
215	Pat Kelly	.08	.06	.03
216	Chris Hammond	.08	.06	.03
217	Rob Deer	.06	.05	.02
218	Cory Snyder	.06	.05	.02
219	Gary Carter	.10	.08	.04
220	Danny Darwin	.05	.04	.02
221	Tom Gordon	.05	.04	.02
222	Gary Sheffield	.10	.08	.04
223	Joe Carter	.20	.15	.08
224	Jay Buhner	.06	.05	.02
225	Jose Offerman	.06	.05	.02
226	Jose Rijo	.06	.05	.02
227	Mark Whiten	.08	.06	.03
228	Randy Milligan	.05	.04	.02
229	Bud Black	.05	.04	.02
230	Gary DiSarcina	.05	.04	.02
231	Steve Finley	.08	.06	.03
232	Dennis Martinez	.08	.06	.03
233	Mike Mussina	.25	.20	.10
234	Joe Oliver	.06	.05	.02
235	Chad Curtis	.25	.20	.10
236	Shane Mack	.08	.06	.03
237	Jaime Navarro	.08	.06	.03
238	Brian McRae	.08	.06	.03
239	Chili Davis	.06	.05	.02
240	Jeff King	.06	.05	.02
241	Dean Palmer	.06	.05	.02
242	Danny Tartabull	.10	.08	.04
243	Charles Nagy	.10	.07	.04
244	Ray Lankford	.15	.11	.06
245	Barry Larkin	.10	.07	.04
246	Steve Avery	.15	.11	.06
247	John Kruk	.08	.06	.03
248	Derrick May	.08	.06	.03
249	Stan Javier	.05	.04	.02
250	Roger McDowell	.05	.04	.02
251	Dan Gladden	.05	.04	.02
252	Wally Joyner	.08	.06	.03
253	Pat Listach	.08	.06	.03
254	Chuck Knoblauch	.08	.06	.03
255	Sandy Alomar Jr.	.10	.08	.04
256	Jeff Bagwell	.25	.20	.10
257	Andy Stankiewicz	.10	.07	.04
258	Darrin Jackson	.06	.05	.02
259	Brett Butler	.08	.06	.03
260	Joe Orsulak	.06	.05	.02
261	Andy Benes	.10	.08	.04
262	Kenny Lofton	.25	.20	.10
263	Robin Ventura	.20	.15	.08
264	Ron Gant	.10	.07	.04
266	Juan Guzman	.10	.07	.04
267	Wes Chamberlain	.08	.06	.03
268	John Smiley	.06	.05	.02
269	Franklin Stubbs	.05	.04	.02
270	Tom Browning	.06	.05	.02
271	Dennis Eckersley	.12	.09	.05
272	Carlton Fisk	.08	.06	.03
273	Lou Whitaker	.08	.06	.03
274	Phil Plantier	.10	.07	.04
275	Bobby Bonilla	.10	.08	.04
276	Ben McDonald	.08	.06	.03
277	Bob Zupcic	.10	.08	.04
278	Terry Steinbach	.06	.05	.02
279	Terry Mulholland	.06	.05	.02
280	Lance Johnson	.06	.05	.02
281	Willie McGee	.06	.05	.02
282	Bret Saberhagen	.08	.06	.03
283	Randy Myers	.08	.06	.03
284	Randy Tomlin	.08	.06	.03
285	Mickey Morandini	.08	.06	.03
286	Brian Williams	.08	.06	.03
287	Tino Martinez	.08	.06	.03
288	Jose Melendez	.08	.06	.03
289	Jeff Huson	.05	.04	.02
290	Joe Grahe	.05	.04	.02
291	Mel Hall	.06	.05	.02
292	Otis Nixon	.06	.05	.02
293	Todd Hundley	.08	.06	.03
294	Casey Candaele	.05	.04	.02
295	Kevin Seitzer	.06	.05	.02
296	Eddie Taubensee	.10	.08	.04
297	Moises Alou	.10	.08	.04
298	Scott Radinsky	.05	.04	.02
299	Thomas Howard	.05	.04	.02
300	Kyle Abbott	.08	.06	.03
301	Omar Vizquel	.05	.04	.02
302	Keith Miller	.05	.04	.02
303	Rick Aguilera	.08	.06	.03
304	Bruce Hurst	.08	.06	.03
305	Ken Caminiti	.06	.05	.02
306	Mike Pagiarulo	.05	.04	.02
307	Frank Seminara	.12	.09	.05
308	Andre Dawson	.10	.07	.04
309	Jose Lind	.06	.05	.02
310	Joe Boever	.05	.04	.02
311	Jeff Parrett (FC)	.05	.04	.02
312	Alan Mills	.05	.04	.02
313	Kevin Tapani	.08	.06	.03
314	Daryl Kile	.08	.06	.03
315	Checklist 211-315 (Will Clark)	.05	.04	.02
316	Mike Sharperson	.05	.04	.02
317	John Orton	.05	.04	.02
318	Bob Tewksbury	.08	.06	.03
319	Xavier Hernandez	.05	.04	.02
320	Paul Assenmacher	.05	.04	.02
321	John Franco	.08	.06	.03
322	Mike Timlin	.06	.05	.02
323	Jose Guzman	.06	.05	.02
324	Pedro Martinez	.10	.07	.04
325	Bill Spiers	.06	.05	.02
326	Melido Perez	.06	.05	.02
327	Mike Macfarlane	.06	.05	.02
328	Ricky Bones	.06	.05	.02
329	Scott Bankhead	.06	.05	.02
330	Rich Rodriguez	.05	.04	.02
331	Geronimo Pena	.06	.05	.02
332	Bernie Williams	.10	.08	.04
333	Paul Molitor	.20	.15	.08
334	Roger Mason	.05	.04	.02
335	David Cone	.05	.04	.02
336	Randy Johnson	.06	.05	.02
337	Pat Mahomes	.08	.06	.03
338	Erik Hanson	.08	.06	.03
339	Duane Ward	.06	.05	.02
340	Al Martin	.10	.07	.04
341	Pedro Munoz	.08	.06	.03
342	Greg Colbrunn	.06	.05	.02
343	Julio Valera	.06	.05	.02
344	John Olerud	.15	.11	.06
345	George Bell	.08	.06	.03
346	Devon White	.08	.06	.03
347	Donovan Osborne	.15	.11	.06
348	Mark Gardner	.06	.05	.02
349	Zane Smith	.06	.05	.02
350	Wilson Alvarez	.06	.05	.02
351	*Kevin Koslofski*	.15	.11	.06
352	Roberto Hernandez	.10	.08	.04
353	Glenn Davis	.08	.06	.03
354	Reggie Sanders	.15	.11	.06
355	Ken Griffey, Jr.	1.50	1.25	.60
356	Marquis Grissom	.10	.07	.04
357	Jack McDowell	.10	.07	.04
358	Jimmy Key	.06	.05	.02
359	Stan Belinda	.05	.04	.02
360	Gerald Williams	.10	.08	.04
361	Sid Fernandez	.08	.06	.03
362	Alex Fernandez	.10	.07	.04
363	John Smoltz	.10	.08	.04
364	Travis Fryman	.20	.15	.08
365	Jose Canseco	.20	.15	.08
366	Dave Justice	.25	.20	.10
367	*Pedro Astacio*	.15	.11	.06
368	Tim Belcher	.08	.06	.03
369	Steve Sax	.08	.06	.03
370	Gary Gaetti	.06	.05	.02
371	*Jeff Frye*	.12	.09	.05
372	Bob Wickman	.10	.07	.04
373	*Ryan Thompson*	.15	.11	.06
374	*David Hulse*	.15	.11	.06
375	Cal Eldred	.10	.07	.04
376	Ryan Klesko	1.00	.75	.40
377	*Damion Easley*	.12	.09	.05
378	*John Kiely*	.10	.07	.04
379	*Jim Bullinger* (FC)	.12	.09	.05
380	Brian Bohanon	.08	.06	.03
381	Rod Brewer	.08	.06	.03
382	*Fernando Ramsey*	.15	.11	.06
383	Sam Militello	.15	.11	.06
384	Arthur Rhodes	.15	.11	.06
385	Eric Karros	.10	.07	.04
386	Rico Brogna	.12	.09	.05
387	*John Valentin*	.12	.09	.05
388	*Kerry Woodson*	.12	.09	.05
389	*Ben Rivera*	.12	.09	.05
390	*Matt Whiteside*	.15	.11	.06
391	Henry Rodriguez	.25	.20	.10
392	John Wetteland	.08	.06	.03
393	Kent Mercker	.06	.05	.02
394	Bernard Gilkey	.08	.06	.03
395	Doug Henry	.08	.06	.03
396	Mo Vaughn	.12	.09	.05
397	Scott Erickson	.08	.06	.03
398	Bill Gullickson	.08	.06	.03
399	Mark Guthrie	.05	.04	.02
400	Dave Martinez	.05	.04	.02
401	*Jeff Kent*	.15	.11	.06
402	Chris Hoiles	.15	.11	.06
403	Mike Henneman	.08	.06	.03
404	Chris Nabholz	.08	.06	.03
405	Tom Pagnozzi	.08	.06	.03
406	Kelly Gruber	.08	.06	.03
407	Bob Welch	.08	.06	.03
408	Frank Castillo	.08	.06	.03
409	John Dopson	.05	.04	.02
410	Steve Farr	.06	.05	.02
411	Henry Cotto	.05	.04	.02
412	Bob Patterson	.05	.04	.02
413	Todd Stottlemyre	.06	.05	.02
414	Greg A. Harris	.05	.04	.02
415	Denny Neagle	.08	.06	.03
416	Bill Wegman	.06	.05	.02
417	Willie Wilson	.06	.05	.02
418	Terry Leach	.05	.04	.02
419	Willie Randolph	.06	.05	.02
420	Checklist 316-420 (Mark McGwire)	.05	.04	.02
421	Calvin Murray (Top Prospects Checklist)	.25	.20	.10
422	Pete Janicki (Top Prospect)	.10	.08	.04
423	Todd Jones (FC) (Top Prospect)	.06	.05	.02
424	Mike Neill (Top Prospect)	.10	.08	.04
425	Carlos Delgado (Top Prospect)	1.00	.75	.40
426	Jose Oliva (Top Prospect)	.20	.15	.08
427	Tyrone Hill (Top Prospect)	.15	.11	.06
428	Dmitri Young (Top Prospect)	.12	.09	.05
429	*Derek Wallace* (Top Prospect)	.20	.15	.08
430	*Michael Moore* (Top Prospect)	.50	.40	.20
431	Cliff Floyd (Top Prospect)	1.25	.90	.50
432	Calvin Murray (Top Prospect)	.15	.11	.06
433	Manny Ramirez (Top Prospect)	1.25	.90	.50
434	Marc Newfield (Top Prospect)	.25	.20	.10
435	Charles Johnson (Top Prospect)	.50	.40	.20
436	Butch Huskey (Top Prospect)	.35	.25	.14
437	Brad Pennington (Top Prospect)	.08	.06	.03
438	*Ray McDavid* (Top Prospect)	.30	.25	.12
439	Chad McConnell (Top Prospect)	.25	.20	.10
440	*Midre Cummings* (Top Prospect)	.40	.30	.15
441	Benji Gil (Top Prospect)	.20	.15	.08
442	Frank Rodriguez (Top Prospect)	.20	.15	.08
443	*Chad Mottola* (Top Prospect)	.75	.60	.30
444	*John Burke* (Top Prospect)	.25	.20	.10
445	Michael Tucker (Top Prospect)	.60	.45	.25
446	Rick Greene (Top Prospect)	.20	.15	.08
447	Rich Becker (Top Prospect)	.20	.15	.08
448	Mike Robertson (Top Prospect)	.08	.06	.03
449	*Derek Jeter* (Top Prospect)	.60	.45	.25
450	Checklist 451-470 Inside the Numbers (David McCarty/Ivan Rodriguez)	.10	.07	.04
451	Jim Abbott (Inside the Numbers)	.10	.08	.04
452	Jeff Bagwell (Inside the Numbers)	.20	.15	.08
453	Jason Bere (Inside the Numbers)	.25	.20	.10
454	Delino DeShields (Inside the Numbers)	.08	.06	.03
455	Travis Fryman (Inside the Numbers)	.15	.11	.06
456	Alex Gonzalez (Inside the Numbers)	.20	.15	.08
457	Phil Hiatt (Inside the Numbers)	.15	.11	.06
458	Dave Hollins (Inside the Numbers)	.10	.08	.04
459	Chipper Jones (Inside the Numbers)	.20	.15	.08
460	Dave Justice (Inside the Numbers)	.25	.20	.10
461	Ray Lankford (Inside the Numbers)	.08	.06	.03
462	David McCarty (Inside the Numbers)	.10	.07	.04
463	Mike Mussina (Inside the Numbers)	.15	.11	.06
464	Jose Offerman (Inside the Numbers)	.08	.06	.03
465	Dean Palmer (Inside the Numbers)	.12	.09	.05
466	Geronimo Pena (Inside the Numbers)	.06	.05	.02
467	Eduardo Perez (Inside the Numbers)	.15	.11	.06
468	Ivan Rodriguez (Inside the Numbers)	.12	.09	.05

470 Bernie Williams (Inside the Numbers) .08 .06 .03
471 Checklist 472-485 Team Stars (Barry Bonds/Matt Williams/Will Clark) .20 .15 .08
472 Strike Force (John Smoltz, Steve Avery, Greg Maddux, Tom Glavine) .15 .11 .06
473 Red October (Jose Rijo/Rob Dibble/Roberto Kelly/Reggie Sanders/Barry Larkin) .08 .06 .03
474 Four Corners (Gary Sheffield/Phil Plantier/Tony Gwynn/Fred McGriff) .20 .15 .08
475 Shooting Stars (Doug Drabek/Craig Biggio/Jeff Bagwell) .08 .06 .03
476 Giant Sticks (Will Clark, Barry Bonds, Matt Williams) .20 .15 .08
477 Boyhood Friends (Eric Davis/Darryl Strawberry) .06 .05 .02
478 Rock Solid (Dante Bichette/Dave Nied/Andres Galarraga) .12 .09 .05
479 Inaugural Catch (Dave Magadan/Orestes Destrade/Bret Barbarie/Jeff Conine) .12 .09 .05
480 Steel City Champions (Tim Wakefield/Andy Van Slyke/Jay Bell) .06 .05 .02
481 "Les Grandes Etoiles" (Marquis Grissom/Delino DeShields/Dennis Martinez/Larry Walker) .15 .11 .06
482 Runnin' Redbirds (Geronimo Pena/Ray Lankford/Ozzie Smith/Bernard Gilkey) .06 .05 .02
483 Ivy Leaguers (Ryne Sandberg, Mark Grace, Randy Myers) .15 .11 .06
484 Big Apple Power Switch (Eddie Murray/Howard Johnson/Bobby Bonilla) .08 .06 .03
485 Hammers & Nails (John Kruk/Dave Hollins/Darren Daulton/Lenny Dykstra) .12 .09 .05
486 Barry Bonds (Award Winners) .25 .20 .10
487 Dennis Eckersley (Award Winners) .06 .05 .02
488 Greg Maddux (Award Winners) .10 .08 .04
489 Dennis Eckersley (Award Winners) .06 .05 .02
490 Eric Karros (Award Winners) .08 .06 .03
491 Pat Listach (Award Winners) .08 .06 .03
492 Gary Sheffield (Award Winners) .10 .08 .04
493 Mark MCGwire (Award Winners) .08 .06 .03
494 Gary Sheffield (Award Winners) .10 .08 .04
495 Edgar Martinez (Award Winners) .06 .05 .02
496 Fred McGriff (Award Winners) .15 .11 .06
497 Juan Gonzalez (Award Winners) .40 .30 .15
498 Darren Daulton (Award Winners) .08 .06 .03
499 Cecil Fielder (Award Winners) .10 .08 .04
500 Checklist 501-510 Diamond Debuts (Brent Gates) .20 .15 .08
501 Tavo Alvarez (Diamond Debuts) .08 .06 .03
502 Rod Bolton (Diamond Debuts) .06 .05 .02
503 *John Cummings* (Diamond Debuts) .15 .11 .06
504 Brent Gates (Diamond Debuts) .30 .25 .12
505 Tyler Green (Diamond Debuts) .10 .08 .04
506 *Jose Martinez* (Diamond Debuts) .15 .11 .06
507 Troy Percival (Diamond Debuts) .08 .06 .03
508 Kevin Stocker (Diamond Debuts) .20 .15 .08
509 *Matt Walbeck* (Diamond Debuts) .15 .11 .06
510 Rondell White (Diamond Debuts) .35 .25 .14
511 Billy Ripken .06 .05 .02
512 Mike Moore .06 .05 .02
513 Jose Lind .06 .05 .02
514 Chito Martinez .06 .05 .02
515 Jose Guzman .06 .05 .02
516 Kim Batiste .06 .05 .02
517 Jeff Tackett .06 .05 .02
518 Charlie Hough .06 .05 .02
519 Marvin Freeman .06 .05 .02
520 Carlos Martinez .06 .05 .02
521 Eric Young .12 .09 .05
522 Pete Incaviglia .06 .05 .02
523 Scott Fletcher .06 .05 .02
524 Orestes Destrade .08 .06 .03
525 Checklist 421-525 (Ken Griffey, Jr.) .10 .07 .04
526 Ellis Burks .06 .05 .02
527 Juan Samuel .06 .05 .02
528 Dave Magadan .06 .05 .02
529 Jeff Parrett .06 .05 .02
530 Bill Krueger .06 .05 .02
531 Frank Bolick .06 .05 .02
532 Alan Trammell .09 .07 .04
533 Walt Weiss .06 .05 .02
534 David Cone .06 .05 .02
535 Greg Maddux .15 .11 .06
536 Kevin Young .20 .15 .08
537 Dave Hansen .08 .06 .03
538 Alex Cole .06 .05 .02
539 Greg Hibbard .06 .05 .02
540 Gene Larkin .06 .05 .02
541 Jeff Reardon .06 .05 .02
542 Felix Jose .06 .05 .02
543 Jimmy Key .06 .05 .02
544 Reggie Jefferson .06 .05 .02
545 Gregg Jefferies .08 .06 .03
546 Dave Stewart .08 .06 .03
547 Tim Wallach .06 .05 .02
548 Spike Owen .06 .05 .02
549 Tommy Greene .06 .05 .02
550 Fernando Valenzuela .06 .05 .02
551 Rich Amaral .06 .05 .02
552 Bret Barberie .06 .05 .02
553 Edgar Martinez .06 .05 .02
554 Jim Abbott .12 .09 .05
555 Frank Thomas 1.50 1.25 .60
556 Wade Boggs .10 .08 .04
557 Tom Henke .06 .05 .02
558 Milt Thompson .06 .05 .02
559 Lloyd McClendon .06 .05 .02
560 Vinny Castilla .06 .05 .02
561 Ricky Jordan .06 .05 .02
562 Andujar Cedeno .06 .05 .02
563 Greg Vaughn .08 .06 .03
564 Cecil Fielder .15 .11 .06
565 Kirby Puckett .25 .20 .10
566 Mark McGwire .12 .09 .05
567 Barry Bonds .50 .40 .20
568 Jody Reed .06 .05 .02
569 Todd Zeile .06 .05 .02
570 Mark Carreon .06 .05 .02
571 Joe Girardi .06 .05 .02
572 Luis Gonzalez .06 .05 .02
573 Mark Grace .10 .08 .04
574 Rafael Palmeiro .08 .06 .03
575 Darryl Strawberry .08 .06 .03
576 Will Clark .20 .15 .08
577 Fred McGriff .25 .20 .10
578 Kevin Reimer .06 .05 .02
579 Dave Righetti .06 .05 .02
580 Juan Bell .06 .05 .02
581 Jeff Brantley .06 .05 .02
582 Brian Hunter .06 .05 .02
583 Tim Naehring .06 .05 .02
584 Glenallen Hill .06 .05 .02
585 Cal Ripken, Jr. .35 .25 .14
586 Albert Belle .30 .25 .12
587 Robin Yount .25 .20 .10
588 Chris Bosio .06 .05 .02
589 Pete Smith .06 .05 .02
590 Chuck Carr .08 .06 .03
591 Jeff Blauser .06 .05 .02
592 Kevin McReynolds .06 .05 .02
593 Andres Galarraga .08 .06 .03
594 Kevin Maas .06 .05 .02
595 Eric Davis .08 .06 .03
596 Brian Jordan .10 .08 .04
597 Tim Raines .06 .05 .02
598 Rick Wilkins .06 .05 .02
599 Steve Cooke .10 .07 .04
600 Mike Gallego .06 .05 .02
601 Mike Munoz .06 .05 .02
602 Luis Rivera .06 .05 .02
603 Junior Ortiz .06 .05 .02
604 Brent Mayne .06 .05 .02
605 Luis Alicea .08 .06 .03
606 Damon Berryhill .06 .05 .02
607 Dave Henderson .06 .05 .02
608 Kirk McCaskill .06 .05 .02
609 Jeff Fassero .08 .06 .03
610 Mike Harkey .06 .05 .02
611 Francisco Cabrera .06 .05 .02
612 Rey Sanchez .06 .05 .02
613 Scott Servais .06 .05 .02
614 Darrin Fletcher .06 .05 .02
615 Felix Fermin .06 .05 .02
616 Kevin Seitzer .06 .05 .02
617 Bob Scanlan .06 .05 .02
618 Billy Hatcher .06 .05 .02
619 John Vander Wal .06 .05 .02
620 Joe Hesketh .06 .05 .02
621 Hector Villanueva .06 .05 .02
622 Randy Milligan .06 .05 .02
623 *Tony Tarasco* .60 .45 .25
624 Russ Swan .06 .05 .02
625 Willie Wilson .06 .05 .02
626 Frank Tanana .06 .05 .02
627 Pete O'Brien .06 .05 .02
628 Lenny Webster .06 .05 .02
629 Mark Clark .08 .06 .03
630 Checklist 526-630 (Roger Clemens) .06 .05 .02
631 Alex Arias .10 .08 .04
632 Chris Gwynn .06 .05 .02
633 Tom Bolton .06 .05 .02
634 Greg Briley .06 .05 .02
635 Kent Bottenfield .06 .05 .02
636 Kelly Downs .06 .05 .02
637 Manuel Lee .06 .05 .02
638 Al Leiter .06 .05 .02
639 Jeff Gardner .06 .05 .02
640 Mike Gardiner .06 .05 .02
641 Mark Gardner .06 .05 .02
642 Jeff Branson .06 .05 .02
643 Paul Wagner .06 .05 .02
644 Sean Berry .10 .08 .04
645 Phil Hiatt .12 .09 .05
646 Kevin Mitchell .06 .05 .02
647 Charlie Hayes .08 .06 .03
648 Jim Deshaies .06 .05 .02
649 Dan Pasqua .06 .05 .02
650 Mike Maddux .06 .05 .02
651 *Domingo Martinez* .12 .09 .05
652 *Greg McMichael* .20 .15 .08
653 *Eric Wedge* .15 .11 .06
654 Mark Whiten .08 .06 .03
655 Bobby Kelly .08 .06 .03
656 Julio Franco .07 .05 .03
657 Gene Harris .06 .05 .02
658 Pete Schourek .06 .05 .02
659 Mike Bielecki .06 .05 .02
660 Ricky Gutierrez .10 .08 .04
661 Chris Hammond .08 .06 .03
662 Tim Scott .08 .06 .03
663 Norm Charlton .06 .05 .02
664 Doug Drabek .07 .05 .03
665 Dwight Gooden .08 .06 .03
666 Jim Gott .06 .05 .02
667 Randy Myers .06 .05 .02
668 Darren Holmes .06 .05 .02
669 Tim Spehr .06 .05 .02
670 Bruce Ruffin .06 .05 .02
671 Bobby Thigpen .06 .05 .02
672 Tony Fernandez .06 .05 .02
673 Darrin Jackson .08 .06 .03
674 Gregg Olson .06 .05 .02
675 Rob Dibble .06 .05 .02
676 Howard Johnson .08 .06 .03
677 *Mike Lansing* .25 .20 .10
678 Charlie Leibrandt .06 .05 .02
679 Kevin Bass .06 .05 .02
680 Hubie Brooks .06 .05 .02
681 Scott Brosius .08 .06 .03
682 Randy Knorr .06 .05 .02
683 Dante Bichette .06 .05 .02
684 Bryan Harvey .08 .06 .03
685 Greg Gohr .06 .05 .02
686 Willie Banks .06 .05 .02
687 Robb Nen .06 .05 .02
688 Mike Scioscia .06 .05 .02
689 John Farrell .06 .05 .02
690 John Candelaria .06 .05 .02
691 Damon Buford .10 .08 .04
692 Todd Worrell .06 .05 .02
693 Pat Hentgen .25 .20 .10
694 John Smiley .06 .05 .02
695 Greg Swindell .06 .05 .02
696 Derek Bell .12 .09 .05
697 Terry Jorgensen .06 .05 .02
698 Jimmy Jones .06 .05 .02
699 David Wells .06 .05 .02
700 Dave Martinez .06 .05 .02
701 Steve Bedrosian .06 .05 .02
702 Jeff Russell .06 .05 .02
703 Joe Magrane .06 .05 .02
704 Matt Mieske .06 .05 .02
705 Paul Molitor .15 .11 .06
706 Dale Murphy .06 .05 .02
707 Steve Howe .06 .05 .02
708 Greg Gagne .06 .05 .02
709 Dave Eiland .06 .05 .02
710 David West .06 .05 .02
711 Luis Aquino .06 .05 .02
712 Joe Orsulak .06 .05 .02
713 Eric Plunk .06 .05 .02
714 Mike Felder .06 .05 .02
715 Joe Klink .06 .05 .02
716 Lonnie Smith .06 .05 .02
717 Monty Fariss .06 .05 .02
718 Craig Lefferts .06 .05 .02
719 John Habyan .06 .05 .02
720 Willie Blair .06 .05 .02
721 Darnell Coles .06 .05 .02
722 Mark Williamson .06 .05 .02
723 Bryn Smith .06 .05 .02
724 Greg W. Harris .06 .05 .02
725 *Graeme Lloyd* .10 .07 .04
726 Cris Carpenter .06 .05 .02
727 Chico Walker .06 .05 .02
728 Tracy Woodson .06 .05 .02
729 Jose Uribe .06 .05 .02
730 Stan Javier .06 .05 .02
731 Jay Howell .06 .05 .02
732 Freddie Benavides .06 .05 .02
733 Jeff Reboulet .06 .05 .02
734 Scott Sanderson .06 .05 .02
735 Checklist 631-735 (Ryne Sandberg) .06 .05 .02
736 Archi Cianfrocco .06 .05 .02
737 Daryl Boston .06 .05 .02
738 Craig Grebeck .06 .05 .02
739 Doug Dascenzo .06 .05 .02
740 Gerald Young .08 .06 .03
741 Candy Maldonado .06 .05 .02
742 Joey Cora .06 .05 .02
743 Don Slaught .06 .05 .02
744 Steve Decker .06 .05 .02
745 Blas Minor .06 .05 .02
746 Storm Davis .06 .05 .02
747 Carlos Quintana .06 .05 .02
748 Vince Coleman .06 .05 .02
749 Todd Burns .06 .05 .02
750 Steve Frey .06 .05 .02
751 Ivan Calderon .06 .05 .02
752 *Steve Reed* .15 .11 .06
753 Danny Jackson .06 .05 .02
754 Jeff Conine .08 .06 .03
755 Juan Gonzalez 1.00 .70 .40
756 Mike Kelly .15 .11 .06
757 John Doherty .10 .07 .04
758 Jack Armstrong .06 .05 .02
759 John Wehner .06 .05 .02
760 Scott Bankhead .06 .05 .02
761 Jim Tatum .10 .07 .04
762 *Scott Pose* .12 .09 .05
763 Andy Ashby .06 .05 .02
764 Ed Sprague .06 .05 .02
765 Harold Baines .06 .05 .02
766 Kirk Gibson .06 .05 .02
767 Troy Neel .25 .20 .10
768 Dick Schofield .06 .05 .02
769 Dickie Thon .06 .05 .02
770 Butch Henry .06 .05 .02
771 Junior Felix .06 .05 .02
772 *Ken Ryan* .10 .08 .04
773 Trevor Hoffman .06 .05 .02
774 Phil Plantier .10 .08 .04
775 Bo Jackson .15 .11 .06
776 Benito Santiago .06 .05 .02
777 Andre Dawson .06 .05 .02
778 Bryan Hickerson .06 .05 .02
779 Dennis Moeller .06 .05 .02
780 Ryan Bowen .08 .06 .03
781 Eric Fox .06 .05 .02
782 Joe Kmak .06 .05 .02
783 Mike Hampton .06 .05 .02
784 *Darrell Sherman* .10 .08 .04
785 J.T. Snow .15 .11 .06
786 Dave Winfield .15 .11 .06
787 Jim Austin .08 .06 .03
788 Craig Shipley .06 .05 .02
789 Greg Myers .06 .05 .02
790 Todd Benzinger .06 .05 .02
791 Cory Snyder .06 .05 .02
792 David Segui .06 .05 .02
793 Armando Reynoso .06 .05 .02
794 Chili Davis .06 .05 .02
795 Dave Nilsson .06 .05 .02
796 Paul O'Neill .06 .05 .02
797 Jerald Clark .06 .05 .02

798	Jose Mesa	.06	.05	.02
799	Brian Holman	.06	.05	.02
800	Jim Eisenreich	.06	.05	.02
801	Mark McLemore	.06	.05	.02
802	Luis Sojo	.06	.05	.02
803	Harold Reynolds	.06	.05	.02
804	Dan Plesac	.06	.05	.02
805	Dave Stieb	.06	.05	.02
806	Tom Brunansky	.06	.05	.02
807	Kelly Gruber	.06	.05	.02
808	Bob Ojeda	.06	.05	.02
809	Dave Burba	.06	.05	.02
810	Joe Boever	.06	.05	.02
811	Jeremy Hernandez	.08	.06	.03
812	Angels Checklist (Tim Salmon)	.40	.30	.15
813	Astros Checklist (Jeff Bagwell)	.15	.11	.06
814	Athletics Checklist (Mark McGwire)	.08	.06	.03
815	Blue Jays Checklist (Roberto Alomar)	.15	.11	.06
816	Braves Checklist (Steve Avery)	.10	.07	.04
817	Brewers Checklist (Pat Listach)	.08	.06	.03
818	Cardinals Checklist (Gregg Jefferies)	.06	.05	.02
819	Cubs Checklist (Sammy Sosa)	.06	.05	.02
820	Dodgers Checklist (Darryl Strawberry)	.08	.06	.03
821	Expos Checklist (Dennis Martinez)	.06	.05	.02
822	Giants Checklist (Robby Thompson)	.08	.06	.03
823	Indians Checklist (Albert Belle)	.15	.11	.06
824	Mariners Checklist (Randy Johnson)	.08	.06	.03
825	Marlins Checklist (Nigel Wilson)	.10	.07	.04
826	Mets Checklist (Bobby Bonilla)	.06	.05	.02
827	Orioles Checklist (Glenn Davis)	.08	.06	.03
828	Padres Checklist (Gary Sheffield)	.10	.08	.04
829	Phillies Checklist (Darren Daulton)	.08	.06	.03
830	Pirates Checklist (Jay Bell)	.06	.05	.02
831	Rangers Checklist (Juan Gonzalez)	.40	.30	.15
832	Red Sox Checklist (Andre Dawson)	.06	.05	.02
833	Reds Checklist (Hal Morris)	.08	.06	.03
834	Rockies Checklist (David Nied)	.12	.09	.05
835	Royals Checklist (Felix Jose)	.06	.05	.02
836	Tigers Checklist (Travis Fryman)	.12	.09	.05
837	Twins Checklist (Shane Mack)	.06	.05	.02
838	White Sox Checklist (Robin Ventura)	.10	.08	.04
839	Yankees Checklist (Danny Tartabull)	.06	.05	.02
840	Checklist 736-840 (Roberto Alomar)	.06	.05	.02
----	3,000 Hits (Robin Yount/George Brett) (SP5)	4.00	3.00	1.50

1993 Upper Deck Clutch Performers

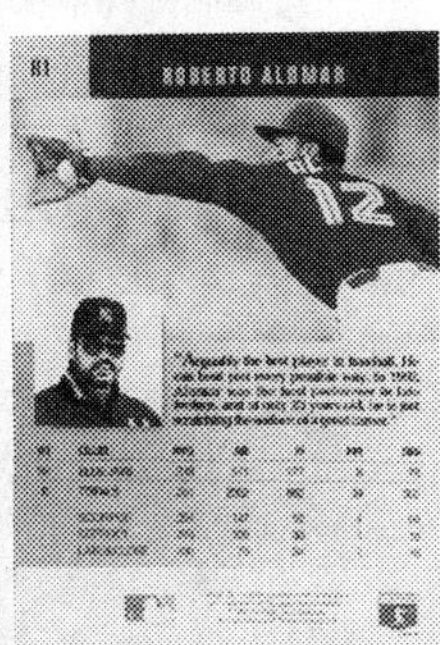

Reggie Jackson has selected the players who perform the best under pressure for this 20-card insert set. Cards were available only in Series II retail packs and use the prefix R for numbering. Fronts have a black bottom panel with "Clutch Performers" printed in dark gray. Jackson's facsimile autograph is overprinted in gold foil. On back, under a second player photo, is Jackson's picture and his assessment of the player. There are a few lines of stats to support the player's selection to this exclusive company.

		MT	NR MT	EX
Complete Set (20):		30.00	22.00	12.00
Common Player:		.75	.60	.30
1	Roberto Alomar	2.00	1.50	.80
2	Wade Boggs	1.00	.75	.40
3	Barry Bonds	3.50	2.75	1.50
4	Jose Canseco	1.25	.90	.50
5	Joe Carter	1.50	1.25	.60
6	Will Clark	1.50	1.25	.60
7	Roger Clemens	1.50	1.25	.60
8	Dennis Eckersley	.75	.60	.30
9	Cecil Fielder	1.50	1.25	.60
10	Juan Gonzalez	6.00	4.50	2.50
11	Ken Griffey, Jr.	8.00	6.00	3.25
12	Rickey Henderson	1.25	.90	.50
13	Barry Larkin	.75	.60	.30
14	Don Mattingly	1.50	1.25	.60
15	Fred McGriff	2.00	1.50	.80
16	Terry Pendleton	.75	.60	.30
17	Kirby Puckett	1.75	1.25	.70
18	Ryne Sandberg	2.00	1.50	.80
19	John Smoltz	.75	.60	.30
20	Frank Thomas	8.00	6.00	3.25

1993 Upper Deck 5th Anniversary

This 15-card insert set features 15 of Upper Deck's most popular cards from its first five years. Foil stamping and a fifth anniversary logo appear on the cards, which are reproductions of the originals. The prefix A appears before each card number. The cards were available in Series II hobby packs only.

		MT	NR MT	EX
Complete Set (15):		20.00	15.00	8.00
Common Player:		.75	.60	.30
1	Ken Griffey, Jr.	6.00	4.50	2.50
2	Gary Sheffield	1.00	.75	.40
3	Roberto Alomar	1.50	1.25	.60
4	Jim Abbott	.75	.60	.30
5	Nolan Ryan	4.00	3.00	1.50
6	Juan Gonzalez	5.00	3.75	2.00
7	Dave Justice	2.00	1.50	.80
8	Carlos Baerga	1.50	1.25	.60
9	Reggie Jackson	1.00	.75	.40
10	Eric Karros	.75	.60	.30
11	Chipper Jones	1.25	.90	.50
12	Ivan Rodriguez	.75	.60	.30
13	Pat Listach	.75	.60	.30
14	Frank Thomas	7.00	5.25	2.75
15	Tim Salmon	2.00	1.50	.80

1993 Upper Deck Future Heroes

This insert set includes eight player cards, a checklist and an unnumbered header card. The cards are numbered 55-63 as a continuation of previous Heroes sets, but this one features more than one player; previous sets featured only one player. Card fronts have a Future Heroes logo and a facsimile autograph. The player's name is revealed using a peeled-back paper effect. Cards were randomly inserted in Series II foil packs.

		MT	NR MT	EX
Complete Set (10):		15.00	11.00	6.00
Common Player:		1.00	.70	.40
Header Card:		2.50	2.00	1.00
55	Roberto Alomar	1.50	1.25	.60
56	Barry Bonds	3.00	2.25	1.25
57	Roger Clemens	1.50	1.25	.60
58	Juan Gonzalez	4.00	3.00	1.50
59	Ken Griffey, Jr.	6.00	4.50	2.50
60	Mark McGwire	1.00	.70	.40
61	Kirby Puckett	1.50	1.25	.60
62	Frank Thomas	6.00	4.50	2.50
63	Checklist	1.00	.70	.40

1993 Upper Deck Home Run Heroes

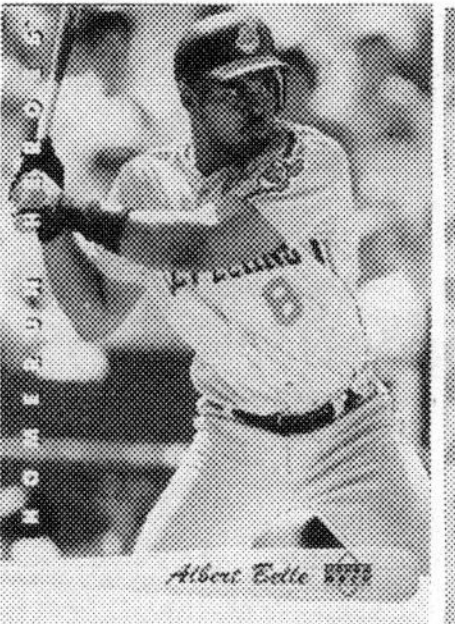

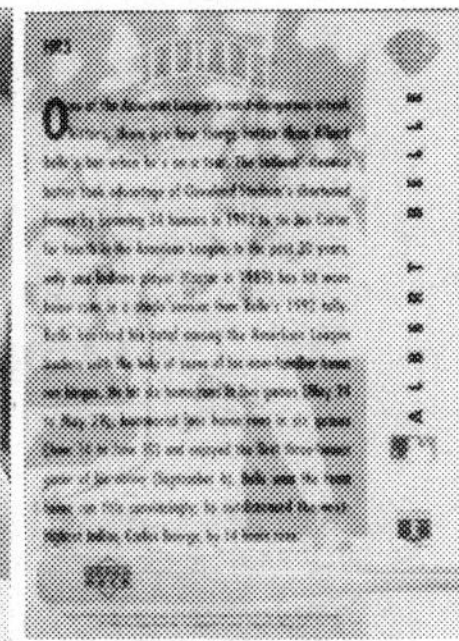

This 28-card insert set features the top home run hitters from each team for 1992. Cards, inserted in Series I jumbo packs, are numbered with an HR prefix. The card fronts say Home Run Heroes along the side; a bat with the player's name and an Upper Deck trademark appears along the bottom.

		MT	NR MT	EX
Complete Set (28):		20.00	15.00	8.00
Common Player:		.50	.40	.20
1	Juan Gonzalez	3.50	2.75	1.50
2	Mark McGwire	.75	.60	.30
3	Cecil Fielder	1.00	.75	.40
4	Fred McGriff	1.50	1.25	.60
5	Albert Belle	1.50	1.25	.60
6	Barry Bonds	3.00	2.25	1.25
7	Joe Carter	1.25	.90	.50
8	Darren Daulton	.60	.45	.25
9	Ken Griffey, Jr.	6.00	4.50	2.50
10	Dave Hollins	.60	.45	.25
11	Ryne Sandberg	2.00	1.50	.80
12	George Bell	.50	.40	.20
13	Danny Tartabull	.50	.40	.20
14	Mike Devereaux	.50	.40	.20
15	Greg Vaughn	.50	.40	.20
16	Larry Walker	.75	.60	.30
17	Dave Justice	2.00	1.50	.80
18	Terry Pendleton	.50	.40	.20
19	Eric Karros	.75	.60	.30
20	Ray Lankford	.50	.40	.20
21	Matt Williams	.75	.60	.30
22	Eric Anthony	.50	.40	.20
23	Bobby Bonilla	.50	.40	.20
24	Kirby Puckett	2.00	1.50	.80
25	Mike Macfarlane	.50	.40	.20
26	Tom Brunansky	.50	.40	.20

1993 Upper Deck Iooss Collection

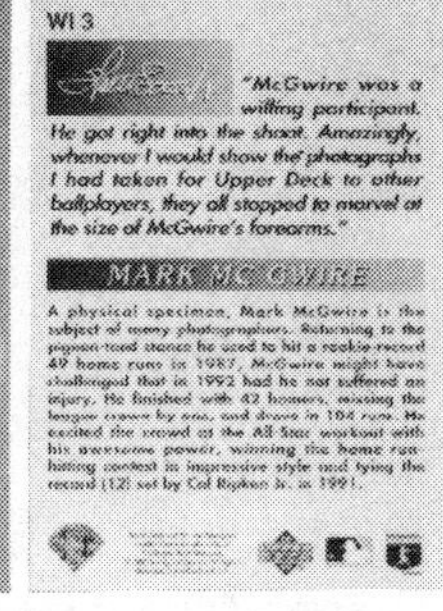

Sports photographer Walter Iooss Jr. has captured 26 current players in this insert set featuring their candid portraits. Cards have full-bleed photos and gold foil stamping. Backs have biographical sketches and are numbered using a WI prefix. They are available in Series I retail packs.

		MT	NR MT	EX
Complete Set (27):		22.00	16.50	8.75
Common Player:		.50	.40	.20
Header Card:		1.00	.75	.40
1	Tim Salmon	2.00	1.50	.80
2	Jeff Bagwell	1.50	1.25	.60
3	Mark McGwire	.75	.60	.30
4	Roberto Alomar	1.75	1.25	.70
5	Steve Avery	1.00	.75	.40
6	Paul Molitor	1.00	.75	.40
7	Ozzie Smith	1.00	.75	.40
8	Mark Grace	.50	.40	.20
9	Eric Karros	.75	.60	.30
10	Delino DeShields	.60	.45	.25
11	Will Clark	1.25	.90	.50
12	Albert Belle	2.00	1.50	.80
13	Ken Griffey, Jr.	6.00	4.50	2.50

14	Howard Johnson	.50	.40	.20
15	Cal Ripken, Jr.	2.00	1.50	.80
16	Fred McGriff	1.50	1.25	.60
17	Darren Daulton	.75	.60	.30
18	Andy Van Slyke	.60	.45	.25
19	Nolan Ryan	6.00	4.50	2.50
20	Wade Boggs	1.00	.75	.40
21	Barry Larkin	.60	.45	.25
22	George Brett	2.00	1.50	.80
23	Cecil Fielder	.75	.60	.30
24	Kirby Puckett	2.00	1.50	.80
25	Frank Thomas	6.00	4.50	2.50
26	Don Mattingly	1.50	1.25	.60

1993 Upper Deck Willie Mays Heroes

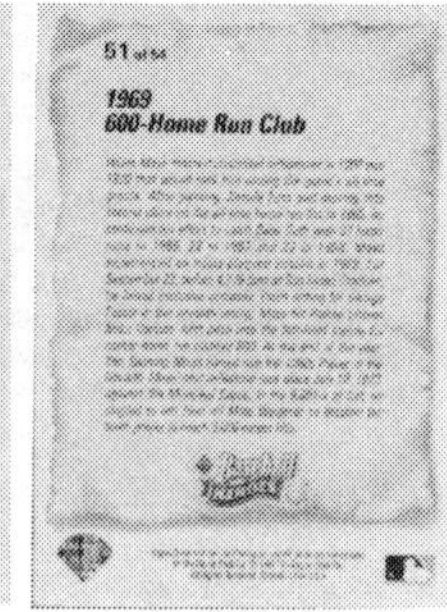

This 10-card insert set includes eight individually-titled cards, an illustrated checklist and one header card. The set is a continuation of Upper Deck's previous Heroes efforts, honoring greats such as Hank Aaron, Nolan Ryan and Reggie Jackson, and is numbered 46-54. Cards were randomly inserted into Series I foil packs.

		MT	NR MT	EX
Complete Set (10):		5.00	3.75	2.00
Common Mays:		.50	.40	.20
	Header card	3.00	2.25	1.25
46	1951 Rookie-of-the-Year	.50	.40	.20
47	1954 The Catch	.50	.40	.20
48	1956-57 30-30 Club	.50	.40	.20
49	1961 Four-Homer Game	.50	.40	.20
50	1965 Most Valuable Player	.50	.40	.20
51	1969 600-Home Run Club	.50	.40	.20
52	1972 New York Homecoming	.50	.40	.20
53	1979 Hall of Fame	.50	.40	.20
54	Checklist - Heroes 46-54	.50	.40	.20

1993 Upper Deck On Deck

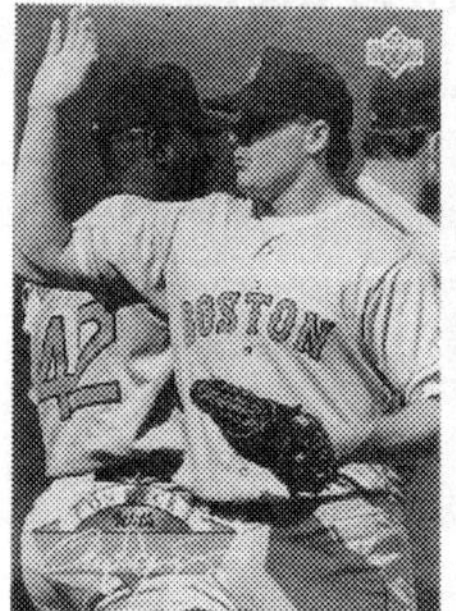
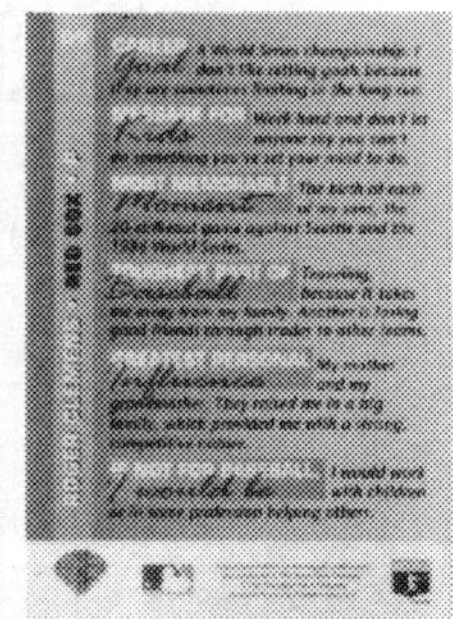

These UV-coated cards feature 25 of the game's top players. Each card has a full-bleed photo on the front and questions and answers on the back. Available only in Series II jumbo packs, the cards have a D prefix for numbering.

		MT	NR MT	EX
Complete Set (25):		24.00	18.00	9.50
Common Player:		.50	.40	.20
1	Jim Abbott	.75	.60	.30
2	Roberto Alomar	2.00	1.50	.80
3	Carlos Baerga	1.50	1.25	.60
4	Albert Belle	1.75	1.25	.70
5	Wade Boggs	.75	.60	.30
6	George Brett	1.75	1.25	.70
7	Jose Canseco	.75	.60	.30
8	Will Clark	1.00	.70	.40
9	Roger Clemens	1.50	1.25	.60
10	Dennis Eckersley	.50	.40	.20
11	Cecil Fielder	1.00	.70	.40
12	Juan Gonzalez	4.00	3.00	1.50
13	Ken Griffey, Jr.	4.50	3.50	1.75
14	Tony Gwynn	.75	.60	.30
15	Bo Jackson	.75	.60	.30
16	Chipper Jones	1.50	1.25	.60
17	Eric Karros	.75	.60	.30
18	Mark McGwire	.75	.60	.30
19	Kirby Puckett	1.50	1.25	.60
20	Nolan Ryan	4.50	3.50	1.75
21	Tim Salmon	3.50	2.75	1.50
22	Ryne Sandberg	2.00	1.50	.80
23	Darryl Strawberry	.50	.40	.20
24	Frank Thomas	6.00	4.50	2.50
25	Andy Van Slyke	.50	.40	.20

1993 Upper Deck Then And Now

This 18-card lithogram set features both Hall of Famers and current players. The cards feature a combination of four-color player photos and a holographic background. They were random inserts in both Series I and Series II packs. Numbering includes the prefix TN.

		MT	NR MT	EX
Complete Set (18):		70.00	52.00	28.00
Common Player:		1.50	1.25	.60
1	Wade Boggs	1.50	1.25	.60
2	George Brett	4.00	3.00	1.50
3	Rickey Henderson	2.00	1.50	.80
4	Cal Ripken, Jr.	5.00	3.75	2.00
5	Nolan Ryan	11.00	8.25	4.50
6	Ryne Sandberg	5.00	3.75	2.00
7	Ozzie Smith	2.00	1.50	.80
8	Darryl Strawberry	1.50	1.25	.60
9	Dave Winfield	3.00	2.25	1.25
10	Dennis Eckersley	1.50	1.25	.60
11	Tony Gwynn	2.00	1.50	.80
12	Howard Johnson	1.50	1.25	.60
13	Don Mattingly	3.00	2.25	1.25
14	Eddie Murray	2.00	1.50	.80
15	Robin Yount	3.00	2.25	1.25
16	Reggie Jackson	4.00	3.00	1.50
17	Mickey Mantle	18.00	13.50	7.25
18	Willie Mays	10.00	7.50	4.00

1993 Upper Deck "Highlights"

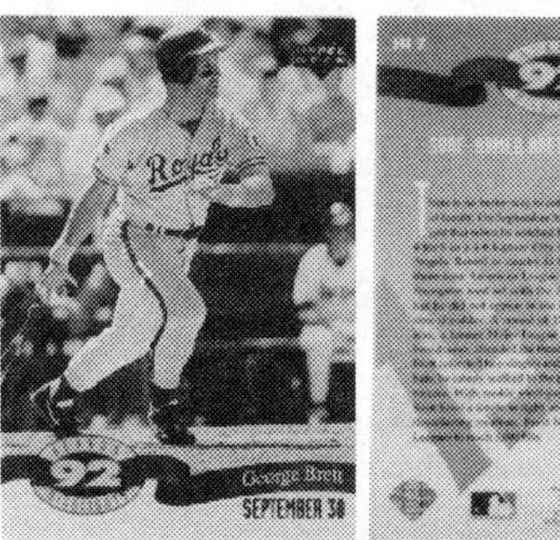

These 20 insert cards commemorate highlights from the 1992 season. Cards, which were randomly inserted in 1993 Upper Deck Series II packs, have a '92 Season Highlights logo on the bottom, with the player's name inside a banner trailing from the logo. The date of the significant event is under the player's name. Card backs have the logo at the top and are numbered with an HI prefix. A headline desscribes what highlight occurred, while the text describes the event. 1992 is faded across the background.

		MT	NR MT	EX
Complete Set (20):		70.00	52.00	28.00
Common Player:		1.00	.70	.40
1	Roberto Alomar	6.00	4.50	2.50
2	Steve Avery	3.00	2.25	1.25
3	Harold Baines	1.00	.70	.40
4	Damon Berryhill	1.00	.70	.40
5	Barry Bonds	9.00	6.75	3.50
6	Bret Boone	1.00	.75	.40
7	George Brett	8.00	6.00	3.25
8	Francisco Cabrera	1.00	.70	.40
9	Ken Griffey, Jr.	20.00	15.00	8.00
10	Rickey Henderson	3.00	2.25	1.25
11	Kenny Lofton	4.00	3.00	1.50
12	Mickey Morandini	1.00	.70	.40
13	Eddie Murray	1.50	1.25	.60
14	David Nied	3.00	2.25	1.25
15	Jeff Reardon	1.00	.70	.40
16	Bip Roberts	1.00	.70	.40
17	Nolan Ryan	18.00	13.50	7.25
18	Ed Sprague	1.00	.70	.40
19	Dave Winfield	3.00	2.25	1.25
20	Robin Yount	3.50	2.75	1.50

1993 Upper Deck Heroes of Baseball Previews

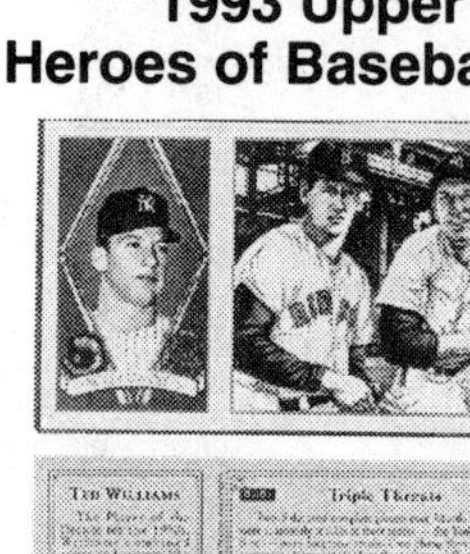

This four-card preview set was produced in conjunction with the All-Star Fan Fest in Baltimore to re-introduce the concept of T202-style "triplefolder" baseball cards. The preview set came in a specially decorated box. The 5-1/4" x 2-1/4" cards feature Ted Williams, Mickey Mantle and Reggie Jackson in various combinations of photos and artwork on each card. Backs are printed in red and gold and include an infield-shaped hologram. Written summaries of the players and their careers are featured. Cards have an "HOB" prefix to their number.

		MT	NR MT	EX
Complete Set (4):		6.00	4.50	2.50
Common Card:		2.00	1.50	.80
1	Triple Threat (Mickey Mantle, Ted Williams)	3.00	2.25	1.25
2	Changing of the Guard (Mickey Mantle, Reggie Jackson)	2.00	1.50	.80
3	Night and Day (Reggie Jackson, Ted Williams)	2.00	1.50	.80
4	Hall-of-Fame Trio (Reggie Jackson, Mickey Mantle, Ted Williams)	3.00	2.25	1.25

1993 Upper Deck All-Time Heroes

This 1993 Upper Deck set pays homage to one of the classiest, turn-of-the-century card sets, the T202 Hassan Triple Folders. The All-Time Heroes cards are 2-1/4" by 5-1/4" and feature two side panels and a larger middle panel, which features an action shot of the player. A portrait of the player and the Baseball Assistance Team (BAT) logo flank the action photo. Card backs have a biography and career summary. A Classic Combinations subset of 35 cards features artwork or photographs of two or more great players together, plus individual photos on the side panels. Production was limited to 5,140 numbered cases; cards were packaged in 12-card foil packs. Ten T202 reprints were also produced and were randomly inserted in the foil packs.

		MT	NR MT	EX
Complete Set:		45.00	34.00	18.00
Common Player:		.10	.08	.04
1	Hank Aaron	2.00	1.50	.80
2	Tommie Agee	.10	.08	.04
3	Bob Allison	.10	.08	.04
4	Matty Alou	.10	.08	.04
5	Sal Bando	.10	.08	.04
6	Hank Bauer	.10	.08	.04
7	Don Baylor	.10	.08	.04
8	Glenn Beckert	.10	.08	.04
9	Yogi Berra	.50	.40	.20
10	Buddy Biancalana	.10	.08	.04
11	Jack Billingham	.10	.08	.04
12	Joe Black	.15	.11	.06
13	Paul Blair	.10	.08	.04
14	Steve Blass	.10	.08	.04
15	Ray Boone	.10	.08	.04
16	Lou Boudreau	.25	.20	.10
17	Ken Brett	.10	.08	.04
18	Nellie Briles	.10	.08	.04
19	Bobby Brown	.15	.11	.06
20	Bill Buckner	.10	.08	.04
21	Don Buford	.10	.08	.04
22	Al Bumbry	.10	.08	.04
23	Lew Burdette	.10	.08	.04
24	Jeff Burroughs	.10	.08	.04
25	Johnny Callison	.10	.08	.04
26	Bert Campaneris	.10	.08	.04
27	Rico Carty	.10	.08	.04
28	Dave Cash	.10	.08	.04
29	Cesar Cedeno	.10	.08	.04
30	Frank Chance	.25	.20	.10
31	Joe Charboneau	.10	.08	.04
32	Ty Cobb	2.00	1.50	.80
33	Jerry Coleman	.10	.08	.04
34	Cecil Cooper	.10	.08	.04
35	Frankie Crossetti	.10	.08	.04
36	Alvin Dark	.10	.08	.04
37	Tommy Davis	.10	.08	.04
38	Dizzy Dean	.35	.25	.14
39	Doug DeCinces	.10	.08	.04
40	Bucky Dent	.10	.08	.04
41	Larry Dierker	.10	.08	.04
42	Larry Doby	.10	.08	.04
43	Moe Drabowsky	.10	.08	.04
44	Dave Dravecky	.10	.08	.04
45	Del Ennis	.10	.08	.04
46	Carl Erskine	.10	.08	.04
47	Johnny Evers	.25	.20	.10
48	Elroy Face	.10	.08	.04
49	Rick Ferrell	.25	.20	.10
50	Mark Fidrych	.10	.08	.04
51	Curt Flood	.10	.08	.04
52	Whitey Ford	.50	.40	.20
53	George Foster	.10	.08	.04
54	Jimmie Foxx	.25	.20	.10
55	Jim Fregosi	.10	.08	.04
56	Phil Garner	.10	.08	.04
57	Ralph Garr	.10	.08	.04
58	Lou Gehrig	2.00	1.50	.80
59	Bobby Grich	.10	.08	.04
60	Jerry Grote	.10	.08	.04
61	Harvey Haddix	.10	.08	.04
62	Toby Harrah	.10	.08	.04
63	Bud Harrelson	.10	.08	.04
64	Jim Hegan	.10	.08	.04
65	Gil Hodges	.25	.20	.10
66	Ken Holtzman	.10	.08	.04
67	Bob Horner	.10	.08	.04
68	Rogers Hornsby	.25	.20	.10
69	Carl Hubbell	.25	.20	.10
70	Ron Hunt	.10	.08	.04
71	Monte Irvin	.25	.20	.10
72	Reggie Jackson	.50	.40	.20
73	Larry Jansen	.10	.08	.04
74	Ferguson Jenkins	.25	.20	.10
75	Tommy John	.15	.11	.06
76	Cliff Johnson	.10	.08	.04
77	Davey Johnson	.10	.08	.04
78	Walter Johnson	.50	.40	.20
79	George Kell	.25	.20	.10
80	Don Kessinger	.10	.08	.04
81	Vern Law	.10	.08	.04
82	Dennis Leonard	.10	.08	.04
83	Johnny Logan	.10	.08	.04
84	Mickey Lolich	.10	.08	.04
85	Jim Lonborg	.10	.08	.04
86	Bill Madlock	.10	.08	.04
87	Mickey Mantle	3.00	2.25	1.25
88	Billy Martin	.25	.20	.10
89	Christy Mathewson	.50	.40	.20
90	Lee May	.10	.08	.04
91	Willie Mays	2.00	1.50	.80
92	Bill Mazeroski	.15	.11	.06
93	Gil McDougald	.10	.08	.04
94	Sam McDowell	.10	.08	.04
95	Minnie Minoso	.10	.08	.04
96	Johnny Mize	.25	.20	.10
97	Rick Monday	.10	.08	.04
98	Wally Moon	.10	.08	.04
99	Manny Mota	.10	.08	.04
100	Bobby Murcer	.10	.08	.04
101	Ron Necciai	.10	.08	.04
102	Al Oliver	.10	.08	.04
103	Mel Ott	.25	.20	.10
104	Mel Parnell	.10	.08	.04
105	Jimmy Piersall	.10	.08	.04
106	Johnny Podres	.10	.08	.04
107	Bobby Richardson	.15	.11	.06
108	Robin Roberts	.25	.20	.10
109	Al Rosen	.10	.08	.04
110	Babe Ruth	4.00	3.00	1.50
111	Joe Sambito	.10	.08	.04
112	Manny Sanguillen	.10	.08	.04
113	Ron Santo	.10	.08	.04
114	Bill Skowron	.15	.11	.06
115	Enos Slaughter	.25	.20	.10
116	Warren Spahn	.25	.20	.10
117	Tris Speaker	.25	.20	.10
118	Frank Thomas	.10	.08	.04
119	Bobby Thomson	.10	.08	.04
120	Andre Thornton	.10	.08	.04
121	Marv Throneberry	.10	.08	.04
122	Luis Tiant	.10	.08	.04
123	Joe Tinker	.25	.20	.10
124	Honus Wagner	.50	.40	.20
125	Bill White	.10	.08	.04
126	Ted Williams	1.00	.70	.40
127	Earl Wilson	.10	.08	.04
128	Joe Wood	.10	.08	.04
129	Cy Young	.50	.40	.20
130	Richie Zisk	.10	.08	.04
131	Babe Ruth, Lou Gehrig	.10	.08	.04
132	Ted Williams, Rogers Hornsby	.10	.08	.04
133	Lou Gehrig, Babe Ruth	.10	.08	.04
134	Babe Ruth, Mickey Mantle	.10	.08	.04
135	Mickey Mantle, Reggie Jackson	.10	.08	.04
136	Mel Ott, Carl Hubbell	.10	.08	.04
137	Mickey Mantle, Willie Mays	.10	.08	.04
138	Cy Young, Walter Johnson	.10	.08	.04
139	Honus Wagner, Rogers Hornsby	.10	.08	.04
140	Mickey Mantle, Whitey Ford	.10	.08	.04
141	Mickey Mantle, Billy Martin	.10	.08	.04
142	Cy Young, Walter Johnson	.10	.08	.04
143	Christy Mathewson, Walter Johnson	.10	.08	.04
144	Warren Spahn, Christy Mathewson	.10	.08	.04
145	Honus Wagner, Ty Cobb	.10	.08	.04
146	Babe Ruth, Ty Cobb	.10	.08	.04
147	Joe Tinker, Johnny Evers	.10	.08	.04
148	Johnny Evers, Frank Chance	.10	.08	.04
149	Hank Aaron, Babe Ruth	.10	.08	.04
150	Willie Mays, Hank Aaron	.10	.08	.04
151	Babe Ruth, Willie Mays	.10	.08	.04
152	Babe Ruth, Whitey Ford	.10	.08	.04
153	Larry Doby, Minnie Minoso	.10	.08	.04
154	Joe Black, Monte Irvin	.10	.08	.04
155	Joe Wood, Christy Mathewson	.10	.08	.04
156	Christy Mathewson, Cy Young	.10	.08	.04
157	Cy Young, Joe Wood	.10	.08	.04
158	Cy Young, Whitey Ford	.10	.08	.04
159	Cy Young, Ferguson Jenkins	.10	.08	.04
160	Ty Cobb, Rogers Hornsby	.10	.08	.04
161	Tris Speaker, Ted Williams	.10	.08	.04
162	Rogers Hornsby, Ted Williams	.10	.08	.04
163	Willie Mays, Monte Irvin	.10	.08	.04
164	Willie Mays, Bobby Thomson	.10	.08	.04
165	Reggie Jackson, Mickey Mantle	.10	.08	.04

1993 Upper Deck All-Time Heroes T202 Reprints

A series of 10 reprints of the classic 1912 Hassan "Triplefolders" baseball cards on which the All-Time Heroes set was patterned was included as random inserts in the Upper Deck old-timers set. The reprints measure 5-1/4" x 2-1/4" (same as the originals). The Hassan cigarette ads on the backs of the originals have been replaced on the reprints by an Upper Deck hologram and the logos of the card company, B.A.T., Major League Baseball and the Cooperstown Collection. The Hassan cards are known as T202, their designation in the "American Card Catalog." The reprints are unnumbered and are checklisted here alphabetically in order of the player appearing on the left end of each card.

		MT	NR MT	EX
Complete Set (10):		10.00	7.50	4.00
Common Player:		.50	.40	.20
(1)	Art Devlin/ Christy Mathewson	1.00	.70	.40
(2)	Hugh Jennings/ Ty Cobb	2.00	1.50	.80
(3)	John Kling/ Cy Young	1.00	.70	.40
(4)	Jack Knight/ Walter Johnson	.75	.60	.30
(5)	John McGraw/ Hugh Jennings	.50	.40	.20
(6)	George Moriarty/ Ty Cobb	2.00	1.50	.80
(7)	Charley O'Leary/ Ty Cobb	2.00	1.50	.80
(8)	Charley O'Leary/ Ty Cobb	2.00	1.50	.80
(9)	Joe Tinker/ Frank Chance	1.00	.70	.40
(10)	Joe Wood/ Tris Speaker	.50	.40	.20

1993 Upper Deck Iooss Collection Super

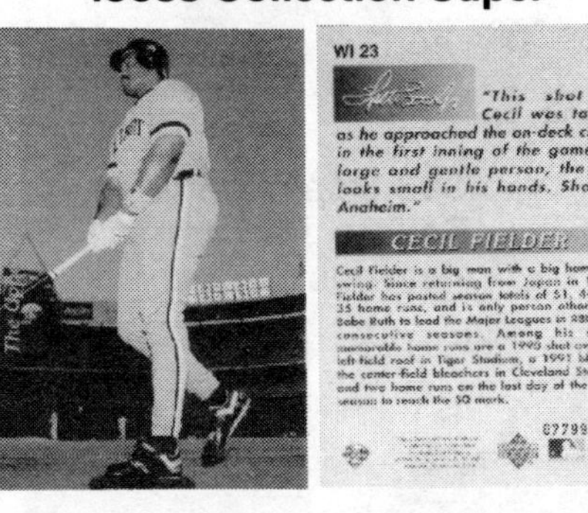

The Upper Deck Co. issued a series of 27 individually numbered oversized cards identical to the Iooss Collection insert cards in the regular Upper Deck set in 1993. The cards are 3-1/2" by 5" and each card is numbered to a limit of 10,000. The cards were available in retail outlets such as WalMart, packaged in blister packs with two foil packs of 1993 Upper Deck cards for a retail price of around $4.97.

		MT	NR MT	EX
Complete Set:		85.00	64.00	34.00
Common Player:		3.00	2.25	1.25
1	Tim Salmon	6.00	4.50	2.50
2	Jeff Bagwell	4.00	3.00	1.50
3	Mark McGwire	5.00	3.75	2.00
4	Roberto Alomar	5.00	3.75	2.00
5	Steve Avery	4.00	3.00	1.50
6	Paul Molitor	4.00	3.00	1.50
7	Ozzie Smith	4.00	3.00	1.50
8	Mark Grace	3.00	2.25	1.25
9	Eric Karros	4.00	3.00	1.50
10	Delino DeShields	3.00	2.25	1.25
11	Will Clark	4.00	3.00	1.50
12	Albert Belle	3.00	2.25	1.25
13	Ken Griffey, Jr.	7.50	5.75	3.00
14	Howard Johnson	3.00	2.25	1.25
15	Cal Ripken, Jr.	6.00	4.50	2.50
16	Fred McGriff	3.50	2.75	1.50
17	Darren Daulton	3.00	2.25	1.25
18	Andy Van Slyke	3.00	2.25	1.25
19	Nolan Ryan	7.50	5.75	3.00
20	Wade Boggs	4.00	3.00	1.50
21	Barry Larkin	3.50	2.75	1.50
22	George Brett	5.00	3.75	2.00
23	Cecil Fielder	4.00	3.00	1.50
24	Kirby Puckett	4.00	3.00	1.50
25	Frank Thomas	7.50	5.75	3.00
26	Don Mattingly	4.00	3.00	1.50
27	Iooss Header	3.00	2.25	1.25

1993 Upper Deck 5th Anniversary Super

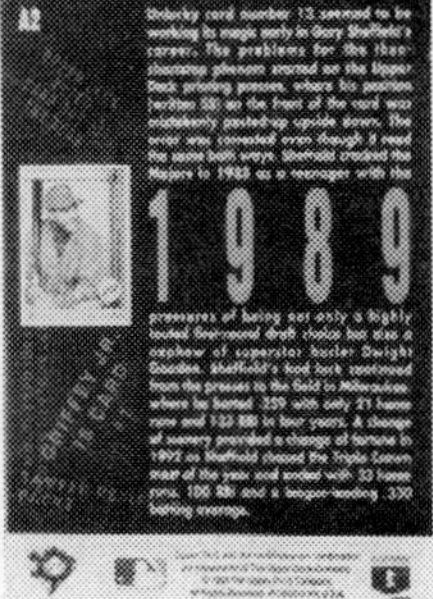

This set of oversized (3-1/2" by 5") cards is simply an enlarged version of the Upper Deck 5th Anniversary subset that was inserted with the company's 1993 cards. There are 15 cards in the set, which are reprinted versions of some of the most popular cards in the last five years from Upper Deck. Each of the cards carries a number on the back out of a limit of 10,000 total. The cards were sold individually in blister packs at retail outlets along with two packs of 1993 Upper Deck.

		MT	NR MT	EX
Complete Set:		52.50	39.00	21.00
Common Player:		3.00	2.25	1.25
1	Ken Griffey, Jr.	9.00	6.75	3.50
2	Gary Sheffield	3.00	2.25	1.25
3	Roberto Alomar	4.00	3.00	1.50
4	Jim Abbott	4.00	3.00	1.50
5	Nolan Ryan	7.50	5.75	3.00
6	Juan Gonzalez	5.00	3.75	2.00

7	David Justice	4.00	3.00	1.50
8	Carlos Baerga	3.50	2.75	1.50
9	Reggie Jackson	4.00	3.00	1.50
10	Eric Karros	3.50	2.75	1.50
11	Chipper Jones	3.00	2.25	1.25
12	Ivan Rodriguez	3.00	2.25	1.25
13	Pat Listach	3.00	2.25	1.25
14	Frank Thomas	7.50	5.75	3.00
15	Tim Salmon	6.00	4.50	2.50

1993 Upper Deck Reggie Jackson Heroes Super

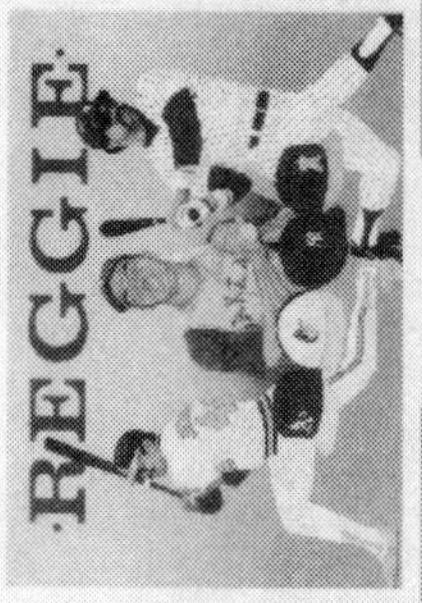

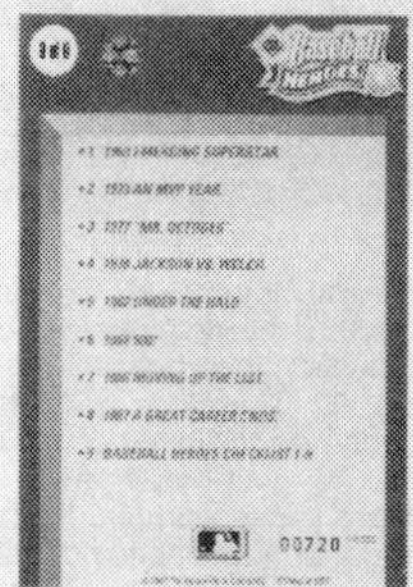

Upper Deck issued a large version of its 1990 Heroes Reggie Jackson cards that was available in retail outlets. Just as in the case of the regular issue Jackson insert cards, there are 10 cards (nine numbered and one unnumbered header card). The cards are 3-1/2" by 5" and identical to the smaller Heroes cards in every other respect. Each of the individual cards carries a sequential number out of a limit of 10,000. The cards were sold one to a package that also included two packs of 1993 Upper Deck cards for about $4.97.

		MT	NR MT	EX
Complete Set:		35.00	26.00	14.00
Common Card:		5.00	3.75	2.00
1	1969 Emerging Superstar (Reggie Jackson)	5.00	3.75	2.00
2	1973 An MVP Year (Reggie Jackson)	5.00	3.75	2.00
3	1977 "Mr. October" (Reggie Jackson)	5.00	3.75	2.00
4	1978 Jackson vs. Welch (Reggie Jackson)	5.00	3.75	2.00
5	1982 Under the Halo (Reggie Jackson)	5.00	3.75	2.00
6	1984 500! (Reggie Jackson)	5.00	3.75	2.00
7	1986 Moving Up the List (Reggie Jackson)	5.00	3.75	2.00
8	1987 A Great Career Ends (Reggie Jackson)	5.00	3.75	2.00
9	Heroes Checklist (Reggie Jackson)	5.00	3.75	2.00
----	Header card	5.00	3.75	2.00

1993 Upper Deck Triple Crown

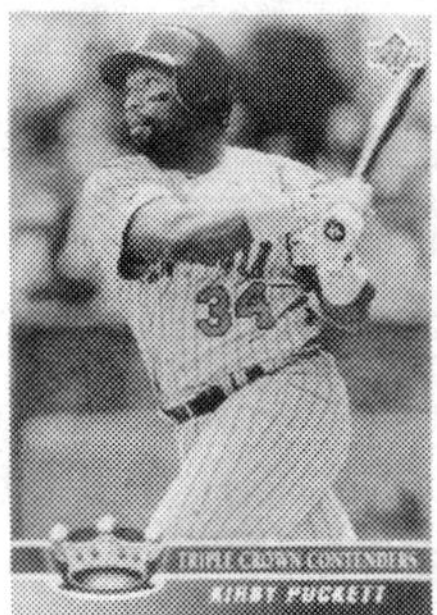

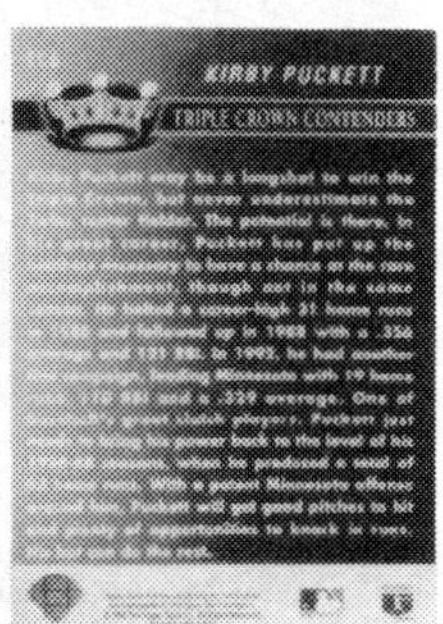

These insert cards were available in 1993 Upper Deck Series I foil packs sold by hobby dealers. The set features 10 players who are candidates to win baseball's Triple Crown. Card fronts have a crown and the player's name at the bottom. Backs put that material at the top and explain why the player might lead the league in home runs, batting average and runs batted in.

		MT	NR MT	EX
Complete Set (10):		30.00	22.00	12.00
Common Player:		1.50	1.25	.60
1	Barry Bonds	5.00	3.75	2.00
2	Jose Canseco	1.75	1.25	.70
3	Will Clark	2.00	1.50	.80
4	Ken Griffey, Jr.	10.00	7.50	4.00
5	Fred McGriff	2.50	2.00	1.00
6	Kirby Puckett	4.50	3.50	1.75
7	Cal Ripken, Jr.	4.50	3.50	1.75
8	Gary Sheffield	1.50	1.25	.60
9	Frank Thomas	10.00	7.50	4.00
10	Larry Walker	1.50	1.25	.60

1993 Upper Deck Diamond Gallery

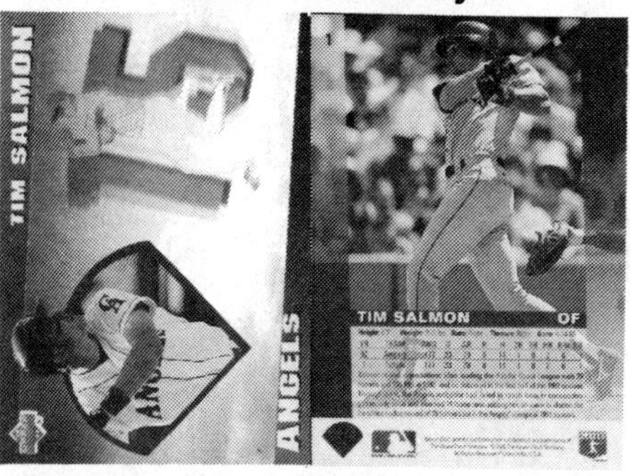

Utilizing something the company calls lithogram technology, Upper Deck produced a 36-card set in 1993 that combined four-colr photography and a holographic image. It featured one star from each of the 28 teams, along with a subset spot-lighting top rookies from 1993 and cards saluting Nolan Ryan, Rickey Henderson and Ozzie Smith. The set came in a specially- designed box, with a numbered checklist card. The set was limited to a total of 123,600.

		MT	NR MT	EX
Complete Set:		35.00	26.00	14.00
Common Player:		.50	.40	.20
1	Tim Salmon	3.00	2.25	1.25
2	Jeff Bagwell	.75	.60	.30
3	Mark McGwire	1.50	1.25	.60
4	Roberto Alomar	2.00	1.50	.80
5	Terry Pendleton	.50	.40	.20
6	Robin Yount	3.00	2.25	1.25
7	Ray Lankford	.75	.60	.30
8	Ryne Sandberg	4.00	3.00	1.50
9	Darryl Strawberry	1.00	.70	.40
10	Marquis Grissom	.50	.40	.20
11	Barry Bonds	3.00	2.25	1.25
12	Carlos Baerga	1.00	.70	.40
13	Ken Griffey, Jr.	5.00	3.75	2.00
14	Benito Santiago	.75	.60	.30
15	Dwight Gooden	.75	.60	.30
16	Cal Ripken, Jr.	4.00	3.00	1.50
17	Tony Gwynn	1.00	.70	.40
18	Dave Hollins	.50	.40	.20
19	Andy Van Slyke	.75	.60	.30
20	Juan Gonzalez	3.50	2.75	1.50
21	Roger Clemens	1.50	1.25	.60
22	Barry Larkin	1.00	.70	.40
23	Dave Nied	1.50	1.25	.60
24	George Brett	4.00	3.00	1.50
25	Travis Fryman	.75	.60	.30
26	Kirby Puckett	3.00	2.25	1.25
27	Frank Thomas	5.00	3.75	2.00
28	Don Mattingly	3.00	2.25	1.25
29	Rickey Henderson	3.00	2.25	1.25
30	Nolan Ryan	5.00	3.75	2.00
31	Ozzie Smith	3.00	2.25	1.25
32	Wilfredo Cordero	1.50	1.25	.60
33	Phil Hyatt	1.50	1.25	.60
34	Mike Piazza	3.50	2.75	1.50
35	J.T. Snow	1.50	1.25	.60
36	Kevin Young	1.50	1.25	.60

1993 Upper Deck SP

This is Upper Deck's first ever super premium baseball card set. There are 290 cards in the single-series set; 252 are individual player cards, while the remainder includes a Premier Prospects subset featuring top prospects (20 cards), 18 All-Stars and a Platinum Power insert set of 20 top home run hitters. Cards, which were available in 12-card foil packs, feature full-bleed color photos and UV coating on the front, plus a special logo using lenticular printing. Foil is also used intricately in the design. Backs have a larger color photo and statistics. Cards are numbered and color-coded by team.

		MT	NR MT	EX
Complete Set (290):		95.00	71.00	38.00
Common Player:		.15	.11	.06
1	Roberto Alomar	1.00	.75	.40
2	Wade Boggs	.30	.25	.12
3	Joe Carter	.75	.60	.30
4	Ken Griffey, Jr.	10.00	7.50	4.00
5	Mark Langston	.15	.11	.06
6	John Olerud	1.25	.90	.50
7	Kirby Puckett	1.50	1.25	.60
8	Cal Ripken, Jr.	1.50	1.25	.60
9	Ivan Rodriguez	.25	.20	.10
10	Barry Bonds	2.00	1.50	.80
11	Darren Daulton	.20	.15	.08
12	Marquis Grissom	.20	.15	.08
13	Dave Justice	1.00	.75	.40
14	John Kruk	.15	.11	.06
15	Barry Larkin	.15	.11	.06
16	Terry Mulholland	.15	.11	.06
17	Ryne Sandberg	1.25	.90	.50
18	Gary Sheffield	.35	.25	.14
19	Chad Curtis	.20	.15	.08
20	Chili Davis	.15	.11	.06
21	Gary DiSarcina	.15	.11	.06
22	Damion Easley	.15	.11	.06
23	Chuck Finley	.15	.11	.06
24	Luis Polonia	.15	.11	.06
25	Tim Salmon	4.50	3.50	1.75
26	*J.T. Snow*	1.00	.75	.40
27	Russ Springer	.15	.11	.06
28	Jeff Bagwell	1.00	.75	.40
29	Craig Biggio	.25	.20	.10
30	Ken Caminiti	.15	.11	.06
31	Andujar Cedeno	.15	.11	.06
32	Doug Drabek	.15	.11	.06
33	Steve Finley	.15	.11	.06
34	Luis Gonzalez	.15	.11	.06
35	Pete Harnisch	.15	.11	.06
36	Darryl Kile	.15	.11	.06
37	Mike Bordick	.15	.11	.06
38	Dennis Eckersley	.15	.11	.06
39	Brent Gates	.75	.60	.30
40	Rickey Henderson	.30	.25	.12
41	Mark McGwire	.30	.25	.12
42	Craig Paquette	.15	.11	.06
43	Ruben Sierra	.20	.15	.08
44	Terry Steinbach	.15	.11	.06
45	Todd Van Poppel	.25	.20	.10
46	Pat Borders	.15	.11	.06
47	Tony Fernandez	.15	.11	.06
48	Juan Guzman	.25	.20	.10
49	Pat Hentgen	.70	.50	.30
50	Paul Molitor	.60	.45	.25
51	Jack Morris	.15	.11	.06
52	Ed Sprague	.15	.11	.06
53	Duane Ward	.15	.11	.06
54	Devon White	.15	.11	.06
55	Steve Avery	.50	.40	.20
56	Jeff Blauser	.15	.11	.06
57	Ron Gant	.20	.15	.08
58	Tom Glavine	.40	.30	.15
59	Greg Maddux	.60	.45	.25
60	Fred McGriff	.50	.40	.20
61	Terry Pendleton	.15	.11	.06
62	Deion Sanders	.40	.30	.15
63	John Smoltz	.15	.11	.06
64	Cal Eldred	.20	.15	.08
65	Darryl Hamilton	.15	.11	.06
66	John Jaha	.20	.15	.08
67	Pat Listach	.15	.11	.06
68	Jaime Navarro	.15	.11	.06
69	Kevin Reimer	.15	.11	.06
70	B.J. Surhoff	.15	.11	.06
71	Greg Vaughn	.15	.11	.06
72	Robin Yount	.75	.60	.30
73	*Rene Arocha*	.40	.30	.15
74	Bernard Gilkey	.15	.11	.06
75	Gregg Jefferies	.20	.15	.08
76	Ray Lankford	.15	.11	.06
77	Tom Pagnozzi	.15	.11	.06
78	Lee Smith	.15	.11	.06
79	Ozzie Smith	.40	.30	.15
80	Bob Tewksbury	.15	.11	.06
81	Mark Whiten	.15	.11	.06
82	Steve Buechele	.15	.11	.06
83	Mark Grace	.15	.11	.06
84	Jose Guzman	.15	.11	.06
85	Derrick May	.15	.11	.06
86	Mike Morgan	.15	.11	.06
87	Randy Myers	.15	.11	.06
88	*Kevin Roberson*	.75	.60	.30
89	Sammy Sosa	.20	.15	.08
90	Rick Wilkins	.15	.11	.06
91	Brett Butler	.15	.11	.06
92	Eric Davis	.15	.11	.06
93	Orel Hershiser	.15	.11	.06
94	Eric Karros	.15	.11	.06
95	Ramon Martinez	.15	.11	.06
96	Raul Mondesi	7.50	5.50	3.00
97	Jose Offerman	.15	.11	.06
98	Mike Piazza	12.00	9.00	4.75
99	Darryl Strawberry	.15	.11	.06
100	Moises Alou	.25	.20	.10
101	Wil Cordero	.20	.15	.08
102	Delino DeShields	.15	.11	.06

103	Darrin Fletcher	.15	.11	.06
104	Ken Hill	.15	.11	.06
105	*Mike Lansing*	.60	.45	.25
106	Dennis Martinez	.15	.11	.06
107	Larry Walker	.20	.15	.08
108	John Wetteland	.15	.11	.06
109	Rod Beck	.15	.11	.06
110	John Burkett	.15	.11	.06
111	Will Clark	.75	.60	.30
112	Royce Clayton	.15	.11	.06
113	Darren Lewis	.15	.11	.06
114	Willie McGee	.15	.11	.06
115	Bill Swift	.15	.11	.06
116	Robby Thompson	.15	.11	.06
117	Matt Williams	.15	.11	.06
118	Sandy Alomar Jr.	.15	.11	.06
119	Carlos Baerga	1.00	.75	.40
120	Albert Belle	1.50	1.25	.60
121	Reggie Jefferson	.15	.11	.06
122	Kenny Lofton	.50	.40	.20
123	Wayne Kirby	.15	.11	.06
124	Carlos Martinez	.15	.11	.06
125	Charles Nagy	.15	.11	.06
126	Paul Sorrento	.15	.11	.06
127	Rich Amaral	.15	.11	.06
128	Jay Buhner	.15	.11	.06
129	Norm Charlton	.15	.11	.06
130	Dave Fleming	.15	.11	.06
131	Erik Hanson	.15	.11	.06
132	Randy Johnson	.15	.11	.06
133	Edgar Martinez	.15	.11	.06
134	Tino Martinez	.15	.11	.06
135	Omar Vizquel	.15	.11	.06
136	Bret Barberie	.15	.11	.06
137	Chuck Carr	.15	.11	.06
138	Jeff Conine	.15	.11	.06
139	Orestes Destrade	.15	.11	.06
140	Chris Hammond	.15	.11	.06
141	Bryan Harvey	.15	.11	.06
142	Benito Santiago	.15	.11	.06
143	Walt Weiss	.15	.11	.06
144	*Darrell Whitmore*	.80	.60	.30
145	*Tim Bolger*	.20	.15	.08
146	Bobby Bonilla	.15	.11	.06
147	Jeromy Burnitz	.20	.15	.08
148	Vince Coleman	.15	.11	.06
149	Dwight Gooden	.15	.11	.06
150	Todd Hundley	.15	.11	.06
151	Howard Johnson	.15	.11	.06
152	Eddie Murray	.15	.11	.06
153	Bret Saberhagen	.15	.11	.06
154	Brady Anderson	.15	.11	.06
155	Mike Devereaux	.15	.11	.06
156	Jeffrey Hammonds	2.50	2.00	1.00
157	Chris Hoiles	.15	.11	.06
158	Ben McDonald	.12	.09	.05
159	Mark McLemore	.15	.11	.06
160	Mike Mussina	.75	.60	.30
161	Gregg Olson	.15	.11	.06
162	David Segui	.15	.11	.06
163	Derek Bell	.15	.11	.06
164	Andy Benes	.15	.11	.06
165	Archi Cianfrocco	.15	.11	.06
166	Ricky Gutierrez	.15	.11	.06
167	Tony Gwynn	.50	.40	.20
168	Gene Harris	.15	.11	.06
169	Trevor Hoffman	.15	.11	.06
170	*Ray McDavid*	.90	.70	.35
171	Phil Plantier	.15	.11	.06
172	Mariano Duncan	.15	.11	.06
173	Len Dykstra	.40	.30	.15
174	Tommy Greene	.15	.11	.06
175	Dave Hollins	.20	.15	.08
176	Pete Incaviglia	.15	.11	.06
177	Mickey Morandini	.15	.11	.06
178	Curt Schilling	.15	.11	.06
179	Kevin Stocker	1.50	1.25	.60
180	Mitch Williams	.15	.11	.06
181	Stan Belinda	.15	.11	.06
182	Jay Bell	.15	.11	.06
183	Steve Cooke	.15	.11	.06
184	Carlos Garcia	.20	.15	.08
185	Jeff King	.15	.11	.06
186	Orlando Merced	.15	.11	.06
187	Don Slaught	.15	.11	.06
188	Andy Van Slyke	.12	.09	.05
189	Kevin Young	.25	.20	.10
190	Kevin Brown	.15	.11	.06
191	Jose Canseco	.60	.45	.25
192	Julio Franco	.15	.11	.06
193	Benji Gil	.60	.45	.25
194	Juan Gonzalez	4.00	3.00	1.50
195	Tom Henke	.15	.11	.06
196	Rafael Palmeiro	.25	.20	.10
197	Dean Palmer	.15	.11	.06
198	Nolan Ryan	7.50	5.50	3.00
199	Roger Clemens	1.00	.75	.40
200	Scott Cooper	.15	.11	.06
201	Andre Dawson	.15	.11	.06
202	Mike Greenwell	.15	.11	.06
203	Carlos Quintana	.15	.11	.06
204	Jeff Russell	.15	.11	.06
205	Aaron Sele	4.00	3.00	1.50
206	Mo Vaughn	.75	.60	.30
207	Frank Viola	.15	.11	.06
208	Rob Dibble	.15	.11	.06
209	Roberto Kelly	.15	.11	.06
210	Kevin Mitchell	.15	.11	.06
211	Hal Morris	.15	.11	.06
212	Joe Oliver	.15	.11	.06
213	Jose Rijo	.15	.11	.06
214	Bip Roberts	.15	.11	.06
215	Chris Sabo	.15	.11	.06
216	Reggie Sanders	.15	.11	.06
217	Dante Bichette	.15	.11	.06
218	Jerald Clark	.15	.11	.06
219	Alex Cole	.15	.11	.06
220	Andres Galarraga	.12	.09	.05
221	Joe Girardi	.15	.11	.06
222	Charlie Hayes	.15	.11	.06
223	*Robert Mejia*	1.00	.75	.40
224	Armando Reynoso	.15	.11	.06
225	Eric Young	.15	.11	.06
226	Kevin Appier	.15	.11	.06
227	George Brett	1.00	.75	.40
228	David Cone	.15	.11	.06
229	Phil Hiatt	.25	.20	.10
230	Felix Jose	.15	.11	.06
231	Wally Joyner	.15	.11	.06
232	Mike Macfarlane	.15	.11	.06
233	Brian McRae	.15	.11	.06
234	Jeff Montgomery	.15	.11	.06
235	Rob Deer	.15	.11	.06
236	Cecil Fielder	.40	.30	.15
237	Travis Fryman	1.00	.75	.40
238	Mike Henneman	.15	.11	.06
239	Tony Phillips	.15	.11	.06
240	Mickey Tettleton	.15	.11	.06
241	Alan Trammell	.15	.11	.06
242	David Wells	.15	.11	.06
243	Lou Whitaker	.15	.11	.06
244	Rick Aguilera	.15	.11	.06
245	Scott Erickson	.15	.11	.06
246	Brian Harper	.15	.11	.06
247	Kent Hrbek	.15	.11	.06
248	Chuck Knoblauch	.12	.09	.05
249	Shane Mack	.15	.11	.06
250	David McCarty	.50	.40	.20
251	Pedro Munoz	.15	.11	.06
252	Dave Winfield	.40	.30	.15
253	Alex Fernandez	.30	.25	.12
254	Ozzie Guillen	.15	.11	.06
255	Bo Jackson	.25	.20	.10
256	Lance Johnson	.15	.11	.06
257	Ron Karkovice	.15	.11	.06
258	Jack McDowell	.25	.20	.10
259	Tim Raines	.15	.11	.06
260	Frank Thomas	10.00	7.50	4.00
261	Robin Ventura	.40	.30	.15
262	Jim Abbott	.15	.11	.06
263	Steve Farr	.15	.11	.06
264	Jimmy Key	.15	.11	.06
265	Don Mattingly	1.00	.75	.40
266	Paul O'Neill	.15	.11	.06
267	Mike Stanley	.15	.11	.06
268	Danny Tartabull	.15	.11	.06
269	Bob Wickman	.20	.15	.08
270	Bernie Williams	.15	.11	.06
271	Jason Bere	4.00	3.00	1.50
272	*Roger Cedeno*	1.50	1.25	.60
273	*Johnny Damon*	1.00	.70	.40
274	*Russ Davis*	2.00	1.50	.80
275	Carlos Delgado	4.50	3.50	1.75
276	Carl Everett	.75	.60	.30
277	Cliff Floyd	6.00	4.50	2.50
278	Alex Gonzalez	2.50	2.00	1.00
279	*Derek Jeter*	2.00	1.50	.80
280	Chipper Jones	2.00	1.50	.80
281	Javier Lopez	6.00	4.50	2.50
282	*Chad Mottola*	3.00	2.25	1.25
283	Marc Newfield	1.25	.90	.50
284	Eduardo Perez	1.50	1.25	.60
285	Manny Ramirez	7.50	5.50	3.00
286	*Todd Steverson*	.75	.60	.30
287	Michael Tucker	1.75	1.25	.60
288	Allen Watson	1.25	.90	.50
289	Rondell White	3.00	2.25	1.25
290	Dmitri Young	1.00	.75	.40

1993 Upper Deck SP Platinum Power

This 20-card insert set features 20 of the game's top home run hitters. The top of each insert card features a special die cut treatment. Backs are numbered with a PP prefix.

		MT	NR MT	EX
Complete Set (20):		175.00	130.00	70.00
Common Player:		4.00	3.00	1.50
1	Albert Belle	12.00	9.00	4.75
2	Barry Bonds	14.00	10.50	5.50
3	Joe Carter	8.00	6.00	3.25
4	Will Clark	6.50	5.00	2.75
5	Darren Daulton	4.00	3.00	1.50
6	Cecil Fielder	7.00	5.25	2.75
7	Ron Gant	4.50	3.50	1.75
8	Juan Gonzalez	24.00	18.00	9.50
9	Ken Griffey, Jr.	40.00	30.00	15.00
10	Dave Hollins	4.00	3.00	1.50
11	Dave Justice	11.00	8.25	4.50
12	Fred McGriff	8.00	6.00	3.25
13	Mark McGwire	4.00	3.00	1.50
14	Dean Palmer	4.50	3.50	1.75
15	Mike Piazza	32.00	24.00	13.00
16	Tim Salmon	20.00	15.00	8.00
17	Ryne Sandberg	10.00	7.50	4.00
18	Gary Sheffield	5.00	3.75	2.00
19	Frank Thomas	40.00	30.00	15.00
20	Matt Williams	4.50	3.50	1.75

1993 Upper Deck Fun Packs

Aimed at the younger audience, this Upper Deck product features 150 "regular" player cards and 75 specialty cards in a varietty of subsets, plus two different types of insert cards. The basic player cards feature a photo (generally an action shot) set onto a background of purple, green and red, highlighted by yellow and orange stripes. On back is a white panel set against a red, yellow and orange blended stripes. In the panel are a cartoon, a trivia question and answer about the player, and some brief biographical details, stats and career summary. The basic player cards are arranged within the set in alphabetical order by team. The teams are also arranged alphabetically, according to their popular nickname. Leading off each team's roster in the set is a "Glow Stars" sticker. These feature a color player photo against a parti-colored background. The area around the photo is die-cut to allow the player's picture to be separated from the background and stuck to a wall, where the white and green outlines glow in the dark. Cards #1-9 are designated as "Stars of Tomorrow". Both front and back have a background of a star-studded purple sky. On front, the player's name appears in white in a stadium setting at bottom. The player is pictured in an action pose above the stadium, outlined as a constellation. On back is a portrait photo, a prediction of future greatness and a few stats and biographical details. Cards 10-21 are "Hot Shots" - heat-sensitive cards. When touched the black textured ink which surrounds the player photo turns clear, revealing a colored pattern beneath. Backs, which are not heat-sensitive, have a short career write-up. Cards 22-27 are "Kid Stars" and feature a childhood photo and a clue to the player's identity against a background of blue, pink and purple question marks. Pink and orange backs have a color photo of the player. Cards 28-37 are checklisted as "Upper Deck Heroes", though that designation does not appear on the cards. The subset is done in comic-book art style, and feature a blackboard motiff on front and back, on which player photos are superimposed and annotated with basketball playing tips. Cards 216-220 are designated "Foldouts" and are double-size (2-1/2"x7"). Fronts have a purple background photo of the player, with a full-color action photo superimposed. The player's name and position are in blue on a vertical yellow band at right. Backs have previous year and career stats and a player profile. Inside the Foldout is a full-color version of the front background photo, showing the playing leadping or diving to make a play. Yellow strips at left and right have the player's name. The five checklist cards which conclude the set have player photos on front.

		MT	NR MT	EX
Complete Set (225):		30.00	22.00	12.00
Common Player:		.10	.08	.04
1	Wil Cordero (Stars of Tomorrow)	.50	.40	.20
2	Brent Gates (Stars of Tomorrow)	.20	.15	.08
3	Benji Gil (Stars of Tomorrow)	.20	.15	.08
4	Phil Hiatt (Stars of Tomorrow)	.20	.15	.08
5	David McCarty (Stars of Tomorrow)	.25	.20	.10
6	Mike Piazza (Stars of Tomorrow)	2.00	1.50	.80
7	Tim Salmon (Stars of Tomorrow)	1.50	1.25	.60
8	J.T. Snow (Stars of Tomorrow)	.40	.30	.15
9	Kevin Young (Stars of Tomorrow)	.50	.40	.20
10	Roberto Alomar (Hot Shots)	.50	.40	.20
11	Barry Bonds (Hot Shots)	.60	.45	.25

12	Jose Canseco (Hot Shots)	.20	.15	.08
13	Will Clark (Hot Shots)	.50	.40	.20
14	Roger Clemens (Hot Shots)	.35	.25	.14
15	Juan Gonzalez (Hot Shots)	.50	.40	.20
16	Ken Griffey, Jr. (Hot Shots)	.80	.60	.30
17	Mark McGwire (Hot Shots)	.35	.25	.14
18	Nolan Ryan (Hot Shots)	.80	.60	.30
19	Ryne Sandberg (Hot Shots)	.60	.45	.25
20	Gary Sheffield (Hot Shots)	.25	.20	.10
21	Frank Thomas (Hot Shots)	.80	.60	.30
22	Roberto Alomar (Kid Stars)	.10	.08	.04
23	Roger Clemens (Kid Stars)	.10	.08	.04
24	Ken Griffey, Jr. (Kid Stars)	.25	.20	.10
25	Gary Sheffield (Kid Stars)	.10	.08	.04
26	Nolan Ryan (Kid Stars)	.25	.20	.10
27	Frank Thomas (Kid Stars)	.25	.20	.10
28	Reggie Jackson (Heroes)	.15	.11	.06
29	Roger Clemens (Heroes)	.10	.08	.04
30	Ken Griffey, Jr. (Heroes)	.25	.20	.10
31	Bo Jackson (Heroes)	.15	.11	.06
32	Cal Ripken, Jr. (Heroes)	.15	.11	.06
33	Nolan Ryan (Heroes)	.25	.20	.10
34	Deion Sanders (Heroes)	.15	.11	.06
35	Ozzie Smith (Heroes)	.10	.08	.04
36	Frank Thomas (Heroes)	.10	.08	.04
37	Tim Salmon (Glow Stars)	.25	.20	.10
38	Chili Davis	.10	.08	.04
39	Chuck Finley	.10	.08	.04
40	Mark Langston	.10	.08	.04
41	Luis Polonia	.10	.08	.04
42	Jeff Bagwell (Glow Stars)	.20	.15	.08
43	Jeff Bagwell	.15	.11	.06
44	Craig Biggio	.10	.08	.04
45	Ken Caminiti	.10	.08	.04
46	Doug Drabek	.10	.08	.04
47	Steve Finley	.12	.09	.05
48	Mark McGwire (Glow Stars)	.25	.20	.10
49	Dennis Eckersley	.12	.09	.05
50	Rickey Henderson	.20	.15	.08
51	Mark McGwire	.20	.15	.08
52	Ruben Sierra	.15	.11	.06
53	Terry Steinbach	.10	.08	.04
54	Roberto Alomar (Glow Stars)	.25	.20	.10
55	Roberto Alomar	.25	.20	.10
56	Joe Carter	.15	.11	.06
57	Juan Guzman	.10	.08	.04
58	Paul Molitor	.25	.20	.10
59	Jack Morris	.12	.09	.05
60	John Olerud	.20	.15	.08
61	Tom Glavine (Glow Stars)	.15	.11	.06
62	Steve Avery	.15	.11	.06
63	Tom Glavine	.12	.09	.05
64	Dave Justice	.20	.15	.08
65	Greg Maddux	.15	.11	.06
66	Terry Pendleton	.10	.08	.04
67	Deion Sanders	.20	.15	.08
68	John Smoltz	.12	.09	.05
69	Robin Yount (Glow Stars)	.25	.20	.10
70	Cal Eldred	.12	.09	.05
71	Pat Listach	.10	.08	.04
72	Greg Vaughn	.10	.08	.04
73	Robin Yount	.35	.25	.14
74	Ozzie Smith (Glow Stars)	.20	.15	.08
75	Gregg Jefferies	.20	.15	.08
76	Ray Lankford	.15	.11	.06
77	Lee Smith	.12	.09	.05
78	Ozzie Smith	.20	.15	.08
79	Bob Tewksbury	.10	.08	.04
80	Ryne Sandberg (Glow Stars)	.25	.20	.10
81	Mark Grace	.15	.11	.06
82	Mike Morgan	.10	.08	.04
83	Randy Myers	.10	.08	.04
84	Ryne Sandberg	.75	.60	.30
85	Sammy Sosa	.15	.11	.06
86	Eric Karros (Glow Stars)	.20	.15	.08
87	Brett Butler	.10	.08	.04
88	Orel Hershiser	.15	.11	.06
89	Eric Karros	.20	.15	.08
90	Ramon Martinez	.10	.08	.04
91	Jose Offerman	.10	.08	.04
92	Darryl Strawberry	.20	.15	.08
93	Marquis Grissom (Glow Stars)	.15	.11	.06
94	Delino DeShields	.20	.15	.08
95	Marquis Grissom	.15	.11	.06
96	Ken Hill	.10	.08	.04
97	Dennis Martinez	.12	.09	.05
98	Larry Walker	.15	.11	.06
99	Barry Bonds (Glow Stars)	.25	.20	.10
100	Barry Bonds	.35	.25	.14
101	Will Clark	.35	.25	.14
102	Bill Swift	.10	.08	.04
103	Robby Thompson	.10	.08	.04
104	Matt Williams	.15	.11	.06
105	Carlos Baerga (Glow Stars)	.20	.15	.08
106	Sandy Alomar, Jr.	.10	.08	.04
107	Carlos Baerga	.25	.20	.10
108	Albert Belle	.20	.15	.08
109	Kenny Lofton	.15	.11	.06
110	Charles Nagy	.10	.08	.04
111	Ken Griffey, Jr. (Glow Stars)	.50	.40	.20
112	Jay Buhner	.15	.11	.06
113	Dave Fleming	.10	.08	.04
114	Ken Griffey, Jr.	1.00	.70	.40
115	Randy Johnson	.15	.11	.06
116	Edgar Martinez	.15	.11	.06
117	Benito Santiago (Glow Stars)	.20	.15	.08
118	Bret Barberie	.10	.08	.04
119	Jeff Conine	.15	.11	.06
120	Brian Harvey	.12	.09	.05
121	Benito Santiago	.20	.15	.08
122	Walt Weiss	.10	.08	.04
123	Dwight Gooden (Glow Stars)	.20	.15	.08
124	Bobby Bonilla	.15	.11	.06
125	Tony Fernandez	.12	.09	.05
126	Dwight Gooden	.20	.15	.08
127	Howard Johnson	.15	.11	.06
128	Eddie Murray	.15	.11	.06
129	Bret Saberhagen	.12	.09	.05
130	Cal Ripken, Jr. (Glow Stars)	.25	.20	.10
131	Brady Anderson	.12	.09	.05
132	Mike Devereaux	.10	.08	.04
133	Ben McDonald	.10	.08	.04
134	Mike Mussina	.15	.11	.06
135	Cal Ripken, Jr.	.75	.60	.30
136	Fred McGriff (Glow Stars)	.20	.15	.08
137	Andy Benes	.12	.09	.05
138	Tony Gwynn	.20	.15	.08
139	Fred McGriff	.20	.15	.08
140	Phil Plantier	.10	.08	.04
141	Gary Sheffield	.20	.15	.08
142	Darren Daulton (Glow Stars)	.15	.11	.06
143	Darren Daulton	.12	.09	.05
144	Len Dykstra	.15	.11	.06
145	Dave Hollins	.12	.09	.05
146	John Kruk	.15	.11	.06
147	Mitch Williams	.10	.08	.04
148	Andy Van Slyke (Glow Stars)	.15	.11	.06
149	Jay Bell	.15	.11	.06
150	Zane Smith	.10	.08	.04
151	Andy Van Slyke	.15	.11	.06
152	Tim Wakefield	.10	.08	.04
153	Juan Gonzalez (Glow Stars)	.25	.20	.10
154	Kevin Brown	.10	.08	.04
155	Jose Canseco	.20	.15	.08
156	Juan Gonzalez	.35	.25	.14
157	Rafael Palmeiro	.20	.15	.08
158	Dean Palmer	.15	.11	.06
159	Ivan Rodriguez	.15	.11	.06
160	Nolan Ryan	1.00	.70	.40
161	Roger Clemens (Glow Stars)	.20	.15	.08
162	Roger Clemens	.20	.15	.08
163	Andre Dawson	.20	.15	.08
164	Mike Greenwell	.15	.11	.06
165	Tony Pena	.10	.08	.04
166	Frank Viola	.10	.08	.04
167	Barry Larkin (Glow Stars)	.15	.11	.06
168	Rob Dibble	.10	.08	.04
169	Roberto Kelly	.15	.11	.06
170	Barry Larkin	.15	.11	.06
171	Kevin Mitchell	.12	.09	.05
172	Bip Roberts	.10	.08	.04
173	Andres Galarrage (Glow Stars)	.20	.15	.08
174	Dante Bichette	.12	.09	.05
175	Jerald Clark	.10	.08	.04
176	Andres Galarraga	.20	.15	.08
177	Charlie Hayes	.12	.09	.05
178	David Nied	.12	.09	.05
179	David Cone (Glow Stars)	.15	.11	.06
180	Kevin Appler	.10	.08	.04
181	George Brett	.60	.45	.25
182	David Cone	.10	.08	.04
183	Felix Jose	.10	.08	.04
184	Wally Joyner	.15	.11	.06
185	Cecil Fielder (Glow Stars)	.20	.15	.08
186	Cecil Fielder	.20	.15	.08
187	Travis Fryman	.15	.11	.06
188	Tony Phillips	.10	.08	.04
189	Mickey Tetteton	.12	.09	.05
190	Lou Whitaker	.15	.11	.06
191	Kirby Puckett (Glow Stars)	.25	.20	.10
192	Scott Erickson	.12	.09	.05
193	Chuck Knoblauch	.12	.09	.05
194	Shane Mack	.12	.09	.05
195	Kirby Puckett	.25	.20	.10
196	Dave Winfield	.35	.25	.14
197	Frank Thomas (Glow Stars)	.50	.40	.20
198	George Bell	.10	.08	.04
199	Bo Jackson	.20	.15	.08
200	Jack McDowell	.15	.11	.06
201	Tim Raines	.15	.11	.06
202	Frank Thomas	1.00	.70	.40
203	Robin Ventura	.20	.15	.08
204	Jim Abbott (Glow Stars)	.25	.20	.10
205	Jim Abbott	.20	.15	.08
206	Wade Boggs	.25	.20	.10
207	Jimmy Key	.10	.08	.04
208	Don Mattingly	.25	.20	.10
209	Danny Tartabull	.15	.11	.06
210	Brett Butler (All-Star Advice)	.10	.08	.04
211	Tony Gwynn (All-Star Advice)	.10	.08	.04
212	Rickey Henderson (All-Star Advice)	.10	.08	.04
213	Ramon Martinez (All-Star Advice)	.10	.08	.04
214	Nolan Ryan (All-Star Advice)	.35	.25	.14
215	Ozzie Smith (All-Star Advice)	.10	.08	.04
216	Marquis Grissom (Fold-Out)	.20	.15	.08
217	Dean Palmer (Fold-Out)	.20	.15	.08
218	Cal Ripken, Jr. (Fold-Out)	.50	.40	.20
219	Deion Sanders (Fold-Out)	.35	.25	.14
220	Darryl Strawberry (Fold-Out)	.25	.20	.10
221	David McCarty (Checklist)	.10	.08	.04
222	Barry Bonds (Checklist)	.10	.08	.04
223	Juan Gonzalez (Checklist)	.10	.08	.04
224	Ken Griffey, Jr. (Checklist)	.10	.08	.04
225	Frank Thomas (Checklist)	.10	.08	.04

The values quoted are intended to reflect the market price.

1993 Upper Deck Fun Packs All-Star Scratch-Offs

Randomly inserted into Fun Packs was a series of nine "All-Star Scratch-Off" game cards. Fronts and backs have a star-studded blue background. Inside the folded, double-size (2-1/2" x 7") cards are American and National League line-ups which can be used to play a baseball game, the rules of which are explained on the card backs. On front are photos of two of the players in the line-up, matched by position from each league. The inserts are numbered with an "AS" prefix.

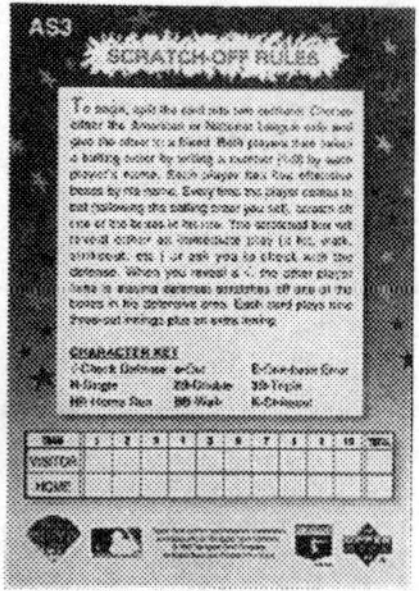

		MT	NR MT	EX
Complete Set (9):		21.00	15.50	8.50
Common Card:		1.00	.70	.40
1	Fred McGriff vs. Frank Thomas	5.00	3.75	2.00
2	Darren Daulton vs. Ivan Rodriguez	1.00	.70	.40
3	Mark McGwire vs. Will Clark	2.50	2.00	1.00
4	Ryne Sandberg vs. Roberto Alomar	3.00	2.25	1.25
5	Robin Ventura vs. Terry Pendleton	1.00	.70	.40
6	Cal Ripken, Jr. vs. Ozzie Smith	4.00	3.00	1.50
7	Barry Bonds vs. Juan Gonzalez	4.00	3.00	1.50
8	Marquis Grissom vs. Ken Griffey, Jr.	5.00	3.75	2.00
9	Tony Gwynn vs. Kirby Puckett	2.00	1.50	.80

1993 Upper Deck Fun Packs Mascot Madness

Upper Deck's high-tech lithogram process of combining color photos and holograms was used to create the five-card "Mascot Madness" inserts which were randomly found in Fun Packs. The mascot's name appears in pink and purple boxes vertically at left. Against a fading orange background are a color photo and a hologram of the mascot. Backs have a description of the mascot and explain his role with the team.

		MT	NR MT	EX
Complete Set (5):		5.00	3.75	2.00
Common Card:		1.00	.70	.40
1	Phillie Phanatic	1.00	.70	.40
2	Pirate Parrot	1.00	.70	.40
3	Fredbird	1.00	.70	.40
4	BJ Birdy	1.00	.70	.40
5	Youppi	1.00	.70	.40

1994 Upper Deck Collector's Choice Promo

Upper Deck used a single promo card to preview new 1994 Collector's Choice brand. Ken Griffey was was featured on the promo, though both the front and back photos differ from those which appear on the the regular-issue card, as does the card number. "For Promotional Use Only" is printed diagonally in black on both the front and back of the card.

50	Ken Griffey, Jr.	6.00	4.50	2.50

1994 Upper Deck Collector's Choice

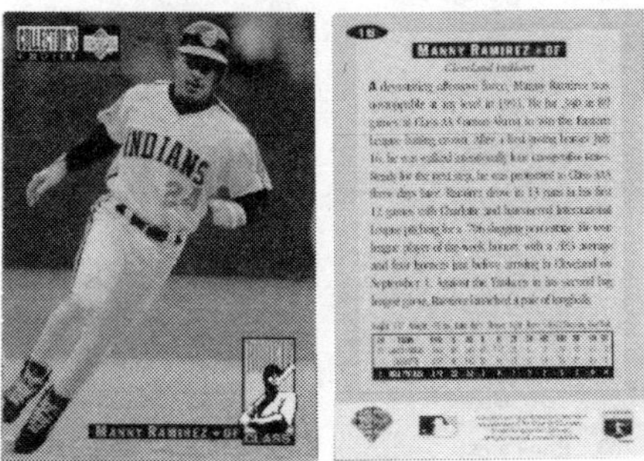

This 1994 Upper Deck set, released in two series, is more widely available than the regular 1994 UD-brand set. The cards, which feature the traditional UV coating and holograms, have large photos with a narrow pinstripe border. Backs have stats and a color photo. Series I has 320 cards and subsets titled Rookie Class, Draft Picks and Top Performers. Series II's subsets are Up Close and Personal, Future Foundation and Rookie Class. Each of the set's player cards can also be found with either a gold- (1 in 36 packs) or silver-foil replica autograph card. One silver-signature card appears in every pack.

		MT	NR MT	EX
	Complete Set (320):	15.00	11.00	6.00
	Gold Signature 40X-75X			
	Silver Signature 4X-8X			
	Common Player:	.05	.04	.02
1	*Rich Becker*	.15	.11	.06
2	Greg Blosser	.10	.07	.04
3	Midre Cummings	.30	.25	.12
4	Carlos Delgado	.90	.70	.35
5	*Steve Dreyer*	.15	.11	.06
6	*Carl Everett*	.15	.11	.06
7	Cliff Floyd	1.00	.70	.40
8	Alex Gonzalez	.60	.45	.25
9	Shawn Green	.20	.15	.08
10	*Butch Huskey*	.10	.08	.04
11	*Mark Hutton*	.15	.11	.06
12	*Miguel Jimenez*	.15	.11	.06
13	Steve Karsay	.20	.15	.08
14	Marc Newfield	.15	.11	.06
15	Luis Ortiz	.10	.08	.04
16	Manny Ramirez	.75	.60	.30
17	Johnny Ruffin	.10	.07	.04
18	*Scott Stahoviak*	.15	.11	.06
19	Salomon Torres	.20	.15	.08
20	*Gabe White*	.10	.08	.04
21	*Brian Anderson*	.15	.11	.06
22	*Wayne Gomes*	.15	.11	.06
23	*Jeff Granger*	.20	.15	.08
24	*Steve Soderstrom*	.20	.15	.08
25	*Trot Nixon*	.75	.60	.30
26	*Kirk Presley*	.15	.11	.06
27	*Matt Brunson*	.15	.11	.06
28	*Brooks Kieschnick*	.50	.40	.20
29	*Billy Wagner*	.15	.11	.06
30	*Matt Drews*	.15	.11	.06
31	Kurt Abbott	.05	.04	.02
32	Luis Alicea	.05	.04	.02
33	Roberto Alomar	.20	.15	.08
34	Sandy Alomar Jr.	.05	.04	.02
35	Moises Alou	.05	.04	.02
36	Wilson Alvarez	.05	.04	.02
37	Rich Amaral	.05	.04	.02
38	Eric Anthony	.05	.04	.02
39	Luis Aquino	.05	.04	.02
40	Jack Armstrong	.05	.04	.02
41	Rene Arocha	.10	.08	.04
42	Rich Aude	.05	.04	.02
43	Brad Ausmus	.05	.04	.02
44	Steve Avery	.15	.11	.06
45	Bob Ayrault	.05	.04	.02
46	Willie Banks	.05	.04	.02
47	Bret Barberie	.05	.04	.02
48	Kim Batiste	.05	.04	.02
49	Rod Beck	.05	.04	.02
50	*Jason Bere*	1.00	.70	.40
51	Sean Berry	.05	.04	.02
52	Dante Bichette	.05	.04	.02
53	Jeff Blauser	.05	.04	.02
54	Mike Blowers	.05	.04	.02
55	Tim Bogar	.05	.04	.02
56	Tom Bolton	.05	.04	.02
57	Ricky Bones	.05	.04	.02
58	Bobby Bonilla	.05	.04	.02
59	Bret Boone	.05	.04	.02
60	Pat Borders	.05	.04	.02
61	Mike Bordick	.05	.04	.02
62	Daryl Boston	.05	.04	.02
63	Ryan Bowen	.05	.04	.02
64	Jeff Branson	.05	.04	.02
65	George Brett	.15	.11	.06
66	Steve Buechele	.05	.04	.02
67	Dave Burba	.05	.04	.02
68	John Burkett	.05	.04	.02
69	Jeromy Burnitz	.10	.08	.04
70	Brett Butler	.05	.04	.02
71	Rob Butler	.05	.04	.02
72	Ken Caminiti	.05	.04	.02
73	Cris Carpenter	.05	.04	.02
74	Vinny Castilla	.05	.04	.02
75	Andujar Cedeno	.05	.04	.02
76	Wes Chamberlain	.05	.04	.02
77	Archi Cianfrocco	.05	.04	.02
78	Dave Clark	.05	.04	.02
79	Jerald Clark	.05	.04	.02
80	Royce Clayton	.10	.08	.04
81	David Cone	.05	.04	.02
82	Jeff Conine	.05	.04	.02
83	Steve Cooke	.05	.04	.02
84	Scott Cooper	.05	.04	.02
85	Joey Cora	.05	.04	.02
86	Tim Costa	.05	.04	.02
87	Chad Curtis	.10	.08	.04
88	Ron Darling	.05	.04	.02
89	Danny Darwin	.05	.04	.02
90	Rob Deer	.05	.04	.02
91	Jim Deshaies	.05	.04	.02
92	Delino DeShields	.05	.04	.02
93	Rob Dibble	.05	.04	.02
94	Gary DiSarcina	.05	.04	.02
95	Doug Drabek	.05	.04	.02
96	Scott Erickson	.05	.04	.02
97	Rikkert Faneyte	.05	.04	.02
98	Jeff Fassero	.15	.11	.06
99	Alex Fernandez	.10	.08	.04
100	Cecil Fielder	.15	.11	.06
101	Dave Fleming	.05	.04	.02
102	Darrin Fletcher	.05	.04	.02
103	Scott Fletcher	.05	.04	.02
104	Mike Gallego	.05	.04	.02
105	Carlos Garcia	.05	.04	.02
106	Jeff Gardner	.05	.04	.02
107	Brent Gates	.15	.11	.06
108	Benji Gil	.20	.15	.08
109	Bernard Gilkey	.05	.04	.02
110	Chris Gomez	.05	.04	.02
111	Luis Gonzalez	.05	.04	.02
112	Tom Gordon	.05	.04	.02
113	Jim Gott	.05	.04	.02
114	Mark Grace	.05	.04	.02
115	Tommy Greene	.05	.04	.02
116	Willie Greene	.05	.04	.02
117	Ken Griffey, Jr.	.75	.60	.30
118	Bill Gullickson	.05	.04	.02
119	Ricky Gutierrez	.05	.04	.02
120	Juan Guzman	.05	.04	.02
121	Chris Gwynn	.05	.04	.02
122	Tony Gwynn	.20	.15	.08
123	Jeffrey Hammonds	.40	.30	.15
124	Erik Hanson	.05	.04	.02
125	Gene Harris	.05	.04	.02
126	Greg Harris	.05	.04	.02
127	Bryan Harvey	.05	.04	.02
128	Billy Hatcher	.05	.04	.02
129	Hilly Hathaway	.05	.04	.02
130	Charlie Hayes	.05	.04	.02
131	Rickey Henderson	.15	.11	.06
132	Mike Henneman	.05	.04	.02
133	Pat Hentgen	.05	.04	.02
134	Roberto Hernandez	.05	.04	.02
135	Orel Hershiser	.05	.04	.02
136	Phil Hiatt	.15	.11	.06
137	Glenallen Hill	.05	.04	.02
138	Ken Hill	.05	.04	.02
139	Eric Hillman	.05	.04	.02
140	Chris Hoiles	.05	.04	.02
141	Dave Hollins	.05	.04	.02
142	David Hulse	.15	.11	.06
143	Todd Hundley	.05	.04	.02
144	Pete Incaviglia	.05	.04	.02
145	Danny Jackson	.05	.04	.02
146	John Jaha	.05	.04	.02
147	Domingo Jean	.05	.04	.02
148	Gregg Jefferies	.05	.04	.02
149	Reggie Jefferson	.05	.04	.02
150	Lance Johnson	.05	.04	.02
151	Bobby Jones	.05	.04	.02
152	Chipper Jones	.25	.20	.10
153	Todd Jones	.05	.04	.02
154	Brian Jordan	.05	.04	.02
155	Wally Joyner	.05	.04	.02
156	David Justice	.25	.20	.10
157	Ron Karkovice	.05	.04	.02
158	Eric Karros	.15	.11	.06
159	Jeff Kent	.05	.04	.02
160	Jimmy Key	.05	.04	.02
161	Mark Kiefer	.05	.04	.02
162	Darryl Kile	.05	.04	.02
163	Jeff King	.05	.04	.02
164	Wayne Kirby	.05	.04	.02
165	Ryan Klesko	.20	.15	.08
166	Chuck Knoblauch	.05	.04	.02
167	Chad Kreuter	.05	.04	.02
168	John Kruk	.10	.08	.04
169	Mark Langston	.05	.04	.02
170	Mike Lansing	.10	.08	.04
171	Barry Larkin	.05	.04	.02
172	Manuel Lee	.05	.04	.02
173	Phil Leftwich	.05	.04	.02
174	Darren Lewis	.05	.04	.02
175	Derek Lilliquist	.05	.04	.02
176	Jose Lind	.05	.04	.02
177	Albie Lopez	.05	.04	.02
178	Javier Lopez	.35	.25	.14
179	Torey Lovullo	.05	.04	.02
180	Scott Lydy	.05	.04	.02
181	Mike Macfarlane	.05	.04	.02
182	Shane Mack	.05	.04	.02
183	Shane Maddux	.05	.04	.02
184	Dave Magadan	.05	.04	.02
185	Joe Magrane	.05	.04	.02
186	Kirt Manwaring	.05	.04	.02
187	Al Martin	.10	.08	.04
188	Pedro A. Martinez	.05	.04	.02
189	Pedro J. Martinez	.10	.08	.04
190	Ramon Martinez	.05	.04	.02
191	Tino Martinez	.05	.04	.02
192	Don Mattingly	.15	.11	.06
193	Derrick May	.05	.04	.02
194	David McCarty	.10	.08	.04
195	Ben McDonald	.05	.04	.02
196	Roger McDowell	.05	.04	.02
197	Fred McGriff	.20	.15	.08
198	Mark McLemore	.05	.04	.02
199	Greg McMichael	.10	.08	.04
200	Jeff McNeely	.10	.08	.04
201	Brian McRae	.05	.04	.02
202	Pat Meares	.05	.04	.02
203	Roberto Mejia	.05	.04	.02
204	Orlando Merced	.05	.04	.02
205	Jose Mesa	.05	.04	.02
206	Blas Minor	.05	.04	.02
207	Angel Miranda	.05	.04	.02
208	Paul Molitor	.20	.15	.08
209	Raul Mondesi	.15	.11	.06
210	Jeff Montgomery	.05	.04	.02
211	Mickey Morandini	.05	.04	.02
212	Mike Morgan	.05	.04	.02
213	Jamie Moyer	.05	.04	.02
214	Bobby Munoz	.05	.04	.02
215	Troy Neel	.20	.15	.08
216	Dave Nilsson	.05	.04	.02
217	John O'Donoghue	.05	.04	.02
218	Paul O'Neill	.05	.04	.02
219	Jose Offerman	.05	.04	.02
220	Joe Oliver	.05	.04	.02
221	Greg Olson	.05	.04	.02
222	Donovan Osborne	.05	.04	.02
223	Jayhawk Owens	.05	.04	.02
224	Mike Pagliarulo	.05	.04	.02
225	Craig Paquette	.05	.04	.02
226	Roger Pavlik	.05	.04	.02
227	Brad Pennington	.05	.04	.02
228	Eduardo Perez	.05	.04	.02
229	Mike Perez	.05	.04	.02
230	Tony Phillips	.05	.04	.02
231	Hipolito Pichardo	.05	.04	.02
232	Phil Plantier	.05	.04	.02
233	*Curtis Pride*	.75	.60	.30
234	Tim Pugh	.05	.04	.02
235	Scott Radinsky	.05	.04	.02
236	Pat Rapp	.05	.04	.02
237	Kevin Reimer	.05	.04	.02
238	Armando Reynoso	.05	.04	.02
239	Jose Rijo	.05	.04	.02
240	Cal Ripken Jr.	.25	.20	.10
241	Kevin Roberson	.25	.20	.10
242	Kenny Rogers	.05	.04	.02
243	Kevin Rogers	.05	.04	.02
244	Mel Rojas	.05	.04	.02
245	John Roper	.05	.04	.02
246	*Kirk Rueter*	1.00	.70	.40
247	Scott Ruffcorn	.15	.11	.06
248	Ken Ryan	.05	.04	.02
249	Nolan Ryan	.40	.30	.15
250	Bret Saberhagen	.05	.04	.02
251	Tim Salmon	1.00	.70	.40
252	Reggie Sanders	.05	.04	.02
253	Curt Schilling	.05	.04	.02
254	David Segui	.05	.04	.02
255	Aaron Sele	.20	.15	.08
256	Scott Servais	.05	.04	.02
257	Gary Sheffield	.10	.08	.04
258	Ruben Sierra	.10	.08	.04
259	Don Slaught	.05	.04	.02
260	Lee Smith	.05	.04	.02
261	Cory Snyder	.05	.04	.02
262	Paul Sorrento	.05	.04	.02
263	Sammy Sosa	.10	.08	.04
264	Bill Spiers	.05	.04	.02
265	Mike Stanley	.05	.04	.02
266	Dave Staton	.05	.04	.02
267	Terry Steinbach	.05	.04	.02
268	Kevin Stocker	.60	.45	.25
269	Todd Stottlemyre	.05	.04	.02
270	Doug Strange	.05	.04	.02
272	Kevin Tapani	.05	.04	.02
273	Tony Tarasco	.30	.25	.12
274	Julian Tavarez	.05	.04	.02
275	Mickey Tettleton	.05	.04	.02
276	Ryan Thompson	.05	.04	.02
277	Chris Turner	.05	.04	.02
278	John Valentin	.05	.04	.02
279	Todd Van Poppel	.10	.08	.04
280	Andy van Slyke	.05	.04	.02
281	Mo Vaughn	.10	.08	.04
282	Robin Ventura	.15	.11	.06
283	Frank Viola	.05	.04	.02
284	Jose Vizcaino	.05	.04	.02
285	Omar Vizquel	.05	.04	.02
286	Larry Walker	.10	.08	.04
287	Duane Ware	.05	.04	.02
288	Allen Watson	.20	.15	.08
289	Bill Wegman	.05	.04	.02
290	Turk Wendell	.05	.04	.02
291	Lou Whitaker	.05	.04	.02
292	Devon White	.10	.08	.04
293	Rondell White	.50	.40	.20
294	Mark Whiten	.05	.04	.02

295 Darrell Whitmore .05 .04 .02
296 Bob Wickman .05 .04 .02
297 Rick Wilkins .05 .04 .02
298 Bernie Williams .05 .04 .02
299 Matt Williams .05 .04 .02
300 Woody Williams .05 .04 .02
301 Nigel Wilson .20 .15 .08
302 Dave Winfield .15 .11 .06
303 Anthony Young .05 .04 .02
304 Eric Young .05 .04 .02
305 Todd Zeile .05 .04 .02
306 Jack McDowell (Top Performers, John Burkett, Tom Glavine) .10 .08 .04
307 Randy Johnson (Top Performers) .10 .08 .04
308 Randy Myers (Top Performers) .05 .04 .02
309 Jack McDowell (Top Performers) .10 .08 .04
310 Mike Piazza (Top Performers) 1.00 .75 .40
311 Barry Bonds (Top Performers) .40 .30 .15
312 Andres Galarraga (Top Performers) .10 .08 .04
313 Juan Gonzalez (Top Performers, Barry Bonds) .50 .40 .20
314 Albert Belle (Top Performers) .25 .20 .10
315 Kenny Lofton (Top Performers) .15 .11 .06
316 Checklist 1-64 (Bonds) .10 .07 .04
317 Checklist 65-128 (Griffey, Jr.) .25 .20 .10
318 Checklist 129--192 (Piazza) .15 .11 .06
319 Checklist 193-256 (Puckett) .10 .07 .04
320 Checklist 257-320 (Ryan) .15 .11 .06
321 Checklist 321-370 .05 .04 .02
322 Checklist 371-420 .05 .04 .02
323 Checklist 421-470 Gonzalez .15 .11 .06
324 Checklist 471-520 (Griffey, Jr) .30 .25 .12
325 Checklist 521-570 .10 .08 .04
326 Checklist 571-620 .05 .04 .02
327 Checklist 621-670 (Thomas) .25 .20 .10
328 California Angels .15 .11 .06
329 Houston Astros .10 .08 .04
330 Oakland Athletics .05 .04 .02
331 Toronto Blue Jays .10 .08 .04
332 Atlanta Braves .10 .08 .04
333 Milwaukee Brewers .05 .04 .02
334 St. Louis Cardinals .05 .04 .02
335 Chicago Cubs .10 .08 .04
336 Los Angeles Dodgers (Piazza) .25 .20 .10
337 Montreal Expos (Floyd) .20 .15 .08
338 San Francisco Giants (Bonds) .15 .11 .06
339 Cleveland Indians (Belle) .15 .11 .06
340 Seattle Mariners (Griffey, Jr) .50 .40 .20
341 Florida Marlins
342 New York Mets
343 Baltimore Orioles (Ripken, Jr.) .20 .15 .08
344 San Diego Padres .08 .06 .03
345 Philadelphia Phillies .05 .04 .02
346 Pittsburgh Pirates .05 .04 .02
347 Texas Rangers (Gonzalez) .25 .20 .10
348 Boston Red Sox .10 .08 .04
349 Cincinnati Reds .05 .04 .02
350 Colorado Rockies .05 .04 .02
351 Kansas City Royals .05 .04 .02
352 Detroit Tigers .05 .04 .02
353 Minnesota Twins (Puckett) .15 .11 .06
354 Chicago White Sox (Thomas) .50 .40 .20
355 New York Yankees .10 .08 .04
356 Bo Jackson .06 .05 .02
357 Randy Johnson .05 .04 .02
358 Darren Daulton .05 .04 .02
359 Charlie Hough .05 .04 .02
360 Andres Galarraga .07 .05 .03
361 Mike Felder .05 .04 .02
362 Chris Hammond .05 .04 .02
363 Shawon Dunston .05 .04 .02
364 Junior Felix .05 .04 .02
365 Ray Lankford .06 .05 .02
366 Darryl Strawberry .05 .04 .02
367 Dave Magadan .05 .04 .02
368 Gregg Olson .05 .04 .02
369 Len Dykstra .05 .04 .02
370 Darrin Jackson .05 .04 .02
371 Dave Stewart .05 .04 .02
372 Terry Pendleton .05 .04 .02
373 Arthur Rhodes .05 .04 .02
374 Benito Santiago .05 .04 .02
375 Travis Fryman .15 .11 .06
376 Scott Brosius .05 .04 .02
377 Stan Belinda .05 .04 .02
378 Derek Parks .06 .05 .02
379 Kevin Seitzer .05 .04 .02
380 Wade Boggs .10 .08 .04
381 Wally Whitehurst .05 .04 .02
382 Scott Leius .05 .04 .02
383 Danny Tartabull .05 .04 .02
384 Harold Reynolds .05 .04 .02
385 Tim Raines .05 .04 .02
386 Darryl Hamilton .05 .04 .02
387 Felix Fermin .05 .04 .02
388 Jim Eisenreich .05 .04 .02
389 Kurt Abbott .10 .08 .04
390 Kevin Appier .05 .04 .02
391 Chris Bosio .05 .04 .02
392 Randy Tomlin .05 .04 .02
393 Bob Hamelin .07 .05 .03
394 Kevin Gross .05 .04 .02
395 Wil Cordero .06 .05 .02
396 Joe Girardi .05 .04 .02
397 Orestes Destrade .05 .04 .02
398 Chris Haney .05 .04 .02
399 Xavier Hernandez .05 .04 .02
400 Mike Piazza .75 .60 .30
401 Alex Arias .05 .04 .02
402 Tom Candiotti .05 .04 .02
403 Kirk Gibson .06 .05 .02
404 Chuck Carr .05 .04 .02
405 Brady Anderson .05 .04 .02
406 Greg Gagne .05 .04 .02
407 Bruce Ruffin .05 .04 .02
408 Scott Hemond .05 .04 .02
409 Keith Miller .05 .04 .02
410 John Wetteland .05 .04 .02
411 Eric Anthony .05 .04 .02
412 Andre Dawson .06 .05 .02
413 Doug Henry .05 .04 .02
414 John Franco .05 .04 .02
415 Julio Franco .05 .04 .02
416 Dave Hansen .05 .04 .02
417 Mike Harkey .05 .04 .02
418 Jack Armstrong .05 .04 .02
419 Joe Orsulak .05 .04 .02
420 John Smoltz .05 .04 .02
421 Scott Livingstone .05 .04 .02
422 Darren Holmes .05 .04 .02
423 Ed Sprague .05 .04 .02
424 Jay Buhner .05 .04 .02
425 Kirby Puckett .25 .20 .10
426 Phil Clark .05 .04 .02
427 Anthony Young .05 .04 .02
428 Reggie Jefferson .05 .04 .02
429 Mariano Duncan .05 .04 .02
430 Tom Glavine .10 .08 .04
431 Dave Henderson .05 .04 .02
432 Melido Perez .05 .04 .02
433 Paul Wagner .05 .04 .02
434 Tim Worrell .05 .04 .02
435 Ozzie Guillen .05 .04 .02
436 Mike Butcher .05 .04 .02
437 Jim Deshaies .05 .04 .02
438 Kevin Young .05 .04 .02
439 Tom Browning .05 .04 .02
440 Mike Greenwell .05 .04 .02
441 Mike Stanton .05 .04 .02
442 John Doherty .05 .04 .02
443 John Dopson .05 .04 .02
444 Carlos Baerga .20 .15 .08
445 Jack McDowell .08 .06 .03
446 Kent Mercker .05 .04 .02
447 Ricky Jordan .05 .04 .02
448 Jerry Browne .05 .04 .02
449 Fernando Vina .05 .04 .02
450 Jim Abbott .05 .04 .02
451 Teddy Higuera .05 .04 .02
452 Tim Naehring .05 .04 .02
453 Jim Leyritz .05 .04 .02
454 Frank Castillo .05 .04 .02
455 Joe Carter .20 .15 .08
456 Craig Biggio .06 .05 .02
457 Geronimo Pena .05 .04 .02
458 Alejandro Pena .05 .04 .02
459 Mike Moore .05 .04 .02
460 Randy Myers .05 .04 .02
461 Greg Myers .05 .04 .02
462 Greg Hibbard .05 .04 .02
463 Jose Guzman .05 .04 .02
464 Tom Pagnozzi .05 .04 .02
465 Marquis Grissom .07 .05 .03
466 Tim Wallach .05 .04 .02
467 Joe Grahe .05 .04 .02
468 Bob Tewksbury .05 .04 .02
469 B.J. Surhoff .05 .04 .02
470 Kevin Mitchell .05 .04 .02
471 Bobby Witt .05 .04 .02
472 Milt Thompson .05 .04 .02
473 John Smiley .05 .04 .02
474 Alan Trammell .05 .04 .02
475 Mike Mussina .10 .08 .04
476 Rick Aguilera .05 .04 .02
477 Jose Valentin .05 .04 .02
478 Harold Baines .05 .04 .02
479 Bip Roberts .05 .04 .02
480 Edgar Martinez .05 .04 .02
481 Rheal Cormier .05 .04 .02
482 Hal Morris .06 .05 .02
483 Pat Kelly .05 .04 .02
484 Roberto Kelly .05 .04 .02
485 Chris Sabo .05 .04 .02
486 Kent Hrbek .05 .04 .02
487 Scott Kamieniecki .05 .04 .02
488 Walt Weiss .05 .04 .02
489 Karl Rhodes .06 .05 .02
490 Derek Bell .06 .05 .02
491 Chili Davis .05 .04 .02
492 Brian Harper .05 .04 .02
493 Felix Jose .05 .04 .02
494 Trevor Hoffman .05 .04 .02
495 Dennis Eckersley .05 .04 .02
496 Pedro Astacio .06 .05 .02
497 Jay Bell .05 .04 .02
498 Randy Velarde .05 .04 .02
499 David Wells .05 .04 .02
500 Frank Thomas 1.00 .70 .40
501 Mark Lemke .05 .04 .02
502 Mike Devereaux .05 .04 .02
503 Chuck McElroy .05 .04 .02
504 Luis Polonia .05 .04 .02
505 Damion Easley .06 .05 .02
506 Greg A. Harris .05 .04 .02
507 Chris James .05 .04 .02
508 Terry Mulholland .05 .04 .02
509 Pete Smith .05 .04 .02
510 Rickey Henderson .07 .05 .03
511 Sid Fernandez .05 .04 .02
512 Al Leiter .05 .04 .02
513 Doug Jones .05 .04 .02
514 Steve Farr .05 .04 .02
515 Chuck Finley .05 .04 .02
516 Bobby Thigpen .05 .04 .02
517 Jim Edmonds .10 .08 .04
518 Graeme Lloyd .07 .05 .03
519 Dwight Gooden .07 .05 .03
520 Pat Listach .05 .04 .02
521 Kevin Bass .05 .04 .02
522 Willie Banks .05 .04 .02
523 Steve Finley .05 .04 .02
524 Delino DeShields .05 .04 .02
525 Mark McGwire .07 .05 .03
526 Greg Swindell .05 .04 .02
527 Chris Nabholz .05 .04 .02
528 Scott Sanders .05 .04 .02
529 David Segui .05 .04 .02
530 Howard Johnson .05 .04 .02
531 Jaime Navarro .05 .04 .02
532 Jose Vizcaino .05 .04 .02
533 Mark Lewis .05 .04 .02
534 Pete Harnisch .05 .04 .02
535 Robby Thompson .05 .04 .02
536 Marcus Moore .05 .04 .02
537 Kevin Brown .05 .04 .02
538 Mark Clark .08 .06 .03
539 Sterling Hitchcock .05 .04 .02
540 Will Clark .20 .15 .08
541 Denis Boucher .05 .04 .02
542 Jack Morris .05 .04 .02
543 Pedro Munoz .05 .04 .02
544 Bret Boone .05 .04 .02
545 Ozzie Smith .10 .08 .04
546 Dennis Martinez .05 .04 .02
547 Dan Wilson .05 .04 .02
548 Rick Sutcliffe .05 .04 .02
549 Kevin McReynolds .05 .04 .02
550 Roger Clemens .15 .11 .06
551 Todd Benzinger .05 .04 .02
552 Bill Haselman .05 .04 .02
553 Bobby Munoz .05 .04 .02
554 Ellis Burks .05 .04 .02
555 Ryne Sandberg .20 .15 .08
556 Lee Smith .05 .04 .02
557 Danny Bautista .05 .04 .02
558 Rey Sanchez .05 .04 .02
559 Norm Charlton .05 .04 .02
560 Jose Canseco .15 .11 .06
561 Tim Belcher .05 .04 .02
562 Denny Neagle .05 .04 .02
563 Eric Davis .05 .04 .02
564 Jody Reed .05 .04 .02
565 Kenny Lofton .15 .11 .06
566 Gary Gaetti .05 .04 .02
567 Todd Worrell .05 .04 .02
568 Mark Portugal .05 .04 .02
569 Dick Schofield .05 .04 .02
570 Andy Benes .05 .04 .02
571 Zane Smith .05 .04 .02
572 Bobby Ayala .05 .04 .02
573 Chip Hale .05 .04 .02
574 Bob Welch .05 .04 .02
575 Deion Sanders .10 .08 .04
576 Dave Nied .08 .06 .03
577 Pat Mahomes .06 .05 .02
578 Charles Nagy .05 .04 .02
579 Otis Nixon .05 .04 .02
580 Dean Palmer .05 .04 .02
581 Roberto Petagine .05 .04 .02
582 Dwight Smith .05 .04 .02
583 Jeff Russell .05 .04 .02
584 Mark Dewey .05 .04 .02
585 Greg Vaughn .05 .04 .02
586 Brian Hunter .05 .04 .02
587 Willie McGee .05 .04 .02
588 Pedro J. Martinez .05 .04 .02
589 Tim Davis .05 .04 .02
590 Jeff Bagwell .15 .11 .06
591 Spike Owen .05 .04 .02
592 Jeff Reardon .05 .04 .02
593 Erik Pappas .05 .04 .02
594 Brian Williams .05 .04 .02
595 Eddie Murray .08 .06 .03
596 Henry Rodriguez .07 .05 .03
597 Erik Hanson .05 .04 .02
598 Stan Javier .05 .04 .02
599 Mitch Williams .05 .04 .02
600 John Olerud .15 .11 .06
601 Vince Coleman .05 .04 .02
602 Damon Berryhill .05 .04 .02
603 Tom Brunansky .05 .04 .02
604 Robb Nen .05 .04 .02
605 Rafael Palmeiro .06 .05 .02
606 Cal Eldred .06 .05 .02
607 Jeff Brantley .05 .04 .02
608 Alan Mills .05 .04 .02
609 Jeff Nelson .05 .04 .02
610 Barry Bonds .35 .25 .14
611 *Carlos Pulido* .15 .11 .06
612 *Tim Hyers* .20 .15 .08
613 Steve Howe .05 .04 .02
614 *Brian Turang* .10 .08 .04
615 Leo Gomez .05 .04 .02
616 Jesse Orosco .05 .04 .02
617 Dan Pasqua .05 .04 .02
618 Marvin Freeman .05 .04 .02
619 Tony Fernandez .05 .04 .02
620 Albert Belle .20 .15 .08
621 Eddie Taubensee .05 .04 .02
622 Mike Jackson .05 .04 .02
623 Jose Bautista .05 .04 .02
624 Jim Thome .15 .11 .06
625 Ivan Rodriguez .10 .08 .04
626 Ben Rivera .05 .04 .02
627 Dave Valle .05 .04 .02
628 Tom Henke .05 .04 .02
629 Omar Vizquel .05 .04 .02
630 Juan Gonzalez .50 .40 .20
631 Roberto Alomar (Up Close) .10 .08 .04
632 Barry Bonds (Up Close) .25 .20 .10
633 Juan Gonzalez (Up Close) .40 .30 .15
634 Ken Griffey, Jr. (Up Close) .75 .60 .30
635 Michael Jordan (Up Close) 3.00 2.25 1.25
636 Dave Justice (Up Close) .10 .08 .04
637 Mike Piazza (Up Close) .40 .30 .15
638 Kirby Puckett (Up Close) .25 .20 .10
639 Tim Salmon (Up Close) .25 .20 .10
640 Frank Thomas (Up Close) .75 .60 .30
641 *Alan Benes* .50 .40 .20
642 Johnny Damon .10 .08 .04
643 *Brad Fullmer* .25 .20 .10
644 Derek Jeter .20 .15 .08
645 *Derrek Lee* .40 .30 .15

646	Alex Ochoa	.08	.06	.03
647	*Alex Rodriguez*	1.50	1.25	.60
648	*Jose Silva*	.50	.40	.20
649	*Terrell Wade*	.75	.60	.30
650	Preston Wilson	.15	.11	.06
651	Shane Andrews	.08	.06	.03
652	James Baldwin	.40	.30	.15
653	*Ricky Bottalico*	.20	.15	.08
654	Fausto Cruz	.08	.06	.03
655	Darren Dreifort	.20	.15	.08
656	Joey Eischen	.08	.06	.03
657	Rick Helling	.08	.06	.03
658	Todd Hollandsworth	.20	.15	.08
659	Brian Hunter	.25	.20	.10
660	Charles Johnson	.25	.20	.10
661	*Michael Jordan*	7.50	5.75	3.00
662	Jeff Juden	.08	.06	.03
663	James Mouton	.50	.40	.20
665	Chan Ho Park	.50	.40	.20
666	Pokey Reese	.06	.05	.02
667	*Ruben Santana*	.15	.11	.06
668	Paul Spoljaric	.10	.08	.04
669	Steve Trachsel	.15	.11	.06
670	Matt Walbeck	.08	.06	.03

1994 Collectors Choice Home Run All-Stars

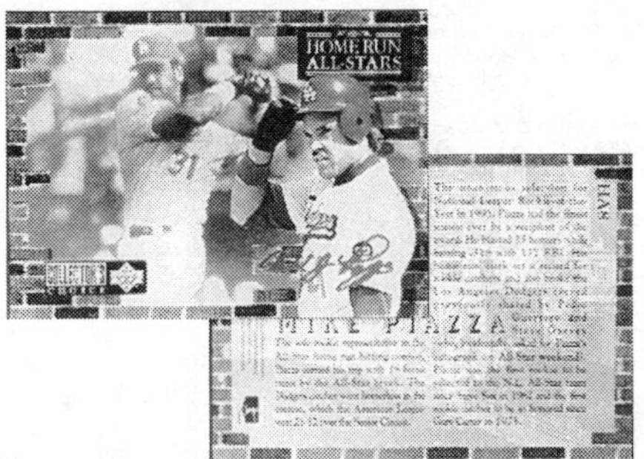

While among the most attractive of the 1994 chase cards, the perceived high production (just over a million sets according to stated odds of winning) of this set keeps it affordable. Sets were available by a mail-in offer to persons who found a winner card in Series I foil packs. Odds of finding such a winner card were about one per foil box. Cards feature a combination of brick-bordered hologram and color player photo on front, along with a gold-foil facsimile autograph. On back the brick border is repeated, as is the photo used for the hologram, though this time in four color. There is a stadium photo in the background, over which is printed a description of the player's home run prowess. A numbering error resulted in two cards numbered HA4 and no card with the HA5 number.

		MT	NR MT	EX
Complete Set (8):		8.00	6.00	3.25
Common Player:		.50	.40	.20
1HA	Juan Gonzalez	1.50	1.25	.60
2HA	Ken Griffey, Jr.	3.00	2.25	1.25
3HA	Barry Bonds	1.25	.90	.50
4HAa	Bobby Bonilla	.50	.40	.20
4HAb	Cecil Fielder	1.00	.70	.40
6HA	Albert Belle	1.25	.90	.50
7HA	David Justice	1.00	.70	.40
8HA	Mike Piazza	1.75	1.25	.70

1994 Upper Deck Team vs. Team Scratch-Off

		MT	NR MT	EX
Complete Set (15):		3.00	2.25	1.25
Common Card:		.25	.20	.10
1	Blue Jays-White Sox	.50	.40	.20
2	Phillies-Braves	.75	.60	.30
3	Mariners-Rangers	.75	.60	.30
4	Dodgers-Giants	.40	.30	.15
5	Red Sox-Yankees	.25	.20	.10
6	Reds-Astros	.25	.20	.10
7	Orioles-Tigers	.25	.20	.10
8	Cubs-Cardinals	.30	.25	.12
9	Athletics-Angels	.25	.20	.10
10	Pirates-Expos	.25	.20	.10
11	Brewers-Indians	.35	.25	.14
12	Rockies-Padres	.25	.20	.10
13	Twins-Royals	.35	.25	.14
14	Mets-Marlins	.25	.20	.10
15	N.L. All-Stars-A.L. All-Stars	.25	.20	.10

A player's name in italic type indicates a rookie card. An (FC) indicates a player's first card for that particular card company.

1994 Upper Deck

Upper Deck's 1994 offering was a typical presentation for the company, combining high-quality regular-issue cards with innovative subsets and high-tech chase cards. Series I, besides the standard player cards, featured subsets included 30 Star Rookies, with metallic borders, 10 "Fantasy Team" stars who excelled in Rotisserie League stats, 14 Home Field Advantage cards showcasing National League stadiums and hometeam stars, and, 15 stars under the age of 25 in a subset titled, "The Future is Now." Regular issue cards feature a color photo on front and a second, black-and-white version of the same photo at left in a vertically stretched format. The player's name, team and Upper Deck logo appear on front in copper foil. Backs have a color photo, recent and career major league stats and an in-field shaped hologram.

		MT	NR MT	EX
Complete Set (550):		32.00	24.00	13.00
Common Player:		.10	.08	.04
Electric Diamonds 5X				
1	Brian Anderson (Star Rookie)	.10	.08	.04
2	Shane Andrews (Star Rookie)	.10	.08	.04
3	James Baldwin (Star Rookie)	.20	.15	.08
4	Rich Becker (Star Rookie)	.10	.08	.04
5	Greg Blosser (Star Rookie)	.10	.08	.04
6	Ricky Bottalico (Star Rookie)	.10	.08	.04
7	Midre Cummings (Star Rookie)	.15	.11	.06
8	Carlos Delgado (Star Rookie)	1.00	.70	.40
9	Steve Dreyer (Star Rookie)	.10	.08	.04
10	*Joey Eischen* (Star Rookie)	.20	.15	.08
11	Carl Everett (Star Rookie)	.12	.09	.05
12	Cliff Floyd (Star Rookie)	1.50	1.25	.60
13	Alex Gonzalez (Star Rookie)	1.25	.90	.50
14	Jeff Granger (Star Rookie)	.20	.15	.08
15	Shawn Green (Star Rookie)	.15	.11	.06
16	Brian Hunter (Star Rookie)	.10	.08	.04
17	Butch Huskey (Star Rookie)	.20	.15	.08
18	Mark Hutton (Star Rookie)	.20	.15	.08
19	*Michael Jordan* (Star Rookie)	10.00	7.50	4.00
20	Steve Karsay (Star Rookie)	.50	.40	.20
21	Jeff McNeely (Star Rookie)	.12	.09	.05
22	Marc Newfield (Star Rookie)	.40	.30	.15
23	Manny Ramirez (Star Rookie)	1.50	1.25	.60
24	*Alex Rodriguez* (Star Rookie)	3.00	2.25	1.25
25	Scott Ruffcorn (Star Rookie)	.15	.11	.06
26	Paul Spoljaric (Star Rookie)	.10	.08	.04
27	*Scott Stahoviak* (Star Rookie)	.12	.09	.05
28	Salomon Torres (Star Rookie)	.15	.11	.06
29	*Steve Trachsel* (Star Rookie)	.50	.40	.20
30	Chris Turner (Star Rookie)	.12	.09	.05
31	Randy Johnson (Fantasy Team)	.10	.08	.04
32	John Wetteland (Fantasy Team)	.10	.08	.04
33	Mike Piazza (Fantasy Team)	1.25	.90	.50
34	Rafael Palmeiro (Fantasy Team)	.12	.09	.05
35	Roberto Alomar (Fantasy Team)	.25	.20	.10
36	Matt Williams (Fantasy Team)	.10	.08	.04
37	Travis Fryman (Fantasy Team)	.20	.15	.08
38	Barry Bonds (Fantasy Team)	.60	.45	.25
39	Marquis Grissom (Fantasy Team)	.12	.09	.05
40	Albert Belle (Fantasy Team)	.25	.20	.10
41	Steve Avery (Future/Now)	.20	.15	.08
42	Jason Bere (Future/Now)	.75	.60	.30
43	Alex Fernandez (Future/Now)	.12	.09	.05
44	Mike Mussina (Future/Now)	.20	.15	.08
45	Aaron Sele (Future/Now)	.75	.60	.30
46	Rod Beck (Future/Now)	.10	.08	.04
47	Mike Piazza (Future/Now)	1.50	1.25	.60
48	John Olerud (Future/Now)	.25	.20	.10
49	Carlos Baerga (Future/Now)	.25	.20	.10
50	Gary Sheffield (Future/Now)	.12	.09	.05
51	Travis Fryman (Future/Now)	.20	.15	.08
52	Juan Gonzalez (Future/Now)	1.50	1.25	.60
53	Ken Griffey, Jr. (Future/Now)	2.50	2.00	1.00
54	Tim Salmon (Future/Now)	.75	.60	.30
55	Frank Thomas (Future/Now)	2.50	2.00	1.00
56	Tony Phillips	.10	.08	.04
57	Julio Franco	.10	.08	.04
58	Kevin Mitchell	.10	.08	.04
59	Raul Mondesi	1.25	.90	.50
60	Rickey Henderson	.15	.11	.06
61	Jay Buhner	.10	.08	.04
62	Bill Swift	.10	.08	.04
63	Brady Anderson	.10	.08	.04
64	Ryan Klesko	1.00	.70	.40
65	Darren Daulton	.10	.08	.04
66	Damion Easley	.15	.11	.06
67	Mark McGwire	.20	.15	.08
68	John Roper	.12	.09	.05
69	Dave Telgheder	.12	.09	.05
70	Dave Nied	.20	.15	.08
71	Mo Vaughn	.12	.09	.05
72	Tyler Green	.10	.08	.04
73	Dave Magadan	.10	.08	.04
74	Chili Davis	.10	.08	.04
75	Archi Cianfrocco	.10	.08	.04
76	Joe Girardi	.10	.08	.04
77	Chris Hoiles	.10	.08	.04
78	Ryan Bowen	.10	.08	.04
79	Greg Gagne	.10	.08	.04
80	Aaron Sele	.75	.60	.30
81	Dave Winfield	.20	.15	.08
82	Chad Curtis	.15	.11	.06
83	Andy Van Slyke	.10	.08	.04
84	Kevin Stocker	.25	.20	.10
85	Deion Sanders	.20	.15	.08
86	Bernie Williams	.10	.08	.04
87	John Smoltz	.10	.08	.04
88	Chris Nabholz	.10	.08	.04
89	Dave Stewart	.10	.08	.04
90	Don Mattingly	.40	.30	.15
91	Joe Carter	.30	.25	.12
92	Ryne Sandberg	.50	.40	.20
93	Chris Gomez	.10	.08	.04
94	Tino Martinez	.10	.08	.04
95	Terry Pendleton	.10	.08	.04
96	Andre Dawson	.10	.08	.04
97	Wil Cordero	.12	.09	.05
98	Kent Hrbek	.10	.08	.04
99	John Olerud	.40	.30	.15
100	Kirt Manwaring	.10	.08	.04
101	Tim Bogar	.10	.08	.04
102	Mike Mussina	.25	.20	.10
103	Nigel Wilson	.15	.11	.06
104	Ricky Gutierrez	.10	.08	.04
105	Roberto Mejia	.15	.11	.06
106	Tom Pagnozzi	.10	.08	.04
107	Mike Macfarlane	.10	.08	.04
108	Jose Bautista	.10	.08	.04
109	Luis Ortiz	.10	.08	.04
110	Brent Gates	.40	.30	.15
111	Tim Salmon	1.50	1.25	.60
112	Wade Boggs	.20	.15	.08
113	*Tripp Cromer*	.12	.09	.05
114	Denny Hocking	.10	.08	.04
115	Carlos Baerga	.35	.25	.14
116	*J.R. Phillips*	.50	.40	.20
117	Bo Jackson	.20	.15	.08
118	Lance Johnson	.10	.08	.04
119	Bobby Jones	.25	.20	.10
120	Bobby Witt	.10	.08	.04
121	Ron Karkovice	.10	.08	.04
122	Jose Vizcaino	.10	.08	.04
123	Danny Darwin	.10	.08	.04
124	Eduardo Perez	.75	.60	.30
125	Brian Looney	.10	.08	.04
126	Pat Hentgen	.20	.15	.08
127	Frank Viola	.10	.08	.04
128	Darren Holmes	.10	.08	.04
129	Wally Whitehurst	.10	.08	.04
130	Matt Walbeck	.10	.08	.04
131	Albert Belle	.40	.30	.15
132	Steve Cooke	.10	.08	.04
133	Kevin Appier	.10	.08	.04
134	Joe Oliver	.10	.08	.04
135	Benji Gil	.20	.15	.08
136	Steve Buechele	.10	.08	.04
137	Devon White	.10	.08	.04
138	Sterling Hitchcock	.12	.09	.05
139	*Phil Leftwich*	.20	.15	.08
140	Jose Canseco	.25	.20	.10
141	Rick Aguilera	.10	.08	.04
142	Rod Beck	.10	.08	.04
143	Jose Rijo	.10	.08	.04
144	Tom Glavine	.25	.20	.10
145	Phil Plantier	.12	.09	.05
146	Jason Bere	1.00	.70	.40
147	Jamie Moyer	.10	.08	.04
148	Wes Chamberlain	.10	.08	.04
149	Glenallen Hill	.10	.08	.04
150	Mark Whiten	.10	.08	.04
151	Bret Barberie	.10	.08	.04
152	Chuck Knoblauch	.10	.08	.04
153	Trevor Hoffman	.10	.08	.04
154	Rick Wilkins	.10	.08	.04
155	Juan Gonzalez	2.00	1.50	.80
156	Ozzie Guillen	.10	.08	.04
157	Jim Eisenreich	.10	.08	.04
158	Pedro Astacio	.12	.09	.05
159	Joe Magrane	.10	.08	.04
160	Ryan Thompson	.10	.08	.04
161	Jose Lind	.10	.08	.04
162	Jeff Conine	.10	.08	.04
163	Todd Benzinger	.10	.08	.04
164	Roger Salkeld	.10	.08	.04
165	Gary DiSarcina	.10	.08	.04
166	Kevin Gross	.10	.08	.04
167	Charlie Hayes	.10	.08	.04
168	Tim Costo	.10	.08	.04
169	Wally Joyner	.10	.08	.04
170	Johnny Ruffin	.10	.08	.04
171	*Kirk Rueter*	.60	.45	.25
172	Len Dykstra	.15	.11	.06
173	Ken Hill	.10	.08	.04
174	Mike Bordick	.10	.08	.04
175	Billy Hall	.12	.09	.05
176	Rob Butler	.20	.15	.08
177	Jay Bell	.10	.08	.04
178	Jeff Kent	.10	.08	.04
179	David Wells	.10	.08	.04
180	Dean Palmer	.12	.09	.05
181	Mariano Duncan	.10	.08	.04
182	Orlando Merced	.10	.08	.04
183	Brett Butler	.10	.08	.04
184	Milt Thompson	.10	.08	.04
185	Chipper Jones	.50	.40	.20
186	Paul O'Neill	.10	.08	.04
187	Mike Greenwell	.10	.08	.04
188	Harold Baines	.10	.08	.04

189 Todd Stottlemyre .10 .08 .04
190 Jeromy Burnitz .12 .09 .05
191 Rene Arocha .12 .09 .05
192 Jeff Fassero .12 .09 .05
193 Robby Thompson .10 .08 .04
194 Greg W. Harris .10 .08 .04
195 Todd Van Poppel .12 .09 .05
196 Jose Guzman .10 .08 .04
197 Shane Mack .10 .08 .04
198 Carlos Garcia .10 .08 .04
199 Kevin Roberson .40 .30 .15
200 David McCarty .15 .11 .06
201 Alan Trammell .10 .08 .04
202 Chuck Carr .10 .08 .04
203 Tommy Greene .10 .08 .04
204 Wilson Alvarez .10 .08 .04
205 Dwight Gooden .10 .08 .04
206 *Tony Tarasco* .40 .30 .15
207 Darren Lewis .10 .08 .04
208 Eric Karros .10 .08 .04
209 Chris Hammond .10 .08 .04
210 Jeffrey Hammonds 1.25 .90 .50
211 Rich Amaral .10 .08 .04
212 Danny Tartabull .10 .08 .04
213 Jeff Russell .10 .08 .04
214 Dave Staton .10 .08 .04
215 Kenny Lofton .20 .15 .08
216 Manuel Lee .10 .08 .04
217 Brian Koelling .10 .08 .04
218 Scott Lydy .10 .08 .04
219 Tony Gwynn .20 .15 .08
220 Cecil Fielder .25 .20 .10
221 Royce Clayton .15 .11 .06
222 Reggie Sanders .12 .09 .05
223 Brian Jordan .10 .08 .04
224 Ken Griffey, Jr. 3.00 2.25 1.25
224a Ken Griffey, Jr. (promo card) 6.00 4.50 2.50
225 Fred McGriff .35 .25 .14
226 Felix Jose .10 .08 .04
227 Brad Pennington .10 .08 .04
228 Chris Bosio .10 .08 .04
229 Mike Stanley .10 .08 .04
230 Willie Greene .10 .08 .04
231 Alex Fernandez .12 .09 .05
232 Brad Ausmus .10 .08 .04
233 Darrell Whitmore .10 .08 .04
234 Marcus Moore .10 .08 .04
235 Allen Watson .40 .30 .15
236 Jose Offerman .10 .08 .04
237 Rondell White .50 .40 .20
238 Jeff King .10 .08 .04
239 Luis Alicea .10 .08 .04
240 Dan Wilson .10 .08 .04
241 Ed Sprague .10 .08 .04
242 Todd Hundley .10 .08 .04
243 Al Martin .10 .08 .04
244 Mike Lansing .20 .15 .08
245 Ivan Rodriguez .12 .09 .05
246 Dave Fleming .10 .08 .04
247 John Doherty .10 .08 .04
248 Mark McLemore .12 .09 .05
249 Bob Hamelin .12 .09 .05
250 Curtis Pride .50 .40 .20
251 Zane Smith .10 .08 .04
252 Eric Young .10 .08 .04
253 Brian McRae .10 .08 .04
254 Tim Raines .12 .09 .05
255 Javier Lopez .75 .60 .30
256 Melvin Nieves .10 .08 .04
257 Randy Myers .10 .08 .04
258 Willie McGee .10 .08 .04
259 Jimmy Key .10 .08 .04
260 Tom Candiotti .10 .08 .04
261 Eric Davis .10 .08 .04
262 Craig Paquette .10 .08 .04
263 Robin Ventura .20 .15 .08
264 Pat Kelly .10 .08 .04
265 Gregg Jefferies .10 .08 .04
266 Cory Snyder .10 .08 .04
267 Dave Justice (Home Field Advantage) .50 .40 .20
268 Sammy Sosa (Home Field Advantage) .12 .09 .05
269 Barry Larkin (Home Field Advantage) .12 .09 .05
270 Andres Galarraga (Home Field Advantage) .12 .09 .05
271 Gary Sheffield (Home Field Advantage) .12 .09 .05
272 Jeff Bagwell (Home Field Advantage) .20 .15 .08
273 Mike Piazza (Home Field Advantage) 1.25 .90 .50
274 Larry Walker (Home Field Advantage) .12 .09 .05
275 Bobby Bonilla (Home Field Advantage) .12 .09 .05
276 John Kruk (Home Field Advantage) .12 .09 .05
277 Jay Bell (Home Field Advantage) .10 .08 .04
278 Ozzie Smith (Home Field Advantage) .12 .09 .05
279 Tony Gwynn (Home Field Advantage) .15 .11 .06
280 Barry Bonds (Home Field Advantage) .50 .40 .20
281 Cal Ripken, Jr. .60 .45 .25
282 Mo Vaughn .12 .09 .05
283 Tim Salmon .75 .60 .30
284 Frank Thomas 2.00 1.50 .80
285 Albert Belle .35 .25 .14
286 Cecil Fielder .20 .15 .08
287 Wally Joyner .10 .08 .04
288 Greg Vaughn .10 .08 .04
289 Kirby Puckett .50 .40 .20
290 Don Mattingly .40 .30 .15
291 Terry Steinbach .10 .08 .04
292 Ken Griffey, Jr. 2.00 1.50 .80
293 Juan Gonzalez 1.00 .70 .40
294 Paul Molitor .25 .20 .10
295 Tavo Alvarez .20 .15 .08
296 Matt Brunson .20 .15 .08
297 Shawn Green .35 .25 .14
298 Alex Rodriguez 1.50 1.25 .60
299 Shannon Stewart .12 .09 .05
300 Frank Thomas 1.50 1.25 .60
301 Mickey Tettleton .10 .08 .04
302 Pedro Munoz .10 .08 .04
303 Jose Valentin .10 .08 .04
304 Orestes Destrade .10 .08 .04
305 Pat Listach .10 .08 .04
306 Scott Brosius .10 .08 .04
307 Darren Oliver .10 .08 .04
308 Rob Dibble .10 .08 .04
309 Mike Blowers .10 .08 .04
310 Jim Abbott .10 .08 .04
311 Mike Jackson .10 .08 .04
312 Craig Biggio .10 .08 .04
313 Kurt Abbott .25 .20 .10
314 Chuck Finley .10 .08 .04
315 Andres Galarraga .15 .11 .06
316 Mike Moore .10 .08 .04
317 Doug Strange .10 .08 .04
318 Pedro J. Martinez .15 .11 .06
319 Kevin McReynolds .10 .08 .04
320 Greg Maddux .35 .25 .14
321 Mike Henneman .10 .08 .04
322 Scott Leius .10 .08 .04
323 John Franco .10 .08 .04
324 Jeff Blauser .10 .08 .04
325 Kirby Puckett .60 .45 .25
326 Darryl Hamilton .10 .08 .04
327 John Smiley .10 .08 .04
328 Derrick May .10 .08 .04
329 Jose Vizcaino .10 .08 .04
330 Randy Johnson .10 .08 .04
331 Jack Morris .10 .08 .04
332 Graeme Lloyd .12 .09 .05
333 Dave Valle .10 .08 .04
334 Greg Myers .10 .08 .04
335 John Wetteland .10 .08 .04
336 Jim Gott .10 .08 .04
337 Tim Naehring .10 .08 .04
338 Danny Bautista .10 .08 .04
339 Jeff Montgomery .10 .08 .04
340 Rafael Palmeiro .15 .11 .06
342 Xavier Hernandez .10 .08 .04
343 Bobby Munoz .15 .11 .06
344 Bobby Bonilla .10 .08 .04
345 Travis Fryman .35 .25 .14
346 Steve Finley .10 .08 .04
347 Chris Sabo .10 .08 .04
348 Armando Reynoso .10 .08 .04
349 Ramon Martinez .10 .08 .04
350 Will Clark .40 .30 .15
351 Moises Alou .15 .11 .06
352 Jim Thome .25 .20 .10
353 Bob Tewksbury .10 .08 .04
354 Andujar Cedeno .10 .08 .04
355 Orel Hershiser .10 .08 .04
356 Mike Devereaux .10 .08 .04
358 Dennis Martinez .10 .08 .04
359 Dave Nilsson .10 .08 .04
360 Ozzie Smith .25 .20 .10
361 Eric Anthony .10 .08 .04
362 Scott Sanders .10 .08 .04
363 Paul Sorrento .10 .08 .04
364 Tim Belcher .10 .08 .04
365 Dennis Eckersley .10 .08 .04
366 Mel Rojas .10 .08 .04
367 Tom Henke .10 .08 .04
368 Randy Tomlin .10 .08 .04
369 B.J. Surhoff .10 .08 .04
370 Larry Walker .12 .09 .05
371 Joey Cora .10 .08 .04
372 Mike Harkey .10 .08 .04
373 John Valentin .10 .08 .04
374 Doug Jones .10 .08 .04
375 Dave Justice .25 .20 .10
376 Vince Coleman .10 .08 .04
377 David Hulse .10 .08 .04
378 Kevin Seitzer .10 .08 .04
379 Pete Harnisch .10 .08 .04
380 Ruben Sierra .12 .09 .05
381 Mark Lewis .10 .08 .04
382 Bip Roberts .10 .08 .04
383 Paul Wagner .10 .08 .04
384 Stan Javier .10 .08 .04
385 Barry Larkin .10 .08 .04
386 Mark Portugal .10 .08 .04
387 Roberto Kelly .10 .08 .04
388 Andy Benes .12 .09 .05
389 Felix Fermin .10 .08 .04
390 Marquis Grissom .15 .11 .06
391 Troy Neel .15 .11 .06
392 Chad Kreuter .10 .08 .04
393 Gregg Olson .10 .08 .04
394 Charles Nagy .10 .08 .04
395 Jack McDowell .15 .11 .06
396 Luis Gonzalez .10 .08 .04
397 Benito Santiago .10 .08 .04
398 Chris James .10 .08 .04
399 Terry Mulholland .10 .08 .04
400 Barry Bonds .50 .40 .20
401 Joe Grahe .10 .08 .04
402 Duane Ward .10 .08 .04
403 John Burkett .10 .08 .04
404 Scott Servais .10 .08 .04
405 Bryan Harvey .10 .08 .04
406 Bernard Gilkey .12 .09 .05
407 Greg McMichael .12 .09 .05
408 Tim Wallach .10 .08 .04
409 Ken Caminiti .10 .08 .04
410 John Kruk .12 .09 .05
411 Darrin Jackson .10 .08 .04
412 Mike Gallego .10 .08 .04
413 David Cone .10 .08 .04
414 Lou Whitaker .10 .08 .04
415 Sandy Alomar Jr. .10 .08 .04
416 Bill Wegman .10 .08 .04
417 Pat Borders .10 .08 .04
418 Roger Pavlik .10 .08 .04
419 Pete Smith .10 .08 .04
420 Steve Avery .25 .20 .10
421 David Segui .10 .08 .04
422 Rheal Cormier .10 .08 .04
423 Harold Reynolds .10 .08 .04
424 Edgar Martinez .10 .08 .04
425 Cal Ripken, Jr. .50 .40 .20
426 Jaime Navarro .10 .08 .04
427 Sean Berry .10 .08 .04
428 Bret Saberhagen .10 .08 .04
429 Bob Welch .10 .08 .04
430 Juan Guzman .10 .08 .04
431 Cal Eldred .10 .08 .04
432 Dave Hollins .12 .09 .05
433 Sid Fernandez .10 .08 .04
434 Willie Banks .10 .08 .04
435 Darryl Kile .10 .08 .04
436 Henry Rodriguez .15 .11 .06
437 Tony Fernandez .10 .08 .04
438 Walt Weiss .10 .08 .04
439 Kevin Tapani .10 .08 .04
440 Mark Grace .10 .08 .04
441 Brian Harper .10 .08 .04
442 Kent Mercker .10 .08 .04
443 Anthony Young .10 .08 .04
444 Todd Zeile .10 .08 .04
445 Greg Vaughn .10 .08 .04
446 Ray Lankford .12 .09 .05
447 David Weathers .15 .11 .06
448 Bret Boone .10 .08 .04
449 Charlie Hough .10 .08 .04
450 Roger Clemens .40 .30 .15
451 Mike Morgan .10 .08 .04
452 Doug Drabek .10 .08 .04
453 Danny Jackson .10 .08 .04
454 Dante Bichette .10 .08 .04
455 Roberto Alomar .30 .25 .12
456 Ben McDonald .15 .11 .06
457 Kenny Rogers .10 .08 .04
458 Bill Gullickson .10 .08 .04
459 Darrin Fletcher .10 .08 .04
460 Curt Schilling .10 .08 .04
461 Billy Hatcher .10 .08 .04
462 Howard Johnson .10 .08 .04
463 Mickey Morandini .10 .08 .04
464 Frank Castillo .10 .08 .04
465 Delino DeShields .10 .08 .04
466 Gary Gaetti .10 .08 .04
467 Steve Farr .10 .08 .04
468 Roberto Hernandez .10 .08 .04
469 Jack Armstrong .10 .08 .04
470 Paul Molitor .25 .20 .10
471 Melido Perez .10 .08 .04
472 Greg Hibbard .10 .08 .04
473 Jody Reed .10 .08 .04
474 Tom Gordon .10 .08 .04
475 Gary Sheffield .12 .09 .05
476 John Jaha .12 .09 .05
477 Shawon Dunston .10 .08 .04
478 Reggie Jefferson .10 .08 .04
479 Don Slaught .10 .08 .04
480 Jeff Bagwell .20 .15 .08
481 Tim Pugh .10 .08 .04
482 Kevin Young .10 .08 .04
483 Ellis Burks .10 .08 .04
484 Greg Swindell .10 .08 .04
485 Mark Langston .10 .08 .04
486 Omar Vizquel .12 .09 .05
487 Kevin Brown .10 .08 .04
488 Terry Steinbach .10 .08 .04
489 Mark Lemke .10 .08 .04
490 Matt Williams .15 .11 .06
491 Pete Incaviglia .10 .08 .04
492 Karl Rhodes .12 .09 .05
493 Rick White .15 .11 .06
494 Hal Morris .10 .08 .04
495 Derek Bell .10 .08 .04
496 Luis Polonia .10 .08 .04
497 Otis Nixon .10 .08 .04
498 Ron Darling .10 .08 .04
499 Mitch Williams .10 .08 .04
500 Mike Piazza 1.50 1.25 .60
501 Pat Meares .15 .11 .06
502 Scott Cooper .10 .08 .04
503 Scott Erickson .10 .08 .04
504 Jeff Juden .10 .08 .04
505 Lee Smith .10 .08 .04
506 Bobby Ayala .10 .08 .04
507 Dave Henderson .10 .08 .04
508 Erik Hanson .10 .08 .04
509 Bob Wickman .10 .08 .04
510 Sammy Sosa .10 .08 .04
511 Hector Carrasco .10 .08 .04
512 Tim Davis .15 .11 .06
513 Darren Dreifort .60 .45 .25
514 Robert Eenhoom .20 .15 .08
515 Jorge Fabregas .12 .09 .05
516 Rick Helling .10 .08 .04
517 Rod Henderson .15 .11 .06
518 Ray Holbert .15 .11 .06
519 Mike Kelly .12 .09 .05
520 James Mouton .75 .60 .30
521 Chan Ho Park .75 .60 .30
522 Roberto Petagine .15 .11 .06
523 Ryan Hancock .25 .20 .10
524 Billy Wagner .20 .15 .08
525 Jason Giambi .15 .11 .06
526 Jose Silva .15 .11 .06
527 Terrell Wade .35 .25 .14
528 Todd Dunn .15 .11 .06
529 Alan Benes .75 .60 .30
530 Brooks Kieschnick 1.50 1.25 .60
531 Todd Hollandsworth .25 .20 .10
532 Brad Fullmer .20 .15 .08
533 Steve Soderstrom .15 .11 .06

No.	Player	MT	NR MT	EX
534	Daron Kirkreit	.15	.11	.06
535	Arquimedez Pozo	.15	.11	.06
536	Charles Johnson	.35	.25	.14
537	Preston Wilson	.25	.20	.10
538	Alex Ochoa	.25	.20	.10
539	Derrek Lee	.15	.11	.06
540	Wayne Gomes	.15	.11	.06
541	Jermaine Allensworth	.15	.11	.06
542	Mike Bell	.20	.15	.08
543	Trot Nixon	2.00	1.50	.80
544	Pokey Reese	.15	.11	.06
545	Neifi Perez	.15	.11	.06
546	Johnny Damon	.25	.20	.10
547	Matt Brunson	.20	.15	.08
548	LaTroy Hawkins	.15	.11	.06
549	Eddie Pearson	.15	.11	.06
550	Derek Jeter	.35	.25	.14

1994 Upper Deck Electric Diamond

Each of the regular issue and subset cards from 1994 Upper Deck was also produced in a limited edition premium pack insert "Electric Diamond" version. Where the regular cards have the Upper Deck logo, player and team name in copper foil, the Electric Diamond version has those elements in a silver prismatic foil, along with an "Electric Diamond" identification line next to the UD logo. Backs are identical to regular cards. Electric Diamond cards are found about every other pack, on average.

	MT	NR MT	EX
Complete Set:	350.00	250.00	150.00
Common Player:	.50	.40	.20

Star cards: Valued about 5X to 7X regular cards

1994 Upper Deck Diamond Collection

The premium chase cards in 1994 Upper Deck are a series of Diamond Collection cards issued in regional subsets. Ten cards are found unique to each of three geographic areas of distribution. Western region cards carry a "W" prefix to the card number, Central cards have a "C" prefix and Eastern cards have an "E" prefix. The region is also indicated in silver foil printing on the front of the card, with a large "W, C" or "E" in a compass design. The player's name and team are also presented in a foil strip at bottom. A "Diamond Collection" logo is shown in embossed-look typography in the background. Diamond Collection cards are inserted only in hobby packs.

	MT	NR MT	EX
Complete Set (30):	350.00	260.00	140.00
Complete Central (10):	180.00	135.00	72.50
Complete East (10):	60.00	45.00	24.00
Complete West (10):	125.00	95.00	50.00
Common Player:	4.00	3.00	1.50

No.	Player	MT	NR MT	EX
1C	Michael Jordan	75.00	56.00	30.00
2C	Jeff Bagwell	10.00	7.50	4.00
3C	Barry Larkin	4.50	3.50	1.75
4C	Kirby Puckett	15.00	11.00	6.00
5C	Manny Ramirez	20.00	15.00	8.00
6C	Ryne Sandberg	15.00	11.00	6.00
7C	Ozzie Smith	9.00	6.75	3.50
8C	Frank Thomas	45.00	34.00	18.00
9C	Andy Van Slyke	4.00	3.00	1.50
10C	Robin Yount	8.00	6.00	3.25
1E	Roberto Alomar	9.00	6.75	3.50
2E	Roger Clemens	10.00	7.50	4.00
3E	Len Dykstra	6.00	4.50	2.50
4E	Cecil Fielder	6.00	4.50	2.50
5E	Cliff Floyd	16.00	12.00	6.50
6E	Dwight Gooden	4.00	3.00	1.50
7E	Dave Justice	8.00	6.00	3.25
8E	Don Mattingly	9.00	6.75	3.50
9E	Cal Ripken, Jr.	18.00	13.50	7.25
10E	Gary Sheffield	5.00	3.75	2.00
1W	Barry Bonds	17.50	13.00	7.00
2W	Andres Galarraga	4.50	3.50	1.75
3W	Juan Gonzalez	25.00	18.00	10.00
4W	Ken Griffey, Jr.	45.00	34.00	18.00
5W	Tony Gwynn	6.00	4.50	2.50
6W	Rickey Henderson	4.50	3.50	1.75
7W	Bo Jackson	6.00	4.50	2.50
8W	Mark McGwire	7.00	5.25	2.75
9W	Mike Piazza	30.00	22.00	12.00
10W	Tim Salmon	17.00	12.50	6.75

1994 Upper Deck Mickey Mantle's Long Shots

Retail packaging was the exclusive venue for this insert set of contemporary long-ball sluggers. Horizontal fronts feature color player action photos with holographic foil rendering of the background. In one of the lower corners appears the logo "1994 Mickey Mantle's Long Shots". Backs have a color player photo at top, with a photo of Mantle beneath and a statement by him about the featured player. Previous season and career stats are included. Cards are numbered with an "MM" prefix. Besides the 20 current player cards there is a Mickey Mantle card and two trade cards which could be redeemed for complete insert card sets.

	MT	NR MT	EX
Complete Set (21):	100.00	75.00	40.00
Common Player:	3.00	2.25	1.25
Mickey Mantle Trade	75.00	56.00	30.00
Mickey Mantle Trade	140.00	105.00	55.00

No.	Player	MT	NR MT	EX
1MM	Jeff Bagwell	6.00	4.50	2.50
2MM	Albert Belle	7.00	5.50	3.00
3MM	Barry Bonds	10.00	7.50	4.00
4MM	Jose Canseco	5.00	3.75	2.00
5MM	Joe Carter	5.00	3.75	2.00
6MM	Carlos Delgado	7.50	5.50	3.00
7MM	Cecil Fielder	4.00	3.00	1.50
8MM	Cliff Floyd	8.00	6.00	3.25
9MM	Juan Gonzalez	10.00	7.50	4.00
10MM	Ken Griffey, Jr.	20.00	15.00	8.00
11MM	Dave Justice	7.00	5.25	2.75
12MM	Fred McGriff	5.00	3.75	2.00
13MM	Mark McGwire	4.00	3.00	1.50
14MM	Dean Palmer	3.00	2.25	1.25
15MM	Mike Piazza	12.00	9.00	4.75
16MM	Manny Ramirez	8.00	6.00	3.25
17MM	Tim Salmon	7.00	5.25	2.75
18MM	Frank Thomas	18.00	13.50	7.25
19MM	Mo Vaughn	3.00	2.25	1.25
20MM	Matt Williams	4.00	3.00	1.50
21MM	Mickey Mantle (Header)	10.00	7.50	4.00

Definitions for grading conditions are located in the Introduction of this price guide.

1994 Upper Deck Jumbo Checklists

Each hobby foil box of 1994 Upper Deck cards contains one jumbo checklist card. In Series I, the 5" x 7" cards feature Ken Griffey, Jr. There is a large color action photo along with a hologram of the

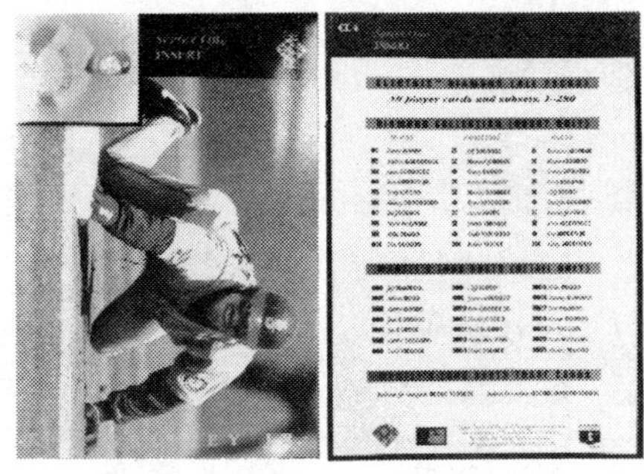

player. Card fronts are highlighted by copper-foil printing. Backs have one of four checklists and are numbered with a CL prefix.

	MT	NR MT	EX
Complete Set:	12.00	9.00	4.75
Common Card:	3.00	2.25	1.25

No.	Card	MT	NR MT	EX
1CL	Numerical Checklist (Ken Griffey, Jr.)	3.00	2.25	1.25
2CL	Alphabetical Checklist (Ken Griffey, Jr.)	3.00	2.25	1.25
3CL	Team Checklist (Ken Griffey, Jr.)	3.00	2.25	1.25
4CL	Insert Checklist (Ken Griffey, Jr.)	3.00	2.25	1.25

1994 Upper Deck Fun Packs

In its second year this product aimed at the young collector again offered a basic set of some 160 players, surrounded by several special subsets. The first nine cards feature Stars of Tomorrow. There is a group of 18 Stand Out cards on which the background can be folded to create a player figure. Profiles cards feature playing tips from six young stars. A group of nine Headline Stars cards features two players on each which fold back to reveal a holographic photo. What's the Call cards offer game problems and cartoon caricatures of nine players. There are nine Fold Outs cards which open to reveal action photos. The subsets concluded with seven heat-activated Fun Cards on which the background temporarily appears when body heat is applied. Each five-card foil pack also includes a scratch-off game card; one for each major league team and one All-Star team for each league.

	MT	NR MT	EX
Complete Set (240):	35.00	26.00	14.00
Common Player:	.05	.04	.02

No.	Player	MT	NR MT	EX
1	Manny Ramirez (Stars of Tomorrow)	1.00	.70	.40
2	Cliff Floyd (Stars of Tomorrow)	1.00	.70	.40
3	Rondell White (Stars of Tomorrow)	.40	.30	.15
4	Carlos Delgado (Stars of Tomorrow)	.60	.45	.25
5	Chipper Jones (Stars of Tomorrow)	.20	.15	.08
6	Javier Lopez (Stars of Tomorrow)	.75	.60	.30
7	Ryan Klesko (Stars of Tomorrow)	1.00	.70	.40
8	Steve Karsay (Stars of Tomorrow)	.20	.15	.08
9	Rich Becker (Stars of Tomorrow)	.10	.08	.04
10	Gary Sheffield	.05	.04	.02
11	Jeffrey Hammonds	.50	.40	.20
12	Roberto Alomar	.25	.20	.10
13	Brent Gates	.15	.11	.06
14	Andres Galarraga	.05	.04	.02
15	Tim Salmon	.60	.45	.25
16	Dwight Gooden	.05	.04	.02
17	Mark Grace	.05	.04	.02
18	Andy Van Slyke	.05	.04	.02
19	Juan Gonzalez	1.00	.70	.40
20	Mickey Tettleton	.05	.04	.02
21	Roger Clemens	.25	.20	.10
22	Will Clark	.25	.20	.10
23	Dave Justice	.35	.25	.14

24	Ken Griffey, Jr.	2.50	2.00	1.00
25	Barry Bonds	.75	.60	.30
26	Bill Swift	.05	.04	.02
27	Fred McGriff	.20	.15	.08
28	Randy Myers	.05	.04	.02
29	Joe Carter	.25	.20	.10
30	Nigel Wilson	.08	.06	.03
31	Mike Piazza	1.50	1.25	.60
32	Dave Winfield	.20	.15	.08
33	Steve Avery	.25	.20	.10
34	Kirby Puckett	.60	.45	.25
35	Frank Thomas	2.50	2.00	1.00
36	Aaron Sele	.60	.45	.25
37	Ricky Gutierrez	.05	.04	.02
38	Curt Schilling	.05	.04	.02
39	Mike Greenwell	.05	.04	.02
40	Andy Benes	.05	.04	.02
41	Kevin Brown	.05	.04	.02
42	Mo Vaughn	.05	.04	.02
43	Dennis Eckersley	.05	.04	.02
44	Ken Hill	.05	.04	.02
45	Cecil Fielder	.20	.15	.08
46	Bobby Jones	.20	.15	.08
47	Tom Glavine	.20	.15	.08
48	Wally Joyner	.05	.04	.02
49	Ellis Burks	.05	.04	.02
50	Jason Bere	.50	.40	.20
51	Randy Johnson	.05	.04	.02
52	Darryl Kile	.05	.04	.02
53	Jeff Montgomery	.05	.04	.02
54	Alex Fernandez	.05	.04	.02
55	Kevin Appier	.05	.04	.02
56	Brian McRae	.05	.04	.02
57	John Wetteland	.05	.04	.02
58	Bob Tewksbury	.05	.04	.02
59	Todd Van Poppel	.05	.04	.02
60	Ryne Sandberg	.40	.30	.15
61	Bret Barberie	.05	.04	.02
62	Phil Plantier	.05	.04	.02
63	Chris Hoiles	.05	.04	.02
64	Tony Phillips	.05	.04	.02
65	Salomon Torres	.08	.06	.03
66	Juan Guzman	.05	.04	.02
67	Paul O'Neill	.05	.04	.02
68	Dante Bichette	.05	.04	.02
69	Len Dykstra	.10	.08	.04
70	Ivan Rodriguez	.06	.05	.02
71	Dean Palmer	.05	.04	.02
72	Brett Butler	.05	.04	.02
73	Rick Aguilera	.05	.04	.02
74	Robby Thompson	.05	.04	.02
75	Jim Abbott	.05	.04	.02
76	Al Martin	.05	.04	.02
77	Roberto Hernandez	.05	.04	.02
78	Jay Buhner	.05	.04	.02
79	Devon White	.05	.04	.02
80	Travis Fryman	.25	.20	.10
81	Jeromy Burnitz	.05	.04	.02
82	John Burkett	.05	.04	.02
83	Orlando Merced	.05	.04	.02
84	Jose Rijo	.05	.04	.02
85	Eddie Murray	.05	.04	.02
86	Howard Johnson	.05	.04	.02
87	Chuck Carr	.05	.04	.02
88	Pedro J. Martinez	.10	.08	.04
89	Charlie Hayes	.05	.04	.02
90	Matt Williams	.05	.04	.02
91	Steve Finley	.05	.04	.02
92	Pat Listach	.05	.04	.02
93	Sandy Alomar, Jr.	.05	.04	.02
94	Delino DeShields	.05	.04	.02
95	Rod Beck	.05	.04	.02
96	Todd Zeile	.05	.04	.02
97	Duane Ward	.05	.04	.02
98	Darryl Hamilton	.05	.04	.02
99	John Olerud	.35	.25	.14
100	Andre Dawson	.05	.04	.02
101	Ozzie Smith	.15	.11	.06
102	Rick Wilkins	.05	.04	.02
103	Alan Trammell	.05	.04	.02
104	Jeff Blauser	.05	.04	.02
105	Bret Boone	.05	.04	.02
106	J.T. Snow	.08	.06	.03
107	Kenny Lofton	.20	.15	.08
108	Cal Ripken, Jr.	.75	.60	.30
109	Carlos Baerga	.40	.30	.15
110	Bip Roberts	.05	.04	.02
111	Barry Larkin	.05	.04	.02
112	Mark Langston	.05	.04	.02
113	Ozzie Guillen	.05	.04	.02
114	Chad Curtis	.05	.04	.02
115	Dave Hollins	.07	.05	.03
116	Reggie Sanders	.05	.04	.02
117	Jeff Conine	.08	.06	.03
118	Mark Whiten	.05	.04	.02
119	Tony Gwynn	.30	.25	.12
120	John Kruk	.07	.05	.03
121	Eduardo Perez	.15	.11	.06
122	Walt Weiss	.05	.04	.02
123	Don Mattingly	.40	.30	.15
124	Rickey Henderson	.15	.11	.06
125	Mark McGwire	.10	.08	.04
126	Wade Boggs	.15	.11	.06
127	Bobby Bonilla	.07	.05	.03
128	Jeff King	.05	.04	.02
129	Jack McDowell	.08	.06	.03
130	Albert Belle	.50	.40	.20
131	Greg Maddux	.25	.20	.10
132	Dennis Martinez	.05	.04	.02
133	Jose Canseco	.35	.25	.14
134	Bryan Harvey	.05	.04	.02
135	Dave Fleming	.05	.04	.02
136	Larry Walker	.08	.06	.03
137	Ken Caminiti	.05	.04	.02
138	Doug Drabek	.05	.04	.02
139	Ron Gant	.06	.05	.02
140	Darren Daulton	.05	.04	.02
141	Ruben Sierra	.07	.05	.03
142	Kirk Rueter	.15	.11	.06
143	Raul Mondesi	1.50	1.25	.60
144	Greg Vaughn	.05	.04	.02
145	Danny Tartabull	.05	.04	.02
146	Eric Karros	.05	.04	.02
147	Chuck Knoblauch	.05	.04	.02
148	Mike Mussina	.25	.20	.10
149	Brady Anderson	.05	.04	.02
150	Paul Molitor	.25	.20	.10
151	Bo Jackson	.08	.06	.03
152	Jeff Bagwell	.25	.20	.10
153	Gregg Jefferies	.05	.04	.02
154	Rafael Palmeiro	.07	.05	.03
155	Orel Hershiser	.05	.04	.02
156	Derek Bell	.05	.04	.02
157	Jeff Kent	.15	.11	.06
158	Craig Biggio	.05	.04	.02
159	Marquis Grissom	.07	.05	.03
160	Matt Mieske	.05	.04	.02
161	Jay Bell	.05	.04	.02
162	Sammy Sosa	.05	.04	.02
163	Robin Ventura	.10	.08	.04
164	Deion Sanders	.20	.15	.08
165	Jimmy Key	.05	.04	.02
166	Cal Eldred	.05	.04	.02
167	David McCarty	.08	.06	.03
168	Carlos Garcia	.05	.04	.02
169	Willie Greene	.05	.04	.02
170	Michael Jordan	9.00	6.75	3.50
171	Roberto Mejia	.08	.06	.03
172	Phil Hiatt	.05	.04	.02
173	Marc Newfield	.20	.15	.08
174	Kevin Stocker	.08	.06	.03
175	Randy Johnson (Standouts)	.05	.04	.02
176	Ivan Rodriguez (Standouts)	.05	.04	.02
177	Frank Thomas (Standouts)	1.00	.70	.40
178	Roberto Alomar (Standouts)	.20	.15	.08
179	Travis Fryman (Standouts)	.15	.11	.06
180	Cal Ripken, Jr. (Standouts)	.40	.30	.15
181	Juan Gonzalez (Standouts)	.60	.45	.25
182	Ken Griffey, Jr. (Standouts)	1.00	.70	.40
183	Albert Belle (Standouts)	.30	.25	.12
184	Greg Maddux (Standouts)	.15	.11	.06
185	Mike Piazza (Standouts)	.75	.60	.30
186	Fred McGriff (Standouts)	.15	.11	.06
187	Robby Thompson (Standouts)	.05	.04	.02
188	Matt Williams (Standouts)	.10	.08	.04
189	Jeff Blauser (Standouts)	.05	.04	.02
190	Barry Bonds (Standouts)	.35	.25	.14
191	Len Dykstra (Standouts)	.10	.08	.04
192	Dave Justice (Standouts)	.20	.15	.08
193	Ken Griffey, Jr. (Profiles)	1.00	.70	.40
194	Barry Bonds (Profiles)	.40	.30	.15
195	Frank Thomas (Profiles)	1.00	.70	.40
196	Juan Gonzalez (Profiles)	.60	.45	.25
197	Randy Johnson (Profiles)	.05	.04	.02
198	Chuck Carr (Profiles)	.05	.04	.02
199	Barry Bonds, Juan Gonzalez (Headline Stars)	1.50	1.25	.60
200	Ken Griffey, Jr., Don Mattingly (Headline Stars)	2.50	2.00	1.00
201	Roberto Alomar, Carlos Baerga (Headline Stars)	1.00	.70	.40
202	Dave Winfield, Robin Yount (Headline Stars)	.75	.60	.30
203	Mike Piazza, Tim Salmon (Headline Stars)	2.00	1.50	.80
204	Albert Belle, Frank Thomas (Headline Stars)	2.50	2.00	1.00
205	Cliff Floyd, Rondell White (Headline Stars)	.75	.60	.30
206	Kirby Puckett, Tony Gwynn (Headline Stars)	1.50	1.25	.60
207	Roger Clemens, Greg Maddux (Headline Stars)	1.25	.90	.50
208	Mike Piazza (What's The Call)	.75	.60	.30
209	Jose Canseco (What's The Call)	.15	.11	.06
210	Frank Thomas (What's The Call)	1.00	.70	.40
211	Roberto Alomar (What's The Call)	.15	.11	.06
212	Barry Bonds (What's The Call)	.35	.25	.14
213	Rickey Henderson (What's The Call)	.08	.06	.03
214	John Kruk (What's The Call)	.08	.06	.03
215	Juan Gonzalez (What's The Call)	.60	.45	.25
216	Ken Griffey, Jr. (What's The Call)	1.00	.70	.40
217	Roberto Alomar (Foldouts)	.35	.25	.14
218	Craig Biggio (Foldouts)	.10	.08	.04
219	Cal Ripken, Jr. (Foldouts)	.90	.70	.35
220	Mike Piazza (Foldouts)	1.50	1.25	.60
221	Brent Gates (Foldouts)	.15	.11	.06
222	Walt Weiss (Foldouts)	.10	.08	.04
223	Bobby Bonilla (Foldouts)	.10	.08	.04
224	Ken Griffey, Jr. (Foldouts)	2.50	2.00	1.00
225	Barry Bonds (Foldouts)	.75	.60	.30
226	Barry Bonds (Fun Cards)	.40	.30	.15
227	Joe Carter (Fun Cards)	.20	.15	.08
228	Mike Greenwell (Fun Cards)	.10	.08	.04
229	Ken Griffey, Jr. (Fun Cards)	1.00	.70	.40
230	John Kruk (Fun Cards)	.10	.08	.04
231	Mike Piazza (Fun Cards)	.75	.60	.30
232	Kirby Puckett (Fun Cards)	.30	.25	.12
233	John Smoltz (Fun Cards)	.10	.08	.04
234	Rick Wilkins (Fun Cards)	.10	.08	.04
235	Checklist 1-40 (Ken Griffey, Jr.)	.50	.40	.20
236	Checklist 41-80 (Frank Thomas)	.50	.40	.20
237	Checklist 81-120 (Barry Bonds)	.20	.15	.08
238	Checklist 121-160 (Mike Piazza)	.35	.25	.14
239	Checklist 161-200 (Tim Salmon)	.20	.15	.08
240	Checklist 201-240 (Juan Gonzalez)	.25	.20	.10

Scratch Off Game Cards

(1)	National League	.05	.04	.02
(2)	Atlanta Braves	.05	.04	.02
(3)	Chicago Cubs	.05	.04	.02
(4)	Cincinnati Reds	.05	.04	.02
(5)	Colorado Rockies	.05	.04	.02
(6)	Florida Marlins	.05	.04	.02
(7)	Houston Astros	.05	.04	.02
(8)	Los Angeles Dodgers	.05	.04	.02
(9)	Montreal Expos	.05	.04	.02
(10)	New York Mets	.05	.04	.02
(11)	Philadelphia Phillies	.05	.04	.02
(12)	Pittsburgh Pirates	.05	.04	.02
(13)	St. Louis Cardinals	.05	.04	.02
(14)	San Diego Padres	.05	.04	.02
(15)	San Francisco Giants	.05	.04	.02
(1)	American League	.05	.04	.02
(2)	Baltimore Orioles	.05	.04	.02
(3)	Boston Red Sox	.05	.04	.02
(4)	California Angels	.05	.04	.02
(5)	Chicago White Sox	.05	.04	.02
(6)	Cleveland Indians	.05	.04	.02
(7)	Detroit Tigers	.05	.04	.02
(8)	Kansas City Royals	.05	.04	.02
(9)	Milwaukee Brewers	.05	.04	.02
(10)	Minnesota Twins	.05	.04	.02
(11)	New York Yankees	.05	.04	.02
(12)	Seattle Mariners	.05	.04	.02
(13)	Texas Rangers	.05	.04	.02
(14)	Toronto Blue Jays	.05	.04	.02

1990 U.S. Playing Card All-Stars

Sold as a box set, these cards are in the standard 2-1/2" x 3-1/2" format but feature rounded corners. Each card features a color player photo with the upper-left and lower-right corners inset to provide for playing card designations. A team logo appears in the lower-left corner. On American League players' cards (Clubs and Spades) the player's name and position appear in white in a blue box beneath the photo. On National Leaguers' cards (Hearts and Diamonds) the box is red and the printing black. Card backs are identical, with blue borders and a multi-colored "1990 Baseball Major League All-Stars" logo on a pinstriped white center panel. The U.S. Playing Card Co. logo is at bottom.

		MT	NR MT	EX
Complete Set (56):		4.00	3.00	1.50
Common Player:		.05	.04	.02
	HEARTS			
J	Bobby Bonilla	.10	.08	.04
Q	Kevin Mitchell	.10	.08	.04
K	Darryl Strawberry	.10	.08	.04
A	Ramon Martinez	.05	.04	.02
2	Mike Scioscia	.05	.04	.02
3	Jeff Brantley	.05	.04	.02
4	Ryne Sandberg	.40	.30	.15
5	Chris Sabo	.10	.08	.04
6	Ozzie Smith	.20	.15	.08
7	John Franco	.05	.04	.02
8	Matt Williams	.10	.08	.04
9	Andre Dawson	.20	.15	.08
10	Benito Santiago	.10	.08	.04
	CLUBS			
J	Wade Boggs	.30	.25	.12
Q	George Bell	.10	.08	.04
K	Rickey Henderson	.25	.20	.10
A	Bob Welch	.05	.04	.02
2	Lance Parrish	.05	.04	.02
3	Bret Saberhagen	.05	.04	.02
4	Gregg Olson	.05	.04	.02
5	Brook Jacoby	.05	.04	.02
6	Ozzie Guillen	.10	.08	.04
7	Ellis Burks	.10	.08	.04
8	Dennis Eckersley	.10	.08	.04
9	Bobby Thigpen	.05	.04	.02
10	Dave Stieb	.05	.04	.02
	DIAMONDS			
J	Tony Gwynn	.25	.20	.10
Q	Will Clark	.30	.25	.12
K	Barry Bonds	.35	.25	.14
A	Frank Viola	.05	.04	.02
2	Greg Olson	.05	.04	.02
3	Dennis Martinez	.10	.08	.04
4	Roberto Alomar	.25	.20	.10
5	Tim Wallach	.05	.04	.02
6	Barry Larkin	.10	.08	.04
7	Neal Heaton	.05	.04	.02
8	Dave Smith	.05	.04	.02
9	Lenny Dykstra	.10	.08	.04
10	Shawon Dunston	.05	.04	.02
	SPADES			
J	Ken Griffey, Jr.	.50	.40	.20
Q	Dave Parker	.20	.15	.08
K	Cecil Fielder	.20	.15	.08
A	Roger Clemens	.10	.08	.04
2	Sandy Alomar	.05	.04	.02
3	Randy Johnson	.10	.08	.04

4	Steve Sax	.05	.04	.02
5	Kelly Gruber	.05	.04	.02
7	Doug Jones	.05	.04	.02
8	Kirby Puckett	.20	.15	.08
9	Chuck Finley, Cal Ripken, Jr.	.05	.04	.02
10	Alan Trammell	.10	.08	.04
	WILD CARDS/JOKERS			
----	Jack Armstrong (Joker)	.05	.04	.02
----	Julio Franco (Joker)	.05	.04	.02
----	Rob Dibble (Wild Card, Randy Myers	.05	.04	.02
----	Mark McGwire (Wild Card, Jose Canseco	.25	.20	.10

1991 U.S. Playing Card All-Stars

In standard 2-1/2" x 3-1/2" format, though with rounded corners, this 56-card set was produced by the country's leading maker of playing cards and sold as a boxed set. Fronts have a color player photo with the top-left and bottom-right corners inset to include playing card designations. A team logo appears in the upper-right corner. On American Leaguers' cards (Hearts and Diamonds), the player's name and position appear in white in a green stripe beneath the photo. National League players (Clubs and Spades) have a yellow stripe with black printing. Backs are red-bordered with a colorful "1991 Baseball Major League All-Stars" logo on a pinstriped white center panel. The U.S. Playing Card Co. logo is at bottom.

		MT	NR MT	EX
	Complete Set (56):	4.00	3.00	1.50
	Common Player:	.05	.04	.02
	HEARTS			
J	Rickey Henderson	.20	.15	.08
Q	Roberto Alomar	.20	.15	.08
K	Dave Henderson	.05	.04	.02
A	Jack Morris	.05	.04	.02
2	Ozzie Guillen	.05	.04	.02
3	Jack McDowell	.10	.08	.04
4	Joe Carter	.10	.08	.04
5	Mark Langston	.05	.04	.02
6	Julio Franco	.05	.04	.02
7	Rick Aguilera	.05	.04	.02
8	Paul Molitor	.15	.11	.06
9	Ruben Sierra	.10	.08	.04
10	Roger Clemens	.10	.08	.04
	CLUBS			
J	Andre Dawson	.15	.11	.06
Q	Chris Sabo	.10		
K	Ivan Calderon	.05	.04	.02
A	Tony Gwynn	.15	.11	.06
2	Paul O'Neill	.05	.04	.02
3	John Smiley	.05	.04	.02
4	Howard Johnson	.10	.08	.04
5	Mike Morgan	.05	.04	.02
6	Barry Larkin	.10	.08	.04
7	Frank Viola	.05	.04	.02
8	Juan Samuel	.05	.04	.02
9	Craig Biggio	.10	.08	.04
10	Lee Smith	.05	.04	.02
	DIAMONDS			
J	Sandy Alomar	.05	.04	.02
Q	Cecil Fielder	.20	.15	.08
K	Cal Ripken, Jr.	.40	.30	.15
A	Ken Griffey, Jr.	.50	.40	.20
2	Carlton Fisk	.15	.11	.06
3	Scott Sanderson	.05	.04	.02
4	Kirby Puckett	.20	.15	.08
5	Jeff Reardon	.05	.04	.02
6	Rafael Palmeiro	.15	.11	.06
7	Bryan Harvey	.05	.04	.02
8	Jimmy Key	.05	.04	.02
9	Harold Baines	.05	.04	.02
10	Dennis Eckersley	.10	.08	.04
	SPADES			
J	Benito Santiago	.05	.04	.02
Q	Ryne Sandberg	.40	.30	.15
K	Ozzie Smith	.20	.15	.08
A	Tom Glavine	.10	.08	.04
2	Eddie Murray	.15	.11	.06
3	Pete Harnisch	.05	.04	.02
4	John Kruk	.10	.08	.04
5	Tom Browning	.05	.04	.02
6	George Bell	.05	.04	.02
7	Dennis Martinez	.10	.08	.04
8	Brett Butler	.05	.04	.02
9	Terry Pendleton	.10	.08	.04
10	Rob Dibble	.05	.04	.02
----	Bobby Bonilla (Joker)	.10	.08	.04
----	Danny Tartabull	.10	.08	.04
----	Wade Boggs (Wild Card)	.25	.20	.12
----	Will Clark (Wild Card)	.25	.20	.10

1992 U.S. Playing Card Aces

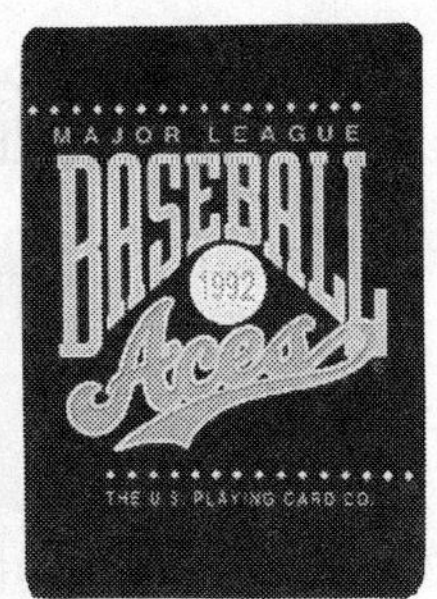

This 56-card boxed sets features 13 top players in each of four major statistical categories, ranked by performance. Hearts feature RBI leaders, Clubs depict home run hitters, batting average leaders are featured on Diamonds and Spades have pitchers with lowest ERAs. Card fronts feature full-bleed color photos, with the playing card suit and rank overprinted in the upper-left and lower-right corners. A team logo is in the lower-left, along with a black box containing the player's name and position in gold. Backs have a red, white and gold "Major League Baseball 1992 Aces" against a black background. The 2-1/2" x 3-1/2" cards have rounded corners.

		MT	NR MT	EX
	Complete Set (56):	6.00	4.50	2.50
	Common Player:	.05	.04	.02
	HEARTS			
J	Will Clark	.20	.15	.08
Q	Howard Johnson	.10	.08	.04
K	Jose Canseco	.25	.20	.10
A	Cecil Fielder	.20	.15	.08
2	Juan Gonzalez	.30	.25	.12
3	Andre Dawson	.15	.11	.06
4	Ron Gant	.15	.11	.06
5	Fred McGriff	.15	.11	.06
6	Joe Carter	.10	.08	.04
7	Frank Thomas	.50	.40	.20
8	Cal Ripkin (Ripken)	.40	.30	.15
9	Ruben Sierra	.10	.08	.04
10	Barry Bonds	.25	.20	.10
	CLUBS			
J	Cal Ripkin (Ripken)	.40	.30	.15
Q	Howard Johnson	.10	.08	.04
K	Cecil Fielder	.20	.15	.08
A	Jose Canseco	.25	.20	.10
2	Chili Davis	.10	.08	.04
3	Mickey Tettleton	.10	.08	.04
4	Danny Tartabull	.10	.08	.04
5	Fred McGriff	.15	.11	.06
6	Andre Dawson	.15	.11	.06
7	Frank Thomas	.50	.40	.20
8	Ron Gant	.15	.11	.06
9	Joe Carter	.10	.08	.04
10	Matt Williams	.10	.08	.04
	DIAMONDS			
J	Ken Griffey, Jr.	.50	.40	.20
Q	Willie Randolph	.05	.04	.02
K	Wade Boggs	.25	.20	.10
A	Julio Franco	.05	.04	.02
2	Danny Tartabull	.10	.08	.04
3	Tony Gwynn	.15	.11	.06
4	Frank Thomas	.50	.40	.20
5	Hal Morris	.10	.08	.04
6	Kirby Puckett	.20	.15	.08
7	Terry Pendleton	.10	.08	.04
8	Rafael Palmeiro	.15	.11	.06
9	Cal Ripkin (Ripken)	.40	.30	.15
10	Paul Molitor	.15	.11	.06
	SPADES			
J	Tim Belcher	.05	.04	.02
Q	Tom Glavine	.10	.08	.04
K	Jose Rijo	.10	.08	.04
A	Dennis Martinez	.05	.04	.02
2	Mike Moore	.05	.04	.02
3	Nolan Ryan	.50	.40	.20
4	Jim Abbott	.10	.08	.04
5	Bill Wegman	.05	.04	.02
6	Mike Morgan	.05	.04	.02
7	Jose DeLeon	.05	.04	.02
8	Pete Harnisch	.05	.04	.02
9	Tom Candiotti	.05	.04	.02
10	Roger Clemens	.10	.08	.04
----	Roger Clemens (Joker)	.10	.08	.04
----	Tom Glavine (Joker)	.10	.08	.04
----	Home Run Rummy Game Instructions	.05	.04	.02
----	Header Card	.05	.04	.02

1992 U.S. Playing Card Team Sets - Braves

Besides several All-Star sets, the U.S. Playing Card Co. in 1992 issued playing card team sets for five teams. All were issued as 56-card boxed sets in a similar format. Cards are 2-1/2" x 3-1/2" with rounded corners. Fronts feature player photos with insets at the upper-left and lower-right corners to allow playing card suit designations and ratings. The player's name and position appears in a colored strip beneath the photo. Backs feature a large color tema logo set again a gray background with either dark blue or red pinstriping and heavy vertical side bars.

		MT	NR MT	EX
	Complete Set (56):	4.50	3.50	1.75
	Common Player:	.05	.04	.02
	HEARTS			
J	Dave Justice	.25	.20	.10
Q	Juan Berenguer	.05	.04	.02
K	Ron Gant	.15	.11	.06
A	Otis Nixon	.10	.08	.04
2	Deion Sanders	.20	.15	.08
3	Mike Stanton	.05	.04	.02
4	Sid Bream	.05	.04	.02
5	Armando Reynoso	.05	.04	.02
6	Brian Hunter	.05	.04	.02
7	Kent Mercker	.05	.04	.02
8	Lonnie Smith	.05	.04	.02
9	Jeff Treadway	.05	.04	.02
10	Tom Glavine	.15	.11	.06
	CLUBS			
J	Pete Smith	.05	.04	.02
Q	Jeff Blauser	.10	.08	.04
K	Charlie Leibrandt	.05	.04	.02
A	Terry Pendleton	.15	.11	.06
2	Mark Lemke	.10	.08	.04
3	Armadno Reynoso	.05	.04	.02
4	Kent Mercker	.05	.04	.02
5	Marvin Freeman	.05	.04	.02
6	Rico Rossy	.05	.04	.02
7	Dave Justice	.25	.20	.10
8	Juan Berenguer	.05	.04	.02
9	Ron Gant	.15	.11	.06
10	Otis Nixon	.10	.08	.04
	DIAMONDS			
J	Brian Hunter	.05	.04	.02
Q	Rafael Belliard	.05	.04	.02
K	Greg Olson	.05	.04	.02
A	Steve Avery	.15	.11	.06
2	Marvin Freeman	.05	.04	.02
3	Pete Smith	.05	.04	.02
4	Mike Heath	.05	.04	.02
5	Jeff Blauser	.10	.08	.04
6	Jim Clancy	.05	.04	.02
7	Rico Rossy	.05	.04	.02
8	John Smoltz	.15	.11	.06
9	Charlie Leibrandt	.05	.04	.02
10	Terry Pendleton	.15	.11	.06
	SPADES			
J	John Smoltz	.15	.11	.06
Q	Lonnie Smith	.05	.04	.02
K	Jeff Treadway	.05	.04	.02
A	Tom Glavine	.15	.11	.06
2	Jim Clancy	.05	.04	.02
3	Deion Sanders	.20	.15	.08
4	Mark Lemke	.10	.08	.04
5	Mike Heath	.05	.04	.02
6	Mike Stanton	.05	.04	.02
7	Sid Bream	.05	.04	.02
8	Rafael Belliard	.05	.04	.02
9	Greg Olson	.05	.04	.02
10	Steve Avery	.15	.11	.06
----	N.L. Logo (Joker)	.05	.04	.02
----	N.L. Logo (Joker)	.05	.04	.02
----	'92 Braves Home Schedule	.05	.04	.02
----	Atlanta Braves History	.05	.04	.02

1992 U.S. Playing Card Team Sets - Cubs

		MT	NR MT	EX
	Complete Set (56):	4.50	3.50	1.75
	Common Player:	.05	.04	.02
	HEARTS			
J	Jerome Walton	.05	.04	.02

		MT	NR MT	EX
Q	Chico Walker	.05	.04	.02
K	Chuck McElroy	.05	.04	.02
A	Andre Dawson	.20	.15	.08
2	Dwight Smith	.05	.04	.02
3	Rick Wilkins	.15	.11	.06
4	Doug Dascenzo	.05	.04	.02
5	Bob Scanlan	.05	.04	.02
6	Chico Walker	.05	.04	.02
7	Paul Assenmacher	.05	.04	.02
8	Mark Grace	.15	.11	.06
9	Ryne Sandberg	.35	.25	.14
10	Danny Jackson	.05	.04	.02
	CLUBS			
J	Hector Villanueva	.05	.04	.02
Q	Doug Dascenzo	.05	.04	.02
K	Shawon Dunston	.10	.08	.04
A	George Bell	.10		
2	Greg Scott	.05	.04	.02
3	Jose Vizcaino	.10	.08	.04
4	Heathcliff Slocumb	.05	.04	.02
5	Danny Jackson	.05	.04	.02
6	Shawn Boskie	.05	.04	.02
7	Luis Salazar	.05	.04	.02
8	Chuck McElroy	.05	.04	.02
9	Andre Dawson	.20	.15	.08
10	Dave Smith	.05	.04	.02
	DIAMONDS			
J	Frank Castillo	.05	.04	.02
Q	Les Lancaster	.05	.04	.02
K	Paul Assenmacher	.05	.04	.02
A	Greg Maddux	.20	.15	.08
2	Shawn Boskie	.05	.04	.02
3	Ced Landrum			
4	Gary Scott	.05	.04	.02
5	Ced Landrum	.05	.04	.02
6	Jose Vizcaino	.10	.08	.04
7	Mike Harkey	.05	.04	.02
8	Jerome Walton	.05	.04	.02
9	George Bell	.10	.08	.04
10	Frank Castillo	.05	.04	.02
	SPADES			
J	Bob Scanlan	.05	.04	.02
Q	Luis Salazar	.05	.04	.02
K	Mark Grace	.15	.11	.06
A	Ryne Sandberg	.35	.25	.14
2	Frank Castillo	.05	.04	.02
3	Mike Harkey	.05	.04	.02
4	Dave Smith	.05	.04	.02
5	Les Lancaster	.05	.04	.02
6	Hector Villanueva	.05	.04	.02
7	Shawon Dunston	.10	.08	.04
8	Heathcliff Slocumb	.05	.04	.02
9	Greg Maddux	.20	.15	.08
10	Dwight Smith	.05	.04	.02
----	N.L. Logo (Joker)	.05	.04	.02
----	N.L. Logo (Joker)	.05	.04	.02
----	'92 Cubs Home Schedule	.05	.04	.02
----	Chicago Cubs Team History	.05	.04	.02

1992 U.S. Playing Card Team Sets - Red Sox

		MT	NR MT	EX
	Complete Set (56):	4.50	3.50	1.75
	Common Player:	.05	.04	.02
	HEARTS			
J	Jack Clark	.05	.04	.02
Q	Jeff Gray	.05	.04	.02
K	Greg Harris	.05	.04	.02
A	Roger Clemens	.25	.20	.10
2	Matt Young	.05	.04	.02
3	John Marzano	.05	.04	.02
4	Dennis Lamp	.05	.04	.02
5	Danny Darwin	.05	.04	.02
6	Jeff Reardon	.10	.08	.04
7	Phil Plantier	.20	.15	.08
8	Tony Fossas	.05	.04	.02
9	Carlos Quintana	.05	.04	.02
10	Wade Boggs	.30	.25	.12
	CLUBS			
J	Luis Rivera	.05	.04	.02
Q	John Marzano	.05	.04	.02
K	Jody Reed	.05	.04	.02
A	Mike Greenwell	.15	.11	.06
2	Danny Darwin	.05	.04	.02
3	Dan Petry	.05	.04	.02
4	Dana Kiecker	.05	.04	.02
5	Greg Harris	.05	.04	.02
6	Tony Pena	.10	.08	.04
7	Dan Petry	.05	.04	.02
8	Jeff Gray	.05	.04	.02
9	Jack Clark	.05	.04	.02
10	Roger Clemens	.25	.20	.10
	DIAMONDS			
J	Tom Brunansky	.05	.04	.02
Q	Mo Vaughn	.25	.20	.10
K	Ellis Burks	.10	.08	.04
A	Joe Hesketh	.05	.04	.02
2	Steve Lyons	.05	.04	.02
3	Dana Kiecker	.05	.04	.02
4	Tony Fossas	.05	.04	.02
5	Matt Young	.05	.04	.02
6	Luis Rivera	.05	.04	.02
7	Tom Bolton	.05	.04	.02
8	Kevin Morton	.05	.04	.02
9	Jody Reed	.05	.04	.02
10	Mike Greenwell	.15	.11	.06
	SPADES			
J	Tony Pena	.10	.08	.04
Q	Phil Plantier	.20	.15	.08
K	Carlos Quintana	.05	.04	.02
A	Wade Boggs	.30	.25	.12
2	Tom Bolton	.05	.04	.02
3	Mo Vaughn	.25	.20	.10
4	Kevin Morton	.05	.04	.02
5	Steve Lyons	.05	.04	.02
6	Tom Brunansky	.05	.04	.02
7	Dennis Lamp	.05	.04	.02
8	Joe Hesketh	.05	.04	.02
9	Ellis Burks	.10	.08	.04
10	Jeff Reardon	.10	.08	.04
----	A.L. Logo (Joker)	.05	.04	.02
----	A.L. Logo (Joker)	.05	.04	.02
----	'92 Red Sox Home Schedule	.05	.04	.02
----	Boston Red Sox Team History	.05	.04	.02

1992 U.S. Playing Card Team Sets - Tigers

		MT	NR MT	EX
	Complete Set (56):	4.50	3.50	1.75
	Common Player:	.05	.04	.02
	HEARTS			
J	Lloyd Moseby	.05	.04	.02
Q	Walt Terrell	.05	.04	.02
K	Mickey Tettleton	.15	.11	.06
A	Cecil Fielder	.25	.20	.10
2	Andy Allanson	.05	.04	.02
3	Dave Bergman	.05	.04	.02
4	Steve Searcy	.05	.04	.02
5	Dan Gakeler	.05	.04	.02
6	Jerry Don Gleaton	.05	.04	.02
7	Paul Gibson	.05	.04	.02
8	Alan Trammell	.20	.15	.08
9	Frank Tanana	.05	.04	.02
10	John Cerutti	.05	.04	.02
	CLUBS			
J	Rob Deer	.05	.04	.02
Q	Skeeter Barnes	.05	.04	.02
K	Pete Incaviglia	.10	.08	.04
A	Tony Phillips	.10	.08	.04
2	Dan Gakeler	.05	.04	.02
3	Walt Terrell	.05	.04	.02
4	David Haas	.05	.04	.02
5	Pete Incaviglia	.10	.08	.04
6	Travis Fryman	.15	.11	.06
7	Scott Aldred	.05	.04	.02
8	Skeeter Barnes	.05	.04	.02
9	Mickey Tettleton	.15	.11	.06
10	Cecil Fielder	.25	.20	.10
	DIAMONDS			
J	Milt Cuyler	.05	.04	.02
Q	Travis Fryman	.15	.11	.06
K	Lou Whitaker	.20	.15	.08
A	Bill Gullickson	.05	.04	.02
2	John Cerutti	.05	.04	.02
3	Steve Searcy	.05	.04	.02
4	David Haas	.05	.04	.02
5	Lloyd Moseby	.05	.04	.02
6	Scott Livingstone	.10	.08	.04
7	John Shelby	.05	.04	.02
8	Mike Henneman	.10	.08	.04
9	Dave Bergman	.05	.04	.02
10	Tony Phillips	.10	.08	.04
	SPADES			
J	Alan Trammell	.20	.15	.08
Q	Jerry Don Gleaton	.05	.04	.02
K	Mike Henneman	.10	.08	.04
A	Frank Tanana	.05	.04	.02
2	Scott Aldred	.05	.04	.02
3	Scott Livingstone	.10	.08	.04
4	John Shelby	.05	.04	.02
5	Rob Deer	.05	.04	.02
6	Milt Cuyler	.05	.04	.02
7	Andy Allanson	.05	.04	.02
8	Paul Gibson	.05	.04	.02
9	Lou Whitaker	.15	.11	.06
10	Bill Gullickson	.05	.04	.02
----	A.L. Logo (Joker)	.05	.04	.02
----	A.L. Logo (Joker)	.05	.04	.02
----	'92 Tigers Home Schedule	.05	.04	.02
----	Detroit Tigers Team History	.05	.04	.02

1992 U.S. Playing Card Team Sets - Twins

		MT	NR MT	EX
	Complete Set (56):	4.50	3.50	1.75
	Common Player:	.05	.04	.02
	HEARTS			
J	Scott Leius	.10	.08	.04
Q	Rick Aguilera	.10	.08	.04
K	Jack Morris	.05	.04	.02
A	Kirby Puckett	.25	.20	.10
2	Junior Ortiz	.05	.04	.02
3	Paul Abbott	.05	.04	.02
4	Steve Bedrosian	.05	.04	.02
5	Pedro Munoz	.10	.08	.04
6	Mike Pagliarulo	.10	.08	.04
7	Greg Gagne	.10	.08	.04
8	Chuck Knoblauch	.15	.11	.06
9	Kevin Tapani	.05	.04	.02
10	Scott Erickson	.10	.08	.04
	CLUBS			
J	Carl Willis	.05	.04	.02
Q	Dan Gladden	.10	.08	.04
K	Kent Hrbek	.20	.15	.08
A	Shane Mack	.15	.11	.06
2	Allan Anderson	.05	.04	.02
3	Al Newman	.10	.08	.04
4	Junior Ortiz	.05	.04	.02
5	Mike Pagliarulo	.10	.08	.04
6	Terry Leach	.05	.04	.02
7	Scott Leius	.10	.08	.04
8	Rick Aguilera	.10	.08	.04
9	Jack Morris	.05	.04	.02
10	Kirby Puckett	.25	.20	.10
	DIAMONDS			
J	Gene Larkin	.10	.08	.04
Q	Randy Bush	.05	.04	.02
K	Chili Davis	.15	.11	.06
A	Brian Harper	.10	.08	.04
2	Al Newman	.05	.04	.02
3	Allan Anderson	.05	.04	.02
4	David West	.05	.04	.02
5	Terry Leach	.05	.04	.02
6	Mark Guthrie	.05	.04	.02
7	Carl Willis	.05	.04	.02
8	Dan Gladden	.10	.08	.04
9	Kent Hrbek	.20	.15	.08
10	Shane Mack	.15	.11	.06
	SPADES			
J	Greg Gagne	.10	.08	.04
Q	Chuck Knoblauch	.15	.11	.06
K	Kevin Tapani	.05	.04	.02
A	Scott Erickson	.10	.08	.04
2	Paul Abbott	.05	.04	.02
3	David West	.05	.04	.02
4	Steve Bedrosian	.05	.04	.02
5	Mark Guthrie	.05	.04	.02
6	Pedro Munoz	.10	.08	.04
7	Gene Larkin	.10	.08	.04
8	Randy Bush	.05	.04	.02
9	Chili Davis	.15	.11	.06
10	Brian Harper	.10	.08	.04
----	A.L. Logo (Joker)	.05	.04	.02
----	A.L. Logo (Joker)	.05	.04	.02
----	'92 Twins Home Schedule	.05	.04	.02
----	Minnesota Twins Team History	.05	.04	.02

1989 Very Fine Pirates

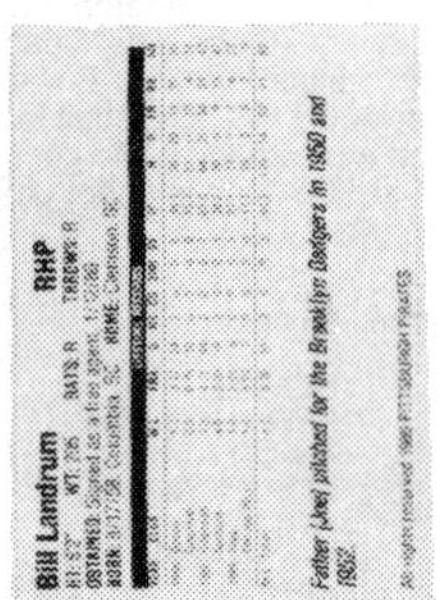

This 30-card set Pittsburgh Pirates team set was sponsored by Veryfine fruit juices, and was issued in the form of two uncut, perforated panels, each containing 15 standard-size cards. A third panel featured color action photographs. The panels were distributed in a stadium promotion to fans attending the April 23 Pirates game at Three Rivers Stadium. The cards display the Pirates traditional black and gold color scheme, and include the player's names and uniform number along the bottom. The "Veryfine" logo appears in the lower right corner. The backs include player data and complete stats.

		MT	NR MT	EX
	Complete 3-Panel Set:	20.00	15.00	8.00
	Complete Singles Card Set:	12.00	9.00	4.75
	Common Player:	.20	.15	.08
0	Junior Ortiz	.20	.15	.08
2	Gary Redus	.30	.25	.12
3	Jay Bell	.40	.30	.15
5	Sid Bream	.30	.25	.12
6	Rafael Belliard	.25	.20	.10
10	Jim Leyland	.30	.25	.12
11	Glenn Wilson	.30	.25	.12
12	Mike La Valliere	.30	.25	.12
13	Jose Lind	.40	.30	.15
14	Ken Oberkfell	.25	.20	.10
15	Doug Drabek	.70	.50	.30
16	Bob Kipper	.20	.15	.08
17	Bob Walk	.25	.20	.10
18	Andy Van Slyke	1.00	.70	.40
23	R.J. Reynolds	.30	.25	.12
24	Barry Bonds	3.00	2.25	1.25
25	Bobby Bonilla	1.50	1.25	.60
26	Neal Heaton	.30	.25	.12
30	Benny Distefano	.30	.25	.12
35	Jim Gott	.35	.25	.14
41	Mike Dunne	.30	.25	.12
43	Bill Landrum	.40	.30	.15
44	John Cangelosi	.25	.20	.10
49	Jeff Robinson	.35	.25	.12
52	Dorn Taylor	.30	.25	.12

54	Brian Fisher	.25	.20	.10
57	John Smiley	.50	.40	.20
----	Ray Miller (31-37, Tommy Sandt	.20	.15	.08
----	Bruce Kimm (32-36)	.20	.15	.08
----	Gene Lamont (32-36)	.20	.15	.08
----	Milt May (39-45)	.20	.15	.08
----	Rich Donnelly (39-45)	.20	.15	.08

1915 Victory Tobacco (T214)

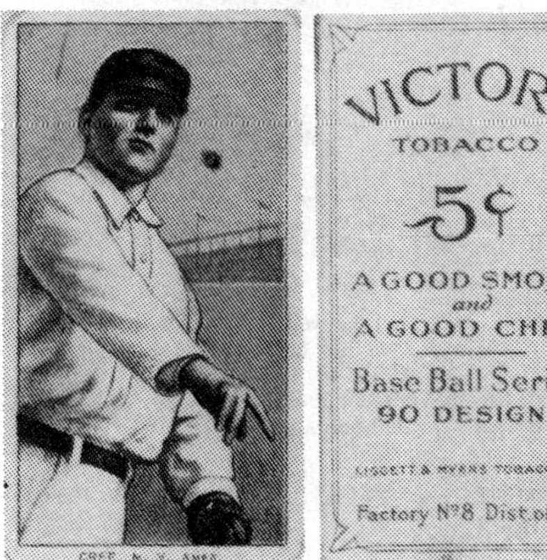

The T214 Victory set of 1915 is another obscure series of tobacco cards that is sometimes mistaken for the better-known T206 "White Border" set. The confusion is understandable because identical player poses were used for both sets. The Victory Tobacco set can be easily identified, however, by the advertising for the Victory brand on the back of the cards. The set features players from the Federal League, both major leagues and at least one minor leaguer. While card backs advertise "90 Designs," fewer subjects have surfaced to date. The set had such limited distribution - apparently restricted to just the Louisiana area - and the cards are so rare that it may be virtually impossible to ever checklist the set completely. Except for the advertising on the backs, the Victory cards are almost identical to the "Type II" Coupon cards (T213), another obscure Louisiana tobacco set issued during the same period. Of the several tobacco sets issued in Louisana in the early part of the 20th Century, the T214 Victory cards are considered the most difficult to find.

		NR MT	EX	VG
	Common Player:	950.00	475.00	285.00
(1)	Chief Bender	1500.	750.00	450.00
(2)	Roger Bresnahan	1500.	750.00	450.00
(3)	Howie Camnitz	950.00	475.00	285.00
(4)	Hal Chase (portrait)	1100.	550.00	330.00
(5)	Hal Chase (throwing)	1100.	550.00	330.00
(6)	Ty Cobb	3000.	1500.	900.00
(7)	Doc Crandall	950.00	475.00	285.00
(8)	Birdie Cree	950.00	475.00	285.00
(9)	Josh Devore	950.00	475.00	285.00
(10)	Ray Demmitt	950.00	475.00	285.00
(11)	Mickey Doolan	950.00	475.00	285.00
(12)	Mike Donlin	950.00	475.00	285.00
(13)	Tom Downey	950.00	475.00	285.00
(14)	Kid Elberfeld	950.00	475.00	285.00
(15)	Russ Ford	950.00	475.00	285.00
(16)	Art Fromme	950.00	475.00	285.00
(17)	Chick Gandil	1250.	625.00	375.00
(18)	Rube Geyer	950.00	475.00	285.00
(19)	Clark Griffith	1500.	750.00	450.00
(20)	Bob Groom	950.00	475.00	285.00
(21)	Hughie Jennings	1500.	750.00	450.00
(22)	Walter Johnson	2000.	1000.	600.00
(23)	Ed Konetchy	950.00	475.00	285.00
(24)	Nap Lajoie	1500.	750.00	450.00
(25)	Ed Lennox	950.00	475.00	285.00
(26)	Sherry Magee	950.00	475.00	285.00
(27)	Rube Marquard	1500.	750.00	450.00
(28)	Chief Meyers (catching)	950.00	475.00	285.00
(29)	Chief Meyers (portrait)	950.00	475.00	285.00
(30)	George Mullin	950.00	475.00	285.00
(31)	Red Murray	950.00	475.00	285.00
(32)	Tom Needham	950.00	475.00	285.00
(33)	Rebel Oakes	950.00	475.00	285.00
(34)	Dode Paskert	950.00	475.00	285.00
(35)	Jack Quinn	950.00	475.00	285.00
(36)	Germany Schaefer	950.00	475.00	285.00
(37)	Wildfire Schulte	950.00	475.00	285.00
(38)	Frank Smith	950.00	475.00	285.00
(39)	Tris Speaker	1350.	675.00	395.00
(40)	Ed Summers	950.00	475.00	285.00
(41)	Bill Sweeney	950.00	475.00	285.00
(42)	Jeff Sweeney	950.00	475.00	285.00
(43)	Ira Thomas	950.00	475.00	285.00
(44)	Joe Tinker	1500.	750.00	450.00
(45)	Heinie Wagner	950.00	475.00	285.00
(46)	Zack Wheat	1500.	750.00	450.00
(47)	Kaiser Wilhelm	950.00	475.00	285.00
(48)	Hooks Wiltse	950.00	475.00	285.00

1913 Voskamp's Coffee Pittsburgh Pirates

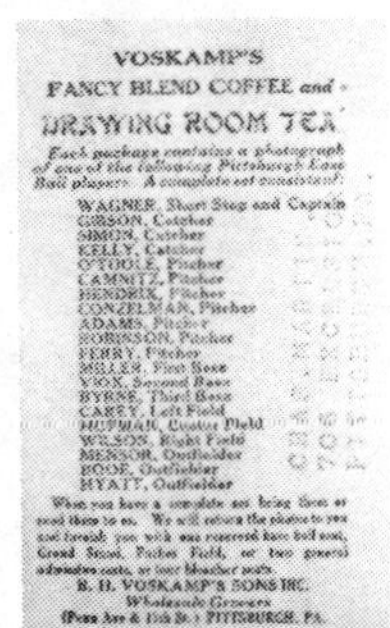

The 1913 Pittsburgh Pirates are featured in this set of cards given away in packages of coffee and tea and redeemable for seats at Pirates games. The 2-1/4" x 3-5/8" cards have player photos on a plain white background. The player's last name and "Pittsburgh" are in black in a lower corner, along with a "Photo by Johnston" credit line. The black-and-white back has a checklist of the set and details of the ticket redemption program. Pose variations of the Hofman and O'Toole cards are reported to exist. The checklist for the unnumbered cards is presented here alphabetically. Because the set was issued just after the great tobacco card era, several of the Pirates in this set are not found on any other cards.

		NR MT	EX	VG
	Complete Set (20):	3500.	1750.	1000.
	Common Player:	150.00	75.00	45.00
(1)	Babe Adams	150.00	75.00	45.00
(2)	Everitt Booe	150.00	75.00	45.00
(3)	Bobby Byrne	150.00	75.00	45.00
(4)	Howie Camnitz	150.00	75.00	45.00
(5)	Max Carey	350.00	175.00	100.00
(6)	Joe Conzelman	150.00	75.00	45.00
(7)	Jack Ferry	150.00	75.00	45.00
(8)	George Gibson	150.00	75.00	45.00
(9)	Claude Hendrix	150.00	75.00	45.00
(10)	Solly Hofman	150.00	75.00	45.00
(11)	Ham Hyatt	150.00	75.00	45.00
(12)	Bill Kelly	150.00	75.00	45.00
(13)	Ed Mensor	150.00	75.00	45.00
(14)	Dots Miller	150.00	75.00	45.00
(15)	Marty O'Toole	150.00	75.00	45.00
(16)	Hank Robinson	150.00	75.00	45.00
(17)	Mike Simon	150.00	75.00	45.00
(18)	Jim Viox	150.00	75.00	45.00
(19)	Honus Wagner	800.00	400.00	240.00
(20)	Owen Wilson	150.00	75.00	45.00

1922 W501

This "strip card" set, known as W501 in the American Card Catalog, is closely connected to the more popular E121 American Caramel set of 1921 and 1922. Measuring the same 2" by 3-1/2", the cards are actually reproductions of the E121 120-card series distributed as strip cards. The W501 cards are numbered in the upper left corner and have the notation "G-4-22" in the upper right corner, apparrently indicating the cards were issued in April of 1922.

		NR MT	EX	VG
	Complete Set:	6000.	3000.	1800.
	Common Player:	25.00	12.50	7.50
1	Ed Rounnel (Rommel)	25.00	12.50	7.50
2	Urban Shocker	25.00	12.50	7.50
3	Dixie Davis	25.00	12.50	7.50
4	George Sisler	40.00	20.00	12.00
5	Bob Veach	25.00	12.50	7.50
6	Harry Heilman (Heilmann)	40.00	20.00	12.00
7a	Ira Falgstead (name incorrect)	25.00	12.50	7.50
7b	Ira Flagstead (name correct)	25.00	12.50	7.50
8	Ty Cobb	700.00	350.00	210.00
9	Oscar Vitt	25.00	12.50	7.50
10	Muddy Ruel	25.00	12.50	7.50
11	Derrill Pratt	25.00	12.50	7.50
12	Ed Gharrity	25.00	12.50	7.50
13	Joe Judge	25.00	12.50	7.50
14	Sam Rice	40.00	20.00	12.00
15	Clyde Milan	25.00	12.50	7.50
16	Joe Sewell	40.00	20.00	12.00
17	Walter Johnson	200.00	100.00	60.00
18	Jack McInnis	25.00	12.50	7.50
19	Tris Speaker	60.00	30.00	18.00
20	Jim Bagby	25.00	12.50	7.50
21	Stanley Coveleskie (Coveleski)	40.00	20.00	12.00
22	Bill Wambsganss	30.00	15.00	9.00
23	Walter Mails	25.00	12.50	7.50
24	Larry Gardner	25.00	12.50	7.50
25	Aaron Ward	25.00	12.50	7.50
26	Miller Huggins	40.00	20.00	12.00
27	Wally Schang	25.00	12.50	7.50
28	Tom Rogers	25.00	12.50	7.50
29	Carl Mays	30.00	15.00	9.00
30	Everett Scott	25.00	12.50	7.50
31	Robert Shawkey	30.00	15.00	9.00
32	Waite Hoyt	40.00	20.00	12.00
33	Mike McNally	25.00	12.50	7.50
34	Joe Bush	30.00	15.00	9.00
35	Bob Meusel	30.00	15.00	9.00
36	Elmer Miller	25.00	12.50	7.50
37	Dick Kerr	25.00	12.50	7.50
38	Eddie Collins	40.00	20.00	12.00
39	Kid Gleason	25.00	12.50	7.50
40	Johnny Mostil	25.00	12.50	7.50
41	Bib Falk (Bibb)	25.00	12.50	7.50
42	Clarence Hodge	25.00	12.50	7.50
43	Ray Schalk	40.00	20.00	12.00
44	Amos Strunk	25.00	12.50	7.50
45	Eddie Mulligan	25.00	12.50	7.50
46	Earl Sheely	25.00	12.50	7.50
47	Harry Hooper	40.00	20.00	12.00
48	Urban Faber	40.00	20.00	12.00
49	Babe Ruth	1000.	500.00	300.00
50	Ivy B. Wingo	25.00	12.50	7.50
51	Earle Neale	30.00	15.00	9.00
52	Jake Daubert	30.00	15.00	9.00
53	Ed Roush	40.00	20.00	12.00
54	Eppa J. Rixey	40.00	20.00	12.00
55	Elwood Martin	25.00	12.50	7.50
56	Bill Killifer (Killefer)	25.00	12.50	7.50
57	Charles Hollocher	25.00	12.50	7.50
58	Zeb Terry	25.00	12.50	7.50
59	Grover Alexander	60.00	30.00	18.00
60	Turner Barber	25.00	12.50	7.50
61	John Rawlings	25.00	12.50	7.50
62	Frank Frisch	40.00	20.00	12.00
63	Pat Shea	25.00	12.50	7.50
64	Dave Bancroft	40.00	20.00	12.00
65	Cecil Causey	25.00	12.50	7.50
66	Frank Snyder	25.00	12.50	7.50
67	Heinie Groh	25.00	12.50	7.50
68	Ross Young (Youngs)	40.00	20.00	12.00
69	Fred Toney	25.00	12.50	7.50
70	Arthur Nehf	25.00	12.50	7.50
71	Earl Smith	25.00	12.50	7.50
72	George Kelly	40.00	20.00	12.00
73	John J. McGraw	50.00	25.00	15.00
74	Phil Douglas	25.00	12.50	7.50
75	Bill Ryan	25.00	12.50	7.50
76	Jess Haines	40.00	20.00	12.00
77	Milt Stock	25.00	12.50	7.50
78	William Doak	25.00	12.50	7.50
79	George Toporcer	25.00	12.50	7.50
80	Wilbur Cooper	25.00	12.50	7.50
81	George Whitted	25.00	12.50	7.50
82	Chas. Grimm	30.00	15.00	9.00
83	Rabbit Maranville	40.00	20.00	12.00
84	Babe Adams	25.00	12.50	7.50
85	Carson Bigbee	25.00	12.50	7.50
86	Max Carey	40.00	20.00	12.00
87	Whitey Glazner	25.00	12.50	7.50
88	George Gibson	25.00	12.50	7.50
89	Bill Southworth	25.00	12.50	7.50
90	Hank Gowdy	25.00	12.50	7.50
91	Walter Holke	25.00	12.50	7.50
92	Joe Oeschger	25.00	12.50	7.50
93	Pete Kilduff	25.00	12.50	7.50
94	Hy Myers	25.00	12.50	7.50
95	Otto Miller	25.00	12.50	7.50
96	Wilbert Robinson	40.00	20.00	12.00
97	Zach Wheat	40.00	20.00	12.00
98	Walter Ruether	25.00	12.50	7.50
99	Curtis Walker	25.00	12.50	7.50
100	Fred Williams	30.00	15.00	9.00
101	Dave Danforth	25.00	12.50	7.50
102	Ed Rounnel (Rommel)	25.00	12.50	7.50
103	Carl Mays	30.00	15.00	9.00
104	Frank Frisch	40.00	20.00	12.00
105	Lou DeVormer	25.00	12.50	7.50
106	Tom Griffith	25.00	12.50	7.50
107	Harry Harper	25.00	12.50	7.50
108a	John Lavan	25.00	12.50	7.50
108b	John J. McGraw	60.00	30.00	18.00
109	Elmer Smith	25.00	12.50	7.50
110	George Dauss	25.00	12.50	7.50
111	Alexander Gaston	25.00	12.50	7.50
112	John Graney	25.00	12.50	7.50
113	Emil Muesel	25.00	12.50	7.50
114	Rogers Hornsby	100.00	50.00	30.00

115	Leslie Nunamaker	25.00	12.50	7.50
116	Steve O'Neill	25.00	12.50	7.50
117	Max Flack	25.00	12.50	7.50
118	Bill Southworth	25.00	12.50	7.50
119	Arthur Nehf	25.00	12.50	7.50
120	Chick Fewster	25.00	12.50	7.50

1928 W502

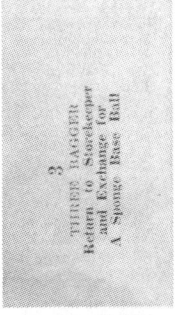

Issued in 1927, this 63-card set is closely related to the York Caramel set (E210) of the same year. The black and white cards measure 1-3/8" by 2-1/2" and display the player's name at the bottom in capital letters preceded by a number in parenthesis. The backs of the cards read either "One Bagger," "Three Bagger" or "Home Run", and were apparently designed to be used as part of a baseball game. There are tow cards known to exist for cards numbers 26, 38, 40, 55 and 59. The set carries the American Card Catalog designation W502.

		NR MT	EX	VG
Complete Set:		4950.	2450.	1400.
Common Player:		25.00	12.50	7.50
1	Burleigh Grimes	65.00	32.00	19.50
2	Walter Reuther	25.00	12.50	7.50
3	Joe Dugan	35.00	17.50	10.50
4	Red Faber	65.00	32.00	19.50
5	Gabby Hartnett	65.00	32.00	19.50
6	Babe Ruth	1100.	550.00	330.00
7	Bob Meusel	35.00	17.50	10.50
8	Herb Pennock	65.00	32.00	19.50
9	George Burns (photo is George J., not George H. Burns)	25.00	12.50	7.50
10	Joe Sewell	65.00	32.00	19.50
11	George Uhle	25.00	12.50	7.50
12	Bob O'Farrell	25.00	12.50	7.50
13	Rogers Hornsby	175.00	87.00	52.00
14	Pie Traynor	65.00	32.00	19.50
15	Clarence Mitchell	25.00	12.50	7.50
16	Eppa Rixey	65.00	32.00	19.50
17	Carl Mays	35.00	17.50	10.50
18	Adolfo Luque	25.00	12.50	7.50
19	Dave Bancroft	65.00	32.00	19.50
20	George Kelly	65.00	32.00	19.50
21	Earl Combs (Earle)	65.00	32.00	19.50
22	Harry Heilmann	65.00	32.00	19.50
23	Ray W. Schalk	65.00	32.00	19.50
24	Johnny Mostil	25.00	12.50	7.50
25	Hack Wilson (photo actually Art Wilson)	65.00	32.00	19.50
26a	Lou Gehrig	1000.	500.00	300.00
26b	Stanley Harris	25.00	12.50	7.50
27	Ty Cobb	1000.	500.00	300.00
28	Tris Speaker	125.00	62.00	37.00
29	Tony Lazzeri	50.00	25.00	15.00
30	Waite Hoyt	65.00	32.00	19.50
31	Sherwood Smith	25.00	12.50	7.50
32	Max Carey	65.00	32.00	19.50
33	Eugene Hargrave	25.00	12.50	7.50
34	Miguel L. Gonzales	25.00	12.50	7.50
35	Joe Judge	25.00	12.50	7.50
36	E.C. (Sam) Rice	65.00	32.00	19.50
37	Earl Sheely	25.00	12.50	7.50
38a	Sam Jones	25.00	12.50	7.50
38b	Emory E. Rigney	25.00	12.50	7.50
39	Bib A. Falk (Bibb)	25.00	12.50	7.50
40a	Nick Altrock	25.00	12.50	7.50
40b	Willie Kamm	25.00	12.50	7.50
42	John J. McGraw	125.00	62.00	37.00
43	Artie Nehf	25.00	12.50	7.50
44	Grover Alexander	125.00	62.00	37.00
45	Paul Waner	65.00	32.00	19.50
46	William H. Terry	100.00	50.00	30.00
47	Glenn Wright	25.00	12.50	7.50
48	Earl Smith	25.00	12.50	7.50
49	Leon (Goose) Goslin	65.00	32.00	19.50
50	Frank Frisch	65.00	32.00	19.50
51	Joe Harris	25.00	12.50	7.50
52	Fred (Cy) Williams	35.00	17.50	10.50
53	Eddie Roush	65.00	32.00	19.50
54	George Sisler	65.00	32.00	19.50
55a	Ed Rommel	25.00	12.50	7.50
55b	L. Waner (photo actually Paul Waner)	65.00	32.00	19.50
56	Roger Peckinpaugh	25.00	12.50	7.50
57	Stanley Coveleskie (Coveleski)	65.00	32.00	19.50
58	Lester Bell	25.00	12.50	7.50
59a	Dave Bancroft	65.00	32.00	19.50
59b	L. Waner	65.00	32.00	19.50
60	John P. McInnis	25.00	12.50	7.50

1922 W503

Issued circa 1923, this 64-card set of blank-backed cards, measuring 1-3/4" by 2-3/4", feature black and white player photos surrounded by a white border. The player's name and team appear on the card, along with a card number in either the left or right bottom corner. There is no indication of the set's producer, although it is believed the cards were issued with candy or gum. The set carries a W503 American Card Catalog designation.

		NR MT	EX	VG
Complete Set:		3700.	1850.	1110.
Common Player:		35.00	17.50	10.50
1	Joe Bush	25.00	12.50	7.50
2	Wally Schang	35.00	17.50	10.50
3	Dave Robertson	35.00	17.50	10.50
4	Wally Pipp	35.00	17.50	10.50
5	Bill Ryan	35.00	17.50	10.50
6	George Kelly	90.00	45.00	27.00
7	Frank Snyder	35.00	17.50	10.50
8	Jimmy O'Connell	35.00	17.50	10.50
9	Bill Cunningham	35.00	17.50	10.50
10	Norman McMillan	35.00	17.50	10.50
11	Waite Hoyt	90.00	45.00	27.00
12	Art Nehf	35.00	17.50	10.50
13	George Sisler	90.00	45.00	27.00
14	Al DeVormer	35.00	17.50	10.50
15	Casey Stengel	200.00	100.00	60.00
16	Ken Williams	35.00	17.50	10.50
17	Joe Dugan	35.00	17.50	10.50
18	"Irish" Meusel	35.00	17.50	10.50
19	Bob Meusel	35.00	17.50	10.50
20	Carl Mays	35.00	17.50	10.50
22	Jess Barnes	35.00	17.50	10.50
23	Walter Johnson	90.00	45.00	27.00
24	Claude Jonnard	35.00	17.50	10.50
25	Dave Bancroft	90.00	45.00	27.00
26	Johnny Rawlings	35.00	17.50	10.50
27	"Pep" Young	35.00	17.50	10.50
28	Earl Smith	35.00	17.50	10.50
29	Willie Kamm	35.00	17.50	10.50
30	Art Fletcher	35.00	17.50	10.50
31	"Kid" Gleason	35.00	17.50	10.50
32	"Babe" Ruth	900.00	450.00	270.00
33	Guy Morton	35.00	17.50	10.50
34	Heinie Groh	35.00	17.50	10.50
35	Leon Cadore	35.00	17.50	10.50
36	Joe Tobin	35.00	17.50	10.50
37	"Rube" Marquard	90.00	45.00	27.00
38	Grover Alexander	125.00	62.00	37.00
39	George Burns	35.00	17.50	10.50
40	Joe Oeschger	35.00	17.50	10.50
41	"Chick" Shorten	35.00	17.50	10.50
42	Roger Hornsby (Rogers)	200.00	100.00	60.00
43	Adolfo Luque	35.00	17.50	10.50
44	Zack Wheat	125.00	62.00	37.00
45	Herb Pruett (Hub)	35.00	17.50	10.50
46	Rabbit Maranville	125.00	62.00	37.00
47	Jimmy Ring	35.00	17.50	10.50
48	Sherrod Smith	35.00	17.50	10.50
49	Lea Meadows (Lee)	35.00	17.50	10.50
50	Aaron Ward	35.00	17.50	10.50
51	Herb Pennock	125.00	62.00	37.00
52	Carlson Bigbee (Carson)	35.00	17.50	10.50
53	Max Carey	125.00	62.00	37.00
54	Charles Robertson	35.00	17.50	10.50
55	Urban Shocker	35.00	17.50	10.50
56	Dutch Ruether	35.00	17.50	10.50
57	Jake Daubert	35.00	17.50	10.50
58	Louis Guisto	35.00	17.50	10.50
59	Ivy Wingo	35.00	17.50	10.50
60	Bill Pertica	35.00	17.50	10.50
61	Luke Sewell	35.00	17.50	10.50
62	Hank Gowdy	35.00	17.50	10.50
63	Jack Scott	35.00	17.50	10.50
64	Stan Coveleskie (Coveleski)	125.00	62.00	37.00

1926 W512

One of the many "strip card" sets of the period (so-called because the cards were sold in strips), the W512 set was issued in 1926 and includes 20 baseball players among its 60 cards. Also featured are boxers, golfers, tennis players, aviators, movie stars and other celebrities. The tiny (1-3/8" by 2-1/4") cards feature rather crude color drawings of the subjects with their names below. The card number appears in the lower left corner. Baseball players lead off the set and are numbered from 1 to 20. Eight of the players are Hall of Famers. Like most strip cards, they have blank backs.

		NR MT	EX	VG
Complete Set:		500.00	250.00	150.00
Common Player:		15.00	7.50	4.50
1	Dave Bancroft	40.00	20.00	12.00
2	Grover Alexander	65.00	32.00	19.50
3	"Ty" Cobb	175.00	87.00	52.00
4	Tris Speaker	65.00	32.00	19.50
5	Glen Wright (Glenn)	15.00	7.50	4.50
6	"Babe" Ruth	200.00	100.00	60.00
7	Everett Scott	15.00	7.50	4.50
8	Frank Frisch	40.00	20.00	12.00
9	Rogers Hornsby	80.00	40.00	24.00
10	Dazzy Vance	40.00	20.00	12.00

1926 W513

This "strip card" set, issued in 1928 was actually a continuation of the W512 set issued two years earlier and is numbered starting with number 61 where the W512 set ended. The blank-backed cards measure 1-3/8" by 2-1/4" and display color drawings of the various celebrities featured in the set, which includes the 26 baseball palyers listed here. (Ten are Hall of Famers.) The cards are numbered in the lower left corner.

		NR MT	EX	VG
Complete Set:		550.00	275.00	165.00
Common Player:		15.00	7.50	4.50
61	Eddie Roush	30.00	15.00	9.00
62	Waite Hoyt	30.00	15.00	9.00
63	"Gink" Hendrick	15.00	7.50	4.50
64	"Jumbo" Elliott	15.00	7.50	4.50
65	John Miljus	15.00	7.50	4.50
66	Jumping Joe Dugan	18.00	9.00	5.50
67	Smiling Bill Terry	40.00	20.00	12.00
68	Herb Pennock	30.00	15.00	9.00
69	Rube Benton	15.00	7.50	4.50
70	Paul Waner	30.00	15.00	9.00
71	Adolfo Luque	15.00	7.50	4.50
72	Burleigh Grimes	30.00	15.00	9.00
73	Lloyd Waner	30.00	15.00	9.00
74	Hack Wilson	30.00	15.00	9.00
75	Hal Carlson	15.00	7.50	4.50
76	L. Grantham	15.00	7.50	4.50
77	Wilcey Moore (Wilcy)	15.00	7.50	4.50
78	Jess Haines	30.00	15.00	9.00
79	Tony Lazzeri	18.00	9.00	5.50
80	Al DeVormer	15.00	7.50	4.50
81	Joe Harris	15.00	7.50	4.50
82	Pie Traynor	30.00	15.00	9.00
83	Mark Koenig	15.00	7.50	4.50
84	Babe Herman	18.00	9.00	5.50
85	George Harper	15.00	7.50	4.50
86	Earl Coombs (Earle Combs)	30.00	15.00	9.00

1919 W514

88
BOB VEACH
LEFT FIELD
DETROIT "TIGERS" A. L.

Consisting of 120 cards, the W514 set is the largest of the various "strip card" issues, so called because the cards were sold in strips. Dating to 1919, it is also one of the earliest and most widely-collected. The color drawings measure 1-3/8" by 2-1/2" and display the card number in the lower corner inside the frame that surrounds the picture. The player's name, position and team appear in the bottom border of the blank-backed cards. The set contains two dozen Hall of Famers and holds an additional interest for baseball historians because it includes seven of the eight Chicago "Black Sox" who were banned from baseball for their alleged role in throwing the 1919 World Series. The most famous of them, "Shoeless" Joe Jackson, makes his only strip card appearance in this set.

		NR MT	EX	VG
Complete Set:		2900.	1450.	870.00
Common Player:		18.00	9.00	5.50
1	Ira Flagstead	18.00	9.00	5.50
2	Babe Ruth	350.00	175.00	105.00
3	Happy Felsch	20.00	10.00	6.00
4	Doc Lavan	18.00	9.00	5.50
5	Phil Douglas	18.00	9.00	5.50
6	Earle Neale	20.00	10.00	6.00
7	Leslie Nunamaker	18.00	9.00	5.50
8	Sam Jones	18.00	9.00	5.50
9	Claude Hendrix	18.00	9.00	5.50
10	Frank Schulte	18.00	9.00	5.50
11	Cactus Cravath	20.00	10.00	6.00
12	Pat Moran	18.00	9.00	5.50
13	Dick Rudolph	18.00	9.00	5.50
14	Arthur Fletcher	18.00	9.00	5.50
15	Joe Jackson	500.00	250.00	150.00
16	Bill Southworth	18.00	9.00	5.50
17	Ad Luque	18.00	9.00	5.50
18	Charlie Deal	18.00	9.00	5.50
19	Al Mamaux	18.00	9.00	5.50
20	Stuffy McInness (McInnis)	18.00	9.00	5.50
21	Rabbit Maranville	35.00	17.50	10.50
22	Max Carey	35.00	17.50	10.50
23	Dick Kerr	18.00	9.00	5.50
24	George Burns	18.00	9.00	5.50
25	Eddie Collins	35.00	17.50	10.50
26	Steve O'Neil (O'Neill)	18.00	9.00	5.50
27	Bill Fisher	18.00	9.00	5.50
28	Rube Bressler	18.00	9.00	5.50
29	Bob Shawkey	20.00	10.00	6.00
30	Donie Bush	18.00	9.00	5.50
31	Chick Gandil	20.00	10.00	6.00
32	Ollie Zeider	18.00	9.00	5.50
33	Vean Gregg	18.00	9.00	5.50
34	Miller Huggins	35.00	17.50	10.50
35	Lefty Williams	20.00	10.00	6.00
36	Tub Spencer	18.00	9.00	5.50
37	Lew McCarty	18.00	9.00	5.50
38	Hod Eller	18.00	9.00	5.50
39	Joe Gedeon	18.00	9.00	5.50
40	Dave Bancroft	35.00	17.50	10.50
41	Clark Griffith	35.00	17.50	10.50
42	Wilbur Cooper	18.00	9.00	5.50
43	Ty Cobb	300.00	150.00	90.00
44	Roger Peckinpaugh	18.00	9.00	5.50
45	Nic Carter (Nick)	18.00	9.00	5.50
46	Bob Roth	18.00	9.00	5.50
47	Heinie Groh	18.00	9.00	5.50
48	Frank Davis	18.00	9.00	5.50
49	Leslie Mann	18.00	9.00	5.50
50	Fielder Jones	18.00	9.00	5.50
51	Bill Doak	18.00	9.00	5.50
52	John J. McGraw	24.00	12.00	7.25
53	Charles Hollocher	18.00	9.00	5.50
54	Babe Adams	18.00	9.00	5.50
55	Dode Paskert	18.00	9.00	5.50
56	Roger Hornsby (Rogers)	18.00	9.00	5.50
57	Max Rath	60.00	30.00	18.00
58	Jeff Pfeffer	18.00	9.00	5.50
59	Nick Cullop	18.00	9.00	5.50
60	Ray Schalk	35.00	17.50	10.50
61	Bill Jacobson	18.00	9.00	5.50
62	Nap Lajoie	25.00	12.50	7.50
63	George Gibson	18.00	9.00	5.50
64	Harry Hooper	35.00	17.50	10.50
65	Grover Alexander	24.00	12.00	7.25
66	Ping Bodie	18.00	9.00	5.50
67	Hank Gowdy	18.00	9.00	5.50
68	Jake Daubert	20.00	10.00	6.00
69	Red Faber	35.00	17.50	10.50
70	Ivan Olson	18.00	9.00	5.50
71	Pickles Dilhoefer	18.00	9.00	5.50
72	Christy Mathewson	60.00	30.00	18.00
73	Ira Wingo (Ivy)	18.00	9.00	5.50
74	Fred Merkle	20.00	10.00	6.00
75	Frank Baker	35.00	17.50	10.50
76	Bert Gallia	18.00	9.00	5.50
77	Milton Watson	18.00	9.00	5.50
78	Bert Shotten (Shotton)	18.00	9.00	5.50
79	Sam Rice	35.00	17.50	10.50
80	Dan Greiner	18.00	9.00	5.50
81	Larry Doyle	18.00	9.00	5.50
82	Eddie Cicotte	20.00	10.00	6.00
83	Hugo Bezdek	18.00	9.00	5.50
84	Wally Pipp	12.00	6.00	3.50
85	Eddie Rousch (Roush)	35.00	17.50	10.50
86	Slim Sallee	18.00	9.00	5.50
87	Bill Killifer (Killefer)	18.00	9.00	5.50
88	Bob Veach	18.00	9.00	5.50
89	Jim Burke	18.00	9.00	5.50
90	Everett Scott	18.00	9.00	5.50
91	Buck Weaver	20.00	10.00	6.00
92	George Whitted	18.00	9.00	5.50
93	Ed Konetchy	18.00	9.00	5.50
94	Walter Johnson	60.00	30.00	18.00
95	Sam Crawford	35.00	17.50	10.50
96	Fred Mitchell	18.00	9.00	5.50
97	Ira Thomas	18.00	9.00	5.50
98	Jimmy Ring	18.00	9.00	5.50
99	Wally Shange (Schang)	18.00	9.00	5.50
100	Benny Kauff	18.00	9.00	5.50
101	George Sisler	35.00	17.50	10.50
102	Tris Speaker	24.00	12.00	7.25
103	Carl Mays	20.00	10.00	6.00
104	Buck Herzog	18.00	9.00	5.50
105	Swede Risberg	20.00	10.00	6.00
106	Hugh Jennings	35.00	17.50	10.50
107	Pep Young	18.00	9.00	5.50
108	Walter Reuther	18.00	9.00	5.50
109	Joe Gharrity	18.00	9.00	5.50
110	Zach Wheat	35.00	17.50	10.50
111	Jim Vaughn	18.00	9.00	5.50
112	Kid Gleason	18.00	9.00	5.50
113	Casey Stengel	60.00	30.00	18.00
114	Hal Chase	20.00	10.00	6.00
115	Oscar Stange (Stanage)	18.00	9.00	5.50
116	Larry Shean	18.00	9.00	5.50
117	Steve Pendergast	18.00	9.00	5.50
118	Larry Kopf	18.00	9.00	5.50
119	Charles Whiteman	18.00	9.00	5.50
120	Jess Barnes	18.00	9.00	5.50

1923 W515

Cards in the 60-card "strip set" measure 1-5/8" by 2-3/8" and feature color drawings. The card number along with the player's name, position and team appear in the bottom border. Most cards also display a "U&U" copyright line, indicating that the drawings for the blank-backed set were provided by Underwood & Underwood, a major news photo service of the day. The set has a heavy emphasis on New York players with 39 of the 60 cards depicting members of the Yankees, Dodgers or Giants. Babe Ruth appears on two cards and two other cards picture two players each. The set includes 23 Hall of Famers.

		NR MT	EX	VG
Complete Set:		1750.	875.00	525.00
Common Player:		22.00	11.00	6.50
1	Bill Cunningham	22.00	11.00	6.50
2	Al Mamaux	22.00	11.00	6.50
3	"Babe" Ruth	350.00	175.00	105.00
4	Dave Bancroft	35.00	17.50	10.50
5	Ed Rommel	22.00	11.00	6.50
6	"Babe" Adams	22.00	11.00	6.50
7	Clarence Walker	22.00	11.00	6.50
8	Waite Hoyt	35.00	17.50	10.50
9	Bob Shawkey	25.00	12.50	7.50
10	"Ty" Cobb	300.00	150.00	90.00
11	George Sisler	35.00	17.50	10.50
12	Jack Bentley	22.00	11.00	6.50
13	Jim O'Connell	22.00	11.00	6.50
14	Frank Frisch	35.00	17.50	10.50
15	Frank Baker	35.00	17.50	10.50
16	Burleigh Grimes	35.00	17.50	10.50
17	Wally Schang	22.00	11.00	6.50
18	Harry Heilman (Heilmann)	35.00	17.50	10.50
19	Aaron Ward	22.00	11.00	6.50
20	Carl Mays	25.00	12.50	7.50
21	The Meusel Bros. (Bob Meusel, Irish Meusel)	22.00	11.00	6.50
22	Arthur Nehf	22.00	11.00	6.50
23	Lee Meadows	22.00	11.00	6.50
24	"Casey" Stengel	55.00	27.00	16.50
25	Jack Scott	22.00	11.00	6.50
26	Kenneth Williams	25.00	12.50	7.50
27	Joe Bush	25.00	12.50	7.50
28	Tris Speaker	45.00	22.00	13.50
29	Ross Young (Youngs)	22.00	11.00	6.50
30	Joe Dugan	25.00	12.50	7.50
31	The Barnes Bros. (Jesse Barnes, Virgil Barnes)	25.00	12.50	7.50
32	George Kelly	35.00	17.50	10.50
33	Hugh McQuillen (McQuillan)	22.00	11.00	6.50
34	Hugh Jennings	35.00	17.50	10.50
35	Tom Griffith	22.00	11.00	6.50
36	Miller Huggins	35.00	17.50	10.50
37	"Whitey" Witt	22.00	11.00	6.50
38	Walter Johnson	55.00	27.00	16.50
39	"Wally" Pipp	22.00	11.00	6.50
40	"Dutch" Reuther	22.00	11.00	6.50
41	Jim Johnston	22.00	11.00	6.50
42	Willie Kamm	22.00	11.00	6.50
43	Sam Jones	22.00	11.00	6.50
44	Frank Snyder	22.00	11.00	6.50
45	John McGraw	45.00	22.00	13.50
46	Everett Scott	22.00	11.00	6.50
47	"Babe" Ruth	350.00	175.00	105.00
48	Urban Shocker	22.00	11.00	6.50
49	Grover Alexander	45.00	22.00	13.50
50	"Rabbit" Maranville	35.00	17.50	10.50
51	Ray Schalk	35.00	17.50	10.50
52	"Heinie" Groh	22.00	11.00	6.50
53	Wilbert Robinson	35.00	17.50	10.50
54	George Burns	22.00	11.00	6.50
55	Rogers Hornsby	50.00	25.00	15.00
56	Zack Wheat	35.00	17.50	10.50
57	Eddie Roush	35.00	17.50	10.50
58	Eddie Collins	35.00	17.50	10.50
59	Charlie Hollocher	22.00	11.00	6.50
60	Red Faber	35.00	17.50	10.50

1920 W516-1

This "strip card" set consists of 30 cards featuring featuring drawings - either portraits or full-length action poses. The blank-backed cards measure 1-1/2" by 2-1/2". The player's name, position and team appear beneath the photo, along with the card number. The set can be identified by an "IFS" copyright symbol. representing International Feature Service. The set includes a dozen Hall of Famers.

		NR MT	EX	VG
Complete Set:		1050.	525.00	315.00
Common Player:		23.00	11.50	7.00
1	Babe Ruth	350.00	175.00	105.00
2	Heinie Groh	23.00	11.50	7.00
3	Ping Bodie	23.00	11.50	7.00
4	Ray Shalk (Schalk)	35.00	17.50	10.50
5	Tris Speaker	45.00	22.00	13.50
6	Ty Cobb	300.00	150.00	90.00
7	Roger Hornsby (Rogers)	55.00	27.00	16.50
8	Walter Johnson	55.00	27.00	16.50
9	Grover Alexander	45.00	22.00	13.50
10	George Burns	23.00	11.50	7.00
11	Jimmy Ring	23.00	11.50	7.00
12	Jess Barnes	23.00	11.50	7.00
13	Larry Doyle	23.00	11.50	7.00
14	Arty Fletcher	23.00	11.50	7.00
15	Dick Rudolph	23.00	11.50	7.00
16	Benny Kauf (Kauff)	23.00	11.50	7.00
17	Art Nehf	23.00	11.50	7.00
18	Babe Adams	23.00	11.50	7.00
19	Will Cooper	23.00	11.50	7.00
20	R. Peckinpaugh	23.00	11.50	7.00

21	Eddie Cicotte	25.00	12.50	7.50
22	Hank Gowdy	23.00	11.50	7.00
23	Eddie Collins	35.00	17.50	10.50
24	Christy Mathewson	55.00	27.00	16.50
25	Clyde Milan	23.00	11.50	7.00
26	M. Kelley (should be G. Kelly)	35.00	17.50	10.50
27	Ed Hooper (Harry)	35.00	17.50	10.50
28	Pep. Young	23.00	11.50	7.00
29	Eddie Rousch (Roush)	35.00	17.50	10.50
30	Geo. Bancroft (Dave)	55.00	27.00	16.50

1921 W516-2

This set is essentially a re-issue of the W516-1 set of the previous year with one major change. The cards are identical to the W516-1 set, except the numbers have been changed and the pictures have all been reversed. The blank-backed cards measure 1-1/2" by 2-1/2" and feature color drawings with the player's name, position and team beneath the picture, along with the card number. The cards display an "IFS" copyright symbol.

		NR MT	EX	VG
Complete Set:		1200.	600.00	360.00
Common Player:		20.00	10.00	6.00
1	George Burns	20.00	10.00	6.00
2	Grover Alexander	90.00	45.00	27.00
3	Walter Johnson	150.00	75.00	45.00
4	Roger Hornsby (Rogers)	100.00	50.00	30.00
5	Ty Cobb	325.00	162.00	97.00
6	Tris Speaker	90.00	45.00	27.00
7	Ray Shalk (Schalk)	42.00	21.00	12.50
8	Ping Bodie	20.00	10.00	6.00
9	Heinie Groh	20.00	10.00	6.00
10	Babe Ruth	400.00	200.00	120.00
11	R. Peckinpaugh	20.00	10.00	6.00
12	Will. Cooper	20.00	10.00	6.00
13	Babe Adams	20.00	10.00	6.00
14	Art Nehf	20.00	10.00	6.00
15	Benny Kauf (Kauff)	20.00	10.00	6.00
16	Dick Rudolph	20.00	10.00	6.00
17	Arty. Fletcher	20.00	10.00	6.00
18	Larry Doyle	20.00	10.00	6.00
19	Jess Barnes	20.00	10.00	6.00
20	Jimmy Ring	20.00	10.00	6.00
21	George Bancroft (Dave)	32.00	16.00	9.50
22	Eddie Rousch (Roush)	42.00	21.00	12.50
23	Pep Young	20.00	10.00	6.00
24	Ed Hooper (Harry)	32.00	16.00	9.50
25	M. Kelley (should be G. Kelly)	32.00	16.00	9.50
26	Clyde Milan	20.00	10.00	6.00
27	Christy Mathewson	150.00	75.00	45.00
28	Eddie Collins	42.00	21.00	12.50
29	Hank Gowdy	20.00	10.00	6.00
30	Eddie Cicotte	30.00	15.00	9.00

1931 W517

The 54-card W517 set is a scarce issue of 3" by 4" cards which are generally found in a sepia color. There are, however, other known colors of W517s, and they tend to bring higher prices from specialists. The cards feature a player picture as well as his name and team. The card number appears in a small circle on the front, while the backs are blank. The set is heavy in stars of the period including two Babe Ruths (#'s 4 and 20). Not actively collected by many, the set is a relatively inexpensive way to obtain cards of many contemporary Hall of Famers.

		NR MT	EX	VG
Complete Set:		4500.	2250.	1350.
Common Player:		45.00	22.00	13.50
1	Earl Combs (Earle)	95.00	47.00	28.00
2	Pie Traynor	45.00	22.00	13.50
3	Eddie Rausch (Roush)	45.00	22.00	13.50
4	Babe Ruth	850.00	425.00	255.00
5a	Chalmer Cissell (Chicago)	45.00	22.00	13.50
5b	Chalmer Cissell (Cleveland)	45.00	22.00	13.50
6	Bill Sherdel	45.00	22.00	13.50
7	Bill Shore	45.00	22.00	13.50
8	Geo. Earnshaw	45.00	22.00	13.50
9	Bucky Harris	65.00	32.00	19.50
10	Charlie Klein	45.00	22.00	13.50
11a	Geo. Kelly (Reds)	45.00	22.00	13.50
11b	Geo. Kelly (Brooklyn)	45.00	22.00	13.50
12	Travis Jackson	45.00	22.00	13.50
13	Willie Kamm	45.00	22.00	13.50
14	Harry Heilman (Heilmann)	45.00	22.00	13.50
15	Grover Alexander	95.00	47.00	28.00
16	Frank Frisch	45.00	22.00	13.50
17	Jack Quinn	45.00	22.00	13.50
18	Cy Williams	45.00	22.00	13.50
19	Kiki Cuyler	45.00	22.00	13.50
20	Babe Ruth	850.00	425.00	255.00
21	Jimmie Foxx	100.00	50.00	30.00
22	Jimmy Dykes	45.00	22.00	13.50
23	Bill Terry	95.00	47.00	28.00
24	Freddy Lindstrom	45.00	22.00	13.50
25	Hughey Critz	45.00	22.00	13.50
26	Pete Donahue	45.00	22.00	13.50
27	Tony Lazzeri	65.00	32.00	19.50
28	Heine Manush (Heinie)	45.00	22.00	13.50
29a	Chick Hafey (Cardinals)	45.00	22.00	13.50
29b	Chick Hafey (Cincinnati)	45.00	22.00	13.50
30	Melvin Ott	95.00	47.00	28.00
31	Bing Miller	45.00	22.00	13.50
32	Geo. Haas	45.00	22.00	13.50
33a	Lefty O'Doul (Phillies)	45.00	22.00	13.50
33b	Lefty O'Doul (Brooklyn)	45.00	22.00	13.50
34	Paul Waner	45.00	22.00	13.50
35	Lou Gehrig	700.00	350.00	210.00
36	Dazzy Vance	45.00	22.00	13.50
37	Mickey Cochrane	45.00	22.00	13.50
38	Rogers Hornsby	115.00	57.00	34.00
39	Lefty Grove	95.00	47.00	28.00
40	Al Simmons	45.00	22.00	13.50
41	Rube Walberg	45.00	22.00	13.50
42	Hack Wilson	45.00	22.00	13.50
43	Art Shires	45.00	22.00	13.50
44	Sammy Hale	45.00	22.00	13.50
45	Ted Lyons	45.00	22.00	13.50
46	Joe Sewell	45.00	22.00	13.50
47	Goose Goslin	45.00	22.00	13.50
48	Lou Fonseca (Lew)	45.00	22.00	13.50
49	Bob Muesel (Meusel)	45.00	22.00	13.50
50	Lu Blue	45.00	22.00	13.50
52	Eddy Collins (Eddie)	95.00	47.00	28.00
53	Joe Judge	45.00	22.00	13.50
54	Mickey Cochrane	125.00	62.00	37.00

1920 W519 - Numbered

Cards in this 20-card "strip set" measure 1-1/2" by 2-1/2" and feature player drawings set against a background of either red, blue, orange, yellow, violet or green. The card number appears in the lower left corner followed by the player's name, which is printed in all capital letters. The player drawings are all posed portraits, except fot Joe Murphy and Ernie Kreuger, who are shown catching. Like all strip cards, the cards were sold in strips and have blank backs. The W519 set was issued circa 1920.

		NR MT	EX	VG
Complete Set:		575.00	287.00	172.00
Common Player:		25.00	12.50	7.50
1	Guy Morton	25.00	12.50	7.50
2	Rube Marquard	50.00	25.00	15.00
3	Gabby Cravath (Gavvy)	25.00	12.50	7.50
4	Ernie Krueger	25.00	12.50	7.50
5	Babe Ruth	350.00	175.00	105.00
6	George Sisler	50.00	25.00	15.00
7	Rube Benton	25.00	12.50	7.50
8	Jimmie Johnston	25.00	12.50	7.50
9	Wilbur Robinson (Wilbert)	50.00	25.00	15.00
10	Johnny Griffith	25.00	12.50	7.50
11	Frank Baker	50.00	25.00	15.00
12	Bob Veach	25.00	12.50	7.50
13	Jesse Barnes	25.00	12.50	7.50
14	Leon Cadore	25.00	12.50	7.50
15	Ray Schalk	50.00	25.00	15.00
16	Kid Gleasen (Gleason)	25.00	12.50	7.50
17	Joe Murphy	25.00	12.50	7.50
18	Frank Frisch	50.00	25.00	15.00
19	Eddie Collins	50.00	25.00	15.00
20	Wallie Schang	25.00	12.50	7.50

1920 W519 - Unnumbered

Cards in this 10-card set are identical in design and size (1-1/2" by 2-1/2") to the W519 Numbered set, except the player drawings are all set against a blue background and the cards are not numbered. With the lone exception of Eddie Ciotte, all of the subjects in the unnumbered set also appear in the numbered set.

		NR MT	EX	VG
Complete Set:		175.00	87.00	52.00
Common Player:		25.00	12.50	7.50
(1)	Eddie Cicotte	25.00	12.50	7.50
(2)	Eddie Collins	50.00	25.00	15.00
(3)	Gabby Cravath (Gavvy)	25.00	12.50	7.50
(4)	Frank Frisch	50.00	25.00	15.00
(5)	Kid Gleasen (Gleason)	25.00	12.50	7.50
(6)	Ernie Kreuger	25.00	12.50	7.50
(7)	Rube Marquard	50.00	25.00	15.00
(8)	Guy Morton	25.00	12.50	7.50
(9)	Joe Murphy	25.00	12.50	7.50
(10)	Babe Ruth	350.00	175.00	105.00

1920 W520

Another "strip card" set issued circa 1920, cards in this set measure 1-3/8" by 2-1/4" and are numbered in the lower right corner from 1 to 20. The first nine cards in the set display portrait poses, while the rest are full-length action poses. Some of the poses in this set are the same as those in the W516 issue with the pictures reversed. The player's last name appears in the border beneath the picture. The cards are blank-backed.

		NR MT	EX	VG
Complete Set:		1400.	700.00	420.00
Common Player:		32.00	16.00	9.50
1	Dave Bancroft	90.00	45.00	27.00
2	Christy Mathewson	225.00	112.00	67.00
3	Larry Doyle	32.00	16.00	9.50
4	Jess Barnes	32.00	16.00	9.50
5	Art Fletcher	32.00	16.00	9.50
6	Wilbur Cooper	32.00	16.00	9.50
7	Mike Gonzales	32.00	16.00	9.50
8	Zach Wheat	90.00	45.00	27.00
9	Tris Speaker	150.00	75.00	45.00
10	Benny Kauff	32.00	16.00	9.50
11	Zach Wheat	90.00	45.00	27.00
12	Phil Douglas	32.00	16.00	9.50
13	Babe Ruth	500.00	250.00	150.00
14	Stan Koveleski (Coveleski)	90.00	45.00	27.00
15	Goldie Rapp	32.00	16.00	9.50
16	Pol Perritt	32.00	16.00	9.50
17	Otto Miller	32.00	16.00	9.50
18	George Kelly	90.00	45.00	27.00
19	Mike Gonzales	32.00	16.00	9.50
20	Les Nunamaker	32.00	16.00	9.50

1921 W521

This issue is closely related to the W519 Numbered set. In fact, it uses the same color drawings as that set with the pictures, reversed, resulting in a mirror-image of the W519 cards. The player poses and the numbering system are identical, as are the various background colors. The W521 cards are blank-backed and were sold in strips.

		NR MT	EX	VG
Complete Set:		500.00	250.00	150.00
Common Player:		20.00	10.00	6.00
1	Guy Morton	20.00	10.00	6.00
2	Rube Marquard	40.00	20.00	12.00
3	Gabby Cravath (Gavvy)	10.00	5.00	3.00
4	Ernie Krueger	20.00	10.00	6.00
5	Babe Ruth	300.00	150.00	90.00
6	George Sisler	40.00	20.00	12.00
7	Rube Benton	20.00	10.00	6.00
8	Jimmie Johnston	20.00	10.00	6.00
9	Wilbur Robinson (Wilbert)	40.00	20.00	12.00
10	Johnny Griffith	20.00	10.00	6.00
11	Frank Baker	40.00	20.00	12.00
12	Bob Veach	20.00	10.00	6.00
13	Jesse Barnes	20.00	10.00	6.00
14	Leon Cadore	20.00	10.00	6.00
15	Ray Schalk	40.00	20.00	12.00
16	Kid Gleasen (Gleason)	20.00	10.00	6.00
17	Joe Murphy	20.00	10.00	6.00
18	Frank Frisch	40.00	20.00	12.00
19	Eddie Collins	40.00	20.00	12.00
20	Wallie Schang	20.00	10.00	6.00

1918 W522

The 20 cards in this "strip card" set, issued circa 1920, are numbered from 31-50 and use the same players and drawings as the W520 set, issued about the same time. The cards measure 1-3/8" by 2-1/4" and are numbered in the lower left corner followed by the player's name. The cards have blank backs.

		NR MT	EX	VG
Complete Set:		1200.	600.00	360.00
Common Player:		32.00	16.00	9.50
31	Benny Kauf (Kauff)	32.00	16.00	9.50
32	Tris Speaker	100.00	50.00	30.00
33	Zach Wheat	32.00	16.00	9.50
34	Mike Gonzales	32.00	16.00	9.50
35	Wilbur Cooper	32.00	16.00	9.50
36	Art Fletcher	32.00	16.00	9.50
37	Jess Barnes	32.00	16.00	9.50
38	Larry Doyle	32.00	16.00	9.50
39	Christy Mathewson	225.00	112.00	67.00
40	Dave Bancroft	75.00	37.00	22.00
41	Les Nunamaker	32.00	16.00	9.50
42	Mike Gonzales	32.00	16.00	9.50
43	George Kelly	75.00	37.00	22.00
44	Otto Miller	32.00	16.00	9.50
45	Pol Perritt	32.00	16.00	9.50
46	Goldie Rapp	32.00	16.00	9.50
47	Stan Koveleski (Coveleski)	75.00	37.00	22.00
48	Babe Ruth	500.00	250.00	150.00
49	Phil Douglas	32.00	16.00	9.50
50	Zach Wheat	75.00	37.00	22.00

1922 W551

Another "strip set" issued circa 1920, these ten cards measure 1-3/8" by 2-1/4" and feature color drawings. The cards are unnumbered and blank-backed.

		NR MT	EX	VG
Complete Set:		1250.	625.00	375.00
Common Player:		45.00	22.00	13.50
(1)	Frank Baker	100.00	50.00	30.00
(2)	Dave Bancroft	100.00	50.00	30.00
(3)	Jess Barnes	45.00	22.00	13.50
(4)	Ty Cobb	400.00	200.00	120.00
(5)	Walter Johnson	200.00	100.00	60.00
(6)	Wally Pipp	45.00	22.00	13.50
(7)	Babe Ruth	425.00	212.00	127.00
(8)	George Sisler	100.00	50.00	30.00
(9)	Tris Speaker	150.00	75.00	45.00
(10)	Casey Stengel	200.00	100.00	60.00

1907 W555

Designated as W555 in the American Card Catalog, very little is known about this obscure set. The nearly sqaure cards measure a tiny 1-1/8" by 1-3-16" and feature a sepia-colored player photo. Sixty-six different cards have been discovered to date, but more are very likely to exist. The manufacturer of the set is unknown, but the sets appear to be related to a series of four early candy cards that carry the ACC designations of E93, E94, E97 and E98, because, with only two exceptions, the players and poses are the same. It is not known how the cards were issued. There is speculation that they may have been issued as "strip" cards or as part of a candy box.

		NR MT	EX	VG
Complete Set:		4300.	2150.	1290.
Common Player:		45.00	22.00	13.50
(1)	Red Ames	45.00	22.00	13.50
(2)	Jimmy Austin	45.00	22.00	13.50
(3)	Johnny Bates	45.00	22.00	13.50
(4)	Chief Bender	125.00	62.00	37.00
(5)	Bob Bescher	45.00	22.00	13.50
(6)	Joe Birmingham	45.00	22.00	13.50
(7)	Bill Bradley	45.00	22.00	13.50
(8)	Kitty Bransfield	45.00	22.00	13.50
(9)	Mordecai Brown	125.00	62.00	37.00
(10)	Bobby Byrne	45.00	22.00	13.50
(11)	Frank Chance	60.00	30.00	18.00
(12)	Hal Chase	70.00	35.00	21.00
(13)	Ed Cicotte	55.00	27.00	16.50
(14)	Fred Clarke	125.00	62.00	37.00
(15)	Ty Cobb	600.00	300.00	180.00
(16)	Eddie Collins (dark uniform)	125.00	62.00	37.00
(17)	Eddie Collins (light uniform)	125.00	62.00	37.00
(18)	Harry Coveleskie (Coveleski)	45.00	22.00	13.50
(19)	Sam Crawford	125.00	62.00	37.00
(20)	Harry Davis	45.00	22.00	13.50
(21)	Jim Delehanty	45.00	22.00	13.50
(22)	Art Devlin	45.00	22.00	13.50
(23)	Josh Devore	45.00	22.00	13.50
(24)	Wild Bill Donovan	45.00	22.00	13.50
(25)	Red Dooin	45.00	22.00	13.50
(26)	Mickey Doolan	45.00	22.00	13.50
(27)	Bull Durham	45.00	22.00	13.50
(28)	Jimmy Dygert	45.00	22.00	13.50
(29)	Johnny Evers	125.00	62.00	37.00
(30)	Russ Ford	45.00	22.00	13.50
(31)	George Gibson	45.00	22.00	13.50
(32)	Clark Griffith	125.00	62.00	37.00
(33)	Topsy Hartsell (Hartsel)	45.00	22.00	13.50
(34)	Bill Heinchman (Hinchman)	45.00	22.00	13.50
(35)	Ira Hemphill	45.00	22.00	13.50
(36)	Hughie Jennings	125.00	62.00	37.00
(37)	Davy Jones	45.00	22.00	13.50
(38)	Addie Joss	125.00	62.00	37.00
(39)	Wee Willie Keeler	45.00	22.00	13.50
(40)	Red Kleinow	45.00	22.00	13.50
(41)	Nap Lajoie	200.00	100.00	60.00
(42)	Joe Lake	45.00	22.00	13.50
(43)	Tommy Leach	45.00	22.00	13.50
(44)	Sherry Magee	55.00	27.00	16.50
(45)	Christy Mathewson	225.00	112.00	67.00
(46)	Amby McConnell	45.00	22.00	13.50
(47)	John McGraw	175.00	87.00	52.00
(48)	Chief Meyers	45.00	22.00	13.50
(49)	Earl Moore	45.00	22.00	13.50
(50)	Mike Mowery	45.00	22.00	13.50
(51)	George Mullin	45.00	22.00	13.50
(52)	Red Murray	45.00	22.00	13.50
(53)	Nichols	45.00	22.00	13.50
(54)	Jim Pastorious (Pastorius)	45.00	22.00	13.50
(55)	Deacon Phillippi (Phillippe)	45.00	22.00	13.50
(56)	Eddie Plank	55.00	27.00	16.50
(57)	Fred Snodgrass	45.00	22.00	13.50
(58)	Harry Steinfeldt	55.00	27.00	16.50
(59)	Joe Tinker	125.00	62.00	37.00
(60)	Hippo Vaughn	45.00	22.00	13.50
(61)	Honus Wagner	600.00	300.00	180.00
(62)	Rube Waddell	125.00	62.00	37.00
(63)	Hooks Wiltse	45.00	22.00	13.50
(64a)	Cy Young (standing, full name on front)	175.00	87.00	52.00
(64b)	Cy Young (standing, last name on front)	175.00	87.00	52.00
(65)	Cy Young (portrait)	175.00	87.00	52.00

1927 W560

Although assigned a "W" number, this set is not a "strip card" issue in the same sense as the rest of the "W" sets, although W560 cards are frequently found in uncut sheets of three or four across or down. Uncut sheets of 16 cards, in four rows of four cards each, are also known to exist. Cards in the W560 set measure 1-3/4" by 2-3/4" and are designed like a deck of playing cards, with the pictures on the various suits - either hearts, clubs, spades, diamonds or jokers. The set includes movie stars, aviators and other athletes, in addition to baseball players. Because they are designed as a deck of playing cards, the cards are printed in either red or black.

		NR MT	EX	VG
Complete Set:		2000.	1000.	600.00
Common Player:		20.00	10.00	6.00
(1)	Vic Aldridge	20.00	10.00	6.00
(2)	Lester Bell	20.00	10.00	6.00
(3)	Larry Benton	20.00	10.00	6.00
(4)	Max Bishop	20.00	10.00	6.00
(5)	Del Bissonette	20.00	10.00	6.00
(6)	Jim Bottomley	35.00	17.50	10.50
(7)	Guy Bush	20.00	10.00	6.00
(8)	W. Clark	20.00	10.00	6.00
(9)	Andy Cohen	20.00	10.00	6.00
(10)	Mickey Cochrane	35.00	17.50	10.50
(11)	Hugh Critz	20.00	10.00	6.00
(12)	Kiki Cuyler	35.00	17.50	10.50
(13)	Taylor Douthit	20.00	10.00	6.00
(14)	Fred Fitzsimmons	20.00	10.00	6.00
(15)	Jim Foxx	225.00	112.00	67.00
(16)	Lou Gehrig	350.00	175.00	105.00

(17)	Goose Goslin	35.00	17.50	10.50
(18)	Sam Gray	20.00	10.00	6.00
(19)	Lefty Grove	100.00	50.00	30.00
(20)	Jesse Haines	35.00	17.50	10.50
(21)	Babe Herman	25.00	12.50	7.50
(22)	Roger Hornsby (Rogers)	125.00	62.00	37.00
(23)	Waite Hoyt	35.00	17.50	10.50
(24)	Henry Johnson	20.00	10.00	6.00
(25)	Walter Johnson	125.00	62.00	37.00
(26)	Willie Kamm	20.00	10.00	6.00
(27)	Remy Kremer	20.00	10.00	6.00
(28)	Fred Lindstrom	35.00	17.50	10.50
(29)	Fred Maguire	20.00	10.00	6.00
(30)	Fred Marberry	20.00	10.00	6.00
(31)	Johnny Mostil	20.00	10.00	6.00
(32)	Buddy Myer	20.00	10.00	6.00
(33)	Herb Pennock	35.00	17.50	10.50
(34)	George Pipgras	20.00	10.00	6.00
(35)	Flint Rhem	20.00	10.00	6.00
(36)	Babe Ruth	500.00	250.00	150.00
(37)	Luke Sewell	20.00	10.00	6.00
(38)	Willie Sherdel	20.00	10.00	6.00
(39)	Al Simmons	35.00	17.50	10.50
(40)	Thomas Thevenow	20.00	10.00	6.00
(41)	Fresco Thompson	20.00	10.00	6.00
(42)	George Uhle	20.00	10.00	6.00
(43)	Dazzy Vance	35.00	17.50	10.50
(44)	Rube Walberg	20.00	10.00	6.00
(45)	Lloyd Waner	35.00	17.50	10.50
(46)	Paul Waner	35.00	17.50	10.50
(47)	Fred "Cy" Williams	25.00	12.50	7.50
(48)	Jim Wilson	20.00	10.00	6.00
(49)	Glen Wright (Glenn)	20.00	10.00	6.00

1923 W572

This set, designated as W572 by the American Card Catalog, measures 1-5/16" x 2-1/2" and are blank-backed. These "strip cards" feature black and white player photos, although some sepia-toned cards have also been found. The set is closely related to the popular E120 American Caramel set issued in 1922 and, with the exception of Ty Cobb, it uses the same photos. The cards were originally issued as strips of ten, with five baseball players and five boxers. They are found on either a white, slick stock or a dark, coarser one. The player's name on the front of the cards appears in script. All cards have on front a copyright symbol and one of several alphabetical combinations indicating the source of the photo.

		NR MT	EX	VG
Complete Set:		4000.	2000.	1200.
Common Player:		20.00	10.00	6.00
(1)	Eddie Ainsmith	20.00	10.00	6.00
(2)	Vic Aldridge	20.00	10.00	6.00
(3)	Grover Alexander	65.00	32.00	19.50
(4)	Walt Barbare	20.00	10.00	6.00
(5)	Jess Barnes	20.00	10.00	6.00
(6)	John Bassler	20.00	10.00	6.00
(7)	Lu Blue	20.00	10.00	6.00
(8)	Norman Boeckel	20.00	10.00	6.00
(9)	George Burns	20.00	10.00	6.00
(10)	Joe Bush	20.00	10.00	6.00
(11)	Leon Cadore	20.00	10.00	6.00
(12)	Virgil Cheevers (Cheeves)	20.00	10.00	6.00
(13)	Ty Cobb	700.00	350.00	210.00
(14)	Eddie Collins	50.00	25.00	15.00
(15)	John Collins	20.00	10.00	6.00
(16)	Wilbur Cooper	20.00	10.00	6.00
(17)	Stanley Coveleski	50.00	25.00	15.00
(18)	Walton Cruise	20.00	10.00	6.00
(19)	Dave Danforth	20.00	10.00	6.00
(20)	Jake Daubert	20.00	10.00	6.00
(21)	Hank DeBerry	20.00	10.00	6.00
(22)	Lou DeVormer	20.00	10.00	6.00
(23)	Bill Doak	20.00	10.00	6.00
(24)	Pete Donohue	20.00	10.00	6.00
(25)	Pat Duncan	20.00	10.00	6.00
(26)	Jimmy Dykes	20.00	10.00	6.00
(27)	Urban Faber	50.00	25.00	15.00
(28)	Bib Falk (Bibb)	20.00	10.00	6.00
(29)	Frank Frisch	50.00	25.00	15.00
(30)	C. Galloway	20.00	10.00	6.00
(31)	Ed Gharrity	20.00	10.00	6.00
(32)	Chas. Glazner	20.00	10.00	6.00
(33)	Hank Gowdy	20.00	10.00	6.00
(34)	Tom Griffith	20.00	10.00	6.00
(35)	Burleigh Grimes	50.00	25.00	15.00
(36)	Ray Grimes	20.00	10.00	6.00
(37)	Heinie Groh	20.00	10.00	6.00
(38)	Joe Harris	20.00	10.00	6.00
(39)	Stanley Harris	50.00	25.00	15.00
(40)	Joe Hauser	20.00	10.00	6.00
(41)	Harry Heilmann	50.00	25.00	15.00
(42)	Walter Henline	20.00	10.00	6.00
(43)	Chas. Hollocher	20.00	10.00	6.00
(44)	Harry Hooper	50.00	25.00	15.00
(45)	Rogers Hornsby	150.00	75.00	45.00
(46)	Waite Hoyt	50.00	25.00	15.00
(47)	Wilbur Hubbell	20.00	10.00	6.00
(48)	Wm. Jacobson	20.00	10.00	6.00
(49)	Chas. Jamieson	20.00	10.00	6.00
(50)	S. Johnson	20.00	10.00	6.00
(51)	Walter Johnson	150.00	75.00	45.00
(52)	Jimmy Johnston	20.00	10.00	6.00
(53)	Joe Judge	20.00	10.00	6.00
(54)	Geo. Kelly	50.00	25.00	15.00
(55)	Lee King	20.00	10.00	6.00
(56)	Larry Kopff (Kopf)	20.00	10.00	6.00
(57)	Geo. Leverette	20.00	10.00	6.00
(58)	Al Mamaux	20.00	10.00	6.00
(59)	"Rabbit" Maranville	50.00	25.00	15.00
(60)	"Rube" Marquard	50.00	25.00	15.00
(61)	Martin McManus	20.00	10.00	6.00
(62)	Lee Meadows	20.00	10.00	6.00
(63)	Mike Menosky	20.00	10.00	6.00
(64)	Bob Meusel	30.00	15.00	9.00
(65)	Emil Meusel	20.00	10.00	6.00
(66)	Geo. Mogridge	20.00	10.00	6.00
(67)	John Morrison	20.00	10.00	6.00
(68)	Johnny Mostil	20.00	10.00	6.00
(69)	Roliene Naylor	20.00	10.00	6.00
(70)	Art Nehf	20.00	10.00	6.00
(71)	Joe Oeschger	20.00	10.00	6.00
(72)	Bob O'Farrell	20.00	10.00	6.00
(73)	Steve O'Neill	20.00	10.00	6.00
(74)	Frank Parkinson	20.00	10.00	6.00
(75)	Ralph Perkins	20.00	10.00	6.00
(76)	H. Pillette	20.00	10.00	6.00
(77)	Ralph Pinelli	20.00	10.00	6.00
(78)	Wallie Pipp	35.00	17.50	10.50
(79)	Ray Powell	20.00	10.00	6.00
(80)	Jack Quinn	20.00	10.00	6.00
(81)	Goldie Rapp	20.00	10.00	6.00
(82)	Walter Reuther	20.00	10.00	6.00
(83)	Sam Rice	50.00	25.00	15.00
(84)	Emory Rigney	20.00	10.00	6.00
(85)	Eppa Rixey	50.00	25.00	15.00
(86)	Ed Rommel	20.00	10.00	6.00
(87)	Eddie Roush	50.00	25.00	15.00
(88)	Babe Ruth	900.00	450.00	270.00
(89)	Ray Schalk	20.00	10.00	6.00
(90)	Wallie Schang	20.00	10.00	6.00
(91)	Walter Schmidt	20.00	10.00	6.00
(92)	Joe Schultz	20.00	10.00	6.00
(93)	Hank Severeid	20.00	10.00	6.00
(94)	Joe Sewell	50.00	25.00	15.00
(95)	Bob Shawkey	20.00	10.00	6.00
(96)	Earl Sheely	20.00	10.00	6.00
(97)	Will Sherdel	20.00	10.00	6.00
(98)	Urban Shocker	20.00	10.00	6.00
(99)	George Sisler	50.00	25.00	15.00
(100)	Earl Smith	20.00	10.00	6.00
(101)	Elmer Smith	20.00	10.00	6.00
(102)	Jack Smith	20.00	10.00	6.00
(103)	Bill Southworth	20.00	10.00	6.00
(104)	Tris Speaker	65.00	32.00	19.50
(105)	Arnold Statz	35.00	17.50	10.50
(106)	Milton Stock	20.00	10.00	6.00
(107)	Jim Tierney	20.00	10.00	6.00
(108)	Harold Traynor	20.00	10.00	6.00
(109)	Geo. Uhle	50.00	25.00	15.00
(110)	Bob Veach	20.00	10.00	6.00
(111)	Clarence Walker	20.00	10.00	6.00
(112)	Curtis Walker	20.00	10.00	6.00
(113)	Bill Wambsganss	20.00	10.00	6.00
(114)	Aaron Ward	20.00	10.00	6.00
(115)	Zach Wheat	50.00	25.00	15.00
(116)	Fred Williams	30.00	15.00	9.00
(117)	Ken Williams	30.00	15.00	9.00
(118)	Ivy Wingo	20.00	10.00	6.00
(119)	Joe Wood	30.00	15.00	9.00
(120)	J.T. Zachary	20.00	10.00	6.00

Values quoted in this guide reflect the retail price of a card – the price a collector can expect to pay when buying a card from a dealer. The wholesale price – that which a collector can expect to receive from a dealer when selling cards – will be significantly lower, depending on desirability and condition.

1922 W573

These cards, identified as W573 in the American Card Catalog, appear to be blank-backed versions of the popular E120 American Caramel set. In reality they were "strip cards," produced in 1923 and sold in strips of ten for a penny. The cards feature black and

white photos. To date 144 different subjects have been found, but it is likely that all 240 poses from the E120 set actually exist.

		NR MT	EX	VG
Complete Set:		4500.	2250.	1350.
Common Player:		45.00	22.00	13.50
(1)	Babe Adams	45.00	22.00	13.50
(2)	Eddie Ainsmith	45.00	22.00	13.50
(3)	Vic Aldridge	45.00	22.00	13.50
(4)	Grover Alexander	125.00	62.00	37.00
(5)	Home Run Baker	100.00	50.00	30.00
(6)	Dave Bancroft	100.00	50.00	30.00
(7)	Walt Barbare	45.00	22.00	13.50
(8)	Turner Barber	45.00	22.00	13.50
(9)	Jess Barnes	45.00	22.00	13.50
(10)	John Bassler	45.00	22.00	13.50
(11)	Carson Bigbee	45.00	22.00	13.50
(12)	Lu Blue	45.00	22.00	13.50
(13)	Norman Boeckel	45.00	22.00	13.50
(14)	Geo. Burns (Boston)	45.00	22.00	13.50
(15)	Geo. Burns (Cincinnati)	45.00	22.00	13.50
(16)	Marty Callaghan	45.00	22.00	13.50
(17)	Max Carey	100.00	50.00	30.00
(18)	Jimmy Caveney	45.00	22.00	13.50
(19)	Virgil Cheeves	45.00	22.00	13.50
(20)	Vern Clemons	45.00	22.00	13.50
(21)	Ty Cobb	750.00	375.00	225.00
(22)	Bert Cole	45.00	22.00	13.50
(23)	Eddie Collins	100.00	50.00	30.00
(24)	Pat Collins	45.00	22.00	13.50
(25)	Wilbur Cooper	45.00	22.00	13.50
(26)	Elmer Cox	45.00	22.00	13.50
(27)	Bill Cunningham	45.00	22.00	13.50
(28)	George Cutshaw	45.00	22.00	13.50
(29)	Dave Danforth	45.00	22.00	13.50
(30)	George Dauss	45.00	22.00	13.50
(31)	Dixie Davis	45.00	22.00	13.50
(32)	Hank DeBerry	45.00	22.00	13.50
(33)	Lou DeVormer	45.00	22.00	13.50
(34)	Bill Doak	45.00	22.00	13.50
(35)	Joe Dugan	75.00	37.00	22.00
(36)	Howard Ehmke	45.00	22.00	13.50
(37)	Frank Ellerbe	45.00	22.00	13.50
(38)	Urban Faber	100.00	50.00	30.00
(39)	Bib Falk (Bibb)	45.00	22.00	13.50
(40)	Max Flack	45.00	22.00	13.50
(41)	Ira Flagstead	45.00	22.00	13.50
(42)	Art Fletcher	45.00	22.00	13.50
(43)	Horace Ford	45.00	22.00	13.50
(44)	Jack Fournier	45.00	22.00	13.50
(45)	Frank Frisch	100.00	50.00	30.00
(46)	Ollie Fuhrman	45.00	22.00	13.50
(47)	C. Galloway	45.00	22.00	13.50
(48)	Walter Gerber	45.00	22.00	13.50
(49)	Ed Gharrity	45.00	22.00	13.50
(50)	Chas. Glazner	45.00	22.00	13.50
(51)	Leon Goslin	100.00	50.00	30.00
(52)	Hank Gowdy	45.00	22.00	13.50
(53)	John Graney	45.00	22.00	13.50
(54)	Ray Grimes	45.00	22.00	13.50
(55)	Heinie Groh	45.00	22.00	13.50
(56)	Jesse Haines	100.00	50.00	30.00
(57)	Earl Hamilton	45.00	22.00	13.50
(58)	Bubbles Hargrave	45.00	22.00	13.50
(59)	Bryan Harris	45.00	22.00	13.50
(60)	Cliff Heathcote	45.00	22.00	13.50
(61)	Harry Heilmann	100.00	50.00	30.00
(62)	Clarence Hodge	45.00	22.00	13.50
(63)	Chas. Hollocher	45.00	22.00	13.50
(64)	Harry Hooper	100.00	50.00	30.00
(65)	Rogers Hornsby	150.00	75.00	45.00
(66)	Waite Hoyt	100.00	50.00	30.00
(67)	Ernie Johnson	45.00	22.00	13.50
(68)	S. Johnson	45.00	22.00	13.50
(69)	Walter Johnson	45.00	22.00	13.50
(70)	Doc Johnston	200.00	100.00	60.00
(71)	Sam Jones	45.00	22.00	13.50
(72)	Ben Karr	45.00	22.00	13.50
(73)	Johnny Lavan	45.00	22.00	13.50
(74)	Geo. Leverette	45.00	22.00	13.50
(75)	"Rabbit" Maranville	100.00	50.00	30.00
(76)	Cliff Markle	45.00	22.00	13.50
(77)	Carl Mays	75.00	37.00	22.00
(78)	Hervey McClellan	45.00	22.00	13.50
(79)	Martin McManus	45.00	22.00	13.50
(80)	Lee Meadows	45.00	22.00	13.50
(81)	Mike Menosky	45.00	22.00	13.50
(82)	Emil Meusel	45.00	22.00	13.50
(83)	Clyde Milan	45.00	22.00	13.50
(84)	Bing Miller	45.00	22.00	13.50
(85)	Elmer Miller	45.00	22.00	13.50

(86)	Lawrence Miller	45.00	22.00	13.50
(87)	Clarence Mitchell	45.00	22.00	13.50
(88)	Geo. Mogridge	45.00	22.00	13.50
(89)	John Morrison	45.00	22.00	13.50
(90)	Johnny Mostil	45.00	22.00	13.50
(91)	Elmer Meyers	45.00	22.00	13.50
(92)	Roliene Naylor	45.00	22.00	13.50
(93)	Les Nunamaker	45.00	22.00	13.50
(94)	Bob O'Farrell	45.00	22.00	13.50
(95)	George O'Neil	45.00	22.00	13.50
(96)	Steve O'Neill	45.00	22.00	13.50
(97)	Herb Pennock	100.00	50.00	30.00
(98)	Ralph Perkins	45.00	22.00	13.50
(99)	Tom Phillips	45.00	22.00	13.50
(100)	Val Picinich	45.00	22.00	13.50
(101)	H. Pillette	45.00	22.00	13.50
(102)	Ralph Pinelli	45.00	22.00	13.50
(103)	Wallie Pipp	75.00	37.00	22.00
(104)	Clark Pittenger	45.00	22.00	13.50
(105)	Derrill Pratt	45.00	22.00	13.50
(106)	Goldie Rapp	45.00	22.00	13.50
(107)	John Rawlings	45.00	22.00	13.50
(108)	Walter Reuther	45.00	22.00	13.50
(109)	Emory Rigney	45.00	22.00	13.50
(110)	Charles Robertson	45.00	22.00	13.50
(111)	Ed Rommel	45.00	22.00	13.50
(112)	Muddy Ruel	45.00	22.00	13.50
(113)	Babe Ruth	1000.	500.00	300.00
(114)	Ray Schalk	100.00	50.00	30.00
(115)	Wallie Schang	45.00	22.00	13.50
(116)	Ray Schmidt	45.00	22.00	13.50
(117)	Walter Schmidt	45.00	22.00	13.50
(118)	Joe Schultz	45.00	22.00	13.50
(119)	Hank Severeid	45.00	22.00	13.50
(120)	Joe Sewell	100.00	50.00	30.00
(121)	Bob Shawkey	75.00	37.00	22.00
(122)	Earl Sheely	45.00	22.00	13.50
(123)	Ralph Shinner	45.00	22.00	13.50
(124)	Urban Shocker	45.00	22.00	13.50
(125)	George Sisler	100.00	50.00	30.00
(126)	Earl Smith (Washington)	45.00	22.00	13.50
(127)	Earl Smith (New York)	45.00	22.00	13.50
(128)	Jack Smith	45.00	22.00	13.50
(129)	Al Sothoron	45.00	22.00	13.50
(130)	Tris Speaker	125.00	62.00	37.00
(131)	Amos Strunk	45.00	22.00	13.50
(132)	Jim Tierney	45.00	22.00	13.50
(133)	John Tobin	45.00	22.00	13.50
(134)	George Toporcer	45.00	22.00	13.50
(135)	Geo. Uhle	45.00	22.00	13.50
(136)	Bob Veach	45.00	22.00	13.50
(137)	John Watson	45.00	22.00	13.50
(138)	Zach Wheat	100.00	50.00	30.00
(139)	Fred Williams	75.00	37.00	22.00
(140)	Ken Williams	45.00	22.00	13.50
(141)	Lawrence Woodall	45.00	22.00	13.50
(142)	Russell Wrightstone	45.00	22.00	13.50
(143)	Ross Young (Youngs)	100.00	50.00	30.00
(144)	J.T. Zachary	45.00	22.00	13.50

1932 W574

Issued circa 1932, cards in the W574 set measure 2-1/4" by 2-7/8". They are unnumbered and are listed here in alphabetical order.

		NR MT	EX	VG
	Complete Set:	1600.	800.00	480.00
	Common Player:	45.00	22.00	13.50
(1)	Dale Alexander	45.00	22.00	13.50
(2)	Luke Appling	125.00	62.00	37.00
(3)	Earl Averill	125.00	62.00	37.00
(4)	Ivy Paul Andrews	45.00	22.00	13.50
(5)	Geore Blaeholder	45.00	22.00	13.50
(6)	Irving Burns	45.00	22.00	13.50
(7)	Pat Caraway	45.00	22.00	13.50
(8)	Chalmer Cissell	45.00	22.00	13.50
(9)	Harry Davis	45.00	22.00	13.50
(10)	Jimmy Dykes	70.00	35.00	21.00
(11)	George Earnshaw	45.00	22.00	13.50
(12)	Urban Faber	125.00	62.00	37.00
(13)	Lewis Fonseca	45.00	22.00	13.50
(14)	Jimmy Foxx	225.00	112.00	67.00
(15)	Victor Frasier	45.00	22.00	13.50
(16)	Robert Grove	200.00	100.00	60.00
(17)	Frank Grube	45.00	22.00	13.50
(18)	Irving Hadley	45.00	22.00	13.50
(19)	Willie Kamm	45.00	22.00	13.50
(20)	Bill Killefer	45.00	22.00	13.50
(21)	Ralph Kress	45.00	22.00	13.50
(22)	Fred Marberry	45.00	22.00	13.50
(23)	Roger Peckinpaugh	45.00	22.00	13.50
(24)	Frank Reiber	45.00	22.00	13.50
(25)	Carl Reynolds	45.00	22.00	13.50
(26)	Al Simmons	125.00	62.00	37.00
(27)	Joe Vosmik	45.00	22.00	13.50
(28)	Gerald Walker	45.00	22.00	13.50
(29)	Whitlow Wyatt	45.00	22.00	13.50

1922 W575-1

Designated as W575 in the American Card Catalog, these "strip cards" are blank-backed. Issued circa 1922, cards in this set measure 2" by 3-1/4". The subjects for the set were taken from the E121 set and include representatives of all 16 major league teams, with heavier emphasis on the New York teams.

		NR MT	EX	VG
	Complete Set:	8500.	4250.	2550.
	Common Player:	30.00	15.00	9.00
(1)	Chas. "Babe" Adams	30.00	15.00	9.00
(2)	G.C. Alexander	100.00	50.00	30.00
(3)	Grover Alexander	100.00	50.00	30.00
(4)	Jim Bagby	30.00	15.00	9.00
(5a)	J. Franklin Baker	85.00	42.00	25.00
(5b)	Frank Baker	85.00	42.00	25.00
(6)	Dave Bancroft (batting)	85.00	42.00	25.00
(7)	Dave Bancroft (fielding)	85.00	42.00	25.00
(8)	Jesse Barnes	30.00	15.00	9.00
(9)	Howard Berry	30.00	15.00	9.00
(10)	L. Bigbee (should be C.)	30.00	15.00	9.00
(11)	Ping Bodie	30.00	15.00	9.00
(13)	"Ed" Brown	30.00	15.00	9.00
(14)	George Burns	30.00	15.00	9.00
(15)	Geo. J. Burns	30.00	15.00	9.00
(16)	"Bullet Joe" Bush	30.00	15.00	9.00
(17)	Owen Bush	30.00	15.00	9.00
(18)	Max Carey (batting)	85.00	42.00	25.00
(19)	Max Carey (hands on hips)	85.00	42.00	25.00
(20)	Ty Cobb	750.00	375.00	225.00
(21)	Eddie Collins	100.00	50.00	30.00
(22)	"Rip" Collins	30.00	15.00	9.00
(23)	Stanley Coveleskie (Coveleski)	85.00	42.00	25.00
(24)	Bill Cunningham	30.00	15.00	9.00
(25)	Jake Daubert	40.00	20.00	12.00
(26)	George Dauss	30.00	15.00	9.00
(27)	"Dixie" Davis	30.00	15.00	9.00
(28)	Charles Deal (dark uniform)	30.00	15.00	9.00
(29)	Charles Deal (light uniform)	30.00	15.00	9.00
(30)	Lou DeVormer	30.00	15.00	9.00
(31)	William Doak	30.00	15.00	9.00
(32)	Bill Donovan	30.00	15.00	9.00
(33)	"Phil" Douglas	30.00	15.00	9.00
(34a)	Johnny Evers (Mgr.)	85.00	42.00	25.00
(34b)	Johnny Evers (Manager)	85.00	42.00	25.00
(35a)	Urban Faber (dark uniform)	85.00	42.00	25.00
(35b)	Urban Faber (white uniform)	85.00	42.00	25.00
(36)	Bib Falk (Bibb)	30.00	15.00	9.00
(37)	Alex Ferguson	30.00	15.00	9.00
(38)	Wm. Fewster	30.00	15.00	9.00
(39)	Eddie Foster	30.00	15.00	9.00
(40)	Frank Frisch	85.00	42.00	25.00
(41)	W.L. Gardner	30.00	15.00	9.00
(42)	Alexander Gaston	30.00	15.00	9.00
(43)	E.P. Gharrity	30.00	15.00	9.00
(44)	Chas. "Whitey" Glazner	30.00	15.00	9.00
(45)	"Kid" Gleason	30.00	15.00	9.00
(46)	"Mike" Gonzalez	30.00	15.00	9.00
(47)	Hank Gowdy	30.00	15.00	9.00
(48a)	John Graney (Util. o.f.)	30.00	15.00	9.00
(49b)	John Graney (O.F.)	30.00	15.00	9.00
(50)	Tom Griffith	30.00	15.00	9.00
(51)	Chas. Grimm	40.00	20.00	12.00
(52a)	Heinie Groh (Cincinnati)	30.00	15.00	9.00
(52b)	Heinie Groh (New York)	30.00	15.00	9.00
(53)	Jess Haines	85.00	42.00	25.00
(54)	Harry Harper	30.00	15.00	9.00
(55)	"Chicken" Hawks	30.00	15.00	9.00
(56)	Harry Heilman (Heilmann) (holding bat)	85.00	42.00	25.00
(57)	Harry Heilman (Heilmann) (running)	85.00	42.00	25.00
(58)	Fred Hoffman	30.00	15.00	9.00
(59a)	Walter Holke (1st B., portrait)	30.00	15.00	9.00
(59b)	Walter Holke (1B, portrait)	30.00	15.00	9.00
(60)	Walter Holke (throwing)	30.00	15.00	9.00
(61a)	Charles Hollacher (name incorrect)	30.00	15.00	9.00
(61b)	Charles Hollocher (name correct)	30.00	15.00	9.00
(62)	Harry Hooper	30.00	15.00	9.00
(63a)	Rogers Hornsby (2nd B.)	150.00	75.00	45.00
(63b)	Rogers Hornsby (O.F.)	150.00	75.00	45.00
(64)	Waite Hoyt	85.00	42.00	25.00
(65)	Miller Huggins	85.00	42.00	25.00
(66)	Wm. C. Jacobson	30.00	15.00	9.00
(67)	Hugh Jennings	30.00	15.00	9.00
(68)	Walter Johnson (arms at chest)	200.00	100.00	60.00
(69)	Walter Johnson (throwing)	200.00	100.00	60.00
(70)	James Johnston	30.00	15.00	9.00
(71)	Joe Judge (batting)	30.00	15.00	9.00
(73a)	George Kelly (1st B.)	85.00	42.00	25.00
(73b)	George Kelly (1B.)	85.00	42.00	25.00
(74)	Dick Kerr	30.00	15.00	9.00
(75)	P.J. Kilduff	30.00	15.00	9.00
(76)	Bill Killefer	30.00	15.00	9.00
(77)	John Lavan	30.00	15.00	9.00
(78)	"Nemo" Leibold	30.00	15.00	9.00
(79)	Duffy Lewis	30.00	15.00	9.00
(80)	Al. Mamaux	30.00	15.00	9.00
(81)	"Rabbit" Maranville	85.00	42.00	25.00
(81b)	Carl Mays (name correct)	40.00	20.00	12.00
(82a)	Carl May (name incorrect)	40.00	20.00	12.00
(83)	John McGraw	110.00	55.00	33.00
(84)	Jack McInnis	30.00	15.00	9.00
(85)	M.J. McNally	30.00	15.00	9.00
(86)	Emil Muesel	30.00	15.00	9.00
(87)	R. Meusel	50.00	25.00	15.00
(88)	Clyde Milan	30.00	15.00	9.00
(89)	Elmer Miller	30.00	15.00	9.00
(90)	Otto Miller	30.00	15.00	9.00
(91a)	John Mitchell (S.S.)	30.00	15.00	9.00
(91b)	John Mitchell (3rd B.)	30.00	15.00	9.00
(92)	Guy Morton	30.00	15.00	9.00
(94)	Eddie Mulligan	30.00	15.00	9.00
(95)	Eddie Murphy	30.00	15.00	9.00
(96a)	"Hy" Myers (C.F./O.F.)	30.00	15.00	9.00
(96b)	Hy Myers (O.F.)	30.00	15.00	9.00
(97)	A.E. Neale	60.00	30.00	18.00
(98)	Arthur Nehf	30.00	15.00	9.00
(99)	Joe Oeschger	30.00	15.00	9.00
(100)	Chas. O'Leary	30.00	15.00	9.00
(101)	Steve O'Neill	30.00	15.00	9.00
(101a)	Jeff Pfeffer (Brooklyn)	30.00	15.00	9.00
(101b)	Jeff Pfeffer (St. Louis)	30.00	15.00	9.00
(102a)	Roger Peckinbaugh (name incorrect)	30.00	15.00	9.00
(102b)	Roger Peckinpaugh (name correct)	30.00	15.00	9.00
(104)	Walter Pipp	60.00	30.00	18.00
(105)	Jack Quinn	30.00	15.00	9.00
(106a)	John Rawlings (2nd B.)	30.00	15.00	9.00
(106b)	John Rawlings (2B.)	30.00	15.00	9.00
(107a)	E.S. Rice (name incorrect)	85.00	42.00	25.00
(107b)	E.C. Rice (name correct)	85.00	42.00	25.00
(108)	Eppa Rixey, Jr.	85.00	42.00	25.00
(109)	Wilbert Robinson	85.00	42.00	25.00
(110)	Tom Rogers	30.00	15.00	9.00
(111)	Ed Rounnel (Rommel)	30.00	15.00	9.00
112	Robert Roth (Rommel)	30.00	15.00	9.00
(113a)	Ed Roush (O.F.)	85.00	42.00	25.00
(113b)	Ed Roush (C.F.)	85.00	42.00	25.00
(114)	"Muddy" Ruel	30.00	15.00	9.00
(115a)	"Babe" Ruth (R.F.)	900.00	450.00	270.00
(115b)	Babe Ruth (L.F.)	900.00	450.00	270.00
(116)	Bill Ryan	30.00	15.00	9.00
(117)	"Slim" Sallee (ball in hand)	30.00	15.00	9.00
(118)	"Slim" Sallee (no ball in hand)	30.00	15.00	9.00
(119)	Ray Schalk (bunting)	85.00	42.00	25.00
(120)	Ray Schalk (catching)	85.00	42.00	25.00
(121a)	Walter Schang	30.00	15.00	9.00
(121b)	Wally Schang	30.00	15.00	9.00
(122a)	Fred Schupp (name incorrect)	30.00	15.00	9.00
(122b)	Ferd Schupp (name correct)	30.00	15.00	9.00
(123a)	Everett Scott (Boston)	30.00	15.00	9.00
(123b)	Everett Scott (New York)	30.00	15.00	9.00
(124)	Hank Severeid	30.00	15.00	9.00
(125)	Robert Shawkey	40.00	20.00	12.00
(126a)	"Pat" Shea	30.00	15.00	9.00
(126b)	Pat Shea	30.00	15.00	9.00
(127)	Earl Sheely	30.00	15.00	9.00
(128)	Urban Shocker	30.00	15.00	9.00
(129)	George Sisler (batting)	100.00	50.00	30.00
(130)	George Sisler (throwing)	100.00	50.00	30.00
(131)	Earl Smith	30.00	15.00	9.00
(132)	Elmer Smith	30.00	15.00	9.00
(133)	Frank Snyder	30.00	15.00	9.00
(134a)	Tris Speaker (large projection)	110.00	55.00	33.00
(134b)	Tris Speaker (small projection)	110.00	55.00	33.00
(135)	Charles Stengel (batting)	225.00	112.00	67.00
(136)	Charles Stengel (portrait)	225.00	112.00	67.00
(137)	Milton Stock	30.00	15.00	9.00
(138a)	Amos Strunk (C.F.)	30.00	15.00	9.00
(138b)	Amos Strunk (O.F.)	30.00	15.00	9.00
(139)	Zeb Terry	30.00	15.00	9.00
(140)	Chester Thomas	30.00	15.00	9.00
(141)	Fred Toney (both feet on ground)	30.00	15.00	9.00
(142)	Fred Toney (one foot in air)	30.00	15.00	9.00
(143)	George Toporcer	30.00	15.00	9.00
(144)	George Tyler	30.00	15.00	9.00
(145)	Jim Vaughn (plain uniform)	30.00	15.00	9.00
(146)	Jim Vaughn (striped uniform)	30.00	15.00	9.00
(147)	Bob Veach (arm raised)	30.00	15.00	9.00
(148)	Bob Veach (arms folded)	30.00	15.00	9.00
(149)	Oscar Vitt	30.00	15.00	9.00
(150)	Curtis Walker	30.00	15.00	9.00
(151)	W. Wambsganss	40.00	20.00	12.00
(152)	Zach Wheat	85.00	42.00	25.00
(153)	George Whitted	30.00	15.00	9.00
(154)	Fred Williams	40.00	20.00	12.00
(155)	Ivy B. Wingo	30.00	15.00	9.00
(156)	Lawton Witt	30.00	15.00	9.00
(157)	Joe Wood	40.00	20.00	12.00
(158)	Pep Young	30.00	15.00	9.00
(159)	Ross Young (Youngs)	85.00	42.00	25.00

A card number in parentheses () indicates the set is unnumbered.

Values for recent cards and sets are listed in Mint (MT), Near Mint (NM), reflecting the fact that many cards from recent years have been preserved in top condition. Recent cards and sets in less than Excellent condition have little collector interest.

1922 W575-2

The black and white cards in this set measure 2-1/8" by 3-3/8". Because of the design of the cards the set is sometimes called the "autograph on shoulder" series.

		NR MT	EX	VG
	Complete Set:	2900.	1450.	870.00
	Common Player:	35.00	17.50	10.50
(1)	Dave Bancroft	75.00	37.00	22.00
(2)	Johnnie Bassler	35.00	17.50	10.50
(3)	Joe Bush	40.00	20.00	12.00
(4)	Ty Cobb	750.00	375.00	225.00
(5)	Eddie Collins	75.00	37.00	22.00
(6)	Stan Coveleskie (Coveleski)	75.00	37.00	22.00
(7)	Jake Daubert	40.00	20.00	12.00
(8)	Joe Dugan	40.00	20.00	12.00
(9)	Red Faber	75.00	37.00	22.00
(10)	Frank Frisch	75.00	37.00	22.00
(11)	Walter H. Gerber	35.00	17.50	10.50
(12)	Harry Heilmann	75.00	37.00	22.00
(13)	Harry Hooper	75.00	37.00	22.00
(14)	Rogers Hornsby	250.00	125.00	75.00
(15)	Waite Hoyt	75.00	37.00	22.00
(16)	Joe Judge	35.00	17.50	10.50
(17)	Geo. Kelly	75.00	37.00	22.00
(18)	Rabbit Maranville	75.00	37.00	22.00
(19)	Rube Marquard	75.00	37.00	22.00
(20)	Guy Morton	35.00	17.50	10.50
(21)	Art Nehf	35.00	17.50	10.50
(22)	Derrill B. Pratt	35.00	17.50	10.50
(23)	Jimmy Ring	35.00	17.50	10.50
(24)	Eppa Rixey	75.00	37.00	22.00
(25)	Gene Robertson	35.00	17.50	10.50
(26)	Ed Rommell (Rommel)	35.00	17.50	10.50
(27)	Babe Ruth	1000.	500.00	300.00
(28)	Wally Schang	35.00	17.50	10.50
(29)	Everett Scott	35.00	17.50	10.50
(30)	Henry Severeid	35.00	17.50	10.50
(31)	Joe Sewell	75.00	37.00	22.00
(32)	Geo. Sisler	75.00	37.00	22.00
(33)	Tris Speaker	100.00	50.00	30.00
(34)	Riggs Stephenson	40.00	20.00	12.00
(35)	Zeb Terry	35.00	17.50	10.50
(36)	Bobbie Veach	35.00	17.50	10.50
(37)	Clarence Walker	35.00	17.50	10.50
(38)	Johnnie Walker	35.00	17.50	10.50
(39)	Zach Wheat	75.00	37.00	22.00
(40)	Kenneth Williams	40.00	20.00	12.00

1938 W711-1 Reds

WALLY BERGER, Outfielder

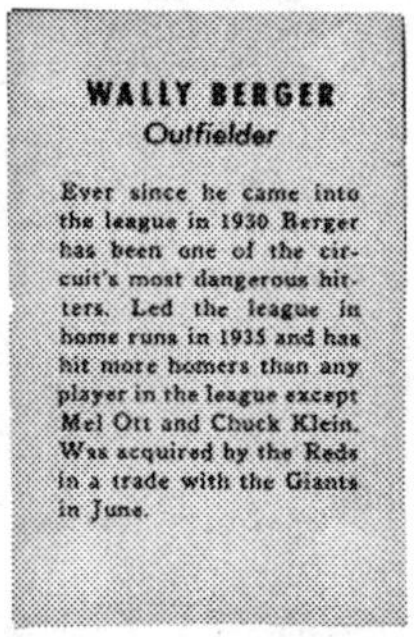

WALLY BERGER
Outfielder
Ever since he came into the league in 1930 Berger has been one of the circuit's most dangerous hitters. Led the league in home runs in 1935 and has hit more homers than any player in the league except Mel Ott and Chuck Klein. Was acquired by the Reds in a trade with the Giants in June.

This 32-card set is a challenging one of particular interest to Cincinnati team collectors. The 2" by 3" cards were sold at the ballpark. Fronts feature a picture of the player while backs have the player's name, position and a generally flattering description of the player's talents. The cards are not numbered.

		NR MT	EX	VG
	Complete Set:	300.00	150.00	90.00
	Common Player:	10.00	5.00	3.00
(1)	Wally Berger ("... in a trade with the Giants in June.")	15.00	7.50	4.50
(2)	Joe Cascarella	25.00	12.50	7.50
(3)	Allen "Dusty" Cooke	25.00	12.50	7.50
(4)	Harry Craft	10.00	5.00	3.00
(5)	Ray "Peaches" Davis	10.00	5.00	3.00
(6)	Paul Derringer ("Won 22 games ... this season.")	15.00	7.50	4.50
(7)	Linus Frey ("... only 25 now.")	25.00	12.50	7.50
(8)	Lee Gamble ("... Syracuse last year.")	25.00	12.50	7.50
(9)	Ival Goodman (no mention of 30 homers)	25.00	12.50	7.50
(10)	Harry "Hank" Gowdy	10.00	5.00	3.00
(11)	Lee Grissom (no mention of 1938)	25.00	12.50	7.50
(12)	Willard Hershberger	15.00	7.50	4.50
(13)	Ernie Lombardi (no mention of 1938 MVP)	30.00	15.00	9.00
(14)	Frank McCormick	15.00	7.50	4.50
(15)	Bill McKechnie ("Last year he led ...")	25.00	12.50	7.50
(16)	Lloyd "Whitey" Moore ("... last year with Syracuse.")	25.00	12.50	7.50
(17)	Billy Myers ("... in his fourth year.")	25.00	12.50	7.50
(18)	Lee Riggs ("... in his fourth season ...")	25.00	12.50	7.50
(19)	Eddie Roush	25.00	12.50	7.50
(20)	Gene Schott	25.00	12.50	7.50
(21)	Johnny Vander Meer (pitching pose)	20.00	10.00	6.00
(22)	Wm. "Bucky" Walter ("... won 14 games ...")	15.00	7.50	4.50
(23)	Jim Weaver	10.00	5.00	3.00

1939 W711-1 Reds

WALLY BERGER, Outfielder

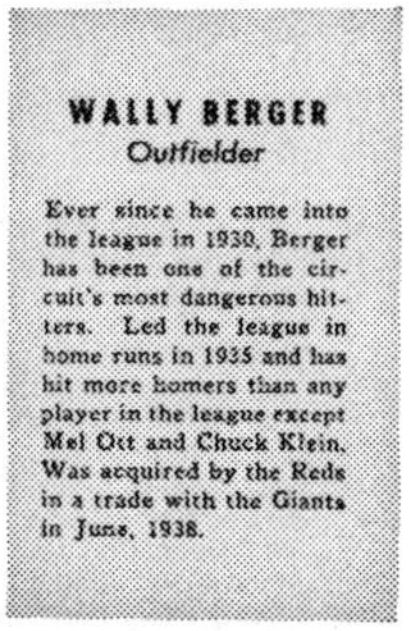

WALLY BERGER
Outfielder
Ever since he came into the league in 1930, Berger has been one of the circuit's most dangerous hitters. Led the league in home runs in 1935 and has hit more homers than any player in the league except Mel Ott and Chuck Klein. Was acquired by the Reds in a trade with the Giants in June, 1938.

An updating by one season of the team-issued 1938 W711-1 issue, most of the players and poses on the 2" by 3" cards remained the same. A close study of the career summary on the card's back is necessary to determine which year of issue is at hand.

		NR MT	EX	VG
	Complete Set:	500.00	250.00	150.00
	Common Player:	20.00	10.00	6.00
(1)	Wally Berger ("... in a trade with the Giants in June, 1938.")	30.00	15.00	9.00
(2)	Nino Bongiovanni	30.00	15.00	9.00
(3)	Stanley "Frenchy" Bordagaray	30.00	15.00	9.00
(4)	Harry Craft	20.00	10.00	6.00
(5)	Ray "Peaches" Davis	20.00	10.00	6.00
(6)	Paul Derringer ("Won 22 games ... last year.")	30.00	15.00	9.00
(7)	Linus Frey ("... only 26 now.")	12.00	6.00	3.50
(8)	Lee Gamble ("... Syracuse in 1937.")	12.00	6.00	3.50
(9)	Ival Goodman (mentions hitting 30 homers)	12.00	6.00	3.50
(10)	Harry "Hank" Gowdy	20.00	10.00	6.00
(11)	Lee Grissom (mentions 1938)	12.00	6.00	3.50
(12)	Willard Hershberger	30.00	15.00	9.00
(13)	Eddie Joost	12.00	6.00	3.50
(14)	Wes Livengood	80.00	40.00	24.00
(15)	Ernie Lombardi (mentions MVP of 1938)	30.00	15.00	9.00
(16)	Frank McCormick	30.00	15.00	9.00
(17)	Bill McKechnie ("In 1937 he led ...")	50.00	25.00	15.00
(18)	Lloyd "Whitey" Moore ("... in 1937 with Syracuse.")	12.00	6.00	3.50
(19)	Billy Myers ("... in his fifth year ...")	12.00	6.00	3.50
(20)	Lee Riggs ("... in his fifth season...")	12.00	6.00	3.50
(21)	Les Scarsella	30.00	15.00	9.00
(22)	Eugene "Junior" Thompson	12.00	6.00	3.50
(23)	Johnny Vander Meer (portrait)	20.00	10.00	6.00
(24)	Wm. "Bucky" Walters ("Won 15 games ...")	30.00	15.00	9.00
(25)	Jim Weaver	20.00	10.00	6.00
(26)	Bill Werber	12.00	6.00	3.50
(27)	Jimmy Wilson	12.00	6.00	3.50

Values quoted in this guide reflect the retail price of a card – the price a collector can expect to pay when buying a card from a dealer. The wholesale price – that which a collector can expect to receive from a dealer when selling cards – will be significantly lower, depending on desirability and condition.

1940 W711-2 Harry Hartman Reds

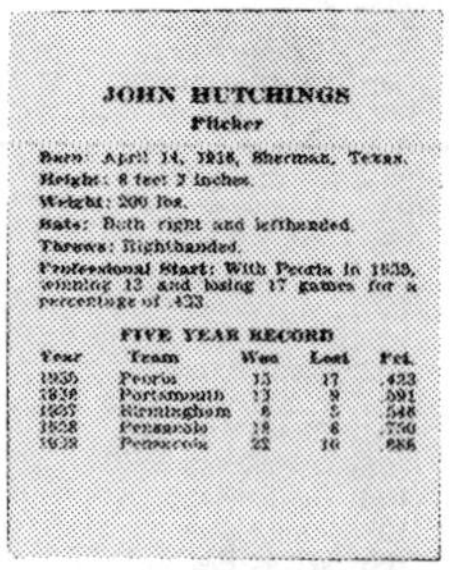

JOHN HUTCHINGS
Pitcher
FIVE YEAR RECORD

Another early set of the Cincinnati Reds, this 32-card set of 2-1/8" by 2-5/8" cards contains a number of interesting items. The black and white cards carry no numbers and feature a picture of the player on the front and name, position and biographical information on the back. As the Reds were World Champions in 1940 after defeating Detroit in four games to three, the set features special cards for the World Series title, making it one of the first to feature events as well as individuals. The set takes it name from Reds' announcer Harry Hartman, who has a card in the issue and supposedly was instrumental in its issue.

		NR MT	EX	VG
	Complete Set:	450.00	225.00	135.00
	Common Player:	12.00	6.00	3.50
(1)	Morris Arnovich	12.00	6.00	3.50
(2)	William (Bill) Baker	12.00	6.00	3.50
(3)	Joseph Beggs	12.00	6.00	3.50
(4)	Harry Craft	12.00	6.00	3.50
(5)	Paul Derringer	20.00	10.00	6.00
(6)	Linus Frey	12.00	6.00	3.50
(7)	Ival Goodman	12.00	6.00	3.50
(8)	Harry (Hank) Gowdy	12.00	6.00	3.50
(9)	Witt Guise	12.00	6.00	3.50
(10)	Harry (Socko) Hartman	12.00	6.00	3.50
(11)	Willard Hershberger	15.00	7.50	4.50
(12)	John Hutchings	12.00	6.00	3.50
(13)	Edwin Joost	12.00	6.00	3.50
(14)	Ernie Lombardi	55.00	27.00	16.50
(15)	Frank McCormick	20.00	10.00	6.00
(16)	Myron McCormick	12.00	6.00	3.50
(17)	William Boyd McKechnie	30.00	15.00	9.00
(18)	Lloyd (Whitey) Moore	12.00	6.00	3.50
(19)	William (Bill) Myers	12.00	6.00	3.50
(20)	Lewis Riggs	12.00	6.00	3.50
(21)	Elmer Riddle	12.00	6.00	3.50
(22)	James A. Ripple	12.00	6.00	3.50
(23)	Milburn Shoffner	12.00	6.00	3.50
(24)	Eugene Thompson	12.00	6.00	3.50
(25)	James Turner	12.00	6.00	3.50
(26)	John Vander Meer	30.00	15.00	9.00
(27)	Wm. (Bucky) Walters	20.00	10.00	6.00
(28)	William (Bill) Werber	12.00	6.00	3.50
(29)	James Wilson	15.00	7.50	4.50
(30)	The Cincinnati Reds	12.00	6.00	3.50
(31)	The Cincinnati Reds World Champions	12.00	6.00	3.50
(32)	Tell The World About The Cincinnati Reds	12.00	6.00	3.50
(33)	Tell The World About The Cincinnati Reds World (Champions)	12.00	6.00	3.50
(34)	Results 1940 World's Series	15.00	7.50	4.50
(35)	Debt of Gratitude to Wm. Koehl Co.	12.00	6.00	3.50

1941 W753 St. Louis Browns

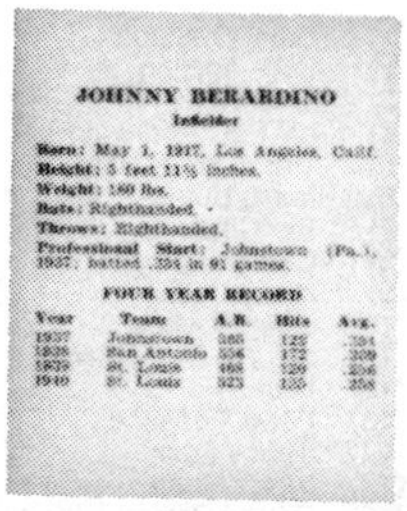

JOHNNY BERARDINO
Infielder
FOUR YEAR RECORD

Measuring 2-1/8" by 2-5/8", this unnumbered set of cards features the St. Louis Browns in black and white portrait photos. There are 29 cards in the set which featured a photo on the front and the player's name, position and personal and statistical information. There are also cards for coaches and one of the the club's two managers that season (Luke

Sewell). As the Browns weren't much of a team in 1941 (or in most seasons for that matter) there are no major stars in the set.

		NR MT	EX	VG
Complete Set:		400.00	200.00	120.00
Common Player:		15.00	7.50	4.50
(1)	Johnny Allen	15.00	7.50	4.50
(2)	Elden Auker (Eldon)	15.00	7.50	4.50
(3)	Donald L Barnes	15.00	7.50	4.50
(4)	Johnny Berardino	20.00	10.00	6.00
(5)	George Caster	15.00	7.50	4.50
(6)	Harlond Benton (Darky) Clift	15.00	7.50	4.50
(7)	Roy J. Cullenbine	15.00	7.50	4.50
(8)	William O. DeWitt	15.00	7.50	4.50
(9)	Roberto Estalella	15.00	7.50	4.50
(10)	Richard Benjamin (Rick) Ferrell	60.00	30.00	18.00
(11)	Dennis W. Galehouse	15.00	7.50	4.50
(12)	Joseph L. Grace	15.00	7.50	4.50
(13)	Frank Grube	15.00	7.50	4.50
(14)	Robert A. Harris	15.00	7.50	4.50
(15)	Donald Henry Heffner	15.00	7.50	4.50
(16)	Fred Hofmann	15.00	7.50	4.50
(17)	Walter Franklin Judnich	15.00	7.50	4.50
(18)	John Henry (Jack) Kramer	15.00	7.50	4.50
(19)	Chester (Chet) Laabs	15.00	7.50	4.50
(20)	John Lucadello	15.00	7.50	4.50
(21)	George Hartley McQuinn	15.00	7.50	4.50
(22)	Robert Cleveland Muncrief, Jr.	15.00	7.50	4.50
(23)	John Niggeling	15.00	7.50	4.50
(24)	Fred Raymond (Fritz) Ostermueller	20.00	10.00	6.00
(25)	James Luther (Luke) Sewell	15.00	7.50	4.50
(26)	Alan Cochran Strange (Cochrane)	15.00	7.50	4.50
(27)	Robert Virgil (Bob) Swift	15.00	7.50	4.50
(28)	James W. (Zack) Taylor	15.00	7.50	4.50
(29)	William Felix (Bill) Trotter	15.00	7.50	4.50
(30)	Presentation Card/Order Form	25.00	12.50	7.50

1941 W754 St. Louis Cardinals

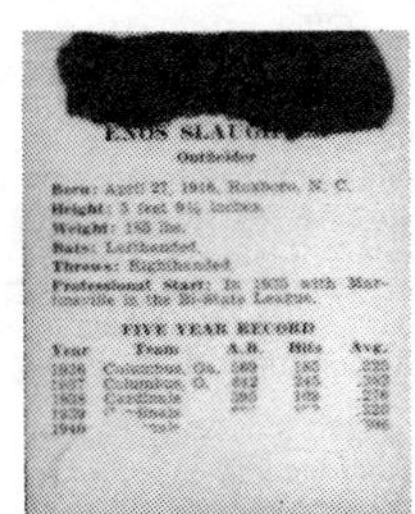

A companion set to W753, this time featuring the other team in St. Louis. Cards measure 2-1/8" by 2-5/8" and are unnumbered. Like the Browns set, there are 29 cards featuring black and white photos on the front and the individual's name, position and personal and statistical information on the back. One interesting addition to the set is a card of Branch Rickey which, coupled with cards of Enos Slaughter and Johnny Mize, gives the set a bit more appeal than the Browns set.

		NR MT	EX	VG
Complete Set:		500.00	250.00	150.00
Common Player:		15.00	7.50	4.50
(1)	Sam Breadon	15.00	7.50	4.50
(2)	James Brown	15.00	7.50	4.50
(3)	Morton Cooper	15.00	7.50	4.50
(4)	William Walker Cooper	15.00	7.50	4.50
(5)	Estel Crabtree	15.00	7.50	4.50
(6)	Frank Crespi	15.00	7.50	4.50
(7)	William Crouch	15.00	7.50	4.50
(8)	Miguel Mike Gonzalez	15.00	7.50	4.50
(9)	Harry Gumbert	15.00	7.50	4.50
(10)	John Hopp	15.00	7.50	4.50
(11)	Ira Hutchinson	15.00	7.50	4.50
(12)	Howard Krist	15.00	7.50	4.50
(13)	Edward E. Lake	15.00	7.50	4.50
(14)	Hubert Max Lanier	20.00	10.00	6.00
(15)	Gus Mancuso	15.00	7.50	4.50
(16)	Martin Marion	25.00	12.50	7.50
(17)	Steve Mesner	15.00	7.50	4.50
(18)	John Mize	60.00	30.00	18.00
(19)	Capt. Terry Moore	20.00	10.00	6.00
(20)	Sam Nahem	15.00	7.50	4.50
(21)	Don Padgett	15.00	7.50	4.50
(22)	Branch Rickey	60.00	30.00	18.00
(23)	Clyde Shoun	15.00	7.50	4.50
(24)	Enos Slaughter	60.00	30.00	18.00
(25)	William H. (Billy) Southworth	15.00	7.50	4.50
(26)	Herman Coaker Triplett	15.00	7.50	4.50
(27)	Clyde Buzzy Wares	15.00	7.50	4.50
(28)	Lou Warneke	15.00	7.50	4.50
(29)	Ernest White	15.00	7.50	4.50
(30)	Presentation Card/Order Form	25.00	12.50	7.50

1888 WG1 Base Ball Playing Cards

This little-known set of playing cards featuring drawings of real baseball players in action poses was issued in 1888 and includes members of the eight National League teams in existence at the time. Each club is represented by nine players - one at each position - making the set complete at 72 cards. The cards measure 2-1/2" x 3-1/2" and have a blue-patterned design on the back. The cards were sold as a boxed set. They were designed to resemble a deck of regular playing cards, and the various positions were all assigned the same denomination (for example, all of the pitchers were kings, catchers were aces, etc.). There are no cards numbered either two, three, four or five; and rather than the typical hearts, clubs, diamonds and spades, each team represents a different "suit." The actual rules of the game remain open to speculation because no instructions have ever been found. The set has an American Card Catalog designation of WG1.

		NR MT	EX	VG
Complete Set:		40000.	20000.	1200.
Common Player:		300.00	150.00	90.00
(1)	Ed Andrews	300.00	150.00	90.00
(2)	Cap Anson	3000.	1500.	900.00
(3)	Charles Bassett	300.00	150.00	90.00
(4)	Charles Bastian	300.00	150.00	90.00
(5)	Charles Bennett	300.00	150.00	90.00
(6)	Handsome Boyle	300.00	150.00	90.00
(7)	Dan Brouthers	1500.	750.00	450.00
(8)	Thomas Brown	300.00	150.00	90.00
(9)	Thomas Burns	300.00	150.00	90.00
(10)	Frederick Carroll	300.00	150.00	90.00
(11)	Daniel Casey	1000.	500.00	300.00
(12)	John Clarkson	1500.	750.00	450.00
(13)	Jack Clements	300.00	150.00	90.00
(14)	John Coleman	300.00	150.00	90.00
(15)	Roger Connor	1500.	750.00	450.00
(16)	Abner Dalrymple	300.00	150.00	90.00
(17)	Jerry Denny	300.00	150.00	90.00
(18)	Jim Donelly	300.00	150.00	90.00
(19)	Sure Shot Dunlap	300.00	150.00	90.00
(20)	Dude Esterbrook	300.00	150.00	90.00
(21)	Buck Ewing	1500.	750.00	450.00
(22)	Sid Farrar	300.00	150.00	90.00
(23)	Silver Flint	300.00	150.00	90.00
(24)	Jim Fogarty	300.00	150.00	90.00
(25)	Elmer Foster	300.00	150.00	90.00
(26)	Pud Galvin	1500.	750.00	450.00
(27)	Charlie Getzein	300.00	150.00	90.00
(28)	Pebbly Jack Glasscock	1000.	500.00	300.00
(29)	Piano Legs Gore	300.00	150.00	90.00
(30)	Ned Hanlon	300.00	150.00	90.00
(31)	Paul Hines	300.00	150.00	90.00
(32)	Joe Hornung	300.00	150.00	90.00
(33)	Dummy Hoy	1000.	500.00	300.00
(34)	Cutrate Irwin (Philadelphia)	300.00	150.00	90.00
(35)	John Irwin (Washington)	300.00	150.00	90.00
(36)	Dick Johnston	300.00	150.00	90.00
(37)	Tim Keefe	1500.	750.00	450.00
(38)	King Kelly	1500.	750.00	450.00
(39)	Willie Kuehne	300.00	150.00	90.00
(40)	Connie Mack	2500.	1250.	750.00
(41)	Smiling Al Maul	300.00	150.00	90.00
(42)	Al Meyers (Myers) (Washington)	300.00	150.00	90.00
(43)	George Meyers (Myers) (Indianapolis)	300.00	150.00	90.00
(44)	Honest John Morrill	300.00	150.00	90.00
(45)	Joseph Mulvey	300.00	150.00	90.00
(46)	Billy Nash	300.00	150.00	90.00
(47)	Billy O'Brien	300.00	150.00	90.00
(48)	Orator Jim O'Rourke	1500.	750.00	450.00
(49)	Bob Pettit	300.00	150.00	90.00
(50)	Fred Pfeffer	300.00	150.00	90.00
(51)	Danny Richardson (New York)	300.00	150.00	90.00
(52)	Hardy Richardson (Detroit)	300.00	150.00	90.00
(53)	Jack Rowe	300.00	150.00	90.00
(54)	Jimmy Ryan	300.00	150.00	90.00
(55)	Emmett Seery	300.00	150.00	90.00
(56)	George Shoch	300.00	150.00	90.00
(57)	Otto Shomberg (Schomberg)	300.00	150.00	90.00
(58)	Pap Smith	300.00	150.00	90.00
(59)	Marty Sullivan	300.00	150.00	90.00
(60)	Billy Sunday	1500.	750.00	450.00
(61)	Ezra Sutton	300.00	150.00	90.00
(62)	Big Sam Thompson	1500.	750.00	450.00
(63)	Silent Mike Tiernan	300.00	150.00	90.00
(64)	Larry Twitchell	300.00	150.00	90.00
(65)	Rip Van Haltren	300.00	150.00	90.00
(66)	Monte Ward	1500.	750.00	450.00
(67)	Deacon White	300.00	150.00	90.00
(68)	Grasshopper Whitney	300.00	150.00	90.00
(69)	Ned Williamson	300.00	150.00	90.00
(70)	Watt Wilmot	300.00	150.00	90.00
(71)	Medoc Wise	300.00	150.00	90.00
(72)	George "Dandy" Wood	300.00	150.00	90.00

1985 Wendy's Tigers

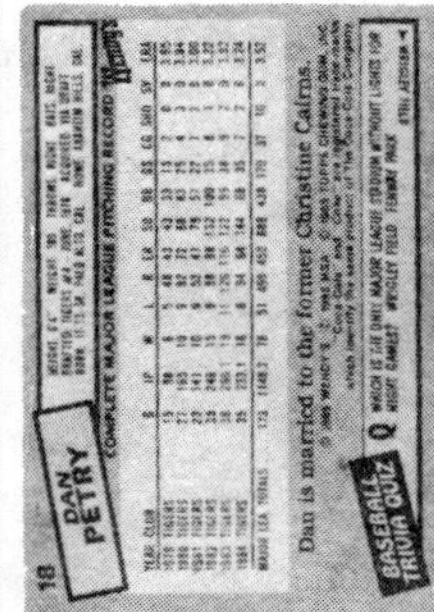

This set contains 22 cards measuring 2-1/2" x 3-1/2", which carry both Wendy's Hamburgers and Coca-Cola logos and were produced by Topps. The cards feature a color photo with the player's team, name and position underneath the picture and the Wendy's logo in the lower left and Coke logo in the upper right. Backs are identical to 1985 Topps cards except they have different card numbers and are done in a red and black color scheme. Cards were distributed three to a pack along with a "Header" checklist in a cellophane package at selected Wendy's outlets in Michigan only.

		MT	NR MT	EX
Complete Set:		8.00	6.00	3.25
Common Player:		.15	.11	.06
1	Sparky Anderson	.30	.25	.12
2	Doug Bair	.15	.11	.06
3	Juan Berenguer	.15	.11	.06
4	Dave Bergman	.15	.11	.06
5	Tom Brookens	.15	.11	.06
6	Marty Castillo	.15	.11	.06
7	Darrell Evans	.40	.30	.15
8	Barbaro Garbey	.15	.11	.06
9	Kirk Gibson	.60	.45	.25
10	Johnny Grubb	.15	.11	.06
11	Willie Hernandez	.25	.20	.10
12	Larry Herndon	.15	.11	.06
13	Rusty Kuntz	.15	.11	.06
14	Chet Lemon	.25	.20	.10
15	Aurelio Lopez	.15	.11	.06
16	Jack Morris	1.00	.70	.40
17	Lance Parrish	.80	.60	.30
18	Dan Petry	.25	.20	.10
19	Bill Scherrer	.15	.11	.06
20	Alan Trammell	1.00	.70	.40
21	Lou Whitaker	.80	.60	.30
22	Milt Wilcox	.15	.11	.06

1974 Weston Expos

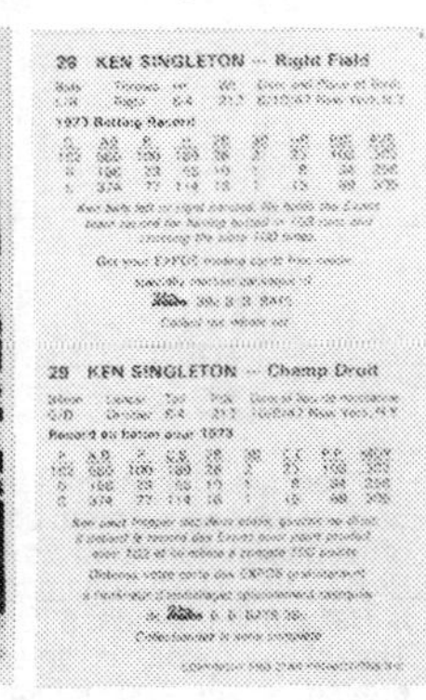

This 10-card set features members of the Montreal Expos. Each full-color card measures 3-1/2" by 5-1/2" and includes a facsimile autograph in black ink with the player's name printed along the bottom. The backs are distinct because they are divided in half. The top of the card lists player data and 1973 statistics in English, while the bottom carries the same information in French. The cards are numbered according to the player's uniform number.

		NR MT	EX	VG
Complete Set:		12.00	6.00	3.75
Common Player:		1.50	.70	.45
3	Bob Bailey	1.50	.70	.45
8	Boots Day	1.50	.70	.45
12	John Boccabella	1.50	.70	.45
16	Mike Jorgensen	1.50	.70	.45
18	Steve Renko	1.50	.70	.45
19	Tim Foli	1.50	.70	.45
21	Ernie McAnally	1.50	.70	.45
26	Bill Stoneman	1.50	.70	.45
29	Ken Singleton	2.00	1.00	.60
33	Ron Hunt	1.50	.70	.45

1993 Whataburger Nolan Ryan

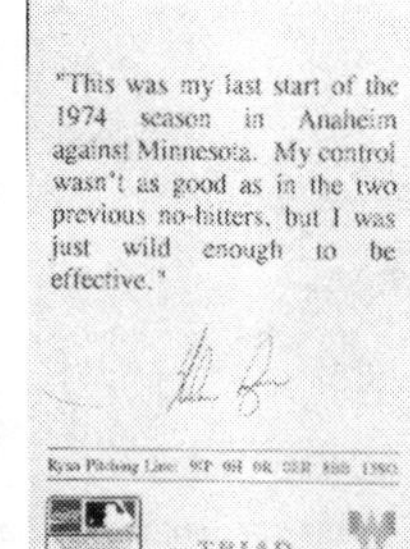

Issued in two-card cello packs at Whataburger restaurants, this set honors the career of Nolan Ryan. Cards have action photos set against colorized backgrounds and overlayed with ribbed plastic to create a 3-D effect. A card title is printed in white in the lower-left corner, with the logo of Triad (the card's maker) in the lower-right. In the upper-left corner is a red "Nolan Ryan's Recollections" logo. Backs have color logos of the hamburger chain, Triad, Coca-Cola and Major League Baseball, along with a quote from Ryan about the career highlight and a facsimile autograph. The cards are unnumbered.

		MT	NR MT	EX
Complete Set (10):		10.00	7.50	4.00
Common Card:		1.00	.70	.40
(1)	1st No-Hitter	1.00	.70	.40
(2)	2nd No-Hitter	1.00	.70	.40
(3)	3rd No-Hitter	1.00	.70	.40
(4)	4th No-Hitter	1.00	.70	.40
(5)	5th No-Hitter	1.00	.70	.40
(6)	6th No-Hitter	1.00	.70	.40
(7)	7th No-Hitter	1.00	.70	.40
(8)	5,000th Strikeout	1.00	.70	.40
(9)	300th Win	1.00	.70	.40
10	Nolan Ryan (on horse)	1.00	.70	.40

1935 Wheaties - Series 1

This set of 25 major leaguers was issued on the back of Wheaties cereal boxes in 1935 and because of its design, is known as "Fancy Frame with Script Signature." The unnumbered cards measure 6" by 6-1/4" with frame, and 5" by 5-1/2" without the frame. The player photo is tinted blue, while the background is blue and orange. A facsimilie autograph appears at the bottom of the photo.

		NR MT	EX	VG
Complete Set:		1600.	800.00	480.00
Common Player:		25.00	12.50	7.50
(1)	Jack Armstrong (batting)	25.00	12.50	7.50
(2)	Jack Armstrong (throwing)	25.00	12.50	7.50
(3)	Wally Berger	25.00	12.50	7.50
(4)	Tommy Bridges	25.00	12.50	7.50
(5a)	Mickey Cochrane (black hat)	50.00	25.00	15.00
(5b)	Michey Cochrane (white hat)	250.00	125.00	75.00
(6)	James "Rip" Collins	25.00	12.50	7.50
(7)	Dizzy Dean	100.00	50.00	30.00
(8)	Dizzy Dean, Paul Dean	70.00	35.00	21.00
(9)	Paul Dean	30.00	15.00	9.00
(10)	William Delancey	25.00	12.50	7.50
(11)	"Jimmie" Foxx	70.00	35.00	21.00
(12)	Frank Frisch	40.00	20.00	12.00
(13)	Lou Gehrig	350.00	175.00	105.00
(14)	Goose Goslin	40.00	20.00	12.00
(15)	Lefty Grove	60.00	30.00	18.00
(16)	Carl Hubbell	50.00	25.00	15.00
(17)	Travis C. Jackson	40.00	20.00	12.00
(18)	"Chuck" Klein	40.00	20.00	12.00
(19)	Gus Mancuso	25.00	12.50	7.50
(20)	Johnny "Pepper" Martin	30.00	15.00	9.00
(21)	Pepper Martin	30.00	15.00	9.00
(22)	Joe Medwick	40.00	20.00	12.00
(23)	Melvin Ott	60.00	30.00	18.00
(24)	Harold Schumacher	25.00	12.50	7.50
(25)	Al Simmons	40.00	20.00	12.00
(26)	"Jo Jo" White	25.00	12.50	7.50

1936 Wheaties - Series 3

Consisting of 12 unnumbered cards, this set is similar in size (6" by 6-1/4" with frame) and design to the Wheaties of the previous year, but is known as "Fancy Frame with Printed Name and Data" because the cards also include a few printed words describing the player.

		NR MT	EX	VG
Complete Set:		750.00	375.00	225.00
Common Player:		25.00	12.50	7.50
(1)	Earl Averill	40.00	20.00	12.00
(2)	Mickey Cochrane	50.00	25.00	15.00
(3)	Jimmy Foxx	60.00	30.00	18.00
(4)	Lou Gehrig	350.00	175.00	105.00
(5)	Hank Greenberg	50.00	25.00	15.00
(6)	"Gabby" Hartnett	40.00	20.00	12.00
(7)	Carl Hubbell	50.00	25.00	15.00
(8)	"Pepper" Martin	30.00	15.00	9.00
(9)	Van L. Mungo	25.00	12.50	7.50
(10)	"Buck" Newsom	25.00	12.50	7.50
(11)	"Arky" Vaughan	40.00	20.00	12.00
(12)	Jimmy Wilson	25.00	12.50	7.50

1936 Wheaties - Series 4

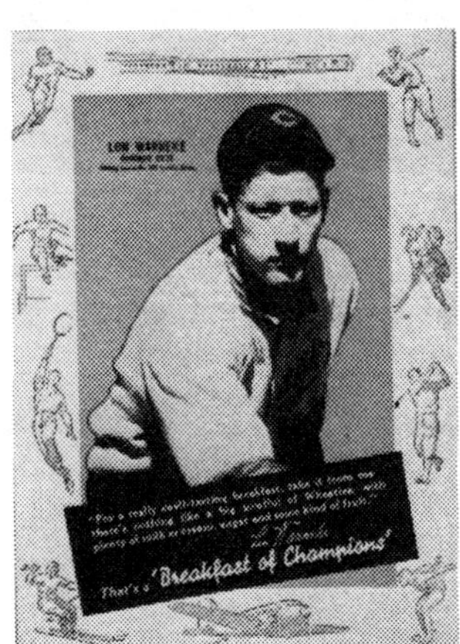

This larger size (8-1/2" by 6") card also made up the back of a Wheaties box, and because of its distinctive border which featured drawings of small athletic figures, it is referred to as "Thin Orange Border/ Figures in Border." Twelve major leaguers are pictured in the unnumbered set. The photos are enclosed in a 4" by 6-1/2" box. Below the photo is an endorsement for Wheaties, the "Breakfast of Champions," and a facsimilie autograph.

		NR MT	EX	VG
Complete Set:		750.00	375.00	225.00
Common Player:		25.00	12.50	7.50
(1)	Curt Davis	25.00	12.50	7.50
(2)	Lou Gehrig	350.00	175.00	105.00
(3)	Charley Gehringer	50.00	25.00	15.00
(4)	Lefty Grove	60.00	30.00	18.00
(5)	Rollie Hemsley	25.00	12.50	7.50
(6)	Billy Herman	40.00	20.00	12.00
(7)	Joe Medwick	40.00	20.00	12.00
(8)	Mel Ott	60.00	30.00	18.00
(9)	Schoolboy Rowe	25.00	12.50	7.50
(10)	Arky Vaughan	40.00	20.00	12.00
(11)	Joe Vosmik	25.00	12.50	7.50
(12)	Lon Warneke	25.00	12.50	7.50

1936 Wheaties - Series 5

Often referred to as "How to Play Winning Baseball", this 12-card set features a large player photo surrounded by blue and white drawings that illustrate various playing tips. Different major leaguers offer advice on different aspects of the game. The cards again made up the back panel of a Wheaties box and measure 8-1/2" by 6-1/2". The cards are numbered from 1 through 12, and some of the panels are also found with a small number "28" followed by a letter from "A" through "L."

		NR MT	EX	VG
Complete Set:		600.00	300.00	180.00
Common Player:		25.00	12.50	7.50
1	Lefty Gomez	50.00	25.00	15.00
2	Billy Herman	40.00	20.00	12.00
3	Luke Appling	40.00	20.00	12.00
4	Jimmie Foxx	60.00	30.00	18.00
5	Joe Medwick	40.00	20.00	12.00
6	Charles Gehringer	40.00	20.00	12.00
7a	Mel Ott (tips in vertical sequence)	60.00	30.00	18.00
7b	Mel Ott (tips in two horizontal rows)	60.00	30.00	18.00
8	Odell Hale	25.00	12.50	7.50
9	Bill Dickey	60.00	30.00	18.00
10	"Lefty" Grove	60.00	30.00	18.00
11	Carl Hubbell	50.00	25.00	15.00
12	Earl Averill	40.00	20.00	12.00

1937 Wheaties - Series 6

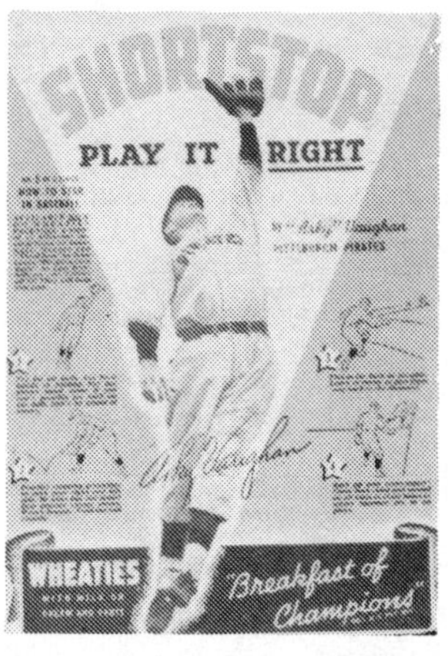

Similar to the Series 5 set, this numbered, 12-card series is known as "How to Star in Baseball" and again includes a large player photo with small instructional drawings to illustrate playing tips. The cards measure 8-1/4" by 6" and include a facsimilie autograph.

		NR MT	EX	VG
Complete Set:		750.00	375.00	225.00
Common Player:		25.00	12.50	7.50
1	Bill Dickey	60.00	30.00	18.00
2	Red Ruffing	40.00	20.00	12.00
3	Zeke Bonura	25.00	12.50	7.50
4	Charlie Gehringer	50.00	25.00	15.00
5	"Arky" Vaughn (Vaughan)	40.00	20.00	12.00
6	Carl Hubbell	50.00	25.00	15.00
7	John Lewis	25.00	12.50	7.50
8	Heinie Manush	40.00	20.00	12.00
9	"Lefty" Grove	60.00	30.00	18.00
10	Billy Herman	40.00	20.00	12.00
11	Joe DiMaggio	350.00	175.00	105.00
12	Joe Medwick	40.00	20.00	12.00

1937 Wheaties - Series 7

This 15-card set of 6" by 8-1/4" panels contains several different card designs. One style (picturing Lombardi, Travis and Mungo) has a white background with an orange border and a large orange circle behind the player. Another design (showing Bonura, DiMaggio and Bridges) has the player outlined against a bright orange background with a Wheaties endorsement along the bottom. A third format (picturing Moore, Radcliff and Martin) has a distinctive red, white and blue border. And a fourth design (featuring Trosky, Demaree and Vaughan) has a tilted picture against an orange background framed in blue and white. The set also includes three Pacific Coast League Players. The cards are numbered with a small "29" followed by a letter from "A" through "P." Card number "29N," which may be another PCL player, is unknown.

		NR MT	EX	VG
Complete Set:		700.00	350.00	210.00
Common Player:		25.00	12.50	7.50
29A	"Zeke" Bonura	25.00	12.50	7.50
29B	Cecil Travis	25.00	12.50	7.50
29C	Frank Demaree	25.00	12.50	7.50
29D	Joe Moore	25.00	12.50	7.50
29E	Ernie Lombardi	40.00	20.00	12.00
29F	John L. "Pepper" Martin	30.00	15.00	9.00
29G	Harold Trosky	25.00	12.50	7.50
29H	Raymond Radcliff	25.00	12.50	7.50
29I	Joe DiMaggio	350.00	175.00	105.00
29J	Tom Bridges	25.00	12.50	7.50
29K	Van L. Mungo	25.00	12.50	7.50
29L	"Arky" Vaughn (Vaughan)	40.00	20.00	12.00
29M	Arnold Statz	150.00	75.00	45.00
29N	Unknown			
29O	Fred Muller (Mueller)	150.00	75.00	45.00
29P	Gene Lillard	150.00	75.00	45.00

A card number in parentheses () indicates the set is unnumbered.

1937 Wheaties - Series 8

Another series printed on the back of Wheaties boxes in 1937, the eight cards in this set are unnumbered and measure 8-1/2" by 6". There are several different designs, but in all of them the player photo is surrounded by speckles of color, causing this

series to be known as the "Speckled Orange, White and Blue" series. A facsimilie autograph is included, along with brief printed 1936 season statistics.

		NR MT	EX	VG
Complete Set:		700.00	350.00	210.00
Common Player:		40.00	20.00	12.00
(1)	Luke Appling	40.00	20.00	12.00
(2)	Earl Averill	40.00	20.00	12.00
(3)	Joe DiMaggio	350.00	175.00	105.00
(4)	Robert Feller	110.00	55.00	33.00
(5)	Chas. Gehringer	50.00	25.00	15.00
(6)	Lefty Grove	60.00	30.00	18.00
(7)	Carl Hubbell	50.00	25.00	15.00
(8)	Joe Medwick	40.00	20.00	12.00

1937 Wheaties - Series 9

This unnumbered set includes one player from each of the 16 major league teams and is generally referred to as the "Color Series." The cards measure 8-1/2" by 6" and were the back panels of Wheaties boxes. The player photos are shown inside or against large stars, circles, "V" shapes, rectangles and other geometrical designs. A facsimilie autograph and team designation are printed near the photo, while a Wheaties endorsement and a line of player stats appear along the bottom.

		NR MT	EX	VG
Complete Set:		950.00	475.00	285.00
Common Player:		25.00	12.50	7.50
(1)	Zeke Bonura	25.00	12.50	7.50
(2)	Tom Bridges	25.00	12.50	7.50
(3)	Harland Clift (Harlond)	25.00	12.50	7.50
(4)	Kiki Cuyler	40.00	20.00	12.00
(5)	Joe DiMaggio	350.00	175.00	105.00
(6)	Robert Feller	110.00	55.00	33.00
(7)	Lefty Grove	60.00	30.00	18.00
(8)	Billy Herman	40.00	20.00	12.00
(9)	Carl Hubbell	50.00	25.00	15.00
(10)	Buck Jordan	25.00	12.50	7.50
(11)	"Pepper" Martin	30.00	15.00	9.00
(12)	John Moore	25.00	12.50	7.50
(13)	Wally Moses	25.00	12.50	7.50
(14)	Van L. Mungo	25.00	12.50	7.50
(15)	Cecil Travis	25.00	12.50	7.50
(16)	Arky Vaughan	40.00	20.00	12.00

The values quoted are intended to reflect the market price.

1937 Wheaties - Series 14

Much reduced in size (2-5/8" by 3-7/8"), these unnumbered cards made up the back panels of single-serving size Wheaties boxes. The player photo (which is sometimes identical to the photos used in the larger series) is set against an orange or white background. The player's name appears in large capital letters with hisposition and team in smaller capitals. A facsimilie autograph and Wheaties endorsement is also included. Some cards are also found with the number "29" followed by a letter.

		NR MT	EX	VG
Complete Set:		1400.	700.00	420.00
Common Player:		50.00	25.00	15.00
(1)	"Zeke" Bonura	50.00	25.00	15.00
(2)	Tom Bridges	50.00	25.00	15.00
(3)	Dolph Camilli	50.00	25.00	15.00
(4)	Frank Demaree	50.00	25.00	15.00
(5)	Joe DiMaggio	450.00	225.00	135.00
(6)	Billy Herman	90.00	45.00	27.00
(7)	Carl Hubbell	100.00	50.00	30.00
(8)	Ernie Lombardi	90.00	45.00	27.00
(9)	"Pepper" Martin	60.00	30.00	18.00
(10)	Joe Moore	50.00	25.00	15.00
(11)	Van Mungo	50.00	25.00	15.00
(12)	Mel Ott	125.00	62.00	37.00
(13)	Raymond Radcliff	50.00	25.00	15.00
(14)	Cecil Travis	50.00	25.00	15.00
(15)	Harold Trosky	50.00	25.00	15.00
(16a)	"Arky" Vaughan (29L on card)	90.00	45.00	27.00
(16b)	"Arky" Vaughan (no 29L on card)	90.00	45.00	27.00

1938 Wheaties - Series 10

One player from each major league team is included in this 16-card set, referred to as the "Biggest Thrills in Baseball" series. Measuring 8-1/2" by 6", each numbered card was the back panel of a Wheaties box and pictures a player along with a printed description of his biggest thrill in baseball and facsimilie autograph. All 16 cards in this series have also been found on paper stock.

		NR MT	EX	VG
Complete Set:		600.00	300.00	180.00
Common Player:		25.00	12.50	7.50
1	Bob Feller	110.00	55.00	33.00
2	Cecil Travis	25.00	12.50	7.50
3	Joe Medwick	40.00	20.00	12.00
4	Gerald Walker	25.00	12.50	7.50
5	Carl Hubbell	50.00	25.00	15.00
6	Bob Johnson	25.00	12.50	7.50
7	Beau Bell	25.00	12.50	7.50
8	Ernie Lombardi	40.00	20.00	12.00
9	Lefty Grove	60.00	30.00	18.00
10	Lou Fette	25.00	12.50	7.50
11	Joe DiMaggio	350.00	175.00	105.00

12	Art Whitney	25.00	12.50	7.50
13	Dizzy Dean	110.00	55.00	33.00
14	Charley Gehringer	50.00	25.00	15.00
15	Paul Waner	40.00	20.00	12.00
16	Dolf Camilli	25.00	12.50	7.50

1938 Wheaties - Series 11

Cards in this unnumbered, eight-card series measure 8-1/2" by 6" and show the players in street clothes either eating or getting ready to enjoy a bowl of Wheaties. Sometimes a waitress or other person also appears in the photo. The set is sometimes called the "Dress Clothes" or "Civies" series.

		NR MT	EX	VG
	Complete Set:	225.00	112.00	67.00
	Common Player:	25.00	12.50	7.50
(1)	Lou Fette	25.00	12.50	7.50
(2)	Jimmie Foxx	75.00	37.00	22.00
(3)	Charlie Gehringer	50.00	25.00	15.00
(4)	Lefty Grove	60.00	30.00	18.00
(5)	Hank Greenberg, Roxie Lawson	50.00	25.00	15.00
(6)	Lee Grissom, Ernie Lombardi	40.00	20.00	12.00
(7)	Joe Medwick	40.00	20.00	12.00
(8)	Lon Warneke	25.00	12.50	7.50

1938 Wheaties - Series 15

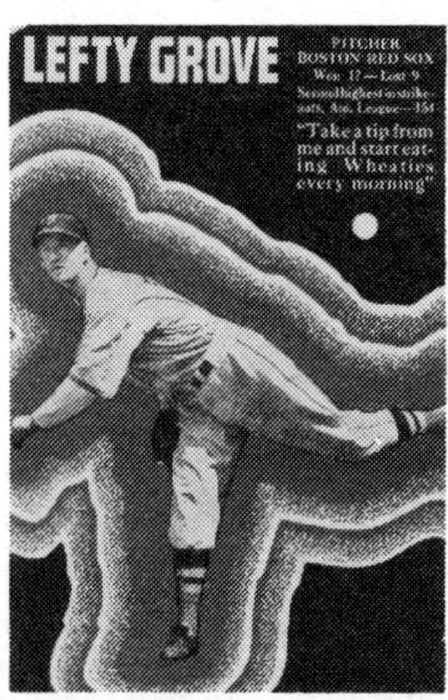

Another set of small (2-5/8" by 3-7/8") cards, the photos in this unnumbered series made up the back panels of single-serving size Wheaties boxes. The panels have orange, blue and white backgrounds, and some of the photos are the same as those used in the larger Wheaties panels.

		NR MT	EX	VG
	Complete Set:	1500.	750.00	450.00
	Common Player:	50.00	25.00	15.00
(1)	"Zeke" Bonura	50.00	25.00	15.00
(2)	Joe DiMaggio	450.00	225.00	135.00
(3)	Charles Gehringer (batting)	125.00	62.00	37.00
(4)	Chas. Gehringer (leaping)	125.00	62.00	37.00
(5)	Hank Greenberg	125.00	62.00	37.00
(6)	Lefty Grove	150.00	75.00	45.00
(7)	Carl Hubbell	110.00	55.00	33.00
(8)	John (Buddy) Lewis	50.00	25.00	15.00
(9)	Heinie Manush	90.00	45.00	27.00
(10)	Joe Medwick	90.00	45.00	27.00
(11)	Arky Vaughan	90.00	45.00	27.00

1939 Wheaties - Series 12

The nine cards in this numbered series, known as the "Personal Pointers" series, measure 8-1/4" by 6" and feature an instructional format similar to earlier Wheaties issues. The cards feature a player photo along with printed tips on various aspects of hitting and pitching.

		NR MT	EX	VG
	Complete Set:	450.00	225.00	135.00
	Common Player:	25.00	12.50	7.50
1	Ernie Lombardi	40.00	20.00	12.00
2	Johnny Allen	25.00	12.50	7.50
3	Lefty Gomez	45.00	22.00	13.50
4	Bill Lee	25.00	12.50	7.50
5	Jimmie Foxx	90.00	45.00	27.00
6	Joe Medwick	40.00	20.00	12.00
7	Hank Greenberg	60.00	30.00	18.00
8	Mel Ott	60.00	30.00	18.00
9	Arky Vaughn (Vaughan)	40.00	20.00	12.00

1939 Wheaties - Series 13

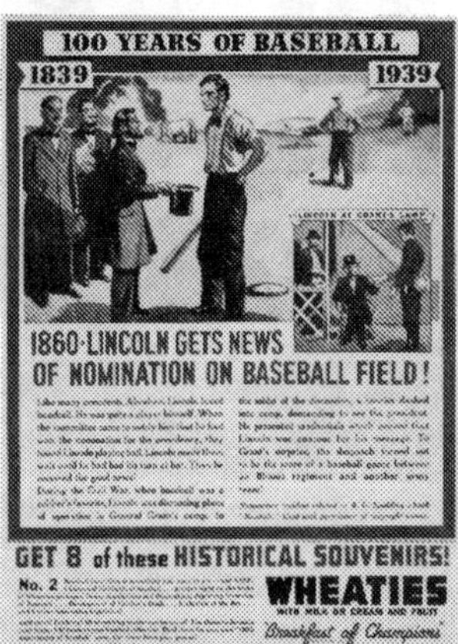

Issued in baseball's centennial year of 1939, this set of eight 6" by 6-3/4" cards commemorates "100 Years of Baseball," each of the numbered panels illustrates a significant event in baseball history.

		NR MT	EX	VG
	Complete Set:	200.00	100.00	60.00
	Common Panel:	25.00	12.50	7.50
1	Design of First Diamond - 1838 (Abner Doubleday)	25.00	12.50	7.50
2	Gets News of Nomination on Field - 1860 (Abraham Lincoln)	25.00	12.50	7.50
3	Crowd Boos First Baseball Glove - 1869	25.00	12.50	7.50
4	Curve Ball Just an Illusion - 1877	25.00	12.50	7.50
5	Fencer's Mask is Pattern - 1877	25.00	12.50	7.50
6	Baseball Gets "All Dressed Up" - 1895	25.00	12.50	7.50
7	Modern Bludgeon Enters Game - 1895	25.00	12.50	7.50
8	"Casey at the Bat"	25.00	12.50	7.50

A player's name in italic type indicates a rookie card. An (FC) indicates a player's first card for that particular card company.

1940 Wheaties Champs of the USA

This numbered set consists of 13 panels, each picturing one baseball player and two other athletes (football stars, golfers, skaters, racers, etc.). The entire panel measures approximately 8-1/4" by 6", while the actual card measures approximately 6" square. Each athlete is pictured in what looks like a postage stamp with a serrated edge. A brief biography appears alongside the "stamp." Some variations are known to exist among the first nine panels. The cards are numbered in the upper right corner.

		NR MT	EX	VG
	Complete Set:	900.00	450.00	270.00
	Common Panel:	25.00	12.50	7.50
1A	Bob Feller	75.00	37.00	22.00
1A	Lynn Patrick	75.00	37.00	22.00
1A	Charles "Red" Ruffling	75.00	37.00	22.00
1B	Leo Durocher	50.00	25.00	15.00
1B	Lynn Patrick	50.00	25.00	15.00
1B	Charles "Red" Ruffing	50.00	25.00	15.00
2A	Joe DiMaggio	250.00	125.00	75.00
2A	Don Duge	250.00	125.00	75.00
2A	Hank Greenberg	250.00	125.00	75.00
2B	Joe DiMaggio	250.00	125.00	75.00
2B	Mel Ott	250.00	125.00	75.00
2B	Ellsworth Vines	250.00	125.00	75.00
3	Bernie Bierman, Bill Dickey, Jimmie Foxx	75.00	37.00	22.00
4	Morris Arnovich, Capt R.K. Baker, Earl "Dutch" Clark	25.00	12.50	7.50
5	Madison (Matty) Bell, Ab Jenkins, Joe Medwick	25.00	12.50	7.50
6A	Ralph Guldahl	25.00	12.50	7.50
6A	John Mize	25.00	12.50	7.50
6A	Davey O'Brien	25.00	12.50	7.50
6B	Bob Feller	50.00	25.00	15.00
6B	John Mize	50.00	25.00	15.00
6B	Rudy York	50.00	25.00	15.00
6C	Ralph Guldahl	25.00	12.50	7.50
6C	Gabby Hartnett	25.00	12.50	7.50
6C	Davey O'Brien	25.00	12.50	7.50
7A	Joe Cronin	25.00	12.50	7.50
7A	Cecil Isbell	25.00	12.50	7.50
7A	Byron Nelson	25.00	12.50	7.50
7B	Joe Cronin	40.00	20.00	12.00
7B	Hank Greenberg	40.00	20.00	12.00
7B	Byron Nelson	40.00	20.00	12.00
7C	Paul Derringer	25.00	12.50	7.50
7C	Cecil Isbell	25.00	12.50	7.50
7C	Byron Nelson	25.00	12.50	7.50
8A	Ernie Lombardi	25.00	12.50	7.50
8A	Jack Manders	25.00	12.50	7.50
8A	George I. Myers	25.00	12.50	7.50
8B	Paul Derringer	25.00	12.50	7.50
8B	Ernie Lombardi	25.00	12.50	7.50
8B	George I. Myers	25.00	12.50	7.50
9	Bob Bartlett, Captain R.C. Hanson, Terrell Jacobs	25.00	12.50	7.50
10	Lowell "Red" Dawson, Billy Herman, Adele Inge	25.00	12.50	7.50
11	Dolph Camilli, Antoinette Concello, Wallace Wade	25.00	12.50	7.50
12	Luke Appling, Stanley Hack, Hugh McManus	25.00	12.50	7.50
13	Felix Adler, Hal Trosky, Mabel Vinson	25.00	12.50	7.50

Grading Guide

Mint (MT): A perfect card. Well-centered with all corners sharp and square. No creases, stains, edge nicks, surface marks, yellowing or fading.

Near Mint (NM): A nearly perfect card. At first glance, a NM card appears to be perfect. May be slightly off-center. No surface marks, creases or loss of gloss.

Excellent (EX): Corners are still fairly sharp with only moderate wear. Borders may be off-center. No creases or stains on fronts or backs, but may show slight loss of surface luster.

Very Good (VG): Shows obvious handling. May have rounded corners, minor creases, major gum or wax stains. No major creases, tape marks, writing, etc.

Good (G): A well-worn card, but exhibits no intentional damage. May have major or multiple creases. Corners may be rounded well beyond card border.

1941 Wheaties Champs of the USA

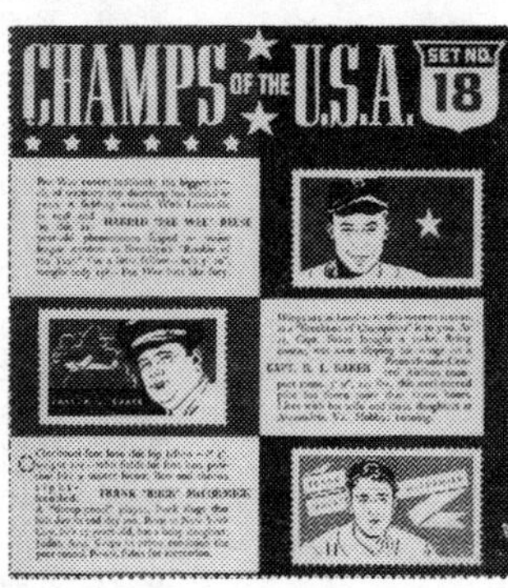

This eight-card series is actually a continuation of the previous year's Wheaties set, and the format is identical. The set begins with number 14, starting where the 1940 set ended.

	NR MT	EX	VG
Complete Set:	425.00	212.00	127.00
Common Panel:	25.00	12.50	7.50

		NR MT	EX	VG
14	Felix Adler, Jimmie Foxx, Capt. R.G. Hanson	50.00	25.00	15.00
15	Bernie Bierman, Bob Feller, Jessie McLeod	50.00	25.00	15.00
16	Lowell "Red" Dawson, Hank Greenberg, J.W. Stoker	30.00	15.00	9.00
17	Antoniette Concello, Joe DiMaggio, Byron Nelson	250.00	125.00	75.00
18	Capt. R.L. Baker, Frank "Buck" McCormick, Harold "Pee Wee" Reese	50.00	25.00	15.00
19	William W. Robbins, Gene Sarazen, Gerald "Gee" Walker	25.00	12.50	7.50
20	Harry Danning, Barney McCosky, Bucky Walters	25.00	12.50	7.50
21	Joe "Flash" Gordon, Stan Hack, George I. Myers	25.00	12.50	7.50

1951 Wheaties

Printed as the backs of single-serving size boxes of Wheaties, the six-card 1951 set includes three baseball players and one football player, basketball player and golfer. Well-trimmed cards measure 2-1/2" by 3-1/4". The cards feature blue line drawings of the athletes with a facsimile autograph and descriptive title below. There is a wide white border.

	NR MT	EX	VG
Complete Set:	600.00	300.00	180.00
Common Player:	75.00	37.00	22.00

		NR MT	EX	VG
(1)	Bob Feller (baseball)	125.00	62.00	37.00
(2)	John Lujack (football)	75.00	38.00	23.00
(3)	George K. Mikan (basketball)	125.00	62.00	37.00
(4)	Stan Musial (baseball)	175.00	87.00	52.00
(5)	Sam Snead (golfer)	75.00	37.00	22.00
(6)	Ted Williams (baseball)	200.00	100.00	60.00

1952 Wheaties

These 2" by 2-3/4" cards appeared on the back of the popular cereal boxes. Actually, sports figures had been appearing on the backs of the boxes for many years, but in 1952, of the 30 athletes depicted, 10 were baseball players. That means there are 20 baseball cards, as each player appears in both a portrait and an action drawing. The cards have a blue line drawing on an orange background with a white border. The player's name, team, and position appear at the bottom. The cards have rounded corners and are not widely collected because they have

an outdated look, are mixed with other athletes and are often poorly cut from the boxes.

	NR MT	EX	VG
Complete Set:	800.00	400.00	240.00
Common Player:	15.00	7.50	4.50

		NR MT	EX	VG
(1)	Larry "Yogi" Berra (portrait)	50.00	25.00	15.00
(2)	Larry "Yogi" Berra (action pose)	50.00	25.00	15.00
(3)	Roy Campanella (portrait)	50.00	25.00	15.00
(4)	Roy Campanella (action pose)	50.00	25.00	15.00
(5)	Bob Feller (portrait)	40.00	20.00	12.00
(6)	Bob Feller (action pose)	40.00	20.00	12.00
(7)	George Kell (portrait)	18.00	9.00	5.50
(8)	George Kell (action pose)	18.00	9.00	5.50
(9)	Ralph Kiner (portrait)	25.00	12.50	7.50
(10)	Ralph Kiner (action pose)	25.00	12.50	7.50
(11)	Bob Lemon (portrait)	25.00	12.50	7.50
(12)	Bob Lemon (action pose)	25.00	12.50	7.50
(13)	Stan Musial (portrait)	75.00	37.00	22.00
(14)	Stan Musial (action pose)	75.00	37.00	22.00
(15)	Phil Rizzuto (portrait)	30.00	15.00	9.00
(16)	Phil Rizzuto (action pose)	30.00	15.00	9.00
(17)	Elwin "Preacher" Roe (portrait)	15.00	7.50	4.50
(18)	Elwin "Preacher" Roe (action pose)	15.00	7.50	4.50
(19)	Ted Williams (portrait)	100.00	50.00	30.00
(20)	Ted Williams (action pose)	100.00	50.00	30.00

1982 Wheaties Indians

These 2-13/16" by 4-1/8" cards were given out ten at a time during three special promotional games; later the complete set was placed on sale at the Indians' gift shop. The 30-card set represented the first time in 30 years that Wheaties had been associated with a baseball card set. The cards feature color photos surrounded by a wide white border with the player's name and position below the picture. The Indians logo is in the lower left corner while the Wheaties logo is in the lower right. Card backs have a Wheaties ad.

	MT	NR MT	EX
Complete Set:	8.00	6.00	3.25
Common Player:	.25	.20	.10

		MT	NR MT	EX
(1)	Chris Bando	.25	.20	.10
(2)	Alan Bannister	.25	.20	.10
(3)	Len Barker	.25	.20	.10
(4)	Bert Blyleven	.75	.60	.30
(5)	Tom Brennan	.25	.20	.10
(6)	Joe Charboneau	.40	.30	.15
(7)	Rodney Craig	.25	.20	.10
(8)	John Denny	.25	.20	.10
(9)	Miguel Dilone	.25	.20	.10
(10)	Jerry Dybzinski	.25	.20	.10
(11)	Mike Fischlin	.25	.20	.10
(12)	Dave Garcia	.25	.20	.10
(13)	Johnny Goryl	.25	.20	.10
(14)	Mike Hargrove	.40	.30	.15
(15)	Toby Harrah	.40	.30	.15
(16)	Ron Hassey	.25	.20	.10
(17)	Von Hayes	.35	.25	.14
(18)	Dennis Lewallyn	.25	.20	.10
(19)	Rick Manning	.25	.20	.10
(20)	Bake McBride	.25	.20	.10
(21)	Tommy McCraw	.25	.20	.10
(22)	Jack Perconte	.25	.20	.10
(23)	Mel Queen	.25	.20	.10
(24)	Dennis Sommers	.25	.20	.10
(25)	Lary Sorensen	.25	.20	.10
(26)	Dan Spillner	.25	.20	.10
(27)	Rick Sutcliffe	.60	.45	.25
(28)	Andre Thornton	.40	.30	.15
(29)	Rick Waits	.25	.20	.10
(30)	Eddie Whitson	.35	.25	.14

1983 Wheaties Indians

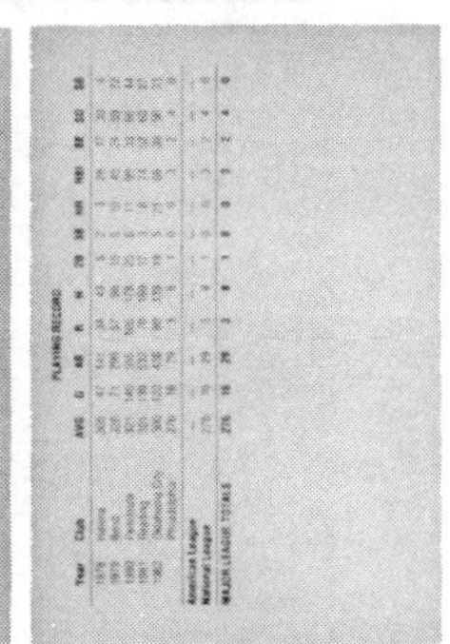

A 32-card set marked the second year of Wheaties involvement with the Indians. Distribution of the 2-13/16" by 4-1/8" cards changed slightly in that the entire set was given away on the day of the special promotional game. As happened in 1982, the set was then placed on sale at the team's gift shop. The set includes 27 players, four coaches and the manager. The format of the cards remained basically the same on the front although the backs of player cards were changed to include complete major and minor league statistics.

	MT	NR MT	EX
Complete Set:	8.00	6.00	3.25
Common Player:	.15	.11	.06

		MT	NR MT	EX
(1)	Bud Anderson	.15	.11	.06
(2)	Jay Baller	.15	.11	.06
(3)	Chris Bando	.15	.11	.06
(4)	Alan Bannister	.15	.11	.06
(5)	Len Barker	.25	.20	.10
(6)	Bert Blyleven	.60	.45	.25
(7)	Wil Culmer	.15	.11	.06
(8)	Miguel Dilone	.15	.11	.06
(9)	Juan Eichelberger	.15	.11	.06
(10)	Jim Essian	.15	.11	.06
(11)	Mike Ferraro	.15	.11	.06
(12)	Mike Fischlin	.15	.11	.06
(13)	Julio Franco	1.75	1.25	.70
(14)	Ed Glynn	.15	.11	.06
(15)	Johnny Goryl	.15	.11	.06
(16)	Mike Hargrove	.25	.20	.10
(17)	Toby Harrah	.25	.20	.10
(18)	Ron Hassey	.15	.11	.06
(19)	Neal Heaton	.35	.25	.14
(20)	Rick Manning	.15	.11	.06
(21)	Bake McBride	.15	.11	.06
(22)	Don McMahon	.15	.11	.06
(23)	Ed Napoleon	.15	.11	.06
(24)	Broderick Perkins	.15	.11	.06
(25)	Dennis Sommers	.15	.11	.06
(26)	Lary Sorensen	.15	.11	.06
(27)	Dan Spillner	.15	.11	.06
(28)	Rick Sutcliffe	.30	.25	.12
(29)	Andre Thornton	.35	.25	.14
(30)	Manny Trillo	.15	.11	.06
(31)	George Vukovich	.15	.11	.06
(32)	Rick Waits	.15	.11	.06

1984 Wheaties Indians

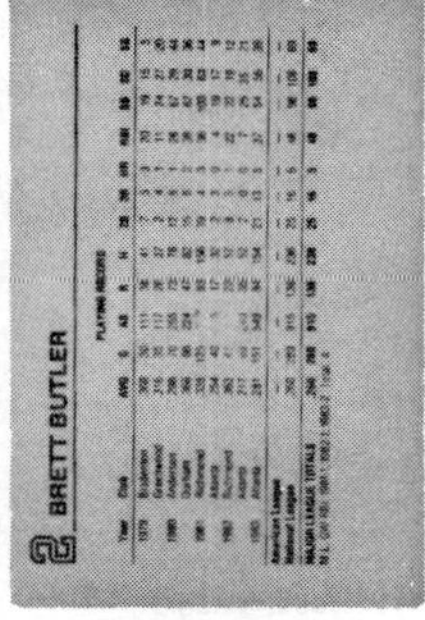

The 2-13/16" by 4-1/8" cards again were given out at Municipal Stadium as part of a promotion involving Wheaties and the Indians on July 22. The set was down from 32 cards in 1983 to 29. There are 26 players as well as cards for the manager, coaches and team mascot, Tom-E-Hawk. Designs of the cards are identical to prior years. The 1984 set is numbered by uniform number. A total of 15,000 sets were printed and any left over from the promotion were placed on sale in the team's gift shop.

		MT	NR MT	EX
Complete Set:		10.00	7.50	4.00
Common Player:		.15	.11	.06
2	Brett Butler	.40	.30	.15
4	Tony Bernazard	.15	.11	.06
8	Carmelo Castillo	.15	.11	.06
10	Pat Tabler	.20	.15	.08
13	Ernie Camacho	.15	.11	.06
14	Julio Franco	1.50	1.25	.60
15	Broderick Perkins	.15	.11	.06
16	Jerry Willard	.15	.11	.06
18	Pat Corrales	.15	.11	.06
21	Mike Hargrove	.25	.20	.10
22	Mike Fischlin	.15	.11	.06
23	Chris Bando	.15	.11	.06
24	George Vukovich	.15	.11	.06
26	Brook Jacoby	.30	.25	.12
27	Steve Farr	.25	.20	.10
28	Bert Blyleven	.60	.45	.25
29	Andre Thornton	.35	.25	.14
30	Joe Carter	2.50	2.00	1.00
31	Steve Comer	.15	.11	.06
33	Roy Smith	.15	.11	.06
34	Mel Hall	.25	.20	.10
36	Jamie Easterly	.15	.11	.06
37	Don Schulze	.15	.11	.06
38	Luis Aponte	.15	.11	.06
44	Neal Heaton	.25	.20	.10
46	Mike Jeffcoat	.15	.11	.06
54	Tom Waddell	.15	.11	.06
----	Coaching Staff (Bobby Bonds, John Goryl, Don McMahon, Ed Napoleon, Dennis Sommers)	.15	.11	.06
----	Tom-E-Hawk (mascot)	.15	.11	.06

1954 Wilson Franks

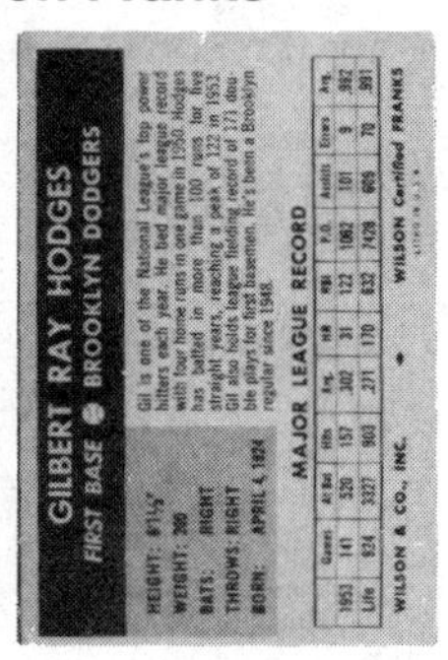

The 2-5/8" by 3-3/4" cards are among the most popular and difficult to find baseball card sets issued with hot dogs during the 1950s. The cards feature color-added photos on the front where the player's name, team and position appear at the top. The front also has a facsimile autograph and a color picture of a package of Wilson's frankfurters. The card backs feature personal information, a short career summary and 1953 and career statistics. The 20-card set includes players from a number of teams and was distributed nationally in the frankfurter packages. The problem with such distribution is that the cards are very tough to find without grease stains from the hot dogs.

		NR MT	EX	VG
Complete Set:		7000.	3500.	2000.
Common Player:		160.00	80.00	48.00
(1)	Roy Campanella	750.00	375.00	225.00
(2)	Del Ennis	160.00	80.00	48.00
(3)	Carl Erskine	300.00	150.00	90.00
(4)	Ferris Fain	160.00	80.00	48.00
(5)	Bob Feller	600.00	300.00	180.00
(6)	Nelson Fox	300.00	150.00	90.00
(7)	Johnny Groth	160.00	80.00	48.00
(8)	Stan Hack	160.00	80.00	48.00
(9)	Gil Hodges	500.00	250.00	150.00
(10)	Ray Jablonski	160.00	80.00	48.00
(11)	Harvey Kuenn	300.00	150.00	90.00
(12)	Roy McMillan	160.00	80.00	48.00
(13)	Andy Pafko	160.00	80.00	48.00
(14)	Paul Richards	160.00	80.00	48.00
(15)	Hank Sauer	160.00	80.00	48.00
(16)	Red Schoendienst	300.00	150.00	90.00
(17)	Enos Slaughter	450.00	225.00	135.00
(18)	Vern Stephens	160.00	80.00	48.00
(19)	Sammy White	160.00	80.00	48.00
(20)	Ted Williams	3000.	1500.	900.00

Values for recent cards and sets are listed in Mint (MT), Near Mint (NM), reflecting the fact that many cards from recent years have been preserved in top condition. Recent cards and sets in less than Excellent condition have little collector interest.

1923 Willard Chocolate (V100)

Issued circa 1923, this set was produced by the Willard Chocolate Company of Canada and features sepia-toned photographs on cards measuring 3-1/4" by 2-1/16". The cards are blank-backed and feature the player's name in script on the front. The set is complete at 180 cards and nearly one-fourth of the photos used in the set are identical to the better known E120 American Caramel set. The Willard set is identified as V100 in the American Card Catalog.

		NR MT	EX	VG
Complete Set (180):		16500.	5750.	3450.
Common Player:		65.00	32.00	19.50
(1)	Chas. B. Adams	65.00	32.00	19.50
(2)	Grover C. Alexander	325.00	162.00	97.00
(3)	J.P. Austin	65.00	32.00	19.50
(4)	J.C. Bagby	65.00	32.00	19.50
(5)	J. Franklin Baker	290.00	145.00	87.00
(6)	David J. Bancroft	275.00	137.00	82.00
(7)	Turner Barber	65.00	32.00	19.50
(8)	Jesse L. Barnes	65.00	32.00	19.50
(9)	J.C. Bassler	65.00	32.00	19.50
(10)	L.A. Blue	65.00	32.00	19.50
(11)	Norman D. Boeckel	65.00	32.00	19.50
(12)	F.L. Brazil (Brazill)	65.00	32.00	19.50
(13)	G.H. Burns	65.00	32.00	19.50
(14)	Geo. J. Burns	65.00	32.00	19.50
(15)	Leon Cadore	65.00	32.00	19.50
(16)	Max G. Carey	275.00	137.00	82.00
(17)	Harold G. Carlson	65.00	32.00	19.50
(18)	Lloyd R Christenberry (Christenbury)	65.00	32.00	19.50
(19)	Vernon J. Clemons	65.00	32.00	19.50
(20)	T.R. Cobb	1550.	775.00	465.00
(21)	Bert Cole	65.00	32.00	19.50
(22)	John F. Collins	65.00	32.00	19.50
(23)	S. Coveleskie (Coveleski)	275.00	137.00	82.00
(24)	Walton E. Cruise	65.00	32.00	19.50
(25)	G.W. Cutshaw	65.00	32.00	19.50
(26)	Jacob E. Daubert	75.00	37.00	22.00
(27)	Geo. Dauss	65.00	32.00	19.50
(28)	F.T. Davis	65.00	32.00	19.50
(29)	Chas. A. Deal	65.00	32.00	19.50
(30)	William L. Doak	65.00	32.00	19.50
(31)	William E. Donovan	65.00	32.00	19.50
(32)	Hugh Duffy	275.00	137.00	82.00
(33)	J.A. Dugan	75.00	37.00	22.00
(34)	Louis B. Duncan	65.00	32.00	19.50
(35)	James Dykes	75.00	37.00	22.00
(36)	H.J. Ehmke	65.00	32.00	19.50
(37)	F.R. Ellerbe	65.00	32.00	19.50
(38)	E.G. Erickson	65.00	32.00	19.50
(39)	John J. Evers	275.00	137.00	82.00
(40)	U.C. Faber	275.00	137.00	82.00
(41)	B.A. Falk	65.00	32.00	19.50
(42)	Max Flack	65.00	32.00	19.50
(43)	Lee Fohl	65.00	32.00	19.50
(44)	Jacques F. Fournier	65.00	32.00	19.50
(45)	Frank F. Frisch	290.00	145.00	87.00
(46)	C.E. Galloway	65.00	32.00	19.50
(47)	W.C. Gardner	65.00	32.00	19.50
(48)	E.P. Gharrity	65.00	32.00	19.50
(49)	Geo. Gibson	65.00	32.00	19.50
(50)	Wm. Gleason	65.00	32.00	19.50
(51)	William Gleason	65.00	32.00	19.50
(52)	Henry M. Gowdy	65.00	32.00	19.50
(53)	I.M. Griffin	65.00	32.00	19.50
(54)	Tom Griffith	125.00	62.00	37.00
(55)	Burleigh A. Grimes	275.00	137.00	82.00
(56)	Charles J. Grimm	75.00	37.00	22.00
(57)	Jesse J. Haines	275.00	137.00	82.00
(58)	S.R. Harris	275.00	137.00	82.00
(59)	W.B. Harris	65.00	32.00	19.50
(60)	R.K. Hasty	65.00	32.00	19.50
(61)	H.E. Heilman (Heilmann)	275.00	137.00	82.00
(62)	Walter J. Henline	65.00	32.00	19.50
(63)	Walter L. Holke	65.00	32.00	19.50
(64)	Charles J. Hollocher	65.00	32.00	19.50
(65)	H.B. Hooper	275.00	137.00	82.00
(66)	Rogers Hornsby	400.00	200.00	120.00
(67)	W.C. Hoyt	275.00	137.00	82.00
(68)	Miller Huggins	275.00	137.00	82.00
(69)	W.C. Jacobsen (Jacobson)	65.00	32.00	19.50
(70)	C.D. Jamieson	65.00	32.00	19.50
(71)	Ernest Johnson	65.00	32.00	19.50
(72)	W.P. Johnson	600.00	300.00	180.00
(73)	James H. Johnston	65.00	32.00	19.50
(74)	R.W. Jones	65.00	32.00	19.50
(75)	Samuel Pond Jones	65.00	32.00	19.50
(76)	J.I. Judge	65.00	32.00	19.50
(77)	James W. Keenan	65.00	32.00	19.50
(78)	Geo. L. Kelly	275.00	137.00	82.00
(79)	Peter J. Kilduff	65.00	32.00	19.50
(80)	William Killefer	65.00	32.00	19.50
(81)	Lee King	65.00	32.00	19.50
(82)	Ray Kolp	65.00	32.00	19.50
(83)	John Lavan	65.00	32.00	19.50
(84)	H.L. Leibold	65.00	32.00	19.50
(85)	Connie Mack	300.00	150.00	90.00
(86)	J.W. Mails	65.00	32.00	19.50
(87)	Walter J. Maranville	275.00	137.00	82.00
(88)	Richard W. Marquard	275.00	137.00	82.00
(89)	C.W. Mays	75.00	37.00	22.00
(90)	Geo. F. McBride	65.00	32.00	19.50
(91)	H.M. McClellan	65.00	32.00	19.50
(92)	John J. McGraw	275.00	137.00	82.00
(93)	Austin B. McHenry	65.00	32.00	19.50
(94)	J. McInnis	65.00	32.00	19.50
(95)	Douglas McWeeney (McWeeny)	65.00	32.00	19.50
(96)	M. Menosky	65.00	32.00	19.50
(97)	Emil F. Meusel	65.00	32.00	19.50
(98)	R. Meusel	75.00	37.00	22.00
(99)	Henry W. Meyers	65.00	32.00	19.50
(100)	J.C. Milan	65.00	32.00	19.50
(101)	John K. Miljus	65.00	32.00	19.50
(102)	Edmund J. Miller	65.00	32.00	19.50
(103)	Elmer Miller	65.00	32.00	19.50
(104)	Otto L. Miller	65.00	32.00	19.50
(105)	Fred Mitchell	65.00	32.00	19.50
(106)	Geo. Mogridge	65.00	32.00	19.50
(107)	Patrick J. Moran	65.00	32.00	19.50
(108)	John D. Morrison	65.00	32.00	19.50
(109)	J.A. Mostil	65.00	32.00	19.50
(110)	Clarence F. Mueller	65.00	32.00	19.50
(111)	A. Earle Neale	175.00	87.00	52.00
(112)	Joseph Oeschger	65.00	32.00	19.50
(113)	Robert J. O'Farrell	65.00	32.00	19.50
(114)	J.C. Oldham	65.00	32.00	19.50
(115)	I.M. Olson	65.00	32.00	19.50
(116)	Geo. M. O'Neil	65.00	32.00	19.50
(117)	S.F. O'Neill	65.00	32.00	19.50
(118)	Frank J. Parkinson	65.00	32.00	19.50
(119)	Geo. H. Paskert	65.00	32.00	19.50
(120)	R.T. Peckinpaugh	65.00	32.00	19.50
(121)	H.J. Pennock	275.00	137.00	82.00
(122)	Ralph Perkins	65.00	32.00	19.50
(123)	Edw. J. Pfeffer	65.00	32.00	19.50
(124)	W.C. Pipp	125.00	62.00	37.00
(125)	Charles Elmer Ponder	65.00	32.00	19.50
(126)	Raymond R. Powell	65.00	32.00	19.50
(127)	D.B. Pratt	65.00	32.00	19.50
(128)	Joseph Rapp	65.00	32.00	19.50
(129)	John H. Rawlings	65.00	32.00	19.50
(130)	E.S. Rice (should be E.C.)	275.00	137.00	82.00
(131)	Branch Rickey	350.00	175.00	105.00
(132)	James J. Ring	65.00	32.00	19.50
(133)	Eppa J. Rixey	275.00	137.00	82.00
(134)	Davis A. Robertson	65.00	32.00	19.50
(135)	Edwin Rommel	65.00	32.00	19.50
(136)	Edd J. Roush	275.00	137.00	82.00
(137)	Harold Ruel (Herold)	65.00	32.00	19.50
(138)	Allen Russell	65.00	32.00	19.50
(139)	G.H. Ruth	2200.	1100.	660.00
(140)	Wilfred D. Ryan	65.00	32.00	19.50
(141)	Henry F. Sallee	65.00	32.00	19.50
(142)	W.H. Schang	65.00	32.00	19.50
(143)	Raymond H. Schmandt	65.00	32.00	19.50
(144)	Everett Scott	65.00	32.00	19.50
(145)	Henry Severeid	65.00	32.00	19.50
(146)	Jos. W. Sewell	275.00	137.00	82.00
(147)	Howard S. Shanks	65.00	32.00	19.50
(148)	E.H. Sheely	65.00	32.00	19.50
(149)	Ralph Shinners	65.00	32.00	19.50
(150)	U.J. Shocker	65.00	32.00	19.50
(151)	G.H. Sisler	275.00	137.00	82.00
(152)	Earl L. Smith	65.00	32.00	19.50
(153)	Earl S. Smith	65.00	32.00	19.50
(154)	Geo. A. Smith	65.00	32.00	19.50
(155)	J.W. Smith	65.00	32.00	19.50
(156)	Tris E. Speaker	325.00	162.00	97.00
(157)	Arnold Staatz (Statz)	65.00	32.00	19.50
(158)	J.R. Stephenson	75.00	37.00	22.00
(159)	Milton J. Stock	65.00	32.00	19.50
(160)	John L. Sullivan	65.00	32.00	19.50
(161)	H.F. Tormahlen	65.00	32.00	19.50
(162)	Jas. A. Tierney	65.00	32.00	19.50
(163)	J.T. Tobin	65.00	32.00	19.50
(164)	Jas. L. Vaughn	65.00	32.00	19.50
(165)	R.H. Veach	65.00	32.00	19.50
(166)	C.W. Walker	65.00	32.00	19.50
(167)	A.L. Ward	65.00	32.00	19.50
(168)	Zack D. Wheat	275.00	137.00	82.00
(169)	George B. Whitted	65.00	32.00	19.50
(170)	Irvin K. Wilhelm	65.00	32.00	19.50
(171)	Roy H. Wilkinson	65.00	32.00	19.50
(172)	Fred C. Williams	75.00	37.00	22.00
(173)	K.R. Williams	75.00	37.00	22.00
(174)	Sam'l W. Wilson	65.00	32.00	19.50
(175)	Ivy B. Wingo	65.00	32.00	19.50
(176)	L.W. Witt	65.00	32.00	19.50
(177)	Joseph Wood	75.00	37.00	22.00
(178)	E. Yaryan	65.00	32.00	19.50
(179)	R.S. Young	65.00	32.00	19.50
(180)	Ross Young (Youngs)	275.00	137.00	82.00

1911 Williams Baking Philadelphia A's (D359)

The 1911 Williams Baking set, an 18-card Philadelphia Athletics set, is among the scarcest early 20th Century baking company issues. The set commemorates the Athletics' 1910 Championship season, and, except for pitcher Jack Coombs, the checklist includes nearly all key members of the club, including manager Connie Mack. The cards are the standard size for the era, 1-1/2" by 2-5/8". The front of each card features a player portrait set against a colored background. The player's name and the word "Athletics" appear at the bottom, while "World's Champions 1910" is printed along the top. The backs of the cards advertise the set as the "Athletics Series." Collectors should be aware that the same checklist was used for a similar Athletics set issued by Rochester Baking and Cullivan's Fireside tobacco (T208) and also that blank-backed versions are also known to exist, but these are classified as E104 cards in the American Card Catalog.

		NR MT	EX	VG
Complete Set:		13000.	6500.	3900.
Common Player:		500.00	250.00	150.00
(1)	Home Run Baker	1500.	750.00	450.00
(2)	Jack Barry	500.00	250.00	150.00
(3)	Chief Bender	1500.	750.00	450.00
(4)	Eddie Collins	1500.	750.00	450.00
(5)	Harry Davis	500.00	250.00	150.00
(6)	Jimmy Dygert	500.00	250.00	150.00
(7)	Topsy Hartsel	500.00	250.00	150.00
(8)	Harry Krause	500.00	250.00	150.00
(9)	Jack Lapp	500.00	250.00	150.00
(10)	Paddy Livingstone (Livingston)	500.00	250.00	150.00
(11)	Bris Lord	500.00	250.00	150.00
(12)	Connie Mack	2000.	1000.	600.00
(13)	Cy Morgan	500.00	250.00	150.00
(14)	Danny Murphy	500.00	250.00	150.00
(15)	Rube Oldring	500.00	250.00	150.00
(16)	Eddie Plank	2000.	1000.	600.00
(17)	Amos Strunk	500.00	250.00	150.00
(18)	Ira Thomas	500.00	250.00	150.00

1910 Williams Caramels (E103)

FRED TENNY, 1st B., N. Y.
The Williams Caramel Co. Oxford, Pa.

This 30-card set issued by the Williams Caramel Co. of Oxford, Pa., in 1910 can be differentiated from other similar sets because it was printed on a thin paper stock rather than cardboard. Measuring approximately 1-1/2" by 2-3/4", each card features a player portrait set against a red background. The bottom of the card lists the player's last name, position and team, followed by a line reading "The Williams Caramel Co. Oxford Pa." Nearly all of the photos in the set, which is designated E103 by the ACC, are identical to those in the M116 Sporting Life set.

		NR MT	EX	VG
Complete Set:		18000.	9000.	5400.
Common Player:		200.00	100.00	60.00
(1)	Chas. Bender	700.00	350.00	210.00
(2)	Roger Bresnahan	700.00	350.00	210.00
(3)	Mordecai Brown	700.00	350.00	210.00
(4)	Frank Chance	700.00	350.00	210.00
(5)	Hal Chase	500.00	250.00	125.00
(6)	Ty Cobb	5000.	2500.	1500.
(7)	Edward Collins	700.00	350.00	210.00
(8)	Sam Crawford	700.00	350.00	210.00
(9)	Harry Davis	200.00	100.00	60.00
(10)	Arthur Devlin	200.00	100.00	60.00
(11)	William Donovan	200.00	100.00	60.00
(12)	Chas. Dooin	200.00	100.00	60.00
(13)	L. Doyle	200.00	100.00	60.00
(14)	John Ewing	200.00	100.00	60.00
(15)	George Gibson	200.00	100.00	60.00
(16)	Hugh Jennings	700.00	350.00	210.00
(17)	David Jones	200.00	100.00	60.00
(18)	Tim Jordan	200.00	100.00	60.00
(19)	N. Lajoie	1500.	750.00	300.00
(20)	Thomas Leach	200.00	100.00	60.00
(21)	Harry Lord	200.00	100.00	60.00
(22)	Chris. Mathewson	2500.	1200.	500.00
(23)	John McLean	200.00	100.00	60.00
(24)	Geo. W. McQuillan	200.00	100.00	60.00
(25)	Pastorius	200.00	100.00	60.00
(26)	N. Rucker	200.00	100.00	60.00
(27)	Fred Tenny (Tenney)	200.00	100.00	60.00
(28)	Ira Thomas	200.00	100.00	60.00
(29)	Hans Wagner	3500.	1750.	750.00
(30)	Robert Wood	200.00	100.00	60.00

1888 E.R. Williams Card Game

This 1889 set of 52 playing cards came packed in its own box that advertised the set as the "Egerton R. Williams Popular Indoor Base Ball Game." Designed to look like a conventional deck of playing cards, the set included various players from the National League and the American Association. Although the set contains 52 cards (like a typical deck of playing cards) only 19 actually feature color drawings of players. Each of these cards pictures two different players (one at the top and a second at the bottom, separated by sepia-colored crossed bats in the middle), resulting in 38 different players. The remaining 33 cards in the deck are strictly game cards showing a specific baseball play (such as "Batter Out on Fly" or "Two Base Hit," etc.). The cards have green-tinted backs and measure 2-7/16" by 3-1/2". Each one carries an 1889 copyright line by E.R. Williams.

		NR MT	EX	VG
Complete Set:		10000.	5000.	3000.
Common Player:		250.00	125.00	75.00
(1)	Cap Anson, Buck Ewing	700.00	350.00	210.00
(2)	Dan Brouthers, Arlie Latham	375.00	187.00	112.00
(3)	Charles Buffinton, Parisian Bob Carruthers	250.00	125.00	75.00
(4)	Hick Carpenter, Cliff Carroll	250.00	125.00	75.00
(5)	Charles Comiskey, Roger Connor	500.00	250.00	150.00
(6)	Pop Corkhill, Jim Fogarty	250.00	125.00	75.00
(7)	John Clarkson, Tim Keefe	500.00	250.00	150.00
(8)	Jerry Denny, Silent Mike Tiernan	250.00	125.00	75.00
(9)	Dave Foutz, King Kelly	400.00	200.00	120.00
(10)	Pud Galvin, Dave Orr	375.00	187.00	112.00
(11)	Pebbly Jack Glasscock, Foghorn Tucker	250.00	125.00	75.00
(12)	Mike Griffin, Ed McKean	250.00	125.00	75.00
(13)	Dummy Hoy, Long John Reilley (Reilly)	250.00	125.00	75.00
(14)	Arthur Irwin, Ned Williamson	250.00	125.00	75.00
(15)	Silver King, John Tener	250.00	125.00	75.00
(16)	Al Myers, Cub Stricker	250.00	125.00	75.00
(17)	Fred Pfeffer, Chicken Wolf	250.00	125.00	75.00
(18)	Toad Ramsey, Gus Weyhing	250.00	125.00	75.00
(19)	Monte Ward, Curt Welch	375.00	187.00	112.00

1993 Ted Williams Card Co. Premier Edition

Without a license from the players' union, the premiere issue of the Ted Williams Card Company relied on innovative subsets to create interest in its "old-timers" set. The first 96 cards in the set comprise the base issue. Those cards feature a black-and-white or color action photo set against a background of a second ghost-image photo. The player's name is at bottom with the card company logo conspicuous at top. Backs have some biographical detail, a career summary, the player's five best seasons' and career stats. Subsets numbered contiguously with the base set include a 19-card Negro Leagues series highlighted with green-foil; five cards featuring the All-American Girls Professional Baseball League; a 10-card "Ted's Greatest Hitters"

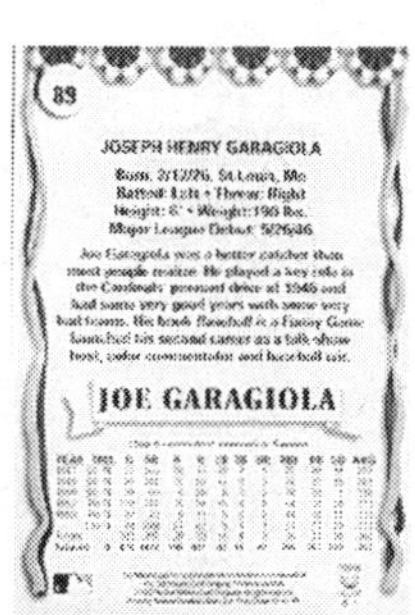

series; 10 "Barrier Breakers" cards featuring Negro Leagues veterans who later played in the majors; a 10-card "Goin' North subset featuring major league stars of the 1940s-1970s in minor league photos, and, a pair of five-card "Dawning of a Legacy" series featuring Juan Gonzalez and Jeff Bagwell. There were also several insert card series which are checklisted separately. The cards were packaged with pog cards, featuring a pair of die-cut player or team logo pogs. The team logo pogs included those of the Negro Leagues.

		MT	NR MT	EX
Complete Set (160):		32.00	24.00	13.00
Common Player:		.10	.08	.04
1	Ted Williams	3.00	2.25	1.25
2	Rick Ferrell	.25	.20	.10
3	Jim Lonborg	.10	.08	.04
4	Mel Parnell	.10	.08	.04
5	Jim Piersall	.25	.20	.10
6	Luis Tiant	.10	.08	.04
7	Carl Yastrzemski	.75	.60	.30
8	Ralph Branca	.10	.08	.04
9	Roy Campanella	.50	.40	.20
10	Ron Cey	.10	.08	.04
11	Tommy Davis	.10	.08	.04
12	Don Drysdale	.75	.60	.30
13	Carl Erskine	.10	.08	.04
14	Steve Garvey	.20	.15	.08
15	Don Newcombe	.10	.08	.04
16	Duke Snider	.50	.40	.20
17	Maury Wills	.40	.30	.15
18	Jim Fregosi	.10	.08	.04
19	Bobby Grich	.10	.08	.04
20	Bill Buckner	.10	.08	.04
21	Billy Herman	.10	.08	.04
22	Ferguson Jenkins	.20	.15	.08
23	Ron Santo	.10	.08	.04
24	Billy Williams	.30	.25	.12
25	Luis Aparicio	.25	.20	.10
26	Luke Appling	.25	.20	.10
27	Minnie Minoso	.10	.08	.04
28	Johnny Bench	1.00	.70	.40
29	George Foster	.10	.08	.04
30	Joe Morgan	.60	.45	.25
31	Buddy Bell	.10	.08	.04
32	Lou Boudreau	.40	.30	.15
33	Rocky Colavito	.25	.20	.10
34	Jim "Mudcat" Grant	.10	.08	.04
35	Tris Speaker	.40	.30	.15
36	Ray Boone	.10	.08	.04
37	Darrell Evans	.10	.08	.04
38	Al Kaline	.50	.40	.20
39	George Kell	.25	.20	.10
40	Mickey Lolich	.10	.08	.04
41	Cesar Cedeno	.10	.08	.04
42	Sal Bando	.10	.08	.04
43	Vida Blue	.10	.08	.04
44	Bert Campaneris	.10	.08	.04
45	Ken Holtzman	.10	.08	.04
46	Lew Burdette	.10	.08	.04
47	Bob Horner	.10	.08	.04
48	Warren Spahn	.75	.60	.30
49	Cecil Cooper	.10	.08	.04
50	Tony Oliva	.30	.25	.12
51	Bobby Bonds	.25	.20	.10
52	Alvin Dark	.10	.08	.04
53	Dave Dravecky	.10	.08	.04
54	Monte Irvin	.10	.08	.04
55	Willie Mays	1.25	.90	.50
56	Bud Harrelson	.10	.08	.04
57	Dave Kingman	.10	.08	.04
58	Yogi Berra	.60	.45	.25
59	Don Baylor	.10	.08	.04
60	Jim Bouton	.10	.08	.04
61	Bobby Brown	.10	.08	.04
62	Whitey Ford	.50	.40	.20
63	Lou Gehrig	1.00	.70	.40
64	Charlie Keller	.10	.08	.04
65	Eddie Lopat	.10	.08	.04
66	Johnny Mize	.40	.30	.15
67	Bobby Murcer	.10	.08	.04
68	Graig Nettles	.20	.15	.08
69	Bobby Shantz	.10	.08	.04
70	Richie Ashburn	.10	.08	.04
71	Larry Bowa	.10	.08	.04
72	Steve Carlton	.40	.30	.15
73	Robin Roberts	.30	.25	.12
74	Matty Alou	.10	.08	.04
75	Harvey Haddix	.10	.08	.04
76	Ralph Kiner	.40	.30	.15
77	Bill Madlock	.10	.08	.04

78	Bill Mazeroski	.20	.15	.08
79	Al Oliver	.10	.08	.04
80	Manny Sanguillen	.10	.08	.04
81	Willie Stargell	.25	.20	.10
82	Al Brumbry	.10	.08	.04
83	Davey Johnson	.10	.08	.04
84	Boog Powell	.10	.08	.04
85	Earl Weaver	.10	.08	.04
86	Lou Brock	.50	.40	.20
87	Orlando Cepeda	.10	.08	.04
88	Curt Flood	.10	.08	.04
89	Joe Garagiola	.10	.08	.04
90	Bob Gibson	.50	.40	.20
91	Rogers Hornsby	.50	.40	.20
92	Enos Slaughter	.25	.20	.10
93	Joe Torre	.10	.08	.04
94	Gaylord Perry	.10	.08	.04
95	Checklist 1-49	.10	.08	.04
96	Checklist 50-96	.10	.08	.04
97	Cool Papa Bell	.25	.20	.10
98	Garnett Blair	.10	.08	.04
99	Gene Benson	.10	.08	.04
100	Lyman Bostock, Sr.	.25	.20	.10
101	Marlin Carter	.10	.08	.04
102	Oscar Charleston	.10	.08	.04
103	Ray Dandridge	.10	.08	.04
104	Mahlon Duckett	.10	.08	.04
105	Josh Gibson	.50	.40	.20
106	Cowan Hyde	.10	.08	.04
107	"Judy" Johnson	.25	.20	.10
108	Buck Leonard	.25	.20	.10
109	John Henry Lloyd	.25	.20	.10
110	Lester Lockett	.10	.08	.04
111	Max Manning	.10	.08	.04
112	Satchel Paige	1.00	.70	.40
113	Armando Vazquez	.10	.08	.04
114	Smokey Joe Williams	.50	.40	.20
115	Negro Leagues Checklist	.10	.08	.04
116	Alice Hohlmeyer	.10	.08	.04
117	Dotty Kamenshek	.10	.08	.04
118	Pepper Davis	.10	.08	.04
119	Marge Wenzell	.10	.08	.04
120	AAGPBA Checklist	.10	.08	.04
121	The Babe (Babe Ruth)	1.00	.70	.40
122	The Iron Horse (Lou Gehrig)	.75	.60	.30
123	Double X (Jimmie Foxx)	.50	.40	.20
124	Rajah (Rogers Hornsby)	.50	.40	.20
125	The Georgia Peach (Ty Cobb)	.75	.60	.30
126	The Say Hey Kid (Willie Mays)	.75	.60	.30
127	Ralph (Ralph Kiner)	.30	.25	.12
128	The Grey Eagle (Tris Speaker)	.30	.25	.12
129	The Big Cat (Johnny Mize)	.30	.25	.12
130	Ted's Greatest Hitters Checklist	.10	.08	.04
131	Satchel Paige	.75	.60	.30
132	Joe Black	.10	.08	.04
133	Roy Campanella	.75	.60	.30
134	Larry Doby	.10	.08	.04
135	Jim Gilliam	.10	.08	.04
136	Monte Irvin	.25	.20	.10
137	Sam Jethroe	.10	.08	.04
138	Willie Mays	.75	.60	.30
139	Don Newcombe	.10	.08	.04
140	Barrier Breakers Checklist	.10	.08	.04
141	Roy Campanella	.50	.40	.20
142	Bob Gibson	.50	.40	.20
143	Boog Powell	.10	.08	.04
144	Willie Mays	.50	.40	.20
145	Johnny Mize	.25	.20	.10
146	Monte Irvin	.10	.08	.04
147	Earl Weaver	.10	.08	.04
148	Ted Williams	1.50	1.25	.60
149	Jim Gilliam	.10	.08	.04
150	Goin' North Checklist	.10	.08	.04
151	Juan Gonzalez (Footsteps to Greatness)	1.50	1.25	.60
152	Juan Gonzalez (Sign 'em Up)	1.50	1.25	.60
153	Juan Gonzalez (The Road to Success)	1.50	1.25	.60
154	Juan Gonzalez (Looking Ahead)	1.50	1.25	.60
155	"Dawning of a Legacy" Checklist	.10	.08	.04
156	Jeff Bagwell (Born with Red Sox Blood)	.40	.30	.15
157	Jeff Bagwell (Movin' Up, Then Out)	.40	.30	.15
158	Jeff Bagwell (Year 1)	.40	.30	.15
159	Jeff Bagwell (Year 2)	.40	.30	.15
160	"Dawning of a Legacy" Checklist	.10	.08	.04

1993 Ted Williams Co. Etched in Stone

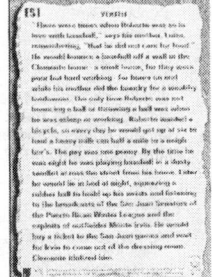

This 10-card insert set documents the career of Roberto Clemente, using sepia-toned and color photographs on the card front, highlighted by a gold-foil embossed "Tribute '93" logo in the lower-left corner and an "Etched in Stone" logo at upper-right. Backs have a detailed biography. Cards are numbered ES1 through ES10.

		MT	NR MT	EX
	Complete Set (10):	1.00	.70	.40
	Common Card:	.10	.08	.04
1ES	Youth (Roberto Clemente)	.10	.08	.04
2ES	Sign Up (Roberto Clemente)	.10	.08	.04
3ES	Try-Out (Roberto Clemente)	.10	.08	.04
4ES	Playing Mad (Roberto Clemente)	.10	.08	.04
5ES	Minor Leagues (Roberto Clemente)	.10	.08	.04
6ES	1955-1959 (Roberto Clemente)	.10	.08	.04
7ES	1960 (Roberto Clemente)	.10	.08	.04
8ES	1963 (Roberto Clemente)	.10	.08	.04
9ES	1970 (Roberto Clemente)	.10	.08	.04
10ES	Etched in Stone Checklist	.10	.08	.04

1993 Ted Williams Co. Brooks Robinson

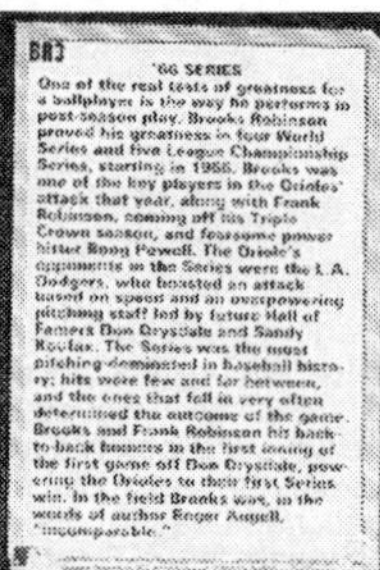

This 10-card insert set, numbered BR1 through BR10, traces the baseball career of Hall of Fame Orioles third baseman Brooks Robinson. Card fronts feature sepia-toned or color photos highlighted yb the player's name in gold foil down the left side and a "Brooks Robinson Collection" diamond logo at lower-right. Backs include a career summary or batting or fielding stats.

		MT	NR MT	EX
	Complete Set (10):	1.00	.70	.40
	Common Card:	.10	.08	.04
1BR	Salad Days (Brooks Robinson)	.10	.08	.04
2BR	Career Batting Stats (Brooks Robinson)	.10	.08	.04
3BR	'66 World Series (Brooks Robinson)	.10	.08	.04
4BR	Career Fielding Stats (Brooks Robinson)	.10	.08	.04
5BR	'70 Series #2 (Brooks Robinson)	.10	.08	.04
6BR	'70 Series #1 (Brooks Robinson)	.10	.08	.04
7BR	Comin' Up (Brooks Robinson)	.10	.08	.04
8BR	All Star Games (Brooks Robinson)	.10	.08	.04
9BR	1964 (Brooks Robinson)	.10	.08	.04
10BR	Brooks Robinson Collection Checklist	.10	.08	.04

1993 Ted Williams Co. Locklear Collection

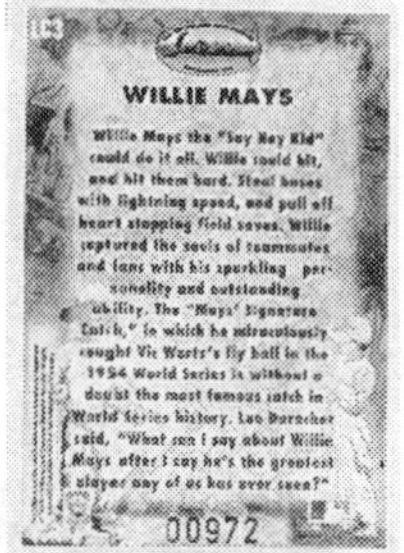

The painting of former major leaguer Gene Locklear is featured in this 10-card insert set The central image of the player is set against a background of multiple player images in orange, red and purple tones. The player's name is in dark blue on the left edge and a "Gene Locklear Collection" logo is in lower-right. On back is a commentary on the player, a card number with an "LC" prefix and, at bottom center, a serial number.

		MT	NR MT	EX
	Complete Set (10):	65.00	49.00	26.00
	Common Player:	4.00	3.00	1.50
1LC	Yogi Berra	6.00	4.50	2.50
2LC	Lou Brock	5.00	3.75	2.00
3LC	Willie Mays	9.00	6.75	3.50
4LC	Johnny Mize	4.00	3.00	1.50
5LC	Satchel Paige	9.00	6.75	3.50
6LC	Babe Ruth	12.00	9.00	4.75
7LC	Enos Slaughter	4.00	3.00	1.50
8LC	Carl Yastrzemski	6.00	4.50	2.50
9LC	Ted Williams	15.00	11.00	6.00
10LC	Locklear Collection Checklist	6.00	4.50	2.50

1993 Ted Williams Co. Memories

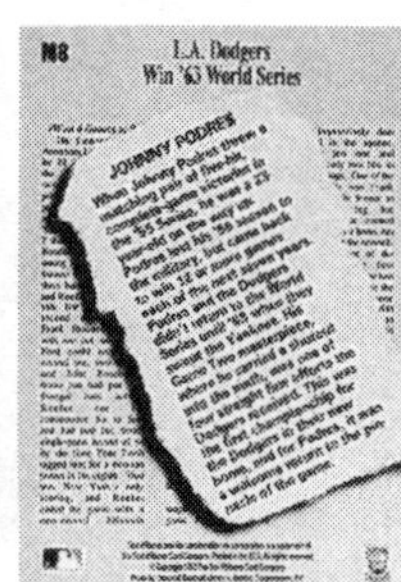

Four historical World Series of the 1950s-1970s are featured in five-card runs within the "Memories" insert set. Fronts have black-and-white or color player photos. In the lower-left corner is a vintage press camera with "Memories" and the year emanating from the flashbulb. The Ted Williams Card Co. logo is at upper-right. The player's name is in white at bottom-center. Cards are numbered with an "M" prefix on back and feature a headline announcing the team's World Series victory and a summary of the featured player's performance in that Fall Classic.

		MT	NR MT	EX
	Complete Set (20):	2.00	1.50	.80
	Common Player:	.10	.08	.04
	1955 BROOKLYN DODGERS			
1	Roy Campanella	.10	.08	.04
2	Jim Gilliam	.10	.08	.04
3	Gil Hodges	.10	.08	.04
4	Duke Snider	.10	.08	.04
5	1955 Dodgers Checklist	.10	.08	.04
	1963 LOS ANGELES DODGERS			
6	Don Drysdale	.10	.08	.04
7	Tommy Davis	.10	.08	.04
8	Johnny Podres	.10	.08	.04
9	Maury Wills	.10	.08	.04
10	1963 Dodgers Checklist	.10	.08	.04
	1971 PITTSBURGH PIRATES			
11	Roberto Clemente	.10	.08	.04
12	Al Oliver	.10	.08	.04
13	Manny Sanguillen	.10	.08	.04
14	Willie Stargell	.10	.08	.04
15	1971 Pirates Checklist	.10	.08	.04
	1975 CINCINNATI REDS			
16	Johnny Bench	.10	.08	.04
17	George Foster	.10	.08	.04
18	Joe Morgan	.10	.08	.04
19	Tony Perez	.10	.08	.04
20	1975 Red Checklist	.10	.08	.04

1994 Ted Williams Card Company

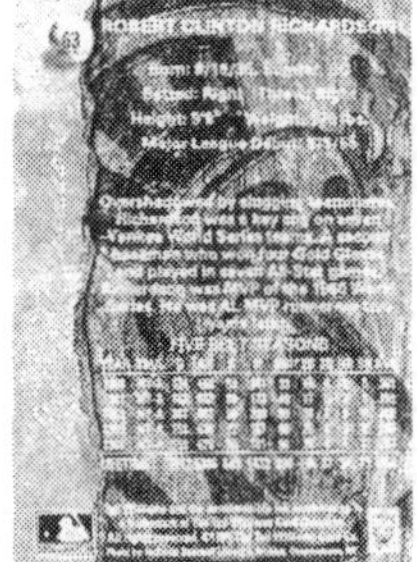

Because the lack of a players' association license again limited the company to using two major leaguers in its card set, the Ted Williams Card Co. spiced up its 1994 edition with hot prospects in the minor leagues, more high-tech production values and innovative subsets and chase cards. The base set for 1994 includes 162 cards. The first 92 cards feature retured or deceased players. Those cards feature a color or colorized photo set against a background of a second ghost-image photo or the actual photo background. Vertically at right is a stone image on which the player's name is printed in extremely difficult to read gold letters. The edge of the stone and the card company logo are embossed. Backs have biographical and career details, a career summary and stats for the player's five top seasons and his career. Subsets numbered consecutively with the base cards include a seven-card "Women of Baseball" series; 18 Negro Leaguers, 18 current minor leaguers in a series titled "The Campaign;" 10 "Goin' North cards of former superstars as minor leaguers; nine "Swingin' for the Fences" cards of home run hitters, and, a nine-card "Dawning of a Legacy" series featuring Cliff Floyd and Tim Salmon. The several insert card series are checklisted separately.

		MT	NR MT	EX
Complete Set (162):		20.00	15.00	8.00
Common Player:		.10	.08	.04
1	Ted Williams	2.50	2.00	1.00
2	Bernie Carbo	.10	.08	.04
3	Bobby Doerr	.10	.08	.04
4	Fred Lynn	.10	.08	.04
5	Johnny Pesky	.10	.08	.04
6	Rico Petrocelli	.10	.08	.04
7	Cy Young	.40	.30	.15
8	Paul Blair	.10	.08	.04
9	Andy Etchebarren	.10	.08	.04
10	Brooks Robinson	.50	.40	.20
11	Gil Hodges	.15	.11	.06
12	Tommy John	.10	.08	.04
13	Rick Monday	.10	.08	.04
14	Dean Chance	.10	.08	.04
15	Doug DeCinces	.10	.08	.04
16	Gabby Hartnett	.10	.08	.04
17	Don Kessinger	.10	.08	.04
18	Bruce Sutter	.10	.08	.04
19	Eddie Collins	.10	.08	.04
20	Nellie Fox	.25	.20	.10
21	Carlos May	.10	.08	.04
22	Ted Kluszewski	.10	.08	.04
23	Vada Pinson	.10	.08	.04
24	Johnny Vander Meer	.10	.08	.04
25	Bob Feller	.40	.30	.15
26	Mike Garcia	.10	.08	.04
27	Sam McDowell	.10	.08	.04
28	Al Rosen	.10	.08	.04
29	Norm Cash	.10	.08	.04
30	Ty Cobb	.60	.45	.25
31	Mark Fidrych	.10	.08	.04
32	Hank Greenberg	.10	.08	.04
33	Denny McLain	.10	.08	.04
34	Virgil Trucks	.10	.08	.04
35	Enos Cabell	.10	.08	.04
36	Mike Scott	.10	.08	.04
37	Bob Watson	.10	.08	.04
38	Amos Otis	.10	.08	.04
39	Frank White	.10	.08	.04
40	Joe Adcock	.10	.08	.04
41	Rico Carty	.10	.08	.04
42	Ralph Garr	.10	.08	.04
43	Eddie Mathews	.35	.25	.14
44	Ben Oglivie	.10	.08	.04
45	Gorman Thomas	.10	.08	.04
46	Earl Battey	.10	.08	.04
47	Rod Carew	.25	.20	.10
48	Jim Kaat	.10	.08	.04
49	Harmon Killebrew	.40	.30	.15
50	Gary Carter	.10	.08	.04
51	Steve Rogers	.10	.08	.04
52	Rusty Staub	.10	.08	.04
53	Sal Maglie	.10	.08	.04
54	Juan Marichal	.25	.20	.10
55	Mel Ott	.10	.08	.04
56	Bobby Thomson	.25	.20	.10
57	Tommie Agee	.10	.08	.04
58	Tug McGraw	.10	.08	.04
59	Elston Howard	.10	.08	.04
60	Sparky Lyle	.10	.08	.04
61	Billy Martin	.10	.08	.04
62	Thurman Munson	.25	.20	.10
63	Bobby Richardson	.10	.08	.04
64	Bill Skowron	.10	.08	.04
65	Mickey Cochrane	.10	.08	.04
66	Rollie Fingers	.10	.08	.04
67	Lefty Grove	.40	.30	.15
68	Catfish Hunter	.10	.08	.04
69	Connie Mack	.50	.40	.20
70	Al Simmons	.10	.08	.04
71	Dick Allen	.10	.08	.04
72	Bob Boone	.10	.08	.04
73	Del Ennis	.10	.08	.04
74	Chuck Klein	.10	.08	.04
75	Mike Schmidt	.60	.45	.25
76	Dock Ellis	.10	.08	.04
77	Elroy Face	.10	.08	.04
78	Phil Garner	.10	.08	.04
79	Bill Mazeroski	.10	.08	.04
80	Pie Traynor	.25	.20	.10
81	Honus Wagner	1.00	.75	.40
82	Dizzy Dean	.10	.08	.04
83	Red Schoendienst	.10	.08	.04
84	Randy Jones	.10	.08	.04
85	Nate Colbert	.10	.08	.04
86	Jeff Burroughs	.10	.08	.04
87	Jim Sundberg	.10	.08	.04
88	Frank Howard	.10	.08	.04
89	Walter Johnson	.50	.40	.20
90	Eddie Yost	.10	.08	.04
91	Checklist 1-46	.10	.08	.04
92	Checklist 47-92	.10	.08	.04
93	Faye Dancer	.10	.08	.04
94	Snookie Doyle	.10	.08	.04
95	Maddy English	.10	.08	.04
96	Nickie Fox	.10	.08	.04
97	Sophie Kurys	.10	.08	.04
98	Alma Ziegler	.10	.08	.04
99	Women of Baseball Checklist	.10	.08	.04
100	Newton Allen	.10	.08	.04
101	Willard Brown	.10	.08	.04
102	Larry Brown	.10	.08	.04
103	Leon Day	.20	.15	.08
104	John Donaldson	.10	.08	.04
105	Rube Foster	.10	.08	.04
106	Bud Fowler	.10	.08	.04
107	Vic Harris	.10	.08	.04
108	Webster McDonald	.10	.08	.04
109	John "Buck" O'Neil	.10	.08	.04
110	Ted "Double Duty" Radcliffe	.10	.08	.04
111	Wilber "Bullet" Rogan	.10	.08	.04
112	Toni Stone	.10	.08	.04
113	Jim Taylor	.10	.08	.04
114	Moses "Fleetwood" Walker	.10	.08	.04
115	George Wilson	.20	.15	.08
116	Judson Wilson	.10	.08	.04
117	Negro Leagues Checklist	.20	.15	.08
118	Howard Battle	.15	.11	.06
119	John Burke	.10	.08	.04
120	Brian Dubose	.10	.08	.04
121	Alex Gonzalez	.25	.20	.10
122	Jose Herrera	.10	.08	.04
123	Jason Giambi	.15	.11	.06
124	Derek Jeter	.20	.15	.08
125	Charles Johnson	.20	.15	.08
126	Daron Kirkreit	.15	.11	.06
127	Jason Moler	.10	.08	.04
128	Vince Moore	.10	.08	.04
129	Chad Mottola	.40	.30	.15
130	Jose Silva	.15	.11	.06
131	Makato Suzuki	.10	.08	.04
132	Brien Taylor	.20	.15	.08
133	Michael Tucker	.25	.20	.10
134	Billy Wagner	.10	.08	.04
135	The Campaign Checklist	.10	.08	.04
136	Gary Carter	.10	.08	.04
137	Tony Conigliaro	.10	.08	.04
138	Sparky Lyle	.10	.08	.04
139	Roger Maris	.40	.30	.15
140	Vada Pinson	.10	.08	.04
141	Mike Schmidt	.50	.40	.20
142	Frank White	.10	.08	.04
143	Ted Williams	2.50	2.00	1.00
144	Goin' North Checklist	.10	.08	.04
145	Joe Adcock	.10	.08	.04
146	Rocky Colavito	.25	.20	.10
147	Lou Gehrig	1.50	1.25	.60
148	Gil Hodges	.20	.15	.08
149	Bob Horner	.10	.08	.04
150	Willie Mays	1.00	.75	.40
151	Mike Schmidt	.50	.40	.20
152	Pat Seery	.10	.08	.04
153	Swingin' for the Fences Checklist	.10	.08	.04
154	Cliff Floyd (The Honors Begin)	.75	.60	.30
155	Cliff Floyd (The Top Polecat)	.75	.60	.30
156	Cliff Floyd (Minor League Team of the Year)	.75	.60	.30
157	Cliff Floyd (Major League Debut)	.75	.60	.30
158	Tim Salmon (Award Winner)	.60	.45	.25
159	Tim Salmon (Early Professional Career)	.60	.45	.25
160	Tim Salmon (An MVP Season)	.60	.45	.25
161	Tim Salmon (Rookie of the Year)	.60	.45	.25
162	Dawning of a Legacy Checklist	.10	.08	.04

1994 Ted Williams Card Co. Etched in Stone

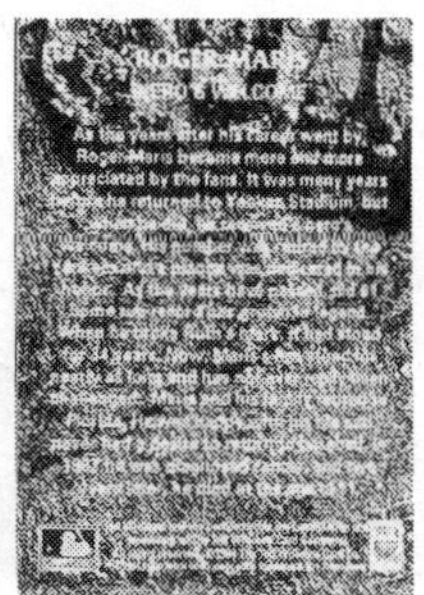

A metallized effect highlights the front design of this nine-card insert series commemorating the career of Roger Maris. Color and colorized photos appear to have been revealed by chiseling away a rock face which forms much of the front border. Backs have career write-ups overprinted on a design which forms a large "Etched in Stone" design when the cards are laid together in order. Cards have an "ES" prefix to the card number.

		MT	NR MT	EX
Complete Set (9):		20.00	15.00	8.00
Common Player:		3.00	2.25	1.25
1ES	Roger Maris (Scouting Report)	3.00	2.25	1.25
2ES	Roger Maris (Traded)	3.00	2.25	1.25
3ES	Roger Maris (Career Year)	3.00	2.25	1.25
4ES	Roger Maris (1961)	3.00	2.25	1.25
5ES	Roger Maris (Silent Accomplishments)	3.00	2.25	1.25
6ES	Roger Maris (Team Player)	3.00	2.25	1.25
7ES	Roger Maris (Reborn)	3.00	2.25	1.25
8ES	Roger Maris (Hero's Welcome)	3.00	2.25	1.25
9ES	Checklist (Roger Maris)	3.00	2.25	1.25

1994 Ted Williams Card Company The 500 Club

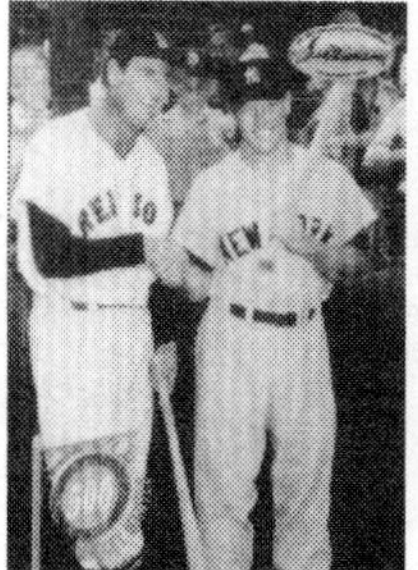

Major leaguers with 500 or more career home runs are featured in this nine-card insert set. Fronts have full-bleed metallized photos, some in color and some which have been colorized. A logo picturing hanging "The 500 Club" sign appears at lower-left, with the player's name in gold. Backs have a basic design that looks for all the world like a toilet seat, in which the player's home run prowess is recalled. Cards are numbered with a "5C" prefix.

		MT	NR MT	EX
Complete Set (9):		32.00	24.00	13.00
Common Player:		3.00	2.25	1.25
1	Hank Aaron	4.50	3.50	1.75
2	Reggie Jackson	4.00	3.00	1.50
3	Harmon Killebrew	3.00	2.25	1.25
4	Mickey Mantle	7.00	5.25	2.75
5	Jimmie Foxx	3.00	2.25	1.25
6	Babe Ruth	7.00	5.25	2.75
7	Mike Schmidt	3.50	2.75	1.50
8	Ted Williams	6.00	4.50	2.50
9	Checklist	3.00	2.25	1.25

1994 Ted Williams Card Company Dan Gardiner Collection

Sports artist Dan Gardiner was commissioned to produce a series of nine insert cards depicting hot minor league propsects for this insert set. Players are depicted in posed portraits on front and in action paintings on the back. Cards carry a "DG" prefix to the card number and each card is serially numbered in the upper-left corner.

		MT	NR MT	EX
Complete Set (9):		25.00	18.50	10.00
Common Player:		2.50	2.00	1.00
1DG	Michael Jordan	8.00	6.00	3.25
2DG	Michael Tucker	3.00	2.25	1.25

3DG	Derek Jeter	3.50	2.75	1.50
4DG	Charles Johnson	3.00	2.25	1.25
5DG	Howard Battle	2.50	2.00	1.00
6DG	Quilvio Vergas	2.50	2.00	1.00
7DG	Brian Hunter	3.00	2.25	1.25
8DG	Brien Taylor	3.00	2.25	1.25
9DG	Checklist	2.50	2.00	1.00

1994 Ted Williams Co. Locklear Collection

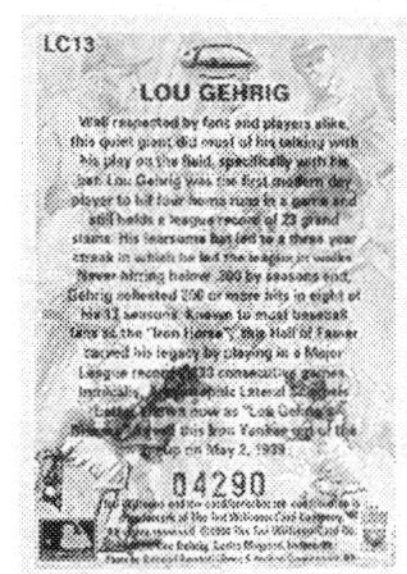

Paintings of eight Hall of Famers plus a checklist are featured in this insert set. The art is the work of former major leaguer Gene Locklear. The cards are numbered with an "LC" prefix.

		MT	NR MT	EX
Complete Set (9):		40.00	30.00	15.00
Common Player:		3.00	2.25	1.25
11LC	Ty Cobb	5.00	3.75	2.00
12LC	Bob Feller	4.00	3.00	1.50
13LC	Lou Gehrig	7.00	5.25	2.75
14LC	Josh Gibson	4.00	3.00	1.50
15LC	Walter Johnson	4.00	3.00	1.50
16LC	Casey Stengel	4.00	3.00	1.50
17LC	Honus Wagner	7.00	5.25	2.75
18LC	Cy Young	7.00	5.25	2.75
19LC	Checklist	3.00	2.25	1.25

1994 Ted Williams Card Company Memories

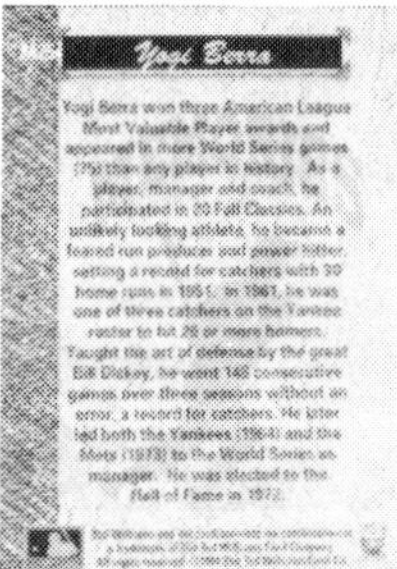

Continuing the card numbers from the 1993 Memories insert set, the 1994 version features highlights of the 1954, 1961, 1968 and 1975 World Series. Card fronts feature metallized images in a snapshot format. The year is noted in large pink numbers at lower-left. Backs describe each player's participation in that particular World Series and are numbered with an "M" prefix.

		MT	NR MT	EX
Complete Set (20):		10.00	7.50	4.00
Common Player:		.50	.40	.20
21M	Monte Irvin (1954 Giants)	.50	.40	.20
22M	Sal Maglie (1954 Giants)	.50	.40	.20
23M	Dusty Rhodes (1954 Giants)	.50	.40	.20
24M	Hank Thompson (1954 Giants)	.50	.40	.20
25M	Yogi Berra (1961 Yankees)	1.50	1.25	.60
26M	Elston Howard (1961 Yankees)	.75	.60	.30
27M	Roger Maris (1961 Yankees)	2.50	2.00	1.00
28M	Bobby Richardson (1961 Yankees)	.75	.60	.30
29M	Norm Cash (1968 Tigers)	.50	.40	.20
30M	Al Kaline (1968 Tigers)	1.25	.90	.50
31M	Mickey Lolich (1968 Tigers)	.50	.40	.20
32M	Denny McLain (1968 Tigers)	.60	.45	.25
33M	Bernie Carbo (1975 Red Sox)	.50	.40	.20
34M	Fred Lynn (1975 Red Sox)	.50	.40	.20
35M	Rico Petrocelli (1975 Red Sox)	.50	.40	.20
36M	Luis Tiant (1975 Red Sox)	.50	.40	.20
37M	Checklist	.50	.40	.20

1994 Ted Williams Card Co. LP Cards

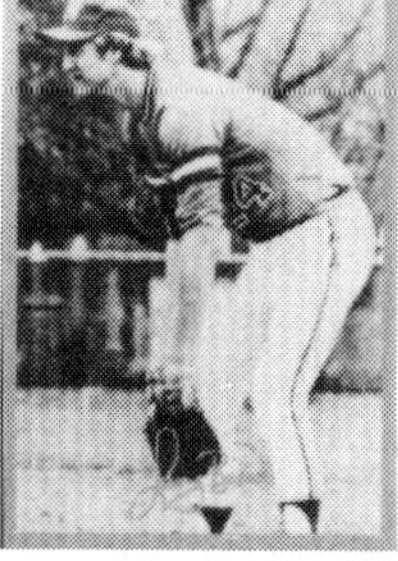
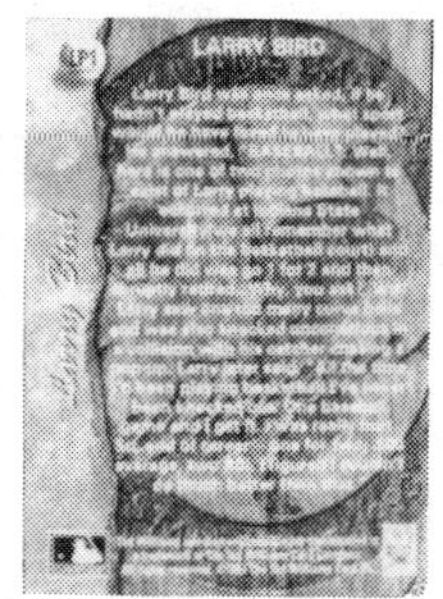

Two premium insert cards in the 1994 Ted Williams Co. set carry an "LP" card number prefix. One depicts basketball superstar Larry Bird playing baseball during his college days at Indiana State University. The other card depicts Ted Williams speaking at the opening of the Ted Williams Museum. Fronts use a metallized technology. Backs describe the action.

		MT	NR MT	EX
Complete Set (2):		15.00	11.00	6.00
Common Player:		5.00	3.75	2.00
1	Larry Bird	8.00	6.00	3.25
2	Ted Williams	12.00	9.00	4.75

1994 Ted Williams Co. Mike Schmidt Collection

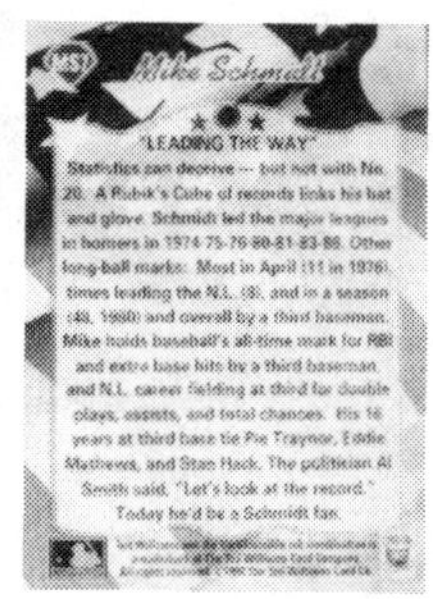

This nine-card insert set honors the career of Hall of Fame Phillies third baseman Mike Schmidt. Fronts feature full-bleed metallized color photos. Backs have a Phillies flag design with a career biography. Cards are numbered with an "MS" prefix.

		MT	NR MT	EX
Complete Set (9):		15.00	11.00	6.00
Common Card:		2.00	1.50	.80
1MS	Mike Schmidt (Mike)	2.00	1.50	.80
2MS	Mike Schmidt (The White House)	2.00	1.50	.80
3MS	Mike Schmidt (Soaping Up)	2.00	1.50	.80
4MS	Mike Schmidt (The Promised Land)	2.00	1.50	.80
5MS	Mike Schmidt (Who's Who)	2.00	1.50	.80
6MS	Mike Schmidt (The Call)	2.00	1.50	.80
7MS	Mike Schmidt (Leading the Way)	2.00	1.50	.80
8MS	Mike Schmidt (Award Winner)	2.00	1.50	.80
9MS	Checklist	2.00	1.50	.80

1988 Woolworth

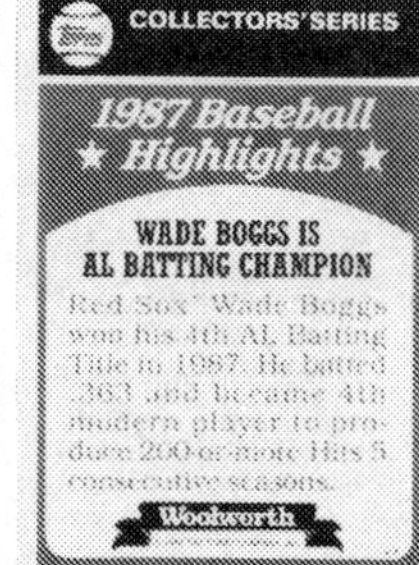

This 33-card boxed set was produced by Topps for exclusive distribution at Woolworth stores. The set includes 18 individual player cards and 15 World Series game action photo cards. World Series cards include two for each game of the Series, plus a card of 1987 Series MVP Frank Viola. Card front carry a Woolworth's Baseball Highlights heading on a red and yellow banner above the blue-bordered super glossy player photo. A white-lettered caption beneath the photo consists of either the player's name or a World Series game notation. Card backs are red, white and blue and contain the Topps logo, card number and "Collector's Series" label above a "1987 Baseball Highlights" logo and a brief description of the photo on the front.

		MT	NR MT	EX
Complete Set:		4.00	3.00	1.50
Common Player:		.09	.07	.04
1	Don Baylor	.12	.09	.05
2	Vince Coleman	.15	.11	.06
3	Darrell Evans	.12	.09	.05
4	Don Mattingly	.90	.70	.35
5	Eddie Murray	.30	.25	.12
6	Nolan Ryan	.90	.70	.35
7	Mike Schmidt	.45	.35	.20
8	Andre Dawson	.20	.15	.08
9	George Bell	.15	.11	.06
10	Steve Bedrosian	.12	.09	.05
11	Roger Clemens	.50	.40	.20
12	Tony Gwynn	.35	.25	.14
13	Wade Boggs	.40	.30	.15
14	Benny Santiago	.25	.20	.10
15	Mark McGwire	.30	.25	.12
16	Dave Righetti	.15	.11	.06
17	Jeffrey Leonard	.09	.07	.04
18	Gary Gaetti	.12	.09	.05
19	World Series Game #1 (Frank Viola)	.12	.09	.05
20	World Series Game #1 (Dan Gladden)	.09	.07	.04
21	World Series Game #2 (Bert Blyleven)	.12	.09	.05
22	World Series Game #2 (Gary Gaetti)	.12	.09	.05
23	World Series Game #3 (John Tudor)	.12	.09	.05
24	World Series Game #3 (Todd Worrell)	.12	.09	.05
25	World Series Game #4 (Tom Lawless)	.09	.07	.04
26	World Series Game #4 (Willie McGee)	.12	.09	.05
27	World Series Game #5 (Danny Cox)	.09	.07	.04
28	World Series Game #5 (Curt Ford)	.09	.07	.04
29	World Series Game #6 (Don Baylor)	.12	.09	.05
30	World Series Game #6 (Kent Hrbek)	.15	.11	.06
31	World Series Game #7 (Kirby Puckett)	.25	.20	.10
32	World Series Game #7 (Greg Gagne)	.09	.07	.04
33	World Series MVP (Frank Viola)	.12	.09	.05

1989 Woolworth

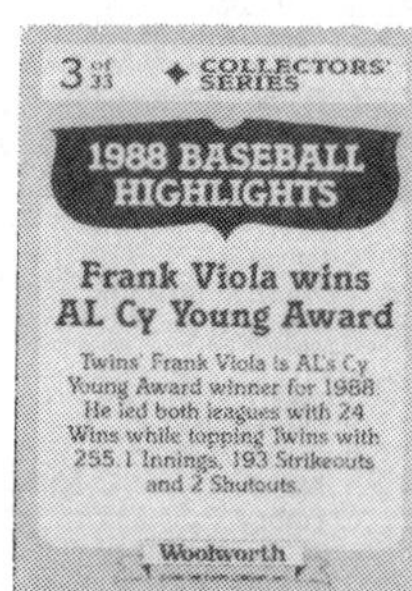

This 33-card set was produced by Topps for the Woolworth store chain and was sold in a special box with a checklist on the back. The glossy-coated cards commemorate the most memorable moments in baseball from the the 1988 season, and include the logo "Woolworth's Baseball Highlights" along the top. The player photos are framed in red, yellow and white and feature the player's name beneath the photo. The backs include a description of the various highlights. Orel Hershiser is pictured on four of the cards, and Jose Canseco appears on two.

		MT	NR MT	EX
Complete Set:		5.00	3.75	2.00
Common Player:		.09	.07	.04
1	Jose Canseco	.70	.50	.30
2	Kirk Gibson	.15	.11	.06
3	Frank Viola	.15	.11	.06
4	Orel Hershiser	.15	.11	.06

5	Walt Weiss	.15	.11	.06
6	Chris Sabo	.15	.11	.06
7	George Bell	.15	.11	.06
8	Wade Boggs	.50	.40	.20
9	Tom Browning	.12	.09	.05
10	Gary Carter	.15	.11	.06
11	Andre Dawson	.15	.11	.06
12	John Franco	.09	.07	.04
13	Randy Johnson	.15	.11	.06
14	Doug Jones	.09	.07	.04
15	Kevin McReynolds	.15	.11	.06
16	Gene Nelson	.09	.07	.04
17	Jeff Reardon	.09	.07	.04
18	Pat Tabler	.09	.07	.04
19	Tim Belcher	.15	.11	.06
20	Dennis Eckersley	.25	.15	.08
21	Orel Hershiser	.20	.15	.08
22	Gregg Jefferies	.25	.20	.10
23	Jose Canseco	.70	.50	.30
24	Kirk Gibson	.15	.11	.06
25	Orel Hershiser	.15	.11	.06
26	Mike Marshall	.09	.07	.04
27	Mark McGwire	.30	.25	.12
28	Rick Honeycutt	.09	.07	.04
29	Tim Belcher	.20	.15	.08
30	Jay Howell	.12	.09	.05
31	Mickey Hatcher	.09	.07	.04
32	Mike Davis	.09	.07	.04
33	Orel Hershiser	.15	.11	.06

1990 Woolworth

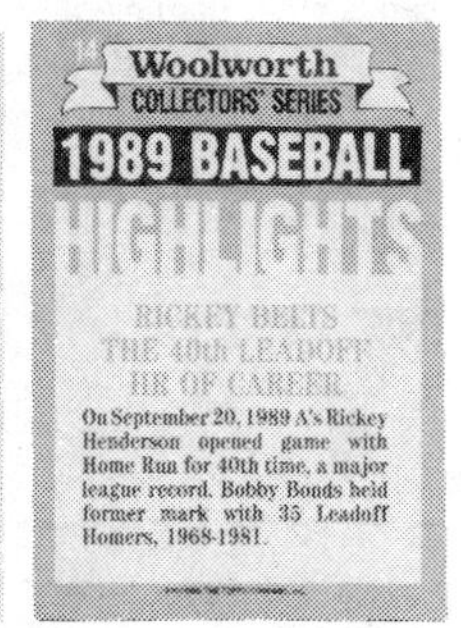

This 33-card set highlights the great baseball moments of 1989. The cards are styled like past Woolworth sets. The set features award winners and regular and post-season highlights.

		MT	NR MT	EX
Complete Set:		3.00	2.25	1.25
Common Player:		.06	.05	.02
1	Robin Yount	.20	.15	.08
2	Kevin Mitchell	.15	.11	.06
3	Bret Saberhagen	.10	.08	.04
4	Mark Davis	.06	.05	.02
5	Gregg Olson	.10	.08	.04
6	Jerome Walton	.06	.05	.02
7	Bert Blyleven	.10	.08	.04
8	Wade Boggs	.25	.20	.10
9	George Brett	.20	.15	.08
10	Vince Coleman	.10	.08	.04
11	Andre Dawson	.20	.15	.08
12	Dwight Evans	.10	.08	.04
13	Carlton Fisk	.20	.15	.08
14	Rickey Henderson	.40	.30	.15
15	Dale Murphy	.20	.15	.08
16	Eddie Murray	.20	.15	.08
17	Jeff Reardon	.08	.06	.03
18	Rick Reuschel	.06	.05	.02
19	Cal Ripken, Jr.	.40	.30	.15
20	Nolan Ryan	.50	.40	.20
21	Ryne Sandberg	.35	.25	.14
22	Robin Yount	.20	.15	.08
23	Rickey Henderson	.40	.30	.15
24	Will Clark	.40	.30	.15
25	Dave Stewart	.10	.08	.04
26	Walt Weiss	.08	.06	.03
27	Mike Moore	.06	.05	.02
28	Terry Steinbach	.08	.06	.03
29	Dave Henderson	.08	.06	.03
30	Matt Williams	.25	.15	.08
31	Rickey Henderson	.40	.30	.15
32	Kevin Mitchell	.15	.11	.06
33	Dave Stewart	.10	.08	.04

Values for recent cards and sets are listed in Mint (MT), Near Mint (NM), reflecting the fact that many cards from recent years have been preserved in top condition. Recent cards and sets in less than Excellent condition have little collector interest.

1991 Woolworth

This 33-card boxed set was produced by Topps for distribution at Woolworth stores. Yellow borders are featured on the fronts of the glossy cards. The back feature baseball highlights from the previous season. Award winners, regular season and World Series highlights are showcased. The cards are numbered on back.

		MT	NR MT	EX
Complete Set:		4.00	3.00	1.50
Common Player:		.08	.06	.03
1	Barry Bonds	.25	.20	.10
2	Rickey Henderson	.25	.20	.10
3	Doug Drabek	.10	.08	.04
4	Bob Welch	.10	.08	.04
5	Dave Justice	.40	.30	.15
6	Sandy Alomar, Jr.	.08	.06	.03
7	Bert Blyleven	.10	.08	.04
8	George Brett	.25	.20	.10
9	Andre Dawson	.15	.11	.06
10	Dwight Evans	.10	.08	.04
11	Alex Fernandez	.20	.15	.08
12	Carlton Fisk	.20	.15	.08
13	Kevin Maas	.08	.06	.03
14	Dale Murphy	.20	.15	.08
15	Eddie Murray	.20	.15	.08
16	Dave Parker	.15	.11	.06
17	Jeff Reardon	.15	.11	.06
18	Cal Ripken, Jr.	.60	.45	.25
19	Nolan Ryan	.75	.60	.30
20	Ryne Sandberg	.60	.45	.25
21	Bobby Thigpen	.10	.08	.04
22	Robin Yount	.20	.15	.08
23	Nasty Boys	.10	.08	.04
24	Dave Stewart	.10	.08	.04
25	Eric Davis	.15	.11	.06
26	Rickey Henderson	.25	.20	.10
27	Billy Hatcher	.08	.06	.03
28	Joe Oliver	.08	.06	.03
29	Chris Sabo	.15	.11	.06
30	Barry Larkin	.15	.11	.06
31	Jose Rijo	.10	.08	.04
32	Reds Celebrate	.10	.08	.04
33	Jose Rijo	.10	.08	.04

1933 World Wide Gum (Canadian Goudey, V353)

Also known as "Canadian Goudeys," this 94-card set drew heavily on its U.S. contemporary. Card fronts are identical to the '33 Goudeys and the backs are nearly so. The first 52 cards in the set carry the same card numbers as their American counterparts, while cards #53-94 have different numbers than the U.S. version. Card backs can be found printed entirely in English, or in English and French; the former being somewhat scarcer. Cards measure approximately 2-3/8" x 2-7/8".

		NR MT	EX	VG
Complete Set (94):		26000.	13000.	7800.
Common Player:		115.00	57.00	34.00
1	Benny Bengough	1200.	600.00	360.00
2	Arthur (Dazzy) Vance	300.00	150.00	90.00
3	Hugh Critz	115.00	57.00	34.00
4	Henry (Heinie) Schuble	115.00	57.00	34.00
5	Floyd (Babe) Herman	175.00	87.00	52.00
6	Jimmy Dykes	175.00	87.00	52.00
7	Ted Lyons	275.00	137.00	82.00
8	Roy Johnson	115.00	57.00	34.00
9	Dave Harris	115.00	57.00	34.00
10	Glenn Myatt	115.00	57.00	34.00
11	Billy Rogell	115.00	57.00	34.00
12	George Pipgras	115.00	57.00	34.00
13	Lafayette Thompson	115.00	57.00	34.00
14	Henry Johnson	115.00	57.00	34.00
15	Victor Sorrell	115.00	57.00	34.00
16	George Blaeholder	115.00	57.00	34.00
17	Watson Clark	115.00	57.00	34.00
18	Herold (Muddy) Ruel	115.00	57.00	34.00
19	Bill Dickey	425.00	212.00	127.00
20	Bill Terry	300.00	150.00	90.00
21	Phil Collins	115.00	57.00	34.00
22	Harold (Pie) Traynor	275.00	137.00	82.00
23	Hazen (Ki-Ki) Cuyler	275.00	137.00	82.00
24	Horace Ford	115.00	57.00	34.00
25	Paul Waner	300.00	150.00	90.00
26	Chalmer Cissell	115.00	57.00	34.00
27	George Connally	115.00	57.00	34.00
28	Dick Bartell	115.00	57.00	34.00
29	Jimmy Foxx	550.00	275.00	165.00
30	Frank Hogan	115.00	57.00	34.00
31	Tony Lazzeri	275.00	137.00	82.00
32	John (Bud) Clancy	115.00	57.00	34.00
33	Relph Kress	115.00	57.00	34.00
34	Bob O'Farrell	115.00	57.00	34.00
35	Al Simmons	275.00	137.00	82.00
36	Tommy Thevenow	115.00	57.00	34.00
37	Jimmy Wilson	115.00	57.00	34.00
38	Fred Brickell	115.00	57.00	34.00
39	Mark Koenig	115.00	57.00	34.00
40	Taylor Douthit	115.00	57.00	34.00
41	Gus Mancuso	115.00	57.00	34.00
42	Eddie Collins	300.00	150.00	90.00
43	Lew Fonseca	115.00	57.00	34.00
44	Jim Bottomley	300.00	150.00	90.00
45	Larry Benton	115.00	57.00	34.00
46	Ethan Allen	115.00	57.00	34.00
47	Henry "Heinie" Manush	275.00	137.00	82.00
48	Marty McManus	115.00	57.00	34.00
49	Frank Frisch	350.00	175.00	105.00
50	Ed Brandt	115.00	57.00	34.00
51	Charlie Grimm	125.00	62.00	37.00
52	Andy Cohen	115.00	57.00	34.00
53	Jack Quinn	115.00	57.00	34.00
54	Urban (Red) Faber	300.00	150.00	90.00
55	Lou Gehrig	3900.	1950.	1170.
56	John Welch	115.00	57.00	34.00
57	Bill Walker	115.00	57.00	34.00
58	Frank (Lefty) O'Doul	150.00	75.00	45.00
59	Edmund (Bing) Miller	115.00	57.00	34.00
60	Waite Hoyt	300.00	150.00	90.00
61	Max Bishop	115.00	57.00	34.00
62	"Pepper" Martin	150.00	75.00	45.00
63	Joe Cronin	300.00	150.00	90.00
64	Burleigh Grimes	275.00	137.00	82.00
65	Milton Gaston	115.00	57.00	34.00
66	George Grantham	115.00	57.00	34.00
67	Guy Bush	115.00	57.00	34.00
68	Willie Kamm	115.00	57.00	34.00
69	Gordon (Mickey) Cochrane	300.00	150.00	90.00
70	Adam Comorosky	115.00	57.00	34.00
71	Alvin Crowder	115.00	57.00	34.00
72	Willis Hudlin	115.00	57.00	34.00
73	Eddie Farrell	115.00	57.00	34.00
74	Leo Durocher	275.00	137.00	82.00
75	Walter Stewart	115.00	57.00	34.00
76	George Walberg	115.00	57.00	34.00
77	Glenn Wright	125.00	62.00	37.00
78	Charles (Buddy) Myer	115.00	57.00	34.00
79	James (Zack) Taylor	115.00	57.00	34.00
80	George Herman (Babe) Ruth	6500.	3250.	1950.
81	D'Arcy (Jake) Flowers	115.00	57.00	34.00
82	Ray Kolp	115.00	57.00	34.00
83	Oswald Bluege	115.00	57.00	34.00
84	Morris (Moe) Berg	175.00	87.00	52.00
85	Jimmy Foxx	550.00	275.00	165.00
86	Sam Byrd	115.00	57.00	34.00
87	Danny Mcfayden (McFayden)	115.00	57.00	34.00
88	Joe Judge	115.00	57.00	34.00
89	Joe Sewell	275.00	137.00	82.00
90	Lloyd Waner	275.00	137.00	82.00
91	Luke Sewell	115.00	57.00	34.00
92	Leo Mangum	115.00	57.00	34.00
93	George Herman (Babe) Ruth	6500.	3250.	1950.
94	Al Spohrer	115.00	57.00	34.00

1934 World Wide Gum (Canadian Goudey, V354)

Again a near-clone of the American issue, the '34 "Canadian Goudeys" feature the same number (96) and size (2-3/8" x 2-7/8") of cards. Player selection is considerably different, however. Cards #1-48 feature the same front design as the '33 World Wide/ Goudey sets. Cards #49-96 have the "Lou Gehrig says..." graphic on the front. Backs can be found in either all-English or English and French.

		NR MT	EX	VG
Complete Set (96):		21000.	10500.	6300.
Common Player:		115.00	57.00	34.00
1	Rogers Hornsby	875.00	437.00	262.00
2	Eddie Morgan	115.00	57.00	34.00
3	Valentine J. (Val) Picinich	115.00	57.00	34.00
4	Rabbit Maranville	265.00	132.00	79.00
5	Flint Rhem	115.00	57.00	34.00
6	Jim Elliott	115.00	57.00	34.00
7	Fred (Red) Lucas	115.00	57.00	34.00
8	Fred Marberry	115.00	57.00	34.00
9	Clifton Heathcote	115.00	57.00	34.00
10	Bernie Friberg	115.00	57.00	34.00
11	Elwood (Woody) English	115.00	57.00	34.00
12	Carl Reynolds	115.00	57.00	34.00
13	Ray Benge	115.00	57.00	34.00
14	Ben Cantwell	115.00	57.00	34.00
15	Irvin (Bump) Hadley	115.00	57.00	34.00
16	Herb Pennock	265.00	132.00	79.00
17	Fred Lindstrom	265.00	132.00	79.00
18	Edgar (Sam) Rice	265.00	132.00	79.00
19	Fred Frankhouse	115.00	57.00	34.00
20	Fred Fitzsimmons	115.00	57.00	34.00
21	Earl Combs (Earle)	265.00	132.00	79.00
22	George Uhle	115.00	57.00	34.00
23	Richard Coffman	115.00	57.00	34.00
24	Travis C. Jackson	265.00	132.00	79.00
25	Robert J. Burke	115.00	57.00	34.00
26	Randy Moore	115.00	57.00	34.00
27	John Henry (Heinie) Sand	115.00	57.00	34.00
28	George Herman (Babe) Ruth	6500.	3250.	1950.
29	Tris Speaker	350.00	175.00	105.00
30	Perce (Pat) Malone	115.00	57.00	34.00
31	Sam Jones	115.00	57.00	34.00
32	Eppa Rixey	265.00	132.00	79.00

33	Floyd (Pete) Scott	115.00	57.00	34.00
34	Pete Jablonowski	115.00	57.00	34.00
35	Clyde Manion	115.00	57.00	34.00
36	Dibrell Williams	115.00	57.00	34.00
37	Glenn Spencer	115.00	57.00	34.00
38	Ray Kremer	115.00	57.00	34.00
39	Phil Todt	115.00	57.00	34.00
40	Russell Rollings	115.00	57.00	34.00
41	Earl Clark	115.00	57.00	34.00
42	Jess Petty	115.00	57.00	34.00
43	Frank O'Rourke	115.00	57.00	34.00
44	Jesse Haines	265.00	132.00	79.00
45	Horace Lisenbee	115.00	57.00	34.00
46	Owen Carroll	115.00	57.00	34.00
47	Tom Zachary	115.00	57.00	34.00
48	Charlie Ruffing	265.00	132.00	79.00
49	Ray Benge	115.00	57.00	34.00
50	Elwood (Woody) English	115.00	57.00	34.00
51	Ben Chapman	115.00	57.00	34.00
52	Joe Kuhel	115.00	57.00	34.00
53	Bill Terry	275.00	137.00	82.00
54	Robert (Lefty) Grove	300.00	150.00	90.00
55	Jerome (Dizzy) Dean	350.00	175.00	105.00
56	Charles (Chuck) Klein	265.00	132.00	79.00
57	Charley Gehringer	300.00	150.00	90.00
58	Jimmy Foxx	375.00	187.00	112.00
59	Gordon (Mickey) Cochrane	300.00	150.00	90.00
60	Willie Kamm	115.00	57.00	34.00
61	Charlie Grimm	125.00	62.00	37.00
62	Ed Brandt	115.00	57.00	34.00
63	Tony Piet	115.00	57.00	34.00
64	Frank Frisch	300.00	150.00	90.00
65	Alvin Crowder	115.00	57.00	34.00
66	Frank Hogan	115.00	57.00	34.00
67	Paul Waner	265.00	132.00	79.00
68	Henry (Heinie) Manush	265.00	132.00	79.00
69	Leo Durocher	275.00	137.00	82.00
70	Floyd Vaughan	265.00	132.00	79.00
71	Carl Hubbell	300.00	150.00	90.00
72	Hugh Critz	115.00	57.00	34.00
73	John (Blondy) Ryan	115.00	57.00	34.00
74	Roger Cramer	125.00	62.00	37.00
75	Baxter Jordan	115.00	57.00	34.00
76	Ed Coleman	115.00	57.00	34.00
77	Julius Solters	115.00	57.00	34.00
78	Charles (Chick) Hafey	265.00	132.00	79.00
79	Larry French	115.00	57.00	34.00
80	Frank (Don) Hurst	115.00	57.00	34.00
81	Gerald Walker	115.00	57.00	34.00
82	Ernie Lombardi	265.00	132.00	79.00
83	Walter (Huck) Betts	115.00	57.00	34.00
84	Luke Appling	265.00	132.00	79.00
85	John Frederick	115.00	57.00	34.00
86	Fred Walker	115.00	57.00	34.00
87	Tom Bridges	115.00	57.00	34.00
88	Dick Porter	115.00	57.00	34.00
89	John Stone	115.00	57.00	34.00
90	James (Tex) Carleton	115.00	57.00	34.00
91	Joe Stripp	115.00	57.00	34.00
92	Lou Gehrig	3900.	1950.	1170.
93	George Earnshaw	115.00	57.00	34.00
94	Oscar Melillo	115.00	57.00	34.00
95	Oral Hildebrand	115.00	57.00	34.00
96	John Allen	115.00	57.00	34.00

1936 World Wide Gum (Canadian Goudey, V355)

This black and white Canadian set was issued by World Wide Gum in 1936. The cards measure approximately 2-1/2" by 2-7/8", and the set includes both portrait and action photos. The card number and player's name (appearing in all capital letters) are printed inside a white box below the photo.

		NR MT	EX	VG
Complete Set (134):		22250.	10250.	6150.
Common Player:		125.00	62.00	37.00
1	Jimmy Dykes	300.00	150.00	90.00
2	Paul Waner	285.00	142.00	85.00
3	Cy Blanton	125.00	62.00	37.00
4	Sam Leslie	125.00	62.00	37.00
5	Johnny Louis Vergez	125.00	62.00	37.00
6	Arky Vaughan	285.00	142.00	85.00
7	Bill Terry	285.00	142.00	85.00
8	Joe Moore	125.00	62.00	37.00
9	Gus Mancuso	125.00	62.00	37.00
10	Fred Marberry	125.00	62.00	37.00
11	George Selkirk	125.00	62.00	37.00
12	Spud Davis	125.00	62.00	37.00
13	Chuck Klein	285.00	142.00	85.00
14	Fred Fitzsimmons	125.00	62.00	37.00
15	Bill Delancey	125.00	62.00	37.00
16	Billy Herman	285.00	142.00	85.00
17	George Davis	125.00	62.00	37.00
18	Rip Collins	125.00	62.00	37.00
19	Dizzy Dean	550.00	275.00	165.00
20	Roy Parmelee	125.00	62.00	37.00
21	Vic Sorrell	125.00	62.00	37.00
22	Harry Danning	125.00	62.00	37.00
23	Hal Schumacher	125.00	62.00	37.00
24	Cy Perkins	125.00	62.00	37.00
25	Speedy Durocher	300.00	150.00	90.00
26	Glenn Myatt	125.00	62.00	37.00
27	Bob Seeds	125.00	62.00	37.00
28	Jimmy Ripple	125.00	62.00	37.00
29	Al Schacht	125.00	62.00	37.00
30	Pete Fox	125.00	62.00	37.00
31	Del Baker	125.00	62.00	37.00
32	Flea Clifton	125.00	62.00	37.00
33	Tommy Bridges	125.00	62.00	37.00
34	Bill Dickey	350.00	175.00	105.00
35	Wally Berger	125.00	62.00	37.00
36	Slick Castleman	125.00	62.00	37.00
37	Dick Bartell	125.00	62.00	37.00
38	Red Rolfe	125.00	62.00	37.00
39	Waite Hoyt	285.00	142.00	85.00
40	Wes Ferrell	125.00	62.00	37.00
41	Hank Greenberg	375.00	187.00	112.00
42	Charlie Gehringer	285.00	142.00	85.00
43	Goose Goslin	285.00	142.00	85.00
44	Schoolboy Rowe	125.00	62.00	37.00
45	Mickey Cochrane	300.00	150.00	90.00
46	Joe Cronin	285.00	142.00	85.00
47	Jimmie Foxx	350.00	175.00	105.00
48	Jerry Walker	125.00	62.00	37.00
49	Charlie Gelbert	125.00	62.00	37.00
50	Roy Hayworth (Ray)	125.00	62.00	37.00
51	Joe DiMaggio	3000.	1500.	900.00
52	Billy Rogell	125.00	62.00	37.00
53	Joe McCarthy	300.00	150.00	90.00
54	Phil Cavaretta (Cavarretta)	125.00	62.00	37.00
55	Kiki Cuyler	285.00	142.00	85.00
56	Lefty Gomez	300.00	150.00	90.00
57	Gabby Hartnett	285.00	142.00	85.00
58	Johnny Marcum	125.00	62.00	37.00
59	Burgess Whitehead	125.00	62.00	37.00
60	Whitey Whitehill	125.00	62.00	37.00
61	Buckey Walters	125.00	62.00	37.00
62	Luke Sewell	125.00	62.00	37.00
63	Joey Kuhel	125.00	62.00	37.00
64	Lou Finney	125.00	62.00	37.00
65	Fred Lindstrom	285.00	142.00	85.00
66	Paul Derringer	125.00	62.00	37.00
67	Steve O'Neil (O'Neill)	125.00	62.00	37.00
68	Mule Haas	125.00	62.00	37.00
69	Freck Owen	125.00	62.00	37.00
70	Wild Bill Hallahan	125.00	62.00	37.00
71	Bill Urbanski	125.00	62.00	37.00
72	Dan Taylor	125.00	62.00	37.00
73	Heinie Manush	285.00	142.00	85.00
74	Jo-Jo White	125.00	62.00	37.00
75	Mickey Medwick (Ducky)	285.00	142.00	85.00
76	Joe Vosmik	125.00	62.00	37.00
77	Al Simmons	285.00	142.00	85.00
78	Shag Shaughnessy	125.00	62.00	37.00
79	Harry Smythe	125.00	62.00	37.00
80	Benny Tate	125.00	62.00	37.00
81	Billy Rhiel	125.00	62.00	37.00
82	Lauri Myllykangas	125.00	62.00	37.00
83	Ben Sankey	125.00	62.00	37.00
84	Crip Polli	125.00	62.00	37.00
85	Jim Bottomley	285.00	142.00	85.00
86	William Clark	125.00	62.00	37.00
87	Ossie Bluege	125.00	62.00	37.00
88	Lefty Grove	300.00	150.00	90.00
89	Charlie Grimm	125.00	62.00	37.00
90	Ben Chapman	125.00	62.00	37.00
91	Frank Crosetti	200.00	100.00	60.00
92	John Pomorski	125.00	62.00	37.00
93	Jesse Haines	285.00	142.00	85.00
94	Chick Hafey	285.00	142.00	85.00
95	Tony Piet	125.00	62.00	37.00
96	Lou Gehrig	3600.	1800.	1080.
97	Bill Jurges	125.00	62.00	37.00
98	Smead Jolley	125.00	62.00	37.00
99	Jimmy Wilson	125.00	62.00	37.00
100	Lonnie Warneke	125.00	62.00	37.00
101	Lefty Tamulis	125.00	62.00	37.00
102	Charlie Ruffing	285.00	142.00	85.00
103	Earl Grace	125.00	62.00	37.00
104	Rox Lawson	125.00	62.00	37.00
105	Stan Hack	125.00	62.00	37.00
106	August Galan	125.00	62.00	37.00
107	Frank Frisch	285.00	142.00	85.00
108	Bill McKechnie	285.00	142.00	85.00
109	Bill Lee	125.00	62.00	37.00
110	Connie Mack	300.00	150.00	90.00
111	Frank Reiber	125.00	62.00	37.00
112	Zeke Bonura	125.00	62.00	37.00
113	Luke Appling	285.00	142.00	85.00
114	Monte Pearson	125.00	62.00	37.00
115	Bob O'Farrell	125.00	62.00	37.00
116	Marvin Duke	125.00	62.00	37.00
117	Paul Florence	125.00	62.00	37.00
118	John Berley	125.00	62.00	37.00
119	Tom Oliver	125.00	62.00	37.00
120	Norman Kies	125.00	62.00	37.00
121	Hal King	125.00	62.00	37.00
122	Tom Abernathy	125.00	62.00	37.00
123	Phil Hensick	125.00	62.00	37.00
124	Roy Schalk (Ray)	285.00	142.00	85.00
125	Paul Dunlap	125.00	62.00	37.00
126	Benny Bates	125.00	62.00	37.00
127	George Puccinelli	125.00	62.00	37.00
128	Stevie Stevenson	125.00	62.00	37.00
129	Rabbit Maranville	285.00	142.00	85.00
130	Bucky Harris	285.00	142.00	85.00
131	Al Lopez	285.00	142.00	85.00
132	Buddy Myer	125.00	62.00	37.00
133	Cliff Bolton	125.00	62.00	37.00
134	Estel Crabtree	125.00	62.00	37.00

1988 Worth Jose Canseco

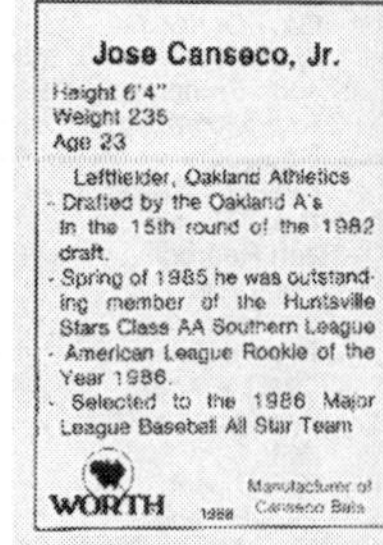

Jose Canseco, Jr.
Height 6'4"
Weight 235
Age 23
Leftfielder, Oakland Athletics
- Drafted by the Oakland A's in the 15th round of the 1982 draft.
- Spring of 1985 he was outstanding member of the Huntsville Stars Class AA Southern League
- American League Rookie of the Year 1986.
- Selected to the 1986 Major League Baseball All Star Team
WORTH 1988 Manufacturer of Canseco Bats

This one-card "set" was issued in conjunction with Jose Canseco's endorsement of Worth bats in 1988. Printed in black-and-white on thin cardboard, the front features a photo of Canseco in civilian clothes with a white facsimile autograph at the bottom. His name appears in black block letters at the bottom. The back has a few biographical details and career highlights, along with the Worth logo. The card measures the standard 2-1/2" x 3-1/2". Thousands of the card made their way into the hobby via one New York dealer at the time of issue and it remains common today.

	MT	NR MT	EX
Jose Canseco	.50	.40	.20

1928 Yeungling's Ice Cream

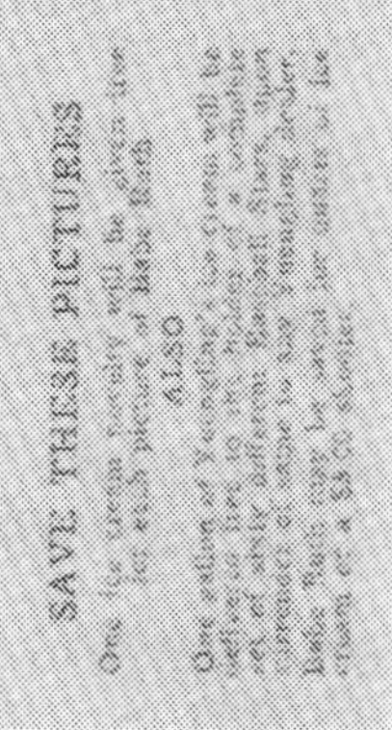

Issued in 1928, the Yeungling's Ice Cream issue consists of 60 black and white cards that measure 1-3/8" by 2-1/2". The photos are similar to those used in the E210 and W502 sets. Other ice cream companies such as Harrington's and Tharp's produced sets closely related to the Yeungling's issue. Collectors could redeem an entire set of Yeungling's cards for a gallon of ice cream or turn in a Babe Ruth card from the set for quarts of ice cream or a scooter valued at $5.

		NR MT	EX	VG
Complete Set:		2900.	1450.	870.00
Common Player:		25.00	12.50	7.50
1	Burleigh Grimes	40.00	20.00	12.00
2	Walter Reuther	25.00	12.50	7.50
3	Joe Dugan	25.00	12.50	7.50
4	Red Faber	40.00	20.00	12.00
5	Gabby Hartnett	40.00	20.00	12.00
6	Babe Ruth	650.00	325.00	195.00
7	Bob Meusel	25.00	12.50	7.50
8	Herb Pennock	40.00	20.00	12.00
9	George Burns	25.00	12.50	7.50
10	Joe Sewell	40.00	20.00	12.00
11	George Uhle	25.00	12.50	7.50
12	Bob O'Farrell	25.00	12.50	7.50
13	Rogers Hornsby	125.00	60.00	40.00
14	"Pie" Traynor	40.00	20.00	12.00
15	Clarence Mitchell	25.00	12.50	7.50
16	Eppa Rixey	40.00	20.00	12.00
17	Carl Mays	25.00	12.50	7.50

18	Adolfo Luque	25.00	12.50	7.50
19	Dave Bancroft	40.00	20.00	12.00
20	George Kelly	40.00	20.00	12.00
21	Earl (Earle) Combs	40.00	20.00	12.00
22	Harry Heilmann	40.00	20.00	12.00
23	Ray W. Schalk	40.00	20.00	12.00
24	Johnny Mostil	25.00	12.50	7.50
25	Hack Wilson	40.00	20.00	12.00
26	Lou Gehrig	400.00	200.00	120.00
27	Ty Cobb	400.00	200.00	120.00
28	Tris Speaker	55.00	27.00	16.50
29	Tony Lazzeri	40.00	20.00	12.00
30	Waite Hoyt	40.00	20.00	12.00
31	Sherwood Smith	25.00	12.50	7.50
32	Max Carey	25.00	12.50	7.50
33	Eugene Hargrave	25.00	12.50	7.50
34	Miguel L. Gonzales	25.00	12.50	7.50
35	Joe Judge	25.00	12.50	7.50
36	E.C. (Sam) Rice	40.00	20.00	12.00
37	Earl Sheely	25.00	12.50	7.50
38	Sam Jones	25.00	12.50	7.50
39	Bib (Bibb) A. Falk	25.00	12.50	7.50
40	Willie Kamm	25.00	12.50	7.50
41	Stanley Harris	40.00	20.00	12.00
42	John J. McGraw	40.00	20.00	12.00
43	Artie Nehf	25.00	12.50	7.50
44	Grover Alexander	55.00	27.00	16.50
45	Paul Waner	40.00	20.00	12.00
46	William H. Terry	40.00	20.00	12.00
47	Glenn Wright	25.00	12.50	7.50
48	Earl Smith	25.00	12.50	7.50
49	Leon (Goose) Goslin	40.00	20.00	12.00
50	Frank Frisch	40.00	20.00	12.00
51	Joe Harris	25.00	12.50	7.50
52	Fred (Cy) Williams	25.00	12.50	7.50
53	Eddie Roush	40.00	20.00	12.00
54	George Sisler	40.00	20.00	12.00
55	Ed. Rommel	25.00	12.50	7.50
56	Roger Peckinpaugh	25.00	12.50	7.50
57	Stanley Coveleskie (Coveleski)	40.00	20.00	12.00
58	Lester Bell	25.00	12.50	7.50
59	Lloyd Waner	40.00	20.00	12.00
60	John P. McInnis	25.00	12.50	7.50

1959 Yoo-Hoo

Issued as a promotion for Yoo-Hoo chocolate flavored soft drink (it's a New York thing), this issue features five New York Yankees players. The black-and-white blank-backed cards measure 2-7/16" x 5-1/8", including a tab at the bottom which could be redeemed for various prizes. The top of the card features a posed spring training photo and includes a facsimile autograph and "Me for Yoo-Hoo" slogan. Prices shown here are for complete cards; cards without tabs would be valued at one-half of these figures. A Mickey Mantle advertising piece in larger size is often collected as an adjunct to the set, but no card of Mantle was issued. The Berra card is considerably scarcer than the others.

		NR MT	EX	VG
Complete Set (5):		750.00	375.00	225.00
Common Player:		75.00	37.00	22.00
(1)	Yogi Berra	400.00	200.00	120.00
(2)	Whitey Ford	150.00	75.00	45.00
(3)	Tony Kubek	75.00	37.00	22.00
(4)	Gil McDougald	75.00	37.00	22.00
(5)	Bill Skowron	90.00	45.00	27.00

A player's name in italic type indicates a rookie card. An (FC) indicates a player's first card for that particular card company.

1993 Yoo-Hoo

The Yoo Hoo beverage company, which had a promotional affiliation with Yogi Berra as far back as the 1950's, made Berra the #1 card in a 1993 set of 20 baseball legends that was released in two series. All of the players included in the set are retired, and all but five are Hall of Famers (at this printing). The

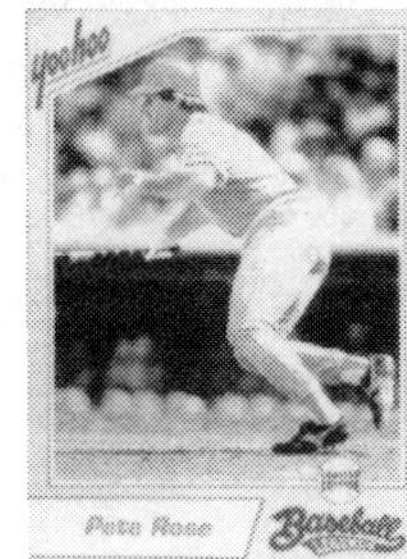

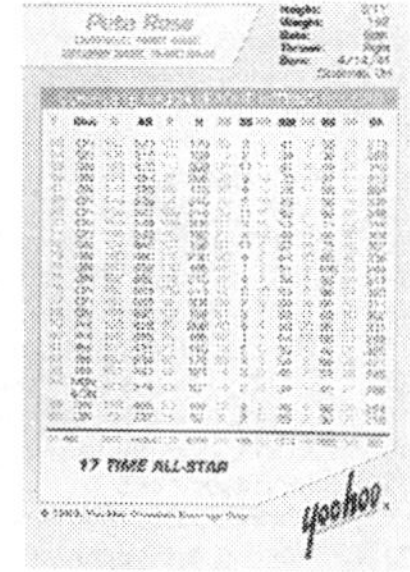

unnumbered cards feature a yellow border with a color photo on the front; the backs have the player's statistics and biographical information.

		MT	NR MT	EX
Complete Set:		10.00	7.50	4.00
Common Player:		.25	.20	.10
	Series I			
(1)	Yogi Berra	.75	.60	.30
(2)	Joe Morgan	.35	.25	.14
(3)	Duke Snider	.75	.60	.30
(4)	Steve Garvey	.30	.25	.12
(5)	Jim Rice	.25	.20	.10
(6)	Bob Feller	.45	.35	.20
(7)	Pete Rose	.60	.45	.25
(8)	Rod Carew	.60	.45	.25
(9)	Gaylord Perry	.40	.30	.15
(10)	Graig Netles	.25	.20	.10
	Series II			
(1)	Johnny Bench	.40	.30	.15
(2)	Lou Brock	.40	.30	.15
(3)	Stan Musial	1.00	.70	.40
(4)	Willie McCovey	.60	.45	.25
(5)	Whitey Ford	.50	.40	.20
(6)	Phil Rizzuto	.50	.40	.20
(7)	Tom Seaver	.60	.45	.25
(8)	Willie Stargell	.40	.30	.15
(9)	Brooks Robinson	.45	.35	.20
(10)	Al Kaline	.45	.35	.20

1994 Yoo-Hoo

		MT	NR MT	EX
Complete Set (20):		8.00	6.00	3.25
Common Player:		.25	.20	.10
1	Luis Aparicio	.35	.25	.14
2	Bobby Bonds	.25	.20	.10
3	Bob Boone	.25	.20	.10
4	Steve Carlton	.40	.30	.15
5	Roberto Clemente	1.00	.70	.40
6	Bob Gibson	.40	.30	.15
7	Keith Hernandez	.25	.20	.10
8	Jim Kaat	.25	.20	.10
9	Roger Maris	.75	.60	.30
10	Don Mattingly	.60	.45	.25
11	Thurman Munson	.60	.45	.25
12	Phil Rizzuto	.50	.40	.20
13	Brooks Robinson	.45	.35	.20
14	Ryne Sandberg	.60	.45	.25
15	Mike Schmidt	.60	.45	.25
16	Carl Yastrzemski	.45	.35	.20
17	Fact card	.25	.20	.10
18	Fact card	.25	.20	.10
19	Fact card	.25	.20	.10
20	Fact card	.25	.20	.10

1927 York Caramels Type I (E210)

Issued in 1927 by the York Caramel Co. of York, Pa., these black and white cards are among the last of the caramel issues. Measuring 1-3/8" by 2-1/2",

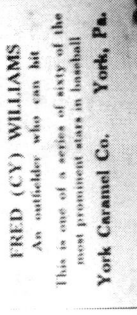

they are similar in appearance to earlier candy and tobacco cards. The front of the card carries the player's name in capital letters beneath the photo preceded by a number in parenthesis. The back also lists the player's name in capital letters, along with a brief phrase describing him and the line "This is one of a series of sixty of the most prominent stars in baseball." The bottom of the cards reads "York Caramel Co. York, Pa." The set includes several variations and is desgniated in the ACC as E210. It is closely related to the W502 set of the same year. The E210-2s differ from the E210-1s in that the card stock is close to being glossy as opposed to the dull appearance of E210-1.

		NR MT	EX	VG
Complete Set:		5000.	2500.	1500.
Common Player:		32.00	16.00	9.50
1	Burleigh Grimes	90.00	45.00	25.00
2	Walter Reuther (Ruether)	32.00	16.00	9.50
3	Joe Duggan (Dugan)	40.00	20.00	12.00
4	Red Faber	70.00	35.00	21.00
5	Gabby Hartnett	70.00	35.00	21.00
6	Babe Ruth	1200.	600.00	360.00
7	Bob Meusel	40.00	20.00	12.00
8	Herb Pennock	70.00	35.00	21.00
9	George Burns	32.00	16.00	9.50
10	Joe Sewell	70.00	35.00	21.00
11	George Uhle	32.00	16.00	9.50
12	Bob O'Farrel (O'Farrell)	32.00	16.00	9.50
13	Rogers Hornsby	125.00	62.00	37.00
14	Pie Traynor	70.00	35.00	21.00
15	Clarence Mitchell	32.00	16.00	9.50
16	Eppa Jepha Rixey (Jeptha)	70.00	35.00	21.00
17	Carl Mays	40.00	20.00	12.00
18	Adolph Luque (Adolfo)	32.00	16.00	9.50
19	Dave Bancroft	70.00	35.00	21.00
20	George Kelly	70.00	35.00	21.00
21	Ira Flagstead	32.00	16.00	9.50
22	Harry Heilmann	70.00	35.00	21.00
23	Raymond W. Shalk (Schalk)	70.00	35.00	21.00
24	Johnny Mostil	32.00	16.00	9.50
25	Hack Wilson (photo actually Art Wilson)	70.00	35.00	21.00
26	Tom Zachary	32.00	16.00	9.50
27	Ty Cobb	800.00	400.00	240.00
28	Tris Speaker	90.00	45.00	27.00
29	Ralph Perkins	32.00	16.00	9.50
30	Jess Haines	70.00	35.00	21.00
31	Sherwood Smith (photo actually Jack Coombs)	32.00	16.00	9.50
32	Max Carey	70.00	35.00	21.00
33	Eugene Hargraves	32.00	16.00	9.50
34	Miguel L. Gonzales	32.00	16.00	9.50
35a	Clifton Heathcot (incorrect spelling)	32.00	16.00	9.50
35b	Clifton Heathcote (correct spelling)	32.00	16.00	9.50
36	E.C. (Sam) Rice	70.00	35.00	21.00
37	Earl Sheely	32.00	16.00	9.50
38	Emory E. Rigney	32.00	16.00	9.50
39	Bib A. Falk (Bibb)	32.00	16.00	9.50
40	Nick Altrock	32.00	16.00	9.50
41	Stanley Harris	70.00	35.00	21.00
42	John J. McGraw	80.00	40.00	24.00
43	Wilbert Robinson	70.00	35.00	21.00
44	Grover Alexander	80.00	40.00	24.00
45	Walter Johnson	150.00	75.00	45.00
46	William H. Terry (photo actually Zeb Terry)	90.00	45.00	27.00
47	Edward Collins	70.00	35.00	21.00
48	Marty McManus	32.00	16.00	9.50
49	Leon (Goose) Goslin	70.00	35.00	21.00
50	Frank Frisch	70.00	35.00	21.00
51	Jimmie Dykes	35.00	17.50	10.50
52	Fred (Cy) Williams	35.00	17.50	10.50
53	Eddie Roush	70.00	35.00	21.00
54	George Sisler	70.00	35.00	21.00
55	Ed Rommel	32.00	16.00	9.50
56	Rogers Peckinpaugh (Roger)	35.00	17.50	10.50
57	Stanley Coveleskie (Coveleski)	70.00	35.00	21.00
58	Clarence Gallaway (Galloway)	32.00	16.00	9.50
59	Bob Shawkey	35.00	17.50	10.50
60	John P. McInnis	45.00	16.00	9.50

1927 York Caramels Type II (E210)

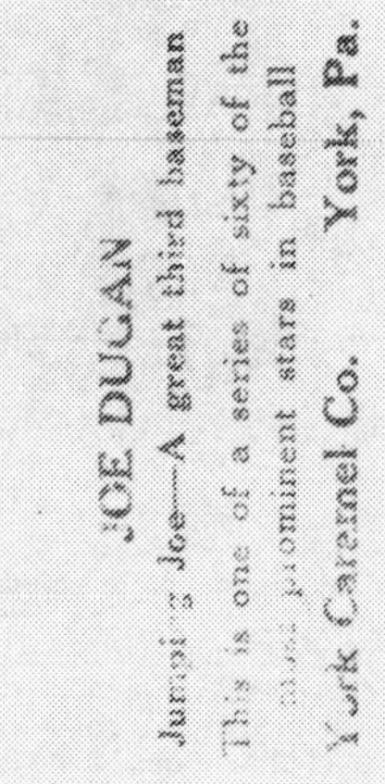

		NR MT	EX	VG
Complete Set:		3800.	1900.	1140.
Common Player:		50.00	25.00	15.00
1	Burleigh Grimes	90.00	45.00	27.00
2	Walter Reuther (Ruether)	50.00	25.00	15.00
3	Joe Dugan	60.00	30.00	18.00
6	Babe Ruth	1200.	600.00	360.00
12	Bob O'Farrell	50.00	25.00	15.00
14	Pie Traynor	90.00	45.00	27.00
16	Eppa Rixey	90.00	45.00	27.00
18	Adolfo Luque	50.00	25.00	15.00
22	Harry Heilmann	90.00	45.00	27.00
23	Ray W. Schalk	90.00	45.00	27.00
24	Johnny Mostil	50.00	25.00	15.00
27	Ty Cobb	800.00	400.00	240.00
29	Tony Lazzeri	75.00	37.00	22.00
31	Sherwood Smith (photo actually Jack Coombs)	50.00	25.00	15.00
32	Max Carey	90.00	45.00	27.00
33	Eugene Hargrave (Hargraves)	50.00	25.00	15.00
34	Miguel L. Gonzales	50.00	25.00	15.00
35	Joe Judge	50.00	25.00	15.00
40	Willie Kamm	50.00	25.00	15.00
43	Artie Nehf	50.00	25.00	15.00
46	William H. Terry (photo actually Zeb Terry)	110.00	55.00	33.00
51	Joe Harris	50.00	25.00	15.00
54	George Sisler	90.00	45.00	27.00
55	Ed Rommel	50.00	25.00	15.00
57	Stanley Coveleskie (Coveleski)	90.00	45.00	27.00
58	Lester Bell	45.00	25.00	15.00

1888 Yum Yum Tobacco (N403)

An extremely rare series of tobacco cards, this set was issued in 1888 by August Beck & Co. of Chicago. The cards, which vary slightly in size but average 1-3/8" by 2-3/4", were distributed in packages of the company's Yum Yum smoking and chewing tobacco. Yum Yum cards carry the American Card Catalog designation N403 and are found in two distinct types: photographic portraits and full-length action drawings that appear to be copied from photos used in the Old Judge sets of the same period. In both types, the player's name and position appear in capital letters below the photo, while the very bottom of the card states: "Smoke and Chew "Yum Yum" Tobacco. A. Beck & Co. Chicago, Ill." Players from all eight National League clubs, plus Brooklyn of the American Association, are included in the set.

		NR MT	EX	VG
Complete Set:		40000.	20000.	12500.
Common Line Drawing:		600.00	300.00	175.00
Common Portrait:		750.00	375.00	230.00
(1)	Cap Anson	10000.	5000.	3000.
(2)	Lady Baldwin	600.00	300.00	175.00
(3)	Dan Brouthers	1000.	500.00	300.00
(4)	Bill "California" Brown	600.00	300.00	175.00
(5)	Buffington (Buffinton)	600.00	300.00	180.00
(6)	Thomas Burns (portrait)	750.00	375.00	230.00
(7)	Thomas Burns (with bat)	600.00	300.00	175.00
(8)	John Clarkson (portrait)	1800.	900.00	550.00
(9)	John Clarkson (throwing)	1000.	500.00	300.00
(10)	John Coleman	750.00	375.00	230.00
(11)	Larry Corcoran	750.00	375.00	230.00
(12)	Tido Daily (Daly) (photo actually Billy Sunday)	750.00	375.00	230.00
(13)	Tom Deasley	750.00	375.00	230.00
(14)	Mike Dorgan	750.00	375.00	230.00
(15)	Buck Ewing (portrait)	1800.	900.00	550.00
(16)	Buck Ewing (with bat)	1000.	500.00	300.00
(17)	Silver Flint	750.00	375.00	230.00
(18)	Pud Galvin	1000.	500.00	300.00
(19)	Joe Gerhardt	750.00	375.00	230.00
(20)	Pete Gillespie	750.00	375.00	230.00
(21)	Pebbly Jack Glasscock	600.00	300.00	175.00
(22)	Ed Greer	750.00	375.00	230.00
(23)	Tim Keefe (pitching)	1000.	500.00	300.00
(24)	Tim Keefe (portrait)	1800.	900.00	550.00
(25)	King Kelly	1200.	600.00	350.00
26	King Kelly (photo)	5000.	2500.	1500.
(27)	Gus Krock	750.00	375.00	230.00
(28)	Connie Mack	1400.	700.00	425.00
(29)	Kid Madden	600.00	300.00	175.00
(30)	Doggie Miller	600.00	300.00	175.00
(31)	Billy Nash	600.00	300.00	175.00
(32)	O'Rourke (portrait)	1800.	900.00	550.00
(33)	O'Rourke (with bat)	1000.	500.00	300.00
(34)	Danny Richardson	750.00	375.00	230.00
(35)	Chief Roseman	750.00	375.00	230.00
(36)	Jimmy Ryan (portrait)	750.00	375.00	230.00
(37)	Jimmy Ryan (throwing)	600.00	300.00	175.00
(38)	Little Bill Sowders	600.00	300.00	175.00
(39)	Marty Sullivan	750.00	375.00	230.00
(40)	Billy Sunday (line drawing)	900.00	450.00	275.00
(41)	Billy Sunday (portrait)	1500.	750.00	450.00
(42)	Ezra Sutton	600.00	300.00	175.00
(43)	Tiernan (portrait)	750.00	375.00	230.00
(44)	Tiernan (with bat)	600.00	300.00	175.00
(45)	Rip Van Haltren (photo not Van Haltren)	750.00	375.00	230.00
(46)	Mickey Welch (hands clasped at chest)	1000.	500.00	300.00
(47)	Mickey Welch (portrait)	1800.	900.00	550.00
(48)	Mickey Welch (right arm extended)	1000.	500.00	300.00
(49)	Grasshopper Whitney	600.00	300.00	175.00
(50)	George "Dandy" Wood	600.00	300.00	175.00

1982 Zellers Expos

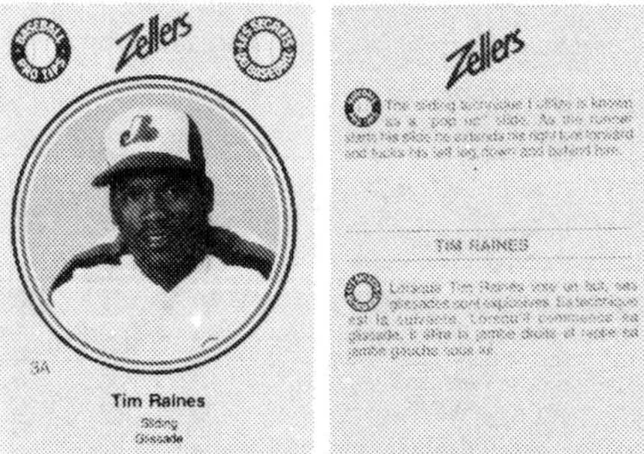

Produced and distributed by the Zellers department stores in Canada, this 60-card set was produced in the form of 20 three-card panels. The cards feature a photo of the player surrounded by rings and a yellow background. A red "Zellers" is above the photo and on either side of it are the words "Baseball Pro Tips" in English on the left and in French on the right. The player's name and the title of the playing tip are under the photo. Backs have the playing tip in both languages. Single cards measure 2-1/2" by 3-1/2" while the whole panel is 7-1/2" by 3-1/2". Although a number of stars are depicted, this set is not terribly popular as collectors do not generally like the playing tips idea. Total panels are worth more than separated cards.

		MT	NR MT	EX
Complete Set:		16.00	12.00	6.50
Common Player:		.40	.30	.15
1	Gary Carter (Catching Position)	1.50	1.25	.60
2	Steve Rogers (Pitching Stance)	.50	.40	.20
3	Tim Raines (Sliding)	1.25	.90	.50
4	Andre Dawson (Batting Stance)	2.00	1.50	.80
5	Terry Francona (Contact Hitting)	.40	.30	.15
6	Gary Carter (Fielding Pop Fouls)	1.50	1.25	.60
7	Warren Cromartie (Fielding at First Base)	.40	.30	.15
8	Chris Speier (Fielding at Shortstop)	.40	.30	.15
9	Billy DeMars (Signals)	.40	.30	.15
10	Andre Dawson (Batting Stroke)	2.00	1.50	.80
11	Terry Francona (Outfield Throws)	.40	.30	.15
12	Woodie Fryman (Holding the Runner-Left Handed)	.40	.30	.15
13	Gary Carter (Fielding Low Balls)	1.50	1.25	.60
14	Andre Dawson (Playing Centerfield)	2.00	1.50	.80
15	Bill Gullickson (The Slurve)	.50	.40	.20
16	Gary Carter (Catching Stance)	1.50	1.25	.60
17	Scott Sanderson (Fielding as a Pitcher)	.40	.30	.15
18	Warren Cromartie (Handling Bad Throws)	.40	.30	.15
19	Gary Carter (Hitting Stride)	1.50	1.25	.60
20	Ray Burris (Holding the Runner-Right Handed)	.40	.30	.15

1978 Zest Soap

Produced by Topps for a Zest Soap promotion, the five cards in this set are almost identical to the regular 1978 Topps issue, except the backs are printed in both Spanish and English and the card numbers are different. The cards measure 2-1/2" by 3-1/2". Because of the player selection and the bilingual backs, it seems obvious that this set was aimed at the Hispanic community.

		NR MT	EX	VG
Complete Set:		6.00	3.00	1.75
Common Player:		.90	.45	.25
1	Joaquin Andujar	1.25	.60	.40
2	Bert Campaneris	1.50	.70	.45
3	Ed Figueroa	.90	.45	.25
4	Willie Montanez	.90	.45	.25
5	Manny Mota	1.50	.70	.45

1992 Ziploc

Dow Brands produced an 11-card set of All-Stars in 1992 that featured mostly Hall of Famers, with the exception only of Nellie Fox. The cards were included in specially-marked Ziploc packages, and also could be purchased by mail.

		MT	NR MT	EX
Complete Set (11):		7.00	5.25	2.75
Common Player:		.50	.40	.20
1	Warren Spahn	.50	.40	.20
2	Bob Gibson	.50	.40	.20
3	Rollie Fingers	.50	.40	.20
4	Carl Yastrzemski	.75	.60	.30
5	Brooks Robinson	.75	.60	.30
6	Pee Wee Reese	.60	.45	.25
7	Willie McCovey	.60	.45	.25
8	Willie Mays	1.00	.70	.40
9	Nellie Fox	.50	.40	.20
10	Yogi Berra	.75	.60	.30
11	Hank Aaron	1.00	.70	.40

Regional interest may affect the value of a card.

Grading Guide

Mint (MT): A perfect card. Well-centered with all corners sharp and square. No creases, stains, edge nicks, surface marks, yellowing or fading.

Near Mint (NM): A nearly perfect card. At first glance, a NM card appears to be perfect. May be slightly off-center. No surface marks, creases or loss of gloss.

Excellent (EX): Corners are still fairly sharp with only moderate wear. Borders may be off-center. No creases or stains on fronts or backs, but may show slight loss of surface luster.

Very Good (VG): Shows obvious handling. May have rounded corners, minor creases, major gum or wax stains. No major creases, tape marks, writing, etc.

Good (G): A well-worn card, but exhibits no intentional damage. May have major or multiple creases. Corners may be rounded well beyond card border.

MINOR LEAGUE ISSUES

1960 Armour Meats Denver Bears

Ten cards from this Class AA farm team of the Detroit Tigers have been checklisted, with others possibly to be discovered. The black-and-white blank-backed cards measure 2-1/2" x 3-1/4" and appear to have been issued on some manner of perforated sheet. The unnumbered cards are checklisted here alphabetically.

		NR MT	EX	VG
Complete Set:		650.00	325.00	195.00
Common Player:		75.00	37.00	22.00
(1)	George Alusik	75.00	37.00	22.00
(2)	Tony Bartirome	75.00	37.00	22.00
(3)	Edward J. Donnelly	75.00	37.00	22.00
(4)	James R. McDaniel	75.00	37.00	22.00
(5)	Charlie Metro	75.00	37.00	22.00
(6)	Harry Perkowski	75.00	37.00	22.00
(7)	Vernon E. Rapp	75.00	37.00	22.00
(8)	James Stump	75.00	37.00	22.00
(9)	Ozzie Virgil	75.00	37.00	22.00
(10)	Robert Walz	75.00	37.00	22.00

Values for recent cards and sets are listed in Mint (MT), Near Mint (NM), reflecting the fact that many cards from recent years have been preserved in top condition. Recent cards and sets in less than Excellent condition have little collector interest.

1940 Associated Stations San Francisco Seals

This album and sticker set was created as a premium by a Northern California gas company. Individual stickers were given away each week at participating service stations. The blank-backed, 1-3/4" x 2-5/8" stickers have the player's name in a black strip at the bottom. Pages in the accompanying 3-1/2" x 6" album have space for an autograph and a few career highlights for each player. The checklist is presented in page order of the album.

		NR MT	EX	VG
Complete Set With Album:		250.00	125.00	75.00
Common Player:		10.00	5.00	3.00
Album:		50.00	25.00	15.00
(1)	"Lefty" O'Doul	25.00	12.50	7.50
(2)	Sam Gibson	10.00	5.00	3.00
(3)	Brooks Holder	10.00	5.00	3.00
(4)	Ted Norbert	10.00	5.00	3.00
(5)	Win Ballou	10.00	5.00	3.00
(6)	Al Wright	10.00	5.00	3.00
(7)	Al Epperly	10.00	5.00	3.00
(8)	Orville Jorgens	10.00	5.00	3.00
(9)	Larry Powell	10.00	5.00	3.00
(10)	Joe Sprinz	10.00	5.00	3.00
(11)	Harvey Storey	10.00	5.00	3.00
(12)	Jack Burns	10.00	5.00	3.00
(13)	Bob Price	10.00	5.00	3.00
(14)	Larry Guay	10.00	5.00	3.00
(15)	Frank Dasso	10.00	5.00	3.00
(16)	Eddie Stutz	10.00	5.00	3.00
(17)	John Barrett	10.00	5.00	3.00
(18)	Eddie Botelho	10.00	5.00	3.00
(19)	Ferris Fain	20.00	10.00	6.00
(20)	Larry Woodall	10.00	5.00	3.00
(21)	Ted Jennings	10.00	5.00	3.00
(22)	Jack Warner	10.00	5.00	3.00
(23)	Wil Leonard	10.00	5.00	3.00
(24)	Gene Kiley	10.00	5.00	3.00
(25)	Bob Jensen	10.00	5.00	3.00

1910 A.W.H. Caramels Virginia League (E222)

This rare set of cards picturing players from the Virginia League was issued by the A.W.H. Caramel Company in 1910. The cards measure 1-1/2" by 2-3/4" and feature player portraits in either red, black, brown, or blue and white. To date examples of 10 different cards have been found. The set carries the ACC designation of E222. The front of the card displays the player's last name and team below his photo. The back states "A.W.H. Brand Caramels" in large letters with "Base Ball Series/Va. State League" below.

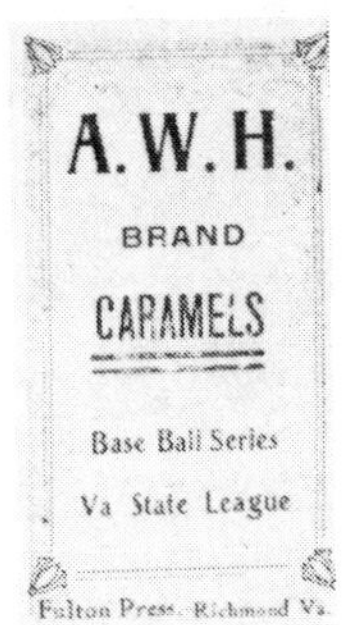

		NR MT	EX	VG
Complete Set:		4000.	2000.	1200.
Common Player:		450.00	198.00	117.00
(1)	Tom Guiheen	450.00	198.00	117.00
(2)	Hooker	450.00	198.00	117.00
(3)	Ison	450.00	198.00	117.00
(4)	McCauley	450.00	198.00	117.00
(5)	Otey	450.00	198.00	117.00
(6)	Revelle	450.00	198.00	117.00
(7)	Ryan	450.00	198.00	117.00
(8)	Shaugnessy	450.00	198.00	117.00
(9)	Sieber	450.00	198.00	117.00
(10)	Smith	450.00	198.00	117.00
(11)	Titman	450.00	198.00	117.00

1961 Bee Hive Starch Toronto Maple Leafs

This 24-card set features players of the Toronto Maple Leafs, an independent team in the International League which featured future Hall of Fame Manager Sparky Anderson as its second baseman. The black-and-white cards are printed on thin, blank-backed stock and measure approximately 2-1/2" x 3-1/4". As the cards are not numbered, the checklist below is presented alphabetically.

		NR MT	EX	VG
Complete Set:		500.00	250.00	150.00
Common Player:		16.00	8.00	4.75
(1)	George Anderson	150.00	75.00	45.00
(2)	Fritzie Brickell	16.00	8.00	4.75
(3)	Ellis Burton	16.00	8.00	4.75
(4)	Bob Chakales	16.00	8.00	4.75
(5)	Rip Coleman	16.00	8.00	4.75
(6)	Steve Demeter	16.00	8.00	4.75
(7)	Joe Hannah	16.00	8.00	4.75
(8)	Earl Hersh	16.00	8.00	4.75
(9)	Lou Jackson	16.00	8.00	4.75
(10)	Ken Johnson	16.00	8.00	4.75
(11)	Lou Johnson	16.00	8.00	4.75
(12)	John Lipon	16.00	8.00	4.75
(13)	Carl Mathias	16.00	8.00	4.75
(14)	Bill Moran	16.00	8.00	4.75
(15)	Ron Negray	16.00	8.00	4.75
(16)	Herb Plews	16.00	8.00	4.75
(17)	Dave Pope	16.00	8.00	4.75
(18)	Steve Ridzik	16.00	8.00	4.75
(19)	Raul Sanchez	16.00	8.00	4.75
(20)	Pat Scantlebury	16.00	8.00	4.75
(21)	Bill Smith	16.00	8.00	4.75
(22)	Bob Smith	16.00	8.00	4.75
(23)	Chuck Tanner	45.00	22.00	13.50
(24)	Tim Thompson	16.00	8.00	4.75

1911 Big Eater Sacramento Solons

This very rare set was issued circa 1911 and includes only members of the Pacific Coast League Sacramento Solons. The black-and-white cards measure 2-1/8" by 4" and feature action photos. The lower part of the card contains a three-line caption that includes the player's last name, team designation (abbreviated to "Sac'to"), and the promotional line: "He Eats 'Big Eaters'." (Although the exact origin is undetermined, it is believed that "Big Eaters" were a candy novelty.)

		NR MT	EX	VG
Complete Set:		2750.	1375.	825.00
Common Player:		110.00	55.00	33.00
(1)	Arellanes	110.00	55.00	33.00
(2)	Baum	110.00	55.00	33.00
(3)	Byram	110.00	55.00	33.00
(4)	Danzig	110.00	55.00	33.00
(5)	Fitzgerald	110.00	55.00	33.00
(6)	Gaddy	110.00	55.00	33.00
(7)	Heister	110.00	55.00	33.00
(8)	Hunt	110.00	55.00	33.00
(9)	Kerns	110.00	55.00	33.00
(10)	LaLonge	110.00	55.00	33.00
(11)	Lerchen	110.00	55.00	33.00
(12)	Lewis	110.00	55.00	33.00
(13)	Mahoney	110.00	55.00	33.00
(14)	Nebinger	110.00	55.00	33.00
(15)	O'Rourke	110.00	55.00	33.00
(16)	Shinn	110.00	55.00	33.00
(17)	Thomas	110.00	55.00	33.00
(18)	Thompson	110.00	55.00	33.00
(19)	Thornton	110.00	55.00	33.00
(20)	Van Buren	110.00	55.00	33.00

Grading Guide

Mint (MT): A perfect card. Well-centered with all corners sharp and square. No creases, stains, edge nicks, surface marks, yellowing or fading.

Near Mint (NM): A nearly perfect card. At first glance, a NM card appears to be perfect. May be slightly off-center. No surface marks, creases or loss of gloss.

Excellent (EX): Corners are still fairly sharp with only moderate wear. Borders may be off-center. No creases or stains on fronts or backs, but may show slight loss of surface luster.

Very Good (VG): Shows obvious handling. May have rounded corners, minor creases, major gum or wax stains. No major creases, tape marks, writing, etc.

Good (G): A well-worn card, but exhibits no intentional damage. May have major or multiple creases. Corners may be rounded well beyond card border.

1910 Bishop & Co. P.C.L. Teams (E221)

A very rare issue, this series of team pictures of clubs in the Pacific Coast League, was distributed by Bishop & Compnay of Los Angeles in 1910. The team photos were printed on a thin, newsprint-type paper that measures an elongated 2-3/4" x 10". Although there were six teams in the PCL at the time, only five clubs have been found - Los Angeles, San Francisco, Portland, Vernon and Oakland. The sixth team, Sacramento, was apparently never issued. The cards indicate that they were issued with five-cent packages of Bishop's Milk Chocolate and that the photos were taken by the Los Angeles Examiner. The black-and-white team photos are found with either a red or green background. The set has been designated E221.

		NR MT	EX	VG
Complete Set:		6000.	3000.	1800.
Common Team:		1200.	600.00	360.00
(1)	Los Angeles	1200.	600.00	360.00
(2)	Oakland	1200.	600.00	360.00
(3)	Portland	1200.	600.00	360.00
(4)	San Francisco	1200.	600.00	360.00
(5)	Vernon	1200.	600.00	360.00

1910 Bishop & Co. P.C.L. (E99)

Briggs, c. f. Sacramento

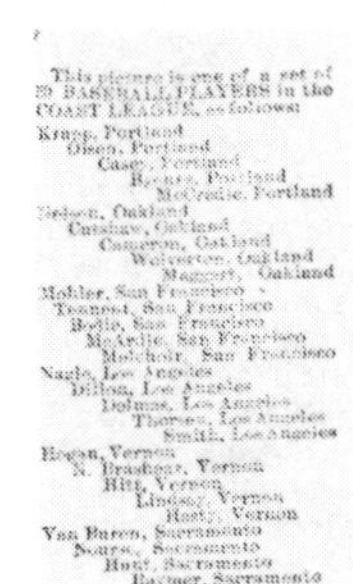

This picture is one of a set of 30 BASEBALL PLAYERS in the COAST LEAGUE, as follows:
Krapp, Portland
Olsen, Portland
Casey, Portland
Byones, Portland
McCredie, Portland
Nelson, Oakland
Cutshaw, Oakland
Cameron, Oakland
Wolverton, Oakland
Maggert, Oakland
Mohler, San Francisco
Tennent, San Francisco
Bodie, San Francisco
McArdle, San Francisco
Melchoir, San Francisco
Nagle, Los Angeles
Dillon, Los Angeles
Delmas, Los Angeles
Thorsen, Los Angeles
Smith, Los Angeles
Hogan, Vernon
N. Brashear, Vernon
Hitt, Vernon
Lindsay, Vernon
Hasty, Vernon
Van Buren, Sacramento
Nourse, Sacramento
Hunt, Sacramento
Raymer, Sacramento
Briggs, Sacramento

The first of two obscure sets produced by the Los Angeles candy maker Bishop & Co., this 30-card set was issued in 1910 and depicts players from the Pacific Coast League, showing five players from each of the six teams. The cards measure approximately 1-1/2" x 2-3/4" and feature black and white player photos with colored backgrounds (either green, blue, purple or yellow). The player's last name, position and team appear along the bottom. The backs of the cards contain the complete checklist in groups of five, according to team, with each name indented slightly more than the name above. Cards in the 1910 set, which has been designated E99 by the ACC, do not contain the name "Bishop & Company, California" along the bottom on the back.

		NR MT	EX	VG
Complete Set:		10000.	4500.	2500.
Common Player:		250.00	125.00	75.00
(1)	Bodie	350.00	175.00	95.00
(2)	N. Brashear	250.00	125.00	75.00
(3)	Briggs	250.00	125.00	75.00
(4)	Byones (Byrnes)	250.00	125.00	75.00
(5)	Cameron	250.00	125.00	75.00
(6)	Casey	250.00	125.00	75.00
(7)	Cutshaw	250.00	125.00	75.00
(8)	Delmas	250.00	125.00	75.00
(9)	Dillon	250.00	125.00	75.00
(10)	Hasty	250.00	125.00	75.00
(11)	Hitt	250.00	125.00	75.00
(12)	Hap. Hogan	250.00	125.00	75.00
(13)	Hunt	250.00	125.00	75.00
(14)	Krapp	250.00	125.00	75.00
(15)	Lindsay	250.00	125.00	75.00
(16)	McArdle	250.00	125.00	75.00
(17)	McCredie (McCreedle)	250.00	125.00	75.00
(18)	Maggert	250.00	125.00	75.00
(19)	Melchoir	250.00	125.00	75.00
(20)	Mohler	250.00	125.00	75.00
(21)	Nagle	250.00	125.00	75.00
(22)	Nelson	250.00	125.00	75.00
(23)	Nourse	250.00	125.00	75.00
(24)	Olsen	250.00	125.00	75.00
(25)	Raymer	250.00	125.00	75.00
(26)	Smith	250.00	125.00	75.00
(27)	Tennent (Tennant)	250.00	125.00	75.00
(28)	Thorsen	250.00	125.00	75.00
(29)	Van Buren	250.00	125.00	75.00
(30)	Wolverton	250.00	125.00	75.00

1911 Bishop & Co. P.C.L. Type I (E100)

Suter, p. San Francisco

This picture is one of a set of 30 BASEBALL PLAYERS in the COAST LEAGUE, as follows
Seaton, Portland
Steen, Portland
Rapps, Portland
Peckinpaugh, Portland
McCredie, Portland
Tozer, Los Angeles
Delhi, Los Angeles
Daley, Los Angeles
Delmas, Los Angeles
Moore, Los Angeles
Tennant, San Francisco
Mohler, San Francisco
Powell, San Francisco
Suter, San Francisco
Weaver, San Francisco
Hap Hogan, Vernon
Burrell, Vernon
Carlisle, Vernon
Hitt, Vernon
Patterson, Vernon
Pfyle, Oakland
Cutshaw, Oakland
Nelson, Oakland
Pearce, Oakland
Wares, Oakland
Baum, Sacramento
Danzig, Sacramento
O'Rourke, Sacramento
Thomas, Sacramento
Lerchen, Sacramento
Bishop & Company, California

This 30-card set, designated E100 by the ACC, was issued in 1911 by the California confectioner Bishop & Company of Los Angeles, which had produced a similar set a year earlier. Both sets showcased star players from the Pacific Coast League. The cards measure approximately 1-1/2" x 2-3/4" and feature black-and-white photos with a background of either green, blue, yellow or red. The backs contain the complete checklist of the set, listing the players in groups of five by team, with one line indented slightly more than the previous one. In addition to the checklist, the 1911 set can be differentiated from the previous year because the line "Bishop & Company, California" appears along the bottom. Variations have been discovered in recent years for many of the cards in the E100 set. The variations, known as "Type II" have either orange or green backgrounds with more tightly cropped photos and blank backs.

		NR MT	EX	VG
Complete Set:		82000.	41000.	24600.
Common Player:		250.00	125.00	75.00
(1)	Spider Baum	250.00	125.00	75.00
(2)	Burrell	250.00	125.00	75.00
(3)	Carlisle	250.00	125.00	75.00
(4)	Cutshaw	250.00	125.00	75.00
(5)	Pete Daley	250.00	125.00	75.00
(6)	Danzig	250.00	125.00	75.00
(7)	Delhi	250.00	125.00	75.00
(8)	Delmas	250.00	125.00	75.00
(9)	Hitt	250.00	125.00	75.00
(10)	Hap Hogan (actually Walter Bray)	250.00	125.00	75.00
(11)	Lerchen	250.00	125.00	75.00
(12)	McCreddie (McCreedie)	250.00	125.00	75.00
(13)	Mohler	250.00	125.00	75.00
(14)	Moore	250.00	125.00	75.00
(15)	Slim Nelson	250.00	125.00	75.00
(16)	P. O'Rourke	250.00	125.00	75.00
(17)	Patterson	250.00	125.00	75.00
(18)	Bunny Pearce	250.00	125.00	75.00
(19)	Peckinpaugh	250.00	125.00	60.00
(20)	Monte Pfyle (Pfyl)	250.00	125.00	75.00
(21)	Powell	250.00	125.00	75.00
(22)	Rapps	250.00	125.00	75.00
(23)	Seaton	250.00	125.00	75.00
(24)	Steen	250.00	125.00	75.00
(25)	Suter	250.00	125.00	75.00
(26)	Tennant	250.00	125.00	75.00
(27)	Thomas	250.00	125.00	75.00
(28)	Tozer	250.00	125.00	75.00
(29)	Clyde Wares	250.00	125.00	75.00
(30)	Weaver	700.00	350.00	210.00

Grading Guide

Mint (MT): A perfect card. Well-centered with all corners sharp and square. No creases, stains, edge nicks, surface marks, yellowing or fading.

Near Mint (NM): A nearly perfect card. At first glance, a NM card appears to be perfect. May be slightly off-center. No surface marks, creases or loss of gloss.

Excellent (EX): Corners are still fairly sharp with only moderate wear. Borders may be off-center. No creases or stains on fronts or backs, but may show slight loss of surface luster.

VeryGood (VG) : Shows obvious handling. May have rounded corners, minor creases, major gum or wax stains. No major creases, tape marks, writing, etc.

Good (G): A well-worn card, but exhibits no intentional damage. May have major or multiple creases. Corners may be rounded well beyond card border.

1911 Bishop & Co. P.C.L. Type II (E100)

Sutor, p., Frisco.

		NR MT	EX	VG
Complete Set:		4750.	2375.	1425.
Common Player:		225.00	112.00	67.00
(1)	Burrell	225.00	112.00	67.00
(2)	Danzig	225.00	112.00	67.00
(3)	Delhi	225.00	112.00	67.00
(4)	Hitt	225.00	112.00	67.00
(5)	Lerchen	225.00	112.00	67.00
(6)	McCreddie	225.00	112.00	67.00
(7)	Slim Nelson	225.00	112.00	67.00
(8)	P. O'Rourke	225.00	112.00	67.00
(9)	Patterson	225.00	112.00	67.00
(10)	Bunny Pearce	225.00	112.00	67.00
(11)	Monte Pfyle	225.00	112.00	67.00
(12)	Rapps	225.00	112.00	67.00
(13)	Seaton	225.00	112.00	67.00
(14)	Steen	225.00	112.00	67.00
(15)	Suter	225.00	112.00	67.00
(16)	Tennant	225.00	112.00	67.00
(17)	Weaver	600.00	300.00	180.00

1958 Bond Bread Buffalo Bisons

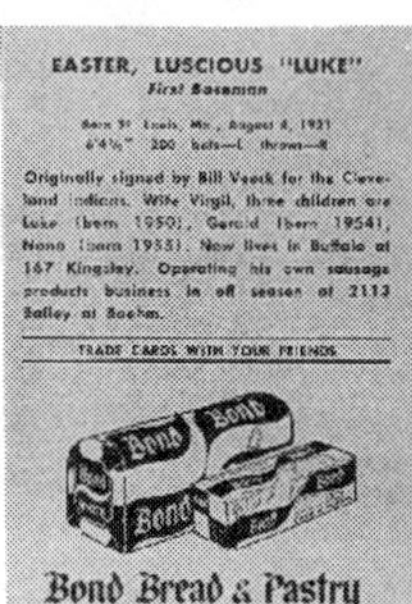

Nine members of the International League affiliate of the Kansas City Athletics are featured in this set. The 2-1/2" x 3-1/2" cards are printed on very thin cardboard. Fronts have a black-and-white player photo, the player's name and position, and an ad for a TV Western. Card backs are printed in red and blue and include a few biographical details and a career summary, along with an ad for bread and pastry.

		NR MT	EX	VG
Complete Set:		150.00	75.00	45.00
Common Player:		15.00	7.50	4.50
(1)	Al Aber	15.00	7.50	4.50
(2)	Joe Caffie	15.00	7.50	4.50
(3)	Phil Cavaretta	15.00	7.50	4.50
(4)	Rip Coleman	15.00	7.50	4.50
(5)	Luke Easter	35.00	17.50	10.50
(6)	Ken Johnson	15.00	7.50	4.50
(7)	Lou Ortiz	15.00	7.50	4.50
(8)	Jack Phillips	15.00	7.50	4.50
(9)	Jim Small	15.00	7.50	4.50

1949 Bowman Pacific Coast League

One of the scarcest issues of the post-war period, the 1949 Bowman PCL set was issued only on the West Coast. Like the 1949 Bowman regular issue, the cards contain black-and-white photos

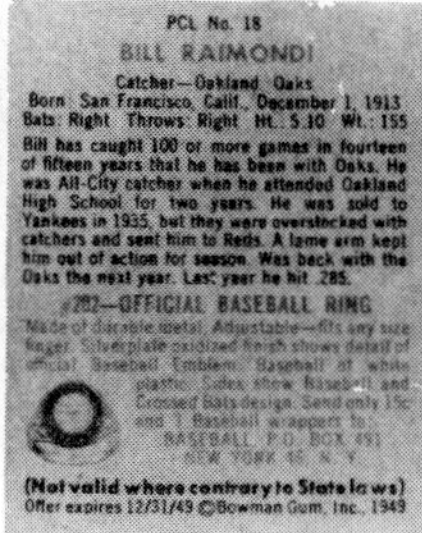

overprinted with various pastel colors. Thirty-six cards, which measure 2-1/16" x 2-1/2", make up the set. It is believed that the cards may have been issued only in sheets and not sold in gum packs.

		NR MT	EX	VG
Complete Set:		5500.	2750.	1650.
Common Player:		150.00	75.00	45.00
1	Lee Anthony	150.00	75.00	45.00
2	George Metkovich	150.00	75.00	45.00
3	Ralph Hodgin	150.00	75.00	45.00
4	George Woods	150.00	75.00	45.00
5	Xavier Rescigno	150.00	75.00	45.00
6	Mickey Grasso	150.00	75.00	45.00
7	Johnny Rucker	150.00	75.00	45.00
8	Jack Brewer	150.00	75.00	45.00
9	Dom D'Allessandro	150.00	75.00	45.00
10	Charlie Gassaway	150.00	75.00	45.00
11	Tony Freitas	150.00	75.00	45.00
12	Gordon Maltzberger	150.00	75.00	45.00
13	John Jensen	150.00	75.00	45.00
14	Joyner White	150.00	75.00	45.00
15	Harvey Storey	150.00	75.00	45.00
16	Dick Lajeski	150.00	75.00	45.00
17	Albie Glossop	150.00	75.00	45.00
18	Bill Raimondi	150.00	75.00	45.00
19	Ken Holcombe	150.00	75.00	45.00
20	Don Ross	150.00	75.00	45.00
21	Pete Coscarart	150.00	75.00	45.00
22	Tony York	150.00	75.00	45.00
23	Jake Mooty	150.00	75.00	45.00
24	Charles Adams	150.00	75.00	45.00
25	Les Scarsella	150.00	75.00	45.00
26	Joe Marty	150.00	75.00	45.00
27	Frank Kelleher	150.00	75.00	45.00
28	Lee Handley	150.00	75.00	45.00
29	Herman Besse	150.00	75.00	45.00
30	John Lazor	150.00	75.00	45.00
31	Eddie Malone	150.00	75.00	45.00
32	Maurice Van Robays	150.00	75.00	45.00
33	Jim Tabor	150.00	75.00	45.00
34	Gene Handley	150.00	75.00	45.00
35	Tom Seats	150.00	75.00	45.00
36	Ora Burnett	150.00	75.00	45.00

1933 Buffalo Bisons Jigsaw Puzzles

Produced as a stadium promotional giveaway, this set consists of 19 player puzzles and one for Hall of Fame Manager Ray Schalk. Each of the 11" x 14", 200-piece, black-and-white puzzles was produced in an edition of 10,000. Puzzles carried a red serial number, and certain numbers could be redeemed for tickets and other prizes. The known puzzles are checklisted below in alphabetical order.

		NR MT	EX	VG
Complete Set:		650.00	325.00	195.00
Common Player:		50.00	30.00	15.00
(1)	Joe Bartulis	50.00	30.00	15.00
(2)	Ollie Carnegie	50.00	30.00	15.00
(3)	Clyde "Buck" Crouse	50.00	30.00	15.00
(4)	Harry Danning	50.00	30.00	15.00
(5)	Gilbert English	50.00	30.00	15.00
(6)	Fred Fussell	50.00	30.00	15.00
(7)	Bob Gould	50.00	30.00	15.00
(8)	Len Koenecke	50.00	30.00	15.00
(9)	Clarence Mueller	50.00	30.00	15.00
(10)	Ray Schalk	75.00	37.50	22.50
(11)	Jack Smith	50.00	30.00	15.00
(12)	Roy Tarr	50.00	30.00	15.00
(13)	Johnny Wilson	50.00	30.00	15.00

1943 Centennial Flour Seattle Rainiers

The 25 cards in this 4" x 5" black-and-white set feature players of the Pacific Coast League Seattle Rainiers. Identical in format to the set issued in 1944, the '43s can be identified by the lines of type at the bottom of the card back reading, "Compliments of/CENTENNIAL FLOURING MILLS."

		NR MT	EX	VG
Complete Set:		1000.	500.00	300.00
Common Player:		40.00	20.00	12.00
(1)	John Babich	40.00	20.00	12.00
(2)	Nick Bonarigo ((Buonarigo))	40.00	20.00	12.00
(3)	Eddie Carnett	40.00	20.00	12.00
(4)	Lloyd Christopher	40.00	20.00	12.00
(5)	Joe Demoran	40.00	20.00	12.00
(6)	Joe Dobbins	40.00	20.00	12.00
(7)	Glenn Elliott	40.00	20.00	12.00
(8)	Carl Fischer	40.00	20.00	12.00
(9)	Leonard Gabrielson	40.00	20.00	12.00
(10)	Stanley Gray	40.00	20.00	12.00
(11)	Dick Gyselman	40.00	20.00	12.00
(12)	Jim Jewell	40.00	20.00	12.00
(13)	Syl Johnson	40.00	20.00	12.00
(14)	Pete Jonas	40.00	20.00	12.00
(15)	Bill Kats	40.00	20.00	12.00
(16)	Lynn King	40.00	20.00	12.00
(17)	Bill Lawrence	40.00	20.00	12.00
(18)	Clarence Marshall	40.00	20.00	12.00
(19)	Bill Matheson	40.00	20.00	12.00
(20)	Ford Mullen	40.00	20.00	12.00
(21)	Bill Skiff	40.00	20.00	12.00
(22)	Byron Speece	40.00	20.00	12.00
(23)	Hal Sueme	40.00	20.00	12.00
(24)	Hal Turpin	40.00	20.00	12.00
(25)	John Yelovic	40.00	20.00	12.00

1944 Centennial Flour Seattle Rainers

Identical in format to the previous year's issue, the 25 black-and-white 4" x 5" cards issued in 1944 can be differentiated from the 1943 set by the two lines of type at the bottom of each card's back. In the 1944 set, it reads, "Compliments of/CENTENNIAL HOTCAKE AND WAFFLE FLOUR."

		NR MT	EX	VG
Complete Set:		1000.	500.00	300.00
Common Player:		40.00	20.00	12.00
(1)	John Babich	40.00	20.00	12.00
(2)	Paul Carpenter	40.00	20.00	12.00
(3)	Lloyd Christopher	40.00	20.00	12.00
(4)	Joe Demoran	40.00	20.00	12.00
(5)	Joe Dobbins	40.00	20.00	12.00
(6)	Glenn Elliott	40.00	20.00	12.00
(7)	Carl Fischer	40.00	20.00	12.00
(8)	Bob Garbould ((Gorbould))	40.00	20.00	12.00
(9)	Stanley Gray	40.00	20.00	12.00
(10)	Dick Gyselman	40.00	20.00	12.00
(11)	Gene Holt	40.00	20.00	12.00
(12)	Roy Johnson	40.00	20.00	12.00
(13)	Syl Johnson	40.00	20.00	12.00
(14)	Al Libke	40.00	20.00	12.00
(15)	Bill Lyman	40.00	20.00	12.00
(16)	Bill Matheson	40.00	20.00	12.00
(17)	Jack McClure	40.00	20.00	12.00
(18)	Jimmy Ripple	40.00	20.00	12.00
(19)	Bill Skiff	40.00	20.00	12.00
(20)	Byron Speece	40.00	20.00	12.00
(21)	Hal Sueme	40.00	20.00	12.00
(22)	Frank Tincup	40.00	20.00	12.00
(23)	Jack Treece	40.00	20.00	12.00
(24)	Hal Turpin	40.00	20.00	12.00
(25)	Sicks Stadium	40.00	20.00	12.00

A player's name in italic type indicates a rookie card. An (FC) indicates a player's first card for that particular card company.

1945 Centennial Flour Seattle Rainiers

The 27 black-and-white cards in the third consecutive issue for this Pacific Coast League team are distinguished from the two previous issues by the borderless photo on the front and the fact that the name and team are printed in a black bar at the bottom. The set can be distinguished from the 1947 issue by virtue of the fact that the player biography on back is not surrounded by a frame. The cards measure slightly narrower but longer than the 1943-44 issues, at 3-7/8" x 5-1/8".

		NR MT	EX	VG
Complete Set:		1000.	500.00	300.00
Common Player:		40.00	20.00	12.00
(1)	Charley Aleno	40.00	20.00	12.00
(2)	Dick Briskey	40.00	20.00	12.00
(3)	John Carpenter	40.00	20.00	12.00
(4)	Joe Demoran	40.00	20.00	12.00
(5)	Joe Dobbins	40.00	20.00	12.00
(6)	Glenn Elliott	40.00	20.00	12.00
(7)	Bob Finley	40.00	20.00	12.00
(8)	Carl Fischer	40.00	20.00	12.00
(9)	Keith Frazier	40.00	20.00	12.00
(10)	Johnny Gill	40.00	20.00	12.00
(11)	Bob Gorbould	40.00	20.00	12.00
(12)	Chet Johnson	40.00	20.00	12.00
(13)	Syl Johnson	40.00	20.00	12.00
(14)	Bill Kats	40.00	20.00	12.00
(15)	Billy Lyman	40.00	20.00	12.00
(16)	Bill Matheson	40.00	20.00	12.00
(17)	George McDonald	40.00	20.00	12.00
(18)	Ted Norbert	40.00	20.00	12.00
(19)	Alex Palica	40.00	20.00	12.00
(20)	Joe Passero	40.00	20.00	12.00
(21)	Hal Patchett	40.00	20.00	12.00
(22)	Bill Skiff	40.00	20.00	12.00
(23)	Byron Speece	40.00	20.00	12.00
(24)	Hal Sueme	40.00	20.00	12.00
(25)	Eddie Taylor	40.00	20.00	12.00
(26)	Hal Turpin	40.00	20.00	12.00
(27)	Jack Whipple	40.00	20.00	12.00

1947 Centennial Flour Seattle Rainiers

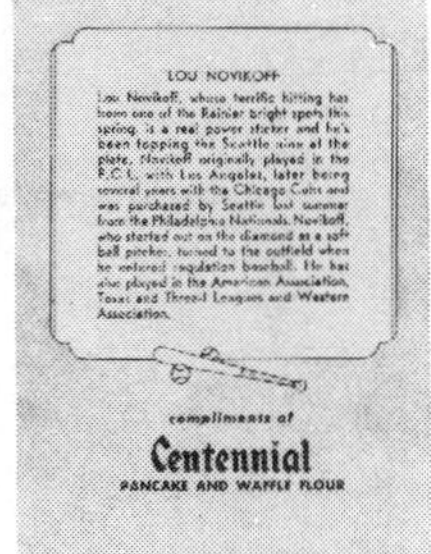

After a lapse of one year, Centennial Flour returned to issue a final black-and-white 32-card set for 1947. Identical in size (3-7/8"x5-1/8") and front format to the 1945 issue, the '47s can be identified by the white framed box on back containing the player's biography.

		NR MT	EX	VG
Complete Set:		850.00	425.00	250.00
Common Player:		30.00	15.00	9.00
(1)	Dick Barrett	40.00	20.00	12.00
(2)	Joe Buzas	30.00	15.00	9.00
(3)	Paul Carpenter	30.00	15.00	9.00
(4)	Rex Cecil	30.00	15.00	9.00
(5)	Tony Criscola	30.00	15.00	9.00
(6)	Walter Dubiel	30.00	15.00	9.00
(7)	Doug Ford	30.00	15.00	9.00
(8)	Rollie Hemsley	45.00	22.00	13.50
(9)	Jim Hill	30.00	15.00	9.00
(10)	Jim Hopper	30.00	15.00	9.00
(11)	Sigmund Jakucki	30.00	15.00	9.00
(12)	Bob Johnson	45.00	22.00	13.50
(13)	Pete Jonas	30.00	15.00	9.00
(14)	Joe Kaney	30.00	15.00	9.00
(15)	Hillis Layne	30.00	15.00	9.00
(16)	Lou Novikoff	45.00	22.00	13.50
(17)	Johnny O'Neil	30.00	15.00	9.00
(18)	John Orphal	30.00	15.00	9.00
(19)	Ike Pearson	30.00	15.00	9.00
(20)	Bill Posedel	30.00	15.00	9.00
(21)	Don Pulford	30.00	15.00	9.00
(22)	Tom Reis	30.00	15.00	9.00
(23)	Charley Ripple	30.00	15.00	9.00
(24)	Mickey Rocco	30.00	15.00	9.00
(25)	Johnny Rucker	30.00	15.00	9.00
(26)	Earl Sheely	30.00	15.00	9.00
(27)	Bob Stagg	30.00	15.00	9.00
(28)	Hal Sueme	30.00	15.00	9.00
(29)	Eddie Taylor	30.00	15.00	9.00

(30)	Ed Vanni	30.00	15.00	9.00
(31)	JoJo White	30.00		
(32)	Tony York	30.00		

1910 Contentnea 1st Series (T209)

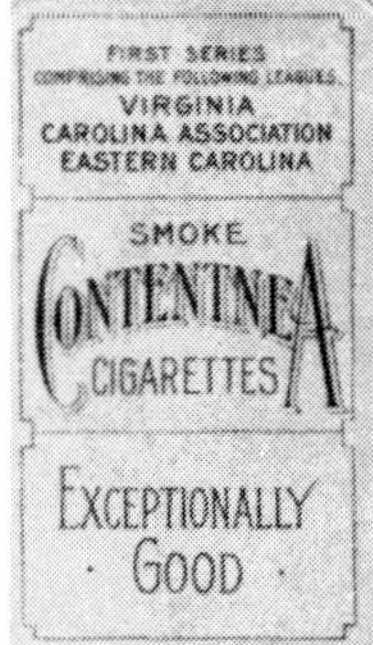

The 1910 Contentnea minor league set actually consists of two distinctively different series, both featuring players from the Virginia League, Carolina Association and Eastern Carolina League. The cards were distributed in packages of Contentnea cigarettes. The first series, featuring color photographs, consists of just 16 cards, each measuring 1-9/16" x 2-11/16". The front of the card has the player's last name and team printed at the bottom, while the back identifies the card as "First Series" and carries an advertisement for Contentnea cigarettes. The second series, believed to have been issued later in 1910, is a massive 221-card set consisting of black-and-white player photos. The cards in this series are slightly larger, measuring 1-5/8" x 2-3/4". They carry the words "Photo Series" on the back, along with the cigarette advertisement. Only a handful of the players in the Contentnea set ever advanced to the major leagues and the set contains no major stars. Subsequently, it generally holds interest only to collectors who specialize in the old Southern minor leagues.

		NR MT	EX	VG
Complete Set:		2000.	1000.	600.00
Common Player:		125.00	62.00	37.00
(1)	Armstrong	125.00	62.00	37.00
(2)	Booles	125.00	62.00	37.00
(3)	Bourquise (Bourquoise)	125.00	62.00	37.00
(4)	Cooper	125.00	62.00	37.00
(5)	Cowell	125.00	62.00	37.00
(6)	Crockett	125.00	62.00	37.00
(7)	Fullenwider	125.00	62.00	37.00
(8)	Gilmore	125.00	62.00	37.00
(9)	Hoffman	125.00	62.00	37.00
(10)	Lane	125.00	62.00	37.00
(11)	Martin	125.00	62.00	37.00
(12)	McGeehan	125.00	62.00	37.00
(13)	Pope	125.00	62.00	37.00
(14)	Sisson	125.00	62.00	37.00
(15)	Stubbe	125.00	62.00	37.00
(16)	Walsh	125.00	62.00	37.00

1910 Contentnea Photo Series (T209)

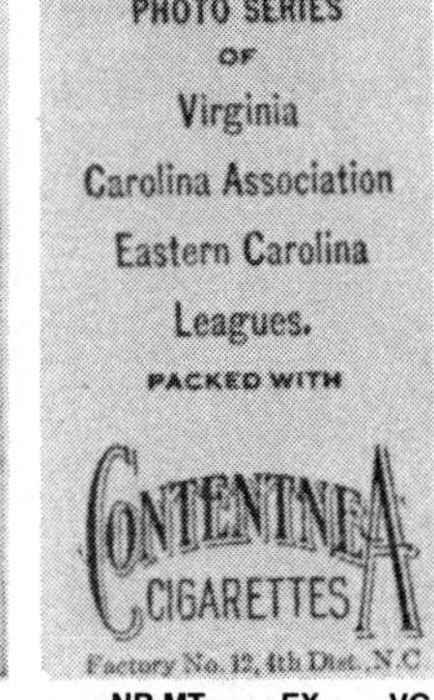

		NR MT	EX	VG
Complete Set:		6000.	3000.	1800.
Common Player:		30.00	15.00	9.00
(1)	Abercrombie	30.00	15.00	9.00
(2)	Andrada	30.00	15.00	9.00
(3)	Armstrong	30.00	15.00	9.00
(4)	Averett	30.00	15.00	9.00
(5)	Baker	30.00	15.00	9.00
(6)	Banner (Bonner)	30.00	15.00	9.00
(7)	Bausewein (Bansewein)	30.00	15.00	9.00
(8)	Beatty	30.00	15.00	9.00
(9)	Bentley	30.00	15.00	9.00
(10)	Beusse	30.00	15.00	9.00
(11)	Biel	30.00	15.00	9.00
(12)	Bigbie (Raleigh)	30.00	15.00	9.00
(13)	Bigbie (Richmond)	30.00	15.00	9.00
(14)	Blackstone	30.00	15.00	9.00
(15)	Bonner	30.00	15.00	9.00
(16)	Bourquin	30.00	15.00	9.00
(17)	Bowen	30.00	15.00	9.00
(18)	Boyle	30.00	15.00	9.00
(19)	Brandon	30.00	15.00	9.00
(20)	Brazelle (Brazell)	30.00	15.00	9.00
(21)	Brent	30.00	15.00	9.00
(22)	Brown	30.00	15.00	9.00
(23)	Busch	30.00	15.00	9.00
(24)	Bussey	30.00	15.00	9.00
(25)	Byrd	30.00	15.00	9.00
(26)	Cafalu (Cefalu)	30.00	15.00	9.00
(27)	Callahan	30.00	15.00	9.00
(28)	Chandler	30.00	15.00	9.00
(29)	Clapp	30.00	15.00	9.00
(30)	Clark (Clarke)	30.00	15.00	9.00
(31)	Clemens	30.00	15.00	9.00
(32)	Clunk	30.00	15.00	9.00
(33)	Cooper	30.00	15.00	9.00
(34)	Corbett	30.00	15.00	9.00
(35)	Cote	30.00	15.00	9.00
(36)	Coutts	30.00	15.00	9.00
(37)	Cowan (Cowen)	30.00	15.00	9.00
(38)	Cowells (Cowell)	30.00	15.00	9.00
(39)	Creagan (Cregan)	30.00	15.00	9.00
(40)	Crockett	30.00	15.00	9.00
(41)	Cross	30.00	15.00	9.00
(42)	Dailey	30.00	15.00	9.00
(43)	C. Derrck (Derrick)	30.00	15.00	9.00
(44)	F. Derrick	30.00	15.00	9.00
(45)	Doak (Greensboro)	30.00	15.00	9.00
(46)	Doak (Wilmington)	30.00	15.00	9.00
(47)	Dobard	30.00	15.00	9.00
(48)	Dobson	30.00	15.00	9.00
(49)	Doyle	30.00	15.00	9.00
(50)	Drumm	30.00	15.00	9.00
(51)	Duvie	30.00	15.00	9.00
(52)	Ebinger	30.00	15.00	9.00
(53)	Eldridge	30.00	15.00	9.00
(54)	Evvans	30.00	15.00	9.00
(55)	Fairbanks	30.00	15.00	9.00
(56)	Farmer	30.00	15.00	9.00
(57)	Ferrell	30.00	15.00	9.00
(58)	Fisher	30.00	15.00	9.00
(59)	Flowers	30.00	15.00	9.00
(60)	Fogarty	30.00	15.00	9.00
(61)	Foltz	30.00	15.00	9.00
(62)	Foreman	30.00	15.00	9.00
(63)	Forque	30.00	15.00	9.00
(64)	Francis	30.00	15.00	9.00
(65)	Fulton	30.00	15.00	9.00
(66)	Galvin	30.00	15.00	9.00
(67)	Gardin	30.00	15.00	9.00
(68)	Garman	30.00	15.00	9.00
(69)	Gastmeyer	30.00	15.00	9.00
(70)	Gaston	30.00	15.00	9.00
(71)	Gates	30.00	15.00	9.00
(72)	Gehring	30.00	15.00	9.00
(73)	Gillespie	30.00	15.00	9.00
(74)	Gorham	30.00	15.00	9.00
(75)	Griffin (Danville)	30.00	15.00	9.00
(76)	Griffin (Lynchburg)	30.00	15.00	9.00
(77)	Guiheen	30.00	15.00	9.00
(78)	Gunderson	30.00	15.00	9.00
(79)	Hale	30.00	15.00	9.00
(80)	Halland (Holland)	30.00	15.00	9.00
(81)	Hamilton	30.00	15.00	9.00
(82)	Hammersley	30.00	15.00	9.00
(83)	Handiboe	30.00	15.00	9.00
(84)	Hannifen (Hannifan)	30.00	15.00	9.00
(85)	Hargrave	30.00	15.00	9.00
(86)	Harrington	30.00	15.00	9.00
(87)	Harris	30.00	15.00	9.00
(88)	Hart	30.00	15.00	9.00
(89)	Hartley	30.00	15.00	9.00
(90)	Hawkins	30.00	15.00	9.00
(91)	Hearne (Hearn)	30.00	15.00	9.00
(92)	Hicks	30.00	15.00	9.00
(93)	Hobbs	30.00	15.00	9.00
(94)	Hoffman	30.00	15.00	9.00
(95)	Hooker	30.00	15.00	9.00
(96)	Howard	30.00	15.00	9.00
(97)	Howedel (Howedell)	30.00	15.00	9.00
(98)	Hudson	30.00	15.00	9.00
(99)	Humphrey	30.00	15.00	9.00
(100)	Hyames	30.00	15.00	9.00
(101)	Irvine	30.00	15.00	9.00
(102)	Irving	30.00	15.00	9.00
(103)	Jackson (Greensboro)	30.00	15.00	9.00
(104)	Jackson (Spartanburg)	30.00	15.00	9.00
(105)	Jenkins (Greenville)	30.00	15.00	9.00
(106)	Jenkins (Roanoke)	30.00	15.00	9.00
(107)	Jobson	30.00	15.00	9.00
(108)	Johnson	30.00	15.00	9.00
(109)	Keating	30.00	15.00	9.00
(110)	Kelley	30.00	15.00	9.00
(111)	Kelly (Anderson)	30.00	15.00	9.00
(112)	Kelly (Goldsboro)	30.00	15.00	9.00
(113)	"King" Kelly	30.00	15.00	9.00
(114)	King	30.00	15.00	9.00
(115)	Kite	30.00	15.00	9.00
(116)	Kunkle	30.00	15.00	9.00
(117)	Landgraff	30.00	15.00	9.00
(118)	Lane	30.00	15.00	9.00
(119)	Lathrop	30.00	15.00	9.00
(120)	Lavoia	30.00	15.00	9.00
(121)	Levy	30.00	15.00	9.00
(122)	Lloyd	30.00	15.00	9.00
(123)	Loval	30.00	15.00	9.00
(124)	Lucia	30.00	15.00	9.00
(125)	Luyster	30.00	15.00	9.00
(126)	MacConachie	30.00	15.00	9.00
(127)	Malcolm	30.00	15.00	9.00
(128)	Martin	30.00	15.00	9.00
(129)	Mayberry	30.00	15.00	9.00
(130)	A. McCarthy	30.00	15.00	9.00
(131)	J. McCarthy	30.00	15.00	9.00
(132)	McCormick	30.00	15.00	9.00
(133)	McFarland	30.00	15.00	9.00
(134)	McFarlin	30.00	15.00	9.00
(135)	C. McGeehan	30.00	15.00	9.00
(136)	Dan McGeehan	30.00	15.00	9.00
(137)	McHugh	30.00	15.00	9.00
(138)	McKeavitt (McKevitt)	30.00	15.00	9.00
(139)	Merchant	30.00	15.00	9.00
(140)	Midkiff	30.00	15.00	9.00
(141)	Miller	30.00	15.00	9.00
(142)	Missitt	30.00	15.00	9.00
(143)	Morgan	30.00	15.00	9.00
(144)	Morrissey (Morrisey)	30.00	15.00	9.00
(145)	Mullany (Mullaney)	30.00	15.00	9.00
(146)	Mullinix	30.00	15.00	9.00
(147)	Mundell	30.00	15.00	9.00
(148)	Munsen (Munson)	30.00	15.00	9.00
(149)	Murdock (Murdoch)	30.00	15.00	9.00
(150)	Newton	30.00	15.00	9.00
(151)	Noojin	30.00	15.00	9.00
(152)	Novak	30.00	15.00	9.00
(153)	Ochs	30.00	15.00	9.00
(154)	Painter	30.00	15.00	9.00
(155)	Peloguin	30.00	15.00	9.00
(156)	Phealean (Phelan)	30.00	15.00	9.00
(157)	Phoenix	30.00	15.00	9.00
(158)	Powell	30.00	15.00	9.00
(159)	Presley (Pressley, Pritchard	30.00	15.00	9.00
(160)	Priest	30.00	15.00	9.00
(161)	Prim	30.00	15.00	9.00
(162)	Pritchard	30.00	15.00	9.00
(163)	Rawe (Rowe)	30.00	15.00	9.00
(164)	Redfern (Redfearn)	30.00	15.00	9.00
(165)	Reggy	30.00	15.00	9.00
(166)	Richardson	30.00	15.00	9.00
(167)	Rickard	30.00	15.00	9.00
(168)	Rickert	30.00	15.00	9.00
(169)	Ridgeway (Ridgway)	30.00	15.00	9.00
(170)	Roth	30.00	15.00	9.00
(171)	Salve	30.00	15.00	9.00
(172)	Schmidt	30.00	15.00	9.00
(173)	Schrader	30.00	15.00	9.00
(174)	Schumaker	30.00	15.00	9.00
(175)	Sexton	30.00	15.00	9.00
(176)	Shanghnessy (Shaughnessy)	30.00	15.00	9.00
(177)	Sharp	30.00	15.00	9.00
(178)	Shaw	30.00	15.00	9.00
(179)	Simmons	30.00	15.00	9.00
(180)	A. Smith	30.00	15.00	9.00
(181)	D. Smith	30.00	15.00	9.00
(182)	Spratt	30.00	15.00	9.00
(183)	Springs	30.00	15.00	9.00
(184)	Stewart	30.00	15.00	9.00
(185)	Stoehr	30.00	15.00	9.00
(186)	Stouch	30.00	15.00	9.00
(187)	Sullivan	30.00	15.00	9.00
(188)	Swindell	30.00	15.00	9.00
(189)	Taxis	30.00	15.00	9.00
(190)	Templin	30.00	15.00	9.00
(191)	Thompson	30.00	15.00	9.00
(192)	B.E. Thompson	30.00	15.00	9.00
(193)	Tiedeman	30.00	15.00	9.00
(194)	Titman	30.00	15.00	9.00
(195)	Toner	30.00	15.00	9.00
(196)	Turner	30.00	15.00	9.00
(197)	Tydeman	30.00	15.00	9.00
(198)	Vail	30.00	15.00	9.00
(199)	Verbout	30.00	15.00	9.00
(200)	Vickery	30.00	15.00	9.00
(201)	Walker (Norfolk)	30.00	15.00	9.00
(202)	Walker (Spartanburg)	30.00	15.00	9.00
(203)	Wallace	30.00	15.00	9.00
(204)	Walsh	30.00	15.00	9.00
(205)	Walters	30.00	15.00	9.00
(206)	Watters	30.00	15.00	9.00
(207)	Waymack	30.00	15.00	9.00
(208)	Webb	30.00	15.00	9.00
(209)	Wehrell	30.00	15.00	9.00
(210)	Weldon	30.00	15.00	9.00
(211)	Welsher	30.00	15.00	9.00
(212)	Westlake	30.00	15.00	9.00
(213)	Williams	30.00	15.00	9.00
(214)	Willis	30.00	15.00	9.00
(215)	Wingo	30.00	15.00	9.00
(216)	Wolf	30.00	15.00	9.00
(217)	Wood	30.00	15.00	9.00
(218)	Woolums	30.00	15.00	9.00
(219)	Workman	30.00	15.00	9.00
(220)	Wright	30.00	15.00	9.00
(221)	Wynne	30.00	15.00	9.00

1940 Crowley's Milk

Nine members of the Binghampton, N.Y., Eastern League team are known in this set of 3" x 5" cards. Some have been seen with stamped postcard backs. Blue-and-white player photos are framed by a red rendition of a ballpark scene on the front of the unnumbered cards. Each card has a facsimile autograph ostensibly written by the pictured player. It is unknown whether the checklist below is complete. Several of the players later appeared with the N.Y. Yankees and other teams.

		NR MT	EX	VG
Complete Set:		650.00	325.00	195.00
Common Player:		75.00	37.50	22.50
(1)	Jimmy Adlam	75.00	37.00	22.00
(2)	Russ Bergman	75.00	37.00	22.00
(3)	Jack Graham	75.00	37.00	22.00
(4)	Al Gurske	75.00	37.00	22.00

		NR MT	EX	VG
(5)	Mike Milosevich	75.00	37.00	22.00
(6)	Aaron Robinson	75.00	37.00	22.00
(7)	Frankie Silvanic	75.00	37.00	22.00
(8)	Pete Suder	75.00	37.00	22.00
(9)	Ray Volps	75.00	37.00	22.00

1959 Darigold Farms Spokane Indians

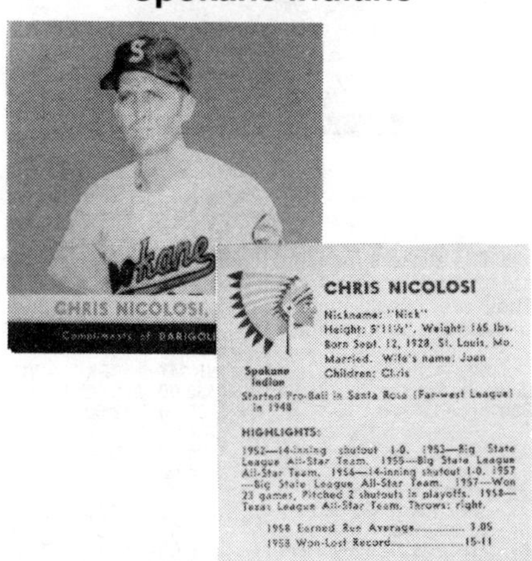

The 22 unnumbered cards in this set were glued to milk cartons by a folded tab at the top of each card. The basic card measures 2-1/2" x 2-3/8", with a 2-1/2" x 2-1/8" tab. Black-and-white player photos are set against colored backgrounds of yellow (1-8), red (9-16) and blue (17-22). Player biographical details and stats are printed in black on the back.

		NR MT	EX	VG
Complete Set:		475.00	240.00	140.00
Common Player:		20.00	10.00	6.00
(1)	Facundo Barragan	20.00	10.00	6.00
(2)	Steve Bilko	25.00	12.50	7.50
(3)	Bobby Bragan	30.00	15.00	9.00
(4)	Chuck Churn	20.00	10.00	6.00
(5)	Tom Davis	40.00	20.00	12.00
(6)	Dom Domenichelli	20.00	10.00	6.00
(7)	Bob Giallombardo	20.00	10.00	6.00
(8)	Connie Grob	20.00	10.00	6.00
(9)	Fred Hatfield	20.00	10.00	6.00
(10)	Bob Lillis	25.00	12.50	7.50
(11)	Lloyd Merritt	20.00	10.00	6.00
(12)	Larry Miller	20.00	10.00	6.00
(13)	Chris Nicolosi	20.00	10.00	6.00
(14)	Allen Norris	20.00	10.00	6.00
(15)	Phil Ortega	20.00	10.00	6.00
(16)	Phillips Paine	20.00	10.00	6.00
(17)	Bill Parsons	20.00	10.00	6.00
(18)	Hisel Patrick	20.00	10.00	6.00
(19)	Tony Roig	20.00	10.00	6.00
(20)	Tom Saffell	20.00	10.00	6.00
(21)	Norm Sherry	25.00	12.50	7.50
(22)	Ben Wade	20.00	10.00	6.00

1960 Darigold Farms Spokane Indians

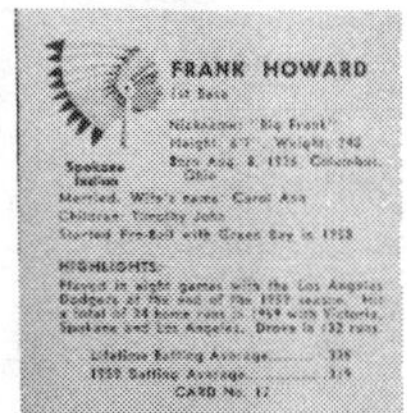

For its second annual baseball card set, the dairy added two cards, for a total of 24, and numbered the issue on the back. Card fronts were black-and-white photos against colored backgrounds of yellow (1-8), green (9-16) and red (17-24). A facsimile autograph appears on the front, as well. The basic card measures 2-3/8" x 2-11/16", with a folded 2-3/8" x 2-1/16" tab at the top, by which the card was glued to a milk carton. Backs are black-and-white.

		NR MT	EX	VG
Complete Set:		425.00	210.00	125.00
Common Player:		15.00	7.50	4.50
1	Chris Nicolosi	15.00	7.50	4.50
2	Jim Pagliaroni	15.00	7.50	4.50
3	Roy Smalley	15.00	7.50	4.50
4	Bill Bethel	15.00	7.50	4.50
5	Joe Liscio	15.00	7.50	4.50
6	Curt Roberts	15.00	7.50	4.50
7	Ed Palmquist	15.00	7.50	4.50
8	Willie Davis	45.00	22.00	13.50
9	Bob Giallombardo	15.00	7.50	4.50
10	Pedro Gomez	15.00	7.50	4.50
11	Mel Nelson	15.00	7.50	4.50
12	Charlie Smith	15.00	7.50	4.50
13	Clarence Churn	15.00	7.50	4.50
14	Ramon Conde	15.00	7.50	4.50
15	George O'Donnell	15.00	7.50	4.50
16	Tony Roig	15.00	7.50	4.50
17	Frank Howard	50.00	25.00	15.00
18	Billy Harris	15.00	7.50	4.50
19	Mike Brumley	15.00	7.50	4.50
20	Earl Robinson	15.00	7.50	4.50
21	Ron Fairly	25.00	12.50	7.50
22	Joe Farzier	15.00	7.50	4.50
23	Allen Norris	15.00	7.50	4.50
24	Ford Young	15.00	7.50	4.50

1928 Exhibits Pacific Coast League

This regional series of 32 cards pictures players from the six California teams in the Pacific Coast League. Like the 1928 major league Exhibits, the PCL cards have a blue tint and are not numbered. They are blank-backed and measure 3-3/8" x 5-3/8". The set includes several misspellings. Cards are occasionally found with a corner clipped, the card corner to be used as a coupon with redemption value.

		NR MT	EX	VG
Complete Set:		1500.	750.00	450.00
Common Player:		40.00	20.00	12.00
1	"Buzz" Arlett	70.00	35.00	20.00
2	Earl Averill	150.00	75.00	45.00
3	Carl Berger (Walter)	70.00	35.00	20.00
4	"Ping" Bodie	60.00	30.00	18.00
5	Carl Dittmar	40.00	20.00	12.00
6	Jack Fenton	40.00	20.00	12.00
7	Neal "Mickey" Finn (Cornelius)	40.00	20.00	12.00
8	Ray French	40.00	20.00	12.00
9	Tony Governor	40.00	20.00	12.00
10	"Truck" Hannah	40.00	20.00	12.00
11	Mickey Heath	40.00	20.00	12.00
12	Wally Hood	40.00	20.00	12.00
13	"Fuzzy" Hufft	40.00	20.00	12.00
14	Snead Jolly (Smead)	40.00	20.00	12.00
15	Bobby "Ducky" Jones	40.00	20.00	12.00
16	Rudy Kallio	40.00	20.00	12.00
17	Ray Keating	40.00	20.00	12.00
18	Johnny Kerr	40.00	20.00	12.00
19	Harry Krause	40.00	20.00	12.00
20	Lynford H. Larry (Lary)	40.00	20.00	12.00
21	Dudley Lee	40.00	20.00	12.00
22	Walter "Duster" Mails	40.00	20.00	12.00
23	Jimmy Reese	50.00	25.00	15.00
24	"Dusty" Rhodes	40.00	20.00	12.00
25	Hal Rhyne	40.00	20.00	12.00
26	Hank Severied (Severeid)	40.00	20.00	12.00
27	Earl Sheely	40.00	20.00	12.00
28	Frank Shellenback	40.00	20.00	12.00
29	Gordon Slade	40.00	20.00	12.00
30	Hollis Thurston	40.00	20.00	12.00
31	"Babe" Twombly	40.00	20.00	12.00
32	Earl "Tex" Weathersby	40.00	20.00	12.00

Grading Guide

Mint (MT): A perfect card. Well-centered with all corners sharp and square. No creases, stains, edge nicks, surface marks, yellowing or fading.

Near Mint (NM): A nearly perfect card. At first glance, a NM card appears to be perfect. May be slightly off-center. No surface marks, creases or loss of gloss.

Excellent (EX): Corners are still fairly sharp with only moderate wear. Borders may be off-center. No creases or stains on fronts or backs, but may show slight loss of surface luster.

VeryGood (VG) : Shows obvious handling. May have rounded corners, minor creases, major gum or wax stains. No major creases, tape marks, writing, etc.

Good (G): A well-worn card, but exhibits no intentional damage. May have major or multiple creases. Corners may be rounded well beyond card border.

1966 Foremost Milk St. Petersburg Cardinals

This 20-card black-and-white set includes players and the manager, Sparky Anderson, of the Florida State League farm club of the St. Louis Cardinals. The unnumbered, blank-backed cards measure 3-1/2" x 5-1/2".

		NR MT	EX	VG
Complete Set:		100.00	50.00	30.00
Common Player:		4.00	2.00	1.20
(1)	George "Sparky" Anderson	25.00	12.50	7.50
(2)	Dave Bakenhaster	4.00	2.00	1.25
(3)	Leonard Boyer	10.00	5.00	3.00
(4)	Ron Braddock	4.00	2.00	1.25
(5)	Thomas "Chip" Coulter	4.00	2.00	1.25
(6)	Ernest "Sweet Pea" Davis	4.00	2.00	1.25
(7)	Phil Knuckles	4.00	2.00	1.25
(8)	Doug Lukens	4.00	2.00	1.25
(9)	Terry Milani	4.00	2.00	1.25
(10)	Tim Morgan	4.00	2.00	1.25
(11)	Harry Parker	4.00	2.00	1.25
(12)	Jerry Robertson	4.00	2.00	1.25
(13)	Francisco Rodriguez	4.00	2.00	1.25
(14)	John "Sonny" Ruberto	4.00	2.00	1.25
(15)	Charlie Stewart	4.00	2.00	1.25
(16)	Gary L. Stone	4.00	2.00	1.25
(17)	Charles "Tim" Thompson	4.00	2.00	1.25
(18)	Jose Villar	4.00	2.00	1.25
(19)	Archie L. Wade	4.00	2.00	1.25
(20)	Jim Williamson	4.00	2.00	1.25

1951 Globe Printing Fresno Cardinals

These 2" x 3" black-and-white, unnumbered, blank-backed cards were one of many minor league team sets issued by Globe Printing of San Jose, Calif., in the early 1950s. Cards were usually given away at the ballpark on a one-per-week or one-per-homestand basis, accounting for the rarity of surviving sets. The team was a California League (Class C) affiliate of the St. Louis Cardinals.

		NR MT	EX	VG
Complete Set:		250.00	125.00	75.00
Common Player:		15.00	7.50	4.50
(1)	Hal Atkinson	15.00	7.50	4.50
(2)	Larry Barton	15.00	7.50	4.50
(3)	Charlie Brooks	15.00	7.50	4.50
(4)	Bill Burton	15.00	7.50	4.50
(5)	Ray Herrera	15.00	7.50	4.50
(6)	Earl Jones	15.00	7.50	4.50
(7)	Jim King	15.00	7.50	4.50
(8)	Whitey Lageman	15.00	7.50	4.50
(9)	Wally Lamers	15.00	7.50	4.50
(10)	John McNamara	30.00	15.00	9.00
(11)	Gerry Mertz	15.00	7.50	4.50
(12)	Frank Olasin	15.00	7.50	4.50
(13)	Howie Phillips	15.00	7.50	4.50
(14)	Jack Ramsey	15.00	7.50	4.50
(15)	Tony Stathos	15.00	7.50	4.50
(16)	Whit Ulrich	15.00	7.50	4.50
(17)	Pete Younie	15.00	7.50	4.50

1951 Globe Printing San Jose Red Sox

These 2" x 3" black-and-white, unnumbered, blank-backed cards were one of many minor league team sets issued by Globe Printing of San Jose, Calif., in the early 1950s. Cards were usually given away at the ballpark on a one-per-week or one-per-homestand basis, accounting for the rarity of surviving sets. The team was a Class C farm club for the Boston Red Sox in the California League.

		NR MT	EX	VG
Complete Set:		250.00	125.00	75.00
Common Player:		15.00	7.50	4.50
(1)	Ken Aspromonte	25.00	12.50	7.50
(2)	Joe Buck	15.00	7.50	4.50
(3)	Harold Buckwalter	15.00	7.50	4.50
(4)	Al Curtis	15.00	7.50	4.50
(5)	Marvin Eyre	15.00	7.50	4.50
(6)	Jack Heinen	15.00	7.50	4.50
(7)	John Kinney	15.00	7.50	4.50
(8)	Walt Lucas	15.00	7.50	4.50
(9)	Syl McNinch	15.00	7.50	4.50
(10)	Stan McWilliams	15.00	7.50	4.50
(11)	Marvin Owen	15.00	7.50	4.50
(12)	Dick Piedrotti	15.00	7.50	4.50
(13)	Al Schroll	15.00	7.50	4.50
(14)	Ed Sobczak	15.00	7.50	4.50
(15)	Joe Stephenson	15.00	7.50	4.50
(16)	George Storti	15.00	7.50	4.50
(17)	Allan Van Alstyne	15.00	7.50	4.50
(18)	Floyd Warr	15.00	7.50	4.50

1952 Globe Printing Columbus Cardinals

This set of 17 cards was given away at Golden Park during the 1952 season. The cards measure 2-1/8" x 3-3/8" and have black-and-white photos of players with the player's name in a white box in the left bottom corner of the photograph. The backs are blank. The cards are unnumbered and listed in alphabetical order.

		NR MT	EX	VG
Complete Set:		250.00	125.00	75.00
Common Player:		15.00	7.50	4.50
(1)	Chief Bender	15.00	7.50	4.50
(2)	Bob Betancourt	15.00	7.50	4.50
(3)	Tom Burgess	15.00	7.50	4.50
(4)	Jack Byers	15.00	7.50	4.50
(5)	Mike Curnan	15.00	7.50	4.50
(6)	Gil Daley	15.00	7.50	4.50
(7)	Bill Harris	15.00	7.50	4.50
(8)	Ev Joyner	15.00	7.50	4.50
(9)	Bob Kerce	15.00	7.50	4.50
(10)	Ted Lewandowski	15.00	7.50	4.50
(11)	John Mackey	15.00	7.50	4.50
(12)	Bill Paolisso	15.00	7.50	4.50
(13)	Dennis Reeder	15.00	7.50	4.50
(14)	Whit Ulrich	15.00	7.50	4.50
(15)	Norman Shope	15.00	7.50	4.50
(16)	Don Swartz	15.00	7.50	4.50
(17)	Len Wile	15.00	7.50	4.50

1952 Globe Printing Co. Miami Beach Flamingos

These 2" x 3" black-and-white, unnumbered, blank-backed cards were one of many minor league team sets issued by Globe Printing of San Jose, Calif., in the early 1950s. Cards were usually given away at the ballpark on a one-per-week or one-per-homestand basis, accounting for the rarity of surviving sets. An embossed album is known for most of the team sets issued in 1952 or later. The Flamingos were an unaffiliated team in the Class B Florida International League.

		NR MT	EX	VG
Complete Set, With Album:		300.00	150.00	90.00
Common Player:		15.00	7.50	4.50
Album:		50.00	25.00	15.00
(1)	Billy Barrett	15.00	7.50	4.50
(2)	Art Bosch	15.00	7.50	4.50
(3)	Jack Caro	15.00	7.50	4.50
(4)	Chuck Ehlman	15.00	7.50	4.50
(5)	Oscar Garmendia	15.00	7.50	4.50
(6)	George Handy	15.00	7.50	4.50
(7)	Clark Henry	15.00	7.50	4.50
(8)	Dario Jiminez	15.00	7.50	4.50
(9)	Jesse Levan	15.00	7.50	4.50
(10)	Bobby Lyons	15.00	7.50	4.50
(11)	Pepper Martin	40.00	20.00	12.00
(12)	Dick McMillin	15.00	7.50	4.50
(13)	Pete Morant	15.00	7.50	4.50
(14)	Chico Morilla	15.00	7.50	4.50
(15)	Ken Munroe	15.00	7.50	4.50
(16)	Walt Nothe	15.00	7.50	4.50
(17)	Marshall O'Coine	15.00	7.50	4.50
(18)	Whitey Platt	15.00	7.50	4.50
(19)	Johnny Podgajny	15.00	7.50	4.50
(20)	Knobby Rosa	15.00	7.50	4.50
(21)	Harry Raulerson	15.00	7.50	4.50
(22)	Mort Smith	15.00	7.50	4.50
23	Tommy Venn	15.00	7.50	4.50
(24)	George Wehmeyer	15.00	7.50	4.50
(25)	Ray Williams	15.00	7.50	4.50

A player's name in italic type indicates a rookie card. An (FC) indicates a player's first card for that particular card company.

1952 Globe Printing Oshkosh Giants

These 2" x 3" black-and-white, unnumbered, blank-backed cards were one of many minor league team sets issued by Globe Printing of San Jose, Calif., in the early 1950s. Cards were usually given away at the ballpark on a one-per-week or one-per-homestand basis, accounting for the rarity of surviving sets. An embossed album is known for most of the team sets issued in 1952 or later. The O-Giants were the Wisconsin State League affiliate of the N.Y. Giants. For a Class D team, a surprising number of the Oshkosh players graduated to the major leagues.

		NR MT	EX	VG
Complete Set, With Album:		300.00	150.00	90.00
Common Player:		15.00	7.50	4.50
Album:		50.00	25.00	15.00
(1)	Dan Banaszak	15.00	7.50	4.50
(2)	Paul Bentley	15.00	7.50	4.50
(3)	Joe Berke	15.00	7.50	4.50
(4)	Joe De Bellis	15.00	7.50	4.50
(5)	Ron Edwards	15.00	7.50	4.50
(6)	Dave Garcia	15.00	7.50	4.50
(7)	Weldon Grimesley	15.00	7.50	4.50
(8)	Cam Lewis	15.00	7.50	4.50
(9)	Paul McAuley	15.00	7.50	4.50
(10)	Don Mills	15.00	7.50	4.50
(11)	Ed Opich	15.00	7.50	4.50
(12)	John Practico	15.00	7.50	4.50
(13)	Rob R. Schmidt	15.00	7.50	4.50
(14)	Rob W. Schmidt	15.00	7.50	4.50
(15)	Frank Szekula	15.00	7.50	4.50
(16)	Victor Vick	15.00	7.50	4.50
(17)	Donald Wall	15.00	7.50	4.50
(18)	Ken Whitehead	15.00	7.50	4.50
(19)	Gordon Windhorn	15.00	7.50	4.50

1952 Globe Printing San Diego Padres

		NR MT	EX	VG
Complete Set:		250.00	125.00	75.00
(1)	Al Benton	15.00	7.50	4.50
(2)	Dain Clay	15.00	7.50	4.50
(3)	John Davis	15.00	7.50	4.50
(4)	Dick Faber	15.00	7.50	4.50
(5)	Ben Flowers	15.00	7.50	4.50
(6)	Murray Franklin	15.00	7.50	4.50
(7)	Herb Gorman	15.00	7.50	4.50
(8)	Jack Graham	15.00	7.50	4.50
(9)	Memo Luna	15.00	7.50	4.50
(10)	Lefty O'Doul (Portrait to waist)	25.00	12.50	7.50
(11)	Lefty O'Doul (second pose unknown)	25.00	12.50	7.50
(12)	Al Olsen	15.00	7.50	4.50
(13)	Jimmie Reese	15.00	7.50	4.50
(14)	Al Richter	15.00	7.50	4.50
(15)	Jack Salveson	15.00	7.50	4.50
(16)	Lou Stringer	15.00	7.50	4.50
(17)	Lonnie Summers	15.00	7.50	4.50
(18)	Jack Tobin	15.00	7.50	4.50

1952 Globe Printing Ventura Braves

These 2" x 3" black-and-white, unnumbered, blank-backed cards were one of many minor league team sets issued by Globe Printing of San Jose, Calif., in the early 1950s. Cards were usually given away at the ballpark on a one-per-week or one-per-homestand basis, accounting for the rarity of surviving sets. An embossed album is known for most of the team sets issued in 1952 or later. It is known that 18 V-Braves were issued in this set, though only six have been checklisted to date. The team was a Class C California League farm club of the Boston Braves. The complete set price is not available.

		NR MT	EX	VG
Complete Set With Album:				
Common Player:		15.00	7.50	4.50
Album:		50.00	25.00	15.00
(1)	Al Aguilar	15.00	7.50	4.50
(2)	Bud Belardi	15.00	7.50	4.50
(3)	Lee Kast	15.00	7.50	4.50
(4)	Richie Morse	15.00	7.50	4.50
(5)	Bob Sturgeon	15.00	7.50	4.50
(6)	Billy Wells	15.00	7.50	4.50

1957 Golden State Dairy S.F. Seals Stickers

There are 23 stickers known in this set, featuring the last minor league team in San Francisco. Virtually every player who appeared in more than 10 games for the Seals that season is included in the

set. The stickers measure approximately 2" x 2-1/2", are printed in black-and-white, and blank-backed. They are checklisted here alphabetically, as the stickers are unnumbered.

		NR MT	EX	VG
Complete Set:		550.00	275.00	165.00
Common Player:		25.00	12.50	7.50
(1)	William "Bill" Abernathie	25.00	12.50	7.50
(2)	Kenneth "Chip" Aspromonte	25.00	12.50	7.50
(3)	Harry "Fritz" Dorish	25.00	12.50	7.50
(4)	Joe "Flash" Gordon	25.00	12.50	7.50
(5)	Grady Hatton Jr.	25.00	12.50	7.50
(6)	Thomas "Tommy" Hurd	25.00	12.50	7.50
(7)	Frank Kellert	25.00	12.50	7.50
(8)	Richard "Marty" Keough	25.00	12.50	7.50
(9)	Leo "Black Cat" Kiely	25.00	12.50	7.50
(10)	Harry William Malmberg	25.00	12.50	7.50
(11)	John McCall	25.00	12.50	7.50
(12)	Albert "Albie" Pearson	40.00	20.00	12.00
(13)	Jack Phillips	25.00	12.50	7.50
(14)	William "Bill" Renna	25.00	12.50	7.50
(15)	Edward "Ed" Sadowski	25.00	12.50	7.50
(16)	Robert W. Smith	25.00	12.50	7.50
(17)	Jack Spring	25.00	12.50	7.50
(18)	Jospeh H. Tanner	25.00	12.50	7.50
(19)	Salvador "Sal" Taormina	25.00	12.50	7.50
(20)	Maynard "Bert" Thiel	25.00	12.50	7.50
(21)	Anthony "Nini" Tornay	25.00	12.50	7.50
(22)	Thomas "Tommy" Umphlett	25.00	12.50	7.50
(23)	Glenn "Cap" Wright	25.00	12.50	7.50

1943 Grand Studio Milwaukee Brewers

It's unknown how these blank-backed, black-and-white, 3-1/2" x 5-1/2" pictures were distributed. The only identification is "PHOTO BY GRAND STUDIO" in the lower-right corner. It's likely the pictures were sold as a set at Borchert Field.

		NR MT	EX	VG
Complete Set:		400.00	200.00	120.00
Common Player:		20.00	10.00	6.00
(1)	Joe Berry	20.00	10.00	6.00
(2)	Bob Bowman	20.00	10.00	6.00
(3)	Earl Caldwell	20.00	10.00	6.00
(4)	Grey Clarke	20.00	10.00	6.00
(5)	Merv Conner	20.00	10.00	6.00
(6)	Paul Erickson	20.00	10.00	6.00
(7)	Charlie Grimm	30.00	15.00	9.00
(8)	Hank Helf	20.00	10.00	6.00
(9)	Don Johnson	20.00	10.00	6.00
(10)	Wes Livengood	20.00	10.00	6.00
(11)	Hershell Martin	20.00	10.00	6.00
(12)	Tommy Nelson	20.00	10.00	6.00
(13)	Ted Norbert	20.00	10.00	6.00
(14)	Bill Norman	20.00	10.00	6.00
(15)	Henry Oana	20.00	10.00	6.00
(16)	Jimmy Pruett	20.00	10.00	6.00
(17)	Bill Sahlin	20.00	10.00	6.00
(18)	Frank Secroy	20.00	10.00	6.00
(19)	Red Smith	20.00	10.00	6.00
(20)	Hugh Todd	20.00	10.00	6.00
(21)	Tony York	20.00	10.00	6.00

1949 Hage's Dairy

Hage's Dairy of California began a three-year run of regional baseball cards featuring Pacific Coast League players in 1949. Despite being produced by the local dairy, the cards were actually distributed inside popcorn boxes at the concession stand in Lane Field Park, home of the P.C.L. San Diego Padres. The 1949 set, like the following two years, was printed on a thin stock measuring 2-5/8" x 3-1/8". The checklist consists of 105 different cards, including several different poses for some of the players. Cards were continually being added or withdrawn to reflect roster changes on the minor league clubs. The Hage's sets were dominated by San Diego players, but also included representatives from the seven other P.C.L. teams. The 1949 cards can be found in four different tints - sepia,

green, blue, and black and white. The unnumbered cards have blank backs. The player's name and team appear inside a box on the front of the card, and the 1949 cards can be dated by the large (quarter-inch) type used for the team names, which are sometimes referred to by city and other times by nickname.

A card number in parentheses () indicates the set is unnumbered.

		NR MT	EX	VG
	Complete Set:	2800.	1400.	840.00
	Common Player:	25.00	12.50	7.50
(1)	"Buster" Adams	25.00	12.50	7.50
(2)	"Red" Adams	25.00	12.50	7.50
(3)	Lee Anthony	25.00	12.50	7.50
(4)	Rinaldo Ardizoia	25.00	12.50	7.50
(5)	Del Baker	25.00	12.50	7.50
(6)	Ed Basinski	25.00	12.50	7.50
(7)	Jim Baxes	25.00	12.50	7.50
(8)	Heinz Becker	25.00	12.50	7.50
(9)	Herman Besse	25.00	12.50	7.50
(10)	Tom Bridges	30.00	15.00	9.00
(11)	Gene Brocker	25.00	12.50	7.50
(12)	Ralph Bucton	25.00	12.50	7.50
(13)	Mickey Burnett	25.00	12.50	7.50
(14)	Dain Clay (pose)	25.00	12.50	7.50
(15)	Dain Clay (batting)	25.00	12.50	7.50
(16)	Dain Corriden, Jim Reese	25.00	12.50	7.50
(17)	Pete Coscarart	25.00	12.50	7.50
(18)	Dom Dallessandro	25.00	12.50	7.50
(19)	Con Dempsey	25.00	12.50	7.50
(20)	Vince DiBiasi	25.00	12.50	7.50
(21)	Luke Easter (batting stance)	30.00	15.00	9.00
(22)	Luke Easter (batting follow thru)	30.00	15.00	9.00
(23)	Ed Fernandez	25.00	12.50	7.50
(24)	Les Fleming	25.00	12.50	7.50
(25)	Jess Flores	25.00	12.50	7.50
(26)	Cecil Garriott	25.00	12.50	7.50
(27)	Charles Gassaway	25.00	12.50	7.50
(28)	Mickey Grasso	25.00	12.50	7.50
(29)	Will Hafey (pitching)	25.00	12.50	7.50
(30)	Will Hafey (pose)	25.00	12.50	7.50
(31)	"Jeep" Handley	25.00	12.50	7.50
(32)	"Bucky" Harris (pose)	40.00	20.00	12.00
(33)	"Bucky" Harris (shouting)	40.00	20.00	12.00
(34)	Roy Helser	25.00	12.50	7.50
(35)	Lloyd Hittle	25.00	12.50	7.50
(36)	Ralph Hodgin	25.00	12.50	7.50
(37)	Leroy Jarvis	25.00	12.50	7.50
(38)	John Jensen	25.00	12.50	7.50
(39)	Al Jurisich	25.00	12.50	7.50
(40)	Herb Karpel	25.00	12.50	7.50
(41)	Frank Kelleher	25.00	12.50	7.50
(42)	Bill Kelly	25.00	12.50	7.50
(43)	Bob Kelly	25.00	12.50	7.50
(44)	Frank Kerr	25.00	12.50	7.50
(45)	Thomas Kipp	25.00	12.50	7.50
(46)	Al Lien	25.00	12.50	7.50
(47)	Lyman Linde (pose)	25.00	12.50	7.50
(48)	Lyman Linde (pitching)	25.00	12.50	7.50
(49)	Dennis Luby	25.00	12.50	7.50
(50)	"Red" Lynn	25.00	12.50	7.50
(51)	Pat Malone	25.00	12.50	7.50
(52)	Billy Martin	80.00	40.00	24.00
(53)	Joe Marty	25.00	12.50	7.50
(54)	Cliff Melton	25.00	12.50	7.50
(55)	Steve Mesner	25.00	12.50	7.50
(56)	Leon Mohr	25.00	12.50	7.50
(57)	"Butch" Moran	25.00	12.50	7.50
(58)	Glen Moulder	25.00	12.50	7.50
(59)	Steve Nagy	25.00	12.50	7.50
(60)	Roy Nicely	25.00	12.50	7.50
(61)	Walt Nothe	25.00	12.50	7.50
(62)	John O'Neill	25.00	12.50	7.50
(63)	"Pluto" Oliver	25.00	12.50	7.50
(64)	Al Olsen (pose)	25.00	12.50	7.50
(65)	Al Olsen (throwing)	25.00	12.50	7.50
(66)	Johnny Ostrowski	25.00	12.50	7.50
(67)	Ray Partee	25.00	12.50	7.50
(68)	Bill Raimondi	25.00	12.50	7.50
(69)	Bill Ramsey	25.00	12.50	7.50
(70)	Len Ratto	25.00	12.50	7.50
(71)	Xavier Rescigno	25.00	12.50	7.50
(72)	John Ritchey (batting)	25.00	12.50	7.50
(73)	John Ritchey (catching)	25.00	12.50	7.50
(74)	Mickey Rocco	25.00	12.50	7.50
(75)	John Rucker	25.00	12.50	7.50
(76)	Clarence Russell	25.00	12.50	7.50
(77)	Jack Salverson	25.00	12.50	7.50
(78)	Bill Schuster	25.00	12.50	7.50
(79)	Tom Seats	25.00	12.50	7.50
(80)	Neil Sheridan	25.00	12.50	7.50
(81)	Vince Shupe	25.00	12.50	7.50
(82)	Joe Sprinz	25.00	12.50	7.50
(83)	Chuck Stevens	25.00	12.50	7.50
(84)	Harvey Storey	25.00	12.50	7.50
(85)	Jim Tabor (Sacramento)	25.00	12.50	7.50
(86)	Jim Tabor (Seattle)	25.00	12.50	7.50
(87)	"Junior" Thompson	25.00	12.50	7.50
(88)	Arky Vaughn	45.00	22.00	13.50
(89)	Jackie Warner	25.00	12.50	7.50
(90)	Jim Warner	25.00	12.50	7.50
(91)	Dick Wenner	25.00	12.50	7.50
(92)	Max West (pose)	25.00	12.50	7.50
(93)	Max West (batting swing)	25.00	12.50	7.50
(94)	Max West (batting follow-thru)	25.00	12.50	7.50
(95)	Hank Weyse	25.00	12.50	7.50
(96)	"Fuzzy" White	25.00	12.50	7.50
(97)	Jo Jo White	25.00	12.50	7.50
(98)	Artie Wilson	25.00	12.50	7.50
(99)	Bill Wilson	25.00	12.50	7.50
(100)	Bobbie Wilson (pose)	25.00	12.50	7.50
(101)	Bobbie Wilson (pitching)	25.00	12.50	7.50
(102)	"Pinky" Woods	25.00	12.50	7.50
(103)	Tony York	25.00	12.50	7.50
(104)	Del Young	25.00	12.50	7.50
(105)	Frank Zak	25.00	12.50	7.50

1950 Hage's Dairy

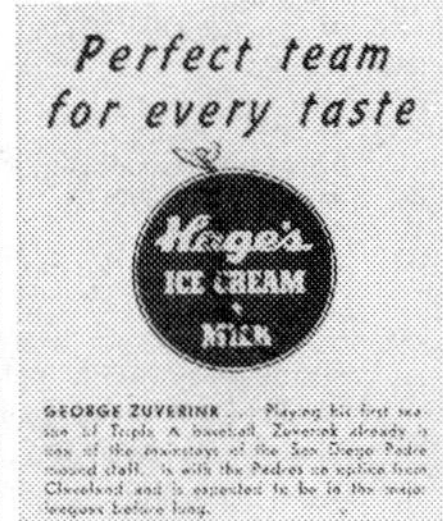

Perfect team
for every taste
Hage's
ICE CREAM
MILK
GEORGE ZUVERINK

The 1950 P.C.L. set from Hage's Dairy was similar in design and size (2-5/8" x 3-1/8") to the previous year and was again distributed in popcorn boxes at the San Diego stadium. The 1950 set is found with either a blank back or a back containing an advertisement for Hage's Ice Cream, "Your Favorite Brand". The advertising backs also contain the player's name and brief 1949 statistics at the bottom. There are 126 different cards in the 1950 set, including different poses for some of the players. Again, Padres dominate the unnumbered set with lesser representation from the other P.C.L. clubs. For the 1950 edition all team names are referred to by city (no nicknames) and the typeface is smaller.

		NR MT	EX	VG
	Complete Set:	2000.	1000.	600.00
	Common Player:	15.00	7.50	4.50
(1)	"Buster" Adams (kneeling)	15.00	7.50	4.50
(2a)	"Buster" Adams (batting follow-thru, with inscription)	15.00	7.50	4.50
(2b)	"Buster" Adams (batting follow-thru, no inscription)	15.00	7.50	4.50
(2c)	"Buster" Adams (batting follow-thru, body to left)	15.00	7.50	4.50
3a	"Buster" Adams (batting stance, caption box touching waist)	15.00	7.50	4.50
(3b)	"Buster" Adams (batting stance, caption box not touching waist)	15.00	7.50	4.50
(4)	"Red" Adams	15.00	7.50	4.50
(5)	Dewey Adkins (photo actually Albie Glossop)	15.00	7.50	4.50
(6)	Rinaldo Ardizoia	15.00	7.50	4.50
(7)	Jose Bache	15.00	7.50	4.50
(8a)	Del Baker (bat visible at lower right)	15.00	7.50	4.50
(8a)	Jim Reese (bat visible at lower right)	15.00	7.50	4.50
(8b)	Del Baker (no bat visible)	15.00	7.50	4.50
(8b)	Jim Reese (no bat visible)	15.00	7.50	4.50
(9)	George Bamberger	15.00	7.50	4.50
(10)	Richard Barrett	15.00	7.50	4.50
(11)	Frank Baumholtz	25.00	12.50	7.50
(12)	Henry Behrman	15.00	7.50	4.50
(13)	Bill Bevens	25.00	12.50	7.50
(14)	Ernie Bickhaus	15.00	7.50	4.50
(15)	Bill Burgher (pose)	15.00	7.50	4.50
(16)	Bill Burgher (catching)	15.00	7.50	4.50
(17)	Mark Christman	15.00	7.50	4.50
(18)	Clint Conaster	15.00	7.50	4.50
(19)	Herb Conyers (fielding)	15.00	7.50	4.50
(20)	Herb Conyers (batting)	15.00	7.50	4.50
(21)	Jim Davis	15.00	7.50	4.50
(22)	Ted Del Guercio	15.00	7.50	4.50
(23)	Vince DiBiasi	15.00	7.50	4.50
(24)	Jess Dobernic	15.00	7.50	4.50
(25)	"Red" Embree (pose)	15.00	7.50	4.50
(26)	"Red" Embree (pitching)	15.00	7.50	4.50
(27)	Elbie Fletcher	15.00	7.50	4.50
(28)	Guy Fletcher	15.00	7.50	4.50
(29)	Tony Freitas	15.00	7.50	4.50
(30)	Denny Galehouse	15.00	7.50	4.50
(31)	Jack Graham (pose, looking to left)	15.00	7.50	4.50
(32)	Jack Graham (pose, looking straight ahead)	15.00	7.50	4.50
(33)	Jack Graham (batting swing)	15.00	7.50	4.50
(34)	Jack Graham (batting stance)	15.00	7.50	4.50
(35)	Orval Grove	15.00	7.50	4.50
(36)	Lee Handley	15.00	7.50	4.50
(37)	Ralph Hodgin	15.00	7.50	4.50
(38)	Don Johnson	15.00	7.50	4.50
(39)	Al Jurisich (pose)	15.00	7.50	4.50
(40)	Al Jurisich (pitching wind-up)	15.00	7.50	4.50
(41)	Al Jurisich (pitching follow-thru)	15.00	7.50	4.50
(42)	Bill Kelly	15.00	7.50	4.50
(43)	Frank Kerr	15.00	7.50	4.50
(44)	Tom Kipp (pose)	15.00	7.50	4.50
(45)	Tom Kipp (pitching)	15.00	7.50	4.50
(46)	Mel Knezovich	15.00	7.50	4.50
(47)	Red Kress	15.00	7.50	4.50
(48)	Dario Lodigiani	15.00	7.50	4.50
(49)	Dennis Luby (pose)	15.00	7.50	4.50
(50)	Dennis Luby (throwing)	15.00	7.50	4.50
(51)	Al Lyons	15.00	7.50	4.50
(52)	Clarence Maddern	15.00	7.50	4.50
(53)	Joe Marty	15.00	7.50	4.50
(54)	Bob McCall	15.00	7.50	4.50
(55)	Cal McIrvin	15.00	7.50	4.50
(56)	Orestes Minoso (batting follow-thru)	40.00	20.00	12.00
(57)	Orestes Minoso (bunting)	40.00	20.00	12.00
(58)	Leon Mohr	15.00	7.50	4.50
(59)	Dee Moore (batting)	15.00	7.50	4.50
(60)	Dee Moore (catching)	15.00	7.50	4.50
(61)	Jim Moran	15.00	7.50	4.50
(62)	Glen Moulder	15.00	7.50	4.50
(63)	Milt Neilsen (pose)	15.00	7.50	4.50
(64)	Milt Neilsen (batting)	15.00	7.50	4.50
(65)	Milt Neilsen (throwing)	15.00	7.50	4.50
(66)	Rube Novotney	15.00	7.50	4.50
(67)	Al Olsen	15.00	7.50	4.50
(68)	Manny Perez	15.00	7.50	4.50
(69)	Bill Raemondi (Raimondi)	15.00	7.50	4.50
(70)	Len Ratto	15.00	7.50	4.50
(71)	Mickey Rocco	15.00	7.50	4.50
(72)	Marv Rotblatt	15.00	7.50	4.50
(73)	Lynwood Rowe (pose)	25.00	12.50	7.50
(74)	Lynwood Rowe (pitching)	25.00	12.50	7.50
(75)	Clarence Russell	15.00	7.50	4.50
(76)	Hal Saltzman (pitching follow-thru)	15.00	7.50	4.50
(77)	Hal Saltzman (pitching wind-up)	15.00	7.50	4.50
(78)	Hal Saltzman (pitching, leg in air)	15.00	7.50	4.50
(79)	Bob Savage (pose)	15.00	7.50	4.50
(80)	Bob Savage (pitching)	15.00	7.50	4.50
(81)	Charlie Schanz	15.00	7.50	4.50
(82)	Bill Schuster	15.00	7.50	4.50
(83)	Neil Sheridan	15.00	7.50	4.50
(84)	Harry Simpson (batting swing)	15.00	7.50	4.50
(85)	Harry Simpson (batting stance)	15.00	7.50	4.50
(86)	Harry Simpson (batting stance, close up)	15.00	7.50	4.50
(87)	Harry Simpson (batting follow-thru)	15.00	7.50	4.50
(88)	Elmer Singleton	15.00	7.50	4.50
(89)	Al Smith (pose)	15.00	7.50	4.50
(90)	Al Smith (batting stance)	15.00	7.50	4.50
(91)	Al Smith (fielding)	15.00	7.50	4.50
(92)	Alphonse Smith (glove above knee)	15.00	7.50	4.50
(93)	Alphonse Smith (glove below knee)	15.00	7.50	4.50
(94)	Steve Souchock	15.00	7.50	4.50
(95)	Jim Steiner	15.00	7.50	4.50
(96)	Harvey Storey (batting stance)	15.00	7.50	4.50
(97)	Harvey Storey (swinging bat)	15.00	7.50	4.50
(98)	Harvey Storey (throwing)	15.00	7.50	4.50
(99)	Harvey Storey (fielding, ball in glove)	15.00	7.50	4.50
(100)	Max Surkont	15.00	7.50	4.50
(101)	Jim Tabor	15.00	7.50	4.50
(102)	Forrest Thompson	15.00	7.50	4.50
(103)	Mike Tresh (pose)	15.00	7.50	4.50
(104)	Mike Tresh (catching)	15.00	7.50	4.50
(105)	Kenny Washington	15.00	7.50	4.50
(106)	Bill Waters (pose)	15.00	7.50	4.50
(107)	Bill Waters (pitching)	15.00	7.50	4.50
(108)	Roy Welmaker (pose)	15.00	7.50	4.50
(109)	Roy Welmaker (pitching)	15.00	7.50	4.50
(110)	Max West (pose)	15.00	7.50	4.50
(111)	Max West (batting stance)	15.00	7.50	4.50
(112)	Max West (kneeling)	15.00	7.50	4.50
(113)	Max West (batting follow-thru)	15.00	7.50	4.50
(114)	Al White	15.00	7.50	4.50
(115)	"Whitey" Wietelmann (pose)	15.00	7.50	4.50
(116)	"Whitey" Wietelmann (bunting)	15.00	7.50	4.50
(117)	"Whitey" Wietelmann (batting stance)	15.00	7.50	4.50
(118)	"Whitey" Wietelmann (throwing)	15.00	7.50	4.50
(119)	Bobbie Wilson	15.00	7.50	4.50
(120)	Bobby Wilson	15.00	7.50	4.50
(121)	Roy Zimmerman	15.00	7.50	4.50
(122)	George Zuverink	15.00	7.50	4.50

1951 Hage's Dairy

The final year of the Hage's P.C.L. issues saw the set reduced to 52 different unnumbered cards, all but 12 of them Padres. The set also includes six cards of Cleveland Indians players, which were issued during an exhibition series with the major league club, and six cards picturing members of the

Hollywood Stars. No other P.C.L. teams are represented. The cards maintained the same size and style of the previous two years but were printed in more color tints, including blue, green, burgundy, gold, gray and sepia (but not black-and-white). The 1951 cards have blank backs and were again distributed in popcorn boxes at the San Diego stadium. The 1951 cards are the most common of the three sets issued by Hage's Dairy. The Indians and Stars players were issued in lesser quantities than the Padres, however, and command a higher value.

The values quoted are intended to reflect the market price.

		NR MT	EX	VG
Complete Set:		1000.	500.00	300.00
Common Player:		15.00	7.50	4.50
(1)	"Buster" Adams	15.00	7.50	4.50
(2)	Del Baker	15.00	7.50	4.50
(3)	Ray Boone	25.00	12.50	7.50
(4)	Russ Christopher	15.00	7.50	4.50
(5)	Allie Clark	25.00	12.50	7.50
(6)	Herb Conyers	15.00	7.50	4.50
(7)	"Red" Embree (pitching, foot in air)	15.00	7.50	4.50
(8)	"Red" Embree (pitching, hands up)	15.00	7.50	4.50
(9)	Jess Flores	25.00	12.50	7.50
(10)	Murray Franklin	25.00	12.50	7.50
(11)	Jack Graham (portrait)	15.00	7.50	4.50
(12)	Jack Graham (batting)	15.00	7.50	4.50
(13)	Gene Handley	25.00	12.50	7.50
(14)	Charles Harris	15.00	7.50	4.50
(15)	Sam Jones (pitching, hands back)	15.00	7.50	4.50
(16)	Sam Jones (pitching, hands up)	15.00	7.50	4.50
(17)	Sam Jones (pitching, leg in air)	15.00	7.50	4.50
(18)	Al Jurisich	15.00	7.50	4.50
(19)	Frank Kerr (batting)	15.00	7.50	4.50
(20)	Frank Kerr (catching)	15.00	7.50	4.50
(21)	Dick Kinaman	15.00	7.50	4.50
(22)	Clarence Maddern (batting)	15.00	7.50	4.50
(23)	Clarence Maddern (fielding)	15.00	7.50	4.50
(24)	Harry Malmberg (bunting)	15.00	7.50	4.50
(25)	Harry Malmberg (batting follow-thru)	15.00	7.50	4.50
(26)	Harry Malmberg (fielding)	15.00	7.50	4.50
(27)	Gordon Maltzberger	25.00	12.50	7.50
(28)	Al Olsen (Cleveland)	25.00	12.50	7.50
(29)	Al Olsen (San Diego)	15.00	7.50	4.50
(30)	Jimmy Reese (clapping)	20.00	10.00	6.00
(31)	Jimmy Reese (hands on knees)	20.00	10.00	6.00
(32)	Al Rosen	45.00	22.00	13.50
(33)	Joe Rowell	15.00	7.50	4.50
(34)	Mike Sandlock	25.00	12.50	7.50
(35)	George Schmees	25.00	12.50	7.50
(36)	Charlie Sipple	15.00	7.50	4.50
(37)	Harvey Storey (batting follow-thru)	15.00	7.50	4.50
(38)	Harvey Storey (batting stance)	15.00	7.50	4.50
(39)	Harvey Storey (fielding)	15.00	7.50	4.50
(40)	Jack Tobin	15.00	7.50	4.50
(41)	Frank Tornay	15.00	7.50	4.50
(42)	Thurman Tucker	15.00	7.50	4.50
(43)	Ben Wade	25.00	12.50	7.50
(44)	Roy Welmaker	15.00	7.50	4.50
(45)	Leroy Wheat	15.00	7.50	4.50
(46)	Don White	15.00	7.50	4.50
(47)	"Whitey" Wietelman (batting)	15.00	7.50	4.50
(48)	"Whitey" Wietelman (fielding)	15.00	7.50	4.50
(49)	Bobby Wilson (batting)	15.00	7.50	4.50
(50)	Bobby Wilson (fielding)	15.00	7.50	4.50
(51)	Tony York	15.00	7.50	4.50
(52)	George Zuverink	25.00	12.50	7.50

A card number in parentheses () indicates the set is unnumbered.

1960 Henry House Wieners Seattle Rainiers

Eighteen different cards are known in this hot dog set; most players played major league baseball prior to their appearance with the Pacific Coast

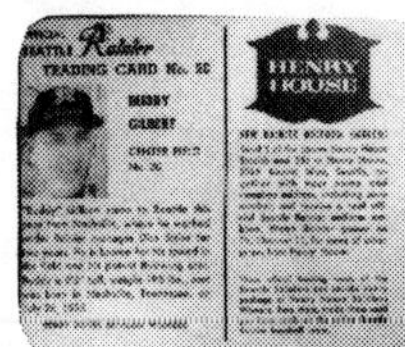

League Seattle Rainiers in 1960. Printed in red, the 4-1/2" x 3-3/4" cards are skip-numbered by player uniform number.

		NR MT	EX	VG
Complete Set:		3500.	1750.	1000.
Common Player:		150.00	37.50	22.50
2	Harry Malmberg	150.00	75.00	45.00
3	Francisco Obregon	150.00	75.00	45.00
4	Johnny O'Brien	200.00	100.00	60.00
5	Gordon Coleman	200.00	100.00	60.00
6	Bill Hain	150.00	75.00	45.00
8	Dick Sisler	200.00	100.00	60.00
9	Jerry Zimmerman	150.00	75.00	45.00
10	Hal Bevan	150.00	75.00	45.00
14	Rudy Regaldo	150.00	75.00	45.00
15	Paul Pettit	200.00	100.00	60.00
16	Buddy Gilbert	150.00	75.00	45.00
21	Erv Palica	150.00	75.00	45.00
22	Joe Taylor	150.00	75.00	45.00
25	Bill Kennedy	150.00	75.00	45.00
26	Dave Stenhouse	150.00	75.00	45.00
28	Ray Ripplemeyer	150.00	75.00	45.00
30	Charlie Beamon	150.00	75.00	45.00
33	Don Rudolph	150.00	75.00	45.00

Values for recent cards and sets are listed in Mint (MT), Near Mint (NM), reflecting the fact that many cards from recent years have been preserved in top condition. Recent cards and sets in less than Excellent condition have little collector interest.

1888 S.F. Hess California League (N388-1)

This tobacco card set picturing players from the California League is one of the rarest of all 19th century issues. Issued in the late 1880s by S.F. Hess & Co. of Rochester, these 2-7/8" by 1-1/2" cards are so rare that only several examples are known to exist. Some of the photos in the N338-1 set are identical to the drawings in the N321 set, issued by S.F. Hess in 1888. The N338-1 cards are found with the words "California League" printed in an arc either above or below the player photo. The player's name appears below the photo. At the bottom of the card the words "S.F. Hess & Co.'s Creole Cigarettes" are printed in a rolling style.

		NR MT	EX	VG
Complete Set:		16000.	8000.	4800.
Common Player:		1000.	500.00	300.00
(1)	Borsher	1000.	500.00	300.00
(2)	Carroll	1000.	500.00	300.00
(3)	C. Ebright	1000.	500.00	300.00
(4)	P. Incell	1000.	500.00	300.00
(5)	C.F. Lawton	1000.	500.00	300.00
(6)	C.F. Levy (throwing)	1000.	500.00	300.00
(7)	C.F. Levy (with bat)	1000.	500.00	300.00
(8)	C. McDonald	1000.	500.00	300.00
(9)	PMeegan	1000.	500.00	300.00
(10)	S.S. Newhert	1000.	500.00	300.00
(11)	P. Noonan	1000.	500.00	300.00
(12)	R.F. Perrier	1000.	500.00	300.00
(13)	Perrier, H. Smith	1000.	500.00	300.00
(14)	Ryan	1000.	500.00	300.00
(15)	J. Smith, N. Smith	1000.	500.00	300.00
(16)	P. Sweeney	1000.	500.00	300.00

1888 S.F. Hess Newsboys League (N333)

Although not picturing actual baseball players, this 44-card set issued by S.F. Hess and Co. has a baseball theme. Cards measure 2-7/8" by 1-1/2" and feature pictures of newspaper boys from eight different papers in eight different cities (Rochester, Cleveland, Philadelphia, Boston, Albany, Detroit, New York and Syracuse). The boys are pictured in a portrait photo wearing a baseball-style shirt bearing the name of their newspaper. The boy's name, position and newspaper are printed below, while the words "Newsboys League" appears in capital letters at the top of the card. No identification is provided for the four Philadelphia newsboys, so a photo description is provided in topdhe checklist that follows.

		NR MT	EX	VG
Complete Set:		3000.	1500.	900.00
Common Player:		70.00	35.00	21.00
(1)	R.J. Bell	70.00	35.00	21.00
(2)	Binden	70.00	35.00	21.00
(3)	Bowen	70.00	35.00	21.00
(4)	Boyle	70.00	35.00	21.00
(5)	Britcher	70.00	35.00	21.00
(6)	Caine	70.00	35.00	21.00
(7)	I. Cohen	70.00	35.00	21.00
(8)	R. Cohen	70.00	35.00	21.00
(9)	Cross	70.00	35.00	21.00
(10)	F. Cuddy	70.00	35.00	21.00
(11)	E. Daisey	70.00	35.00	21.00
(12)	Davis	70.00	35.00	21.00
(13)	B. Dinsmore	70.00	35.00	21.00
(14)	Donovan	70.00	35.00	21.00
(15)	A. Downer	70.00	35.00	21.00
(16)	Fanelly	70.00	35.00	21.00
(17)	J. Flood	70.00	35.00	21.00
(18)	C. Gallagher	70.00	35.00	21.00
(19)	M.H. Gallagher	70.00	35.00	21.00
(20)	D. Galligher	70.00	35.00	21.00
(21)	J. Galligher	70.00	35.00	21.00
(22)	Haskins	70.00	35.00	21.00
(23)	Herze	70.00	35.00	21.00
(24)	F. Horan	70.00	35.00	21.00
(25)	Hosler	70.00	35.00	21.00
(26)	Hyde	70.00	35.00	21.00
(27)	Keilty	70.00	35.00	21.00
(28)	C. Kellogg	70.00	35.00	21.00
(29)	Mahoney	70.00	35.00	21.00
(30)	Mayer	70.00	35.00	21.00
(31)	I. McDonald	70.00	35.00	21.00
(32)	McGrady	70.00	35.00	21.00
(33)	O'Brien	70.00	35.00	21.00
(34)	E.C. Murphy	70.00	35.00	21.00
(35)	Sabin	70.00	35.00	21.00
(36)	Shedd	70.00	35.00	21.00
(37)	R. Sheehan	70.00	35.00	21.00
(38)	Smith	70.00	35.00	21.00
(39)	Talbot	70.00	35.00	21.00
(40)	Walsh	70.00	35.00	21.00
(41)	Philadelphia newsboy (hair parted on right side)	70.00	35.00	21.00
(42)	Philadelphia newsboy (hair parted on left side)	70.00	35.00	21.00
(43)	Philadelphia newsboy (no part in hair)	70.00	35.00	21.00
(44)	Philadelphia newsboy (head shaved)	70.00	35.00	21.00

1912 Home Run Kisses (E136)

Save HOME RUN KISSES Pictures
for valuable premiums
List will be issued July 15, 1912
COLLINS-McCARTHY CANDY CO.
San Francisco, Cal.

This 90-card set of Pacific Coast League players, known by the ACC designation E136, was produced in 1912 by the San Francisco candy company of Collins-McCarthy. Each card measures a large 2-1/4" x 4-1/4" and features sepia-toned player photos surrounded by an ornate frame. The front of the card has the words "Home Run Kisses" above the player's name. Most cards found are blank-backed, but others exist with a back that advises "Save

Home Run Kisses Pictures for Valuable Premiums" along with other details of the Collins-McCarthy promotion.

		NR MT	EX	VG
Complete Set:		8750.	4375.	2625.
Common Player:		120.00	60.00	36.00
(1)	Ables	120.00	60.00	36.00
(2)	Agnew	120.00	60.00	36.00
(3)	Altman	120.00	60.00	36.00
(4)	Arrelanes	120.00	60.00	36.00
(5)	Auer	120.00	60.00	36.00
(6)	Bancroft	250.00	125.00	75.00
(7)	Bayless	120.00	60.00	36.00
(8)	Berry	120.00	60.00	36.00
(9)	Boles	120.00	60.00	36.00
(10)	Brashear	120.00	60.00	36.00
(11)	Brooks (Los Angeles)	120.00	60.00	36.00
(12)	Brooks (Oakland)	120.00	60.00	36.00
(13)	Brown	120.00	60.00	36.00
(14)	Burrell	120.00	60.00	36.00
(15)	Butler	120.00	60.00	36.00
(16)	Carlisle	120.00	60.00	36.00
(17)	Carson	120.00	60.00	36.00
(18)	Castleton	120.00	60.00	36.00
(19)	Chadbourne	120.00	60.00	36.00
(20)	Check	120.00	60.00	36.00
(21)	Core	120.00	60.00	36.00
(22)	Corhan	120.00	60.00	36.00
(23)	Coy	120.00	60.00	36.00
(24)	Daley	120.00	60.00	36.00
(25)	Dillon	120.00	60.00	36.00
(26)	Doane	120.00	60.00	36.00
(27)	Driscoll	120.00	60.00	36.00
(28)	Fisher	120.00	60.00	36.00
(29)	Flater	120.00	60.00	36.00
(30)	Gaddy	120.00	60.00	36.00
(31)	Gregg	120.00	60.00	36.00
(32)	Gregory	120.00	60.00	36.00
(33)	Harkness	120.00	60.00	36.00
(34)	Heitmuller	120.00	60.00	36.00
(35)	Henley	120.00	60.00	36.00
(36)	Hiester	120.00	60.00	36.00
(37)	Hoffman	120.00	60.00	36.00
(38)	Hogan	120.00	60.00	36.00
(39)	Hosp	120.00	60.00	36.00
(40)	Howley	120.00	60.00	36.00
(41)	Ireland	120.00	60.00	36.00
(42)	Johnson	120.00	60.00	36.00
(43)	Kane	120.00	60.00	36.00
(44)	Klawitter	120.00	60.00	36.00
(45)	Kreitz	120.00	60.00	36.00
(46)	Krueger	120.00	60.00	36.00
(47)	Leard	120.00	60.00	36.00
(48)	Leverencz	120.00	60.00	36.00
(49)	Lewis	120.00	60.00	36.00
(50)	Lindsay	120.00	60.00	36.00
(51)	Litschi	120.00	60.00	36.00
(52)	Lober	120.00	60.00	36.00
(53)	Malarkey	120.00	60.00	36.00
(54)	Martinoni	120.00	60.00	36.00
(55)	McArdle	120.00	60.00	36.00
(56)	McCorry	120.00	60.00	36.00
(57)	McDowell	120.00	60.00	36.00
(58)	McIver	120.00	60.00	36.00
(59)	Metzger	120.00	60.00	36.00
(60)	Miller	120.00	60.00	36.00
(61)	Mundorf	120.00	60.00	36.00
(62)	Nagle	120.00	60.00	36.00
(63)	Noyes	120.00	60.00	36.00
(64)	Olmstead	120.00	60.00	36.00
(65)	O'Rourke	120.00	60.00	36.00
(66)	Page	120.00	60.00	36.00
(67)	Parkins	120.00	60.00	36.00
(68)	Patterson (Oakland)	120.00	60.00	36.00
(69)	Patterson (Vernon)	120.00	60.00	36.00
(70)	Pernoll	120.00	60.00	36.00
(71)	Powell	120.00	60.00	36.00
(72)	Price	120.00	60.00	36.00
(73)	Raftery	120.00	60.00	36.00
(74)	Raleigh	120.00	60.00	36.00
(75)	Rogers	120.00	60.00	36.00
(76)	Schmidt	120.00	60.00	36.00
(77)	Schwenk	120.00	60.00	36.00
(78)	Sheehan	120.00	60.00	36.00
(79)	Shinn	120.00	60.00	36.00
(80)	Slagle	120.00	60.00	36.00
(81)	Smith	120.00	60.00	36.00
(82)	Stone	120.00	60.00	36.00
(83)	Swain	120.00	60.00	36.00
(84)	Taylor	120.00	60.00	36.00
(85)	Tiedeman	120.00	60.00	36.00
(86)	Toner	120.00	60.00	36.00
(87)	Tozer	120.00	60.00	36.00
(88)	Van Buren	120.00	60.00	36.00
(89)	Williams	120.00	60.00	36.00
(90)	Zacher	120.00	60.00	36.00

The values quoted are intended to reflect the market price.

1940 Hughes Frozen Confections Sacramento Solons

These borderless 2 x 3" black-and-white cards of the Sacramento Solons can be found in two versions, either blank-backed or with the 1940 Solons

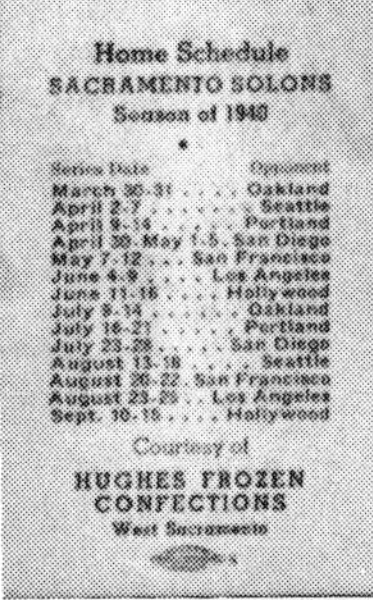

Pacific Coast League schedule printed on back. Fronts featured action poses with a facsimile autograph.

		NR MT	EX	VG
Complete Set:		1500.	750.00	450.00
Common Player:		75.00	37.00	22.00
(1)	Mel Almada	75.00	37.00	22.00
(2)	Frank Asbell	75.00	37.00	22.00
(3)	Larry Barton	75.00	37.00	22.00
(4)	Robert Blattner	75.00	37.00	22.00
(5)	Bennie Borgmann	75.00	37.00	22.00
(6)	Tony Freitas	75.00	37.00	22.00
(7)	Art Garibaldi	75.00	37.00	22.00
(8)	Jim Grilk	75.00	37.00	22.00
(9)	Gene Handley	75.00	37.00	22.00
(10)	Oscar Judd	75.00	37.00	22.00
(11)	Lynn King	75.00	37.00	22.00
(12)	Norbert Kleinke	75.00	37.00	22.00
(13)	Max Marshall	75.00	37.00	22.00
(14)	William McLaughlin	75.00	37.00	22.00
(15)	Bruce Ogrodowski	75.00	37.00	22.00
(16)	Franich Riel	75.00	37.00	22.00
(17)	Bill Schmidt	75.00	37.00	22.00
(18)	Melvin Wasley	75.00	37.00	22.00
(19)	Chet Wieczorek	75.00	37.00	22.00
(20)	Deb Williams	75.00	37.00	22.00

1957 Hygrade Meats Seattle Rainiers

While the front of the cards mentions a complete set of 22 cards, only a dozen have been checklisted to date. The round-cornered cards measure 4-1/2 x 3-3/4" and are printed in red on white. Backs are blank. The cards feature only players of the Pacific Coast League Seattle Rainiers. The cards are unnumbered.

		NR MT	EX	VG
Common Player:		150.00	75.00	45.00
(1)	Dick Aylward	150.00	75.00	45.00
(2)	Bob Balcena	150.00	75.00	45.00
(3)	Jim Dyck	150.00	75.00	45.00
(4)	Marion Fricano	150.00	75.00	45.00
(5)	Bill Glynn	150.00	75.00	45.00
(6)	Larry Jansen	150.00	75.00	45.00
(7)	Bill Kennedy	150.00	75.00	45.00
(8)	Jack Lohrke	150.00	75.00	45.00
(9)	Frank O'Doul	250.00	125.00	75.00
(10)	Ray Orteig	150.00	75.00	45.00
(11)	Joe Taylor	150.00	75.00	45.00
(12)	Morrie (Maury) Wills	250.00	125.00	75.00

1912 Imperial Tobacco (C46)

This minor league set, issued in 1912 by the Imperial Tobacco Company, is the only tobacco baseball set issued in Canada. Designated as C46 in the American Card Catalog, each sepia-toned card measures 1-1/2" x 2-5/8" and features a distinctive card design that pictures the player inside an oval surrounded by a simulated woodgrain background featuring a bat, ball and glove in the borders.

The player's last name appears in capital letters in a panel beneath the oval. (An exception is the card of James Murray, whose caption includes both first and last names.) The backs include the player's name and team at the top, followed by a brief biography. The 90 subjects in the set are members of the eight teams in the Eastern League (Rochester, Toronto, Buffalo, Newark, Providence, Baltimore, Montreal and Jersey City), even though the card backs refer to it as the International League. The set contains many players with major league experience, including Hall of Famers Joe Kelley and Joe "Iron Man" McGinnity.

		NR MT	EX	VG
Complete Set:		4200.	2100.	1260.
Common Player:		35.00	17.50	10.50
1	William O'Hara	100.00	50.00	30.00
2	James McGinley	50.00	25.00	15.00
3	"Frenchy" LeClaire	35.00	17.50	10.50
4	John White	35.00	17.50	10.50
5	James Murray	35.00	17.50	10.50
6	Joe Ward	35.00	17.50	10.50
7	"Whitey" Alperman	35.00	17.50	10.50
8	"Natty" Nattress	35.00	17.50	10.50
9	Fred Sline	35.00	17.50	10.50
10	Royal Rock	35.00	17.50	10.50
11	Ray Demmitt	35.00	17.50	10.50
12	"Butcher Boy" Schmidt	35.00	17.50	10.50
13	Samuel Frock	35.00	17.50	10.50
14	Fred Burchell	35.00	17.50	10.50
15	Jack Kelley	35.00	17.50	10.50
16	Frank Barberich	35.00	17.50	10.50
17	Frank Corridon	35.00	17.50	10.50
18	"Doc" Adkins	35.00	17.50	10.50
19	Jack Dunn	35.00	17.50	10.50
20	James Walsh	35.00	17.50	10.50
21	Charles Hanford	35.00	17.50	10.50
22	Dick Rudolph	35.00	17.50	10.50
23	Curt Elston	35.00	17.50	10.50
24	Silton	35.00	17.50	10.50
25	Charlie French	35.00	17.50	10.50
26	John Ganzel	35.00	17.50	10.50
27	Joe Kelley	200.00	100.00	60.00
28	Benny Meyers	35.00	17.50	10.50
29	George Schirm	35.00	17.50	10.50
30	William Purtell	35.00	17.50	10.50
31	Bayard Sharpe	35.00	17.50	10.50
32	Tony Smith	35.00	17.50	10.50
33	John Lush	35.00	17.50	10.50
34	William Collins	35.00	17.50	10.50
35	Art Phelan	35.00	17.50	10.50
36	Edward Phelps	35.00	17.50	10.50
37	"Rube" Vickers	35.00	17.50	10.50
38	Cy Seymour	35.00	17.50	10.50
39	"Shadow" Carroll	35.00	17.50	10.50
40	Jake Gettman	35.00	17.50	10.50
41	Luther Taylor	35.00	17.50	10.50
42	Walter Justis	35.00	17.50	10.50
43	Robert Fisher	35.00	17.50	10.50
44	Fred Parent	35.00	17.50	10.50
45	James Dygert	35.00	17.50	10.50
46	Johnnie Butler	35.00	17.50	10.50
47	Fred Mitchell	35.00	17.50	10.50
48	Heinie Batch	35.00	17.50	10.50
49	Michael Corcoran	35.00	17.50	10.50
50	Edward Doescher	35.00	17.50	10.50
51	Wheeler	35.00	17.50	10.50
52	Elijah Jones	35.00	17.50	10.50
53	Fred Truesdale	35.00	17.50	10.50
54	Fred Beebe	35.00	17.50	10.50
55	Louis Brockett	35.00	17.50	10.50
56	Wells	35.00	17.50	10.50
57	"Lew" McAllister	35.00	17.50	10.50
58	Ralph Stroud	35.00	17.50	10.50
59	Manser	35.00	17.50	10.50
60	"Ducky" Holmes	35.00	17.50	10.50
61	Rube Dessau	35.00	17.50	10.50
62	Fred Jacklitsch	35.00	17.50	10.50
63	Graham	35.00	17.50	10.50
64	Noah Henline	35.00	17.50	10.50
65	"Chick" Gandil	50.00	25.00	15.00
66	Tom Hughes	35.00	17.50	10.50
67	Joseph Delehanty	35.00	17.50	10.50
68	Pierce	35.00	17.50	10.50
69	Gaunt	35.00	17.50	10.50
70	Edward Fitzpatrick	35.00	17.50	10.50
71	Wyatt Lee	35.00	17.50	10.50
72	John Kissinger	35.00	17.50	10.50
73	William Malarkey	35.00	17.50	10.50
74	William Byers	35.00	17.50	10.50
75	George Simmons	35.00	17.50	10.50
76	Daniel Moeller	35.00	17.50	10.50

77	Joseph McGinnity	200.00	100.00	60.00
78	Alex Hardy	35.00	17.50	10.50
79	Bob Holmes	35.00	17.50	10.50
80	William Baxter	35.00	17.50	10.50
81	Edward Spencer	35.00	17.50	10.50
82	Bradley Kocher	35.00	17.50	10.50
83	Robert Shaw	35.00	17.50	10.50
84	Joseph Yeager	35.00	17.50	10.50
85	Carlo	35.00	17.50	10.50
86	William Abstein	35.00	17.50	10.50
87	Tim Jordan	35.00	17.50	10.50
88	Dick Breen	35.00	17.50	10.50
89	Tom McCarty	50.00	25.00	15.00
90	Ed Curtis	100.00	50.00	30.00

1962 Kahn's Wieners Atlanta "Crackers"

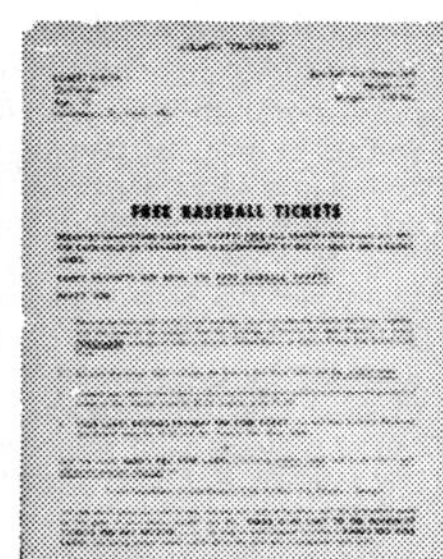

Kahn's made a single foray into the minor league market in 1962 with a separate 24-card set of Atlanta Crackers. The cards feature the same basic format, 3-1/4" x 4", borderless black and white photos with a Kahn's ad message in a white panel below the picture, as the major league issue. The backs are slightly different, having a free ticket offer in place of the player stats. Atlanta was the top farm club of the St. Louis Cardinals in 1962. The most famous alumnus in the set is Tim McCarver.

		NR MT	EX	VG
Complete Set:		400.00	200.00	120.00
Common Player:		15.00	7.50	4.50
(1)	James (Jimmy) Edward Beauchamp	15.00	7.50	4.50
(2)	Gerald Peter Buchek	15.00	7.50	4.50
(3)	Robert Burda	15.00	7.50	4.50
(4)	Hal Deitz	15.00	7.50	4.50
(5)	Robert John Duliba	15.00	7.50	4.50
(6)	Harry Michael Fanok	15.00	7.50	4.50
(7)	Phil Gagliano	15.00	7.50	4.50
(8)	John Glenn	15.00	7.50	4.50
(9)	Leroy Gregory	15.00	7.50	4.50
(10)	Richard (Dick) Henry Hughes	15.00	7.50	4.50
(11)	John Charles Kucks, Jr.	15.00	7.50	4.50
(12)	Johnny Joe Lewis	15.00	7.50	4.50
(13)	James (Mac - Timmie) Timothy McCarver	35.00	17.50	10.50
(14)	Robert F. Milliken	15.00	7.50	4.50
(15)	Joe Morgan	15.00	7.50	4.50
(16)	Ronald Charles Plaza	15.00	7.50	4.50
(17)	Bob Sadowski	15.00	7.50	4.50
(18)	Jim Saul	15.00	7.50	4.50
(19)	Willard Schmidt	15.00	7.50	4.50
(20)	Joe Schultz	15.00	7.50	4.50
(21)	Thomas Michael (Mike) Shannon	20.00	10.00	6.00
(22)	Paul Louis Toth	15.00	7.50	4.50
(23)	Andrew Lou Vickery	15.00	7.50	4.50
(24)	Fred Dwight Whitfield	15.00	7.50	4.50

1952 Knowles Service Stations Stockton Ports

Contemporary, and sharing a format with, the many Globe minor league issues of the early '50s, this set of Stockton Ports (California State League) cards carries the advertising of Knowles Service Stations. The blank-backed, black-and-white cards measure 2-1/4" x 3-1/2" and are unnumbered. It is likely the checklist here is incomplete, so no complete set price is given.

		NR MT	EX	VG
Common Player:		15.00	7.50	4.50
(1)	Wayne Clary	15.00	7.50	4.50
(2)	Harry Clements	15.00	7.50	4.50
(3)	John Crocco	15.00	7.50	4.50
(4)	Tony Freitas	15.00	7.50	4.50
(5)	Fibber Hirayama	15.00	7.50	4.50
(6)	Dave Mann	15.00	7.50	4.50
(7)	Larry Mann	15.00	7.50	4.50
(8)	Hank Moreno	15.00	7.50	4.50
(9)	Frank Romero	15.00	7.50	4.50
(10)	Chuck Thomas	15.00	7.50	4.50
(11)	Bud Watkins	15.00	7.50	4.50

1952 Laval Dairy Provincial League

This rare Canadian minor league issue includes only players from the Class C Provincial League, centered in Quebec. The black-and-white cards are blank-backed and measure 1-3/4" x 2-1/2". The player name, position, date and place of birth and card number is in French. Teams represented in the set are Quebec (Braves), St. Jean (Pirates), Three Rivers (independent), Drummondville (Senators), Granby (Phillies) and Ste. Hyacinthe (Philadelphia A's).

		NR MT	EX	VG
Complete Set (114):		1250.	625.00	350.00
Common Player:		15.00	7.50	4.50
1	Georges McQuinn	15.00	7.50	4.50
2	Cliff Statham	15.00	7.50	4.50
3	Frank Wilson	15.00	7.50	4.50
4	Unknown			
5	Georges Maranda	15.00	7.50	4.50
6	Unknown			
7	Roger McCardell	15.00	7.50	4.50
8	Joseph Janiak	15.00	7.50	4.50
9	Herbert Shankman	15.00	7.50	4.50
10	Joe Subbiondo	15.00	7.50	4.50
11	Jack Brenner	15.00	7.50	4.50
12	Donald Buchanan	15.00	7.50	4.50
13	Robert Smith	15.00	7.50	4.50
14	Raymond Lague	15.00	7.50	4.50
15	Mike Fandozzi	15.00	7.50	4.50
16	Dick Moler	15.00	7.50	4.50
17	Edward Bazydio	15.00	7.50	4.50
18	Unknown			
19	Edwin Charles	15.00	7.50	4.50
20	Jack Nullaney	15.00	7.50	4.50
21	Bob Bolan	15.00	7.50	4.50
22	Bob Long	15.00	7.50	4.50
23	Cleo Lewright	15.00	7.50	4.50
24	Herb Taylor	15.00	7.50	4.50
25	Frankie Gaeta	15.00	7.50	4.50
26	Bill Truitt	15.00	7.50	4.50
27	Jean Prats	15.00	7.50	4.50
28	Tex Taylor	15.00	7.50	4.50
29	Ron Delbianco	15.00	7.50	4.50
30	Joe DiLorenzo	15.00	7.50	4.50
31	Johnny Paszek	15.00	7.50	4.50
32	Ken Suess	15.00	7.50	4.50
33	Harry Sims	15.00	7.50	4.50
34	William Jackson	15.00	7.50	4.50
35	Jerry Mayers	15.00	7.50	4.50
36	Gordon Maltzberger	15.00	7.50	4.50
37	Gerry Cabana	15.00	7.50	4.50
38	Gary Rutkey	15.00	7.50	4.50
39	Ken Hatcher	15.00	7.50	4.50
40	Vincent Cosenza	15.00	7.50	4.50
41	Edward Yaeger	15.00	7.50	4.50
42	Jimmy Orr	15.00	7.50	4.50
43	Johnny Di Matino	15.00	7.50	4.50
44	Lenny Wisneski	15.00	7.50	4.50
45	Pete Caniglia	15.00	7.50	4.50
46	Guy Coleman	15.00	7.50	4.50
47	Herb Fleischer	15.00	7.50	4.50
48	Charles Yahrling	15.00	7.50	4.50
49	Roger Bedard	15.00	7.50	4.50
50	Al Barillari	15.00	7.50	4.50
51	Hugh Mulcahy	15.00	7.50	4.50
52	Vincent Canepa	15.00	7.50	4.50
53	Bob Loranger	15.00	7.50	4.50
54	Georges Carpentier	15.00	7.50	4.50
55	Bill Hamilton	15.00	7.50	4.50
56	Hector Lopez	15.00	7.50	4.50
57	Joel Taylor	15.00	7.50	4.50
58	Alonzo Brathwaite	15.00	7.50	4.50
59	Carl McQuillen	15.00	7.50	4.50
60	Robert Trice	15.00	7.50	4.50
61	John Dworak	15.00	7.50	4.50
62	Al Pinkston	15.00	7.50	4.50
63	William Shannon	15.00	7.50	4.50
64	Stanley Wotychowisz	15.00	7.50	4.50
65	Roger Herbert	15.00	7.50	4.50
66	Troy Spencer	15.00	7.50	4.50
67	Johnny Rohan	15.00	7.50	4.50
68	Unknown			
69	Ramon Mason	15.00	7.50	4.50
70	Tom Smith	15.00	7.50	4.50
71	Douglas McBean	15.00	7.50	4.50
72	Bill Babik	15.00	7.50	4.50
73	Dante Cozzi	15.00	7.50	4.50
74	Melville Doxtater	15.00	7.50	4.50
75	William Gilray	15.00	7.50	4.50
76	Armando Diaz	15.00	7.50	4.50
77	Ackroyd Smith	15.00	7.50	4.50
78	Germain Pizarro	15.00	7.50	4.50
79	Jim Heap	15.00	7.50	4.50
80	Herbert Crompton	15.00	7.50	4.50
81	Howard Bodell	15.00	7.50	4.50
82	Andre Schreiser	15.00	7.50	4.50
83	John Wingo	15.00	7.50	4.50
84	Salvatore Arduini	15.00	7.50	4.50
85	Fred Pallito	15.00	7.50	4.50
86	Aaron Osofsky	15.00	7.50	4.50
87	Jack DiGrace	15.00	7.50	4.50
88	Alphonso Chico Girard	15.00	7.50	4.50
89	Manuel Trabous	15.00	7.50	4.50
90	Tom Barnes	15.00	7.50	4.50
91	Humberto Robinson	15.00	7.50	4.50
92	Jack Bukowatz	15.00	7.50	4.50
93	Marco Mainini	15.00	7.50	4.50
94	Claude St. Vincent	15.00	7.50	4.50
95	Fernand Brosseau	15.00	7.50	4.50
96	John Malangone	15.00	7.50	4.50
97	Pierre Nantel	15.00	7.50	4.50
98	Donald Stevens	15.00	7.50	4.50
99	Jim Prappas	15.00	7.50	4.50
100	Richard Fitzgerald	15.00	7.50	4.50
101	Yves Aubin	15.00	7.50	4.50
102	Frank Novosel	15.00	7.50	4.50
103	Tony Campos	15.00	7.50	4.50
104	Gelso Oviedo	15.00	7.50	4.50
105	Guly Becker	15.00	7.50	4.50
106	Aurelio Ala	15.00	7.50	4.50
107	Orlando Andux	15.00	7.50	4.50
108	Tom Hackett	15.00	7.50	4.50
109	Guillame Vargas	15.00	7.50	4.50
110	Fransisco Salfran	15.00	7.50	4.50
111	Jean-Marc Blais	15.00	7.50	4.50
112	Vince Pizzitola	15.00	7.50	4.50
113	John Olsen	15.00	7.50	4.50
114	Jacques Monette	15.00	7.50	4.50

1954 MD Super Service Sacramento Solons

Probably an issue of the Globe company, which produced many contemporary minor league sets, this issue features only players of the Pacific Coast League Sacremento Solons. The unnumbered cards are printed in black-and-white and carry an ad for a local gas station. The borderless, blank-backed cards measure 2-1/8" x 3-3/8". Because of the likelihood that this checklist is incomplete, no price is quoted for a complete set.

		NR MT	EX	VG
Common Player:		15.00	7.50	4.50
(1)	Joe Brovia	15.00	7.50	4.50
(2)	Al Cicotte	15.00	7.50	4.50
(3)	Nippy Jones	15.00	7.50	4.50
(4)	Richie Meyers	15.00	7.50	4.50
(5)	Hank Schenz	15.00	7.50	4.50
(6)	Bud Sheeley	15.00	7.50	4.50

A player's name in italic type indicates a rookie card. An (FC) indicates a player's first card for that particular card company.

1963 Milwaukee Sausage Seattle Rainiers

Inserted into meat packages by a Seattle sausage company, the 11 cards known in this set are all Seattle Rainiers players, several of whom had big league experience. Cards measure approximately 4-1/4"-square and are printed in blue, red and yellow. The unnumbered cards are checklisted in alphabetical order.

		NR MT	EX	VG
Complete Set:		1500.	750.00	450.00
Common Player:		150.00	75.00	45.00
(1)	Dave Hall	150.00	75.00	45.00
(2)	Bill Harrell	150.00	75.00	45.00
(3)	Pete Jernigan	150.00	75.00	45.00
(4)	Bill McLeod	150.00	75.00	45.00
(5)	Mel Parnell	200.00	100.00	60.00
(6)	Elmer Singleton	150.00	75.00	45.00
(7)	Archie Skeen	150.00	75.00	45.00
(8)	Paul Smith	150.00	75.00	45.00
(9)	Pete Smith	150.00	75.00	45.00
(10)	Bill Spanswick	150.00	75.00	45.00
(11)	George Spencer	150.00	75.00	45.00

1911 Mono Cigarettes (T217)

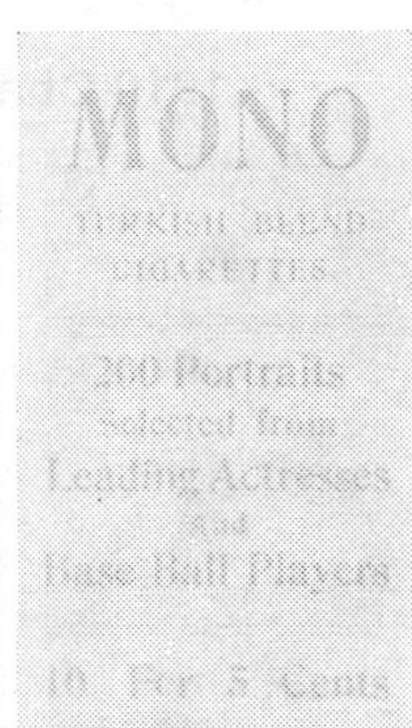

As was common with many tobacco issues of the period, the T217 set - distributed on the West Coast by Mono Cigarettes - feature both baseball players and "Leading Actresses." The 23 baseball players in the Mono set are all from the Pacific Coast League. Two of the players (Delhi and Hughie Smith) are shown in two poses, resulting in a total of 25 different cards. The players are pictured in black-and-white photos on a card that measures approximately 1-1/2" x 2-5/8", the standard size of a tobacco card. The player's name and team appear at the bottom, while the back of the card carries an advertisement for Mono Cigarettes. The Mono set, which can be dated to the 1909-1911 period, is among the rarest of all tobacco cards.

		NR MT	EX	VG
Complete Set:		6250.	3125.	1875.
Common Player:		225.00	112.00	67.00
(1)	Aiken	225.00	112.00	67.00
(2)	Curtis Bernard	225.00	112.00	67.00
(3)	L. Burrell	225.00	112.00	67.00
(4)	Chadbourn	225.00	112.00	67.00
(5)	R. Couchman	225.00	112.00	67.00
(6)	Elmer Criger	225.00	112.00	67.00
(7)	Pete Daley	225.00	112.00	67.00
(8)	W. Delhi (glove at chest level)	225.00	112.00	67.00
(9)	W. Delhi (glove at shoulder level)	225.00	112.00	67.00
(10)	Bert Delmas	225.00	112.00	67.00
(11)	Ivan Howard	225.00	112.00	67.00
(12)	Kitty Knight	225.00	112.00	67.00
(13)	Gene Knapp (Krapp)	225.00	112.00	67.00
(14)	Metzger	225.00	112.00	67.00
(15)	Carl Mitze	225.00	112.00	67.00
(16)	J. O'Rourke	225.00	112.00	67.00
(17)	R. Peckinpaugh	250.00	125.00	75.00
(18)	Walter Schmidt	225.00	112.00	67.00
(19)	Hughie Smith (batting)	225.00	112.00	67.00
(20)	Hughie Smith (fielding)	225.00	112.00	67.00
(21)	Wm. Stein	225.00	112.00	67.00
(22)	Elmer Thorsen	225.00	112.00	67.00
(23)	Oscar Vitt	225.00	112.00	67.00
(24)	Clyde Wares	225.00	112.00	67.00
(25)	Geo. Wheeler	225.00	112.00	67.00

A card number in parentheses () indicates the set is unnumbered.

1947 Morley Studios Tacoma Tigers

This set of Tacoma Tigers (Western International League) features borderless black-and-white posed action photos with a facsimile autograph on front. A "Morley Sports Photos" credit line appears at the bottom. Backs of the first six cards are blank, while the others feature player biographies and a Series A through F designation. The unnumbered cards measure 2-1/2" x 3-1/2".

		NR MT	EX	VG
Complete Set:		1000.	500.00	300.00
Common Player:		50.00	25.00	15.00
(1)	Hank Bartolomew	50.00	25.00	15.00
(2)	Rod Belcher	50.00	25.00	15.00
(3)	Tip Berg	50.00	25.00	15.00
(4)	Gene Cligh	50.00	25.00	15.00
(5)	Clay Huntington	50.00	25.00	15.00
(6)	Donald Mooney	50.00	25.00	15.00
(7)	Richard A. Greco	50.00	25.00	15.00
(8)	Cy Greenlaw	50.00	25.00	15.00
(9)	Bob Joratz	50.00	25.00	15.00
(10)	Earl Kuper	50.00	25.00	15.00
(11)	Red Harvel	50.00	25.00	15.00
(12)	Julian Morgan	50.00	25.00	15.00
(13)	Pete Tedeschi	50.00	25.00	15.00
(14)	Stanley Gilson	50.00	25.00	15.00
(15)	Cleve Ramsey	50.00	25.00	15.00
(16)	Harry Wygard	50.00	25.00	15.00
(17)	Mitch Chetkovich	50.00	25.00	15.00
(18)	Carl Shaply	50.00	25.00	15.00
(19)	Glenn Stetter	50.00	25.00	15.00
(20)	Bob Hedington	50.00	25.00	15.00
(21)	Ed Keehan	50.00	25.00	15.00
(22)	Gordon Walden	50.00	25.00	15.00
(23)	Maury Donovan	50.00	25.00	15.00
(24)	Guy Miller	50.00	25.00	15.00

1952 Mother's Cookies

This is one of the most popular regional minor league sets ever issued. Cards of Pacific Coast League players were included in packages of cookies. Distribution was limited to the West Coast. The 64 cards feature full color photos on a colored background, with player name and team. The cards measure 2-13/16" x 3-1/2", though the cards' rounded corners cause some variation in listed size. Card backs feature a very brief player statistic, card numbers and an offer for purchasing postage stamps. Five cards (11, 16, 29, 37 and 43) are considered scarce, while card #4 (Chuck Connors) is the most popular.

		NR MT	EX	VG
Complete Set:		1500.	750.00	450.00
Common Player:		24.00	12.00	7.25
1	Johnny Lindell	35.00	17.50	10.50
2	Jim Davis	24.00	12.00	7.25
3	Al Gettle (Gettel)	24.00	12.00	7.25
4	Chuck Connors	200.00	100.00	60.00
5	Joe Grace	24.00	12.00	7.25
6	Eddie Basinski	24.00	12.00	7.25
7	Gene Handley	24.00	12.00	7.25
8	Walt Judnich	24.00	12.00	7.25
9	Jim Marshall	24.00	12.00	7.25
10	Max West	24.00	12.00	7.25
11	Bill MacCawley	50.00	25.00	15.00
12	Moreno Peiretti	24.00	12.00	7.25
13	Fred Haney	35.00	17.50	10.50
14	Earl Johnson	24.00	12.00	7.25
15	Dave Dahle	24.00	12.00	7.25
16	Bob Talbot	50.00	25.00	15.00
17	Smokey Singleton	24.00	12.00	7.25
18	Frank Austin	24.00	12.00	7.25
19	Joe Gordon	35.00	17.50	10.50
20	Joe Marty	24.00	12.00	7.25
21	Bob Gillespie	24.00	12.00	7.25
22	Red Embree	24.00	12.00	7.25
23	Lefty Olsen	24.00	12.00	7.25
24	Whitey Wietelmann	24.00	12.00	7.25
25	Frank O'Doul	35.00	17.50	10.50
26	Memo Luna	24.00	12.00	7.25
27	John Davis	24.00	12.00	7.25
28	Dick Faber	24.00	12.00	7.25
29	Buddy Peterson	125.00	62.00	37.00
30	Hank Schenz	24.00	12.00	7.25
31	Tookie Gilbert	24.00	12.00	7.25
32	Mel Ott	60.00	30.00	18.00
33	Sam Chapman	24.00	12.00	7.25
34	Dick Cole	24.00	12.00	7.25
35	John Ragni	24.00	12.00	7.25
36	Tom Saffell	24.00	12.00	7.25
37	Roy Welmaker	50.00	25.00	15.00
38	Lou Stringer	24.00	12.00	7.25
39	Artie Wilson	24.00	12.00	7.25
40	Chuck Stevens	24.00	12.00	7.25
41	Charlie Schanz	24.00	12.00	7.25
42	Al Lyons	24.00	12.00	7.25
43	Joe Erautt	125.00	62.00	37.00
44	Clarence Maddern	24.00	12.00	7.25
45	Gene Baker	24.00	12.00	7.25
46	Tom Heath	24.00	12.00	7.25
47	Al Lien	24.00	12.00	7.25
48	Bill Reeder	24.00	12.00	7.25
49	Bob Thurman	24.00	12.00	7.25
50	Ray Orteig	24.00	12.00	7.25
51	Joe Brovia	24.00	12.00	7.25
52	Jim Russell	24.00	12.00	7.25
53	Fred Sanford	24.00	12.00	7.25
54	Jim Gladd	24.00	12.00	7.25
55	Clay Hopper	24.00	12.00	7.25
56	Bill Glynn	24.00	12.00	7.25
57	Mike McCormick	24.00	12.00	7.25
58	Richie Myers	24.00	12.00	7.25
59	Vinnie Smith	24.00	12.00	7.25
60	Stan Hack	35.00	17.50	10.50
61	Bob Spicer	24.00	12.00	7.25
62	Jack Hollis	24.00	12.00	7.25
63	Ed Chandler	24.00	12.00	7.25
64	Bill Moisan	35.00	17.50	10.50

1953 Mother's Cookies

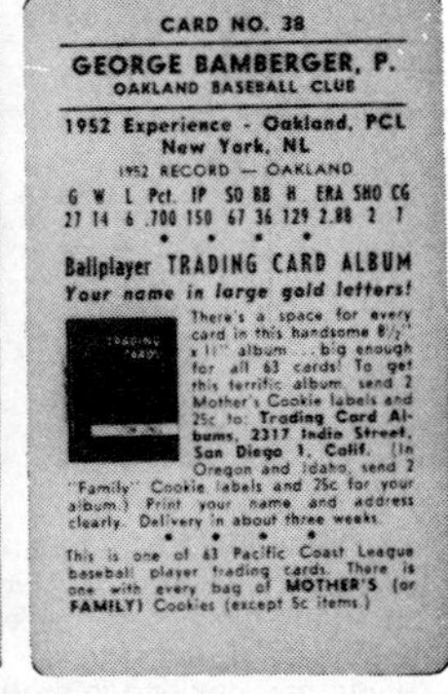

The 1953 Mother's Cookies cards are again 2-3/16" x 3-1/2", with rounded corners. There are 63 players from Pacific Coast League teams included. The full-color fronts have facsimile autographs rather than printed player names, and card backs offer a trading card album. Cards are generally more plentiful than in the 1952 set, with 11 of the cards apparently double printed.

		NR MT	EX	VG
Complete Set:		425.00	213.00	128.00
Common Player:		12.00	6.00	3.50
1	Lee Winter	16.00	8.00	4.75
2	Joe Ostrowski	12.00	6.00	3.50
3	Will Ramsdell	12.00	6.00	3.50
4	Bobby Bragan	16.00	8.00	4.75
5	Fletcher Robbe	12.00	6.00	3.50
6	Aaron Robinson	12.00	6.00	3.50
7	Augie Galan	12.00	6.00	3.50
8	Buddy Peterson	12.00	6.00	3.50
9	Frank Lefty O'Doul	18.00	9.00	5.50
10	Walt Pocekay	12.00	6.00	3.50
11	Nini Tornay	12.00	6.00	3.50
12	Jim Moran	12.00	6.00	3.50
13	George Schmees	12.00	6.00	3.50
14	Al Widmar	12.00	6.00	3.50
15	Ritchie Myers	12.00	6.00	3.50
16	Bill Howerton	12.00	6.00	3.50
17	Chuck Stevens	12.00	6.00	3.50
18	Joe Brovia	12.00	6.00	3.50

19	Max West	12.00	6.00	3.50
20	Eddie Malone	12.00	6.00	3.50
21	Gene Handley	12.00	6.00	3.50
22	William D. McCawley	12.00	6.00	3.50
23	Bill Sweeney	12.00	6.00	3.50
24	Tom Alston	12.00	6.00	3.50
25	George Vico	12.00	6.00	3.50
26	Hank Arft	12.00	6.00	3.50
27	Al Benton	12.00	6.00	3.50
28	"Pete" Milne	12.00	6.00	3.50
29	Jim Gladd	12.00	6.00	3.50
30	Earl Rapp	12.00	6.00	3.50
31	Ray Orteig	12.00	6.00	3.50
32	Eddie Basinski	12.00	6.00	3.50
33	Reno Cheso	12.00	6.00	3.50
34	Clarence Maddern	12.00	6.00	3.50
35	Marino Pieretti	12.00	6.00	3.50
36	Bill Raimondi	12.00	6.00	3.50
37	Frank Kelleher	12.00	6.00	3.50
38	George Bamberger	18.00	9.00	5.50
39	Dick Smith	12.00	6.00	3.50
40	Charley Schanz	12.00	6.00	3.50
41	John Van Cuyk	12.00	6.00	3.50
42	Lloyd Hittle	12.00	6.00	3.50
43	Tommy Heath	12.00	6.00	3.50
44	Frank Kalin	12.00	6.00	3.50
45	Jack Tobin	12.00	6.00	3.50
46	Jim Davis	12.00	6.00	3.50
47	Claude Christie	12.00	6.00	3.50
48	Elvin Tappe	12.00	6.00	3.50
49	Stan Hack	16.00	8.00	4.75
50	Fred Richards	12.00	6.00	3.50
51	Clay Hopper	12.00	6.00	3.50
52	Roy Welmaker	12.00	6.00	3.50
53	Red Adams	12.00	6.00	3.50
54	Piper Davis	12.00	6.00	3.50
55	Spider Jorgensen	12.00	6.00	3.50
56	Lee Walls	12.00	6.00	3.50
57	Jack Phillips	12.00	6.00	3.50
58	Red Lynn	12.00	6.00	3.50
59	Eddie Beckman	12.00	6.00	3.50
60	Gene Desautels	12.00	6.00	3.50
61	Bob Dillinger	12.00	6.00	3.50
62	Al Federoff	12.00	6.00	3.50
63	Bill Boemler	12.00	6.00	3.50

1960 National Bank Washington/Tacoma Giants

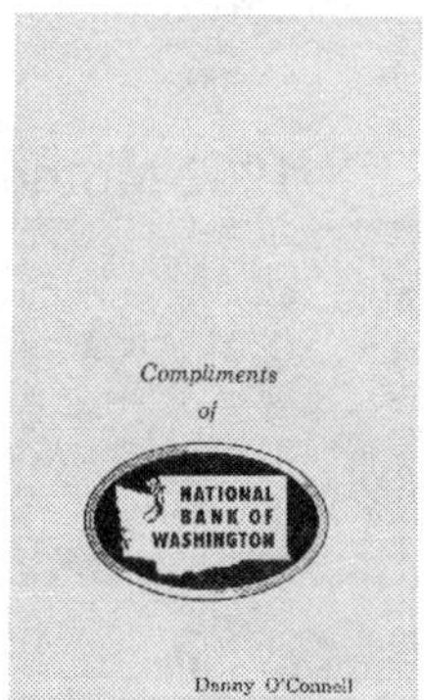

Compliments of
NATIONAL BANK OF WASHINGTON
Danny O'Connell

These 3"x5" unnumbered cards have color photos on front and can be found either with no advertising on the back, or a black-and-white bank ad. Only members of the Pacific Coast League Tacoma Giants are included in the set. The set contains the first card issued of Hall of Fame pitcher Juan Marichal. Unfortunately, fellow Hall of Famer Willie McCovey, who played in 17 games for Tacoma in 1960 is not included in the set.

		NR MT	EX	VG
Complete Set:		850.00	425.00	255.00
Common Player:		20.00	10.00	6.00
(1)	Matty Alou	60.00	30.00	18.00
(2)	Ossie Alvarez	20.00	10.00	6.00
(3)	Don Choate	20.00	10.00	6.00
(4)	Red Davis	20.00	10.00	6.00
(5)	Bob Farley	20.00	10.00	6.00
(6)	Eddie Fisher	20.00	10.00	6.00
(7)	Tom Haller	20.00	10.00	6.00
(8)	Sherman Jones	20.00	10.00	6.00
(9)	Juan Marichal	400.00	200.00	120.00
(10)	Ray Monzant	20.00	10.00	6.00
(11)	Danny O'Connell	25.00	12.50	7.50
(12)	Jose Pagan	20.00	10.00	6.00
(13)	Bob Perry	20.00	10.00	6.00
(14)	Dick Phillips	20.00	10.00	6.00
(15)	Bobby Prescott	20.00	10.00	6.00
(16)	Marshall Renfroe	20.00	10.00	6.00
(17)	Frank Reveira	20.00	10.00	6.00
(18)	Dusty Rhodes	25.00	12.50	7.50
(19)	Sal Taormina	20.00	10.00	6.00
(20)	Verle Tiefenthaler	20.00	10.00	6.00
(21)	Dom Zanni	20.00	10.00	6.00

1909 Obak (T212)

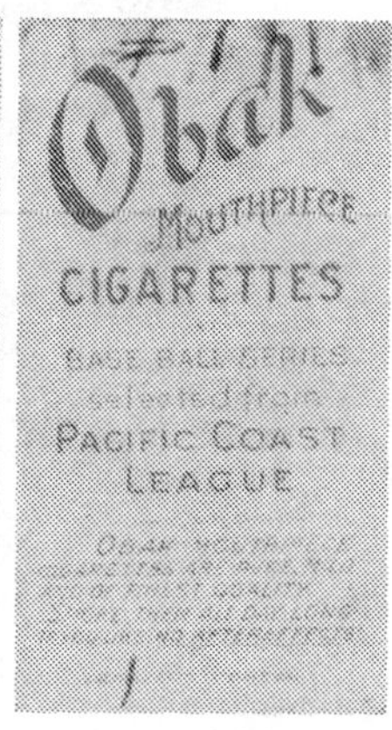

Collectors of early Pacific Coast League memorabilia consider the Obak Cigarette cards to be among the most signifiacant of all the 20th Century minor league tobacco issues. Produced annually from 1909 to 1911, the Obak cards were actually three separate and distinct sets, but because they were all grouped together under a single T212 designation in the American Card Catalog, they are generally collected that way today. The Obak sets are closely related in style to the more popular T206 "White Border" set issued over the same three-year period, and, in fact, were produced by the California branch of the same American Tobacco Company conglomerate. The Obaks are the standard tobacco card size, 1-1/2" x 2-5/8" and feature a colored lithograph, along with the player's name and team, on the front of the card. The year of issue can easily be determined by examing the back. The 1909 issue has blue printing with the name "Obak" appearing in an "Old English" type style; for 1910 the type face was changed to straight block letters; and in 1911 the backs were printed in red and included a brief biography and player statistics. There are 269 different players in the three issues, but, because many of the subjects appeared in more than one year, Obak collectors generally consider the set complete at 426 different cards. The 1909 edition featured only teams from the Pacific Coast League, while the 1910 and 1911 sets were expanded to also include players from the Northwestern League. The Obak sets offer advanced collectors a challenging number of variations, and they have additional appeal because about 40 percent of the checklisted players had major league experience.

		NR MT	EX	VG
Complete Set:		2300.	1150.	690.00
Common Player:		30.00	15.00	9.00
(1)	Baum	30.00	15.00	9.00
(2)	Bernard	30.00	15.00	9.00
(3)	Berry	30.00	15.00	9.00
(4)	Bodie	30.00	15.00	9.00
(5)	Boyce	30.00	15.00	9.00
(6)	Brackenridge	30.00	15.00	9.00
(7)	N. Brashear	30.00	15.00	9.00
(8)	Breen	30.00	15.00	9.00
(9)	Brown	30.00	15.00	9.00
(10)	D. Brown	30.00	15.00	9.00
(11)	Browning	30.00	15.00	9.00
(12)	Byrnes	30.00	15.00	9.00
(13)	Cameron	30.00	15.00	9.00
(14)	Carroll	30.00	15.00	9.00
(15)	Carson	30.00	15.00	9.00
(16)	Christian	30.00	15.00	9.00
(17)	Coy	30.00	15.00	9.00
(18)	Delmas	30.00	15.00	9.00
(19)	Dillon	30.00	15.00	9.00
(20)	Eagan	30.00	15.00	9.00
(21)	Easterly (Eastley)	30.00	15.00	9.00
(22)	Flannagan	30.00	15.00	9.00
(23)	Fisher	30.00	15.00	9.00
(24)	Fitzgerald	30.00	15.00	9.00
(25)	Gandil	45.00	22.00	13.50
(26)	Garrett	30.00	15.00	9.00
(27)	Graham	30.00	15.00	9.00
(28)	Graney	30.00	15.00	9.00
(29)	Griffin	30.00	15.00	9.00
(30)	Guyn	30.00	15.00	9.00
(31)	Haley	30.00	15.00	9.00
(32)	Harkins	30.00	15.00	9.00
(33)	Henley	30.00	15.00	9.00
(34)	Hitt	30.00	15.00	9.00
(35)	Hogan	30.00	15.00	9.00
(36)	W. Hogan	30.00	15.00	9.00
(37)	Howard	30.00	15.00	9.00
(38)	Howse	30.00	15.00	9.00
(39)	Jansing	30.00	15.00	9.00
(40)	LaLonge	30.00	15.00	9.00
(41)	C. Lewis	30.00	15.00	9.00
(42)	D. Lewis	35.00	17.50	10.50
(43)	J. Lewis	30.00	15.00	9.00
(44)	Martinez	30.00	15.00	9.00
(45)	McArdle	30.00	15.00	9.00
(46)	McCredie	30.00	15.00	9.00
(47)	McKune	30.00	15.00	9.00
(48)	Melchoir	30.00	15.00	9.00
(49)	Mohler	30.00	15.00	9.00
(50)	Mott	30.00	15.00	9.00
(51)	Mundorff	30.00	15.00	9.00
(52)	Murphy	30.00	15.00	9.00
(53)	Nagle	30.00	15.00	9.00
(54)	Nelson	30.00	15.00	9.00
(55)	Olson	30.00	15.00	9.00
(56)	Ornsdorff	30.00	15.00	9.00
(57)	Ort	30.00	15.00	9.00
(58)	Ragan	30.00	15.00	9.00
(59)	Raymer	30.00	15.00	9.00
(60)	Raymond	30.00	15.00	9.00
(61)	Reidy	30.00	15.00	9.00
(62)	Ryan	30.00	15.00	9.00
(63)	Shinn	30.00	15.00	9.00
(64)	Smith	30.00	15.00	9.00
(65)	Speas	30.00	15.00	9.00
(66)	Stoval (Stovall)	30.00	15.00	9.00
(67)	Tennant	30.00	15.00	9.00
(68)	Whalen	30.00	15.00	9.00
(69)	Wheeler	30.00	15.00	9.00
(70)	Wiggs	30.00	15.00	9.00
(71)	Willett	30.00	15.00	9.00
(72)	J. Williams	30.00	15.00	9.00
(73)	R. Williams	30.00	15.00	9.00
(74)	Willis	30.00	15.00	9.00
(75)	Zeider	30.00	15.00	9.00

1910 Obak (T212)

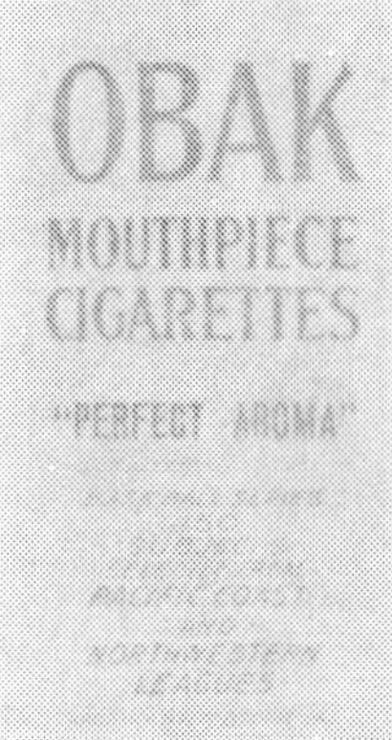

		NR MT	EX	VG
Complete Set:		3200.	1600.	960.00
Common Player:		15.00	7.50	4.50
(1)	Agnew	15.00	7.50	4.50
(2)	Akin	15.00	7.50	4.50
(3)	Ames	15.00	7.50	4.50
(4)	Annis	15.00	7.50	4.50
(5a)	Armbuster (Armbruster) ("150 subjects" back)	15.00	7.50	4.50
(5b)	Armbuster (Armbruster) ("175 subjects" back)	15.00	7.50	4.50
(6)	Baker	15.00	7.50	4.50
(7)	Bassey	15.00	7.50	4.50
(8)	Baum	15.00	7.50	4.50
(9)	Beall	15.00	7.50	4.50
(10)	Bennett	15.00	7.50	4.50
(11)	Bernard	15.00	7.50	4.50
(12a)	Berry ("150 subjects" back)	15.00	7.50	4.50
(12b)	Berry ("175 subjects" back)	15.00	7.50	4.50
(13)	Blankenship	15.00	7.50	4.50
(14)	Boardman	15.00	7.50	4.50
(15)	Bodie	15.00	7.50	4.50
(16)	Bonner	15.00	7.50	4.50
(17a)	Brackenridge ("150 subjects" back)	15.00	7.50	4.50
(17b)	Brackenridge ("175 subjects" back)	15.00	7.50	4.50
(18a)	N. Brashear ("150 subjects" back)	15.00	7.50	4.50
(18b)	N. Brashear ("175 subjects" back)	15.00	7.50	4.50
(19)	R. Brashear	15.00	7.50	4.50
(20)	Breen	15.00	7.50	4.50
(21a)	Briggs ("150 subjects" back)	15.00	7.50	4.50
(21b)	Briggs ("175 subjects" back)	15.00	7.50	4.50
(22)	Brinker	15.00	7.50	4.50
(23)	Briswalter	15.00	7.50	4.50
(24)	Brooks	15.00	7.50	4.50
(25)	Brown (Sacramento)	15.00	7.50	4.50
(26)	Brown (Vancouver)	15.00	7.50	4.50
(27)	D. Brown	15.00	7.50	4.50
(28)	Browning	15.00	7.50	4.50
(29)	Burrell, Byrd	15.00	7.50	4.50
(30)	Byrnes	15.00	7.50	4.50
(31a)	Cameron ("150 subjects" back)	15.00	7.50	4.50
(31b)	Cameron ("175 subjects" back)	15.00	7.50	4.50
(32)	Capren (Capron)	15.00	7.50	4.50
(33)	Carlisle	15.00	7.50	4.50
(34)	Carroll	15.00	7.50	4.50
(35)	Cartwright	15.00	7.50	4.50
(36)	Casey	15.00	7.50	4.50
(37)	Casleton (Castleton)	15.00	7.50	4.50
(38)	Chenault	15.00	7.50	4.50
(39)	Christian	15.00	7.50	4.50

(40) Coleman 15.00 7.50 4.50
(41) Cooney 15.00 7.50 4.50
(42a) Coy ("150 subjects" back) 15.00 7.50 4.50
(42b) Coy ("175 subjects" back) 15.00 7.50 4.50
(43a) Criger ("150 subjects" back) 15.00 7.50 4.50
(43b) Criger ("175 subjects" back) 15.00 7.50 4.50
(44) Custer 15.00 7.50 4.50
(45) Cutshaw 15.00 7.50 4.50
(46) Daley 15.00 7.50 4.50
(47a) Danzig ("150 subjects" back) 15.00 7.50 4.50
(47b) Danzig ("175 subjects" back) 15.00 7.50 4.50
(48) Daringer 15.00 7.50 4.50
(49) Davis 15.00 7.50 4.50
(50) Delhi 15.00 7.50 4.50
(51) Delmas 15.00 7.50 4.50
(52a) Dillon ("150 subjects" back) 15.00 7.50 4.50
(52b) Dillon ("175 subjects" back) 15.00 7.50 4.50
(53) Dretchko 15.00 7.50 4.50
(54) Eastley 15.00 7.50 4.50
(55) Erickson 15.00 7.50 4.50
(56) Flannagan 15.00 7.50 4.50
(57) Fisher (Portland) 15.00 7.50 4.50
(58a) Fisher (Vernon, "150 subjects" back)
15.00 7.50 4.50
(58b) Fisher (Vernon, "175 subjects" back)
15.00 7.50 4.50
(59) Fitzgerald 15.00 7.50 4.50
(60) Flood 15.00 7.50 4.50
(61) Fournier 15.00 7.50 4.50
(62) Frisk 15.00 7.50 4.50
(63) Gaddy 15.00 7.50 4.50
(64) Gardner 15.00 7.50 4.50
(65) Garrett 15.00 7.50 4.50
(66) Greggs (Gregg) 15.00 7.50 4.50
(67a) Griffin ("150 subjects" back) 15.00 7.50 4.50
(67b) Griffin ("175 subjects" back) 15.00 7.50 4.50
(68) Gurney 15.00 7.50 4.50
(69) Hall (Seattle) 15.00 7.50 4.50
(70) Hall (Tacoma) 15.00 7.50 4.50
(71) Harkins 15.00 7.50 4.50
(72) Hartman 15.00 7.50 4.50
(73) Hendrix 15.00 7.50 4.50
(74a) Henley ("150 subjects" back) 15.00 7.50 4.50
(74b) Henley ("175 subjects" back) 15.00 7.50 4.50
(75) Hensling 15.00 7.50 4.50
(76) Hetling 15.00 7.50 4.50
(77) Hickey 15.00 7.50 4.50
(78a) Hiester ("150 subjects" back) 15.00 7.50 4.50
(78b) Hiester ("175 subjects" back) 15.00 7.50 4.50
(79) Hitt 15.00 7.50 4.50
(80) Hogan (Oakland) 15.00 7.50 4.50
(81a) Hogan (Vernon, "150 subjects" back)
15.00 7.50 4.50
(81b) Hogan (Vernon, "175 subjects" back)
15.00 7.50 4.50
(82) Hollis 15.00 7.50 4.50
(83) Holm 15.00 7.50 4.50
(84a) Howard ("150 subjects" back) 15.00 7.50 4.50
(84b) Howard ("175 subjects" back) 15.00 7.50 4.50
(85) Hunt 15.00 7.50 4.50
(86) James 15.00 7.50 4.50
(87) Jansing 15.00 7.50 4.50
(88) Jensen 15.00 7.50 4.50
(89) Johnston 15.00 7.50 4.50
(90) Keener 15.00 7.50 4.50
(91) Killilay 15.00 7.50 4.50
(92) Kippert 15.00 7.50 4.50
(93) Klein 15.00 7.50 4.50
(94a) Krapp ("150 subjects" back) 15.00 7.50 4.50
(94b) Krapp ("175 subjects" back) 15.00 7.50 4.50
(95) Kusel 15.00 7.50 4.50
(96a) LaLonge ("150 subjects" back) 15.00 7.50 4.50
(96b) LaLonge ("175 subjects" back) 15.00 7.50 4.50
(97) Lewis 15.00 7.50 4.50
(98) J. Lewis 15.00 7.50 4.50
(99) Lindsay 15.00 7.50 4.50
(100) Lively 15.00 7.50 4.50
(101) Lynch 15.00 7.50 4.50
(102a) Manush ("150 subjects" back) 15.00 7.50 4.50
(102b) Manush ("175 subjects" back) 15.00 7.50 4.50
(103) Martinke 15.00 7.50 4.50
(104a) McArdle ("150 subjects" back) 15.00 7.50 4.50
(104b) McArdle ("175 subjects" back) 15.00 7.50 4.50
(105a) McCredie ("150 subjects" back)15.00 7.50 4.50
(105b) McCredie ("175 subjects" back)15.00 7.50 4.50
(106a) Melchoir ("150 subjects" back) 15.00 7.50 4.50
(106b) Melchoir ("175 subjects" back) 15.00 7.50 4.50
(107) Miller (San Francisco) 15.00 7.50 4.50
(108) Miller (Seattle) 15.00 7.50 4.50
(109) Mitze 15.00 7.50 4.50
(110a) Mohler ("150 subjects" back) 15.00 7.50 4.50
(110b) Mohler ("175 subjects" back) 15.00 7.50 4.50
(111a) Moser ("150 subjects" back) 15.00 7.50 4.50
(111b) Moser ("175 subjects" back) 15.00 7.50 4.50
(112) Mott 15.00 7.50 4.50
(113a) Mundorf (name incorrect, "150 subjects" back)
50.00 25.00 15.00
(113b) Mundorff (name correct, "175 subjects" back)
15.00 7.50 4.50
(114a) Murphy ("150 subjects" back) 15.00 7.50 4.50
(114b) Murphy ("175 subjects" back) 15.00 7.50 4.50
(115) Nagle 15.00 7.50 4.50
(116) Nelson 15.00 7.50 4.50
(117) Netzel 15.00 7.50 4.50
(118) Nourse 15.00 7.50 4.50
(119) Nordyke 15.00 7.50 4.50
(120) Olson 15.00 7.50 4.50
(121) Orendorff (Orsnsdorff) 15.00 7.50 4.50
(122a) Ort ("150 subjects" back) 15.00 7.50 4.50
(122b) Ort ("175 subjects" back) 15.00 7.50 4.50
(123) Ostdiek 15.00 7.50 4.50
(124) Pennington 15.00 7.50 4.50
(125) Perrine 15.00 7.50 4.50
(126a) Perry ("150 subjects" back) 15.00 7.50 4.50
(126b) Perry ("175 subjects" back) 15.00 7.50 4.50
(127) Persons 15.00 7.50 4.50
(128a) Rapps ("150 subjects" back) 15.00 7.50 4.50
(128b) Rapps ("175 subjects" back) 15.00 7.50 4.50
(129) Raymer 15.00 7.50 4.50
(130) Raymond 15.00 7.50 4.50
(131) Rockenfield 15.00 7.50 4.50
(132) Roth 15.00 7.50 4.50
(133) D. Ryan 15.00 7.50 4.50
(134) J. Ryan 15.00 7.50 4.50
(135) Scharnweber 15.00 7.50 4.50
(136) Schmutz 15.00 7.50 4.50
(137) Seaton (Portland) 15.00 7.50 4.50
(138) Seaton (Seattle) 15.00 7.50 4.50
(139) Shafer 15.00 7.50 4.50
(140) Shaw 15.00 7.50 4.50
(141) Shea 15.00 7.50 4.50
(142) Shinn 15.00 7.50 4.50
(143) Smith 15.00 7.50 4.50
(144a) H. Smith ("150 subjects" back) 15.00 7.50 4.50
(144b) H. Smith ("175 subjects" back) 15.00 7.50 4.50
(145a) J. Smith ("150 subjects" back) 15.00 7.50 4.50
(145b) J. Smith ("175 subjects" back) 15.00 7.50 4.50
(146) Speas 15.00 7.50 4.50
(147) Spiesman 15.00 7.50 4.50
(148) Starkell 15.00 7.50 4.50
(149a) Steen ("150 subjects" back) 15.00 7.50 4.50
(149b) Steen ("175 subjects" back) 15.00 7.50 4.50
(150) Stevens 15.00 7.50 4.50
(151a) Stewart ("150 subjects" back) 15.00 7.50 4.50
(151b) Stewart ("175 subjects" back) 15.00 7.50 4.50
(152) Stovell (Stovall) 15.00 7.50 4.50
(153) Streib 15.00 7.50 4.50
(154) Sugden 15.00 7.50 4.50
(155) Sutor 15.00 7.50 4.50
(156) Swain 15.00 7.50 4.50
(157a) Swander ("150 subjects" back) 15.00 7.50 4.50
(157b) Swander ("175 subjects" back) 15.00 7.50 4.50
(158) Tennant 15.00 7.50 4.50
(159) Thomas 15.00 7.50 4.50
(160) Thompson 15.00 7.50 4.50
(161) Thorsen 15.00 7.50 4.50
(162a) Tonnesen ("150 subjects" back)
15.00 7.50 4.50
(162b) Tonnesen ("175 subjects" back)
15.00 7.50 4.50
(163) Tozer 15.00 7.50 4.50
(164) Van Buren 15.00 7.50 4.50
(165) Vitt 15.00 7.50 4.50
(166) Wares 15.00 7.50 4.50
(167) Waring 15.00 7.50 4.50
(168) Warren 15.00 7.50 4.50
(169) Weed 15.00 7.50 4.50
(170a) Whalen ("150 subjects" back) 15.00 7.50 4.50
(170b) Whalen ("175 subjects" back) 15.00 7.50 4.50
(171a) Willett ("150 subjects" back) 15.00 7.50 4.50
(171b) Willett ("175 subjects" back) 15.00 7.50 4.50
(172a) Williams ("150 subjects" back) 15.00 7.50 4.50
(172b) Williams ("175 subjects" back) 15.00 7.50 4.50
(173a) Willis ("150 subjects" back) 15.00 7.50 4.50
(173b) Willis ("175 subjects" back) 15.00 7.50 4.50
(174a) Wolverton ("150 subjects" back)
15.00 7.50 4.50
(174b) Wolverton ("175 subjects" back)
15.00 7.50 4.50
(175) Zackert 15.00 7.50 4.50

1911 Obak (T212)

PFYL, OAKLAND, P. C. L.
PFYL, considered a good first baseman, covers lots of ground around first and plays a snappy game. Is a good hitter and very fast on bases. Is a left-handed thrower and hitter. Enthusiastic worker, with a good supply of "ginger."
A.B. B.H. P.C.
1908....104 28 269
1909....464 166 358
1910....181 45 249
OBAK
SPEAKS QUALITY
IN ANY COMPANY

	NR MT	EX	VG
Complete Set:	2500.	1250.	750.00
Common Player:	15.00	7.50	4.50

(1) Abbott 15.00 7.50 4.50
(2) Ables 15.00 7.50 4.50
(3) Adams 15.00 7.50 4.50
(4) Agnew 15.00 7.50 4.50
(5) Akin 15.00 7.50 4.50
(6) Annis 15.00 7.50 4.50
(7) Arrelanes (Arellanes) 15.00 7.50 4.50
(8) Barry 15.00 7.50 4.50
(9) Bassey 15.00 7.50 4.50
(10) Baum 15.00 7.50 4.50
(11) Bennett 15.00 7.50 4.50
(12) Bernard 15.00 7.50 4.50
(13) Berry 15.00 7.50 4.50
(14) Bloomfield 15.00 7.50 4.50
(15) Bonner 15.00 7.50 4.50
(16) Brackenridge 15.00 7.50 4.50
(17) Brashear 15.00 7.50 4.50
(18) R. Brashear 15.00 7.50 4.50
(19) Brinker 15.00 7.50 4.50
(20) Brown 15.00 7.50 4.50
(21) Browning 15.00 7.50 4.50
(22) Bues 15.00 7.50 4.50
(23) Burrell 15.00 7.50 4.50
(24) Burns 15.00 7.50 4.50
(25) Butler 15.00 7.50 4.50
(26) Byram 15.00 7.50 4.50
(27) Carlisle 15.00 7.50 4.50
(28) Carson 15.00 7.50 4.50
(29) Cartwright 15.00 7.50 4.50
(30) Casey 15.00 7.50 4.50
(31) Castleton 15.00 7.50 4.50
(32) Chadbourne 15.00 7.50 4.50
(33) Christian 15.00 7.50 4.50
(34) Coleman 15.00 7.50 4.50
(35) Cooney 15.00 7.50 4.50
(36) Coy 15.00 7.50 4.50
(37) Criger 15.00 7.50 4.50
(38) Crukshank 15.00 7.50 4.50
(39) Cutshaw 15.00 7.50 4.50
(40) Daley 15.00 7.50 4.50
(41) Danzig 15.00 7.50 4.50
(42) Dashwood 15.00 7.50 4.50
(43) Davis 15.00 7.50 4.50
(44) Delhi 15.00 7.50 4.50
(45) Delmas 15.00 7.50 4.50
(46) Dillon 15.00 7.50 4.50
(47) Engel 15.00 7.50 4.50
(48) Erickson 15.00 7.50 4.50
(49) Fitzgerald 15.00 7.50 4.50
(50) Flater 15.00 7.50 4.50
(51) Frisk 15.00 7.50 4.50
(52) Fullerton 15.00 7.50 4.50
(53) Garrett 15.00 7.50 4.50
(54) Goodman 15.00 7.50 4.50
(55) Gordon 15.00 7.50 4.50
(56) Grindle 15.00 7.50 4.50
(57) Hall 15.00 7.50 4.50
(58) Harris 15.00 7.50 4.50
(59) Hasty 15.00 7.50 4.50
(60) Henderson 15.00 7.50 4.50
(61) Henley 15.00 7.50 4.50
(62) Hetling 15.00 7.50 4.50
(63) Hiester 15.00 7.50 4.50
(64) Higgins 15.00 7.50 4.50
(65) Hitt 15.00 7.50 4.50
(66) Hoffman 15.00 7.50 4.50
(67) Hogan 15.00 7.50 4.50
(68) Holm 15.00 7.50 4.50
(69) Householder 15.00 7.50 4.50
(70) Hosp 15.00 7.50 4.50
(71) Howard 15.00 7.50 4.50
(72) Hunt 15.00 7.50 4.50
(73) James 15.00 7.50 4.50
(74) Jensen 15.00 7.50 4.50
(75) Kading 15.00 7.50 4.50
(76) Kane 15.00 7.50 4.50
(77) Kippert 15.00 7.50 4.50
(78) Knight 15.00 7.50 4.50
(79) Koestner 15.00 7.50 4.50
(80) Krueger 15.00 7.50 4.50
(81) Kuhn 15.00 7.50 4.50
(82) LaLonge 15.00 7.50 4.50
(83) Lamline 15.00 7.50 4.50
(84) Leard 15.00 7.50 4.50
(85) Lerchen 15.00 7.50 4.50
(86) Lewis 15.00 7.50 4.50
(87) Madden 15.00 7.50 4.50
(88) Maggert 15.00 7.50 4.50
(89) Mahoney 15.00 7.50 4.50
(90) McArdle 15.00 7.50 4.50
(91) McCredie 15.00 7.50 4.50
(92) McDonnell 15.00 7.50 4.50
(93) Meikle 15.00 7.50 4.50
(94) Melchoir 15.00 7.50 4.50
(95) Mensor 15.00 7.50 4.50
(96) Metzger 15.00 7.50 4.50
(97) Miller (Oakland) 15.00 7.50 4.50
(98) Miller (San Francisco) 15.00 7.50 4.50
(99) Ten Million 15.00 7.50 4.50
(100) Mitze 15.00 7.50 4.50
(101) Mohler 15.00 7.50 4.50
(102) Moore 15.00 7.50 4.50
(103) Morse 15.00 7.50 4.50
(104) Moskiman 15.00 7.50 4.50
(105) Mundorff 15.00 7.50 4.50
(106) Murray 15.00 7.50 4.50
(107) Netzel 15.00 7.50 4.50
(108) Nordyke 15.00 7.50 4.50
(109) Nourse 15.00 7.50 4.50
(110) O'Rourke 15.00 7.50 4.50
(111) Ostdiek 15.00 7.50 4.50
(112) Patterson 15.00 7.50 4.50
(113) Pearce 15.00 7.50 4.50
(114) Peckinpaugh 15.00 7.50 4.50
(115) Pernoll 15.00 7.50 4.50
(116) Pfyl 15.00 7.50 4.50
(117) Powell 15.00 7.50 4.50
(118) Raleigh 15.00 7.50 4.50
(119) Rapps 15.00 7.50 4.50
(120) Raymer 15.00 7.50 4.50
(121) Raymond 15.00 7.50 4.50
(122) Reddick 15.00 7.50 4.50
(123) Roche 15.00 7.50 4.50
(124) Rockenfield 15.00 7.50 4.50
(125) Rogers 15.00 7.50 4.50
(126) Ross 15.00 7.50 4.50
(127) Ryan 15.00 7.50 4.50
(128) J. Ryan 15.00 7.50 4.50
(129) Scharnweber 15.00 7.50 4.50
(130) Schmidt 15.00 7.50 4.50
(131) Schmutz 15.00 7.50 4.50
(132) Seaton (Portland) 15.00 7.50 4.50
(133) Seaton (Seattle) 15.00 7.50 4.50
(134) Shaw 15.00 7.50 4.50
(135) Shea 15.00 7.50 4.50
(136) Sheehan (Portland) 15.00 7.50 4.50
(137) Sheehan (Vernon) 15.00 7.50 4.50
(138) Shinn 15.00 7.50 4.50
(139) Skeels 15.00 7.50 4.50
(140) H. Smith 15.00 7.50 4.50

(141)	Speas	15.00	7.50	4.50
(142)	Spencer	15.00	7.50	4.50
(143)	Spiesman	15.00	7.50	4.50
(144)	Starkel	15.00	7.50	4.50
(145)	Steen	15.00	7.50	4.50
(146)	Stewart	15.00	7.50	4.50
(147)	Stinson	15.00	7.50	4.50
(148)	Stovall	15.00	7.50	4.50
(149)	Strand	15.00	7.50	4.50
(150)	Sutor	15.00	7.50	4.50
(151)	Swain	15.00	7.50	4.50
(152)	Tennant	15.00	7.50	4.50
(153)	Thomas (Sacramento)	15.00	7.50	4.50
(154)	Thomas (Victoria)	15.00	7.50	4.50
(155)	Thompson	15.00	7.50	4.50
(156)	Thornton	15.00	7.50	4.50
(157)	Thorsen	15.00	7.50	4.50
(158)	Tiedeman	15.00	7.50	4.50
(159)	Tozer	15.00	7.50	4.50
(160)	Van Buren	15.00	7.50	4.50
(161)	Vitt	15.00	7.50	4.50
(162)	Ward	15.00	7.50	4.50
(163)	Wares	15.00	7.50	4.50
(164)	Warren	15.00	7.50	4.50
(165)	Weaver	20.00	10.00	6.00
(166)	Weed	15.00	7.50	4.50
(167)	Wheeler	15.00	7.50	4.50
(168)	Wiggs	15.00	7.50	4.50
(169)	Willett	15.00	7.50	4.50
(170)	Williams	15.00	7.50	4.50
(171)	Wolverton	15.00	7.50	4.50
(172)	Zacher	15.00	7.50	4.50
(173)	Zackert	15.00	7.50	4.50
(174)	Zamlock	15.00	7.50	4.50
(175)	Zimmerman	15.00	7.50	4.50

1911 Obak Cabinets (T4)

Among the scarcest of all the 20th Century tobacco issues, the T4 Obak Premiums were cabinet-sized cards distributed in conjunction with the more popular and better-known Obak T212 card set. Both sets were issued in 1911 by Obak "mouthpiece" cigarettes and featured players from the Pacific Coast League. The Obak Premiums measured a large 5" x 7" and wre printed on a cardboard-like paper. The attractive cards featured a greyish monochome player photo inside a 3-1/2" x 5" oval. There was no printing on the front of the card to identify the player or indicate the Manufacturer, and the backs of the cards were blank. In most cases the photos used for the premiums were identical to the T212 photos, except for some cropping differences. Under the Obak mail-in promotion, 50 coupons from cigarette packages were required to obtain just one premium card, which may explain their extreme scarcity today. According to the coupon, all 175 players pictured in the regular T212 set were available as premium cards, but todate 30 different players have been found in the larger cabinet size. Most of the Obak premiums that exist in original condition contain a number, written in pencil on the back of the card, that corresponds to the checklist printed on the coupon. Because of their extreme scarcity, these cards are quite expensive and generally appeal only to the very advanced Pacific Coast League collectors.

		NR MT	EX	VG
Complete Set:		9500.	4750.	2850.
Common Player:		300.00	150.00	90.00
3	Howard	300.00	150.00	90.00
22	Christian	300.00	150.00	90.00
24	Maggert	300.00	150.00	90.00
33	Flater	300.00	150.00	90.00
34	Zacher	300.00	150.00	90.00
37	Ryan	300.00	150.00	90.00
49	Kuhn	300.00	150.00	90.00
59	Baum	300.00	150.00	90.00
71	Melchoir	300.00	150.00	90.00
72	Vitt	300.00	150.00	90.00
74	Berry	300.00	150.00	90.00
75	Miller	300.00	150.00	90.00
76	Tennant	300.00	150.00	90.00
77	Mohler	300.00	150.00	90.00
79	Sutor	300.00	150.00	90.00
80	Browning	300.00	150.00	90.00
81	Ryan	300.00	150.00	90.00
82	Powell	300.00	150.00	90.00
83	Schmidt	300.00	150.00	90.00
84	Meikle	300.00	150.00	90.00
85	Madden	300.00	150.00	90.00
87	Moskiman	300.00	150.00	90.00
88	Zamlock	300.00	150.00	90.00
92	Carlisle	300.00	150.00	90.00
97	Stewart	300.00	150.00	90.00
111	Mundorff	300.00	150.00	90.00
140	Annis	300.00	150.00	90.00
159	Dashwood	300.00	150.00	90.00
167	Spencer	300.00	150.00	90.00

1955 Old Homestead Franks Des Moines Bruins

A very rare minor league issue, this set features players of the Class A Western League farm team of the Chicago Cubs. Many of the players were future major leaguers. Cards measure about 2-1/2" x 3-3/4" and have black-and-white portrait photos of the players with a facsimile autograph across the jersey. A black strip at the bottom of the card has the player and team name, and the position. Backs have an ad for the issuing hot dog company.

		NR MT	EX	VG
Complete Set:		650.00	325.00	195.00
Common Player:		35.00	17.50	10.50
(1)	Bob Andersoon	35.00	17.50	10.50
(2)	Ray Bellino	35.00	17.50	10.50
(3)	Don Biebel	35.00	17.50	10.50
(4)	Bobby Cooke	35.00	17.50	10.50
(5)	Dave Cunningham	35.00	17.50	10.50
(6)	Bert Flammini	35.00	17.50	10.50
(7)	Gene Fodge	35.00	17.50	10.50
(8)	Eddie Haas	35.00	17.50	10.50
(9)	Paul Hoffmeister	35.00	17.50	10.50
(10)	Pepper Martin	60.00	30.00	18.00
(11)	Jim McDaniel	35.00	17.50	10.50
(12)	Bob McKee	35.00	17.50	10.50
(13)	Paul Menking	35.00	17.50	10.50
(14)	Vern Morgan	35.00	17.50	10.50
(15)	Joe Pearson	35.00	17.50	10.50
(16)	John Pramesa	35.00	17.50	10.50
(17)	Joe Stanka	35.00	17.50	10.50
(18)	Jim Stoddard	35.00	17.50	10.50
(19)	Bob Thorpe	35.00	17.50	10.50
(20)	Burdy Thurlby	35.00	17.50	10.50
(21)	Don Watkins	35.00	17.50	10.50

1910 Old Mill Cigarettes Series 1 (T210)

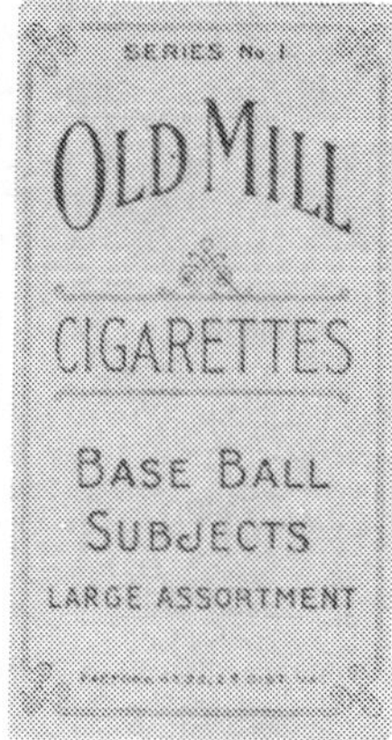

Because of their distinctive red borders, this 1910 minor league tobacco issue is often called the Red Border set by collectors. A massive set, it consists of eight different series and totals some 640 cards, each measuring 1-1/2" x 2-5/8". The fronts of the cards feature a glossy black-and-white photo, while the backs carry an ad for Old Mill Cigarettes. Each of the eight series is devoted to a different minor league. Series 1 features players from the South Atlantic League; Series 2 pictures players from the Virginia League; Series 3 is devoted to the Texas League; Series 4 features the Virginia Valley League; Series 5 pictures players from the Carolina Associations; Series 6 spotlights the Blue Grass League; Series 7 is devoted to the Eastern Carolina League; and Series 8 show players from the the Southern Association. The various series are identified by number along the top on the back of the cards. Collectors generally agree that Series 7 cards (Eastern Carolina League players) are the most difficult to find, while Series 2 cards (Virginia League) are the most common. The relative scarcity of the various series is reflected in the prices listed. Collectors should be aware that some Series 3 cards (Texas League) can be found with orange, rather than red, borders - apparently because not enough red ink was used during part of the print run.

		NR MT	EX	VG
Complete Set:		900.00	450.00	270.00
Common Player:		15.00	7.50	4.50
(1)	Bagwell	15.00	7.50	4.50
(2)	Balenti	15.00	7.50	4.50
(3)	Becker	15.00	7.50	4.50
(4)	Bensen	15.00	7.50	4.50
(5)	Benton	15.00	7.50	4.50
(6)	Bierkortte	15.00	7.50	4.50
(7)	Bierman	15.00	7.50	4.50
(8)	Breitenstein	15.00	7.50	4.50
(9)	Bremmerhof	15.00	7.50	4.50
(10)	Carter	15.00	7.50	4.50
(11)	Cavender	15.00	7.50	4.50
(12)	Collins	15.00	7.50	4.50
(13)	DeFraites	15.00	7.50	4.50
(14)	Dudley	15.00	7.50	4.50
(15)	Dwyer	15.00	7.50	4.50
(16)	Edwards	15.00	7.50	4.50
(17)	Enbanks	15.00	7.50	4.50
(18)	Eubank	15.00	7.50	4.50
(19)	Fox	15.00	7.50	4.50
(20)	Hannifan	15.00	7.50	4.50
(21)	Hartley	15.00	7.50	4.50
(22)	Hauser	15.00	7.50	4.50
(23)	Hille	15.00	7.50	4.50
(24)	Howard	15.00	7.50	4.50
(25)	Hoyt	15.00	7.50	4.50
(27)	Ison	15.00	7.50	4.50
(28)	Jones	15.00	7.50	4.50
(29)	Kalkhoff	15.00	7.50	4.50
(30)	Krebs	15.00	7.50	4.50
(31)	Lawrence	15.00	7.50	4.50
(32)	Lee (Jacksonville)	15.00	7.50	4.50
(33)	Lee (Macon)	15.00	7.50	4.50
(34)	Lewis (Columbia)	15.00	7.50	4.50
(35)	Lewis (Columbus)	15.00	7.50	4.50
(36)	Lipe (batting)	15.00	7.50	4.50
(37)	Lipe (portrait)	15.00	7.50	4.50
(38)	Long	15.00	7.50	4.50
(39)	Magoon	15.00	7.50	4.50
(40)	Manion	15.00	7.50	4.50
(41)	Marshall	15.00	7.50	4.50
(42)	Martin	15.00	7.50	4.50
(43)	Martina	15.00	7.50	4.50
(44)	Massing	15.00	7.50	4.50
(45)	McLeod	15.00	7.50	4.50
(46)	McMahon	15.00	7.50	4.50
(47)	Morse	15.00	7.50	4.50
(48)	Mullane	15.00	7.50	4.50
(49)	Mulldowney	15.00	7.50	4.50
(50)	Murch	15.00	7.50	4.50
(51)	Norcum	15.00	7.50	4.50
(52)	Pelkey	15.00	7.50	4.50
(53)	Petit	15.00	7.50	4.50
(54)	Pierce	15.00	7.50	4.50
(55)	Pope	15.00	7.50	4.50
(56)	Radebaugh	15.00	7.50	4.50
(57)	Raynolds	15.00	7.50	4.50
(58)	Reagan	15.00	7.50	4.50
(59)	Redfern (Redfearn)	15.00	7.50	4.50
(60)	Reynolds	15.00	7.50	4.50
(61)	Schulz	15.00	7.50	4.50
(62)	Schulze	15.00	7.50	4.50
(63)	Schwietzka	15.00	7.50	4.50
(64)	Shields	15.00	7.50	4.50
(65)	Sisson	15.00	7.50	4.50
(66)	Smith	15.00	7.50	4.50
(67)	Sweeney	15.00	7.50	4.50
(68)	Taffee	15.00	7.50	4.50
(69)	Toren	15.00	7.50	4.50
(70)	Viola	15.00	7.50	4.50
(71)	Wagner	15.00	7.50	4.50
(72)	Wahl	15.00	7.50	4.50
(73)	Weems	15.00	7.50	4.50
(74)	Wells	15.00	7.50	4.50
(75)	Wohlleben	15.00	7.50	4.50

1910 Old Mill Cigarettes Series 2 (T210)

		NR MT	EX	VG
Complete Set:		900.00	450.00	270.00
Common Player:		12.00	6.00	3.50
(1)	Andrada	12.00	6.00	3.50
(2)	Archer	12.00	6.00	3.50
(3)	Baker	12.00	6.00	3.50
(4)	Beham	12.00	6.00	3.50
(5)	Bonner	12.00	6.00	3.50
(6)	Bowen	12.00	6.00	3.50
(7)	Brandon	12.00	6.00	3.50

		NR MT	EX	VG
(8)	Breivogel	12.00	6.00	3.50
(9)	Brooks	12.00	6.00	3.50
(10)	Brown	12.00	6.00	3.50
(11)	Busch	12.00	6.00	3.50
(12)	Bussey	12.00	6.00	3.50
(13)	Cefalu	12.00	6.00	3.50
(14)	Chandler	12.00	6.00	3.50
(15)	Clarke	12.00	6.00	3.50
(16)	Clunk	12.00	6.00	3.50
(17)	Cote	12.00	6.00	3.50
(18)	Cowan	12.00	6.00	3.50
(19)	Decker	12.00	6.00	3.50
(20)	Doyle	12.00	6.00	3.50
(21)	Eddowes	12.00	6.00	3.50
(22)	Fisher	12.00	6.00	3.50
(23)	Fox	12.00	6.00	3.50
(24)	Foxen	12.00	6.00	3.50
(25)	Gaston	12.00	6.00	3.50
(26)	Gehring	12.00	6.00	3.50
(27)	Griffin (Danville)	12.00	6.00	3.50
(28)	Griffin (Lynchburg)	12.00	6.00	3.50
(29)	Hale	12.00	6.00	3.50
(30)	Hamilton	12.00	6.00	3.50
(31)	Hanks	12.00	6.00	3.50
(32)	Hannafin	12.00	6.00	3.50
(33)	Hoffman	12.00	6.00	3.50
(34)	Holland	12.00	6.00	3.50
(35)	Hooker	12.00	6.00	3.50
(36)	Irving	12.00	6.00	3.50
(37)	Jackson (Lynchburg)	12.00	6.00	3.50
(38)	Jackson (Norfolk)	12.00	6.00	3.50
(39)	Jackson (Portsmouth)	12.00	6.00	3.50
(40)	Jackson (Richmond)	12.00	6.00	3.50
(41)	Jenkins	12.00	6.00	3.50
(42)	Keifel	12.00	6.00	3.50
(43)	Kirkpatrick	12.00	6.00	3.50
(44)	Kunkel	12.00	6.00	3.50
(45)	Landgraff	12.00	6.00	3.50
(46)	Larkins	12.00	6.00	3.50
(47)	Laughlin	12.00	6.00	3.50
(48)	Lawlor	12.00	6.00	3.50
(49)	Levy	12.00	6.00	3.50
(50)	Lloyd	12.00	6.00	3.50
(51)	Loos	12.00	6.00	3.50
(52)	Lovell	12.00	6.00	3.50
(53)	Lucia	12.00	6.00	3.50
(54)	MacConachie	12.00	6.00	3.50
(55)	Mayberry	12.00	6.00	3.50
(56)	McFarland	12.00	6.00	3.50
(57)	Messitt	12.00	6.00	3.50
(58)	Michel	12.00	6.00	3.50
(59)	Mullaney	12.00	6.00	3.50
(60)	Munson	12.00	6.00	3.50
(61)	Neuton	12.00	6.00	3.50
(62)	Nimmo	12.00	6.00	3.50
(63)	Norris	12.00	6.00	3.50
(64)	Peterson	12.00	6.00	3.50
(65)	Powell	12.00	6.00	3.50
(66)	Pressly (Pressley)	12.00	6.00	3.50
(67)	Pritchard	12.00	6.00	3.50
(68)	Revelle	12.00	6.00	3.50
(69)	Rowe	12.00	6.00	3.50
(70)	Schmidt	12.00	6.00	3.50
(71)	Schrader	12.00	6.00	3.50
(72)	Sharp	12.00	6.00	3.50
(73)	Shaw	12.00	6.00	3.50
(74)	Smith (Lynchburg, batting)	12.00	6.00	3.50
(75)	Smith (Lynchburg, catching)	12.00	6.00	3.50
(76)	Smith (Portsmouth)	12.00	6.00	3.50
(77)	Spicer	12.00	6.00	3.50
(78)	Titman	12.00	6.00	3.50
(79)	Toner	12.00	6.00	3.50
(80)	Tydeman	12.00	6.00	3.50
(81)	Vail	12.00	6.00	3.50
(82)	Verbout	12.00	6.00	3.50
(83)	Walker	12.00	6.00	3.50
(84)	Wallace	12.00	6.00	3.50
(85)	Waymack	12.00	6.00	3.50
(86)	Woolums	12.00	6.00	3.50
(87)	Zimmerman	12.00	6.00	3.50

1910 Old Mill Cigarettes Series 3 (T210)

		NR MT	EX	VG
Complete Set:		1100.	550.00	330.00
Common Player:		15.00	7.50	4.50
(1)	Alexander	15.00	7.50	4.50
(2)	Ash	15.00	7.50	4.50
(3)	Bandy	15.00	7.50	4.50
(4)	Barenkemp	15.00	7.50	4.50
(5)	Belew	15.00	7.50	4.50
(6)	Bell	15.00	7.50	4.50
(7)	Bennett	15.00	7.50	4.50
(8)	Berlck	15.00	7.50	4.50
(9)	Billiard	15.00	7.50	4.50
(10)	Blanding	15.00	7.50	4.50
(11)	Blue	15.00	7.50	4.50
(12)	Burch	15.00	7.50	4.50
(13)	Burk	15.00	7.50	4.50
(14)	Carlin	15.00	7.50	4.50
(15)	Conaway	15.00	7.50	4.50
(16)	Corkhill	15.00	7.50	4.50
(17)	Cowan	15.00	7.50	4.50
(18)	Coyle	15.00	7.50	4.50
(19)	Crable	15.00	7.50	4.50
(20)	Curry	15.00	7.50	4.50
(21)	Dale	15.00	7.50	4.50
(22)	Davis	15.00	7.50	4.50
(23)	Deardorff	15.00	7.50	4.50
(24)	Donnelley	15.00	7.50	4.50
(25)	Doyle	15.00	7.50	4.50
(26)	Druke	15.00	7.50	4.50
(27)	Dugey	15.00	7.50	4.50
(28)	Ens	15.00	7.50	4.50
(29)	Evans	15.00	7.50	4.50
(30)	Fillman	15.00	7.50	4.50
(31)	Firestine	15.00	7.50	4.50
(32)	Francis	15.00	7.50	4.50
(33)	Galloway	15.00	7.50	4.50
(34)	Gardner	15.00	7.50	4.50
(35)	Gear	15.00	7.50	4.50
(36)	Glawe	15.00	7.50	4.50
(37)	Gordon	15.00	7.50	4.50
(38)	Gowdy	15.00	7.50	4.50
(39)	Harbison	15.00	7.50	4.50
(40)	Harper	15.00	7.50	4.50
(41)	Hicks	15.00	7.50	4.50
(42)	Hill	15.00	7.50	4.50
(43)	Hinninger	15.00	7.50	4.50
(44)	Hirsch	15.00	7.50	4.50
(45)	Hise	15.00	7.50	4.50
(46)	Hooks	15.00	7.50	4.50
(47)	Hornsby	15.00	7.50	4.50
(48)	Howell	15.00	7.50	4.50
(49)	Johnston	15.00	7.50	4.50
(50)	Jolley	15.00	7.50	4.50
(51)	Jones	15.00	7.50	4.50
(52)	Kaphan	15.00	7.50	4.50
(53)	Kipp	15.00	7.50	4.50
(54)	Leidy	15.00	7.50	4.50
(55)	Malloy	15.00	7.50	4.50
(56)	Maloney	15.00	7.50	4.50
(57)	Meagher	15.00	7.50	4.50
(58)	Merritt	15.00	7.50	4.50
(59)	McKay	15.00	7.50	4.50
(60)	Mills	15.00	7.50	4.50
(61)	Morris	15.00	7.50	4.50
(63)	Munsell	15.00	7.50	4.50
(64)	Nagel	15.00	7.50	4.50
(65)	Northen	15.00	7.50	4.50
(66)	Ogle	15.00	7.50	4.50
(67)	Onslow	15.00	7.50	4.50
(68)	Pendleton	15.00	7.50	4.50
(69)	Powell	15.00	7.50	4.50
(70)	Riley	15.00	7.50	4.50
(71)	Robertson	15.00	7.50	4.50
(72)	Rose	15.00	7.50	4.50
(73)	Salazor	15.00	7.50	4.50
(74)	Shindel	15.00	7.50	4.50
(75)	Shontz	15.00	7.50	4.50
(76)	Slaven	15.00	7.50	4.50
(77)	Smith (bat over shoulder)	15.00	7.50	4.50
(78)	Smith (bat at hip level)	15.00	7.50	4.50
(79)	Spangler	15.00	7.50	4.50
(80)	Stadeli	15.00	7.50	4.50
(81)	Stinson	15.00	7.50	4.50
(82)	Storch	15.00	7.50	4.50
(83)	Stringer	15.00	7.50	4.50
(84)	Tesreau	15.00	7.50	4.50
(85)	Thebo	15.00	7.50	4.50
(86)	Tullas	15.00	7.50	4.50
(87)	Walsh	15.00	7.50	4.50
(88)	Watson	15.00	7.50	4.50
(89)	Weber	15.00	7.50	4.50
(90)	Weeks	15.00	7.50	4.50
(91)	Wertherford	15.00	7.50	4.50
(92)	Wickenhofer	15.00	7.50	4.50
(93)	Williams	15.00	7.50	4.50
(94)	Woodburn	15.00	7.50	4.50
(95)	Yantz	15.00	7.50	4.50

1910 Old Mill Cigarettes Series 4 (T210)

		NR MT	EX	VG
Complete Set:		625.00	312.00	187.00
Common Player:		15.00	7.50	4.50
(1)	Aylor	15.00	7.50	4.50
(2)	Benney	15.00	7.50	4.50
(3)	Best	15.00	7.50	4.50
(4)	Bonno	15.00	7.50	4.50
(5)	Brown	15.00	7.50	4.50
(6)	Brumfield	15.00	7.50	4.50
(7)	Campbell	15.00	7.50	4.50
(8)	Canepa	15.00	7.50	4.50
(9)	Carney	15.00	7.50	4.50
(10)	Carter	15.00	7.50	4.50
(11)	Cochrane	15.00	7.50	4.50
(12)	Coller	15.00	7.50	4.50
(13)	Connolly	15.00	7.50	4.50
(14)	Davis	15.00	7.50	4.50
(15)	Connell	15.00	7.50	4.50
(16)	Doshmer	15.00	7.50	4.50
(17)	Dougherty	15.00	7.50	4.50
(18)	Erlewein	15.00	7.50	4.50
(19)	Farrell	15.00	7.50	4.50
(20)	Geary	15.00	7.50	4.50
(21)	Halterman	15.00	7.50	4.50
(22)	Headly	15.00	7.50	4.50
(23)	Hollis	15.00	7.50	4.50
(24)	Hunter	15.00	7.50	4.50
(25)	Johnson	15.00	7.50	4.50
(26)	Kane	15.00	7.50	4.50
(27)	Kuehn	15.00	7.50	4.50
(28)	Leonard	15.00	7.50	4.50
(29)	Lux	15.00	7.50	4.50
(30)	McClain	15.00	7.50	4.50
(31)	Mollenkamp	15.00	7.50	4.50
(32)	Moore	15.00	7.50	4.50
(33)	Moye	15.00	7.50	4.50
(34)	O'Connor	15.00	7.50	4.50
(36)	Pick	15.00	7.50	4.50
(37)	Pickels	15.00	7.50	4.50
(38)	Schafer	15.00	7.50	4.50
(39)	Seaman	15.00	7.50	4.50
(40)	Spicer	15.00	7.50	4.50
(41)	Stanley	15.00	7.50	4.50
(42)	Stockum	15.00	7.50	4.50
(43)	Titlow	15.00	7.50	4.50
(44)	Waldron	15.00	7.50	4.50
(45)	Wills	15.00	7.50	4.50
(46)	Witter	15.00	7.50	4.50
(47)	Womach	15.00	7.50	4.50
(48)	Young	15.00	7.50	4.50
(49)	Zurlage	15.00	7.50	4.50

1910 Old Mill Cigarettes Series 5 (T210)

		NR MT	EX	VG
Complete Set:		1100.	550.00	330.00
Common Player:		15.00	7.50	4.50
(1)	Abercrombie	15.00	7.50	4.50
(2)	Averett	15.00	7.50	4.50
(3)	Bansewein	15.00	7.50	4.50
(4)	Bentley	15.00	7.50	4.50
(5)	C.G. Beusse	15.00	7.50	4.50
(6)	Fred Beusse	15.00	7.50	4.50
(7)	Bigbie	15.00	7.50	4.50
(8)	Eivens	15.00	7.50	4.50
(9)	Blackstone	15.00	7.50	4.50
(10)	Brannon	15.00	7.50	4.50
(11)	Brazell	15.00	7.50	4.50
(12)	Brent	15.00	7.50	4.50
(13)	Bullock	15.00	7.50	4.50
(14)	Cashion	15.00	7.50	4.50
(15)	Corbett	15.00	7.50	4.50
(16)	Corbett	15.00	7.50	4.50
(17)	Coutts	15.00	7.50	4.50
(18)	Lave Cross	15.00	7.50	4.50
(19)	Crouch	15.00	7.50	4.50
(20)	C.L. Derrick	15.00	7.50	4.50
(21)	F.B. Derrick	15.00	7.50	4.50
(22)	Dobard	15.00	7.50	4.50
(23)	Drumm	15.00	7.50	4.50
(24)	Duvie	15.00	7.50	4.50
(25)	Ehrhardt	15.00	7.50	4.50
(26)	Eldridge	15.00	7.50	4.50
(27)	Fairbanks	15.00	7.50	4.50
(28)	Farmer	15.00	7.50	4.50
(29)	Ferrell	15.00	7.50	4.50
(30)	Finn	15.00	7.50	4.50
(31)	Flowers	15.00	7.50	4.50
(32)	Fogarty	15.00	7.50	4.50
(33)	Francisco	15.00	7.50	4.50
(34)	Gardin	15.00	7.50	4.50
(35)	Gilmore	15.00	7.50	4.50
(36)	Gorham	15.00	7.50	4.50
(37)	Gorman	15.00	7.50	4.50
(38)	Guss	15.00	7.50	4.50
(39)	Hammersley	15.00	7.50	4.50
(40)	Hargrave	15.00	7.50	4.50
(41)	Harrington	15.00	7.50	4.50
(42)	Harris	15.00	7.50	4.50
(43)	Hartley	15.00	7.50	4.50
(44)	Hayes	15.00	7.50	4.50
(45)	Hicks	15.00	7.50	4.50
(46)	Humphrey	15.00	7.50	4.50
(47)	Jackson	15.00	7.50	4.50
(48)	James	15.00	7.50	4.50
(49)	Jenkins	15.00	7.50	4.50
(50)	Johnston	15.00	7.50	4.50
(51)	Kelly	15.00	7.50	4.50
(52)	Laval	15.00	7.50	4.50
(53)	Lothrop	15.00	7.50	4.50
(54)	MacConachie	15.00	7.50	4.50
(55)	Mangum	15.00	7.50	4.50
(56)	A. McCarthy	15.00	7.50	4.50
(57)	J. McCarthy	15.00	7.50	4.50
(58)	McEnroe	15.00	7.50	4.50
(59)	McFarlin	15.00	7.50	4.50
(60)	McHugh	15.00	7.50	4.50
(61)	McKevitt	15.00	7.50	4.50
(62)	Midkiff	15.00	7.50	4.50
(63)	Moore	15.00	7.50	4.50
(64)	Noojin	15.00	7.50	4.50
(65)	Ochs	15.00	7.50	4.50
(66)	Painter	15.00	7.50	4.50
(67)	Redfern (Redfearn)	15.00	7.50	4.50
(68)	Reis	15.00	7.50	4.50
(69)	Rickard	15.00	7.50	4.50
(70)	Roth (batting)	15.00	7.50	4.50
(71)	Roth (fielding)	15.00	7.50	4.50
(72)	Smith	15.00	7.50	4.50
(73)	Springs	15.00	7.50	4.50
(74)	Stouch	15.00	7.50	4.50
(75)	Taxis	15.00	7.50	4.50
(76)	Templin	15.00	7.50	4.50
(77)	Thrasher	15.00	7.50	4.50
(78)	Trammell	15.00	7.50	4.50
(79)	Walker	15.00	7.50	4.50
(80)	Walters	15.00	7.50	4.50
(81)	Wehrell	15.00	7.50	4.50
(82)	Weldon	15.00	7.50	4.50
(83)	Williams	15.00	7.50	4.50
(84)	Wingo	15.00	7.50	4.50
(85)	Workman	15.00	7.50	4.50
(86)	Wynne	15.00	7.50	4.50
(87)	Wysong	15.00	7.50	4.50

1910 Old Mill Cigarettes Series 6 (T210)

		NR MT	EX	VG
Complete Set:		2800.	1400.	840.00
Common Player:		16.00	8.00	4.75
(1)	Angermeier (fielding)	16.00	8.00	4.75
(2)	Angermeir (portrait)	16.00	8.00	4.75
(3)	Atwell	16.00	8.00	4.75
(4)	Badger	16.00	8.00	4.75
(5)	Barnett	16.00	8.00	4.75

(6)	Barney	16.00	8.00	4.75
(7)	Beard	16.00	8.00	4.75
(8)	Bohannon	16.00	8.00	4.75
(9)	Callahan	16.00	8.00	4.75
(10)	Chapman	16.00	8.00	4.75
(11)	Chase	16.00	8.00	4.75
(12)	Coleman	16.00	8.00	4.75
(13)	Cornell (Frankfort)	16.00	8.00	4.75
(14)	Cornell (Winchester)	16.00	8.00	4.75
(15)	Creager	16.00	8.00	4.75
(16)	Dailey	16.00	8.00	4.75
(17)	Edington	16.00	8.00	4.75
(18)	Elgin	16.00	8.00	4.75
(19)	Ellis	16.00	8.00	4.75
(20)	Everden	16.00	8.00	4.75
(21)	Gisler	16.00	8.00	4.75
(22)	Goodman	16.00	8.00	4.75
(23)	Goostree (hands behind back)	16.00	8.00	4.75
(24)	Goostree (leaning on bat)	16.00	8.00	4.75
(25)	Haines	16.00	8.00	4.75
(26)	Harold	16.00	8.00	4.75
(27)	Heveron	16.00	8.00	4.75
(28)	Hicks	16.00	8.00	4.75
(29)	Hoffmann	16.00	8.00	4.75
(30)	Horn	16.00	8.00	4.75
(31)	Kaiser	16.00	8.00	4.75
(32)	Keifel	16.00	8.00	4.75
(33)	Kimbrough	16.00	8.00	4.75
(34)	Kirchen	16.00	8.00	4.75
(35)	Kircher	16.00	8.00	4.75
(36)	Kuhlman	16.00	8.00	4.75
(37)	Kuhlmann	16.00	8.00	4.75
(38)	L'Heureux	16.00	8.00	4.75
(39)	Mulvain	16.00	8.00	4.75
(40)	McKernan	16.00	8.00	4.75
(41)	Meyers	16.00	8.00	4.75
(42)	Moloney	16.00	8.00	4.75
(43)	Mullin	16.00	8.00	4.75
(44)	Olson	16.00	8.00	4.75
(45)	Oyler	16.00	8.00	4.75
(46)	Reed	16.00	8.00	4.75
(47)	Ross	16.00	8.00	4.75
(48)	Scheneberg (fielding)	16.00	8.00	4.75
(49)	Scheneberg (portrait)	16.00	8.00	4.75
(50)	Schultz	16.00	8.00	4.75
(51)	Scott	16.00	8.00	4.75
(52)	Sinex	16.00	8.00	4.75
(53)	Stengel	2500.	1250.	750.00
(54)	Thoss	16.00	8.00	4.75
(55)	Tilford	16.00	8.00	4.75
(56)	Toney	16.00	8.00	4.75
(57)	Van Landingham (Valladingham) (Lexington)	16.00	8.00	4.75
(58)	Van Landingham (Valladingham) (Shelbyville)	16.00	8.00	4.75
(59)	Viox	16.00	8.00	4.75
(60)	Walden	16.00	8.00	4.75
(61)	Whitaker	16.00	8.00	4.75
(62)	Wills	16.00	8.00	4.75
(63)	Womble	16.00	8.00	4.75
(64)	Wright	16.00	8.00	4.75
(65)	Yaeger	16.00	8.00	4.75
(66)	Yancey	16.00	8.00	4.75

1910 Old Mill Cigarettes Series 7 (T210)

		NR MT	EX	VG
Complete Set:		1300.	650.00	390.00
Common Player:		18.00	9.00	5.50
(1)	Armstrong	18.00	9.00	5.50
(2)	Beatty	18.00	9.00	5.50
(3)	Biel	18.00	9.00	5.50
(4)	Bonner	18.00	9.00	5.50
(5)	Brandt	18.00	9.00	5.50
(6)	Brown	18.00	9.00	5.50
(7)	Cantwell	18.00	9.00	5.50
(8)	Carrol	18.00	9.00	5.50
(9)	Cooney	18.00	9.00	5.50
(10)	Cooper	18.00	9.00	5.50
(11)	Cowell	18.00	9.00	5.50
(12)	Creager (Cregan)	18.00	9.00	5.50
(13)	Crockett	18.00	9.00	5.50
(14)	Dailey	18.00	9.00	5.50
(15)	Dobbs	18.00	9.00	5.50
(16)	Dussault	18.00	9.00	5.50
(17)	Dwyer	18.00	9.00	5.50
(18)	Evans	18.00	9.00	5.50
(19)	Forgue	18.00	9.00	5.50
(20)	Fulton	18.00	9.00	5.50
(21)	Galvin	18.00	9.00	5.50
(22)	Gastmeyer (batting)	18.00	9.00	5.50
(23)	Gastmeyer (fielding)	18.00	9.00	5.50
(24)	Gates	18.00	9.00	5.50
(25)	Gillespie	18.00	9.00	5.50
(26)	Griffin	18.00	9.00	5.50
(27)	Gunderson	18.00	9.00	5.50
(28)	Ham	18.00	9.00	5.50
(29)	Handibe (Handiboe)	18.00	9.00	5.50
(30)	Hart	18.00	9.00	5.50
(31)	Hartley	18.00	9.00	5.50
(32)	Hobbs	18.00	9.00	5.50
(33)	Hyames	18.00	9.00	5.50
(34)	Irving	18.00	9.00	5.50
(35)	Kaiser	18.00	9.00	5.50
(36)	Kelley	18.00	9.00	5.50
(37)	Kelly	18.00	9.00	5.50
(38)	Kelly (mascot)	18.00	9.00	5.50
(39)	Luyster	18.00	9.00	5.50
(40)	MacDonald	18.00	9.00	5.50
(41)	Malcolm	18.00	9.00	5.50
(42)	Mayer	18.00	9.00	5.50
(43)	McCormac (McCormick)	18.00	9.00	5.50
(44)	McGeeham (McGeehan)	18.00	9.00	5.50
(45)	Merchant	18.00	9.00	5.50
(46)	Mills	18.00	9.00	5.50
(47)	Morgan	18.00	9.00	5.50
(48)	Morris	18.00	9.00	5.50
(49)	Munson	18.00	9.00	5.50
(50)	Newman	18.00	9.00	5.50
(51)	Noval (Novak)	18.00	9.00	5.50
(52)	O'Halloran	18.00	9.00	5.50
(53)	Phelan	18.00	9.00	5.50
(54)	Prim	18.00	9.00	5.50
(55)	Reeves	18.00	9.00	5.50
(56)	Richardson	18.00	9.00	5.50
(57)	Schumaker	18.00	9.00	5.50
(58)	Sharp	18.00	9.00	5.50
(59)	Sherrill	18.00	9.00	5.50
(60)	Simmons	18.00	9.00	5.50
(61)	Steinbach	18.00	9.00	5.50
(62)	Stohr	18.00	9.00	5.50
(63)	Taylor	18.00	9.00	5.50
(64)	Webb	18.00	9.00	5.50
(65)	Whelan	18.00	9.00	5.50
(66)	Wolf	18.00	9.00	5.50
(67)	Wright	18.00	9.00	5.50

1910 Old Mill Cigarettes Series 8 (T210)

		NR MT	EX	VG
Complete Set:		5000.	2500.	1500.
Common Player:		16.00	8.00	4.75
(1)	Allen (Memphis)	16.00	8.00	4.75
(2)	Allen (Mobile)	16.00	8.00	4.75
(3)	Anderson	16.00	8.00	4.75
(4)	Babb	16.00	8.00	4.75
(5)	Bartley	16.00	8.00	4.75
(6)	Bauer	16.00	8.00	4.75
(7)	Bay	16.00	8.00	4.75
(8)	Bayliss	16.00	8.00	4.75
(9)	Berger	16.00	8.00	4.75
(10)	Bernhard	16.00	8.00	4.75
(11)	Bitroff	16.00	8.00	4.75
(12)	Breitenstein	16.00	8.00	4.75
(13)	Bronkie	16.00	8.00	4.75
(14)	Brooks	16.00	8.00	4.75
(15)	Burnett	16.00	8.00	4.75
(16)	Cafalu	16.00	8.00	4.75
(17)	Carson	16.00	8.00	4.75
(18)	Case	16.00	8.00	4.75
(19)	Chappelle	16.00	8.00	4.75
(20)	Cohen	16.00	8.00	4.75
(21)	Collins	16.00	8.00	4.75
(22)	Crandall	16.00	8.00	4.75
(23)	Cross	16.00	8.00	4.75
(24)	Jud. Daly	16.00	8.00	4.75
(25)	Davis	16.00	8.00	4.75
(26)	Demaree	16.00	8.00	4.75
(27)	DeMontreville	16.00	8.00	4.75
(28)	E. DeMontreville	16.00	8.00	4.75
(29)	Dick	16.00	8.00	4.75
(30)	Dobbs	16.00	8.00	4.75
(31)	Dudley	16.00	8.00	4.75
(32)	Dunn	16.00	8.00	4.75
(33)	Elliot	16.00	8.00	4.75
(34)	Emery	16.00	8.00	4.75
(35)	Erloff	16.00	8.00	4.75
(36)	Farrell	16.00	8.00	4.75
(37)	Fisher	16.00	8.00	4.75
(38)	Fleharty	16.00	8.00	4.75
(39)	Flood	16.00	8.00	4.75
(40)	Foster	16.00	8.00	4.75
(41)	Fritz	16.00	8.00	4.75
(42)	Greminger	16.00	8.00	4.75
(43)	Gribbon	16.00	8.00	4.75
(44)	Griffin	16.00	8.00	4.75
(45)	Gygli	16.00	8.00	4.75
(46)	Hanks	16.00	8.00	4.75
(47)	Hart	16.00	8.00	4.75
(48)	Hess	16.00	8.00	4.75
(49)	Hickman	16.00	8.00	4.75
(50)	Hohnhorst	16.00	8.00	4.75
(51)	Huelsman	16.00	8.00	4.75
(52)	Jackson	3500.	1750.	1050.
(53)	Jordan	16.00	8.00	4.75
(54)	Kane	16.00	8.00	4.75
(55)	Kelly	16.00	8.00	4.75
(56)	Kerwin	16.00	8.00	4.75
(57)	Keupper	16.00	8.00	4.75
(58)	LaFitte	16.00	8.00	4.75
(59)	Larsen	16.00	8.00	4.75
(60)	Lindsay	16.00	8.00	4.75
(61)	Lynch	16.00	8.00	4.75
(62)	Manuel	16.00	8.00	4.75
(63)	Manush	16.00	8.00	4.75
(64)	Marcan	16.00	8.00	4.75
(65)	Maxwell	16.00	8.00	4.75
(66)	McBride	16.00	8.00	4.75
(67)	McCreery	16.00	8.00	4.75
(68)	McGilvray	16.00	8.00	4.75
(69)	McLaurin	16.00	8.00	4.75
(70)	McTigue	16.00	8.00	4.75
(71)	Miller (Chattanooga)	16.00	8.00	4.75
(72)	Miller (Montgomery)	16.00	8.00	4.75
(73)	Molesworth	16.00	8.00	4.75
(74)	Moran	16.00	8.00	4.75
(75)	Newton	16.00	8.00	4.75
(76)	Nolley	16.00	8.00	4.75
(77)	Osteen	16.00	8.00	4.75
(78)	Owen	16.00	8.00	4.75
(79)	Paige	16.00	8.00	4.75
(80)	Patterson	16.00	8.00	4.75
(81)	Pepe	16.00	8.00	4.75
(82)	Perdue	16.00	8.00	4.75
(83)	Peters	16.00	8.00	4.75
(84)	Phillips	16.00	8.00	4.75
(85)	Pratt	16.00	8.00	4.75
(86)	Rementer	16.00	8.00	4.75
(87)	Rhodes	16.00	8.00	4.75
(88)	Rhoton	16.00	8.00	4.75
(89)	Robertson	16.00	8.00	4.75
(90)	Rogers	16.00	8.00	4.75
(91)	Rohe	16.00	8.00	4.75
(92)	Seabough (Seabaugh)	16.00	8.00	4.75
(93)	Seitz	16.00	8.00	4.75
(94)	Schlitzer	16.00	8.00	4.75
(95)	Schopp	16.00	8.00	4.75
(96)	Siegle	16.00	8.00	4.75
(97)	Smith	16.00	8.00	4.75
(98)	Sid. Smith	16.00	8.00	4.75
(99)	Steele	16.00	8.00	4.75
(100)	Swacina	16.00	8.00	4.75
(101)	Sweeney	16.00	8.00	4.75
(102)	Thomas (fielding)	16.00	8.00	4.75
(103)	Thomas (portrait)	16.00	8.00	4.75
(104)	Vinson	16.00	8.00	4.75
(105)	Wagner (Birmingham)	16.00	8.00	4.75
(106)	Wagner (Mobile)	16.00	8.00	4.75
(107)	Walker	16.00	8.00	4.75
(108)	Wanner	16.00	8.00	4.75
(109)	Welf	16.00	8.00	4.75
(110)	Whiteman	16.00	8.00	4.75
(111)	Whitney	16.00	8.00	4.75
(112)	Wilder	16.00	8.00	4.75
(113)	Wiseman	16.00	8.00	4.75
(114)	Yerkes	16.00	8.00	4.75

1958 Omaha Cardinals Picture Pak

This rare late-1950s minor league issue contains the first card of Hall of Fame pitcher Bob Gibson. Probably sold as a complete set in format similar to major league picture packs of the era, there are 23 player cards and a header card. Cards measure 3-3/8"x4-3/8", have a black-and-white player picture and facsimile autograph. They are blank-backed. The checklist of the unnumbered cards is printed here in alphabetical order.

		NR MT	EX	VG
Complete Set:		450.00	225.00	135.00
Common Player:		10.00	5.00	3.00
Header Card		10.00	5.00	3.00
(1)	Tony Alomar	15.00	7.50	3.00
(2)	Dave Benedict	10.00	5.00	3.00
(3)	Bill Bergesch	15.00	7.50	4.50
(4)	Bob Blaylock	10.00	5.00	3.00
(5)	Prentice "Pidge" Browne	10.00	5.00	3.00
(6)	Chris Cannizzaro	10.00	5.00	3.00
(7)	Nels Chittum	10.00	5.00	3.00
(8)	Don Choate	10.00	5.00	3.00
(9)	Phil Clark	10.00	5.00	3.00
(10)	Jim Frey	20.00	10.00	6.00
(11)	Bob Gibson	200.00	100.00	60.00
(12)	Ev Joyner	10.00	5.00	3.00
(13)	Johnny Keane	12.00	6.00	3.50
(14)	Paul Kippels	10.00	5.00	3.00
(15)	Boyd Linker	10.00	5.00	3.00
(16)	Bob Mabe	10.00	5.00	3.00
(17)	Bernard Mateosky	10.00	5.00	3.00
(18)	Ronnie Plaza	10.00	5.00	3.00
(19)	Bill Queen	10.00	5.00	3.00
(20)	Bill Smith	10.00	5.00	3.00
(21)	Bobby G. Smith	10.00	5.00	3.00
(22)	Lee Tate	10.00	5.00	3.00
(23)	Benny Valenzuela	10.00	5.00	3.00

1962 Team Omaha Dodgers

Dodgers

This unnumbered black-and-white set measures 3-3/8"x4-1/4" and is blank-backed.

		NR MT	EX	VG
Complete Set:		250.00	125.00	75.00
Common Player:		12.00	6.00	3.50
(1)	Joe Altobelli	18.00	9.00	5.50
(2)	Jim Barbieri	12.00	6.00	3.50
(3)	Scott Breeden	12.00	6.00	3.50
(4)	Mike Brumley	12.00	6.00	3.50
(5)	Jose Cesar	12.00	6.00	3.50
(6)	Bill Hunter	12.00	6.00	3.50
(7)	Don LeJohn	12.00	6.00	3.50
(8)	Jack Lutz	12.00	6.00	3.50

(9)	Ken McMullen	12.00	6.00	3.50
(10)	Danny Ozark	12.00	6.00	3.50
(11)	Curt Roberts	12.00	6.00	3.50
(12)	Ernie Rodriguez	12.00	6.00	3.50
(13)	Dick Scarbrough	12.00	6.00	3.50
(14)	Bart Shirley	12.00	6.00	3.50
(15)	Dick Smith	12.00	6.00	3.50
(16)	Jack Smith	12.00	6.00	3.50
(17)	Nate Smith	12.00	6.00	3.50
(18)	Gene Snyder	12.00	6.00	3.50
(19)	Burbon Wheeler	12.00	6.00	3.50
(20)	Nick Wilhite (Willhite)	12.00	6.00	3.50
(21)	Jim Williams	12.00	6.00	3.50
(22)	Larry Williams	12.00	6.00	3.50

1952 Parkhurst

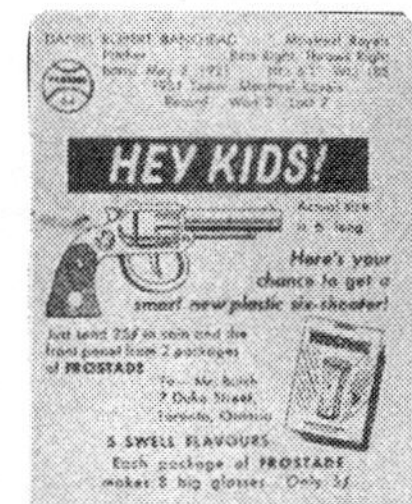

Produced by a Canadian competitor to Kool-aid, this 100-card set features players from three International League teams, the Toronto Maple Leafs, Montreal Royals and Ottawa Athletics, along with cards featuring baseball playing tips and quizzes. Measuring 2" x 2-1/2", the cards feature black-and-white player photos on front. Backs are printed in red and have a few biographical details, 1951 stats and an ad for Frostade.

		NR MT	EX	VG
Complete Set (100):		1900.	950.00	550.00
Common Card (1-25, 49-100):		20.00	10.00	6.00
Common Card (26-48):		10.00	5.00	3.00
1	Joe Becker	100.00	30.00	10.00
2	Bobby Rhawn	20.00	10.00	6.00
3	Aaron Silverman	20.00	10.00	6.00
4	Russ Bauers	20.00	10.00	6.00
5	Bill Jennings	20.00	10.00	6.00
6	Grover Bowers	20.00	10.00	6.00
7	Vic Lombardi	20.00	10.00	6.00
8	Billy DeMars	25.00	12.50	7.50
9	Frank Colman	20.00	10.00	6.00
10	Charley Grant	20.00	10.00	6.00
11	Irving Medlinger	20.00	10.00	6.00
12	Burke McLaughlin	20.00	10.00	6.00
13	Lew Morton	20.00	10.00	6.00
14	Red Barrett	20.00	10.00	6.00
15	Leon Foulk	20.00	10.00	6.00
16	Neil Sheridan	20.00	10.00	6.00
17	Ferrell Anderson	20.00	10.00	6.00
18	Roy Shore	20.00	10.00	6.00
19	Duke Markell	20.00	10.00	6.00
20	Bobby Balcena	20.00	10.00	6.00
21	Wilmer Fields	20.00	10.00	6.00
22	Charlie White	20.00	10.00	6.00
23	Red Fahr	20.00	10.00	6.00
24	Jose Bracho	20.00	10.00	6.00
25	Ed Stevens	20.00	10.00	6.00
26	Maple Leaf Stadium	25.00	12.50	7.50
27	Throwing Home	10.00	5.00	3.00
28	Regulation Baseball Diamond	10.00	5.00	3.00
29	Gripping the Bat	10.00	5.00	3.00
30	Hiding the Pitch	10.00	5.00	3.00
31	Catcher's Stance	10.00	5.00	3.00
32	Quiz: "How long does..."	10.00	5.00	3.00
33	Finger and Arm Exercises	10.00	5.00	3.00
34	First Baseman	10.00	5.00	3.00
35	Pitcher's Stance	10.00	5.00	3.00
36	Swinging Bats	10.00	5.00	3.00
37	Quiz: "Can a player advance"	10.00	5.00	3.00
38	Watch the Ball	10.00	5.00	3.00
39	Quiz: "Can a team..."	10.00	5.00	3.00
40	Quiz: "Can a player put..."	10.00	5.00	3.00
41	How to Bunt	10.00	5.00	3.00
42	Wrist Snap	10.00	5.00	3.00
43	Pitching Practice	10.00	5.00	3.00
44	Stealing Bases	10.00	5.00	3.00
45	Pitching 1	10.00	5.00	3.00
46	Pitching 2	10.00	5.00	3.00
47	Signals	10.00	5.00	3.00
48	Regulation Baseballs	10.00	5.00	3.00
49	Al Ronning	20.00	10.00	6.00
50	Bill Lane	20.00	10.00	6.00
51	Will Sampson	20.00	10.00	6.00
52	Charlie Thompson	20.00	10.00	6.00
53	Ezra McGlothin	20.00	10.00	6.00
54	Spook Jacobs	25.00	12.50	7.50
55	Art Fabbro	20.00	10.00	6.00
56	Jim Hughes	20.00	10.00	6.00
57	Don Hoak	60.00	30.00	18.00
58	Tommy Lasorda	225.00	112.00	67.00
59	Gil Mills	20.00	10.00	6.00
60	Malcolm Mallette	20.00	10.00	6.00
61	Rocky Nelson	30.00	15.00	9.00
62	John Simmons	20.00	10.00	6.00
63	Bob Alexander	20.00	10.00	6.00
64	Dan Bankhead	40.00	20.00	12.00
65	Solomon Coleman	20.00	10.00	6.00
66	Walt Alston	125.00	62.00	37.00
67	Walt Fiala	20.00	10.00	6.00
68	Jim Gilliam	60.00	30.00	18.00
69	Jim Pendleton	25.00	12.50	7.50
70	Gino Cimoli	30.00	15.00	9.00
71	Carmen Mauro	20.00	10.00	6.00
72	Walt Moryn	25.00	12.50	7.50
73	Jim Romano	20.00	10.00	6.00
74	Joe Lutz	20.00	10.00	6.00
75	Ed Roebuck	25.00	12.50	7.50
76	Johnny Podres	60.00	30.00	18.00
77	Walter Novik	20.00	10.00	6.00
78	Lefty Gohl	20.00	10.00	6.00
79	Tom Kirk	20.00	10.00	6.00
80	Bob Betz	20.00	10.00	6.00
81	Bill Hockenbury	20.00	10.00	6.00
82	Al Rubeling	20.00	10.00	6.00
83	Julius Watlington	20.00	10.00	6.00
84	Frank Fanovich	20.00	10.00	6.00
85	Hank Foiles	25.00	12.50	7.50
86	Lou Limmer	20.00	10.00	6.00
87	Ed Hrabcsak	20.00	10.00	6.00
88	Bob Gardner	20.00	10.00	6.00
89	John Metkovich	20.00	10.00	6.00
90	Jean-Pierre Roy	20.00	10.00	6.00
91	Frank Skaff	20.00	10.00	6.00
92	Harry Desert	20.00	10.00	6.00
93	Stan Jok	20.00	10.00	6.00
94	Russ Swingle	20.00	10.00	6.00
95	Bob Wellman	20.00	10.00	6.00
96	John Conway	20.00	10.00	6.00
97	George Maskovich	20.00	10.00	6.00
98	Charlie Bishop	20.00	10.00	6.00
99	Joe Murray	20.00	10.00	6.00
100	Mike Kume	20.00	10.00	6.00

1962 Pepsi-Cola Tulsa Oilers

(Texas League) (2-1/2" x 3-1/2") (unnumbered)

		NR MT	EX	VG
Complete Set:		240.00	120.00	72.50
Common Player:		12.00	6.00	3.50
(1)	Bob Blaylock	12.00	6.00	3.50
(2)	Bud Bloomfield	12.00	6.00	3.50
(3)	Dick Hughes	12.00	6.00	3.50
(4)	Gary Kolb	12.00	6.00	3.50
(5)	Chris Krug	12.00	6.00	3.50
(6)	Hank Kuhlmann	12.00	6.00	3.50
(7)	Whitey Kurowski	15.00	7.50	4.50
(8)	Johnny Joe Lewis	12.00	6.00	3.50
(9)	Elmer Lindsey	12.00	6.00	3.50
(10)	Jeoff Long	12.00	6.00	3.50
(11)	Pepper Martin	20.00	10.00	6.00
(12)	Jerry Marx	12.00	6.00	3.50
(13)	Weldon Maudin	12.00	6.00	3.50
(14)	Dal Maxvill	18.00	9.00	5.50
(15)	Bill McNamee	12.00	6.00	3.50
(16)	Joe Patterson	12.00	6.00	3.50
(17)	Gordon Richardson	12.00	6.00	3.50
(18)	Daryl Robertson	12.00	6.00	3.50
(19)	Tom Schwaner	12.00	6.00	3.50
(20)	Joe Shipley	12.00	6.00	3.50
(21)	Jon Smith	12.00	6.00	3.50
(22)	Clint Stark	12.00	6.00	3.50
(23)	Terry Tucker	12.00	6.00	3.50
(24)	Bill Wakefield	12.00	6.00	3.50

1963 Pepsi-Cola Tulsa Oilers

(Texas League) (2-1/2" x 3-1/2") (unnumbered)

		NR MT	EX	VG
Complete Set:		200.00	100.00	60.00
Common Player:		10.00	5.00	3.00
(1)	Dennis Aust	10.00	5.00	3.00
(2)	Jim Beauchamp	15.00	7.50	4.50
(3)	Bud Bloomfield	10.00	5.00	3.00
(4)	Felix DeLeon	10.00	5.00	3.00
(5)	Don Dennis	10.00	5.00	3.00
(6)	Lamar Drummonds	10.00	5.00	3.00
(7)	Tom Hilgendorf	10.00	5.00	3.00
(8)	Gary Kolb	10.00	5.00	3.00
(9)	Chris Krug	10.00	5.00	3.00
(10)	Bee Lindsey	10.00	5.00	3.00
(11)	Ray Majtyka	12.00	6.00	3.50
(12)	Pepper Martin	16.00	8.00	4.75
(13)	Jerry Marx	10.00	5.00	3.00
(14)	Hunkey Mauldin	10.00	5.00	3.00
(15)	Joe Paterson	10.00	5.00	3.00
(16)	Grover Resinger	10.00	5.00	3.00
(17)	Gordon Richardson	10.00	5.00	3.00
(18)	Jon Smith	10.00	5.00	3.00
(19)	Chuck Taylor	10.00	5.00	3.00
(20)	Terry Tucker	10.00	5.00	3.00
(21)	Lou Vickery	10.00	5.00	3.00
(22)	Bill Wakefield	10.00	5.00	3.00
(23)	Harry Watts	10.00	5.00	3.00
(24)	Jerry Wild	10.00	5.00	3.00

1966 Pepsi-Cola Tulsa Oilers

(Pacific Coast League) (2-1/2" x 3-1/2") (unnumbered)

		NR MT	EX	VG
Complete Set:		200.00	100.00	60.00
Common Player:		10.00	5.00	3.00
(1)	Florian Ackley	10.00	5.00	3.00
(2)	Dennis Aust	10.00	5.00	3.00
(3)	Elio Chacon	10.00	5.00	3.00
(4)	James Cosman	10.00	5.00	3.00
(5)	Mack Creager	10.00	5.00	3.00
(6)	Robert Dews	10.00	5.00	3.00
(7)	Harold Gilson	10.00	5.00	3.00
(8)	Larry Jaster	10.00	5.00	3.00
(9)	Alex Johnson	10.00	5.00	3.00
(10)	George Kernek	10.00	5.00	3.00
(11)	Jose Laboy	12.00	6.00	3.50
(12)	Richard LeMay	10.00	5.00	3.00
(13)	Charles Metro	10.00	5.00	3.00
(14)	David Pavlesic	10.00	5.00	3.00
(15)	Robert Pfeil	10.00	5.00	3.00
(16)	Ronald Piche	10.00	5.00	3.00
(17)	Robert Radovich	10.00	5.00	3.00
(18)	David Ricketts	10.00	5.00	3.00
(19)	Theodore Savage	12.00	6.00	3.50
(20)	George Schultz	10.00	5.00	3.00
(21)	Edward Spiezio	10.00	5.00	3.00
(22)	Clint Stark	10.00	5.00	3.00
(23)	Robert Tolan	10.00	5.00	3.00
(24)	Walter Williams	10.00	5.00	3.00

1910 Red Sun Southern Association (T211)

The 1910 minor league tobacco set issued by Red Sun Cigarettes features 75 players from the Southern Association. Known by the American Card Catalog designation T211, the Red Sun issue is similar in size and style to the massive 640-card Old Mill set (T210) issued the same year. Cards in both sets measure 1-1/2" x 2-5/8" and feature glossy black-and-white player photos. Unlike the Old Mill set, however, the Red Sun cards have a green border surrounding the photograph and a bright red and white advertisement for Red Sun Cigarettes on the back. A line at the bottom promotes the cards as "First Series 1 to 75," implying that additional sets would follow, but apparently none ever did. Each of the 75 subjects in the Red Sun set was also pictured in Series Eight of the Old Mill set. Because of the "glossy" nature of the photographs, cards in both the Old Mill and Red Sun sets were susceptible to cracking, making condition and proper grading of these cards especially important to collectors.

		NR MT	EX	VG
Complete Set:		2700.	1350.	810.00
Common Player:		35.00	17.50	10.50
(1)	Allen	35.00	17.50	10.50
(2)	Anderson	35.00	17.50	10.50
(3)	Babb	35.00	17.50	10.50
(4)	Bartley	35.00	17.50	10.50
(5)	Bay	35.00	17.50	10.50
(6)	Bayliss	35.00	17.50	10.50
(7)	Berger	35.00	17.50	10.50
(8)	Bernard	35.00	17.50	10.50
(9)	Bitroff	35.00	17.50	10.50
(10)	Breitenstein	35.00	17.50	10.50
(11)	Bronkie	35.00	17.50	10.50
(12)	Brooks	35.00	17.50	10.50
(13)	Cafalu	35.00	17.50	10.50
(14)	Case	35.00	17.50	10.50
(15)	Chappelle	35.00	17.50	10.50
(16)	Cohen	35.00	17.50	10.50
(17)	Cross	35.00	17.50	10.50
(18)	Jud. Daly	35.00	17.50	10.50
(19)	Davis	35.00	17.50	10.50

		NR MT	EX	VG
(20)	DeMontreville	35.00	17.50	10.50
(21)	E. DeMontreville	35.00	17.50	10.50
(22)	Dick	35.00	17.50	10.50
(23)	Dunn	35.00	17.50	10.50
(24)	Erloff	35.00	17.50	10.50
(25)	Fisher	35.00	17.50	10.50
(26)	Flood	35.00	17.50	10.50
(27)	Foster	35.00	17.50	10.50
(28)	Fritz	35.00	17.50	10.50
(29)	Greminger	35.00	17.50	10.50
(30)	Gribbon	35.00	17.50	10.50
(31)	Griffin	35.00	17.50	10.50
(32)	Gygli	35.00	17.50	10.50
(33)	Hanks	35.00	17.50	10.50
(34)	Hart	35.00	17.50	10.50
(35)	Hess	35.00	17.50	10.50
(36)	Hickman	35.00	17.50	10.50
(37)	Hohnhorst	35.00	17.50	10.50
(38)	Huelsman	35.00	17.50	10.50
(39)	Jordan	35.00	17.50	10.50
(40)	Kane	35.00	17.50	10.50
(41)	Kelly	35.00	17.50	10.50
(42)	Kerwin	35.00	17.50	10.50
(43)	Keupper	35.00	17.50	10.50
(44)	LaFitte	35.00	17.50	10.50
(45)	Lindsay	35.00	17.50	10.50
(46)	Lynch	35.00	17.50	10.50
(47)	Manush	35.00	17.50	10.50
(48)	McCreery	35.00	17.50	10.50
(49)	Miller	35.00	17.50	10.50
(50)	Molesworth	35.00	17.50	10.50
(51)	Moran	35.00	17.50	10.50
(52)	Nolley	35.00	17.50	10.50
(53)	Paige	35.00	17.50	10.50
(54)	Pepe	35.00	17.50	10.50
(55)	Perdue	35.00	17.50	10.50
(56)	Pratt	35.00	17.50	10.50
(57)	Rhoton	35.00	17.50	10.50
(58)	Robertson	35.00	17.50	10.50
(59)	Rogers	35.00	17.50	10.50
(60)	Rohe	35.00	17.50	10.50
(61)	Seabaugh	35.00	17.50	10.50
(62)	Seitz	35.00	17.50	10.50
(63)	Siegle	35.00	17.50	10.50
(64)	Smith	35.00	17.50	10.50
(65)	Sid. Smith	35.00	17.50	10.50
(66)	Steele	35.00	17.50	10.50
(67)	Swacina	35.00	17.50	10.50
(68)	Sweeney	35.00	17.50	10.50
(69)	Thomas	35.00	17.50	10.50
(70)	Vinson	35.00	17.50	10.50
(71)	Wagner	35.00	17.50	10.50
(72)	Walker	35.00	17.50	10.50
(73)	Welf	35.00	17.50	10.50
(74)	Wilder	35.00	17.50	10.50
(75)	Wiseman	35.00	17.50	10.50

1946 Remar Bread Oakland Oaks

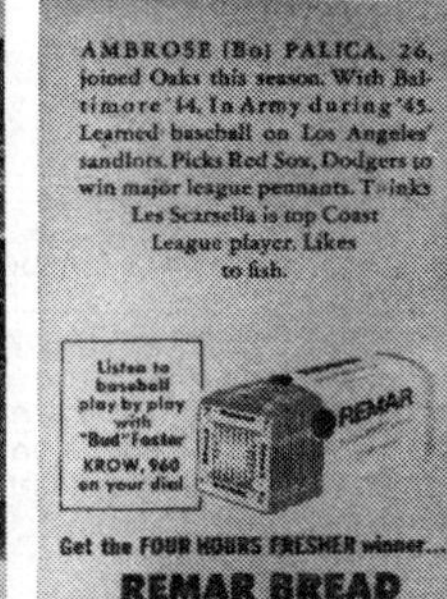

AMBROSE (Bo) PALICA, 26, joined Oaks this season. With Baltimore '44. In Army during '45. Learned baseball on Los Angeles' sandlots. Picks Red Sox, Dodgers to win major league pennants. Thinks Les Scarsella is top Coast League player. Likes to fish.
Listen to baseball play by play with "Bud" Foster KROW, 960 on your dial
REMAR
Get the FOUR HOURS FRESHER winner...
REMAR BREAD

Remar Baking Company issued several baseball card sets in the northern California area from 1946-1950, all picturing members of the Oakland Oaks of the Pacific Coast League. The 1946 set consists of 23 cards (five unnumbered, 18 numbered). Measuring 2" x 3", the cards were printed on heavy paper and feature black and white photos with the player's name, team and position at the bottom. The backs contain a brief write-up plus an ad for Remar Bread printed in red. The cards were distributed one per week. The first five cards were unnumbered. The rest of the set is numbered on the front, but begins with number "5", rather than "6".

		NR MT	EX	VG
Complete Set:		375.00	187.00	112.00
Common Player:		15.00	7.50	4.50
5	Hershell Martin (Herschel)	15.00	7.50	4.50
6	Bill Hart	15.00	7.50	4.50
7	Charlie Gassaway	15.00	7.50	4.50
8	Wally Westlake	15.00	7.50	4.50
9	Mickey Burnett	15.00	7.50	4.50
10	Charles (Casey) Stengel	80.00	40.00	24.00
11	Charlie Metro	15.00	7.50	4.50
12	Tom Hafey	15.00	7.50	4.50
13	Tony Sabol	15.00	7.50	4.50
14	Ed Kearse	15.00	7.50	4.50
15	Bud Foster (announcer)	15.00	7.50	4.50
16	Johnny Price	15.00	7.50	4.50
17	Gene Bearden	15.00	7.50	4.50
18	Floyd Speer	15.00	7.50	4.50
19	Bryan Stephens	15.00	7.50	4.50
20	Rinaldo (Rugger) Ardizoia	15.00	7.50	4.50
21	Ralph Buxton	15.00	7.50	4.50
22	Ambrose (Bo) Palica	15.00	7.50	4.50
----	Brooks Holder	15.00	7.50	4.50
----	Henry (Cotton) Pippen	15.00	7.50	4.50
----	Billy Raimondi	60.00	30.00	18.00
----	Les Scarsella	15.00	7.50	4.50
----	Glen (Gabby) Stewart	15.00	7.50	4.50

1947 Remar Bread Oakland Oaks

CHARLES (Casey) STENGEL
Oaks Manager 8

Fiery CHARLES (CASEY) STENGEL has been in baseball 36 years. During his playing days, Stengel—a fast, hard-hitting outfielder — was with Brooklyn Dodgers, Boston Braves, New York Giants. Has managed Dodgers, Braves and Milwaukee of American Association. He's noted for his ability to develop young players.
"Let's Be Friends"
Listen to baseball play by play with "Bud" Foster KROW, 960 on your dial
REMAR BAKING CO.

Remar's second set consisted of 25 numbered cards, again measuring 2" x 3". The cards are nearly identical to the previous year's set, except the loaf of bread on the back is printed in blue, rather than red.

		NR MT	EX	VG
Complete Set:		350.00	175.00	105.00
Common Player:		15.00	7.50	4.50
1	Billy Raimondi	15.00	7.50	4.50
2	Les Scarsella	15.00	7.50	4.50
3	Brooks Holder	15.00	7.50	4.50
4	Charlie Gassaway	15.00	7.50	4.50
5	Mickey Burnett	15.00	7.50	4.50
6	Ralph Buxton	15.00	7.50	4.50
7	Ed Kearse	15.00	7.50	4.50
8	Charles (Casey) Stengel	70.00	35.00	21.00
9	Bud Foster (announcer)	15.00	7.50	4.50
10	Ambrose (Bo) Palica	15.00	7.50	4.50
11	Tom Hafey	15.00	7.50	4.50
12	Hershel Martin (Herschel)	15.00	7.50	4.50
13	Henry (Cotton) Pippen	15.00	7.50	4.50
14	Floyd Speer	15.00	7.50	4.50
15	Tony Sabol	15.00	7.50	4.50
16	Will Hafey	15.00	7.50	4.50
17	Ray Hamrick	15.00	7.50	4.50
18	Maurice Van Robays	15.00	7.50	4.50
19	Dario Lodigiani	15.00	7.50	4.50
20	Mel (Dizz) Duezabou	15.00	7.50	4.50
21	Damon Hayes	15.00	7.50	4.50
22	Gene Lillard	15.00	7.50	4.50
23	Aldon Wilkie	15.00	7.50	4.50
24	Dewey Soriano	15.00	7.50	4.50
25	Glen Crawford	15.00	7.50	4.50

1948 Remar Bread Oakland Oaks

(3-1/4" x 5-1/2") (the set is one team picture card) (black and white) (PCL)

	NR MT	EX	VG
Team Picture	1200.	600.00	360.00

1949 Remar Bread Oakland Oaks

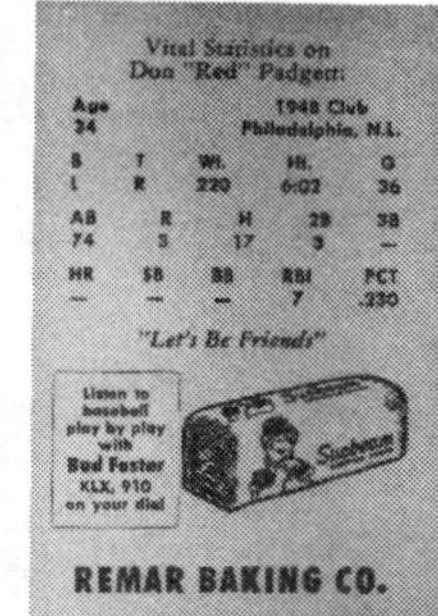

The 1949 Remar Bread issue was increased to 32 cards, again measuring 2" x 3". Unlike the two earlier sets, photos in the 1949 Remar set are surrounded by a thin, white border and are unnumbered. The player's name, team and position appear below the black and white photo. The backs are printed in blue and include the player's 1948 statistics and the distinctive loaf of bread.

		NR MT	EX	VG
Complete Set:		350.00	175.00	105.00
Common Player:		12.00	6.00	3.50
(1)	Ralph Buxton	12.00	6.00	3.50
(2)	Milo Candini	15.00	7.50	4.50
(3)	Rex Cecil	15.00	7.50	4.50
(4)	Loyd Christopher (Lloyd)	12.00	6.00	3.50
(5)	Charles Dressen	20.00	10.00	6.00
(6)	Mel Duezabou	12.00	6.00	3.50
(7)	Bud Foster (sportscaster)	12.00	6.00	3.50
(8)	Charlie Gassaway	12.00	6.00	3.50
(9)	Ray Hamrick	12.00	6.00	3.50
(10)	Jack Jensen	20.00	10.00	6.00
(11)	Earl Jones	12.00	6.00	3.50
(12)	George Kelly	18.00	9.00	5.50
(13)	Frank Kerr	15.00	7.50	4.50
(14)	Richard Kryhoski	12.00	6.00	3.50
(15)	Harry Lavagetto	12.00	6.00	3.50
(16)	Dario Lodigiani	12.00	6.00	3.50
(17)	Billy Martin	80.00	40.00	24.00
(18)	George Metkovich	12.00	6.00	3.50
(19)	Frank Nelson	12.00	6.00	3.50
(20)	Don Padgett	12.00	6.00	3.50
(21)	Alonzo Perry	15.00	7.50	4.50
(22)	Bill Raimondi	12.00	6.00	3.50
(23)	Earl Rapp	12.00	6.00	3.50
(24)	Eddie Samcoff	12.00	6.00	3.50
(25)	Les Scarsella	12.00	6.00	3.50
(26)	Forest Thompson (Forrest)	15.00	7.50	4.50
(27)	Earl Toolson	12.00	6.00	3.50
(28)	Lou Tost	15.00	7.50	4.50
(29)	Maurice Van Robays	12.00	6.00	3.50
(30)	Jim Wallace	12.00	6.00	3.50
(31)	Arthur Lee Wilson	18.00	9.00	5.50
(32)	Parnell Woods	15.00	7.50	4.50

1950 Remar Bread Oakland Oaks

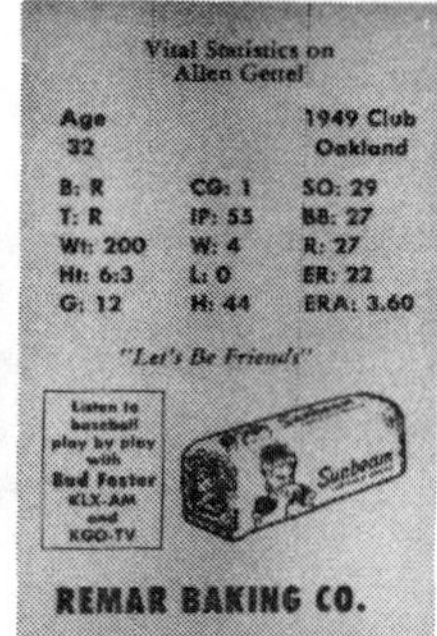

The most common of the Remar Bread issues, the 1950 set contains 27 unnumbered cards, again measuring 2" x 3" and featuring members of the Oakland Oaks. The cards are nearly identical to the previous year's set but can be differentiated by the 1949 statistics on the back.

		NR MT	EX	VG
Complete Set:		200.00	100.00	60.00
Common Player:		12.00	6.00	3.50
(1)	George Bamberger	15.00	7.50	4.50
(2)	Hank Behrman	12.00	6.00	3.50
(3)	Loyd Christopher (Lloyd)	12.00	6.00	3.50
(4)	Chuck Dressen	15.00	7.50	4.50
(5)	Mel Duezabou	12.00	6.00	3.50
(6)	Augie Galan	12.00	6.00	3.50
(7)	Charlie Gassaway	12.00	6.00	3.50
(8)	Allen Gettel	12.00	6.00	3.50
(9)	Ernie W. Groth	12.00	6.00	3.50
(10)	Ray Hamrick	12.00	6.00	3.50
(11)	Earl Harrist	12.00	6.00	3.50
(12)	Billy Herman	18.00	9.00	5.50
(13)	Bob Hofman	12.00	6.00	3.50
(14)	George Kelly	18.00	9.00	5.50
(15)	Harry Lavagetto	12.00	6.00	3.50
(16)	Eddie Malone	12.00	6.00	3.50
(17)	George Metkovich	12.00	6.00	3.50
(18)	Frank Nelson	12.00	6.00	3.50
(19)	Rafael (Ray) Noble	12.00	6.00	3.50
(20)	Don Padgett	12.00	6.00	3.50
(21)	Earl Rapp	12.00	6.00	3.50
(22)	Clyde Shoun	12.00	6.00	3.50
(23)	Forrest Thompson	12.00	6.00	3.50
(24)	Louis Tost	12.00	6.00	3.50
(25)	Dick Wakefield	12.00	6.00	3.50
(26)	Artie Wilson	15.00	7.50	4.50
(27)	Roy Zimmerman	12.00	6.00	3.50

The values quoted are intended to reflect the market price.

1966 Royal Crown Cola Columbus Yankees

This set of 20 cards was distributed in eight packs of Royal Crown Cola, then based in Columbus, Ga. They were part of a strip that measured 2-1/4" wide. The first 3" of the 9-1/2" strip had a black-and-white photo of the player with his name, position and other bio information, along with an RC logo in blue and red print. The bottom portion of the card has a promotion sponsored by the ballclub and RC, offering a case of cola for turning in a complete set in an album provided for the cards. Those who turned in the cards were also eligible to win baseball equipment or picnic coolers in a giveaway at a game July 31 of that year. Most cards have the advertisement removed. Those cards that include the advertisement should be considered more valuable. The cards are unnumbered and listed in alphabetical order.

		NR MT	EX	VG
Complete Set:		375.00	187.50	110.00
Common Player:		20.00	10.00	6.00
(1)	Gil Blanco	20.00	10.00	6.00
(2)	Ronnie Boyer	25.00	12.50	7.50
(3)	Jim Brenneman	20.00	10.00	6.00
(4)	Butch Cretara	20.00	10.00	6.00
(5)	Bill Henry	20.00	10.00	6.00
(6)	Joe Jeran	20.00	10.00	6.00
(7)	Jerry Kenney	20.00	10.00	6.00
(8)	Ronnie Kirk	20.00	10.00	6.00
(9)	Tom Kowalski	20.00	10.00	6.00
(10)	Jim Marrujo	20.00	10.00	6.00
(11)	Dave McDonald	20.00	10.00	6.00
(12)	Ed Merritt	20.00	10.00	6.00
(13)	Jim Palma	20.00	10.00	6.00
(14)	Cecil Perkins	20.00	10.00	6.00
(15)	Jack Reed	20.00	10.00	6.00
(16)	Ellie Rodriguez	25.00	12.50	7.50
(17)	John Schroeppel	20.00	10.00	6.00
(18)	Dave Truelock	20.00	10.00	6.00
(19)	Steve Whitaker	20.00	10.00	6.00
(20)	Earl Willoughby	20.00	10.00	6.00

1950 San Francisco Seals Popcorn

These 3-1/4" x 4-1/2" black-and-white cards were issued with the purchase of caramel corn at Sicks Stadium.

		NR MT	EX	VG
Complete Set:		150.00	75.00	45.00
Common Player:		12.00	6.00	3.50
(1)	Dick Briskey	12.00	6.00	3.50
(2)	Ralph Buxton	12.00	6.00	3.50
(3)	Harry Feldman	12.00	6.00	3.50
(4)	Chet Johnson	12.00	6.00	3.50
(5)	Al Lien	12.00	6.00	3.50
(6)	Dario Lodigiani	12.00	6.00	3.50
(7)	Cliff Melton	12.00	6.00	3.50
(8)	Roy Nicely	12.00	6.00	3.50
(9)	Roy Partee	12.00	6.00	3.50
(10)	Manny Perez	12.00	6.00	3.50
(11)	Neill Sheridan	12.00	6.00	3.50
(12)	Elmer Singleton	12.00	6.00	3.50
(13)	Jack Tobin	12.00	6.00	3.50

1953 Team Issue San Francisco Seals

This set of 24 cards was sold at Sicks Stadium and by mail for 25 cents. Fronts of the 4" x 5" black-and-white cards contain a player photo with facsimile autograph. The player's name, team and position are printed in the white bottom border. Backs of the unnumbered cards are blank.

		NR MT	EX	VG
Complete Set:		350.00	175.00	100.00
Common Player:		15.00	7.50	4.50
(1)	Bill Boemler	15.00	7.50	4.50
(2)	Bill Bradford	15.00	7.50	4.50
(3)	Reno Cheso	15.00	7.50	4.50
(4)	Harlond Clift	15.00	7.50	4.50
(5)	Walt Clough	15.00	7.50	4.50
(6)	Cliff Coggin	15.00	7.50	4.50
(7)	Tommy Heath	15.00	7.50	4.50
(8)	Leo Hughes (Trainer)	15.00	7.50	4.50
(9)	Frank Kalin	15.00	7.50	4.50
(10)	Al Lien	15.00	7.50	4.50
(11)	Al Lyons	15.00	7.50	4.50
(12)	John McCall	15.00	7.50	4.50
(13)	Bill McCawley	15.00	7.50	4.50
(14)	Jim Moran	15.00	7.50	4.50
(15)	Bob Muncrief	15.00	7.50	4.50
(16)	Leo Righetti	18.00	9.00	5.50
(17)	Ted Shandor	15.00	7.50	4.50
(18)	Elmer Singleton	15.00	7.50	4.50
(19)	Lou Stringer	15.00	7.50	4.50
(20)	Sal Taormina	15.00	7.50	4.50
(21)	Will Tiesiera	15.00	7.50	4.50
(22)	Nini Tornay	15.00	7.50	4.50
(23)	George Vico	15.00	7.50	4.50
(24)	Jerry Zuvela	15.00	7.50	4.50

1963 Scheible Press Rochester Red Wings

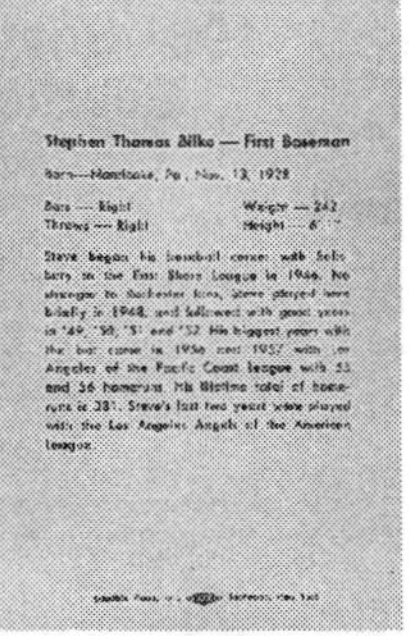
Stephen Thomas Bilko — First Baseman

Bats — Right
Throws — Right

Apparently sold as a stadium concession stand item in a paper and cellophane envelope, the nine full-color 3-13/16" x 5-7/8" cards are printed on heavy paper with a black-and-white back. The '63 Red Wings were the International League affiliate of the Baltimore Orioles.

		NR MT	EX	VG
Complete Set:		225.00	112.50	67.50
Common Player:		20.00	10.00	6.00
(1)	Joe Altobelli	25.00	12.50	7.50
(2)	Steve Bilko	20.00	10.00	6.00
(3)	Sam E. Bowens	20.00	10.00	6.00
(4)	Don Brummer	20.00	10.00	6.00
(5)	Luke Easter	30.00	15.00	9.00
(6)	Darrell Johnson, Chris Krug	25.00	12.50	7.50
(7)	Fred Valentine	20.00	10.00	6.00
(8)	Ozzie Virgil	20.00	10.00	6.00
(9)	Ray Youngdahl	20.00	10.00	6.00

1954 Seattle Popcorn Seattle Rainiers

One of the longest-running minor league baseball card promotions in hobby history were the Seattle popcorn cards of 1954-68. Similar in format throughout that period, the cards were 2" x 3" in size, black-and-white, usually featuring portrait photos on the front with the players name or name and position below. In some years the cards were printed on semi-glossy stock. In some years card backs were blank, in other years, backs featured ads for various local businesses as sponsors; in a few years, cards could be found with both blank and printed backs. Many photo and spelling variations are known throughout the series; most are noted in the appropriate checklists. The unnumbered cards are checklisted alphabetically. It is possible a few stragglers will be added to these checklists in the future.

		NR MT	EX	VG
Complete Set:		350.00	175.00	100.00
Common Player:		15.00	7.50	4.50
(1)	Gene Bearden	15.00	7.50	4.50
(2)	Al Brightman	15.00	7.50	4.50
(3)	Jack Burkowatz	15.00	7.50	4.50
(4)	Tommy Byrne	15.00	7.50	4.50
(5)	Joe Erautt	15.00	7.50	4.50
(6)	Bill Evans	15.00	7.50	4.50
(7)	Van Fletcher	15.00	7.50	4.50
(8)	Bob Hall	15.00	7.50	4.50
(9)	Pete Hernandez	15.00	7.50	4.50
(10)	Lloyd Jenney	15.00	7.50	4.50
(11)	Joe Joshua	15.00	7.50	4.50
(12)	Vern Kindsfather	15.00	7.50	4.50
(13)	Tom Lovrich	15.00	7.50	4.50
(14)	Clarence Maddern	15.00	7.50	4.50
(15)	Don Mallott	15.00	7.50	4.50
(16)	Loren Meyers	15.00	7.50	4.50
(17)	Steve Nagy	15.00	7.50	4.50
(18)	Ray Orteig	15.00	7.50	4.50
(19)	Gerry Priddy	15.00	7.50	4.50
(20)	George Schmees	15.00	7.50	4.50
(21)	Bill Schuster	15.00	7.50	4.50
(22)	Leo Thomas	15.00	7.50	4.50
(23)	Jack Tobin	15.00	7.50	4.50
(24)	Al Widmer	15.00	7.50	4.50
(25)	Artie Wilson	18.00	9.00	5.50
(26)	Al Zarilla	15.00	7.50	4.50

1955 Seattle Popcorn Seattle Rainiers

		NR MT	EX	VG
Complete Set:		300.00	150.00	90.00
Common Player:		15.00	7.50	4.50
(1)	Bob Balcena	15.00	7.50	4.50
(2)	Monty Basgall	15.00	7.50	4.50
(3)	Ewell Blackwell	22.00	11.00	6.50
(4)	Bill Brenner	15.00	7.50	4.50
(5)	Jack Burkowatz	15.00	7.50	4.50
(6)	Van Fletcher	15.00	7.50	4.50
(7)	Joe Ginsberg	15.00	7.50	4.50
(8)	Jehosie Heard	18.00	9.00	5.50
(9)	Fred Hutchinson	22.00	11.00	6.50
(10)	Larry Jansen	15.00	7.50	4.50
(11)	Bob Kelly	15.00	7.50	4.50
(12)	Bill Kennedy	15.00	7.50	4.50
(13)	Lou Kretlow	15.00	7.50	4.50
(14)	Rocco Krsnich	15.00	7.50	4.50
(15)	Carmen Mauro	15.00	7.50	4.50
(16)	John Oldham	15.00	7.50	4.50
(17)	George Schmees	15.00	7.50	4.50
(18)	Elmer Singleton	15.00	7.50	4.50
(19)	Alan Strange	15.00	7.50	4.50
(20)	Gene Verble	15.00	7.50	4.50
(21)	Marv Williams	15.00	7.50	4.50
(22)	Harvey Zernia	15.00	7.50	4.50

1956 Seattle Popcorn Seattle Rainiers

		NR MT	EX	VG
Complete Set:		350.00	175.00	100.00
Common Player:		15.00	7.50	4.50
(1)	Fred Baczewski	15.00	7.50	4.50
(2)	Bob Balcena	15.00	7.50	4.50
(3)	Bill Brenner	15.00	7.50	4.50
(4)	Sherry Dixon	15.00	7.50	4.50
(5)	Don Fracchia	15.00	7.50	4.50
(6)	Bill Glynn	15.00	7.50	4.50
(7)	Larry Jansen	15.00	7.50	4.50
(8)	Howie Judson	15.00	7.50	4.50
(9)	Bill Kennedy	15.00	7.50	4.50
(10)	Jack Lohrke	15.00	7.50	4.50
(11)	Vic Lombardi	15.00	7.50	4.50
(12)	Carmen Mauro	15.00	7.50	4.50
(13)	Ray Orteig	15.00	7.50	4.50
(14)	Bud Podbielan	15.00	7.50	4.50
(15)	Leo Righetti	15.00	7.50	4.50
(16)	Jim Robertson	15.00	7.50	4.50
(17)	Art Shallock	15.00	7.50	4.50
(18)	Art Schult	15.00	7.50	4.50
(19)	Luke Sewell	20.00	10.00	6.00
(20)	Elmer Singleton	15.00	7.50	4.50
(21a)	Milt Smith (portrait)	15.00	7.50	4.50
(21b)	Milt Smith (action)	15.00	7.50	4.50
(22)	Vern Stephens	15.00	7.50	4.50
(23)	Alan Strange	15.00	7.50	4.50
(24)	Joe Taylor	15.00	7.50	4.50
(25)	Artie Wilson	20.00	10.00	6.00
(26)	Harvey Zernia	15.00	7.50	4.50

1957 Seattle Popcorn Seattle Rainiers

By presenting any nine different pictures to either of **GIL'S DRIVE-INS** you will receive **FREE** an 8" x 10" player picture of your choice and you still keep your nine small pictures.

Three locations to serve you

GIL'S DRIVE-IN
4406 Rainier Avenue
1 mile south of Sicks' Stadium
•
3500 Avalon Way
35th S.W. and Avalon Way
West Seattle
•
Burien
1st South and South 152nd

		NR MT	EX	VG
Complete Set:		350.00	175.00	100.00
Common Player:		15.00	7.50	4.50
(1)	Dick Aylward	15.00	7.50	4.50
(2)	Bob Balcena	15.00	7.50	4.50
(3)	Eddie Basinki	15.00	7.50	4.50
(4)	Hal Bevan	15.00	7.50	4.50
(5)	Joe Black	24.00	12.00	7.25
(6)	Juan Delis	15.00	7.50	4.50
(7)	Jim Dyck	15.00	7.50	4.50
(8)	Marion Fricano	15.00	7.50	4.50
(9)	Bill Glynn	15.00	7.50	4.50
(10)	Larry Jansen	15.00	7.50	4.50
(11)	Howie Judson	15.00	7.50	4.50
(12)	Bill Kennedy	15.00	7.50	4.50
(13)	Jack Lohrke	15.00	7.50	4.50
(14)	Carmen Mauro	15.00	7.50	4.50
(15)	George Munger	15.00	7.50	4.50
(16)	Lefty O'Doul	25.00	12.50	7.50
(17)	Ray Orteig	15.00	7.50	4.50
(18)	Duane Pillette	15.00	7.50	4.50
(19)	Bud Podbielan	15.00	7.50	4.50
(20)	Charley Rabe	15.00	7.50	4.50

(21)	Leo Righetti	15.00	7.50	4.50
(22)	Joe Taylor	15.00	7.50	4.50
(23)	Edo Vanni	15.00	7.50	4.50
(24)	Morrie (Maury) Wills	60.00	30.00	18.00

1958 Seattle Popcorn Seattle Rainiers

		NR MT	EX	VG
Complete Set:		225.00	110.00	65.00
Common Player:		12.00	6.00	3.50
(1)	Bob Balcena	12.00	6.00	3.50
(2)	Ed Basinki	12.00	6.00	3.50
(3)	Hal Bevan	12.00	6.00	3.50
(4)	Jack Bloomfield	12.00	6.00	3.50
(5)	Juan Delis	12.00	6.00	3.50
(6)	Dutch Dotterer	12.00	6.00	3.50
(7)	Jim Dyck	12.00	6.00	3.50
(8)	Al Federoff	12.00	6.00	3.50
(9)	Art Fowler	12.00	6.00	3.50
(10)	Bill Kennedy	12.00	6.00	3.50
(11)	Marty Kutyna	12.00	6.00	3.50
(12)	Ray Orteig	12.00	6.00	3.50
(13)	Duane Pillette	12.00	6.00	3.50
(14)	Vada Pinson	35.00	17.50	10.50
(15)	Connie Ryan	12.00	6.00	3.50
(16)	Phil Sartzer	12.00	6.00	3.50
(17)	Max Surkont	12.00	6.00	3.50
(18)	Gale Wade	12.00	6.00	3.50
(19)	Ted Wieand	12.00	6.00	3.50

1959 Seattle Popcorn Seattle Rainiers

		NR MT	EX	VG
Complete Set:		400.00	200.00	120.00
Common Player:		12.00	6.00	3.50
(1)	Bobby Adams	12.00	6.00	3.50
(2)	Frank Amaya	12.00	6.00	3.50
(3)	Hal Bevan	12.00	6.00	3.50
(4)	Jack Bloomfield	12.00	6.00	3.50
(5)	Clarence Churn	12.00	6.00	3.50
(6)	Jack Dittmer	12.00	6.00	3.50
(7)	Jim Dyck	12.00	6.00	3.50
(8)	Dee Fondy	12.00	6.00	3.50
(9)	Mark Freeman	12.00	6.00	3.50
(10)	Dick Hanlon	12.00	6.00	3.50
(11)	Carroll Hardy	12.00	6.00	3.50
(12)	Bobby Henrich	12.00	6.00	3.50
(13)	Jay Hook	12.00	6.00	3.50
(14)	Fred Hutchinson	18.00	9.00	5.50
(15)	Jake Jenkins	12.00	6.00	3.50
(16)	Eddie Kazak	12.00	6.00	3.50
(17)	Bill Kennedy	12.00	6.00	3.50
(18)	Harry Lowrey	12.00	6.00	3.50
(19a)	Harry Malmbeg (Malmberg)	12.00	6.00	3.50
(19b)	Harry Malmberg	12.00	6.00	3.50
(20)	Bob Mape	12.00	6.00	3.50
(21)	Darrell Martin	12.00	6.00	3.50
(22)	John McCall	12.00	6.00	3.50
(23)	Claude Osteen	15.00	7.50	4.50
(24)	Paul Pettit	12.00	6.00	3.50
(25)	Charley Rabe	12.00	6.00	3.50
(26)	Rudy Regalado	12.00	6.00	3.50
(27)	Eric Rodin	12.00	6.00	3.50
(28)	Don Rudolph	12.00	6.00	3.50
(29)	Lou Skizas	12.00	6.00	3.50
(30)	Dave Stenhouse	12.00	6.00	3.50
(31)	Alan Strange	12.00	6.00	3.50
(32)	Max Surkont	12.00	6.00	3.50
(33)	Ted Tappe	12.00	6.00	3.50
(34)	Elmer Valo	12.00	6.00	3.50
(35)	Gale Wade	12.00	6.00	3.50
(36)	Bill Wight	12.00	6.00	3.50
(37)	Ed Winceniak	12.00	6.00	3.50

1960 Seattle Popcorn Seattle Rainiers

		NR MT	EX	VG
Complete Set:		200.00	100.00	60.00
Common Player:		12.00	6.00	3.50
(1)	Charlie Beamon	12.00	6.00	3.50
(2)	Hal Bevan	12.00	6.00	3.50
(3)	Whammy Douglas	12.00	6.00	3.50
(4)	Buddy Gilbert	12.00	6.00	3.50
(5)	Hal Jeffcoat	12.00	6.00	3.50
(6)	Leigh Lawrence	12.00	6.00	3.50
(7)	Darrell Martin	12.00	6.00	3.50
(8)	Francisco Obregon	12.00	6.00	3.50
(9)	Johnny O'Brien	12.00	6.00	3.50
(10)	Paul Pettitt	12.00	6.00	3.50
(11)	Ray Ripplemeyer	12.00	6.00	3.50
(12)	Don Rudolph	12.00	6.00	3.50
(13)	Willard Schmidt	12.00	6.00	3.50
(14)	Dick Sisler	12.00	6.00	3.50
(15)	Lou Skizas	12.00	6.00	3.50
(16)	Joe Taylor	12.00	6.00	3.50
(17)	Bob Thurman	12.00	6.00	3.50
(18)	Gerald Zimmerman	12.00	6.00	3.50

1961 Seattle Popcorn Seattle Rainiers

		NR MT	EX	VG
Complete Set:		200.00	100.00	60.00
Common Player:		12.00	6.00	3.50
(1)	Galen Cisco	12.00	6.00	3.50
(2a)	Marlan Coughtry	12.00	6.00	3.50
(2b)	Marlin Coughtry	12.00	6.00	3.50
(3)	Pete Cronin	12.00	6.00	3.50
(4)	Arnold Earley	12.00	6.00	3.50
(5)	Bob Heffner	12.00	6.00	3.50
(6)	Curt Jenson	12.00	6.00	3.50
(7a)	Harry Malmberg (coach)	12.00	6.00	3.50
(7b)	Harry Malmberg (player-coach)	12.00	6.00	3.50
(8)	Dave Mann	12.00	6.00	3.50
(9)	Darrell Martin	12.00	6.00	3.50
(10a)	Erv Palica	12.00	6.00	3.50
(10b)	Ervin Palica	12.00	6.00	3.50
(11)	Johnny Pesky	15.00	7.50	4.50
(12)	Dick Radatz	12.00	6.00	3.50
(13a)	Ted Schreiber	12.00	6.00	3.50
(13b)	Ted Shreiber	12.00	6.00	3.50
(14)	Paul Smith	12.00	6.00	3.50
(15a)	John Tillman (infielder)	12.00	6.00	3.50
(15b)	Bob Tillman (catcher)	12.00	6.00	3.50
(16)	Bob Toft	12.00	6.00	3.50
(17)	Tom Umphlett	12.00	6.00	3.50
(18)	Earl Wilson	12.00	6.00	3.50
(19)	Ken Wolfe	12.00	6.00	3.50

1962 Seattle Popcorn Seattle Rainiers

		NR MT	EX	VG
Complete Set:		200.00	100.00	60.00
Common Player:		12.00	6.00	3.50
(1)	Dave Hall	12.00	6.00	3.50
(2)	Billy Harrell	12.00	6.00	3.50
(3)	Curt Jensen	12.00	6.00	3.50
(4)	Stew MacDonald	12.00	6.00	3.50
(5)	Bill MacLeod	12.00	6.00	3.50
(6)	Dave Mann	12.00	6.00	3.50
(7)	Dave Morehead	12.00	6.00	3.50
(8a)	John Pesky	15.00	7.50	4.50
(8b)	Johnny Pesky	15.00	7.50	4.50
(9a)	Ted Schreiber (second baseman)	12.00	6.00	3.50
(9b)	Ted Schreiber (infielder)	12.00	6.00	3.50
(10)	Elmer Singleton	12.00	6.00	3.50
(11)	Archie Skeen	12.00	6.00	3.50
(12)	Pete Smith	12.00	6.00	3.50
(13)	George Spencer	12.00	6.00	3.50
(14)	Bob Toft	12.00	6.00	3.50
(15)	Tom Umphlett	12.00	6.00	3.50
(16)	Ken Wolfe	12.00	6.00	3.50

1963 Seattle Popcorn Seattle Rainiers

		NR MT	EX	VG
Complete Set:		150.00	75.00	45.00
Common Player:		10.00	5.00	3.00
(1)	Don Gile	10.00	5.00	3.00
(2)	Dave Hall	10.00	5.00	3.00
(3)	Billy Harrell	10.00	5.00	3.00
(4)	Pete Jernigan	10.00	5.00	3.00
(5)	Stan Johnson	10.00	5.00	3.00
(6)	Dalton Jones	10.00	5.00	3.00
(7)	Mel Parnell	10.00	5.00	3.00
(8)	Joe Pedrazzini	10.00	5.00	3.00
(9)	Elmer Singleton	10.00	5.00	3.00
(10)	Archie Skeen	10.00	5.00	3.00
(11)	Rac Slider	10.00	5.00	3.00
(12)	Pete Smith	10.00	5.00	3.00
(13)	Bill Spanswick	10.00	5.00	3.00
(14)	George Spencer	10.00	5.00	3.00
(15)	Wilbur Wood	20.00	10.00	6.00

1964 Seattle Popcorn Seattle Rainiers

		NR MT	EX	VG
Complete Set:		150.00	75.00	45.00
Common Player:		10.00	5.00	3.00
(1)	Earl Averill	10.00	5.00	3.00
(2)	Billy Gardner	10.00	5.00	3.00
(3)	Russ Gibson	10.00	5.00	3.00
(4)	Guido Grilli	10.00	5.00	3.00
(5)	Bob Guindon	10.00	5.00	3.00
(6)	Billy Harrell	10.00	5.00	3.00
(7)	Fred Holmes	10.00	5.00	3.00
(8)	Stan Johnson	10.00	5.00	3.00
(9)	Hal Kolstad	10.00	5.00	3.00
(10)	Felix Maldonado	10.00	5.00	3.00
(11)	Gary Modrell	10.00	5.00	3.00
(12)	Merlin Nippert	10.00	5.00	3.00
(13)	Rico Petrocelli	16.00	8.00	4.75
(14)	Jay Ritchie	10.00	5.00	3.00
(15)	Barry Shetrone	10.00	5.00	3.00
(16)	Pete Smith	10.00	5.00	3.00
(17)	Bill Tuttle	10.00	5.00	3.00
(18)	Edo Vanni	10.00	5.00	3.00

1965 Seattle Popcorn Seattle Rainiers

		NR MT	EX	VG
Complete Set:		200.00	100.00	60.00
Common Player:		10.00	5.00	3.00
(1)	Earl Averill	10.00	5.00	3.00
(2)	Tom Burgmeier	10.00	5.00	3.00
(3)	Bob Guindon	10.00	5.00	3.00
(4)	Jack Hernandez	10.00	5.00	3.00
(5)	Fred Holmes	10.00	5.00	3.00
(6)	Ed Kirkpatrick	10.00	5.00	3.00
(7)	Hal Kolstad	10.00	5.00	3.00
(8)	Joe Koppe	10.00	5.00	3.00
(9)	Les Kuhnz	10.00	5.00	3.00
(10)	Bob Lemon	18.00	9.00	5.50
(11)	Bobby Locke	10.00	5.00	3.00
(12)	Jim McGlothlin	10.00	5.00	3.00
(13)	Bob Radovich	10.00	5.00	3.00
(14)	Merritt Ranew	10.00	5.00	3.00
(15)	Jimmie Reese	12.50	6.25	3.75
(16)	Rick Reichardt	10.00	5.00	3.00
(17)	Tom Satriano	10.00	5.00	3.00
(18)	Dick Simpson	10.00	5.00	3.00
(19)	Jack Spring	10.00	5.00	3.00
(20)	Ed Sukla	10.00	5.00	3.00
(21)	Jackie Warner	10.00	5.00	3.00
(22)	Stan Williams	10.00	5.00	3.00

1966 Seattle Popcorn Seattle Angels

		NR MT	EX	VG
Complete Set:		250.00	125.00	75.00
Common Player:		10.00	5.00	3.00
(1)	Del Bates	10.00	5.00	3.00
(2)	Tom Burgmeier	10.00	5.00	3.00
(3)	Jim Campanis	12.50	6.25	3.75
(4)	Jim Coates	10.00	5.00	3.00
(5)	Tony Cortopassi	10.00	5.00	3.00
(6)	Chuck Estrada	10.00	5.00	3.00
(7)	Ray Hernandez	10.00	5.00	3.00
(8)	Jay Johnstone	15.00	7.50	4.50
(9)	Bill Kelso	10.00	5.00	3.00
(10)	Vic LaRose	10.00	5.00	3.00
(11)	Bobby Locke	10.00	5.00	3.00
(12)	Rudy May	10.00	5.00	3.00
(13)	Andy Messersmith	12.50	7.50	4.50
(14)	Bubba Morton	10.00	5.00	3.00
(15)	Cotton Nash	10.00	5.00	3.00
(16)	John Olerud	16.00	8.00	4.75
(17)	Marty Pattin	10.00	5.00	3.00
(18)	Merritt Ranew	10.00	5.00	3.00
(19)	Minnie Rojas	10.00	5.00	3.00
(20)	George Rubio	10.00	5.00	3.00
(21)	Al Spangler	10.00	5.00	3.00
(22)	Ed Sukla	10.00	5.00	3.00
(23)	Felix Torres	10.00	5.00	3.00
(24)	Ken Turner	10.00	5.00	3.00
(25)	Chuck Vinson	10.00	5.00	3.00
(26)	Don Wallace	10.00	5.00	3.00
(27)	Jack D. Warner	10.00	5.00	3.00
(28)	Mike White	10.00	5.00	3.00

1967 Seattle Popcorn Seattle Angels

		NR MT	EX	VG
Complete Set:		150.00	75.00	45.00
Common Player:		9.00	4.50	2.75
(1)	George Banks	9.00	4.50	2.75
(2)	Tom Burgmeier	9.00	4.50	2.75
(3)	Jim Coates	9.00	4.50	2.75
(4)	Chuck Cottier	12.00	6.00	3.50
(5)	Tony Curry	9.00	4.50	2.75
(6)	Vern Geishert	9.00	4.50	2.75

(11)	Bobby Locke	9.00	4.50	2.75
(12)	Bill Murphy	9.00	4.50	2.75
(13)	Marty Pattin	9.00	4.50	2.75
(14)	Merritt Ranew	9.00	4.50	2.75
(15)	Bob Sadowski	9.00	4.50	2.75
(16)	Ed Sukla	9.00	4.50	2.75
(17)	Hector Torres	9.00	4.50	2.75
(18)	Chuck Vinson	9.00	4.50	2.75
(19)	Don Wallace	9.00	4.50	2.75

1968 Seattle Popcorn Seattle Angels

		NR MT	EX	VG
Complete Set:		150.00	75.00	45.00
Common Player:		9.00	4.50	2.75
(1)	Ethan Blackaby	9.00	4.50	2.75
(2)	Jim Coates	9.00	4.50	2.75
(3)	Tom Egan	9.00	4.50	2.75
(4)	Larry Elliott	9.00	4.50	2.75
(5)	Jim Englehardt	9.00	4.50	2.75
(6)	Gus Gil	9.00	4.50	2.75
(7)	Bill Harrelson	9.00	4.50	2.75
(8)	Steve Hovley	9.00	4.50	2.75
(9)	Jim Mahoney	9.00	4.50	2.75
(10)	Mickey McGuire	9.00	4.50	2.75
(11)	Joe Overton	9.00	4.50	2.75
(12)	Marty Pattin	9.00	4.50	2.75
(13)	Larry Sherry	9.00	4.50	2.75
(14)	Marv Staehle	9.00	4.50	2.75
(15)	Ed Sukla	9.00	4.50	2.75
(16)	Jarvis Tatum	9.00	4.50	2.75
(17)	Hawk Taylor	9.00	4.50	2.75
(18)	Chuck Vinson	9.00	4.50	2.75

1947 Signal Gasoline Pacific Coast League

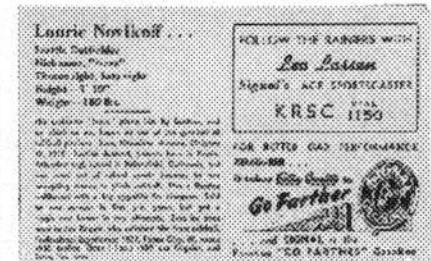

Five of the eight PCL teams participated in this baseball card promotion, giving away cards of hometeam players. Because of vagaries of local distribution, some teams, notably Sacramento and Seattle, are scarcer than others, and there are specific palyer rarities among other teams. The black-and-white cards are 5-9/16" x 3-1/2" and feature on the front a drawing of the player and several personal or career highlights in cartoon form. The artwork was done by former N.Y. Giants pitcher Al Demaree. On the backs are player biographical details, an ad for Signal gas and an ad for the co-sponsoring radio station in each local. Cards are unnumbered.

	NR MT	EX	VG
Complete Set:	2250.	1125.	675.00
Common Player:	8.00	4.00	2.40

1947 Hollywood Stars

(1)	Ed Albosta	8.00	4.00	2.50
(2)	Carl Cox	8.00	4.00	2.50
(3)	Frank Dasso	8.00	4.00	2.50
(4)	Tod Davis	8.00	4.00	2.50
(5)	Jim Delsing	8.00	4.00	2.50
(6)	Jimmy Dykes	15.00	7.50	4.50
(7)	Paul Gregory	8.00	4.00	2.50
(8)	Fred Haney	12.00	6.00	3.50
(9)	Frank Kelleher	8.00	4.00	2.50
(10)	Joe Krakauskas	8.00	4.00	2.50
(11)	Al Libke	8.00	4.00	2.50
(12)	Tony Lupien	8.00	4.00	2.50
(13)	Xaiver Rescigno	8.00	4.00	2.50
(14)	Jack Sherman	8.00	4.00	2.50
(15)	Andy Skurski	8.00	4.00	2.50
(16)	Glen (Glenn) Stewart	8.00	4.00	2.50
(17)	Al Unser	8.00	4.00	2.50
(18)	Fred Vaughn	8.00	4.00	2.50
(19)	Woody Williams	175.00	87.00	52.00
(20)	Dutch (Gus) Zernial	15.00	7.50	4.50

1947 Los Angeles Angels

(1)	Red Adams	8.00	4.00	2.50
(2)	Larry Barton	8.00	4.00	2.50
(3)	Cliff Chambers	8.00	4.00	2.50
(4)	Lloyd Christopher	8.00	4.00	2.50
(5)	Cece Garriott	8.00	4.00	2.50
(6)	Al Glossop	8.00	4.00	2.50
(7)	Bill Kelly	8.00	4.00	2.50
(8)	Red Lynn	8.00	4.00	2.50
(9)	Eddie Malone	8.00	4.00	2.50
(10)	Dutch McCall	8.00	4.00	2.50
(11)	Don Osborne	8.00	4.00	2.50
(12)	John Ostrowski	8.00	4.00	2.50
(13)	Reggie Otero	8.00	4.00	2.50
(14)	Ray Prim	8.00	4.00	2.50
(15)	Ed Sauer	8.00	4.00	2.50
(16)	Bill Schuster	8.00	4.00	2.50
(17)	Tuck Stainback	8.00	4.00	2.50
(18)	Lou Stringer	8.00	4.00	2.50

1947 Oakland Oaks

(1)	Vic Buccola	8.00	4.00	2.50
(2)	Mickey Burnett	8.00	4.00	2.50
(3)	Ralph Buxton	8.00	4.00	2.50
(4)	Vince DiMaggio	75.00	37.00	22.00
(5)	Dizz Duezabou	8.00	4.00	2.50
(6)	Bud Foster	8.00	4.00	2.50
(7)	Sherriff Gassaway	8.00	4.00	2.50
(8)	Tom Hafey	8.00	4.00	2.50
(9)	Brooks Holder	8.00	4.00	2.50
(10)	Gene Lillard	8.00	4.00	2.50
(11)	Dario Lodigiani	8.00	4.00	2.50
(12)	Hershel Martin	8.00	4.00	2.50
(13)	Cotton Pippen	8.00	4.00	2.50
(14)	Billy Raimondi	8.00	4.00	2.50
(15)	Tony Sabol	8.00	4.00	2.50
(16)	Les Scarsella	8.00	4.00	2.50
(17)	Floyd Speer	8.00	4.00	2.50
(18)	Casey Stengel	90.00	45.00	27.00
(19)	Maurice Van Robays	8.00	4.00	2.50

1947 Sacramento Solons

(1)	Bud Beasley	35.00	17.50	10.50
(2)	Frank Dasso	35.00	17.50	10.50
(3)	Ed Fitzgerald (Fitz Gerald)	35.00	17.50	10.50
(4)	Guy Fletcher	35.00	17.50	10.50
(5)	Tony Freitas	35.00	17.50	10.50
(6)	Red Mann	35.00	17.50	10.50
(7)	Joe Marty	35.00	17.50	10.50
(8)	Steve Mesner	35.00	17.50	10.50
(9)	Bill Ramsey	35.00	17.50	10.50
(10)	Charley Ripple	150.00	75.00	45.00
(11)	John Rizzo	150.00	75.00	45.00
(12)	Al Smith	150.00	75.00	45.00
(13)	Ronnie Smith	150.00	75.00	45.00
(14)	Tommy Thompson	150.00	75.00	45.00
(15)	Jim Warner	65.00	32.00	19.50
(16)	Ed Zipay	65.00	32.00	19.50

1947 Seattle Rainiers

(1)	Kewpie Barrett	55.00	27.00	16.50
(2)	Herman Besse	45.00	22.00	13.50
(3)	Guy Fletcher	45.00	22.00	13.50
(4)	Jack Jakucki	45.00	22.00	13.50
(5)	Bob Johnson	60.00	30.00	18.00
(6)	Pete Jonas	60.00	30.00	18.00
(7)	Hillis Layne	60.00	30.00	18.00
(8)	Red Mann	60.00	30.00	18.00
(9)	Lou Novikoff	60.00	30.00	18.00
(10)	John O'Neill	60.00	30.00	18.00
(11)	Bill Ramsey	60.00	30.00	18.00
(12)	Mickey Rocco	60.00	30.00	18.00
(13)	George Scharein	60.00	30.00	18.00
(14)	Hal Sueme	60.00	30.00	18.00
(15)	Jo Jo White	60.00	30.00	18.00
(16)	Tony York	60.00	30.00	18.00

1948 Signal Gasoline Oakland Oaks

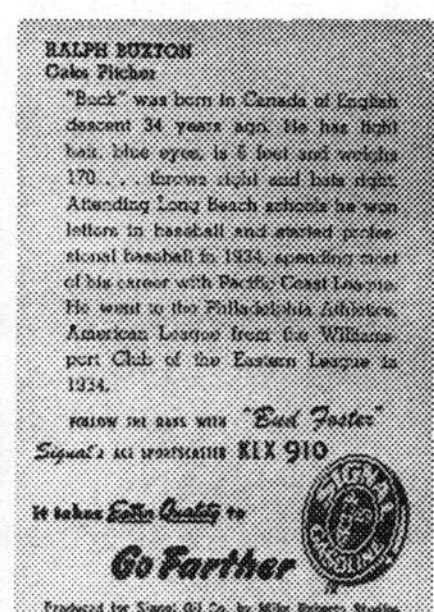

Issued by Signal Oil in the Oakland area in 1948, this 24-card set features members of the Oakland Oaks of the Pacific Coast League. The unnumbered cards, measuring 2-3/8" x 3-1/2", were given away at gas stations. The front consists of a color photo, while the backs (printed in either blue or black) contain a brief player write-up along with a Signal Oil ad and logo.

		NR MT	EX	VG
Complete Set:		475.00	237.00	142.00
Common Player:		18.00	9.00	5.50
(1)	John C. Babich	18.00	9.00	5.50
(2)	Ralph Buxton	18.00	9.00	5.50
(3)	Loyd E. Christopher (Lloyd)	18.00	9.00	5.50
(4)	Merrill Russell Combs	18.00	9.00	5.50
(5)	Melvin E. Deuzabou	18.00	9.00	5.50
(6)	Nicholas ("Nick") Etten	20.00	10.00	6.00
(7)	Bud Foster (announcer)	18.00	9.00	5.50
(8)	Charles Gassaway	18.00	9.00	5.50
(9)	Will Hafey	18.00	9.00	5.50
(10)	Ray Hamrick	18.00	9.00	5.50
(11)	Brooks Richard Holder	20.00	10.00	6.00
(12)	Earl Jones	18.00	9.00	5.50
(13)	Harry "Cookie" Lavagetto	18.00	9.00	5.50
(14)	Robert E. Lillard	18.00	9.00	5.50
(15)	Dario Lodigiani	18.00	9.00	5.50
(16)	Ernie Lombardi	30.00	15.00	9.00
(17a)	Alfred Manuel Martin (born 1921)	90.00	45.00	27.00
17b	Alfred Manuel Martin (born 1928)	90.00	45.00	27.00
(18)	George Michael Metkovich	18.00	9.00	5.50
(19)	William L. Raimondi	18.00	9.00	5.50
(20)	Les George Scarsella	18.00	9.00	5.50
(21)	Floyd Vernie Speer	18.00	9.00	5.50
(22)	Charles "Casey" Stengel	90.00	45.00	27.00
(23)	Maurice Van Robays	18.00	9.00	5.50
(24)	Aldon Jay Wilkie	18.00	9.00	5.50

1947 Smith's Oakland Oaks

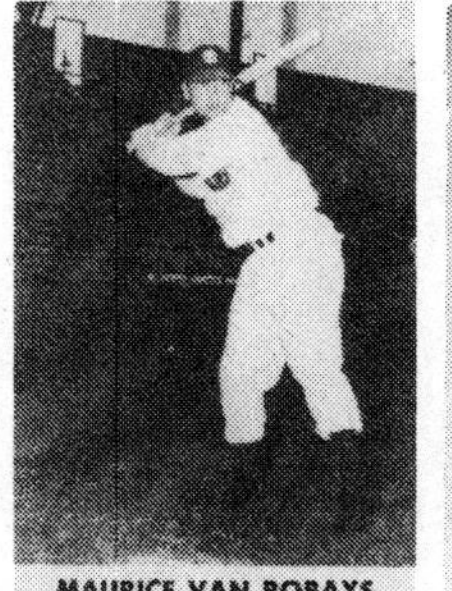

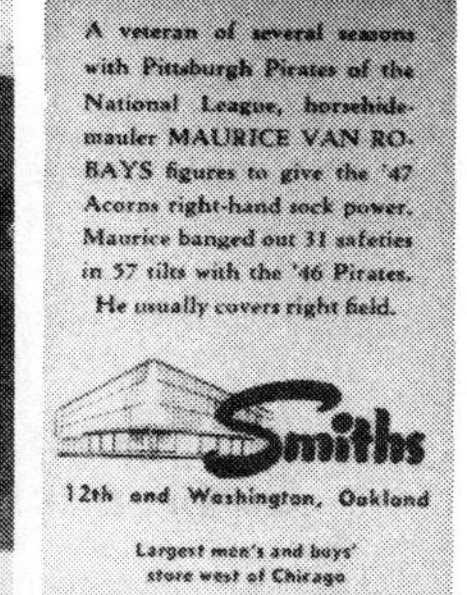

A veteran of several seasons with Pittsburgh Pirates of the National League, horsehide-mauler MAURICE VAN ROBAYS figures to give the '47 Acorns right-hand sock power. Maurice banged out 31 safeties in 57 tilts with the '46 Pirates. He usually covers right field.
Smiths
12th and Washington, Oakland
Largest men's and boys' store west of Chicago

This regional set of Oakland Oaks (Pacific Coast League) cards was issued in 1947 by Smith's Clothing stores and is numbered in the lower right corner. The card fronts include a black and white photo with the player's name, team and position below. The backs carry a brief player write-up and an advertisement for Smith's Clothing. The cards measure 2" x 3". The Max Marshall card was apparently short-printed and is much scarcer than the rest of the set.

		NR MT	EX	VG
Complete Set:		575.00	287.00	172.00
Common Player:		18.00	9.00	5.50
1	Charles (Casey) Stengel	90.00	45.00	27.00
2	Billy Raimondi	18.00	9.00	5.50
3	Les Scarsella	18.00	9.00	5.50
4	Brooks Holder	18.00	9.00	5.50
5	Ray Hamrick	18.00	9.00	5.50
6	Gene Lillard	18.00	9.00	5.50
7	Maurice Van Robays	18.00	9.00	5.50
8	Charlie (Sheriff) Gassaway	18.00	9.00	5.50
9	Henry (Cotton) Pippen	18.00	9.00	5.50
10	James Arnold	18.00	9.00	5.50
11	Ralph (Buck) Buxton	18.00	9.00	5.50
12	Ambrose (Bo) Palica	18.00	9.00	5.50
13	Tony Sabol	18.00	9.00	5.50
14	Ed Kearse	18.00	9.00	5.50
15	Bill Hart	18.00	9.00	5.50
16	Donald (Snuffy) Smith	18.00	9.00	5.50
17	Oral (Mickey) Burnett	18.00	9.00	5.50
18	Tom Hafey	18.00	9.00	5.50
19	Will Hafey	18.00	9.00	5.50
20	Paul Gillespie	25.00	6.00	3.50
21	Damon Hayes	25.00	6.00	3.50
22	Max Marshall	125.00	6.00	3.50
23	Mel (Dizz) Duezabou	18.00	9.00	5.50
24	Mel Reeves	18.00	9.00	5.50
25	Joe Faria	25.00	6.00	3.50

1948 Smith's Oakland Oaks

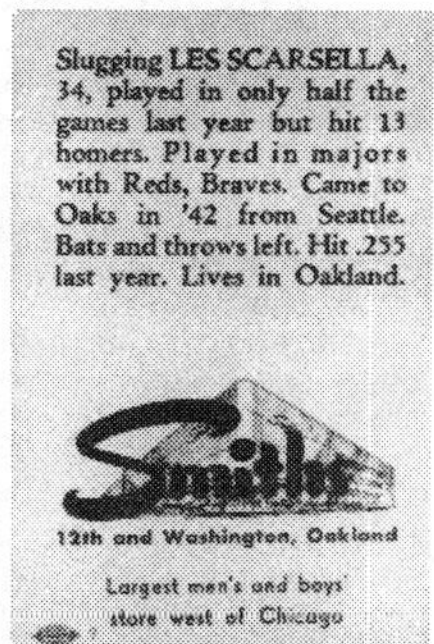

Slugging LES SCARSELLA, 34, played in only half the games last year but hit 13 homers. Played in majors with Reds, Braves. Came to Oaks in '42 from Seattle. Bats and throws left. Hit .255 last year. Lives in Oakland.
Smiths
12th and Washington, Oakland
Largest men's and boys' store west of Chicago

The 1948 Smith's Clothing issue was another 25-card regional set featuring members of the Oakland Oaks of the Pacific Coast League. Almost identical to the 1947 Smith's issue, the black and white cards again measure 2" x 3" but were printed on heavier, glossy stock. The player's name, team and position appear below the photo with the card number in the lower right corner. The back has a brief player write-up and an ad for Smith's clothing.

		NR MT	EX	VG
Complete Set:		500.00	250.00	150.00
Common Player:		18.00	9.00	5.50
1	Billy Raimondi	18.00	9.00	5.50
2	Brooks Holder	18.00	9.00	5.50
3	Will Hafey	20.00	6.00	3.50
4	Nick Etten	18.00	9.00	5.50
5	Lloyd Christopher	18.00	9.00	5.50
6	Les Scarsella	18.00	9.00	5.50
7	Ray Hamrick	18.00	9.00	5.50
8	Gene Lillard	18.00	9.00	5.50
9	Maurice Van Robays	18.00	9.00	5.50
10	Charlie Gassaway	18.00	9.00	5.50
11	Ralph (Buck) Buxton	18.00	9.00	5.50
12	Tom Hafey	18.00	9.00	5.50
13	Damon Hayes	18.00	9.00	5.50
14	Mel (Dizz) Duezabou	18.00	9.00	5.50
15	Dario Lodigiani	18.00	9.00	5.50
16	Vic Buccola	18.00	9.00	5.50
17	Billy Martin	90.00	45.00	27.00
18	Floyd Speer	18.00	9.00	5.50
19	Eddie Samcoff	18.00	9.00	5.50
20	Charles (Casey) Stengel	90.00	45.00	27.00
21	Lloyd Hittle	18.00	9.00	5.50
22	Johnny Babich	18.00	9.00	5.50
23	Merrill Combs	18.00	9.00	5.50
24	Eddie Murphy	18.00	9.00	5.50
25	Bob Klinger	18.00	9.00	5.50

1948 Sommer & Kaufmann San Francisco Seals

One of the more common of the many Pacific Coast League issues of the late 1940s, this emission from the San Francisco boys' clothier features 30 black-and-white 2" x 3" cards. Fronts have a player photo, name position and card numbers. Backs have a few biographical details and stats, along with an ad. The 1948 issue can be differentiated from the 1949 issue by the words "BOYS SHOP" above the company logo on back.

		NR MT	EX	VG
Complete Set:		750.00	375.00	225.00
Common Player:		25.00	12.50	7.50
1	Lefty O'Doul	40.00	20.00	12.00
2	Jack Brewer	25.00	12.50	7.50
3	Con Dempsey	25.00	12.50	7.50
4	Tommy Fine	25.00	12.50	7.50
5	Kenneth Gables	25.00	12.50	7.50
6	Robert Joyce	25.00	12.50	7.50
7	Al Lien	25.00	12.50	7.50
8	Cliff Melton	25.00	12.50	7.50
9	Frank Shofner	25.00	12.50	7.50
10	Don Trower	25.00	12.50	7.50
11	Joe Brovia	25.00	12.50	7.50
12	Dino Paul Restelli	25.00	12.50	7.50
13	Gene Woodling	30.00	15.00	9.00
14	Ben Guintini	25.00	12.50	7.50
15	Felix Mackiewicz	25.00	12.50	7.50
16	John Patrick Tobin	25.00	12.50	7.50
17	Manuel Perez	25.00	12.50	7.50
18	Bill Werle	25.00	12.50	7.50
19	Homer Howell	25.00	12.50	7.50
20	Wilfred Leonard	25.00	12.50	7.50
21	Bruce Ogrodowski	25.00	12.50	7.50
22	Dick Lejeskie	25.00	12.50	7.50
23	Hugh Luby	25.00	12.50	7.50
24	Roy Nicely	25.00	12.50	7.50
25	Ray Orteig	25.00	12.50	7.50
26	Michael Rocco	25.00	12.50	7.50
27	Del Young	25.00	12.50	7.50
28	Joe Sprinz	25.00	12.50	7.50
29	Doc Hughes	25.00	12.50	7.50
30	Batboys	25.00	12.50	7.50

1949 Sommer & Kaufmann San Francisco Seals

Twenty-eight black-and-white cards numbered 1-29 (#24 unknown) make up the second and final card issue of the "Frisco area clothier". Measuring 2" x 3", the cards are nearly identical to the '48 issue. The '49s can be identified by the mention of "Hot Rod" shoes on the back. Fronts feature a borderless player photo with a panel at the bottom giving name, position and card number. Backs have the ad for the boy's shop and a brief biographical and player sketch.

		NR MT	EX	VG
Complete Set:		700.00	350.00	210.00
Common Player:		25.00	12.50	7.50
1	Lefty O'Doul	40.00	20.00	12.00
2	Jack Brewer	25.00	12.50	7.50
3	Kenneth Gables	25.00	12.50	7.50
4	Con Dempsey	25.00	12.50	7.50
5	Al Lien	25.00	12.50	7.50
6	Cliff Melton	25.00	12.50	7.50
7	Steve Nagy	25.00	12.50	7.50
8	Manny Perez	25.00	12.50	7.50
9	Roy Jarvis	25.00	12.50	7.50
10	Roy Partee	25.00	12.50	7.50
11	Reno Cheso	25.00	12.50	7.50
12	Dick Lajeskie	25.00	12.50	7.50
13	Roy Nicely	25.00	12.50	7.50
14	Mickey Rocco	25.00	12.50	7.50
15	Frank Shofner	25.00	12.50	7.50
16	Richard Holder	25.00	12.50	7.50
17	Dino Restelli	25.00	12.50	7.50
18	Floyd J. "Arky" Vaughan	50.00	25.00	15.00
19	Jackie Baccioccu	25.00	12.50	7.50
20	Bob Drilling	25.00	12.50	7.50
21	Del Young	25.00	12.50	7.50
22	Joe Sprinz	25.00	12.50	7.50
23	Doc Hughes	25.00	12.50	7.50
24	Unknown			
25	Bert Singleton	25.00	12.50	7.50
26	John Brocker	25.00	12.50	7.50
27	Jack Tobin	25.00	12.50	7.50
28	Walt Judnich	25.00	12.50	7.50
29	Hal Foldman	25.00	12.50	7.50

1946 Sunbeam Bread Sacramento Solons

The 21 unnumbered cards in this Pacific Coast League team set are printed with black-and-white fronts containing a borderless player photo with a panel beneath containing name, position and a photo credit. Backs are printed in blue, red and yellow and contain a brief career summary and an ad for the bread brand. The cards measure approximately 2" x 3". Players are checklisted here in alphabetical order.

		NR MT	EX	VG
Complete Set:		300.00	150.00	90.00
Common Player:		15.00	7.50	4.50
(1)	Bud Beasley	15.00	7.50	4.50
(2)	Jack Calvey	15.00	7.50	4.50
(3)	Gene Crobett	15.00	7.50	4.50
(4)	Bill Conroy	15.00	7.50	4.50
(5)	Guy Fletcher	15.00	7.50	4.50
(6)	Tony Freitas	15.00	7.50	4.50
(7)	Ted Greenhalgh	15.00	7.50	4.50
(8)	Al Jarlett	15.00	7.50	4.50
(9)	Jesse Landrum	15.00	7.50	4.50
(10)	Gene Lillard	15.00	7.50	4.50
(11)	Garth Mann	15.00	7.50	4.50
(12)	Lilo Marcucci	15.00	7.50	4.50
(13)	Joe Marty	15.00	7.50	4.50
(14)	Steve Mesner	15.00	7.50	4.50
(15)	Herm Pillette	15.00	7.50	4.50
(16)	Earl Sheely	15.00	7.50	4.50
(17)	Al Smith	15.00	7.50	4.50
(18)	Gerald Staley	20.00	10.00	6.00
(19)	Averett Thompson	15.00	7.50	4.50
(20)	Jo Jo White	15.00	7.50	4.50
(21)	Bud Zipay	15.00	7.50	4.50

1947 Sunbeam Bread Sacramento Solons

Similar in format to the 1946 issue, the 26 cards in the '47 set again featured black-and-white player photos on front, with a panel beneath giving player name, position and photo credit. Backs of the 2" x 3" cards had a color depiction of a loaf of the sponsoring company's bread. The unnumbered cards are alphabetically checklisted here.

		NR MT	EX	VG
Complete Set:		375.00	185.00	110.00
Common Player:		15.00	7.50	4.50
(1)	Gene Babbit	15.00	7.50	4.50
(2)	Bob Barthelson	15.00	7.50	4.50
(3)	Bud Beasley	15.00	7.50	4.50
(4)	Chuck Cronin	15.00	7.50	4.50
(5)	Eddie Fernandes	15.00	7.50	4.50
(6)	Ed Fitzgerald (Fitz Gerald)	15.00	7.50	4.50
(7)	Guy Fletcher	15.00	7.50	4.50
(8)	Tony Freitas	15.00	7.50	4.50
(9)	Garth Mann	15.00	7.50	4.50
(10)	Joe Marty	15.00	7.50	4.50
(11)	Lou McCollum	15.00	7.50	4.50
(12)	Steve Mesner	15.00	7.50	4.50
(13)	Frank Nelson	15.00	7.50	4.50
(14)	Tommy Nelson	15.00	7.50	4.50
(15)	Joe Orengo	15.00	7.50	4.50
(16)	Hugh Orphan	15.00	7.50	4.50
(17)	Nick Pesut	15.00	7.50	4.50
(18)	Bill Ramsey	15.00	7.50	4.50
(19)	Johnny Rizzo	15.00	7.50	4.50
(20)	Mike Schemer	15.00	7.50	4.50
(21)	Al Smith	15.00	7.50	4.50
(22)	Tommy Thompson	15.00	7.50	4.50
(23)	Jim Warner	15.00	7.50	4.50
(24)	Mel Wasley	15.00	7.50	4.50
(25)	Leo Wells	15.00	7.50	4.50
(26)	Eddie Zipay	15.00	7.50	4.50

1949 Sunbeam Bread Stockton Ports

(California League) (2" x 3") (unnumbered)

		NR MT	EX	VG
Complete Set:		600.00	300.00	180.00
(1)	Lou Bronzan	50.00	25.00	15.00
(2)	Jimmie Brown	50.00	25.00	15.00
(3)	Rocco Cardinale	50.00	25.00	15.00
(4)	Harry Clements	50.00	25.00	15.00
(5)	Nino Bongiovanni	50.00	25.00	15.00
(6)	Norm Grabar	50.00	25.00	15.00
(7)	Bud Guldborg	50.00	25.00	15.00
(8)	Carl Hoberg	50.00	25.00	15.00
(9)	Eddie Murphy	50.00	25.00	15.00
(10)	Sandy Sandel	50.00	25.00	15.00
(11)	Dick Stone	50.00	25.00	15.00
(12)	Matt Zidich	50.00	25.00	15.00

1950 Sunbeam Bread Stockton Ports

(California League) (2" x 3") (black and white) (unnumbered)

		NR MT	EX	VG
Complete Set:		600.00	300.00	180.00
(1)	Richard L. Adams	50.00	25.00	15.00
(2)	James Edward Brown	50.00	25.00	15.00
(3)	Harry Clements	50.00	25.00	15.00
(4)	John Burton Goldborg	50.00	25.00	15.00
(5)	Gerald Lee Haines	50.00	25.00	15.00
(6)	Alfred Michael Heist	50.00	25.00	15.00
(7)	Don Masterson	50.00	25.00	15.00
(8)	Lauren Hugh Monroe	50.00	25.00	15.00
(9)	Frank E. Murray	50.00	25.00	15.00
(10)	Lauren Keith Simon Jr.	50.00	25.00	15.00
(11)	George Anthony Stanich	50.00	25.00	15.00
(12)	Robert Louis Stevens	50.00	25.00	15.00
(13)	Harold Lee Zurcher	50.00	25.00	15.00

1966 Toledo Mud Hens

(3-1/4" x 5-1/2") (unnumbered)

		NR MT	EX	VG
Complete Set:		400.00	200.00	120.00
Common Player:		15.00	7.50	4.50
(1)	Loren Babe	15.00	7.50	4.50
(2)	Stan Bahnsen	15.00	7.50	4.50
(3)	Bill Bethea	15.00	7.50	4.50
(4)	Wayne Comer	15.00	7.50	4.50
(5)	Jack Cullen	15.00	7.50	4.50
(6)	Jack Curtis	15.00	7.50	4.50
(7)	Gil Downs	15.00	7.50	4.50
(8)	Joe Faroci	15.00	7.50	4.50
(9)	Frank Fernandez	15.00	7.50	4.50
(10)	Mike Ferraro	15.00	7.50	4.50
(11)	Doc Foley	15.00	7.50	4.50
(12)	Mike Hegan	15.00	7.50	4.50
(13)	Jim Horsford	15.00	7.50	4.50
(14)	Elvio Jiminez	15.00	7.50	4.50
(15)	Bob Lasko	15.00	7.50	4.50
(16)	Jim Merritt	15.00	7.50	4.50
(17)	Archie Moore	15.00	7.50	4.50
(18)	Bobby Murcer	35.00	17.50	10.50
(19)	Tony Preybycian	15.00	7.50	4.50
(20)	Bob Schmidt	15.00	7.50	4.50
(21)	Charlie Senger, Loren Babe Bill Shantz	15.00	7.50	4.50
(22)	Bill Shantz	15.00	7.50	4.50
(23)	Paul Toth	15.00	7.50	4.50
(24)	Jerry Walker	15.00	7.50	4.50

1964 True-Aid Buffalo Bisons

(International League) (2-1/4" x 5-1/2") (unnumbered)

		NR MT	EX	VG
Complete Set:		150.00	75.00	45.00
(1)	Ed Bauta	40.00	20.00	12.00
(2)	Choo Choo Coleman	60.00	30.00	18.00
(3)	Cleon Jones	60.00	30.00	18.00

1961 Union Oil Pacific Coast League

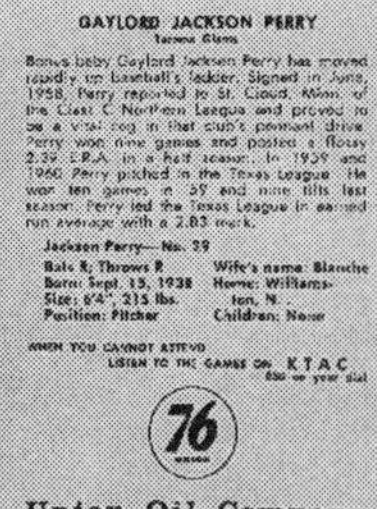

The last of three Union Oil PCL issues, the 67 cards in this set feature sepia-toned borderless photos on front in a 3" x 4" format. Backs are printed in blue and feature biographical data, a career summary, and ads by the issuing oil company and participating radio station co-sponsors. Six of the eight teams in the '61 PCL are featured, with Salt Lake City and Vancouver not participating in the promotion. Presumably because of smaller print runs, the cards distributed in Hawaii and Spokane bring a premium price. Hall of Fame pitcher Gaylord Perry is featured on his first baseball card in this set. Only the Tacoma cards are numbered, and they are skip-numbered.

	NR MT	EX	VG
Complete Set:	750.00	375.00	225.00
Common Player:	8.00	4.00	2.40

1961 Hawaii Islanders

(1)	Ray Jablonski	18.00	9.00	5.40
(2)	Jim McManus	12.00	6.00	3.60
(3)	George Prescott	50.00	25.00	15.00
(4)	Diego Segui	12.00	6.00	3.60
(5)	Rachel Slider	12.00	6.00	3.60
(6)	Jim Small	12.00	6.00	3.60
(7)	Milt Smith	12.00	6.00	3.60
(8)	Dave Thies	12.00	6.00	3.60
(9)	Jay Ward	12.00	6.00	3.60
(10)	Bill Werle	12.00	6.00	3.60

1961 Portland Beavers

(1)	Ed Bauta	8.00	4.00	2.50
(2)	Vern Benson	8.00	4.00	2.50
(3)	Jerry Buchek	8.00	4.00	2.50
(4)	Bob Burda	8.00	4.00	2.50
(5)	Duke Carmel	8.00	4.00	2.50
(6)	Don Choate	8.00	4.00	2.50
(7)	Phil Gagliano	8.00	4.00	2.50
(8)	Jim Hickman	8.00	4.00	2.50
(9)	Ray Katt	8.00	4.00	2.50
(10)	Mel Nelson	8.00	4.00	2.50
(11)	Jim Shaffer	8.00	4.00	2.50
(12)	Mike Shannon	8.00	4.00	2.50
(13)	Clint Stark	8.00	4.00	2.50

1961 Sacramento Solons

(1)	Galen Cisco	8.00	4.00	2.50
(2)	Lu Clinton	8.00	4.00	2.50
(3)	Marlan Coughtry	8.00	4.00	2.50
(4)	Harry Malmberg	8.00	4.00	2.50
(5)	Dave Mann	8.00	4.00	2.50
(6)	Derrell Martin	8.00	4.00	2.50
(7)	Erv Palica	8.00	4.00	2.50
(8)	Johnny Pesky	8.00	4.00	2.50
(9)	Bob Tillman	8.00	4.00	2.50
(10)	Marv Toft	8.00	4.00	2.50
(11)	Tom Umphlett	8.00	4.00	2.50

1961 San Diego Padres

(1)	Dick Barone	8.00	4.00	2.50
(2)	Jim Bolger	8.00	4.00	2.50
(3)	Kent Hadley	8.00	4.00	2.50
(4)	Mike Hershberger	12.00	6.00	3.60
(5)	Stan Johnson	8.00	4.00	2.50
(6)	Dick Lines	8.00	4.00	2.50
(7)	Jim Napier	8.00	4.00	2.50
(8)	Tony Roig	8.00	4.00	2.50
(9)	Herb Score	25.00	12.50	7.50
(10)	Harry Simpson	12.00	6.00	3.50
(11)	Joe Taylor	8.00	4.00	2.50
(12)	Ben Wade	8.00	4.00	2.50

1961 Spokane Indians

(1)	Doug Camilli	10.00	5.00	3.00
(2)	Ramon Conde	10.00	5.00	3.00
(3)	Bob Giallombardo	10.00	5.00	3.00
(4)	Mike Goliat	10.00	5.00	3.00
(5)	Preston Gomez	40.00	20.00	12.00
(6)	Rod Graber	10.00	5.00	3.00
(7)	Tim Harkness	10.00	5.00	3.00
(8)	Jim Harwell	10.00	5.00	3.00
(9)	Howie Reed	10.00	5.00	3.00
(10)	Curt Roberts	10.00	5.00	3.00
(11)	Rene Valdes	10.00	5.00	3.00

1961 Tacoma Giants

10	Red Davis	8.00	4.00	2.50
12	Dick Phillips	8.00	4.00	2.50
17	Gil Garrido	8.00	4.00	2.50
20	Georges Maranda	8.00	4.00	2.50
25	John Orsino	8.00	4.00	2.50
26	Dusty Rhodes	12.00	6.00	3.60
28	Ron Herbel	8.00	4.00	2.50
29	Gaylord Perry	75.00	37.50	22.50
30	Rafael Alomar	12.00	6.00	3.60
34	Bob Farley	8.00	4.00	2.50

1960 Tulsa Oilers

		NR MT	EX	VG
Complete Set:		240.00	120.00	72.50
Common Player:		25.00	12.50	7.50
(1)	Bob Blaylock	25.00	12.50	7.50
(2)	Artie Burnett	25.00	12.50	7.50
(3)	Bill Carpenter	25.00	12.50	7.50
(4)	Julio Gotay	25.00	12.50	7.50
(5)	Ray Katt	25.00	12.50	7.50
(6)	Harry Keister	25.00	12.50	7.50
(7)	Fred Koenig	25.00	12.50	7.50
(8)	Rich Rogers	25.00	12.50	7.50
(9)	Lynn Rube	25.00	12.50	7.50
(10)	Jim Schaffer	25.00	12.50	7.50
(11)	Ted Thiem	25.00	12.50	7.50
(12)	Dixie Walker	25.00	12.50	7.50

1958 Union Oil Sacramento Solons

Ten members of the independent Pacific Coast League team were included in a black-and-white card set distributed at Union 76 gas stations in that locale. Fronts feature borderless player photos with a wide white strip at the bottom on which is printed the player team name and the position. Backs have brief stats, a "76 Sports Club" pennant and information about a specific game for which the card can be exchanged for admission by a child. Cards measure approximately 2-1/2" x 3-1/4".

		NR MT	EX	VG
Complete Set:		120.00	60.00	35.00
Common Player:		10.00	5.00	3.00
(1)	Marshall Bridges	20.00	10.00	6.00
(2)	Dick Cole	10.00	5.00	3.00
(3)	Jim Greengrass	10.00	5.00	3.00
(4)	Al Heist	10.00	5.00	3.00
(5)	Nippy Jones	10.00	5.00	3.00
(6)	Carlos Paula	10.00	5.00	3.00
(7)	Kal Segrist	10.00	5.00	3.00
(8)	Sibbi Sisti	10.00	5.00	3.00
(9)	Joe Stanka	20.00	10.00	6.00
(10)	Bud Watkins	10.00	5.00	3.00

1960 Union Oil Seattle Rainiers

Given away at Union 76 gas stations in the Seattle area, this set of nine full-color cards measure approximately 3-1/8" x 4". Backs have brief biographical data, a career summary and a large Union 76 logo. The cards are skip-numbered.

		NR MT	EX	VG
Complete Set:		175.00	87.50	50.00
Common Player:		10.00	5.00	3.00
4	Francisco Obregon	20.00	10.00	6.00
6	Drew Gilbert	10.00	5.00	3.00
7	Bill Hain	10.00	5.00	3.00
10	Ray Ripplemeyer	75.00	37.50	22.50
13	Joe Taylor	10.00	5.00	3.00
15	Lou Skizas	10.00	5.00	3.00
17	Don Rudolph	10.00	5.00	3.00
19	Gordy Coleman	15.00	7.50	4.50
22	Hal Breven	10.00	5.00	3.00

1961 Union Oil Taiyo Whales

This three-card set was produced in conjunction with an exhibition series played in October, 1961, between the Taiyo Whales of Japan's Central League, and the Hawaii Islanders, a Class AAA Pacific Cost League farm club of the K.C. Athletics. The player cards measure just over 3" x 4", while the team photo card is 5" x 3-3/4". Cards are black and have some player biography and ads for Union Oil Co., and the English - and Japanese - language radio stations that carried the games.

		NR MT	EX	VG
Complete Set:		50.00	25.00	15.00
(1)	Akihito Kondo	15.00	7.50	4.50
(2)	Gentaro Shimada	15.00	7.50	4.50
(3)	Taiyo Whales Team	20.00	10.00	6.00

1951 Vancouver Capilanos Popcorn Issue

(2" x 3") (unnumbered) (black and white) (1950 stats) (Sears and Roebuck) (NWL)

		NR MT	EX	VG
Complete Set:		350.00	175.00	100.00
Common Player:		15.00	7.50	4.50
(1)	Chuck Abernathy	15.00	7.50	4.50
(2)	Jerry Barta	15.00	7.50	4.50
(3)	Bud Beasley	15.00	7.50	4.50
(4)	Gordy Brunswick	15.00	7.50	4.50
(5)	Reno Cheso	15.00	7.50	4.50
(6)	Ken Chorlton	15.00	7.50	4.50
(7)	Carl Gunnarson	15.00	7.50	4.50
(8)	Pete Hernandez	15.00	7.50	4.50
(9)	Vern Kindsfather	15.00	7.50	4.50
(10)	Bobby McGuire	15.00	7.50	4.50
(11)	Bob McLean	15.00	7.50	4.50
(12)	Charlie Mead	15.00	7.50	4.50
(13)	Jimmy Moore	15.00	7.50	4.50
(14)	George Nicholas	15.00	7.50	4.50
(15)	Johnny Ritchie	15.00	7.50	4.50
(16)	Sandy Robertson	15.00	7.50	4.50
(17)	Bill Schuster	15.00	7.50	4.50
(18)	Dick Sinovic	15.00	7.50	4.50
(19)	Ron Smith	15.00	7.50	4.50
(20)	Bob Snyder	15.00	7.50	4.50
(21)	Don Tisnerat	15.00	7.50	4.50
(22)	Ray Tran	15.00	7.50	4.50
(23)	Reg Wallis (trainer)	15.00	7.50	4.50
(24)	Bill Whyte	15.00	7.50	4.50

1952 Vancouver Capilanos Popcorn Issue

(2" x 3") (black and white) (1951 stats) (Sears and Roebuck) (NWL)

		NR MT	EX	VG
Complete Set:		300.00	150.00	90.00
Common Player:		15.00	11.00	6.00
(1)	Gordie Brunswick	15.00	7.50	4.50
(2)	Bob Duretto	15.00	7.50	4.50
(3)	Van Fletcher	15.00	7.50	4.50
(4)	John Guldborg	15.00	7.50	4.50
(5)	Paul Jones	15.00	7.50	4.50
(6)	Eddie Locke	15.00	7.50	4.50
(7)	Tom Lovrich	15.00	7.50	4.50
(8)	Jimmy Moore	15.00	7.50	4.50
(9)	George Nicholas	15.00	7.50	4.50
(10)	John Ritchey	15.00	7.50	4.50
(11)	Johnny Ritchie	15.00	7.50	4.50
(12)	Bill Schuster	15.00	7.50	4.50
(13)	Bob Snyder	15.00	7.50	4.50
(14)	Len Tran	15.00	7.50	4.50
(15)	Ray Tran	15.00	7.50	4.50
(16)	Edo Vannie	15.00	7.50	4.50
(17)	Jim Wert	15.00	7.50	4.50
(18)	Bill Whyte	15.00	7.50	4.50
(19)	Jesse Williams	15.00	7.50	4.50
(20)	Jessie Williams	15.00	7.50	4.50

1953 Vancouver Capilanos Popcorn Issue

(2-1/8" x 3-1/8") (black and white) (1952 stats) (Sears and Roebuck) (NWL)

		NR MT	EX	VG
Complete Set:		250.00	125.00	75.00
Common Player:		15.00	11.00	6.00
(1)	Dick Briskey	15.00	7.50	4.50
(2)	Jack Bukowatz	15.00	7.50	4.50
(3)	Ken Chorlton	15.00	7.50	4.50
(4)	Van Fletcher	15.00	7.50	4.50
(5)	John Guldborg	15.00	7.50	4.50
(6)	Carl Gunnerson	15.00	7.50	4.50
(7)	Jim Hedgecock	15.00	7.50	4.50
(8)	Gordon Hernandez	15.00	7.50	4.50
(9)	Pete Hernandez	15.00	7.50	4.50
(10)	Jim Leavitt	15.00	7.50	4.50
(11)	Rod MacKay	15.00	7.50	4.50
(12)	Frank Mascaro	15.00	7.50	4.50
(13)	Lonnie Myers	15.00	7.50	4.50
(14)	Rod Owen	15.00	7.50	4.50
(15)	Harvey Storey	15.00	7.50	4.50
(16)	Bob Stuart	15.00	7.50	4.50
(17)	Dale Thomason	15.00	7.50	4.50
(18)	Jim Wert	15.00	7.50	4.50

1954 Vancouver Capilanos Popcorn Issue

(2-3/16" x3-5/16") (black and white) (backs are blank) (Sears and Roebuck) (NWL)

		NR MT	EX	VG
Complete Set:		200.00	100.00	60.00
Common Player:		12.50	6.25	3.75
(1)	Bill Brenner	12.50	6.25	3.75
(2)	Ken Chorlton	12.50	6.25	3.75
(3)	John Cordell	12.50	6.25	3.75
(4)	Bob Duretto	12.50	6.25	3.75
(5)	Dick Greco	12.50	6.25	3.75
(6)	Arnie Hallgren	12.50	6.25	3.75
(7)	Danny Holden	12.50	6.25	3.75
(8)	Rod McKay	12.50	6.25	3.75
(9)	George Nicholas	12.50	6.25	3.75

		NR MT	EX	VG
(10)	Nick Pesut	12.50	6.25	3.75
(11)	Ken Richardson	12.50	6.25	3.75
(12)	Bob Roberts	12.50	6.25	3.75
(13)	Bob Wellman	12.50	6.25	3.75
(14)	Marvin Williams	12.50	6.25	3.75

1933 Worch Cigar American Association

Though the issuer is not identified anywhere on these blank-backed, 3-7/16" x 5-7/16" black-and-white cards, the individual player photos were available as premiums for redemption of cigar bands, by the Worch Cigar Co., of St. Paul. The issue is similar in format to the Minneapolis Star major league cards of the same era, and indeed the cards were offered together. Most collectors prefer to chase either the major leaguers or the minor leaguers independently, so they are cataloged in that fashion. The set encompasses players from the 1932-33 Minneapolis Millers, the 1933 St. Paul Saints and a handful from the Columbus Redbirds and Kansas City Blues. The unnumbered cards are checklisted below alphabetically. The complete set price is not available. Hauser and Richards are worth $25-$12.50-$7.50.

		NR MT	EX	VG
Complete Set:		900.00	450.00	275.00
Common Player:		22.00	11.00	6.50
(1)	Bancroft	22.00	11.00	6.50
(2)	Clyde Beck	22.00	11.00	6.50
(3)	Rube Benton	22.00	11.00	6.50
(4)	W. Berger	22.00	11.00	6.50
(5)	Brannon	22.00	11.00	6.50
(6)	Andy Cohen	25.00	12.50	7.50
(7)	Nick Cullop	22.00	11.00	6.50
(8)	Day	22.00	11.00	6.50
(9)	Bob Fenner	22.00	11.00	6.50
(10)	Fischall	22.00	11.00	6.50
(11)	Fitzgerald	22.00	11.00	6.50
(12)	Gaffke	22.00	11.00	6.50
(13)	Foster Ganzel	22.00	11.00	6.50
(14)	Louis Garland	22.00	11.00	6.50
(15)	Joe Glenn	22.00	11.00	6.50
(16)	Wesley Griffin	22.00	11.00	6.50
(17)	Angelo Guiliani	22.00	11.00	6.50
(18)	Slim Harriss	22.00	11.00	6.50
(19)	Spencer Harris	22.00	11.00	6.50
(20)	Joe Hauser	30.00	15.00	9.00
(21)	Walter Henline	22.00	11.00	6.50
(22)	Frank "Dutch" Henry	22.00	11.00	6.50
(23)	Phil Hensick	22.00	11.00	6.50
(24)	Walter Hilcher	22.00	11.00	6.50
(25)	Hill	22.00	11.00	6.50
(26)	Jesse Hill	22.00	11.00	6.50
(27)	Bob Holand	22.00	11.00	6.50
(28)	Harry Holsclaw	22.00	11.00	6.50
(29)	Meredith Hopkins	22.00	11.00	6.50
(30)	Irvine Jeffries	22.00	11.00	6.50
(31)	Fred Koster	22.00	11.00	6.50
(32)	Walter Mails	22.00	11.00	6.50
(33)	Emmett McCann	22.00	11.00	6.50
(34)	Joe Mowry	22.00	11.00	6.50
(35)	Les Munns	22.00	11.00	6.50
(36)	George Murray	22.00	11.00	6.50
(37)	Floyd Newkirk	22.00	11.00	6.50
(38)	Leo Norris	22.00	11.00	6.50
(39)	Frank Packard	22.00	11.00	6.50
(40)	Ben Paschal	22.00	11.00	6.50
(41)	Jess Petty	22.00	11.00	6.50
(42)	Ray Radcliff	22.00	11.00	6.50
(43)	Paul Richards	25.00	12.50	7.50
(44)	Rodda	22.00	11.00	6.50
(45)	Rose	22.00	11.00	6.50
(46)	Larry Rosenthal	22.00	11.00	6.50
(47)	Art Ruble	22.00	11.00	6.50
(48)	Rosy Ryan	22.00	11.00	6.50
(49)	Sheehan (Mps. announcer)	22.00	11.00	6.50
(50)	Art Shires	22.00	11.00	6.50
(51)	Ed Sicking	22.00	11.00	6.50
(52)	Ernest Smith	22.00	11.00	6.50
(53)	Walter Tauscher	22.00	11.00	6.50
(54)	Myles Thomas	22.00	11.00	6.50
(55)	Phil Todt	22.00	11.00	6.50
(56)	Gene Trow	22.00	11.00	6.50
(57)	Harold Vandenberg	22.00	11.00	6.50
(58)	Elam Van Gilder	22.00	11.00	6.50
(59)	Charles Wilson	22.00	11.00	6.50
(60)	Emil Yde	22.00	11.00	6.50

1950 World Wide Gum

International League players are featured in this 48-card set. Measuring 3-1/4" x 2-5/8", the blank-backed cards are printed in blue-on-white with English and French stats and biographical data. Connors and Lasorda are worth $400-$200-$120; Cimoli, Gionfriddo and Bridges are worth $50-$25-$15.

		NR MT	EX	VG
Complete Set (48):		2800.	1400.	825.00
Common Player:		50.00	25.00	15.00
1	Rocky Bridges	85.00	42.00	25.00
2	Chuck Connors	500.00	250.00	150.00
3	Jake Wade	50.00	25.00	15.00
4	Al Cihocki	50.00	25.00	15.00
5	John Simmons	50.00	25.00	15.00
6	Frank Trechock	50.00	25.00	15.00
7	Steve Lembo	50.00	25.00	15.00
8	Johnny Welaj	50.00	25.00	15.00
9	Seymour Block	50.00	25.00	15.00
10	Pat McGlothlin	50.00	25.00	15.00
11	Bryan Stephens	50.00	25.00	15.00
12	Clarence Podbielan	55.00	27.00	16.50
13	Clem Hausmann	50.00	25.00	15.00
14	Turk Lown	55.00	27.00	16.50
15	Joe Payne	50.00	25.00	15.00
16	Coacker Triplett	50.00	25.00	15.00
17	Nick Strincevich	50.00	25.00	15.00
18	Charlie Thompson	50.00	25.00	15.00
19	Erick Silverman	50.00	25.00	15.00
20	George Schmees	50.00	25.00	15.00
21	George Binks	50.00	25.00	15.00
22	Gino Cimoli	75.00	37.00	22.00
23	Marty Tabacheck	50.00	25.00	15.00
24	Al Gionfriddo	65.00	32.00	19.50
25	Ronnie Lee	50.00	25.00	15.00
26	Clyde King	50.00	25.00	15.00
27	Harry Heslet	50.00	25.00	15.00
28	Jerry Scala	50.00	25.00	15.00
29	Boris Woyt	50.00	25.00	15.00
30	Jack Collum	50.00	25.00	15.00
31	Chet Laabs	50.00	25.00	15.00
32	Carden Gillwater	50.00	25.00	15.00
33	Irving Medlinger	50.00	25.00	15.00
34	Toby Atwell	50.00	25.00	15.00
35	Charlie Marshall	50.00	25.00	15.00
36	Johnny Mayo	50.00	25.00	15.00
37	Gene Markland	50.00	25.00	15.00
38	Russ Kerns	50.00	25.00	15.00
39	Jim Prendergast	50.00	25.00	15.00
40	Lou Welaj	50.00	25.00	15.00
41	Clyde Kluttz	60.00	30.00	18.00
42	Bill Glynn	50.00	25.00	15.00
43	Don Richmond	50.00	25.00	15.00
44	Hank Biasatti	50.00	25.00	15.00
45	Tom Lasorda	400.00	200.00	120.00
46	Al Roberge	50.00	25.00	15.00
47	George Byam	50.00	25.00	15.00
48	Dutch Mele	50.00	25.00	15.00

1911 Zeenut Pacific Coast League (E136)

Produced for 28 straight years, these Pacific Coast League cards were among the longest-running and most popular baseball issues ever to appear on the West Coast. Issued by the Collins-McCarthy Candy Co. (later known as the Collins-Hencke Candy Co. and then simply the Collins Candy Co.) of San Francisco, Zeenut cards were inserted in boxes of the company's products: Zeenuts, Ruf-Neks and Home Run Kisses. All Zeenut cards issued from 1913 to 1937 included a half-inch coupon at the bottom that could be redeemed for various prizes. Since most of these coupons were removed (and many not too carefully) Zeenuts are difficult to find in top condition today, and only a very small percentage survived with the coupon intact. (The sizes listed in the following descriptions are for cards without coupons.) Over the 28-year span, it is estimated that nearly 3,700 different cards were issued as part of the Zeenuts series, but new discoveries are still being made, and the checklist continues to grow. It is sometimes difficult to differentiate one year from another after 1930. Because it is so rare to find Zeenuts cards with the coupon still attached, values listed are for cards without the coupon. Cards with the coupon still intact will generally command an additional 25-35 percent premium. The first Zeenut cards measure 2-1/8" x 4" and feature a sepia-toned photo on a brown background surrounded by an off-white border. The backs of the cards are blank. Although the 1911 cards did not include the coupon bottom, some cards have been found with punch holes, indicating they may have also been used for premiums. A total of 122 different players have been found.

		NR MT	EX	VG
Complete Set:		3300.	1650.	975.00
Common Player:		32.00	16.00	9.50
(1)	Abbott	32.00	16.00	9.50
(2)	Ables	32.00	16.00	9.50
(3a)	Agnew (large pose)	32.00	16.00	9.50
(3b)	Agnew (small pose)	32.00	16.00	9.50
(4a)	Akin (large pose)	32.00	16.00	9.50
(4b)	Akin (small pose)	32.00	16.00	9.50
(5)	Arellanes	32.00	16.00	9.50
(6a)	Arlett (large pose)	32.00	16.00	9.50
(6b)	Arlett (middle size pose)	32.00	16.00	9.50
(6c)	Arlett (small pose)	32.00	16.00	9.50
(7)	Barry	32.00	16.00	9.50
(8)	Baum	32.00	16.00	9.50
(9)	Bernard	32.00	16.00	9.50
(10)	Berry	32.00	16.00	9.50
(11)	Bohen	32.00	16.00	9.50
(12)	Brackenridge	32.00	16.00	9.50
(13)	Brashear	32.00	16.00	9.50
(14a)	Brown (large pose)	32.00	16.00	9.50
(14b)	Brown (small pose)	32.00	16.00	9.50
(15)	Browning	32.00	16.00	9.50
(16a)	Burrell (large pose)	32.00	16.00	9.50
(16b)	Burrell (small pose)	32.00	16.00	9.50
(17)	Byram	32.00	16.00	9.50
(18)	Carlisle	32.00	16.00	9.50
(19)	Carman	32.00	16.00	9.50
(20a)	Carson (large pose)	32.00	16.00	9.50
(20b)	Carson (middle size pose)	32.00	16.00	9.50
(20c)	Carson (small pose)	32.00	16.00	9.50
(21)	Castleton	32.00	16.00	9.50
(22)	Chadbourne	32.00	16.00	9.50
(23)	Christian	32.00	16.00	9.50
(24)	Couchman	32.00	16.00	9.50
(25)	Coy	32.00	16.00	9.50
(26)	Criger	32.00	16.00	9.50
(27)	Cutshaw	32.00	16.00	9.50
(28)	Daley	32.00	16.00	9.50
(29)	Danzig	32.00	16.00	9.50
(30)	Delhi	32.00	16.00	9.50
(31a)	Delmas (large pose)	32.00	16.00	9.50
(31b)	Delmas (small pose)	32.00	16.00	9.50
(32)	Dillon	32.00	16.00	9.50
(33a)	Discoll (name incorrect)	32.00	16.00	9.50
(33b)	Driscoll (name correct)	32.00	16.00	9.50
(34)	Dulin	32.00	16.00	9.50
(35)	Fanning	32.00	16.00	9.50
(36)	Fitzgerald	32.00	16.00	9.50
(37)	Flater	32.00	16.00	9.50
(38)	French	32.00	16.00	9.50
(39)	Fullerton	32.00	16.00	9.50
(40)	Gleason	32.00	16.00	9.50
(41)	Gregory	32.00	16.00	9.50
(42)	Halla	32.00	16.00	9.50
(43)	Harkness	32.00	16.00	9.50
(44a)	Heitmuller (large pose)	32.00	16.00	9.50
(44b)	Heitmuller (small pose)	32.00	16.00	9.50
(45)	Henley	32.00	16.00	9.50
(46)	Hetling	32.00	16.00	9.50
(47)	Hiester	32.00	16.00	9.50
(48a)	Hitt (large pose)	32.00	16.00	9.50
(48b)	Hitt (small pose)	32.00	16.00	9.50
(50)	Hoffman	32.00	16.00	9.50
(51)	Hogan	32.00	16.00	9.50
(52a)	Holland (large pose)	32.00	16.00	9.50
(52b)	Holland (small pose)	32.00	16.00	9.50
(53)	Hosp	32.00	16.00	9.50
(54a)	Howard (large pose)	32.00	16.00	9.50
(54b)	Howard (small pose)	32.00	16.00	9.50
(55)	Kane	32.00	16.00	9.50
(56)	Kerns	32.00	16.00	9.50
(57)	Kilroy	32.00	16.00	9.50
(58)	Knight	32.00	16.00	9.50
(59)	Koestner	32.00	16.00	9.50
(60)	Krueger	32.00	16.00	9.50
(61)	Kuhn	32.00	16.00	9.50
(62)	LaLonge	32.00	16.00	9.50
(63)	Lerchen	32.00	16.00	9.50
(64)	Leverenz	32.00	16.00	9.50
(65)	Lewis	32.00	16.00	9.50
(66)	Lindsay	32.00	16.00	9.50
(67)	Lober	32.00	16.00	9.50
(68)	Madden	32.00	16.00	9.50
(69)	Maggert	32.00	16.00	9.50
(70)	Mahoney	32.00	16.00	9.50
(71)	Martinoni	32.00	16.00	9.50
(72)	McArdle	32.00	16.00	9.50
(73)	McCredie	32.00	16.00	9.50
(74)	McDonnell	32.00	16.00	9.50
(75a)	McKune (large pose)	32.00	16.00	9.50
(75b)	McKune (middle size pose)	32.00	16.00	9.50

No.	Player	NR MT	EX	VG
(75c)	McKune (small pose)	32.00	16.00	9.50
(76)	Meikle	32.00	16.00	9.50
(77)	Melchoir	32.00	16.00	9.50
(78)	Metzger	32.00	16.00	9.50
(79)	Miller	32.00	16.00	9.50
(80)	Mitze	32.00	16.00	9.50
(81)	Mohler	32.00	16.00	9.50
(82a)	Moore (large pose)	32.00	16.00	9.50
(82b)	Moore (small pose)	32.00	16.00	9.50
(83a)	Moskiman (lettering size large)	32.00	16.00	9.50
(83b)	Moskiman (lettering size small)	32.00	16.00	9.50
(84)	Murray	32.00	16.00	9.50
(85)	Naylor	32.00	16.00	9.50
(86)	Nebinger	32.00	16.00	9.50
(87)	Nourse	32.00	16.00	9.50
(88a)	Noyes (large pose)	32.00	16.00	9.50
(88b)	Noyes (small pose)	32.00	16.00	9.50
(89)	O'Rourke	32.00	16.00	9.50
(90)	Patterson (Oakland)	32.00	16.00	9.50
(91)	Patterson (Vernon)	32.00	16.00	9.50
(92)	Pearce	32.00	16.00	9.50
(93)	Peckinpaugh	30.00	15.00	9.00
(94)	Pernoll	32.00	16.00	9.50
(95)	Pfyl	32.00	16.00	9.50
(96)	Powell	32.00	16.00	9.50
(97a)	Raleigh (large pose)	32.00	16.00	9.50
(97b)	Raleigh (small pose)	32.00	16.00	9.50
(98)	Rapps	32.00	16.00	9.50
(99)	Rodgers	32.00	16.00	9.50
(100a)	Ryan (Portland, box around name and team)	45.00	22.00	13.50
(100b)	Ryan (Portland, no box around name and team)	32.00	16.00	9.50
(101)	Ryan (San Francisco)	32.00	16.00	9.50
(102)	Seaton	32.00	16.00	9.50
(103)	Shaw	32.00	16.00	9.50
(104)	Sheehan	32.00	16.00	9.50
(105)	Shinn	32.00	16.00	9.50
106a	Smith (Los Angeles, large pose)	32.00	16.00	9.50
(106b)	Smith (Los Angeles, small pose)	32.00	16.00	9.50
(107a)	Smith (San Francisco, large pose)	32.00	16.00	9.50
(107b)	Smith (San Francisco, small pose)	32.00	16.00	9.50
(108)	Steen	32.00	16.00	9.50
(109)	Stewart	32.00	16.00	9.50
(110a)	Stinson (large pose)	32.00	16.00	9.50
(110b)	Stinson (small pose)	32.00	16.00	9.50
(111)	Sutor	32.00	16.00	9.50
(112)	Tennant	32.00	16.00	9.50
(113)	Thomas	32.00	16.00	9.50
(114)	Thompson	32.00	16.00	9.50
(115)	Thornton	32.00	16.00	9.50
(116)	Tiedeman	32.00	16.00	9.50
(117)	Van Buren	32.00	16.00	9.50
(118)	Vitt	32.00	16.00	9.50
(119)	Wares	32.00	16.00	9.50
(120)	Weaver	135.00	65.00	40.00
(121)	Wolverton	32.00	16.00	9.50
(122)	Zacher	32.00	16.00	9.50
(123)	Zamloch	32.00	16.00	9.50

1912 Zeenut Pacific Coast League (E136)

The second series of Zeenut cards measure 2-1/8" x 4-1/8" and featured sepia-toned photographs on a brown background with no border. Most cards have blank backs, but some have been found with printing advising collectors to "Save Zeenut pictures for valuable premiums." The checklist consists of 158 subjects, but more cards are still being discovered.

		NR MT	EX	VG
	Complete Set:	4000.	2000.	1200.
	Common Player:	32.00	16.00	9.50
(1)	Abbott	32.00	16.00	9.50
(2)	Ables	32.00	16.00	9.50
(3)	Agnew	32.00	16.00	9.50
(4)	Altman	32.00	16.00	9.50
(5)	Arellanes	32.00	16.00	9.50
(6)	Auer	32.00	16.00	9.50
(7)	Baker (horizontal pose)	32.00	16.00	9.50
(8)	Baker (vertical pose)	32.00	16.00	9.50
(9)	Bancroft	65.00	32.00	19.50
(10)	Baum	32.00	16.00	9.50
(11)	Bayless	32.00	16.00	9.50
(12)	Berger	32.00	16.00	9.50
(13)	Berry	32.00	16.00	9.50
(14)	Bohen	32.00	16.00	9.50
(15)	Boles	32.00	16.00	9.50
(16)	Bonner			
(17)	Boone	32.00	16.00	9.50
(18)	Brackenridge	32.00	16.00	9.50
(19)	Brashear	32.00	16.00	9.50
(20)	Breen			
(21)	Brooks (Los Angeles)	32.00	16.00	9.50
(22)	Brooks (Oakland)	32.00	16.00	9.50
(23)	Brown	32.00	16.00	9.50
(24)	Burch	32.00	16.00	9.50
(25)	Burrell	32.00	16.00	9.50
(26)	Butcher	32.00	16.00	9.50
(27)	Butler	32.00	16.00	9.50
(28)	Byram	32.00	16.00	9.50
(29)	Carlisle	32.00	16.00	9.50
(30)	Carson	32.00	16.00	9.50
(31)	Castleton	32.00	16.00	9.50
(32)	Chadbourne	32.00	16.00	9.50
(33)	Chech	32.00	16.00	9.50
(34)	Cheek	32.00	16.00	9.50
(35)	Christian	32.00	16.00	9.50
(36)	Cook	32.00	16.00	9.50
(37)	Core	32.00	16.00	9.50
(38)	Corhan	32.00	16.00	9.50
(39)	Coy	32.00	16.00	9.50
(40)	Daley	32.00	16.00	9.50
(41)	Delhi	32.00	16.00	9.50
(42)	Dillon	32.00	16.00	9.50
(43)	Doane	32.00	16.00	9.50
(44)	Driscoll	32.00	16.00	9.50
(45)	Durbin	32.00	16.00	9.50
(46)	Fanning	32.00	16.00	9.50
(47)	Felts	32.00	16.00	9.50
(48)	Fisher	32.00	16.00	9.50
(49)	Fitzgerald	32.00	16.00	9.50
(50)	Flater	32.00	16.00	9.50
(51)	Frick	32.00	16.00	9.50
(52)	Gaddy	32.00	16.00	9.50
(53)	Gedeon	32.00	16.00	9.50
(54)	Gilligan	32.00	16.00	9.50
(55)	Girot	32.00	16.00	9.50
(56)	Gray	32.00	16.00	9.50
(57)	Gregg	32.00	16.00	9.50
(58)	Gregory	32.00	16.00	9.50
(59)	Halla	32.00	16.00	9.50
(60)	Hamilton (Oakland)	32.00	16.00	9.50
(61)	Hamilton (San Francisco)	32.00	16.00	9.50
(62)	Harkness	32.00	16.00	9.50
(63)	Hartley	32.00	16.00	9.50
(64)	Heitmuller	32.00	16.00	9.50
(65)	Henley	32.00	16.00	9.50
(66)	Hetling (glove open)	32.00	16.00	9.50
(67)	Hetling (glove closed)	32.00	16.00	9.50
(68)	Hiester	32.00	16.00	9.50
(69)	Higginbottom	32.00	16.00	9.50
(70)	Hitt	32.00	16.00	9.50
(71)	Hoffman	32.00	16.00	9.50
(72)	Hogan	32.00	16.00	9.50
(73)	Hosp	32.00	16.00	9.50
(74)	Howard	32.00	16.00	9.50
(75)	Howley	32.00	16.00	9.50
(76)	Ireland	32.00	16.00	9.50
(77)	Jackson	32.00	16.00	9.50
(78)	Johnson	32.00	16.00	9.50
(79)	Kane	32.00	16.00	9.50
(80)	Killilay	32.00	16.00	9.50
(81)	Klawitter	32.00	16.00	9.50
(82)	Knight	32.00	16.00	9.50
(83)	Koestner ("P" visible)	32.00	16.00	9.50
(84)	Koestner (no "P" visible)	32.00	16.00	9.50
(85)	Kreitz	32.00	16.00	9.50
(86)	Krueger	32.00	16.00	9.50
(87)	LaLonge	32.00	16.00	9.50
(88)	Leard	32.00	16.00	9.50
(89)	Leverenz	32.00	16.00	9.50
(90)	Lewis	32.00	16.00	9.50
(91)	Lindsay	32.00	16.00	9.50
(92)	Litschi	32.00	16.00	9.50
(93)	Lober	32.00	16.00	9.50
(94)	Madden	32.00	16.00	9.50
(95)	Mahoney	32.00	16.00	9.50
(96)	Malarkey	32.00	16.00	9.50
(97)	Martinoni	32.00	16.00	9.50
(98)	McArdle	32.00	16.00	9.50
(99)	McAvoy	32.00	16.00	9.50
(100)	McCorrey	32.00	16.00	9.50
(101)	McCredie	32.00	16.00	9.50
(102)	McDonald	32.00	16.00	9.50
(103)	McDowell	32.00	16.00	9.50
(104)	McIver	32.00	16.00	9.50
(105)	Meikle	32.00	16.00	9.50
(106)	Metzger	32.00	16.00	9.50
(107)	Miller (Sacramento)	32.00	16.00	9.50
(108)	Miller (San Francisco)	32.00	16.00	9.50
(109)	Mitze	32.00	16.00	9.50
(110)	Mohler	32.00	16.00	9.50
(111)	Moore	32.00	16.00	9.50
(112)	Mundorf (batting)	32.00	16.00	9.50
(113)	Mundorf (fielding)	32.00	16.00	9.50
(114)	Nagle	32.00	16.00	9.50
(115)	Noyes	32.00	16.00	9.50
(116)	O'Rourke	32.00	16.00	9.50
(117)	Olmstead	32.00	16.00	9.50
(118)	Orr	32.00	16.00	9.50
(119)	Page	32.00	16.00	9.50
(120)	Parkins	32.00	16.00	9.50
(121)	Patterson (Oakland)	32.00	16.00	9.50
(122)	Patterson (Vernon)	32.00	16.00	9.50
(123)	Pernol	32.00	16.00	9.50
(124)	Pope	32.00	16.00	9.50
(125)	Powell	32.00	16.00	9.50
(126)	Price	32.00	16.00	9.50
(127)	Raftery	32.00	16.00	9.50
(128)	Raleigh	32.00	16.00	9.50
(129)	Rapps ("P" visible)	32.00	16.00	9.50
(130)	Rapps (no "P" visible)	32.00	16.00	9.50
(131)	Reidy	32.00	16.00	9.50
(132)	Rodgers	32.00	16.00	9.50
(133)	Rohrer	32.00	16.00	9.50
(134)	Schmidt	32.00	16.00	9.50
(135)	Schwenk	32.00	16.00	9.50
(136)	Sharpe	32.00	16.00	9.50
(137)	Sheehan	32.00	16.00	9.50
(138)	Shinn	32.00	16.00	9.50
(139)	Slagle	32.00	16.00	9.50
(140)	Smith	32.00	16.00	9.50
(141)	Stewart	32.00	16.00	9.50
(142)	Stinson	32.00	16.00	9.50
(143)	Stone	32.00	16.00	9.50
(144)	Sullivan	32.00	16.00	9.50
(145)	Swain	32.00	16.00	9.50
(146)	Taylor	32.00	16.00	9.50
(147)	Temple	32.00	16.00	9.50
(148)	Tiedeman	32.00	16.00	9.50
(149)	Toner	32.00	16.00	9.50
(150)	Tozer	32.00	16.00	9.50
(151)	Van Buren	32.00	16.00	9.50
(152)	Wagner	32.00	16.00	9.50
(153)	Whalen	32.00	16.00	9.50
(154)	Williams (Sacramento)	32.00	16.00	9.50
(155)	Williams (San Francisco)	32.00	16.00	9.50
(156)	Joe Williams	32.00	16.00	9.50
(157)	Wuffli	32.00	16.00	9.50
(158)	Zacher	32.00	16.00	9.50
(159)	Zimmerman	32.00	16.00	9.50

1913 Zeenut Pacific Coast League (E136)

		NR MT	EX	VG
	Complete Set:	3800.	1900.	1100.
	Common Player:	32.00	16.00	9.50
(1)	Abbott	32.00	16.00	9.50
(2)	Ables	32.00	16.00	9.50
(3)	Arelanes	32.00	16.00	9.50
(4)	Arlett	32.00	16.00	9.50
(5)	Baker	32.00	16.00	9.50
(6)	Baum	32.00	16.00	9.50
(7)	Bayless	32.00	16.00	9.50
(8)	Becker	32.00	16.00	9.50
(9)	Berry	32.00	16.00	9.50
(10)	Bliss	32.00	16.00	9.50
(11)	Boles	32.00	16.00	9.50
(12)	Brackenridge	32.00	16.00	9.50
(13)	Brashear	32.00	16.00	9.50
(14)	Brooks	32.00	16.00	9.50
(15)	Byrnes	32.00	16.00	9.50
(16)	Cadreau	32.00	16.00	9.50
(17)	Carlisle	32.00	16.00	9.50
(18)	Carson	32.00	16.00	9.50
(19)	Cartwright	32.00	16.00	9.50
(20)	Chadbourne	32.00	16.00	9.50
(21)	Charles	32.00	16.00	9.50
(22)	Cheek	32.00	16.00	9.50
(23)	Christian	32.00	16.00	9.50
(24)	Clarke	32.00	16.00	9.50
(25)	Clemons	32.00	16.00	9.50
(26)	Cook	32.00	16.00	9.50
(27)	Corhan	32.00	16.00	9.50
(28)	Coy	32.00	16.00	9.50
(29)	Crabb	32.00	16.00	9.50
(30)	Crisp	32.00	16.00	9.50
(31)	Derrick	32.00	16.00	9.50
(32)	DeCanniere	32.00	16.00	9.50
(33)	Dillon	32.00	16.00	9.50
(34)	Doane	32.00	16.00	9.50
(35)	Douglass	32.00	16.00	9.50
(36)	Downs	32.00	16.00	9.50
(37)	Driscoll	32.00	16.00	9.50
(38)	Drucke	32.00	16.00	9.50
(39)	Elliott	32.00	16.00	9.50
(40)	Ellis	32.00	16.00	9.50
(41)	Fanning	32.00	16.00	9.50
(42)	Fisher	32.00	16.00	9.50

(43)	Fitzgerald	32.00	16.00	9.50
(44)	Gardner	32.00	16.00	9.50
(45)	Gill	32.00	16.00	9.50
(46)	Goodwin	32.00	16.00	9.50
(47a)	Gregory (large pose)	32.00	16.00	9.50
(47b)	Gregory (small pose)	32.00	16.00	9.50
(48)	Grey	32.00	16.00	9.50
(49)	Guest	32.00	16.00	9.50
(50)	Hagerman	32.00	16.00	9.50
(51)	Halla	32.00	16.00	9.50
(52)	Hallinan	32.00	16.00	9.50
(53)	Heilmann	100.00	50.00	30.00
(54)	Henley	32.00	16.00	9.50
(55)	Hetling	32.00	16.00	9.50
(56)	Higginbotham	32.00	16.00	9.50
(57)	Hitt	32.00	16.00	9.50
(58)	Hoffman	32.00	16.00	9.50
(59)	Hogan (San Francisco)	32.00	16.00	9.50
(60)	Hogan (Vernon)	32.00	16.00	9.50
(61)	Hosp	32.00	16.00	9.50
(62)	Howard (Los Angeles)	32.00	16.00	9.50
(63)	Howard (San Francisco)	32.00	16.00	9.50
(64)	Hughes	32.00	16.00	9.50
(65)	Jackson	32.00	16.00	9.50
(66)	James	32.00	16.00	9.50
(67)	Johnson	32.00	16.00	9.50
(68)	Johnston	32.00	16.00	9.50
(69)	Kane	32.00	16.00	9.50
(70)	Kaylor	32.00	16.00	9.50
(71)	Kenworthy	32.00	16.00	9.50
(72)	Killilay	32.00	16.00	9.50
(73)	Klawitter	32.00	16.00	9.50
(74)	Koestner	32.00	16.00	9.50
(75)	Kores	32.00	16.00	9.50
(76)	Krapp	32.00	16.00	9.50
(77)	Kreitz	32.00	16.00	9.50
(78)	Krause	32.00	16.00	9.50
(79)	Krueger	32.00	16.00	9.50
(80)	Leard	32.00	16.00	9.50
(81)	Leifield	32.00	16.00	9.50
(82)	Lewis	32.00	16.00	9.50
(83)	Lindsay	32.00	16.00	9.50
(84)	Litschi	32.00	16.00	9.50
(85)	Lively	32.00	16.00	9.50
(86)	Lober	32.00	16.00	9.50
(87)	Lohman	32.00	16.00	9.50
(88)	Maggart	32.00	16.00	9.50
(89)	Malarky	32.00	16.00	9.50
(90)	McArdle	32.00	16.00	9.50
(91)	McCarl	32.00	16.00	9.50
(92)	McCormick	32.00	16.00	9.50
(93)	McCorry	32.00	16.00	9.50
(94)	McCredie	32.00	16.00	9.50
(95)	McDonnell	32.00	16.00	9.50
(96)	Meloan	32.00	16.00	9.50
(97)	Metzger	32.00	16.00	9.50
(98)	Miller	32.00	16.00	9.50
(99)	Mitze	32.00	16.00	9.50
(100)	Moore	32.00	16.00	9.50
(101)	Moran	32.00	16.00	9.50
(102)	Mundorf	32.00	16.00	9.50
(103)	Munsell	32.00	16.00	9.50
(104)	Ness	32.00	16.00	9.50
(105)	O'Rourke	32.00	16.00	9.50
(106)	Overall	32.00	16.00	9.50
(107)	Page	32.00	16.00	9.50
(108)	Parkin	32.00	16.00	9.50
(109)	Patterson	32.00	16.00	9.50
(110)	Pearce	32.00	16.00	9.50
(111)	Pernoll	32.00	16.00	9.50
(112)	Perritt	32.00	16.00	9.50
(113)	Pope	32.00	16.00	9.50
(114)	Pruitt	32.00	16.00	9.50
(115)	Raleigh	32.00	16.00	9.50
(116)	Reitmyer	32.00	16.00	9.50
(117)	Riordan	32.00	16.00	9.50
(118)	Rodgers	32.00	16.00	9.50
(119)	Rogers	32.00	16.00	9.50
(120)	Rohrer	32.00	16.00	9.50
(121)	Ryan	32.00	16.00	9.50
(122)	Schaller	32.00	16.00	9.50
(123)	Schirm	32.00	16.00	9.50
(124)	Schmidt	32.00	16.00	9.50
(125)	Schulz	32.00	16.00	9.50
(126)	Sepulveda	32.00	16.00	9.50
(127)	Shinn	32.00	16.00	9.50
(128)	Spenger	32.00	16.00	9.50
(129)	Stanley	32.00	16.00	9.50
(130)	Stanridge	32.00	16.00	9.50
(131)	Stark	32.00	16.00	9.50
(132)	Sterritt	32.00	16.00	9.50
(133)	Stroud	32.00	16.00	9.50
(134)	Tennant	32.00	16.00	9.50
(135)	Thomas	32.00	16.00	9.50
(136)	Todd	32.00	16.00	9.50
(137)	Tonneman	32.00	16.00	9.50
(138)	Tozer	32.00	16.00	9.50
(139)	Van Buren	32.00	16.00	9.50
(140)	Wagner	32.00	16.00	9.50
(141)	West	32.00	16.00	9.50
(142)	Williams	32.00	16.00	9.50
(143)	Wolverton	32.00	16.00	9.50
(144)	Wotell	32.00	16.00	9.50
(145)	Wuffli	32.00	16.00	9.50
(146)	Young	32.00	16.00	9.50
(147)	Zacher	32.00	16.00	9.50
(148)	Zimmerman	32.00	16.00	9.50

A player's name in italic type indicates a rookie card. An (FC) indicates a player's first card for that particular card company.

1914 Zeenut Pacific Coast League (E136)

The 1914 Zeenut cards measure 2" x 3-1/2" without the coupon, and feature black and white photos on a gray, borderless background. To date, 146 different poses have been found. The backs are blank.

		NR MT	EX	VG
Complete Set:		3100.	1550.	925.00
Common Player:		26.00	13.00	7.75
(1)	Ables	26.00	13.00	7.75
(2)	Abstein	26.00	13.00	7.75
(3)	Alexander	26.00	13.00	7.75
(4)	Arbogast	26.00	13.00	7.75
(5)	Arlett	26.00	13.00	7.75
(6)	Arrelanes	26.00	13.00	7.75
(7)	Bancroft	130.00	65.00	40.00
(8)	Barham	26.00	13.00	7.75
(9)	Barrenkamp	26.00	13.00	7.75
(10)	Barton	26.00	13.00	7.75
(11)	Baum	26.00	13.00	7.75
(12)	Bayless	26.00	13.00	7.75
(13a)	Bliss (large pose)	26.00	13.00	7.75
(13b)	Bliss (small pose)	26.00	13.00	7.75
(14)	Boles	26.00	13.00	7.75
(15)	Borton	26.00	13.00	7.75
(16)	Brashear	26.00	13.00	7.75
(17)	Brenegan	26.00	13.00	7.75
(18)	Brooks	26.00	13.00	7.75
(19)	Brown	26.00	13.00	7.75
(20)	Butler	26.00	13.00	7.75
(21)	Calvo	26.00	13.00	7.75
(22)	Carlisle	26.00	13.00	7.75
(23)	Cartwright	26.00	13.00	7.75
(24)	Charles	26.00	13.00	7.75
(25)	Chech	26.00	13.00	7.75
(26)	Christian	26.00	13.00	7.75
(27)	Clarke	26.00	13.00	7.75
(28)	Colligan	26.00	13.00	7.75
(29)	Cook	26.00	13.00	7.75
(31)	Coy	26.00	13.00	7.75
(32)	Crabb	26.00	13.00	7.75
(33)	Davis	26.00	13.00	7.75
(34)	Derrick	26.00	13.00	7.75
(35)	Devlin	26.00	13.00	7.75
(36)	DeCannier	26.00	13.00	7.75
(37)	Dillon	26.00	13.00	7.75
(38)	Doane	26.00	13.00	7.75
(39)	Downs	26.00	13.00	7.75
(40)	Ehmke	12.00	6.00	3.50
(41)	Ellis	26.00	13.00	7.75
(42)	Evans	26.00	13.00	7.75
(43)	Fanning	26.00	13.00	7.75
(44)	Fisher	26.00	13.00	7.75
(45)	Fitzgerald	26.00	13.00	7.75
(46)	Fleharty	26.00	13.00	7.75
(47)	Frambach	26.00	13.00	7.75
(48)	Gardner	26.00	13.00	7.75
(49)	Gedeon	26.00	13.00	7.75
(50)	Geyer	26.00	13.00	7.75
(51)	Gianini	26.00	13.00	7.75
(52)	Gregory	26.00	13.00	7.75
(53)	Guest	26.00	13.00	7.75
(54)	Hallinan	26.00	13.00	7.75
(55)	Hannah	26.00	13.00	7.75
(56)	Harkness (batting)	26.00	13.00	7.75
(57)	Haworth (batting)	26.00	13.00	7.75
(58)	Haworth (catching)	26.00	13.00	7.75
(59)	Henderson	26.00	13.00	7.75
(60)	Henley	26.00	13.00	7.75
(61)	Hern	26.00	13.00	7.75
(62)	Hettling	26.00	13.00	7.75
(63)	Higginbotham	26.00	13.00	7.75
(64)	Hitt	26.00	13.00	7.75
(65)	Hogan	26.00	13.00	7.75
(66a)	Hosp (large pose)	26.00	13.00	7.75
(66b)	Hosp (small pose)	26.00	13.00	7.75
(67)	Howard	26.00	13.00	7.75
(68)	Hughes (Los Angeles)	26.00	13.00	7.75
(69)	Hughes (San Francisco)	26.00	13.00	7.75
(70)	Johnson	26.00	13.00	7.75
(71)	Kane	26.00	13.00	7.75
(72)	Kaylor	26.00	13.00	7.75
(73)	Killilay	26.00	13.00	7.75
(74)	Klawitter	26.00	13.00	7.75
(75)	Klepfler	26.00	13.00	7.75
(76)	Kores	26.00	13.00	7.75
(77)	Kramer	26.00	13.00	7.75
(78)	Krause	26.00	13.00	7.75
(79a)	Leard (large pose)	26.00	13.00	7.75
(79b)	Leard (small pose)	26.00	13.00	7.75
(80)	Liefeld	26.00	13.00	7.75
(81)	Litschi	26.00	13.00	7.75
(82)	Lober	26.00	13.00	7.75
(83)	Loomis	26.00	13.00	7.75
(84)	Love	26.00	13.00	7.75
(85)	Lynn	26.00	13.00	7.75
(86)	Maggart	26.00	13.00	7.75
(87)	Malarkey	26.00	13.00	7.75
(88)	Martinoni	26.00	13.00	7.75
(89)	McArdle	26.00	13.00	7.75
(90)	McCredie	26.00	13.00	7.75
(91)	McDonald	26.00	13.00	7.75
(92)	Meek	26.00	13.00	7.75
(93)	Meloan	26.00	13.00	7.75
(94)	Menges	26.00	13.00	7.75
(95)	Metzger	26.00	13.00	7.75
(96)	Middleton	26.00	13.00	7.75
(97)	Mitze	26.00	13.00	7.75
(98)	Mohler	26.00	13.00	7.75
(99)	Moore	26.00	13.00	7.75
(100)	Moran	26.00	13.00	7.75
(101)	Mundorf	26.00	13.00	7.75
(102)	Murphy	26.00	13.00	7.75
(103)	Musser	26.00	13.00	7.75
(104)	Ness	26.00	13.00	7.75
(105)	O'Leary	26.00	13.00	7.75
(106)	Orr	26.00	13.00	7.75
(107)	Page	26.00	13.00	7.75
(108)	Pape	26.00	13.00	7.75
(109)	Parkin	26.00	13.00	7.75
(110a)	Peet (large pose)	26.00	13.00	7.75
(110b)	Peet (small pose)	26.00	13.00	7.75
(111)	Perkins	26.00	13.00	7.75
(112)	Pernoll	26.00	13.00	7.75
(113)	Perritt	26.00	13.00	7.75
(114)	Powell	26.00	13.00	7.75
(115)	Prough	26.00	13.00	7.75
(116)	Pruiett	26.00	13.00	7.75
(117)	Quinlan	26.00	13.00	7.75
(118a)	Raney (incorrect spelling)	26.00	13.00	7.75
(118b)	Ramey (correct spelling)	26.00	13.00	7.75
(119)	Rieger	26.00	13.00	7.75
(120)	Rodgers	26.00	13.00	7.75
(121)	Rogers	26.00	13.00	7.75
(122)	Rohrer	26.00	13.00	7.75
(123)	Ryan	26.00	13.00	7.75
(124)	Ryan	26.00	13.00	7.75
(125)	Sawyer	26.00	13.00	7.75
(126)	Schaller	26.00	13.00	7.75
(127)	Schmidt	26.00	13.00	7.75
(128)	Sepulveda	26.00	13.00	7.75
(129)	Shinn	26.00	13.00	7.75
(130)	Slagle	26.00	13.00	7.75
(131)	Speas	26.00	13.00	7.75
(132)	Stanridge	26.00	13.00	7.75
(133)	Stroud	26.00	13.00	7.75
(134)	Tennant	26.00	13.00	7.75
(135)	Tobin	26.00	13.00	7.75
(136)	Tozer	26.00	13.00	7.75
(137)	Van Buren	26.00	13.00	7.75
(138)	West	26.00	13.00	7.75
(139)	White	26.00	13.00	7.75
(140)	Wolter	26.00	13.00	7.75
(141)	Wolverton	26.00	13.00	7.75
(142)	Yantz	26.00	13.00	7.75
(143)	Young	26.00	13.00	7.75
(144)	Zacher	26.00	13.00	7.75
(145)	Zumwalt	26.00	13.00	7.75

1915 Zeenut Pacific Coast League (E137)

The 1915 Zeenut cards are dated on the front, making identification very easy. They measure 2" x 3-1/8" without the coupon and feature a black and white photo on a light background. To date 141 different cards are known to exist. This year is among the toughest of all Zeenuts to find.

	NR MT	EX	VG
Complete Set:	4250.	2125.	1275.
Common Player:	35.00	17.50	10.50
(1) Ables	35.00	17.50	10.50
(2) Abstein	35.00	17.50	10.50
(3) Alcock	35.00	17.50	10.50
(4) Arbogast	35.00	17.50	10.50
(5) Baerwald	35.00	17.50	10.50
(6) Barbour	35.00	17.50	10.50
(7) Bates	35.00	17.50	10.50
(8) Baum	35.00	17.50	10.50
(9) Bayless	35.00	17.50	10.50
(10) Beatty	35.00	17.50	10.50
(11) Beer	35.00	17.50	10.50
(12) Benham	35.00	17.50	10.50
(13) Berger	35.00	17.50	10.50
(14) Beumiller	35.00	17.50	10.50
(15) Blankenship	35.00	17.50	10.50
(16) Block	35.00	17.50	10.50
(17) Bodie	45.00	22.00	13.50
(18) Boles	35.00	17.50	10.50
(19) Boyd	35.00	17.50	10.50
(20) Bromley	35.00	17.50	10.50
(21) Brown	35.00	17.50	10.50
(22) Burns	35.00	17.50	10.50
(23) Carlisle	35.00	17.50	10.50
(24) Carrisch	35.00	17.50	10.50
(25) Charles	35.00	17.50	10.50
(26) Chech	35.00	17.50	10.50
(27) Christian	35.00	17.50	10.50
(28) Clarke	35.00	17.50	10.50
(29) Couch	35.00	17.50	10.50
(30) Covaleski (Coveleski)	130.00	65.00	40.00
(31) Daniels	35.00	17.50	10.50
(32) Davis	35.00	17.50	10.50
(33) DeCanniere	35.00	17.50	10.50
(34) Dent	35.00	17.50	10.50
(35) Derrick	35.00	17.50	10.50
(36) Dillon	35.00	17.50	10.50
(37) Doane	35.00	17.50	10.50
(38) Downs	35.00	17.50	10.50
(39) Elliott	35.00	17.50	10.50
(40) F. Elliott	35.00	17.50	10.50
(41) Ellis	35.00	17.50	10.50
(42) Evans	35.00	17.50	10.50
(43) Fanning	35.00	17.50	10.50
(44) Faye	35.00	17.50	10.50
(45) Fisher	35.00	17.50	10.50
(46) Fittery	35.00	17.50	10.50
(47) Fitzgerald	35.00	17.50	10.50
(48) Fromme	35.00	17.50	10.50
(49) Gardiner	35.00	17.50	10.50
(50) Gedeon	35.00	17.50	10.50
(51) Gleischmann	35.00	17.50	10.50
(52) Gregory	35.00	17.50	10.50
(53) Guest	35.00	17.50	10.50
(54) Hall	35.00	17.50	10.50
(55) Halla	35.00	17.50	10.50
(56) Hallinan	35.00	17.50	10.50
(57) Hannah	35.00	17.50	10.50
(58) Harper	35.00	17.50	10.50
(59) Heilmann	130.00	65.00	40.00
(60) Henley	35.00	17.50	10.50
(61) Hetling	35.00	17.50	10.50
(62) Higginbotham	35.00	17.50	10.50
(63) Hilliard	35.00	17.50	10.50
(64) Hitt (winding up)	35.00	17.50	10.50
(65) Hitt (throwing)	35.00	17.50	10.50
(66) Hogan	35.00	17.50	10.50
(67) Hosp	35.00	17.50	10.50
(68) Howard	35.00	17.50	10.50
(69) Hughes	35.00	17.50	10.50
(70) Johnson	35.00	17.50	10.50
(71) Jones	35.00	17.50	10.50
(72) Kahler	35.00	17.50	10.50
(73) Kane	35.00	17.50	10.50
(74) Karr	35.00	17.50	10.50
(75) Killilay	35.00	17.50	10.50
(76) Klawitter	35.00	17.50	10.50
(77) Koerner	35.00	17.50	10.50
(78) Krause	35.00	17.50	10.50
(79) Kuhn	35.00	17.50	10.50
(80) LaRoy	35.00	17.50	10.50
(81) Leard	35.00	17.50	10.50
(82) Lindsay	35.00	17.50	10.50
(83) Litschi	35.00	17.50	10.50
(84) Lober	35.00	17.50	10.50
(85) Love	35.00	17.50	10.50
(86) Lush	35.00	17.50	10.50
(87) Maggart	35.00	17.50	10.50
(88) Malarkey	35.00	17.50	10.50
(89) Manda	35.00	17.50	10.50
(90) Marcan	35.00	17.50	10.50
(91) Martinoni	35.00	17.50	10.50
(92) McAvoy	35.00	17.50	10.50
(93) McCredie	35.00	17.50	10.50
(94) McDonell	35.00	17.50	10.50
(95) McMullen	90.00	45.00	27.00
(96) Meek	35.00	17.50	10.50
(97) Meloan	35.00	17.50	10.50
(98) Metzger	35.00	17.50	10.50
(99) Middleton	35.00	17.50	10.50
(100) Mitchell	35.00	17.50	10.50
(101) Mitze	35.00	17.50	10.50
(102) Morgan	35.00	17.50	10.50
(103) Mundorff	35.00	17.50	10.50
(104) Murphy	35.00	17.50	10.50
(105) Ness	35.00	17.50	10.50
(106) Nutt	35.00	17.50	10.50
(107) Orr	35.00	17.50	10.50
(108) Pernoll	35.00	17.50	10.50
(109) Perritt	35.00	17.50	10.50
(110) Piercey	35.00	17.50	10.50
(111) Price	35.00	17.50	10.50
(112) Prough	35.00	17.50	10.50
(113) Prueitt	35.00	17.50	10.50
(114) Purtell	35.00	17.50	10.50
(115) Reed	35.00	17.50	10.50
(116) Reisigl	35.00	17.50	10.50
(117) Remneas	35.00	17.50	10.50
(118) Risberg	90.00	45.00	27.00
(119) Rohrer	35.00	17.50	10.50
(120) Russell	35.00	17.50	10.50
(121) Ryan (Los Angeles)	35.00	17.50	10.50
(122) Ryan	35.00	17.50	10.50
(123) Schaller	35.00	17.50	10.50
(124) Schmidt	35.00	17.50	10.50
(125) Scoggins	35.00	17.50	10.50
(126) Sepulveda	35.00	17.50	10.50
(127) Shinn	35.00	17.50	10.50
(128) Smith	35.00	17.50	10.50
(129) Speas	35.00	17.50	10.50
(130) Spencer	35.00	17.50	10.50
(132) Tennant	35.00	17.50	10.50
(133) Terry	35.00	17.50	10.50
(134) Tobin	35.00	17.50	10.50
(135) West	35.00	17.50	10.50
(136) White	35.00	17.50	10.50
(137) C. Williams	90.00	45.00	27.00
(138) J. Williams	35.00	17.50	10.50
(139) Wolter	35.00	17.50	10.50
(140) Wolverton	35.00	17.50	10.50
(141) Zacher	35.00	17.50	10.50

1916 Zeenut Pacific Coast League (E137)

The 1916 Zeenuts measure 2" x 3-1/8" without the coupon and are dated on the front (some cards were misdated 1916, however). The card fronts feature black and white photos on a blue background. There are 144 known subjects. The 1916 series was among the more difficult.

	NR MT	EX	VG
Complete Set:	3600.	1800.	1000.
Common Player:	30.00	15.00	9.00
(1) Autrey	30.00	15.00	9.00
(2) Barbeau	30.00	15.00	9.00
(3) Barry	30.00	15.00	9.00
(4) Bassler	30.00	15.00	9.00
(5) Bates	30.00	15.00	9.00
(6) Baum	30.00	15.00	9.00
(7) Bayless	30.00	15.00	9.00
(8) Beer	30.00	15.00	9.00
(9) Berg	30.00	15.00	9.00
(10) Berger	30.00	15.00	9.00
(11) Blankenship	30.00	15.00	9.00
(12) Block	30.00	15.00	9.00
(13) Bodie	45.00	22.00	13.50
(14) Bohne	30.00	15.00	9.00
(15) Boles	30.00	15.00	9.00
(16) Boyd	30.00	15.00	9.00
(17) Brief	30.00	15.00	9.00
(18) Brooks	30.00	15.00	9.00
(19) Brown	30.00	15.00	9.00
(20) Butler	30.00	15.00	9.00
(21) Callahan	30.00	15.00	9.00
(22) Carrisch	30.00	15.00	9.00
(23) Chance	130.00	65.00	40.00
(24) Claxton	150.00	75.00	45.00
(25) Coffey	30.00	15.00	9.00
(26) Cook	30.00	15.00	9.00
(27) Corbett	30.00	15.00	9.00
(28) Couch	30.00	15.00	9.00
(29) Crandall	30.00	15.00	9.00
(30) Dalton	30.00	15.00	9.00
(31) Davis	30.00	15.00	9.00
(32) Derrick	30.00	15.00	9.00
(33) Doane	30.00	15.00	9.00
(34) Downs	30.00	15.00	9.00
(35) Dugan	30.00	15.00	9.00
(36) Eldred	30.00	15.00	9.00
(37) F. Elliott	30.00	15.00	9.00
(38) H. Elliott	30.00	15.00	9.00
(39) Ellis	30.00	15.00	9.00
(40) Erickson	30.00	15.00	9.00
(41) Fanning	30.00	15.00	9.00
(42) Fisher	30.00	15.00	9.00
(43) Fittery	30.00	15.00	9.00
(44) Fitzgerald	30.00	15.00	9.00
(45) Fromme	30.00	15.00	9.00
(46) Galloway	30.00	15.00	9.00
(47) Gardner	30.00	15.00	9.00
(48) Gay	30.00	15.00	9.00
(49) Gleischmann	30.00	15.00	9.00
(50) Griffith	30.00	15.00	9.00
(51) Griggs	30.00	15.00	9.00
(52) Guisto	30.00	15.00	9.00
(53) Hagerman	30.00	15.00	9.00
(54) Hall	30.00	15.00	9.00
(55) Hallinan	30.00	15.00	9.00
(56) Hannah	30.00	15.00	9.00
(57) Harstadt	30.00	15.00	9.00
(58) Haworth	30.00	15.00	9.00
(59) Hess	30.00	15.00	9.00
(60) Higginbotham	30.00	15.00	9.00
(61) Hitt	30.00	15.00	9.00
(62) Hogg	30.00	15.00	9.00
(63) Hollocher	30.00	15.00	9.00
(64) Horstman	30.00	15.00	9.00
(65) Houck	30.00	15.00	9.00
(66) Howard	30.00	15.00	9.00
(67) Hughes	30.00	15.00	9.00
(68) E. Johnston	30.00	15.00	9.00
(69) G. Johnston	30.00	15.00	9.00
(70) Jones	30.00	15.00	9.00
(71) Kahler	30.00	15.00	9.00
(72) Kane	30.00	15.00	9.00
(73) Kelly	30.00	15.00	9.00
(74) Kenworthy	30.00	15.00	9.00
(75) Klawitter	30.00	15.00	9.00
(76) Klein	30.00	15.00	9.00
(77) Koerner	30.00	15.00	9.00
(78) Krause	30.00	15.00	9.00
(79) Kuhn	30.00	15.00	9.00
(80) Lane	30.00	15.00	9.00
(81) Larsen	30.00	15.00	9.00
(82) Lush	30.00	15.00	9.00
(83) Machold	30.00	15.00	9.00
(84) Maggert	30.00	15.00	9.00
(85) Manser	30.00	15.00	9.00
(86) Martin	30.00	15.00	9.00
(87) Mattick	30.00	15.00	9.00
(88) McCredie	30.00	15.00	9.00
(89) McGaffigan	30.00	15.00	9.00
(90) McLarry	30.00	15.00	9.00
(91) Menges	30.00	15.00	9.00
(92) Middleton	30.00	15.00	9.00
(93) Mitchell	30.00	15.00	9.00
(94) Mitze	30.00	15.00	9.00
(95) Munsell	30.00	15.00	9.00
(96) Murphy	30.00	15.00	9.00
(97) Nixon	30.00	15.00	9.00
(98) Noyes	30.00	15.00	9.00
(99) Nutt	30.00	15.00	9.00
(100) O'Brien	30.00	15.00	9.00
(101) Oldham	30.00	15.00	9.00
(102) Orr	30.00	15.00	9.00
(103) Patterson	30.00	15.00	9.00
(104) Perritt	30.00	15.00	9.00
(105) Prough	30.00	15.00	9.00
(106) Prueitt	30.00	15.00	9.00
(107) Quinlan	30.00	15.00	9.00
(108) Quinn (Portland)	30.00	15.00	9.00
(109) Quinn (Vernon)	30.00	15.00	9.00
(110) Rader	30.00	15.00	9.00
(111) Randall	30.00	15.00	9.00
(112) Rath	30.00	15.00	9.00
(113) Reisegl	30.00	15.00	9.00
(114) Reuther	30.00	15.00	9.00
(115) Risberg	90.00	45.00	27.00
(116) Roche	30.00	15.00	9.00
(117) Ryan	30.00	15.00	9.00
(118) Ryan	30.00	15.00	9.00
(119) Scoggins	30.00	15.00	9.00
(120) Sepulveda	30.00	15.00	9.00
(121) Schaller	30.00	15.00	9.00
(122) Sheehan	30.00	15.00	9.00
(123) Shinn	30.00	15.00	9.00
(124) Smith	30.00	15.00	9.00
(125) Sothoron	30.00	15.00	9.00
(126) Southworth	30.00	15.00	9.00
(127) Speas	30.00	15.00	9.00
(128) Spencer	30.00	15.00	9.00
(129) Standridge	30.00	15.00	9.00
(130) Steen	30.00	15.00	9.00
(131) Stumpf	30.00	15.00	9.00
(132) Vann	30.00	15.00	9.00
(133) Vaughn	30.00	15.00	9.00
(134) Ward	30.00	15.00	9.00
(135) Whalling	30.00	15.00	9.00
(136) Wilie	30.00	15.00	9.00
(137) Williams	30.00	15.00	9.00
(138) Wolverton	30.00	15.00	9.00
(139) Wuffli	30.00	15.00	9.00
(140) Zabel	30.00	15.00	9.00
(141) Zacher	30.00	15.00	9.00
(142) Zimmerman	30.00	15.00	9.00

A card number in parentheses () indicates the set is unnumbered.

1917 Zeenut Pacific Coast League (E137)

The 1917 Zeenuts measure 1-3/4" x 3-1/2" and feature black and white photos on a light background. They are dated on the front and have blank backs. An advertising poster has been found listing

119 players (two pose variations brings the total to 121), but to date, six players on the list have not been found.

		NR MT	EX	VG
Complete Set:		2600.	1300.	775.00
Common Player:		26.00	13.00	7.75
(1)	Arlett	26.00	13.00	7.75
(2)	Arrelanes	26.00	13.00	7.75
(3)	Baker (catching)	26.00	13.00	7.75
(4)	Baker (throwing)	26.00	13.00	7.75
(5)	Baldwin	26.00	13.00	7.75
(6)	Bassler	26.00	13.00	7.75
(7)	Baum	26.00	13.00	7.75
(8)	Beer	26.00	13.00	7.75
(9)	Bernhard	26.00	13.00	7.75
(10)	Bliss	26.00	13.00	7.75
(11)	Boles	26.00	13.00	7.75
(12)	Brenton	26.00	13.00	7.75
(13)	Brief	26.00	13.00	7.75
(14)	Brown	26.00	13.00	7.75
(15)	Burns	26.00	13.00	7.75
(16)	Callahan	26.00	13.00	7.75
(17)	Callan	26.00	13.00	7.75
(18)	Calvo	26.00	13.00	7.75
(19)	Chadbourne	26.00	13.00	7.75
(20)	Chance	130.00	65.00	40.00
(21)	Coltrin	26.00	13.00	7.75
(22)	Connifer	26.00	13.00	7.75
(23)	Corhan	26.00	13.00	7.75
(24)	Crandall (Los Angeles)	26.00	13.00	7.75
(25)	Crandall (Salt Lake)	26.00	13.00	7.75
(26)	Cress	26.00	13.00	7.75
(27)	Davis	26.00	13.00	7.75
(28)	DeCanniere	26.00	13.00	7.75
(29)	Doane	26.00	13.00	7.75
(30)	Dougan	26.00	13.00	7.75
(31)	Dougherty	26.00	13.00	7.75
(32)	Downs	26.00	13.00	7.75
(33)	Dubuc	26.00	13.00	7.75
(34)	Ellis	26.00	13.00	7.75
(35)	Erickson	26.00	13.00	7.75
(36)	Evans	26.00	13.00	7.75
(37)	Farmer	26.00	13.00	7.75
(38)	Fincher	26.00	13.00	7.75
(39)	Fisher	26.00	13.00	7.75
(40)	Fitzgerald	26.00	13.00	7.75
(41)	Fournier	26.00	13.00	7.75
(42)	Fromme	26.00	13.00	7.75
(43)	Galloway	26.00	13.00	7.75
(44)	Gislason	26.00	13.00	7.75
(45)	Goodbred	26.00	13.00	7.75
(46)	Griggs	26.00	13.00	7.75
(47)	Groehling	26.00	13.00	7.75
(48)	Hall (Los Angeles)	26.00	13.00	7.75
(49)	Hall (San Francisco)	26.00	13.00	7.75
(50)	Hannah	26.00	13.00	7.75
(51)	Harstad	26.00	13.00	7.75
(52)	Helfrich	26.00	13.00	7.75
(53)	Hess	26.00	13.00	7.75
(54)	Hitt	26.00	13.00	7.75
(55)	Hoff	26.00	13.00	7.75
(56)	Hollacher	26.00	13.00	7.75
(57)	Hollywood	26.00	13.00	7.75
(58)	Houck	26.00	13.00	7.75
(59)	Howard	26.00	13.00	7.75
(60)	Hughes	26.00	13.00	7.75
(61)	Johnson	26.00	13.00	7.75
(62)	Kilhullen	26.00	13.00	7.75
(63)	Killiffer	26.00	13.00	7.75
(64)	Koerner	26.00	13.00	7.75
(65)	Krause	26.00	13.00	7.75
(66)	Lane	26.00	13.00	7.75
(67)	Lapan	26.00	13.00	7.75
(68)	Leake	26.00	13.00	7.75
(69)	Lee	26.00	13.00	7.75
(70)	Leverenz	26.00	13.00	7.75
(71)	Maggert	26.00	13.00	7.75
(72)	Maisel	26.00	13.00	7.75
(73)	Mattick	26.00	13.00	7.75
(74)	McCreedie	26.00	13.00	7.75
(75)	McLarry	26.00	13.00	7.75
(76)	Mensor	26.00	13.00	7.75
(77)	Meusel	35.00	17.50	10.50
(78)	Middleton	26.00	13.00	7.75
(79)	Miller (batting)	26.00	13.00	7.75
(80)	Miller (throwing)	26.00	13.00	7.75
(81)	Mitchell	26.00	13.00	7.75
(82)	Mitze	26.00	13.00	7.75
(83)	Murphy	26.00	13.00	7.75
(84)	Murray	26.00	13.00	7.75
(85)	O'Brien	26.00	13.00	7.75
(86)	O'Mara	26.00	13.00	7.75
(87)	Oldham	26.00	13.00	7.75
(88)	Orr	26.00	13.00	7.75
(89)	Penelli	26.00	13.00	7.75
(90)	Penner	26.00	13.00	7.75
(91)	Pick	26.00	13.00	7.75
(92)	Prough	26.00	13.00	7.75
(93)	Pruiett	26.00	13.00	7.75
(94)	Quinlan	26.00	13.00	7.75
(95)	Quinn	26.00	13.00	7.75
(96)	Rath	26.00	13.00	7.75
(97)	Roche	26.00	13.00	7.75
(98)	Ryan (Los Angeles)	26.00	13.00	7.75
(99)	Ryan (Salt Lake)	26.00	13.00	7.75
(100)	Schaller	26.00	13.00	7.75
(101)	Schinkle	26.00	13.00	7.75
(102)	Schultz	26.00	13.00	7.75
(103)	Sheehan	26.00	13.00	7.75
(104)	Sheeley	26.00	13.00	7.75
(105)	Shinn	26.00	13.00	7.75
(106)	Siglin	26.00	13.00	7.75
(107)	Simon	26.00	13.00	7.75
(108)	Smith	26.00	13.00	7.75
(109)	Snyder	26.00	13.00	7.75
(110)	Stanridge	26.00	13.00	7.75
(111)	Steen	26.00	13.00	7.75
(112)	Stovall	26.00	13.00	7.75
(113)	Stumpf	26.00	13.00	7.75
(114)	Sullivan	26.00	13.00	7.75
(115)	Terry	26.00	13.00	7.75
(116)	Tobin	26.00	13.00	7.75
(117)	Valencia	26.00	13.00	7.75
(118)	Vaughn	26.00	13.00	7.75
(119)	Whalling	26.00	13.00	7.75
(120)	Wilie	26.00	13.00	7.75
(121)	Wolverton	26.00	13.00	7.75

1918 Zeenut Pacific Coast League (E137)

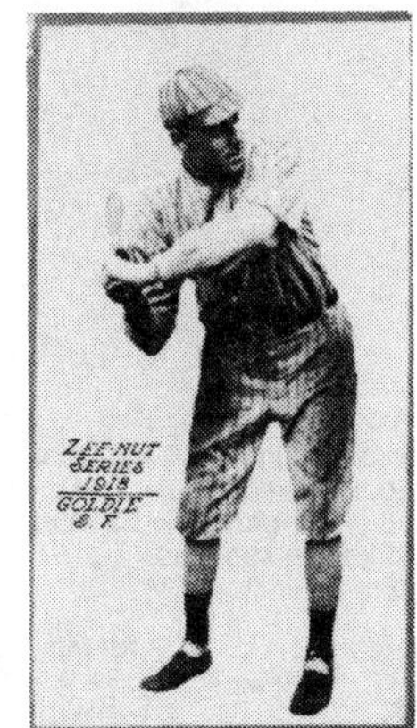

The 1918 Zeenuts are among the most distinctive because of their red borders surrounding the photos. They measure 1-3/4" x 3-1/8" and are among the more difficult years to find.

		NR MT	EX	VG
Complete Set:		3000.	1500.	900.00
Common Player:		35.00	17.50	10.50
(1)	Alcock	35.00	17.50	10.50
(2)	Arkenburg	35.00	17.50	10.50
(3)	A. Arlett	35.00	17.50	10.50
(4)	Baum	35.00	17.50	10.50
(5)	Boles	35.00	17.50	10.50
(6)	Borton	35.00	17.50	10.50
(7)	Brenton	35.00	17.50	10.50
(8)	Bromley	35.00	17.50	10.50
(9)	Brooks	35.00	17.50	10.50
(10)	Brown	35.00	17.50	10.50
(11)	Caldera	35.00	17.50	10.50
(12)	Camm	35.00	17.50	10.50
(13)	Chadbourne	35.00	17.50	10.50
(14)	Chappell	35.00	17.50	10.50
(15)	Codington	35.00	17.50	10.50
(16)	Conwright	35.00	17.50	10.50
(17)	Cooper	35.00	17.50	10.50
(18)	Cox	35.00	17.50	10.50
(19)	Crandall (Los Angeles)	35.00	17.50	10.50
(20)	Crandall (Salt Lake)	35.00	17.50	10.50
(21)	Crawford	35.00	17.50	10.50
(22)	Croll	35.00	17.50	10.50
(23)	Davis	35.00	17.50	10.50
(24)	DeVormer	35.00	17.50	10.50
(25)	Dobbs	35.00	17.50	10.50
(26)	Downs	35.00	17.50	10.50
(27)	Dubuc	35.00	17.50	10.50
(28)	Dunn	35.00	17.50	10.50
(29)	Easterly	35.00	17.50	10.50
(30)	Eldred	35.00	17.50	10.50
(31)	Elliot	35.00	17.50	10.50
(32)	Ellis	35.00	17.50	10.50
(33)	Essick	35.00	17.50	10.50
(34)	Farmer	35.00	17.50	10.50
(35)	Fisher	35.00	17.50	10.50
(36)	Fittery	35.00	17.50	10.50
(37)	Forsythe	35.00	17.50	10.50
(38)	Fournier	35.00	17.50	10.50
(39)	Fromme	35.00	17.50	10.50
(40)	Gardner (Oakland)	35.00	17.50	10.50
(41)	Gardner (Sacramento)	35.00	17.50	10.50
(42)	Goldie	35.00	17.50	10.50
(43)	Griggs	35.00	17.50	10.50
(44)	Hawkes	35.00	17.50	10.50
(45)	Hollander	35.00	17.50	10.50
(46)	Hosp	35.00	17.50	10.50
(47)	Howard	35.00	17.50	10.50
(48)	Hummel	35.00	17.50	10.50
(49)	Hunter	35.00	17.50	10.50
(50)	Johnson	35.00	17.50	10.50
(51)	G. Johnson	35.00	17.50	10.50
(52)	Kantlehner	35.00	17.50	10.50
(53)	Killefer	35.00	17.50	10.50
(54)	Koerner	35.00	17.50	10.50
(55)	Konnick	35.00	17.50	10.50
(56)	Kremer	35.00	17.50	10.50
(57)	Lapan	35.00	17.50	10.50
(58)	Leake	35.00	17.50	10.50
(59)	Leathers	35.00	17.50	10.50
(60)	Leifer	35.00	17.50	10.50
(61)	Leverenz	35.00	17.50	10.50
(62)	Llewlyn	35.00	17.50	10.50
(63)	Martin	35.00	17.50	10.50
(64)	McCabe	35.00	17.50	10.50
(65)	McCredie	35.00	17.50	10.50
(66)	McKee	35.00	17.50	10.50
(67)	McNulty	35.00	17.50	10.50
(68)	Mensor	35.00	17.50	10.50
(69)	Middleton	35.00	17.50	10.50
(70)	Miller (Oakland)	35.00	17.50	10.50
(71)	Miller (Salt Lake)	35.00	17.50	10.50
(72)	J. Mitchell	35.00	17.50	10.50
(73)	R. Mitchell	35.00	17.50	10.50
(74)	Mitze	35.00	17.50	10.50
(75)	Moore	35.00	17.50	10.50
(76)	Morton	35.00	17.50	10.50
(77)	Murray	35.00	17.50	10.50
(78)	O'Doul	90.00	45.00	27.00
(79)	Orr	35.00	17.50	10.50
(80)	Pepe	35.00	17.50	10.50
(81)	Pertica	35.00	17.50	10.50
(82)	Phillips	35.00	17.50	10.50
(83)	Pick	35.00	17.50	10.50
(84)	Pinelli	45.00	22.00	13.50
(85)	Prentice	35.00	17.50	10.50
(86)	Prough	35.00	17.50	10.50
(87)	Quinlan	35.00	17.50	10.50
(88)	Ritchie	35.00	17.50	10.50
(89)	Rogers	35.00	17.50	10.50
(90)	Ryan	35.00	17.50	10.50
(91)	Sand	35.00	17.50	10.50
(92)	Shader	35.00	17.50	10.50
(93)	Sheely	35.00	17.50	10.50
(94)	Siglin	35.00	17.50	10.50
(95)	Smale	35.00	17.50	10.50
(96)	Smith	35.00	17.50	10.50
(97)	Smith	35.00	17.50	10.50
(98)	Stanbridge	35.00	17.50	10.50
(99)	Terry	35.00	17.50	10.50
(100)	Valencia	35.00	17.50	10.50
(101)	West	35.00	17.50	10.50
(102)	Wilie	35.00	17.50	10.50
(103)	Williams	35.00	17.50	10.50
(104)	Wisterzill	35.00	17.50	10.50

1919 Zeenut Pacific Coast League (E137)

The 1919-1921 Zeenuts cards were dated on the front and measure 1-3/4" x 3-1/8". They featured borderless, sepia-toned photos. To date, 144 subjects exist in the 1919 series; 151 have been found for 1920; and 168 different subjects have been discovered for 1921 (even though a promotional flier indicates 180 players).

		NR MT	EX	VG
Complete Set:		3000.	1500.	900.00
Common Player:		20.00	10.00	6.00
(1)	Ally	20.00	10.00	6.00
(2)	Fatty Arbuckle	350.00	175.00	100.00
(3)	A. Arlett	20.00	10.00	6.00
(4)	R. Arlett	24.00	12.00	7.25

(5)	Baker	20.00	10.00	6.00
(6)	Baldwin	20.00	10.00	6.00
(7)	Baum	20.00	10.00	6.00
(8)	Beck	20.00	10.00	6.00
(9)	Bigbee	20.00	10.00	6.00
(10)	Blue	20.00	10.00	6.00
(11)	Bohne	20.00	10.00	6.00
(12)	Boles	20.00	10.00	6.00
(13)	Borton	20.00	10.00	6.00
(14)	Bowman	20.00	10.00	6.00
(15)	Brooks	20.00	10.00	6.00
(16)	Brown	20.00	10.00	6.00
(17)	Byler	20.00	10.00	6.00
(18)	Caldera	20.00	10.00	6.00
(19)	Cavaney	20.00	10.00	6.00
(20)	Chadbourne	20.00	10.00	6.00
(21)	Chech	20.00	10.00	6.00
(22)	Church	20.00	10.00	6.00
(23)	Clymer	20.00	10.00	6.00
(24)	Coleman	20.00	10.00	6.00
(25)	Compton	20.00	10.00	6.00
(26)	Conkwright	20.00	10.00	6.00
(27)	Connolly	20.00	10.00	6.00
(28)	Cook	20.00	10.00	6.00
(29)	Cooper (Los Angeles)	20.00	10.00	6.00
(30)	Cooper (Oakland)	20.00	10.00	6.00
(31)	Cooper (Portland)	20.00	10.00	6.00
(32)	Corhan	20.00	10.00	6.00
(33)	Couch	20.00	10.00	6.00
(34)	Cox	20.00	10.00	6.00
(35)	Crandall (Los Angeles)	20.00	10.00	6.00
(36)	Crandall (San Francisco)	20.00	10.00	6.00
(37)	Crespi	20.00	10.00	6.00
(38)	Croll	20.00	10.00	6.00
(39)	Cunningham	20.00	10.00	6.00
(40)	Dawson	20.00	10.00	6.00
(41)	Dell	20.00	10.00	6.00
(42)	DeVormer	20.00	10.00	6.00
(43)	Driscoll	20.00	10.00	6.00
(44)	Eastley	20.00	10.00	6.00
(45)	Edington	20.00	10.00	6.00
(46)	Eldred	20.00	10.00	6.00
(47)	Elliott	20.00	10.00	6.00
(48)	Ellis	20.00	10.00	6.00
(49)	Essick	20.00	10.00	6.00
(50)	Fabrique	20.00	10.00	6.00
(51)	Falkenberg	20.00	10.00	6.00
(52)	Fallentine	20.00	10.00	6.00
(53)	Finneran	20.00	10.00	6.00
(54)	Fisher (Sacramento)	20.00	10.00	6.00
(55)	Fisher (Vernon)	20.00	10.00	6.00
(56)	Fitzgerald	20.00	10.00	6.00
(57)	Flannigan	20.00	10.00	6.00
(58)	Fournier	20.00	10.00	6.00
(59)	French	20.00	10.00	6.00
(60)	Fromme	20.00	10.00	6.00
(61)	Gibson	20.00	10.00	6.00
(62)	Griggs	20.00	10.00	6.00
(63)	Haney	20.00	10.00	6.00
(64)	Harper	20.00	10.00	6.00
(65)	Henkle	20.00	10.00	6.00
(66)	Herr	20.00	10.00	6.00
(67)	Hickey	20.00	10.00	6.00
(68)	High	20.00	10.00	6.00
(69)	Holling	20.00	10.00	6.00
(70)	Hosp	20.00	10.00	6.00
(71)	Houck	20.00	10.00	6.00
(72)	Howard	20.00	10.00	6.00
(73)	Kamm	20.00	10.00	6.00
(74)	Kenworthy	20.00	10.00	6.00
(75)	Killefer	20.00	10.00	6.00
(76)	King	20.00	10.00	6.00
(77)	Koehler	20.00	10.00	6.00
(78)	Koerner	20.00	10.00	6.00
(79)	Kramer (Oakland)	20.00	10.00	6.00
(80)	Kramer (San Francisco)	20.00	10.00	6.00
(81)	Land	20.00	10.00	6.00
(82)	Lane	20.00	10.00	6.00
(83)	Lapan	20.00	10.00	6.00
(84)	Larkin	20.00	10.00	6.00
(85)	Lee	20.00	10.00	6.00
(86)	Long	20.00	10.00	6.00
(87)	Mails	20.00	10.00	6.00
(88)	Mains	20.00	10.00	6.00
(89)	Maisel	20.00	10.00	6.00
(90)	Mathes	20.00	10.00	6.00
(91)	McCredie	20.00	10.00	6.00
(92)	McGaffigan	20.00	10.00	6.00
(93)	McHenry	20.00	10.00	6.00
(94)	McNulty	20.00	10.00	6.00
(95)	Meusel	12.00	6.00	3.50
(96)	Middleton	20.00	10.00	6.00
(97)	Mitchell	20.00	10.00	6.00
(98)	Mitze	20.00	10.00	6.00
(99)	Mulory	20.00	10.00	6.00
(100)	Murphy	20.00	10.00	6.00
(101)	Murray	20.00	10.00	6.00
(102)	Niehoff (Los Angeles)	20.00	10.00	6.00
(103)	Niehoff (Seattle)	20.00	10.00	6.00
(104)	Norse	20.00	10.00	6.00
(105)	Oldham	20.00	10.00	6.00
(106)	Orr	20.00	10.00	6.00
(107)	Penner	20.00	10.00	6.00
(108)	Pennington	20.00	10.00	6.00
(109)	Piercy	20.00	10.00	6.00
(110)	Pinelli	25.00	12.50	7.50
(111)	Prough	20.00	10.00	6.00
(112)	Rader	20.00	10.00	6.00
(113)	Reiger	20.00	10.00	6.00
(114)	Ritchie	20.00	10.00	6.00
(115)	Roach	20.00	10.00	6.00
(116)	Rodgers	20.00	10.00	6.00
(117)	Rumler	20.00	10.00	6.00
(118)	Sands	20.00	10.00	6.00
(119)	Schick	20.00	10.00	6.00
(120)	Schultz	20.00	10.00	6.00
(121)	Scott	20.00	10.00	6.00
(122)	Seaton	20.00	10.00	6.00
(123)	Sheely	20.00	10.00	6.00
(124)	Siglin	20.00	10.00	6.00
(125)	Smith	20.00	10.00	6.00
(126)	Bill Smith	20.00	10.00	6.00
(127)	Snell	20.00	10.00	6.00
(128)	Spangler	20.00	10.00	6.00
(129)	Speas	20.00	10.00	6.00
(130)	Spencer	20.00	10.00	6.00
(131)	Starasenich	20.00	10.00	6.00
(132)	Stumpf	20.00	10.00	6.00
(133)	Sutherland	20.00	10.00	6.00
(134)	Vance	20.00	10.00	6.00
(135)	Walker	20.00	10.00	6.00
(136)	Walsh	20.00	10.00	6.00
(137)	Ware	20.00	10.00	6.00
(138)	Weaver	20.00	10.00	6.00
(139)	Westerzil	20.00	10.00	6.00
(140)	Wilhoit	20.00	10.00	6.00
(141)	Wilie	20.00	10.00	6.00
(142)	Willets	20.00	10.00	6.00
(143)	Zamloch	20.00	10.00	6.00
(144)	Zweifel	20.00	10.00	6.00

1920 Zeenut Pacific Coast League (E137)

		NR MT	EX	VG
Complete Set:		2200.	1100.	650.00
Common Player:		18.00	9.00	5.50
(1)	Adams	18.00	9.00	5.50
(2)	Agnew	18.00	9.00	5.50
(3)	Alcock	18.00	9.00	5.50
(4)	Aldrige	18.00	9.00	5.50
(5)	Andrews	18.00	9.00	5.50
(6)	Anfinson	18.00	9.00	5.50
(7)	A. Arlett	18.00	9.00	5.50
(8)	R. Arlett	20.00	10.00	6.00
(9)	Baker	18.00	9.00	5.50
(10)	Baldwin	18.00	9.00	5.50
(11)	Bassler	18.00	9.00	5.50
(12)	Baum	18.00	9.00	5.50
(13)	Blue	18.00	9.00	5.50
(14)	Bohne	18.00	9.00	5.50
(15)	Brenton	18.00	9.00	5.50
(16)	Bromley (dark hat)	18.00	9.00	5.50
(17)	Bromley (light hat)	18.00	9.00	5.50
(18)	Brown	18.00	9.00	5.50
(19)	Butler	18.00	9.00	5.50
(20)	Caveney	18.00	9.00	5.50
(21)	Chadbourne	18.00	9.00	5.50
(22)	Compton	18.00	9.00	5.50
(23)	Connolly	18.00	9.00	5.50
(24)	Cook	18.00	9.00	5.50
(25)	Corhan	18.00	9.00	5.50
(26)	Cox	18.00	9.00	5.50
(27)	K. Crandall	18.00	9.00	5.50
(28)	O. Crandall	18.00	9.00	5.50
(29)	Crawford	18.00	9.00	5.50
(30)	Cullop	18.00	9.00	5.50
(31)	Cunningham	18.00	9.00	5.50
(32)	DeVitalis	18.00	9.00	5.50
(33)	DeVormer	18.00	9.00	5.50
(34)	Dooley	18.00	9.00	5.50
(35)	Dorman	18.00	9.00	5.50
(36)	Dumovich	18.00	9.00	5.50
(37)	Dylar	18.00	9.00	5.50
(38)	Edington	18.00	9.00	5.50
(39)	Eldred	18.00	9.00	5.50
(40)	Ellis	18.00	9.00	5.50
(41)	Essick	18.00	9.00	5.50
(42)	Fisher	18.00	9.00	5.50
(43)	Fitzgerald	18.00	9.00	5.50
(44)	Fromme	18.00	9.00	5.50
(45)	Gardner	18.00	9.00	5.50
(46)	Ginglardi	18.00	9.00	5.50
(47)	Gough	18.00	9.00	5.50
(48)	Griggs	18.00	9.00	5.50
(49)	Guisto	18.00	9.00	5.50
(50)	Hamilton	18.00	9.00	5.50
(51)	Hanicy	18.00	9.00	5.50
(52)	Hartford	18.00	9.00	5.50
(53)	High	18.00	9.00	5.50
(54)	Hill	18.00	9.00	5.50
(55)	Hodges	18.00	9.00	5.50
(56)	Howard	18.00	9.00	5.50
(57)	James	18.00	9.00	5.50
(58)	Jenkins	18.00	9.00	5.50
(59)	Johnson (Portland)	18.00	9.00	5.50
(60)	Johnson (Salt Lake)	18.00	9.00	5.50
(61)	Jones	18.00	9.00	5.50
(62)	Juney	18.00	9.00	5.50
(63)	Kallio	18.00	9.00	5.50
(64)	Kamm	18.00	9.00	5.50
(65)	Keating	18.00	9.00	5.50
(66)	Kenworthy	18.00	9.00	5.50
(67)	Killeen	18.00	9.00	5.50
(68)	Killefer	18.00	9.00	5.50
(69)	Kingdon	18.00	9.00	5.50
(70)	Knight	18.00	9.00	5.50
(71)	Koehler	18.00	9.00	5.50
(72)	Koerner	18.00	9.00	5.50
(73)	Kopp	18.00	9.00	5.50
(74)	Kremer	18.00	9.00	5.50
(75)	Krug	18.00	9.00	5.50
(76)	Kunz	18.00	9.00	5.50
(77)	Lambert	18.00	9.00	5.50
(78)	Lane	18.00	9.00	5.50
(79)	Larkin	18.00	9.00	5.50
(80)	Leverenz	18.00	9.00	5.50
(81)	Long	18.00	9.00	5.50
(82)	Love	18.00	9.00	5.50
(83)	Maggart	18.00	9.00	5.50
(84)	Mails	18.00	9.00	5.50
(85)	Maisel	18.00	9.00	5.50
(86)	Matterson	18.00	9.00	5.50
(87)	Matteson	18.00	9.00	5.50
(88)	McAuley	18.00	9.00	5.50
(89)	McCredie	18.00	9.00	5.50
(90)	McGaffigan	18.00	9.00	5.50
(91)	McHenry	18.00	9.00	5.50
(92)	McQuaid	18.00	9.00	5.50
(93)	Miller	18.00	9.00	5.50
(94)	Mitchell	18.00	9.00	5.50
(95)	J. Mitchell	18.00	9.00	5.50
(96)	Mitchell	18.00	9.00	5.50
(97)	Mitze	18.00	9.00	5.50
(98)	Moffitt	18.00	9.00	5.50
(99)	Mollwitz	18.00	9.00	5.50
(100)	Morse	18.00	9.00	5.50
(101)	Mulligan	18.00	9.00	5.50
(102)	Murphy	18.00	9.00	5.50
(103)	Niehoff	18.00	9.00	5.50
(104)	Nixon	18.00	9.00	5.50
(105)	O'Shaughnessy	18.00	9.00	5.50
(106)	Orr	18.00	9.00	5.50
(107)	Paull	18.00	9.00	5.50
(108)	Penner	18.00	9.00	5.50
(109)	Pertica	18.00	9.00	5.50
(110)	Peterson	18.00	9.00	5.50
(111)	Polson	18.00	9.00	5.50
(112)	Prough	18.00	9.00	5.50
(113)	Reagan	18.00	9.00	5.50
(114)	Reiger	18.00	9.00	5.50
(115)	Reilly	18.00	9.00	5.50
(116)	Rheinhart	18.00	9.00	5.50
(117)	Rodgers	18.00	9.00	5.50
(118)	Ross	18.00	9.00	5.50
(119)	Rumler	18.00	9.00	5.50
(120)	Russell	18.00	9.00	5.50
(121)	Sands	18.00	9.00	5.50
(122)	Schaller	18.00	9.00	5.50
(123)	Schang	18.00	9.00	5.50
(124)	Schellenback	18.00	9.00	5.50
(125)	Schick	18.00	9.00	5.50
(126)	Schorr	18.00	9.00	5.50
(127)	Schroeder	18.00	9.00	5.50
(128)	Scott	18.00	9.00	5.50
(129)	Seaton	18.00	9.00	5.50
(130)	Sheely	18.00	9.00	5.50
(131)	Siebold	18.00	9.00	5.50
(132)	Siglin	18.00	9.00	5.50
(133)	Smith	18.00	9.00	5.50
(134)	G. Smith	18.00	9.00	5.50
(135)	Spellman	18.00	9.00	5.50
(136)	Spranger	18.00	9.00	5.50
(137)	Stroud	18.00	9.00	5.50
(138)	Stumpf	18.00	9.00	5.50
(139)	Sullivan	18.00	9.00	5.50
(140)	Sutherland	18.00	9.00	5.50
(141)	Thurston (dark hat)	18.00	9.00	5.50
(142)	Thurston (light hat)	18.00	9.00	5.50
(143)	Walsh	18.00	9.00	5.50
(144)	Wares	18.00	9.00	5.50
(145)	Weaver	18.00	9.00	5.50
(146)	Willie	18.00	9.00	5.50
(147)	Winn	18.00	9.00	5.50
(148)	Wisterzill	18.00	9.00	5.50
(149)	Worth	18.00	9.00	5.50
(150)	Yelle	18.00	9.00	5.50
(151)	Zamlock	18.00	9.00	5.50
(152)	Zeider	18.00	9.00	5.50

Grading Guide

Mint (MT): A perfect card. Well-centered with all corners sharp and square. No creases, stains, edge nicks, surface marks, yellowing or fading.

Near Mint (NM): A nearly perfect card. At first glance, a NM card appears to be perfect. May be slightly off-center. No surface marks, creases or loss of gloss.

Excellent (EX): Corners are still fairly sharp with only moderate wear. Borders may be off-center. No creases or stains on fronts or backs, but may show slight loss of surface luster.

VeryGood (VG) : Shows obvious handling. May have rounded corners, minor creases, major gum or wax stains. No major creases, tape marks, writing, etc.

Good (G): A well-worn card, but exhibits no intentional damage. May have major or multiple creases. Corners may be rounded well beyond card border.

1921 Zeenut Pacific Coast League (E137)

	NR MT	EX	VG
Complete Set:	2300.	1150.	675.00
Common Player:	18.00	9.00	5.50

		NR MT	EX	VG
(1)	Adams	18.00	9.00	5.50
(2)	Alcock	18.00	9.00	5.50
(3)	Aldridge	18.00	9.00	5.50
(4)	Alton	18.00	9.00	5.50
(5)	Anfinson	18.00	9.00	5.50
(6)	Arlett	22.00	11.00	6.50
(7)	Baker	18.00	9.00	5.50
(8)	Baldwin	18.00	9.00	5.50
(9)	Bates	18.00	9.00	5.50
(10)	Berry	18.00	9.00	5.50
(11)	Blacholder	18.00	9.00	5.50
(12)	Blossom	18.00	9.00	5.50
(13)	Bourg	18.00	9.00	5.50
(14)	Brinley	18.00	9.00	5.50
(15)	Bromley	18.00	9.00	5.50
(16)	Brown	18.00	9.00	5.50
(17)	Brubaker	18.00	9.00	5.50
(18)	Butler	18.00	9.00	5.50
(19)	Byler	18.00	9.00	5.50
(20)	Carroll	18.00	9.00	5.50
(21)	Casey	18.00	9.00	5.50
(22)	Cather	18.00	9.00	5.50
(23)	Caveney	18.00	9.00	5.50
(24)	Chadbourne	18.00	9.00	5.50
(25)	Compton	18.00	9.00	5.50
(26)	Connel	18.00	9.00	5.50
(27)	Cook	18.00	9.00	5.50
(28)	Cooper	18.00	9.00	5.50
(29)	Couch	18.00	9.00	5.50
(30)	Cox	18.00	9.00	5.50
(31)	Crandall	18.00	9.00	5.50
(32)	Cravath	18.00	9.00	5.50
(33)	Crawford	120.00	60.00	36.00
(34)	Crumpler	18.00	9.00	5.50
(35)	Cunningham	18.00	9.00	5.50
(36)	Daley	18.00	9.00	5.50
(37)	Dell	18.00	9.00	5.50
(38)	Demaree	18.00	9.00	5.50
(39)	Douglas	18.00	9.00	5.50
(40)	Dumovich	18.00	9.00	5.50
(41)	Elliott	18.00	9.00	5.50
(42)	Ellis	18.00	9.00	5.50
(43)	Ellison	18.00	9.00	5.50
(44)	Essick	18.00	9.00	5.50
(45)	Faeth	18.00	9.00	5.50
(46)	Fisher	18.00	9.00	5.50
(47)	Fittery	18.00	9.00	5.50
(48)	Fitzgerald	18.00	9.00	5.50
(49)	Flaherty	18.00	9.00	5.50
(50)	Francis	18.00	9.00	5.50
(51)	French	18.00	9.00	5.50
(52)	Fromme	18.00	9.00	5.50
(53)	Gardner	18.00	9.00	5.50
(54)	Geary	18.00	9.00	5.50
(55)	Gennin	18.00	9.00	5.50
(56)	Gorman	18.00	9.00	5.50
(57)	Gould	18.00	9.00	5.50
(58)	Griggs	18.00	9.00	5.50
(59)	Hale	18.00	9.00	5.50
(60)	Hannah	18.00	9.00	5.50
(61)	Hansen	18.00	9.00	5.50
(62)	Hesse	18.00	9.00	5.50
(63)	High	18.00	9.00	5.50
(64)	Hughes	18.00	9.00	5.50
(65)	Hyatt	18.00	9.00	5.50
(66)	Jackson	18.00	9.00	5.50
(67)	Jacobs	18.00	9.00	5.50
(68)	Jacobs	18.00	9.00	5.50
(69)	Jenkins	18.00	9.00	5.50
(70)	Johnson	18.00	9.00	5.50
(71)	Jones	18.00	9.00	5.50
(72)	Jourden	18.00	9.00	5.50
(73)	Kallio	18.00	9.00	5.50
(74)	Kamm	18.00	9.00	5.50
(75)	Kearns	18.00	9.00	5.50
(76)	Kelly	18.00	9.00	5.50
(77)	Kersten	18.00	9.00	5.50
(78)	Kifer	18.00	9.00	5.50
(79)	Killefer	18.00	9.00	5.50
(80)	King	18.00	9.00	5.50
(81)	Kingdon	18.00	9.00	5.50
(82)	Knight	18.00	9.00	5.50
(83)	Koehler	18.00	9.00	5.50
(84)	Kopp	18.00	9.00	5.50
(85)	Krause	18.00	9.00	5.50
(86)	Kremer	18.00	9.00	5.50
(87)	Krug	18.00	9.00	5.50
(88)	Kunz	18.00	9.00	5.50
(89)	Lane	18.00	9.00	5.50
(90)	Leverenz	18.00	9.00	5.50
(91)	Lewis	18.00	9.00	5.50
(92)	Lindimore	18.00	9.00	5.50
(93)	Love	18.00	9.00	5.50
(94)	Ludolph	18.00	9.00	5.50
(95)	Lynn	18.00	9.00	5.50
(96)	Lyons	18.00	9.00	5.50
(97)	McAuley	18.00	9.00	5.50
(98)	McCredie	18.00	9.00	5.50
(99)	McGaffigan	18.00	9.00	5.50
(100)	McGraw	18.00	9.00	5.50
(101)	McQuaid	18.00	9.00	5.50
(102)	Merritt	18.00	9.00	5.50
(103)	Middleton	18.00	9.00	5.50
(104)	Miller	18.00	9.00	5.50
(105)	Mitchell	18.00	9.00	5.50
(106)	Mitze	18.00	9.00	5.50
(107)	Mollwitz	18.00	9.00	5.50
(108)	Morse	18.00	9.00	5.50
(109)	Murphy (Seattle)	18.00	9.00	5.50
(110)	Murphy (Vernon)	18.00	9.00	5.50
(111)	Mustain	18.00	9.00	5.50
(112)	Nickels	18.00	9.00	5.50
(113)	Niehaus	18.00	9.00	5.50
(114)	Niehoff	18.00	9.00	5.50
(115)	Nofziger	18.00	9.00	5.50
(116)	O'Connell	18.00	9.00	5.50
(117)	O'Doul	45.00	22.00	13.50
(118)	O'Malia	18.00	9.00	5.50
(119)	Oldring	18.00	9.00	5.50
(120)	Oliver	18.00	9.00	5.50
(121)	Orr	18.00	9.00	5.50
(122)	Paton	18.00	9.00	5.50
(123)	Penner	18.00	9.00	5.50
(124)	Pick	18.00	9.00	5.50
(125)	Pillette	18.00	9.00	5.50
(126)	Pinelli	22.00	11.00	6.50
(127)	Polson	18.00	9.00	5.50
(128)	Poole	18.00	9.00	5.50
(129)	Prough	18.00	9.00	5.50
(130)	Rath	18.00	9.00	5.50
(131)	Read	18.00	9.00	5.50
(132)	Reinhardt	18.00	9.00	5.50
(133)	Rieger	18.00	9.00	5.50
(134)	Rogers	18.00	9.00	5.50
(135)	Rose (Sacramento)	18.00	9.00	5.50
(136)	Rose (Salt Lake)	18.00	9.00	5.50
(137)	Ross (Portland)	18.00	9.00	5.50
(138)	Ross (Sacramento)	18.00	9.00	5.50
(139)	Ryan	18.00	9.00	5.50
(140)	Sand	18.00	9.00	5.50
(141)	Schick	18.00	9.00	5.50
(142)	Schneider	18.00	9.00	5.50
(143)	Scott	18.00	9.00	5.50
(144)	Shang	18.00	9.00	5.50
(145)	Sheehan	18.00	9.00	5.50
(146)	Shore	18.00	9.00	5.50
(147)	Shorr	18.00	9.00	5.50
(148)	Shultis	18.00	9.00	5.50
(149)	Siebold	18.00	9.00	5.50
(150)	Siglin	18.00	9.00	5.50
(151)	Smallwood	18.00	9.00	5.50
(152)	Smith	18.00	9.00	5.50
(153)	Spencer	18.00	9.00	5.50
(154)	Stanage	18.00	9.00	5.50
(155)	Statz	18.00	9.00	5.50
(156)	Stumph	18.00	9.00	5.50
(157)	Thomas	18.00	9.00	5.50
(158)	Thurston	18.00	9.00	5.50
(159)	Tyrrell	18.00	9.00	5.50
(160)	Van Osdoll	18.00	9.00	5.50
(161)	Walsh	18.00	9.00	5.50
(162)	White	18.00	9.00	5.50
(163)	Wilhoit	18.00	9.00	5.50
(164)	Wilie	18.00	9.00	5.50
(165)	Winn	18.00	9.00	5.50
(166)	Wolfer	18.00	9.00	5.50
(167)	Yelle	18.00	9.00	5.50
(168)	Young	18.00	9.00	5.50
(169)	Zeider	18.00	9.00	5.50

Values quoted in this guide reflect the retail price of a card – the price a collector can expect to pay when buying a card from a dealer. The wholesale price – that which a collector can expect to receive from a dealer when selling cards – will be significantly lower, depending on desirability and condition.

1922 Zeenut Pacific Coast League (E137)

The 1922 Zeenuts are dated on the front, measure 1-7/8" x 3-1/8" and feature black and white photos with sepia highlights. There are 162 subjects,

and four of them (Koehler, Williams, Gregg and Schneider) have been found with variations in color tones.

	NR MT	EX	VG
Complete Set:	4000.	2000.	1200.
Common Player:	18.00	9.00	5.50

		NR MT	EX	VG
(1)	J. Adams	18.00	9.00	5.50
(2)	S. Adams	18.00	9.00	5.50
(3)	Agnew	18.00	9.00	5.50
(4)	Anfinson	18.00	9.00	5.50
(5)	Arlett	22.00	11.00	6.50
(6)	Baldwin	18.00	9.00	5.50
(7)	Barney	18.00	9.00	5.50
(8)	Bell	18.00	9.00	5.50
(9)	Blaeholder	18.00	9.00	5.50
(10)	Bodie	22.00	11.00	6.50
(11)	Brenton	18.00	9.00	5.50
(12)	Bromley	18.00	9.00	5.50
(13)	Brovold	18.00	9.00	5.50
(14)	Brown	18.00	9.00	5.50
(15)	Brubaker	18.00	9.00	5.50
(16)	Burger	18.00	9.00	5.50
(17)	Byler	18.00	9.00	5.50
(18)	Canfield	18.00	9.00	5.50
(19)	Carroll	18.00	9.00	5.50
(20)	Cartwright	18.00	9.00	5.50
(21)	Chadbourne	18.00	9.00	5.50
(22)	Compton	18.00	9.00	5.50
(23)	Connolly	18.00	9.00	5.50
(24)	Cook	18.00	9.00	5.50
(25)	Cooper	18.00	9.00	5.50
(26)	Coumbe	18.00	9.00	5.50
(27)	Cox	18.00	9.00	5.50
(28)	Crandall	18.00	9.00	5.50
(29)	Crumpler	18.00	9.00	5.50
(30)	Cueto	18.00	9.00	5.50
(31)	Dailey	18.00	9.00	5.50
(32)	Daly	18.00	9.00	5.50
(33)	Deal	18.00	9.00	5.50
(34)	Dell	18.00	9.00	5.50
(35)	Doyle	18.00	9.00	5.50
(36)	Dumovich	18.00	9.00	5.50
(37)	Eldred	18.00	9.00	5.50
(38)	Eller	18.00	9.00	5.50
(39)	Elliott	18.00	9.00	5.50
(40)	Ellison	18.00	9.00	5.50
(41)	Essick	18.00	9.00	5.50
(42)	Finneran	18.00	9.00	5.50
(43)	Fittery	18.00	9.00	5.50
(44)	Fitzgerald	18.00	9.00	5.50
(45)	Freeman	18.00	9.00	5.50
(46)	French	18.00	9.00	5.50
(47)	Gardner	18.00	9.00	5.50
(48)	Geary	18.00	9.00	5.50
(49)	Gibson	18.00	9.00	5.50
(50)	Gilder	18.00	9.00	5.50
(51)	Gould	18.00	9.00	5.50
(52)	Gregg	18.00	9.00	5.50
(53)	Gressett	18.00	9.00	5.50
(54)	Griggs	18.00	9.00	5.50
(55)	Hampton	18.00	9.00	5.50
(56)	Hannah	18.00	9.00	5.50
(57)	Hawks	18.00	9.00	5.50
(58)	Henke	18.00	9.00	5.50
(59)	High (Portland)	18.00	9.00	5.50
(60)	High (Vernon)	18.00	9.00	5.50
(61)	Houck	18.00	9.00	5.50
(62)	Howard	18.00	9.00	5.50
(63)	Hughes	18.00	9.00	5.50
(64)	Hyatt	18.00	9.00	5.50
(65)	Jacobs	18.00	9.00	5.50
(66)	James	18.00	9.00	5.50
(67)	Jenkins	18.00	9.00	5.50
(68)	Jones	18.00	9.00	5.50
(69)	Kallio	18.00	9.00	5.50
(70)	Kamm	18.00	9.00	5.50
(71)	Keiser	18.00	9.00	5.50
(72)	Kelly	18.00	9.00	5.50
(73)	Kenworthy	18.00	9.00	5.50
(74)	Kilduff	18.00	9.00	5.50
(75)	Killefer	18.00	9.00	5.50
(76)	Killhullen	18.00	9.00	5.50
(77)	King	18.00	9.00	5.50
(78)	Knight	18.00	9.00	5.50
(79)	Koehler	18.00	9.00	5.50
(80)	Kremer	18.00	9.00	5.50
(81)	Kunz	18.00	9.00	5.50
(82)	Lafayette	18.00	9.00	5.50
(83)	Lane	18.00	9.00	5.50

(84)	Lazzeri	120.00	60.00	36.00
(85)	Lefevre	18.00	9.00	5.50
(86)	D. Lewis	22.00	11.00	6.50
(87)	S. Lewis	18.00	9.00	5.50
(88)	Lindimore	18.00	9.00	5.50
(89)	Locker	18.00	9.00	5.50
(90)	Lyons	18.00	9.00	5.50
(91)	Mack	18.00	9.00	5.50
(92)	Marriott	18.00	9.00	5.50
(93)	May	18.00	9.00	5.50
(94)	McAuley	18.00	9.00	5.50
(95)	McCabe	18.00	9.00	5.50
(96)	McCann	18.00	9.00	5.50
(97)	McCredie	18.00	9.00	5.50
(98)	McNeely	18.00	9.00	5.50
(99)	McQuaid	18.00	9.00	5.50
(100)	Miller	18.00	9.00	5.50
(101)	Mitchell	18.00	9.00	5.50
(102)	Mitze	18.00	9.00	5.50
(103)	Mollwitz	18.00	9.00	5.50
(104)	Monahan	18.00	9.00	5.50
(105)	Murphy (Seattle)	18.00	9.00	5.50
(106)	Murphy (Vernon)	18.00	9.00	5.50
(107)	Niehaus	18.00	9.00	5.50
(108)	O'Connell	18.00	9.00	5.50
(109)	Orr	18.00	9.00	5.50
(110)	Owen	18.00	9.00	5.50
(111)	Pearce	18.00	9.00	5.50
(112)	Pick	18.00	9.00	5.50
(113)	Ponder	18.00	9.00	5.50
(114)	Poole	18.00	9.00	5.50
(115)	Prough	18.00	9.00	5.50
(116)	Read	18.00	9.00	5.50
(117)	Richardson	18.00	9.00	5.50
(118)	Rieger	18.00	9.00	5.50
(119)	Ritchie	18.00	9.00	5.50
(120)	Ross	18.00	9.00	5.50
(121)	Ryan	18.00	9.00	5.50
(122)	Sand	18.00	9.00	5.50
(123)	Sargent	18.00	9.00	5.50
(124)	Sawyer	18.00	9.00	5.50
(125)	Schang	18.00	9.00	5.50
(126)	Schick	18.00	9.00	5.50
(127)	Schneider	18.00	9.00	5.50
(128)	Schorr	18.00	9.00	5.50
(129)	Schulte (Oakland)	18.00	9.00	5.50
(130)	Schulte (Seattle)	18.00	9.00	5.50
(131)	Scott	18.00	9.00	5.50
(132)	See	18.00	9.00	5.50
(133)	Shea	18.00	9.00	5.50
(134)	Sheehan	18.00	9.00	5.50
(135)	Siglin	18.00	9.00	5.50
(136)	Smith	18.00	9.00	5.50
(137)	Soria	18.00	9.00	5.50
(138)	Spencer	18.00	9.00	5.50
(139)	Stanage	18.00	9.00	5.50
(140)	Strand	18.00	9.00	5.50
(141)	Stumpf	18.00	9.00	5.50
(142)	Sullivan	18.00	9.00	5.50
(143)	Sutherland	18.00	9.00	5.50
(144)	Thomas	18.00	9.00	5.50
(145)	Thorpe	2000.	1000.	600.00
(146)	Thurston	18.00	9.00	5.50
(147)	Tobin	18.00	9.00	5.50
(148)	Turner	18.00	9.00	5.50
(149)	Twombly	18.00	9.00	5.50
(150)	Valla	18.00	9.00	5.50
(151)	Vargas	18.00	9.00	5.50
(152)	Viveros	18.00	9.00	5.50
(153)	Wallace	18.00	9.00	5.50
(154)	Walsh	18.00	9.00	5.50
(155)	Wells	18.00	9.00	5.50
(156)	Westersil	18.00	9.00	5.50
(157)	Wheat	18.00	9.00	5.50
(158)	Wilhoit	18.00	9.00	5.50
(159)	Wilie	18.00	9.00	5.50
(160)	Williams	18.00	9.00	5.50
(161)	Yelle	18.00	9.00	5.50
(162)	Zeider	18.00	9.00	5.50

1923 Zeenut Pacific Coast League (E137)

This is the only year that Zeenuts cards were issued in two different sizes. Cards in the "regular" series measure 1-7/8" x 3", feature black and white photos and are dated 1923. A second series, containing just 24 cards (all San Francisco and Oakland players), were actually re-issues of the 1922 series with a "1923" date.

		NR MT	EX	VG
Complete Set:		3000.	1500.	900.00
Common Player:		18.00	9.00	5.50
(1)	Agnew (1923 photo)	18.00	9.00	5.50
(2)	Agnew (1922 photo re-dated)	20.00	10.00	6.00
(3)	Alten	18.00	9.00	5.50
(4)	Anderson	18.00	9.00	5.50
(5)	Anfinson	18.00	9.00	5.50
(6)	Arlett	22.00	11.00	6.50
(7)	Baker	18.00	9.00	5.50
(8)	Baldwin	18.00	9.00	5.50
(9)	Barney	18.00	9.00	5.50
(10)	Blake	18.00	9.00	5.50
(11)	Bodie	22.00	11.00	6.50
(12)	Brazil	18.00	9.00	5.50
(13)	Brenton	11.00	5.50	3.25
(14)	Brown (Oakland)	11.00	5.50	3.25
(15)	Brown (Sacramento)	18.00	9.00	5.50
(16)	Brubaker	18.00	9.00	5.50
(17)	Buckley	18.00	9.00	5.50
(18)	Canfield	18.00	9.00	5.50
(19)	Carroll	18.00	9.00	5.50
(20)	Cather	18.00	9.00	5.50
(21)	Chadbourne	18.00	9.00	5.50
(22)	Charvez	18.00	9.00	5.50
(23)	Cochrane	18.00	9.00	5.50
(24)	Colwell	18.00	9.00	5.50
(25)	Compton	18.00	9.00	5.50
(26)	Cook	18.00	9.00	5.50
(27)	Cooper (1923 photo)	18.00	9.00	5.50
(28)	Cooper (1922 photo re-date)	20.00	10.00	6.00
(29)	Coumbe	18.00	9.00	5.50
(30)	Courtney	18.00	9.00	5.50
(31)	Crandall	18.00	9.00	5.50
(32)	Crane	18.00	9.00	5.50
(33)	Crowder	18.00	9.00	5.50
(34)	Crumpler	18.00	9.00	5.50
(35)	Daly (Los Angeles)	18.00	9.00	5.50
(36)	Daly (Portland)	18.00	9.00	5.50
(37)	Deal	18.00	9.00	5.50
(38)	Doyle	18.00	9.00	5.50
(39)	Duchalsky	18.00	9.00	5.50
(40)	Eckert	18.00	9.00	5.50
(41)	Eldred	18.00	9.00	5.50
(42)	Eley	18.00	9.00	5.50
(43)	Eller	18.00	9.00	5.50
(44)	Ellison (1923 photo)	18.00	9.00	5.50
(45)	Ellison (1922 photo re-dated)	20.00	10.00	6.00
(46)	Essick	18.00	9.00	5.50
(47)	Fittery	18.00	9.00	5.50
(48)	Flashkamper	18.00	9.00	5.50
(49)	Frederick	18.00	9.00	5.50
(50)	French	18.00	9.00	5.50
(51)	Geary (1923 photo)	18.00	9.00	5.50
(52)	Geary (1922 photo re-dated)	20.00	10.00	6.00
(53)	Gilder	18.00	9.00	5.50
(54)	Golvin	18.00	9.00	5.50
(55)	Gorman	18.00	9.00	5.50
(56)	Gould	18.00	9.00	5.50
(57)	Gressett	18.00	9.00	5.50
(58)	Griggs	18.00	9.00	5.50
(59)	Hannah (Los Angeles)	18.00	9.00	5.50
(60)	Hannah (Vernon)	18.00	9.00	5.50
(61)	Hemingway	18.00	9.00	5.50
(62)	Hendryx	18.00	9.00	5.50
(63)	High	18.00	9.00	5.50
(64)	H. High	18.00	9.00	5.50
(65)	Hodge	18.00	9.00	5.50
(66)	Hood	18.00	9.00	5.50
(67)	Houghs	18.00	9.00	5.50
(68)	Howard (1923 photo)	18.00	9.00	5.50
(69)	Howard (1922 photo re-date)	20.00	10.00	6.00
(70)	Del Howard	18.00	9.00	5.50
(71)	Jacobs	18.00	9.00	5.50
(72)	James	18.00	9.00	5.50
(73)	Johnson	18.00	9.00	5.50
(74)	Johnston	18.00	9.00	5.50
(75)	Jolly	18.00	9.00	5.50
(76)	Jones (Los Angeles)	18.00	9.00	5.50
(77)	Jones (Oakland)	18.00	9.00	5.50
(78)	Jones (Portland)	18.00	9.00	5.50
(79)	Kallio	18.00	9.00	5.50
(80)	Kearns	18.00	9.00	5.50
(81)	Keiser	18.00	9.00	5.50
(82)	Keller	18.00	9.00	5.50
(83)	Kelly (San Francisco)	18.00	9.00	5.50
(84)	Kelly (Seattle)	18.00	9.00	5.50
(85)	Kenna	18.00	9.00	5.50
(86)	Kilduff	18.00	9.00	5.50
(87)	Killifer	18.00	9.00	5.50
(88)	King	18.00	9.00	5.50
(89)	Knight (1923 photo)	18.00	9.00	5.50
(90)	Knight (1922 photo re-dated)	20.00	10.00	6.00
(91)	Koehler	18.00	9.00	5.50
(92)	Kopp	18.00	9.00	5.50
(93)	Krause	18.00	9.00	5.50
(94)	Kremer	18.00	9.00	5.50
(95)	Krug	18.00	9.00	5.50
(96)	Lafayette (1923 photo)	18.00	9.00	5.50
(97)	Lafayette (1922 photo re-dated)	20.00	10.00	6.00
(98)	Lane	18.00	9.00	5.50
(99)	Lefevre	18.00	9.00	5.50
(100)	Leslie	18.00	9.00	5.50
(101)	Levere	18.00	9.00	5.50
(102)	Leverenz	18.00	9.00	5.50
(103)	Lewis	18.00	9.00	5.50
(104)	Lindimore	18.00	9.00	5.50
(105)	Locker	18.00	9.00	5.50
(106)	Lyons	18.00	9.00	5.50
(107)	Maderas	18.00	9.00	5.50
(108)	Mails	18.00	9.00	5.50
(109)	Marriott	18.00	9.00	5.50
(110)	Matzen	18.00	9.00	5.50
(111)	McAuley	18.00	9.00	5.50
(112)	McAuliffe	18.00	9.00	5.50
(113)	McCabe (Los Angeles)	18.00	9.00	5.50
(114)	McCabe (Salt Lake)	18.00	9.00	5.50
(115)	McCann	18.00	9.00	5.50
(116)	McGaffigan	18.00	9.00	5.50
(117)	McGinnis	18.00	9.00	5.50
(118)	McNeilly	18.00	9.00	5.50
(119)	McWeeney	18.00	9.00	5.50
(120)	Middleton	18.00	9.00	5.50
(121)	Miller	18.00	9.00	5.50
(122)	Mitchell (1923 photo)	18.00	9.00	5.50
(123)	Mitchell (1922 photo re-date)	20.00	10.00	6.00
(124)	Mitze	18.00	9.00	5.50
(125)	Mulligan	18.00	9.00	5.50
(126)	Murchio	18.00	9.00	5.50
(127)	D. Murphy	18.00	9.00	5.50
(128)	R. Murphy	18.00	9.00	5.50
(129)	Noack	18.00	9.00	5.50
(130)	O'Brien	18.00	9.00	5.50
(131)	Onslow	18.00	9.00	5.50
(132)	Orr	18.00	9.00	5.50
(133)	Pearce	18.00	9.00	5.50
(134)	Penner	18.00	9.00	5.50
(135)	Peters	18.00	9.00	5.50
(136)	Pick	18.00	9.00	5.50
(137)	Pigg	18.00	9.00	5.50
(138)	Plummer	18.00	9.00	5.50
(139)	Ponder	18.00	9.00	5.50
(140)	Poole	18.00	9.00	5.50
(141)	Ramage	18.00	9.00	5.50
(142)	Read (1923 photo)	18.00	9.00	5.50
(143)	Read (1922 photo re-dated)	20.00	10.00	6.00
(144)	Rhyne	18.00	9.00	5.50
(145)	Ritchie	18.00	9.00	5.50
(146)	Robertson	18.00	9.00	5.50
(147)	Rohwer (Sacramento)	18.00	9.00	5.50
(148)	Rohwer (Seattle)	18.00	9.00	5.50
(149)	Ryan	18.00	9.00	5.50
(150)	Sawyer	18.00	9.00	5.50
(151)	Schang	18.00	9.00	5.50
(152)	Schneider	18.00	9.00	5.50
(153)	Schroeder	18.00	9.00	5.50
(154)	Scott	18.00	9.00	5.50
(155)	See	18.00	9.00	5.50
(156)	Shea	18.00	9.00	5.50
(157)	M. Shea	18.00	9.00	5.50
(158)	Spec Shea	18.00	9.00	5.50
(159)	Sheehan	18.00	9.00	5.50
(160)	Shellenback	18.00	9.00	5.50
(161)	Siglin	18.00	9.00	5.50
(162)	Singleton	18.00	9.00	5.50
(163)	Smith	18.00	9.00	5.50
(164)	M.H. Smith	18.00	9.00	5.50
(165)	Stanton	18.00	9.00	5.50
(166)	Strand	18.00	9.00	5.50
(167)	Stumpf	18.00	9.00	5.50
(168)	Sutherland	18.00	9.00	5.50
(169)	Tesar	18.00	9.00	5.50
(170)	Thomas (Los Angeles)	18.00	9.00	5.50
(171)	Thomas (Oakland)	18.00	9.00	5.50
(172)	Tobin	18.00	9.00	5.50
(173)	Twombly	18.00	9.00	5.50
(174)	Valla	18.00	9.00	5.50
(175)	Vargas	18.00	9.00	5.50
(176)	Vitt	18.00	9.00	5.50
(177)	Wallace	18.00	9.00	5.50
(178)	Walsh (San Francisco)	18.00	9.00	5.50
(179)	Walsh (Seattle)	18.00	9.00	5.50
(180)	Paul Waner	120.00	60.00	36.00
(181)	Wells (Oakland)	18.00	9.00	5.50
(182)	Wells (San Francisco)	18.00	9.00	5.50
(183)	Welsh	18.00	9.00	5.50
(184)	Wilhoit	18.00	9.00	5.50
(185)	Wilie (1923 photo)	18.00	9.00	5.50
(186)	Wilie (1922 photo re-dated)	20.00	10.00	6.00
(187)	Williams	18.00	9.00	5.50
(188)	Witzel	18.00	9.00	5.50
(189)	Wolfer	18.00	9.00	5.50
(190)	Wolverton	18.00	9.00	5.50
(191)	Yarrison	18.00	9.00	5.50
(192)	Yaryan	18.00	9.00	5.50
(193)	Yelle (1923 photo)	18.00	9.00	5.50
(194)	Yelle (1922 photo re-dated)	20.00	10.00	6.00
(195)	Moses Yellowhorse	50.00	25.00	15.00
(196)	Zeider	18.00	9.00	5.50

Grading Guide

Mint (MT): A perfect card. Well-centered with all corners sharp and square. No creases, stains, edge nicks, surface marks, yellowing or fading.

Near Mint (NM): A nearly perfect card. At first glance, a NM card appears to be perfect. May be slightly off-center. No surface marks, creases or loss of gloss.

Excellent (EX): Corners are still fairly sharp with only moderate wear. Borders may be off-center. No creases or stains on fronts or backs, but may show slight loss of surface luster.

Very Good (VG): Shows obvious handling. May have rounded corners, minor creases, major gum or wax stains. No major creases, tape marks, writing, etc.

Good (G): A well-worn card, but exhibits no intentional damage. May have major or multiple creases. Corners may be rounded well beyond card border.

1924 Zeenut Pacific Coast League (E137)

Zeenut cards in 1924 and 1925 measure 1-3/4" x 2-7/8" and display the date on the front. The cards include a full photographic background. There are 144 subjects known in the 1924 series and 162 known for 1925.

		NR MT	EX	VG
Complete Set:		2000.	1000.	600.00
Common Player:		16.00	8.00	4.75
(1)	Adams	16.00	8.00	4.75
(2)	Agnew	16.00	8.00	4.75
(3)	Arlett	18.00	9.00	5.50
(4)	Baker	16.00	8.00	4.75
(5)	E. Baldwin	16.00	8.00	4.75
(6)	T. Baldwin	16.00	8.00	4.75
(7)	Beck	16.00	8.00	4.75
(8)	Benton	16.00	8.00	4.75
(9)	Bernard	16.00	8.00	4.75
(10)	Bigbee	16.00	8.00	4.75
(11)	Billings	16.00	8.00	4.75
(12)	Blakesly	16.00	8.00	4.75
(13)	Brady	16.00	8.00	4.75
(14)	Brazil	16.00	8.00	4.75
(15)	Brown	16.00	8.00	4.75
(16)	Brubaker	16.00	8.00	4.75
(17)	Buckley	16.00	8.00	4.75
(18)	Burger	16.00	8.00	4.75
(19)	Byler	16.00	8.00	4.75
(20)	Cadore	16.00	8.00	4.75
(21)	Cather	16.00	8.00	4.75
(22)	Chadbourne	16.00	8.00	4.75
(23)	Christian	16.00	8.00	4.75
(24)	Cochrane (Portland)	120.00	60.00	36.00
(25)	Cochrane (Sacramento)	16.00	8.00	4.75
(26)	Cooper	16.00	8.00	4.75
(27)	Coumbe	16.00	8.00	4.75
(28)	Cox	16.00	8.00	4.75
(29)	Crandall	16.00	8.00	4.75
(30)	Daly	16.00	8.00	4.75
(31)	Deal	16.00	8.00	4.75
(32)	Distel	16.00	8.00	4.75
(33)	Durst	16.00	8.00	4.75
(34)	Eckert	16.00	8.00	4.75
(35)	Eldred	16.00	8.00	4.75
(36)	Ellison	16.00	8.00	4.75
(37)	Essick	16.00	8.00	4.75
(38)	Flashkamper	16.00	8.00	4.75
(39)	Foster	16.00	8.00	4.75
(40)	Fredericks	16.00	8.00	4.75
(41)	Geary	16.00	8.00	4.75
(42)	Goebel	16.00	8.00	4.75
(43)	Golvin	16.00	8.00	4.75
(44)	Gorman	16.00	8.00	4.75
(45)	Gould	16.00	8.00	4.75
(46)	Gressett	16.00	8.00	4.75
(47)	Griffin (San Francisco)	16.00	8.00	4.75
(48)	Griffin (Vernon)	16.00	8.00	4.75
(49)	Guisto	16.00	8.00	4.75
(50)	Gunther	16.00	8.00	4.75
(51)	Hall	16.00	8.00	4.75
(52)	Hannah	16.00	8.00	4.75
(53)	Hendryx	16.00	8.00	4.75
(54)	High	16.00	8.00	4.75
(55)	Hodge	16.00	8.00	4.75
(56)	Hood	16.00	8.00	4.75
(57)	Ivan Howard	16.00	8.00	4.75
(58)	Hughes (Los Angeles)	16.00	8.00	4.75
(59)	Hughes (Sacramento)	16.00	8.00	4.75
(60)	Jacobs	16.00	8.00	4.75
(61)	James	16.00	8.00	4.75
(62)	Jenkins	16.00	8.00	4.75
(63)	Johnson	16.00	8.00	4.75
(64)	Jones	16.00	8.00	4.75
(65)	Keck	16.00	8.00	4.75
(66)	Kelley	16.00	8.00	4.75
(67)	Kenworthy	16.00	8.00	4.75
(68)	Kilduff	16.00	8.00	4.75
(69)	Killifer	16.00	8.00	4.75
(70)	Kimmick	16.00	8.00	4.75
(71)	Kopp	16.00	8.00	4.75
(72)	Krause	16.00	8.00	4.75
(73)	Krug	16.00	8.00	4.75
(74)	Kunz	16.00	8.00	4.75
(75)	Lafayette	16.00	8.00	4.75
(76)	Lennon	16.00	8.00	4.75
(77)	Leptich	16.00	8.00	4.75
(78)	Leslie	16.00	8.00	4.75
(79)	Leverenz	16.00	8.00	4.75
(80)	Lewis	16.00	8.00	4.75
(81)	Maderas	16.00	8.00	4.75
(82)	Mails	16.00	8.00	4.75
(83)	McAuley	16.00	8.00	4.75
(84)	McCann	16.00	8.00	4.75
(85)	McDowell	16.00	8.00	4.75
(86)	McNeely	16.00	8.00	4.75
(87)	Menosky	16.00	8.00	4.75
(88)	Meyers	16.00	8.00	4.75
(89)	Miller	16.00	8.00	4.75
(90)	Mitchell	16.00	8.00	4.75
(91)	Mulligan	16.00	8.00	4.75
(92)	D. Murphy	16.00	8.00	4.75
(93)	R. Murphy	16.00	8.00	4.75
(94)	Osborne	16.00	8.00	4.75
(95)	Paynter	16.00	8.00	4.75
(96)	Penner	16.00	8.00	4.75
(97)	Peters (Sacramento)	16.00	8.00	4.75
(98)	Peters (Salt Lake)	16.00	8.00	4.75
(99)	Pick	16.00	8.00	4.75
(100)	Pillette	16.00	8.00	4.75
(101)	Poole	16.00	8.00	4.75
(102)	Prough	16.00	8.00	4.75
(103)	Querry	16.00	8.00	4.75
(104)	Read	16.00	8.00	4.75
(105)	Rhyne	16.00	8.00	4.75
(106)	Ritchie	16.00	8.00	4.75
(107)	Root	12.00	6.00	3.50
(108)	Rowher	16.00	8.00	4.75
(109)	Schang	16.00	8.00	4.75
(110)	Schneider	16.00	8.00	4.75
(111)	Schorr	16.00	8.00	4.75
(112)	Schroeder	16.00	8.00	4.75
(113)	Scott	16.00	8.00	4.75
(114)	Sellers	16.00	8.00	4.75
(115)	"Speck" Shay	16.00	8.00	4.75
(116)	Shea (Sacramento)	16.00	8.00	4.75
(117)	Shea (San Francisco)	16.00	8.00	4.75
(118)	Shellenback	16.00	8.00	4.75
(119)	Siebold	16.00	8.00	4.75
(120)	Siglin	16.00	8.00	4.75
(121)	Slade	16.00	8.00	4.75
(122)	Smith (Sacramento)	16.00	8.00	4.75
(123)	Smith (San Francisco)	16.00	8.00	4.75
(124)	Stanton	16.00	8.00	4.75
(125)	Tanner	16.00	8.00	4.75
(126)	Twomley	16.00	8.00	4.75
(127)	Valla	16.00	8.00	4.75
(128)	Vargas	16.00	8.00	4.75
(129)	Vines	16.00	8.00	4.75
(130)	Vitt	16.00	8.00	4.75
(131)	Wallace	16.00	8.00	4.75
(132)	Walsh	16.00	8.00	4.75
(133)	Paul Waner	120.00	60.00	36.00
(134)	Warner (fielding)	16.00	8.00	4.75
(135)	Warner (throwing)	16.00	8.00	4.75
(136)	Welsh	16.00	8.00	4.75
(137)	Wetzel	16.00	8.00	4.75
(138)	Whalen	16.00	8.00	4.75
(139)	Wilhoit	16.00	8.00	4.75
(140)	Williams (San Francisco)	16.00	8.00	4.75
(141)	Williams (Seattle)	16.00	8.00	4.75
(142)	Wolfer	16.00	8.00	4.75
(143)	Yelle	16.00	8.00	4.75
(144)	Moses Yellowhorse	45.00	22.00	13.50

1925 Zeenut Pacific Coast League (E137)

		NR MT	EX	VG
Complete Set:		2200.	1100.	650.00
Common Player:		16.00	8.00	4.75
(1)	Adeylatte	16.00	8.00	4.75
(2)	Agnew	16.00	8.00	4.75
(3)	Arlett	12.00	6.00	3.50
(4)	Bagby	16.00	8.00	4.75
(5)	Bahr	16.00	8.00	4.75
(6)	Baker	16.00	8.00	4.75
(7)	E. Baldwin	16.00	8.00	4.75
(8)	Barfoot	16.00	8.00	4.75
(9)	Beck	16.00	8.00	4.75
(10)	Becker	16.00	8.00	4.75
(11)	Blakesley	16.00	8.00	4.75
(12)	Boehler	16.00	8.00	4.75
(13)	Brady	16.00	8.00	4.75
(14)	Brandt	16.00	8.00	4.75
(15)	Bratcher	16.00	8.00	4.75
(16)	Brazil	16.00	8.00	4.75
(17)	Brower	16.00	8.00	4.75
(18)	Brown	16.00	8.00	4.75
(19)	Brubaker	16.00	8.00	4.75
(20)	Bryan	16.00	8.00	4.75
(21)	Canfield	16.00	8.00	4.75
(22)	W. Canfield	16.00	8.00	4.75
(23)	Cather	16.00	8.00	4.75
(24)	Chavez	16.00	8.00	4.75
(25)	Christain	16.00	8.00	4.75
(26)	Cochrane	16.00	8.00	4.75
(27)	Connolly	16.00	8.00	4.75
(28)	Cook	16.00	8.00	4.75
(29)	Cooper	16.00	8.00	4.75
(30)	Coumbe	16.00	8.00	4.75
(31)	Crandall	16.00	8.00	4.75
(32)	Crane	16.00	8.00	4.75
(33)	Crockett	16.00	8.00	4.75
(34)	Crosby	16.00	8.00	4.75
(35)	Cutshaw	16.00	8.00	4.75
(36)	Daly	16.00	8.00	4.75
(37)	Davis	16.00	8.00	4.75
(38)	Deal	16.00	8.00	4.75
(39)	Delaney	16.00	8.00	4.75
(40)	Dempsey	16.00	8.00	4.75
(41)	Dumovich	16.00	8.00	4.75
(42)	Eckert	16.00	8.00	4.75
(43)	Eldred	16.00	8.00	4.75
(44)	Elliott	16.00	8.00	4.75
(45)	Ellison	16.00	8.00	4.75
(46)	Emmer	16.00	8.00	4.75
(47)	Ennis	16.00	8.00	4.75
(48)	Essick	16.00	8.00	4.75
(49)	Finn	16.00	8.00	4.75
(50)	Flowers	16.00	8.00	4.75
(51)	Frederick	16.00	8.00	4.75
(52)	Fussell	16.00	8.00	4.75
(53)	Geary	16.00	8.00	4.75
(54)	Gorman	16.00	8.00	4.75
(55)	Griffin (San Francisco)	16.00	8.00	4.75
(56)	Griffin (Vernon)	16.00	8.00	4.75
(57)	Grimes	16.00	8.00	4.75
(58)	Guisto	16.00	8.00	4.75
(59)	Hannah	16.00	8.00	4.75
(60)	Haughy	16.00	8.00	4.75
(61)	Hemingway	16.00	8.00	4.75
(62)	Hendryx	16.00	8.00	4.75
(63)	Herman	24.00	12.00	7.25
(64)	High	16.00	8.00	4.75
(65)	Hoffman	16.00	8.00	4.75
(66)	Hood	16.00	8.00	4.75
(67)	Horan	16.00	8.00	4.75
(68)	Horton	16.00	8.00	4.75
(69)	Howard	16.00	8.00	4.75
(70)	Hughes	16.00	8.00	4.75
(71)	Hulvey	16.00	8.00	4.75
(72)	Hunnefield	16.00	8.00	4.75
(73)	Jacobs	16.00	8.00	4.75
(74)	James	16.00	8.00	4.75
(75)	Keating	16.00	8.00	4.75
(76)	Keefe	16.00	8.00	4.75
(77)	Kelly	16.00	8.00	4.75
(78)	Kilduff	16.00	8.00	4.75
(79)	Kohler	16.00	8.00	4.75
(80)	Kopp	16.00	8.00	4.75
(81)	Krause	16.00	8.00	4.75
(82)	Krug	16.00	8.00	4.75
(83)	Kunz	16.00	8.00	4.75
(84)	Lafayette	16.00	8.00	4.75
(85)	Lazzeri	100.00	50.00	30.00
(86)	Leslie	16.00	8.00	4.75
(87)	Leverenz	16.00	8.00	4.75
(88)	Duffy Lewis	22.00	11.00	6.50
(89)	Lindemore	16.00	8.00	4.75
(90)	Ludolph	16.00	8.00	4.75
(91)	Makin	16.00	8.00	4.75
(92)	Martin (Sacramento)	16.00	8.00	4.75
(93)	Martin (Portland)	16.00	8.00	4.75
(94)	McCabe	16.00	8.00	4.75
(95)	McCann	16.00	8.00	4.75
(96)	McCarren	16.00	8.00	4.75
(97)	McDonald	16.00	8.00	4.75
(98)	McGinnis (Portland)	16.00	8.00	4.75
(99)	McGinnis (Sacramento)	16.00	8.00	4.75
(100)	McLaughlin	16.00	8.00	4.75
(101)	Milstead	16.00	8.00	4.75
(102)	Mitchell	16.00	8.00	4.75
(103)	Moudy	16.00	8.00	4.75
(104)	Mulcahy	16.00	8.00	4.75
(105)	Mulligan	16.00	8.00	4.75
(106)	O'Doul	45.00	22.00	13.50
(107)	O'Neil	16.00	8.00	4.75
(108)	Ortman	16.00	8.00	4.75
(109)	Pailey	16.00	8.00	4.75
(110)	Paynter	16.00	8.00	4.75
(111)	Peery	16.00	8.00	4.75
(112)	Penner	16.00	8.00	4.75
(113)	Pfeffer	16.00	8.00	4.75
(114)	Phillips	16.00	8.00	4.75
(115)	Pickering	16.00	8.00	4.75
(116)	Piercy	16.00	8.00	4.75
(117)	Pillette	16.00	8.00	4.75
(118)	Plummer	16.00	8.00	4.75
(119)	Ponder	16.00	8.00	4.75
(120)	Pruett	16.00	8.00	4.75
(121)	Rawlings	16.00	8.00	4.75
(122)	Read	16.00	8.00	4.75
(123)	Jimmy Reese	24.00	12.00	7.25
(124)	Rhyne	16.00	8.00	4.75
(125)	Riconda	16.00	8.00	4.75
(126)	Ritchie	16.00	8.00	4.75
(127)	Rohwer	16.00	8.00	4.75
(128)	Rowland	16.00	8.00	4.75

(129)	Ryan	16.00	8.00	4.75
(130)	Sandberg	16.00	8.00	4.75
(131)	Schang	16.00	8.00	4.75
(132)	Shea	16.00	8.00	4.75
(133)	M. Shea	16.00	8.00	4.75
(134)	Shellenbach	16.00	8.00	4.75
(135)	Sherling	16.00	8.00	4.75
(136)	Siglin	16.00	8.00	4.75
(137)	Slade	16.00	8.00	4.75
(138)	Spencer	16.00	8.00	4.75
(139)	Steward	16.00	8.00	4.75
(140)	Stivers	16.00	8.00	4.75
(141)	Suhr	16.00	8.00	4.75
(142)	Sutherland	16.00	8.00	4.75
(143)	Thomas (Portland)	16.00	8.00	4.75
(144)	Thomas (Vernon)	16.00	8.00	4.75
(145)	Thompson	16.00	8.00	4.75
(146)	Tobin	16.00	8.00	4.75
(147)	Twombly	16.00	8.00	4.75
(148)	Valla	16.00	8.00	4.75
(149)	Vinci	16.00	8.00	4.75
(150)	O. Vitt	16.00	8.00	4.75
(151)	Wachenfeld	16.00	8.00	4.75
(152)	Paul Waner	120.00	60.00	36.00
(153)	Lloyd Waner	120.00	60.00	36.00
(154)	Warner	16.00	8.00	4.75
(155)	Watson	16.00	8.00	4.75
(156)	Weinert	16.00	8.00	4.75
(157)	Whaley	16.00	8.00	4.75
(158)	Whitney	16.00	8.00	4.75
(159)	Williams	16.00	8.00	4.75
(160)	Winters	16.00	8.00	4.75
(161)	Wolfer	16.00	8.00	4.75
(162)	Woodring	16.00	8.00	4.75
(163)	Yeargin	16.00	8.00	4.75
(164)	Yelle	16.00	8.00	4.75

1926 Zeenut Pacific Coast League (E137)

Except for their slightly smaller size (1-3/4" x 2-3/4"), the 1926 Zeenut cards are nearly identical to the previous two years. Considered more difficult than other Zeenuts series of this era, the 1926 set consists of more than 170 known subjects.

		NR MT	EX	VG
Complete Set:		2700.	1350.	800.00
Common Player:		18.00	9.00	5.50
(1)	Agnew	18.00	9.00	5.50
(2)	Allen	18.00	9.00	5.50
(3)	Alley	18.00	9.00	5.50
(4)	Averill	100.00	50.00	30.00
(5)	Bagwell	18.00	9.00	5.50
(6)	Baker	18.00	9.00	5.50
(7)	T. Baldwin	18.00	9.00	5.50
(8)	Berry	18.00	9.00	5.50
(9)	Bool	18.00	9.00	5.50
(10)	Boone	18.00	9.00	5.50
(11)	Boyd	18.00	9.00	5.50
(12)	Brady	18.00	9.00	5.50
(13)	Brazil	18.00	9.00	5.50
(14)	Brower	18.00	9.00	5.50
(15)	Brubaker	18.00	9.00	5.50
(16)	Bryan	18.00	9.00	5.50
(17)	Burns	18.00	9.00	5.50
(18)	C. Canfield	18.00	9.00	5.50
(19)	W. Canfield	18.00	9.00	5.50
(20)	Carson	18.00	9.00	5.50
(21)	Christian	18.00	9.00	5.50
(22)	Cole	18.00	9.00	5.50
(23)	Connolly	18.00	9.00	5.50
(24)	Cook	18.00	9.00	5.50
(25)	Couch	18.00	9.00	5.50
(26)	Coumbe	18.00	9.00	5.50
(27)	Crockett	18.00	9.00	5.50
(28)	Cunningham	18.00	9.00	5.50
(29)	Cutshaw	18.00	9.00	5.50
(30)	Daglia	18.00	9.00	5.50
(31)	Danning	18.00	9.00	5.50
(32)	Davis	18.00	9.00	5.50
(33)	Delaney	18.00	9.00	5.50
(34)	Eckert	18.00	9.00	5.50
(35)	Eldred	18.00	9.00	5.50
(36)	Elliott	18.00	9.00	5.50
(37)	Ellison	18.00	9.00	5.50
(38)	Ellsworth	18.00	9.00	5.50
(39)	Elsh	18.00	9.00	5.50
(40)	Fenton	18.00	9.00	5.50
(41)	Finn	18.00	9.00	5.50
(42)	Flashkamper	18.00	9.00	5.50
(43)	Fowler	18.00	9.00	5.50
(44)	Frederick	18.00	9.00	5.50
(45)	Freeman	18.00	9.00	5.50
(46)	French	18.00	9.00	5.50
(47)	Garrison	18.00	9.00	5.50
(48)	Geary	18.00	9.00	5.50
(49)	Gillespie	18.00	9.00	5.50
(50)	Glazner	18.00	9.00	5.50
(51)	Gould	18.00	9.00	5.50
(52)	Governor	18.00	9.00	5.50
(53)	Griffin (Missions)	18.00	9.00	5.50
(54)	Griffin (San Francisco)	18.00	9.00	5.50
(55)	Guisto	18.00	9.00	5.50
(56)	Hamilton	18.00	9.00	5.50
(57)	Hannah	18.00	9.00	5.50
(58)	Hansen	18.00	9.00	5.50
(59)	Hasty	18.00	9.00	5.50
(60)	Hemingway	18.00	9.00	5.50
(61)	Hendryx	18.00	9.00	5.50
(62)	Hickok	18.00	9.00	5.50
(63)	Hillis	18.00	9.00	5.50
(64)	Hoffman	18.00	9.00	5.50
(65)	Hollerson	18.00	9.00	5.50
(66)	Holmes	18.00	9.00	5.50
(67)	Hood	18.00	9.00	5.50
(68)	Howard	18.00	9.00	5.50
(69)	Hufft	18.00	9.00	5.50
(70)	Hughes	18.00	9.00	5.50
(71)	Hulvey	18.00	9.00	5.50
(72)	Hurst	18.00	9.00	5.50
(73)	R. Jacobs	18.00	9.00	5.50
(74)	Jahn	18.00	9.00	5.50
(75)	Jenkins	18.00	9.00	5.50
(76)	Johnson	18.00	9.00	5.50
(77)	Jolly	18.00	9.00	5.50
(78)	Jones	18.00	9.00	5.50
(79)	Kallio	18.00	9.00	5.50
(80)	Keating	18.00	9.00	5.50
(81)	Kerr (Hollywood)	18.00	9.00	5.50
(82)	Kerr (San Francisco)	18.00	9.00	5.50
(83)	Kilduff	18.00	9.00	5.50
(84)	Killifer	18.00	9.00	5.50
(85)	Knight	18.00	9.00	5.50
(86)	Koehler	18.00	9.00	5.50
(87)	Kopp	18.00	9.00	5.50
(88)	Krause	18.00	9.00	5.50
(89)	Krug	18.00	9.00	5.50
(90)	Kunz	18.00	9.00	5.50
(91)	Lafayette	18.00	9.00	5.50
(92)	Lane	18.00	9.00	5.50
(93)	Lang	18.00	9.00	5.50
(94)	Lary	18.00	9.00	5.50
(95)	Leslie	18.00	9.00	5.50
(96)	Lindemore	18.00	9.00	5.50
(97)	Ludolph	18.00	9.00	5.50
(98)	Makin	18.00	9.00	5.50
(99)	Mangum	18.00	9.00	5.50
(100)	Martin	18.00	9.00	5.50
(101)	McCredie	18.00	9.00	5.50
(102)	McDowell	18.00	9.00	5.50
(103)	McKenry	18.00	9.00	5.50
(104)	McLoughlin	18.00	9.00	5.50
(105)	McNally	18.00	9.00	5.50
(106)	McPhee	18.00	9.00	5.50
(107)	Meeker	18.00	9.00	5.50
(108)	Metz	18.00	9.00	5.50
(109)	Miller	18.00	9.00	5.50
(110)	Mitchell (Los Angeles)	18.00	9.00	5.50
(111)	Mitchell (San Francisco)	18.00	9.00	5.50
(112)	Monroe	18.00	9.00	5.50
(113)	Moudy	18.00	9.00	5.50
(114)	Mulcahy	18.00	9.00	5.50
(115)	Mulligan	18.00	9.00	5.50
(116)	Murphy	18.00	9.00	5.50
(117)	O'Doul	45.00	22.00	13.50
(118)	O'Neill	18.00	9.00	5.50
(119)	Oeschger	18.00	9.00	5.50
(120)	Oliver	18.00	9.00	5.50
(121)	Ortman	18.00	9.00	5.50
(122)	Osborn	18.00	9.00	5.50
(123)	Paynter	18.00	9.00	5.50
(124)	Peters	18.00	9.00	5.50
(125)	Pfahler	18.00	9.00	5.50
(126)	Pillette	18.00	9.00	5.50
(127)	Plummer	18.00	9.00	5.50
(128)	Prothro	18.00	9.00	5.50
(129)	Pruett	18.00	9.00	5.50
(130)	Rachac	18.00	9.00	5.50
(131)	Ramsey	18.00	9.00	5.50
(132)	Rathjen	18.00	9.00	5.50
(133)	Read	18.00	9.00	5.50
(134)	Redman	18.00	9.00	5.50
(135)	Jimmy Reese	24.00	12.00	7.25
(136)	Rodda	18.00	9.00	5.50
(137)	Rohwer	18.00	9.00	5.50
(138)	Ryan	18.00	9.00	5.50
(139)	Sandberg	18.00	9.00	5.50
(140)	Sanders	18.00	9.00	5.50
(141)	E. Shea	18.00	9.00	5.50
(142)	M. Shea	18.00	9.00	5.50
(143)	Sheehan	18.00	9.00	5.50
(144)	Shellenbach	18.00	9.00	5.50
(145)	Sherlock	18.00	9.00	5.50
(146)	Siglin	18.00	9.00	5.50
(147)	Slade	18.00	9.00	5.50
(148)	E. Smith	18.00	9.00	5.50
(149)	M. Smith	18.00	9.00	5.50
(150)	Staley	18.00	9.00	5.50
(151)	Statz	18.00	9.00	5.50
(152)	Stroud	18.00	9.00	5.50
(153)	Stuart	18.00	9.00	5.50
(154)	Suhr	18.00	9.00	5.50
(155)	Swanson	18.00	9.00	5.50
(156)	Sweeney	18.00	9.00	5.50
(157)	Tadevich	18.00	9.00	5.50
(158)	Thomas	18.00	9.00	5.50
(159)	Thompson	18.00	9.00	5.50
(160)	Tobin	18.00	9.00	5.50
(161)	Valla	18.00	9.00	5.50
(162)	Vargas	18.00	9.00	5.50
(163)	Vinci	18.00	9.00	5.50
(164)	Walters	18.00	9.00	5.50
(165)	Waner	75.00	38.00	23.00
(166)	Weis	18.00	9.00	5.50
(167)	Whitney	18.00	9.00	5.50
(168)	Williams	18.00	9.00	5.50
(169)	Wright	18.00	9.00	5.50
(170)	Yelle	18.00	9.00	5.50
(171)	Zaeffel	18.00	9.00	5.50
(172)	Zoellers	18.00	9.00	5.50

1927 Zeenut Pacific Coast League (E137)

The 1927 Zeenuts are the same size and color as the 1926 issue, except the year is expressed in just two digits (27), a practice that continued through 1930. There are 144 subjects known.

		NR MT	EX	VG
Complete Set:		2000.	1000.	600.00
Common Player:		16.00	8.00	4.75
(1)	Agnew	16.00	8.00	4.75
(2)	Arlett	22.00	11.00	6.50
(3)	Averill	100.00	50.00	30.00
(4)	Backer	16.00	8.00	4.75
(5)	Bagwell	16.00	8.00	4.75
(6)	Baker	16.00	8.00	4.75
(7)	D. Baker	16.00	8.00	4.75
(8)	Ballenger	16.00	8.00	4.75
(9)	Baumgartner	16.00	8.00	4.75
(10)	Bigbee	16.00	8.00	4.75
(11)	Boehler	16.00	8.00	4.75
(12)	Bool	16.00	8.00	4.75
(13)	Borreani	16.00	8.00	4.75
(14)	Brady	16.00	8.00	4.75
(15)	Bratcher	16.00	8.00	4.75
(16)	Brett	16.00	8.00	4.75
(17)	Brown	16.00	8.00	4.75
(18)	Brubaker	16.00	8.00	4.75
(19)	Bryan	16.00	8.00	4.75
(20)	Callaghan	16.00	8.00	4.75
(21)	Caveney	16.00	8.00	4.75
(22)	Christian	16.00	8.00	4.75
(23)	Cissell	16.00	8.00	4.75
(24)	Cook	16.00	8.00	4.75
(25)	Cooper (Oakland)	16.00	8.00	4.75
(26)	Cooper (Sacramento)	16.00	8.00	4.75
(27)	Cox	16.00	8.00	4.75
(28)	Cunningham	16.00	8.00	4.75
(29)	Daglia	16.00	8.00	4.75
(30)	Dickerman	16.00	8.00	4.75
(31)	Dumovitch	16.00	8.00	4.75
(32)	Eckert	16.00	8.00	4.75
(33)	Eldred	16.00	8.00	4.75
(34)	Ellison	16.00	8.00	4.75
(35)	Fenton	16.00	8.00	4.75
(36)	Finn	16.00	8.00	4.75
(37)	Fischer	16.00	8.00	4.75
(38)	Frederick	16.00	8.00	4.75
(39)	French	16.00	8.00	4.75
(40)	Fullerton	16.00	8.00	4.75
(41)	Geary	16.00	8.00	4.75
(42)	Gillespie	16.00	8.00	4.75
(43)	Gooch	16.00	8.00	4.75
(44)	Gould	16.00	8.00	4.75
(45)	Governor	16.00	8.00	4.75
(46)	Guisto	16.00	8.00	4.75
(47)	Hannah	16.00	8.00	4.75
(48)	Hasty	16.00	8.00	4.75
(49)	Hemingway	16.00	8.00	4.75
(50)	Hoffman	16.00	8.00	4.75
(51)	Hood	16.00	8.00	4.75
(52)	Hooper	100.00	50.00	30.00
(53)	Hudgens	16.00	8.00	4.75

(54)	Hufft	16.00	8.00	4.75
(55)	Hughes	16.00	8.00	4.75
(56)	Jahn	16.00	8.00	4.75
(57)	Johnson (Portland)	16.00	8.00	4.75
(58)	Johnson (Seals)	16.00	8.00	4.75
(59)	Jolly	16.00	8.00	4.75
(60)	Jones	16.00	8.00	4.75
(61)	Kallio	16.00	8.00	4.75
(62)	Keating	16.00	8.00	4.75
(63)	Keefe	16.00	8.00	4.75
(64)	Killifer	16.00	8.00	4.75
(65)	Kimmick	16.00	8.00	4.75
(66)	Kinney	16.00	8.00	4.75
(67)	Knight	16.00	8.00	4.75
(68)	Koehler	16.00	8.00	4.75
(69)	Kopp	16.00	8.00	4.75
(70)	Krause	16.00	8.00	4.75
(71)	Krug	16.00	8.00	4.75
(72)	Kunz	16.00	8.00	4.75
(73)	Lary	16.00	8.00	4.75
(74)	Leard	16.00	8.00	4.75
(75)	Lingrel	16.00	8.00	4.75
(76)	Ludolph	16.00	8.00	4.75
(77)	Mails	16.00	8.00	4.75
(78)	Makin	16.00	8.00	4.75
(79)	Martin	16.00	8.00	4.75
(80)	May	16.00	8.00	4.75
(81)	McCabe	16.00	8.00	4.75
(82)	McCurdy	16.00	8.00	4.75
(83)	McDaniel	16.00	8.00	4.75
(84)	McGee	16.00	8.00	4.75
(85)	McLaughlin	16.00	8.00	4.75
(86)	McMurtry	16.00	8.00	4.75
(87)	Metz	16.00	8.00	4.75
(88)	Miljus	16.00	8.00	4.75
(89)	Mitchell	16.00	8.00	4.75
(90)	Monroe	16.00	8.00	4.75
(91)	Moudy	16.00	8.00	4.75
(92)	Mulligan	16.00	8.00	4.75
(93)	Murphy	16.00	8.00	4.75
(94)	O'Brien	16.00	8.00	4.75
(95)	O'Doul	45.00	22.00	13.50
(96)	Oliver	16.00	8.00	4.75
(97)	Osborn	16.00	8.00	4.75
(98)	Parker (Missions, batting)	16.00	8.00	4.75
(99)	Parker (Missions, throwing)	16.00	8.00	4.75
(100)	Parker (Portland)	16.00	8.00	4.75
(101)	Peters	16.00	8.00	4.75
(102)	Pillette	16.00	8.00	4.75
(103)	Ponder	16.00	8.00	4.75
(104)	Prothro	16.00	8.00	4.75
(105)	Rachac	16.00	8.00	4.75
(106)	Ramsey	16.00	8.00	4.75
(107)	Read	16.00	8.00	4.75
(108)	Jimmy Reese	24.00	12.00	7.25
(109)	Rodda	16.00	8.00	4.75
(110)	Rohwer	16.00	8.00	4.75
(111)	Rose	16.00	8.00	4.75
(112)	Ryan	16.00	8.00	4.75
(113)	Sandberg	16.00	8.00	4.75
(114)	Sanders	16.00	8.00	4.75
(115)	Severeid	16.00	8.00	4.75
(116)	Shea	16.00	8.00	4.75
(117)	Sheehan (Hollywood)	16.00	8.00	4.75
(118)	Sheehan (Seals)	16.00	8.00	4.75
(119)	Sherlock	16.00	8.00	4.75
(120a)	Shinners (date is "1927")	25.00	12.50	7.50
(120b)	Shinners (date is "27")	16.00	8.00	4.75
(121)	Singleton	16.00	8.00	4.75
(122)	Slade	16.00	8.00	4.75
(123)	E. Smith	16.00	8.00	4.75
(124)	Sparks	16.00	8.00	4.75
(125)	Stokes	16.00	8.00	4.75
(126)	J. Storti	16.00	8.00	4.75
(127)	L. Storti	16.00	8.00	4.75
(128)	Strand	16.00	8.00	4.75
(129)	Suhr	16.00	8.00	4.75
(130)	Sunseri	16.00	8.00	4.75
(131)	Swanson	16.00	8.00	4.75
(132)	Tierney	16.00	8.00	4.75
(133)	Valla	16.00	8.00	4.75
(134)	Vargas	16.00	8.00	4.75
(135)	Vitt	16.00	8.00	4.75
(136)	Weinert	16.00	8.00	4.75
(137)	Weis	16.00	8.00	4.75
(138)	Wendell	16.00	8.00	4.75
(139)	Whitney	16.00	8.00	4.75
(140)	Williams	16.00	8.00	4.75
(141)	Guy Williams	16.00	8.00	4.75
(142)	Woodson	16.00	8.00	4.75
(143)	Wright	16.00	8.00	4.75
(144)	Yelle	16.00	8.00	4.75

Grading Guide

Mint (MT): A perfect card. Well-centered with all corners sharp and square. No creases, stains, edge nicks, surface marks, yellowing or fading.

Near Mint (NM): A nearly perfect card. At first glance, a NM card appears to be perfect. May be slightly off-center. No surface marks, creases or loss of gloss.

Excellent (EX): Corners are still fairly sharp with only moderate wear. Borders may be off-center. No creases or stains on fronts or backs, but may show slight loss of surface luster.

VeryGood (VG) : Shows obvious handling. May have rounded corners, minor creases, major gum or wax stains. No major creases, tape marks, writing, etc.

Good (G): A well-worn card, but exhibits no intentional damage. May have major or multiple creases. Corners may be rounded well beyond card border.

1928 Zeenut Pacific Coast League (E137)

Zeenut cards from 1928 through 1930 maintain the same size and style as the 1927 series. The 1928 and 1929 series consist of 168 known subjects, while the 1930 series has 186. There are some lettering variations in the 1930 series.

		NR MT	EX	VG
Complete Set:		2200.	1100.	650.00
Common Player:		16.00	8.00	4.75
(1)	Agnew	16.00	8.00	4.75
(2)	Earl Averill	90.00	45.00	27.00
(3)	Backer	16.00	8.00	4.75
(4)	Baker	16.00	8.00	4.75
(5)	Baldwin	16.00	8.00	4.75
(6)	Barfoot	16.00	8.00	4.75
(7)	Bassler	16.00	8.00	4.75
(8)	Berger	16.00	8.00	4.75
(9)	Bigbee (Los Angeles)	16.00	8.00	4.75
(10)	Bigbee (Portland)	16.00	8.00	4.75
(11)	Bodie	22.00	11.00	6.50
(12)	Boehler	16.00	8.00	4.75
(13)	Bool	16.00	8.00	4.75
(14)	Boone	16.00	8.00	4.75
(15)	Borreani	16.00	8.00	4.75
(16)	Bratcher	16.00	8.00	4.75
(17)	Brenzel	16.00	8.00	4.75
(18)	Brubaker	16.00	8.00	4.75
(19)	Bryan	16.00	8.00	4.75
(20)	Burkett	16.00	8.00	4.75
(21)	Camilli	18.00	9.00	5.50
(22)	W. Canfield	16.00	8.00	4.75
(23)	Caveney	16.00	8.00	4.75
(24)	Cohen	16.00	8.00	4.75
(25)	Cook	16.00	8.00	4.75
(26)	Cooper	16.00	8.00	4.75
(27)	Craghead	16.00	8.00	4.75
(28)	Crosetti	30.00	15.00	9.00
(29)	Cunningham	16.00	8.00	4.75
(30)	Daglia	16.00	8.00	4.75
(31)	Davis	16.00	8.00	4.75
(32)	Dean	16.00	8.00	4.75
(33)	Dittmar	16.00	8.00	4.75
(34)	Donovan	16.00	8.00	4.75
(35)	Downs	16.00	8.00	4.75
(36)	Duff	16.00	8.00	4.75
(37)	Eckert	16.00	8.00	4.75
(38)	Eldred	16.00	8.00	4.75
(39)	Ellsworth	16.00	8.00	4.75
(40)	Fenton	16.00	8.00	4.75
(41)	Finn	16.00	8.00	4.75
(42)	Fitterer	16.00	8.00	4.75
(43)	Flynn	16.00	8.00	4.75
(44)	Frazier	16.00	8.00	4.75
(45)	French (Portland)	16.00	8.00	4.75
(46)	French (Sacramento)	16.00	8.00	4.75
(47)	Fullerton	16.00	8.00	4.75
(48)	Gabler	16.00	8.00	4.75
(49)	Gomes	16.00	8.00	4.75
(50)	Gooch	16.00	8.00	4.75
(51)	Gould	16.00	8.00	4.75
(52)	Governor	16.00	8.00	4.75
(53)	Graham ("S" on uniform)	16.00	8.00	4.75
(54)	Graham (no "S" on uniform)	16.00	8.00	4.75
(55)	Guisto	16.00	8.00	4.75
(56)	Hannah	16.00	8.00	4.75
(57)	Hansen	16.00	8.00	4.75
(58)	Harris	16.00	8.00	4.75
(59)	Hasty	16.00	8.00	4.75
(60)	Heath	16.00	8.00	4.75
(61)	Hoffman	16.00	8.00	4.75
(62)	Holling	16.00	8.00	4.75
(63)	Hood	16.00	8.00	4.75
(64)	House	16.00	8.00	4.75
(65)	Howard	16.00	8.00	4.75
(66)	Hudgens	16.00	8.00	4.75
(67)	Hufft	16.00	8.00	4.75
(68)	Hughes	16.00	8.00	4.75
(69)	Hulvey	16.00	8.00	4.75
(70)	Jacobs	16.00	8.00	4.75
(71)	Johnson (Portland)	16.00	8.00	4.75
(72)	Johnson (San Francisco)	16.00	8.00	4.75
(73)	Jolley	16.00	8.00	4.75
(74)	Jones (batting)	16.00	8.00	4.75
(75)	Jones (throwing)	16.00	8.00	4.75
(76)	Kallio	16.00	8.00	4.75
(77)	Keating	16.00	8.00	4.75
(78)	Keefe	16.00	8.00	4.75
(79)	Keesey	16.00	8.00	4.75
(80)	Kerr	16.00	8.00	4.75
(81)	Killifer	16.00	8.00	4.75
(82)	Kinney	16.00	8.00	4.75
(83)	Knight	16.00	8.00	4.75
(84)	Knothe	16.00	8.00	4.75
(85)	Koehler	16.00	8.00	4.75
(86)	Kopp	16.00	8.00	4.75
(87)	Krause	16.00	8.00	4.75
(88)	Krug	16.00	8.00	4.75
(89)	Lary	16.00	8.00	4.75
(90)	LeBourveau	16.00	8.00	4.75
(91)	Lee	16.00	8.00	4.75
(92)	Ernie Lombardi	90.00	45.00	27.00
(93)	Mails	16.00	8.00	4.75
(94)	Martin (Missions)	16.00	8.00	4.75
(95)	Martin (Seattle)	16.00	8.00	4.75
(96)	May	16.00	8.00	4.75
(97)	McCabe	16.00	8.00	4.75
(98)	McCrea	16.00	8.00	4.75
(99)	McDaniel	16.00	8.00	4.75
(100)	McLaughlin	16.00	8.00	4.75
(101)	McNulty	16.00	8.00	4.75
(102)	Mellano	16.00	8.00	4.75
(103)	Muesel (Meusel)	20.00	10.00	6.00
(104)	Middleton	16.00	8.00	4.75
(105)	Mishkin	16.00	8.00	4.75
(106)	Mitchell	16.00	8.00	4.75
(107)	Monroe	16.00	8.00	4.75
(108)	Moudy	16.00	8.00	4.75
(109)	Mulcahy	16.00	8.00	4.75
(110)	Muller	16.00	8.00	4.75
(111)	Mulligan	16.00	8.00	4.75
(112)	W. Murphy	16.00	8.00	4.75
(113)	Nance	16.00	8.00	4.75
(114)	Nelson	16.00	8.00	4.75
(115)	Osborn	16.00	8.00	4.75
(116)	Osborne	16.00	8.00	4.75
(117)	Parker	16.00	8.00	4.75
(118)	Peters	16.00	8.00	4.75
(119)	Pillette	16.00	8.00	4.75
(120)	Pinelli	16.00	8.00	4.75
(121)	Plitt	16.00	8.00	4.75
(122)	Ponder	16.00	8.00	4.75
(123)	Rachac	16.00	8.00	4.75
(124)	Read	16.00	8.00	4.75
(125)	Reed	16.00	8.00	4.75
(126)	Jimmy Reese	22.00	11.00	6.50
(127)	Rego	16.00	8.00	4.75
(128)	Rhodes	16.00	8.00	4.75
(129)	Rhyne	16.00	8.00	4.75
(130)	Rodda	16.00	8.00	4.75
(131)	Rohwer	16.00	8.00	4.75
(132)	Rose	16.00	8.00	4.75
(133)	Roth	16.00	8.00	4.75
(134)	Ruble	16.00	8.00	4.75
(135)	Ryan	16.00	8.00	4.75
(136)	Sandberg	16.00	8.00	4.75
(137)	Schulmerich	16.00	8.00	4.75
(138)	Severeid	16.00	8.00	4.75
(139)	Shea	16.00	8.00	4.75
(140)	Sheely	16.00	8.00	4.75
(141)	Shellenback	16.00	8.00	4.75
(142)	Sherlock	16.00	8.00	4.75
(143)	Sigafoos	16.00	8.00	4.75
(144)	Singleton	16.00	8.00	4.75
(145)	Slade	16.00	8.00	4.75
(146)	Smith	16.00	8.00	4.75
(147)	Sprinz	16.00	8.00	4.75
(148)	Staley	16.00	8.00	4.75
(149)	Suhr	16.00	8.00	4.75
(150)	Sunseri	16.00	8.00	4.75
(151)	Swanson	16.00	8.00	4.75
(152)	Sweeney	16.00	8.00	4.75
(153)	Teachout	16.00	8.00	4.75
(154)	Twombly	16.00	8.00	4.75
(155)	Vargas	16.00	8.00	4.75
(156)	Vinci	16.00	8.00	4.75
(157)	Vitt	16.00	8.00	4.75
(158)	Warhop	16.00	8.00	4.75
(159)	Weathersby	16.00	8.00	4.75
(160)	Weiss	16.00	8.00	4.75
(161)	Welch	16.00	8.00	4.75
(162)	Wera	16.00	8.00	4.75
(163)	Wetzel	16.00	8.00	4.75
(164)	Whitney	16.00	8.00	4.75
(165)	Williams	16.00	8.00	4.75
(166)	Wilson	16.00	8.00	4.75
(167)	Wolfer	16.00	8.00	4.75
(168)	Yerkes	16.00	8.00	4.75

Values quoted in this guide reflect the retail price of a card – the price a collector can expect to pay when buying a card from a dealer. The wholesale price – that which a collector can expect to receive from a dealer when selling cards – will be significantly lower, depending on desirability and condition.

Values for recent cards and sets are listed in Mint (MT), Near Mint (NM), reflecting the fact that many cards from recent years have been preserved in top condition. Recent cards and sets in less than Excellent condition have little collector interest.

1929 Zeenut Pacific Coast League (E137)

		NR MT	EX	VG
Complete Set:		2250.	1125.	675.00
Common Player:		16.00	8.00	4.75
(1)	Albert	16.00	8.00	4.75
(2)	Almada	16.00	8.00	4.75
(3)	Anderson	16.00	8.00	4.75
(4)	Anton	16.00	8.00	4.75
(5)	Backer	16.00	8.00	4.75
(6)	Baker	16.00	8.00	4.75
(7)	Baldwin	16.00	8.00	4.75
(8)	Barbee	16.00	8.00	4.75
(9)	Barfoot	16.00	8.00	4.75
(10)	Bassler	16.00	8.00	4.75
(11)	Bates	16.00	8.00	4.75
(12)	Berger	16.00	8.00	4.75
(13)	Boehler	16.00	8.00	4.75
(14)	Boone	16.00	8.00	4.75
(15)	Borreani	16.00	8.00	4.75
(16)	Brenzel	16.00	8.00	4.75
(17)	Brooks	16.00	8.00	4.75
(18)	Brubaker	16.00	8.00	4.75
(19)	Bryan	16.00	8.00	4.75
(20)	Burke	16.00	8.00	4.75
(21)	Burkett	16.00	8.00	4.75
(22)	Burns	16.00	8.00	4.75
(23)	Bush	16.00	8.00	4.75
(24)	Butler	16.00	8.00	4.75
(25)	Camilli	18.00	9.00	5.50
(26)	Carlyle	16.00	8.00	4.75
(27)	Carlyle	16.00	8.00	4.75
(28)	Cascarella	16.00	8.00	4.75
(29)	Caveney	16.00	8.00	4.75
(30)	Childs	16.00	8.00	4.75
(31)	Christensen	16.00	8.00	4.75
(32)	Cole	16.00	8.00	4.75
(33)	Collard	16.00	8.00	4.75
(34)	Cooper	16.00	8.00	4.75
(35)	Couch	16.00	8.00	4.75
(36)	Cox	16.00	8.00	4.75
(37)	Craghead	16.00	8.00	4.75
(38)	Crandall	16.00	8.00	4.75
(39)	Cronin	16.00	8.00	4.75
(40)	Crosetti	24.00	12.00	7.25
(41)	Daglia	16.00	8.00	4.75
(42)	Davis	16.00	8.00	4.75
(43)	Dean	16.00	8.00	4.75
(44)	Dittmar	16.00	8.00	4.75
(45)	Donovan	16.00	8.00	4.75
(46)	Dumovich	16.00	8.00	4.75
(47)	Eckardt	16.00	8.00	4.75
(48)	Ellsworth	16.00	8.00	4.75
(49)	Fenton	16.00	8.00	4.75
(50)	Finn	16.00	8.00	4.75
(51)	Fisch	16.00	8.00	4.75
(52)	Flynn	16.00	8.00	4.75
(53)	Frazier	16.00	8.00	4.75
(54)	Freitas	16.00	8.00	4.75
(55)	French	16.00	8.00	4.75
(56)	Gabler	16.00	8.00	4.75
(57)	Glynn	16.00	8.00	4.75
(58)	Gomez	100.00	50.00	30.00
(59)	Gould	16.00	8.00	4.75
(60)	Governor	16.00	8.00	4.75
(61)	Graham	16.00	8.00	4.75
(62)	Hand	16.00	8.00	4.75
(63)	Hannah	16.00	8.00	4.75
(64)	Harris	16.00	8.00	4.75
(65)	Heath	16.00	8.00	4.75
(66)	Heatherly	16.00	8.00	4.75
(67)	Hepting	16.00	8.00	4.75
(68)	Hillis	16.00	8.00	4.75
(69)	Hoffman	16.00	8.00	4.75
(70)	Holling	16.00	8.00	4.75
(71)	Hood	16.00	8.00	4.75
(72)	House	16.00	8.00	4.75
(73)	Howard	16.00	8.00	4.75
(74)	Hubbell	16.00	8.00	4.75
(75)	Hufft	16.00	8.00	4.75
(76)	Hurst	16.00	8.00	4.75
(77)	Jacobs (Los Angeles)	16.00	8.00	4.75
(78)	Jacobs (San Francisco)	16.00	8.00	4.75
(79)	Jahn	16.00	8.00	4.75
(80)	Jeffcoat	16.00	8.00	4.75
(81)	Johnson	16.00	8.00	4.75
(82)	Jolley	16.00	8.00	4.75
(83)	Jones	16.00	8.00	4.75
(84)	Jones	16.00	8.00	4.75
(85)	Kallio	16.00	8.00	4.75
(86)	Kasich	16.00	8.00	4.75
(87)	Keane	16.00	8.00	4.75
(88)	Keating	16.00	8.00	4.75
(89)	Keesey	16.00	8.00	4.75
(90)	Killifer	16.00	8.00	4.75
(91)	Knight	16.00	8.00	4.75
(92)	Knothe	16.00	8.00	4.75
(93)	Knott	16.00	8.00	4.75
(94)	Koehler	16.00	8.00	4.75
(95)	Krasovich	16.00	8.00	4.75
(96)	Krause	16.00	8.00	4.75
(97)	Krug (Hollywood)	16.00	8.00	4.75
(98)	Krug (Los Angeles)	16.00	8.00	4.75
(99)	Kunz	16.00	8.00	4.75
(100)	Langford	16.00	8.00	4.75
(101)	Lee	16.00	8.00	4.75
(102)	Ernie Lombardi	90.00	45.00	27.00
(103)	Mahaffey	16.00	8.00	4.75
(104)	Mails	16.00	8.00	4.75
(105)	Maloney	16.00	8.00	4.75
(106)	McCabe	16.00	8.00	4.75
(107)	McDaniel	16.00	8.00	4.75
(108)	McEvoy	16.00	8.00	4.75
(109)	McIssacs	16.00	8.00	4.75
(110)	McQuaid	16.00	8.00	4.75
(111)	Miller	16.00	8.00	4.75
(112)	Monroe	16.00	8.00	4.75
(113)	Muller	16.00	8.00	4.75
(114)	Mulligan	16.00	8.00	4.75
(115)	Nance	16.00	8.00	4.75
(116)	Nelson	16.00	8.00	4.75
(117)	Nevers	16.00	8.00	4.75
(118)	Oana	16.00	8.00	4.75
(119)	Olney	16.00	8.00	4.75
(120)	Ortman	16.00	8.00	4.75
(121)	Osborne	16.00	8.00	4.75
(122)	Ostenberg	16.00	8.00	4.75
(123)	Peters	16.00	8.00	4.75
(124)	Pillette	16.00	8.00	4.75
(125)	Pinelli	20.00	10.00	6.00
(126)	Pipgras	16.00	8.00	4.75
(127)	Plitt	16.00	8.00	4.75
(128)	Polvogt	16.00	8.00	4.75
(129)	Rachac	16.00	8.00	4.75
(130)	Read	16.00	8.00	4.75
(131)	Reed	16.00	8.00	4.75
(132)	Jimmy Reese	24.00	12.00	7.25
(133)	Rego	16.00	8.00	4.75
(134)	Ritter	16.00	8.00	4.75
(135)	Roberts	16.00	8.00	4.75
(136)	Rodda	16.00	8.00	4.75
(137)	Rodgers	16.00	8.00	4.75
(138)	Rohwer	16.00	8.00	4.75
(139)	Rollings	16.00	8.00	4.75
(140)	Rumler	16.00	8.00	4.75
(141)	Ryan	16.00	8.00	4.75
(142)	Sandberg	16.00	8.00	4.75
(143)	Schino	16.00	8.00	4.75
(144)	Schmidt	16.00	8.00	4.75
(145)	Schulmerich	16.00	8.00	4.75
(146)	Scott	16.00	8.00	4.75
(147)	Severeid	16.00	8.00	4.75
(148)	Shanklin	16.00	8.00	4.75
(149)	Sherlock	16.00	8.00	4.75
(150)	Slade	16.00	8.00	4.75
(151)	Staley	16.00	8.00	4.75
(152)	Statz	16.00	8.00	4.75
(153)	Steinecke	16.00	8.00	4.75
(154)	Suhr	16.00	8.00	4.75
(155)	Taylor	16.00	8.00	4.75
(156)	Thurston	16.00	8.00	4.75
(157)	Tierney	16.00	8.00	4.75
(158)	Tolson	16.00	8.00	4.75
(159)	Tomlin	16.00	8.00	4.75
(160)	Vergez	16.00	8.00	4.75
(161)	Vinci	16.00	8.00	4.75
(162)	Volkman	16.00	8.00	4.75
(163)	Walsh	16.00	8.00	4.75
(164)	Warren	16.00	8.00	4.75
(165)	Webb	16.00	8.00	4.75
(166)	Weustling	16.00	8.00	4.75
(167)	Williams	16.00	8.00	4.75
(168)	Wingo	16.00	8.00	4.75

1930 Zeenut Pacific Coast League (E137)

		NR MT	EX	VG
Complete Set:		2400.	1200.	725.00
Common Player:		16.00	8.00	4.75
(1)	Allington	16.00	8.00	4.75
(2)	Almada	16.00	8.00	4.75
(3)	Andrews	16.00	8.00	4.75
(4)	Anton	16.00	8.00	4.75
(5)	Arlett	20.00	10.00	6.00
(6)	Backer	16.00	8.00	4.75
(7)	Baecht	16.00	8.00	4.75
(8)	Baker	16.00	8.00	4.75
(9)	Baldwin	16.00	8.00	4.75
(10)	Ballou	16.00	8.00	4.75
(11)	Barbee	16.00	8.00	4.75
(12)	Barfoot	16.00	8.00	4.75
(13)	Bassler	16.00	8.00	4.75
(14)	Bates	16.00	8.00	4.75
(15)	Beck	16.00	8.00	4.75
(16)	Boone	16.00	8.00	4.75
(17)	Bowman	16.00	8.00	4.75
(18)	Brannon	16.00	8.00	4.75
(19)	Brenzel	16.00	8.00	4.75
(20)	Brown	16.00	8.00	4.75
(21)	Brubaker	16.00	8.00	4.75
(22)	Brucker	16.00	8.00	4.75
(23)	Bryan	16.00	8.00	4.75
(24)	Burkett	16.00	8.00	4.75
(25)	Burns	16.00	8.00	4.75
(26)	Butler	16.00	8.00	4.75
(27)	Camilli	20.00	10.00	6.00
(28)	Carlyle	16.00	8.00	4.75
(29)	Caster	16.00	8.00	4.75
(30)	Caveney	16.00	8.00	4.75
(31)	Chamberlain	16.00	8.00	4.75
(32)	Chatham	16.00	8.00	4.75
(33)	Childs	16.00	8.00	4.75
(34)	Christensen	16.00	8.00	4.75
(35)	Church	16.00	8.00	4.75
(36)	Cole	16.00	8.00	4.75
(37)	Coleman	16.00	8.00	4.75
(38)	Collins	16.00	8.00	4.75
(39)	Coscarart	16.00	8.00	4.75
(40)	Cox	16.00	8.00	4.75
(41)	Coyle	16.00	8.00	4.75
(42)	Craghead	16.00	8.00	4.75
(43)	Cronin	16.00	8.00	4.75
(44)	Crosetti	22.00	11.00	6.50
(45)	Daglia	16.00	8.00	4.75
(46)	Davis	16.00	8.00	4.75
(47)	Dean	16.00	8.00	4.75
(48)	DeViveiros	16.00	8.00	4.75
(49)	Dittmar	16.00	8.00	4.75
(50)	Donovan	16.00	8.00	4.75
(51)	Douglas	16.00	8.00	4.75
(52)	Dumovich	16.00	8.00	4.75
(53)	Edwards	16.00	8.00	4.75
(54)	Ellsworth	16.00	8.00	4.75
(55)	Falk	16.00	8.00	4.75
(56)	Fisch	16.00	8.00	4.75
(57)	Flynn	16.00	8.00	4.75
(58)	Freitas	16.00	8.00	4.75
(59)	French (Portland)	16.00	8.00	4.75
(60)	French (Sacramento)	16.00	8.00	4.75
(61)	Gabler	16.00	8.00	4.75
(62)	Gaston	16.00	8.00	4.75
(63)	Gazella	16.00	8.00	4.75
(64)	Gould	16.00	8.00	4.75
(65)	Governor	16.00	8.00	4.75
(66)	Green	16.00	8.00	4.75
(67)	Griffin	16.00	8.00	4.75
(68)	Haney	16.00	8.00	4.75
(69)	Hannah	16.00	8.00	4.75
(70)	Harper	16.00	8.00	4.75
(71)	Heath	16.00	8.00	4.75
(72)	Hillis	16.00	8.00	4.75
(73)	Hoag	16.00	8.00	4.75
(74)	Hoffman	16.00	8.00	4.75
(75)	Holland	16.00	8.00	4.75
(76)	Hollerson	16.00	8.00	4.75
(77)	Holling	16.00	8.00	4.75
(78)	Hood	16.00	8.00	4.75
(79)	Horn	16.00	8.00	4.75
(80)	House	16.00	8.00	4.75
(81)	Hubbell	16.00	8.00	4.75
(82)	Hufft	16.00	8.00	4.75
(83)	Hurst	16.00	8.00	4.75
(84)	Jacobs (Los Angeles)	16.00	8.00	4.75
(85)	Jacobs (Oakland)	16.00	8.00	4.75
(86)	Jacobs	16.00	8.00	4.75
(87)	Jahn	16.00	8.00	4.75
(88)	Jeffcoat	16.00	8.00	4.75
(89)	Johns	16.00	8.00	4.75
(90)	Johnson (Portland)	16.00	8.00	4.75
(91)	Johnson (Seattle)	16.00	8.00	4.75
(92)	Joiner	16.00	8.00	4.75
(93)	Kallio	16.00	8.00	4.75
(94)	Kasich	16.00	8.00	4.75
(95)	Keating	16.00	8.00	4.75
(96)	Kelly	16.00	8.00	4.75
(97)	Killifer	16.00	8.00	4.75
(98)	Knight	16.00	8.00	4.75
(99)	Knothe	16.00	8.00	4.75
(100)	Koehler	16.00	8.00	4.75
(101)	Kunz	16.00	8.00	4.75
(102)	Lamanski	16.00	8.00	4.75
(103)	Lawrence	16.00	8.00	4.75
(104)	Lee	16.00	8.00	4.75
(105)	Leishman	16.00	8.00	4.75
(106)	Lelivelt	16.00	8.00	4.75
(107)	Lieber	16.00	8.00	4.75
(108)	Ernie Lombardi	90.00	45.00	27.00
(109)	Mails	16.00	8.00	4.75
(110)	Maloney	16.00	8.00	4.75
(111)	Martin	16.00	8.00	4.75
(112)	McDougal	16.00	8.00	4.75
(113)	McLaughlin	16.00	8.00	4.75
(114)	McQuaide	16.00	8.00	4.75
(115)	Mellana	16.00	8.00	4.75
(116)	Miljus ("S" on uniform)	16.00	8.00	4.75
(117)	Miljus ("Seals" on uniform)	16.00	8.00	4.75
(118)	Monroe	16.00	8.00	4.75
(119)	Montgomery	16.00	8.00	4.75
(120)	Moore	16.00	8.00	4.75

		NR MT	EX	VG
(121)	Mulana	16.00	8.00	4.75
(122)	Muller	16.00	8.00	4.75
(123)	Mulligan	16.00	8.00	4.75
(124)	Nelson	16.00	8.00	4.75
(125)	Nevers	16.00	8.00	4.75
(126)	Odell	16.00	8.00	4.75
(127)	Olney	16.00	8.00	4.75
(128)	Osborne	16.00	8.00	4.75
(129)	Page	16.00	8.00	4.75
(130)	Palmisano	16.00	8.00	4.75
(131)	Parker	16.00	8.00	4.75
(132)	Pasedel	16.00	8.00	4.75
(133)	Pearson	16.00	8.00	4.75
(134)	Penebskey	16.00	8.00	4.75
(135)	Perry	16.00	8.00	4.75
(136)	Peters	16.00	8.00	4.75
(137)	Petterson	16.00	8.00	4.75
(138)	H. Pillette	16.00	8.00	4.75
(139)	T. Pillette	16.00	8.00	4.75
(140)	Pinelli	20.00	10.00	6.00
(141)	Pipgrass	16.00	8.00	4.75
(142)	Porter	16.00	8.00	4.75
(143)	Powles	16.00	8.00	4.75
(144)	Read	16.00	8.00	4.75
(145)	Reed	16.00	8.00	4.75
(146)	Rehg	16.00	8.00	4.75
(147)	Ricci	16.00	8.00	4.75
(148)	Roberts	16.00	8.00	4.75
(149)	Rodda	16.00	8.00	4.75
(150)	Rohwer	16.00	8.00	4.75
(151)	Rosenberg	16.00	8.00	4.75
(152)	Rumler	16.00	8.00	4.75
(153)	Ryan	16.00	8.00	4.75
(154)	Schino	16.00	8.00	4.75
(155)	Severeid	16.00	8.00	4.75
(156)	Shanklin	16.00	8.00	4.75
(157)	Sheely	16.00	8.00	4.75
(158)	Sigafoos	16.00	8.00	4.75
(159)	Statz	16.00	8.00	4.75
(160)	Steinbacker	16.00	8.00	4.75
(161)	Stevenson	16.00	8.00	4.75
(162)	Sulik	16.00	8.00	4.75
(163)	Taylor	16.00	8.00	4.75
(164)	Thomas (Sacramento)	16.00	8.00	4.75
(165)	Thomas (San Francisco)	16.00	8.00	4.75
(166)	Trembly	16.00	8.00	4.75
(167)	Turner	16.00	8.00	4.75
(168)	Turpin	16.00	8.00	4.75
(169)	Uhalt	16.00	8.00	4.75
(170)	Vergez	16.00	8.00	4.75
(171)	Vinci	16.00	8.00	4.75
(172)	Vitt	16.00	8.00	4.75
(173)	Wallgren	16.00	8.00	4.75
(174)	Walsh	16.00	8.00	4.75
(175)	Ward	16.00	8.00	4.75
(176)	Warren	16.00	8.00	4.75
(177)	Webb	16.00	8.00	4.75
(178)	Wetzell	16.00	8.00	4.75
(179)	F. Wetzel	16.00	8.00	4.75
(180)	Williams	16.00	8.00	4.75
(181)	Wilson	16.00	8.00	4.75
(182)	Wingo	16.00	8.00	4.75
(183)	Wirts	16.00	8.00	4.75
(184)	Woodall	16.00	8.00	4.75
(185)	Zamlack	16.00	8.00	4.75
(186)	Zinn	16.00	8.00	4.75

1931 Zeenut Pacific Coast League (E137)

Beginning in 1931, Zeenuts cards were no longer dated on the front, and cards without the coupon are very difficult to date. The words "Zeenuts Series" was also dropped from the front and replaced with just the words "Coast League." Zeenut cards in 1931 and 1932 measure 1-3/4" x 2-3/4".

		NR MT	EX	VG
Complete Set:		1550.	750.00	450.00
Common Player:		16.00	8.00	4.75
(1)	Abbott	16.00	8.00	4.75
(2)	Andrews	16.00	8.00	4.75
(3)	Anton	16.00	8.00	4.75
(4)	Backer	16.00	8.00	4.75
(5)	Baker	16.00	8.00	4.75
(6)	Baldwin	16.00	8.00	4.75
(7)	Barbee	16.00	8.00	4.75
(8)	Barton	16.00	8.00	4.75
(9)	Bassler	16.00	8.00	4.75
(10)	Berger (Missions)	16.00	8.00	4.75
(11)	Berger (Portland)	16.00	8.00	4.75
(12)	Biggs	16.00	8.00	4.75
(13)	Bowman	16.00	8.00	4.75
(14)	Brenzel	16.00	8.00	4.75
(15)	Bryan	16.00	8.00	4.75
(16)	Burns	16.00	8.00	4.75
(17)	Camilli	20.00	10.00	6.00
(18)	Campbell	16.00	8.00	4.75
(19)	Carlyle	16.00	8.00	4.75
(20)	Caveney	16.00	8.00	4.75
(21)	Chesterfield	16.00	8.00	4.75
(22)	Cole	16.00	8.00	4.75
(23)	Coleman	16.00	8.00	4.75
(24)	Coscarart	16.00	8.00	4.75
(25)	Crosetti	20.00	10.00	6.00
(26)	Davis	16.00	8.00	4.75
(27)	DeBerry	16.00	8.00	4.75
(28)	Demaree	16.00	8.00	4.75
(29)	Dean	16.00	8.00	4.75
(30)	Delaney	16.00	8.00	4.75
(31)	Dondero	16.00	8.00	4.75
(32)	Donovan	16.00	8.00	4.75
(33)	Douglas	16.00	8.00	4.75
(34)	Ellsworth	16.00	8.00	4.75
(35)	Farrell	16.00	8.00	4.75
(36)	Fenton	16.00	8.00	4.75
(37)	Fitzpatrick	16.00	8.00	4.75
(38)	Flagstead	16.00	8.00	4.75
(39)	Flynn	16.00	8.00	4.75
(40)	Frazier	16.00	8.00	4.75
(41)	Freitas	16.00	8.00	4.75
(42)	French	16.00	8.00	4.75
(43)	Fullerton	16.00	8.00	4.75
(44)	Gabler	16.00	8.00	4.75
(45)	Gazella	16.00	8.00	4.75
(46)	Hale	16.00	8.00	4.75
(47)	Hamilton	16.00	8.00	4.75
(48)	Haney	16.00	8.00	4.75
(49)	Hannah	16.00	8.00	4.75
(50)	Harper	16.00	8.00	4.75
(51)	Henderson	16.00	8.00	4.75
(52)	Herrmann	16.00	8.00	4.75
(53)	Hoffman	16.00	8.00	4.75
(54)	Holland	16.00	8.00	4.75
(55)	Holling	16.00	8.00	4.75
(56)	Hubbell	16.00	8.00	4.75
(57)	Hufft	16.00	8.00	4.75
(58)	Hurst	16.00	8.00	4.75
(59)	Jacobs	16.00	8.00	4.75
(60)	Kallio	16.00	8.00	4.75
(61)	Keating	16.00	8.00	4.75
(62)	Keesey	16.00	8.00	4.75
(63)	Knothe	16.00	8.00	4.75
(64)	Knott	16.00	8.00	4.75
(65)	Kohler	16.00	8.00	4.75
(66)	Lamanski	16.00	8.00	4.75
(67)	Lee	16.00	8.00	4.75
(68)	Lelivelt	16.00	8.00	4.75
(69)	Lieber	16.00	8.00	4.75
(70)	Lipanovic	16.00	8.00	4.75
(71)	McDonald	16.00	8.00	4.75
(72)	McDougall	16.00	8.00	4.75
(73)	McLaughlin	16.00	8.00	4.75
(74)	Monroe	16.00	8.00	4.75
(75)	Moss	16.00	8.00	4.75
(76)	Mulligan	16.00	8.00	4.75
(77)	Ortman	16.00	8.00	4.75
(78)	Orwoll	16.00	8.00	4.75
(79)	Parker	16.00	8.00	4.75
(80)	Penebskey	16.00	8.00	4.75
(81)	H. Pillette	16.00	8.00	4.75
(82)	Pillette	16.00	8.00	4.75
(83)	Pinelli	20.00	10.00	6.00
(84)	Pool	16.00	8.00	4.75
(85)	Posedel	16.00	8.00	4.75
(86)	Powers	16.00	8.00	4.75
(87)	Read	16.00	8.00	4.75
(88)	Jimmy Reese	24.00	12.00	7.25
(89)	Rhiel	16.00	8.00	4.75
(90)	Ricci	16.00	8.00	4.75
(91)	Rohwer	16.00	8.00	4.75
(92)	Ryan	16.00	8.00	4.75
(93)	Schino	16.00	8.00	4.75
(94)	Schulte	16.00	8.00	4.75
(95)	Severeid	16.00	8.00	4.75
(96)	Sharpe	16.00	8.00	4.75
(97)	Shellenback	16.00	8.00	4.75
(98)	Simas	16.00	8.00	4.75
(99)	Steinbacker	16.00	8.00	4.75
(100)	Summa	16.00	8.00	4.75
(101)	Tubbs	16.00	8.00	4.75
(102)	Turner	16.00	8.00	4.75
(103)	Turpin	16.00	8.00	4.75
(104)	Uhalt	16.00	8.00	4.75
(105)	Vinci	16.00	8.00	4.75
(106)	Vitt	16.00	8.00	4.75
(107)	Wade	16.00	8.00	4.75
(108)	Walsh	16.00	8.00	4.75
(109)	Walters	16.00	8.00	4.75
(110)	Wera	16.00	8.00	4.75
(111)	Wetzel	16.00	8.00	4.75
(112)	Williams (Portland)	16.00	8.00	4.75
(113)	Williams (San Francisco)	16.00	8.00	4.75
(114)	Wingo	16.00	8.00	4.75
(115)	Wirts	16.00	8.00	4.75
(116)	Wise	16.00	8.00	4.75
(117)	Woodall	16.00	8.00	4.75
(118)	Yerkes	16.00	8.00	4.75
(119)	Zamlock	16.00	8.00	4.75
(120)	Zinn	16.00	8.00	4.75

A player's name in italic type indicates a rookie card. An (FC) indicates a player's first card for that particular card company.

1932 Zeenut Pacific Coast League (E137)

		NR MT	EX	VG
Complete Set:		1550.	750.00	450.00
Common Player:		16.00	8.00	4.75
(1)	Abbott	16.00	8.00	4.75
(2)	Almada	16.00	8.00	4.75
(3)	Anton	16.00	8.00	4.75
(4)	Babich	16.00	8.00	4.75
(5)	Backer	16.00	8.00	4.75
(6)	Baker	16.00	8.00	4.75
(7)	Ballou	16.00	8.00	4.75
(8)	Bassler	16.00	8.00	4.75
(9)	Berger	16.00	8.00	4.75
(10)	Blackerby	16.00	8.00	4.75
(11)	Bordagaray	16.00	8.00	4.75
(12)	Brannon	16.00	8.00	4.75
(13)	Briggs	16.00	8.00	4.75
(14)	Brubaker	16.00	8.00	4.75
(15)	Callaghan	16.00	8.00	4.75
(16)	Camilli	20.00	10.00	6.00
(17)	Campbell	16.00	8.00	4.75
(18)	Carlyle	16.00	8.00	4.75
(19)	Caster	16.00	8.00	4.75
(20)	Caveney	16.00	8.00	4.75
(21)	Chamberlain	16.00	8.00	4.75
(22)	Cole	16.00	8.00	4.75
(23)	Collard	16.00	8.00	4.75
(24)	Cook	16.00	8.00	4.75
(25)	Coscarart	16.00	8.00	4.75
(26)	Cox	16.00	8.00	4.75
(27)	Cronin	16.00	8.00	4.75
(28)	Daglia	16.00	8.00	4.75
(29)	Dahlgren	24.00	12.00	7.25
(30)	Davis	16.00	8.00	4.75
(31)	Dean	16.00	8.00	4.75
(32)	Delaney	16.00	8.00	4.75
(33)	Demaree	16.00	8.00	4.75
(34)	Devine	16.00	8.00	4.75
(35)	DeViveiros	16.00	8.00	4.75
(36)	Dittmar	16.00	8.00	4.75
(37)	Donovan	16.00	8.00	4.75
(38)	Ellsworth	16.00	8.00	4.75
(39)	Fitzpatrick	16.00	8.00	4.75
(40)	Frazier	16.00	8.00	4.75
(41)	Freitas	16.00	8.00	4.75
(42)	Garibaldi	16.00	8.00	4.75
(43)	Gaston	16.00	8.00	4.75
(44)	Gazella	16.00	8.00	4.75
(45)	Gillick	16.00	8.00	4.75
(46)	Hafey	16.00	8.00	4.75
(47)	Haney	16.00	8.00	4.75
(48)	Hannah	16.00	8.00	4.75
(49)	Henderson	16.00	8.00	4.75
(50)	Herrmann	16.00	8.00	4.75
(51)	Hipps	16.00	8.00	4.75
(52)	Hofman	16.00	8.00	4.75
(53)	Holland	16.00	8.00	4.75
(54)	House	16.00	8.00	4.75
(55)	Hufft	16.00	8.00	4.75
(56)	Hunt	16.00	8.00	4.75
(57)	Hurst	16.00	8.00	4.75
(58)	Jacobs	16.00	8.00	4.75
(59)	Johns	16.00	8.00	4.75
(60)	Johnson (Missions)	16.00	8.00	4.75
(61)	Johnson (Portland)	16.00	8.00	4.75
(62)	Johnson (Seattle)	16.00	8.00	4.75
(63)	Joiner	16.00	8.00	4.75
(64)	Kallio	16.00	8.00	4.75
(65)	Kasich	16.00	8.00	4.75
(66)	Keesey	16.00	8.00	4.75
(67)	Kelly	16.00	8.00	4.75
(68)	Koehler	16.00	8.00	4.75
(69)	Lee	16.00	8.00	4.75
(70)	Lieber	16.00	8.00	4.75
(71)	Mailho	16.00	8.00	4.75
(72)	Martin (Oakland)	16.00	8.00	4.75
(73)	Martin (San Francisco)	16.00	8.00	4.75
(74)	McNeely	16.00	8.00	4.75
(75)	Miljus	16.00	8.00	4.75
(76)	Monroe	16.00	8.00	4.75
(77)	Mosolf	16.00	8.00	4.75
(78)	Moss	16.00	8.00	4.75
(79)	Muller	16.00	8.00	4.75
(80)	Mulligan	16.00	8.00	4.75

(81)	Oana	16.00	8.00	4.75
(82)	Osborn	16.00	8.00	4.75
(83)	Page	16.00	8.00	4.75
(84)	Penebsky	16.00	8.00	4.75
(85)	H. Pillette	16.00	8.00	4.75
(86)	Pinelli	20.00	10.00	6.00
(87)	Poole	16.00	8.00	4.75
(88)	Quellich	16.00	8.00	4.75
(89)	Read	16.00	8.00	4.75
(90)	Ricci	16.00	8.00	4.75
(91)	Salvo	16.00	8.00	4.75
(92)	Sankey	16.00	8.00	4.75
(93)	Sheehan	16.00	8.00	4.75
(94)	Shellenback	16.00	8.00	4.75
(95)	Sherlock (Hollywood)	16.00	8.00	4.75
(96)	Sherlock (Missions)	16.00	8.00	4.75
(97)	Shores	16.00	8.00	4.75
(98)	Simas	16.00	8.00	4.75
(99)	Statz	16.00	8.00	4.75
(100)	Steinbacker	16.00	8.00	4.75
(101)	Sulik	16.00	8.00	4.75
(102)	Summa	16.00	8.00	4.75
(103)	Thomas	16.00	8.00	4.75
(104)	Uhalt	16.00	8.00	4.75
(105)	Vinci	16.00	8.00	4.75
(106)	Vitt	16.00	8.00	4.75
(107)	Walsh (Missions)	16.00	8.00	4.75
(108)	Walsh (Oakland)	16.00	8.00	4.75
(109)	Walters	16.00	8.00	4.75
(110)	Ward	16.00	8.00	4.75
(111)	Welsh	16.00	8.00	4.75
(112)	Wera	16.00	8.00	4.75
(113)	Williams	16.00	8.00	4.75
(114)	Willoughby	16.00	8.00	4.75
(115)	Wirts	16.00	8.00	4.75
(116)	Wise	16.00	8.00	4.75
(117)	Woodall	16.00	8.00	4.75
(118)	Yde	16.00	8.00	4.75
(119)	Zahniser	16.00	8.00	4.75
(120)	Zamloch	16.00	8.00	4.75

1933 Zeenut PCL (sepia) (E137)

This is the most confusing era for Zeenut cards. The cards of 1933-36 are nearly identical, displaying the words, "Coast League" in a small rectangle (with rounded corners), along with the player's name and team. The photos were black and white (except 1933 Zeenuts have also been found with sepia photos). Because no date appears on the photos, cards from these years are impossible to tell apart without the coupon bottom that lists an expiration date. To date over 161 subjects have been found, with some known to exist in all four years. There are cases where the exact same photo was used from one year to the next (sometimes with minor cropping differences). All cards of Joe and Vince DiMaggio have their last name misspelled "DeMaggio."

		NR MT	EX	VG
Complete Set:		700.00	350.00	200.00
Common Player:		15.00	7.50	4.50
(1)	L. Almada	15.00	7.50	4.50
(2)	Anton	15.00	7.50	4.50
(3)	Bassler	15.00	7.50	4.50
(4)	Bonnelly	15.00	7.50	4.50
(5)	Bordagary	15.00	7.50	4.50
(6)	Bottarini	15.00	7.50	4.50
(7)	Brannan	15.00	7.50	4.50
(8)	Brubaker	15.00	7.50	4.50
(9)	Bryan	15.00	7.50	4.50
(10)	Burns	15.00	7.50	4.50
(11)	Camilli	18.00	9.00	5.50
(12)	Chozen	15.00	7.50	4.50
(13)	Cole	15.00	7.50	4.50
(14)	Cronin	15.00	7.50	4.50
(15)	Dahlgren	18.00	9.00	5.50
(16)	Donovan	15.00	7.50	4.50
(17)	Douglas	15.00	7.50	4.50
(18)	Flynn	15.00	7.50	4.50
(19)	French	15.00	7.50	4.50
(20)	Frietas	15.00	7.50	4.50
(21)	Galan	15.00	7.50	4.50
(22)	Hofmann	15.00	7.50	4.50
(23)	Kelman	15.00	7.50	4.50
(24)	Lelivelt	15.00	7.50	4.50
(25)	Ludolph	15.00	7.50	4.50
(26)	McDonald	15.00	7.50	4.50
(27)	McNeely	15.00	7.50	4.50
(28)	McQuaid	15.00	7.50	4.50
(29)	Moncrief	15.00	7.50	4.50
(30)	Nelson	15.00	7.50	4.50
(31)	Osborne	15.00	7.50	4.50
(32)	Petersen	15.00	7.50	4.50
(33)	Reeves	15.00	7.50	4.50
(34)	Scott	15.00	7.50	4.50
(35)	Shellenback	15.00	7.50	4.50
(36)	J. Sherlock	15.00	7.50	4.50
(37)	V. Sherlock	15.00	7.50	4.50
(38)	Steinbacker	15.00	7.50	4.50
(39)	Stine	15.00	7.50	4.50
(40)	Strange	15.00	7.50	4.50
(41)	Sulik	15.00	7.50	4.50
(42)	Sweetland	15.00	7.50	4.50
(43)	Uhalt	15.00	7.50	4.50
(44)	Vinci	15.00	7.50	4.50
(45)	Vitt	15.00	7.50	4.50
(46)	Wetzel	15.00	7.50	4.50
(47)	Woodall	15.00	7.50	4.50
(48)	Zinn	15.00	7.50	4.50

1933 - 36 Zeenut PCL (black and white) (E137)

		NR MT	EX	VG
Complete Set:		6000.	3000.	1800.
Common Player:		15.00	7.50	4.50
(1a)	Almada (large pose)	15.00	7.50	4.50
(1b)	Almada (small pose)	15.00	7.50	4.50
(2a)	Anton (large pose)	15.00	7.50	4.50
(2b)	Anton (small pose)	15.00	7.50	4.50
(3)	Babich	15.00	7.50	4.50
(4)	Backer	15.00	7.50	4.50
(5)	Ballou (black stockings)	15.00	7.50	4.50
(6a)	Ballou (stockings with band, large pose)	15.00	7.50	4.50
(6b)	Ballou (stockings with band, small pose)			
(7)	Barath	15.00	7.50	4.50
(8)	Beck	15.00	7.50	4.50
(9)	C. Beck	15.00	7.50	4.50
(10)	W. Beck	15.00	7.50	4.50
(11)	Becker	15.00	7.50	4.50
(12)	Biongovanni	15.00	7.50	4.50
(13)	Blackerby	15.00	7.50	4.50
(14)	Blakely	15.00	7.50	4.50
(15)	Borja (Sacramento)	15.00	7.50	4.50
(16)	Borja (Seals)	15.00	7.50	4.50
(17)	Brundin	15.00	7.50	4.50
(18)	Carlyle	15.00	7.50	4.50
(19a)	Caveney (name incorrect)	15.00	7.50	4.50
(19b)	Cavaney (name correct)	15.00	7.50	4.50
(20)	Chelini	15.00	7.50	4.50
(21)	Cole (with glove)	15.00	7.50	4.50
(22)	Cole (no glove)	15.00	7.50	4.50
(23)	Connors	15.00	7.50	4.50
(24)	Coscarart (Missions)	15.00	7.50	4.50
(25)	Coscarart (Seattle)	15.00	7.50	4.50
(26)	Cox	15.00	7.50	4.50
(27)	Davis	15.00	7.50	4.50
(28)	J. DeMaggio (DiMaggio) (batting)	2000.	1000.	600.00
(29)	J. DeMaggio (DiMaggio) (throwing)	2000.	1000.	600.00
(30)	V. DeMaggio (DiMaggio)	400.00	200.00	120.00
(31)	DeViveiros	15.00	7.50	4.50
(32)	Densmore	15.00	7.50	4.50
(33)	Dittmar	15.00	7.50	4.50
(34)	Donovan	15.00	7.50	4.50
(35)	Douglas (Oakland)	15.00	7.50	4.50
(36)	Douglas (Seals)	15.00	7.50	4.50
(37a)	Duggan (large pose)	15.00	7.50	4.50
(37b)	Duggan (small pose)	15.00	7.50	4.50
(38)	Durst	15.00	7.50	4.50
(39a)	Eckhardt (large pose)	15.00	7.50	4.50
(39b)	Eckhardt (small pose)	15.00	7.50	4.50
(40)	Ellsworth	15.00	7.50	4.50
(41)	Fenton	15.00	7.50	4.50
(42)	Fitzpatrick	15.00	7.50	4.50
(43)	Francovich	15.00	7.50	4.50
(44)	Funk	15.00	7.50	4.50
(45a)	Garibaldi (large pose)	15.00	7.50	4.50
(45b)	Garibaldi (small pose)	15.00	7.50	4.50
(46)	Gibson (black sleeves)	15.00	7.50	4.50
(47)	Gibson (white sleeves)	15.00	7.50	4.50
(48)	Gira	15.00	7.50	4.50
(49)	Glaister	15.00	7.50	4.50
(50)	Graves	15.00	7.50	4.50
(51a)	Hafey (Missions, large pose)	15.00	7.50	4.50
(51b)	Hafey (Missions, middle-size pose)	15.00	7.50	4.50
(51c)	Hafey (Missions, small pose)	15.00	7.50	4.50
(52)	Hafey (Sacramento)	15.00	7.50	4.50
(53)	Haid (Oakland)	15.00	7.50	4.50
(54)	Haid (Seattle)	15.00	7.50	4.50
(55)	Haney	15.00	7.50	4.50
(56a)	Hartwig (Sacramento, large pose)	15.00	7.50	4.50
(56b)	Hartwig (Sacramento, small pose)	15.00	7.50	4.50
(57)	Hartwig (Seals)	15.00	7.50	4.50
(58)	Henderson	15.00	7.50	4.50
(59)	Herrmann	15.00	7.50	4.50
(60)	B. Holder	15.00	7.50	4.50
(61)	Holland	15.00	7.50	4.50
(62)	Horne	15.00	7.50	4.50
(63)	House	15.00	7.50	4.50
(64)	Hunt	15.00	7.50	4.50
(65)	A.E. Jacobs	15.00	7.50	4.50
(66)	Johns	15.00	7.50	4.50
(67)	D. Johnson	15.00	7.50	4.50
(68)	L. Johnson	15.00	7.50	4.50
(69)	Joiner	15.00	7.50	4.50
(70)	Jolly, Jorgensen	15.00	7.50	4.50
(71)	Joost, Kallio	15.00	7.50	4.50
(74)	Kamm	15.00	7.50	4.50
(75)	Kampouris	15.00	7.50	4.50
(76)	E. Kelly (Oakland)	15.00	7.50	4.50
(77)	E. Kelly (Seattle)	15.00	7.50	4.50
(78)	Kenna	15.00	7.50	4.50
(79)	Kintana	15.00	7.50	4.50
(80)	Lahman	15.00	7.50	4.50
(81)	Lieber	15.00	7.50	4.50
(82)	Ludolph	15.00	7.50	4.50
(83)	Mailho	15.00	7.50	4.50
(84a)	Mails (large pose)	15.00	7.50	4.50
(84b)	Mails (small pose)	15.00	7.50	4.50
(85)	Marty (black sleeves)	15.00	7.50	4.50
(86)	Marty (white sleeves)	15.00	7.50	4.50
(87)	Massuci (different pose)	15.00	7.50	4.50
(88)	Masucci (different pose)	15.00	7.50	4.50
(89a)	McEvoy (large pose)	15.00	7.50	4.50
(89b)	McEvoy (small pose)	15.00	7.50	4.50
(90)	McIsaacs	15.00	7.50	4.50
(91)	McMullen (Oakland)	15.00	7.50	4.50
(92)	McMullen (Seals)	15.00	7.50	4.50
(93)	Mitchell	15.00	7.50	4.50
(94a)	Monzo (large pose)	15.00	7.50	4.50
(94b)	Monzo (small pose)	15.00	7.50	4.50
(95)	Mort (throwing)	15.00	7.50	4.50
(96)	Mort (batting)	15.00	7.50	4.50
(97a)	Muller (Oakland, large pose)	15.00	7.50	4.50
(97b)	Muller (Oakland, small pose)	15.00	7.50	4.50
(98)	Muller (Seattle)	15.00	7.50	4.50
(99)	Mulligan (hands showing)	15.00	7.50	4.50
(100)	Mulligan (hands not showing)	15.00	7.50	4.50
(101)	Newkirk	15.00	7.50	4.50
(102)	Nicholas	15.00	7.50	4.50
(103)	Nitcholas	15.00	7.50	4.50
(103a)	Norbert (large pose)	15.00	7.50	4.50
(103b)	Norbert (small pose)	15.00	7.50	4.50
(105)	O'Doul (black sleeves)	45.00	22.00	13.50
(106)	O'Doul (white sleeves)	45.00	22.00	13.50
(107)	Oglesby	15.00	7.50	4.50
(108)	Ostenberg	15.00	7.50	4.50
(109)	Outen (throwing)	15.00	7.50	4.50
(110)	Outen (batting)	15.00	7.50	4.50
(111)	Page (Hollywood)	15.00	7.50	4.50
(112)	Page (Seattle)	15.00	7.50	4.50
(113)	Palmisano	15.00	7.50	4.50
(114)	Parker	15.00	7.50	4.50
(115)	Phebus	15.00	7.50	4.50
(116)	T. Pillette	15.00	7.50	4.50
(117)	Pool	15.00	7.50	4.50
(118)	Powers	15.00	7.50	4.50
(119)	Quellich	15.00	7.50	4.50
(120)	Radonitz	15.00	7.50	4.50
(121a)	Raimondi (large pose)	15.00	7.50	4.50
(121b)	Raimondi (small pose)	15.00	7.50	4.50
(122a)	Jimmy Reese (large pose)	24.00	12.00	7.25
(122b)	Jimmy Reese (small pose)	24.00	12.00	7.25
(123)	Rego	15.00	7.50	4.50
(124)	Rhyne (front)	15.00	7.50	4.50
(125)	Rosenberg	15.00	7.50	4.50
(126)	Salinsen	15.00	7.50	4.50
(127)	Salkeld	15.00	7.50	4.50
(128)	Salvo	15.00	7.50	4.50
(129)	Sever	15.00	7.50	4.50
(130)	Sheehan (black sleeves)	15.00	7.50	4.50
(131)	Sheehan (white sleeves)	15.00	7.50	4.50
(132a)	Sheely (large pose)	15.00	7.50	4.50
(132b)	Sheely (small pose)	15.00	7.50	4.50
(134)	Sprinz	15.00	7.50	4.50
(135)	Starritt	15.00	7.50	4.50
(136)	Statz	15.00	7.50	4.50
(137a)	Steinbacker (large pose)	15.00	7.50	4.50
(137b)	Steinbacker (small pose)	15.00	7.50	4.50
(138)	Stewart	15.00	7.50	4.50
(139)	Stitzel (Los Angeles)	15.00	7.50	4.50
(140)	Stitzel (Missions)	15.00	7.50	4.50
(141)	Stitzel (Seals)	15.00	7.50	4.50
(142)	Stoneham	15.00	7.50	4.50
(143)	Street	15.00	7.50	4.50
(144)	Stroner	15.00	7.50	4.50
(145)	Stutz	15.00	7.50	4.50
(146)	Sulik	15.00	7.50	4.50
(147a)	Thurston (Mission)	15.00	7.50	4.50
(147b)	Thurston (Missions)	15.00	7.50	4.50
(148)	Vitt (Hollywood)	15.00	7.50	4.50
(149)	Vitt (Oakland)	15.00	7.50	4.50
(150)	Wallgren	15.00	7.50	4.50
(151)	Walsh	15.00	7.50	4.50
(152)	Walters	15.00	7.50	4.50

(153)	West	15.00	7.50	4.50
(154a)	Wirts (large pose)	15.00	7.50	4.50
(154b)	Wirts (small pose)	15.00	7.50	4.50
(155)	Woodall (batting)	15.00	7.50	4.50
(156)	Woodall (throwing)	15.00	7.50	4.50
(157)	Wright (facing to front)	15.00	7.50	4.50
(158)	Wright (facing to left)	15.00	7.50	4.50
(159)	Zinn	15.00	7.50	4.50

1937 - 38 Zeenut Pacific Coast League (E137)

The 1937 and 1938 Zeenuts are similar to the 1933-1936 issues, except the black rectangle containing the player's name and team has square (rather than rounded) corners. Again, it is difficult to distinguish between the two years. In 1938, Zeenuts eliminated the coupon bottom and began including a separate coupon in the candy package along with the baseball card. The final two years of the Zeenuts issues, the 1937 and 1938 cards, are among the more difficult to find.

		NR MT	EX	VG
Complete Set:		2850.	1425.	850.00
Common Player:		32.00	16.00	9.50
(1)	Annunzio	32.00	16.00	9.50
(2)	Baker	32.00	16.00	9.50
(3)	Ballou	32.00	16.00	9.50
(4)	C. Beck	32.00	16.00	9.50
(5)	W. Beck	32.00	16.00	9.50
(6)	Bolin	32.00	16.00	9.50
(7)	Bongiavanni	32.00	16.00	9.50
(8)	Boss	32.00	16.00	9.50
(9)	Carson	32.00	16.00	9.50
(10)	Clabaugh	32.00	16.00	9.50
(11)	Clifford	32.00	16.00	9.50
(12)	B. Cole	32.00	16.00	9.50
(13)	Coscarart	32.00	16.00	9.50
(14)	Cronin	32.00	16.00	9.50
(15)	Cullop	32.00	16.00	9.50
(16)	Daglia	32.00	16.00	9.50
(17)	D. DeMaggio (DiMaggio)	400.00	200.00	120.00
(18)	Douglas	32.00	16.00	9.50
(19)	Frankovich	32.00	16.00	9.50
(20)	Frazier	32.00	16.00	9.50
(21)	Fredericks	32.00	16.00	9.50
(22)	Freitas	32.00	16.00	9.50
(23)	Gabrielson (Oakland)	32.00	16.00	9.50
(24)	Gabrielson (Seattle)	32.00	16.00	9.50
(25)	Garibaldi	32.00	16.00	9.50
(26)	Gibson	32.00	16.00	9.50
(27)	Gill	32.00	16.00	9.50
(28)	Graves	32.00	16.00	9.50
(29)	Guay	32.00	16.00	9.50
(30)	Gudat	32.00	16.00	9.50
(31)	Haid	32.00	16.00	9.50
(32)	Hannah	32.00	16.00	9.50
(33)	Hawkins	32.00	16.00	9.50
(34)	Herrmann	32.00	16.00	9.50
(35)	Holder	32.00	16.00	9.50
(36)	Jennings	32.00	16.00	9.50
(37)	Judnich	32.00	16.00	9.50
(38)	Klinger	32.00	16.00	9.50
(39)	Koenig	32.00	16.00	9.50
(40)	Koupal	32.00	16.00	9.50
(41)	Koy	32.00	16.00	9.50
(42)	Lamanski	32.00	16.00	9.50
(43)	Leishman (Oakland)	32.00	16.00	9.50
(44)	Leishman (Seattle)	32.00	16.00	9.50
(45)	G. Lillard	32.00	16.00	9.50
(46)	Mann	32.00	16.00	9.50
(47)	Marble (Hollywood)	32.00	16.00	9.50
(49)	Miller	32.00	16.00	9.50
(50)	Mills	32.00	16.00	9.50
(51)	Monzo	32.00	16.00	9.50
(52)	B. Mort (Hollywood)	32.00	16.00	9.50
(53)	B. Mort (Missions)	32.00	16.00	9.50
(54)	Muller	32.00	16.00	9.50
(55)	Murray	32.00	16.00	9.50
(56)	Newsome	32.00	16.00	9.50
(57)	Nitcholas	32.00	16.00	9.50
(58)	Olds	32.00	16.00	9.50
(59)	Orengo	32.00	16.00	9.50
(60)	Osborne	32.00	16.00	9.50
(61)	Outen	32.00	16.00	9.50
(62)	C. Outen (Hollywood)	32.00	16.00	9.50
(63)	C. Outen (Missions)	32.00	16.00	9.50
(64)	Pippin	32.00	16.00	9.50
(65)	Powell	32.00	16.00	9.50
(66)	Radonitz	32.00	16.00	9.50
(67)	Raimondi (Oakland)	32.00	16.00	9.50
(68)	Raimondi (San Francisco)	32.00	16.00	9.50
(69)	A. Raimondi	32.00	16.00	9.50
(70)	W. Raimondi	32.00	16.00	9.50
(71)	Rhyne	32.00	16.00	9.50
(72)	Rosenberg (Missions)	32.00	16.00	9.50
(73)	Rosenberg (Portland)	32.00	16.00	9.50
(74)	Sawyer	32.00	16.00	9.50
(75)	Seats	32.00	16.00	9.50
(76)	Sheehan (Oakland)	32.00	16.00	9.50
(77)	Sheehan (San Francisco)	32.00	16.00	9.50
(78)	Shores	32.00	16.00	9.50
(79)	Slade (Hollywood)	32.00	16.00	9.50
(80)	Slade (Missions)	32.00	16.00	9.50
(81)	Sprinz (Missions)	32.00	16.00	9.50
(82)	Sprinz (San Francisco)	32.00	16.00	9.50
(83)	Statz	32.00	16.00	9.50
(84)	Storey	32.00	16.00	9.50
(85)	Stringfellow	32.00	16.00	9.50
(86)	Stutz	32.00	16.00	9.50
(87)	Sweeney	32.00	16.00	9.50
(88)	Thomson	32.00	16.00	9.50
(89)	Tost (Hollywood)	32.00	16.00	9.50
(90)	Tost (Missions)	32.00	16.00	9.50
(91)	Ulrich	32.00	16.00	9.50
(92)	Vergez	32.00	16.00	9.50
(93)	Vezelich	32.00	16.00	9.50
(94)	Vitter (Hollywood)	32.00	16.00	9.50
(95)	Vitter (San Francisco)	32.00	16.00	9.50
(96)	West	32.00	16.00	9.50
(97)	Wilson	32.00	16.00	9.50
(98)	Woodall	32.00	16.00	9.50
(99)	Wright	32.00	16.00	9.50

DiMaggio's first cards are Zeenuts' best

Without a doubt, the most sought-after of the more than 3,000 Zeenuts cards issued from 1911 and 1938 are the pair depicting Joe DiMaggio during his four-year minor league career with the San Francisco Seals (1932-35).

Both cards, a throwing pose issued in 1935 and a batting pose presumably issued the previous year, identify the player as "J. DeMAGGIO." Contemporary cards of his brothers Vince and Dom also spelled the family name "DeMaggio," as did many of the early newspaper accounts of the future Hall of Famer.

Valued at $2,000 apiece in Near Mint condition without the bottom coupon, the few surviving examples with coupon command a significant premium, with sales records approaching $4,000.

1970 Mac's Wichita Aeros

(Indians) (black and white) (2-1/2" x 3-1/4") (Card backs are blank)

	NR MT	EX	VG
Complete Set:	300.00	150.00	90.00

(1) Ken Aspromonte
(2) Frank Baker
(3) Larry Burchard
(4) Lou Camilli
(5) Mike Carruthers
(6) Chris Chambliss
(7) Ed Farmer
(8) Pedro Gonzales
(9) Jerry Hinsley
(10) Luis Isaac
(11) John Lowenstein
(12) Cap Peterson
(13) Jim Rittwage
(14) Bill Rohr
(15) Richie Scheinblum
(16) John Scruggs
(17) Ken Suarez
(18) Dick Tidrow

1971 Currie Press Richmond Braves

(Atlanta Braves) (black and white) (3-3/8" x 5-5/16")

	NR MT	EX	VG
Complete Set:	150.00	75.00	45.00

(1) Tommie Aaron
(2) Sam Ayoub
(3) Dusty Baker
(4) Jim Breazeale
(5) Jack Crist
(6) Shaun Fitzmaurice
(7) Jim French
(8) Larry Jaster
(9) Van Kelly
(10) Rich Kester
(11) Clyde King
(12) Dave Lobb
(13) Larry Maxie
(14) Hank McGraw
(15) Gary Neibauer
(16) Guy Rose
(17) Fred Velazquez
(18) Bobby Young

1971 Jeff Morey Syracuse Chiefs

(New York Yankees) (black and white)

	NR MT	EX	VG
Complete Set:	90.00	45.00	27.00

(1) Len Boehmer
(2) Ossie Chavarria
(3) Alan Closter
(4) Fred Frazier
(5) Rob Gardner
(6) George Pena
(7) Rusty Torres
(8) Denny Walton

1972 TCMA Cedar Rapids Cardinals

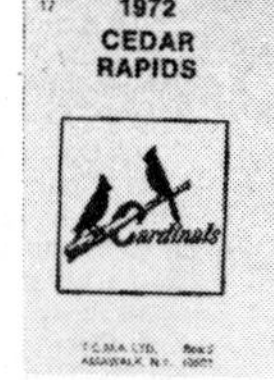

(St. Louis Cardinals, A) (complete set price includes the scarce team photo card which measures 3-1/4" x 5")

	NR MT	EX	VG
Complete Set:	125.00	65.00	40.00

1 Bill Pinkham
2 Mark Hale
3 Tom Zimmer
4 Don Buchheister
5 Jethro Mills
6 John Sawatski
7 Jim Gregory
8 Duke Wheeler
9 Victor Diaz
10 Jim Dunham
11 Mike Carmuso
12 Bruce Henderson
13 Manny Abreu
14 Luis Gonzales
15 Gary Trumbauer
16 Randy Rencor
17 Gary Geiger
18 Burt Nordstrom
19 Mike Proffitt
20 Milo Voskovitch
21 Jim Silvey
22 Joe Mazzella
23 Craig Burns
24 Leon Lee
25 Larry Aubel
26 Mark Mueller
27 Tony Velasquez
28 Bill Poe
29 Monte Bolinger
30 Team Photo

1972 Team Seattle Rainiers

(Independent) (black and white) (sold as 4-player sheets) (unnumbered)

	NR MT	EX	VG
Complete Set:	45.00	33.75	18.00

(1) Rafael Amiami
(2) Greg Brust
(3) Wade Carpenter
(4) Mike Peters
(5) Jose Gomez
(6) Gene Lanthorn
(7) Jeff McKay
(8) Jay Tatar
(9) Rocky Hernandez
(10) Tony Pepper
(11) Roger Rasmussen
(12) Jack Winchester
(13) Wes Dixon
(14) Ray Ewing
(15) Ken Roll
(16) Rich Thompson
(17) Willy Adams
(18) Bill Kindoll
(19) Kevin Kooyman
(20) Wendell Stephens
(21) Steve Mezich
(22) John Ownes
(23) Jose Sencion
(24) Ray Washburn

1972 Team Tacoma Twins

(Minnesota Twins) (black and white) (2-3/8" x 3-3/16") (backs are blank)

	NR MT	EX	VG
Complete Set:	32.50	24.00	13.00

(1) Mike Adams
(2) Glen Borgmann
(3) Mike Brooks
(4) Ezell Carter
(5) Mike Derrick
(6) Glenn Ezell
(7) Ken Gill
(8) Hal Haydel
(9) Ron Herbel
(10) Jim Holt
(11) Tom Kelly
(12) Steve Luebber
(13) Cap Peterson
(14) Dennis Saunders
(15) Jim Strickland
(16) Jerry Terrell

1973 TCMA Cedar Rapids Astros

(Houston Astros, A) (cards are slightly smaller than the standard 2-1/2" x 3-1/2" size)

	NR MT	EX	VG
Complete Set:	80.00	40.00	24.00

1 Arturo Gonzales
2 Ramon Perez
3 Al Williams
4 Guillermo Foster
5 Bob Dean
6 Fred Mims
7 Art Gardner
8 Jesus Reyes
9 Don Buchheister
10 Neil Rasmussen
11 Luis Pujols
12 George Vasquez
13 Paulo DeLeon
14 Mike Stanton
15 Luis Sanchez
16 Jose Sosa
17 Luis Melendez
18 Steve Englishby
19 Rafael Tatis
20 Richard Williams
21 Alfredo Javier
22 Romaldo Blanco
23 Bob Youse
24 Eleno Cuen
25 Leo Posada
26 Team Photo
27 Pancho Lopez
28 Jorge Moreno

1973 Team Sherbrooke Pirates

(Pittsburgh Pirates) (black and white) (4-1/4"x3-1/4") (unnumbered, blank backs)

	NR MT	EX	VG
Complete Set:	180.00	90.00	55.00

(1) Tony Armas
(2) David Arrington
(3) Mel Civil
(4) Pablo Cruz
(5) Frank Frontive
(6) Brad Gratz
(7) Roberto Guenns
(8) Juan Jiminez
(9) Ken Macha
(10) Mario Mendoza
(11) Jim Minshall
(12) Ron Mitchell
(13) Luther Quinn
(14) Jim Sadowski
(15) Kent Tekulve
(16) John Vance
(17) Bud Whileyman
(18) Alfredo Zavala

1973 Team Syracuse Chiefs

(Yankees) (black and white) (Includes late-issue Pazik card)

	NR MT	EX	VG
Complete Set:	200.00	100.00	60.00

(1) Felipe Alou
(2) Matty Alou
(3) Ron Blomberg
(4) John Callison
(5) Horace Clark
(6) Alan Closter
(7) Joe DiMaggio
(8) Lou Gehrig
(9) Larry Gowell
(10) Ralph Houk
(11) Mike Kekich
(12) Ron Klimkowski
(13) Steve Kline
(14) Sparky Lyle
(15) Mickey Mantle
(16) Lindy McDaniel
(17) George Medich
(18) Gene Michael
(19) Thurman Munson
(20) Bobby Murcer
(21) Graig Nettles
(22) Mike Pazik
(23) Fritz Peterson
(24) Babe Ruth
(25) Cellie Sanchez
(26) Mel Stottlemyre
(27) Frank Tepedino
(28) Otto Velez
(29) Roy White
(30) George Zeber

1973 Caruso Tacoma Twins

(Minnesota Twins) (black and white) (2-3/8" x 3-1/8") (blank backs)

	NR MT	EX	VG
Complete Set:	20.00	15.00	8.00

(1) Vic Albury
(2) Glen Borgmann
(3) Mike Brooks
(4) Bill Campbell
(5) Glenn Ezell
(6) Kerby Ferrell
(7) Dan Fife
(8) Bob Gebhard
(9) Ken Gill
(10) Bucky Guth
(11) Jim Hoppe
(12) Tom Kelly
(13) Craig Kusick
(14) John Matias
(15) Mike McCormick
(16) Jim Nettles
(17) Tim Norton
(18) Rick Renick
(19) Eric Soderholm
(20) Bob Storm
(21) Jim Strickland

1973 Kansas State Bank Wichita Aeros

(Cubs) (black and white) (Price includes letter-size variations for Hibbs and Tomplins)

	NR MT	EX	VG
Complete Set:	95.00	47.00	28.00

(1) Matt Alexander
(2) Tom Badcock
(3) Clinton Compton
(4) Jim Hibbs
4 a Jim Hibbs
(5) Pete LaCock
(6) Tony LaRussa
(7) Tom Lundstedt
(8) Jim Marshall
(9) J.C. Martin
(10) Al Montreuil
(11) Joe Ortiz
(12) Griggy Porter
(13) Paul Reuschel
(14) Ralph Rickey
(15) Dave Rosello
(16) Jim Todd
(17) Chris Ward
(18) Ron Tompkins
(18 a) Ron Tompkins
(19) Floyd Weaver

1974 Caruso Albuquerque Dukes

(Los Angeles Dodgers) (black and white) (2-7/8" x 3-7/8") (backs are blank)

	NR MT	EX	VG
Complete Set:	20.00	15.00	8.00

64 Henry Cruz
65 Tom Tischinski
66 Orlando Alvarez
67 Terry McDermott
68 Ivan DeJesus
69 Kevin Pasley
70 Phil Keller
71 Eddie Solomon
72 Charlie Manuel
73 Greg Shanahan
74 Lee Robinson
75 P.R. Powell

76 Jerry Royster
77 Stan Wasiak
78 Bobby Randall
79 Jim Allen

1974 Dukes Team

(Los Angeles Dodgers) (black and white) (2-1/2" x 4-1/8") (backs are blank)

	NR MT	EX	VG
Complete Set:	350.00	175.00	100.00

(1) Orlando Alvarez
(2) Bernie Beckman
(3) Wayne Burney
(4) Henry Cruz
(5) Ivan De Jesus
(6) Greg Heydeman
(7) Rex Hudson
(8) Phil Keller
(9) Charlie Manuel
(10) Terry McDermott
(11) Rick Nitz
(12) Kevin Pasley
(13) P.R. Powell
(14) Bobby Randall
(15) Rick Rhoden
(16) Lee Robinson
(17) Jerry Royster
(18) Greg Shanahan
(19) Eddie Solomon
(20) Mike Strahler
(21) Tom Tischinski
(22) Stan Wall
(23) Stan Wasiak

1974 TCMA Cedar Rapids Astros

(Houston Astros, A)

	NR MT	EX	VG
Complete Set:	90.00	45.00	27.00

1 Bob Renninger
2 Bob Youse
3 Jesus Reyes
4 Arturo Gonzalez
5 Tom Rima
6 Joe Sambito
7 Dave Aloi
8 Mike Jones
9 Calvin Partley
10 Alejandro Taveras
11 Luis Pujols
12 Eric Brown
13 Luis Sanchez
14 Jose Alfaro
15 Jorge Moreno
16 Fred Mims
17 Fernando Tatis
18 Tom Tellman
19 Kevin Drake
20 Guillermo Foster
21 Pastor Perez
22 Bob Cluck
23 Larry Elenes
24 Jose Sosa
25 Leo Posada
26 Mike Holland
27 Pablo DeLeon
28 Don Buchheister

Values for recent cards and sets are listed in Mint (MT), Near Mint (NM), reflecting the fact that many cards from recent years have been preserved in top condition. Recent cards and sets in less than Excellent condition have little collector interest.

1974 TCMA Gastonia Rangers

(Texas Rangers, A)

	NR MT	EX	VG
Complete Set:	80.00	40.00	24.00

(1) Curt Arnett
(2) Jon Astroth
(3) Mike Bacsik
(4) Len Barker
(5) Don Bodenhamer
(6) Don Bright
(7) Gary Cooper
(8) Rich Donnelly
(9) Dan Duran
(10) Dave Fendrick
(11) Lindsey Graham
(12) Tim Murphy
(13) Fred Nichols
(14) Drew Nickerson
(15) Ed Nottle
(16) Wally Pontiff
(17) Ray Rainbolt
(18) Rich Shubert
(19) Rick Simon
(20) Keith Smith
(21) John Sutton
(22) Mark Tanner
(23) Don Thomas
(24) Bobby Thompson

1974 Caruso Hawaii Islanders

(San Diego Padres) (black and white) (2-7/8" x 3-7/8") (backs are blank)

	NR MT	EX	VG
Complete Set:	20.00	10.00	6.00

101 Gene Locklear
102 Gary Jestadt
103 Hector Torres
104 Ed Acosta
105 Pat Corrales
106 Bill Almon
107 Rich Chiles
108 Roy Hartsfield

1974 Falstaff Beer Omaha Royals

(Kansas City Royals) (black and white) (8" x 10") (unnumbered) (backs are blank)

	NR MT	EX	VG
Complete Set:	180.00	90.00	55.00

(1) Jose Arcia
(2) Ed Bernard
(3) Jim Clark
(4) Jim Foor
(5) Tom Harmon
(6) Dennis Leonard
(7) Jose Martinez
(8) Dennis Paepke
(9) Paul Peiz
(10) Tom Poquette

1974 Caruso Phoenix Giants

(San Francisco Giants) (black and white) (2-3/4" x 3-7/8") (backs are blank)

	NR MT	EX	VG
Complete Set:	20.00	10.00	6.00

80 Skip James
81 Mike Sadek
82 Leon Brown
83 Glenn Redmon
84 Ed Sukla
85 Glenn Adams
86 Bruce Christiansen
87 Jimmy Rosario
88 Frank Johnson
89 Glenn Ezell
90 Rocky Bridges

1974 Caruso Sacramento Solons

(Milwaukee Brewers) (black and white) (2-7/8" x 3-7/8") (backs are blank)

	NR MT	EX	VG
Complete Set:	22.50	11.25	6.75

46 Tom Reynolds
47 Art Kusnyer
48 Gorman Thomas
49 Bill McNulty
50 Tom Bianco
51 Gary Cavallo
52 Tom Hausman
53 Roger Miller
54 Tom King
55 Craig Glassco
56 Jose Salado
57 Sixto Lezcano
58 Steve McCartney
59 Juan Lopez
60 Jack Lind
61 Rob Ellis
62 Bob Lemon
63 Bob Sheldon

1974 Caruso Salt Lake City Angels

(California Angels) (black and white) (2-7/8" x 3-7/8") (backs are blank)

	NR MT	EX	VG
Complete Set:	20.00	10.00	6.00

91 Rudy Meoli
92 Bob Marcano
93 Frankie George
94 Dave Chorley
95 Morrie Nettles
96 Bruce Bochte
97 Norm Sherry
98 Jerry Bell
99 Paul Dade
100 Danny Briggs

1974 Team Seattle Rainiers

(co-op) (black and white)

	NR MT	EX	VG
Complete Set:	175.00	85.00	50.00

(1) Mike Armstrong
(2) Keith Haigerson
(3) Sam Hessley
(4) Rick Kuhn
(5) Carl Christiansen
(6) Bob Cummings
(7) Lynn Jones
(8) Jerry Rogers
(9) Tim Doerr
(10) Steve Meade
(11) Peter Savute
(12) Jim Turner
(13) Mike McNiel
(14) Steve Moore
(15) John Underwood
(16) Alan Viebrock
(17) Ron Gibson
(18) Doug Peterson
(19) Greg Riddock
(20) Bill Taoukalas

1974 Caruso Spokane Indians

(Texas Rangers) (black and white) (2-7/8" x 3-7/8") (backs are blank)

	NR MT	EX	VG
Complete Set:	20.00	10.00	6.00

28 Steve Dunning
29 Bob Johnson
30 Rick Henninger
31 Jim Schellenback
32 Rick Waits
33 Dave Driscione
34 Bill Fahey
35 Don Castle
36 Bob Jones
37 Dave Moates
38 Tom Robson
39 Mike Cubbage
40 Steve Greenberg
41 Roy Howell
42 Pete Mackanin
43 Vern Wilkens
44 Marty Martinez
45 Del Wilber

1974 Team Syracuse Chiefs

(Yankees) (black and white) (Frazier is a scarce, late issue)

	NR MT	EX	VG
Complete Set:	175.00	85.00	50.00

(1) Rich Bladt
(2) Ron Blomberg
(3) Tom Buskey
(4) Rick Dempsey
(5) Joe DiMaggio
(6) Pat Dobson
(7) Fred Frazier
(8) Whitey Ford
(9) Lou Gehrig
(10) Roger Hambright
(11) Mike Hegan
(12) Elston Howard
(13) Steve Kline
(14) Sparky Lyle
(15) Mickey Mantle
(16) Sam McDowell
(17) George Medich
(18) Gene Michael
(19) Thurman Munson
(20) Bobby Murcer
(21) Graig Nettles
(22) Dave Paga
(23) Fritz Peterson
(24) Babe Ruth
(25) Celerino Sanchez
(26) Fred Stanley
(27) Mel Stottlemyre
(28) Otto Velez
(29) Bill Virdon
(30) Roy White

1974 Caruso Tacoma Twins

(Minnesota Twins) (black and white) (2-7/8" x 3-7/8") (backs are blank)

	NR MT	EX	VG
Complete Set:	20.00	10.00	6.00

1 Jim Obradovich
2 Dale Soderholm
3 Craig Kusick
4 Cal Ermer
5 Eddie Bane
6 Dan Fife
7 Jim Hughes
8 Mike Pazik
9 Frank Schuster
10 Coley Smith
11 Earl Stephenson
12 Juan Vientidos
13 Dan Vossler
14 Mark Wiley
15 Sam Ceci
16 George Pena
17 Sergio Ferrer
18 Doug Howard
19 Bill Ralston
20 Rick Renick
21 Jim Van Wyck
22 Mike Adams
23 Lyman Bostock
24 Jim Fairey
25 Tom Kelly
26 Ed Palat
27 Danny Walton

The values quoted are intended to reflect the market price.

1974 One Day Film Wichita Aeros

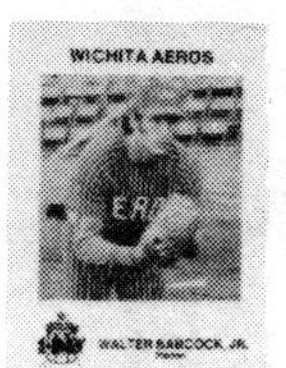

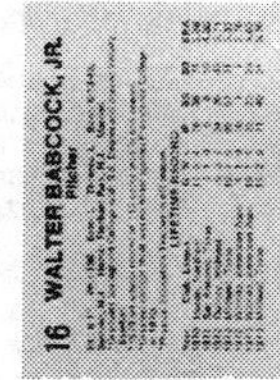

(Chicago Cubs) (black and white) (Includes the scarce Badcock card)

	NR MT	EX	VG
Complete Set:	90.00	45.00	27.00

101 Francisco Lopez
102 Paul Zahn
103 Walter Babcock Jr, Tom Babcock
104 Roberto Rodriguez
105 George Manz
106 Tom Dettore Jr.
107 David LaRoche
108 Daniel Corder
109 Mike Roarke
110 James Todd Jr.
111 Wilford Prail
112 Paul Reuschel
113 Cleo James
114 Al Montreuil
115 Ron Matney
116 Robert Sperring
117 Jack Hiatt
118 Griggy Porter Jr.
119 Ron Dunn
120 Gene Hiser
121 Alfredo Zavala
122 Dave Arrington
123 Steven Swisher
124 Pete LaCock
125 Scipio R. Spinks
126 Bob Drew
127 John Wallenstein
128 Paul "Doc" St. Onge

1975 Caruso Albuquerque Dukes

(Los Angeles Dodgers) (black and white) (2-3/4" x 3-7/8")

	NR MT	EX	VG
Complete Set:	22.50	11.25	6.75

1 Orlando Alvarez
2 Joe Simpson
3 Jerry Royster
4 Lee Robinson
5 John Hale
6 Bobby Randall
7 Terry McDermott
8 Terry Collins
9 Cleo Smith
10 Wayne Burney
11 Dick Selma
12 Greg Shanahan
13 Rex Hudson
14 Stan Wasiak
15 Pablo Peguero
16 Rick Nitz
17 Stan Wall
18 Jim Allen
19 Jim Haller
20 Dennis Lewallyn
21 Wayne Miller

Regional interest may affect the value of a card.

1975 TCMA Anderson Rangers

(Texas Rangers, A) (black and white)

	NR MT	EX	VG
Complete Set:	40.00	20.00	12.00

1 Tommy Smith
2 Rick Lisi
3 Mark Miller
8 Tim Brookens
9 Keath Chauncey
10 Glenn Purvis
15 Gary Grey
16 Curt Runyon
17 Terry Olson
18 Jim Crall
20 Dave McCarthy
23 Kerry Gettery
25 Danny Tidwell
28 Wes Goodale
29 Jeff Byrd
32 Jim Clancy
37 Bob Carroll
39 Bill Patten
42 Freeman Evans
43 Don Bright
46 Joe Russell
47 Ward Smith
57 Drew Nickerson
67 Darrel Frolin
---- Ed Nottle

1975 TCMA Appleton Foxes

(Chicago White Sox, A) (black and white)

	NR MT	EX	VG
Complete Set:	35.00	17.50	10.50

(1) Fred Anyzeski
(2) Kevin Bell
(3) Robert Bianco
(4) Paul Bock
(5) Bobby Combs
(6) Roy Coulter
(7) Bob Flynn
(8) Bill Kautzer
(9) Tom King
(10) Bob Klein
(11) Odie Koehnke
(12) Tony Komadina
(13) Juan Leonardo
(14) Ted Loehr
(15) Gordon Lund
(16) Bobby McClellan
(17) Candy Mercado
(18) Larry Monroe
(19) Johnny Narron
(20) Phil Nerone
(21) Ed Olszta
(22) Bob Palmer
(23) Harris Price
(24) Scott Richartz
(25) Silvano Robles
(26) Eric Thomas
(27) Tom Toman
(28) Ed Wheeler
(29) Batboys

1975 TCMA Burlington Bees

(Milwaukee Brewers, A) (black and white) (2-1/2" x 3-1/2")

	NR MT	EX	VG
Complete Set:	45.00	22.00	13.50

(1) John Buffamoyer
(2) Gary Conn
(3) Barry Cort
(4) Marty DeMerritt
(5) "Butch" Edge
(6) Terry Erwin
(7) Matt Galante
(8) Miguel Garcia
(9) Frank Gaton
(10) "Moose" Hass (Haas)
(11) Dennis Holmberg
(12) Sam Jones
(13) Sam Killingsworth
(14) Esteban Maria
(15) Victor Marichal
(16) Marcos Majias
(17) Sam Monteau
(18) Willie Mueller
(19) Abelino Pena
(20) Neil Rasmussen
(21) Alex Rodriquez
(22) Sal Rosario
(23) Pedro Sanchez
(24) Carey Scarborough
(25) Joe Slaymaker
(26) Ron Smith
(27) Gil Stafford
(28) Dave Sylvia
(29) John Whiting

1975 TCMA Cedar Rapids Giants

(San Francisco Giants, A) (black and white)

	NR MT	EX	VG
Complete Set:	35.00	17.50	10.50

1 Tom Hughes
2 Mike Wilbins
3 Steve Cline
4 Joe Heinen
5 German de los Santos
6 John Riddle
7 Bob Thompson
8 Jeff Yurak
9 Terry Lee
10 Dan Beitey
11 John Nix
12 Don Sasser
13 Brian Felda
14 John Johnson
15 Mike Cash
16 Jim Ray
17 Dan Smith
18 Don Buchheister
19 Bob Hartsfield
20 Barney Wilson
21 Frank Ferrell
22 Mike Dodd
23 Jim Ayers
24 Jerry Stamps
25 Mark Woodbrey
26 Don Benedetti
27 Ron Hodges
28 Wayne Bradley
29 Calvin Moore
30 Garet Strong
31 Terry Kenny
32 Ernie Young

1975 TCMA Clinton Pilots

(Detroit Tigers, A) (black and white)

	NR MT	EX	VG
Complete Set:	80.00	40.00	24.00

1 Jim Leyland
2 Dave Rozema
3 Dwight Carter
4 Brian Kelly
5 Greg Kline
6 Steve Gamby
7 Bill Michael
8 Randy Haas
9 Issac Gimenez
10 Ray Gimenez
11 Jim Murray
12 John Dinkelmeyer
13 Larry Feola
14 Tom Lantz
15 Not Issued
16 Mike Uremovich
17 Kevin Slattery
18 Mark Wagner
19 Ben Hunt
20 Greg Shippy
21 Luis Atilano
22 Tom Perkins
23 Al Baker
24 Steve Trella
24a Jose Centeno
24b Steve Trella
25 Harry Schulz
26 Not Issued
27 Mike Bartell
28 Al Callis
29 Venoy Garrison
30 Jeff Reinke
---- Dave Holm

1975 TCMA Dubuque Packers

(Houston Astros, A) (black and white)

	NR MT	EX	VG
Complete Set:	35.00	17.50	10.50

1 Clancy (Mascot)
2 Terry Puhl
3 Jeff Smith
4 Tom Rima
5 Arnaldo Alvarado
6 Fay Thompson
7 Bob Dean
8 Mike Mendoza
9 John McLaren
10 Bob Cluck
11 Romo Blanco
12 Roger Polanco
13 Eleno Cuen
14 Rick Haynes
15 J.J. Cannon
16 Fernando Tatis
17 Mike Weeber
18 Alan Knicely
19 Tom Dixon
20 Paulo DeLeon
21 Luis Pujols
22 Jose Alfaro
23 Gordon Pladson
24 Dave Aloi
25 Jorge Moreno
26 Tom Twellman
27 George Lazarique (Lauzerique)
28 Arnie Costell
29 Kevin Drake
30 Mike Hasley
31 Jack Goetz
32 Alvin Osofsky

1975 Sussman Ft. Lauderdale Yankees

(New York Yankees) (black and white) (backs are blank) (Price includes the scarce Figueroa card)

	NR MT	EX	VG
Complete Set:	80.00	40.00	24.00

1 Scott Norris
2 Mike Ferraro
3 Benny Perez
4 Neil Liebovitz
5 Dave Wright
6 Rich Meltz
7 Dave Rajsick
8 Greg Diehl
9 Tony Derosa
10 Rick Fleshman
11 Pat Peterson
12 Jim Sullivan
13 Marv Thompson
14 Joe Alvarez
15 Ken Kruppa
16 Jim Bierman
17 Doug Melvin
18 Joe Kwasny
19 Mike Heath
20 Sheldon Gill
21 Dennis Werth
22 Jesus Figueroa
23 Wilson Plunkett
24 Jose Alcantara
25 Leo Pasada
26 Garth Iorg
27 Scott Delgatti
28 Mike Rusk
29 Team Photo
30 Jerry Narron

1975 Caruso Hawaii Islanders

(San Diego Padres) (black and white) (2-7/8" x 3-7/8")

	NR MT	EX	VG
Complete Set:	20.00	10.00	6.00

1 Gus Gil
2 Steve Huntz
3 Bob Davis
4 Randy Elliott
5 Dave Roberts
6 Rod Gaspar
7 Jim Fairey
8 Jerry Turner
9 Marv Galliher
10 Sonny Jackson
11 Bill Almon
12 Brent Strom
13 Frank Linzy
14 Jim Shellenback
15 Larry Hardy
16 Gary Ross
17 Bob Strampe
18 Jerry Johnson
19 Butch Metzer
20 Dave Wehrmeister
21 Bob Miller

1975 TCMA International League

(AAA)

	NR MT	EX	VG
Complete Set:	40.00	30.00	15.00

1 Jerry White
2 Dyar Miller
3 Mike Krizmanich
4 Earl Stephenson
5 Mike Reinbach
6 Jerry White
7 John Stearns
8 Lee Elia
9 Dave Pagan
10 Rob Andrews
11 Jim Hutto
12 Chris Coletta
13 Ron Clark
14 Bill Kirkpatrick
15 Fred Frazier
16 Joe Altobelli
17 Jim Hutto
18 Mike Willis
19 Glenn Stitzel
20 Fred Frazier
21 Gary Carter
22 Steve Dillard
23 Mike Krizmanich
24 Hank Webb
25 Karl Kuehl
26 Lee Elia
27 Chris Coletta
28 Mike Willis
29 Bob Gebhard
30 Dick Wissel
31 Dick Wissel

1975 TCMA Iowa Oaks

(Houston Astros, AAA)

	NR MT	EX	VG
Complete Set:	80.00	40.00	24.00

(1) Carlos Alfonso
(2) Ron Boone
(3) Ray Busse
(4) Mike Cosgrove
(5) Jerry Davannon (DaVanon)
(6) Bob Didier
(7) Mike Easler
(8) Art Gardner
(9) Alfredo Javier
(10) Jesus de la Rosa
(11) Ramon de los Santos
(12) Joe Niekro
(13) George Pena
(14) Ramon Perez
(15) Russ Rothermal
(16) Ron Roznovsky
(17) Paul Siebert
(18) Joe Sparks
(19) Scipio Spinks
(20) Mike Stanton
(21) Alejandro Taveras

1975 TCMA Lafayette Drillers

(San Francisco, AA)

	NR MT	EX	VG
Complete Set:	100.00	50.00	30.00

1 Chico Del Orbe
2 Wendell Kim
3 Joey Martin
4 Scott Wolfe
5 Tommy Smith
6 Jake Brown
7 Gary Atwell
8 Ernie Young
9 Craig Barnes
10 John Yeglinski
11 Tom Stedman
12 Gary Alexander
13 Jack Clark
14 Reggie Walton
15 Frank Riccelli
16 Rob Dressler
17 Kyle Hypes
18 Jay Dillard
19 Jeff Little
20 Julio Division
21 Silvano Quezada
22 David Fuqua
23 Terry Cornutt
24 John Steigerwald
25 Bob Drew
26 Don Steele
27 Al Stuckeman
28 Dan Adams
29 Ducky Crandall
30 Denny Sommers
31 Clark Field
32 Batboys

1975 TCMA Lynchburg Rangers

(Texas Rangers, A)

	NR MT	EX	VG
Complete Set:	50.00	25.00	15.00

(1) Rich Albert
(2) Curt Arnett
(3) George Ban
(4) Mel Barrow
(5) Larry Bradford
(6) Bobby Buford
(7) Bobby Cuellar
(8) Amado Dinzey
(9) Brian Doyle
(10) Dan Duran
(11) Chuck Hammond
(12) Eddie Holman
(13) William Johnson
(14) Jerome Johnson
(15) Robert Long
(16) Ken Miller
(17) Brian Nakamoto
(18) Pat Putnam
(19) Ray Rainbolt
(20) Ron Rockhill
(21) Jeff Scott
(22) Glenn Smith
(23) Mark Tanner
(24) Wayne Terwilliger
(25) Don Thomas
(26) Bobby Thompson

1975 Team Oklahoma City 89'ers

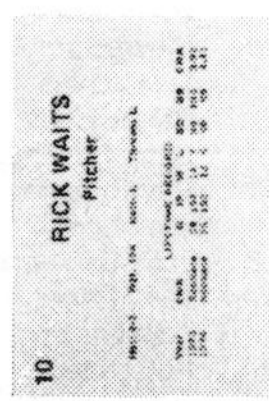

(Cleveland Indians) (black and white)

	NR MT	EX	VG
Complete Set:	12.00	6.00	3.50

1 Robert Grossman
2 Barry Lersch
3 Thomas Mc Gough
4 Richard Henninger
5 Thomas Brennan
6 Bruce Ellingsen
7 Larry Andersen
8 James Kern
9 James Strickland
10 Rick Waits
11 John Siracusa
12 Benjamin Heise
13 Orlando Gonzalez
14 Brian Ostrosser
15 Tommy Smith
16 Thomas Mc Millan
17 James Norris
18 Mike Hannah
19 Nelson Garcia
20 Joseph Lis
21 Gene Dusan
22 Michael Brooks
23 John Davis
24 Rex Rosser

1975 Top Trophies Omaha Royals

(Kansas City Royals) (black and white) (8" x 10")

	NR MT	EX	VG
Complete Set:	60.00	30.00	18.00

Norm Angelini
Al Autry
Hal Baird
Greg Chlan
Mickey Cobb
Bobby Floyd
Ruppert Jones
Gary Lance
Mark Littell
Keith Marshall
Gary Martz
Frank Ortenzio
Craig Perkins
Jamie Quirk
Steve Staggs
George Throop
U. L. Washington
John Wathan

1975 Caruso Phoenix Giants

(San Francisco Giants) (black and white) (2-7/8" x 3-7/8") (card backs are blank)

	NR MT	EX	VG
Complete Set:	20.00	15.00	8.00

1 Leon Brown
2 Jim Williams
3 Horace Speed
4 Tony Pepper
5 Skip James
6 Jack Mull
7 Rick Bradley
8 Glenn Redmon
9 Larry Herndon
10 Bruce Christensen
11 Mike Edan
12 John LeMaster
13 Tom Heintzelman
14 Rod Dressler
15 Greg Minton
16 Bob Knepper
17 Tommy Toms
18 Ed Sulka
19 Tony Gonzalez
20 Kyle Hydes
21 Don Rose

1975 Circle K Foods Phoenix Giants

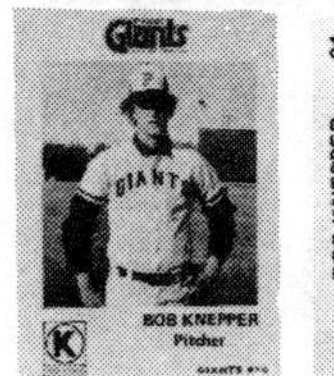

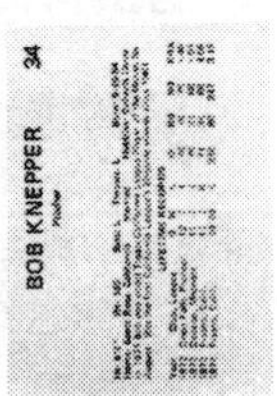

(San Francisco Giants) (black and white)

	NR MT	EX	VG
Complete Set:	12.00	6.00	3.50

1 Rocky Bridges
2 Jack Mull
3 Mike Sadek
4 Bob Nolan
5 Tony Gonzalez
6 Ed Sukla
7 Don Rose
8 Greg Minton
9 Tom Bradley
10 Bob Knepper
11 Rob Dressler
12 John Le Master
13 Glen Redmon
14 Skip James
15 Bruce Christiansen
16 Mike Eden
17 Tom Heintzelman
18 Tony Pepper
19 Jim Williams
20 Larry Herndon
21 Leon Brown
22 Horace Speed
23 Frank Johnson
24 Henry K Jordan
25 Ethan Blackaby
26 Michael J Cramer

1975 TCMA Quad City Angels

(California Angels, A)

	NR MT	EX	VG
Complete Set:	50.00	25.00	15.00

1 Rick Young
2 Ralph Botting
3 Willie Aikens
4 Bryant Fahrow
5 Stan Cliburn
6 Bobby Knoop
7 Jim Dorsey
8 Julio Cruz
9 Carl Person
10 Steve Mulliniks
11 Alex Guerrero
12 Manuel Jiminez
13 Rafael Kelly
14 Mike Howard
15 Carl Meche
16 Carlos Perez
17 Pat Kelly
18 John Hund
19 Mark Wulfemeyer
20 Steve Powers
21 John Roslund
22 Doug Slettvet
23 Billy Taylor
24 Mal Washington
25 Paul Hartzell
26 Steve Kelley
27 Andy Castillo
28 Danny Miller
29 Thad Bosley
30 Steve Brisbin
31 Kim Allen
32 Mark Stipetich
33 Mike Martinson
34 John Caneira

1975 Caruso Sacramento Solons

(Milwaukee Brewers) (black and white) (2-3/4" x 3-7/8") (backs are blank)

	NR MT	EX	VG
Complete Set:	22.00	16.50	8.75

1 Bob Hansen
2 Dave Lindsey
3 Tommie Reynolds
4 Jack Lind
5 Toby Bianco
6 Bill Mc Nulty
7 Duane Espy
8 Bob Sheldon
9 George Vasquez
10 Art Kusnyer
11 Rob Ellis
12 Jimmy Rosario
13 Steve Bowling
14 Rick Austin
15 Tom Widmar
16 Carl Austerman
17 Carlos Velasquez
18 Gordy Crane
19 Roger Miller
20 Bill Travers
21 Pat Osburn
22 Juan Lopez

1975 Caruso Salt Lake City Gulls

(California Angels) (black and white) (2-3/4" x 3-7/8") (backs are blank)

	NR MT	EX	VG
Complete Set:	20.00	10.00	6.00

1 Rusty Torres
2 Dave Collins
3 John Balaz
4 Ron Jackson
5 Dan Briggs
6 John Doherty
7 Frankie George
8 Mike Miley
9 Darrell Darrow
10 Rocky Jordan

11 Ike Hampton
12 Gary Wheelock
13 Charlie Hockenberry
14 Gary Ryerson
15 Barry Raziano
16 Louis Quintana
17 Sid Monge
18 Charlie Hudson
19 Steve Blateric
20 Norm Sherry

1975 TCMA San Antonio Brewers

(Cleveland Indians, AA) (black and white)

	NR MT	EX	VG
Complete Set:	30.00	15.00	9.00

(1) Wil Aaron
(2) Ed Arsenault
(3) Jerry Bell
(4) Mike Brooks
(5) Gary Cleverly
(6) Joe Garcia
(7) Bob Grossman
(8) Rich Guerra
(9) Mike Hannah
(10) Bob Hickey
(11) Bill Hiss
(12) Dennis Kinney
(13) Manny Lantigua
(14) Tom Linnert
(15) Tony Manning
(16) Steve Rametta
(17) Andy Rodriguez
(18) Ron Salyer
(19) Woody Smith
(20) Paul Starkovich
(21) Gary Weese
(22) Norm Werd

1975 TCMA Shreveport Captains

(Pittsburgh Pirates, AA) (black and white)

	NR MT	EX	VG
Complete Set:	50.00	25.00	15.00

(1) Paul Djakonow
(2) Mike Edwards
(3) Mike Gonzalez
(4) Frank Grundler
(5) Randy Hopkins
(6) Tim Jones
(7) Mike Kavanagh
(8) Rick Langford
(9) Don Leshnock
(10) Ken Melvin
(11) Ron Mitchell
(12) Tim Murtaugh
(13) Dave Nelson
(14) Doug Nelson
(15) Steve Nicosa (Nicosia)
(16) Max Oliveras
(17) Mitchell Page
(18) Harry Saferight
(19) Randy Sealy
(20) Jim Sexton
(21) Rich Standart
(22) Tom Thomas
(23) Steve Williams

1975 Caruso Spokane Indians

(Milwaukee Brewers) (black and white) (2-3/4" x 3-7/8")

	NR MT	EX	VG
Complete Set:	20.00	10.00	6.00

1 Tom Robson
2 Dave Moates
3 Rudy Kinard
4 Charlie Bordes
5 Rick Guarnera
6 Roy Smalley
7 Ken Pape
8 Tommy Cruz
9 Bob Jones
10 Doug Ault
11 Ron Pruitt
12 Dave Criscione
13 John Astroth
14 Mike Cubbage
15 Rick Kemp
16 Rick Waits
17 Jerry Bostic
18 Mike Bacsik
19 Dave Moharter
20 Art De Filippis
21 Ron Norman

1975 Team Syracuse Chiefs

(New York Yankees) (black and white) (Bladt is a scare, late issue)

	NR MT	EX	VG
Complete Set:	225.00	170.00	90.00

(1) Rick Bladt
(2) Ron Blomberg
(3) Bobby Cox
(4) Rick Dempsey
(5) Pat Dobson
(6) Whitey Ford
(7) Elston Howard
(8) Gerry Kenney
(9) Sparky Lyle
(10) Mickey Mantle
(11) Tippy Martinez
(12) Scott McGregor
(13) George Medich
(14) Thurman Munson
(15) Graig Nettles
(16) Dave Pagan
(17) Billy Parker
(18) Babe Ruth
(19) Rick Sawyer
(20) Fred Stanley
(21) Mel Stottlemyre
(22) Otto Velez
(23) Bill Virdon
(24) Roy White
25 Terry Whitfield

1975 KMO Radio Tacoma Twins

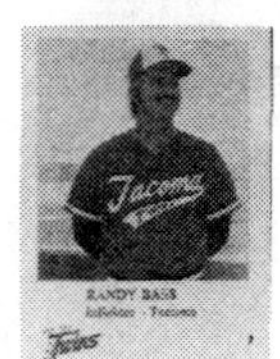

(Minnesota Twins) (black and white) (2-3/4" x 3-7/8")

	NR MT	EX	VG
Complete Set:	20.00	10.00	6.00

1 Mark Wiley
2 Dave Mc Kay
3 Jerry Terrell
4 Tom Lunstedt
5 Bill Ralston
6 Randy Beach
7 Randy Bass
8 Rick Renick
9 Bob Gorinski
10 Cal Ermer
11 Tom Johnson
12 Rocky Stone
13 Eddie Bane
14 Mike Pazik
15 Greg Thayer
16 Brad Cutler
17 Coley Smith
18 Juan Vientidos
19 Tom Kelly
20 Ed Palat
21 Mike Poepping

1975 Stewart Sandwiches Tidewater Tides

(New York Mets) (black and white) (2-1/2" x 3-1/2")

	NR MT	EX	VG
Complete Set:	125.00	60.00	35.00

(1) Benny Ayala
(2) Bob Bartlett
(3) Dwight Bernard
(4) Kent Biggerstaff
(5) Bruce Boisclair
(6) Nardi Contreras
(7) Jerry Cram
(8) Mark De John
(9) Ron Diggle
(10) Nino Espinosa
(11) Leo Foster
(12) Joe Frazier
(13) Ron Hodges
(14) Jay Kleven
(15) Bill Laxton
(16) Gary Manderbach
(17) Brock Pemberton
(18) Terry Senn
(19) Roy Staiger
(20) Randy Sterling
(21) Craig Swan
(22) George Theodore
(23) Mike Vail
(24) Mike Wegener

1975 Caruso Tucson Toros

(Oakland A's) (black and white) (2-7/8" x 3-7/8") (card backs are blank)

	NR MT	EX	VG
Complete Set:	20.00	15.00	8.00

1 Bill Grabarkewitz
2 Tom Sandt
3 Ramon Webster
4 Gaylen Pitts
5 Buzz Nitschke
6 Mike Weathers
7 Dale Sanner
8 Charlie Chant
9 Ike Blessitt
10 Keith Lieppman
11 Rich McKinney
12 Juan Gomez
13 Lew Krausse
14 Craig Mitchell
15 Leo Mazzone
16 Skip Lockwood
17 Leon Hooten
18 Alan Griffin
19 Skip Pitlock
20 Roger Nelson
21 Hank Aguirre

1975 Team Tucson Toros

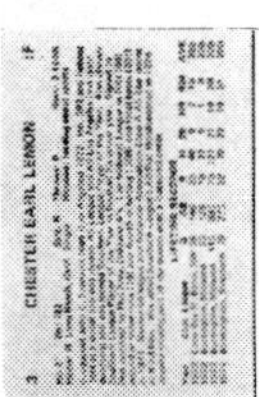

(Oakland A's) (black and white)

	NR MT	EX	VG
Complete Set:	35.00	17.50	10.50

Autograph Card
1 Hank Aguirre
2 Charlie Chant
3 Juan Gomez
4 Bill Grabarkewitz
5 Alan Griffin
6 Leon Hooten
7 Lew Krausse
8 Chester Lemon
9 Skip Lockwood
10 Leo Mazzone
11 Rich Mc Kinney
12 Craig Mitchell
13 Roger Nelson
14 Buzz Nitschke
15 Orlando Pena
16 Gaylen Pitts
17 Charlie Sands
18 Tom Sandt
19 Dale Sanner
20 Mike Weathers
21 Ramon Webster
22 Larry Davis
23 Freddie The Toro

A card number in parentheses () indicates the set is unnumbered.

1975 7-11 Tulsa Oliers

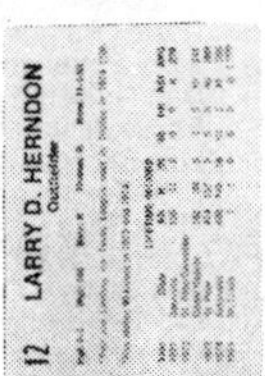

(St. Louis Cardinals) (black and white)

	NR MT	EX	VG
Complete Set:	80.00	40.00	24.00

1 Hector Cruz
2 Leon Lee
3 Kenton "Ken" Boyer
4 Kenneth Reynolds
5 Richard Leon
6 Kenneth Crosby
7 Michael Kelleher
8 Harold Lanier
9 James Willoughby
10 William Parsons
11 Harold Rasmussen
12 Larry Herndon
13 Douglas Howard
14 Michael Proly
15 Gregory Terlecky
16 Jerry Mumphrey
17 Randall Wiles
18 Joseph Lindsey
19 John Johnson
20 James Foor
21 Sergio Robles
22 Thomas Harmon
23 Mario Guerreo
24 Richard Billings

1975 TCMA Waterbury Dodgers

(Los Angeles Dodgers, AA) (black and white)

	NR MT	EX	VG
Complete Set:	35.00	17.50	10.50

(1) Tom Badcock
(2) Jose Baez
(3) Glenn Burke
(4) Larry Corrigan
(5) Bob Detherage
(6) Mike Dimmel
(7) Art Fischetti
(8) Dewey Forry
(9) Rafael Landestoy
(10) Dave Lanfair
(11) Don LeJohn
(12) Bob Lesslie
(13) Rich Magner
(14) Barney Mestek
(15) Steve Patchin
(16) Thad Philyaw
(17) Lance Rautzham
(18) Jim Riggleman
(19) Don Standley
(20) Tim Steele
(21) Jim Van Der Beck
(22) Marvin Webb

1975 TCMA Waterloo Royals

(Kansas City Royals, A) (complete set price includes both Barranca variations)

	NR MT	EX	VG
Complete Set:	80.00	40.00	24.00

(1a) German Barranca (Waterloo Royals logo on back)
(1b) German Barranca (Dubuque Packers logo and #17 on back)
(2) Al Bartlinski
(3) John Bass
(4) Charlie Beamon
(5) Roy Branch
(6) Brenda Brun, Dave Brunk)
(7) Willie Clark
(8) Pat Curran
(9) Karel Deleeuw
(10) Bobby Edmonson
(11) Bobby Falcon
(12) Craig Flanders
(13) Joe Gates
(14) Luis Gonzalez
(15) John Hart
(16) Dave Hrovat

(17) Steve Lacy
(18) Kevin Lahey
(19) Tom Laseter
(20) Manuel Moreta
(21) Lou Olsen
(22) Darrell Parker
(23) Jerry Peterson
(24) Dan Quisenberry
(25) Ed Sempsprott
(26) Luis Silverio
(27) Dick Smotherman
(28) Mark Souza
(29) John Sullivan
(30) Roy Tanner
(31) Hal Thomasson
(32) Gary Williams
(33) Mike Williams
(34) Willie Wilson

1975 Sussman West Palm Beach Expos

(Montreal Expos) (black and white) (Price includes late-issue cards for Whitacre, Krause and Bernazand)

	NR MT	EX	VG
Complete Set:	50.00	25.00	15.00

1 Julio Perez
2 Gary Gingrich
3 Jim Baby
4 1975 Expos (Fred Whitacre) (GM)
5 Mark Ewell
6 Jose Bastian
7 Roberto Ramos
8 Carlos Ledezma
9 Joe Kerrigan
10 Hal Dues
11 Marcel Lacheman
12 Godfrey Evans
13 Jerry Fry
14 Ron Staggs
15 Mike Curran
16 William Welsh
17 Gordon Mac Kenzie
18 Chris Wood
19 Mike Grabowski
20 Bob Woodland
21 Shane Rawley
22 Gary Horstmann
23 Mike Finlayson
24 Dave Mac Quarrie
25 Larry Horn
26 Mark Knose
27 Ron Sorey
28 Guy Krause
29 Antonio Bernazand, Guy Krause
30 Antonio Bernazand

1976 TCMA Appleton Foxes

(Chicago White Sox, A) (black and white)

	NR MT	EX	VG
Complete Set:	30.00	15.00	9.00

(1) Jay Attardi
(2) Roy Coulter
(3) Curt Etchandy
(4) Rick Evans
(5) Mike Farrell
(6) Bob Flynn
(7) Jim Handley
(8) Marshal Harper
(9) Tom Joyce
(10) Bill Kautzer
(11) Bill Lehman
(12) Mitch Lukevics
(13) Bob Madden
(14) Pete Maropis
(15) Candy Mercado
(16) Phil Nerone
(17) Mike Nored
(18) Ed Olszta
(19) Harris Price
(20) Curt Ramstack
(21) Scott Richartz
(22) Silvano Robles
(23) Ted Schultz
(24) Randy Seltzer
(25) Mike Smith
(26) Tommy Toman
(27) Ed Yesenchak
(28) Ed Holt, Jim Napier)
(29) Batboys

1976 TCMA Arkansas Travelers

(St. Louis Cardinals, AA) (cards are slightly larger than the standard 2-1/2" by 3-1/2" size)

	NR MT	EX	VG
Complete Set:	90.00	45.00	27.00

(1) Cardell Camper
(2) Manny Castillo
(3) Bill Caudill
(4) Jack Krol
(5) Ryan Kurosaki
(6) Terry Landrum
(7) Ken Oberkfell
(8) Mike Ramsey
(9) John Urrea
(10) Bill Valentine
(11) Randy Wiles
(12) John Young

1976 TCMA Asheville Tourists

(Texas Rangers, A) (black & white)

	NR MT	EX	VG
Complete Set:	50.00	25.00	15.00

1 Joe Russell
2 Randy Reynolds
3 Paul Mirabella
4 David Rivera
5 Bob Carroll
6 Bill Stone
7 Riccardo Lisi
8 Ward Smith
9 Harold Kelly
10 David McCarthy
11 Wayne Pinkerton
12 Richard Couch
13 Mike Arrington
14 Jerry Gaines
15 Patrick Putnam
16 Patrick Moock
17 Mark Miller
18 Larue Washington
19 Danny Tidwell
20 Wayne Terwilliger
21 Glenn Furvis
22 Len Glowzenski
23 Mark Soroko
24 Edward Miller
25 Joseph Stewart

1976 Team Batavia Trojans

(Cleveland Indians, A) (black & white) (back of cards are blank)

	NR MT	EX	VG
Complete Set:	100.00	50.00	30.00

(1) Ron Arp
(2) John Brown
(3) Rocky Bullard
(4) John Buszka
(5) Al Cajide
(6) Jack Cassini
(7) Denny Doss
(8) Dave Fowlkes
(9) Ray Gault
(10) Tim Glass
(11) Larry Harmon
(12) Craig Harvey
(13) Kevin Jeansonne
(14) Bill Mitchell
(15) Steve Narleski
(16) Ken Preseren
(17) Nate Puryear
(18) Julian Rodriguez
(19) Mike Rowe
(20) Reggie Smith
(21) John Spence
(22) Sam Spence
(23) Paul Tasker
(24) John Teising
(25) Jeff Tomski
(26) Tony Toups
(27) Terry Tyson
(28) Troy Wilder
(29) Bubba Wilson

1976 TCMA Baton Rouge Cougars

(No affiliation, A) (black & white)

	NR MT	EX	VG
Complete Set:	40.00	20.00	12.00

(1) Sterling Allen
(2) Nick Baltz
(3) Matt Batts
(4) Randy Benson
(5) Mike Brooks
(6) Tom Brown
(7) Jim Carruth
(8) Winston Cole
(9) Robbie Cox
(10) Kevin Fogg
(11) Gary Grunsky
(12) Larry Keenum
(13) Paul Kennemur
(14) Terry Leach
(15) Mickey Miller
(16) Dave Obal
(17) Ken Palmer
(18) Gerry Poche
(19) Ed Stephenson
(20) Bob Taylor
(21) Curtis Wallace

1976 TCMA Burlington Bees

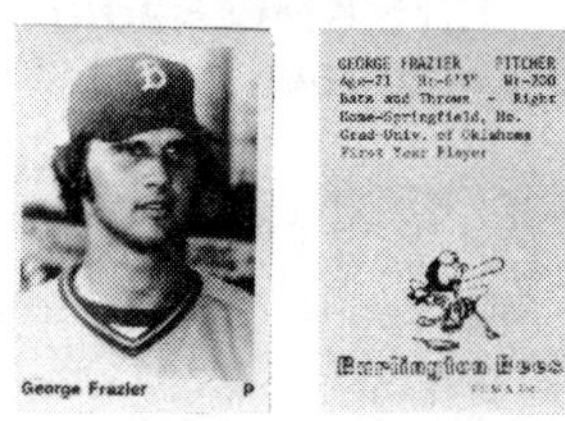

(Milwaukee Brewers, A) (black & white)

	NR MT	EX	VG
Complete Set:	30.00	15.00	9.00

(1) Greg Anderson
(2) Gary Conn
(3) Roger Danson
(4) John Dempsey
(5) Bill Dick
(6) Alvin Edge
(7) Butch Edge
(8) Miguel Encarcion
(9) Adalberto Flores
(10) Rich Ford
(11) Elliott Franklin
(12) George Frazier
(13) Matt Galante
(14) Frank Gaton
(15) Gary Gingrich
(16) Dave Globig
(17) John Hannon
(18) Dennis Holmberg
(19) Sam Jones
(20) Gary Larocque
(21) Shawn McCarthy
(22) Sam Monteau
(23) Willie Mueller
(24) Rick O'Keeffe
(25) Jay Passmore
(26) Abelino Pena
(27) Eric Restin
(28) Edgardo Romero
(29) Chuck Ross
(30) Dave Smith
(31) Ron Smith
(32) Talmage Tanks
(33) Ron Wrona

1976 TCMA Cedar Rapids Giants

(San Francisco Giants, A) (complete set price includes all variations)

	NR MT	EX	VG
Complete Set:	65.00	32.00	19.50

(1) Terry Adams
(2) Dave Anderson
(3) Ted Barnicle
(4) Jose Barrios
(5) Ken Barton
(6) Bryan Boyne
(7) Don Buchheister
(8) Ken Burton
(9) Wayne Cato
(10) Mike Glinatsis
(11a) Steve Grimes (incorrect name on back)
(11b) Steve Grimes (correct name on back)
(12) Ron Hodges
(13) John Johnson
(14) Steven McKown
(15) Dave Mendoza
(16) Stan Moline
(17) Dick Murray
(18) Billy Ray Parker
(19) Francis Parker
(20) Wayne Pechek
(21) Tim Peterson
(22) Jim Pryor
(23) Mike Rex
(24) Pat Roy
(25) German de los Santos
(26) Don Sasser
(27) Ted Schoenhaus
(28) Steve Sherman
(29) Bill Tullish
(30) Lozando Washington
(31) Steve Watson
(32) Steve Wilkins
(33) Barney Wilson
(34a) Mark Woodbrey (incorrect name on back)
(34b) Mark Woodbrey (correct name on back)
(35) Ernie Young
(36) Jeff Yurak
(37) Team Photo

1976 TCMA Clinton Pilots

(Detroit Tigers, A) (complete set price includes scarce Kline and Robles cards)

	NR MT	EX	VG
Complete Set:	95.00	47.00	28.00

(1) Phil Bauer
(2) Mike Bigusiak
(3) Ken Bokek
(4) Bobby Buford
(5) Dave Burress
(6) Felan Byrd
(7) Tom Carlson
(8) George David
(9) Fred DePietro
(10) Julian Ditto
(11) Tim Doerr
(12) Mike Elders
(13) Freeman Evans
(14) Popilio Fermin
(15) Don Fletcher
(16) Miguel Garcia
(17) Kerry Getter
(18) Juan Gonzalez
(19) Bob Hartsfield
(20) Kent Hunziker
(21) Joe Jackson
(22) Tom King
(23) Greg Kline
(24) Willie Mueller
(25) Denzil Palmer
(26) Jack Parish
(27) Gene Quick
(28) Silvano Robles
(29) Phil Trucks
(30) Jackie Uhey
(31) Mike Vaughn
(32) Paul Vavruska
(33) Larry Walbring
(34) Mal Washington
(35) Ward Wilson
(36) Dave Wood
(37) Donna Colschen, Fritz Colschen

1976 TCMA Dubuque Packers

(Houston Astros, A) (black & white)

	NR MT	EX	VG
Complete Set:	65.00	32.00	19.50

(1) Jose Alvarez
(2) Edward Anderson
(3) Reno Aragon
(4) Bruce Boehy
(5) Leroy Clark
(6) John Clothery
(7) Robert Cluck
(8) Neal Cooper
(9) Martin DeMerritt
(10) Jeff Ellison
(11) Larry Eubanks
(12) Barry Glabman
(13) Larry Green
(14) Robert Hallgren
(15) Michael Hasley
(16) Ray Hutchinson
(17) Alan Knicely
(18) Kenneth Lahonta
(19) George Lauzerique
(20) John Lee
(21) William Melendez
(22) Michael Mendoza
(23) Richard Miller

(24) Raul Nieves
(25) Martin Perez
(26) Donald Pisker
(27) Joseph Pittman
(28) Gordon Pladson
(29) Pedro Prieto
(30) Bill Roberts
(31) Alberto Rondon
(32) Simon Rosario
(33) Randy Rouse
(34) Jeffrey Smith
(35) Fay Thompson
(36) Tom Twellman
(37) Michael Tyler
(38) Jerry Willeford
(39) Gary Wilson
(40) Robert Cluck, Steve Greenberg, George Lauzerique

1976 Sussman Ft. Lauderdale Yankees

(New York Yankees, A) (black & white) All cards in this set have blank backs.

	NR MT	EX	VG
Complete Set:	65.00	32.00	19.50

1 Jesus Figueroa
2 Duke Drawdy
3 Jerry Narron
4 Joe Alcantara
5 Jim Mc Donald
6 Tom Davis
7 Bernardo Estevez
8 Jim Lysgaard
9 Domingo Ramos
10 Ken Kruppa
11 Nate Chapman
12 Antonio Bautista
13 Darnell Waters
14 Mike Heath
15 Damaso Garcia
16 Marty Caffrey
17 Mike Ferraro
18 Orlando Pena
19 Dave Wright
20 Greg Diehl
21 Willie Upshaw
22 Roger Slagle
23 Rick Stenholm
24 Benny Perez
25 Tim Lewis
26 Bevan Luis
27 Doug Melvin
28 Randy Niemann
29 Juan Espino
30 Sandy Valdespino

1976 Caruso Hawaii Islanders

(San Diego Padres, AAA) (black & white) (cards are appromimately 3-5/8" x 2-3/4" in size)

	NR MT	EX	VG
Complete Set:	25.00	12.50	7.50

1 Chuck Hartenstein
2 Jim Shellenback
3 Eddie Watt
4 Roy Hartsfield
5 Dave Roberts
6 Bobby Valentine
7 John Scott
8 Jerry Stone
9 Dave Hilton
10 Bill Almon
11 Joe Pepitone
12 Gaylen Mc Spadden
13 Gene Richards
14 Ken Reynolds
15 Jim Fairey
16 Dave Freisleben
17 Kala Kaaihue
18 Rod Gaspar
19 Jerry Johnson
20 Steve Huntz
21 Mike Champion

1976 Team Indianapolis Indians

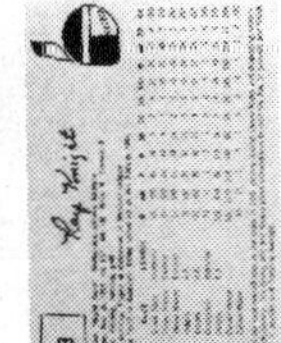

(Cincinnati Reds, AAA) (color) (co-sponsored by Tom Aikens)

	NR MT	EX	VG
Complete Set:	35.00	17.50	10.50

Checklist
1 Jim Snyder
2 Larry Payne
3 Ray Knight
4 Arturo De Freites
5 Joe Henderson
6 Tom Spencer
7 Dave Revering
8 Jeff Sovern
9 Tom Hume
10 Rudy Meoli
11 Sonny Ruberto
12 Tom Carroll
13 Junior Kennedy
14 Lorin Grow
15 Dave Schneck
16 Manny Sarmiento
17 Don Werner
18 Mike Thompson
19 Keith Marshall
20 Rich Hinton
21 John Knox
22 Carlos Alfonso
23 Tony Franklin
24 Mac Scarce
25 Ron Mc Clain

1976 Team Oklahoma City 89'ers

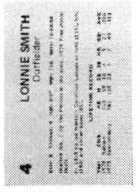

(Philadelphia Phillies, AAA) (black & white) This set is numbered as it appears on the cards.

	NR MT	EX	VG
Complete Set:	65.00	32.00	19.50

1 Terry R. Jones
2 Sergio Ferrer
3 Ronald B. Clark
4 Lonnie Smith
6 James F. Morrison
7 Mickael T. Buskey
8 Dane C. Iorg
10 Richard A. Bosetti
12 Fred Andrews
14 James Bunning
15 Randy L. Lerch
16 Danny J. Boitano
18 Willie Hernandez
19 William G. Nahorodny
20 Ruben Amaro
21 David Wallace
22 Wayne O. Nordhagen
23 Quency Hill
24 John M. Bastable
25 John E. Montague Jr.
26 Manuel M. Seoane
28 Larry G. Kiser
30 Robert L. Oliver

1976 Top Trophies Omaha Royals

(Kansas City Royals, AAA) (black & white) (cards are 8" x 10" in size and have blank backs)

	NR MT	EX	VG
Complete Set:	85.00	42.00	25.00

(1) Hall Of Fame Members
(2) Hal Baird
(3) Cowboy (Mark Ballinger)
(4) Tom Bruno
(5) Jerry Cram
(6) Dave Cripe
(7) Dave Hasbach
(8) Bob Johnson
(9) Ruppert Jones
(10) Gary Lance
(11) Sheldon Mallory
(12) Gary Martz
(13) Bob Mc Clure
(14) Lynn Mc Kinney
(15) Brian Murphy
(16) Roger Nelson
(17) Lew Olsen
(18) Moose (Frank Ortenzio)
(19) Steve Patchin
(20) Max Patkin
(21) Craig Perkins
(22) Steve Staggs
(23) Bill Sudakis
(24) George Throop
(25) U. L. Washington
(26) Duke (John Wathan)
(27) Joe Zdeb

1976 Valley Nat'l Bank Phoenix Giants

(San Francisco Giants, AAA) (black & white) This set lists no positions. Cards are approximately 4-3/8" x 3-3/8" in size. All cards in this set have blank backs and stamped autographs on their fronts.

	NR MT	EX	VG
Complete Set:	12.00	6.00	3.50

(1) Gary Alexander
(2) Rocky Bridges (Sitting in dugout)
(3) Rocky Bridges (Standing in field)
(4) Bruce Christiansen (Standing in field)
(5) Jack Clark (Standing in field)
(6) Terry Cornutt (Standing in field)
(7) Jay Dillard (Standing in field)
(8) Bob Gallagher (Standing in field)
(9) Don Hahn (Standing in field)
(10) Tom Heintzelman (Standing in field)
(11) Kyle Hypes (Standing in field)
(12) Skip James (Fielding)
(13) Skip James (Throwing)
(14) Harry Jordan (Throwing)
(15) Bob Knepper (Throwing)
(16) Johnny Le Master (Throwing)
(17) Joey Martin (Throwing)
(18) Bruce Miller (Throwing)
(19) Greg Minton (Throwing)
(20) Jack Mull (Throwing)
(21) Ed Plank (Throwing)
(22) Silvano Quezada (Throwing)
(23) Frank Ricelli (Throwing)
(24) Horace Speed (Throwing)
(25) Tommy Toms (Throwing)
(26) Mike Wegener (Throwing)

1976 Caruso Phoenix Giants

(San Francisco Giants, AAA) (black & white) (yellow card stock) This set is approximately 3-5/8" x 2-3/4" in size.

	NR MT	EX	VG
Complete Set:	25.00	12.50	7.50

1 John Le Master
2 Bruce Christensen
3 Kyle Hypes
4 Silvano Quezada
5 Skip James
6 Rocky Bridges
7 Frank Ricelli
8 Horace Speed
9 Terry Cornutt
10 Mike Wegener
11 Gary Alexander
12 Tommy Toms
13 Bob Gallagher
14 Mike Eden
15 Bob Knepper
16 Tom Heintzelman
17 Joey Martin
18 Ed Plank
19 Jack Clark
20 Bruce Miller

1976 Cramer Phoenix Giants

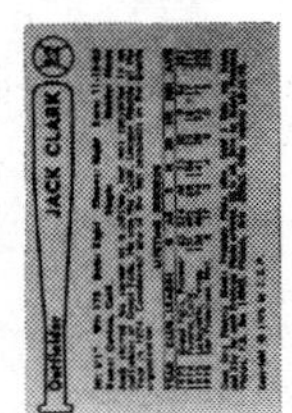

(San Fransico Giants, AAA) This set is numbered as it appears on the backs on the cards.

	NR MT	EX	VG
Complete Set:	20.00	10.00	6.00

2 Johnnie LeMaster
10 Jack Mull
11 Larry Herndon
14 Bruce Miller
15 Skip James
17 Bruce Christensen
18 Bob Gallagher
19 Mike Eden
20 Horace Speed
22 Jack Clark
23 Tom Heintzelman
25 Gary Alexander
26 Rocky Bridges
28 Ed Plank
30 Frank Ricelli
32 Silvano Quezoda
33 Tommy Toms
34 Bob Knepper
35 Mike Wegener
36 Kyle Hypes
37 Rob Dressler
38 Terry Cornutt
---- Ethan Blackaby, Trainer/Stad. Super Card, Checklist

1976 Coke Phoenix Giants

(San Francisco Giants, AAA) This black and white set lists no positions, is approximately 4-3/8" x 3-3/8" in size, and has a Coca-Cola emblem on each card. Stamped autographs appear on the card fronts, backs are blank.

	NR MT	EX	VG
Complete Set:	20.00	10.00	6.00

(1) Gary Alexander
(2) Bruce Christensen
(3) Jack Clark
(4) Terry Cornutt
(5) Rob Dressler
(6) Mike Eden
(7) Bob Gallagher
(8) Tom Heintzelman
(9) Larry Herndon
(10) Kyle Hypes
(11) Bob Knepper
(12) Johnnie Lemaster
(13) Bruce Miller
(14) Jack Mull
(15) Ed Plank
(16) Silvano Quezada
(17) Frank Riccelli
(18) Horace Speed
(19) Tommy Toms
(20) Mike Wegener
(21a) Rocky Bridges
(21b) Rocky Bridges
(22a) Skip James
(22b) Skip James

1976 TCMA Quad City Angels

(California Angels, A) (black & white) (with scarce, late issue Mercedes card)

	NR MT	EX	VG
Complete Set:	130.00	65.00	40.00

(1) Dan Beerbrower
(2) Ned Bergert
(3) Ralph Botting
(4) Bob Boyd
(5) Gary Boyle
(6) Rich Brewster
(7) Jim Brown
(8) Jerry Brust
(9) Bob Clark
(10) Mark Clear
(11) Stan Cliburn
(12) Steve Eddy
(13) Bill Ewing
(14) Bob Ferris
(15) John Flannery
(16) David Hollifield
(17) Rafael Kelly
(18) Carney Lansford
(19) Joe Maddon
(20) Mike Martinson
(21) Manuel Mercedes
(22) Scott Moffit
(23) Don Mraz
(24) Mystery Infielder
(25) Jim Officer
(26) Harry Pells
(27) Charles Porter
(28) Jerry Quigley
(29) John Ricanelli
(30) Bob Slater
(31) Doug Slettvet
(32) Randy Smith
(33) Bob Starks
(34) Dave Steck
(35) Larry Stubing
(36) Billy Taylor
(37) Steve Tebbetts
(38) Richard Thon
(39) Steve Whitehead
(40) Ken Wright

1976 Caruso Sacramento Solons

(Texas Rangers, AAA) (black & white)

	NR MT	EX	VG
Complete Set:	25.00	12.50	7.50

1 Dave Criscione
2 Keith Smith
3 Dave Moharter
4 Craig Skok
5 Bob Jones
6 Mike Bacsik
7 Tommy Cruz
8 Tommy Boggs
9 Doug Ault
10 Greg Pryor
11 Charlie Bordes
12 Art De Filippis
13 John Sutton
14 Ed Nottle
15 Jim Gideon
16 Don Thomas
17 Bump Wills
18 Lew Beasley
19 Jerry Bostic
20 Len Barker
21 David Clyde
22 Rick Donnelly
23 Greg Mohlberg

1976 Caruso Salt Lake City Gulls

(California Angels, AAA) (black & white)

	NR MT	EX	VG
Complete Set:	20.00	10.00	6.00

1 Darrell Darrow
2 Gary Wheelock
3 Mike Overy
4 Frankie George
5 Carlos Lopez
6 Mike Miley
7 Mike Martinson
8 Ed Kurpici
9 Billy Smith
10 Pat Cristelli
11 Orlando Alvarez
12 Ike Hampton
13 Chuck Hockenbery
14 Wayne Simpson
15 Dick Lange
16 Skip Pitlock
17 Luis Quintana
18 Paul Dade
19 Dave Collins
20 Dan Briggs
21 Charlie Hudson
22 Gil Flores

1976 Knowlton's San Antonio Brewers

(Texas Rangers, AA) (black & white)

	NR MT	EX	VG
Complete Set:	50.00	25.00	15.00

(1) Mel Barrow
(2) Frank Bolick
(3) Don Bright
(4) Mike Bucci
(5) Jeffrey Byrd
(6) Keith Chauncey
(7) Jim Clancy
(8) Bobby Cuellar
(9) Doug Duncan
(10) Dan Duran
(11) Gary Gray
(12) Ed Holman
(13) Rudy Jaramillo
(14) Marty Martinez
(15) Brian Nakamoto
(16) Ron Norman
(17) Wayne Pinkerton
(18) John Poloni
(19) Ray Rainbolt
(20) Rich Shubert
(21) Mike Steen
(22) Blair Stouffer
(23) Don G. Thomas
(24) Jim Thomas
(25) Bobby Thompson
(26) Dan Wheat

A player's name in italic type indicates a rookie card. An (FC) indicates a player's first card for that particular card company.

1976 Cramer Seattle Rainiers

(No Affiliations, A) (black & white, 2" x 3")

	NR MT	EX	VG
Complete Set:	18.00	9.00	5.50

2 Steve Stillwell
5 Doug Peterson
6 Steve Watson
7 Bob Kraft
8 Russ Attebery
9 Terry Sheehan
11 George Benson
12 Dave Stewart
14 Paul Gilmartin
17 Ken May
18 Kevin Gilmartin
19 Ken Kanikeberg
20 Xavier Dixon
21 Vince Barbisan
23 Ken Peters
26 Dave Sloan
27 Jimmy Williams
30 Danny Miller
35 Art Peterson
37 Dennis Peterson

1976 TCMA Shreveport Captains

(Pittsburgh Pirates, AA) (set price includes scarce Weinberg, team cards)

	NR MT	EX	VG
Complete Set:	175.00	85.00	50.00

1 Gary Hargis
2 Rich Standart
3 Rich Anderson
4 Doug Nelson
5 Luke Wrenn
6 Mike Gonzalez
7 Rod Scurry
8 Jim Sexton
9 Paul Djakonow
10 Dave Nelson
11 Mike Edwards
12 Randy Sealy
13 John Lipon
14 Albert Louis
15 Silvio Martinez
16 Steve Blomberg
17 Frank Grundler
18 Harry Saferight
19 Chet Gunter
20 Rafael Cariel
21 Ron Mitchell
22 Randy Hopkins
23 Barry Weinberg
---- Tim Murtaugh, Team Card

1976 Caruso Spokane Indians

(Milwaukee Brewers, AAA) (black & white)

	NR MT	EX	VG
Complete Set:	25.00	12.50	7.50

1 Bobby Sheldon
2 Jimy Rosario
3 Sam Ceci
4 Tom Widmar
5 Ron Jacobs
6 Bob Ellis
7 Juan Lopez
8 Kevin Kobel
9 Bob Stampe
10 Moose Haas
11 Perry Danforth
12 Art Kuysner
13 Frank Howard
14 Gary Beare
15 Kurt Bevacqua
16 Tommie Reynolds
17 Bob Hansen
18 Steve Bowling
19 Lenn Sakata
20 Toby Bianco
21 Rick Austin

1976 Dairy Queen Tacoma Twins

(Minnesota Twins, AAA) (black & white)

	NR MT	EX	VG
Complete Set:	20.00	10.00	6.00

(1) Paul Ausman
(2) Randy Bass
(3) Bill Butler
(4) Larry Cox
(5) Tom Epperly
(6) Cal Ermer
(7) Jim Gideon
(8) Bob Gorinski
(9) Tom Johnson
(10) Jack Maloof
(11) Bob Maneely
(12) Davis May
(13) Dave Mc Kay
(14) Willie Norwood
(15) Mike Pazik
(16) Mike Peopping
(17) Rick Rennick
(18) Tommy Sain
(19) Dale Solderholm
(20) Jim Van Wyck
(21) Juan Vientidos
(22) Mark Wiley
(23) Rob Wilfong
(24) Al Woods

1976 Caruso Tucson Toros

(Texas Rangers, AAA) (black & white)

	NR MT	EX	VG
Complete Set:	20.00	10.00	6.00

1 Bob Picciolo
2 Don Hopkins
3 Keith Lieppman
4 Gary Woods
5 Mike Weathers
6 Angel Manguel
7 Bob Lacey
8 Rich McKinney
9 Harry Bright
10 Wayne Gross
11 Jim Holt
12 Leon Hooten
13 Alan Griffin
14 Gaylen Pitts
15 Craig Mitchell
16 Tom Bradley
17 Rick Lysander
18 Charlie Hudson
19 Jeff Newman
20 Charlie Sands

1976 Cramer Tucson Toros

(Texas Rangers, AAA) (black and white, 2-3/8" x 3-1/2") This set is numbered as it appears on the cards.

	NR MT	EX	VG
Complete Set:	15.00	7.50	4.50

2 Mike Weathers
3 Gary Woods
6 Keith Lieppman
8 Angel Manguel
9 Rob Picciolo
10 Chris Batton
11 Don Hopkins
12 Jeff Newman
14 Dale Sanner
15 Wayne Kirby
16 Leon Hooten
19 Bob Lacey
22 Rich McKinney
23 Harry Bright
25 Wayne Gross
28 Rick Lysander
32 Craig Mitchell
33 Juan Gomez
34 Alan Griffin
35 Tom Bradley
37 Jim Holt
39 Charlie Sands
42 Gaylen Pitts
44 Skip Pitlock

1976 Goof's Pants Tulsa Oilers

(St. Louis Cardinals, AAA) (black & white)

	NR MT	EX	VG
Complete Set:	150.00	75.00	45.00

1 Ken Boyer
2 Lloyd Allen
3 Tom Harmon
4 Stan Butkus
5 Doug Clary
6 Mike Easler
7 Doug Capilla
8 Stan Mejias
9 Ed Crosby
10 Jimmy Freeman
11 John Tamargo
12 Leon Lee
13 Leron Lagrow
14 Luis Alvarado
15 Mike Potter
16 Mike Proly
17 Bill Rothan
18 Garry Templeton
19 Tom Walker
20 Charlie Chant
21 Steve Waterbury
22 Randy Wiles
23 Satchel Paige (autographed)
24 Paul Dean (autographed)
25 Earl Bass
26 Lee Landers

1976 TCMA Wausau Mets

(New York Mets, A) (black & white)

	NR MT	EX	VG
Complete Set:	35.00	17.50	10.50

(1) Gene Bardot
(2) Bob Barger
(3) Dave Bedrosian
(4) Butch Benton
(5) Keith Bodie
(6) Randy Brown
(7) Paul Cacciatore
(8) Larry Calufetti
(9) Ed Cipot
(10) Russell Clark
(11) Steve Darnell
(12) Tony Echols
(13) Ed Hicks
(14) Steve Kessels
(15) Steve Love
(16) Luis Lunar
(17) Jeryl McIves
(18) Jim Mills
(19) Juan Monasterio
(20) Bill Monbouquette
(21) Ted O'Neill
(22) Mario Ramirez
(23) Willie Simon
(24) Fred Westfall
(25) Jim Brown, Mike Feder

1976 TCMA Waterloo Royals

(Kansas City Royals, A) (black & white)

	NR MT	EX	VG
Complete Set:	65.00	32.00	19.50

(1) Bob Barr
(2) German Barranca
(3) Steve Beene
(4) Kent Cvejdlik
(5) Karel De Leeuw
(6) Rich Dubee
(7) Craig Eaton
(8) Richard Gale
(9) Danny Garcia
(10) Kevin Gillen
(11) Dale Hrovat
(12) Jack Hudson

(13) Clint Hurdle
(14) Bryan Jones
(15) Ron Kainer
(16) Steve Lacy
(17) Tom Laseter
(18) Fernando Llodrat
(19) Manuel Moreta
(20) Darrell Parker
(21) Ricky Passalacqua
(22) Jerry Peterson
(23) Ken Phelps
(24) Dan Quisenberry
(25) Ed Sempsrott
(26) Luis Silverio
(27) Ron Smith
(28) Mark Souza
(29) John Sullivan
(30) Roy Tanner
(31) Hal Thomasson
(32) Alan Viebrock
(33) Mike Williams

1976 TCMA Williamsport Tomahawks

(Cleveland Indians, AA) (black & white)

	NR MT	EX	VG
Complete Set:	35.00	17.50	10.50

(1) Wil Aaron
(2) Ed Arsenault
(3) Stan Bockewitz
(4) Wayne Cage
(5) Red Davis
(6) Bob Grossman
(7) Rich Guerra
(8) Mike Hannah
(9) Tom Linnert
(10) Tom McGough
(11) Mike Dolf
(12) Lou Isaac
(13) Pete Ithier
(14) Dennis Kinney
(15) George Mahan
(16) Tim Norrid
(17) Rick Oliver
(18) Bob Servoss
(19) Glenn Redmon
(20) Pat Wasko
(21) Gary Weese
(22) Kris Yoder
(23) Checklist

1977 TCMA Appleton Foxes

(Chicago White Sox, A) (complete set price includes scarce Minoso variation)

	NR MT	EX	VG
Complete Set:	125.00	65.00	35.00

(1) Tim Bright
(2) Brad Calhoun
(3) Bobby Combs
(4) Marvis Foley
(5) Lorenzo Gray
(6) Marshal Harper
(7) Greg Herman
(8) Clay Hicks
(9) A.J. Hill
(10) Fred Howard
(11) Kent Hunziker
(12) Bob Madden
(13) John Martin
(14) Candy Mercado
(15a) Orestes Minosi, Jr. (name incorrect)
(15b) Orestes Minoso, Jr. (name correct)
(16) Ed Olszta
(17) Andy Pasillas
(18) Joel Perez
(19) Carlos Rios
(20) Keith Rokosz
(21) Randy Seltzer
(22) Michael Sivik
(23) Paul Soth
(24) Leo Sutherland
(25) Rick Thoren
(26) Steve Trout
(27) Mike Tulacz
(28) Ed Yesenchak
(29) Appleton Foxes Staff

1977 TCMA Arkansas Travelers

(St. Louis Cardinals, AA) (set includes all late-issue logo variations) (black & white)

	NR MT	EX	VG
Complete Set:	225.00	110.00	65.00

(1) Carlton Roy Keller
(2) Carlton Roy Keller
(3) Ryan Kurosaki
(4) Ryan Kurosaki
(5) Terry Landrum
(6) Teto Landrum
(7) Nick Leyva
(8) Nick Leyva
(9) Mike Murphy
(10) Mike Ramsey
(11) Mike Ramsey
(12) Andy Replogle
(13) Andy Replogle
(14) Jim Riggleman
(15) Jim Riggleman
(16) Steve Staniland
(17) John Yeglinski
(18) John Yeglinski
(19) John Young
(20) John Young
(21) Ray Winder Field

1977 TCMA Asheville Tourists

(Texas Rangers, A) (black & white)

	NR MT	EX	VG
Complete Set:	25.00	12.50	7.50

(1) Bryan Allard
(2) Steve Bianchi
(3) Richard Couch
(4) Dennis Doyle
(5) Steve Finch
(6) Jerry Gaines
(7) Mike Griffin
(8) Mike Hicks
(9) Mike Jaccar
(10) Stan Jakubowski
(11) Greg Jemison
(12) Kerry Keenan
(13) Vic Mabee
(14) Dave McCarthy
(15) Arnold McCrary
(16) Ron Patrick
(17) Scott Peterson
(18) Dave Rivera
(19) Phil Roddy
(20) Jeff Scott
(21) Bill Simpson
(22) John Takas
(23) Wayne Terwilliger
(24) Al Thomson
(25) Phil Watson
(26) Len Whitehouse
(27) Wayne Wilkerson
(28) Glenn Williams
(29) Mike Williamson

1977 TCMA Bristol Red Sox

(Boston Red Sox, A) (black & white)

	NR MT	EX	VG
Complete Set:	140.00	70.00	42.50

(1) Erwin Bryant
(2) Mark Buba
(3) Jose Caldera
(4) Tom Farias
(5) Joel Finch
(6) Glenn Fisher
(7) Otis Foster
(8) Ken Huizenga
(9) Ed Jurak
(10) Dave Koza
(11) Joe Kranich
(12) Dave Labossiere
(13) Breen Newcomer
(14) Mike O'Berry
(15) Gary Purcell
(16) Win Remmerswael (Remmerswaal)
(17) Burke Suter
(18) Steve Tarbell
(19) John Tudor
(20) Rich Waller

1977 TCMA Burlington Bees

(Milwaukee Brewers, A) (complete set price includes scarce Halls and Mercado cards) (black & white)

	NR MT	EX	VG
Complete Set:	80.00	40.00	24.00

(1) Daryl Bailey
(2) Tim Bannister
(3) Mike Dempsey
(4) Bill Dick
(5) Gary Donovan
(6) Larry Edwards
(7) Bert Flores
(8) Richard Ford
(9) Gary Gingerich
(10) Steve Greene
(11) Gary Halls
(12) Dave Hersh
(13) Al Manning
(14) Brad Meagher
(15) Candy Mercado
(16) Dennis Menke
(17) Larry Montgomery
(18) Willie Mueller
(19) Jose Oppenheimer
(20) Glenn Partridge
(21) Jay Passmore
(22) Rene Quinones
(23) Eric Restin
(24) Chuck Ross
(25) Terry Shoebridge
(26) Steve Splitt
(27) Jesus Vega

1977 TCMA Cedar Rapids Giants

(San Francisco Giants, A) (complete set price includes scarce Laubhan card)

	NR MT	EX	VG
Complete Set:	100.00	50.00	30.00

1 Rich Murray
2 Bob Brenly
3 Dave Anderson
4 John Sylvester
5 Ken Feinburg
6 Brian Moulton
7 Phil Nastu
8 Henry Marcias
9 Gary Ledbetter
10 Ken Barton
11 Jack Mull
12 Drew Nickerson
13 Jim Pryor
14 Mike Wardlow
15 Dave Myers
16 Bart Bass
17 Steve Sherman
18 Jon Harper
19 Don Buchheister
20 Mark Kuecker
21 Dan Hartwig
22 Chris Bourjos
23 Jeff Shourds
24 Steve Pearce
---- John Laubhan

1977 TCMA Charleston Patriots

(Pittsburgh Pirates, A) (black & white)

	NR MT	EX	VG
Complete Set:	35.00	17.50	10.50

(1) Tom Burke III
(2) Jorge Carty
(3) Arcadio Cruz
(4) Bienvenido de la Rosa
(5) Rick Evans
(6) Stan Floyd
(7) Skip Leech
(8) Jim Mahoney
(9) Jim Miller
(10) Adalberto Ortiz
(11) Jim Parke
(12) Pascual Perez
(13) Eric Peterson
(14) Fred Rein
(15) Martin Rivas
(16) Bob Rock
(17) Richard Rodriquez
(18) Chuck Rouse
(19) Simon Santana
(20) Brian Schwerman
(21) Bob Semerano
(22) Jim Smith
(23) Alfredo Torres
(24) Candido Ventura
(25) Jerry Yandrick

1977 TCMA Clinton Dodgers

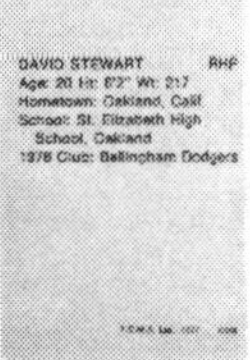

(Los Angeles Dodgers, A) (black & white) (Baltimore Orioles, AAA)

	NR MT	EX	VG
Complete Set:	115.00	55.00	33.00

(1) Paul Bain
(2) Paul Bock
(3) Dave Cohea
(4) Gerry de la Cruz
(5) Jim Del Vecchio
(6) Charles Dorgan
(7) Jim Evans
(8) Chuck Gardner
(9) Rich Goulding
(10) Dan Henry
(11) Tim Jones
(12) George Kaage
(13) Ron Kittle
(14) Mark Kryka
(15) Mickey Lashley
(16) Don LeJohn, Jr.
(17) Dick McLaughlin
(18) Damon Middleton
(19) Jim Peterson
(20) Jose Reyes
(21) Tim Roche
(22) Eric Schmidt
(23) Mike Scioscia
(24) Hilario Soriano
(25) Dave Stewart
(26) Bill Swoope
(27) Ken Townsend
(28) Max Venable
(29) Mike Wilson

1977 TCMA Cocoa Astros

(Houston Astros, A) (black & white)

	NR MT	EX	VG
Complete Set:	30.00	15.00	9.00

(1) Ed Anderson
(2) Reno Aragon
(3) Bruce Bochy
(4) Jeff Ellison
(5) Larry Eubanks
(6) Bob Hallgren
(7) Don Harkness
(8) Phil Klimas
(9) Randy Lamb
(10) Ramon Leader
(11) Diago Melendez
(12) Mark Miggins
(13) Dennis Miscik
(14) Jose Mota
(15) Jim Pankovits
(16) Gordy Pladson
(17) George Ploucher
(18) Pete Prieto
(19) Gary Rajsich
(20) Bert Roberge
(21) Simon Rosario
(22) Randy Rouse
(23) Dave Smith
(24) Tom Wiedenbauer
(25) Cocoa Astros Staff

1977 TCMA Columbus Clippers

(Pittsburgh Pirates, AAA) (complete set price includes variations) (black & white)

	NR MT	EX	VG
Complete Set:	280.00	140.00	82.00

(1) Dave Augustine
(2) Chris Batton
(3) Dale Berra
(4) Mike Easler
(5) Mike Edwards
(6) Gary Hargis
(7) Red Hartman
(8) Randy Hopkins
(9) Tim Jones
(10a) Alberto Lois (photo actually Lowell Palmer)
(10b) Alberto Lois (correct photo)
(11) Ken Macha
(12) Ron Mitchell
(13) Tim Murtaugh
(14) Doug Nelson
(15) Jim Nettles
(16) Steve Nicosa (Nicosia)
(17) Bob Oliver
(18a) Lowell Palmer (photo actually Alberto Lois)
(18b) Lowell Palmer (correct photo)
(19) Ray Price
(20) Fred Scherman
(21) Rich Standart
(22) Ed Whitson

1977 TCMA Daytona Beach Islanders

(Kansas City Royals, A) (black & white)

	NR MT	EX	VG
Complete Set:	20.00	10.00	6.00

(1) Steve Beene
(2) Ed Cowan
(3) Rich Dubee
(4) Craig Eaton
(5) Bob Engelmeyer
(6) Jack Fleming
(7) Henry Greene
(8) Ben Grzybeck
(9) John Hoscheidt
(10) Sam Jones
(11) Tom Krattli
(12) Steve Lacey
(13) Mel Lowman
(14) Jose Martinez
(15) Ken Phelps
(16) Ray Prince
(17) Phil Pulido
(18) Tim Riley
(19) Cliff Roberts
(20) Juan Rodriquez
(21) Ed Sempsrott
(22) Marty Serrano
(23) Brad Simmons
(24) Paul Stevens
(25) Roy Tanner
(26) Hal Thomasson
(27) Buddy Yarbrough

1977 TCMA Evansville Triplets

(Detroit Tigers, AAA) (black & white)

	NR MT	EX	VG
Complete Set:	360.00	180.00	110.00

(1) Bob Adams
(2) Julio Alonso
(3) Tom Bianco
(4) Tom Brookens
(5) George Cappuzzello
(6) Tim Corcoran
(7) Charles Day
(8) Pio DiSalva
(9) Jim Eschen
(10) Gary Geiger
(11) Eddie Glynn
(12) Dan Gonzales
(13) Glenn Gulliver
(14) Frank Harris
(15) Roric Harrison
(16) Artie James
(17) Marvin Lane
(18) Jerry Manuel
(19) Bob Molinaro
(20) Jack Morris
(21) Len Moss
(22) Lance Parrish
(23) Bruce Taylor
(24) John Valle
(25) Milt Wilcox

1977 Sussman Ft. Lauderdale Yankees

(New York Yankees, A) (black & white) (all cards have blank backs)

	NR MT	EX	VG
Complete Set:	75.00	37.50	22.00

1 Pat Callahan
2 Woody Keys
3 Johnny Crawford
4 Jose Alcantara
5 Mark Theil
6 Joe Le Febvre
7 Beban Luis
8 Ted Wilborn
9 Gerry Gaube
10 Nat Showalter
11 Mark Softy
12 Jose Paulino
13 Roger Holt
14 Jim Mc Donald
15 Tim Kibbee
16 Tim Guess
17 Sam Ellis
18 Pat Tabler
19 Dave Wright
20 Steve Peters
21 Don Hogestyn
22 Scott Delgatti
23 Don Fisk
24 Stan Saleski
25 Jimmy De Paola
26 Mark Burlingame
27 Gus Gil
28 Butch Riggar
29 Juan Espino
30 Tony Cameron
31 Eddie Napoleon

1977 Chong Hawaii Islanders

	NR MT	EX	VG
Complete Set:	17.50	8.75	5.25

1 Manny Estrada
3 Jim Wilhelm
4 Lin Hamilton
5 Luis Melendez
7 Pedro Garcia
8 Warren Hacker
9 Kala Kaaihu
10 Chuck Baker
11 Jerry Stone
12 Jim Fairey
14 John D'Acquisto
15 Jay Franklin
16 Dick Phillips
17 Bob Kammeyer
18 Rick Sweet
20 John McAllen
21 Mike DuPree
22 Steve Mura
23 Vic Bernal
24 Clay Kirby
25 Mark Wiley
28 Steve Huntz
29 Eddie Watt
30 Chris Ward

1977 Caruso Hawaii Islanders

(San Diego Padres, AAA) (black & white) This set is numbered as they appear on the cards.

	NR MT	EX	VG
Complete Set:	20.00	10.00	6.00

1 Manny Estrada
3 Jim Wilhelm
4 Lin Hamilton
5 Luis Melendez
7 Pedro Garcia
8 Warren Hacker
9 Kala Kaaihu
10 Chuck Baker
11 Jerry Stone
12 Jim Fairey
14 John D'Acquisto
15 Jay Franklin
16 Dick Phillips
17 Bob Kammeyer
18 Rick Sweet
20 John Mc Allen
21 Mike Du Pree
22 Steve Mura
23 Vic Bernal
24 Clay Kirby
25 Mark Wiley
28 Steve Huntz
29 Eddie Watt
30 Chris Ward

1977 TCMA Holyoke Millers

(Milwaukee Brewers, AA) (black & white)

	NR MT	EX	VG
Complete Set:	25.00	12.50	7.50

(1) Ike Blessitt
(2) Mark Bomback
(3) John Buffamoyer
(4) Doug Clarey
(5) Garry Conn
(6) Gene Delyon
(7) Bill Dick
(8) Greg Erardi
(9) Rick Ford
(10) George Frazier
(11) Matt Galante
(12) John Hannon
(13) Lynn B. Herzig
(14) Gary Holle
(15) Dale Hrovat
(16) Ron Jacobs
(17) Tom Kayser
(18) Gary LaRocque
(19) Lanny Phillips
(20) Neil Rasmussen
(21) Ed Rasmussen
(22) Ed Romero
(23) Bill Severns
(24) Rich Shubert
(25) Dave Smith
(26) Ron Wrona
(27) Jeff Yurak

1977 Team Indianapolis Indians

(Cincinnati Reds, AAA) (color)

	NR MT	EX	VG
Complete Set:	20.00	10.00	6.00

2 Roy Majtyka
3 Joe Henderson
4 Dave Revering
5 Tom Hume
6 Ron Oester
7 Larry Payne
8 Don Werner
9 Paul Moskau
10 Dan Norman
11 Mike LaCoss
12 Mike Grace
13 Dan Dumoulin
14 Steve Henderson
15 Mac Scarce
16 Tommy Mutz
17 Larry Rothschild
18 Rudy Meoli
19 Raul Ferreyra
20 Arturo DeFreites
21 Mario Soto
22 Hugh Yancy
23 Barry Moss
24 Jack Maloof
25 Manny Sarmiento
26 Ron McClain
---- Team Photo
---- Checklist

1977 TCMA Jacksonville Suns

(Kansas City Royals, AA) (black & white)

	NR MT	EX	VG
Complete Set:	75.00	37.50	22.00

(1) Mark Ballanger
(2) German Barranca
(3) Steve Burke
(4) Mike Denevi
(5) Rich Gale
(6) Joe Gates
(7) Jim Gaudet
(8) Kevin Gillen
(9) Bobby Glass
(10) Tim Ireland
(11) Dennis Kaspryzak
(12) Pete Koegel
(13) Gordon MacKenzie
(14) Frank McCann
(15) Randy McGilberry
(16) Lew Olsen
(17) Darrell Parker
(18) Bill Paschall
(19) Ken Phelps
(20) Dan Quisenberry
(21) Luis Silverio
(22) Gary Williams

1977 TCMA Lodi Dodgers

(Los Angeles Dodgers, A) (black & white)

	NR MT	EX	VG
Complete Set:	45.00	22.50	13.50

(1) Charles Barrett
(2) Mark Bradley
(3) Merv Garrison
(4) Brad Gulden
(5) Dan Henry
(6) Ubaldo Heredia
(7) Hank Jones
(8) Mike Lake
(9) Rudy Law
(10) Tony Martin
(11) Dave Patterson
(12) Pable Peguero
(13) Jack Perconte
(14) Charlie Phillips
(15) Don Ruzek
(16) Rick Sander
(17) Ed Santos
(18) Rod Scheller
(19) Steve Shirley
(20) Kelly Snider
(21) Mike Tennant
(22) Miguel Vallaran
(23) Stan Wasiak
(24) Myron White
(25) Mike Williams

1977 TCMA Lynchburg Mets

(New York Mets, A) (complete set price includes scarce Reardon card plus Allen, Benton and Greenstein variations)

	NR MT	EX	VG
Complete Set:	220.00	110.00	65.00

(1) Jack Aker
(2a) Neil Allen (Pirates logo)
(2b) Neil Allen (Mets Logo)
(3) Gene Bardot
(4a) Butch Benton (knee showing)
(4b) Butch Benton (ankle showing)
(5) George Bradbury
(6) Mike Brown
(7) Randy Brown
(8) Robert Bryant
(9) Russell Clark
(10) Carmen Coppol
(11) Dave Covert
(12) Curt Fisher
(13) Ron Gill
(14) Scott Goodfarb
(15) Bob Grant
(16) Stu Greenstein (knee to head photo)
(17) Stu Greenstein (waist to.head photo)
(18) Bob Healy
(19) Steve Keesses
(20) Jerry McIver
(21) Juan Monasterio
(22) Ted O'Neill
(23) Pacho Perez
(24) Mario Ramirez
(25) Jeff Reardon
(26) Bob Rossen
(27) Cliff Speck
(28) Randy Tate
(29) David Von Ohlen
(30) Fred Westfall
(31) Ward Wilson
(32) Steve Yost

1977 Chong Modesto A's

(Oakland A's, A) (black & white)

	NR MT	EX	VG
Complete Set:	1300.	650.00	400.00

1 Ted Smith
2 Barry Wright
3 Craig Minetto
4 Dominic Scala
5 Rickey Henderson
6 Jesse Wright
7 Mike Rodriguez
8 Ernie Camacho
9 Pat Dempsey
10 Randy Green
11 Mike Patterson

12 Mace Harrison
13 Rod Patterson
14 Monte Bothwell
15 Bart Braun
16 Rich Oziomiela
17 Tom Trebelhorn
18 Rod Mc Neely
19 Ron Beaurivage
20 Brian Meyl
21 John Eisinger
22 Juan Gomez, Tom Trebelhorn
---- Chong Distributor Card

1977 TCMA Newark Co-Pilots

(Milwaukee Brewers, A) (black & white)

	NR MT	EX	VG
Complete Set:	35.00	17.50	10.50

(1) Kevin Bass
(2) Manuel Betemit
(3) Rick Broas
(4) Ronald Buggs
(5) Chris Carstensen
(6) Pablo Cauallo
(7) Stan Davis
(8) Steve Day
(9) Tom DeRosa
(10) Ron Driver
(11) Gerry Erb
(12) Brian Fisher
(13) Adalberto Flores
(14) Bill Foley
(15) Eric Frey
(16) Jeff Harryman
(17) Dennis Holmberg
(18) Gary House
(19) Jerry Jenkins
(20) Tim Jordan
(21) David LaPoint
(22) Joe Mitchell
(23) Steve Manderfield
(24) Chester Nelson
(25) Rick Nicholson
(26) Joe Polese
(27) James Quinn
(28) John Roesch
(29) John Skorockocki

1977 Top Trophies Omaha Royals

(Kansas City Royals, AAA) (black & white) (cards are approximately 6-1/2" x 8-1/4" in size)

	NR MT	EX	VG
Complete Set:	95.00	42.50	28.50

(1) Mark Ballinger
(2) Steve Barr
(3) Charlie Beamon
(4) Jerry Cram
(5) Dave Cripe
(6) Rich Gale
(7) Dave Hasbach
(8) Clint Hurdle
(9) Rudy Kinard
(10) Pete Koegel
(11) Joe Lahoud
(12) Gary Lance
(13) Lynn Mc Kinney
(14) Ken Melvin
(15) Brian Murphy
(16) Greg Shanahan
(17) John Sullivan
(18) U. L. Washington
(19) Gary Wright

1977 TCMA Orlando Twins

(Minnesota Twins, AA) (black & white) (includes scarce, late-issue Felton card)

	NR MT	EX	VG
Complete Set:	80.00	40.00	24.00

(1) Archie Amerson
(2) Paul Ausman
(3) Terry Bulling
(4) John Castino
(5) Wayne Caughey
(6) Julian Ditto
(7) Tom Epperly
(8) Frank Estes
(9) John Felton
(10) Greg Field
(11) Mike Gatlin
(12) John Goryl
(13) Bill Harris
(14) Bruce MacPherson
(15) Dennis Mattick
(16) Johnny Pittman
(17) Brian Rothrock
(18) Gary Serum
(19) Dale Soderholm
(20) Mark Souza
(21) Greg Thayer
(22) Steve Wagner
(23) Jeff Youngbauer

1977 Coke Premium Phoenix Giants

(San Francisco Giants, AAA) This black and white set is approximately 4-3/8" x 3-3/8" in size, and lists no positions. It can further be identified by its red bottom border and the Coca-Cola emblem in the top corner. All cards except Rick Bradley's have stamped autographs on their fronts.

	NR MT	EX	VG
Complete Set:	20.00	10.00	6.00

(1) Gary Alexander
(2) Chris Arnold
(3) Rick Bradley
(4) Rocky Bridges
(5) Rob Dressler
(6) Don Hahn
(7) Vic Harris
(8) Dave Heaverlo
(9) Kyle Hypes
(10) Skip James
(11) Skip James
(12) Garry Jestadt
(13) Harry Jordan
(14) Junior Kennedy
(15) Wendell Kim
(16) Bob Knepper
(17) Joey Martin
(18) Greg Minton
(19) Ed Plank
(20) Frank Riccelli
(21) Rick Sanderlin
(22) Horace Speed
(23) Tommy Toms
(24) Mike Wegener

1977 Cramer Phoenix Giants

(San Francisco Giants, AAA) (color, 2-3/8" x 3-1/2") (co-sponsored by Coca-Cola) (set is numbered as it appears on backs of cards)

	NR MT	EX	VG
Complete Set:	12.00	6.00	3.50

2 Wendell Kim
4 Vic Harris
6 Junior Kennedy
7 Greg Minton
9 Garry Jestadt
10 Rick Sanderlin
11 Don Hahn
12 Frank Riccelli
15 Skip James
16 Rob Dressler
17 Chris Arnold
18 Rick Bradley
20 Horace Speed
21 Bob Knepper
22 Michael Wegener
23 Tommy Toms
24 Dave Heaverlo
25 Gary Alexander
26 Rocky Bridges
27 Joey Martin
28 Ed Plank
29 Kyle Hypes
---- Ethan Blackaby
---- Harry Jordan

1977 Valley Nat'l Bank Phoenix Giants

(San Francisco Giants, AAA) (black & white) This lists no positions and is approximately 4-3/8" x 3-3/8" in size. It can further be identified by its blue bottom border. Also all cards are stamped with autographs except the Rick Bradley card.

	NR MT	EX	VG
Complete Set:	15.00	7.50	4.50

(1) Chris Arnold
(2) Rick Bradley
(3) Rocky Bridges
(4) Terry Cornutt
(5) Rob Dressler
(6) Monroe Greenfield
(7) Don Hahn
(8) Randy Hammon
(9) Tom Heintzelman
(10) Kyle Hypes
(11) Skip James
(12) Garry Jestadt
(13) Harry Jordan
(14) Junior Kennedy
(15) Wendell Kim
(16) Bob Knepper
(17) Joey Martin
(18) Greg Minton
(19) Ed Plank
(20) Frank Riccelli
(21) Rick Sanderlin
(22) Horace Speed
(23) Tommy Toms
(24) Mike Wegener

1977 TCMA Quad City Angels

(California Angels, A) (black & white)

	NR MT	EX	VG
Complete Set:	35.00	17.50	10.50

(1) Jim Ball
(2) Gary Balla
(3) Ned Bergert
(4) Mike Bishop
(5) Arturo Bonitto
(6) Bob Boyd
(7) Rich Brewster
(8) Scott Carnes
(9) Mark Clear
(10) Keith Comstock
(11) Frank Coppenbarger
(12) Chuck Cottier
(13) Joel Crisler
(14) John Harris
(15) Bob Healy
(16) John Henderson
(17) Craig Hendrickson
(18) Dave Hollifield
(19) Greg Johnson
(20) Donny Jones
(21) Scott Moffitt
(22) Steve Oliva
(23) Harry Pells
(24) Ken Schrom
(25) Rick Sentlinger
(26) Doug Slettvet
(27) Fernando Tarin
(28) Steve Tebbetts
(29) Ken Wright

1977 TCMA Reading Phillies

(Philadelphia Phillies, AA) (black & white)

	NR MT	EX	VG
Complete Set:	200.00	100.00	60.00

(1) Gary Begnaud
(2) George Benson
(3) Todd Brenizer
(4) Franco Ciammachilli
(5) Narda Contreras
(6) Rafael Contreras
(7) Phil Convertino
(8) Todd Cruz
(9) Bobby Demeo
(10) Lee Elia
(11) Dan Greenhalgh
(12) Glenn Gregson
(13) John Guarnaccia
(14) Jesus Hernaiz
(15) Mark Klein
(16) Pete Manos
(17) Jose Moreno
(18) Ed Olivaros
(19) Mel Roberts
(20) Kevin Saucier
(21) Tom Siliacato
(22) Rocky Skalisky
(23) Tom White

1977 McCurdy's Rochester Red Wings

(Baltimore Orioles, AAA) This black and white set was also produced in the form of 4 uncut sheets measuring 7-1/2" x 11" in size. The listing is typed as the players appear on the uncut sheets (six players per sheet).

	NR MT	EX	VG
Complete Set:	85.00	42.00	25.00

(1) David Criscione
(2) Pedro Liranzo
(3) Michael Parrott
(4) Taylor Duncan
(5) David Ford
(6) Earl Stephenson
(7) Blake Doyle
(8) Richard Bladt
(9) Terry Crowley
(10) Tony Chavez
(11) John Flinn
(12) Larry Harlow
(13) John O'Rear
(14) Randy Miller
(15) Mike Fiore
(16) Creighton Tevlin
(17) Ed Farmer
(18) John McCall
(19) Myrl Smith
(20) Gersan Jarquin
(21) Dave Harper
(22) Dennis Blair
(23) Kevin Kennedy
(24) Ken Boyer

1977 TCMA St. Petersburg Cardinals

(St. Louis Cardinals, A) (black & white) (includes scarce, late-issue Nagle card)

	NR MT	EX	VG
Complete Set:	65.00	32.00	19.50

1 Kelly Parris (Paris)
2 William Bowman
3 Felipe Zayas
4 John Littlefield
5 Denzel Martindale
6 John Fulgham
7 Raymond Searage
8 Frank Hundsacker
9 Michael Stone
10 Terry Gray
11 Daniel O'Brien
12 Jorge Arazamendi
13 Hub Kittle
14 Thomas Herr
15 Raymond Donaghue
16 Henry Mays
17 Scott Boras
18 Claude Crockett
19 Michael Pisarkiewicz
20 Robert Harrison
21 Hector Eduardo
22 Alfred Meyer
23 David Pennial
24 Benny Joe Edelen
25 Ralph Miller, Jr.
26 Mike Nagle

1977 TCMA Salem Pirates

(Pittsburgh Pirates, A) (complete set price includes variations) (black & white)

	NR MT	EX	VG
Complete Set:	180.00	90.00	54.00

(1) Paul Anthony
(2) Jim Brady
(3) Randy Bryandt
(4) Bryan Clark
(5) Casey Clatk
(6) Stewart Cliburn
(7) Wink Cole
(8) Eugenio Cotes
(9) Pablo Cruz (no shadow on face)
(10) Pablo Cruz (shadow on face)
(11) Dennis Davis
(12) John Dean (waist to cap photo)
(13) John Dean (chest to cap photo)
(14) Dan DeBattista
(15) Steve Demeter
(16) Bob Mazur
(17) Jerry McDonald (waist to cap photo)
(18) Jerry McDonald (chest to cap photo)
(19) Ossie Oliveras (chest to cap photo)
(20) Ossie Oliveras (batting)
(21) Tony Pena
(22) Alphie Perdue
(23) Jeff Pinkus
(24) Steve Powers (logo on left)
(25) Steve Powers (logo on right)
(26) Fred Rein
(27) Dave Rodgers
(28) Luis Salazar
(29) Chuck Valley
(30) Rafael Vasquez
(31) Dick Walterhouse (logo on right)
(32) Dick Walterhouse (logo on left)
(33) Bob Weismiller (logo on left)
(34) Bob Weismiller (logo on right)
(35) Ernie Young

Definitions for grading conditions are located in the Introduction of this price guide.

1977 Cramer Salt Lake City Gulls

(California Angels, AAA) (color, 2-3/8" x 3-1/2") (co-sponsored by Coca-Cola)

	NR MT	EX	VG
Complete Set:	11.00	5.50	3.50

1 Jimy Williams
2 Fred Frazier
4 Rance Mulliniks
5 Gilberto Flores
6 Chuck Dobson
7 Danny Goodwin
8 Tom Donohue
9 Thad Bosley
10 Pat Cristelli
11 Dave Machemer
12 Fred Kuhaulua
13 Orlando Alvarez
14 Frankie George
15 Bob Nolan
16 Luis Quintana
17 Stan Perzanowski
18 John Caneira
19 Frank Panick
20 Dick Lange
21 Mike Barlow
22 Willie Aikens
24 Mike Overy
25 Butch Alberts
---- Leonard Garcia

1977 Mr. Chef's San Jose Missions

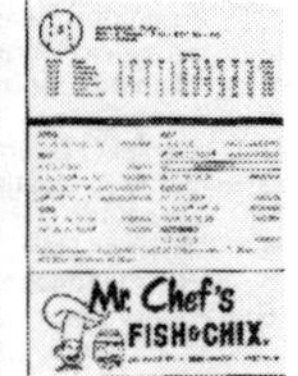

(Oakland A's, AAA) (color)

	NR MT	EX	VG
Complete Set:	15.00	7.50	4.50

1 Team Card/Checklist
2 Rene Lachemann
3 Blue Moon Odom
4 Derek Bryant
5 Milt Ramirez
6 Mark Williams
7 Jim Tyrone
8 Greg Sinatro
9 Charlie Beamon
10 Tim Hosley
11 Denny Haines
12 Mike Weathers
13 Don Hopkins
14 Bob Lacey
15 Craig Mitchell
16 Randy Boyd
17 Denny Walling
18 Randy Scarbery
19 Brian Kingman
20 Ron Bell
21 Randy Taylor
22 Jimmy Sexton
23 Brian Abraham
24 Dave Johnson
25 Paul Mitchell

1977 TCMA Shreveport Captains

(Pittsburgh Pirates, AA) (black & white)

	NR MT	EX	VG
Complete Set:	80.00	40.00	24.00

(1) Doe Boyland
(2) Fred Breining
(3) Jim Busby
(4) Juan Deliza
(5) Paul Djakonow
(6) Chet Gunter
(7) Al Holland
(8) Rick Honeycutt
(9) Rusty Johnston
(10) Mike Kavanagh
(11) Jim Kidder
(12) John Lipon
(13) Larry Littleton
(14) Tim Murtaugh
(15) Doug Nelson
(16) Nelson Norman
(17) Leo Ortiz
(18) Don Robinson
(19) Felix Rodriquez
(20) Harry Saferight
(21) Rod Scurry
(22) Tommy Thomas
(23) Luke Wrenn

1977 TCMA Spartanburg Phillies

(Philadelphia Phillies, A) (black & white)

	NR MT	EX	VG
Complete Set:	75.00	37.50	22.00

1 Pablo Minier
2 Tom Brunswick
3 Marty Bystrom
4 Jim Nickerson
5 Jarrell Whaley
6 Wally Nunn
7 Henry Mack
8 Jim Lasek
9 Joe Jones
10 Nick Popovich
11 Ricky Burdette
12 Armand Abreu
13 Ronnie Mattson
14 Glenn Ballard
15 Tony Gonzalez
16 Brian Watts
17 Elijah Bonaparte
18 Jeff Kraus
19 Mike Comptom
20 Bob Roman
21 Ozzie Virgil
22 Barry Janney
23 Sam Welborn
24 Ken Berger

1977 Cramer Spokane Indians

(Milwaukee Brewers, AAA) (color, 2-3/8" x 3-1/2") (co-sponsored by Coca-Cola)

	NR MT	EX	VG
Complete Set:	17.50	8.75	5.50

1 Duane Espy
2 Bill McLaurine
4 Jim Gantner
6 Bill Sharp
7 Perry Danforth
8 Steve Ruling
10 Art Kusnyer
11 Lenn Sakata
12 Bob Sheldon
13 Gorman Thomas
14 Juan Lopez
15 Tommie Reynolds
16 Ron Diggle
17 Sam Hinds
18 Tom Hausman
19 Lary Sorensen
20 Ken Sanders
21 Dick Davis
22 Kevin Kobel
24 Bob Ellis
25 Roger Miller
26 John Felske
28 Rich Folkers
---- Mark Voorhees

1977 Dairy Queen Tacoma Twins

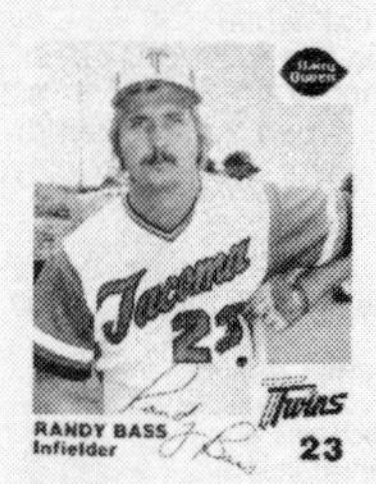

(Minnesota Twins, AAA) (black & white)

	NR MT	EX	VG
Complete Set:	35.00	17.50	10.50

1 Jim Van Wyck
2a Luis Gomez
2b Wayne Caughey
3 Dave Edwards
4 Sam Perlozzo
5 Sal Butera
6 Hosken Powell
7 Tommy Sain
8 Willie Norwood
9 John Lonchar
10 Tom Kelly
11 Eddie Bane
12 Davis May
13 Tom Hall
14 Gregg Bemis
15 Gary Ward
16 Gary Serum
17 Mike Proly
18 Steve Luebber
19 Art DeFillippis
20 Jim Gideon
21 Jim Hughes
22 Juan Veintidos
23 Randy Bass
24 Bill Butler
25 Dan Graham
26 Del Wilber
---- Tim Loberg
---- Rob Wilfong
---- Jeff Holly

1977 Cramer Tucson Toros

(Texas Rangers, AAA) (color, 2-3/8" x 3-1/2") (co-sponsored by Orange Crush)

	NR MT	EX	VG
Complete Set:	7.00	3.50	2.10

2 Dave Moates
4 Lew Beasley
5 Ken Pape
6 Wayne Pinkerton
7 Larue Washington
8 Greg Mahlberg
11 Keith Smith
12 Keathel Chauncey
13 David Moharter
14 Rich Donnelly
17 Rick Stelmaszek
19 Gary Gray
20 Bob Babcock
27 Ed Nottle
32 David Clyde
33 Kurt Bevacqua
35 John Poloni
40 Len Barker
45 Mark Soroko
51 Pat Putnam
52 Mike Bacsik
53 Bobby Cuellar
59 David Harper
---- Chip Steger

1977 TCMA Visalia Oaks

(Minnesota Twins, A) (black & white)

	NR MT	EX	VG
Complete Set:	20.00	10.00	6.00

(1) John Altman
(2) Leland Byrd
(3) Bob Carroll
(4) Tim Costello
(5) Doug Duncan
(6) Rick Green
(7) James LaFountain
(8) Roy McMillan
(9) Dean Olson
(10) Glenn Purvis
(11) Frank Quintero
(12) Charlie Renneau
(13) Ray Smith
(14) Rick Sofield
(15) Kevin Stanfield
(16) Joe Stewart
(17) Bill Stone

1977 TCMA Waterloo Indians

(Cleveland Indians, A) (complete set price includes scarce Arnold and Strickfaden cards plus Brennan variations)

	NR MT	EX	VG
Complete Set:	150.00	75.00	45.00

(1) Craig Adams
(2) John Arnold
(3a) Thomas Brennan (Texas League logo on front)
(3b) Thomas Brennan (Midwest League logo on front)
(4) John Buszka
(5) Norman Churchhill
(6) Dennis Doss
(7) Gene Dusan
(8) David Fowlkes
(9) Pedro Garcia
(10) Raymond Gault
(11) Craig Harvey
(12) William Hiss
(13) Rick Howerton
(14) Kevin Jeansonne
(15) Steven Narleski
(16) Thomas Pulchinski
(17) Nathaniel Puryear
(18) Junior Roman
(19) David Schuler
(20) Daniel Skiba
(21) Forest Smith
(22) Samuel Spence
(23) Dave Strickfaden
(24) Jeffery Tomski
(25) Tony Toups
(26) Terry Tyson
(27) Michael Vaughn
(28) Patrick Washko
(29) Steven Widner
(30) Al Wihtal (Whitol)
(31) Dwain Wilson

1977 TCMA Wausau Mets

(New York Mets, A) (black & white)

	NR MT	EX	VG
Complete Set:	60.00	30.00	18.00

(1) Kevan Aman
(2) Rick Armer
(3) Paul Cacciatore
(4) Buddy Cardwell
(5) Kelvin Chapman
(6) Alexander Coghan
(7) Gary Corrado
(8) Tom Egan
(9) Bob Grant
(10) James Hammer
(11) Randy Holman
(12) Luis Lunar
(13) Bill Muth
(14) Bob Pappageorgas
(15) Rick Patterson
(16) Don Pearson
(17) Dennis Sandoval
(18) Kim Seaman
(19) Keith Shermeyer
(20) Tony Thomas
(21) Tom Thurberg
(22) Alex Trevino
(23) Charlie Warren
(24) Rick Wolf

1977 TCMA West Haven Yankees

(New York Yankees, AA) (black & white)

	NR MT	EX	VG
Complete Set:	150.00	75.00	45.00

(1) Richard Anderson
(2) Antonie Bautista
(3) Jim Beattie
(4) Donald Castle
(5) Steven Coulson
(6) Duke Drawdy
(7) Michael Ferraro
(8) Jesus Figueroa
(9) Richard Fleshman
(10) Damaso Garcia
(11) Michael Heath
(12) Lloyd Kern
(13) Timothy Lewis
(14) Jim Lysgaard
(15) Douglas Melvin
(16) Carl Merrill
(17) Jerry Narron
(18) Nelson Pichardo
(19) Domingo Ramos
(20) Roger Slagle
(21) Garry Smith
(22) Richard Stenholm
(23) Sandy Valdespino
(24) Will Verhoeff
(25) Bob Zeig

1978 Cramer Albuquerque Dukes

(Los Angeles Dodgers, AAA) (color, 2-3/8" x 3-1/2") This set is numbered as they appear on the backs of the cards.

	NR MT	EX	VG
Complete Set:	35.00	17.50	10.50

1 Dell Crandall (Del)
2 Terry Collins
3 Rudy Law
4 Enzo Hernandez
5 Ron Washington
6 Joe Simpson
7 Rafael Landestoy
9 Pablo Peguero
11 Bob Welch
12 John O'Rear
13 Hank Webb
14 Dennis Lewallyn
16 Pedro Guerrero
17 Joe Beckwith
19 Claude Westmoreland
20 Brad Gulden
21 Rick Sutcliffe
24 Kevin Keefe
29 Bill Butler
---- Team Logo & Schedule

1978 TCMA Appleton Foxes

(Chicago White Sox, A) (black and white)

	NR MT	EX	VG
Complete Set:	30.00	15.00	9.00

(1) Rod Allen
(2) Edward Bahns
(3) Phil Bauer
(4) Ross Baumgarten
(5) Harry Chappas
(6) Roy Coulter
(7) David Daniels
(8) Mark Esser
(9) Curt Etchandy
(10) Lorenzo Gray
(11) John Hanely
(12) Dave Hersh
(13) Clay Hicks
(14) Lamar Hoyt (LaMarr)
(15) Dewey Robinson
(16) Mike Sivik
(17) Jackie Smith
(18) Paul Soth
(19) Leo Sutherland
(20) Richard Thoren
(21) Tom Toman
(22) Phil Trucks
(23) Michael Tulacz
(24) Jeffery Vuksan
(25) Victor Walters

1978 TCMA Arkansas Travelers

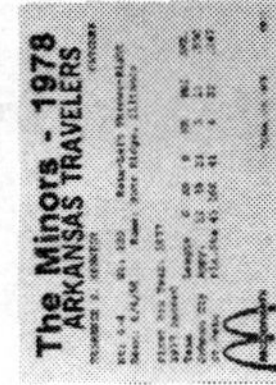

(St. Louis Cardinals, AA) (black and white)

	NR MT	EX	VG
Complete Set:	150.00	75.00	45.00

(1) Jose Aranzamendi
(2) Earl Bass
(3) Dave Boyer
(4) Glenn Brummer
(5) Mike Calise
(6) Roy Donaghue
(7) Gene Dotson
(8) Leon Durham
(9) Joe Edelen
(10) John Fulgham
(11) Nelson Garcia
(12) R.J. Harrison
(13) Terry Herr (Tommy)
(14) Terry Kennedy
(15) Ryan Kurosaki
(16) Jim Lentine
(17) John Littlefield
(18) Dan O'Brien
(19) Dave Penniall
(20) Len Strelitz
(21) Randy Thomas
(22) Tommy Thompson
(23) Fred Tisdale

1978 TCMA Asheville Tourists

(Texas Rangers, A) (black and white)

	NR MT	EX	VG
Complete Set:	25.00	12.50	7.50

(1) Jim Barbe
(2) John Butch
(3) Jim Capowski
(4) Ron Carney
(5) Joe Carrol
(6) Ted Davis
(7) Luis Gonzalez
(8) Issie Gutierrez
(9) Bob Hallgren
(10) Dave Hibner
(11) Mike Jirschele
(12) Bobby Johnson
(13) Chuck Lamson
(14) Bill LaRosa
(15) Ed Lynch
(16) Jim Mathews
(17) Arnold McCrary
(18) Mark Mercer
(19) Linvel Mosby
(20) Pat Nelson
(21) Steve Nielsen
(22) Scott Peterson
(23) Miguel Pizarro
(24) Steve Righetti
(25) Bill Simpson
(26) Mike Vickers
(27) Len Whitehouse
(28) Arnold Wilhoite
(29) George Wright

1978 TCMA Burlington Bees

(Milwaukee Brewers, A) (black and white)

	NR MT	EX	VG
Complete Set:	30.00	15.00	9.00

(1) John Adam
(2) Daryl Bailey
(3) Tim Bannister
(4) Kevin Bass
(5) Manuel Betemit
(6) Terry Bevington
(7) Chris Cartensen
(8) Tom DeRosa
(9) Bill Dick
(10) Frank DiPino
(11) Alvin Edge
(12) Larry Edwards
(13) Bill Foley
(14) Ed Gilliam
(15) Jeff Harryman
(16) Jerry Jenkins
(17) Jim Jordan
(18) David LaPoint
(19) Doug Loman
(20) Melvin Manning
(21) Larry Montgomery
(22) Steve Reed
(23) Ivan Rodriquez
(24) Terry Shoebridge
(25) Lee Sigman
(26) John Skorochocki
(27) Bob Smith
(28) Weldon Swift

1978 TCMA Cedar Rapids Giants

(San Francisco Giants, A) (black and white)

	NR MT	EX	VG
Complete Set:	95.00	47.00	28.00

(1) Pat Alexander
(2) Darnell Baker
(3) Jeff Borruel
(4) De Wayne Buice
(5) Don Buchheister
(6) Raymondo Cosio
(7) Charles (Chili) Davis
(8) Ken Feinberg
(9) Rob Henderson
(10) Craig Hedrick
(11) Steve Holman
(12) Bob Kearney
(13) Craig Landis
(14) Doug Landuyt
(15) Javier Lopez
(16) Henry Macias
(17) Louis Marietta
(18) Jack Mull
(19) Venice Murray
(20) Bob Omo
(21) Juan Oppenheimer
(22) Ron Pisel
(23) Francisco Rojas
(24) Alfonso Rosario
(25) John Smith
(26) Jeff Stadler
(27) Jeff Stember
(28) Frankie Thon
(29) Veterans Memorial Stadium

1978 TCMA Charleston Charlies

(Houston Astros, AAA) (black and white)

	NR MT	EX	VG
Complete Set:	12.00	6.00	3.50

(1) Dave Augustine
(2) Jim Beauchamp
(3) Craig Cacek
(4) Joe Cannon
(5) Bob Coluccio
(6) Keith Drumright
(7) Mike Fischlin
(8) Larry Hardy
(9) Bo McLaughton (McLaughlin)
(10) Jim O'Bradovich
(11) Ramon Perez
(12) Don Pisker
(13) Luis Pujols
(14) Vern Ruhle
(15) Jose Sosa
(16) Rob Sperring
(17) Roy Thomas
(18) Mike Tyler
(19) Randy Wiles
(20) Rick Williams

1978 TCMA Charleston Pirates

(Pittsburgh Pirates, A) (black and white)

	NR MT	EX	VG
Complete Set:	25.00	12.50	7.50

(1) Doug Britt
(2) Bryan Clark
(3) Casey Clark
(4) Steve Farr
(5) Rick Federici
(6) Doug Frobel
(7) Tim Ganch
(8) Gene Gentile
(9) Luis Giminez
(10) Wendell Hihhett
(11) Woody Huyke
(12) Jean Leduc
(13) Brian Lucas
(14) Ed Lynch
(15) Vic Marte
(16) Tony Nicely
(17) Adalberto Ortiz
(18) Mike Pill
(19) Charlie Powell
(20) Wascar Reyes
(21) Carlos Rios
(22) Brian Schwerman
(23) Billy Scripture
(24) Ed Vargas

1978 TCMA Clinton Dodgers

(Los Angeles Dodgers, A) (black and white)

	NR MT	EX	VG
Complete Set:	35.00	17.50	10.50

(1) Jan Bac, Rich Bach)
(2) Jerry Bass
(3) Rocky Cordova
(4) Dean Craig
(5) Mark Elliott
(6) Larry Ferst
(7) Rick Ford
(8) Doug Foster
(9) Miguel Franjul
(10) Doug Harrison
(11) Leonardo Hernandez
(12) Mike Holt
(13) Mike Howard
(14) Tim Jones
(15) Kevin Joyce
(16) Mark Kryka
(17) Don LeJohn
(18) Jack Littrell
(19) Evon Martinson
(20) Rusty McDonald
(21) Dick McLaughlin
(22) Chris Mulden
(23) Rick Ollar
(24) Joe Purpura
(25) German Rivera
(26) Mike Stone
(27) Steve Sunker
(28) Bill Swoope
(29) Mark Van Bever
(30) Mitch Webster
(31) Larry Wright
(32) Clinton Batboys
(33) Clinton's Riverview Stadium

1978 TCMA Columbus Clippers

(Pittsburgh Pirates, AAA) (color)

	NR MT	EX	VG
Complete Set:	25.00	12.50	7.50

(1) Dale Berra
(2) Dorian Boyland
(3) Fred Breining
(4) Cot Deal
(5) Mike Easler
(6) Mike Fiore
(7) Jim Fuller
(8) Fernando Gonzales (Gonzalez)
(9) Gary Hargis
(10) Al Holland
(11) Randy Hopkins
(12) Odell Jones
(13) John Lipon
(14) Alberto Lois
(15) Ken Macha
(16) Ron Mitchell
(17) Roger Nelson
(18) Steve Nicosia
(19) Ossie Olivares
(20) Dave Pagan
(21) Harry Saferight
(22) Mickey Scott
(23) Rod Scurry
(24) Tom Shopay
(25) Randy Tate
(26) Tom Walker
(27) Ed Whitson

1978 TCMA Daytona Beach Astros

(Houston Astros, A) (black and white)

	NR MT	EX	VG
Complete Set:	20.00	10.00	6.00

(1) Ricky Adams
(2) Rick Aponte
(3) Julio Beltran
(4) Al Cajide
(5) John Cloherty
(6) Paul Cooper
(7) Steve Englishby
(8) George Gross
(9) Don Harkness
(10) Pete Hernandez
(11) Kevin Houston
(12) Doug Jackson
(13) Ramon Leader
(14) Del Leatherwood
(15) Stan Leland
(16) Scott Loucks
(17) Jim MacDonald
(18) Diego Melendez
(19) Fred Morris
(20) Jose Mota
(21) Leo Posado
(22) Simon Rosario
(23) Randy Rouse
(24) Billy Smith
(25) Jose Turnes
(26) Randy Walraven

1978 Tiefel & Associates Denver Bears

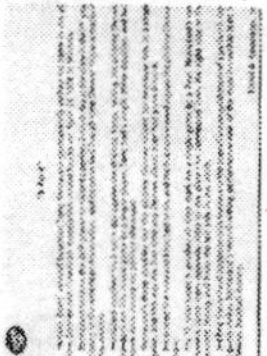

(Montreal Expos, AAA) (color)

	NR MT	EX	VG
Complete Set:	20.00	10.00	6.00

1 Tony Bernazard
2 Tony Bernazard ("6 for 6")
3 Ossie Blanco

4 Leonel Carrion
5 Joe Carroll
6 Ed Creech
7 Don Demola
8 Doc Edwards
9 Jerry Fry
10 Dave Gronlund
11 Mike Hart
12 Tim Jones
13 Joe Keener
14 Larry Landreth
15 Pete Mackanin
16 Randy Miller
17 Frank Ortenzio
18 Bob Pate
19 Roberto Ramos
20 Steve Ratzer
21 Rick Resnick
22 Ken Rushing
23 Dan Schatzeder
24 Bryn Smith
25 Frank Orenzio, Bobby Pate, Rick Resnick

1978 TCMA Dunedin Blue Jays

(Toronto Blue Jays, A) (black and white)

	NR MT	EX	VG
Complete Set:	45.00	22.00	13.50

(1) Jesse Barfield
(2) Larry Bullard
(3) Jeff Carsley
(4) Rick Counts
(5) Tom Dejak
(6) Eduardo Dennis
(7) Wayne DeWright
(8) Roberto Galvez
(9) Miguel Gomez
(10) Scott Gregory
(11) Rick Hertel
(12) Darryl Hill
(13) Jack Hollis
(14) Dennis Homberg
(15) Mike Lebo
(16) Denis Menke
(17) Benny Perez
(18) Jay Robertson
(19) Dave Rohm
(20) Jose Rosario
(21) Pete Rowe
(22) Ron Sorey
(23) Fay Thompson
(24) Greg Wells
(25) Ralph Wheeler
(26) Randy Wiens
(27) Andre Wood

1978 Team Geneva Cubs

(Chicago Cubs, A) This set is numbered as it appears on the cards. It was also produced in a set of 4 uncut sheets.

	NR MT	EX	VG
Complete Set:	90.00	45.00	27.00

4 Jeff Doyle
7 Bob Hartsfield
8 Mike Turgeon
10 Bill Morgan
11 Jerry Ahlert
14 Bubba Kizer
18 J.W. Mitchell
21 Joe Cole
22 Bill Ross
25 Joe Hicks
26 Mike Godley
27 Mark Parker
28 Ted Trevino
29 Mark Gilbert
30 Lou Whetstone
31 Ted May
37 Joe McClain
39a Ennis Lamont
39b Doug McCracken
41 Tom Spino
44 Bill Earley
45 Randy Clark
49 Joe Stethers
---- Team Card

1978 TCMA Greenwood Braves

(Atlanta Braves, A) (black and white)

	NR MT	EX	VG
Complete Set:	15.00	7.50	4.50

(1) Terry Abbot
(2) Tom Ballard
(3) Tim Barr
(4) Clete Boyer
(5) Smokey Burgess
(6) Tim Cole
(7) Joe Cowley
(8) John Dyer
(9) Andre Forbes
(10) Alan Gallagher
(11) Bill Haley
(12) Steve Hammond
(13) Bill Haslerig
(14) Danny Lucia
(15) Jeff Matthews
(16) Tommy Mee
(17) Alvin Moore
(18) Felix Pettaway
(19) Bob Porter
(20) Rafael Ramirez
(21) George Ramos
(22) Andre Sams
(23) Brian Snitker
(24) Scott Thayer
(25) Bruce Tonascia
(26) Wyatt Tonkin
(27) William Tucker
(28) Bob Veale
(29) Richard Wieters

1978 TCMA Holyoke Millers

(Milwaukee Brewers, AA) (color)

	NR MT	EX	VG
Complete Set:	12.00	6.00	3.50

(1) Jeff Barker
(2) Ken Biggerstaff
(3) Ed Carroll
(4) Mike Dempsey
(5) Bill Dick
(6) Ronnie Driver
(7) Marshall Edwards
(8) George Farson
(9) Steve Green
(10) Steve Grimes
(11) Mike Henderson
(12) Lynn B. Herzig
(13) Gary Holle
(14) Ron Jacobs
(15) Bernado Leonard
(16) Willie Mueller
(17) Rick Nicholson
(18) Neil Rasmussen
(19) Chuck Ross
(20) Dave Smith
(21) Steve Splitt
(22) Esteban Texidor
(23) Don Whiting
(24) Jeff Yurak

1978 Team Indianapolis Indians

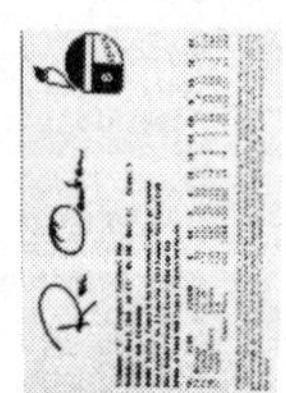

(Cincinnati Reds, AAA) (color) This set was co-sponsored by Tom Aikens.

	NR MT	EX	VG
Complete Set:	25.00	12.50	7.50

1 Team Photo
2 Roy Majtyka
3 Paul Moskau
4 Harry Spilman
5 Mike LaCoss
6 Ron Oester
7 Dan Dumoulin
8 Ed Armbrister
9 Mario Soto
10 Tommy Mutz
11 Dave Moore
12 John Summers
13 Larry Payne
14 John Valle
15 George Cappuzzello
16 Mike Grace
17 Rafael Santo Domingo
18 Angel Torres
19 Vic Correll
20 Lynn Jones
21 Raul Ferreyra
22 Arturo Defreites
23 Frank Pastore
24 Randy Davidson
25 Jeff Sovern
26 Ron McClain
27 Checklist

1978 TCMA Knoxville Knox Sox

(Chicago White Sox, AA) (black and white)

	NR MT	EX	VG
Complete Set:	210.00	105.00	60.00

(1) Harold Baines
(2) Richard Barnes
(3) Richard Dotson
(4) Marvis Foley
(5) Ken Frailing
(6) Fred Frazier
(7) Joe Gates
(8) Quency Hill
(9) Fred Howard
(10) Rusty Kuntz
(11) Tony LaRussa
(12) Mitch Lukevics
(13) Larry Monroe
(14) Bill Moran
(15) Mark Naehring
(16) Chris Nyman
(17) Andy Pasillas
(18) Donn Seidholz
(19) Duane Shaffer
(20) Ken Silvestri
(21) Tom Spencer
(22) Willie Thompson
(23) Tommy Toman
(24) Steve Trout
(25) Mike Wolf

1978 TCMA Lodi Dodgers

(Los Angeles Dodgers, A) (black and white) (set includes corrected Scheller card)

	NR MT	EX	VG
Complete Set:	30.00	15.00	9.00

(1) Paul Bain
(2) Bobby Brown
(3) H.P. Drake
(4) Larry Fobbs
(5) Marv Garrison
(6) Rick Goulding
(7) Brian Hayes
(8) Ubalso Heredia
(9) Hank Jones
(10) George Kaage
(11) Mike Lake
(12) Mickey Lashley
(13) Dave Richards
(14) Tim Roche
(15) Ron Roenicke
(16) Don Ruzek
(17a) Rod Scheller (incorrect name on back)
(17b) Rod Scheller (correct name on back)
(18) Eric Schmidt
(19) Steve Shirley
(20) John Shoemaker
(21) Mike Stone
(22) Ken Townsend
(23) Max Venable
(24) John Walker
(25) Stan Wasiak

1978 Brittling's Memphis Chicks

(Montreal Expos, AA) (black & white, 3-7/8" x 2-13/16")

	NR MT	EX	VG
Complete Set:	20.00	10.00	6.00

(1) Felipe Alou
(2) Ray Crowley
(3) Godfrey Evans
(4) Larry Goldetsky
(5) Warren Hemm
(6) Dale McMullen
(7) Julio Perez
(8) Joe Pettini
(9) John Scoras
(10) Rick Williams

1978 Chong Modesto A's

3) MIKE DAVIS - OF
1978 Modesto A's
CALIFORNIA LEAGUE

(Oakland A's, A) (black & white)

	NR MT	EX	VG
Complete Set:	75.00	37.50	22.00

1 Pat Dempsey
2 Ed Nottle
3 Mike Davis
4 Bruce Fournier
5 Dana Berry
6 Dave Mc Carthy
7 Doug Hunt
8 Dave Beard
9 Shooty Babbit
10 Dennis Wysznski
11 Mike Mc Lellan
12 Don Van Marter
13 Don Schubert
14 Craig Harris
15 Paul Mize
16 Chip Kniss
17 Tom Eagan
18 Jim Bennett
19 Robert Moore
20 John Lavery
21 Ken Palmer
22 Eric Attaway
23 Bob Markham
24 Dan Darichuk
25 Ted Nowakowski
26 Gaylen Pitts

1978 TCMA Newark Wayne Co-Pilots

(Milwaukee Brewers, A) (black and white)

	NR MT	EX	VG
Complete Set:	25.00	12.50	7.50

(1) Bert Acosta
(2) Sally Beal
(3) Randy Boyce
(4) Eddie Brunson
(5) Ron Bugga
(6) Pablo Cavallo
(7) Rafael Cuevas
(8) Stan Davis
(9) Greg Dellart
(10) Jorge DeJesus
(11) Roberto Diaz
(12) Duke Duncan
(13) Lance Ediger
(14) Willie Flowers
(15) Steve Gibson
(16) Sam Gierhan
(17) Dan Gilmartin
(18) Dean Hall
(19) Rocky Hall
(20) Nick Hernandez
(21) Doug Jones
(22) Tim Jordan
(23) Eliqio Kelly
(24) Harvey Kuenn
(25) David Lebron
(26) Jerry Lewis
(27) Steve Manderfield
(28) Ray Manship
(29) Dan Maxson
(30) Tom McLish
(31) Steve Norwood
(32) Rick Olsen
(33) Jim Padula
(34) Vince Pone
(35) Luis Ramirez
(36) Russell Ramirez
(37) Kenny Richardson
(38) Jim Robinson
(39) John Roesch
(40) Pat Seegers
(41) Tom Soto
(42) John Stevenson
(43) Al Wesolowski
(44) Nick Willhite
(45) Porter Wyatt

1978 Team Oklahoma City 89'ers

(Philadelphia Phillies) (black and white) (Price includes the late-issue, scarce Wright card)

	NR MT	EX	VG
Complete Set:	80.00	40.00	24.00

1 Fred Ray Beene
3 Ramon Aviles
4 Lonnie Smith
5 Robert Michael DeMeo
6 James Forrest Morrison
7 Michael T. Buskey
8 Kerry Michael Dineen
9 Rogers Lee Brown
10 Steven Craig Waterbury
11 Orlando Alvarez
12 Todd Ruben Cruz
14 Kevin Andrew Saucier
15 Mike Anderson
16 Danny Jon Boitano
17 Charles Edward Kniffin
18 Daniel Dean Warthen
19 Bobby Keith Moreland
20 Orlando Gonzalez
21 Michael Sherman Wallace
22 John C. Vuckovich
23 John William Poff
25 Jackson A. Todd
26 Arnaldo Contreras Jr.
27 Michael James Ryan
28 Tom Harmon
29 William Connors
30 James L. Wright Jr.

1978 TCMA Orlando Twins

(Minnesota Twins, AA) (black and white)

	NR MT	EX	VG
Complete Set:	15.00	7.50	4.50

(1) Terry Bulling
(2) John Castino
(3) Mark Clapham
(4) Rich Dalton
(5) Rick Duncan
(6) Frank Estes
(7) John Goryl
(8) Jeff Holly
(9) Darrell Jackson
(10) Curt Lewis
(11) Bruce MacPherson
(12) Dennis Mantick
(13) Marty Maxwell
(14) Kevin McWhinter
(15) Warren Mertens
(16) Frank Quintero
(17) Tom Sain
(18) Terry Sheehan
(19) Ray Smith
(20) Dan Spain
(21) Jesus Vega
(22) Steve Wagner
(23) Kurt Whittmayer

1978 Cramer Phoenix Giants

(San Francisco Giants, AAA) (color, 2-3/8" x 3-1/2") (co-sponsored by Pepsi-Cola)

	NR MT	EX	VG
Complete Set:	9.00	4.50	2.75

2 Wendell Kim
3 Greg Johnston
5 Howie Mitchell
6 Joe Strain
7 Greg Minton
10 Rick Sanderlin
11 Guy Sularz
12 Phil Nastu
13 Rocky Bridges
14 Mike Rowland
15 Mike Cash
16 Rob Dressler
17 Casey Parsons
18 Randy Hammon
19 Terry Cornutt
21 Jeff Little
22 Rich Murray
23 Don Carrithers
24 Art Gardner
25 Rick Bradley
27 Dennis Littlejohn
28 Ed Plank
29 Kyle Hypes
---- Ethan Blackaby
---- Harry Jordan

1978 TCMA Quad City Angels

(California Angels, A) (black and white)

	NR MT	EX	VG
Complete Set:	80.00	40.00	24.00

(1) Gary Balla
(2) Ned Bergert
(3) Jeff Bertoni
(4) Joe Blyleven
(5) Arturo Bonnitto
(6) Bob Border
(7) Jeff Connor
(8) Brian Harper
(9) Brad Havens
(10) Mike Heaton
(11) Don Jones
(12) Guy Jones
(13) Monte Mendenhall
(14) Mark Miller
(15) Charles Nash
(16) Steve Oliva
(17) Harry Pells
(18) John Pound
(19) Melvin Quarles
(20) Bran Riffle (Riffel)
(21) Greg Ris
(22) Andy Rodriguez
(23) Wade Schexnayder
(24) Darryl Sconiers
(25) Mike Stover
(26) Doug Thompson
(27) Jim Vallone
(28) Steve Van Deren
(29) Alan Wiggins
(30) Waterloo Municipal Stadium

1978 TCMA Richmond Braves

(Atlanta Braves, AAA) (color)

	NR MT	EX	VG
Complete Set:	25.00	12.50	7.50

(1) Tommie Aaron
(2) James Arline
(3) Bruce Benedict
(4) Larry Bradford
(5) Glenn Hubbard
(6) Frank LaCorte
(7) Michael Macha
(8) Jerry Maddox
(9) Richard Mahler
(10) Joey McLaughlin
(11) Edward Miller
(12) Jon Richardson
(13) Chico Ruiz
(14) John Sain
(15) Hank Small
(16) Duane Theiss
(17) Larry Whisenton
(18) Kris Yoder
(19) Front Office
(20) Chief Powa Hitta, Seymore Baseball (Team mascots)

1978 TCMA Rochester Red Wings

(Baltimore Orioles, AAA) (color)

	NR MT	EX	VG
Complete Set:	25.00	12.50	7.50

(1) Ray Bare
(2) Tom Bianco
(3) Don Cardoza
(4) Tony Chevez
(5) Tom Chism
(6) Dave Criscione
(7) Mike Dimmel
(8) Blake Doyle
(9) Skeeter Jarquin
(10) Kevin Kennedy
(11) Wayne Krenchicki
(12) Rafael Liranzo
(13) Marty Parrill
(14) Jeff Rineer
(15) Frank Robinson
(16) Earl Stephenson
(17) Tim Stoddard

1978 TCMA St. Petersburg Cardinals

(St. Louis Cardinals, A) (black and white)

	NR MT	EX	VG
Complete Set:	25.00	12.50	7.50

(1) Fulvio Bertolotti
(2) Jack Boag
(3) Mark Bumstead
(4) Tom Chamberlain
(5) Donnie Chesire
(6) Dennis Cirbo
(7) Glenn Comoletti
(8) Chris Davis
(9) Hector Eduardo
(10) Neil Fiala
(11) Julian Gutierrez
(12) Brett Houser
(13) Dave Johnson
(14) Dave Jorn
(15) Arno Kirchenwitz
(16) Terry Landrum
(17) Hal Lanier
(18) Chris Lombardo
(19) Ralph Miller, Jr.
(20) Kelly Paris
(21) Mike Pisarkiewicz
(22) Mike Pope
(23) Jim Reeves
(24) Gene Roof
(25) Larry Silver
(26) Elliot Waller
(27) Ray Williams
(28) Hal Witt
(29) Felipe Zayas

1978 TCMA Salem Pirates

(Pittsburgh Pirates, A) (black and white)

	NR MT	EX	VG
Complete Set:	15.00	7.50	4.50

(1) Juan Arias
(2) Pablo Cruz
(3) Phil Cyburt
(4) Rickey Evans
(5) Marc Gelinas
(6) Sandy Hill
(7) Rick Lancelotti
(8) Robert Long
(9) Jim Mahoney
(10) Frank Miloszewski
(11) Bob Parsons
(12) Rick Peterson
(13) Luis Salazar
(14) Dean Rick
(15) Bob Rock
(16) Luis Salazar
(17) Rick Peterson
(18) Alfredo Torres
(19) Chich Valley
(20) Ben Wiltbank

1978 Cramer Salt Lake City Gulls

(California Angels, AAA) (color, 2-3/8" x 3-1/2") (co-sponsored by Coca-Cola) This set is numbered as it appears on the cards.

	NR MT	EX	VG
Complete Set:	9.00	4.50	2.75

1 Tommy Smith
2 Jim Anderson
3 Dave Machemer
4 Dickie Thon
5 Kim Allen
6 Gil Flores
7 Deron Johnson
8 Tom Donohue
9 Steve Stroughter
10 Pat Cristelli
11 John Racanelli
14 Stan Cliburn
15 Bobby Jones
16 Gil Kubski
17 Chuck Porter
18 John Caneira
19 Bob Ferris
20 Dave Schuler
21 Mike Barlow
22 Willie Aikens
24 Mike Overy
25 Dave Frost
26 Carlos Perez
---- Leonard Garcia

Values for recent cards and sets are listed in Mint (MT), Near Mint (NM), reflecting the fact that many cards from recent years have been preserved in top condition. Recent cards and sets in less than Excellent condition have little collector interest.

1978 Mr. Chef's San Jose Missions

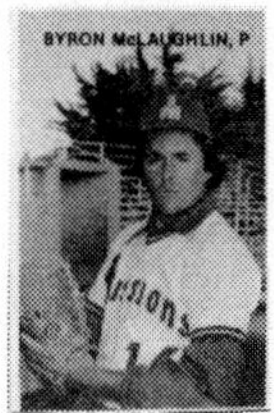
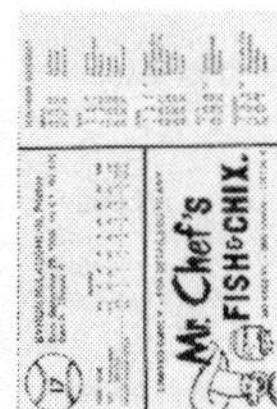

(Seattle Mariners, AAA) (color)

	NR MT	EX	VG
Complete Set:	25.00	12.50	7.50

1 Team logo & checklist
2 Rene Lachemann
3 Greg Biercevicz
4 Frank Mac Cormack
5 Ed Crosby
6 Joe Decker
7 Jose Elguezabal
8 Gary Wheelock
9 Alan Griffin
10 Pete Ithier
11 Rick Baldwin
12 Charlie Beamon
13 Juan Berhnardt
14 Luis Delgado
15 Steve Hamrick
16 Tom Brown
17 Byron Mc Laughlin
18 Tommy Mc Millan
19 Bill Plummer
20 George Mitterwald
21 Archie Amerson
22 Manny Estrada
23 Jack Pierce
24 Mike Kekich

1978 Cramer Spokane Indians

(Milwaukee Brewers, AAA) (black and white, 2-3/8" x 3-1/2")

	NR MT	EX	VG
Complete Set:	9.00	4.50	2.75

1 Duane Espy
2 William L. McLaurine
3 Ronnie Jay "Ron" Diggle
4 Dale M. Hrovat
5 James P. Quirk
6 Lanny A. Phillips
7 Billy E. Severns
8 Tony Muser
9 Jack S. Heidemann
10 Edgardo Romero
11 Stephen M. Ruling
12 Creighton J. Tevlin
13 (I.) Juan Lopez
14 Not Issued
15 Tommie D. Reynolds
16 Not Issued
17 Ron R. Wrona
18 Barry L. Cort
19 Samuel H. Hinds
20 John A. Buffamoyer
21 Robert J. Galasso, Jr.
22 Edward J. Farmer
23 Not Issued
24 Lynn E. McKinney
25 Not Issued
26 John F. Felske
27 Gary R. Beare
28 Edgar F. "Ned" Yost

1978 Richard West Springfield Cardinals

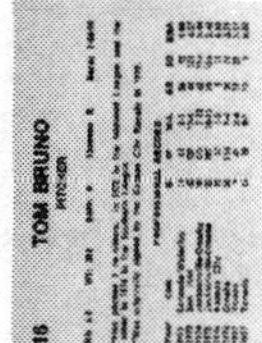

(St. Louis Cardinals) (black and white) (Price includes the scarce, late-issue Oberkfell and Frazier cards)

	NR MT	EX	VG
Complete Set:	70.00	35.00	21.00

1 Ken Oberkfell
2 Ron Farkas
3 Mike Potter
4 John Scott
5 Mike Ramsey
6 Nyls Nyman
7 David Bialas
8 Benny Ayala
9 Manny Castillo
10 John Tamargo
11 Eddie Daves
12 Lee Landers
13 Jimy Williams
14 Tommy Toms
15 Al Autry
16 Tom Bruno
17 Frank Riccelli
18 Silvio Martinez
19 Bill Rothan
20 Gregory Terlecky
21 Ron Selak
22 Aurelio Lopez
23 George Frazier
24 Ken Rudolph

1978 TCMA Syracuse Chiefs

(Toronto Blue Jays, AAA) (color)

	NR MT	EX	VG
Complete Set:	25.00	12.50	7.50

(1) Danny Ainge
(2) Butch Alberts
(3) Vern Benson
(4) Jeff Byrd
(5) Victor Cruz
(6) Mike Darr
(7) Andy Dyes
(8) Butch Edge
(9) Sam Ewing
(10) Chuck Fore
(11) Steve Grilli
(12) Pat Kelly
(13) Sheldon Mallory
(14) Luis Melendez
(15) Ken Pape
(16) Ken Reynolds
(17) Tom Sandt
(18) Mike Stanton
(19) Hector Torres
(20) Ernie Whitt
(21) Alvis Woods
(22) Gary Woods

1978 Cramer Tacoma Yankees

(New York Yankees, AAA) (color, 2-3/8" x 3-1/2") (co-sponsored by Puget Sound National Bank)

	NR MT	EX	VG
Complete Set:	10.00	5.00	3.00

1 Mike Ferraro
8 Ed Napoleon
9 Dennis Werth
10 Roger Slagle
14 Dennis Irwin
15 Darryl Jones
17 Domingo Ramos
18 Jim Lysgaard
19 Jim Curnal
20 George Zeber
21 Bob Kammeyer
22 Marv Thompson
23 Roy Staiger
25 Steve Taylor
27 Dell Alston (Del)
28 Dave Rajsich
29 Larry McCall
38 Jerry Narron
39a Brian Doyle
39b Garry Smith
42 Damaso Garcia
43 Bob Polinsky
44 Tommy Cruz
47 Hoyt Wilhelm
54 Neal Mersch

1978 TCMA Tidewater Tides

(New York Mets, AAA) (color) (complete set price includes scarce Verdi card)

	NR MT	EX	VG
Complete Set:	20.00	10.00	6.00

(1) Neil Allen
(2) Fred Andrews
(3) Juan Berenguer
(4) Dwight Bernard
(5) Marshall Brant
(6) Mike Bruhart
(7) Ed Cipot
(8) Mardie Cornejo
(9) Sergio Ferrer
(10) Tom Hausman
(11) Roy Lee Jackson
(12) Ed Kurpiel
(13) Pepe Mangual
(14) Rich Miller
(15) Bob Myrick
(16) Dan Norman
(17) John Pacella
(18) Greg Pavlick
(19) Marty Perez
(20) Mario Ramirez
(21) Randy Rogers
(22) Luis Rosado
(23) Mike Scott
(24) Dan Smith
(25) Alex Trevino
(26) Mike Van De Casteele
(27) Frank Verdi

1978 Cramer Tucson Toros

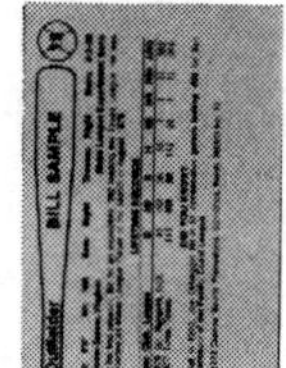

(Texas Rangers, AAA) (color, 2-3/8" x 3-1/2") (co-sponsored by Orange Crush)

	NR MT	EX	VG
Complete Set:	9.00	4.50	2.75

2 Larue Washington
4 Nelson Norman
9 Wayne Pinkerton
10 Paul Mirabella
12 Keathel Chauncey
13 David Moharter
14 Bill Fahey
15a Mike Bucci
15b Keith Smith
19 Bill Sample
20 Bob Babcock
21 Don Bright
22 Stan Thomas
24 Greg Mahlberg
27 Gary Gray
28 Danny Darwin
32 Pat Putnam
35 Rusty Torres
39 Jackie Brown
42 Rich Donnelly
45 Mike Bacsik
46 Bobby Cuellar
48 Jerry Reedy
59a David Harper
59b Jim Hughes

1978 TCMA Waterloo Indians

(Cleveland Indians, A) (black and white)

	NR MT	EX	VG
Complete Set:	15.00	7.50	4.50

(1) Tom Anderson
(2) Ken Bolek
(3) Juan Bonilla
(4) Tim Brill
(5) John Buszka
(6) Bob Conley
(7) Sammy Davis
(8) Jack DuBeau
(9) Jerry Dybzinski
(10) Robin Fuson
(11) Tim Glass
(12) Vic Homstedt
(13) Don Hubbard
(14) Angelo Lo Grande
(15) Carl Nicholson
(16) Thomas Pulchinski
(17) Al Rauch
(18) Kevin Rhomberg
(19) Ramon Romero
(20) Ed Saavedra
(21) Forest Smith
(22) Sam Spence
(23) John Teising
(24) Lloyd Turner
(25) Glenn Wendt
(26) Troy Wilder

1978 TCMA Wausau Mets

(New York Mets, A) (black and white)

	NR MT	EX	VG
Complete Set:	25.00	12.50	7.50

(1) Curt Baker
(2) Don Brazell
(3) Stewart Bringhurst
(4) Greg Brown
(5) Bill Chamberlain
(6) Al Coghen
(7) Ed Cuervo
(8) Bruce Ferguson
(9) Jeff Franklin
(10) Brent Gaff
(11) John Hinkel
(12) Chris Jones
(13) Ken Jones
(14) Chris Kirby
(15) Randy Lamb
(16) Steve Lowe
(17) Mike Lowry
(18) Dan Monzon
(19) Jim Noonan
(20) Darryl Paquette
(21) Don Pearson
(22) Junior Roman
(23) Frank Sanchez
(24) Keith Shermeyer
(25) John McDonald Stadium

1978 TCMA Wisconsin Rapids Twins

(Minnesota Twins, A) (black and white)

	NR MT	EX	VG
Complete Set:	15.00	7.50	4.50

(1) Greg Allen
(2) Paul Croft
(3) George Dierburger
(4) Gary Dobbs
(5) Mark Funderburk
(6) Michael Gustave
(7) Lance Hallberg
(8) Elmore Hill
(9) Joe Keith Isaac
(10) Abner Johnson
(11) Elmer Lingerman
(12) Ronnie Mears
(13) John Minarcin
(14) Dean Moranda
(15) Eric Prevost
(16) Clyde Reichard
(17) Harold Rowe
(18) Richard Stelmaszek

1979 TCMA Albuquerque Dukes

(Los Angeles Dodgers, AAA) (color)

	NR MT	EX	VG
Complete Set:	70.00	35.00	21.00

1 Pablo Peguero
2 Mike Tennent
3 Mike Williams
4 Bill Swiacki
5 Dave Stewart
6 Dave Patterson
7 Dennis Lewallyn
8 Kevin Keefe
9 Gerry Hannahs
10 Mike Scioscia
11 Mickey Hatcher
12 John O'Rear
13 Jack Perconte
14 Kelly Snider
15 Alex Taveras
16 Pedro Guerrero
17 Rich Magner
18 Bobby Mitchell
19 Rudy Law
20 Joe Beckwith
21 Claude Westmoreland
22 Bobby Castillo
23 Bobby Padilla

1979 University Volkswagen Albuquerque Dukes

(Los Angeles Dodgers, AAA)

	NR MT	EX	VG
Complete Set:	200.00	100.00	60.00

(1) Joe Beckwith
(2) Robert Castillo
(3) Del Crandall
(4) Pedro Guerrero
(5) Gerald Hannahs
(6) Mickey Hatcher
(7) Kevin Keefe
(8) Rudy Law
(9) Dennis Lewallyn
(10) Rich Magner
(11) Bobby Mitchell
(12) John O'Rear
(13) Dave Patterson
(14) Pablo Peguero
(15) Jack Perconte
(16) Mike Scioscia
(17) Kelly Snider
(18) Dave Stewart
(19) Bill Swiacki
(20) Alex Taveras
(21) Mike Tennant
(22) Claude Westmoreland
(23) Mike Williams

1979 TCMA Appleton Foxes

(Chicago White Sox, A) (black and white)

	NR MT	EX	VG
Complete Set:	30.00	15.00	9.00

1 Paul Soth
2 Dennis Keating
3 Vito Lucarelli
4 Ed Bahns
5 Dave White
6 Kevin Hickey
7 Clancy Woods
8 Jeff Vuksan
9 Lorenzo Gray
10 Mike Johnson
11 Dave Daniels
12 Ivan Mesa
13 Mike Sivik
14 Phil Bauer
15 Mart Teutsch
16 Luis Estrada
17 Jim Breazeale
18 Vince Bienek
19 Bob Umdenstock
20 Mike Maitland
21 Duane Shaffer
22 Mark Platel
23 Don Kraeger
24 Vic Walters
25 Paul Gbur

1979 TCMA Arkansas Travelers

(St. Louis Cardinals, AA) (color)

	NR MT	EX	VG
Complete Set:	15.00	7.50	4.50

1 Arno Kirchenwitz
2 Len Strelitz
3 Raymond Williams
4 Terry Landrum
5 Jim Riggleman
6 John Littlefield
7 Thomas N. Thompson
8 Joseph Dotson
9 Elliott Waller
10 Joseph DeSa
11 Fred Tisdale
12 Jorge Aranzamendi
13 Neil Fiala
14 Mike McCormick
15 Fulvio Bertolotti
16 Dennis Delany
17 Chris Davis
18 Randy Thomas
19a Tom Chamberlain
19b Hector Eduardo
20 Ray Searage
21 David Johnson
22 Gene Roof

1979 TCMA Asheville Tourists

(Texas Rangers, A) (black and white)

	NR MT	EX	VG
Complete Set:	75.00	37.50	22.00

1 Luis Gonzalez
2 Tracy Cowger
3 Tom McGivney
4 Lynvel Mosby
5 Wayne Terwilliger
6 Jim Farr
7 Dave Chapman
8 Andy Tam
9 Jeff Zitek
10 George Wright
11 Dave Miller
12 Wes Williams
13 Jim McWilliams

14 Al Ortiz
15 Steve Righetti
16 Bobby Tanzi
17 Amos Lewis
18 Arnold Wilhoite
19 Pat Nelson
20 Mike Childs
21 Mike Vickers
22 Jeff Scott
23 Dan Dixon
24 Chuck Kwolek
25 Dave Hibner
26 Mike Richardt
27 Stan Reese
28 Gene Nelson

1979 TCMA Buffalo Bisons

(Pittsburgh Pirates, AA) (black and white)

	NR MT	EX	VG
Complete Set:	80.00	40.00	24.00

1 Dave Dravecky
2 Stu Cliburn
3 Rick Lancellotti
4 Joe Galante
5 Tony Pena
6 Jerry McDonald
7 Steve Demeter
8 Ernie Young
9 Bubba Evans
10 Marc Galinas
11 Juan Arias
12 Harry Doris, Bob Weismiller)
13 Fred Breining
14 Chick Valley
15 Tom McMillan
16 Luis Salazar
17 Jim Smith
18 Al Torres
19 Dick Walterhouse
20 Robert Long
21 Paul Djakonow

1979 TCMA Burlington Bees

(Milwaukee Brewers, A) (black and white)

	NR MT	EX	VG
Complete Set:	15.00	7.50	4.50

1 Larry Edwards
2 Russell Ramirez
3 Pat Seegers
4 Jim Robinson
5 Sam Gierham
6 Rocky Hall
7 Willie Lozado
8 Nick Hernandez
9 Ron Buggs
10 Dan Gilmartin
11 Mark Lepson
12 Doug Jones
13 Steve Gibson
14 Bob Gibson
15 Johnny Evans
16 Roberto Diaz
17 Duane Espy
18 Vince Bailey
19 Randy Boyce
20 Greg DeHart
21 Stan Davis
22 Vince Pone
23 Jim Padula
24 Steve Norwood
25 Steve Manderfield

1979 TCMA Cedar Rapids Giants

(San Francisco Giants, A) (black and white)

	NR MT	EX	VG
Complete Set:	70.00	35.00	21.00

1 Steve Duckhorn
2 Jesus Cruz
3 Mark Benson
4 Jorge Mundroig
5 John Rabb
6 Robbie Henderson
7 Jeff Stadler
8 Matt Sutherland
9 Francisco Rojas
10 Rick Doss
11 Bruce Oliver
12 Bill Bellomo
13 Glenn Fisher
14 Bud Curran
15 Wayne Cato
16 Jeff Stember
17 Paul Plinski
18 Jose Chue
19 Rick Kean
20 George Torassa
21 Ned Raines
22 Lou Merietta
23 Craig Hedrick

24 Kelly Anderson
25 Harry Wing
26 Juan Oppenhiemer
27 Ray Cosio
28 Bob Deer (Rob)
29 Don Buchheister
30 Phil Sutton
31 Doug Linduyt
32 Bob Cummins

1979 TCMA Charleston Charlies

(Houston Astros, AAA) (color) (complete set price includes corrected cards)

	NR MT	EX	VG
Complete Set:	40.00	20.00	12.00

1 Keith Drumright
2 Jim Beauchamp
3 Russ Rothermel
4 Reggie Baldwin
5 Gary Woods
6 Mike Fischlin
7 Mike Tyler
8 Dave Bergman
9 Ramon Perez
10a Mark Miggins (Dave Smith photo, no mustache)
10b Mark Miggins (correct photo, with mustache)
11a David Smith (Mark Miggins photo, with mustache)
11b David Smith (correct photo, no mustache)
12 Dave Augustine
13 Gordy Pladson
14 Luis Pujols
15 Larry Hardy
16 Rob Sperring
17 Wilbur Howard
18 Gary Wilson
19 Mike Mendoza

1979 TCMA Clinton Dodgers

(Los Angeles Dodgers, A) (black and white)

	NR MT	EX	VG
Complete Set:	110.00	55.00	33.00

1 Mark Eliott
2 Clay Smith
3 Johnny Lee Robbins
4 Roberto Alexander
5 Matt Reeves
6 Alan Wiggins
7 Otis Bradley
8 Paul Popovich
9 Alejandro Pena
10 Steve Sax
11 Mitch Webster
12 Eric Schmidt
13 Chris Gancy
14 Kent Johnson
15 Marcos Rodriguez
16 Leonardo Hernandez
17 Dick McLaughlin
18 Dave Sax
19 Dave LaPointe
20 Rod Nelson
21 Bob Giesecke
22 Larry Wright
23 Steve Maples
24 Kevin Joyce
25 Bob White
26 Candido Maldonado
27 Frank Wilczewski
28 Larry Ferst

1979 TCMA Columbus Clippers

(New York Yankees, AAA) (color)

	NR MT	EX	VG
Complete Set:	15.00	7.50	4.50

1 Brad Gulden
2 Roy Staiger
3 Paul Semall
4 Damaso Garcia
5 Garry Smith
6 Stan Williams
7 Gene Michael
8 Jim Beattie
9 Gerry McNertney
10 Dennis Werth
11 Mark Letendre
12 Marvin Thompson
13 Tommy Cruz
14 Ron Davis
15 Bob Polinsky
16 Bruce Robinson
17 Greg Cochran
18 Rodger Holt
19 Dennis Sherrill

20 Steve Taylor
21 Rich Anderson
22 Nathan Chapman
23 Bob Kammeyer
24 Chris Welsh
25 Howard Cassidy
26 Paul Mirabella
27 Bobby Brown
28 Daryl Jones
29 Mickey Vernon

1979 TCMA Elmira Pioneers

(Boston Red Sox, A) (black and white)

	NR MT	EX	VG
Complete Set:	40.00	20.00	12.00

1 Lloyd Bessard
2 Jay Fredlund
3 Ken Hagemann
4 Danny Huffstickler
5 Arturo Samaniego
6 Glenn Eddins, Jr.
7 Joaquin Gutierrez
8 Tom McCarthy
9 Steve Fortune
10 Don Hayford
11 Eddie Lee
12 Russell Lee Pruitt
13 Scott Gering
14 Dave Holt
15 Steve Schaefer
16 Tony Cleary
17 Andy Serrano
18 Francisco Vasquez
19 Gus Malespin
20 Hal Natupsky
21 Dick Berardino
22 Ed Berroa
23 Bill Limoncelli
24 Bob Birrell
25 Wayne Tremblay
26 Tom Brunner
27 Tom DeSanto
28 Mark Saunders

1979 TCMA Hawaii Islanders

(San Diego Padres, AAA) (color)

	NR MT	EX	VG
Complete Set:	9.00	4.50	2.75

1 Bob Mitchell
2 Lynn McKinney
3 Rick Sweet
4 Craig Stimac
5 Andy Dyes
6 Dick Phillips
7 Jim Wilhelm
8 Vic Bernal
9 Gary Lucas
10 Jim Beswick
11 Sam Perlozzo
12 Steve Brye
13 Don Reynolds
14 Steve Smith
15 Al Zarilla
16 Chuck Baker
17 Alan Fitzmorris
18 Dennis Kinney
19 Mike Dupree
20 Fred Kuhaulua
21 Juan Eichelberger
22 Dennis Blair
23 Tom Tellmann
24 Tony Castillo

1979 Cramer Hawaii Islanders

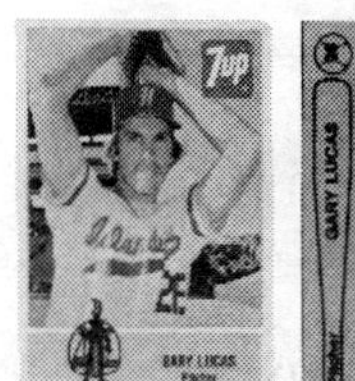

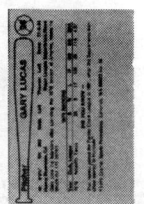

(San Diego Padres, AAA) (color, 2-3/8" x 3-1/2") (co-sponsored by 7-Up)

	NR MT	EX	VG
Complete Set:	7.50	4.50	2.75

3 Al Zarilla
5 Sam Perlozzo

8 Tucker Ashford
9 Steve Brye
10 Vic Bernal
11 Chuck Baker
12 Bob Mitchell
13 Juan Eichelberger
14 Craig Stimac
16 Tom Tellmann
17 Dennis Kinney
18 Rick Sweet
19 Al Fitzmorris
20 Lynn McKinney
21 Jim Beswick
22 Randy Fierbaugh
23 Fred Kuhaulua
24 Dick Phillips
25 Jim Wilhelm
26 Gary Lucas
27 Tony Castillo
28 Andy Dyes
29 Dave Wehrmeister
---- Team Logo & Schedule

1979 TCMA Holyoke Millers

(Milwaukee Brewers, AA) (color)

	NR MT	EX	VG
Complete Set:	9.00	4.50	2.75

1 Rene Quinones
2 Terry Bevington
3 Bill Foley
4 Ed Carroll
5 Kevin Bass
6 Bobby Smith
7 Mark Schuster
8 George Farson
9 Rick Olsen
10 Tom Soto
11 Ron Driver
12 Tom Cook
13 Gersan Jarquin
14 Rick Duran
15 Don Whiting
16 Brian Thorson
17 Mike Henderson
18 Butch Riggar
19 Steve Splitt
20 Larry Rush
21 Steve Reed
22 Darryl Bailey
23 Weldon Swift
24 Rocky Hall
25 Lance Rautzhan
26 Barry Cort
27 "Duke" Duncan
28 Jeff Yurak
29 Sam Hinds
30 Tom Kayser

1979 Team Indianapolis Indians

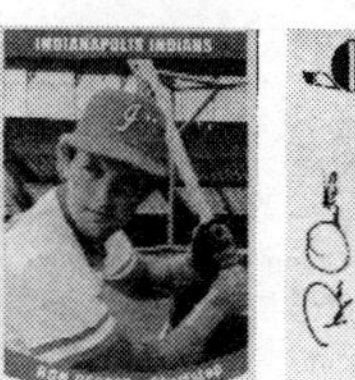

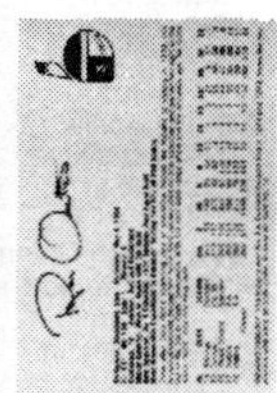

(Cincinnati Reds, AAA) (color)

	NR MT	EX	VG
Complete Set:	25.00	12.50	7.50

1 Team Photo
2 Roy Majtyka
3 Ron Oester
4 Dave Moore
5 Harry Spilman
6 The Outfielders
7 Charlie Leibrandt
8 Tommy Mutz
9 Larry Rothschild
10 Eddie Milner
11 The Infielders
12 Doug Corbett
13 Randy Davidson
14 Bruce Berenyl
15 Don Lyle
16 George Cappuzzello
17 The Catchers
18 Mike Grace
19 Geoff Combe
20 Steve Bowling
21 Manny Sarmiento
22 Don Werner
23 The Relievers
24 Jay Howell
25 John Valle
26 Dan Dumoulin
27 Mickey Duval
28 Mario Soto

29 The Starters
30 Ron McClain
31 Bush Stadium
32 Checklist

1979 Police Iowa Oaks

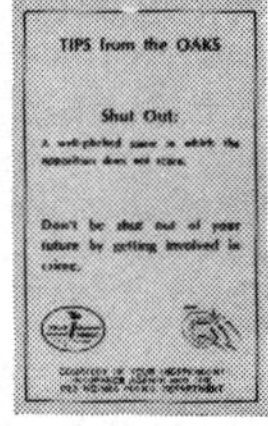

(Chicago White Sox, AAA) (black and white)

	NR MT	EX	VG
Complete Set:	125.00	62.50	37.50

(1) Lloyd Allen
(2) Harold Baines
(3) Kevin Bell
(4) Harry Chappas
(5) Mike Colbern
(6) Fred Frazier
(7) Guy Hoffman
(8) Dewey Hoyt
(9) Art Kusnyer
(10) Tony LaRussa
(11) Bob Molinaro
(12) Chris Nyman
(13) Dewey Robinson
(14) John Sutton

1979 TCMA Jackson Mets

(New York Mets, AA) (color) (includes scarce front office staff card)

	NR MT	EX	VG
Complete Set:	12.00	6.00	3.50

1 "Paco" Perez
2 Wally Backman
3 Hubie Brooks
4 Wayne Sexton
5 Paul Wiener
6 Bob Wellman
7 Jodie Davis
8 Bob Grote
9 Sergio Beltre
10 Paul Cacciatore
11 Keith Bodie
12 Pete Hamner
13 Luis Lunar
14 Mike Howard
15 Dave Von Ohlen
16 Rick Anderson
17 Dan Smith
18 Rich Miller, Jr.
19 Bobby Bryant
20 Russell Clark
21 Greg Harris
22a Front Office Staff
22b Stan Hough
23 Ronald MacDonald
24 Fred Martinez

1979 TCMA Knoxville White Sox

(Chicago White Sox, AA) (black and white)

	NR MT	EX	VG
Complete Set:	70.00	35.00	21.00

1 Mark Naehring
2 Phil Trucks
3 Luis Guzman
4 Gordy Lund
5 Richard Barnes
6 Britt Burns
7 Leo Sutherland
8 Richard Dotson
9 Don Seidholz
10 John Flannery
11 Mitch Lukevics
12 Ron Kittle
13 Willie Gutierrez
14 Larry Monroe
15 John Hanley
16 Joel Perez
17 Jackie Smith
18 Bruce Dal Canton
19 Ray Murillo
20 Andy Pasillas
21 Ted Barnicle
22 A.J. Hill
23 Ray Torres
24 Rod Allen
25 Tom Spencer
26 Willie Thompson

1979 TCMA Lodi Dodgers

(Los Angeles Dodgers, A) (black and white)

	NR MT	EX	VG
Complete Set:	60.00	30.00	18.00

1 Rod Kemp
2 Augie Ruiz
3 Paul Bain
4 Alfredo Mejia
5 Skip Mann
6 Mike Marshall
7 Rocky Cordova
8 Steve Perry
9 Jesse Baez
10 Jim Nobles
11 Larry Powers
12 Johnny Walker
13 Bill Swoope
14 Stan Wasiak
15 Miguel Franjul
16 Jerry Bass
17 Bob Foster
18 Chris Malden
19 Brian Hayes
20 Hank Jones
21 Evon Martinson

1979 TCMA Memphis Chicks

(Montreal Expos, AA) (black and white)

	NR MT	EX	VG
Complete Set:	260.00	130.00	77.00

1 Steve Lovins
2 Steve Michael
3 Bill Armstrong
4 Julio Perez
5 Bryn Smith
6 Larry Goldetsky
7 Doug Simunic
8 Charlie Lea
9 Dave Hostetler
10 Anthony Johnson
11 Randy Schafer
12 Mike Finlayson
13 Rick Williams
14 Rick Engle
15 Bob Teneini
16 Ray Crowley
17 John Scoras
18 Jeff Gingrich
19 Dennis Sherow
20 Tim Raines
21 Billy Gardner
22 Pat Rooney
23 Warren Hemm
24 Godfrey Evans

1979 Chong Modesto A's

(Oakland A's, A) (black and white) (cards are gold on front, and have blank backs)

	NR MT	EX	VG
Complete Set:	55.00	27.00	16.50

Logo Card
1 Gaylen Pitts
2 Rich Morales
3 Frank Kneuer
4 Pat Dempsey
5 Fred Devito
6 Dana Berry
7 Paul Stevens
8 Mike Woodard
9 Jay Greb
10 Kelvin Moore
11 Mike Davis
12 Bob Markham
13 Don Morris
14 Don Schubert
15 Craig Harris
16 Mike Yesenchak
17 Chuck Dougherty
18 Don Van Marter
19 Walt Bigos
20 John Gosse
21 Fritz Lund
22 Dave Mc Carthy
23 Ron Jensen

1979 Team Nashville Sounds

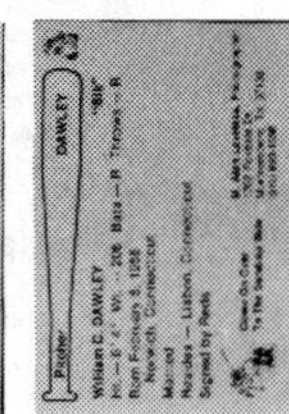

(Cincinnati Reds, AA) (color) (co-sponsored by Sundrop)

	NR MT	EX	VG
Complete Set:	24.00	12.00	7.25

(1) Mike Armstrong
(2) Skeeter Barnes
(3) Scott Brown
(4) Geoff W. Combe
(5) Bill Dawley
(6) Rick Duncan
(7) Rayl Ferreyra
(8) Bob Hamilton
(9) Paul Householder
(10) Greg Hughes
(11) Bill Kelly
(12) Bob Mayer
(13) Gene Menees
(14) Mark Miller
(15) Eddie Milner
(16) Farrell Owens
(17) Joe Price
(18) R. Santo Domingo
(19) George R. Scherger
(20) Larry Schmittou
(21) Tom Sohns
(22) Dave Van Gorder
(23) Duane Walker
(----) Team Photo
(----) 1979 Soundettes

1979 TCMA Newark Co-Pilots

(No affiliation, A) (black and white)

	NR MT	EX	VG
Complete Set:	18.00	9.00	5.50

1 Tom Dann
2 Steve Nicastro
3 Joe Rigoli
4 Bob Bill
5 Mike Overton
6 Mike Fichman
7 Steve Dembowski
8 Mal Oleskak
9 Don Clatterbuck
10 Michael LaCasse
11 Kevin MacDonald
12 Joe McCann
13 Harry White
14 Mark Grier
15 Carl Adams
16 Bob Cross
17 Billy Clay
18 Keith Gainer
19 Richard Block
20 Kevin Rose
21 Mitch Wright
22 Len Spicer
23 Lance Viola
24 Andy Pascarella

1978 Team Oklahoma City 89'ers

(Philadelphia Phillies, AAA)

	NR MT	EX	VG
Complete Set:	45.00	22.00	13.50

1 Fred Beene
3 Ramon Aviles
4 Lonnie Smith
5 Robert DeMeo
6 James Morrison
7 Michael T. Buskey
8 Kerry Dineen
9 Rogers Brown
10 Steven Waterbury
11 Orlando Alvarez
12 Todd Cruz
14 Kevin Saucier
15 Mike Anderson
16 Danny Boitano
17 Charles Kniffin
18 Daniel Warthen
19 Bobby Moreland
20 Orlando Gonzalez
21 Michael Wallace
22 John C. Vukovich
23 John Poff
25 Jackson Todd
26 Arnaldo Contreras, Jr.
27 Michael Ryan
28 Tom Harmon
29 William Connors
30 William Connors

1979 TCMA Ogden A's

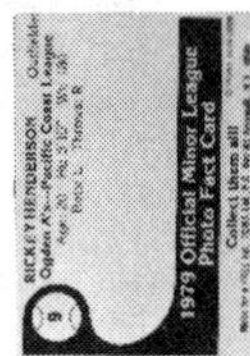

(Oakland A's, AAA) (color)

	NR MT	EX	VG
Complete Set:	225.00	110.00	65.00

1 Terry Enyart
2 Tim Hosley
3 Mike Morgan
4 Mike Rodriguez
5 Craig Mitchell
6 Jose Pagan
7 Mack Harrison
8 Dennis Haines
9 Rickey Henderson
10 Brian Abraham
11 Richard Lysander
12 Jeff Cox
13 Brian Kingman
14 Royle Stillman
15 Danny Goodwin
16 Rya Cosey
17 Mark Souza
18 Mark Budaska
19 Frank Kolarek
20 Pat Dempsey
21 Craig Mitchell
22 Allen Wirth
23 Jeff Jones
24 Mike Patterson
25 Bob Grandas
26 Keith Liepman

1979 Cramer 1970s P.C.L. All-Stars

(AAA)

	NR MT	EX	VG
Complete Set:	60.00	30.00	18.00

(1) Brian Abraham (San Jose)
(2) Willie Mays Aikens (Salt Lake City)
(3) Gary Alexander (Phoenix)
(4) Dell Alston (Tacoma)
(5) Orlando Alvarez (Albuquerque)
(6) Chris Arnold (Phoenix)
(7) Gerry Augustine (Sacramento)
(8) Doug Ault (Sacramento)
(9) Rick Austin (Sacramento)
(10) Chuck Baker (Hawaii)
(11) Eddie Bane (Tacoma)
(12) Len Barker (Sacramento)
(13) Mike Barlow (Salt Lake City)
(14) Randy Bass (Tacoma)
(15) Charlie Beamon, Jr. (San Jose)
(16) Lew Beasley (Sacramento)
(17) Joe Beckwith (Albuquerque)
(18) Ron Bell (Vancouver)
(19) Juan Berenguer (Tacoma)
(20) Vic Bernal (Hawaii)
(21) Dale Berra (Portland)
(22) Kurt Bevacqua (Tucson)
(23) Dan Boone (Salt Lake City)
(24) Jerry Bostic (Sacramento)
(25) Steve Bowling (Sacramento)
(26) Rocky Bridges (Phoenix)
(27) Derek Bryant (San Jose)
(28) Mark Budaska (Ogden)
(29) Steve Burke (Spokane)

(30) Bill Butler (Tacoma)
(31) Keathel Chauncey (Tucson)
(32) Jack Clark (Phoenix)
(33) Stan Cliburn (Salt Lake City)
(34) David Clyde (Tucson)
(35) Terry Cornutt (Phoenix)
(36) Ray Cosey (Ogden)
(37) Jeff Cox (Ogden)
(38) Del Crandell (Albuquerque)
(39) Ed Crosby (Spokane)
(40) Ed Crosby (San Jose)
(41) Tommy Cruz (Sacramento)
(42) Darrell Darrow (Salt Lake City)
(43a) Rich Donnelly (Sacramento)
(43b) Jim Dorsey (Salt Lake City)
(44) Brian Doyle (Sacramento)
(45) Rob Dressler (Phoenix)
(46) Andy Dyes (San Jose)
(47) Rob Ellis (Spokane)
(48) Terry Enyart (Ogden)
(49) Cal Ermer (Tacoma)
(50) Manny Estrada (Hawaii)
(51) Greg Field (Portland)
(52) Randy Fierbaugh (Hawaii)
(53) Rick Foley (Salt Lake City)
(54) Jay Franklin (Hawaii)
(55) Pedro Garcia (Hawaii)
(56) Mike Garman (Portland)
(57) Jerry Garvin (Tacoma)
(58) Pedro Guerrero (Albuquerque)
(59) Moose Haas (Spokane)
(60) Tom Hall (Tacoma)
(61) Bob Hansen (Spokane)
(62) Vic Harris (Vancouver)
(63) Tom Heinzelman (Phoenix)
(64) Enzo Hernandez (Albuquerque)
(65) Frank Howard (Spokane)
(66) Phil Huffman (Vancouver)
(67) Jim Hughes (Tacoma)
(68) Skip James (Phoenix)
(69) Garry Jestadt (Phoenix)
(70) Bobby Jones (Salt Lake City)
(71) Bob Kammeyer (Hawaii)
(72) Kevin Keefe (Albuquerque)
(73) Wendall Kim (Phoenix)
(74) Kevin Kobel (Spokane)
(75) Gil Kubski (Salt Lake City)
(76) Fred Kuhaulua (Hawaii)
(77) Craig Kusick (Tacoma)
(78) Art Kusnyer (Sacramento)
(79) Rafael Lanestoy (Albuquerque)
(80) Rudy Law (Albuquerque)
(81) Vance Law (Portland)
(82) John Lemaster (Phoenix)
(83) Jeff Leonard (Albuquerque)
(84) Sixto Lezcano (Sacramento)
(85) Jack Lind (Sacramento)
(86) Larry Lintz (San Jose)
(87) Jeff Little (Phoenix)
(88) Dennis Littlejohn (Phoenix)
(89) Juan Lopez (Spokane)
(90) Steve Luebber (Tacoma)
(91) Greg Mahlberg (Tucson)
(92) Sheldon Mallory (San Jose)
(93) Jack Maloof (Tacoma)
(94) Davis May (Tacoma)
(95) Steve McCatty (Vancouver)
(96) Dave McKay (Tacoma)
(97) Lynn McKinney (Hawaii)
(98) Tom McMillan (San Jose)
(99) Bill McNulty (Sacramento)
(100) Luis Melendez (Hawaii)
(101) Greg Minetto (Vancouver)
(102) Craig Mitchell (Vancouver)
(103) Dave Moharter (Spokane)
(104) Rance Mulliniks (Salt Lake City)
(105) Steve Mura (Hawaii)
(106) Larry Murray (San Jose)
(107) Tony Muser (Spokane)
(108) Phil Natsu (Phoenix)
(109) Mike Norris (San Jose)
(110) Willie Norwood (Tacoma)
(111) Kunio Ogawa (Vancouver)
(112) Oswaldo Olivares (Portland)
(113) Dan Osborn (Sacrameento)
(114) Tom Paciorek (San Jose)
(115) Ken Pape (Tucson)
(116) Dave Patterson (Albuquerque)
(117) Mike Pazik (Tacoma)
(118) Sammy Perlozzo (Tacoma)
(119) Ed Plank (Phoenix)
(120) Bill Plummer (Spokane)
(121) John Poloni (Tucson)
(122) Mike Potter (Spokane)
(123) Hoskin Powell (Tacoma)
(124) Mike Proly (Tacoma)
(125) Pat Putnam (Tucson)
(126) Gus Quiros (Vancouver)
(127) Milt Ramirez (San Jose)
(128) Barry Raziano (Salt Lake City)
(129) Rick Rennick (Tacoma)
(130) Tommie Reynolds (Sacramento)
(131) Frank Ricelli (Phoenix)
(132) Bruce Robinson (Vancouver)
(133) Craig Ryan (Vancouver)
(134) Lenn Sakata (Spokane)
(135) Mike Scioscia (Albuquerque)
(136) Bill Severns (Vancouver)
(137) Rob Sheldon (Spokane)
(138) Joe Simpson (Albuquerque)
(139) Wayne Simpson (Albuquerque)
(140) Coley Smith (Tacoma)
(141) Keith Smith (Tucson)
(142) Royle Stillman (Ogden)
(143) Craig Stok (Sacramento)
(144) Jerry Stone (Hawaii)
(145) Joe Strain (Phoenix)
(146) Brent Strom (Hawaii)
(147) Steve Strougher (Salt Lake City)
(148) Rick Sutcliffe (Albuquerque)
(149) John Sutton (Sacramento)
(150) Rick Sweet (Hawaii)
151 Danny Walton (Spokane)
(152) Mark Weathers (San Josse)
(153) Dave Wehrmeister (Hawaii)
(154) Claude Westmorland (Albuquerque)
(155) Mark Wiley (Hawaii)
(156) Rob Wilfong (Tacoma)
(157) Bump Wills (Sacramento)
(158) Dick Woodson (Spokane)
(159) Jeff Yurak (Vancouver)

1979 Cramer Phoenix Giants

(San Francisco Giants, AAA) (color, 2-7/16" x 3-1/2") (co-sponsored by Valley National Bank)

	NR MT	EX	VG
Complete Set:	6.00	3.00	1.75

1 Doug Schafer
2 Kyle Hypes
3 Mike Rowland
4 Jeff Little
5 Rocky Bridges
6 Phil Nastu
7 Bill Bordley
8 Ed Plank
9 Joe Strain
10 Greg Johnston
11 Don Carrithers
12 Tom Heintzelman
13 Randy Harmon
14 Rick Bradley
15 Terry Cornutt
16 Chris Bourjos
17 Casey Parsons
18 Rich Murray
19 Dennis Littlejohn
20 Mark Kuecker
21 Rick Sanderlin
22 Guy Sularz
23 Mike Rex
24 Ethan Blackaby
---- Tommy Gonzales
---- Harry Jordan

1979 TCMA Portland Beavers

(Pittsburgh Pirates, AAA) (color)

	NR MT	EX	VG
Complete Set:	16.00	8.00	4.75

1 Al Holland
2 Ossie Oliveras
3 Greg Field
4 Ben Wiltbank
5 Vance Law
6 Tom Sandt
7 Dorian Boyland
8 Ron Mitchell
9 John Lipon
10 Gene Cotes
11 Joe Coleman
12 Gene Pentz
13 Gary Hargis
14 Alberto Lois
15 Mike Garman
16 Manny Lantigua
17 Dan Warthen
18 Craig Cacek
19 Larry Littleton
20 Pascual Perez
21 Harry Saferight
22 Rod Scurry
23 Rick Jones
24 Rod Gilbreath

1979 TCMA Quad City Cubs

(Chicago Cubs, A) (black and white)

	NR MT	EX	VG
Complete Set:	30.00	15.00	9.00

1 Mike Wright
2 Ed Mohr
3 Ed Moore
4 Roger Crow
5 Bill Morgan
6 Wayne Rohlfing
7 Ted May
8 Joe McClain
9 Rich McClure
10 J.W. Mitchell
11 Joe Hicks
12 Mark Gilbert
13 Joey Cole
14 Randy Clark
15 Hal Kizer
16 Craig Kornfeld
17 Bob Maddon
18 Gordon Hodgson
19 John Bargfeldt
20 Andy Walker
21 Freddy Forgeur
22 Jim Napier
23 Tom Spino
24 Mike Shepston
25 Steve Viskas
26 Bob Oliver
27 Norm Churchill

1979 TCMA Richmond Braves

(Atlanta Braves, AAA) (color)

	NR MT	EX	VG
Complete Set:	10.00	5.00	3.00

1 Joey McLaughlin
2 Mike Reynolds
3 John Sain
4 Larry Whisenton
5 Larry Owen
6 Jerry Maddox
7 Jon Richardson
8 Seymour Baseball, Chief Powa-Hitta (Team Mascots)
9 Radio Voices
10 Front Office
11 Jamie Easterly
12 Roger Alexander
13 Chico Ruiz
14 Terry Harper
15 Tom Burgess
16 Duane Thesis
17 Larry Bradford
18 Dan Morogiello
19 Jerry Keller
20 Pat Rockett
21 Rick Camp
22 Tommy Boggs
23 Jim Arline
24 Ed Miller
25 Tony Brizzolara

1979 TCMA Rochester Red Wings

(Baltimore Orioles, AAA) (color)

	NR MT	EX	VG
Complete Set:	15.00	7.50	4.50

1 Jeff Youngbauer
2 Joe Kerrigan
3 Kevin Kennedy
4 Blake Doyle
5 Willie Royster
6 Art James
7 Tony Franklin
8 Carlos Lopez
9 Mike Eden
10 Howard Edwards
11 Tom Bianco
12 Gerry Pirtle
13 Jim Smith
14 Ken Diggle
15 Mark Corey
16 Jeff Rineer
17 Jose Bastian
18 Tom Chism
19 Tony Chevez
20 Dave Ford

1979 TCMA Salt Lake City Gulls

(California Angels, AAA) (color)

	NR MT	EX	VG
Complete Set:	15.00	7.50	4.50

9 Mike Overy
10 Bob Ferris
11 Rance Mulliniks
12 Bob Clark
13 Bill Ewing
14 Jim Dorsey
15 Joel Crisler
16a John Harris
16b Gil Kubski
17a Darrell Darrow
17b Dave Schuler
18a Rick Foley
18b Carlos Perez
19a Chuck Porter
19b Dan Whitmer
20a Jay Peters
20b Floyd Rayford
21a Bobby Ramos
21b Bob Slater
22a Pepe Manguel
22b Jim Williams
23a Daniel Boone
23b Leonard Garcia

1979 TCMA Savannah Braves

(Atlanta Braves, AA) (color)

	NR MT	EX	VG
Complete Set:	20.00	10.00	6.00

1 Dom Chiti
2 Gary Cooper
3 Not Issued
4 Bill Haslerig
5 Brian Snitker
6 Tim Brill
7 Tim Graven
8 Sonny Jackson
9 Mike Shields
10 Greg Johnson
11 Clay Elliott
12 Jose Alvarez
13 Kris Yoder
14 Steve Bedrosian
15 Joe Cowley
16 Richard Witers (correct picture, wrong name & stats)
17 Leo Mazzone
18 Eddie Hass (correct picture, wrong name & stats)
19 Terry Leach
20 Tim Cole
21 Louis Pratt
22 Bob Porter
23 Rafael Ramirez
24 Kenny Smith
25 Mike Miller
26 Jim Wessinger
---- Rufino Linares

1979 TCMA Spokane Indians

(Seattle Mariners, AAA) (color)

	NR MT	EX	VG
Complete Set:	12.00	6.00	3.50

1 Ed Crosby
2 Royle Stillman
3 Mike Potter
4 Danny Walton
5 Rod Craig
6 Charlie Beamon
7 Jack L. Pierce
8 Ken Pape
9 Reggie Walton
10 Bill Plummer
11 Gary Lance
12 George Decker
13 Jim Lewis
14 Mike Davey
15 Jack Heidemann
16 Rene Lachemann
17 Gary Wheelock
18 Rob Pietroburgo
19 Rob Dressler
20 Karl Anderson
21 Greg Biercevicz
22 Steve Burke
23 Terry Bulling
24 Moncho Berhardt
25 Manny Estrada

1978 Richard West Springfield Redbirds

(St. Louis Cardinals, AAA) This set is numbered as it appears on the cards.

	NR MT	EX	VG
Complete Set:	75.00	37.50	22.00

2 Ron Farkas
3 Mike Potter
4 John Scott
5 Mike Ramsey
6 Nyls Nyman
7 David Bialas
8 Benny Ayala
9 Manny Castillo
10 John Tamargo
11 Eddie Daves
12 Lee Landers
13 Jimy Williams
14 Tommy Toms
15 Al Autry
16 Tom Bruno
17 Frank Riccelli
18 Silvio Martinez
19 Bill Rothan
20 Gregory Terlecky
21 Ron Selak
22 Aurelio Lopez
24 Ken Rudolph

Definitions for grading conditions are located in the Introduction of this price guide.

1979 TCMA Syracuse Chiefs

(Toronto Blue Jays, AAA) (color)

	NR MT	EX	VG
Complete Set:	18.00	9.00	5.50

1 Greg Wells
2 Vern Benson
3 Ernie Whitt
4 Willie Upshaw
5 Mark Wiley
6 Domingo Ramos
7 Joe Cannon
8 Don Pisker
9 Butch Edge
10 Mike Sember
11 Dave Baker
12 Garth Iorg
13 Jackson Todd
14 Chuck Fore
15 Doug Ault
16 Davis May
17 Steve Grilli
18 Luis Rosado
19 Ken Raynolds
20 Steve Luebber

1979 Team Syracuse Chiefs

(Toronto Blue Jays, AAA) This set is numbered as it appears on the cards. Cards are approximately 4" x 6" in size with blank backs. No positions are listed.

	NR MT	EX	VG
Complete Set:	50.00	25.00	15.00

1 Domingo Ramos
2 Papo Rosado
3 Chuck Scrivener
4 Danny Ainge
5 Dave Baker
6 Pat Kelly
7 Don Pisker
8 Vern Benson
9 Garth Iorg
10 Mike Sember
12 Ernie Whitt
14 Butch Alberts
15 Ken Reynolds
16 Jackson Todd
17 Doug Ault
19 Butch Edge
21 Steve Grilli
22 Davis May
23 Joe Cannon
25 Jerry Garvin
26 Willie Upshaw
27 Mark Wiley
29 Tom Buskey
31 Steve Luebber

1979 TCMA Tacoma Tugs

(Cleveland Indians, AAA) (color)

	NR MT	EX	VG
Complete Set:	20.00	10.00	6.00

1 Ron Hassey
2 Tom Brown
3 Rick Borchers
4 Larry Andersen
5 Tom Brennan
6 Juan Berenguer
7 Bobby Cuellar
8 Todd Heimer
9 Gary Melson
10 Hugh Yancy
11 Sal Rende
12 Dave Oliver
13 Jerry Dybzinski
14 Mike Champion
15 Bob Allietta
16 Sandy Whitol
17 Nate Puryear
18 Carl Nicholson
19 Del Alston
20 Rich Chiles
21 Sheldon Mallory
22 Tim Norrid
23 Rob Ellis
24 Gene Dusan
25 Fred Gladding
26 Wayne Cage

1979 TCMA Tidewater Tides

(New York Mets, AAA) (color)

	NR MT	EX	VG
Complete Set:	35.00	17.50	10.50

1 Roy Lee Jackson
2 John Pacella
3 Jose Moreno
4 Frank Verdi
5 Jeff Reardon
6 Dwight Bernard
7 Mookie Wilson
8 Butch Benton
9 Ron Washington
10 Jim Buckner
11 Dan Norman
12 Mario Ramirez
13 Marshall Brant
14 Ed Cipot
15 Mike Scott
16 Stan Hough
17 Scott Holman
18 Kelvin Chapman
19 Mike Van De Casteele
20 Greg Pavlick
21 Bobby Bryant
22 Russell Clark
23 Jesse Orosco
24 Bob Gorinski
25 Earl Stephenson

1979 TCMA Toledo Mud Hens

(Minnesota Twins, AAA) (color)

	NR MT	EX	VG
Complete Set:	8.00	4.00	2.50

1 Gary Ward
2 Paul Thormodsgard
3 Cal Ermer
4 Archie Amerson
5 Kevin Stanfield
6 Dan Graham
7 Dave Engle
8 Sal Butera
9 Terry Felton
10 Terry Sheehan
11 Wayne Caughey
12 John Verhoeven
13 Buck Chamberlin
14 Jim Buckner
15 Tom Sain
16 Greg Thayer
17 Dave Coleman
18 Darrell Jackson
19 Frank Vilorio
20 Jesus Vega
21 Dennis Mantick
22 Ray Smith

1979 TCMA Tucson Toros

(Texas Rangers, AAA) (color)

	NR MT	EX	VG
Complete Set:	9.00	4.50	2.75

1 Gary Gray
2 Myrl Smith
3 Mike Bruhardt
4 Brian Allard
5 Mike Bucci
6 Stan Jakubowski
7 Ron Gooch
8 Rich Donnelly
9 Steve Bianchi
10 Marty Scott
11 Don Kainer
12 Wayne Pinkerton
13 Fla Strawn
14 Tom Grieve
15 Greg Mahlberg
16 Dave Moharter
17 Mike Hart
18 Odie Davis
19 Keathel Chauncey
20 Ed Lynch
21 Bob Myrick
22 Mel Barrow
23 Larry McCall
24 Jim Umbarger

1979 TCMA Tulsa Drillers

(Texas Rangers, AA) (color)

	NR MT	EX	VG
Complete Set:	16.00	8.00	4.75

1 Wayne Tolleson
2 Joe Russell
3 Len Whitehouse
4 Jim Capowski
5 Fla Strawn
6 Steve Finch
7 Dan Dixon
8 Ray Rainbolt
9 Steve Nielsen
10 Mark Mercer
11 Ron Gooch
12 Jack Ramirez
13 Jim Schaffer
14 Rick Lisi
15 Terry Bogener
16 John Butcher
17 Jim Barbe
18 Ron Carney
19 Dave Crutcher
20 Nick Capra
21 Mel Barrow
22 Hal Kelly
23 Bill Rollings
24 Roy Clark

1979 TCMA Vancouver Canadians

(Milwaukee Brewers, AAA) (color)

	NR MT	EX	VG
Complete Set:	12.00	6.00	3.50

1 Skip James
2 Vic Harris
3 Ron Jacobs
4 Marshall Edwards
5 Craig Ryan
6 Tim Nordbrook
7 Mark Bomback
8 Andy Replogle
9 Danny Boitano
10 Rickey Keeton
11 Gus Quiros
12 Juan Lopez
13 Ned Yost
14 Clay Carroll
15 Kuni Ogawa
16 Randy Stein
17 Ed Romero
18 Jeff Yurak
19 Sam Hinds
20 John Felske
21 Billy Severns
22a Kent Biggerstaff
22b Lenn Sakata
23a Willie Mueller
23b Creighton Tevlin

1979 TCMA Waterbury A's

(Oakland A's, AA) (black and white)

	NR MT	EX	VG
Complete Set:	60.00	30.00	18.00

1 Dennis De Barr
2 Rick Tronerud
3 Walt Horn
4 Bart Braun
5 Dennis Wysznaski
6 Keith Atherton
7 Leroy Robbins
8 Frank Kolarek
9 Ed Nottle
10 Al Armstead
11 Shooty Babitt
12 Randy Green
13 Bob Klebba
14 Mike Patterson
15 Mike Davis
16 Al Minker
17 Larry Groover
18 Paul Mize
19 Bruce Fournier
20 Bob Grandas
21 Ron McNeely
22 Tim Conroy
23 Scott Meyer
24 Dave Beard
25 Robert Moore

1979 TCMA Waterloo Indians

(Cleveland Indians, A) (black and white)

	NR MT	EX	VG
Complete Set:	45.00	22.50	13.50

1a Matt Bullinger
1b Lynn Garrett
2a Lou Ganci
2b Tim Glass
3a Bill Hallstrom
3b Ron Linfonte
4a Keith Hendry
4b Jeff Klein
5 Troy Wilder
6 Jerry Stuzrien
7 Frank Regan
8 Gary Hinson
9 Steve McMurray
10 Sammy Davis
11 Rick Barnhart
12 John Asbell
13 Tom Anderson
14 Dane Anthony
15 Reid Cassidy
16 Scott Dwyer
17 Randy Rambis
18 Marcus Clark
19 Carmelo Castello (Castillo)
20 Rick Colzie
21 Ed Saavedra
22 Bob Diering
23 Mel Queen
24 Cal Emory
25 Peter Peltz
26 Tommy Martinez
27 Robbie Alvarez
28 John Walters
29 Dave Hudgins
30 Greg Johnson
31 Rod Hudson
32 Ray Richard

1979 TCMA Wausau Timbers

(No affiliation, A) (black and white)

	NR MT	EX	VG
Complete Set:	20.00	10.00	6.00

1 Brent Gaff
2 Jerry Stutzriem
3 Todd Winterfeldt
4 Kerry Keenan
5 Dave Stockstill
6 Vic Mabee
7 Israel Gutierrez
8 Wally Goff
9 Joe Nemeth
10 Lloyd Turner
11 John Zisk
12 Bob Johnson
13 Rick Barnhart
14 Ramon Romero
15 Jack Littrell
16 Tom Robson
17 Donald Lowe
18 Dean Craig
19 Alex Christianson
20 Ted Davis
21 Mike Jirschele
22 Cameron Killebrew
23 Arnold McCrary
24 Jim Payne
25 Tom Owens

1979 TCMA West Haven Yankees

(New York Yankees, AA) (color)

	NR MT	EX	VG
Complete Set:	50.00	25.00	15.00

1 Mark Johnston
2 Ed Napoleon
3 Don Cooper
4 Brian Dayett
5 Dan Schmitz
6 Pat Callahan
7 Nat Showalter
8 Carl Merrill
9 Dan Ledduke
10 Jim McDonald
11 Tom Filer
12 Kenny Baker
13 Willie McGee
14 Andy McGaffigan
15 Greg Jemison
16 Mark Softy
17 Mike Griffin
18 Tim Lewis
19 Steve Donohue
20 Tim Lollar
21 Dave Righetti
22 Batboys
23 Robert Zeig
24 Juan Espino
25 Joe Lefebvre
26 Mark Harris
27 Hoyt Wilhelm
28 Lloyd Kern
29 Front Office Staff
30 Neal Mersch

1979 TCMA Wisconsin Rapids Twins

(Minnesota Twins, A) (black and white)

	NR MT	EX	VG
Complete Set:	20.00	10.00	6.00

1 Antonio Lopez
2 Mike Ungs
3 Mike Riley
4 George Dierberger
5 Bob Blake

6 Alex Dovalis
7 Ron Grout
8 Matt Henderson
9 Steve Mapel
10 John Minarcin
11 Kim Nelson
12 Scott Stoltenberg
13 Bob Bohnet
14 Tarry Boelter
15 Gary Dobbs
16 Stan Cannon
17 Luis Bravo
18 Rubio Malone
19 Ted Kromy
20 Chuck Belk
21 Jose Rodriques
22 Jack Schumate
23 Rich Stelmaszek

1980 TCMA Albuquerque Dukes

(Los Angeles Dodgers, AAA) (color)

	MT	NR MT	EX
Complete Set:	55.00	41.00	22.00

1 Dave Stewart
2 Joe Beckwith
3 Pablo Peguero
4 Kelly Snider
5 Bill Swiacki
6 Ron Roenicke
7 John O'Rear
8 Dennis Lewallyn
9 Doug Harrison
10 Dave Patterson
11 Claude Westmoreland
12 Myron White
13 Gary Weiss
14 Teddy Martinez
15 Mike Wilson
16 Jack Perconte
17 Kevin Keefe
18 Wayne Caughey
19 Terry Collins
20 Bobby Mitchell
21 Mark Nipp
22 Ted Power
23 Del Crandall
24 Paul Padilla
25 Gerald Hannahs
26 Mike Scioscia
27 Don Crow

1980 TCMA Anderson Braves

(Atlanta Braves, A) (color)

	MT	NR MT	EX
Complete Set:	25.00	18.50	10.00

1 Dan Church
2 Arcilio Castaigne
3 Duane Theiss
4 Tim Fuller
5 Larry Edwards
6 Tim Alexander
7 Dave Coghill
8 Sonny Jackson
9 Scott Patterson
10 Ken Ames
11 Felipe Arroyo
12 Dave Chase
13 Mark Moses
14 Bill Nice
15 Mike Payne
16 Carlos Rymer
17 Buddy Bailey
18 Roy North
19 Randy Whistler
20 Eric Ayala
21 Mike Koperda
22 Mike Garcia
23 Ken Scanlon
24 Miguel Sosa
25 Harold Williams
26 Brett Butler
27 Brook Jacoby
28 Brad Komminsk
29 Rafael Quezada

1980 TCMA Appleton Foxes

(Chicago White Sox, A) (black and white)

	MT	NR MT	EX
Complete Set:	70.00	52.00	28.00

1 Luis Estrada
2 Bob Fallon
3 Diego Melendez
4 William Mills
5 Rick Naumann
6 J.B. Brown
7 Jeff Vuksan
8 Vito Lucarelli
9 Ron Kittle
10 Larry Wright
11 Dennis Vasquez
12 Nelson Rodreguez
13 Steve Pastrovich
14 Daniel Ortega
15 Keith Brown
16 Jim English
17 A.J. Hill
18 Mitch Olson
19 Greg Stewart
20 Greg Walker
21 David White
22 Tim Carroll
23 Dave Daniels
24 Dennis Keatting
25 Bill Luzinski
26 Lary Doby
27 Larry Hall
28 Mike Maitland
29 Gordy Lund
30 Ron Wollenhaupt

1980 TCMA Arkansas Travelers

(St. Louis Cardinals, AA) (color)

	MT	NR MT	EX
Complete Set:	15.00	11.00	6.00

1 Benny (Joe) Edelen
2 George Bjorkman
3 Jorge Aranzamendi
4 Jame Riggleman
5 John Ruberto
6 Mike Calise
7 Luis DeLeon
8 Mike Dimmel
9 Andrew Rincon
10 Dave Penniall
11 Alan Olmsted
12 James McIntyre
13 Ryan Kurosaki
14 David Johnson
15 Frank Hunsaker
16 Julian Gutierrez
17 Nelson Garcia
18 Freddie Tisdale
19 Felipe Zayas
20 Ray Williams
21 John Murphy
22 Kelly Paris
23 Bill Valentine
24 Mike McCormick
25 David Jorn

1980 TCMA Asheville Tourists

(Texas Rangers, A) (color)

	MT	NR MT	EX
Complete Set:	16.00	12.00	6.50

1 Billy Goodman
2 Tom Robson
3 George Gomez
4 Melvin Gilliam
5 Andy Hancock
6 Jim Schaefer
7 Toni Fossas
8 Dave Hibner
9 Ron McKee
10 Bobby Ball
11 Jimmy Tjader
12 Joe Nemeth
13 Pete O'Brien
14 Ron Carney
15 Kerry Kenan
16 Jim Maxwell
17 Jay Pettibone
18 Bill Taylor
19 Daryl Smith
20 Linvel Mosby
21 Donnie Scott
22 Larry Donofrio
23 Frank Garcia
24 Rick Burdette
25 Dave Schmidt
26 Greg Eason
27 Shelton McMath
28 Mike Jirschele

1980 TCMA Batavia Trojans

(Cleveland Indians, A) (black and white)

	MT	NR MT	EX
Complete Set:	85.00	64.00	34.00

1 Angelo Gilbert
2 Terry Norman
3 Mark Bajus
4 Todd Richards
5 Mike Kolodny
6 Kirk Jones
7 Tom Blackmon
8 Tom Burns
9 Monty Holland
10 Mike Schwarber
11 Orestes Moldes
12 Chuck Hollowell
13 Tom Stiboro
14 Brian Meier
15 Rick Elkin
16 Luis Duarte
17 Chuck Melito
18 Darold Ellison
19 Kevin Malone
20 Andy Alvis
21 Kelly Gruber
22 Rick Colzie
23 Justo Saavedra
24 Matt Minium
25 Dave Gallagher
26 Pat Grady
27 Chris Rehbaum
28 Jeff Moronko
29 Nelson Ruiz
30 Mark Wright

1980 TCMA Buffalo Bisons

(Pittsburgh Pirates, AA) (color)

	MT	NR MT	EX
Complete Set:	12.50	9.50	5.00

1 Mike Barnes
2 Ron Mitchell
3 Rick Federici
4 Dave Dravecky
5 Jim Buckner
6 Drew Macauley
7 Steve Farr
8 Rick Evans
9 Not Issued
10 Paul Djakonow
11 Mike Allen
12 Bob Rock
13 Al Torres
14 Larry Nicholson
15 Ed Vargas
16 Steve Demeter
---- Al Ortiz, Jr.

1980 TCMA Burlington Bees

(Milwaukee Brewers, A) (black and white)

	MT	NR MT	EX
Complete Set:	25.00	18.50	10.00

1 Steve Gibson
2 Kevin McCoy
3 Mike Donovan
4 Mark Lepson
5 Dave Grier
6 Greg Dehart
7 Orlando Gonzalez
8 Steve Manderfield
9 Brian Thorson
10 Duane Espy
11 Vince Pone
12 Jesse Vasquez
13 Al Walker
14 Ty Coleman
15 Steve Norwood
16 Rich Bach
17 Greg Cicotte
18 Mike Anderson
19 Kurt Kingsolver
20 Walt Steele
21 Jorge DeJesus
22 Juan Castillo
23 Mark Higgins
24 Kirk Downs
25 John Evans
26 Curt Watanabe
27 Stan Levi
28 Karl McKay
29 Bengie Biggus

1980 TCMA Cedar Rapids Reds

(Chicago White Sox, A) (color)

	MT	NR MT	EX
Complete Set:	8.00	6.00	3.25

1 Mark Moore
2 Newt Box
3 Dave Hoenstine
4 Emil Drzayich
5 Larry Buckle
6 Carlos Porte
7 Eski Viltz
8 Steve Hughes
9 Tony Masone
10 Bob Lapple
11 Rick Jendra
12 Charlie McKinney
13 Jose Mota
14 Steve Skaggs
15 Frank DeJulio
16 Mark Miller
17 Les Straker
18 Paul Gibson
19 Jeff Jones
20 Mike Messaros
21 Don "Bucky" Buchheister
22 Jim Lett
23 Mike Kripner
24 Steve Daniels
25 Kevin Waller
26 Wayne Guinn

1980 TCMA Charleston Charlies

(Texas Rangers, AAA) (color)

	MT	NR MT	EX
Complete Set:	8.00	6.00	3.25

1 Tom Burgess
2 Mark Scott
3 Wayne Pinkerton
4 Nelson Norman
5 Brian Allard
6 Greg Mahlberg
7 Dave Moharter
8 Mike Richardt
9 Richard Lisi
10 Mike Hart
11 Mark Mercer
12 Dan Duran
13 John Butcher
14 Fla Strawn
15 Odie Davis
16 Tucker Ashford
17 Bob Babcock

1980 Team Charlotte O's

(Baltimore Orioles, AA) (set is bordered in orange, but a blue-bordered set was also issued. The blue set has four addition cards - Doc Cole, Marshall Hester, a team photo and a team logo.

	MT	NR MT	EX
Complete Set:	1800.	1350.	720.00

(1) Larry Anderson
(2) John Buffamoyer
(3) Brooks Carey
(4) John Denman
(5) Tommy Eaton
(6) Kurt Fabrizio
(7) Will George
(8) Jose Gonzales
(9) Drungo Hazewood
(10) Dave Huppert
(11) Minnie Mendoza
(12) Edwin Neal
(13) Russ Pensiero
(14) Billy Presley
(15) Luis Quintana
(16) Dan Ramirez
(17) Cal Ripken, Jr.
(18) Willie Royster
(19) John Shelby
(20) Tommy Smith
(21) Don Welchel
(22) Cat Whitfield
(23) Jimmy Williams
(24) "The Pepper Girls"

1980 WBTV Charlotte O's

(Baltimore Orioles, AA)

	MT	NR MT	EX
Complete Set:	950.00	712.50	380.00

1 John Shelby
3 John Buffamoyer
4 Tommy Eaton
6 Cat Whitfield
9 Tommy Smith
11 Curt Fabrizio
13 Willie Royster
14 Drungo Hazewood
16 Cal Ripken Jr.
17 John Denman
18 Larry Anderson
19 David Huppert
20 Billy Presley
21 Brooks Carey
22 Russ Pensiero
24 Dan Ramierz
25 Jose Gonzales
27 Luis Quintana
30 Don Welchel
31 Will George
32 Edwin Neal
---- Logo Card
---- Team Photo
---- The Pepper Girls
---- Minnie Mendoza
---- Doc Cole
---- Marshall Hester

1980 TCMA Clinton Giants

(San Francisco Giants, A) (black and white)

	MT	NR MT	EX
Complete Set:	80.00	60.00	32.00

1 Dave Wilhelmi
2 Dennis Rathjen
3 Jose Chue
4 Ramon Bautista
5 Jerry Stoval
6 Chris Goodchild
7 Ron Matrisciano
8 Ken Schwab
9 Tim Hagemann
10 Scott Garrelts
11 Art Maebe
12 Kevin Johnson
13 David Fonseca
14 Randy Kutcher
15 Tim Painton
16 Chris Brown
17 Frank Thon
18 Rafael Estepan
19 Glen Moon
20 Rob Deer
21 Ron Perodin
22 Stan Morton
23 Richard Figueroa
24 Bob Cummings
25 Gilbert Albright
26 Wayne Cato
27 Tommy Jones

1980 TCMA Columbus Astros

(Houston Astros, AA) (black and white)

	MT	NR MT	EX
Complete Set:	25.00	18.50	10.00

1 Greg Cypret
2 Val Primmante
3 Tim Tolman
4 Stan Leland
5 Del Letherwood
6 Chick Valley
7 Johnny Ray
8 Bert Pena
9 Doug Stokke
10 Matt Galante
11 Greg Dahl
12 Rod Boxberger
13 John Hessler
14 Simone Rosario
15 Reggie Waller
16 Riccardo Aponte
17 Scott Loucks
18 Keith Bodie
19 Ron Meredith
20 Jim MacDonald
21 Mark Miggins
22 Rex Jones

1980 Police/Fire Safety Columbus Clippers

This minor league police safety set was issued by the Columbus, Ohio Police Department. The Columbus Clippers were affiliated with the New York Yankees in 1980. This set contains 25 cards, including one of

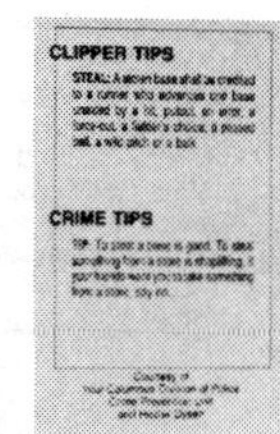

Dave Righetti. The cards are printed with full-color fronts and player statistics on the back along with a safety message. The cards are 2-3/8" by 3-3/4" size.

	MT	NR MT	EX
Complete Set:		25.00	12.50

2 Brian Doyle
11 Roger Holt
12 Dennis Sherrill
14 Joe Lefebvre
15 Garry Smith
16 Joe Altibelli (Altobelli)
17 Dave Coleman
18 Roger Slagle
20 Brad Gulden
21 Jim Lewis
22 Marv Thompson
23 Tim Lollar
24 Dave Righetti
25 Roy Staiger
26 Bruce Robinson
27 Greg Cochran
28 Jim Nettles
29 Bob Kammeyer
30 Dave Wehrmeister
31 Jim McDonald
33 Marshall Brandt (Brant)
34 Chris Welsh
36 Ken Clay
---- George H. Sisler Jr. (general manager)
---- Coaches/Trainer Card (Sammy Ellis, Mark Letendre, Jerry McNertney)

1980 TCMA Columbus Clippers

(New York Yankees, AAA) (color)

	MT	NR MT	EX
Complete Set:	25.00	18.50	10.00

1 Tim Lollar
2 Roger Stagle
3 Chris Welsh
4 Wayne Harer
5 Garry Smith
6 Brad Gulden
7 Roger Holt
8 Joe Altobelli
9 Roy Staiger
10 Bob Kammeyer
11 Jim McDonald
12 Jim Nettles
13 Brian Doyle
14 Sammy Ellis
15 Bruce Robinson
16 Jim Lewis
17 Dave Righetti
18 Mark Letendre
19 Dave Coleman
20 Marshall Brant
21 Greg Cochran
22 Jerry McNertney
23 Dennis Sherrill
24 Marv Thompson
25 Dave Wehrmeister
26 Joe Lefebvre
27 George Sisler, Jr.
28 Juan Espino

1980 Team Columbus Clippers

(New York Yankees, AAA)

	MT	NR MT	EX
Complete Set:	15.00	11.00	6.00

(1) Joe Altibelli (Altobelli)
(2) Marshall Brandt
(3) Ken Clay
(4) Greg Cochan
(5) Dave Coleman
(6) Brian Doyle
(7) Brad Gulden
(8) Roger Holt
(9) Bob Kammeyer
(10) Joe Lefebvre
(11) Jim Lewis
(12) Tim Lollar
(13) Jim McDonald
(14) Jim Nettles
(15) Dave Righetti
(16) Bruce Robinson
(17) Dennis Sherrill
(18) George H. Sisler Jr.
(19) Roger Slagle
(20) Roy Staiger
(21) Marv Thompson
(22) Dave Wehrmeister
(23) Chris Welsh
(24) Coaches/Trainer Card (Jerry McNertney, Sammy Ellis, Mark Letendre)
(25) Garry Smith

1980 TCMA Elmira Pioneers

(Boston Red Sox, A) (black and white)

	MT	NR MT	EX
Complete Set:	60.00	45.00	24.00

1 Alan Banes
2 Tom Bolton
3 Allan Bowlin
4 Dennis Boyd
5 Brice Cote
6 Steve Garrett
7 George Greco
8 Ty Herman
9 Ron Hill
10 Kevin Keenan
11 Jeff Hall
12 John Ackley
13 Mark Weinbrecht
14 Bob Sandling
15 Brandon Plainte
16 George Mecerod
17 Tom McCarthy
18 Mitch Johnson
19 Don Leach
20 Tim Duncan
21 Jeff Hunter
22 Tony Stevens
23 Ron Oddo
24 Wolf Ramos
25 Mike Bryant
26 Gus Burgess
27 Mike Ciampa
28 Simon Glenn
29 Dick Berardino
30 Parker Wilson
31 Brian Zell
32 Gilberto Gonzalez
33 Bob Crandall
34 Marve Handler
34a Marve Handler
34b Bill Limoncelli
35 Brian Butera
36 Sam Mele
37 Frank Malzone
38 Charlie Wagner
39 Jay La Bare
40 Charlie Lynch
41 Alan Mintz
42 Rodolfo Santana
43 Miguel Valdez

1980 TCMA El Paso Diablos

(California Angels, AA) (color)

	MT	NR MT	EX
Complete Set:	15.00	11.00	6.00

1 Brandt Humphrey
2 Dennis Gilbert
3 Scott Garnes
4 Rick Steirer
5 Tom Chevolek
6 Rich Rommel
7 Jim Saul
8 Mark Miller
9 Brian Harper
10 Bob Border
11 Joel Crisler
12 Mike Bishop
13 Tom Bhagwat
14 Daryl Sconiers
15 Don Smelser
16 Steve Brown
17 Tom Brunansky
18 Donny Jones
19 Perry Morrison
20 Rich Brewster
21 Rick Adams
22 Mike Walters
23 Jamie Hamilton
24 Charlie Phillips

Values for recent cards and sets are listed in Mint (MT), Near Mint (NM), reflecting the fact that many cards from recent years have been preserved in top condition. Recent cards and sets in less than Excellent condition have little collector interest.

1980 TCMA Evansville Triplets

(Detroit Tigers, AAA) (color)

	MT	NR MT	EX
Complete Set:	12.00	9.00	4.75

1 Roger Weaver
2 Mark DeJohn
3 James Gaudet
4 David Steffen
5 Michael Chris
6 Mark Fidrych
7 Ed Putnam
8 Altar Greene
9 David Rucker
10 Gerald Ujdur
11 Darrell Brown
12 Steve Baker
13 Go Giannotta
14 John Martin
15 Ralph Treuel
16 David Machemer
17 Jim Leyland
18 Bruce Robbins
19 Martin Castillo
20 Dan Gonzales
21 Glenn Gulliver
22 Steve Patchin
23 Juan Lopez
24 Richard Leach

1980 TCMA Glens Falls White Sox

(Chicago White Sox, AA) (black and white)

	MT	NR MT	EX
Complete Set:	95.00	71.00	38.00

1 Steve Pastrovich
2 Len Bradley
3 Tom Johnson
4 Randy Evans
5 Mark Platel
6 Luis Rois
7 Rick Seilheimer
8 Ray Torres
9 Reggie Patterson
10 Kevin Hickey
11 Ted Barnicle
12 Rick Wieters
13 Mark Teutsch
14 Mark Esser
15 Andy Pasillas
16 Julio Perez
17 Ron Perry
18 Randy Johnson
19 Dom Fucci
20 Vince Bienek
21 A.J. Hill
22 Lorenzo Gray
23 Fran Mullins
24 Mike Pazik
25 Duane Shaffer
26 Orlando Cepeda
27 Allan Haines
28 Batboys
29 Bob Bolster

1980 TCMA Glens Falls White Sox

(Chicago White Sox, AA) (color)

	MT	NR MT	EX
Complete Set:	15.00	11.00	6.00

1 Ron Perry
2 Len Bradley
3 Mark Teutsch
4 Randy Johnson
5 Mark Esser
6 Andy Pasillas
7 Kevin Hickey
8 Rick Seilheimer
9 Mark Platel
10 Julio Perez
11 Vince Bienek
12 Fran Mullins
13 Rick Wieters
14 Dom Fucci
15 Randy Evans
16 Steve Pastrovich
17 Luis Rois
18 Reggie Patterson
19 Ted Barnicle
20 Sox Infield (Dom Fucci, Lorenzo Gray, A.J. Hill)
21 Mike Pazik
22 Allan Haines
23 Bob Bolster
24 Duane Shaffer
25 Orlando Cepeda
26 Lorenzo Gray
27 Ray Torres
28 Tom Johnson
29 Batboys
30 A.J. Hill

1980 TCMA Hawaii Islanders

(San Diego Padres, AAA) (color)

	MT	NR MT	EX
Complete Set:	12.00	9.00	4.75

1 Chuck Baker
2 Doug Rader
3 Bob Duensing
4 Juan Eichelberger
5 Eric Mustad
6 Craig Stimac
7 Graig Kusick
8 Jim Beswick
9 Dennis Blair
10 Bobby Mitchell
11 Chuck Hartenstein
12 John Yandle
13 Greg Wilkes
14 Tom Tellmann
15 George Stablein
16 Mike Armstrong
17 Mark Lee
18 Steve Smith
19 Tim Flannery
20 Rick Sweet
21 Tony Castillo
22 Broderick Perkins
23 Don Reynolds
24 Andy Dyes
25 Fred Kuhaulua

1980 Team Indianapolis Indians

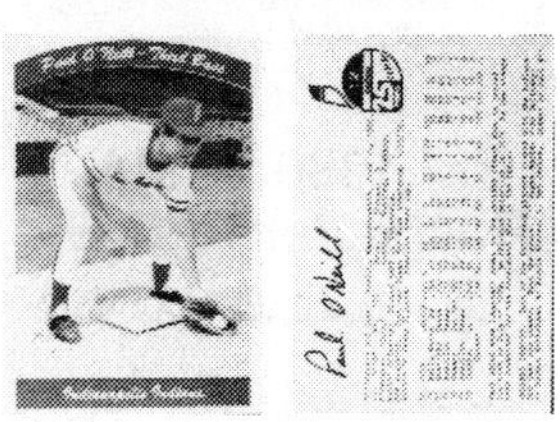

(Cincinnati Reds, AAA)

	MT	NR MT	EX
Complete Set:	20.00	15.00	8.00

1 Team Photo
2 Jim Beauchamp
3 Sheldon Burnside
4 Mike Grace
5 Joe Price
6 John Hale
7 Geoff Combe
8 Dave Van Gorder
9 Bruce Berenyi
10 Eddie Milner
11 Jay Howell
12 Paul O'Neill
13 The Braintrust
14 Larry Rothschild
15 Paul Householder
16 The Relievers
17 Scott Brown
18 Mark Milner
19 The Starters
20 Blake Doyle
21 Gene Menees
22 Rafael Santo Domingo
23 Bill Kelly
24 Don Lyle
25 Bill Dawley
26 Duane Walker
27 Angel Torres
28 The Catchers
29 The Infielders
30 The Outfielders
31 John Young
32 Checklist

1980 TCMA Holyoke Millers

(Milwaukee Brewers, AA) (color)

	MT	NR MT	EX
Complete Set:	9.00	6.75	3.50

1 Rick Kranitz
2 John Skorochocki
3 Mark Schuster
4 Barry Cort
5 Frank Thomas
6 Ivan Rodriguez
7 Eddie Brunson
8 Kuni Ogawa
9 Terry Shoebridge
10 Tom Kayser
11 Weldon Swift
12 Frank DiPino
13 Kevin Bass
14 David Green
15 Doug Loman
16 John Adams
17 Steve Lake
18 Steve Reed
19 Ed Carroll
20 Larry Montgomery
21 Terry Lee
22 Dave Curran
23 Gerald Ako
24 Tony Torres
25 Lee Stigman

1980 Police Iowa Oaks

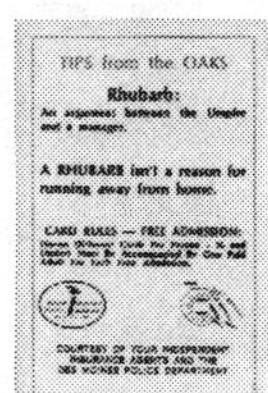

(Chicago White Sox, AAA) (set includes both variations)

	MT	NR MT	EX
Complete Set:	275.00	210.00	110.00

(1) Richard Barnes
(2) Nardi Contreras
(3) Henry Cruz
(4) Fred Frazier
(5) Joe Gates
(6) Guy Hoffman
(7) Lamar Hoyt
(8) Chris Nyman
(9) Dewey Robinson
(10) Leo Sutherland
(11) Pete Ward
(12) Mike Wolf
(13a) Mike Colbern (A Walk)
(13b) Mike Colbern (Rhubarb)
(14a) Raymundo Torres (Rhubarb)
(14b) Raymundo Torres (A Walk)

1980 TCMA Knoxville Blue Jays

(Toronto Blue Jays, AA) (black and white)

	MT	NR MT	EX
Complete Set:	100.00	75.00	40.00

1 Chuck Fore
2 Gene Petralli
3 John Poloni
4 Pete Rowe
5 Paul Hodgson
6 Mark Stober
7 Davis May
8 Jesse Flores
9 Bob Silverman
10 Shaun McCarthy
11 Ralph Santana
12 Mike Cuellar, Jr.
13 Jesse Barfield
14 Ed Dennis
15 Tim Thompson
16 Tom Dejak
17 Pedro Hernandez
18 Larry Hardy
19 Dave Gibson
20 Jesus de la Rosa
21 Charlie Puelo
22 Andre Wood
23 Keith Walker
24 "Rocket" Wheeler
25 Bob Humphreys
26 Rick Morgan
27 Duane Larson
28 Ed Holtz

1980 TCMA Lynn Sailors

(Seattle Mariners, AA) (color)

	MT	NR MT	EX
Complete Set:	8.00	6.00	3.25

1 Mike Moore
2 Larry Patterson
3 Rodney Hobbs
4 Bobby Floyd
5 Chuck Lindsay
6 Rob Simond
7 Mike Hart
8 Don Minnick
9 Orlando Mercado
10 Miguel Negron
11 Karl Best
12 Jeff Cary
13 Manny Estrada
14 Gary Pellant
15 Mickey Bowers
16 Tom Hunt
17 Joe Georger
18 Jammie Allen
19 R.J. Harrison
20 Roy Clark
21 Sam Welborn
22 Lloyd Kern
23 Ron Musselman

1980 TCMA Memphis Chicks

(Montreal Expos, AA) (black and white)

	MT	NR MT	EX
Complete Set:	30.00	22.00	12.00

1 Steve Lovins
2 Charlie Lea
3 Anthony Johnson
4 Tom Gorman
5 Greg Bargar
6 Joe Abone
7 Larry Goldetsky
8 Larry Bearnarth
9 Mike Gates
10 Glen Franklin
11 Ray Crowley
12 Leonel Carrion
13 Terry Francona
14 Kevin Mendon
15 Brad Mills
16 Tony Phillips
17 Pat Rooney
18 Dennis Sherow
19 Tommy Joe Shimp
20 Bryn Smith
21 Chris Smith
22 Doug Simunic
23 Bob Tenenini
24 Grayling Tobias
25 Tom Wieghaus
26 Rick Williams
27 Steve Winfield
28 Frank Wren
29 Bud Yanus
30 Audie Thor

1980 Chong Modesto A's

(Oakland A's, A)

	MT	NR MT	EX
Complete Set:	45.00	34.00	18.00

1 Don Schubert
2 Steve Gelfarb
3 Mike Woodard
4 Paul Stockley
5 Gordon Eakin
6 Kevin Jacobson
7 Al Armstead
8 Jim Bennett
9 Lynn Garrett
10 Bob Garrett
11 Rich Hatcher
12 Jim Durrman
13 Frank Kneuer
14 Frank Kolarek
15 John Gosse
16 Ron Mantsch
17 Rick Holloway
18 Ken Corzel
19 Don Van Marter
20 Chuck Dougherty
21 Tom Brunswick
22 Ed Retzer
23 Mark Ferguson
24 Roy Moretti
25 Keith Call
26 Bob Wood
27 Keith Lieppman
28 Brad Fischer
29 Dan Kiser

Regional interest may affect the value of a card.

1980 Team Nashville Sounds

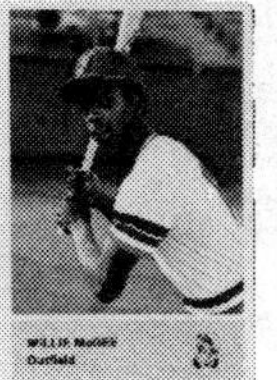

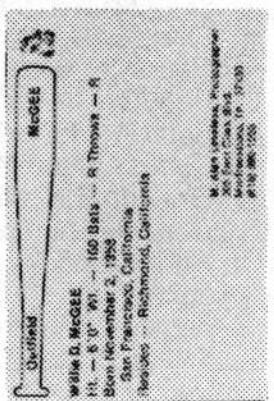

(New York Yankees, AA)

	MT	NR MT	EX
Complete Set:	25.00	18.75	10.00

(1) Ken Baker
(2) Steve Balboni
(3) Paul Boris
(4) Pat Callahan
(5) Nate Chapman
(6) Don Cooper
(7) Brian Dayett
(8) Pat Dobson
(9) Tom Filer
(10) Brad Gulden
(11) Greg Jemison
(12) Dan Ledduke
(13) Andy Mc Gaffigan
(14) Willie Mc Gee
(15) Stump (Carl Merrill)
(16) Eddie Napoleon
(17) Brian Ryde, Brian Ryder)
(18) Rafel Santana (S/B RAFAEL)
(19) Danny Schmitz
(20) Buck Showalter
(21) Roger Slagle
(22) Pat Tabler
(23) Steve Taylor
(24) James Werly
(25) Ted Wilborn

1980 TCMA Ogden A's

(Oakland A's, AAA) (color)

	MT	NR MT	EX
Complete Set:	12.00	9.00	4.75

1 Tim Hosley
2 Ray Cosey
3 Craig Minetto
4 Derek Bryant
5 Randy Green
6 Rich Lysander
7 Mark Busaska
8 Terry Enyart
9 Brian Abraham
10 Mark Souza
11 Bob Grandas
12 Frank Harris
13 John Sutton
14 Milt Ramirez
15 David Beard
16 Bruce Fournier
17 Allen Wirth
18 Royle Stillman
19 Jeff Cox
20 Kelvin Moore
21 "Shooty" Babbitt (Babitt)
22 Pat Dempsey
23 Jose Pagan

1980 Team Oklahoma City 89'ers

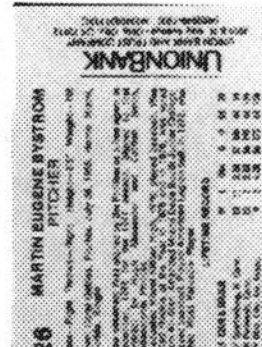

(Philadelphia Phillies, AAA) This set is numbered as it appears on the cards.

	MT	NR MT	EX
Complete Set:	35.00	26.00	14.00

1 John Loviglio
3 Luis Aguayo
4 Mike Anderson
6 Jim Snyder
7 Orlando Isales
8 Billy Smith

9 Luis Rodriguez
10 Ramon Lora
11 Jose Martinez
12 Leonard Matuszek
14 Orlando Sanchez
15 Elijah B. Bonaparte
16 Ruben Arroyo
17 Paul G. Thormodsgard
18 Scott A. Munninghoff
19 Porfirio Altamirano
20 Orlando E. Gonzalez
21 Donald McCormack
22 Robert Speck
23 John Poff
24 James L. Wright Jr.
25 William Suter Jr.
26 Martin Bystrom
28 Jerry Reed

1980 Team Omaha Royals

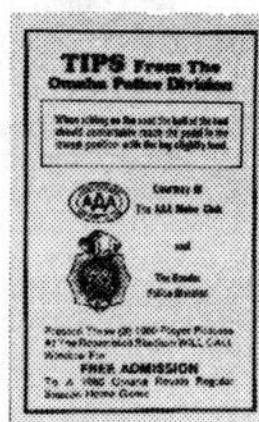

(Kansas City Royals, AAA)

	MT	NR MT	EX
Complete Set:	35.00	26.00	14.00

(1) Dave Augustine
(2) German Barranca
(3) Leon Brown
(4) Steve Busby
(5) Manny Castillo
(6) Craig Chamberlain
(7) Jerry Cram
(8) Ken Cvejdlik
(9) Bob Detherage
(10) Keith Drumright
(11) Dan Fischer
(12) Danny Garcia
(13) Jim Gaudet
(14) Kelly Heath
(15) Tim Ireland
(16) Bill Laskey
(17) Randy McGilberry
(18) Mike Morley
(19) Tom Mutz
(20) Bill Paschall
(21) Ken Phelps
(22) Jeff Schattinger
(23) Joe Sparks
(24) Jeff Twitty

1980 TCMA Orlando Twins

(Minnesota Twins, AA) (black and white)

	MT	NR MT	EX
Complete Set:	80.00	60.00	32.00

1 Wade Adamson
2 Tim Barr
3 Tom Biko
4 Steve Green
5 Eddie Hodge
6 Steve Mapel
7 Jose Reyes
8 Lance Hallberg
9 F. Estes
10 Lenny Faedo
11 Steve Benson
12 Tim Laudner
13 A. Cadahia
14 G. Ballard
15 Mike Ungs
16 Terry Sheehan
17 Steve McManaman
18 Alex Ramirez
19 Mark Funderburk
20 Kevin McWhirter
21 Scott Ullger
22 Roy McMillan

1980 TCMA Peninsula Pilots

(Philadelphia Phillies, A) (black and white); sponsored by Pepsi Cola.

	MT	NR MT	EX
Complete Set:	65.00	49.00	26.00

1 Phil Teston
2 Daryl Adams
3 Carlos Cabassa
4 Miguel Alicea
5 Fred Warner
6 Kelly Faulk
7 Wally Goff
8 Wil Culmer
9 Keith Washington
10 Bob Tiefenauer
11 Don Carman
12 Roy Smith
13 Jim Wright
14 Randy Greer
15 Joe Bruno
16 Al White
17 Paul Kiess
18 Russ Hamric
19 Ray Borucki
20 Ron Smith
21 Julio Franco
22 Jeff Ulrich
23 Herb Orensky
24 John Fierro
25 Bob Neal
26 Frank Funk
27 Bill Dancy

1980 TCMA Peninsula Pilots

(Philadelphia Phillies, A) (color); sponsored by Burger King.

	MT	NR MT	EX
Complete Set:	30.00	22.00	12.00

1 Phil Teston
2 Daryl Adams
3 Carlos Cabassa
4 Roy Smith
5 Don Carman
6 Miguel Alicea
7 Jim Wright
8 Fred Warner
9 Bob Neal
10 John Fierro
11 George Farson
12 Bill Dancy
13 Kelly Faulk
14 Wally Goff
15 Herb Orensky
16 Jeff Ulrich
17 Julio Franco
18 Keith Washington
19 Wil Culmer
20 Randy Greer
21 Joe Bruno
22 Al White
23 Paul Kiess
24 Russ Hamric
25 Ray Borucki
26 Ron Smith
27 Bob Tiefenauer

1980 Valley Nat'l Bank Phoenix Giants

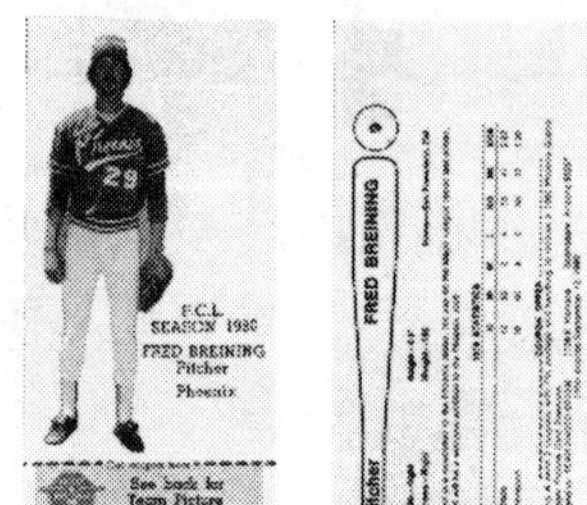

(San Francisco Giants, AAA) (2" x 5")

	MT	NR MT	EX
Complete Set:	8.00	6.00	3.25

1 Mike Williams
2 Bob Tufts
3 Doug Schaefer
4 Mike Rowland
5 Larry Prewitt
6 Ed Plank
7 Phil Nastu
8 Terry Cornutt
9 Fred Breining
10 Bill Bordley
11 Chris Bourjos
12 Max Venable
13 Casey Parsons
14 Craig Landis
15 Bob Kearney
16 Dennis Littlejohn
17 Jose Barrios
18 Mike Rex
19 Rich Murray
20 Joe Pettini
21 Guy Sularz
22 Rocky Bridges
23 Jim Duffalo
24 Ethan Blackaby
25 Tommy Gonzales
26 Harry Jordan

1980 TCMA Portland Beavers

(Pittsburgh Pirates, AAA) (color)

	MT	NR MT	EX
Complete Set:	20.00	15.00	8.00

1 Mike Tyler
2 Dorian Boyland
3 Craig Cacek
4 Jerry McDonald
5 Rob Ellis
6 Jim Mahoney
7 Pascual Perez
8 Tommy Sandt
9 Vance Law
10 Mickey Mahler
11 Dick Pole
12 Bill Fortinberry
13 Stewart Cliburn
14 Harry Dorish
15 Gary Hargis
16 Not Issued
17 Odell Jones
18 Tom Trebelhorn
19 Mike Davey
20 Rick Lancellotti
21 Robert Long
22 Rod Gilbreath
23 Larry Anderson (Andersen)
24 Tony Pena
25 Gene Pentz
26 Dan Warthen
27 Rick Rhoden

1980 TCMA Quad Cities Cubs

(Chicago Cubs, A) (black and white)

	MT	NR MT	EX
Complete Set:	60.00	45.00	24.00

1 Mike Thompson
2 Gerry Mims
3 Tim Millner
4 Ed Moore
5 Tom Morris
6 Glenn Swaggerty
7 Ray Soff
8 Carlos Gil
9 Richard Renwick
10 Mark Wilkins
11 Bob Maddon
12 Norm Churchill
13 Mike Diaz
14 Pete Bazan
15 Ted Trevino
16 Jack Upton
17 Craig Kornfeld
18 Jim Payne
19 Glenn Millhauser
20 Bruce Compton
21 Mike Kelley
22 Dennis Mork
23 Gordy Hodgson
24 Wayne Rohlfing
25 Phil Belmonte
26 Mike Wilson
27 Rich DeLoach
28 John Stockstill
29 Carmelo Martinez
30 Jim Napier
31 Davey Nesmoe
32 Roger Crow

1980 TCMA Reading Phillies

(Philadelphia Phillies, AA) (black and white)

	MT	NR MT	EX
Complete Set:	750.00	550.00	300.00

1 Wayne Williams
2 Jose Castro
3 Ozzie Virgil
4 Mark Davis
5 Don Fowler
6 Miguel Ibarra
7 Joe Jones
8 Jeff Kraus
9 Tommy Hart
10 Ernie Gause
11 Darren Burroughs
12 Tom Lombarski
13 Jorge Bell
14 John Devincenzo
15 Bob Dernier
16 Manny Abreu
17 Ron Clark
18 Rollie Dearmas
19 Cliff Speck
20 Dan Prior
21 Tony McDonald
22 Ryne Sandberg
23 Jesus Herniz
24 Steve Curry

1980 TCMA Richmond Braves

(Atlanta Braves, AAA) (color)

	MT	NR MT	EX
Complete Set:	9.00	6.75	3.50

1 Danny Morogiello
2 Rafael Ramirez
3 Butch Edge
4 Larry Whisenton
5 Fred Hatfield
6 Steve Hammond
7 Tony Brizzolara
8 Gary Melson
9 John Sain
10 Danny O'Brien
11 Rick Mahler
12 Charlie Keller
13 Butch Metzger
14 Horace Speed
15 Glenn Hubbard
16 Harry Saferight
17 Terry Harper
18 Ken Smith
19 Bob Beall
20 Craig Skok
21 Jim Wessinger
22 Eddie Miller
23 Bo McLaughlin

1980 TCMA Rochester Red Wings

(Baltimore Orioles, AAA) (color)

	MT	NR MT	EX
Complete Set:	12.00	9.00	4.75

1 Bob Bonner
2 Dallas Williams
3 Vern Thomas
4 Dan Logan
5 Mark Corey
6 Mike Boddicker
7 Larry Jones
8 Jeff Rineer
9 Tom Rowe
10 Jeff Schneider
11 Kevin Kennedy
12 Mike Eden
13 Doc Edwards
14 John Valle
15 Steve Luebber
16 Wayne Krenchicki
17 Jim Smith
18 Floyd Rayford
19 Tom Smith
20 Larry Johnson
21 Pete Torrez

1980 TCMA Salt Lake City Gulls

(California Angels, AAA) (color) (complete set price includes scarce card #'s 18-21)

	MT	NR MT	EX
Complete Set:	12.00	9.00	4.75

1 Ralph Botting
2 Dan Whitmer
3 Craig Eaton
4 Scott Moffitt
5 Mark Nocciolo
6 Dave Schuler
7 Ken Schrom
8 Charlie Phillips
9 Jeff Bertoni
10 Rick Oliver
11 Jay Peters
12 John Harris
13 Carlos Perez
14 Steve Lubratich
15 Rick Foley
16 Jim Dorsey
17 Steve Eddy
18 Moose Stubing
19 Leonard Garcia
20 Sterling Gull
21 Gil Kubski
22 Pete Mangual
23 Bob Clark
24 Bob Ferris
25 Fernando Gonzalez
26 Mike Overy

1980 Jack In The Box San Jose Missions

(No affiliation, AAA) (2" x 3")

	MT	NR MT	EX
Complete Set:	25.00	18.50	10.00

1 Bill Plummer
2 Ed Aponte
3 Mark Batten
4 Bud Black
5 Mark Chellette
6 Ramon Estepa
7 Chris Flammang
8 Bill Gaffney
9 Rick Graser
10 Tim Hallgren
11 Tracy Harris
12 Steve Knight
13 Chris Krajewski
14 Jed Murray
15 Tito Nanni
16 Brian Snyder
18 Jeff Stottlemyre
19 Scott Stranski
20 Dave Valle
21 Checklist

1980 TCMA Spokane Indians

(Seattle Mariners, AAA) (color)

	MT	NR MT	EX
Complete Set:	25.00	18.50	10.00

1 Bob Stoddard
2 Dave Smith
3 Greg Biercevicz
4 Carlos Diaz
5 Joe Coleman
6 Ron McGee
7 Roy Branch
8 Bryan Clark
9 Vance McHenry
10 Terry Bulling
11 Kip Young
12 Manny Sarmiento
13 Randy Stein
14 Jim Maler
15 Dave Elder
16 Dave Henderson
17 Gary Wheelock
18 Rene Lachemann
19 Kim Allen
20 Rich Anderson
21 Reggie Walton
22 Dan Firova
23 Steve Stroughter
24 Charlie Beamon

1980 TCMA Syracuse Chiefs

(Toronto Blue Jays, AAA) (color)

	MT	NR MT	EX
Complete Set:	15.00	11.00	6.00

1 Garth Iorg
2 Doug Ault
3 Kevin Pasley
4 Jackson Todd
5 Pat Rockett
6 Jay Robertson
7 Mike Willis
8 Tom Brown
9 Phil Huffman
10 Butch Alberts
11 Jack Kucek
12 Mitchell Webster
13 Mike Barlow
14 Greg Wells
15 Pat Kelly
16 Lloyd Moseby
17 Dave Baker
18 Randy Benson
19 Harry Warner
20 Danny Ainge
21 Willie Upshaw
22 Domingo Ramos
23 Don Pisker

A card number in parentheses () indicates the set is unnumbered.

1980 Team Syracuse Chiefs

(Toronto Blue Jays, AAA) This set is numbered as it appears on the cards, is 3-1/4" x 5" in size, with blank backs.

	MT	NR MT	EX
Complete Set:	45.00	34.00	18.00

4 Don Pisker
5 Dave Baker
9 Garth Iorg
11 Kevin Pasley
12 Steve Davis
14 Butch Alberts
15 Lloyd Moseby
16 Jackson Todd
17 Mitchell Webster
18 Pat Rockett
19 Tom Brown
20 Jack Kucek
21 Steve Grilli
22 Phil Huffman
23 Mike Willis
24 Harry Warner
25 Doug Ault
26 Pat Kelly
27 Randy Benson
28 Luis Leal
29 Mike Barlow
30 Jay Robertson
32 Greg Wells
---- Tony DeRosa (Trainer)

1980 TCMA Tacoma Tigers

(Cleveland Indians, AAA) (color)

	MT	NR MT	EX
Complete Set:	9.00	6.75	3.50

1 Not Issued
2 Tim Norrid
3 Larry Littleton
4 Wayne Cage
5 Don Collins
6 Bobby Cuellar
7 Mel Queen
8 Larry McCall
9 Raphael Vasquez
10 Sandy Whitol
11 Bob Allietta
12 Tom Brennan
13 Mike Bucci
14 Sal Rende
15 Dave Oliver
16 Mike Champion
17 Gary Gray
18 Todd Heimer
19 John Bonilla
20 Kevin Rhomberg
21 Rick Borchers
22 Art Popham
23 Gene Dusan
24 Del Alston
25 Eric Wilkins
26 Steve Ciszczon
27 Miek Paxton
27a Louis DeLeon
27b Mike Paxton
---- Rob Pietroburgo

1980 TCMA Tidewater Tides

(New York Mets, AAA) (color)

	MT	NR MT	EX
Complete Set:	18.00	13.50	7.25

1 Dave Von Ohlen
2 Jose Moreno
3 Juan Berenguer
4 Wally Backman
5 Sergio Ferrer
6 Gil Flores
7 Ed Cipot
8 Butch Benton
9 Ron MacDonald
10 Dyar Miller
11 Greg Harris
12 Tom Dixon
13 Reggie Baldwin
14 Fred Beene
15 Hubie Brooks
16 Not Issued
17 Mookie Wilson
18 Kelvin Chapman
19 Roy Lee Jackson
20 Jimmy Smith
21 Ed Lynch
22 Papo Rosado
23 Mike Scott
24 Frank Verdi
25 Randy McGilberry

1980 TCMA Toledo Mud Hens

(Minnesota Twins, AAA) (color)

	MT	NR MT	EX
Complete Set:	10.00	7.50	4.00

1 Steve Mapel
2 Bob Randall
3 Cal Ermer
4 Bruce MacPherson
5 Gary Serum
6 Ron Washington
7 Terry Felton
8 Randy Bush
9 John Walker
10 Willie Norwood
11 Jesus Vega
12 Wilfredo Sarmiento
13 Steve Herz
14 Buck Chamberlin
15 Dave Engle
16 Ray Smith
17 Al Williams
18 Jeff Brueggemann
19 Bob Veselic
20 Kurt Seibert

1980 TCMA Tucson Toros

(Houston Astros, AAA) (color)

	MT	NR MT	EX
Complete Set:	12.00	9.00	4.75

1 Danny Heep
2 Jimmy Sexton
3 Joe Pittman
4 Rick Williams
5 Gary Wilson
6 Bob Sprowl
7 Jack Fleming
8 Tom Wiedenbauer
9 Jimmy Johnson
10 George Gross
11 Billy Smith
12 Dave LaBossiere
13 Dennis Miscik
14 Alan Knicely
15 Tom Spencer
16 Gary Rajsich
17 Mike Fischlin
18 Gordy Pladson
19 Jim Pankovits
20 Brent Strom
21 Mike Mendoza
22 Gary Woods
23 Bert Roberge
24 Doug Stokke

1980 TCMA Tulsa Drillers

(Texas Rangers, AA) (color)

	MT	NR MT	EX
Complete Set:	8.00	6.00	3.25

1 Jerry Gleaton
2 Dave Crutcher
3 Tony Hudson
4 Ted Davis
5 Mike Roberts
6 Jack Lozorko
7 Jim Farr
8 Nick Capra
9 Larry Reynolds
10 George Wright
11 Mel Barrow
12 Frank Garcia
13 Phil Klimas
14 Luis Gonzalez
15 Mike Jirschele
16 Wayne Tolleson
17 Ronnie Gooch
18 Tracy Cowger
19 Steve Nielsen
20 Chuck Lamson
21 Bobby Johnson
22 Dave Schmidt
23 Darrell Ortiz
24 Wayne Terwilliger
25 Mike Vickers
26 Mitch Fletcher

1980 TCMA Utica Blue Jays

(Toronto Blue Jays, A) (black & white)

	MT	NR MT	EX
Complete Set:	35.00	26.00	14.00

1 Larry Hardy
2 Rich White
3 Carlos Cabrera
4 Jim Baker
5 Felix Feliciano
6 Rafael Harris
7 Tom Norko
8 Silverio Valdez
9 Jon Woodworth
10 Bob Wilbur
11 Hector Torres
12 Tomas Castillo
13 Juan Castillo
14 Roberto Cerrud
15 Jose Escobar
16 Tony Gilmore
17 Luis Guzman
18 Toby Hernandez
19 Mark Holton
20 Dennis Howard
21 Miguel Ortiz
22 Tom O'Dowd
23 Al Montgomery
24 Bob McNair
25 Tom Lukish
26 Herman Lewis
27 Carlos Leal
28 Paul Langfield
29 Mike Hurdle
30 Bill Reade
31 Rafael Rivas
32 Miguel Rodriguez
33 Rico Sutton

1980 TCMA Vancouver Canadians

(Milwaukee Brewers, AAA) (color)

	MT	NR MT	EX
Complete Set:	7.00	5.25	2.75

1 Lawrence Rush
2 Willie Mueller
3 Ned Yost
4 Gus Quiros
5 Bobby Glen Smith
6 Terry Bevington
7 Dave LaPoint
8 Billy Severns
9 Lance Rautzhan
10 Tim Nordbrook
11 Bob Didier
12 Kent Biggerstaff
13 Ed Romero
14 Dan Boitano
15 Craig Ryan
16 Rene Quinones
17 Mike Henderson
18 Fred Holdsworth
19 Marshall Edwards
20 Bob Galasso
21 Vic Harris
22 Rick Olsen

1980 TCMA Waterbury Reds

(Cincinnati Reds, AA) (black & white)

	MT	NR MT	EX
Complete Set:	90.00	67.00	36.00

1 Nick Fiorillo
2 Jeff Lahti
3 Steve Christmas
4 Doug Neuenschwander
5 Paul Herring
6 Randy Town
7 Bill Scherer (Scherrer)
8 Scott Dye
9 Lee Garrett
10 Mike Compton
11 Rick O'Keefe
12 Jose Brito
13 Bob Hamilton
14 Mark Gilbert
15 Skeeter Barnes
16 Tom Sohns
17 Dan Sarrett
18 Tom Lawless
19 Tom Foley
20 Russ Aldrich
21 Nick Esasky
22 Greg Hughes

1980 TCMA Waterloo Indians

(Cleveland Indians, A) (black & white)

	MT	NR MT	EX
Complete Set:	45.00	34.00	18.00

1 John Hoban
2 Dane Anthony
3 Ron Leach
4 Larry White
5 Tim Glass

6 Ramon Romero
7 Alan Willis
8 Jack Nuismer
9 John Bohnet
10 John Asbell
11 Larry Hrynko
12 Kirk Jones
13 Rick Barnhart
14 Daryl Fazzio
15 Bryan Meier
16 Chris Rehbaum
17 Sammy Torres
18 Bruce Chaney
19 Erik Peterson
20 George Cechetti
21 Robert Bohnet
22 Don Nicolet
23 Gary Hinson
24 Frank Regan
25 Everett Rey
26 Rick Baker
27 Carmelo Castillo
28 Tommy Martinez
29 Mike Taylor
30 Cal Emery
31 Chuck Stobbs
32 Bob Gariglio
33 Rich Blumeyer
34 Wes Mitchell
35 Von Hayes

1980 TCMA Wausau Timbers

(Seattle Mariners, A) (black & white)

	MT	NR MT	EX
Complete Set:	25.00	18.50	10.00

1 Tom Brennan
2 John Burden
3 Mark Cahill
4 Tony Jordan
5 Martin Little
6 Edwin Nunez
7 Steve Roche
8 Elias Salva
9 Mark Softy
10 John Zisk
11 Takashi Upshur
12 Bobby Tanzi
13 Jimmy Presley
14 Mario Diaz
15 Enrique Diaz
16 Mike Hood
17 Chris Henry
18 Rick Graser
19 Mike Frierson
20 Kevin King
21 Werner Lajszky
22 Arnie McCrary
23 Orlando Martinez

1980 TCMA West Haven White Caps

(Oakland A's, AA) (color)

	MT	NR MT	EX
Complete Set:	7.00	5.25	2.75

1 Al Minker
2 Dennis Wyszynski
3 Leroy Robbins
4 Don Morris
5 Bruce Fournier
6 Rob Klebba
7 Paul Stevens
8 Paul Mize
9 Scott Meyer
10 Bert Bradley
11 Craig Harris
12 Bobby Markham
13 Fred Devito
14 Darryl Ciaz
15 Mike Patterson
16 Keith Atherton
17 Shooty Babbitt (Babitt)
18a Nick Beamon
18b Staff
19a Keith Comstock
19b John Gosse
20a David Goldstein
20b Ed Nottle
21a Keathel Chauncey
21b Rich Lynch
21c Bob Moore
22a Tim Conroy
22b Aggie Maggio
23a Coach Benson
23b Randy Sealy
24 Rick Tronerud

A player's name in italic type indicates a rookie card. An (FC) indicates a player's first card for that particular card company.

1980 TCMA Wichita Aeros

(Chicago Cubs, AAA) (color)

	MT	NR MT	EX
Complete Set:	60.00	45.00	24.00

1 Karl Pagel
2 Jim Tracy
3 Kim Buettemeyer
4 Mark Parker
5 Bill Hayes
6 Danny Rohn
7 Randy Martz
8 Jack Hiatt
9 Jesus Figeroa
10 Ignacio Javier
11 Mike Turgeon
12 Lee Smith
13 Mike Allen
14 Jesus Alfaro
15 Paul Semall
16 Jared Martin
17 Brian Rosinski
18 Steve Macko
19 Vince Valentini
20 George Riley
21 Manny Seoane
22 Mark Lemongello

1980 TCMA Wisconsin Rapids Twins

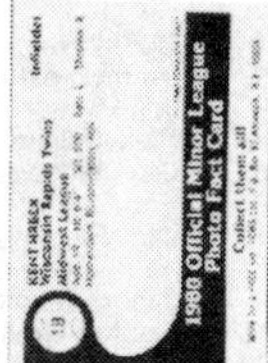

(Minnesota Twins, A) (black & white)

	MT	NR MT	EX
Complete Set:	180.00	135.00	70.00

1 Sam Arrington
2 Luis Santos
3 Robert Mulilgan
4 Larry May
5 Manuel Lunar
6 William Lamkey
7 Bob Konepa
8 Hal Jackson
9 Ken Francingues
10 Conrad Everett
11 Chris Thomas
12 Paul Voight
13 Richard Ray Austin
14 Glenn Ballard
15 James Christensen
16 Manuel Colletti
17 Gary Gaetti
18 Kent Hrbek
19 Kevin Miller
20 Norberto Molina
21 Brad Carlson
22 Matt Henderson
23 Joe Kubit
24 Bruce Stocker
25 Ray Stein
26 Rich Stelmaszek
27 Tony Oliva

1981 TCMA Albuquerque Dukes

(Los Angeles Dodgers, AAA) (color) (Koufax was a scarce, withdrawn card)

	MT	NR MT	EX
Complete Set:	80.00	60.00	32.00

1 Dave Moore
2 Dave Patterson
3 Steve Shirley
4 Alejandro Pena
5 Ted Power
6 Bill Swiacki
7 Ricky Wright
8 Dave Richards
9 Ron Roenicke
10 Brian Holton
11 Kevin Keefe
12 Brent Strom
13 Don Crow
14 Wayne Caughey
15 Larry Fobbs
16 Mike Marshall
17 Jack Perconte
18 Alex Taveras
19 Gary Weiss
20 Rudy Law
21 Candy Maldonado
22 Bobby Mitchell
23a Sandy Koufax
23b Tack Wilson
24 Del Crandall
25 Dick McLaughlin

1981 TCMA Appleton Foxes

(Chicago White Sox, A) (color)

	MT	NR MT	EX
Complete Set:	9.00	6.75	3.50

1 Jesse Anderson
2 Jeff Barnard
3 Keith Desjarlais
4 Kevin Flannery
5 Tom Mullen
6 Rick Naumann
7 Dan Ortega
8 Steve Pastrovich
9 Mark Platel
10 Jim Siwy
11 Roy Schumacher
12 Wayne Schukert
13 Larry Donofrio
14 Cecil Espy
15 Leo Garcia
16 Ike Golden
17 John Hanley
18 A.J. Hill
19 Scott Meier
20 Mike Morse
21 Dave Nix
22 Gary Robinette
23 Ramon Romero
24 Mark Seeger
25 Ray Torres
26 Wes Kent
27 Dave Wall
28 Sam Ewing
29 Doug Wiesner

1981 TCMA Arkansas Travelers

(St. Louis Cardinals, AA) (black & white)

	MT	NR MT	EX
Complete Set:	15.00	11.00	6.00

1 Felipe Zayas
2 Steve Turco
3 Donald Moore
4 Dennis Delany
5 Fred Tisdale
6 Rhadames Mills
7 Jeffrey Doyle
8 Jorge Aranzamendi
9 David Kable
10 Kerry Burchett
11 Jerry Johnson
12 David Jorn
13 Rafael Pimentel
14 Mark Riggins
15 Daniel Winslow
16 Kevin Hagen
17 James Gott
18 Ralph Citarella
19 James Riggleman
20 Louis Pratt
21 Gaylen Pitts
22 Jerry McKune
23 Arkansas Travelerettes

1981 TCMA Batavia Trojans

(Cleveland Indians, A) (black & white)

	MT	NR MT	EX
Complete Set:	12.50	9.50	5.00

1 Mark Bajus
2 Tom Burns
3 Jose Roman
4 Steve Cushing
5 Mike Poindexter
6 Todd Richard
7 Brian Silvas
8 Phil Deriso
9 Bart Mackie
10 Adalberto Nieves
11 Rick Elkin
12 Arnold Cochran
13 Ray Martinez
14 Jerry Nalley
15 Junior Noboa
16 Ed Tanner
17 Sam Martin
18 John Merchant
19 Scott Collins
20 Bernardo Brito
21 Gary Holden
22 Eric Jones
23 Chris Rehbaum
24 Randy Washington
25 George Alpert
26 Miguel Roman
27 Dave Oliver
28 Luis Isaac
29 Paul Seymour
30 John Jakubowski

1981 TCMA Birmingham Barons

(Detroit Tigers, AA) (black & white)

	MT	NR MT	EX
Complete Set:	95.00	71.00	38.00

1 John Lackey
2 Roy Majtyka
3 Dwight Lowry
4 Manny Seoane
5 Ron Mathis
6 Bruce Robbins
7 Mark Dacko
8 Mike Laga
9 Frank Hunsaker
10 Glenn Wilson
11 Gary Bozich
12 Howard Johnson
13 Jeff Kenaga
14 Bob Nandin
15 Jack Smith
16 Bruce Chaney
17 Stan Younger
18 Nick O'Connor
19 Dick Pole
20 Stine Poole
21 Darrell Woodard
22 Barbaro Garbey
23 Augie Ruiz
24 Paul Josephson
25 Mike Beecroft

1981 TCMA Bristol Red Sox

(Boston Red Sox, AA) (color)

	MT	NR MT	EX
Complete Set:	16.00	12.00	6.50

1 Craig Brooks
2 Bill Moloney
3 Kevin Kane
4 Gene Gentile
5 Reggie Whittemore
6 Jim Wilson
7 Brian Denman
8 Tony Torchia
9 Dave Schoppee
10 Rick Colbert
11 Chuck Sandberg
12 Ed Jurak
13 Jerry King
14 Kenny Young
15 Jay Fredlund
16 Erwin Bryant
17 Steve Shields
18 Glenn Eddins
19 Dave Tyler
20 Clint Johnson
21 Dennis Burtt
22 Jim Watkins

1981 TCMA Buffalo Bisons

(Pittsburgh Pirates, AA) (color)

	MT	NR MT	EX
Complete Set:	12.00	9.00	4.75

1 John Lipon
2 John Holland
3 Doug Britt
4 Jose DeLeon
5 Ben Wiltbank
6 Benny de la Rosa
7 Drew Macauley
8 Carlos Ledezema
9 Stew Cliburn
10 Bob Rock
11 Rafael Vasquez
12 Dan Wortham
13 Jose Rodriguez
14 Billy Waag
15 Gary Hargis
16 Jose Calderon
17 Angel Barez
18 Steve Farr
19 Carlos Rios
20 Tony Incavigua
21 Terry Salazar
22 Doug Frobel
23 Eddie Vargas
24 Frank Riccelli
25 Reggie Buchanan

1981 TCMA Burlington Bees

(Milwaukee Brewers, A) (black & white)

	MT	NR MT	EX
Complete Set:	30.00	22.00	12.00

1 Dave Morris
2 Vince Pone
3 Kevin McCoy
4 Steve Noewood
5 Gene Smith
6 Raymond Gallo
7 Craig Herberholz
8 Not Issued
9 Mark Lepson
10 Tim Crews
11 Steve Gibson
12 Johnson Wood
13 Murphy Susa
14 Angel Morris
15 Henry Contreras
16 Steve Jordan
17 Randy Ready
18 Butch Kirby
19 Mike Samuel
20 Juan Castillo
21 Brad DeKraai
22 Carlos Ponce
23 Mark Higgins
24 Gerry Miller
25 Ronnie Jones
26 Karl McKay
27 Joel Parker
28 Bill Nowlan
29 Lawrence Avery
30 Terry Bevington

1981 TCMA Cedar Rapids Reds

(Cincinnati Reds, A) (color)

	MT	NR MT	EX
Complete Set:	20.00	15.00	8.00

1 Larry Jackson
2 Kurt Kepshire
3 Brad Lesley
4 Rick Myles
5 Mike Raines
6 Ron Robinson
7 Mark Rothey
8 Ray Corbett
9 Dave Miley
10 Emil Drzavich
11 Kevin Hinds
12 Dave Hoenstine
13 Dean Seats
14 Mike Sorel
15 Tom Wesley
16 Jeff Jones
17 Ken Scarpace
18 Scott Terry
19 Randy Davidson
20 Don Buchheister
21 Jeff Clay
22 Mark Bowden
23 Bob Buchanan
24 Scott Ender
25 Greg McKinney
26 Dave Hall

1981 TCMA Charleston Charlies

(Cleveland Indians, AAA) (color)

	MT	NR MT	EX
Complete Set:	14.00	10.50	5.50

1 Tom Brennan
2 Bobby Cuellar
3 Gordy Glaser
4 Ed Glynn
5 Mike Paxton
6 Eric Wilkins
7 Sandy Whitol
8 Chris Bando
9 Tim Norrid
10 Kenny Barton
11 Mike Bucci
12 Len Faedo
13 Mike Fischlin
14 Angelo Logrande
15 Von Hayes
16 Odie Davis
17 Jim Lentine
18 Karl Pagel
19 Rodney Craig
20 Vassie Gardner
21 Mel Queen
22 Nate Puryear
23 Rob Petroburgo
24 Cal Emery

1981 TCMA Charleston Royals

(Kansas City Royals, A) (black & white)

	MT	NR MT	EX
Complete Set:	12.50	9.50	5.00

1 Greg Jonson
2 Hector Arroyo
3 David Wong
4 Mike Olson
5 Hal Hatcher
6 Roger Hansen
7 Glenn Ray
8 Theo Shaw
9 Dave Albright
10 Bob Hegman
11 Fran Cutty
12 Doug Cook
13 Russell Stephans
14 Chuck McMichael
15 Ben Cadahia
16 Cliff Pastornicky
17 Jeff Gladden
18 Mark Huismann
19 Abner Johnson
20 Randy Meyer
21 Bill Best
22 Larry Grahek
23 Rick Rizzo
24 Tad Venger
25 Willie Neal
26 Rick Mathews

1981 Team Charlotte O's

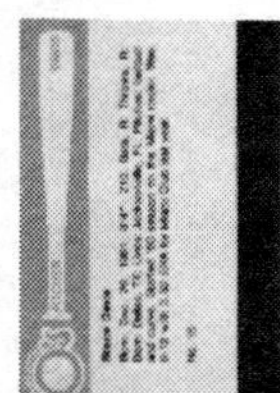

(Baltimore Orioles, AA)

	MT	NR MT	EX
Complete Set:	65.00	49.00	26.00

(1) Juan Arias
(2) Don Bowman
(3) Scott Budner
(4) Storm Davis
(5) John Denman
(6) Tim Derryberry
(7) Allen Edwards
(8) Will George
(9) Tim Graven
(10) Drungo Hazewood
(11) Ricky Jones
(12) Mark Naehring
(13) Earl Neal
(14) Paul O'Neill
(15) Victor Rodriguez
(16) Willie Royster
(17) John Shelby
(18) Mark Smith
(19) Cliff Speck
(20) Bill Swaggerty
(21) Don Welchel
(22) Cat Whitfield
(23) Mark Wiley
(24) "The Pepper Girls"
(25) Team Logo

1981 TCMA Chattanooga Lookouts

(Cleveland Indians, AA) (black & white)

	MT	NR MT	EX
Complete Set:	15.00	11.00	6.00

1 Robert Gariglio
2 John Burden
3 Robbie Alvarez
4 Luis DeLeon
5 Steve Narleski
6 Matt Bullinger
7 Jack Nuismer
8 Steve Roche
9 Everett Rey
10 Todd Heimer
11 Tim Glass
12 Jeff Moronko
13 John Bohnet
14 George Cecchetti
15 Ricky Baker
16 Carmelo Castillo
17 Sal Rende
18 Rick Burchers
19 Chuck Stobbs
20 Craig Adams
21 Larry White
22 Jeff Tomski
23 Kevin Rhomberg
24 Woody Smith
25 Bud Anderson

1981 TCMA Clinton Giants

(San Francisco Giants, A) (black & white)

	MT	NR MT	EX
Complete Set:	15.00	11.00	6.00

1 Joe Banach
2 Wendell Kim
3 Steve Cline
4 Dave Wilhelmi
5 Bruce Oliver
6 Ben Callo
7 Jose Chue
8 Art Gomez
9 Kevin Smay
10 Greg Bangert
11 Mark O'Connell
12 Matt Young
13 Dennis Schafer
14 Louis D'Amore
15 Gus Stokes
16 Kirk Ortega
17 John Taylor
18 Ken Frazier
19 James Johnson
20 Sean Toerner
21 Dave Wilson
22 Joe Henderson
23 Mike Lenti
24 Tom McLaughlin
25 Greg McSparron
26 Rolloa Adams
27 Lance Junker
28 Rich Figueroa
29 Mark Tudor

1981 TCMA Columbus Clippers

(New York Yankees, AAA) (color)

	MT	NR MT	EX
Complete Set:	20.00	15.00	8.00

1 Dick Stenholm
2 Tucker Ashford
3 Andre Robertson
4 Pat Callahan
5 Danny Schmitz
6 Jim Lewis
7 Paul Boris
8 Andy McGaffigan
9 Dave Righetti
10 Mike Griffin
11 Steve Balboni
12 Greg Cochran
13 Marshall Bryant
14 Brian Ryder
15 Juan Espino
16 Pat Tabler
17 Frank Verdi
18 Dave Coleman
19 Wayne Harer
20 Bill Showalter
21 Gary Smith
22 John Pacella
23 Dave Wehrmister (Wehrmeister)
24 Tom Filer
25 Mark Letenore
26 Sam Ellis
27 George H. Sisler
28 Jerry McNertney

1981 Police Columbus Clippers

(New York Yankees, AAA)

	MT	NR MT	EX
Complete Set:	12.00	9.00	4.75

(1) Tucker Ashford
(2) Steve Balboni
(3) Paul Boris
(4) Marshall Brant
(5) Pat Callahan
(6) Greg Cochran
(7) Dave Coleman
(8) Juan Espino
(9) Mike Griffin
(10) Wayne Harer
(11) Jim Lewis
(12) John Pacella
(13) Dave Righetti
(14) Andre Robertson
(15) Brian Ryder
(16) Dan Schmitz
(17) Buck Showalter
(18) George H. Sisler Jr.
(19) Garry Smith
(20) Rick Stenholm
(21) Pat Tabler
(22) Frank Verdi
(23) Dave Wehrmeister
(24) Coaches/Trainer Card (Jerry McNertney, Sammy Ellis, Mark Letendre)
(25) Sgt. Dick Hoover (Columbus Police Dept.)

1981 TCMA Durham Bulls

(Atlanta Braves, A) (black & white)

	MT	NR MT	EX
Complete Set:	15.00	11.00	6.00

1 Miguel Sosa
2 Mike Garcia
3 Kevin Rigby
4 Ken Scanlon
5 Tommy Thompson
6 Gary Cooper
7 Tom Hayes
8 Harold Williams
9 Keith Hagman
10 Brad Komminsk
11 Glen Bockhorn
12 Jeff Vuksan
13 Alvin Moore
14 Alan Gallagher
15 Rick Behenna
16 Rick Coatney
17 Jeff Dedmon
18 Glen Germer
19 Hoot Gibson
20 Danny Lucia
21 Roy North
22 Scott Patterson
23 Mike Payne
24 Gary Reiter

1981 Red Rooster Edmonton Trappers

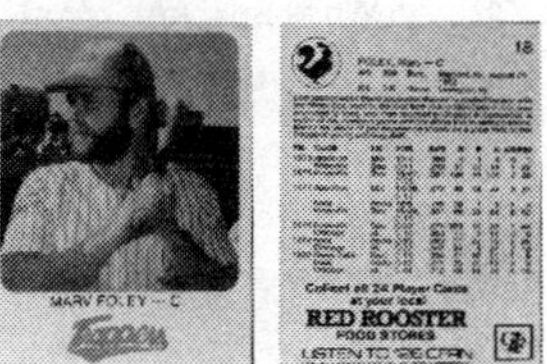

(Chicago White Sox, AAA)

	MT	NR MT	EX
Complete Set:	18.00	13.50	7.25

1 Gary Holle
2 John Poff
3 Dan Williams
4 Nardi Contreras
5 Juan Agosto
6 Guy Hoffman
7 Chris Nyman
8 Gord Lund
9 Vern Thomas
10 Rich Barnes
11 John Flannery
12 Bill Atkinson
13 Hector Eduardo
14 Leo Sutherland
15 Ray Murillo
16 Joe Gates
17 Julio Perez
18 Marv Foley
19 Mike Colbern
20 Fran Mullins
21 Rod Allen
22 Reggie Patterson
23 Jay Loviglio
24 Mark Teutsch

1981 TCMA El Paso Diablos

(Milwaukee Brewers, AA) (color)

	MT	NR MT	EX
Complete Set:	12.00	9.00	4.75

1 Ed Irvine
2 Willie Lozado
3 Al Manning
4 John Skorochocki
5 Terry Showbridge
6 Stan Davis
7 Jerry Lane
8 Doug Loman
9 Gerry Ako

10 Jim Koontz
11 Doug Jones
12 Larry Motgomery
13 Bill Schroeder
14 Mike Madden
15 Bob Skubbe (Skube)
16 Chick Valley
17 Rick Krantiz
18 Tony Torres
19 Weldon Swift
20 Tim Cook
21 Johnny Evans
22 Tom Candiotti
23 Tony Muser
24 Al Price

1981 TCMA Evansville Triplets

(Detroit Tigers, AAA) (color)

	MT	NR MT	EX
Complete Set:	8.00	6.00	3.25

1 Jim Leyland
2 George Cappuzzello
3 Mike Chris
4 Mark Fidrych
5 Larry Pashnick
6 Larry Rothschild
7 Manny Seoane
8 Jerry Ujdur
9 Pat Underwood
10 Roger Weaver
11 Marty Castillo
12 Larry Johnson
13 Mark DeJohn
14 Vern Followell
15 Glenn Gulliver
16 Craig Kusick
17 Juan Lopez
18 Tim Corcoran
19 Les Filkins
20 Eddie Gates
21 Ken Houston
22 Dennis Kinney

1981 TCMA Glens Falls White Sox

(Chicago White Sox, AA) (color)

	MT	NR MT	EX
Complete Set:	25.00	18.50	10.00

1 Luis Estrada
2 Randy Evans
3 Robert Fallon
4 Chuck Johnson
5 Mickey Maitland
6 Tom Mullen
7 Dennis Vasquez
8 Richard Wieters
9 Ricky Seilheimer
10 Andy Pasillas
11 Dom Fucci
12 Tim Hulett
13 Ivan Mesa
14 Peter Peltz
15 Ron Perry
16 Greg Walker
17 Vince Bienek
18 Randy Johnson
19 Ron Kittle
20 Luis Rois
21 Raymundo Torres
22 Jim Mahoney
23 Len Bradley
24 Larry Edwards

1981 TCMA Hawaii Islanders

(San Diego Padres, AAA) (color)

	MT	NR MT	EX
Complete Set:	7.00	5.25	2.75

1 Tim Flannery
2 Jose Moreno
3 Gary Ashby
4 Steve Smith
5 Doug Gwosdz
6 Tony Castillo
7 Jim Beswick
8 Alan Wiggins
9 Rick Lancellotti
10 Curtis Reed
11 Mike Armstrong
12 Steve Fireovid
13 Alan Olmsted
14 George Stablein
15 Tom Tellmann
16 Kim Seaman
17 Fred Kuhualua
18 Floyd Chiffer
19 Eric Show
20 Larry Duensing
21 Doug Rader
22 Chuck Hartenstein
23 Mario Ramirez

1981 TCMA Holyoke Millers

(California Angels, AA) (color)

	MT	NR MT	EX
Complete Set:	10.00	7.50	4.00

1 Ed Rodriguez
2 Jim Saul
3 Tom Kayser
4 T.J. Byrne
5 D. Comfort, D. Thomas)
6 John Yandle
7 Ricky Adams
8 Mike Brown
9 Chris Clark
10 Dennis Gilbert
11 Curt Brown
12 Jeff Connor
13 Lonnie Dugger
14 Dave Duran
15 Rick Foley
16 Pat Keedy
17 Darrell Miller
18 Mark Nocciolo
19 Les Pearsey
20 Gary Pettis
21 Gustavo Polidor
22 Brandt Humphry
23 Bill Mooneyham
24 Perry Morrison
25 Dennis Rasmussen
26 Rick Rommell

1981 Team Holyoke Millers

(California Angels, AA) This set features blank back cards, and was also produced in the form of an uncut poster.

	MT	NR MT	EX
Complete Set:	60.00	45.00	24.00

(1) Rick Adams
(2) Mike Brown
(3) T.J. Byrne
(4) Chris Clark
(5) Jeff Connor
(6) Lonnie Dugger
(7) Dave Duran
(8) Rick Foley
(9) Dennis Gilbert
(10) Brandt Humphry
(11) Tom Kayser
(12) Pat Keedy
(13) Darrell Miller
(14) Bill Mooneyham
(15) Jerry Morrison
(16) Mark Nocciolo
(17) Les Pearsey
(18) Gary Pettis
(19) Gustavo Polidor
(20) Dennis Rasmussen
(21) Ed Rodriguez
(22) Rich Rommel
(23) Jim Saul
(24) Dave Thomas
(25) John Yandle

1981 Team Indianapolis Indians

(Cincinnati Reds, AAA) (co-sponsored by Tom Aikens)

	MT	NR MT	EX
Complete Set:	15.00	11.00	6.00

1 Team Photo
2 Jim Beauchamp
3 Geoff Combe
4 Paul Householder
5 Charlie Leibrandt
6 Dave Van Gorder
7 Tom Foley
8 Kip Young
9 Eddie Milner
10 The Relievers
11 Jose Brito
12 Greg Mahlberg
13 Bill Bonham
14 The Teachers
15 Nick Esasky
16 Jeff Lahti
17 The Lightening Squad
18 Gene Menees
19 Scott Brown
20 The Outfielders
21 Duane Walker
22 Bill Kelly
23 The Infielders
24 Joe Kerrigan
25 German Barranca
26 The Starters
27 Paul Herring
28 Bill Dawley
29 Skeeter Barnes
30 The Catchers
31 Sergio Ferrer
32 John Young

1981 TCMA Lynn Sailors

(Seattle Mariners, AA) (color)

	MT	NR MT	EX
Complete Set:	18.00	13.50	7.25

1 Karl Best
2 Bud Black
3 Mark Cahill
4 Joe Georger
5 Tracy Harris
6 R.J. Harrison
7 Steve Krueger
8 Jed Murray
9 Dave Sheriff
10 Rob Simond
11 Dave Smith
12 Matt Young
13 Jim Nelson
14 Dave Valle
15 Edwin Aponte
16 Billy Crone
17 Mario Diaz
18 Paul Serna
19 Mike White
20 Al Chambers
21 Ramon Estepa
22 Rodney Hobbs
23 Tito Nanni
24 Bobby Floyd
25 Mickey Bowers
26 Bob Randolp, Lloyd D. Kern)
27 Jeff Stottlemyre
28 Clark Crist

1981 TCMA Miami Orioles

(Baltimore Orioles, A) (black and white) (complete set price includes scarce Willsher and Young cards)

	MT	NR MT	EX
Complete Set:	110.00	82.50	45.00

1 Ron Dillard
2 Al Pardo
3 Freddie Smith
4 Mark Brown
5 Don Murelli
6 Minnie Mendoza
7 John DeLeon
8 Pat Dumouchelle
9 Satch Sanders
10 Francisco Oliveras
11 Mike Alvarez
12 Skip Clark
13 Andy Timko
14 Frank Ferroni
15 Lonnie Ivie
16 Neal Herrick
17 Leon Hoke
18 Tim Maples
19 Jeff Williams
20 Bret Gold
21 Scott Johnson
22 Chris Willsher
23 Mike Young

1981 Chong Modesto A's

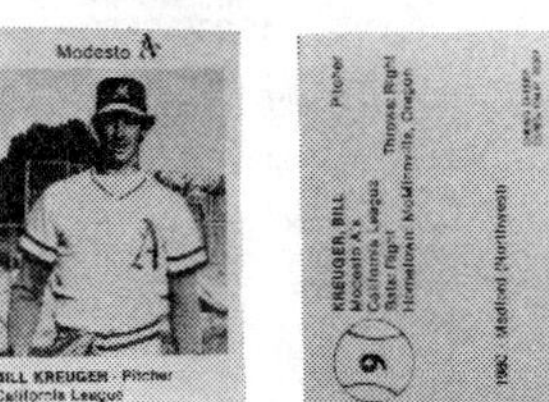

(Oakland A's, A)

	MT	NR MT	EX
Complete Set:	30.00	22.00	12.00

1 Rick Arnold
2 Ron Mantsch
3 Robert Moore
4 Ed Retzer
5 Don Van Marter
6 Robert Wood
7 Mark Ferguson
8 Ron Jensen
9 Bill Kreuger
10 Greg Mine
11 Mike Altobelli
12 Gordon Eakin
13 Terry Byrum
14 Paul Stockley
15 Monte Mc Abee
16 Selwyn Young
17 Kevin Jacobson
18 Joe Williams
19 Tom Colburn
20 Terry Harper
21 Jay Schellin
22 Dennis Stowe
23 Joe Soprano
24 Wayne Rudolph
25 Frank Harris
26 Keith Lieppman
27 Brad Fischer
28 Dwight Adams
29 Phil Danielson
30 Rod Murphy

1981 Arby's Nashville Sounds

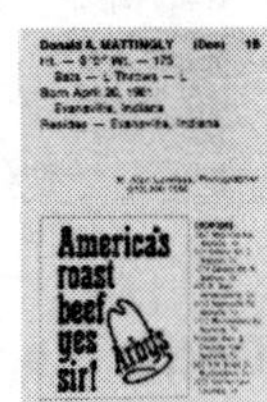

(New York Yankees, AA)

	MT	NR MT	EX
Complete Set:	25.00	18.50	10.00

(1) Manager, Trainer & Coaches
(2) Team Photo
(3) Rod Boxberger
(4) Pat Callahan
(5) Nate Chapman
(6) Brian Dayett
(7) Dan Hanggie
(8) Bob Jamison
(9) Curt Kaufman
(10) Dan Led Duke
(11) Don Mattingly
(12) Willie Mc Gee
(13) Mike Morgan
(14) Otis Nixon
(15) Erik Peterson
(16) Brian Poldberg
(17) Frank Ricci
(18) Wes Robbins
(19) Buck Showalter
(20) Roger Slagle
(21) Jeff Taylor
(22) Steve Taylor
(23) Rafael Villaman
(24) Jamie Werly
(25) Ted Wilborn

1981 TCMA Oklahoma City 89'ers

(Philadelphia Phillies, AAA) (color)

	MT	NR MT	EX
Complete Set:	175.00	131.25	70.00

1 Porfirio Altamirano
2 Carlos Arroyo
3 Eli Bonaparte
4 Warren Brusstar
5 Bob Dernier
6 Mark Davis
7 Dan Larsen
8 Orlando Isales
9 Don McCormack
10 Lenny Matuszek
11 Dennis Miscik
12 Manny McDonald
13 Scott Munninghoff
14 Dickie Noles
15 Jon Reelhorn
16 Luis Rodriguez
17 Ryne Sandberg
18 Bill Suter
19 Osvaldo (Ozzie) Virgil
20 George Vukovich
21 Bob Demeo
22 Ellis Deal
23 Jim Snyder
24 Jose Castro
25 Jim Rasmussen
26 Jeff Ulrich

1981 TCMA Omaha Royals

(Kansas City Royals, AAA) (color)

	MT	NR MT	EX
Complete Set:	10.00	7.50	4.00

1 Joe Sparks
2 Jerry Cram
3 Paul McGannon
4 Craig Chamberlain
5 Gary Christenson
6 Altee Hammaker
7 Dan Fischer
8 Don Hood
9 Mike Jones
10 Bill Laskey
11 Bill Paschall
12 Jeff Schattinger
13 Jim Gaudet
14 Greg Keatley
15 Manny Castillo
16 Onix Concepcion
17 Kelly Heath
18 Tim Ireland
19 Ron Johnson
20 Jim Buckner
21 Bob Detherage
22 Darryl Motley
23 Bombo Rivera
24 Pat Sheridan

1981 TCMA Pawtucket Red Sox

(Boston Red Sox, AAA) (color)

	MT	NR MT	EX
Complete Set:	125.00	95.00	50.00

1 Joel Finch
2 Mike Howard
3 Bruce Hurst
4 Keith MacWhorther
5 Bob Ojeda
6 Danny Parks
7 Win Remmerswaal
8 Luis Aponte
9 Jim Dorsey
10 Manny Sarmiento
11 Mike Smithson
12 Joe Morgan
13 Dale Robertson
14 Marty Barrett
15 Wade Boggs
16 Dave Koza
17 Julio Valdez
18 Sam Bowen
19 Lee Graham
20 Russ Laribee
21 Mike Ongarato
22 Chico Walker
23 Roger LaFrancois
24 Rich Gedman

1981 Valley Nat'l Bank Phoenix Giants

(San Francisco Giants, AAA) (3-3/8" x 2-1/4")

	MT	NR MT	EX
Complete Set:	9.00	6.75	3.50

1 Phoenix Booster Rooster/Checklist
2 Harry Jordan
3 Bob Tufts
4 Bob Brenly
5 Jeff Stember
6 Max Venable
7 Doug Shaefer
8 Mike Williams
9 Mark Clavert
10 Mike Rowland
11 Mike Rex
12 Jose Barrios
13 Al Hargesheimer
14 Dave Wiggins
15 Guy Sularz
16 Tommy Jones
17 Phil Hinrichs
18 Dennis Littlejohn
19 Wayne Pechek
20 Gene Pentz
21 Joe Pettini
22 Jeff Ransom
23 Tom Runnells
24 Rich Murray
25 Rocky Bridges
26 Tommy Gonzales
27 Ethan Blackaby

1981 TCMA Portland Beavers

(Pittsburgh Pirates, AAA) (color)

	MT	NR MT	EX
Complete Set:	14.00	10.50	5.50

1 Pete Ward
2 Tom Trebelhorn
3 Santo Alcala
4 Matt Alexander
5 Mike Anderson
6 Dave Augustine
7 Bob Beall
8 Doe Boyland
9 Craig Cacek
10 Cecilio Guante
11 Dave Hilton
12 Willie Horton
13 Odell Jones
14 Vance Law
15 Mark Lee
16 Robert Long
17 Dale Mohorgic
18 Bobby Mitchell
19 Junior Ortiz
20 Pascual Perez
21 Tommy Sandt
22 Jimmy Smith
23 Luis Tiant
24 Alfredo Torres
25 Rusty Torres
26 Eleno Cuen
27 Kent Biggerstaff

1981 TCMA Quad City Cubs

(Chicago Cubs, A) (black & white)

	MT	NR MT	EX
Complete Set:	12.00	9.00	4.75

1 Dave Pagel
2 Don Hyman
3 Greg Tarnow
4 Rusty Piggot
5 Fritz Connally
6 Mike Buckley
7 Shane Allen
8 Mickey Tenney
9 Dennis Webb
10 Kevin Schoendienst
11 Jim Walsh
12 Terry Austin
13 Tom Johnson
14 Gary Monroe
15 Henry Cotto
16 Dan Cataline
17 Mike King
18 Tom Smith
19 Stan Kyles
20 Joe Housey
21 John Miglio
22 Ken Pryce
23 Ray Soff
24 Mark Vaji
25 Glenn Swaggerty
26 Craig Weissman
27 Jim Gerlach
28 Mark Wilkins
29 Don Schultze
30 Rich Morales
31 Gene Oliver
32 Roger Crow
33 Mike Palmer

1981 TCMA Reading Phillies

(Philadelphia Phillies, AA) (black & white)

	MT	NR MT	EX
Complete Set:	125.00	95.00	50.00

1 Jerry Reed
2 Kelly Faulk
3 Tom Hart
4 Darren Burroughs
5 Dan Prior
6 Miguel Alicea
7 Leroy Smith
8 Don Carman
9 Carlos Cabassa
10 Wally Goff
11 Herb Orensky
12 Miguel Ibarra
13 Jim Wright
14 Russ Hamric
15 Ron Smith
16 Tom Lombarski
17 Julio Franco
18 Ray Borucki
19 Keith Washington
20 Joe Bruno
21 Wil Culmer
22 Al Sanchez
23 Ron Clark
24 George Culver

1981 TCMA Redwood Pioneers

(California Angels, A) (black & white)

	MT	NR MT	EX
Complete Set:	13.00	9.75	5.25

1 Robert Bastian
2 Brian Buckley
3 Tom Crisler
4 Jay Kibbe
5 Ron Romanick
6 Jeff Smith
7 Ron Sylvia
8 Mike Venezia
9 Doug Rau
10 Aldo Bagiotti
11 Duffy Ryan
12 Wade Schexnayder
13 Harry Francis
14 Matt Gundelfinger
15 Ron Hunt
16 Marion Hunter
17 Tim Krauss
18 Mark Sproesser
19 Leo Lemon
20 Ken Tillman
21 Luis Zambrana
22 Warren Spahn
23 Tom Leonard
24 Kathy Leonard
25 David Levinson
26 Ralph Hartman
27 Chris Bankowski
28 Chris Cannizzaro
29 Barton Braun
30 Steve Levinson

1981 TCMA Richmond Braves

(Atlanta Braves, AAA) (color)

	MT	NR MT	EX
Complete Set:	35.00	26.00	14.00

1 John Sain
2 Tony Brizzolara
3 Jerry Keller
4 Ken Smith
5 Cragi Landis
6 Larry Whisenton
7 Bob Porter
8 Brett Butler
9 Chico Ruiz
10 Paul Runge
11 Butch Edge
12 Steve Bedrosian
13 Carlos Diaz
14 Larry McWilliams
15 Jose Alvarez
16 Steve Hammond
17 Steve Curry
18 Dan O'Brien
19 Ken Dayley
20 Matt Sinatro
21 Eddie Haas
22 Randy Johnson
23 Craig Robinson
24 Harry Saferight
25 Sam Ayoub

1981 TCMA Rochester Red Wings

(Baltimore Orioles, AAA) (color)

	MT	NR MT	EX
Complete Set:	225.00	165.00	85.00

1 Mike Boddicker
2 Bill Bonner
3 Brooks Carey
4 Tom Chism
5 Tom Eaton
6 Johnny Hale
7 Mike Hart
8 Drungo Hazewood
9 Dave Huppert
10 Kevin Kennedy
11 Dan Logan
12 Steve Luebber
13 Ed Putnam
14 Floyd Rayford
15 Cal Ripken, Jr.
16 Tom Rowe
17 John Valle
18 Don Welchel
19 Larry Jones
20 Richie Bancells
21 Chris Bourjos
22 Doc Edwards
23 Dallas Williams

1981 WTF Co. Rochester Red Wings

(Baltimore Orioles, AAA)

	MT	NR MT	EX
Complete Set:	280.00	210.00	110.00

1 Calvin Ripken Jr.
2 Dallas Williams
3 Chris Bourjos
4 Mark Corey
5 Doc Edwards
6 Thomas Rowe
7 Jeffrey Schneider
8 James Umbarger
9 Don Welchel
10 Larry Jones
11 Dan Logan
12 Steve Luebber
13 Eddy Putman
14 Floyd Rayford
15 David Huppert
16 Drungo Hazewood
17 James Hart
18 John Hale
19 Tom Eaton
20 Checklist
21 Bob Bonner
22 Brooks Carey
23 Mike Boddicker
24 Thomas Chism
25 Silver Stadium

1981 TCMA Salt Lake City Gulls

(California Angels, AAA) (color)

	MT	NR MT	EX
Complete Set:	11.00	8.25	4.50

1 Leonard Garcia
2 Ralph Botting
3 Steve Brown
4 Craig Eaton
5 Bob Ferris
6 Dave Frost
7 Christian Knapp
8 Mike Mahler
9 Alfredo Martinez
10 Carlos Perez
11 Dave Schuler
12 Ricky Steirer
13 Mike Walters
14 Mike Bishop
15 Brian Harper
16 Jeff Bertoni
17 Scott Carnes
18 Fernando Gonzalez
19 Steve Lubratich
20 Daryl Sconier
21 Tom Brunansky
22 Pepe Mangual
23 Scott Moffitt
24 Don Pisker
25 Moose Stubing
26 Bob Davis

1981 TCMA Shreveport Captains

(Pittsburgh Pirates, AA) (black & white)

	MT	NR MT	EX
Complete Set:	12.50	9.50	5.00

1 Jack Mull
2 John Rabb
3 Jim Dunn
4 Tom O'Malley
5 Jim Wojcik
6 Glenn Fisher
7 Alan Fowlkes

8 Mike Tucker
9 Dan Gladden
10 Brad Bauman
11 Mark Dempsey
12 Paul Szymarek
13 Jim Duffalo
14 Doug Landuyt
15 Doran Perdue
16 Greg Baker
17 Ron Quick
18 Doug Wabeke
19 Jim Rothford
20 Scott Garrelts
21 Mark Lohuis
22 Greg Moyer
23 Pat Alexander

1981 TCMA Spokane Indians

(Seattle Mariners, AAA) (color)

	MT	NR MT	EX
Complete Set:	7.00	5.25	2.75

1 Chris Flammang
2 Manny Estrada
3 Scott Stranski
4 Sam Welborn
5 Orlando Mercado
6 Roy Clark
7 Mike Hart
8 Greg Biercevicz
9 Bob Galasso
10 Brian Allard
11 Steve Finch
12 Doug Merrifield
13 Rene Lachemann
14 Reggie Walton
15 Ed Vande Berg
16 Ted Cox
17 Ron Musselman
18 Bob Stoddard
19 Joe Coleman
20 Vance McHenry
21 Ken Pape
22 Jim Mahler
23 Larry Patterson
24 Randy Stein
25 Allen Wirth
26 Casey Parsons
27 Kim Allen
28 Rich Anderson
29 Jim Beattie
30 Brad Gulden
31 Jamie Allen
32 Marty Martinez

1981 TCMA Syracuse Chiefs

(Toronto Blue Jays, AAA) (color)

	MT	NR MT	EX
Complete Set:	7.50	5.50	3.00

1 Steve Baker
2 Tom Brown
3 Chuck Fore
4 Steve Grilli
5 Phil Huffman
6 Jack Kucek
7 Dale Murray
8 Kevin Pasley
9 Gene Petralli
10 Ramon Lora
11 Dave Baker
12 Charlie Beamon
13 Keith Chapman
14 Mike Davis
15 Pedro Hernandez
16 Greg Wells
17 Joe Cannon
18 Gil Kubski
19 Creighton Tevlin
20 Marv Thomson
21 Ken Schrom
22 Dave Tomlin
23 Bob Humphreys
24 Tony DeRosa

1981 Team Syracuse Chiefs

(Toronto Blue Jays, AAA) All cards are postcard size with blank backs.

	MT	NR MT	EX
Complete Set:	35.00	26.00	14.00

2 Pedro Hernandez
3 Kelvin Chapman
5 Steve Baker
6 Domingo Ramos
8 Dan Whitmer
9 Gere Petralli
10 Charlie Beamon
12 Steve Davis

14 Paul Mirabella
15 Ramon Lora
16 Dave Tomlin
17 Creighton Tevlin
19 Tom Brown
20 Jack Kucek
22 Marv Thompson
23 J.J. Cannon
24 Phil Huffman
25 Bob Humphreys
26 Jim Wright
27 Dale Murray
28 Steve Baker
29 Ken Schrom
31 Chuck Fore
32 "Boomer" Wells

1981 TCMA Tacoma Tigers

(Oakland A's, AAA) (color)

	MT	NR MT	EX
Complete Set:	7.00	5.25	2.75

1 Larry Davis
2 Rick Randahl
3 Art Popham
4 Eric Mustad
5 Bob Kearney
6 Ed Nottle
7 Pat Dempsey
8 Dave Hamilton
9 Derek Bryant
10 Rich Bordi
11 Mike Davis
12 Jim Nettles
13 Mark Budaska
14 Don Fowler
15 Jim Sexton
16 Paul Mize
17 Keith Drumright
18 Kelvin Moore
19 Jeff Cox
20 Roy Thomas
21 Fred Holdsworth
22 Mark Souza
23 Rick Lysander
24 Dave Beard
25 Kevin Bell
26 Dave Heaverlo
27 Bob Grandas
28 Tigers Mascot
29 Batboys
30 Stan Naccarato
31 Jim Perry
32 Ed Figueroa

1981 TCMA Tidewater Tides

(New York Mets, AAA) (color)

	MT	NR MT	EX
Complete Set:	10.00	7.50	4.00

1 Ricky Sweet
2 Bruce Bochy
3 Ronald McDonald
4 Brian Giles
5 Ron Gardenhire
6 Phil Mankowski
7 Todd Winterfeldt
8 Wally Backman
9 Gary Rajsich
10 Sergio Beltre
11 Gil Flores
12 Mike Howard
13 Charlie Puleo
14 Tom Dixon
15 Scott Dye
16 Ed Lynch
17 Brent Gaff
18 Dave Von Ohlen
19 Mike Mendoza
20 Jesse Orosco
21 Jack Aker
22 Sam Perlozzo
23 Greg Harris
24 Ray Searage
25 Mark Daly
26 Rick Anderson
27 Danny Boitano
28 Dan Norman
29 Terry Leach

1981 TCMA Toledo Mud Hens

(Minnesota Twins, AAA) (color)

	MT	NR MT	EX
Complete Set:	7.50	5.50	3.00

1 Cal Ermer
2 Buck Chamberlin
3 Jose Bastian
4 Terry Felton
5 Gerry Hannahs
6 Mike Kinnunen

7 Buce MacPherson
8 Wally Sarmiento
9 Bob Veselic
10 Ric Williams
11 Aurelio Cadahia
12 Steve Herz
13 Dave Machemer
14 Kurt Seibert
15 Kelly Snider
16 Jesus Vega
17 John Walker
18 Ron Washington
19 Keathel Chauncey
20 Ed Cipot
21 Frank Estes
22 Steve Stroughter

1981 TCMA Tucson Toros

(Houston Astros, AAA) (color)

	MT	NR MT	EX
Complete Set:	15.00	11.00	6.00

1 Greg Cyprt
2 Dell Leayherwood
3 Joe Pittman
4 Alan Knicely
5 Bob Cluck
6 Tom Vessey
7 Bert Pena
8 Simon Rosario
9 Mark Miggins
10 Johnny Ray
11 Scott Loucks
12 Jimmy Johnson
13 Tom Spencer
14 Dave Labossiere
15 Stan Leland
16 Ron Meredith
17 Jim Pankovits
18 Gordon Pladson
19 Pete Ladd
20 Tim Tolman
21 Bert Roberge
22 George Gross
23 Jim MacDonald
24 Billy Smith
25 Jack Donovan
26 Tom Wiedenbauer

1981 TCMA Tulsa Drillers

(Texas Rangers, AA) (color)

	MT	NR MT	EX
Complete Set:	15.00	11.00	6.00

1 George Wright
2 Tracy Cowger
3 Phil Klimas
4 Marty Scott
5 Dave Stockstill
6 Mel Barrow
7 Larry Reynolds
8 Ted Davis
9 Steve Nielsen
10 Ron Carney
11 Joe Nemeth
12 Walt Terrell
13 Don Scott
14 Dennis Long
15 Dave Crutcher
16a Tony Fossas
16b Pete O'Brien
17 Mike Roberts
18 Ron Darling
19 Jack Lazorko
20 Tom Burgess
21 Tony Hudson
22 Kevin Richards
23 Greg Hughes
24 Brooks Wallace
25 Lindy Duncan
26 Bobby Ball
27 Joe Russell
28 Ron Gooch
29 Mike Jirschele

1981 TCMA Vancouver Canadians

(Milwaukee Brewers, AAA) (color)

	MT	NR MT	EX
Complete Set:	7.00	5.25	2.75

1 Jamie Cocanower
2 Chuck Porter
3 Doug Wanz
4 Dwight Bernard
5 Mark Schuster
6 Frank Thomas
7 Brian Thorson
8 Ivan Rodriguez
9 Gil Kubski
10 Baylor Moore
11 Gus Quiros

12 Larry Rush
13 Rich Olsen
14 Terry Lee
15 Willie Mueller
16 Andy Replogle
17 Frank DiPino
18 Rene Quinones
19 Bobby Smith
20 Lee Stigman
21 John Flinn
22 Gerry Ako
23 Tom Soto
24 Kevin Bass
25 Steve Lake

1981 TCMA Vero Beach Dodgers

(Los Angeles Dodgers, A) (black & white)

	MT	NR MT	EX
Complete Set:	15.00	11.00	6.00

1 Ed Amelung
2 Paul Bard
3 Frank Bryant
4 John Debus
5 Dan Forer
6 Art Hammond
7 Bobby Kenyon
8 Tony Lachowetz
9 Dave Lanning
10 Skip Mann
11 Holly Martin
12 Mike O'Malley
13 Felix Oroz
14 Steve Perry
15 Pat Raimondo
16 Curtis Reade
17 R.J. Reynolds
18 Greg Smith
19 Bill Sobbe
20 Terry Sutcliffe
21 Ricky Thomas
22 Brad Thorp
23 Juan Villaescusa
24 Brett Wise
25 David Wallace
26 John Shoemaker
27 Stan Wasiak

1981 TCMA Waterbury Reds

(Cincinnati Reds, AA) (black & white)

	MT	NR MT	EX
Complete Set:	20.00	15.00	8.00

1 Rich Carlucci
2 Keefe Cato
3 Mike Dowless
4 Ken Jones
5 Doug Neuenschwander
6 Rick O'Keefe
7 Bill Scherrer
8 Lester Straker
9 Mike Sullivan
10 Randy Town
11 Anthony Walker
12 Steve Christmas
13 Adolfo Feliz
14 Tom Lawless
15 Gary Redus
16 Hector Rincones
17 Eski Viltz
18 Russ Aldrich
19 Mark Gilbert
20 Dave Bisceglia
21 Tony Walker
22 George Scherger
23 Lee Garrett

1981 TCMA Waterloo Indians

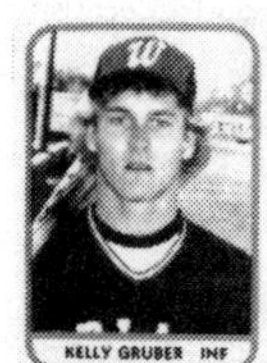

(Cleveland Indians, A) (black & white)

	MT	NR MT	EX
Complete Set:	35.00	26.00	14.00

1 Gomer Hodge
2 Rick Colzie
3 Dennis Brogna
4 Larry Hrynko
5 John Asbell
6 Mark Bajus
7 Tom Burns
8 Mike Dixon
9 John Hoban
10 Mike Jeffcoat
11 Ricky Lintz
12 Tom Owens
13 Greg Pope
14 Ramon Romero
15 Mike Schwarber
16 Rich Thompson
17 Not Issued
18 Jack Fimple
19 John Malkin
20 Arnold Cochran
21 Shanie Dugas
22 Kelly Gruber
23 Marlin Methven
24 Juan Pacho
25 Larry Dotson
26 Dave Gallagher
27 Ed Saavedra
28 Mike Taylor
29 Winston Ficklin
30 Adalberto Nieves
31 Bernardo Brito
32 Steve Cushing
33 Ralph Elpin
34 Bob Feller
---- Louis Duarte

1981 TCMA Wausau Timbers

(Seattle Mariners, A) (black & white)

	MT	NR MT	EX
Complete Set:	30.00	22.00	12.00

1 Kevin Steger
2 Jeff Stottlemyre
3 Bob Hudson
4 Edwin Nunez
5 Tom Brennan
6 Mark Pedersen
7 Brian Snyder
8 Mark Batten
9 Chris Hunger
10 Don McKenzie
11 David Blume
12 Eddie Yampierre
13 Jesse Baez
14 Rick Adair
15 Jeff Cary
16 Enrique Diaz
17 Donnell Nixon
18 Harold Reynolds
19 Darnell Coles
20 Jimmy Presley
21 Clark Crist
22 Omar Minaya
23 Mark Chelette
24 Glenn Walker
25 John Moses
26 Ivan Calderon
27 Kevin King
28 Tom Hunt
29 Bill Plummer

1981 TCMA West Haven A's

(Oakland A's, AA) (color)

	MT	NR MT	EX
Complete Set:	9.00	6.75	3.50

1 Robert Didier
2 Keith Atherton
3 Bert Bradley
4 DeWayne Buice
5 Darryl Cias
6 Keith Comstock
7 Tim Conroy
8 Jim Durrman
9 Bobby Garrett
10 Bruce Fournier
11 Lynn Garrett
12 Steve Gelfarb
13 Rick Holloway
14 Tony Phillips
15 Ricky Tronerud
16 Don Morris
17 Mike Woodard
18 Alan Abraham
19 Dennis Sherow
20 Gorman Heimueller
21 Scott Meyer
22 Dick Lynch
23 Scott Pyle

Regional interest may affect the value of a card.

1981 TCMA Wisconsin Rapids Twins

(Minnesota Twins, A) (black & white)

	MT	NR MT	EX
Complete Set:	30.00	22.00	12.00

1 Ken Staples
2 Tom Leix
3 Smokey Everett
4 Tony Guerrero
5 Larry Harris
6 Kirby Krueger
7 Jeorge Ortiz
8 Adriano Pena
9 Luis Suarez
10 Mike Ungs
11 Mark Wright
12 Richard Yett
13 Ken Chandler
14 Jeff Reed
15 Michael Cole
16 Ken Foster
17 Jim Payne
18 Bill Price
19 Mandy Smith
20 Talbot Aiello
21 Jim Eisenreich
22 John Palica
23 Nelson Suarez

1982 TCMA Albuquerque Dukes

(Los Angeles Dodgers, AAA) (color)

	MT	NR MT	EX
Complete Set:	45.00	34.00	18.00

1 Joe Beckwith
2 John Franco
3 Burt Geiger
4 Orel Hershiser
5 Brian Holton
6 Dave Moore
7 Tom Niedenfuer
8 Steve Shirley
9 Rick Rodas
10 Larry White
11 Rick Wright
12 Don Crow
13 Dave Sax
14 Dave Anderson
15 Greg Brock
16 Larry Fobbs
17 Ross Jones
18 Alex Taveras
19 Mark Bradley
20 Dave Holman
21 Candy Maldonado
22 Mike Marshall
23 Tack Wilson
24 Del Crandall
25 Dave Cohea
26 Dick McLaughlin
27 Brent Strom

1982 TCMA Alexandria Dukes

(Pittsburgh Pirates, A) (black & white)

	MT	NR MT	EX
Complete Set:	17.50	12.00	6.50

1 Johnny Taylor
2 Lee Marcheskie
3 Larry Lamonde
4 Ray Krawczyk
5 Jeffrey Horne
6 Christopher Green
7 Fernando Gonzales
8 Lance Dodd
9 Wilfrido Cordoba
10 Mike Quade
11 Brad Garnett
12 Marvin Clack
13 Nick Castaneda
14 Pete Rowe
15 Burk Goldthorn
16 James Churchill
17 Jeffrey Zaske
18 Timothy Wheeler
19 Brian McCann
20 Dan Warthen
21 John Lipon
22 Joe Orsulak
23 Ken Ford
24 Jim Felt
25 Nelson de la Rosa
26 Andy Smith
27 Rick Renteria

1982 TCMA Amarillo Gold Sox

(San Diego Padres, AA) (black & white)

	MT	NR MT	EX
Complete Set:	16.00	12.00	6.50

1 George Hinshaw
2 Brian Greer
3 John Stevenson
4 Joe Scherger
5 Gerry Davis
6 Bob Macias
7 Jeff Ronk
8 Don Purpura
9 Mike Martin
10 Mark Parent
11 James Steels
12 Jim Coffman
13 John White
14 Tom Biko
15 Neil Bryant
16 Mike Couchee
17 Steve Stone
18 Bill Long
19 Willie Hardwick
20 Marty Kain
21 Randy Kaczmarski
22 Rick Shaw
23 Glen Ezell
24 Mike Hebrard
25 Tom House

1982 Fritsch Appleton Foxes

(Chicago White Sox, A)

	MT	NR MT	EX
Complete Set:	12.00	9.00	4.75

1 Team Logo/Checklist
2 Jeff Overton
3 Leo Garcia
4 Jim Sutton
5 Wade L. Rowdon
6 Ramon Rosario
7a Al Jones (leg showing) (sample card)
7b Al Jones (no leg showing) (regular issue)
8 John Taylor
9 Scott Meier
10 Jess Anderson
11 Steve Pastrovich
12 Curt Reed
13 Wes Kent
14 John Skinner
15 Dave Nix
16 Joseph J. Paglino
17 Don Koch
18 Wayne Schuckert
19 Bill Babcock
20 Eddie Miles
21a Kevin Flannery (elbow showing) (sample card)
21b Kevin Flannery (elbow not showing) (regular issue)
22 Scott Gibson
23 Art Niemann
24 Daryl Boston
25 Michael J. Tanzi
26 Michael J. Buggs
27 Pat Adams
28 Al Heath
29 Doug Wiesner
30 Mike Pazik
31 Adrian Garrett

1982 TCMA Arkansas Travelers

(St. Louis Cardinals, AA) (black & white)

	MT	NR MT	EX
Complete Set:	100.00	75.00	40.00

1 Scott Arigoni
2 Kevin Hagen
3 Rickey Horton
4 Jeff Keener
5 Rafael Pimentel
6 Gerry Perry
7 Mark Riggins
8 Ed Sanford
9 Buddy Schultz
10 Tom Thurberg
11 Mark Salas
12 Tom Nieto
13 Jose Gonzales
14 Greg Guin
15 Peachy Guiterrez
16 Luis Ojeda
17 Don Moore
18 Jim Adduci
19 Andy Van Slyke
20 Jack Ayer
21 Larry Reynolds
22 Gaylen Pitts
23 Dave England
24 Jorge Aranzamendi

1982 TCMA Auburn Astros

(Houston Astros, A) (black & white)

	MT	NR MT	EX
Complete Set:	8.00	6.00	3.25

1 Tom Roarke
2 Bob Hartsfield
3 Jeff Jacobson
4 Mike Stellern
5 Ray Perkins
6 Eric Anderson
7 Jeff Meadows
8 Mike Hogan
9 Larry McIver
10 Bob Hinson
11 Jeff Datz
12 Tracy Dophied
13 Rich Bombard
14 Craig Kizer
15 Tom Riewerts
16 Steve Swain
17 Ricardo Rivera
18 Carlos Alfonso
19 Rick Thompson

1982 Fritsch Beloit Brewers

(Milwaukee Brewers, A)

	MT	NR MT	EX
Complete Set:	12.00	9.00	4.75

1 Team Logo/Checklist
2a Joe Henderson (catching) (sample card)
2b Joe Henderson (batting) (regular issue)
3 Gerry Miller
4 Bill Wegman
5 Johnson C. Wood
6 Ty Van Burkleo
7 John Hoban
8 John Gibbons
9 Fritz Fedor
10 Marcos Gomez
11 Dewey James
12 Mike Myerchin
13 Collin Tanabe
14 Kenny Clayton
15 Butch Kirby
16 Joe Edwin Morales
17 Gary Evans
18 Danny Gilmartin
19 Mike Samuel
20 Bryan Clutterbuck
21 Bill Max
22 Brad DeKraai
23 Martin Antunez
24 Terry Bevington
25 Bill Nowlan
26 Angel Morris Jr.
27a Ted Pallas (glove above head) (sample card)
27b Ted Pallas (glove at waist) (regular issue)

1982 TCMA Birmingham Barons

(Detroit Tigers, AA) (color)

	MT	NR MT	EX
Complete Set:	8.00	6.00	3.25

1 Stan Younger
2 Barbaro Garbey
3 Darrell Woodard
4 Homer Moncrief
5 Dave Gumpert
6 Mike Beecroft
7 Bob Melvin
8 Randy O'Neal
9 Chuck Cary
10 Kenny Baker
11 Bruce Fields
12 Randy Harvey

13 Rondal Rollins
14 Gary Hinson
15 John Flannery
16 Dave Hawarney
17 Kevin Pasley
18 Jerry Bass
19 Frank McCann
20 Steve Quealey
21 Charlie Nail
22 Emilio Carrasquel
23 Paul Gibson
24 Ed Brinkman

1982 TCMA Buffalo Bisons

(Pittsburgh Pirates, AA) (color)

	MT	NR MT	EX
Complete Set:	11.00	8.25	4.50

1 Rich Leggat
2 Bob Misak
3 Connor McGeehee
4 Drew McCauley
5 Greg Pastors
6 John Schaive
7 Al Torres
8 Keith Thibodeaux
9 Tim Wheeler
10 Kevin Houston
11 Ron Wotus
12 John Holland
13 Steve Farr
14 Eleno Cuen
15 Tim Burke
16 Mike Bielecki
17 Rick Peterson
18 Tom Sandt

1982 TCMA Burlington Rangers

(Texas Rangers, A) (black and white) (complete set price includes scarce Avery card)

	MT	NR MT	EX
Complete Set:	40.00	30.00	16.00

1 Timothy Henry
2 Rodney Hodde
3 Anthony Hudson
4 James Jeffries
5 Keith Jones
6 Timothy Maki
7 Larry McLane
8 Michael Schmid
9 Gary Sharp
10 Gregory Tabor
11 Antonio Triplett
12 Raymond Warren
13 Curtis Wilkerson
14 Frank Brosiuos
15 Kevin Buckley
16 Chuckie Canady
17 Glen Cook
18 Douglas Davis
19 Mark Gammage
20 Jorge Gomez
21 Otto Gonzalez
22 Whitney Harry
23 Albert Hartman
24 Dwayne Henry
25 Martin Scott
26 Steven Nielsen
27 Larry Avery

1982 Fritsch Burlington Rangers

(Texas Rangers, A)

	MT	NR MT	EX
Complete Set:	10.00	7.50	4.00

1 Team Logo/Checklist
2 Lawrence Avery
3 Kevin Buckley
4 Dwayne Henry
5 Al Hartman
6 Tony Triplett
7 Ray Warren
8 Frank Brosious
9 Garry Venner
10 Keith Jones
11 Rod Hodde
12 Jorge Gomez
13 Curtis Wilkerson
14 Tim Henry
15 Greg Tabor
16 Chuckie Canady
17 Mark Gammage
18 Mike Schmid
19 Gary Sharp
20 Larry McLane
21 Tony Hudson
22 Doug Davis
23 Glen Cook
24 Whitney Harry
25 Jim Jeffries
26 Greg Campbell
27 Otto Gonzalez
28 Marty Scott
29 Tim Maki
30 Steve Nielsen

1982 TCMA Cedar Rapids Reds

(Cincinnati Reds, A) (color)

	MT	NR MT	EX
Complete Set:	60.00	45.00	24.00

1 Mark Rothey
2 Rob Murphy
3 Curt Heidenreich
4 Steve Lowrey
5 Kurt Kepshire
6 Mike Riley
7 Freddie Toliver
8 Mike Ferguson
9 Mike Hennessy
10 Jim Pettibone
11 Larry Freeburg
12 Danny Lamar
13 Mark Matzen
14 Paul Kirsch
15 Adolfo Feliz
16 Tony Burley
17 Byron Peyton
18 Bill Metil
19 Dave Hall
20 Eric Davis
21 Paul O'Neill
22 Tim Stout
23 Scott Terry
24 Jeff Jones
25 Randy Davidson
26 David Clay
27 Don Buchheister

1982 TCMA Charleston Charlies

(Cleveland Indians, AAA) (color)

	MT	NR MT	EX
Complete Set:	7.00	5.25	2.75

1 Bud Anderson
2 John Bohnet
3 Gordy Glaser
4 Ed Glynn
5 Neal Heaton
6 Larry Hrynko
7 Silvio Martinez
8 Jack Nuismer
9 Rob Pietroburgo
10 Ray Searage
11 Bill Nahorodny
12 Tim Norrid
13 Craig Stimac
14 Luis DeLeon
15 Angelo LoGrande
16 Rich Murray
17 Kevin Rhomberg
18 Dave Rosello
19 Carmelo Castillo
20 Larry Littleton
21 Karl Pagel
22 Dave Riviera
23 Doc Edwards
24 Chuck Estrada

1982 TCMA Charleston Royals

(Kansas City Royals, A) (black and white) (Cone and Psaltis cards have transposed backs)

	MT	NR MT	EX
Complete Set:	65.00	49.00	26.00

1 Jim Miner
2 Roger Hausen
3 Mike Sorrel
4 Tom McHugh
5 John Bryant
6 Danny Jackson
7 Mitch Ashmore
8 Perry Swanson
9 Bert Johnson
10 Chris Bryeans
11 Bob Umdenstock
12 Mike Kingery
13 Tim Ballard
14 Dick Vitato
15 Ron Krauss
16 Ken Patterson
17 Roland Oruna
18 Den Swank
19 Spiro Psaltis (Dave Cone name & bio on card)
20 Dave Cone (Spiro Psaltis name & bio on card)
21 Cliff Pastornicky
22 Willie Neal
23 Mark Farnsworth
24 Roy Tanner

1982 Team Charlotte O's Heroes Aren't Hard

(Baltimore Orioles, AA) (orange & blue border)

	MT	NR MT	EX
Complete Set:	45.00	34.00	18.00

(1) The Heroes
(2) Jesus Alfaro
(3) Juan Arias
(4) Tony Arnold
(5) Chris Bourjos
(6) Don Bowman
(7) Randy Boyd
(8) Mark Brown
(9) Carlos Cabassa
(10) Mark Corey
(11) Dan Craven
(12) John Denman
(13) H. Shelton Drum
(14) Drungo Hazewood
(15) Leo Hernandez
(16) Eddie Hook
(17) Dave Huppert
(18) Bruce Mac Pherson
(19) Minnie Mendoza
(20) Mark Naehring
(21) Phil Nastu
(22) Paul O'Neill
(23) Francisco Oliveras
(24) Russ Pensiero
(25) Julio Perez
(26) Tom Rowe
(27) Jeff Schaeffer
(28) Mark Smith
(29) John Stefero
(30) Matt Tyner
(31) Mark Wiley

1982 TCMA Chattanooga Lookouts

(Cleveland Indians, AA) (black & white)

	MT	NR MT	EX
Complete Set:	22.00	16.50	8.75

1 Nate Puryear
2 Scott Munninghoff
3 Everett Rey
4 Ed Saavedra
5 Richard Thompson
6 Tim Glass
7 Ricky Baker
8 Dane Anthony
9 Tom Owens
10 Mike Schwarber
11 Sal Rende
12 Marlin Methvin
13 Shanie Dugas
14 George Cecchetti
15 Steve Roche
16 Kelly Gruber
17 Dave Gallagher
18 Robin Fuson
19 Steve Narleski
20 Rick Borchers
21 Jeff Moronko
22 Craig Adams
23 Al Gallagher
24 Chuck Stobbs
25 Hank Gaughan

1982 Fritsch Clinton Giants

(San Francisco Giants, A)

	MT	NR MT	EX
Complete Set:	15.00	11.00	6.00

1 Team Logo/Checklist
2 Wendell Kim
3 Steve Cline
4 Matt Nokes
5 Phil Ouellette
6 Glenn Barling
7 Michael Jones
8 Todd Zacher
9 David Nenad
10 Everett Graham
11 Steve Wilcox
12 Randy Saunier
13 Ramon Bautista
14 Mike Dunn
15 Marty Baier
16 Kernan Ronan
17 Gene Lambert
18 Allen Smoot
19 Larry Crews
20 Brian Murtha
21 Glenn Jones
22 Eric Erickson
23 Mark Grant
24 Randy Ebersberger
25 Bob O'Connor
26 Mark Tudor
27 Gus Stokes
28 John Marks
29 Jim Weir
30 Mickey Swenson
31 Mark Swenson
32 Mark Swenson, Mickey Swenson

1982 TCMA Columbus Clippers

(New York Yankees, AAA) (color)

	MT	NR MT	EX
Complete Set:	200.00	150.00	80.00

1 John Pacella
2 Tucker Ashford
3 Wayne Harer
4 Steve Balboni
5 Curt Kaufman
6 Marshall Brant
7 Mike Bruhert
8 Greg Cochran
9 Pete Filson
10 Jamie Werley
11 Dave Wehrmeister
12 Bob Sykes
13 David Stegman
14 Garry Smith
15 Dick Scott
16 Dan Schmitz
17 Andre Robertson
18 Bobby Ramos
19 Scott Patterson
20 Mike Patterson
21 Don Mattingly
22 Jim Lewis
23 Juan Espino
24 Steve Donohue, Sammy Ellis, Jerry McNertney
25 Frank Verdi
26 George H. Sisler, Jr.

1982 Police Columbus Clippers

(New York Yankees, AAA)

	MT	NR MT	EX
Complete Set:	50.00	37.50	20.00

(1) Tucker Ashford
(2) Steve Balboni
(3) Marshall Brant
(4) Mike Bruhert
(5) Greg Cochran
(6) Juan Espino
(7) Pete Filson
(8) Wayne Harper
(9) Curt Kaufman
(10) Jim Lewis
(11) Don Mattingly
(12) John Pacella
(13) Mike Patterson
(14) Scott Patterson
(15) Bobby Ramos
(16) Andre Robertson
(17) Dan Schmitz
(18) George H. Sisler Jr.
(19) Garry Smith
(20) Dave Stegman
(21) Bob Sykes
(22) Frank Verdi
(23) Dave Wehrmeister
(24) Jamie Werly
(25) Coaches/Trainer Card (Sammy Ellis, Jerry McNertney, Steve Donohue)

1982 Fritsch Danville Suns

(California Angels, A)

	MT	NR MT	EX
Complete Set:	18.00	13.50	7.25

1 Team Logo/Checklist
2 Gus Gil
3 Jeff Ahern
4 T.R. Bryden
5 Mark Bingham
6 Bill White
7a Rick Turner (no glove) (sample card)
7b Rick Turner (with glove) (regular issue)

8 Jack Crawford
9 Kevin Price
10 Butch Dowies
11 Carlos Matos
12 Doug Lindsey
13 Tony Gonzalez
14 Marcel Lachemann
15 Richard Zaleski
16 Scott Oliver
17 Ellie Barros
18 Willie D. Williams
19 Freddy Machuca
20 Bill Worden
21 Devon White
22 Joe King
23 Mike Saverino
24 Brian Hartsock
25 Mark Bonner
26 Rafel Lugo
27 Dick Schofield
28 Norman Carrasco

1982 TCMA Daytona Beach Astros

(Houston Astros, A) (black & white)

	MT	NR MT	EX
Complete Set:	40.00	30.00	16.00

1 Guillermo Castro
2 Mitch Coplon
3 Joe Ferrante
4 Scott Gardner
5 Manny Hernandez
6 Uvaldo Regalado
7 Rex Schimpf
8 Ben Snyder
9 Roberto Yan
10 Doug Britt
11 Steve Dunnegan
12 Eric Bullock
13 Ty Gainey
14 Ira Lane
15 Neil Simons
16 Eric Swanson
17 Mark Campbell
18 Robbie McGorkle
19 Jamie Williams
20 Glenn Davis
21 Jim McKnight
22 Val Medina
23 Larry Simcox
24 Phil Smith
25 Mark Strucher

1982 TCMA Durham Bulls

(Atlanta Braves, A) (black & white)

	MT	NR MT	EX
Complete Set:	50.00	37.00	20.00

1 Mike Garcia
2 Keith Hagman
3 Scott Hood
4 Joe Lorenz
5 Bob Luzon
6 Bryan Neal
7 Ken Scanlon
8 Rick Siriano
9 Miguel Sosa
10 Jim Stefanski
11 Tommy Thompson
12 Freddy Tiburcio
13 Bob Tumpane
14 Dave Clay
15 Rick Coatney
16 Jeff Dedmon
17 Brian Fisher
18 Rick Hatcher
19 Mike Payne
20 Gary Reiter
21 Andre Treadway
22 Bruce Dal Canton
23 Buddy Bailey
24 Gene Lane
25 Bob Dews

1982 TCMA Edmonton Trappers

(Chicago White Sox, AAA) (color)

	MT	NR MT	EX
Complete Set:	30.00	22.00	12.00

1 Carlos Ibarra
2 Jose Castro
3 Jim Siwy
4 Steve Dillard
5 Chris Nyman
6 Guy Hoffman
7 Keith Desjarlais
8 Jay Loviglio
9 Fran Mullins
10 Lorenzo Gray
11 Leo Sutherland
12 Woody Agosto
13 Ron Kittle
14 Nardi Contreras
15 Reggie Patterson
16 David Hogg
17 Len Bradley
18 Dom Fucci
19 Rich Barnes
20 Rusty Kuntz
21 Rick Seilheimer
22 Gordy Lund
23 Geoff Combe
24 Dave Grossman
25 Jeff Schattinger

1982 TCMA El Paso Diablos

(Milwaukee Brewers, AA) (color)

	MT	NR MT	EX
Complete Set:	8.00	6.00	3.25

1 Eric Peyton
2 Dion James
3 Ron Koenigsfeld
4 Kurt Kingsolver
5 Dan Davidsmeier
6 Bill Foley
7 Randy Ready
8 Mark Schuster
9 Don Whiting
10 Mark Johnston
11 Joe Hansen
12 Steve Michael
13 Jerry Jenkins
14 Andy Beene
15 Steve Manderfield
16 Bob Schroeck
17 Dave Grier
18 Jack Uhey
19 Steve Parrott
20 Jim Koontz
21 Bob Gibson
22 Derek Tatsuno
23 Tony Muser
24 Al Price

1982 TCMA Evansville Triplets

(Detroit Tigers, AAA) (color)

	MT	NR MT	EX
Complete Set:	8.00	6.00	3.25

1 Howard Bailey
2 Juan Berenguer
3 Mark Dacko
4 Mark Lee
5 Rick Matula
6 Bruce Robbins
7 Larry Rothschild
8 Dave Rucker
9 Augie Ruez
10 Gerald Ujdur
11 Marty Castillo
12 Don McCormack
13 Stine Poole
14 Jeff Cox
15 Paul Djakonow
16 Mike Laga
17 Juan Lopez
18 Vern Followell
19 Les Filkins
20 Eddie Gates
21 Ray Hampton
22 Jeff Kenaga
23 Mark Corey
24 Ken Houston
25 Roy Majtyka

1982 TCMA Fort Myers Royals

(Kansas City Royals, A) (black & white)

	MT	NR MT	EX
Complete Set:	12.50	9.50	5.00

1 Rick Rizzo
2 Hal Hatcher
3 Tommy Thompson
4 Benny Gadahia
5 Warren Oliver
6 Greg Jonson
7 Nick Harsh
8 Mickey Palmer
9 Rick Plautz
10 Duane Gustavson
11 Tony Ferreira
12 Mike Alvarez
13 Jeff Gladden
14 Dave Wong
15 Fran Cutty
16 Mark Huismann
17 James Gleissner
18 Bill Best
19 Lester Strode
20 Mark Newman
21 Bill Pecota
22 Rick Mathews
23 Steve Morrow

1982 TCMA Glens Falls White Sox

(Chicago White Sox, AA) (black & white)

	MT	NR MT	EX
Complete Set:	120.00	90.00	47.50

1 Vince Bienek
2 J.B. Brown
3 Ed Cipot
4 Larry Donofrid
5 Dom Fucci
6 Tim Hulett
7 Phil Klimas
8 Mike Morse
9 Pete Peltz
10 Joel Skinner
11 Vern Thomas
12 Dan Williams
13 Dave Yobs
14 Not Issued
15 Not Issued
16 Larry Edwards
17 Bob Fallopn
18 Jack Hardy
19 Chuck Johnson
20 John Lackey
21 Mike Maitland
22 Tom Mullen
23 Mark Teutsch
24 Mike Withrow
25 Jim Mahoney

1982 TCMA Hawaii Islanders

(San Diego Padres, AAA) (color)

	MT	NR MT	EX
Complete Set:	150.00	112.50	60.00

1 Ron Tingley
2 Dave Richards
3 Steve Smith
4 Jim Pankovits
5 Jerry Johnson
6 Joe Lansford
7 Jerry De Simone
8 Dan Gausepohl
9 Aaron Cain
10 Tony Gwynn
11 Rick Lancellotti
12 Jeff Pyburn
13 Steve Fireovid
14 Andy Hawkins
15 George Stablein
16 Ron Meredith
17 Fred Kuhaulua
18 Tim Hamm
19 Tom Tellmann
20 Dave Dravecky
21 Mark Thurmond
22 Kim Seaman
23 Doug Rader
24 Chuck Hartenstein
25 Larry Duensing

1982 TCMA Holyoke Millers

(California Angels, AA) (color)

	MT	NR MT	EX
Complete Set:	7.00	5.25	2.75

1 Michael Barba
2 Brian Buckely
3 Jeff Conner
4 Lonnie Dugger
5 Dave Duran
6 Bill Mooneyham
7 Perry Morrison
8 Ron Romanick
9 David A. Smith
10 David W. Smith
11 Bob Palmer
12 Larry Patterson
13 Rick Adams
14 Bob Bohnet
15 Ron Hunt
16 Pat Keedy
17 Tim Krauss
18 Gus Polidor
19 Chris Clark
20 Harry Francis
21 Dennis Gilbert
22 Darrell Miller
23 Jack Hiatt
24 Marc Terrazas
25 George Como
26 Ben Surner

1982 Team Holyoke Millers

(California Angels, AA) This set was also produced in the form of a poster. The cards were bordered by stars and measured approximately 1-7/8" x 2-7/8" in size.

	MT	NR MT	EX
Complete Set:	40.00	30.00	16.00

(1) Mike Barba
(2) Jim Beswick
(3) Bob Bohnet
(4) Rod Boxberger
(5) Brian Buckley
(6) Chris Clark
(7) Jeff Conner
(8) Harry Francis
(9) Dennis Gilbert
(10) Mike Gordon
(11) Jack Hiatt
(12) Pat Keedy
(13) Jay Kibbe
(14) Tim Krauss
(15) Steve Liddle
(16) Mark McCormack
(17) Darrell Miller
(18) Bill Mooneyham
(19) Bob Palmer
(20) Larry Patterson
(21) Gustavo Polidor
(22) Ron Romanick
(23) David A. Smith
(24) D.W. Smith
(25) Mark Sproesser
(26) Marc Terrasaz
(27) Craig Thomas
(28) Mike Venezia
(29) Matt Wroth

1982 TCMA Idaho Falls Athletics

(Oakland A's, A) (black & white)

	MT	NR MT	EX
Complete Set:	11.00	8.25	4.50

1 Dave Baehr
2 Jim Bailey
3 Mark Border
4 Eric Brown
5 Tom Conquest
6 Doug Farrow
7 Todd Fischer
8 Angelo Gilbert
9 Mark Kochanski
10 Tim Lambert
11 Dave Leiper
12 Tenoa Stevenson
13 Steve Travers
14 Shawn Gill
15 Russ Wortmann
16 Leon Baham
17 Bill Davis
18 Mark Dye
19 John Michel
20 Clemente Oropeza
21 Greg Robles
22 Kenny Clayton
23 Steve Campbell
24 Rob Loscalzo
25 Eddie Malone
26 Gary McGraw
27 Jorge Oquendo
28 Ricky Thomas
29 Dave Wilder
30 Keith Lieppman
31 Grady Fuson
32 Mark Doberenz
33 Dave Sheriff

1982 Team Indianapolis Indians

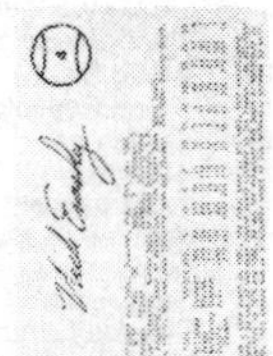

(Cincinnati Reds, AAA) (co-sponsored by Tom Aikens)

	MT	NR MT	EX
Complete Set:	12.00	9.00	4.75

1 Team Photo
2 George Scherger
3 Kip Young
4 Nick Esasky
5 Brad Lesley
6 Duane Walker
7 Bill Dawley
8 The Instructors
9 Brooks Carey
10 Orlando Isales
11 Brian Ryder
12 Dave Van Gorder
13 Greg Harris
14 The Bullpen
15 Tom Lawless
16 Mike Dowless
17 Gary Redus
18 The Catchers
19 Rich Carlucci
20 Tom Foley
21 Ben Hayes
22 Steve Christmas
23 The Outfielders
24 Ron Farkas
25 Dave Tomlin
26 Dallas Williams
27 The Infielders
28 Gil Kubski
29 Neil Fiala
30 The Starting Pitchers
31 Lee Garrett
32 Behind The Scenes

1982 TCMA Iowa Cubs

(Chicago Cubs, AAA) (color)

	MT	NR MT	EX
Complete Set:	20.00	15.00	8.00

1 Alfred Benton
2 Scott Fletcher
3 Tom Grant
4 Mel Hall
5 Bill Hayes
6 Randy LaVigne
7 Jared Martin
8 Danny Rohn
9 Joe Strain
10 Pat Tabler
11 Scot Thompson
12 Jack Upton
13 Elliott Waller
14 Robert Blyth
15 Tom Filer
16 Jay Howell
17 Larry Jones
18 Chris Knapp
19 Ken Kravec
20 Craig Lefferts
21 Mark Parker
22 Mike Proly
23 Herman Segelke
24 Randy Stein
25 Jim Napier
26 Scott Breeden
27 Ken Grandquist
28 Bob Reynolds
29 Tom Butts
30 Frank Macy
31 Kim Hart
32 Dr. Richard Evans

1982 TCMA Jackson Mets

(New York Mets, AA) (color)

	MT	NR MT	EX
Complete Set:	125.00	90.00	47.50

1 Jeff Bittiger
2 Matt Bullinger
3 Ted Davis
4 Scott Dye
5 Steve Ibarguen
6 Jody Johnston
7 Brain Kolbe
8 Jose Rodriguez
9 John Semprini
10 Doug Sisk
11 Ronn Reynolds
12 Dave Duff
13 Rick Poe
14 Mike Anicich
15 Rick McMullen
16 Al Pedrique
17 Jim Woodward
18 Bill Rittweger
19 Billy Beane
20 Terry Blocker
21 Darryl Strawberry
22 Gene Dusan
23 Bob Apodaca
24 Bob Sikes
25 Bill Walberg

1982 TCMA Knoxville Blue Jays

(Toronto Blue Jays, AA) (black & white)

	MT	NR MT	EX
Complete Set:	10.00	7.50	4.00

1 Team Photo
2 Scott Elam
3 Randy Ford
4 Dennis Howard
5 Tom Lukish
6 Colin McLaughlin
7 Keith Walker
8 Matt Williams
9 Brian Stemberger
10 Brian Milner
11 Dan Whitmer
12 Tim Thompson
13 Paul Hodgson
14 Andre Wood
15 Carlos Rios
16 Ed Dennis
17 Vern Ramie
18 J.J. Cannon
19 Vassie Gardner
20 Ron Shepherd
21 Larry Hardy
22 Hector Torres
23 John Woodworth

1982 Ehrler's Dairy Louisville Redbirds

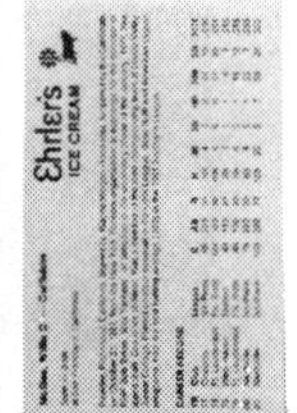

(St. Louis Cardinals, AAA)

	MT	NR MT	EX
Complete Set:	20.00	15.00	8.00

(1) George A. Bjorkman
(2) Jose Oscar Brito
(3) Glen E. Brummer
(4) Michael S. Calise
(5) Ralph A. Citarella
(6) Joseph De Sa
(7) Jeffrey D. Doyle
(8) Joseph F. Frazier
(9) John T. Fulgham
(10) David A. Green
(11) Ricky N. Horton
(12) David B. Kable
(13) Jeffrey Allen Lahti
(14) William Allen Lyons
(15) John R. Martin
(16) Willie D. Mc Gee
(17) Jerry Mc Kune
(18) Dyar K. Miller
(19) Gotay Mills
(20) Daniel J. Morogiello
(21) Alan R. Olmsted
(22) Kelly J. Paris
(23) Gaylen R. Pitts
(24) Andrew J. Rinson
(25) Gene (Eugene L. Roof)
(26) Orlando Sanchez
(27) Rafael Santana
(28) Jed Smith
(29) John A. Stuper
(30) Steven W. Winfield

1982 TCMA Lynchburg Mets

(New York Mets, A) (black & white) (Webster, Johnston and Raeside are late-issue, scarce cards)

	MT	NR MT	EX
Complete Set:	95.00	71.00	37.00

1 Danny Monzon
2 Laschelle Tarver
3 Herman Winningham
4 John De Imonte
5 Bruce Kastelic
6 Kevin Mitchell
7 DeWayne Vaughn
8 Ed Rech
9 Jeff Sunderlage
10 Paul Wilmet
11 Tom Miller
12 Roger Frash
13 Duane Evans
14 Chuck Schonoor
15 Randy Milligan
16 Lloyd McClendon
17 Rick Myles
18 Roger Begue
19 Jay Tibbs
20 Bill Fultz
21 Rich Webster
22 Jody Johnston
23 John Raeside

1982 TCMA Lynn Sailors

(Seattle Mariners, AA) (black & white)

	MT	NR MT	EX
Complete Set:	19.00	14.00	7.50

1 Rick Adair
2 Carl Best (Karl)
3 Kevin Dukes
4 Joe Georger
5 Steve Krueger
6 Jed Murray
7 Jeff Stottlemyre
8 Scott Stranski (photo actually Jeff Stottlemyre)
9 Jim Nelson
10 Clark Crist
11 Bill Crone (photo actually John Moses)
12 Mario Diaz
13 Jim Presley
14 Ramon Estepa (photo acutally Tito Nanni)
15 Tito Nanni
16 Glenn Walker
17 Harold Reynolds
18 Mickey Bowers

1982 Fritsch Madison Muskies

(Oakland A's, A)

	MT	NR MT	EX
Complete Set:	9.75	7.00	4.00

1 Team Logo/Checklist
2 Joel Boni
3 Steve Kiefer
4 Mike Flinn
5 John "Duke" Smith
6 Chuck Kolotka
7 Kevin Coughlon
8 Tom Heckman
9 Gene Ransom
10 Scott Anderson
11 Scot Mitchell
12 Mark Jarrett
13 Jeff Tipton
14 Mark Fellows
15 Monte R. McAbee
16 Ron Wilkinson
17 Allen Edwards
18 Frank Harris
19 Brad Fischer
20 James Feeley
21 Ron Harrison
22 Kevin D. Waller
23 Mike Ashman
24 Rob Vavrock
25 Jeff Kobernus
26 Keith Call
27a Pat O'Hara (batting) (sample card)
27b Pat O'Hara (catching) (regular issue)
28 Thomas Romano
29 Mark "Mac" McDonald
30 Bruce Amador
31 Jeff Cary
32 Hector Perez
33 Ed Janus
34 Bob Drew, Michael Duval

1982 TCMA Miami Marlins

(Baltimore Orioles, A) (black & white)

	MT	NR MT	EX
Complete Set:	10.00	7.50	4.00

1 Will George
2 Mike Glinatsis
3 Marcos Gonzalez
4 Brian McDonough
5 Carlos Moreno
6 Joel Pyfrom
7 Tony Wadley
8 Jose Caballero
9 Ron Cardieri
10 Jorge Curbelo
11 Jorge Llano
12 Robbie Alvarez
13 Julio Beltran
14 Bob Boyce
15 Edgar Castro
16 Rick Rembielak
17 Angel Valdez
18 Raul Tovar
19 Lee Granger
20 Mike Kutner
21 Frank Contreras
22 John Tamargo

1982 Chong Modesto A's

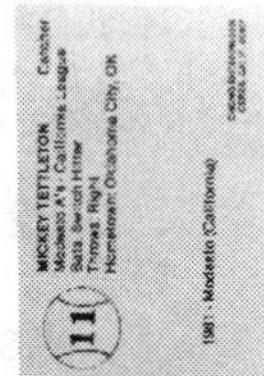

(Oakland A's, A)

	MT	NR MT	EX
Complete Set:	40.00	30.00	16.00

1 Dave Hudgens
2 Rod Murphy
3 Selwyn Young
4 Tom Copeland
5 Thad Reece
6 Rick Tronerud
7 Terry Harper
8 John Hotchkiss
9 Jimmy Camacho
10 Aurdie Colbert
11 Mickey Tettleton
12 Curt Young
13 Wayne Palicia
14 Ed Retzer
15 Paul Josephson
16 Mike Lynes
17 Mark Ferguson
18 Tony Herron
19 Gary Dawson
20 Tim Conroy
21 Rick Rodriguez
22 Don Van Marter
23 Wayne Rudolph
24 Pete Whisenant
25 Jim Durrman
26 Phil Danielson
27 Dan Kiser

1982 Arby's Nashville Sounds

(New York Yankees, AA)

	MT	NR MT	EX
Complete Set:	9.50	7.00	4.00

1 Dave Banes
2 Mike Browning
3 Brian Butterfield
4 Ben Callahan
5 Pat Callahan
6 Nate Chapman
7 Clay Christiansen
8 Dean Craig
9 Brian Dayett
10 Tommie Dodd
11 Guy Elston
12 Ray Fontenot
13 Paul Grayner
14 Rex Hudler
15 Tim Knight
16 Chris Lein
17 Erik Peterson
18 Brian Poldberg
19 Frank Ricci
20 Mark Salas
21 Dan Schmitz
22 Buck Showalter
23 Roger Slagle
24 Garry Smith
25 Bob Sykes
26 Rafael Villaman
27 Stefan Wever
---- Manager & Coaches (Hoyt Wilhelm, John Oates, Eddie Napoleon)

1982 TCMA Oklahoma City 89'ers

(Philadelphia Phillies, AAA) (color)

	MT	NR MT	EX
Complete Set:	35.00	26.00	14.00

1 Mike Willis
2 Rowland Office
3 Tim Corcoran
4 Ramon Aviles
5 Ellis Deal
6 Ron Clark
7 Al Sanchez
8 Len Matuszek
9 Jerry Reed
10 Rusty Hamric
11 Julio Franco
12 Mark Davis
13 Joe Kerrigan
14 Tom Lombarski
15 Tony McDonald
16 Luis Rodriguez
17 Jeff Ulrich
18 Jim Rasmussen
19 Jon Reelhorn
20 Herb Orensky
21 Kelly Downs
22 Marty Decker
23 Darren Burroughs
24 Don Carman
25 Wil Culmer

1982 TCMA Omaha Royals

(Kansas City Royals, AAA) (color) (complete set price includes variations; without the corrected cards)

	MT	NR MT	EX
Complete Set:	50.00	37.00	20.00

1 Mike Armstrong
2 Ralph Botting
3 Keith Creel
4 Dan Fischer
5 Don Hood
6 Phil Huffman
7 Bill Kelly
8 Dave Schuler
9 Bob Tufts
10 Frank Wills
11 Greg Keatley
12 Don Slaught
13 Mitch Ashmore
14 Buddy Biancalana
15 Manuel Colletti
16 Dave Edler
17a Ron Johnson (blue uinform, photo actually Dan Weiser)
17b Ron Johnson (white uniform, correct photo)
18a Dan Weiser (white uniform, photo actually Ron Johnson)
18b Dan Weiser (blue uniform, correct photo)
19 Darryl Motley
20 Bombo Rivera
21 Mark Ryal
22 Pat Sheridan
23 Luis Silverio
24 Bill Gorman
25 Joe Sparks
26 Jerry Cram
27 Paul McGannon

1982 TCMA Oneonta Yankees

(New York Yankees, A) (black & white)

	MT	NR MT	EX
Complete Set:	150.00	110.00	60.00

1 Orestes Destrade
2 Jim Riggs
3 Brent Giesdal
4 Ken Berry
5 Dan O'Regan
6 Q.V. Lowe
7 Stan Sanders
8 Tim Birtsas
9 Steve Campagno
10 Pat Bone
11 Tim Byron
12 Jesus Alcala
13 John Elway
14 Mike Fennell
15 Jim Ferguson
16 Mike Glavin
17 Pedro Medina

1982 TCMA Orlando Twins

(Minnesota Twins, AA) (black & white)

	MT	NR MT	EX
Complete Set:	20.00	15.00	8.00

1 Kevin Williams
2 Lee Belanger
3 Eric Broersma
4 Smokey Everett
5 Jack Hobbs
6 Bob Konopa
7 Mark Funderburk
8 Greg Gagne
9 Dave Meier
10 Mike McCain
11 Tony Pilla
12 Tim Teufel
13 Tom Kelly
14 Rick Austin
15 Chino Cadahia
16 Andre David
17 Steve Douglas
18 Ken Foster
19 Ted Kromy
20 Larry May
21 Bob Mulligan
22 Jay Pettibone
23 Sam Arrington
24 Eddie Hodge

1982 TCMA Orlando Twins Southern League Champs

(Minnesota Twins, AA) (black & white) (set features players from 1981 championship season)

	MT	NR MT	EX
Complete Set:	30.00	22.00	12.00

1 Rod Booker
2 Randy Bush
3 Chino Cadahia
4 Manny Colletti
5 Andre David
6 Steve Douglas
7 Gary Gaetti
8 Tim Laudner
9 Tim Teufel
10 Scott Ulger
11 Lance Hallberg
12 Tom Kelly
13 Eric Broersma
14 Scott Gleckel
15 Steve Green
16 Brad Havens
17 Jack Hobbs
18 Bob Konopa
19 Ted Kromy
20 Steve Mapel
21 Bob Mulligan
22 Jose Reyes
23 Gary Serum
24 Frank Viola

1982 Valley Nat'l Bank Phoenix Giants

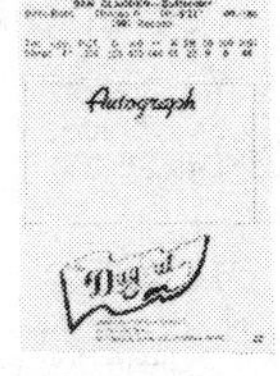

(San Francisco Giants, AAA)

	MT	NR MT	EX
Complete Set:	9.00	6.75	3.50

1 Team Photo
2 Mike Chris
3 Ted Wilborn
4 Mike Rowland
5 John Rabb
6 Paul Szymarek
7 Rocky Bridges
8 Dave Roberts
9 Tommy Gonzalez, Harry Jordan
10 Mike Tucker
11 Ethan Blackaby
12 Craig Chamberlain
13 Ron Pruitt
14 Mark Dempsey
15 Dorian Boyland
16 Jeff Stember
17 Mike Turgeon
18 Giantettes
19 Andy Mc Gaffigan
20 Kelly Smith
21 Tom Runnells
22 Dan Gladden
23 Tom O'Malley
24 Jose Barrios
25 Bill Martin
26 Mike Rex
27 Al Hergesheimer

1982 TCMA Portland Beavers

(Pittsburgh Pirates, AAA) (color)

	MT	NR MT	EX
Complete Set:	12.00	9.00	4.75

1 Jose DeLeon
2 Butch Edge
3 Cecilio Guante
4 Odell Jones
5 Robert Long
6 Randy Nieman
7 Pasqual Perez (Pascual)
8 Manny Sarmiento
9 Lee Tunnell
10 Stan Cliburn
11 Junior Ortiz
12 Wayne Caughey
13 Denny Gonzalez
14 Willie Horton
15 Bobby Mitchell
16 Nelson Norman
17 Eddie Vargas
18 Dave Augustine
19 Trench Davis
20 Doug Frobel
21 Jose Rodriguez
22 Reggie Walton
23 Jim Saul
24 Vern Law, Jim Saul
25 Not Issued
26 Carlos Lezedma

1982 TCMA Quad City Cubs

(Chicago Cubs, A) (black & white)

	MT	NR MT	EX
Complete Set:	7.50	5.50	3.00

1 Darryl Banks
2 Allen Black
3 Russ Brahms
4 Rich Buonantony
5 Jorge Carpio
6 Tim Clarke
7 Mitch Cooke
8 Jeff Fruge
9 Ron Kaufman
10 Vance Lovelace
11 Mike Shulleetta
12 Roger Crow
13 Craig Weissman
14 Lee George
15 Wendell Henderson
16 Jeff Remo
17 James Allen
18 Ken Arnerich
19 Jeff Rutledge
20 Otis Tramble
21 Antonio Cordova
22 Darrin Jackson
23 Scott Miller
24 Rolando Roomes
25 Jim Walsh
26 George Enright
27 Quency Hill
28 Randy Roetter

1982 TCMA Reading Phillies

(Philadelphia Phillies, AA) (black & white)

	MT	NR MT	EX
Complete Set:	20.00	15.00	8.00

1 Jay Baller
2 Kelly Faulk
3 Butch Hughes
4 Kyle Money
5 John Palmieri
6 Dan Prior
7 Jim Rasmussen
8 Leroy Smith
9 Dennis Thomas
10 Richard Wortham
11 Gerry Willard
12 Al Velasquez
13 Dave Enos
14 Paul Fryer
15 Steve Jeltz
16 Jon Lindsey
17 Joe Nemeth
18 Randy Salava
19 Keith Washington
20 Steve Harvey
21 Tony McDonald
22 John Felske

1982 TCMA Redwood Pioneers

(California Angels, A) (black & white)

	MT	NR MT	EX
Complete Set:	8.00	6.00	3.25

1 Michael Brooks
2 Steven Eakes
3 Craig Gerber
4 Kevin Halicki
5 Gordon Jones
6 Tim Kammeyer
7 Steve Liddle
8 James Randall
9 Esmyel Romero
10 Michael Saatzer
11 Mark Smelko
12 Jeff Smith
13 Mark Sproesser
14 Darryl Stephens
15 Richard Sundberg
16 Ronald Sylvia
17 Paul Wright
18 Luis Zambrana
19 Harry Oliver
20 Glen Fisher
21 Ronald Hunt
22 Terry Harper
23 Kevin Jacobson
24 Barton Barun
25 Chris Cannizzaro
26 Brian Parfrey
27 Ralph Hartman

1982 TCMA Richmond Braves

(Atlanta Braves, AAA) (color) (complete set price includes both Brizzolara cards)

	MT	NR MT	EX
Complete Set:	75.00	56.00	30.00

1 Jose Alvarez
2a Tony Brizzolara (catching)
2b Tony Brizzolara (portrait)
3 Tim Cole
4 John D'Acquisto
5 Carlos Diaz
6 Craig McMurtry
7 Donnie Moore
8 Jeff Twitty
9 Roger Weaver
10 Jerry Keller
11 Larry Owen
12 Matt Sinatro
13 Brook Jacoby
14 Gerald Perry
15 Chico Ruiz
16 Paul Runge
17 Paul Zuvella
18 Mike Reynolds
19 Albert Hall
20 Leonel Vargas
21 Bob Porter
22 Mike Colbern
23 Ken Smith
24 Terry Harper
25 Ken Dayley
26 Mike Smith
27 Eddie Haas
28 Johnny Sain
29 Craig Robinson
30 Sam Ayoub
31 Albert Hall, Terry Harper, Brook Jacoby, Gerald Perry, Roger Weaver

1982 TCMA Rochester Red Wings

(Baltimore Orioles, AAA) (color)

	MT	NR MT	EX
Complete Set:	9.00	6.75	3.50

1 Mike Boddicker
2 John Flinn
3 Bruce MacPherson
4 Craig Minetto
5 Allan Ramirez
6 Cliff Speck
7 Bill Swaggerty
8 Don Welchel
9 Tim Derryberry
10 Dan Graham

11 Willie Royster
12 Glenn Gulliver
13 Rick Jones
14 Rick Lisi
15 Dan Logan
16 Vic Rodriguez
17 John Shelby
18 John Valle
19 Mike Young
20 Lance Nichols
21 Tom Chism
22 Ken Rowe

1982 TCMA Salt Lake City Gulls

(Seattle Mariners, AAA) (color)

	MT	NR MT	EX
Complete Set:	9.00	6.75	3.50

1 Doug Merrifield
2 Jamie Allen
3 Rod Allen
4 Rich Bordi
5 Al Chambers
6 Bryan Clark
7 Roy Clark
8 Steve Finch
9 Gary Gray
10 Tracy Harris
11 Mike Hart
12 Vance McHenry
13 Orlando Mercado
14 Ron Musselman
15 Casey Parsons
16 Domingo Ramos
17 Brian Snyder
18 Bob Stoddard
19 Roy Thomas
20 Dave Valle
21 Sammye Welborn
22 Matt Young
23 Manny Estrada
24 Bobby Floyd
25 Joe Decker

1982 TCMA Spokane Indians

(California Angels, AAA) (color)

	MT	NR MT	EX
Complete Set:	9.00	6.75	3.50

1 Steve Brown
2 Craig Eaton
3 Rick Foley
4 Mickey Mahler
5 Fred Martinez
6 Paul Olden
7 Jeff Schneider
8 Rick Steirer
9 Mike Walters
10 Mike Bishop
11 Steve Herz
12 Jerry Narron
13 Jeff Bertoni
14 Craig Cacer
15 Scott Carnes
16 John Harris
17 Steve Lubratich
18 Les Pearsey
19 Mike Brown
20 Tom Brunansky
21 Ron Jackson
22 Pepe Mangual
23 Gary Pettis
24 Moose Stubing
25 Joe Coleman
26 Leonard Garcia

1982 Fritsch Springfield Cardinals

(St. Louis Cardinals, AAA)

	MT	NR MT	EX
Complete Set:	10.00	7.50	4.00

1 Team Logo/Checklist
2 Dave Bialas
3 Bruce "Pic" Miller
4 Bill Lyons
5 Mike Pittman
6 Freddie Silva
7 Robert Hicks
8 Tom Epple
9a Dan Stryffeler (bat on shoulder) (sample card))
9b Dan Stryffeler (bat off shoulder) (regular issue)
10 Gus Malespin
11 Steve Winfield
12 Danny Cox
13 Greg Dunn
14 Bobby Kish
15 Tom Dozier
16 Marty Mason
17 Alan Hunsinger
18 Don Collins
19 Mike Harris
20 Randy Hunt
21 Deron Thomas
22 Harry McCulla
23 Brad Bennett
24 Francisco Batista

1982 TCMA Syracuse Chiefs

(Toronto Blue Jays, AAA) (color) (complete set price includes scarce Larson, O'Keefe and Whitmer cards)

	MT	NR MT	EX
Complete Set:	50.00	37.00	20.00

1 Mike Barlow
2 Tom Dixon
3 Mark Eichhorn
4 Mark Geisel
5 John Littlefield
6 Frank Ricelli
7 Ken Schrom
8 Steve Senteney
9 Jackson Todd
10 Jim Wright
11 Jim Gaudet
12 Ramon Lora
13 Gene Petralli
14 Dave Baker
15 Charlie Beamon
16 Brian Doyle
17 Tony Fernandez
18 Fred Manrique
19 Glenn Adams
20 George Bell
21 Pedro Hernandez
22 Creighton Tevlin
23 Mitch Webster
24 Doug Ault
25 Tom Craig
26 Jim Beauchamp
27a Duane Larson
27b Rick O'Keefe
28 Dan Whitmer

1982 Team Syracuse Chiefs

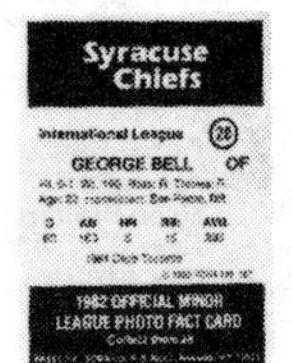

(Toronto Blue Jays, AAA) (cards are postcard size and have blank backs)

	MT	NR MT	EX
Complete Set:	80.00	60.00	32.00

(1) Glenn Adams
(2) Doug Ault
(3) Dave Baker
(4) Mike Barlow
(5) Charlie Beamon
(6) Jim Beauchamp
(7) George Bell
(8) Pete Dempsey
(9) Tom Dixon
(10) Brian Doyle
(11) Mark Eichhorn
(12) Tony Fernandez
(13) Dave Geisel
(14) Pedro Hernandez
(15) John Littlefield
(16) Fred Manrique
(17) Rick O'Keeffe (O'Keefe)
(18) Gino Petralli
(19) Ken Schrom
(20) Steve Senteney
(21) Creighton Tevlin
(22) Jackson Todd
(23) Mitch Webster
(24) Dan Whitmer

1982 TCMA Tacoma Tigers

(Oakland A's, AAA) (color) (complete set price includes scarce Comstock and Sexton cards)

	MT	NR MT	EX
Complete Set:	60.00	45.00	24.00

1 DeWayne Bruce
2 Don Fowler
3 Dave Heaverlo
4 Bill Castro
5 Gorman Heimueller
6 Dennis Kinney
7 Eric Mustad
8 Dave Patterson
9 Bill Swiacki
10 Ed Figueroa
11 Darryl Cias
12 Tim Hosley
13 Kevin Bell
14 Danny Goodwin
15 Paul Mize
16 Johnny Evans
17 Jim Nettles
18 Dennis Sherow
19 Ed Nottle
20 Larry Davis
21 Art Popham
22 Stan Naccarato
23 Keith Atherton
24 Jeff Jones
25 Brian Kingman
26 Pat Dempsey
27 Robert Kearney
28 Mack Babitt
29 Keith Drumright
30 Mike Gallego
31 Kelvin Moore
32 Tony Phillips
33 Rick Bosetti
34 Michael Davis
35 Bob Grandas
36 Mitchell Page
37 Tigers Mascot
38 Johnny Sexton
39 Keith Comstock

1982 TCMA Tidewater Tides

(New York Mets, AAA) (color) (complete set price includes scarce Cubbage card)

	MT	NR MT	EX
Complete Set:	22.00	16.50	8.75

1 Rick Ownbey
2 Kelvin Chapman
3 Mike Davis
4 Mike Fitzgerald
5 Mike Howard
6 Bruce Bochy
7 Gil Flores
8 Brian Giles
9 Phil Mankowski
10 Ronald MacDonald
11 Rusty Tillman
12 Rick Anderson
13 Ron Darling
14 Terry Leach
15 Jose Oquendo
16 Marvell Wynne
17 Greg Biercevicz
18 Scott Holman
19 Jack Aker
20 Brent Gaff
21 Steve Ratzer
22 Bob Schaefer
23 Dave Von Ohlen
24 Walt Terrell
25 Mike Anicich
26 Mike Cubbage

1982 TCMA Toledo Mud Hens

(Minnesota Twins, AAA) (color) (Price includes the late issue, scarce card #s 26-28)

	MT	NR MT	EX
Complete Set:	80.00	60.00	32.00

1 Don Cooper
2 Glenn Dooner
3 Steve Korczyk
4 Jeff Little
5 Jack O'Connor
6 Bob Veselic
7 Frank Viola
8 Mike Walters
9 Rick Williams
10 Harry Saferight
11 Ray Smith
12 Rod Booker
13 Jim Christensen
14 Dave Machemer
15 Ivan Mesa
16 Kelly Snider
17 Greg Wells
18 Mike Sodders
19 Elijah Bonaparte
20 Randy Bush
21 Rick Sofield
22 Scott Ulger
23 Cal Ermer
24 Buck Chamberlin
25 Not Issued
26 Pete Filson
27 Doug Fregin
28 Bob Mitchell

1982 TCMA Tucson Toros

(Houston Astros, AAA) (color)

	MT	NR MT	EX
Complete Set:	8.00	6.00	3.25

1 Bert Pena
2 Chris Jones
3 Mark Ross
4 Tom Vessey
5 Steve Lake
6 Greg Cypret
7 Billy Doran
8 Tim Tolman
9 Jim Tracy
10 Larry Ray
11 Harry Spillman (Spilman)
12 Jim McDonald
13 Rickey Keeton
14 Zacarias Paris
15 Bert Roberge
16 Rick Lysander
17 Mark Miggins
18 Billy Smith
19 Bobby Sprowl
20 George Cappuzzello
21 Gordy Pladson
22 Bill Wood
23 James Hand
24 Jim Johnson
25 Gary Tuck
26 Dennis Menke (Denis)
27 Dave Labossiere
28 Batboys

1982 TCMA Tulsa Drillers

(Texas Rangers, AA) (color) (complete set price includes scarce #s 25-28)

	MT	NR MT	EX
Complete Set:	40.00	30.00	16.00

1 Tom Henke
2 Brad Mengwasser
3 Martin Leach
4 Dennis Long
5 Mike Mason
6 Tim Henry
7 Al Lachowicz
8 Kevin Richards
9 Jim Gideon
10 Tom Dunbar
11 Don Scott
12 Tracy Cowger
13 Steve Moore
14 Carmelo Aguayo
15 Dave Stockstill
16 Oscar Majia
17 Dan Murphy
18 Ron Dillard
19 Mike Jirschele
20 Gerry Neutang
21 Robert Ball
22 Tom Burgess
23 Orlando Gomez
24 Joe Nemeth
25 Curtis Wilkerson
26 Brett Benza
27 Steve Buechele
28 Mike Rubel

1982 TCMA Vancouver Canadians

(Milwaukee Brewers, AAA) (color)

	MT	NR MT	EX
Complete Set:	8.00	6.00	3.25

1 Bob Skube
2 Frank Thomas
3 Bill Schroder (Schroeder)
4 Kevin Bass
5 Willie Lozada (Lozado)
6 John Skorochocki
7 Lawrence Rush
8 Ed Irvine
9 Stan Davis
10 Doug Loman
11 Steve Herz
12 Tim Cook
13 Doug Jones
14 Mike Madden
15 Rich Olsen
16 Frank DiPino
17 Pete Ladd

18 Chuck Valley
19 Rick Kranitz
20 Jaimie Cocanower (Jamie)
21 Chuck Porter
22 Mike Anderson
23 Eli Grba
24 Brian Thorson

1982 TCMA Vero Beach Dodgers

(Los Angeles Dodgers, A) (black & white)

	MT	NR MT	EX
Complete Set:	85.00	64.00	34.00

1 Roberto Alexandro
2 Ernie Borbon
3 Paul Cozzolino
4 Dave Daniel
5 Rich Felt
6 Sid Fernandez
7 Robert Kenyon
8 Steve Martin
9 Peyton Mosher
10 Matt Reeves
11 Robert Slezak
12 Paul Bard
13 Steve Boncore
14 Jack Fimple
15 Robert Allen
16 Carmelo Alvarez
17 Jerry Bendorf
18 Sid Bream
19 Harold Perkins
20 Larry See
21 Ralph Bryant
22 Cecil Espy
23 Tony Lachowetz
24 Stu Pederson
25 Bob Seymour
26 Terry Collins
27 Rob Giesecke
28 Dave Wallace
29 John Shoemaker

1982 TCMA Waterbury Reds

(Cincinnati Reds, AA) (color)

	MT	NR MT	EX
Complete Set:	40.00	30.00	16.00

1 Bill Landrum
2 Larry Buckle
3 Keefe Cato
4 Kenneth Jones
5 Gene Menees
6 Clem Freeman
7 Bob Buchanan
8 Jeff Russell
9 Ronald Robinson
10 Nicholas Fiorillo
11 Raymond Corbett
12 Michael Kripner
13 Skeeter Barnes
14 Danny Tartabull
15 Eski Viltz
16 Paul Herring
17 Glen Franklin
18 Mark Gilbert
19 Kenneth Scarpace
20 Tony Walker
21 Ronald Little
22 Crestwell Pratt
23 Jim Lett

1982 TCMA Waterloo Indians

(Cleveland Indians, A) (black & white) (set includes scarce #s26-28)

	MT	NR MT	EX
Complete Set:	50.00	37.50	20.00

1 Steve Cushing
2 Rich Doyle
3 Ralph Elpin
4 Mike Jeffcoat
5 Wayne Johnson
6 Ricky Lintz
7 Rodney McDonald
8 John Miglio
9 Ramon Romero
10 David Wick
11 Alan Willis
12 John Malkin
13 Phillip Wilson
14 Rod Carraway
15 Winston Ficklin
16 Mike Gertz
17 Sam Martin
18 Junior Noboa
19 Ed Tanner
20 George Albert
21 Jerry Nalley
22 Chris Rehbaum
23 Dwight Taylor
24 Mike Taylor
25 Randy Washington
26 Gomer Hodge
27 Vic Albury
28 Ron Wollenhaupt

1982 Fritsch Waterloo Indians

(Cleveland Indians, A)

	MT	NR MT	EX
Complete Set:	9.00	6.75	3.50

1 Team Logo/Checklist
2 Gomer Hodge
3 Vic Albury
4 Ron Wollenhaupt
5a Rickey Lintz (left wrist not showing) (sample card))
5b Rickey Lintz (left wrist showing) (regular issue)
6 Jerry Nalley
7 Phil Wilson
8 Rod McDonald
9 Rod Carraway
10 Steve Roche
11 Dave Gallagher
12 Ralph Elpin
13 Dave Wick
14 Mike Gertz
15 Steve Cushing
16 John Miglio
17 Chris Rehbaum
18 Marlin Methven
19 Winston Ficklin
20 John Malkin
21 Sammy Martin
22 Ed Tanner
23 Rich Doyle
24 Jose Roman
25 Wayne Johnson
26 Randy Washington
27 George Alpert
28 Junior Noboa

1982 Fritsch Wausau Timbers

(Seattle Mariners, A)

	MT	NR MT	EX
Complete Set:	9.00	6.75	3.50

1 Team Logo/Checklist
2 Team Photo
3 Jack Roeder
4 Stan Edmonds
5 Curtis Kouba
6 Bart Mackie
7 Joe Benes
8 Randy Meier
9 Donell Nixon
10 Ivan Calderon
11 Eric Parent
12 Mike Bucci
13 Bret McAfee
14 Ronn Dixon
15 Martin O. Enriquez
16 Luis Trinidad H. Castillo
17 R.J. Harrison
18 Mike Johnson
19 Mitch Zwolensky
20 Donny Holland
21 Jay Michael Erdahl
22 Mike Evans
23 Gary Pellant
24 Don Diego Pierce
25 Angel Vicente Fonseca
26 Bill Taylor
27 Ric Wilson
28 Chip Conklin
29 Terry Hayes
30 Tom Hunt
31 Bob Gisselman

1982 TCMA West Haven A's

(Oakland A's, AA) (black & white)

	MT	NR MT	EX
Complete Set:	10.00	7.50	4.00

1 Brian Abraham
2 Bert Bradley
3 Jeff Carey
4 Chris Codiroli
5 Keith Comstock
6 Chuck Hensley
7 Bill Krueger
8 Lou Marietta
9 Jack Smith
10 Bill Bathe
11 Chuck Fick
12 Mike Gallego
13 Steve Gelfarb
14 Donnie Hill
15 Monte McAbee
16 Paul Mize
17 Tim Pyznarski
18 Ron Wilkerson
19 Mike Woodard
20 Jim Bennett
21 Lynn Garrett
22 Rodney Hobbs
23 Rusty McNealy
24 Luis Rojas
25 Dennis Sherow
26 Bob Didier
27 Keith Lieppman
28 Scot Pyle
29 Walt Horn

1982 Team Wichita Aeros

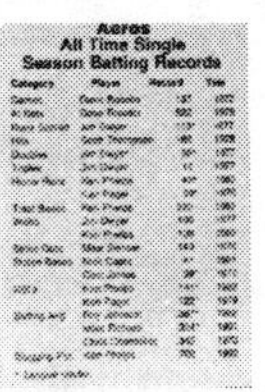

(Montreal Expos, AAA)

	MT	NR MT	EX
Complete Set:	10.00	7.50	4.00

(1) Joseph Abone
(2) Felipe Alou
(3) Douglas Capilla
(4) Michael Gates
(5) Thomas Gorman
(6) Batting Leaders (Roy Johnson)
(7) Roy Johnson
(8) Wally Johnson
(9) Richard Little
(10) Willard Mueller
(11) Richard Murray
(12) Batting Leaders (Ken Phelps)
(13) Kenneth Phelps
(14) Luis Quintana
(15) Richard Ramos
(16) Pat Rooney
(17) William Sattler
(18) Kim Seaman
(19) Christopher Smith
(20) Michael Stenhouse
(21) Thomas Weighaus

1982 Fritsch Wisconsin Rapids Twins

(Minnesota Twins, A)

	MT	NR MT	EX
Complete Set:	9.00	6.75	3.50

1 Team Logo/Checklist
2 Greg Kipfer
3 Ken Staples
4 Mike Weiermiller
5 Dave Hoyt
6 Mark Wright
7 Alvaro "Espi" Espinoza
8 Paul Fleming
9 Johnny Salery
10 Herbert Carter
11 Rick Scheetz
12 Larry James Mikesell
13 Sebby Borriello
14 Mark Portugal
15 Jose Gil
16 Barry "B.C." Houston
17 Dick Henkemeyer
18 Phil Franko
19 John Foster
20 Eric Porter
21 Willi Flores
22 Mark Larcom
23 Steve Aragon
24 Marc J. Page
25 Jeff Arney
26 Craig Henderson
27 Rhett Whisman

1983 TCMA Albany-Colonie A's

(Oakland A's, AA) (black & white)

	MT	NR MT	EX
Complete Set:	120.00	90.00	47.50

1 Jesse Anderson
2 Allen Edwards
3 Mark Fellows
4 Mark Ferguson
5 Paul Josephson
6 Mike Lynes
7 Steve Ontiveros
8 Gary Wex
9 Jim Durrman
10 Charlie O'Brien
11 Mike Ashman
12 Steve Kiefer
13 Tim Pyznarski
14 Luis Quinones
15 Phil Stephenson
16 Sly Young
17 Luis Bravo
18 Ron Harrison
19 Tom Romano
20 Pete Whisenant

1983 TCMA Albuquerque Dukes

(Los Angeles Dodgers, AAA) (color)

	MT	NR MT	EX
Complete Set:	45.00	34.00	18.00

1 Franklin Stubbs
2 Bert Geiger
3 Orel Hershiser
4 Brian Holton
5 Dean Rennicke
6 Rich Rodas
7 Paul Voigt
8 Larry White
9 Steve Perry
10 Alex Taveras
11 Jack Fimple
12 Scotti Madison
13 Brent Strom
14 Candy Maldonado
15 Sid Bream
16 Ross Jones
17 German Rivera
18 Greg Schultz
19 Ed Amelung
20 Tony Brewer
21 Ernesto Borbon
22 Lemmie Miller
23 Del Crandall
24 Dave Cohea
25 Dick McLaughlin

1983 TCMA Alexandria Dukes

(Pittsburgh Pirates, A) (black & white)

	MT	NR MT	EX
Complete Set:	75.00	56.00	30.00

1 Bobby Lyons
2 Sam Khalifa
3 Chuck Meadows
4 Scott Borland
5 Nick Castaneda
6 Jim Opie
7 Marvin Clack
8 Pete Rice
9 Art Ray
10 Scott Bailes
11 John Lipon
12 Johnny Taylor
13 Jim Aulenback
14 Chris Lein
15 David Tumbas
16 Roberto Bonilla
17 Thomas Martinez
18 Sean Faherty
19 Craig Brown
20 David Johnson
21 Steve Susce
22 Jim Felt
23 Nelson de la Russa
24 Eric Zimmerman
25 Steve Lewis
26 Rubin Rodriguez
27 Ravelo Manzanillo
28 Mike Quade
29 Jim Buckmier
30 Dorn Taylor
31 Lorenzo Bundy

1983 TCMA Anderson Braves

(Atlanta Braves, A) (color)

	MT	NR MT	EX
Complete Set:	12.50	9.50	5.00

1 Bill MacKay
2 Rick Albert
3 Skip Weisman
4 Randy Ingle
5 Dave May
6 Buzz Capra
7 John Baker
8 Jose Cano

9 Al Candelaria
10 Chip Reese
11 Ken Lynn
12 Charlie Morelock
13 John Mortillaro
14 Jim Rivera
15 Randy Rogers
16 Maximo Rosario
17 Rudy Torres
18 Sylverio Valdez
19 Ramon Vargas
20 Dave Griffin
21 Ralph Giansanti
22 Jay Palma
23 Andres Thomas
24 Dave Van Horn
25 Russ Anglin
26 Clint Brill
27 Jerry Ragsdale
28 Paul Llewellyn
29 Dave Morris
30 Larry Moser
31 Jay Roberts
32 Rich Thompson
33 Jeff Wagner

1983 Fritsch Appleton Foxes

(Chicago White Sox, A)

	MT	NR MT	EX
Complete Set:	10.00	7.50	4.00

1 Bill Smith
2 Mike Trujillo
3 Dave McLaughlin
4 Kim Christensen
5 Joel Mc Keon
6 Jim Best
7 Rich DeVincenzo
8 Pat Adams
9 Steve Noworyta
10 Craig Smajstrla
11 Mike Henley
12 Rolando Pino
13 John Cangelosi
14 Ken Williams
15 Team Photo
16 Team Photo
17 Edwin Correa
18 Ed Sedar
19 Bill Atkinson
20 Al Jones
21 Greg Tarnow
22 Ron Karkovice
23 David Kinsel
24 Johnny Moses
25 John Boles
26 Garry Keeton
27 Don Ruzek
28 Bill Sandry
29 Al Heath
30 Team Logo/Checklist

1983 TCMA Arkansas Travelers

(St. Louis Cardinals, AA) (black & white)

	MT	NR MT	EX
Complete Set:	110.00	82.50	45.00

1 Mike Rhodes
2 Ruben Gotay
3 Terry Clark
4 Kurt Kepshire
5 Walter Pierce
6 Mike Barba
7 Bill Thomas
8 Steve Winfield
9 Jerry Johnson
10 John Adams
11 Randy Hunt
12 Mark Salas
13 Mike Harris
14 Mike Wolters
15 Terry Pendelton
16 Luis Ojeda
17 Greg Guin
18 Alan Hunsinger
19 Rod Booker
20 Fran Batista
21 Gotay Mills
22 Larry Reynolds
23 Nick Leyva
24 Jorge Aranzamendi
25 Dave England

1983 TCMA Beaumont Golden Gators

(San Diego Padres, AA) (black & white) (card #3 of Steve Johnson is rarely found in Mint condition)

	MT	NR MT	EX
Complete Set:	95.00	71.00	38.00

1 Mike Martin
2 Ozzie Guillen
3 Steve Johnson
4 Randy Kaczmarski
5 Walt Vanderbush
6 Jim Leopold
7 Bob Patterson
8 Mark Williamson
9 Marty Lain
10 Dan Purpura
11 John Kruk
12 Steve Garcia
13 Mark Parent
14 Jeff Ronk
15 Mark Gillaspie
16 Pat Casey
17 Frank Ricci
18 Willie Hardwick
19 Ray Haywood, Jr.
20 James Steels
21 Jack Maloof
22 Allen Gerhardt
23 Gene Confreda

1983 Fritsch Beloit Brewers

(Milwaukee Brewers, A)

	MT	NR MT	EX
Complete Set:	10.00	7.50	4.00

1 Butch Kirby
2 Woolsey Rice
3 Dewey James
4 Jeff Gyarmati
5 John Mitchell
6 John Antonelli
7 Hank Landers
8 Jay Aldrich
9 Bruce Williams
10 Mark Johnston
11 Doug Norton
12 Steve Anderson
13 Bill Nowlan
14 Don Whiting
15 Team Logo/Checklist
16 Tim Nordbrook
17 Dave Tarrolly
18 Brian Finley
19 Jim Teahan
20 Tim Utecht
21 Billy Joe Robidoux
22 Chuck Crim
23 Edgar Diaz
24 Fritz Fedor
25 Dan Scarpetta
26 Hector Quinones
27 Chris Bosio
28 Stan Boroski
29 Joel Weatherford
---- Team Logo/Checklist

1983 TCMA Birmingham Barons

(Detroit Tigers, AA) (color)

	MT	NR MT	EX
Complete Set:	7.50	5.50	3.00

1 Raul Tovar
2 Don Gordon
3 Dan Williams
4 Dwight Lowry
5 Stan Younger
6 Dave Hawarny
7 Mark Smith
8 Doug Baker
9 Don Heinker
10 Bruce Robbins
11 George Foussianes
12 Bob Melvin
13 Greg Norman
14 Chuck Cary
15 Scott Tabor
16 Nelson Simmons
17 Scottie Earl
18 Ted Davis
19 Colin Ward
20 Jon Furman
21 Pedro Chavez
22 Keith Comstock
23 Troy Dixon
24 Roger Mason
25 Roy Majtyka

1983 TCMA Buffalo Bisons

(Cleveland Indians, AA) (color)

	MT	NR MT	EX
Complete Set:	20.00	15.00	8.00

1 Robin Fuson
2 Wayne Johnson
3 Rich Doyle
4 Gordie Glaser
5 Rod McDonald
6 Tom Owens
7 Rich Thompson
8 Jeff Green
9 Ramon Romero
10 John Malkin
11 Tim Glass
12 Everett Rey
13 Sal Rende
14 Jim Wilson
15 Shanie Dugas
16 Kelly Gruber
17 Jeff Moronko
18 Rene Quinones
19 Dave Gallagher
20 Ed Saavedra
21 Dwight Taylor
22 George Cecchetti
23 Joe Charboneau
24 Al Gallagher
25 Jack Aker

1983 TCMA Burlington Rangers

(Texas Rangers, A) (color)

	MT	NR MT	EX
Complete Set:	10.00	7.50	4.00

1 Barry Bass
2 John Buckley
3 Glenn Cook
4 Jose Guzman
5 Dave Hopkins
6 Terry Johnson
7 Chris Joslin
8 Randy Kramer
9 Tim Maki
10 Todd Schulte
11 Mike Soper
12 Elijah Ben
13 Bob Brower
14 George Crum
15 Ron Dillard
16 Bob Gergen
17 Otto Gonzales
18 Whitney Harry
19 Bob Hausladen
20 Brendan Hennessey
21 Jeff Mace
22 Sam Sorce
23 Kevin Stock
24 Mark Sutton
25 Tony Triplett
26 Orlando Gomez
27 Greg Jemison
28 Greg Campbell

1983 Fritsch Burlington Rangers

(Texas Rangers, A)

	MT	NR MT	EX
Complete Set:	10.00	7.50	4.00

1 Bob Hausladen
2 Todd Schulte
3 Sam Sorce
4 George Crum
5 Randy Kramer
6 Antonio Triplett
7 Jose Guzman
8 Elijah Ben
9 Barry Bass
10 Terry Johnson
11 Bobby Brower
12 Glen Cook
13 Bob Gergen
14 Ron Dillard
15 Whitney J. Harry
16 Chris Joslin
17 Otto Gonzalez
18 Brendan Hennessy
19 Tim Maki
20 John Buckley
21 Mark Sutton
22 Kevin Stock
23 David Hopkins
24 Jeff Mace
25 Greg Campbell
26 Greg Jemison
28 Team Logo/Checklist
29 Team Logo/Fritsch Ad
30 Sponsor Card

1983 TCMA Butte Copper Kings

(Kansas City Royals, Rookie) (black & white)

	MT	NR MT	EX
Complete Set:	25.00	18.50	10.00

1 Dennis Boatright
2 Dan Chelini
3 Dave Digirolama
4 Tom Edens
5 Phil George
6 Gary Klein
7 Stefan Lipson
8 Charley Luman
9 Randy Robinson
10 John Serritella
11 Jose Torres
12 Rob Vodvarka
13 Dave Landrith
14 Tom Niemann
15 Stan Oxner
16 Jim Bagnall
17 Vic Davila
18 Jere Longenecker
19 Mike Miller
20 Kevin Seitzer
21 Kevin Stanley
22 Mark Van Blaricom
23 Edward Allen
24 John Devich
25 Tommy Mohr
26 Dave Rooker
27 John Rubel
28 Jeff Schulz
29 Joe Kasunick
30 Tommy Jones
31 Guy Hansen
32 Bruce Platt
33 Tom Osowski

1983 TCMA Cedar Rapids Reds

(Cincinnati Reds, A) (color)

	MT	NR MT	EX
Complete Set:	15.00	11.00	6.00

1 Bruce Kimm
2 Scott Jones
3 Dave Lochner
4 Mike Knox
5 Glenn Spagnola
6 Billy Hawley
7 Mike Konderla
8 Tim Scott
9 Tim Reynolds
10 Joe Stalp
11 Louie Trujillo
12 Steve Padia
13 Rob Murphy
14 Buddy Pryor
15 Scott Radloff
16 Tom Riley
17 Delwyn Young
18 Dave Haberle
19 Terry Lee
20 Mike Manfre
21 Vince Rover
22 Kal Daniels
23 Orsino Hill
24 Jeff Rhodes
25 Jay Munson
26 Don Buchheister
27 Batboys
28 Wayne Harmon

1983 Fritsch Cedar Rapids Reds

(Cincinnati Reds, A)

	MT	NR MT	EX
Complete Set:	10.00	7.50	4.00

1 Tim Reynolds
2 Buddy Pryor
3 Tim Scott
4 Joe Stalp
5 Tom Riley
6 Wayne Harmon
7 Jay Munson
8 Dave Lochner
9 Mike Knox
10 Billy Hawley
11 Dave Haberle
12 Louie Trujillo
13 Terry Lee
14 Mike Konderla
15 Jeff Rhodes
16 Glenn Spagnola
17 Kal Daniels
18 Scott Jones
19 Vin Rover
20 Mike Manfre
21 Scott Radloff
22 Bruce Kimm
23 Orsino Hill
24 Rob Murphy

25 Steve Padia
26 Team Logo/Checklist

1983 TCMA Charleston Charlies

(Cleveland Indians, AAA) (color)

	MT	NR MT	EX
Complete Set:	7.50	5.50	3.00

1 Jay Baller
2 Mike Jeffcoat
3 Larry Hrynko
4 Jerry Reed
5 Roy Smith
6 Sandy Whitol
7 Doug Simunic
8 Jerry Willard
9 Luis DeLeon
10 Angelo Logrande
11 Juan Pacho
12 Karl Pagel
13 Jack Perconte
14 Tim Norrid
15 Rodney Craig
16 Wil Culmer
17 Kevin Rhomberg
18 Otto Velez
19 Ed Glynn
20 Vic Albury
21 Steve Cisczon
22 Doc Edwards

1983 TCMA Charleston Royals

(Kansas City Royals, A) (black & white)

	MT	NR MT	EX
Complete Set:	9.00	6.75	3.50

1 Mark Pirruccello
2 Nicky Richards
3 Joe Szekely
4 Jim Bagnall
5 Chris Bryeans
6 Craig Goodin
7 Keith Hempfield
8 Bill Phillips
9 Rich Vitato
10 Edward Allen
11 Roland Oruna
12 Jack Shuffield
13 Van Snider
14 Richard Aube
15 John Bryant
16 Doug Cook
17 John Davis
18 Bob De Bord
19 Tom Drizmala
20 Rich Goodin
21 Ron McCormack
22 Israel Sanchez
23 John Serritella
24 Roy Tanner
25 Duane Gustavson
26 Mark Farnsworth

1983 TCMA Chattanooga Lookouts

(Seattle Mariners, AA) (black & white)

	MT	NR MT	EX
Complete Set:	180.00	135.00	72.50

1 Darnell Coles
2 Paul Serna
3 Chris Hunger
4 Joe Whitmer
5 Ramon Estepa
6 Danny Tartabull
7 Vic Martin
8 Alvin Davis
9 Mike Bucci
10 Miguel Negron
11 Mark Langston
12 Mickey Bowers
13 Bob Randolph
14 Robert Hudson
15 Don (Clay) Hill
16 Jeff Stottlemyre
17 Tracy Harris
18 Kevin King
19 Kevin Dukes
20 John Burden
21 Mark Cahill
22 Kevin Steger
23 Tom Hunt
24 Chief Lookout
25 Harry Landreth
26 Dave Valle
27 Ivan Calderon
---- Team Photo

1983 Fritsch Clinton Giants

(San Francisco Giants, A)

	MT	NR MT	EX
Complete Set:	10.00	7.50	4.00

1 Bill Kueh, Gus Stokes)
2 Eric Halberg
3 Scott Norman
4 Billy Cabell
5 Jim Weir
6 Greg Lynn
7 Marty Baier
8 Ramon Bautista
9 Scott Rainey
10 Gene Lambert
11 Orlando Blackwell
12 Davis Tavarez
13 Bob Naber
14 Alonzo Powell
15 Mike Empting
16 John Hughes
17 Brian Bargerhuff
18 Alan Marr
19 Ken Mills
20 Kelvin Smith
21 Van Sowards
22 Kurt Mattson
23 Ed Stewart
24 Dennie Taft
25 Marty DeMerritt
26 Scott Blanke
27 Randy Weibel
28 Jeff Gladden
29 Bill Lachemann
30 Team Logo/Checklist

1983 TCMA Columbus Astros

(Houston Astros, AA) (black & white)

	MT	NR MT	EX
Complete Set:	30.00	22.00	12.00

1 George Bjorkman
2 Ed Cuervo
3 John Csefalvay
4 Mike Grace
5 Jim Sherman
6 Mark Strucher
7 Larry Simcox
8 Steve Benson
9 Eric Bullock
10 Ty Gainey
11 Glenn Davis
12 Fransisco Jabalera
13 Jeff Calhoun
14 Jeff Heathcock
15 Jim MacDonald
16 Tim Meckes
17 Zac Paris
18 Pat Perry
19 Ben Snyder
20 Jack Smith
21 Bob Sprowl
22 Jack Hiatt
23 Ken Bolek
24 Rex Jones

1983 TCMA Columbus Clippers

(New York Yankees, AAA) (color)

	MT	NR MT	EX
Complete Set:	20.00	15.00	8.00

1 Johnny Oates
2 Coaching Staff
3 Juan Espino
4 Bradley Gulden
5 Silton Fontenot
6 David Wehrmeister
7 Timothy Burke
8 Dennis Rasmussen
9 Clay Christiansen
10 Stefan Wever
11 Curt Kaufman
12 Jesus Hernaiz
13 Guy Elston
14 Benjamin Callahan III
15 Stephen Balboni
16 Marshall Brant
17 Bert Campaneris
18 Edwin Rodriguez
19 Barry Evans
20 Robert Meacham
21 Clell Hobson, Jr.
22 Michael Patterson
23 Matthew Winters
24 James Hart
25 Otis Nixon
26 Brian Dayett
27 Rowland Office

1983 TCMA Daytona Beach Astros

(Houston Astros, A) (black & white)

	MT	NR MT	EX
Complete Set:	10.00	7.50	4.00

1 Dave Cripe
2 Stan Hough
3 Rich Bombard
4 Mike Callahan
5 Guillermo Castro
6 Manny Hernandez
7 Mark Knudson
8 Mike Hogan
9 Uvaldo Regaldo
10 Ed Reilly
11 Rex Schimpf
12 Jamey Shouppe
13 Tom Wiedenbauer
14 Don Berti
15 Jeff Datz
16 Jamie Williams
17 Randy Braun
18 Glenn Carpenter
19 Juan Delgado
20 Gary D'Onofrio
21 Steve McAllister
22 Ricardo Rivera
23 Jim Thomas
24 Mike Botkin
25 Curtis Burke
26 Louie Meadows
27 Tony Walker

1983 TCMA Durham Bulls

(Atlanta Braves, A) (color)

	MT	NR MT	EX
Complete Set:	16.00	12.00	6.50

1 Chip Childress
2 Steve Chmil
3 Terry Cormack
4 Inocencio Guerrero
5 Johnny Hatcher
6 Pat Hodge
7 Scott Hood
8 Mike Knox
9 Bob Luzon
10 Bryan Neal
11 Tony Neuendorff
12 Ken Scanlon
13 Rick Siriano
14 Freddy Tiburcio
15 Bob Tumpane
16 Mike Bormann
17 Dave Clay
18 Tim Cole
19 Mark Lance
20 Rich Leggatt
21 Dennis Lubert
22 Ike Pettaway
23 Allen Sears
24 Zane Smith
25 Duane Ward
26 Matt West
27 Tim Alexander
28 Brian Snitker
29 Leo Mazzone

1983 TCMA El Paso Diablos

(Milwaukee Brewers, AA) (color)

	MT	NR MT	EX
Complete Set:	6.00	4.50	2.50

1 Dan Burns
2 Eric Peyton
3 Joe Henderson
4 Jim Paciorek
5 Bryan Duquette
6 Stan Davis
7 Mark Effrig
8 Rene Quinones
9 Mike Felder
10 Juan Castillo
11 Stan Levi
12 Garrett Nago
13 Bill Max
14 Ray Gallo
15 Bryan Clutterbuck
16 Steve Parrott
17 Tim Crews
18 Al Price
19 Carlos Ponce
20 Kevin McCoy
21 Earnest Riles
22 Frank Thomas
23 Jack Lazorko
24 Bob Schroeck
25 Lee Sigman

1983 TCMA Erie Cardinals

(St. Louis Cardinals, A) (color)

	MT	NR MT	EX
Complete Set:	15.00	11.00	6.00

1 Paul Mangiardi
2 Joe Rigoli
3 John Rigos
4 Jim ReBoulet
5 Wilfredo Martinez
6 Bill Packer
7 Mark Dougherty
8 Keith Turnbull
9 Jamie Brisco
10 Brian Farley
11 Mike Behrend
12 Mark Angelo
13 Jeff Pasquali
14 Scott Pleis
15 Chuck McGrath
16 Jeff Gass
17 Phil Burwell
18 John Costello
19 Tim Kavanaugh
20 Tom Pagnozzi
21 Tom Rossi
22 Ernie Carrasco
23 Tom Caulfield
24 Mike Robinson
25 Kurt Kaull

1983 TCMA Evansville Triplets

(Detroit Tigers, AAA) (color)

	MT	NR MT	EX
Complete Set:	7.50	5.50	3.00

1 Mark Dacko
2 Craig Eaton
3 David Gumpert
4 Bryan Kelly
5 Steven Luebber
6 Charles Nail
7 Randall O'Neill
8 Larry Pashnick
9 Davis Rucker
10 Patrick Underwood
11 Martin Castillo
12 Willie Royster
13 Jeffery Bertoni
14 Julio Gonzales
15 Mike Laga
16 Juan Lopez
17 Kenneth Baker
18 Barbaro Garbey
19 Bob Grandas
20 Jeffrey Kenaga
21 Darryl Motley
22 Gordon MacKenzie
23 William Armstrong
24 Mark DeJohn
25 German Barranca

1983 TCMA Glens Falls White Sox

(Chicago White Sox, AA) (black & white)

	MT	NR MT	EX
Complete Set:	35.00	26.00	14.00

1 Darryl Boston
2 J.B. Brown
3 Wes Kent
4 Monte McAbee
5 Scott Meier
6 Ed Miles
7 Mike Morse
8 Dave Nix
9 Curt Reed
10 Ramon Romero
11 Pat Kelly
12 Tom Brennan
13 Keith Desjarlais
14 Mike Maitland
15 Homer Moncrief
16 Robert Moore
17 Tom Mullen
18 Steve Pastrovich
19 Wayne Schuckert
20 Mike Tanzi
21 Mike Withrow
22 Adrian Garrett
23 Lori Corcoran
24 Dick Manning

1983 TCMA Greensboro Hornets

(New York Yankees, A) (color)

	MT	NR MT	EX
Complete Set:	25.00	18.50	10.00

1 Johnny Baldwin
2 Scott Beahan

3	Ozzie Canseco
4	Jim Corsi
5	Logan Easley
6	John Caston
7	Steve George
8	Randy Graham
9	Rich Gumbert
10	Daryl Humphrey
11	Steve Ray
12	Dick Seidel
13	Randy White
14	Fredi Gonzalez
15	Phil Lombardi
16	Mark Blaser
17	Maurice Ching
18	Mike Fennell
19	Roberto Kelly
20	Pedro Medina
21	Felix Perdomo
22	Jim Riggs
23	Jose Rivera
24	Stan Javier
25	Joe MacKay
26	Tony Russell
27	Carlos Tosca
28	Bill Evers
29	Q.V. Lowe
30	Don McGann

1983 TCMA Idaho Falls Athletics

(Oakland A's, A) (black & white)

	MT	NR MT	EX
Complete Set:	9.00	6.75	3.50

1	Steve Bowens
2	Steve Chasteen
3	Oscar DeChavez
4	Wayne Giddings
5	Dave Hanna
6	Darel Hansen
7	Perry Johnson
8	Mark Leonette
9	Wade Mangum
10	Camilo Pascual
11	Larry Smith
12	Bob Vantrease
13	Tony Wadley
14	Joe Law
15	Eric Garrett
16	Matt Held
17	Mike Rojas
18	Steve Chumas
19	Darrell Dull
20	Rich Borowski
21	Twayne Harris
22	Rob Nelson
23	Felix Pagan
24	Mike Rantz
25	Mike Wilder
26	Maurice Castain
27	Steve Howard
28	Sly Humphrey
29	Tony Moncrief
30	Jim Nettles
31	Grady Fuson
32	Gary Lance
33	Mark Doberenz
34	Dave Sheriff

1983 Team Indianapolis Indians

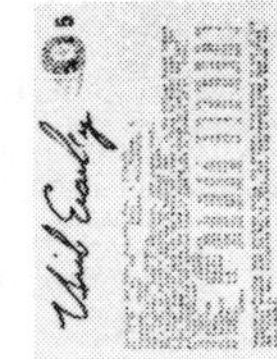

(Cincinnati Reds, AAA) (co-sponsored by Tom Aikens)

	MT	NR MT	EX
Complete Set:	10.00	7.50	4.00

1	Indians Team
2	"Last Season We Won It All"
3	Roy Hartsfield
4	Charlie Leibrandt
5	Nick Esasky
6	Greg Harris
7	Dallas Williams
8	Joe Edelen
9	The Starters (Mike Dowless, Greg Harris, Charlie Leibrandt, Jeff Russell, Freddie Toliver)
10	Willie Lozado
11	Brian Ryder
12	Tom Lawless
13	The Bullpen (Bob Buchanan, Rich Carlucci, Joe Edelen, Brad Lesley, Brian Ryder)
14	Jeff Russell
15	Ray Corbett
16	Rich Carlucci
17	The Infielders (Skeeter Barnes, Nick Esasky, Glen Franklin, John Harris, Tom Lawless, Willie Lozado)
18	Orlando Isales
19	Freddie Toliver
20	Ron Little
21	The Catchers (Ray Corabett, Dave Van Gorder)
22	Mark Gilbert
23	Mike Dowless
24	Glen Franklin
25	The Outfielders (Mark Gilbert, Orlando Isales, Ron Little, Dallas Williams)
26	Brad Lesley
27	Dave Van Gorder
28	Bob Buchanan
29	John Harris
30	The Instructors (Ted Kluszewski, Fred Norman)
31	Skeeter Barnes
32	Lee Garrett

1983 TCMA Iowa Cubs

(Chicago Cubs, AAA) (color) (If the unnumbered Cubby card is included, the set is worth $150 in Mint condition)

	MT	NR MT	EX
Complete Set:	90.00	67.50	36.00

1	Rich Bordi
2	Bill Earley
3	Tom Filer
4	Alan Hargesheimer
5	Larry Jones
6	Dan Larson
7	Reggie Patterson
8	John Perlman (Jon)
9	Don Schulze
10	Randy Stein
11	Mike Diaz
12	Bill Hayes
13	Fritz Connally
14	Joe Hicks
15	Jay Loviglio
16	Carmelo Martinez
17	Jerry Manuel
18	Dave Owen
19	Dan Rohn
20	Joe Carter
21	Henry Cotto
22	Tom Grant
23	Carlos Lezcano
24	Steve Carroll
25	Front Office Team
26	Jim Narier
27	Scott Breeden
28	Kim Hart
29	Ken Grandquist
----	Cubby (team mascot)

1983 Kelly Studios Kinston Blue Jays

(Toronto Blue Jays, A)

	MT	NR MT	EX
Complete Set:	65.00	49.00	26.00

(1)	Jim Bishop
(2)	J.J. Cannon
(3)	Ron Clark
(4)	Scot Elam
(5)	Jose Escobar
(6)	Keith Gilliam
(7)	Devallon Harper
(8)	Moe Hazelette
(9)	Ken Kinnard
(10)	Chris Knapp
(11)	Tom Layton
(12)	Tom Layton
(13)	Perry Lychak
(14)	Peery Mader
(15)	Alex Marte
(16)	Mark Poole
(17)	Joe Pursell
(18)	Steve Reish
(19)	Derrick Reutter
(20)	Ralph Rivas
(21)	Tim Rodgers
(22)	Randy Romagna
(23)	Eddie Santos
(24)	Jay Schroeder
(25)	Mike Sharperson
(26)	Rico Sutton
(27)	Bernie Tatis
(28)	Guillermo Valenzuela
(29)	Dave Wells

1983 TCMA Knoxville Blue Jays

(Toronto Blue Jays, AA) (black & white)

	MT	NR MT	EX
Complete Set:	9.00	6.75	3.50

1	Tom Blackmon
2	Stan Clarke
3	John Cerutti
4	Mercedes Esquer
5	Jack McKnight
6	Chris Phillips
7	Dave Shipanoff
8	Bill Pinkham
9	Dan Whitmer
10	Carry Harris
11	Chris Johnston
12	Augie Schmidt
13	Andre Wood
14	Chris Shaddy
15	Kevin Aitcheson
16	Eddie Dennis
17	Greg Griffin
18	Paul Hodgson
19	John McLaren
20	Doug Ault
21	John Woodworth
22	Gary McCune

1983 BHN Las Vegas Stars

(San Diego Padres, AAA)

	MT	NR MT	EX
Complete Set:	12.00	9.00	4.75

(1)	Greg Booker
(2)	Bobby Brown
(3)	Larry Brown
(4)	Tim Cook
(5)	Gerry Davis
(6)	Gerry De Simone
(7)	Harry Dunlop
(8)	Steve Fireovid
(9)	Larry Harlow
(10)	Geroge Hinshaw
(11)	Tom House
(12)	Jerry Johnson
(13)	Joe Lansford
(14)	Bill Long
(15)	Kevin Mc Reynolds
(16)	Felix Oroz
(17)	Joe Pittman
(18)	Larry Rothschild
(19)	Cecilio Ruiz
(20)	James Steels
(21)	Mark Thurmond
(22)	Ron Tingley

1983 Riley's Louisville Redbirds

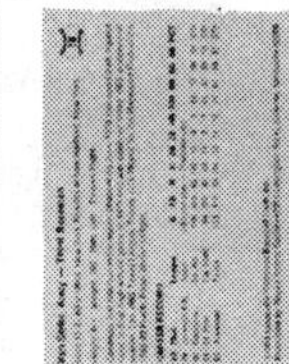

(St. Louis Cardinals, AAA)

	MT	NR MT	EX
Complete Set:	20.00	15.00	8.00

1	Jim Fregosi
2	Gaylen Pitts
3	Jerry Mc Kune
4	Dyar Miller
5	Gene Roof
6	Kevin Hagen
7	Joe De Sa
8	David Von Ohlen
9	Tom Nieto
10	Jeff Keener
11	Jeff Doyle
12	Tito Landrum
13	Jose Gonzalez
14	Jose Brito
15	Gene Dotson
16	Ralph Citarella
17	Andy Rincon
18	Andy Van Slyke
19	Jim Adduci
20	John Fulgham
21	Mike Calise
22	Dennis Werth
23	Ricky Horton
24	Orlando Sanchez
25	Tom Thurberg
26	Todd Worrell
27	Bill Lyons
28	Dave Kable
29	Doyle Harris
30	Jed Smith

The values quoted are intended to reflect the market price.

1983 TCMA Lynchburg Mets

(New York Mets, A) (black & white)

	MT	NR MT	EX
Complete Set:	55.00	41.00	22.00

1	Reggie Jackson
2	Larry McNutt
3	Bill Latham
4	Jeff Bettendorf
5	Bill Fultz
6	Darryl Denby
7	Randy Milligan
8	Greg Olson
9	Bruce Morrison
10	Dwight Gooden
11	Sam Perlozzo
12	Not Issued
13	John Cumberland
14a	Mark Carreon
14b	Dave Cochrane
15	Lenny Dykstra
16	Jay Tibbs
17	John Heller
18	Jeff Sunderlage
19	Dave Wyatt
20	Joe Graves
21	Rich Pickett
22	Ed Hearn
23	Wes Gardner

1983 TCMA Lynn Pirates

(Pittsburgh Pirates, AA) (black & white)

	MT	NR MT	EX
Complete Set:	29.00	21.00	11.00

1	Mike Bielecki
2	Wilfredo Cordoba
3	Fernando Gonzalez
4	John Lackey
5	Lee Marcheskie
6	Dale Mahorcic
7	Craig Pippin
8	Keith Thibodeaux
9	Tim Wheeler
11	Stan Cliburn
12	Burke Goldthorn
13	Peter Rowe
14	Rafael Belliard
15	Nelson Norman
16	Greg Pastors
17	Rich Renteria
18	John Schaive
19	Benny Distefano
20	Ken Ford
21	Connor McGeehee
22	Jose Rodriguez
23	Tommy Sandt
24	Frank Leger
25	Brian McCann
26	Thomas Lynn
27	Gary Fitzpatrick
28	Jay Walsh

1983 Fritsch Madison Muskies

(Oakland A's, A)

	MT	NR MT	EX
Complete Set:	45.00	34.00	18.00

1	B. Dre, E. Janus)
2	S. Charr, M. Du Val)
3	Dave Collins
4	Todd Fischer
5	Dave Wilder
6	Ray Alonzo
7	Dennis Gonsalves
8	Jorge Diaz
9	Thad Reece
10	Ed Retzer
11	Shawn Gill
12	Tom Conquest
13	Jose Canseco
14	Keith Call
15	Bob Loscalzo
16	Bob Hallas
17	Eddie Escribano
18	Gene Ransom
19	John Michel
20	Mikki Jackson
21	Juan Cruz
22	Greg Robles
23	Pete Kendrick
24	Gary Dawson
25	Glenn Godwin
26	John Huey
27	Dave Leiper
28	Brian Graham
29	Hector Perez
30	Frank Trucchio
31	Brad Fischer
32	Team Logo/Checklist

1983 TCMA Memphis Chicks

(Montreal Expos, AA) (black & white)

	MT	NR MT	EX
Complete Set:	12.00	9.00	4.75

1 Shooty Babitt
2 George Cruz
3 Rene Gonzales
4 John Damon
5 Jeff Carl
6 Larry Goldetsky
7 Don Carter
8 Nelson Santovenia
9 Dave Hoeksema
10 Tommy Joe Shimp
11 Tim Cates
12 Bud Yanus
13 Rod Nealeigh
14 Jeff Taylor
15 Leonel Carrion
16 Jim Auten
17 Bob Tenenini
18 Larry Glasscock
19 Joe Hesketh
20 Greg Bargar
21 Razor Shines
22 Jeff Porter
23 Rick Renick
24 Mike Kinnvnen

1983 TCMA Miami Marlins

(San Diego Padres, A) (black & white)

	MT	NR MT	EX
Complete Set:	120.00	90.00	47.50

1 Will George
2 Mike McClain
3 Scott Gardner
4 Francisco Cota
5 Gene Walter
6 Sergio Del Rosario
7 Bill Gerhardt
8 Chuck Kolotka
9 Greg Raymer
10 Kevin Rhodas
11 Jeff Dean
12 Ray Nodell
13 Billy Ireland
14 Jose Gomez
15 Dan Jones
16 Al Simmons
17 Paul Noce
18 Manny Del Rosario
19 John Frierson
20 Benito Santiago
21 Bob Allinger
22 Tim Cannon
23 Tommy Francis
24 Steve Sayles
25 Jim Breazeale
26 Mark Miggins
27 Dennis Maley
28 Todd Hutcheson

1983 TCMA Midland Cubs

(Chicago Cubs, AA) (black & white)

	MT	NR MT	EX
Complete Set:	10.00	7.50	4.00

1 Bill Schammel
2 Tommy Harmon
3 Glen Gregson
4 Jim Walsh
5 Neil Bryant
6 Dennis Brogna
7 Carlos Gil
8 Doug Weleno
9 Tim Millner
10 Bruce Chanye
11 Ken Pryce
12 Darrel Banks
13 Bill Hatcher
14 Tom Lombarski
15 George Borges
16 Trey Brooks
17 Don Hyman
18 Ron Richardson
19 Stan Kyles
20 Mike Anicich
21 Jim Gerlach
22 Ray Soff
23 Tom Johnson
24 Randy LaVigne
25 Rick Baker
26 A.J. Hill

1983 Chong Modesto A's

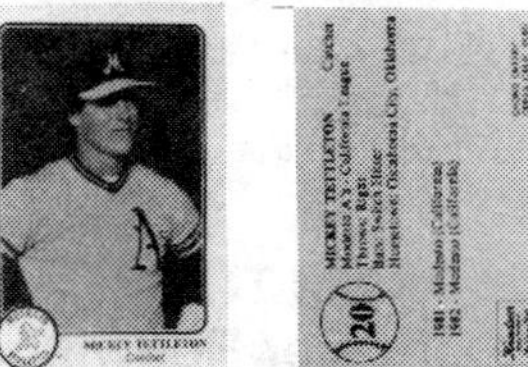

(Oakland A's, A)

	MT	NR MT	EX
Complete Set:	35.00	26.00	14.00

1 Bruce Amador
2 Eric Barry
3 Bob Bathe
4 Tommy Copeland
5 Kevin Coughlon
6 James Eppard
7 Charles Fick
8 Mike Gorman
9 Tony Herron
10 Rodney Hobbs, Mark Jarrett
11 Mark Jarrett
12 Jeff Kaiser
13 Jeff Kobernus
14 Tim Lambert
15 Rod Murphy
16 Ed Myers
17 Davis Peterson
18 Tab Rojas
19 Phil Strom
20 Mickey Tettleton
21 Raymond Thoma
22 Ricky Thomas
23 Robert Vavrock
24 Thomas Zmudosky
25 George Mitterwald
26 Rick Tronerud
27 Keith Lieppman
28 Phil Danielson
29 Dan Kiser
30 Davis Fry

1983 TCMA Nashua Angels

(California Angels, AA) (black & white) (mint cards of Cliburn and Connor are scarce)

	MT	NR MT	EX
Complete Set:	7.50	5.50	3.00

1 Bob Bastian
2 Rod Boxberger
3 Stewart Cliburn
4 Jeff Connor
5 Bill Mooneyham
6 Ron Romanick
7 Mickey Saatzer
8 D.W. Smith
9 Ron Sylvia
10 Steve Liddle
11 Larry Patterson
12 Harry Francis
13 Craig Gerber
14 Gustavo Polidor
15 Darryl Stephens
16 Frank Vilorio
17 Jim Beswick
18 Sap Randall
19 Al Romero
20 Winston Llenas
21 Frank Reberger
22 Richard Zaleski
23 Mark McCormack
24 Ben Surner
25 Jerry Mileur
26 George Como
27 Nashua Angels Chicken

1983 Team Nashville Sounds

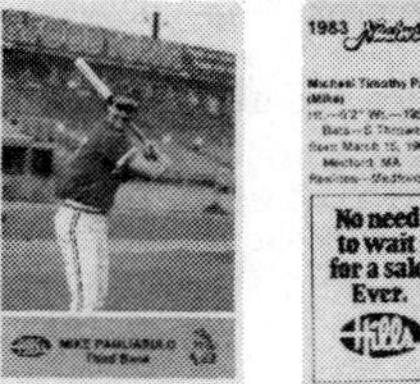

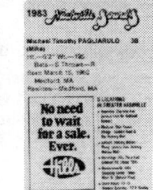

(New York Yankees, AA)

	MT	NR MT	EX
Complete Set:	12.00	9.00	4.75

(1) Scott Bradley
(2) Mike Browning
(3) Tim Burke
(4) Ben Callahan
(5) Pete Dalena
(6) Matt Gallegos
(7) Paul Grayner
(8) Doug Holmquist
(9) Frank Kneuer
(10) Tim Knight
(11) Vic Mata
(12) Derwin Mc Nealy
(13) Ed Olwine
(14) Mike Pagliarulo
(15) Scott Patterson
(16) Erik Peterson
(17) Mike Reddish
(18) Jim Saul
(19) Kelly Scott
(20) Mark Shifflett
(21) Buck Showalter
(22) Mark Silva
(23) Keith Smith
(24) Dave Szymczak
(25) Hoyt Wilhelm

1983 TCMA Oklahoma City 89'ers

(Texas Rangers, AAA) (color)

	MT	NR MT	EX
Complete Set:	10.00	7.50	4.00

1 Bill Stearns
2 Tommy Burgess
3 Terry Bogener
4 Nick Capra
5 Tracy Cowger
6 Victor Cruz
7 Tommy Dunbar
8 Mike Griffin
9 Thomas Henke
10 Michael Jirschele
11 Robert Jones
12 Peter MacKanin
13 Mark Mercer
14 Ron Musselman
15 David Rajsich
16 Paul Semall
17 David Stockstill
18 Don Werner
19 Curt Wilkerson
20 Mike Mason
21 Joe Strain
22 Jim Farr
23 Don Scott
24 Danny Wheat

1983 TCMA Omaha Royals

(Kansas City Royals, AAA) (color)

	MT	NR MT	EX
Complete Set:	30.00	22.00	12.00

1 Mike Alvarez
2 Bud Black
3 Derek Botelho
4 Scott Brown
5 Keith Creel
6 Danny Jackson
7 Mike Parrott
8 Dan St. Clair
9 Dave Schuler
10 Vince Yuhas
11 Brian Poldberg
12 Russ Stephans
13 Buddy Biancalana
14 Jeff Cox
15 Mark Funderburk
16 Kelly Heath
17 Cliff Pastornicky
18 Steve Hammond
19 Bombo Rivera
20 Mark Ryal
21 Pat Sheridan
22 Dave Leeper
23 Bill Gorman
24 Joe Sparks
25 Jerry Cram
26 Paul McCannon

1983 TCMA Orlando Twins

(Minnesota Twins, AA) (color) (complete set price includes scarce Carroll card)

	MT	NR MT	EX
Complete Set:	45.00	34.00	18.00

1 Phil Roof
2 Tony Pilla
3 Jim Weaver
4 Kevin Williams
5 Jeff Reed
6 Steve Lombardozzi
7 Mike McCain
8 John Palica
9 Mike Sodders
10 Chino Cadahia
11 Ken Foster
12 Jerry Lomastro
13 Manny Pena
14 Jay Pettibone
15 Rich Yett
16 Jack Hobbs
17 Ted Kromy
18 Kirby Krueger
19 Eric Broersma
20 Paul Gibson
21 Mike Giordano
22 Tony Guerrero
23 Not Issued
24 Not Issued
25 Carson Carroll

1983 TCMA Pawtucket Red Sox

(Boston Red Sox, AAA) (color)

	MT	NR MT	EX
Complete Set:	45.00	34.00	18.00

1 Bob Birrell
2 Dennis Boyd
3 Dennis Burtt
4 Steve Crawford
5 Brian Denman
6 Jim Dorsey
7 Mark Fidrych
8 Keith MacWhorter
9 Bill Moloney
10 Dave Schoppee
11 Steve Shields
12 Roger LaFrancois
13 John Lickert
14 Marty Barrett
15 Juan Bustabad
16 Mike Davis
17 Dave Koza
18 Jim Wilson
19 Reggie Whittemore
20 Gus Burgess
21 Geno Gentile
22 Lee Graham
23 Juan Pautt
24 Chico Walker
25 Tony Torchia
26 Mike Roarke

1983 Fritsch Peoria Suns

(California Angels, A)

	MT	NR MT	EX
Complete Set:	15.00	11.00	6.00

1 Ray Jimenez
2 Joe King
3 Kevin Davis
4 Scott Glanz
5 Donald Groh
6 Dave Heath
7 Kris Kline
8 Doug McKenzie
9 Mark McLemore
10 Tom Smith
11 Rick Stromer
12 Jose Valdez
13 Don Timberlake
14 Mike Rizzo
15 Jack Crawford
16 Tom Rentschler
17 Jeff Salazar
18 Jay Lewis
19 Al Cristy
20 Rafael Lugo
21 Scott Suehr
22 Devon White
23 Julian Gonzalez
24 Brian Hartsock
25 Bob Kipper
26 Ron Phipps
27 Mike Saverino
28 Eddie Rodriguez
29 Joe Coleman
30 Team Logo/Checklist

Values for recent cards and sets are listed in Mint (MT), Near Mint (NM), reflecting the fact that many cards from recent years have been preserved in top condition. Recent cards and sets in less than Excellent condition have little collector interest.

1983 BHN Phoenix Giants

(San Francisco Giants, AAA)

	MT	NR MT	EX
Complete Set:	15.00	11.00	6.00

1 John Rabb
2 Mark Calvert
3 Scott Garrelts
4 Brian Asselstine
5 Jeff Ransom
6 Rich Murray
7 Jeff Cornell
8 Dan Gladden
9 Tom Runnells
10 Kernan Ronan
11 Phil Hinrichs
12 Kelvin Torve
13 Herman Segelke
14 Guy Sularz
15 Randy Kutcher
16 Ted Wilborn
17 Mike Brecht
18 Butch Hughes
19 Ron Pisel
20 Mark Davis
21 Mark Dempsey
22 Chris Smith
23 Craig Chamberlain
24 Jack Mull
25 Doug Landuyt
26 Ethan Blackaby
27 Phoenix Giants Rooster
28 Tommy Gonzalez

1983 TCMA Portland Beavers

(Philadelphia Phillies, AAA) (black & white) (complete set price includes scarce #s 23-25)

	MT	NR MT	EX
Complete Set:	120.00	90.00	47.50

1 Luis Aguayo
2 Juan Samuel
3 Larry Andersen
4 Kyle Money
5 Kevin Gross
6 Steve Jeltz
7 Jerry Keller
8 Len Matuszek
9 Kelly Downs
10 Ramon Aviles
11 Tim Corcoran
12 George Culver
13 John Felske
14 Chris Bourjos
15 Porfi Altamirano
16 Dick Davis
17 John Russell
18 Marty Decker
19 Charlie Hudson
20 Ed Miller
21 Ron Pruitt
22 Alejandro Sanchez
23 Stan Bahnsen
24 Larry Bradford
25 Kiko Garcia

1983 TCMA Quad City Cubs

(Chicago Cubs, A) (black & white)

	MT	NR MT	EX
Complete Set:	45.00	34.00	18.00

1 Roger Crow
2 Larry Cox
3 Dick Pole
4 Mario Panetta
5 David Barber, Kyle Benjamin
6 Mark Baker
7 Steve Balmer
8 Brad Blevins
9 Mitch Cook
10 Jeff Fruge
11 Rene German
12 Tim Grachen
13 Randy Lockie
14 Rudy Serafini
15 Brian Tuller
16 Steven Roadcap
17 Juan Velazquez
18 Jim Allen
19 Steve Cordner
20 Shawon Dunston
21 Gary Jones
22 Tony Woods
23 Jose Rivera
24 Stan Boderick
25 Damon Farmar
26 Dave Martinez
27 Rolando Roomes

1983 TCMA Reading Phillies

(Philadelphia Phillies, AA) (black & white)

	MT	NR MT	EX
Complete Set:	130.00	97.50	52.50

1 Bud Bartholow
2 Darren Burroughs
3 Don Carman
4 Jay Davisson
5 Rich Gaynor
6 Frankie Griffin
7 Bill Johnson
8 George Riley
9 Denny Thomas
10 Ed Wojna
11 Darren Daulton
12 Mike LaValliere
13 Den Dowell
14 Greg Legg
15 Francisco Melendez
16 Julio Perez
17 Juan Samuel
18 Willie Darkis
19 Randy Salava
20 Jeff Stone
21 Keith Washington
22 Mel Williams
23 Bill Dancy
24 Bob Tiefenauer

1983 TCMA Redwood Pioneers

(California Angels, A) (color)

	MT	NR MT	EX
Complete Set:	8.00	6.00	3.25

1 Jeff Ahern
2 Ken Angulo
3 Kris Bankowski
4 Mark Bonner
5 Norman Carrasco
6 Dave Brady
7 T.R. Bryden
8 Kevin Davis
9 Steve Enkes
10 Lonnie Garza
11 Dennis Gilbert
12 Terry Harper
13 Lee Jones
14 Lance Junker
15 Tim Kammeyer
16 Greg Key
17 Tony Mack
18 Mike Madril
19 Kirk McCaskill
20 Scott Oliver
21 Kevin Price
22 Tom Rentschuler
23 Mark Smelko
24 Rick Turner
25 Bill Worden
26 Goldie Wright
27 Luis Zambrana
28 Don Rowe
29 Bernie Smith
30 Jack Lind
31 Mark Terrazas
32 Pioneer Pete (team mascot)

1983 TCMA Richmond Braves

(Atlanta Braves, AAA) (color)

	MT	NR MT	EX
Complete Set:	14.00	10.50	5.50

1 Jose Alvarez
2 Tony Brizzolara
3 Joe Cowley
4 Ken Daley
5 Greg Field
6 Chuck Fore
7 Sam Ayoub
8 Gary Reiter
9 Augie Ruiz
10 Bob Walk
11 Matt Sinatro
12 Steve Swisher
13 Brook Jacoby
14 Gerald Perry
15 Chico Ruiz
16 Paul Runge
17 Paul Zuvella
18 Albert Hall
19 Brad Komminsk
20 Bob Porter
21 Leonel Vargas
22 Larry Whisenton
23 Eddie Haas
24 Craig Robinson
25 Johnny Sain

1983 TCMA Rochester Redwings

(Baltimore Orioles, AAA) (color)

	MT	NR MT	EX
Complete Set:	12.00	9.00	4.75

1 Lance Nichols
2 Mark Brown
3 John Flinn
4 Dave Ford
5 Craig Minetto
6 Dan Morogiello
7 Allan Ramirez
8 Mark Smith
9 Cliff Speck
10 Bill Swaggerty
11 Dave Huppert
12 Al Pardo
13 Floyd Rayford
14 Bob Bonner
15 Glenn Gulliver
16 Rick Jones
17 Dan Logan
18 John Valle
19 Elijah Bonaparte
20 Drungo Hazewood
21 Ric Lisi
22 Mike Young
23 Tom Chism
24 Richie Bancells
25 Mark Wiley

1983 TCMA St. Petersburg Cardinals

(St. Louis Cardinals, A) (black & white)

	MT	NR MT	EX
Complete Set:	20.00	15.00	8.00

1 Joseph Boever
2 Javier Carranza
3 Henry Carson
4 Danny Cox
5 Thomas Dozier
6 Thomas Epple
7 Michael Hartley
8 Robert Kish
9 John Martin
10 Christian Martinez
11 Mark Riggins
12 Freddie Silva
13 Scott Young
14 Randall Champion
15 Timothy Wallace
16 James Burns
17 Frank Garcia
18 Brad Luther
19 Deron Thomas
20 Francisco Batista
21 Robert Helsom
22 Richard James
23 Jose Rodriguez
24 Barry Sayler
25 Steve F. Turco
26 Stephen Turgion
27 Ralph Miller, Jr.
28 Karl Rogozenski
29 James Riggleman
30 Dave Link

1983 TCMA Salt Lake City Gulls

(Seattle Mariners, AAA) (color)

	MT	NR MT	EX
Complete Set:	9.00	6.75	3.50

1 Edwin Nunez
2 Jerry Gleaton
3 Robert Babcock
4 Brian Snyder
5 Karl Best
6 Brian Allard
7 Mike Moore
8 Rick Adair
9 Jed Murray
10 Joe Decker
11 Phil Bradley
12 Mark Woodmansee
13 Tito Nanni
14 Rod Allen
15 Bud Bulling
16 Jamie Nelson
17 Jim Maler
18 Bill Crone
19 John Moses
20 Glen Walker
21 Al Chambers
22 Harold Reynolds
23 Spike Owen
24 Bobby Floyd
25 Doug Merrifield
26a Manny Estrada
26b Manny Estrada

1983 Barry Colla San Jose Bees

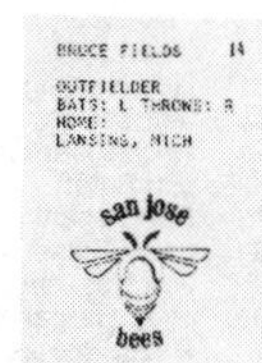

(No affiliation, A)

	MT	NR MT	EX
Complete Set:	7.50	5.50	3.00

1 Frank Verdi
2 Hiromi Wada
3 Charlie Bertucio
4 Lee Granger
5 Brian Mc Donough
6 Gary Springer
7 Dan Mc Inerny
8 Osamu Abe
9 Yukiichi Komazaki
10 Hiro Shirahata
11 Mark Butler
12 Mark Jacob
13 Kerry Cook
14 Bruce Fields
15 Gary Legumina
16 Sadahito Ueda
17 Kraig Priessman
18 Katsuya Soma
19 Mike Daughterty
20 Carl Nichols
21 Jeff Gilbert
22 Jeff Summers
23 Leon Hoke
24 Kurt Leiter
25 Greg Dehart
26 Harry Steve

1983 Fritsch Springfield Cardinals

(St. Louis Cardinals, A)

	MT	NR MT	EX
Complete Set:	10.00	7.50	4.00

1 Pete Stoll
2 David Clements
3 Paul Cherry
4 Sammy Martin
5 Dave Droschak
6 Curtis Ford
7 Marty Mason
8 Ed Tanner
9 Scott Arigoni
10 Brett Benza
11 Mick Shade
12 Joe Silkwood
13 Bob Geren
14 Greg Dunn
15 John Young
16 Dave Hoyt
17 Harry McCulla
18 Matt Gundelfinger
19 Randy Martinez
20 Mike Pittman
21 Dan Stryffeler
22 Dave Bialas
23 Mike Gambeski
24 Allen Morlock
25 Gus Malespin
26 Team Logo/Checklist

1983 TCMA Syracuse Chiefs

(Toronto Blue Jays, AAA) (color)

	MT	NR MT	EX
Complete Set:	35.00	26.00	14.00

1 Jim Beauchamp
2 Bernie Beckman

3 Tommy Craig
4 Jim Baker
5 Mark Bomback
6 Don Cooper
7 Mark Eichhorn
8 Dennis Howard
9 Tom Lukish
10 Colin McLaughlin
11 Jeff Schneider
12 Keith Walker
13 Matt Williams
14 Toby Hernandez
15 Geno Petralli
16 Tony Fernandez
17 Fred Manrique
18 Bob Nandin
19 Jeff Reynolds
20 Tim Thompson
21 George Bell
22 Anthony Johnson
23 Vern Ramie
24 Ron Shepherd
25 Mitch Webster
26 Bob Humphreys

1983 TCMA Tacoma Tigers

(Oakland A's, AAA) (color) (complete set price includes scarce cards of McKay, Moore, Perry, Retzer and Rodriquez)

	MT	NR MT	EX
Complete Set:	90.00	67.00	36.00

1 Keith Atherton
2 Bert Bradley
3 DeWayne Buice
4 Gorman Heimueller
5 Chuck Hensley
6 Jerome King
7 Russ McDonald
8 Curt Young
9 Daryl Cias
10 Bill Bathe
11 Donnie Hill
12 John Hotchkiss
13 Mike Woodard
14 Jim Bennett
15 Lynn Garrett
16 Dave Hudgens
17 Rusty McNealy
18 Bob Didier
19 Stan Naccarato
20 Jim Nettles
21 Dave Heaverlo
22 Larry Davis
23 Art Popham
24 Tigers Mascot
25a Bob Christofferson
25b Danny Goodwin
26 Scott Pyle
27 Dennis Sherow
28 Jeff Jones
29a Dave McKay
29b Rickey Peters
30a Jim Christiansen
30b Dave Rodriguez
31 Ed Retzer
32 Kelvin Moore
33 Shawn Perry

1983 TCMA Tampa Tarpons

(Cincinnati Reds, A) (black & white) (complete sets usually include many miscut cards)

	MT	NR MT	EX
Complete Set:	30.00	22.00	12.00

1 Tony Burley
2 Virg Conley
3 L.C. Culver
4 Tony Evans
5 Tom Browning
6 Not Issued
7 Tim Dodd
8 Jason Felice
9 Adolfo Feliz
10 Fergy Ferguson
11 Jack Foley
12 Clem Freeman, Jr.
13 Orlando Gonzalez
14 Dave Hall
15 Ty Hubbard, III
16 Danny LaMar
17 Ted Langdon
18 Terrence McGriff
19 Paul O'Neil
20 Cressy Pratt
21 Kevin Steinmetz
22 Allen Swindle
23 Scott Terry
24 Tony Threatt
25 Steve Watson
26 Tracy Jones
27 Nick Fiorillo
28 Jim Hoff
29 Mike Sims
30 Bull Norman

1983 TCMA Tidewater Tides

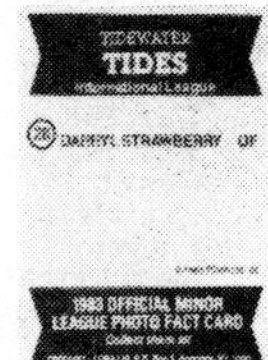

(New York Mets, AAA) (color)

	MT	NR MT	EX
Complete Set:	50.00	40.00	20.00

1 Ron Darling
2 Mike Fitzgerald
3 Wally Backman
4 Clint Hurdle
5 Terry Leach
6 Mike Bishop
7 Kelvin Chapman
8 Gary Rajsich
9 Tim Leary
10 Steve Senteney
11 Tom Gorman
12 Walt Terrell
13 Jeff Bittiger
14 Scott Dye
15 Greg Biercevicz
16 Brent Gaff
17 Dan Schmitz
18 Mike Howard
19 Rusty Tillman
20 Ron Gardenhire
21 Marvell Wynne
22 Gil Flores
23 Davey Johnson
24 Al Jackson
25 Josh Wakana
26 Tucker Ashford
27 Bob Sikes
28 Darryl Strawberry
29 Jose Oquendo

1983 TCMA Toledo Mud Hens

(Minnesota Twins, AAA) (color) (complete set price includes scarce #s 26-29)

	MT	NR MT	EX
Complete Set:	90.00	67.00	36.00

1 Paul Boris
2 Terry Felton
3 Kevin Flannery
4 Ed Hodge
5 Steve Korczyk
6 Jim Lewis
7 Jeff Little
8 Bob Mulligan
9 Ken Schrom
10 Mike Walters
11 Rick Austin
12 Stine Poole
13 Dave Baker
14 Greg Gagne
15 Houston Jimenez
16 Tim Teufel
17 Jesus Vega
18 Michael Wilson
19 Andre David
20 Mike Hart
21 Randy Johnson
22 Dave Meier
23 Cal Ermer
24 Tim Aga, Kevin Flannery)
25 Scott Tellgren
26 Eric Broersma
27 Mike McCain
28 Bryan Oelkers
29 Jack O'Conner

1983 TCMA Tri-Cities Triplets

(Texas Rangers, A) (black & white)

	MT	NR MT	EX
Complete Set:	7.50	5.50	3.00

1 Bob Sebra
2 Steve Kordish
3 Bruce Kipper
4 Kerry Burns
5 Dennis Knight
6 Mark Cipres
7 John Munley
8 Robin Keathley
9 Nick Esposito
10 John Fryhoff
11 Dan Lindquist
12 Jim Allison
13 Bill Hance
14 Tony Carlucci
15 Reggie Mosley
16 Mark Gile
17 Ron Hansen
18 Mike Keehn
19 Vince Sakowski
20 Bert Martinez
21 Greg Bailey
22 Danny Simpson
23 Jim Cesario
24 Brendan Hennessy
25 Clint Curry
26 Dave Oliver
27 Gary Venner
28 Bob Bill

1983 TCMA Tucson Toros

(Houston Astros, AAA) (color) (includes scarce, late-issue Robles card)

	MT	NR MT	EX
Complete Set:	20.00	15.00	8.00

1 Ed Bonine
2 Dan Boone
3 Buster Keeton
4 Ron Mathis
5 Ron Meredith
6 Jeff Morris
7 Gordie Pladson
8 Bert Roberge
9 Bob Veselic
10 Sam Welborn
11 Julio Solano
12 Steve Christmas
13 Luis Pujols
14 Wes Clements
15 Greg Cypret
16 Jim Pankovits
17 Bert Pena
18 Cliff Wherry
19 Chris Jones
20 Larry Ray
21 Bob Pate
22 Scott Loucks
23 Matt Galante
24 Gary Tuck
25 Dave Labossiere
26 Ruben Robles

1983 TCMA Tulsa Drillers

(Texas Rangers, AA) (color)

	MT	NR MT	EX
Complete Set:	9.00	6.75	3.50

1 Jorge Gomez
2 Glen Cook
3 Tony Fossas
4 Rob Clark
5 Billy Taylor
6 Larry McLane
7 Daryl Smith
8 Dennis Long
9 Mitch Zwolensky
10 Tim Henry
11 Dwayne Henry
12 Kirk Killingsworth
13 Bob Brower
14 Chuckie Canady
15 Mike Rubel
16 John Buckley
17 Tracy Cowger
18 Steve Nielsen
19 Joe Nemeth
20 Jim Foit
21 Dan Murphy
22 Steve Buechele
23 Jerry Neufang
24 Terry Johnson
25 Marty Scott

1983 TCMA Vero Beach Dodgers

(Los Angeles Dodgers, A) (black & white)

	MT	NR MT	EX
Complete Set:	25.00	18.50	10.00

1 Mike Beuder
2 Tom Duffy
3 Rick Felt
4 Mike Gentle
5 Brian Innis
6 Charlie Jones
7 Vance Lovelace
8 Morris Madden
9 Rafael Montalvo
10 Bill Scudder
11 Chris Thomas
12 Rob Slezak
13 Luis Rivera
14 Steve Boncore
15 Bob Gilles
16 Mariano Duncan
17 John Gregory
18 Hector Guzman
19 Gary Newsom
20 Harold Perkins
21 Billy White
22 Ralph Bryant
23 Jerald Cain
24 Dan Cataline
25 Reggie Williams
26 John Shoemaker
27 Rob Giesecke
28 Stan Wasiak
29 Dennis Lewallyn

1983 Fritsch Visalia Oaks

(Minnesota Twins, A)

	MT	NR MT	EX
Complete Set:	85.00	64.00	34.00

1 Lee Belanger
2 Jeff Arney
3 Steve Aragon
4 Sam Arrington
5 Phil Franko
6 Kirby Puckett
7 Frank Ramppen
8 Bob DeCosta
9 Jack McMahon
10 Stan Holmes
11 Frank Eufemia
12 Ron McKelvie
13 Harry Warner
14 Jeff Brueggemann
15 Erez Borowsky
16 Mark Cartwright
17 Joe Kubit
18 Curt Wardle
19 Bennie Richie
20 Craig Henderson
21 Greg Howe
22 Curt Kindred
23 Alvaro Espinoza
24 Mark Portugal
25 Brian Rupe

1983 TCMA Waterbury Reds

(Cincinnati Reds, AA) (black & white)

	MT	NR MT	EX
Complete Set:	60.00	45.00	24.00

1 Keefe Cato
2 Bryan Funk
3 Curt Heidenreich
4 Ken Jones
5 Bill Landrum
6 Jim Pettibone
7 Mark Rothey
8 Lester Straker
9 Lloyd McClendon
10 Dave Miley
11 Adolfo Feliz
12 Carlos Porte
13 Hector Rincones
14 Wade Rowdon
15 Eric Davis
16 Dexter Day
17 Leo Garcia
18 Ruben Guzman
19 Jim Lett

1983 Fritsch Waterloo Indians

(Cleveland Indians, A)

	MT	NR MT	EX
Complete Set:	9.00	6.75	3.75

1 Randy Washington
2 Edwin Aponte
3 Ben Piphus
4 Eddie Diaz
5 Andy Ortiz
6 Juan Lopez
7 Nelson Pedraza
8 Junior Noboa
9 Jay Keeler
10 Wilson Valera
11 John Miglio
12 Jose Roman
13 Miguel Roman
14 Phil Wilson

15 Reggie Ritter
16 Pookie Bernstine
17 Bernardo Brito
18 Winston Ficklin
19 Ray Martinez
20 Jeff Barkley
21 Dane Anthony
22 Mike Gertz
23 Wes Pierorazio
24 Mike Poindexter
25 Rich Diaz
26 Rick Henke
27 Vic Albury
28 Gomer Hodge
29 Team Logo/Checklist Card

1983 Fritsch Wausau Timbers

(Seattle Mariners, A)

	MT	NR MT	EX
Complete Set:	9.00	6.75	3.75

1 K.R. Houston
2 John Poloni
3 Gary Pellant
4 Tom Burns
5 Martin Enriquez
6 Brian David
7 Ronn Dixon
8 Tim Slavin
9 Terry Taylor
10 Eric Parent
11 Chip Conklin
12 David Myers
13 Kevin Roy
14 Todd Francis
15 Randy Meier
16 Robby Vollmer
17 Jesse Baez
18 Scott Barnhouse
19 Paul Schneider
20 Scott Roebuck
21 Tom Duggan
22 Bob Baldrick
23 Sam Haley
24 Ron Sismondo
25 Randy Newman
26 John Duncan
27 Dave Smith
28 Wray Begendahl
29 Kenny Briggs
30 R.J. Harrison
31 Team Logo/Checklist Card

1983 Dog-N-Shake Wichita Aeroes

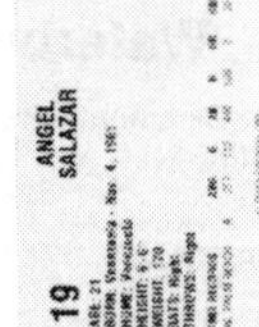

(Montreal Expos, AAA)

	MT	NR MT	EX
Complete Set:	15.00	11.00	6.00

1 Checklist
2 Felipe Alou
3 Shooty Babitt
4 Greg Bargar
5 Butch Benton
6 Tom Dixon
7 Mike Fuentes
8 Mike Gates
9 Gene Glynn
10 Dick Grapenthin
11 Bob James
12 Roy Johnson
13 Brad Mills
14 Eric Mustad
15 Luis Quintana
16 Rick Ramos
17 Bob Reece
18 Pat Rooney
19 Angel Salazar
20 Bill Sattler
21 Mike Stenhouse
22 Rennie Stennett
23 Tom Wieghaus
24 1982 Batting Title (Roy Johnson)

1983 Fritsch Wisconsin Rapids Twins

(Minnesota Twins, A)

	MT	NR MT	EX
Complete Set:	9.00	6.75	3.50

1 Coe Brier
2 Ronnie Scheer
3 Allan Anderson
4 Jeff Wilson
5 Joe Sain
6 Paul Felix
7 Carson Carroll
8 David Steinberg
9 Tim Graupmann
10 John Kearns
11 Bob Ferro
12 Mark Larcom
13 Johnny Salery
14 Bob Costello
15 Leo Cardenas, Jr.
16 Danny Clay
17 Brian Hobaugh
18 Mike Maack
19 Luis Cruz
20 Jim Burnos
21 Ken Klump
22 Paul Mancuso
23 Brad Skoglund
24 Michael Moreno
25 David Baehr
26 John Marks
27 Charlie Manuel
28 Team Logo/Checklist

1984 TCMA Albany-Colonie A'S

(Oakland A's, AA) (color)

	MT	NR MT	EX
Complete Set:	25.00	18.75	10.00

1 Jim Bennett
2 Ron Arnold
3 Gene Gentile
4 Rodney Hobbs
5 Thad Reece
6 Brian Graham
7 Keith Lieppman
8 Rick Tronerud
9 Brian Thorson
10 John Liburdi
11 Tom Dozier
12 Todd Fischer
13 Bob Hallas
14 Pete Kendrick
15 Stan Kyles
16 Erik Bernard
17 Tim Lambert
18 Ed Myers
19 Les Straker
20 Tom Zmudosky
21 Mike Ashman
22 Mickey Tettleton
23 Bob Bathe
24 Jim Eppard
25 Greg Robles
26 Ray Thoma

1984 Cramer Albuquerque Dukes

(Los Angeles Dodgers, AAA) (A limited-edition glossy set set was also produced)

	MT	NR MT	EX
Complete Set:	6.00	4.50	2.50

146 Jack Fimple
147 Rich Rodas
148 R.J. Reynolds
149 Sid Bream
150 Lemmie Miller
151 Franklin Stubbs
152 Dave Sax
153 Alex Taveras
154 Steve Perry
155 Don Smith
156 Robbie Allen
157 Greg Schultz
158 Larry White
159 Ernesto Borbon
160 Dean Rennicke
161 Tony Brewer
162 Larry See
163 Ed Amelung
164 John Debus
165 Ken Howell
166 Roberto Alexander
167 Terry Collins
168 Brian Holton
169 Dick McLaughlin
245 Dave Wallace
246 Mark Sheehy

1984 TCMA Arkansas Travelers

(St. Louis Cardinals, AA) (color)

	MT	NR MT	EX
Complete Set:	8.00	6.00	3.25

1 Eddie Tanner
2 Dave Clements
3 Dan Stryffeler
4 Deron Thomas
5 Tim Wallace
6 Todd Worrell
7 Bob Helson
8 Al Morlock
9 Larry Reynolds
10 Greg Guin
11 Bob Geren
12 John Adams
13 Mark Schulte
14 Dave Bialas
15 Willie Hardwick
16 Curt Ford
17 John Martin
18 Pat Perry
19 Marty Mason
20 Joe Silkwood
21 Gotay Mills
22 John Young
23 Pete Stoll
24 Walt Pierce
25 Andy Hassler
26 Mike Harris

1984 TCMA Beaumont Golden Gators

(San Diego Padres, AA) (color)

	MT	NR MT	EX
Complete Set:	6.00	4.50	2.50

1 Jimmy Jones
2 Pete Kutsukos
3 James Steels
4 Al Newman
5 Mark Gillaspie
6 Ed Vosberg
7 Steve Murray
8 Mark Parent
9 Gene Walter
10 Kevin Towers
11 Bill Long
12 Tim Cook
13 Steve Schefsky
14 Jim Leopold
15 Jimmy Thomas
16 Pat Casey
17 Mark Wasinger
18 Steve Garcia
19 Jerry Johnson
20 Steve Johnson
21 Bobby Tolan
22 Chuck Kolotka
23 Todd Hutcheson
24 Ray Etchebarren
25 Jeff Ronk

1984 TCMA Buffalo Bisons

(Cleveland Indians, AA) (color)

	MT	NR MT	EX
Complete Set:	6.00	4.50	2.50

1 Jeff Moronko
2 George Cecchetti
3 Tim Glass
4 "Junior" Naboa
5 Rene Quinones
6 Doug Simonic
7 Andy Allanson
8 Jose Roman
9 Jay Baller
10 Alec McCullock
11 Rich Doyle
12 Rich Thompson
13 Dave Szymczak
14 John Bohnet
15 Andy Ortiz
16 Ramon Romero
17 Steve Mardsen
18 Jack Aker
19 Ed Aponte
20 Randy Washington
21 Don Carter
22 Ed Saavedra
23 Pookie Bernstine
24 Robin Fuson
25 Doug Helmquist

1984 TCMA Butte Copper Kings

(Seattle Mariners, A) (color)

	MT	NR MT	EX
Complete Set:	8.00	6.00	3.25

1 Manny Estrada
2 John Anderson
3 James Bowden
4 Dan Clark
5 Mike Wood
6 Tom Osowski
7 Carl Moesche
8 Greg Brinkman
9 Tony Diaz
10 Charlie Fonville
11 Steve French
12 Richard Hayden
13 Brad Kinney
14 Dan Larson
15 Mark Machalec
16 Rafael Matos
17 Pablo Monceratt
18 Arvid Morfin
19 Kevin Ochs
20 Bill O'Leary
21 Bregg Ray
22 Paul Steinert
23 Gregg Thienpont
24 George Uribe
25 Nestor Valiente
26 Lazaro Vilella
27 Logan White

1984 TCMA Cedar Rapids Reds

(Cincinnati Reds, A) (color)

	MT	NR MT	EX
Complete Set:	10.00	7.50	4.00

1 Robbie Phillips
2 Ted Langdon
3 Jim Pettibone
4 Doug Barba
5 Paul Kirsch
6 Brian Funk
7 Hugh Kemp
8 Virgil Conley
9 Mike Konderla
10 Jordan Berge
11 Tim Dodd
12 Jim Lett
13 Dexter Day
14 Joe Oliver
15 Tom Riley
16 Lanell Culver
17 Kurt Stillwell
18 Danny LaMar
19 Don Buchheister
20 Ronnie Giddens
21 Mike Manfre
22 Scott Loseke
23 Rod Lich
24 Mike Dowless
25 Lenny Harris
26 Gary Denbo
27 Ron Henika
28 Dave Haberle

1984 TCMA Charlotte O'S

(Baltimore Orioles, AA) (color)

	MT	NR MT	EX
Complete Set:	7.50	5.50	3.00

1 Bob Hice
2 Terry Mauney
3 Charlie Frederick
4 Ronni Salcedo
5 Paul Cameron
6 Carlos Concepcion
7 Al Pardo
8 Jeff Kenaga
9 Peter Torrez
10 Grady Little
11 Chris Willsher
12 Bobby Mariano
13 Pat Dumouchelle
14 Jamie Reed
15 Bob Konopa
16 Dave Falcone
17 Kenny Dixon
18 Jeff Gilbert
19 Jesus Alfaro
20 Jeff Williams
21 Paul Bard
22 Ken Gerhart
23 Kurt Leiter
24 John Tutt
25 Jeff Summers
26 Tony Arnold
27 Herbie Oliveras

1984 TCMA Chattanooga Lookouts

(Seattle Mariners, AA) (color)

	MT	NR MT	EX
Complete Set:	6.00	4.50	2.50

1a Mike Evans
1b Kevin King
2 Ramon Estepa
3 Dan Hanggie

4 Brick Smith
5 Ed Holtz
6 Clark Crist
7 Ross Grimsley
8 Bill Plummer
9 Tom Hunt
10 Donnell Nixon (Donell)
11 John Semprini
12 Paul Serna
13 Mike Johnson
14 Harry Landreth
15 Lee Guetterman
16 Joe Whitmer
17 Not Issued
18 Rick Luecken
19 Tom Rowe
20 A.J. Hill
21 Randy Ramirez
22 Ric Wilson
23 Rick Adair
24 John Moses
25 Mario Diaz
26 Mickey Brantley
27 Don Clay Hill
28 Jeff McDonald
29 Greg Bartley

1984 Police/Fire Safety Columbus Clippers

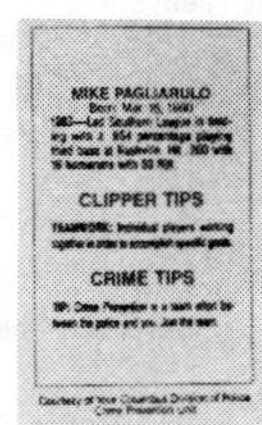

(New York Yankees, AAA) The Columbus Clippers, in conjunction with the Columbus, Ohio, Police Department, issued this, their fourth card set, after skipping 1983. The cards are distributed each season at the Clippers' ballpark and at local police departments. The 1984 set contains 25 cards with full-color fronts and player biographies on the back. The cards measure 2-3/8" by 3-3/4".

	MT	NR MT	EX
Complete Set:	8.00	6.00	3.25

2 Andre Robertson
4 Kelly Heath
12 Rex Hudler
14 Victor Mata
15 Mike O'Berry
17 Butch Hobson
19 Kelly Scott
20 Curt Brown
21 Brian Dayett
23 Dan Briggs
24 Mike Pagliarulo
25 Don Fowler
27 Don Cooper
29 Pat Rooney
31 Scott Patterson
32 Matt Winters
34 George Cappuzzello
36 Joe Cowley
38 Clay Christiansen
39 Dennis Rasmussen
40 Scott Bradley
42 Pete Dalena
---- "Stump" Merrill (manager)
---- George H. Sisler Jr. (general manager)
---- Coaches/Trainer Card (Mark Connor, Steve Donohue, Gil Patterson, Mickey Vernon)

1984 TCMA Columbus Clippers

(New York Yankees, AAA) (color)

	MT	NR MT	EX
Complete Set:	10.00	7.50	4.00

1 Mike Pagliarulo
2 Kelly Heath
3 Pat Rooney
4 Brian Dayett
5 Dan Briggs
6 Don Fowler
7 George Cappuzzello
8 Rex Hudler
9 Andre Robertson
10 Victor Mata
11 Scott Bradley
12 Clay Christianson
13 Joe Cowley
14 Scott Patterson
15 Curt Brown
16 Butch Hobson
17 Don Cooper
18 Pete Dalena
19 Kelly Scott
20 Mike O'Berry
21 Coach, Trainer & Manager
22 Matt Winters
23 Stump Merrill
24 George Sisler, Jr.
25 Dennis Rasmussen

1984 Team Daytona Beach Astros

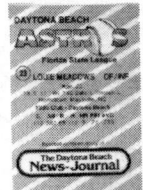

(Houston Astros, A)

	MT	NR MT	EX
Complete Set:	45.00	34.00	18.00

1 Dave Cripe
2 Stan Hough
3 Rich Bombard
4 Mik Crefin
5 Mike Friederich
6 Chuck Mathews
7 Greg Mize
8 Raynor Noble
9 Ray Perkins
10 Uvaldo Reglado
11 Doug Shaab
12 Don Berti
13 Jeff Datz
14 Robbie Wine
15 Glenn Carpenter
16 Bobby Falls
17 Ramon Rodriguez
18 Nelson Rood
19 Jim Sherman
20 Mike Botkin
21 Curtis Burke
22 Juan Delgado
23 Louis Meadows
24 Mike Stellern
25 Larry Lasky

1984 TCMA Durham Bulls

(Atlanta Braves, A) (color)

	MT	NR MT	EX
Complete Set:	12.00	9.00	4.75

1 Simon Rosario
2 Mark Lance
3 Mike Yastrzemski
4 Pat Hodge
5 Johnny Hatcher
6 Terry Cormack
7 Jeff Wagner
8 Dave Griffin
9 Leo Mazzone
10 Tim Alexander
11 Rafael Barbosa
12 Bob Tumpane
13 Chip Childress
14 Andres Thomas
15 Mike Knox
16 Tony Neuendorff
17 Scott Hood
18 Rich Leggatt
19 Todd Lamb
20 Paul Assenmacher
21 Paul Josephson
22 Jose Cano
23 Steve Ziem
24 John Mortillaro
25 Brian Aviles
26 Jim Rivera
27 Marty Schreiber
28 Brian Snitker
29 Randy Ingle
30 Sonny Jackson

A card number in parentheses () indicates the set is unnumbered.

1984 Cramer Edmonton Trappers

(California Angels, AAA) (color) (a limited-edition glossy set was also produced)

	MT	NR MT	EX
Complete Set:	6.00	4.50	2.50

97 Moose Stubing
98 Tim Krauss
99 Angel Moreno
100 Marty Kain
101 Sap Randall
102 Rick Steirer
103 Dave W. Smith
104 Rick Adams
105 Craig Gerber
106 Steve Finch
107 Steve Liddle
108 Chris Clark
109 Darrell Miller
110 Bill Mooneyham
111 Doug Corbett
112 Steve Lubratich
113 Stu Cliburn
114 Mike Browning
115 Joe Simpson
116 Reggie West
117 Mike Brown
118 Pat Keedy
119 Jay Kibbe
120 Ed Ott
242 Frank Reberger
249 Steve Lubratich

1984 TCMA El Paso Diablos

(Milwaukee Brewers, AA) (color)

	MT	NR MT	EX
Complete Set:	12.00	9.00	4.75

1 Mark Effrig
2 Johnson Wood
3 Bob Schroeck
4 Steve Michael
5 Bryan Clutterbuck
6 Chuck Grim
7 Doug Jones
8 Mike Villegas
9 Mike Samuel
10 Tim Crews
11 Bryan Duquette
12 Terry Bevington
13 Kelvin Moore
14 Stan Davis
15 Ted Higuera
16 Juan Castillo
17 Dan Plante
18 Dave Klipstein
19 Alan Cartwright
20 Paul Hartzell
21 Joe Morales
22 Cam Walker
23 Mike Felder
24 Dale Sveum
25 Garrett Nago

1984 TCMA Evansville Triplets

(Detroit Tigers, AAA) (color)

	MT	NR MT	EX
Complete Set:	7.50	5.50	3.00

1 Juan Lopez
2 Howard Bailey
3 Rondal Rollin
4 Gordon McKenzie
5 Pat Larkin
6 Mark Dacko
7 Stan Younger
8 Dave Gumpert
9 Nelson Simmons
10 Len Faedo
11 Bob Melvin
12 Dallas Williams
13 Doug Baker
14 Scotty Earl
15 John Harris
16 Mike Laga
17 Randy O'Neal
18 Jeff Conner
19 Don Heinkel
20 Bill Armstrong
21 Roger Mason
22 Carl Willis

Definitions for grading conditions are located in the Introduction of this price guide.

1984 Cramer Everett Giants

(San Francisco Giants, Rookie) (black & white) (set includes scarce cards)

	MT	NR MT	EX
Complete Set:	12.00	9.00	4.75

1 Greg Litton
2 Lyle Swepson
3a Mike Cicione
3b Darin James
4 Joe Olker
5 Harry Davis
6 a Greg Gilbert
6 b Daren James
7 Kent Cooper
8 Steve Cottrell
9 Kevin Woodhouse
10 Keith Silver
11 Dave Hornsby
12 a Stuart Tate
12 b Jim Ewing
13 a Rob Cosby
13 b Rod Rush
14 a Sixto Martes
14 b Rod Rush
15 Loren Hibbs
16 Dave Hinnrichs
17 Francisco Echevarria
18 Chris Stangel
19 a Paul Blair
19 b T.J. McDonald
20 a Terry Mulholland
20 b T.J. McDonald
21 Davis Tavarez
22 a Brad Porter
22 b T.J. McDonald
23 Francis Calzado
24 a Jim Wasem
24 b T.J. McDonald
25 John Grimes
26 a Todd Moriaty
26 b Tony Perezchica
27a John Ackerman
27b Tony Perezchica
28 a Rocky Bridges
28 b Tony Perezchica
29 Tom Wetzel
30 Tom Messier

1984 TCMA Greensboro Hornets

(New York Yankees, A) (color)

	MT	NR MT	EX
Complete Set:	15.00	11.00	6.00

1 Carlos Tosca
2 Ray Fortaleza
3 Brad Winler
4 Roberto Kelly
5 Jeff Horne
6 Fredi Gonzalez
7 Nattie George
8 Joey MacKay
9 Doug Carpenter
10 Brad Arnsberg
11 Chris Fedor
12 Bill Bulton
13 Dave Smalley
14 Tim Williams
15 Chuck Mathison
16 Eric Parent
17 Ricky Torres
18 Steve George
19 Mark Ferguson
20 Jonis Rodriguez
21 Bob Devlin
22 Moe Ching
23 Pedro Medina
24 Rich Mattocks
25 Mitch Seoane
26 Bill Englehart

1984 Pizza Hut Greenville Braves

	MT	NR MT	EX
Complete Set:	67.50	50.00	27.00

1 Mike Cole
2 Freddie Tiburcio
5 Carlos Rios
6 Joe Johnson
9 Steve Chmil
10 Marty Clary
11 Randy Ingle
12 Glen Bockhorn
14 Augie Ruiz
15 Matt Sinatro
16 Rich Leggett
18 Matt West
19 Doc Estes
20 Bobby Dews
22 Steve Curry
23 Roy North
24 Tommy Thompson
25 Inocencio Guerrero
26 Bob Luzon

27 Leo Mazzone, Duane Ward
28 Tim Cole
29 Mike Bormann
30 Andre Treadway
---- David Clay

1984 Cramer Hawaii Islanders

(Pittsburgh Pirates, AAA) (color) (a limited-edition glossy set was also produced)

	MT	NR MT	EX
Complete Set:	6.00	4.50	2.50

121 Al Pulido
122 Jeff Zaske
123 Kelly Paris
124 Larry Lamonde
125 Paul Semall
126 Dave Tomlin
127 Lorenzo Bundy
128 Ron Wotus
129 Ray Krawczyk
130 Denny Gonzales
131 Mike Bielecki
132 Stan Cliburn
133 Nelson Norman
134 Chuck Hartenstein
135 Mike Howard
136 Bob Miscik
137 Tom Sandt
138 Jim Winn
139 Trench Davis
140 Tim Wheeler
141 Bob Walk
142 Steve Herz
143 Carlos Ledezma
144 Benny Distefano
145 John Malkin

1984 Team Idaho Falls A's

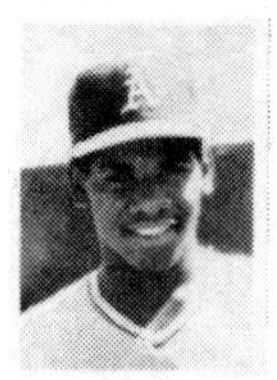

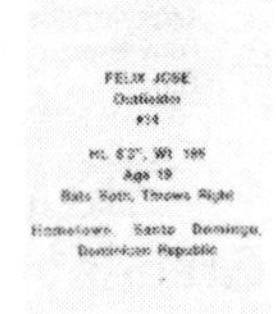

(Oakland A's, A)

	MT	NR MT	EX
Complete Set:	40.00	30.00	16.00

(1) Russ Applegate
(2) Eldridge Armstrong
(3) Darren Balsley
(4) Mickey Boyer
(5) Adan Brito
(6) Antonio Cabrera
(7) Mike Cupples
(8) Arturo Ferreira
(9) Mark Gillespie
(10) John Gonzalez
(11) Bob Hassel
(12) Jesus Hernaz
(13) James Jackson
(14) Tony Johnson
(15) Felix Jose
(16) Mark Leonette
(17) Scott LeVander
(18) Jim Nettles
(19) Ramon Nunez
(20) Ken Patterson
(21) Ted Polakowski
(22) Basilio Reyes
(23) Kevin Russ
(24) Scott Sabo
(25) David Sheriff
(26) Bob Vantrease
(27) Camilo Veras
(28) Mike Walker
(29) Mark Warren
(30) James Wilridge

1984 Team Indianapolis Indians

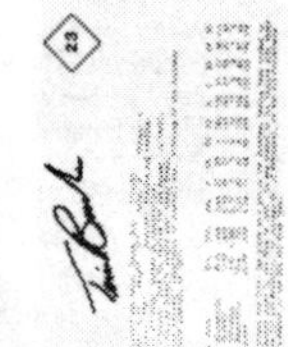

(Montreal Expos, AAA) (co-sponsored by Tom Aikens)

	MT	NR MT	EX
Complete Set:	9.00	6.75	3.50

1 1984 Indianapolis Indians
2 Bob Rodgers
3 Leonel Carrion
4 Chris Welsh
5 Sal Butera
6 Joe Hesketh
7 Roy Johnson
8 Craig Eaton
9 Brad Mills
10 The Catchers (George Bjorkman, Sal Butera)
11 Eric Mustad
12 Mike Fuentes
13 Greg Bargar
14 Shooty Babitt
15 The Outfielders (Shooty Babitt, Mike Fuentes, Roy Johnson, Max Venable)
16 Dick Grapenthin
17 Razor Shines
18 The Starting Pitchers (Greg Bargar, Tim Burke, Joe Hesketh, Eric Mustad, Chris Welsh)
19 Bill Sattler
20 George Bjorkman
21 The Relief Pitchers (Darren Dilks, Craig Eaton, Dick Grapenthin, Bill Sattler)
22 Gene Glynn
23 Tim Burke
24 Ron Johnson
25 Rene Gonzales
26 The Infielders (Mike Gates, Gene Glynn, Rene Gonzales, Ron Johnson, Brad Mills, Razor Shines)
27 Darren Dilks
28 Max Venable
29 Mike Gates
30 Mike Stenhouse
31 Jeff Porter
32 Bush Stadium

1984 TCMA Iowa Cubs

(Chicago Cubs, AA) (color)

	MT	NR MT	EX
Complete Set:	60.00	45.00	24.00

1 Ken Pryce
2 Bill Earley
3 Cubby (team mascot)
4 Dick Easter
5 Ken Grandquist
6 Jon Perlman
7 Thad Bosley
8 Don Rohn
9 Joe Hicks
10 B. Holden, F. Macy
11 Jim Napier
12 Pete Mackanin
13 S. Bernabe, M. Schimming
14 Trey Brooks
15 Bill Hayes
16 Don Werner
17 Tom Lombarski
18 Dave Owen
19 B. Bielenberg, C. McCullough
20 Gil Carlos
21 Dick Cummings
22 Don Schulze
23 Porfirio Altamirano
24 Billy Hatcher
25 Joe Carter
26 Not Issued
27 Ron Meredith
28 Tom Filer
29 Bill Johnson
30 Tom Grant
31 Reggie Patterson
---- Derek Botelho

1984 TCMA Jackson Mets

(New York Mets, AA) (color)

	MT	NR MT	EX
Complete Set:	40.00	30.00	16.00

1 DeWayne Vaughn
2 Rick Myles
3 Mark Lockenmeyer
4 Calvin Schiraldi
5 Reggie Jackson
6 Jeff Innis
7 Bill Fultz
8 Joe Graves
9 Jeff Bettendorf
10 Greg Pavlick
11 Staff (B. Hetrick, S. Massengale, R. Rainer)
12 Bill Max
15 Floyd Youmans
16 Sam Perlozzo
17 Billy Beane
18 Lenny Dykstra
19 Daryl Denby
20 Mark Carreon
21 Dave Cochran
22 Steve Springer
23 Al Pedrique
24 Fermin Ubri
25 Randy Milligan
---- Ed Hearn
---- Greg Olson

1984 Forestry Jackson Mets

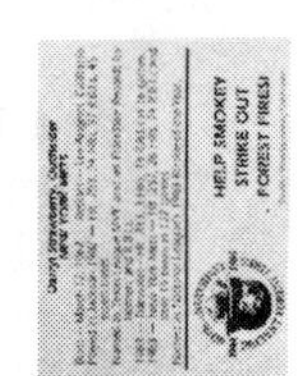

(New York Mets, AA) (3" x 4") This set lists the major league team each player signed with.

	MT	NR MT	EX
Complete Set:	45.00	34.00	18.00

(1) Neil Allen (Cardinals)
(2) Wally Backman (Mets)
(3) Hubie Brooks (Mets)
(4) Jody Davis (Cubs)
(5) Brian Giles (Mets)
(6) Tim Leary (Mets)
(7) Lee Mazzilli (Pirates)
(8) Jesse Orosco (Mets)
(9) Jeff Reardon (Expos)
(10) Doug Sisk (Mets)
(11) Darryl Strawberry (Mets)
(12) Mookie Wilson (Mets)
(13) Marvel Wynne (Pirates)
(14) Ned Yost (Rangers)
(15) Davey Johnson (Mets)

1984 Cramer Las Vegas Stars

(San Diego Padres, AAA) (color) (This set is numbered as they appear on the backs of the cards. A limited-edition, glossy set was also made)

	MT	NR MT	EX
Complete Set:	15.00	11.00	6.00

218 Greg Booker
219 Ray Hayward
220 Joe Lansford
221 Bob Patterson
222 Jerry Davis
223 Jerry DeSimone
224 Fritz Connally
225 Bruce Bochy
226 Marty Decker
227 Mike Martin
228 John Kruk
229 Walt Vanderbush
230 Rick Lancellotti
231 Ed Wojna
232 Tom House
233 Felix Oroz
234 George Hinshaw
235 Darren Burroughs
236 Ozzie Guillen
237 Ron Roenicke
238 Larry Brown
239 Bob Cluck
240 Ed Rodriguez
244 Larry Duensing
250 John Kruk

1984 TCMA Little Falls Mets

(New York Mets, A) (color)

	MT	NR MT	EX
Complete Set:	20.00	15.00	8.00

1 Will Stiles
2 Keith Belcik
3 Mike Westbrook
4 Scott Little
5 Chuck Friedel
6 Ralph Adams
7 Jeff Karr
8 Ray Pereira
9 Keith Traylor
10 Shane Young
11 Owen Moreland, III
12 Jeff Howes
13 Bud Harrelson
14 Terence Johnson
15 Craig Kiley
16 Jeff Ciszkowski
17 Hector Perez
18 Bucky Autry
19 Kevin Elster
20 Alan Wilson
21 Mauro Gozzo
22 Mark Davis
23 Lew Graham
24 David West
25 Rich Rodriguez
26 Ron Dominco

1984 Riley's Louisville Redbirds

(St. Louis Cardinals, AAA)

	MT	NR MT	EX
Complete Set:	18.00	13.50	7.25

1 Jim Fregosi
2 Gaylen Pitts
3 Jerry Mc Kune
4 Dyar Miller
5 Gene Roof
6 Gary Rajsich
7 Doyle Harris
8 Tom Nieto
9 Dave Von Ohlen
10 Jed Smith
11 Kevin Hagen
12 Rod Booker
13 Jose Gonzalez
14 Bill Lyons
15 Terry Pendleton
16 Ralph Citarella
17 Kurt Kenshire
18 Vic Harris
19 Jim Aducci
20 Vince Coleman
21 Jack Ayer
22 Jeff Keener
23 Rick Ownbey
24 Terry Clark
25 Steve Baker
26 Jerry Johnson
27 Mark Salas
28 Mickey Mahler
29 Dave Kable
30 Dennis Werth

1984 T&J SC Madison Muskies

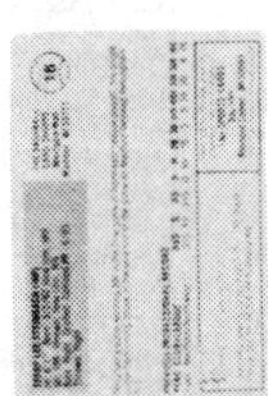

(Oakland A's, A) (black & white)

	MT	NR MT	EX
Complete Set:	12.00	9.00	4.75

1 Darrel Akerfelds
2 Larry Beardman
3 Rich Borowski
4 Maurice Castain
5 Kevin Coughlon
6 Mike Fulmer
7 Eric Garrett
8 Wayne Giddings
9 Shawn Gill
10 Dennis Gonsalves
11 Darel Hansen
12 Jim Jones
13 Bob Loscalzo
14 John Marquardt
15 Rob Nelson
16 Terry Steinbach
17 Tim Belcher
18 Al Heath
19 Luis Polonia
20 Joe Odom
21 Scotty Lee Whaley
22 Mike Wilder
23 Dave Schober
24 Gary Lance
25 Brad Fischer

1984 TCMA Maine Guides

(Cleveland Indians, AAA) (color)

	MT	NR MT	EX
Complete Set:	7.50	5.50	3.00

1 Ramon Romero
2 Jerry Reed
3 Roy Smith
4 Steve Farr
5 Doug Simunic
6 Richard Barnes
7 Dave Gallagher
8 Bud Anderson
9 Vic Albury
10 Doc Edwards
11 Picky DeLeon
12 Lorenzo Gray
13 Guy Elston
14 Wil Culmer
15 Jeff Barkley
16 Karl Pagel
17 Juan Espino
18 Dwight Taylor
19 Rod Craig
20 Luis Quinones
21 Keith MacWhorter
22 Ed Glynn
23 Shanie Dugas

1984 TCMA Memphis Chicks

(Kansas City Royals, AA) (color)

	MT	NR MT	EX
Complete Set:	35.00	26.00	14.00

1 Rick Mathews
2 Rich Dubee
3 Rick Rizzo
4 Art Hartinez
5 Billy Best
6 Reggie Wyatt
7 Mike Kingery
8 Mitch Ashmore
9 Van Snider
10 Jeff Neuzil
11 Bill Wilder
12 Doug Cook
13 Bob Hegma, Not Issued)
14 Lester Strod, Not Issued)
15 Vinnie Yuhas
16 Jim Miner
17 Steve Reish
18 Roger Hansen
19 Doug Gilcrease
20 Hal Hatcher
21 Jose Reyes
22 Steve Morrow
23 Mark Pirruccello
24 Bill Pecota
25 Dave Cone

1984 TCMA Midland Cubs

(Chicago Cubs, AA) (color)

	MT	NR MT	EX
Complete Set:	20.00	15.00	8.00

1 Joe Henderson
2 Antonio Cordova
3 Don Hyman
4 Jim Boudreau
5 John Huey
6 Jorge Carpio
7 Joe Housey
8 Darryl Banks
9 Ray Soff
10 Mike Capel
11 Jeff Moscaret
12 Doug Potestio
13 Dennis Brogna
14 Glenn Gregson
15 George Enright
16 Darrin Jackson
17 Danny Norman
18 Ricky Baker
19 Jim Auten
20 Jeff Jones
21 Paul Noce
22 Shawon Dunston
23 Gary Varsho
24 Tony Woods

Values quoted in this guide reflect the retail price of a card – the price a collector can expect to pay when buying a card from a dealer. The wholesale price – that which a collector can expect to receive from a dealer when selling cards – will be significantly lower, depending on desirability and condition.

1984 Chong Modesto A's

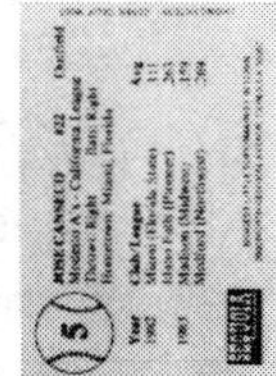

(Oakland A's, A)

	MT	NR MT	EX
Complete Set:	95.00	71.00	38.00

1 Eric Barry
2 Mark Bauer
3 Paul Bradley
4 Greg Cadaret
5 Jose Canseco
6 Chip Conklin
7 Ron Cummings
8 Rocky Coyle
9 Oscar De Chavez
10 Brian Dorsett
11 Mark Ferguson
12 Eric Garret
13 Mike Gorman
14 Juan Cruz
15 Brian Guinn
16 Stan Hilton
17 Joe Law
18 Dave Leiper
19 Tony Moncrief
20 Doug Scherer
21 Keith Thrower
22 Jose Tolentino
23 George Mitterwald
24 Jeff Kobernus
25 Mark Doberenz
26 Dan Kiser
27 Dave Fry
28 Tom Zmudosky

1984 Team Nashville Sounds

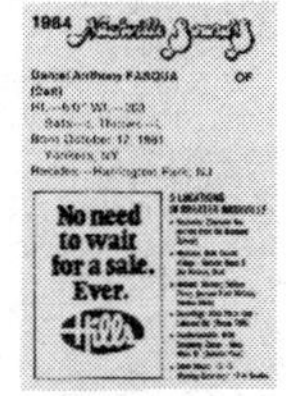

(New York Yankees, AA)

	MT	NR MT	EX
Complete Set:	12.00	9.00	4.75

(1) Johnny Baldwin
(2) Ben Callahan
(3) John Csefalvay
(4) Pete Dalena
(5) Pat Dempsey
(6) Don Fowler
(7) Randy Graham
(8) Johnny Hawkins
(9) Stan Javier
(10) Mike King
(11) Tim Knight
(12) Jim Marshall
(13) Don Mc Gann
(14) Scott Nielsen
(15) Dan Pasqua
(16) Erik Peterson
(17) Jim Rasmussen
(18) Jim Saul
(19) Mark Shiflett
(20) Keith Smith
(21) Bob Tewksbury
(22) Chuck Tomaselli
(23) Hoyt Wilhelm
(24) Bill Worden

1984 TCMA Newark Orioles

(Baltimore Orioles, A) (color) (Set includes the scarce Arnold card)

	MT	NR MT	EX
Complete Set:	9.00	6.75	3.50

1 Randy Riley
2 Eric Bell
3 Troy Howerton
4 David Dahse
5 Dan Mickan
6 Wayne Wilson
7 Dan Fizpatrick
8 Alan Ennis
9 Rich Bair
10 Greg Wirth
11 David Smith
12 Mike Whalen
13 Dan Hayes
14 Tim Smith
15 Frank Velleggia
16 Jim Rooney
17 Rich Caldwell
18 Henry Gonzales
19 Larry Heise
20 Gerry Adams
21 Bob Gutierrez
22 Randy Wilson
23 Jim Hutto
24 Bob Kline
25 Jeff Arnold

1984 TCMA Oklahoma City 89'ers

(Texas Rangers, AAA) (color)

	MT	NR MT	EX
Complete Set:	9.00	6.75	3.50

1 Al Lachowicz
2 Rob Clark
3 Tommy Burgess
4 Cliff Wherry
5 Rusty Gerhardt
6 Dan Larson
7 Mike Griffin
8 Dave Stockstill
9 Mike Jirschele
10 Tom Henke
11 Nick Capra
12 Tony Fossas
13 Steve Buechele
14 Mike Rubel
15 Barry Brunkenkant
16 Kevin Buckley
17 Chuckie Canady
18 Tommy Dunbar
19 Don Scott
20 Victor Cruz
21 Mitch Zwolensky
22 Glenn Cook
23 Dan Murphy
24 German Barranca

1984 TCMA Omaha Royals

(Kansas City Royals, AAA) (color)

	MT	NR MT	EX
Complete Set:	7.50	5.50	3.00

1 Charlie Leibrandt
2 Gene Lamont
3 Tony Ferreira
4 Al Hargesheimer
5 Frank Wills
6 Rickey Keeton
7 Nick Swartz
8 John Morris
9 Mike Brewer
10 Steve Hammond
11 Mike Parrott
12 Marty Wilkerson
13 Jerry Cram
14 Bill Gorman
15 Keith Creel
16 Vinnie Yuhas
17 Theo Shaw
18 Dan St. Clair
19 Mike Alvarez
20 Mike Jones
21 Cliff Pastornicky
22 Dave Leeper
23 Brian Poldberg
24 Mark Ryal
25 Rondin Johnson
26 Russ Stephens
27 Jim Scranton
28 Frank Mancuso
29 Matt Bassett
30 Terry Wendlandt

1984 TCMA Pawtucket Red Sox

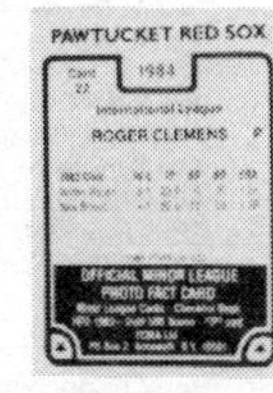

(Boston Red Sox, AAA) (color)

	MT	NR MT	EX
Complete Set:	125.00	95.00	50.00

1 Charlie Mitchell
2 Lee Graham
3a Tony Torcia (name incorrect)
3b Tony Torchia (name correct)
4 Dale Robertson
5 Dennis Burtt
6 Jim Dorsey
7 Chuck Davis (photo actually Mike Davis)
8 Paul Gnacinski
9 Gus Burgess
10a Paul Hundhammer (incorrect name on back)
10b Paul Hundhammer (correct name on back)
11a Tony Herron (incorrect name on back)
11b Tony Herron (correct name on back)
12 Juan Pautt
13 Kevin Romine
14 Steve Crawford
15 Reggie Whittemore
16 Chico Walker
17 Dave Malpeso
18 Steve Lyons
19 Pat Dodson
20 Marc Sullivan
21 Mike Rochford
22 Roger Clemens
23 Rich Gale
24 Brian Denman
25 Juan Bustabad
26 Mike Davis

1984 Cramer Phoenix Giants

(San Francisco Giants, AAA) (color) (A limited-edition, glossy set was also produced)

	MT	NR MT	EX
Complete Set:	8.00	6.00	3.25

1 Phil Oullette
2 Mark Calvert
3 Mark Grant
4 Rob Deer
5 Scott Garrelts
6 Rich Murray
7 Mark Schuster
8 Alejandro Sanchez
9 Jim Farr
10 Herman Segelke
11 Tom O'Malley
12 Jeff Cornell
13 Joe Pettini
14 Tip Lefebvre
15 Brian Kingman
16 Alan Fowlkes
17 Dan Gladden
18 Randy Kutcher
19 Jeff Blobaum
20 Randy Gomez
21 Colin Ward
22 Guy Sularz
23 Chris Brown
24 Jack Mull
241 Tim Blackwell

1984 Cramer Portland Beavers

(Philadelphia Phillies, AAA) (color) (co-sponsored by Coca-Cola) (A limited-edition, glossy set was also produced)

	MT	NR MT	EX
Complete Set:	11.00	8.25	4.50

195 Dave Wehrmeister
196 Stephen Mura
197 Jeff Stone
198 Darren Daulton
199 Francisco Melendez
200 Lee Elia
201 Kelly Downs
202 Bobby Mitchell
203 Randy Salava
204 Don Carman
205 Steve Jeltz
206 George Riley
207 Jose Calderon
208 John Russell
209 Rick Schu
210 Ken Dowell
211 Willie Darkis
212 Richard Gaynor
213 Jay Davisson
214 Steve Fireovid
215 George Culver
216 Russ Hamric

A card number in parentheses () indicates the set is unnumbered.

1984 TCMA Prince William Pirates

(Pittsburgh Pirates, A) (color)

	MT	NR MT	EX
Complete Set:	10.00	7.50	4.00

1 Leon Roberts
2 Jim Buckmier
3 Sean Faherty
4 Shawn Holman
5 Jim Felt
6 Dorn Taylor
7 Mike Berger
8 Pete Piskol
9 John Pavlik
10 Brian Buckley
11 Eric Fink
12 Dorley Downs
13 Wilfredo Cordoba
14 Jim Aulenback
15 Joe Charboneau
16 Felix Fermin
17 Jeff Patton
18 Scott Borland
19 Steve Lewis
20 Don Williams
21 Shawn Stone
22 Sam Haro
23 Rich Sauveur
24 Mitch McKelvey
25 Kim Christenson
26 Craig Brown
27 David Tumbas
28 Leo Sanchez
29 John Lipon
30 Dave Johnson
31 Nick Castaneda
32 Kerry Baker
33 George Borges
34 Stacy Pettis

1984 TCMA Richmond Braves

(Atlanta Braves, AAA) (color)

	MT	NR MT	EX
Complete Set:	8.00	6.00	3.25

1 Mike Reynolds
2 Rufino Linares
3 Ken Smith
4 Paul Boris
5 Larry Whisenton
6 Tom Hayes
7 Vic Lisi
8 Larry Owen
9 Tony Brizzolara
10 Brad Kommins, Leo Vargas)
11 Brad Komminsk
12 Leo Vargas
13 Craig Jones
14 Roger LaFrancois
15 Gary Reiter
16 Bob Galasso
17 Steve Shields
18 Randy Martz
19 Terry Leach
20 Brian Fisher
21 Joe Johnson
22 Sam Ayoub
23 Paul Zuvella
24 Paul Runge
25 Milt Thompson
26 Johnny Sain
27 Eddie Haas

1984 TCMA Rochester Red Wings

(Baltimore Orioles, AAA) (color)

	MT	NR MT	EX
Complete Set:	8.00	6.00	3.25

1 Larry Sheets
2 Rich Carlucci
3 Mark Wiley
4 Jim Hutto
5 Mike Calise
6 John Valle
7 Lee Granger
8 Ismael Oquendo
9 Frank Verdi
10 Jeff Shaefer
11 Glenn Gulliver
12 Luis Rosado
13 Bob Bonner
14 Don Welchel
15 Leo Hernandez
16 Allan Ramirez
17 Bill Swaggerty
18 Joe Kucharski
19 Mike Young

Definitions for grading conditions are located in the Introduction of this price guide.

1984 Cramer Salt Lake City Gulls

(Seattle Mariners, AAA) (color) (co-sponsored by Pennzoil) (A limited-edition, glossy set was also produced)

	MT	NR MT	EX
Complete Set:	20.00	15.00	8.00

170 Danny Tartabull
171 Brian Allard
172 Bill Crone
173 Ivan Calderon
174 Tito Nanni
175 Dave Geisel
176 Dave Valle
177 Jed Murray
178 Brian Snyder
179 Robert Long
180 Jim Lewis
181 Bill Nahorodny
182 Jamie Allen
183 Edwin Nunez
184 Jim Presley
185 Harold Reynolds
186 Jerry Gleaton
187 Glen Walker
188 Al Chambers
189 Karl Best
190 Darnell Coles
191 Bobby Floyd
192 Bobby Cuellar
193 Brad Boylan

1984 TCMA Savannah Cardinals

(St. Louis Cardinals, A) (color)

	MT	NR MT	EX
Complete Set:	7.50	5.50	3.00

1 Sonny James
2 Jeff Lauck
3 Barry McPherson
4 John Costello
5 Kurt Kaull
6 Chuck McGrath
7 Ken Huth
8 Hans Herzog
9 Ted Milner
10 Jim Reboulet
11 Mark Angelo
12 Bob Kish
13 Jamie Brisco
14 Jeff Perry
15 Ernie Carrasco
16 Harry McCulla
17 Bill Packer
18 Glenn Harris
19 Victor Paulino
20 George Vogel
21 Lloyd Merritt
22 Sal Agostinelli
23 Ted Carson
24 Miguel Soto
25 Ken Sinclair
26 Mike Behrend

1984 1st Base Sports Shreveport Captains

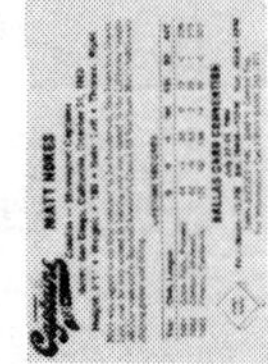

(No affiliation, AA)

	MT	NR MT	EX
Complete Set:	15.00	11.00	6.00

(1) Kevin Bates
(2) Orlando Blackwell
(3) Randy Bockus
(4) Steve Cline
(5) Larry Crews
(6) Bob Cumming
(7) Duane Espy
(8) Bob Gendron
(9) Mike Jones
(10) Chuck Lusted
(11) Kurt Mattson
(12) Bobby Moore
(13) Randy Morse
(14) Matt Nokes
(15) Bob O'Connor
(16) Jessie Reid
(17) Kernan Ronan
(18) Steve Smith
(19) Bryan Snyder
(20) Van Sowards
(21) Steve Stanicek
(22) John Stevenson
(23) Kelvin Torve
(24) Dave Wilhelmi

1984 Team Spokane Indians

(Cleveland Indians) (color)

	MT	NR MT	EX
Complete Set:	25.00	18.50	10.00

1 Rodney McCray
5 Trace Czyzewski
7 Eric Varoz
8 Larry Martin Jr.
9 Jose Lora
10 Jack Maloof
11 Mick Kelleher
14 Mike DeButch
15 Mike Costello
16 Brad Pounders
17 Efrain Valdez
18 Greg Sparks
20 Steve Luebber
23 Robert Perkins
25 John Carlson
26 Mick Gildehaus
27 Joe Filandino
30 Terry Forbes
32 Rusty Ford
34 Rich Scales
42 Joe Bitker
44 Jorge Suris
48 Randell Byers

1984 TCMA Syracuse Chiefs

(Toronto Blue Jays, AAA) (color)

	MT	NR MT	EX
Complete Set:	30.00	22.00	12.00

1 Jim Beauchamp
2 Larry Hardy
3 Tommy Craig
4 Dennis Howard
5 Ron Shephard
6 Rick Leach
7 Anthony Johnson
8 Augie Schmidt
9 Tony Fernandez
10 Jerry Keller
11 Matt Williams
12 Fred Manrique
13 Bobby Nandin
14 Al Woods
15 Toby Hernandez
16 Mike Proly
17 Tim Rodgers
18 Mark Eichhorn
19 Stan Clarke
20 Tom Lukish
21 David Walsh
22 Mike Morgan
23 Mark Bomback
24 Manny Castillo
25 Dave Shipanoff
26 Dave Stenhouse
27 Kelly Gruber
28 Dale Holman
29 Jim Baker
30 Tim Thompson
31 John Cerutti
32 Batboys

1984 Cramer Tacoma Tigers

(Oakland A's, AAA) (color) (This set is numbered as it appears on the backs) (A limited-edition, glossy set was also made)

	MT	NR MT	EX
Complete Set:	6.00	4.50	2.50

73 Bruce Robinson
74 Dave Hudgens
75 Ron Arnold
76 Ramon de los Santos
77 Tom Romano
78 Steve Kiefer
79 Carlos Lezcano
80 Bill Bathe
81 Mike Gallego
82 Jeff Jones
83 Steve Ontiveros
84 Bill Krueger
85 Curt Young
86 Chuck Hensley
87 Tim Pyznarski
88 Phil Stephenson
89 Mark Wagner
90 Ed Nottle
91 Danny Goodwin
92 Bert Bradley
93 John Hotchkiss
94 Dave Ford
95 Gorman Heimueller
96 Dan Meyer
247 Ed Farmer

1984 TCMA Tidewater Tides

(New York Mets, AAA) (color)

	MT	NR MT	EX
Complete Set:	24.00	18.00	9.50

1 Scott Holman
2 Sid Fernandez
3 Wes Gardner
4 John Christensen
5 Herman Winningham
6 Bill Latham
7 Gil Flores
8 Brent Gaff
9 Rusty Tillman
10 Bob Schaefer
11 Ed Olwine
12 Rich Pickett
13 Jeff Bittiger
14 Tom Gorman
15 Jay Tibbs
16 Rafael Santana
17 Bob Sikes
18 Ross Jones
19 Rick Anderson
20 Terry Blocker
21 Laschelle Tarver
22 Al Jackson
23 Kevin Mitchell
24 Brian Giles
25 Ronn Reynolds
26 Terry Leach
27 Kelvin Chapman
28 Clint Hurdle

1984 TCMA Toledo Mud Hens

(Minnesota Twins, AAA) (color)

	MT	NR MT	EX
Complete Set:	7.00	5.25	2.75

1 Steve Lombardozzi
2 Jeffrey Reed
3 Alvaro Espinoza
4 Ray Smith
5 Rich Yett
6 Cal Ermer
7 Dan Schmitz
8 Brad Havens
9 Bob Mulligan
10 Bob Mitchell
11 Andre David
12 Scott Ulger
13 James Weaver
14 Tom Klawitter
15 Jack O'Connor
16 Keith Comstock
17 Eric Broersma
18 Greg Field
19 Tim Agan
20 Dave Baker
21 Jim Shellenback
22 Tack Wilson
23 Rick Lysander
24 Jay Pettibone

1984 Cramer Tucson Toros

(Houston Astros, AAA) (color) (This set is numbered as it appears on the backs of the cards) (A limited-edition, glossy set was also made)

	MT	NR MT	EX
Complete Set:	8.00	6.00	3.25

49 Eric Rasmussen
50 Matt Galante
51 Jose Alvarez
52 Chris Jones
53 Wes Clements
54 Greg Cypert
55 Dwight Bernard
56 Rex Jones
57 Tim Tolman
58 Jaime Williams
59 Manny Hernandez
60 Tye Waller
61 Jim Pankovits
62 Glenn Davis
63 Julio Solano
64 Eddie Bonine
65 Jeff Heathcock
66 Ruben Robles
67 Bert Pena

68 Mark Ross
69 Craig Minetto
70 Larry Ray
71 Luis Pujols
72 Ron Mathis
248 Gary Tuck

1984 Team Tulsa Drillers

(Texas Rangers, AA) This set is numbered as it appears on the cards.

	MT	NR MT	EX
Complete Set:	15.00	11.00	6.00

4 Jorge Gomez
6 Keith Jones
7 Oscar Mejia
14 Greg Jemison
16 Dan Murphy
18 Randy Asadoor
19 Greg Tabor
20 Whitney Harry
22 Barry Bass
23 Orlando Gomez
24 Tim Meckes
26 Bob Gergen
27 John Buckley
28 Bill Hance
29 Jose Guzman
30 Steve Kordish
31 Javier Ortiz
32 Billy Taylor
34 Terry Johnson
36 Dwayne Henry
37 Tommy Joe Shimp
---- Greg Campbell

1984 Cramer Vancouver Canadians

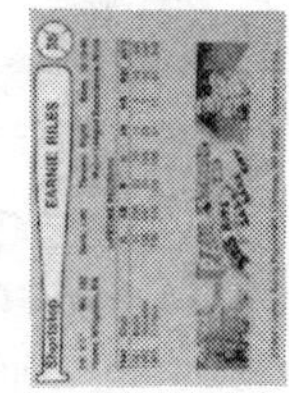

(Milwaukee Brewers, AAA) (color) (co-sponsored by Orange Crush) (A limited-edition, glossy set was also produced)

	MT	NR MT	EX
Complete Set:	6.00	4.50	2.50

25 Ron Koenigsfeld
26 Andy Beene
27 Tony Muser
28 Doug Loman
29 Dan Davidsmeier
30 Ray Searage
31 Kelvin Moore
32 Tom Candiotti
33 Frankie Thomas
34 Carlos Ponce
35 Earnie Riles
36 Dan Boone
37 Dave Huppert
38 Hoskin Powell
39 Doug Jones
40 Bob Gibson
41 Eric Peyton
42 Scott Roberts
43 Jamie Nelson
44 Ed Irvine
45 Jim Koontz
46 Mike Anderson
47 Marshall Edwards
48 Jack Lazorko
243 Don Rowe

1984 TCMA Visalia Oaks

(Minnesota Twins, A) (color)

	MT	NR MT	EX
Complete Set:	7.50	5.50	3.00

1 Bennie Richie
2 Curt Kindred
3 Erez Borowsky
4 Alexis Marte
5 Vincent Ferraro
6 Osvaldo Alfonzo
7 Corey Elliot
8 Phillip Sheppard
9 Leonard Braddy
10 John Hilton
11 Timothy Thompson
12 Brian Hobaugh
13 Tom Reed
14 Jeffrey Schugel
15 Carson Carroll
16 Tim Graupmann
17 Matthew Butcher
18 Paul Mancuso
19 Antonio Codinach
20 Allan Anderson
21 Ronald Scheer
22 Scott Gibson
23 Joseph Tarangelo
---- Steven Aragon
---- Dan Lindquist

1984 Rock's Dugout Wichita Aeros

(Montreal Expos, AAA)

	MT	NR MT	EX
Complete Set:	40.00	30.00	16.00

1 Charlie Puleo
2 Dave Miley
3 Hector Rincones
4 Leo Garcia
5 Tom Browning
6 Charlie Nail
7 Wayne Krenchicki
8 Ron Robinson
9 Curt Heidenrich
10 Dave Van Gorder
11 Tom Runnells
12 Mark Gilbert
13 Terry Bogener
14 Keefe Cato
15 Eric Davis
16 Skeeter Barner
17 Bill Landrum
18 Alan Knicely
19 John Franco
20 Fred Toliver
21 Wade Rowdon
22 Gene Dusan
---- Checklist

1985 TCMA Albany-Colonie Yankees

(New York Yankees, AA) (complete set price includes scarce Lindsey and Hughes cards)

	MT	NR MT	EX
Complete Set:	25.00	18.50	10.00

1 Brad Arnsberg
2 Tim Byron
3 Darin Cloninger
4 Doug Drabek
5 Logan Easley
6 Mark Ferguson
7 Steve Frey
8 Randy Graham
9 Scott Nielsen
10 Scott Patterson
11 Bob Tewksbury
12 Bill Lindsey
13 Phil Lombardi
14 Mark Blaser
15 Ron Chapman
16 Orestes Destrade
17 Rafael Landestoy
18 Jim Riggs
19 Dick Scott
20 Doug Carpenter
21 Tony Russell
22 Brad Winkler
23 Barry Foote
24 Dave LaRoche
25 Jim Saul
26 Mike Fennell
27 Kevin Rand
28 Bernard Bremer
29 Erik Bernard
30 S. Haye, J. Lemperle)
31 Phil Pivnick
32 John Hawkins
33 Tim Knight
34 John Liburdi
35 Keith Hughes

1985 Cramer Albuquerque Dukes

(Los Angeles Dodgers, AAA) (color)

	MT	NR MT	EX
Complete Set:	6.00	4.50	2.50

151 Dean Rennicke
152 Tony Brewer
153 Joe Vavra
154 Dennis Powell
155 Craig Shipley
156 Terry Collins
157 Hector Rincones
158 Ed Amelung
159 Erik Sonberg
160 Dick McLaughlin
161 Ralph Bryant
162 German Rivera
163 Jack Fimple
164 Brian Holton
165 Lemmie Miller
166 Bill Scudder
167 Stu Pederson
168 Larry White
169 Tim Meeks
170 Gil Reyes
171 Don Smith
172 Steve Martin
173 Rafael Montalvo
174 Rich Rodas
175 Franklin Stubbs

1985 TCMA Beaumont Golden Gators

(San Diego Padres, AA) (color)

	MT	NR MT	EX
Complete Set:	20.00	15.00	8.00

1 Jeffrey Childers
2 Rickey Coleman
3 Mark Williamson
4 Shane Mack
5 Edward Vosberg
6 Gregory Smith
7 Peter Kutsukos
8 Jimmy Jones
9 Ulises Sierra
10 Rigo Rodriguez
11 Steven Schefsky
12 Michael McClain
13 Edward Miller
14 Thomas Brassil
15 Frank Castro
16 Mark Poston
17 Michael Mills
18 Gary Green
19 Mark Wasinger
20 David Corman
21 Benito Santiago
22 John Tutt
23 Todd Hutcheson
24 Jack Lamabe
25 Bobby Tolan

1985 TCMA Beloit Brewers

(Milwaukee Brewers, A) (color)

	MT	NR MT	EX
Complete Set:	7.50	5.50	3.00

1 Mike Samuel
2 Walt Pohle
3 Joe Mitchell
4 Jim Rowe
5 Mike Coin
6 Bob Simonson
7 Rob Dewolf
8 Mike Gobbo
9 Tom Steinbach
10 Angel Rodriguez
11 Frank Mattox
12 Bernard Kent
13 Darryel Walters
14 Wes Clements
15 Dean Freeland
16 Mike Frew
17 Greg Simmons
18 Alex Madrid
19 John Ludy
20 Gary Kanwisher
21 Alan Sadler
22 Martin Montano
23 Derek Diaz
24 Miguel Alicea
25 Rob Derksen
26 Dave Machemer

1985 Cramer Bend Phillies

(Philadelphia Phillies, A) (black & white, 2" x 3")

	MT	NR MT	EX
Complete Set:	6.00	4.50	2.50

(1) Dion Beck
(2) Ben Blackmun
(3) Steve Bowden
(4) Rodney Brunelle
(5) Tim Collins
(6) Luis Faccio
(7) Kenley Graves
(8) Nat Green
(9) Jason Grimsley
(10) Steve Harris
(11) Vince Holyfield
(12) John Hurtado
(13) Ron Jones
(14) Bruce Luttrull
(15) Trey McCall
(16) John McKinney
(17) Robert Nazabal
(18) Rick Parker
(19) Mario Perez
(20) Ernie Rodriguez
(21) Floyd Rossum
(22) Steve Sharts
(23) Clifton Walker
(24) Carlos Zayas

1985 Team Birmingham Barons

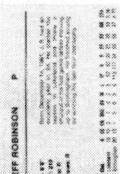

(Detroit Tigers, AA)

	MT	NR MT	EX
Complete Set:	45.00	34.00	18.00

(1) Ricky Barlow
(2) Cary Golbert
(3) Curt Cornwell
(4) Mark Dejohn
(5) Steve Eagar
(6) Bruce Fields
(7) Paul Gibson
(8) Mike Henneman
(9) William Hinz
(10) John Hotchkiss
(11) Duane James
(12) Al Labozzetta
(13) Gordon Mackenzie
(14) Scotti Madison
(15) Steve McInnery
(16) Craig Mills
(17) Dan Norman
(18) Ramon Pena
(19) Joe Perrotte
(20) Jeff Robinson
(21) Ronald Rollin
(22) Benny Ruiz
(23) Gary Springer
(24) Dan St. Clair
(25) Reggie Thomas

1985 TCMA Buffalo Bisons

(Chicago White Sox, AAA) (color)

	MT	NR MT	EX
Complete Set:	7.50	5.50	3.00

1 John Boles
2 Nardi Contreras
3 Greg Latta
4 Steve Christmas
5 Rick Seltheimer
6 Joel Skinner
7 Nelson Barrera
8 Jose Castro
9 Bryan Little
10 Kelvin Moore
11 Ramon Romero

12 Alex Taveras
13 Mark Gilbert
14 Randy Johnson
15 Mark Ryal
16 Dave Yobs
17 Bob Fallon
18 Steve Fireovid
19 Jerry Gleaton
20 Jim Hickey
21 Bill Long
22 Joel McKeon
23 Tom Mullen
24 Scott Stranski
25 Bruce Tanner
26 Dave Wehrmeister

1985 TCMA Burlington Rangers

(Texas Rangers, A) (color)

	MT	NR MT	EX
Complete Set:	6.00	4.50	2.50

1 Joe Grayston
2 Mike Page
3 Larry Klein
4 Brad Hill
5 Steve Cullers
6 Neil Reilly
7 Dale Lanok
8 George Threadgill
9 Dave Darretta
10 Mike Bucci
11 Steve Neilsen
12 Sid Akins
13 Angelo Vasquez
14 Tim Owen
15 Jim St. Laurent
16 Bob O'Hearn
17 Jim Jagnow
18 Mark Kramer
19 Carlos Hernandez
20 Bryan Dial
21 Ty Harden
22 Robin Keathley
23 Stu Rogers
24 Darrell Whitaker
25 Steve Daniel
26 Ross Jones
27 Jim Allison
28 Jim Bridges

1985 Cramer Calgary Cannons

(Seattle Mariners, AAA) (color)

	MT	NR MT	EX
Complete Set:	15.00	11.00	6.00

76 Karl Best
77 Jim Lewis
78 Bobby Floyd
79 Paul Serna
80 Al Chambers
81 Don Scott
82 Roy Thomas
83 John Moses
84 Bobby Cuellar
85 Frank Wills
86 Pat Casey
87 Dave Tobik
88 Mickey Brantley
89 Paul Mirabella
90 Bob Stoddard
91 Ricky Nelson
92 Brian Snyder
93 Bill Crone
94 Danny Tartabull
95 Bob Long
96 Darnell Coles
97 Ron Tingley
98 Rick Luecken
99 Joe Whitmer
100 Clay Hill

1985 TCMA Cedar Rapids Reds

(Cincinnati Reds, A) (color)

	MT	NR MT	EX
Complete Set:	18.00	13.50	7.25

1 John Boyles
2 Mark Cieslak
3 Mike Coffey
4 Virgil Conley
5 Clay Daniel
6 Rob Dibble
7 Barry Fick
8 Mike Goedde
9 Doug Kampsen
10 Steve Oliverio
11 Jim Pettibone
12 Danny Smith
13 Ozzie Soto
14 Mark Berry
15 Greg Toler
16 Gary Denbo
17 Gerg Monda
18 Carlos Porte
19 Brian Robinson
20 Eddie Williams
21 Dan Boever
22 Elvin Fulgencio
23 Tubby Pace
24 Darren Riley
25 Allen Sigler
26 Paul Kirsch
27 Jay Ward
28 Don Buchheister
29 Rod Licht
30 Bud Curren
31 Tom Riley
32 Scott Breeden

1985 TCMA Charlotte O'S

(Baltimore Orioles, A) (complete set price includes scarce Gilbert and Nichols cards)

	MT	NR MT	EX
Complete Set:	9.00	6.75	3.50

1 Kenny Gerhart
2 Lee Granger
3 Jeff Jacobson
4 Rick Lockwood
5 John Stefero
6 Dave Thielker
7 Kelvin Torve
8 Tony Arnold
9 Carl Nichols
10 Mike Reddish
11 Ron Salcedo
12 Jeff Schaefer
13 Dom Chiti
14 John Hart
15 Francisco Oliveras
16 Jeff Summers
17 Jeff Wood
18 Bobby Mariano
19 Rich Caldwell
20 Jeff Gilbert
21 John Babyan
22 John Hoover
23 Ricky Jones
24 John Flinn
25 Alan Ramirez
26 Jose Brito
27 Bob Hice
28 Terry Mauney
29 Charlie Frederick
30 Paul Cameron
31 Mike Couche

1985 Team Chattanooga Lookouts

(Seattle Mariners, AAA) All cards have blank backs.

	MT	NR MT	EX
Complete Set:	65.00	49.00	26.00

(1) Rick Adair
(2) Brian Bargerhuff
(3) Greg Bartley
(4) Randy Braun
(5) Renard Brown
(6) Jim Bryant
(7) Clark Crist
(8) Brian David
(9) Mario Diaz
(10) Mike Evans
(11) Dan Firova
(12) Ross Grimsley
(13) Dave Hengel
(14) Paul Hollins
(15) Tom "Radar" Hunt
(16) Ken Jones
(17) Vic Martin
(18) Jeff McDonald
(19) Rusty McNealy
(20) Jed Murray
(21) Dave Myers
(22) Randy Newman
(23) Bill Plummer
(24) Brick Smith
(25) Terry Taylor
(26) Ric Wilson

1985 Police/Fire Safety Columbus Clippers

(New York Yankees, AAA) The 1985 edition of this minor league team issue was, once again, 25 cards. The Columbus Clippers were affiliated with the New York Yankees and had issued sets each year (except 1983) since 1980. The cards are 2-3/8" by 3-3/4". They have a full-color player picture on the front and a brief biography with a safety tip on the back.

	MT	NR MT	EX
Complete Set:	7.00	5.25	2.75

1 Kelly Heath
3 Tom Barrett
5 Kelly Scott
11 Alphonso Pulido (Alfonso)
12 Rex Hudler
14 Pete Dalena
15 Tim Knight
16 Bert Bradley
17 Butch Hobson
18 Matt Winters
19 Keith Smith
20 Curt Brown
21 Dan Pasqua
23 Dan Briggs
26 Al Williams
27 Don Cooper
29 Juan Espino
37 Brian Fisher
38 Jim Deshaies
39 Clay Christiansen
42 Mark Silva
44 Kelly Faulk
---- Carl "Stump" Merrill (manager)
---- Coaches/Trainer Card (Steve Donohue, Q.V. Lowe, Jerry McNertney, Mickey Vernon)
---- George H. Sisler Jr. (general manager)

1985 TCMA Columbus Clippers

(New York Yankees, AAA) (complete set price includes scarce Bonilla and Mata cards)

	MT	NR MT	EX
Complete Set:	15.00	11.00	6.00

1 Vic Mata
2 Bert Bradley
3 Curt Brown
4 Clay Christiansen
5 Don Cooper
6 Kelly Faulk
7 Brian Fisher
8 Alphonso Pulido
9 Kelly Scott
10 Al Williams
11 Juan Espino
12 Mike O'Berry
13 Tom Barrett
14 Dan Briggs
15 Pete Dalena
16 Kelly Heath
17 Butch Hobson
18 Rex Hudler
19 Keith Smith
20 Tim Knight
21 Dan Pasqua
22 Matt Winters
23 Jim Deshaies
24 Mark Silva
25 Doug Holmquist
26 Juan Bonilla
29 George Sisler
---- Coaches (Steve Donohue, Q.V. Lowe, Jerry McNertney, Mickey Vernon)

1985 Team Daytona Beach Islanders

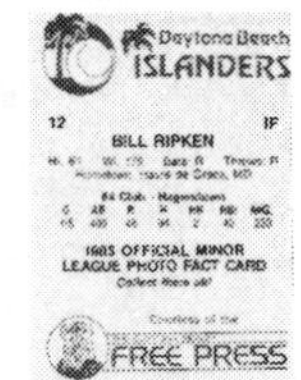

(Cleveland Indians, A) This set is numbered as they appear on the cards.

	MT	NR MT	EX
Complete Set:	50.00	37.00	20.00

1 Tim Haller
2 Michael Holm
3 Dave Murray
4 Mike Halasaz
5 Ray Corbett
6 Jeff Hubbard
7 Perry Hill
8 Kurt Beamesderfer
10 Rick Poznanski
11 Tony Triplett
12 Bill Ripken
14 Pat Vanheyningen
15 Dan Van Cleve
16 Larry Heise
17 Jim Hutto
18 Tim Smith
19 Robert Gutierrez
20 Rob Amble
22 Chris Willsher
23 Eric Dersin
24 Rich Rice
25 Jeff Melrose
26 Carm Lo Sauro
27 Edward Rohan
28 Ben Bianchi
29 Justin Gannon
30 Bruce Kipper
31 Ron Johnson
---- Brian Robinson
---- Thomas Petrizzo

1985 TCMA Durham Bulls

(Atlanta Braves, A) (color)

	MT	NR MT	EX
Complete Set:	12.00	9.00	4.75

1 Paul Assenmacher
2 Vince Barger
3 Kevin Blankenship
4 Mike Bormann
5 Kevin Coffman
6 Maximo Del Rosario
7 David Jones
8 Dave Morris
9 Mac Rogers
11 Mike Santiago
12 Marty Schrieber
13 Troy Tomsick
14 Harry Bright
15 Jim Grant
16 Bob Porter
17 Mike Delao
18 Flavio Alfaro
19 Chris Baird
20 Chip Childress
21 Terry Cormack
22 Sal D'Alessandro
23 Juan Fredymond
24 Dave Griffin
25 Wayne Harrison
26 Johnny Hatcher
27 Roger LaFrancois
28 Mike Nipper
29 Bob Posey
30 Mike Reynolds
31 Jeff Wagner
32 Mike Yastrzemski

1985 Cramer Edmonton Trappers

(California Angels, AAA) (color)

	MT	NR MT	EX
Complete Set:	15.00	11.00	6.00

1 Pat Keedy
2 Wally Joyner
3 Mike Madril
4 Don Groh
5 Scott Oliver
6 Tony Mack
7 Kirk McCaskill
8 Reggie West
9 Rafael Lugo
10 James Randall
11 Marty Kain
12 Gus Polidor
13 Steve Liddle
14 Winston Llenas
15 Bob Ramos
16 Dave Smith
17 Tim Krauss
18 Chris Clark
19 Stewart Cliburn
20 Curt Kaufman
21 Bob Bastian
22 Norman Carrasco
23 Frank Reberger
24 Jack Howell
25 Al Romero

1985 TCMA Elmira Pioneers

(Boston Red Sox, A) (color)

	MT	NR MT	EX
Complete Set:	20.00	15.00	8.00

1 John Abbot
2 Brady Anderson
3 Mike Carista

4 Dell Carter
5 Jim Cox
6 Roberto Fuentes
7 Dan Gabriele
8 Gary Gouldrup
9 Brock Knight
10 Eric Laseke
11 Derek Livernois
12 Greg Lotzar
13 Greg Magistri
14 Josias Manzanillo
15 Donnie McGowan
16 Bill Plante
17 Todd Pratt
18 Carlos Quintana
19 Marte Rogers
20 Victor Rosario
21 Tim Speakman
22 John Toale
23 Luis Vasquez
24 Kerman Williams
25 Bill Zupka

1985 Cramer Everett Giants - Series I

(San Francisco Giants, A) (black & white) (cards measure 2" x 3")

	MT	NR MT	EX
Complete Set:	6.00	4.50	2.50

(1) David Blakely
(2) George Bonilla (pitching)
(3) George Bonilla (portrait)
(4) Ty Dabney
(5) Tom Ealy
(6) Kim Flowers (portrait)
(7) Kim Flowers (with glove)
(8) George Jones (portrait)
(9) George Jones (with bat)
(10) Joe Kmak
(11) Alan Marr
(12) Willie Mijares
(13) Todd Miller
(14) Rick Nelson (holding bat)
(15) Rick Nelson (swinging bat)
(16) Tom Osowski
(17) Darren Pearson (standing in shadow)
(18) Darren Pearson (sunlight on right side)
(19) Brian Petty
(20) Steve Santora
(21) Howard Townsend (portrait)
(22) Howard Townsend (with glove)
(23) John Verducci
(24) Mike Whitt

1985 Cramer Everett Giants - Series II

(San Francisco Giants, A) (black & white) (cards measure 2" x 3")

	MT	NR MT	EX
Complete Set:	6.00	4.50	2.50

1 Jeff Carter
2 Mike Dandos
3 Bruce Graham
4 Dave Hornsby
5 Lloyd Jackson
6 Robert Jackson
7 Darrin James
8 Joe Jordan
9 Randy McCament
10 Timber Mead
11 Dave Morris
12 Curt Motton
13 Brian Ohnoutka
14 Doug Robertson
15 Darrell Rodgers
16 Steve Santora
17 Billy Smith
18 Joe Strain
19 Jack Uhey
20 John Van Kempen
21 Paul Van Stone
22 Mike Whitt
23 Rick Wilson
24 Trevor Wilson

1985 Smokey Fresno Giants

	MT	NR MT	EX
Complete Set:	60.00	45.00	24.00

1 Wendell Kim
2 Marty De Merritt
3 Charles Culberson
4 Angel Escobar
5 Dave Allen
6 Mike Jones
7 Jim Wasem
8 Mackey Sasser
9 Deron Mc Cue
10 Greg Gilbert
11 Charlie Hayes
12 Greg Litton
13 Romy Cucjen
14 John Grimes
15 Ed Puikunas
16 Dan Winters
17 Charlie Corbell
18 Jay Reid
19 Stuart Tate
20 Al Candelaria
21 Todd Kuhn
22 John Burkett
23 Steve Smith
24 Rich Henning
25 Tommy Alexander
26 Todd Oakes
27 Don Wolfe
28 Paul Nef, Paul Reyne)
29 Bill Thompson
30 Curt Goldgrabe
31 Mary Driscoll

1985 TCMA Ft. Myers Royals

(Kansas City Royals, A) (color)

	MT	NR MT	EX
Complete Set:	20.00	15.00	8.00

1 Ed Bass
2 Todd Mabe
3 Brad Davis
4 Craig Walter
5 Don Sparling
6 Tom Niemann
7 Angel Morris
8 Jeff Hull
9 Kevin Seitzer
10 Mark Van Blaricom
11 Phil George
12 Jose DeJesus
13 Jose Nunez
14 Jeff Brown
15 Israel Sanchez
16 Chito Martinez
17 Doug Gilcrease
18 Gary Thurman
19 Tommy Mohr
20 Theo Shaw
21 Mark Farnsworth
22 Steve DeSalvo
23 Mike Keckler
24 Jackie Blackburn
25 Jim Moore
26 Duane Gustavson
27 Mike Alvarez
28 Luis Santos
29 Derek Vanacore
30 Jose Rodiles

1985 Pizza Hut Greenville Braves

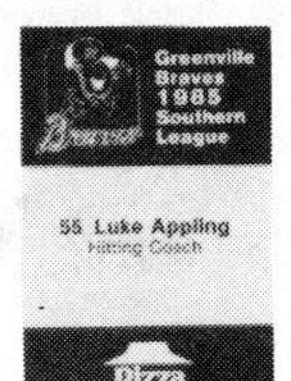

(Atlanta Braves, AA) This set is numbered as it appears on the backs of the cards, and is in the form of a poster. The complete poster is approximately 16-1/2" x 21" in size.

	MT	NR MT	EX
Complete Set:	30.00	22.00	12.00

4a Bob Luzon
4b Bill Slack
5 Mike Knox
6 Maximo Rosario
7 Tom Hayes
8 Andres Thomas
11 Jeff Ransom
12 Glen Bockhorn
14 Randy Ingle
15 Rich Leggatt
16 Paul Assenmacher
17 Rick Albert
19 Todd Lamb
20 Tommy Thompson
22 Leo Vargas
25 Inocencio Guerrero
27 Steve Ziem
30 Andre Treadway
31 Larry Bradford
32 Jim Beauchamp
40 Ben Callahan
55 Luke Appling
---- Bob Tumpane
---- Ken Smith
---- Team logo card (in white)
---- Team logo card (in navy blue)

1985 Team Greenville Braves

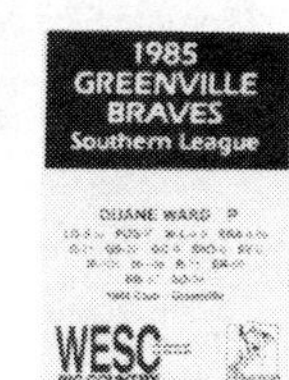

(Atlanta Braves, AA)

	MT	NR MT	EX
Complete Set:	30.00	22.00	12.00

(1) Rick Albert
(2) Brian Aviles
(3) Jim Beauchamp
(4) Glen Bockhorn
(5) Larry Bradford
(6) Inocencio Guerrero
(7) Tom Hayes
(8) Randy Ingle
(9) Joe Johnson
(10) Mike Knox
(11) Todd Lamb
(12) Rich Leggatt
(13) Bob Luzon
(14) Simon Rosario
(15) Matt Sinatro
(16) Bill Slack
(17) Jeff Taylor
(18) Andre Thomas
(19) Tommy Thompson
(20) Freddie Tiburcio
(21) Andre Treadway
(22) Bob Tumpane
(23) Leo Vargas
(24) Duane Ward
(25) Larry Whisenton
(26) Steve Ziem

1985 TCMA Greensboro Hornets

(Boston Red Sox, A) (color)

	MT	NR MT	EX
Complete Set:	7.00	5.25	2.75

1 Doug Camilli
2 Alan Ashikinazy
3 Tary Scott
4 Manuel Jose
5 Thomas Bonk
6 Bruce Lockhart
7 Christopher Moritz
8 Joseph Skripko
9 Zachary Crouch
10 Roberto Zambrano
11 Joseph Stephenson
12 Wayne Tremblay
13 Eduardo Zambrano
14 Pat Dewechter
15 Roy Hall
16 James Corsi
17 Daryl Irvine
18 Eric Hetzel
19 David Peterson
20 Daniel Cakeler
21 Ernest Abril
22 Patrick Jelks
23 Jose Flores
24 Eugene Barrios
25 Anthony DeFrancesco
26 Leverne Jackson
27 Bradley Mettler
28 John DePrimo

1985 Cramer Hawaii Islanders

(Pittsburgh Pirates, AAA) (color)

	MT	NR MT	EX
Complete Set:	6.00	4.50	2.50

226 Jim Opie
227 Sam Khalifa
228 Scott Loucks
229 Denio Gonzalez
230 Rick Reuschel
231 Benny Distefano
232 Paul Semall
233 Tommy Sandt
234 Mitchell Page
235 Steve Shirley
236 Hedi Vargas
237 Jim Winn
238 Trench Davis
239 Bobby Miscik
240 Chris Green
241 Dave Tomlin
242 Stan Cliburn
243 Bob Walk
244 Steve Herz
245 Ray Krawczyk
246 John Henry Johnson
247 John Malkin
248 Manny Sarmiento
249 Jeff Zaske
250 Jerry Dybzinski

1985 Team Huntsville Stars

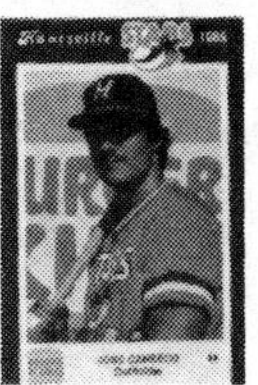

(Oakland A's, AA) (co-sponsored by Burger King)

	MT	NR MT	EX
Complete Set:	10.00	7.50	4.00

Brian Thorson
11 Luis Polonia
14 Brian Graham
15 Tom Dozier
16 Terry Steinbach
17 Chip Conklin
18 John Marquardt
19 Ray Thoma
20 Stan Javier
21 Bill Monneyham
22 Brian Dorsett
23 Scott Whaley
24 Gary lance
25 Brad Fischer
26 Mark Bauer
30 Larry Smith
31 Tim Belcher
32 Darrel Akerfelds
33 Eric Plunk
34 Greg Cadaret
40 Joe Law
41 Rob Nelson
42 Wayne Giddings
43 Rick Stromer
44 Jose Canseco

1985 Team Indianapolis Indians

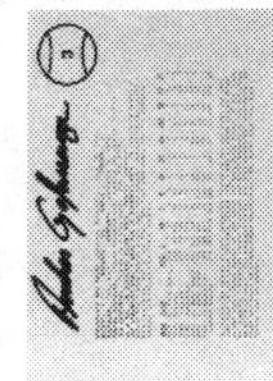

(Cincinnati Reds, AAA)

	MT	NR MT	EX
Complete Set:	25.00	18.50	10.00

1 Team photo
2 Felipe Alou
3 Andres Galarraga
4 Rich Stoll
5 Roy Johnson
6 Steve Baker
7 Mike Fuentes
8 Tim Cates
9 Max Venable
10 Fred Breining
11 Rene Gonzales
12 Fred Manrique
13 Greg Bargar
14 Al Newman
15 Sal Butera
16 Mickey Mahler
17 Dave Hostetler
18 Paul Hertzler
19 Randy St. Claire
20 George Bjorkman
21 Wally Johnson
22 Jack O'Connor
23 Dave Hocksema
24 Steve Brown
25 Casey Candaele

26 Coaches/Trainer Card
27 The Broadcasters
28 Ray Knight (Indianapolis alumni)
29 Dave Revering (Indianapolis alumni)
30 Ron Oester (Indianapolis alumni)
31 Mario Soto (Indianapolis alumni)
32 Bruce Berenyi (Indianapolis alumni)
33 Charlie Leibrandt (Indianapolis alumni)
34 Gary Redus (Indianapolis alumni)
35 Nick Esasky (Indianapolis alumni)
36 Bob Rodgers (Indianapolis alumni)

1985 TCMA International League All-Stars

(AAA) (Complete set price includes includes scarce Greenwell, Mitchell and Slider cards)

	MT	NR MT	EX
Complete Set:	35.00	26.00	14.00

1 Bob Shaffer
2 Bob Tumpane
3 Miguel Sosa
4 Kevin Mitchell
5 Carlos Rios
6 Lasbelle Tarver
7 Billy Beane
8 Doc Estes
9 Larry Owen
10 Ed Hearn
11 Tony Brizzolara
12 John Rabb
13 Billy Springer (Steve Springer)
14 Al Pedrique
15 John Gibbons
16 Terry Blocker
17 Joe Johnson
18 Charlie Mitchell (withdrawn from set - scarce)
19 Rick Anderson
20 Jeff Bittiger
21 Wes Gardner
22 Roy Majtyka
23 Bruce Dal Canton
24 Doc Edwards
25 Jim Wilson
26 Juan Bonilla
27 Scott Ullger
28 Kelly Paris
29 Rick Leach
30 Mike Hart
31 Kelly Heath
32 Juan Espino
33 Dan Briggs
34 Jim Deshaies
35 Dave Gallagher
36 Dan Rohn
37 Kelly Gruber
38 Jeff Reed
39 Dennis Burtt
40 Brad Havens
41 Tom Henke
42 Tom Rowe
43 Brian Allard
44 Mike Greenwell (withdrawn from set - scarce)
45 Rac Slider (withdrawn from set - scarce)

1985 TCMA Iowa Cubs

(Chicago Cubs, AAA) (color)

	MT	NR MT	EX
Complete Set:	10.00	7.50	4.50

1 Tony Castillo
2 Bill Hayes
3 Trey Brooks
4 Tom Lombarski
5 Paul Noce
6 Dave Owen
7 Julio Valdez
8 Brian Dayett
9 Tom Grant
10 Billy Hatcher
11 Chico Walker
12 Jay Baller
13 Derek Botelho
14 Dave Gumpert
15 Scott Holman
16 Bill Johnson
17 Ron Meridith
18 Sam Bernabe
19 Jon Perlman
20 Ken Pryce
21 Larry Rothschild
22 Mark Gillaspie
23 Dave Hostetler
24 Greg Hoffmann
25 Dick Cummings
26 Ken Grandquist
27 Don Silverman
28 Larry Cox
29 Jim Colborn

30 Steve Carroll
31 Steve Weck
33 Bruce Bielenberg
35 Cubby (mascot, Del Roy Smith (batboy), Danny Woolis (batboy))
36 Steve Rodiles

1985 TCMA Kinston Blue Jays

(Toronto Blue Jays, A) (color)

	MT	NR MT	EX
Complete Set:	22.00	16.50	8.75

1 Mark Clemons
2 Omar Bencomo
3 Tony Castillo
4 Mike Cullen
5 Mark Dickman
6 Perry Lychak
7 Alan McKay
8 Jose Mesa
9 Pablo Reyes
10 Jose Segura
11 Willie Shanks
12 Mark Cooper
13 Nelson Liriano
14 Randy Romagna
15 Pat Borders
16 Webster Garrison
17 Omar Malave
18 Joselito Reyes
19 Glen-Allen Hill
20 Drex Roberts
21 Geronimo Berroa
22 Ken Whitfield
23 Eric Yelding
24 Grady Little
25 Rocket Wheeler
26 Tex Drake

1985 Cramer Las Vegas Stars

(San Diego Padres, AAA) (color)

	MT	NR MT	EX
Complete Set:	20.00	15.00	8.00

101 Victor Rodriguez
102 Rusty Tillman
103 John Kruk
104 Ray Hayward
105 Mark Parent
106 Steve Lubratich
107 Marty Decker
108 Ed Rodriguez
109 Lance McCullers
110 Bob Cluck
111 Walt Vanderbush
112 Gene Walter
113 George Hinshaw
114 Ray Smith
115 Steve Garcia
116 Randy Asadoor
117 Bob Patterson
118 Keefe Cato
119 Jim Leopold
120 Ed Wojna
121 Sonny Siebert
122 Tim Pyznarski
123 Mike Couchee
124 Kevin Kristan
125 James Steels

1985 TCMA Little Falls Mets

(New York Mets, A) (color)

	MT	NR MT	EX
Complete Set:	9.00	6.75	3.50

1 Mike Anderson
2 Kevin Armstrong
3 Steve Brueggemann
4 Ron Dominico
5 Brian Givens
6 Lorin Jundy
7 Kelvin Page
8 Chris Rauth
9 Jeff Richardson
10 John Touzzo
11 Tom Wachs
12 Todd Welborn
13 Mark Brunswick
14 Ron Narcisse
15 Rob Colescott
16 Kurt DeLuca
17 Andres Espinoza
18 Dave Gelatt
19 T.J. Johnson
20 Luis Natera
21 Craig Repoz
22 Joaquin Contreras
23 Cliff Gonzalez
24 Maury Gooden
25 Dean Johnson
26 Johnny Monell
27 Bryant Robertson

1985 Riley's Louisville Redbirds

(St. Louis Cardinals, AAA)

	MT	NR MT	EX
Complete Set:	15.00	11.00	6.00

1 Jim Fregosi
2 Joe Rigoli
3 Frank Evans
4 Jerry Mc Kune
5 Vince Coleman
6 Andy Hassler
7 Kevin Hagen
8 Jeff Keener
9 Dave Kable
10 Jed Smith
11 Randy Hunt
12 Joe Pettini
13 Curt Ford
14 Dave Clements
15 Jose Oquendo
16 Matt Keough
17 Bill Lyons
18 Pat Perry
19 Willie Lozado
20 Fred Martinez
21 Jack Ayer
22 Mike Lavalliere
23 John Morris
24 Mick Shade
25 Ben Hayes
26 Rick Ownby
27 Casey Parsons
28 Todd Worrell
29 Mike Anderson
30 Ron Jackson

1985 TCMA Lynchburg Mets

(New York Mets, A) (color)

	MT	NR MT	EX
Complete Set:	15.00	11.00	6.00

1 Mike Cubbage
2 Jim Bibby
3 Dave Tresch
4 Jeff Innis
5 Reggie Dobie
6 Mickey Weston
7 Wray Bergendahl
8 Dave Jensen
9 Jose Bautista
10 David Wyatt
11 Tom Burns
12 Kyle Hartshorn
13 Joe Klink
14 Kevin Burrell
15 Al Carmichael
16 Steve Philips
17 Chris Maloney
18 Keith Miller
19 Kevin Elster
20 Frank Moscat
21 Wilmer Caraballo
22 Andy Lawrence
23 Rey Martinez
24 John Wilson
25 Shawn Abner
26 George Doggett
27 Scott Little

1985 TCMA Madison Muskies

(Oakland A's, A) (color)

	MT	NR MT	EX
Complete Set:	9.00	6.75	3.50

1 Scott Sabo
2 Faustoe Santos
3 Scott Whaley
4 Roy Anderson
5 Russell Applegate
6 Antionio Arias
7 Gregory Brake
8 Todd Burns
9 Brian Criswell
10 Michael Cupples
11 Brian Dorsett
12 Patrick Dietrick
13 Jose Ferreira
14 Robert Gould

15 Darel Hansen
16 Mark Howie
17 Domingo Jose
18 John Kanter
19 Russell Kibler
20 Joseph Kramer
21 Andrew Krause
22 Mark Leonette
23 James Nettles
24 Richard Wise
25 David Schober

1985 T&J SC Madison Muskies

(Oakland A's, A)

	MT	NR MT	EX
Complete Set:	12.00	9.00	4.75

1 Roy Anderson
2 Russ Applegate
3 Tony Arias
4 Greg Brake
5 Todd Burns
6 Brian Criswell
7 Mike Cupples
8 Brian Dorsett
9 P.J. Dietrick
10 Arturo Ferreira
11 Bob Gould
12 Darel Hansen
13 Mark Howie
14 Felix Jose
15 John Kanter
16 Russ Kibler
17 Joe Kramer
18 Andy Krause
19 Mark Leonette
20 Jim Nettles
21 Scott Sabo
22 Faustoe Santos
23 Dave Schober
24 Scotty Lee Whaley
25 Rick Wise

1985 TCMA Maine Guides

(Cleveland Indians, AAA) (color)

	MT	NR MT	EX
Complete Set:	7.50	5.50	3.00

1 Jeff Barkley
2 Dave Beard
3 Jose Calderon
4 Mark Calvert
5 Bryan Clark
6 Keith Creel
8 Jerry Reed
9 Tommy Rowe
10 Roy Smith
11 Rich Thompson
12 Jim Siwy
13 Jose Roman
14 Pat Dempsey
15 Kevin Buckley
16 Geno Petralli
17 Shanie Dugas
18 Barry Evans
19 Jeff Moronko
20 Junior Noboa
21 Luis Quinones
22 Danny Rohn
23 Orlando Sanchez
24 Jim Wilson
26 Mike Brewer
27 Dave Gallagher
28 Dwight Taylor
29 Doc Edwards
30 Brian Allard
31 Steve Ciszczon
32 Scott Tellgren

1985 TCMA Tigers De Mexico

(Mexican League, AAA) (color)

	MT	NR MT	EX
Complete Set:	7.00	5.25	2.75

1 Jesus Rios
2 Roberto Mendez
3 Maurillo Arangure

4 Oswaldo Alvarez
5 Martin Buitimea
6 Ramon Villegas
7 Rodolfo Dimas
8 Francisco Montano
9 Ildefonso Velazquel
10 Lorenzo Retes
11 Francisco Coto
12 Juan Palafox
13 Martin Torres
14 Jose Aguilar
15 Jose Alvarado
16 Ismael Jaime
17 Homar Rojas
18 Adulfo Camacho
19 Jose De Jesus
20 Manuel Morales
21 Amado Peralta
22 Ricardo Renteria
23 Nicolas Castaneda
24 Antionio Castro
25 Matias Caprillo
26 Javier Cruz
27 Juan Bellacetin
28 Luis Ibarra
29 "Chano" & The Chicken

1985 TCMA Midland Angels

(California Angels, AA) (color)

	MT	NR MT	EX
Complete Set:	30.00	22.50	16.00

1 Tito Nanni
2 Bryan Price
3 Greg Key
4 Fred Wilburn
5 Mark Bonner
6 David Heath
7 Doug McKenzie
8 Devon White
9 Dan Murphy
10 Joe Maddon
11 Tom Bryden
12 Don Timberlake
13 Steve Finch
14 Doug Davis
15 Ken Angulo
16 Spiro Psaltis
17 Mark McLemore
18 Kevin Davis
19 Billie Merrifield
20 Aurelio Monteagudo
21 Scott Suehr
22 Ed Delzer
23 Juan Cruz
24 Reggie Montgomery
25 Julian Gonzalez

1985 Chong Modesto A's

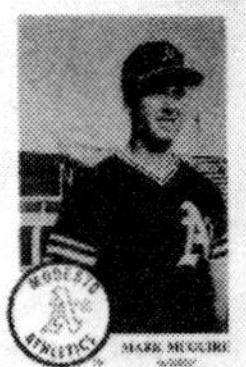

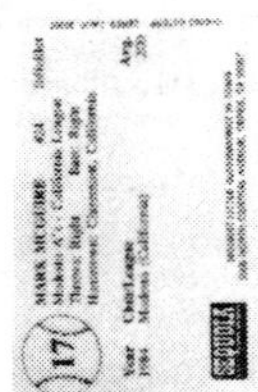

(Oakland A's, A) (with the misspelled McGuire card, the set is worth $100)

	MT	NR MT	EX
Complete Set:	120.00	90.00	47.50

1 Kevin Stock
2 Paul Bradley
3 Antonio Cabrera
4 Twayne Harris
5 Oscar De Chavez
6 Eric Garrett
7 Brian Guinn
8 Allan Heath
9 Joe Strong
10 Mike Fulmer
11 Randy Harvey
12 Kevin Coughlon
13 Jim Eppard
14 Pete Kendrick
15 Jim Jones
16 Steve Howard
17a Mark McGuire (misspelled)
17b Mark McGwire (corrected)
18 Rick Rodriguez
19 Mark Bauer
20 Damon Farmar
21 Dave Wilder
22 Stan Hilton
23 Doug Scherer
24 Bob Loscalzo
25 Joe Odom
26 George Mitterwald
27 Rick Tronerud
28 John Cartelli

1985 TCMA Nashua Pirates

(Pittsburgh Pirates, AA) (color)

	MT	NR MT	EX
Complete Set:	7.50	5.50	3.00

1 Scott Bailes
2 Kerry Baker
3 Mike Berger
4 Craig Brown
5 Kim Christenson
6 Nelson de la Rosa
7 Dorley Downs
8 Stan Fansler
9 Felix Fermin
10 Ken Ford
11 Sam Haro
12 Dave Johnson
13 Tony Laird
14 Larry Lamonde
15 Ravelo Manzanillo
16 Lee Marcheskie
17 Steve McAllister
18 Mitch McKelvy
19 Pete Rice
20 Leon Roberts
21 Ruben Rodriguez
22 Leo Sanchez
23 Rich Sauveur
24 Don Taylor
25 Dave Tumbas
26 Donald Williams
27 John Lipon
28 George Como
29 Jerome Mileur

1985 Team Nashville Sounds

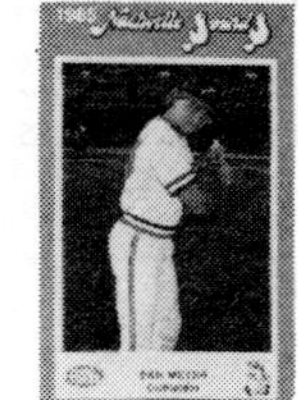

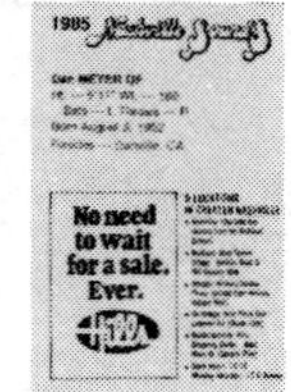

(Detroit Tigers, AA)

	MT	NR MT	EX
Complete Set:	8.00	6.00	3.25

(1) Doug Baker
(2) Darrell Brown
(3) Chuck Cary
(4) Jeff Conner
(5) Brian Denman
(6) Scott Earl
(7) Bryan Kelly
(8) Rusty Kuntz
(9) Mike Laga
(10) Dwight Lowry
(11) Scotti Madison
(12) Don Mc Gann
(13) Gordy Mc Kenzie
(14) Dan Meyer
(15) Bobby Mitchell
(16) Rich Monteleone
(17) John Pacella
(18) Chris Pittaro
(19) Joe Pittman
(20) Leon Roberts
(21) Steve Shirley
(22) Nelson Simmons
(23) Robert Stoddard
(24) Paul Voight
(25) Don Werner

1985 TCMA Newark Orioles

(Baltimore Orioles, A) (color)

	MT	NR MT	EX
Complete Set:	7.00	5.25	2.75

1 Scott Williams
2 Randy King
3 Ty Nichols
4 Greg Talamantez
5 Jeff Tackett
6 Hemmy McFarlane
7 Tony Rohan
8 Mike Holm
9 Gerald Adams
10 Henry Gonzalez
11 Wayne Wilson
12 Benny Bautista
13 Sherwin Cijntje
14 Rico Rossy
15 Robert Gutierrez
16 Mark Schockman
17 Rob Dromerhauser
18 Ray Crone
19 Chris Gaeta
20 Pat Van Heyningen
21 Pete Mancini
22 Jesse Vazquez
23 Matt Skinner
24 Kevin Burke
25 Frank Bellino

1985 Team Osceola Astros

(Houston Astros, A)

	MT	NR MT	EX
Complete Set:	60.00	45.00	24.00

(1) Troy Afenir
(2) Karl Allaire
(3) Mark Baker
(4) Curtis Burke
(5) Ken Caminiti
(6) Earl Cash
(7) Mike Cerefin
(8) Dave Cripe
(9) Greg Dube
(10) Mike Friederich
(11) Tony Hampton
(12) Scott Houp
(13) Ryan Job
(14) Kevin Jones
(15) Kirk Jones
(16) Clarke Lange
(17) Larry Lasky
(18) Arbrey Lucas
(19) Rob Mallicoat
(20) Mark Mangham
(21) Chuck Mathews
(22) Jim O'Dell
(23) Bob Parker
(24) Mark Reynolds
(25) David Rosen
(26) Doug Shaab
(27) Glenn Sherlock
(28) Mike Stellern
(29) Charley Taylor
(30) Gerald Young

1985 TCMA Oklahoma City 89'ers

(Texas Rangers, AAA) (color)

	MT	NR MT	EX
Complete Set:	12.50	9.50	5.00

1 Orlando Mercado
2 Mitch Zwolensky
3 Jeff Kunkel
4 Mike Jirchele
5 Geno Petralli
6 Jim Anderson
7 Tommy Boggs
8 Glen Cook
9 Ricky Wright
10 Tony Fossas
11 Jose Guzman
12 Mike Parrott
13 Tommy Shimp
14 Greg Cambell
15 Dave Oliver
16 George Wright
17 Steve Buechele
18 Oddibie McDowell
19 Bob Sebra
20 Jim Maler
21 Bob Brower
22 Mike Rubel
23 Dave Stockstill
24 Rusty Gerhardt
25 Nick Capra
26 Dale Mohorcic
27 Dale Murray
28 Greg Tabor
29 Chuckie Canady
30 Bill Earley

1985 TCMA Omaha Royals

(Kansas City Royals, AAA) (color)

	MT	NR MT	EX
Complete Set:	20.00	15.00	8.00

1 Bil Gorman
2 Matt Bassett
3 Nick Swartz
4 Frank Mancuso
5 Terry Wendlandt
6 Gus Cherry
7 Les Strode
8 Rich Murray
9 Pat Putnam
10 Tony Ferreira
11 Rich Dubee
12 Butch Davis
13 Mike Griffin
14 Renie Martin
15 Mark Huismann
16 Jamie Quirk
17 Jim Scranton
18 Mike Kinnunen
19 John Morris
20 Marty Wilkerson
21 Rondin Johnson
22 Gene Lamont
23 Mike Kingery
24 Dave Leeper
25 Dave Cone
26 Al Hargesheimer
27 Kenny Baker
28 Buster Keeton
29 Bill Pecota
30 Bob Hegman
31 Brian Pohlberg

1985 TCMA Orlando Twins

(Minnesota Twins, AA) (color)

	MT	NR MT	EX
Complete Set:	7.00	5.25	2.75

1 Steve Aragon
2 Erez Borowsky
3 Mark Davison
4 Paul Felix
5 Mark Funderburk
6 Dan Hanggie
7 Alexis Marte
8 Mike Moreno
9 Greg Morhardt
10 Bobby Ralston
11 Sam Sorce
12 Jeff Trout
13 Mike Verkuilen
14 Ossie Alfonzo
15 Al Cardwood
16 Danny Clay
17 Ken Klump
18 Paul Mancuso
19 Bob Mulligan
20 Les Straker
21 Tim Wiseman
22 Charlie Manuel
23 Wayne Hattaway
24 Dave Williams
25 Gorman Heimueller
26 Craig Henderson

1985 TCMA Pawtucket Red Sox

(Boston Red Sox, AAA) (color)

	MT	NR MT	EX
Complete Set:	40.00	30.00	16.00

1 Gus Burgess
2 Juan Bustabad
3 Pat Dodson
4 Mike Greenwell
5 Paul Hundhammer
6 Not Issued
7 Dave Malpeso
8 Mike Mesh
9 Garry Miller-Jones
10 Sam Nattile
11 Kevin Romine
12 Danny Sheaffer
13 Robin Fuson
14 Rac Slider
15 Dave Sax
16 Tony Herron
17 Tom McCarthy
18 Kevin Kane
19 Mitch Johnson
20 Charlie Mitchell
21 George Mercerod

1985 Cramer Phoenix Giants

(San Francisco Giants, AAA) (color)

	MT	NR MT	EX
Complete Set:	6.00	4.50	2.50

176 Jack Lazorko
177 Randy Kutcher
178 Larry Crews
179 Randy Gomez
180 Fran Mullins
181 Mike Woodard
182 Phil Oullette
183 John Rabb
184 Jeff Robinson
185 Mark Schuster
186 Pat Adams

187 Jim Lefebvre
188 Ricky Adams
189 Kelly Downs
190 Roger Mason
191 Bob Lacey
192 Doug Mansalino
193 Kevin Rhomberg
194 Augie Schmidt
195 Tack Wilson
196 Greg Schultz
197 Bobby Cummings
198 Colin Ward
199 Mark Grant
200 Jeff Cornell

1985 Cramer Portland Beavers

(Philadelphia Phillies, AAA) (color)

	MT	NR MT	EX
Complete Set:	20.00	15.00	8.00

26 David Rucker
27 Gib Seibert
28 Dave Shipanoff
29 Chris James
30 Steve Moses
31 Rocky Childress
32 Alan LeBoeuf
33 Arturo Gonzalez
34 Rick Schu
35 Bill Dancy
36 Jim Olander
37 Randy Salava
38 Mike Maddux
39 Bill Nahorodny
40 Tony Ghelfi
41 Jay Davisson
42 Darren Daulton
43 Francisco Melendez
44 Ralph Citarella
45 Rodger Cole
46 Ken Dowell
47 Bob Tiefenauer
48 Greg Legg
49 Rick Surhoff
50 Mike Diaz

1985 TCMA Prince Williams Pirates

(Pittsburgh Pirates, A) (color)

	MT	NR MT	EX
Complete Set:	12.50	9.50	5.00

1 Orlando Lind
2 Scott Neal
3 Barry Jones
4 Jose Melendez
5 Chip Cunningham
6 Terry Adkins
7 Robby Russell
8 Dimas Gutierrez
9 Steve Lewis
10 Jim Neidlinger
11 Steve Barnard
12 Mike Folga
13 Chris Lein
14 Lance Belen
15 Scott Borland
16 Shawn Holman
17 Jose Lind
18 Tony Blasucci
19 Gary Grudzinski
20 Reggie Barringer
21 Kevin Gordon
22 John Smiley
23 Ed Ott
24 Mike Stevens
25 Van Evans
26 Frank Klopp
27 J.B. Moore
28 Dave Butters
29 Scott Knox
30 Burk Goldthorn
31 Brian Jones

1985 ProCards Reading Phillies

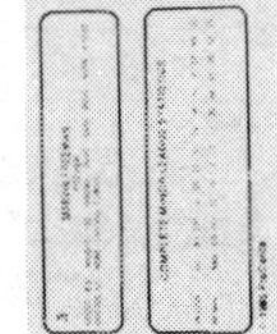

(Philadelphia Phillies, AA) This was the first and only set produced by ProCards in 1985.

	MT	NR MT	EX
Complete Set:	9.00	6.75	3.50

1 George Culver
2 Randy Day
3 Marvin Freeman
4 Bruce Long
5 Ramon Caraballo
6 Kevin Ward
7 Keith Miller
8 Jose Escobar
9 Ken Kinnard
10 Todd Soares
11 Greg Jelks
12 Ken Jackson
13 Tony Brown
14 Joe Cipolloni
15 Wilfredo Tejada
16 Rob Hicks
17 Scott Wright
18 Bryan Hobbie
19 Mark Bowden
20 Jim Olson
21 Steve Labay
22 Tony Evetts
23 Darryl Menard
24 Rich Gaynor
25 Barney Nugent

1985 TCMA Richmond Braves

(Atlanta Braves, AAA) (color)

	MT	NR MT	EX
Complete Set:	7.00	5.25	2.75

1 Tony Brizzolara
2 Marty Clary
3 David Clay
4 Jeff Dedmon
5 Dan Morogiello
6 Mike Payne
7 Gary Reiter
8 Dave Schuler
9 Steve Shields
10 Matt West
11 John Lickert
12 Larry Owen
13 Glenn Gulliver
14 Randy Johnson
15 Carlos Rios
16 Ken Smith
17 Miguel Sosa
18 Doc Estes
19 Lee Graham
20 Gene Roof
21 Milt Thompson
22 John Rabb
23 Bruce Dal Canton
24 Sam Ayoub
25 Sonny Jackson
26 Roy Majtyka

1985 TCMA Rochester Red Wings

(Baltimore Orioles, AAA) (complete set price includes scarce Biercevicz and Bjorkman cards)

	MT	NR MT	EX
Complete Set:	12.00	9.00	4.75

1 Raymond Corbett
2 Al Pardo
3 Luis Rosado
4 Dave Falcone
5 Leonardo Hernandez
6 Ricky Jones
7 Nelson Norman
8 Kelly Paris
9 James Traber
10 Roderick Allen
11 Darrel Brown
12 Robert Molinaro
13 John Shelby
14 Gerald Augustine
15 Jose Brito
16 Bradley Havens
17 Phillip Huffman
18 Jerry Johnson
19 Odell Jones
20 Joseph Kucharski
21 David Rajsich
22 William Swaggerty
23 Donald Welchel
24 Frank Verdi
25 Sandy Valdespino
26 "The Braintrust"
27 D. Gordo, J. Kurcharski)
28 Jamie Reed
29 Mark Wiley
30 Greg Biercevicz
31 George Bjorkman

1985 Cramer Spokane Indians

(San Diego Padres, A) (black & white) (cards measure 2" x 3")

	MT	NR MT	EX
Complete Set:	6.00	4.50	2.50

(1) Eric Bauer
(2) Bill Blount
(3) Jerald Clark
(4) Joey Cora
(5) Adam Ging
(6) Greg Hall
(7) Greg Harris
(8) Nate Hill
(9) Chris Knabenshue
(10) Glen Kuiper
(11) Joe Lynch
(12) Jack Maloof
(13) Matt Maysey
(14) Tom Meagher
(15) Maurice Morton
(16) Jay Nieporte
(17) Eric Nolte
(18) Juan Paris
(19) Jeff Parks
(20) Ramon Rodriguez
(21) Norm Sherry
(22) Bill Stevenson
(23) Jorge Suris
(24) Jim Tatum

1985 Cramer Spokane Indians All-Time Greats

(black & white) (cards measure 2" x 3")

	MT	NR MT	EX
Complete Set:	9.50	7.25	3.75

(1) Doyle Alexander
(2) John Billingham
(3) Bill Buckner
(4) Willie Crawford
(5) Jim Fairey
(6) Alan Foster
(7) Steve Garvey
(8) Charlie Hough
(9) Tommy Hutton
(10) Von Joshua
(11) Ray Lamb
(12) Tom Lasorda
(13) Dave Lopes
(14) Joe Moeller
(15) Tom Paciorek
(16) John Purdin
(17) Bill Russell
(18) Ted Sizemore
(19) Gus Sposito
(20) Jack Spring
(21) Bob Stinson
(22) Bob Valentine
(23) Sandy Vance
(24) Geoff Zahn

1985 TCMA Springfield Cardinals

(St. Louis Cardinals, A) (color)

	MT	NR MT	EX
Complete Set:	7.00	5.25	2.75

1 John Rigos
2 Rich Embser
3 Jim Fregosi
4 Jim Van Houten
5 John Costello
6 Todd Demeter
7 John Digioia
8 Greg Dunn
9 John Fassero
10 Lloyd Merrit
11 Mike Fitzgerald
12 Craig Wilson
13 Mike Hartley
14 Matt Kinzer
15 Ron Leon
16 Brad Luther
17 Harry McCulla
18 Steve Turco
19 Steve Turgeon
20 Charles McGrath
21 Jay North
22 Angleo Nunley
23 Pete Stoll
25 Mike Robinson
30 Paul Wilmet

1985 TCMA Syracuse Chiefs

(Toronto Blue Jays, AAA) (color)

	MT	NR MT	EX
Complete Set:	120.00	90.00	47.50

1 Gibson Alba
2 Fred McGriff
3 Gary Allenson
4 Stan Clark (Clarke)
5 Dale Holman
6 Tom Filer
7 Keith Gilliam
8 Tom Henke
9 Dennis Howard
10 John Woodworth
11 Rick Leach
12 Matt Williams
13 Don Gordon
14 Alex Infante
15 Colin McLaughlin
16 Pat Rooney
17 Mark Poole
18 Jerry Keller
19 Mike Sharperson
20 John Mayberry
21 Doug Ault
22 Kelly Gruber
23 Vance McHenry
24 "Red" Coughlin
25 Dale Holma, Fred McGriff)
26 Batboys
27 John Cerutti
28 Dennis Homberg
29 Derwin McNealy
30 Cloyd Boyer
31 Dave Stegman

1985 Cramer Tacoma Tigers

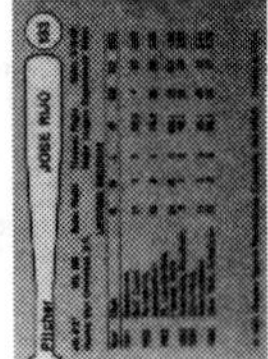

(Oakland A's, AAA) (color)

	MT	NR MT	EX
Complete Set:	7.50	5.50	3.00

126 Keith Lieppman
127 Jose Tolentino
128 Keith Thrower
129 Chuck Estrada
130 Ricky Peters
131 Tom Romano
132 Phil Stephenson
133 Jose Rijo
134 Danny Goodwin
135 Thad Reece
136 Mike Ashman
137 Ron Harrison
138 Stan Kyles
139 Steve Kiefer
140 Tim Lambert
141 Doug Scherer
142 Steve Ontiveros
143 Bob Bathe
144 Bob Owchinko
145 Tom Dozier
146 Joe Lansford
147 Steve Mura
148 Bill Bathe
149 Mike Chris
150 Tom Tellman (Tellmann)

1985 TCMA Tidewater Tides

(New York Mets, AAA) (Complete set price includes scarce card #16)

	MT	NR MT	EX
Complete Set:	50.00	37.00	20.00

1 Rick Lancellotti
2 Terry Leach
3 Sid Fernandez
4 Jeff Bettendorf
5 Calvin Schiraldi
6 Rick Anderson
7 Randy Niemann
8 Jeff Bittiger
9 Wes Gardner
10 Bill Latham
11 Rick Aguilera
12 Ed Olwine
13 Laschelle Tarver
14 Billy Beane
15 John Gibbons
16 Steve Springer (black bat, photo actually Ed Hearn)
17 Steve Springer (white bat, correct photo)
18 Kevin Mitchell

19 Terry Blocker
20 Len Dykstra
21 Ed Hearn
22 Ross Jones
23 Mike Davis
24 Alfredo Pedrique
25 Mark Carreon
26 John Cumberland
27 Bob Schaefer
28 Rick Rainer

1985 TCMA Toldeo Mud Hens

(Minnesota Twins, AAA) (Complete set price includes scarce Chiffer card)

	MT	NR MT	EX
Complete Set:	15.00	11.00	6.00

1 Allan Anderson
2 Eric Broersma
3 Mark Brown
4 Dennis Burtt
6 Frank Eufemia
8 Ed Hodge
10 Mark Portugal
11 Mike Walters
12 Len Whitehouse
13 Toby Hernandez
14 Jeff Reed
15 Alvaro Espinoza
16 Houston Jiminez
17 Steve Lombardozzi
18 Scott Ullger
19 Reggie Whittemore
20 Andre David
21 Mike Hart
22 Stan Holmes
23 Greg Howe
24 Jerry Lomastro
25 Al Woods
26 Cal Ermer
27 Jim Shellenback
30 Rich Yett
32 Floyd Cliffer

1985 Cramer Tucson Toros

(Houston Astros, AAA) (color)

	MT	NR MT	EX
Complete Set:	7.50	5.50	3.00

51 Chris Jones
52 Eric Bullock
53 Jimmy Johnson
54 Mark Ross
55 Larry Acker
56 Manny Hernandez
57 Vern Followell
58 Larry Montgomery
59 Rick Colbert
60 Mark Knudson
61 Rafael Landestoy
62 Stan Hough
63 Mike Calise
64 Tye Waller
65 Glenn Davis
66 Randy Martz
67 Chuck Jackson
68 John Mizerock
69 Ty Gainey
70 Eddie Bonine
71 Pedro Hernandez
72 James Miner
73 Charlie Kerfeld
74 Rex Jones
75 Brad Mills

1985 Team Tulsa Drillers

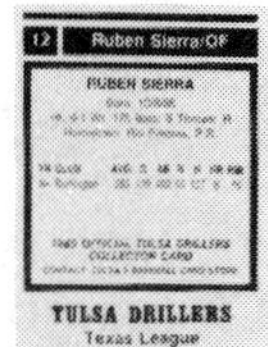

(Texas Rangers, AA) (This set is numbered as it appears on the card backs) (The set price includes the scarce Sierra card)

	MT	NR MT	EX
Complete Set:	100.00	75.00	40.00

1 Ken Reitz
4 George Crum
6 George Foussianes
7 Oscar Mejia
9 Jamie Doughty
10 Mark Gile
12 Ruben Sierra
14 Barry Brunenkant
17 Larry Pott
18 Bobby Witt
19 Duane James
20 Tony Hudson
22 Jeff Moronko
23 Orlando Gomez
24 Jeff Mace
25 Bob Gergen
26 Barry Bass
27 Rob Clark
28 Bill Fahey
29 Dwayne Henry
30 Terry Johnson
31 Javier Ortiz
32 Kirk Killingsworth
33 Scott Anderson
34 Bill Taylor
35 Otto Gonzalez
36 Al Lachowicz
37 Clyde Reichard

1985 TCMA Utica Blue Sox

(No Affiliation, A) (color) Although the Utica Blue Jays set is classified as a Co-op team, players were furnished from the Expos, Phillies, Rangers and Tigers.

	MT	NR MT	EX
Complete Set:	35.00	26.00	14.00

1 Jim Allison
2 Ross Jones
3 Dave Linton
4 Paulino Paixao
5 Bob Sudo
6 Darren Travels
7 Sergio Valdez
8 Rob Williams
9 Roger Dean
10 Pancho Hedfelt
11 Al Hibbs
12 Esteben Beltre
13 Rodney Clark
14 Jeff Scheaffer
15 Alfonso Traverez
16 Larry Walker
17 Bob Brown
18 Andy Donatelli
19 Ray Garcia
20 Raymond Noble
21 Fred Perez
22 Troy Ricker
23 Steve St. Claire
24 Ken Brett
25 Gene Glynn
26 Dan Gazzilli

1985 Cramer Vancouver Canadians

(Milwaukee Brewers, AAA) (color)

	MT	NR MT	EX
Complete Set:	6.00	4.50	2.50

201 Dan Davidsmeier
202 Brad Lesley
203 Tim Leary
204 Bobby Clark
205 Juan Castillo
206 Jim Aducci
207 Earnie Riles
208 Mike Paul
209 Dale Sveum
210 Jaime Cocanower
211 Mike Felder
212 Brian Duquette
213 Jim Paciorek
214 Bob Skube
215 Tom Trebelhorn
216 Bill Wegman
217 Mike Martin
218 Scott Roberts
219 Rick Waits
220 Chuck Crim
221 Jaime Nelson
222 Brian Clutterbuck
223 Garret Nago
224 Carlos Ponce
225 Al Price

1985 TCMA Vero Beach Dodgers

(Los Angeles Dodgers, A) (color)

	MT	NR MT	EX
Complete Set:	7.00	5.25	2.75

1 Bobby Hamilton
2 Tracy Woodson
3 John Schlichting
4 Gary Newsom
5 Manuel Francois
6 Joe Szekley
7 Felipe Gutierrez
8 Wayne Kirby
9 Gary Legumina
10 Ed Jacobo
11 Henry Gatewood
12 Norberto Flores
13 Harry Ritch
14 Joe Karmeris
15 William Brennan
16 Bob Jacobsen
17 Vince Beringhele
18 Mike Schweignoffer
19 Bary Wohler
20 Greg Mayberry
21 Luis Lopez
22 Mike Pesavento
23 Mike Cherry
24 Rob Giesecke
25 Dennis Lewallyn
26 Stan Wasiak
27 John Shoemaker

1985 TCMA Visalia Oaks

(Minnesota Twins, A) (color)

	MT	NR MT	EX
Complete Set:	7.50	5.50	3.00

1 Phil Wilson
2 Doug Palmer
3 Perry Husband
4 Bill O'Connor
5 Sal Nicolosi
6 Jeff Schugel
7 Brad Bierley
8 Jay Bell
9 Chris Forgione
10 Robert Calley
11 Tom DiCeglio
12 Chris Calvert
13 Dave Vetsch
14 Gene Larkin
15 Bob Lee
16 Ray Velasquez
17 Todd Budke
18 Jeff Rojas
19 Wes Pierorazio
20 Neil Landmark
21 Tony Guerrero
22 Jose Dominguez
23 Scott Klingbell
24 Troy Galloway
25 Danny Schmitz

1985 TCMA Waterbury Indians

(Cleveland Indians, AA) (color)

	MT	NR MT	EX
Complete Set:	18.00	13.50	7.25

1 Nelson Pedraza
2 Wilson Valera
3 Randy Washington
4 Winston Ficklin
5 Glenn Edwards
6 Richard Doyle
7 Mickey Street
8 John Miglio
9 Cal Santarelli
10 Wayne Johnson
11 Reggie Ritter
12 Doug Jones
13 Marty Leach
14 Jeff Arney
15 Dave Clark
16 Ron Wallenhaupt
17 German Barranca
18 Tim Glass
19 Jim Driscoll
20 George Cecchetti
21 John Farrell
22 Jack Aker
23 Cory Snyder
24 Andy Allanson
25 Dain Syverson

1986 TCMA Albany-Colonie Yankees

(New York Yankees, AA) (color)

	MT	NR MT	EX
Complete Set:	12.00	9.00	4.75

1 Jim Riggs
2 Roberto Kelly
3 Carson Carroll
4 Miguel Sosa
5 Tom Barrett
6 Ferdi Gonzalez
7 Keith Hughes
8 Bill Monobouquette
9 Carlos Martinez
10 Tony Russell
11 Mike Heifferon
12 Eric Bernard
13 John Liburdi
14 Eric Dersin
15 Jeff Pries
16 Jim Saul
17 Logan Easley
18 Mo Ching
19 John Lemperie
20 Chuck Yaeger
21 Eric Schmidt
22 Bill Lindsey
23 Darren Reed
24 John Kennedy
25 Aris Tirado
26 Bill Fulton
27 Joe Impagliazzo
28 Clay Christensen
29 Steve George
30 Brent Blum
31 Bob Davidson
32 Bullpen Action (Brent Blum, Logan Easley, Bill Monobouquette)

1986 ProCards Albuquerque Dukes

(Los Angeles Dodgers, AAA)

	MT	NR MT	EX
Complete Set:	7.00	5.25	2.75

(1) Ed Amelung
(2) Ralph Bryant
(3) Terry Collins
(4) Lenny Currier
(5) Jon Debus
(6) Dave Eichhorn
(7) Jack Fimple
(8) Balvino Galvez
(9) Jose Gonzalez
(10) Jeff Hamilton
(11) Mark Heuer
(12) Brian Holton
(13) Dennis Livingston
(14) Scott May
(15) Dick McLaughlin
(16) Adrian Meagher
(17) Tim Meeks
(18) Gary Newsom
(19) Stu Pederson
(20) Gil Reyes
(21) Mike Schweighoffer
(22) Larry See
(23) Craig Shipley
(24) Steve Shirley
(25) Joe Vavra
(26) Dave Wallace
(27) Mike Watters
(28) Reggie Williams

1986 ProCards Appleton Foxes

(Chicago White Sox, A)

	MT	NR MT	EX
Complete Set:	6.00	4.50	2.50

(1) Tony Bartolomucci
(2) John Boling
(3) Glen Braxton
(4) Kurt Brown
(5) Buzz Capra
(6) Tony Cento
(7) William Eveline
(8) James Filippi
(9) Cornelio Garcia
(10) Tom Hartley
(11) Richard Issac
(12) Scott Kershaw
(13) William Magallanes
(14) Steve McLaughlin
(15) Eric Milholand
(16) Steve Moran
(17) Donn Pall
(18) Luis Peraza
(19) David Reynolds
(20) Jesus Sandoval
(21) Ron Scruggs
(22) Dave Sheldon
(23) Duke Sims
(24) John Stein
(25) George Stone
(26) Randy Velarde
(27) Aubrey Waggoner
(28) Marty Warren

1986 ProCards Arkansas Travelers

(St. Louis Cardinals, AA)

	MT	NR MT	EX
Complete Set:	12.00	9.00	4.75

(1) Tom Almante
(2) Rod Booker

(3) Ernie Carrasco
(4) Paul Cherry
(5) Dave Clements
(6) Mark Dougherty
(7) Rich Embser
(8) Lance Johnson
(9) Dave Kable
(10) Jeff Kenner
(11) Jeff Ledbetter
(12) Joe Magrane
(13) John Martin
(14) Henry McCulla
(15) Curt Metzger
(16) Allen Morlock
(17) Mike Rhodes
(18) Mark Riggins
(19) James Riggleman
(20) Mike Robinson
(21) Jose Rodriguez
(22) Mark Schulte
(23) Ray Soff
(24) Eddie Tanner
(25) Tim Wallace
(26) Scott Young

1986 ProCards Ashville Tourists

(Houston Astros, A)

	MT	NR MT	EX
Complete Set:	7.00	5.25	2.75

(1) Tim Arnsburg
(2) Jeff Baldwin
(3) Ken Bolek
(4) Chris Clawson
(5) Carlo Colombino
(6) Todd Credeur
(7) Pedro DeLeon
(8) Cameron Drew
(9) Jeff Edwards
(10) John Elliot
(11) Stan Fascher
(12) Fred Gladding
(13) Neder Horta
(14) Bert Hunter
(15) Blaise Ilsley
(16) Richard Johnson
(17) Larry Lasky
(18) Scott Markley
(19) David Meads
(20) Tony Metoyer
(21) Gary Murphy
(22) Carlos Reyes
(23) A. Rodriguez
(24) Ron Roebuck
(25) Wayne Rogalski
(26) Joe Schulte
(27) Shawn Talbott
(28) Dan Walters
(29) Terry Wells

1986 ProCards Auburn Astros

(Houston Astros, A)

	MT	NR MT	EX
Complete Set:	6.00	4.50	2.50

(1) Troy Aleshire
(2) Dave Banks
(3) Keith Bodie
(4) Daven Bond
(5) Bill Bonham
(6) Damon Brooks
(7) Gary Cooper
(8) Jeff Edwards
(9) Joel Estes
(10) Scott Gray
(11) Carl Grovom
(12) Trent Hubbard
(13) Bert Hunter
(14) Gayron Jackson
(15) Rusty Kryzanowski
(16) Brian Meyer
(17) Guy Nomrand
(18) Jimmy Olson
(19) Dave Potts
(20) Ron Roebuck
(21) Dave Rohde
(22) Pedro Sanchez
(23) Richie Simon
(24) Matt Stennett
(25) Jim Vike
(26) Kevin Wasilewski
(27) Ed Whited

1986 ProCards Bakersfield Dodgers

(Los Angeles Dodgers, A)

	MT	NR MT	EX
Complete Set:	20.00	15.00	8.00

(1) Dave Alarid
(2) Mike Batesole
(3) Manuel Benitez
(4) Mike Burke
(5) Dave Carlucci
(6) Jovon Edwards
(7) Mike Fiala
(8) Bert Flores
(9) Rick Gahbrielson
(10) Rene Garcia
(11) Darryl Gilliam
(12) Anthony Hardwick
(13) Ted Holcomb
(14) Jay Hornacek
(15) Ron Jackson
(16) Stan Jonston
(17) Tim Kelly
(18) Brian Kopetsky
(19) Don "Ducky" LeJohn
(20) Ramon Martinez
(21) Andy Naworski
(22) Jeff Nelson
(23) Jay Ray
(24) Jack Savage
(25) Bryan Smith
(26) Dan Smith
(27) Walt Stull
(28) John Wetteland
(29) Mike White

1986 ProCards Beaumont Golden Gators

(Houston Astros, AA)

	MT	NR MT	EX
Complete Set:	15.00	11.00	6.00

(1) Santos Alomar
(2) Joe Bitker
(3) Tom Brassil
(4) Randy Byers
(5) Frank Castro
(6) Joe Chavez
(7) Joey Cora
(8) Mike Costello
(9) Mike Debutch
(10) Rich Doyle
(11) Rusty Ford
(12) Brent Gjesdal
(13) Eric Hardgrave
(14) Steve Lubratich
(15) Steve Luebber
(16) Shane Mack
(17) Paul Mancuso
(18) Mike McClain
(19) Mike Mills
(20) Mark Poston
(21) Candy Sierra
(22) Todd Simmons
(23) Steve Smith
(24) Eric Varoz
(25) Bill Wrona

1986 Cramer Bellingham Mariners

(Seattle Mariners, Rookie)

	MT	NR MT	EX
Complete Set:	6.00	4.50	2.50

101 David Hartnett
102 Jim Bowie, Jr.
103 Michael McDonald
104 Jose Bennet
105 Deron Johnson, Jr.
106 Wendell Bolar
107 Gregory Briley
108 Jose Tartabull, Jr.
109 Thomas Little
110 Jerry Goff
111 Michael Thorpe
112 Brad Rohde
113 James Pritikin
114 Bret Simmermacher
115 Tim Fortugno
116 Arvid Morfin
117 Jody Ryan
118 Troy Williams
119 Randy Little
120 James Blueberg
121 Richard DeLuca
122 Daniel Disher
123 Ted Williams
124 Raul Mendez
125 Fausto Ramirez
126 Clay Gunn
127 Rudy Webster
128 Patrick Lennon
129 Mark Wooden

1986 ProCards Beloit Brewers

(Milwaukee Brewers, A)

	MT	NR MT	EX
Complete Set:	6.00	4.50	2.50

(1) Shon Ashley
(2) Rich Bosley
(3) Bob Caci
(4) Isaiah Clark
(5) Carlos Escalera
(6) Frank Fazzini
(7) Dan Fitzpatrick
(8) Ed Greene
(9) Joe Haney
(10) Doug Henry
(11) Gomer Hodge
(12) Tom Kleean
(13) Lance Lincoln
(14) Rusty McGinnis
(15) Charlie McGrew
(16) Carl Moraw
(17) Ray Ojeda
(18) Warren Olson
(19) Juan Reyes
(20) Jim Rowe
(21) Greg Simmons
(22) Bob Simonson
(23) Jeff Smith
(24) Jose Ventura
(25) Randy Veres
(26) Larry Whitford

1986 Cramer Bend Phillies

(Philadelphia Phillies, A)

	MT	NR MT	EX
Complete Set:	6.00	4.50	2.50

130 Roderick Robertson
131 Quinn Williams
132 Al Hibbs
133 Scott Ruckman
134 Doug Hodo
135 Stephen Scarsone
136 Charles Malone
137 Keith Greene
138 Donald Church
139 Andrew Ashby
140 Elvis Romero
141 Glen Anderson
142 Kenny Miller
143 Fred Christopher
144 Brad Moore
145 Leroy Ventress
146 John Gianukakis
147 Chris Limbach
148 Tim Sossamon
149 Ryan Silva
150 Gary Berman
151 Bubba Allison
152 Juan Ascencio
153 Jeff Myaer
154 Garland Kiser

1986 ProCards Buffalo Bisons

(Chicago White Sox, AAA)

	MT	NR MT	EX
Complete Set:	6.00	4.50	2.50

(1) Glen Bockhorn
(2) Dick Bosman
(3) Daryl Boston
(4) Scott Bradley
(5) Tony Brizzolara
(6) Darren Burroughs
(7) Nick Capra
(8) Bryan Clark
(9) Joe Cowley
(10) Joe Desa
(11) Pete Filson
(12) Jerry Don Gleaton
(13) Al Jones
(14) Tim Krauss
(15) Greg Latta
(16) Bill Long
(17) Jim Marshall
(18) Steve McCatty
(19) Russ Morman
(20) Chris Nyman
(21) Bruce Tanner
(22) Tom Thomson
(23) Dave Wehrmeister
(24) Ken Williams
(25) Matt Winters
(26) Dave Yobs

1986 ProCards Burlington Expos

(Montreal Expos, Kansas City Royals, A)

	MT	NR MT	EX
Complete Set:	15.00	11.00	6.00

(1) Tom Arrington
(2) Daryl Asbe
(3) Luis Corcino
(4) Matt Crouch
(5) Geff Davis
(6) Pat Dougherty
(7) Fritz Fedor
(8) Cesar Hernandez
(9) Jim Hunter
(10) Jeff Huson
(11) Juan Jimenez
(12) Tom Johnson
(13) Frank Laureano
(14) Tim Lemons
(15) Andy Leonard
(16) J.R. Miner
(17) Melido Perez
(18) Jose Rodriguez
(19) Brad Shores
(20) Joe Slotnick
(21) Stuart Stauffacher
(22) Bob Sudo
(23) Scott Sundgren
(24) Alfonso Tavarez
(25) Larry Walker
(26) Bob Williams
(27) John Williams
(28) Team Photo

1986 ProCards Calgary Cannons

(Seattle Mariners, AAA)

	MT	NR MT	EX
Complete Set:	10.00	7.50	4.00

(1) Greg Bartley
(2) Mickey Brantley
(3) Randy Braun
(4) Pat Casey
(5) Bill Crone
(6) Mario Diaz
(7) Jerry Dybzinski
(8) Steve Fireovid
(9) Dan Firova
(10) Ross Grimsley
(11) Dave Hengel
(12) Clay Hill
(13) Vic Martin
(14) Doug Merrifield
(15) Rich Montelone
(16) John Moses
(17) Jed Murray
(18) Ricky Nelson
(19) Randy Newman
(20) Jack O'Conner
(21) Bill Plummer
(22) Jerry Reed
(23) Harold Reynolds
(24) Dave Valle
(25) Bill Wilkinson
(26) Joe Witmer

1986 TCMA Cedar Rapids Reds

(Cincinnati Reds, A) (color)

	MT	NR MT	EX
Complete Set:	6.00	4.50	2.50

1 Dan Belinskas
2 Brad Brusky
3 Mike Converse
4 Mike Campbell
5 Tim Deltz
6 Curt Kindred
7 Gino Mintelli
8 Mike Roesler
9 Greg Simpson
10 Mike Smith
11 Greg Toler
12 Mike Vincent
13 Rod Zeratsky
14 Marty Brown
15 Joe Dunlap
16 Mark Germann
17 Scott Hilgenberg
18 Randy Hindman
19 Cal Cain
20 Mark Jackson
21 Chris Jones
22 Allen Sigler
23 John Bryant
24 Paul Kirsch
25 Gene Dusan
26 Neal Davenport
27 "Bucky" Buchheister
28 Lamar the Dog (mascot)

1986 ProCards Charleston Rainbows

(San Diego Padres, A)

	MT	NR MT	EX
Complete Set:	40.00	30.00	16.00

(1) Carlos Baerega
(2) Miguel Batista (with bat)
(3) Miguel Batista (with glove)
(4) Billy Blount
(5) Victor Cabrera
(6) Rafael Chaves
(7) Jeff Cisco

(8) Roberto Clemente, Jr.
(9) Jim Daniel
(10) Carl Ferraro
(11) Greg Harris
(12) Pat Kelly
(13) Chris Knabenshue
(14) Jim Lewis
(15) Bill Marx
(16) Matt Maysey
(17) Rod McCray
(18) Tom Meagher
(19) Jaime Moreno
(20) Eric Nolte
(21) Juan Paris
(22) Joe Pleasac
(23) Ramon Rodriguez
(24) Greg Sparks
(25) Bill Stevenson
(26) Jim Tatum
(27) Kevin Towers
(28) Rafael Valez
(29) Jim Wasem

1986 WBTV Charlotte O's

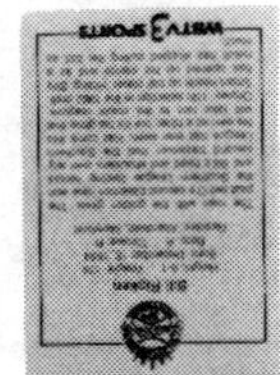

(Baltimore Orioles, AA)

	MT	NR MT	EX
Complete Set:	22.00	16.50	8.75

(1) Kurt Beamesderfer
(2) Eric Bell
(3) Greg Biagini
(4) Terry Bogner
(5) Jim Boudreau
(6) Mark Brown
(7) Paul Cameron (sportscaster)
(8) Tom Dodd
(9) Dave Falcone
(10) John Flinn
(11) Charlie Frederick (sportscaster)
(12) Lee Granger
(13) Bob Hice (sportscaster)
(14) Jerry Holtz
(15) John Hoover
(16) Joe Kucharski
(17) Terry Mauney (sportscaster)
(18) Carl Nichols
(19) Francisco Oliveras
(20) Chris Padget
(21) Mike Raczka
(22) Joe Redfield
(23) Rich Rice
(24) Billy Ripken
(25) Rico Rossy
(26) Ron Salcedo
(27) Dave Smith
(28) Scott Stranski
(29) Jeff Wood
(30) O's Fans

1986 ProCards Chattanooga Lookouts

(Seattle Mariners, AA)

	MT	NR MT	EX
Complete Set:	10.00	7.50	4.00

(1) Ben Amaya
(2) Bob Baldrick
(3) Brian Bargerhuff
(4) Terry Bell
(5) Jim Bryant
(6) John Burden
(7) Scott Buss
(8) Brian David
(9) John Duncun
(10) Bob Gunnarson
(11) Matt Hall
(12) R.J. Harrison
(13) Paul Hollins
(14) Tom Hunt
(15) Ross Jones
(16) Rick Luecken
(17) Edgar Martinez
(18) Jeff McDonald
(19) Rusty McNealy
(20) Rick Moore
(21) Dave Myers
(22) Paul Schneider
(23) Brick Smith
(24) Terry Taylor
(25) Mike Wishnevski

1986 ProCards Clearwater Phillies

(Philadelphia Phillies, A)

	MT	NR MT	EX
Complete Set:	7.50	5.50	3.00

(1) Carlos Arroyo
(2) Bruce Carter
(3) Travis Chambers
(4) Ron Clark
(5) Pat Coveney
(6) Shawn Dantzler
(7) Greg Edge
(8) Jim Fortenberry
(9) Todd Frohwirth
(10) Billy Jester
(11) Ronald Jones
(12) Bart Kaiser
(13) Jeff Kaye
(14) Jeff Knox
(15) Ken Kraft
(16) Scott Madden
(17) Mike Miller
(18) Tom Newell
(19) Segio Perez
(20) Mark Pottinger
(21) Walley Ritchie
(22) Bob Scanlan
(23) Scott Steen
(24) Rodney Wheeler
(25) Steven Williams
(26) Ted Zipeto

1986 ProCards Clinton Giants

(San Francisco Giants, A) (Price includes the scarce Hutchins card)

	MT	NR MT	EX
Complete Set:	7.50	5.50	3.00

(1) John Barry
(2) Dave Blakely
(3) George Bonilla
(4) Jeff Carter
(5) Todd Cash
(6) Tom Ealy
(7) Bill Evers
(8) Perry Flowers
(9) Dean Freeland
(10) Dave Hornsby
(11) Lance Hutchins
(12) Lloyd Jackson
(13) Timber Mead
(14) Todd Miller
(15) Dave Morris
(16) Jack Mull
(17) Rick Nelson
(18) Eric Pawling
(19) Darren Pearson
(20) Jose Pena
(21) C.L. Penigar
(22) Eric Pilkington
(23) Doug Robertson
(24) Dobie Swepson
(25) Howard Townsend
(26) Paul Van Stone
(27) Matt Walker
(28) Mike Whitt
(29) Trevor Wilson
(30) Team Photo

1986 ProCards Columbia Mets

(New York Mets, AA)

	MT	NR MT	EX
Complete Set:	35.00	26.00	14.00

(1) Bob Apodaca
(2) Jaime Archibald
(3) Kevin Armstrong
(4) Brandon Bailey
(5) Chris Bayer
(6) Mark Brunswick
(7) Joaquin Contreras
(8) Kurt Deluca
(9) Tom Doyle
(10) Dave Gelatt
(11) Brian Givens (blue jersey)
(12) Brian Givens (white jersey)
(13) Alan Hayden
(14) Barry Hightower
(15) Troy James
(16) Scott Jaster
(17) Greg Jeffries (Jefferies)
(18) Geary Jones
(19) Johnny Monell
(20) Felix Perdomo
(21) Chris Rauth
(22) Craig Repoz
(23) Robert Rinehart, Jr.
(24) Daniel Siblerud
(25) William Stiles
(26) John Thozzo
(27) Thomas Wachs
(28) Mark Willoughby

1986 ProCards Columbus Astros

(Houston Astros, AA)

	MT	NR MT	EX
Complete Set:	6.00	4.50	2.50

(1) Troy Afenir
(2) Karl Allaire
(3) Mark Baker
(4) Jeff Bettendorf
(5) Rich Bombard
(6) Pen Caminiti
(7) Mitch Cook
(8) Dave Cripe
(9) Jeff Datz
(10) Juan Delgado
(11) Ed Duke
(12) Bobby Falls
(13) Mike Friederich
(14) Tom Funk
(15) Ryan Job
(16) Tony Kelley
(17) Rob Mallicoat
(18) Chuck Mathews
(19) Joe Mikulik
(20) Jim O'Dell
(21) Bob Parker
(22) Larry Ray
(23) Roger Samuels
(24) Chuck Taylor
(25) Gerald Young

1986 ProCards Columbus Clippers

(New York Yankees, AAA)

	MT	NR MT	EX
Complete Set:	7.50	5.50	3.00

(1) Mike Armstrong
(2) Brad Arnsburg
(3) Clay Christiansen
(4) Pete Dalena
(5) Orestes Destrade
(6) Doug Drabek
(7) Juan Espino
(8) Kelly Faulk
(9) Barry Foote
(10) Randy Graham
(11) Leo Hernandez
(12) Al Holland
(13) Brian Butterfiel, Dave LaRoche, Kevin Rand)
(14) Phil Lombardi
(15) Victor Mata
(16) Derwin McNealy
(17) Dan Pasqua
(18) Scott Patterson
(19) Jeff Pries
(20) Alfonso Pulido
(21) Andre Robertson
(22) Mark Silva
(23) Keith Smith
(24) Mike Soper
(25) Miguel Sosa
(26) Dave Stegman

1986 Team Columbus Clippers

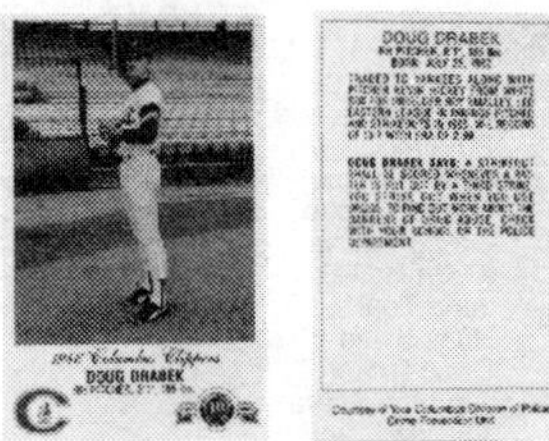

(New York Yankees, AAA)

	MT	NR MT	EX
Complete Set:	10.00	7.50	4.00

(1) Mike Armstrong
(2) Brad Arnsberg
(3) Clay Christiansen
(4) Pete Dalena
(5) Orastes Destrade
(6) Doug Drabek
(7) Juan Espino
(8) Kelly Faulk
(9) Randy Graham
(10) Leo Hernandez
(11) Al Holland
(12) Phil Lombardi
(13) Victor Mata
(14) Derwin McNealy
(15) Dan Pasqua
(16) Scott Patterson
(17) Jeff Pries
(18) Alfonso Pulido
(19) Andre Robertson
(20) Mark Silva
(21) Keith Smith
(22) Mike Soper
(23) Dave Stegman
(24) Manager Card (George Sisler Jr., Barry Foote)
(25) Coaches/Trainer Card (Dave La Roche, Brian Butterfield, Kevin Rand)

1986 ProCards Daytona Beach Islanders

(No Affiliation, A)

	MT	NR MT	EX
Complete Set:	6.00	4.50	2.50

(1) Jim Allison
(2) Regan Bass
(3) Warren Busick
(4) Chino Cadihia
(5) Tony Clark
(6) Rafael Cruz
(7) Mike Dotzler
(8) Darrin Garner
(9) Otto Gonzalez
(10) Ty Harden
(11) David Hausterman
(12) Perry W. Hill
(13) Paul James
(14) Ross Jones
(15) Mark Kramer
(16) Dave Linton
(17) Carmen Losauro
(18) Jimmy Meadows
(19) Jeff Melrose
(20) Tim Owen
(21) Larry Pardo
(22) Dave Rolland
(23) Ron Russell
(24) Travis Sheffield
(25) Ed Soto
(26) Jim St. Laurent
(27) George Threadgill
(28) Tom West

1986 ProCards Durham Bulls

(Atlanta Braves, A)

	MT	NR MT	EX
Complete Set:	40.00	30.00	16.00

(1) Buddy Bailey
(2) Jeff Blauser
(3) Johnny Cash
(4) Bill Clossen
(5) Kevin Coffman
(6) Tim Criswell
(7) Chris Cron
(8) Maximo Del Rosario
(9) Drew Denson
(10) Todd Dewey
(11) Juan Fredymond
(12) Ronnie Gant
(13) Wayne Harrison
(14) Larry Jaster
(15) Cesar Jiminez
(16) John Kilner
(17) Todd Lamb
(18) Mike Merrill
(19) Charlie Morelock
(20) Mike Nipper
(21) Bob Posey
(22) Mike Reynolds
(23) Jim Rockey
(24) Mac Rogers
(25) Rick Siebert
(26) Gerald Wagner
(27) Phil Wellman

1986 ProCards Edmonton Trappers

(California Angels, AAA)

	MT	NR MT	EX
Complete Set:	15.00	11.00	6.00

(1) Robert Bastien
(2) Norman Carrasco
(3) Ray Chadwick
(4) Bobby Clark
(5) The Cliburns (Stan Cliburn, Stewart Cliburn)
(6) Stan Cliburn
(7) Stewart Cliburn
(8) Steven Finch

(9) Todd Fischer
(10) Tony Fossas
(11) Alan Kim Fowlkes
(12) Leonard Garcia
(13) Craig Gerber
(14) Chris Green
(15) Jack Howell
(16) Pat Keedy
(17) Steven Liddle
(18) Rufino Linares
(19) Winston Llenas
(20) Tony Lynn Mack
(21) Reggie Montgomery
(22) Gus Polidor
(23) Frank Reberger
(24) Al Romero
(25) Mark Ryal
(26) David Wayne Smith
(27) Devon White

1986 ProCards Elmira Pioneers

(Boston Red Sox, A)

	MT	NR MT	EX
Complete Set:	15.00	11.00	6.00

(1) Mike Baker
(2) Steve Bast
(3) Ken Bourne
(4) Tim Buheller
(5) Mike Coffey
(6) Scott Cooper
(7) Roger Haggerty
(8) Bart Haley
(9) Keith Harrison
(10) Tony Hill
(11) Joe Marchese
(12) Dave Milstien
(13) Jim Morrison
(14) Glen O'Donnell
(15) Lem Pilkinton
(16) Chris Rawdon
(17) Julio Rosario
(18) Ken Ryan
(19) Ed Sardinha
(20) Curt Schilling
(21) Thom Sepela
(22) Scott Sommers
(23) Joaquin Tejada
(24) Al Thorton
(25) David Walters
(26) Ron Warren
(27) Stuart Weidie
(28) Mike Whiting
(29) Kerman Williams
(30) Paul Williams

1986 ProCards El Paso Diablos

(Milwaukee Brewers, AA)

	MT	NR MT	EX
Complete Set:	6.00	4.50	2.50

(1) Jay Aldrich
(2) Robby Allen
(3) Jesus Alfaro
(4) Bill Bates
(5) Alan Cartwright
(6) Dave Clay
(7) Tim Crews
(8) Derek Diaz
(9) Duffy Dyer
(10) Brian Finley
(11) Lavell Freeman
(12) John Gibbons
(13) Dave Huppert
(14) Pete Hendrick
(15) Pete Kolb
(16) Dan Murphy
(17) Garrett Nago
(18) Bob Nandin
(19) Steve Stanicek
(20) Dave Stapleton
(21) John Thorton
(22) Jackson Todd
(23) Cam Walker

1986 ProCards Erie Cardinals

(St. Louis Cardinals, A) (Complete set price includes scarce Hershman card)

	MT	NR MT	EX
Complete Set:	30.00	22.00	12.00

(1) Luis Alicea
(2) Tom Baine
(3) Mark Behny
(4) Brad Bluestone
(5) Randy Butts
(6) Rick Christain
(7) Bien Figueroa
(8) Robert Glisson
(9) Stephen Graff
(10) Kerry Griffith
(11) John Hackett
(12) Scott Hamilton
(13) William Hershman
(14) Eric Hohn
(15) Joe Hollinshed
(16) David Horton
(17) Glen Kuiper
(18) Scott Lawrence
(19) Roberto Marte
(20) Steve Meyer
(21) Carey Nemeth
(22) Robert Nettles
(23) Carrol Parker
(24) Francisco Perez
(25) Kyle Reese
(26) Joe Rigoli
(27) Steve Shade
(28) Greg Smith
(29) Steve Turgeon
(30) Stanley Zaltsman
(31) Todd Zeile

1986 Cramer Eugene Emeralds

(Kansas City Royals, A) This set is numbered as they appear on the cards.

	MT	NR MT	EX
Complete Set:	8.00	6.00	3.25

26 Rob Wolkoys
27 David Tinkle
28 Brian McRae
29 Mike Oblesbee
30 Carlos Escalera
31 Pat Bailey
32 Tim Goff
33 Ondra Ford
34 Robert Bell
35 John Larios
36 Jim Larsen
37 Kenny Jackson
38 Sean Berry
39 Randy Goodenough
40 Mike Butcher
41 Kevin Karcher
42 Chuck Mount
43 Greg Hibbard
44 Boo Champagne
45 Gary Blouin
46 Ken Adams
47 Gus Jones
48 Joe Skodny
49 Mike Tresmer
50 Dennis Moeller

1986 Cramer Everett Giants - Color

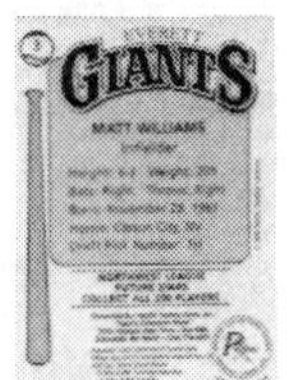

(San Francisco Giants, A) (color)

	MT	NR MT	EX
Complete Set:	20.00	15.00	8.00

1 Kevin Fitzgerald
2 Paul McClellan
3 Matt Williams
4 Brad Gambee
5 Gregg Ritchie
6 Kevin Redick
7 John Toal
8 Russ Swan
9 Drew Ricker
10 Jim McNamara
11 Andrew Dixon
12 David Patterson
13 Tim McCoy
14 James Pena
15 Marty Newton
16 Chuck Tate
17 Jim Massey
18 Chris Stubberfield
19 John Rannow
20 Shaun MacKenzie
21 Tod Ronson
22 Chris Shultis
23 Brock Birch
24 Keith Krafve
25 James Jones
180 Joe Strain
181 Todd Wilson
182 Mark Leonard
183 Robin Riemer
184 David Nash
185 Chuck Higson
186 Matt Walker

1986 Cramer Everett Giants - Black and White

(San Francisco Giants, A) (2" x 3")

	MT	NR MT	EX
Complete Set:	9.00	6.75	3.50

(1) James "Earl" Averill
(2) Brock Birch
(3) Andrew Dixon
(4) Kevin Fitzgerald
(5) Ricky Fleming
(6) Brad Gambee
(7) Bruce Graham
(8) Chuck Higson
(9) James Jones
(10) Keith Krafve
(11) Mark Leonard
(12) Shaun MacKenzie
(13) Jim Massey
(14) Paul McClellan
(15) Tim McCoy
(16) Jim McNamara
(17) Willie Mijares
(18) Dave Nash
(19) Marty Newton
(20) Dave Patterson
(21) James Pena
(22) John Rannow
(23) Kevin Redick
(24) Drew Ricker
(25) Robin Reimer
(26) Gregg Ritchie
(27) Tod Ronson
(28) Chris Shultis
(29) Damon Skyta
(30) Joe Strain
(31) Chris Stubberfield
(32) Chuck Tate
(33) John Toal
(34) Jack Uhey
(35) Matt Walker
(36) Todd Wilson

1986 ProCards Florida State League All-Stars

(Class A) (A)

	MT	NR MT	EX
Complete Set:	50.00	37.00	20.00

(1) Odie Abril
(2) Julio Alcala
(3) Chris Alvarez
(4) Brady Anderson
(5) Scott Arnold
(6) Tim Arnold
(7) Mark Berry
(8) Dave Bialas
(9) Marc Bombard
(10) Norman Brock
(11) Alax Cole
(12) Rufus Ellis
(13) Jeff Fassero
(14) Jeff Fischer
(15) John Fishel
(16) Jim Fortenberry
(17) Pete Geist
(18) Otto Gonzalez
(19) Maurice Guercio
(20) Matt Harrison
(21) John Hawkins
(22) Brad Henderson
(23) Ted Higgins
(24) Dave Holt
(25) Jim Jefferson
(26) Ron Johns
(27) Ron Jones
(28) Dan Juenke
(29) Tim Leiper
(30) Joel Lono
(31) Luis Lopez
(32) Rob Lopez
(33) Greg Lotzar
(34) Walt McConnell
(35) Jim Meadows
(36) Chris Morgan
(37) Max Oliveras
(38) Ray Perkins
(39) Dody Rather
(40) Jim Reboulet
(41) Darren Riley
(42) Don Rowland
(43) Tary Scott
(44) Mike Sears
(45) Doug Strange
(46) George Threadgill
(47) Shane Turner
(48) Luis Vasquez
(49) Tom West
(50) John Wockenfuss

1986 Smokey Bear Fresno Giants

(San Francisco Giants, A)

	MT	NR MT	EX
Complete Set:	40.00	30.00	16.00

1 Tim Blackwell (manager)
2 Gary Davenport (coach)
3 Vince Sferrazza (trainer)
4 Gary Jones
5 Felipe Gonzalez
6 Joe Kmak
7 Greg Gilbert
8 Sam Moore
9 Mike Villa
10 Tom Messier
11 Randy McCament
12 Joe Olker
13 Dave Hinnrichs
14 Eric Erickson
15 Darrell Rodgers
16 Dennis Cook
17 Steve Smith
18 Hector Quinones
19 Ty Dabney
20 Tony Perezchica
21 Scott Thompson
22 Tom Mathews
23 John Skurla
24 T.J. McDonald
25 Charles Culberson
26 Harry Davis
27 Kenny Compton (batboy)
28 Tony Vitale (groundskeeper)
29 Smokey Bear (batting)
30 Smokey Bear (throwing)
31 Smokey Bear (saluting)
---- Introductory Card

1986 ProCards Ft. Lauderdale Yankees

(New York Yankees, A)

	MT	NR MT	EX
Complete Set:	6.00	4.50	2.50

(1) Chris Alverez
(2) Anthony Balabon
(3) Douglas Carpenter
(4) Chris Carroll
(5) Gary Cathcart
(6) Mike Christopher
(7) Ysidro Giron
(8) Fred Gonzalez
(9) Robert Green
(10) Maurice Guerico
(11) Mathew Harrison
(12) Johnny Hawkins
(13) Theodore Higgins
(14) Harvey Lee
(15) Jason Maas
(16) Michael McClear
(17) Kenneth Patterson
(18) Johnnie Pleicones
(19) Norman Santiago
(20) Robert Sepanek
(21) Scott Shaw
(22) Aristarco Tirado
(23) Shane Turner

1986 ProCards Ft. Myers Royals

(Kansas City Royals, A)

	MT	NR MT	EX
Complete Set:	6.00	4.50	2.50

(1) Julio Alcala
(2) Mike Alvarez
(3) Jeff Bedell
(4) Stan Boroski
(5) Pete Carey
(6) Bob Davis
(7) Jose DeJesus
(8) Rafael DeLeon
(9) Rufus Ellis
(10) Mark Farnsworth
(11) Phil George
(12) Carlos Gonzalez
(13) Duane Gustavson
(14) Jeff Hull

(15) Chris Jelic
(16) Kevin Koslofski
(17) Deric Ladnier
(18) Mike Loggins
(19) Mitch McKelvey
(20) Bill Mulligan
(21) Geoff Peterson
(22) Henry Robinson
(23) Ricky Rojas
(24) Gregg Schmidt
(25) Mark Van Blaricom
(26) Bob Van Vuren
(27) Troy Watkins
(28) Dejon Watson
(29) Don Woyce

1986 ProCards Geneva Cubs

(Chicago Cubs, A)

	MT	NR MT	EX
Complete Set:	6.00	4.50	2.50

(1) Jim Bullinger
(2) Todd Cloninger
(3) Tony Collins
(4) Mike Curtis
(5) Sergio Espinal
(6) Jimmie Gardner
(7) John Green
(8) Tony Hamza
(9) Derrick Hardamon
(10) Phil Harrison
(11) Clint Harwick
(12) Joe Housey
(13) Ced Landrum
(14) Jerry Lapenta
(15) Tony LaPoint
(16) Jay Loviglio
(17) Kelly Mann
(18) Jim Matas
(19) Steve Melendez
(20) Chuck Oertli
(21) Brian Otten
(22) Randy Penvose
(23) Parnell Perry
(24) Harry Shelton
(25) Jose Soto
(26) Bob Strickland
(27) Fernando Zarranz

1986 ProCards Glens Falls Tigers

(Detroit Tigers, AAA)

	MT	NR MT	EX
Complete Set:	6.00	4.50	2.50

(1) Ricky Barlow
(2) Willie Darkins
(3) Allen Duffy
(4) Paul Felix
(5) Marty Freeman
(6) Paul Gibson
(7) Mike Gorman
(8) Ruben Guzman
(9) Jeff Herman
(10) John Hiller
(11) Al Labozzetta
(12) Scott Lusader
(13) Morris Madden
(14) Frank Masters
(15) Steve McInerney
(16) Craig Mills
(17) Rey Palacios
(18) Roman Pena
(19) Benny Ruiz
(20) Bob Schaefer
(21) Steve Searcy
(22) Max Soto
(23) James Walewander
(24) Craig Weissmann

1986 ProCards Greensboro Hornets

(Boston Red Sox, A)

	MT	NR MT	EX
Complete Set:	7.50	5.50	3.00

(1) John Abbott
(2) Alan Ashkinazy
(3) Doug Camilli
(4) Kevin Camilli
(5) Jose Flores
(6) Dan Gabriele
(7) Chris Gaeckle
(8) Dan Gakeler
(9) Mike Goff
(10) Dan Hale
(11) Ray Hansen
(12) Tom Kane
(13) Derek Livernois
(14) Don McGowan
(15) Jim Orsag
(16) Billy Plante
(17) Todd Pratt
(18) Carlos Quintana
(19) Ray Revak
(20) John Roberts
(21) Victor Rosario
(22) Larry Shikles
(23) John Toale
(24) Paul Toutsis
(25) Pete Youngman
(26) Eddie Zambrano
(27) Bill Zupka

1986 ProCards Greenville Braves

(Atlanta Braves, AA) The set was also produced in the form of a 16" x 20" poster with a logo card included. The regular set does not contain the logo card.

	MT	NR MT	EX
Complete Set:	30.00	22.00	12.00

(1) Rick Albert
(2) Jose Alvarez
(3) Jim Beauchamp
(4) Kevin Blankenship
(5) Chip Childress
(6) Steve Curry
(7) Sal D'Alessandro
(8) Darryl Denby
(9) Tom Glavine
(10) Paul Gnacinski
(11) Dave Griffin
(12) Jeff Groves
(13) Inocencio Guerrero
(14) Randy Ingle
(15) Carlos Rios
(16) Mike Scott
(17) Bill Slack
(18) Pete Smith
(19) Thornton Stringfellow
(20) Freddy Tiburcio
(21) Greg Tubbs
(22) Bob Tumpane
(23) Steve Ziem
(24) Logo card (featured in poster set only)

1986 ProCards Hagerstown Suns

(Baltimore Orioles, A)

	MT	NR MT	EX
Complete Set:	7.00	5.25	2.75

(1) Jeff Ballard
(2) Frank Bellino
(3) Mickey Billmeyer
(4) Sherwin Clintje
(5) Brian Dudois
(6) Chris Eagelston
(7) Glenn Gulliver
(8) Scott Khoury
(9) Tom Magrann
(10) Paul McNeal
(11) Bob Milacki
(12) Bob Molinaro
(13) Ty Nichols
(14) Pete Palermo
(15) Tim Richardson
(16) Norman Roberts
(17) Geraldo Sanchez
(18) Dana Smith
(19) Chuck Stanhope
(20) Pete Stanicek
(21) Earl Stephenson
(22) Scott Stranski
(23) Craig Strobel
(24) Greg Talamantez
(25) Paul Thorpe
(26) Jesse Vasquez
(27) Ted Wilborn
(28) Wayne Wilson
(29) Craig Worthington

1986 ProCards Hawaii Islanders

(Pittsburgh Pirates, AAA)

	MT	NR MT	EX
Complete Set:	7.50	5.50	3.00

(1) Jackie Brown
(2) Glenn Brummer
(3) Trench Davis
(4) Benny Distefano
(5) Cecil Espy
(6) Tom Fandt
(7) Stan Fansler
(8) Ed Farmer
(9) Felix Fermin
(10) Burk Goldthorn
(11) Sam Haro
(12) Dave Johnson
(13) Barry Jones
(14) Ray Krawczyk
(15) Carlos Ledezma
(16) Dave Leeper
(17) Bobby Miscik
(18) Scott Neal
(19) Bob Patterson
(20) Rick Renteria
(21) Lee Tunnell
(22) Ron Wotus
(23) Jeff Zaske

1986 Team Huntsville Stars

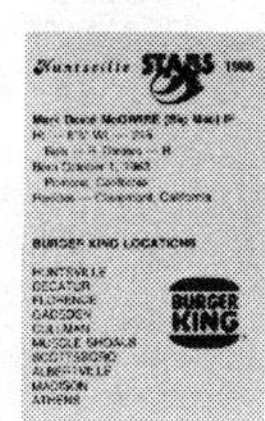

(Oakland A's, AA)

	MT	NR MT	EX
Complete Set:	15.00	11.25	6.00

10 Amin David
11 Gary Jones
12 Dave Nix
14 Dave Wilder
15 Rocky Coyle
16 Terry Steinbach
18 Damon Farmar
19 Ray Thoma
20 Brian Guinn
21 Todd Burns
22 Stan Hilton
23 Wally Whitehurst
24 Jose Tolentino
25 Brad Fischer
26 Mark Leonette
30 Stan Kyles
31 Tim Belcher
32 Scott Whaley
33 Mark McGwire
34 Greg Cadaret
40 Doug Scherer
41 John Cox
42 Kirk McDonald
44 Rick Tronerud
45 Roy Johnson

1986 Team Indianapolis Indians

(Montreal Expos, AAA)

	MT	NR MT	EX
Complete Set:	7.50	5.50	3.00

1 Team logo
2 Owen J. Bush
3 Joe Sparks
4 Rich Stoll
5 Jack Glasscock
6 Randy Hunt
7 Tom Romano
8 Amos Rusie
9 Bob Owchinko
10 Rene Gonzales
11 Authentic document
12 John Dopson
13 Derrell Baker
14 1928 Indianapolis team photo
15 Randy St. Claire
16 "Skeeter" Barnes
17 Rodger Cole
18 "Lefty Bob" Logan
19 Wally Johnson
20 Len Barker
21 Al Lopez
22 Mike Hocutt
23 Bob Sebra
24 Herb Score
25 Curt Brown
26 Dallas Williams
27 Larry Groves
28 Luis Rivera
29 Don Buford
30 Tom Nieto
31 Dave Tomlin
32 "Champ" Summers
33 Casey Candaele
34 Tim Barrett
35 Billy Moore
36 Coaches/Trainer (Jerry Manuel, Lee Garrett, Rick Williams)

1986 ProCards Iowa Cubs

(Chicago Cubs, AAA)

	MT	NR MT	EX
Complete Set:	7.00	5.25	2.75

(1) Johnny Abrego
(2) Bob Bathe
(3) Pookie Berustine
(4) Trey Brooks
(5) Mike Brumley
(6) Steve Christmas
(7) Jim Colborn
(8) Jeff Cornell
(9) Larry Cox
(10) Steve Engel
(11) Terry Francona
(12) Dave Grossman
(13) Dave Gumpert
(14) Steve Hammond
(15) Joe Hicks
(16) Guy Hoffman
(17) Dave Martinez
(18) Ron Meridith
(19) Brad Mills
(20) Paul Noce
(21) Gary Parmenter
(22) Doug Potestio
(23) Ken Pryce
(24) Bobby Ramos
(25) Julio Valdez
(26) Chico Walker

1986 TCMA Jackson Mets

(New York Mets, AA) (color)

	MT	NR MT	EX
Complete Set:	11.00	8.25	4.50

1 Jim Adamczak
2 Reggie Dobie
3 Wray Bergendahl
4 Tom Edens
5 Kyle Hartshorn
6 Jeff Innis
7 Kurt Lundgren
8 Ed Pruitt
9 Mike Santiago
10 Mickey Weston
11 Doug Gwosdz
12 Greg Olson
13 Kevin Elster
14 Dennis Glynn
15 Paul Hertzler
16 Andy Lawrence
17 Jeff McKnight
18 Rick Lockwood
19 Shawn Abner
20 Jason Felice
21 Scott Little
22 Johnny Wilson
23 Sam McCrary
24 Mike Cubbage
25 Glenn Abbott
26 Randy Milligan
27 Keith Miller

1986 TCMA Jacksonville Expos

(Montreal Expos, AA) (color)

	MT	NR MT	EX
Complete Set:	7.50	5.50	3.00

1 Tony Nicometi
2 Johnny Paredes
3 Jim Cecchini
4 Armando Moreno
5 Tom Traen
6 Peter Camelo
7 John Trautwein
8 Nelson Santovenia
9 Leonel Carrion
10 Q.V. Lowe
11 Joe Graves
12 Greg Raymer
13 Matt Sferrazza
14 Kevin Price
15 Mark Gardner
16 Troy McKay
17 Gary Weinberger
18 Wilfredo Tejada
19 Tommy Thompson
20 Mark Corey
21 Jeff Reynolds
22 Norman Nelson
23 Brian Holman
24 Bill Cutshall
25 Jack Daugherty
26 Tim McCormack

1986 ProCards Jamestown Expos

(Montreal Expos, A)

	MT	NR MT	EX
Complete Set:	7.50	5.50	3.00

(1) Michael Blowers
(2) Don Burke
(3) C. Scott Clemo
(4) William D'Boever
(5) Kody Duey
(6) Jerome Duke
(7) Kenneth Fox
(8) Paul Frye
(9) Chan Galbato
(10) Robert Gaylor
(11) Michael Haines
(12) Mark Hardy
(13) Gene Harris
(14) Steven King
(15) Paul Peter Martineau
(16) James McDonald
(17) David Morrow
(18) Jeffrey Oller
(19) Troy Ricker
(20) Michael Robertson
(21) Dean Rockweiler
(22) Robert Shannon
(23) Steve St. Claire
(24) Joe Beely Sims
(25) Jeffrey Tabaka
(26) Darren Travels
(27) Sal Vaccaro
(28) Jeffrey Wedvick
(29) Frank Welborn
(30) Yippee (team mascot)

1986 ProCards Kenosha Twins

(Minnesota Twins, A)

	MT	NR MT	EX
Complete Set:	6.00	4.50	2.50

(1) Paul Abbott
(2) Larry Blackwell
(3) Jeff Bumgarner
(4) James Cook
(5) Mark Davis
(6) Tom DiCeglio
(7) Julio Delancer
(8) Rafael DeLima
(9) Tom Fiore
(10) Steven Gasser
(11) Marty Lanoux
(12) Bob Lee
(13) Don Leppert
(14) Jerry Mack
(15) Howard Manzon
(16) Ted Miller
(17) Edgar Naveda
(18) Tim O'Conner
(19) Yorkis Perez
(20) Bob Perry
(21) Mike Redding
(22) Bob Strube
(23) Luis Tapais
(24) Gary Thomason
(25) Leonard Webster

1986 ProCards Kinston Eagles

(No Affiliation, A)

	MT	NR MT	EX
Complete Set:	6.00	4.50	2.50

(1) Howard Akers
(2) Bubba Brevell
(3) Scott Cannon
(4) Ed Delzer
(5) Van Evans
(6) Bruce Fischback
(7) Gene Gentile
(8) Al Heath
(9) Mike Ingle
(10) Lindsey Johnson
(11) Roger Johnson
(12) Randy Kramer
(13) Dan Larsen
(14) Perry Lychak
(15) Scott Melvin
(16) Paul Moralez
(17) Marty Reed
(18) Emmett Robinson
(19) Gabriel Robles
(20) Randy Romagna
(21) Melvin Rosario
(22) John Schofield
(23) Dave Trembley
(24) Ken Whitfield

1986 ProCards Knoxville Blue Jays

(Toronto Blue Jays, AA)

	MT	NR MT	EX
Complete Set:	9.00	6.75	3.50

(1) Kash Beauchamp
(2) Jim Bishop
(3) Pat Borders
(4) Sal Campusano
(5) J.J. Cannon
(6) Eddie Dennis
(7) Tim Englund
(8) Keith Gilliam
(9) Larry Hardy
(10) Glenallen Hill
(11) Randy Holland
(12) Jim Howard
(13) Tony Hudson
(14) Manny Lee
(15) Nelson Liriano
(16) Colin McLaughlin
(17) Greg Moore
(18) Oswald Peraza
(19) Jose Segura
(20) Chris Shaddy
(21) Kevin Sliwinski
(22) Matt Stark
(23) Bernie Tatis
(24) Norm Tonnucci
(25) Dave Walsh
(26) Mike Yearout
(27) Cliff Young

1986 ProCards Lakeland Tigers

(Detroit Tigers, A)

	MT	NR MT	EX
Complete Set:	20.00	15.00	8.00

(1) Jeff Agar
(2) Bernie Anderson
(3) Tommy Burgess
(4) Bill Cooper
(5) Steve Eagar
(6) Ken Gohmann
(7) Keith Hoskinson
(8) Mark Lee
(9) Tim Leiper
(10) Al Liebert
(11) Tony Long
(12) Porfi Martinez
(13) Chip McHugh
(14) Jeff Minick
(15) Dave Minnema
(16) Chris Morgan
(17) Rod Poissant
(18) Laney Prioleau
(19) Art Raubolt
(20) Donnie Rowland
(21) Joseph Slavic
(22) Terry Smith
(23) John Smoltz
(24) Doug Strange
(25) Mike York

1986 ProCards Las Vegas Stars

(San Diego Padres, AAA) Las Vegas sets sold through ProCards dealer distributions did not include Larry Bowa Manager card.

	MT	NR MT	EX
Complete Set:	15.00	11.00	6.00

(1) Randy Asadoor
(2) Greg Booker
(3) Steve Garcia
(4) Dick Grapenthin
(5) Gary Green
(6) Ray Hayward
(7) Todd Hutcheson
(8) Jimmy Jones
(9) Steve Kemp
(10) Steve Lubratich
(11) Mark Parent
(12) Tim Pyznarski
(13) Edwin Rodriguez
(14) Benito Santiago
(15) James Siwy
(16) Gregory Smith
(17) Brian Snyder
(18) James Steels
(19) Bob Stoddard
(20) John Tutt
(21) Ed Vosberg
(22) Mark Wasinger
(23) Mark Williamson
(24) Ed Wojna
(25) Gary Woods
---- Larry Bowa (included only in ballpark giveaway sets)

1986 ProCards Little Falls Mets

(New York Mets, A)

	MT	NR MT	EX
Complete Set:	7.00	5.25	2.75

(1) Mike Anderson
(2) Pete Bauer
(3) Lou Berge
(4) Rick Brown
(5) Genaro Castro
(6) Rob Colescott
(7) Pat Crosby
(8) Mark DiVincenzo
(9) Rick Duant
(10) Ken Farmer
(11) Mark Fiedler
(12) Cliff Gonzalez
(13) Ceoric Hawkins
(14) Rob Hernandez
(15) Alex Jiminez
(16) Lorin Jundy
(17) Rich Lundahl
(18) Dan McMurtrie
(19) Rich Miller
(20) Rodney Murrel
(21) Ron Narcisse
(22) Luis Natera
(23) Fritz Polka
(24) Jaime Roseboro
(25) Joel Sklar
(26) Heath Slocumb
(27) Andy Taylor
(28) Tony Thompson
(29) Todd Welborn

1986 Team Louisville Redbirds

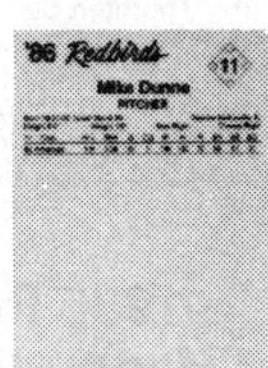

(St. Louis Cardinals, AAA)

	MT	NR MT	EX
Complete Set:	9.00	6.75	3.50

1 Jim Fregosi
2 Dyar Miller
3 David Hudson
4 Jack Ayer
5 Steve Braun
6 Joe Boever
7 Rod Booker
8 Rich Buonantony
9 Ralph Citarella
10 Greg Dunn
11 Mike Dunne
12 Bill Farley
13 Curt Ford
14 Kurt Kepshire
15 Alan Knicely
16 Jim Lindeman
17 Bill Lyons
18 Fred Manrique
19 Fred Martinez
20 John Morris
21 Tom Pagnozzi
22 Casey Parsons
23 Joe Pettini
24 Marty Pevey
25 Dave Rajsich
26 Ray Soff
27 Dan Stryffeler
28 Tim Wallace
29 Jed Smith
30 Mascots (B. Johnson & D. Harris)

1986 ProCards Lynchburg Mets

(New York Mets, A)

	MT	NR MT	EX
Complete Set:	7.50	5.50	3.00

(1) Ralph Adams
(2) Jim Bibby
(3) Desi Brooks
(4) Kevin Brown
(5) Wilmer Caraballo
(6) Al Carmichael
(7) Jeff Ciszkowski
(8) Angelo Cuevas
(9) Bobby Floyd
(10) Jeff Gardner
(11) Steve Gay
(12) Ronnie Gideon
(13) Mauro Gozzo
(14) Marcus Lawton
(15) Chuck Lynn
(16) Hector Perez
(17) Steve Phillips
(18) Jeff Richardson
(19) Rich Rodriguez
(20) Zoilo Sanchez
(21) Eric Stampel
(22) Dave Tresch
(23) Wilson Valera
(24) Juan Villanueva
(25) Dave West
(26) Mike Westbrook
(27) Dan Winters
(28) Shane Young

1986 ProCards Macon Pirates

(Pittsburgh Pirates, A)

	MT	NR MT	EX
Complete Set:	7.50	5.50	3.00

(1) Ben Abner
(2) Kevin Andersh
(3) Kirk Berry
(4) Dwight Bernard
(5) Octavio Cepeda
(6) Tony Chance
(7) Jim Davins
(8) Dorley Downs
(9) Kevin Franchi
(10) Ron Giddens
(11) Andy Hall
(12) Todd Hansen
(13) Rob Hatfield
(14) Guillermo Mercedes
(15) Orlando Merced
(16) Douglas Moreno
(17) Rafael Muratti
(18) Luis Pena
(19) Julio Perez
(20) Mike Quade
(21) Gilbert Roca
(22) Jeff Satzinger
(23) Brian Stackhouse
(24) Mike Stevanus
(25) Keith Swartzlander
(26) Jay Wollenburg
(27) Joey Zellner

1986 ProCards Madison Muskies

(Oakland A's, A)

	MT	NR MT	EX
Complete Set:	7.50	5.50	3.00

(1) Douglas Ames
(2) Tony Arias
(3) Larry Arnot
(4) Antonio Cabrera
(5) Ron Carter
(6) Brian Criswell
(7) Michael Cupples
(8) Patrick Dietrick
(9) Bobby Gould
(10) Marty Hall
(11) Mark Howie
(12) Andre Jacas
(13) Russell Kibler
(14) Kirk McDonald
(15) James Nettles
(16) Dave Nix
(17) David Otto
(18) Kevin Russ
(19) Scott Sabo
(20) Dave Schober
(21) Jeffrey Shaver
(22) Dave Shillinglaw
(23) Nelson Silverio
(24) Robert Stocker
(25) Camilo Veras
(26) Walter Weiss
(27) Walter Whitehurst
(28) Rick Wise

1986 Daniels Madison Muskies

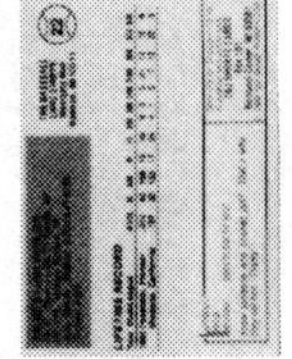

(Oakland A's, A)

	MT	NR MT	EX
Complete Set:	12.50	9.50	5.00

1 Doug Ames
2 Tony Arias
3 Larry Arndt
4 Tony Cabrera
5 Ron Carter
6 Brian Criswell
7 Mike Cupples
8 Pat Dietrick
9 Bobby Gould
10 Marty Hall
11 Mark Howie
12 Andre Jacas
13 Russ Kibler
14 Kirk McDonald
15 Dave Nix
16 Dave Otto
17 Scott Sabo
18 Jeff Shaver
19 Nelson Silverio
20 Bob Stocker
21 Camilo Veras
22 Walt Weiss
23 Wally Whitehurst
24 Jim Nettles
25 Dave Schober
26 Dave Schillinglaw
27 Rick Wise

1986 ProCards Maine Guides

(Cleveland Indians, AAA)

	MT	NR MT	EX
Complete Set:	7.00	5.25	2.75

(1) Barry Bruenkant
(2) Kevin Buckley
(3) George Cecchetti
(4) Steve Ciszczon
(5) Dave Clark
(6) Steve Commer
(7) Keith Creel
(8) Barry Evans
(9) Dave Gallagher
(10) Kevin Hagen
(11) Doug Jones
(12) Jim Napier
(13) Junior Noboa
(14) Bryan Oelkers
(15) Craig Pippen
(16) Reggie Ritter
(17) Scott Roberts
(18) Jose Roman
(19) Tommy Rowe
(20) Cory Snyder
(21) Curt Wardle
(22) Randy Washington
(23) Jim Weaver
(24) Frank Wills
(25) Jim Wilson
(26) Rich Yett

1986 Cramer Medford A's

(Oakland A's, A) This set is numbered as it appears on the backs of the cards.

	MT	NR MT	EX
Complete Set:	9.00	6.75	3.50

51 William Savarino
52 James Reiser
53 David Veres
54 Mark Stancel
55 Mark Beavers
56 William Reynolds
57 Luis Martinez
58 Bill Coonan
59 Pat Gilbert
60 Larry Ritchey
61 Glenn Hoffinger
62 Robbie Gilbert
63 Todd Hartley
64 Kevin Tapani
65 Weston Weber
66 Jeff Kopyta
67 Dann Howitt
68 Jeff Glover
69 Lance Blankenship
70 Kevin Kunkel
71 James Carroll
72 Darrin Duffy
73 John Kent
74 Vincent Teixeira
75 Keith Wentz

Values for recent cards and sets are listed in Mint (MT), Near Mint (NM), reflecting the fact that many cards from recent years have been preserved in top condition. Recent cards and sets in less than Excellent condition have little collector interest.

1986 Time Out Sports Memphis Chicks

(Kansas City Royals, AA) (This set is numbered as it appears on the cards)

	MT	NR MT	EX
Complete Set, Gold:	20.00	15.00	8.00
Complete Set, Silver:	30.00	22.00	12.00

1 Tommy Jones
3 Gary Thurman
5 Gene Morgan
6 Mike Miller
7 Hector Rincones
9 Van Snider
10 Chito Martinez
11 Phil George
12 Art Martinez
14 Israel Sanchez
15 Doug Gilcrease
16 Jere Longenecker
18 Joe Jarrell
20 Angel Morris
21 Mitch McKelvey
23 Rick Goodin
24 Jimmy Daniel
25 Rich Dubee
26 Ken Crew
27 Terry Bell
28 Bo Jackson
29 John Davis
32 Jose Rodiles
33 Luis De Los Santos
35 Mike McFarlane
---- Steve Morrow

1986 ProCards Miami Marlins

(Baltimore Orioles, A)

	MT	NR MT	EX
Complete Set:	6.00	4.50	2.50

(1) German Bautista
(2) Juan Bellver
(3) Mike Browning
(4) Rick Carrano
(5) Tim Dulin
(6) Todd Edwards
(7) Marc Estes
(8) John Harrington
(9) Fred Hatfield
(10) Tommy Hearn
(11) Alan Hixon
(12) Lance Hudson
(13) Dan Juenke
(14) Bob Latmore
(15) Kurt Leiter
(16) Pedro Llanes
(17) Jerry Miller
(18) Curt Morgan
(19) Luis Ojeda
(20) Ray Perkins
(21) Eric Rasmussen
(22) Elem Rossy
(23) Todd Smith
(24) Phil Taylor
(25) Dave Van Ohlen
(26) Greg Wallace
(27) Phil Wielegman
(28) Roger Wilson
(29) John Wockenfuss

1986 ProCards Midland Angels

(California Angels, AA)

	MT	NR MT	EX
Complete Set:	7.00	5.25	2.75

(1) Doug Banning
(2) Brian Brady
(3) DeWayne Buice
(4) Vinicio Cedeno
(5) Terry Clark
(6) Mike Cook
(7) Sherman Corbett
(8) Doug Davis
(9) Brian Hartsock
(10) Dave Heath
(11) John Hotchkiss
(12) Kevin King
(13) Vance Lovelace
(14) Joe Maddon
(15) Mike Madril
(16) Mark McLemore
(17) Bill Merrifield
(18) Aurelio Monteagudo
(19) Rafael Pimental
(20) James Randall
(21) Jeff Schaffer
(22) Don Timberlake
(23) Raul Tovar
(24) Phil Venturino
(25) Glen Walker
(26) Richard Zaleski

1986 ProCards Modesto A's

(Oakland A's, A) (Price includes scarce Anderson catching card)

	MT	NR MT	EX
Complete Set:	10.00	7.50	4.00

(1) Roy Anderson (catching)
(2) Roy Anderson (with bat)
(3) Russell Applegate
(4) Darren Balsley
(5) Tyler Brilinski
(6) John "Doc" Cartelli
(7) Jerry Deguero
(8) Mike Duncan
(9) Vic Figueroa
(10) Steve Gorey
(11) Darel Hansen
(12) Twayne Harris
(13) Mike Hogan
(14) Steve Howard
(15) Butch Hughes
(16) Jim Jones
(17) Felix Jose
(18) John Kanter
(19) Joe Kramer
(20) Rich Martig
(21) Jerome Nelson
(22) Tommie Reynolds
(23) Bob Sharpnack
(24) Jim Strichek
(25) Joe Strong
(26) Mark Tortorice
(27) Bruce Walton

1986 Chong Modesto A's

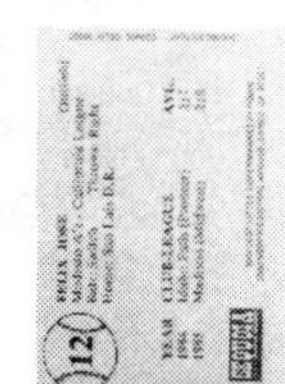

(Oakland A's, A)

	MT	NR MT	EX
Complete Set:	15.00	11.00	6.00

1 Roy Anderson
2 Russ Applegate
3 Darren Baisley
4 Bo Kent
5 Tyler Brilinski
6 Pat Dietrick
7 Mike Duncan
8 Darel Hansen
9 Twayne Harris
10 Steve Howard
11 James Jones
12 Felix Jose
13 Lance Blankenship
14 Richard Martig
15 Shannon Mendenhall
16 Jerome Nelson
17 Jose Peguero
18 Bob Sharpnack
19 Mark Tortorice
20 Bruce Walton
21 Joe Xavier
22 Kevin Tapani
23 Mark Beavers
24 Butch Hughes
25 Tommie Reynolds
26 John Cartelli
27 Jeff Koryta

A player's name in italic type indicates a rookie card. An (FC) indicates a player's first card for that particular card company.

1986 ProCards Nashua Pirates

(Pittsburgh Pirates, AA)

	MT	NR MT	EX
Complete Set:	7.50	5.50	3.00

(1) Mike Ashman
(2) Kerry Baker
(3) Mike Berger
(4) Craig Brown
(5) Matias Carrillo
(6) Scott Fiepke
(7) Ken Ford
(8) Kevin Gordon
(9) Tommy Gregg
(10) Dimas Gutierrez
(11) Reggie Hammonds
(12) Martin Hernandez
(13) Shawn Holman
(14) Tony Laird
(15) Jim Leopold
(16) Jose Lind
(17) Orlando Lind
(18) Steve McAllister
(19) Jim Neidlinger
(20) Jim Opie
(21) Hipolito Pena
(22) Pete Rice
(23) Ruben Rodriguez
(24) Dennis Rogers
(25) Rich Sauveur
(26) Dorn Taylor
(27) Spin Williams
(28) "H" Williams

1986 Team Nashville Sounds

(Detroit Tigers, AAA)

	MT	NR MT	EX
Complete Set:	12.00	9.00	4.75

(1) Doug Baker
(2) Fred Breining
(3) Chuck Cary
(4) Pedro Chavez
(5) Jeff Conner
(6) Brian Denman
(7) Scott Earl
(8) Bruce Fields
(9) Paul Gibson
(10) Brian Harper
(11) Don Heinkel
(12) Mike Henneman
(13) Rodney Hobbs
(14) Bryan Kelly
(15) Jack Lazorko
(16) Scotti Madison
(17) Don McGann
(18) Matt Nokes
(19) Chris Nyman
(20) German Rivera
(21) Leon Roberts
(22) Jeff Robinson
(23) Gene Roof
(24) Tim Tolman

1986 ProCards New Britain Red Sox

(Boston Red Sox, AA)

	MT	NR MT	EX
Complete Set:	35.00	26.00	14.00

(1) Andy Araujo
(2) Tony Beal
(3) Jose Birriel
(4) Ellis Burks
(5) Pete Cappadona
(6) Robert Chadwick
(7) Jim Corsi
(8) Steve Curry
(9) Chuck Davis
(10) Steve Ellsworth
(11) Eduardo Estrada
(12) Demarlo Hale
(13) Sam Horn
(14) Pat Jelks
(15) Dana Kiecker
(16) John Marzano
(17) Bill McInnis
(18) Mark Meleski
(19) Sam Nattile

(20) Dave Peterson
(21) Jody Reed
(22) Paul Slifko
(23) Hector Steward
(24) Tony Torchia
(25) Scott Wade

1986 ProCards Oklahoma City 89'ers

(Texas Rangers, AAA)

	MT	NR MT	EX
Complete Set:	10.50	7.25	4.25

(1) Bob Brower
(2) Greg Campbell
(3) Rob Clark
(4) Glen Cook
(5) Tommy Dunbar
(6) Dave Geisel
(7) Rusty Gerhardt
(8) Bobby Jones
(9) Jeff Kunkel
(10) Willie Lozado
(11) Jim Maler
(12) Orlando Mercado
(13) Dale Mohoric (Mohorcic)
(14) Jeff Moronko
(15) Dave Oliver
(16) Dave Owen
(17) Mike Parrott
(18) Luis Pujols
(19) Jeff Russell
(20) Tommy Joe Shimp
(21) Ruben Sierra
(22) Rick Surhoff
(23) Greg Tabor
(24) Don Welchel
(25) Don Werner
(26) Matt Williams

1986 ProCards Omaha Royals

(Kansas City Royals, AAA)

	MT	NR MT	EX
Complete Set:	10.00	7.50	4.00

(1) Scott Bankhead
(2) John Boles
(3) Mike Brewer
(4) Keefe Cato
(5) Joe Citari
(6) David Cone
(7) Frank Funk
(8) Mike Griffin
(9) Roger Hansen
(10) Bill Hayes
(11) Bob Hegman
(12) Rondin Johnson
(13) Mike Kingery
(14) Renie Martin
(15) Mike Miller
(16) Tom Mullen
(17) Bill Pecota
(18) Jose Reyes
(19) Dave Schuler
(20) Jeff Schulz
(21) Jim Scranton
(22) Kevin Seitzer
(23) Theo Shaw
(24) Russ Stephans
(25) Lester Strode
(26) Nick Swartz
(27) Scott Taber
(28) Mike Warren
(29) Marty Wilkerson

1986 TCMA Omaha Royals

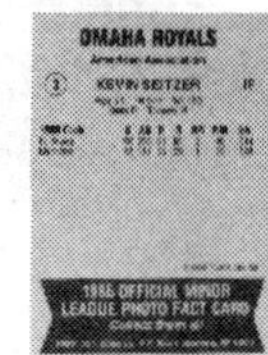

(Kansas City Royals, AA) (color)

	MT	NR MT	EX
Complete Set:	15.00	11.00	6.00

1 Bill Hayes
2 Ron Johnson
3 Kevin Seitzer
4 Mike Kingery
5 Roger Hansen
6 Jeff Schultz
7 Jim Scranton
8 Bob Hegman
9 Marty Wilkerson
10 Russ Stephans
11 Dwight Taylor
12 Bill Pecota
13 Mike Brewer
14 Joe Citari
15 Mike Griffin
16 Dave Cone
17 Scott Tabor
18 Jim Strode
19 Dave Schuler
20 Theo Shaw
21 Alan Hargesheimer
22 Tom Mullen
23 John Boles
24 Frank Funk
25 Scott Bankhead

1986 ProCards Orlando Twins

(Minnesota Twins, AA)

	MT	NR MT	EX
Complete Set:	6.00	4.50	2.50

(1) Steve Aragon
(2) Brad Bierley
(3) Todd Budke
(4) Mark Clemons
(5) Jose Dominguez
(6) Troy Galloway
(7) Steve Gomez
(8) Stan Holmes
(9) Joe Klink
(10) Gene Larkin
(11) John Marquardt
(12) George Mitterwald
(13) Greg Morhardt
(14) Steve Padia
(15) Doug Palmer
(16) Ray Ramirez
(17) Robbie Smith
(18) Alan Sontag
(19) Sam Sorce
(20) Jeff Taylor
(21) Jeff Trout
(22) Dave Vetsch
(23) Kevin Wiggins
(24) Phil Wilson

1986 ProCards Osceola Astros

(Houston Astros, A)

	MT	NR MT	EX
Complete Set:	6.00	4.50	2.50

(1) Norman Brock
(2) Mike Brown
(3) Scott Camp
(4) Jesus Carrion
(5) Earl Cash
(6) Don Dunster
(7) Francois Durocher
(8) John Fishel
(9) Terry Green
(10) Anthony Hampton
(11) Geysi Heredia
(12) Stan Hough
(13) Ken Houston
(14) Chris Huchingson
(15) Calvin James
(16) Joe Kwolek
(17) Jeff Livin
(18) Darryl Menard
(19) Pete Mueller
(20) Randy Randle
(21) Dody Rather
(22) Marty Schreiber
(23) Glenn Sherlock
(24) Doug Snyder
(25) Mel Stottlemyre
(26) Gary Tuck
(27) Jose Vargas
(28) Tom Wiedenbauer
(29) Jamie Williams

1986 ProCards Palm Springs Angels

(California Angels, A)

	MT	NR MT	EX
Complete Set:	12.00	9.00	4.75

(1) Kent Anderson
(2) Bobby Bell
(3) Dante Bichette
(4) Paul Bilak
(5) Mike Butler
(6) Richie Carter
(7) Pete Coachman
(8) Larry Cook
(9) Barry Dacus
(10) John DiGioia
(11) Mark Doran
(12) Todd Eggertsen
(13) William Fraser
(14) Miguel Garcia
(15) Billy Geivett
(16) Bryan Harvey
(17) Chuck Hernandez
(18) Doug Jennings
(19) Tom Kotchman
(20) Reggie Lambert
(21) Scott Marrott
(22) David Martinez
(23) Dave Montanari
(24) Dario Nunez
(25) Erik Pappas
(26) Stacey Pettis
(27) Bryan Price
(28) Mike Romanovsky
(29) Ty Van Burkleo

1986 Smokey Bear Palm Springs Angels

(California Angels, A)

	MT	NR MT	EX
Complete Set:	16.00	12.00	6.50

1 Tom Osowski (general manager)
2 Tom Kotchman (manager)
3 Chuck Hernandez (coach)
4 Paul Bilak (trainer)
5 Bobby Bell
6 Eric Pappas
7 John DiGioia
8 Miguel Garcia
9 William Fraser
10 Mike Romanovsky
11 Larry Cook
12 Bryan Harvey
13 Scott Marrett
14 Richie Carter
15 Bryan Price
16 Todd Eggertson
17 Mick Butler
18 Phil Venturino
19 Barry Dacus
20 Ty Van Burkleo
21 David Montanari
22 Pete Coachman
23 Billy Geivett
24 Mitch Seoane
25 Dario Nunez
26 Doug Jennings
27 Reggie Lambert
---- Introductory Card

1986 ProCards Pawtucket Red Sox

(Boston Red Sox, AAA)

	MT	NR MT	EX
Complete Set:	35.00	26.00	14.00

(1) Todd Benzinger
(2) Dick Berardino
(3) Mike Brown
(4) Chris Cannizzaro
(5) John Christensen (glove on right hand)
(6) John Christensen (glove on left hand)
(7) Tony Cleary
(8) Mike Dalton
(9) Pat Dodson
(10) Mike Greenwell
(11) Mitch Johnson
(12) John Leister
(13) George Mecerod
(14) Mike Mesh
(15) Gary Miller-Jones
(16) Ed Nottle
(17) Rey Quinonez
(18) Mike Rochford
(19) Kevin Romine
(20) Calvin Schiraldi
(21) Jeff Sellers
(22) Danny Sheaffer
(23) Mike Stenhouse
(24) Laschelle Tarver
(25) Gary Tremblay
(26) Mike Trujillo
(27) Dana Williams
(28) Rob Woodard

1986 ProCards Peninsula White Sox

(Chicago White Sox, A)

	MT	NR MT	EX
Complete Set:	6.00	4.50	2.50

(1) Jorge Alcazar
(2) Larry Allen
(3) Jeff Anderson
(4) Bob Bailey
(5) Jerry Bertolani
(6) Virgil Conley
(7) Dan Cronkright
(8) Tom Drees
(9) Wayne Edwards
(10) Duane Engram
(11) Chuck Hartenstein
(12) Mark Henry
(13) Tom Hildebrand
(14) Chris Jefts
(15) Tom Lahrman
(16) Jim Markert
(17) Glen McElroy
(18) Mike Moore
(19) John Pawlowski
(20) Adam Peterson
(21) Darrell Pruitt
(22) Kevin Renz
(23) Ron Scheer
(24) Ed Sedar
(25) Pete Venturini
(26) Dave Wallwork
(27) Eric Wilson
(28) Jim Winters

1986 ProCards Peoria Chiefs

(Chicago Cubs, A)

	MT	NR MT	EX
Complete Set:	40.00	30.00	16.00

(1) Scott Anders
(2) Dick Canan
(3) Tony Collins
(4) Leonard Damian
(5) Bill Danek
(6) John Fierro
(7) Jim Gardner
(8) Mark Grace
(9) John Green
(10) Tony Hamza
(11) Jeff Hirsch
(12) Greg Kallevig
(13) Joe Kraemer
(14) John Lewis
(15) Dave Liddell
(16) Tom Lombarski
(17) Pete Mackanin
(18) Bob Mandeville
(19) Bill Phillips
(20) Kris Roth
(21) Tad Scowik
(22) Jeff Small
(23) Dwight Smith
(24) John Turner
(25) Tim Wallace
(26) Jim Wright
(27) Fernando Zarranz

1986 ProCards Phoenix Firebirds

(San Francisco Giants, AAA)

	MT	NR MT	EX
Complete Set:	8.00	6.00	3.25

(1) Rick Adams
(2) Mike Aldrete
(3) Randy Bockus
(4) Kelly Downs
(5) Duane Espy
(6) Randy Gomez
(7) Everett Graham
(8) Mark Grant
(9) Chuck Hensley
(10) Mike Jeffcoat
(11) Randy Johnson
(12) Cris Jones
(13) Randy Kutcher
(14) Rick Lancellotti
(15) Jim Lefebvre
(16) Jack McNight
(17) Bob Moore
(18) Terry Mulholland
(19) Phil Ouellette
(20) Jon Perlman
(21) Luis Quinones
(22) Jesse Reid
(23) Cliff Shidawara
(24) Frank Williams
(25) Jack Wilson
(26) Mike Woodard

1986 ProCards Pittsfield Cubs

(Chicago Cubs, AA)

	MT	NR MT	EX
Complete Set:	70.00	52.00	28.00

(1) Rich Amaral
(2) Damon Berryhill

(3) Mike Capel
(4) Bruce Crabbe
(5) Luis Cruz
(6) Jackie Davidson
(7) Jim Dickerson
(8) Drew Hall
(9) Carl Hamilton
(10) Darrin Jackson
(11) Dave Kopf
(12) Mike Lacer
(13) Dave Lenderman
(14) Greg Maddux
(15) Mike Martin
(16) Allen McKay
(17) Jamie Moyer
(18) Rafael Palmeiro
(19) Dick Pole
(20) Steve Roadcap
(21) Jeff Rutledge
(22) Tom Spencer
(23) Phil Stephenson
(24) Gary Varsho
(25) Tony Woods

1986 Team Pittsfield Cubs

(Chicago Cubs, AA) This set is in the form of a 10-7/8" x 16-3/4" poster.

	MT	NR MT	EX
Complete Set:	60.00	45.00	24.00

(1) Rich Amaral
(2) Damon Berryhill
(3) Brad Blevins
(4) Mike Capel
(5) Troy Chestnut
(6) Bruce Crabbe
(7) Luis Cruz
(8) Jackie Davidson
(9) Drew Hall
(10) Carl Hamilton
(11) Darrin Jackson
(12) Dave Kopf
(13) Tom Layton
(14) Dave Lenderman
(15) Mike Martin
(16) Alan McKay
(17) Paul Noce
(18) Rafael Palmeiro
(19) Rolando Roomes
(20) Phil Stephenson
(21) Gary Varsho
(22) Tony Woods

1986 ProCards Portland Beavers

(Philadelphia Phillies, AAA) (Price includes the scarce Miller card)

	MT	NR MT	EX
Complete Set:	9.00	6.75	3.50

(1) Jeff Bittiger
(2) Dave Bulls
(3) Joe Cipolloni
(4) Randy Day
(5) Ken Dowell
(6) Arturo Gonzalez
(7) Tom Gorman
(8) Kevin Hickey
(9) Rob Hicks
(10) Chris James
(11) Greg Jelks
(12) Tim Knight
(13) Alan LeBoeuf
(14) Randy Lerch
(15) Mike Maddux
(16) Francisco Melendez
(17) Keith Miller
(18) Kyle Money
(19) Ronn Reynolds
(20) Dave Shipanoff
(21) Jeff Stone
(22) Bobby Tiefenauer
(23) Fred Toliver

1986 ProCards Prince William Pirates

(Pittsburgh Pirates, A)

	MT	NR MT	EX
Complete Set:	7.00	5.25	2.75

(1) Reggie Barringer
(2) Lance Belen
(3) Tony Blasucci
(4) Rocky Bridges
(5) Tony Chance
(6) Carey Cheek
(7) Jeff Cook
(8) Ron Delucchi
(9) Tim Drummond
(10) Sal Ferreiras
(11) Brett Gideon
(12) Mike Goodwin
(13) Brian Jones
(14) Bob Koopman
(15) Tim McMillan
(16) Jose Melendez
(17) Larry Melton
(18) Page Odle
(19) Chris Pierce
(20) Tom Prince
(21) Chris Ritter
(22) Dave Rooker
(23) Rob Russell
(24) John Smiley
(25) Greg Stading
(26) Mike Stevens
(27) Kyle Todd

1986 ProCards Quad Cities Angels

(California Angels, A)

	MT	NR MT	EX
Complete Set:	12.00	9.00	4.75

(1) Edgar Alfonso
(2) Tom Alfredson
(3) Bob Auth
(4) Gerald Baker
(5) Mark Ban
(6) Tim Burcham
(7) Chris Collins
(8) Frank DiMichele
(9) Santiago Espinosha
(10) Andres Esponisa (Espinoza)
(11) Chuck Finley
(12) Ken Grant
(13) Dan Grunard
(14) Randy Harvey
(15) Dave Johnson
(16) Sam Joseph
(17) Scott Kannenberg
(18) Bill Lachemann
(19) Jeff Manto
(20) Mark Marino
(21) Ed Marquez
(22) Steve McGuire
(23) Glenn Meyers
(24) Richerd Morehouse
(25) Gary Nalls
(26) Giovanny Reyes
(27) Edwin Rivera
(28) Ed Rodriguez
(29) Robert Rose
(30) Mickey Saatzer
(31) Glenn Washington
(32) Roger Zottneck
(33) Team Card

1986 ProCards Reading Phillies

(Philadelphia Phillies, AA)

	MT	NR MT	EX
Complete Set:	7.00	5.25	2.75

(1) Ramon Aviles
(2) Shawn Barton
(3) Mark Bowden
(4) Tony Brown
(5) Jose Cecena
(6) George Culver
(7) Steve DeAngelis
(8) Marvin Freeman
(9) Ramon Henderson
(10) Ken Jackson
(11) Michael Jackson
(12) Ricky Jordan
(13) Steve Labay
(14) Jose Leiva
(15) Bruce Long
(16) Darren Loy
(17) Keith Miller
(18) Steve Moses
(19) Howard Nichols, Jr.
(20) Barney Nugent
(21) Jim Olander
(22) Ray Ramon
(23) Bruce Ruffin
(24) Mike Shelton
(25) Kevin Ward
(26) Lenny Watts

1986 ProCards Richmond Braves

(Atlanta Braves, AAA)

	MT	NR MT	EX
Complete Set:	7.50	5.50	3.00

(1) Sam Ayoub
(2) Dave Beard
(3) Steve Curry
(4) Bruce Dal Canton
(5) Juan Eichelberger
(6) Doc Estes
(7) Lee Graham
(8) Al Hall
(9) Kelly Heath
(10) Mike Jones
(11) Brad Komminsk
(12) Robert Long
(13) Roy Majtyka
(14) Ed Olwine
(15) Larry Owen
(16) Gerald Perry
(17) Charlie Puleo
(18) John Rabb
(19) Paul Runge
(20) Steve Shields
(21) Cliff Speck
(22) Mark Strucher
(23) Ron Tingley
(24) Andre Treadway
(25) Matt West
(26) Paul Zuvella

1986 ProCards Rochester Red Wings

(Baltimore Orioles, AAA)

	MT	NR MT	EX
Complete Set:	7.50	5.50	3.00

(1) Tony Arnold
(2) Dom Chiti
(3) Ken Gerhart
(4) Glenn Gulliver
(5) John Habyan
(6) John Hart
(7) Mike Hart
(8) Rex Hudler
(9) Phil Hoffman
(10) Odell Jones
(11) Rick Jones
(12) Mick Kinnunen
(13) Curt Motton
(14) Tom O'Malley
(15) Al Pardo
(16) Kelly Paris
(17) Eric Rasmussen
(18) Mike Reddish
(19) Don Scott
(20) Nelson Simmons
(21) Mike Skinner
(22) Ken Smith
(23) Kelvin Torve
(24) Jim Traber
(25) Jeff Williams
(26) Silver Stadium

1986 ProCards St. Petersburg Cards

(St. Louis Cardinals, A)

	MT	NR MT	EX
Complete Set:	8.00	6.00	3.25

(1) Sal Agostinelli
(2) Scott Arnold
(3) Richard Arzola
(4) David Bilalis
(5) Henry Carson
(6) Alex Cole
(7) John Costello
(8) Jeff Fassero
(9) Jim Fregosi, Jr.
(10) Brad Henderson
(11) Hans Herzog
(12) Stephen Hill
(13) Howard Hilton
(14) Ken Infante
(15) Ronald Johns
(16) Bill Jones
(17) Matt Kinzer
(18) Martin Mason
(19) Charles McGrath
(20) Jesus Mendez
(21) Scott Murray
(22) Jay North
(23) Mauricio Nunez
(24) Steven Petitt
(25) Jim Puzey
(26) Jim Reboulet
(27) John Rigos
(28) Roy Silver
(29) Mike Theisen

1986 ProCards Salem Red Birds

(Texas Rangers, A)

	MT	NR MT	EX
Complete Set:	7.00	5.25	2.75

(1) Kevin Bootay
(2) Mike Bucci
(3) Joel Cartaya
(4) Jeff Clay
(5) Bryan Dial
(6) Tom Duggan
(7) Riley Epps
(8) Al Farmer
(9) Greg Ferlenda
(10) Stephen Glasker
(11) Tim Hallgren
(12) Brad Hill
(13) Duane James
(14) Ron King
(15) Steve Kordish
(16) Chad Kreuter
(17) Steve Lankard
(18) Jeff Mays
(19) Tim McLoughlin
(20) Bob Mortimer
(21) Dave Murray
(22) Bob O'Hearn
(23) Kevin Reimer
(24) Dave Satnat
(25) Mitch Thomas
(26) Jose Vargas
(27) Jim Vlcek
(28) Darrell Whitaker
(29) Mike Winbush

1986 Cramer Salem Angels

(California Angels, A) This set is numbered as it appears on the backs of the cards.

	MT	NR MT	EX
Complete Set:	6.00	4.50	2.50

76 Colin Charland
77 Giovanny Reyes
78 Jeff Gay
79 Julio Granco
80 Brandy Vann
81 Alan Mills
82 Gary Gorski
83 Bobby Cabello
84 Bill Vanderwel
85 Greg Jackson
86 Scott Cerny
87 Michael Knapp
88 Daryl Green
89 Colby Ward
90 James Bisceglia
91 Greg Fix
92 Luis Merejo
93 Tony Bonura
94 David Grilione
95 Terence Carr
96 Lee Stevens
97 Michael Fetters
98 Santiaga Espinosa
99 Mike Spearnock
100 Roberto Hernandez

1986 ProCards San Jose Bees

(No Affiliation, A)

	MT	NR MT	EX
Complete Set:	6.00	4.50	2.50

(1) Freddie Arroyo
(2) Shawn Barton
(3) Mike Bigusiak
(4) Randy Bispo
(5) James Bolt
(6) Darryl Cias
(7) Ken Foster
(8) Darren Garrick
(9) Lorenzo Gray
(10) Steven Howe
(11) Brian Kubala
(12) Edward McCarter
(13) Ted Milner
(14) Yoshi Nakashima
(15) Mike Nittoli
(16) Dave Okubo
(17) Ken Reitz
(18) Daryl Sconiers
(19) Harry Steve
(20) Nori Tanabe
(21) Jim Tinkey
(22) Mike Verdi
(23) Hank Wada
(24) Mickey Yamano
(25) George Yokota

1986 ProCards Shreveport Captains

(San Francisco Giants, AA)

	MT	NR MT	EX
Complete Set:	13.00	9.75	5.25

(1) Jeff Brantley
(2) John Burkett
(3) Kevin Burrell
(4) Alan Cockrell
(5) Charlie Corbell
(6) Marty Demerritt
(7) Angel Escobar
(8) George Ferran
(9) John Grimes
(10) Dean Hummel

(11) Charlie Hayes
(12) Mike Jones
(13) Wendell Kim
(14) Marty Demerritt
(15) Greg Litton
(16) Daryl Masuyama
(17) Deron McCue
(18) Scott Medvin
(19) Steve Miller
(20) Brian Ohnoutka
(21) Ed Phikunas
(22) Mackey Sasser
(23) Keith Silver
(24) Stu Tate
(25) Todd Thomas
(26) John Verducci
(27) Colin Ward
(28) Team Card

1986 Donn Jennings Southern League All-Stars

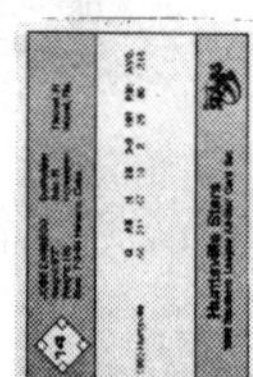

(AA) All cards in this set are listed as 1986 All Stars with the exception of Jose Canseco, listed as 1985 MVP, and Bo Jackson, listed as 1986 Future Star.

	MT	NR MT	EX
Complete Set:	15.00	11.00	6.00

1 Bill Ripken
2 Mike Yastrzemski
3 Mark McGwire
4 Gary Thurman
5 Karkovice Ron
6 Jose Tolentino
7 Chris Padget
8 Brian Guinn
9 Luis De Los Santos
10 Terry Steinback
11 Larry Ray
12 Tom Dodd
13 Bo Jackson
14 Jose Canseco
15 Alonzo Powell
16 Glenallen Hill
17 Brick Smith
18 Todd Burns
19 Dave White
20 Paul Schneider
21 Brian Holman
22 Anthony Kelly
23 Tom Glavine
24 Cliff Young
25 Kevin Price

1986 Cramer Spokane Indians

(San Diego Padres, A) This set is numbered as it appears on the backs of the cards.

	MT	NR MT	EX
Complete Set:	15.00	11.00	6.00

155 Brian Wood
156 Bob Lutticken
157 Jim Navilliat
158 Carl Holmes
159 Ronald Moore
160 George Brett
161 Greg Harris
162 Dave Brockil
163 Ricky Bones
164 Brian Harrison
165 Paul Quinzer
166 Mark Sampson
167 Mike Basso
168 Craig Cooper
169 Tom Levasseur
170 Terry McDevitt
171 Thomas Howard
172 Tony Pellegrino
173 Keith Harrison
174 Warren Newson
175 Kevin Coentopp
176 Jeff Yurtin
177 Rob Picciolo
178 James Austin
179 William Taylor

1986 University City Spokane Indians

(San Diego Padres) (color)

	MT	NR MT	EX
Complete Set:	10.00		7.50

6 James Austin
7 Terry McDevitt
8 Bob Picciolo
9 Tommy LeVasseur
10 Rickey Bones
11 Brian Harrison
12 Bob Lutticken
14 William Taylor
15 Jeff Yurtin
16 Tony Pellegrino
17 Greg Harris
20 Kevin Koentopp
21 Thomas Howard
22 Brian Wood
23 Sonny Siebert
24 Keith Harrison
25 Doug Brucail
26 Mike Basso
27 Paul Quinzer
28 Jim Navilliat
30 Craig Cooper
31 Warren Newson
32 Dave Collinshaw
34 Mark Sampson

1986 TCMA Stars Of The Future Post Card Set

(AAA)

	MT	NR MT	EX
Complete Set:	25.00	18.75	10.00

1 Cooper Stadium Home of the Clippers
2 Team & Barry Foote, Mgr.
3 Pitchers (Alfonso Pulido, Doug Drabek, Mike Armstrong, Brad Arnsberg)
4 Catchers (Juan Espino, Phil Lombardi, Darwin McNeely, Dave Stegman)
5 1st base, 2nd base shortstop (Orestes Destrade, Andre Robertson, Mike Soper, Leo Hernandez)
6 Doug Potestio
7 Julio Valdez
8 Dave Martinez, Steve Hammond, Mike Brumley, Bobby Ramos
9 Dave Gumpert, Ken Price
10 Trey Brooks
11 Joe Hicks
12 Pookie Bernstine
13 Johnny Abrego
14 Dennis Livingston
15 Mike Watters (2nd base)
16 Stu Pederson (Outfielder)
17 Ralph Bryant
18 Jeff Hamilton (3rd base)
19 Balvino Galvez (Pitcher)
20 Ed Amelung (Outfielder)
21 Alvis Woods
22 Scott Ullger
23 Andre David
24 Dennis Burtt
25 Geraldo "Jerry" Lomastro
26 Fred McGriff
27 Alex Infante
28 Stan Clark, Rondal Rollin)
29 Chris Johnston
30 Jeff Hearron
31 Stan Jefferson
32 Dave Magadan
33 John Gibbons
34 John Mitchell
35 Tony Ferreira
36 Jesse Reid
37 Jim Lefebvre
38 Mike Aldrete
39 Terry Mulholland
40 Mark Grant

1986 ProCards Stockton Ports

(Milwaukee Brewers, A)

	MT	NR MT	EX
Complete Set:	6.00	4.50	2.50

(1) John Beuerlein
(2) Jamie Brisco
(3) Todd Brown
(4) Tim Casey
(5) Rob Derksen
(6) Rob DeWolf
(7) Todd France
(8) Mike Frew
(9) Mike Fulmer
(10) Mike Gobbo
(11) Gary Kanwisher
(12) Matt Kent
(13) John Ludy

(14) Dave Machaemer
(15) Joe Mitchell
(16) Mario Monico
(17) Martin Montano
(18) Frank Mattox
(19) Doug Norton
(20) Jeff Peterek
(21) Walter Pohle
(22) Danny Ratliff
(23) Jeff Reece
(24) Alan Sadler
(25) Darryel Walters
(26) Fred Williams

1986 ProCards Sumter Braves

(Atlanta Braves, A)

	MT	NR MT	EX
Complete Set:	45.00	34.00	18.00

(1) Tom Abrell
(2) John Alva
(3) Ron Bianco
(4) Johnny Cuevas
(5) Shawn Frazier
(6) Jeff Greene
(7) Tom Greene
(8) Kevin Harmon
(9) Mike Hennessy
(10) Dennis Hood
(11) Dodd Johnson
(12) Barry Jones
(13) Clarence Jones
(14) David Jones
(15) Dave Justice
(16) Mark Lemke
(17) Al Martin
(18) Ed Mathews
(19) Leo Mazzone
(20) Bob McNally
(21) Bob Pfaff
(22) Ellis Roby
(23) Matt Rowe
(24) Jim Salisbury
(25) David Seitz
(26) Brian Snitker
(27) Andy Tomberlain
(28) Rob Tomberlain
(29) Danny Weems
(30) Jeff Wetherby

1986 ProCards Syracuse Chiefs

(Toronto Blue Jays, AAA)

	MT	NR MT	EX
Complete Set:	25.00	18.50	10.00

(1) Gibson Alba
(2) Luis Aquino
(3) Doug Ault
(4) Joe Beckwith
(5) Stan Clarke
(6) Rich Carlucci
(7) Jose Castro
(8) John Cerutti
(9) Don Cooper
(10) Red Coughlin
(11) Otis Green
(12) Dale Holman
(13) Dennis Howard
(14) Alex Infante
(15) Joe Johnston
(16) Luis Leal
(17) Manny Lee
(18) Fred McGriff
(19) Steve Mingori
(20) Ron Musselman
(21) Mark Poole
(22) Mike Sharperson
(23) Ron Shepherd
(24) Dave Stenhouse
(25) Lou Thornton
(26) Rockett Wheeler
(27) John Woodworth

1986 ProCards Tacoma Tigers

(Oakland A's, AAA)

	MT	NR MT	EX
Complete Set:	11.00	8.25	4.50

(1) Darrel Ackerfelds
(2) Ralph Citarella
(3) Brian Dorsett
(4) Tom Dozier
(5) Jim Eppard
(6) Chuck Estrada
(7) Mike Gallego
(8) Walt Horn
(9) Brian Javier
(10) Jeff Kaiser
(11) Tim Lambert
(12) Dave Leiper
(13) Keith Lieppman

(14) Joey McLaughlin
(15) Rob Nelson
(16) Eric Plunk
(17) Luis Polonia
(18) Thad Reece
(19) Rick Rodriguez
(20) Lenn Sakata
(21) Ray Smith
(22) Keith Thrower
(23) Rusty Tillman
(24) Jerry Willard
(25) Curt Young

1986 ProCards Tampa Tarpons

(Cincinnati Reds, A)

	MT	NR MT	EX
Complete Set:	6.00	4.50	2.50

(1) Carlos Acosta
(2) Tim Barker
(3) Mark Berry
(4) Phil Dale
(5) Chuck Donahue
(6) Jeff Hayward
(7) Jim Jefferson
(8) Dave Keller
(9) Ted Langdon
(10) Rod Lich
(11) Joel Lond
(12) Rob Lopez
(13) Tim Mirabito
(14) Angelo Nunley
(15) Mike Ramsey
(16) Darren Riley
(17) Dusty Rogers
(18) Isidro Rondon
(19) Francisco Silverio
(20) Jack Smith
(21) Ozzie Soto
(22) Tom Summer
(23) Francisco Tenacen
(24) Don Wakamatsu
(25) Brant Weatherford
(26) Jeff Wilson
(27) Tom Wilson

1986 ProCards Tidewater Tides - Tides Emblem

(New York Mets, AAA)

	MT	NR MT	EX
Complete Set:	10.00	7.50	4.00

(1) Rick Anderson
(2) Terry Blocker
(3) Tom Burns
(4) Mark Carreon
(5) Tim Corcoran
(6) John Cumberland
(7) Mike Davis
(8) Tony Ferreira
(9) Doug Frobel
(10) Ron Gardenhire
(11) John Gibbons
(12) Ed Glynn
(13) Ed Hearn
(14) Stan Jefferson
(15) Terry Leach
(16) Barry Lyons
(17) Dave Magadan
(18) Tom McCarthy
(19) Marlin McPhail
(20) Randy Milligan
(21) John Mitchell
(22) Randy Myers
(23) Alfredo Pedrique
(24) Sam Perlozzo
(25) Rick Rainer
(26) Doug Sisk
(27) Steve Springer
(28) DeWayne Vaughn
(29) Dave Wyatt

1986 ProCards Tidewater Tides - Mets Emblem

(New York Mets, AAA)

	MT	NR MT	EX
Complete Set:	10.00	7.50	4.00

(1) Richard Anderson
(2) Terry Blocker
(3) Tom Burns
(4) Mark Carreon
(5) Tim Corcoran
(6) John Cumberland
(7) Michael Davis
(8) Tony Ferreira
(9) Doug Frobel
(10) Ronald Gardenhire
(11) John Gibbons

(12) Edward Glynn
(13) Edward Hearn
(14) Stanley Jefferson
(15) Terry Leach
(16) Barry Lyons
(17) David Magadan
(18) Marlin McPhail
(19) Tom McCarthy
(20) Randy Milligan
(21) John Mitchell
(22) Randy Myers
(23) Sam Perlozzo
(24) Alfredo Pedrique
(25) Rick Rainer
(26) Doug Sisk
(27) Steven Springer
(28) DeWayne Vaughn
(29) David Wyatt

1986 ProCards Toledo Mud Hens

(Houston Astros, AAA)

	MT	NR MT	EX
Complete Set:	6.00	4.50	2.50

(1) Allen Anderson
(2) Brad Boylan
(3) Eric Broersma
(4) Mark Brown
(5) Danny Clay
(6) Mark Davidson
(7) Andre David
(8) Pat Dempsey
(9) Alvaro Espinosa
(10) Frank Eufemia
(11) Mark Funderburk
(12) Gorman Heimueller
(13) Richard Leggatt
(14) Jerry Lomastro
(15) Charlie Manuel
(16) Alex Morte
(17) Charlie Mitchell
(18) Bob Ralston
(19) Mario Ramirez
(20) Ramon Romero
(21) Les Straker
(22) Scott Ullger
(23) Ron Washington
(24) Al Woods

1986 Cramer Tri-Cities Triplets

(No Affiliation, A)

	MT	NR MT	EX
Complete Set:	7.00	5.25	2.75

180 Joe Strain
181 Tod Wilson
182 Mark Leonard
183 Robin Riomer
184 David Nash
185 Chuck Higso
186 Matt Walke,)
187 Andy Naworski
188 Kevin Brockway
189 Bruce Carter
190 Dan Adriance
191 Tony Rasmus
192 Kendall Walling
193 Eric Pawling
194 Joe Giola
195 John Jaha
196 Daron Connelly
197 David Connelly
198 Andy Hall
199 Darryl Gilliam
200 Thomas Ealy

1986 ProCards Tucson Toros

(Houston Astros, AAA)

	MT	NR MT	EX
Complete Set:	6.00	4.50	2.50

(1) Larry Acker
(2) Carlos Alfonso
(3) Don August
(4) Glen Carpenter
(5) Ty Gainey
(6) Jeff Heathcock
(7) Manny Hernandez
(8) Chuck Jackson
(9) Rex Jones
(10) Mark Knudson
(11) Rob Mallicoat
(12) Ron Mathis
(13) Louie Meadows
(14) Jim Miner
(15) John Mizerock
(16) Rafael Montalvo
(17) Ray Noble
(18) Bert Pena
(19) Nelson Rood
(20) Mark Ross
(21) Jim Sherman
(22) Jim Thomas
(23) Duane Walker
(24) Ty Waller
(25) Eddie Watt
(26) Robbie Wine

1986 Team Tulsa Drillers

(Texas Rangers, AA)

	MT	NR MT	EX
Complete Set:	10.00	7.50	4.00

1 Mark Poole
2 Tony Triplett
3 Kirk Killingsworth
4 Mike Couchee
5 Art Gardner
6 Bill Stearns
7 Tim Rodgers
8 Mike Loynd
9a Jerry Browne
9b Rick Knapp
10 Steve Wilson
11 Jamie Doughty
12 Benny Cadahia
14 Bob Gergen
15 Greg Ferlenda
16 Kevin Bootay
17 Javier Ortiz
18 Greg Bailey
19 Dan Olsson
20 Paul Kilgus
21 Jeff Melrose
22 Rick Raether
23 Randy Kramer
24 Larry Klein
25 Mike Stanley
26 Bob Bill
27 Jose Mota

1986 ProCards Vancouver Canadians

(Milwaukee Brewers, AAA)

	MT	NR MT	EX
Complete Set:	12.00	9.00	4.75

(1) Jim Adduci
(2) Terry Bevington
(3) Mike Birkbeck
(4) Chris Bosio
(5) Glenn Braggs
(6) Mark Ciardi
(7) Bryan Clutterbuck
(8) Chuck Crim
(9) Dan Davidsmeier
(10) Ed Diaz
(11) Bryan Duquette
(12) Bob Gibson
(13) Dion James
(14) John Johnson
(15) Steve Kiefer
(16) Dave Klipstein
(17) Joe Meyer
(18) Ed Myers
(19) Charlie O'Brien
(20) Jim Paciorek
(21) Mike Paul
(22) Chuck Porter
(23) Ray Searage
(24) B.J. Surhoff
(25) Dale Sveum
(26) Rich Thompson
(27) Rick Waits

1986 ProCards Ventura Gulls

(Toronto Blue Jays, A)

	MT	NR MT	EX
Complete Set:	11.00	8.25	4.50

(1) Geronimo Berroa
(2) Hugh Brinson
(3) Francisco Cabrera
(4) Mark Dickmon
(5) Rob Ducey
(6) Oscar Escobar
(7) Glenn Ezell
(8) Sandy Guerrero
(9) Mike Jones
(10) Ken Kinnard
(11) Darryl Landrum
(12) Omar Malave
(13) Domingo Martinez
(14) Jose Mesa
(15) Steve Mumaw
(16) Jeff Musselman
(17) Greg Myers
(18) Al Olsen
(19) Alfredo Ortiz
(20) Zack Paris
(21) Todd Provence
(22) Pablo Reyes
(23) Luis Reyna
(24) Willie Shanks
(25) Todd Stottlemyre
(26) Tom Wasilewski
(27) Dave Wells
(28) Eric Yelding

1986 ProCards Vermont Reds

(Cincinnati Reds, AA)

	MT	NR MT	EX
Complete Set:	9.00	6.75	3.50

(1) Jordan Berge
(2) John Boyles
(3) Norm Charlton
(4) Jeff Cox
(5) Clay Daniel
(6) Gary Denbo
(7) Rob Dibble
(8) Jeff Gray
(9) Lenny Harris
(10) Billy Hawley
(11) Ron Henika
(12) Mike Manfre
(13) Greg Monda
(14) Steve Oliverio
(15) Buddy Pryor
(16) Brian Robinson
(17) Jim Scott
(18) Brooks Shumake
(19) Mike Sims
(20) Danny Smith
(21) Glen Spagnola
(22) Jeff Treadway
(23) Jay Ward
(24) Delwyn Young

1986 ProCards Vero Beach Dodgers

(Los Angeles Dodgers, A)

	MT	NR MT	EX
Complete Set:	18.00	13.50	7.25

(1) Andy Anthony
(2) Kevin Ayers
(3) Michael Cherry
(4) Carl Cox
(5) Kevin Devine
(6) Peter Geist
(7) Rob Giesecke
(8) Juan Guzman
(9) Jeff Hartman
(10) Darren Holmes
(11) Michael Hoff
(12) Ed Jacobo
(13) Robert Jacobsen
(14) Wayne Kirby
(15) Ken Lampert
(16) Luis Lopez
(17) Walt McConnell
(18) Domingo Michel
(19) Jon Pequignot
(20) Rod Rochie
(21) John Schlichting
(22) Jorge Sepulveda
(23) John Shoemaker
(24) Felix Tejeda
(25) Bob Tucker
(26) Jesus Vila
(27) Stan Wasiak

1986 ProCards Visalia Oaks

(Minnesota Twins, A)

	MT	NR MT	EX
Complete Set:	6.00	4.50	2.50

(1) Mike Adams
(2) Joey Aragon
(3) Ben Bianchi
(4) Gary Borg
(5) Bob Callfy
(6) Alfredo Cardwood
(7) DeWayne Coleman
(8) Rob Cramer
(9) Chris Forgione
(10) Henry Gatewood
(11) Donnie Iasparro
(12) Chris Kroener
(13) Sal Nicolosi
(14) Bill O'Conner
(15) Wes Pierorazio
(16) Shannon Raybon
(17) Scott Rohlof
(18) Danny Schmitz
(19) Tom Schwarz
(20) Tim Senne
(21) Bob Tabeling
(22) Tom Thomas
(23) Ray Velasquez
(24) Eddie Yanes

1986 ProCards Waterbury Indians

(Cleveland Indians, AA)

	MT	NR MT	EX
Complete Set:	7.00	5.25	2.75

(1) Jeff Arney
(2) Chris Beasley
(3) Mike Bellaman
(4) Jay Bell
(5) Bernardo Brito
(6) George Crum
(7) Jim Driscoll
(8) Luis Encarnacion
(9) John Farrell
(10) Winston Ficklin
(11) Orlando Gomez
(12) Milt Harper
(13) Rick Henke
(14) Bob Link
(15) Don Lovell
(16) Oscar Mejia
(17) Kent Murphy
(18) Michael Murphy
(19) Cliff Pastornicky
(20) Miguel Roman
(21) Cal Santarelli
(22) Craig Smajstra
(23) Daryl Smith
(24) Dain Syverson
(25) Steve Whitmyer
(26) Bill Worden

1986 ProCards Waterloo Indians

(Cleveland Indians, A)

	MT	NR MT	EX
Complete Set:	6.00	4.50	2.50

(1) Brian Allard
(2) David Alvis
(3) Keith Bennett
(4) Dave Bresnahan
(5) Claudio Carrasco
(6) Glen Fairchild
(7) Mike Farr
(8) Myron Gardner
(9) Andy Ghelfi
(10) John Githens
(11) Mark Higgins
(12) Trey Hillman
(13) Steve Johnson
(14) Scott Jordan
(15) Greg Karpuk
(16) Lee Kuntz
(17) Greg LaFever
(18) Luis Medina
(19) Manny Mercado
(20) Rod Nichols
(21) Mike Poehl
(22) John Power
(23) Mike Rountree
(24) Don Santo
(25) Charles Scott
(26) Rob Swain
(27) Steve Swisher
(28) Chuck Todd
(29) Kevin Trudeau
(30) Casey Webster
(31) Greg Williamson
(32) Mike Workman

1986 ProCards Watertown Pirates

(Pittsburgh Pirates, A)

	MT	NR MT	EX
Complete Set:	9.50	7.25	3.75

(1) Steve Adams
(2) Moises Alou
(3) Jeff Banister
(4) Daryl Boyd
(5) Lawrence Brady
(6) Guy Conti
(7) Bill Copp
(8) Jeff Gurtcheff
(9) Craig Heakins
(10) Mike Khoury
(11) Tim Kirk
(12) Blaine Lockley
(13) Dino Moran
(14) Douglas Moreno
(15) Steve Moser
(16) Ed Ott
(17) Al Quintana
(18) Randy Robicheaux
(19) Carl Rose
(20) Scott Runge
(21) Bill Sampen
(22) Butch Schlopy
(23) Tom Shields
(24) Tracy Toy
(25) Glenn Trudo
(26) Miguel Varverde
(27) Mike Walker

1986 ProCards Wausau Timbers

(Seattle Mariners, A)

	MT	NR MT	EX
Complete Set:	7.00	5.25	2.75

(1) Robert Bernardo
(2) Fremio Cabrera
(3) John Clem
(4) Don Cohoon
(5) Bobby Cuellar
(6) Mike Darby
(7) Bret Davis
(8) William Diaz
(9) Tom Eccleston
(10) Joe Georger
(11) Bob Gibree
(12) Dan Larson
(13) Benito Malave
(14) Brian McCann
(15) Dave McCorkle
(16) Tim McLain
(17) Pablo Moncerratt
(18) Clay Parker
(19) Jeff Roberts
(20) Brad Rohde
(21) Mike Schooler
(22) Rich Slominski
(23) Paul Serna
(24) Bob Siegel
(25) Dave Snell
(26) Jorge Uribe
(27) Omar Visquel
(28) Anthony Woods
(29) Clint Zavarras

1986 ProCards West Palm Beach Expos

(Montreal Expos, A)

	MT	NR MT	EX
Complete Set:	10.00	7.50	4.00

(1) Felipe Alou
(2) Tim Arnold
(3) Scott Ayers
(4) Kent Bachman
(5) Esteban Beltre
(6) Mark Blaser
(7) Edgar Caceres
(8) Allen Collins
(9) Kerry Cook
(10) Bill Cunningham
(11) Mike Day
(12) Bob Devlin
(13) Eddie Dixon
(14) Kevin Dunton
(15) Jeff Fischer
(16) George Flower
(17) Keith Foley
(18) Gene Glynn
(19) Sam Haley
(20) Melvin Houston
(21) Randy Johnson
(22) Jim Kahmann
(23) Scott Mann
(24) Alonzo Powell
(25) Iggy Rodriguez
(26) Tim Thiessen
(27) Gary Wayne
(28) Bud Yanus

1986 ProCards Winston-Salem Spirits

(Chicago Cubs, A)

	MT	NR MT	EX
Complete Set:	7.00	5.25	2.75

(1) Bob Bafia
(2) Greg Bell
(3) Brent Casteel
(4) Doug Dacenzo (Dascenzo)
(5) Jim Essian
(6) Ron Ewart
(7) Rick Hopkins
(8) Brian House
(9) Rick Krantiz
(10) Lester Lancaster
(11) Dave Masters
(12) Steve Maye
(13) Julius McDougal
(14) Mark McMorris
(15) William Menendez
(16) David Pavlas
(17) Jim Phillip
(18) Jeff Pico
(19) Cohen Renfroe
(20) Tim Rice
(21) Don Richardson
(22) Rolando Roomes
(23) Mike Tullier
(24) Hector Villanueva
(25) Darcy Walker
(26) Rick Wrona
(27) Ernie Shore Stadium
(28) Ernie Shore Stadium
(29) Team Photo

1986 ProCards Winter Haven Red Sox

(Boston Red Sox, A)

	MT	NR MT	EX
Complete Set:	7.50	5.50	3.00

(1) Odie Abril
(2) Brady Anderson
(3) Gregg Barrios
(4) Greg Bochesa
(5) Mike Carista
(6) Mike Clarkin
(7) Tony DeFrancesco
(8) Robert Fuentes
(9) Angel Gonzalez
(10) Dave Holt
(11) Daryl Irvine
(12) Laverne Jackson
(13) Manny Jose
(14) Eric Laseke
(15) Bruce Lockhart
(16) Greg Lotzar
(17) Tim McGee
(18) Chris Moritz
(19) Rob Parkins
(20) John Sanderski
(21) Tary Scott
(22) Mike Sears
(23) Scott Skripko
(24) Jim Snediker
(25) Dan Sullivan
(26) Luis Vasquez
(27) Robert Zambrano

1987 ProCards Albany-Colonie Yankees

(New York Yankees, AA)

	MT	NR MT	EX
Complete Set:	9.00	6.75	3.50

739 Steve Rosenberg
740 Tony Russell
741 Bob Barker
742 Eric Schmidt
743 Robert Geren
744 Maurice Guercio
745 Randy Velarde
746 Ted Higgins
747 Gary Cathcart
749 Tim Layana
750 Jim Howard
751 Matthew Harrison
752 Carson Carroll
753 Chris Alvarez
754 Darren Reed
755 Jeff Knox
756 Jeffrey Pries
757 Tommy Jones
758 Fredi Gonzalez
759 Hal Morris
760 Brent Blum
761 Steve Frey
762 Jerry McNertney

1987 Team Albuquerque Dukes

(Los Angeles Dodgers, AAA)

	MT	NR MT	EX
Complete Set:	10.00	7.50	4.00

1 Terry Collins (manager)
2 Ben Hines (coach)
3 Brent Strom (coach)
4 Lenny Currier (trainer)
5 William Brennan
6 Dennis Burtt
7 Jaime Cocanower
8 Tim Crews
9 Jeff Edwards
10 Hector Heredia
11 Shawn Hillegas
12 Pete Ladd
13 Dennis Livingston
14 Tim Meeks
15 Jon Debus
16 Orlando Mercado
17 Gilberto Reyes
18 Shanie Dugas
19 Jeff Hamilton
20 Jack Perconte
21 Larry See
22 Craig Shipley
23 Brad Wellman
24 Tracy Woodson
25 Ralph Bryant
26 Jose Gonzalez
27 Chris Gwynn
28 George Hinshaw
29 Stu Pederson
30 Mike Ramsey

1987 ProCards Appleton Foxes

(Kansas City Royals, A)

	MT	NR MT	EX
Complete Set:	6.00	4.50	2.50

513 Chuck Mount
514 Bill Gilmore
515 John Larios
516 Pete Capello
517 D.J. Watson
518 Carlos Escalera
519 Frank Laureano
520 Deric Ladnier
521 Mike Tresemer
522 Mike Butcher
523 Joe Skodny
524 Darren Watkins
525 Ben Lee
526 Carlos Gonzalez
527 Charlie Eisenreich
528 Tom Gilles
529 Brian Poldberg
530 Mike Alvarez
531 Pat Bailey
532 Jose Rodriquez
533 Rob Wolkovs
534 Mike Leon
535 Tony Pickett
536 Ken Barry
537 Luke Nocas
538 Dennis Moeller
539 Greg Hibbard
540 Kenny Jackson
541 Phil McKinzie
542 Jim Willis

1987 ProCards Arkansas Travelers

(St. Louis Cardinals, AA)

	MT	NR MT	EX
Complete Set:	7.00	5.25	2.75

570 Dennis Carter
571 Mike Robinson
572 Charles McGrath
573 Jose Calderon
574 Kennedy Infante
575 Jeff Passero
576 James Riggleman
577 Randall Champion
578 Steven Peters
579 Paul Wilmet
580 James Fregosi
581 Roy Silver
582 Scott Arnold
583 Tim Jones
584 Sal Agostinelli
585 Luis Alicea
586 Craig Weissmann
587 Jeff Oyster
588 Kenneth Hill
589 Alex Cole
590 Mike Fitzgerald
591 Ray Stevens
592 James Reboult
593 Brad Henderson
594 John Costello

1987 ProCards Asheville Tourists

(Houston Astros, A)

	MT	NR MT	EX
Complete Set:	7.50	5.75	3.00

1818 Karl Rhodes
1819 Trent Hubbard
1820 Gene Confreda
1821 Keith Bodie
1822 Ryan Bowen
1823 Daven Bond
1824 Lou Frazier
1825 Doug Gonring
1826 Jim Olson
1827 Marty Hall
1828 Charlie Taylor
1829 Kevin Wasilewski
1830 Guy Normand
1831 Mike Stoker
1832 Nedar Horta
1833 Bert Hunter
1834 Mike Simms
1835 Shawn Talbott
1836 Victor Hithe
1837 Sam August
1838 Todd McClure
1839 Mike Oglesbee
1840 Lou Deiley
1841 Ed Whited
1842 Jeff Edwards
1843 Gorky Perez
1844 Pedro Sanchez
1845 John Sheehan

1987 ProCards Auburn Astros

(Houston Astros, A)

	MT	NR MT	EX
Complete Set:	6.00	4.50	2.50

2446 John Massarelli
2447 Rusty Harris
2448 Todd McClure
2449 Not Issued
2450 Damon Brooks
2451 Billy Paul Carver
2452 Andres Mota
2453 Dan Lewis
2454 Steve Polverini
2455 Randy Hennis
2456 Chris Hawkins
2457 Gary Tuck
2458 Dan Nyssen
2459 Carlos Laboy
2460 Gorky Perez
2461 Robert Romo
2462 Todd Newman
2463 Greg Johnson
2464 Rick Aponte
2465 Hector Herrera
2466 Ken Dickson
2467 Al Osuna
2468 Edison Renteria
2469 Dean Hartgraves
2470 Richie Simon
2471 Douglas Royalty

1987 ProCards Bakersfield Dodgers

(Los Angeles Dodgers, A)

	MT	NR MT	EX
Complete Set:	16.00	12.00	6.50

1406 Mike Hartley
1407 Dan Montgomery
1408 Macario Gastelum
1409 Miguel Mota
1410 Juan Guzman
1411 Billy Brooks
1412 Juan Bell
1413 Todd Kroll
1414 John Stein
1415 Luis Lopez
1416 Jim Kating
1417 Mike White
1418 Doug Cox
1419 Stan Johnston
1420 Kevin Kennedy
1421 Mark Sheehy
1422 Rod Roche
1423 Ted Holcomb
1424 Eric Managham
1425 Fred Farwell
1426 Dave Hansen
1427 Tim Anderson
1428 Wayne Kirby
1429 Paul Moralez
1430 Carlos Hernandez
1431 Mike Siler
1432 Mike Munoz
1433 Mike Pitz
1434 Willie Pinelli

1987 Team Bellingham Mariners

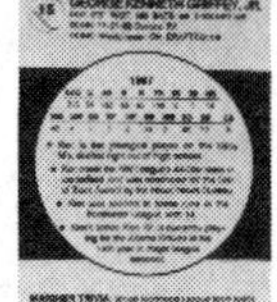

(Seattle Mariners, A)

	MT	NR MT	EX
Complete Set:	50.00	37.00	20.00

1 Jeffrey Hooper
2 Erick Bryant
3 Brian Wilkerson
4 Dorian Daughtry
5 Kevin Reichardt
6 Keith Helton
7 John Hoffman
8 Victor Manguel

9 Chuck Carr
10 Tom Peters
11 Todd Haney
12 Joe Georger
13 Jeff Morrison
14 Wade Taylor
15 Ken Griffey, Jr.
16 Spyder Webb
17 Otis Patrick
18 Mike Goff
19 Brian Baldwin
20 Tony Cayson
21 Mike Sisco
22 Mike McGuire
23 Ruben Gonzalez
24 Rick Sweet
25 Daryl Burrus
26 Scott Stoerck
27 Fausto Ramirez
28 Salty Parker
29 Steve Bieksha
30 Paul Togneri
31 Corey Paul
32 Batboys
33 Team Photo
---- Marty Reese
---- Team Logo Card

1987 ProCards Beloit Brewers

(Milwaukee Brewers, A)

	MT	NR MT	EX
Complete Set:	12.00	9.00	4.75

1266 Randy Veres
1267 Greg Vaughn
1268 John Jaha
1269 Shon Ashley
1270 Steve Monson
1271 Steve Kostichka
1272 Jamie Cangemi
1273 Robert Jones
1274 Brian Stone
1275 Brian Drahman
1276 Jim Rowe
1277 Doug Henry
1278 Rusty McGinnis
1279 Lance Lincoln
1280 Terry Brown
1281 Ron Harrison
1282 Tim Barker
1283 Gomer Hodge
1284 Dave Carley
1285 Hector Alberro
1286 Tim Watkins
1287 Ray Ojeda
1288 Dan Adriance
1289 Manny Chireno
1290 Dave Taylor
1291 Tim McIntosh

1987 Best Birmingham Barons

(Chicago White Sox, AA)

	MT	NR MT	EX
Complete Set:	7.50	5.75	3.00

1 Rico Petrocelli
2 Sam Hairston, Sr.
3 Moe Drabowsky
4 James Wesley (Jim) O'Dell
5 Marlin McPhail
6 Wil Caraballo
7 Rondal Rollin
8 Larry Acker
9 Jeff Bettendorf
10 Antonio G. (Tony) Menendez
11 Richard Kent (Rich) Gaynor
12 John Robert Boling
13 Adam Charles Peterson
14 Gardner C. (Grady) Hall
15 Donn Steven Pall
16 James Joseph (Jim) Hickey
17 John Pawlowski
18 John Graydon (Jack) Hardy
19 Rolando Pino
20 Kenton Craig (Kent) Torve
21 Darrell Ray Pruitt
22 Peter Paul Venturini
23 Manual Victor Salinas
24 James A. (Jim) Winters
25 Troy Gene Thomas
26 William Donald (Bill) Lindsey
27 Jorge Enrique Alcazar
28 Rick DeHart (trainer)

Values quoted in this guide reflect the retail price of a card – the price a collector can expect to pay when buying a card from a dealer. The wholesale price – that which a collector can expect to receive from a dealer when selling cards – will be significantly lower, depending on desirability and condition.

1987 Team Buffalo Bisons

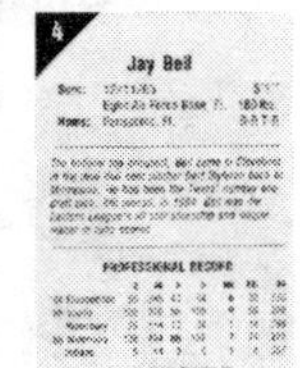

(Cleveland Indians, AAA) (co-sponsored by Pucko)

	MT	NR MT	EX
Complete Set:	10.00	7.50	4.00

1 Don Lovell
2 Kent Murphy
3 Andy Allanson
4 Jay Bell
5 Barry Brunkenkant
6 Dave Clark
7 Doug Frobel
8 Junior Noboa
9 Casey Parsons
10 Craig Smajstria
11 Ron Tingley
12 Randy Washington
13 Eddie Williams
14 Gibson Alba
15 John Farrell
16 Jeff Kaiser
17 Mike Murphy
18 Bryan Oelkers
19 Reggie Ritter
20 Scott Roberts
21 Jose Roman
22 Don Shulze
23 Frank Wills
24 Rod Allen
25 Orlando Gomez
26 Mike Bucci, Rick Peterson
27 Mike Billoni
28 Donald "Butcher" Palmer
29 John Murphy, Pete Weber

1987 ProCards Burlington Expos

(Montreal Expos, A)

	MT	NR MT	EX
Complete Set:	7.00	5.25	2.75

1067 Leonard Kelly
1068 James Vincent Olson
1069 Nels Jacobsen
1070 Tony Welborn
1071 Kent Bottenfield
1072 Sal Vaccaro
1073 Doug Duke
1074 Jeff Oller
1075 Mike Dull
1076 Jose Alou
1077 Steven St. Claire
1078 Ben Spitale
1079 Kevin Finigan
1080 Russ Schueler
1081 Delwyn Young
1082 Jeff Wedvick
1083 David Morrow
1084 Bobby Gaylor
1085 Mike Ishmael
1086 Mark Hardy
1087 Buzz Capra
1088 John Howes
1089 Bobby Pate
1090 J.R. Miner
1091 Sean Cunningham
1092 Dan Larson
1093 Mel Rojas
1094 Robin DeYoung
1095 Doug Vontz

1987 ProCards Calgary Cannons

(Seattle Mariners, AAA)

	MT	NR MT	EX
Complete Set:	7.00	5.25	2.75

2309 Edgar Martinez
2310 Mike Watters
2311 Jim Weaver
2312 Bill Plummer
2313 Ross Grimsley
2314 Dennis Powell
2315 Mike Brown
2316 Paul Schneider
2317 Dave Hengel
2318 Karl Best
2319 Mario Diaz
2320 Brick Smith
2321 Roy Thomas
2322 Mike Campbell
2323 Randy Braun
2324 Mike Wishnevski
2325 Terry Taylor
2326 Stan Clarke
2327 Donell Nixon
2328 Tony Ferreira
2329 Jerry Narron
2330 Dave Gallagher
2331 Doug Gwosdz
2332 Rich Monteleone

1987 ProCards Cedar Rapids Reds

(Cincinnati Reds, A)

	MT	NR MT	EX
Complete Set:	6.00	4.50	2.50

1010 Al Lobozzetta
1011 Phil Dale
1012 Scott Willis
1013 Curt Kindred
1014 Joe Lazor
1015 Joel Lono
1016 Scott Scudder
1017 Ron Mullins
1018 Mendy Espinal
1019 Keith Brown
1020 Dusty Rogers
1021 Joe Bruno
1022 Keith Lockhart
1023 Reggie Jefferson
1024 Greg Lonigro
1025 Don Wakamatsu
1026 Brian Robinson
1027 Cal Cain
1028 Mike Vincent
1029 Ted Wilborn
1030 John Stewart
1031 Don Brown
1032 Francisco Silverio
1033 Paul Kirsch
1034 Bernie Walker
1035 Rich Bombard
1036 Jim Knudtson
1037 Lamar (mascot)

1987 ProCards Charleston Rainbows

(San Diego Padres, A)

	MT	NR MT	EX
Complete Set:	7.50	5.75	3.00

1984 Brian Brooks
1985 Carlos Baerga
1986 Gregg S. Harris
1987 Michael J. King
1988 Gregory Hall
1989 William Taylor
1990 James P. Austin
1991 Brian Lee Harrison
1992 Gary Lance
1993 Mike Young
1994 James Navilliat
1995 Terry McDevitt
1996 Omar Olivares
1997 Matt Maysey
1998 Rafael Valdez
1999 Warren Newson
2000 Tony Torchia
2001 Jamie Norena
2002 Jimmy Tatum, Jr.
2003 Michael A. Basso
2004 Ricardo Bones
2005 Keith Harrison
2006 Doug Brocail

1987 ProCards Charleston Wheelers

(No Affiliation, A)

	MT	NR MT	EX
Complete Set:	6.00	4.50	2.50

2135 William Melvin
2136 James Hendrix
2137 Gilbert Villaueva
2138 Alan Wilson
2139 Steven Scarsone
2140 Peter Callas
2141 Rodney Brunelle
2142 Bob Gsellman
2143 Steven Mehl
2144 Gary Pifer
2145 Larry Allen
2146 John Knapp
2147 Danny Weems
2148 Hal Dyer
2149 Carl Grovom
2150 Kevin Main
2151 Timothy McMillian
2152 Robert Strickland
2153 J. Anthony LaPoint
2154 Jimmie Gardiver
2155 Steven O'Quinn
2156 Christopher Keshock
2157 L. Timothy Sossamon
2158 Jack Peel
2159 Norberto Martin
2160 Thomas Abrell
2161 Randall Robinson
2162 Doyle Balthazar

1987 Team Charlotte O's

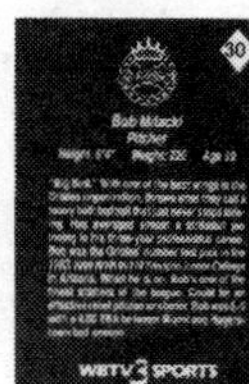

(Baltimore Orioles, AA)

	MT	NR MT	EX
Complete Set:	8.00	6.00	3.25

(1) Miguel Alicea
(2) Kurt Beamesderfer
(3) Greg Biagini
(4) Paul Cameron
(5) Sherwin Cijntje
(6) Matt Cimo
(7) Jim Daniel
(8) Tom Dodd
(9) Dave Falcone
(10) John Flinn
(11) Charlie Frederick
(12) Bob Hice
(13) Jerry Holtz
(14) John Hoover
(15) Paul Householder
(16) Joe Jarrell
(17) Ricky Jones
(18) Joe Kucharski
(19) Robert Long
(20) Terry Mauney
(21) Bob Milacki
(22) Francisco Javier Oliveras
(23) Mike Raczka
(24) Rico Rossy
(25) Chester Durwood Stanhope
(26) Pete Stanicek
(27) Jack Tackett
(28) Greg Talamantez
(29) Jeff Wood
(30) Crockett Park

1987 Best Chattanooga Lookouts

(Seattle Mariners, AA) A second identical set was also printed in a limited quantity of 1,000 with the cards featuring Coca-Cola emblems.

	MT	NR MT	EX
Complete Set:	7.50	5.75	3.00

1 Sal Rende
2 Dan Warthen
3 Gregory Bartley
4 James Parker
5 James Walker
6 Calvin Jones
7 James Bryant
8 Michael Schooler
9 Douglas Givler
10 Erik Hanson
11 Michael Christ
12 Kenneth Spratke
13 Robert Gunnarson
14 Roger Hansen
15 Bill McGuire
16 Eric Fox
17 Greg Briley
18 Gregory Fulton
19 Nesi Balelo
20 David Myers
21 Matthew Hall
22 John Gibbons
23 Brian David
24 William Mendek
25 Andre Robertson
26 Tom Hunt (trainer)

1987 ProCards Clearwater Phillies

(Philadelphia Phillies, A)

	MT	NR MT	EX
Complete Set:	6.00	4.50	2.50

1521 Rick Parker
1522 Brad Moore
1523 Curt Befort
1524 Chuck Malone
1525 Olen Parker
1526 Carlos Zayas
1527 Bobby Behnsch
1528 Jeff Kaye
1529 Harvey Brumfield
1530 Shawn Dantzier
1531 Ramon Caraballo
1532 Eric Boudreaux
1533 Garry Clark
1534 Warren Magec
1535 Carlos Arroyo
1536 Steve Sharts
1537 Gary White
1538 Gary Berman
1539 Rollie DeArmas
1540 Dave Brundage
1541 Julio Machado
1542 Juan Sanchez
1543 Brad Brink
1544 Allen Wisdom
1545 Bart Kaiser
1546 Todd Howey
1547 Travis Warren

1987 ProCards Clinton Giants

(San Francisco Giants, A)

	MT	NR MT	EX
Complete Set:	6.00	4.50	2.50

981 Doug Robertson
982 John Toal
983 Dave Patterson
984 Gregg Ritchie
985 Jim Anderson
986 Willie Mijares
987 Felipe Gonzales
988 Tod Ronson
989 Jim McNamara
990 John Rannow
991 Bill Carlson
992 Tom Ealy
993 Kevin Redick
994 Mark Leonard
995 Dee Dixon
996 Kim Flowers
997 Bill Evers
998 Todd Oakes
999 Jim Pena
1000 Brock Birch
1001 Paul McClellan
1002 Drew Ricker
1003 Sam Moore
1004 Daron Connelly
1005 Bob Richmond
1006 Ray Velasquaz
1007 Trevor Wilson
1008 Bryan Hickerson
1009 Team Photo

1987 ProCards Columbia Mets

(New York Mets, AA)

	MT	NR MT	EX
Complete Set:	7.00	5.25	2.75

1623 Barry Hightower
1624 Bob Apodaca
1625 Brandon Bailey
1626 Cliff Gonzalez
1627 David Lau
1628 Jaime Roseboro
1629 Rich Lundahl
1630 Adam Ging
1631 Johnny Monell
1632 Butch Hobson
1633 Steve Kennelley
1634 Rick Brown
1635 David Liddell
1636 Luis Natera
1637 Bobby Hernandez
1638 Victor Garcia
1639 Scott Henion
1640 Juan Marina
1641 Dan McMurtrie
1642 Mike Anderson
1643 Fritz Polka
1644 Rodney Murrell
1645 Tom Doyle
1646 Danny Naughton
1647 Rick Durant
1648 Julio Valera
1649 Rob Colescott
1650 Alex Jiminez
1651 Todd Welborn

1987 ProCards Columbus Astros

(Houston Astros, AA)

	MT	NR MT	EX
Complete Set:	8.00	6.00	3.25

841 Al Chambers
842 Jeff Datz
843 Fred Gladding
844 Troy Afenir
845 Jim Thomas
846 Mel Stottlemyre
847 Cameron Drew
848 Blaise Isley
849 Mitch Cook
850 Rob Parker
851 Jim Van Houten
852 John Fishel
853 Mark Baker
854 Karl Allaire
855 Joe Mikulik
856 Tom Wiedenbauer
857 Dody Rather
858 Jose Rodiles
859 Earl Cash
860 Jeff Livin
861 Larry Lasky
862 Rob Mallicoat
863 Rich Johnson
864 Norman Brock
865 Ken Caminiti

1987 ProCards Columbus Clippers

(New York Yankees, AAA)

	MT	NR MT	EX
Complete Set:	10.00	7.50	4.00

24 Bucky Dent
25 Clete Boye, Jerry McNertney, Kevin Rand, Ken Rowe, Champ Summers
26 Glenn Sherlock
27 Juan Espino
28 Mitch Lyden
29 Bobby Meacham
30 Pete Dalena
31 Orestes Destrade
32 Shane Turner
33 Bryan Little
34 Jeff Moronko
35 Phil Lombardi
36 Dick Scott
37 Roberto Kelly
38 Jay Buhner
39 Henry Cotto
40 Keith Hughes
41 Rich Bordi
42 Randy Graham
43 Alfonso Pulido
44 Mike Armstrong
45 Al Holland
46 Ron Romanick
47 Brad Arnsberg
48 Pete Filson
49 Al Leiter
50 Bill Fulton

1987 TCMA Columbus Clippers

(New York Yankees, AAA) (Withdrawn cards in this set are very scarce; they are generally not found in many sets)

	MT	NR MT	EX
Complete Set:	75.00	56.00	30.00

(1) Mike Armstrong
(2) Brad Arnsberg
(3) Rich Bordi
(4) Jay Buhner
(5) Pete Dalena
(6) Bucky Dent
(7) Oretes Destrade
(8) Juan Espino
(9) Pete Filson
(10) Bill Fulton
(11) Randy Graham
(12) Al Holland
(13) Keith Hughes
(14) Roberto Kelly
(15) Al Leiter
(16) Bryan Little
(17) Phil Lombardi
(18) Phil Lombardi (variation - withdrawn from set)
(19) Mitch Lyden
(20) Bobby Meacham
(21) Jeff Moronko (withdrawn from set)
(22) Pulido Alfonso
(23) Ron Romanick
(24) Glenn Sherlock
(25) George Sisler
(26) Shane Turner
(27) Coaches (Clete Boyer, John Summers, Jerry McNertney, Ken Rowe)

1987 Police/Fire Safety Columbus Clippers

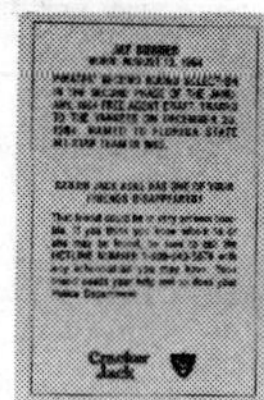

(New York Yankees, AAA)

	MT	NR MT	EX
Complete Set:	9.00	6.75	3.50

1 Brad Arnsberg
2 Rich Bordi
3 Pete Filson
4 Bill Fulton
5 Randy Graham
6 Al Holland
7 Alfonso Pulido
8 Ron Romanick
9 Bob Tewksbury
10 Juan Espino
11 Mitch Lyden
12 Pete Dalena
13 Orestes Destrade
14 Bryan Little
15 Phil Lombardi
16 Bobby Meacham
17 Jeff Moronko
18 Shane Turner
19 Jay Buhner
20 Henry Cotto
21 Keith Hughes
22 Roberto Kelly
23 Bucky Dent
24 Jerry McNertney, Kevin Rand, Ken Rowe, Champ Summers
25 Glenn Sherlock

1987 ProCards Daytona Beach Admirals

(Chicago White Sox, A)

	MT	NR MT	EX
Complete Set:	6.00	4.50	2.50

2283 Todd Trafton
2284 Carl Sullivan
2285 Eric Milholland
2286 Tom Drees
2287 Tony Blasucci
2288 Carlos de la Cruz
2289 Ken Reed
2290 Doug Little
2291 James Brennen
2292 Mark Henry
2293 Francisco Abreu
2294 Conde Cortez
2295 Patrick Coveny
2296 Matt Mercullo
2297 Wayne Edwards
2298 Chris Jefts
2299 Frank Potesto
2300 Billy Eveline
2301 Ed Sedar
2302 Chris Cota
2303 Gralyn Engram
2304 Jerry Bertolani
2305 Andy Nieto
2306 Dan Cronkright
2307 Mike Gellinger
2308 Glen McElroy

1987 ProCards Denver Zephyrs

(Milwaukee Brewers, AAA)

	MT	NR MT	EX
Complete Set:	7.50	5.75	3.00

212 David Clay
213 Tim Pyznarski
214 Al Price
215 Jay Aldrich
216 Joey Meyer
217 Brad Komminsk
218 Billy Bates
219 Ron Harrison
220 Paul Mirabella
221 Alex Madrid
222 Dave Schuler
223 Dave Klipstein
224 Terry Bevington
225 John Beuerlein
226 Dan Scarpetta
227 Jim Adduci
228 Don August
229 Steve Kiefer
230 Alan Cartwright
231 Mark Knudson
232 Jackson Todd
233 David Davidsmeier
234 Bryan Clutterbuck
235 Charlie O'Brien
236 Keith Smith
237 Al Jones
238 Steve Stanicek

1987 ProCards Dunedin Blue Jays

(Toronto Blue Jays, A)

	MT	NR MT	EX
Complete Set:	9.00	6.75	3.50

923 Carlos Diaz
924 Steve Cummings
925 Bob Watts
926 Mike Jones
927 Hugh Brinson
928 Bob Bailor
929 Dennis Holmberg
930 Dana Johnson
931 Darren Baisley
932 Steve Mumaw
933 Daryl Landrum
934 Tony Castillo
935 Steve Mingori
936 Ric Moreno
937 Webster Garrison
938 Hector de la Cruz
939 Chris Jones
940 Ray Young
941 Kevin Batiste
942 Greg David
943 Shawn Jeter
944 Willie Blair
945 Domingo Martinez
946 Earl Sanders
947 Jerry Schunk
948 Pedro Munoz
949 Ken Rivers
950 Derek Ware
951 Pat Saitta

1987 ProCards Durham Bulls

(Atlanta Braves, A)

	MT	NR MT	EX
Complete Set:	7.00	5.25	2.75

1652 Cesar Jimenez
1653 Barry Jones
1654 Jeff Weiss
1655 Bob Pfaff
1656 Sid Akins
1657 Brian G. Smitker
1658 Tim Criswell
1659 Johnny Cuevas
1660 Gary Newsom
1661 Ellis Roby
1662 Dave Miller
1663 Kent Mercker
1664 John Stewart
1665 Alex Smith
1666 Bill Slack
1667 Eddie Matthews (Mathews)
1668 Mike Merrill
1669 Rick Siebert
1670 Gary Eave
1671 Rick Morris
1672 Juan Fredymond
1673 Jeff Greene
1674 D.J. Jones
1675 Jim Salisbury
1676 John Alva
1677 Mark Lemke
1678 Dennis Hood
1679 Dodd Johnson

1987 ProCards Edmonton Trappers

(California Angels, AAA)

	MT	NR MT	EX
Complete Set:	6.00	4.50	2.50

2061 Jim Eppard
2062 Jack Lazorko
2063 David Heath
2064 Bobby Misick
2065 Dave Shippanoff (Shipanoff)
2066 Michael Ramsey
2067 Doug Banning
2068 Kevin King
2069 Allen Morelock
2070 Tack Wilson
2071 Ed Amelung
2072 Tom Kotchman

2073 Pete Coachman
2074 Bill Merrifield
2075 Richard Zaleski
2076 James Randall
2077 Frank Reberger
2078 Sherman Corbett
2079 Norm Carrasco
2080 Tony Fossas
2081 T.R. Bryden
2082 Terry Clark
2083 Jack Fimple

1987 Team Elmira Pioneers - Black

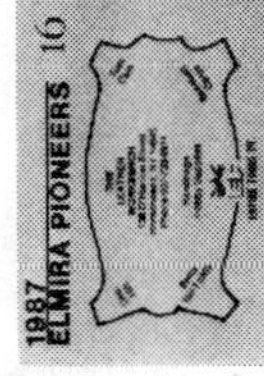

(Boston Red Sox, A)

	MT	NR MT	EX
Complete Set:	6.00	4.50	2.50

1 Clyde Smoll (president/general manager)
2 Bill Limoncelli (manager)
3 Dave Sullivan (assistant general manager)
4 Miguel Monegro
5 Larry Scanneli
6 Kendrick Bourne
7 Robert Echevarria
8 Julio Rosario
9 Brian Warfel
10 Terry Marrs
11 Sam Melton
12 Scott Powers
13 Al Thornton
14 Luis Dorante
15 Mike Kelly
16 Vincent Degifico
17 Tony Mosley
18 Craig Wilson
19 Steve Michael
20 Thom Sepela
21 Tony Romero
22 Johnny Diaz
23 Greg McCollum
24 Edward Banasiak
25 Joaquin Tejeda
26 Jose Pemberton
27 Ronnie Richardson
28 Bernie Stento
29 Al Bumbry (instructor)
30 Felix Maldonado (instructor)
31 Frank Malzone (instructor)
32 Eddie Popowski (instructor)
33 Charlie Wagner (instructor)
34 Paul Brown

1987 Team Elmira Pioneers - Red

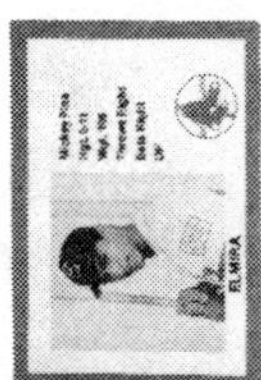

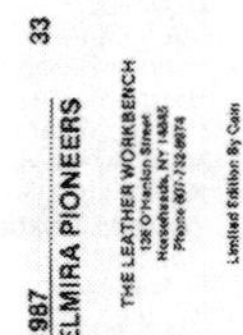

(Boston Red Sox, A)

	MT	NR MT	EX
Complete Set:	45.00	34.00	18.00

1 Clyde Smoll
2 Bill Limoncelli
3 Dave Sullivan
4 Miguel Monegro
5 Larry Scanneli
6 Kendrick Bourne
7 Robert Echevarria
8 Julio Rosario
9 Brian Warfel
10 Terry Marrs
11 Sam Melton
12 Scott Powers
13 Al Thornton
14 Luis Dorante
15 Mike Kelly
16 Vincent Degifico
17 Tony Mosley
18 Craig Wilson
19 Steve Michael
20 Thom Sepela
21 Tony Romero
22 Johnny Diaz
23 Greg McCollum
24 Edward Banasiak
25 Joaquin Tejada
26 Jose Pemberton
27 Ronnie Richardson
28 Bernie Stento
29 Al Bumbry
30 Reggie Harris
31 Bob Zupcic
32 Mike Dillard
33 Mickey Pine
34 Phillip Plantier
35 Checklist
36 Checklist

1987 ProCards El Paso Diablos

(Milwaukee Brewers, AA)

	MT	NR MT	EX
Complete Set:	6.00	5.25	2.75

1548 Lavell Freeman
1549 Joseph Mitchell
1550 Donald Scott
1551 Peter Kendrick
1552 Garrett Nago
1553 Robert DeWolf
1554 Eric Hardgrave
1555 Frank Mattox
1556 Pete Kolb
1557 Jamie Brisco
1558 Mark Ambrose
1559 John Miglio
1560 Tim Casey
1561 Duffy Dyer
1562 Jesus Alfaro
1563 Derek Diaz
1564 Todd Brown
1565 Cameron Walker
1566 Walter Pohle
1567 Paul Lindblad
1568 Darryel Walters
1569 Daniel Murphy, Jr.
1570 Jeffrey Peterek
1571 Alan Sadler
1572 Ramon Serna
1573 Michael Gobbo
1574 Barry Bass

1987 ProCards Erie Cardinals

(St. Louis Cardinals, A)

	MT	NR MT	EX
Complete Set:	6.00	4.50	2.50

2566 Rick Christian
2567 Opie Moran
2568 Joe Rigoli
2569 Reed Olmstead
2570 Ron Leon
2571 Steve Jeffers
2572 Eddie Carter
2573 Steve Jongewaard
2574 Ernie Radcliffe
2575 Roberto Marte
2576 Gregg Smith
2577 Antron Grier
2578 Keith Bennett
2579 Tim Meamber
2580 Scott Broadfoot
2581 Tony Russo
2582 Mike Evans
2583 Orlando Thomas
2584 Brad Harvick
2585 Kevin Robinson
2586 Dave Payton
2587 Scott Halama
2588 Jerry Daniels
2589 Chris Houser
2590 Darren Nelson
2591 Jeremy Hernandez
2592 Pat Moore
2593 Mike Hinkle
2594 Tim Redman

1987 ProCards Eugene Emeralds

(Kansas City Royals, A)

	MT	NR MT	EX
Complete Set:	11.00	8.25	4.50

2648 Darryl Robinson
2649 Antoine Pickett
2650 Doug Hupke
2651 Erv Houston
2652 Stu Cole
2653 Bob Moore
2654 James Campbell
2655 Archie Smith
2656 Doug Bock
2657 Doug Nelson
2658 Ben Pierce
2659 Keith Shibata
2660 Pete Alborano
2661 Brian McCormack
2662 Trey Gainous
2663 Derek Sholl
2664 Darren Watkins
2665 Bud Adams
2666 Luis Mallea
2667 Tony Clements
2668 Jorge Pedre
2669 Juan Berrios
2670 Montie Phillips
2671 Jim Hudson
2672 Kevin Appier
2673 Tom Gordon
2674 Terry Shumpert
2675 Don Wright
2676 Kevin Pickens
2677 Dennis Studeman

1987 Cramer Everett Giants

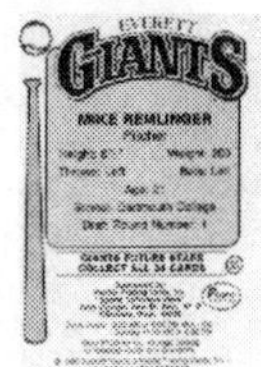

(San Francisco Giants, A)

	MT	NR MT	EX
Complete Set:	6.00	4.50	2.50

1 Matt Walker
2 Gilbert Heredia
3 Scott Goins
4 Anthony Piazza
5 Lonnie Phillips
6 Richard Aldrete
7 Andy Rohn
8 Kip Southland
9 Jamie Cooper
10 Glenn Abraham
11 Randy Lind
12 Joe Strain
13 Eric Gunderson
14 Chris Kocman
15 Tony Michalak
16 Tom Hostetler
17 Michael Ham
18 Todd Hawkins
19 Jimmy Terrill
20 Shaun MacKenzie
21 Jim Massey
22 Rob Wilson
23 Donn Perno
24 Gary Geiger
25 Bill Bluhm
26 Jeff Morris
27 Brad Comstock
28 Dickens Benoit
29 Brad Gambee
30 Mark Owens
31 Mike Remlinger
32 Mark Dewey
33 Bruce Graham
34 Checklist

1987 ProCards Fayetteville Generals

(Detroit Tigers, A)

	MT	NR MT	EX
Complete Set:	8.00	6.00	3.25

1292 Hector Berrios
1293 Jose Ramos
1294 Dan O'Neill
1295 Steve Parascand
1296 Basilio Cabrera
1297 Ramon Solano
1298 Zach Doster
1299 Milt Cuyler
1300 Wade Phillips
1301 Darryl Martin
1302 Scott Aldred
1303 Manny Mantrana
1304 Darren Hursey
1305 Carlos Rivera
1306 Allen Liebert
1307 Paul Foster
1308 John Lipon
1309 Juan Lopez
1310 Arnie Beyeler
1311 Marcos Gonzalez
1312 Liliano Castro
1313 Luis Melendez
1314 Phil Clark
1315 Ron Rightnowar
1316 Ken Williams
1317 Rob Friesen
1318 Glenn Belcher

1987 ProCards Ft. Lauderdale Yankees

(New York Yankees, A)

	MT	NR MT	EX
Complete Set:	12.00	9.00	4.75

669 Jose Laboy
680 Tim Becker
681 Marty Bystrom
682 Steve Frey
683 Troy Evers
684 Chris Carroll
685 Bob Green
686 Scott Shaw
687 Mike Christopher
688 Dana Ridenour
689 Andy Stankiewicz
690 George Berube
691 Max Ward
692 Dan Arendas
693 Paul Lassard
694 Ron Rub
695 Bill Voeltz
696 Scott Gay
697 Rich Scheid
698 Kevin Mass
700 Bernie Williams
701 Steve Adkins
702 John Johnson
703 Jim Leyritz
704 Jeff Hellman
705 Mel Rosario
706 Mark Manering
707 Steve Brow
708 Fred Carter
709 Ken Patterson

1987 ProCards Fort Myers Royals

(Kansas City Royals, A)

	MT	NR MT	EX
Complete Set:	12.00	9.00	4.75

2220 Bill Mulligan
2221 Stan Boroski
2222 Gary Blouin
2223 Mike Trapp
2224 David Tinkle
2225 Greg Hibbard
2226 Sean Berry
2227 Boo Champagne
2228 Andy Naworski
2229 Tim Odom
2230 Jesus DeLeon
2231 Mark Schulte
2232 Dennis Studeman
2233 Gus Jones
2234 Charles Culberson
2235 Vasquez Aquedo
2236 Tim Goff
2237 Rufus Ellis
2238 Tom Johnson
2239 Ricky Rojas
2240 Terry Jones
2241 Luis Corcino
2242 Randy Goodenough
2243 Kevin Koslofski
2244 Tom Gordon
2245 Brian McRae
2246 Kyle Reese
2247 Ken Kravec
2248 Jerry Terrell
2249 Angel Morris
2250 Mark Farnsworth
2251 David Howard
2252 Jacob Brumfield
2253 Ron Johnson

1987 ProCards Gastonia Rangers

(Texas Rangers, A)

	MT	NR MT	EX
Complete Set:	45.00	34.00	18.00

1761 Felipe Castillo
1762 Glenn Patterson
1763 Aurelio Cadania
1764 Juan Gonzalez
1765 Bob Gross
1766 Saul M. Barretto
1767 Phil Bryant
1768 Dean Palmer
1769 Rivert (Ortiz) Lino
1770 Allen Gerhardt
1771 Bob Malloy
1772 Gus Meizosa
1773 Raphael Cruz
1774 Ed Soto

1775 Roger Pavlik
1776 Paul Postier
1777 Ross Jones
1778 Wayne Rosenthal
1779 Michael Scanlin
1780 Ronald Jackson
1781 James McCutcheon
1782 Darrin Garner
1783 Richard Ramirez
1784 Art Gardner
1785 Jose Velez
1786 Darrell Whitaker
1787 John Burgos
1788 Francisco Sanchez
1789 Samuel Sosa

1987 ProCards Geneva Cubs

(Chicago Cubs, A)

	MT	NR MT	EX
Complete Set:	6.00	4.50	2.50

2622 Mike Aspray
2623 Brett Robinson
2624 Mark North
2625 Tom Spencer
2626 Steve Melendez
2627 Ken Reynolds
2628 Rick Wilkins
2629 Herberto Andrade
2630 Ray Mullino
2631 Fernando Ramsey
2632 Derrick Moore
2633 Mike Boswell
2634 Marty Rivero
2635 Mike Reeder
2636 Gabby Rodriguez
2637 Bill Melvin
2638 Henry Gomez
2639 Ed Caballero
2640 Jeff Massicotte
2641 Simeon Mejias
2642 Kevin Main
2643 Phil Mannion
2644 Eddie Williams
2645 Vaughn Williams
2646 Glenn Sullivan
2647 Steve Owens

1987 ProCards Glens Falls Tigers

(Detroit Tigers, AA)

	MT	NR MT	EX
Complete Set:	8.00	6.00	3.25

349 Ruben Guzman
350 Chris Hoiles
351 Tom Burgess
352 Jeff Jones
353 Wes Clements
354 Kevin Ritz
355 Steve McInerney
356 Bill Cooper
357 Tim Leiper
358 Doug Strange
359 Ron Marigny
360 Jeff Agar
361 Matt Sferrazza
362 Benny Ruiz
363 Mark Lee
364 Rod Poissant
365 Chris Morgan
366 Jeff Hermann
367 Paul Felix
368 Ramon Pena
369 Pedro Chavez
370 Dan DiMascio
371 John Duffy
372 John Smoltz
373 Chip McHugh

1987 ProCards Greensboro Hornets

(Boston Red Sox, A)

	MT	NR MT	EX
Complete Set:	9.00	6.75	3.50

1704 Tom Kane
1705 Curt Schilling
1706 Dick Berardino
1707 Pete Youngman
1708 Mike Carista
1709 Ken Ryan
1710 Chuck Wacha
1711 John Roberts
1712 Scott Summers
1713 Scott Cooper
1714 Joe Marchese
1715 Juan Paris
1716 Juan Molero
1717 Tony Hill
1718 Gilberto Martinez
1719 Tim McGee
1720 Ray Hansen
1721 Alex Flores
1722 Victor Rosario
1723 Dan Hale
1724 Mike Baker
1725 Jim Morrison
1726 Lem Pilkinton
1727 John Sanderski
1728 Chris Gaeckle
1729 David Walters

1987 Best Greenville Braves

(Atlanta Braves, AA)

	MT	NR MT	EX
Complete Set:	40.00	30.00	16.00

1 James Beauchamp
2 Leo D. Mazzone
3 Roland T. Jackson
4 Randy Ingle
5 Carlos Rafael Rios
6 Ronald Nipper
7 Andrew Denson
8 Adrian Charles Wills
9 David Justice
10 Todd Alan Dewey
11 Willie John Childress
12 Edgar Yost
13 Ronald Edwin Gant
14 John Steven Kilner
15 Brian Keith Aviles
16 Bryan Pierce Farmer
17 Inocencio Guerrero
18 Maximo Del Rosario
19 Kevin Blankenship
20 Kevin Reese Coffman
21 Jeffrey Wetherby
22 Larry Wayne Heise
23 Ira Thomas Greene
24 Peter John Smith
25 Johnny Hatcher
26 Gregory Alan Tubbs
27 Kenneth Joe Kinnard
28 Michael William Scott

1987 ProCards Hagerstown Suns

(Baltimore Orioles, A)

	MT	NR MT	EX
Complete Set:	7.00	5.25	2.75

1465 Mike Borgatti
1466 Paul McNeal
1467 Will George
1468 Brian Dubois
1469 Leo Gomez
1470 Benny Bautista
1471 Gerry Lomastro
1472 Craig Strobel
1473 Randy Struek
1474 Tim Dulin
1475 Glenn Gulliver
1476 Blaine Beatty
1477 John Posey
1478 Louie Paulino
1479 Steve Bowden
1480 Wayne Wilson
1481 Pete Palermo
1482 Rick Carriger
1483 Tim Richardson
1484 Kevin Burke
1485 Frank Bellino
1486 Rafael Skeetl
1487 Paul Thorpe
1488 Mel Mallinak
1489 Gordon Dillard
1490 Scott Khoury
1491 Ernie Young
1492 Geraldo Sanchez
1493 Doug Cinnella

1987 ProCards Harrisburg Senators

(Pittsburgh Pirates, AA)

	MT	NR MT	EX
Complete Set:	7.00	5.25	2.75

374 Shawn Holman
375 Dave Trembley
376 Tom Prince
377 David Rooker
378 Jose Melendez
379 Felix Fermin
380 Phillip Wellman
381 Craig Brown
382 Scott Neal
383 Jeff Cook
384 Lance Belen
385 Rob Russell
386 Kyle Todd
387 Orlando Lind
388 Don Williams
389 Dave Douglas
390 Brian Jones
391 Brett Gideon
392 Tommy Gregg
393 Jim Neidlinger
394 Gino Gentile
395 Dimas Gutierrez
396 Mike Walker
397 Rich Sauveur
398 Chris Ritter
399 Ben Abner

1987 ProCards Hawaii Islanders

(Chicago White Sox, AAA)

	MT	NR MT	EX
Complete Set:	7.00	5.25	2.75

185 Mike Yastrzemski
186 Ken Williams
187 Jack Hardy
188 David White
189 Derek Tatsuno
190 Ralph Citarella
191 Tom Forrester
192 Brian Giles
193 Tommy Thompson
194 Don Rowe
195 Jim Rasmussen
196 Mike Taylor
197 Dave Cochrane
198 Tim Scott
199 Scott Nielson
200 Bill Long
201 Ray Krawczyk
202 Kevin Hickey
203 Joey McLaughlin
204 Kala Kaaihue
205 Carlos Martinez
206 Russ Norman
207 Tim Krauss
208 Randy Gomez
209 Greg Latta
210 Bob Bailey
211 Pat Keedy

1987 Team Huntsville Stars

(Oakland A's, AA)

	MT	NR MT	EX
Complete Set:	10.00	7.50	4.00

1 Roy Anderson
2 Larry Arndt
3 Tim Birtsas
4 Lance Blankenship
5 Tyler Brilinski
6 Todd Burns
7 Jim Corsi
8 Brian Criswell
9 Pat Dietrick
10 Darrin Duffy
11 Brad Fischer
12 Scott Hemond
13 Steve Howard
14 Mark Howie
15 Jimmy Jones
16 Felix Jose
17 Russ Kibler
18 Joe Kramer
19 Reese Lambert
20 Doug Scherer
21 Jeff Shaver
22 Jose Tolentino
23 Walt Weiss
24 Wally Whitehurst
25 Joe Xavier

1987 ProCards Idaho Falls Braves

(Atlanta Braves, A)

	MT	NR MT	EX
Complete Set:	6.00	4.50	2.50

2595 Mike Wilson
2596 Anthony Ferrebee
2597 Phillip Maldonado
2598 Mark Martin
2599 Jeff Allison
2600 Richard Duke
2601 Chuck Lavrusky
2602 Kevin McNees
2603 Rod Gilbreath
2604 Teddy Williams
2605 Walter Hawkins
2606 Chris Bryant
2607 A.J. Waznik
2608 Mike Lomeli
2609 Gregg Gilbert
2610 Jim Procopio
2611 Bill Wright
2612 Herb Hippauf
2613 Matthew Williams
2614 Joe Koh
2615 Daerren Cox
2616 Steve Glass
2617 Frank Ramirez
2618 John Mitchell
2619 Jeff Dodig
2620 Pat Abbatiello
2621 Greg Ziegler

1987 Team Indianapolis Indians

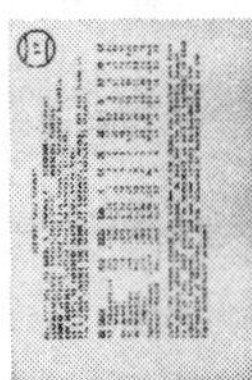

(Montreal Expos, AAA) (co-sponsored by Tom Aikens) All cards in this set have a Pepsi-Cola emblem on the front.

	MT	NR MT	EX
Complete Set:	8.00	6.00	3.25

1 Team Photo
2 It Was Magic
3 The Magic Continues
4 Joe Sparks (manager)
5 Jerry Manuel (coach)
6 Luis Pujols
7 Dave Tomlin
8 Razor Shines
9 Tim Barrett
10 Jack Daugherty
11 Ubaldo Heredia
12 Ron Shepherd
13 Curt Brown
14 Tom Romano
15 Jeff Fischer
16 Jeff Reynolds
17 Jeff Parrett
18 Billy Moore
19 Mark Gardner
20 Johnny Paredes
21 Sergio Valdez
22 Dallas Williams
23 Mike Smith
24 Kelly Faulk
25 Wilfredo Tejada
26 Pascual Perez
27 Luis Rivera
28 Scott Clemo
29 Nelson Norman
30 Mark Corey
31 Dennis Martinez
32 Tim McCormack (trainer)
33 Alonzo Powell
34 The Voices of the Indians (Tom Akins, Howard Kellman)
35 The Bat Boys (Kenny Akins, Sean Schnaiter, Mark Schumacher)
36 Bill Rowley (clubhouse man)

1987 ProCards International League All-Stars

	MT	NR MT	EX
Complete Set:	14.00	10.50	5.50

1 Jeff Moronko
2 Jay Buhner

3 Brad Arnsberg
4 Roberto Kelly
5 Randy Milligan
6 Kevin Elster
7 Sam Horn
8 Nelson Liriano
9 Ed Nottle
10 Don Gordo
11 Rey Palacios
12 Mark Carreon
13 Randy Velarde
14 Bruce Fields
15 Mike Henneman
16 Scott Lusader
17 Jim Walewander
18 Keith Miller
19 John Marzano
20 Todd Benzinger
21 Jody Reed
22 Tom Bolton
23 Orestes Destrade
24 Sylvester Campusano
25 Todd Sotttlemyre
26 Rob Ducey
27 Bill Ripken
28 Jeff Ballard
29 Pete Stanicek
30 Craig Worthington
31 Chris Padget
32 Tom Glavine
33 Jeff Blauser
34 Marty clary
35 David Griffin
36 Keith Miller
37 Travis Chambers
38 Al Leiter
39 Columbus Clippers Team
40 Tidewater Tides Team
41 Pawtucket Red Sox Team
42 Syracuse Chiefs Team
43 Toledo Mud Hens Team
44 Rochester Red Wings Team
45 Maine Guides Team

1987 Team Iowa Cubs

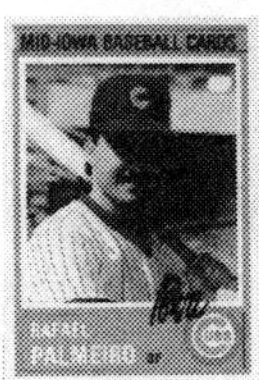

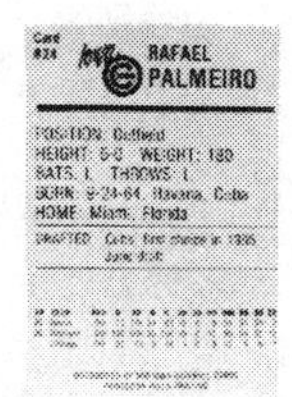

(Chicago Cubs, AA)

	MT	NR MT	EX
Complete Set:	30.00	22.00	12.00

1 Carl Hamilton
2 Drew Hall
3 Jackie Davidson
4 Mike Capel
5 Jay Baller
6 Doug Potestio
7 Gary Parmenter
8 tom Layton
9 Joe Kraemer
10 Dave Kopf
11 Paul Noce
12 Bruce Crabbe
13 Mike Brumley
14 Bill Hayes
15 Damon Berryhill
16 Pookie Bernstine
17 Julio Valdez
18 Phil Stephenson
19 Wade Rowdon
20 Luis Quinones
21 Dick Pole
22 Larry Cox
23 Gary Varsho
24 Rafael Palmeiro
25 Darrin Jackson

1987 Team Jackson Mets

(New York Mets, AA)

	MT	NR MT	EX
Complete Set:	11.00	8.25	4.50

1 Dan Winters
2 Jeff McKnight
3 Jose Bautista
4 Tucker Ashford
5 Tom McCarthy
6 Zoilo Sanchez
7 Shane Young
8 Kurt Lundgren
9 Jeff Gardner
10 Mike Hocutt
11 Mickey Weston
12 Al Carmichael
13 Sam McCrary
14 Ed Pruitt
15 Joaquin Contreras
16 Marcus Lawton
17 Johnny Wilson
18 Steve Phillips
19 Kyle Hartshorn
20 Glenn Abbott
21 Tom Burns
22 Alan Hayden
23 Dave West
24 Gregg Jefferies
25 Mike Santiago

1987 TCMA International League All-Stars

(AAA)

	MT	NR MT	EX
Complete Set:	13.00	9.75	5.25

1 Jeff Moronko
2 Jay Buhner
3 Brad Arnsberg
4 Roberto Kelly
5 Randy Milligan
6 Kevin Elster
7 Sam Horn
8 Nelson Liriano
9 Ed Nottle
10 Don Gordon
11 Rey Palacios
12 Mark Carreon
13 Randy Velarde
14 Bruce Fields
15 Mike Henneman
16 Scott Lusader
17 Jim Walewander
18 Keith Miller
19 John Marzano
20 Todd Benzinger
21 Jody Reed
22 Tom Bolton
23 Orestes Destrade
24 Sylvester Campusano
25 Todd Stottlemyre
26 Rob Ducey
27 Bill Ripken
28 Jeff Ballard
29 Pete Stanicek
30 Craig Worthington
31 Chris Padget
32 Tom Glavine
33 Jeff Blauser
34 Marty Clary
35 David Griffin
36 Keith Miller
37 Travis Chambers
38 Al Leiter
39 Columbus Clippers Team
40 Tidewater Tides Team
41 Pawtucket Red Sox Team
42 Syracuse Chiefs Team
43 Toledo Mud Hens Team
44 Rochester Red Wings Team
45 Maine Guides Team

1987 ProCards Jacksonville Expos

(Montreal Expos, AA)

	MT	NR MT	EX
Complete Set:	10.00	7.50	4.00

429 Larry Walker
430 Tim Arnold
431 Norm Santiago
432 Pete Camelo
433 Nelson Santovenia
434 Mike Berger
435 Andy Lawrence
436 Scott Mann
437 Edgar Caceres
438 Gary Weinberger
439 Esteban Beltre
440 Armando Moreno
441 James Opie
442 Mike Shade
443 Dave Graybill
444 Mike Payne
445 Bill Cunningham
446 Bob Devlin
447 Bob Sudo
448 Kevin Price
449 John Trautwein
450 Gary Wayne
451 Randy Johnson
452 Brian Holman
453 Tommy Thompson
454 Joe Kerrigan
455 Mike Quade
456 Jim Kahmann
457 Team Photo

1987 ProCards Jamestown Expos

(Montreal Expos, A)

	MT	NR MT	EX
Complete Set:	7.00	5.25	2.75

2538 Russ Martin
2539 Angelo Cianfrocco
2540 Michael Ishmael
2541 Scott McHugh
2542 Not Issued
2543 Jesus Paredes
2544 F. Boi Rodriguez
2545 Joe B. Sims
2546 Larry Doss
2547 Terrel E. Hansen
2548 Jorge Mitchell
2549 Kelvin Shephard
2550 Troy Landon Ricker
2551 John Vander Wal
2552 Corey Viltz
2553 Gene Glynn
2554 Brian Braden
2555 Bob Natal
2556 Scott Ayers
2557 Mario Brito
2558 Bob Kerrigan
2559 Gilles Bergeron
2560 Danilo Leon
2561 Howard Earl Farmer
2562 Matt Shiflett
2563 Kevin Cavalier
2564 Jeff Carter
2565 Chris Marchok
2678 Q.V. Lowe
2679 Jeff Wedrick

1987 ProCards Kenosha Twins

(Minnesota Twins, A)

	MT	NR MT	EX
Complete Set:	7.50	5.75	3.00

1155 Jim Davins
1156 Robert Hernandez
1157 Michael Randle
1158 Kendall Snyder
1159 Edgar Naveda
1160 Rafael DeLima
1161 Buddy Buzzard
1162 Burt Beattie
1163 Rusty Kryzanowski
1164 Michael Lexa
1165 Mike Dyer
1166 David Jacas
1167 Robert Tinkey
1168 Jarvis Brown
1169 Dana Heinle
1170 Dwight Bernard
1171 Jeff Satzinger
1172 Carl Thomas
1173 Derek Parks
1174 Lenny Webster
1175 Scott Leius
1176 Chris Forgione
1177 Elvis Romero
1178 Paul Abbott
1179 Miguel Murphy
1180 German Gonzalez
1181 Don Leppert
1182 John Skelton
1183 Enrique Rios

1987 ProCards Kinston Indians

(Cleveland Indians, A)

	MT	NR MT	EX
Complete Set:	6.00	4.50	2.50

1680 Bill Shamblin
1681 Kevin Wickander
1682 Mark Gilles
1683 Charles Soos
1684 Scott Buss
1685 Phillip Dillmore
1686 Lewis Kent
1687 Jim Grossman
1688 Michael Poehl
1689 Fritz Fedor
1690 Brian Graham
1691 Scott Jordan
1692 Casey Webster
1693 Michael Workman
1694 Michael Farr
1695 Andrew Ghelfi
1696 James Bruske
1697 Robert Swain
1698 Trey Hillman
1699 Doyle Wilson
1700 Thomas Hinzo
1701 Milton Harper
1702 Kerry Richardson
1703 Rodney Nichols

1987 ProCards Knoxville Blue Jays

(Toronto Blue Jays, AA)

	MT	NR MT	EX
Complete Set:	7.00	5.25	2.75

1494 Jose Mesa
1495 Chris Shaddy
1496 Mike Yearout
1497 Omar Malave
1498 Aurelio Monteagudo
1499 Rocky Coyle
1500 Troy Chestnut
1501 Tim Englund
1502 Luis Reyna
1503 Kevin Silwinski
1504 Todd Provence
1505 Eric Yelding
1506 Keith Gilliam
1507 Omar Bencomo
1508 Geronimo Berroa
1509 Bernie Tatis
1510 Enrique Burgos
1511 Oswald Peraza
1512 Dave Walsh
1513 Pat Borders
1514 Jeff Hearron
1515 Randy Holland
1516 Glenn Ezell
1517 Kevin Kierst
1518 Norm Tomucci
1519 J.J. Cannon
1520 Cliff Young

1987 ProCards Lakeland Tigers

(Detroit Tigers, A)

	MT	NR MT	EX
Complete Set:	6.00	4.50	2.50

2333 Wayne Housie
2334 Keith Nicholson
2335 Craig Mills
2336 Rich Wieligman
2337 Scott Schultz
2338 Donnie Rowland
2339 Kevin Bradshaw
2340 Doyle Balthazar
2341 Ron Marigny
2342 Bernie Anderson
2343 Terry Smith
2344 Rocky Cusack
2345 Richard Carter
2346 Rich Lacko
2347 Wade Phillips
2348 Mike Hansen
2349 Mark Lee
2350 Pat Austin
2351 Bob Thomson
2352 Mark Pottinger
2353 Robinson Garces
2354 Blane Fox
2355 Dave Cooper
2356 Adam Dempsay
2357 Paul Wenson
2358 Ken Gohmann

1987 ProCards Las Vegas Stars

(San Diego Padres, AAA)

	MT	NR MT	EX
Complete Set:	7.00	5.25	2.75

106 Joe Bitker
107 Shawn Abner
108 Jack Kroll
109 Joe Lansford
110 Scott Parsons
111 Sonny Seibert
112 Randy Asadoor
113 Kevin John Buckley
114 Rusty Ford
115 Mark Poston
116 Todd Simmons
117 Ray Hayward
118 Todd Hutcheson
119 Randell Byers
120 Brian Snyder
121 Bill Blount
122 Jimmy Jones
123 Shane Mack
124 Edwin Rodriguez
125 Steve Garcia
126 Craig Wiley
127 Gary Green
128 Leon Roberts

129 Ed Vosberg
130 James Siwy
131 Rob Piccolo
132 Mark Wasinger

1987 ProCards Little Falls Mets

(New York Mets, A)

	MT	NR MT	EX
Complete Set:	7.50	5.75	3.00

2382 Terry Bross
2383 Pat Disabato
2384 Terry Griffin
2385 Eric Hillman
2386 Lorin Jundy
2387 Steve LaRose
2388 Jim McAnarney
2389 Mike Miller
2390 Steve Newton
2391 Jeff Smith
2392 Dave Trautwein
2393 Butch Wallen
2394 Anthony Young
2395 Javier Gonzalez
2396 Todd Hundley
2397 Tim Bogar
2398 Ron Height
2399 Alex Jiminez (Jimenez)
2400 Dave Joiner
2401 Bob Olah
2402 Radhames Polanco
2403 Rob Lemle
2404 Terry McDaniel
2405 Danny Naughton
2406 Titi Roche
2407 Jim Tesmer
2409 Rich Miller
2410 Al Jackson
2411 Rick McWane

1987 Team Louisville Redbirds

(St. Louis Cardinals, AAA)

	MT	NR MT	EX
Complete Set:	9.00	6.75	3.50

1 Mike Jorgensen
2 Joe Pettini
3 Jack Ayer
4 Greg Bargar
5 Joe Boever
6 Rod Booker
7 Rich Buontatony
8 Jose Calderon
9 Paul Cherry
10 Rick Colbert
11 Mark Dougherty
12 Dan Driessen
13 Bill Earley
14 Dick Grapenthin
15 David Green
16 Lance Johnson
17 Tim Jones
18 Mickey Mahler
19 John A. Martin
20 John Morris
21 John Murphy
22 Tom Pagnozzi
23 Mike Laga
24 Bill Lyons
25 Joe Magrane
26 Victor Rodriguez
27 Ray Soff
28 Duane Walker
29 David "Hap" Hudson
30 Billy Johnson

1987 ProCards Lynchburg Mets

(New York Mets, A)

	MT	NR MT	EX
Complete Set:	6.00	4.50	2.50

2163 Craig Repoz
2164 Juan Villanueva
2165 Tom Wachs
2166 Chris Jelic
2167 Kip Gross
2168 Desi Brooks
2169 Eric Erickson
2170 Ron Gideon
2171 James Archibald
2172 Hector Perez
2173 Alan Hayden
2174 Felix Perdomo
2175 Jeff Ciszkowski
2176 Pete Bauer
2177 Chris Rauth
2178 Bill Stiles
2179 Geary Jones
2180 Dave Gelatt
2181 Rich Rodriguez
2182 Jim Bibby
2183 Scott Jaster
2184 John Tamargo
2185 Troy James
2186 Jeff Richardson
2187 Mark Brunswick
2188 Wilson Valera
2189 Scott Lawrenson
2190 Brian Givens

1987 ProCards Macon Pirates

(Pittsburgh Pirates, A)

	MT	NR MT	EX
Complete Set:	6.00	4.50	2.50

1184 Ernesto Santana
1185 Tracy Toy
1186 Joel Forrest
1187 Jeff Banister
1188 Tony Mealy
1189 John Love
1190 Mike York
1191 Tony Longmire
1192 Tim Vaughn
1193 Richard Reed
1194 Pete Murphy
1195 Blane Lockley
1196 Steve Adams
1197 Julio Perez
1198 Doug Ellis
1199 Julio Peguero
1200 Stan Belinda
1201 Damon Hansel
1202 Craig Heakins
1203 Ed Yacopino
1204 Glenn Trudo
1205 Scott Ruskin
1206 Tonny Cohen
1207 Dennis Rogers
1208 Dave Moharter

1987 ProCards Madison Muskies

(Oakland A's, A)

	MT	NR MT	EX
Complete Set:	7.00	5.25	2.75

488 Bert Bradley
489 David D. Schober
490 Scott Hemond
491 James Nettles
492 Vince Teixeira
493 Ozzie Canseco
494 Pat Gilbert
495 Luis Martinez
496 Doug Ortman
497 Jamie Reiser
498 Weston Weber
499 Gerry Barragan
500 Leland Maddox
501 Ken Jones
502 Camilo Veras
503 Mike Cupples
504 Jeffrey Glover
505 Jeff Kopyta
506 Kevin Kunkel
507 Mark Beavers
508 Jim Carroll
509 Blaine Deabenderfer, Jr.
510 Reese Lambert
511 Luis Salcedo
512 Bob Sharpnack

1987 T&J SC Madison Muskies

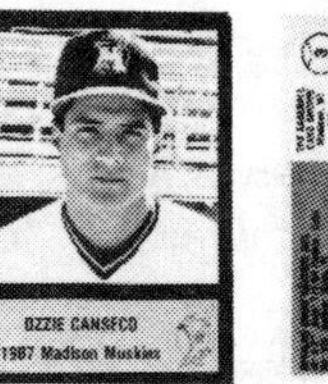

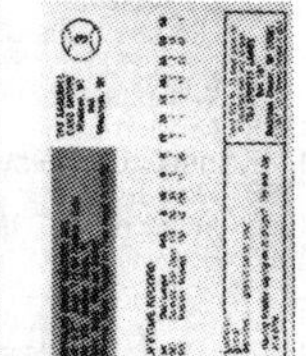

(Madison Muskies, A)

	MT	NR MT	EX
Complete Set:	13.00	9.75	5.25

1 Gerry Barragan
2 Mark Beavers
3 Ozzie Canseco
4 Jim Carroll
5 Mike Cupples
6 Blaine Deabenberfer
7 Pat Gilbert
8 Jeff Glover
9 Scott Hemond
10 Jeff Kopyta
11 Kevin Kunkel
12 Luis Martinez
13 Doug Ortman
14 Dave Otto
15 Jamie Reiser
16 Luis Salcedo
17 Bob Sharpnack
18 Bob Stocker
19 Vinnie Teixeira
20 Camilo Veras
21 Wes Weber
22 Jim Nettles
23 Dave Schober

1987 ProCards Maine Guides

(Philadelphia Phillies, AAA)

	MT	NR MT	EX
Complete Set:	7.50	5.75	3.00

1 Jim Olander
2 Doug Bair
3 Len Watts
4 Greg Legg
5 Fred Tolliver (Toliver)
6 Shawn Barton
7 Ken Jackson
8 Keith Miller
9 Greg Jelks
10 Barney Nugent
11 Jeff Stone
12 Marvin Freeman
13 Steve DeAngelis
14 Jeff Calhoun
15 Gib Seibert
16 Ken Dowell
17 Wally Ritchie
18 Joe Cipolloni
19 Travis Chambers
20 Tom Newell
21 Darren Loy
22 Alan LeBoeuf
23 Ron Jones

1987 TCMA Maine Guides

(Philadelphia Phillies, AAA) (Cards 26 & 27 were withdrawn; "Maine: was misspelled as "Main" on card fronts)

	MT	NR MT	EX
Complete Set:	8.50	6.50	3.50

1 Shawn Barton
2 Jeff Calhoun
3 Travis Chambers
4 Marvin Freeman
5 Mike Maddux
6 Tom Newell
7 Fred Toliver
8 Joe Cipolloni
9 Darren Loy
10 Ken Dowell
11 Ken Jackson
12 Greg Jelks
13 Alan LeBoeuf
14 Greg Legg
15 Keith Miller
16 Gib Seibert
17 Ron Jones
18 Jim Olander
19 Jeff Stone
20 Len Watts
21 Darren Daulton
22 Kevin Ward
23 Bill Dancy
24 Tim Corcoran
25 Mike Willis
26 Barney Nugent (withdrawn)
27 Mike Mixon (withdrawn)

1987 Best Memphis Chicks

(Kansas City Royals, AA)

	MT	NR MT	EX
Complete Set:	7.00	5.25	2.75

1 Bob Schaefer
2 Duane Gustavson
3 Rich Dubee
4 Jose Rivera
5 Julio Alcala
6 Mark Van Blaricom
7 Jim Bennett
8 Ken Crew
9 Jose DeJesus
10 Scott Stranski
11 Phil George
12 Theo Shaw
13 Mark Shiflett
14 Don Sparling
15 Mike Miller
16 Tim Lambert
17 Gene Morgan
18 Mike Loggins
19 Jere Longenecker
20 Mauro Gozza
21 Jim Eisenreich
22 Rick Luecken
23 Terry Bell
24 Matt Winters
25 Mike Fuentes
26 Jamie Nelson
27 Steve Morrow (trainer)

1987 ProCards Memphis Chicks

(Kansas City Royals, AA)

	MT	NR MT	EX
Complete Set:	7.50	5.75	3.00

625 Mike Fuentes
626 Phil George
627 Mauro Gozzo
628 Mike Loggins
629 Jose DeJesus
630 Mark Shiflett
631 Matt Winters
632 Jamie Nelson
633 Jere Longenecker
634 Bob Schafer
635 Rich Dubee
636 Mark Van Blaricom
637 Tim Lambert
638 Scott Stranski
639 Theo Shaw
640 Gene Morgan
641 Terry Bell
642 Rick Luecken
643 Don Sparling
644 Ken Crew
645 Duane Gustavson
646 Mike Miller
647 Jose Rivera
648 Julio Alcala
649 Jim Bennett
650 Steve Morrow
651 Jim Eisenreich

1987 ProCards Miami Marlins

(Baltimore Orioles, A)

	MT	NR MT	EX
Complete Set:	6.00	4.50	2.50

710 Kenny King
711 Jim Falzone
712 Stacey Burdick
713 Scott Evans
714 Tony Woods
715 Not Issued
716 Doug Carpenter
717 Rick Richardi
718 Tony Rohan
719 Bobby Latmore
720 Mickey Billmeyer
721 Masahito Watanabe
722 Shuji Inagaki
723 Scott Diez
724 Mike Browning
725 Frank Colston
726 Not Issued
727 Ken Adderly
728 Greg Daniels
729 John Harrington
730 Fred de la Mata
731 Hideharu Matsuo
732 Larry Mims
733 Tom Magrann
734 Toshimitsu Suetsugu
735 Luis Ojeda
---- Mamoru Sugiura

1987 ProCards Midland Angels

(California Angels, AA)

	MT	NR MT	EX
Complete Set:	7.50	5.75	3.00

595 Miguel Garcia
596 David Martinez
597 Bill Geivett
598 Chris Collins
599 Brian Brady

600 Doug Banning
601 Ty Van Burkleo
602 Vinicio Cedeno
603 Al Olson
604 Doug Davis
605 John Hotchkiss
606 Edwin Marquez
607 Joe Redfield
608 Damon Farmar
609 Max Oliveras
610 Doug Jennings
611 Stan Holmes
612 Chuck Hernandez
613 Toby Mack
614 Mitch Seoane
615 Mark Doran
616 Mike Romanovsky
617 Robbie Allen
618 Vance Lovelace
619 Brian Harvey
620 Steve McGuire
621 Marty Reed
622 Barry Dacus
623 Phil Venturino
624 Team Photo

1987 ProCards Modesto A's

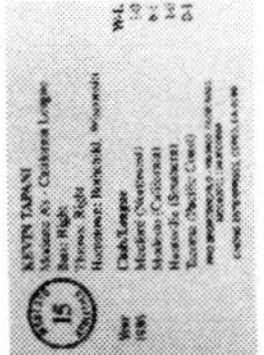

(Oakland A's, A)

	MT	NR MT	EX
Complete Set:	8.00	6.00	3.25

266 John Kent
267 William Savarino III
268 David Veres
269 Michael Duncan
270 Jerome Nelson
271 Michael Bordick
272 John Minch
273 Steve Gokey
274 Butch Hughes
275 Lance Blankenship
276 Robert Gould
277 Kevin Tapani
278 Chris Hayes
279 Bruce Walton
280 Steve Iannini
281 Kevin Williamson
282 Jerry Peguero
283 Bob Fingers
284 Joseph Law
285 Dann Howitt
286 Patrick Britt
287 John Cartelli
288 Tommie D. Reynolds
289 Scott Holcomb
290 Jim Corsi

1987 Chong Modesto A's

(Oakland A's, A)

	MT	NR MT	EX
Complete Set:	7.00	5.25	2.75

1 Mike Bordick
2 Pat Britt
3 Jim Corsi
4 David Gavin
5 Robert Gould
6 Scott Holcomb
7 Dann Howitt
8 Steve Iannini
9 Bo Kent
10 Joe Law
11 John Minch
12 Jerome Nelson
13 Jose Peguero
14 Bill Savarino
15 Kevin Tapini
16 David Veres
17 Bruce Walton
18 Kevin Williamson
19 Chris Hayes
20 Frank Masters
21 Jeff Whitney
22 Drew Stratton
23 Tommie Reynolds
24 Butch Huges
25 John Cartelli
26 Bob Fingers
27 Gary Gorski
28 The Pro Sportsworld Team
1 Tony LaRussa (Pro Sportsworld Special Edition card)
2 Joe Rudi (Pro Sportsworld Special Edition card)
3 Dave Duncan (Pro Sportsworld Special Edition card)
4 Dave Leiper (Pro Sportsworld Special Edition card)

1987 ProCards Myrtle Beach Blue Jays

(Toronto Blue Jays, A)

	MT	NR MT	EX
Complete Set:	15.00	11.00	6.00

1435 Julian Yan
1436 Oscar Escobar
1437 Jose Diaz
1438 Darren Hall
1439 Doug Linton
1440 Vince Horsman
1441 Barry Foote
1442 Mike Murray
1443 Leroy Stanton
1444 Patrick Hentgen
1445 Tom Quinlan
1446 Randy Knorr
1447 Dennis Jones
1448 Cesar Mejia
1449 Lindsay Foster
1450 Jim Tracy
1451 John Poloni
1452 John Shea
1453 Rocket Wheeler
1454 Wayne Davis
1455 Junior Felix
1456 Rich Depastino
1457 Victor Diaz
1458 Mark Whiten
1459 Joe Humphries
1460 Bob Guehther
1461 Andy Dziadkowiec
1462 Francisco Cabrera
1463 Luis Sojo
1464 Paul Rodgers

1987 Team Nashville Sounds

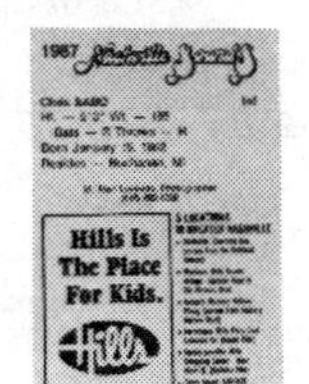

(Cincinnati Reds, AA) (Price includes the scarce Hill card)

	MT	NR MT	EX
Complete Set:	13.00	9.75	5.25

(1) Mark Berry
(2) Norm Charlton
(3) Bill Cutshall
(4) Rob Dibble
(5) Leo Garcia
(6) Wayne Garland
(7) Orlando Gonzalez
(8) Jeff Gray
(9) Lenny Harris
(10) Ron Henika
(11) Bob Jamison
(12) Duncan Stewart
(13) Hugh Kemp
(14) Mike Konderla
(15) Jack Lind
(16) Mike Manfre
(17) Jeff Montgomery
(18) Pat Pacillo
(19) Buddy Pryor
(20) Chris Sabo
(21) Eddie Tanner
(22) Scott Terry
(23) Jeff Treadway
(24) Max Venable
(25) Carl Willis
(26) John Young

1987 ProCards Newark Orioles

(Baltimore Orioles, A)

	MT	NR MT	EX
Complete Set:	6.00	4.50	2.50

2769 David Esquer
2770 Mike Lehman
2771 Mike Hart
2772 Earl Stephenson
2773 John Oliphant
2774 Gary Arnold
2775 Jack Voigt
2776 Tom Michno
2777 Frank Bryan
2778 Craig Lopez
2779 Steve Culkar
2780 Mike Sander
2781 Bob Shoulders
2782 Joe Gast
2783 Bob Williams
2784 Mike Elmore
2785 Chaun Wilson
2786 Danny Hartline
2787 Don Buford, Jr.
2788 Jeff Ahr
2789 Steven Finley
2790 Dickie Winzenread
2791 Scott Evans
2792 Mike Eberle
2793 Ernie Young
2794 Thomas Shannon
2795 Randy Strijek
2796 Tom Harms
2797 Luis Pena

1987 ProCards New Britain Red Sox

(Boston Red Sox, AA)

	MT	NR MT	EX
Complete Set:	8.00	6.00	3.25

763 Mike Clarkin
764 Zach Crouch
765 Bill Zupka
766 Angel Gonzalez
767 Luis Vasquez
768 Greg Lotzar
769 Brady Anderson
770 Bill McInnis
771 Bob Chadwick
772 Scott Skripko
773 Steve Bast
774 Carlos Quintana
775 Greg Bochesa
776 Daryl Irvine
777 Tony DeFrancesco
778 Dana Williams
779 Dana Kiecker
780 Dave Holt
781 Dan Gakeler
782 Roberto Zambrano
783 Josias Manzanillo
784 Tary Scott
785 Chris Mortiz
786 Jose Birriel
787 Ed Estrada

1987 ProCards Oklahoma City 89'ers

(Texas Rangers, AAA)

	MT	NR MT	EX
Complete Set:	7.50	5.75	3.00

133 Paul Kilgus
134 Gary Wheelock
135 Dave Owen
136 Frank Pastore
137 Don Werner
138 Dave Meier
139 Keith Creel
140 Mike Stanley
141 Kirk Killingsworth
142 Mike Jeffcoat
143 Steve Kemp
144 Toby Harrah
145 Ron Meridith
146 Glen Cook
147 Javier Ortiz
148 Cecil Espy
149 Tim Rodgers
150 Dwayne Henry
151 Greg Smith
152 Tom O'Malley
153 Greg Tabor
154 Alan Knicely
155 Nick Capra
156 Ray Ramirez
157 Bill Taylor
158 Jeff Zaske
159 Dave Rucker

1987 ProCards Omaha Royals

(Kansas City Royals, AAA)

	MT	NR MT	EX
Complete Set:	7.50	5.75	3.00

2084 Frank Funk
2085 Jose Angero
2086 John Wathan
2087 Van Snider
2088 Nick Swartz
2089 Gary Thurman
2090 Chito Martinez
2091 Dwight Taylor
2092 Joe Citari
2093 Derek Botelho
2094 Rondin Johnson
2095 Bob Stoddard
2096 Al Hargesheimer
2097 Steve Shirley
2098 Craig Pippin
2099 Adrian Garrett
2100 Scott Madison
2101 Israel Sanchez
2102 John Davis
2103 Ron Wotus
2104 Bobby Ramos
2105 Rick Anderson
2106 Jeff Schulz
2107 Mike MacFarlane (Macfarlane)
2108 Luis Delos de las Santos
2109 Tom Muller

1987 ProCards Oneonta Yankees

(New York Yankees, A)

	MT	NR MT	EX
Complete Set:	8.00	6.00	3.25

2505 Lew Hill
2506 Anthony Morrison
2507 Darrel Tingle
2508 Bernie Williams
2509 Hector Vargas
2510 Gerald Williams
2511 Dan Roman
2512 Steve Erickson
2513 Tom Popplewell
2514 Doug Gogolewski
2515 Bill DaCoste
2516 David Turgeon
2517 Tom Weeks
2518 Brian Butterfield
2519 Freddie Hailey
2520 Julio Ramon
2521 Dave Eiland
2522 Jay Makemson
2523 Bill Voeltz
2524 Chris Byrnes
2525 Randy Foster
2526 Mark Mitchell
2527 Ron Ehrhard
2528 Gary Allenson
2529 Rod Imes
2530 Mark Marris
2531 Bobby Dickerson
2532 Tim Bishop
2533 Dean Kelley
2534 Ed Martel
2535 Luc Berube
2536 Jack Gills
2537 Tom Cloninger

1987 ProCards Orlando Twins

(Minnesota Twins, AA)

	MT	NR MT	EX
Complete Set:	6.00	4.50	2.50

866 Jeff Bumgarner
867 Robbie Smith
868 Dan Smith
869 John Eccles
870 Henry Gatewood
871 Bobby Ralston
872 Jim Shellenback
873 Ken Koch
874 George Mitterwald
875 Mark Clemons
876 Steve Gasser
877 Toby Nivens
878 Steve Gomez
879 Brad Bierley
880 Jeff Reboulet
881 Gary Borg
882 Doug Palmer
883 Tom Schwarz
884 Eddie Yanes
885 Not Issued
886 Jeff Bronkey
887 Wes Pierorazio
888 Allan Sontag
889 Darrell Higgs
890 Mark Funderburk
891 Larry Blackwell
892 Dave Vetsch

1987 ProCards Osceola Astros

(Houston Astros, A)

	MT	NR MT	EX
Complete Set:	6.00	4.50	2.50

952 Terry Wells
953 Juan Lopez

954 Mike Brown
955 Carlo Colobino
956 Randy Randle
957 Ken Bolek
958 Calvin James
959 Dan Walters
960 Doug Snyder
961 Jeff Baldwin
962 Stan Fascher
963 Tony Metoyer
964 Brian Meyer
965 Joe Schulte
966 Jose Vargas
967 David Potts
968 John Elliott
969 Jack Billingham
970 Don Dunster
971 Joel Estes
972 Gary Cooper
973 Juan Delgrado
974 Scott Markley
975 Ken Houston
976 Terry Green
977 Tim Arnsberg
978 Jose Cano
979 Todd Credeur
980 David Rohde

1987 ProCards Palm Springs Angels

(California Angels, A)

	MT	NR MT	EX
Complete Set:	7.00	5.25	2.75

291 Mike Spearnock
292 Al Heath
293 David Johnson
294 Jeff Manto
295 Reggie Lambert
296 Paul Bilak
297 Kenny Grant
298 Dan Grunhard
299 Colin Charland
300 Mike Shull
301 Paul Sorrento
302 Lee Stevens
303 Bill Vanderwel
304 Colby Ward
305 Glenn Washington
306 Roger Zottneck
307 Bill Lachemann
308 Tim Kelly
309 Tom Alfredson
310 Edgar Alfonso
311 Tim Burham
312 Dario Nunez
313 Erik Pappas
314 Michael Anderson
315 Bobby Bell
316 Mike Fetters
317 Frank DiMichele
318 Richard Morehouse
319 Todd Eggertsen
320 Mark Marino
321 Andres Espinoza
322 Gary Nalls

1987 ProCards Pawtucket Red Sox

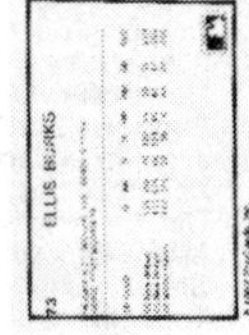

(Boston Red Sox, AAA)

	MT	NR MT	EX
Complete Set:	9.00	6.75	3.50

51 John Marzano
52 Sam Horn
53 Stephen Curry
54 Kevin Romine
55 John Leister
56 Jody Reed
57 Todd Benzinger
58 Mitchell Johnson
59 Mike Rochford
60 LaSchelle Tarver
61 Hector Stewart
62 Tom Bolten
63 Glenn Hoffman
64 Andy Araujo
65 Tony Cleary
66 Mike Dalton
67 Steve Ellsworth
68 Mike Mesh
69 Gary Miller-Jones
70 Gary Tremblay
71 Scott Wade
72 Ed Nottle
73 Ellis Burks
74 Chuck Davis
75 Mark Meleski
76 Dana Williams
77 Chris Cannizzaro

1987 TCMA Pawtucket Red Sox

(Boston Red Sox, AAA)

	MT	NR MT	EX
Complete Set:	15.00	11.00	6.00

1 Andy Araujo
2 Chris Cannizzaro
3 Steve Curry
4 Mike Dalton
5 Chuck Davis
6 Steve Ellsworth
7 Mitch Johnson
8 Danny Sheaffer
9 Mike Rochford
10 Hector Stewart
11 John Marzano
12 Gary Tremblay
13 Todd Benzinger
14 Sam Horn
15 Mike Mesh
16 Gary Miller-Jones
17 Jody Reed
18 Kevin Romine
19 LaSchelle Tarver
20 Scott Wade
21 Ed Nottle
22 Ellis Burks
23 Rob Woodard
24 Pat Dodson
25 Dave Sax
26 John Leister
27 Tom Bolton
28 Mark Meleski

1987 ProCards Peninsula White Sox

(Chicago White Sox, A)

	MT	NR MT	EX
Complete Set:	6.00	4.50	2.50

1872 Mark Davis
1873 Kevin Renz
1874 Chet Diemidc
1875 Mark Foley
1876 Daniel Tauken
1877 Joe Singley
1878 Dewey Robinson
1879 Aubrey Waggoner
1880 Mike Ollom
1881 Craig Grebeck
1882 Dave Reynolds
1883 Scott Radinsky
1884 Miguel Audain
1885 Bruce Hulstrom
1886 Tom Sutryk
1887 Glenn Braxton
1888 Ron Scheer
1889 Dave Wallwork
1890 Tom Reichel
1891 Jeff Greene
1892 Kelsey Isa
1893 Tom Lahrman
1894 Bo Kennedy
1895 Todd Hall
1896 Ron Scruggs
1897 Kurt Brown
1898 Virgil Conley
1899 Tony Cento
1900 Dan Wagner

1987 ProCards Peoria Chiefs

(Chicago Cubs, A)

	MT	NR MT	EX
Complete Set:	9.00	6.75	3.50

400 Ray Mullino
401 Butch Garcia
402 John Green
403 Sergio Espinal
404 Dick Canan
405 Jerry Lapenta
406 Steve Hill
407 Shawn Boskie
408 Greg Iaverone
409 John Berringer
410 Joe Housey
411 Derrick May
412 Pat Gomez
413 Greg Smith
414 Brian Otten
415 David Rosario
416 Elvin Paulino
417 Edwards Williams
418 Harry Shelton
419 Jerome Walton
420 Simeon Mejias
421 Parnell Perry
422 Phil Harrison
423 Steve Parker
424 Kelly Mann
425 Mike Folga
426 Jim Tracy
427 William Kazmierczak
428 Fernando Zarranz

1987 Pizza World Peoria Chiefs

(Chicago Cubs, A) This set is 5-1/2" x 4-1/2" in size and is co-sponsored by station WCT-106.

	MT	NR MT	EX
Complete Set:	35.00	26.00	14 00

(1) Butch Garcia
(2) Pat Gomez
(3) John Green
(4) Steve Hill
(5) Jerome Walton
(6) Chief Rainout

1987 ProCards Phoenix Firebirds

(San Francisco Giants, AAA)

	MT	NR MT	EX
Complete Set:	15.00	11.00	6.00

78 Chris Jones
79 Matt Williams
80 Randy Bockus
81 George Ferran
82 Terry Mulholland
83 Charlie Corbell
84 Angel Escobar
85 Kevin Burrell
86 Colin Ward
87 Mike Woodard
88 Larry Hardy
89 Randy Kutcher
90 Jon Perlman
91 Jack McKnight
92 Alan Cockrell
93 Jessie Reid
94 Joe Price
95 John Verducci
96 Cliff Shidawara
97 Mackey Sasser
98 Pat Adams
99 Duane Espy
100 Wendell Kim
101 Atlee Hammaker
102 Francisco Melendez
103 Steve Miller
104 Mike Rubel
105 Jeff Brantly

1987 ProCards Pittsfield Cubs

(Chicago Cubs, A)

	MT	NR MT	EX
Complete Set:	45.00	34.00	18.00

323 Ray Thoma
324 Greg Bell
325 Hector Villanueva
326 Jim Essian
327 Jim Wright
328 Brian McCann
329 Brian House
330 Laddy Renfroe
331 Mike Miller
332 Mark Grace
333 Brian Guinn
334 Jim Phillips
335 Leonard Damian
336 Dave Masters
337 Dave Pavlas
338 Mark Leonette
339 Rick Wrona
340 David Wilder
341 Jeff Pico
342 Rick Hopkins
343 Roger Williams
344 Rich Amaral
345 Doug Dascenzo
346 Tim Rice
347 Rolando Roomes
348 Dwight Smith

1987 Team Pittsfield Cubs

(Chicago Cubs, AA) This set is in the form of a 10-7/8" x 16-3/4" poster.

	MT	NR MT	EX
Complete Set:	125.00	94.00	50.00

(1) Rick Amaral
(2) Greg Bell
(3) Leonard Damian
(4) Doug Dascenzo
(5) Jim Essian
(6) Mark Grace
(7) Rick Hopkins
(8) Brian House
(9) Dave Masters
(10) Brian McCann
(11) Dave Pavlas
(12) Jim Phillips
(13) Jeff Pico
(14) Laddie Renfroe
(15) Tim Rice
(16) Rolando Roomes
(17) Dwight Smith
(18) Ray Thomas
(19) Hector Villanueva
(20) Ben Webber
(21) Roger Williams
(22) Jim Wright
(23) Rick Wrona

1987 The Bon Pocatello Giants

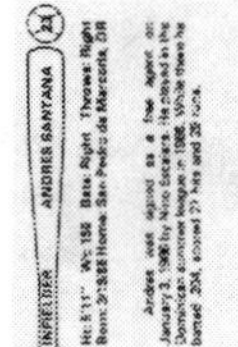

(San Francisco Giants, A)

	MT	NR MT	EX
Complete Set:	65.00	49.00	26.00

1 Doug Messer
2 Rafael Landestoy
3 Brett Lewis
4 Steve Connolly
5 Steve Lienhard
6 Kevin Meier
7 Jim Jones
8 Reid Gunter
9 Mike Greenwood
10 Jim Malseed
11 Domingo DeLaRosa
12 Matt Williams
13 Bill Carlson
14 John Vuz
15 Dominick Johnson
16 Jim Myers
17 Dave Edwards
18 Ron McLintock
19 Mike Williams
20 Mike Wandler
21 Karl Breitenbucher
22 Keith James
23 Andres Santana
24 Rocco Bofolino
25 Jesus Figueroa
26 Francisco Arias
27 Juan Guerrero
28 Jesus Laya
29 Erik Johnson
30 Diego Segui
31 Glenn Abraham
32 Jose Linarez

1987 ProCards Port Charlotte Rangers

(Texas Rangers, A)

	MT	NR MT	EX
Complete Set:	7.50	5.75	3.00

2034 Ken Clawson
2035 John Schofield
2036 Steve Lankard
2037 Scott Morse
2038 John Barfield
2039 Mitch Thomas
2040 Marty Cerny
2041 Edwin Morales
2042 Rick Raether
2043 Steve Wilson
2044 Jeff Mays
2045 Jeff Andrews
2046 Greg Harrell
2047 Fred Samson
2048 Stephen Glasker
2049 Mick Billmeyer
2050 Jose Vargas
2051 Rick Bernardo
2052 Mark Kramer
2053 Julio DeLeon

2054 Joel Cartaya
2055 Chris Colon
2056 Gar Millay
2057 Jim Skaalen
2058 Chad Kreuter
2059 Kevin Reimer
2060 Joe Pearn

1987 ProCards Portland Beavers

(Minnesota Twins, AAA)

	MT	NR MT	EX
Complete Set:	7.00	5.25	2.75

160 Jeff Bittiger
161 Pat Dempsey
162 Randy Niemann
163 Allan Anderson
164 Billy Beane
165 Chris Pittaro
166 Pat Casey
167 Roy Smith
168 Phil Wilson
169 Steve Liddle
170 Danny Clay
171 Julius McDougal
172 Kevin Hagen
173 Alvaro Espinosa
174 Kevin Trudeau
175 Ben Bianchi
176 Alex Marte
177 Bill Latham
178 Gene Larkin
179 Greg Morhardt
180 Ron Musselman
181 Charlie Manuel
182 Ken Silvestri
183 Brad Boylan
184 Ron Gardenhire

1987 ProCards Prince William Yankees

(New York Yankees, A)

	MT	NR MT	EX
Complete Set:	9.00	6.75	3.50

2254 Hensley Meulens
2255 Yanko Hauradou
2256 Bob Davidson
2257 Ricky Torres
2258 Ralph Kraus
2259 Scott Kamieniecki
2260 Alan Mills
2261 Art Calvert
2262 Rick Balabon
2263 Rob Sepanek, Jr.
2264 Chris Howard
2265 Mickey Tresh
2266 Chris Lombardozzi
2267 Mike Heifferon
2268 Bill Clossen
2269 Bill Voeltz
2270 Ysidro Giron
2271 Aris Tirado
2272 Amalio Carreno
2273 Steve Adkins
2274 Hector Vargas
2275 Fernando Figuerda (Figueroa)
2276 Ramon Manon
2277 Jason Maas
2278 Rob Lambert
2279 Joe Hicks
2280 Tony Gwinn
2281 John Ramos
2282 William Morales

1987 ProCards Quad City Angels

(California Angels, A)

	MT	NR MT	EX
Complete Set:	6.00	4.50	2.50

1096 Terrence Carr
1097 Troy Giles
1098 Edgar Rodriguez
1099 Santiago Espinosa
1100 Giovanny Reyes
1101 Lawrence Pardo
1102 Jose Tapia
1103 Roberto Hernandez
1104 Scott Kannenberg
1105 Daryl Green
1106 Luis Merejo
1107 Brandy Vann
1108 Mike Kelser
1109 Jim Bisceglia
1110 Rafael Pineda
1111 Elvin Rivera
1112 Greg Fix
1113 Eddie Rodriguez
1114 Don Long
1115 Gary Ruby
1116 Jim McCollom
1117 Chris Graves
1118 Chris Cron
1119 Scott Cerney
1120 Kendall Walling
1121 Jeff Gay
1122 Michael Knapp
1123 Ken Bandy
1124 Dave Grilione
1125 Greg Jackson
1126 Luis Gallardo

1987 ProCards Reading Phillies

(Philadelphia Phillies, AA)

	MT	NR MT	EX
Complete Set:	7.50	5.75	3.00

788 George Culver
789 Tony Brown
790 Joe Lefebvre
791 Greg Edge
792 Miguel Vargas
793 Dan Giesen
794 Tom Barrett
795 Dion Beck
796 Mike Shelton
797 Bruce Long
798 Ray Roman
799 Kevin Ward
800 Rick Lundblade
801 Howard Nichols
802 Ramon Henderson
803 Ricky Jordan
804 Mark Bowden
805 Steve Blackshear
806 Todd Frohwirth
807 Bob Scanlon
808 Jim Fortenberry
809 Jose Leiva
810 John McLarnan
811 Steve Williams
812 Michael Miller
813 Rob Hicks

1987 Bob's Photo Richmond Braves

(Atlanta Braves, AAA) This team issued set measures 5" x 3-7/8" in size.

	MT	NR MT	EX
Complete Set:	55.00	41.00	22.00

(1) Chuck Cary
(2) Floyd Chiffer
(3) Marty Clary
(4) Sal D'Alessandro
(5) Trench Davis
(6) Juan Eichelberger
(7) Mike Fischlin
(8) Tom Glavine
(9) Dave Griffin
(10) Inocencio Guerrero
(11) Kelly Heath
(12) Chuck Hensley
(13) Dale Holman
(14) John Mizerock
(15) Darryl Motley
(16) Ed Olwine
(17) John Rabb
(18) Paul Runge
(19) Cliff Speck
(20) Matt West
(21) Steve Ziem

1987 Crown Oil Richmond Braves

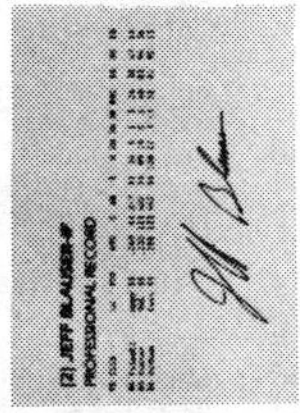

(Atlanta Braves, AAA) This set is numbered as it appears on the cards. Also, originally in the form of a perforated 11" x 28-1/2" sheet.

	MT	NR MT	EX
Complete Set:	25.00	18.50	10.00

1 Kelly Heath
2 Jeff Blauser
5 Mark Strueher
6 Roy Majtyka
8 John Mizerock
9 Bob Tumpane
10 Sal D'Alessandro
12 Paul Runge
14 Tom Glavine
15 Juan Eichelberger
18 Mike Fischlin
19 Steve Zlem
20 John Rabb
24 David Griffin
25 Dale Holman
26 Rick Albert
28 Floyd Chiffer
29 Stan Cliburn
30 Darryl Motley
31 Bean Stringfellow
32 Trench Davis
34 Marty Clary
37 Chuck Hensley
39 Cliff Speck
42 Mike Brown
43 Nardi Contreras
45 Matt West
47 Chuck Cary
---- Sam Ayoub

1987 TCMA Richmond Braves

(Atlanta Braves, AAA)

	MT	NR MT	EX
Complete Set:	20.00	15.00	8.00

1 Chuck Cary
2 Floyd Chiffer
3 Marty Clary
4 Juan Eichelberger
5 Tom Glavine
6 Chuck Hensley
7 Bean Stringfellow
8 Matt West
9 Steve Ziem
10 John Mizerock
11 Jeff Blauser
12 Mike Fischlin
13 David Griffin
14 Paul Runge
15 Mark Strucher
16 Bob Tumpane
17 Trench Davis
18 Kelly Heath
19 Darryl Motley
20 John Rabb
21 Roy Majtyka
22 Nardi Contreras
23 Dale Holman
24 Jim McManus
25 Cliff Speck
26 Rich Albert
27 Mike Brown
28 Stan Cliburn
29 Sam Ayoub

1987 ProCards Rochester Red Wings

(Baltimore Orioles, AAA)

	MT	NR MT	EX
Complete Set:	9.00	6.75	3.50

1901 Phil Hoffman
1902 Dave Van Gorder
1903 John Hart
1904 Ron Salcedo
1905 Mike Skinner
1906 Chris Padget
1907 Scott Ullger
1908 Eric Rasmussen
1909 Mike Griffin
1910 Mike Hart
1911 Carl Nichols
1912 Bill Ripken
1913 Curt Motton
1914 D.L. Smith
1915 Dom Chiti
1916 Luis DeLeon
1917 Brad Havens
1918 Nelson Simmons
1919 Ron Washington
1920 Jack O'Connor
1921 Kelvin Torve
1922 Jamie Reed
1923 Craig Worthington
1924 John Habyan
1925 Jeff Ballard
1926 Jim Traber
1927 Bob Molinaro

1987 TCMA Rochester Red Wings

(Baltimore Orioles, AAA)

	MT	NR MT	EX
Complete Set:	13.00	9.75	5.25

1 Jeff Ballard
2 Luis DeLeon
3 Mike Griffin
4 John Habyan
5 Brad Havens
6 Phil Huffman
7 Jack O'Connor
8 Eric Rasmussen
9 Mike Skinner
10 Carl Nichols
11 Dave Van Gorder
12 Chris Padget
13 Bill Ripken
14 David Lee Smith
15 Kelvin Torve
16 Ron Washington
17 Craig Worthington
18 Mike Hart
19 Ron Salcedo
20 Jim Traber
21 Scott Ullger
22 Chris Green
23 Curt Motton
24 John Hart
25 Dom Chiti
26 Jerry Lomastro
27 Joe Kucharski
28 Rex Mudler
29 Don Gordon, Joe Kucharski

1987 ProCards St. Petersburg Cardinals

(St. Louis Cardinals, A)

	MT	NR MT	EX
Complete Set:	7.00	5.25	2.75

2007 Dave Osteen
2008 Craig Wilson
2009 Jesus Mendez
2010 Mike Sassone
2011 Mike Robertson
2012 Mauricio Nunez
2013 Brett Harrison
2014 Joe Cunningham
2015 Michael Senne
2016 Tom Amante
2017 Mike Fox
2018 Dave Horton
2019 John Murphy
2020 David DeCordova
2021 Chris Forrest
2022 Hans Herzog
2023 Tom Mauch
2024 Dave Bialas
2025 Marty Mason
2026 Crucito Lara
2027 William Hershmann
2028 Benito Malave
2029 Gregory Becker
2030 Randy Butts
2031 Jay North
2032 Pete Fagan
2033 Rob Livchak

1987 ProCards Salem Angels

(California Angels, A)

	MT	NR MT	EX
Complete Set:	7.00	5.25	2.75

2412 Edgar Rodriguez
2413 Gary Buckels
2414 Jay Bobel, Jr.
2415 Troy Giles
2416 Robert Wassenaar
2417 John Orton
2418 Mario Molina
2419 Bill Robinson
2420 Greg Jackson
2421 Eric Reinholtz
2422 Jorge Montero
2423 Ramon Martinez
2424 Reed Peters
2425 Tony Rasmus
2426 Jim Townsend
2427 Frnak Mutz
2428 Ruben Amaro
2429 Santiago Espinosa
2430 Wiley Lee, Jr.
2431 Paul List
2432 Rafael Pineda
2433 Kevin Flora
2434 Mikael Musolino
2435 Mike Erb
2436 Luis Gallardo
2437 Cary Grubb
2438 Lanny Abshier
2439 Freddie Davis, Jr.
2440 Scott Randolph
2441 Jeff Goettsch
2442 Jesse Flores
2443 Mark Weidemaier
2444 Chris Smith
2445 Derek Winchell

1987 ProCards Salem Buccaneers

(Pittsburgh Pirates, A)

	MT	NR MT	EX
Complete Set:	7.00	5.25	2.75

1236 Kevin Franchi
1237 Mike Stevens
1238 Larry Melton
1239 Rob Hatfield
1240 Octavio Cepeda
1241 Greg Stading
1242 Pete Rice
1243 Tim Kirk
1244 Ben Morrow
1245 Matias Carrillo
1246 Martin Hernandez
1247 Mike Dotzher
1248 Steve Moser
1249 John Rigos
1250 Harold Williams
1251 Gilberto Roca
1252 Rafael Muratti
1253 Jim Thrift
1254 Bill Copp
1255 Bob Koopmann
1256 Bill Sampen
1257 Mike Stevanus
1258 Reggie Barringer
1259 Jeff King
1260 Tony Chance
1261 Todd Smith
1262 Doug Pittman
1263 Chris Lein
1264 Steve Demeter
1265 Kevin Davis

1987 Police Salinas Spurs

(A)

	MT	NR MT	EX
Complete Set:	65.00	49.00	26.00

1 Keith Foley
2 Jorge Uribe
3 Dave Snell
4 Maryann Hudson
5 Mike Brants
6 William Diaz
7 Andrea Fine
8 Dave "Doc" Mosley
9 John Clem
10 Rick Moore
11 Greg Brinkman
12 Dave McCorkle
13 Bob Bernardo
14 Tom Eccelston
15 Danny Larson
16 Jovan Edwads
17 Michael Darby
18 Buddy Meachum
19 Omar Visquel
20 Robert Gibree
21 Tom Krause
22 Steve Murray
23 Pablo Moncerratt
24 Tom Newberg
25 Jeff Hull
26 Tim Fortugno
27 Jeff Nelson
28 Mike Kolovitz
29 John Burden
30 Clint Zavaras
31 Smokey Bear
32 Greg Mahlberg

Values for recent cards and sets are listed in Mint (MT), Near Mint (NM), reflecting the fact that many cards from recent years have been preserved in top condition. Recent cards and sets in less than Excellent condition have little collector interest.

1987 Team San Antonio Dodgers

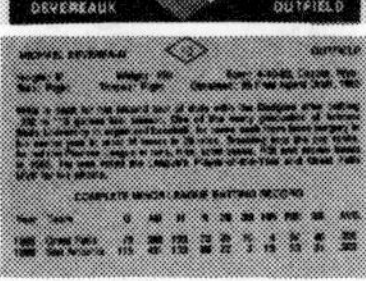

(Los Angeles Dodgers, AA) (Sets sold at the ballpark did not include logo cards)

	MT	NR MT	EX
Complete Set:	8.00	6.00	3.25

1 Jeff Schaefer
2 Andres Mena
3 Manager/Coaches (Gary LaRocque, Dennis Lewallyn, Jim Stoeckel)
4 Tim Scott
5 Alonzo Tellez
6 Rob Rowen
7 Domingo Michel
8 Barry Wohler
9 Juan Bustabad
10 Mike Devereaux
11 Scott May
12 Jeff Brown
13 Mike Schweighoffer
14 Walt McConnell
15 Felix Tejeda
16 Mike Huff
17 Joe Szekely
18 Bob Hamilton
19 Jon Pequignot
20 Dave Eichhorn
21 Homar Rojas
22 Jack Savage
23 Ken Harvey
24 Mark Heuer

1987 ProCards San Bernadino Spirits

(No Affiliation, A)

	MT	NR MT	EX
Complete Set:	6.00	4.50	2.50

2359 Steve Walker
2360 Larry Smith
2361 Jeff Edwards
2362 Don Stearns
2363 Randy Harvey
2364 Stan Sanchez
2365 Rich Dauer
2366 Ron Carter
2367 Mark Combs
2368 James Filippi
2369 Delwyn Young
2370 Vince Shinholster
2371 Brian Hartsock
2372 Leon Baham
2373 Scott Marrett
2374 Mike Brocki
2375 Brian Morrison
2376 Walt Stull
2377 Robert Greenlee
2378 Todd Cruz
2379 Tony Triplett
2380 Todd Hayes
2381 Tom Thompson

1987 ProCards San Jose Bees

(No Affiliation, A)

	MT	NR MT	EX
Complete Set:	7.00	5.25	2.75

2191 Sam Hirose
2192 Hector Nakamura
2193 Ken Reitz
2194 Sal Vaccaro
2195 Harvey Lee
2196 Charlie Moore
2197 Rocky Osaka
2198 Kat Kamei
2199 Frank Bryan
2200 Ted Haraguchi
2201 Mickey Yamano
2202 Dan Mori
2203 Tom Nabekawa
2204 Rattoo Akimoto
2205 David Rolland
2206 Mark Seay
2207 Paco Burgos
2208 Elias Sosas
2209 Mike Verdi
2210 Rick Tracy
2211 Warren Brusstar
2212 Lawrence Feola
2213 Roger Erickson
2214 Julian Gonzales
2215 Eddie Gonzales
2216 Steve McCatty
2217 Rusty McNealy
2218 Daryl Sconiers
2219 Shawn Barton
---- Brian Kubala

1987 ProCards Savannah Cardinals

(St. Louis Cardinals, A)

	MT	NR MT	EX
Complete Set:	7.00	5.25	2.75

1846 Bobby DeLoach
1847 Chuck Johnson
1848 David Krebs
1849 Geronimo Pena
1850 Eric Hahn
1851 Scott Nichols
1852 Jay Martel
1853 Greg Ward
1854 Pat Hewes
1855 Mike Henry
1856 Mark Grater
1857 Mark Davis
1858 Pedro Llanes
1859 Carroll Parker
1860 Chico Singletary
1861 Carey Nemeth
1862 Reed Olmstead
1863 Eddie Looper
1864 Julian Martinez
1865 Franklin Abreu
1866 Don Dumas
1867 Stan Zaltsman
1868 Lenny Picota
1869 Mark Behny
1870 Scott Lawrence
1871 Mark DeJohn

1987 Team Salt Lake City Trappers

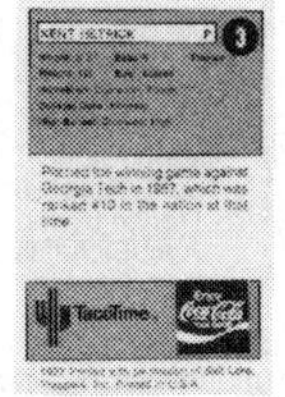

(No affiliation, A) (An unnumbered card for coach Barry Moss is also included.) (The set price includes the scarce card for Kim and Joie Casey)

	MT	NR MT	EX
Complete Set:	7.00	5.25	2.75

1 Kurt Strange
2 Michael Malinak
3 Kent Hetrick
4 Jon Beuder
5 Neil Reynolds
6 James Ferguson
7 Coach/Bat Boys (Lance Bagshaw, Ryan Bagshaw, Andy Iacona, Reuben Rodriguez)
8 John Groennert
9 Isaac Alleyne
10 Todd Noonan
11 Jim Gilligan (manager)
12 David Ward
13 Ed Citronnelli
14 General Manager/Public Relations (Steve Pearson, Glenn Seninger)
15 Kouichi Ikeue
16 Mike Humphrey
17 Niles Creekmore
18 Frank Colston
19 Adam Casillas
20 Yasuhiro Hiyama
21 Trainer/Announcer (Steve Fong, Randy Kerdoon)
22 Anthony Blackmon
23 Matt Huff
24 Jon Leake
25 Tim Peters
26 Steve Scott
27 David Poss
28 Team Photo/Checklist
---- Barry Most, Kim & Joie Casey

1987 ProCards Shreveport Captains

(San Francisco Giants, AA)

	MT	NR MT	EX
Complete Set:	11.00	8.25	4.50

458 Everett Graham
459 Paul Meyers
460 Ty Dabney
461 Dennis Cook
462 Dean Freeland
463 Tony Perezchica
464 Scott Medvin
465 Greg Litton
466 Romy Cucjen
467 Kirt Manwaring
468 Todd Thomas
469 Brian Ohnoutka
470 Jeff Brantley
471 John Burkett
472 Ed Puikunas
473 Randy McCament
474 Charlie Hayes
475 T.J. McDonald
476 Deron McCue
477 Stuart Tate
478 Tom Wasilewski
479 John Grimes
480 Vince Sferazza
481 Marty DeMerritt
482 Jack Mull

1987 Donn Jennings Southern League All-Stars

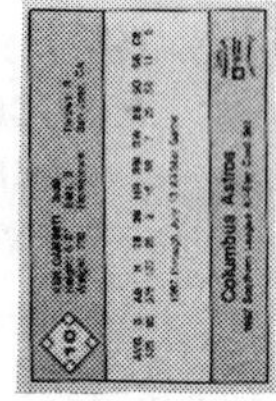

(AA)

	MT	NR MT	EX
Complete Set:	6.00	4.50	2.50

1 Dave Falcone
2 Rondal Rollin
3 Geronimo Berroa
4 Bernie Tatis
5 Nelson Santovenia
6 Tom Dodd
7 Cameron Drew
8 Larry Walker
9 Matt Winters
10 Ken Caminiti
11 Dave Myers
12 Jimmy Jones
13 Ronnie Gant
14 John Trautwein
15 Rob Mallicoat
16 Randy Johnson
17 Kevin Price
18 Steve Gasser
19 Kevin Coffman
20 Adam Peterson
21 Jeff Bettendorf
22 Jim Beauchamp (manager)
23 Rico Petrocelli (coach)
24 Greg Biagini (coach)
25 Leo Mazzone (coach)

1987 ProCards Spartanburg Phillies

(Philadelphia Phillies, A)

	MT	NR MT	EX
Complete Set:	6.00	4.50	2.50

1790 Jim Platts
1791 Peter Maldonado
1792 Gene Bierscheid
1793 Jeff Stark
1794 Charles McElroy
1795 Mark Sims
1796 Garry Clark
1797 Keith Greene
1798 Kenny Miller
1799 Michel Lamarche
1800 Ramon Aviles
1801 Ron Nelson
1802 Andy Ashby
1803 Trey McCall
1804 Todd Crosby
1805 Cliff Walker
1806 Martin Foley

1807 Luis Iglesias
1808 Elbi Romero
1809 Vince Holyfield
1810 Jeff Grotewald
1811 Bob Tiefanauer
1812 Vladimir Perez
1813 Cesar Delrosa
1814 Phillip Price
1815 Scott Hufford
1816 Fred Christopher
1817 Mike Colpitt

1987 ProCards Spokane Indians

(San Diego Padres, A)

	MT	NR MT	EX
Complete Set:	9.00	6.75	3.50

2680 Osvaldo Sanchez
2681 Darrin Reichle
2682 Tony Lewis
2683 Saul Soltero
2684 Jay Estrada
2685 Rich Holsman
2686 Andy Skeels
2687 David Hollins
2688 Charles Hilleman
2689 Steve Lubratich
2690 Reggie Farmer
2691 Monte Brooks
2692 Bobby Sheridan
2693 Kevin Farmer
2694 Francisco de la Cruz
2695 David Bond
2696 Paul Faries
2697 Bob Lutticken
2698 Terry Gilmore
2699 Pedro Aquino
2700 Todd Torchia
2701 Steve Hendricks
2702 Jose Valentin
2703 Mike Myers
2704 Dustin Picciolo ((Mgr. son), Rob Picciolo)

1987 Best Springfield Cardinals

(St. Louis Cardinals, A)

	MT	NR MT	EX
Complete Set:	20.00	15.00	8.00

1 Gaylen Pitts
2 Mark A. Riggins
3 Alexander Ojea
4 Stephen W. Meyer
5 James W. Puzey
6 Ronald M. Johns
7 Tim Lemons
8 John T. Baine
9 Jeffrey L. Graham
10 William E. Bivens
11 Robert J. Faron
12 Stephen F. Hill
13 Howard Hilton
14 David Takach
15 Michael I. Perez
16 David J. Sala
17 Scott W. Hamilton
18 Robert A. Glisson
19 Michael S. Raziano
20 Brian Farley
21 Larry R. Breedlove
22 Bienvendo Figueroa
23 Vincent L. Kindred
24 Scott Melvin
25 Otis B. Gilkey
26 Todd E. Zeile
27 Bluestone Brad
28 Scott Norman

1987 ProCards Stockton Ports

(Milwaukee Brewers, A)

	MT	NR MT	EX
Complete Set:	15.00	11.00	6.00

239 Gary Sheffield
240 Rob Derksen
241 Dave Machemer
242 Sandy Guerrero
243 Todd France
244 Danny Fitzpatrick
245 Mario Monico
246 Daryl Hamilton
247 Renard Brown
248 Angel Rodriguez
249 Isaiah Clark
250 Charley McGrew
251 Martin Montano
252 Ruben Escalera
253 Mike Frew
254 John Ludy
255 Luis Castillo
256 George Canale
257 Jim Hunter
258 Keith Fleming
259 Carl Moraw
260 Tim Torricelli
261 Jim Morris
263 Gary Kanwisher
264 Fred Williams
265 Ed Puig

1987 ProCards Sumter Braves

(Atlanta Braves, A)

	MT	NR MT	EX
Complete Set:	6.00	4.50	2.50

1349 Jerald Frost
1350 William Turner
1351 Miguel Sabino
1352 Walt Williams
1353 Bob McNally
1354 Clarence Jones
1355 Kevin Brown
1356 Rusty Richards
1357 Paul Marak
1358 Buddy Bailey
1359 Mark Clark
1360 Kevin Harmon
1361 David Plumb
1362 Carl Jones
1363 Rich Longuil
1364 Mike Bell
1365 Jesse Minton
1366 Rich Maloney
1367 Jim Czajkowski
1368 Jim Lemasters
1369 Larry Jaster
1370 Danny Rogers
1371 Ken Pennington
1372 Al Martin
1373 James Nowlin
1374 Brian Deak
1375 Sean Ross
1376 Gerald Wagner
1377 David Butts
1378 Jay Johnson

1987 ProCards Syracuse Chiefs

(Toronto Blue Jays, AAA)

	MT	NR MT	EX
Complete Set:	8.00	6.00	3.25

1928 Silve Campusano
1929 Nelson Liriano
1930 Lou Thornton
1931 Greg Myers
1932 Don Gordon
1933 Steve Firevoid
1934 Doug Ault
1935 Alex Infante
1936 Jose Segura
1937 Luis Aquino
1938 Todd Stottlemyre
1939 Tony Hudson
1940 Dave Stenhouse
1941 Manny Lee
1942 Otis Green
1943 Rob Ducey
1944 Jose Escobar
1945 Jose Castro
1946 Dave LaRoche
1947 Hector Torres
1948 Steve Davis
1949 Doc Estes
1950 Glenallen Hill

1987 TCMA Syracuse Chiefs

(Toronto Blue Jays, AAA)

	MT	NR MT	EX
Complete Set:	11.50	8.75	4.50

1 Luis Aquino
2 Steve Davis
3 Jeff Hearron
4 Don Gordon
5 Odell Jones
6 Colin McLaughlin
7 Jose Segura
8 Todd Stottlemyre
9 David Wells
10 Greg Myers
11 Dave Stenhouse
12 Jose Castro
13 Jose Escobar
14 Otis Green
15 Alex Infante
16 Manny Lee
17 Nelson Liriano
18 Silvester Campusano
19 Rob Ducey
20 Glenallen Hill
21 Lou Thornton
22 Doc Estes
23 Doug Ault
24 Dave LaRoche
25 Hector Torres
26 Don Gordo, Joe Kucharski)
27 Joseph Coyle
28 Mel Queen
29 Kash Beauchamp
30 Steve Fireovid
31 Randy Day
32 Eddie Mahar
33 Red Coughlin

1987 ProCards Tacoma Tigers

(Oakland A's, AAA)

	MT	NR MT	EX
Complete Set:	8.00	7.25	3.75

1575 Tim Dozier
1576 Darrel Akerfelds
1577 Stan Kyles
1578 Bobby Clark
1579 Gary Jones
1580 Wayne Krenchicki
1581 Dave Van Ohlen
1582 Bruce Tanner
1583 Matt Sinatro
1584 Thad Reece
1585 Eric Broersma
1586 Chuck Estrada
1587 Steve Henderson
1588 Keith Lieppman
1589 Roy Johnson
1590 Dan Rohn
1591 Jose Tolentino
1592 Bill Mooneyham
1593 Jerry Willard
1594 Alejandro Sanchez
1595 Tim Belcher
1596 Brian Dorsett
1597 Tim Birtsas

1987 ProCards Tampa Tarpons

(Cincinnati Reds, A)

	MT	NR MT	EX
Complete Set:	7.00	5.25	2.75

1319 Gary Denbo
1320 Pete Carey
1321 Mike Converse
1322 Ken Huseby
1323 Mike Roesler
1324 Kevin Pearson
1325 Juan Pinol
1326 Marc Bombard
1327 Tim Swob
1328 Dwayne Williams
1329 Tom Novak
1330 Jeff Richardson
1331 Bret Williamson
1332 Jack Smith
1333 Chris Hammond
1334 Timber Mead
1335 Kent Willis
1336 Mark Jackson
1337 Steve Davis
1338 Gino Minutelli
1339 Mike Campbell
1340 Chris Fernandez
1341 Neal Davenport
1342 Scott Hilgenberg
1343 Jeff Forney
1344 Billy Hawley
1345 Pete Beeler
1346 Rod Zeratsky
1347 Rich Sapienza
1348 Mike Villa

1987 Texas League All-Stars

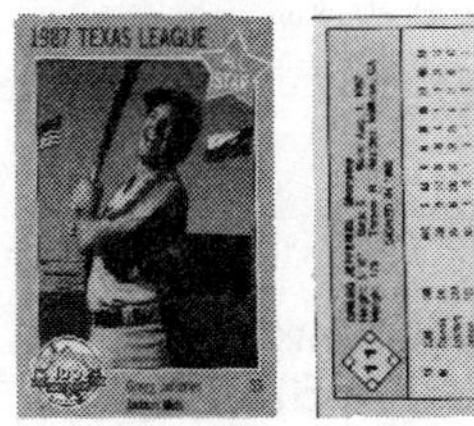

	MT	NR MT	EX
Complete Set:	20.00	15.00	8.00

1 Mike Debutch
2 Roy Silver
3 Joe Lynch
4 Doug Jennings
5 Brad Pounders
6 Jack Mull
7 Jeff Gardner
8 Roberto Alomar
9 Ed Jurak
10 Sandy Alomar, Jr.
11 Gregg Jefferies
12 Joe Redfield
13 Steve Smith
14 Shane Young
15 Marty Reed
16 Joaquin Contreras
17 Jim St. Laurent
18 Thomas Howard
19 Steve Peters
20 John Miglio
21 Scott Arnold
22 Kirt Manwaring
23 Greg Harris
24 Marcus Lawton
25 Lavel Freeman
26 Mike Fitzgerald
27 Charlie Hayes
28 Mike Devereaux
29 David West
30 Jesus Alfaro
31 Ray Stephens
32 Ty Dabney
33 John Burkett
34 Jack Savage
35 Joe Szckely

1987 ProCards Tidewater Tides

(New York Mets, AAA)

	MT	NR MT	EX
Complete Set:	8.50	6.50	3.50

2472 Clint Hurdle
2473 DeWayne Vaugh
2474 Reggie Dobie
2475 Jeff McKnight
2476 Terry Blocker
2477 John Gibbons
2478 Jason Felice
2479 Jeff Innis
2480 Tom Edens
2481 Keith Miller
2482 Steve Springer
2483 Mike Cubbage
2484 Tom McCarthy
2485 Dave Wyatt
2486 Ed Glynn
2487 Ricky Nelson
2488 Tom Lombarski
2489 John Cumberland
2490 Greg Olson
2491 John Mitchell
2492 Mark Carreon
2493 Bill Latham
2494 Jose Roman
2495 Andre David
2496 Don Schulze
2497 Bob Buchanan
2498 Gene Walter
2499 Randy Milligan
2500 Rob Evans
2501 Rick Rainer
2502 Dwight Gooden
2503 Kevin Elster
2504 Bob Gibson

1987 TCMA Tidewater Tides

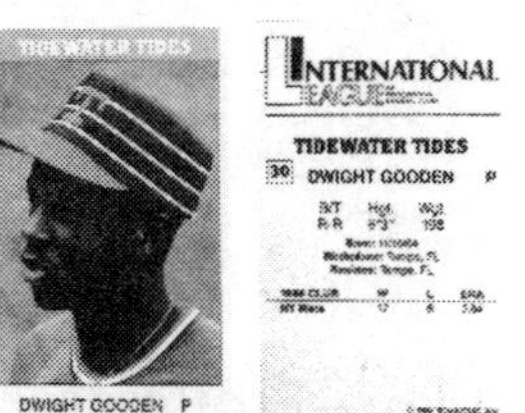

(New York Mets, AAA)

	MT	NR MT	EX
Complete Set:	12.50	9.50	5.00

1 Reggie Dobie
2 Tom Edens
3 Bob Gibson
4 Ed Glynn
5 Jeff Innis
6 Tom McCarthy
7 John Mitchell
8 DeWayne Vaughn
9 Dave Wyatt
10 John Gibbons
11 Greg Olson
12 Andre David
13 Kevin Elster

14 Tom Lombarski
15 Jeff McKnight
16 Keith Miller
17 Randy Milligan
18 Steve Springer
19 Terry Blocker
20 Mark Carreon
21 Gene Walter
22 Clint Hurdle
23 Mike Cubbage
24 John Cumberland
25 Rick Rainer
26 Don Schulze
27 Bob Buchanan
28 Bill Latham
29 Jose Roman
30 Dwight Gooden

1987 ProCards Toledo Mud Hens

(Detroit Tigers, AAA)

	MT	NR MT	EX
Complete Set:	9.00	6.75	3.50

1954 Scott Earl
1955 Steve Searcy
1956 Scott Lusader
1957 German Rivera
1958 Jim Walewander
1959 Ricky Wright
1960 Don Heinkel
1961 John Pacella
1962 Ricky Barlow
1963 Paul Gibson
1964 Fred Tiburcio
1965 Tim Tolman
1966 Jed Murray
1967 Bruce Fields
1968 Rey Palacios
1969 Mike Henneman
1970 Doug Baker
1971 Morris Madden
1972 Mike Stenhouse
1973 Leon Roberts
1974 Bill Laskey
1975 Gene Roof
1976 Don McGann
1977 Jeff Ransom
1978 John Hiller
1979 Billy Bean
1980 Willie Hernandez
1981 Kirk Gibson
1982 Bryan Kelly
1983 Jerry Davis

1987 TCMA Toledo Mud Hens

(Detroit Tigers, AAA)

	MT	NR MT	EX
Complete Set:	8.00	6.00	3.25

1 Rey Palacios
2 Don Heinkel
3 German Rivera
4 Bill Laskey
5 Mike Stenhouse
6 Fred Tiburcio
7 Jim Walewander
8 Scott Lusader
9 Bruce Fields
10 Scott Earl
11 Jeff Ransom
12 James R. Wright
13 Mike Henneman
14 John Pacella
15 Morris Madden
16 Steve Searcy
17 Paul Gibson
18 Jed Murray
19 Ricky Barlow
20 Doug Baker
21 Leon Roberts
22 Gene Roof
23 Tim Tolman
24 Jerry Davis
25 Dwight Lowry

1987 ProCards Tucson Toros

(Houston Astros, AAA)

	MT	NR MT	EX
Complete Set:	7.00	5.25	2.75

2110 Juan Agosto
2111 Glenn Carpenter
2112 Robbie Wine
2113 Bill Crone
2114 Rafael Montalvo
2115 Tye Waller
2116 Manny Hernandez
2117 Dale Berra
2118 Louie Meadows
2119 Rocky Childress
2120 Gerald Young
2121 Ray Fontenot
2122 Jim Miner
2123 Ron Mathis
2124 Nelson Rood
2125 Bert Pena
2126 Kevin Hagen
2127 Jeff Heathcock
2128 Eric Bullock
2129 Ronn Reynolds
2130 Anthony Kelley
2131 Eddie Watt
2132 Ty Gainey
2133 Bob Didier
2134 Tom Funk

1987 Jones Photo Tucson Toros

(Houston Astros, AAA) No positions are listed on these cards which measure 3" x 5-1/8" in size.

	MT	NR MT	EX
Complete Set:	40.00	30.00	16.00

(1) Dale Berra
(2) Eric Bullock
(3) Glenn Carpenter
(4) Bill Crone
(5) Bob Dider
(6) Jeff Edwards
(7) Tom Funk
(8) TY Gainey
(9) Jeff Heathcock
(10) Manny Hernandez
(11) Paul Householder
(12) Chuck Jackson
(13) Anthony Kelley
(14) Ron Mathis
(15) Louie Meadows
(16) Jim Miner
(17) Rafael Montaivo
(18) Raynor Noble
(19) Ronn Reynolds
(20) Nelson Rood
(21) Tye Waller
(22) Ed Watt
(23) Robbie Wine
(24) Gerald Young

1987 Team Tulsa Drillers

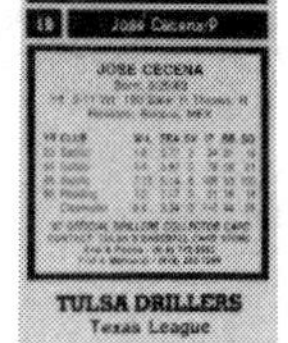

(Texas Rangers, AA)

	MT	NR MT	EX
Complete Set:	7.50	5.75	3.00

1 Dave Murray
2 Brad Hill
3 Mike Jirschele
4 Bobby Jones
5 Mike Couchee
6 Bill Stearns
7 Dave Harman
8 Greg Ferlenda
9 Jeff Melrose
10 Otto Gonzalez
11 Eddie Jurak
12 Jim St. Laurent
13 Howard Hilton, Dave Pavlas
14 Ruben Guzman
15 Tom Duggan
16 George Threadgill
17 Ken Rogers
18 Rick Knapp
19 Jose Cecena
20 Bob Malloy
21 Darrell Whitaker
22 Rick Odekirk
23 Larry Klein
24 Tommy West
25 Jose Mota
26 Gary Mielke
27 Rob Bill
28 Rod Lung

1987 ProCards Utica Blue Sox

(Philadelphia Phillies, A)

	MT	NR MT	EX
Complete Set:	8.00	6.00	3.25

2705 Manlio Perez
2706 Leroy Ventress
2707 Rafael Bustamante
2708 Kim Batiste
2709 Scott Ruckman
2710 Shelby McDonald
2711 Troy Zerb
2712 Robert Jones
2713 Jim Vatcher
2714 Doug Lindsey
2715 Jeffrey Scott
2716 Gary White
2717 Mark Cobb
2718 Bob Chadwick
2719 David Monterio
2720 Marc Lopez
2721 Rick Trlicek
2722 Steve Kirkpatrick
2723 Darrell Coulter
2724 Scott Reaves
2725 Joe Williams
2726 Royal Thomas
2727 John LaRosa
2728 Timothy Peek
2729 Andy Ashby
2730 Matt Rambo
2731 Jaime Barragan
2732 Robert Hurta
2733 Phil Fagnano
2734 Corey Smith
2735 Ike Galloway
2736 Dave Allen
2737 Greg McCarthy

1987 ProCards Vancouver Canadians

(Pittsburgh Pirates, AAA)

	MT	NR MT	EX
Complete Set:	8.00	6.00	3.25

1598 Mike Bielecki
1599 Jackie Brown
1600 Jeff Cox
1601 Carlos LeDezma
1602 Mark Ross
1603 Tommy Dunbar
1604 Stan Fansler
1605 Rocky Bridges
1606 Dave Johnson
1607 Sammy Haro
1608 Sammy Khalifa
1609 Houston Jimenez
1610 Tim Drummond
1611 Dave Leeper
1612 Mike Dunne
1613 Randy Kramer
1614 Butch Davis
1615 Hipolito Pena
1616 Jose Lind
1617 Larry Ray
1618 Danny Bilardello
1619 Vincente Palacios
1620 Ruben Rodriquez
1621 Dorn Taylor
1622 U.L. Washington

1987 ProCards Vermont Reds

(Cincinnati Reds, A)

	MT	NR MT	EX
Complete Set:	7.50	5.75	3.00

814 Brad Brusky
815 Jim Jefferson
816 Ted Langdon
817 Francisco Tenacen
818 Marty Brown
819 Greg Simpson
820 Ramon Sambo
821 Tim Mirabito
822 Rob Lopez
823 Joe Dunlap
824 Tom Dietz
825 Mike Smith
826 Angelo Nunley
827 Steve Oliverio
828 John Bryant
829 Tom Runnells
830 Dave Miley
831 Glenn Spagnolia
832 Joe Oliver
833 Mark Germann
834 Greg Monita
835 Chris Jones
837 Mark Berry
838 Darren Riley
839 Marvin Haynes
840 Rod Lich

1987 ProCards Vero Beach Dodgers

(Los Angeles Dodgers, A)

	MT	NR MT	EX
Complete Set:	12.00	9.00	4.75

1730 John Wetteland
1731 Jose Tapia
1732 Joe Spagnuolo
1733 Dan Pena
1734 Darren Holmes
1735 Pete Feist
1736 Ramon Martinez
1737 Pat Zachry
1738 Fred Gegan
1739 Ken Lambert
1740 Manny Francois
1741 Mancy Benitez
1742 Mike Garner
1743 Tom Thomas
1744 Mike Batesole
1745 Jeff Brown
1746 Kevin Campbell
1747 Rob Giesecke
1748 Joe Kesselmark
1749 Jay Hornacek
1750 Felipe Esteban
1751 Tom Beyers
1752 Kevin Devine
1753 Bryan Smith
1754 Mike Burke
1755 Bill Bartels
1756 Rene Garcia
1757 Lee Langley
1758 Kevin Shea
1759 John Shoemaker
1760 Phil Torres

1987 ProCards Visalia Oaks

(Minnesota Twins, A)

	MT	NR MT	EX
Complete Set:	6.00	4.50	2.50

543 Jamie Williams
544 Glen Myers
545 Kenny Morgan
546 Tim Cota
547 Bob Strube
548 Bob Lee
549 Jeff Perry
550 Kurt Walker
551 Troy Galloway
552 Dave Blakely
553 Park Pittman
554 Ike Goldstein
555 Chris Calvert
556 Tim Senne
557 Kenny Davis
558 Mike Redding
559 Tim O'Connor
560 Todd Burke
561 Joey Aragon
562 Joey Zellner
563 John Pust
564 Mike Adams
565 Marty Lanoux
566 Gordon Heimueller
567 Dan Schmitz
568 Clark Lange
569 Shannon Raybon

1987 ProCards Waterloo Indians

(Cleveland Indians, A)

	MT	NR MT	EX
Complete Set:	6.00	4.50	2.50

1038 Fidel Compres
1039 Manny Mercado
1040 Jim Richardson
1041 Steve Johnigan
1042 Brad Wolten
1043 Mark Pike
1044 Dave Alvis
1045 Tom Gamba
1046 Scott Johnson
1047 Glenn Adams
1048 Todd Gonzales
1049 Kevin Kuykendall
1050 John Githens
1052 Mike Walker
1053 Jeff Shaw
1054 Carl Chambers
1055 Rudy Seanez
1056 Paul Kuzniar
1057 Don Santos
1058 Keith Seifert
1059 Ray Williamson
1060 Tom Lampkin
1061 Riley Polk
1062 Glenn Fairchild
1063 Claudio Carrasco
1064 Lenny Randle
1065 Dan Redmond
1066 Rick Adair

1987 ProCards Watertown Pirates

(Pittsburgh Pirates, A)

	MT	NR MT	EX
Complete Set:	12.00	9.00	4.75

2798 Ben Webb
2799 Rodger Castner

2800 Robert Harris
2801 Ed Shea
2802 Scott Runge
2803 Chip Duncan
2804 Scott Barczi
2805 Keith Raisanen
2806 Pete Freeman
2807 Steve Carter
2808 Kevin Burdick
2809 Wesley Chamberlain
2810 Domingo Merejo
2811 Junior Vizcaino
2812 Keith Shepherd
2813 Ed Hartman
2814 Jose Acosta
2815 Jim Garrison
2816 Jody Williams
2817 Mark Thomas
2818 Rob Barnwell
2819 Jeff Griffith
2820 Joe Pacholec
2821 Pete Murphy
2822 Mark Koller
2823 Joe Macavage
2824 Moises Alou
2825 Doug Torberg
2826 Charlie Green
2827 Jeff Cox
2828 Mike Sandoval

1987 ProCards Wausau Timbers

(Seattle Mariners, A) (Price includes the scarce #1152 card)

	MT	NR MT	EX
Complete Set:	6.00	4.50	2.50

1127 Bobby Cuellar
1128 Jim Bluerberg
1129 Jody Ryan
1130 Dan Disher
1131 Howard Townsend
1132 Troy Williams
1133 Patrick Lennon
1134 Jose Tartabull
1135 Wendell Bolar
1136 Clay Gunn
1137 Jose Bennett
1138 Ted Williams
1139 Anthony Woods
1140 Drew Kosco
1141 Jim Bowie
1142 Mark Wooden
1143 Jerry Goff
1144 Deron Johnson
1145 Mike Thorpe
1146 Michael McDonald
1147 Trent Intorcia
1148 Dave Hartnott
1149 Mark Gold
1150 Pat Rice
1151 Rudy Webster
1152 Unidentified Player
1153 Ric Wilson
1154 Tim Erickson

1987 ProCards West Palm Beach Expos

(Montreal Expos, A)

	MT	NR MT	EX
Complete Set:	7.50	5.75	3.00

652 Rob Leary
653 Tim Touma
654 Paul Frye
655 Alfredo Cardwood
656 Jeff Tabaka
657 Rob Williams
658 Derrell Baker
659 Pat Sipe
660 Kevin Dean
661 Bob Caffrey
662 Bud Yanus
663 Don Burke
664 Mike Blowers
665 Cesar Hernandez
666 Al Collins
667 Yorkis Perez
668 Charlie Lea
669 Omer Munoz
670 Mel Houston
671 Tommy Traen
672 Eddie Dixon
673 Kevin Kristan
674 Jeff Huson
675 Don Burke
676 Steve Rousey
677 Gene Harris
678 Geff Davis
679 John Spinosa

A card number in parentheses () indicates the set is unnumbered.

1987 ProCards Williamsport Bills

(Cleveland Indians, AA)

	MT	NR MT	EX
Complete Set:	6.00	4.50	2.50

1379 Dain Syverson
1380 Keith Bennett
1381 Winston Ficklin
1382 Oscar Mejia
1383 Luis Encarnacion
1384 Steve Moses
1385 Bobby Link
1386 Jim Bishop
1387 Mark Higgins
1388 Mike Bellaman
1389 Ivan Murrell
1390 Daryl Smith
1391 Miguel Roman
1392 Dave Bresnahan
1393 Rick Henke
1394 Brian Allard
1395 Greg LaFever
1396 Steve Swosher
1397 Greg Dube
1398 Scott Sabo
1399 Roger Wilson
1400 Chris Beasley
1401 Bernardo Brito
1402 Luis Medina
1403 Turner Gill
1404 Greg Karpuk
1405 Joe Skalski

1987 ProCards Winston-Salem Spirits

(Chicago Cubs, A)

	MT	NR MT	EX
Complete Set:	7.00	5.25	2.75

1209 Mark McMorris
1210 Greg Kallevig
1211 Todd Cloninger
1212 Cedric Landrum
1213 Bill Danek
1214 Phil Hannon
1215 Heath Slocumb
1216 Bob Bafia
1217 Luis Cruz
1218 Jim Bullinger
1219 Tad Slowik
1220 Glenn Gregson
1221 Jay Loviglio
1222 Lee Grimes
1223 Tim Wallace
1224 John Lewis
1225 Joe Girardi
1226 Gabby Robles
1227 Mike Tullier
1228 Mike Miller
1229 Chuck Oertli
1230 Kris Roth
1231 Jeff Hirsch
1232 Jeff Small
1233 DeWayne Coleman
1234 Jim Matas
1235 Mike Curtis

1987 ProCards Winter Haven Red Sox

(Boston Red Sox, A)

	MT	NR MT	EX
Complete Set:	6.00	4.50	2.50

893 Tim Buheller
894 Felix Dedos
895 Livio Padilla
896 Larry Shikles
897 Ronnie McGowan
898 Bart Haley
899 Erik Laseke
900 Leverne Jackson
901 Daniel Sullivan
902 Dan Gabrielle
903 Mike Coffey
904 Stuart Weidie
905 Bruce Lockhart
906 David Milstein
907 Odie Abril
908 John Toale
909 Manny Jose
910 Wayne Murphy
911 Mike Sears
912 Paul Slifko
913 Eduardo Zambrano
914 Eric Hetzel
915 Derek Livernois
916 Doug Camilli
917 Mike Ickes
918 Roger Haggerty
919 Paul Thoutsis
920 Jim Orsag
921 Todd Pratt
922 Dana Gomez

1987 Team Wichita Pilots

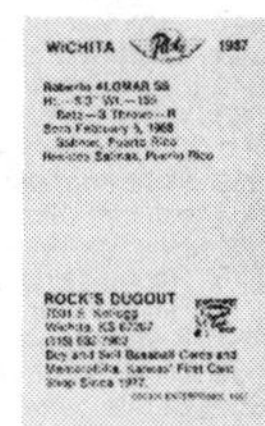

(San Diego Padres) (color) (Rock's Dugout)

	MT	NR MT	EX
Complete Set:	35.00	26.00	14.00

10 Mike Debutch
11 Kevin Armstrong
12 Tommy Alexander
14 Roberto Alomar
15 Sandy Alomar, Jr.
17 Nate Colbert
18 Chris Knabenshue
19 Brad Pounders
20 Steve Smith
21 Joe Lynch
22 Greg Harris
23 Eric Nolte
24 Thomas Howard
25 Jeff Reece
26 Mike Costello
27 Scott Rainey
28 Jeff Stewart
29 Dave Cortez
30 Tom Brassil
31 Candy Sierra
32 Kevin Brown
33 Eric Bauer
42 Steve Luebber
43 Jerald Clark
44 Cam Walker

1987 ProCards Wytheville Cubs

(Chicago Cubs, A)

	MT	NR MT	EX
Complete Set:	7.00	5.25	2.75

2738 Anthony Whitson
2739 Matt Walbeck
2740 Horace Tucker
2741 Scott Taylor
2742 Derek Stroud
2743 Dave Sommer
2744 Jossy Rosario
2745 Victor Quiles
2746 Eric Perry
2747 Elvin Paulino
2748 Nelson Nunex
2749 Greg Jackson
2750 John Gardner
2751 Edger Galarza
2752 Henry Fleming
2753 Matthew Franco
2754 Francisco Espino
2755 Darren Eggleston
2756 Jay Eddings
2757 Braz Davis
2758 Frank Castillo
2759 Danny Carpenter
2760 Carlos Canino
2761 Frank Campos
2762 Matt Cakora
2763 Warren Arrington
2764 Alex Arias
2765 Tom King
2766 Rick Kranitz
2767 Brad Mills
2768 Team Photo

1988 ProCards Albany-Colonie Yankees

(New York Yankees, AA)

	MT	NR MT	EX
Complete Set:	8.00	6.00	3.25

1329 Amalio Carreno
1330 Andy Stankiewicz
1331 Bob Green
1332 Rob Sepanek
1333 Tim Layana
1334 Bobby Davidson
1335 Gary Cathcart
1336 Dave Eiland
1337 Mike Christopher
1338 Rick Torres
1339 Tony Ferreira
1340 Troy Evers
1341 Tim Becker
1342 Dana Ridenour
1343 Melvin Rosario
1344 Jim Leyritz
1345 Scott Shaw
1346 Jason Mass
1347 Oscar Azocar
1348 Aris Tirado
1349 Hensley Meulens
1350 Dickie Scott
1351 Deron Johnson
1352 Tommy Jones
1353 Tony Cloninger
1354 Mike Heifferon
---- Checklist

1988 CMC Albuquerque Dukes

(Los Angeles Dodgers, AAA)

	MT	NR MT	EX
Complete Set:	8.00	6.00	3.25

1 Shawn Hillegas
2 Stan Kyles
3 Bill Krueger
4 Ray Searage
5 Tony Arnold
6 Bill Brennan
7 Dennis Burtt
8 Tim Crews
9 Mike Hartley
10 Chuck Hensley
11 Hector Heredia
12 Chris Gwynn
13 Hinshaw George
14 Mike Ramsey
15 Jon Debus
16 Mike Sharperson
17 Tracy Woodson
18 Mike Devereaux
19 Jose Gonzalez
20 John Gibbons
21 Gil Reyes
22 Shanie Dugas
23 Mariano Duncan
24 Steve Garcia
25 Terry Collins

1988 ProCards Albuquerque Dukes

(Los Angeles Dodgers, AAA)

	MT	NR MT	EX
Complete Set:	8.00	6.00	3.25

249 Steve Garcia
250 Bill Brennan
251 Brent Strom
252 Mike Devereaux
253 Mike Sharperson
254 Von Joshua
255 Mariano Duncan
256 Tracy Woodson
257 Gilberto Reyes
258 Jose Gonzalez
259 Chris Gwynn
260 John Gibbons
261 Tony Arnold
262 Ray Searage
263 Mike Hartley
264 Tim Crews
265 Shawn Hillegas
266 Shanie Dugas
267 Mike Ramsey
268 George Hinshaw
269 Jon Debus
270 Terry Collins
271 Bill Krueger
272 Lenny Currier
273 Chuck Hensley
274 Hector Heredia
275 Stan Kyles
276 Dennis Burtt
---- Checklist

1988 ProCards Appleton Foxes

(Kansas City Royals, A)

	MT	NR MT	EX
Complete Set:	7.00	9.75	5.25

137 Jorge Pedre
138 Luis Mallea
139 Brian Meyers
140 Kevin Shaw
141 Doug Nelson
142 Terry Shumpert

143 Linton Dyer
144 Darryl Robinson
145 Dave Howard
146 Don Wright
147 Bill Stonikas
148 Karl Drezek
149 Tom Gordon
150 Tim Odom
151 Trey Gainous
152 Brian McCormack
153 Keith Shibata
154 Frank Henderson
155 Jesus DeLeon
156 Chris Gurchiek
157 Doug Bock
158 Jeff Baum
159 Andre Rabouin
160 Dennis Moeller
161 Bobby Knecht
162 Brian Poldberg
163 Mike Leon
164 Larry Dawson
165 Team Photo Card
---- Checklist

1988 Grand Slam Arkansas Travelers

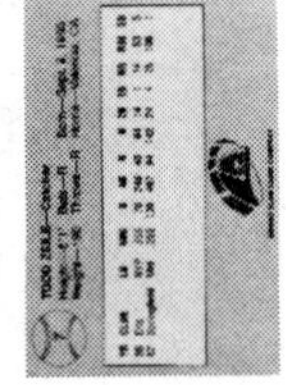

(St. Louis Cardinals, AA)

	MT	NR MT	EX
Complete Set:	10.00	7.50	4.00

1 Rick Colbert
2 Brad Henderson
3 Steve Engel
4 Jim Riggleman
5 Jeff Fassero
6 Bien Figueroa
7 Todd Zeile
8 Tom Baine
9 Bob Faron
10 Mauricio Nunez
11 Ken Infante
12 Howard Hilton
13 Brett Harrison
14 Matt Kinzer
15 Jesus Mendez
16 Jim Fregosi
17 Benito Malave
18 Mike Sassone
19 Mike Robinson
20 Mike Robertson
21 Mike Perez
22 Jim Puzey
23 Dave Osteen
24 Jeff Oyster
25 Mike Senne

1988 ProCards Asheville Tourists

(Houston Astros, A)

	MT	NR MT	EX
Complete Set:	6.00	5.25	2.75

1049 Billy Carver
1050 Kenny Dickson
1051 Greg Johnson
1052 Andy Harter
1053 Ramon Cedeno
1054 Mike Beams
1055 Joe Charno
1056 Carlos Laboy
1057 Neder Horta
1058 Ed Renteria
1059 Chris Lee
1060 Harold Allen
1061 Dan Lewis
1062 Gorky Perez
1063 Fred Costello
1064 Joe Locke
1065 Doug Royalty
1066 Joe Ortiz
1067 Charley Taylor
1068 Gary Tuck
1069 Richie Simon
1070 Dennis Tafoya
1071 Danny Newman
1072 Dean Hartgraves
1073 Mike Hook
1074 Carlos Henry
1075 Dave Cunningham
1076 Gene Confreda
1077 Ron McKee
1078 Todd Weber
---- Checklist

1988 ProCards Auburn Astros

(Houston Astros, A)

	MT	NR MT	EX
Complete Set:	10.00	7.50	4.00

1947 Larry Lamphere
1948 Scott Spurgeon
1949 Chris Small
1950 Wally Trice
1951 Dennis Tafoya
1952 Pat Penafeather
1953 Kenny Lofton
1954 Ron Porterfield
1955 Rodney Windes
1956 Harry Fuller
1957 Ken Morris
1958 Dave Shermet
1959 Bernie Jenkins
1960 Rod Scheckla
1961 John Massarelli
1962 Mike Beams
1963 Rick Wise
1964 Bob Neal
1965 Neder Horta
1966 Andy Mota
1967 Frank Cacciatore
1968 Jim DeSapio
1969 Rick Dunnum
1970 Gordy Farmer
1971 John Graham
1972 David Klinefelter
1973 Luis Gonzalez
1974 Mica Lewis
---- Checklist

1988 ProCards Augusta Pirates

(Pittsburgh Pirates, A)

	MT	NR MT	EX
Complete Set:	18.00	13.50	7.25

359 Wes Chamberlain
360 Moises Alou
361 Miguel Valverde
362 Mickey Peyton
363 Jeff Griffith
364 Orlando Merced
365 Carlos Garcia
366 Eddie Hartman
367 Pete Freeman
368 Scott Barczi
369 Jimmy Garrison
370 Ben Shelton
371 Jose Acosta
372 Joe Macavage
373 Joe Pacholec
374 Butch Schlopy
375 Keith Shepherd
376 Scott Runge
377 Willie Smith
378 Ron Downs
379 Tracy Toy
380 Tonny Cohen
381 Joel Forrest
382 Jeff Cox
383 Dave Moharter
384 Glenn Trudo
385 S. Carter
386 Robert Harris
387 Jmaes Rhoades
388 Paul Day
389 Len Monheimer
1576 Mark Merchant
---- Checklist

1988 Cal Cards Bakersfield Dodgers

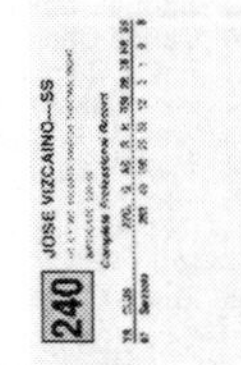

(Los Angeles Dodgers, A)

	MT	NR MT	EX
Complete Set:	8.00	6.00	3.25

234 Jeff Brown
235 Dan Henley
236 John Knapp
237 Alan Lewis
238 Dan Montgomery
239 Jose Munoz
240 Jose Vizcaino
241 Amilcar Valdez
242 Adam Brown
243 Carlos Hernandez
244 Billy Argo
245 Jay Hornacek
246 John Beuder
247 Bruce Dostal
248 Steve Green
249 Wayne Kirby
250 Billy Brooks
251 Carlos Carrasco
252 Chris Cerny
253 Chris Gettler
254 Ken King
255 Todd Kroll
256 Lee Langley
257 Dan Pena
258 Tim Scott
259 Zak Shinall
260 Dennis Springer
261 John Wanish
262 Gary La Rogue
263 Guy Conti
264 Stan Johnston
265 Tommy Davis
266 Jack Patton
267 Rick Smith

1988 Best/ProCards Baseball America AA Prospects

(AA)

	MT	NR MT	EX
Complete Set:	15.00	11.00	6.00

1AA Hensley Meulens (Albany)
2AA Mike Harkey (Pittsfield)
3AA Rob Ritchie (Glens Falls)
4AA Omar Vizquel (Vermont)
5AA Jerome Walton (Pittsfield)
6AA Chuck Malone (Reading)
7AA Tom Lampkin (Williamsport)
8AA Joe Girardi (Pittsfield)
9AA Kevin Wickander (Williamsport)
10AA Bill McGuire (Vermont)
11AA Pete Harnisch (Charlotte)
12AA Derek Park (Orlando)
13AA Alex Sanchez (Knoxville)
14AA Jose DeJesus (Memphis)
15AA Rafael DeLima (Orlando)
16AA Mark Lemke (Greenville)
17AA Chris Hammond (Chattanooga)
18AA German Gonzalez (Orlando)
19AA Dennis Jones (Knoxville)
20AA Francisco Cabrera (Knoxville)
21AA Ramon Martinez (San Antonio)
22AA Gary Sheffield (El Paso)
23AA Juan Bell (San Antonio)
24AA Greg Vaughn (El Paso)
25AA Kevin Brown (Tulsa)
26AA Mike Munoz (San Antonio)
27AA Trevor Wilson (Shreveport)
28AA John Wetteland (San Antonio)
29AA Jeff Manto (Midland)
30AA Buddy Bailey (Greenville)

1988 Star Co. Baseball City Royals

(Kansas City Royals, A) (Price includes the scarce Silverio card and the corrected Vasquez and Walker cards)

	MT	NR MT	EX
Complete Set:	11.00	8.25	4.50

1 Bud Adams
2 Ken Adams
3 Jon Alexander
4 Jose Anglero
5 Kevin Appier
6 Sean Berry
7 Mike Butcher
8 Dera Clark
9 Tony Bridges-Clements
10 Jeff Conine
11 Carlos Escalera
12 Carlos Gonzalez
13 Dan Harlan
14 Kenny Jackson
15 Kevin Koslofski
16 Richie LeBlanc Jr.
17 Brian McRae
18 Bobby Moore
19 Harvey Pulliam Jr.
20a Tom Rice
20b Luis Silverio (late issue, misnumbered, gold rather than blue border)
21 Joe Skodny
22 Mike Tresemer
23a Aguedo Vasquez (correct name & stats, wrong picture)
23b Aguedo Vasquez (corrected)
24a Steve Walker (correct name & stats, wrong picture)
24b Steve Walker (corrected)
25 DeJon Watson

1988 ProCards Batavia Clippers

(Philadelphia Phillies, A)

	MT	NR MT	EX
Complete Set:	6.00	4.50	2.50

Checklist
1662 Bob Tiefenauer
1663 Dave Cash
1664 Don McCormack
1665 Tony Trevino
1666 Leroy Ventress
1667 Nicio Martinez
1668 Scott Drury
1669 Wayne Fuller
1670 Rick Trlicek
1671 Eric Enos
1672 Mark Bradford
1673 Erik Bratlien
1674 Tim Dell
1675 Mike Owens
1676 Tom Marsh
1677 Chris Walker
1678 Nick Santa Cruz
1679 Joe Tenhunfeld
1680 Ike Galloway
1681 Rich Walker
1682 Todd Elam
1683 Matt Viggiano
1684 Dave Allen
1685 Rich Tracy
1686 Fred Felton III
1687 Andy Barrick
1688 Gary Wilson
1689 Brian Cummings
1690 Troy Zerb
1691 Brad Rogers

1988 Team Bellingham Mariners

	MT	NR MT	EX
Complete Set:	9.00	6.75	3.50

1 Jeff Hooper
2 Erick Bryant
3 Brian Wilkinson
4 Dorian Daughty
5 Kevin Reichardt
6 Keith Helton
7 John Hoffman
8 Victor Mangual
9 Chuck Carr
10 Tom Peters
11 Todd Haney
12 Joe Georger
13 Jeff Morrison
14 Wade Taylor
15 Ken Griffey, Jr.
16 Spyder Webb
17 Otis Patrick
18 Mike Goff
19 Brian Baldwin
20 Tony Cayson
21 Mike Sisco
22 Mike McGuire
23 Ruben Gonzalez
24 Rick Sweet
25 Daryl Burrus
26 Scott Stoerck
27 Fausto Ramirez
28 Salty Parker
29 Steve Beiksha
30 Paul Togneri
31 Corey Paul
32 Chris Van Buren
33 Team Photo/Checklist

1988 Legoe Bellingham Mariners

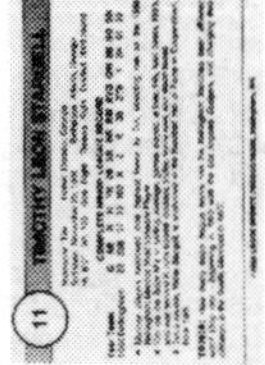

(Seattle Mariners, A)

	MT	NR MT	EX
Complete Set:	6.00	11.25	6.00

1 Ricky Candelari
2 Dorian Daughtry
3 Tony Cayson
4 Ellerton Maynard
5 Mike McLaughlin
6 Tom McNamara
7 Greg Prikl
8 Julio Reyan
9 Jeff Miller

10 Pete Schmidt
11 Tim Stargell
12 Gary Wheelock
13 Brian Wilkinson
14 Lee Hancock
15 John Kohli
16 Jim Kosnik
17 Tom Liss
18 Victor Mangual
19 Scott Pitcher
20 Keith Barrett
21 Scott Stoerck
22 Nick Felix
23 Ted Eldredge
24 Chris Doll
25 Erick Bryant
26 Mike Beiras
27 Otis Patrick
28 P.J. Carey
29 Donnie Reynolds
30 Batboys (Jeff Crnich, Mike Thompson)
31 Spyder Webb
---- Logo card

1988 Grand Slam Beloit Brewers

(Milwaukee Brewers, A)

	MT	NR MT	EX
Complete Set:	6.00	4.50	2.50

1 Gomer Hodge
2 Gary Robson
3 Jim Poulin
4 Frank Bolick
5 Tim Raley
6 Dan Adriance
7 Charlie McGrew
8 Juan Uribe
9 Bob Simonson
10 Mark Chapman
11 Bob Sobczyk
12 Bryan Foster
13 Kent Hetrick
14 Torricelli Tim
15 Mike Guerrero
16 Curt Krippner
17 Tim Wahl
18 Leonardo Perez
19 Dave Nilsson
20 Dan Peters
21 Randy Moore
22 Mike Whitlock
23 Chris Cassels
24 Steve Sparks
25 Chris Johnson

1988 Legoe Bend Bucks

(California Angels) (color)

	MT	NR MT	EX
Complete Set:		12.50	9.50

1 Angel Carrasquillo
2 Jeff Kipila
3 Shawn Cunningham
4 Jeff Oberdank
5 Ramon Martinez
6 Frank Brito
7 Gary DiSarcina
8 Steve Kirwin
9 Jeff Kelso
10 Jim Edmonds
11 Dave Patrick
12 Chris Threadgill
13 Huascar Mateo
14 Tim Taft
15 Dave Sturdivant
16 Enrique Tejeda
17 Miguel Batista
18 Bruce Vegely
19 Dave Neal
20 John Fritz
21 Glenn Carter
22 Mark Holzemer
23 Todd James
24 John Marchese
25 Justin Martin
26 Don Vidmar
27 Don Long
28 Howie Gershberg
29 Rick Ingalls
30 Derek Winchell
31 Gary Murphy
32 Paul List
33 Shawn Cunningham, Gary DiSarcina, Jeff Oberdank
34 Bucky Buck (Mascot/ckecklist on back)
35 Charles Phillips
---- Logo Card

1988 ProCards Billings Mustangs

(Cincinnati Reds, A)

	MT	NR MT	EX
Complete Set:	7.00	5.25	2.75

Checklist
1802 David Keller
1803 John Groninger
1804 Jim Brune
1805 Duane Mulville
1806 Glenn Sutko
1807 Scott Sellner
1808 Michael Mulvaney
1809 Doug Bond
1810 Steve Reyes
1811 Tony Terzariel
1812 Dante Johnson
1813 Danny Perozo
1814 Scott Economy
1815 John Groennert
1816 Tomas Rodriguez
1817 Steve McCarthy
1818 Steve Foster
1819 Brian Nichols
1820 Brian Landy
1821 Jerry Spradlin
1822 Reggie Sanders
1823 C.L. Thomas
1824 Vicente Javier
1825 Johnny Almaraz
1826 Carl Stewart
1827 Jim Hoff
1828 Kurt Dempster
1829 Michael Songini
1830 Benny Colvard
1831 Carl Nordstrom

1988 Best Birmingham Barons

(Chicago White Sox, AA)

	MT	NR MT	EX
Complete Set:	7.00	5.25	2.75

1 Wayne Edwards
2 Tony Biasucci
3 Tom Drees
4 Ray Chadwick
5 Jim Markert
6 Dave Wallwork
7 Moe Drabowsky
8 Rico Petrocelli
9 Todd Trafton
10 Tommy Tompson
11 Pete Venturini
12 Tom Forrester
13 Dan Wagner
14 Mark Davis
15 Rick Pollack
16 Carlos Martinez
17 Rich Gaynor
18 John Boling
19 Daryl Smith
20 Tony Menedez
21 Dan Cronkright
22 Matt Merullo
23 Jerry Bertolani
24 Craig Grebeck
25 Willie Magallanes
26 Doug Little
27 Chuck Mount
28 Kevin Renz
29 Checklist/Hoover Metro Stadium

1988 ProCards Boise Hawks

(No affiliation, A)

	MT	NR MT	EX
Complete Set:	6.00	4.50	2.50

Checklist
1605 John Bilello
1606 Michael Tate
1607 Wendell Bolar
1608 Michael Moore
1609 Christopher Gurchiek
1610 James Qualls
1611 Mike Shambaugh
1612 Edward Holub
1613 Christopher Shultis
1614 Barry Griffin
1615 Larry Lundeen
1616 Jeff Mace
1617 Earl Malone
1618 Jerry Backus
1619 Randy Janikowski
1620 Michael Larson
1621 Chuck Lavrusky
1622 Michael Lomeli
1623 Bill Wenrick
1624 Charles Douglas
1625 Mark Krumback
1626 Joseph Mancini
1627 Daren De Pew
1628 Keven Bottenfield
1629 Tim MacKinnon
1630 Frank Jury
1631 Robert Winterburn
1632 Mal Fichman

1988 ProCards Bristol Tigers

	MT	NR MT	EX
Complete Set:	7.00	5.25	2.75

1862 Rick Mag
1863 Carlos Maldonado
1864 Doug Biggs
1865 Tim Brader
1866 Juan Estevez
1867 Bob Frassa
1868 Rusty Meacham
1869 Julio Rosa
1870 Ron Howard
1871 Mike Davidson
1872 Rich Rowland
1873 Freddy Padilla
1874 Jimmy Hayes
1875 Chris Gollehon
1876 Eric Shoup
1877 Mike Rendina
1878 Duane Walker
1879 Blaine Rudolph
1880 Mike Koller
1881 Tom Aldrich
1882 Marcos Bentances
1883 Mick Delas
1884 Bret Roach
1885 Rico Brogna
1886 Ed Ferm
1887 Kurt Shea
1888 Rob Thomas
1889 Mike Jones
1890 Paul Nozling
1891 Tookie Spann
1892 Benny Castillo
---- Checklist

1988 CMC Buffalo Bisons

(Pittsburgh Pirates, AAA)

	MT	NR MT	EX
Complete Set:	7.00	5.25	2.75

1 Logan Easley
2 Stan Fansler
3 Brett Gideon
4 Dave Johnson
5 Randy Kramer
6 Morris Madden
7 Bob Patterson
8 Dave Rucker
9 Dorn Taylor
10 Scott Medvin
11 Benny Distefano
12 Tommy Gregg
13 Tom Romano
14 Bernie Tatis
15 Denny Gonzalez
16 Bryan Little
17 Jim Reboulet
18 Rico Rossy
19 Tom Prince
20 Orestes Destrade
21 Felix Fermin
22 Dave Sax
23 Skeeter Barnes
24 Stan Cliburn
25 Rocky Bridges

1988 ProCards Buffalo Bisons

(Pittsburgh Pirates, AAA)

	MT	NR MT	EX
Complete Set:	7.00	5.25	2.75

1464 Randy Kramer
1465 Felix Fermin
1466 Morris Madden
1467 Bob Patterson
1468 Dorn Taylor
1469 Stan Fansler
1470 Jim Reboulet
1471 Rico Rossy
1472 Dave Rucker
1473 Denny Gonzalez
1474 Tommy Gregg
1475 Bernie Tatis
1476 Dave Johnson
1477 Donald Palmer
1478 Rocky Bridges
1479 Jackie Brown
1480 Stan Cliburn
1481 Carlos Ledezma
1482 Kevin Hodge
1483 Dave Sax
1484 Scott Medvin
1485 Tom Romano
1486 Orestes Destrade
1487 Skeeter Barnes
1488 Tom Prince
1489 Benny Distefano
1490 Logan Easley
1491 Bryan Little
1492 Brett Gideon
1493 Pilot Field
---- Checklist

1988 Team Buffalo Bisons

(Pittsburgh Pirates, AAA) This set is in the form of a 14" x 14" poster.

	MT	NR MT	EX
Complete Set:	15.00	11.00	6.00

(1) Rocky Bridges
(2) Benny Distefano
(3) Dave Johnson
(4) Bryan Little
(5) Morris Madden
(6) Jim Reboulet
(7) Tom Romano
(8) Dorn Taylor

1988 ProCards Burlington Braves

(Atlanta Braves, A)

	MT	NR MT	EX
Complete Set:	9.00	6.75	3.50

1106 Lynn Robinson
1107 Carl Pointer-Jones
1108 Mike Stanton
1109 Chad Smith
1110 Matt Turner
1111 Pat Tilman
1112 Brian Murphy
1113 Jerald Frost
1114 Steve Glass
1115 Brian Champion
1116 Grady Little
1117 Brian Cummings
1118 Jim Lemasters
1119 Jeff Greene
1120 Jim Nowlin
1121 Dave Karasinski
1122 Jaime Cuesta
1123 Dave Grilone
1124 Albert Martin
1125 Sean Ross
1126 Rich Casarotti
1127 Rick Berg
1128 Eduardo Perez
1129 Andy Tomberlin
1130 Brian Hunter
1131 Gil Garrido, Jr.
1132 Brian Deak
1133 John Mitchell
1134 Jack Aker
1135 Paul Egins III
---- Checklist

1988 ProCards Burlington Indians

(Cleveland Indians, A)

	MT	NR MT	EX
Complete Set:	6.00	4.50	2.50

1772 Brent Roberts
1773 Rick Falkner
1774 Lenny Gilmore
1775 Martin Eddy
1776 Randy Mazey
1777 Vince Barranco
1778 Sean Baron
1779 Jeff Bonchek
1780 Rouglas Odor
1781 Axel Castillo
1782 Todd Butler
1783 Carlos Mota
1784 Scott Allen
1785 Charles Alexander
1786 Mike Bucci
1787 Pedro Arias
1788 Pablo Gomez
1789 David Oliveras
1790 Doug Piatt
1791 Barry Blundin
1792 Jeff Mutis
1793 Mike Ashworth
1794 Bob Kairis
1795 Brett Merriman
1796 Greg McMichael
1797 Andre Halle
1798 Brian Johnson
1799 Dan Williams
1800 Mark Lewis
1801 Ray Borowicz
---- Checklist

The values quoted are intended to reflect the market price.

1988 Sport Pro Butte Copper Kings

	MT	NR MT	EX
Complete Set:	8.00	6.00	3.25

1 Mike Hamilton
2 Jim Hivizda
3 Greg Kuzman
4 Tim MacNeil
5 Robb Nen
6 Ken Penland
7 Carl Randle
8 Bill Schorr
9 Cedrick Shaw
10 Kyle Spencer
11 Kenny Shiozaki
12 Denny Tomori
13 Bill Losa
14 Jeff Frye
15 Rob Maurer
16 Dom Pierce
17 Joe Wardlow
18 Trey McCoy
19 Rod Morris
20 Mike Spear
21 Thayer Swain
22 Monty Farriss
23 Travis Law
24 Brad Fontes
25 Jeff Hainline
26 Steve Allen
27 Ev Cunningham
28 Ernie Rodriquez
29 Bump Wills

1988 CMC Calgary Cannons

(Seattle Mariners, AAA)

	MT	NR MT	EX
Complete Set:	8.50	6.50	3.50

1 Darren Burroughs
2 Paul Schneider
3 Rich Monteleone
4 Dennis Powell
5 Jay Baller
6 Mike Christ
7 Jim Walker
8 Matt West
9 Mike Schooler
10 Rod Scurry
11 Donell Nixon
12 Phil Ouellette
13 Greg Briley
14 Dave Cochrane
15 Brian Giles
16 Edgar Martinez
17 John Christensen
18 Dave Hengel
19 Nelson Simmons
20 Mike Wishnevski
21 Roger Hansen
22 Doug Merrifield
23 Mike Watters
24 Bill Plummer
25 Dan Warthen

1988 ProCards Calgary Cannons

(Seattle Mariners, AAA) This is also a police set.

	MT	NR MT	EX
Complete Set:	7.50	5.75	3.00

779 Rod Scurry
780 Darren Burroughs
781 Terry Taylor
782 Edgar Martinez
783 Mike Wishnevski
784 Brian Giles
785 Dave Cocrane
786 Erik Hanson
787 Doug Merrifield
788 Matt West
789 Dan Warthen
790 Roger Hansen
791 Jim Walker
792 Jay Baller
793 Paul Schneider
794 John Christensen
795 Mike Schooler
796 Dennis Powell
797 Rich Monteleone
798 Mike Watters
799 Greg Briley
800 Bill Plummer
801 Phil Ouellette
802 Nelson Simmons
803 Brick Smith
804 Mario Diaz
1550 Dave Hengel
---- Checklist

1988 Cal Cards California League All-Stars

(A)

	MT	NR MT	EX
Complete Set:	15.00	11.00	6.00

1 Jose Offerman
2 Eric Karros
3 Mark Merchant
4 Willie Banks
5 Lance Rice
6 Carlos Capellan
7 Jose Valentin
8 Dave Jacas
9 Braulio Castillo
10 Mike Humphreys
11 Wiley Lee
12 Ruben Gonzalez
13 Johnny Ard
14 Mike Goff
15 Jeff Hartsock
16 James Wray
17 Doug Simons
18 Jerry Brooks
19 Eddie Pye
20 Andy Skeels
21 Sean Snedeker
22 Steve Finken
23 Tim Johnson
24 Guy Conti
25 Scott Ullger
26 Tim Terrio
27 Bill Weiss
28 Don Drysdale
29 Charlie Montoyo
30 Jim Jones
31 Stan Royer
32 Bobby Jones
33 Darren Lewis
34 Gary Borg
35 Steve Hecht
36 Gary Nalls
37 John Dalfanz
38 Chris George
39 Mike Ignasiak
40 Kevin Meier
41 Joe Strong
42 Shawn Barton
43 Mark Dewey
44 Bill Savarino
45 John Jaha
46 Joe Kmak
47 Steve Lienhard
48 Greg Sparks
49 Duane Espy
50 Todd Oakes
51 Scott Wilson
52 Brent Howard
53 Erik DeSonnaville
54 Bob Brooks
55 George Ulrich
56 Joe Gagliardi

1988 Star Co. Carolina League All-Stars

(A)

	MT	NR MT	EX
Complete Set:	9.00	6.75	3.50

1 Jay Ward
2 Mike Hart
3 Stan Belinda
4 Royal Clayton
5 Scott Cooper
6 Brian DuBois
7 Mike Eberle
8 Andy Hall
9 Chris Howard
10 Dean Kelley
11 Tim Kirk
12 Joe Marchese
13 Jim Orsag
14 Julio Peguero
15 John Ramos
16 Enrique Rios
17 Randy Strijek
18 Junior Vizcaino
19 Bernie Williams
20 Bob Zupcic
21 Glenn Adams
22 Pete Alborano
23 Beau Allred
24 Kevin Bearse
25 Mike Bell
26 Luis Cruz
27 Butch Garcia
28 Phil Harrison
29 Allen Liebert
30 Kelly Mann
31 Kent Mercker
32 Rick Morris
33 Charles Ogden
34 Dave Plumb
35 Greg Smith
36 Rob Swain
37 Theron Todd
38 Mike Twardoski
39 Danny Weems
40 Mike Westbrook

1988 ProCards Cedar Rapids Reds

(Cincinnati Reds, A)

	MT	NR MT	EX
Complete Set:	7.00	5.25	2.75

1136 Don Buchheister
1137 Greg Simpson
1138 Bill Dodd
1139 Mike Moscrey
1140 Sandy Krume
1141 Chico Fernandez
1142 Freddy Benavides
1143 Gary Denbo
1144 Marc Bombard
1145 Bruce Colson
1146 Reggie Jefferson
1147 Pete Beeler
1148 Rich Sapienza
1149 Ramon Sambo
1150 Steve Davis
1151 Jeff Forney
1152 Greg Lonigro
1153 Doug Eastman
1154 Jim Brune
1155 Eddie Rush
1156 Brad Brusky
1157 Scott Scudder
1158 Carl Nordstrom
1159 Butch Henry
1160 Sam Chavez
1161 Bud Curran
1162 Darrell Rodgers
1163 Milton Hill
1164 Mike Malinak
1165 Jim Bishop
---- Checklist

1988 ProCards Charleston Rainbows

(San Diego Padres, A)

	MT	NR MT	EX
Complete Set:	6.00	4.50	2.50

1193 Willie Forbes
1194 Tony Pellegrino
1195 Jim Wasem
1196 David Bond
1197 Charles Hillemann
1198 Jose Valentin
1199 Mike Myers
1200 Osvaldo Sanchez
1201 Rafael Valdez
1202 Mike King
1203 Guillermo Velazquez
1204 Monte Brooks
1205 Mark Kleven
1206 Todd Hansen
1207 Keith Harrison
1208 Darrin Reichle
1209 Todd Torchia
1210 Omar Olivares
1211 Doug Brocail
1212 Gary Lance
1213 Jay Estrada
1214 Tony Lewis
1215 Saul Soltero
1216 Reggie Farmer
1217 Bob Lutticken
1218 Jaime Moreno
1219 Jack Krol
1220 Nelson Silverio
1221 Tim Barker
---- Checklist

1988 Best Charleston Wheelers

(Chicago Cubs, A)

	MT	NR MT	EX
Complete Set:	6.00	4.50	2.50

1 Matt Walbeck
2 Brad Mills
3 Greg Mahlberg
4 Scott Taylor
5 Mike Reeder
6 Lee Grimes
7 Eric Perry
8 Steve Owens
9 Alex Arias
10 Darren Eggleston
11 Tony Duenas
12 Jay Eddings
13 Patrick Gomez
14 Henry Gomez
15 John Gardner
16 Marcus Lopez
17 Matt Cakora
18 Don Cohoon
19 DeWayne Coleman
20 Braz Davis
21 Harry Shelton
22 Fernando Ramsey
23 Elio Jose
24 Frank Campos
25 Ray Mullino
26 Nick Rameriez
27 Bob Grimes
28 Checklist/Wheelers Stadium

1988 Team Charlotte Knights

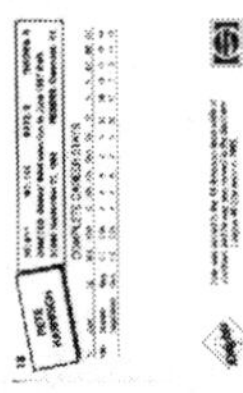

(Baltimore Orioles, AA)

	MT	NR MT	EX
Complete Set:	9.00	6.75	3.50

1 Brian Householder
2 Bob Williams
3 Butch Davis
4 Kevin Price
5 Tim Dulin
6 Rob Walton
7 Jim O'Dell
8 Jeff Tackett
9 Joe Jarrell
10 Jeff Wood
11 John Posey
12 Craig Chamberlain
13 Rocky Cusak
14 Mike Pazik
15 Rafel Skeete
16 Jim Daniel
17 Paul Thorpe
18 Pete Harnish
19 Jerry Holtz
20 Gordon Dillard
21 Dana Smith
22 Ty Nichols
23 Greg Biagini
24 Curt Brown
25 Sherwin Cijntje

1988 Star Co. Charlotte Rangers

(Texas Rangers) (color) (Price includes late-issue Jones and Sanchez cards)

	MT	NR MT	EX
Complete Set:	45.00	34.00	18.00

1 Rick Bernardo
2 Brian Bohanon
3 Omar Brewer
4 Phil Bryant
5 Paco Burgos
6 Rufus Ellis
7 Darrin Garner
8 Juan Gonzalez
9 Bill Haselman
10 Jonathan Hurst
11 Mark Kramer
12 Adam Lamie
13 Darren Loy
14 Barry Manual
15 Terry Mathews
16 Jeff Mays
17 Darren Niethammer
18 Dean Palmer
19 Mark Petkovsek
20 Lino Rivera
21 Wayne Rosenthal
22 Tony Scruggs
23 Sammy Sosa
---- Rey Sanchez

1988 Best Chattanooga Lookouts

(Cincinnati Reds, AA)

	MT	NR MT	EX
Complete Set:	6.00	4.50	2.50

1 Timber Mead
2 Chris Hammond
3 Keith Brown
4 Joe Lazor
5 Rich Bombard
6 Chris Jones
7 Tony DeFrancasco
8 Hedi Vargas
9 Keith Lockhart
10 Mark Germann
11 Darrell Pruitt
12 Don Wakamatsu
13 Brian Finley
14 Tom Runnells
15 Tim Deitz
16 Gino Minutelli
17 Joe Bruno
18 Phil Dale
19 Jim Jefferson
20 Lary Sorenson
21 Mike Smith
22 Jeff Richardson
23 Bernie Walker
24 Darren Riley
25 Angelo Nunley
26 Logo & checklist card

1988 Team Chattanooga Lookout Legends #I

(Cincinnati Reds, AA)

	MT	NR MT	EX
Complete Set:	12.00	9.00	4.75

(1) Chris Bando
(2) Juan Bonilla
(3) Joe Charboneau
(4) Pat Corrales
(5) Ellis Clary
(6) Gil Coan
(7) Jeff Cox
(8) Sonny Dixon
(9) Lee Elia
(10) Joe Engel
(11) Engel Stadium
(12) Cal Ermer
(13) Don Grate
(14) Roy Hawes
(15) "Spook" Jacobs
(16) Jim Kaat
(17) Matt Keough
(18) Harmon Killebrew
(19) Rene Lacheman
(20) Hillis Layne
(21) Jesse Levan
(22) Frank Lucchesi
(23) Jackie Mitchell
(24) Louis "Bobo" Newsom
(25) Sal Rende
(26) Kevin Rhomberg
(27) Costen Shockley
(28) Al Sima
(29) Buck Varner
(30) Gene Verble
(31) Junior Wooten
(32) Checklist

1988 Star Co. Clearwater Phillies

(Philadelphia Phillies, A) (Price includes late issue Hamner card)

	MT	NR MT	EX
Complete Set:	11.00	8.25	4.50

1 Steve Bates
2 Cliff Brantley
3 Rod Brunelle
4 Pete Callas
5a Chris Calvert
5b Luis Iglesias (misnumbered)
6 Ramon Caraballo
7 Fred Christopher
8 Garry Clark
9 Todd Crosby
10 Shawn Dantzler
11 Kevin Fynan
12a Jason Grimsley
12b Granny Hamner (late issue, misnumbered, gold rather than red border)
13 Jeff Grotewold
14 Todd Howey
15 Not Issued
16 Steve Kirkpatrick
17 Chris Limbach
18 Pete Maldonado
19 Trey McCall
20 Scott Reaves
21 Mark Sims
22 Steve Scarsone
23 Brad Smith
24 Tim Taft
25 Royal Thomas
26 Travis Walden

1988 ProCards Clinton Giants

(San Francisco Giants, A)

	MT	NR MT	EX
Complete Set:	9.00	6.75	3.50

693 John Vuz
694 Steve Lienhard
695 Rod Beck
696 Steve Connelly
697 Tom Hostetler
698 Scott Nelson
699 Mark Poling
700 Bill Carlson
701 Juan Guerrero
702 Jimmy Terrill
703 Jim Anderson
704 Mark Owens
705 Andres Santana
706 Todd Miller
707 Craig Colbert
708 Erik Johnson
709 Mike Ham
710 Tony Michalak
711 Mark Dewey
712 Bill Evers
713 Mike Stanfield
714 Robert Lucero
715 Jamie Cooper
716 Elanis Westbrooks
717 Jeff Morris
718 Tom Ealy
719 Mike Villa
720 Lonnie Phillips
---- Checklist

1988 CMC Colorado Springs Sky Sox

(Cleveland Indians, AAA)

	MT	NR MT	EX
Complete Set:	7.00	5.25	2.75

1 Darrel Akerfelds
2 Mlke Brown
3 Don Gordon
4 Jeff Kaiser
5 Ron Mathis
6 Jon Perlman
7 Reggie Ritter
8 Rick Rodrigez
9 Charlie Scott
10 Joe Skalski
11 John Stefano
12 Ron Tingley
13 Mark Higgins
14 Tommy Hinzo
15 Don Lovell
16 Domingo Ramos
17 Eddie Williams
18 Paul Zuvella
19 Rod Allen
20 Terry Francona
21 Luis Medina
22 Randy Washington
23 Reggie Williams
24 Steve Swisher
25 Aurelio Rodriguez

1988 ProCards Colorado Springs Sky Sox

(Cleveland Indians, AAA)

	MT	NR MT	EX
Complete Set:	7.00	5.25	2.75

1522 John Stefero
1523 Don Lovell
1524 Reggie Williams
1525 Randy Washington
1526 Mike Brown
1527 Tommy Hinzo
1528 Paul Zuvella
1529 Charles Scott
1530 Rick Peterson
1531 Jeff Kaiser
1532 Ron Tingley
1533 Joe Skalski
1534 Domingo Ramos
1535 Keith Bennett
1536 Aurelio Rodriguez
1537 Darrel Akerfelds
1538 Don Gordon
1539 Steve Ciszczon
1540 Reggie Ritter
1541 Terry Francona
1542 Jon Perlman
1543 Luis Medina
1544 Mark Higgins
1545 Rod Allen
1546 Steve Swisher
1547 Eddie Williams
1548 Ron Mathis
1549 Rick Rodriguez
---- Checklist

1988 Grand Slam Columbia Mets

(New York Mets, A)

	MT	NR MT	EX
Complete Set:	6.00	4.50	2.50

1 Butch Hobson
2 Pete Bauer
3 Rick Durant
4 Rocky Elli
5 Eric Hillman
6 Steve Larose
7 Juan Marina
8 James McAnarney
9 Mike Miller
10 Kevin Ponder
11 Julio Valera
12 Javier Gonzalez
13 David Lau
14 Alex Diaz
15 Alex Jimenez
16 David Joiner
17 Rodney Murrell
18 Fred Hina
19 Manny Mantrana
20 Scott Spoolstra
21 Rob Lemle
22 Terry McDaniel
23 Danny Naughton
24 Jaime Roseboro
25 Scott Jaster
26 Chris Donnels
28 Joel Horlen

1988 Best Columbus Astros

(Houston Astros, AA)

	MT	NR MT	EX
Complete Set:	7.00	5.25	2.75

1 Charlie Kerfeld
2 Don Dunster
3 Terry Wells
4 Glenn Spagnola
5 Brian Meyer
6 Ken Crew
7 Doug Givler
8 Jose Vargas
9 Kyle Todd
10 Juan Lopez
11 David Rohde
12 Dan Walters
13 John Elliott
14 Rich Johnson
15 Larry Lasky
16 Jeff Edwards
17 Blaise Ilsley
18 Tom Funk
19 Carlo Colombino
20 Fred Gladding
21 Gary Cooper
22 Terry Green
23 Troy Afenir
24 Dayton Preston
25 Tom Wiedenbauer
26 Clavin James
27 Norman Brock
28 Team photo & checklist card

1988 Police Columbus Clippers

(New York Yankees, AAA)

	MT	NR MT	EX
Complete Set:	8.00	6.00	3.25

(1) Chris Alvarez
(2) Jay Buhner
(3) Pat Clements
(4) Casey Close
(5) Pete Dalena
(6) Alvaro Espinoza
(7) Bill Fulton
(8) Bob Geren
(9) Matt Harrison
(10) Mike Kinnunen
(11) Rick Langford
(12) Jeff Moronko
(13) Hal Morris
(14) Jamie Nelson
(15) Scott Nielson
(16) Clay Parker
(17) Bert Pena
(18) Hipolito Pena
(19) Eric Schmidt
(20) Steve Shields
(21) Cliff Speck
(22) Randy Velarde
(23) Ward Turner
(24) Coaches/Trainer card (Champ Summers, Kevin Rand, Ken Rowe)
(25) Managers card (George Sisler, Bucky Dent)

1988 CMC Columbus Clippers

(New York Yankees, AAA)

	MT	NR MT	EX
Complete Set:	10.00	7.50	4.00

1 Pat Clements
2 Clay Parker
3 Scott Nielsen
4 Bill Fulton
5 Matt Harrison
6 Steve Shields
7 Hipolito Pena
8 Eric Schmidt
9 Mike Kinnuenen
10 Rick Langford
11 Bob Geren
12 Jamie Nelson
13 Berton Pena
14 Rob Lambert
15 Alvaro Espinoza
16 Pete Dalena
17 Randy Velarde
18 Jeff Moronko
19 Turner Ward
20 Hal Morris
21 Casey Close
22 Cliff Speck
23 Jay Buhner
24 Chris Alvarez
25 Bucky Dent
26 Governors Cup

1988 ProCards Columbus Clippers

(New York Yankees, AAA)

	MT	NR MT	EX
Complete Set:	10.00	7.50	4.00

303 Bob Geren
304 Glenn Sherlock
305 Jamie Nelson
306 Bucky Dent
307 Field Staff
308 Rick Langford
309 Clay Parker
310 Scott Nielsen
311 Cliff Speck
312 Bill Fulton
313 Eric Schmidt
314 Steve Shields
315 Hipolito Pena
316 Mike Kinnunen
317 Matt Harrison
318 Pat Clements
319 Rob Lambert
320 Alvaro Espinoza

321 Pete Dalena
322 Berto Pena
323 Chris Alvarez
324 Randy Velarde
325 Casey Close
326 Max Ward
327 Hal Morris
328 Jeff Moronko
329 Jay Buhner
330 Team Photo
---- Checklist

1988 CMC Denver Zephyrs

(Milwaukee Brewers, AAA)

	MT	NR MT	EX
Complete Set:	7.00	5.25	2.75

1 Mark Knudson
2 Mike Konderla
3 Alex Madrid
4 John Miglio
5 Paul Mirabella
6 Tim Watkins
7 Jay Aldrich
8 Don August
9 Mark Ciardi
10 Tom Filer
11 Tim Pyznarski
12 German Rivera
13 Billy Jo Robidoux
14 Keith Smith
15 Charlie O'Brien
16 Ronn Reynolds
17 Billy Bates
18 Kiki Diaz
19 Todd Brown
20 Lavell Freeman
21 Brad Komminsk
22 Steve Stanicek
23 Darryel Walters
24 Darryl Hamilton
25 Duffy Dyer

1988 ProCards Denver Zephyrs

(Milwaukee Brewers, AAA)

	MT	NR MT	EX
Complete Set:	7.00	5.25	2.75

1250 Todd Jackson
1251 Alex Madrid
1252 Peter Kolb
1253 German Rivera
1254 Bill Mooneyham
1255 Darryel Walters
1256 Kiki Diaz
1257 Tom Filer
1258 Paul Mirabella
1259 Don August
1260 John Miglio
1261 Keith Smith
1262 Ronn Reynolds
1263 Brad Komminsk
1264 Duffy Dyer
1265 Tim Watkins
1266 Steve Stanicek
1267 Billy Jo Robidoux
1268 Charlie O'Brien
1269 Pete Kendrick
1270 Jay Aldrich
1271 Billy Bates
1272 Mark Ciardi
1273 Tim Pyznarski
1274 Darryl Hamilton
1275 Mark Knudson
1276 Mike Konderla
1277 Lavell Freeman
1278 Todd Brown
---- Checklist

1988 Star Co. Dunedin Blue Jays

(Toronto Blue Jays, A) (Price includes late-issue Ault card)

	MT	NR MT	EX
Complete Set:	9.00	6.75	3.50

1 Francisco Cabrera
2 Tony Castillo
3a Wayne Davis
3b Doug Ault (late issue, misnumbered, gold rather than aqua border)
4 Jose Diaz
5 Richard DePastino
6 Lindsay Foster
7 Peter Geist
8 Darren Hall
9 Pat Hentgen
10 Vince Horsman
11 Shawn Jeter
12 Steve Mumaw
13 Pedro Munoz
14 Paul Rodgers
15 Earl Sanders
16 Jerry Schunk
17 Jason Townley
18 James Tracy
19 Darrin Wade
20 Bob Watts
21 Mark Whiten
22 Bob Wishnevski
23 Julian Yan
24 Mark Young

1988 Star Co. Durham Bulls (Blue)

(Atlanta Braves, A) The Costner Gold cards in this set were issued late and are misnumbered. Many of them were sold as single cards and not included in sets. The Gold card in sets should be considered quite scare. The Costner no number card was re-issued as a blue card at the request of the ball club and again were sold as singles even though they should be included in the sets.

	MT	NR MT	EX
Complete Set:	16.00	12.00	6.50

1 Michael Bell
2 Scott Bohlke
3 David Butts
4a Jim Czajowski
4b Buddy Bailey (Gold)
5 Jeff Dodig
6 Mike Fowler
7 Ted Holcomb
8 Cesar Jimenez
9a Dodd Johnson
9b Kevin Costner (Gold)
10 Rich Longuil
11 Phil Maldinado
12 Rich Maloney
13 Paul Marak
14 Kent Mercker
15 Rick Morris
16 Kenneth Pennington
17 Dave Plumb
18 Ellis Roby
19 Doug Stockam
20 Mike Stoker
21 Theron Todd
22 Lee Upshaw
23 Danny Weems
24 Walt Williams
---- Kevin Costner (Blue)

1988 Star Co. Durham Bulls (Orange)

(Atlanta Braves, A)

	MT	NR MT	EX
Complete Set:	10.00	7.50	4.00

1 Michael Bell
2 Scott Bohlke
3 David Butts
4 Jim Czajowski
5 Jeff Dodig
6 Mike Fowler
7 Ted Holcomb
8 Cesar Jimenez
9 Dodd Johnson
10 Rich Longuil
11 Phil Maldonado
12 Rich Maloney
13 Paul Marak
14 Kent Mercker
15 Rick Morris
16 Kenneth Pennington
17 Dave Plumb
18 Ellis Roby
19 Doug Stockam
20 Mike Stoker
21 Theron Todd
22 Lee Upshaw
23 Danny Weems
24 Walt Williams
25 Buddy Bailey
26 Kevin Costner

1988 ProCards Eastern League All-Stars

(Class AA)

	MT	NR MT	EX
Complete Set:	10.00	7.50	4.00

1 Dave Eiland
2 Kevin Maas
3 Hensley Meulens
4 Dana Ridenour
5 Andy Stankiewicz
6 Dan Dimascio
7 Shawn Holman
8 Tobey Lovullo
9 Julius McDougal
10 Cesar Mejia
11 Rob Richie
12 Delwyn Young
13 Jeff Cook
14 Kevin Davis
15 Dimas Gutierrez
16 Jeff King
17 Larry Melton
18 Paul Wilmet
19 Jose Birriel
20 Mike Carista
21 Ed Estrada
22 Todd Pratt
23 John Roberts
24 Luis Vasquez
25 Joe Girardi
26 Mike Harkey
27 Bryan House
28 Hector Villanueva
29 Jerome Walton
30 Dean Wilkins
31 Tony Brown
32 Greg Edge
33 Warren Magee
34 Chuck Malone
35 Jeff Hull
36 Ricky Rojas
37 Omar Vizquel
38 Jim Wilson
39 Mark Howie
40 Scott Jordan
41 Tom Lampkin
42 Mike Poehl
43 Casey Webster
44 Kevin Wickander
45 Dave Trembley
46 Harold Williams
47 Jim Essian
48 Grant Jackson
49 Brian McCann
50 Brian Allard
51 Brian Graham
52 Mike Hargroce

1988 CMC Edmonton Trappers

(California Angels, AAA)

	MT	NR MT	EX
Complete Set:	7.00	5.25	2.75

1 Terry Clark
2 Mike Cook
3 Jack Lazorko
4 Vance Lovelace
5 Bryan Harvey
6 Urbano Lugo
7 Joe Johnson
8 Philip Venturino
9 Marty Reed
10 Barry Dacus
11 Miguel Alicea
12 Darrell Miller
13 Pete Coachman
14 Stan Holmes
15 Bob Miscik
16 Brian Brady
17 Kent Anderson
18 Doug Davis
19 Edwin Marquez
20 Joe Redfield
21 Jim Eppard
22 Tom Kotchman
23 Dante Bichette
24 Mark Doran
25 Kevin King

1988 ProCards Edmonton Trappers

(California Angels, AAA)

	MT	NR MT	EX
Complete Set:	7.00	5.25	2.75

555 Joe Redfield
556 Jack Lazorko
557 Vance Lovelace
558 Jim Eppard
559 Doug Davis
560 Joe Johnson
561 Chico Walker
562 Marty Reed
563 Chuck Hernandez
564 Junior Noboa
565 Frank Dimichele
566 Phil Venturino
567 Mike Cook
568 Barry Dacus
569 Terry Clark
570 Mark Doran
571 Stan Holmes
572 Brian Brady
573 Kevin King
574 Kent Anderson
575 Edwin Marquez
576 Dante Bichette
577 Bobby Miscik
578 Pete Coachman
579 Darrell Miller
580 Tom Kotchman
581 Urbano Lugo
582 Miguel Alicea
583 Craig Gerber
584 Al Olson
---- Checklist

1988 Cain Elmira Pioneers

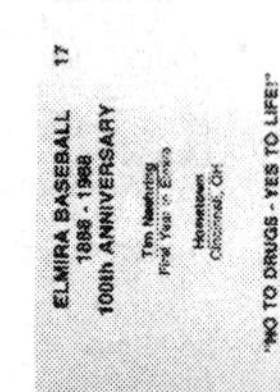

(Boston Red Sox, A)

	MT	NR MT	EX
Complete Set:	8.00	6.00	3.25

1 Logo card
2 Alberto Pratts
3 Steve Michael
4 Scott Taylor
5 Bernie Dzafic
6 Dan Kite
7 John Dolan
8 Peter Estrada
9 Tim Stange
10 Al Sanders
11 Carlos Rivera
12 Luis Dorante
13 John Flaherty
14 Pedro Matilla
15 David Monegro
16 Lou Munoz
17 Tim Naehring
18 Julio Rosario
19 Willie Tatum
20 Al Thornton
21 Chris Whitehead
22 Terry Marrs
23 Mickey Rivers Jr.
24 Larry Scannell
25 John Spencer
26 Brian Warfel
27 Bill Limoncelli
28 John Post
29 Dennis Robarge
30 Clyde Smoll

1988 Cain Elmira Pioneers Test Issue

(Boston Red Sox, A) (Test Issue) This is a withdrawn set with only 2,000 sets produced.

	MT	NR MT	EX
Complete Set:	150.00	112.00	60.00

(1) Reggie Harris
(2) Tony Mosley
(3) Mickey Pina
(4) Ronnie Richardson
(5) Packy Rogers
(6) Tony Romero
(7) Julio Rosario
(8) Brian Warfel
(9) Bob Zupcic
(10) Team Photo (1941)
(11) Team photo (1967)
(12) Team photo (1979)

1988 Best El Paso Diablos

(Milwaukee Brewers, AA)

	MT	NR MT	EX
Complete Set:	12.00	9.00	4.75

1 Gary Sheffield
2 Donald Scott
3 Daniel Scarpetta
4 Jamie Brisco
5 George Canale
6 Dave Machemer
7 Ramon Serna
8 Luis Castillo
9 Bill Mooneyham
10 Paul Lindblad
11 Jim Rowe

12 Matias Carrillo
13 Alan Cartwright
14 Robert DeWolf
15 Mark Ambrose
16 Andy Anderson
17 Barry Bass
18 Bradley Wheeler
19 Fred Williams
20 Gregory Vaughn
21 Jeffrey Peterek
22 Edward Puig
23 Angel Rodriguez
24 Adrian Meagher
25 Joseph Mitchell
26 Mario Monico
27 Rob Hicks
28 James Hunter
29 Frankie Mattox
30 Checklist/Dudley Dome

1988 Best El Paso Diablos Limited Edition

(Milwaukee Brewers, AA) This set includes the same players as listed in the regular set. The fronts of the cards are silver & black and the backs of the cards are royal blue as opposed to the gray backs of the regular set. Only 1,300 of these sets were made.

	MT	NR MT	EX
Complete Set:	20.00	15.00	8.00

1988 Best Eugene Emeralds

(Kansas City Royals, A)

	MT	NR MT	EX
Complete Set:	6.00	4.50	2.50

1 Bob Hamblin
2 Steve Hoeme
3 Greg Harvey
4 Steve Otto
5 Bill Drohan
6 Hector Wagner
7 Kyle Irvin
8 Jim Smith
9 Brad Hopper
10 Randy Vaughn
11 Joel Johnston
12 David Rolls
13 Rob Buchanan
14 Jeff Hulse
15 Fred Russell
16 Jeff Garber
17 Kelvin Davis
18 Ron Collins
19 Bill Gardner
20 Steve Preston
21 Karl Drezek
22 Bobby Holley
23 Frank Henderson
24 John Gilcrist
25 Derek Sholl
26 Gerald Ingram
27 Milt Richardson
28 Frankie Watson
29 Keith Shibata
30 Logo & checklist card

1988 ProCards Fayetteville Generals

(Detroit Tigers, A)

	MT	NR MT	EX
Complete Set:	9.00	6.75	3.50

1079 Keith Nicholson
1080 Glenn Belcher
1081 Steve Pegues
1082 Andy Toney
1083 Luis Melendez
1084 Larry Coker
1085 Mark Adler
1086 Jose Ramos
1087 Robinson Garces
1088 Steve Parascand
1089 Chuck Duquette
1090 Zack Doster
1091 Duben Bello
1092 Charles Steward
1093 Felix Liriano
1094 Travis Fryman
1095 Dave Richards
1096 Ron Cook
1097 Chris Schnurbursh
1098 Randy Luciani
1099 Kevin Camilli
1100 Miguel Murphy
1101 Liliano Castro
1102 Bill Henderson
1103 Michael Wilkins
1104 Leon Roberts
1105 Mike DeLao
---- Checklist

1988 Star Co. Florida State All-Stars

(A)

	MT	NR MT	EX
Complete Set:	8.00	6.00	3.25

1 John Shoemaker
2 Felipe Alou
3 Keith Bodie
4 Doug Cinnella
5 Scott Diez
6 Kip Gross
7 Dave Hansen
8 Randy Hennis
9 Nels Jacobsen
10 Chris Limbach
11 Luis Martinez
12 Todd McClure
13 Brian Morrison
14 Bob Natal
15 Chris Nichting
16 Geronimo Pena
17 Fritz Polka
18 Karl Rhodes
19 Homar Rojas
20 Miguel Santana
21 Mike Simms
22 Greg Talamantez
23 John Vanderwal
24 Juan Villaneuva
25 Mike White
26 Masahiro Yamaoto
27 Buck Showalter
28 John Lipon
29 Russ Meyer
30 Luis Silverio
31 Phil Clark
32 Milt Cuyler
33 Jose Diaz
34 Carlos Escalera
35 Greg Everson
36 Blame Fox
37 Cornelio Garcia
38 Darrin Garner
39 Mike Hansen
40 Brent Knackert
41 Adam Lamle
42 Richie LeBlanc
43 Ravelo Manzanillo
44 Kevin Mmahat
45 Tony Morrison
46 Livio Padilla
47 Dean Palmer
48 Dan Rohrmeier
49 Carl Sullivan
50 Aquedo Vasquez
51 Don Vesling
52 Julian Yan

1988 Cal Cards Fresno Suns

(A)

	MT	NR MT	EX
Complete Set:	6.00	4.50	2.50

1 Tony Triplett
2 Marc Combs
3 Joe Mancini
4 Jon Hobbs
5 Ernie Young
6 Dan Simonds
7 Tracy Pancoski
8 Frank Bellino
9 Todd Hawkins
10 John Barry
11 Kim Flowers
12 Jim Malseed
13 Dave Nash
14 Richard Yagi
15 Hector Miyauchi
16 Steve Bowden
17 Frank Bryan
18 John Bilello
19 Rob Rowen
20 Anthony Tagi
21 Bullet Manabe
22 Chuck Higson
23 Gary Geiger
24 Rocco Buffolino
25 Brad Comstock
26 Dean Treanor
27 Tom Bell

1988 ProCards Fresno Suns

(No Affiliation, A)

	MT	NR MT	EX
Complete Set:	6.00	4.50	2.50

1222 Frank Bryan
1223 Kim Flowers
1224 John Bilello
1225 Chuck Higson
1226 Brad Comstock
1227 John Barry
1228 Dave Nash
1229 Gary Geiger
1230 Dan Simonds
1231 Rocco Buffolino
1232 Jim Malseed
1233 H Miyauchi
1234 Antony Tagi
1235 Bullet Manabe
1236 Dean Treanor
1237 Jon Hobbs
1238 Joe Ueda
1239 Richard Yagi
1240 Tracey Pancoski
1241 Ernie Young
1242 Todd Hawkins
1243 Tony Triplett
1244 Rob Rowen
1245 Marty Montano
1246 George Omachi
1247 Joe Mancini
1248 Tom Bell
1249 Donna Van Duzer
---- Checklist

1988 Star Co. Ft. Lauderdale Yankees

(New York Yankees, A) (Price includes late-issue Showalter card)

	MT	NR MT	EX
Complete Set:	9.00	6.75	3.50

1 Dan Arendas
2 Luc Berube
3 Art Calvert
4 Darrin Chapin
5 Bob Dickerson
6 Jim Ehrhard
7 Steve Erickson
8 Fernando Figueroa
9 Scott Gay
10 Doug Gogolewski
11 Fred Hailey
12 Rodney Imes
13 Scoitt Kamieniecki
14 Ralph Kraus
15 Mark Mitchell
16 Kevin Mmahat
17 Tony Morrison
18 Carlos Rodriguez
19a Gabriel Rodriguez
19b Buck Showalter (late issue, misnumbered, gold rather than purple border)
20 Dan Roman
21 Wade Taylor
22 David Turgeon
23 Bill Voeltz
24 Thomas Weeks

1988 ProCards Gastonia Rangers

(Texas Rangers, A)

	MT	NR MT	EX
Complete Set:	11.00	8.25	4.50

995 Marv Rockman
996 Bob Lavender
997 Bill Findlay
998 Mike Taylor
999 Jay Baker
1000 Rick Knapp
1001 Chris Shiflett
1002 Luke Sable
1003 Robb Nan
1004 Jim McCutcheon
1005 Cris Colon
1006 Joe Pearn
1007 Brant Alyea
1008 Felipe Castillo
1009 Orlando Gomez
1010 Kevin Belcher
1011 Jose Velez
1012 Jeff Melrose
1013 Bill Losa
1014 Pat Garman
1015 Brad Meyer
1016 Marty Cerny
1017 Wilson Alvarez
1018 Brian Steiner
1019 Spencer Wilkinson
1020 Roger Pavlik
1021 Glenn Patterson
1022 Saul Barretto
1023 Chuck Marguardt
---- Checklist

1988 ProCards Geneva Cubs

(Chicago Cubs, A)

	MT	NR MT	EX
Complete Set:	6.00	4.50	2.50

1633 Eric Perry
1634 Nick Ramirez
1635 Eric Williams
1636 Gary Arnold
1637 Ray Figueroa
1638 Jim Murphy
1639 Skip Eggleston
1640 Rick Mundy
1641 Dave Goodwin
1642 Mike Sodders
1643 Tim Ellis
1644 Dan Johnston
1645 Matt Leonard
1646 Eligio Rodriguez
1647 Tracy Smith
1648 Francisco Espino
1649 Derrick Stroud
1650 Bill St. Peter
1651 Scott Taylor
1652 Ben Shreve
1653 Chris Lutz
1654 Bill Hayes
1655 Carlos Canino
1656 Ken Shepard
1657 George Brzezinski
1658 Marty Owens
1659 Dave Oster
1660 Sheila Arnold
1661 Quinn's Cards
---- Checklist

1988 ProCards Glens Falls Tigers

(Detroit Tigers, AA)

	MT	NR MT	EX
Complete Set:	7.00	5.25	2.75

913 Wayne Housie
914 Pat Austin
915 Eric Hardgrave
916 Delwyn Young
917 John Wockenfuss
918 Ken Williams
919 Julius McDougal
920 Rich Lacko
921 Paul Wenson
922 Rich Wieligman
923 Torey Lovullo
924 Cesar Mejia
925 Rob Richie
926 Kevin Ritz
927 Mike Schwabe
928 Bernie Anderson
929 Shawn Holman
930 Ken Gotmann
931 Dan Dimascio
932 Adam Dempsay
933 Bill Cooper
934 Kevin Bradshaw
935 Hector Berrios
936 Jeff Jones
937 Robert Link
938 Tim Leiper
---- Checklist

1988 Team Great Falls Dodgers

(Los Angeles Dodgers, R)

	MT	NR MT	EX
Complete Set:	12.00	9.00	4.75

1 Bill Bene
2 Eric Karros
3 Brett Magnusson
4 Ernie Carr
5 Chris Morrow
6 Mike McHugh
7 Lance Rice
8 Jeff Castillo
9 Eddie Pye
10 Dan Opperman
11 Jerry Brooks
12 Don Carroll

13 Jim Wray
14 John Braase
15 Steve Finken
16 Brock McMurray
17 Bill Wengert
18 John Huebner
19 Bryan Beals
20 Sean Snedeker
21 Jeff Hartsock
22 Jose Oferman
23 Mike James
24 Cam Biberdorf
25 Ramon Valdes
26 Tim Johnson
27 Goose Gregson

1988 ProCards Greensboro Hornets

(Cincinnati Reds, A)

	MT	NR MT	EX
Complete Set:	7.00	5.25	2.75

1551 Bill Risley
1552 Quinn Marsh
1553 Scott Jeffery
1554 Keith Thomas
1555 Brian Lane
1556 Shane Letterio
1557 Brad Robinson
1558 Eddie Taubenese
1559 Joe Turek
1560 Kevin Pearson
1561 Ron Mullins
1562 Adam Casillias
1563 Tony Mealy
1564 Ken Huseby
1565 Scott Westermann
1566 Mack Jenkins
1567 Rosario Rodriguez
1568 Andy Rickman
1569 Jack Smith
1570 Steve Hester
1571 Jimmy Mee
1572 Don Brown
1573 Keith Kaiser
1574 Joey Vierra
1575 Mark Berry
---- Checklist

1988 Best Greenville Braves

(Atlanta Braves, AA)

	MT	NR MT	EX
Complete Set:	7.00	5.25	2.75

1 Ed Whited
2 Terry Bell
3 Sal D'Alessandro
4 Inocencio Guerrero
5 Dennis Hood
6 John Alva
7 Miguel Sabino
8 Barry Jones
9 Drew Denson
10 Mark Lemke
11 Jim Lovell
12 Dale Polley
13 Bryan Farmer
14 Dave Miller
15 Steve Ziem
16 Kevin Blankenship
17 Maximo Del Rosario
18 Tom Dozier
19 Andy Nezelek
20 John Kilner
21 Tom Dunbar
22 Eddie Mathews
23 Mike Fischlin
24 Logo & checklist card

1988 Star Co. Hagerstown Suns

(Baltimore Orioles, AA) (Price includes late-issue Hart card and corrected (b) cards

	MT	NR MT	EX
Complete Set:	7.00	5.25	2.75

1 Jeff Ahr
2 Dave Bettendorf
3 Don Buford Jr.
4 Mike Eberle
5 Scott Evans
6 Craig Faulkner
7 Steve Finley
8 Tom Harms
9 Walt Harris
10 Bob Latmore
11a Kevin McNees
11b Mike Hart (late issue, misnumbered, gold rather than orange border)
12 Larry Mims
13 Chris Myers
14 Matt Nowak
15 Louie Paulino
16a Pete Palermo (correct name & stats, wrong picture)
16b Pete Palermo (corrected picture, however listed as Carolina League rather than Hagerstown)
17a Chris Pinder (correct name & stats, wrong picture)
17b Chris Pinder (corrected picture, however listed as Carolina League rather than Hagerstown)
18 Mike Sander
19 David Secui
20 Steve Sonneberger
21 Randy Strijek
22 Anthony Telford
23 Jack Voigt
24 Bob Williams
25 Chaun Wilson

1988 ProCards Hamilton Redbirds

(St. Louis Cardinals, A)

	MT	NR MT	EX
Complete Set:	6.00	4.50	2.50

1 Checklist
1719 Chris Houser
1720 Scott Halama
1721 John Cebuhar
1722 Brad Duvall
1723 Antron Grier
1724 Rick Christian
1725 Mark Battell
1726 Lee Plemel
1727 Mike Ross
1728 Dale Kisten
1729 Tim Redman
1730 Kevin Robinson
1731 Cory Saterfield
1732 Dan Radison
1733 Luis Melendez
1734 Mike Evans
1735 Randy Butts
1736 Mark Clark
1737 John Lepley
1738 Joe Federico
1739 Steve Fanning
1740 Rodney Brooks
1741 Tom Malchesky
1742 Ed Lampe
1743 J.P. Gentleman
1744 Dean Weese
1745 Steve Graham
1746 Frank Moran
1747 Joe Hall

1988 ProCards Harrisburg Senators

(Pittsburgh Pirates, AA)

	MT	NR MT	EX
Complete Set:	7.00	5.25	2.75

834 John Rigos
835 Jeff Cook
836 Tommy Shields
837 Kevin Davis
838 Scott Little
839 Spin Williams
840 Rick Reed
841 Dimas Gutierrez
842 Jim Neidlinger
843 Mike Curtis
844 Lance Belen
845 Chris Ritter
846 Dave Trembley
847 Orlando Lind
848 Jose Melendez
849 Ron Johns
850 Mike Walker
851 Gilberto Roca
852 Paul Wilmet
853 Bill Copp
854 Tony Chance
855 Jeff Banister
856 Gino Gentile
857 Larry Melton
858 Robby Russell
859 Jeff King
860 Clay Daniel
861 Harold Williams
862 Scott Kautz
---- Checklist

1988 Team Huntsville Stars

(Oakland A's, A)

	MT	NR MT	EX
Complete Set:	8.00	6.00	3.25

(2) Scott Chiamparino
(3) Brian Criswell
(4) Pat Dietrick
(5) DeMarlo Hale
(6) Scott Hemond
(7) Scott Holcomb
(8) Steve Howard
(9) Jimmy Jones
(10) Bo Kent
(11) Kirk McDonald
(12) John Minch
(13) Jerome Nelson
(14) Jerry Peguero
(15) Tommie Reynolds
(16) Andre Robertson
(17) Will Schock
(18) Bob Sharpnack
(19) Dave Shotkoski
(20) Kevin Sliwinski
(21) Greg Sparks
(22) Bruce Tanner
(23) Camilo Veras
(24) Dave Veres
(25) Bruce Walton
(26) Mike Bordick

1988 ProCards Idaho Falls Braves

(Atlanta Braves, A)

	MT	NR MT	EX
Complete Set:	6.00	4.50	2.50

1832 The Clubhouse
1833 Team photo & checklist
1834 Daryl Blanks
1835 Marco Paddy
1836 Gary Schoonover
1837 Glenn Mitchell
1838 Rodney Richey
1839 John Albertson
1840 Lamar Hall
1841 Dave Monteiro
1842 Matthew Williams
1843 Chris Jones
1844 Ramces Guerrero
1845 Donovan Campbell
1846 Kevin Henry
1847 Greg Harper
1848 Al Bacosa
1849 Pat Stivers
1850 Keith LeClair
1851 Eric Kuhlman
1852 Rai Henninger
1853 Jim Procopio
1854 Paul Opdyke
1855 Rudy Gardey
1856 Mark Eskins
1857 Daniel Lehnerz
1858 Jim Kortright
1859 Steve Lopez
1860 Herb Hippauf
1861 Rich Pohle
---- Checklist

1988 CMC Indianapolis Indians

(Montreal Expos, AAA)

	MT	NR MT	EX
Complete Set:	8.00	6.00	3.25

1 Randy Johnson
2 Kurt Kepshire
3 Bob Sebra
4 Steve Shirley
5 Tim Barrett
6 Jeff Fischer
7 Mike Smith
8 Sergio Valdez
9 Brian Holman
10 Rex Hudler
11 Johnny Paredes
12 Razor Shines
13 Billy Moore
14 Otis Nixon
15 Alonzo Powell
16 Ron Shepherd
17 Tim Hulett
18 Nelson Santovenia
19 Wilfredo Tejada
20 Mike Berger
21 Jack Daugherty
22 Garrett Nago
23 Mel Houston
24 Joe Sparks
25 Mike Colber, Joe Kerrigan, Nelson Norman)

1988 ProCards Indianapolis Indians

(Montreal Expos, AAA)

	MT	NR MT	EX
Complete Set:	7.00	5.25	2.75

496 Joe Sparks
497 Billy Moore
498 Tim McCormack
499 Mike Colber, Joe Kerrigan)
500 Nelson Santovenia
501 Sergio Valdez
502 Tim Barrett
503 Jeff Fischer
504 Brian Holman
505 Steve Shirley
506 Kurt Kepshire
507 Mel Houston
508 Gary Wayne
509 Mike Smith
510 Randy Johnson
511 Bob Sebra
512 Joe Hesketh
513 Rex Hudler
514 Razor Shines
515 Garrett Nago
516 Johnny Paredes
517 Nelson Norman
518 Otis Nixon
519 Mike Berger
520 Alonzo Powell
521 Jack Daugherty
522 Tim Hulett
523 Wil Tejada
524 Ron Shepherd
525 Tom Akin, Howard Kellman)
---- Checklist

1988 CMC Iowa Cubs

(Chicago Cubs, AAA)

	MT	NR MT	EX
Complete Set:	15.00	11.00	6.00

1 Mike Capel
2 Len Damian
3 Jeff Pico
4 Laddie Renfroe
5 Bob Tewksbury
6 Jeff Hirsch
7 Joe Kraemer
8 Bill Landrum
9 Dave Masters
10 Rich Surhoff
11 Roger Williams
12 Damon Berryhill
13 Bruce Crabbe
14 Mark Grace
15 Brian Guinn
16 Paul Noce
17 Phil Stephenson
18 Greg Tabor
19 Doug Dascenzo
20 Dave Meier
21 Dwight Smith
22 Gary Varsho
23 Bill Bathe
24 Pete Mackanin
25 Jim Wright

1988 ProCards Iowa Cubs

(Chicago Cubs, AAA)

	MT	NR MT	EX
Complete Set:	18.00	13.50	7.25

526 Brian Guinn
527 Bill Bathe

528 Doug Dascenzo
529 Rick Surhoff
530 Dwight Smith
531 Dave Grossman
532 Jeff Hirsch
533 Dave Masters
534 Bob Tewksbury
535 Gary Varsho
536 Dave Meier
537 Damon Berryhill
538 Paul Noce
539 Mark Grace
540 Phil Stephenson
541 Bill Landrum
542 Jim Wright
543 Pete Mackanin
544 Leonard Damian
545 Roger Williams
546 Jeff Pico
547 Mike Capel
548 Greg Tabor
549 Joe Kraemer
550 Bruce Crabbe
551 Laddie Renfroe
552 Front Office
553 More Front Office
554 Cubbie Bear (mascot)
---- Checklist

1988 Grand Slam Jackson Mets

(New York Mets, AA)

	MT	NR MT	EX
Complete Set:	8.00	6.00	3.25

1 Ron Gideon
2 Zoilo Sanchez
3 Geary Jones
4 Tucker Ashford
5 Glenn Abbott
6 Kyle Hartshorn
7 Tom Doyle
8 Chris Jelic
9 Mike Santiago
10 Jeff Gardner
11 Virgil Conley
12 Craig Shipley
13 Rich Rodriguez
14 Brian Given
15 Blaine Beatty
16 Todd Welborn
17 Miguel Roman
18 Manny Salinas
19 Shawn Barton
20 Joaquin Contreras
21 Angelo Cuevas
22 Mickey Weston
23 Kevin Tapani
24 Felix Perdomo
25 Alan Hayden

1988 Best Jacksonville Expos

(Montreal Expos, AA)

	MT	NR MT	EX
Complete Set:	7.00	5.25	2.75

1 Rick Carriger
2 Mike Shade
3 Rich Sauver
4 John Hoover
5 Gene Harris
6 Eddie Dixon
7 Mark Gardner
8 Mark Clemons
9 Tommy Alexander
10 Richie Lewis
11 Yorkis Perez
12 Orsino Hill
13 Kevin Dean
14 Derrell Baker
15 Bill Mann
16 Mike Blowers
17 Esteban Beltre
18 Jeff Huson
19 Andy Lawrence
20 Pat Sipe
21 Randy Braun
22 Doug Duke
23 Nardi Contreras
24 Tommy Thompson
25 Bob Caffrey
26 Jim Yalmann
27 Armando Moreno
28 Gary Engelkin
29 Checklist/Sam W. Wolfson Stadium

1988 ProCards Jacksonville Expos

(Montreal Expos, AA)

	MT	NR MT	EX
Complete Set:	7.00	5.25	2.75

964 Scott Mann
965 Orsino Hill
966 Jeffrey Huson
967 Eddie Dixon
968 Derrell Baker
969 Nardi Contreras
970 Doug Duke
971 Tommy Thompson
972 Andy Lawrence
973 Yorkis Perez
974 Jim Kahmann
975 Mike Blowers
976 Randy Braun
977 Mark Clemons
978 Todd Soares
979 Bob Caffrey
980 Gene Harris
981 Pat Sipe
982 Tommy Alexander
983 Armando Moreno
984 Kevin Dean
985 Mike Shade
986 Rich Sauver
987 Mark Gardner
988 Rick Carriger
989 John Hoover
990 Gary Engelkin
991 Esteban Belter
992 Richie Lewis
993 Team Photo
994 Sam Molfson Park
---- Checklist

1988 ProCards Jamestown Expos

(Montreal Expos, A)

	MT	NR MT	EX
Complete Set:	9.00	6.75	3.50

1893 Kevin P. Malone
1894 Roger LaFrancois
1895 Wilfredo Nieva
1896 Bryn Kosco
1897 Bret Davis
1898 Rob Kerrigan
1899 Daniel Freed
1900 Angel Rivera
1901 Jeff Atha
1902 Tim Piechowski
1903 Isaac Alleyne
1904 Tim Laker
1905 Rodney Boddie
1906 Idaiberto Echemendia
1907 Brian Sajonia
1908 Joe Siddall
1909 Joe Klancnik
1910 Marquis Grissom
1911 Keith Kaub
1912 Jose Solarte
1913 Danilo Leon
1914 Steve Overeem
1915 Kevin Finigan
1916 Jorge Mitchell
1917 Javan Reagans
1918 Darrin Winston
1920 Dan Archibald
1921 Martin Robitaille
2039 Q.V. Lowe
---- Checklist

1988 ProCards Kenosha Twins

(Minnesota Twins, A)

	MT	NR MT	EX
Complete Set:	7.00	5.25	2.75

1379 Bob Tinkey
1380 Willie Banks
1381 Dwight Bernard
1382 Fred White
1383 Rusty Kryzanowski
1384 Steve Stowell
1385 Alex Perez
1386 Chad Swanson
1387 Tom Gilles
1388 Doug Pittman
1389 Dave Jacas
1390 Jarvis Brown
1391 David Smith
1392 Lenny Webster
1393 Frank Valdez
1394 Mark Ericson
1395 Michael Lexa
1396 Carlos Capellan
1397 Chris Martin
1398 Pete Delkus
1399 Don Leppert
1400 John Skelton
1401 Shane Jenny
1402 Ron Gardenhire
1403 Bob Lee
1404 Basil Meyer
1405 Tom Marten
1406 Pat Bangtson
---- Checklist

1988 Star Co. Kinston Indians

(Cleveland Indians, A) (Price includes late-issue Adams card)

	MT	NR MT	EX
Complete Set:	12.00	9.00	4.75

1a Beau Allread
1b Glen Adams (late issue, misnumbered, gold rathern than violet border)
2 Kevin Bearse
3 Joey Belle
4 Steven Bird
5 Glenn Fairchild
6 Greg Ferlinda
7 Mark Gilles
8 John Githens
9 Todd Gonzales
10 David Harwell
11 Christopher Isaacson
12 Scott Johnson
13 Carl Kelipuleole
14 Lewis Kent
15 Allen Liebert
16 Everado Magallanes
17 Mark Maloney
18 Charles Ogden
19 James Richardson
20 Charles Soos
21 Robert Swain
22 Michael Twardoski
23 Michael Westbrook
24 Raymond Williamson

1988 Best Knoxville Blue Jays

(Toronto Blue Jays, AA)

	MT	NR MT	EX
Complete Set:	6.00	4.50	2.50

1 Alex Sanchez
2 Sanchez Felix
3 John Shea
4 Mike Jones
5 Jimy Kelly
6 Domingo Martinez
7 Kevin Batiste
8 Hector Delacruz
9 Kash Beauchamp
10 Darren Balsley
11 Doug Scherer
12 Carlos Diaz
13 Jose Escobar
14 Ken Rivers
15 Doug Linton
16 Chris Jones
17 Omar Bencomo
18 Correa Guzman
19 Dennis Jones
20 Steve Cummings
21 Gary McCune
22 Tim Ringler
23 John Poloni
24 Hugh Brinson
25 Tom Quinlan
26 Logo & checklist card

1988 Star Co. Lakeland Tigers

(Detroit Tigers, A) (Price includes late-issue Lipon card)

	MT	NR MT	EX
Complete Set:	8.00	6.00	3.25

1 Scott Aldred
2 Doyle Balthazar
3 Arnie Beyeler
4 Basilio Cabrera
5 Luis Galindo
6 Richard Carter
7 Phil Clark
8 Milt Cuyler
9 Dean Decillis
10 Gregory Everson
11 Paul Foster
12 Blane Fox
13 Mike Hansen
14 Lance Hudson
15a Scott Hufford
15b John Lipon (late issue, misnumbered, gold rather than violet border)
16 Darren Hursey
17 Mark Lee
18 Randy Nosek
19 Dan O'Neill
20 Wade Phillips
21 Gary Pifer
22 Ron Rightnowar
23 Joseph Slavik
24 Bob Thomson
25 Donald Vesling

1988 CMC Las Vegas Stars

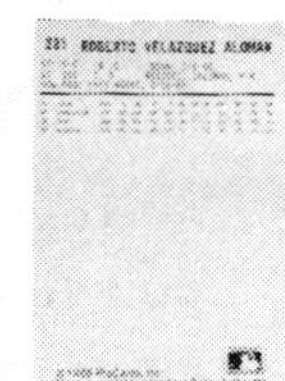

(San Diego Padres, AAA)

	MT	NR MT	EX
Complete Set:	18.00	13.50	7.25

1 Joe Bitker
2 Keith Comstock
3 Greg Harris
4 Joel McKeon
5 Pete Roberts
6 Todd Simmons
7 Ed Vosberg
8 Kevin Towers
9 Joe Lynch
10 Shane Mack
11 Thomas Howard
12 Jerald Clark
13 Randy Byers
14 Bip Roberts
15 Brad Pounders
16 Rob Nelson
17 Gary Green
18 Joey Cora
19 Mike Brumley
20 Roberto Alomar
21 Bruce Bochy
22 Sandy Alomar, Jr.
23 Tom Brassil
24 Steve Smith
25 Sonny Siebert

1988 ProCards Las Vegas Stars

(San Diego Padres, AAA)

	MT	NR MT	EX
Complete Set:	18.00	13.50	7.25

222 Edward Vosberg
223 Joe Lynch
224 Randell Byers
225 Joel McKeon
226 Todd Hutcheson
227 Greg Harris
228 Pete Roberts
229 Jerald Clark
230 Joe Bitker
231 Roberto Alomar
232 Gary Green
233 Shane Mack
234 Joey Cora
235 Mike Brumley
236 Sandy Alomar
237 Rob Nelson
238 Tom Brassil
239 Thomas Howard
240 Todd Simmons
241 Bruce Bochy
242 Kevin Towers
243 Steve Lubratich
244 Steve Smith
245 Bip Roberts
246 Keith Comstock
247 Brad Pounders
248 Sonny Siebert
---- Checklist

1988 Pucko Little Falls Mets

	MT	NR MT	EX
Complete Set:	9.00	6.75	3.50

1 Lee May
2 Kevin Baez
3 Tom Bales
4 Tom Becker
5 Ron Height
6 Todd Hundley
7 Michael Noelke
8 Bob Olah

9 Steve Piskor
10 Radhames Polanco
11 Titi Roche
12 Sammye Sanchez
13 Greg Turtletaub
14 Lonnie Walker
15 Terry Bross
16 Terry Griffin
17 Chris Hill
18 Steve Newton
19 Vladimir Perez
20 Dale Plummer
21 Dave Proctor
22 Pete Schourek
23 John Wenrick
24 Anthony Young
25 Brian Zimmerman
26 Bill Stein
27 Al Jackson
28 Rick McWane
29 Frenk Minnissale

1988 CMC Louisville Redbirds

(St Louis Cardinals, AAA)

	MT	NR MT	EX
Complete Set:	7.00	5.25	2.75

1 John Costello
2 Dick Grapenthin
3 John Martin
4 Randy O'Neal
5 Tim Conroy
6 Gibson Alba
7 Rich Buonantony
8 Chris Carpenter (Cris)
9 Dave Rajsich
10 Jim Leopold
11 Alex Cole
12 Bill Lyons
13 Tim Jones
14 David Green
15 Craig Wilson
16 John Murphy
17 Duane Walker
18 Mike Fitzgerald
19 Carl Ray Stephens
20 Luis Alicea
21 Sal Agostinelli
22 Roy Silver
23 Mark Dougherty
24 Joe Pettini
25 Mike Jorgenson (Jorgensen)

1988 ProCards Louisville Redbirds

(St. Louis Cardinals, AAA)

	MT	NR MT	EX
Complete Set:	7.50	5.75	3.00

421 David Green
422 Carl Ray Stephens
423 John Martin
424 Sal Agostinelli
425 Duane Walker
426 Dick Grapenthin
427 Mike Fitzgerald
428 Chris Carpenter (Cris)
429 John Murphy
430 Randy O'Neal
431 Roy Silver
432 Bill Lyons
433 Tim Jones
434 David Hudson
435 Joe Pettini
436 Luis Alicea
437 Jim Leopold
438 Alex Cole
439 Craig Wilson
440 John Costello
441 Mike Jorgenson (Jorgensen)
442 Gibson Alba
443 Dave Rajsich
444 Mark Dougherty
445 Rich Bounantony
---- Checklist

1988 Team Louisville Redbirds

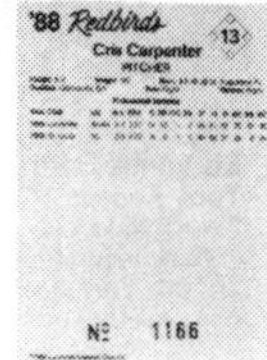

(St. Louis Cardinals, AAA)

	MT	NR MT	EX
Complete Set:	9.00	6.75	3.50

1 Mike Jorgensen
2 Joe Pettini
3 Darold Knowles
4 Steve Braun
5 Sal Agostinelli
6 Gibson Alba
7 Luis Alicea
8 Scott Arnold
9 Greg Bargar
10 Rod Booker
11 Derek Botelho
12 Rich Buonantony
13 Cris Carpenter
14 Alex Cole
15 Tim Conroy
16 John Costello
17 Danny Cox
18 Mark Dougherty
19 Mike Fitzgerald
20 Dick Grapenthin
21 David Green
22 Mike Hocutt
23 Tim Jones
24 Matt Kinzer
25 Wayne Krenchicki
26 Mike Laga
27 Jim Leopold
28 Jim Lindeman
29 Rick Lockwood
30 Bill Lyons
31 Joe Magrane
32 John A. Martin
33 Greg Mathews
34 Ron Meridith
35 John Morris
36 John V. Murphy
37 Randy O'Neal
38 Jeff Oyster
39 Steve Peters
40 Jim Puzey
41 Dave Rajsich
42 Mike Robinson
43 Mark Ryal
44 Roy Silver
45 Carl Ray Stephens
46 Lester Strode
47 Scott Terry
48 Lee Tunnell
49 Duane Walker
50 Craig Wilson
51 David "Hap" Hudson
52 Billy "Bird" Johnson
53 Billings & Burnett
54 Checklist
---- Logo card

1988 Star Co. Lynchburg Red Sox

(Boston Red Sox, A) (Price includes the late-issue Berardino card)

	MT	NR MT	EX
Complete Set:	9.00	6.75	3.50

Team logo card
1 Billy Bartels
2 Paul Brown
3 Tim Buheller
4 Randy Cina
5a Scott Cooper
5b Dick Berardino (late issue, misnumbered, gold rather than sea-green border)
6 Paul Devlin
7 David Gray
8 Bart Haley
9 Reggie Harris
10 Joseph Marchese
11 Gilberto Martinez
12 Gregory McCollum
13 Timothy McGee
14 Shannon Mendenhall
15 Juan Molero
16 Jim Orsag
17 Mickey Pina
18 Jeffrey Plympton
19 Scott Powers
20 Ronnie Richardson
21 Enrique Rios
22 Kenneth Ryan
23 Scott Sommers
24 David Walters
25 Stuart Weidie
26 Craig Wilson
27 Robert Zupcic

Values for recent cards and sets are listed in Mint (MT), Near Mint (NM), reflecting the fact that many cards from recent years have been preserved in top condition. Recent cards and sets in less than Excellent condition have little collector interest.

1988 T&J SC Madison Muskies

(Oakland A's, A) (color, 2-3/8" x 3-3/8")

	MT	NR MT	EX
Complete Set:	7.00	5.25	2.75

1 Rob Alexander
2 Bruce Arola
3 Pedro Baez
4 Bert Bradley
5 Scott Brosius
6 Nasusel Cabrera
7 Ozzie Canseco
8 Felix Caraballo
9 Jim Carroll
10 Jim Chenevey
11 Dave Gavin
12 Chris Gust
13 Demarlo Hale
14 Fred Hanker
15 Frank Masters
16 Jim Nettles
17 Bob Parry
18 Jamie Reiser
19 Dion Reyna
20 Marteese Robinson
21 Will Schock
22 Matt Siuda
23 Bob Stocker
24 Brian Thorson
25 Pat Wernig

1988 CMC Maine Phillies

(Philadelphia Phillies, AAA)

	MT	NR MT	EX
Complete Set:	8.00	6.00	3.25

1 Marty Bystrom
2 Travis Chambers
3 Barney Nugent
4 Marvin Freeman
5 Brad Brink
6 John McLarnan
7 Mike Shelton
8 Tom Newell
9 Bob Scanlan
10 Todd Frohwirth
11 Ricky Jordon (Jordan)
12 John Russell
13 Shane Turner
14 Ron Jones
15 Rick Lundblade
16 Tommy Barrett
17 Kenny Jackson
18 Greg Jelks
19 Ramon Henderson
20 Keith Miller
21 Jim Olander
22 Kevin Ward
23 George Culver
24 Ramon Aviles
25 Joe Lefebvre

1988 ProCards Maine Phillies

(Philadelphia Phillies, AAA)

	MT	NR MT	EX
Complete Set:	8.00	6.00	3.25

277 Jim Olander
278 Kevin Ward
279 Marvin Freeman
280 Ron Jones
281 John McLarnan
282 Mike Shelton
283 Travis Chambers
284 Tom Barrett
285 John Russell
286 Ricky Jordan
287 Ken Jackson
288 Shane Turner
289 Brad Brink
290 Keith Miller
291 Rick Lundblade
292 Marty Bystrom
293 Tom Newell
294 Bob Scanlan
295 Ramon Henderson
296 Todd Frohwirth
297 Danny Clay
298 Greg Jelks
299 Barney Nugent
300 George Culver
301 Joe Lefebvre
302 Ramon Aviles
---- Checklist

1988 Star Co. Martinsville Phillies

(Philadelphia Phillies, R) (A blue-bordered set was also issued)

	MT	NR MT	EX
Complete Set:	6.00	4.50	2.50

1 John Anderson
2 Kenneth Bean
3 Al Bennett
4 Toby Borland
5 Greg Breaux
6 Tim Churchill
7 Dan Coccia
8 Matt Current
9 Mike Dafforn
10 Rollie DeArmas
11 Tom Doyle
12 Donnie Elliot
13 John Escobar
14 Paul Fletcher
15 Reggie Garcia
16 Brian Harper
17 Dennis Hoffman
18 Luther Johnson
19 Craig Johnston
20 Troy Kent
21 Darrell Lindsey
22 Antonio Linares
23 Aurelio Llanos
24 Chris Lowe
25 Nick Macaluso
26 John Marshall
27 Eulogio Perez
28 Edwin Rosado
29 Victor Rosario
30 Francisco Tejada
31 Chris Toney
32 Ray Walker

1988 Best Memphis Chicks

(Kansas City Royals, AA)

	MT	NR MT	EX
Complete Set:	7.00	5.25	2.75

1 Mel Stottlemyre
2 Rich Thompson
3 Mark Van Blaricom
4 Steve Morrow
5 Ken Bowen
6 Jacob Brumfield
7 Larry Acker
8 Matt Crouch
9 Casey Parson
10 Jim Campbell
11 Kevin Burrell
12 Luis Encarnacion
13 Mark Gillaspie
14 Ken Kravec
15 Randy Hunt
16 Mauro Gozzo
17 Charlie Culberson
18 Jose DeJesus
19 Matt Winters
20 Rick Lueken
21 Chito Martinez
22 Mike Miller
23 Ken Spratke
24 Thad Reece
25 Jose Rivera
26 Sal Rende
27 Tim McCarver Stadium
28 Checklist

1988 Grand Slam Midland Angels

(California Angels, AA)

	MT	NR MT	EX
Complete Set:	7.50	5.50	3.00

1 Max Oliveras
2 Kurt Walker
3 Tim Kelly
4 Vinicio Cedeno
5 Shane Young
6 Tim Burcham
7 Chris Collins
8 Frank Dimichelle
9 Todd Eggertsen
10 Mike Fetters
11 Colby Ward
12 Steve McGuire
13 Mike Knapp

14 Erik Pappas
15 Tom Alfredson
16 Danny Grunhard
17 C.L. Penigar
18 Lee Stevens
19 Jesus Alfaro
20 David Martinez
21 Jeff Manto
22 Jim McCollom
23 Jim Thomas
24 Craig Gerber
25 Norm Carrasco

1988 Grand Slam Midwest League All-Stars

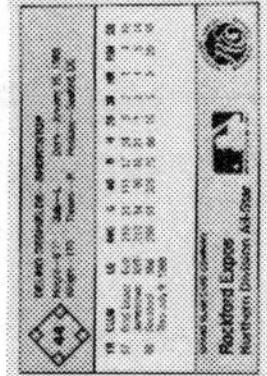

(A)

	MT	NR MT	EX
Complete Set:	10.00	7.50	4.00

1 Mark Owens (Clinton)
2 Andres Santana (Clinton)
3 Erik Johnson (Clinton)
4 Jamie Cooper (Clinton)
5 Rod Beck (Clinton)
6 Stephen Connolly (Clinton)
7 Tom Hostetler (Clinton)
8 Pete Beeler (Cedar Rapids)
9 Greg Lonigro (Cedar Rapids)
10 Jeff Forney (Cedar Rapids)
11 Bill Dodd (Cedar Rapids)
12 Butch Henry (Cedar Rapids)
13 Darrell Rodgers (Cedar Rapids)
14 Scott Scudder (Cedar Rapids)
15 Marc Bombard (Cedar Rapids)
16 Brian Deak (Burlington)
17 Rich Casarotti (Burlington)
18 Brian Hunter (Burlington)
19 Al Martin (Burlington)
20 Jim Lemasters (Burlington)
21 Troy Neel (Waterloo)
22 Tommy Kramer (Waterloo)
23 Bob Rose (Quad City)
24 Wiley Lee (Quad City)
25 Gary Buckels (Quad City)
26 Ray Lankford (Springfield)
27 Greg Becker (Springfield)
28 Greg Kallevig (Peoria)
29 Fernando Zarranz (Peoria)
30 Steve Olin (Waterloo)
31 Lenny Webster (Kenosha)
32 Shawn Gilbert (Kenosha)
33 Jarvis Brown (Kenosha)
34 Pat Bangston (Kenosha)
35 Pete Delkus (Kenosha)
36 Ron Gardenhire (Kenosha)
37 Jorge Pedre (Appleton)
38 Darryl Robinson (Appleton)
39 Jesus Deleon (Appleton)
40 Tom Gordon (Appleton)
41 Bobby Knecht (Appleton)
42 Greg Colbrunn (Rockford)
43 John Mello (Rockford)
44 Delino DeShields (Rockford)
45 Mario Brito (Rockford)
46 Howard Farmer (Rockford)
47 Tim Peters (Rockford)
48 Mike Maksudian (S. Bend)
49 Ray Payton (S. Bend)
50 Scott Brosius (Madison)
51 Ozzie Canseco (Madison)
52 Jim Chenevey (Madison)
53 Pat Wernig (Madison)
54 Will Schock (Madison)
55 Mike McDonald (Wausau)
56 Chuck Carr (Wausau)
57 Mike Goff (Wausau)
58 Kurt Stange (Wausau)
59 Mark Chapman (Beloit)

1988 Star Co. Miami Marlins

(A) (Price includes the late-issue Santiago card)

	MT	NR MT	EX
Complete Set:	6.00	4.50	2.50

1 Jeff Allison
2 Mick Billmeyer
3 Ron Brevell
4 Mike Browning
5 Hector Cotto
6 Tony Diaz
7 Scott Diez
8 Orlando Gonzalez
9 Clay Hill
10 Matt Huff
11 Kanenori Tarumi
12 Shuji Inagaki
13 Trent Intorcia
14 Masao Kida
15 Brian Morrison
16 Rafael Muratti
17a Mitsuru Ogiwara
17b Jose Santiago (late issue, misnumbered, gold rather than green border)
18 Julio Perez
19 Arnie Prieto
20 Rick Richardi
21 Sal Roldan
22 Tony Rohan
23 Motokuni Sano
24 Dave Von Ohlen

1988 Cal Cards Modesto A's

(Oakland A's, A)

	MT	NR MT	EX
Complete Set:	7.50	5.50	3.00

56 David Veres
57 David Shotkoski
58 Ray Young
59 Kevin Williamson
60 Jeff Glover
61 Mark Beavers
62 Gary Gorski
63 Jeff Kopyta
64 Scott Chiamparino
65 Mark Stancel
66 Steve Maye
67 Dann Howitt
68 Jorge Brito
69 Drew Stratton
70 David Finley
71 Keith Watkins
72 Ron Coomer
73 Gerry Barragan
74 Luis Martinez
75 Bill Savarino
76 Heriberto Done
77 Randy Randle
78 Francis Ciprian
79 Patrick Gilbert
80 Vince Teixeira
81 Jeff Newman
82 Pete Richert
83 Dave Hollenback

1988 Team Modesto A's

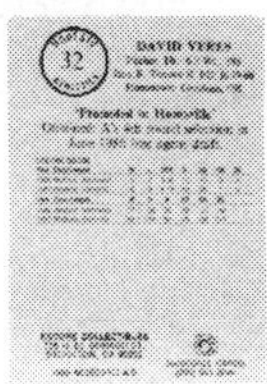

(Oakland A's, A)

	MT	NR MT	EX
Complete Set:	8.00	6.00	3.25

1 Jeff Newman
2 Pete Richert
3 Dave Hollenback
4 Rich Berg
5 Felix Caraballo
6 Jim Carroll
7 Jeff Childers
8 Scott Chiamparino
9 Jim Foley
10 Jeff Glover
11 Gary Gorski
12 Jeff Kopta
13 Steve Maye
14 Mark Stancel
15 Weston Weber
16 Ray Young
17 Jorge Brito
18 Francis Ciprian
19 Tony Arias
20 Isaiah Clark
21 Ron Coomer
22 Darrin Duffy
23 Dave Finley
24 Angel Martinez
25 Dan Russell
26 Pat Gilbert
27 Dann Howitt
28 Antoine Pickett
29 Drew Stratton
30 Steve Gokey
31 Dave Shotkoski
32 David Veres
33 Mike Gallego
34 Walt Weiss
35 Greg Cadaret
36 Checklist

1988 ProCards Myrtle Beach Blue Jays

(Toronto Blue Jays, A)

	MT	NR MT	EX
Complete Set:	8.00	6.00	3.25

1166 Steve Wapnick
1167 Graeme Lloyd
1168 Denis Boucher
1169 Bernardino Nunez
1170 Edgar Marquez
1171 Derek Bell
1172 Steve Woide
1173 Chris Floyd
1174 Nate Cromwell
1175 Juan de la Rosa
1176 Greg David
1177 Dan Etzweiler
1178 Xavier Hernandez
1179 Mike Murray
1180 Leroy Stanton
1181 Omar Malave
1182 Randy Knorr
1183 Greg Vella
1184 Mike Timlin
1185 Steve Towey
1186 Williams Suero
1187 Allan Silverstein
1188 Richard Hebner
1189 Luis Sojo
1190 Jimmy Rogers
1191 Rob MacDonald
1192 Todd Provence
---- Checklist

1988 CMC Nashville Sounds

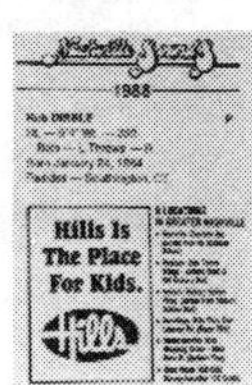

(Cincinnati Reds, AAA)

	MT	NR MT	EX
Complete Set:	7.50	5.50	3.00

1 Jack Armstrong
2 Tim Birtsas
3 Norm Charlton
4 Rob Dibble
5 Jeff Gray
6 Mike Jones
7 Hugh Kemp
8 Rob Lopez
9 Steve Oliverio
10 Pat Pacillo
11 Mike Roesler
12 Lenny Harris
13 Greg Monda
14 Luis Quinones
15 Dan Boever
16 Doug Gwosdz
17 Joe Oliver
18 Marty Brown
19 Scott Earl
20 Dave Klipstein
21 Ron Roenicke
22 Van Snider
23 Jack Lind
24 Wayne Garland
25 John Young

1988 ProCards Nashville Sounds

(Cincinnati Reds, AAA)

	MT	NR MT	EX
Complete Set:	7.00	5.25	2.75

471 Scott Earl
472 Pat Pacillo
473 Van Snider
474 Dave Klipstein
475 Ron Roenicke
476 Dan Boever
477 Tim Birtsas
478 Jeff Gray
479 Hugh Kemp
480 Doug Gwosdz
481 Marty Brown
482 Steve Oliverio
483 Joe Oliver
484 Jack Armstrong
485 Mike Jones
486 Jack Lind
487 Rob Lopez
488 Norm Charlton
489 Lenny Harris
490 Luis Quinones
491 Greg Monda
492 Mike Roesler
493 Robbie Dibble
494 Wayne Garland
495 John R. Young
---- Checklist

1988 Team Nashville Sounds

(Cincinnati Reds, AAA)

	MT	NR MT	EX
Complete Set:	9.00	6.75	3.50

(1) Jack Armstrong
(2) Skeeter Barnes
(3) Dan Boever
(4) Marty Brown
(5) Norm Charlton
(6) Tony DeFrancesco
(7) Rob Dibble
(8) Scottie Earl
(9) Jeff Gray
(10) Doug Gwosdz
(11) Lenny Harris
(12) Jim Jefferson
(13) Mike Jones
(14) Hugh Kemp
(15) Terry McGriff
(16) Charlie Mitchell
(17) Steve Oliverio
(18) Luis Quinones
(19) Ron Roenicke
(20) Candy Sierra
(21) Van Snider
(22) Eddie Tanner
(23) Hedi Vargas
(24) Manager/Coach/Trainer card (John Young, Frank Lucchesi, Wayne Garland)

1988 ProCards New Britain Red Sox

(Boston Red Sox, AA)

	MT	NR MT	EX
Complete Set:	4.00	3.00	1.50

889 Luis Vasquez
890 Daryl Irvine
891 Mike Clarkin
892 Doug Palmer
893 Bob Chadwick
894 John Roberts
895 Eduardo Zambrano
896 Mike Dalton
897 Manny Jose
898 Dan Gabrielle
899 Larry Shikles
900 Greg Bochesa
901 Tim McGee
902 Jose Birriel
903 Ed Estrada
904 Dan Gakeler
905 Tito Stewart
906 Todd Pratt
907 Chris Moritz
908 Curt Schilling
909 Mike Carista
910 Angel Gonzalez
911 Roberto Zambrano
912 Jason Jackson
---- Checklist

1988 CMC Oklahoma City 89'ers

(Texas Rangers, AAA)

	MT	NR MT	EX
Complete Set:	7.00	5.25	2.75

1 Scott Anderson
2 Dwayne Henry
3 Scott May
4 Craig McMurtry
5 Gary Mielke
6 Ferguson Jenkins
7 Ray Hayward
8 Ed Vande Berg
9 Tony Fossas
10 Rick Odekirk
11 Darrell Whitaker
12 Otto Gonzalez
13 Gar Millay
14 Jose Tolentino
15 Bill Merrifield
16 Barbaro Garbey
17 Larry Klein

18	Jeff Kunkel
19	Tom O'Malley
20	Dan Rohn
21	Don Werner
22	Robby Wine
23	Jim St. Laurent
24	James Steels
25	Toby Harrah

1988 ProCards Oklahoma City 89'ers

(Texas Rangers, AAA) Cards in this set have a Pizza Hut emblem on their backs.

	MT	NR MT	EX
Complete Set:	7.00	5.25	2.75

27	Scott May
28	Bill Taylor
29	Rick Odekirk
30	Jeff Kunkel
31	Dan Rohn
32	Larry Klein
33	Dwayne Henry
34	Tony Fossas
35	Gary Mielke
36	Bill Merrifield
37	Don Werner
38	James Steels
39	Jim St Laurent
40	Gar Millay
41	Jose Tolentino
42	Robbie Wine
43	Darrell Whitaker
44	Craig McMurtry
45	Barbaro Garbey
46	Toby Harrah
47	Otto Gonzalez
48	Tom O'Malley
49	Ray Hayward
50	Ferguson Jenkins
51	Ray Ramirez
52	Ed Vande Berg
----	Checklist

1988 CMC Omaha Royals

(Kansas City Royals, AAA)

	MT	NR MT	EX
Complete Set:	7.00	5.25	2.75

1	Rick Anderson
2	Luis Aquino
3	Bob Buchanan
4	Steve Fireovid
5	Jerry Don Gleaton
6	Al Hargesheimer
7	Jeff Montgomery
8	Tom Mullen
9	Bill Swaggerty
10	Rondin Johnson
11	Israel Sanchez
12	Nick Capra
13	Mike Loggins
14	Gary Thurman
15	Jeff Schulz
16	Dave Owen
17	Dann Bilardello
18	Larry Owen
19	Tom Dodd
20	Buddy Biancalana
21	Joe Citari
22	Luis de los Santos
23	Rich Dubee
24	Jose Castro
25	Glenn Ezell

1988 ProCards Omaha Royals

(Kansas City Royals, AAA)

	MT	NR MT	EX
Complete Set:	4.00	3.00	1.50

1494	Rich Dubee
1495	Tom Poquette
1496	Israel Sanchez
1497	Jerry Gleaton
1498	Bill Swaggerty
1499	Nick Capra
1500	Nick Swartz
1501	Jeff Montgomery
1502	Buddy Biancalana
1503	Glenn Ezell
1504	Mike Loggins
1505	Tom Dodd
1506	Luis de los Santos
1507	Tom Mullen
1508	Jeff Schulz
1509	Jose Castro
1510	Dave Owen
1511	Don Welchel
1512	Rick Anderson
1513	Steve Fireovid
1514	Bob Buchanan
1515	Ron Johnson
1516	Larry Owen
1517	Al Hargesheimer
1518	Dann Bilardello
1519	Joe Citari
1520	Luis Aquino
1521	Gary Thurman
----	Checklist

1988 ProCards Oneonta Yankees

(New York Yankees, A)

	MT	NR MT	EX
Complete Set:	8.00	6.00	3.25

	Checklist
2040	Ed Martel
2041	Andy Cook
2042	Todd Brill
2043	Pat Kelly
2044	Bob DeJardin
2045	Jason Bridges
2046	Herb Erhardt
2047	Ken Greer
2048	Skip Nelloms
2049	Hector Vargas
2050	John Seeburger
2051	Craig Brink
2052	Jeff Livesey
2053	Rey Fernandez
2054	Miguel Torres
2055	Jorge Candelaria
2056	Bob Hunter
2057	Jeff Hoffman
2058	Bob Zeihen
2059	Mike Draper
2060	Art Canestro
2061	Bruce Prybylinski
2062	Jerry Nielsen
2063	Jay Makemson
2064	Gary & Kelvin Allenson
2065	Tim Weston
2066	Alan Warren
2067	Jay Knoblauh
2068	Mark Martin
2069	Jeff Johnson
2070	Jeff Taylor
2071	Frank Seminara
2072	Rod Ehrhard

1988 Best Orlando Twins

(Minnesota Twins, AA)

	MT	NR MT	EX
Complete Set:	7.50	5.50	3.00

1	Derek Parks
2	Tim O'Connor
3	Duane Gustavson
4	Eddie Yanes
5	Mark Funderburk
6	Toby Nivens
7	Steven Comer
8	James Pittman
9	Mike Dyer
10	Jaime Williams
11	Joey Aragon
12	Gary Borg
13	Jeff Satzinger
14	Kevin Trudeau
15	Terry Jorgensen
16	Chris Forgione
17	German Gonzalez
18	Chip Hale
19	Jeff Reboulet
20	Larry Casian
21	Mike Dotzler
22	Rafael DeLima
23	Steve Gasser
24	Francisco Oliveras
25	Shannon Raybon
26	Wayne Hattaway
27	Bill Cutshall
28	Bernardo Brito
29	Checklist/Tinker Field

1988 Star Co. Osceola Astros

(Houston Astros, A) (Price includes the late-issue Bodie card)

	MT	NR MT	EX
Complete Set:	7.00	5.25	2.75

1	Manuel Acta
2	Samuel August
3	Jeff Baldwin
4	Daven Bond
5	Ryan Bowen
6	Todd Credeur
7a	Louis Deiley
7b	Keith Bodie (late issue, misnumbered, gold rather than orange border)
8	Pedro DeLeon
9	Tony Eusebio
10	Lou Frazier
11	Carl Grovom
12	Rusty Harris
13	Randall Hennis
14	Victor Hithe
15	Trent Hubbard
16	Bert Hunter
17	Todd McClure
18	Guy Normand
19	Dan Nyssen
20	Alfonso Osuna
21	David Potts
22	Karl Rhodes
23	Pedro Sanchez
24	John Sheenan
25	Mike Simms

1988 Cal Cards Palm Springs Angels

(California Angels, A)

	MT	NR MT	EX
Complete Set:	7.00	5.25	2.75

85	Colin Charland
86	Mike Erb
87	John Fritz
88	Scott Kannenberg
89	Jim Long
90	Luis Merejo
91	Rich Morehouse
92	Jeff Richardson
93	Jose Tapia
94	Bill Vanderwel
95	Dan Ward
96	Edgar Alfonzo
97	Ruben Amaro
98	Mike Anderson
99	Mark Baca
100	Jeff Barns
101	Scott Cerny
102	Cris Cron
103	Ted Dyson
104	Jim McAnany
105	Mike Musolino
106	Gary Nalls
107	John Orton
108	Reed Peters
109	Giovanny Reyes
110	Paul Sorrento
111	Glenn Washington
112	Bill Lachemann
113	Reggie Lambert
114	Gary Ruby
115	Bill Durney

1988 ProCards Palm Springs Angels

(California Angels, A)

	MT	NR MT	EX
Complete Set:	7.00	5.25	2.75

1433	John Orton
1434	Ruben Amaro
1435	J. Gary Ruby
1436	Bill Lacheman
1437	Luis Merejo
1438	Mike Anderson
1439	Reed Peters
1440	Scott Cerny
1441	Chris Cron
1442	Dan Ward
1443	Mike Erb
1444	Scott Kannenberg
1445	John Fritz
1446	Jose Tapia
1447	Colin Charland
1448	Dario Nunez
1449	Richard Morehouse
1450	Paul Sorrento
1451	Jeff Barns
1452	Jim McAnany
1453	Tim Dyson
1454	Gary Nalls
1455	Glenn Washington
1456	Mark Baca
1457	Bill Vanderwel
1458	Jim Bisceglia
1459	Bobby Bell
1460	Jimmy Long
1461	Reggie Lambert
1462	Bill Durney
1463	Jeff Richardson
----	Checklist

1988 CMC Pawtucket Red Sox

(Boston Red Sox, AAA)

	MT	NR MT	EX
Complete Set:	7.50	5.50	3.00

1	Rob Woodward
2	Mike Rochford
3	Mitch Johnson
4	John Leister
5	Andy Araujo
6	Zack Crouch
7	Steve Curry
8	Eric Hetzel
9	Tom Bolton
10	Dana Kiecker
11	Randy Kutcher
12	Bill McInnis
13	Glenn Hoffman
14	Tony Cleary
15	Chris Cannizzaro
16	Pat Dodson
17	Angel Gonzalez
18	Mike Mesh
19	Gary Miller-Jones
20	Carlos Quintana
21	Dana Williams
22	Gary Tremblay
23	Scott Wade
24	Ed Nottie
25	Mark Meleski

1988 ProCards Pawtucket Red Sox

(Boston Red Sox, AAA)

	MT	NR MT	EX
Complete Set:	7.50	5.50	3.00

446	Andy Araujo
447	Mike Rochford
448	Rob Woodward
449	Eric Hetzel
450	Gary Tremblay
451	Chris Cannizzaro
452	Tom Bolton
453	Carlos Quintana
454	Mark Meleski
455	Mitch Johnson
456	Bill McInnis
457	Zack Crouch
458	Scott Wade
459	Gary Miller-Jones
460	Dana Williams
461	Dana Kiecker
462	Angel Gonzalez
463	Mike Mesh
464	Randy Kutcher
465	Glenn Hoffman
466	Pat Dodson
467	Tony Cleary
468	Steve Curry
469	Ed Nottie
470	John Leister
----	Checklist

1988 Team Peoria Chiefs

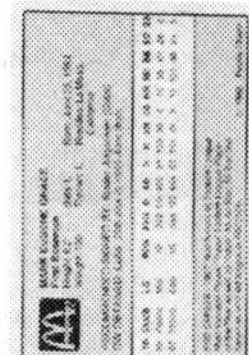

(Chicago Cubs, AA)

	MT	NR MT	EX
Complete Set:	50.00	40.00	20.00

(1)	Herbie Andrade
(2)	Warren Arrington
(3)	Mike Aspray
(4)	Lenny Bell
(5)	Pookie Bernstine
(6)	Mike Boswell
(7)	Ed Caballero
(8)	Chiefs' Alumni
(9)	Rusty Crockett
(10)	Sergio Espinal
(11)	Mark Grace
(12)	Carl Hamilton
(13)	Phil Hannon
(14)	Hersey Hawkins
(15)	Greg Kallevig
(16)	Rick Kranitz
(17)	Jerry Lapenta
(18)	Greg Maddux
(19)	Jeff Massicotte
(20)	Steve Melendez
(21)	Bill Melvin
(22)	Mark North
(23)	Rafael Palmeiro
(24)	Elvin Pulino
(25)	Pete & Harry
(26)	Jeff Pico
(27)	Marty Rivero
(28)	Brett Robinson
(29)	Gabby Rodriguez
(30)	Stars of the Future
(31)	Jim Tracy
(32)	Rick Wilkins

(33) Eddie Williams
(34) Jerome Walton
(35) Fernando Zarranz

1988 CMC Phoenix Firebirds

(San Francisco Giants, AAA)

	MT	NR MT	EX
Complete Set:	15.00	11.00	6.00

1 Randy Bockus
2 John Burkett
3 Dennis Cook
4 Roger Mason
5 Jeff Brantley
6 Mike Hogan
7 Brian Ohnoutka
8 Roger Samuels
9 Randy McCament
10 Terry Mullholland
11 Ed Puikunas
12 Kirt Manwaring
13 Bobby Ramos
14 Angel Escobar
15 Charlie Hayes
16 Tony Perezchica
17 Mark Wasinger
18 Matt Williams
19 Alan Cockrell
20 Everett Graham
21 Rusty Tillman
22 Ty Dabney
23 Deron McCue
24 Wendell Kim
25 Tim Blackwell, Marty DeMarrite

1988 ProCards Phoenix Firebirds

(San Francisco Giants, AAA)

	MT	NR MT	EX
Complete Set:	10.00	7.50	4.00

53 Tim Blackwell
54 Mark Wasinger
55 Randy Bockus
56 Matt Williams
57 Charlie Hayes
58 Deron McCue
59 Rusty Tillman
60 Everett Graham
61 Kirt Manwaring
62 Roger Mason
63 Angel Escobar
64 Francisco Melendez
65 Wendell Kim
66 Cliff Shidawara
67 Marty DeMerritt
68 Alan Cockrell
69 Bobby Ramos
70 Roger Samuels
71 Randy McCament
72 Ty Dabney
73 Mike Hogan
74 Ed Puikunas
75 Tony Perezchica
76 John Burkett
77 Terry Mulholland
78 Jeff Brantley
79 Brian Ohnoutka
80 Dennis Cook
---- Checklist

1988 ProCards Pittsfield Cubs

(Chicago Cubs, AA)

	MT	NR MT	EX
Complete Set:	8.00	6.00	3.25

1355 Hector Villanueva
1356 Mitch Zwolensky
1357 Julio Valdez
1358 Ray Thoma
1359 Joe Girardi
1360 Jim Essian
1361 Bryan House
1362 Rich Amaral
1363 Bob Bafia
1364 Brian McCann
1365 Mike Tullier
1366 Jerry Lapenta
1367 Jim Bullinger
1368 Dean Wilkins
1369 Steve Parker
1370 Ced Landrum
1371 Mark Leonette
1372 Rich Scheid
1373 Dave Kopf
1374 Jerome Walton
1375 Jackie Davidson
1376 Kris Roth
1377 Mike Harkey
1378 Gary Parmenter
---- Checklist

1988 Team Pittsfield Cubs

(Chicago Cubs, AA) This set is in the form of a 10-7/8" x 16-3/4" poster.

	MT	NR MT	EX
Complete Set:	21.00	15.50	8.50

(1) Rich Amaral
(2) Bob Bafia
(3) Jim Bullinger
(4) Jackie Davidson
(5) Jim Essian
(6) Joe Girardi (not pictured)
(7) Mike Harkey
(8) Bryan House
(9) Grant Jackson (not pictured)
(10) Dave Kopf
(11) Cedric Landrum
(12) Jerry LaPenta
(13) Mark Leonette
(14) Brian McCann
(15) Alan McKay
(16) E.J. Narcise (not pictured)
(17) Steve Parker
(18) Gary Parmenter
(19) Kris Roth
(20) Rich Scheid
(21) Jeff Small
(22) Ray Thoma
(23) Mike Tullier (not pictured)
(24) Hector Villanueva
(25) Robin Wadsworth (not pictured)
(26) Jerome Walton (not pictured)
(27) Matt & Ben Webber
(28) Dean Wilkens
(29) Rick Wrona
(30) Mitch Zwolensky

1988 ProCards Pocatello Giants

(San Francisco Giants, R)

	MT	NR MT	EX
Complete Set:	7.00	5.25	2.75

Checklist
2073 Don Brock
2074 David Wuthrich
2075 Andre George
2076 Jim Myers
2077 Carlos Sanchez
2078 Francisco (Arias)
2079 Sean Thompson
2080 Scott Ebert
2081 Adam Hilpert
2082 Steve Reed
2083 Lance Burnett
2084 Dave Edwards
2085 Marino Hernandez
2086 Greg Lee
2087 Reuben Smiley
2088 Daris Toussaint
2089 Victor Cruz
2090 Brett Hewatt
2091 Kevin Rodgers
2092 Adam Smith
2093 Kevin Hall
2094 David Slavin
2095 Dobie (Swepson)
2096 Jesus Laya
2097 Joey Speaks
2098 David Booth
2099 Carl Hanselman
2100 Diego Segui
2101 Jack Hiatt
2102 Jack Penrod

1988 Star Co. Port Charlotte Rangers

(Texas Rangers, A) Team is located in Port Charlotte, Florida.

	MT	NR MT	EX
Complete Set:	30.00	22.00	12.00

1 Rick Bernardo
2 Brian Bohanon
3 Omar Brewer
4 Phil Bryant
5 Paco Burgos
6 Rufus Ellis
7 Darrin Garner
8 Juan Gonzalez
9 Bill Haselman
10 Jonathan Hurst
11 Mark Kramer
12 Adam Lamle
13 Darren Loy
14a Barry Manuel
14b Bobby Jones (late issue, misnumbered)
15 Terry Mathews
16 Jeff Mays
17 Darren Niethammer
18 Dean Palmer
19 Mark Petkovsek
20 Lino Rivera
21 Wayne Rosenthal
22 Tony Scruggs
23 Sammy Sosa
---- Rey Sanchez

1988 CMC Portland Beavers

(Minnesota Twins, AAA)

	MT	NR MT	EX
Complete Set:	7.00	5.25	2.75

1 Andy Anderson
2 Karl Best
3 T.R. Bryden
4 Jeff Bumgarner
5 Mark Portugal
6 Roy Smith
7 Ray Soff
8 Freddie Toliver
9 Jim Winn
10 Jim Davins
11 Brian Harper
12 Steve Liddle
13 Doug Baker
14 Ricky Jones
15 Kelvin Torve
16 Brad Bierly
17 Eric Bullock
18 Winston Ficklin
19 Chris Pittaro
20 Vic Rodriguez
21 Robby Ralston
22 John Moses
23 Phil Wilson
24 Jim Mahoney
25 Jim Shellenback

1988 ProCards Portland Beavers

(Minnesota Twins, AAA)

	MT	NR MT	EX
Complete Set:	7.00	5.25	2.75

639 Brad Bierley
640 Eric Bullock
641 Kelvin Torve
642 Jim Winn
643 John Moses
644 Jim Shellenback
645 Roy Smith
646 Karl Best
647 Doug Baker
648 Brad Boylan
649 Vic Rodrigeuz
650 Jim Mahoney
651 Brian Harper
652 Winston Ficklin
653 Chris Pittaro
654 Allan Anderson
655 Steve Liddle
656 Ricky Jones
657 Bobby Ralston
658 Mark Portugai
659 Jeff Bumgarner
660 Jim Davins
661 Phil Wilson
662 Ray Soff
663 T.R. Bryden
664 Fred Toliver
---- Checklist

1988 Star Co. Prince William Yankees

(New York Yankees, A) There was no manager card produced in this set.

	MT	NR MT	EX
Complete Set:	8.00	6.00	3.25

1 Steve Adkins
2 Tim Bishop
3 Brent Blum
4 Dennis Brow
5 Ken Brown
6 Royal Clayton
7 Bill Dacosta
8 Luis Faccio
9 Reynaldo Fernandez
10 Randy Foster
11 Victor Garcia
12 Chris Howard
13 Dean Kelly
14 Jose Laboy
15 Kevin Maas
16 Mark Marris
17 Alan Mills
18 William Morales
19 Tom Popplewell
20 John Ramos
21 Jerry Rub
22 Darrell Tingle
23 Mickey Tresh
24 Bernie Williams
25 Gerald Williams

1988 ProCards Pulaksi Braves

(Atlanta Braves, R)

	MT	NR MT	EX
Complete Set:	7.00	5.25	2.75

Checklist
1748 Phillip Wellman
1749 Fred Koenig
1750 Smoky Burgess
1751 Scott Goselin
1752 Scott Grove
1753 John Greenwood
1754 Tom Rizzo
1755 Steve Wendell
1756 Glen Gardner
1757 David Reis
1758 Errol Flynn
1759 Paul Reis
1760 Calvain Culberson
1761 Ricky Rigsby
1762 Brent McCoy
1763 Chris Mitta
1764 Mike Urman
1765 David Piela
1766 Roger Hailey
1767 Robert Minaya
1768 Randy Simmons
1769 Ron Thomas
1770 Cloyd Boyer
1771 Don Bowman

1988 ProCards Reading Phillies

(Philadelphia Phillies, AA)

	MT	NR MT	EX
Complete Set:	6.00	4.50	2.50

863 Tom Schwarz
864 Alan Leboeuf
865 Steve Sharts
866 Brad Moore
867 Tony Brown
868 Scott Service
869 Chuck Malone
870 Tim Sossamon
871 Warren Magee
872 Jeff Kaye
873 Gary Berman
874 Dan Giesen
875 Chuck McElroy
876 Tim Fortugno
877 Steve Deangelis
878 Rick Parker
879 Howard Nichols
880 Greg Edge
881 Harvey Brumfield
882 Greg Legg
883 Vince Holyfield
884 Jose Leiva
885 Ray Roman
886 Chris Calvert
887 Tim Corcoran
888 Carlos Arroyo
---- Checklist

1988 Grand Slam Quad City Angels

(California Angels, A)

	MT	NR MT	EX
Complete Set:	6.00	4.50	2.50

1 Eddie Rodriguez
2 Mike Couchee
3 Bill Zick
4 Wiley Lee
5 Kevin Flora
6 Larry Pardo
7 Edgal Rodriguez
8 Bill Robinson
9 Terence Carr
10 Steve Dunn
11 David Holdridge
12 Frank Mutz
13 Daryl Green
14 Bob Rose
15 Troy Giles
16 Rod Lung
17 Jim Townsend
18 Mario Molina
19 Edgar Alfonzo
20 Roberto Hernandez
21 Kenny Grant
22 Jim Aylward
23 Cesar DeLaRosa
24 Charlie Romero
25 Rob Wassenaar

26 Tim McKinnis
27 Chris Graves
28 Gary Buckels
29 Brandy Vann
30 Mike Musolino

1988 Cal Cards Reno Silver Sox

(No affiliation) (A)

	MT	NR MT	EX
Complete Set:	6.00	4.50	2.50

268 Alan Fowlkes
269 Elvin Rivera
270 Tony LaCerra
271 Reggie Glover
272 Bill Shamblin
273 Scott Madden
274 Joe Strong
275 John Savage
276 Frank Mutz
277 Mike Garner
278 Kinney Sims
279 Jamie Allison
280 Jim Aylward
281 Cary Grubb
282 Chris Holmes
283 Robbie Rogers
284 Mike Rountree
285 Joe Ortiz
286 Gregg Ward
287 Dave Liddell
288 Jim Pace
289 Pete Houston
290 Fred Carter
291 Nate Oliver

1988 Bob's Photo Richmond Braves

(Atlanta Braves, AAA) (3-7/8" x 5")

	MT	NR MT	EX
Complete Set:	45.00	34.00	18.00

1 Joe Boever
2 Bean Stringfellow
3 Carlos Rios
4 Sid Akins
5 Lonnie Smith
6 Jeff Blauser
7 Derek Lilliquist
8 John Smoltz
9 Juan Espino
10 John Mizerock
11 Marty Clary
12 Mike Fischlin
13 David Justice
14 Dave Griffin
15 Tommy Greene
16 Alex Smith
17 Jeff Wetherby
18 Gary Eave
19 Greg Tubbs
20 Dave Miller
21 Kevin Coffman
22 Tommy Dunbar
23 John Grubb
24 Barry Jones

1988 CMC Richmond Braves

(Atlanta Braves, AAA)

	MT	NR MT	EX
Complete Set:	26.00	22.50	12.00

1 Tommy Green
2 Derek Lilliquist
3 John Smoltz
4 Bean Stringfellow
5 Gary Eave
6 Juan Eichelberger
7 Sid Akins
8 Jose Alvarez
9 Joe Boever
10 Marty Clary
11 Todd Dewey
12 Ron Gant
13 Alex Smith
14 Lonnie Smith
15 Greg Tubbs
16 Jeff Wetherby
17 David Justice
18 Carlos Rios
19 Dave Griffin
20 Juan Espino
21 John Mizerock
22 Jeff Blauser
23 Jim Beauchamp
24 Leo Mazzone
25 Clarence Jones

1988 ProCards Richmond Braves

(Atlanta Braves, AAA)

	MT	NR MT	EX
Complete Set:	20.00	15.00	8.00

1 Lonnie Smith
2 Tommy Greene
3 Ronnie Gant
4 Todd Dewey
5 Greg Tubbs
6 Sam Ayoub
7 Juan Espino
8 Carlos Rios
9 Jeff Wetherby
10 Juan Eichelberger
11 Marty Clary
12 Jose Alvarez
13 Bean Stringfellow
14 Sid Akins
15 Jim Beauchamp
16 Leo Mazzone
17 Clarence Jones
18 Jeff Blauser
19 John Mizerock
20 Dave Griffin
21 Derek Lilliquist
22 Joe Boever
23 John Smoltz
24 Dave Justice
25 Alex Smith
26 Gary Eave
---- Checklist

1988 Team Richmond Braves

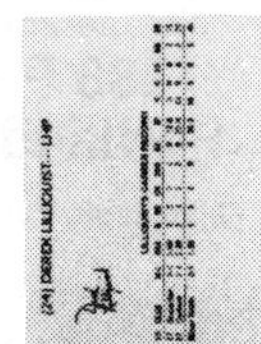

(Atlanta Braves, AAA) This set is also sponsored by station 35-WRLH.

	MT	NR MT	EX
Complete Set:	21.00	15.50	8.50

1 Sam Ayoub
2 Jeff Blauser
4 Mike Fischlin
5 Lonnie Smith
6 Carlos Rios
9 Jim Beauchamp
14 Terry Bell
15 Greg Tubbs
16 Sid Akins
18 Dave Justice
19 Bean Strinfellow
20 Dave Miller
22 Jeff Wetherby
24 Derek Lilliquist
25 John Mizerock
26 John Smoltz
27 Johnny Grubb
28 Steve Ziem
29 Juan Espino
30 Alex Smith
31 Gary Eave
32 Marty Clary
33 Tommy Greene
34 Dave Griffin
36 Joe Boever
---- Team Photo

1988 Cal Cards Riverside Red Wave

(A)

	MT	NR MT	EX
Complete Set:	8.00	6.00	3.75

206 Kevin Armstrong
207 James Austin
208 Ricky Bones
209 Rafael Chaves
210 Brian Harrison
211 Richard Holsman
212 James Lewis
213 Steve Loubier
214 Bill Marx
215 Brian Wood
216 Brian Brooks
217 Paul Faries
218 Kevin Farmer
219 Greg Hall
220 Kevin Garner
221 Steve Hendricks
222 Dave Hollins
223 Tom Levasseur
224 Terry McDevitt
225 Warren Newsom
226 Andy Skeels
227 Bill Taylor
228 Pat Jelks
229 Tony Torchia
230 William Blount
231 Jim Danile
232 Ron Oglesby
233 Tye Waller

1988 ProCards Riverside Red Wave

(San Diego Padres, A)

	MT	NR MT	EX
Complete Set:	8.00	6.00	3.75

1407 Ron Oglesby
1408 Kevin Farmer
1409 Steve Hendricks
1410 Brian Brooks
1411 Pat Jelks
1412 Jim Daniel
1413 Tony Torchia
1414 Tye Waller
1415 Greg Hall
1416 Warren Newson
1417 Tom Levasseur
1418 Dave Hollins
1419 Bill Taylor
1420 Brian Wood
1421 Bill Blount
1422 Paul Faries
1423 Jim Lewis
1424 Bill Marx
1425 Andy Skeels
1426 Ricky Bones
1427 Rich Holsman
1428 Brian Harrison
1429 Rafel Chavez
1430 Terry McDevitt
1431 Kevin Garner
1432 Steve Loubier
---- Checklist

1988 ProCards Rochester Red Wings

(Baltimore Orioles, AAA)

	MT	NR MT	EX
Complete Set:	9.00	6.75	3.50

193 Dale Berra
194 Eric Bell
195 Dave Smith
196 Bob Gibson
197 Vic Mata
198 Sherwin Cinjntje
199 Jeff Ballard
200 Ron Salcedo
201 Jay Tibbs
202 Mickey Tettleton
203 Matt Cimo
204 Chris Padget
205 Pete Stanicek
206 Jose Mesa
207 Reg Montgomery
208 Mark Bowden
209 Bill Scherrer
210 Mike Griffin
211 Johnny Oates
212 Dom Chiti
213 Keith Hughes
214 Jamie Reed
215 John Habyan
216 Jerry Narron
217 Craig Worthington
218 Curt Motton
219 Dickie Noles
220 Jay Colley
221 Silver Stadium
---- Checklist

1988 Pucko Rochester Red Wings

	MT	NR MT	EX
Complete Set:	9.00	6.75	3.50

1 Rochester Red Wings
2 Mark Bowden
3 Dale Berra
4 Curt Brown
5 Matt Cimo
6 Gordon Dillard
7 Steve Finley
8 Mike Griffin
9 John Habyan
10 Pete Harnisch
11 Kevin Hickey
12 Gerry Holtz
13 Keith Hughes
14 Ken Landreaux
15 Vic Mata
16 Bob Milacki
17 Jerry Narron
18 Carl Nichols
19 Dickie Noles
20 Chris Padget
21 Tim Pyznarski
22 Mike Raczka
23 Wade Rowdon
24 Ron Salcedo
25 Chuck Stanhope
26 Jeff Stone
27 Craig Worthington
28 Dom Chiti
29 Curt Motton
30 Johnny Oates
31 Jamie Reed
32 Bob Goughan
33 Rochester Red Wings
34 Rochester Red Wings
35 Rochester Red Wings
36 Rochester Red Wings

1988 CMC Rochester Red Wings

(Baltimore Orioles, AAA)

	MT	NR MT	EX
Complete Set:	9.00	6.75	3.50

1 Jeff Ballard
2 Eric Bell
3 Jose Mesa
4 Mark Bowden
5 Bob Gibson
6 John Habyan
7 Mike Griffin
8 Dickie Noles
9 Bill Scherrer
10 Jay Tibbs
11 Matt Cimo
12 Dale Berra
13 Chris Padget
14 Jerry Narron
15 Keith Hughes
16 Ron Salcedo
17 David Lee Smith
18 Pete Stanicek
19 Craig Worthington
20 Sherwin Cinjtje
21 Mickey Tettleton
22 Tito Landrum
23 Vic Mata
24 Johnny Oates
25 Curt Motton

1988 Team Rochester Red Wings

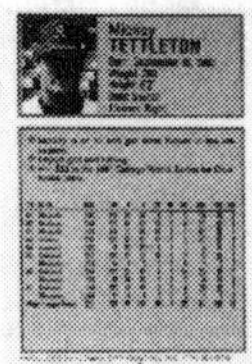

(Baltimore Orioles, AAA)

	MT	NR MT	EX
Complete Set:	9.00	6.75	3.50

(1) Jeff Ballard
(2) Eric Bell
(3) Dale Berra
(4) Mark Bowden
(5) Dom Chiti
(6) Sherwin Cijntje
(7) Matt Cimo
(8) Bob Gibson
(9) Mike Griffin
(10) John Habyan
(11) Keith Hughes
(12) Vic Mata
(13) Jose Mesa
(14) Curt Motton
(15) Jerry Narron
(16) Dickie Noles
(17) Johnny Oates
(18) Chris Padget
(19) Ron Salcedo
(20) Bill Scherrer
(21) Dave (D.L.) Smith
(22) Pete Stanicek
(23) Mickey Tettleton
(24) Jay Tibbs
(25) Jim Traber
(26) Craig Worthington

Definitions for grading conditions are located in the Introduction of this price guide.

1988 Team Rockford Expos

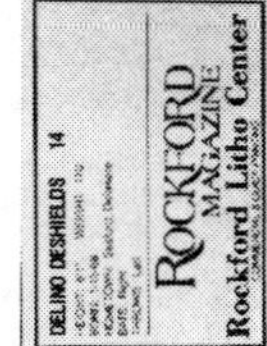

(Montreal Expos, A)

	MT	NR MT	EX
Complete Set:	12.00	9.00	4.75

1 Alan Bannister
3 Gene Glynn
4 Trevor Penn
6 Steve Pearse
9 Jesus Paredes
13 Arci Cianfrocco
14 Delino DeShields
15 Kent Willis
17 Paul Frye
20 Mike Parrott
22 Kevin Sheary
23 Rob Kerrigan
27 Greg Colburn (Colbrunn)
28 Mario Brito
33 James Faulk
35 John Mello
39 Chris Pollack
41 Dave Clark
42 Chris Lariviere
44 Troy Ricker
45 Jeff Carter
46 Chris Marchok
47 Cesar Hernandez
48 Howard Farmer
49 Rob Leary
51 Scott Bromby
55 Nate Minchey
---- John Cain
---- Sean Cunningham
---- Jeff Hauser
---- Scott Lane
---- Bill Larsen
---- Thomas Shannon
----- Dan Deweerdt

1988 ProCards St. Catharines Blue Jays

(Toronto Blue Jays, A)

	MT	NR MT	EX
Complete Set:	7.00	5.25	2.75

2005 Armando Pagliari
2006 Luis Salazar
2007 Timothy Brown
2008 Jose Villa
2009 Benigno Placeres
2010 Brad Evaschuk
2011 Jose Guarache
2012 Pablo Castro
2013 Donn Wolfe
2014 Eddie Dennis
2015 Mike McAlpin
2016 Timithy Hodge
2017 Nigel Wilson
2018 Daniel Dodd
2019 Greg Williams
2020 Greg McCutcheon
2021 Robert Montalvo
2022 Curtis Johnson
2023 David Weathers
2024 Jose Martinez
2025 Edgar Marquez
2026 Rafael Martinez
2027 Jason Townley
2028 Marcos Tavaras
2029 Greg Harding
2030 Bryan Dixon
2031 Mike Jockish
2032 Mike Taylor
2033 Rick Vaughn
2034 Anthony Ward
2035 Ryan Thompson
2036 Darrin Wade
2037 Armando Serra
2038 Patrick Guerrero
---- Checklist

1988 Star Co. St. Petersburg Cardinals

(St. Louis Cardinals, A) (Price includes the late-issue cards for Bialas, Fagan and Riggins)

	MT	NR MT	EX
Complete Set:	8.00	6.00	3.25

1 John Balfanz
2 Scott Braodfoot
3 Dennis Carter
4 Joseph Cunningham
5 Jerry Daniels
6a Terry Elliot
6b David Bialas (late issue, misnumbered, gold rather than red border)
7 James Fernandez
8 Scott Hamilton
9 Patrick Hews
10 Stephen Hill
11 Crucito Lara
12 Scott Lawrence
13 Robert Livchak
14 Lonnie Maclin
15 Julian Martinez
16 Thomas Mauch
17 Kevin Maxey
18 Scott Melvin
19 Darren Nelson
20 Jay North
21 Geronimo Pena
22 Lenin Picota
23 Larry Pierson
24 Terrence Thomas
25 Stanley Zaltsman
26 Mark Riggins (late issue)
27 Pete Fagan (late issue)

1988 Star Co. St. Lucie Mets

(New York Mets, A) (Price includes the late-issue Hurdle card)

	MT	NR MT	EX
Complete Set:	7.00	3.75	2.00

1 Brandon Bailey
2 Chris Bayer
3 Kevin Brown
4 Rick Brown
5 Jeff Ciszkowski
6 Chris Donnels
7 Jovon Edwards
8 Dave Gelatt
9 Adam Ging
10 Kip Gross
11 Rob Hernandez
12 Andre Jacas
13a Scott Jaster
13b Clint Hurdle (late issue, misnumbered, gold rather than violet border)
14 Geary Jones
15 Manny Mantrana
16 Gus Meizoso
17 Doug Myres
18 Hector Perez
19 Fritz Polka
20 Craig Repoz
21 Bill Stiles
22 Greg Talamantez
23 John Toale
24 Dave Trautwein
25 Juan Villanueva

1988 Star Co. Salem Buccaneers

(Pittsburgh Pirates, A) (Price includes the late-issue Ward card)

	MT	NR MT	EX
Complete Set:	7.00	7.25	3.75

1 Steve Adams
2 Stan Belinda
3 Kevin Burdick
4 Terry Crowley
5 Chip Duncan
6 Oscar Escobar
7 Andy Hall
8 Scott Henion
9 Tim Kirk
10 Tony Longmire
11 John Love
12 Tim McKinley
13 Tim McMillan
14 Pete Murphy
15 Julio Peguero
16 Keith Raisnen
17 Richard Reed
18 Scott Ruskin
19 Mike Stevanus
20 Dave Takach
21a Doug Torborg
21b Jay Ward (late issue, misnumbered, gold rather than aqua border)
22 Junior Vizcaino
23 Ben Webb
24 Ed Yacopino
25 Mike York

1988 Team Salt Lake City Trappers

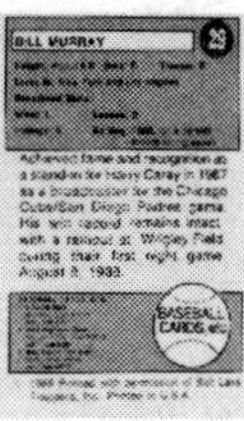

(A)

	MT	NR MT	EX
Complete Set:	9.00	6.75	3.50

1 Patrick Waid
2 Murray Brothers
3 Coaches
4 Front office & announcer
5 Chris Sloniger
6 Bullpen Coach & Bat boys
7 Ray Karczewski
8 Kelly Zane
9 Jeff Allison
10 Tommy Boyce
11 Bobby Edwards
12 Rick L. Hurni
13 Will Ambos
14 Greg "Tank" Ehmig
15 Michael Gibbons
16 Promo/Bus mgr & Scout
17 Kerry Shaw
18 Barry Moss
19 Doug Howard
20 Myron "Pops" Gardner
21 Fred Riscen
22 Martin Peralta
23 Terence "T-Can" Glover
24 Tim McKercher
25 Mando Verdugo
26 Bill Wenrick
27 Sal Roldan
28 Lee Carballo
29 Sean Johnson
30 Bill Murray

1988 Best San Antonio Missions

(Los Angeles Dodgers, AA)

	MT	NR MT	EX
Complete Set:	11.00	8.25	4.50

1 Ramon Martinez
2 Barry Wohler
3 Michael Pitz
4 Greg LaFever
5 Tony Mack
6 Domingo Michel
7 Michael Munoz
8 Wayne Kirby
9 Jim Kating
10 Mike Schweighoffer
11 Joe Kesselmark
12 Juan Bustabad
13 David Eichhorn
14 Manuel Francois
15 Darrin Fletcher
16 Walter McConnell
17 Phil Torres
18 Jose Mota
19 Mike Huff
20 Joe Humphries
21 John Wetteland
22 Javier Ortiz
23 Kevin Kennedy
24 Juan Bell
25 Mark Sheehy
26 Luis Lopez
27 Pat Zachry
28 Logo & checklist card

1988 Best San Antonio Missions Ltd. Edition

(Los Angeles Dodgers, AA) The set contains the same players as listed in the regular set. The fronts of the cards are silver & black and the backs of the cards are royal blue as opposed to the gray backs of the regular set. Only 1,300 of these sets were made.

	MT	NR MT	EX
Complete Set:	20.00	15.00	8.00

1988 Best San Bernadino Spirit

(Seattle Mariners, A)

	MT	NR MT	EX
Complete Set:	70.00	52.00	28.00

1 Ken Griffey Jr.
2 Don Reynolds
3 Lee Townsend
4 Ted Williams
5 Anthony Woods
6 Pat Rice
7 Jody Ryan
8 Rich DeLucia
9 William Diaz
10 Dan Disher
11 Ted Eldredge
12 Jerry Goff
13 Jose Tartabull
14 Ralph Dick
15 Jim Blueburg
16 Jim Bowie Jr.
17 Dave Burba
18 Clay Gunn
19 Keith Helton
20 Steve Hisey
21 Joe Kemp
22 Bryan King
23 Jeff Nelson
24 Rich Doyle
25 Todd Hayes
26 Mike Brocki
27 Bobby Cuellar
28 Checklist/Fiscalini Field

1988 Best San Bernadino Spirit Ltd. Edition

This set features the same players as listed in the regular set. Fronts of cards are silver & black and the backs are royal blue as opposed to the gray backs of the regular set. Only 1,300 of these sets were made.

	MT	NR MT	EX
Complete Set:	80.00	60.00	32.50

1988 Cal Cards San Bernadino Spirit

(Seattle Mariners, A)

	MT	NR MT	EX
Complete Set:	30.00	22.50	12.00

29 Steve Murray
30 Jim Bowie Jr.
31 Dan Disher
32 Clay Gunn
33 Jerry Goff
34 Ken Griffey Jr.
35 Joe Kemp
36 Jose Tartabull
37 William Diaz
38 Ted Williams
39 Steve Hisey
40 Mike Brocki
41 Ted Eldredge
42 Jody Ryan
43 Pat Rice
44 Keith Helton
45 Howard Townsend
46 Tim McLain
47 Jim Blueberg
48 Jeff Nelson
49 David Burba
50 Rich DeLucia
51 Todd Hayes
52 Rich Doyle
53 Ralph Dick
54 Bobby Cuellar

Definitions for grading conditions are located in the Introduction of this price guide.

1988 Cal Cards San Jose Giants

(San Francisco Giants, A)

	MT	NR MT	EX
Complete Set:	6.50	4.75	2.50

116 Rich Aldrete
117 Paul Blair
118 Greg Conner
119 Tad Hanyuda
120 Joe Jodo
121 Gary Jones
122 Mark Leonard
123 Jim McNamara
124 William Mijares
125 Scott Murray
126 Dave Patterson
127 Gregg Ritchie
128 Tod Ronson
129 Ken Suzuki
130 Daron Connelly
131 Eric Gunderson
132 Gil Heredia
133 Koji Maeda
134 Tom Meagher
135 Kevin Meier
136 Eric Pilkington
137 Doug Robertson
138 Russ Swan
139 Ray Velasquez
140 Masa Yamamoto
141 Duane Espy
142 Sam Hirose
143 Todd Oakes
144 Lance Hutchins

1988 ProCards San Jose Giants

(San Francisco Giants, A)

	MT	NR MT	EX
Complete Set:	7.00	5.25	2.75

108 Koli Maeda
109 Paul Blair
110 Willie Mijares
111 Dave Peterson
112 Gary Jones
113 Scott Murray
114 Eric Gunderson
115 Doug Robertson
116 Ray Velasquez
117 Masa Yamamoto
118 Russ Swan
119 Rich Aldrete
120 Tom Meagher
121 Ken Suzuki
122 Todd Oakes
123 Sam Hirose
124 Lance Hutchins
125 Duane Espy
126 Tod Ronson
127 Eric Pilkington
128 Tad Hanyuda
129 Greg Conner
130 Gil Heredia
131 Gregg Ritchie
132 Kevin Meier
133 Jim McNamara
134 Mark Leonard
135 Daron Connelly
136 Joe Johdo
---- Checklist

1988 ProCards Savannah Cardinals

(St. Louis Cardinals, A)

	MT	NR MT	EX
Complete Set:	7.00	5.25	2.75

331 Mike Hinkle
332 Ken Smith
333 Tony Russo
334 Tim Sherrill
335 Rob Colescott
336 Martin Mason
337 Keith Champion
338 Dave Krebs
339 Mark Behny
340 Bill Hershman
341 Roberto Marte
342 Hal Hempen
343 Clint Horsley
344 Tim Meamber
345 Brad Harvick
346 Reed Olmstead
347 John Sellick
348 Jim Ferguson
349 Stan Barrs
350 Eddie Looper
351 Kris Huffman
352 Ryan Johnston
353 Mike Alvarez
354 Eddie Carter
355 Antron Grier
356 Jean Gentleman
357 Greg Doss
358 Francisco Rosario
---- Checklist

1988 ProCards Shreveport Captains

(San Francisco Giants, AA)

	MT	NR MT	EX
Complete Set:	7.00	5.25	2.75

1279 Jack Mull
1280 Joe Kmak
1281 Jose Dominguez
1282 Joe Olker
1283 Mike Benjamin
1284 Vince Sferrazza
1285 Dean Freeland
1286 Steve Cline
1287 Andy Dixon
1288 Paul Meyers
1289 George Bonilla
1290 Paul McClellan
1291 Jeff Carter
1292 Jose Pena
1293 Romy Cucjen
1294 Rick Nelson
1295 Stuart Tate
1296 Mike Remlinger
1297 John Skurla
1298 Trevor Wilson
1299 Harry Davis
1300 Tim McCoy
1301 Ed Puikunas
1302 T.J. McDonald
---- Checklist

1988 Grand Slam South Atlantic League All-Stars

(A)

	MT	NR MT	EX
Complete Set:	9.00	6.75	3.50

1 Richie Hebner (Myrtle Beach)
2 Mel Roberts (Spartanburg)
3 Ned Yost (Sumter)
4 Bill Paul Carver (Asheville)
5 Ron Downs (Augusta)
6 Eddie Taubensee (Greensboro)
7 Brian Lane (Greensboro)
8 Joe Turek (Greensboro)
9 Ron Mullins (Greensboro)
10 Omar Olivares (Charleston)
11 Darrin Reichle (Charleston)
12 Guillermo Velazquez
13 Alex Arias (Charleston)
14 Mike Miller (Columbia)
15 Anthony Toney (Fayetteville)
16 Brant Alyea (Gastonia)
17 Williams Suero (Myrtle Beach)
18 Luis Sojo (Myrtle Beach)
19 Greg Vella (Myrtle Beach)
20 Derek Bell (Myrtle Beach)
21 Xavier Hernandez (Myrtle Beach)
22 Jimmy Rogers (Myrtle Beach)
23 Denis Boucher (Myrtle Beach)
24 Rob Colescott (Savannah)
25 John Sellick (Sumter)
26 James Vatcher (Spartanburg)
27 Andy Carter (Spartanburg)
28 Dennis Burlingame (Sumter)

1988 Grand Slam South Bend White Sox

(A)

	MT	NR MT	EX
Complete Set:	6.00	4.50	2.50

1 Cesar Bernhardt
2 Larry Allen
3 Javier Ocasio
4 Kevin Murdock
5 Ed Smith
6 Ray Payton
7 Dwayne Hosey
8 Rod McCray
9 Kinnis Pledger
10 Mike Maksudian
11 Wilson Valera
12 Bernando Cruz
13 Kurt Brown
14 Don Cooper
15 Steve Dillard
16 Jim Reinebold
17 Ed Sedar
18 Argenis Conde
19 Mike Girouard
20 Julian Gonzalez
21 Curt Hasler
22 John Hudek
23 Bo Kennedy
24 Rob Resnikoff
25 Randy Robinson
26 Steve Schrenik
27 Mark Tortorice
28 Stanley Coveleski

1988 Donn Jennings Southern League All-Stars

(AA)

	MT	NR MT	EX
Complete Set:	9.00	6.75	3.50

1 Matt Winters (Memphis)
2 Kevin Burrell (Memphis)
3 Steve Howard (Huntsville)
4 Mike Bordick (Huntsville)
5 Keith Lockhart (Chattanooga)
6 Darrell Pruitt (Chattanooga)
7 Matt Merullo (Birmingham)
8 Jerry Bertolani (Birmingham)
9 Tim Dulin (Charlotte)
10 Carlo Columbino (Columbus)
11 Rafael Delima (Orlando)
12 Derek Parks (Orlando)
13 Bernardo Brito (Orlando)
14 Barry Jones (Greenville)
15 Mark Lemke (Greenville)
16 Ed Whited (Greenville)
17 Drew Denson (Greenville)
18 Jeff Huson (Jacksonville)
19 Bob Caffrey (Jackson)
20 Randy Braun (Jackson)
21 Armando Moreno (Jackson)
22 Frrancisco Cabreba (Knoxville)
23 Webster Garrison (Knoxville)
24 Junior Felix (Knoxville)
25 Domingo Martinez (Knoxville)
26 Alex Sanchez (Knoxville)
27 Steve Cummings (Knoxville)
28 Kevin Blankenship (Greenville)
29 Larry Casian (Orlando)
30 German Gonzales (Orlando)
31 Brian Meyer (Columbus)
32 Pete Harnisch (Charlotte)
33 Brian Householder (Charlotte)
34 Tom Drees (Birmingham)
35 Joe Lazor (Chattanooga)
36 Chris Hammond (Chattanooga)
37 Joe Bruno (Chattanooga)
38 Rico Petrocelli (Birmingham)
39 Tommy Thompson (Jacksonville)
40 Nardi Contreres (Jacksonville)

1988 ProCards Southern Oregon A's

(Oakland A's, A)

	MT	NR MT	EX
Complete Set:	7.00	5.25	2.75

1692 Jim Buccheri
1693 Tim Vannaman
1694 Richard Rozman
1695 Nick Venuto
1696 Tony Ariola
1697 Joel Smith
1698 DeWayne Jones
1699 Tom Carcione
1700 Josue Espinal
1701 Stan Royer
1702 Rod Correia
1703 Joel Chimelis
1704 Mike Messerly
1705 Dean Borelli
1706 Lee Tinsley
1707 Tony Floyd
1708 Greg Ferguson
1709 Kevin MacLeod
1710 Mike Mungin
1711 Dan Eskew
1712 Jim Lawson
1713 Ray Harris
1714 J.P. Ricciardi
1715 Jerry Rizza
1716 Joe Hillman
1717 Lenny Sakata
1718 Jesus Hernaiz
---- Checklist

1988 ProCards Spartanburg Phillies

(Philadelphia Phillies, A)

	MT	NR MT	EX
Complete Set:	8.50	6.25	3.50

1024 Jeff Stark
1025 Matt Rambo
1026 Bob Hurta
1027 Tim Peek
1028 Greg McCarthy
1029 Darrell Coulter
1030 Shelby McDonald
1031 John Larosa
1032 Phil Fagnano
1033 Mel Roberts
1034 Rod Robertson
1035 Kim Batista
1036 Jaime Barragan
1037 Scott Ruckman
1038 Marty Foley
1039 Carlos Zayas
1040 Tony Trevino
1041 Gary Maasberg
1042 Doug Lindsey
1043 Todd Felton
1044 Gary White
1045 Jim Vatcher
1046 Bob Britt
1047 Buzz Capra
1048 Jim Platts
---- Checklist

1988 Star Co. Spartanburg Phillies

(Philadelphia Phillies, A) (The set price is for the red-bordered set. A blue-bordered set was also issued)

	MT	NR MT	EX
Complete Set:	7.00	5.25	2.75

1 Jimmy Barragan
2 Kim Batiste
3 Andy Carter
4 Mark Cobb
5 Darrell Coulter
6 Paul Ellison
7 Martin Foley
8 Bobby Hurta
9 Stephen Kirkpatrick
10 John Larosa
11 Doug Lindsey
12 Tim Mauser
13 Greg McCarthy
14 Sheebie McDonald
15 Timothy Peek
16 Matt Rambo
17 Scott Reaves
18 Rod Robertson
19 Scott Ruckman
20 Royal Thomas Jr.
21 James Vatcher
22 Mel Roberts
23 Buzz Capra
24 Brett Massie

1988 ProCards Spokane Indians

(San Diego Padres, A)

	MT	NR MT	EX
Complete Set:	8.00	6.00	3.25

Checklist
1922 Greg Conley
1923 Tye Waller
1924 Rob Cantwell
1925 Kelly Lifgren
1926 Mike Humphreys
1927 Squeezer Thompson
1928 Steve Lubratich
1929 Pedro Aquino
1930 Luis Lopez
1931 Craig Bigham
1932 Greg Smith
1933 A.J. Sager
1934 John Kuehl
1935 Chad Kuhn
1936 Nicko Riesgo
1937 Brad Hoyer
1938 David Briggs
1939 Bob Curnow
1940 Brian Cisarik
1941 Renay Bryand
1942 Barry Hightower
1943 Mark Verstandig
1944 Craig Proctor
1945 Chris Haslock
1946 Ron Morton

1988 Best Springfield Cardinals

(St. Louis Cardinals, A)

	MT	NR MT	EX
Complete Set:	16.00	12.00	4.75

1 Robert Glisson
2 Mark Grater
3 Jeremy Hernandez
4 Michael Henry
5 Gregory Becker
6 Shawn Hathaway
7 William Bivens
8 Andrew Taylor
9 James Gibbs
10 Frank Postio
11 Bob Sudo
12 Charles Johnson
13 Bernard Gilkey
14 Raymond Lankford
15 David Payton
16 Michael Raziano
17 Alex Ojea
18 Stephen Meyer
19 Rodney Brewer
20 Steven Jeffers
21 Franklin Abreu
22 John Murphy
23 Gary Nichols
24 Ed Fulton
25 Chris Maloney
26 Mark De John
27 Brad Bluestone
28 Logo & checklist card

1988 Cal Cards Stockton Ports

(Milwaukee Brewers, A)

	MT	NR MT	EX
Complete Set:	7.00	5.25	2.75

175 Steve Monson
176 Ron Romanick
177 Doug Henry
178 Brian Stone
179 Randy Veres
180 Angel Miranda
181 Alan Sadler
182 Jaime Navarro
183 Narcisco Elvira
184 Carl Moraw
185 Keith Fleming
186 Brian Drahman
187 Danny Fitzpatrick
188 Gil Villanueva
189 Tim McIntosh
190 Robert Jones
191 Mark Aguilar
192 Robert Smith
193 John Jaha
194 Shon Ashley
195 Dave Taylor
196 Sandy Guerrero
197 Bill Spiers
198 Angel Rodriguez
199 Charlie Montoyo
200 Ruben Escalera
201 Rob Derksen
202 'Dave Huppert
203 Jay Williams
204 Don Miller
205 Dan Chapman

1988 ProCards Stockton Ports

(Milwaukee Brewers, A)

	MT	NR MT	EX
Complete Set:	6.00	4.50	2.50

721 Rob Derkson
722 Steve Monson
723 Mark Aguilar
724 Shon Ashley
725 Keith Fleming
726 Alan Sadler
727 Sandy Guerrero
728 Gil Villanueva
729 Dave Taylor
730 Randy Veres
731 Ron Romanick
732 Bobby Jones
733 Tim McIntosh
734 Brian Drahman
735 Ruben Escalera
736 Jaime Navarro
737 Charlie Montoyo
738 Bill Spiers
739 Brian Stone
740 Dave Hoppert
741 Rob Smith
742 Angel Rodriguez
743 John Jaha
744 Jay Williams
745 Danny Fitzpatrick
746 Carl Moraw
747 Doug Henry
748 Narcisso Elvira
749 Angel Miranda
750 Don Miller
751 Dan Chapman
752 Mike Conro, Mark Marine)
---- Checklist

1988 ProCards Sumter Braves

(Atlanta Braves, A)

	MT	NR MT	EX
Complete Set:	13.50	10.25	5.50

390 Keith Mitchell
391 Tony Baldwin
392 Bob Cole
393 Dennis Burlingame
394 John Reilley
395 Wes Currin
396 Mark Davis
397 Johnny Cuevas
398 Jesus Mendoza
399 Jose Valencia
400 Winnie Relaford
401 Greg Harper
402 Rick Siebert
403 Marcos Vezquez
404 Skipper Wright
405 Gregg Gilbert
406 Greg Cloninger
407 A J Waznik
408 Glenn Mitchell
409 Juan Fredymond
410 Ben Rivera
411 David Colon
412 Tom Redington
413 Dave Nied
414 Ned Yost
415 Larry Jaster
416 Rick Albert
417 Willy Johnson
418 Ralph Meister
419 Teddy Williams
420 Ed Holtz
---- Checklist

1988 CMC Syracuse Chiefs

(Toronto Blue Jays, AAA)

	MT	NR MT	EX
Complete Set:	7.00	5.25	2.75

1 Steve Davis
2 Randy Holland
3 Colin McLaughlin
4 Jose Nunez
5 Mark Ross
6 Norm Tonucci
7 Bob Shirley
8 Cliff Young
9 Doug Bair
10 Jack O'Connor
11 Frank Wills
12 Luis Reyna
13 Geronimo Berroa
14 Rob Ducey
15 Glenallen Hill
16 Sal Butera
17 Eric Yelding
18 Greg Myers
19 Otis Green
20 Kelly Heath
21 Alexis Infante
22 Chris Shaddy
23 Hector Torres
24 Bob Bailor
25 Galen Cisco

1988 ProCards Syracuse Chiefs

(Toronto Blue Jays, AAA)

	MT	NR MT	EX
Complete Set:	7.00	5.25	2.75

805 Jack O'Connor
806 Luis Leal
807 Cliff Young
808 Geronimo Berroa
809 Norm Tonucci
810 Luis Reyna
811 Kelly Hetah
812 Glenallen Hill
813 Alexis Infante
814 Steve Davis
815 Enrique Burgos
816 Doug Bair
817 Bob Bailor
818 Galen Cisco
819 Red Coughlin
820 Jose Nunez
821 Greg Myers
822 Hector Torres
823 Colin McLaughlin
824 Mark Ross
825 Rob Ducey
826 Sal Butera
827 Bob Shirley
828 Marc DeBottis
829 Randy Holland
830 Frank Wills
831 Otis Green
832 Eric Yelding
833 Chris Shaddy
---- Checklist

1988 CMC Tacoma Tigers

(Oakland A's, AAA)

	MT	NR MT	EX
Complete Set:	9.00	6.75	3.50

1 Rich Bordi
2 Todd Burns
3 Charlie Corbell
4 Reese Lambert
5 Tim Meeks
6 Jeff Zaske
7 Jim Corsi
8 Jeff Shaver
9 Brian Snyder
10 Bob Stoddard
11 Lance Blakenship
12 Tyler Brilinski
13 Ed Jurak
14 Wayne Krenchicki
15 Roy Johnson
16 Luis Polonia
17 Alex Sanchez
18 Matt Sinatro
19 Andre Robertson
20 Kevin Sliwinski
21 Jimmy Jones
22 Orlando Mercado
23 Gary Jones
24 Felix Jose
25 Joe Xavier

1988 ProCards Tacoma Tigers

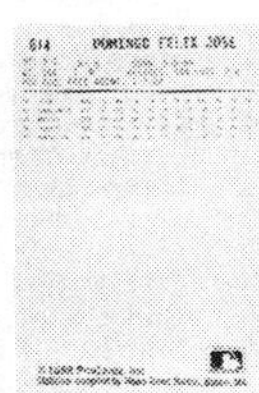

(Oakland A's, AAA)

	MT	NR MT	EX
Complete Set:	9.00	6.75	3.50

612 Gary Jones
613 Joe Xavier
614 Felix Jose
615 Eddie Jurak
616 Matt Sinatro
617 Tyler Brilinski
618 Jim Jones
619 Jeff Shaver
620 Stan Naccarato
621 Roy Johnson
622 Brad Fischer
623 Chuck Estrada
624 Orlando Mercado
625 Jim Corsi
626 Kevin Sliwinski
627 Rich Bordi
628 Bob Stoddard
629 Brian Snyder
630 Lance Blankenship
631 Reese Lambert
632 Todd Burns
633 Tim Meeks
634 Andre Robertson
635 Wayne Krenchicki
636 Charlie Corbell
637 Alex Sanchez
638 Luis Polonia
---- Checklist

1988 Star Co. Tampa Tarpons

(Chicago White Sox, A) (Price includes the late-issue Foley card)

	MT	NR MT	EX
Complete Set:	6.00	4.50	2.50

1 Hernan Adames
2 Leon Baham
3 Kurt Brown
4 Chris Cauley
5 Brian Davis
6 Bill Eveline
7 Cornelio Garcia
8 Jeff Greene
9 Buddy Groom
10a Todd Hall
10b Marv Foley (late issue, misnumbered, gold rather than navy border)
11 Brent Knackert
12 Jerry Kutzler
13 Tom Lahrman
14 Ravelo Manzanillo
15 Norberto Martin
16 Pat Mehrtens
17 Eric Milholland
18 Kevin Murdock
19 Mike Ollom
20 Jack Peel
21 Dave Reynolds
22 Dan Rohrmeier
23 Carl Sullivan
24 Tony Woods
---- Team logo card

1988 CMC Tidewater Tides

(New York Mets, AAA) (Price is for the set with the misspelled Jefferies card; with the corrected card, the set is worth $15 in Mint condition)

	MT	NR MT	EX
Complete Set:	15.00	11.00	6.00

1 Jack Savage
2 David West
3 Jeff Innis
4 Tim Drummond
5 Tom Edens
6 Steve Frey
7 Tom McCarthy
8 John Mitchell
9 Jose Roman
10 Randy Niemann
11 Wally Whitehurst
12 Phil Lombardi
13 Greg Olson
14 Ken Dowell
15a Gregg Jeffries (name incorrect)
15b Gregg Jefferies (name correct)
16 Darren Reed
17 Joaquin Contreas
18 Andre David
19 Jeff McKnight
20 Keith Miller
21 Steve Springer
22 Mark Carreon
23 Tim Tolman
24 Mike Cubbage
25 John Cumberland
26 Rich Miller

1988 ProCards Tidewater Tides

(New York Mets, AAA)

	MT	NR MT	EX
Complete Set:	15.00	11.00	6.00

1577 John Mitchell
1578 Phil Lombardi
1579 John Cumberland
1580 Sam McCrary
1581 Tom Edens
1582 Jeff Innis
1583 Jack Savage
1584 Tim Tolman
1585 Rich Miller
1586 Mike Cubbage
1587 Jeff McKnight
1588 Mark Carren
1589 Wally Whitehurst
1590 Reggie Dobie
1591 Marcus Lawton
1592 Dave West
1593 Tim Drummond
1594 Al Pardo
1595 Ken Dowell
1596 Andre David
1597 Greg Olson
1598 Steve Springer
1599 Tom McCarthy
1600 Gregg Jefferies
1601 Jose Roman
1602 Steve Frey
1603 Darren Reed
1604 Keith Miller
---- Checklist

1988 SG & CC Tidewater Tides

(New York Mets, AAA) This set is numbered as it appears on the cards. The set is also in the form of a perforated uncut sheet. The team photo measures approximately 9-1/2" x 11" in size.

	MT	NR MT	EX
Complete Set:	20.00	18.75	8.00

4 Steve Frey
5 Ken Dowell
9 Gregg Jeffries
10 Steve Springer
11 Darren Reed
16 Tim Tolman
17 Andre David
18 Jeff McKnight
19 Jose Roman
21 Wally Whitehurst
22 Joaquin Contreras
23 Jack Savage
25 Keith Miller
26 Mike Cubbage
27 John Miller
28 Tom Edens
29 Greg Olson
30 Dave West
31 Mark Carreon
33 Phil Lombardi
34 John Cumberland
35 Tim Drummond
36 Tom McCarthy
37 Rich Miller
39 Randy Niemann
40 Jeff Innis
---- Sam McCrary
---- Dave Rosenfield
---- R.C. Reuteman
---- Tony Mercurio
---- Team photo

1988 CMC Toledo Mud Hens

(Detroit Tigers, AAA)

	MT	NR MT	EX
Complete Set:	7.00	5.25	2.75

1 Dave Beard
2 Stan Clarke
3 Don Schulze
4 Steve Searcy
5 Eric King
6 Roman Pena
7 Mike Trujillo
8 Dave Cooper
9 Paul Cherry
10 John Duffy
11 Mark Huisman
12 Billy Bean
13 Scott Lusader
14 Doug Strange
15 Jeff Reynolds
16 Benny Ruis
17 Pedro Chavez
18 Rey Palacios
19 Chris Hoiles
20 Paul Felix
21 Tim Leiper
22 Donnie Rowland
23 Pete Rice
24 Mike Brown
25 Pat Corrales

1988 ProCards Toledo Mud Hens

(Detroit Tigers, AAA)

	MT	NR MT	EX
Complete Set:	7.00	5.25	2.75

585 Jeff Reynolds
586 Dave Beard
587 Doug Strange
588 Mark Huismann
589 Donnie Rowland
590 Pat Corrales
591 Paul Cherry
592 Eric King
593 Mike Trujillo
594 Scott Lusader
595 Billy Bean
596 John Duffy
597 Chris Hoiles
598 Pete Rice
599 Gene Roof
600 Paul Felix
601 Pedro Chavez
602 Benny Ruiz
603 Tim Leiper
604 Don Schulze
605 Rey Palacios
606 Don McGann
607 Stan Clarke
608 Dave Cooper
609 Steve Searcy
610 Ramon Pena
611 Mike Brown
---- Checklist

1988 Grand Slam Texas League All-Stars

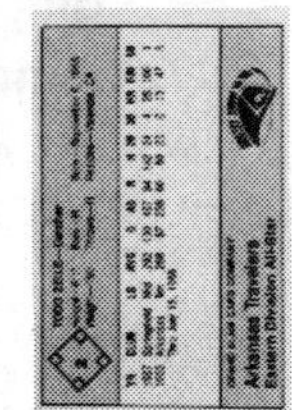

(AA)

	MT	NR MT	EX
Complete Set:	9.00	6.75	3.50

1 Jack Mull (Shreveport)
2 Todd Zeile (Arkansas)
3 Chad Kreuter (Tulsa)
4 Gary Alexander (Tulsa)
5 Steve Wilson (Tulsa)
6 Dan Scarpetta (El Paso)
7 John Wetteland (San Antonio)
8 Joe Olker (Shreveport)
9 Kevin Bootay (Tulsa)
10 Angelo Cuevas (Jackson)
11 Mike Benjamin (Shreveport)
12 Scott Coolbaugh (Tulsa)
13 Brett Harrison (Arkansas)
14 Manny Salinas (Jackson)
15 John Skurla (Shreveport)
16 Tom Baine (Arkansas)
17 John Barfield (Tulsa)
18 Blaine Beatty (Jackson)
19 Jose Dominguez (Shreveport)
20 Scott Arnold (Arkansas)
21 Dave Pavlas (Tulsa)
22 Kevin Kennedy (San Antonio)
23 Mike Basso (Wichita)
24 Mario Monico (El Paso)
25 Fred Williams (El Paso)
26 Gary Sheffield (El Paso)
27 Jim McCollom (Midland)
28 Ramon Martinez (San Antonio)
29 Terry Gilmore (Wichita)
30 Mike Munoz (San Antonio)
31 Ed Puig (El Paso)
32 Carlos Baerga (Wichita)
33 Mike Huff (San Antonio)
34 Chris Knabenshue (Wichita)
35 Greg Vaughn (El Paso)
36 Mike Knapp (Midland)
37 Luis Lopez (San Antonio)
38 Frank Mattox (El Paso)
39 Jeff Manto (Midland)

1988 CMC Triple A All-Stars

(AAA)

	MT	NR MT	EX
Complete Set:	12.00	9.00	4.75

1 Bill Bathe (Iowa)
2 Luis De Los Santos (Omaha)
3 Johnny Paredes (Indianapolis)
4 Tom O'Malley (Oklahoma City)
5 Felix Fermin (Buffalo)
6 Billy Moore (Indianapolis)
7 Ronaldo Roomes (Iowa)
8 Van Snider (Nashville)
9 German Rivera (Denver)
10 Lavell Freeman (Denver)
11 Dorn Taylor (Buffalo)
12 Norm Charlton (Nashville)
13 Randy Johnson (Indianapolis)
14 Gary Sheffield (Denver)
15 Mike Harkey (Iowa)
16 Bob Geren (Columbus)
17 Dave Griffin (Richmond)
18 Tom Barrett (Maine)
19 Craig Worthington (Rochester)
20 Randy Velarde (Columbus)
21 Steve Finley (Rochester)
22 Carlos Quintana (Pawtucket)
23 Mark Carreon (Tidewater)
24 Lonnie Smith (Richmond)
25 Steve Searcy (Toledo)
26 Mark Huismann (Toledo)
27 Gregg Jefferies (Tidewater)
28 Ricky Jordan (Maine)
29 Dave West (Tidewater)
30 John Smoltz (Richmond)
31 Sandy Alomar Jr. (Las Vegas)
32 Francisco Melendez (Phoenix)
33 Mike Woodard (Vancouver)
34 Edgar Martinez (Calgary)
35 Mike Brumley (Las Vegas)
36 Mike Deverax (Albuquerque)
37 Cameron Drew (Tucson)
38 Luis Medina (Colorado Springs)
39 Rod Allen (Colorado Springs)
40 George Henshaw (Albuquerque)
41 Bill Brenna (Albuquerque)
42 Bill Krueger (Albuquerque)
43 Karl Best (Portland)
44 Juan Bell (Albuquerque)
45 Ramon Martinez (Albuquerque)

1988 ProCards Triple-A All-Stars

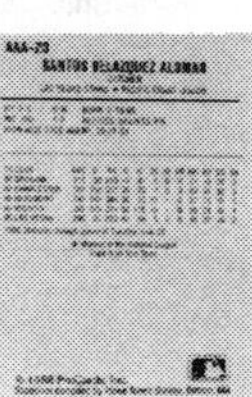

(AAA) AAA precedes all card numbers on the backs of the cards.

	MT	NR MT	EX
Complete Set:	12.00	9.00	4.75

1 Mike Devereaux
2 Chris Gwynn
3 Tracy Woodson
4 Benny Distefano
5 Tom Prince
6 Eddie Jurak
7 Phil Ouellette
8 Luis Medina
9 Bob Geren
10 Mike Kinnunen
11 Scott Nielsen
12 Lavell Freeman
13 Tim Pyznarski
14 German Rivera
15 Urbano Lugo
16 Bill Bathe
17 Bob Sebra
18 Mike Bielecki
19 Dwight Smith
20 Sandy Alomar
21 Mike Brumley
22 Joey Cora
23 Greg Harris
24 Dick Grapenthin
25 Mike Shelton
26 Marty Brown
27 Hugh Kemp
28 Tom O'Malley
29 Steve Finley
30 Luis de los Santos
31 Steve Curry
32 Tony Perezchica
33 Roy Smith
34 Joe Boever
35 Bob Milacki
36 Geronimo Berroa
37 Eric Yelding
38 Lance Blankenship
39 Mark Carreon
40 Gregg Jefferies
41 David West
42 Mark Huismann
43 Rey Palacios
44 Cameron Drew
45 Donn Pall
46 Sap Randall
47 Terry Collins
48 Carlos Ledezma
49 Bill Plummer
50 Joe Sparks
51 Toby Harrah
52 Ed Nottle
53 Randy Holland
54 Mike Cubbage
---- Checklist

1988 CMC Tucson Toros

(Houston Astros, AAA)

	MT	NR MT	EX
Complete Set:	10.00	7.50	4.00

1 Manny Hernandez
2 Anthony Kelley
3 Mike Loynd
4 Dave Meads
5 Kevin Hagen
6 Rafael Montalvo
7 Jose Cano
8 Rocky Childress
9 Jeff Datz
10 Luis DeLeon
11 Ken Caminiti
12 Glenn Carpenter
13 Nelson Rood
14 Cameron Drew
15 Craig Biggio
16 Alex Trevino
17 Karl Allaire
18 Joe Mikulik
19 John Fishel
20 Louie Meadows
21 Jim Weaver
22 Pat Keedy
23 Craig Smajstrla
24 Bob Didier
25 Eddie Watt

1988 Jones Photo Tucson Toros

(Houston Astros, AAA) No positions are listed on cards which measure 3" x 5-1/8" in size. Each set comes in a protective miniature binder.

	MT	NR MT	EX
Complete Set:	40.00	30.00	16.00

(1) Karl Allaire
(2) Craig Biggio
(3) Ken Caminiti
(4) Jose Cano
(5) Glenn Carpenter
(6) Rocky Childress
(7) Jeff Datz
(8) Luis DeLeon
(9) Bob Didier
(10) Drew Cameron
(11) John Fishel
(12) Kevin Hagen
(13) Manny Hernandez
(14) Pat Keedy
(15) Anthony Kelley
(16) Dave Meads
(17) Joe Mikulik
(18) Rafael Montalvo
(19) Nelson Rood
(20) Joe Sambito
(21) Alex Trevino
(22) Eddie Watt
(23) Jim Weaver
(24) Craig Smajstria

1988 ProCards Tucson Toros

(Houston Astros, AAA)

	MT	NR MT	EX
Complete Set:	10.00	7.50	4.00

166 Craig Biggio
167 Karl Allaire
168 Craig Smajstrla
169 Manny Hernandez
170 Rafael Montalvo
171 Jose Cano
172 Jim Weaver
173 Glenn Carpenter
174 Luis DeLeon
175 Pat Keedy
176 Joe Mikulik
177 Louie Meadows
178 John Fishel
179 Clay Christiansen
180 Kevin Hagen
181 Rocky Childress
182 Ken Caminiti
183 Dave Meads
184 Eddie Watt
185 Mike Loynd
186 Anthony Kelley
187 Jeff Datz
188 Cameron Drew
189 Ernie Camacho
190 Bob Didier
191 Nelson Rood
192 Rex Jones
---- Checklist

1988 Team Tulsa Drillers

(Texas Rangers, AA)

	MT	NR MT	EX
Complete Set:	12.00	9.00	4.75

1 Mike Scanlin
2 George Threadgill

3 Monty Fariss
4 Mitch Thomas
5 Efrain Valdez
6 Darrell Whitaker
7 Jose Vargas
8 Steve Wilson
9 Jeff Andrews
10 Jim Skaalen
11 Stan Hough
12 Gary Alexander
13 Kevin Bootay
14 John Barfield
15 Kevin Brown
16 Joel Cartaya
17 Bubba Jackson
18 Scott Coolbaugh
19 Chad Kreuter
20 Steve Lankard
21 Gar Millay
22 Bob Malloy
23 Dave Pavlas
24 Paul Fostier
25 Kevin Reimer
26 Rick Raether
27 Greg Harrel
28 Kenny Rogers

1988 Pucko Utica Blue Sox

(Chicago White Sox, A)

	MT	NR MT	EX
Complete Set:	6.00	4.50	2.50

1 Rob Lukachyk
2 Clemente Alvarez
3 Brett Berry
4 Mark Chasey
5 Paul Fuller
6 Vince Harris
7 Derek Lee
8 Steve Mehl
9 Jesus Merejo
10 Eugenio Tejada
11 Marcus Trammell
12 Randy Warren
13 John Zaksek
14 John Chafin
15 Virgil Cooper
16 Fred Dabney
17 Carlos De LaCruz
18 Keith Felden
19 Scott Fuller
20 Mike Galvan
21 Pat Mehrtens
22 Frank Merigliano
23 Jose Pena
24 Ron Stephens
25 Ed Walsh
26 Rick Patterson
27 Preston Douglas
28 Steve Jessup
29 Joanne Gerace

1988 CMC Vancouver Canadians

(Chicago White Sox, AAA)

	MT	NR MT	EX
Complete Set:	7.00	5.25	2.75

1 Jeff Bittiger
2 Joel Davis
3 Steve Rosenberg
4 Carl Willis
5 Ed Wojna
6 Ken Patterson
7 Adam Peterson
8 Grady Hall
9 Donn Pall
10 Jack Hardy
11 Greg Hibbard
12 Kelly Paris
13 Santiago Garcia
14 Mike Woodwood
15 Ron Karkovice
16 Bill Lindsey
17 Russ Morman
18 Troy Thomas
19 Mike Yastrzemski
20 James Randall
21 Jeff Schafer
22 Daryl Sconiers
23 Jorge Alcazar
24 Dave Gallagher
25 Marlin McPhail

1988 ProCards Vancouver Canadians

(Chicago White Sox, AAA)

	MT	NR MT	EX
Complete Set:	7.00	5.25	2.75

753 Jeff Schaefer
754 Steve Rosenberg
755 Jack Hardy
756 Edward Wojna
757 Ken Patterson
758 Bill Lindsey
759 Donn Pall
760 Russ Morman
761 Grady Hall
762 Carl Willis
763 Joel Davis
764 Santiago Garcia
765 James Randall
766 Daryl Sconiers
767 Mike Woodard
768 Ron Jackson
769 Eli Grba
770 Greg Hibbard
771 Dave Gallagher
772 Jorge Alcazar
773 Ron Karkovice
774 Mike Yastrzemski
775 Troy Thomas
776 Adam Peterson
777 Marlin McPhail
778 Terry Bevington
---- Checklist

1988 ProCards Vermont Mariners

(Seattle Mariners, AA)

	MT	NR MT	EX
Complete Set:	7.50	5.50	3.00

939 Mark Wooden
940 Bryan Price
941 Dave Schuler
942 Greg Fulton
943 Bill McGuire
944 Jim Wilson
945 Eric Fox
946 Omar Vizquel
947 Pat Lennon
948 Keith Foley
949 Nezi Balelo
950 John Gibbons
951 Dave Brundage
952 Dave Myers
953 Jorge Uribe
954 Rich Morales
955 Tom Newberg
956 Dave Snell
957 Greg Brinkman
958 Bill Mendek
959 Ricky Rojas
960 Clint Zavaras
961 Jeff Hull
962 Calvin Jones
963 Dave McCorkle
---- Checklist

1988 Star Co. Vero Beach Dodgers

(Los Angeles Dodgers, A) (Price includes the late-issue Shoemaker card)

	MT	NR MT	EX
Complete Set:	7.00	5.25	2.75

1 Michael Batesole
2 Kevin Campbell
3 Timothy Cash
4 Doug Cox
5 Thomas DeMerit
6 Felipe Esteban
7 Howard Freiling
8 Henry Goshay
9 David Hansen
10 Jeffrey Hartman
11 Gordon Hershiser
12 Carl Johnson
13 Eric Mangham
14 Angel Martinez
15 Gregory Mayberry
16 Frank Mustari
17 Jeffrey Mons
18a Christopher Nichting
18b John Shoemaker (late issue, misnumbered, gold rather than red border)
19 Hidetsugu Nishimura
20 Douglas Noch
21 Jay Ray
22 Homar Rojas
23 Miguel Santana
24 Mike White
25 Stephen Wood
26 Masahiro Yamamoto

1988 Star Co. Virginia Generals

(A) (Price includes the late-issue Breeden, Ford and Phillippe cards and the corrected Joslyn card)

	MT	NR MT	EX
Complete Set:	9.00	6.75	3.50

1 Pete Alborano
2 Mike Borgatti
3 Kevin Brooks
4 Pete Capello
5 Lee Carballo
6 Luis Corcino
7 Steve Culkaf
8a Brian Dubois
8b Joe Breeden (late issue, misnumbered, gold rather than navy border)
9 Kent Headley
10 Jimi Hendrix
11 Tom Johnson
12a John Joslyn (correct name & stats, wrong picture)
12b John Joslyn (corrected)
13 Frank Laureano
14 Carmelo Losauro
15 Pat McKinley
16 Angel Morris
17 Gregory Papageorge
18 Phil Price
19 Ruben Pujols
20 Ernest Radcliffe Jr.
21 Kyle Reese
22 Kent Willis
23 Ondra Ford
---- Team logo card
---- Gilinda Phillippe (late issue - very scarce)

1988 Cal Cards Visalia Oaks

(Minnesota Twins, A)

	MT	NR MT	EX
Complete Set:	7.00	5.25	2.75

145 Kenny Davis
146 Ken Morgan
147 Mike Randle
148 Joey Zellner
149 Tim Arnold
150 John Eccles
151 Shawn Gilbert
152 Kenny Grant
153 Marty Lanoux
154 Scott Leius
155 Jose Marzan
156 Ed Naveda
157 A.J. Richardson
158 Doug Snyder
159 Larry Blackwell
160 Mike Reddings
161 Steve Scanlon
162 Bob Strube
163 Jim Williams
164 Troy James
165 Paul Abbott
166 Jeff Bronkey
167 Mark Guthrie
168 Dana Heinle
169 Doug Kline
170 Scott Ullger
171 Bruce Bucz
172 Andy Seidensticker
173 Mark Jones
174 Gorman Heimueller

1988 ProCards Visalia Oaks

(Minnesota Twins, A)

	MT	NR MT	EX
Complete Set:	7.00	5.25	2.75

81 Kenny Davis
82 Dana Heinle
83 Larry Blackwell
84 John Eccles
85 Mike Randle
86 Kenny Grant
87 A.J. Richardson
88 Troy James
89 Jose Marzan
90 Kenny Morgan
91 Shawn Gilbert
92 Paul Abbott
93 Mike Redding
94 Steve Scanlon
95 Jeff Bronkey
96 Slim Williams
97 Tim Arnold
98 Joey Zellner
99 Scott Ullger
100 Doug Snyder
101 Bob Strube
102 Scott Leius
103 Edgar Naveda
104 Marty Lanoux
105 Gorman Heimueller
106 Andy Seidensticker
107 Doug Kline
---- Checklist

1988 ProCards Waterloo Indians

(Cleveland Indians, A)

	MT	NR MT	EX
Complete Set:	7.00	5.25	2.75

665 Tommy Kurczewski
666 Andy Casano
667 Angel Ortiz
668 Bill Bluhm
669 John Stutz
670 Willie Garza
671 Jim Baxter
672 Scott Khoury
673 T.J. Gamba
674 Bill Narleski
675 Julio Liriano
676 Ramon Bautista
677 Ivan McBride
678 Keith Seifert
679 Steve Colavito
680 Sam Ferretti
681 Troy Neel
682 Peter Kuld
683 Mark Pike
684 Keith Bennett
685 Roger Hill
686 Eric Rasmussen
687 Ken Bolek
688 Steve Olin
689 Tom Kramer
690 Tony Scaglione
691 Greg Roscoe
692 Rudy Seanez
---- Checklist

1988 Pucko Watertown Pirates

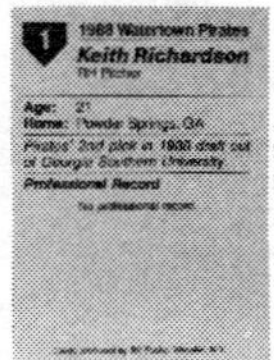

(Pittsburgh Pirates, A)

	MT	NR MT	EX
Complete Set:	7.00	5.25	2.75

1 Keith Richardson
2 Joe Ausanio
3 Steve Buckholz
4 Rodger Castner
5 Joel Forrest
6 Tim Holmes
7 Mark Koller
8 Craig Lewis
9 Dan Nielson
10 Ernesto Santana
11 Mike Stevanus
12 Randy Tomlin
13 Bobby Underwood
14 Bryan Arnold
15 Jay Bluthardt
16 Ken Buksa
17 Ralph Denkenberger
18 Chris Estep
19 Mike Huyler
20 Deron Johnson
21 Domingo Merejo
22 Steve Montejo
23 Darwin Pennye
24 Paul Spalt
25 Dave Stone
26 Mike Valla
27 Tim Wakefield
28 John Wehner
29 Flavio Williams
30 John Young
31 Stan Cliburn
32 Tom Barnard
33 Robert Bill
34 Gene Sunnen
35 Bob Burgess & Bob Morgia

1988 Grand Slam Wausau Timbers

(Seattle Mariners, A)

	MT	NR MT	EX
Complete Set:	6.00	4.50	2.50

1 Rick Sweet
2 Chuck Kniffen
3 Fausto Ramirez
4 Chris Doll
5 Lorenzo Sisney
6 Ruben Gonzalez
7 Keith Frink

8 Chuck Carr
9 John Hoffman
10 Kurt Stange
11 Mike McDonald
12 Jim Pritikin
13 Ray Williams
14 Todd Haney
15 Todd Azar
16 Jeff Hooper
17 Rudy Webster
18 Steve Bieksha
19 Chuck Webb
20 Mike McGuire
21 Brian Baldwin
22 Tony Woods
23 Scott Stoerick
24 Frank Colston
25 Mike Gardiner
26 Dru Kosco
27 Mike Goff
28 Randy Roetter

1988 ProCards Williamsport Bills

(Cleveland Indians, AA)

	MT	NR MT	EX
Complete Set:	7.00	5.25	2.75

1303 Lee Kuntz
1304 Tom Lampkin
1305 Kent Murphy
1306 Mike Hargrove
1307 Mike Farr
1308 Andy Ghelfi
1309 Jeff Shaw
1310 Mike Walker
1311 Brian Allard
1312 Turner Gill
1313 Brian Graham
1314 Tony Ghelfi
1315 Kevin Wickander
1316 Stan Hilton
1317 Casey Webster
1318 Theo Shaw
1319 Darryl Landrum
1320 Claudio Carrasco
1321 Paul Kuzniar
1322 Mark Howie
1323 Jim Bruske
1324 Doyle Wilson
1325 Mike Poehl
1326 Scott Jordan
1327 Milt Harper
1328 Kerry Richardson
---- Checklist

1988 Rock's Dugout Wichita Pilots

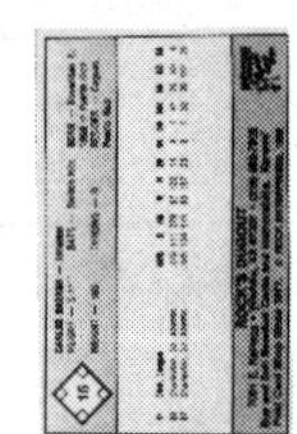

(San Diego Padres, AA) This set is numbered by the player's uniforms.

	MT	NR MT	EX
Complete Set:	9.00	6.75	3.50

10 Mike DeButch
11 Jeff Yurtin
12 Craig Wiley
14 Chris Knabenshue
15 Carlos Baerga
16 Mike Basso
17 Nate Colbert
18 Jim Tatum
19 Gregg Harris
20 Terry Gilmore
21 Bill Wrona
22 Jimmy Lester
23 Paul Quinzer
24 Craig Cooper
25 James Austin
26 Mike Costello
27 Jeff Hermann
28 Pat Jelks
29 Bill Stevenson
30 Jeff Childers
31 Mike Mills
32 Kevin Brown
33 Eric Bauer
40 Pat Kelly
41 Rusty Ford
42 Steve Luebber
43 Matt Maysey
---- Joe Chavez
---- Logo card

1988 Star Co. West Palm Beach Expos

(Montreal Expos, A) (Price includes the late-issue Felipe Alou card)

	MT	NR MT	EX
Complete Set:	9.50	7.25	3.75

1 Pat Adams
2a Jose Alou
2b Felipe Alou (late issue, misnumbered, gold rather than sea-green border)
3 Kent Bottenfield
4 Kevin Cavalier
5 Doug Cinnella
6 Scott Clemo
7 Al Collins
8 Rob DeYoung
9 Mike Dull
10 Bobby Gaylor
11 John Howes
12 Nels Jacobsen
13 Ross Jones
14 Tyrone Kingwood
15 Danilo Leon
16 Guinn Mack
17 Rob Mason
18 Omer Munoz
19 Bob Natal
20 Jeff Oller
21 Boi Rodriguez
22 Norm Santiago
23 Jeff Tabaka
24 John Vanderwal
25 Corey Viltz
26 Tony Welborn

1988 Star Co. Winston-Salem Spirits

(Chicago Cubs, A) (Price includes the late-issue Loviglio card)

	MT	NR MT	EX
Complete Set:	9.50	7.25	3.75

1 John Berringer
2 Luis Cruz
3 Victor Garcia
4 Henry Gatewood
5 Phil Harrison
6 Steve Hill
7 Bill Kazmierczak
8 John Lewis
9 Kelly Mann
10 Jim Matas
11 Derrick May
12 Tom Michno
13 Brian Otten
14 Gregg Patterson
15 David Rosario
16a Heath Slocumb
16b Jay Loviglio (late issue, misnumbered, gold rather than green border)
17 Greg Smith
18 Glen Sullivan
19 Jeff Schwarz
20 Francisco Tenacen
21 Tim Wallace
22 Eric Woods

1988 Star Co. Winter Haven Red Sox

(Boston Red Sox, A)

	MT	NR MT	EX
Complete Set:	8.00	6.00	3.25

1 John Abbott
2 Odie Abril
3 Mike Baker
4 Eddie Banasiak
5 Ken Bourne
6 Dale Burgo
7 Johnny Diaz
8 Donald Florence
9 Roger Haggerty
10 Michael Kelly
11 Jorge Kuilan
12 Donnie McGowan
13 David Milstien
14 Miguel Monegro
15 Tony Mosley
16 Luis Munoz
17 Warren Olson
18 Livio Padilla
19 Juan Paris
20 Phil Plantier
21 Carlos Rivera
22 Julio Rosario
23 Michael Thompson
24 Doug Treadway
25 Leslie Wallin
26 Brian Warfel
27 Paul Williams Jr.

1988 ProCards Wytheville Cubs

	MT	NR MT	EX
Complete Set:	7.00	5.25	2.75

1975 Milciades Uribe
1976 Rob Bonneau
1977 Wayne Weinheimer
1978 Kevin Roberson
1979 Brad Huff
1980 Victor Cancel
1981 Sean Reed
1982 Marvin Cole
1983 Bill Paynter
1984 Tony Whitson
1985 Daren Burns
1986 Roberto Smalls
1987 Bubba Browder
1988 Julio Valdez
1989 Bill Earley
1990 Woody Smith
1991 Steve Roadcap
1992 Benny Shreve
1993 Mike Galdu
1994 Kenny Holley
1995 Ivan Marteniz
1996 Matt Leonard
1997 Juan Adams
1998 Jason Doss
1999 Marc Caosielli
2000 Billy Gamble
2001 Ronnie Rasp
2002 Jerome Williams
2003 Troy Bailey
2004 Team Photo
---- Checklist

1989 CMC AAA All-Stars

(AAA) (color)

	MT	NR MT	EX
Complete Set:	9.00	6.75	3.50

1 Todd Zeile
2 Luis de los Santos
3 Junior Noboa
4 Jeff Huson
5 Scott Coolbaugh
6 Skeeter Barnes
7 Larry Walker
8 Greg Vaughn
9 Steve Henderson
10 Mark Gardner
11 Morris Madden
12 Jack Armstrong
13 Stan Belinda
14 Alex Cole
15 Orlando Merced
16 Frank Cabrera
17 Hal Morris
18 Mark Lemke
19 Randy Velarde
20 Tom O'Malley
21 Butch Davis
22 Glenallen Hill
23 Greg Tubbs
24 Kevin Maas
25 Alex Sanchez
26 Mark Eichhorn
27 Mickey Pina
28 Julio Machado
29 Rob Richie
30 Tim Naehring
31 Sandy Alomar
32 Kelvin Torve
33 Joey Cora
34 Paul Zuvella
35 Matt Williams
36 Bruce Fields
37 Jerald Clark
38 Mike Huff
39 Jim Wilson
40 Ramon Martinez
41 Bryan Clark
42 Steve Olin
43 Andy Benes
44 Lee Stevens
45 Adam Peterson

1989 Best Albany Yankees

(New York Yankees, AA) (color)

	MT	NR MT	EX
Complete Set:	12.00	9.00	4.75

1 Deion Sanders
2 Jim Leyritz
3 Bob Davidson
4 Scott Shaw
5 Tim Layana
6 Royal Clayton
7 Glenn Sherlock
8 Buck Showalter
9 Rob Sepanek
10 Bob Geren
11 Ricky Torres
12 Jerry Rub
13 John Ramos
14 Mitch Lyden
15 Andy Stankiewicz
16 Bobby Dickerson
17 Hensley Meulens
18 Aris Tirado
19 Oscar Azocar
20 Tim Becker
21 Rodney Imes
22 Mike Christopher
23 Kevin Mmahat
24 Jason Maas
25 Scott Kamieniecki
26 Dale McConachie
27 Russ Meyer
28 Bob Mariano
29 Tim Weston
30 Checklist

1989 Best Limited-Edition Albany Yankees

(New York Yankees, A) This Limited Edition set has a platinum colored border as opposed to the white border of the regular set. Also the backs of the cards are blue & white as opposed to the yellow backs of the regular set.

	MT	NR MT	EX
Complete Set:	18.00	13.50	7.25

1 Deion Sanders
2 Jim Leyritz
3 Bob Davidson
4 Scott Shaw
5 Tim Layana
6 Royal Clayton
7 Glenn Sherlock
8 Buck Showalter
9 Rob Sepanek
10 Bob Geren
11 Ricky Torres
12 Jerry Rub
13 John Ramos
14 Mitch Lyden
15 Andy Stankiewicz
16 Bobby Dickerson
17 Hensley Meulens
18 Aris Tirado
19 Oscar Azocar
20 Tim Becker
21 Rodney Immes
22 Mike Christopher
23 Kevin Mmahat
24 Jason Maas
25 Scott Kamieniecki
26 Dale McConachie
27 Russ Meyer
28 Bob Mariano
29 Tim Weston
30 Checklist

1989 Best All-Decade Albany Yankees

(New York Yankees, A)

	MT	NR MT	EX
Complete Set:	9.00	6.75	3.50

1 Deion Sanders
2 Mike Ashman
3 Roberto Kelly
4 Bob Geren
5 Logan Easley
6 Jim Leyritz
7 Steve Ontiveros
8 Matt Harrison
9 Scott Nielsen
10 Royal Clayton
11 Tim Layana
12 Kevin Maas
13 Bob Tewksbury
14 Phil Stephenson
15 Tom Barrett
16 Rod Imes
17 Andy Stankiewicz
18 Hal Morris
19 Randy Velarde
20 Darren Reed
21 Orestes Destrade
22 Doug Drabeck
23 Hensley Meulens
24 Tim Lambert
25 Kevin Mmahat
26 Dave Eiland
27 Brad Arnsberg
28 Steve Adkins
29 Rob Spanek
30 Steve Rosenberg

31 Mickey Tettleton
32 Keith Hughes
33 Bernie Williams
34 Mitch Lyden
35 Thad Reece
36 Logo & checklist card

1989 ProCards Albany Yankees

(New York Yankees, A) (color)

	MT	NR MT	EX
Complete Set:	9.00	6.75	3.50

313 Checklist
314 Rodney Imes
315 Tim Becker
316 Scott Kamieniecki
317 Scott Shaw
318 Royal Clayton
319 Bobby Dickerson
320 Mitch Lyden
321 Mike Christopher
322 Russ Meyer
323 Tim Weston
324 Bob Mariano
325 Jim Leyritz
326 Buck Showalter
327 Bobby Davidson
328 Jerry Rub
329 Tim Layana
330 Rob Sepanek
331 Aris Tirado
332 Oscar Azocar
333 Andy Stankiewicz
334 Jason Maas
335 Ricky Torres
336 John Ramos
337 Hensley Meulens
338 Deion Sanders
339 Glenn Sherlock
340 Darrin Chapin
341 Kevin Mmahat

1989 Star Co. Albany-Colonie Yankees

(New York Yankees, AA) (color) (Price include the late-issue Sanders card)

	MT	NR MT	EX
Complete Set:	11.00	8.25	4.50

1 Oscar Azocar
2 Tim Becker
3 Darrin Chapin
4 Mike Christopher
5 Royal Clayton
6 Bobby Davidson
7 Bobby Dickerson
8 Rodney Imes
9 Tim Layana
10 Jim Leyritz
11 Mitch Lyden
12 Jason Maas
13 Hensley Meulens
14 Kevin Mmahat
15 John Ramos
16 Jerry Rub
17 Rob Sepanek
18 Scott Shaw
19 Andy Stankiewicz
20 Aris Tirado
21 Ricky Torres
22 Buck Showalter
23 Deion Sanders

1989 CMC Albuquerque Dukes

(Los Angeles Dodgers, AAA) (color)

	MT	NR MT	EX
Complete Set:	8.00	6.00	3.25

1 William Brennan
2 Dennis Burtt
3 Jeff Fischer
4 Mike Hartley
5 Hector Heredia
6 Dave Eichhorn
7 Ramon Martinez
8 Mike Munoz
9 Jim Neidlinger
10 Dave Walsh
11 John Wetteland
12 Jon Debus
13 Shanie Dugas
14 Mike Sharperson
15 Chris Gwynn
16 Tracy Woodson
17 Jose Gonzalez
18 Darrin Fletcher
19 Joe Szekely
20 Juan Bustabad
21 Walt McConnell
22 Domingo Michel
23 Jose Vizcaino
24 Mike Huff
25 Javier Ortiz

1989 ProCards Albuquerque Dukes

(Los Angeles Dodgers, AAA)

	MT	NR MT	EX
Complete Set:	8.00	6.00	3.25

58 Darrin Fletcher
59 Mike Sharperson
60 Brent Strom
61 Dave Eichhorn
62 Mike Munoz
63 John Wetteland
64 Chris Gwynn
65 William Brennan
66 Hector Heredia
67 Mike Hartley
68 Dennis Burtt
69 Ramon Martinez
70 Dave Walsh
71 Jim Neidlinger
72 Kevin Kennedy
73 Von Joshua
74 Stan Johnston
75 Tracy Woodson
76 Jon Debus
77 Joe Szekely
78 Juan Bustabad
79 Mike Huff
80 Jose Gonzalez
81 Domingo Michel
82 Jose Vizcaino
83 Walt McConnell
84 Javier Ortiz
85 Shanie Dugas
86 Jeff Fischer
87 Checklist

1989 Tribune Albuquerque Dukes

(Los Angeles Dodgers, AAA) (co-sponsored by the Albuquerque Tribune)

	MT	NR MT	EX
Complete Set:	25.00	18.50	10.00

(1) Bill Brennan
(2) Dennis Burtt
(3) Juan Bustabad
(4) Jon Debus
(5) Shanie Dugas
(6) Dave Eichhorn
(7) Jeff Fischer
(8) Darrin Fletcher
(9) Jose Gonzalez
(10) Chris Gwynn
(11) Mike Hartley
(12) Stan Johnston
(13) Von Joshua
(14) Kevin Kennedy
(15) Ramon Martinez
(16) Walt McConnell
(17) Domingo Michel
(18) Mike Munoz
(19) Jim Neidlinger
(20) Javier Ortiz
(21) Mike Sharperson
(22) Brent Strom
(23) Joe Szekely
(24) Jose Vizcaino
(25) Dave Walsh
(26) John Wetteland
(27) Tracy Woodson
(28) Hector Heredia
(29) Mike Huff

1989 ProCards Appleton Foxes

(Kansas City Royals, A) (color)

	MT	NR MT	EX
Complete Set:	6.00	4.50	2.50

848 Checklist
849 Hector Wagner
850 Randy Vaughn
851 Dennis Studeman
852 Steve Hoeme
853 Greg Harvey
854 Bill Drohan
855 Don Wright
856 Hugh Walker
857 Frank Henderson
858 Greg Prusia
859 Ondra Ford
860 Darryl Robinson
861 Steve Preston
862 Chris Garibaldo
863 Jeff Garber
864 Mike Beall
865 Pete Capello
866 Jeff Hulse
867 Linton Dyer
868 Rob Buchanan
869 Brad Shores
870 Allard Baird
871 Andre Rabouin
872 Brian Poldberg
873 John McCormick
874 Ben Pierce
875 Mark Parnell
876 Steve Otto
877 Luke Nocas
878 John Hofer

1989 Grand Slam Arkansas Travelers

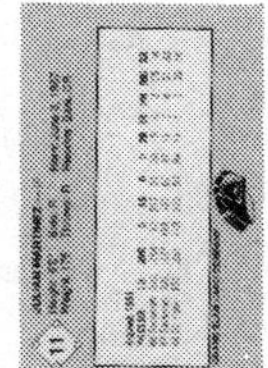

(St. Louis Cardinals, AA) (color)

	MT	NR MT	EX
Complete Set:	9.00	6.75	3.50

1 Gaylen Pitts
2 Chris Maloney
3 Rod Brewer
4 Dennis Carter
5 Mike Fox
6 Bernard Gilkey
7 Steve Hill
8 Mike Hinkle
9 Ray Lankford
10 John Lepley
11 Julian Martinez
12 Chuck McGarth
13 Opie Moran
14 Steve Mumaw
15 Dave Osteen
16 Jeff Oyster
17 Mike Perez
18 Len Picota
19 Frank Potestio
20 Andy Rincon
21 Mike Robertson
22 Roy Silver
23 Ray Stephens
24 Craig Weissmann
25 Craig Wilson

1989 ProCards Asheville Tourists

(Houston Astros, A) (color)

	MT	NR MT	EX
Complete Set:	7.00	5.25	2.75

939 Checklist
940 Matthew McKee
941 Vitas Laniauskas
942 Ron McKee
943 Kevin Day
944 Charley Taylor
945 John Massarelli
946 Roddy Scheckla
947 Rodney Windes
948 Dave Shermet
949 Rafael Campos
950 Willie Ansley
951 Pedro Delossantos
952 Andujar Cedeno
953 Gordon Farmer
954 Brian Bennett
955 Brian Griffiths
956 Troy Dovey
957 Harry Fuller
958 Scott Spurgeon
959 Gregory Johnson
960 Dean Hartgraves
961 Jim Coveney
962 Joe Charno
963 Francisco Perez
964 Rick Dunnum
965 Carlos Henry
966 Mica Lewis
967 Lawrence Lamphere
968 Mike Beams

1989 ProCards Auburn Astros

(Houston Astros, A) (color)

	MT	NR MT	EX
Complete Set:	8.00	6.00	3.25

2159 Checklist
2160 Edwin Valentin
2161 Shane Reynolds
2162 Ted Campusano
2163 Scott Makarewicz
2164 Lance Madsen
2165 Jose Santana
2166 Ken Lofton
2167 Toncie Reed
2168 Reggie Waller
2169 Brian Porter
2170 Cole Hyson
2171 Ben Gonzales
2172 Jim Desapio
2173 Mike McDowell
2174 Francisco Perez
2175 Howard Prager
2176 Luther Johnson
2177 John Graham
2178 Bob Neal
2179 Darin Bruehl
2180 P.J. Riley
2181 Roger Marrero
2182 Donne Wall
2183 Kevin Scott
2184 Doug Simunic
2185 Dave Henderson
2186 Mica Lewis
2187 Rick Wise
2188 Mark Small
2189 Daryl Wooten

1989 ProCards (Poster) Auburn Astros

(Houston Astros, A)

	MT	NR MT	EX
Complete Set:	30.00	22.00	12.00

2159 Checklist card
2160 Edwin Valentin
2161 Shane Reynolds
2162 Ted Campusano
2163 Scott Makarewicz
2164 Lance Madsen
2165 Jose Santana
2166 Ken Lofton
2167 Toncie Reed
2168 Reggie Waller
2169 Brian Porter
2170 Cole Hyson
2171 Ben Gonzales
2172 Jim Desapio
2173 Mike McDowell
2174 Francisco Perez
2175 Howard Prager
2176 Luther Johnson
2177 John Graham
2178 Bob Neal
2179 Darin Bruehl
2180 P.J. Riley
2181 Roger Marrero
2182 Donne Wall
2183 Kevin Scott
2184 Doug Simunic
2185 Dave Henderson
2186 Mica Lewis
2187 Rick Wise
2188 Mark Small
2189 Daryl Wooten

1989 ProCards Augusta Pirates

(Pittsburgh Pirates, A) (color)

	MT	NR MT	EX
Complete Set:	6.00	4.50	2.50

490 Checklist
491 Jeff Kuder
492 Jose Acosta
493 Tim Odom
494 Jeff Osborne
495 Jeff Neely
496 Mark Merchant
497 Felix Antigua
498 Mandy Romero
499 Chris Estep
500 Bobby Underwood
501 Jeff Stout
502 Mike Stevanus
503 Ken Huseby
504 Darwin Pennye
505 Flavio Williams
506 Keith Raisanen
507 Mark Thomas
508 Glenn McNabb
509 Mike Huyler
510 Antonio Felix
511 Ben Shelton
512 Kevin Andersh
513 Bruce Klein
514 Stan Cliburn
515 Terry Abbott
516 Pete Blohm

517 Greg Sims
518 Rod Byerly
519 Jay Snead
520 Chris Scheuer
521 Kyle Fisher

1989 Cal League Bakersfield Dodgers

(Los Angeles Dodgers, A) (color)

	MT	NR MT	EX
Complete Set:	8.00	6.00	3.25

180 David Dawson
181 Sean Snedeker
182 Kevin Campbell
183 Jeff Hartsock
184 Bill Bene
185 Macario Gastelum
186 Mike James
187 Rob Piscetta
188 Bill Wengert
189 James Wray
190 Cam Biberdorf
191 Bill Parham
192 Lance Rice
193 Eric Boddie
194 Jose Offerman
195 Scott Marabell
196 John Huebner
197 Bryan Beals
198 Eddie Pye
199 K.G. White
200 Ernie Carr
201 Eric Karros
202 Braulio Castillo
203 Jerry Brooks
204 Chris Morrow
205 Steve Finken
206 Tim Johnson
207 Guy Conti
208 Tim Terrio

1989 Best-ProCards Baseball America Prospects

(AA)

	MT	NR MT	EX
Complete Set:	24.00	18.00	9.50

1 Wes Chamberlain
2 Travis Fryman
3 Steve Adkins
4 Jason Grimsley
5 Bernie Williams
6 Tino Martinez
7 Beau Allred
8 Rodney Imes
9 Scott Cooper
10 Pat Combs
11 Eric Anthony
12 Darryl Kile
13 Steve Avery
14 Marquis Grissom
15 Delino Deshields
16 Brian Lane
17 Bob Hamelin
18 Scott Leius
19 Paul Sorrento
20 Howard Farmer
21 Robin Ventura
22 Wayne Edwards
23 Ray Lankford
24 Andy Benes
25 Jose Offerman
26 Juan Gonzalez
27 Dean Palmer
28 Julio Valera
29 Sammy Sosa
30 Gary Disarcina
---- Checklist card

1989 Star Co. Baseball City Royals

(Kansas City Royals, A) (color) (Price includes the late-issue Watson and coaches cards)

	MT	NR MT	EX
Complete Set:	8.00	6.00	3.25

1 Ken Adams
2 Pete Alborano
3 Jon Alexander
4 Jose Anglero
5 Sean Berry
6 Jeff Conine
7 Carlos Gonzalez
8 Kevin Shaw
9 Dave Howard
10 Jim Hudson
11 Tom Johnson
12 Joel Johnston
13 Lorin Jundy
14 Kevin Koslofski
15 Francisco Laureano
16 Brian McCormack
17 Dennis Moeller
18 Bobby Moore
19 Doug Nelson
20 Jorge Pedre
21 Kevin Pickens
22 Ruben Pujols
23 Keith Shepherd
24 Bill Stonikas
26 DeJon Watson (Late Issue)
27 Coaches (Luis Silverio, Ron Johnson, Mike Alvarez) (Late Issue)

1989 ProCards Batavia Clippers

(Philadelphia Phillies, A) (color)

	MT	NR MT	EX
Complete Set:	6.00	4.50	2.50

1915 Checklist
1916 Tony Lozinski
1917 Jeff Etheredge
1918 Robert Mendonca
1919 Tim Churchill
1920 Albert Bennett
1921 Paul Fletcher
1922 Joe Millette
1923 Steve Parris
1924 Matt Stevens
1925 Donnie Elliott
1926 David Agado
1927 Todd Goergen
1928 Robert Gaddy
1929 Mike Sullivan
1930 Michael Owens
1931 Mickey Hyde
1932 Dana Brown
1933 Joe Urbon
1934 Steve Bieser
1935 Field Staff
1936 Pat Woodruff
1937 Sam Taylor
1938 Greg Gunderson
1939 Eduardo Ortega
1940 John Escobar
1941 Eric Bratlein
1942 Josh Lowery
1943 Brian Cummings
1944 Edwin Rosado
1945 Robby Corsaro

1989 Star Beloit Brewers

(Milwaukee Brewers, A)

	MT	NR MT	EX
Complete Set:	6.00	4.50	2.50

1 Frank Bolick
2 Kevin Carmody
3 Don Erickson
4 John Faccio
5 Dave Fitzgerald
6 Librado Garcia
7 Mike Grayson
8 Mike Guerrero
9 Bert Hefferman
10 Chris Johnson
11 Mark Kiefer
12 Ken Kremer
13 Greg Landry
14 Heath Lane
15 Oreste Marrero
16 Vilato Marrero
17 Don Meyett
18 Bob Muhammad
19 Troy O'Leary
20 Joe Ortiz
21 Jose Peguero
22 Rich Pfaff
23 Dave Voit
24 Tim Wahl
25 Bob Watts
26 Alex Taveras & Gary Robson

1989 Star Co. Beloit Brewers

(Milwaukee Brewers, A)

	MT	NR MT	EX
Complete Set:	6.00	4.50	2.50

1 Frank Bolick
2 Arthur Butcher
3 John Byington
4 Jamie Cangemi
5 Kevin Carmody
6 Larry Carter
7 Steve Diaz
8 Calvin Eldred
9 John Finn
10 Dave Fitzgerald
11 Librado Garcia
12 Ron Hanisch
13 Mitch Hannahs
14 Bert Heffernan
15 Kenny Jackson
16 Chris Johnson
17 Mark Kiefer
18 Ken Kremer
19 Curt Krippner
20 Vilato Marrero
21 Don Meyett
22 Angel Miranda
23 Rich Pfaff
24 Guillermo Sandoval
25 Alex Taveras

1989 Legoe Bellingham Mariners

(Seattle Mariners, A)

	MT	NR MT	EX
Complete Set:	7.00	5.25	2.75

1 Greg Pirki
2 Julio Reyan
3 Keith Bryant
4 Jeff Darwin
5 Anthony Gordon
6 Jim Gutierrez
7 Michael LeBlanc
8 Tom Liss
9 Richard Lodding
10 Scott Lodgek
11 Darin Loe
12 Oscar Rivas
13 Roger Salkeld
14 Glenn Twardy
15 Johnny Wiggs
16 Kerry Woodson
17 Lash Bailey
18 Doug Davis
19 Pedro Roa
20 Brian Turang
21 Mark Brakebill
22 Jeremy Mathews
23 Bonel Chevalier
24 Alvin Rittman
25 Tony Cayson
26 Rich Hanlin
27 Corey Paul
28 Willie Romay
29 Dave Smith
30 P.J. Carey
31 Mauro Mazzotti
32 Gary Wheelock
33 Spyder Webb
34 Bill Tucker
35 Jerry Walker
36 Batboys & checklist card-Logo card

1989 Legoe Bend Bucks

	MT	NR MT	EX
Complete Set:	12.50	9.50	5.00

1 Erik Bennett
2 Marvin Cobb
3 Chris Cota
4 Wayne Helm
5 James Jones
6 Jaun Reyes
7 Fili Martinez
8 Marcus Moore
9 David Rice
10 Paul Swingle
11 Willie Warrecker
12 Joe Warren
13 David Neville
14 Richard Parker
15 Tom Rudstrom
16 Damion Easley
17 Corey Kapano
18 Jeff Kipila
19 Brian Specyalski
20 Rick Hirtensteiner
21 Bobby Jones
22 Jeff Kelso
23 Tim Salmon
24 Terry Taylor
25 Russell Lundgren
26 Don Long
27 Howie Gershberg
28 Rick Ingalls
29 Bill Durney
30 Bucky (Mascot)

1989 ProCards Billings Mustangs

(Cincinnati Reds, A) (color)

	MT	NR MT	EX
Complete Set:	6.00	4.50	2.50

2038 Checklist
2039 Kevin Hudson
2040 Travis Teegarden
2041 Trey Wilburn
2042 K.C. Gillum
2043 Brian Nichols
2044 Tomas Rodriquez
2045 Rick Allen
2046 Chris Gill
2047 Kyle Reagan
2048 David Keller
2049 Mike Goedde
2050 Brian Parrotte
2051 Brian Fry
2052 Sean Doty
2053 Kurt Dempster
2054 Mark Cerny
2055 Rob Dombrowski
2056 Andy Duke
2057 Steve Vondran
2058 Danny Perozo
2059 Harry Henderson IV
2060 Bob Blankenship
2061 Eric Bates
2062 Chris Keim
2063 Scott Pose
2064 Tim Pugh
2065 Gill Galloway
2066 Mark Borcherding
2067 Darron Cox
2068 Trevor Hoffman

1989 Best Birmingham Barons

(Chicago White Sox, AA) (color)

	MT	NR MT	EX
Complete Set:	10.00	7.50	4.00

1 Robin Ventura
2 Mike Ollom
3 Tony Menendez
4 Victor Diaz
5 Dan Wagner
6 Kevin Davis
7 Doug Frobel
8 Aubrey Waggoner
9 Chidez Garcia
10 Tony Blascucci
11 Grady Hall
12 Jerry Bertolani
13 Ravelo Manzanillo
14 Rich Amaral
15 Jerry Kutzler
16 Don Wakamatsu
17 Craig Grebeck
18 Chuck Mount
19 Todd Trafton
20 Ken Berry
21 Wayne Edwards
22 Doug Little
23 C.L. Penigar
24 Buddy Groom
25 Dave Wallwork
26 Ron Jackson
27 Tommy Thompson
28 Rick Peterson
29 Sam Hairston
30 Checklist

1989 Best Limited-Edition Birmingham Barons

(Chicago White Sox, AA) This set has a platinum colored border as opposed to the white border of the regular set. Also the backs of the cards are white as opposed to the yellow & white backs of the regular set.

	MT	NR MT	EX
Complete Set:	16.00	12.00	6.50

1 Robin Ventura
2 Mike Ollom
3 Tony Menendez
4 Victor Diaz
5 Dan Wagner
6 Kevin Davis
7 Doug Frobel
8 Aubrey Waggoner
9 Chidez Garcia
10 Tony Blascucci
11 Grady Hall
12 Jerry Bertolani
13 Ravelo Manzanillo
14 Rich Amaral
15 Jerry Kutzler
16 Don Wakamatsu

17 Craig Grebeck
18 Chuck Mount
19 Todd Trafton
20 Ken Berry
21 Wayne Edwards
22 Doug Little
23 C.L. Penigar
24 Buddy Groom
25 Dave Wallwork
26 Ron Jackson
27 Tommy Thompson
28 Rick Peterson
29 Sam Hairston
30 Checklist

1989 Best All-Decade Birmingham Barons

(Chicago White Sox, AA)

	MT	NR MT	EX
Complete Set:	9.00	6.75	3.50

1 Robin Ventura
2 Howard Johnson
3 Ken Berry
4 Doug Baker
5 Keith Comstock
6 Ken Baker
7 Tom Drees
8 Scotty Earl
9 Wayne Edwards
10 Bruce Fields
11 Tom Forrester
12 George Foussianes
13 Barbaro Garbey
14 Paul Gibson
15 Craig Grebeck
16 Dave Gumpert
17 Don Heinkel
18 Mike Henneman
19 Ron Karkovice
20 Mike Laga
21 Roy Majtyka
22 Carlos Martinez
23 Bob Melvin
24 Tony Menendez
25 Matt Merullo
26 Donn Pall
27 Adam Peterson
28 Rico Petrocelli
29 Rondall Rollin
30 Bobby Thigpen
31 Glenn Wilson
32 Mike Yastrzemski
33 Stan Younger
34 Logo & checklist card

1989 ProCards Birmingham Barons

(Chicago White Sox, A) (color)

	MT	NR MT	EX
Complete Set:	9.00	6.75	3.50

88 Checklist
89 Ken Berry
90 Dan Wagner
91 Rich Amaral
92 Chuck Mount
93 Doug Little
94 Tony Blasucci
95 Mike Ollom
96 Dave Wallwork
97 Todd Trafton
98 Kevin Davis
99 Rick Peterson
100 Jerry Bertolani
101 Victor Diaz
102 Cornelio Garcia
103 Tony Menendez
104 Tommy Thompson
105 Doug Frobel
106 Robin Ventura
107 Don Wakamatsu
108 Grady Hall
109 Buddy Groom
110 Wayne Edwards
111 Craig Grebeck
112 Sam Hairston, Sr.
113 Ron Jackson
114 Aubrey Waggoner
115 C.L. Penigar
116 Glen McElroy
117 Jerry Kutzler
118 Hoover Stadium

1989 Star Co. Bluefield Orioles

(Baltimore Orioles, R) (color) (Price includes the late-issue card #s 26-30)

	MT	NR MT	EX
Complete Set:	9.00	6.75	3.50

1 Eric Alexander
2 Manny Alexander
3 Chris Batiste
4 Mattie Belen
5 Cristian Benitez
6 Sergio Cairo
7 Bo Davis
8 Cesar Devares
9 John Fowler
10 Israel Frias
11 Shawn Heiden
12 Keith Kessinger
13 T.R. Lewis
14 John Marett
15 Tom Martin
16 Victor Medina
17 Jimmy Roso
18 Brad Pennington
19 Arron Norwood
20 Keith Schmidt
21 Al Sieradzki
22 Rob Stiegele
23 Doug Sutton
24 Tommy Taylor
25 Joe Teixeira
26 Mat Anderson (Late Issue)
27 Daryl Noore (Late Issue)
28 Bob Wheatcroft (Late Issue)
29 Earl Williams
30 Coaches (Jose Soto, Mike Young, Chet Nichols) (Late Issue)

1989 ProCards Boise Hawks

(No affiliation, A) (color)

	MT	NR MT	EX
Complete Set:	6.00	4.50	2.50

1976 Checklist
1977 Jeff Mace
1978 Boise Batboys (J.D. Schmidt, Nick Baltes, Kevin Kuenzi, Bill Church)
1979 Chip Reese
1980 Scott Jurgens
1981 David Perry
1982 Stan Cook
1983 Eric Doucet
1984 Tommy Griffith
1985 Jeff Gyarmati
1986 Darrell MacMillan
1987 Rod Tafoya
1988 Jeff Thrams
1989 Steve Mattingly
1990 Jack Malone
1991 Joe Mancini
1992 Ruben Rodriguez
1993 Bob Sobczyk
1994 Tim Wallace
1995 Dan Olson
1996 Bruce Arola
1997 John Bilello
1998 Jorge Candelaria
1999 Chris Cernay
2000 Brian Currie
2001 Chris Forreset
2002 Steve King
2003 Michael Larson
2004 Mike Lomeli
2005 Garry Wurm
2006 Paul Cluff

1989 Star Co. Bristol Tigers

(Detroit Tigers, A) (color) (Price includes the late-issue card #s 28-31)

	MT	NR MT	EX
Complete Set:	6.00	4.50	2.50

1 Michael Bowman
2 Jeff Braley
3 Aurturo Caines
4 Pedro Checo
5 Matthew Coleman
6 Lance Daniels
7 Robert Davis
8 Fredie Gamble
9 Mike Garcia
10 Jose Guzman
11 Chris Hall
12 Ricky Ibarguen
13 Travis Kinyoun
14 Ken Lewis
15 Ron Maietta
16 Steve Matchett
17 Kasy McKeon
18 Joe Neidinger
19 Kelley O'Neal
20 Rudy Pemberton
21 Mike Rendina
22 Juan Reyes
23 Eddie Rodriguez
24 Jose Rodriquez
25 Brian Rountree
26 Mac Siebert
27 Mario Stefani
28 Brad Wilson
29 Ruben Amaro
30 Steve Webber
31 Boyce Cox

1989 CMC Buffalo Bisons

(Pittsburgh Pirates, AAA) (color)

	MT	NR MT	EX
Complete Set:	7.00	5.25	2.75

1 Mike Billoni
2 Bill Landrum
3 Carlos Ledezma
4 Jay Bell
5 Dave Rucker
6 Scott Medvin
7 Miguel Garcia
8 Larry Melton
9 Rick Reed
10 Andy Hall
11 Benny Distefano
12 Mascot (Buster T. Bison)
13 Dann Bilardello
14 Steve Henderson
15 Sammy Khalifa
16 Jeff King
17 Bobby Meacham
18 Jim Pankovits
19 Ron Krauza
20 Scott Little
21 Tom Romano
22 Lue Thornton
23 Reggie Williams
24 Terry Collins
25 Jackie Brown

1989 ProCards Buffalo Bisons

(Pittsburgh Pirates, AAA) (color)

	MT	NR MT	EX
Complete Set:	7.00	5.25	2.75

1661 Checklist
1662 Dave Rucker
1663 Bobby Meacham
1664 Jim Pankovits
1665 Steve Carter
1666 Mascot
1667 Sammy Khalifa
1668 Terry Collins
1669 Lou Thornton
1670 Tom Romano
1671 Jeff King
1672 Andy Hall
1673 Larry Melton
1674 Bill Landrum
1675 Rick Reed
1676 Steve Henderson
1677 Dann Bilardello
1678 Carlos Ledezma
1679 Jay Bell
1680 Scott Medvin
1681 Scott Little
1682 Benny Distefano
1683 Jackie Brown
1684 Bob Patterson
1685 Reggie Williams
1686 Miguel Garcia
1687 Orestes Destrade

1989 ProCards Burlington Braves

(Atlanta Braves, A) (color)

	MT	NR MT	EX
Complete Set:	6.00	4.50	2.50

1596 Checklist
1597 Johnny Cuevas
1598 Lee Upshaw
1599 Mark Davis
1600 Joe Saccomanno
1601 Greg Cloninger
1602 Gary Schoonover
1603 Tom Kurczewski
1604 Preston Watson
1605 Jesus Mendoza
1606 Bob Pfaff
1607 Steve Glass
1608 Tony Baldwin
1609 Keith Mitchell
1610 Tom Redington
1611 Dave Karasinski
1612 Allan Waznik
1613 Steve Curry
1614 Ross Grimsley
1615 Jim Saul
1616 Steve Wendell
1617 Chris Czarnik
1618 Brian Cummings
1619 Dave Reis
1620 Don Campbell
1621 Daryl Blanks
1622 Teddy Williams
1623 Kevin Kelly
1624 Rich Longuil
1625 Paul C. Egins, III
1626 Skipper Wright
1627 Robert Cole

1989 Star Co. Burlington Braves

(Atlanta Braves, A) (color) (Price includes the late-issue card #s 26-29)

	MT	NR MT	EX
Complete Set:	6.00	4.50	2.50

1 Tony Baldwin
2 Daryl Blanks
3 Donovan Campbell
4 Greg Cloninger
5 Bob Cole
6 Johnny Cuevas
7 Brian Cummings
8 Chris Czarnik
9 Mark Davis
10 Steve Glass
11 Dave Karasinski
12 Kevin Kelly
13 Jesus Mendoza
14 Rich Longuil
15 Keith Mitchell
16 Bob Pfaff
17 Thomas Redington
18 David Reis
19 Joseph Saccomanno
20 Gary Schoonover
21 Lee Upshaw
22 Preston Watson
23 Allen Waznik
24 Steven Wendell
25 Teddy Williams
26 Skipper Wright
27 Jim Saul
28 Ross Grimsely
29 Steve Curry
30 Not Issued

1989 Star Co. Burlington Indians

(Cleveland Indians, A) (color) (Price includes the late-issue card #s 26-29 and Persons)

	MT	NR MT	EX
Complete Set:	8.00	6.00	3.25

1 Chad Allen
2 Andy Baker
3 Stacy Brown
4 Mark Charbonnet
5 Chris Cole
6 John Cotton
7 Mike Davis
8 Anthony Dela Cruz
9 Mark Delpiano
10 Carey Elston
11 Mike Gonzalez
12 Brian Hart
13 Avery Johnson
14 Tom Lachmann
15 Nolan Lane
16 Jesse Levis
17 Dean Meddaugh
18 David Nebraska
19 Ramon Ortiz
20 Cecil Pettiford
21 Clyde Pough
22 Roberto Rivera
23 Tommy Tillman
24 Ramon Torres
25 Reynaldo Ventura
26 Olonzo Woodfin (Late Issue)
27 Jim Cabella (Late Issue)
28 Coaches (Mark Oestreich, Stan Hilton) (Late Issue)
29 Teddy Blackwell (Late Issue)
---- Robert Persons (Late Issue)

1989 Sport Pro Butte Copper Kings

(Texas Rangers, R) (color)

	MT	NR MT	EX
Complete Set:	7.00	5.25	2.75

1 Stacy Parker
2 David Perez
3 Brian Roper
4 Donald Harris
5 Eric Bickhardt
6 Brian Romero
7 Barry Winford
8 Brian Crowley
9 Jose Borges
10 Steve Rowley
11 Jim Clinton
12 Jose Oliva
13 Joe Eischen
14 Chris Shiflett
15 Geoff Flinn
16 Troy Eklund
17 Jay Franklin
18 Brian Steiner
19 Manny Garcia
20 Randy Marshall

21 John Graves
22 Mark Young
23 Darrin Hays
24 Bump Wills
25 Buddy Micheu
26 Timmie Morrow
27 Dan Peltier
28 Ernie Rodriguez
29 Marvin White
30 Dave Freisleben

1989 CMC Calgary Cannons

(Seattle Mariners, AAA) (color)

	MT	NR MT	EX
Complete Set:	7.00	5.25	2.75

1 Luis DeLeon
2 Chuck Hensley
3 Colin McLaughlin
4 Steve Oliverio
5 Reggie Dobie
6 Bill Wilkinson
7 Rich Doyle
8 Jeff Hull
9 Bryan Price
10 Glenn Spagnola
11 Clint Zavaras
12 Dan Boever
13 Jay Buhner
14 Dave Cochrane
15 Roger Hansen
16 Paul Noce
17 Jim Bowie
18 Joe Dunlap
19 Bruce Fields
20 Mike Kingery
21 Bill McGuire
22 Jim Wilson
23 Omar Visquel
24 Rich Morales
25 Dan Warthen

1989 ProCards Calgary Cannons

(Seattle Mariners, AAA) (color)

	MT	NR MT	EX
Complete Set:	6.50	4.75	2.50

522 Checklist
523 Dan Warthen
524 Greg Fulton
525 Jim Bowie
526 Jeff Hull
527 Glenn Spagnola
528 Reggie Dobie
529 Joe Dunlap
530 Roger Hansen
531 Chuck Hensley
532 Colin McLaughlin
533 Bill McGuire
534 Bruce Fields
535 Dan Boever
536 Jim Wilson
537 Omar Vizquel
538 Rich Morales
539 Paul Noce
540 Bryan Price
541 Rich Doyle
542 Dave Cochrane
543 Steve Oliverio
544 Jay Buhner
545 Mike Kingery

1989 California League All-Stars

(A) (color)

	MT	NR MT	EX
Complete Set:	9.00	6.75	3.50

1 Jose Offerman
2 Eric Karros
3 Mark Merchant
4 Willie Banks
5 Lance Rice
6 Carlos Capellan
7 Jose Valentin
8 David Jacas
9 Braulio Castillo
10 Mike Humphreys
11 Miley Lee
12 Ruben Gonzelez
13 Johnny Ard
14 Mike Goff
15 Jeff Hartsock
16 James Wray
17 Doug Simons
18 Jerry Brooks
19 Eddie Pye
20 Andy Skeels
21 Sean Snedeker
22 Steve Finken
23 Tim Johnson
24 Guy Conti
25 Scott Ullger
26 Tim Terrio
27 Bill Weiss
28 Don Drysdale
29 Charlie Montoyo
30 Jim Jones
31 Stan Royer
32 Bobby Jones
33 Darren Lewis
34 Gary Borg
35 Steve Hecht
36 Gary Nalls
37 John Balfanz
38 Chris George
39 Mike Ignasiak
40 Kevin Meier
41 Joe Strong
42 Shawn Barton
43 Mark Dewey
44 Bill Savarino
45 John Jaha
46 Joe Kmak
47 Steve Lienhard
48 Greg Sparks
49 Duane Espy
50 Todd Oakes
51 Scott Wilson
52 Brent Howard
53 Erik deSonnaville
54 Bob Brooks
55 George Ulrich
56 Joe Gagliardi

1989 Best Canton-Akron Indians

(Cleveland Indians, AA) (color)

	MT	NR MT	EX
Complete Set:	6.00	4.50	2.50

1 Kevin Bearse
2 Julius McDougal
3 Jeff Shaw
4 Beau Allred
5 Casey Webster
6 Efrain Valdez
7 Dan Boever
8 William Williams
9 Dan Redmond
10 Tom Magrann
11 Eric Rasmussen
12 Michael Twardoski
13 Mark Gilles
14 Gregory Ferlenda
15 Lindsay Foster
16 Todd Gonzales
17 Bob Molinaro
18 Carl Keliipuleole
19 Scott Khoury
20 Paul Kuzniar
21 Allen Liebert
22 Jose Leiva
23 Everado Magallanes
24 Gregory McMichael
25 Troy Neel
26 Robert Swain
27 Charles Ogden
28 Checklist

1989 ProCards Canton-Akron Indians

(Cleveland Indians, AA) (color)

	MT	NR MT	EX
Complete Set:	6.00	4.50	2.50

1297 Checklist
1298 Jeff Shaw
1299 Mike Twardoski
1300 Carl Keliipueole
1301 Not Used
1302 Beau Allred
1303 Rob Swain
1304 Lindsay Foster
1305 Paul Kuznair
1306 Kevin Bearse
1307 Sam Ferretti
1308 Eric Rasmussen
1309 Everado Magallanes
1310 Scott Khoury
1311 Efrain Valdez
1312 Jose Leiva
1313 Tom Magrann
1314 Allen Liebert
1315 Greg McMichael
1316 Jeff Edwards
1317 Billy Williams
1318 Casey Webster
1319 Bob Molinaro
1320 Todd Gonzales
1321 Julius McDougal
1322 Todd Ogden
1323 Mark Gilles
1324 Troy Neel
1325 Dan Boever

1989 Star Co. Canton-Akron Indians

(Cleveland Indians, AA) (color)

	MT	NR MT	EX
Complete Set:	9.00	6.75	3.50

1 Beau Allred
2 Coaching Staff (Bob Molinaro, Eric Rasmussen, Billy Williams)
3 Dan Boever
4 Jeff Edwards
5 Greg Ferlenda
6 Lindsay Foster
7 Mark Gilles
8 Todd Gonzales
9 Carl Keliipuleole
10 Scott Khoury
11 Paul Kuzniar
12 Allen Liebert
13 Everado Magallanes
14 Tom Magrann
15 Julius McDougal
16 Greg McMichael
17 Troy Neel
18 Todd Ogden
19 Jeff Shaw
20 Rob Swain
21 Mike Twardoski
22 Efrain Valdez
23 Casey Webster
24 Jose Leiva
25 Joey Belle

1989 Best Cedar Rapids Reds

(Cincinnati Reds, A) (color)

	MT	NR MT	EX
Complete Set:	7.50	5.50	3.00

1 Jeff Branson
2 Stephen Foster
3 Scott Jeffrey
4 Quinn Marsh
5 Michael Myers
6 William Risley
7 Joseph Turek
8 Joseph Vierra
9 Scott Economy
10 Steve McCarthy
11 Duane Mulville
12 Eddie Taubensee
13 Andy Rickman
14 Adam Casillas
15 Kennedy Infante
16 Chris Schnurbusch
17 Scott Sellner
18 Norm Brock
19 Benny Colvard
20 Doug Eastman
21 Tony Mealy
22 Dave Miley
23 Gerry Groninger
24 Don Buchheister
25 Tom Spencer
26 Larry Rothchild
27 Tony Vasquez
28 Chris Lombardozzi
29 Steve Hester
30 Checklist

1989 Best All-Decade Cedar Rapids Reds

(Cincinnati Reds, A)

	MT	NR MT	EX
Complete Set:	9.00	6.75	3.50

1 Eric Davis
2 Kal Daniels
3 Lenny Harris
4 Chris Sabo
5 Paul O'Neill
6 Kurt Stillwell
7 Scott Terry
8 Joe Oliver
9 Reggie Jefferson
10 Eddie Williams
11 Eddie Taubensee
12 Keith Lockhart
13 Bob Murphy
14 Ron Robinson
15 Scott Scudder
16 Rob Dibble
17 Ron Henika
18 Adam Casillas
19 Jeff Jones
20 Jeff Branson
21 Brad Lesley
22 Phil Dale
23 Butch Henry
24 Rosario Rodriquez
25 Ray Corbett
26 Eski Viltz
27 Bruce Kimm
28 Marc Bombard
29 Marty Brown
30 Scott Bryant
31 Ross Powell
32 Keith Brown
33 Dan Boever
34 Don Buchheister
35 Lamar
36 Team photo & checklist

1989 ProCards Cedar Rapids Reds

(Cincinnati Reds, A) (color)

	MT	NR MT	EX
Complete Set:	7.00	6.00	3.25

910 Checklist
911 Mike Malinak
912 Bill Risley
913 Scott Jeffery
914 Steve McCarthy
915 Joey Vierra
916 Benny Colvard
917 Tom Spencer
918 Mike Myers
919 Steve Hester
920 Joe Turek
921 Scott Economy
922 Adam Casillas
923 Doug Eastman
924 Duane Mulville
925 Scott Sellner
926 Tony Mealy
927 Dave Miley
928 Jeff Branson
929 Quinn Marsh
930 Gerry Groninger
931 Don Buchheister
932 Andy Rickman
933 Larry Rothschild
934 Chris Schnurbusch
935 Chris Lombardozzi
936 Steve Foster
937 Eddie Taubensee
938 Norm Brock

1989 Star Co. Cedar Rapids Reds

(Cincinnati Reds, A) (color) (Price includes the late-issue Powell card)

	MT	NR MT	EX
Complete Set:	7.00	5.25	2.75

1 Jeff Branson
2 Norm Brock
3 Adam Casillas
4 Benny Colvard
5 Doug Eastman
6 Scott Eonomy
7 Steve Foster
8 Steve Hester
9 Scott Jeffery
10 Quinn Marsh
11 Steve McCarthy
12 Tony Mealy
13 Duane Mulville
14 Mike Myers
15 Andy Rickman
16 Bill Risley
17 Chris Schnurbusch
18 Scott Sellner
19 Eddie Taubensee
20 Joe Turek
21 Joey Vierra
22 Dave Miley
23 Gerry Groninger
24 Tom Spencer
25 Pete Beeler
26 Don Brown
27 Steve Hester
28 Kennedy Infante
29 Mike Malinak
30 Ross Powell

1989 ProCards Charleston Rainbows

(San Diego Padres, A) (color)

	MT	NR MT	EX
Complete Set:	6.00	4.50	2.50

969 Checklist
970 Team picture
971 A.J. Sager
972 Vance Tucker
973 Bob Brucato
974 Greg Conley
975 Brian Span
976 Vince Harris
977 Stan Tukes
978 Ron Oglesby
979 Greg Smith
980 Gerard Cifarelli
981 Chris Haslock

982 Joe Murdock
983 Bryce Florie
984 Luis Lopez
985 Matt Witkowski
986 John Kuehl
987 Jeff Hart
988 Scot Welish
989 Jimmy Lester
990 Mark Verstandig
991 Jack Krol
992 Pedro Martinez
993 David Bond
994 Dave Briggs
995 Nicko Riesgo
996 Renay Bryand

1989 Best Charleston Wheelers

(Chicago Cubs, A) (color)

	MT	NR MT	EX
Complete Set:	6.50	4.75	2.75

1 Wayne Weinheimer
2 Eric Williams
3 Miliciades Uribe
4 Kraig Washington
5 Scott Taylor
6 William St. Peter
7 Kevin Roberson
8 Jossy Rosario
9 Mathew Leonard
10 James Murphy
11 Matthew Franco
12 Luis Benitez
13 Herberto Andrade
14 Anthony Whitson
15 Roberto Smalls
16 Sean Reed
17 Ronnie Rasp
18 David Goodwin
19 John Gardner
20 Jason Doss
21 Jay Eddings
22 Matthew Cakora
23 Frank Campos
24 William Earley
25 Greg Mahlberg
26 Jim O'Reilly
27 Watt Powell Park

1989 ProCards Charleston Wheelers

(Chicago Cubs, A) (color)

	MT	NR MT	EX
Complete Set:	6.00	4.50	2.50

1743 Checklist
1744 Miliciades Uribe
1745 James Murphy
1746 Jim O'Reilly
1747 Kevin Roberson
1748 Matt Franco
1749 Luis Benitez
1750 Jossy Rosario
1751 Wayne Weinheimer
1752 Kraig Washington
1753 Bill Saint Peter
1754 Bill Earley
1755 Greg Mahlberg
1756 Eric Williams
1757 Scott Taylor
1758 Mathew Leonard
1759 Herberto Andrade
1760 Christopher Lutz
1761 Roberto Smalls
1762 Sean Reed
1763 Tony Whitson
1764 Ronnie Rasp
1765 Jason Doss
1766 Jay Eddings
1767 Frank Campos
1768 David Goodwin
1769 John Gardner
1770 Matt Cakora

1989 Best Chattanooga Lookouts

(Cincinnat Reds, AA) (color)

	MT	NR MT	EX
Complete set:	6.00	4.50	2.50

1 Reggie Jefferson
2 Keith Kaiser
3 Tony DeFrancesco
4 Brian Lane
5 Joe Lazor
6 Milton Hill
7 Jim Tracy
8 Rich Bombard
9 Butch Henry
10 Terry Lee
11 Pete Beeler
12 Alfredo Benavides
13 Timber Mead
14 Bill Dodd
15 Darrell Rodgers
16 Greg Lonigro
17 Chris Lombardozzi
18 Kevin Pearson
19 Mike Moscrey
20 Bernie Walker
21 Joe Bruno
22 Don Brown
23 Jerome Nelson
24 Sandy Krum
25 Alan Hayden
26 Checklist

1989 Grand Slam Chattanooga Lookouts

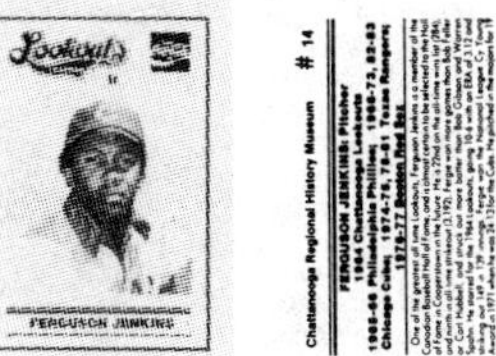

(Cincinnati Reds, AA) (color)

	MT	NR MT	EX
Complete Set:	6.00	4.50	2.50

1 Jim Tracy
2 Rich Bombard
3 Sandy Krum
4 Pete Beeler
5 Fred Benavides
6 Don Brown
7 Joe Bruno
8 Tony DeFrancesco
9 Bill Dodd
10 Milton Hill
11 Butch Henry
12 Reggie Jefferson
13 Keith Kaiser
14 Brian Lane
15 Joe Lazor
16 Terry Lee
17 Greg Lonigro
18 Mike Moscrey
19 Jerome Nelson
20 Kevin Pearson
21 Darrell Rodgers
22 Bernie Walker
23 Alan Hayden
24 Timber Mead
25 Chris Lombardozzi

1989 Team Chattanooga Lookouts

(Cincinnati Reds, AA) (black & white)

	MT	NR MT	EX
Complete Set:	8.00	15.00	8.00

1 Ted Abernathy
2 Bob Allison
3 John Boozer
4 Jimmy Bragan
5 Mickey Brantley
6 Keith Brown
7 Bob Costas
8 Alan Davis
9 Kid Elberfeld
10 Dave Gallagher
11 Erik Hanson
12 Dave Hengel
13 Grant Jackson
14 Ferguson Jenkins
15 Bill Lee
16 Charlie Letchas
17 Robert Long
18 Jim Morgan
19 Jeff Moronko
20 Al Neiger
21 Sammy Stang Nicklin
22 Bob Oldis
23 Ernie Oravetz
24 Jim Presley
25 Tom Runnells
26 Frank Sacka
27 Mike Schooler
28 Brick Smith
29 Danny Tartabull
30 Dave Valle
31 Hedi Vargas
32 Denny Walling
---- Chattanooga Regional History Museum

1989 Star Co. Charlotte Rangers

(Texas Rangers, A) (Price includes the three late-issue, unnumberd cards)

	MT	NR MT	EX
Complete Set:	8.00	6.00	3.25

1 Wilson Alvarez
2 Rick Bernardo
3 Mick Billmeyer
4 Paco Burgos
5 Joel Cartaya
6 Felipe Castillo
7 Brian Evans
8 Pat Garman
9 Stephan Glaskar
10 Rob Maurer
11 Rob Lavender
12 Travis Law
13 Bruce Lipscomb
14 Bill Losa
15 Jonathon Hurst
16 Rod Morris
17 Scott Morse
18 Ed Ohman
19 Roger Pavlik
20 Wayne Rosenthal
21 Luke Sable
22 Cedric Shaw
23 Jeff Shore
24 John Sipple
25 Mike Taylor
26 Bobby Jones
27 Rusty Gerhardt
28 Jeff Hubbard
---- Jonathon Hurst (Late issue)
---- Rob Lavender (Late issue)
---- Rob Maurer (Late issue)

1989 Team Charlotte Knights

(Chicago Cubs, AA) (color)

	MT	NR MT	EX
Complete Set:	9.00	6.75	3.50

1 Laddie Renfroe
2 Jim Essian
3 Grant Jackson
4 Ced Landrum
5 Derrick May
6 Jim Bullinger
7 Butch Garcia
8 Luis Cruz
9 Kelly Mann
10 Glenn Sullivan
11 Greg Smith
12 Erik Pappas
13 David Rosario
14 Ty Griffin
15 Tom Michno
16 Greg Kallevig
17 Shawn Boskie
18 Jeff Hirsch
19 Jackie Davidson
20 Matt Cakora
21 Phil Harrison
22 Bob Bafia
23 Brian McCann
24 Orsino Hill
25 Pablo Rivera

1989 Star Co. Clearwater Phillies

(Philadelphia Phillies, A) (color) (Price includes the late-issue card #26 and anniversary card)

	MT	NR MT	EX
Complete Set:	7.00	5.25	2.75

1 Jaime Barragan
2 Kim Batiste
3 Kendrick Bourne
4 Jim Carroll
5 Andy Carter
6 Fred Christopher
7 Mark Cobb
8 Pat Combs
9 Kevin Fynan
10 Jeff Grotewold
11 Dave Holdridge
12 Steve Kirkpatrick
13 Lee Langley
14 Tim Mauser
15 Trey McCall
16 Shelby McDonald
17 Matt Rambo
18 Scott Reaves
19 Rod Robertson
20 Mark Sims
21 Royal Thomas
22 Tony Trevino
23 Jim Vatcher
24 Chris Walker
25 Carlos Zayas
26 Glenn Gulliver, Tim Corcoran (Late Issue)
---- Clearwater Phillies 5th Anniversary Card

1989 ProCards Clinton Giants

(San Francisco Giants, A) (color)

	MT	NR MT	EX
Complete Set:	9.00	6.75	3.50

879 Checklist
880 Dave Bohnenkamp
881 Kevin Temperly
882 Adell Davenport
883 Adam Hilpert
884 Marino Hernandez
885 Chris Fye
886 Jimmy Myers
887 Gary Sharko
888 Karl Breitenbucher
889 Shane Borchert
890 Chris Hancock
891 Kevin Rogers
892 Jeffry Bonner
893 Reggie Williams
894 Rueben Smiley
895 Royce Clayton
896 Robbie Kemper
897 Scooter Tucker
898 Keith Bodie
899 Steve Gray
900 Julio Fernandez
901 Jeff Morris
902 Shannon Coppell
903 Carl Hanselman
904 Dominick Johnson
905 Domingo Delarosa
906 Steve Reed
907 Bill Gibbons
908 Steve Pratt
909 Dave Slavin

1989 CMC Colorado Springs Sky Sox

(Cleveland Indians, AAA) (color)

	MT	NR MT	EX
Complete Set:	6.00	4.50	2.50

1 Steve Davis
2 Don Gordon
3 Jeff Kaiser
4 Ed Wonjna
5 Kevin Wickander
6 Neil Allen
7 Joel Davis
8 Charles Scott
9 Joe Skalski
10 Mike Hargrove
11 Ron Tingley
12 Pete Dalena
13 Brian Giles
14 Denny Gonzales
15 Mark Higgins
16 Tommy Hinzo
17 Paul Zuvella
18 Dave Hengel
19 Dwight Taylor
20 Mark Salas
21 Danny Sheaffer
22 Ty Gainey
23 Rick Adair
24 Rich Dauer
25 Steve Ciczczon

1989 ProCards Colorado Springs Sky Sox

(Cleveland Indians, AAA) (color)

	MT	NR MT	EX
Complete set:	7.00	5.25	2.75

233 Checklist
234 Dwight Taylor
235 Pete Dalena
236 Ed Wojna

237 Joel Davis
238 Kevin Wickander
239 Mike Walker
240 Mark Salas
241 Danny Sheaffer
242 Rich Dauer
243 Dave Hengel
244 Stan Hilton
245 Paul Zuvella
246 Mike Hargrove
247 Rick Adair
248 Denny Gonzalez
249 Steve Davis
250 Steve Ciszczon
251 Mike Young
252 Steve Olin
253 Brian Giles
254 Tom Lampkin
255 Mark Higgins
256 Tommy Hinzo
257 Ron Tingley
258 Ty Gainey
259 Theo Shaw
260 Don Gordon

1989 Best Columbia Mets

(New York Mets, A) (color)

	MT	NR MT	EX
Complete Set:	8.00	6.00	3.25

1 Todd Hundley
2 Vladimir Perez
3 Derrick Young
4 Rob Lemle
5 Archie Corbin
6 Dan Fumanik
7 Bob Olah
8 Dave Joiner
9 Michael Noelke
10 Lee May
11 Eric Hillman
12 Kevin Baez
13 Chris Hill
14 Pete Schourek
15 Jim Morrisette
16 Anthony Young
17 John Wenrick
18 Steve Newton
19 Andy Reich
20 Doug Saunders
21 Radhames Polanco
22 Bill Stein
23 Jack Fisher
24 Pat Hyman
25 Rich Bomgardner
26 Frank Harris
27 Lonnie Walker
28 Kevin Maloney
29 Al Jimenez
30 Checklist

1989 Grand Slam Columbia Mets

(New York Mets, A) (color)

	MT	NR MT	EX
Complete Set:	8.00	6.00	3.25

() Team logo
1 Bill Stein
2 Jack Fisher
3 Rich Bomgardner
4 Skip Weisman
5 Kevin Maloney
6 Kevin Baez
7 Archie Corbin
8 Dan Furmanik
9 Chris Hill
10 Eric Hillman
11 Todd Hundley
12 Alex Jimenez
13 Dave Joiner
14 Rob Lemle
15 Lee May
16 James Morrisette
17 Steve Newton
18 Mike Noelke
19 Bob Olah
20 Vladimir Perez
21 Radhames Polanco
22 Andy Reich
23 Doug Saunders
24 Pete Schourek
25 Julian Vasquez
26 Lonnie Walker
27 John Wenrick
28 Anthony Young
29 Derrick Young

1989 CMC Columbus Clippers

(New York Yankees, AAA) (color)

	MT	NR MT	EX
Complete Set:	10.00	7.50	4.50

1 Bill Fulton
2 Scott Nielsen
3 Dickie Noles
4 Clay Parker
5 Hipolito Pena
6 Don Schulze
7 Chuck Cary
8 Dave Eiland
9 Jimmy Jones
10 Balvino Galvez
11 Bob Geren
12 Mike Woodard
13 Randy Velarde
14 Brian Dorsett
15 Steve Kiefer
16 Hal Morris
17 Kevin Maas
18 John Fishel
19 Darrell Miller
20 Bob Green
21 Bernie Williams
22 Mark Wasinger
23 Dick Grapenthin
24 Coaches (Ken Rowe, Champ Summers, Gary Tuck, Mike Heifferon)
25 Bucky Dent
26 Dave Sax
27 Dave Griffin
28 Stanley Jefferson
29 Mark Leiter
30 Darrin Chapin

1989 Police Columbus Clippers

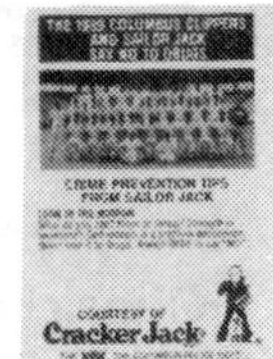

(New York Yankees, AAA) (color)

	MT	NR MT	EX
Complete Set:	7.00	5.25	2.75

1 Chuck Cary
2 Dave Eiland
3 Bill Fulton
4 Balvino Galvez
5 Dick Grapethin
6 Jimmy Jones
7 Scott Nielsen
8 Duckie Noles
9 Clay Parker
10 Hipolito Pena
11 Don Schulze
12 Brian Dorsett
13 Bob Geren
14 Darrell Miller
15 Steve Kiefer
16 Hal Morris
17 Randy Velarde
18 Mark Wasinger
19 Mike Woodard
20 John Fishel
21 Bobby Green
22 Kevin Maas
23 Bernie Williams
24 Coaches (Ken Rowe, Champ Summers, Mike Heifferon, Gary Tuck)
25 George Sisler, Bucky Dent

1989 ProCards Columbus Clippers

(New York Yankees, AAA) (color)

	MT	NR MT	EX
Complete Set:	7.50	5.50	3.00

732 Checklist
733 Darrel Miller
734 Bobby Green
735 John Fishel
736 Bernie Williams
737 Kevin Maas
738 Mark Wasinger
739 Chris Alvarez
740 Steve Kiefer
741 Randy Velarde
742 Mike Woodard
743 Hal Morris
744 Hipolito Pena
745 Chuck Cary
746 Bill Fulton
747 Dick Grapenthin
748 Balvino Galvez
749 Dickie Noles
750 Dave Eiland
751 Clay Parker
752 Jimmy Jones
753 Don Schulze
754 Scott Nielsen
755 Field Staff (Ken Rowe, Bucky Dent, Champ Summers, Mike Heifferon, Gary Tuck)
756 Dave Sax
757 Bucky Dent
758 Bob Geren
759 Brian Dorsett

1989 Best Columbus Mudcats

(Houston Astros, AA) (color)

	MT	NR MT	EX
Complete Set:	8.00	6.00	3.25

1 Eric Anthony
2 Manny Acta
3 Garret Nago
4 Darryl Kile
5 David Salaiz
6 Pedro Sanchez
7 Michael Simms
8 Tom Weidenbrauer
9 Randy Hennis
10 Fred Gladding
11 Doug Givler
12 Lou Frazier
13 Jeff Baldwin
14 Blane Fox
15 Tony Eusebio
16 Fred Costello
17 Mike Browning
18 Ryan Bowen
19 Jim Hickey
20 Bobby Ramos
21 David Rohde
22 Karl Rhodes
23 Billy Carver
24 Steve Oliverio
25 Jose Cano
26 Todd Credeur
27 Phil Torres
28 Checklist

1989 Best Limited-Edition Columbus Mudcats

(Houston Astros, AA)

	MT	NR MT	EX
Complete Set:	12.00	9.00	4.75

1 Eric Anthony
2 Manny Acta
3 Garret Nago
4 Darryl Kile
5 David Salaiz
6 Pedro Sanchez
7 Michael Simms
8 Tom Weidenbrauer
9 Randy Hennis
10 Fred Gladding
11 Doug Givler
12 Lou Frazier
13 Jeff Baldwin
14 Blane Fox
15 Tony Eusebio
16 Fred Costello
17 Mike Browning
18 Ryan Bowen
19 Jim Hickey
20 Bobby Ramos
21 David Rohde
22 Karl Rhodes
23 Billy Carver
24 Steve Oliverio
25 Jose Cano
26 Todd Credeur
27 Phil Torres
28 Checklist

1989 ProCards Columbus Mudcats

(Houston Astros) (color)

	MT	NR MT	EX
Complete Set:	8.00	6.00	3.25

119 Checklist
120 Team Logo
121 Bobby Ramos
122 Mike Browning
123 Dave Rohde
124 Doug Givler
125 Tony Eusebio
126 Ryan Bowen
127 Pedro Sanchez
128 Joel Estes
129 Fred Costello
130 Tom Wiedenbauer
131 Rob Mallicoat
132 Trent Hubbard
133 Darryl Kile
134 Eric Anthony
135 Jeff Baldwin
136 Manny Acta
137 Randy Hennis
138 David Salaiz
139 Fred Gladding
140 Sam August
141 Mike Simms
142 Karl Rhodes
143 Blane Fox
144 Terry Wells
145 Lou Frazier
146 Garrett Nago
147 Mike Loynd
148 Bert Hunter
149 Team Picture

1989 Star Co. Columbus Mudcats

(Houston Astros, AA) (color) (Price includes late-issue coaching staff card)

	MT	NR MT	EX
Complete Set:	8.00	6.00	3.25

1 Manny Mota
2 Eric Anthony
3 Jeff Baldwin
4 Ryan Bowen
5 Mike Browning
6 Fred Costello
7 Joel Estes
8 Tony Eusebio
9 Blane Fox
10 Lou Frazier
11 Doug Givier
12 Randy Hennis
13 Trent Hubbard
14 Bert Hunter
15 Darryl Kile
16 Mike Loynd
17 Rob Mallicoatt
18 Garret Nago
19 Karl Rhodes
20 David Rohde
21 Pedro Sanchez
22 Mike Sims
23 Terry Wells
24 Coaches (Tom Wiedenbauer, Bobby Ramos, Fred Gladding)

1989 CMC Denver Zephyrs

(Milwaukee Brewers, AAA) (color)

	MT	NR MT	EX
Complete Set:	8.00	6.00	3.25

1 Jay Aldrich
2 Tim Watkins
3 Tony Fossas
4 Mike Kinnuenen
5 Mike Costello
6 Donnie Scott
7 Ray Krawczyk
8 Jeff Petarek
9 Al Sadler
10 Todd Simmons
11 Bob Stoddard
12 Kiki Diaz
13 Darryl Hamilton
14 Lavell Freeman
15 Billy Bates
16 Darryel Walters
17 Jimmy Jones
18 Ruben Rodriguez
19 George Canale
20 Joe Mitchell
21 Joe Xavier
22 Matias Carrillo
23 Greg Vaughn
24 Jackson Todd
25 Dave Machemer

1989 ProCards Denver Zephyrs

(Milwaukee Brewers, AAA) (color)

	MT	NR MT	EX
Complete Set:	8.00	6.00	3.25

30 Todd Simmons
31 Bob Stoddard
32 Ray Krawczyk
33 Mike Kinnunen
34 Ruben Rodriguez
35 George Canale
36 Greg Vaughn
37 Dave Machemer
38 Billy Bates
39 Darryl Hamilton
40 Jim Jones
41 Tim Watkins
42 Jay Aldrich
43 Joe Mitchell
44 Alan Sadler
45 Mike Costello
46 Jeff Peterek

47 Kiki Diaz
48 Lavell Freeman
49 Matias Carrillo
50 Peter Kolb
51 Jackson Todd
52 Donnie Scott
53 Joe Xavier
54 Darryel Walters
55 Tony Fossas
56 Norm Jones
57 Checklist

1989 Star Co. Dunedin Blue Jays

(Toronto Blue Jays, A) (color) (Price includes the late-issue coaches card)

	MT	NR MT	EX
Complete Set:	8.00	6.00	3.25

1 Denis Boucher
2 Enrique Burgos
3 Nate Cromwell
4 Andy Dziadkowiec
5 Henry Lee Goshay
6 Darren Hall
7 Pat Hentgen
8 Vince Horsman
9 Jimy Kelly
10 Randy Knorr
11 Mike Mills
12 Bernardino Nunez
13 Paul Rodgers
14 Earl Sanders
15 Al Silverstein
16 Ed Sprague
17 Williams Suero
18 Marcos Taveras
19 Mike Tomlin
20 Relito Uribe
21 Greg Vella
22 Steve Wapnick
23 Woody Williams
24 Julian Yan
25 Mark Young
26 Coaches (Doug Ault, Dennis Holmberg, Steve Mingori - Late Issue)

1989 Star Co. Durham Bulls

(Atlanta Braves, A) (color) (Price includes the scarce, late-issue card #s 26-29)

	MT	NR MT	EX
Complete Set:	16.00	12.00	6.50

1 Steve Avery
2 Dennis Burlingame
3 David Butts
4 Rich Casarotti
5 Brian Champion
6 Jamie Cuesta
7 Wes Currin
8 Jim Czajkowski
9 Brian Deak
10 Todd Dewey
11 Mike Fowler
12 Jerald Frost
13 Phil Maldonado
14 Rich Maloney
15 Al Martin
16 David Nied
17 Ken Pennington
18 Ben Rivera
19 Sean Ross
20 Mike Stoker
21 Pat Tilmon
22 Theron Todd
23 Andy Tomberlin
24 Matt Turner
25 Steve Ziem
26 Grady Little
27 Larry Jaster
28 Inocencio Guerrero
29 Kevin Costner

1989 Team Durham Bulls

(Atlanta Braves, A) (color) (co-sponsored by 28 WPTF-TV & Kodak)

	MT	NR MT	EX
Complete Set:	16.00	12.00	6.50

(1) Team Photo
(2) Steve Avery
(3) Dennis Burlingame
(4) David Butts
(5) Rich Casarotti
(6) Brian Champion
(7) Jamie Cuesta
(8) Wes Currin
(9) Jim Czajkowski
(10) Brian Deak
(11) Todd Dewey
(12) Mike Fowler
(13) Jerald Frost
(14) Phil Maldonado
(15) Rich Maloney
(16) David Nied
(17) Al Martin
(18) Ken Pennington
(19) Ben Rivera
(20) Sean Ross
(21) Mike Stoker
(22) Pat Tilmon
(23) Theron Todd
(24) Andy Tomberlin
(25) Matt Turner
(26) Steve Ziem
(27) Ino Guerrero
(28) Larry Jaster
(29) Grady Little

1989 ProCards Eastern League All-Stars

(AA)

	MT	NR MT	EX
Complete Set:	8.00	6.00	3.25

1 Index
2 Andy Stankiewicz
3 Leo Gomez
4 Travis Fryman
5 Wes Chamberlain
6 Beau Allred
7 Troy Neel
8 Rob Sepanek
9 Jim Leyritz
10 Rodney Imes
11 Steve Adkins
12 Daryl Irvine
13 Dan Gabriele
14 Tim Layana
15 Scott Kamieniecki
16 Jason Grimsley
17 Josias Manzanillo
18 Tino Martinez
19 Casey Webster
20 Jack Smith
21 Victor Hithe
22 John Ramos
23 Jeff Bannister
24 Tim Mauser
25 Rick Parker
26 Buck Showalter

1989 ProCards Eastern League Diamond Diplomacy

(AA)

	MT	NR MT	EX
Complete Set:	6.00	4.50	2.50

1 Index
2 Vitalyi Romanov
3 German Gulbit
4 Sergey Korolev
5 Vadim Kulakov
6 Evgenyi Puchkov
7 Alexei Koshevoy
8 Sergey Zhigalov
9 Edmuntas Matusyavichus
10 Alexander Dundik
11 Sergei Onichuk
12 Boris Rogascozv
13 Andrei Fzelykovskyi
14 Alexander Krupenchenkov
15 Leonid Korneev
16 Roman Stepanov
17 Ilya Bogatyrev
18 Alexander Kozyrez
19 Timur Tritonenkov
20 Audrey Popov
21 Igor Mahambitov
22 Kevin Burdick
23 Dave Milstien
24 Dave Walters
25 Steve Scarsone
26 Tommy Shields
27 Steve Adams
28 Jeff Banister
29 Dan Simonds
30 Joe Dunlap
31 Leverne Jackson
32 Rich Doyle
33 Glenn Spagnola
34 Chris Calvert
35 Mike Twardoski
36 Ted Williams
37 Troy Neel
38 Don Buford
39 Frank Bellino
40 Mike Sander
41 Jeff Edwards
42 Eastern League group photo
43 Rich Gale
44 Stump Merrill
45 Rob Thomson
46 Dave Trembley
47 Dick Groch
48 Potte, Fitzgerald, Kellogg)
49 Kevin Rand
50 David Hays

1989 CMC Edmonton Trappers

(California Angels, AAA) (color)

	MT	NR MT	EX
Complete Set:	6.00	4.50	2.50

1 Jack Lazorko
2 Rich Monteleone
3 Carl Willis
4 Cliff Young
5 Tim Burcham
6 Colin Charland
7 Stu Cliburn (edmonton)
8 Sherman Corbett
9 Mike Fetters
10 Colby Ward
11 Stan Holmes
12 Pete Coachman
13 Edwin Marquez
14 Jim Eppard
15 Doug Davis
16 Mike Ramsey
17 Kent Anderson
18 Mike Brown
19 Jamie Nelson
20 Jeff Manto
21 Lee Stevens
22 Jim Thomas
23 Max Venable
24 Chuck Hernandez
25 Tom Kotchman

1989 ProCards Edmonton Trappers

(California Angels, AAA) (color)

	MT	NR MT	EX
Complete Set:	6.00	4.50	2.50

546 Checklist
547 Sherm Corbett
548 Jim Eppard
549 Tom Kotchman
550 Jim Thomas
551 Doug Davis
552 Edwin Marquez
553 Tim Burcham
554 Lee Stevens
555 Stan Holmes
556 Max Venable
557 Cliff Young
558 Mike Brown
559 Vance Lovelace
560 Don McGann
561 Mike Ramsey
562 Chuck Hernandez
563 Pete Coachman
564 Rich Monteleone
565 Colin Charland
566 Stewart Cliburn
567 Carl Willis
568 Colby Ward
569 Jamie Nelson
570 Jeff Manto

1989 Pucko Elmira Pioneers

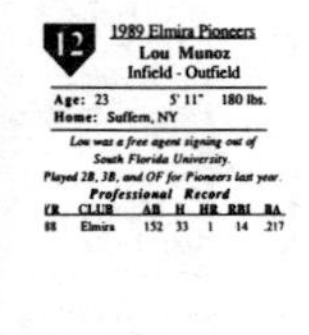

(Boston Red Sox) (color) (Price includes late-issue cards #2, 29-32)

	MT	NR MT	EX
Complete Set:	7.00	5.25	2.75

1 Dave Alvarez
2 Johnny Diaz
3 Luis Dorante
4 Chris Hanks
5 Pete Hoy
6 Garrett Jenkins
7 Steve Michael
8 Jim Morrison
9 Bart Moore
10 Frank Morelli
11 Tony Mosley
12 Lou Munoz
13 Ender Perozo
14 Ed Riley
15 Carlos Rivera
16 Julio Rosario
17 Chris Rosfelder
18 Andy Rush
19 Al Sanders
20 John Spencer
21 Richard Witherspoon
22 Mike Verdi
23 Dave Kennedy
24 Dunn Field
25 Clyde Smoll
26 Dennis Robarge
27 Kevin Morton
28 Michael Thompson
29 John Locker
30 Jeff McNeely
31 Paul Quantrill
32 Eric Wedge

1989 Star Co. Elizabethton Twins

(Minnesota Twins, A) (color)

	MT	NR MT	EX
Complete Set:	7.50	5.50	3.00

1 Bryan Asp
2 Tom Benson
3 Jayson Best
4 David Bigham
5 Marty Cordoua
6 Sandy Diaz
7 Steve Dunn
8 Rick Freeman
9 Randy Gentile
10 Jody Harrington
11 Mike Hinde
12 Mike House
13 Karl Johnson
14 Jose Leon
15 Mike Lloyd
16 Angel Lugo
17 Bob McCreary
18 Jeff Milene
19 Mike Misuraca
20 Steve Morris
21 Willie Mota
22 Dennis Neagle
23 Tim Nedin
24 Rex De La Nuez
25 Kerry Taylor
26 Amadeo Garcia
27 Wade Wacker
28 Phil Wiese
29 Ray Smith
30 Coaching Staff (Rick Tomlin, Jim Lemon)
31 Jeff Chambers

1989 Grand Slam El Paso Diablos

(Milwaukee Brewers, AA) (color)

	MT	NR MT	EX
Complete Set:	6.00	4.50	2.50

1 Marc Bombard
2 Paul Lindblad
3 James Austin
4 Mark Chapman
5 Mike Costello
6 Brian Drahman
7 Keith Fleming
8 Doug Henry
9 Jim Hunter
10 John Miglio
11 Steve Monson
12 Carl Moraw
13 Jaime Navarro
14 Ed Puig
15 Tim Watkins
16 Teddy Higuera
17 Randy Veres
18 Tim McIntosh
19 Tim Torricelli
20 Jesus Alfaro
21 Greg Edge
22 Sandy Guerrero
23 Frank Mattox
24 D.L. Smith
25 Shon Ashley
26 Andre David
27 Ruben Escalera
28 Ramon Sambo
29 Darryel Walters
30 Mario Monico

1989 Star Co. Erie Orioles

(Baltimore Orioles, A) (color) (Price includes the late-issue, card #s 26-29)

	MT	NR MT	EX
Complete Set:	8.00	6.00	3.25

1 Tony Beasley
2 Dan Berthel
3 John Bowen
4 Dave Brown
5 Pat Hedge
6 John Hemmerly
7 Aman Hicks
8 Brad Hildreth
9 Ed Horowitz
10 Zack Kerr
11 Pat Leinen
12 Rich Meek
13 Carey Metts
14 Cary Moore
15 Steve Nicosia
16 Mike Oquist
17 Jamie Pena
18 Doug Reynolds
19 Art Rhodes
20 Mike Richardson
21 David Riddle
22 Pete Rose Jr.
23 Mark Rupp
24 Gary Shingledecker
25 Melvin Wearing
26 Steve Williams (Late issue)
27 Bobby Tolan (Late issue)
28 Mark Brown (Late issue)
29 Dave Werner (Late issue)

1989 Best Eugene Emeralds

(Kansas City Royals, A) (color)

	MT	NR MT	EX
Complete Set:	6.00	4.50	2.50

1 Chris Schaeffer
2 Mike Webster
3 Kirk Baldwin
4 Jake Jacobs
5 Don Lindsey
6 Matt Karchner
7 Scott Centala
8 Ben Pardo
9 Ed Pierce
10 Kirk Thompson
11 Dave Ritchie
12 David Solseth
13 Colin Ryan
14 Kevin Long
15 Javier Alvarez
16 Rich Tunison
17 Kerwin Moore
18 Milt Richardson
19 Fred Russell
20 Ron Collins
21 Rob Buchanan
22 John Gilcrist
23 Brian Ahern
24 Sean Collins
25 Checklist

1989 Star Co. Everett Giants

(San Francisco Giants, A) (color)

	MT	NR MT	EX
Complete Set:	6.00	4.50	2.50

1 Maximo Aleys
2 Clayton Bellinger
3 Steve Callahan
4 Teodoro Cespedes
5 Ron Crowe
6 Brian Dour
7 Scott Ebert
8 Mike Grahovac
9 Edward Gustafson
10 Kevin Hall
11 Chris Hancock
12 Carl Hanselman
13 Dan Hendrickson
14 David Hocking
15 Steve Hosey
16 Randy Johnson
17 Kevin Jones
18 Kevin Kasper
19 Jesus Laya
20 Mike McDonald
21 Troy Mentzer
22 Dan Montes
23 Vince Palyan
24 Ed Quesada
25 Jon Schiller
26 Greg Brummett
27 Greg Lund
28 Jason McFarlin
29 Glen Warren
30 Joe Strain
31 Diego Segui
32 Bryce Welch

1989 ProCards Fayetteville Generals

(Detroit Tigers, A) (color)

	MT	NR MT	EX
Complete Set:	6.00	4.50	2.50

1567 Checklist
1568 Glenn Belcher
1569 Leo Torres
1570 Jeff Jones
1571 Rob Thomas
1572 Linty Ingram
1573 Lino Rivera
1574 Marcos Betances
1575 Rusty Meacham
1576 Mike Koller
1577 Gene Roof
1578 Rich Rowland
1579 Blaine Rudolph
1580 Benny Castillo
1581 Randy Marshall
1582 Kurt Shea
1583 Tim Brader
1584 Mike Rendina
1585 Darryl Martin
1586 Jim Murphy
1587 Julio Rosa
1588 Freddy Torres
1589 Brett Roach
1590 Micky Delas
1591 Paul Nozling
1592 Ron Howard
1593 Mike Davidson
1594 Steve Peques
1595 Freddy Padilla

1989 Team Fayetteville Generals

(Detroit Tigers, A)

	MT	NR MT	EX
Complete Set:	6.00	4.50	2.50

(1) Mark Cole
(2) John DeSilva
(3) Don Erickson
(4) Mark Ettles
(5) Ed Ferm
(6) Greg Gohr
(7) Pat Pesavento
(8) Dan Raley
(9) Andy Toney
(10) Duane Walker

1989 Star Co. Fort Lauderdale Yankees

(New York Yankees, A) (color) (Price includes the scarce, late-issue card #s 26-29)

	MT	NR MT	EX
Complete Set:	7.00	5.25	2.75

1 Steve Adkins
2 Russell Davis
3 Herb Erhardt
4 Steve Erickson
5 Victor Garcia
6 Doug Gogolewski
7 John Green
8 Freddie Hailey
9 Mike Hook
10 Chris Howard
11 Dean Kelly
12 Ralph Kraus
13 Mark Leiter
14 Ramon Manon
15 Ed Martel
16 Alan Mills
17 Red Morrison
18 Skip Nelloms
19 Tom Popplewell
20 Mike Rhodes
21 Carlos Rodriguez
22 Garriel Rodriguez
23 Dan Roman
24 Melvin Rosario
25 John Seeburger
26 Bob Zeihen
27 Clete Boyer
28 Jack Hubbard
29 David Schuler

1989 Star Co. Frederick Keys

(Baltimore Orioles, A) (color) (Price includes the scarce, late-issue card #s 25 A-27)

	MT	NR MT	EX
Complete Set:	8.00	6.00	3.25

1 Stacey Burdick
2 Mike Cavers
3 Andres Constant
4 Francisco Dela Rosa
5 Mike Deutsch
6 Oneri Fleita
7 Roy Gilbert
8 Ricky Gutierrez
9 Tom Harms
10 Paris Hayden
11 Stacey Jones
12 Mike Lehman
13 Mike Linskey
14 Rodney Lofton
15 Scott Meadows
16 Luis Mercedes
17 Dave Miller
18 Steve Mondile
19 Chris Myers
20 Luis Paulino
21 David Segui
22 Dan Simonds
23 Anthony Telford
24 Jack Voight
25A Jerry Narron (Error, with glasses, late issue)
25B Jerry Narron (Corrected)
26 Mike Pazik (Late issue)
27 Pete Rose, Jr. (Late issue)

1989 ProCards Gastonia Rangers

(Texas Rangers, A) (color)

	MT	NR MT	EX
Complete Set:	8.00	6.00	3.25

997 Checklist
998 Joe Wardlow
999 Spencer Wilkinson
1000 Everett Cunningham
1001 Dominic Pierce
1002 Kyle Spencer
1003 Robb Nen
1004 Kevin Belcher
1005 Carl Randle
1006 Ivan Rodriguez
1007 Joe Lewis
1008 Eric McCray
1009 Anthony Berry
1010 Chuck Marquardt
1011 Jim McCutcheon
1012 Trey McCoy
1013 Doug Cronk
1014 Cris Colon
1015 Jim Crawford
1016 Ronaldo Romero
1017 Orlando Gomez
1018 Jose Hernandez
1019 Jim Hvizda
1020 Francisco Valdez
1021 Darren Oliver
1022 Steve Allen
1023 Jeff Frye
1024 Tim MacNeil
1025 Oscar Acosta
1026 Mike Mendazona

1989 Star Co. Gastonia Rangers

(Texas Rangers, A) (color)

	MT	NR MT	EX
Complete Set:	9.00	6.75	3.50

1 Steve Allen
2 Kevin Belcher
3 Tony Berry
4 Cris Colon
5 Doug Cronk
6 Everett Cunningham
7 Jeff Frye
8 Jose Hernandez
9 Jim Hvizda
10 Joe Lewis
11 Tim MacNeil
12 Trey McCoy
13 Eric McCray
14 Jim McCutchen
15 Mike Mendazona
16 Robb Nen
17 Darren Oliver
18 Dominic Pierce
19 Carl Randle
20 Ivan Rodriguez
21 Rolando Romero
22 Kyle Spencer
23 Frank Valdez
24 Joe Wardlow
25 Spencer Wilkinson
---- Coaching staff

1989 ProCards Geneva Cubs

(Chicago Cubs, A) (color)

	MT	NR MT	EX
Complete Set:	6.00	4.50	2.50

1856 Checklist
1857 Quinn's Cards
1858 Front Office Staff
1859 Grounds Crew (Ed Smaldone, Dave Mungo)
1860 Frankie Espino
1861 Ed Smaldone
1862 Rene Francisco
1863 Darrin Beep
1864 Doug Welch
1865 Kevin Gore
1866 David Swartzbaugh
1867 Travis Willis
1868 Jeff Cesari
1869 Jeff Ludwig
1870 Luis Benitez
1871 Richie Grayum
1872 Kalani Bush
1873 Jim Sweeney
1874 Al Stacey
1875 Tony Colon
1876 Chris Ebright
1877 Gary Scott
1878 Mark Linden
1879 Pablo Delgado
1880 Micah Murphy
1881 Shannon Jones
1882 Gregg Patterson
1883 Rick Mundy
1884 Billy White
1885 Ken Reynolds
1886 Pookie Bernstine

1989 Sport Pro Great Falls Dodgers

(Los Angeles Dodgers, R) (color)

	MT	NR MT	EX
Complete Set:	7.00	5.25	2.75

1 Tom Goodwin
2 Michael Frame
3 Rich Crane
4 Michael Potthoff
5 Jamie McAndrew
6 Tony Helmick
7 Javier Loera
8 Audelle Cummings
9 Joe Vavra
10 Jason Brosnan
11 Ray Bielanin
12 Michael Wismer
13 Yale Fowler
14 Tim Barker
15 Joey Seals
16 Lee DeLoach
17 John Deutsch
18 Kiki Jones
19 Bryan Baar
20 Barry Parisotto
21 Frank Humber
22 Anthony Collier
23 Mathew Howard
24 Erik Madsen
25 Stephen O'Donnell
26 Rod Harvell
27 Bobby Fletcher
28 Mike Galle
29 Craig White
30 Ray Calhoun
31 Bill Miller
32 Matt Wilson
33 Goose Gregson

1989 ProCards Greensboro Hornets

(Cincinnati Reds, A) (color)

	MT	NR MT	EX
Complete Set:	7.00	5.25	2.75

403 Checklist
404 Gary Denbo
405 Mark Berry
406 Lavell Cudjo
407 Victor Garcia
408 Igor Baez
409 Danny Perozo
410 Mike Mulvaney
411 Dave McAuliffe
412 Brian Landy
413 Jerry Spradlin
414 Jason Satre
415 Reggie Sanders
416 Eugene Jones
417 Dante Johnson
418 Eddie Rush
419 Jim Wolfer
420 Glenn Sutko
421 Mike Songini
422 Vicente Javier

423 Mo Sanford
424 Mike Malley
425 Mark Krumback
426 Kurt Dempster
427 Phil Dale
428 Mike Anderson
429 Carl Nordstrom
430 Tom Iverson
431 Johnny Almaraz

1989 Best Greenville Braves

(Atlanta Braves, AA) (color) (A limited-edition set was also produced)

	MT	NR MT	EX
Complete Set:	15.00	11.00	6.00

1 Dennis Hood
2 Brian Hunter
3 Darrell Pruitt
4 Mike Bell
5 Rick Morris
6 Edwin Alicea
7 John Alva
8 Juan Pacho
9 Ellis Roby
10 Jim Lemasters
11 Maximo Del Rosario
12 Tim Deitz
13 Danny Weems
14 Mike Stanton
15 Dale Polley
16 Doug Stockam
17 Paul Marak
18 Bill Slack
19 Terry Bell
20 Buddy Bailey
21 Randy Ingle
22 Jim Lovell
23 German Jimenez
24 Jimmy Kremers
25 Dave Plumb
26 Tommy Dunbar
27 Miguel Sabino
28 Steven Avery
29 Checklist

1989 ProCards Greenville Braves

(Atlanta Braves, AA) (color)

	MT	NR MT	EX
Complete Set:	7.00	5.25	2.75

1150 Checklist
1151 Sid Adkins
1152 Greg Tubbs
1153 German Jimenez
1154 John Alva
1155 Juan Pacho
1156 Edwin Alicea
1157 Danny Weems
1158 Brian Hunter
1159 Ellis Roby
1160 Dale Polley
1161 Maximo Delrosario
1162 Terry Bell
1163 Jimmy Kremers
1164 Dale Plumb
1165 Doug Stockam
1166 Mike Stanton
1167 Jim Lovell
1168 Bill Slack
1169 Dennis Hood
1170 Miguel Sabino
1171 Darrell Pruitt
1172 Rick Morris
1173 Mike Bell
1174 Paul Marak
1175 Tim Deitz
1176 Jim Lemasters
1177 Randy Ingle
1178 Buddy Bailey
1179 Tommy Dunbar

1989 Star Co. Greenville Braves

(Atlanta Braves, AA) (color)

	MT	NR MT	EX
Complete Set:	7.00	5.25	2.75

1 Edwin Alicea
2 John Alva
3 Mike Bell
4 Terry Bell
5 Tim Dietz
6 Maximo Del Rosario
7 Tommy Dunbar
8 Dennis Hood
9 Brian Hunter
10 German Jimenez
11 John Kilner
12 Jimmy Kremers
13 Jim Lemasters
14 Paul Marak
15 Rick Morris
16 Juan Pacho
17 Dave Plumb
18 Dale Polley
19 Darrell Pruitt
20 Ellis Roby
21 Miguel Sabino
22 Mike Stanton
23 Doug Stockam
24 Danny Weems
25 Coaching Staff (Buddy Bailey, Bill Slack, Randy Ingle)

1989 Best Hagerstown Suns

(Baltimore Orioles, AA) (color)

	MT	NR MT	EX
Complete Set:	7.00	5.25	2.75

1 Leo Gomez
2 John Githens
3 Jose Mesa
4 Robert Latmore
5 Victor Hithe
6 Maduro Garces
7 Sherwin Cijntje
8 Steve Culkar
9 Dave Bettendorf
10 Jimmie Schaffer
11 Tom Brown
12 Mike Eberle
13 Brian Dubois
14 Craig Faulkner
15 Don Buford
16 Brian Ebel
17 Chuck Stanhope
18 Erik Sonberg
19 Paul Thorpe
20 Randy Strijek
21 Dana Smith
22 Rafel Skeete
23 Dan Simonds
24 Jeff Schwarz
25 Mike Sander
26 John Posey
27 Chris Pinder
28 Ty Nichols
29 Checklist

1989 Best All-Decade Hagerstown Suns

(Baltimore Orioles, AA)

	MT	NR MT	EX
Complete Set:	7.00	5.25	2.75

1 Jeff Ballard
2 Blaine Beatty
3 Eric Bell
4 Dave Bettendorf
5 Dave Corman
6 Paul Croft
7 Brian Dubois
8 Pat Dumouchelle
9 Dave Falcone
10 Steve Finley
11 Ken Gerhart
12 Leo Gomez
13 Ed Hook
14 Bob Konopa
15 Mike Linskey
16 Grady Little
17 Bob Mollinaro
18 Chris Myers
19 Gregg Olson
20 Al Pardo
21 Tim Richardson
22 Bill Ripken
23 Ramon Romero
24 Ron Salcedo
25 Mike Sander
26 Dave Segui
27 Larry Sheets
28 Chuck Stanhope
29 Pete Stanicek
30 John Stefero
31 Scott Stranski
32 Andy Timko
33 Jim Traber
34 Matt Tyner
35 Craig Worthington
36 Logo & checklist card

1989 ProCards Hagerstown Suns

(Baltimore Orioles, AA) (color)

	MT	NR MT	EX
Complete Set:	7.00	5.25	2.75

261 Checklist
262 John Githens
263 Jeff Schwarz
264 Larry Mims
265 Randy Strijek
266 Craig Faulkner
267 Erik Sonberg
268 Chris Pinder
269 Chuck Stanhope
270 Mike Eberle
271 Bob Latmore
272 Victor Hithe
273 Dave Bettendorf
274 Brian Dubois
275 Mike Sander
276 Steve Culkar
277 Don Buford
278 Rafel Skeete
279 Ty Nichols
280 Leo Gomez
281 Robinson Garces
282 Jim Schaffer
283 Tom Brown
284 Brian Ebel
285 Paul Thorpe
286 Dana Smith

1989 Star Co. Hagerstown Suns

(Baltimore Orioles, AA) (color)

	MT	NR MT	EX
Complete Set:	7.00	5.25	2.75

1 Dave Bettendorf
2 Don Buford
3 Sherwin Cijntje
4 Steve Culkar
5 Brian Dubois
6 Mike Eberle
7 Craig Faulkner
8 Robinson Garces
9 John Githens
10 Leo Gomez
11 Victor Hithe
12 Bob Latmore
13 Ty Nichols
14 John Posey
15 Mike Sander
16 Jeff Schwarz
17 Rafel Skeete
18 Dana Smith
19 Randy Strijek
20 Pete Stanicek
21 Paul Thorpe
22 Coaching Staff (Jimmie Schaffer, Tom Brown)

1989 Star Co. Hamilton Redbirds

(St. Louis Cardinals, A) (color) (Price includes the scarce, late-issue card #s 7, 25-29)

	MT	NR MT	EX
Complete Set:	6.00	4.50	2.50

1 Scott Banton
2 Mark Battell
3 Allan Biggers
4 Mark Bowlan
5 David Boss
6 Cliff Brannon
7 Mike Campas
8 John Cebuhar
9 David Cassidy
10 Tripp Cromer
11 Jose Fernandez
12 Randy Berlin
13 Steve Graham
14 Larry Gryskevich
15 Chris Gorton
16 Brian Golden
17 Sean Grubb
18 Don Green
19 Tom Infante
20 Tim Lata
21 Mike Milchin
22 Tim Redman
23 Dan Shannon
24 Jose Trujillo
25 Stan Tukes
26 Mark Wilson
27 Joseph Pettini
28 Joseph Cunningham
29 Mike Evans

1989 ProCards Harrisburg Senators

(Pittsburgh Pirates, AA) (color)

	MT	NR MT	EX
Complete Set:	8.00	6.00	3.25

287 Checklist
288 TIm Conroy
289 Rico Rossy
290 Bill Sampen
291 Ed Yacopino
292 Dave Trembley
293 Junior Vizcaino
294 Julio Peguero
295 Steve Adams
296 Wes Chamberlain
297 Kevin Burdick
298 Tommy Shields
299 Orlando Merced
300 Orlando Lind
301 Chris Lein
302 Harold Williams
303 Robby Russell
304 Jeff Cook
305 Stan Belinda
306 Jeff Banister
307 Julio Perez
308 Pete Murphy
309 Jim Tracy
310 Mike York
311 Ben Webb
312 Tim McKinley

1989 Star Co. Harrisburg Senators

(Pittsburgh Pirates, AA) (color)

	MT	NR MT	EX
Complete Set:	7.00	5.25	2.75

1 Steve Adams
2 Jeff Banister
3 Stan Belinda
4 Kevin Burdick
5 Wes Chamberlain
6 Jeff Cook
7 Orlando Lind
8 Tim McKinley
9 Orlando Merced
10 Pete Murphy
11 Julio Peguero
12 Julio Perez
13 Rico Rossy
14 Rob Russell
15 Bill Sampen
16 Tommy Shields
17 Jim Tracy
18 Junior Vizcaino
19 Ben Webb
20 Ed Yacopino
21 Mike York
22 Dave Trembley
23 Chris Lein

1989 Sport Pro Helena Brewers

(Milwaukee Brewers, A) (color)

	MT	NR MT	EX
Complete Set:	6.00	4.50	2.50

1 Joe Andrzejewski
2 Angel Diaz
3 Reggie Brown
4 Pat Rehwinkel
5 Tim Wilson
6 Rusty Rugg
7 Troy Haugen
8 Tony Diggs
9 Bill Brakeley
10 Greg Landry
11 Troy O'Leary
12 David Volt
13 Joe Roebuck
14 Gustavo Federico
15 Ramser Correa
16 Reed Charpia
17 Bo Dodson
18 Bob Vancho
19 Bob Kappesser
20 Eric Patton
21 David Weldin
22 Sam Drake
23 Kevin Tannahill
24 Scott Muscat
25 Darrin White
26 Ray Burris
27 Dusty Rhodes

1989 Best Huntsville Stars

(Oakland A's, AA) (color)

	MT	NR MT	EX
Complete Set:	7.00	5.25	2.75

1 Scott Hemond
2 William Schock
3 Troy Afenir
4 William Savarino
5 David Veres
6 Jim Kating
7 Dann Howitt
8 Robert Strocker
9 Eric Fox
10 Stephen Maye
11 Robert Sharpnack
12 Scott Brosius
13 Weston Weber

14 Tim Casey
15 David Shotkoski
16 Scott Holcomb
17 Gary Jones
18 Rick Tronerud
19 Dave Schober
20 Jeffrey Newman
21 Pat Gilbert
22 Kevin Ward
23 Patrick Wernig
24 Raymond Young
25 Angel Escobar
26 Jose Mota
27 Joe Klink
28 Ozzie Canseco
29 Checklist

1989 ProCards Idaho Falls Braves

(Atlanta Braves, R) (color)

	MT	NR MT	EX
Complete Set:	6.00	4.50	2.50

2007 Checklist
2008 Field Staff (Mike Boyer, Randy Smith, Cloyd Boyer)
2009 Brian Wright
2010 Ramces Guerrero
2011 Jimmie Pullins
2012 Lionel Adams III
2013 Rickey Rigsby
2014 Ken Harring, Jr.
2015 Jose Olmeda
2016 Fred Lopez
2017 Ricky Gore
2018 Daniel Sims, Jr.
2019 Dave Waldenberger
2020 Billy Miller
2021 Tyler Houston
2022 Chris Burton
2023 Michael Sweeney
2024 Chris Sparrow
2025 Jim Baranoski
2026 Tony Valle
2027 Doug Rogers
2028 Eric Kuhlman
2029 Jeff Zona
2030 Tom Eckhardt
2031 Jim Kortright
2032 Scott Osmon
2033 Don Lemon
2034 Randy White
2035 Mike Parker
2036 Tom Newman
2037 Kevin Haeberle

1989 CMC Indianapolis Indians

(Montreal Expos, AAA) (color)

	MT	NR MT	EX
Complete Set:	7.50	5.25	2.75

1 Tim Barrett
2 Sergio Valdez
3 Steve Frey
4 Pat Pacillo
5 Brett Gideon
6 Scott Anderson
7 Jay Baller
8 Mark Gardner
9 Tim McCormack
10 Rich Thompson
11 Gil Reyes
12 Razor Shines
13 Billy Moore
14 Mike Blowers
15 Marty Pevey
16 Randy Braun
17 Lorenzo Bundy
18 Jeff Huson
19 Armando Moreno
20 Junio Noboa
21 Kevin Dean
22 Darryl Motley
23 Larry Walker
24 Coaches (Dave Van Gorder, Joe Kerrigan, Nelson Norman)
25 Tom Runnells

1989 ProCards Indianapolis Indians

(Montreal Expos, AAA) (color)

	MT	NR MT	EX
Complete Set:	7.50	5.50	3.00

1209 Checklist
1210 Alonzo Powell
1211 Billy Moore
1212 Joel McKeon
1213 Randy Braun
1214 Jeff Dedmon
1215 Sergio Valdez
1216 Howard Kellman, Tom Akins
1217 Marty Pevey
1218 Steve Frey
1219 Razor Shines
1220 Tom Runnells
1221 Mike Blowers
1222 Armando Moreno
1223 Lorenzo Bundy
1224 Mark Gardner
1225 Kevin Dean
1226 Tim McCormack
1227 Coaches (Dave Van Gorder, Joe Kerrigan, Nelson Norman)
1228 Rich Sauveur
1229 Tim Barrett
1230 Brett Gideon
1231 Jay Baller
1232 Urbano Lugo
1233 Jeff Huson
1234 Scott Anderson
1235 Junior Noboa
1236 Pat Picillo
1237 Rich Thompson
1238 Darryl Motley
1239 Larry Walker
1240 Gilberto Reyes

1989 CMC Iowa Cubs

(Chicago Cubs, AAA) (color)

	MT	NR MT	EX
Complete Set:	7.00	5.25	2.75

1 Mike Capel
2 Len Damian
3 Joe Kraemer
4 Ed Vande Berg
5 Mike Harkey
6 Dave Masters
7 Kevin Blankenship
8 Lester Lancaster
9 Rich Scheid
10 Dean Wilkins
11 Butch Garcia
12 Lloyd McClendon
13 Hector Villanueva
14 Bruce Crabbe
15 Luis Cruz
16 Brian Guinn
17 Bryan House
18 Howard Nichols
19 Dave Owen
20 Doug Dascenzo
21 Winston Ficklin
22 Dwight Smith
23 Mike Tullier
24 Jim Wright
25 Pete Mackanin

1989 ProCards Iowa Cubs

(Chicago Cubs, AAA) (color)

	MT	NR MT	EX
Complete Set:	7.50	5.50	3.00

1688 Checklist
1689 Les Lancaster
1690 Dean Wilkins
1691 Roger Williams
1692 Luis Cruz
1693 Butch Garcia
1694 Dave Owen
1695 Lloyd McClendon
1696 Hector Villanueva
1697 Jim Wright
1698 Dave Masters
1699 Kevin Blankenship
1700 Bryan House
1701 Mike Tullier
1702 Doug Dascenzo
1703 Dave Grossman
1704 Mike Harkey
1705 Len Damian
1706 Mike Capel
1707 Pete Mackanin
1708 Dwight Smith
1709 Brian Guinn
1710 Ed Vandeberg
1711 Winston Ficklin
1712 Howard Nichols
1713 Rich Scheid
1714 Bruce Crabbe
1715 Joe Kraemer

1989 Grand Slam Jackson Mets

(New York Mets, AA) (color)

	MT	NR MT	EX
Complete Set:	5.00	3.75	2.00

1 Greg Talamantez
2 Chuck Carr
3 Tim Bogar
4 Craig Repoz
5 Chris Jelic
6 Toby Nivens
7 Todd Welborn
8 Dave Trautwein
9 Gus Meizoso
10 Jeff Bumgarner
11 Julio Machado
12 Juan Villanueva
13 Manny Salinas
14 Angelo Cuevas
15 Zoilo Sanchez
16 Johnny Monell
17 Gilberto Roca
18 Howie Freiling
19 Mike DeButch
20 Steve Swisher
21 Bob Apodaca
22 Kip Gross
23 Pete Bauer
24 Chris Rauth
25 Dave Liddell
26 Kevin Brown
27 Brian Givens
28 Dale Plummer
29 Julio Valera
30 Alan Hayden

1989 Best Jacksonville Expos

(Montreal Expos, AA) (color) (A limited-edition set was also produced)

	MT	NR MT	EX
Complete Set:	12.00	9.00	4.75

1 Marquis Grissom
2 Alan Bannister
3 Mel Houston
4 Chris Marchok
5 Eddie Dixon
6 Doug Duke
7 Mike Dull
8 Pat Sipe
9 Kent Bottenfield
10 Travis Chambers
11 Archie Cianfrocco
12 Howard Farmer
13 Tim Peters
14 Quinn Mack
15 Delino Deshields
16 Boi Rodriguez
17 Rob Natal
18 Fred Williams
19 Rick Carriger
20 Gomer Hodge
21 Danilo Leon
22 Sean Cunningham
23 Peter Bragan
24 Dan Gakeler
25 John Vanderwal
26 Nardi Contreas
27 Gene Glynn
28 Melquiades Rojas
29 Checklist Rojas

1989 ProCards Jacksonville Expos

(Montreal Expos, AA) (color)

	MT	NR MT	EX
Complete Set:	11.00	8.25	4.50

150 Checklist
151 Alan Bannister
152 Delino Deshields
153 Quinn Mack
154 Tim Peters
155 Howard Farmer
156 Mel Rojas
157 Dan Gakeler
158 Sean Cunningham
159 Eddie Dixon
160 Archie Cianfrocco
161 John Vanderwal
162 Travis Chambers
163 Kent Bottenfield
164 Mike Dull
165 Pat Sipe
166 Chris Marchok
167 Doug Duke
168 Rick Carriger
169 Danilo Leon
170 Mel Houston
171 Phil Wilson
172 Fred Williams
173 Nardi Contreras
174 Gene Glynn
175 Marquis Grissom
176 Rob Natal
177 Boi Rodriguez
178 Team Photo

1989 ProCards Jamestown Expos

(Montreal Expos, A) (color)

	MT	NR MT	EX
Complete Set:	6.00	4.50	2.50

2129 Checklist
2130 Dale Buzzard
2131 Buena Rodriquez
2132 F.P. Santangelo
2133 Robert Small
2134 Tyrone Woods
2135 Paul Ciaglo
2136 Pete Young
2137 Tim Laker
2138 Gary Pipik
2139 Troy Wessel
2140 Steve Whitehead
2141 Matt Stairs
2142 Dan Archibald
2143 Pat Heiderscheit
2144 David Sommer
2145 Scott Davison
2146 Todd Mayo
2147 Isaac Elder
2148 Ken Lake
2149 Gary Engelken
2150 Don Werner
2151 Steve Mandl
2152 Q.V. Lowe
2153 Alejandro Tejada
2154 Gary Regira
2155 Joe Klancnik
2156 Rusty Kilgo
2157 John Thoden
2158 Joe Logan, Jr.

1989 Star Co. Johnson City Cardinals

(St. Louis Cardinals, R) (color)

	MT	NR MT	EX
Complete Set:	7.00	5.25	2.75

1 Jim Allen
2 Juan Andujar
3 Alan Botkin
4 Johnny Calzado
5 Frank Cimorelli
6 Paul Coleman
7 Ernie Baker
8 Steve Dixon
9 Chuck Edwards
10 Bryan Eversgerd
11 Willie Espinal
12 Bill Felitz
13 Jeff Fayne
14 Scott Halama
15 Mike Kraft
16 Tony Ochs
17 Al Pacheco
18 Ahmed Rodriguez
19 Odails Savinon
20 Richard Shackle
21 John Stevens
22 Ron Weber
23 Denny Wiseman
24 Coaching Staff (Mark DeJohn, Dick Sisler)
25 Alfredo Ortiz
26 Robert Harrison

1989 ProCards Kenosha Twins

(Minnesota Twins, A) (color)

	MT	NR MT	EX
Complete Set:	7.00	5.25	2.75

1057 Checklist
1058 Bob Lee
1059 Mike Mathiot
1060 Steve Morris
1061 Mark North
1062 Brad Fontes
1063 Jay Kvasnicka
1064 Deryk Gross
1065 Carl Johnson
1066 Dom Rovasio
1067 Pat Mahomes
1068 Terry Brown
1069 Bryan Roskom
1070 Don Leppert
1071 Mike Misuraca
1072 J.P. Wright
1073 Steve Dunn
1074 J.T. Bruett
1075 Gary Resetar
1076 Rich Garces
1077 Rusty Kryzanowski
1078 Chad Swanson
1079 Steve Muh
1080 Brian Allard
1081 Mike Pomeranz
1082 Rolando Pino
1083 Cheo Garcia
1084 Steve Liddle
1085 Dan Fox

1989 Star Co. Kenosha Twins

(Minnesota Twins, A) (color) (Price includes the late-issue, Fox and Allred cards)

	MT	NR MT	EX
Complete Set:	6.00	4.50	2.50

1 Tom Boyce
2 Terry Brown
3 J.T. Bruett
4 Steve Dunn
5 Brad Fontes
6 Rich Garces
7 Cheo Garcia
8 Deryk Gross
9 Carl Johnson
10 Rusty Kryzanowski
11 Jay Kvasnicka
12 Pat Mahomes
13 Mike Mathiot
14 Todd McClure
15 Mike Misuraca
16 Steve Morris
17 Steve Muh
18 Mark North
19 Rolando Pino
20 Mike Pomeranz
21 Gary Resetar
22 Bryan Roskom
23 Dom Rovasio
24 J.P. Wright
25 Steve Liddle
26 Dan Fox
27 Brian Allard

1989 Star Co. Kingsport Mets

(New York Mets, R) (color) (Price includes the scarce, late-issue card #s 26-30)

	MT	NR MT	EX
Complete Set:	7.00	5.25	2.75

1 Dan Auchard
2 Tim Buhe
3 Chris Butle
4 Hector Carrasco
5 Albert Castillo
6 Nick Davis
7 Alberto Diaz
8 Tom Engle
9 Andy Fidler
10 Brook Fordyce
11 Rob Guzik
12 James Harris
13 Reid Hartmann
14 Craig Johnston
15 Mike Lehnerz
16 Tim McClinton
17 Wallace Minnifield
18 Rich Ostopowicz
19 Nicolas Polanco
20 Deron Sample
21 Craig Scott
22 Jim Sheffler
23 Eric Thornton
24 Ed Vazquez
25 Kyle Washington
26 Jim Eschen
27 Dan Norman
28 Mike Murray
29 Bat Boys (Tyler Hobbs, Josh Brickey, Ben Smith, Travis Nelson)
30 Dottie Elsea

1989 Star Co. Kinston Indians

(Cleveland Indians, A) (color) (Price includes the late-issue, Brown and George cards)

	MT	NR MT	EX
Complete Set:	7.00	5.25	2.75

1 Jamie Allison
2 Ramon Bautista
3 Barry Blackwell
4 Jim Bruske
5 Andy Casano
6 Daren Epley
7 Richard Falkner
8 Greg Ferlenda
9 Sam Ferretti
10 Brian Johnson
11 Tommy Kramer
12 Mark Lewis
13 Jeff Mutis
14 Charles Nagy
15 Rouglas Odor
16 David Oliveras
17 Angel Ortiz
18 Doug Piatt
19 Mark Pike
20 Jim Richardson
21 Greg Roscoe
22 Tony Scaglione
23 Rudy Seanez
24 Ken Whitfield
25 Ken Bolek
26 Mike Brown
27 Will George

1989 Best Knoxville Blue Jays

(Toronto Blue Jays, AA) Error cards #22 & #23 were corrected.

	MT	NR MT	EX
Complete Set:	9.00	6.75	3.50
Complete Set:			

1 Derek Bell
2 Kevin Batiste
3 Darren Balsley
4 Carlos Diaz
5 Jose Diaz
6 Webster Garrison
7 Tom Gilles
8 Mauro Gozzo
9 Xavier Hernandez
10 Shawn Jeter
11 Chris Jones
12 Dennis Jones
13 Rob MacDonald
14 Omar Malave
15 Domingo Martinez
16 Mike Mills
17 Brian Morrison
18 Pedro Munoz
19 Joe Newcomb
20 Tom Quinlan
21 Ken Rivers
22 Jimmy Rogers (Schunk pictured on card's back.)
23 Jerry Schunk (Rogers pictured on card's back.)
24 John Shea
25 J.J. Cannon
26 Mark Whiten
27 Bob Wisheuski
28 Barry Foote
29 John Poloni
30 Tim Ringler
31 Logo & checklist card

1989 ProCards Knoxville Blue Jays

(Toronto Blue Jays, AA) (color)

	MT	NR MT	EX
Complete Set:	8.00	6.00	3.25

1119 Checklist
1120 Bill Dyke
1121 Gary McCune
1122 Tim Ringler
1123 Tom Quinlan
1124 Kevin Batiste
1125 Carlos Diaz
1126 Pedro Munoz
1127 Omar Malave
1128 Barry Foote
1129 J.J. Cannon
1130 Shawn Jeter
1131 Webster Garrison
1132 Ken Rivers
1133 Jimmy Rogers
1134 Chris Jones
1135 Joe Newcomb
1136 Dennis Jones
1137 Darren Balsley
1138 Bob Wishnevski
1139 Rob MacDonald
1140 John Shea
1141 Mike Mills
1142 Jerry Schunk
1143 Tom Gilles
1144 Xavier Hernandez
1145 Goose Gozzo
1146 Brian Morrison
1147 John Paul Poloni
1148 Domingo Martinez
1149 Derek Bell

1989 Star Co. Knoxville Blue Jays

(Toronto Blue Jays, AA)

	MT	NR MT	EX
Complete Set:	8.00	6.00	3.25

1 Derek Bell
2 Carlos Diaz
3 Jose Diaz
4 Webster Garrison
5 Darren Balsley
6 Goose Gozzo
7 Kevin Batiste
8 Shawn Jeter
9 Chris Jones
10 Dennis Jones
11 Rob MacDonald
12 Domingo Martinez
13 Omar Malave
14 Pedro Munoz
15 Joe Dean Newcomb
16 Tom Quinlan
17 Ken Rivers
18 Jimmy Rogers
19 Jerry Schunk
20 John Shea
21 Mark Whiten
22 Bob Wishnevski
23 Mike Mills
24 J.J. Cannon
25 John Poloni

1989 Star Co. Lakeland Tigers

(Detroit Tigers, A) (color) (Price includes late-issue card #s 26-28)

	MT	NR MT	EX
Complete Set:	6.00	4.50	2.50

1 Marcos Adler
2 Jim Baxter
3 Rico Brogna
4 Basilio Cabrera
5 Ron Cook
6 Luis Gilindo
7 Dave Haas
8 Shawn Hare
9 Bill Henderson
10 Riccardo Ingram
11 Mike Jones
12 John Kiely
13 Kurt Knudsen
14 Mike Lumley
15 Ron Marigny
16 Dan O'Neill
17 Dan Raley
18 Dave Richards
19 Tookie Spann
20 Chuck Steward
21 Eric Stone
22 Steve Strong
23 Andy Toney
24 Mike Wilkins
25 Marty Willis
26 John Lipon
27 Kenn Cunningham
28 Ralph Treuel

1989 CMC Las Vegas Stars

(San Diego Padres, AAA) (color)

	MT	NR MT	EX
Complete Set:	9.00	6.75	3.50

1 Joe Bitker
2 Keith Comstock
3 Joe Lynch
4 Terry Gilmore
5 Tony Ghelfi
6 Matt Maysey
7 Dan Murphy
8 Eric Nolte
9 Pete Roberts
10 Bill Taylor
11 Sandy Alomar
12 Randy Byers
13 Jerald Clark
14 Joey Cora
15 Thomas Howard
16 Rob Nelson
17 Jeff Hearron
18 Carlos Baerga
19 Bill Wrona
20 Jeff Yurtin
21 Paul Runge
22 Shawn Abner
23 Chris Knabenshue
24 Steve Smith
25 Coaches (Tony Torchia, Steve Luebber)

1989 ProCards Las Vegas Stars

(San Diego Padres, AAA) (color)

	MT	NR MT	EX
Complete Set:	9.00	6.75	3.50

1 Tony Ghelfi
2 Dan Murphy
3 Billy Taylor
4 Joe Bitker
5 Matt Maysey
6 Randy Byers
7 Sandy Alomar
8 Thomas Howard
9 Carlos Baerga
10 Jerald Clark
11 Jeff Hearron
12 Eric Nolte
13 Pete Roberts
14 Keith Comstock
15 Pat Clements
16 Terry Gilmore
17 Roger Smithberg
18 Billy Wrona
19 Chris Knabenshue
20 Jeff Yurtin
21 Shawn Abner
22 Joe Lynch
23 Joey Cora
24 Rob Nelson
25 Steve Smith
26 Steve Luebber
27 Tony Torchia
28 Todd Hutcheson
29 Checklist

1989 ProCards London Tigers

(Detroit Tigers, AA) (color)

	MT	NR MT	EX
Complete Set:	10.00	7.50	4.00

1356 Checklist
1357 Steve Howe
1358 Bob Gilson
1359 Bob Eaman
1360 Bill Wilkinson
1361 Dan Ross
1362 Dave Cooper
1363 Donnie Rowland
1364 Bernie Anderson
1365 John Toale
1366 Travis Fryman
1367 Mike DeLao
1368 Scott Aldred
1369 Ron Rightnowar
1370 Darren Hursey
1371 Arnie Beyeler
1372 Dean Decillis
1373 Tim Leiper
1374 Don Vesling
1375 Mike Schwabe
1376 Mike Hansen
1377 Randy Nosek
1378 Chris Chambliss
1379 Rob Thomson
1380 Greg Everson
1381 Scott Livingstone
1382 Wayne Housie
1383 Phil Clark
1384 Doyle Balthazar
1385 Manny Jose
1386 Tom Aldrich
1387 Jose Ramos

1989 ProCards Louisville Redbirds

(St. Louis Cardinals, AAA) (color)

	MT	NR MT	EX
Complete Set:	8.50	6.25	3.50

1241 Checklist
1242 Roger Erickson
1243 Jim Puzey
1244 Bryan Oelkers
1245 Randy Byers
1246 Jeff Fassero
1247 Steve Peters
1248 Scott Arnold
1249 Ted Power
1250 Bob Tewksbury
1251 Howard Hilton
1252 Gibson Alba
1253 David "Hap" Hudson
1254 Mark Riggins
1255 Matt Kinzer
1256 Mike Jorgensen
1257 Romy Cucjen
1258 Greg Jelks
1259 Mike Fitzgerald
1260 Leon Durham
1261 Ron Shepherd
1262 Bien Figueroa
1263 Luis Alicea
1264 Rod Booker
1265 Tom Baine
1266 Alex Cole
1267 Todd Zeile
1268 Ken Hill

1989 Team Louisville Redbirds

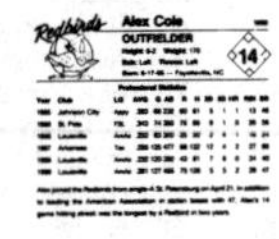

(St. Louis Cardinals, AAA) (color)

	MT	NR MT	EX
Complete Set:	10.00	7.50	4.00

1 Billy Bird (mascot)
2 Todd Zeile
3 Todd Zeile
4 Todd Zeile
5 Todd Zeile
6 Mike Jorgensen
7 Gibson Alba
8 Luis Alicea
9 Scott Arnold
10 Tom Baine
11 Rod Booker
12 Randell Byers
13 Cris Carpenter
14 Alex Cole
15 Romy Cucjen
16 Leon Durham
17 Roger Erickson
18 Jeff Fassero
19 Bien Figueroa
20 Mike Fitzgerald
21 Don Heinkel
22 Ken Hill
23 Howard Hilton
24 Greg Jelks
25 Matt Kinzer
26 Jim Lindeman
27 Willie McGee
28 Chuck McGrath
29 Bryan Oelkers
30 Steve Peters
31 Frank Potestio
32 Ted Power
33 Jim Puzey
34 Ron Shepherd
35 Bob Tewksbury
36 Craig Wilson
37 Todd Worrell
38 Hap Hudson

1989 Team Louisville Cardinals

(St. Louis Cardinals) (color) (glossy red backs)

	MT	NR MT	EX
Complete Set:	50.00	37.50	20.00

1 Billy Bird (mascot)
2 Todd Zeile
3 Todd Zeile
4 Todd Zeile
5 Todd Zeile
6 Mike Jorgensen
7 Gibson Alba
8 Luis Alicea
9 Scott Arnold
10 Tom Baine
11 Rod Booker
12 Randall Byers
13 Cris Carpenter
14 Alex Cole
15 Romy Cucjen
16 Leon Durham
17 Roger Erickson
18 Jeff Fassero
19 Bien Figueroa
20 Mike Fitzgerald
21 Don Heinkel
22 Ken Hill
23 Howard Hilton
24 Greg Jelks
25 Matt Kinzer
26 Jim Lindeman
27 Willie McGee
28 Chuck McGrath
29 Bryan Oelkers
30 Steve Peters
31 Frank Potestio
32 Ted Power
33 Jim Puzey
34 Ron Shepherd
35 Bob Tewksbury
36 Craig Wilson
37 Todd Worrell
38 "Hap" Hudson

1989 Star Co. Lynchburg Red Sox

(Boston Red Sox, A) (color) (Price includes late-issue card #s 26-30)

	MT	NR MT	EX
Complete Set:	8.00	6.00	3.25

1 Mike Baker
2 Jose Birriel
3 Tim Buheller
4 Dale Burgo
5 Fred Davis
6 Paul Devlin
7 John Dolan
8 Tom Fischer
9 Dave Gray
10 Bart Haley
11 Mike Kelly
12 Derek Livernois
13 Gil Martinez
14 Juan Molero
15 Tim Naehring
16 David Owen
17 Juan Paris
18 Phil Plantier
19 Scott Powers
20 Leslie Wallin
21 Stu Weidie
22 Craig Wilson
23 Gary Allenson
24 Jim Bibby
25 Scott Skripko
26 Roger Hagger
27 Zack Dzafic
28 Ronnie Richardson
29 Rodney Taylor

1989 Star Co. Madison Muskies

(Oakland A's, A) (color)

	MT	NR MT	EX
Complete Set:	6.00	4.50	2.50

1 Mark Aguilar
2 Tony Ariola
3 Rich Berg
4 Dean Borelli
5 James Buccheri
6 Tom Carcione
7 Mike Messerly
8 Jim Foley
9 Lorenzo Furcal
10 Apolinar Garcia
11 Dwayne Hosey
12 Jim Lawson
13 Will Love
14 Angel Martinez
15 Frank Masters
16 Luis Mateo
17 Jim Nettles
18 Bronswell Patrick
19 Ed Ricks
20 Billy Taylor
21 Lee Tinsley
22 Tim Vannaman

1989 Star Co. Martinsville Phillies

(Philadelphia Phillies, R) (color)

	MT	NR MT	EX
Complete Set:	6.00	4.50	2.50

1 Al Baur
2 Kenneth Bean
3 Luis Brito
4 Williams Carmona
5 Paul Carson
6 Cancio Casado
7 Jim Cosman
8 Ismael Cruz
9 Matt Current
10 Mike Dafforn
11 Lamar Foster
12 Darrell Goedhart
13 Elliot Gray
14 Tom Hardgrove
15 Charles Hurst
16 Jeff Jackson
17 Aurelio Llanos
18 Stewart Lovdal
19 Chris Lowe
20 Facanel Medina
21 Rick Meyer
22 Sixto Montero
23 Jeff Patterson
24 Eulogio Perez
25 Jimmy Phillips
26 Mark Randall
27 David Ross
28 Chuck Shive
29 Calvin Talford
30 Cory Thomas
31 Gil Valencia
32 Julio Vargas
33 Dan Welch
34 Scott Wiegandt
35 Coaching Staff (Roly DeArmas, Al LeBoeuf, John Martin)

1989 Best Medford A's

(Oakland A's, A) (color)

	MT	NR MT	EX
Complete Set:	6.00	4.50	2.50

1 Michael Conte
2 Scott Schockey
3 Frank Harris
4 James Gibbs
5 Scott Erwin
6 Mike Grimes
7 Brad Eagar
8 Scott Lydy
9 Fred Cooley
10 Dionini Guzman
11 Pedro Pena
12 Dave Latter
13 Darin Kracl
14 Nick Venuto
15 Ken Ritter
16 Trent Weaver
17 Lorenzo Furcal
18 Grady Fuson
19 Steve Lemuth
20 Steve Chitren
21 Russ Cormier
22 Craig Paquette
23 Tim Annee
24 Marco Armas
25 Jimmy Waggoner
26 Enoch Simmons
27 Kurt Abbott
28 Dana Allison
29 Galvin Osteen
30 Todd Smith
31 Checklist

1989 Best Memphis Chicks

(Kansas City Royals, AA) (color)

	MT	NR MT	EX
Complete Set:	9.00	6.75	3.50

1 Bob Hamelin
2 John Duffy
3 Jacob Brunfield
4 Mark Lee
5 Aguedo Vasquez
6 Julio Alcala
7 Tony Bridges-Clement
8 Kenny Bowen
9 Stewart Cole
10 Carlos Escalera
11 Deric Ladnier
12 Chito Martinez
13 Brian McRae
14 Angel Morris
15 Harvey Pulliam
16 Kyle Reese
17 Jim Campbell
18 Dora Clark
19 Victor Cole
20 Luis Encarnacion
21 Mike Magnante
22 Mike Tresemer
23 Steve Walker
24 Jeff Cox
25 Joe Breeden
26 Guy Hansen
27 Mike Leon
28 Checklist

1989 ProCards Memphis Chicks

(Kansas City Royals, AA) (color)

	MT	NR MT	EX
Complete Set:	8.00	6.00	3.25

1180 Checklist
1181 John Duffy
1182 Carlos Escalera
1183 Julio Alcala
1184 Stu Cole
1185 Victor Cole
1186 Aguedo Vasquez
1187 Luis Encarnacion
1188 Jacob Brumfield
1189 Deric Ladnier
1190 Mark Lee
1191 Mike Leon
1192 Guy Hansen
1193 Joe Breeden
1194 Jim Campbell
1195 Jeff Cox
1196 Steve Walker
1197 Mike Tresemer
1198 Mike Magnante
1199 Dera Clark
1200 Chito Martinez
1201 Rob Hamelin
1202 Tony Bridges-Clements
1203 Angel Morris
1204 Harvey Pulliam
1205 Brian McRae
1206 Kyle Reese
1207 Ken Bowen

1989 Star Co. Memphis Chicks

(Kansas City Royals, AA) (color)

	MT	NR MT	EX
Complete Set:	9.00	6.75	3.50

1 Julio Alcala
2 Kenny Bowen
3 Tony Bridges-Clements
4 Jacob Brumfield
5 Jim Campbell
6 Dera Clark
7 Stu Cole
8 Victor Cole
9 John Duffy
10 Luis Encarnacion
11 Carlos Escalera
12 Bob Hamelin
13 Deric Ladnier
14 Mark Lee
15 Mike Magnante
16 Chito Martinez
17 Brian McRae
18 Angel Morris
19 Harvey Pulliam
20 Kyle Reese
21 Mike Tresemer
22 Aguedo Vasquez
23 Steve Walker
24 Coaching Staff (Jeff Cox, Guy Hansen, Joe Breeden)

1989 Star Co. Miami Miracle

(No affiliation, A)

	MT	NR MT	EX
Complete Set:	6.00	4.50	2.50

1 Rick Bernardo
2 Tommy Boyce
3 Not issued
4 Fernando Figueroa
5 Longo Garcia
6 Jim Gattis
7 Lindsey Johnson
8 Randy Kotchman
9 Mark Kramer
10 Adam Lamle
11 Shane Letterio
12 Tony Mack
13 Tony Metoyer
14 Ronald Mullins
15 Michael Maksudian
16 Kevin Ponder
17 Chris Sloniger
18 Doug Torborg
19 Al Torres
20 Luis Verdugo
21 Front Office
22 Miracle team photo
---- Marty Cerny

1989 Grand Slam Midland Angels

(California Angels, A) (color)

	MT	NR MT	EX
Complete Set:	7.50	5.50	3.00

1 Max Oliveras
2 Nate Oliver
3 Gary Ruby
4 Tom Alfredson
5 Jeff Barns
6 Gary Buckels
7 Tim Burcham
8 Mike Butcher
9 Vinicio Cedeno
10 Scott Cerny
11 Chris Cron
12 Frank DiMichele
13 Gary DiSarcina
14 Mark Doran
15 Otto Gonzalez
16 Everett Graham
17 Danny Grunhard
18 Roberto Hernandez
19 Mark Howie
20 Mike Knapp
21 Scott Lewis
22 David Martinez
23 Luis Merejo
24 Rich Morehouse
25 John Orton
26 Reed Peters

27 Bobby Rose
28 Kevin Trudeau
29 Hediberto Vargas
30 Shane Young

1989 Chong Modesto A's

(Oakland A's, A) (black and white)

	MT	NR MT	EX
Complete Set:	8.00	6.00	3.25

1 Ted Kubiak
2 Pete Richert
3 Dave Hollenback
4 Dan Kiser
5 Mike Cobleigh
6 Steve Gokey
7 Rob Alexander
8 Pedro Baez
9 Steve Dye
10 Dan Eskew
11 Daryl Green
12 Gary Gorski
13 Kirk McDonald
14 William Perez
15 Joe Slusarski
16 Steve Towey
17 Brian Veilleux
18 Weston Weber
19 Tom Carcione
20 Henry Mercedes
21 Bill Savarino
22 Joel Chimelis
23 Rod Correia
24 Francisco Matos
25 Stan Royer
26 Daryl Vice
27 Ron Witmeyer
28 David Gavin
29 Joe Hillman
30 Darren Lewis
31 Bob Parry
32 Keith Thomas
33 Ricky Henderson
34 Jose Canseco
35 Mark McGwire
36 Checklist

1989 Cal League Modesto A's

(Oakland A's) (color)

	MT	NR MT	EX
Complete Set:	7.00	5.25	2.75

266 Joe Slusarki
267 Pedro Baez
268 Brian Veilleux
269 Steve Dye
270 Rob Alexander
271 Darren Green
272 Jeff Kopyta
273 Kevin MacLeod
274 Kirk McDonald
275 Joe Hillman
276 Stan Royer
277 Rod Correia
278 Darren Lewis
279 Joel Chimelis
280 Joe Kemp
281 Ron Witmeyer
282 Jorge Brito
283 Francisco Matos
284 Charlie McGrew
285 Marteese Robinson
286 Bob Parry
287 Pete Richert
288 Lenn Sakata
289 Steve Gokey
290 David Hollenback

1989 ProCards Myrtle Beach Blue Jays

(Toronto Blue Jays, A) (color)

	MT	NR MT	EX
Complete Set:	7.00	5.25	2.75

1450 Checklist
1451 Leroy Stanton
1452 Mark Young
1453 Eddie Mendez
1454 Greg David
1455 Todd Provence
1456 Domingo Cedeno
1457 Tim Hodge
1458 Juan DeLaRosa
1459 Jose Monzon
1460 Eric Brooks
1461 Mike Seal
1462 Mike Taylor
1463 Mike Ogliaruso
1464 Tim Brown
1465 Mike Fischlin
1466 Bill Monbouquette
1467 Rafael Martinez
1468 Greg Harding
1469 Ray Giannelli
1470 Curtis Johson
1471 Dan Dodd
1472 Jose Olivares
1473 Jesse Cross
1474 Terry Wilson
1475 David Weathers
1476 Mike Brady
1628 Rich Depastino
1629 Rick Vaughan
1630 Anthony Ward

1989 CMC Nashville Sounds

(Cincinnati Reds, AA) (color)

	MT	NR MT	EX
Complete Set:	6.00	4.50	2.50

1 Charlie Mitchell
2 Keith Brown
3 Jeff Gray
4 Mike Griffin
5 Hugh Kemp
6 Rob Lopez
7 Mike Roesler
8 Scott Scudder
9 John Young
10 Luis Vasquez
11 Doug Gwosdz
12 Joe Oliver
13 Skeeter Barnes
14 Marty Brown
15 Mark Germann
16 Keith Lockhart
17 Luis Quinones
18 Jeff Richardson
19 Eddie Tanner
20 Chris Jones
21 Scotti Madison
22 Rolando Roomes
23 Van Snider
24 Ray Rippelmeyer
25 Frank Lucchesi

1989 ProCards Nashville Sounds

(Cincinnati Reds, AA) (color)

	MT	NR MT	EX
Complete Set:	7.00	5.25	2.75

1269 Checklist
1270 Jeff Sellers
1271 Scotti Madison
1272 Luis Quinones
1273 Charlie Mitchell
1274 Mike Griffin
1275 Mark Germann
1276 John Young
1277 Doug Gwosdz
1278 Keith Lockhart
1279 Chris Hammond
1280 Ray Rippelmeyer
1281 Van Snider
1282 Mike Roesler
1283 Joe Oliver
1284 Frank Lucchesi
1285 Luis Vasquez
1286 Rolando Roomes
1287 Eddie Tanner
1288 Jeff Gray
1289 Skeeter Barnes
1290 Chris Jones
1291 Jeff Richardson
1292 Marty Brown
1293 Scott Scudder
1294 Hugh Kemp
1295 Rob Lopez
1296 Keith Brown

1989 Team Nashville Sounds

(New York Yankees, AA)

	MT	NR MT	EX
Complete Set:	12.00	9.00	4.75

1 Skeeter Barnes
2 Freddie Benavides
3 Keith Brown
4 Marty Brown
5 George Dyce
6 Jeff Gray
7 Mike Griffin
8 Doug Gwosdz
9 Chris Hammond
10 Alan Hayden
11 Hugh Kemp
12 Tito Landrum
13 Keith Lockhart
14 Rob Lopez
15 Frank Lucchesi
16 Scotti Madison
17 Terry McGriff
18 Charlie Mitchell
19 Joe Oliver
20 Kevin Pearson
21 Jeff Reynolds
22 Jeff Richardson
23 (Ray Rippelmeyer & John Young)
24 Mike Roesler
25 Larry Schmittou
26 Scott Scudder
27 Van Snider
28 Eddie Tanner
29 Luis Vasquez
30 (Bob Walters & Bob Jamison)

1989 ProCards New Britain Red Sox

(Boston Red Sox, AA) (color)

	MT	NR MT	EX
Complete Set:	9.00	6.75	3.50

598 Checklist
599 Ed Zambrano
600 Bob Zupcic
601 Pete Youngman
602 Rich Gale
603 Chris Moritz
604 Dan Gabriele
605 Mike Carista
606 Josias Manzanillo
607 Mike Dalton
608 Steve Bast
609 Scott Cooper
610 Jim Orsag
611 Daryl Irvine
612 Zach Crouch
613 Larry Shikles
614 Dave Walters
615 Leverne Jackson
616 Joe Marchese
617 Butch Hobson
618 Randy Randle
619 Mickey Pina
620 Livio Padilla
621 Dave Milstien
622 Jeff Plympton
623 Scott Sommers
624 Todd Pratt

1989 Star Co. New Britain Red Sox

(Boston Red Sox, AA) (color)

	MT	NR MT	EX
Complete Set:	9.00	6.75	3.50

1 Ed Estrada
2 Leverne Jackson
3 Scott Cooper
4 Zach Crouch
5 Titi Srewart
6 Don Gabriele
7 Daryl Irvine
8 Josias Manzanillo
9 Joe Marchese
10 David Milstien
11 Chris Moritz
12 Jim Orsag
13 Lavid Padilla
14 Mickey Pina
15 Todd Pratt
16 Jeff Plympton
17 Randy Randle
18 Larry Shikles
19 Scott Sommers
20 David Walters
21 Ed Zambrano
22 Robert Zupcic
23 Butch Hobson
24 Rich Gale
25 Pete Youngman

1989 Pucko Niagara Falls Rapids

(Detroit Tigers, A) (color)

	MT	NR MT	EX
Complete Set:	6.00	4.50	2.50

1 Don Pedersen
2 Eric Albright
3 Marcos Betances
4 Brian Cornelius
5A Luis Ivan Cruz
5B Dave Keating
6 John DeSilva
7 John Doherty
8 Mark Ettles
9 Jeff Goodale
10 Jim Heins
11 Tim Herrmann
12 Jody Hurst
13 Kieth Kimberlin
14 Keith Langston
15 Matt Logue
16 Doug Marcero
17 Craig Middlekauff
18 Mario Moccia
19 Gustavo Pinto
20 Bob Reimink
21 Rick Sellers
22 Freddy Torres
23 Craig Wiley
24 David Wilson
25 Rick Magnante
26 Juan Lopez
27 Ron Ross
28 Tom Prohaska
29 Sal Maglie Stadium

1989 CMC Oklahoma City 89'ers

(Texas Rangers, AAA) (color)

	MT	NR MT	EX
Complete Set:	6.50	4.75	2.50

1 Darrel Akerfelds
2 John Barfield
3 Bill Scherrer
4 Mike Jeffcoat
5 Scott May
6 Gary Mielke
7 Dave Miller
8 Dave Pavlas
9 Paul Wilmet
10 Darrell Whitaker
11 Mike Berger
12 John Gibbons
13 Jack Daugherty
14 Andre Robertson
15 Dan Rohn
16 Ron Roenicke
17 Jim St. Laurent
18 Rey Sanchez
19 Kevin Reimer
20 Darren Loy
21 Scott Coolbaugh
22 Tack Wilson
23 Jim Skaalen
24 Stan Hough
25 Ferguson Jenkins

1989 ProCards Oklahoma City 89'ers

(Texas Rangers, AAA) (color)

	MT	NR MT	EX
Complete Set:	8.00	6.00	3.25

1506 Checklist
1507 (Abner 89er)
1508 Jim Skaalen
1509 Paul Wilmet
1510 Jeff Stone
1511 Rey Sanchez
1512 Scott Coolbaugh
1513 Ferguson Jenkins
1514 Andre Robertson
1515 Mike Berger
1516 Darrel Whitaker
1517 Drew Hall
1518 John Barfield
1519 Ron Roanicke
1520 Mike Jeffcoat
1521 Stan Hough
1522 Dave Miller
1523 Scott May
1524 Jim St. Laurent
1525 Jack Daugherty
1526 Darren Loy
1527 Kevin Reimer
1528 Gary Mielke
1529 Dave Pavlas
1530 Dan Rohn
1531 John Gibbons
1532 Darrel Akerfelds
1533 Ray Ramirez
1534 Tack Wilson

1989 CMC Omaha Royals

(Kansas City Royals, AAA) (color)

	MT	NR MT	EX
Complete Set:	7.00	5.25	2.75

1 Bob Buchanan
2 Stan Clarke
3 Steve Fireovid
4 Kevin Appier
5 Matt Crouch
6 Jose DeJesus
7 Rick Luecken
8 Ed Olwine
9 Ken Spratke
10 Kevin Burrell
11 Tom Dodd
12 Ed Hearn
13 Nick Castaneda
14 Jose Castro
15 Bill Pecota
16 Mike Mesh

17 Mike Jirschele
18 Terry Shumpert
19 Nick Capra
20 Mike Loggins
21 Matt Winters
22 Jeff Schulz
23 Sal Rende
24 Steve Morrow
25 Coaching Staff (Tom Poquette, Rich Dubee)

1989 ProCards Omaha Royals

(Kansas City Royals, AAA) (color)

	MT	NR MT	EX
Complete Set:	6.00	4.50	2.50

1716 Checklist
1717 Matt Crouch
1718 Steve Fireovid
1719 Ken Spratke
1720 Kevin Appier
1721 Terry Shumpert
1722 Nick Casteneoa
1723 Steve Morrow
1724 Bob Buchanan
1725 Ed Olwine
1726 Tim Pyznarski
1727 Tom Dodd
1728 Matt Winters
1729 Luis Delossantos
1730 Mike Mesh
1731 Jose Castro
1732 Ed Hearn
1733 Kevin Burrell
1734 Rick Luecken
1735 Jose DeJesus
1736 Jeff Schulz
1737 Stan Clarke
1738 Mike Loggins
1739 Rich Dubee
1740 Sal Rende
1741 Tom Poquette
1742 Nick Capra

1989 ProCards Oneonta Yankees

(New York Yankees, A) (color)

	MT	NR MT	EX
Complete Set:	8.00	6.00	3.25

2097 Checklist
2098 Brian Butterfield
2099 John Barrilleaux
2100 Enrique Hernandez
2101 Jeff Taylor
2102 Sherman Obando
2103 Mike Gardella
2104 Art Canestro
2105 James Moody
2106 Larry Stanford
2107 Scott Chase
2108 Kelly Sharitt
2109 Russ Davis
2110 Brad Ausmus
2111 Lew Hill
2112 J.T. Snow
2113 David Howell
2114 Ken Juarbe
2115 Aaron Van Scoyoc
2116 Ricky Strickland
2117 Richard Barnwell
2118 Mark Hutton
2119 Dave Kent
2120 Rich Arena
2121 Frank Seminara
2122 Todd Malone
2123 Ricky Rhodes
2124 Orlando Miller
2125 Joe Ross
2126 Jose Vazquez
2127 Paul Oster
2128 John Brubaker

1989 Best Orlando Twins

(Minnesota Twins, AA) (color)

	MT	NR MT	EX
Complete Set:	7.50	5.50	3.00

1 Paul Sorrento
2 Jimmy Williams
3 Mark Funderburk
4 Dwight Bernard
5 Ron Gardenhire
6 Jim Kahmann
7 Paul Abbott
8 Tim Arnold
9 Pat Bangston
10 Ben Bianchi
11 Larry Blackwell
12 Jeff Bronkey
13 Pete Delkus
14 Mark Guthrie
15 Terry Jorgensen
16 Scott Leius
17 Ken Morgan
18 Edger Naveda
19 Derek Parks
20 Park Pittman
21 Mike Randle
22 Mike Redding
23 A.J. Richardson
24 Jeff Satzinger
25 Doug Snyder
26 Marty Lanoux
27 Wayne Hattaway
28 Shereen Samonds
29 Jamie Lowe
30 Greg Brinkman
31 Checklist

1989 ProCards Orlando Twins

(Minnesota Twins, AA) (color)

	MT	NR MT	EX
Complete Set:	6.00	4.50	2.50

1326 Checklist
1327 Doug Snyder
1328 Marty Lanoux
1329 Ben Bianchi
1330 Jeff Gatzinger
1331 Pete Delkus
1332 Scott Leius
1333 Mike Redding
1334 Park Pittman
1335 Mark Guthrie
1336 Wayne Hattaway
1337 Jeff Bronkey
1338 Pat Bangston
1339 Mike Randle
1340 Larry Blackwell
1341 Ken Morgan
1342 Dwight Bernard
1343 Paul Sorrento
1344 Mike Funderburk
1345 Jeff Reboulet
1346 A.J. Richardson
1347 Edgar Naveda
1348 Paul Abbott
1349 Jim Kahmann
1350 Derek Parks
1351 John Eccles
1352 Terry Jorgensen
1353 Tim Arnold
1354 Jimmy Williams
1355 Ron Gardenhire

1989 Star Co. Osceola Astros

(Houston Astros, A) (color) (Price includes the late-issue Vargas and Sweet cards)

	MT	NR MT	EX
Complete Set:	7.50	5.50	3.00

1 Harold Allen
2 David Bond
3 Billy Paul Carver
4 Ramon Cedeno
5 Todd Credeur
6 Luis Gonzalez
7 Rusty Harris
8 Blaise Ilsley
9 Bernie Jenkins
10 Carlos Laboy
11 Dan Lewis
12 Andy Mota
13 Guy Normand
14 Dan Nyssen
15 Joe Ortiz
16 Al Osuna
17 Gorky Perez
18 David Potts
19 Ed Renteria
20 Scott Servais
21 John Sheehan
22 Dave Silvestri
23 Richie Simon
24 Dennis Tafoya
25 Willie Trice
26 Jose Vargas (Late Issue)
27 Rick Sweet (Late Issue)

1989 Cal League Palm Springs Angels

(California Angels, A) (color)

	MT	NR MT	EX
Complete Set:	6.00	4.50	2.50

32 Troy Giles
33 Dave Sturdivant
34 Jeff Gay
35 Ronnie Ortegon
36 Charlie Romero
37 Mario Marlina
38 Ramon Martinez
39 Wiley Lee
40 Christopher Graves
41 Ed Rodriquez
42 Christopher Threadgill
43 Cesar DeLaRosa
44 Edgar Alfonzo
45 Fred Carter
46 Jose Valez
47 Frank Bryan
48 James Townsend
49 David Neal
50 Donald Vidmar
51 Jeffrey Richardson
52 James Bisceglia
53 Brandy Vann
54 Steve McGuire
55 Miguel Alicia
56 Todd James
57 Tim McCoy
58 Chris Beardsley
59 David Graybill
60 Don Long
61 Al Olson
62 Kernan Ronan
63 Bill Lacheman

1989 ProCards Palm Springs Angels

(California Angels, A) (color)

	MT	NR MT	EX
Complete Set:	7.00	5.25	2.75

462 Checklist
463 Jim Townsend
464 Edgar Alfonzo
465 Edgar Rodriguez
466 Jeff Gay
467 Ramon Martinez
468 Tim McCoy
469 Jeff Richardson
470 Charlie Romero
471 Brandy Vann
472 Chris Treadgill
473 Troy Giles
474 Dave Neal
475 Cesar DeLaRosa
476 Don Long
477 Mario Molina
478 Ronnie Ortegon
479 Fred Carter
480 Al Olson
481 Keenan Ronan
482 Don Vidmar
483 Chris Graves
484 Jose Velez
485 Wiley Lee
486 Dave Sturdivant
487 Frank Bryan
488 Chris Beasley
489 Bill Lachemann

1989 CMC Pawtucket Red Sox

(Boston Red Sox, AAA) (color)

	MT	NR MT	EX
Complete Set:	7.50	5.50	3.00

1 Tom Bolton
2 Steve Currey
3 Eric Hetzel
4 Dana Kiecker
5 John Leister
6 Mike Rochford
7 Steve Ellsworth
8 Andy Araujjo
9 John Trautwein
10 Rob Woodward
11 Chris Canizzaro
12 Gary Miller-Jones
13 Carlos Quintana
14 Gary Tremblay
15 Scott Wade
16 Dana Williams
17 John Marzano
18 Kevin Romine
19 Jackie Gutierrez
20 Luis Rivera
21 John Roberts
22 Angel Gonzales
23 Eduardo Estrade
24 Mark Meleski
25 Ed Nottle

1989 Dunkin' Donuts Pawtucket Red Sox

(Boston Red Sox, AAA) This set is in the form of an 11" x 19" perforated poster.

	MT	NR MT	EX
Complete Set:	25.00	18.50	10.00

(1) Andy Araujo
(2) Steve Bast
(3) Tom Bolton
(4) Chris Cannizzaro
(5) Tony Cleary
(6) Steve Curry
(7) Mike Dalton
(8) Steve Ellsworth
(9) Angel Gonzalez
(10) Jackie Gutierrez
(11) Eric Hetzel
(12) Dana Kiecker
(13) Rick Lancellotti
(14) John Leister
(15) John Marzano
(16) Mark Meleski
(17) Gary Miller-Jones
(18) Ed Nottle
(19) Carlos Quintana
(20) Luis Rivera
(21) John Roberts
(22) Mike Rochford
(23) Kevin Romine
(24) Lee Stange
(25) John Trautwein
(26) Gary Tremblay
(27) Scott Wade
(28) Dana Williams
(29) Rob Woodward
(30) Logo card
(31) Team card

1989 ProCards Pawtucket Red Sox

(Boston Red Sox, AAA) (color)

	MT	NR MT	EX
Complete Set:	8.00	6.00	3.25

677 Checklist
678 Ed Nottle
679 Andy Araujo
680 Tom Bolton
681 John Leister
682 Kevin Romine
683 Tony Cleary
684 Angel Gonzalez
685 John Troutwein
686 Chris Cannizzaro
687 John Marzano
688 Carlos Quintana
689 Gary Miller-Jones
690 Dana Williams
691 Steve Curry
692 Lee Stange
693 John Roberts
694 Jackie Gutierrez
695 Scott Wade
696 Mark Meleski
697 Luis Rivera
698 Ed Estrada
699 Rob Woodward
700 Mike Rochford
701 Dana Kiecker
702 Gary Tremblay
703 Eric Hetzel
704 Steve Ellsworth

1989 Star Co. Peninsula Pilots

(No affiliation, A) (color) (Price includes the late-issue coaching staff card)

	MT	NR MT	EX
Complete Set:	6.00	4.50	2.50

1 Dave Bauer
2 Chris Bushing
3 Jeff Champ
4 Hernan Cortes
5 Tom Fine
6 Joe Gast
7 Pat Hewes
8 Dodd Johnson
9 Tim Kirk
10 Jay Knoblaugh
11 Al Lombardi
12 Julian Machado
13 Jay Makemson
14 Sam Manti
15 Matt Michael
16 Rodney Murrell
17 Greg Papageorge
18 Hector Perez
19 Lem Pilkenton
20 Tad Powers
21 Clyde Reichard

22 Rick Seibert
23 Todd Stephan
24 Len Thigpen
25 Micky Tresh
26 Coaching Staff (Jim Thrift, Clyde Reichard - Late Issue)

1989 Team Peoria Chiefs

(Chicago Cubs, A) (color) (error set)

	MT	NR MT	EX
Complete Set:	12.00	9.00	4.75

1 Ty Griffin
2 Braz Davis
3 Frankie Espino
4 Marcos Lopez
5 Jeff Massicotte
6 Jay Eddings
7 Brett Robinson
8 John Salles
9 Heathcliff Slocumb
10 Mike Sodders
11 Derek Stroud
12 Rick Mundy
13 Billy Paynter
14 Peoria's Past Chicago's Future
15 Matt Walbeck
16 Juan Adames
17 Alex Arias
18 Eddie Williams
19 Eric Perry
20 Tracy Smith
21 Peoria's Olympic Stars (Fernando Ramsey, Ty Griffin)
22 Woody Smith
23 Warren Arrington
24 Elvin Paulino
25 Fernando Ramsey
26 Harry Shelton
27 Greg Eberle
28 (Jeff Pico, Greg Maddux, Paul Kilgus)
29 Pookie Bernstine
30 Brad Mills
31 Rick Kranitz
32 Bob Grimes
33 Clar Krusinski
34 Front Office Staff
---- McDonalds Coupon

1989 Kodak Gold 200 Peoria Chiefs

(Chicago Cubs, A) (color) (corrected set)

	MT	NR MT	EX
Complete Set:	11.00	8.25	4.50

1 Ty Griffin
2 Braz Davis
3 Frankie Espino
4 Marcos Lopez
5 Jeff Massicotte
6 Jay Eddings
7 Brett Robinson
8 John Salles
9 Heathcliff Slocumb
10 Mike Sodders
11 Derek Stroud
12 Rick Mundy
13 Billy Paynter
14 Peoria's Pas,)
15 Matt Walbeck
16 Juan Adames
17 Alex Arias
18 Eddie Williams
19 Eric Perry
20 Tracy Smith
21 Peoria's Olympic Stars (Fernando Ramsey, Ty Griffin)
22 Woddy Smith
23 Warren Arrington
24 Elvin Paulino
25 Fernando Ramsey
26 Harry Shelton
27 Greg Eberle
28 Jeff Pico, Greg Maddux, Paul Kilgus
29 Pookie Bernstine
30 Brad Mills
31 Rick Kranitz
32 Bob Grimes
33 Clar Krusinski
34 Front Office Staff
---- McDonalds Coupon

1989 CMC Phoenix Firebirds

(San Francisco Giants, AAA) (color)

	MT	NR MT	EX
Complete Set:	10.00	7.50	4.00

1 John Burkett
2 Ed Puikunas
3 Dennis Cook
4 Terry Mullholland
5 Mark Leonard
6 Ernie Camacho
7 Marty DeMarrite
8 Joe Olker
9 Stu Tate
10 Trevor Wilson
11 Bill Bathe
12 Wilfredo Tejada
13 Charlie Hayes
14 Tony Perezchica
15 Rusty Tillman
16 Mike Benjamin
17 Mike Laga
18 Matt Williams
19 Ron Wotus
20 Ken Gerhart
21 Jack Mull
22 Paul Meyers
23 John Skurla
24 George Wright
25 Gordie McKenzie

1989 ProCards Phoenix Firebirds

(San Francisco Giants, AAA) (color)

	MT	NR MT	EX
Complete Set:	9.00	6.75	3.50

1477 Checklist
1478 Mike Hamm
1479 Rusty Tillman
1480 Terry Mulholland
1481 Trevor Wilson
1482 Dennis Cook
1483 John Burkett
1484 George Wright
1485 Matt Williams
1486 Marty DeMerritt
1487 Charlie Hayes
1488 Bruce Graham
1489 Wil Tejada
1490 Paul Meyers
1491 Stu Tate
1492 Ed Puikunas
1493 Mike Laga
1494 Ernie Camacho
1495 Bill Bathe
1496 John Skurla
1497 Joe Olker
1498 Mark Leonard
1499 Ken Gerhart
1500 Mike Benjamin
1501 Ron Wotus
1502 Tony Perezchica
1503 Jack Mull
1504 Gordy MacKenzie
1505 Ron Davis

1989 Star Co. Pittsfield Mets

(New York Mets, A) (color) (Price includes ate-issue card #s 26-29)

	MT	NR MT	EX
Complete Set:	6.00	4.50	2.50

1 Chris Butterfield
2 Stanton Cameron
3 Joe Dellicarri
4 Chris Dorn
5 Steve Gasser
6 Dennis Harriger
7 Mike Hemmerich
8 Derek Henderson
9 Tim Hines
10 Tim Howard
11 Pat Howell
12 Paul Johnson
13 John Johnstone
14 Greg Langbehn
15 Medina Luciano
16 Lee May, Jr.
17 Joe McCann
18 Norberto Navarro
19 Steve Piskor
20 Curtis Pride
21 Ryan Richmond
22 Dave Telgheder
23 Mark Willoughby
24 Tim Blackwell
25 Dan Sequi
26 Steve Jacobucci
27 Jamie Hoffner
28 Jim Tesmer
29 Alan Zinter

1989 CMC Portland Beavers

(Minnesota Twins, AAA) (color)

	MT	NR MT	EX
Complete Set:	6.00	4.50	2.50

1 Jim Davins
2 Manny Hernandez
3 Kurt Kepshire
4 Steve Shields
5 Ray Soff
6 Lee Tunnell
7 Larry Cadian
8 Mike Dyer
9 Francisco Oliveras
10 Les Straker
11 Randy St. Claire
12 Orlando Mercado
13 Greg Olson
14 Doug Baker
15 Bobby Ralston
16 Kelvin Torve
17 Vic Rodriquez
18 Brad Bierly
19 John Christensen
20 Alan Cockrell
21 Bernardo Brito
22 Mark Davidson
23 Rafael Delima
24 Chip Hale
25 Jim Shellenback

1989 ProCards Portland Beavers

(Minnesota Twins, AAA) (color)

	MT	NR MT	EX
Complete Set:	7.00	5.25	2.75

207 Checklist
208 Chip Hale
209 Orlando Mercado
210 Victor Rodriquez
211 Jim Davins
212 Bernardo Brito
213 Randy St. Claire
214 John Christensen
215 Kurt Kepshire
216 Ray Soff
217 Lee Tunnell
218 Steve Shields
219 Lester Straker
220 Kelvin Torve
221 Manny Hernandez
222 Rafael Delima
223 Larry Casian
224 Alan Cockrell
225 Greg Olson
226 Jim Shellenback
227 Mark Davidson
228 Mike Dyer
229 Francisco Oliveras
230 Doug Baker
231 Brad Bierley
232 Bobby Ralston

1989 Star Co. Princeton Pirates

(Pittsburgh Pirates, R) (color) (Price includes late-issue card #s 26-28)

	MT	NR MT	EX
Complete Set:	6.00	4.50	2.50

1 Adrian Adkins
2 Felix Antiqua
3 Tim Curley
4 John Curtis
5 Alberto De Los Santos
6 Marvin Dooley
7 Marc Biordano
8 Z.B. Hamilton
9 Bill Holmes
10 David Howard
11 Wade Lytle
12 Ramon Martinez
13 Troy Mooney
14 Eric Parkinson
15 Darryl Ratliff
16 Andre Redmond
17 Jose Rodriquez
18 Roman Rodriquez
19 Delvy Santiago
20 Bruce Schreiber
21 Jesse Torres
22 Ramon Valdez
23 Dave Watson
24 Bobby West
25 Kelly Woods
26 Julio Garcia
27 Tom Dettore
28 Ken Crenshaw

1989 Star Co. Prince William Cannons

(New York Yankees, A) (color) (Price includes late-issue card #s 26-29)

	MT	NR MT	EX
Complete Set:	7.00	5.25	2.75

1 Jason Bridges
2 Dennis Brow
3 Andy Cook
4 Bob DeJardin
5 Pedro DeLeon
6 Mike Draper
7 Rob Ehrhard
8 Ken Greer
9 Jeff Johnson
10 Pat Kelly
11 Jeff Livesey
12 Mark Marris
13 Bill Masse
14 Gerald Nielsen
15 Mark Ohlms
16 Vince Phillips
17 Bruce Prybylinski
18 Frank Seminara
19 Don Sparks
20 Don Stanford
21 Wade Taylor
22 Dave Turgeon
23 Hector Vargas
24 Tom Weeks
25 Gerald Williams
26 Mauricio Zazueta (Late Issue)
27 Mark Weidemaier (Late Issue)
28 Dave Jorn (Late Issue)
29 Trey Hillman (Late Issue)

1989 ProCards Pulaski Braves

(Atlanta Braves, R) (color)

	MT	NR MT	EX
Complete Set:	9.00	6.75	3.50

1887 Checklist
1888 Dave Dickman
1889 Ron Thomas
1890 Mike Pisacreta
1891 Bat Boys
1892 Javier Lopez
1893 Melvin Nieves
1894 Brent McCoy
1895 Don Strange
1896 Dan Snover
1897 Earl Jewett
1898 Shaun Sottile
1899 Tab Brown
1900 Fred Koenig
1901 Phillip Wellman
1902 Matt West
1903 Mike Cerame
1904 Tony Tarasco
1905 Darren Ritter
1906 Jarrod Parker
1907 Roger Hailey
1908 Mark Wohlers
1909 Sean Hutchinson
1910 Jeff Clark
1911 Lee Heath
1912 Greg Arnold
1913 John Kupsey
1914 Steve Swail

1989 Best Quad City Angels

(California Angels, A) (color)

	MT	NR MT	EX
Complete Set:	8.00	6.00	3.25

1 Glenn Carter
2 Eddie Rodriquez
3 Joe Georger
4 Bill Zick
5 Jeff Oberdank
6 Kevin Flora
7 David Esquer
8 Jim Aylward
9 Mark Holzemer
10 Mike Erb
11 Justin Martin
12 Larry Pardo
13 Frank Mutz
14 Steve McGuire
15 Bill Vanderwel
16 Gary Murrhy
17 Mark Zappelli
18 John Marchese
19 Bruce Vegely
20 Mike Musolino
21 Larry Gonzales
22 J.R. Phillips
23 Claudio Carrasco
24 Dave Partrick
25 Mitch Seoane
26 Bill Eveline
27 Jim Edmonds
28 Beban Perez
29 Steve De Angelis
30 Ruben Amaro, Jr.
31 Checklist

1989 Grand Slam Quad City Angels

(California Angels, A) (color)

	MT	NR MT	EX
Complete Set:	8.00	6.00	3.25

1 Eddie Rodriguez
2 Mitch Seoane
3 Joe Georger
4 Bill Zick
5 Mark Zappelli
6 Jim Edmonds
7 J.R. Phillips
8 Glenn Carter
9 Dave Patrick
10 John Marchese
11 Kevin Flora
12 Bruce Vegely
13 Kyle Abbott
14 Mike Erb
15 Mike Musolino
16 Bill Vanderwell
17 Steve McGuire
18 Ruben Amaro, Jr.
19 Gary Murphy
20 Jeff Oberdank
21 Mark Holzemer
22 Frank Mutz
23 Beban Perez
24 Larry Pardo
25 David Esquer
26 Steve Deangelis
27 Jim Aylward
28 Larry Gonzales
29 Claudio Carrasco
30 Bill Eveline

1989 Best Reading Phillies

(Philadelphia Phillies, AA) (color)

	MT	NR MT	EX
Complete Set:	6.00	4.50	2.50

1 Chuck McElroy
2 Warren Magee
3 Chuck Malone
4 Steve Scarsone
5 Stephen Sharts
6 Scott Service
7 Jeff Tabaka
8 Bob Scanlan
9 Rick Parker
10 Jason Grimsley
11 Cliff Brantley
12 Shane Turner
13 Ramon Henderson
14 Vince Holyfield
15 Martin Foley
16 Gregory Edge
17 Bobby Edmonds
18 Frank Bellinio
19 Eric Boudreaux
20 Harvey Brumfield
21 Chris Calvert
22 Sal Agostinelli
23 Jeffrey Williams
24 Mark Ruffner
25 Ramon Aviles
26 Mike Hart
27 Checklist

1989 ProCards Reading Phillies

(Philadelphia Phillies, AA) (color)

	MT	NR MT	EX
Complete Set:	7.00	5.25	2.75

650 Checklist
651 Steve Sharts
652 Bob Scanlan
653 Ramon Henderson
654 Sal Agostinelli
655 Shane Turner
656 Chuck Malone
657 Scott Service
658 Mike Hart
659 Frank Bellino
660 Rick Parker
661 Vince Holyfield
662 Cliff Brantley
663 Jeff Tabaka
664 Chris Calvert
665 Steve Scarsone
666 Greg Edge
667 Harvey Brumfield
668 Eric Boudreaux
669 Chuck McElroy
670 Jason Grimsley
671 Ramon Aviles
672 Marty Foley
673 Bobby Joe Edmonds
674 Warren Magee
675 Jeff Williams
676 Pat Combs

1989 Star Co. Reading Phillies

(Philadelphia Phillies, AA) (Price includes late-issue coaching staff and Hart cards)

	MT	NR MT	EX
Complete Set:	7.00	5.25	2.75

1 Sal Agostinelli
2 Frank Bellino
3 Erik Bratlien
4 Harvey Brumfield
5 Chris Calvert
6 Amalio Carreno
7 Fred Christopher
8 Joe Citari
9 Pat Combs
10 Bobby Joe Edmonds
11 Marty Foley
12 Jason Grimsley
13 Ramon Henderson
14 Gerald Holtz
15 Vince Holyfield
16 Warren Magee
17 Chuck Malone
18 Chuck McElroy
19 Rick Parker
20 Victor Rosario
21 Bob Scanlan
22 Steve Scarsone
23 Scott Service
24 Shane Turner
25 Jeff Williams
26 Mike Hart, Ramon Aviles, George Culver

1989 Cal League Reno Silver Sox

(No affiliation, A) (color)

	MT	NR MT	EX
Complete Set:	6.00	4.50	2.50

239 Mike Anderson
240 Bob Ayrault
241 John Bilelo
242 Jeorge Candelaria
243 Carlos Carrasco
244 Tim Fortugno
245 Joe Strong
246 Brian Sullivan
247 Gil Villanueva
248 Mike Warren
249 Brian Hartsock
250 Gary Nalls
251 Mike Westbrook
252 Joe Kmak
253 Mike Bosco
254 Doug Carpenter
255 Terence Carr
256 Framl Dominguez
257 Kaha Wong
258 Brian Palma
259 Claudio Carrasco
260 Shawn Barton
261 John Balfanz
262 Bill Bluhm
263 Jack Patton
264 Jerry Maldonado
265 Eli Grba

1989 Bob's Photo Richmond Braves

(Atlanta Braves, AAA) (color)

	MT	NR MT	EX
Complete Set:	45.00	34.00	18.00

1 Andy Nezelek
2 Carlos Rios
3 Terry Blocker
4 Kent Mercker
5 Eddie Mathews
6 Kash Beauchamp
7 Bryan Farmer
8 Gary Eave
9 Chris Shaddy
10 Dwayne Henry
11 Tommy Greene
12 Ed Whited
13 Dave Justice
14 Rusty Richards
15 Robbie Wine
16 John Mizerock
17 Mark Lemke
18 Barry Jones
19 Alex Smith
20 Drew Denson
21 Jim Beauchamp
22 Leo Mazzone
23 Sonny Jackson
24 John Grubb
25 Greg Tubbs
26 Joel McKeon
27 Steve Ziem
28 Dave Plumb
29 Charlie Puleo

1989 CMC Richmond Braves

(Atlanta Braves, AAA) (color)

	MT	NR MT	EX
Complete Set:	11.00	8.25	4.50

1 Marty Clary
2 Gary Eave
3 Tommy Green
4 Dwayne Henry
5 Kent Mercker
6 Andy Nezelek
7 Rusty Richards
8 Bryan Farmer
9 Bob Black
10 Eddie Mathews
11 Robby Wine
12 John Mizerock
13 Carlos Rios
14 Sam Ayoub
15 David Justice
16 Jeff Wetherby
17 Terry Blocker
18 Drew Denson
19 Mark Lemke
20 Barry Jones
21 Ed Whited
22 Chris Shaddy
23 Kash Beauchamp
24 Coaching Staff (Leo Mazzone, Sonny Jackson, John Grubb)
25 Jim Beauchamp

1989 ProCards Richmond Braves

(Atlanta Braves, AAA) (color)

	MT	NR MT	EX
Complete Set:	11.00	8.25	4.50

817 Checklist
818 Team Photo
819 Clubhouse Manager)
820 Sam Ayoub
821 John Grubb
822 Jim Beauchamp
823 Greg Tubbs
824 Chris Shaddy
825 Mark Eichhorn
826 Mark Clary
827 John Mizerock
828 Gary Eave
829 Rusty Richards
830 Mark Lemke
831 Tommy Greene
832 Sonny Jackson
833 Leo D. Mazzone
834 Bryan Farmer
835 Kent Mercker
836 Kash Beauchamp
837 Ed Whited
838 Dave Justice
839 Andy Nezelek
840 Jeff Wetherby
841 Alex Smith
842 Carlos Rios
843 Robbie Wine
844 Dwayne Henry
845 Eddie Mathews
846 Barry Jones
847 Drew Denson

1989 Team Richmond Braves

(Atlanta Braves, AAA) (color)

	MT	NR MT	EX
Complete Set:	12.00	9.00	4.75

(1) Team Photo
(2) Jim Beauchamp
(3) Coaching Staff (John Grubb)
(4) Coaching Staff (Leo Mazzone)
(5) Coaching Staff (Sonny Jackson)
(6) Coaching Staff (Sam Ayoub)
(7) Carlos Rios
(8) Kash Beauchamp
(9) Chris Shaddy
(10) Bryan Farmer
(11) Alex Smith
(12) Mark Lemke
(13) Barry Jones
(14) Terry Blocker
(15) Dave Justice
(16) Jeff Weatherby
(17) Kent Mercker
(18) John Mizerock
(19) Eddie Mathews
(20) Robbie Wine
(21) John Kilner
(22) Gary Eave
(23) Marty Clary
(24) Tommy Greene
(25) Andy Nezelek
(26) Ed Whited
(27) Dwayne Henry
(28) Drew Denson
(29) Rusty Richards

1989 Best Riverside Red Wave

(San Diego Padres, A) (color)

	MT	NR MT	EX
Complete Set:	7.50	5.50	3.00

1 Bob Lutticken
2 Mark Beavers
3 Scott Bigham
4 Jay Estrada
5 Kevin Farmer
6 Todd Hansen
7 Brian Harrison
8 Mike Humphreys
9 Tony Lewis
10 Kelly Lifgren
11 Stephen Loubier
12 Bill Marx
13 Tim McWilliam
14 Darrin Reichle
15 Andy Skeels
16 Saul Soltero
17 William Taylor
18 Rafael Valdez
19 Jose Valentin
20 Guillermo Valasquez
21 Mike Young
22 Steve Lubratich
23 Jon Matlack
24 Nate Colbert
25 Bruce Bochy
26 Greg Hall
27 Monte Brooks
28 Jim Daniel
29 Isaiah Clark
30 Checklist

1989 Cal League Riverside Red Wave

(San Diego Padres, A) (color)

	MT	NR MT	EX
Complete Set:	7.50	5.50	3.00

1 Scott Bigham
2 Tim McWilliams
3 Gil Valasquez
4 Rafael Valdez
5 Mike Humphreys
6 Greg Hall
7 Kevin Farmer
8 Jose Valentin
9 Isaiah Clark
10 Montie Brooks
11 Bob Lutticken
12 Andy Skeels
13 Will Taylor
14 Bill Marx
15 Darren Reichle
16 Kelly Lifgren
17 Brian Harrison
18 Mike Young
19 Bobby Sheridan
20 Steve Loubier
21 Jay Estrada
22 Todd Hansen
23 Mark Beavers
24 Tony Lewis
25 Steve Lubratich
26 Jon Matlack
27 Nate Colbert
28 Jim Daniels
29 Bruce Bochy
30 Tye Waller
31 Saul Soltero

1989 ProCards Riverside Red Wave

(San Diego Padres, A) (color)

	MT	NR MT	EX
Complete Set:	6.50	4.75	2.50

1388 Checklist
1389 Steve Loubier
1390 Mark Beavers
1391 Nate Colbert
1392 Kelly Lifgren
1393 Darrin Reichle
1394 Guillermo Valazquez
1395 Tony Lewis
1396 Scott Bigham
1397 Greg Hall
1398 Rafael Valdez
1399 Mike Young
1400 Mike Humphreys
1401 Tim McWilliams
1402 Will Taylor
1403 Bob Lutticken
1404 Isaiah Clark
1405 Bruce Bochy
1406 Saul Soltero
1407 Jim Daniels
1408 Jon Matlack
1409 Jay Estrada
1410 Brian Harrison
1411 Steve Lubratich

1412 Kevin Farmer
1413 Todd Hansen
1414 Andy Skeels
1415 Jose Valentin
1416 Bill Marx
1417 Monte Brooks
1418 Bobby Sheridan

1989 CMC Rochester Red Wings

(Baltimore Orioles, AAA) (color)

	MT	NR MT	EX
Complete Set:	7.50	5.50	3.00

1 Mike Jones
2 Chuck Stanhope
3 Francisco Melendez
4 Cesar Mejia
5 Mike Raczka
6 Mickey Weston
7 Curt Shilling
8 Mike Smith (Height 6'1")
9 Mike Smith (Height 6'3")
10 Mark Huismann
11 Dave Johnson
12 John Posey
13 Keith Hughes
14 Chris Padget
15 Sherwin Cijntje
16 Tim Hulett
17 Jeff Tackett
18 Harold Perkins
19 Waly Harris
20 Tim Dulin
21 Juan Bell
22 Butch Davis
23 Rick Schu
24 Rick Bosman
25 Greg Biagini

1989 ProCards Rochester Red Wings

(Baltimore Orioles, A) (color)

	MT	NR MT	EX
Complete Set:	7.00	5.25	2.75

1631 Checklist
1632 Sherwin Cijntje
1633 Jay Tibbs
1634 Mike Smith (height 6'1")
1635 Cesar Mejia
1636 Jose Mesa
1637 Mike Smith (height 6'3")
1638 Micky Weston
1639 Steve Finley
1640 Chris Hoyles
1641 Dick Bosman
1642 Rick Schu
1643 Harold Perkins
1644 Chris Padget
1645 Jeff Tackett
1646 Tim Dulin
1647 Billy Moore
1648 Mike Raczka
1649 Pete Harnisch
1650 Mark Huismann
1651 Walt Harris
1652 Butch Davis
1653 Tim Hulett
1654 Francisco Melendez
1655 Curt Schilling
1656 Dave Johnson
1657 Mike Jones
1658 Juan Bell
1659 Keith Hughes
1660 Greg Biagini

1989 Team Rockford Expos

(Montreal Expos, A)

	MT	NR MT	EX
Complete Set:	8.00	6.00	3.25

(1) Isaac Alleyne
(2) Derrell Baker
(3) Esteban Beltre
(4) Rod Boddie
(5) Scott Bromby
(6) Reid Cornelius
(7) Bret Davis
(8) Kevin Foster
(9) Dan Freed
(10) Michael Gibbons
(11) Terrel Hansen
(12) Dan Hargis
(13) Ben Howze
(14) Keith Kaub
(15) Rob Kerrigan
(16) Bryn Kosco
(17) Rob Mason
(18) Nate Minchey
(19) Chris Nabholz
(20) Dave Oropeza
(21) Jesus Paredes
(22) Mike Parrott
(23) Mike Quade
(24) Kelvin Shephard
(25) Matt Shiflett
(26) Joe Siddall
(27) Joel Smith
(28) Adam Terris
(29) Jay Williams
(30) Darrin Williams
(31) Kelly Zane

1989 ProCards St. Catharines Blue Jays

(Toronto Blue Jays, A) (color)

	MT	NR MT	EX
Complete Set:	7.00	5.25	2.75

2069 Checklist
2070 Gregg Martin
2071 Bill Abere
2072 Ryan Thompson
2073 Daren Brown
2074 Scott Hutson
2075 Oscar Garcia
2076 Daren Kizziah
2077 Carlos Delgado
2078 Mike Jockish
2079 Greg O'Halloran
2080 Hector Mercedes
2081 Nigel Wilson
2082 Billy Parese
2083 Gonzalo Vargas
2084 Anton Mobley
2085 Chris Beacom
2086 John Wanish
2087 Ernesto Santana
2088 Rob Blumberg
2089 Sterling Stock
2090 Greg Bicknell
2091 Jeff Kent
2092 Armondo Pagliardi
2093 Mike McAlpin
2094 Greg McCutcheon
2095 Bob Shirley
2096 Rick Holifield

1989 Star Co. Saint Lucie Mets

(New York Mets, A) (color) (Price includes late-issue Horlen and Hina cards)

	MT	NR MT	EX
Complete Set:	7.00	5.25	2.75

1 Brant Alyea
2 Terry Bross
3 Alex Diaz
4 Tony Diaz
5 Chris Donnels
6 Clint Hurdle
7 Ron Gideon
8 Terry Griffin
9 Rudy Hernandez
10 Tim Hines
11 Scott Jaster
12 Crucito Lara
13 Steve LaRose
14 David Lau
15 Juan Marina
16 Terry McDaniel
17 Mike Miller
18 Danny Naughton
19 Dale Plummer
20 Dave Proctor
21 Titi Roche
22 Jamie Roseboro
23 Julio Valera
24 Mike Whitlock
25 Vince Zawaski
26 Joel Horlen
27 Fred Hina

1989 Star Co. Saint Petersburg Cardinals

(St. Louis Cardinals, A) (color) (Price includes late-issue card #s 26-29)

	MT	NR MT	EX
Complete Set:	7.00	5.25	2.75

1 Franklin Abreu
2 Greg Becker
3 Bill Bivens
4 Art Calvert
5 Greg Carmona
6 Ric Christian
7 Alex Cole
8 Rheal Cormier
9 Todd Crosby
10 Terry Elliot
11 Joe Federico
12 Joey Fernandez
13 Ed Fulton
14 Mark Grater
15 Joe Hall
16 Shawn Hathaway
17 Jeremy Hernandez
18 Rich Hoffman
19 Chuck Johnson
20 Scott Melvin
21 Scott Nichols
22 Larry Pierson
23 Tony Russo
24 Tim Sherrill
25 Ken Smith
26 Paul Thoutsis (Late Issue)
27 Dave Bialas (Late Issue)
28 Marty Mason (Late Issue)
29 Team Photo (Late Issue)

1989 Star Co. Salem Buccaneers

(Pittsburgh Pirates, A) (color) (Price includes late-issue Garcia, Harris and Williams cards)

	MT	NR MT	EX
Complete Set:	9.00	6.75	3.50

1 Moises Alou
2 Fernando Arguelles
3 Joe Ausanio
4 Scott Barczi
5 Terry Crowley
6 Ron Downs
7 Chip Duncan
8 Mike Fortuna
9 Carlos Garcia
10 Ed Hartman
11 Trent Jewett
12 Domingo Merejo
13 Paul Miller
14 Blas Minor
15 Albert Molina
16 Joseph Pacholec
17 Keith Richardson
18 Scott Ruskin
19 Butch Schlopy
20 Winston Seymour
21 Willie Smith
22 Randy Tomlin
23 Miguel Valverde
24 John Wehner
25 Rocky Bridges
26 Julio Garcia (Late Issue)
27 Spin Williams (Late Issue)
---- Robert Harris (Late Issue)

1989 Team Salem Dodgers

(Los Angeles Dodgers, A)

	MT	NR MT	EX
Complete Set:	50.00	37.00	20.00

1 Tom Beyers
2 Burt Hooton
3 Anthony Garcia
4 Geoff Clark
5 Jorge Alvarez
6 Garrett Beard
7 Bill Bene
8 Paul Branconier
9 Don Carroll
10 Clayton Enno
11 Gary Forrester
12 Larry Gonzalez
13 Sebastian Goodlow
14 John Kries
15 Ken Luckham
16 Brock McMurray
17 Bill Miller
18 Chris Morrow
19 Robin Nina
20 Hector Ortiz
21 Jorge Pascual
22 Jose Perez
23 Pedro Perez
24 Rex Peters
25 Mike Piazza
26 Rafael Rijo
27 Napoleon Robinson
28 Chris Sperry
29 Dan Stupur
30 Ramon Taveras

1989 Cal League Salinas Spurs

(No affiliation, A) (color)

	MT	NR MT	EX
Complete Set:	6.00	4.50	2.50

123 Ray Velasquez
124 Dan Adriance
125 Doug Messer
126 Larry Carter
127 Scott Nelson
128 Dave Horan
129 Dave Cantrell
130 Yuki Kaseda
131 Chikada Toyotoshi
132 Dragon Taguchi
133 Yuji Yamaguchi
134 Masa Kuoda
135 Yasu Suzuki
136 Toshi Yoshinaga
137 Dickens Benoit
138 Pat Brady
139 Mark Standford
140 Matt Williams
141 Greg Lee
142 Jeff Kaiser
143 Tod Ronson
144 Kerry Shaw
145 Jim McNamara
146 Tim Ireland
147 Jerry Nyman
148 Ken Kajima
149 Brian Castello

1989 ProCards Salinas Spurs

(No affiliation, A) (color)

	MT	NR MT	EX
Complete Set:	6.00	4.50	2.50

1799 Checklist
1800 Dave Horan
1801 Mark Standiford
1802 Steve Gray
1803 Kerry Shaw
1804 Masa Kuoda
1805 Jeff Kaiser
1806 Greg Lee
1807 Ray Valasquez
1808 Yuki Kaseda
1809 Dragon Taguchi
1810 Yoshi Yoshinaga
1811 Jim McNamara
1812 Honen Chikida
1813 Yuji Yamaguchi
1814 Yasu Suzuki
1815 Pat Brady
1816 Larry Carter
1817 Doug Messer
1818 Dan Adriance
1819 Greg Sparks
1820 Jerry Nyman
1821 Tod Ronson
1822 Tim Ireland
1823 Scott Gay
1824 Scott Nelson
1825 Matt Williams
1826 Dave Cantrell
1827 Dickens Benoit
1828 Brian John Costello

1989 Best San Antonio Missions

(Los Angeles Dodgers, AA) (color) (A limited-edition set was also produced)

	MT	NR MT	EX
Complete Set:	9.50	7.00	3.75

1 Mike White
2 Manuel Francois
3 Eric Mangham
4 Darren Holmes
5 Tony Arnold
6 Kevin Armstrong
7 Gordon Hershiser
8 Wayne Kirby
9 Joseph Kesselmark
10 Adam Brown
11 Brian Traxler
12 Dan Henley
13 Carlos Hernandez
14 Louie Martinez
15 Louie Lopez
16 Isidrio Marquez
17 Dave Hansen
18 Dan Scarpetta
19 Greg Mayberry
20 Dennis Springer
21 Homar Rojas
22 Chris Nichting
23 Michael Pitz
24 Tim Scott
25 John Shoemaker
26 Claude Osteen
27 Jose Offerman
28 Checklist

1989 Best San Bernadino Spirit

(Seattle Mariners, A) (color)

	MT	NR MT	EX
Complete Set:	6.00	4.50	2.50

1 Jim Companis
2 Dorian Daughtry
3 Richard Carter
4 Rick Balabon
5 Greg Burlingame
6 Jim Blueburg
7 Daniel Barbara
8 Brian Baldwin
9 Willie Ambos
10 Chuck Kniffin
11 Ralph Dick
12 Jorge Uribe
13 Kurt Stange
14 Jim Pritikin
15 Steve Hill
16 Lee Hancock
17 Anthony Woods
18 Jose Tarabull
19 Scott Runge
20 Bryan King
21 Jody Ryan
22 Mike McDonald
23 Ruben Gonzalez
24 Mike Goff
25 Todd Haney
26 Stan Sanchez
27 Mark Merchant
28 Rich Dauer, Mark Harmon
29 Checklist

1989 Cal League San Bernadino Spirit

(Seattle Mariners, A) (color)

	MT	NR MT	EX
Complete Set:	6.00	4.50	2.50

64 Calvin Jones
65 Troy Evans
66 Will Ambos
67 Jody Ryan
68 Richard Carter
69 Kurt Strange
70 Greg Burlingame
71 Lee Hancock
72 Mike Goff
73 Brian Baldwin
74 Rick Balabon
75 Rodney Poissant
76 Dan Barbara
77 John Hoffman
78 Jorge Uribe
79 Jose Tartabull
80 Bryan King
81 Todd Haney
82 Ruben Gonzalez
83 Anthony Woods
84 Steve Hill
85 Jim Campanis
86 Jim Pritikin
87 Mike McDonald
88 Dorian Daughtry
89 Chuck Kniffen
90 Ralph Dick
91 Stan Sanchez
92 Chris Verna
93 Mark Merchant
---- The Bug (mascot)

1989 Best San Jose Giants

(San Francisco Giants, A) (color)

	MT	NR MT	EX
Complete Set:	7.00	5.25	2.75

1 Andres Santana
2 Rod Beck
3 Jamie Cooper
4 James Terrill
5 Lonnie Phillips
6 Don Brock
7 Mark Dewey
8 Dan Fernandez
9 Bill Carlson
10 David Booth
11 Steve Decker
12 Montie Phillips
13 Elanis Westbrook
14 Tom Ealy
15 Bryan Hickerson
16 James Pena
17 Scott Wilson
18 Kevin Meier
19 Tom Hostetler
20 Steve Lienhard
21 Juan Guerrero
22 James Malseed
23 Jim Jones
24 Steve Hecht
25 T.J. McDonald
26 Mike Ham
27 Scott Goins
28 Duanne Espy
29 Todd Oakes
30 Ernie Sierra
31 Checklist

1989 Cal League San Jose Giants

(San Francisco Giants, A) (color)

	MT	NR MT	EX
Complete Set:	9.00	6.75	3.50

209 Rod Beck
210 Don Brock
211 Mark Dewey
212 Bryan Hickerson
213 Tom Hostetler
214 Steve Leinhard
215 Kevin Meier
216 Jim Pena
217 Lonnie Phillips
218 Jim Terrill
219 Juan Guerrero
220 Mike Ham
221 Steve Hecht
222 Jim Jones
223 Jim Malseed
224 T.J. McDonald
225 Elanis Westbrooks
226 Andrew Santana
227 Steve Decker
228 David Booth
229 Bill Carlson
230 Jamie Cooper
231 Tom Ealy
232 Dan Fernandez
233 Scoot Goins
234 Scott Wilson
235 Duane Espy
236 Todd Oakes
237 Harry Steve
238 Dave Hilton

1989 ProCards San Jose Giants

(San Francisco Giants, A) (color)

	MT	NR MT	EX
Complete Set:	7.50	5.50	3.00

432 Checklist
433 Montie Phillips
434 Tom Ealy
435 Elanis Westbrooks
436 T.J. McDonald
437 Jim Malseed
438 Scott Goins
439 Bill Carlson
440 David Booth
441 Dan Fernandez
442 Don Brock
443 Bryan Hickerson
444 Tom Hostetler
445 Jim Pena
446 Steve Decker
447 Kevin Meier
448 Mark Dewey
449 Jim Terrill
450 Andres Santana
451 Juan Guerrero
452 Lonnie Phillips
453 Duane Espy
454 Scott Wilson
455 Todd Oakes
456 Steve Lienhard
457 Steve Hecht
458 Jamie Cooper
459 Rod Beck
460 Jim Jones
461 Mike Ham

1989 Star Co. San Jose Giants

(San Francisco Giants, A) (Price includes late-issue card #s 26-29)

	MT	NR MT	EX
Complete Set:	7.50	5.50	3.00

1 Rod Beck
2 Dave Booth
3 Don Brock
4 Bill Carlson
5 Jamie Cooper
6 Steve Decker
7 Mark Dewey
8 Tom Ealy
9 Dan Fernandez
10 Scott Goins
11 Juan Guerrero
12 Mike Ham
13 Steven Hecht
14 Bryan Hickerson
15 Tom Hostetler
16 Jim Jones
17 Steve Lienhard
18 James Malseed
19 T.J. McDonald
20 Kevin Meier
21 James Pena
22 Montie Phillips
23 Andres Santana
24 James Terrill
25 Elanis Westbrooks
26 Todd Oakes
27 Duane Espy
28 Scott Wilson

1989 Star Co. Sarasota White Sox

(Chicago White Sox, R) (color)

	MT	NR MT	EX
Complete Set:	6.00	4.50	2.50

1 Kurt Brown
2 Eddie Caceres
3 Darrin Campbell
4 Chris Cauley
5 Bob Fletcher
6 Paul Fuller
7 Ken Gohmann
8 Cliff Gonzalez
9 Todd Hall
10 Curt Hasler
11 John Hudek
12 Bo Kennedy
13 Brent Knackert
14 Rodney McCray
15 Jim Morris
16 Javier Ocasio
17 Raymond Payton
18 Jack Peel
19 Bob Resnikoff
20 Dave Reynolds
21 Dan Rohrmeier
22 Ron Stephens
23 Carl Sullivan
24 Scott Tedder
25 Coaching Staff (Tony Franklin, Don Cooper, Pat Roessler)

1989 ProCards Savannah Cardinals

(St. Louis Cardinals, A) (color)

	MT	NR MT	EX
Complete Set:	6.00	4.50	2.50

342 Checklist
343 Jay North
344 Keith Champion
345 Gabriel Ozuna
346 Bobby Deloach
347 Dan Doyel
348 Dean Weese
349 Orlando Thomas
350 Luis Martinez
351 John Burgos
352 Tim Pettengill
353 Ahmed Rodriguez
354 Jim Ferguson
355 Vince Kindred
356 Juan Belbru
357 Mauricio Nunez
358 Eddie Carter
359 Mateo Ozuna
360 Lorenzo Calzado
361 Julio Mendez
362 Al Biggers
363 Steve Fanning
364 Mike Hensley
365 Brad Harvick
366 Bill Hershman
367 David Sala
368 Andy Taylor
369 Dan Hitt
370 Mark Clark
371 John Ericks

1989 CMC Scranton-Wilkes Barre Red Barons

(Philadelphia Phillies, AAA) (color)

	MT	NR MT	EX
Complete Set:	6.00	4.50	2.50

1 Marvin Freeman
2 Barney Nugent
3 John Martin
4 Bob Sebra
5 Alex Madrid
6 Dave Cash
7 Gordon Dillard
8 Brad Moore
9 Wally Ritchie
10 Randy O'Neal
11 Tommy Barrett
12 Steve Stanicek
13 Keith Miller
14 Matt Cimo
15 Jim Olander
16 Ron Salcedo
17 Ken Jackson
18 Joe LaFebvre
19 Greg Legg
20 Joe Redfield
21 Al Pardo
22 Floyd Rayford
23 Victor Rosario
24 Kevin Bootay
25 Bill Dancy

1989 ProCards Scanton-Wilkes Barre Red Barons

(Philadelphia Phillies, AAA) (color)

	MT	NR MT	EX
Complete Set:	7.00	5.25	2.75

705 Checklist
706 Danny Clay
707 Ron Salcedo
708 Greg Legg
709 Brad Moore
710 Victor Rosario
711 Al Pardo
712 Barney Nugent
713 Kevin Bootay
714 Gordon Dillard
715 Wally Ritchie
716 Keith Miller
717 Steve Stanicek
718 Bob Sebra
719 John Martin
720 Alex Madrid
721 Brad Brink
722 Joe LeFebvre
723 Jim Olander
724 George Culver
725 Tommy Barrett
726 Randy O'Neal
727 Floyd Rayford
728 Bruce Ruffin
729 Ken Johnson
730 Matt Cimo
731 Joe Redfield
1208 Bill Dancy

1989 ProCards Shreveport Captains

(San Francisco Giants, AA) (color)

	MT	NR MT	EX
Complete Set:	6.00	4.50	2.50

1829 Checklist
1830 Steve Connolly
1831 Russ Swan
1832 Mike Remlinger
1833 Eric Gunderson
1834 Paul Blair
1835 Jim Anderson
1836 Dee Dixon
1837 Steve Cline
1838 Bill Evers
1839 Greg Connor
1840 Mike Senne
1841 Gregg Ritchie
1842 Ted Wood
1843 David Patterson
1844 Craig Colbert
1845 Erik Johnson
1846 Jeff Carter
1847 Rich Aldrete
1848 Jose Pena
1849 Markus Owens
1850 Paul McClellan
1851 Doug Robertson
1852 Dean Freeland
1853 Randy McCament
1854 Jose Dominquez
1855 George Bonilla

1989 Grand Slam So. Atlantic League All-Stars

(A) (color)

	MT	NR MT	EX
Complete Set:	9.00	6.75	3.50

1 Stan Cliburn
2 Orlando Gomez
3 Willie Ansley
4 Larry Lamphere
5 Greg Sims
6 Glen McNabb

7 Jeff Neely
8 Brian Wood
9 Keith Raisanen
10 Mandy Romero
11 Pedro Martinez
12 John Kuehl
13 Scott Taylor
14 Matt Franco
15 Chris Hill
16 Andy Reich
17 Todd Hundley
18 Bob Olah
19 Kevin Baez
20 James Morrisette
21 Lino Rivera
22 Anthony Young
23 Reggie Sanders
24 Darren Oliver
25 Jim Hvizda
26 Ivan Rodriguez
27 Jeff Frye
28 Trey McCoy
29 Doug Cronk
30 Kevin Belcher
31 Mo Sanford
32 Dave McAuliffe
33 Mike Mulvaney
34 Lavell Codjo
35 Ray Giannelli
36 John Ericks
37 Gabriel Ozuna
38 Mauricio Nunez
39 Darryl Martin
40 Francisco Valdez
41 Leroy Ventress
42 Glen Gardner
43 Everett Cunningham
44 Randy Simmons
45 Pete Blohm
46 Jeff Osborne

1989 Donn Jennings Southern League All-Stars

(AA) (color)

	MT	NR MT	EX
Complete Set:	9.00	6.75	3.50

1 Harvey Pulliam
2 Robin Ventura
3 Eric Anthony
4 Kelly Mann
5 Delino DeShields
6 Scott Leius
7 Bernie Walker
8 Jimmy Kremers
9 Bob Hamelin
10 Todd Trafton
11 Greg Smith
12 Terry Jorgensen
13 Paul Sorrento
14 Paul Abbott
15 Jerry Kutzler
16 Wayne Edwards
17 Buddy Groom
18 Joe Bruno
19 Mark Guthrie
20 Mel Rojas
21 Rob Wishnevski
22 Luis Encarnacion
23 Buddy Bailey
24 Barry Foote
25 Jeff Newman

1989 Grand Slam South Bend White Sox

(Chicago White Sox, A) (color)

	MT	NR MT	EX
Complete Set:	7.00	5.25	2.75

1 Craig Wallin
2 Rick Patterson
3 Jim Reinebold
4 Roger LaFrancois
5 Kirk Champion
6 Scott Johnson
7 Scott Radinsky
8 Frank Merigliano
9 Sam Chavez
10 Virgil Cooper
11 Fred Dabney
12 Carlos Delacruz
13 Bret Marshall
14 Mike Mitchner
15 Steve Schrenk
16 Jose Ventura
17 Randy Warren
18 Steve Mehl
19 Kinnis Pledger
20 John Zaksek
21 Mark Chasey
22 Rob Lukachyk
23 Wayne Busby
24 Cesar Bernhardt
25 Eugenio Tejada

26 Greg Roth
27 Derek Lee
28 Ed Smith
29 Jay Hornacek
30 Clemente Alvarez

1989 ProCards Spartanburg Phillies

(Philadelphia Phillies, A) (color)

	MT	NR MT	EX
Complete Set:	7.00	5.25	2.75

1027 Checklist
1028 Todd Elam
1029 Ed Rosado
1030 Mickey Morandini
1031 Jon Szynal
1032 Rick Jones
1033 Troy Kent
1034 Greg McCarthy
1035 Mike Carlin
1036 Gary Wilson
1037 Toby Borland
1038 Jason Backs
1039 Reggie Garcia
1040 Darrell Lindsey
1041 Paul Ellison
1042 Darrell Coulter
1043 Nick Santacruz
1044 Leroy Ventress
1045 John Marshall
1046 Antonio Linares
1047 Tom Marsh
1048 Reed Olmstead
1049 Chris Sementelli
1050 Mel Roberts
1051 Pedro Zayas
1052 Tim Dell
1053 Tim Churchill
1054 John Larosa
1055 Steve Keller
1056 Don "Moose" DeMuth

1989 Star Co. Spartanburg Phillies

(Philadelphia Phillies, A) (color) (Price includes late-issue coaching staff card)

	MT	NR MT	EX
Complete Set:	7.00	5.25	2.75

1 Jason Backs
2 Toby Borland
3 Mike Carlin
4 Tim Churchill
5 Darrell Coulter
6 Tim Dell
7 Todd Elam
8 Paul Ellison
9 Reggie Garcia
10 Steve Keller
11 Troy Kent
12 John LaRosa
13 Antonio Linares
14 Darrell Lindsey
15 Tom Marsh
16 John Marshall
17 Greg McCarthy
18 Mike Morandini
19 Reed Olmstead
20 Ed Rosado
21 Nick Santa Cruz
22 Jon Szynal
23 Leory Ventress
24 Gary Wilson
25 Pedro Zayas
26 Coaching Staff (Mel Roberts, Rick Jones, Buzz Capra - Late Issue)

1989 Sport Pro Spokane Indians

(San Diego Padres, A) (color)

	MT	NR MT	EX
Complete Set:	7.00	5.25	2.75

1 Dave Staton
2 Eddie Zinter
3 Rod Billingsley
4 Bruce Bochy
5 Tony McGee
6 John Phelan
7 Joe Buckley
8 Greg Hall
9 Terry Rupp
10 Dan Deville
11 Rick Davis
12 Bill Johnson
13 Tom Brassel
14 Kerry Knox
15 Brian Span

16 Scot Welish
17 Troy Cunningham
18 Steve Martin
19 Kevin Higgins
20 Chris Gollehon
21 Jeff Barton
22 Bobby Sheridan
23 Kevin Towers
24 Rico Coleman
25 Steve Bethea
26 Darrell Sherman

1989 Best Springfield Cardinals

(St. Louis Cardinals, A) (color)

	MT	NR MT	EX
Complete Set:	6.00	4.50	2.50

1 Mike Fiore
2 Dave Grimes
3 Antron Grier
4 Brad DuVall
5 Bob Colescott
6 Scott Broadfoot
7 Luis Faccio
8 Winston Brown
9 Kris Huffman
10 Michael Ross
11 Lee Plemel
12 Jeff Shireman
13 Scott Lawrence
14 John Sellick
15 David Payton
16 David Richardson
17 Charlie White
18 Cory Satterfield
19 Tom Malchesky
20 Dale Kisten
21 Roberto Marte
22 Ti Meamber
23 Edward Looper
24 Fred Langiotti
25 Lonnie Maclin
26 Vince Sferrezza
27 Rick Colbert
28 Dan Moushon
29 Dan Radison
30 Checklist

1989 Best All-Decade Springfield Cardinals

(St. Louis Cardinals, A) (color)

	MT	NR MT	EX
Complete Set:	9.00	6.75	3.50

1 Todd Zeile
2 Craig Wislon
3 Harry McCulla
4 Tom Amante
5 Frankie Batista
6 Ed Tanner
7 Alan Hunsinger
8 Tom Dozier
9 Danny Cox
10 John Costello
11 Jeff Oyster
12 John Young
13 Matt Kinzer
14 Joe Boever
15 Mike Hartley
16 Paul Wilmet
17 Pat Perry
18 Scott Arnold
19 Dale Kisten
20 Steve Peters
21 Robert Faron
22 Dave Bialas
23 Tom Baine
24 Ray Lankford
25 Mike Perez
26 Mike Milchin
27 Gaylen Pitts
28 Bob Geren
29 Jim Lindeman
30 Curt Ford
31 Vince Coleman
32 Bill Lyons
33 Randy Hunt
34 Mike Fitzgerald
35 Tom Pagnozzi
36 Logo & Checklist card

1989 Best Stockton Ports

(Milwaukee Brewers, A) (color)

	MT	NR MT	EX
Complete Set:	7.50	5.50	3.00

1 Dave Nilsson
2 Chris George
3 Mike Ignasiak
4 Steve Monson
5 Carl Moraw
6 Jamie Cangemi
7 Richard Durant
8 Steve Sparks
9 Kent Hetrick
10 Mark Ambrose
11 Jeff Ciszekowski
12 Danny Fitzpatrick
13 Leo Perez
14 Charlie Montoyo
15 Larry Oedewaldt
16 John Jaha
17 Randy Snyder
18 Gary Borg
19 Chris Cassels
20 Tim Raley
21 Bryan Foster
22 Pat Listach
23 Rob Smith
24 Bobby Jones
25 Jim Poulin
26 Batboys (Chris Moreno, Mike Wickhan)
27 Don Miller
28 Dan Chapman
29 Dave Huppert
30 Rob Derksen
31 (Mark Marino, Mike Conroy)
32 Checklist

1989 Cal League Stockton Ports

(Milwaukee Brewers, A) (color)

	MT	NR MT	EX
Complete Set:	8.00	6.00	3.25

150 Jaime Cangemi
151 Dan Fitzpatrick
152 Steve Sparks
153 Chris George
154 Jeff Ciszkowski
155 Rick Durant
156 Carl Moraw
157 Mike Ignasiak
158 Leo Perez
159 Mark Ambrose
160 Steve Monson
161 Kent Hetrick
162 Dave Nillson
163 Chris Cassels
164 Gary Borg
165 John Jaha
166 Bobby Jones
167 Larry Oedewaldt
168 Rob Smith
169 Tim Raley
170 Randy Snyder
171 Bryan Foster
172 Charlie Montoya
173 Pat Listach
174 Dan Chapman
175 Don "Killer" Miller
176 Dave Huppert
177 Rob Derkson
178 Jim Poulin
179 Julio Cruz

1989 ProCards Stockton Ports

(Milwaukee Brewers, A) (color)

	MT	NR MT	EX
Complete Set:	7.00	5.25	2.75

372 Checklist
373 Leo Perez
374 Dave Nilsson
375 Larry Oedewaldt
376 Kent Hetrick
377 Mark Ambrose
378 Carl Moraw
379 Pat Listach
380 John Jaha
381 Charlie Montoyo
382 Randy Snyder
383 Bobby Jones
384 Steve Monson
385 Rob Derksen
386 Dave Huppert
387 Jim Poulin
388 Rick Durant
389 Jamie Cangemi
390 Steve Sparks
391 Chris George
392 Chris Cassels
393 Bryan Foster
394 Rob Smith
395 Dan Fitzpatrick
396 Gary Borg
397 Don Miller
398 Dan Chapman
399 Jeff Ciszkowski
400 Mike Ignasiak
401 Tim Raley
402 Compliment Card

1989 Star Co. Stockton Ports

(Milwaukee Brewers, A)

	MT	NR MT	EX
Complete Set:	8.00	6.00	3.25

1 Gary Borg
2 Larry Oedewaldt
3 John Jaha
4 Pat Listach
5 Mike Ignasiak
6 Elvira Narciso
7 Tim Fortugno
8 Chris George
9 Tim Raley
10 Kent Hetrick
11 Steve Sparks
12 Charlie Montoyo
13 Jamie Cangemi
14 Chris Cassels
15 Bobby Jones
16 Randy Synder
17 Jeff Ciszkowski
18 Ron Smith
19 Richard Durrant
20 Bryan Foster
21 Dave Nilsson
22 Dave Huppert, James Poole
23 Dan Chapman
24 Don Miller
25 Rob Derksen
26 (Marsh/Wickam)
27 Jim Poulin
28 (Marino/Conroy)

1989 ProCards Sumter Braves

(Atlanta Braves, R) (color)

	MT	NR MT	EX
Complete Set:	7.00	5.25	2.75

1086 Checklist
1087 Tom Rizzo
1088 Ed Holtz
1089 Billy Partin
1090 Paul Reis
1091 Ralph Rowe
1092 Willy Johnson
1093 Elias Sosa
1094 Gil Garrido
1095 Ned Yost
1096 Steve Lopez
1097 Glen Gardner
1098 Lionel Adams
1099 Mark Wohlers
1100 Dave Dickman
1101 Calvain Culberson
1102 Judd Johnson
1103 Winnie Relaford
1104 Rod Richey
1105 Johnny Maldonado
1106 Lamar Hall
1107 Scott Goselin
1108 Chad Smith
1109 Mike Urman
1110 Randy Simmons
1111 Roberto Minaya
1112 Eduardo Perez
1113 Roberto DeLeon
1114 Scott Grove
1115 Marcos Vazquez
1116 Glenn Mitchell
1117 Greg Harper
1118 Jeff Meier

1989 CMC Syracuse Chiefs

(Toronto Blue Jays, AAA) (color)

	MT	NR MT	EX
Complete Set:	8.50	6.25	3.50

1 Doug Bair
2 Joe Nunez
3 Jack O'Connor
4 Mark Ross
5 Frank Wills
6 Willie Blair
7 Steve Cummings
8 DeWayne Buice
9 Juan Guzman
10 Alex Sanchez
11 Sal Butera
12 Otis Green
13 Randy Holland
14 Tim Tolman
15 Glenallen Hill
16 Stu Pederson
17 Kelly Heath
18 Hector De La Cruz
19 Junio Felix
20 Frank Cabrera
21 Sil Campusano
22 Luis Sojo
23 Chico Walker
24 Coaching Staff (Galen Cisco, Hector Torres)
25 Bob Bailor

1989 ProCards Syracuse Chiefs

(Toronto Blue Jays, AAA) (color)

	MT	NR MT	EX
Complete Set:	10.00	7.50	4.00

790 Checklist
791 Francisco Cabrera
792 Chico Walker
793 Otis Green
794 Frank Wills
795 Randy Holland
796 Bob Bailor
797 Juan Guzman
798 Stu Pederson
799 Galen Cisco
800 Kelly Heath
801 Hector Torres
802 Sal Butera
803 Steve Cummings
804 Glenallen Hill
805 Willie Blair
806 Jose Nunez
807 Doug Bair
808 Sil Campusano
809 Luis Sojo
810 Junior Felix
811 DeWayne Buice
812 Jack O'Connor
813 Alex Sanchez
814 Mark Ross
815 Tim Tolman
816 Hector Delacruz

1989 Team Syracuse Chiefs

The Chiefs gave away a single-sheet photo album on a promotional night. The sheet folds into a 8-3/8" x 11" sheet. There are 30 cards on this sheet, each measuring 2-1/8" x 2-5/8" and separated by perforations to facilitate separation of the cards. The cards are skip-numbered according to uniform number and have statistics on the back.

	MT	NR MT	EX
Complete Set:	8.50	6.25	3.50

(1) Otis Green
(2) Jose Escobar
(3) Junior Felix
(4) Kelly Heath
(6) Sil Campusano
(8) Stu Pederson
(9) Timothy Tolman
(10) Chico Walker
(12) Hector Delacruz
(15) Willie Blair
(16) Juan Guzman
(17) Luis Sojo
(21) DeWayne Buice
(23) Alex Sanchez
(24) Glenallen Hill
(25) Francisco Cabrera
(26) Sal Butera
(27) Jose Nunez
(28) Mark Ross
(29) Zavier Hernandez
(32) Steven Cummings
(36) Jack O'Connor
(40) Doug Bair
(44) Frank Wills

1989 CMC Tacoma Tigers

(Oakland A's, AAA) (color)

	MT	NR MT	EX
Complete Set:	7.00	5.25	2.75

1 Rich Bordi
2 Jim Corsi
3 Reese Lambert
4 Brian Snyder
5 Bill Dawley
6 Joe Law
7 Bryan Clark
8 Bruce Walton
9 Chuck Estrada
10 Dave Otto
11 Jeff Shaver
12 Lance Blankenship
13 Tyler Brilinski
14 Felix Jose
15 Buddy Pryor
16 Russ McGinnis
17 Jessie Reid
18 Donnie Hill
19 Doug Jennings
20 Dick Scott
21 Steve Howard
22 Larry Arndt
23 Mike Bordick
24 Pat Dietrick
25 Brad Fischer

1989 ProCards Tacoma Tigers

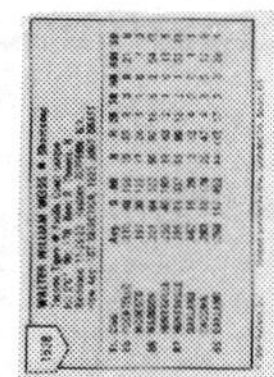

(Oakland A's, AAA) (color)

	MT	NR MT	EX
Complete Set:	9.00	6.75	3.50

1535 Checklist
1536 Jose Canseco
1537 Mark McGwire
1538 Walt Weiss
1539 Lance Blankenship
1540 Bruce Tanner
1541 Doug Jennings
1542 Felix Jose
1543 Walt Horn
1544 Rich Bordi
1545 Brian Snyder
1546 Bruce Walton
1547 Dave Otto
1548 Reese Lambert
1549 Jessie Reid
1550 Joe Law
1551 Brad Fischer
1552 Steve Howard
1553 Pat Dietrick
1554 Dickie Scott
1555 Bill Dawley
1556 Russ McGinnis
1557 Larry Arndt
1558 Buddy Pryor
1559 Jeff Shaver
1560 Jim Corsi
1561 Tyler Brilinski
1562 Donnie Hill
1563 Bryan Clark
1564 Chuck Estrada
1565 Mike Bordick
1566 Stan Naccaratto

1989 Grand Slam Texas League All-Stars

(AA) (color)

	MT	NR MT	EX
Complete Set:	9.00	6.75	3.50

1 Pat Kelly
2 Chris Cron
3 Bobby Rose
4 Gary Disarcina
5 Scott Lewis
6 Luis Merejo
7 Paul Faries
8 Warren Newson
9 Charlie Hillemann
10 Andy Benes
11 Omar Olivares
12 Rich Holsman
13 Tim McIntosh
14 Shon Ashley
15 Ramon Sambo
16 D.L. Smith
17 Carlos Hernandez
18 Dennis Springer
19 Gaylen Pitts, Chris Mahoney
20 Julian Martinez
21 Ray Stephens
22 Ray Lankford
23 Dave Osteen
24 Mike Perez
25 Bill Bivens
26 Julio Valera
27 Dave Trautwein
28 Chuck Carr
29 Jeff Carter
30 Craig Colbert
31 Gary Alexander
32 Dean Palmer
33 Bill Haselman
34 Juan Gonzalez
35 Steve Lankard
36 Mark Petkovsek
37 Bob Malloy
38 Roy Silver
39 Not used
40 Carl Sawatski
---- League Logo

1989 Candl Coins Fold-Out Set Tidewater Tides

(New York Mets, AAA) (color) This set is in calendar form and measures approximately 11" x 28-1/2".

	MT	NR MT	EX
Complete Set:	10.00	7.50	4.00

1 Danny Frisella
2 Roy Foster
3 Jon Matlack
4 Amos Otis
5 Choo Choo Coleman
6 Mike Vail
7 Nino Espinosa
8 George Theodore
9 Craig Swan
10 Roy Staiger
11 Don Schulze
12 Clint Hurdle
13 Randy Milligan
14 Mark Carreon
15 Kevin Elster
---- Tides Team photo
---- 1975 Tides Team photo
---- 1987 Tides Team photo

1989 CMC Tidewater Tides

(New York Mets, AAA) (color)

	MT	NR MT	EX
Complete Set:	7.50	5.50	3.00

1 Tim Drummond
2 Tom Edens
3 Jeff Innis
4 John Mitchell
5 Jack Savage
6 Wally Whitehurst
7 Dave West
8 Shawn Barton
9 Blaine Beatty
10 Kevin Tapini
11 Ken Dowell
12 Phil Lombardi
13 Jeff McKnight
14 Keith Miller
15 Tom O'Malley
16 Joaquin Contreras
17 Darren Reed
18 Dave Liddell
19 Rick Lundblade
20 Jeff Gardner
21 Mike Cubbage
22 Craig Shipley
23 Marcus Lawton
24 Mark Carreon
25 Rich Miller
26 Glenn Abbott
27 Tony Brown
28 Sam McCrary
29 Mark Bailey

1989 ProCards Tidewater Tides

(New York Mets, AAA) (color)

	MT	NR MT	EX
Complete Set:	5.00	3.75	2.00

1946 Checklist
1947 Field Staff (Mike Cubbage, Glenn Abbott, Sam McCrary, Rich Miller)
1948 Keith Miller
1949 Mark Bailey
1950 Jeff Innis
1951 Manny Salinas
1952 Tim Drummond
1953 Jeff McKnight
1954 Lou Thornton
1955 Bill Scherrer
1956 Tom Edens
1957 Darren Reed
1958 Wally Whitehurst
1959 Mike DeButch
1960 Joaquin Contreras
1961 Craig Shipley
1962 Kevin Brown
1963 Ken Dowell
1964 Blaine Beatty
1965 Tom O'Malley
1966 Jeff Gardner
1967 Marcus Lawton
1968 Rick Lundblade
1969 Shawn Barton
1970 John Mitchell
1971 Jack Savage
1972 Kevin Tapani
1973 Dave West
1974 Tony Brown
1975 Phil Lombardi

1989 CMC Toledo Mud Hens

(Detroit Tigers, AAA) (color)

	MT	NR MT	EX
Complete Set:	6.00	4.50	2.50

1 Randy Bockus
2 Ramon Pena
3 Mike Trujillo
4 Dave Palmer
5 Shawn Holman
6 Bob Link
7 Kevin Ritz
8 Paul Wenson
9 Kenny Williams
10 Dave Beard
11 Jeff Datz
12 Dave Griffin
13 Doug Strange
14 Larry See
15 Jim Walewander
16 Leo Garcia
17 Dan Dimascio
18 Pat Austin
19 Kevin Bradshaw
20 Norman Carrasco
21 Milt Cuyler
22 Delwyn Young
23 Rich Wieligman
24 Steve McInerney
25 John Wockenfuss

1989 ProCards Toledo Mud Hens

(Detroit Tigers, AAA) (color)

	MT	NR MT	EX
Complete Set:	7.00	5.25	2.75

760 Checklist
761 Jeff Datz
762 Steve McInerney
763 Kenny Williams
764 Delwyn Young
765 Rob Richie
766 Pat Austin
767 Leo Garcia
768 Norman Carrasco
769 Randy Bockus
770 Jim Walewander
771 John Wockenfuss
772 Billy Bean
773 Edwin Nunez
774 Ivan DeJesus
775 Rich Wieligman
776 Mike Trujillo
777 Dave Beard
778 Bob Link
779 Ramon Pena
780 Paul Wenson
781 Shawn Holman
782 Doug Strange
783 Kevin Bradshaw
784 Larry See
785 Dave Griffin
786 Kevin Ritz
787 Milt Cuyler
788 Dan DeMascio
789 Dave Palmer

1989 ProCards Triple A All-Star Game

(AAA) (color)

	MT	NR MT	EX
Complete Set:	9.00	6.75	3.50

1 Checklist
2 Scotti Madison
3 Mike Heifferon
4 Ed Hearn
5 Kent Mercker
6 Sandy Alomar
7 Jay Bell
8 Junior Noboa
9 Dorn Taylor
10 Mark Gardner
11 Jeff Huson
12 Hap Hudson
13 Tom O'Malley
14 Todd Zeile
15 Skeeter Barnes
16 Francisco Cabrera
17 Tom Bolton
18 Kevin Maas
19 Randy Velarde
20 Hal Morris
21 Bucky Dent
22 Steve Henderson
23 Keith Hughes
24 Keith Miller
25 Mike Trujillo
26 Scott Coolbaugh
27 Terry Clark
28 Tom Kotchman
29 Tom Drees
30 Lance Johnson
31 Glenallen Hill
32 Jim Wilson
33 Paul Zuvella
34 Steve Olin
35 Tom Lampkin
36 Pete Dalena
37 Sal Rende
38 Rick Luecken
39 Bryan Clark
40 Victor Rodriguez
41 Billy Bates
42 Greg Vaughn
43 Pete Mackanin
44 Kevin Blankenship
45 Carl Nichols
46 Javier Ortiz
47 Ramon Martinez
48 Mike Huff
49 Jerald Clark
50 Steve Smith
51 Matt Williams
52 Stu Tate
53 Jim Beauchamp
54 Tommy Greene
55 Mark Lemke

1989 CMC Tucson Toros

(Houston Astros, AAA) (color)

	MT	NR MT	EX
Complete Set:	7.00	5.25	2.75

1 Rocky Childress
2 Mitch Johnson
3 Anthony Kelley
4 Roger Mason
5 Dave Meads
6 Ed Vosberg
7 Jeff Heathcock
8 Charlie Kerfeld
9 Brian Meyer
10 Dan Schatzeder
11 Matt Sinatro
12 Craig Smajstrla
13 Jose Tolentino
14 Louie Meadows
15 Carl Nichols
16 Casey Candaele
17 Brick Smith
18 Harry Spillman
19 Ron Washington
20 Chuck Jackson
21 Carlo Columbino
22 Gary Cooper
23 Steve Lombardozzi
24 Coaching Staff (Eddie Watt, Frank Cacciatore)
25 Bob Skinner

1989 Jones Photo Tucson Toros

(Houston Astros, AAA) (color)

	MT	NR MT	EX
Complete Set:	25.00	18.50	10.00

(1) Eric Anthony
(2) Frank Cacciatore
(3) Casey Candaele
(4) Rocky Childress
(5) Carlo Colombino
(6) Gary Cooper
(7) Jeff Heathcock
(8) Chuck Jackson
(9) Mitch Johnson
(10) Anthony Kelley
(11) Charley Kerfeld
(12) Darryl Kile
(13) Steve Lombardozzi
(14) Roger Mason
(15) Louie Meadows
(16) Dave Meads
(17) Brian Meyer
(18) Carl Nichols
(19) Dave Rohde
(20) Dan Schatzede
(21) Craig Smajstrla
(22) Brick Smith
(23) Harry Spilman
(24) Jose Tolentino
(25) Ed Vosberg
(26) Ron Washington

1989 ProCards Tucson Toros

(Houston Astros, AAA) (color)

	MT	NR MT	EX
Complete Set:	7.50	5.50	3.00

179 Checklist
180 Dave Meads
181 Steve Lombardozzi
182 Larry Lasky
183 Jose Tolentino
184 Gary Cooper
185 Carl Nichols
186 Anthony Kelly
187 Mitch Johnson
188 Charley Kerfeld
189 Brian Meyer
190 Ron Washington
191 Louie Meadows
192 Ed Vosberg
193 Brick Smith
194 Rocky Childress
195 Roger Mason
196 Jeff Heathcock
197 Casey Candaele
198 Dan Schatzeder
199 Harry Spilman
200 Craig Smajstrla
201 Matt Sinatro
202 Frank Cacciatore
203 Bob Skinner
204 Eddie Watt
205 Chuck Jackson
206 Carlo Colombino

1989 Best Tulsa Drillers

(Texas Rangers, AA)

	MT	NR MT	EX
Complete Set:	15.00	11.00	6.00

1 Scott Collbaugh
2 Chuckie Canady
3 Wayne Tolleson
4 Pete O'Brien
5 Dean Palmer
6 Mike Stanley
7 Jim St. Laurent
8 Bob Sebra
9 Steve Wilson
10 Rick Raether
11 Walt Terrell
12 Mike Rubel
13 Jack Lazorko
14 Kevin Buckley
15 Steve Buechele
16 David Lynch
17 Jerry Gleaton
18 Ron Darling
19 Tom Henke
20 Mike Jirschele
21 Eddie Jurak
22 Phil Klimas
23 Chad Kreuter
24 Tommy Dunbar
25 Juan Gonzalez
26 Mel Barrow
27 Jerry Browne
28 Tom Burgess
29 Jim Skaalen
30 Kevin Reimer
31 Sammy Sosa
32 Kevin Brown
33 Rob Clark
34 Marty Scott
35 Ruben Sierra
36 Logo & checklist card

1989 Grand Slam Tulsa Drillers

(Texas Rangers, AA) (color)

	MT	NR MT	EX
Complete Set:	15.00	11.00	6.00

1 Tommy Thompson
2 Walt Williams
3 Jeff Andrews
4 Greg Harrel
5 Gary Alexander
6 Phil Bryant
7 Felipe Castillo
8 Monty Fariss
9 Darrin Garner
10 Juan Gonzalez
11 Bill Haselman
12 Adam Lamle
13 Steve Lankard
14 David Lynch
15 Bob Malloy
16 Barry Manuel
17 Terry Mathews
18 Gar Millay
19 Dean Palmer
20 Mark Petkovsek
21 Paul Postier
22 Marv Rockman
23 Fred Samson
24 Tony Scruggs
25 Sammy Sosa
26 George Threadgill

1989 Tulsa BB Card Shop Tulsa Drillers

(Texas Rangers) (color)

	MT	NR MT	EX
Complete Set:	25.00	18.50	10.00

1 Gary Alexander
2 Wilson Alvarez
3 Jeff Andrews
4 Phil Bryant
5 Filipe Castillo
6 Monty Fariss
7 Darrin Garner
8 Juan Gonzalez
9 Greg Harrel
10 Bill Haselman
11 John Hoover
12 Darren Loy
13 Bob Mallow
14 Alex Marte
15 Terry Mathews
16 Gar Millay
17 Dean Palmer
18 Mark Petkovsek
19 Paul Postier
20 Marv Rockman
21 Wayne Rosenthal
22 Frederic Samson
23 Tony Scruggs
24 Sammy Sosa
25 Tommy Thompson (Manager)
26 Walt Williams (Coach)
27 Ruben Sierra (Past star)

1989 Pucko Utica Blue Sox

(Chicago White Sox, A) (color)

	MT	NR MT	EX
Complete Set:	6.00	4.50	2.50

1 Dave Van Winkle
2 Glen Braxton
3 Kenny Burroughs
4 Ken Coleman
5 Mike Davino
6 Brian Davis
7 John Furch
8 Mike Galvan
9 Dave Gorman
10 Keith Harris
11 Jeff Ingram
12 Brian Keyser
13 Greg Kobza
14 Rich Long
15 Pat Mehrtens
16 Jesus Merejo
17 Greg Perschke
18 Ron Plemmons
19 Johnny Ruffin
20 Lance Sanders
21 Joe Singley
22 John Smith
23 Scott Stevens
24 Dean Tatarain
25 Robert Thompson
26 Dennis Walker
27 Jerry Wolak
28 Ron Vaughn
29 Bill Ballou
30 Mike Gellinger
31 Rick Ray
32 Joanne Gerace
33 Strike-O
34 Murnane Field

1989 CMC Vancouver Canadians

(Chicago White Sox, AAA) (color)

	MT	NR MT	EX
Complete Set:	7.50	5.50	3.00

1 Jeff Bittiger
2 Adam Peterson
3 Greg Hibbard
4 Tom McCarthy
5 Jack Hardy
6 Jose Segura
7 John Pawlowski
8 Rick Rodriguez
9 John Davis
10 Tom Drees
11 Kelly Paris
12 Steve Springer
13 Keith Smith
14 Jim Weaver
15 Marlin McPhail
16 Russ Morman
17 Carlos Martinez
18 Lance Johnson
19 Jerry Willard
20 Tom Forrester
21 Cal Emery
22 Mark Davis

23 Marv Foley
24 Jeff Schaefer
25 Moe Drabowsky

1989 ProCards Vancouver Canadians

(Chicago White Sox, AAA) (color)

	MT	NR MT	EX
Complete Set:	9.00	6.75	3.50

571 Checklist
572 Cal Emery
573 Marv Foley
574 Greg Latta
575 Doug Mansolino
576 Lance Johnson
577 Jack McDowell
578 Keith Smith
579 Carlos Martinez
580 Rick Rodriguez
581 Moe Drabowsky
582 John Davis
583 Jim Weaver
584 Greg Hibbard
585 Mark Davis
586 Jack Hardy
587 Jerry Willard
588 Tom Drees
589 Adam Peterson
590 Russ Morman
591 Jose Segura
592 Steve Springer
593 Tom McCarthy
594 Kelly Paris
595 John Pawlowski
596 Marlin McPhail
597 Tom Forrester

1989 Star Co. Vero Beach Dodgers

(Los Angeles Dodgers, A) (color) (Price includes the corrected cards, late-issue card #s 26-29, and the two unnumbered cards)

	MT	NR MT	EX
Complete Set:	12.00	9.00	4.75

1 William Argo
2 Anthony Barron
3 Rafael Bournigal
4 Albert Bustillos
5 J. Dale Coleman
6 Sherman Collins
7 Bruce Dostal
8 Dino Ebel
9 Stephen Green
10 Mark Griffin
11 Dana Heinle
12 Masaaki Kamanaka
13 Yasuhiro Kawabata
14 John Knapp
15 Alan Lewis
16 Brett Magnusson
17 Danny Montgomery
18a Jose Munoz
18b Jose Monoz (corrected)
19a Douglas Noch
19b Douglas Noch (corrected)
20a Daniel Opperman
20b Daniel Opperman (corrected)
21a Hector Ortiz
21b Hector Ortiz (corrected)
22a James Poole
22b James Poole (corrected)
23a Henry Rodriguez
23b Henry Rodriguez (corrected)
24a Michael Sampson
24b Michael Sampson (corrected)
25a Zakary Shinall
25b Zakary Shinall (corrected)
26 Jeff Van Zytveld
27 Joe Alvarez
28 Dennis Lewallyn
29 Jun Irisawa
---- Amilcar Valdez
---- Compliment Card

1989 Cal League Visalia Oaks

(Minnesota Twins, A) (color)

	MT	NR MT	EX
Complete Set:	7.00	5.25	2.75

94 Basil Meyer
95 Doug Simons
96 Johnny Ard
97 Steve Stowell
98 Rob Wassenaar
99 Bob Strube
100 Howard Townsend
101 Willie Banks
102 Fred White
103 Kiyoshi Sagawa
104 Shawn Gilbert
105 Mike Dotzler
106 Jarvis Brown
107 Loy McBride
108 Frank Valdez
109 Dave Jacas
110 Lenny Webster
111 Jose Marzan
112 Carlos Capellan
113 Vince Teixeira
114 Kouichi Ozawa
115 Minoru Yojo
116 Ken Fujimoto
117 David Smith
118 Scott Ullger
119 Gorman Heimueller
120 Takashi Yoshida
121 Acey Kohlogi
122 Rick McWane

1989 ProCards Visalia Oaks

(Minnesota Twins, A) (color)

	MT	NR MT	EX
Complete Set:	5.00	3.75	2.00

1419 Checklist
1420 Gorman Heimueller
1421 Howard Townsend
1422 Kouichi Ozawa
1423 Vince Teixeira
1424 Minoru Yojo
1425 Rob Wassenaar
1426 Willie Banks
1427 Johnny Ard
1428 Greg Brinkman
1429 Bob Strube
1430 Takashi Yoshida
1431 Rick McWane
1432 Kenji Fujimoto
1433 Scott Ullger
1434 Kiyoshi Sagawa
1435 Doug Simons
1436 Todd McClure
1437 Jarvis Brown
1438 Mike Dotzler
1439 Shawn Gilbert
1440 Frank Valdez
1441 Carlos Capellan
1442 Lenny Webster
1443 Jose Marzan
1444 Steve Stowell
1445 Basil Meyer
1446 Fred White
1447 David Jacas
1448 David Smith
1449 Loy McBride

1989 ProCards Waterloo Diamonds

(No affiliation, A) (color)

	MT	NR MT	EX
Complete Set:	6.00	4.50	2.50

1771 Checklist
1772 Steve Hendricks
1773 Scott Meadows
1774 Alexis Figueroa
1775 Jose LeBron
1776 Dave Gavin
1777 Bob Curnow
1778 James Nolan
1779 Tim Holland
1780 Rob Cantwell
1781 Jeff Hart
1782 Ron Morton
1783 Chuck Ricci
1784 Mark Littell
1785 Jamie Moreno
1786 Osvaldo Sanchez
1787 Mike King
1788 Billy Reed
1789 Luis Galindez
1790 Pedro Lopez
1791 Ray Holbert
1792 Don Fowler
1793 Mike Borgatti
1794 Brad Hoyer
1795 Dave Cunningham
1796 Reggie Farmer
1797 Chad Kuhn
1798 Rich Slomkowski

1989 Star Co. Waterloo Diamonds

(No affiliation, A) (color)

	MT	NR MT	EX
Complete Set:	6.00	4.50	2.50

1 Mike Borgatti
2 Rob Cantwell
3 Dave Cunningham
4 Bob Curnow
5 Reggie Farmer
6 Alex Figueroa
7 Don Fowler
8 Luis Galindez
9 Dave Gavin
10 Darrin Hart
11 Steve Hendricks
12 Ray Holbert
13 Tim Holland
14 Brad Hoyer
15 Mike King
16 Chad Kuhn
17 Jose LeBron
18 Pedro Lopez
19 Rich Slomkowski
20 Scott Meadows
21 Ron Morton
22 James Noland
23 Billy Reed
24 Chuck Ricci
25 Osvaldo Sanchez
26 Jaime Moreno
27 Mark Littell
28 George Paulis
29 Mark Gieseke
30 Darrin Hart
31 Terry McDivitt
32 Scott McNaney

1989 Star Co. Watertown Indians

(Cleveland Indians, A) (color) (Price includes late-issue card #s 26-29)

	MT	NR MT	EX
Complete Set:	10.00	7.50	4.00

1 Chuck Alexander
2 Keith Bevenour
3 Jerry Dipoto
4 Martin Durkin
5 Bruce Egloff
6 Alex Farran
7 Cornell Foggie
8 Fabio Gomez
9 Jeff Hancock
10 Joey James
11 Brian Graham
12 Garland Kiser
13 Ty Kovach
14 Brett Merriman
15 Carlos Mota
16 Scott Neill
17 Rouglas Odor
18 Doug Piatt
19 Tim Riemer
20 Greg Roscoe
21 Marc Tepper
22 Will Vespe
23 Dan Williams
24 Don Young
25 Erik Young
26 Ken Silvertri
27 Frank Kelbe
28 Rich Saint John
29 Brad DesJardins

1989 Grand Slam Wausau Timbers

(Seattle Mariners, A) (color)

	MT	NR MT	EX
Complete Set:	6.00	4.50	2.50

1 Mike McGuire
2 Tommy Jones
3 Ernest Castro
4 Bob Burton
5 John Reilley
6 John Boyles
7 Ellerton Maynard
8 Scott Pitcher
9 Ted Eldridge
10 Ben Burnau
11 Scott Taylor
12 Mark Razook
13 Brian Wilkinson
14 Scott Stoerck
15 Jeremy Matthews
16 Nick Felix
17 Jim Bennett
18 Hunter Hoffman
19 Jorge Robles
20 Steve Murray
21 Rick Candelari
22 Kevin Kerkes
23 Jeff Miller
24 Jeff Keitges
25 Erick Bryant
26 Tim Stargell
27 Chris Howard
28 Mike Gardner

1989 Pucko Welland Pirates

(Pittsburgh Pirates, A) (color)

	MT	NR MT	EX
Complete Set:	8.00	6.00	3.25

1 William Pennyfeather
2 Scott Arvesen
3 Robert Bailey, Jr.
4 Angel Beltram
5 David Bird
6 Mike Brewington
7 Kim Broome
8 Rod Byerly
9 Nelson Caraballo
10 Tom Deller
11 Raymond Doss
12 Mike Fortuna
13 Valentine Henderson
14 Deron Johnson
15 Paul Keefer
16 Jeff Kuder
17 John Latham
18 Javier Magria
19 Erik Nelson
20 Rob Peterson
21 Winston Seymour
22 Garland Slaughter
23 Mark Thomas
24 Ken Trusky
25 Tom Tuholski
26 Paul Wagner
27 Tim Wakefield
28 Ron Way
29 Flavio Williams
30 U.L. Washington
31 Larry Smith
32 Paul Allen
33 Bill Kuehn
34 Bob Burgess
35 John Belfor, Norma Chaney)

1989 Star Co. West Palm Beach Expos

(Montreal Expos, A) (color) (Price includes the late-issue logo card and card #s25-29)

	MT	NR MT	EX
Complete Set:	9.00	8.25	4.50

1 Jose Alou
2 Bret Barberie
3 Chris Bennett
4 Daryl Boyd
5 Jeff Carter
6 Doug Cinnella
7 Greg Colbrunn
8 Will Cordero
9 Rob DeYoung
10 Bert Echemendia
11 Jim Fregosi
12 Scott Henion
13 Ross Jones
14 Doug Kline
15 Rob Leary
16 John Mello
17 Yorkis Perez
18 Alonzo Powell
19 Troy Ricker
20 Hector Rivera
21 Trevor Penn
22 Matt Stairs
23 Corey Viltz
24 David Wainhouse
25 Pat Murphy
26 a Willie P. Banana mascot
26 b Luis Puljols
27 Felipe Alou
28 Dave Tomlin
29 Dave Jauss
---- Team Logo

1989 Rock's Dugout Wichita Wranglers

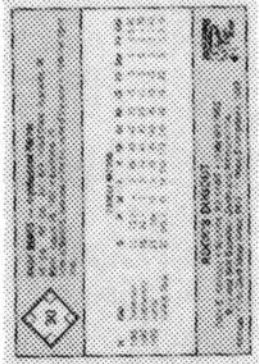

(San Diego Padres, AA) (color)

	MT	NR MT	EX
Complete Set:	9.00	6.75	3.50

(1) Mike Basso
(2) Andy Benes

(3) Ricky Bones
(4) Doug Brocail
(5) Brian Brooks
(6) Joe Chavez
(7) Rafael Chavez
(8) Brian Cisarik
(9) Craig Cooper
(10) Robert DeWolf
(11) Paul Faries
(12) Kevin Garner
(13) Greg Harris
(14) Charlie Hillemann
(15) David Hollins
(16) Rich Holsman
(17) Pat Kelly
(18) Gary Lance
(19) Tom LeVasseur
(20) Jim Lewis
(21) Bryan Little
(22) Warren Newson
(23) Omar Olivares
(24) Tony Pellegrino
(25) Paul Quinzer
(26) Rich Rodriguez
(27) Dan Walters
(28) Brian Wood
(29) Team Logo
(30) Rock's Dugout Card

1989 Rock's Dugout Wichita Wrangers

(San Diego Padres, AA) (color) (stadium set)

	MT	NR MT	EX
Complete Set:	11.00	8.25	4.50

1 Compliment Card
2 Warren Nelson
3 Tony Pellegrino
4 Charlie Hillemann
5 Brian Cisarik
6 Larry Mims
7 Steve Hendricks
8 Andy Benes
9 Mike Basso
10 Compliment Card
11 Omar Olivares
12 Dave Hollins
13 Doug Brocail
14 Jim Lewis
15 Pat Kelly
16 Ricky Bones
17 Kevin Garner
18 Paul Faries
19 Rich Rodriguez
20 Rich Holsman
21 Compliment Card
22 Title Card
23 Saul Soltero
24 Steve Loubier
25 Rafael Chavez
26 Tom LeVasseur
27 Bryan Little
28 Gary Lance
29 Cookie (mascot)
30 Compliment Card

1989 Rock's Dugout Wichita Wrangers

(San Diego Padres, AA) (color) (highlight set)

	MT	NR MT	EX
Complete Set:	7.00	5.25	2.75

1 Title Card
2 Home Run Threats (Warren Newson, Rob DeWolf, Brian Brooks, Kevin Garner)
3 Wranglers Celebrate
4 Pitching Round-Up (Rich Rogriguez, Rich Holsman, Doug Brocial, Brian Wood, Omar Olivares, Rafael Chavez)
5 Paul Faries
6 Tribute to A. Bartlett Giamatti
7 Jose Mota
8 300 Club (Warren Newson, Brian Cisarik, Rob DeWolf, Tom LeVasseur, Paul Faries)
9 Tom LeVasseur
10 Mike Basso
11 Dave Hollins
12 Warren Newson
13 Newson Scoring
14 Holson's Wind Up
15 Kelly's Direction
16 Pitching Sensation (Valdez)
17 DeWolf's Grand Slam
18 Omar Olivares
19 Benes Delivers
20 Ricky Bones

A player's name in italic type indicates a rookie card. An (FC) indicates a player's first card for that particular card company.

1989 Rock's Dugout Wichita Wrangers Update

(San Diego Padres, AA) (color) (update set)

	MT	NR MT	EX
Complete Set:	7.00	5.25	2.75

1 Title Card
2 Pat Kelly
3 Paul Faries
4 Omar Olivares
5 Andy Benes
6 Charlie Hillemann
7 Warren Newson
8 Craig Cooper
9 Saul Soltero
10 Rafael Valdez
11 Jose Mota
12 Brian Brooks
13 Larry Mims
14 Steve Loubler
15 Rob DeWolf
16 Paul Quinzer
17 Home Run Threats (Warren Newson, Rob DeWolf, Brian Brooks, Kevin Garner)
18 Jose Valentin
19 Andy Benes
20 Rich Holsman

1989 ProCards Williamsport Bills

(Seattle Mariners, AA) (color)

	MT	NR MT	EX
Complete Set:	8.00	6.00	3.25

625 Checklist
626 Dru Kosco
627 Bobby Cuellar
628 Mark Wooden
629 Mike Brocki
630 David Burba
631 Jerry Goff
632 Pat Lennon
633 Jose Melendez
634 Randy Roetter
635 Tino Martinez
636 Ted Williams
637 Jeff Nelson
638 Scott Runge
639 Jeff Hooper
640 William Diaz
641 Harry Davis
642 Dave Brundage
643 Jack Smith
644 Brad Brusky
645 Keith Helton
646 Pat Rice
647 Dana Ridenour
648 Greg Fulton
649 Rich Delucia

1989 Star Co. Williamsport Bills

(Seattle Mariners, AA) (color) (Price includes late-issue Burba card)

	MT	NR MT	EX
Complete Set:	7.00	5.25	2.75

1 Dave Brundage
2 Brad Brusky
3 Bobby Cuellar
4 Harry Davis
5 Rich DeLucia
6 William Diaz
7 Jeff Goff
8 Todd Haney
9 Keith Helton
10 Jeff Hooper
11 Calvin Jones
12 Patrick Lennon
13 Tino Martinez
14 Jose Melendez
15 Jeff Nelson
16 Bryan Price
17 Mark Razook
18 Patrick Rice
19 Richardo Rojas
20 Jack Smith
21 Glen Spagnola
22 Ted Williams
23 Mark Wooden
24 Jay Ward
25 David Burba (Late Issue)

1989 Star Co. Winston-Salem Spirit

(Chicago Cubs, A) (color)

	MT	NR MT	EX
Complete Set:	9.50	7.25	3.75

() Team Photo 7.00
1 Lenney Bell
2 Ed Caballero
3 Dick Canan
4 Frank Castillo
5 Don Cohoon
6 Rusty Crockett
7 Darren Duffy
8 Pat Gomez
9 Phillip Hannon
10 John Jensen
11 Dan Kennedy
12 Ray Mullino
13 Steve Parker
14 Marty Rivero
15 Bob Strickland
16 Francisco Tenacen
17 Rick Wilkins
18 Eric Woods
19 Jay Loviglio
20 Joe Housey
21 Steve Melendez

1989 Star Co. Winter Haven Red Sox

(Boston Red Sox, A) (color) (Price includes late-issue card #s 26-29)

	MT	NR MT	EX
Complete Set:	7.00	5.25	2.75

1 Odie Abril
2 Jim Byrd
3 Felix DeDos
4 Vincent Degifico
5 Bernie Dzafic
6 Peter Estrada
7 John Flaherty
8 Donald Florence
9 Chris Hanks
10 Reggie Harris
11 Howard Landry
12 Erik Laseke
13 Chris Leach
14 Terry Marrs
15 Pedro Matilla
16 Meredith Moore
17 Alfredo Pratts
18 Mickey Rivers
19 Ken Ryan
20 Al Sanders
21 Larry Scannell
22 Hector Stewart
23 Willie Tatum
24 Mike Thompson
25 John Valentin
26 Charles Wacha
27 James Whitehead
28 Doug Camilli
29 David Holt

1989 Star Co. Wytheville Cubs

(Chicago Cubs, R) (color) (Price includes late-issue card #s 26-30)

	MT	NR MT	EX
Complete Set:	6.00	4.50	2.50

1 Newland Aponte
2 Troy Bailey
3 Ronnie Brown
4 Victor Cancel
5 Pedro Castelland
6 Amilcar Correa
7 Dale Craig
8 Earl Cunningham
9 Kevin Dalson
10 Eddie Fowler
11 Jac Gelb
12 Don Gillespie
13 Fred Hill
14 Brad Huff
15 Calvin Ford
16 Jesse Hollins
17 Eric Jaques
18 Dan Kennedy
19 Greg Kessler
20 Mike Little
21 Raymond Mack
22 Recardo Medina
23 Leo Perez
24 Randy Sodders
25 Aaron Taylor
26 Scott Teague (Late)
27 Paul Torres (Late)
28 Clinton Write (Late)
29 Coaching Staff (Late)
30 Greg Keuter (Late)

1989 Star Minor League Baseball

In 1989, Star Company became the first minor league producer to venture into the wax pack market when it issued its first set of 100 cards. The cards were numbered 1-100 with players randomly selected. Several months later, Wax II was issued, again in a 100-card series numbered 101-200. There were no sets issued, nor was there a checklist available to the collector. Common cards are 5 cents. Unlike its predecessor, which had borders of various colors, the second wax series sported red borders. Individual card prices are for Mint condition.

	MT	NR MT	EX
Complete Set:	26.00	19.50	10.50

1 Eric Anthony 1.00
2 David Rohde (Photo of Karl Rhodes-not corrected) .20
3 Mike Simms
4 John Faccio
5 Oreste Marrero
6 Troy O'Leary .40
7 Rob Maurer .15
8 Rod Morris
9 Ed Ohman
10 Jim Byrd
11 Mark Cobb
12 pat Combs
13 Tim Mauser
14 Jim Vatcher
15 Luis Gonzalez .40
16 Andres Mota
17 Scott Servais .20
18 David Silvestri .15
19 Kevin Burdick
20 Tommy Shields
21 Mike York
22 Mike Anaya
23 Dale Plummer
24 Titi Roche
25 Vincent Zawaski
26 Anthony Barron
27 Rafael Bournigal
28 Albert Bustillos
29 Mark Griffin
30 Brett Magnusson
31 Mike Jones
32 Bret Barberie .30
33 Bert Echemendia
34 Mike Bell .10
35 Brian Hunter .20
36 Jim LeMasters
37 Rick Morris
38 Dominic Pierce
39 Joey Wardlow
40 Dera Clark
41 Stu Cole
42 Bob Hamelin .25
43 Deric Ladnier
44 Brian McRae
45 Mike Tresemer
46 Steve Walker
47 Greg Becker
48 Art Calvert
49 Todd Crosby
50 Shawn Hathaway
51 Rich Garces .15
52 Todd McClure
53 Steve Morris
54 Tim Dell
55 Antonio Linares
56 John Marshall
57 Mike Morandini .20
58 Paul Fuller
59 John Hudek
60 Ron Stephens
61 Scott Tedder
62 Pete Alborano
63 Kevin Shaw
64 Anthony Ariola
65 James Buccheri
66 William Love
67 Steve Avery 3.00
68 Rich Casarotti
69 Brian Champion
70 Wes Currin
71 Brian Deak
72 Ken Pennington
73 Theron Todd

74 Andy Tomberlin
75 Richard Falkner
76 Tommy Kramer .15
77 Charles Nagy .40
78 Chris Howard
79 Mike Rhodes
80 Gabriel Rodriguez
81 Bob Zeihen
82 Rod Beck 1.00
83 Jamie Cooper
84 Steve Decker .30
85 Mark Dewey
86 Juan Guerrero .30
87 Andres Santana .15
88 Pedro DeLeon
89 Pat Kelly .30
90 Bill Masse .10
91 Jerry Nielson
92 Mark Ohims
93 Moises Alou .50
94 Ed Hartman
95 Keith Richardson
96 Royal Clayton .30
97 Bobby Davidson
98 Mitch Lyden
99 Hensley Meulen, Hensley Meulens)
100 John Ramos
101 Robin Ventura 2.50
102 Luis Mercedes .15
103 Dave Miller
104 Randy Berlin
105 Mike Campas
106 Jose Trujillo
107 Lem Pikenton
108 Frank Bolick .10
109 Bert Heffernan
110 Chris Czarnik
111 Andy Benes 1.50
112 Skipper Wright
113 Eric Alexander
114 Manny Alexander .20
115 Jimmy Roso
116 Chris Donnels
117 Jaime Roseboro
118 Julian Yan
119 Vincent Degifico
120 Mike Morandini .25
121 Goose Gozzo
122 Pedro Munoz .40
123 Keith Helton
124 Tino Martinez .50
125 Sandy Alomar .40
126 Scott Cooper .75
127 Daryl Irvine
128 Jim Orsag
129 Mickey Pina
130 Scott Sommers
131 Ed Zambrano
132 Dave Bettendorf
133 Steve Allen
134 Kevin Belcher
135 Doug Cronk
136 Tito Stewart
137 Jeff Frye .15
138 Trey McCoy .20
139 Robb Nen .20
140 Jim Hvizda
141 Tommy Boyce
142 Michael Maksudian
143 Matt Current
144 Tom Hardgrove
145 Julio Vargas
146 Dan Welch
147 Steve Dunn .50
148 Mike Musuraca
149 Mike House
150 Deion Sanders 2.00
151 Willie Mota
152 Tim Nedin
153 Kerry Taylor .15
154 Beau Alred
155 Troy Neel .40
156 Shawn Hare
157 Chris Butterfield
158 Tim Hines
159 Pat Howell
160 Paul Johnson
161 Ryan Richmond
162 Ernie Baker
163 Pedro Castellano .25
164 Eric Jaques
165 Mark Willoughby
166 Dan Segui
167 Richard Skackle
168 Mark Lewis .40
169 John Johnstone
170 Phil Plantier 2.00
171 Wes Chamberlain .50
172 James Harris
173 Felix Antigua
174 Bruce Schreiber
175 Pete Rose Jr.
176 Kelly Woods
177 Anthony DeLaCruz
178 Charles Nagy .40
179 Nolan Lane
180 Fabio Gomez
181 Chris Butler
182 Brett Merriman
183 Carlos Mota
184 Doug Piatt
185 Marc Tepper
186 Dan Williams
187 Maximo Aleys
188 Ken Lewis
189 Joey Vierra
190 Ron Morton
191 Brook Fordyce .30
192 Steve McCarthy
193 Steve Hosey 1.00
194 Steve Foster .15
195 Ron Crowe
196 Steve Callahan
197 Benny Colvard
198 Adam Casillas
199 Joey Belle 4.00
200 Ben McDonald .60

1990 Best Albany Yankees

(New York Yankees) (color)

	MT	NR MT	EX
Complete Set:	6.00	4.50	2.50

1 Bernie Williams
2 Andy Cook
3 Ramon Manon
4 Tom Newell
5 Scott Kamienicki
6 Russell Meyer
7 Willie Smith
8 Don Stanford
9 Wade Taylor
10 Ricky Torres
11 Mitch Lyden
12 John Ramos
13 Andy Skeels
14 Bobby DeJardin
15 Bobby Dickerson
16 Pat Kelly
17 Tim Weston
18 Donald Sparks
19 Greg Sparks
20 Freddie Hailey
21 Billy Masse
22 Vince Phillips
23 Royal Clayton
24 Robert Zeihen
25 Joseph Lefebvre
26 Checklist

1990 ProCards Albany Yankees

(New York Yankees) (color)

	MT	NR MT	EX
Complete Set:	6.00	4.50	2.50

1028 Checklist
1029 Darrin Chapin
1030 Royal Clayton
1031 Andrew Cook
1032 Douglas Gogolewski
1033 Christian Howard
1034 Scott Kamieniecki
1035 Ronald Rub
1036 Donald Stanford
1037 Mitchell Lyden
1038 Andrew Skeels
1039 Robert Dejardin
1040 Bobby Dickerson
1041 Patrick Kelly
1042 Donald Sparks
1043 Joseph Sparks
1044 Freddie Hailey
1045 William Masse
1046 Vincent Phillips
1047 Robert Zeihen
1175 Ramon Manon
1176 Wade Taylor
1177 John Ramos
1178 Carlos Rodriquez
1179 Bernabe Williams
1180 Rick Down
1181 Joe Lefebvre
1182 Russell Meyer
1183 Glenn Sherlock

1990 Star Co. Albany Yankees

(New York Yankees) (color)

	MT	NR MT	EX
Complete Set:	6.00	4.50	2.50

1 Darrin Chapin
2 Royal Clayton
3 Andy Cook
4 Bobby Dickerson
5 Gogo Gogolewski
6 Freddie Hailey
7 Scott Kamieniecki
8 Pat Kelly
9 Mitch Lyden
10 Ramon Manon
11 Billy Masse
12 Vince Phillips
13 John Ramos
14 Carlos Rodriquez
15 Jerry Rub
16 Andy Skeels
17 Don Sparks
18 Greg Sparks
19 Don Stanford
20 Wade Taylor
21 Ricky Torres
22 Bernie Williams
23 Bob Zeihen
24 Rick Down
25 Joe Lefebvre
26 Glenn Sherlock
27 Mark Shiflett
28 Tim Weston

1990 CMC Albuquerque Dukes

(Los Angeles Dodgers) (color)

	MT	NR MT	EX
Complete Set:	7.00	5.25	2.75

1 Mike Christopher
2 Jeff Bittiger
3 Jeff Fischer
4 Steve Davis
5 Morris Madden
6 Darren Holmes
7 Greg Mayberry
8 Mike Maddux
9 Tim Scott
10 Jim Neidlinger
11 Dave Walsh
12 Dennis Springer
13 Terry Wells
14 Adam Brown
15 Darrin Fletcher
16 Carlos Hernandez
17 Dave Hansen
18 Dan Henley
19 Jose Offerman
20 Jose Vizcaino
21 Luis Lopez
22 Butch Davis
23 Wayne Kirby
24 Mike Huff
25 Billy Bean
26 Glenn Hoffman
27 Kevin Kennedy
28 Dukes Coaches (Claude Osteen, Von Joshua, Walt McConnel)

1990 ProCards Albuquerque Dukes

(Los Angeles Dodgers) (color)

	MT	NR MT	EX
Complete Set:	7.00	5.25	2.75

334 Checklist
335 Jeff Bittiger
336 Mike Christopher
337 Steve Davis
338 Jeff Fischer
339 Darren Holmes
340 Morris Madden
341 Mike Maddux
342 Greg Mayberry
343 Jim Neidlinger
344 Tim Scott
345 Dave Walsh
346 Terry Wells
347 Adam Brown
348 Darrin Fletcher
349 Carlos Hernandez
350 Dave Hanson
351 Dan Henley
352 Glenn Hoffman
353 Walt McConnel
354 Jose Offerman
355 Jose Vizcaino
356 Billy Bean
357 Butch Davis
358 Mike Huff
359 Wayne Kirby
360 Luis Lopez
361 Kevin Kennedy
362 Von Joshua
363 Claude Osteen

1990 Box Scores Appleton Foxes

(Kansas City Royals) (color)

	MT	NR MT	EX
Complete Set:	3.00	2.25	1.25

1 Team Checklist
2 Brian Ahern
3 Francisco Baez
4 Kirk Baldwin
5 Joe Breeden
6 Gary Caraballo
7 John Conner
8 Francisco Garcia
9 John Gilcrest
10 Grant Griesser
11 John Gross
12 Arned Hernandez
13 Jake Jacobs
14 Mike Jirschele
15 Matt Karchner
16 David King
17 Herb Milton
18 Giovanni Miranda
19 Kerwin Moore
20 Andre Rabouin
21 Fred Russell
22 Colin Ryan
23 Chris Schaefer
24 Steve Shifflett
25 Dave Solseth
26 Rod Stillwell
27 Louis Talbert
28 Rich Tunison
29 Pedro Vazquez
30 Skip Wiley

1990 Diamond Appleton Foxes

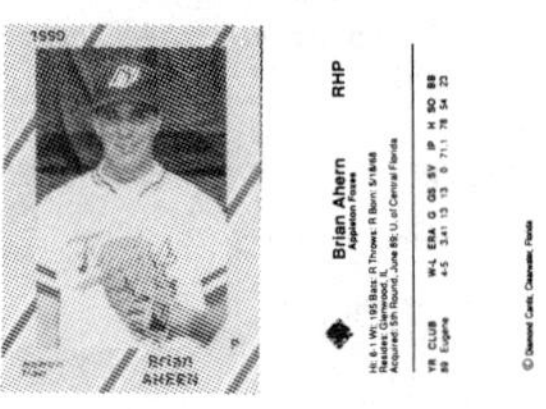

(Kansas City Royals) (color)

	MT	NR MT	EX
Complete Set:	3.00	2.25	1.25

1 Brian Ahern
2 Francisco Baez
3 Kirk Baldwin
4 Gary Caraballo
5 John Conner
6 Francisco Garcia
7 John Gilcrist
8 Grant Griesser
9 John Gross
10 Arned Hernandez
11 Jake Jacobs
12 Matt Karchner
13 David King
14 Herbert Milton
15 Giovanni Miranda
16 Kerwin Moore
17 Not Issued
18 Colin Ryan
19 Chris Schaefer
20 Steve Shifflett
21 Dave Solseth
22 Rod Stillwell
23 Louis Talbert
24 Rich Tunison
25 Fred Russell
26 Pedro Vazquez, Skip Wiley
27 Joe Breeden
28 Mike Jirschele
29 Andre Rabouin
30 Brad Shores

1990 ProCards Appleton Foxes

(Kansas City Royals) (color)

	MT	NR MT	EX
Complete Set:	3.00	2.25	1.25

2085 Checklist
2086 Brian Ahern
2087 Francisco Baez
2088 Kirk Baldwin
2089 John Conner
2090 Develon Jacobs
2091 Matthew D. Karchner
2092 Herbert Milton
2093 Christopher Schaefer
2094 Stephen Shifflett
2095 Louis Talbert
2096 Warren Wiley
2097 Grant Griesser
2098 Colin Ryan
2099 David Solseth
2100 Edgardo P. Caraballo
2101 David King
2102 Giovanni Miranda
2103 Frederick Russell
2104 Rod Stillwell
2105 Richard Tunison
2106 Pedro Vazquez

2107 Francisco Garcia
2108 John Gilcrest
2109 Kerwin Moore
2110 Arned Hernandez
2111 Joe Breeden
2112 Mike Jirschele
2113 Andre Rabouin

1990 Grand Slam Arkansas Travelers

(St. Louis Cardinals) (color)

	MT	NR MT	EX
Complete Set:	6.00	4.50	2.50

1 Dave Bialas
2 Marty Mason
3 Dan Doyle
4 Frankie Abreu
5 Isaac Alleyne
6 John Burgos
7 Greg Carmona
8 Ric Christan
9 Rheal Cormier
10 John Ericks
11 Steve Fanning
12 Joey Fernandez
13 Mike Fitzgerald
14 Ed Fulton
15 Mark Grater
16 Joe Hall
17 Rich Hoffman
18 Brian Jordan
19 Dale Kisten
20 John Lepley
21 Scott Melvin
22 Dave Osteen
23 Gab Ozuna
24 Len Picota
25 Larry Pierson
26 Mike Ross
27 Brian Stone
28 Paul Thoutsis
29 Jose Vargas
30 Charlie White

1990 ProCards Asheville Tourists

(Houston Astros) (color)

	MT	NR MT	EX
Complete Set:	4.00	3.00	1.50

2738 Checklist
2739 Troy Dovey
2740 Benjamin Gonzales
2741 Christopher Gardner
2742 Anthony Gutierrez
2743 Michael McDowell
2744 Julio Munoz
2745 Franciso Perez
2746 Limbert Rivas
2747 Eliezel Rosario
2748 Mark Allen
2749 Donnel Wall
2750 Kenneth Wheeler
2751 Edward Beuerlein
2752 Kevin Scott
2753 Craig Curtis
2754 David Hajeck
2755 Brett Holum
2756 Justin McCray
2757 Orlando Miller
2758 Edward Quijada
2759 Gershow Dallas
2760 Juan Encarnacion
2761 Brian Hunter
2762 Luther Johnson
2763 Jose Santan
2764 Frank Cacciatore
2765 Rick Aponte

1990 Best Auburn Astros

(Houston Astros) (color)

	MT	NR MT	EX
Complete Set:	3.00	2.25	1.25

1 Manny Mota, Jr.
2 Robert Hurta
3 Steve Veit
4 David Wilson
5 Efrain Barreiro
6 Jose Flores
7 Bob Hurlbutt
8 Doug Ketchen
9 Jeff Ball
10 Vince Roman
11 Steve Powers
12 Bryan Smith
13 Michael Irwin
14 Mark Hampton
15 Marty Jones
16 Dave Allen
17 Lincoln Gumbs, Jr.
18 Fletcher Thompson
19 Tyrone Scott
20 John Graham
21 Brian Porter
22 Marc Techman
23 Don Alexander
24 Mark Copeland
25 Checklist

1990 ProCards Auburn Astros

(Houston Astros) (color)

	MT	NR MT	EX
Complete Set:	3.00	2.25	1.25

3393 Checklist
3394 Ray Montgomery
3395 Chris Hatcher
3396 Layne Lambert
3397 Tony Gilmore
3398 Manny Mota, Jr.
3399 Bob Hurta
3400 Steve Veit
3401 Mark Hampton
3402 Tyrone Scott
3403 Marty Jones
3404 David Wilson
3405 Vince Roman
3406 Bryan Smith
3407 Steve Powers
3408 Jeff Ball
3409 Lincoln Gumbs
3410 Fletcher Thompson
3411 Jose Flores
3412 Michael Irwin
3413 Efrain Barreiro
3414 Dave Allen
3415 J.B. Ketchen
3416 Robert Hurlbutt
3417 Ricky Peters
3418 Don Alexander

1990 ProCards Augusta Pirates

(Pittsburgh Pirates) (color)

	MT	NR MT	EX
Complete Set:	4.00	3.00	1.50

2454 Checklist
2455 Scott Arveson
2456 David Bird
2457 Brent Honeywell
2458 Ramon Martinez
2459 Wayne Masters
2460 Eric Parkinson
2461 Kevin Rychel
2462 Delvy Santiago
2463 Bobby Underwood
2464 Paul Wagner
2465 Ron Way
2466 Felix Antiqua
2467 Jason Nixon
2468 Jessie Torres
2469 Rich Aude
2470 Willie Greene
2471 Bill Holmes
2472 Deron Johnson
2473 Austin Manahan
2474 Roman Rodriguez
2475 Winston Seymour
2476 Mike Brewington
2477 William Pennyfeather
2478 Daryl Ratliff
2479 Kenneth Trusky
2480 Lee Driggers

1990 Cal League Bakersfield Dodgers

(Los Angeles Dodgers) (color)

	MT	NR MT	EX
Complete Set:	5.00	3.75	2.00

230 Kiki Jones
231 Fausto Tatis
232 Baltazar Mesa
233 Napoleon Robinson
234 Jason Brosnan
235 Rich Crane
236 Mike Frame
237 Jamie McAndrew
238 Tony Helmick
239 Frank Humber
240 Mike Pothoff
241 John Brasse
242 Barry Parisotto
243 Craig Bishop
244 Tom Beyers
245 Anthony Garcia
246 Goose Gregson
247 Chris Morrow
248 Steve O'Donnell
249 John Deutsch
250 Brock McMurray
251 Gary Forrester
252 Garrett Teel
253 Matt Howard
254 Brett Magnusson
255 Tim Barker
256 Bryan Barr
257 Bryan Beals
258 John Munoz
259 Bill Lott
260 Bill Ashley
261 Tom Goodwin

1990 Star Co. Baseball City Royals

(Kansas City Royals) (color)

	MT	NR MT	EX
Complete Set:	4.00	3.00	1.50

1 Jose Anglero
2 Mike Beall
3 Jacob Brumfield
4 Sean Collins
5 Huascar de Leon
6 Bill Drohan
7 Linton Dyer
8 Jeff Garber
9 Chris Garibaldo
10 Greg Harvey
11 Steve Hoeme
12 Bobby Holley
13 Brad Hopper
14 Gary Koenig
15 Kevin Long
16 John McCormick
17 Steve Otto
18 Mark Parnell
19 Hipolito Pichardo
20 Ben Pierce
21 Darryl Robinson
22 Kevin Shaw
23 Randy Vaughn
24 Hugh Walker
25 Daren Watkins
26 Mike Webster
27 Don Wright
28 Brian Poldberg
29 Mike Alzarez
30 Ron Johnson
31 Mike Farnsworth

1990 ProCards Batavia Clippers

(Philadelphia Phillies) (color)

	MT	NR MT	EX
Complete Set:	3.00	2.25	1.25

3055 Checklist
3056 Al Baur
3057 Elliot Gray
3058 Eric Hill
3059 Charlie Hurst
3060 Tom Jones
3061 John Ingram
3062 Stewart Lovdal
3063 Steve McGovern
3064 Michael Montgomery
3065 Steven Parris
3066 Lamont Ross
3067 Michael Williams
3068 Porfirio Pena
3069 Ryan Ridenour
3070 Willie Smith
3071 Ismael Cruz
3072 Erik Judson
3073 R.A. Neitzel
3074 Michael Owens
3075 Eulogio Perez
3076 Sean Ryan
3077 James Savage
3078 Steven Bieser
3079 Robert Hartwig
3080 Jeffrey Jackson
3081 Field Staff
3082 Tom Nuneviller
3083 Gilbert Valencia
3084 Gary Morgan

1990 Legoe Bellingham Mariners

(Seattle Mariners) (color)

	MT	NR MT	EX
Complete Set:	3.00	2.25	1.25

1 Sean Twitty
2 Richard Lodding
3 Ruben Santana
4 Rick Green
5 Doug Tegtmeir
6 David Adam
7 James Converse
8 Doug Fitzer
9 James Magill
10 Rob Callistro
11 John Cummings
12 John Hoffman
13 Greg Hunter
14 Kevin King
15 Clay Klavitter
16 Matthew Kluge
17 Tony Kounas
18 Bobby Magallanes
19 David McDonald
20 Fred McNair
21 Lipso Nava
22 Robert Nichols
23 Glenn Raasch
24 Randy Rivera
25 Willie Romay
26 Brian Stephens
27 James Terrell
28 Willie Wilder
29 Willie Wilkerson
30 Tyler Williams
31 Kevin Yianacopolos
32 Todd Youngblood
33 Kyle Duke
34 P.J. Carey (Manager)
35 Wheelock, Pines, Webb
36 Bill Tucker
37 Jerry Walker

1990 Best Beloit Brewers

(Milwaukee Brewers) (color)

	MT	NR MT	EX
Complete Set:	3.00	2.25	1.25

1 Ramser Correa
2 Bill Robertson
3 Joe Andrejewski
4 Larry Carter
5 Troy O'Leary
6 Sam Drake
7 Tim Fortugno
8 Scott Kimball
9 Greg Landry
10 Scott Muscatt
11 Brett Snyder
12 Vilato Marrero
13 Randy Snyder
14 Darrin White
15 John Byington
16 Daren Cornell
17 Leon Glenn
18 Oreste Marrero
19 Henry Reynoso
20 Arthur Butcher
21 Jeff Nate
22 Scott Meissner
23 Bob Vancho
24 Troy Haugen
25 Keith Fleming
26 Robert Decksen
27 Checklist

1990 Star Co. Beloit Brewers

(Milwaukee Brewers) (color)

	MT	NR MT	EX
Complete Set:	3.00	2.25	1.25

1 Joe Andrzejewski
2 Arthur Butcher
3 John Byington
4 Larry Carter
5 Tim Clark
6 Sam Drake
7 Keith Fleming
8 Tim Fortugno
9 Leon Glenn
10 Troy Haugen
11 Scott Kimball
12 Oreste Marrero
13 Vilato Marrero
14 Tom McGraw
15 Scott Muscat
16 Troy O'Leary
17 Henry Reynoso
18 Bill Robertson
19 Rob Smith
20 Brett Snyder
21 Randy Snyder
22 Bob Vancho
23 Darrin White
24 Dave Wrona
25 Rob Derksen
26 Jeff Nate
27 Scott Meissner

Values quoted in this guide reflect the retail price of a card – the price a collector can expect to pay when buying a card from a dealer. The wholesale price – that which a collector can expect to receive from a dealer when selling cards – will be significantly lower, depending on desirability and condition.

1990 Legoe Bend Bucks

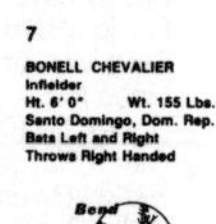

(California Angels) (color)

	MT	NR MT	EX
Complete Set:	3.00	2.25	1.25

1 Bucky (Mascot)
2 Gene Dusan
3 Sean Krokroskia
4 Micky Hyde
5 Marty Hunter
6 Kelly Ahrens
7 Bonell Chevalier
8 Mike Bubalo
9 Lonnie Potter
10 Jason Klonoski
11 Bob Blankenship
12 Dan Henrikson
13 Jose Reyes
14 Todd Russell
15 Russ Miller
16 Darrell Wagner
17 Glenn McCormick
18 Steve Avent
19 Chuck Wanke
20 Dan Vannell
21 Doug Twitty
22 Lee Sammons
23 Mario Lyons
24 Amner Reyes
25 Pedro Frias
26 Gary Ross
27 Pedro Roa
28 Shannon Hunt
29 Audy Mesa
30 Jim Gibbs
31 Checklist & Bat Boys (Matt Russell, Jason Lundren)

1990 ProCards Billings Mustangs

(Cincinnati Reds) (color)

	MT	NR MT	EX
Complete Set:	3.00	2.25	1.25

3210 Checklist
3211 Kevin Berry
3212 Sean Doty
3213 Scott Duff
3214 Michael Ferry
3215 Brian Fry
3216 Christopher Keim
3217 Larry Luebbers
3218 Greg Margheim
3219 Ernesto Nieves
3220 Scott Robinson
3221 Carl Steward
3222 Kevin Tatar
3223 Ryan Edwards
3224 Brian Nichols
3225 Roy Hammargren
3226 Dave Wheeler
3227 Bobby Filotei
3228 Keith Gordon
3229 Kevin Jones
3230 Rob Perna
3231 Kevin Riggs
3232 Todd Wilson
3233 Eric Burroughs
3234 Elliot Quinones
3235 Chris Vasquez
3236 Victor Perez
3237 K.C. Gillum
3238 Gerry Groninger
3239 Mack Jenkins

1990 Best Birmingham Barons

(Chicago White Sox) (color)

	MT	NR MT	EX
Complete Set:	60.00	45.00	24.00

1 Frank Thomas
2 Kurt Brown
3 Matt Merrullo
4 Matt Stark
5 Tom Alfredson
6 Cesar Bernhardt
7 Edgar Caceres
8 Greg Roth
9 Cornelio Garcia
10 Derek Lee
11 Willie Magallanes
12 Rodney McCray
13 Aubrey Waggoner
14 Carlos Delacruz
15 Brian Drahman
16 Buddy Groom
17 Todd Hall
18 Roberto Hernandez
19 John Hudek
20 Bo Kennedy
21 Dave Reynolds
22 Rich Scheid
23 Ron Stephens
24 Mike Gellinger
25 Rick Peterson
26 Sam Hairston
27 Dave Wallwork
28 Ken Berry
29 Pat Roessler
30 Checklist & Bat Boys

1990 ProCards Birmingham Barons

(Chicago White Sox) (color)

	MT	NR MT	EX
Complete Set:	30.00	22.00	12.00

1101 Checklist
1102 Carlos Delacruz
1103 Brian Drahman
1104 Buddy Groom
1105 Todd Hall
1106 Roberto Hernandez
1107 John Hudek
1108 Bo Kennedy
1109 Dave Reynolds
1110 Rich Scheid
1111 Kurt Brown
1112 Matt Merullo
1113 Matt Stark
1114 Cesar Bernhardt
1115 Greg Roth
1116 Frank Thomas
1117 Cornelio Garcia
1118 Derek Lee
1119 Rodney McCray
1120 Aubrey Waggoner
1393 Ron Stephens
1394 Tom Alfredson
1395 Edgar Caceres
1396 Will Magallanes
1397 Ken Berry
1398 Sam Hairston
1399 Pat Roessler
1400 Mike Gellinger

1990 Star Co. Bluefield Orioles

(Baltimore Orioles) (color) Two cards are numbered #21

	MT	NR MT	EX
Complete Set:	4.00	3.00	1.50

1 Matt Anderson
2 Mattie Asencio
3 Derek Bell
4 Brett Benge
5 Robert Burgillos
6 Allen Davis
7 Doug Flowers
8 Gordon Graham
9 Roy Hodge
10 Ihosvany Marquez
11 Juan Mercedes
12 Jose Millares
13 Shawn O'Connell
14 John O'Donoghue
15 German Paredes
16 Dan Ramirez
17 Estuar Ruiz
18 Keith Schmidt
19 Scott Sprick
20 Mike Thomas
21a Brad Tippitt
21b Mike Wiley

1990 ProCards Boise Hawks

(California Angels) (color)

	MT	NR MT	EX
Complete Set:	6.00	4.50	2.50

3304 Checklist
3305 Randy Powers
3306 Phil Leftwich
3307 Todd McCray
3308 Ken Edenfield
3309 Louie Pakele
3310 Jeff Ball
3311 Hilly Hathaway
3312 Paul Swingle
3313 Darryl Scott
3314 Dan Stenz
3315 Wayne Helm
3316 Michael Search
3317 Bob Gomez
3318 Jose Santana
3319 J.R. Phillips
3320 P.J. Forbes
3321 Brian Grebeck
3322 Brian Specyalski
3323 Joe Williams
3324 Mark D'Alesandro
3325 Randy Kotchman
3326 J.R. Showalter
3327 Dave Patrick
3328 Dave Staydohar
3329 Rich Sheppard
3330 Clifton Garrett
3331 Tom Kotchman
3332 Orv Franchuk
3333 Howie Gershberg
3334 Fausto Tejero
3335 Troy Percival
3336 Danny Gil

1990 ProCards Bristol Tigers

(Detroit Tigers) (color)

	MT	NR MT	EX
Complete Set:	5.00	3.75	2.00

3148 Checklist
3149 Carlos Fermin
3150 Keith Roberts
3151 Kevin Miller
3152 Adrian Jordan
3153 Luis Hernandez
3154 Daniel Bautista
3155 Chris Hall
3156 Jose Lima
3157 Alex Ubinas
3158 Ron Maitta
3159 Greg Haeger
3160 Shannon Withem
3161 Robert Riker
3162 Daniel Cruz
3163 Brian Dubose
3164 Luis Salazar
3165 Felipe Lira
3166 Mike Guifoyle
3167 Brian Warren
3168 Jimmy Alder
3169 Vince Bradford
3170 Paul Reinisch
3171 Jimmy Henry
3172 Brad Wilson
3173 Tony Clark
3174 Ken Cunningham
3175 Ruben Amaro
3176 Rich Henning

1990 Star Co. Bristol Tigers

(Detroit Tigers) (color)

	MT	NR MT	EX
Complete Set:	4.00	3.00	1.50

1 Jimmy Alder
2 Vincent Bradford
3 Tony Clark
4 Danny Cruz
5 Brian DuBose
6 Carlos Fermin
7 Mike Guilfoyle
8 Greg Haeger
9 Chris Hall
10 Jimmy Henry
11 Luis Hernandez
12 Adrian Jordan
13 Dave Keating
14 Jose Lima
15 Felipa Lira
16 Ron Maietta
17 Mike Mauro
18 Kevin Miller
19 Paul Reinisch
20 Robert Riker
21 Keith Roberts
22 Luis Salazar
23 Randy Stokes
24 Alex Ubina
25 Brad Wilson
26 Shannon Withem
27 Ken Cunningham
28 Rich Henning
29 Steve Webber
30 Boyce Cox

1990 CMC (TCMA) Buffalo Bisons

(Pittsburgh Pirates) (color)

	MT	NR MT	EX
Complete Set:	6.00	4.50	2.50

1 Stan Belinda
2 Gordon Dillard
3 Terry Collins
4 Mark Huismann
5 Hugh Kemp
6 Scott Medvin
7 Vicente Palacios
8 Rick Reed
9 Mark Ross
10 Dorn Taylor
11 Mike York
12 Jeff Richardson
13 Dann Bilardello
14 Tom Prince
15 Danny Sheaffer
16 Kevin Burdick
17 Steve Kiefer
18 Orlando Merced
19 Armando Moreno
20 Mark Ryal
21 Tommy Shields
22 Steve Carter
23 Wes Chamberlain
24 Jeff Cook
25 Scott Little

1990 ProCards Buffalo Bisons

(Pittsburgh Pirates) (color)

	MT	NR MT	EX
Complete Set:	6.00	4.50	2.50

364 Checklist
365 Stan Belinda
366 Gordon Dillard
367 Mark Huismann
368 Hugh Kemp
369 Scott Medvin
370 Vicente Palacios
371 Rick Reed
372 Mark Ross
373 Dorn Taylor
374 Mike York
375 Dann Bilardello
376 Tom Prince
377 Danny Sheaffer
378 Kevin Burdick
379 Steve Kiefer
380 Orlando Merced
381 Armando Moreno
382 Jeff Richardson
383 Mark Ryal
384 Tommy Shields
385 Steve Carter
386 Wes Chamberlain
387 Jeff Cook
388 Scott Little
389 Terry Collins
390 Jackie Brown
391 Steve Henderson

1990 Team Buffalo Bisons

(Pittsburgh Pirates) (color)

	MT	NR MT	EX
Complete Set:	8.00	6.00	3.25

6 Armando Moreno
7 Dann Bilardello
13 Dan Sheaffer
15 Steve Kiefer
17 Hugh Kemp
18 Jeff Richardson
19 Moses Alou
22 Tom Prince
23 Scott Little
24 Kevin Burdick
25 Mike York
26 Tommy Shields
27 Mark Huismann
29 Mark Ryal
30 Dorn Taylor
31 Orlando Merced
32 Steve Carter
37 Mark Ross
38 Vicente Palacios
39 Roger Mason
42 Randy Kramer
44 Wes Chamberlain
54 Mike Roecler
---- Jackie Brown
---- Terry Collins
---- Steve Henderson
---- Carlos Ledezma
---- Sponsor's Card

1990 Best Burlington Braves

(Atlanta Braves) (color)

	MT	NR MT	EX
Complete Set:	9.00	6.75	3.50

1 Pedro Borbon
2 Matt Murray
3 Glenn Gardner
4 Ramon Caraballo

5 Tom Bruck
6 Oswaldo Apolinario
7 Dave Reis
8 Tony Valle
9 Steve Swail
10 Jeff Calderone
11 Roberto Deleon
12 Eddie Watt
13 Tim Gillis
14 Walt Roy
15 Dickey Marze
16 Jeff Clark
17 Paul Reis
18 Scott Grove
19 Tony Baldwin
20 Javy Lopez
21 Kevin Kelly
22 Greg Harper
23 Daryl Blanks
24 Randy Simmons
25 Darren Ritter
26 Rod Byerly
27 Brent McCoy
28 Jim Saul
29 Gene Lane
30 Checklist

1990 ProCards Burlington Braves

(Atlanta Braves) (color)

	MT	NR MT	EX
Complete Set:	9.00	6.75	3.50

2339 Checklist
2340 Pedro Borbon
2341 Tom Bruck
2342 Rod Byerly
2343 Jeff Caderone
2344 Scott Grove
2345 Kevin Kelly
2346 Matt Murray
2347 Dave Reis
2348 Darren Ritter
2349 Walt Roy
2350 Tony Valle
2351 Roberto Deleon
2352 Javier Lopez
2353 Steve Swail
2354 Oswaldo Apolinario
2355 Glen Gardner
2356 Tim Gillis
2357 Dicky Marze
2358 Brent McCoy
2359 Paulo Reis
2360 Ramon Caraballo
2361 Tony Baldwin
2362 Daryl Banks
2363 Jeff Clark
2364 Randy Simmons
2365 Jim Saul
2366 Gil Garrido
2367 Eddie Watt
2368 Phillip Wellman

1990 Star Co. Burlington Braves

(Atlanta Braves) (color)

	MT	NR MT	EX
Complete Set:	9.00	6.75	3.50

1 Oswaldo Apolinario
2 Tony Baldwin
3 Daryl Blanks
4 Pedro Borbon
5 Tom Bruck
6 Rodney Byerly
7 Jeff Calderone
8 Ramon Carabello
9 Jeff Clark
10 Roberto Deleon
11 Glen Gardner
12 Tim Gillis
13 Scott Grove
14 Greg Harper
15 Kevin Kelly
16 Javy Lopez
17 Dickey Marze
18 Brent McCoy
19 Matt Murray
20 Dave Reis
21 Paul Reis
22 Darren Ritter
23 Walt Roy
24 Randy Simmons
25 Steve Swail
26 Tony Valle
27 Jim Saul
28 Gil Garrido
29 Eddie Watt
30 Phil Wellman
31 Gene Lane

1990 ProCards Burlington Indians

(Cleveland Indians) (color)

	MT	NR MT	EX
Complete Set:	6.00	4.50	2.50

3000 Checklist
3001 Sam Baker
3002 Dickie Brown
3003 Shawn Bryant
3004 Alan Embree
3005 Steve Gajkowsi
3006 Carl Johnson
3007 Shawn McElfish
3008 Tony Tillman
3009 Alan Walden
3010 Von Wechsberg
3011 Roberto Jimenez
3012 John Martinez
3013 Miguel Flores
3014 Matt Gilmore
3015 Frank Monastero
3016 Mike Pinckes
3017 Tim Thomas
3018 Jim Thome
3019 Jeff Brohm
3020 Sam Hence
3021 Pedro Henderson
3022 Ramon Ortiz
3023 Tracy Sanders
3024 Ramon Torres
3025 Darrell Whitemore
3026 David Keller
3027 Stan Hilton
---- Dan Devoe

1990 Sport Pro Butte Copper Kings

(Texas Rangers) (color)

	MT	NR MT	EX
Complete Set:	6.00	4.50	2.50

1 Rodney Busha
2 Greg Blevins
3 Miguel Castellano
4 Rusty Greer
5 Terry Burrows
6 Gary Posey
7 Dan Smith
8 David Hulse
9 Jose Cardona
10 Steve Dreyer
11 Paul Matachum
12 Malvin Matos
13 Scott Erickson
14 Shane Patterson
15 Brian Mercado
16 Kevin Murray
17 Steve Ramharter
18 Bobby St. Pe
19 Brian Scheetz
20 Victor Reyes
21 Brian Mouton
22 Chris Geis
23 Steve Surico
24 Sahnnon Penn
25 Tyrone Washington
26 Jon Shave
27 Andy Watson
28 Tim Wells
29 Matt Whiteside
30 Todd Guggiana

1990 CMC (TMCA) Calgary Cannons

(Seattle Mariners) (color)

	MT	NR MT	EX
Complete Set:	7.00	5.25	2.75

1 Pat Pacillo
2 Tony Blasucci
3 Mike Walker
4 Pat Rice
5 Terry Taylor
6 David Burba
7 Vance Lovelace
8 Ed Vande Berg
9 Greg Fulton
10 Ed Jurak
11 Dave Cochrane
12 Edgar Martinez
13 Matt Sinatro
14 Bill McGuire
15 Mickey Brantley
16 Tom Dodd
17 Jim Weaver
18 Todd Haney
19 Casey Close
20 Theo Shaw
21 Keith Helton
22 Jose Melendez
23 Tom Jones
24 Dan Warthen
25 Randy Roetter

1990 ProCards Calgary Cannons

(Seattle Mariners) (color)

	MT	NR MT	EX
Complete Set:	5.00	3.75	2.00

643 Checklist
644 Tony Blasucci
645 Dave Burba
646 Keith Helton
647 Vance Lovelace
648 Jose Melendez
649 Pat Pacillo
650 Pat Rice
651 Terry Taylor
652 Mike Walker
653 Bill Mcguire
654 Matt Sinatro
655 Mario Diaz
656 Greg Fulton
657 Todd Haney
658 Ed Jurak
659 Tino Martinez
660 Jeff Schaefer
661 Casey Close
662 Tom Dodd
663 Jim Weaver
664 Tommy Jones
665 Dan Warthen

1990 Cal League All-Stars

(All-Stars) (color)

	MT	NR MT	EX
Complete Set:	7.00	5.25	2.75

1 Dave Staton
2 Brett Magnusson
3 John Deutsch
4 Jose Garcia
5 Vince Harris
6 Jim Edmonds
7 Steve Hendricks
8 Tim Barker
9 Carlos Capellan
10 Darrell Sherman
11 Frank Bolick
12 Chris Morrow
13 J.T. Bruett
14 Matt Howard
15 Troy Buckley
16 George Tsamis
17 Jason Brosnan
18 Richard Garces
19 Kerry Woodson
20 Kiki Jones
21 Roger Salkeld
22 Jamie McAndrew
23 Jim Newlin
24 Denny Neagle
25 Scott Ullger
26 Brian Allard
27 Joe Gagliardi
28 Sal Artiaga
29 Chris Bando
30 Mitch Zwolensky
31 Levenda & Weiss
32 Kevin Dykstra
33 Bob Brooks
34 Brian Laxamana
35 Brent Howard
36 Pat Listach
37 Scooter Tucker
38 Bo Dodson
39 Tom Eiterman
40 Dan Lewis
41 Chris Cassels
42 Dwayne Hosey
43 Ron Witmeyer
44 Shikato Yanagida
45 Rueben Smiley
46 Mike Sarbaugh
47 Adell Davenport
48 Bob Kappesser
49 Royce Clayton
50 Kevin Rogers
51 Angel Miranda
52 Mike Soper
53 Dan Rambo
54 Dave Fitzgerald
55 Cecil Pettiford
56 Chris Johnson

1990 Best Canton-Akron Indians

(Cleveland Indians) (color)

	MT	NR MT	EX
Complete Set:	5.00	3.75	2.00

1 Mark Lewis
2 Will George
3 Lee Kuntz
4 Ken Bolek
5 Darren Epley
6 Allen Liebert
7 Sam Ferretti
8 Manny Francois
9 Jim Orsag
10 Joe Kesselmark
11 Rob Swain
12 Jim Tatum
13 Lee Jackson
14 Delwyn Young
15 Miguel Sabino
16 Franciso Melendez
17 Rob Wine
18 Jim Bruske
19 Jeff Fassero
20 Bruce Egloff
21 Carl Keliipuleole
22 Jeff Mutis
23 Greg Roscoe
24 Rudy Seanez
25 Allen Collins
26 Mike Curtis
27 Charles Nagy
28 Checklist

1990 ProCards Canton-Akron Indians

(Cleveland Indians) (color)

	MT	NR MT	EX
Complete Set:	6.00	4.50	2.50

1284 Checklist
1285 Jim Bruske
1286 Allen Collins
1287 Mike Curtis
1288 Bruce Egloff
1289 Jeff Fassero
1290 Carl Keliipuleole
1291 Jeff Mutis
1292 Charles Nagy
1293 Rudy Seanez
1294 Allen Liebert
1295 Robbie Wine
1296 Darren Epley
1297 Sam Ferretti
1298 Manny Francois
1299 Mark Lewis
1300 Francisco Melendez
1301 Rob Swain
1302 Jimmy Tatum
1303 Leverne Jackson
1304 Joe Kesselmark
1305 Miguel Sabino
1306 Delwyn Young
1307 Roberto Zambrano
1308 Greg Roscoe
1309 Ken Bolek
1363 Will George

1990 Star Co. Canton-Akron Indians

(Cleveland Indians) (color)

	MT	NR MT	EX
Complete Set:	7.00	5.25	2.75

1 Jim Bruske
2 Allen Collins
3 Mike Curtis
4 Darren Epley
5 Jeff Fassero
6 Sam Ferretti
7 Jason Jackson
8 Carl Keliipuleole
9 Mark Lewis
10 Allen Liebert
11 Greg McMichael
12 Francisco Melendez
13 Jeff Mutis
14 Charles Nagy
15 Greg Roscoe
16 Miguel Sabino
17 Casey Webster
18 Delwyn Young
19 Roberto Zambrano
20 Ken Bolek
21 Lee Kuntz

1990 Carolina League All-Stars

(All-Stars) (color)

	MT	NR MT	EX
Complete Set:	6.00	4.50	2.50

1 Zachary Kerr
2 Mike Oquist
3 Todd Stephan
4 Ricky Gutierrez
5 Tim Holland
6 Dan Berthel
7 Wally Moon
8 Bill Murray
9 Brian Conroy
10 Freddie Davis
11 Paul Williams
12 Greg Blosser
13 James Byrd

14 Frank Seminara
15 Mike Gardella
16 Mauricio Zazueta
17 J.T. Snow
18 Russ Davis
19 Gary Denbo
20 Mike Pomeranz
21 Mandy Romeo
22 Mike Huyler
23 Bruce Schreiber
24 Darwin Pennye
25 Chris Estep
26 Paul Miller
27 Skipper Wright
28 Mike Mordecai
29 Keith Mitchell
30 Popeye Cole
31 Brian Champion
32 Brian Graham
33 Dennis Noonan
34 Ty Kovach
35 Greg Ferlenda
36 Gerard DiPoto
37 Garland Kiser
38 Tommy Kramer
39 Jesse Levis
40 Brian Johnson
41 Rouglas Odor
42 Nolan Lane
43 Ken Ramos
44 Lem Pilkinton
45 Rick Balabon
46 Shannon Jones
47 John Salles
48 Elvin Paulino
49 Gary Scott
50 Billy White
51 Brad Mills
52 Steve DiBartolomeo

1990 Best Cedar Rapids Reds

(Cincinnati Reds) (color)

	MT	NR MT	EX
Complete Set:	5.00	3.75	2.00

1 Scott Bryant
2 Glenn Sutko
3 Edward Taubensee
4 Vicente Javier
5 Terry Abbott
6 Edward Rush
7 Michael Mulvaney
8 Richard Allen
9 Lavell Cudjo
10 Anthony Terzarial
11 Reginald Sanders
12 Mark Krumback
13 Tom Spencer
14 William Risley
15 Robert Ayala
16 Victoriano Garcia
17 Ramon Manon
18 Joseph Turek
19 Dave Miley
20 Michael Anderson
21 Douglas King
22 David McAuLiffee
23 Meredith Sanford
24 Mark Borcherding
25 Scott Jeffrey
26 Steve Hester
27 Howard James

1990 ProCards Cedar Rapids Reds

(Cincinnati Reds) (color) Most of these cards have printers marks on them

	MT	NR MT	EX
Complete Set:	6.00	4.50	2.50

2312 Checklist
2313 Bill Risley
2314 Bobby Ayala
2315 Victor Garcia
2316 Ramon Manon
2317 Scott Economy
2318 Mike Anderson
2319 Steve McCarthy
2320 Dave McAuliffe
2321 Mo Stanford
2322 Jerry Spradlin
2323 Steve Hester
2324 Frank Kremblas
2325 Eddie Taubensee
2326 Brian Nichols
2327 Vicente Javier
2328 Bob Dombroski
2329 Eddie Rush
2330 Mike Mulvaney
2331 Rick Allen
2332 Lavell Cudjo
2333 Tony Terzarial
2334 Reggie Sanders
2335 Mark Krumback
2336 Scott Bryant
2337 Dave Miley
2338 Terry Abbott

1990 Best Charleston Rainbows

(San Diego Padres) (color)

	MT	NR MT	EX
Complete Set:	3.00	2.25	1.25

1 Russ Garside
2 Lance Banks
3 Jeff Barton
4 Brian Beck
5 Julio Bruno
6 Rico Coleman
7 Troy Cunningham
8 Bob Curnow
9 Roberto Arredono
10 Pedro Guzman
11 Lee Henderson
12 Bill Johnson
13 Pedro Lopez
14 Pablo Martinez
15 Jose Mateo
16 William Marx
17 Joe Murdock
18 Danny Pickett
19 Craig Pueschner
20 Rafael Santiago
21 Charles Thompson
22 William Thompson
23 Ed Zinter
24 John Maxwell
25 Mark Littell
26 Jack Krol
27 Jimmy Lester
28 Checklist

1990 ProCards Charleston Rainbows

(San Diego Padres) (color)

	MT	NR MT	EX
Complete Set:	3.00	2.25	1.25

2029 Checklist
2030 Squeezer Thompson
2031 Rafael Santiago
2032 Lance Banks
2033 Danny Pickett
2034 Troy Cunningham
2035 Charles Thompson
2036 Joe Murdock
2037 Pete Guzman
2038 Russ Garside
2039 Ed Zinter
2040 Bill Johnson
2041 Lee Henderson
2042 Rob Curnow
2043 Pedro Lopez
2044 Pablo Martinez
2045 Roberto Arredondo
2046 Julio Bruno
2047 Jose Mateo
2048 Monte Brooks
2049 Scott Bream
2050 Brian Beck
2051 Jeff Barton
2052 Craig Pueschner
2053 Rico Coleman
2054 Jack Krol
2055 Mark Littell
2056 Jimmy Lester

1990 Best Charleston Wheelers

(Cincinnati Reds) (color) Card is spelled Scott Pelmmons on front of card

	MT	NR MT	EX
Complete Set:	4.00	3.00	1.50

1 Darron Cox
2 Chris Hook
3 Mike Malley
4 Steve McCarthy
5 Ernie Nieves
6 Scott Plemmons
7 Tim Pugh
8 Johnny Ray
9 Jason Satre
10 Jerry Spradlin
11 Trey Wilburn
12 Timothy Cecil
13 Brian Nichols
14 Raphael Bustamante
15 Chris Gill
16 Trevor Hoffman
17 Kevin Jones
18 Noel Velez
19 Todd Watson
20 Mark Arland
21 Jack Hollis
22 Eugene Jones
23 Danny Perozo
24 Scott Pose
25 Mark Berry
26 Jim Lett
27 Mike Griffith
28 Tom Iverson
29 Checklist

1990 ProCards Charleston Wheelers

(Cincinnati Reds) (color)

	MT	NR MT	EX
Complete Set:	4.00	3.00	1.50

2231 Checklist
2232 Mark Borcherding
2233 Tim Cecil
2234 Chris Hook
2235 Doug King
2236 Mike Malley
2237 Ernesto Nieves
2238 Scott Plemmons
2239 Tim Pugh
2240 Johnny Ray
2241 Jason Satre
2242 Trey Wilburn
2243 Darron Cox
2244 Jon Fuller
2245 Raphael Bustamante
2246 Chris Gill
2247 Trevor Hoffman
2248 Noel Velez
2249 Todd Watson
2250 Mark Arland
2251 K.C. Gillum
2252 Jack Hollis
2253 Eugene Jones
2254 Danny Perozo
2255 Scott Pose
2256 Mark Berry
2257 Jim Lett
2258 Mike Griffin

1990 Team Charlotte Knights

(Chicago Cubs) (color)

	MT	NR MT	EX
Complete Set:	5.00	3.75	2.00

1 Lance Dickson
2 Phil Hannon
3 Dick Canan
4 Darrin Duffy
5 Alex Arias
6 Heathcliff Slocumb
7 Chico Walker
8 John Posey
9 John Stefero
10 Butch Garcia
11 Glenn Sullivan
12 Fernando Zarranz
13 Bill Kazmierczak
14 Ty Griffin
15 Ray Mullino
16 Jay Loviglio
17 Brett Robinson
18 Chuck Mount
19 Tommy Helms
20 Frank Castillo
21 Rusty Crockett
22 Rick Wilkins
23 Richie Grayum
24 Bob Grimes
25 Rick Kranitz

1990 Star Co. Charlotte Rangers

(Texas Rangers) (color)

	MT	NR MT	EX
Complete Set:	8.00	6.00	3.25

1 Gerald Alexander
2 Rob Brown
3 Cris Colon
4 Fidel Compres
5 Doug Cronk
6 Everett Cunningham
7 Jeff Frye
8 Bryan Gore
9 Daren Hays
10 Jose Hernandez
11 Jim Hvizda
12 Barry Manuel
13 Trey McCoy
14 Rod Morris
15 Robb Nen
16 Darren Niethammer
17 Darren Oliver
18 Jeff Oller
19 Roger Pavlik
20 Jack Peel
21 David Perez
22 Ivan Rodriquez
23 Bill Losa
24 Steve Rowley
25 Luke Sable
26 Fred Samson
27 Kyle Spencer
28 Thayer Swain
29 Bobby Jones
30 Jeff Hubbard

1990 Grand Slam Chattanooga Lookouts

(Cincinnati Reds) (color)

	MT	NR MT	EX
Complete Set:	4.00	3.00	1.50

1 Jim Tracy
2 Don Gullett
3 Gregg Crain
4 Doug Banning
5 Freddie Benavides
6 Jeff Branson
7 Joe Bruno
8 Adam Casillas
9 Ben Colvard
10 Tony DeFrancesco
11 Bill Dodd
12 Brian Lee Finley
13 Jeff Forney
14 Steve Foster
15 Alan Hayden
16 Butch Henry
17 Keith Kaiser
18 Joe Lazor
19 Terry Lee
20 Greg Lonigro
21 Gino Minutelli
22 Mike Moscrey
23 Jerome Nelson
24 Ross Powell
25 Rosario Rodriquez
26 Melvin Rosario
27 Scott Sellner

1990 Star Co. Clearwater Phillies

(Philadelphia Phillies) (color)

	MT	NR MT	EX
Complete Set:	3.00	2.25	1.25

1 Jim Barragan
2 Toby Borland
3 Cliff Brantley
4 Andy Carter
5 Tim Dell
6 Todd Elam
7 Kevin Frynan
8 Jeff Hulse
9 Kennedy Infante
10 Lee Langley
11 Darrell Lindsey
12 Tony Lozinski
13 Greg McCarthy
14 Terry McDevitt
15 Shelby McDonald
16 Joe Millette
17 Jeff Patterson
18 Mark Randall
19 Ed Rosado
20 Steve Scarsone
21 Joe Tenhunfeld
22 Tony Trevino
23 Leroy Ventress
24 Cary Williams
25 Pat Woodruff
26 Lee Elia
27 LeBoeu, Martin)

1990 Best Clinton Giants

(San Francisco Giants) (color)

	MT	NR MT	EX
Complete Set:	3.00	2.25	1.25

1 Clay Bellinger
2 Steve Callahan
3 Kelly Ahrens
4 Frank Cary
5 Jeff Bonner
6 Ed Gustafson
7 Greg Brummett
8 Chris Hancock
9 Jack Mull
10 Steve Cline
11 Gus Vollmer
12 Brian Costello
13 Jason McFarlin
14 Carl Hanselman
15 Randy Johnson
16 Marino Hernandez
17 Kevin Kasper
18 Steward Hillman
19 Roger Miller
20 Joey James
21 Ron Crowe
22 Maximo Aleys
23 Pat Rapp
24 Rafael Novoa

25 Steve Rolen
26 Vince Palyan
27 Rob Taylor
28 Jon Pattin
29 Checklist

1990 ProCards Clinton Giants

(San Francisco Giants) (color)

	MT	NR MT	EX
Complete Set:	3.00	2.25	1.25

2539 Checklist
2540 Carl Hanselman
2541 Rafael Novoa
2542 Steward Hillman
2543 Chris Hancock
2544 Rob Taylor
2545 Steve Callahan
2546 Greg Brummett
2547 Pat Rapp
2548 Max Aleys
2549 Jim Foley
2550 Ed Gustafson
2551 Kelly Ahrens
2552 Jon Pattin
2553 Roger Miller
2554 Joey James
2555 Frank Carey
2556 Kevin Kasper
2557 Ron Crowe
2558 Clay Bellinger
2559 Steve Rolen
2560 Jeffrey Bonner
2561 Randy Johnson
2562 Gus Vollmer
2563 Jason McFarlin
2564 Vince Palyan
2565 Jack Mull
2566 Steve Cline
2567 Ron Wotus

1990 CMC (TCMA) Colorado Springs Sky Sox

(Cleveland Indians) (color)

	MT	NR MT	EX
Complete Set:	5.00	3.75	2.00

1 Mike Walker
2 Colby Ward
3 Joe Skalski
4 Efrain Valdez
5 Doug Robertson
6 Jeff Edwards
7 Greg McMichael
8 Carl Willis
9 Beau Allred
10 Jeff Kaiser
11 Ty Gainey
12 Tom Lampkin
13 Ever Magallanes
14 Tom Magrann
15 Jeff Manto
16 Luis Medina
17 Troy Neel
18 Steve Springer
19 Rick Adair
20 Turner Ward
21 Casey Webster
22 Jeff Wetherby
23 Alan Cockrell
24 Bobby Molinaro

1990 ProCards Colorado Springs Sky Sox

(Cleveland Indians) (color)

	MT	NR MT	EX
Complete Set:	6.00	4.50	2.50

30 Checklist
31 Greg McMichael
32 Doug Robertson
33 Jeff Shaw
34 Joe Skalski
35 Efrain Valdez
36 Mike Walker
37 Colby Ward
38 Carl Willis
39 Tom Lampkin
40 Tom Magrann
41 Juan Castillo
42 Ever Magallanes
43 Jeff Manto
44 Luis Medina
45 Troy Neel
46 Steve Springer
47 Casey Webster
48 Beau Allred
49 Alan Cockrell
50 Ty Gainey
51 Dwight Taylor
52 Turner Ward
53 Jeff Wetherby
54 Bobby Molinaro
55 Buddy Bell
56 Rick Adair

1990 Grand Slam Columbia Mets

(New York Mets) (color)

	MT	NR MT	EX
Complete Set:	4.00	3.00	1.50

Team Picture
1 Bill Stein
2 Jack Fisher
3 Tim McClinton
4 Jarrod Parker
5 Nick Davis
6 Joe McCann
7 James Harris
8 Ried Hartmann
9 Pat Howell
10 Deron Sample
11 Tim Howard
12 Brian Davis
13 Tito Navarro
14 Alberto Diaz
15 Julian Vasquez
16 Greg Langbehn
17 Art Emm
18 Ryan Richmond
19 Alberto Castillo
20 Chris Dorn
21 Joe Vitko
22 Brook Fordyce
23 Kevin Carroll
24 Mark Thomas
25 Stanton Cameron
26 Dave Telgheder
27 Robert Burton
28 Tim Marting
29 Jay Brazeau
30 Checklist

1990 Team (Play II) Columbia Mets

(New York Mets) (color)

	MT	NR MT	EX
Complete Set:	4.00	3.00	1.50

Series I
1 Bill Stein
2 Alberto Castillo
3 Joe Vitko
4 Reid Hartman
5 Joe McCann
6 Tim Howard
7 Gregg Langbehn
Series II
1 Deron Sample
2 Kevin Carroll
3 Julian Vasquez
4 Stanton Cameron
5 Brian Davis
6 Tito Navarro
Series III
1 Art Emm
2 Alberto Diaz
3 Ryan Richmond
4 Mark Thomas
5 Chris Dorn
6 Nick Davis
7 Tim McClinton
Series IV
1 David Telgheder
2 Jarrod Parker
3 Pat Howell
4 Brook Fordyce
5 James Harris
6 Jack Fisher
7 Team Photo

1990 CMC (TCMA) Columbus Clippers

(New York Yankees) (color)

	MT	NR MT	EX
Complete Set:	9.00	6.75	3.50

1 Steve Adkins
2 Dave Eiland
3 John Habyan
4 Mark Leiter
5 Kevin Mmahat
6 Hipolito Pena
7 Willie Smith
8 Rich Monteleone
9 Hensley Meulens
10 Andy Stankiewicz
11 Jim Leyritz
12 Jim Walenwander
13 Oscar Azocar
14 John Fishel
15 Jason Maas
16 Van Snider
17 Kevin Maas
18 Ricky Torres
19 Jeff Date, Dave Sax
20 Darrin Chapin
21 Rob Sepanek
22 Mark Wasinger
23 Jimmy Jones
24 Clipper Coaches
25 Carl Merrill
26 Bob Davidson

1990 Police Columbus Clippers

(New York Yankees) (black and white) (error set)

	MT	NR MT	EX
Complete Set:	11.00	8.25	4.50

1 Ken Rowe
2 Clete Boyer
3 Stump Merrill
4 Kevin Maas (Error) (Mispelled on back of card)
5 Jim Leyritz
6 John Fishel
7 Dave Sax
8 Jason Maas
9 Ron Davis
10 Bob Davidson
11 Mark Leiter
12 Oscar Azocar
13 Dave Eiland
14 Willie Smith
15 Van Snider
16 John Habyan
17 Steve Adkins
18 Brian Dorsett
19 Jimmy Jones
20 Kevin Mmahat
21 Jim Walewander
22 Rob Sepanek
23 Hensley Meulens
24 Andy Stankiewicz
25 Mark Wasinger

1990 Police Columbus Clippers

(New York Yankees) (black and white) (corrected set)

	MT	NR MT	EX
Complete Set:	6.00	4.50	2.50

1 Ken Rowe
2 Clete Boyer
3 Stump Merrill
4 Kevin Maas
5 Jim Leyritz
6 John Fishel
7 Dave Sax
8 Jason Maas
9 Ron Davis
10 Bob Davidson
11 Mark Leiter
12 Oscar Azocar
13 Dave Eiland
14 Willie Smith
15 Van Snider
16 John Habyan
17 Steve Adkins
18 Brian Dorsett
19 Jimmy Jones
20 Kevin Mmahat
21 Jim Walewander
22 Rob Sepanek
23 Hensley Meulens
24 Andy Stankiewicz
25 Mark Wasinger

1990 ProCards Columbus Clippers

(New York Yankees) (color)

	MT	NR MT	EX
Complete Set:	6.00	4.50	2.50

666 Checklist
667 Steve Adkins
668 Darrin Chapin
669 Bob Davidson
670 Dave Eiland
671 John Habyan
672 Jimmy Jones
673 Mark Leiter
674 Kevin Mmahat
675 Rich Monteleone
676 Willie Smith
677 Ricky Torres
678 Jeff Datz
679 Brian Dorsett
680 Dave Sax
681 Jim Leyritz
682 Hensley Meulens
683 Carlos Rodriguez
684 Rob Sepanek
685 Andy Stankiewicz
686 Jim Walewander
687 Mark Wasinger
688 Oscar Azocar
689 John Fishel
690 Jason Maas
691 Kevin Maas
692 Van Snider
693 Field Staff

1990 Team Columbus Clippers

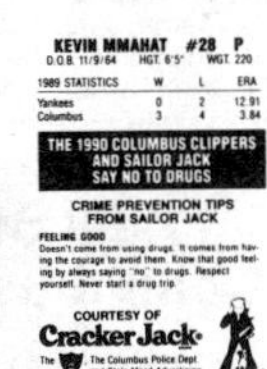

(New York Yankees) (color) (fold out)

	MT	NR MT	EX
Complete Set:	12.00	9.00	4.75

2 Mark Wasinger
4 Jim Walewander
9 Oscar Azocar
13 Bob Davidson
14 Jim Leyritz
16 Dave Sax
18 Andy Stankiewicz
21 John Fishel
22 Stump Merrill
23 Darrin Chapin
24 John Habyan
25 Dave Eiland
26 Jason Maas
27 Mark Leiter
28 Kevin Mmahat
29 Van Snider
30 Rich Monteleone
31 Hensley Meulens
34 Brian Dorsett
35 Steve Adkins
37 Kevin Maas
38 Rob Sepanek
40 Jimmy Jones
44 Clay Parker
---- Team Photo

1990 Best Columbus Mudcats

(Houston Astros) (color)

	MT	NR MT	EX
Complete Set:	8.00	6.00	3.25

1 Willie Ansley
2 Andy Mota
3 Andujar Cedeno
4 Luis Gonzalez
5 Tony Eusebio
6 Dean Hartgraves
7 Rusty Harris
8 Burt Hunter
9 Jeff Baldwin
10 Bernie Jenkins
11 Harold Allen
12 Shane Reynolds
13 Rich Simon
14 Daven Bond
15 Wally Trice
16 Fred Costello
17 Todd Credeur
18 John Sheehan
19 Al Osuna
20 Mike Browning
21 Charley Taylor
22 Joe Mikulik
23 Ed Renteria
24 Dennis Tafoya
25 Jose Cano
26 Checklist

1990 ProCards Columbus Mudcats

(Houston Astros) (color)

	MT	NR MT	EX
Complete Set:	8.00	6.00	3.25

1336 Checklist
1337 Harold Allen
1338 Daven Bond
1339 Mike Browning
1340 Jose Cano
1341 Fred Costello

1342 Todd Credeur
1343 Dean Hartgraves
1344 Al Osuna
1345 Shane Reynolds
1346 John Sheehan
1347 Richie Simon
1348 Dennis Tafoya
1349 Wally Trice
1350 Tony Eusebio
1351 Andujar Cedeno
1352 Luis Gonzalez
1353 Rusty Harris
1354 Andy Mota
1355 Ed Renteria
1356 Willie Ansley
1357 Jeff Baldwin
1358 Bert Hunter
1359 Bernie Jenkins
1360 Joe Mikulik
1361 Rick Sweet
1362 Charley Taylor

1990 Star Co. Columbus Mudcats

(Houston Astros) (color)

	MT	NR MT	EX
Complete Set:	8.00	6.00	3.25

1 Harold Allen
2 Willie Ansley
3 Eric Anthony
4 Jeff Baldwin
5 Daven Bond
6 Mike Browning
7 Andujar Cedeno
8 Fred Costello
9 Todd Credeur
10 Tony Eusebio
11 Luis Gonzalez
12 Rusty Harris
13 Dean Hartgraves
14 Bert Hunter
15 Bernie Jenkins
16 Joe Mikulik
17 Andy Mota
18 Joe Ortiz
19 Al Osuna
20 Ed Renteria
21 John Sheehan
22 Rich Simon
23 Dennis Tafoya
24 Wally Trice
25 Coaching Staff
26 Ron Porterfield
27 Diamond Jim
28 Mason Dixon
29 Belinda Kay

1990 CMC (TCMA) Denver Zephyrs

(Milwaukee Brewers) (color)

	MT	NR MT	EX
Complete Set:	4.00	3.00	1.50

1 Jeff Peterek
2 Ed Puig
3 Tim Watkins
4 Tom Edens
5 Mike Capel
6 Darryel Walters
7 Joe Xavier
8 Tim Torricelli
9 Joe Redfield
10 D.L. Smith
11 Billy Moore
12 Joe Mitchell
13 Mario Monico
14 Frank Mattox
15 Tim McIntosh
16 Mark Higgins
17 George Canale
18 Don Gordon
19 Al Sadler
20 Don August
21 Mike Birkbeck
22 Dennis Powell
23 Chuck McGrath
24 Ruben Escalera
25 Dave Machemer
26 Jackson Todd

1990 ProCards Denver Zephyrs

(Milwaukee Brewers) (color)

	MT	NR MT	EX
Complete Set:	4.00	3.00	1.50

615 Checklist
616 Don August
617 Mike Birkbeck
618 Mike Capel
619 Logan Easley
620 Tom Edens
621 Don Gordon
622 Chuck McGrath
623 Jeff Peterek
624 Dennis Powell
625 Ed Puig
626 Al Sadler
627 Tim Watkins
628 Tim McIntosh
629 Tim Torricelli
630 George Canale
631 Mark Higgins
632 Frank Mattrox
633 Joe Mitchell
634 Joe Redfield
635 D.L. Smith
636 Joe Xavier
637 Ruben Escalera
638 Mario Monico
639 Billy Moore
640 Darryel Walters
641 Dave Machemer
642 Jackson Todd

1990 Star Co. Dunedin Blue Jays

(Toronto Blue Jays) (color)

	MT	NR MT	EX
Complete Set:	9.00	6.75	3.50

1 Chris Beacom
2 Denis Boucher
3 Pete Blohm
4 Tim Brown
5 Domingo Cedeno
6 Jesse Cross
7 Juan DeLa Rosa
8 Rich Depastino
9 Ray Giannelli
10 Tim Hodge
11 Vince Horsman
12 Jeffrey Irish
13 Jeff Kent
14 Greg O'Halloran
15 Blaine Rudolph
16 Al Silverstein
17 Marcos Taveras
18 Mike Taylor
19 Ryan Thompson
20 Mike Timlin
21 Jason Townley
22 Rick Trlicek
23 Anthony Ward
24 Dave Weathers
25 Mark Young
26 Dennis Holmberg
27 Bill Monbouquette
28 Jon Woodworth

1990 Sportsprint Durham Bulls

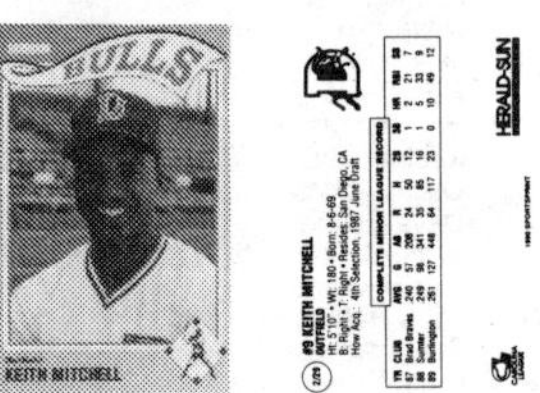

(Atlanta Braves) (color)

	MT	NR MT	EX
Complete Set:	5.00	3.75	2.00

1 Team Picture
2 Keith Mitchell
3 Brian Champion
4 Brian Deak
5 Ken Harring
6 Kevin Castleberry
7 Mike Mordecai
8 D.C. Campbell
9 Chris Czarnik
10 Marcos Vazquez
11 Skipper Wright
12 Popeye Cole
13 Edwin Alicea
14 Pat Tilmon
15 Theron Todd
16 Johnny Cuevas
17 David Nied
18 Josman Robles
19 Brian Cummings
20 Dave Brust
21 Rich Longuil
22 Phil Maldonado
23 Chad Smith
24 Rodney Richey
25 Todd Dewey
26 Dave Karasinski
27 Nate Minchey
28 Larry Jaster
29 Grady Little

1990 Sportsprint Durham Bulls

(Atlanta Braves) (color) (update set)

	MT	NR MT	EX
Complete Set:	11.00	8.25	4.50

1 Lee Johnson
2 Pedro Bourbon (Borbon)
3 Scott Diaz
4 Ben Rivera
5 Rod Byerly
6 Dan Snover
7 Ron Klesko (Ryan)
8 The Mechanical Bull

1990 CMC (TCMA) Edmonton Trappers

(California Angels) (color)

	MT	NR MT	EX
Complete Set:	5.00	3.75	2.00

1 Cliff Young
2 Max Oliveras (Manager)
3 Gary Buckels
4 Timothy Burcham, Chris Beasley
5 Sherman Corbett
6 Mike Erb
7 Mike Fetters
8 Chuck Hernandez
9 Jeff Heathcock
10 Scott Lewis
11 Rafael Montalvo
12 John Skurla
13 Lee Stevens
14 Nelson Rood
15 Bobby Rose
16 Dan Grunhard
17 Reed Peters
18 Doug Davis
19 Gary DiSarcina
20 Pete Coachman
21 Chris Cron
22 Karl Allaire
23 Ron Tingley

1990 ProCards Edmonton Trappers

(California Angels) (color)

	MT	NR MT	EX
Complete Set:	5.00	3.75	2.00

508 Checklist
509 Chris Beasley
510 Gary Buckels
511 Tim Burcham
512 Sherman Corbett
513 Mike Erb
514 Mike Fetters
515 Jeff Heathcock
516 Scott Lewis
517 Rafael Montalvo
518 Cliff Young
519 Doug Davis
520 Ron Tingley
521 Karl Allaire
522 Pete Coachman
523 Chris Cron
524 Gary DiSarcina
525 Nelson Rood
526 Bobby Rose
527 Lee Stevens
528 Dan Grunhard
529 Reed Peters
530 John Skurla
531 Max Oliveras
532 Chuck Hernandez

1990 Star Co. Elizabethton Twins

(Minnesota Twins) (color)

	MT	NR MT	EX
Complete Set:	3.00	2.25	1.25

1 Rich Becker
2 Tom Benson
3 Jose Bethancourt
4 David Bigham
5 Todd Blakeman
6 Brent Brede
7 Matt Brown
8 Sandy Diaz
9 Roger Dixon
10 Tom Gavin
11 John Gumpf
12 Jon Henry
13 Damian Miller
14 Matt Morse
15 Devin Peppers
16 Tim Pershing
17 Kurt Pfeffer
18 Cisco Pichardo
19 Todd Ritchie
20 Paul Russo
21 Tony Spaan
22 Steve Taylor
23 Chris Wallgren
24 Ray Smith
25 Lemo, Tomlin)
26 Joe Hubbard

1990 Pucko Elmira Pioneers

(Chicago White Sox) (color)

	MT	NR MT	EX
Complete Set:	3.00	2.25	1.25

1 Tim Graham
2 Dave Alvarez
3 Randy Brown
4 Tim Davis
5 Jason Friedman
6 Larry Grant
7 Jeff Limoncelli
8 Shea Wardwell
9 Willie Dukes
10 Jose Lora
11 Jose Malave
12 Jeff McNeely
13 Joe Demus
14 John Lammon
15 Chris Davis
16 Jim Dennison
17 Gar Finnvold
18 John Locker
19 Erik Plantenberg
20 Dave Ring
21 Silverio Santa Maria
22 Cedric Santiago
23 Tim Smith
24 Brian Young
25 Mike Verdi
26 Mike Quatrine
27 Old Pioneer (Mascot)

1990 Grand Slam El Paso Diablos

(Milwaukee Brewers) (color)

	MT	NR MT	EX
Complete Set:	5.00	3.75	2.00

1 Dave Huppert
2 Paul Lindblad
3 Jesus Alfaro
4 Shon Ashley
5 James Austin
6 Mark Chapman
7 Craig Cooper
8 Dee Dixon
9 Greg Edge
10 Cal Eldred
11 Ruben Escalera
12 Dean Freeland
13 Robinson Garces
14 Chris George
15 Sandy Guerrero
16 Mitch Hannahs
17 Bert Heffeman
18 Mike Ignasiak
19 Joe Kmak
20 Scott May
21 Charles McGrath
22 Steve Monson
23 Charlie Montoyo
24 Ed Puig
25 Rafael Skeete

1990 Star Co. Erie Sailors

(Baltimore Orioles) (color)

	MT	NR MT	EX
Complete Set:	3.00	2.25	1.25

1 Joe Boyce
2 Mark Cerny
3 Stan Cook
4 Brian Currie
5 Gary Daniels
6 D.J. Floyd
7 Brian Golden
8 Van Golmont
9 Mike Holland
10 Mike Jockish
11 Robbie Kemper
12 Mike Larson
13 Mike Lomeli
14 Darryll MacMillan
15 Greg McCutheon
16 Linc Mikkelson
17 Thomas Mitchell
18 Andy Postema
19 Brian Reimsnyder
20 Jerry Rizza
21 Ruben Rodriguez

22 Joe Roebuck
23 Shaun Sanderson
24 Mike Songini
25 Al Stacey
26 Rod Tafoya
27 Steve Woide
28 Garry Wurm
29 Mal Fichman
30 David Voit
31 Brad Weitzel

1990 Grand Slam Eugene Emeralds

(Kansas City Royals) (color)

	MT	NR MT	EX
Complete Set:	4.00	3.00	1.50

1 Javier Alvarez
2 Francisco Baez
3 Ramy Brooks
4 Jay Caraballo
5 Scott Davis
6 Weddison Ebanks
7 Sean Franceschi
8 Chuck Frederick
9 Harry Guanchez
10 Rafael Gutierrez
11 Dave Haber
12 Donny Harrel
13 Doug Harris
14 Phil Hiatt
15 Dave Hierholzer
16 Brad Holman
17 Darron Johnson
18 Tony Long
19 Giovanni Miranda
20 Ricky Moser
21 Gabriel Pineda
22 Doug Peters
23 Damon Pollard
24 Shayne Rea
25 Dave Rolls
26 Arnie Sambel
27 Doug Shields
28 Vernon Slater
29 Brady Steward
30 Shannon Strong

1990 Best Everett Giants

(San Francisco Giants) (color)

	MT	NR MT	EX
Complete Set:	4.00	3.00	1.50

1 Adam Hyzdu
2 Dan Varnell
3 Dan Carlson
4 Dan Flanagan
5 Frank Gould
6 Jim Huslig
7 The Walker (Mascot)
8 Brian McLeod
9 Mike Myers
10 Kurt Peltzer
11 Joe Rosselli
12 Mark Yockey
13 Eric Christopherson
14 Marcus Jensen
15 Jason Sievers
16 Mate Borgono
17 Brian Dakin
18 Mike Helms
19 Tony Spires
20 Ricky Ward
21 Jason Young
22 Courtney Davis
23 Shelby Hart
24 Lenny Ayres
25 John Jackson
26 Derek Reid
27 Kieth Ringgold
28 Dave Edwards (Checklist)

1990 ProCards Everett Giants

(San Francisco Giants) (color)

	MT	NR MT	EX
Complete Set:	4.00	3.00	1.50

3116 Checklist
3117 Lenny Ayres
3118 Scott Ebert
3119 Dan Carlson
3120 Dan Flanagan
3121 Frank Gould
3122 James Huslig
3123 Kevin McGehee
3124 Brian McLeod
3125 Mike Myers
3126 Kurt Peltzer
3127 Joe Rosselli
3128 Mark Yockey
3129 Eric Christopherson
3130 Marcus Jensen
3131 Jason Sievers
3132 Mate Borgono
3133 Brian Dakin
3134 Mike Helms
3135 Tony Spires
3136 Rick Ward
3137 Jason Young
3138 Courtney Davis
3139 Shelby Hart
3140 Adam Hyzdu
3141 John Jackson
3142 Derek Reid
3143 Kieth Ringgold
3144 Dan Varnell
3145 Deron McCue
3146 Diego Sequi
3147 Juan Lopez

1990 ProCards Fayetteville Generals

(Detroit Tigers) (color)

	MT	NR MT	EX
Complete Set:	3.00	2.25	1.25

2396 Checklist
2397 Jeff Braley
2398 Mike Garcia
2399 Frank Gonzales
2400 Jose Guzman
2401 Tim Herrmann
2402 Linty Ingram
2403 Mike Kollar
2404 Randy Marshall
2405 Brian Rountree
2406 Mac Seibert
2407 Marino Stefany
2408 Leo Torres
2409 Mike Gillette
2410 Hunter Hoffman
2411 Kasey McKeon
2412 Rick Sellers
2413 Ron Howard
2414 Don Pederson
2415 Pat Pesavento
2416 Mike Rendina
2417 Gino Tagliferri
2418 Freddy Torres
2419 Artuno Caines
2420 Brian Cornelius
2421 Rudy Pemberton
2422 Team Picture
2423 Gene Roof

1990 Star Co. Florida State League All-Stars

(All-Stars) (color)

	MT	NR MT	EX
Complete Set:	7.00	5.25	2.75

1 Cam Biberdorf
2 Bobby DeLoach
3 Bruce Dostal
4 D.J. Dozier
5 Jim Faulk
6 Dan Freed
7 John Johnstone
8 Jeff Juden
9 Anthony Kelley
10 George Kerfut
11 Kenny Lofton
12 Scott Makarewicz
13 John Massarelli
14 John Mello
15 Joe Millette
16 Nikco Riesgo
17 Roman Taveras
18 Tony Trevino
19 Jeff Vanzytveld
20 Eric Young
21 Pete Young
22 Alan Zinter
23 Felipe Alou
24 Tim Blackwell
25 Doyle Balthazar
26 Jacob Brumfield
27 Jesse Cross
28 Ivan Cruz
29 Everett Cunningham
30 John DeSilva
31 Greg Harvey
32 Garrett Jenkins
33 Jeff Kent
34 Keith Kimberlin
35 Jay Knoblaugh
36 Barry Manuel
37 Javier Ocasio
38 Greg O'Halloran
39 David Perez
40 Tom Popplewell
41 Ivan Rodriguez
42 Fred Samson
43 Larry Stanford
44 Scott Tedder
45 Mike Timlin
46 Jason Townley
47 Anthony Ward
48 Dennis Holmberg
49 John Lipon
50 Bobby Jones

1990 Star Ft. Lauderdale Yankees

(New York Yankees) (color) (Price includes late-issue Erhardt card and the corrected Ehrhard card)

	MT	NR MT	EX
Complete Set:	7.00	5.25	2.75

1 Rich Barnwell
2 John Brubaker
3 Hernan Cortes
4 Todd Devereaux
5 Mike Draper
6 Kirk Dulom
7a Rod Ehrhard (Photo Error)
7b Rod Ehrhard (Corrected)
8 Victor Garcia Jr.
9 Ken Greer
10 Jeff Johnson
11 Jay Knoblaugh
12 Jeff Livesey
13 Skip Nelloms
14 Tom Newell
15 Rey Noriega
16 Mark Ohlms
17 Ed Pimentel
18 Tom Popplewell
19 Larry Stanford
20 Dave Turgeon
21 Hector Vargas
22 Gerald Williams
23 Mike Hart
24 Dave Schuller
25 Rob Thomson
26 Mark Zettelmeyer
27 Adam Wagner
---- Herb Erhardt

1990 Sportsprint Frederick Keys

(Baltimore Orioles) (color)

	MT	NR MT	EX
Complete Set:	9.00	6.75	3.50

1 Wally Moon
2 Mike Pazik
3 Bobby Miscik
4 Tony Beasley
5 Mike Deutsch
6 Mike Richardson
7 Steve Mondile
8 Rich Slomkowski
9 Doug Reynolds
10 Zachary Kerr
11 Anthony Telford
12 Stacy Jones
13 Paris Hayden
14 Roy Gilbert
15 Tim Holland
16 Mike Lehman
17 Ken Shamburg
18 Ricky Gutierrez
19 Dan Berthel
20 Pete Rose II
21 Ed Horowitz
22 Mike Oquist
23 Rob Stiegele
24 Todd Stephan
25 Andres Constant
26 Chuck Ricci
27 Jeff Bumgarner
28 Pat Hedge
29 Art Rhodes
30 Brad Hildreth

1990 Best Gastonia Rangers

(Texas Rangers) (color)

	MT	NR MT	EX
Complete Set:	3.00	2.25	1.25

1 Tony Scruggs
2 Ronaldo Romero
3 Carl Randle
4 Travis Buckley
5 Ken Powell
6 Joey Eischen
7 Brian Romero
8 Buddy Micheu
9 Jonathan Hurst
10 Joey Wardlow
11 Jay Franklin
12 Troy Eklund
13 Brian Evans
14 Eric Bickhardt
15 Brian Steiner
16 Barry Winford
17 Timmie Morrow
18 Randy Marshall
19 Michael Arner
20 Joe Lewis
21 Jose Oliva
22 Craig Newkirk
23 John Graves
24 James Clinton
25 Orlando Gomez
26 Marvin White
27 Randy Whisler
28 Tom Tisdale
29 Ramon Santiago
30 Checklist

1990 ProCards Gastonia Rangers

(Texas Rangers) (color)

	MT	NR MT	EX
Complete Set:	3.00	2.25	1.25

2510 Checklist
2511 Mike Arner
2512 Eric Bickhardt
2513 Travis Buckley
2514 Joey Eischen
2515 Brian Evans
2516 Jay Franklin
2517 John Graves
2518 Johathan Hurst
2519 Carl Randle
2520 Brian Romero
2521 Ronaldo Romero
2522 Brian Steiner
2523 Joe Lewis
2524 Buddy Micheu
2525 Barry Winford
2526 Mike Burton
2527 Jim Clinton
2528 Randy Marshall
2529 Craig Newkirk
2530 Jose Oliva
2531 Joey Wardlow
2532 Troy Eklund
2533 Timmie Morrow
2534 Kenny Powell
2535 Tony Scruggs
2536 Orlando Gomez
2537 Randy Whisler
2538 Marvin White

1990 Star Co. Gastonia Rangers

(Texas Rangers) (color)

	MT	NR MT	EX
Complete Set:	3.00	2.25	1.25

1 Michael Arner
2 Eric Bickhardt
3 Travis Buckley
4 Michael Burton
5 James Clinton
6 Joey Eischen
7 Troy Eklund
8 Brian Evans
9 Jay Franklin
10 John Graves
11 Jonathan Hurst
12 Joe Lewis
13 Randy Marshall
14 Buddy Micheu
15 Timmie Morrow
16 Craig Newkirk
17 Jose Oliva
18 Ken Powell
19 Carl Randle
20 Brian Romero
21 Ronaldo Romero
22 Tony Scruggs
23 Brian Steiner
24 Joey Wardlow
25 Barry Winford
26 Orlando Gomez
27 Marvin White
28 Perry Hill
29 Randy Whisler

1990 ProCards Gate City Pioneers

(Co-op) (color)

	MT	NR MT	EX
Complete Set:	3.00	2.25	1.25

3337a Checklist
3337b Keith Casey (checklisted as #3338)
3339 Akihiko Chiyomaru
3340 Hiroyuki Satoh
3341 Hector Ortega
3342 Hidiki Misuzawa
3343 Carlos Espinoza
3344 William Martinez
3345 Itsuki Asai
3346 Jim Heilgeist
3347 Tony Marabella
3348 Tyrone Horne

3349 Hector Rivera
3350 Mike Fier
3351 Paul Hutto
3352 Gary Adams
3353 Buck Atwater
3354 Angelo Santiago
3355 Trey Wilburn
3356 Doug Noce
3357 Chris Emerick
3358 Takashi Maema
3359 Kelly Frederikson
3360 Perry Sanchez
3361 David Carter
3362 Keiji Abe
3363 Eddie Bonine

1990 Sport Pro Gate City Pioneers

(Co-op) (color)

	MT	NR MT	EX
Complete Set:	3.00	2.25	1.25

1 Gary Adams
2 Itsuki Asai
3 Tyrone Atwater
4 David Carter
5 Keith Casey
6 Akihiko Chiyomaru
7 Chris Emerick
8 Trey Wilburn
9 Mike Fier
10 Kelly Fredericksen
11 Jim Heilgeist
12 Tyrone Horne
13 Paul Hutto
14 Takashi Maema
15 Tony Marabella
16 Angelo Santiago
17 Hideki Mizusawa
18 Doug Noce
19 Hiroyuki Satoh
20 Hector Rivera
21 Perry Sanchez
22 Ed Bonine
23 Keiji Abe
24 Ed Creech

1990 ProCards Geneva Cubs

(Chicago Cubs) (color)

	MT	NR MT	EX
Complete Set:	3.00	2.25	1.25

3028 Checklist
3029 Lance Dickson
3030 Troy Bradford
3031 Ricardo Medina
3032 Brad Huff
3033 Brad Erdman
3034 Victor Cancel
3035 Charlie Fiacco
3036 Phil Dauphin
3037 Greg Kessler
3038 Joe Porcelli
3039 German Diaz
3040 Bill Paynter
3041 Jessie Hollins
3042 Clinton White
3043 John Dericco
3044 Andrew Hartung
3045 Tim Delgado
3046 Mike Young
3047 Stephen Coffey
3048 Paul Torres
3049 Tim Parker
3050 Luis Benitez
3051 Amilcar Correa
3052 Roberto Smalls
3053 Bill Hayes
3054 Joe Housey

1990 Star Co. Geneva Cubs

(Chicago Cubs) (color) (Includes the six unnumbered cards)

	MT	NR MT	EX
Complete Set:	15.00	11.00	6.00

1 Luis Benitez
2 Troy Bradford
3 Victor Cancel
4 Stephen Coffey
5 Amilcar Correa
6 Phil Dauphin Jr.
7 Paul Torres
8 John DeRicco
9 German Diaz
10 Lance Dickson
11 Brad Erdman
12 Charlie Fiacco
13 Andrew Hartung
14 Jesse Hollins
15 Brad Huff
16 Greg Kessler
17 Ricardo Medina
18 Tim Parker
19 Bill Payner
20 Joe Porcelli
21 Gabby Rodriguez
22 Roberto Smalls
23 Carl Stanley
24 Clinton White
25 Michael Young
26 Bill Hayes
---- Dan Bensen
---- Ken Burlew
---- Tim Delgado
---- Kevin Heilbronner
---- Dave Oster
---- Ken Shepard

1990 Sport Pro Great Falls Dodgers

(Los Angeles Dodgers) (color) Cards #9 & #10 are twin brothers

	MT	NR MT	EX
Complete Set:	9.00	6.75	3.50

1 Ron Walden
2 Dan Gray
3 Mike Busch
4 Raul Mondesi
5 James Daspit
6 Ed Lund
7 Lonnie Webb
8 Keoki Farrish
9 Mark Mimbs
10 Mike Mimbs
11 Burgess Watts
12 Pedro Martinez
13 Jason Kerr
14 Eric Blackwell
15 David Baumann
16 Junior Perez
17 Don Meyers
18 Garey Ingram
19 Ken Hamilton
20 Gordon Tipton
21 Mike Frauenhoffer
22 Dan Andrews
23 Brian Piotrowicz
24 John Dejardl
25 Tim Griffin
26 Ed Stryker
27 Ron Mauer
28 Ira Smith
29 Guy Conti
30 Joe Vavra

1990 Best Greensboro Hornets

(New York Yankees) (color)

	MT	NR MT	EX
Complete Set:	4.00	3.00	1.50

1 Todd Malone
2 Sterling Hitchcock
3 Jeff Hoffman
4 Mark Hutton
5 Dan Johnston
6 Ken Juarbe
7 Jim Haller
8 Roberto Munoz
9 Cesar Perez
10 Rafael Quirico
11 Ricky Rhodes
12 Steve Tucker
13 Brian Johnson
14 John Jarvis
15 Larry Walker
16 Andy Fox
17 Ramon Jimenez
18 Scott Romano
19 Daniel Sanchez
20 Aaron Van Scoyoc
21 Tim Garland
22 Sean Gilliam
23 Lew Hill
24 Michael Rhodes
25 Jason Robertson
26 Brian Turner
27 Brian Butterfield
28 Ted Uhlaender
29 Rich Arena
30 Dave Jorn

1990 ProCards Greensboro Hornets

(New York Yankees) (color)

	MT	NR MT	EX
Complete Set:	4.00	3.00	1.50

2652 Checklist
2653 Jim Haller
2654 Sterling Hitchcock
2655 Jeff Hoffman
2656 Mark Hutton
2657 Dan Johnston
2658 Ken Juarbe
2659 Todd Malone
2660 Roberto Munoz
2661 Cesar Perez
2662 Rafael Quirico
2663 Ricky Rhodes
2664 Steve Tucker
2665 Brian Johnson
2666 John Jarvis
2667 Larry Walker
2668 Andy Fox
2669 Ramom Jimenez
2670 Scott Romano
2671 Daniel Sanchez
2672 Aaron Van Scoyoc
2673 Tim Garland
2674 Sean Gilliam
2675 Lew Hill
2676 Mike Rhodes
2677 Jason Robertson
2678 Brian Turner
2679 Brian Butterfield
2680 Dave Jorn
2681 Rich Arena
2682 Ted Uhlaender

1990 Star Co. Greensboro Hornets

(New York Yankees) (color)

	MT	NR MT	EX
Complete Set:	4.00	3.00	1.50

1 Andy Fox
2 Tim Garland
3 Sean Gilliam
4 Jim Haller
5 Sterling Hitchcock
6 Jeff Hoffman
7 Mark Hutton
8 John Jarvis
9 Ramon Jimenez
10 Brain Johnson
11 Dan Johnston
12 Ken Juarbe
13 Todd Malone
14 Roberto Munoz
15 Cesar Perez
16 Rafael Quirico
17 Mike Rhodes
18 Ricky Rhodes
19 Jason Robertson
20 Scott Romano
21 Daniel Sanchez
22 Tuck Tucker
23 Brian Turner
24 Aaron Van Scoyoc
25 Larry Walker
26 Field Personnel

1990 Best Greenville Braves

(Atlanta Braves) (color) #10 card is incorrectly spelled on checklist

	MT	NR MT	EX
Complete Set:	4.00	3.00	1.50

1 Lee Upshaw
2 David Plumb
3 Brian Champion
4 Pat Gomez
5 Tom Redington
6 Ben Rivera
7 Brian Boltz
8 Turk Wendell
9 Kelly Mann
10 Rich Casrotti
11 Rick Morris
12 Matt Turner
13 Judd Johnson
14 Rich Maloney
15 Doug Stockam
16 Dan Weems
17 Al Martin
18 Kevin Batiste
19 Andy Tomberlin
20 Rolando Pino
21 John Kilner
22 Checklist

1990 ProCards Greenville Braves

(Atlanta Braves) (color)

	MT	NR MT	EX
Complete Set:	4.00	3.00	1.50

1121 Checklist
1122 Brian Boltz
1123 Maximo Del Rosario
1124 Lee Johnson
1125 John Kilner
1126 Ben Rivera
1127 Doug Stockam
1128 Matt Turner
1129 Preston Watson
1130 Danny Weems
1131 Turk Wendell
1132 Kelly Martin
1133 David Plumb
1134 Mike Bell
1135 Rich Casarotti
1136 Rick Morris
1137 Tom Redington
1138 Rico Rossy
1139 Rich Maloney
1140 Kevin Batiste
1141 Al Martin
1142 Andy Tomberlin
1143 Buddy Bailey
1144 Bill Slack
1145 Terry Harper
1146 Randy Ingle

1990 Star Co. Greenville Braves

(Atlanta Braves) (color)

	MT	NR MT	EX
Complete Set:	4.00	3.00	1.50

1 John Alva
2 Kevin Batiste
3 Michael Bell
4 Brian Boltz
5 Rich Casarotti
6 Kevin Dean
7 Maximo Del Rosario
8 Judd Johnson
9 Lee Johnson
10 John Kilner
11 Rich Maloney
12 Kelly Mann
13 Gene Martin
14 Rich Morris
15 David Plumb
16 Thomas Redington
17 Ben Rivera
18 Doug Stockam
19 Andy Tomberlin
20 Matt Turner
21 Preston Watson
22 Danny Weems
23 Steven Wendell
24 Coaching Staff

1990 Best Hagerstown Suns

(Baltimore Orioles) (color)

	MT	NR MT	EX
Complete Set:	6.00	4.50	2.50

1 Ben McDonald
2 Dan Simonds
3 Doug Robbins
4 Mike Eberle
5 Tom Brown
6 Joe Durhamm
7 Bobby Latmore
8 Ty Nichols
9 Rodney Lofton
10 Craig Faulkner
11 Paris Haden
12 Luis Mercedes
13 Scott Meadows
14 Victor Hithe
15 Jack Voigt
16 Steve Culkar
17 Stacey Burdick
18 Chris Myers
19 Mike Borgatti
20 Mike Linskey
21 Mike Sander
22 Joel McKeon
23 Francisco Delarosa
24 Dave Miller
25 Mike Cavers
26 Paul Thorpe
27 Ozzie Peraza
28 Jose Mesa
29 Jerry Narron
30 Checklist (Mascot)

1990 ProCards Hagerstown Suns

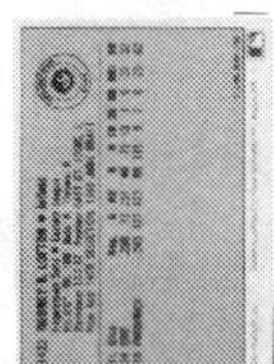

(Baltimore Orioles) (color)

	MT	NR MT	EX
Complete Set:	6.00	4.50	2.50

1401 Checklist
1402 Mike Borgatti
1403 Stacey Burdick
1404 Mike Cavers
1405 Steve Culkar
1406 Francisco Delarosa
1407 Mike Linskey
1408 Ben McDonald
1409 Joel McKeon
1410 Jose Mesa
1411 Dave Miller
1412 Chris Myers
1413 Mike Sander
1414 Paul Thorpe
1415 Mike Eberle
1416 Doug Robbins
1417 Dan Simonds
1418 Pat Austin
1419 Dave Bettendorf
1420 Don Buford
1421 Craig Faulkner
1422 Bobby Latmore
1423 Rodney Lofton
1424 Rick Lundblade
1425 Ty Nichols
1426 Victor Hithe
1427 Paris Hayden
1428 Scott Meadows
1429 Luis Mercedes
1430 Jack Voight
1431 Jerry Narron
1432 Tom Brow, Joe Durham)

1990 Star Co. Hagerstown Suns

(Baltimore Orioles) (color)

	MT	NR MT	EX
Complete Set:	4.00	3.00	1.50

1 Pat Austin
2 Mike Borgatti
3 Don Buford
4 Stacey Burdick
5 Mike Cavers
6 Steve Culkar
7 Francisco DeLaRosa
8 Mike Eberle
9 Craig Faulkner
10 Walt Harris
11 Paris Hayden
12 Bobby Latmore
13 Rod Lofton
14 Joel McKeon
15 Scott Meadows
16 Luis Mercedes
17 Jose Mesa
18 Dave Miller
19 Chris Myers
20 Ty Nichols
21 Doug Robbins
22 Mike Sander
23 Tony Telford
24 Paul Thorpe
25 Jack Voigt
26 Jerry Narron
27 Tom Brown
28 Joe Durham

1990 Best Hamilton Redbirds

(St. Louis Cardinals) (color)

	MT	NR MT	EX
Complete Set:	3.00	2.25	1.25

1 Donovan Osborne
2 Roy Bailey
3 Marcos Betances
4 Chris Maloney
5 Tom Fusco
6 Kevin McLeod
7 Mark Smith
8 David Boss
9 George Sells
10 Troy Salvior
11 Mike Newby
12 Rich Rupkey
13 Paul Ellis
14 Marc Ronan
15 Joe Turvey
16 Wander Pimentel
17 Ahmed Rodriguez
18 Ozzie Perez
19 Gary Cooper
20 Rodney Eldridge
21 Mark MacArthur
22 Chris Alesio
23 Terry Bradshaw
24 John Thomas
25 Jeff Payne
26 Juan Belbru
27 Luis Melendez
28 Checklist

1990 Star Co. Hamilton Redbirds

(St. Louis Cardinals) (color)

	MT	NR MT	EX
Complete Set:	3.00	2.25	1.25

Logo Card
1 Chris Alesio
2 Jose Arias
3 Roy Bailey
4 Andy Beasly
5 Juan Belbru
6 Marcos Betances
7 David Boss
8 Alan Botkin
9 Gary Cooper
10 Rodney Eldridge
11 Paul Ellis
12 Jeff Fayne
13 Tom Fusco
14 Chris Lowe
15 Mark MacArthur
16 Kevin McLeod
17 Mike Newby
18 Ozzie Perez
19 Wander Pimentel
20 Ahmed Rodriguez
21 Rich Rupkey
22 Troy Salvior
23 George Sells
24 Mark Smith
25 John Thomas
26 Luis Melendez
27 Chris Maloney
28 Robert Harrison

1990 ProCards Harrisburg Senators

(Pittsburgh Pirates) (color)

	MT	NR MT	EX
Complete Set:	8.00	6.00	3.25

1184 Checklist
1185 Steve Adams
1186 Joe Ausanio
1187 Jim Czajkowski
1188 Miguel Garcia
1189 Blas Minor
1190 Pete Murphy
1191 Keith Richardson
1192 Randy Tomlin
1193 Jim Tracy
1194 Ben Webb
1195 Jeff Banister
1196 Scott Barczi
1197 Trent Jewett
1198 Terry Crowley
1199 Carlos Garcia
1200 Jeffrey Osborne
1201 Julio Perez
1202 Junior Vizcaino
1203 John Wehner
1204 Moises Alou
1205 Robert Harris
1206 Julio Peguero
1207 Ed Yacopino
1208 Marc Bombard
1209 Spin Williams

1990 Star Co. Harrisburg Senators

(Pittsburgh Pirates) (color)

	MT	NR MT	EX
Complete Set:	8.00	6.00	3.25

1 Steve Adams
2 Moises Alou
3 Jeff Banister
4 Scott Barczi
5 Terry Crowley
6 Jim Czajkowski
7 Carlos Garcia
8 Miguel Garcia
9 Robert Harris
10 Trent Jewett
11 Blas Minor
12 Pete Murphy
13 Jeffrey Osborne
14 Julio Peguero
15 Julio Perez
16 Keith Richardson
17 Randy Tomlin
18 Jim Tracy
19 Junior Vizcaino
20 Ben Webb
21 John Wehner
22 Ed Yacopino
23 Marc Bombard
24 Spin Williams
25 Mike Sandoval

1990 Sport Pro Helena Brewers

(Milwaukee Brewers) (color)

	MT	NR MT	EX
Complete Set:	3.00	2.25	1.25

1 Tim Carter
2 Mike Hooper
3 Juan Flores
4 Tony Coble
5 Kevin McDonald
6 Chris Wheat
7 Pat Miller
8 Scott Moseley
9 Tony Diggs
10 Jason Zimbauer
11 Mike Couture
12 Gordon Powell
13 Larue Baber
14 Mark Stephens
15 Kurt Archer
16 Vince Castaldo
17 Geoffery Kellogg
18 Eric Patten
19 Todd Edwards
20 Don Pruitt
21 Mark Rupp
22 Charles Rambadt
23 Tim Wilson
24 Mike Carter
25 Brian Souza
26 Mike Norris
27 Bill Brakeley
28 Mike Coombs
29 Gary Calhoun

1990 ProCards Huntington Cubs

(Chicago Cubs) (color)

	MT	NR MT	EX
Complete Set:	3.00	2.25	1.25

3271 Checklist
3272 Miguel Camarena
3273 Sean Cheetham
3274 Scott Gardner
3275 Tyson Godfrey
3276 Ryan Hawblitzel
3277 Chuck Kirk
3278 Ken Krahenbuhl
3279 Tom Mann
3280 Nelson Ramirez
3281 Adrian Sanchez
3282 Dave Stephens
3283 Aaron Taylor
3284 Mike Gabbani
3285 Matt Walbeck
3286 Jim Wolf
3287 Morris Craig
3288 No Card Issued
3289 Ceasar Montero
3290 Tim Moore
3291 Micah Murphy
3292 J.P. Postiff
3293 Humberto Saa
3294 Rafael Soto
3295 Jose Viera
3296 Pablo Delgado
3297 Rolando Fernandez
3298 Calvin Ford
3299 Willie Gardner
3300 Ed Larregui
3301 Mike Little
3302 Jason Sehorn
3303 Steve Roadcap

1990 Best Huntsville Stars

(Oakland Athletics) (color)

	MT	NR MT	EX
Complete Set:	4.00	3.00	1.50

1 Darren Lewis
2 Richard Berg
3 Samuel Chavez
4 Stephen Chitren
5 Daniel Eskew
6 Daryl Green
7 Dannie Harris
8 Kevin MacLeod
9 William Schock
10 Joe Slusarski
11 Mark Stancel
12 Brian Veilleux
13 Jorge Brito
14 Peter Kuld
15 Scott Brosius
16 Ronald Coomer
17 Jim Kating
18 Robert Ralston
19 Stan Royer
20 Tony Brown
21 Ozzie Canseco
22 Nelson Simmons
23 Tack Wilson

24 Jeff Newman
25 Glenn Abbott
26 Brian Thorson
27 Checklist

1990 ProCards Idaho Falls Braves

(Atlanta Braves) (color)

	MT	NR MT	EX
Complete Set:	3.00	2.25	1.25

3240 Checklist
3241 Brian Dare
3242 Steve Hodges
3243 Tom Newman
3244 Michael Hoog
3245 Scott Ryder
3246 Tom Rizzo
3247 Don'l Dease
3248 Tommy Owen
3249 John Wood
3250 John Surane
3251 Grant Brittain
3252 Geoff Orr
3253 Joe Markulike
3254 Paul DiPino
3255 Rick Karcher
3256 Corby Fister
3257 Kevin O'Connor
3258 Michael Sweeney
3259 Chris Burton
3260 Nathan Fults
3261 Stu McMillan
3262 Steve Curry
3263 Randy Smith
3264 Doc Halliday
3265 Bill Bates
3266 Shawn Rohrwild
3267 Bill Kooiman
3268 Marek Drabinski
3269 Ed Giovanola
3270 Loren Gress

1990 CMC (TCMA) Indianapolis Indians

(Montreal Expos) (color)

	MT	NR MT	EX
Complete Set:	4.00	3.00	1.50

1 Steve Fireovid
2 Danny Clay
3 Howard Farmer
4 Travis Chambers
5 Chris Marchok
6 Dan Gakeler
7 Scott Anderson
8 Dale Mohorcic
9 Richard Thompson
10 Eddie Dixon
11 Jim Davins
12 Edwin Marquez
13 Jerry Goff
14 Dwight Lowry
15 Jim Steels
16 Quinn Mack
17 Eric Bullock
18 Otis Green
19 Randy Braun
20 Mel Houston
21 Jesus Paredes
22 Romy Cucjen
23 Jose Castro
24 Esteban Beltre
25 Tim Johnson

1990 ProCards Indianapolis Indians

(Montreal Expos) (color)

	MT	NR MT	EX
Complete Set:	4.50	3.50	1.75

279 Checklist
280 Scott Anderson
281 Esteban Beltre
282 Travis Chambers
283 Randy Braun
284 Danny Clay
285 Eric Bullock
286 Jim Davins
287 Jose Castro
288 Eddie Dixon
289 Romy Cucjen
290 Howard Farmer
291 Jerry Goff
292 Steve Fireovid
293 Otis Green
294 Dan Gakeler
295 Mel Houston
296 Balvino Galvez
297 Dwight Lowry
298 Dale Mohorcic
299 Quinn Mack
300 Chris Marchok
301 Edwin Marquez

302 Mel Rojas
303 Johnny Paredes
304 Rich Thompson
305 German Rivera
306 James Steels
307 Tim Johnson
308 Gomer Hodge
309 Joe Kerrigan

1990 CMC (TCMA) Iowa Cubs

(Chicago Cubs) (color)

	MT	NR MT	EX
Complete Set:	5.00	3.75	2.00

1 Shawn Boskie
2 Dave Masters
3 Kevin Blankenship
4 Greg Kallevig
5 Steve Parker
6 David Pavlas
7 Jeff Pico
8 Laddie Renfroe
9 Dean Wilkins
10 Paul Wilmet
11 Bob Bafia
12 Brian Guinn
13 Greg Smith
14 Derrick May
15 Glenn Sullivan
16 Bill Wrona
17 Erik Pappas
18 Hector Villanueva
19 Ced Landrum
20 Jeff Small
21 Gary Varsho
22 Brad Bierly
23 Jeff Hearron
24 Jim Essian
25 Brian McCann

1990 ProCards Iowa Cubs

(Chicago Cubs) (color)

	MT	NR MT	EX
Complete Set:	5.00	3.75	2.00

310 Checklist
311 Kevin Blankenship
312 Shawn Boskie
313 Mark Bowden
314 Greg Kallevig
315 Dave Masters
316 Steve Parker
317 Dave Pavlas
318 Laddie Renfroe
319 Paul Wilmet
320 Jeff Hearron
321 Erik Pappas
322 Hector Villanueva
323 Bob Bafia
324 Brian Guinn
325 Jeff Small
326 Greg Smith
327 Glen Sullivan
328 Bill Wrona
329 Brad Bierley
330 Cedric Landrum
331 Derrick May
332 Gary Varsho
333 Jim Essian

1990 Grand Slam Jackson Mets

(New York Mets) (color)

	MT	NR MT	EX
Complete Set:	8.00	6.00	3.25

Logo Car,)
1 Todd Hundley
2 Doug Kline
3 Alex Jimenez
4 Bob Apodaca
5 Clint Hurdle
6 Fred Hina
7 Terry Bross
8 Steve Larose
9 Joe Delli Carri
10 Jamie Roseboro
11 Howie Freiling
12 Chris Donnels
13 Javier Gonzalez
14 Dave Proctor
15 Doug Cinnella
16 Kevin Baez
17 Toby Nivens
18 Mike Miller
19 Aguedo Vasquez
20 Joe Whipps
21 Rudy Hernandez
22 Rocky Elli
23 Ron Gideon
24 Chuck Carr
25 Crucito Lara
26 Anthony Young
27 Terry McDaniel
28 Steve Davis

1990 Best Jacksonville Expos

(Montreal Expos) (color)

	MT	NR MT	EX
Complete Set:	8.00	6.00	3.25

(Team Photo)
1 Greg Colbrunn
2 Rob Natal
3 Bret Barberie
4 Archi Cianfrocco
5 Wilfredo Cordero
6 Bryn Kosco
7 Omer Munoz
8 Boi Rodriguez
9 Terrell Hansen
10 Cesar Hernandez
11 Trevor Penn
12 Miguel Santana
13 John Vanderwal
14 Brian Barnes
15 Chris Bennett
16 Kent Brottenfield
17 Mario Brito
18 Jeff Carter
19 Bob Malloy
20 Richie Lewis
21 Chris Nabholz
22 Yorkis Perez
23 Hector Rivera
24 Darrin Winston
25 Jerry Manuel
26 Nardi Contreras
27 Lorenzo Bundy
28 Jay Williams
29 Edwin Marquez
30 Checklist

1990 ProCards Jacksonville Expos

(Montreal Expos) (color)

	MT	NR MT	EX
Complete Set:	8.00	6.00	3.25

1364 Checklist
1365 Brian Barnes
1366 Chris Bennett
1367 Kent Bottenfield
1368 Mario Brito
1369 Jeff Carter
1370 Bob Malloy
1371 Chris Nabholz
1372 Yorkis Perez
1373 Tim Peters
1374 Hector Rivera
1375 Tim Sossamon
1376 Darrin Winston
1377 Greg Colbrunn
1378 Rob Natal
1379 Bret Barbarie
1380 Archi Cianfrocco
1381 Wil Cordero
1382 Bryn Kosco
1383 Omer Munoz
1384 Terrel Hansen
1385 Cesar Hernandez
1386 Trevor Penn
1387 Miguel Santana
1388 John Vanderwal
1389 Lorenzo Bundy
1390 Team Picture
1391 Jerry Manuel
1392 Nardi Contreas

1990 Pucko Jamestown Expos

(Montreal Expos) (color)

	MT	NR MT	EX
Complete Set:	3.00	2.25	1.25

1 Theodore Ciesia
2 Robert Fitzpatrick
3 Domingo Matos
4 Abimael Rodriguez
5 Mark Tsitouris
6 Randon Wilstead
7 Jeff Barry
8 Robert Katzaroff
9 Glenn Murray
10 Jerry Nyman
11 Todd Samples
12 Michael Friedland
13 Derek Aucoin
14 Robert Baxter
15 Billy Brewer
16 Ralph Diaz
17 Ranbir Grewal
18 Chris Haney
19 Darrin Kotch
20 Steve Long
21 Michael Mathile
22 Felix Moya
23 Joe Morris
24 John Polasek
25 Troy Ricker
26 Troy Wessel
27 Pat Daugherty
28 Q.V. Lowe
29 Jose Castro
30 Scott Yurcisin
31 Tom O'Reilley & Staff
32 Yuppi (Mascot)
33 College Stadium
34 Dan Hargis

1990 Star Co. Johnson City Cardinals

(St. Louis Cardinals) (color)

	MT	NR MT	EX
Complete Set:	3.00	2.25	1.25

1 Hector Alberro
2 Joe Aversa
3 Scott Baker
4 Harrison Ball
5 Duff Brumley
6 Kevin Carpenter
7 Jerry Davis
8 John Dempsey
9 Tremayne Donald
10 Tracey Ealy
11 Ben Ellsworth
12 Ron French
13 Cecilio Gonzalez
14 Aaron Holbert
15 Tim Jordan
16 John Kelly
17 Jose Lopez
18 Jeremy McGarity
19 David Norris
20 Sean Page
21 Beto Rodriguez
22 Manuel Rodriguez
23 Craig Ruyak
24 Frank Speek
25 Jim Spivey
26 Brian Sullivan
27 Tom Urbani
28 Coaching Staff
29 Joe Cunningham
30 Mike Gaddie

1990 Best Kenosha Twins

(Minnesota Twins) (color)

	MT	NR MT	EX
Complete Set:	3.00	2.25	1.25

1 Steve Dunn
2 Rex DeLa Nuez
3 Randy Gentile
4 Deryk Gross
5 Troy Hoerner
6 Mike Lloyd
7 Mike Mathiot
8 Jeff Milene
9 Steve Morris
10 Willi Mota
11 Alex Nunez
12 Francisco Pichardo
13 Rob Schiel
14 Joe Siwa
15 Bryan Roskom
16 Darren Musselwhite
17 Jayson Best
18 Sandy Diaz
19 Jody Harrington
20 Marc Lipson
21 Mike Misuraca
22 Tim Nedin
23 Alan Newman
24 Carlos Pulido
25 Scott Robles
26 Jeff Thelen
27 Steve Liddle
28 Rick Anderson
29 Dan Fox
30 Checklist

1990 ProCards Kenosha Twins

(Minnesota Twins) (color)

	MT	NR MT	EX
Complete Set:	3.00	2.25	1.25

2285 Checklist
2286 Jayson Best
2287 Sandy Diaz
2288 Jody Harrington
2289 Marc Lipson
2290 Mike Misuraca
2291 Tim Nedin
2292 Alan Newman
2293 Carlos Pulido
2294 Scott Robles
2295 Jeff Thelen
2296 Jeff Milene
2297 Willie Mota
2298 Joe Siwa
2299 Steve Dunn
2300 Randy Gentile
2301 Mike Lloyd
2302 Mike Mathiot
2303 Alex Nunez
2304 Rob Schiel
2305 Rex DeLa Nuez
2306 Deryk Gross
2307 Troy Hoerner
2308 Steve Morris
2309 Francisco Pichardo
2310 Steve Liddle
2311 Rick Anderson

1990 Star Co. Kenosha Twins

(Minnesota Twins) (color)

	MT	NR MT	EX
Complete Set:	3.00	2.25	1.25

1 Jayson Best
2 Sandy Diaz
3 Steve Dunn
4 Randy Gentile
5 Deryk Gross
6 Jody Harrington
7 Troy Hoerner
8 Rex DeLa Nuez
9 Marc Lipson
10 Mike Lloyd
11 Mike Mathiot
12 Jeff Milene
13 Mike Misuraca
14 Steve Morris
15 Willi Mota
16 Tim Nedin
17 Alan Newman
18 Alex Nunez
19 Francisco Pichardo
20 Carlos Pulido
21 Scott Robles
22 Rob Schiel
23 Joe Siwa
24 Jeffrey Thelen
25 Steve Liddle
26 Rick Anderson
27 Dan Fox
28 Darren Musselwhite
29 Bryan Roskom

1990 Best Kingsport Mets

(New York Mets) (color)

	MT	NR MT	EX
Complete Set:	3.00	2.25	1.25

1 Aaron Ledesma
2 Darian Lindsay
3 Gerrod Davis
4 Wayne Mathis
5 Bernie Millan
6 Mason Rudolph
7 Micah Franklin
8 Ray Martinez
9 Tony Moore
10 Rob Carpenter
11 Edward Fully
12 Nicholas Polanco
13 Omar Garcia
14 Rob Rees
15 Mike Anaya
16 Hector Carrasco
17 Tim Sandy
18 Nate Benson
19 Casper Van Rybach
20 Tom Wegmann
21 Rich Bristow
22 Tom Engle
23 Marcel Johnson
24 Charlie Williams
25 Jim Thrift
26 Gil Rondon
27 Dan Norman
28 Checklist

1990 Star Co. Kingsport Mets

(New York Mets) (color)

	MT	NR MT	EX
Complete Set:	3.00	2.25	1.25

1 Mike Anaya
2 Nate Benson
3 Richie Bristow
4 Rob Carpenter
5 Hector Carrasco
6 Jay Davis

7 Tom Engle
8 Micah Franklin
9 Edward Fully
10 Omar Garcia
11 Butch Huskey
12 Marcel Johnson
13 Aaron Ledesma
14 Darian Lindsay
15 Ray Martinez
16 Wayne Mathis
17 Bernie Millan
18 Tony Moore
19 Nicholas Polanco
20 Rob Rees
21 Mason Rudolph
22 Tim Sandy
23 Casper Van Rybach
24 Tom Wegmann
25 Charlie Williams
26 Jim Thrift
27 Gil Rondon
28 Dave Fricke
29 Dottie Elsea
30 Bat Boys

1990 Sportsprint Kinston Indians

(Cleveland Indians) (color) (Price includes late-issue Costo card)

	MT	NR MT	EX
Complete Set:	3.00	2.25	1.25

1 Jerry DiPoto
2 Tommy Kramer
3 Rouglas Odor
4 Ty Kovach
5 Curtis Leskanic
6 Brian Johnson
7 Fabio Gomez
8 Jesse Levis
9 Ken Ramos
10 Nolan Lane
11 Marc Tepper
12 Garland Kiser
13 Jamie Allison
14 Lindsay Foster
15 Will Vespe
16 Ramon Bautista
17 David Oliveras
18 Rick Falkner
19 Greg Ferlenda
20 Chris Pinder
21 Mando Verdugo
22 Dan Williams
23 Robert Person
24 Scott Neill
25 Eddie Zambrano
26 Tim Ellis
27 Fred Gladding
28 Brian Graham
29 Dennis Noonan
---- Tim Costo
---- Checklist

1990 Diamond Cards Kissimmee Dodgers

(Los Angeles Dodgers) (color)

	MT	NR MT	EX
Complete Set:	3.00	2.25	1.25

1 Henry Blanco
2 Jake Botts
3 Jimmy Brown
4 Jason Broyles
5 Donnie Carroll
6 Nelson Castro
7 Jose Cruz
8 Kieth Daniel
9 Greg Davis
10 Andres Diaz
11 Ross Farnsworth
12 Dirk Gorman
13 Randy Graves
14 Rob Hoffman
15 Andres Macu
16 Al Maldonado
17 Tom Mathews
18 Domingo Mota
19 Peter Nurre
20 Jose Parra
21 Jose Perez
22 Alton Pinkney
23 Javier Puchales
24 Mike Racobaldo
25 Frank Smith
26 Rob Sweeney
27 Jose Valdez
28 Leroy Williams
29 Ivan DeJesus

A player's name in italic type indicates a rookie card. An (FC) indicates a player's first card for that particular card company.

1990 Best Knoxville Blue Jays

(Toronto Blue Jays) (color)

	MT	NR MT	EX
Complete Set:	6.00	4.50	2.50

1 Eddie Zosky
2 Jimmy Rogers
3 Pete Blohm
4 Pat Hentgen
5 William Suero
6 Shawn Jeter
7 Doug Merrifield
8 Juan Guzman
9 John Stearns
10 J.J. Cannon
11 Mike Maksudian
12 Paul Rodgers
13 Julian Yan
14 Bernie Nunez
15 Domingo Martinez
16 Chris Rauth
17 Andy Dziadkowiec
18 Woody Williams
19 John Poloni
20 Chris Jones
21 Darren Hall
22 Tom Quinlan
23 Earl Sanders
24 Dennis Jones
25 Jerry Schunk
26 Randy Knorr
27 Nate Cromwell
28 Checklist

1990 ProCards Knoxville Blue Jays

(Toronto Blue Jays) (color)

	MT	NR MT	EX
Complete Set:	6.00	4.50	2.50

1237 Checklist
1238 Nate Cromwell
1239 Woody Williams
1240 Pat Hentgen
1241 Jimmy Rogers
1242 Juan Guzman
1243 Chris Jones
1244 Darren Hall
1245 Earl Sanders
1246 Pete Blohm
1247 Bob MacDonald
1248 Randy Knorr
1249 William Suero
1250 Jerry Schunk
1251 Eddie Zosky
1252 Tom Quinlan
1253 Julian Yan
1254 Domingo Martinez
1255 Paul Rodgers
1256 Bernie Nunez
1257 Shawn Jeter
1258 Mike Maksudian
1259 John Stearns
1260 J.J. Cannon
1261 John Poloni

1990 Star Co. Knoxville Blue Jays

(Toronto Blue Jays) (color)

	MT	NR MT	EX
Complete Set:	5.00	3.75	2.00

1 Pete Blohm
2 Nate Cromwell
3 Andy Dziadkowiec
4 Darren Hall
5 Pat Hentgen
6 Shawn Jeter
7 Chris Jones
8 Dennis Jones
9 Randy Knorr
10 Bob MacDonald
11 Mike Maksudian
12 Domingo Martinez
13 Bernie Nunez
14 Tom Quinlan
15 Paul Rodgers
16 Jimmy Rogers
17 Earl Sanders
18 Jerry Schunk
19 Williams Suero
20 Woody Williams
21 Rob Wishnevski
22 Julian Yan
23 Eddie Zosky
24 John Stearns
25 J.J. Cannon
26 John Poloni

1990 Star Co. Lakeland Tigers

(Detroit Tigers) (color) (Price includes corrected cards)

	MT	NR MT	EX
Complete Set:	6.00	4.50	2.50

1 Eric Albright
2 Doyle Balthazar
3 Hector Barrios
4 Mark Cole
5 Ron Cook
6 Ivan Cruz
7 John Doherty
8 John DeSilva
9 Mark Ettles
10 Ed Ferm
11 Greg Gohr
12 Jeff Goodale
13 Darren Hursey
14 Jody Hurst
15 Keith Kimberlin
16 Kurt Knudsen
17 Todd Krum
18a Ron Marigny (wrong photo)
18b Ron Marigny (corrected)
19 Darryl Martin
20 Dan Raley
21a Robert Reimink (wrong photo)
21b Robert Reimink (corrected)
22 Lino Rivera
23a Tookie Spann (wrong photo)
23b Tookie Spann (corrected)
24 Mike Tresh
25 Marty Willis
26 John Lipon
27 Doug Carpenter
28 Terry Smith

1990 CMC (TCMA) Las Vegas Stars

(San Diego Padres) (color)

	MT	NR MT	EX
Complete Set:	6.00	4.50	2.50

1 Roger Smithberg
2 Steve Peters
3 Matt Maysey
4 Terry Gilmore
5 Eric Nolte
6 Jim Lewis
7 Pete Roberts
8 Dan Murphy
9 Rich Rodriguez
10 Joe Lynch
11 Mike Basso
12 Ronn Reynolds
13 Jose Mota
14 Paul Faries
15 Warren Newson
16 Alex Cole
17 Tom Levasseur
18 Charles Hillemann
19 Jeff Yurtin
20 Rafael Valdez
21 Brian Ohnoutka
22 Pat Kelley
23 Gary Lance
24 Tony Torchia
25 Todd Hutcheson

1990 ProCards Las Vegas Stars

(San Diego Padres) (color)

	MT	NR MT	EX
Complete Set:	6.00	4.50	2.50

112 Checklist
113 Terry Gilmore
114 Jim Lewis
115 Joe Lynch
116 Matt Maysey
117 Dan Murphy
118 Eric Nolte
119 Brian Ohnoutka
120 Steve Peters
121 Paul Quinzer
122 Pete Roberts
123 Rich Rodriguez
124 Roger Smithberg
125 Rafael Valdez
126 Mike Basso
127 Ronn Reynolds
128 Paul Faries
129 Tom LeVasseur
130 Jose Mota
131 Eddie Williams
132 Jeff Yurtin
133 Alex Cole
134 Charles Hillemann
135 Thomas Howard
136 Warren Newson
137 Pat Kelly
138 Gary Lance
139 Tony Torchia

1990 ProCards London Tigers

(Detroit Tigers) (color)

	MT	NR MT	EX
Complete Set:	4.00	3.00	1.50

1262 Checklist
1263 David Haas
1264 John Kiely
1265 Mike Lumley
1266 Rusty Meacham
1267 Dave Richards
1268 Ron Rightnowar
1269 Mike Wilkins
1270 Ken Williams
1271 Rich Rowland
1272 Tom Aldrich
1273 Chris Alvarez
1274 Arnie Beyeler
1275 Rico Brogna
1276 Lou Frazier
1277 Luis Galindo
1278 Basilio Cabrera
1279 Steve Green
1280 Richardo Ingram
1281 Tim Leiper
1282 Steve Pegues
1283 John Toale

1990 CMC (TCMA) Louisville Redbirds

(St. Louis Cardinals) (color)

	MT	NR MT	EX
Complete Set:	7.00	5.25	2.75

1 Scott Arnold
2 Gibson Alba
3 Cris Carpenter
4 Stan Clarke
5 Mike Hinkle
6 Howard Hilton
7 Dave Osteen
8 Mike Perez
9 Bernard Gilkey
10 Dennis Carter
11 Julian Martinez
12 Rod Brewer
13 Ray Stephens
14 Ray Lankford
15 Craig Wilson
16 Roy Silver
17 Bien Figueroa
18 Jesus Mendez
19 Geronimo Pena
20 Omar Olivares
21 Mark Grater
22 Tim Sherrill
23 Pat Austin
24 Todd Crosby
25 Gary Nichols
26 Mauricio Nunez
27 Gaylen Pitts
28 Mark Riggins
29 Brad Bluestone

1990 ProCards Louisville Redbirds

(St. Louis Cardinals) (color)

	MT	NR MT	EX
Complete Set:	7.00	5.25	2.75

392 Checklist
393 Gibson Alba
394 Scott Arnold
395 Cris Carpenter
396 Stan Clarke
397 Mark Grater
398 Howard Hilton
399 Mike Hinkle
400 Omar Olivares
401 Dave Osteen
402 Mike Perez
403 Tim Sherrill
404 Scott Nichols
405 Ray Stephens
406 Pat Austin
407 Rod Brewer
408 Todd Crosby
409 Bien Figueroa
410 Julian Martinez
411 Jesus Mendez
412 Geronimo Pena
413 Craig Wilson
414 Dennis Carter
415 Bernard Gilkey
416 Ray Lankford
417 Mauricio Nunez
418 Roy Silver
419 Gaylen Pitts
420 Mark Riggins

1990 Team Louisville Redbirds

(St. Louis Cardinals) (color)

	MT	NR MT	EX
Complete Set:	11.00	8.25	4.50

1 Billy Bird/Checklist
2 Bernard Gilkey
3 Gaylen Pitts
4 Mark Riggins
5 Gibson Alba
6 Luis Alicea
7 Scott Arnold
8 Rod Brewer
9 Ernie Camacho
10 Cris Carpenter
11 Stan Clarke
12 Rheal Cormier
13 Danny Cox
14 Todd Crosby
15 Bien Figueroa
16 Terry Francona
17 Ed Fulton
18 Bernard Gilkey
19 Ken Hill
20 Howard Hilton
21 Mike Hinkle
22 Dale Kisten
23 Ray Lankford
24 Lonnie Maclin
25 Julian Martinez
26 Greg Mathews
27 Jesus Mendez
28 Scott Nichols
29 Tom Niedenfuer
30 Mauricio Nunez
31 Omar Olivares
32 Dave Osteen
33 Geronimo Pena
34 Mike Perez
35 Dave Richardson
36 Stan Royer
37 Tim Sherrill
38 Roy Silver
39 Ray Stephens
40 Bob Tewksbury
41 Steve Trout
42 Craig Wilson

1990 Sportprint Lynchburg Red Sox

(Boston Red Sox) (color)

	MT	NR MT	EX
Complete Set:	3.00	2.25	1.25

1 Greg Blosser
2 Chris Leach
3 Ed Perozo
4 Mickey Rivers Jr.
5 James Byrd
6 Miguel Monegro
7 Scott Powers
8 Willie Tatum
9 Les Wallin
10 Chris Whitehead
11 Luis Dorante
12 Chris Hanks
13 Paul Williams
14 Odie Abril
15 Paul Brown
16 Brian Conroy
17 Freddie Davis
18 Peter Estrada
19 Howard Landry
20 Tato Pratts
21 Ken Ryan
22 Rennie Scott
23 Tim Stange
24 Scott Taylor
25 David Duchin
26 Jim Bibby
27 Gary Allenson

1990 Best Madison Muskies

(Oakland A's) (color)

	MT	NR MT	EX
Complete Set:	5.00	3.75	2.00

1 Todd Van Poppel
2 Ed Tredway
3 Kurt Abbott
4 Marcos Armas
5 Eric Campa
6 Fred Cooley
7 Scott Henry
8 Glenn Osinski
9 Jim Waggoner
10 Enoch Simmons
11 Keith Thomas
12 Lee Tinsley
13 Leandro Mejia
14 Gerbacio Deleon
15 Jim Gibbs
16 Hugh Gulledge
17 Chad Kuhn
18 Dave Latter
19 Jim Lawson
20 Mike Mohler
21 Gavin Osteen
22 Bronswell Patrick
23 Timothy Peek
24 Bill Taylor
25 Casey Parsons
26 Bert Bradley
27 Shane Borchert
28 Wynn Beck
29 Checklist

1990 ProCards Madison Muskies

(Oakland A's) (color)

	MT	NR MT	EX
Complete Set:	3.00	2.25	1.25

2259 Checklist
2260 Brad Brimall
2261 Matthew Grott
2262 Darin Kracl
2263 Chad Kuhn
2264 Dave Latter
2265 Ray Martinez
2266 Leandro Mejia
2267 Mike Mohler
2268 Gavin Osteen
2269 Steve Peck
2270 Pedro Pena
2271 Wynn Beck
2272 Henry Mercedes
2273 Ed Tredway
2274 Kurt Abbott
2275 Fred Cooley
2276 Mike Conte
2277 Glenn McCormick
2278 Scott Shockey
2279 Carlos Tamarez
2280 Darryl Vice
2281 Enoch Simmons
2282 Lee Tinsley
2283 Casey Parsons
2284 Bert Bradley

1990 ProCards Martinsville Phillies

(Philadelphia Phillies) (color)

	MT	NR MT	EX
Complete Set:	3.00	2.25	1.25

3177 Checklist
3178 Rick Meyer
3179 Lamar Foster
3180 Facanel Medina
3181 Williams Carmona
3182 Mike Farmer
3183 Darren Hedley
3184 Bill Higgins
3185 Winston Wheeler
3186 Patrico Medina
3187 Maurice Hines
3188 David Croak
3189 Bob Badacour
3190 Gary Bennett
3191 Gary Lance
3192 Ray Domeco
3193 Pete Freeman
3194 Francisco Rosario
3195 Antonio Grissom
3196 J.J. Munoz
3197 Mike Lieberthal
3198 Mike Murphy
3199 Robbie KAmerschen
3200 Darren Cooper
3201 Jeff Borgese
3202 Terry Tewell
3203 Jorge Pascual
3204 David Agado
3205 Chad Anderson
3206 Domingo Tejada
3207 German Arias
3208 Dagoberto Tapia
3209 Derek Botelh, Roly DeArmas)
3419 Alberto Vicente

1990 Best Medicine Hat Blue Jays

(Toronto Blue Jays) (color)

	MT	NR MT	EX
Complete Set:	3.00	2.25	1.25

1 Mike Coolbaugh
2 Jason Reese
3 Tim Hyers
4 Travis Burley
5 Kyle Duey
6 Mark Choate
7 Richard Orman
8 Greg Wilcox
9 Lonell Roberts
10 Brent Bowers
11 Felix Septino
12 Ned Barley
13 Anastacio Garcia
14 Keith Hines
15 Scott Miller
16 Morgan Adams
17 Dave Fletcher
18 Dale Kistaitis
19 John Gilligan
20 Kris Harmes
21 Lee Daniel
22 Ronold Reams
23 Thomas Hotchkiss
24 Marc Loeb
25 Raphael Garcia
26 Howard Battle
27 Hector Taravez
28 Checklist

1990 Best Memphis Chicks

(Kansas City Royals) (color)

	MT	NR MT	EX
Complete Set:	8.00	6.00	3.25

1 Brent Mayne
2 Jorge Pedre
3 Pete Alborano
4 Stu Cole
5 David Howard
6 Sean Berry
7 Frank Laureano
8 Jeff Conine
9 Bobby Moore
10 Kevin Koslofski
11 Tommy Dunbar
12 Kyle Reese
13 Brian McRae
14 Scott Centala
15 Greg Everson
16 Richie LeBlanc
17 Joel Johnston
18 Hector Wagner
19 Brian McCormack
20 Vicotr Cole
21 Carlos Maldonado
22 Jim Campbell
23 Andres Cruz
24 Doug Nelson
25 Guy Hansen
26 Jeff Cox
27 Mike Leon
28 Brian Peterson
29 Checklist

1990 ProCards Memphis Chicks

(Kansas City Royals) (color) Cards #1 thru #25 are numbered # of 30 cards but card #26 thru #31 are numbered # of 31 cards.

	MT	NR MT	EX
Complete Set:	8.00	6.00	3.25

1000 Checklist
1001 Scott Centala
1002 Jim Campbell
1003 Andres Cruz
1004 Doug Nelson
1005 Greg Everson
1006 Victor Cole
1007 Carlos Maldonado
1008 Hector Wagner
1009 Brian McCormack
1010 Joel Johnson
1011 Kyle Reese
1012 Brent Mayne
1013 Jorge Pedre
1014 Stu Cole
1015 Dave Howard
1016 Sean Berry
1017 Jeff Conine
1018 Frank Laureano
1019 Bobby Moore
1020 Pete Alborano
1021 Kevin Koslofski
1022 Brian McRae
1023 Tommy Dunbar
1024 Richie LeBlanc
1025 Jeff Cox
1026 Guy Hansen
1027 Brian Peterson

1990 Star Co. Memphis Chicks

(Kansas City Royals) (color)

	MT	NR MT	EX
Complete Set:	8.00	6.00	3.25

1 Pete Alborano
2 Sean Berry
3 Jim Campbell
4 Scott Centala
5 Stu Cole
6 Victor Cole
7 Jeff Conine
8 Andres Cruz
9 Tommy Dunbar
10 Chuck Everson
11 David Howard
12 Kevin Koslofski
13 Frank Laureano
14 Richie LeBlanc
15 Carlos Maldonado
16 Brent Mayne
17 Brian McCormack
18 Brian McRae
19 Dennis Moeller
20 Bobby Moore
21 Doug Nelson
22 Jorge Pedre
23 Kyle Reese
24 Daryl Smith
25 Hector Wagner
26 Coaching Staff
27 Mike Leon

1990 Star Miami Miracle I

(Independent) (color)

	MT	NR MT	EX
Complete Set:	3.00	2.25	1.25

1 Dave Alexander
2 Joe Beaulac
3 Tommy Boyce
4 Tim Delgado
5 Marty Durkin
6 Eddie Garczyk
7 Marc Giordano
8 Pierre Gomez
9 Jackie Gutierrez
10 Lance Hudson
11 Anthony Kelley
12 George Kerfut
13 Dennis Kidd
14 Angel Lugo
15 Tim MacNeil
16 Javier Magria
17 Tim McKinley
18 Bill Miller
19 Angel Morris
20 Jorge Pascual
21 Kevin Ponder
22 Mike Reitzel
23 Harry Shelton
24 Dave Taylor
25 Pat Varni
26 Mike Easler
27 Bob Fralick
28 Fredi Gonzalez
29 Seth Fogler
30 Office Personnel
31 Jericho (Mascot)

1990 Star Miami Miracle II

(Independent) (color) Card #21, #26 Rigsby and #22, #27 Rogers each appear in set on two different cards.

	MT	NR MT	EX
Complete Set:	3.00	2.25	1.25

1 Miah Bradbury
2 Matt Cakora
3 Paul Carey
4 Greg D'Alexander
5 Clay Daniel
6 Marty Durkin
7 Mike Ericson
8 Librado Garcia
9 Marc Giordano
10 Brad Gregory
11 Jackie Gutierrez
12 Dennis Kidd
13 Anthony Kelly
14 George Kerfut
15 Tito Landrum
16 Mike Lansing
17 Tom Mincho
18 Bill Miller
19 Jorge Pascual
20 Tom Raffo
21 Tim Rigsby
22 Charlie Rogers
23 Rich Sauveur
24 Harry Shelton
25 Chad Smith
26 Tim Rigsby
27 Charlie Rogers
28 Coaching Staff
29 Michael Veek
30 Jericho (Mascot)
31 Team Photo

1990 Grand Slam Midland Angels

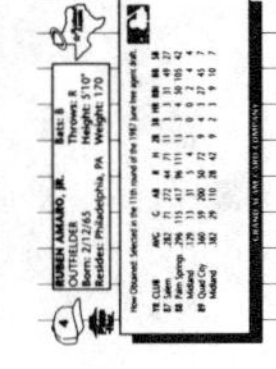

(California Angels) (color)

	MT	NR MT	EX
Complete Set:	4.50	3.50	1.75

1 Eddie Rodriguez
2 Gary Ruby
3 Steve DeAngelis
4 Ruben Amaro Jr.
5 Kyle Abbott
6 Mark Zappelli
7 Mark Howie
8 Scott Cerny
9 Jeff Barns
10 Mark Davis
11 Wiley Lee
12 Joe Grahe
13 Mike Knapp
14 Jim Aylward
15 Mike Butcher
16 Mark Holzemer
17 Carl Hamilton
18 Glenn Carter
19 Kevin Trudeau
20 Dan Wagner
21 Andy Hall
22 Frank DiMichele
23 Luis Merejo
24 Kevin Flora
25 Scott Sowell
---- Juice the Moose (Mascot)
---- Midland Angels Logo Card
---- Pizza Hut Admission Card

1990 1 Hour Photo Midland Angels

(California Angels) (color)

	MT	NR MT	EX
Complete Set:	15.00	11.00	6.00

1 Kyle Abbott
2 Luis Aguayo
3 Ruben Amaro Jr.
4 Jim Aylward
5 Jeff Barns
6 Mike Butcher
7 Glenn Carter
8 Scott Cerny
9 Doug Davis
10 Mark Davis
11 Steve DeAngelis
12 Frank DiMichele
13 Mark Doran
14 Mike Erb
15 Kevin Flora
16 Joe Grahe
17 Andy Hall
18 Carl Hamilton
19 Mark Holzemer
20 Mike Hook
21 Mark Howie
22 Mike Knapp
23 Wiley Lee
24 Dave Martinez
25 Tim Meeks
26 Robert Moore
27 Reed Peters
28 Eddie Rodriguez
29 Gary Ruby
30 Scott Sowell
31 Dave Sturdivant
32 Kevin Trudeau
33 Brandy Vann
34 Don Vidmar
35 Mark Zappelli

1990 Grand Slam Midwest League All-Stars

(All-Stars) (color)

	MT	NR MT	EX
Complete Set:	7.00	5.25	2.75

1 Kurt Abbott
2 Joe Andrzejewski
3 Jayson Best
4 Doug Bochtler
5 Len Brutcher
6 John Byington
7 Scott Cepicky
8 Fred Cooley
9 Steve Dunn
10 Mike Eatinger
11 Rusty Kilgo
12 Scott Kimball
13 Tim Laker
14 Marc Lipson
15 Danny Matznick
16 Henry Mercedes
17 Alan Newman
18 Randy Snyder
19 Tom Taylor
20 Lee Tinsley
21 Rich Tunison
22 Bob Vancho
23 Jerry Wolak
24 Tyrone Woods
25 John Zaksek
26 Northern Division Staff
27 Ramon Caraballo
28 Frank Carey
29 Pedro Castellano
30 Chad Curtis
31 Damion Easley
32 Luis Galindez
33 Victor Garcia
34 Chris Hancock
35 Mike Hook
36 Joey James
37 Clyde Keller
38 Javy Lopez
39 Chris Lutz
40 Fili Martinez
41 Dave McAuliffe
42 Brent McCoy
43 Roger Miller
44 Mike Mulvaney
45 Matt Murray
46 J.D. Noland
47 Dave Reis
48 Reggie Sanders
49 Mo Sanford
50 Ed Taubensee
51 Rob Taylor
52 Matt Witkowski
53 Southern Division Staff
54 Matt Grott
55 Darin Kracl
56 Pedro Pena
57 Rafael Novoa
58 Pedro Borbon

1990 Cal League Modesto A's

(Oakland A's) (color)

	MT	NR MT	EX
Complete Set:	3.00	2.25	1.25

149 Scott Erwin
150 John Briscoa
151 Todd Smith
152 James Lawson
153 Dana Allison
154 William Taylor
155 Bronswell Patrick
156 Timothy McCoy
157 William Love
158 Joseph Ortiz
159 Timothy Vannaman
160 Michael Messerly
161 Keith Thomas
162 James Buccheri
163 Ronald Correia
164 Dean Borelli
165 Ronald Witmeyer
166 James Waggoner
167 Thomas Carcione
168 Francisco Matos
169 Dwayne Hosey
170 Kevin Lofthus
171 Ted Kubiak
172 Pete Richert
173 Dave Hollenback

1990 Chong Modesto A's

(Oakland A's) (black and white)

	MT	NR MT	EX
Complete Set:	4.00	3.00	1.50

(1) Dean Borelli
(2) John Briscoe
(3) James Buccheri
(4) Thomas Carcione
(5) Joe Chimelies
(6) Michael Conte
(7) Russel Cormier
(8) Ronald Correia
(9) Scott Erwin
(10) Severino Garcia
(11) Matthew Grott
(12) Ramon Guzman
(13) Brettly Hendley
(14) Dave Hollenback
(15) Dwayne Hosey
(16) Ted Kubiak
(17) Mike Kennedy
(18) Ruben Lardizabal
(19) William Love
(20) Francisco Matos
(21) Tim McCoy
(22) Mike Messerly
(23) Robert Parry
(24) Craig Paquette
(25) Bronswell Patrick
(26) Steven Peck
(27) Pedro Pena
(28) Pete Richert
(29) Richard Shockey
(30) Todd Smith
(31) Richard Strebeck
(32) Darryl Vice
(33) James Waggoner
(34) Ronald Witmeyer
---- Modesto A's Emblem
---- Checklist

1990 ProCards Modesto A's

	MT	NR MT	EX
Complete Set:	3.00	2.25	1.25

2202 Checklist
2203 Dana Allison
2204 John Briscoe
2205 Scott Erwin
2206 Apolinar Garcia
2207 Johnny Guzman
2208 Tim McCoy
2209 Jim Lawson
2210 Will Love
2211 Bronswell Patrick
2212 Todd Smith
2213 Bill Taylor
2214 Dean Borrelli
2215 Tom Carcione
2216 Joe Ortiz
2217 James Buccheri
2218 Rod Correia
2219 Kevin Lofthus
2220 Francisco Matos
2221 Mike Messerly
2222 Craig Paquette
2223 James Waggoner
2224 Ron Witmeyer
2225 Dwayne Hosey
2226 Keith Thomas
2227 Tim Vannaman
2228 Bob Parry
2229 Ted Kubiak
2230 Pete Richert

1990 ProCards Myrtle Beach Blue Jays

(Toronto Blue Jays) (color)

	MT	NR MT	EX
Complete Set:	3.00	2.25	1.25

2766 Checklist
2767 Greg Bicknell
2768 Rob Blumberg
2769 Eric Bradley
2770 Daren Brown
2771 Scott Hutson
2772 Daren Kizziah
2773 Gregg Martin
2774 Rick Nowak
2775 Mike Ogliaruso
2776 Jose Olivares
2777 Aaron Small
2778 John Wanish
2779 Ken Rivers
2780 Juan Jaime
2781 Bill Abare
2782 Brad Mengel
2783 Hector Mercedes
2784 Scott Miller
2785 Robert Montalvo
2786 Bill Parese
2787 Rickey Holifield
2788 Shawn Holtzclaw
2789 Anton Mobley
2790 Todd Provence
2791 Nigel Wilson
2792 Mike Fischlin
2793 Steve Mingori
2794 Leroy Stanton

1990 CMC (TCMA) Nashville Sounds

(Cincinnati Reds) (color)

	MT	NR MT	EX
Complete Set:	6.00	4.50	2.50

1 Milt Hill
2 Robert Moore
3 Joey Vierra
4 Terry McGriff
5 Chris Hammond
6 Charlie Mitchell
7 Rodney Imes
8 Rob Lopez
9 Keith Brown
10 Scott Scudder
11 Bob Sebra
12 Donnie Scott
13 Skeeter Barnes
14 Paul Noce
15 Leo Garcia
16 Chris Jones
17 Kevin Pearson
18 Darryl Motley
19 Keith Lockhart
20 Brian Lane
21 Eddie Tanner
22 Reggie Jefferson
23 Neil Allen
24 Pete Mackanin
25 Ray Ripplemeyer
26 John Young

1990 ProCards Nashville Sounds

(Cincinnati Reds) (color)

	MT	NR MT	EX
Complete Set:	6.00	4.50	2.50

222 Checklist
223 Neil Allen
224 Keith Brown
225 Chris Hammond
226 Milton Hill
227 Rodney Imes
228 Rob Lopez
229 Charlie Mitchell
230 Robert Moore
231 Rosario Rodriguez
232 Scott Scudder
233 Bob Sebra
234 Joey Vierra
235 Tony DeFrancesco
236 Terry McGriff
237 Donnie Scott
238 Reggie Jefferson
239 Brian Lane
240 Chris Lombardozzi
241 Paul Noce
242 Kevin Pearson
243 Eddie Tanner
244 Skeeter Barnes
245 Leo Garcia
246 Chris Jones
247 Keith Lockhart
248 Darryl Motley
249 Pete Mackanin
250 Ray Ripplemeyer

1990 Team-Hill's Nashville Sounds

(Cincinnati Reds) (color)

	MT	NR MT	EX
Complete Set:	9.00	6.75	3.50

(1) Skeeter Barnes
(2) Billy Bates
(3) Freddie Benavides
(4) Keith Brown
(5) Leo Garcia
(6) Kip Gross
(7) Chris Hammond
(8) Milt Hill
(9) Rodney Imes
(10) Reggie Jefferson
(11) Chris Jones
(12) Brian Lane
(13) Joe Lazor
(14) Terry Lee
(15) Keith Lockhart
(16) Rob Lopez
(17) Pete Mackanin
(18) Terry McGriff
(19) Gino Minutelli
(20) Charlie Mitchell
(21) Jerome Nelson
(22) Paul Noce
(23) Ray Ripplemeyer
(24) Larry Schmittou
(25) Donnie Scott
(26) Scott Scudder
(27) Eddie Tanner
(28) Luis Vasquez
(29) Joey Vierra
(30) John Young

1990 Best New Britain Red Sox

(Boston Red Sox) (color)

	MT	NR MT	EX
Complete Set:	12.00	9.00	4.75

1 Eric Wedge
2 Tom Fisher
3 Julius McDougal
4 Josias Manzanillo

5 Dave Milstien
6 Bob Zupcic
7 Jeff Bagwell
8 Craig Wilson
9 Mike Twardoski
10 Donald Florence
11 Mike Kelly
12 Mike Carista
13 Stu Weidie
14 Kevin Morton
15 Gordon Hurlbert
16 Vince Degifico
17 Juan Paris
18 Dave Owen
19 Randy Randle
20 Jeff Plympton
21 John Valentin
22 Todd Pratts
23 Butch Hobson
24 Derek Livernois
25 David Walters
26 Rich Gale
27 Bob Spencer
28 The Staff
29 Checklist

1990 ProCards New Britain Red Sox

(Boston Red Sox) (color)

	MT	NR MT	EX
Complete Set:	12.00	9.00	4.75

1310 Checklist
1311 Mike Carista
1312 Tom Fischer
1313 Don Florence
1314 Derek Livernois
1315 Josias Manzanillo
1316 Kevin Morton
1317 Dan O'Neill
1318 Dave Owen
1319 Jeff Plympton
1320 Dave Walters
1321 Todd Pratt
1322 Eric Wedge
1323 Craig Wilson
1324 Jeff Bagwell
1325 Vinnie Degifico
1326 Julius McDougal
1327 Dave Milstein
1328 Randy Randle
1329 Mike Twardorski
1330 Mike Kelly
1331 Juan Parris
1332 Stu Weidie
1333 Bob Zupcic
1334 Butch Hobson
1335 Rich Gale

1990 Star Co. New Britain Red Sox

(Boston Red Sox) (color)

	MT	NR MT	EX
Complete Set:	12.00	9.00	4.75

1 Jeff Bagwell
2 Mike Carista
3 Vinnie Degifico
4 Tom Fischer
5 Donald Florence
6 Michael Kelly
7 Kooz Kuzniar
8 Derek Livernois
9 Josias Manzanillo
10 Julius McDougal
11 David Milstien
12 Kevin Morton
13 David Owen
14 Juan Paris
15 Jeff Plympton
16 Todd Pratt
17 Randy Randle
18 Mike Twardoski
19 John Valentin
20 David Walters
21 Eric Wedge
22 Stuart Weidie
23 Craig Wilson
24 Robert Zupcic
25 Butch Hobson
26 Rich Gale
27 Gordon Hurlbert

1990 Pucko Niagara Falls Rapids

(Detroit Tigers) (color)

	MT	NR MT	EX
Complete Set:	3.00	2.25	1.25

1 Danny Rogers
2 Doug Kimbler
3 Tim Kirt
4 Denny McNamara
5 Dave Mastropietro
6 Kirk Mendenhall
7 Mario Moccia
8 Kelley O'Neal
9 Brian Saltzgaber
10 Warran Sawkiw
11 Gino Tagliaferri
12 Gernaro DeBrand
13 Gregg Radachowsky
14 Sean Sadler
15 Francisco Alcantara
16 Greg Coppeta
17 Tom Drell
18 Rob Fazekas
19 Kevin Keon
20 Eric Leimeister
21 Doug Marcero
22 Brian Nelson
23 Eddy Rodriguez
24 Brian Schubert
25 Arthur Thigpen
26 Bob Undorf
27 Steve Wolf
28 Juan Lopez
29 Joe Decker
30 Chris Rogaliner
31 Joe DeDario
32 Larry & Barbara Tiermey
33 Dinger the Duck (Mascot)

1990 CMC (TCMA) Oklahoma City 89ers

(Texas Rangers) (color)

	MT	NR MT	EX
Complete Set:	15.00	11.00	6.00

1 Jack Hardy
2 Steve Lankard
3 John Hoover
4 David Lynch
5 Mark Petkovsek
6 David Miller
7 Brad Arnsberg
8 Jeff Satzinger
9 John Barfield
10 Mike Berger
11 John Russell
12 Pat Garman
13 Gary Green
14 Bryan House
15 Ron Washington
16 Nick Capra
17 Juan Gonzalez
18 Gar Millay
19 Kevin Reimer
20 Bernie Tatis
21 Steve Smith
22 Dick Egan
23 Stan Hough
24 Ray Ramirez

1990 ProCards Oklahoma City 89ers

(Texas Rangers) (color)

	MT	NR MT	EX
Complete Set:	15.00	11.00	6.00

421 Checklist
422 Gerald Alexander
423 Brad Arnsberg
424 John Barfield
425 Jack Hardy
426 Ray Hayward
427 John Hoover
428 Steve Lankard
429 David Lynch
430 Craig McMurty
431 David Miller
432 Mark Petkovsek
433 Jeff Satzinger
434 Mike Berger
435 Dave Engle
436 John Russell
437 Pat Dodson
438 Pat Garman
439 Gary Green
440 Bryan House
441 Dean Palmer
442 Ron Washington
443 Nick Capra
444 Juan Gonzalez
445 Gar Millay
446 Kevin Reimer
447 Bernie Tatis
448 Steve Smith
449 Dick Egan
450 Stan Hough

1990 CMC (TCMA) Omaha Royals

(Kansas City Royals) (color)

	MT	NR MT	EX
Complete Set:	8.00	6.00	3.25

1 Jat Baller
2 Ray Chadwick
3 Dera Clark
4 Luis Encarnation
5 Jim LeMasters
6 Mike Magnante
7 Mel Stottlemyre
8 Tony Ferreira
9 Pete Filson
10 Andy McGaffigan
11 Luis de los Santos
12 Mike Loggins
13 Chito Martinez
14 Bobby Meacham
15 Russ Morman
16 Bill Pecota
17 Harvey Pulliam
18 Jeff Schultz
19 Gary Thurman
20 Thad Reece
21 Tim Spehr
22 Paul Zuvella
24 Bob Hameli, Tom Poquette, Rich Dubee
25 Sal Rende

1990 ProCards Omaha Royals

(Kansas City Royals) (color)

	MT	NR MT	EX
Complete Set:	9.00	6.75	3.50

57 Checklist
58 Ray Chadwick
59 Dera Clark
60 Luis Encarnacion
61 Tony Ferreira
62 Pete Filson
63 Jim LeMasters
64 Mike Magnante
65 Mike Tresemer
66 Mel Stottlemyre
67 Bill Wilkinson
68 Kevin Burrell
69 Tim Spehr
70 Luis de los Santos
71 Bob Hamelin
72 Bobby Meacham
73 Russ Morman
74 Thad Reece
75 Paul Zuvella
76 Mike Loggins
77 Chito Martinez
78 Harvey Pulliam
79 Jeff Schulz
80 Sal Rende
81 Tom Poquette
82 Rich Dubee

1990 ProCards Oneonta Yankees

(New York Yankees) (color)

	MT	NR MT	EX
Complete Set:	4.00	3.00	1.50

3365 Checklist
3366 Luis Gallardo
3367 Adin Lohry
3368 Todd Malone
3369 Cesar Perez
3370 Steve Perry
3371 Rafael Quirico
3372 Dedrick Strickland
3373 Scott Romano
3374 Brian Turner
3375 Jovino Carvajal
3376 Ron Frazier
3377 Darren Hodges
3378 Sam Militello
3379 Pat Morphy
3380 Kirk Ojala
3381 Bo Siberz
3382 Matt Dunbar
3383 Doug Demetre
3384 Robert Eeehoorn
3385 Mike Hankins
3386 Kevin Jordan
3387 Rich Lantrip
3388 Bob Deller
3389 Trey Hillman
3390 Ken Dominguez
3391 Mark Shiflett
3392 Brian Miller
3420 Jalal Leach

Values for recent cards and sets are listed in Mint (MT), Near Mint (NM), reflecting the fact that many cards from recent years have been preserved in top condition. Recent cards and sets in less than Excellent condition have little collector interest.

1990 Best Orlando Sun Rays

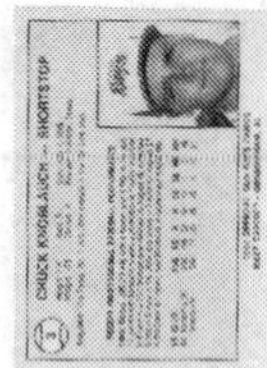

(Minnesota Twins) (color)

	MT	NR MT	EX
Complete Set:	10.00	7.50	4.00

1 Willie Banks
2 John Eccles
3 Chuck Knoblauch
4 Shawn Gilbert
5 Ed Naveda
6 Jose Marzan
7 Reed Olmstead
8 Jeff Hull
9 Jarvis Brown
10 Kenny Morgan
11 Mike Randle
12 Gary Resetar
13 Lenny Webster
14 Frank Valdez
15 Greg Johnson
16 Scott Erickson
17 Basil Meyer
18 Rob Wassenaar
19 Mike Redding
20 Steve Muh
21 Doug Simons
22 Steve Stowell
23 Johnny Ard
24 Groman Heimueller
25 Rick McWane
26 Wayne Hattaway
27 Jeff Reboulet
28 Ron Gardenhire
29 Mark Funderbunk
30 Checklist

1990 ProCards Orlando Sun Rays

(Minnesota Twins) (color)

	MT	NR MT	EX
Complete Set:	10.00	7.50	4.00

1074 Checklist
1075 Johnny Ard
1076 Willie Banks
1077 Scott Erickson
1078 Greg Johnson
1079 Basil Meyer
1080 Steve Muh
1081 Mike Redding
1082 Doug Simons
1083 Steve Stowell
1084 Rob Wassenaar
1085 Jeff Hull
1086 John Eccles
1087 Gary Resetar
1088 Lenny Webster
1089 Shawn Gilbert
1090 Chuck Knoblauch
1091 Jose Marzan
1092 Reed Olmstead
1093 Jeff Reboulet
1094 Frank Valdez
1095 Jarvis Brown
1096 Kenny Morgan
1097 Mike Randle
1098 Ron Gardenhire
1099 Mark Funderburk
1100 Gorman Heimueller

1990 Star Co. Orlando Sun Rays

(Minnesota Twins) (color)

	MT	NR MT	EX
Complete Set:	10.00	7.50	4.00

1 Johnny Ard
2 Willie Banks
3 Jarvis Brown
4 John Eccles
5 Scott Erickson
6 Shawn Gilbert
7 Greg Johnson
8 Chuck Knoblauch
9 Orlando Lind
10 Jose Marzan
11 Basil Meyer
12 Kenny Morgan
13 Denny Neagle
14 Reed Olmstead

15 Mike Randle
16 Jeff Reboulet
17 Mike Redding
18 Gary Resetar
19 Doug Simons
20 Steve Stowell
21 Frank Valdez
22 Rob Wassenaar
23 Lenny Webster
24 Ron Gardenhire
25 Mark Funderburk
26 Gorman Heimueller
27 Rick McWane
28 Wayne Hattaway

1990 Star Co. Osceola Astros

(Houston Astros) (color)

	MT	NR MT	EX
Complete Set:	7.00	5.25	2.75

1 Manny Acta
2 Donald Angotti
3 Peter Bauer
4 Michael Beams
5 Chris Colombino
6 Troy Dovey
7 Rick Dunnum
8 Brian Griffiths
9 David Henderson
10 Cole Hyson
11 Jeff Juden
12 Todd Jones
13 Frank Kellner
14 Lawrence Lamphere
15 Mica Lewis
16 Kenneth Lofton
17 Ken Luckham
18 Lance Madsen
19 Scott Makarewicz
20 John Massarelli
21 Dan Nyssen
22 Edward Ponte
23 Howard Prager
24 Toncie Reed
25 Gabriel Rodriguez
26 Rodney Windes
27 Sal Butera
28 Jack Billingham
29 Bobby Ramos
30 Gene Confreda

1990 Cal League Palm Springs Angels

(California Angels) (color)

	MT	NR MT	EX
Complete Set:	15.00	11.00	6.00

203 Terence Carr
204 David Esquer
205 Jeff Kipila
206 Jeff Oberdank
207 J.R. Phillips
208 Terry Taylor
209 Frank Dominguez
210 Richard Parker
211 David Sturdivant
212 Davis Patrick
213 Beban Perez
214 Jeff Kelso
215 Tim Salmon
216 Tim Wallace
217 David Martinez
218 Brandy Vann
219 Marvin Cobb
220 Stephen Dunn
221 John Fritz
222 Michael Shull
223 Michael Search
224 William Warrecker
225 Donald Vidmar
226 Clement Acosta
227 TIm Meeks
228 Nate Oliver
229 Kernan Ronan

1990 ProCards Palm Springs Angels

(California Angels) (color)

	MT	NR MT	EX
Complete Set:	13.00	9.75	5.25

2568 Checklist
2569 Clement Acosta
2570 Marvin Cobb
2571 Steve Dunn
2572 John Fritz
2573 David Martinez
2574 Brett Merriman
2575 Larry Pardo
2576 Michael Search
2577 Brandy Vann
2578 Don Vidmar
2579 Willy Warrecker
2580 Frank Dominguez
2581 Richard Parker
2582 Dave Sturdivant
2583 Dave Esquer
2584 Jeff Kipila
2585 Jeff Oberdank
2586 J.R. Phillips
2587 Terry Taylor
2588 Tim Wallace
2589 Terry Carr
2590 Jeff Kelso
2591 Dave Patrick
2592 Beban Perez
2593 Tim Salmon
2594 Nate Oliver
2595 Kernan Rohan

1990 CMC (TCMA) Pawtucket Red Sox

(Boston Red Sox) (color)

	MT	NR MT	EX
Complete Set:	11.00	8.25	4.50

1 Tito Stewart
2 John Trautwein
3 Mike Rochford
4 Larry Shikles
5 Daryl Irvine
6 John Leister
7 Joe Johnson
8 Mark Meleski
9 Steven Bast
10 Ed Nottle
11 John Flaherty
12 John Marzano
13 Gary Tremblay
14 Scott Cooper
15 Angel Gonzalez
16 Julius McDougal
17 Tim Naehring
18 Jim Pankovits
19 Rick Lancellotti
20 Mickey Pina
21 Phil Plantier
22 Jeff Stone
23 Scott Wade
24 Mike Dalton
25 Jeff Gray

1990 ProCards Pawtucket Red Sox

(Boston Red Sox) (color)

	MT	NR MT	EX
Complete Set:	15.00	11.00	6.00

451 Checklist
452 Steve Bast
453 Tom Bolton
454 Steve Curry
455 Mike Dalton
456 Jeff Gray
457 Daryl Irvine
458 Joe Johnson
459 John Leister
460 Mike Rochford
461 Larry Shikles
462 Tito Steward
463 John Trautwein
464 John Flaherty
465 John Marzano
466 Gary Tremblay
467 Scott Cooper
468 Angel Gonzalez
469 Tim Naehring
470 Jim Pankovits
471 Mo Vaughn
472 Rick Lancellotti
473 Mickey Pina
474 Phil Plantier
475 Jeff Stone
476 Scott Wade
477 Ed Nottle
478 Mark Meleski
479 Lee Strange

1990 Star Co. Peninsula Pilots

(Seattle Mariners) (color)

	MT	NR MT	EX
Complete Set:	3.00	2.25	1.25

1 Lash Bailey
2 Rick Balabon
3 Dan Barbara
4 Mark Brakebill
5 Jimmy Campanis
6 Jeff Darwin
7 Kyle Duke
8 Marcos Garcia
9 Anthony Gordon
10 Jim Gutierrez
11 Scott Lodgek
12 Darin Loe
13 Ron Mullins
14 Ron Pezzoni
15 Lem Pilkington
16 Rod Poissant
17 Oscar Rivas
18 Jorge Robles
19 Damon Saetre
20 Ruben Santana
21 Jesus Tavarez
22 Delvin Thomas
23 Kelvin Thomas
24 Landon Williams
25 Jim Nettles
26 Ross Grimsley
27 Allan Lovinger

1990 Team Sully's Pub Peoria Chiefs

(Chicago Cubs) (color)

	MT	NR MT	EX
Complete Set:	6.00	4.50	2.50

1 Timothy "Earl" Cunningham
2 Shawn Boskie
3 Front Office Personnel
4 Bradley Erdman
5 William Payner
6 Richard Mundy
7 Kraig Washington
8 Pedro Castellano
9 Cub's Top Prospects
10 Curley Johnson
11 Matthew Franco
12 William St. Peter
13 Arthur Smith
14 Paul Torres
15 Victor Cancel
16 Christopher Ebright
17 Rene Francisco
18 Jerrome Williams
19 Jason Doss
20 Peoria's Famous Five
21 Jay Eddings
22 Jac Gelb
23 Henrique Gomez
24 Eric Jaques
25 Christopher Lutz
26 Ray Mullino
27 Ronnie Rasp
28 David Swartzbaugh
29 Travis Willis
30 Mark Young
31 Greg Mahlberg
32 James Strobe
33 Jim O'Reilly
34 Bill Harford
35 Richad Zisk
36 Sully's Bar
37 Joseph Bosco

1990 Team Peoria Chiefs

(Chicago Cubs) (color) (update set)

	MT	NR MT	EX
Complete Set:	4.00	3.00	1.50

1 Lance Dickson
2 Jim Robinson
3 Damon Berryhill
4 Matthew Walbeck
5 Marvin Cole
6 James Sweeney
7 James Murphy

1990 CMC (TCMA) Phoenix Firebirds

(San Francisco Giants) (color)

	MT	NR MT	EX
Complete Set:	7.00	5.25	2.75

1 Paul McClellan
2 Randy McCament
3 Gil Heredia
4 George Bonilla
5 Russ Swan
6 Ed Vosberg
7 Eric Gunderson
8 Trevor Wilson
9 Greg Booker
10 Kirt Manwaring
11 Mike Kingery
12 Brian Brady
13 Mark Bailey
14 Gregg Ritchie
15 George Hinshaw
16 Craig Colbert
17 Kash Beauchamp
18 Jeff Carter
19 Mark Leonard
20 Tony Perezchica
21 Mike Laga
22 Mike Benjamin
23 Timber Mead
24 Duane Epsy
25 Time Ireland
26 Larry Hardy

1990 ProCards Phoenix Firebirds

(San Francisco Giants) (color)

	MT	NR MT	EX
Complete Set:	9.00	6.75	3.50

1 Checklist
2 George Bonilla
3 Greg Booker
4 Rich Bordi
5 John Burkett
6 Gil Heredia
7 Bob Knepper
8 Randy McCament
9 Paul McClellan
10 Timber Mead
11 Ed Vosberg
12 Trevor Wilson
13 Mark Bailey
14 Kirt Manwaring
15 Mike Benjamin
16 Brian Brady
17 Jeff Carter
18 Craig Colbert
19 Erik Johnson
20 Greg Litton
21 Kash Beauchamp
22 George Hinshaw
23 Mike Kingery
24 Mark Leonard
25 Gregg Richie
26 Rick Parker
27 Duane Epsy
28 Tim Ireland
29 Larry Hardy

1990 Pucko Pittsfield Mets

(New York Mets) (color)

	MT	NR MT	EX
Complete Set:	4.00	3.00	1.50

1 Phillip Scott
2 Kyle Washington
3 Eric Thornton
4 Wallace Minnifield
5 Robbi Guzik
6 Joe Arrendondo
7 Jarrod Parker
8 Jason King
9 Tim Buhe
10 Tim McClinton
11 Nicki Davis
12 Brian Dunn
13 Todd Douma
14 Steve Thomas
15 Mike Sciortino
16 Peter Walker
17 Tom Wilson
18 Mike Thomas
19 Andy Fidler
20 Juan Castillo
21 Jim Scheffler
22 Ed Vazquez
23 Alberto Castillo
24 Mike Freitas
25 Jim Eschen
26 Randy Niemann
27 Billy Gardner Jr.
28 Joe Hawkins
29 The Clubhouse Boys
30 Walconah Park
31 Jeromy Burnitz
32 Tommy Allison

1990 CMC (TCMA) Portland Beavers

(Minnesota Twins) (color)

	MT	NR MT	EX
Complete Set:	8.00	6.00	3.25

1 Paul Abbott
2 Pat Bangtson
3 Larry Casian
4 Mike Cook
5 Pete Delkus
6 Mike Dyer
7 Charles Scott
8 Francisco Oliveras
9 Park Pittman
10 Jimmy Williams
11 Rich Yett
12 Vic Rodriguez
13 Jamie Nelson
14 Derek Parks
15 Ed Naveda
16 Scott Lewis
17 Terry Jorgensen

18 Doug Baker
19 Chip Hale
20 Dave Jacas
21 Jim Shellenback
22 Rafael DeLima
23 Bernardo Brito
24 J.T. Bruett
25 Paul Sorrento

1990 ProCards Portland Beavers

(Minnesota Twins) (color)

	MT	NR MT	EX
Complete Set:	7.00	5.25	2.75

167 Checklist
168 Paul Abbott
169 Pat Bangtson
170 Larry Casian
171 Mike Cook
172 Pete Delkus
173 Mike Dyer
174 Mark Guthrie
175 Orlando Lind
176 Francisco Oliveras
177 Park Pittman
178 Charles Scott
179 Jimmy Williams
180 Jamie Nelson
181 Derek Parks
182 Doug Baker
183 Chip Hale
184 Terry Jorgensen
185 Scott Leius
186 Larty Lanoux
187 Edgar Naveda
188 Victor Rodriguez
189 Paul Sorrento
190 Bernardo Brito
191 Rafael DeLima
192 David Jacas
193 Alonzo Powell
194 Jim Shellenbach

1990 Diamond Cards Princeton Patriots

(Co-op) (color)

	MT	NR MT	EX
Complete Set:	3.00	2.25	1.25

1 Joel Adamson
2 Ron Blazier
3 Luis Brito
4 Patrick Cheek
5 Jerome Edwards
6 Samuel Edwards
7 Jesus Garces
8 Mario Garcia
9 Jeffrey Gunn
10 David Hammond
11 Brad Hassinger
12 Steve Hollins
13 Aurelio Llanos
14 Ron Lockett
15 Bryan Manicchia
16 Jeff Repoz
17 Troy Rusk
18 Chad Silver
19 Terry Smith
20 Chris Snyder
21 Jose Sosa
22 Mark Steffens
23 Bill Stohr
24 Francisco Tejada
25 Julio Vargas
26 Juan Villareal
27 Matt Whisenant
28 Eli Grba
29 Ramon Henderson
30 Brent Leiby

1990 Sportprint Prince William Cannons

(New York Yankees) (color)

	MT	NR MT	EX
Complete Set:	5.00	3.75	2.00

1 Mike Brown
2 Gary Denbo
3 Darren London
4 Bob Mariano
5 Brad Ausmus
6 Jason Bridges
7 Art Canestro
8 Russ Davis
9 Herb Erhardt
10 Mike Gardella
11 Cullen Hartzog
12 Enrique Hernandez
13 Dave Howell
14 Ed Martel
15 James Moody
16 Gerald Nielsen
17 Sherman Obando
18 Paul Oster
19 Rich Polak
20 Bruce Prybylinski
21 Curtis Ralph
22 Andres Rodriguez
23 Frank Seminara
24 Dave Silvestri
25 J.T. Snow
26 John Viera
27 Tom Weeks
28 Jim Wiley
29 Mauricio Zazueta
30 Team Photo

1990 Best Pulaski Braves

(Atlanta Braves) (color)

	MT	NR MT	EX
Complete Set:	3.00	2.25	1.25

1 Brian Bark
2 Barry Chiles
3 Travis Dunlap
4 Steward Ford
5 Brett Grebe
6 Keith Morrison
7 Larry Owens
8 Mike Place
9 Joe Roa
10 Mike Shepherd
11 Henry Werland
12 David Williams
13 Wallace Gonzalez
14 Vincent Jiminez
15 Jamie Crump
16 Patrick Dando
17 Hector Roa
18 Karl Rudison
19 George Virgilio
20 Troy Hughes
21 Anthony Johnson
22 Brian Kowitz
23 Jimmie Pullins
24 Armando Rodriguez
25 Juan Williams
26 Randy Ingle
27 Randy Phillips
28 Cloyd Boyer
29 Checklist

1990 ProCards Pulaski Braves

(Atlanta Braves) (color)

	MT	NR MT	EX
Complete Set:	3.00	2.25	1.25

3085 Checklist
3086 Anthony Johnson
3087 Brian Kowitz
3088 Troy Hughes
3089 George Virgilio
3090 Raymond Mack
3091 David Williams
3092 Vincent Jimenez
3093 Wallace Gonzalez
3094 Karl Rudison
3095 Jamie Crump
3096 Pat Dando
3097 Hector Roa
3098 Steward Ford
3099 Travis Dunlap
3100 Barry Chiles
3101 Brian Bark
3102 Larry Owens
3103 Brett Grebe
3104 Keith Morrison
3105 Mike Sheppard
3106 Michael Place
3107 Joe Roa
3108 Henry Werland
3109 Armando Rodriguez
3110 Jimmie Pullins
3111 Juan Williams
3112 Johnny Walker
3113 Cloyd Boye, Randy Phillips)
3114 Randy Ingle
3115 Team Photo

1990 Grand Slam Quad City Angels

(California Angels) (color)

	MT	NR MT	EX
Complete Set:	4.00	3.00	1.50

1 Don Long
2 Joe Georger
3 Mitch Seoane
4 Robert Horowitz
5 Dave Neal
6 Mike Hook
7 Bruce Vegely
8 Roberto Castillo
9 Justin Martin
10 Steve King
11 Les Haffner
12 Dave Adams
13 Marcus Moore
14 Erik Bennett
15 John Marchese
16 Jeff Gay
17 Lawrence Gonzales
18 Mick Billmeyer
19 Corey Kapano
20 Henry Threadgill
21 Chad Curtis
22 Ron Ortegon
23 Ray Martinez
24 Damion Easley
25 Fili Martinez
26 Reggie Williams
27 Rick Hirtensteiner
28 Egal Rodriguez
29 Chris Threadgill
30 Bobby Jones

1990 Best Reading Phillies

(Philadelphia Phillies) (color)

	MT	NR MT	EX
Complete Set:	4.00	3.00	1.50

1 David Holdridge
2 Robert Ayrault
3 Eric Boudreaux
4 John McLaman
5 Amalio Carreno
6 Ramon Aviles
7 Andy Ashby
8 Timothy Mauser
9 Warren Magee
10 Mark Sims
11 Gary Wilson
12 Douglas Lindsay
13 Sal Agosinalli
14 Gary Alexander
15 Kim Batiste
16 Martin Foley
17 Jeff Grotewold
18 Roderick Robertson
19 Casey Waller
20 Frank Bellino
21 Vince Holyfield
22 Stephen Kirkpatrick
23 Thomas Marsh
24 Don McCormack
25 George Culver
26 Checklist

1990 ProCards Reading Phillies

(Philadelphia Phillies) (color)

	MT	NR MT	EX
Complete Set:	4.00	3.00	1.50

1210 Checklist
1211 Andy Ashby
1212 Bob Ayrault
1213 Amalio Carreno
1214 Eric Boudreaux
1215 Fred Christopher
1216 David Holdridge
1217 Tim Mauser
1218 Warren Magee
1219 John McLarnan
1220 Mark Sims
1221 Gary Wilson
1222 Sal Agostinelli
1223 Doug Linsey
1224 Gary Alexander
1225 Kim Batiste
1226 Marty Foley
1227 Jeff Grotewold
1228 Rod Robertson
1229 Casey Waller
1230 Frank Bellino
1231 Vince Holyfield
1232 Steve Kirkpatrick
1233 Tom Marsh
1234 Don McCormack
1235 George Culver
1236 Ramon Aviles

1990 Star Co. Reading Phillies

(Philadelphia Phillies) (color)

	MT	NR MT	EX
Complete Set:	4.00	3.00	1.50

1 Sal Agostinelli
2 Gary Alexander
3 Andy Ashby
4 Bob Ayrault
5 Kim Batiste
6 Frank Bellino
7 Eric Boudreaux
8 Cliff Brantley
9 Richard Buonantony
10 Jeff Grotewold
11 Amalio Carreno
12 Marty Foley
13 David Holdridge
14 Vince Holyfield
15 Steve Kirkpatrick
16 Doug Lindsey
17 Warren Magee
18 Tom Marsh
19 Tim Mauser
20 John McLarnan
21 Rod Robertson
22 Mark Sims
23 Casey Waller
24 Gary Wilson
25 Floyd Youmans
26 Don McCormack
27 Ramon Aviles
28 George Culver

1990 Cal League Reno Silver Sox

(Cleveland Indians) (color)

	MT	NR MT	EX
Complete Set:	3.00	2.25	1.25

262 Ken Whitfield
263 Tom Eiterman
264 Clyde Pough
265 Alexander Ferran
266 Mike Easley
267 Joel Chimelis
268 Todd Blackwell
269 Mark Charbonnet
270 Tim Donahue
271 Carlos Mota
272 Shawn Barton
273 Kaha Wong
274 Gary Nalls
275 Milt Harper
276 Keith Shepherd
277 Michael Soper
278 Jeff Whitney
279 Cecil Pettiford
280 William Wertz
281 Felix Caraballo
282 Greg Paxton
283 Howard Cole
284 Garry Clark
285 Tad Powers
286 Mike Brown
287 Ben Gallo
288 Dean Trenor
289 Rich St. John
290 Jerry Maldonado
291 Todd Karli
292 Jack Patton

1990 Bob's Camera Richmond Braves

(Atlanta Braves) (color) Card #22 was not included in most sets. A set with this card should bring a premium.

	MT	NR MT	EX
Complete Set:	30.00	22.00	12.00

1 Ed Olwine
2 Steve Ziem
3 Bill Laskey
4 Brian Snyder
5 Bruce Crabbe
6 John Mizerock
7 Steve Avery
8 Kent Merker
9 Tommy Greene
10 Paul Marak
11 Barry Jones
12 Jimmy Kremers
13 Andy Nezelek
14 Dale Polley
15 Geronimo Berroa
16 Ed Whited
17 Rusty Richards
18 Dennis Hood
19 Rico Rossy
20 Andy Tomberlin
21 Kelly Mann
22 Ric Berg

1990 CMC (TCMA) Richmond Braves

(Atlanta Braves) (color)

	MT	NR MT	EX
Complete Set:	15.00	11.00	6.00

1 Steve Avery
2 Not Issued
3 Dale Polley
4 Rusty Richards
5 Andy Nezelek
6 Ed Olwine
7 Jim Beauchamp

8 Paul Marak
9 Dave Justice
10 Jimmy Kremers
11 Drew Denson
12 Barry Jones
13 Francisco Cabrera
14 Bruce Crabbe
15 Dennis Hood
16 Geronimo Berroa
17 Ed Whited
18 Sam Ayoub
19 Brian Hunter
20 Tommy Greene
21 John Mizerock
22 Ken Dowell
23 John Alva
24 Bill Laskey
25 Brian Snyder
26 Rick Lueken
27 Kent Mercker
---- Braves' Coaches

1990 ProCards Richmond Braves

(Atlanta Braves) (color)

	MT	NR MT	EX
Complete Set:	15.00	11.00	6.00

251 Checklist
252 Steve Avery
253 Tommy Greene
254 Bill Laskey
255 Paul Marak
256 Andy Nezelek
257 Ed Olwine
258 Dale Polley
259 Rusty Richards
260 Brian Snyder
261 Jimmy Kremers
262 John Mizerock
263 John Alva
264 Francisco Cabrera
265 Bruce Crabbe
266 Drew Denson
267 Ken Dowell
268 Ed Whited
269 Geronimo Berroa
270 Dennis Hood
271 Brian Hunter
272 Barry Jones
273 Dave Justice
274 Jim Beauchamp
275 John Grubb
276 Leo Mazzone
277 Sonny Jackson
278 Rick Berg

1990 Team Richmond Braves

(Atlanta Braves) (color) (fold out)

	MT	NR MT	EX
Complete Set:	24.00	18.00	9.50

5 Ken Dowell
7 Jimmy Kremers
8 Dennis Hood
9 Jim Beauchamp
11 Steve Avery
12 Bruce Crabbe
15 David Justice
16 Sonny Jackson
20 Francisco Cabrera
22 Geronimo Berroa
24 Ed Whited
27 Brian Hunter
29 John Mizerock
30 Paul Marak
31 Ed Olwine
33 Leo Mazzone
34 Dale Polley
37 Rusty Richards
38 Rick Ber, Bill Laskey)
39 Drew Denson
40 Andy Nezelek
42 Tommy Greene
43 Brian Snyder
45 Barry Jones
46 Kent Mercker
49 John Grubb
54 Rick Luecken

1990 Team 25th Anniversary Richmond Braves

(Atlanta Braves) (black and white)

	MT	NR MT	EX
Complete Set:	11.00	8.25	4.50

1 Tommie Aaron
2 Sam Ayoub
3 Dusty Baker
4 Jim Beauchamp
5 Tony Brizzolara
6 Brett Butler
7 Ken Dayley
8 Darell Evans
9 Ralph Garr
10 Tom House
11 Glenn Hubbard
12 Brook Jacoby
13 Jerry Keller
14 Brad Komminsky
15 Rick Mahler
16 Larry Maxie
17 Dale Murphy
18 Larry Owen
19 Gerald Perry
20 Ron Reed
21 Chico Ruiz
22 Pablo Torrealba
23 Paul Zuvella

1990 Best Riverside Red Wave

(San Diego Padres) (color)

	MT	NR MT	EX
Complete Set:	4.00	3.00	1.50

1 Dave Staton
2 Steve Bethea
3 Scott Bigham
4 Renay Bryand
5 Rick Davis
6 Dan Deville
7 Jay Estrada
8 Reggie Farmer
9 Vince Harris
10 Brian Harrison
11 Chris Haslock
12 Steve Hendricks
13 Kevin Higgins
14 Kerry Knox
15 Kelly Lifgren
16 Tony McGee
17 Darrell Sherman
18 Greg Smith
19 Nate Colbert
20 Steve Kuebber
21 Jim Daniel
22 Bruce Bochy
23 Candy Sierra
24 Darrin Reichle
25 Royal Thomas
26 Heath Lane
27 Checklist

1990 Cal League Riverside Red Wave

(San Diego Padres) (color)

	MT	NR MT	EX
Complete Set:	4.00	3.00	1.50

1 Dave Staton
2 Greg Smith
3 Darrell Sherman
4 Tony McGee
5 Luis Lopez
6 Kevin Higgins
7 Steve Bethea
8 Scott Bigham
9 Reggie Farmer
10 Mark Gieske
11 Steve Hendricks
12 Vince Harris
13 Renay Bryand
14 Rick Davis
15 Dan Deville
16 Jay Estrada
17 Brian Harrison
18 Chris Haslock
19 Heath Lane
20 Bill Marx
21 Royal Thomas
22 Kelly Lifgren
23 Darrin Reichele
24 Bruce Bochy
25 Steve Luebber
26 Nate Colbert
27 Tye Waller

1990 ProCards Riverside Red Wave

(San Diego Padres) (color)

	MT	NR MT	EX
Complete Set:	4.00	3.00	1.50

2596 Checklist
2597 Renay Bryand
2598 Rick Davis
2599 Dan DeVille
2600 Jay Estrada
2601 Brian Harrison
2602 Chris Haslock
2603 Kerry Knox
2604 Heath Lane
2605 Kelly Lifgren
2606 Bill Marx
2607 Darrin Reichle
2608 Royal Thomas
2609 Candy Sierra
2610 Kevin Higgins
2611 Tony McGee
2612 Steve Bethea
2613 Scott Bigham
2614 Mark Gieseke
2615 Steve Hendricks
2616 Luis Lopez
2617 Dave Staton
2618 Reggie Farmer
2619 Vince Harris
2620 Darrell Sherman
2621 Greg Smith
2622 Nate Colbert
2623 Steve Luebber

1990 CMC (TCMA) Rochester Red Wings

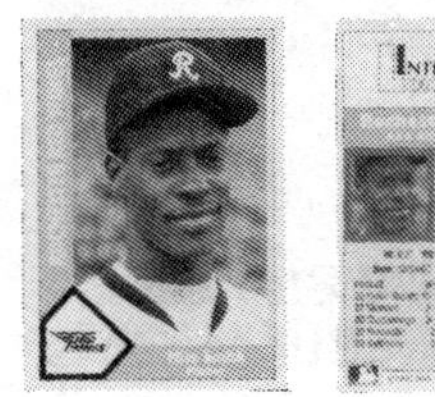

(Baltimore Orioles) (color)

	MT	NR MT	EX
Complete Set:	10.00	7.50	4.00

1 Ben McDonald
2 Rob Woodward
3 Mickey Weston
4 Mike Jones
5 Curtis Schilling
6 Jay Aldrich
7 Paul Blair
8 Mike Smith
9 Jeff Tackett
10 Leo Gomez
11 Donell Nixon
12 Jeff McKnight
13 Juan Bell
14 Chris Hoiles
15 Steve Stanicek
16 Tim Dulin
17 Chris Padget
18 Greg Walker
19 Tony Chance
20 J.J. Bautista
21 John Mitchell
22 Not Issued
23 Vic Hithe
24 Darrell Miller
25 Shane Turner
26 Greg Biagini
27 Dick Bosman
28 Danny Boone

1990 ProCards Rochester Red Wings

(Baltimore Orioles) (color)

	MT	NR MT	EX
Complete Set:	10.00	7.50	4.00

694 Checklist
695 Jay Aldrich
696 Jose Bautista
697 Eric Bell
698 Dan Boone
699 Ben McDonald
700 John Mitchell
701 Curt Schilling
702 Mike Smith
703 Rob Woodward
704 Chris Hoiles
705 Darrell Miller
706 Jeff Tackett
707 Juan Bell
708 Tim Dulin
709 Leo Gomez
710 Jeff McKnight
711 Shane Tucker
712 Greg Walker
713 Tony Chance
714 Victor Hithe
715 Donell Nixon
716 Chris Padget
717 Pete Stanicek
718 Mike Linskey
719 Joaquin Contreras
720 Greg Biagini
721 Dick Bosman
722 Paul Blair

1990 Team Rochester Red Wings

(Baltimore Orioles) (color)

	MT	NR MT	EX
Complete Set:	20.00	15.00	8.00

() Checklist
1 Governor's Cup
2 David Segui
3 Ben McDonald
4 Chris Hoiles
5 Tim Dulin
6 Leo Gomez
7 Jeff McNight
8 Donnell Nixon
9 Juan Bell
10 Mickey Weston
11 Sam Horn
12 Mike Mussina
13 Jeff Tackett
14 Curt Schilling
15 Dan Boone
16 Eric Bell
17 Marty Brown
18 Rob Woodward
19 Tony Chance
20 Mike Linskey
21 Chris Padget
22 Shane Turner
23 Mike Smith
24 Victor Hithe
25 Joaquin Contreras
26 Joel McKeon
27 Brad Komminsk
28 Jose Bautista
29 Francisco Delarosa
30 Anthony Kelley
31 Ken Shamburg
32 Brian Holton
33 Dan Lunetta
34 Greg Biagini
35 Dick Bosman

1990 ProCards Rockford Expos

(Montreal Expos) (color)

	MT	NR MT	EX
Complete Set:	3.00	2.25	1.25

2683 Checklist
2684 Dan Archibald
2685 Rusty Kilgo
2686 John Thoden
2687 Steve Whitehead
2688 Gary Regira
2689 Joe Logan
2690 Brian Sullivan
2691 Jim Eddy
2692 Brian Wilkinson
2693 Martin Martinez
2694 Doug Bochtler
2695 Chris Bushing
2696 Tim Laker
2697 Rob Leary
2698 Bill Cramer
2699 Scott Davidson
2700 Ron Krause
2701 Deryk Hudson
2702 Michael Grace
2703 J.D. Ramirez
2704 Keith Kaub
2705 Buen Rodriguez
2706 Isaac Elder
2707 Jeff Ramsey
2708 Troy Ricker
2709 Tyrone Woods
2710 Mike Quade
2711 Sid Monge

1990 Team-Lithocenter Rockford Expos

(Montreal Expos) (color)

	MT	NR MT	EX
Complete Set:	4.00	3.00	1.50

6 Scotty Davidson
9 Issac Elder
11 J.D Ramirez
13 Tim Laker
19 Steve Whitehead
21 Ron Leary
22 Rusty Kilgo
23 Brian Wilkinson
27 Dan Archibald
28 Gary Regira
32 C.L. Smith
34 Michael Grace
37 Jeff Ramsey
39 Chris Bushing
40 Ben Howze
43 Joe Logan
44 Troy Ricker
45 Martin Martine, Sid Monge)

46 John Thoden
47 Buen Rodriguez
48 Bill Cramer
49 Doug Bochtler
51 Tyrone Woods
55 Deryk Hudson
56 Ron Krause
58 Jim Eddy
82 Mike Quade
---- Expos Team (John Cain)

1990 ProCards Saint Catharine's Blue Jays

(Toronto Blue Jays) (color)

	MT	NR MT	EX
Complete Set:	10.00	7.50	4.00

3451 Checklist
3452 Matt Hudik
3453 Juan Querecuto
3454 Carlos Delgado
3455 Edgar Marquez
3456 Robert Perez
3457 Tom Singer
3458 Scott Brow
3459 Sam Mandia
3460 Matt Watson
3461 Joe Ganote
3462 Frank Kowar
3463 Dave Marcon
3464 Paul Menhart
3465 Bobby Aylmer
3466 Rob Montalvo
3467 Ciro Ambrosio
3468 Rusty Filter
3469 Allen Rhea
3470 Huck Flener
3471 Dave Tollison
3472 Steve Karsay
3473 Rick Steed
3474 Mike Taylor
3475 Jeff Irish
3476 Andy Carlton
3477 Wally Heckel
3478 Wilberto Rojas
3479 Anton Mobley
3480 Shawn Scott
3481 Jacinto Yorro
3482 Doug Ault
3483 Mike McAlpin
3484 Daren Balsley

1990 Star Co. Saint Lucie Mets

(New York Mets) (color) (Price includes late-issue corrected cards for Donnie Brown and James Morrisette) condition)

	MT	NR MT	EX
Complete Set:	8.00	6.00	3.25

1 Mike Brady
2a Kevin Brown
2b Donnie Brown
3 Chris Butterfield
4 Archie Corbin
5 Joe Delli Carri
6 D.J. Dozier
7 Dan Furmanik
8 Kenny Graves
9 Denny Harriger
10 Chris Hill
11 Paul Johnson
12 John Johnstone
13 Jimy Kelly
14 Vega Marina
15 Lee May
16 Loy McBride
17a Jim Morrisette
17b James Morrisette
18 Steve Newton
19 Bob Olah
20 Vladimir Perez
21 Andy Reich
22 Nikco Riesgo
23 Bryan Rogers
24 Doug Saunders
25 Pete Schourek
26 Derrick Young
27 Al Zinter
28 Tim Blackwell
29 Joel Horlen
30 Steve Jacobucci
31 Marc Goldberg

1990 Star Co. Saint Petersburg Cardinals

(St. Louis Cardinals) (color)

	MT	NR MT	EX
Complete Set:	3.00	2.25	1.25

1 Ed Carter
2 Mark Clark
3 Tripp Cromer
4 Bobby DeLoach
5 Brad DuVall
6 John Ericks
7 Jose Fernandez
8 Mike Flore
9 Steve Graham
10 Antron Grier
11 David Grimes
12 Henry Hernandez
13 Daniel Hitt
14 Lonnie Maclin
15 Steffen Majer
16 Tim Meamber
17 Mike Milchin
18 Lee Plemel
19 Tim Redman
20 Dave Richardson
21 Cory Satterfield
22 John Sellick
23 Jeff Shireman
24 Jose Trujillo
25 Dean Weese
26 Pettini, North

1990 Star Co. Salem Buccaneers

(Pittsburgh Pirates) (color)

	MT	NR MT	EX
Complete Set:	4.00	3.00	1.50

1 Robert Bailey
2 Steve Buckholz
3 Tom Deller
4 Chip Duncan
5 Chris Estep
6 Antonio Felix
7 Tim Hines
8 Mike Huyler
9 John Latham
10 Tim McDowell
11 Glen McNabb
12 Domingo Merejo
13 Paul Miller
14 Brian Morrison
15 Darwin Pennye
16 Mike Pomeranz
17 Keith Raisanen
18 Mandy Romero
19 Butch Schlopy
20 Bruce Schreiber
21 Ben Shelton
22 Greg Sims
23 Tim Wakefield
24 Flavio Williams
25 Stan Cliburn
26 Chris Lein
27 Sandy Krum

1990 Cal League Salinas Spurs

(Independent) (color)

	MT	NR MT	EX
Complete Set:	5.00	3.75	2.00

117 Steve Howe
118 Shigehi Sasaki
119 Seiichi Murakami
120 Kenichi Ootsuka
121 Kouichi Emoto
122 Kenichi Uchiyama
123 Rudy Gardey
124 Quinn Marsh
125 Ray Velasquez
126 Greg Page
127 Carlos Carrasco
128 Steve Maye
129 John Reilly
130 Ed Landphere
131 Bill Carlson
132 Gregg Mannion
133 Paul Alegre
134 Brent Hahn
135 Jerry Peguero
136 Steve Meredith
137 Sean Thompson
138 Jim Shevlin
139 Shikato Yanagida
140 Kenichi Yamanouchi
141 Yoshiki Ootsuka
142 Hide Koga
143 Takayuki Kohno
144 John Jonas
145 Mike Spiers
146 Pete Rowe
147 Yoshi Okamoto
148 Masahiro Kuboto

1990 ProCards Salinas Spurs

(Co-op) (color)

	MT	NR MT	EX
Complete Set:	3.00	2.25	1.25

2712 Checklist
2713 Kenichi Uchiyama
2714 Greg Page
2715 Kouichi Emoto
2716 Kenichi Ohtsuka
2717 Seiichi Murakami
2718 Carlos Carrasco
2719 Shigeki Sasaki
2720 John Reilley
2721 Quinn Marsh
2722 Yoshiki Ohtsuka
2723 Shikato Yanagita
2724 Kenichi Yamanouchi
2725 Brent Hahn
2726 Jerry Peguero
2727 Jim Shevlin
2728 Ed Landphere
2729 Paul Alegre
2730 Bill Carlson
2731 Wayne Housie
2732 Scott Jaster
2733 Corey Paul
2734 Sean Thompson
2735 Hide Koga
2736 Takayuki Kohno
2737 Pete Rowe

1990 BBC, etc. Salt Lake City Trappers

(Independent) (color)

	MT	NR MT	EX
Complete Set:	8.00	6.00	3.25

2 Checklist, Jeff McFarlane, Ryan Bagshaw, Andy Iacona, Steve Evans)
3 Darren Garrick (Coach, Reuben Rodriguez, Dan Shwam)
4 Dave Baggott
5 Mike Nyquist
6 Travis Tarchione
7 Ray Karczewski
8 Dan Ryan
9 Ed Garczyk
10 Holly Andrett, John Stein, Kurt Wilson
11 J.D. Ramirez
12 Shingo Matsukubo, Akihiro Fukushima, Shigeki Taguchi
13 Mike Steinkamp
14 Mike Grace
15 Barry Moss
16 Anthony St. John
17 Shaun Sanderson
18 Van Schley
19 Chris Skryd
20 Max Tripodi
21 Mike Bible
22 Dave Alexander
23 Scott Bray
24 Joe Beaulac
25 Phil Evans
26 Gerard Giustino
27 James Troup
28 Michael Ashworth
29 Bill Murray
30 John Stewart

1990 Grand Slam San Antonio Missions

(Los Angeles Dodgers) (color)

	MT	NR MT	EX
Complete Set:	12.00	9.00	4.75

1 John Shoemaker
2 Burt Hooton
3 Jon Debus
4 Rob Giesecke
5 Rafael Bournigal
6 Jerry Brooks
7 Adam Brown
8 Kevin Campbell
9 Ernie Carr
10 Braulio Castillo
11 Dale Coleman
12 Steve Finken
13 Tom Goodwin
14 Jeff Hartsock
15 Mike James
16 Eric Karros
17 Isidrio Marquez
18 Luis Martinez
19 Dan Opperman
20 Mike Pitz
21 Jim Poole
22 Eddie Pye
23 Lance Rice
24 Henry Rodriguez
25 Homar Rojas
26 Zak Shinall
27 Dennis Springer
28 Mica Valdez
29 Mike White
30 James Wray

1990 Best San Bernadino Spirit

(Seattle Mariners) (color)

	MT	NR MT	EX
Complete Set:	5.00	3.75	2.00

1 Roger Salkeld
2 Rich Delucia
3 Calvin Jones
4 Jim Bennett
5 Dave Evans
6 Jeff Keitges
7 Isaiah Clark
8 Chuck Kniffin
9 Patrick Lennon
10 Roberto Del Pozo
11 Manuel Furcal
12 Bob Magallanes
13 Tom Maynard
14 Greg Pirkl
15 Scott Taylor
16 Fernando Arguelies
17 Scott Pitcher
18 Brian Turang
19 Steve Murray
20 David Smith
21 Johnny Wiggs
22 Ray Williams
23 Jim Newlin
24 Tim Stargell
25 Kerry Woodson
26 Keith Bodie
27 Mascot "The Bug"
28 Batboys/Checklist

1990 Cal League San Bernardino Spirit

(Seattle Mariners) (color)

	MT	NR MT	EX
Complete Set:	5.00	3.75	2.00

Robert Harve, The Bug)
87 Roger Salkeld
88 Rich Delucia
89 Jim Newlin
90 Kerry Woodson
91 Jim Bennett
92 Nick Felix
93 Scott Taylor
94 Johnny Wiggs
95 Scott Pitcher
96 Calvin Jones
97 Dave Evans
98 Manuel Furcal
99 Dave Smith
100 Fernando Arguelles
101 Pat Lennon
102 Tyrone Kingwood
103 Isaiah Clark
104 Roberto Del Pozo
105 Greg Pirkl
106 Brian Turang
107 Bobby Magallenes
108 Tim Stargell
109 Rich Morales
110 Jeff Keitges
111 Ellerton Maynard
112 Ray Williams
113 Steve Murray
114 Keith Bodie
115 Chuck Kniffin
116 Lance Bland

1990 ProCards San Bernadino Spirit

(Seattle Mariners) (color)

	MT	NR MT	EX
Complete Set:	5.00	3.75	2.00

2624 Checklist
2625 Jim Bennett
2626 Rich DeLucia
2627 Dave Evans
2628 Manuel Furcal
2629 Calvin Jones
2630 Jim Newlin
2631 Scott Pitcher
2632 Roger Salkeld
2633 Scott Taylor
2634 Johnny Wiggs
2635 Kerry Woodson
2636 Fernando Arguelles
2637 Greg Pirkl
2638 Isaiah Clark
2639 Jeff Keitges

2640 Bob Magallanes
2641 Tim Stargell
2642 Brian Turang
2643 Roberto Del Pozo
2644 Tyrone Kingwood
2645 Patrick Lennon
2646 Ellerton Maynard
2647 Dave Smith
2648 Bo Williams
2649 Keith Bodie
2650 Chuck Kniffin
2651 Steve Murray

1990 Best San Jose Giants

(San Francisco Giants) (color)

	MT	NR MT	EX
Complete Set:	6.00	4.50	2.50

1 Steve Hosey
2 Kerry Shaw
3 Rueben Smiley
4 Pat Brady
5 Jeff Brauning
6 Craig Cala
7 Royce Clayton
8 Adell Davenport
9 John Patterson
10 Troy Mentzer
11 Jim Jones
12 Dan Fernandez
13 Eddie Tucker
14 Elanis Westbrook
15 Jim Myers
16 Chris Fye
17 Joel Estes
18 Don Brock
19 Gary Sharko
20 Vince Herring
21 Brian Dour
22 John Vuz
23 Dan Rambo
24 Kevin Rogers
25 Dom Johnson
26 Jeff Morris
27 Scott Wilson
28 Dick Dietz
29 Tom Spenser
30 1990 Keystone Combo

1990 Cal League San Jose Giants

(San Francisco Giants) (color)

	MT	NR MT	EX
Complete Set:	6.00	4.50	2.50

28 Steve Hosey
29 Kerry Shaw
30 Rueben Smiley
31 Pat Brady
32 Elanis Westbrooks
33 John Patterson
34 Jeff Brauning
35 Craig Cala
36 Royce Clayton
37 Scooter Tucker
38 Jim Jones
39 Adell Davenport
40 Dan Fernanadez
41 Troy Mentzer
42 Brian Dour
43 Chris Fye
44 Dan Rambo
45 Joel Estes
46 Gary Sharko
47 Dominic Johnson
48 Vince Herring
49 Jim Myers
50 Don Brock
51 Kevin Rogers
52 John Vuz
53 Tom Spencer
54 Jeff Morris
55 Scott Wilson

1990 ProCards San Jose Giants

(San Francisco Giants) (color)

	MT	NR MT	EX
Complete Set:	6.00	4.50	2.50

2000 Checklist
2001 John Vuz
2002 Chris Fye
2003 Kevin Rogers
2004 Don Brock
2005 Gary Sharko
2006 Dan Rambo
2007 Joel Estes
2008 Jim Myers
2009 Brian Dour
2010 Vince Herring
2011 Dom Johnson
2012 Dan Fernandez
2013 Troy Mentzer
2014 Eddie Tucker
2015 Jeff Brauning
2016 Jim Jones
2017 John Patterson
2018 Royce Clayton
2019 Adell Davenport
2020 Kerry Shaw
2021 Elanis Westbrooks
2022 Craig Cala
2023 Pat Brady
2024 Rueben Smiley
2025 Steve Hosey
2026 Tom Spencer
2027 Dick Dietz
2028 Jeff Morris
2172 Pitching Stars

1990 Star Co. San Jose Giants

(San Francisco Giants) (color)

	MT	NR MT	EX
Complete Set:	6.00	4.50	2.50

1 Pat Brady
2 Jeff Brauning
3 Don Brock
4 Craig Cala
5 Royce Clayton
6 Adell Davenport
7 Brian Dour
8 Joel Estes
9 Dan Fernandez
10 Chris Fye
11 Vince Herring
12 Steve Hosey
13 Dominic Johnson
14 Jim Jones
15 Troy Mentzer
16 Jim Myers
17 John Patterson
18 Dan Rambo
19 Kevin Rogers
20 Gary Sharko
21 Kerry Shaw
22 Rueben Smiley
23 Scooter Tucker
24 John Vuz
25 Elanis Westbrooks
26 Hose, Brady, Smiley)
27 Tom Spencer
28 Dick Dietz
29 Jeff Morris
30 Scott Wilson

1990 Star Co. Sarasota White Sox

(Chicago White Sox) (color)

	MT	NR MT	EX
Complete Set:	4.00	3.00	1.50

1 Clemente Alvarez
2 Wayne Busby
3 Darrin Campbell
4 Mark Chasey
5 Nandi Cruz
6 Fred Dabney
7 Mike Davino
8 Horace Gaither
9 Mike Galvan
10 Ramon Garcia
11 Cliff Gonzalez
12 Jay Hornacek
13 Brian Keyser
14 Rob Lukachyk
15 Frank Merigliano
16 Scott Middaugh
17 Javier Ocasio
18 Ray Payton
19 Greg Perschke
20 Kinnis Pledger
21 Rob Resnikoff
22 Ed Smith
23 Carl Sullivan
24 Scott Tedder
25 Jose Ventura
26 Tony Franklin
27 Don Cooper
28 Ron Jackson
29 Steve Davis
30 Serbi, Flath)

1990 ProCards Savannah Cardinals

(St. Louis Cardinals) (color)

	MT	NR MT	EX
Complete Set:	4.00	3.00	1.50

2057 Checklist
2058 Jose Arias
2059 Ernie Baker
2060 Marcos Betances
2061 Steve Dixon
2062 Bill Espinal
2063 Luis Faccio
2064 Dennis Fletcher
2065 Russ Gaston
2066 Donald Green
2067 Al Pacheco
2068 Rick Shackle
2069 Mark Tolbert
2070 Tony Ochs
2071 Joe Turvey
2072 Ignacio Duran
2073 Larry Gryskevich
2074 Mike Keating
2075 Jim Ferguson
2076 Nicio Martinez
2077 Mateo Ozuna
2078 Kevin Tahan
2079 Scott Banton
2080 Cliff Brannon
2081 Johnny Calzado
2082 Paul Coleman
2083 Anthony Lewis
2084 Field Staff

1990 CMC (TCMA) Scranton-Wilkes Barre Red Barons

(Philadelphia Phillies) (color)

	MT	NR MT	EX
Complete Set:	5.00	3.75	2.00

1 Eric Boudreaux
2 Marvin Freeman
3 Jason Grimsley
4 Chuck Malone
5 Dickie Noles
6 Wally Ritchie
7 Bob Scanlan
8 Scott Service
9 Steve Sharts
10 John Gibbons
11 Sal Agostinelli
12 Jim Adduci
13 Kelly Heath
14 Micky Morandini
15 Victor Rosario
16 Steve Stanicek
17 Jim Vatcher
18 Bill Dancy
19 Ron Jones
20 Chris Knabenshue
21 Keith Miller
22 Floyd Rayford
23 Jim Wright
24 Todd Frohwirth
25 Barney Nugent

1990 ProCards Scranton-Wilkes Barre Red Barons

(Philadelphia Phillies) (color)

	MT	NR MT	EX
Complete Set:	5.00	3.75	2.00

591 Checklist
592 Jose DeJesus
593 Marvin Freeman
594 Todd Frohwirth
595 Jason Grimsley
596 Chuck Malone
597 Brad Moore
598 Wally Ritchie
599 Bob Scanlan
600 Scott Service
601 Steve Sharts
602 John Gibbons
603 Tom Nieto
604 Jim Adduci
605 Kelly Heath
606 Mickey Morandini
607 Victor Rosario
608 Steve Stanicek
609 Greg Legg
610 Ron Jones
611 Chris Knabenshue
612 Keith Miller
613 Jim Vatcher
614 Jim Wright

1990 Star Co. Shreveport Captains

(San Francisco Giants) (color)

	MT	NR MT	EX
Complete Set:	3.00	2.25	1.25

1 Rich Aldrete
2 Rod Beck
3 Steve Connolly
4 Jamie Cooper
5 Steve Decker
6 Mark Dewey
7 Tom Ealy
8 Juan Guerrero
9 Mike Ham
10 Steve Hecht
11 Bryan Hickerson
12 Tom Hostetler
13 Erik Johnson
14 Steve Lienhard
15 Kevin Meier
16 Rick Nelson
17 Mark Owens
18 Dave Patterson
19 Jim Pena
20 Steve Reed
21 Mike Remlinger
22 Andres Santana
23 Randy Strijek
24 Ted Wood
25 Bill Evers
26 Todd Oakes
27 Tony Taylor

1990 Star Co. South Atlantic League All-Stars

(League All-Stars) (color)

	MT	NR MT	EX
Complete Set:	7.00	5.25	2.75

1 Mike Arner
2 Jeff Braley
3 Mike Burton
4 Cris Colon
5 Darron Cox
6 Andy Fox
7 Bob Gaddy
8 Mike Garcia
9 John Graves
10 David Hajek
11 Jeff Hoffman
12 Jonathan Hurst
13 Ramon Jimenez
14 Brian Johnson
15 Chris Limbach
16 Orlando Miller
17 Rudy Pemberton
18 Pat Pesavento
19 Scott Pose
20 Mike Rendina
21 Brian Romero
22 Tony Scruggs
23 Gene Rook
24 Orlando Gomez
25 Kelly Sharitt
26 Felix Antigua
27 Rob Blumberg
28 Vinicio Castilla
29 Brian Davis
30 Brooke Fordyce
31 Roger Hailey
32 James Harris
33 Shawn Holtzclaw
34 Tim Howard
35 Pat Howell
36 Austin Manahan
37 Tito Navarro
38 Mike Ogliaruso
39 William Pennyfeather
40 Craig Pueschner
41 Deron Sample
42 Rick Shackle
43 Don Strange
44 Ken Trusky
45 Joe Vitko
46 Bill Stein
47 Mike Fischlin
48 Bob Burton

1990 Best South Bend White Sox

(Chicago White Sox) (color)

	MT	NR MT	EX
Complete Set:	3.00	2.25	1.25

1 Len Brutcher
2 Scott Cepicky
3 John Hairston
4 David Vanwinkle
5 Jeff Ingram
6 Leo Tejada
7 Ron Plemmons
8 Jorge Ramos
9 Joe Singley
10 Richard Long
11 Craig Teter
12 Dennis Walker
13 Jerry Wolak
14 John Zaksek
15 Greg Kobza
16 Steve Schrenk
17 Mike Mitchner
18 Michael Eatinger
19 Thomas Forrester
20 Danny Matznick
21 Michael Mongiello
22 Scott Stevens
23 Bill Vanderwel

24 Rick Patterson
25 Scott Johnson
26 Mike Barnett
27 Kirk Champion
28 Robert Wickman
29 Jim Reinbol,)

1990 Grand Slam South Bend White Sox

(Chicago White Sox) (color)

	MT	NR MT	EX
Complete Set:	3.00	2.25	1.25

1 Lenny Brutcher
2 Scott Cepicky
3 Mike Eatinger
4 Tom Forrester
5 John Hairston
6 Jeff Ingram
7 Earnie Johnson
8 Scott Johnson
9 Rich Long
10 Dan Matznick
11 Mike Mitchener
12 Mike Mongiello
13 Ron Plemmons
14 Jorge Ramos
15 Johnny Ruffin
16 Steve Schrenk
17 Scott Stevens
18 Eugenio Tejada
19 Dave Vanwinkle
20 Dennis Walker
21 Jerry Wolak
22 John Zaksek
23 Frank Campos
24 Greg Kobza
25 Joe Singley
26 Craig Teter
27 Rick Patterson
28 Kirk Champion
29 Jim Reinebold
30 Mike Barnett

1990 DJ Southern League All-Stars

(All-Stars) (color)

	MT	NR MT	EX
Complete Set:	11.00	8.25	4.50

1 Tony Brown
2 Jeff Conine
3 Will Magallanes
4 Mike Maksudian
5 Brian McRae
6 Kenny Morgan
7 Jorge Pedre
8 Stan Royer
9 Matt Stark
10 William Suero
11 Frank Thomas
12 Lenny Webster
13 Ed Zosky
14 Scott Centala
15 Steve Chitren
16 Greg Johnson
17 Carlos Maldonado
18 Will Schock
19 Doug Simons
20 Woody Williams
21 Rob Wishnevski
22 Mike Bell
23 Adam Casillas
24 Greg Colbrunn
25 Benny Colvard
26 Wil Cordero
27 Tony Eusebio
28 Jeff Forney
29 Luis Gonzalez
30 Terrell Hansen
31 Brian Hunter
32 Andy Mota
33 Tom Redington
34 Chico Walker
35 Doug Banning
36 Brian Bames
37 Kent Bottenfield
38 John Kilner
39 Gino Minutelli
40 Heath SLocumb
41 Fernando Zarranz
42 Mike Bell
43 Jeff Conine
44 Frank Thomas
45 Andy Mota
46 Frank Thoma, Jeff Conine)
47 Ed Zosk, Mike Bell)
48 Ken Berr, Buddy Bailey)
49 Coaches
50 VIPs

1990 Best Southern Oregon Athletics

(Oakland A's) (color)

	MT	NR MT	EX
Complete Set:	7.00	5.25	2.75

1 Todd Van Poppel
2 Eric Helfand
3 Kirk Dressendorfer
4 Kevin Dattaola
5 Doug Johns
6 Luis Lan Franco
7 Bill Picketts
8 Todd Revenig
9 Craig Sudbury
10 Eric Booker
11 Jim Dillon
12 Manny Martinez
13 Jeff Clifford
14 Chaon Garland
15 Ernie Young
16 Mark Craft
17 Curtis Shaw
18 Chris Hart
19 Carlos Salazar
20 Craig Connolly
21 Dan Vizzini
22 Brad Brimhall
23 Dave Tripp
24 Dave Zancanaro
25 Don Peters
26 Mike Muhlethaler
27 Eric Myers
28 Glen Osinski
29 Scott Henry
30 Checklist

1990 ProCards Southern Oregon Athletics

(Oakland A's) (color)

	MT	NR MT	EX
Complete Set:	7.00	5.25	2.75

3421 Checklist
3422 Todd Van Poppel
3423 Dave Zancanaro
3424 Don Peters
3425 Kirk Dressendorfer
3426 Eric Helfand
3427 Curtis Shaw
3428 Chaon Garland
3429 Eric Booker
3430 Craig Sudbury
3431 Chris Hart
3432 Luis Lan Franco
3433 Manny Martinez
3434 Rafael Mercado
3435 Bill Picketts
3436 Carlos Salazar
3437 Carlos Tamarez
3438 Ernie Young
3439 Brad Brimhall
3440 Jeff Clifford
3441 Craig Connolly
3442 Mark Craft
3443 Jim Dillon
3444 Eric Myers
3445 Todd Revening
3446 Dave Tripp
3447 Dan Vizzini
3448 Mike Muhlethaler
3449 Grady Fuson
3450 Scott Budner

1990 Best Spartanburg Phillies

(Philadelphia Phillies) (color)

	MT	NR MT	EX
Complete Set:	3.00	2.25	1.25

1 Tom Hardgrove
2 Paul Fletcher
3 Robert Gaddy
4 Darrell Goedhart
5 Todd Goergen
6 Greg Gunderson
7 Chris Limbach
8 Matt Stevens
9 Michael Sullivan
10 Bob Wells
11 Scott Wiegandt
12 Brian Adams
13 Matt Current
14 Tim Churchill
15 John Escobar
16 Donnie Elliott
17 Eduardo Ortega
18 Nick Santa Cruz
19 Dana Brown
20 Antonio Linares
21 Dan Shannon
22 Joe Urbon
23 Gil Valencia
24 Dan Welch
25 Mel Roberts
26 Buzz Capra
27 Rick Jones
28 Tom Marsh
29 Rick Zolzer
30 Craig Strobel

1990 ProCards Spartanburg Phillies

(Philadelphia Phillies) (color)

	MT	NR MT	EX
Complete Set:	3.00	2.25	1.25

2481 Checklist
2482 Donnie Elliott
2483 Paul Fletcher
2484 Robert Gaddy
2485 Darrell Goedhart
2486 Todd Goergen
2487 Greg Gunderson
2488 Chris Limbach
2489 Matt Stevens
2490 Mike Sullivan
2491 Bob Wells
2492 Scott Wiegandt
2493 Brian Adams
2494 Matt Current
2495 Tom Marsh
2496 Tim Churchill
2497 John Escobar
2498 Tom Hardgrove
2499 Eduardo Ortega
2500 Eulogio Perez
2501 Nick SantaCruz
2502 Dana Brown
2503 Antonio Linares
2504 Dan Shannon
2505 Joe Urbon
2506 Gil Valencia
2507 Dan Welch
2508 Mel Roberts (Manager, Buzz Capra)
2509 Rick Jones

1990 Star Co. Spartanburg Phillies

(Philadelphia Phillies) (color)

	MT	NR MT	EX
Complete Set:	3.00	2.25	1.25

1 Brian Adams
2 Dana Brown
3 Tim Churchill
4 Matt Current
5 Donnie Elliott
6 John Escobar
7 Paul Fletcher
8 Robert Gaddy
9 Darrell Goedhart
10 Todd Goergen
11 Greg Gunderson
12 Tom Hardgrove
13 Chris Limbach
14 Antonio Linares
15 Tom Marsh
16 Eduardo Ortega
17 Eulogio Perez
18 Nick Santa Cruz
19 Dan Shannon
20 Matt Stevens
21 Michael Sullivan
22 Joe Urbon
23 Gil Valencia
24 Dan Welch
25 Bob Wells
26 Scott Wiegandt
27 Coaching Staff
28 Craig Strobeo
29 Rick Zulzer

1990 Sport Pro Spokane Indians

(San Diego Padres) (color)

	MT	NR MT	EX
Complete Set:	3.00	2.25	1.25

1 Keith McKoy
2 Jeff Ordway
3 Rusty Silcox
4 Tony Mortensen
5 Larry Hawks
6 Bill Ostermeyer
7 Russ Garside
8 Dave Adams
9 Rob Hays
10 Brent Bish
11 Jim Elliott
12 Jay Gainer
13 Steve Siebert
14 Scott Sanders
15 Jim West
16 Scott Fredrickson
17 Jeff Pearce
18 Mike Bradley
19 Matt Mieske
20 Julio Bruno
21 Lance Painter
22 Bruce Bensching
23 Kevin Farlow
24 Darius Gash
25 Ryan Thibault
26 Gene Glynn
27 Bruce Tanner
28 Kevin Towers

1990 Best Springfield Cardinals

(St. Louis Cardinals) (color)

	MT	NR MT	EX
Complete Set:	3.00	2.25	1.25

1 Juan Andujar
2 Alvin Rittman
3 David Bell
4 Randy Berlin
5 Alan Botkin
6 Mike Campas
7 Troy Clemens
8 Joe Federico
9 Ezequiel Herrera
10 Vince Kindred
11 Mike Kraft
12 Carlos Landinez
13 Fred Langiotti
14 Luis Martinez
15 Orlando Thomas
16 Tim Lata
17 Tom Infante
18 Clyde Keller
19 Mike Hensley
20 Chris Gorton
21 Steve Gewecke
22 John Corona
23 Frank Cimorelli
24 Ron Weber
25 Dennis Wiseman
26 Keith Champion
27 Roger Erickson
28 Mike Evans
29 Team Photo

1990 Best Stockton Ports

(Milwaukee Brewers) (color)

	MT	NR MT	EX
Complete Set:	5.00	3.75	2.00

1 Cal Eldred
2 Dave Nilsson
3 Steve Diaz
4 Bob Kappesser
5 Pat Listach
6 Remigio Diaz
7 Frank Bolick
8 Mike Guerrero
9 Sylvester Love
10 Jim Sass
11 John Finn
12 Ken Jackson
13 Tim Raley
14 Chris Cassels
15 Chris Johnson
16 Mike Ignasiak
17 Dave Fitzgerald
18 Juan Uribe
19 Scott Hamilton
20 Kevin Carmody
21 Jamie Cangemi
22 Guillermo Sandoval
23 Ron Hanisch
24 Leo Perez
25 Angel Miranda
26 Bo Dodson
27 Chris Bando
28 Mitch Zwolensky
29 Checklist

1990 Cal League Stockton Ports

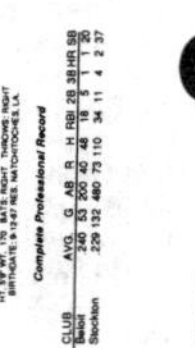

(Milwaukee Brewers) (color)

	MT	NR MT	EX
Complete Set:	5.00	3.75	2.00

174 Cal Eldred
175 Angel Miranda
176 Chris Johnson
177 Mike Ignasiak
178 Dave Fitzgerald
179 Juan Uribe
180 Scott Hamilton
181 Kevin Carmody
182 Jamie Cangemi
183 Guillermo Sandoval
184 Doug Henry
185 Curt Krippner
186 Leo Perez
187 Dave Nilsson
188 Steve Diaz
189 Bob Kappesser
190 Bo Dodson
191 Pat Listach
192 Remigio Diaz
193 Frank Bolick
194 Sylvester Love
195 Jim Sass
196 John Finn
197 Ken Jackson
198 Tim Raley
199 Chris Cassels
200 Chris Bando
201 Mitch Zwolensky
202 Ron Hanisch

1990 ProCards Stockton Ports

(Milwaukee Brewers) (color)

	MT	NR MT	EX
Complete Set:	5.00	3.75	2.00

2173 Checklist
2174 Chris Johnson
2175 Angel Miranda
2176 Mike Ignasiak
2177 Dave Fitzgerald
2178 Calvin Eldred
2179 Juan Uribe
2180 Scott Hamilton
2181 Kevin Carmody
2182 Jamie Cangemi
2183 Guillermo Sandoval
2184 Curt Krippner
2185 Leo Perez
2186 Dave Nilsson
2187 Steve Diaz
2188 Bob Kappesser
2189 Bob Dodson
2190 Pat Listach
2191 Remigio Diaz
2192 Frank Bolick
2193 Mike Guerrero
2194 Sylvester Love
2195 James Sass
2196 John Finn
2197 Kenny Jackson
2198 Tim Raley
2199 Chris Cassels
2200 Chris Bando
2201 Mitch Zwolensky

1990 Best Sumter Braves

(Atlanta Braves) (color)

	MT	NR MT	EX
Complete Set:	11.00	8.25	4.50

1 Tyler Houston
2 Tab Brown
3 Mike Gabriele
4 Roger Hailey
5 Lee Heath
6 Ron Thomas
7 Earl Jewett
8 Pat Kelly
9 Ryan Klesko
10 John Kupsey
11 Gene Martin
12 Eddie Mathews
13 Miguel Mendez
14 Tom Newman
15 Melvin Nieves
16 Jose Olmeda
17 Eduardo Perez
18 Bill Schafer
19 Fred Lopez
20 Dan Sims
21 Shawn Sottile
22 Earl Steinmetz
23 Tony Tarasco
24 Don Strange
25 Mark Wohlers
26 Willy Johnson
27 Kevin Haeberle
28 Vinico Castilla
29 Steve Glass
30 Checklist (Ned Yost)

1990 ProCards Sumter Braves

(Atlanta Braves) (color)

	MT	NR MT	EX
Complete Set:	11.00	8.25	4.50

2424 Checklist
2425 Tab Brown
2426 Mike Gabriele
2427 Kevin Haeberle
2428 Roger Hailey
2429 Earl Jewett
2430 Bill Schafer
2431 Shaun Sottile
2432 Earl Steinmetz
2433 Don Strange
2434 Ron Thomas
2435 Mark Wohlers
2436 Tyler Houston
2437 Fred Lopez
2438 Eduardo Perez
2439 Vinicio Castilla
2440 Pat Kelly
2441 Ryan Klesko
2442 John Kupsey
2443 Miguel Mendez
2444 Jose Olmeda
2445 Lee Heath
2446 Gene Martin
2447 Melvin Nieves
2448 Daniel Sims
2449 Tony Tarasco
2450 Ned Yost
2451 Matt West
2452 Steve Glass
2453 Ralph Rowe

1990 CMC (TCMA) Syracuse Chiefs

(Toronto Blue Jays) (color)

	MT	NR MT	EX
Complete Set:	8.00	6.00	3.25

1 Alex Sanchez
2 Mauro Gozzo
3 Steve Cummings
4 Tom Gilles
5 Doug Linton
6 Mike Loynd
7 Bob Shirley
8 John Shea
9 Paul Kilgus
10 Carlos Diaz
11 Joe Szekely
12 Rick Lysander
13 Jim Eppard
14 Derek Bell
15 Jose Escobar
16 Webster Garrison
17 Paul Runge
18 Luis Sojo
19 Ed Sprague
20 Hector Delacruz
21 Bob Ducey
22 Ozzie Virgil
23 Stu Pederson
24 Mark Whiten
25 Andy Dziadkowiec
26 Bob Bailor
27 Steve Wapnick
28 Ralph Wheeler

1990 ProCards Syracuse Chiefs

(Toronto Blue Jays) (color)

	MT	NR MT	EX
Complete Set:	8.00	6.00	3.25

563 Checklist
564 Tom Gilles
565 Mauro Gozzo
566 Paul Kilgus
567 Doug Linton
568 Mike Loynd
569 Rick Lysander
570 Alex Sanchez
571 John Shea
572 Steve Wapnick
573 Andy Dziadkowiec
574 Joe Szekely
575 Ozzie Vrgil
576 Jim Eppard
577 Jose Escobar
578 Webster Garrison
579 Paul Runge
580 Luis Sojo
581 Ed Sprague
582 Derek Bell
583 Hector DeLaCruz
584 Rob Ducey
585 Pedro Munoz
586 Stu Pederson
587 Mark Whiten
588 Bob Bailor
589 Bob Shirley
590 Rocket Wheeler

1990 Team Syracuse Chiefs

The Chiefs gave away a single-sheet photo album on a promotional night. The sheet folds into a 9-1/2" x 10-1/2" sheet. There are 30 cards on this sheet, each measuring 2-1/8" x 3-1/8" and separated by perforations to facilitate separation of the cards. The cards are unnumbered and have statistics and a facsimile autograph on the back. The cards are listed in the order in which they appear on the sheet.

	MT	NR MT	EX
Complete Set:	9.00	6.75	3.50

(1) Bob Bailor
(2) Bob Shirley
(3) Rocket Wheeler
(4) Randy Holland
(5) Derek Bell
(6) Steve Cummings
(7) Hector Delacruz
(8) Carlos Diaz
(9) Rob Ducey
(10) Jim Eppard
(11) Jose Escobar
(12) Webster Garrison
(13) Tom Gilles
(14) Mauro Gozzo
(15) Paul Kilgus
(16) Doug Linton
(17) Mike Loynd
(18) Rick Lysander
(19) Pedro Munoz
(20) Stu Pederson
(21) Paul Runge
(22) Alex Sanchez
(23) John Shea
(24) Luis Sojo
(25) Ed Sprague
(26) Joe Szekely
(27) Ozzie Virgil
(28) Steve Wapnick
(29) Mark Whiten
(30) Rob Wishnevski

1990 CMC (TCMA) Tacoma Tigers

(Oakland A's) (color)

	MT	NR MT	EX
Complete Set:	7.00	5.25	2.75

1 Ray Young
2 Dave Veres
3 Scott Chiamparino
4 Tony Ariola
5 Weston Weber
6 Bruce Walton
7 Dave Otto
8 Reese Lambert
9 Joe Bitker
10 Joe Law
11 Ed Wojna
12 Timothy Casey
13 Patrick Dietrick
14 Bruce Fields
15 Eric Fox
16 Scott Hemond
17 Steve Howard
18 Doug Jennings
19 Al Pedrique
20 Dann Howitt
21 Russ McGinnis
22 Troy Afenir
23 Larry Arndt
24 Dickie Scott
25 Kevin Ward

1990 ProCards Tacoma Tigers

(Oakland A's) (color)

	MT	NR MT	EX
Complete Set:	7.00	5.25	2.75

83 Checklist
84 Tony Ariola
85 Joe Bitker
86 Scott Chiamparino
87 Reese Lambert
88 Joe Law
89 Dave Otto
90 Dave Veres
91 Bruce Walton
92 Wes Weber
93 Ed Wojna
94 Ray Young
95 Troy Afenir
96 Russ McGuinnis
97 Larry Arnt
98 Mike Bordick
99 Scott Hemond
100 Dann Howitt
101 Doug Jennings
102 Al Pedrique
103 Dick Scott
104 Tim Casey
105 Pat Dietrick
106 Bruce Fields
107 Eric Fox
108 Steve Howard
109 Kevin Ward
110 Brad Fisher
111 Chuck Estrada

1990 Diamond Tampa Yankees

(New York Yankees) (color)

	MT	NR MT	EX
Complete Set:	6.00	4.50	2.50

1 Tim Cooper
2 Abdiel Cumberbatch
3 Tim Demerson
4 Ryan Eberly
5 Carl Everett
6 Brian Faw
7 Nathanael Felix
8 Michael Figga
9 Brent Gilbert
10 Adolfo Harris
11 Jim Hayes
12 Richard Hines
13 Frank Laviano
14 Ricardo Ledee
15 Johnny Leon
16 Jeff Matouzas
17 Mariano Rivera
18 Tim Rumer
19 Edwin Salcedo
20 Alexis Santaella
21 Sandi Santiago
22 Tate Seefried
23 Keith Seiler
24 Michael Smith
25 Shane Spencer
26 John Thibert
27 Rich Turrentine
28 Coaching Staff

1990 Grand Slam Texas League All-Stars

(All-Stars) (color)

	MT	NR MT	EX
Complete Set:	7.00	5.25	2.75

1 Eric Karros
2 Eddie Pye
3 Greg David
4 Charlie Montoya
5 Bert Heffernan
6 Mike Knapp
7 Mike Humphreys
8 Henry Rodriguez
9 Dee Dixon
10 Jesus Alfardo
11 Jeff Barnes
12 Ricky Bones
13 Jeremy Hernandez
14 Mike James
15 Dennis Springer
16 Kevin Campbell
17 Chris George
18 Dave Huppert
19 Rob Giesecke
20 Rob Maurer
21 Rudy Hernandez
22 Dave Patterson
23 Andres Santana
24 Steve Decker
25 Bill Haselman
26 Kevin Belcher
27 Ted Wood
28 Terry McDaniel
29 Dan Rohrmeier
30 Joe Hall
31 Anthony Young
32 Terry Bross
33 Peter Schourek
34 Dave Osteen
35 Jim Pena
36 Steve Allen
37 Bill Evers
38 Greg Harrel

1990 CMC (TCMA) Tidewater Tides

(New York Mets) (color)

	MT	NR MT	EX
Complete Set:	6.00	4.50	2.50

1 Shawn Barton
2 Kevin Brown

3 Rocky Childress
4 Brian Givens
5 Manny Hernandez
6 Jeff Innis
7 Cesar Mejia
8 Scott Nielsen
9 Dale Plummer
10 Ray Soff
11 Lou Thornton
12 Dave Trautwein
13 Julio Valera
14 Tim Bogar
15 Mike DeButch
16 Jeff Gardner
17 Denny Gonzalez
18 Chris Jelic
19 Roger Samuels
20 Dave Liddell
21 Orlando Mercado
22 Kevin Torve
23 Alex Diaz
24 Keith Hughes
25 Darren Reed
26 Zolio Sanchez
27 Steve Swisher
28 John Cumberland
29 Rich Miller
30 Scott Lawrenson

1990 ProCards Tidewater Tides

(New York Mets) (color)

	MT	NR MT	EX
Complete Set:	6.00	4.50	2.50

533 Checklist
534 Shawn Barton
535 Kevin Brown
536 Rocky Childress
537 Brian Givins
538 Manny Hernandez
539 Jeff Innis
540 Cesar Mejia
541 Scott Nielsen
542 Dale Plummer
543 Roger Samuels
544 Ray Soff
545 Dave Trautwein
546 Julio Valera
547 Dave Liddell
548 Orlando Mercado
549 Tim Boger
550 Mike DeButch
551 Jeff Gardner
552 Denny Gonzalez
553 Chris Jelic
554 Kelvin Torve
555 Alex Diaz
556 Keith Hughes
557 Darren Reed
558 Zolio Sanchez
559 Lou Thornton
560 Steve Swisher
561 John Cumberland
562 Rich Miller

1990 Team-WTAR Tidewater Tides

(New York Mets) (color)

	MT	NR MT	EX
Complete Set:	9.00	6.75	3.50

1 Lou Thornton
4 Denny Gonzales
7 Zolio Sanchez
9 Steve Swisher
10 Mike DeButch
11 Cesar Mejia
12 Keith Hughes
13 Tim Bogar
14 Jeff Gardner
18 Kevin Torve
19 Alex Diaz
22 Dale Plummer
24 Orlando Mercado
27 Dave Liddell
28 Ray Soff
30 Shawn Barton
31 Chris Jelic
32 Kevin Brown
33 Roger Samuels
35 Manny Hernandez
36 Darren Reed
37 Rich Miller
39 Scott Nielsen
40 Jeff Innis
42 Dave Trautwein
44 Brian Givins
47 Rocky Childress
48 Julio Valera
---- John Cumberland
---- Scott Lawenson
---- 1990 Tidewater Team Picture

1990 CMC (TCMA) Toledo Mud Hens

(Detroit Tigers) (color)

	MT	NR MT	EX
Complete Set:	11.00	8.25	4.50

1 Don Vesling
2 Scott Aldred
3 Dennis Burtt
4 Shawn Holman
5 Matt Kinzer
6 Randy Nosek
7 Jose Ramos
8 Kevin Ritz
9 Mike Schwabe
10 Steve Searcy
11 Eric Stone
12 Domingo Michel
13 Phil Ouellette
14 Shawn Hare
15 Jim Lindeman
16 Scott Livingstone
17 Lavel Freeman
18 Travis Fryman
19 Scott Lusader
20 Dean Decillis
21 Milt Cuyler
22 Tom Gamboa
23 Phil Clark
24 Torey Lovullo
25 Aurelio Rodriguez
26 Jeff Jones
27 Steve McInerney

1990 ProCards Toledo Mud Hens

(Detroit Tigers) (color)

	MT	NR MT	EX
Complete Set:	11.00	8.25	4.50

140 Checklist
141 Scott Aldred
142 Dennis Burtt
143 Shawn Holman
144 Matt Kinzer
145 Randy Nosek
146 Jose Ramos
147 Kevin Ritz
148 Mike Schwabe
149 Steve Searcy
150 Eric Stone
151 Don Vesling
152 Phil Clark
153 Phil Ouellette
154 Dean DeCillis
155 Travis Fryman
156 Jim Lindeman
157 Scott Livingstone
158 Torey Luvullo
159 Domingo Michel
160 Milt Cuyler
161 Lavel Freeman
162 Shawn Hare
163 Scott Lusader
164 Tom Gamboa
165 Jeff Jones
166 Aurelio Rodriguez

1990 ProCards Triple A All-Stars

(All-Stars) (color)

	MT	NR MT	EX
Complete Set:	7.00	5.25	2.75

1 Checklist
2 Mark Whiten
3 Luis Sojo
4 Dave Polley
5 Kelvin Torve
6 Keith Hughes
7 Keith Miller
8 Paul Faries
9 German Rivera
10 Leo Gomez
11 Bob Bailor
12 Juan Gonzalez
13 Hensley Meulens
14 Brian Dorsett
15 Kevin Mmahat
16 Tim Naehring
17 Steve Carter
18 Terry Gilmore
19 Bernard Gilkey
20 Steve Searcy
21 Mike Cook
22 Dorn Taylor
23 Pete Filson
24 Tim McIntosh
25 Joe Redfield
26 Dave Machemer
27 Bill Dancy
28 Eddie Williams
29 Mike Perez
30 Travis Fryman
31 Jose Offerman
32 Kevin Kenndy
33 Dave Walsh
34 Erik Pappas
35 Jeff Small
36 Terry Collins
37 Jerry Willard
38 Tom Drees
39 Marv Foley
40 Craig Smajstrla
41 Orsino Hill
42 Lee Stevens
43 Todd Haney
44 Darrin Fletcher
45 Dave Hansen
46 Mike Huff
47 Joe Bitker
48 Ray Young
49 Scott Chiamparino
50 Alan Cockrell
51 Chris Hammond
52 Mark Leonard
53 Ken Hill
54 David Segul

1990 CMC (TCMA) Tucson Toros

(Houston Astros) (color)

	MT	NR MT	EX
Complete Set:	4.00	3.00	1.50

1 Ryan Bowen
2 Brian Meyer
3 Terry Clark
4 Darryl Kile
5 Randy St. Claire
6 Randy Hennis
7 Lee Tunnell
8 William Brennan
9 Craig Smajstrla
10 Gary Cooper
11 Carl Nichols
12 Louie Meadows
13 Jose Tolentino
14 Harry Spillman
15 Javier Ortiz
16 Doug Strange
17 Jim Olander
18 Karl Rhodes
19 Dave Rohde
20 Mike Simms
21 Scott Servais
22 Pedro Sanchez
23 Kevin Dean
24 Brian Fisher
25 Bob Skinner

1990 ProCards Tucson Toros

(Houston Astros) (color)

	MT	NR MT	EX
Complete Set:	4.00	3.00	1.50

195 Checklist
196 Ryan Bowen
197 William Brennan
198 Terry Clark
199 Brian Fisher
200 Randy Hennis
201 Darryl Kile
202 Brian Meyer
203 Randy St. Claire
204 Lee Tunnell
205 Carl Nichols
206 Scott Servais
207 Pedro Sanchez
208 Mike Simms
209 Craig Smajstrla
210 Harry Spilman
211 Doug Strange
212 Jose Tolentino
213 Gary Cooper
214 Kevin Dean
215 Louie Meadows
216 Jim Olander
217 Javier Ortiz
218 Karl Rhodes
219 Bob Skinner
220 Brent Strom
221 Tim Tolman

1990 ProCards Tulsa Drillers

(Texas Rangers) (color)

	MT	NR MT	EX
Complete Set:	7.00	5.25	2.75

1147 Checklist
1148 Steve Allen
1149 Phil Bryant
1150 Felipe Castillo
1151 Eric McCray
1152 Marv Rockman
1153 Wayne Rosenthall
1154 Cedric Shaw
1155 Chris Shiflett
1156 Mike Taylor
1157 Mitch Thomas
1158 Bill Haselman
1159 Greg Iavarone
1160 Paco Burgos
1161 Monty Fariss
1162 Darrin Garner
1163 Rob Maurer
1164 Paul Postier
1165 Brant Alyea
1166 Kevin Belcher
1167 Donald Harris
1168 Dan Peltier
1169 Dan Rohrmeier
1170 Dean Palmer
1171 Terry Mathews
1172 Tom Thompson
1173 Walt Williams
1174 Jeff Andrews

1990 Tulsa BB Card Shop Tulsa Drillers

(Texas Rangers) (color)

	MT	NR MT	EX
Complete Set:	6.00	4.50	2.50

1 Steve Allen
2 Jeffrey Andrews
3 Kevin Belcher
4 Paco Burgos
5 Felipe Castillo
6 Everett Cunningham
7 Monty Fariss
8 Darrin Garner
9 Greg Harrel
10 Donald Harris
11 William Haselman
12 Jim Hvizda
13 Greg Iavarone
14 David Lynch
15 Terry Mathews
16 Rob Maurer
17 Eric McCray
18 Roger Pavlik
19 Dan Peltier
20 Paul Postier
21 Mary Rockman
22 Dan Rohrmeier
23 Cedric Shaw
24 Mike Taylor
25 Tom Thompson
26 George Threadgill
27 Walt Williams
28 Tom Henke

1990 Pucko Utica Blue Sox

(Chicago White Sox) (color)

	MT	NR MT	EX
Complete Set:	4.00	3.00	1.50

1 Kevin Coughlin
2 Todd Martin
3 Dan Monzon
4 Rogelio Nunez
5 Rafael Ochoa
6 Adam Sanders
7 Joe Solimine
8 Chris Sparrow
9 Keith Strange
10 Dean Tatarian
11 Craig Teter
12 Kerry Valrie
13 Barry Williams
14 Rodney Bolton
15 Frank Campos
16 Rolando Caridad
17 Chris Fruge
18 Dave Gorman
19 Todd Hotz
20 Pat Hulme
21 Johnathan Jenkins
22 Ernesto Santana
23 John Smith
24 Kevin Tolar
25 Tom Thompson
26 Thompson's Staff
27 Morgana
28 Murnane Field
29 Mike Bradish
30 Lee Dorsey

1990 CMC (TCMA) Vancouver Canadians

(Chicago White Sox) (color)

	MT	NR MT	EX
Complete Set:	6.00	4.50	2.50

1 Wilson Alvarez
2 Adam Peterso
3 Tom Drees

4 Ravelo Manzanillo
5 Marv Foley
6 Grady Hall
7 Shawn Hillegas, Mike Campbell
8 Not Issued
9 C.L. Penigar
10 John Pawlowski
11 Steve Rosenberg
12 Jose Segura
13 Rich Amaral
14 Pete Dalena
15 Ramon Sambo
16 Marcus Lawton
17 Orsino Hill
18 Marlin McPhail
19 Keith Smith
20 Todd Trafton
21 Norberto Martin
22 Don Wakamatsu
23 Jerry Willard
24 Dana Williams
25 Tracy Woodson
26 Moe Drabowsky (Coach)
27 Roger LaFrancois (Coach)

1990 ProCards Vancouver Canadians

(Chicago White Sox) (color)

	MT	NR MT	EX
Complete Set:	6.00	4.50	2.50

480 Checklist
481 Wilson Alvarez
482 Mike Campbell
483 Tom Drees
484 Grady Hall
485 Shawn Hillegas
486 Ravelo Manzanillo
487 John Pawloski
488 Adam Peterson
489 Steve Rosenberg
490 Jose Sequra
491 Don Wakamatsu
492 Jerry Willard
493 Rich Amaral
494 Pete Dalena
495 Norberto Martin
496 Keith Smith
497 Todd Trafton
498 Tracy Woodson
499 Orsino Hill
500 Marcus Lawton
501 Marlin McPhail
502 C.L. Penigar
503 Ramon Sambo
504 Dana Williams
505 Marv Foley
506 Moe Drabowski
507 Roger LeFrancois

1990 Star Co. Vero Beach Dodgers

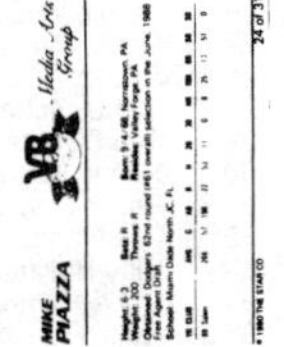

(Los Angeles Dodgers) (color)

	MT	NR MT	EX
Complete Set:	5.00	3.75	2.00

Sponser's Card
1 Jorge Alvarez
2 Pedro Astacio
3 Tony Barron
4 Bill Bene
5 Cam Biberdorf
6 Eric Boddie
7 Ray Calhoun
8 Anthony Collier
9 Edwin Correa
10 Javier Delahoya
11 Bruce Dostal
12 Dino Ebel
13 Bob Fletcher
14 Freddy Gonzales
15 Pete Gonzales
16 Marc Griffin
17 John Knapp
18 Alan Lewis
19 Scott Marabell
20 Robin Nina
21 Tim Patrick
22 Pedro Perez
23 Rex Peters
24 Mike Piazza
25 Ramon Taveras
26 Jeff Vanzytvelo
27 Bill Wengert
28 Mike Wismer
29 Eric Young
30 Alvare, Lewallyn)
31 Matt Wilson

1990 Cal League Visalia Oaks

(Minnesota Twins) (color)

	MT	NR MT	EX
Complete Set:	7.00	5.25	2.75

56 Denny Neagle
57 Chad Swanson
58 Mike Trombley
59 Mike Aspray
60 Pat Mahomes
61 Tom Fine
62 Richard Garces
63 Fred White
64 Phil Wiese
65 George Tsamis
66 Carl Fratcelli
67 Dan Masteller
68 Ramon Cedeno
69 Bob McCreary
70 Ray Ortiz
71 Carlos Capellan
72 Jay Kausnicka
73 Mike House
74 J.T. Bruett
75 Troy Buckley
76 Todd Logan
77 Daniel Segui
78 Jose Garcia
79 Scott Ullger
80 Brian Allard
81 Bruce Bucz
82 Joel Safly
83 Joseph Bucz
84 Jason Elick
85 Robert Spurlock
86 Darren Holt

1990 ProCards Visalia Oaks

(Minnesota Twins) (color)

	MT	NR MT	EX
Complete Set:	7.00	5.25	2.75

2146 Checklist
2147 Tom Fine
2148 Richard Garces
2149 Pat Mahomes
2150 Denny Neagle
2151 Mike Aspray
2152 Chad Swamson
2153 Mike Trombley
2154 George Tsamis
2155 Fred White
2156 Phil Wiese
2157 Troy Buckley
2158 Todd Logan
2159 Carlos Capellan
2160 Carl Fraticelli
2161 Jose Garcia
2162 Dan Masteller
2163 Bob McCreary
2164 Dan Segui
2165 J.T. Bruett
2166 Ramon Cedeno
2167 Mike House
2168 Jay Kvasnicka
2169 Ray Ortiz
2170 Scott Ullger
2171 Brian Allard

1990 Best Waterloo Diamonds

(San Diego Padres) (color)

	MT	NR MT	EX
Complete Set:	3.00	2.25	1.25

1 Ray Holbert
2 David Colon
3 Bryce Florie
4 Todd Embry
5 Luis Galindez
6 Jeff Hart
7 Rod Billingsly
8 Brad Hoyer
9 Tony Lewis
10 Steven Martin
11 Brian McKeon
12 Ron Morton
13 J.D. Noland
14 Billy Reed
15 Terry Rupp
16 Osvaldo Sanchez
17 Shawn Whalen
18 Matt Witlowski
19 Bryan Little
20 Ron Oglesby
21 George Poulis
22 Greg Conley
23 Gene Glynn
24 Matt Toole
25 Mark Verstanding
26 Tom Doyle
27 Jose Lebron
28 Checklist

1990 ProCards Waterloo Diamonds

(San Diego Padres) (color)

	MT	NR MT	EX
Complete Set:	3.00	2.25	1.25

2369 Checklist
2370 Todd Embry
2371 Bryce Florie
2372 Luis Galindez
2373 Jeff Hart
2374 Brad Hoyer
2375 Jose LeBron
2376 Tony Lewis
2377 Brian McKeon
2378 Ron Morton
2379 Billy Reed
2380 Rod Billingsley
2381 Greg Conley
2382 Mark Verstanding
2383 Tom Doyle
2384 Ray Holbert
2385 Steve Martin
2386 Terry Rupp
2387 Matt Toole
2388 Matt Witlowski
2389 David Colon
2390 J.D. Noland
2391 Osvaldo Sanchez
2392 Shawn Whalen
2393 Bryan Little
2394 Ron Oglesby
2395 Gene Glynn

1990 Star Co. Watertown Indians

(Cleveland Indians) (color)

	MT	NR MT	EX
Complete Set:	3.00	2.25	1.25

1 Chad Allen
2 William Canate
3 Mark Charbonnet
4 Brian Cofer
5 John Cotton
6 Mike Davis
7 Marc Del Piano
8 Tim Ellis
9 Brian Giles
10 Mike Gonzalez
11 Dane Kallevig
12 Dennis Kluss
13 John Lorms
14 Oscar Munoz
15 Joe Perez
16 Clyde Pough
17 Roberto Rivera
18 Bobby Ryan
19 Keith Shepherd
20 Kelly Stinnett
21 Paulino Tena
22 Ken Welch
23 Bill Wertz
24 Jim Gabella
25 Ken Silvestri
26 Teddy Blackwell
27 Tom Van Schaack
28 Tracy Richardson

1990 Best Wausau Timbers

(Baltimore Orioles) (color)

	MT	NR MT	EX
Complete Set:	3.00	2.25	1.25

1 T.R. Lewis
2 Steven Williams
3 Pat Leinen
4 Tom Martin
5 Daryl Moore
6 Matt Anderson
7 Richard Smith
8 Brad Pennington
9 Thomas Taylor
10 Bob Wheatcroft
11 Joe Teixeira
12 David Riddle
13 Shawn Heiden
14 Sergio Cairo
15 Greg Zaun
16 Jim Roso
17 Caesar Devares
18 Keith Kessinger
19 Garye Shingledecker
20 Manuel Alexander
21 John Fowler
22 Christan Benitez
23 Melvin Wearing Jr.
24 Aman Hicks
25 Hector Bautista
26 Allen Davis
27 Keith Schmidt
28 Not Issued
29 Checklist

1990 ProCards Wausau Timbers

(Baltimore Orioles) (color)

	MT	NR MT	EX
Complete Set:	3.00	2.25	1.25

2114 Checklist
2115 Steve Williams
2116 Pat Leinen
2117 Tom Martin
2118 Daryl Moore
2119 Matt Anderson
2120 Rich Smith
2121 Brad Pennington
2122 Tom Taylor
2123 Rob Wheatcroft
2124 Joe Teixeira
2125 Dave Riddle
2126 Shawn Heiden
2127 John Marett
2128 Greg Zaun
2129 Jimmy Roso
2130 Cesar Devares
2131 Keith Kessinger
2132 Gary Shingledecker
2133 T.R. Lewis
2134 John Fowler
2135 Manny Alexander
2136 Christan Benitez
2137 Melvin Wearing
2138 Aman Hicks
2139 Hector Bautista
2140 Bo Davis
2141 Keith Schmidt
2142 Sergio Cairo
2143 Mike Young
2144 Chet Nichols
2145 Onen Fleita

1990 Star Co. Wausau Timbers

(Baltimore Orioles) (color)

	MT	NR MT	EX
Complete set:	3.00	2.25	1.25

1 Matthew Anderson
2 Hector Bautista
3 Christan Benitez
4 John Boothby
5 Sergio Cairo
6 Bo Davis
7 Cesar Devares
8 John Fowler
9 Shawn Heiden
10 Aman Hicks
11 Brad Hildreth
12 Robert Kessinger
13 Michael Leinen
14 T.R. Lewis
15 John Marett
16 Thomas Martin
17 John Moore
18 Brad Pennington
19 David Riddle
20 James Roso
21 Keith Schmidt
22 Richard Smith
23 Tommy Taylor
24 Melvin Wearing
25 Robert Wheatcroft
26 Steven Williams
27 Gregory Zaun
28 Coaching staff
29 Mitch Bibb

1990 Pucko Welland Pirates

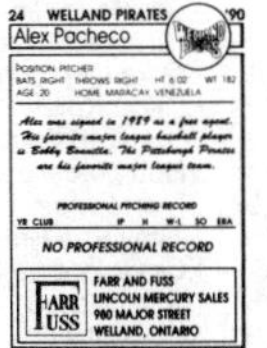

(Pittsburgh Pirates) (color)

	MT	NR MT	EX
Complete Set:	3.00	2.25	1.25

1 Kurt Miller
2 Michael Brown

3 Genaro Campusano
4 Jon Martin
5 Janiero Feliz
6 Ben Johnson
7 Steve Polewski
8 Kevin Young
9 John Schulte
10 Anthony Brown
11 Scott Bullett
12 John Curtis
13 Thomas Green
14 Joe Ronca
15 Wes Grisham
16 Tim Edge
17 Marcus Hanel
18 Rob Peterson
19 Lynn Carlson
20 Stephen Cooke
21 Mark Futrell
22 Jeff Lyle
23 Troy Mooney
24 Alex Pacheco
25 Andre Redmond
26 Richard Robertson
27 Steve Roeder
28 Brian Shouse
29 Shelton Simpson
30 David Tellers
31 Michael Zimmerman
32 Jim Mallon
33 Mallon's Staff
34 Bob Burgess
35 Farr and Fuss
36 Welland Sports Center

1990 Star Co. West Palm Beach Expos

(Montreal Expos) (color)

	MT	NR MT	EX
Complete Set:	4.00	3.00	1.50

1 Rod Boddie
2 Paul Ciaglo
3 Reid Cornelius
4 Bret Davis
5 Jim Faulk
6 Rob Fletcher
7 Kevin Foster
8 Dan Freed
9 Dan Gakeler
10 Eddie Gonzalez
11 Rob Kerrigan
12 Ken Lake
13 Richie Lewis
14 Rob Mason
15 Todd Mayo
16 John Mello
17 Doug Piatt
18 Chris Pollack
19 F.P. Santangelo
20 Joe Siddall
21 David Sommer
22 Joel Smith
23 Matt Stairs
24 Adam Terris
25 David Wainhouse
26 John Wenrick
27 Fred Williams
28 Pete Young
29 Felipe Alou
30 Dave Jauss
31 Sean Cunningham

1990 Rocks Dugout Wichita Wranglers

(San Diego Padres) (color)

	MT	NR MT	EX
Complete Set:	5.00	3.75	2.00

1 Checklist
2 Ricky Bones
3 Doug Brocail
4 Rafael Chavez
5 Brian Cisarik
6 Gregory David
7 Todd Hansen
8 Jeremy Hernandez
9 Charles Hilleman
10 Richard Holsman
11 Mike Humphreys
12 Dean Kelley
13 Stephen Loubier
14 Bob Lutticken
15 Pedro Martinez
16 Tim McWilliam
17 Craig Repoz
18 A.J. Sager
19 William Taylor
20 Jose Valentin
21 Guillermo Valasquez
22 Juan Villanueva
23 Dan Walters
24 Brian Wood
25 Steve Lubratich
26 Lonnie Keeter
27 Jon Matlack
28 Cookie

1990 Best Williamsport Bills

(Seattle Mariners) (color)

	MT	NR MT	EX
Complete Set:	3.00	2.25	1.25

1 Lee Hancock
2 Jim Blueberg
3 Jim Bowie
4 Troy Evers
5 Fernando Figueroa
6 Mike Gardiner
7 Mike Goff
8 Ruben Gonzalez
9 Chuck Hensley
10 Jeff Hooper
11 Chris Howard
12 Bryan King
13 Dru Kosco
14 Shane Letterio
15 Mike McDonald
16 Mark Merchant
17 Jeff Nelson
18 Ken Pennington
19 Mark Razook
20 Dana Ridenour
21 Ricky Rojas
22 Ted Williams
23 Mark Wooden
24 Chris Verna
25 Rich Morales
26 Bobby Cuellar
27 Checklist

1990 ProCards Williamsport Bills

(Seattle Mariners) (color)

	MT	NR MT	EX
Complete Set:	3.00	2.25	1.25

1048 Checklist
1049 Jim Blueberg
1050 Troy Evers
1051 Fernando Figueroa
1052 Mike Gardiner
1053 Mike Goff
1054 Lee Hancock
1055 Chuck Hensley
1056 Jeff Nelson
1057 Dana Ridenour
1058 Ricky Rojas
1059 Mark Wooden
1060 Jeff Hooper
1061 Chris Howard
1062 Ruben Gonzalez
1063 Bryan King
1064 Shane Letterio
1065 Ken Pennington
1066 Mark Razook
1067 Jim Bowie
1068 Dru Kosco
1069 Mike McDonald
1070 Mark Merchant
1071 Ted Williams
1072 Rich Morales
1073 Bobby Cuellar

1990 Star Co. Williamsport Bills

(Seattle Mariners) (color)

	MT	NR MT	EX
Complete Set:	3.00	2.25	1.25

1 Jim Blueberg
2 Jim Bowie
3 Dave Brundage
4 Rich DeLucia
5 Troy Evers
6 Fernando Figueroa
7 Mike Gardiner
8 Mike Goff
9 Lee Hancock
10 Chuck Hensley
11 Jeff Hooper
12 Chris Howard
13 Bryan King
14 Dru Kosco
15 Shane Letterio
16 Mike McDonald
17 Mark Merchant
18 Jeff Nelson
19 Ken Pennington
20 Mark Razook
21 Dana Ridenour
22 Ricky Rojas
23 Ted Williams
24 Mark Wooden
25 Rich Morales
26 Bobby Cuellar
27 Chris Verna

1990 Sportprint Winston-Salem Spirit

(Chicago Cubs) (color)

	MT	NR MT	EX
Complete Set:	5.00	3.75	2.00

1 Gary Scott
2 Billy White
3 John Salles
4 Paul Blair
5 Bill Melvin
6 John Gardner
7 Doug Welch
8 Dale Craig
9 Derek Stroud
10 Kevin Roberson
11 Fernando Ramsey
12 Shannon Jones
13 Ronnie Rasp
14 Jim Murphy
15 John Jensen
16 Steve DiBartolomeo
17 Jim Bulinger
18 Ed Caballero
19 Tim Moore
20 Jeff Massicotte
21 Tracy Smith
22 Scott Taylor
23 Julio Strauss
24 Elvin Paulino
25 Eddie Williams
26 Lickety Split
27 Steve Melendez
28 Bill Early
29 Brad Mills
30 Team Photo

1990 Star Co. Winter Haven Red Sox

(Boston Red Sox) (color)

	MT	NR MT	EX
Complete Set:	5.00	3.75	2.00

1 Tracy Allen
2 Felix Colon
3 Freddie Davis
4 Alex Delgado
5 Jim Dennison
6 Colin Dixon
7 Willie Dukes
8 Ray Fagnant
9 Jason Friedman
10 Greg Hansell
11 Pete Hoy
12 Garrett Jenkins
13 Dan Kite
14 Pedro Matilla
15 Jeff McNeely
16 Steven Michael
17 Bart Moore
18 Boo Moore
19 Tony Mosley
20 Lou Munoz
21 Paul Quantrill
22 Ed Riley
23 Andy Rush
24 Al Sanders
25 Richard Witherspoon
26 Dave Holt
27 Doug Camilli
28 Jim Stricek

1990 Golden Cards Yakima Bears

(Los Angeles Dodgers) (color)

	MT	NR MT	EX
Complete Set:	5.00	3.75	2.00

1 Garrett Beard
2 Javier Delahoya
3 Mike Sampson
4 Helms Borhinger
5 Juan Bustabad
6 Kurt Olson
7 Jeff Brummer
8 Ken Burroughs
9 Erik Madsen
10 Daniel Cardenas
11 Hector Ortiz
12 Pedro Astacio
13 Raphael Rijo
14 Tim Patrick
15 Scott Doffek
16 Ben O'Connor
17 Joe Kelly
18 Billy Lott
19 Tony Arnold
20 Steve Ford
21 Faurot/Moen
22 Sean Sena
23 Jerry Royster
24 Craig White
25 Nolberto Troncoso
26 Mike Galle
27 Craig Bishop
28 Scott Freeman
29 Steve Mintz
30 Eric Blackwell
31 Paul Branconier
32 Yale Fowler
33 Fausto Tatis
34 Jose Perez
35 Jorge Cantres
36 Pedro Perez

1990 Best Minor League Baseball

Best made its debut in the single card market in 1990 with a 324 card set. The cards were issued in foil packs and not available as a complete set. Common players are 15 cents each. Prices listed are for cards in Mint condition.

		MT	NR MT	EX
	Complete Set:	90.00	67.00	36.00
	Common Player:	.15	.11	.06
1	Frank Thomas	22.00		
2	Eric Wedge	.20		
3	Willie Ansley	.40		
4	Mark Lewis	.40		
5	Greg Colbrunn	.20		
6	David Staton	.60		
7	Ben McDonald	1.00		
8	Brent Mayne	.25		
9	Ray Holbert	.20		
10	T.R. Lewis	.20		
11	Willie Banks	.50		
12	Steve Dunn	.30		
13	Juan Andujar	.30		
14	Roger Salkeld	.75		
15	Steve Hosey	.75		
16	Tyler Houston	.35		
17	David Holdridge	.25		
18	Todd Malone	.30		
19	Tony Scruggs	.25		
20	Darron Cox	.15		
21	Mike Linskey	.15		
22	Darren Lewis	1.25		
23	Eddie Zoskey	.25		
24	Ramser Correa	.20		
25	Lee Upshaw	.20		
26	Bernie Williams	.75		
27	Brian Harrison (Last name incorrect on checklist.)	.20		
28	Len Brutcher	.20		
29	Scott Centala	.20		
30	Kenny Morgan	.20		
31	Pedro Borbon	.30		
32	Lee Hancock	.25		
33	Clay Bellinger	.25		
34	Chris Meyers	.25		
35	Russ Garside	.25		
36	Ron Plemmons	.15		
37	Jose LeBron	.15		
38	Tom Hardgrove	.15		
39	Alan Newman	.30		
40	Ramon Jimenez	.40		
41	Ezequiel Herrera (First name misspelled on checklist.)	.20		
42	Jason Satre	.15		
43	Bob Malloy	.15		
44	William Suero	.20		
45	Lenny Webster	.35		
46	Andy Ashby	.50		
47	Darren Ritter (First name misspelled on checklist.)	.20		
48	Andy Mota	.20		
49	Pat Gomez	.15		
50	Ron Stephens	.15		
51	Daniel Eskew	.15		
52	Joe Andrzejewski	.15		
53	Doug Robbins	.15		
54	Noel Velez	.15		
55	Dana Ridenour	.15		
56	Luis Martinez	.15		
57	Dave Fleming	1.00		
58	Adell Davenport	.20		
59	Brent McCoy	.20		
60	Johnny Ard	.20		
61	Cal Eldred	1.50		
62	Tab Brown	.15		
63	Scott Kamieniecki	.35		
64	Scott Bryant	.25		
65	Brad Pennington	.25		
66	Bernie Jenkins	.15		
67	Frank Carey	.15		
68	Matt Witkowski	.15		

69 Checklist 1-48 .15
70 Josias Manzanillo .25
71 Checklist 49-96 .15
72 Andujar Cedeno (First name misspelled on card front.) 1.00
73 Rick Rojas .20
74 Scott Brosius .30
75 Tom Redington .20
76 Kevin Rogers .25
77 Jerry Wolak .25
78 Rick Davis .15
79 Juan Guzman 2.00
80 Cesar Bernhardt .20
81 Randy Simmons .20
82 Clyde Keller .20
83 Anthony Manahan .25
84 Tom Maynard .30
86 Sean Berry .30
87 Brian Boltz .30
88 Shawn Gilbert .30
89 Rafael Novoa .30
90 John Vanderwal .30
91 Scott Pose .35
92 Don Stanford .20
93 Joe Federico .25
94 Todd Watson .25
95 Luis Gonzalez (Last name misspelled on checklist.) 1.00
96 Pat Leinen .30
97 Joel Estes (First name misspelled on card front.) .15
98 Troy O'Leary .50
99 Matt Stark .35
100 Tony Tarasco 1.50
101 Marc Lipson .20
102 Kevin Higgins .15
103 Jack Voight (Last name misspelled on card back.) .20
104 Steve Schrenk .20
105 Jonathan Hurst (Last name misspelled on card front.) .15
106 Scott Erickson .50
107 Javier Lopez 6.00
108 Bob Zupcic (Last name misspelled on card front.) .35
109 Edwin Marquez .20
110 Shawn Heiden .15
111 Mike Maksudian .20
112 Tony Eusebio (Last name misspelled on card front.) .20
113 Chris Hancock .20
114 Royce Clayton 1.25
115 Tim Mauser .15
116 Ckecklist 97-144 .15
117 Carlos Maldonado .20
118 Rex DeLa Nuez .20
119 Mike Curtis .20
120 Roger Miller .20
121 Daryl Moore .20
122 Turk Wendell .35
123 Dan Rambo .15
124 Scott Kimball .15
125 Willie Magallanes .15
126 Dannie Harris .15
127 Joey James .15
128 Wil Cordero 1.50
129 Rob Taylor .20
130 Bryce Florie .15
131 Mike Mitchner (Last name misspelled on checklist.) .15
132 Jeff Bagwell 9.00
133 Caesar Devares .15
134 Tim Gillis .15
135 Victor Hithe .15
136 Earl Steinmetz .15
137 Carl Keliipuleole .15
138 Ted Williams .15
139 Jorge Pedre .15
140 Amalio Carreno .15
141 Chris Gill .15
142 Dennis Wiseman .15
143 Checklist 145-192 .15
144 Derek Lee .25
145 Brett Snyder .20
146 Chuck Knoblauch 1.50
147 Rafael Quirico .15
148 Julian Yan .15
149 John Thelen .15
150 Checklist 193-240 .15
151 Darrin Reichle .20
152 John Ramos .20
153 Patrick Lennon .25
154 Wade Taylor .25
155 Mike Twardoski .15
156 Jeff Conine 2.00
157 Kelly Mann .25
158 Gary Wilson .15
159 Chris Frye .15
160 Roger Hailey .30
161 Harold Allen .20
162 Ozzie Canseco .20
163 Checklist 241-288 .15
164 Rudy Seanez .25
165 John Zaksek .15
166 Roberto DeLeon (Last name misspelled on checklist.) .20
167 Matt Merullo .20
168 Checklist 289-324 (Wrong numbers listed on checklist.) .15
169 Terrell Hansen .20
170 Ron Crowe .15
171 Luis Galindez .15
172 Vilato Marrero .15
173 Scott Cepicky .30
174 Gary Resetar .15
175 Rich Scheid (First name misspelled on card front.) .15
176 Jimmy Rogers .15
177 Ken Pennington .20
178 Tom Martin .20
179 Mitch Lyden .15
180 Jorge Brito .15
181 Chris Gorton .15
182 Mark Sims .20
183 Jose Olmeda .15
184 Ed Taubensee .25
185 Steve Morris .15
186 Tim Pugh .25
187 Barry Winford .15
188 Allen Leibert (Last name misspelled on card back.) .15
189 Kurt Brown .15
190 Kelly Lifgren .15
191 Mike Kelly .50
192 Robert Munoz .25
193 Judd Johnson .15
194 Hector Wagner .15
195 Dave Reis .15
196 Isaiah Clark .15
197 William Schock .15
198 Ruben Gonzalez .15
199 Mike Eberle .15
200 Michael Arner .15
201 Raphael Bustamante .15
202 John Patterson .15
203 Joe Slusarski .20
204 Rodney McCray .20
205 Wally Trice .15
206 Edgar Caceres .15
207 Eugene Jones .15
208 Joey Wardlow .15
209 Steven Martin .15
210 Woody Williams .15
211 Kevin Morton .15
212 Bobby DeJardin (Last name misspelled on checklist.) .15
213 Chris Bennett .20
214 Brian Johnson .15
215 Randy Snyder .15
216 Roberto Hernandez .50
217 Glen Gardner .20
218 Fred Costello .15
219 Melvin Nieves .60
220 Al Martin 1.00
221 Kerry Knox .20
222 Mike Eatinger .20
223 Jim Myers .20
224 Jay Owens .25
225 Jayson Best .20
226 Mike McDonald .20
227 Kim Bateste .30
228 Rich Delucia .30
229 Chris Delarwelle .15
230 Jeff Hoffman .15
231 Bobby Moore .15
232 Dan Wilson .30
233 Greg Pirkl (Last name misspelled everywhere.) .60
234 Criag Newkirk .15
235 Mike Hensley .15
236 Ryan Klesko 8.00
237 Donald Sparks .15
238 J.D. Noland .15
239 Chris Howard .15
240 Stan Royer .30
241 Manuel Alexander .25
242 Jeff Plympton .20
243 Jeff Juden .35
244 Charles Nagy 1.00
245 Ryan Bowen .35
246 Scott Taylor .15
247 Tom Quinlan .15
248 Royal Thomas .15
249 Ricky Rhodes .15
250 Alex Fernandez 3.00
251 Bruce Egloff .15
252 Greg Sparks .15
253 Brian Dour .15
254 John Byington .20
255 Stacey Burdick .20
256 Danny Matznick .20
257 Reed Olmstead .20
258 Jim Bowie .15
259 Jim Newlan .15
260 Ramon Caraballo .20
261 Brian Barnes .15
262 Mike Gardiner .20
263 Andy Fox .20
264 Brian McKeon .15
265 Andy Tomberlin .25
266 Frank Bellino .15
267 Tim Lata .15
268 Mike Burton .15
269 Jim Orsag .15
270 Scott Romano .15
271 Leon Glenn .15
272 Mike Misuraca .15
273 Randy Knorr .25
274 Eddie Tucker .25
275 Ken Powell .15
276 Brian McRae 1.25
277 Mark Merchant .25
278 Vinicio Castilla .15
279 Stephen Chitren .25
280 Marteese Robinson .15
281 Osvaldo Sanchez .15
282 Mike Mongiello .15
283 John Valentin .50
284 Timmie Morrow .15
285 Matt Murray .15
286 Darrell Sherman .25
287 Royal Clayton .20
288 Jason Robertson .15
289 John Kilner .15
290 Jeff Mutis .25
291 Gary Alexander .25
292 Oreste Marrero .15
293 Melvin Wearing .15
294 Scott Meadows .15
295 Pat Hentgen 3.00
296 John Hudek .60
297 Tim Stargell .15
298 Tony Brown .15
299 Scott Plemmons .15
300 Chris Nabholz .35
301 Brian Romero .15
302 Vince Kindred .15
303 Robert Ayrault .15
304 Steve Stowell .15
305 Don Strange .20
306 Tim Nedin .15
307 Derek Livernois .15
308 Kerry Woodson .15
309 Sam Ferretti .15
310 Reuben Smiley (First name misspelled on checklist.) .20
311 Jim Campbell .15
312 Al Osuna .25
313 Luis Mercedes .25
314 Billy Reed .20
315 Vince Harris .15
316 Jeff Carter .15
317 Dave Riddle .15
318 Frank Thomas 14.00
319 Eric Wedge .15
320 Mark Lewis .25
321 Alex Fernandez 2.00
322 Chuck Knoblauch 1.25
323 Charles Nagy .60
324 Tyler Houston .25

1990 Collectors Marketing Corp. Pre-Rookie

This set was originated by combining CMC team sets with cards produced by ProCards and purchased by CMC. The ProCards were were given a glossy facing and randomly inserted in wax packs along with CMC cards. The set was catalogued at 880 cards, however, card #660, Mario Brito, was never issued. The cards were numbered at their bottom right corners, on their backs. These numbers were not coordinated with the original CMC team sets, and therefore many team sets were separated with ProCards cards between them. The CMC cards in this set differ from the original CMC team sets by the color of their backs (yellow in lieu of green) and the players are pictured in place of the team logos. A checklist was available through the company. Shortly after the cards hit the market, the CMC company was sold to Impel Marketing. Since the original CMC team sets were issued as one complete AAA set in a special wooden box, there were packaging problems with duplicates and/or missing cards. To its credit, Impel did attempt to rectify the situation by replacing any cards that were missing from the sets as issued by CMC. Commons are 20 cents. Individual card prices are for Mint condition.

	MT	NR MT	EX
Complete Set:	80.00	60.00	32.00
Common Player:	.05	.04	.02

1 Stan Belinda .20
2 Gordon Dillard .05
3 Terry Collins .05
4 Mark Huisman .05
5 Hugh Kemp .05
6 Scott Medvin .05
7 Vincente Palacios .05
8 Rick Reed .05
9 Mark Ross .05
10 Dorn Taylor .05
11 Mike York .05
12 Jeff Richardson .05
13 Dann Bilardello .05
14 Tom Prince .05
15 Danny Sheaffer .05
16 Kevin Burdick .05
17 Steve Kiefer .05
18 Orlando Merced .75
19 Armando Moreno .05
20 Mark Ryal .05
21 Tommy Shields .05
22 Steve Carter .05
23 Wes Chamberlain .20
24 Jeff Cook .05
25 Scott Little .05
26 Jeff Peterek .05
27 Ed Puig .05
28 Tim Watkins .05
29 Tom Edens .05
30 Mike Capel .05
31 Darryel Walters .05
32 Joe Xavier .05
33 Tim Torricelli .05
34 Joe Redfield .05
35 D.L. Smith .05
36 Billy Moore .05
37 Joe Mitchell .05
38 Mario Monico .05
39 Frank Mattox .05
40 Tim McIntosh .05
41 Mark Higgins .05
42 George Canale .05
43 Don Grodon .05
44 Al Sadler .05
45 Don August .05
46 Mike Birkbeck .05
47 Dennis Powell .05
48 Chuck McGrath .05
49 Ruben Escalera .05
50 Dave Machemer .05
51 Steve Fireovid .05
52 Danny Clay .05
53 Howard Farmer .05
54 Travis Chambers .05
55 Chris Marchok .05
56 Dan Gakeler .05
57 Scott Anderson .05
58 Dale Mohorcic .05
59 Richard Thompson .05
60 Eddie Dixon .05
61 Jim Davins .05
62 Edwin Marquez .05
63 Jerry Goff .05
64 Dwight Lowery .05
65 Jim Steels .05
66 Quinn Mack .05
67 Eric Bullock .05
68 Otis Green .05
69 Randy Braun .05
70 Mel Houston .05
71 Johnny Paredes .05
72 Romy Cucjen .05
73 Jose Castro .05
74 Esteban Beltre .05
75 Tim Johnson .05
76 Shawn Boskie .05
77 Dave Masters .05
78 Kevin Blankenship .05
79 Greg Kallevig .05
80 Steve Parker .05
81 David Pavlas .05
82 Jeff Pico .05
83 Laddie Renfroe .05
84 Dean Wilkins .05
85 Paul Wilmet .05
86 Bob Bafia .05
87 Brian Guinn .05
88 Greg Smith .05
89 Derrick May .40
90 Glenn Sullivan .05
91 Bill Wrona .05
92 Eric Pappas .05
93 Hector Villanueva .05
94 Ced Landrum .05
95 Jeff Small .05
96 Gary Varsho .05
97 Brad Bierly .05
98 Jeff Hearron .05
99 Jim Essian .05
100 Brian McCann .05
101 Scott Arnold .05
102 Gibson Alba .05
103 Cris Carpetner .05
104 Stan Clarke .05
105 Mike Hinkle .05
106 Howard Hilton .05
107 Dave Osteen .05
108 Mike Perez .20
109 Bernard Gilkey 1.25
110 Dennis Carter .05
111 Julian Martinez .05
112 Rod Brewer .05
113 Ray Stephens .05
114 Ray Lankford 1.25
115 Craig Wilson .05
116 Roy Silver .05
117 Bien Figueroa .05
118 Jesus Mendez .05
119 Geronimo Pena .25
120 Omar Olivares .15
121 Mark Grater .05
122 Tim Sherrill .05
123 Pat Austin .05
124 Todd Crosby .05
125 Scott Nichols .05
126 Milt Hill .05
127 Robert Moore .05
128 Joey Vierra .05
129 Terry McGriff .05
130 Chris Hammond .25
131 Charlie Mitchell .05
132 Rodney Imes .05
133 Rob Lopez .05
134 Keith Brown .05
135 Scott Scudder .20
136 Bob Sebra .10
137 Donnie Scott .05
138 Skeeter Barnes .10
139 Paul Noce .05
140 Leo Garcia .05
141 Chris Jones .05
142 Kevin Pearson .05
143 Darryl Motley .05
144 Keith Lockhart .10
145 Brian Lane .10
146 Eddie Tanner .05
147 Reggie Jefferson .50

148 Neil Allen .05
149 Pete Mackanin .05
150 Ray Ripplemeyer .05
151 Jack Hardy .05
152 Steve Lankard .05
153 John Hoover .05
154 David Lynch .05
155 Mark Petkovsek .05
156 David Miller .05
157 Brad Arnsberg .05
158 Jeff Satzinger .05
159 John Barfield .05
160 Mike Berger .05
161 John Russell .05
162 Pat Garman .05
163 Gary Green .05
164 Bryan House .05
165 Ron Washington .05
166 Nick Capra .05
167 Juan Gonzalez 15.00
168 Gar Millay .05
169 Kevin Reimer .15
170 Bernie Tatis .05
171 Steve Smith .05
172 Dick Egan .05
173 Stan Hough .05
174 Ray Ramirez .05
175 Moe Drabowsky .05
176 Jay Baller .05
177 Ray Chadwick .05
178 Dera Clark .05
179 Luis Encarnacion .05
180 Jim LeMasters .05
181 Mike Magnante .05
182 Mel Stottlemyre .05
183 Tony Ferreira .05
184 Pete Filson .05
185 Andy McGaffigan .05
186 Luis DeLos Santos .05
187 Mike Loggins .05
188 Chito Martinez .05
189 Bobby Meacham .05
190 Russ Morman .05
191 Bill Pecota .05
192 Harvey Pulliam .20
193 Jeff Schulz .05
194 Gary Thurman .10
195 Thad Reece .05
196 Tim Spehr .20
197 Paul Zuvella .05
198 Not Issued .05
199 Poquette & Dubee, Bob Hamelin .05
200 Sal Rende .05
201 Steve Adkins .05
202 Dave Eiland .05
203 John Habyan .05
204 Mark Leiter .05
205 Kevin Mmahat .05
206 Hipolito Pena .05
207 Willie Smith .05
208 Rich Monteleone .05
209 Hensley Meulens .05
210 Andy Stankiewicz .15
211 Jim Leyritz .10
212 Jim Walewander .05
213 Oscar Azocar .05
214 John Fishel .05
215 Jason Maas .05
216 Van Snider .05
217 Kevin Maas .20
218 Ricky Torres .05
219 Dave Sax .05
220 Darrin Chapin .05
221 Rob Sepanek .05
222 Mark Wasinger .05
223 Jimmy Jones .05
224 Clippers Coaches .05
225 Stump Merrill .05
226 Bob Davidson .05
227 Eric Boudreaux .05
228 Marvin Freeman .05
229 Jason Grimsley .05
230 Chuck Malone .05
231 Dickie Moles .05
232 Wally Ritchie .05
233 Bob Scanlan .05
234 Scott Service .05
235 Steve Sharts .05
236 John Gibbons .05
237 Sal Agostinelli .05
238 Jim Adduci .05
239 Kelly Heath .05
240 Mickey Marandini .75
241 Victor Rosario .05
242 Steve Stanicek .05
243 Jim Vatcher .05
244 Bill Dancy .05
245 Ron Jones .05
246 Chris Knabenshue .05
247 Keith Miller .05
248 Floyd Rayford .05
249 Jim Wright .05
250 Todd Frohwirth .05
251 Barney Nugent .05
252 Tito Stewart .05
253 John Trautwein .05
254 Mike Rochford .05
255 Larry Shikles .05
256 Daryl Irvine .05
257 John Leister .05
258 Joe Johnson .05
259 Mark Meleski .05
260 Steven Bast .05
261 Ed Nottle .05
262 John Flaherty .05
263 John Marzano .05
264 Gary Tremblay .05
265 Scott Cooper 1.50
266 Angel Gonzalez .05
267 Julius McDougal .05
268 Tim Naehring .50
269 Jim Pankovits .05
270 Rick Lancelotti .05
271 Mickey Pina .05
272 Phil Plantier 2.50
273 Jeff Stone .05
274 Scott Wade .05
275 Mike Dalton .05
276 Jeff Gray .05
277 Steve Avery 3.00
278 Braves Coaches .05
279 Dale Polley .05
280 Rusty Richards .05
281 Andy Nezelek .05
282 Ed Olwine .05
283 Jim Beauchamp .05
284 Paul Marak .05
285 Dave Justice 5.00
286 Jimmy Kremmers .05
287 Drew Denson .05
288 Barry Jones .05
289 Francisco Cabrera .10
290 Bruce Crabbe .05
291 Dennis Hood .05
292 Geronimo Berroa .40
293 Ed Whited .05
294 Sam Ayoub .05
295 Brian Hunter .30
296 Tommy Green .15
297 John Mizerock .05
298 Ken Dowell .05
299 John Alva .05
300 Bill Lasky .05
301 Brian Snyder .05
302 Ben McDonald .50
303 Rob Woodward .05
304 Mickey Weston .05
305 Mike Jones .05
306 Curtis Schilling .15
307 Jay Aldrich .05
308 Paul Blair .05
309 Mike Smith .05
310 Jeff Tackett .05
311 Leo Gomez .35
312 Juan Bell .10
313 Chris Hoiles 1.75
314 Donell Nixon .05
315 Steve Stanicek .05
316 Tim Dulin .05
317 Chris Padget .05
318 Greg Walker .05
319 Tony Chance .05
320 Jeff McKnight .05
321 J.J. Bautista .10
322 John Mitchell .05
323 Vic Hithe .05
324 Darrell Miller .05
325 Shane Turner .05
326 Greg Biagini .05
327 Alex Sanchez .08
328 Mauro Gozzo .08
329 Steven Cummings .05
330 Tom Gilles .05
331 Douglas Linton .05
332 Mike Loynd .05
333 Bob Shirley .05
334 John Shea .05
335 Paul Kilgus .10
336 Carlos Diaz .05
337 Joe Szekely .05
338 Rick Lysander .05
339 Jim Eppard .05
340 Derek Bell 1.75
341 Jose Escobar .05
342 Webster Garrison .05
343 Paul Runge .05
344 Luis Sojo .10
345 Ed Sprague .35
346 Hector Delacruz .05
347 Rob Ducey .05
348 Ozzie Virgil .08
349 Stu Pederson .05
350 Mark Whiten 1.25
351 Andy Dziadkowiec .05
352 Shawn Barton .05
353 Kevin Brown .05
354 Rocky Childress .05
355 Brian Givens .05
356 Manny Hernandez .05
357 Jeff Innis .05
358 Cesar Mejia .05
359 Scott Nielson .05
360 Dale Plummer .05
361 Ray Soff .05
362 Lou Thornton .05
363 Dave Trautwein .05
364 Julio Valera .15
365 Tim Bogar .05
366 Mike DeButch .05
367 Jeff Gardner .05
368 Denny Gonzalez .05
369 Chris Jelic .05
370 Roger Samuels .05
371 Dave Liddell .05
372 Orlando Mercado .05
373 Kelvin Torva .05
374 Alex Diaz .05
375 Keith Hughes .05
376 Darren Reed .05
377 Zolio Sanchez .05
378 Do Vesling .05
379 Scott Aldred .05
380 Dennis Burtt .05
381 Shawn Holman .05
382 Matt Kinzer .05
383 Randy Mosek .05
384 Jose Ramos .05
385 Kevin Ritz .05
386 Mike Schwabe .05
387 Steve Searcy .05
388 Eric Stone .05
389 Domingo Michel .05
390 Phil Ouellette .05
391 Shawn Hare .05
392 Jim Lindeman .05
393 Scott Livingstone .15
394 Lavel Freeman .05
395 Travis Fryman 6.00
396 Scott Lusader .05
397 Dean Decillis .05
398 Milt Cuyler .35
399 Not Issued .05
400 Phil Clark .25
401 Torey Lovullo .05
402 Aurelio Rodriguez .05
403 Mike Christopher .05
404 Jeff Bittiger .05
405 Jeff Fischer .05
406 Steve Davis .05
407 Morris Madden .05
408 Darren Holmes .15
409 Greg Mayberry .05
410 Mike Maddux .08
411 Tim Scott .05
412 Jim Neidlinger .05
413 Dave Walsh .05
414 Dennis Springer .05
415 Terry Wells .05
416 Adam Brown .05
417 Darrin Fletcher .40
418 Carlos Hernandez .15
419 Dave Hansen .15
420 Dan Henley .05
421 Jose Offerman .35
422 Jose Vizcaino .15
423 Luis Lopez .05
424 Butch Davis .05
425 Wayne Kirby .10
426 Mike Huff .10
427 Billy Bean .05
428 Pat Pacillo .05
429 Tony Blasucci .10
430 Mike Walker .05
431 Pat Rice .05
432 Terry Taylor .05
433 David Burba .05
434 Vance Lovelace .05
435 Ed Vande Berg .05
436 Greg Fulton .05
437 Ed Jurak .05
438 Dave Cochrane .05
439 Edgar Martinez .75
440 Matt Sinatro .05
441 Bill McGuire .05
442 Mickey Brantley .05
443 Tom Dodd .05
444 Jim Weaver .05
445 Todd Haney .05
446 Casey Close .05
447 Theo Shaw .05
448 Keith Helton .05
449 Jose Melendez .05
450 Tom Jones .05
451 Dan Warthen .05
452 Randy Roetter .05
453 Mike Walker .05
454 Colby Ward .05
455 Joe Skalski .05
456 Efrain Valdez .05
457 Doug Robertson .05
458 Jeff Edwards .05
459 Greg McMichael .05
460 Carl Willis .05
461 Beau Allred .05
462 Jeff Kaiser .05
463 Ty Gainey .05
464 Tom Lampkin .05
465 Ever Magallanes .05
466 Tom Magrann .05
467 Jeff Manto .05
468 Luis Medina .05
469 Troy Neel .60
470 Steve Springer .05
471 Not Issued .05
472 Turner Ward .15
473 Casey Webster .05
474 Jeff Weatherly .05
475 Alan Cockrell .05
476 Rick Adain, Steve McInerny .05
477 Bobby Molinaro .05
478 Cliff Young .05
479 Michael Arner .05
480 Gary Buckels .05
481 Timothy Burcham .05
482 Sherman Corbett .05
483 Mike Erb .05
484 Mike Fetters .05
485 Chuck Hernandez .05
486 Jeff Heathcock .05
487 Scott Lewis .05
488 Rafael Montalvo .05
489 John Skuria .05
490 Lee Stevens .05
491 Nelson Rood .05
492 Bobby Rose .05
493 Dan Grunhard .05
494 Reed Peters .05
495 Doug Davis .05
496 Gary DiSarcina .15
497 Pete Coachman .05
498 Chris Cron .05
499 Karl Allaire .05
500 Ron Tingley .05
501 Chris Beasley .05
502 Max Oliveras .05
503 Roger Smithberg .05
504 Steve Peters .05
505 Matt Maysey .05
506 Terry Gilmore .05
507 Jeff Datz .05
508 Eric Nolte .05
509 Jim Lewis .05
510 Pete Roberts .05
511 Dan Murphy .05
512 Rich Rodriguez .05
513 Joe Lynch .05
514 Mike Basso .05
515 Ronn Reynolds .05
516 Jose Mota .05
517 Paul Faries .05
518 Warren Newsome .05
519 Alex Cole .25
520 Tom Levasseur .05
521 Charles Hillemann .05
522 Jeff Yurtin .05
523 Rafael Valdez .05
524 Brian Ohnoutka .05
525 Pat Kelley .05
526 Gary Lance .05
527 Tony Torchia .05
528 Paul McClellan .05
529 Randy McCament .05
530 Gil Heredia .05
531 George Bonilla .05
532 Russ Swan .05
533 Ed Vosberg .05
534 Eric Gunderson .05
535 Trevor Wilson .10
536 Greg Booker .05
537 Kirt Manwaring .10
538 Mike Kingery .05
539 Brian Brady .05
540 Mark Bailey .05
541 Gregg Ritchie .05
542 George Hinshaw .05
543 Craig Colbert .05
544 Kash Beauchamp .05
545 Jeff Carter .05
546 Mark Leonard .05
547 Tony Perezchica .05
548 Mike Laga .05
549 MIke Benjamin .05
550 Timber Mead .05
551 Duane Espy .05
552 Tim Ireland .05
553 Paul Abbott .05
554 Pat Bangston .05
555 Larry Casian .05
556 Mike Cook .05
557 Pete Delkus .05
558 Mike Dyer .05
559 Charlie Scott .05
560 Francisco Oliveras .05
561 Park Pittman .05
562 Jimmy Williams .05
563 Rich Yett .05
564 Vic Rodriguez .05
565 Jamie Nelson .05
566 Derek Parks .20
567 Ed Naveda .05
568 Scott Leius .10
569 Terry Jorgensen .05
570 Doug Baker .05
571 Chip Hale .10
572 Dave Jacas .05
573 Jim Shellenback .05
574 Rafael DeLima .05
575 Bernardo Brito .05
576 J.T. Bruett .10
577 Paul Sorrento .40
578 Ray Young .05
579 Dave Veres .05
580 Scott Chiamparino .10
581 Tony Ariola .05
582 Weston Weber .05
583 Bruce Walton .05
584 Dave Otto .05
585 Reese Lambert .05
586 Joe Bitker .05
587 Joe Law .05
588 Ed Wojna .05
589 Timothy Casey .05
590 Patrick Dietrick .05
591 Bruce Fields .05
592 Eric Fox .10
593 Scott Hemond .10
594 Steve Howard .05
595 Doug Jennings .05
596 Al Pedrique .05
597 Dann Howitt .05
598 Russ McGinnis .05
599 Troy Afenir .05
600 Larry Arndt .05
601 Dickie Scott .05
602 Kevin Ward .05
603 Ryan Bowen .15
604 Brian Meyer .05
605 Terry Clark .05
606 Darryl Kile 1.00
607 Randy St. Claire .05
608 Randy Hennis .05
609 Lee Tunnell .05
610 Bill Brennan .05
611 Craig Smajstrla .05
612 Gary Cooper .05
613 Carl Nichols .05
614 Louie Meadows .05
615 Jose Tolentino .05
616 Harry Spillman .05
617 Javier Ortiz .05
618 Doug Strange .05

619 Jim Olander .05
620 Karl Rhodes .60
621 David Rohde .05
622 Mike Simms .05
623 Scott Servais .25
624 Pedro Sanchez .05
625 Kevin Dean .05
626 Brian Fisher .05
627 Bob Skinner .05
628 Wilson Alvarez 1.75
629 Adam Peterson .05
630 Tom Drees .05
631 Ravelo Manzanillo .05
632 Marv Foley .05
633 Grady Hall .05
634 Mike Campbell .05
635 Shawn Hillegas .05
636 C.L. Penigar .05
637 John Pawlowski .05
638 Steve Rosenberg .05
639 Jose Segura .05
640 Rich Amaral .05
641 Pete Dalena .05
642 Ramon Sambo .05
643 Marcus Lawton .05
644 Orsino Hill .05
645 Marlin McPhail .05
646 Keith Smith .05
647 Todd Trafton .05
648 Norberto Martin .05
649 Don Wakamatsu .05
650 Jerry Willard .05
651 Dana Williams .05
652 Tracy Woodson .05
653 Glenn Hoffman .05
654 Anthony Scruggs .05
655 Reggie Sanders 1.25
656 Rick Lueken .05
657 Kent Mercker .20
658 Dukes Coaches .05
659 Richard Shockey (Picture is of Mo Sanford) .15
660 Brian Barney, Mario Brito .15
661 Not Issued .05
662 Ed Quijada .05
663 Steve Wapnick .05
664 Kevin Tahan .05
665 Johnny Guzman .15
666 Bronswell Patrick .05
667 Kevin Kennedy .05
668 Orlando Miller .25
669 Mauricio Nunez .05
670 Hector Rivera .05
671 Roger LaFrancois .05
672 Jackson Todd .05
673 John Young .05
674 Bob Bailor .05
675 David Hajeck .05
676 Ralph Wheeler .05
677 Anthony Gutierrez .05
678 Gaylen Pitts .05
679 Mark Riggins .05
680 Brad Bluestone .05
681 Dick Bosman .05
682 Wil Cordero .75
683 Todd Hutcheson .05
684 Steve Swisher .05
685 John Cumberland .05
686 Rich Miller .05
687 Scott Lawrenson .05
688 Larry Hardy .05
689 Danny Boone .05
690 Terrel Hansen .05
691 Tom Gamboa, Jeff Jones .05
692 Gavin Osteen .05
693 Dave Riddle .05
694 Tim Pugh .15
695 Eugene Jones .05
696 Scott Pose .10
697 Ramon Jimenez .05
698 Fred Russell .05
699 Louis Talbert .05
700 J.D. Noland .05
701 Osvaldo Sanchez .05
702 David Colon .05
703 Jeff Hart .05
704 Jeff Hoffman .05
705 Sean Gilliam .05
706 Al Pacheco .05
707 Jason Satre .05
708 Tim Cecil .05
709 Phil Wiese .05
710 Larry Pardo .05
711 Clemente Acosta .05
712 Chris Johnson .05
713 Frank Bolick .15
714 Jose Garcia .05
715 Adell Davenport .05
716 Kevin Rogers .20
717 Dan Rambo .05
718 Vince Harris .05
719 Darrell Sherman .10
720 Isaiah Clark .05
721 Miguel Sabino .05
722 Frank Valdez .05
723 Giovanni Miranda .05
724 Daryl Ratliff .05
725 Mike Brewinton .05
726 Eric Parkinson .05
727 Vin Castilla .05
728 Roger Hailey .15
729 Earl Steinmetz .05
730 Doug Gogolewski .05
731 Andy Cook .05
732 John Toale .05
733 Mike Curtis .05
734 Delwyn Young .05
735 Scott Meadows .05
736 Don Sparks .05
737 Gary Wilson .05
738 Blas Minor .15
739 Jeff Bagwell 8.00
740 Phil Bryant .05
741 Felipe Castillo .05
742 Craig Faulkner .05
743 Jeff Conine 1.50
744 Kevin Belcher .05
745 Bill Haselman .05
746 Matt Stark .05
747 Todd Hall .05
748 Scott Centala .05
749 Doug Simons .05
750 Shawn Gilbert .05
751 Kenny Morgan .05
752 Andy Mota .05
753 Jeff Baldwin .05
754 Reed Olmstead .05
755 Basil Meyer .05
756 Mark Razook .05
757 Ken Pennington .05
758 Shane Letterio .05
759 Ted Williams .05
760 Luis Gonzalez .50
761 Carlos Garcia .40
762 Terry Crowley .05
763 Julio Peguero .05
764 Francisco Delarosa .05
765 Rodney Lofton .05
766 Eric McCray .05
767 Mike Wilkins .05
768 John Kiely .05
769 Derek Lee .05
770 Bo Kennedy .05
771 John Hudek .05
772 Bernie Nunez .05
773 Tom Quinlan .05
774 Jim Tatum .20
775 Casey Waller .05
776 Doug Lindsey .05
777 Roberto Zambrano .05
778 Wade Taylor .10
779 Carlos Maldonado .05
780 Brent Mayne .10
781 Jerry Rub .05
782 Vincent Phillips .05
783 Eric Wedge .10
784 Andrew Ashby .15
785 Royal Clayton .05
786 Jeffrey Osbourne .05
787 Pat Kelly .20
788 John Wehner .05
789 Bernie Williams .75
790 Moises Alou 1.25
791 Mark Merchant .05
792 Chris Myers .05
793 Donald Harris .05
794 Michael McDonald .05
795 Jim Blueberg .05
796 James Bowie .05
797 Ruben Gonzalez .05
798 Rob Maurer .05
799 Monty Farris .05
800 Bob Ayrault .05
801 Tim Mauser .05
802 David Holdridge .05
803 Kim Batiste .25
804 Dan Peltier .15
805 Derek Livernois .10
806 Thomas Fischer .05
807 Chuck Knoblauch 1.50
808 Willie Banks .50
809 Johnny Ard .05
810 Willie Ansley .20
811 Andujar Cedeno 1.25
812 Eddie Zoskey .15
813 Randy Knorr .10
814 Juan Guzman 1.50
815 Jimmy Rogers .05
816 Nate Cromwell .05
817 Aubrey Waggoner .05
818 Frank Thomas 18.00
819 Matt Merullo .05
820 Roberto Hernandez .60
821 Cesar Bernhardt .05
822 Sterling Hitchcock .25
823 Ricky Rhodes .05
824 Todd Malone .05
825 Andy Fox .05
826 Ryan Klesko 7.50
827 Tyler Houston .15
828 Tab Brown .05
829 Brian McRae .60
830 Victor Cole .20
831 Mark Lewis .35
832 Rudy Seanez .10
833 Charles Nagy .75
834 Jeff Mutis .10
835 Carl Keliipuleole .05
836 Steve Pegues .05
837 Mike Lumley .05
838 Tim Leiner .05
839 Dave Evans .05
840 Darron Cox .10
841 Tony Ochs .05
842 Paul Coleman .15
843 Rafael Novoa .10
844 Clay Bellinger .05
845 Jason McFarlin .05
846 Craig Paquette .40
847 Timmie Morrow .05
848 Brian Hunter .75
849 Willie Greene .40
850 Austin Manahan .05
851 Rich Aude .20
852 Luis Lopez .05
853 Darrin Reichle .05
854 Tim Salmon 10.00
855 Royce Clayton 1.00
856 Steve Hosey .20
857 Kerry Woodson .05
858 Roger Salkeld .50
859 Tim Stargell .05
860 Greg Pirkl .35
861 Pat Mahomes .50
862 Denny Naegle .20
863 Troy Buckley .05
864 Ray Ortiz .05
865 Leo Perez .05
866 Cal Eldred 1.00
867 Darin Kracl .05
868 Lee Tinsley .15
869 T.R. Lewis .15
870 Jim Roso .05
871 Tom Taylor .05
872 Matt Anderson .05
873 Kerwin Moore .15
874 Rich Tunison .05
875 Brian Ahern .05
876 Eddie Taubensee .20
877 Scott Bryant .10
878 Steve Martin .05
879 Josias Mazanillo .05
880 Bob Zupcic .20

1990 ProCards A & AA Minor League Stars

This set was originally marketed for ProCards in wax packs by Progressive Sports Images in 1991 and, later, was distributed as a complete set. Commons are 20 cents each. Indvidual card prices are for Mint condition.

	MT	NR MT	EX
Complete Set (200):	15.00	11.00	6.00
Common Player:	.05	.04	.02

1 Mike Linskey .05
2 Ben McDonald .50
3 Francisco DeLaRosa .05
4 Jose Mesa .05
5 Kevin Morton .05
6 Dan O'Neill .05
7 Dave Owen .05
8 Jeff Plympton .05
9 Charles Nagy .25
10 Rudy Seanez .10
11 Bruce Egloff .05
12 Joe Ausanio .05
13 Jim Tracy .05
14 Randy Tomlin .10
15 Jim Campbell .05
16 Mike Gardiner .05
17 Rusty Meacham .05
18 John Kiely .05
19 Darrin Chapin .05
20 Wade Taylor .05
21 Don Stanford .05
22 Andy Ashby .05
23 Bob Ayrault .05
24 Luis Mercedes .10
25 Scott Meadows .05
26 Jeff Bagwell 3.00
27 Mark Lewis .10
28 Carlos Garcia .25
29 Moises Alou .75
30 Rico Brogna .10
31 Bernie Williams .20
32 Pat Kelly .15
33 Mitch Lyden .05
34 Hector Wagner .05
35 Carlos Maldonado .05
36 Brian Barnes .10
37 Chris Nabholz .10
38 Jeff Carter .05
39 Johnny Ard .05
40 Willie Banks .20
41 Scott Erickson .15
42 Greg Johnson .05
43 Al Asuna .05
44 Bob MacDonald .05
45 Pat Hentgen 1.75
46 Frank Thomas 9.00
47 Matt Stark .05
48 Jeff Conine .75
49 Sean Berry .15
50 Brian McRae .25
51 Bobby Moore .05
52 Brent Mayne .10
53 Greg Colbrunn .15
54 Terrel Hansen .05
55 Lenny Webster .05
56 Chuck Knoblauch .75
57 Willie Ansley .10
58 Andujar Cedeno .25
59 Luis Gonzalez .25
60 Eddie Zosky .10
61 William Suero .05
62 Tom Quinlan .05
63 Kelly Mann .05
64 Mike Bell .05
65 Mark Dewey .05
66 Tom Hostetler .05
67 Kevin Belcher .05
68 Bill Haselman .05
69 Bob Maurer .05
70 Dan Rohrmeier .05
71 Dan Peltier .10
72 Steven Decker .05
73 Dave Patterson .05
74 Ed Zinter .05
75 David Bird .05
76 Willie Espinal .05
77 Dennis Fletcher .05
78 Travis Buckley .05
79 Brian Romero .05
80 Mike Arner .05
81 Brian Evans .05
82 John Graves .05
83 Randy Marshall .05
84 Mike Garcia .05
85 Jeff Braley .05
86 Ricky Rhodes .05
87 Jim Haller .05
88 Sterling Hitchcock .15
89 Rob Blumberg .05
90 Mike Ogliaruso .05
91 Gregg Martin .05
92 Tim Pugh .10
93 Roger Hailey .10
94 Don Strange .05
95 Robert Gaddy .05
96 Willie Greene .20
97 Austin Manahan .05
98 Tony Scruggs .05
99 Mike Burton .05
100 Shawn Holtzclaw .05
101 Orlando Miller .15
102 David Hajek .05
103 Scott Pose .05
104 Tyler Houston .10
105 Melvin Nieves .25
106 Ryan Klesko 2.50
107 Daryl Moore .05
108 Skip Wiley .05
109 Brian McKeon .05
110 Rusty Kilgo .05
111 Chris Bushing .05
112 Alan Newman .05
113 Marc Lipson .05
114 Darin Kracl .05
115 Matt Grott .05
116 Rafael Novoa .05
117 Pat Rapp .05
118 Ed Gustafson .05
119 Chris Hancock .05
120 Mo Sanford .15
121 Bill Risley .05
122 Victor Garcia .05
123 Dave McAuliffe .05
124 Pedro Borbon .05
125 Rich Tunlson .05
126 Fred Cooley .05
127 Joey James .05
128 Reggie Sanders .50
129 Scott Bryant .05
130 Brent McCoy .05
131 Ramon Caraballo .05
132 Javier Lopez 2.00
133 Brian Harrison .05
134 Rich DeLucia .10
135 Roger Salkeld .25
136 Kerry Woodson .05
137 Chris Johnson .05
138 Cal Eldred .40
139 Angel Miranda .20
140 Richard Garces .10
141 Pat Mahomes .25
142 Denny Neagle .10
143 George Tsamis .05
144 Johnny Guzman .15
145 Dan Rambo .05
146 Jim Myers .05
147 Darrell Sherman .35
148 Dave Staton .20
149 Brian Turang .05
150 Bo Dodson .15
151 Dave Nilsson .35
152 Frank Bolick .10
153 Ray Ortiz .05
154 J.T. Bruett .05
155 John Patterson .05
156 Royce Clayton .40
157 Hilly Hathaway .15
158 Phil Leftwich .40
159 Randy Powers .05
160 Todd Van Poppel .40
161 Don Peters .05
162 Dave Zancanaro .05
163 Kirk Dressendorfer .05
164 Curtis Shaw .15
165 Joe Rosselli .10
166 Mark Dalesandro .05
167 Eric Helfand .05
168 Eric Booker .05
169 Adam Hyzdu .20
170 Eric Christopherson .10
171 Marcus Jensen .05
172 Derek Reid .05
173 Lance Dickson .10
174 Tim Parker .05
175 Jessie Hollins .05
176 Sam Militello .25
177 Darren Hodges .05
178 Kirt Ojala .05
179 Steve Karsay 1.00
180 Andrew Hartung .15
181 Kevin Jordan .15
182 Robert Eenhoorn .05
183 Jalal Leach .05
184 Carlos Delgado 2.00
185 Sean Cheetham .05
186 J.J. Munoz .05
187 Jim Thome .40
188 Tracy Sanders .10
189 Tony Clark .10

190 Jose Viera .05
191 Pat Dando .05
192 Brian Kowitz .10
193 Mike Lieberthal .20
194 Jeff Borgese .05
195 Mike Ferry .05
196 K.C. Gillum .05
197 Elliott Quinones .05
198 Grant Brittain .05
199 Checklist 1-100 .05
200 Checklist 101-200 .05

1990 ProCards Future Stars AAA Baseball

This was series was the second produced for ProCards by Progressive Sports Images. Its predecessor in 1989 had simply been AAA players from the regular ProCards team sets with 1989 stats added. The 1990 series, complete with 1990 stats, featured cards from all AAA teams in a completely different format from the regular 1990 team sets. Although the cards were numbered consecutively 1-700, an attempt was made to maintain team integrity. The series was later issued in complete sets. Commons are 15 cents each. Due to a scarcity of certain cards in inventory and additional labor costs to dealers, the consumer can be expected to pay a minimum of $6-$8 for team sets from this product. Individual card prices are for Mint condition.

	MT	NR MT	EX
Complete Set (700):	25.00	18.00	10.00
Common Player:	.05	.04	.02

1 Terry Gilmore .05
2 Jim Lewis .05
3 Joe Lynch .05
4 Matt Maysey .05
5 Dan Murphy .05
6 Eric Nolte .05
7 Brian Ohnoutka .05
8 Steve Peters .05
9 Paul Quinzer .05
10 Pete Roberts .05
11 Rich Rodriguez .05
12 Roger Smithberg .05
13 Rafael Valdez .05
14 Mike Basso .05
15 Ronn Reynolds .05
16 Paul Faries .05
17 Tom LeVasseur .05
18 Jose Mota .05
19 Eddie Williams .05
20 Jeff Yurtin .05
21 Alex Cole .10
22 Charles Hillemann .05
23 Thomas Howard .05
24 Warren Newsome .05
25 Pat Kelly .10
26 Gary Lance .05
27 Tony Torchia .05
28 George Bonilla .05
29 Greg Booker .05
30 Rich Bordi .05
31 John Burkett .50
32 Gil Heredia .10
33 Bob Knepper .05
34 Randy McCament .05
35 Paul McClellan .05
36 Timber Mead .05
37 Ed Vosberg .05
38 Trevor Wilson .20
39 Mark Bailey .05
40 Kirt Manwaring .05
41 Mike Benjamin .05
42 Brian Brady .05
43 Jeff Carter .05
44 Craig Colbert .05
45 Erik Johnson .05
46 Greg Litton .05
47 Kash Beauchamp .05
48 George Hinshaw .05
49 Mike Kingery .05
50 Mark Leonard .05
51 Gregg Ritchie .05
52 Rick Parker .05
53 Duane Espy .05
54 Tim Ireland .05
55 Larry Hardy .05
56 Jeff Bittiger .05
57 Mike Christopher .05
58 Steve Davis .05
59 Jeff Fischer .05
60 Darren Holmes .05
61 Morris Madden .05
62 Mike Maddux .05
63 Greg Mayberry .05
64 Jim Neidlinger .05
65 Tim Scott .05
66 Dave Walsh .05
67 Terry Wells .05
68 Adam Brown .05
69 Darrin Fletcher .05
70 Carlos Hernandez .15
71 Dave Hansen .10
72 Dan Henley .05
73 Glenn Hoffman .05
74 Walt McConnell .05
75 Jose Offerman .25
76 Jose Vizcaino .10
77 Billy Bean .05
78 Butch Davis .05
79 Mike Huff .05
80 Wayne Kirby .05
81 Luis Lopez .05
82 Kevin Kennedy .05
83 Claude Osteen .05
84 Von Joshua .05
85 Chris Beasley .05
86 Gary Buckels .05
87 Tim Burcham .05
88 Sherman Corbett .05
89 Mike Erb .05
90 Mike Fetters .05
91 Jeff Heathcock .05
92 Scott Lewis .05
93 Rafael Montalvo .05
94 Cliff Young .05
95 Doug Davis .05
96 Ron Tingley .05
97 Karl Allaire .05
98 Pete Coachman .05
99 Chris Cron .05
100 Gary DiSarcina .15
101 Nelson Rood .05
102 Bobby Rose .05
103 Lee Stevens .05
104 Dan Grunhard .05
105 Reed Peters .05
106 John Skurla .05
107 Max Oliveras .05
108 Chuck Hernandez .05
109 Tony Blasucci .05
110 Dave Burba .05
111 Keith Helton .05
112 Vance Lovelace .05
113 Jose Melendez .05
114 Pat Pacillo .05
115 Pat Rice .05
116 Terry Taylor .05
117 Mike Walker .05
118 Bill McGuire .05
119 Matt Sinatro .05
120 Mario Diaz .05
121 Greg Fulton .05
122 Todd Haney .05
123 Ed Jurak .05
124 Tino Martinez .40
125 Jeff Schaefer .05
126 Casey Close .05
127 Tom Dodd .05
128 Jim Weaver .05
129 Tommy Jones .05
130 Dan Warthen .05
131 Tony Ariola .05
132 Joe Bitker .05
133 Scott Chiamparino .05
134 Reese Lambert .05
135 Joe Law .05
136 Dave Otto .05
137 Dave Veres .05
138 Bruce Walton .05
139 Weston Weber .05
140 Ed Wojna .05
141 Ray Young .05
142 Troy Afenir .05
143 Russ McGinnis .05
144 Larry Arndt .05
145 Mike Bordick .15
146 Scott Hemond .05
147 Dann Howitt .05
148 Doug Jennings .05
149 Al Pedrique .05
150 Dick Scott .05
151 Tim Casey .05
152 Pat Dietrick .05
153 Bruce Fields .05
154 Eric Fox .05
155 Steve Howard .05
156 Kevin Ward .05
157 Brad Fischer .05
158 Chuck Estrada .05
159 Wilson Alvarez 1.25
160 Mike Campbell .05
161 Tom Drees .05
162 Grady Hall .05
163 Shawn Hillegas .05
164 Ravelo Manzanillo .05
165 John Pawlowski .05
166 Adam Peterson .05
167 Steve Rosenberg .05
168 Jose Segura .05
169 Don Wakamatsu .05
170 Jerry Willard .05
171 Rich Amaral .05
172 Pete Dalena .05
173 Norberto Martin .05
174 Keith Smith .05
175 Todd Trafton .05
176 Tracy Woodson .05
177 Orsino Hill .05
178 Marcus Lawton .05
179 Marlin McPhall .05
180 C.L. Penigar .05
181 Ramon Sambo .05
182 Dana Williams .05
183 Marv Foley .05
184 Moe Drabowsky .05
185 Roger LaFrancois .05
186 Ryan Bowen .15
187 William Brennan .05
188 Terry Clark .05
189 Brian Fisher .05
190 Randy Hennis .05
191 Darryl Kile .75
192 Brian Meyer .05
193 Randy St. Claire .05
194 Lee Tunnell .05
195 Carl Nichols .05
196 Scott Servais .10
197 Pedro Sanchez .05
198 Mike Simms .05
199 Criag Smajstria .05
200 Harry Spilman .05
201 Doug Strange .05
202 Jose Tolentino .05
203 Gary Cooper .05
204 Kevin Dean .05
205 Louie Meadows .05
206 Jim Olander .05
207 Javier Ortiz .05
208 Karl Rhodes .40
209 Bob Skinner .05
210 Brent Strom .05
211 Tim Tolman .05
212 Greg McMichael .05
213 Doug Robertson .05
214 Jeff Shaw .05
215 Joe Skalski .05
216 Efrain Valdez .05
217 Mike Walker .05
218 Colby Ward .05
219 Carl Willis .05
220 Tom Lampkin .05
221 Tom Magrann .05
222 Juan Castillo .05
223 Ever Magallanes .05
224 Jeff Manto .05
225 Luis Medina .05
226 Troy Neel .30
227 Steve Springer .05
228 Casey Webster .05
229 Beau Allred .05
230 Alan Cockrell .05
231 Ty Gainey .05
232 Dwight Taylor .05
233 Turner Ward .05
234 Jeff Wetherby .05
235 Bobby Molinaro .05
236 Buddy Bell .05
237 Rick Adair .05
238 Paul Abbott .05
239 Pat Bangston .05
240 Larry Casian .05
241 Mike Cook .05
242 Pete Delkus .05
243 Mike Dyer .05
244 Mark Guthrie .05
245 Orlando Lind .05
246 Francisco Oliveras .05
247 Park Pittman .05
248 Charles Scott .05
249 Jimmy Williams .05
250 Jamie Nelson .05
251 Derek Parks .05
252 Doug Baker .05
253 Chip Hale .05
254 Terry Jorgensen .05
255 Scott Leius .10
256 Marty Lanoux .05
257 Ed Naveda .05
258 Victor Rodriguez .05
259 Paul Sorrento .20
260 Berbardo Brito .05
261 Rafael Delima .05
262 David Jacas .05
263 Alonzo Powell .05
264 Jim Shellenback .05
265 Shawn Barton .05
266 Kevin Brown .05
267 Rocky Childress .05
268 Brian Givens .05
269 Manny Hernandez .05
270 Jeff Innis .05
271 Cesar Mejia .05
272 Scott Nielsen .05
273 Dale Plummer .05
274 Rogre Samuels .05
275 Ray Soff .05
276 Dave Trautwein .05
277 Julio Valera .05
278 Dave Liddell .05
279 Oralndo Mercado .05
280 Tim Bogar .05
281 Mike DeButch .05
282 Jeff Gardner .05
283 Denny Gonzalez .05
284 Chris Jelic .05
285 Kelvin Torve .05
286 Alex Diaz .05
287 Keith Hughes .05
288 Darren Reed .05
289 Zollo Sanchez .05
290 Lou Thornton .05
291 Steve Swisher .05
292 John Cumberland .05
293 Rich Miller .05
294 Jose DeJesus .05
295 Marvin Freeman .05
296 Todd Frohwirth .05
297 Jason Grimsley .05
298 Chuck Malone .05
299 Brad Moore .05
300 Wally Ritchie .05
301 Bob Scanlan .05
302 Scott Service .05
303 Steve Sharts .05
304 John Gibbons .05
305 Tom Nieto .05
306 Jim Adduci .05
307 Kelly Heath .05
308 Mickey Morandini .20
309 Victor Rosario .05
310 Steve Stanicek .05
311 Greg Legg .05
312 Ron Jones .05
313 Chris Knabenshue .05
314 Keith Miller .05
315 Jim Vatcher .05
316 Jim Wright .05
317 Steve Adkins .05
318 Darrin Chapin .05
319 Bob Davidson .05
320 Dave Elland .05
321 John Habyan .05
322 Jimmy Jones .05
323 Mark Leiter .05
324 Kevin Mmahat .05
325 Rich Monteleone .05
326 Willie Smith .05
327 Ricky Torres .05
328 Jeff Datz .05
329 Brian Dorsett .05
330 Dave Sax .05
331 Jim Leyritz .05
332 Hensley Meulens .05
333 Carlos Rodriguez .05
334 Rob Sepanek .05
335 Andy Stankiewicz .10
336 Jim Walewander .05
337 Mark Wasinger .05
338 Oscar Azocar .05
339 John Fishel .05
340 Jason Maas .05
341 Kevin Maas .15
342 Van Snider .05
343 Field Staff .05
344 Tom Gilles .05
345 Mauro Gozzo .05
346 Paul Kilgus .05
347 Doug Linton .05
348 Mike Loynd .05
349 Rick Lysander .05
350 Alex Sanchez .05
351 John Shea .05
352 Steve Wapnick .05
353 Andy Dziadkowiec .05
354 Joe Szekely .05
355 Ozzie Virgil .05
356 Jim Eppard .05
357 Jose Escobar .05
358 Webster Garrison .05
359 Paul Runge .05
360 Luis Sojo .10
361 Ed Sprague .15
362 Derek Bell .75
363 Hector DeLaCruz .05
364 Rob Ducey .05
365 Pedro Munoz .20
366 Stu Pederson .05
367 Mark Whiten .75
368 Bob Ballor .05
369 Bob Shirley .05
370 Rocket Wheeler .05
371 Scott Aldred .05
372 Dennis Burtt .05
373 Shawn Holman .05
374 Matt Kinzer .05
375 Randy Nosek .05
376 Jose Ramos .05
377 Kevin Ritz .05
378 Mike Schwabe .05
379 Steve Searcy .05
380 Eric Stone .05
381 Don Vesling .05
382 Phil Clark .10
383 Phil Ouellette .05
384 Dean DeCillis .05
385 Travis Fryman 3.50
386 Jim Lindeman .05
387 Scott Livingstone .10
388 Torey Lovullo .05
389 Domingo Michel .05
390 Milt Cuyler .15
391 Lavell Freeman .05
392 Shawn Hare .05
393 Scott Lusader .05
394 Tom Gamboa .05
395 Jeff Jones .05
396 Aurelio Rodriguez .05
397 Steve Avery 1.50
398 Tommy Greene .25
399 Bill Laskey .05
400 Paul Marak .05
401 Andy Nezelek .05
402 Ed Olwine .05
403 Dale Polley .05
404 Rusty Richards .05
405 Brian Snyder .05
406 Jimmy Kremers .05
407 John Mizerock .05
408 John Alva .05
409 Francisco Cabrera .05
410 Bruce Crabbe .05
411 Drew Denson .05
412 Ken Dowell .05
413 Ed Whited .05
414 Geronimo Berroa .05
415 Dennis Hood .05
416 Brian Hunter .15
417 Barry Jones .05
418 Dave Justice 4.00
419 Jim Beauchamp .05
420 John Grubb .05
421 Leo Mazzone .05
422 Sonny Jackson .05
423 Rick Berg .05

424	Steve Bast	.05
425	Tom Bolton	.05
426	Steve Curry	.05
427	Mike Dalton	.05
428	Jeff Gray	.05
429	Daryl Irvine	.05
430	Joe Johnson	.05
431	John Leister	.05
432	Mike Rochford	.05
433	Larry Shikles	.05
434	Tito Stewart	.05
435	John Trautwein	.05
436	John Flaherty	.05
437	John Marzano	.05
438	Gary Tremblay	.05
439	Scott Cooper	.75
440	Angel Gonzalez	.05
441	Tim Naehring	.20
442	Jim Pankovits	.05
443	Mo Vaughn	2.00
444	Rick Lancellotti	.05
445	Mickey Pina	.05
446	Phil Plantier	1.50
447	Jeff Stone	.05
448	Scott Wade	.05
449	Ed Nottle	.05
450	Mark Meleski	.05
451	Lee Stange	.05
452	Jay Aldrich	.05
453	Jose Bautista	.05
454	Eric Bell	.05
455	Dan Boone	.05
456	Ben McDonald	.50
457	John Mitchell	.05
458	Curt Schilling	.05
459	Mike Smith	.05
460	Rob Woodward	.05
461	Chris Holles	.60
462	Darrell Miller	.05
463	Jeff Tackett	.05
464	Juan Bell	.05
465	Tim Dullin	.05
466	Leo Gomez	.10
467	Jeff McKnight	.05
468	Shane Turner	.05
469	Greg Walker	.05
470	Tony Chance	.05
471	Victor Hithe	.05
472	Donnell Nixon	.05
473	Chris Padget	.05
474	Pete Stanicek	.05
475	Mike Linskey	.05
476	Joaquin Contreras	.05
477	Greg Biagini	.05
478	Dick Bosman	.05
479	Paul Blair	.05
480	Stan Belinda	.10
481	Gordon Dillard	.05
482	Mark Huismann	.05
483	Hugh Kemp	.05
484	Scott Medvin	.05
485	Vincente Palacios	.05
486	Rick Reed	.05
487	Mark Ross	.05
488	Dorn Taylor	.05
489	Mike York	.05
490	Dann Bilardello	.05
491	Tom Prince	.05
492	Danny Sheaffer	.05
493	Kevin Burdick	.05
494	Steve Kiefer	.05
495	Orlando Merced	.50
496	Armando Moreno	.05
497	Jeff Richardson	.05
498	Mark Ryal	.05
499	Tommy Shields	.05
500	Steve Carter	.05
501	Wes Chamberlain	.20
502	Jeff Cook	.05
503	Scott Little	.05
504	Terry Collins	.05
505	Jackie Brown	.05
506	Steve Henderson	.05
507	Gibson Alba	.05
508	Scott Arnold	.05
509	Cris Carpenter	.05
510	Stan Clarke	.05
511	Mark Grater	.05
512	Howard Hilton	.05
513	Mike Hinkle	.05
514	Omar Olivares	.05
515	Dave Osteen	.05
516	Mike Perez	.10
517	Tim Sherrill	.05
518	Scott Nichols	.05
519	Ray Stephens	.05
520	Pat Austin	.05
521	Rod Brewer	.05
522	Todd Crosby	.05
523	Bien Figueroa	.05
524	Julian Martinez	.05
525	Jesus Mendez	.05
526	Geronimo Pena	.25
527	Craig Wilson	.05
528	Dennis Carter	.05
529	Bernard Gilkey	1.00
530	Ray Lankford	1.00
531	Mauricio Nunez	.05
532	Roy Silver	.05
533	Gaylen Pitts	.05
534	Mark Riggins	.05
535	Neil Allen	.05
536	Keith Brown	.05
537	Chris Hammond	.20
538	Milton Hill	.05
539	Rodney Imes	.05
540	Rob Lopez	.05
541	Charlie Mitchell	.05
542	Bobby Moore	.05
543	Rosario Rodriguez	.05
544	Scott Scudder	.05
545	Bob Sebra	.05
546	Joey Vierra	.05
547	Tony DeFrancesco	.05
548	Terry McGriff	.05
549	Donnie Scott	.05
550	Reggie Jefferson	.15
551	Brian Lane	.05
552	Chris Lombardozzi	.05
553	Paul Noce	.05
554	Kevin Pearson	.05
555	Eddie Tanner	.05
556	Skeeter Barnes	.05
557	Leo Garcia	.05
558	Chris Jones	.05
559	Keith Lockhart	.05
560	Darryl Motley	.05
561	Pete Mackanin	.05
562	Ray Ripplemeyer	.05
563	Scott Anderson	.05
564	Esteban Beltre	.05
565	Travis Chambers	.05
566	Randy Braun	.05
567	Danny Clay	.05
568	Eric Bullock	.05
569	Jim Davins	.05
570	Jose Castro	.05
571	Eddie Dixon	.05
572	Romy Cucjen	.05
573	Howard Farmer	.05
574	Jerry Goff	.05
575	Steve Fireovid	.05
576	Otis Green	.05
577	Dan Gakeler	.05
578	Mel Houston	.05
579	Balvino Galvez	.05
580	Dwight Lowery	.05
581	Dale Mohorcic	.05
582	Quinn Mack	.05
583	Chris Marchok	.05
584	Edwin Marquez	.05
585	Mel Rojas	.05
586	Johnny Paredes	.05
587	Rich Thompson	.05
588	German Rivera	.05
589	James Steels	.05
590	Tim Johnson	.05
591	Gomer Hodge	.05
592	Joe Kerrigan	.05
593	Ray Chadwick	.05
594	Dera Clark	.05
595	Luis Encarnacion	.05
596	Tony Ferreira	.05
597	Pete Filson	.05
598	Jim LeMasters	.05
599	Mike Magnante	.05
600	Mike Tresemer	.05
601	Mel Stottlemyre	.05
602	Bill Wilkinson	.05
603	Kevin Burrell	.05
604	Tim Spehr	.05
605	Luis DeLosSantos	.05
606	Bob Hamelin	.35
607	Bobby Meacham	.05
608	Russ Morman	.05
609	Thad Reece	.05
610	Paul Zuvella	.05
611	Mike Loggins	.05
612	Chito Martinez	.05
613	Harvey Pulliam	.10
614	Jeff Schulz	.05
615	Sal Rende	.05
616	Tom Poquette	.05
617	Rich Dubee	.05
618	Kevin Blankenship	.05
619	Shawn Boskie	.05
620	Mark Bowden	.05
621	Greg Kallevig	.05
622	Dave Masters	.05
623	Steve Parker	.05
624	Dave Pavlas	.05
625	Laddie Renfroe	.05
626	Paul Wilmet	.05
627	Jeff Hearron	.05
628	Erik Pappas	.05
629	Hector Villanueva	.05
630	Bob Bafia	.05
631	Brian Guinn	.05
632	Jeff Small	.05
633	Greg Smith	.05
634	Glenn Sullivan	.05
635	Bill Wrona	.05
636	Brad Bierley	.05
637	Cedric Landrum	.05
638	Derrick May	.50
639	Gary Varsho	.05
640	Jim Essian	.05
641	Don August	.05
642	Mike Birkbeck	.05
643	Mike Capel	.05
644	Logan Easley	.05
645	Tom Edens	.05
646	Don Gordon	.05
647	Chuck McGrath	.05
648	Jeff Peterek	.05
649	Dennis Powell	.05
650	Ed Puig	.05
651	Alan Sadler	.05
652	Tim Watkins	.05
653	Tim McIntosh	.05
654	Tim Torricelli	.05
655	George Canale	.05
656	Mark Higgins	.05
658	Joe Mitchell	.05
659	Joe Redfield	.05
660	D.L. Smith	.05
661	Joe Xavier	.05
662	Ruben Escalera	.05
663	Mario Monico	.05
664	Billy Moore	.05
665	Darryel Walters	.05
666	Dave Machemer	.05
667	Jackson Todd	.05
668	Gerald Alexander	.05
669	Brad Arnsberg	.05
670	John Barfield	.05
671	Jack Hardy	.05
672	Ray Hayward	.05
673	John Hoover	.05
674	Steve Lankard	.05
675	David Lynch	.05
676	Craig McMurtry	.05
677	David Miller	.05
678	Mark Petkovsek	.05
679	Jeff Satzinger	.05
680	Mike Berger	.05
681	Dave Engle	.05
682	John Russell	.05
683	Pat Dodson	.05
684	Pat Garman	.05
685	Gary Green	.05
686	Bryan House	.05
687	Dean Palmer	2.50
688	Ron Washington	.05
689	Nick Capra	.05
690	Juan Gonzalez	7.00
691	Gar Millay	.05
692	Kevin Reimer	.10
693	Bernie Tatis	.05
694	Checklist 1 - 100	.05
695	Checklist 101 - 200	.05
696	Checklist 201 - 300	.05
697	Checklist 301 - 400	.05
698	Checklist 401 - 500	.05
699	Checklist 501 - 600	.05
700	Checklist 601 - 700	.05

1990 Star Minor League Baseball Wax

Star finished the 1990 season with another 100 card wax series. This series was closely akin in makeup to its 1989 wax II predecessor. The set featured yellow borders around color photos. There was no checklist and the series was not issued in a set. A second series was planned, but never materialized. Commons are 15 cents each. Individual card prices are for Mint condition.

	MT	NR MT	EX
Complete Set (100):	15.00	11.00	6.00
Common Player:	.05	.04	.02

1	Bruce Schreiber	.05
2	Jeff Juden	.20
3	Kenny Lofton	2.50
4	Scott Makarewicz	.05
5	Al Sanders	.05
6	Rod Boddie	.05
7	Jim Faulk	.05
8	Dan Freed	.05
9	D.J. Dozier	.05
10	Nicko Riesgo	.05
11	Alan Zinter	.15
12	Jim Bruske	.05
13	Mark Lewis	.15
14	Willie Ansley	.15
15	Tony Eusebio	.05
16	Luis Gonzalez	.30
17	Andy Mota	.05
18	Tony Barron	.05
19	Kevin Maas	.10
20	Anthony Collier	.05
21	Ramon Taveras	.05
22	Eric Young	.20
23	Everett Cunningham	.05
24	Barry Manuel	.05
25	David Perez	.05
26	Ivan Rodriguez	2.00
27	Fred Samson	.05
28	Ben McDonald	.40
29	Blas Minor	.15
30	Jeff Blagwell	2.50
31	Mike Twardoski	.05
32	T.R. Lewis	.15
33	Ron Cook	.05
34	Ivan Cruz	.15
35	Jody Hurst	.05
36	Keith Kimberlin	.05
37	Lino Rivera	.05
38	Mike Tresh	.05
39	Hernan Cortes	.05
40	Jay Knoblauch	.05
41	Larry Stanford	.05
42	Hector Vargas	.05
43	Jacob Brumfield	.15
44	Mark Parnell	.05
45	Willie Banks	.25
46	Reed Olmstead	.05
47	Mike Redding	.05
48	Rich DeLucia	.10
49	Mike Gardiner	.05
50	Royal Clayton	.05
51	Darrin Chapin	.05
52	Mitch Lyden	.05
53	Don Sparks	.05
54	Bernie Williams	.40
55	Steve Dunn	.20
56	Alan Newman	.10
57	Brent McCoy	.05
58	Mike Galvan	.05
59	Greg Perschke	.05
60	Rob Resnikoff	.05
61	Sammy Sosa	1.75
62	Bobby DeLoach	.05
63	Jesse Cross	.05
64	Ray Giannelli	.05
65	Jeff Kent	1.00
66	Greg O'Halloran	.05
67	Mike Timlin	.20
68	Brian McRae	.40
69	Anthony Ward	.05
70	Toby Borland	.05
71	Joe Millette	.05
72	Tony Trevino	.05
73	Anthony Kelley	.05
74	George Kerfut	.05
75	Scott Meadows	.05
76	Luis Mercedes	.25
77	Dan Barbara	.05
78	Rod Poissant	.05
79	Gary Alexander	.05
80	Bob Ayrault	.05
81	Kim Batiste	.10
82	Pete Alborano	.05
83	Scott Centala	.05
84	Stu Cole	.05
85	Jeff Conine	1.00
86	Bobby Moore	.05
87	Jorge Pedre	.05
88	Mike Maksudian	.05
89	Jerry Schunk	.05
90	William Suero	.05
91	Eddie Zosky	.10
92	Jeff Hoffman	.05
93	Ramon Jimenez	.05
94	Michael Bell	.05
95	Thomas Redington	.05
96	Michael Arner	.05
97	Brian Romero	.05
98	Tony Scruggs	.05
99	James Harris	.05
100	Tito Navarro	.10

1990 Classic #1 Draft Picks

Todd Van Poppel and Alex Fernandez head up the 24- 1990 first round draft picks featured in this 25-card set. The set is limited with only 150,000 sets released to the hobby. A letter of authenticity accompanies each individually numbered set. Unlike other Classic issues, this set is not designed for use with the trivia board game. Individual card prices are for Mint condition.

	MT	NR MT	EX
Complete Set (26):	12.00	9.00	4.75
Common Player:	.20	.15	.08

1	Chipper Jones	2.00
3	Mike Lieberthal	.35
4	Alex Fernandez	2.00
5	Kurt Miller	.30
6	Marc Newfield	1.50
7	Dan Wilson	.50
8	Tim Costo	.25
9	Ron Walden	.25
10	Carl Everett	.50
11	Shane Andrews	.50
12	Todd Ritchie	.25
13	Donovan Osborne	.40
14	Todd Van Poppel	.75
15	Adam Hyzdu	.20
16	Dan Smith	.20
17	Jeromy Burnitz	1.00
18	Aaron Holbert	.25
19	Eric Christopherson	.20
20	Mike Mussina	3.00
21	Tom Nevers	.20
23	Lance Dickson	.30
24	Rondell White	3.00
25	Robbie Beckett	.20
26	Don Peters	.20
----	Future Stars-Checklist (Chipper Jones/ Rondell White)	1.50

1991 Classic Best Minors - Major League Way

Classic Best followed Best into the single card market in 1991 with a 450 card set. The first 396 cards were issued in poly packs and later available in factory sealed sets. Cards numbered 397-450 were only available in the factory sets. Commons are 15 cents each. Individual card prices are for Mint condition.

	MT	NR MT	EX
Complete Set (450):	24.00	18.00	9.50
Common Player:	.05	.04	.02

1 Mike Schmidt .35
2 Kevin Roberson .40
3 Paul Rodgers .05
4 Marc Newfield 1.00
5 Marc Ronan .05
6 Marty Willis .05
7 Jason Hardtke .05
8 Matt Mieske .35
9 Brian Johnson .05
10 Alex Arias .05
11 Eric Young .15
12 Donald Harris .05
13 Bruce Chick .05
14 Brian Williams .20
15 Brian Cornelius .05
16 Brian Giles .05
17 Brad Ausmus .10
18 Ivan Cruz .10
19 Keven Flora .10
20 Robbie Katzaroff .05
21 Randy Knorr .05
22 Micky Henson .05
23 Chris Haney .05
24 Jeff Mutis .10
25 Barry Winford .05
26 Ray Giannelli .05
27 Donovan Osborne .20
28 Ruben Gonzalez .05
29 Howard Battle .35
30 Greg O'Halloran .05
31 Ben Vanryn .05
32 Rick Hulsman .05
33 Jose Valentin .25
34 Jose Zambrano .05
35 John Gross .05
36 Jessie Hollins .05
37 Kevin Scott .05
38 Kerwin Moore .05
39 Eric Albright .05
40 Ernesto Rodriguez .05
41 Reggie Sanders .75
42 Henry Werland .05
43 Boo Moore .15
44 Mike Messerly .05
45 Mike Lansing .25
46 Mike Gardella .05
47 Mo Sanford .10
48 Tavo Alvarez .25
49 Nick Davis .05
50 Charlie Hillemann .05
51 Jeff Darwin .15
52 Reid Cornelius .10
53 Matt Rambo .05
54 Rich Batchelor .05
55 Ricky Gutierrez .20
56 Rod Bolton .15
57 Pat Bryant .10
58 Hugh Walker .10
59 Keith Schmidt .05
60 Ceasar Morillo .05
61 Gabe White .40
62 Javy Lopez 2.50
63 Carlos Delgado 2.00
64 John Johnstone .05
65 Andres Berumen .05
66 Brian Kowitz .05
67 Shane Reynolds (Photo actually Orlando Miller) .05
68 Jeromy Burnitz .50
69 Scott Bryant .05
70 Jason McFarlin .05
71 John Conner .05
72 Garrett Jenkins .05
73 Greg Kobza .05
74 Mark Swope .05
75 Jerome Williams .05
76 Jeff Bonner .05
77 Jermaine Swinton .05
78 John Cohen .05
79 Johnny Calzado .05
80 Juan Andujar .05
81 Paul Ellis .05
82 Paul Gonzalez .05
83 Scott Taylor .05
84 Stan Spencer .05
85 Steve Martin .05
86 Scott Cepicky .05
87 Max Aleys .05
88 Michael Brown (Photo actually Matt Brown) .05
89 Jim Waggoner .05
90 Mickey Rivers Jr. .05
91 Nate Crowmwell .05
92 Carlos Perez .05
93 Matt Brown (Photo actually Michael Brown) .05
94 Jose Hernandez .05
95 Johnny Ruffin .15
96 Kevin Jordan .15
97 Manny Alexander .10
98 Tony Longmire .05
99 Lonell Roberts .05
100 Doug Lindsey .05
101 Al Harley .05
102 Jerry Thurston .05
103 Mike Williams .10
104 David Bell .15
105 Greg Johnson .05
106 Roger Salkeld .25
107 Mike Milchin .05
108 Jeff Kent .75
109 Tim Stargell .05
110 Miah Bradbury .05
111 Paul Fletcher .05
112 Steven Rolen .05
113 Tony Spires .05
114 Kevin Tolar .05
115 Kevin Dattola .05
116 Sherman Obando .20
117 Sean Ryan .05
118 Carlos Mota .05
119 Steve Karsay 1.00
120 Kelly Lifgren .05
121 Damion Easley .20
122 Fred Russell .05
123 Freddie Davis Jr. .05
124 Dave Zancanaro .05
125 Jeff Jackson .10
126 Steve Pegues .05
127 Gerald Williams .05
128 Eric Helfand .10
129 Gary Painter .05
130 Colin Ryan .05
131 Randy Brown .05
132 Andy Fox .05
133 Mike Ogliaruso .05
134 Matt Franco .05
135 Willie Ansley .15
136 Ivan Rodriguez .75
137 Anthony Lewis .05
138 Bill Wertz .05
139 Tom Kinney .05
140 Brad Hassinger .05
141 Elliot Gray .05
142 Clemente Alvarez .05
143 Mike Hankins .05
144 Jim Haller .05
145 Manuel Martinez .05
146 Nilson Robledo .05
147 Rex DeLa Nuez .05
148 Steve Bethea .05
149 Oscar Munoz .05
150 Sam Militello .15
151 Phil Hiatt .15
152 Alberto de Los Santos .05
153 Darrell Sherman .05
154 Henry Mercedes .10
155 David Holdridge .05
156 Sean Ross .05
157 Brandon Wilson .10
158 William Pennyfeather .10
159 Derek Parks .05
160 Troy O'Leary .25
161 Genaro Campusano .05
162 Robbie Beckett .10
163 Chris Burton .05
164 Jeff Williams .10
165 John Massarelli .05
166 John Kelly .05
167 Jim Wiley .05
168 Mark Mitchelson .05
169 Jeff McNeely .15
170 Keith Kimberlin .05
171 Mike DeKneef .05
172 Rusty Greer .15
173 Pete Castellano .05
174 Paul Torres .05
175 Rod McCall .05
176 Jim Bullinger .05
177 Brian Champion .05
178 Greg Hunter .05
179 Luis Galindez .05
180 Rodney Eldridge .05
181 Rudy Pemberton .05
182 Russ Davis .40
183 Cristobal Colon .05
184 Scott Bream .05
185 Tim Nedin .05
186 Joe Ausanlo .05
187 Shanhon Withem .05
188 Mike Oquist .05
189 Pete Young .05
190 Paul Carey .05
191 Chris Gies .05
192 Gar Finnvold .05
193 Greg Martin .05
194 Oreste Marrero .05
195 Jim Thome .75
196 Bill Ostermeyer .05
197 David Hulse .10
198 Damon Buford .10
199 Jonathan Hurst .05
200 Rich Tunison .05
201 Tom Nevers .05
202 Tracy Sanders .10
203 Troy Buckley .05
204 Todd Gugglana .05
205 Tim Laker .05
206 Dean Locklear .05
207 Lee Tinsley .20
208 Jose Velez .05
209 Greg Zaun .10
210 Bill Ashley .40
211 Gary Caraballo .05
212 Kiki Jones .05
213 Dave Wrona .05
214 Michael Carter .15
215 Leon Glenn Jr. .05
216 Glenn Sutko .05
217 Pat Howell .05
218 Austin Manahan .05
219 Jon Jenkins .05
220 Brook Fordyce .15
221 Kevin Rodgers .10
222 David Allen .05
223 Kurt Archer .05
224 Keith Mitchell .10
225 Bruce Schreiber .05
226 Greg Blosser .20
227 Dave Nilsson .35
228 Fred Colley .05
229 Marc Lipson .05
230 Jay Gainer .05
231 Sean Cheetham .05
232 Tim Howard .05
233 Steve Hosey .15
234 Javier Ocasio .05
235 Ricky Rhodes .05
236 Mark Griffin .05
237 Scott Shockey .05
238 T.R. Lewis .10
239 Kevin Young .20
240 Robb Nen .20
241 Steve Dunn .25
242 Tommy Taylor .05
243 Keith Valrie .05
244 Mateo Ozuna .05
245 Scott Bullett .20
246 Anthony Brown .05
247 Phil Leftwich .15
248 Cliff Garrett .05
249 Wade Fyock .05
250 Shayne Rea .05
251 Royce Clayton .40
252 Martin Martinez .05
253 Dave Patterson .05
254 Robert Fitzpatrick .05
255 John Jackson .05
256 Enoch Simmons .05
257 Dave Proctor .05
258 Garret Anderson .05
259 Mark Delesandro .05
260 Ken Edenfield .05
261 Tom Raffo .05
262 Tim Cecil .05
263 Bobby Magallanes .05
264 Vince Castaldo .05
265 Terry Burrows .05
266 Victor Madrigal .05
267 Tyler Houston .15
268 Chipper Jones 1.00
269 Terry Bradshaw .15
270 Jalal Leach .05
271 Jose Ventura .05
272 Derek Lee .05
273 Derek Reld .05
274 David Wilson .05
275 Patrick .05
276 John Roper .15
277 Rogello Nunez .05
278 Fred White .05
279 J.T. Snow .50
280 Pedro Astacio .25
281 Corey Thomas .05
282 Chris Johnson .05
283 Ignacio Duran .05
284 Dave Fleming .40
285 Wilson Alvarez 1.25
286 Eric Booker .05
287 John Ericks .05
288 Don Peters .05
289 Ed Ferm .05
290 Mike Lieberthal .10
291 John Jaha .15
292 Bryan Baar .05
293 Archie Corbin .05
294 Kevin Tatar .05
295 Shea Wardwell .05
296 Hipilito Pichardo .20
297 Curtis Leskanic .15
298 Sam August .05
299 Tim Pugh .20
300 Mike Huyler .05
301 Mark Parnell .05
302 Jeff Juden .15
303 Carl Sullivan .05
304 Tyrone Kingwood .05
305 Glenn Carter .05
306 Tom Fischer .05
307 Braulio Castillo .05
308 Bob McCreary .05
309 Ty Kovach .05
310 Troy Salvior .05
311 Mike Weimerskirch .05
312 Chistopher Hatcher .10
313 Bryan Smith .05
314 John Patterson .05
315 Scooter Tucker .05
316 Ray Callari .05
317 Mike Moberg .05
318 Midre Cummings .25
319 Todd Ritchie .20
320 Eric Christopherson .05
321 Adam Hyzdu .20
322 Andres Duncan .05
323 Mike Myers .05
324 Salomon Torres .50
325 Tony Gilmore .05
326 Walter Trice .05
327 Tom Redington .05
328 Terry Taylor .05
329 Tim Salmon 3.00
330 Dan Masteller (Last name misspelled on checklist.) .05
331 Mark Wohlers .10
332 Willie Smith .05
333 Todd Jones .05
334 Alan Zinter .05
335 Arthur Rhodes .30
336 Toby Borland .05
337 Shawn Whalen .05
338 Scott Sanders .05
339 Bill Meury .05
340 Amadoz Arias .05
341 Denny Hoppe .05
342 Dave Teigheder .05
343 Paul Bruno .05
344 Paul Russo .05
345 Rich Becker (Photo actually Tim Persing) .10
346 Steve Vondran .05
347 Rich Langford .05
348 Ron Lockett .05
349 Sam Taylor .05
350 Willie Greene .25
351 Tom Houk .05
352 Lance Painter .10
353 Dan Wilson .10
354 John Kuehl (Last name misspelled everywhere.) .05
355 Pedro Martinez .40
356 John Byington .05
357 Scott Freeman .05
358 Bo Dodson .15
359 Julian Vasquez .05
360 Rondell White 2.00
361 Aaron Small .10
362 Doug Fitzer .05
363 Billy White .05
364 Jeff Tuss .05
365 Jeff Barry .05
366 Craig Pueschner .05
367 Julio Bruno .10
368 Jamie Dismuke .05
369 K.C. Gillium .05
370 Jason Klonoski .05
371 Tim Persing (Photo actually Rich Becker) .05
372 Mark Borcherding .05
373 Larry Luebbers .10
374 Carlos Fermin .05
375 Charlie Rogers .05
376 Ramon Caraballo .05
377 Orlando Miller (Photo actually Shane Reynolds) .10
378 Joey James .05
379 Dan Rogers .05
380 Jon Shave .05
381 Frank Bolick .10
382 Frank Seminara .10
383 Mel Wearing Jr. .05
384 Zak Shinall .05
385 Sterling Hitchcock .20
386 Todd Van Poppel .40
387 D.J. Dozier .05
388 Ryan Klesko 1.75
389 Tim Costo .20
390 Brad Pennington .05
391 Checklist 1 - 66 .05
392 Checklist 67 - 132 .05
393 Checklist 133 - 198 .05
394 Checklist 199 - 264 .05
395 Checklist 365 - 330 .05
396 Checklist 331 - 396 .05
397 Frank Rodriguez .40
398 Frank Jacons .05
399 Mike Kelly .60
400 David McCarty .50
401 Scott Stahoviak .20
402 Doug Gianville .20
403 Curt Krippner .05
404 Joe Vitiello .25
405 Justin Thompson .40
406 Trevor Miller .10
407 Tarrick Brock .10
408 Eddie Williams .10
409 Scott Ruffcorn 1.00
410 Chris Durkin .05
411 Jim Kewis .15
412 Calvin Reese .20
413 Toby Rumfield .05
414 Brent Gates 1.00
415 Mike Neill .05
416 Tyler Green .20
417 Ron Allen .05
418 Larry Thomas Jr. .10
419 Chris Weinke .05
420 Matt Brewer .05
421 Dax Jones .05
422 Jon Farrell .25
423 Dan Jones .05
424 Eduardo Perez .75
425 Rodney Pedraza .20
426 Tom McKinnon .10
427 Al Watson 1.00
428 Herbert Perry .10
429 Shawn Estes .20
430 Tommy Adams .25
431 Mike Grace .05
432 Tyson Godfrey .05
433 Andy Hartung .20
434 Shawn Livsey .20
435 Earl Cunningham .05
436 Scott Lydy .25
437 Aaron Sele 2.50
438 Tim Costo .20
439 Tanyon Sturtze .10
440 Ed Ramos .10
441 Buck McNabb .10
442 Scott Hatteberg .20
443 Brian Barber .30
444 Julian Heredia .05
445 Chris Pritchett .10
446 Bubba Smith .25
447 Shawn Purdy .05
448 Jeff Borski .05
449 Jamie Gonzalez .05
450 Checklist 397 - 450 .05

1991 Classic Best Gold Bonus

	MT	NR MT	EX
Complete Set (20):	18.00	13.50	7.25
Common Player:	.25	.20	.10

1 Mike Schmidt .75
2 Marc Newfield 1.50
3 Matt Mieske 1.00
4 Reggie Sanders 1.50
5 Jeromy Burnitz .75
6 Todd Van Poppel 1.00
7 Ivan Rodriguez 1.50
8 Sam Militello .40
9 Jim Thome 2.00
10 Brook Fordyce .50
11 Dave Nilsson 1.00
12 Royce Clayton 1.00
13 Mark Wohlers .25
14 Arthur Rhodes .50
15 Ryan Klesko 3.00
16 Mike Kelly 1.00
17 Frankie Rodriguez 1.00
18 David McCarty 1.00
19 Tyler Green .75
20 Eduardo Perez 1.00

1991 Impel/Line Drive Pre-Rookie AAA

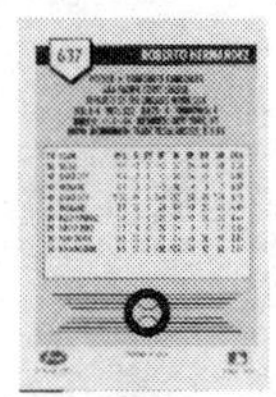

Impel made its maiden voyage into the minor league market in 1991 with this set of AAA cards issued in poly packs. Unlike its predecessor (see CMC 1990 Pre-Rookie) of 1990, this set featured complete team sets of 25 cards each within the overall issued with no other company's product mixed in. The cards were numbered consecutively 1-650 and all cards of a particular team were kept together. The cards were issued only in poly packs and not as a complete set. A checklist was available from the company. Impel is the third company to handle this line. It all started with TCMA in 1972; CMC took over in 1988 and Impel bought out CMC in 1990. Commons are 15 cents each. Due to a scarcity of certain cards in inventory and additional labor costs to dealers, the consumer can be expected to pay a minimum of $6.-$8. for team sets from this product. 1991 Line Drive team sets sold at the stadiums included team checklist cards. Individual card prices are for Mint condition.

	MT	NR MT	EX
Complete Set (650):	20.00	15.00	8.00
Common Player:	.05	.04	.02

1 Billy Bean .05
2 Jerry Brooks .05
3 Mike Christopher .05
4 Dennis Cook .05
5 Butch Davis .05
6 Tom Goodwin .05
7 Dave Hansen .05
8 Jeff Hartsock .05
9 Bert Heffernan .05
10 Carlos Hernandez .05
11 Chris Jones .05
12 Eric Karros .75
13 Dave Lynch .05
14 Luis Martinez .05
15 Jamie McAndrew .05
16 Jim Neidlinger .05
17 Jose Offerman .20
18 Eddie Pye .05
19 Henry Rodriguez .25
20 Greg Smith .05
21 Dave Veres .05
22 Dave Walsh .05
23 John Wetteland .20
24 Kevin Kennedy .05
25 Von Joshua, Claude Osteen .05
26 Jeff Banister .05
27 Cecil Espy .05
28 Steve Fireovid .05
29 Carlos Garcia .15
30 Mark Huismann .05
31 Scott Little .05
32 Tom Magrann .05
33 Roger Mason .05
34 Tim Meeks .05
35 Orlando Merced .20
36 Joey Meyer .05
37 Keith Miller .05
38 Blas Minor .05
39 Armando Moreno .05
40 Jeff Neely .05
41 Joe Redfield .05
42 Rick Reed .05
43 Jeff Richardson .05
44 Rosario Rodriguez .05
45 Jeff Schulz .05
46 Jim Tracy .05
47 Greg Tubbs .05
48 Mike York .05
49 Terry Collins .05
50 Jackie Brown .05
51 Rich Amaral .15
52 Rick Balabon .05
53 Dave Brundage .05
54 Dave Burba .05
55 Dave Cochrane .05
56 Alan Cockrell .05
57 Mike Cook .05
58 Keith Helton .05
59 Dennis Hood .05
60 Chris Howard .05
61 Chuck Jackson .05
62 Calvin Jones .05
63 Pat Lennon .05
64 Shane Letterio .05
65 Vance Lovelace .05
66 Tino Martinez .10
67 John Mitchell .05
68 Dennis Powell .05
69 Alonzo Powell .05
70 Pat Rice .05
71 Ricky Rojas .05
72 Steve Springer .05
73 Ed VandeBerg .05
74 Keith Bodie .05
75 Ross Grimsley .05
76 Eddie Taubensee .10
77 Jeff Bittiger .05
78 Willie Blair .05
79 Marty Brown .05
80 Kevin Burdick .05
81 Steve Cummings .05
82 Mauro Gozzo .05
83 Ricky Horton .05
84 Stan Jefferson .05
85 Brian Johnson .05
86 Barry Jones .05
87 Wayne Kirby .10
88 Mark Lewis .10
89 Rudy Seanez .05
90 Luis Lopez .05
91 Ecer Magallanes .05
92 Luis Medina .05
93 Dave Otto .05
94 Roberto Zambrano .05
95 Jeff Shaw .05
96 Efrain Valdez .05
97 Sergio Valdez .05
98 Kevin Wickander .05
99 Charlie Manuel .05
100 Rick Adair, Jim Gabella .05
101 Steve Adkins .05
102 Daven Bond .05
103 Darrin Chapin .05
104 Royal Clayton .05
105 Steve Howe .05
106 Keith Hughes .05
107 Mike Humphreys .05
108 Jeff Johnson .05
109 Scott Kamieniecki .05
110 Pat Kelly .25
111 Jason Maas .05
112 Alan Mills .05
113 Rich Monteleone .05
114 Hipolito Pena .05
115 John Ramos .05
116 Carlos Rodriguez .05
117 Dave Sax .05
118 Van Snider .05
119 Don Sparks .05
120 Andy Stankiewicz .05
121 Wade Taylor .05
122 Jim Walewander .05
123 Bernie Williams .20
124 Rick Down .05
125 Denby, Boyer, Meyer .05
126 D.L. Smith .05
127 James Austin .05
128 Esteban Beltre .05
129 Mickey Brantley .05
130 George Canale .05
131 Matias Carrillo .05
132 Juan Castillo .05
133 Jim Davins .05
134 Carlos Diaz .05
135 Cal Eldred .40
136 Narciso Elvira .05
137 Brian Fisher .05
138 Chris George .05
139 Sandy Guerrero .05
140 Doug Henry .05
141 Darren Holmes .10
142 Mike Ignasiak .05
143 Jeff Kaiser .05
144 Joe Kmak .05
145 Tim McIntosh .05
146 Charlie Montoyo .05
147 Jim Olander .05
148 Ed Puig .05
149 Tony Muser .05
150 Lamar Johnson, Don Rowe .05
151 Kyle Abbott .05
152 Ruben Amaro .05
153 Kent Anderson .05
154 Mike Erb .05
155 Randy Bockus .05
156 Gary Buckels .05
157 Tim Burcham .05
158 Chris Cron .05
159 Chad Curtis .40
160 Doug Davis .05
161 Mark Davis .05
162 Gary DiSarcina .10
163 Mike Fetters .05
164 Joe Grahe .05
165 Dan Grunhard .05
166 Dave Leiper .05
167 Rafael Montalvo .05
168 Reed Peters .05
169 Bobby Rose .05
170 Lee Stevens .05
171 Ron Tingley .05
172 Ed Vosberg .05
173 Mark Wasinger .05
174 Max Oliveras .05
175 Lenn Sakata, Gary Ruby .05
176 Bret Barbarie .05
177 Kevin Bearse .05
178 Kent Bottenfield .10
179 Wil Cordero .60
180 Mike Davis .05
181 Alex Diaz .05
182 Eddie Dixon .05
183 Jeff Fassero .25
184 Jerry Goff .05
185 Todd Haney .05
186 Steve Hecht .05
187 Jimmy Kremers .05
188 Quinn Mack .05
189 David Masters .05
190 Marlin McPhall .05
191 Doug Piatt .05
192 Dana Ridenour .05
193 Scott Service .05
194 Razor Shines .05
195 Tito Stewart .05
196 Mel Houston .05
197 John Vanderwal .10
198 Darrin Winston .05
199 Jerry Manuel .05
200 Gomer Hodge, Nardi Contreras .05
201 Brad Bierley .05
202 Steve Carter .05
203 Frank Castillo .10
204 Lance Dickson .10
205 Craig Smajstrla .05
206 Brian Guinn .05
207 Joe Kraemer .05
208 Cedric Landrum .05
209 Derrick May .20
210 Scott May .05
211 Ryss McGinnis .05
212 Chuck Mount .05
213 Dave Pavlas .05
214 Laddie Renfroe .05
215 David Rosario .05
216 Rey Sanchez .05
217 Dan Simonds .05
218 Jeff Small .05
219 Doug Strange .05
220 Glenn Sullivan .05
221 Rick Wilkins .50
222 Steve Wilson .05
223 Bob Scanlan .05
224 Jim Essian .05
225 Grant Jackson .05
226 Luis Alicea .05
227 Rod Brewer .05
228 Nick Castaneda .05
229 Stan Clarke .05
230 Marty Clary .05
231 Fidel Compres .05
232 Todd Crosby .05
233 Bob Davidson .05
234 Bien Figueroa .05
235 Ed Fulton .05
236 Mark Grater .05
237 Omar Olivares .05
238 Brian Jordan .40
239 Lonnie Maclin .05
240 Julian Martinez .05
241 Al Nipper .05
242 Dave Osteen .05
243 Leny Picota .05
244 Dave Richardson .05
245 Mike Ross .05
246 Stan Royer .05
247 Tim Sherrill .05
248 Carl Ray Stephens .05
249 Mark DeJohn .05
250 Mark Riggins .05
251 Billy Bates .05
252 Freddie Benavides .05
253 Keith Brown .05
254 Adam Casillas .05
255 Tony DeFrancesco .05
256 Leo Garcia .05
257 Angel Gonzalez .05
258 Denny Gonzalez .05
259 Kip Gross .05
260 Charlie Mitchell .05
261 Milton Hill .05
262 Rodney Imes .05
263 Reggie Jefferson .15
264 Keith Lockhart .05
265 Manny Jose .05
266 Terry Lee .05
267 Rob Lopez .05
268 Gino Minutelli .05
269 Kevin Pearson .05
270 Ross Powell .05
271 Donnie Scott .05
272 Luis Vasquez .05
273 Joey Vierra .05
274 Pete Mackanin .05
275 Don Gullett, Jim Lett .05
276 Oscar Azocar .05
277 Dann Bilardello .05
278 Ricky Bones .10
279 Brian Dorsett .05
280 Scott Coolbaugh .05
281 John Costello .05
282 Terry Gilmore .05
283 Heremy Hernandez .05
284 Kevin Higgins .05
285 Chris Jelic .05
286 Dean Kelley .05
287 Derek Lilliquist .05
288 Jose Meledez .05
289 Jose Mota .05
290 Adam Peterson .05
291 Ed Romero .05
292 Steven Rosenberg .05
293 Tim Scott .05
294 Dave Staton .25
295 Will Taylor .05
296 Jim Vatcher .05
297 Dan Walters .05
298 Kevin Ward .05
299 Jim Riggleman .05
300 Jon Matlack, Tony Torchia .05
301 Gerald Alexander .05
302 Kevin Belcher .05
303 Jeff Andrews .05
304 Tony Scruggs .05
305 Jeff Bronkey .05
306 Paco Burgos .05
307 Nick Capra .05
308 Monty Fariss .05
309 Darrin Garner .05
310 Bill Haselman .05
311 Terry Mathews .05
312 Rob Maurer .05
313 Gar Millay .05
314 Dean Palmer 1.25
315 Roger Pavlik .10
316 Dan Peltier .25
317 Steve Peters .05
318 Mark Petkovsek .05
319 Jim Poole .05
320 Paul Postier .05
321 Wayne Rosenthal .05
322 Dan Smith .20
323 Terry Wells .05
324 Tommy Thompson .05
325 Stan Hough .05
326 Sean Berry .10
327 Jacob Brumfield .10
328 Bob Buchanan .05
329 Kevin Burrell .05
330 Stu Cole .05
331 Victor Cole .15
332 Jeff Conine 1.00
333 Tommy Dunbar .05
334 Luis Encarnacion .05
335 Greg Everson .05
336 Bob Hamelin .35
337 Joel Johnston .05
338 Frank Laureano .05
339 Jim LeMasters .05
340 Mike Magnante .05
341 Carlos Maldonado .05
342 Andy McGaffigan .05
343 Bobby Moore .05
344 Harvey Pulliam .05
345 Daryl Smith .05
346 Tim Spehr .05
347 Hector Wagner .05
348 Paul Zuvella .05
349 Sal Rende .05
350 Brian Poldberg, Guy Hansen .05
351 Luis Aguayo .05
352 Tom Barrett .05
353 Mike Brumley .05
354 Scott Cooper .50
355 Mike Gardiner .05
356 Eric Hetzel .05
357 Mike Twardoski .05
358 Rick Lancellotti .05
359 Derek Livernois .05
360 Mark Meleski .05
361 Kevin Morton .05
362 Dan O'Neill .05
363 Jim Pankovits .05
364 Mickey Pina .05
365 Phil Plantier 1.00
366 Jeff Plympton .05
367 Todd Pratt .05
368 Larry Shikles .05
369 Jeff Stone .05
370 Mo Vaughn 1.50
371 David Walters .05
372 Eric Wedge .05
373 Bob Zupcic .10
374 Butch Hobson .05
375 Rich Gale .05
376 Rich Aldrete .05
377 Mark Bailey .05
378 Rod Beck .25
379 Jeff Carter .05
380 Craig Colbert .05
381 Darnell Coles .05
382 Mark Dewey .05
383 Gil Heredia .05
384 Darren Lewis .35

385 Johnny Ard .05
386 Rafael Novoa .05
387 Francisco Oliveras .05
388 Tony Perezchica .05
389 Mark Thurmond .05
390 Mike Remlinger .05
391 Greg Ritchie .05
392 Rick Rodriguez .05
393 Andres Santana .05
394 Jose Segura .05
395 Stuart Tate .05
396 Jimmy Williams .05
397 Jim Wilson .05
398 Ted Wood .05
399 Duane Espy .05
400 Alan Bannister, Larry Hardy .05
401 Paul Abbott .05
402 Willie Banks .15
403 Bernardo Brito .05
404 Jarvis Brown .05
405 J.T. Bruett .05
406 Tim Drummond .05
407 Tom Edens .05
408 Rich Garces .10
409 Chip Hale .05
410 Terry Jorgensen .05
411 Kenny Morgan .05
412 Pedro Munoz .20
413 Edgar Naveda .05
414 Denny Naegle .05
415 Jeff Reboulet .05
416 Victor Rodriguez .05
417 Jack Savage .05
418 Dan Sheaffer .05
419 Charles Scott .05
420 Paul Sorrento .25
421 George Tsamis .05
422 Lenny Webster .05
423 Carl Willis .05
424 Russ Nixon .05
425 Jim Dwyer, Gordon Heimueller, Paul Kirsch .05
426 John Alva .05
427 Mike Bell .05
428 Tony Castillo .05
429 Bruce Crabbe .05
430 John Davis .05
431 Brian Hunter .25
432 Randy Kramer .05
433 Mike Loggins .05
434 Kelly Mann .05
435 Tom McCarthy .05
436 Yorkis Perez .05
437 Dale Polley .05
438 Armando Reynoso .15
439 Rusty Richards .05
440 Victor Rosario .05
441 Mark Ross .05
442 Rico Rossy .05
443 Randy St. Claire .05
444 Joe Szekely .05
445 Andy Tomberlin .05
446 Matt Turner .05
447 Glenn Wilson .05
448 Tracy Woodson .05
449 Phil Niekro .10
450 Bruce Del Canton, Sonny Jackson .05
451 Tony Chance .05
452 Joaquin Contreras .05
453 Francisco DeLaRosa .05
454 Benny Distefano .05
455 Mike Eberle .05
456 Todd Frohwirth .05
457 Steve Jeltz .05
458 Chito Martinez .05
459 Dave Martinez .05
460 Jeff McKnight .05
461 Luis Mercedes .05
462 Mike Mussina 2.50
463 Chris Myers .05
464 Joe Price .05
465 Israel Sanchez .05
466 David Segui .10
467 Tommy Shields .05
468 Mike Linskey .05
469 Jeff Tackett .05
470 Anthony Telford .05
471 Shane Turner .05
472 Jeff Wetherby .05
473 Rob Woodward .05
474 Greg Biagini .05
475 Mike Young, Dick Bosman .05
476 Sal Agostinelli .05
477 Gary Alexander .05
478 Andy Ashby .05
479 Bob Ayrault .05
480 Kim Batiste .05
481 Amalio Carreno .05
482 Rocky Elli .05
483 Darrin Fletcher .05
484 Jeff Grotewold .05
485 Chris Knabenshue .05
486 Greg Legg .05
487 Jim Lindeman .05
488 Chuck Malone .05
489 Tim Mauser .05
490 Louie Meadows .05
491 Mickey Morandini .15
492 Julio Peguero .05
493 Wally Ritchie .05
494 Bruce Ruffin .05
495 Rick Schu .05
496 Ray Searage .05
497 Scott Wade .05
498 Gary Wilson .05
499 Bill Dancy .05
500 Floyd Rayford, Jim Wright .05
501 Derek Bell .50
502 Rob Ducey .05
503 Julius McDougal .05
504 Juan Guzman 1.00
505 Pat Hentgen 1.50
506 Shawn Jeter .05
507 Doug Linton .05
508 Bob MacDonald .05
509 Mike Maksudian .05
510 Ravelo Manzanillo .05
511 Domingo Martinez .10
512 Stu Pederson .05
513 Marty Pevey .05
514 Tom Quinlan .05
515 Alex Sanchez .05
516 Jerry Schunk .05
517 John Shea .05
518 Ed Sprague .15
519 William Suero .05
520 Steve Wapnick .05
521 Mickey Weston .05
522 John Poloni .05
523 Eddie Zosky .05
524 Bob Bailor .05
525 Rocket Wheeler .05
526 Troy Afenir .05
527 Mike Bordick .15
528 Jorge Brito .05
529 Scott Brosius .15
530 Kevin Campbell .05
531 Pete Coachman .05
532 Dan Eskew .05
533 Eric Fox .05
534 Apolinar Garcia .05
535 Webster Garrison .05
536 Johnny Guzman .05
537 Jeff Pico .05
538 Dann Howitt .05
539 Doug Jennings .05
540 Brad Komminsk .05
541 Tim McCoy .05
542 Jeff Musselman .05
543 Troy Neel .35
544 Will Schock .05
545 Nelson Simmons .05
546 Bruce Walton .05
547 Pat Wernig .05
548 Ron Witmeyer .05
549 Jeff Newman .05
550 Glenn Abbott .05
551 Kevin Baez .05
552 Blaine Beatty .05
553 Doug Cinnella .05
554 Chris Donnels .05
555 Jeff Gardner .05
556 Terrel Hansen .05
557 Manny Hernandez .05
558 Eric Hillman .05
559 Todd Hundley .20
560 Alex Jimenez .05
561 Tim Leiper .05
562 Lee May .10
563 Orlando Mercado .05
564 Brad Moore .05
565 Al Pedrique .05
566 Dale Plummer .05
567 Rich Saveur .05
568 Ray Soff .05
569 Kelvin Torve .05
570 Dave Trautwein .05
571 Julio Valera .10
572 Robbie Wine .05
573 Anthony Young .10
574 Steve Swisher .05
575 Ron Washington, Bob Apodaca .05
576 Scott Aldred .10
577 Karl Allaire .05
578 Skeeter Barnes .05
579 Arnie Beyeler .05
580 Rico Brogna .10
581 Phil Clark .10
582 Mike Dalton .05
583 Curt Ford .05
584 Dan Gakeler .05
585 David Haas .05
586 Shawn Hare .05
587 John Kiely .05
588 Mark Leiter .05
589 Scott Livingstone .05
590 Mitch Lyden .05
591 Eric Mangham .05
592 Rusty Meacham .05
593 Mike Munoz .05
594 Randy Nosek .05
595 Johnny Paredes .05
596 Kevin Ritz .05
597 Rich Rowland .10
598 Don Vesling .05
599 Joe Sparks .05
600 Mark Wagner, Ralph Treuel .05
601 Harold Allen .05
602 Eric Anthony .25
603 Doug Baker .05
604 Ryan Bowen .20
605 Mike Capel .05
606 Andujar Cedeno .30
607 Terry Clark .05
608 Carlo Colombino .05
609 Gary Cooper .05
610 Calvin Schiraldi .05
611 Randy Hennis .05
612 Butch Henry .05
613 Blaise Isley .05
614 Kenny Lofton 2.00
615 Terry McGriff .05
616 Andy Mota .05
617 Javier Ortiz .05
618 Scott Servais .10
619 Mike Simms .05
620 Jose Tolentino .05
621 Lee Tunnell .05
622 Brent Strom .05
623 Gerald Young .05
624 Bob Skinner .05
625 Dave Engle .05
626 Cesar Bernhardt .05
627 Mario Brito .05
628 Kurt Brown .05
629 John Cangelosi .05
630 Jeff Carter .05
631 Tom Drees .05
632 Grady Hall .05
633 Joe Hall .05
634 Curt Hasler .05
635 Danny Heep .05
636 Dan Henley .05
637 Roberto Hernandez .50
638 Orsino Hill .05
639 Jerry Kutzier .05
640 Noberto Martin .05
641 Rod McCray .05
642 Bob Nelson .05
643 Warren Newsome .05
644 Greg Perschke .05
645 Rich Scheid .05
646 Matt Stark .05
647 Ron Stephens .05
648 Don Wakamatsu .05
649 Marv Foley .05
650 Roger LaFrancois, Moe Drabowsky .05

1991 Impel/Line Drive Pre-Rookie AA

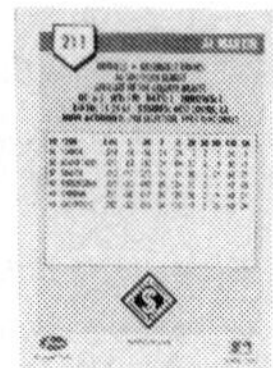

Impel followed its successful AAA wax series with a 650 card AA wax series consisting of team mini sets of 25 cards each. Like the AAA series, a checklist for the AA series was available from the company. Commons are 15 cents each. Due to a scarcity of certain cards in inventory and additional labor costs to dealers, the consumer can be expected to pay a minimum of $6.-$8. for team sets from this product. 1991 Line Drive team sets sold at the stadiums included team checklist cards. Individual card prices are for Mint condition.

	MT	NR MT	EX
Complete Set (650):	18.00	13.50	7.25
Common Player:	.05	.04	.02

1 Andy Cook .05
2 Russell Davis .50
3 Bobby DeJardin .05
4 Mike Draper .05
5 Victor Garcia .05
6 Mike Gardella .05
7 Cullen Hartzog .05
8 Jay Knoblauh .05
9 Billy Masse .05
10 Jeff Livesey .05
11 Edward Martel .05
12 Vince Phillips .05
13 Tom Popplewell .05
14 Jerry Rub .05
15 Dave Silvestri .10
16 Tom Newell .05
17 Willie Smith .05
18 J.T. Snow .40
19 Don Stanford .05
20 Larry Stanford .05
21 John Toale .15
22 Hector Vargas .05
23 Gerald Williams .15
24 Dan Radison .05
25 Dave Jore, Bob Mariano .05
26 Frank Abreu .05
27 Cliff Brannon .05
28 Greg Carmona .05
29 Ric Christian .05
30 John Ericks .10
31 Steve Fanning .05
32 Joey Fernandez .05
33 Jose Fernandez .05
34 Mike Flore .05
35 David Grimes .05
36 Dale Kisten .05
37 John Lepley .05
38 Luis Martinez .05
39 Mike Milchin .05
40 Donovan Osborne .25
41 Gabriel Ozuna .05
42 Lee Plemel .05
43 Don Prybylinski .05
44 John Sellick .05
45 Jeff Shireman .05
46 Brian Stone .05
47 Charlie White .05
48 Dennis Wiseman .05
49 Joe Pettini .05
50 Scott Melvin, Marty Mason .05
51 Wilson Alvarez 1.25
52 Wayne Busby .05
53 Darrin Campbell .05
54 Mark Chasey .05
55 Ron Coomer .05
56 Argenis Cortez .05
57 Mike Davino .05
58 Lindsay Foster .05
59 Ramon Garcia .05
60 Kevin Garner .05
61 Jeff Gay .05
62 Chris Howard .05
63 John Hudek .05
64 Scott Jaster .05
65 Bo Kennedy .05
66 Derek Lee .05
67 Frank Merigliano .05
68 Scott Middaugh .05
69 Javier Ocasio .05
70 Kinnis Pledger .05
71 Greg Roth .05
72 Aubrey Waggoner .05
73 Jose Ventura .05
74 Tony Franklin .05
75 Rick Peterson, Pat Roessler, Sam Halrston .05
76 Ramon Bautista .05
77 Eric Bell .05
78 Jim Bruske .05
79 Tim Costo .20
80 Mike Curtis .05
81 Jerry DiPoto .10
82 Dren Epley .05
83 Sam Ferrelli .05
84 Garland Kiser .05
85 Ty Kovach .05
86 Tom Kramer .05
87 Molan Lane .05
88 Jesse Levis .05
89 Carlos Martinez .05
90 Jeff Mutis .10
91 Rouglas Odor .05
92 Gary Resetar .05
93 Greg Roscoe .05
94 Miguel Sabino .05
95 Bernie Tatis .05
96 Jim Thome .75
97 Ken Ramos .05
98 Ken Whitfield .05
99 Ken Bolek .05
100 Dave Keller .05
101 Steve Adams .05
102 Stan Fansler .05
103 Mandy Romero .05
104 Terry Crowley Jr. .05
105 Chip Duncan .05
106 Greg Edge .05
107 Chris Estep .05
108 Carl Hamilton .05
109 Lee Hancock .05
110 Tim Hines .05
111 Mike Huyler .05
112 Paul Miller .05
113 Pete Murphy .05
114 Darwin Pennye .05
115 Mike Roesler .05
116 Bruce Schreiber .05
117 Greg Sparks .05
118 Dennis Tafoya .05
119 Tim Wakefield .20
120 Ben Webb .05
121 John Wehner .05
122 Ed Yacopino .05
123 Eddie Zambrano .20
124 Marc Bombard .05
125 Trent Jewett, Spin Williams .05
126 Alex Arias .10
127 Paul Blair .05
128 Jim Bullinger .05
129 Dick Canan .05
130 Rusty Crockett .05
131 Steve DiBartolomeo .05
132 John Gardner .05
133 Henry Gomez .05
134 Ty Griffin .05
135 Shannon Jones .05
136 Mike Knapp .05
137 Tim Parker .05
138 Elvin Paulino .05
139 Fernando Ramsey .05
140 Kevin Roberson .40
141 John Salles .05
142 Mike Sodders .05
143 Bill St. Peter .05
144 Julio Strauss .05
145 Scott Taylor .05
146 Tim Watkins .05
147 Doug Welch .05
148 Billy White .05
149 Jay Loviglio .05
150 Rick Kranitz .05
151 Rick Allen .05
152 Mike Anderson .05
153 Bobby Ayala .10
154 Pete Beeler .05
155 Jeff Branson .05
156 Scott Bryant .10
157 Bill Dodd .05
158 Steve Foster .05
159 Victor Garcia .05

160 Frank Kremblas .05
161 Greg Lonigro .05
162 Dave McAuliffe .05
163 Steve McCarthy .05
164 Scott Pose .10
165 Tim Pugh .20
166 Bill Risley .05
167 Reggie Sanders .50
168 Mo Sanford .15
169 Scott Sellner .05
170 Jerry Spradlin .10
171 Glenn Sutko .05
172 Todd Trafton .05
173 Bernie Walker .05
174 Jim Tracy .05
175 Mike Griffin .05
176 Shon Ashley .05
177 John Byington .05
178 Mark Chapman .05
179 Jim Czajkowski .05
180 Ruben Escalera .05
181 Craig Faulkner .05
182 Tim Fortugno .05
183 Don Gordon .05
184 Mitch Hannahs .05
185 Steve Lienhard .05
186 Dave Jacas .05
187 Kenny Jackson .05
188 John Jaha .20
189 Chris Johnson .05
190 Mark Kiefer .15
191 Pat Listach .30
192 Tom McGraw .05
193 Angel Miranda .20
194 Dave Nilsson .40
195 Jeff Schwarz .05
196 Steve Sparks .05
197 Jim Tatum .15
198 Brandy Vann .05
199 Dave Huppert .05
200 Paul Lindblad .05
201 Rich Casarotti .05
202 Vinnie Castilla .05
203 Brian Champion .05
204 Popeye Cole .05
205 Johnny Cuevas .05
206 Brian Deak .05
207 Pat Gomez .05
208 Judd Johnson .05
209 Ryan Klesko 2.00
210 Rich Maloney .05
211 Al Martin .40
212 Keith Mitchell .10
213 Rick Morris .05
214 Ben Rivera .10
215 Napoleon Robinson .05
216 Boi Rodriguez .05
217 Sean Ross .05
218 Earl Sanders .05
219 Scott Taylor .05
220 Lee Upshaw .05
221 Preston Watson .05
222 Turk Wendell .10
223 Mark Wohlers .10
224 Chris Chamblis .05
225 Terry Harper, Bill Slack, Randy Ingle .05
226 Jeff Bumgarner .05
227 Stacey Burdick .05
228 Paul Carey .05
229 Bobby Dickerson .05
230 Roy Gilbert .05
231 Ricky Gutierrez .10
232 Tim Holland .05
233 Stacy Jones .05
234 Tyrone Kingwood .05
235 Mike Lehman .05
236 Rod Lofton .05
237 Kevin Hickey .05
238 Joel McKeon .05
239 Scott Meadows .05
240 Steve Luebber .05
241 Mike Oquist .10
242 Ozzie Peraza .05
243 Tim Raley .05
244 Arthur Rhodes .20
245 Doug Robbins .05
246 Ken Shamburg .05
247 Todd Stephan .05
248 Jack Voight .05
249 Jerry Narron .05
250 Joe Durham .05
251 Chris Cassels .05
252 Archie Clanfrocco (First name misspelled on card.) .10
253 Dan Freed .05
254 Greg Fulton .05
255 Chris Haney .05
256 Cesar Hernandez .05
257 Richard Holsman .05
258 Rob Katzaroff .05
259 Bryan Kosco .05
260 Ken Lake .05
261 Hector Rivera .05
262 Chris Marchok .05
263 Chris Martin .05
264 Matt Maysey .05
265 Omar Munoz .05
266 Bob Natal .05
267 Chris Pollack .05
268 F.P. Santangelo .05
269 Joe Siddall .05
270 Stan Spencer .05
271 Matt Stairs .05
272 David Wainhouse .05
273 Pete Young .05
274 Mike Quade .05
275 Joe Kerrigan, Pete Dalena .05
276 Marco Armas .15
277 Bob Bafia .05
278 Dean Borrelli .05
279 John Briscoe .05
280 James Buccheri .05
281 Tom Carcione .05
282 Joel Chimelis .05
283 Fred Cooley .05
284 Russ Cormier .05
285 Matt Grott .05
286 Dwayne Hosey .10
287 Chad Kuhn .05
288 Dave Latter .05
289 Francisco Matos .05
290 Gavin Osteen .05
291 Tim Peek .05
292 Don Peters .05
293 Scott Shockey .05
294 Will Tejada .05
295 Lee Tinsley .15
296 Todd Van Poppel .40
297 Darryl Vice .05
298 Dave Zancanaro .10
299 Casey Parsons .05
300 Bert Bradley .05
301 Frank Carey .05
302 Larry Carter .05
303 Royce Clayton .40
304 Tom Ealy .05
305 Juan Guerrero .05
306 Bryan Hickerson .05
307 Steve Hosey .20
308 Tom Hostetler .05
309 Erik Johnson .05
310 Dan Lewis .05
311 Paul McClellan .05
312 Jim McNamara .05
313 Kevin Meier .05
314 Jim Myers .05
315 Dave Patterson .05
316 John Patterson .05
317 Jim Pena .05
318 Dan Rambo .05
319 Steve Reed .05
320 Kevin Rogers .20
321 Reuben Smiley .05
322 Scooter Tucker .10
323 Pete Weber .05
324 Bill Evers .05
325 Tony Taylor, Todd Oakes .05
326 Fernando Arguelles .05
327 Shawn Barton .10
328 Jim Blueberg .05
329 Frank Bolick .15
330 Bret Boone .75
331 Jim Bowie .05
332 Jim Campanis .05
333 Gary Eave .10
334 David Evans .05
335 Fernando Figueroa .05
336 Dave Fleming .40
337 Ruben Gonzalez .05
338 Mike McDonald .05
339 Jeff Nelson .05
340 Jim Newlin .05
341 Ken Pennington .05
342 Mike Pitz .05
343 Dave Richards .05
344 Roger Salkeld .25
345 Jack Smith .05
346 Tim Stargell .05
347 Brian Turang .10
348 Ted Williams .05
349 Jim Nettles .05
350 Bobby Cuellar, Lem Pilkinton .05
351 Pete Blohm .05
352 Domingo Cedeno .10
353 Nate Cromwell .05
354 Jesse Cross .05
355 Juan De La Rosa .05
356 Bobby LeLoach .05
357 Ray Giannelli .05
358 Darren Hall .05
359 Mark Young .05
360 Jeff Kent .75
361 Randy Knorr .10
362 Jose Monzon .05
363 Bernie Nunez .05
364 Paul Rodgers .05
365 Jimmy Rogers .05
366 Mike Taylor .05
367 Ryan Thompson .15
368 Jason Townley .05
369 Rick Trlicek .10
370 Anthony Ward .05
371 Dave Weathers .15
372 Woody Williams .10
373 Julian Yan .05
374 John Stearns .05
375 Mike McAlpin, Steve Mingori .05
376 Doyle Balthazar .05
377 Basillo Cabrera .05
378 Ron Cook .05
379 Ivan Cruz .10
380 Dean Decillis .05
381 John DeSilva .10
382 John Doherty .20
383 Lou Frazier .05
384 Luis Galindo .05
385 Greg Gohr .10
386 Bud Groom .05
387 Darren Hursey .05
388 Ricardo Ingram .05
389 Keith Kimberlin .05
390 Todd Krumm .05
391 Randy Marshall .05
392 Domingo Michel .05
393 Steve Pegues .05
394 Jose Ramos .05
395 Bob Reimink .05
396 Ruben Rodriguez .05
397 Eric Stone .05
398 Marty Willis .05
399 Gene Roof .05
400 Jeff Jones, Dan Raley .05
401 Pete Alborano .05
402 Jim Baxter .05
403 Tony Clements .05
404 Archie Corbin .05
405 Andres Cruz .05
406 Jeff Garber .05
407 David Gonzalez .05
408 Kevin Koslofski .05
409 Deric Ladnier .05
410 Mark Parnell .05
411 Jorge Pedre .05
412 Doug Peters .05
413 Hipolito Pichardo .15
414 Eddie Pierce .05
415 Mike Poehl .05
416 Darryl Robinson .05
417 Steve Shifflett .05
418 Jim Smith .05
419 Lou Talbert .05
420 Terry Taylor .05
421 Rich Tunison .05
422 Hugh Walker .10
423 Darren Watkins .05
424 Jeff Cox .05
425 Brian Peterson, Mike Alvarez .05
426 Clemente Acosta .05
427 Jeff Barns .05
428 Mike Butcher .10
429 Glenn Carter .05
430 Marvin Cobb .05
431 Sherman Corbett .05
432 Kevin Davis .05
433 Damion Easley .30
434 Kevin Flora .10
435 Larry Gonzales .10
436 Mark Howie .05
437 Todd James .05
438 Bobby Jones .20
439 Steve King .05
440 Marcus Lawton .05
441 Ken Rivers .05
442 Doug Robertson .05
443 Tim Salmon 4.00
444 Ramon Sambo .05
445 Daryl Sconiers .10
446 Dave Shotkoski .05
447 Terry Taylor .05
448 Mark Zappelli .05
449 Don Long .05
450 Kernan Ronam, Gene Richards .05
451 Michael Beams .05
452 Greg Blosser .25
453 Brian Conroy .05
454 Freddie Davis .05
455 Colin Dixon .05
456 Peter Estrada .05
457 Ray Fagnant .05
458 Tom Fischer .05
459 John Flaherty .10
460 Donald Florence .05
461 Blane Fox .05
462 Steve Hendricks .05
463 Wayne Housie .10
464 Peter Hoy .05
465 Thomas Kane .05
466 David Milstien .05
467 Juan Paris .05
468 Scott Powers .05
469 Paul Quantrill .20
470 Randy Randle .05
471 Al Sanders .05
472 Scott Taylor .05
473 John Valentin .40
474 Gary Allenson .05
475 Rick Wise .05
476 Pat Bangtson .05
477 Carlos Capellan .05
478 Rafael DeLima .05
479 Frank Valdez .05
480 Cheo Garcia .05
481 Shawn Gilbert .05
482 Greg Johnson .05
483 Jay Kvasnicka .05
484 Orlando Lind .10
485 Pat Mahomes .20
486 Jose Marzan .05
487 Dan Masteller .05
488 Bob McCreary .05
489 Steve Muh .05
490 Reed Olmstead .05
491 Ray Ortiz .05
492 Derek Parks .15
493 Joe Siwa .05
494 Steve Stowell .05
495 Mike Trombley .20
496 Jim Shellenback .05
497 Rob Wassenaar .05
498 Phil Wiese .05
499 Scott Ullger .05
500 Mark Funderbuck .05
501 Jason Backs .05
502 Toby Borland .05
503 Cliff Brantley .05
504 Dana Brown .05
505 John Burgos .05
506 Andy Carter .05
507 Bruce Dostal .05
508 Rick Dunnum .05
509 John Martin .05
510 David Holdridge .05
511 Darrell Lindsey .05
512 Doug Lindsey .05
513 Tony Longmire .10
514 Tom Marsh .05
515 Rod Robertson .05
516 Edwin Rosado .05
517 Sean Ryan .05
518 Steve Scarsone .10
519 Mark Sims .05
520 Jeff Tabaka .05
521 Tony Trevino .05
522 Casey Waller .05
523 Cary Williams .05
524 Don McCormack .05
525 Al LeBoeuf .05
526 Steve Allen .05
527 Jorge Alvarez .10
528 Bryan Baar .05
529 Tim Barker .05
530 Tony Barron .05
531 Cam Biberdorf .05
532 Jason Brosnan .05
533 Braulio Castillo .15
534 Steve Finken .05
535 Freddy Gonzalez .05
536 Mike James .05
537 Brett Magnusson .05
538 Jose Munoz .05
539 Lance Rice .05
540 Zak Shinall .05
541 Dennis Springer .05
542 Ramon Taveras .10
543 Jimmy Terrill .05
544 Brian Traxier .05
545 Jody Treadwell .05
546 Mike White .05
547 Mike Wilkins .05
548 Eric Young .25
549 John Shoemaker .05
550 James Wray .05
551 Willie Ansley .10
552 Sam August .05
553 Jeff Baldwin .05
554 Pete Bauer .05
555 Kevin Coffman .05
556 Kevin Dean .05
557 Tony Eusebio .10
558 Dean Freeland .05
559 Rusty Harris .05
560 Dean Hartgraves .05
561 Trent Hubbard .05
562 Bert Hunter .05
563 Bernie Jenkins .05
564 Jeff Juden .20
565 Keith Kalser .05
566 Steve Larose .05
567 Lance Madsen .05
568 Scott Makarewicz .05
569 Rob Mallicoat .05
570 Joe Mikulik .05
571 Orlando Miller .10
572 Shane Reynolds .15
573 Richie Simon .05
574 Rick Sweet .05
575 Don Reynolds, Charlie Taylor .05
576 Rob Brown .05
577 Mike Burton .05
578 Evertt Cunningham .05
579 Jeff Frye .10
580 Pat Garman .05
581 Bryan Gore .05
582 David Green .05
583 Donald Harris .10
584 Jose Hernandez .20
585 Greg Iavarone .05
586 Barry Manuel .10
587 Trey McCoy .10
588 Rod Morris .05
589 Robb Nen .25
590 David Perez .05
591 Bobby Reed .05
592 Ivan Rodriguez .60
593 Dan Rohrmeier .05
594 Brian Romero .05
595 Luke Sable .05
596 Frederic Samson .05
597 Cedric Shaw .10
598 Chris Shiflett .10
599 Bobby Jones .15
600 Oscar Acosta, Jeff Hubbard .05
601 Mike Basso .05
602 Doug Brocail .10
603 Rafael Chavez .10
604 Brian Cisarik .05
605 Greg David .05
606 Rick Davis .05
607 Vince Harris .05
608 Charles Hillemann .05
609 Kerry Knox .05
610 Pete Kuid .05
611 Jim Lewis .05
612 Luis Lopez .20
613 Pedro Martinez .25
614 Tim McWilliam .05
615 Tom Redington .05
616 Darrin Reichle .05
617 A.J. Sager .05
618 Frank Seminara .20
619 Darrell Sherman .10
620 Jose Valentin .15
621 Guillermo Velasquez .10
622 Tim Wallace .05
623 Brian Wood .05
624 Steve Lubratich .05

625 John Cumberland, Jack Maloof .05
626 Tim Bogar .15
627 Jeromy Burnitz (Last name misspelled on card.) .40
628 Hernan Cortez .05
629 Steve Davis .05
630 Joe Delli Carri .05
631 D.J. Dozier .10
632 Javier Gonzalez .05
633 Rudy Hernandez .05
634 Chris Hill .05
635 John Johnstone .10
636 Doug Kline .05
637 Loy McBride .05
638 Joel Horlen .05
639 Tito Navarro .10
640 Toby Nivens .05
641 Bryan Rogers .05
642 David Sommer .05
643 Greg Talamantez .05
644 Dave Telgheder .15
645 Jose Vargas .10
646 Aguedo Vasquez .05
647 Paul Williams .05
648 Alan Zinter .20
649 Clint Hurdie .05
650 Jim Eschen .05

1991 ProCards Tomorrow's Heroes

This is the newest of the issues from Procards and is comprised of an assortment of AAA, AA and A classification players representing all 26 Major League organizations. There are 4 checklists; one for every ninety cards in the set. The cards are individually numbered beginning with Baltimore of the American League and concluding with San Francisco of the National League. Each of the Major League segments then has representation of the best players within their Minor League organization. EX: BALTIMORE ORIOLES AAA - Mussina, Mercedes, Frowirth, Martinez, Sequi AA - Rhodes, Jones A - Moore, Alexander, Williams, Anderson, Lemp, Krivda "Tomorrow's Heroes" in a great title since there are dozens of prospects pictured within this set; many of whom would soon be mainstays on big league rosters. Cards were only available in foil packs. Cards are bordered in white with a prominent pink and gray checkered interior pattern. Card manufacturer, player's name, position, and team are lettered in white and bordered in red. The original plans reportedly called for production of 10,000 cases of Tomorrow's Heroes, but those plans were changed dramatically to a limited production run of 1,007 cases upon the acquisition of Pro Cards by Fleercorp; thereby resulting in this product becoming an extremely scarce and highly sought after commodity. Individual card prices are for Mint condition.

	MT	NR MT	EX
Complete Set (360):	40.00	30.00	16.00
Common Player:	.05	.04	.02

1 Mike Mussina 2.50
2 Luis Mercedes .20
3 Todd Frohwirth .10
4 Chito Martinez .10
5 David Sequi .10
6 Arthur Rhodes .20
7 Stacy Jones .05
8 Daryl Moore .05
9 Manny Alexander .05
10 Jeff Williams .05
11 Matt Anderson .05
12 Chris Lemp .05
13 Rick Krivda .20
14 Phil Plantier 1.50
15 Mo Vaughn 2.50
16 Scott Cooper .75
17 Mike Gardiner .10
18 Kevin Morton .50
19 Jeff Plympton .05
20 Jeff McNeely .25
21 Willie Tatum .05
22 Tim Smith .05
23 Frank Rodriguez .75
24 Chris Davis .05
25 Cory Bailey .10
26 Rob Henkel .05
27 Kyle Abbott .10
28 Lee Stevens .50
29 Chad Curtis .60
30 Ruben Amaro .15
31 Mark Howie .05
32 Tim Salmon 5.00
33 Kevin Flora .10
34 Garret Anderson .25
35 Darryl Scott .05
36 Don Vidmar .05
37 Korey Keling .05
38 Troy Percival .15
39 Eduardo Perez .75
40 Julian Heredia .05
41 Wilson Alvarez 1.50
42 Ramon Garcia .15
43 Johnny Ruffin .25
44 Scott Cepicky .05
45 Rod Bolton .05
46 Rogelio Nunez .05
47 Brandon Wilson .25
48 Marc Kubicki .05
49 Mark Lewis .20
50 Jim Thome 1.00
51 Tim Costo .20
52 Jeff Mutis .05
53 Tracy Sanders .10
54 Mike Soper .05
55 Miguel Flores .05
56 Brian Giles .10
57 Curtis Leskanic .15
58 Kyle Washington .10
59 Jason Hardtke .10
60 Albie Lopez .15
61 Oscar Resendez .05
62 Manny Ramirez 4.00
63 Rico Brogna .10
64 Scott Livingstone .10
65 Greg Gohr .10
66 Scott Aldred .05
67 Brian Warren .05
68 Bob Undorf .05
69 Rob Grable .05
70 Tom Mezzanotte .05
71 Justin Thompson .25
72 Trever Miller .25
73 Joel Johnston .05
74 Kevin Koslofski .05
75 Archie Corbin .05
76 Phil Hiatt .25
77 Danny Miceli .05
78 Joe Randa .15
79 Mark Johnson .05
80 Joe Vitiello .30
81 Cal Eldred .50
82 Doug Henry .05
83 Dave Nilsson .50
84 John Jaha .40
85 Shon Ashley .05
86 Jim Tatum .10
87 Bo Dodson .20
88 Otis Green .05
89 Denny Neagle .10
90 Checklist 1-90 .05
91 Pedro Munoz .20
92 Jarvis Brown .05
93 Pat Mahomes .20
94 Cheo Garcia .05
95 David McCarty .75
96 Chris Delarwelle .10
97 Scott Stahoviak .10
98 Midre Cummings .50
99 Todd Ritchie .20
100 Dave Sartain .05
101 Pedro Grifol .05
102 Eddie Guardado .20
103 Bob Carlson .05
104 Sandy Diaz .05
105 John Ramos .05
106 Bernie Williams .20
107 Wade Taylor .05
108 Pat Kelly .25
109 Jeff Johnson .10
110 Scott Kamieniecki .10
111 Dave Silvestri .15
112 Ed Martel .05
113 Willie Smith .05
114 J.T. Snow .50
115 Gerald Williams .25
116 Larry Stanford .05
117 Bruce Prybylinski .05
118 Rey Noriega .05
119 Rich Batchelor .05
120 Brad Ausmus .10
121 Robert Eenhoorn .05
122 Sam Militello .15
123 Jason Robertson .10
124 Carl Everett .50
125 Kiki Hernandez .20
126 Rafael Quirico .05
127 Lyle Mouton .10
128 Tim Flannelly .15
129 Todd Van Poppel .50
130 Tim Peek .05
131 Henry Mercedes .05
132 Todd Smith .05
133 Brent Gates .60
134 Gary Hust .05
135 Mike Neill .10
136 Russ Brock .10
137 Ricky Kimball .05
138 Tino Martinez .20
139 Calvin Jones .05
140 Roger Salkeld .25
141 Dave Fleming .50
142 Bret Boone .75
143 Jim Campanis .10
144 Marc Newfield 1.50
145 Mike Hampton .05
146 Shawn Estes .20
147 David Lisiecki .05
148 Dean Palmer 1.00
149 Rob Maurer .15
150 Jim Poole .05
151 Terry Mathews .05
152 Monty Fariss .10
153 Ivan Rodriquez 1.00
154 Barry Manuel .05
155 Donald Harris .10
156 Rusty Greer .25
157 Matt Whiteside .05
158 Derek Bell .75
159 Eddie Zosky .10
160 Domingo Martinez .05
161 Juan Guzman .75
162 Ed Sprague .20
163 Rob Ducey .05
164 Vince Horsman .05
165 Darren Hall .05
166 Rick Trlicek .10
167 Dave Weathers .20
168 Robert Perez .05
169 Nigel Wilson .75
170 Carlos Delgado 2.50
171 Steve Karsay 1.00
172 Howard Battle .50
173 Huck Fiener .05
174 Robert Butler .10
175 Giovanni Carrara .05
176 Michael Taylor .05
177 Brian Hunter .10
178 Turk Wendell .10
179 Mark Wohlers .10
180 Checklist 91-180 .05
181 Ryan Klesko 2.50
182 Keith Mitchell .10
183 Vinny Castilla .05
184 Napoleon Robinson .10
185 Mike Kelly .75
186 Javy Lopez 2.50
187 Ramon Caraballo .05
188 David Nied .60
189 Don Strange .05
190 Chipper Jones 1.25
191 Troy Hughes .05
192 Don Robinson .05
193 Lance Marks .05
194 Manuel Jimenez .10
195 Tony Graffagnino .05
196 Brad Woodall .05
197 Kevin Grijak .05
198 Darin Paulino .05
199 Lance Dickson .25
200 Rey Sanchez .15
201 Elvin Paulino .05
202 Alex Arias .10
203 Fernando Ramsey .05
204 Pete Castellano .20
205 Ryan Hawblitzel .10
206 John Jensen .05
207 Jerrone Williams .05
208 Earl Cunningham .80
209 Phil Dauphin .10
210 Doug Glanville .15
211 Jim Robinson .05
212 Ken Arnold .05
213 Reggie Jefferson .20
214 Reggie Sanders .75
215 Mo Sanford .10
216 Steve Foster .05
217 Dan Wilson .10
218 John Roper .15
219 Trevor Hoffman .10
220 Calvin Reese .25
221 John Hrusovsky .05
222 Andy Mota .05
223 Kenny Lofton 1.50
224 Andujar Cedeno .50
225 Ryan Bowen .10
226 Jeff Juden .20
227 Chris Gardner .50
228 Brian Williams .15
229 Ed Ponte .05
230 Chris Hatcher .05
231 Fletcher Thompson .05
232 Wally Trice .05
233 Donne Wall .05
234 Tom Nevers .15
235 Jim Daugherty .05
236 Mark Loughlin .05
237 Jose Offerman .30
238 Dave Hansen .10
239 Carlos Hernandez .05
240 Eric Karros .90
241 Henry Rodriguez .30
242 Jamie McAndrew .05
243 Tom Goodwin .05
244 Pedro Martinez .50
245 Braulio Castillo .10
246 Matt Howard .05
247 Michael Mimbs .05
248 Murph Proctor .05
249 Vernon Spearman .05
250 Jason Kerr .05
251 Mike Sharp .05
252 Pedro Osuna .05
253 Doug Piatt .05
254 Wil Cordero .75
255 John VanderWal .10
256 Bret Barberie .10
257 Todd Haney .05
258 Chris Haney .05
259 Matt Stairs .20
260 David Wainhouse .05
261 Bob Natal .05
262 Rob Katzaroli .05
263 Willie Greene .30
264 Reid Cornelius .05
265 Glenn Murray .10
266 Rondell White 1.50
267 Tavo Alvarez .20
268 Gabe White .50
269 Brian Looney .05
270 Checklist 181-270 .05
271 Derrick White .05
272 Heath Haynes .05
273 Mike Daniel .05
274 Jim Austin .10
275 Chris Donnels .10
276 Julio Valera .05
277 Todd Hundley .40
278 Anthony Young .10
279 Jeff Gardner .05
280 Jeromy Burnitz .50
281 Tito Navarro .10
282 D.J. Dozier .10
283 Julian Vasquez .05
284 Pat Howell .50
285 Brook Fordyce .20
286 Todd Douma .05
287 Jose Martinez .10
288 Ricky Otero .10
289 Quilvio Veras .20
290 Joe Crawford .05
291 Todd Fiegel .10
292 Jason Jacome .05
293 Kim Batiste .10
294 Andy Ashby .20
295 Wes Chamberlain .15
296 Dave Hollins .75
297 Tony Longmire .05
298 Nikco Riesgo .05
299 Cliff Brantley .05
300 Troy Paulsen .05
301 Elliott Gray .05
302 Mike Lieberthal .10
303 Tyler Green .20
304 Dan Brown .05
305 Carlos Garcia .20
306 John Wehner .10
307 Paul Miller .05
308 Tim Wakefield .20
309 Kurt Miller .10
310 Joe Sondrini .05
311 Hector Fajardo .10
312 Scott Bullett .15
313 Jon Farrell .10
314 Marc Pisciotta .05
315 Rheal Cormier .20
316 Omar Olivares .05
317 Donovan Osborne .20
318 Clyde Keller .05
319 John Kelly .05
320 Terry Bradshaw .20
321 Brian Eversgerd .05
322 Dmitri Young .75
323 Eddie Williams .20
324 Brian Barber .20
325 Andy Bruce .05
326 Tom McKinnon .15
327 Jamie Cochran .05
328 Steve Jones .05
329 Jerry Santos .05
330 Allen Watson .60
331 John Mabry .05
332 Jose Melendez .05
333 Dave Staton .20
334 Frank Seminara .10
335 Matt Mieske .40
336 Jay Gaines .10
337 J.D. Noland .10
338 Roberto Arredondo .10
339 Lance Painter .25
340 Darren Lewis .50
341 Ted Wood .05
342 Johnny Ard .05
343 Royce Clayton .50
344 Paul McClellan .05
345 John Patterson .05
346 Steve Hosey .25
347 Larry Carter .05
348 Juan Guerrero .10
349 Bryan Hickerson .10
350 Rich Huisman .10
351 Kevin McGehee .05
352 Gary Sharko .05
353 Salomon Torres .50
354 Eric Christopherson .05
355 Rod Huffman .05
356 Bill VanLandingham .05
357 Frank Charles .05
358 Ken Grundt .05
359 Matt Brewer .05
360 Checklist 271-360 .05

1991 Kraft Albany-Colonie Yankees

(New York Yankees) (color) Set was produced by Classic Best, sponsored by Kraft and Oscar Meyer, and given away at the ballpark on a promotional night.

	MT	NR MT	EX
Complete Set:	15.00	11.00	6.00

1 Pat Kelly
2 Wade Taylor
3 Bernie Williams
4 John Ramos
5 Willie Smith
6 Team Logo

1991 Procards Albany Yankees

(New York Yankees) (color)

	MT	NR MT	EX
Complete Set:	7.00	5.25	2.75

999 Andy Cook
1000 Mike Draper
1001 Victor Garcia
1002 Mike Gardella
1003 Cullen Hartzog
1004 Ed Martel
1005 Tom Newell
1006 Tom Popplewell
1007 Jerry Rub
1008 Willie Smith
1009 Don Stanford
1010 Larry Stanford
1011 Jeff Livesey
1012 Andy Skeels
1013 John Toale
1014 Russ Davis
1015 Bobby DeJardin
1016 Dave Silvestri
1017 J.T. Snow
1018 Hector Vargas
1019 Jay Knoblauh
1020 Billy Masse
1021 Vince Phillips
1022 Gerald Williams
1023 Dan Radison
1024 Dave Jorn
1025 Bob Mariano
1026 Checklist

1991 ProCards Albuquerque Dukes

(Los Angeles Dodgers) (color)

	MT	NR MT	EX
Complete Set:	7.00	5.25	2.75

1134 Mike Christopher
1135 Jeff Hartsock
1136 Chris Jones
1137 Dave Lynch
1138 Jamie McAndrew
1139 Jim Niedlinger
1140 Dan Opperman
1141 Dave Veres
1142 John Wetteland
1143 Bert Heffernan
1144 Carlos Hernandez
1145 Dave Hansen
1146 Eric Karros
1147 Luis Martinez
1148 Walt McConnell
1149 Jose Offerman
1150 Eddie Pye
1151 Greg Smith
1152 Billy Bean
1153 Jerry Brooks
1154 Butch Davis
1155 Tom Goodwin
1156 Henry Rodriguez
1157 Kevin Kennedy
1158 Von Joshua
1159 Claude Osteen
1160 Checklist

1991 Classic Best Appleton Foxes

(Kansas City Royals) (color)

	MT	NR MT	EX
Complete Set:	3.00	2.25	1.25

Foxes Logo
1 Francisco Baez
2 Jim Chrisman
3 Wade Fyock
4 Doug Harris
5 David Hierholzer
6 Herb Milton
7 Vernon Slater
8 Dario Perez
9 Gabriel Pineda
10 Damon Pollard
11 Shayne Rea
12 Donny Harrel
13 Lance Jennings
14 Chad Strickland
15 Gary Caraballo
16 Jeff Clarke
17 George Day
18 Harry Guanchez
19 Giovanni Miranda
20 Brady Stewart
21 Brad Shores
22 Darren Burton
23 Butch Cole
24 Ed Gerald
25 Tom Smith
26 Joe Breeden
27 Mike Jirschele
28 Mike Mason
29 Checklist (Not listed on checklist)

1991 ProCards Appleton Foxes

(Kansas City Royals) (color)

	MT	NR MT	EX
Complete Set:	3.00	2.25	1.25

1707 Francisco Baez
1708 Jim Chrisman
1709 Wade Fyock
1710 Doug Harris
1711 Dave Hierholzer
1712 Herb Milton
1713 Rodney Myers
1714 Dario Perez
1715 Gabriel Pineda
1716 Damon Pollard
1717 Shayne Rea
1718 Donny Harrel
1719 Lance Jennings
1720 Chad Strickland
1721 Gary Caraballo
1722 Jeff Clarke
1723 George Day
1724 Harry Guanchez
1725 Giovanni Miranda
1726 Brady Stewart
1727 Darren Burton
1728 Butch Cole
1729 Ed Gerald
1730 Tom Smith
1731 Joe Breeden
1732 Mike Jirschele
1733 Mike Mason
1734 Checklist

1991 ProCards Arkansas Travelers

(St. Louis Cardinals) (color)

	MT	NR MT	EX
Complete Set:	3.00	2.25	1.25

1276 Fidel Compres
1277 John Ericks
1278 David Grimes
1279 Dale Kisten
1280 John Lepley
1281 Steffen Majer
1282 Mike Milchin
1283 Donovan Osborne
1284 Gabriel Ozuna
1285 Lee Piemel
1286 Dean Weese
1287 Dennis Wiseman
1288 Jose Fernandez
1289 Don Prybylinski
1290 Tim Redman
1291 Greg Carmona
1292 Steve Fanning
1293 Joey Fernandez
1294 Mike Fiore
1295 Scott Melvin
1296 John Sellick
1297 Jeff Shireman
1298 Cliff Brannon
1299 Rick Christian
1300 Luis Martinez
1301 Charlie White
1302 Joe Pettini
1303 Marty Mason
1304 Checklist

1991 Classic Best Ashville Tourists

(Houston Astros) (color)

	MT	NR MT	EX
Complete Set:	3.00	2.25	1.25

Tourists Logo
1 Efrain Barreiro
2 Paul Branconier
3 Duane Brown
4 Jim Daugherty
5 Javier Hernandez
6 Douglas Ketchen
7 Fionel Nieves
8 Steve Powers
9 Mario Prats
10 Dennis Reed
11 David Wilson
12 Nicky Davis
13 Jose Flores
14 Al Harley
15 Alberto Montero
16 Tom Nevers
17 Steve Veit
18 Bob Hurlbutt
19 Raphael Lanfranco
20 Lance Smith
21 John Gonzales
22 Vince Roman
23 Jermaine Swinton
24 David Wallace
25 Jimmy White
26 Frank Cacciatore
27 Rick Aponte
28 Bob Robertson
29 Ron Hanisch

1991 Procards Ashville Tourists

(Houston Astros) (color)

	MT	NR MT	EX
Complete Set:	3.00	2.25	1.25

559 Efrain Barreiro
560 Paul Branconier
561 Duane Brown
562 Jim Daugherty
563 Javier Hernandez
564 Doug Ketchen
565 Fionel Nieves
566 Steve Powers
567 Mario Prats
568 Dennis Reed
569 Dave Wilson
570 Bob Hurlbutt
571 Rafael Lanfranco
572 Lance Smith
573 Nick Davis
574 Jose Flores
575 Al Harley
576 Alberto Montero
577 Tom Nevers
578 Steve Veit
579 John Gonzales
580 Vince Roman
581 Jermaine Swinton
582 David Wallace
583 Jimmy White
584 Frank Cacciatore
585 Ricardo Aponte
586 Bob Robertson
587 Checklist

1991 Classic Best Auburn Astros

(Houston Astros) (color)

	MT	NR MT	EX
Complete Set:	3.00	2.25	1.25

Auburn Logo
1 Mark Loughlin (First name mispelled on checklist.)
2 Tony Miller
3 Jim Lewis
4 Rod Biehl
5 Chris White
6 Louie Martinez
7 Jamie Evans
8 Tom Anderson
9 Joe Sewell
10 Rich Schulte
11 Ron Calini
12 Don Angotti
13 Eric Martinez
14 Mike Murphy
15 Mario Linares
16 Bryant Winslow
17 James Mouton
18 Todd Hobson
19 Chris Durkin
20 Brian McGlone
21 Brian Thompson
22 Jim Waring
23 Mick Matuszak (First name mispelled on checklist.)
24 Clark Crist
25 Don Alexander
26 Steve Dillard
27 Kory Finzer
28 Marc Techman
29 John Graham

1991 ProCards Auburn Astros

(Houston Astros) (color)

	MT	NR MT	EX
Complete Set:	4.00	3.00	1.50

4267 Rod Biehl
4268 Jamie Evans
4269 Jim Lewis
4270 Mark Loughlin
4271 Louie Martinez
4272 Tony Miller
4273 Joe Sewell
4274 Jim Waring
4275 Chris White
4276 Don Angotti
4277 Mario Linares
4278 Mike Murphy
4279 Ron Cacini
4280 Eric Martinez
4281 Brian McGlone
4282 James Mouton
4283 Bryant Winslow
4284 Miguel Cabrera
4285 Chris Durkin
4286 Todd Hobson
4287 Rich Schulte
4288 Brian Thompson
4289 Steve Dillard
4290 Don Alexander
4291 Clark Crist
4292 Checklist

1991 Classic Best Augusta Pirates

(Pittsburgh Pirates) (color)

	MT	NR MT	EX
Complete Set:	3.00	2.25	1.25

1 Julio Garcia
2 Scott Arveson
3 Lynn Carlson
4 Steve Cooke
5 Hector Fajardo
6 Mark Futrell
7 Donnie Gobel
8 Bobby Hunter
9 John Latham
10 Troy Mooney
11 Brian Shouse
12 Rick White
13 Marcus Hanel
14 Jessie Torres
15 Mark Johnson
16 Ramon Martinez
17 Steve Polewski
18 Hector Rodriguez
19 Pasquale Arace
20 Tom Green
21 Paul List
22 Joe Ronca
23 Anthony Brown
24 Mike Brown
25 Scott Bullett
26 Joe Sondrini
27 Rick Keeton
28 Kurt Miller
29 Genaro Campusano
30 Don Werner

1991 ProCards Augusta Pirates

(Pittsburgh Pirates) (color)

	MT	NR MT	EX
Complete Set:	3.00	2.25	1.25

795 Scott Arveson
796 Lynn Carlson
797 Steve Cooke
798 Hector Fajardo
799 Mark Futrell
800 Donnie Gobel
801 John Latham
802 Jeff Lyle
803 Kurt Miller
804 Troy Mooney
805 Andre Redmond
806 Rick White
807 Mark Hanel
808 Jessie Torres
809 Mike Brown
810 Genaro Campusano
811 Mark Johnson
812 Ramon Martinez
813 Steve Polewski
814 Hector Rodriguez
815 Joe Sondrini
816 Pasquale Arace
817 Anthony Brown
818 Scott Bullett
819 Tom Green
820 Paul List
821 Joe Ronca
822 Don Werner
823 Julio Garcia
824 Rick Keeton
825 Checklist

1991 Cal League Bakersfield Dodgers

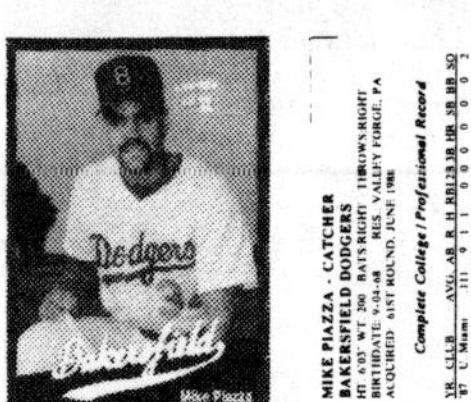

(Los Angeles Dodgers) (color)

	MT	NR MT	EX
Complete Set:	15.00	11.00	6.00

1 Raul Mondesi
2 Rob Maurer
3 Fausto Tatis
4 Gordon Tipton
5 Ed Stryker
6 Rex Peters
7 Mike Piazza
8 Brian Piotrowicz
9 Alan Lewis
10 Domingo Mota
11 Stephen Mintz
12 Mark Mimbs
13 Ed Lund
14 Garey Ingram
15 Billy Lott
16 Mike Galle
17 Greg Hansell
18 Javier Delahoya
19 Dino Ebel
20 Anthony Collier
21 James Daspit
22 Dan Cardenas
23 Garrett Beard
24 Helms Bohringer
25 Mike Busch
26 Al Bustillos
27 Don Carroll
28 Tom Beyers
29 Goose Gregson
30 Glenn Hoffman
31 Terry McFarlin
32 Pedro Martinez

1991 Classic Best Baseball City Royals

(Kansas City Royals) (color)

	MT	NR MT	EX
Complete Set:	3.00	2.25	1.25

1 Andres Berumen
2 John Connor
3 Bubba Dunn
4 John Gross
5 Greg Harvey
6 Brad Hopper
7 Jake Jacobs
8 Matt Karchner
9 Tony Long
10 John McCormick
11 Kevin Shaw
12 Skip Wiley
13 Huascar de Leon
14 Travis Kinyoun
15 Colin Ryan
16 Dave Solseth
17 Phil Hiatt
18 David King
19 Ceasar Morillo
20 Fred Russell
21 John Schreiner
22 Pedro Vazquez
23 Jay Andrews III
24 John Gilcrist
25 Scott Hennessey
26 Kerwin Moore
27 Doug Shields
28 Carlos Tosca
29 Ron Johnson
30 Pete Filson

1991 ProCards Baseball City Royals

(Kansas City Royals) (color)

	MT	NR MT	EX
Complete Set:	3.00	2.25	1.25

1388 Andres Berumen
1389 John Conner
1390 Bubba Dunn
1391 John Gross
1392 Greg Harvey
1393 Brad Hopper
1394 Jake Jacobs
1395 Matt Karchner
1396 Tony Long
1397 John McCormick
1398 Kevin Shaw
1399 Skip Wiley
1400 Travis Klnyoun
1401 Colin Ryan
1402 Dave Solseth
1403 Phil Hiatt
1404 David King
1405 Ceasar Morillo
1406 Fred Russell
1407 John Schreiner
1408 Pedro Vazquez
1409 Jay Andrews
1410 John Gilcrist
1411 Scott Hennessey
1412 Kerwin Moore
1413 Doug Shields
1414 Pete Filson
1415 Ron Johnson
1416 Checklist

1991 Classic Best Batavia Clippers

(Philadelphia Phillies) (color)

	MT	NR MT	EX
Complete Set:	3.00	2.25	1.25

1 Rob Nash (No position listed on card.)
2 Gene Schall
3 Tommy Eason
4 Pat Ruth
5 Julio Vargas
6 Craig Billeci
7 Patrick Cheek
8 Lamar Foster
9 Jesus Garces
10 David Hayden
11 Bruce Smolen
12 Jerome Edwards
13 Antonio Grissom
14 Facaner Medina
15 Tom Vilet
16 Bryan Manicchia
17 Matt Whisenant
18 Carlos Arroyo
19 Glenn Nevill
20 Tyler Green
21 Pat Bojcun
22 Mike Grace
23 John Whisonant
24 Greg Brown
25 Ron Allen
26 Ron Blazier
27 Ramon Aviles
28 Craig Holman (Checklist lists card as Tony Scott.)
29 Chipper the Clipper (Mascot)
30 Gary Beatty

1991 ProCards Batavia Clippers

(Seattle Mariners)(color)

	MT	NR MT	EX
Complete Set:	3.00	2.25	1.25

3474 Ron Allen
3475 Ron Blazier
3476 Pat Bojcun
3477 Greg Brown
3478 Mike Grace
3479 Tyler Green
3480 Craig Holman
3481 Bryan Manicchia
3482 Glenn Nevill
3483 Matt Whisenant
3484 John Whisonant
3485 Tommy Eason
3486 Pat Ruth
3487 Julio Vargas
3488 Craig Billeci
3489 Pat Cheek
3490 Lamar Foster
3491 Jesus Garces
3492 David Hayden
3493 Gene Schall
3494 Bruce Smolen
3495 Jerome Edwards
3496 Antonio Grissom
3497 Facaner Medina
3498 Rob Nash
3499 Tom Vilet
3500 Ramon Aviles
3501 Carlos Arroyo
3502 Tony Scott
3503 Checklist

1991 Classic Best Bellingham Mariners

(Philadelphia Phillies) (color)

	MT	NR MT	EX
Complete Set:	3.00	2.25	1.25

1 Clem Barlow
2 Clay Klavitter
3 Tommy Boudreau
4 Jon Halland
5 Eddy Diaz
6 James Terrell (Last name misspelled on card front.)
7 Sean Twitty
8 Todd Walles
9 Barney Erhard
10 Erik O'Donnell
11 Michael Bond
12 Charles Smith
13 Craig Clayton
14 Willie Speakman
15 Scott Bosarge
16 Tommy Adams
17 Julio Fernandez
18 Trey Witte
19 Doug Anderson
20 Pete Weinbaum
21 Toby Foreman
22 David Lisiecki (Last name misspelled on checklist.)
23 Jeff Borski
24 Charles Wiley (Last name misspelled on card front.)
25 Todd Youngblood
26 Giovanni Polanco
27 Staff
28 LaGrande Russell
29 Shawn Estes
30 Tucker-Walker

1991 ProCards Bellingham Mariners

(Seattle Mariners) (color)

	MT	NR MT	EX
Complete Set:	4.00	3.00	1.50

3654 Doug Anderson
3655 Jeff Borski
3656 Shawn Estes
3657 Toby Foreman
3658 David Lisiecki
3659 Erick O'Donnell
3660 Giovanni Polanco
3661 Julio Reyan
3662 Richard Russell
3663 Pete Weinbaum
3664 Charles Wiley
3665 Trey Witte
3666 Todd Youngblood
3667 Scott Bosarge
3668 Clay Klavitter
3669 Willie Speakman
3670 Michael Bond
3671 Craig Clayton
3672 Eddy Diaz
3673 Barney Erhard
3674 Jon Halland
3675 Bubba Smith
3676 Todd Walles
3677 Tommy Adams
3678 Clem Barlow
3679 Tommy Boudreau
3680 Julio Fernandez
3681 James Terrell
3682 Sean Twitty
3683 Dave Myers
3684 Gary Wheelock
4174 Checklist (Numbered out of sequence.)

1991 Classic Best Beloit Brewers

(Milwaukee Brewers) (color)

	MT	NR MT	EX
Complete Set:	3.00	2.25	1.25

1 William Brakeley
2 Larry Carter
3 Francisco Gamez
4 Geoffrey Kellogg
5 Pat Miller
6 Donald Pruitt
7 Brian Souza
8 Mark Stephens
9 James Sass
10 Jason Zimbauer
11 Steve Diaz
12 Darrin White
13 Juan Cabrera
14 Tim Carter
15 Gordon Powell Jr.
16 Julian Salazar
17 Bobby Benjamin
18 Tony Diggs
19 Todd Edwards
20 Graciano Enriquez
21 Chris Ervin
22 Michael Carter
23 Dave Wrona
24 Leon Glenn
25 Mike Hooper
26 Dave Rajsich
27 Rob Derkson
28 James Hvizda (Checklist Not listed on checklist.)
---- Beloit Logo
---- Brewers Logo

1991 ProCards Beloit Brewers

(Milwaukee Brewers) (color)

	MT	NR MT	EX
Complete Set:	3.00	2.25	1.25

2094 William Brakeley
2095 Larry Carter
2096 Francisco Gamez
2097 Mike Hooper
2098 Jim Hvizda
2099 Geoffrey Kellogg
2100 Pat Miller
2101 Donald Pruitt
2102 Brian Souza
2103 Mark Stephens
2104 Jason Zimbauer
2105 Steve Diaz
2106 Darrin White
2107 Juan Cabrera
2108 Michael Carter
2109 Tim Carter
2110 Leon Glenn
2111 Gordon Powell
2112 Julian Salazar
2113 Dave Wrona
2114 Bobby Benjamin
2115 Tony Diggs
2116 Todd Edwards
2117 Graciano Enriquez
2118 James Sass
2119 Rob Derksen
2120 Dave Rajsich
2121 Checklist

1991 Classic Best Bend Bucks

(Independent) (color)

	MT	NR MT	EX
Complete Set:	3.00	2.25	1.25

Bucks Logo
1 J.R. Cock
2 Tim Cain
3 Stan Kyles
4 Kyle Duke
5 Mark Finney
6 Steve Goucher
7 Darren Haddock
8 Tim Minik
9 Robert Person
10 Geoff Samuels
11 Mike Boker
12 Jim Fregosi Jr.
13 Jim Savage
14 Jerry Schoen
15 Frank Turco
16 Ryan Turner
17 Clifford Williams
18 Anthony Pritchett
19 Keith Ringgold
20 Scott Ollison
21 Stacy Parker
22 Brian McGee
23 Ed Lightner
24 Larry Hawks
25 Loen Glenn
26 Michael Bard
27 Eric Moen
28 Bill Stein
29 Checklist (Not listed on checklist.)

1991 ProCards Bend Bucks

(Independent) (color)

	MT	NR MT	EX
Complete Set:	3.00	2.25	1.25

3685 Mike Boker
3686 Tim Cain
3687 Robbie Castaneda
3688 J.R. Cock
3689 Kyle Duke
3690 Mark Finney
3691 Steve Goucher
3692 Darin Haddock
3693 Tim Minik
3694 Robert Person
3695 Geoff Samuels
3696 Larry Hawks
3697 Brian McGee
3698 Cliff Williams
3699 Mike Bard
3700 Leon Glenn
3701 Ed Lightner
3702 Scott Ollison
3703 Jim Savage
3704 Jerry Schoen
3705 Frank Turco
3706 Stacy Parker
3707 Tony Pritchett
3708 Keith Ringgold
3709 Ryan Turner
3710 Bill Stein

3711 Jim Fregosl Jr.
3712 Stan Kyles
3713 Checklist

1991 ProCards Billings Mustangs

(Cincinnati Reds) (color)

	MT	NR MT	EX
Complete Set:	3.00	2.25	1.25

3745 Mike Coletti
3746 John Courtright
3747 Scott Dodd
3748 Phil Kendall
3749 Rich Langford
3750 Charles McClain
3751 Dave Reeves
3752 Dan Tobin
3753 Domingo Vivas
3754 Chuck Wyatt
3755 Rich Zastoupil
3756 Mike Harrison
3757 Bo Loftin
3758 Trey Wilburn
3759 Joe DeBerry
3760 Ramon Hernandez
3761 Mike Jones
3762 Brian Koelling
3763 Matt Martin
3764 Scott Snead
3765 Pierre Burris
3766 Derick Graham
3767 Bob Jesperson
3768 Damin Montgomery
3769 Gene Taylor
3770 P.J. Carey
3771 Mack Jenkins
3772 Checklist

1991 Sport Pro Billings Mustangs

(Cincinnati Reds) (color)

	MT	NR MT	EX
Complete Set:	4.00	3.00	1.50

1 Charles McClain
2 Pierre Burris
3 Scott Snead
4 Dan Tobin
5 Bo Loftin
6 Trey Wilburn
7 Domingo Vivas
8 Matt Martin
9 Derrick Graham
10 Chuck Wyatt
11 Scott Dodd
12 Damin Montgomery
13 John Coletti
14 Joe DeBerry
15 John Courtright
16 Gene Taylor
17 Ramon Hernandez
18 Mike Jones
19 Rich Langford
20 Brian Koelling
21 Mike Harrison
22 Dave Reeves
23 Rich Zastoupil
24 Bob Jesperson
25 Phil Kendall
26 Kevin Hudson
27 Mack Jenkins
28 Paul "P.J." Carey
29 Blank
30 Blank

1991 ProCards Birmingham Barons

(Chicago White Sox) (color)

	MT	NR MT	EX
Complete Set:	4.00	3.00	1.50

1446 Wilson Alvarez
1447 Conde Cortes
1448 Mike Davino
1449 Ramon Garcia
1450 Chris Howard
1451 John Hudek
1452 Bo Kennedy
1453 Frank Merigliano
1454 Scott Middaugh
1455 Jose Ventura
1456 Darrin Campbell
1457 Jeff Gay
1458 Wayne Busby
1459 Mark Chasey
1460 Ron Coomer
1461 Lindsay Foster
1462 Kevin Garner
1463 Javier Ocasio
1464 Greg Roth
1465 Scott Jaster
1466 Derek Lee
1467 Kinnis Pledger
1468 Aubrey Waggoner
1469 Tony Franklin
1470 Sam Hairston
1471 Rick Peterson
1472 Pat Roessler
1473 Checklist

1991 Classic Best Bluefield Orioles

(Baltimore Orioles) (color)

	MT	NR MT	EX
Complete Set:	3.00	2.25	1.25

1 Kris Gresham
2 Gordie Graham
3 Stewart Ruiz
4 Terry Farrar
5 Mike Thomas
6 Juan Mercedes
7 Vaughan Eshelman
8 Brad Seitzer
9 Basillo Ortiz
10 Mike Coss
11 Eric Alexander
12 Derek Adams
13 Bryan Grejtak
14 Glenn Coleman
15 Doug McConathy
16 Mat Sanders
17 Kevin Ryan
18 Rick Krivda
19 Allen Plaster
20 Steve Firsich
21 Chris Lemp
22 Brett Benge
23 Shawn O'Connell
24 Mike Tullier
25 Chris Lein
26 Checklist (Not listed on checklist.)
---- Bluefield Logo
---- Orioles Logo
---- MLB Logo
---- Schmidt Ad

1991 ProCards Bluefield Orioles

	MT	NR MT	EX
Complete Set:	3.00	2.25	1.25

4119 Brett Benge
4120 Vaughn Eshelman
4121 Terry Farrar
4122 Stevie Firsick
4123 Ricky Krivda
4124 Chris Lemp
4125 Juan Mercedes
4126 Shawn O'Connell
4127 Al Plaster
4128 Kevin Ryan
4129 Matt Sanders
4130 Bryan Grejtak
4131 Kris Gresham
4132 Derk Adams
4133 Mike Coss
4134 Gordie Graham
4135 Doug McConathy
4136 Stu Ruiz
4137 Brad Seitzer
4138 Eric Alexander
4139 Glenn Coleman
4140 Basil Ortiz
4141 Mike Thomas
4142 Chris Lein
4143 Mike Tullier
4144 Checklist

1991 Classic Best Boise Hawks

(California Angels) (color)

	MT	NR MT	EX
Complete Set:	4.00	3.00	1.50

1 Todd Claus
2 Chris Prichett
3 Luis Raven
4 Chance Giedhill
5 Tyrone Boykin
6 James Ruocchio
7 Rod Van Dyke
8 Eduardo Perez
9 Orlando Palmeiro
10 Elgin Bobo
11 Jose Stela
12 Shawn Purdy
13 Mark Mammola
14 John Wylie
15 Mark Sweeney
16 Ron Tallent
17 Chris Turner
18 Brandon Markiewicz (First name misspelled on card front.)
19 Gary Hagy
20 Jim Sears
21 Carlos Polanco
22 Ron Watson
23 Troy Percival
24 Eric Martinez
25 Korey Koling
26 Rob Dodd
27 Chris Robinson
28 Mark Ratekin
29 Julian Heredia
30 Alan Russell

1991 ProCards Boise Hawks

(California Angels) (color)

	MT	NR MT	EX
Complete Set:	4.00	3.00	1.50

3869 Robb Dodd
3870 Chance Giedhill
3871 Julian Heredia
3872 Korey Keling
3873 Mark Mammola
3874 Eric Martinez
3875 Troy Percival
3876 Shawn Purdy
3877 Mark Ratekin
3878 Chris Robinson
3879 Rod Van Dyke
3880 Ron Watson
3881 John Wylie
3882 Elgin Bobo
3883 Jose Stela
3884 Chris Turner
3885 Todd Claus
3886 Gary Hagy
3887 Brandon Markiewicz
3888 Carlos Polanco
3889 Chris Pritchett
3890 James Ruocchio
3891 Jimmy Sears
3892 Ron Tallent
3893 Ty Boykin
3894 Robby Cannon
3895 Orlando Palmeiro (Orlando Palmeiro is a cousin of Texas Ranger Rafael Palmeiro.)
3896 Eduardo Perez
3897 Luis Raven
3898 Mark Sweeney
3899 Tom Kotchman
3900 Joe Caro
3901 Orv Franchuk
3902 Howie Gershberg
3903 Checklist

1991 Classic Best Bristol Tigers

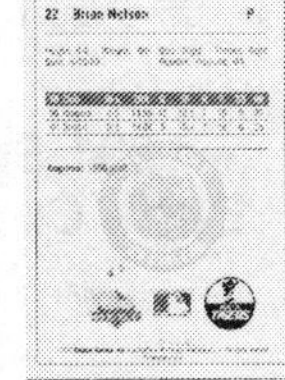

(Detroit Tigers) (color)

	MT	NR MT	EX
Complete Set:	3.00	2.25	1.25

1 James Givens
2 Jorge Caro
3 Justin Mashore
4 Tom Mezzanotte
5 Luis Hernandez
6 Tarrick Brock
7 Rob Yelton
8 Brian Prichard
9 Alex Ubina
10 John Sutey
11 Jose Sanjurjo
12 Keith Kimsey
13 Jorge Moreno
14 Trevor Miller
15 Vince Bradford
16 Greg Raffo
17 Clint Sadowsky
18 Carlos Diaz
19 Blas Cedeno
20 Juan Lopez
21 Matt Bauer
22 Brian Nelson
23 Tom Schwarber
24 Dan Ruff
25 Justin Thompson
26 Brian Edmondson (Last name misspelled on checklist.)
27 Paul Magrini
28 Nelson Perpetuo
29 Art Adams
30 Kevin Bradshaw

1991 ProCards Bristol Tigers

(Detroit Tigers) (color)

	MT	NR MT	EX
Complete Set:	3.00	2.25	1.25

3594 Art Adams
3595 Matt Bauer
3596 Blas Cedeno
3597 Brian Edmondson
3598 Paul Magrini
3599 Trever Miller
3600 Brian Nelson
3601 Nelson Perpetuo
3602 Henry Quiles
3603 Greg Raffo
3604 Clint Sadowsky
3605 Tom Schwarber
3606 Justin Thompson
3607 Tom Mezzanotte
3608 Brian Prichard
3609 Alex Ubina
3610 Rob Yelton
3611 Jorge Caro
3612 Carlos Diaz
3613 James Givens
3614 Luis Hernandez
3615 Jorge Moreno
3616 Dan Ruff
3617 Vince Bradford
3618 Keith Kimsey
3619 Justin Mashore
3620 Jose Sanjurjo
3621 John Sutey
3622 Juan Lopez
3623 Checklist

1991 ProCards Buffalo Bisons

(Pittsburgh Pirates) (color)

	MT	NR MT	EX
Complete Set:	5.00	3.75	2.00

533 Kevin Blankenship
534 Steve Fireovid
535 Mark Huismann
536 Roger Mason
537 Tim Meeks
538 Blas Minor
539 Jeff Neely
540 Rick Reed
541 Rosario Rodriguez
542 Jim Tracy
543 Mike York
544 Jeff Banister
545 Tom Magrann
546 Carlos Garcia
547 Joey Meyer
548 Armando Moreno
549 Joe Redfield
550 Jeff Richardson
551 Cecil Epsy
552 Scott Little
553 Keith Miller
554 Jeff Schulz
555 Greg Tubbs
556 Terry Collins
557 Jackie Brown
558 Checklist

1991 Team Blue Shield Buffalo Bisons

(Pittsburgh Pirates) (color)

	MT	NR MT	EX
Complete Set:	8.00	6.00	3.25

2 Terry Collins
6 Armando Moreno
7 Keith Miller
12 Carlos Garcia
13 Steve Fireovid
14 Cecil Espy
15 Greg Tubbs
17 John Wehner
19 Tim Dulin
22 Tom Prince
23 Scott Little
27 Kevin Blankenship
30 Carlton Hamilton
32 Jeff Schulz
34 Rick Reed
36 Jeff Neely
37 Blas Minor
38 Mike Roesler
39 Roger Mason
41 Jackie Brown
44 Jeff Richardson
45 Joe Ausanio
46 Joey Meyer

47 Tim Meeks
48 Jeff Banister
50 Rosarion Rodriguez
99 Mr. Magoo

1991 Classic Best Burlington Astros

(Houston Astros) (color)

	MT	NR MT	EX
Complete Set:	3.00	2.25	1.25

Houston Logo
1 David Allen
2 Troy Dovey
3 Benjamin Gonzales
4 Anthony Guiterrez
5 Robert Hurta
6 Kevin Lane
7 Michael McDowell
8 Tyrone Scott
9 Walter Trice
10 Donnie Wall
11 Kenneth Wheeler Jr.
12 Manuel Acta
13 Raul Chavez
14 Gary Christopherson
15 David Henderson
16 Layne Lambert
17 Roberto Petagine
18 Fletcher Thompson
19 Ruben Cruz
20 Christopher Hatcher
21 Raymond Montgomery
22 Bryan Smith
23 Jeffery Bennington
24 Michael Burns
25 Tony Gilmore
26 Jim Hickey
27 Tim Tolman
28 Chris Correnti
29 Checklist (Not listed on checklist.)

1991 ProCards Burlington Astros

(Houston Astros) (color)

	MT	NR MT	EX
Complete Set:	3.00	2.25	1.25

2792 Dave Allen
2793 Troy Dovey
2794 Benny Gonzales
2795 Anthony Gutierrez
2796 Bob Hurta
2797 Kevin Lane
2798 Mike McDowell
2799 Tyrone Scott
2800 Wally Trice
2801 Donne Wall
2802 Ken Wheeler
2803 Jeff Bennington
2804 Mike Burns
2805 Tony Gilmore
2806 Manuel Acta
2807 Raul Chavez
2808 Gary Christopherson
2809 Dave Henderson
2810 Layne Lambert
2811 Roberto Petagine
2812 Fletcher Thompson
2813 Ruben Cruz
2814 Chris Hatcher
2815 Ray Montgomery
2816 Bryan Smith
2817 Tim Tolman
2818 Jim Hickey
2819 Checklist

1991 ProCards Burlington Indians

(Cleveland Indians) (color)

	MT	NR MT	EX
Complete Set:	6.00	4.50	2.50

3290 Brandon Bluhm
3291 Jose Colon
3292 Chris Coulter
3293 Carlos Crawford
3294 Ian Doyle
3295 Jesus Gonzalez
3296 Pep Harris
3297 Fernando Hernandez
3298 Danny Key
3299 Rodney Koller
3300 Albie Lopez
3301 Chris Maffett
3302 Oscar Resendez
3303 Pete Guerra
3304 Cale Lawson
3305 Mike Taylor
3306 David Chisum
3307 Felipe Duran
3308 Rodd Hairston
3309 Javier Robles
3310 Jorge Santiago
3311 Jeffrey Whitaker
3312 Todd Whitehurst
3313 Mike Zollars
3314 Ronnie Coleman
3315 Sam Hence
3316 Manny Ramirez
3317 Bobby Schultz
3318 Mike Shirley
3319 Andre White
3320 David Keller
3321 Stan Hilton
3322 Don Jacoby
3323 Checklist

1991 Sport Pro Butte Copper Kings

(Texas Rangers) (color)

	MT	NR MT	EX
Complete Set:	4.00	3.00	1.50

1 James Koehler
2 Jason Ayala
3 Chris Starr
4 Terrell Berthau
5 Andy Watson
6 Paul Dalzachio
7 Michael Crespo
8 Dave Giberti
9 Mike Edwards
10 Chris Curtis (No position listed.)
11 Lanny Williams
12 Shawn Kennedy
13 Todd Gates
14 Kerry Lacey
15 Eric Vargas
16 Lance Schuermann
17 Terrell Lowery
18 Victor Madrigal
19 Charlie Sullivan
20 Franklin Parra
21 Kevin Sisk
22 Bo Magee
23 Greg Wiseman
24 Keith McGough
25 Bryan Roberts
26 Jose Texidor
27 Doug Sisson
28 Chuck Marquardt
29 Jim Benedict
30 Dick Egan

1991 Sport-Pro Butte Copper Kings

(Texas Rangers) (color)

	MT	NR MT	EX
Complete Set:	2.00	1.50	.80

1 Benji Gil
2 Joe Brownholtz (All seven players are pictured on the card., Marty Davis, Paul Paramo, Brad Stuart, Pat Underhill, Robbie McCune, Pat Poyner)

1991 ProCards Calgary Cannons

(Seattle Mariners) (color)

	MT	NR MT	EX
Complete Set:	5.00	3.75	2.00

264 Keith Bodie (Checklist lists card as #530.)
508 Rick Balabon
509 Dave Burba
510 Keith Helton
511 Calvin Jones
512 Vance Lovelace
513 John Mitchell
514 Dennis Powell
515 Pat Rice
516 Ricky Rojas
517 Ed Vandeberg
518 Dave Cochrane
519 Chris Howard
520 Rich Amaral
521 Chuck Jackson
522 Shane Letterio
523 Tino Martinez
524 Steve Springer
525 Dave Brundage
526 Alan Cockrell
527 Dennis Hood
528 Pat Lennon
529 Alonzo Powell
531 Ross Grimsley
532 Checklist

1991 Cal League Cal League All-Stars

(color)

	MT	NR MT	EX
Complete Set:	7.00	5.25	2.75

1 Pedro Martinez
2 Marc Newfield
3 Raul Mondesi
4 Matt Mieske
5 Dave Van Winkle
6 Mike Piazza
7 Jay Gainer
8 Brian Raabe
9 Terry McFarlin
10 Ed Zinter
11 Jesus Tavarez
12 Garey Ingram
13 Alan Newman
14 Greg Hansell
15 Mick Billmeyer
16 Corey Kapano
17 Anthony Collier
18 J.D. Noland
19 Rex Peters
20 Mark Gieseke
21 Ron Maurer
22 Marcos Garcia
23 Tom Beyers
24 Goose Gregson
25 Matt Wilson
26 Joe Gagilardi
27 John Lavenda, Rick Smith
28 Bob Brooks
29 Adell Davenport
30 John Finn
31 Rick Huisman
32 Hideyuki Mifune
33 Joey James
34 Mark Krumback
35 Gary Sharko
36 Troy O'Leary
37 Kevin McGehee
38 Henry Mercedes
39 Pat Rapp
40 Hideyuki Yasuda
41 Clay Bellinger
42 Mike Mohler
43 Jason McFarlin
44 Manny Martinez
45 Carl Hanselman
46 Cliff Gonzalez
47 Ron Wotus
48 Gary Lucas
49 Scott Wilson
50 Brian Laxamana
51 Todd Whitty
52 Mike Stetson
53 Ray Dimuro
54 Dave Lattimer
55 Bo Dodson
56 Timber Mead

1991 ProCards Canton-Akron Indians

(Cleveland Indians) (color)

	MT	NR MT	EX
Complete Set:	5.00	3.75	2.00

971 Eric Bell
972 Mike Birkbeck
973 Jim Bruske
974 Mike Curtis
975 Jerry Dipoto
976 Garland Kiser
977 Ty Kovach
978 Tom Kramer
979 Jeff Mutis
980 Greg Roscoe
981 Jesse Levis
982 Gary Resetar
983 Ramon Bautista
984 Tim Costo
985 Daren Epley
986 Sam Ferretti
987 Carlos Martinez
988 Rouglas Odor
989 Jim Thome
990 Nolan Lane
991 Ken Ramos
992 Miguel Sabino
993 Bernie Tatis
994 Ken Whitefield
995 Ken Bolek
996 Will George
997 Dave Keller
998 Checklist

1991 ProCards Carolina League All-Star Game

(color)

	MT	NR MT	EX
Complete Set:	7.00	5.25	2.75

1 Tim Gilles
2 Javy Lopez
3 Scott Taylor
4 Manny Alexander
5 Tony Beasley
6 Sergio Cairo
7 Cesar Devares
8 Ed Horowitz
9 Mel Wearing
10 Kip Vaughn
11 Chad Allen
12 Mike Easley
13 Tom Eiterman
14 Miguel Flores
15 Brian Giles
16 Brian Graham
17 Garland Kiser
18 Scott Neill
19 Tracy Sanders
20 Mike Soper
21 Buddy Bailey
22 Bruce Chick
23 Jeff McNeely
24 Boo Moore
25 Bill Norris
26 Erik Plantenburg
27 Tim Smith
28 Bobby Holley
29 Ron Pezzoni
30 Andy Fox
31 Mike Hankins
32 Mike Hart
33 Darren Hodges
34 Sam Militello
35 Mark Ohlms
36 Daryl Ratliff
37 Dave Tellers
38 Paul Wagner
39 Troy Bradford
40 Pete Castellano
41 Chris Ebright
42 Ryan Hawblitzel
43 John Jensen
44 Brad Mills
45 Matt Walbeck
46 Travis Willis
47 Checklist

1991 ProCards Carolina Mudcats

(Pittsburgh Pirates) (color)

	MT	NR MT	EX
Complete Set:	4.00	3.00	1.50

1078 Steve Adams
1079 Chip Duncan
1080 Stan Fansler
1081 Carl Hamilton
1082 Lee Hancock
1083 Paul Miller
1084 Pete Murphy
1085 Mike Roesler
1086 Dennis Tafoya
1087 Tim Wakefield
1088 Ben Webb
1089 Tim Hines
1090 Mandy Romero
1091 Terry Crowley
1092 Greg Edge
1093 Mike Huyler
1094 Bruce Schreiber
1095 Greg Sparks
1096 John Wehner
1097 Chris Estep
1098 Darwin Pennye
1099 Ed Yacopino
1100 Eddie Zambrano
1101 Marc Bombard
1102 Spin Williams
1103 Checklist

1991 Classic Best Cedar Rapids Reds

(Cincinnati Reds) (color)

	MT	NR MT	EX
Complete Set:	4.00	3.00	1.50

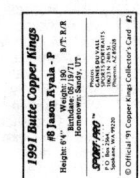

1 Kevin Berry
2 Mark Borcherding
3 Ryan Edwards
4 Mike Ferry
5 Leonard Griffen
6 Trevor Hoffman
7 Rich Langford
8 Larry Luebbers
9 Ramon Manon
10 Greg Margheim

11 Scott Robinson
12 Jason Satre
13 Darron Cox
14 Jon Fuller
15 Matt Giegling
16 Amadoz Arias
17 Jamie Dismuke
18 Vicente Javier (First name misspelled on card back.)
19 Kevin Riggs
20 Steve Vondran
21 Todd Wilson
22 Eugene Jones
23 Danny Perozo
24 Noel Velez
25 K.C. Gillum
26 Frank Funk
27 Mark Berry
28 Mark Jenkins (First name misspelled on checklist.)
29 Gregg Crain
30 Checklist (Not listed on checklist.)

1991 ProCards Cedar Rapids Reds

(Cincinnati Reds) (color)

	MT	NR MT	EX
Complete Set:	4.00	3.00	1.50

2709 Kevin Berry
2710 Mark Borcherding
2711 Ryan Edwards
2712 Mike Ferry
2713 Leonard Griffen
2714 Trevor Hoffman
2715 Rich Langford
2716 Larry Luebbers
2717 Greg Margheim
2718 Scott Robinson
2719 Jason Satre
2720 Darron Cox
2721 Jon Fuller
2722 Matt Giegling
2723 Steve Vondran
2724 Hammadoz Arias
2725 Jamie Dismuke
2726 Bob Filotel
2727 Vincent Javier
2728 Kevin Riggs
2729 Eddie Rush
2730 Todd Wilson
2731 K.C. Gillum
2732 Eugene Jones
2733 Danny Perozo
2734 Noel Velez
2735 Frank Funk
2736 Mark Berry
2737 Mack Jenkins
2738 Checklist

1991 Classic Best Charleston Rainbows

(San Diego Padres) (color)

	MT	NR MT	EX
Complete Set:	3.00	2.25	1.25

Rainbows Logo
1 Robbie Beckett
2 Mike Bradley
3 Jeff Brown
4 Cameron Cairncross
5 Ted Devore
6 Craig Eubanks
7 Jeff Huber
8 Bill Johnson
9 Steve Newton
10 Charles Thompson
11 Joe Waldron
12 Adan Ayala (First name misspelled on checklist.)
13 Jerry Thurston
14 Dave Adams
15 Brent Bish
16 Scott Bream
17 Craig Bullock
18 Tom Doyle
19 Pablo Martinez
20 Brian Beck
21 Ray McDavid
22 Keith McKoy
23 Jeff Pearce
24 Dave Trembley
25 Bruce Tanner
26 Jaime Moreno
27 Tom Ivie
28 John Maxwell
29 Checklist (Not listed on checklist.)

1991 ProCards Charleston Rainbows

(San Diego Padres) (color)

	MT	NR MT	EX
Complete Set:	3.00	2.25	1.25

87 Robbie Beckett
88 Mike Bradley
89 Jeff Brown
90 Cameron Cairncross
91 Ted Devore
92 Craig Eubanks
93 Jeff Huber
94 Bill Johnson
95 Charles Thompson
96 Joe Waldron
97 Adan Ayala
98 Jerry Thurston
99 Dave Adams
100 Brent Bish
101 Scott Bream
102 Craig Bullock
103 Tom Doyle
104 Pablo Martinez
105 Bill Ostermeyer
106 Brian Beck
107 Ray McDavid
108 Keith McKoy
109 Jeff Pearce
110 Dave Trembley
111 Jaime Moreno
112 Bruce Tanner
113 Checklist

1991 Classic Best Charleston Wheelers

(Cincinnati Reds) (color)

	MT	NR MT	EX
Complete Set:	3.00	2.25	1.25

1 Tim Cecil
2 Sean Doty
3 Scott Duff
4 Chris Hook
5 Doug King
6 Reggie Leslie
7 Ernie Nieves
8 Johnny Ray
9 John Roper
10 Carl Stewart
11 Kevin Tatar
12 Roy Hammargren
13 Greg Hammond
14 Dan Wilson
15 Rafael Bustamante
16 Herb Erhardt
17 Chris Gill
18 Bobby Perna
19 Tom Raffo
20 Lenny Wentz
21 Mark Arland
22 Steve Gibralter
23 Keith Gordon
24 Tom Spencer
25 Elliott Quinones
26 Chris Vasquez
27 Derek Botelho
28 Team (Checklist) (Not listed on checklist.)
---- Wheelers Logo
---- Reds Logo

1991 ProCards Charleston Wheelers

(Cincinnati Reds) (color)

	MT	NR MT	EX
Complete Set:	4.00	3.00	1.50

2878 Tim Cecil
2879 Sean Doty
2880 Scott Duff
2881 Chris Hook
2882 Doug King
2883 Reggie Leslie
2884 Ernie Nieves
2885 Johnny Ray
2886 John Roper
2887 Carl Stewart
2888 Kevin Tatar
2889 Roy Hammargren
2890 Greg Hammond
2891 Dan Wilson
2892 Rafael Bustamante
2893 Herb Erhardt
2894 Chris Gill
2895 Bobby Perna
2896 Tom Raffo
2897 Lenny Wentz
2898 Mark Arland
2899 Steve Gibralter
2900 Elliott Quinones
2901 Chris Vasquez
2902 Dave Miley
2903 Derek Botelho
2904 Checklist

1991 ProCards Charlotte Knights

(Chicago Cubs) (color)

	MT	NR MT	EX
Complete Set:	5.00	3.75	2.00

1681 Jim Bullinger
1682 Steve DiBartolomeo
1683 John Gardner
1684 Henry Gomez
1685 Shannon Jones
1686 Tim Parker
1687 John Salles
1688 Mike Sodders
1689 Julio Strauss
1690 Tim Watkins
1691 Michael Knapp
1692 Scott Taylor
1693 Alex Arias
1694 Paul Blair
1695 Dick Canan
1696 Rusty Crockett
1697 Elvin Paulino
1698 Bill St. Peter
1699 Billy White
1700 Ty Griffin
1701 Fernando Ramsey
1702 Kevin Roberson
1703 Doug Welch
1704 Jay Loviglio
1705 Rick Kranitz
1706 Checklist

1991 Classic Best Charlotte Rangers

(Texas Rangers) (color)

	MT	NR MT	EX
Complete Set:	4.00	3.00	1.50

1 Michael Arner
2 Eric Bickhardt
3 Travis Buckley
4 Joey Eischen
5 Nick Felix
6 Barry Goetz
7 Darren Oliver
8 Juan Quero
9 Carl Randle
10 Steve Rowley
11 Kyle Spencer
12 Brian Steiner
13 Darren Niethammer
14 Kevin Tannahill
15 Barry Winford
16 James Clinton
17 Cris Colon
18 Todd Guggiana
19 Craig Newkirk
20 Jose Oliva
21 Rusty Greer
22 David Hulse
23 Timmie Morrow (Last name misspelled on checklist.)
24 Ken Powell
25 Jose Texidor
27a Donna Van Duzer (Trainer, numbered correctly on checklist.)
27b Bob Molinaro
28 Marvin White
29 Walt Williams
30 Checklist (Not listed on checklist.)

1991 ProCards Charlotte Rangers

(Texas Rangers) (color)

	MT	NR MT	EX
Complete Set:	4.00	3.00	1.50

1305 Michael Arner
1306 Eric Bickhardt
1307 Travis Buckley
1308 Joey Eischen
1309 Nick Felix
1310 Barry Goetz
1311 Darren Oliver
1312 Juan Quero
1313 Carl Randle
1314 Stephen Rowley
1315 Kyle Spencer
1316 Brian Steiner
1317 Darren Niethammer
1318 Kevin Tannahill
1319 Barry Winford
1320 Jim Clinton
1321 Cris Colon
1322 Todd Guggiana
1323 Craig Newkirk
1324 Jose Oliva
1325 Rusty Greer
1326 David Hulse
1327 Timmie Morrow
1328 Kenny Powell
1329 Jose Texidor
1330 Bobby Molinaro
1331 Marvin White
1332 Checklist

1991 ProCards Chattanooga Lookouts

(Cincinnati Reds) (color)

	MT	NR MT	EX
Complete Set:	5.00	3.75	2.00

1950 Mike Anderson
1951 Bobby Ayala
1952 Bill Dodd
1953 Steve Foster
1954 Victor Garcia
1955 Scott Jeffery
1956 Dave McAuliffe
1957 Steve McCarthy
1958 Tim Pugh
1959 Bill Risley
1960 Mo Sandford
1961 Jerry Spradlin
1962 Joe Turek
1963 Glenn Sutko
1964 Rick Allen
1965 Jeff Branson
1966 Frank Kremblas
1967 Greg Lonigro
1968 Scott Sellner
1969 Todd Trafton
1970 Scott Bryant
1971 Ben Colvard
1972 Scott Pose
1973 Reggie Sanders
1974 Jim Tracy
1975 Mike Griffin
1976 Checklist

1991 Classic Best Clearwater Phillies

(Philadelphia Phillies) (color)

	MT	NR MT	EX
Complete Set:	3.00	2.25	1.25

1 Elliott Gray (No position on card back.)
2 Paul Fletcher
3 Bob Gaddy
4 Darrell Goedhart
5 Ramon Henderson
6 Chris Limbach
7 Steve Parris
8 Matt Stevens
9 Mike Sullivan
10 Darold Knowles
11 Scott Wiegandt
12 Mike Williams
13 Matt Current
14 Terry Tewell
15 Pat Brady
16 John Escobar
17 Ron Lockett
18 Lee Ella
19 R.A. Neitzel
20 Troy Paulsen
21 Mickey Hyde
22 Tom Nuneviller
23 Stacy Parker
24 Sam Taylor
25 Joe Urbon
26 Leroy Ventress
27 Checklist (Not listed on checklist.)
---- Clearwater Logo
---- Phillies Logo
---- Schmidt Ad

1991 ProCards Clearwater Phillies

(Philadelphia Phillies) (color)

	MT	NR MT	EX
Complete Set:	3.00	2.25	1.25

1613 Paul Fletcher
1614 Bob Gaddy
1615 Darrell Goedhart
1616 Elliott Gray
1617 Chris Limbach
1618 Steve Parris
1619 Matt Stevens
1620 Mike Sullivan
1621 Bob Wells
1622 Scott Wiegandt
1623 Mike Williams
1624 Matt Current
1625 Terry Tewell
1626 Pat Brady
1627 John Escobar
1628 Ron Lockett
1629 Joe Millette
1630 R.A. Neitzel
1631 Troy Paulsen
1632 Mickey Hyde
1633 Tom Nuneviller
1634 Stacy Parker
1635 Sam Taylor
1636 Joe Urbon

1637 Leroy Ventress
1638 Lee Elia
1639 Ramon Henderson
1640 Darold Knowles
1641 Checklist

1991 Classic Best Clinton Giants

(San Francisco Giants) (color)

	MT	NR MT	EX
Complete Set:	5.00	3.75	2.00

1 Dan Carlson
2 Dan Flanagan
3 Dan Henrikson
4 Brett McGonnigal
5 Rod Huffman
6 Joe Rosselli
7 Kurt Peltzer
8 Salomon Torres
9 Jose Reyes
10 Mark Yockey
11 Mate Borgogno
12 Matt Davis
13 Andres Duncan
14 Eric Christopherson
15 Gary Mayse
16 Bill Carpine
17 Shelby Hart
18 Pepe Frias
19 Teodulo Mejias
20 Adam Hyzdu
21 Barry Miller
22 Rikkert Faneyte
23 Greg Brummett
24 Ricky Ward
25 Jason Young
26 Jack Mull
27 Steve Cline
28 Deron McCue
29 Team card/checklist
---- Clinton Logo

1991 ProCards Clinton Giants

(San Francisco Giants) (color)

	MT	NR MT	EX
Complete Set:	5.00	3.75	2.00

826 Dan Carlson
827 Dan Flanagan
828 Dan Henrikson
829 Rod Huffman
830 Brian McLeod
831 Mike Myers
832 Kurt Peltzer
833 Jose Reyes
834 Salomon Torres
835 Mark Yockey
836 Eric Christopherson
837 Mike Grahovac
838 Teodulo Mejias
839 Mate Borgogno
840 Matt Davis
841 Andres Duncan
842 Carlos Lak
843 Barry Miller
844 Ricky Ward
845 Courtney Davis
846 Shelby Hart
847 Adam Hyzdu
848 Roberto Ramirez
849 Dan Rumsey
850 Jason Young
851 Jack Mull
852 Deron McCue
853 Steve Cline
854 Checklist

1991 ProCards Colorado Springs Sky Sox

(Cleveland Indians) (color)

	MT	NR MT	EX
Complete Set:	5.00	3.75	2.00

2176 Jeff Bittiger
2177 Willie Blair
2178 Steve Cummings
2179 Mauro Gozzo
2180 Dave Otto
2181 Rudy Seanez
2182 Jeff Shaw
2183 Efrain Valdez
2184 Sergio Valdez
2185 Kevin Wickander
2186 Brian Johnson
2187 Eddie Taubensee
2188 Marty Brown
2189 Kevin Burdick
2190 Mark Lewis
2191 Luis Lopez
2192 Ever Magallanes
2193 Luis Medina
2194 Bernie Tatis
2195 Geronimo Berroa
2196 Barry Jones
2197 Wayne Kirby
2198 John Moses
2199 Roberto Zambrano
2200 Charlie Manuel
2201 Rick Adair
2202 Jim Gabella
2203 Checklist

1991 Play II Columbia Mets

(New York Mets) (color)

	MT	NR MT	EX
Complete Set:	7.00	5.25	2.75

1 Tim Blackwell
2 Bill Latham
3 Howie Freiling
4 Bob Burton
5 Tom Engle
6 Ed Perozo
7 Tom Allison
8 Rob Rees
9 Omar Garcia
10 Berto Castillo
11 Edwards Fully
12 Richie Bristow
13 Aaron Ledesma
14 Juan Castillo
15 Fernando Vina
16 Mike Thomas
17 Bernie Millan
18 Jake King
19 Brian Dunn (First name different on card back.)
20 Danilo Mompres
21 Tim McClinton
22 Robbi Guzik
23 Mike Freitas
24 Jay Davis
25 Mason Rudolph
26 Rob Carpentier
27 Tom Wegman
28 Jose Martinez
29 Butch Huskey
30 Met Maulers
31 Strike Force
32 Tito Navarro

1991 Police Columbus Clippers

(New York Yankees) (color)

	MT	NR MT	EX
Complete Set:	4.00	3.00	1.50

(1) Steve Adkins
(2) Daven Bond
(3) Darrin Chapin
(4) Royal Clayton
(5) Steve Howe
(6) Keith Hughes
(7) Mike Humphreys
(8) Jeff Johnson
(9) Scott Kamieniecki
(10) Pat Kelly
(11) Jason Maas
(12) Alan Mills
(13) Kevin Mmahat
(14) Rich Montelone
(15) John Ramos
(16) Carlos Rodriguez
(17) Dave Sax
(18) Van Snider
(19) Don Sparks
(20) Andy Stankiewicz
(21) Wade Taylor
(22) Jim Walewander
(23) Bernie Williams
---- Clete Royer, Gary Denbo, Monk Meyer, Rick Down, Ken Schnacks

1991 ProCards Columbus Clippers

(New York Yankees) (color)

	MT	NR MT	EX
Complete Set:	5.00	3.75	2.00

588 Steve Adkins
589 Daven Bond
590 Darrin Chapin
591 Royal Clayton
592 Steve Howe
593 Jeff Johnson
594 Scott Kamieniecki
595 Alan Mills
596 Rich Monteleone
597 Hipolito Pena
598 Wade Taylor
599 John Ramos
600 Dave Sax
601 Keith Hughes
602 Pat Kelly
603 Torey Lovullo
604 Carlos Rodriguez
605 Don Sparks
606 Andy Stankiewicz
607 Jim Walewander
608 Mike Humphreys
609 Jason Maas
610 Pat Sheridan
611 Van Snider
612 Bernie Williams
613 Team picture
614 Rick Down
615 Field Staff
616 Checklist

1991 Classic Best Columbus Indians

(Cleveland Indians) (color)

	MT	NR MT	EX
Complete Set:	3.00	2.25	1.25

1 Raymond Harvey
2 Victor Jones
3 Joe Perez
4 Kyle Washington
5 Mike Pinckes
6 David Milcki
7 Mark Charbonnet
8 Andy Baker
9 Sam Baker
10 Dickie Brown
11 Brian Cofer
12 Alan Embree
13 Steve Gajkowski
14 Mike McLochlin
15 Robert Rivera
16 Delvy Santiago
17 Alan Walden
18 Bill Wertz
19 Chip Winiarski
20 John Lorms
21 Kelly Stinnett
22 David Bell
23 John Cotton
24 Tim Donahue
25 Jason Hardtke
26 Rod McCall
27 Fabio Gamez (Different position on card back.)
28 Robbie Smith
29 Pat Bryant
30 Teddy Blackwell (Checklist)

1991 ProCards Columbus Indians

(Cleveland Indians) (color)

	MT	NR MT	EX
Complete Set:	3.00	2.25	1.25

1475 Andy Baker
1476 Sam Baker
1477 Dickie Brown
1478 Brian Cofer
1479 Alan Embree
1480 Steve Gajkowski
1481 Mike McLochlin
1482 Roberto Rivera
1483 Delvy Santiago
1484 Alan Walden
1485 Bill Wertz
1486 Chip Winiarski
1487 John Lorms
1488 Kelly Stinnett
1489 David Bell
1490 John Cotton
1491 Tim Donahue
1492 Jason Hardtke
1493 Rod McCall
1494 Mike Pinckes
1495 Robbie Smith
1496 Patrick Bryant
1497 Mark Charbonnet
1498 Raymond Harvey
1499 Pedro Henderson
1500 Victor Jones
1501 Joe Perez
1502 Ramon Torres
1503 Kyle Washington
1504 Mike Brown
1505 Dyar Miller (Not listed on checklist.)
1506 Checklist (Not listed on checklist.)

1991 ProCards Denver Zephyrs

(Milwaukee Brewers) (color)

	MT	NR MT	EX
Complete Set:	5.00	3.75	2.00

114 Jim Austin
115 Jim Davins
116 Cal Eldred
117 Narciso Elvira
118 Brian Fisher
119 Chris George
120 Doug Henry
121 Mike Ignasiak
122 Jeff Kalser
123 Ed Pulg
124 Carlos Diaz
125 Joe Kmak
126 Tim McIntosh
127 Esteban Beltre
128 George Canale
129 Juan Castillo
130 Sandy Guerrero
131 Charlie Montoyo
132 D.L. Smith
133 Mickey Brantley
134 Matias Carrillo
135 Jim Olander
136 Rolando Roomes
137 Tony Muser
138 Lamar Johnson
139 Don Rowe
140 Checklist

1991 Classic Best Dunedin Blue Jays

(Toronto Blue Jays) (color)

	MT	NR MT	EX
Complete Set:	4.00	3.00	1.50

1 Scott Brow
2 Daren Brown
3 Tim Brown
4 Daren Kizziah (First name misspelled on checklist.)
5 Graeme Lloyd
6 Gregg Martin
7 Paul Menhart
8 Marcus Moore
9 Mike Ogliaruso
10 Aaron Small
11 John Wanish
12 Eric Brooks
13 Anastacio Garcia
14 Greg O'Halloran
15 Bill Abare
16 Nandi Cruz
17 Brad Mengel
18 Billy Parese
19 David Tollison
20 Tim Hodge
21 Shawn Holtzclaw
22 Robert Perez
23 Shawn Scott
24 Nigel Wilson
25 Dennis Holmberg
26 Bill Monbouquette
27 Pete Rowe
28 Rob Montalvo
29 Kris Harmes
30 Jon Woodworth (Checklist)

1991 ProCards Dunedin Blue Jays

(Toronto Blue Jays) (color)

	MT	NR MT	EX
Complete Set:	4.00	3.00	1.50

197 Scott Brow
198 Daren Brown
199 Tim Brown
200 Daren Kizziah
201 Graeme Lloyd
202 Gregg Martin
203 Paul Menhart
204 Marcus Moore
205 Mike Ogliaruso
206 Aaron Small
207 John Wanish
208 Eric Brooks
209 Anastacio Garcia
210 Kris Harmes
211 Greg O'Halloran
212 Bill Abare
213 Nandi Cruz
214 Brad Mengel
215 Robert Montalvo
216 Billy Parese
217 David Tollison
218 Tim Hodge
219 Shawn Holtzclaw
220 Robert Perez
221 Shawn Scott
222 Nigel Wilson
223 Dennis Holmberg
224 Bill Monbouquette
225 Checklist

1991 Classic Best Durham Bulls

(Atlanta Braves) (color)

	MT	NR MT	EX
Complete Set:	10.50	8.00	4.25

1 Matt Shiflett
2 Brian Bark
3 David Nied
4 Matt Murray
5 Jeff Cronin
6 Mike Kelly
7 Dennis Burlingame
8 Dave Brust
9 Earl Steinmetz
10 Pedro Borbon
11 Steve Swall
12 Eddie Perez
13 Mike Mordecai
14 Ed Giovanola
15 Grady Little
16 Larry Jaster
17 Tim Gillis
18 Pat Dando
19 Javy Lopez
20 Jeff Clark
21 Tony Tarasco
22 Shawn Sottile
23 Brent McCoy
24 Ramon Caraballo
25 Brian Kowitz
26 Phillip Wellman (Checklist)
---- Bulls Logo
---- Braves Logo
---- MLB Logo
---- Schmidt Ad

1991 ProCards Durham Bulls

(Atlanta Braves) (color)

	MT	NR MT	EX
Complete Set:	8.00	6.00	3.25

1535 Brian Bark
1536 Pedro Borbon
1537 Dennis Burlingame
1538 Jeff Cronin
1539 Roger Hailey
1540 Matt Murray
1541 David Nied
1542 Walt Roy
1543 Matt Shiflett
1544 Earl Steinmetz
1545 Don Strange
1546 Scott Taylor
1547 Javy Lopez
1548 Eddie Perez
1549 Steve Swall
1550 Dave Brust
1551 Ramon Caraballo
1552 Pat Dando
1553 Tim Gillis
1554 Ed Giovanola
1555 Pat Kelly
1556 Brent McCoy
1557 Mike Mordecai
1558 Jeff Clark (Checklist error, listed as # 1671.)
1559 Brian Kowitz (Checklist error, listed as # 1672.)
1560 Melvin Nieves (Checklist error, listed as # 1673.)
1561 Randy Simmons (Checklist error, listed as # 1674.)
1675 Tony Tarasco (Numbered out of sequence.)
1676 Grady Little (Numbered out of sequence.)
1677 Gil Garrido (Numbered out of sequence.)
1678 Larry Jaster (Numbered out of sequence.)
1679 Phil Wellman (Numbered out of sequence.)
1680 Checklist (Numbered out of sequence.)

1991 ProCards Durham Bulls Update

(Atlanta Braves) (color)

	MT	NR MT	EX
Complete Set:	4.00	3.00	1.50

1 Mike Kelly
2 Hank Werland
3 Rob Mattson
4 Marcos Vazquez
5 Nate Minchey
6 Darren Ritter
7 Greg McMichael
8 Darren Watkins
9 Checklist

1991 ProCards Edmondton Trappers

(California Angels) (color)

	MT	NR MT	EX
Complete Set:	7.00	5.25	2.75

1507 Kyle Abbott
1508 Chris Beasley
1509 Gary Buckles
1510 Tim Burcham
1511 Mike Erb
1512 Mike Fetters
1513 Joe Grahe
1514 Dave Leiper
1515 Rafael Montalvo
1516 Ed Vosberg
1517 Cliff Young
1518 Doug Davis
1519 Ron Tingley
1520 Kent Anderson
1521 Chris Cron
1522 Chad Curtis
1523 Gary DiSarcina
1524 Bobby Rose
1525 Mark Wasinger
1526 Ruben Amaro
1527 Mark Davis
1528 Dan Grunhard
1529 Reed Peters
1530 Lee Stevens
1531 Max Oliveras
1532 Gary Ruby
1533 Lenn Sakata
1534 Checklist

1991 ProCards Elizabethton Twins

(Minnesota Twins) (color)

	MT	NR MT	EX
Complete Set:	3.00	2.25	1.25

4293 Ron Caridad
4294 Bob Carlson
4295 Sandy Diaz
4296 Eddie Guardado
4297 Melanio Mieses
4298 Rafael Pina
4299 Dave Sartain
4300 Dave Schwartz
4301 Dennis Sweeney
4302 Alvin Brown
4303 Pedro Gritol
4304 Francisco Ramirez
4305 Mike Fernandez
4306 Craig Hawkins
4307 Steve Hazlett
4308 Scott Shell
4309 Ramon Valette
4310 Merritt Bowden
4311 Brent Brede
4312 Tim Moore
4313 Kenny Norman
4314 Kevin Strong
4315 Ray Smith
4316 Jim Lemon
4317 Rick Tomlin
4318 Checklist

1991 Classic Best Elmira Pioneers

(Boston Red Sox) (color)

	MT	NR MT	EX
Complete Set:	6.00	4.50	2.50

1 Brian Bright
2 Felix Colon
3 Jim Crowley
4 John Eierman
5 Jason Fridman (Last name spelled differently on checklist.)
6 Tim Graham
7 John Lammon
8 Dana LeVangle
9 Jose Lora
10 Bill Madril
11 Jose Marin
12 Paul Rappoli
13 Tony Rodriguez
14 Frank Rodriguez
15 Emison Soto
16 Corey Bailey
17 Timothy Budrewicz
18 Chris Davis
19 Richard Delgado
20 Rob Henkel
21 Melvin Gonzalez
22 Mark Konopki
23 John Chafin
24 Todd Miller
25 Mark Mitchelson
26 Alberto Pratts
27 Dave Holt
28 Garry Roggenburk
29 K.K. Cards
30 Steve Jacobucci (Checklist)

1991 ProCards Elmira Pioneers

(Boston Red Sox) (color)

	MT	NR MT	EX
Complete Set:	9.00	6.75	3.50

3261 Cory Bailey
3262 Tim Budrewicz
3263 John Chafin
3264 Chris Davis
3265 Richard Delgado
3266 Melvin Gonzales
3267 Rob Henkel
3268 Mark Konopki
3269 Todd Miller
3270 Mark Mitchelson
3271 Alberto Pratts
3272 John Lammon
3273 Dana LeVangie
3274 Bill Madril
3275 Felix Colon
3276 Jim Crowley
3277 Jason Friedman
3278 Jose Marin
3279 Frank Rodriguez
3280 Tony Rodriguez
3281 Brian Bright
3282 John Eierman
3283 Tim Graham
3284 Jose Lora
3285 Paul Rappoli
3286 Emirson Soto
3287 Dave Holt
3288 Garry Roggenburk
3289 Checklist

1991 ProCards El Paso Diablos

(Milwaukee Brewers) (color)

	MT	NR MT	EX
Complete Set:	8.00	6.00	3.25

2739 Mark Chapman
2740 Jim Czajkowski
2741 Tim Fortugno
2742 Don Gordon
2743 Chris Johnson
2744 Mark Kiefer
2745 Steve Lienhard
2746 Tom McGraw
2747 Angel Miranda
2748 Jeff Schwarz
2749 Steve Sparks
2750 Craig Faulkner
2751 Dave Nilsson
2752 John Byington
2753 Pat Listach
2754 Mike Guerrero
2755 Mitch Hannahs
2756 John Jaha
2757 Jim Tatum
2758 Shon Ashley
2859 Ruben Escalera
2860 Dave Jacas
2861 Kenny Jackson
2862 Dave Huppert
2863 Paul Linblad
2864 Checklist

1991 Classic Best Erie Sailors

(Independent) (color)

	MT	NR MT	EX
Complete Set:	7.00	5.25	2.75

Sailors Logo
1 Amador Arias
2 Rafael Astacio
3 Irene Cabral
4 J.J. Cruz
5 Steve DiMarco
6 Rick Juday
7 Dan Mahony
8 Kenny Marrero
9 Scott Sprick
10 Jeff Stenta
11 Kelvin Thomas
12 Noel Velez
13 Jim Whitman
14 David Carter
15 Joe Andrzejewski
16 Matt Connolly
17 Dom Konleczki
18 Jeff Letourneau
19 Mike Lynch
20 Edwin Millerick
21 Tom Paskievitch
22 Scott Pudlo (Last name misspelled on card front)
23 Tim Roberts
24 Roosevelt Smith
25 Bob Zeihen
26 Roberto Marte
27 Ray Korn
28 Barry Moss
29 ChecklistWJEE News Team (Not listed on checklist)

1991 ProCards Erie Sailors

(Independent) (color)

	MT	NR MT	EX
Complete Set:	6.00	4.50	2.50

4059 Joe Andrzejewski
4060 David Carter
4061 Matt Connolly
4062 Dom Konieczki
4063 Curt Krippner
4064 Jeff Letourneau
4065 Mike Lynch
4066 Edwin Millerick
4067 Tom Paskievitch
4068 Scott Pudlo
4069 Tim Roberts
4070 Roosevelt Smith
4071 J.J. Cruz
4072 Dan Mahony
4073 Ken Marrero
4074 Amador Arias
4075 Rafael Astacio
4076 Rich Juday
4077 Steve DiMarco
4078 Scott Sprick
4079 Jeff Stenta
4080 Irene Cabral
4081 Kelvin Thomas
4082 Noel Velez
4083 Jim Whitman
4084 Barry Moss
4085 Ray Korn
4086 Roberto Marte
4087 Bob Zeihen
4088 Checklist

1991 Classic Best Eugene Emeralds

(Kansas City Royals) (color)

	MT	NR MT	EX
Complete Set:	7.00	5.25	2.75

1 Tony Castro
2 Dave Haber
3 Andy Brookens
4 Shane Halter
5 Troy Babbitt
6 Nick Kaiser
7 Ramie Brooks
8 Paul Sanders
9 Steve Hinton
10 Vernon Slater
11 Mark Johnson
12 Dan Servello
13 Les Norman
14 Joe Randa
15 Joe Vitiello
16 Kevin Kobetitsch
17 Dave Farsaci
18 John Medrick
19 Angel Macias
20 Jeff Smith
21 Danny Miceli
22 John Downs
23 Thomas Lee
24 Roger Landress
25 Mike Bailey
26 Joel Johnson
27 Jason Bryans
28 Kris Glaser (No position listed on card back.)
29 Chris Connolly
30 Checklist (Not listed on set checklist.)

1991 ProCards Eugene Emeralds

(Kansas City Royals) (color)

	MT	NR MT	EX
Complete Set:	6.00	4.50	2.50

3714 Mike Bailey
3715 Jason Bryans
3716 Chris Connolly
3717 J.D. Downs
3718 Dave Farsaci
3719 Kris Glaser
3720 Joel Johnson
3721 Kevin Kobetitsch
3722 Roger Landress
3723 Thomas Lee
3724 Angel Macias
3725 John Medrick
3726 Danny Miceli
3727 Jeff Smith
3728 Rayme Brooks
3729 Paul Sanders
3730 Troy Babbitt
3731 Andy Brookens
3732 Dave Haber
3733 Shane Halter
3734 Steve Hinton
3735 Nick Kaiser
3736 Joe Randa
3737 Tony Castro

3738 Mark Johnson
3739 Les Norman
3740 Dan Servello
3741 Vernon Slater
3742 Hoe Vitiello
3743 Checklist

1991 ProCards Florida State League All Stars

	MT	NR MT	EX
Complete Set:	7.00	5.25	2.75

1 Phil Hiatt
2 Tony Long
3 Kevin Shaw
4 Rusty Greer
5 Darren Niethammer
6 Pat Brady
7 Ron Lockett
8 Troy Paulsen
9 Paul Menhart
10 Migel Wilson
11 Rich Batchelor
12 Jovino Carvajal
13 Mark Hutton
14 Brian Johnson
15 Kevin Jordan
16 Bob Munoz
17 Rey Noriega
18 Russ Springer
19 Jeff Braley
20 Brian Cornelius
21 Kirk Mendenhall
22 Paris Hayden
23 Jonathan Hurst
24 Mike Lansing
25 Tom Michno
26 Montie Phillips
27 Rod Bolton
28 Scott Cepicky
29 Rob Lukachyk
30 Todd Douma
31 Brook Fordyce
32 Pat Howell
33 Curtis Pride
34 Paul Ellis
35 Rick Shackle
36 Adam Brown
37 Ray Calhoun
38 Marc Griffin
39 Matt Howard
40 Michael Mimbs
41 Chris Morrow
42 Reid Cornelius
43 Rusty Kilgo
44 Joe Logan
45 Gary Painter
46 Checklist

1991 Classic Best Everett Giants

(San Francisco Giants) (color)

	MT	NR MT	EX
Complete Set:	7.00	5.25	2.75

1 D.J. Thielen
2 Doug VanderWeele
3 Al Rodriguez (No position listed on card back.)
4 Randy Swank
5 Brett McGonnigal
6 Don Montgomery
7 Ray Jackson
8 Dax Jones
9 Ken Feist
10 Tim Florez
11 Frank Charles
12 Derek Dana
13 Tim Casper
14 Jarod Juelsgaard
15 Tim Luther
16 Shawn Henrichs
17 Rich Hyde
18 Ken Grundt
19 Ken Henderson
20 Moose Adams
21 Matt Brewer
22 Lenny Ayers
23 Eric Stonecipher
24 Bill VanLandingham
25 Chuck Wanke
26 Darren Wittcke
27 Roberto Ramirez
28 Kevin Bellomo
29 Paul Eckard
30 Checklist (Not listed on checklist.)

1991 ProCards Everett Giants

(San Francisco Giants) (color)

	MT	NR MT	EX
Complete Set:	6.00	4.50	2.50

3904 Moose Adams
3905 Lenny Ayres
3906 Ken Grundt
3907 Shawn Henrichs
3908 Rich Hyde
3909 Jarod Juelsgaard
3910 Tim Luther
3911 Eric Stonecipher
3912 Doug VanderWeele
3913 William VanLandingham
3914 Chuck Wanke
3915 Darren Wittcke
3916 Dan Calcagno
3917 Frank Charles
3918 Derek Dana
3919 Don Montgomery
3920 Tim Casper
3921 Tim Florez
3922 Roberto Ramirez
3923 Al Rodriguez
3924 Randy Swank
3925 D.J. Thielen
3926 Kevin Bellomo
3927 Matt Brewer
3928 Ken Feist
3929 Ken Henderson
3930 Ray Jackson
3931 Dax Jones
3932 Brett McGonnigal
3933 giants (Rob Ellis)
3934 Mike Bubalo
3935 Dan Spiliner
3936 Checklist

1991 ProCards Fayetteville Generals

(Detroit Tigers) (color)

	MT	NR MT	EX
Complete Set:	6.00	4.50	2.50

1161 Greg Coppeta
1162 Bob Fazekas
1163 Mike Guilfoyle
1164 Greg Haeger
1165 John Kosenski
1166 Joe Neidinger
1167 Corey Reincke
1168 Eddy Rodriguez
1169 Randy Stokes
1170 Bob Undorf
1171 Brian Warren
1172 Shannon Withem
1173 Sean Sadler
1174 Brian Saltzgaber
1175 Brad Wilson
1176 Jimmy Alder
1177 Carlos Fermin
1178 Doug Kimbler
1179 Carlos Maldonado
1180 Kelley O'Neal
1181 Dan Rogers
1182 Dan Bautista
1183 Steve Looney
1184 Aaron Seja
1185 Mike Weinberg
1186 Gerry Groninger
1187 Rich Bombard
1188 Dwight Lowery
1189 Checklist

1991 Classic Best Fayetteville Generais

(Detroit Tigers) (color)

	MT	NR MT	EX
Complete Set:	7.00	5.25	2.75

1 Greg Coppetta
2 Mike Guilfoyle
3 Greg Haeger
4 John Kosenski
5 Seth Stephens
6 Joe Neidinger
7 Corey Reincke
8 Eddy Rodriguez
9 Bob Fazekas
10 Brad Wilson
11 Dwight Lowery
12 Rich Bombard
13 Shannon Withem
14 Gerry Groninger
15 Dean Sadler
16 Brian Saltzgaber
17 Jimmy Adler
18 Carlos Fermin
19 Doug Kimbler
20 Carlos Maldonado
21 Kelley O'Neal
22 Dan Rogers
23 Dan Bautista
24 Steve Looney
25 Aaron Beja
26 Mike Weinberg
27 Robert Undorf
28 Randall Stokes
29 Brian Warren
30 Mike Delao (Checklist)

1991 Classic Best Ft. Lauderdale Yankees

(New York Yankees) (color)

	MT	NR MT	EX
Complete Set:	7.00	5.25	2.75

1 Rich Batchelor
2 Art Canestro
3 Glenn Sherlock
4 Ken Greer
5 Mark Hutton
6 Ramon Manon
7 Moose Marris
8 Ted Uhlaender
9 Bob Munoz
10 Jerry Nielsen
11 Rich Polak
12 Bruce Prybylinski
13 Tim Rumer
14 Russ Springer
15 Jim Wiley
16 Brian Johnson
17 Jose Pineda
18 Larry Walker
19 Juan Blackwell
20 Dave Howell
21 Kevin Jordan
22 Rey Noriega
23 Andres Rodriguez
24 Rich Barnwell
25 Jovino Carvajal
26 Nookie Garland
27 Jay Leach
28 Rick Strickland
29 Mike Brown
30 Checklist (Not listed on set checklist.)

1991 ProCards Ft. Lauderdale Yankees

(New York Yankees) (color)

	MT	NR MT	EX
Complete Set:	6.00	4.50	2.50

2416 Rich Batchelor
2417 Art Canestro
2418 Ken Greer
2419 Mark Hutton
2420 Ramon Manon
2421 Mark Marris
2422 Bob Munoz
2423 Jerry Nielsen
2424 Rich Polak
2425 Bruce Prybylinski
2426 Tim Rumer
2427 Russ Springer
2428 Jim Wiley
2429 Brian Johnson
2430 Jose Pineda
2431 Larry Walker
2432 Juan Blackwell
2433 Dave Howell
2434 Kevin Jordan
2435 Rey Noriega
2436 Andres Rodriguez
2437 Aaron Van Scoyoc
2438 Rich Barnwell
2439 Jovino Carvajal
2440 Tim Garland
2441 Jalal Leach
2442 Rick Strickland
2443 Glenn Sherlock
2444 Mike Brown
2445 Ted Uhlaender
2446 Checklist

1991 Classic Best Frederick Keys

(Baltimore Orioles) (color)

	MT	NR MT	EX
Complete Set:	7.00	5.25	2.75

1 Mark Carper
2 Andres Constant
3 Shane Hale
4 Mike Hook
5 Zachary Kerr
6 John O'Donoghue Jr.
7 Chuck Ricci
8 David Riddle
9 Jeff Williams
10 Steve Williams
11 Kip Yaughn
12 Cesar Devares
13 Ed Horowitz
14 Doug Reynolds
15 Manny Alexander
16 Tony Beasley
17 Randy Berlin
18 T.R. Lewis
19 Scott Sprick
20 Mel Wearing Jr.
21 Jason Alstead
22 Dan Berthel
23 Damon Buford
24 Sergio Cairo
25 Pat Hedge
26 Wally Moon
27 John O'Donoghue Sr. (Coach)
28 Joel Youngblood
29 Rob Kessinger
30 Mitch Bibb (Checklist)

1991 ProCards Frederick Keys

(Baltimore Orioles) (color)

	MT	NR MT	EX
Complete Set:	6.00	4.50	2.50

2355 Mark Carper
2356 Andres Constant
2357 Shane Hale
2358 Mike Hook
2359 Pat Leinen
2360 Daryl Moore
2361 John O'Donoghue
2362 Chuck Ricci
2363 David Riddle
2364 Jeff Williams
2365 Kip Yaughn
2366 Cesar Devares
2367 Ed Horowitz
2368 Doug Reynolds
2369 Manny Alexander
2370 Tony Beasley
2371 Randy Berlin
2372 T.R. Lewis
2373 Scott Sprick
2374 Mel Wearing
2375 Jason Alstead
2376 Dan Berthel
2377 Damon Buford
2379 Roy Gilbert
2380 Pat Hedge
2381 Wally Moon
2382 Don Buford
2383 Checklist

1991 Classic Best Gastonia Rangers

(Texas Rangers) (color)

	MT	NR MT	EX
Complete Set:	7.00	5.25	2.75

1 Tony Bouton
2 Terry Burrows
3 Jose Cardona
4 Steve Dreyer
5 Scott Erickson
6 Chris Gies
7 Mickey Henson
8 Victor Madrigal
9 Keith McGough
10 Tyrone Washington
11 Tim Wells
12 Matt Whiteside
13 Greg Blevins (Last name spelled differently on checklist.)
14 Michael Crespo
15 Tom Hernandez
16 Miguel Castellano
17 Bump Wills
18 David Lowery
19 Randy Marshall
20 Paul Matachun
21 Shannon Penn
22 Jon Shave
23 Sid Holland
24 Malvin Matos
25 Keith Murray
26 Marty Posey
27 Dell Curry
28 Tom Tisdale
29 Muggsy Bogues
30 Rowdy Ranger (Checklist)

1991 ProCards Gastonia Rangers

(Texas Rangers) (color)

	MT	NR MT	EX
Complete Set:	6.00	4.50	2.50

2678 Tony Bouton
2679 Terry Burrows
2680 Jose Cardona
2681 Steve Dreyer
2682 Scott Erickson
2683 Chris Gies
2684 Mickey Henson
2685 Victor Madrigal
2686 Keith McGough
2687 Tyrone Washington
2688 Tim Wells
2689 Matt Whiteside
2690 Greg Blevins
2691 Mike Crespo

2692 Tom Hernandez
2693 Miguel Castellanos
2694 Pete Laake
2695 David Lowery
2696 Randy Marshall
2697 Paul Matachun
2698 Shannon Penn
2699 Jon Shave
2700 Sid Holland
2701 Malvin Matos
2702 Keith Murray
2703 Marty Posey
2704 Bump Wills
2705 Perry Hill
2706 Jackson Todd
2707 Randy Whisler
2708 Checklist

1991 Classic Best Geneva Cubs

(Chicago Cubs) (color)

	MT	NR MT	EX
Complete Set:	7.00	5.25	2.75

1 Bill Bliss
2 Ben Burlingame
3 Dale Craig
4 Morris Craig
5 Steve Davis
6 Serge Dolron
7 Willie Gardner
8 Rudy Gomez
9 Pat Huston
10 Brian Kenny
11 Ed Larregul
12 Ricardo Medina
13 Tim Moore
14 Leo Perez
15 Pedro Perez
16 Jim Robinson
17 Humberto Saa de la Cruz
18 Joe Sarcia
19 Greg Mahlberg
20 Joe Szczepanski
21 Joey Terilli
22 Mike Tidwell
23 Ozzie Timmons
24 Doug Gianville
25 Scott Weiss
26 Mike Young
27 Carl Schramm
28 Joe Housey
29 Phil Hannon
30 Checklist (Not listed on set checklist.)

1991 ProCards Geneva Cubs

(Chicago Cubs) (color)

	MT	NR MT	EX
Complete Set:	6.00	4.50	2.50

4207 Bill Bliss
4208 Ben Burlingame
4209 Steve Davis
4210 Brian Kenny
4211 Leo Perez
4212 Pedro Perez
4213 Carl Schramm
4214 Dave Stevens
4215 Joe Szczepanski
4216 Mike Tidwell
4217 Steve Trachsel
4218 Scott Weiss
4219 Mike Young
4220 Dale Craig
4221 Serge Doiron
4222 Jim Robinson
4223 Rudy Gomez
4224 Pat Huston
4225 Ricardo Medina
4226 Tim Moore
4227 Humberto Saa
4228 Joe Sarcia
4229 Willie Gardner
4230 Doug Glanville
4231 Ed Larregui
4232 Joey Terilli (Last name misspelled on checklist.)
4233 Ozzie Timmons
4234 Greg Mahlberg
4235 Phil Hannon
4236 Checklist

1991 Sport Pro Great Falls Dodgers

(Los Angeles Dodgers) (color)

	MT	NR MT	EX
Complete Set:	8.00	6.00	3.25

1 Frank Smith
2 Albert Maldonado
3 Mike Brown
4 Nelson Castro
5 Henry Blanco
6 Jose Parra
7 Robert Mejia
8 Larry Jacinto
9 Jacob Botts
10 Joe Seals
11 Ross Farnsworth
12 Mike Boyzuick
13 Stewart Strong
14 Willis Otanez
15 Greg Davis
16 Randall Graves
17 Ken Huckaby
18 Jay Kirkpatrick
19 Daniel Andrews
20 Erik Zammarchi
21 Chris Sinacori
22 Cam Aronetz
23 Mike Walkden
24 Rick Gorecki
25 Todd Williams
26 Juan Castro
27 Patrick Reed
28 Tito Landrum
29 Javier Puchales
30 Alton Pinkney

1991 ProCards Greensboro Hornets

(New York Yankees) (color)

	MT	NR MT	EX
Complete Set:	3.00	2.25	1.25

3050 Matt Dunbar
3051 Bryan Faw
3052 Ron Frazier
3053 Rich Hines
3054 Todd Malone
3055 Pat Morphy
3056 Cesar Perez
3057 Rafael Quirico
3058 Mariano Rivera
3059 Keith Seiler
3060 Bo Siberz
3061 Shad Smith
3062 Kiki Hernandez
3063 Kevin McMullen
3064 Tim Cooper
3065 Luis Gallardo
3066 Rick Lantrip
3067 Scott Romano
3068 Phillip Scott
3069 Brian Turner
3070 Richard Turrentine
3071 Bob Deller
3072 Carl Everett
3073 Sean Gilliam
3074 Lew Hill
3075 Trey Hillman
3076 Brian Milner
3077 Mark Shiflett
3078 Checklist

1991 Classic Best Greenville Braves

(Atlanta Braves) (color)

	MT	NR MT	EX
Complete Set:	7.00	5.25	2.75

Greenville Logo
1 Pat Gomez
2 Judd Johnson
3 Ben Rivera
4 Napoleon Robinson
5 Earl Sanders
6 Bill Taylor
7 Lee Upshaw
8 Preston Watson
9 Turk Wendell
10 Mark Wohlers
11 Johnny Cuevas
12 Brian Deak
13 Fred Lopez
14 Rich Casarotti
15 Vinnie Castilla
16 Brian Champion
17 Ryan Klesko
18 Rich Maloney
19 Rick Morris
20 Popeye Cole
21 Keith Mitchell
22 Sean Ross
23 Al Martin
24 Boi Rodriguez
25 Chris Chambliss
26 Bill Slack
27 Terry Harper
28 Randy Ingle
29 Jim Lovell (Checklist)

1991 ProCards Greenville Braves

(Atlanta Braves) (color)

	MT	NR MT	EX
Complete Set:	7.00	5.25	2.75

2995 Pat Gomez
2996 Judd Johnson
2997 Ben Rivera
2998 Napoleon Robinson
2999 Earl Sanders
3000 Bill Taylor
3001 Lee Upshaw
3002 Preston Watson
3003 Steven Wendell
3004 Mark Wohlers
3005 Johnny Cuevas
3006 Brian Deak
3007 Fred Lopez
3008 Rich Casarotti
3009 Vinny Castilla
3010 Brian Champion
3011 Ryan Klesko
3012 Rich Maloney
3013 Rick Morris
3014 Popeye Cole
3015 Al Martin
3016 Keith Mitchell
3017 Sean Ross
3018 Chris Chambliss
3019 Terry Harper
3020 Bill Slack
3021 Checklist

1991 Sport Pro Gulf Coast Rangers

(Texas Rangers) (color)

	MT	NR MT	EX
Complete Set	3.00	2.25	1.25

1 Mike McCollough
2 Jose Alberro
3 Keith Nalepka
4 David Gandolph
5 Eric Strovink
6 Wilson Heredia
7 Jamie Bethke
8 Mike O'Brien
9 Paul Paramo
10 Kevin Woodall
11 Danny Patterson
12 James Kennedy
13 Billy Seaton
14 Trevor Haughney
15 Pat Underhill
16 Jon Lindsay
17 Jeff Carew
18 Marty Davis
19 George Evangelista
20 Miguel Ubiera
21 Bert Gerhart
22 Daryl Henderson
23 Steve Burton
24 Joey Vallot
25 Reynaldo Tolentino, Roberto Troncoso
26 Heath Vaughn
27 Miguel Soto
28 Bryan Wilson
29 H.B. Awkard
30 Coaching Staff

1991 ProCards Hagerstown Suns

(Baltimore Orioles) (color)

	MT	NR MT	EX
Complete Set:	5.00	3.75	2.00

2447 Jeff Bumgarner
2448 Stacey Burdick
2449 Steve Culkar
2450 Kevin Hickey
2451 Stacy Jones
2452 Pat Leinen
2453 Joel McKeon
2454 Bob Milacki
2455 Mike Oquist
2456 Ozzie Peraza
2457 Arthur Rhodes
2458 Todd Stephan
2459 Mike Lehman
2460 Doug Robbins
2461 Bobby Dickerson
2462 Ricky Gutierrez
2463 Tim Holland
2464 Rod Lofton
2465 Ken Schamburg
2466 Paul Carey
2467 Tyrone Kingwood
2468 Scott Meadows
2469 Tim Raley
2470 Jack Voigt
2471 Jerry Narron
2472 Joe Durham
2473 Steve Luebber
2474 Checklist

1991 Classic Best Hamilton Redbirds

(St. Louis Cardinals) (color)

	MT	NR MT	EX
Complete Set:	3.00	2.25	1.25

1 Joe Castaldo
2 Tim Degrasse
3 John Frascatore
4 Kevin Lucero
5 Mike Badorek
6 Rigo Beltran
7 Al Watson
8 Jeff Pasquale
9 Scott Longaker
10 Duff Brumley
11 Jason Hisey
12 Jeff Tanderys
13 Antonio Boone
14 Gary Taylor
15 Mike DiFelice
16 Garrett Blanton
17 John Mabry
18 John O'Brien
19 Mike Cantu
20 Joe Turvey
21 Ron Warner
22 Brent Bohrofen
23 Keith Black
24 Jim Davenport
25 Ben Ellsworth
26 Rick Mediavilla
27 Ronnie French
28 Larry Meza
29 Rick Colbert
30 Steve Turco (Checklist)

1991 ProCards Hamilton Redbirds

(St. Louis Cardinals) (color)

	MT	NR MT	EX
Complete Set:	3.00	2.25	1.25

4026 Mike Badorek
4027 Rigo Beltran
4028 Antonio Boone
4029 Duff Brumley
4030 Joe Castaldo
4031 Doug Creek
4032 Tim DeGrasse
4033 John Frascatore
4034 Jason Hisey
4035 Scott Longaker
4036 Kevin Lucero
4037 Jeff Pasquale
4038 Scott Simmons
4039 Jeff Tanderys
4040 Allen Watson
4041 Mike DiFelice
4042 Joe Turvey
4043 Keith Black
4044 Mike Cantu
4045 Ben Ellsworth
4046 Larry Meza
4047 John O'Brien
4048 Ron Warner
4049 Garrett Blanton
4050 Brent Bohrofen
4051 Jim Davenport
4052 Ronnie French
4053 John Mabry
4054 Rick Mediavilla
4055 Gary Taylor
4056 Rick Colbert
4057 Steve Turco
4058 Checklist

1991 ProCards Harrisburg Senators

(Montreal Expos) (color)

	MT	NR MT	EX
Complete Set:	6.00	4.50	2.50

617 Dan Freed
618 Chris Haney
619 Rich Holsman
620 Carl Keliipuleole
621 Richie Lewis
622 Chris Marchok
623 Matt Maysey
624 Chris Pollack
625 Hector Rivera
626 Stan Spencer
627 David Wainhouse
628 Pete Young
629 Greg Fulton
630 Bob Natal
631 Joe Siddall
632 Archie Clanfrocco (First name misspelled on card and checklist.)
633 Bryn Kosco
634 Chris Martin
635 Omer Munoz
636 F.P. Santangelo
637 Matt Stairs

638 Chris Cassels
639 Cesar Hernandez
640 Rob Katzaroff
641 Ken Lake
642 Mike Quade
643 Pete Dalena
644 Joe Kerrigan
645 Checklist

1991 Sport Pro Helena Brewers

(Milwaukee Brewers) (color)

	MT	NR MT	EX
Complete Set:	3.00	2.25	1.25

1 John Trisler
2 Derek Ghostlaw
3 Matt Benson
4 Mike Lawn
5 Marshall Boze
6 Scott Lucas
7 Larry Winawer
8 Tyrone Hill
9 LaRue Baber
10 Joe Gmitter
11 Mike Matheny
12 Jeff Cirillo
13 James Wilkie
14 Dave Preikszas
15 Brian Dennison
16 Andy Fairman
17 Todd Iwema
18 Dave Fitzgerald
19 Rusty Rugg
20 Chris Wheat
21 Tom Hickox
22 Robert Tucker
23 Randy Hood
24 Brian Souza
25 Mike Basse
26 Chuck Bush
27 Eric Wilford
28 Roger Caplinger
29 Dusty Rhodes
30 Harry Dunlop

1991 Classic Best High Desert Mavericks

(San Diego Padres) (color)

	MT	NR MT	EX
Complete Set:	4.00	3.00	1.50

1 Renay Bryand (Last name misspelled on checklist.)
2 Dan Deville
3 Jay Estrada
4 Luis Galindez
5 Chris Haslock
6 Jose LeBron
7 Kelly Lifgren
8 Brian McKeon
9 Billy Reed
10 Rusty Silcox
11 Roger Smithberg
12 Royal Thomas Jr.
13 Ed Zinter
14 John Abercrombie Jr.
15 Greg Conley
16 Bob Lutticken
17 Mark Verstandig
18 Steve Bethea
19 Jay Gainer
20 Mark Gieseke
21 Paul Gonzalez
22 Ray Holbert
23 Mat Witkowski
24 Reggie Farmer
25 Steve Martin
26 Matt Mieske
27 J.D. Noland
28 Osvaldo Sanchez
29 Bruce Bochy
30 Mark Littel (Checklist)

1991 ProCards High Desert Mavericks

(San Diego Padres) (color)

	MT	NR MT	EX
Complete Set:	4.00	3.00	1.50

2384 Renay Bryand
2385 Dan Deville
2386 Jay Estrada
2387 Luis Galindez
2388 Chris Haslock
2389 Jose Lebron
2390 Kelly Lifgren
2391 Brian McKeon
2392 Billy Reed
2393 Rusty Silcox
2394 Roger Smithberg
2395 Royal Thomas
2396 Ed Zinter
2397 John Abercrombie
2398 Greg Conley
2399 Bob Lutticken
2400 Mark Verstandig
2401 Steve Bethea
2402 Jay Gainer
2403 Mark Gieseke
2404 Paul Gonzalez
2405 Ray Holbert
2406 Matt Witkowski
2407 Reggie Farmer
2408 Steve Martin
2409 Matt Mieske
2410 J.D. Noland
2411 Osvaldo Sanchez
2412 Bruce Bochy
2413 Lonnie Keeter
2414 Mark Littell
2415 Checklist

1991 Classic Best Huntington Cubs

(Chicago Cubs) (color)

	MT	NR MT	EX
Complete Set:	3.00	2.25	1.25

1 Terry Adams
2 Perry Amos
3 Ken Arnold
4 Randy Belyeu
5 Joaquin Cabral
6 Miguel Camarena
7 Devin Chavez
8 Jose Fernandez
9 Mario Garcia
10 Scott Gardner
11 Kirk Goodson
12 Krandall Hernandez
13 Maceo Houston
14 Jay Meyer
15 Gino Morones
16 Jose Pacheo
17 Richard Perez
18 Mickey Reeves
19 Sergio Reyes
20 Chris Rodriguez
21 Mitchell Root
22 Frank Sample
23 Adrian Sanchez
24 Calvin Smith
25 Darren Tillman
26 Jim Wolff
27 Pedro Valdez
28 Steven Walker
29 Tom Walker
30 Steve Roadcap (Checklist)

1991 ProCards Huntington Cubs

(Chicago Cubs) (color)

	MT	NR MT	EX
Complete Set:	3.00	2.25	1.25

3324 Terry Adams
3325 Perry Amos
3326 Miguel Camarena
3327 Mario Garcia
3328 Scott Gardner
3329 Kirk Goodson
3330 Jay Meyer
3331 Gino Morones
3332 Jose Pacheo
3333 Chris Rodriguez
3334 Frank Sample
3335 Adrian Sanchez
3336 Randy Belyeu (Last name misspelled on checklist.)
3337 Krandell Hernandez
3338 Jim Wolff
3339 Ken Arnold
3340 Joaquin Cabral
3341 Devon Chavez
3342 Richard Perez
3343 Mitchell Root
3344 Calvin Smith
3345 Tom Walker
3346 Jose Fernendez
3347 Maceo Houston
3348 Michael Reeves
3349 Sergio Reyes
3350 Darren Tillman
3351 Pedro Valdez
3352 Steven Walker
3353 Steve Roadcap
3354 Gil Kubski
3355 Checklist

1991 Classic Best Huntsville Stars

(Oakland A's) (color)

	MT	NR MT	EX
Complete Set:	5.00	3.75	2.00

Stars Logo
1 Marcos Armas
2 Bob Bafla
3 Dean Borrelli
4 Mike Conte
5 James Buccheri
6 Tom Carcione
7 Joel Chimelis
8 Fred Cooley
9 Russ Cormier
10 Doc Thorson
11 Matt Grott
12 Dwayne Hosey
13 Chad Kuhn
14 Dave Latter
15 Francisco Matos
16 Gavin Osteen
17 Bert Bradley
18 Tim Peek
19 Don Peters
20 Dave Zancanaro
21 Scott Shockey
22 Casey Parsons
23 Lee Tinsley
24 Todd Van Poppel
25 Darryl Vice
26 Pat Gomez (Checklist)

1991 ProCards Huntsville Stars

(Oakland Athletics) (color)

	MT	NR MT	EX
Complete Set:	5.00	3.75	2.00

1788 Russ Cormier
1789 Matt Grott
1790 Chad Kuhn
1791 Dave Latter
1792 Gavin Osteen
1793 Tim Peek
1794 Don Peters
1795 Todd Van Poppel
1796 Weston Weber
1797 Dave Zancanaro
1798 Dean Borrelli
1799 Tom Carcione
1800 Bob Bafla
1801 James Buccheri
1802 Joel Chimelis
1803 Fred Cooley
1804 Francisco Matos
1805 Scott Shockey
1806 Darryl Vice
1807 Marcos Armas (First name spelled differently on card back.)
1808 Mike Conte
1809 Dwayne Hosey
1810 Lee Tinsley
1811 Casey Parsons
1812 Bert Bradley
1813 Checklist

1991 Burger King Huntsville Stars

This set was given away on a special night, continuing a tradition that began in 1985. The 26-card set measures 2 /8" x 3-1/2", and is unnumbered, listed below in alphabetical order. The cards contain statistical information on the back, and Burger King logos appear on both sides of the card. The format is identical to other team issues in the series from Huntsville. This set may also include a card listing northern Alabama locations of sponsor Burger King.

	MT	NR MT	EX
Complete Set:	6.00		

(1) Kurt Abbott
(2) Dean Borrelli
(3) Bert Bradley
(4) Jorge Brito
(5) James Buccheri
(6) Joel Chimelis
(7) Mike Conte
(8) Rod Correia
(9) Kevin Dattola
(10) Dan Eskew
(11) Apolinar Garcia
(12) Matt Grott
(13) Chad Kuhn
(14) Dave Latter
(15) Troy Neel
(16) Gavin Osteen
(17) Craig Paquette
(18) Casey Parsons
(19) Tim Peek
(20) Don Peters
(21) Scott Shockey
(22) Lee Tinsley
(23) Todd Van Poppel
(24) Darryl Vice
(25) Winston Weber
(26) Dave Zancanaro

1991 ProCards Idaho Falls Braves

(Atlanta Braves) (color)

	MT	NR MT	EX
Complete Set:	3.00	2.25	1.25

4319 Jimmy Armstrong
4320 Scott Behrens
4321 Doug Cook
4322 Wayne Koklys
4323 Jerry Koller
4324 Shannon Ledwick
4325 Carl Majeski
4326 Ricky Petit
4327 Craig Rapp
4328 Matt Viarengo
4329 Brent Weber
4330 Ben Weeks
4331 Brad Woodall
4332 Paul Kelliher
4333 Brad Rippelmeyer
4334 Dave Toth
4335 Anthony Gaffagnino
4336 Loren Gress
4337 Kevin Grijak
4338 Dario Paulino (First name incorrect on checklist.)
4339 Thomas Coates
4340 Armando Rodriguez
4341 Pedro Swann
4342 Dominic Therrien
4344 Steve Curry
4345 Phil Dale
4346 Randy Smith
4347 Checklist

1991 Sport Pro Idaho Falls Braves

(Atlanta Braves) (color)

	MT	NR MT	EX
Complete Set:	3.00	2.25	1.25

1 Ronald York
2 Michael Place
3 Brad Rippelmeyer
4 Amando Rodriguez
5 Anthony Graffignino
6 Tom Coates
7 Richard O'Neil
8 Ben Weeks
9 Greg Reinert
10 Jim Armstrong
11 Travis Dunlap
12 Julio Vasquez
13 Gary Stanton
14 Johnny Walker
15 David Toth
16 Snannon Ledwick
17 Kevin Grijak
18 Cristobal Santoya
19 Wayne Simoneaux
20 Craig Rapp
21 Vincent Jimenez
22 Carl Majeski
23 Dario Paulino
24 Jason Kempfer
25 Pedro Swann
26 Brad Woodall (No position listed.)
27 Blank
28 Blank
29 Blank
30 Blank

1991 ProCards Indianapolis Indians

(Montreal Expos) (color)

	MT	NR MT	EX
Complete Set:	6.00	4.50	2.50

453 Kevin Bearse
454 Chris Bennett
455 Kent Bottenfield
456 Eddie Dixon
457 Jeff Fassero
458 Dave Masters
459 Doug Piatt
460 Dana Ridenour
461 Scott Service
462 Tito Stewart
463 Darrin Winston
464 Jimmy Kremers
465 Bret Barberie

466 Wilfredo Cordero
467 Jerry Goff
468 Todd Haney
469 Mel Houston
470 Marlin McPhail
471 Razor Shines
472 Mike Davis
473 Alex Diaz
474 Steve Hecht
475 Quinn Mack
476 John Vanderwal
477 Jerry Manuel
478 Nardi Contreras
479 Gomer Hodge
480 Checklist

1991 ProCards Iowa Cubs

(Chicago Cubs) (color)

	MT	NR MT	EX
Complete Set:	6.00	4.50	2.50

1053 Lance Dickson
1054 Joe Kraemer
1055 Scott May
1056 Chuck Mount
1057 Jose Nunez
1058 Dave Pavlas
1059 Laddie Renfroe
1060 David Rosario
1061 Bob Scanlan
1062 Steve Wilson
1063 Russ McGinnis
1064 Dan Simonds
1065 Rick Wilkins
1066 Brian Guinn
1067 Ray Sanchez
1068 Gary Scott
1069 Craig Smajstrla
1070 Jeff Small
1071 Doug Strange
1072 Glenn Sullivan
1073 Brad Bierley
1074 Steve Carter
1075 Cedric Landrum
1076 Jim Essian
1077 Grant Jackson
2233 Checklist (Numbered out of sequence.)

1991 ProCards Jackson Generals

(Houston Astros) (color)

	MT	NR MT	EX
Complete Set:	5.00	3.75	2.00

916 Sam August
917 Pete Bauer
918 Kevin Coffman
919 Chris Gardner
920 Carl Grovom
921 Dean Hartgraves
922 Jeff Juden
923 Keith Kaiser
924 Steve Larose
925 Rob Mallicoat
926 Shane Reynolds
927 Richie Simon
928 Tony Eusebio
929 Scott Makarewicz
930 Jeff Baldwin
931 Rusty Harris
932 Trent Hubbard
933 Lance Madsen
934 Orlando Miller
935 Willie Ansley
936 Kevin Dean
937 Bert Hunter
938 Bernie Jenkins
939 Joe Mikulik
940 Rick Sweet
941 Don Reynolds
942 Charlie Taylor
973 Checklist

1991 ProCards Jacksonville Suns

(Seattle Mariners) (color)

	MT	NR MT	EX
Complete Set:	7.00	5.25	2.75

141 Shawn Barton
142 Jim Blueberg
143 Gary Eave
144 David Evans
145 Fernando Figueroa
146 Dave Fleming
147 Jeff Nelson
148 Jim Newlin
149 Michael Pitz
150 Dave Richards
151 Roger Salkeld
152 Fernando Arguelles
153 Jim Campanis
154 Frank Bolick
155 Bret Boone
156 Jim Bowie
157 Ruben Gonzalez
158 Tony Manahan
159 Ken Pennington
160 Jack Smith
161 Brian Turang
162 Mike McDonald
163 Tim Stargell
164 Ted Williams
165 Team Picture
166 Jim Nettles
167 Bobby Cuellar
168 Lem Pilkinton (Name misspelled on back of card.)
169 Checklist

1991 Classic Best Jamestown Expos

(Montreal Expos) (color)

	MT	NR MT	EX
Complete Set:	3.00	2.25	1.25

1 John White
2 Blake Babki
3 Derrick White
4 Mark Grudzielanek
5 Jim Austin
6 Mike Danrel
7 Matt Allen
8 Scott Campbell
9 Chris Falco
10 Scott Dennison
11 Douglas A. O'Neill
12 Mitchel Simons
13 Tommy Owen
14 Domingo Matos
15 Mark LoRosa
16 Duane Ashley
17 Brian Looney
18 Jim Wynne
19 Nick Sproviero
20 Jeff Hostetler
21 Buddy Jenkins Jr.
22 Matt Figueroa
23 James Ferguson
24 Darek Braunecker (First name misspelled on checklist.)
25 Heath Haynes
26 Pete Tarutis
27 Rodney Pedraza
28 Coaching Staff
29 Front Office
30 Checklist (Not listed on checklist.)

1991 ProCards Jamestown Expos

(Montreal Expos) (color)

	MT	NR MT	EX
Complete Set:	3.00	2.25	1.25

3534 Duane Ashley
3535 Darek Braunecker
3536 James Ferguson
3537 Matt Figueroa
3538 Heath Haynes
3539 Jeff Hostetler
3540 Buddy Jenkins
3541 Mark LaRosa
3542 Brian Looney
3543 Rodney Pedraza
3544 Nick Sproviero
3545 Pete Tarutis
3546 Jim Wynne
3547 Matt Allen
3548 Michael Daniel
3549 Tommy Owen
3550 Scott Campbell
3551 Scott Dennison
3552 Chris Faico
3553 Mark Grudzielanek
3554 Domingo Matos
3555 Michael Simons
3556 Derrick White
3557 Jim Austin
3558 Blake Babki
3559 Doug O'Neill
3560 Johnny White
3561 Field Staff
3562 Checklist

1991 Classic Best Johnson City Cardinals

(St. Louis Cardinals) (color)

	MT	NR MT	EX
Complete Set:	5.00	3.75	2.00

1 Eddie Williams
2 John Dempsey
3 Aaire Borzello
4 Pat Murray
5 Andy Bruce
6 Darrel Deak
7 Larry Gilligan
8 Doug Radziewicz
9 Steve Dudek
10 Jesus Ugueto
11 Dimitri Young
12 DaRond Stoval
13 Chris Vlasis
14 Hector Colon
15 Basil Shabazz
16 Keith Jones
17 Jamie Cochran
18 Brian Barber
19 Russell Gaston
20 Dennis Slininger
21 Gerald Santos
22 David Chasin
23 Brian Avram
24 Manuel Rodriguez
25 Steve Jones
26 Cecilio Gonzalez
27 Jose Arias
28 Tom McKinnon
29 Chris Maloney
30 Joe Cunningham (Checklist)

1991 ProCards Johnson City Cardinals

(St. Louis Cardinals) (color)

	MT	NR MT	EX
Complete Set:	5.00	3.75	2.00

3968 Brian Avram
3969 Brian Barber
3970 David Chajin
3971 Jamie Cochran
3972 Cecilio Gonzalez
3973 Bill Hurst
3974 Steve Jones
3975 Tom McKinnon
3976 Manuel Rodriguez
3977 Jerry Santos
3978 Dennis Slinger
3979 John Dempsey
3980 Eddie Williams
3981 Andy Bruce
3982 Darrel Deak
3983 Steve Dudek
3984 Larry Gilligan
3985 Pat Murray
3986 Doug Radziewicz
3987 Jesus Ugueto
3988 Hector Colon
3989 Keith Jones
3990 Basil Shabazz (First name misspelled on Checklist.)
3991 DaRond Stovall
3992 Chris Vlasis
3993 Dmitri Young
3994 Chris Maloney
4172 Joe Cunningham (Numbered out of sequence.)
4173 Checklist (Numbered out of sequence.)

1991 Classic Best Kane County Cougars

(Baltimore Orioles) (color)

	MT	NR MT	EX
Complete Set:	4.00	3.00	1.50

1 Shaun Hrabar
2 Joe Borowski
3 Matt Anderson
4 Rob Blumberg Jr.
5 James Dedrick
6 Michael Hebb
7 Thomas Martin
8 David Paveloff
9 Brad Pennington
10 Tommy Taylor
11 Todd Unrein
12 Michael Wiley
13 Jimmy Roso
14 Greg Zaun
15 Steven DiMarco
16 Manny Garcia
17 Jose Millares
18 Brent Miller
19 Daniel Ramirez
20 Brad Tyler
21 Bo Davis
22 Steven Godin
23 Aman Hicks
24 German Paredes
25 Keith Schmidt
26 Bob Miscik
27 Larry McCall
28 Oneri Fleita
29 Doug Flowers
30 Marc Zello (Checklist)

1991 ProCards Kane County Cougars

(Baltimore Orioles) (color)

	MT	NR MT	EX
Complete Set:	4.00	3.00	1.50

2650 Matt Anderson
2651 Rob Blumberg
2652 Joe Borowski
2653 Jim Dedrick
2654 Mike Hebb
2655 Thomas Martin
2656 Dave Paveloff
2657 Brad Pennington
2658 Todd Unrein
2659 Mike Wiley
2660 Jimmy Roso
2661 Greg Zaun
2662 Steve DiMarco
2663 Manny Garcia
2664 Jose Millares
2665 Brent Miller
2666 Daniel Ramirez
2667 Brad Tyler
2668 Allen Davis
2669 Steven Godin
2670 Aman Hicks
2671 Shaun Hrabar
2672 German Paredes
2673 Keith Schmidt
2674 Bob Miscik
2675 Oneri Fleita
2676 Larry McCall
2677 Checklist

1991 Team Kane County Cougars

(Baltimore Orioles) (color) This set is listed by uniform number.

	MT	NR MT	EX
Complete Set:	6.00	4.50	2.50

3 Gregory Zaun
7 Shaun Hrabar
11 Daniel Ramirez
13 Thomas Taylor
14 Jose Millares
15 Aman Hicks
16 Steve Godin
17 Terry Farrar
18 James Dedrick
20 David Paveloff
21 Jimmy Roso
23 Jim Audley
24 Manny Garcia
25 Bradley Tippitt
27 Brent Miller
28 Tom Martin
29 Michael Wiley
34 Brad Seitzer
35 Doug Reynolds
36 Matthew Anderson
37 Michael Hebb
38 Todd Unrein
39 Joe Borowski
40 Vaughn Eshelman
---- Coaches, Marc Zello
---- Ozzie (Mascot)

1991 Classic Best Kenosha Twins

(Minnesota Twins) (color)

	MT	NR MT	EX
Complete Set:	3.00	2.25	1.25

1 Alvin Brown
2 Willie Mota
3 Todd Blakeman
4 Denny Hocking
5 Matt Morse
6 David Rivera
7 Brent Brede

8 Tim Persing
9 John Gumpf
10 Denny Hoppe
11 Kurt Pfeffer
12 Dave Bigham
13 Dickie Dixon
14 Bart Peterson
15 Pat Russo
16 Kerry Taylor
17 Steve Taylor
18 Jeff Thelen
19 Joel Lepel
20 Rick Anderson
21 Dan Fox
22 Todd Ritchie
23 Paul Bruno
24 Midre Cummings
25 Rich Becker
26 Tom Houk
27 Jason Klonoski
28 Checklist (Not listed on checklist)
---- Kenosha Logo
---- Twins Logo

1991 ProCards Kenosha Twins

(Minnesota Twins) (color)

	MT	NR MT	EX
Complete Set:	3.00	2.25	1.25

2066 Dave Bigham
2067 Dickie Dixon
2068 Denny Hoppe
2069 Jason Klonoski
2070 Tim Persing
2071 Bart Peterson
2072 Todd Ritchie
2073 Pat Russo
2074 Kerry Taylor
2075 Steve Taylor
2076 Jeff Thelen
2077 Alvin Brown
2078 Paul Bruno
2079 Willie Mota
2080 Todd Blakeman
2081 Denny Hocking
2082 Tom Houk
2083 Matt Morse
2084 David Rivera
2085 Paul Russo
2086 Rich Becker
2087 Brent Brede
2088 Midre Cummings
2089 John Gumpf
2090 Kurt Pfeffer
2091 Joel Lepel
2092 Rick Anderson
2093 Checklist

1991 Classic Best Kingsport Mets

(New York Mets) (color)

	MT	NR MT	EX
Complete Set:	3.00	2.25	1.25

Mets Logo
1 Jeff Henderson
2 Demond Smith
3 Darwin Davis
4 Mike Patrizi
5 Suliban Luciano
6 Brian Daubach (First name misspelled on checklist.)
7 Ty Quillin
8 Ricky Otero
9 Paul Meyer (Last name misspelled on checklist.)
10 Quilvio Veras
11 Rafael Hernandez
12 Brett Rossler
13 Randy Len Farmer
14 Guillermo Garcia
15 Todd Fiegel
16 Joe Crawford
17 Eric Corbell
18 Shaun Watson
19 Hector Ramirez
20 Steve Seymour
21 Mark Hokanson
22 Bradley Schorr
23 Jason Jacome
24 Andre David
25 L.D. Bennese
26 Jesus Hernaiz
27 Cesar Diaz
28 Andrew Cotner
29 Checklist (Not listed on checklist.)

1991 ProCards Kingsport Mets

(New York Mets) (color)

	MT	NR MT	EX
Complete Set:	3.00	2.25	1.25

3804 Eric Corbell
3805 Andrew Cotner
3806 Joe Crawford
3807 Todd Fiegel
3808 Jeff Henderson
3809 Mark Hokanson
3810 Jason Jacome
3811 Hector Ramirez
3812 Brad Schorr
3813 Steve Seymour
3814 Shaun Watson
3815 Cesar Diaz
3816 Mike Patrizi
3817 Ross Rossler
3818 Brian Daubach
3819 Darwin Davis
3820 Randy Farmer
3821 Guillermo Garcia
3822 Rafael Hernandez
3823 Paul Meyer
3824 Quilvio Veras
3825 Suliban Luciano
3826 Ricky Otero
3827 Ty Quillin
3828 Demond Smith
3829 Andre David
3830 Jesus Hernaiz
3831 Checklist

1991 Classic Best Kinston Indians

(Cleveland Indians) (color)

	MT	NR MT	EX
Complete Set:	4.00	3.00	1.50

1 Chad Allen
2 Shawn Bryant
3 Carl Johnson
4 Tim Langdon
5 Curtis Leskanic
6 Mike Malley
7 Scott Morgan
8 Oscar Munoz
9 Scott Neill
10 Robert Person
11 Cecil Pettiford
12 Mike Soper
13 Carlos Mota
14 Bill Losa
15 Mike Easley
16 Miguel Flores
17 Fred Gladding
18 Clyde Pough
19 Tim Rigsby
20 Mike Sarbaugh
21 Paulino Tena
22 Marc Tepper
23 William Canate
24 Danny Williams
25 Tom Eiterman
26 Brian Giles
27 Tracy Sanders
28 Brian Graham
29 Dan Devoe
30 North Johnson (No position listed.)
---- Checklist

1991 ProCards Kinston Indians

(Cleveland Indians) (color)

	MT	NR MT	EX
Complete Set:	4.00	3.00	1.50

313 Chad Allen
314 Shawn Bryant
315 Carl Johnson
316 Tim Langdon
317 Curtis Leskanic
318 Mike Malley
319 Scott Morgan
320 Oscar Munoz
321 Scott Neill
322 Robert Person
323 Cecil Pettiford
324 Mike Soper
325 Bill Losa
326 Carlos Mota
327 Mike Easley
328 Miguel Flores
329 Fabio Gomez
330 Clyde Pough
331 Tim Rigsby
332 Mike Sarbaugh
333 Paulino Tena
334 Marc Tepper
335 William Canate
336 Brad DeJardin
337 Tom Eiterman
338 Brian Giles
339 Tracy Sanders
340 Brian Graham
341 Fred Gladding
342 Dan Williams
343 Checklist

1991 ProCards Kissimmee Dodgers

(Los Angeles Dodgers) (color)

	MT	NR MT	EX
Complete Set:	3.00	2.25	1.25

4175 Gary Cope
4176 John Davidson
4177 Dave Fitzpatrick
4178 Michael Iglesias
4179 Martin Lavigne
4180 Clint Minear
4181 Antonio Osuna
4182 Jose Salcedo
4183 Kevin Smith
4184 Young Chul Sohn
4185 Robert Sweeney
4186 Ismael Valdez
4187 Brandon Watts
4188 Chad Zerbe
4189 Anthony Rodriguez
4190 Felix Rodriguez
4191 Carlo Walton
4192 Brent Williams
4193 German Gonzalez
4194 Chris Latham
4195 Sandy Martinez
4196 Todd Soares
4197 Bill Stephens
4198 Dennis Winicki
4199 Gustavo Zapata
4200 Angel Dotel
4201 Lonnie Jackson
4202 Vince Jackson
4203 Clarence Richmond
4204 Mel Warren
4205 Field Staff
4206 Checklist card

1991 ProCards Knoxville Blue Jays

(Toronto Blue Jays) (color)

	MT	NR MT	EX
Complete Set:	5.00	3.75	2.00

1760 Nathaniel Cromwell
1761 Jesse Cross
1762 Darren Hall
1763 Vince Horsman
1764 Jimmy Rogers
1765 Rick Trlicek
1766 Anthony Ward
1767 Dave Weathers
1768 Woody Williams
1769 Rob Wishnevski
1770 Randy Knorr
1771 Jose Monzon
1772 Jason Townley
1773 Domingo Cedeno
1774 Ray Giannelli
1775 Jeff Kent
1776 Mike Taylor
1777 Julian Yan
1778 Mark Young
1779 Juan De La Rosa
1780 Bobby DeLoach
1781 Bernie Nunez
1782 Paul Rodgers
1783 Ryan Thompson
1784 John Stearns
1785 Mike McAlpin
1786 Steve Mingori
1787 Checklist

1991 Classic Best Lakeland Tigers

(Detroit Tigers) (color)

	MT	NR MT	EX
Complete Set:	3.00	2.25	1.25

1 Jeff Braley
2 Tom Drell
3 Mark Ettles
4 Ed Ferm
5 Mike Garcia
6 Frank Gonzales
7 Eric Leimeister
8 Steve Carter
9 Mike Lumley
10 Doug Carpenter
11 Lino Rivera
12 Leonardo Torres
13 Steve Wolf
14 Eric Albright
15 Mike Gillette
16 Rick Sellers
17 Fernando Arroyo
18 Jose Anglero
19 Ron Howard
20 Ron Marigny
21 Kirt Mendenhall
22 Mike Rendina
23 Brian Cornelius
24 Jeff Goodale
25 Dennis McNamara
26 Rudy Pemberton
27 Warren Sawkiw
28 Pat Woodruff
29 John Lipon
30 Checklist (Not listed on checklist.)

1991 ProCards Lakeland Tigers

(Detroit Tigers) (color)

	MT	NR MT	EX
Complete Set:	3.00	2.25	1.25

257 Jeff Braley
258 Tom Drell
259 Mark Ettles
260 Ed Ferm
261 Mike Garcia
262 Frank Gonzales
263 Eric Leimeister
264 Mike Lumley
265 Doug Marcero
266 Lino Rivera
267 Leonardo Torres
268 Steve Wolf
269 Mike Gillette
270 Brad Wilson
271 Jose Anglero
272 Ron Howard
273 Ron Marigny
274 Kirk Mendenhall
275 Mike Rendina
276 Warren Sawkiw
277 Brian Cornelius
278 Jeff Goodale
279 Denny McNamara
280 Rudy Pemberton
281 Pat Woodruff
282 John Lipon
283 Fernando Arroyo
284 Doug Carpenter
285 Checklist

1991 ProCards Las Vegas Stars

(San Diego Padres) (color)

	MT	NR MT	EX
Complete Set:	6.00	4.50	2.50

226 Ricky Bones
227 Pat Clements
228 John Costello
229 Terry Gilmore
230 Jeremy Hernandez
231 Derek Lilliquist
232 Jose Melendez
233 Adam Peterson
234 Steve Rosenberg
235 Tim Scott
236 Rafael Valdez
237 Dann Bilardello
238 Brian Dorsett
239 Kevin Higgins
240 Dan Walters
241 Scott Coolbaugh
242 Dean Kelley
243 Jose Mota
244 Ed Romero
245 Craig Shipley
246 Dave Staton
247 Oscar Azocar
248 Thomas Howard
249 Chris Jelic
250 Will Taylor
251 Jim Vatcher
252 Kevin Ward
253 Jom Riggleman
254 Jon Matlack
255 Tony Torchia
256 Checklist

1991 ProCards London Tigers

(Detroit Tigers) (color)

	MT	NR MT	EX
Complete Set:	3.00	2.25	1.25

1869 John DeSilva
1870 John Doherty
1871 Greg Gohr
1872 Buddy Groom
1873 Darren Hursey
1875 Todd Krumm
1876 Randy Marshall
1877 Jose Ramos
1878 Eric Stone
1879 Marty Willis
1880 Doyle Balthazar
1881 Ruben Rodriguez
1882 Ivan Cruz
1883 Dean Decillis
1884 Luis Galindo
1885 Keith Kimberlin
1886 Domingo Michel
1887 Bob Reimink

1888 Basilio Cabrera
1889 Lou Frazier
1890 Riccardo Ingram
1891 Steve Pegues
1892 Gene Roof
1893 Jeff Jones
1894 Dan Raley
2232a Kurt Knudson (Misnumbered - listed on checklist as #1874.)
2232b Checklist (Numbered out of sequence.)

1991 ProCards Louisville Redbirds

(St. Louis Cardinals) (color)

	MT	NR MT	EX
Complete Set:	6.00	4.50	2.50

2906 Marty Clary
2907 Rheal Cormier
2908 Bob Davidson
2909 Mark Grater
2910 Mike Milchin
2911 Al Nipper
2912 Omar Olivares
2913 Dave Osteen
2914 Len Picota
2915 Dave Richardson
2916 Ed Fulton
2917 Scott Nichols
2918 Ray Stephens
2919 Luis Alicea
2920 Greg Carmona
2921 Nick Castaneda
2922 Todd Crosby
2923 Bien Figueroa
2924 Stan Royer
2925 Rod Brewer
2926 Joey Fernandez
2927 Brian Jordan
2928 Lonnie Maclin
2929 Julian Martinez
2930 Jesus Mendez
2931 Mike Ross
2932 Mark DeJohn
2933 Mark Riggins
2934 Checklist

1991 Team Louisville Redbirds

(St. Louis Cardinals) (color)

	MT	NR MT	EX
Complete Set:	9.00	6.75	3.50

1 Billy Bird (Mascot)
2 Mark Clark
3 Omar Olivares
4 Ken Hill
5 Rheal Cormier
6 Tim Sherrill
7 Mark Grater
8 Jamie Moyer
9 Mike Milchin
10 Mike Hinkle
11 Mike Loynd
12 Mike Perez
13 Todd Worrell
14 Rod Brewer
15 Joey Fernandez
16 Pedro Guerrero
17 Luis Alicea
18 Todd Crosby
19 Tim Jones
20 Bien Figueroa
21 Greg Carmona
22 Stan Royer
23 Bernard Gilkey
24 Brian Jordan
25 Lonnie Maclin
26 Julian Martinez
27 Ray Stephens
28 Ed Fulton
29 Scott Nichols
30 Mark DeJohn
31 Mark Riggins
32 Brian Jordan

1991 Classic Best Lynchburg Red Sox

(Boston Red Sox) (color)

	MT	NR MT	EX
Complete Set:	4.00	3.00	1.50

Lynchburg Logo
1 Dale Burgo
2 Jim Dennison
3 Gar Finnvold
4 Brad Hoyer
5 Tony Mosley
6 Erik Plantenburg
7 Ed Riley
8 Rennie Scott
9 Tim Smith
10 Kevin Uhrhan
11 Denny Berni
12 Joe Luis
13 Craig Wilson
14 Scott Bethea
15 James Byrd
16 Alex Delgado
17 Bill Norris
18 Willie Tatum
19 Gary Villalobos
20 Bruce Chick
21 Chris Leach
22 Jeff McNeely
23 Boo Moore
24 Jose Zambrano
25 Buddy Bailey
26 Jim Bibby
27 David Duchin
28 Andy Rush
29 Checklist (Not listed on checklist.)

1991 ProCards Lynchburg Red Sox

(Boston Red Sox) (color)

	MT	NR MT	EX
Complete Set:	4.00	3.00	1.50

1190 Dale Burgo
1191 Jim Dennison
1192 Gar Finnvold
1193 Brad Hoyer
1194 Tony Mosley
1195 Erik Plantenberg
1196 Ed Riley
1197 Andy Rush
1198 Rennie Scott
1199 Tim Smith
1200 Kevin Uhrhan
1201 Denny Berni
1202 Joe Luis
1203 Graig Wilson
1204 Scott Bethea
1205 Jim Byrd
1206 Alex Delgrado
1207 Bill Norris
1208 Willie Tatum
1209 Gary Villalobos
1210 Bruce Chick
1211 Chris Leach
1212 Jeff McNeely
1213 Boo Moore
1214 Jose Zambrano
1215 Buddy Bailey
1216 Jim Bibby
1217 Checklist

1991 Classic Best Macon Braves

(Atlanta Braves) (color)

	MT	NR MT	EX
Complete Set:	8.50	6.25	3.50

1 Barry Chiles
2 Earl Jewell
3 Thomas Leahy
4 Ray Mack
5 Don Mattson
6 Keith Morrison
7 Darren Ritter
8 Joe Roa
9 Shawn Rohrwild
10 Glenn Hubbard
11 Marcos Vazquez
12 Henry Werland
13 David Williams
14 Marek Drabinski
15 Wallace Gonzalez
16 Tyler Houston
17 Grant Brittain
18 Brian Snitker
19 Chipper Jones
20 Rick Karcher
21 Jose Olmeda
22 Geoff Orr
23 Lee Heath
24 Troy Hughs
25 Kevin O'Connor
26 Raul Robinson
27 Juan Williams
28 Roy Majyka
29 Matt West
30 Bryan Butz (Checklist)

1991 ProCards Macon Braves

(Atlanta Braves) (color)

	MT	NR MT	EX
Complete Set:	7.50	5.50	3.00

855 Barry Chiles
856 Earl Jewett
857 Tom Leahy
858 Ray Mack
859 Rob Mattson
860 Keith Morrison
861 Darren Ritter
862 Joe Roa
863 Shawn Rohrwild
864 Marcos Vazquez
865 Henry Werland
866 David Williams
867 Marek Drabinski
868 Wallace Gonzalez
869 Tyler Houston
870 Grant Brittain
871 Loren Gress
872 Chipper Jones
873 Rick Karcher
874 Jose Olmeda
875 Geoff Orr
876 Lee Heath
877 Troy Hughes
878 Kevin O'Connor
879 Raul Robinson
880 Juan Williams
881 Roy Majtyka
882 Glenn Hubbard
883 Brian Snitker
884 Matt West
885 Checklist

1991 Classic Best Madison Muskies

(Oakland A's) (color)

	MT	NR MT	EX
Complete Set:	3.00	2.25	1.25

Muskie's Logo
1 Todd Russell
2 Tanyon Sturtze
3 Craig Sudbury
4 Michael Grimes
5 Bradley Brimhall
6 Craig Connolly
7 James Dillon
8 William Gulledge
9 Douglas Johns
10 Scott McCarty
11 Leandro Mejia
12 Eric Myers
13 Scott Budner
14 Malcolm Shaw
15 Brett Hendley
16 Islay Molina
17 Scott Henry
18 Ernest Young
19 Gregory Reid
20 Donald Lydy
21 Shane Borchert
22 Gary Jones
23 Luis Lanfranco
24 Carlos Hernandez
25 Robert Carlsen
26 William Picketts
27 Rafael Mercado
28 Lee Sammons
29 Checklist (Not listed on checklist.)

1991 ProCards Madison Muskies

(Oakland Athletics) (color)

	MT	NR MT	EX
Complete Set:	3.00	2.25	1.25

2122 Brad Brimhall
2123 Craig Connolly
2124 Jim Dillon
2125 Hugh Gulledge
2126 Doug Johns
2127 Scott McCarty
2128 Leandro Mejia
2129 Eric Meyers
2130 Todd Revenig
2131 Gary Ross
2132 Curt Shaw
2133 Tanyon Sturtze
2134 Brett Hendley
2135 Scott Henry
2136 Islay Molina
2137 Robert Carlsen
2138 Carlos Hernandez
2139 Luis Lanfranco
2140 Rafael Mercado
2141 Bill Picketts
2142 Scott Lydy
2143 Greg Reid
2144 Keith Thomas
2145 Ernie Young
2146 Gary Jones
2147 Scott Budner
2148 Checklist

1991 Classic Best Martinsville Phillies

(Philadelphia Phillies) (color)

	MT	NR MT	EX
Complete Set:	3.00	2.25	1.25

1 Mike Murphy
2 Eric Mauldin
3 Dan Larson
4 Wayne Johnson
5 Reynoldo De Los Santos
6 Jason Urbanek
7 Andy Sallee
8 Johnny Mallee
9 Joey Jelinek
10 Carlton Hardy
11 Phillip Geisler
12 Lamar Cherry
13 Luis Brito
14 Brent Bell
15 Porfirio Pena
16 Gary Bennett
17 Dean Hopp
18 John Salamon
19 Thane Page
20 Robert Mitchell
21 Fernando Mejias
22 John Ingram
23 Sam Edwards
24 Dominic DeSantis
25 Scott Coleman
26 Dan Brown
27 Chad Anderson
28 Juan Alexis
29 Roly DeArmas
30 Mike Townsend (Checklist)

1991 ProCards Martinsville Phillies

(Philadelphia Phillies) (color)

	MT	NR MT	EX
Complete Set:	3.00	2.25	1.25

3442 Juan Alexi
3443 Chad Anderson
3444 Dan Brown
3445 Scott Coleman
3446 Dominic DeSantis
3447 Sam Edwards
3448 Joel Gilmore
3449 John Ingram
3450 Fernando Mejias
3451 Robert Mitchell
3452 Thane Page
3453 John Salamon
3454 Gary Bennett
3455 Dean Hopp
3456 Porfirio Pena
3457 Brent Bell
3458 Luis Brito
3459 Lamar Cherry
3460 Phil Geisler
3461 Carlton Hardy
3462 Joey Jelinek
3463 John Mallee
3464 Andy Sallee
3465 Jason Urbanek
3466 Reynaldo DeLosSantos
3467 Wayne Johnson
3468 Danny Larson
3469 Eric Mauldin
3470 Mike Murphy
3471 Eli Grba
3472 Checklist

1991 ProCards Medicine Hat Blue Jays

(Toronto Blue Jays) (color)

	MT	NR MT	EX
Complete Set:	3.00	2.25	1.25

4089 Travis Baptist
4090 Isbel Cardona (First name misspelled on checklist.)
4091 Ned Darley
4092 Andrew Dolson
4093 Chris Ermis
4094 Allen Ford
4095 Freddy Lopez
4096 Jose Manuare
4097 Albert Montoya
4098 Mike O'Halloran
4099 Ken Robinson

4100 Steve Sinclair
4101 Mike Taylor
4102 John Lombardi
4103 Brent Lutz
4104 Angel Martinez
4105 D.J. Boston
4106 Felipe Crespo
4107 Ted Langowski
4108 Gabriel Rosario
4109 Hector Tavarez
4110 John Touskalas
4111 Matt Wilke
4112 Emenegilda Alvarez
4113 Stoney Briggs
4114 Lee Daniels
4115 Jose Herrera
4116 Jairo Ramos
4117 J.J. Cannon
4118 Gilbert Rondon
4119 Checklist

1991 Sport Pro Medicine Hat Blue Jays

(Toronto Blue Jays) (color)

	MT	NR MT	EX
Complete Set:	3.00	2.25	1.25

1 Donald Boston
2 Angel Martinez
3 Jose Manuare
4 John Tsoukalas
5 Chris Ermis
6 Hector Tavarez
7 Michael Taylor
8 Jairo Ramos
9 Jose Herrera
10 Travis Baptist
11 Isabel Cardona
12 Steve Sinclair
13 Freddy Lopez
14 Lee Daniels
15 Gabriel Rosario
16 Albert Montoya
17 Andrew Dolson
18 Matt Wilke
19 Ned Darley
20 William Briggs
21 Emeneglida Alvarez
22 Felipe Crespo
23 Mike O'Halloran
24 Gilbert Rondon
25 Geoff Horne
26 J.J. Cannon
27 Blank
28 Blank
29 Blank
30 Blank

1991 ProCards Memphis Chicks

(Kansas City Royals) (color)

	MT	NR MT	EX
Complete Set:	4.00	3.00	1.50

646 Archie Corbin
647 Andres Cruz
648 Mark Parnell
649 Doug Peters
650 Hipolito Pichardo
651 Eddie Pierce
652 Mike Poehl
653 Steve Shifflett
654 Jim Smith
655 Lou Talbert
656 Terry Taylor
657 Jim Baxter
658 Jorge Pedre
659 Tony Bridges-Clements
660 Jeff Garber
661 David Gonzalez
662 Deric Ladnier
663 Darryl Robinson
664 Rich Tunison
665 Pete Alborano
666 Kevin Koslofski
667 Hugh Walker
668 Darren Watkins
669 Jeff Cox
670 Mike Alvarez
671 Brian Peterson
672 Checklist

1991 Classic Best Miami Miracle

(Independent) (color)

	MT	NR MT	EX
Complete Set:	4.00	3.00	1.50

1 Fredi Gonzalez
2 Will McEnaney
3 Rodney Nettnin
4 Billy Walker
5 Scott Asche
6 Mike Ericson
7 John Fritz
8 Jonathan Hurst
9 Tom Michno
10 Nate Minchey (Last name misspelled on checklist.)
11 Charlie Rodgers
12 Ken Whitworth
13 Ken Williams
14 Lee Langley
15 George Kerfut
16 Miah Bradbury
17 Andy Dziadkowiec
18 Kevin Castleberry
19 Greg D'Alexander
20 Marc Giordano
21 Mike Lansing
22 Ray Ledinsky
23 Hector Roa
24 John Urcioll
25 James Morrisette
26 Edwin Alicea
27 Chris Burton
28 Paris Hayden
29 Dennis Kidd
30 Bob Fralick (Checklist)

1991 ProCards Miami Miracle

(Independent) (color)

	MT	NR MT	EX
Complete Set:	4.00	3.00	1.50

399 Scott Asche
400 Mike Ericson
401 John Fritz
402 Jonathan Hurst
403 George Kerfut
404 Lee Langley
405 Tom Michno
406 Nate Minchey
407 Charlie Rogers
408 Ken Whitworth
409 Ken Williams
410 Miah Bradbury
411 Andy Dziadkowiec
412 Kevin Castleberry
413 Greg D'Alexander
414 Marc Giordano
415 Mike Lansing
416 Ray Ledinsky
417 Hector Roa
418 John Urcioli
419 Edwin Alicea
420 Chris Burton
421 Paris Hayden
422 Dennis Kidd
423 Fredi Gonzalez
424 Bob Fralic, Will McEnaney)
425 Checklist

1991 ProCards Midland Angels

(California Angels) (color)

	MT	NR MT	EX
Complete Set:	7.00	5.25	2.75

426 Clemente Acosta
427 Mike Butcher
428 Glenn Carter
429 Marvin Cobb
430 Sherman Corbett
431 Todd James
432 Steve King
433 Doug Robertson
434 Dave Shotkoski
435 Mark Zappelli
436 Larry Gonzales
437 Ken Rivers
438 Jeff Barns
439 Kevin Davis
440 Damion Easley
441 Kevin Flora
442 Mark Howie
443 Daryl Sconiers
444 Terry Taylor
445 Bobby Jones
446 Marcus Lawton
447 Tim Salmon
448 Ramon Sambo
449 Don Long
450 Gene Richards
451 Kernan Ronan
452 Checklist

1991 Team Midland Angels

This 32-card set was issued by the Midland Angels and sponsored by a local camera shop, One Hour Photo. The cards are 5" x 5-1/2", and have player information on the front of the card, with blank backs (since the cards are printed on photographic stock). The cards are unnumbered. They were given away weekly and included an opportunity for fans receiving the cards to get them autographed by the players. Two of the cards don't have the player's name.

	MT	NR MT	EX
Complete Set:	16.00	12.00	6.50

(1) Edgar Alfonso
(2) Don Barbara
(3) Jeff Barnes
(4) Hector Berrios
(5) Mick Billmeyer
(6) Mike Butcher
(7) Marvin Cobb
(8) Sherman Corbett
(9) Kevin Davis
(10) Damion Easley
(11) Kevin Flora
(12) Larry Gonzalez
(13) Mark Howie
(14) Bobby Jones
(15) Steve King
(16) Marcus Lawton
(17) Don Long
(18) Fili Martinez
(19) Walt McConnell
(20) Rafael Montalvo
(21) Gene Richards
(22) Ken Rivers
(23) Doug Robertson
(24) Kernan Ronan
(25) Tim Salmon
(26) Ramon Sambo
(27) Dave Shotkoski
(28) Alan Sontag
(29) Terry Taylor
(30) Don Vidmar
(31) Reggie Williams
(32) Mark Zappelli

1991 ProCards Midwest League All-Star Game

(color)

	MT	NR MT	EX
Complete Set:	7.00	5.25	2.75

1 Darren Burton
2 Gary Caraballo
3 Eric Christopherson
4 Rod Huffman
5 Mike Myers
6 Salomon Torres
7 Phil Dauphin
8 Brad Erdman
9 Jose Vierra
10 Domingo Jean
11 Rogelio Nunez
12 Kevin Tolar
13 Brandon Wilson
14 Clyde Keller
15 Tony Gilmore
16 Chris Hatcher
17 Fletcher Thompson
18 Wally Trice
19 Donne Wall
20 Ken Wheeler
21 Mark Borcherding
22 Larry Luebbers
23 Eddie Rush
24 Don Barbara
25 Mark Dalesandro
26 Cliff Garrett
27 Phil Leftwich
28 Billy Minnis
29 Roberto Arredondo
30 John Kuehl
31 Tim Worrell
32 Larry Carter
33 Mike Carter
34 Don Pruitt
35 Brad Tyler
36 Greg Zaun
37 Denny Hocking
38 Tim Pershing
39 Todd Ritchie
40 Jim Dillon
41 Brett Hendley
42 Rafael Mercado
43 Islay Molina
44 Tanyon Sturtze
45 Ranbir Grewal
46 Shaun Murphy
47 Glenn Murray
48 Corey Powell
49 Mike Weimerskirch
50 Randy Wilstead
51 Checklist

1991 Classic Best Modesto A's

(Oakland Athletics) (color)

	MT	NR MT	EX
Complete Set:	3.00	2.25	1.25

Modesto Log,,)
1 Kurt Abbott
2 Trent Weaver
3 Craig Sudbury
4 Rob Fletcher
5 Chaon Garland
6 Ken Hokuf
7 Ruben Lardizabal
8 Rick Miller
9 Mike Mohler
10 Glenn Osinski
11 Bronswell Patrick
12 Delfino Mejia
13 Scott Rose
14 Todd Smith
15 Rick Strebeck
16 Eric Booker
17 Ted Kubiak
18 Pete Richert
19 Dave Hollenback
20 Mike Messerly
21 Eric Helfand
22 Henry Mercedes
23 Enoch Simmons
24 Manuel Martinez
25 Kevin Dattola
26 Jim Waggoner
27 Checklist (Not listed on checklist.)

1991 Frank Chong Modesto A's

(Oakland A's) (color)

	MT	NR MT	EX
Complete Set:	3.00	2.25	1.25

1 Ted Kubiak (Manager)
2 Pete Richert (Coach)
3 Dave Hollenback (Trainer)
4 Enoch Simmons
5 Fred Cooley
6 Chris Hart
7 Carlos Salazar
8 Brad Parker
9 Mike Messerly
10 Ken Hokuf
11 Henry Mercedes
12 Scott Rose
13 Steve Phoenix
14 Craig Sudbury
15 Rich Strebeck
16 Mike Mohler
17 Kurt Abbott
18 Jimmy Waggoner
19 Will Love
20 Todd Smith
21 Fausto Cruz
22 Scott Erwin
23 Manny Martinez
24 Eric Booker
25 Kevin Dattola
26 Ruben Lardizabal
27 Glenn Osinski
28 Chaon Garland
29 Marcos Armas
30 Bronswell Patrick
31 Francisco Matos
32 Russ Cormier
33 Mike Conte
34 Eric Helfand
---- Modesto Logo Joe Rudi Night

1991 ProCards Modesto A's

(Oakland Athletics) (color)

	MT	NR MT	EX
Complete Set:	3.00	2.25	1.25

3079 Scott Erwin
3080 Chaon Garland
3081 Ken Hokuf
3082 Ruben Lardizabal
3083 Will Love
3084 Mike Mohler
3085 Bronswell Patrick
3086 Steve Phoenix
3087 Scott Rose
3088 Todd Smith
3089 Craig Sudbury
3090 Don Keathley
3091 Henry Mercedes
3092 Kurt Abbott
3093 Marcos Armas (First name spelled differently on back.)
3094 Fred Cooley
3095 Fausto Cruz
3096 Rob Fletcher
3097 Mike Messerly
3098 Glenn Osinski
3099 Carlos Salazar

3100 Jim Waggoner
3101 Eric Booker
3102 Kevin Dattola
3103 Chris Hart
3104 Manuel Martinez
3105 Enoch Simmons
3106 Ted Kubiak
3107 Pete Richert
3108 Checklist

1991 Classic Best Myrtle Beach Hurricanes

(Toronto Blue Jays) (color)

	MT	NR MT	EX
Complete Set:	7.50	5.50	3.00

1 Bobby Aylmer
2 Greg Bicknell
3 Kyle Duey
4 Huck Flener
5 Joe Ganote
6 Raphael Garcia
7 Ricardo Jordan
8 Steve Karsay
9 Sam Mandia
10 Tom Singer
11 Rick Steed
12 Carlos Delgado
13 Juan Jaime
14 Marc Loeb
15 Ciro Ambrosio
16 Howard Battle
17 Andy Carlton
18 Mark Choate
19 Mariano Dotel
20 Tim Hyers
21 Scott Miller
22 Ernesto Rodriguez
23 Brent Bowers
24 Rickey Holifield
25 Ronald Reams
26 Lonell Roberts
27 Garth Iorg
28 Darren Bailsey
29 Leroy Stanton
30 Armando Pagliari (Checklist)

1991 ProCards Myrtle Beach Hurricanes

(Toronto Blue Jays) (color)

	MT	NR MT	EX
Complete Set:	7.50	5.50	3.00

2935 Bobby Aylmer
2936 Greg Bicknell
2937 Kyle Duey
2938 Huck Flener
2939 Joe Ganote
2940 Rafael Garcia
2941 Ricardo Jordan
2942 Steve Karsay
2943 Sam Mandia
2944 Tom Singer
2945 Rick Steed
2946 Carlos Delgado
2947 Juan Jaime
2948 Marc Loeb
2949 Ciro Ambrosio
2950 Howard Battle
2951 Andy Carlton
2952 Mark Choate
2953 Mariano Dotel
2954 Tim Hyers
2955 Scott Miller
2956 Ernesto Rodriguez
2957 Brent Bowers
2958 Rickey Holifield
2959 Ron Reams
2960 Lonell Roberts
2961 Garth Iorg
2962 Darren Baisley
2963 Leroy Stanton
2964 Checklist

1991 ProCards Nashville Sounds

(Cincinnati Reds) (color)

	MT	NR MT	EX
Complete Set:	5.00	3.75	2.00

2149 Keith Brown
2150 Kip Gross
2151 Milton Hill
2152 Rodney Imes
2153 Gino Minutelli
2154 Charlie Mitchell
2155 Ross Powell
2156 Luis Vasquez
2157 Joey Vierra
2158 Pete Beeler
2159 Tony DeFrancesco
2160 Donnie Scott
2161 Freddie Benavides
2162 Angel Gonzalez
2163 Denny Gonzalez
2164 Reggie Jefferson
2165 Terry Lee
2166 Keith Lockhart
2167 Kevin Pearson
2168 Adam Casillas
2169 Leo Garcia
2170 Manny Jose
2171 Bernie Walker
2172 Pete Mackanin
2173 Don Gullett
2174 Jim Lett
2175 Checklist

1991 Team Nashville Sounds

(Cincinnati Reds) (color)

	MT	NR MT	EX
Complete Set:	9.50	7.00	3.75

(1) Jose Alvarez
(2) Billy Bates
(3) Freddie Benavides
(4) Keith Brown
(5) Tony DeFrancesco
(6) Rob Dibble
(7) Steve Foster
(8) Leo Garcia
(9) Angel Gonzalez
(10) Denny Gonzalez
(11) Kip Gross
(12) Don Gullett
(13) Milton Hill
(14) Rodney Imes
(15) Chris Jones
(16) Terry Lee
(17) Jim Lett
(18) Keith Lockhart
(19) Pete Mackanin
(20) Gino Minutelli
(21) Charlie Mitchell
(22) Kevin Pearson
(23) Ross Powell
(24) Tim Pugh
(25) Larry Schmittou
(26) Donnie Scott
(27) Glenn Sutko
(28) Todd Trafton
(29) Joe Turek
(30) Luis Vasquez
(31) Joey Vierra
(32) John Young
(33) Adam Casillas
---- Sponsor Card

1991 ProCards New Britain Red Sox

(Boston Red Sox) (color)

	MT	NR MT	EX
Complete Set:	4.00	3.00	1.50

344 Brian Conroy
345 Freddie Davis
346 Pete Estrada
347 Tom Fischer
348 Don Florence
349 Peter Hoy
350 Tom Kane
351 Paul Quantrilli
352 Al Sanders
353 Scott Taylor
354 Ray Fagnant
355 John Flaherty
356 Colin Dixon
357 Steve Hendricks
358 Dave Milstien
359 Scott Powers
360 Randy Randle
361 John Valentin
362 Mike Beams
363 Greg Blosser
364 Blane Fox
365 Wayne Housie
366 Juan Paris
367 Gary Allenson
368 Rick Wise
369 Checklist

1991 Classic Best Niagara Falls Rapids

(Detroit Tigers) (color)

	MT	NR MT	EX
Complete Set:	3.00	2.25	1.25

1 Kevin Morgan
2 Jimmy Brown
3 Arthur Johnson
4 Thomas Gibson
5 Ryan Haley
6 Jim Van Scoyoc
7 Aaron Seja
8 Clarke Rea
9 Brian Sullivan
10 Brian Dubose
11 Kevin Miller
12 Evan Pratte
13 Tony Clark
14 Ron Grable
15 Robin Higginbotham
16 Peter Feeley
17 Carlos Burguillos
18 Rich Kelley
19 Ben Blomdahl
20 John Reid
21 Dennis Walsh
22 Shawn Turri
23 Doug Martin
24 Sean Bergman
25 Jim Henry
26 Shannon Withem
27 Bob Lemay
28 Corey Reincke
29 Gary Calhoun
30 Stan Luketich (Checklist)

1991 ProCards Niagara Falls Rapids

(Detroit Tigers) (color)

	MT	NR MT	EX
Complete Set:	3.00	2.25	1.25

3624 Sean Bergman
3625 Ben Blomdahl
3626 Scott DuRussel
3627 Jimmy Henry
3628 Rich Kelley
3629 Bob Lemay
3630 Doug Martin
3631 Corey Reincke (First name spelled differently on checklist.)
3632 Shawn Turri
3633 Dennis Walsh
3634 Shannon Withem
3635 Ryan Haley
3636 Kevin Miller
3637 Gregg Radachowsky
3638 Clarke Rea
3639 Jimmy Brown
3640 Brian Dubose
3641 Rob Grable
3642 Kevin Morgan
3643 Evan Pratte
3644 Carlos Burguillos
3645 Tony Clark
3646 Peter Feeley
3647 Robin Higginbotham
3648 Aaron Seja
3649 Brian Sullivan
3650 Gary Calhoun
3651 Stan Luketich
3652 Jim Van Scoyoc
3653 Checklist

1991 ProCards Oklahoma City 89ers

(Texas Rangers) (color)

	MT	NR MT	EX
Complete Set:	7.00	5.25	2.75

170 Gerald Alexander
171 Joe Bitker
172 Jeff Bronkey
173 Terry Matthews
174 Roger Pavlik
175 Steve Peters
176 Jim Poole
177 Mark Petkovsek
178 Wayne Rosenthal
179 Dan Smith
180 Terry Wells
181 Mike Berger
182 Bill Haselman
183 Paco Burgos
184 Monty Fariss
185 Darrin Garner
186 Rob Maurer
187 Dean Palmer
188 Paul Postier
189 Kevin Belcher
190 Nick Capra
191 Gar Millay
192 Dan Peltier
193 Tommy Thompson
194 Jeff Andrews
195 Stan Hough
196 Checklist

1991 ProCards Omaha Royals

(Kansas City Royals) (color)

	MT	NR MT	EX
Complete Set:	5.00	3.75	2.00

1027 Bob Buchanan
1028 Victor Cole
1029 Luis Encarnacion
1030 Greg Everson
1031 Joel Johnston
1032 Jim Lemasters
1033 Mike Magnante
1034 Carlos Maldonado
1035 Daryl Smith
1036 Hector Wagner
1037 Kevin Burrell
1038 Tim Spehr
1039 Sean Berry
1040 Stu Cole
1041 Jeff Conine
1042 Bob Hamelin
1043 Frank Laureano
1044 Paul Zuvella
1045 Jacob Brumfield
1046 Tommy Dunbar
1047 Bobby Moore
1048 Harvey Pulliam
1049 Sal Rende
1050 Guy Hansen
1051 Brian Polberg
1052 Checklist

1991 ProCards Oneonta Yankees

(New York Yankees) (color)

	MT	NR MT	EX
Complete Set:	3.00	2.25	1.25

4145 Dennis Burbank
4146 Billy Coleman
4147 Andy Croghan
4148 Keith Garagozzo
4149 Scott Gully
4150 Bert Inman
4151 Frank Laviano
4152 Steve Munda
4153 Sandi Santiago
4154 Ben Short
4155 Grant Sullivan
4156 Jorge Posada
4157 John Quintell
4158 Tom Wilson
4159 Steve Anderson
4160 Roger Burnett
4161 Tim Flannelly
4162 Steve Livesey
4163 Tate Seefried
4164 Andrew Albrecht
4165 Mark Hubbard
4166 Lyle Mouton
4167 Steve Phillips
4168 Jack Gillis
4169 Mark Rose
4170 Bill Schmidt
4171 Checklist

1991 ProCards Orlando Sun Rays

(Minnesota Twins) (color)

	MT	NR MT	EX
Complete Set:	4.00	3.00	1.50

1842 Pat Bangtson
1843 Pete Delkus
1844 Greg Johnson
1845 Orlando Lind
1846 Pat Mahomes
1847 Steve Muh
1848 Steve Stowell
1849 Mike Trombley
1850 Rob Wassenaar
1851 Phil Wiese
1852 Derek Parks
1853 Joe Siwa
1854 Carlos Capellan
1855 Cheo Garcia
1856 Shawn Gilbert
1857 Jose Marzan
1858 Dan Masteller
1859 Bob McCreary
1860 Reed Olmstead
1861 Rafael Delima
1862 Jay Kvasnicka
1863 Ray Ortiz
1864 Frank Valdez
1865 Scott Ullger
1866 Mark Funderburk
1867 Jim Shellenback
1869 Checklist

1991 Classic Best Osceola Astros

(Houston Astros) (color)

	MT	NR MT	EX
Complete Set:	4.00	3.00	1.50

Astros Logo
1 Fred Costello
2 Gordon Farmer
3 Brian Griffiths
4 Cole Hyson

5 Lee Johnson
6 Todd Jones
7 Ken Luckham
8 Montie Phillips
9 Ed Ponte
10 Matt Rambo
11 Mark Small
12 Brian Williams
13 Rodney Windes
14 Ed Beuerlein
15 John Massarelli
16 Jeff Ball
17 Perry Berry
18 Dave Hajek
19 Frank Kellner
20 Bobby Ramos
21 Ed Renteria
22 Craig Curtis
23 Gershon Dallas
24 Brian Hunter
25 Luther Johnson
26 Sal Butera
27 Mike Freer
28 Kevin Scott
29 Checklist (Not listed on checklist.)

1991 ProCards Osceola Astros

(Houston Astros) (color)

	MT	NR MT	EX
Complete Set:	4.00	3.00	1.50

673 Fred Costello
674 Gordon Farmer
675 Brian Griffiths
676 Cole Hyson
677 Lee Johnson
678 Todd Jones
679 Ken Luckham
680 Montie Phillips
681 Ed Ponte
682 Matt Rambo
683 Robert Resnikoff
684 Mark Small
685 Brian Williams
686 Rodney Windes
687 Ed Beuerlein
688 John Massarelli
689 Kevin Scott
690 Jeff Ball
691 Perry Berry
692 Dave Hajek
693 Frank Kellner
694 Howard Prager
695 Ed Renteria
696 Craig Curtis
697 Gershon Dallas
698 Brian Hunter
699 Luther Johnson
700 Coaching Staff
701 Checklist

1991 ProCards Palm Springs Angels

(Los Angels Angels) (color)

	MT	NR MT	EX
Complete Set:	4.00	3.00	1.50

2007 Hector Berrios
2008 Steve Loubier
2009 Brett Merriman
2010 Louis Pakele
2011 Steve Peck
2012 Randy Powers
2013 Alan Sontag
2014 Paul Swingle
2015 Dave Van Winkle
2016 Bruce Vegely
2017 Don Vidmar
2018 Mick Billmeyer
2019 Frank Dominguez
2020 Danny Gil
2021 Edgar Alfonzo
2022 P.J. Forbes
2023 Corey Kapano
2024 Ramon Martinez
2025 J.R. Phillips
2026 J.R. Showalter
2027 Davie Colon
2028 Jim Edmonds
2029 Carlos Laboy
2030 Dave Patrick
2031 Beban Perez
2032 Edgal Rodriguez
2033 Nate Oliver
2034 Stu Cliburn
2035 Mario Mendoza
2036 Checklist

1991 ProCards Pawtucket Red Sox

(Boston Red Sox) (color)

	MT	NR MT	EX
Complete Set:	8.00	6.00	3.25

31 Mike Gardiner
32 Eric Hetzel
33 Daryl Irvine
34 Derek Livernois
35 Josias Manzanillo
36 Kevin Morton
37 Dan O'Neill
38 Jeff Plympton
39 Larry Shikles
40 David Walters
41 Todd Pratt
42 Eric Wegde
43 Luis Aguayo
44 Tom Barrett
45 Mike Brumley
46 Scott Cooper
47 Rick Lancelotti
48 Jim Pankovits
49 Mo Vaughn
50 Mickey Pina
51 Phil Plantier
52 Jeff Stone
53 Bob Zupcic
54 Butch Hobson
55 Rich Gale
56 Mark Meleski
57 Checklist

1991 Dunkin' Donuts Pawtucket Red Sox

(Boston Red Sox) (color)

	MT	NR MT	EX
Complete Set:	15.00	11.00	6.00

(1) Luis Aguayo
(2) Tom Barrett
(3) Scott Cooper
(4) John Flaherty
(5) Rich Gale
(6) Mike Gardiner
(7) Eric Hetzel
(8) Butch Hobson
(9) Darryl Irvine
(10) Rick Lancelotti
(11) Derek Livernois
(12) Mark Meleski
(13) Kevin Morton
(14) Dan O'Neill
(15) Jim Pankovits
(16) Mickey Pina
(17) Phil Plantier
(18) Jeff Plympton
(19) Todd Pratt
(20) Paul Quantrill
(21) Larry Shikles
(22) Jeff Stone
(23) Scott Taylor
(24) Mike Twardoski
(25) John Valentin
(26) Mo Vaughn
(27) Gene Walter
(28) Dave Walters
(29) Eric Wedge
(30) Rob Zupcic

1991 Classic Best Peninsula Pilots

(Seattle Mariners) (color)

	MT	NR MT	EX
Complete Set:	3.00	2.25	1.25

1 Greg Pirkl
2 Jim Converse
3 Kelvin Thomas
4 Manuel Furcal
5 Brad Holman
6 Kevin King
7 Bill Kostitch
8 Richard Lodding
9 Paul Perkins
10 Scott Schanz
11 Doug Tegtmeier
12 Salvy Urso
13 Johnny Wiggs
14 Tony Kounas
15 Jorge Morales
16 Damon Saetre
17 Willie Romay
18 Mark Brakebill
19 Mike Fermaint
20 Ron Pezzoni
21 Bobby Holley
22 Israel Seda
23 Roberto Del Pozo
24 Mark Merchant
25 Checklist (Not listed on checklist.)
---- Pilots Logo
---- Mariners Logo
---- MLB Logo
---- Schmidt Ad

1991 ProCards Peninsula Pilots

(Seattle Mariners) (color)

	MT	NR MT	EX
Complete Set:	3.00	2.25	1.25

370 Manuel Furcal
371 Brad Holman
372 Kevin King
373 Bill Kostich
374 Richard Lodding
375 Paul Perkins
376 Scott Schanz
377 Doug Tegtmeier
378 Sal Urso
379 Johnny Wiggs
380 Tony Kounas
381 Jorge Morales
382 Glen Raasch
383 Mark Brakebill
384 Mike Fermaint
385 Jon Halland
386 Bobby Holley
387 Israel Seda
388 Roberto Del Poza
389 Mark Merchant
390 Ron Pezzoni
391 Willie Romay
392 Damon Saetre
393 Kelvin Thomas
394 Steve Smith
395 Carlos Lezcano
396 Bryan Price
397 Checklist

1991 Classic Best Peoria Chiefs

(Chicago Cubs) (color)

	MT	NR MT	EX
Complete Set:	7.00	5.25	2.75

Chiefs Logo
1 Dave Ross
2 Pedro Alicano
3 Amilcar Correa
4 Tim Delgado
5 Jason Doss
6 Chuck Kirk
7 Tom Mann
8 Earl Cunningham
9 Aaron Taylor
10 Brad Erdman
11 Rick Mundy
12 Tyson Godfrey
13 Paul Torres
14 Jose Viera
15 Bryan Wilson
16 German Diaz
17 Tim Moore
18 Victor Cancel
19 Rolando Fernandez
20 Willie Gardner
21 Mike Little
22 Bill Hayes
23 Lester Strode
24 Jim O'Reilly
25 Phillip Dauphin
26 Kenneth Krahenbuhl
27 Rafael Soto
28 Andy Hartung
29 Checklist (Not listed on checklist.)

1991 ProCards Peoria Chiefs

(Chicago Cubs) (color)

	MT	NR MT	EX
Complete Set:	4.00	3.00	1.50

1333 Pedro Alicano
1334 Amilcar Correa
1335 Tim Delgado
1336 Jason Doss
1337 Tyson Godfrey
1338 Chuck Kirk
1339 Tom Mann
1340 Pedro Perez
1341 Dave Ross
1342 Dave Swartzbaugh
1343 Aaron Taylor
1344 Brad Erdman
1345 Rick Mundy
1346 Steve Coffey
1347 Morris Craig
1348 German Diaz
1349 Andy Hartung
1350 Tim Moore
1351 Rafael Soto
1352 Jose Vierra
1353 Danny Cancel
1354 Earl Cunningham
1355 Phil Dauphin
1356 Rolando Fernandez
1357 Willie Gardner
1358 Mike Little
1359 Bill Hayes
1360 Lester Strode
1361 Checklist

1991 Team Peoria Chiefs

(Chicago Cubs) (color)

	MT	NR MT	EX
Complete Set:	8.00	6.00	3.25

1 Bill Hayes
2 Lester Strode
3 Jim O'Reilly
4 Pedro Alicano
5 Amlicar Correa
6 Tim Delgado
7 Jason Doss
8 Tyson Godfrey
9 Chuck Kirk
10 Ken Krahenbuhl
11 Tom Mann
12 David Ross
13 Aaron Taylor
14 Brad Erdman
15 Rick Mundy
16 German Diaz
17 Andy Hartung
18 Tim Moore
19 Rafael Soto
20 Paul Torres
21 Jose Viera
22 Bryan Wilson
23 Victor Cancel
24 Earl Cunningham
25 Phil Dauphin
26 Rolando Fernandez
27 Mike Little
28 John Davis
29 Acro (Mascot)
30 Staff
31 Rick Sutcliffe
32 Scott Weiss
33 Darrin Duffy
34 Bill Bliss

1991 ProCards Phoenix Firebirds

(San Francisco Giants) (color)

	MT	NR MT	EX
Complete Set:	7.50	5.50	3.00

58 Johnny Ard
59 Rod Beck
60 Mark Dewey
61 Gil Heredia
62 Rafael Novoa
63 Francisco Oliveras
64 Mike Remlinger
65 Rick Rodriguez
66 Jose Segura
67 Stuart Tate
68 Jimmy Williams
69 Mark Bailey
70 Craig Colbert
71 Jeff Carter
72 Paul Noce
73 Rick Parker
74 Tony Perezchica
75 Ken Phelps
76 Andres Santana
77 Jim Wilson
78 Rich Aldrete
79 Darnell Coles
80 Darren Lewis
81 Gregg Ritchie

82 Ted Wood
83 Duane Espy
84 Alan Bannister
85 Larry Hardy
86 Checklist

1991 Classic Best Pittsfield Mets

(New York Mets)(color)

	MT	NR MT	EX
Complete Set:	3.00	2.25	1.25

Pittsfield Log,)
1 Tny Tijerina
2 Greg Beals
3 Dwight Robinson
4 Frank Jacobs
5 Todd Nace
6 Randy Curtis
7 Jerome Tolliver
8 Tim Sandy
9 Michael Sciortino
10 Danilo Mompres
11 Bernie Millan
12 Micah Franklin
13 Joe Arredondo
14 Casper Van Rynbach
15 Ottis Smith
16 Chris Shanahan
17 Jim Scheffler
18 Jim Manfred
19 Darian Lindsay
20 Mike Lehnerz
21 Hector Carrasco
22 Mike Anaya
23 Chris George
24 Eric Reichenbach
25 Jim Thrift
26 Jerry Koosman
27 Billy Gardner
28 Checklist (Not listed on checklist.)

1991 ProCards Pittsfield Mets

(New York Mets) (color)

	MT	NR MT	EX
Complete Set:	3.00	2.25	1.25

3414 Mike Anaya
3415 Hector Carrasco
3416 Chris George
3417 Mike Lehnerz
3418 Darian Lindsay
3419 Jim Manfred
3420 Eric Reichenbach
3421 Jim Scheffler
3422 Chris Shanahan
3423 Ottis Smith
3424 Casper Van Rynbach
3425 Greg Beals
3426 Tony Tijerina
3427 Joe Arredondo
3428 Micah Franklin
3429 Frank Jacobs
3430 Bernie Millan
3431 Danilo Mompres
3432 Dwight Robinson
3433 Mike Sciortino
3434 Randy Curtis
3435 Todd Nace
3436 Tim Sandy
3437 Jerome Tolliver
3438 Jim Thrift
3439 Billy Gardner
3440 Jerry Koosman
3441 Checklist

1991 ProCards Pocatello Pioneers

(Co-op) (color)

	MT	NR MT	EX
Complete Set:	3.00	2.25	1.25

3773 Derek Atwood (First name spelled differently on checklist.)
3774 Rob Callistro
3775 Rich Ekman
3776 Monty Gibson
3777 Steve Grennan
3778 Steve Mill
3779 Steve Patterson
3780 Jason Reese
3781 Bruce Schenck
3782 Dale Stevens
3783 Von Wechsberg
3784 James Joyce
3785 John Martinez
3786 Marc Morris
3787 Buck Atwater
3788 Dean Banks
3789 Kris Kaelin
3790 Audy Mesa
3791 Jeff Schoizen
3792 Paul Weldon
3793 Kevin Wong
3794 Todd Anderson
3795 William Carmona
3796 Stacey Hamm
3797 Larry Minter
3798 Dino Philyaw
3799 Terry Robinson
3800 Rich Morales Jr.
3801 Rick Rodriguez
3802 Eddie Sedar
3803 Checklist

1991 Sport-Pro Pocatello Pioneers

(Independent) (color)

	MT	NR MT	EX
Complete Set:	3.00	2.25	1.25

1 Larry Minter
2 Rob Callistro
3 Steve Mill
4 Richard Joyce
5 Terry Robinson
6 Bruce Schenck
7 Von Wechsberg
8 John Martinez
9 Rich Ekman
10 Dean Banks
11 Jason Reese
12 Mark Morris
13 Derick Atwood
14 Kevin Wong
15 Steve Patterson
16 Todd Anderson
17 Dale Stevens
18 Monty Gibson
19 Steve Grennan
20 Kris Kaelin
21 Paul Weldon
22 Jeffrey Scholzen
23 Tyrone Atwater
24 Audy Mesa
25 Dino Philyaw
26 Stacey Hamm
27 William Carmona
28 Eddie Sedar
29 Rick Rodriguez
30 Rich Morales Jr.

1991 ProCards Portland Beavers

(Minnesota Twins) (color)

	MT	NR MT	EX
Complete Set:	7.00	5.25	2.75

1558 Paul Abbott
1559 Willie Banks
1560 Tim Drummond
1561 Tom Edens
1562 Richard Garces
1563 Denny Neagle
1564 Jack Savage
1565 Charles Scott
1566 George Tsamis
1567 Carl Willis
1568 Danny Sheaffer
1569 Lenny Webster
1570 Chip Hale
1571 Terry Jorgensen
1572 Jeff Reboulet
1573 Victor Rodriguez
1574 Paul Sorrento
1575 Bernardo Brito
1576 Jarvis Brown
1577 J.T. Bruett
1578 Kenny Morgan
1579 Pedro Munoz
1580 Edgar Naveda
1581 Russ Nixon
1582 Jim Dwyer
1583 Gorman Heimuller
1584 Paul Kirsch
1585 Checklist

1991 Classic Best Princeton Reds

(Cincinnati Reds) (color)

	MT	NR MT	EX
Complete Set:	3.00	2.25	1.25

1 Kevin Aubin
2 Juan Loyola
3 Omar Malpica
4 John Gast
5 Ken Cavazzoni
6 Chris Reed
7 James Miller
8 John Hrusovsky
9 Rodney Steph
10 Rossi Morris
11 Armando Morales
12 Bill Dreisbach
13 Toby Rumfield
14 Dee Jenkins
15 Calvin Reese
16 Rodney Thomas
17 Eli Robinson
18 Jeff Murphy
19 Yamil Conception
20 Blake Bentley
21 Wayne Wilkerson
22 Rory Rhodriquez
23 Kevin Jarvis
24 Bryant Balentine
25 John Brothers
26 Jimmy Wiggins
27 Fermin Garcia
28 Sam Mejias
29 Jim Arendt
30 Tom Iversen (Checklist)

1991 ProCards Princeton Reds

(Cincinnati Reds) (color)

	MT	NR MT	EX
Complete Set:	3.00	2.25	1.25

3504 Bryant Balentine
3505 John Brothers
3506 Fermin Garcia
3507 John Hrusovsky
3508 Kevin Jarvis
3509 Jim Miller
3510 Armando Morales
3511 Jeff Murphy
3512 Chris Reed
3513 Rory Rhodriquez (Last name misspelled on checklist.)
3514 Rodney Steph
3515 Jim Wiggins
3516 Kevin Aubin
3517 Bill Dreisbach
3518 Toby Rumfield
3519 Ken Cavazzoni
3520 Yamil Conception
3521 John Gast
3522 Dee Jenkins
3523 Calvin Reese
3524 Eli Robinson
3525 Blake Bentley
3526 Juan Loyola
3527 Omar Malpica
3528 Rossi Morris
3529 Rodney Thomas
3530 Wayne Wilkerson
3531 Sam Mejias
3532 Doc Rodgers
3533 Checklist

1991 Classic Best Prince William Cannons

(New York Yankees) (color)

	MT	NR MT	EX
Complete Set:	5.00	3.75	2.00

1 Brent Gilbert
2 Sterling Hitchcock
3 Darren Hodges
4 Jeff Hoffman
5 Mike Hankins
6 Dan Johnson
7 Sam Militello Jr.
8 Mark Ohlms
9 Kirt Ojala
10 Curtis Ralph
11 Ricky Rhodes
12 Stephen Tucker
13 Brad Ausmus
14 Michael Figga
15 John Jarvis
16 Robert Eenhoorn
17 Andy Fox
18 Ramon Jimenez
19 Daniel Sanchez
20 Joey Wardlow
21 Paul Oster
22 Jason Robertson
23 John Viera
24 Mike Hart
25 Dave Schuler
26 Rob Thomson
27 Adam Wagner
28 Sherman Obando
29 Jim Haller
30 Prince Willie (Checklist)

1991 ProCards Prince William Cannons

(New York Yankees) (color)

	MT	NR MT	EX
Complete Set:	5.00	3.75	2.00

1417 Brent Gilbert
1418 Jim Haller
1419 Sterling Hitchcock
1420 Darren Hodges
1421 Jeff Hoffman
1422 Dan Johnston
1423 Sam Militello
1424 Mark Ohlms
1425 Kirt Ojala
1426 Curtis Ralph
1427 Ricky Rhodes
1428 Stephen Tucker
1429 Brad Ausmus
1430 Michael Figga
1431 John Jarvis
1432 Robert Eenhoorn
1433 Andy Fox
1434 Mike Hankins
1435 Ramon Jimenez
1436 Daniel Sanchez
1437 Joe Wardlow
1438 Sherman Obando
1439 Paul Oster
1440 Jason Robertson
1441 John Viera
1442 Mike Hart
1443 Dave Schuler
1444 Rob Thomson
1445 Checklist

1991 Classic Best Pulaski Braves

(Atlanta Braves) (color)

	MT	NR MT	EX
Complete Set:	3.00	2.25	1.25

1 Joe Ayrault
2 Paul Kelliher
3 Carlos Lara
4 Carl Archer
5 Keith Chaney
6 Cory Crosnoe
7 Manuel Jimenez
8 Jason Keeline
9 Lansing Marks
10 George Virgilio
11 Mark Chambers
12 Andre Johnson
13 Don Robinson (No position listed on card.)
14 Randy Ingle
15 Javier Rivas
16 Scott Behrens
17 Dirk Blair
18 Stewart Ford
19 Dwayne Fowler
20 Cloyd Boyer
21 Jason Butler
22 Scott Francis (Last name misspelled on checklist.)
23 Fred Koening
24 Eric Lairsey
25 Ricardo Petit
26 Scott Ryder
27 John Wilder
28 Matt Viarengo
29 Kevin Saulter
30 Mike Cerame (Checklist)

1991 ProCards Pulaski Braves

(Atlanta Braves) (color)

	MT	NR MT	EX
Complete Set:	3.00	2.25	1.25

3995 Scott Behrens
3996 Dirk Blair
3997 Jason Butler
3998 Stewart Ford
3999 Dwayne Fowler
4000 Scott Francis
4001 Eric Lairsey
4002 Ricardo Petit
4003 Scott Ryder
4004 Kevin Saulter
4005 Matt Viarengo
4006 John Wilder
4007 Joe Ayrault
4008 Paul Kelliher
4009 Carlos Lara
4010 Carl Archer
4011 Keith Chaney
4012 Cory Crosnoe
4013 Manuel Jiminez
4014 Jason Keeline
4015 Lance Marks
4016 George Virgilio
4017 Mark Chambers
4018 Andre Johnson
4019 Javier Rivas
4020 Don Robinson
4021 Dominic Therrien
4022 Randy Ingle
4023 Cloyd Boyer
4024 Fred Koenig
4025 Checklist

1991 Classic Best Quad City Angels

(California Angels) (color)

	MT	NR MT	EX
Complete Set:	7.00		

Quad City Logo 3.00
1 Dave Adams
2 Brit Craven (First name spelled differently on card front.)
3 Ken Edenfield
4 Bobby Gamez
5 Matt Hyde
6 Bret Lacheman
7 Phil Leftwich
8 Justin Martin
9 Norm Montoya
10 Darryl Scott
11 Victor Silverio
12 Tom Dodge
13 Jose Stela
14 Fausto Tejero
15 Don Barbara
16 Mark Dalesandro
17 Brian Grebeck
18 Jeff Kipila
19 Bill Minnis
20 Jeff Oberdank
21 Carlos Polanco
22 Garret Anderson
23 Emmitt Cohick
24 Cliff Garrett
25 Dan Peiratt
26 Rafael Muratti
27 Mitch Seoane
28 Joe Georger
29 Checklist (Not listed on checklist.)

1991 ProCards Quad City Angels

(California Angels) (color)

	MT	NR MT	EX
Complete Set:	3.00	2.25	1.25

2618 Dave Adams
2619 Britt Craven
2620 Ken Edenfield
2621 Bobby Gamez
2622 Joe Klancnik
2623 Bret Lachemann
2624 Phil Leftwich
2625 Justin Martin
2626 Norm Montoya
2627 Darryl Scott
2628 Victor Silverio
2629 Jon Anderson
2630 Tom Dodge
2631 Jose Stella
2632 Fausto Tejero
2633 Don Barbara
2634 Mark Dalesandro
2635 Gary Forrester
2636 Brian Grebeck
2637 Jeff Kipila
2638 Billy Minnis
2639 Jeff Oberdank
2640 Carlos Polanco
2641 Garret Anderson
2642 Emmitt Cohick
2643 Cliff Garrett
2644 Rafael Muratti
2645 Mitch Seoane
2646 Joe Georger
2647 Matt Hyde
2648 Checklist

1991 ProCards Reading Phillies

(Philadelphia Phillies) (color)

	MT	NR MT	EX
Complete Set:	4.00	3.00	1.50

398 Checklist (Numbered out of sequence.)
1362 Jason Backs
1363 Toby Borland
1364 Cliff Brantley
1365 John Burgos
1366 Andy Carter
1367 Rick Dunnum
1368 David Holdridge
1369 Darrell Lindsey
1370 Mark Sims
1371 Jeff Tabaka
1372 Doug Lindsey
1373 Edwin Rosado
1374 Joe Millette
1375 Nikco Riesgo
1376 Rod Robertson
1377 Sean Ryan
1378 Tony Trevino
1379 Casey Waller
1380 Dana Brown
1381 Bruce Dostal
1382 Tony Longmire
1383 Tom Marsh
1384 Cary Williams
1385 Don McCormack
1386 Al LeBoeuf
1387 John Martin

1991 Cal League Reno Silver Sox

(Independent) (color)

	MT	NR MT	EX
Complete Set:	4.00	3.00	1.50

1 John Rabb
2 Mark Krumback
3 Lonnie Phillips
4 Frank Turco
5 Jim Jones
6 Dom Johnson
7 Cliff Williams
8 Rick Odekirk
9 Andy Postema
10 Joe Warren
11 Doug Messer
12 Cliff Gonzalez
13 Joe Roebuck
14 Tom Mitchell
15 Mike Norris
16 Tom Gilles
17 Troy Clemens
18 Todd McCray
19 Rich Buonantony
20 Francisco Alcantara
21 Mike Songini
22 Dodd Johnson
23 Dion Beck
24 Brian Stephens
25 Joe Olker
26 David Volt
27 Bill Murray
28 Dean Treanor
29 Mal Fichman

1991 Bob's Camera Richmond Braves

(Atlanta Braves) (color) (Photos measure approximately 4" x 8" in size and are printed on Kodak stock. Their backs are blank.)

	MT	NR MT	EX
Complete Set:	35.00	26.00	14.00

2 Bruce Crabbe
5 Gibson Alba
6 John Davis
7 Tony Castillo
8 Randy Kramer
10 Tom McCarthy
11 Andy Nezelek
12 Yorkis Perez
13 Dale Polley
14 Armando Reynoso
15 Mark Ross
16 Randy St. Claire
17 Matt Turner
18 Joe Szekely
19 John Alva
20 Mike Bell
21 Victor Rosario
22 Rico Rossy
23 Tracy Woodson
24 Bruce Fields
25 Brian Hunter
26 Mike Loggins
27 Al Martin
28 Rich Casarotti
29 Vinny Castilla
30 Mark Wohlers
31 Jerome Nelson
32 Jeff Parrett
33 Keith Mitchell
34 Pat Gomez
35 Boi Rodriguez
36 Jerry Willard
37 Deion Sanders
38 Phil Niekro
39 Sonny Jackson
40 Bruce Dal Canton
41 Johnny Grubb
42 Rick Berg
43 Steve Curry
---- Kelly Mann
---- Rusty Richards
---- Andy Tomberlin

1991 ProCards Richmond Braves

(Atlanta Braves) (color)

	MT	NR MT	EX
Complete Set:	6.00	4.50	2.50

2559 Gibson Alba
2560 Tony Castillo
2561 Randy Kramer
2562 Paul Marak
2563 Tom McCarthy
2564 Yorkis Perez
2565 Dale Polley
2566 Armando Reynoso
2567 Mark Ross
2568 Randy St. Claire
2569 Matt Turner
2570 Randy Veres
2571 Kelly Mann
2572 Joe Szekely
2573 Jerry Willard
2574 John Alva
2575 Mike Bell
2576 Bruce Crabbe
2577 Victor Rosario
2578 Rico Rossy
2579 Tracy Woodson
2580 Bruce Fields
2581 Brian Hunter
2582 Glenn Wilson
2583 Phil Niekro
2584 Rick Berg
2585 Bruce Dal Canton
2586 John Grubb
2587 Sonny Jackson
2588 Checklist

1991 ProCards Rochester Red Wings

(Baltimore Orioles) (color)

	MT	NR MT	EX
Complete Set:	7.00	5.25	2.75

1895 Francisco De La Rosa
1896 Todd Frohwirth
1897 Mike Linskey
1898 Dave Martinez
1899 Mike Mussina
1900 Chris Myers
1901 Israel Sanchez
1902 Roy Smith
1903 Anthony Telford
1904 Rob Woodward
1905 Mike Eberle
1906 Jeff Tackett
1907 Benny Distefano
1908 Steve Jeltz
1909 Jeff McKnight
1910 David Segui
1911 Tommy Shields
1912 Shane Turner
1913 Tony Chance
1914 Chito Martinez
1915 Oddibe McDowell
1916 Luis Mercedes
1917 Jeff Wetherby
1918 Greg Biagini
1919 Dick Bosman
1920 Mike Young
1921 Checklist

1991 Classic Best Rockford Expos

(Montreal Expos) (color)

	MT	NR MT	EX
Complete Set:	3.00	2.25	1.25

Checklist
1 Bob Baxter
2 Jim Young
3 Stacey Collins
4 Ralph Diaz
5 Ranbir Grewal
6 Ben Howze
7 Pat Jurado
8 Martin Martinez
9 Mike Mathile
10 Corey Powell
11 Rafael Reyes
12 Bobby Ryan
13 Jose Castro
14 Robert Fitzpatrick
15 Steve Keighley
16 Rich Dubee
17 Ray Callari
18 Ted Ciesia
19 Mike Friedland
20 Chris Malinoski
21 Dan Smith
22 Randy Wilstead
23 Mike Moberg
24 Shaun Murphy
25 Glenn Murray
26 Mike Weimerskirch
27 Pat Kelly
28 Steve Whitehead
29 Dan Hargia (First name incorrect on card front and checklist.)

1991 ProCards Rockford Expos

(Montreal Expos) (color)

	MT	NR MT	EX
Complete Set:	3.00	2.25	1.25

2037 Bob Baxter
2038 Stacey Collins
2039 Ralph Diaz
2040 Ranbir Grewal
2041 Ben Howze
2042 Pat Jurado
2043 Martin Martinez
2044 Mike Mathile
2045 Corey Powell
2046 Rafael Reyes
2047 Bobby Ryan
2048 Steve Whitehead
2049 Robert Fitzpatrick
2050 Dan Hargis
2051 Steve Keighley
2052 Ray Callari
2053 Ted Ciesla
2054 Mike Friedland
2055 Chris Malinoski
2056 Dandy Smith
2057 Randy Wilstead
2058 Mike Moberg
2059 Shaun Murphy
2060 Glenn Murphy
2061 Mike Weimerskirch
2062 Pat Kelly
2063 Jose Castro
2064 Rich Dubee
2065 Checklist

1991 Classic Best St. Catherines Blue Jays

(Toronto Blue Jays) (color)

	MT	NR MT	EX
Complete Set:	4.00	3.00	1.50

St. Cath Logo
1 Mike Morland
2 Keiver Campbell
3 Lou Benbow Jr.
4 Kris Harmes
5 Sharnol Adriana (No position listed.)
6 Chris Weinke
7 Mike Coolbaugh
8 Robert Butler
9 Joe Lis Jr.
10 Craig Quinlan
11 Kurt Heble
12 Keith Hines
13 Giovanni Carrara
14 James O'Conner
15 Gary Miller
16 Dennis Gray Jr.
17 Chris Kotes
18 Paul Barton
19 Ben Weber
20 Paul Spoljaric
21 Tim Lindsay
22 Darin Nolan
23 Angel Lugo
24 Scott Shannon
25 Coco Division
26 Doug Ault
27 Checklist (Not listed on checklist.)
---- Toronto Logo
---- MLB Logo

1991 ProCards St. Catharines Blue Jays

(Toronto Blue Jays)(color)

	MT	NR MT	EX
Complete set:	4.00	3.00	1.50

3386 Paul Barton
3387 Giovanni Carrara
3388 Dennis Gray
3389 Chris Coates
3390 Tim Lindsay
3391 Angel Lugo
3392 Gary Miller
3393 Darin Molan
3394 Jim O'Connor
3395 Paul Spoljaric
3396 Ben Weber
3397 Kris Harmes
3398 Mike Morland
3399 Craig Quinlan
3400 Sharnol Adriana
3401 Louis Benbow
3402 Mike Coolbaugh
3403 Kurt Heble
3404 Joe Lis
3405 Chris Weinke
3406 Robert Butler
3407 Keiver Campbell

3408 Keith Hines
3409 Felix Septimo
3410 Jacinto Yorro
3411 Doug Ault
3412 Julio Division
3413 Checklist

1991 Classic Best St. Lucie Mets

(New York Mets) (color)

	MT	NR MT	EX
Complete Set:	6.00	4.50	2.50

1 Mark Thomas
2 Curtis Pride
3 James Morrisette
4 Stanton Cameron
5 Doug Saunders
6 Jamie Hoffner
7 Derek Henderson
8 James Harris
9 Alberto Diaz
10 Chris Butterfield
11 Brook Fordyce (First name misspelled on checklist.)
12 Kevin Carroll
13 Tom Wegmann
14 Pete Walker
15 Joe Vitko
16 Julian Vasquez
17 Deron Sample
18 Andy Reich
19 Joe McCann
20 Gregg Langbehn
21 Denny Harriger
22 Chris Dorn
23 Tim Howard
24 Todd Douma
25 Pat Howell
26 John Tamargo
27 Ron Gideon
28 Randy Niemann
29 Marc Goldberg
30 Joe Hawkins (Checklist)

1991 ProCards St. Lucie Mets

(New York Mets) (color)

	MT	NR MT	EX
Complete Set:	6.00	4.50	2.50

702 Mike Brad,)
703 Chris Dorn
704 Todd Douma
705 Gregg Langbehn
706 Joe McCann
707 David Proctor
708 Andy Reich
709 Deron Sample
710 Julian Vasquez
711 Joe Vitko
712 Pete Walker
713 Kevin Carroll
714 Brook Fordyce
715 Chris Butterfield
716 Al Diaz
717 James Harris
718 Derek Henderson
719 Jamie Hoffner
720 Tim Howard
721 Doug Saunders
722 Stanton Cameron
723 Brian Davis
724 Pat Howell
725 Curtis Pride
726 Mark Thomas
727 John Tamargo
728 Ron Gideon
729 Randy Niemann

1991 Classic Best St. Petersburg Cardinals

(St. Louis Cardinals) (color)

	MT	NR MT	EX
Complete Set:	4.00	3.00	1.50

1 Ernie Baker
2 Mike Cassidy
3 John Corona
4 Steve Dixon
5 John Thomas
6 Luis Faccio
7 Chris Gorton
8 Daryl Green
9 Dave Bialas
10 Troy Salvior
11 Jay North
12 Rick Shackle
13 Mark Smith
14 Ron Weber
15 Paul Ellis
16 Fred Langiotti
17 Brad Beanblossom
18 Mike Campas
19 Tripp Cromer (Last name misspelled on checklist.)
20 Joe Federico
21 Jonas Hamlin
22 Tony Ochs
23 Jose Trujillo
24 Bill Gale
25 Rich Gonzales
26 Ezequiel Herrera
27 Anthony Lewis
28 Mauricio Nenez
29 Tim Lata
30 Dan Doyel (Checklist)

1991 ProCards St. Petersburg Cardinals

(St. Louis Cardinals) (color)

	MT	NR MT	EX
Complete Set:	4.00	3.00	1.50

2265 Ernie Baker
2266 Dave Cassidy
2267 John Corona
2268 Steve Dixon
2269 Luis Faccio
2270 Chris Gorton
2271 Daryl Green
2272 Mike Hensley
2273 Tim Lata
2274 Troy Salvior
2275 George Sells
2276 Rick Shackle
2277 Ron Weber
2278 Paul Ellis
2279 Fred Langiotti
2280 Brad Beanblossom
2281 Mike Campas
2282 Tripp Cromer
2283 Joe Federico
2284 Jonas Hamlin
2285 Tony Ochs
2286 Jose Trujillo
2287 Bill Gale
2288 Rich Gonzalez
2289 Ezequiel Herrera
2290 Anthony Lewis
2291 Skeets Thomas
2292 Dave Bialas
2293 Jay North
2294 Checklist

1991 Classic Best Salem Buccaneers

(Pittsburgh Pirates) (color)

	MT	NR MT	EX
Complete Set:	3.00	2.25	1.25

Salem Log,,,)
1 Tim Edge
2 Rick Osik
3 Rich Aude
4 Rob Bailey
5 Alberto De Los Santos
6 Austin Manahan
7 Roman Rodriguez
8 Ben Shelton
9 Kevin Young
10 Mike Brewington
11 William Pennyfeather
12 Daryl Ratliff
13 Ken Trusky
14 David Bird
15 Bobby Underwood
16 Tim McDowell
17 Eric Parkinson
18 Rich Robertson
19 Kevin Rychel
20 Dave Tellers
21 Paul Wagner
22 Dave Watson
23 Ron Way
24 Sandy Krum
25 Stan Cliburn
26 Checklist (Not listed on checklist.)

1991 ProCards Salem Buccaneers

(Pittsburgh Pirates) (color)

	MT	NR MT	EX
Complete Set:	3.00	2.25	1.25

944 David Bird
945 Steve Buckholz
946 Tim McDowell
947 Eric Parkinson
948 Rich Robertson
949 Kevin Rychel
950 Dave Tellers
951 Paul Wagner
952 Dave Watson
953 Ron Way
954 Mike Zimmerman
955 Tim Edge
956 Keith Osik
957 Rich Aude
958 Rob Bailey
959 Alberto De Los Santos
960 Austin Manahan
961 Roman Rodriguez
962 Ben Shelton
963 Kevin Young
964 Mike Brewington
965 William Pennyfeather
966 Daryl Ratliff
967 Ken Trusky
968 Stan Cliburn
969 Tom Dettore
970 Checklist

1991 Classic Best Salinas Spurs

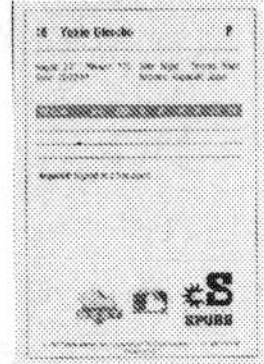

(Independent) (color)

	MT	NR MT	EX
Complete Set:	3.00	2.25	1.25

1 Ken Briggs
2 Rafael Rivera
3 Hideyuki Yasuda (First name misspelled on checklist.)
4 Hideyuki Mifune (First name misspelled on checklist.)
5 Todd Cruz
6 Tommy Griffith
7 Kenichi Yamanouchi
8 Brant McCreadle
9 James Bishop
10 Arihito Muramatsu
11 Rye Kawano
12 Brian Palma
13 Richard Shepperd
14 Katasumasa Ohta
15 Yukitoshi Oka
16 Yukio Ohsubo
17 Steve Maye
18 Tsuyoshi Nishioka
19 John Stewart
20 Dave Karasinski
21 Kazutaka Ikesue
22 Bruce Arola
23 Carlos Carrasco
24 Hide Koga
25 Dick Little
26 Takayuki Kohno
27 Shuzo Arita
28 Dee Marge Goshgarian
29 Greg Swin
30 Bill Carison (Checklist)

1991 ProCards Salinas Spurs

(Independent) (color)

	MT	NR MT	EX
Complete Set:	3.00	2.25	1.25

2234 Bruce Arola
2235 Carlos Carrasco
2236 Kazutaka Ikesue
2237 Dave Karasinski
2238 Steve Maye
2239 Brant McCreadle
2240 Ken Olson
2241 Tsuyoshi Nishioka
2242 Katsumasa Ohta
2243 Yukio Ohtsubo
2244 Yukitoshi Oka
2245 John Stewart
2246 Ken Briggs
2247 Rafael Rivera
2248 Hideyuki Yasuda
2249 Jim Bishop
2250 Bill Carlson
2251 Todd Cruz
2252 Hideyuki Mifune
2253 Greg Swim
2254 Kenichi Yamanouchi
2255 Tommy Griffith
2256 Ryo Kawano
2257 Arihito Mauramatsu
2258 Brian Palma
2259 Rich Shepperd
2260 Hide Koga
2261 Shuzo Arita
2262 Takayuki Kohno
2263 Dick Little
2264 Checklist

1991 ProCards Salt Lake Trappers

(Independent) (color)

	MT	NR MT	EX
Complete Set:	3.00	2.25	1.25

3202 Willie Ambos
3203 Dan Furmanik
3204 John Gilligan
3205 Jim Guidi
3206 Dave Marcon
3207 Kevin McDonald
3208 Geno Mirabella
3209 Tad Powers
3210 Chris Shultea
3211 Mark Stephens
3212 Jon Willard
3213 David Rolls
3214 Willie Smith
3215 Mike Aranzullo
3216 Brian Biggers
3217 Jeff Cooper
3218 Eric Macrina
3219 Eddie Ortega
3220 Keith Rader
3221 Todd Stefan
3222 Ben Castillo
3223 Steve Cunha
3224 Todd Edwards
3225 Rick Hirtensteiner
3226 Jim Martin
3227 Nick Belamonte
3228 Mark Brewer
3229 Dan Shwam
3230 Team picture
3231 Checklist

1991 Sport Pro Salt Lake City Trappers

(Independent) (color)

	MT	NR MT	EX
Complete Set:	3.00	2.25	1.25

1 Keith Radar
2 Dan Furmanik
3 Tad Powers
4 Todd Edwards
5 Kevin McDonald
6 Rick Hirtensteiner
7 Mike Aranzullo
8 Brian Biggers
9 David Rolls
10 Jon Willard
11 Steve Cunha
12 John Gilligan
13 Eric Macrina
14 Jim Martin
15 Willie Smith
16 Ben Castillo
17 Geno Mirabella
18 Eddie Ortega
19 Chris Shultea
20 Mark Stephens
21 Todd Stefan
22 Jeff Copper
23 David Marcon
24 Jim Guidi
25 Willie Ambos
26 Mark Brewer
27 Dan Shwam
28 Nick Belmonte
29 Kelly O'Brien
30 Blank

1991 ProCards San Antonio Missions

(Los Angeles Dodgers) (color)

	MT	NR MT	EX
Complete Set:	7.50	5.50	3.00

2965 Steve Allen
2966 Pedro Astacio
2967 Dale Coleman
2968 Orel Hershiser
2969 Mike James
2970 Isidrio Marquez
2971 Pedro Martinez
2972 Zak Shinall
2973 Dennis Springer
2974 Jimmy Terrill
2975 Jody Treadwell
2976 Mike Wilkins
2977 James Wray
2978 Bryan Baar
2979 Lance Rice
2980 Timothy Barker
2981 Dino Ebel
2982 Steve Finken
2983 Jose Munoz
2984 Brian Traxler
2985 Eric Young
2986 Tony Barron
2987 Braulio Castillo

2988 Brett Magnusson
2989 Scott Marabell
2990 Mike White
2991 John Shoemanker
2992 Burt Hooten
2993 Ron Roenicke
2994 Checklist

1991 Classic Best San Bernardino Spirit

(Seattle Mariners) (color)

	MT	NR MT	EX
Complete Set:	4.00	3.00	1.50

Spirit Log,)
1 John Cummings
2 Jeff Darwin
3 Doug Fitzer
4 Marcos Garcia
5 Jim Gutierrez
6 Mike Hampton
7 Troy Kent
8 Darin Loe
9 Dave McDonald
10 Antonio Pena
11 Scott Pitcher
12 Steve Murray
13 Clay Klavitter
14 Greg Pirkl
15 Greg Hunter
16 Jeff Keitges
17 Bryan King
18 Bobby Magallanes
19 Lipso Nava
20 Ruben Santana
21 Delvin Thomas
22 Tow Maynard
23 Marc Newfield
24 Jesus Tavarez
25 Derrick Young
26 Chuck Kniffin
27 Tommy Jones
28 Sam Vranjes (Checklist)

1991 ProCards San Bernardino Spirit

(Seattle Mariners) (color)

	MT	NR MT	EX
Complete Set:	6.00	4.50	2.50

1977 John Cummings
1978 Jeff Darwin
1979 Doug Fitzer
1980 Marcos Garcia
1981 Jim Gutierrez
1982 Mike Hampton
1983 Troy Kent
1984 Darin Loe
1985 Dave McDonald
1986 Antonio Pena
1987 Scott Pitcher
1988 Oscar Rivas
1989 Clay Klavitter
1990 Greg Pirkl
1991 Sam Vranjes
1992 Greg Hunter
1993 Jeff Keitges
1994 Bryan King
1995 Bobby Magallanes
1996 Lipso Nava
1997 Ruben Santana
1998 Delvin Thomas
1999 Ellerton Maynard
2000 Marc Newfield
2001 Jesus Tavarez
2002 Derrick Young
2003 Tommy Jones
2004 Chuck Kniffin
2005 Steve Murray
2006 Checklist

1991 Classic Best San Jose Giants

(San Francisco Giants) (color)

	MT	NR MT	EX
Complete Set:	3.00	2.25	1.25

1 Dan Fernandez
2 Roger Miller
3 Jon Pattin
4 Clay Bellinger
5 Ron Crowe
6 Adell Davenport
7 Kevin Kasper
8 Tony Spires
9 Jeffry Bonner
10 Jason McFarlin
11 Steven Rolen
12 Eddie Williams
13 Max Aleys
14 Steve Callahan
15 Brian Dour
16 Carl Hanselman
17 Vince Herring
18 Kevin McGehee
19 Pedro Pena
20 Patrick Rapp
21 Gary Sharko
22 Rob Taylor
23 Ron Wotus
24 Gary Lucas
25 Dick Dietz
26 John Jackson
27 Rick Huisman
28 Derek Reid
29 Joey James
30 Scott Wilson (Checklist)

1991 ProCards San Jose Giants

(San Francisco Giants) (color)

	MT	NR MT	EX
Complete Set:	3.00	2.25	1.25

1 Max Aleys
2 Steve Callahan
3 Brian Dour
4 Carl Hanselman
5 Vince Herring
6 Rick Huisman
7 Kevin McGehee
8 Pedro Pena
9 Pat Rapp
10 Gary Sharko
11 Rob Taylor
12 Dan Fernandez
13 Roger Miller
14 Jon Pattin
15 Clay Bellinger
16 Ron Crowe
17 Adell Davenport
18 Joey James
19 Kevin Kasper
20 Steve Rolen
21 Tony Spires
22 Jeff Bonner
23 John Jackson
24 Jason McFarlin
25 Derek Reid
26 Jackso, McFarlin, Reid)
27 Ron Wotus
28 Dick Dietz
29 Gary Lucas
30 Checklist

1991 Classic Best Sarasota White Sox

(Chicago White Sox) (color)

	MT	NR MT	EX
Complete Set:	6.00	4.50	2.50

Sarasota Logo
1 Rod Bolton
2 Lenny Brutcher
3 Fred Dabney
4 Mike Galvan
5 Earnie Johnson
6 Brian Keyser
7 Dan Matznick
8 Mike Mongiello
9 Johnny Ruffin
10 Scott Stevens
11 Robert Wickman
12 Clemente Alvarez
13 Greg McGough
14 Greg Kobza
15 Scott Cepicky
16 Don Cooper
17 Justin McCray
18 Pete Rose II
19 Ed Smith
20 Dean Tatarian
21 Leo Tejada
22 Jerry Wolak
23 Rob Lukachyk
24 Ron Plemmons
25 Carl Sullivan
26 Scott Tedder
27 Rick Patterson
28 Mike Barnett
29 Steve Davis (Checklist)

1991 ProCards Sarasota White Sox

(Chicago White Sox) (color)

	MT	NR MT	EX
Complete Set:	6.00	4.50	2.50

1104 Rod Bolton
1105 Len Brutcher
1106 Fred Dabney
1107 Mike Galvan
1108 Earnie Johnson
1109 Brian Keyser
1110 Danny Matznick
1111 Mike Mongiello
1112 Johnny Ruffin
1113 Scott Stevens
1114 Bob Wickman
1115 Clemente Alvarez
1116 Greg Kobza
1117 Greg McGough
1118 Scott Cepicky
1119 Justin McCray
1120 Pete Rose
1121 Ed Smith
1122 Dean Tatarian
1123 Leo Tejada
1124 Rob Lukachyk
1125 Ron Plemmons
1126 Carl Sullivan
1127 Scott Tedder
1128 Jerry Wolak
1129 Rick Patterson
1130 Mike Barnett
1131 Don Cooper
1132 Chet DiEmidio
1133 Checklist

1991 Classic Best Savannah Cardinals

(St. Louis Cardinals) (color)

	MT	NR MT	EX
Complete Set:	5.00	3.75	2.00

Savannah Logo
1 Roy Bailey
2 Roy Silver
3 Bryan Eversgerd
4 Pete Fagan
5 Russell Gaston
6 Mike Jolley
7 John Kelly
8 Tom Kinney
9 Jose Lopez
10 Jeremy McGarity
11 Frank Speek
12 Matt Tomso
13 Jim Spivey
14 Marc Ronan
15 Mark Taylor
16 Rodney Eldridge
17 Miccal Jackson
18 Carlos Landinez
19 Mark MacArthur
20 Sean Page
21 Ozzie Perez
22 Wander Pimentel
23 Terry Bradshaw
24 Tracey Ealy
25 Anthony Jenkins
26 Tim Jordan
27 Larry Milbourne
28 John Stuper
29 Checklist (Not listed on checklist.)

1991 ProCards Savannah Cardinals

(St. Louis Cardinals) (color)

	MT	NR MT	EX
Complete Set:	5.00	3.75	2.00

1642 Roy Bailey
1643 Scott Baker
1644 Bryan Eversgerd
1645 Thomas Fusco
1646 Russ Gaston
1647 Mike Jolley
1648 John Kelly
1649 Tom Kinney
1650 Jose Lopez
1651 Jeremy McGarity
1652 Frank Speek
1653 Matt Tomso
1654 Marc Ronan
1655 Jim Spivey
1656 Mark Taylor
1657 Rodney Eldridge
1658 Miccal Jackson
1659 Carlos Landinez
1660 Mark MacArthur
1661 Sean Page
1662 Ozzie Perez
1663 Wander Pimentel
1664 Terry Bradshaw
1665 Tracey Ealy
1666 Anthony Jenkins
1667 Tim Jordan
1668 Larry Milbourne
1669 John Stupe, Roy Silver)
1670 Checklist

1991 ProCards Scranton Red Barons

(Philadelphia Phillies) (color)

	MT	NR MT	EX
Complete Set:	7.00	5.25	2.75

2530 Andy Ashby
2531 Bob Ayrault
2532 Amalio Carreno
2533 Rocky Elli
2534 Chuck Malone
2535 Tim Mauser
2536 Wally Ritchie
2537 Bruce Ruffin
2538 Ray Searage
2539 Gary Wilson
2540 Sal Agostinelli
2541 Darrin Fletcher
2542 Gary Alexander
2543 Kim Batiste
2544 Jeff Grotewold
2545 Dave Hollins
2546 Greg Legg
2547 Rick Schu
2548 Steve Scarsone
2549 Sil Campusano
2550 Wes Chamberlain
2551 Chris Knabenshue
2552 Louis Meadows
2553 Julio Peguero
2554 Scott Wade
2555 Bill Dancy
2556 Floyd Rayford
2557 Jim Wright
2558 Checklist

1991 ProCards Shreveport Captains

(San Francisco Giants) (color)

	MT	NR MT	EX
Complete Set:	5.00	3.75	2.00

1814 Larry Carter
1815 Bryan Hickerson
1816 Tom Hostetler
1817 Paul McClellan
1818 Kevin Meier
1819 Jim Myers
1820 Jim Pena
1821 Dan Rambo
1822 Steve Reed
1823 Kevin Rogers
1824 Jim McNamara
1825 Scooter Tucker
1826 Frank Carey
1827 Royce Clayton
1828 Juan Guerrero
1829 Erik Johnson
1830 Dan Lewis
1831 Dave Patterson
1832 John Patterson
1833 Jamie Cooper
1834 Tom Ealy
1835 Steve Hosey
1836 Reuben Smiley
1837 Pete Weber
1838 Bill Evers
1839 Todd Oakes
1840 Tony Taylor
1841 Checklist

1991 ProCards South Atlantic League All-Stars

(All-Star Game) (color)

	MT	NR MT	EX
Complete Set:	7.00	5.25	2.75

1 Jim Daugherty
2 Tom Nevers
3 Scott Bullett
4 Hector Fajardo
5 Bill Ostermeyer
6 Bruce Tanner
7 Steve Gilbralter
8 Dave Miley
9 Bobby Perna
10 Tom Raffo
11 John Roper
12 Tim Blackwell
13 Juan Castillo
14 Gerrod Davis
15 Ed Fully
16 Butch Huskey
17 Jose Martinez
18 Rod McCall
19 Kyle Washington
20 Kelley O'Neal
21 Brian Saltzgaber
22 Steve Dreyer
23 David Lowery
24 Marty Posey
25 Carl Everett
26 Kiki Hernandez
27 Trey Hillman
28 Rich Hines
29 Rafael Quirico
30 Mark Shiflett
31 Greg Spratt
32 Tyler Houston
33 Chipper Jones
34 Roy Majtyka
35 Jose Olmeda
36 Howard Battle
37 Carlos Delgado
38 Joe Ganote
39 Ernesto Rodriguez

40 Rick Steed
41 Terry Bradshaw
42 John Kelly
43 Michael Farmer
44 Mike Lieberthal
45 Corey Thomas
46 William Martinez
47 Todd Samples
48 Checklist

1991 Classic Best South Bend White Sox

(Chicago White Sox) (color)

	MT	NR MT	EX
Complete Set:	5.00	3.75	2.00

South Bend Logo
1 Kevin Tolar
2 Horace Gaither
3 Dan Monzon
4 Jorge Ramos
5 Keith Strange
6 Dennis Walker
7 Brandon Wilson
8 John Hairston
9 Kevin Coughlin
10 Charlers Poe
11 Don Sheppard
12 Todd Altaffer
13 Jason Bere
14 Frank Campos
15 Rolando Caridad
16 Domingo Jean
17 Jon Jenkins
18 Dean Locklear
19 Don Perigny
20 Keith Shepherd
21 Greg Young
22 Rogello Nunez
23 Mark Haley
24 Nilson Robledo
25 Keith Vairie
26 Kirk Champion
27 Tommy Thompson
28 John Hawkins
29 Checklist (Not listed on checklist.)

1991 ProCards South Bend White Sox

(Chicago White Sox) (color)

	MT	NR MT	EX
Complete Set:	5.00	3.75	2.00

2848 Todd Altaffer
2849 Jason Bere
2850 Frank Campos
2851 Rolando Caridad
2852 Domingo Jean
2853 Jon Jenkins
2854 Dean Locklear
2855 Don Perigny
2856 Keith Shepherd
2857 Kevin Tolar
2858 Greg Young
2859 Rogello Nunez
2860 Nilson Robledo
2861 Joe Solimine
2862 Horace Gaither
2863 John Hairston
2864 Jorge Ramos
2865 Keith Strange
2866 Dennis Walker
2867 Brandon Wilson
2868 Kevin Coughlin
2869 Ty Hawkins
2870 Charles Poe
2871 Don Sheppard
2872 Kerry Vairie
2873 Tommy Thompson
2874 Kirk Champion
2875 Mark Haley
2876 Jim Reinebold
2877 Checklist

1991 Classic Best Southern Oregon A's

(Oakland A's) (color)

	MT	NR MT	EX
Complete Set:	4.00	3.00	1.50

1 Joel Wolfe
2 Damon Mashore
3 Tim Smith
4 Tim Doyle
5 George Williams
6 Ricky Kimball
7 Chris Thomsen
8 Rick Norton
9 Todd Ingram
10 Russell Brock
11 Brent Cookson
12 Jason Wood
13 Scott Sheldon
14 Miguel Jemenez (Last name misspelled on checklist.)
15 Mike Neill (No position listed on card back.)
16 Gary Hust
17 Santiago Morillo
18 Michael Evans
19 Tony Scharff
20 Dan Vizzini
21 Mike Kennedy
22 Vicente Francisco
23 Creighton Gubanich (No position listed on card back.)
24 Brent Gates
25 Kirt Endebrock (First name misspelled on checklist.)
26 Michael Thees
27 Dan Nerat
28 Joe Misa
29 Steve Wojciechowski
30 Checklist (Staff)

1991 ProCards Southern Oregon A's

(Oakland Athletics) (color)

	MT	NR MT	EX
Complete Set:	4.00	3.00	1.50

3832 Russell Brock
3833 Tim Doyle
3834 Michael Evans
3835 Todd Ingram
3836 Jeff Jensen
3837 Miguel Jiminez
3838 Ricky Kimball
3839 Joe Misa
3840 Santiago Morillo
3841 Dan Nerat
3842 Tony Scharff
3843 Tim Smith
3844 Brad Stowell
3845 Michael Thees
3846 Dan Vizzini
3847 Steve Wojciechowski
3848 Tod Frick
3849 Mike Kennedy
3850 Creighton Gubanich
3851 George Williams
3852 Juan Cabrera
3853 Kurt Endebrock
3854 Vincente Francisco
3855 Brent Gates
3856 Rick Norton
3857 Scott Sheldon
3858 Chris Thomsen
3859 Jason Wood
3860 Brent Cookson
3861 Chris Hart
3862 Gary Hust
3863 Damon Mashore
3864 Mike Neill
3865 Joel Wolfe
3866 Grady Fuson
3867 Jim Slaton
3868 Checklist

1991 ProCards Southern Oregon A's

(Oakland A's) (color)

	MT	NR MT	EX
Complete Set:	9.00	6.75	3.50

1 Jose Canseco
2 Terry Steinbach
3 Todd Van Poppel
4 Tony Ariola
5 Tony Floyd
6 Darin Kracl
7 Stan Royer
8 Greg Cadaret
9 Jeff Shaver
10 Larry Arndt
11 Kirk Dressendorfer
12 Fred Cooley
13 Kevin Tapani
14 Jose Canseco
15 Steve Chitren
16 Brian Dorsett
17 Dann Howitt
18 Lance Blankenship
19 Dana Allison
20 Kevin Macleod
21 Dave Otto
22 Terry Steinbach
23 Steve Howard
24 Wally Whitehurst
25 Scott Chiamparino
26 Don Peters
27 Jim Eppard
28 Dennis Rogers
29 Craig Paguette
30 Todd Burns
31 Steve Ontiveros
32 Jeff Kaiser
33 Charlie O'Brien
34 Mike Bordick
35 Dave Zancanaro
36 Checklist

1991 Classic Best Spartanburg Phillies

(Philadelphia Phillies) (color)

	MT	NR MT	EX
Complete Set:	4.00	3.00	1.50

1 Scott Carlton
2 Ray Domecq
3 Donnie Elliott
4 Todd Goergen
5 Brad Hassinger
6 Eric Hill
7 Charlie Hurst
8 Bryan Manicchia
9 J.J. Munoz
10 Mike Owens
11 Jeff Patterson
12 Mark Randall
13 Stephen Avent
14 Mike Lieberthal
15 Troy Rusk
16 Erik Judson
17 Eulogio Perez
18 Jim Savage
19 Kenny Sirak
20 Corey Thomas
21 Al Bennett
22 Steve Bieser
23 Michael Farmer
24 Antonio Grissom
25 Rob Hartwig
26 Jeff Jackson
27 Mark Steffens
28 Mel Roberts
29 Buzz Capra
30 Brent Leiby (Checklist)

1991 ProCards Spartanburg Phillies

(Philadelphia Phillies) (color)

	MT	NR MT	EX
Complete Set:	4.00	3.00	1.50

886 Scott Carlton
887 Ray Domecq
888 Donnie Elliott
889 Todd Goergen
890 Brad Hassinger
891 Eric Hill
892 Chuck Hurst
893 Bryan Manicchia
894 J.J. Munoz
895 Mike Owens
896 Jeff Patterson
897 Mark Randall
898 Steve Avent
899 Mike Lieberthal
900 Erik Judson
901 Eulogio Perez
902 Troy Rusk
903 Jim Savage
904 Kenny Sirak
905 Corey Thomas
906 Al Bennett
907 Steve Bieser
908 Michael Farmer
909 Antonio Grissom
910 Rob Hartwig
911 Jeff Jackson
912 Mark Steffens
913 Mel Roberts
914 Buzz Capra
915 Checklist

1991 Classic Best Spokane Indians

(San Diego Padres) (color)

	MT	NR MT	EX
Complete Set:	3.00	2.25	1.25

1 Eric Ciocca
2 Joey Long
3 Jim Campbell
4 Mike Grohs
5 Scotty Pugh
6 Kyle Moody
7 David Leback
8 Derek Vaughn
9 Reggie Stephens
10 Shawn Robertson
11 Jerrold Rountree
12 Mark Anthony
13 Tim Ploeger
14 Drew Overholser
15 Craig Hanson
16 Joe Grygiel
17 Scott Eggleston
18 Jose Davila
19 Cord Corbitt
20 Kevin Johnson
21 Jerrey Thurston
22 John Biancamano
23 Scott Bream
24 Chris Benhardt
25 Alvaro Samboy
26 Tim Hall
27 Joe Frias
28 Danny Garcia
29 Gene Glynn
30 Keith Dugger (Checklist)

1991 ProCards Spokane Indians

(San Diego Padres) (color)

	MT	NR MT	EX
Complete Set:	3.00	2.25	1.25

3937 Chris Benhardt
3938 Jimbo Campbell
3939 Eric Ciocca
3940 Cord Corbitt
3941 J.D. DaVila (Last name spelled differently on checklist.)
3942 Scott Eggleston
3943 Mike Grohs
3944 Joy Grygiel
3945 Chris Hanson
3946 Joe Long
3947 Drew Overholser
3948 Tim Ploeger
3949 Alvaro Samboy
3950 Tim Hall
3951 Kevin Johnson
3952 Jerrey Thurston
3953 Juice Biancamano
3954 Scott Bream
3955 Mel Edwards
3956 Joe Frias
3957 Kyle Moody
3958 Scotty Pugh
3959 Mark Anthony
3960 David Lebak
3961 Shawn Robertson
3962 Jerrold Rountree
3963 Reggie Stephens
3964 Derek Vaughn
3965 Gene Glynn
3966 Danny Garcia
3967 Checklist

1991 Classic Best Springfield Cardinals

(St. Louis Cardinals) (color)

	MT	NR MT	EX
Complete Set:	3.00	2.25	1.25

1 Paul Anderson
2 Juan Andujar
3 Joe Aversa
4 Scott Banton
5 Fernando Barreiro
6 Andy Beasley
7 Alan Botkin
8 Mark Bowlan
9 Johnny Calzado
10 Frank Cimorelli
11 Mike Ramsey
12 John Dempsey
13 Ignacio Duran
14 Dann Eaton
15 Bill Espinal
16 Jeff Fayne
17 Dennis Fletcher
18 Clyde Keller
19 Kevin Nielsen
20 Dave Norris
21 Mateo Ozuna
22 Ahmed Rodriquez
23 Beto Rodriguez
24 Odallis Savinon
25 Kevin Tahan
26 Orlando Thomas
27 Tom Urbani
28 Jose Velez
29 Roger Erickson (No position listed on card front.)
30 Checklist (Mike Evans)

1991 ProCards Springfield Cardinals

(St. Louis Cardinals) (color)

	MT	NR MT	EX
Complete Set:	3.00	2.25	1.25

731 Paul Anderson
732 Fernando Barreiro
733 Alan Botkin
734 Mark Bowlan
735 Frank Cimorelli
736 Dann Eaton
737 Willie Espinal
738 Dennis Fletcher
739 Clyde Keller
740 Kevin Nielsen

741 Dave Norris
742 Tom Urbani
743 Andy Beasley
744 John Dempsey
745 Orlando Thomas
746 Juan Andujar
747 Joe Aversa
748 Ignacio Duran
749 Mateo Ozuna
750 Ahmed Rodriguez
751 Beto Rodriguez
752 Kevin Tahan
753 Scott Banton
754 Johnny Calzado
755 Paul Coleman
756 Jeff Payne
757 Odalis Savinon
758 Jose Velez
759 Mike Ramsey
760 Roger Erickson
761 Checklist

1991 Classic Best Stockton Ports

(Milwaukee Brewers) (color)

	MT	NR MT	EX
Complete Set:	3.00	2.25	1.25

Ports Logo
1 Jamie Cangemi
2 Otis Green
3 Steve Monson
4 Robert Vancho
5 Linc Mikkelsen
6 Oreste Marrero
7 Richard Berg
8 Kurt Archer
9 Sam Drake
10 Guillermo Sandoval
11 Dave Fitzgerald
12 Troy Haugen
13 Remigio Diaz
14 Randy Snyder
15 Michael Couture
16 Randy Hood
17 Troy O'Leary
18 John Finn
19 Vince Castaldo
20 Bo Dodson
21 Vilato Marrero
22 Juan Flores
23 Tim Clark
24 Chris Bando
25 Mitch Zwolensky
26 Checklist (Not listed on checklist.)

1991 ProCards Stockton Ports

(Milwaukee Brewers) (color)

	MT	NR MT	EX
Complete Set:	3.00	2.25	1.25

3023 Kurt Archer
3024 Rich Berg
3025 Jamie Cangemi
3026 Tim Dell
3027 Sam Drake
3028 Otis Green
3029 Lincoln Mikkelsen
3030 Mo Monson
3031 Steve Sparks
3032 Bob Vancho
3033 Brandy Vann
3034 Juan Flores
3035 Randy Snyder
3036 Vince Castaldo
3037 Remigio Diaz
3038 Bo Dodson
3039 Troy Haugen
3040 Oreste Marrero
3041 Vilato Marrero
3042 Tim Clark
3043 Mike Couture
3044 John Finn
3045 Randy Hood
3046 Troy O'Leary
3047 Chris Bando
3048 Mitch Zwolensky
3049 Checklist

1991 Classic Best Sumter Flyers

(Montreal Expos) (color)

	MT	NR MT	EX
Complete Set:	5.00	3.75	2.00

1 Tavo Alvarez
2 Derek Aucoin
3 Matt Conley
4 Kevin Foster
5 Ron Gerstein
6 Darrin Kotch
7 Steve Long
8 William Martinez
9 Joe Norris
10 Shane Andrews
11 Ben Vanryn
12 Gabe White
13 Chris Hirsch
14 Doug Noce
15 Raul Santana
16 Tony Marabella
17 Hector Ortega
18 Claudio Rodriguez
19 Abimael Rodriguez
20 Gus Santiago
21 Marc Tsitouris
22 Gary Adams
23 Tyrone Horne
24 Todd Samples
25 Rondell White
26 Lorenzo Bundy
27 Gary Lance
28 Carlos Ponce
29 Bill Slosson
30 Checklist (Not listed on checklist.)

1991 ProCards Sumter Flyers

(Montreal Expos) (color)

	MT	NR MT	EX
Complete Set:	5.00	3.75	2.00

2324 Tavo Alvarez
2325 Derek Aucoin
2326 Matt Conley
2327 Kevin Foster
2328 Ron Gerstein
2329 Darrin Kotch
2330 Steve Long
2331 William Martinez (First name misspelled on back.)
2332 Joe Norris
2333 Carlos Perez
2334 Ben Van Ryn
2335 Gabe White
2336 Chris Hirsch
2337 Doug Noce
2338 Raul Santana
2339 Shane Andrews
2340 Jolbert Cabrera
2341 Tony Marabella
2342 Hector Ortega
2343 Claudio Ozario
2344 Abimael Rodriguez
2345 Gus Santiago
2346 Marc Tsitouris
2347 Gary Adams
2348 Tyrone Horne
2349 Todd Samples
2350 Rondell White
2351 Lorenzo Bundy
2352 Gary Lance
2353 Carlos Ponce
2354 Checklist

1991 Kraft Syracuse Chiefs

(Toronto Blue Jays) (color)

	MT	NR MT	EX
Complete Set:	15.00	11.00	6.00

(1) Derek Bell
(2) Pat Hentgen
(3) Alex Sanchez
(4) Ed Sprague
(5) Eddie Zosky

1991 Merchants Bank Syracuse Chiefs

(Toronto Blue Jays) (color)

	MT	NR MT	EX
Complete Set:	20.00	15.00	8.00

(1) Bob Bailor
(2) Derek Bell
(3) Pete Blohm
(4) Denis Boucher
(5) Rod Ducey
(6) Juan Guzman
(7) Pat Hentgen
(8) Randy Holland
(9) Shawn Jeter
(10) Randy Knorr
(11) Doug Linton
(12) Rob MacDonald
(13) Mike Maksudian
(14) Ravelo Manzanillo
(15) Domingo Martinez
(16) Julius McDougal
(17) Stu Pederson
(18) Marty Pevey
(19) John Poloni
(20) Tom Quinlan
(21) Alex Sanchez
(22) Jerry Schunk
(23) John Shea
(24) Ed Sprague
(25) William Suero
(26) Steve Wapnick
(27) Mickey Weston
(28) Rocket Wheeler
(29) Frank Wills
(30) Eddie Zosky

1991 ProCards Syracuse Chiefs

(Toronto Blue Jays) (color)

	MT	NR MT	EX
Complete Set:	8.50	6.25	3.50

2475 Pete Blohm
2476 Juan Guzman
2477 Pat Hentgen
2478 Doug Linton
2479 Alex Sanchez
2480 John Shea
2481 Steve Wapnick
2482 Mickey Weston
2483 Marty Pevey
2484 Ed Sprague
2485 Domingo Martinez
2486 Julius McDougal
2487 Tom Quinlan
2488 Jerry Schunk
2489 William Suero
2490 Eddie Zoskey
2491 Derek Bell
2492 Rob Ducey
2493 Shawn Jeter
2494 Mike Maksudian
2495 Stu Pederson
2496 Bob Bailor
2497 John Poloni
2498 Rocket Wheeler
2499 Checklist

1991 Team Syracuse Chiefs

The Chiefs gave away a single sheet photo album on a promotional night. The sheet folds into a 9-1/2" x 10-1/2" sheet. There are 30 cards on this sheet, each measuring 2-1/8" x 3-1/8" and separated by perforations to facilitate separation of the cards. The cards are unnumbered and have statistics and a facsimile autograph on the back. The cards are listed in the order in which they appear on the sheet.

	MT	NR MT	EX
Complete Set:	8.00	6.00	3.25

(1) Bob Bailor
(2) John Poloni
(3) Rocket Wheeler
(4) Randy Holland
(5) Derek Bell
(6) Pete Blohm
(7) Denis Boucher
(8) Rob Ducey
(9) Juan Guzman
(10) Pat Hentgen
(11) Shawn Jeter
(12) Randy Knorr
(13) Doug Linton
(14) Bob MacDonald
(15) Mike Maksudian
(16) Ravelo Manzanillo
(17) Domingo Martinez
(18) Julius McDougal
(19) Stu Pederson
(20) Mary Pevey
(21) Tom Quinlan
(22) Alex Sanchez
(23) Jerry Schunk
(24) John Shea
(25) Ed Sprague
(26) William Suero
(27) Steve Wapnick
(28) Mickey Weston
(29) Frank Wills
(30) Eddie Zosky

1991 ProCards Tacoma Tigers

(Oakland Athletics) (color)

	MT	NR MT	EX
Complete Set:	4.00	3.00	1.50

2295 Dana Allison
2296 Kevin Campbell
2297 Dan Eskew
2298 Apolinar Garcia
2299 Johnny Guzman
2300 Reggie Harris
2301 Jeff Musselman
2302 Clay Parker
2303 Jeff Pico
2304 Will Schock
2305 Joe Slusarski
2306 Bruce Walton
2307 Pat Wernig
2308 Troy Afenir
2309 Jorge Brito
2310 Scott Brosius
2311 Pete Coachman
2312 Rod Correia
2313 Webster Garrison
2314 Scott Hemond
2315 Dann Howitt
2316 Ron Witmeyer
2317 Eric Fox
2318 Troy Noel
2319 Lee Sammons
2320 Nelson Simmons
2321 Jeff Newman
2322 Glenn Abbott
2323 Checklist

1991 Team Tampa Yankees

This 33-card set was produced at the same time as the 1992 Ft. Lauderdale Yankees set. The cards have borderless color photos with the player's name at the bottom of the card. On the back is statistical and biographical information. The cards are unnumbered.

	MT	NR MT	EX
Complete Set:	3.00	2.25	1.25

(1) Rodolfo Albornoz
(2) Rich Arena
(3) Tom Carter
(4) Hop Cassady
(5) Jeff Cindrich
(6) Abdiel Cumberbatch
(7) Ken Dominguez
(8) Shane Ferguson
(9) Jose Garcia
(10) Marcus Gipner
(11) Chris Guth
(12) Elston Hansen
(13) Chris Heaps
(14) Ricardo Ledee
(15) Brian Lewis
(16) Eric Knowles
(17) Jeff Montuzas
(18) Luis Parra
(19) Angel Paulino
(20) Albert Perez
(21) Luis Ramirez
(22) Tom Raynor
(23) Victor Regalado
(24) Angel Reyes
(25) Matt Ruoff
(26) Alex Santaella
(27) Sandi Santiago
(28) Sean Smith
(29) Shane Spencer
(30) John Sutherland
(31) John Thibert
(32) Hoyt Wilhelm
(33) Jason Wuerch

1991 ProCards Tidewater Tides

(New York Mets) (color)

	MT	NR MT	EX
Complete Set:	7.00	5.25	2.75

2500 Blaine Beatty
2501 Terry Bross
2502 Doug Cinnella
2503 Mark Dewey
2504 Manny Hernandez
2505 Eric Hillman
2506 Brad Moore
2507 Dale Plummer
2508 Rich Sauveur
2509 Ray Soff
2510 Dave Trautwein
2511 Julio Valera
2512 Anthony Young
2513 Todd Hundley

2514 Orlando Mercado
2515 Kevin Baez
2516 Chris Donnels
2517 Jeff Gardner
2518 Alex Jimenez
2519 Al Pedrique
2520 Kelvin Torve
2521 Chuck Carr
2522 Terrel Hansen
2523 Tim Leiper
2524 Terry McDaniel
2525 Jaime Roseboro
2526 Steve Swisher
2527 Bob Apodaca
2528 Ron Washington
2529 Checklist

1991 ProCards Toledo Mud Hens

(Detroit Tigers) (color)

	MT	NR MT	EX
Complete Set:	6.00	4.50	2.50

1922 Scott Aldred
1923 Mike Dalton
1924 Dan Gakeler
1925 Greg Gohr
1926 Dave Haas
1927 John Kiely
1928 Rusty Meacham
1929 Mike Munoz
1930 Randy Nosek
1931 Ron Rightnowar
1932 Kevin Ritz
1933 Don Vesling
1934 Phil Clark
1935 Mitch Lyden
1936 Rich Rowland
1937 Karl Allaire
1938 Arnie Beyeler
1939 Rico Brogna
1940 Scott Livingstone
1941 Johnny Paredes
1942 Skeeter Barnes
1943 Curt Ford
1944 Shawn Hare
1945 Eric Mangham
1946 Joe Sparks
1947 Ralph Treuel
1948 Mark Wagner
1949 Checklist

1991 ProCards Triple A All-Star Game

(All-Star Game) (color)

	MT	NR MT	EX
Complete Set:	7.00	5.25	2.75

1 Jerry Brooks
2 Carlos Hernandez
3 Roger Mason
4 Rick Reed
5 Tino Martinez
6 Luis Medina
7 Rich Monteleone
8 Bernie Williams
9 Doug Henry
10 Tim McIntosh
11 Jim Olander
12 Ruben Amaro
13 Chad Curtis
14 Max Oliveras
15 Lee Stevens
16 Dana Ridenour
17 John Vanderwal
18 Russ McGinnis
19 Laddie Renfroe
20 Rey Sanchez
21 Kevin Ward
22 Ray Stephens
23 Terry Lee
24 Pete Mackanin
25 Monty Fariss
26 Rob Maurer
27 Sal Rende
28 Tim Spehr
29 Scott Cooper
30 Daryl Irvine
31 Phil Plantier
32 Mo Vaughn
33 Darren Lewis
34 Andres Santana
35 Tom Edens
36 Denny Neagle
37 Gary Wayne
38 Armando Reynoso
39 Greg Biagini
40 Chito Martinez
41 Steve Scarsone
42 Derek Bell
43 Rob Ducey
44 Eddie Zoskey
45 Kevin Campbell
46 Scott Livingstone
47 Chris Donnels
48 Jeff Gardner
49 Todd Hundley
50 Steve Swisher
51 Gary Cooper
52 Kenny Lofton
53 Bob Skinner
54 Dean Wilkins
55 Checklist

1991 ProCards Tucson Toros

(Houston Astros) (color)

	MT	NR MT	EX
Complete Set:	7.50	5.50	3.00

2204 Harold Allen
2205 Ryan Bowen
2206 Mike Capel
2207 Terry Clark
2208 Dean Freeland
2209 Randy Hennis
2210 Butch Henry
2211 Blaise Isley
2212 Calvin Schiraldi
2213 Lee Tunnell
2214 Dean Wilkins
2215 Terry McGriff
2216 Scott Servais
2217 Doug Baker
2218 Andujar Cedeno
2219 Carlo Colombino
2220 Andy Mota
2221 Mike Simms
2222 Jose Tolentino
2223 Eric Anthony
2224 Gary Cooper
2225 Kenny Lofton
2226 Javier Ortiz
2227 Gerald Young
2228 Bob Skinner
2229 Dave Engle
2230 Brent Strom
2231 Checklist

1991 ProCards Tulsa Drillers

(Texas Rangers) (color)

	MT	NR MT	EX
Complete Set:	7.50	5.50	3.00

2765 Rob Brown
2766 Everett Cunningham
2767 Bryan Gore
2768 Barry Manuel
2769 Robb Nen
2770 David Perez
2771 Bobby Reed
2772 Brian Romero
2773 Cedric Shaw
2774 Chris Shiflett
2775 Greg Iavarone
2776 Ivan Rodriguez
2777 Mike Burton
2778 Jeff Frye
2779 Pat Garman
2780 Jose Hernandez
2781 Trey McCoy
2782 Luke Sable
2783 Frederic Samson
2784 David Green
2785 Donald Harris
2786 Rod Morris
2787 Dan Rohrmeier
2788 Bobby Jones
2789 Oscar Acosta
2790 Jeff Hubbard
2791 Checklist

1991 Team Tulsa Drillers

(Texas Rangers) (color)

	MT	NR MT	EX
Complete Set:	10.00	7.50	4.00

1 Oscar Acosta
2 Rob Brown
3 Paco Burgos
4 Mike Burton
5 Mike Campbell
6 Everett Cunningham
7 Jeff Frye
8 Bryan Gore
9 David Green
10 Greg Harrel
11 Donald Harris
12 Jose Hernandez
13 Jeff Hubbard
14 Greg Iavarone
15 Bobby Jones
16 Barry Manuel
17 Trey McCoy
18 Eric McCray
19 Rod Morris
20 Robb Nen
21 David Perez
22 Bobby Reed
23 Ivan Rodriguez
24 Dan Rohrmeier
25 Brian Romero
26 Steve Rowley
27 Luke Sable
28 Frederic Samson
29 Cedric Shaw
30 Juan Gonzalez

1991 Classic Best Utica Blue Sox

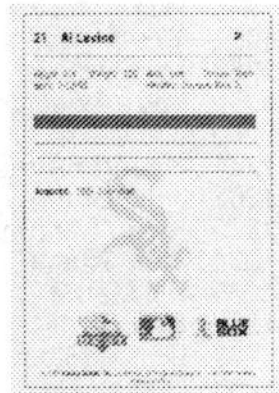

(Chicago White Sox) (color)

	MT	NR MT	EX
Complete Set:	4.00	3.00	1.50

1 Marc Kubici
2 Doug Brady
3 John Herrholtz
4 Mike Bertotti
5 Shawn Buchanan
6 Ray Durham
7 Rob Eillis
8 Mike Heathcott
9 Greg Young
10 Matt Hattabaugh
11 Dean Haase
12 Dave Martorana
13 Jeff Pierce
14 Jonathan Story
15 Steve Siebert
16 Glenn DiSarcina (Last name misspelled on checklist.)
17 Tommy Helms
18 Harold Henry
19 Greg Fritz
20 Larry Thomas Jr.
21 Al Levine
22 Bill Baliou (Coach)
23 Mike Gellinger
24 Charlie Culberson
25 Rick Ray
26 Hank Tagle
27 Troy Fryman
28 Patrick Rollins
29 Rafael Ochoa (First name misspelled on checklist.)
30 Checklist (Not listed on checklist.)

1991 ProCards Utica Blue Sox

(Chicago White Sox) (color)

	MT	NR MT	EX
Complete Set:	4.00	3.00	1.50

3232 Mike Bertotti
3233 Bull Ellis
3234 Greg Fritz
3235 Mike Heathcott
3236 John Herholz (Last name spelled different on checklist.)
3237 Marc Kubicki
3238 Al Levine
3239 Hank Tagle
3240 Larry Thomas
3241 Greg Young
3242 Dean Haase
3243 Matt Hattabaugh
3244 Doug Brady
3245 Glenn DiSarcina
3246 Ray Durham
3247 Troy Fryman
3248 Tommy Helms
3249 Mutta Martorana
3250 Pep Rollins
3251 Steve Siebert
3252 Shawn Buchanan
3253 Harold Henry
3254 Rafael Ochoa
3255 Jeff Pierce
3256 Jonathan Story
3257 Mike Gellinger
3258 Bill Ballou
3259 Charlie Culberson
3260 Checklist

1991 ProCards Vancouver Canadians

(Chicago White Sox) (color)

	MT	NR MT	EX
Complete Set:	4.00	3.00	1.50

1586 Mario Brito
1587 Jeff Carter
1588 Tom Drees
1589 Grady Hall
1590 Curt Hasler
1591 Roberto Hernandez
1592 Jerry Kutzler
1593 Greg Perschke
1594 Rich Scheld
1595 Ron Stephens
1596 Kurt Brown
1597 Matt Stark
1598 Don Wakamatsu
1599 Cesar Bernhardt
1600 Joe Hall
1601 Danny Heep
1602 Dan Henley
1603 Noberto Martin
1604 Rob Nelson
1605 John Cangelosi
1606 Orsino Hill
1607 Rod McCray
1608 Warren Newson
1609 Marv Foley
1610 Moe Drabowsky
1611 Roger LaFrancois
1612 Checklist

1991 Classic Best Vero Beach Dodgers

(Los Angeles Dodgers) (color)

	MT	NR MT	EX
Complete Set:	6.00	4.50	2.50

1 Pedro Astacio
2 Dave Baumann
3 Bill Bene
4 Mike Brady
5 Ray Calhoun
6 Dale Coleman
7 Scott Freeman
8 Kiki Jones
9 Mike Mimbs
10 Tim Patrick
11 Mike Sampson
12 Sean Snedeker
13 Bill Wengert
14 Adam Brown
15 Pedro Gonzalez
16 Hector Ortiz Jr.
17 Rafael Bournigal
18 John Deutsch
19 Scott Doffek
20 Tim Griffin
21 Matt Howard
22 Sean McKamie
23 Steve O'Donnell
24 Bill Ashley
25 Rafael Rijo
26 Jeffrey Vanzytveld
27 Mark Griffin
28 Brock McMurray
29 Chris Morrow
30 Jerry Royster (Checklist)

1991 ProCards Vero Beach Dodgers

(Los Angeles Dodgers) (color)

	MT	NR MT	EX
Complete Set:	6.00	4.50	2.50

762 Pedro Astacio
763 Dave Baumann
764 Bill Bene
765 Mike Brady
766 Ray Calhoun
767 Dale Coleman
768 Scott Freeman
769 Kiki Jones
770 Michael Mimbs
771 Tim Patrick
772 Mike Sampson
773 Sean Snedeker
774 Bill Wengert
775 Adam Brown
776 Pedro Gonzalez
777 Hector Ortiz
778 Rafael Bournigal
779 John Deutsch
780 Scott Doffek
781 Tim Griffin
782 Matt Howard
783 Sean McKamie
784 Steve O'Donnell
785 Billy Ashley
786 Eric Blackwell
787 Mark Griffin
788 Brock McMurray
789 Chris Morrow

790 Rafael Rijo
791 Jerry Royster
792 John Debus
793 Dennis Lewallyn
794 Checklist

1991 Classic Best Visalia Oaks

(Minnesota Twins) (color)

	MT	NR MT	EX
Complete Set:	3.00	2.25	1.25

Oaks Log,,)
1 Jayson Best
2 Ed Gustafson
3 Jon Henry
4 Marc Lipson
5 Mike Misuraca
6 Darren Musselwhite
7 Tim Nedin
8 Al Newman
9 Carlos Pulido
10 Mark Swope
11 Fred White
12 Matt Brown
13 Troy Buckley
14 Chris Delarwelle
15 Steve Dunn
16 Mica Lewis
17 Pat Meares
18 Alex Nunez
19 Brian Raabe
20 John Cohen
21 Rex De Le Nuez
22 Tom Gavin
23 Derrell Rumsey
24 Steve Liddle
25 Bob Kappesser
26 Brian Allard
27 Joel Sefly (Checklist)

1991 ProCards Visalia Oaks

(Minnesota Twins) (color)

	MT	NR MT	EX
Complete Set:	3.00	2.25	1.25

1735 Jayson Best
1736 Ed Gustafson
1737 Jon Henry
1738 Marc Lipson
1739 Mike Misuraca
1740 Darren Musselwhite
1741 Mark Swope
1742 Fred White
1743 Matt Brown
1744 Troy Buckley
1745 Bob Kappesser
1746 Chris Delarwelle
1747 Steve Dunn
1748 Mica Lewis
1749 Pat Meares
1750 Alex Nunez
1751 Brian Raabe
1752 John Cohen
1753 Rex De La Nuez
1754 Tom Gavin
1755 Derrell Rumsey
1756 Greg Sims
1757 Steve Liddle
1758 Brian Allard
1759 Checklist

1991 Classic Best Waterloo Diamonds

(San Diego Padres) (color)

	MT	NR MT	EX
Complete Set:	3.00	2.25	1.25

Diamonds Logo
1 Lance Banks
2 Bruce Bensching
3 Bryce Florie
4 Scott Frederickson
5 Rob Hays
6 Tony Mortensen
7 Lance Painter
8 Scott Sanders
9 Ryan Thibault
10 Tim Worrell
11 Jimmy Lester
12 Lee Henderson
13 Jim West
14 Robreto Arredondo (First name misspelled on checklist.)
15 Julio Bruno
16 Kevin Farlow
17 John Kuehl
18 Bill Meury
19 Bill Rivell
20 Darius Gash
21 Steve Gill
22 Craig Pueschner
23 Reggie Stephens
24 Shawn Whalen
25 Bryan Little
26 Sonny Siebert
27 George Poulis
28 Larry Hawks
29 Jack Grandy (Checklist)

1991 ProCards Waterloo Diamonds

(San Diego Padres) (color)

	MT	NR MT	EX
Complete Set:	3.00	2.25	1.25

1248 Lance Banks
1249 Bruce Bensching
1250 Bryce Florie
1251 Scott Fredrickson
1252 Rob Hays
1253 Tony Mortensen
1254 Lance Painter
1255 Scott Sanders
1256 Ryan Thibault
1257 Tim Worrell
1258 Larry Hawks
1259 Lee Henderson
1260 Jim West
1261 Roberto Arredondo
1262 Julio Bruno
1263 Kevin Farlow
1264 John Kuehl
1265 Bill Meury
1266 Bob Rivell
1267 Darius Gash
1268 Steve Gill
1269 Craig Pueschner
1270 Reggie Stephens
1271 Shawn Whalen
1272 Bryan Little
1273 Jimmy Lester
1274 Sonny Siebert
1275 Checklist

1991 Classic Best Watertown Indians

(Cleveland Indians) (color)

	MT	NR MT	EX
Complete Set:	3.00	2.25	1.25

1 Sam Baker
2 Brian Buzard
3 Grady Davidson
4 Joe Fleet
5 Jason Fronio
6 Steve Gajkowski
7 Mike Jewell
8 Greg Knapland
9 Kevin Logsdon
10 Mike Malley
11 Andy Stemler
12 Gary Taterson
13 Ryan Martindale
14 Mike Moore
15 Jose Moreno
16 Hector Andujar
17 Tommy Bates
18 Brad Kantor
19 Aaron Morris
20 Pat Maxwell
21 Herbert Perry
22 Scott Sharts
23 Bill Vosik
24 Jeff Brohm
25 Ottis Edwards
26 Pedro Henderson
27 Omar Ramirez
28 Tim Thomas
29 Tom Van Tiger
30 Checklist (Not listed on checklist.)

1991 ProCards Watertown Indians

(Cleveland Indians) (color)

	MT	NR MT	EX
Complete Set:	3.00	2.25	1.25

3356 Sam Baker
3357 Brian Buzard
3358 Grady Davidson
3359 Joe Fleet
3360 Jason Fronio
3361 Steve Gajkowski
3362 Mike Jewell
3363 Greg Knapland
3364 Kevin Logsdon
3365 Mike Malley
3366 Andy Stemler
3367 Gary Tatterson
3368 Ryan Martindale
3369 Mike Moore
3370 Jose Moreno
3371 Hector Andujar
3372 Tommy Bates
3373 Brad Kantor
3375 Aaron Morris
3376 Herbert Perry
3377 Scott Sharts
3378 Bill Vosik
3379 Jeff Brohm
3380 Otis Edwards
3381 Pedro Henderson
3382 Omar Ramirez
3383 Tim Thomas
3384 Tom Van Tiger
3385 Darrell Whitmore
3386 Checklist

1991 Classic Best Welland Pirates

(Pittsburgh Pirates) (color)

	MT	NR MT	EX
Complete Set:	3.00	2.25	1.25

1 Jon Farrell
2 Tony Womack
3 Todd Schroeder
4 Don Garvey
5 Antonio Mitchell
6 James Cardona
7 Mitch House
8 James Krevokuch
9 Dean Hinson II
10 Angie Encarnacion
11 Chuck Touch
12 Gregg Leavell
13 Joe McLin Jr.
14 Trace Ragland
15 Craig Shotton
16 Marty Neff
17 Jeff Leatherman
18 Deon Danner
19 Steven Roeder
20 Matt Ruebel
21 John Douris
22 Mike Maguire
23 David Bradley
24 Roberto Ramirez
25 Glenn Coombs
26 John Hope
27 Mike Teich
28 Jason Bullard
29 Dan Jones
30 Checklist (Not listed on checklist.)

1991 ProCards Welland Pirates

(Pittsburgh Pirates) (color)

	MT	NR MT	EX
Complete Set:	3.00	2.25	1.25

3563 Jason Bullard
3564 Glenn Coombs
3565 Deon Danner
3566 J.D. Douris
3567 John Hope
3568 Dan Jones
3569 Mike Maguire
3570 Marc Pisciotta
3571 Roberto Ramrirez
3572 Matt Ruebel
3573 Mike Teich
3574 Angie Encarnacion
3575 Jon Farrell
3576 Dean Hinson
3577 Don Garvey
3578 Mitch House
3579 Krev Krevokuch
3580 Jeff Leatherman
3581 Joe McLin
3582 Todd Schroeder
3583 Chuck Tooch
3584 Tony Womack
3585 James Cardona
3586 Gregg Leavell
3587 Antonio Mitchell
3588 Marty Neff
3589 Trace Ragland
3590 Craig Shotton
3591 Lee Driggers
3592 Jerry Nyman
3593 Checklist

1991 Classic Best West Palm Beach Expos

(Montreal Expos) (color)

	MT	NR MT	EX
Complete Set:	4.00	3.00	1.50

1 Felipe Alou
2 Doug Bochtler
3 Chris Bushing
4 Reid Cornelius
5 Jim Eddy
6 Rusty Kilgo
7 Joe Logan
8 Felix Moya
9 John Polasek
10 Gary Regira
11 Steve Renko
12 John Thoden
13 Jeff Tuss
14 Brian Wilkinson
15 Bill Cramer
16 Tim Laker
17 Perry Sanchez
18 Rob Bargas
19 Scott Davison
20 Willie Greene
21 Ron Krause
22 Chad McDonald
23 J.D. Ramirez
24 Jeff Barry
25 Marty Durkin
26 Todd Mayo
27 Dave Jauss (No position listed on back of card.)
28 Troy Ricker
29 Tyrone Woods
30 Sean Cunningham

1991 ProCards West Palm Beach Expos

(Montreal Expos) (color)

	MT	NR MT	EX
Complete Set:	4.00	3.00	1.50

1218 Doug Bochtler
1219 Chris Bushing
1220 Reid Cornelius
1221 Jim Eddy
1222 Rusty Kilgo
1223 Joe Logan
1224 Felix Moya
1225 John Polasek
1226 Gary Regira
1227 Steve Renko
1228 John Thoden
1229 Jeff Tuss
1230 Brian Wilkinson
1231 Bill Cramer
1232 Tim Laker
1233 Perry Sanchez
1234 Rob Bargas
1235 Scott Davison
1236 Willie Greene
1237 Chad McDonald
1238 J.D. Ramirez
1239 Jeff Barry
1240 Marty Durkin
1241 Todd Mayo
1242 Troy Ricker
1243 Tyrone Woods
1244 Felipe Alou
1245 Dave Jauss
1246 Mike Parrott
1247 Checklist

1991 Procards Wichita Wranglers

(San Diego Padres) (color)

	MT	NR MT	EX
Complete Set:	5.00	3.75	2.00

2590 Doug Brocail
2591 Renay Bryand
2592 Rafael Chavez
2593 Rick Davis
2594 Kerry Knox
2595 Pedro Martinez
2596 Darrin Reichle
2597 A.J. Sager
2598 Frank Seminara
2599 Roger Smithberg
2600 Brian Wood
2601 Mike Basso
2602 Pete Kuid
2603 Greg David
2604 Luis Lopez
2605 Tom Redington
2606 Jose Valentin
2607 Guillermo Velasquez
2608 Tim Wallace
2609 Brian Cisarik
2610 Vince Harris
2611 Charlie Hillemann
2612 Tim McWilliam
2613 Darrell Sherman
2614 Steve Lubratich
2615 John Cumberland
2616 Jack Maloof
2617 Checklist

1991 Rock's-Team Wichita Wranglers

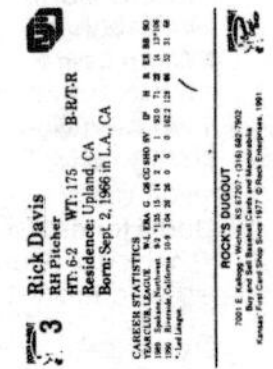

(San Diego Padres) (color)

	MT	NR MT	EX
Complete Set:	6.00	4.50	2.50

1 Doug Brocail
2 Rafel Chavez
3 Rick Davis
4 Kerry Knox
5 Jim Lewis
6 Pedro Martinez
7 Darrin Reichle
8 A.J. Sager
9 Frank Seminara
10 Brian Wood
11 Mike Basso
12 Pete Kuld
13 Greg David
14 Luis Lopez
15 Tom Redington
16 Jose Valentin
17 Guillermo Velasquez
18 Tim Wallace
19 Brian Cisarik
20 Vince Harris
21 Charlie Hileman
22 Tim McWilliam
23 Darrell Sherman
24 Steve Lubratich
25 John Cumberland
26 Jack Maloof
---- Checklist

1991 Rock's-Team Wichita Wranglers

(San Diego Padres) (color)

	MT	NR MT	EX
Complete Set:	6.00	4.50	2.50

Checklist, Sandy Alomar Jr., Andy Benes
1 Doug Brocail
2 Rafel Chavez
3 Rick Davis
4 Kerry Knox
5 Jim Lewis
6 Pedro Martinez
7 Darrin Reichle
8 A.J. Sager
9 Frank Seminara
10 Brian Wood
11 Mike Basso
12 Pete Kuid
13 Greg David
14 Luis Lopez
15 Tom Redington
16 Jose Valentin
17 Guillermo Velasquez
18 Tim Wallace
19 Brian Cisarik
20 Vince Harris
21 Charlie Hileman
22 Tim McWilliam
23 Darrell Sherman
24 Steve Lubratich
25 John Cumberland
26 Jack Maloof

1991 ProCards Williamsport Bills

(New York Mets) (color)

	MT	NR MT	EX
Complete Set:	4.00	3.00	1.50

286 Chris Hall
287 John Johnstone
288 Doug Kline
289 Toby Nivens
290 Bryan Rogers
291 David Sommer
292 Greg Talamantez
293 Dave Telgheder
294 Jose Vargas
295 Aguedo Vasquez
296 Javier Gonzalez
297 Alan Zinter
298 Tim Bogar
299 Hernan Cortes
300 Joe Dellicarri
301 Rudy Hernandez
302 Tito Navarro
303 Paul Williams
304 Jeromy Burnitz
305 Steve Davis
306 D.J. Dozier
307 Lee May
308 Loy McBride
309 Clint Hurdle
310 Jim Eschen
311 Joel Horlen
312 Checklist (Numbered correctly, but not listed on checklist.)

A player's name in italic type indicates a rookie card. An (FC) indicates a player's first card for that particular card company.

1991 Classic Best Winston-Salem Spirits

(Chicago Cubs) (color)

	MT	NR MT	EX
Complete Set:	4.00	3.00	1.50

1 Troy Bradford (First name misspelled on checklist.)
2 Ed Caballero
3 Sean Cheetham
4 Ryan Hawblitzel
5 Jessie Hollins
6 Eric Jaques
7 Billy Melvin
8 Leo Perez
9 Chris Lutz
10 Joe Porcelli
11 Travis Willis
12 Brad Mills
13 Mike Gabbani
14 Brad Huff
15 Matt Walbeck
16 Joe Biasucci
17 Pete Castellano
18 Marvin Cole
19 Matt Franco
20 Mike Grace
21 Bill Earley
22 Bryan Wilson
23 Chris Ebright
24 Richie Grayum
25 John Jensen
26 Paul Torres
27 Jerrone Williams
28 Steve Melendez
29 Checklist (Not listed on checklist.)
---- Spirits Logo

1991 ProCards Winston-Salem Spirits

(Chicago Cubs) (color)

	MT	NR MT	EX
Complete Set:	4.00		

2820 Troy Bradford
2821 Ed Caballero
2822 Sean Cheetham
2823 Ryan Hawblitzel
2824 Jesse Hollins
2825 Eric Jacques
2826 Bill Melvin
2827 Leo Perez
2828 Joe Porcelli
2829 Dave Swartzbaugh
2830 Travis Willis
2831 Mike Gabbani
2832 Matt Walbeck
2833 Joe Biasucci
2834 Pete Castellano
2835 Marvin Cole
2836 Matt Franco
2837 Mike Grace
2838 J.P. Postiff
2839 Bryan Wilson
2840 Chris Ebright
2841 Richie Grayum
2842 John Jensen
2843 Paul Torres
2844 Jerrone Williams
2845 Brad Mills
2846 Bill Earley
2847 Checklist

1991 Classic Best Winter Haven Red Sox

(Boston Red Sox) (color)

	MT	NR MT	EX
Complete Set:	3.00	2.25	1.25

1 Tracy Allen
2 Paul Brown
3 Dan Kite
4 Mark Mitchelson
5 Mike Verdi
6 Gary Painter
7 Terry Powers
8 Kenny Ryan Jr.
9 Silverio Santa Maria
10 Brian Young
11 Joe Demus
12 Lou Dorante
13 Willie Dukes Jr.
14 Pedro Matilla
15 Randy Brown
16 Lee Stange
17 Mike DeKneef
18 Greg Graham
19 Larry Grant
20 John Malzone
21 Les Wallin
22 Garrett Jenkins
23 Jim Morrison
24 Mickey Rivers Jr.
25 Shea Wardwell
26 Joe Marchese
27 Jim Strcek
28 Jose Lora
29 Richard Delgado
30 Checklist

1991 ProCards Winter Haven Red Sox

(Boston Red Sox) (color)

	MT	NR MT	EX
Complete Set:	3.00	2.25	1.25

481 Tracy Allen
482 Paul Brown
483 Dan Kite
484 Mark Mitchelson
485 Tommy Niles
486 Gary Painter
487 Terry Powers
488 Kenny Ryan
489 Silverio Santa Maria
490 Brian Young
491 Joe Demus
492 Lou Dorante
493 Willie Dukes
494 Bill Madril
495 Randy Brown
496 Mike Dekneef
497 Greg Graham
498 Larry Grant
499 John Malzone
500 Les Wallin
501 Garrett Jenkins
502 Jim Morrison
503 Mickey Rivers
504 Shea Wardwell
505 Mike Verdi
506 Joe Marchese
507 Checklist

1991 Classic Best Yakima Bears

(Los Angeles Dodgers) (color)

	MT	NR MT	EX
Complete Set:	3.00	2.25	1.25

1 Vernon Spearman
2 Eric Vorbeck
3 Marc Tramuta
4 Ron Richard
5 Murph Proctor
6 J.J. Johnson
7 Chris Demetral
8 Eric Blackwell
9 Keoki Farrish
10 Dan Gray
11 Tim Griffin
12 Don Meyers
13 Kevin Van DeBrake
14 Burgess Watts
15 Ben O'Connor
16 Jason Keer
17 Ken Hamilton
18 Don Carroll
19 Jason Broyles
20 Brad Boggetto
21 David Bauman
22 Doug Bennett
23 Carlos Castillo
24 Chris Crabtree
25 Rob Legendre
26 Mike Sharp
27 Jo Jo Smith
28 Carlos Thomas
29 Joe Vavra
30 Geoff Clark (Checklist)

1991 ProCards Yakima Bears

(Los Angeles Dodgers) (color)

	MT	NR MT	EX
Complete Set:	3.00	2.25	1.25

4237 Doug Bennett
4238 Brad Boggetto
4239 Jason Broyles
4240 Don Carroll
4241 Carlos Castillo
4242 Chris Crabtree
4243 Kenny Hamilton
4244 Jason Kerr
4245 Rob Legendre
4246 Ben O'Connor
4247 Mike Sharp
4248 Jo Jo Smith
4249 Carlos Thomas
4250 Dan Gray
4251 Don Meyers (Last name misspelled on checklist.)
4252 Chris Demetral
4253 Tim Griffin
4254 Murph Proctor
4255 Ron Richard
4256 Marc Tramuta
4257 Kevin Van de Brake
4258 Burgess Watts
4259 Eric Blackwell
4260 Keoki Farrish
4261 Vernon Spearman
4262 Roger Sweeney
4263 Eric Vorbeck
4264 Joe Vavra
4265 Tony Arnold
4266 Checklist

1991 Classic #1 Draft Picks

After releasing a 26-card draft pick set in 1990, Classic returned with a 50-card issue for 1991. Only 330,000 hobby sets were produced. The card fronts feature gray and maroon borders surrounding full-color photos and the Classic logo in the upper left corner. A special bonus card of Frankie Rodriguez is also included with the set. Each set also includes a certificate of authenticity. Individual card prices are for Mint condition.

	MT	NR MT	EX
Complete Set:	12.00	9.00	4.75
Common Player:	.30	.25	.12

		MT
1	Brien Taylor	3.00
2	Mike Kelly	2.50
3	David McCarty	2.50
4	Dmitri Young	1.50
5	Joe Vitiello	1.50
6	Mark Smith	.80
7	Tyler Green	1.25
8	Shawn Estes	.50
9	Doug Glanville	.80
10	Manny Ramirez	1.50
11	Cliff Floyd	.50
12	Tyrone Hill	.80
13	Eduardo Perez	1.50
14	Al Shirley	.70
15	Benji Gil	.35
16	Calvin Reese	.35
17	Allen Watson	.35
18	Brian Barber	.35
19	Aaron Sele	.50
20	John Farrell	.35
21	Scott Ruffcorn	.40
22	Brent Gates	.40
23	Scott Stahoviak	.50
24	Tom McKinnon	.30
25	Shawn Livsey	.30
26	Jason Pruitt	.30
27	Greg Anthony	.35
28	Justin Thompson	.35
29	Steve Whitaker	.35
30	Jorge Fabregas	.60
31	Jeff Ware	.35
32	Bobby Jones	.60
33	J.J. Johnson	.40
34	Mike Rossiter	.30
35	Dan Chowlowsky	.30
36	Jimmy Gonzalez	.30
37	Trevor Miller	.30
38	Scott Hatteberg	.30
39	Mike Groppuso	.40
40	Ryan Long	.30
41	Eddie Williams	.30
42	Mike Durant	.30
43	Buck McNabb	.30
44	Jimmy Lewis	.30
45	Eddie Ramos	.30
46	Terry Horn	.30
47	Jon Barnes	.30
48	Shawn Curran	.30
49	Tommy Adams	.50
50	Trevor Mallory	.30
----	Frankie Rodriguez (Bonus Card)	2.00

1991 Front Row Draft Picks

Only 240,000 of these sets were produced. The bonus card in the set must be sent in to Front Row in exchange for a special Frankie Rodriguez card. The first 120,000 collectors returning bonus cards also received Front Row's mini-update set. The cards feature full-color photos on both sides. Each set includes an official certificate of authenticity. 1991 marks the premier issue of Front Row baseball draft picks. Individual card prices are for Mint condition.

	MT	NR MT	EX
Complete Set:	8.00	6.00	3.25
Common Player:	.20	.15	.08

1 Frankie Rodriguez 1.25
2 Aaron Sele .75
3 Chad Schoenvogel .20
4 Scott Ruffcorn .40
5 Dan Chowlowski .20
6 Gene Schall .20
7 Trever Miller .25
8 Chris Durkin .20
9 Mike Neill .20
10 Kevin Stocker .40
11 Bobby Jones .50
12 John Farrell .20
13 Ronnie Allen .20
14 Mike Rossiter .20
15 Scott Hatteberg .25
16 Rodney Pedraza .20
17 Mike Durant .20
18 Ryan Long .20
19 Greg Anthony .20
20 Jon Barnes .20
21 Brian Barber .20
22 Brent Gates .35
23 Calvin Reese .30
24 Terry Horn .20
25 Scott Stahoviak .35
26 Jason Pruitt .30
27 Shawn Curran .20
28 Jimmy Lewis .25
29 Alex Ochoa .20
30 Joe Deberry .20
31 Justin Thompson .30
32 Jimmy Gonzalez .30
33 Eddie Ramos .20
34 Tyler Green .50
35 Toby Rumfield .20
36 Dave Doorneweerd .20
37 Jeff Hostetler .20
38 Shawn Livsey .25
39 Mike Groppuso .40
40 Steve Whitaker .30
41 Tom McKinnon .30
42 Buck McNabb .25
43 Al Shirley .50
44 Allan Watson .25
45 Bill Bliss .20
46 Todd Hollandsworth .20
47 Manny Ramirez 1.50
48 J.J. Johnson .25
49 Cliff Floyd 1.00
50 Bonus Card .25

1992 Classic Best

This 400-card wax pack set has an All-American look, with red, white and blue used in the card design. A red and white banner is at the bottom, with the player's name, team and position below the photo. On the back the player's name is stretched horizontally across the back of the card, along with a head shot.

	MT	NR MT	EX
Complete Set (400):	20.00	15.00	8.00
Complete Factory Set (450):	25.00	18.50	10.00

1 Nolan Ryan .75
2 Darius Gash .05
3 Brad Ausmus .10
4 Mike Gardella .05
5 Mark Hutton .05
6 Bobby Munoz .10
7 Don Sparks .05
8 Shane Andrews .25
9 Gary Hymel .05
10 Roberto Arredondo .05
11 Joe Randa .05
12 Pedro Grifol .05
13 Steve Dixon .05
14 John Thomas .05
15 Chris Durkin .05
16 Jeff Conger .05
17 John Farrell .15
18 Antonio Mitchell .05
19 Matt Ruebel .05
20 Darren Burton .10
21 Lance Jennings .05
22 Kerwin Moore .10
23 Julio Bruno .10
24 Joe Vitiello .20
25 Brook Fordyce .05
26 Rob Katzaroff .05
27 Julian Vasquez .05
28 Alan Zinter .10
29 Clemente Alvarez .05
30 Scott Cepicky .05
31 Mike Mongiello .05
32 Tom Redington .05
33 Johnny Ruffin .10
34 Eric Booker .05
35 Manny Martinez .05
36 Mike Grimes .05
37 Paul Byrd .05
38 Brian Giles .05
39 David Mlicki .05
40 Tracy Sanders .05
41 Kyle Washington .05
42 Scott Bullett .05
43 Steve Cooke .20
44 Austin Manahan .05
45 Ben Shelton .05
46 Joe DeBerry .10
47 Steve Gibralter .15
48 Willie Greene .10
49 Brian Koelling .05
50 Larry Luebbers .10
51 Greg "Pepper" Anthony .10
52 Homer Bush .10
53 Manny Cora .05
54 Joey Hamilton .15
55 David Mowry .05
56 Bobby Perna .05
57 Jamie Dismuke .05
58 Kenneth Gillum .05
59 Calvin Reese .10
60 Phil Dauphin .15
61 Ryan Hawblitzel .10
62 Tim Parker .05
63 Dave Swartzbaugh .05
64 Billy White .05
65 Terry Burrows .05
66 Chris Gies .05
67 Kurt Miller .05
68 Timmie Morrow .05
69 Benny Colvard .05
70 Tim Costo .15
71 Mica Lewis .05
72 John Roper .05
73 Kevin Tatar .05
74 Joel Adamson .05
75 Mike Farmer .05
76 Kevin Stocker .75
77 David Tokheim .05
78 Ray Jackson .05
79 Dax Jones .05
80 Randy Curtis .05
81 Eric Reichenbach .10
82 Jerome Tolliver .05
83 Quilvio Veras .05
84 George Evangelista .05
85 Pat Bryant .10
86 Willie Canate .05
87 Brian Lane .05
88 Howard Battle .15
89 Rob Butler .15
90 Carlos Delgado 1.50
91 Tyler Houston .05
92 Troy Hughes .05
93 Chipper Jones .60
94 Mel Nieves .35
95 Jose Olmeda .05
96 John Finn .05
97 Mike Guerrero .05
98 Troy O'Leary .15
99 Ben Blomdahl .15
100 Mike Schmidt .40
101 Carlos Burguillos .05
102 Kiki Hernandez .05
103 Brian Dubose .05
104 Kevin Morgan .05
105 Justin Thompson .25
106 Jason Alstead .05
107 Matt Anderson .05
108 Brad Pennington .05
109 Brad Tyler .05
110 Jovino Carvajal .05
111 Roger Luce .05
112 Ken Powell .05
113 Steve Sadecki .05
114 Craig Clayton .05
115 Russell Davis .35
116 Mike Kelly .35
117 Javier Lopez 1.50
118 Doug Piatt .05
119 Manny Alexander .05
120 Damon Buford .05
121 Erik Schullstrom .05
122 Mark Smith .15
123 Jeff Williams .05
124 Reid Cornelius .05
125 Tim Laker .05
126 Chris Martin .05
127 Mike Mathile .05
128 Derrick White .05
129 Luis Galindez .05
130 John Kuehl .05
131 Ray McDavid .20
132 Sean Mulligan .05
133 Tookie Spann .05
134 Marcos Armas .20
135 Scott Erwin .05
136 Johnny Guzman .10
137 Mike Mohler .05
138 Craig Paquette .10
139 Dean Tatarian .05
140 Orlando Miller .05
141 Tow Maynard .05
142 Marc Newfield .30
143 Greg Pirkl .05
144 Jesus Tavarez .05
145 Tom Smith .05
146 Brad Seitzer .05
147 Brent Brede .05
148 Elston Hansen .05
149 Jamie Ogden .05
150 Rogelio Nunez .05
151 Manny Cervantes .05
152 David Sartain .05
153 Shawn Bryant .05
154 Chad Ogea .15
155 Manny Ramirez 2.00
156 Darrell Whitmore .05
157 Greg O'Halloran .05
158 Tim Brown .05
159 Curtis Pride .20
160 Marcus Moore .05
161 Robert Perez .05
162 Aaron Small .05
163 David Tollison .05
164 Nigel Wilson .40
165 Jim Givens .05
166 Dennis McNamara .05
167 Kelley O'Neal .05
168 Rudy Pemberton .05
169 Joe Perona .05
170 Brian Cornelius .05
171 Ivan Cruz .05
172 Frank Gonzales .05
173 Mike Lumley .05
174 Brian Warren .05
175 Aaron Sele 1.50
176 Gary Caraballo .05
177 Creighton Gubanich .05
178 Brad Parker .05
179 Scott Sheldon .05
180 Archie Corbin .05
181 Phil Hiatt .25
182 Domingo Mota .05
183 Dan Carlson .05
184 Hugh Walker .05
185 Joe Ciccarella .05
186 John Jackson .05
187 Brent Gates .35
188 Eric Helfand .05
189 Damon Mashore .10
190 Malcolm (Curtis) Shaw .05
191 Jason Wood .05
192 Terry Powers .05
193 Steve Karsay .60
194 Greg Blosser .15
195 Gar Finnvold .05
196 Scott Hatteberg .05
197 Derek Livernois .05
198 Jeff McNeely .05
199 Rex DeLaNuez .05
200 Ken Griffey Jr. 1.50
201 Pat Meares .05
202 Alan Newman .05
203 Paul Russo .05
204 Anthony Collier .05
205 Roberto Petagine .25
206 Brian Hunter .25
207 James Mouton .40
208 Tom Nevers .05
209 Garret Anderson .05
210 Clifton Garrett .05
211 Eduardo Perez .25
212 Shawn Purdy .05
213 Darren Bragg .05
214 Glenn Murray .15
215 Ruben Santana .15
216 Charles (Bubba) Smith .15
217 Terry Adams .05
218 William (Bill) Bliss .05
219 German Diaz .05
220 Willie Gardner .05
221 Ed Larregui .05
222 Tim Garland .05
223 Kevin Jordan .05
224 Tim Rumer .05
225 Jason Robertson .05
226 Todd Claus .05
227 Julian Heredia .05
228 Mark Sweeney .05
229 Robert Eenhoorn .05
230 Tyler Green .20
231 Mike Lieberthal .10
232 Ron Lockett .05
233 Tom Nuneviller .05
234 Sean Ryan .05
235 Alvaro Benavides .05
236 Kevin Bellomo .05
237 Tony Bridges .05
238 Eric Whitford .05
239 James Bishop .05
240 Midre Cummings .30
241 Tom Green .05
242 Marcus Hanel .05
243 Billy Ashley .20
244 Matt Howard .05
245 Tommy Adams .10
246 Craig Bryant .05
247 Ron Pezzoni .05
248 Barry Miller .05
249 Jason McFarlin .05
250 Joe Rosselli .05
251 Billy Van Landingham .05
252 Chris Seelbach .05
253 Jason Bere 1.25
254 Eric Christopherson .05
255 Rick Huisman .05
256 Kevin McGehee .05
257 Salomon Torres .25
258 Brian Boehringer .05
259 Glenn DiSarcina .05
260 Jason Schmidt .05
261 Charles Poe .05
262 Ricky Bottalico .05
263 Tommy Eason .05
264 Joel Gilmore .05
265 Pat Ruth .05
266 Gene Schall .05
267 Jim Campbell .05
268 Brian Barber .05
269 Allen Battle .05
270 Marc Ronan .05
271 Scott Simmons .05
272 Dmitri Young .20
273 Butch Huskey .20
274 Frank Jacobs .05
275 Aaron Ledesma .20
276 Jose Martinez .15
277 Andy Beasley .05
278 Paul Ellis .05
279 John Kelly .05
280 Jeremy McGarity .05
281 Mateo Ozuna .05
282 Allen Watson .25
283 Francisco Gamez .05
284 Leon Glenn .05
285 Duane Singleton .10
286 Andy Pettitte .10
287 Donald Harris .05
288 Robb Nen .05
289 Jose Oliva .05
290 Keith Garagozzo .05
291 Dan Smith .05
292 Kiki Jones .05
293 Rich Becker .25
294 Mike Durant .05
295 Denny Hocking .05
296 Mike Lewis .05
297 Troy Ricker .05
298 Todd Ritchie .05
299 Scott Stahoviak .10
300 Brien Taylor .35
301 Jim Austin .05
302 Mike Daniel .05
303 Joseph Eischen .15
304 Ranbir Grewal .05
305 Rondell White .40
306 Mark Hubbard .05
307 Tate Seefried .15
308 Tom Wilson .05
309 Benji Gil .35
310 Mike Edwards .05
311 J.D. Noland .05
312 Jay Gainer .05
313 Lance Painter .05
314 Tim Worell .05
315 Sean Cheetham .05
316 Earl Cunningham .10
317 Brad Erdman .05
318 Paul Torres .05
319 Jose Vierra .15
320 Chris Gambs .10
321 Brandon Wilson .05
322 Brett Donovan .05
323 Larry Thomas .10
324 Brian Griffiths .05
325 Chad Schoenvogel .05
326 Mandy Romero .05
327 Chris Curtis .10
328 Jim Campanis .05
329 Anthony Manahan .05
330 Jason Townley .05
331 Fidel Compres .05
332 John Ericks .05
333 Don Prybylinski .05
334 Jason Best .05
335 Rob Wishnevski .05
336 John Byington .05
337 Omar Garcia .05
338 Tony Eusebio .05
339 Paul Swingle .05
340 Mark Zappelli .05
341 Bobby Jones .40
342 J.R. Phillips .60
343 Jim Edmonds .25
344 Greg Hansell .10
345 Mike Piazza 3.50
346 Mike Busch .05
347 Darrell Sherman .05
348 Shawn Green .15
349 Willie Mota .05
350 David McCarty .25
351 James Dougherty .05
352 Fernando Vina .05
353 Ken Huckaby .05
354 Joe Vitko .05
355 Roberto (Diaz) Mejia .25
356 Willis Otanez .05
357 Billy Lott .05
358 Jason Pruitt .10
359 Jorge Fabregas .15
360 Mike Stefanski .05
361 Robert Saitz .05
362 Scott Talanoa .05
363 LaRue Baber .05
364 Tyrone Hill .25
365 Rick Mediavilla .05
366 Eddie Williams .05
367 Rigo Beltran .05

368	Doug VanderWeele	.05
369	Donnie Elliott	.05
370	Dan Cholowsky	.05
371	Derrell Rumsey	.05
372	Anthony Graffagnino	.05
373	Scott Ruffcorn	.35
374	Mike Rossiter	.15
375	Mike Robertson	.05
376	P.J. Forbes	.05
377	Doug Brady	.05
378	Rick Clelland	.05
379	Ugueth Urbina	.30
380	Cliff Floyd	2.00
381	Danny Young	.05
382	Eddie Ramos	.10
383	Bob Abreu	.05
384	Gary Mota	.10
385	Tony Womack	.05
386	Jeff Motuzas	.05
387	Desi Relaford	.05
388	John Elerman	.05
389	Walt McKeel	.05
390	Tim VanEgmond	.05
391	Frank Rodriguez	.35
392	Paul Carey	.15
393	Michael Matheny	.10
394	George Glinatsis	.05
395	Checklist (1-69)	.05
396	Checklist (70-138)	.05
397	Checklist (139-207)	.05
398	Checklist (208-276)	.05
399	Checklist (277-345)	.05
400	Checklist (346-400)	.05
401	Paul Shuey	.10
402	Derek Jeter	.40
403	Derek Wallace	.15
404	Sean Lowe	.10
405	Jim Pittsley	.15
406	Shannon Stewart	.05
407	Jamie Arnold	.15
408	Jason Kendall	.05
409	Eddie Pearson	.10
410	Todd Steverson	.10
411	Dan Serafini	.10
412	John Burke	.15
413	Jeff Schmidt	.10
414	UER (Sherard Clinkscales)	.20
415	Shon Walker	.10
416	Brandon Cromer	.10
417	Johnny Damon	.15
418	Michael Moore	.10
419	Michael Matthews	.10
420	Brian Sackinsky	.10
421	Jon Lieber	.15
422	Danny Clyburn	.10
423	Chris Smith	.25
424	Dwain Bostic	.10
425	Bob Wolcott	.05
426	Mike Gulan	.05
427	Yuri Sanchez	.05
428	Tony Sheffield	.10
429	Ritchie Moody	.15
430	Andy Hartung	.10
431	Trey Beamon	.10
432	Tim Crabtree	.15
433	Mark Thompson	.10
434	John Lynch	.15
439	Tavo Alvarez	.20
441	Troy Penix	.05
442	Scott Pose	.20
447	Jesus Martinez	.25
449	Chad Fonville	.10
1	Ken Griffey, Jr. (Autograph)	150.00
2	David McCarty (Autograph)	40.00
3	Nolan Ryan (Autograph)	200.00
4	Mike Schmidt (Autograph)	75.00
5	Brien Taylor (Autograph)	40.00

1992 Classic Best Red Bonus

These 20 red bonus cards were randomly inserted in 1992 Classic Best black jumbo packs, one per pack. Cards are numbered with a BC prefix.

	MT	NR MT	EX
Complete Set (20):	25.00	18.50	10.00
Common Player:	.25	.20	.10

1	Nolan Ryan	2.50
2	Mark Hutton	.25
3	Shane Andrews	.40
4	Scott Bullett	.25
5	Kurt Miller	.25
6	Carlos Delgado	5.00
7	Chipper Jones	2.50
8	Dmitri Young	1.50
9	Mike Kelly	1.25
10	Javy Lopez	5.00
11	Aaron Sele	5.00
12	Ken Griffey, Jr.	4.00
13	Midre Cummings	.75
14	Salomon Torres	1.00
15	Brien Taylor	1.00
16	Mike Piazza	10.00
17	David McCarty	1.00
18	Scott Ruffcorn	1.50
19	Cliff Floyd	8.00
20	Frankie Rodriguez	1.50

1992 Classic Best Blue Bonus

These 30 blue bonus cards were randomly inserted into 1992 Classic Best white jumbo packs, one per pack. Cards are numbered with a BC prefix. There were also 2,000 autographed Royce Clayton cards randomly inserted into the packs.

	MT	NR MT	EX
Complete Set (30):	30.00	22.00	12.00
Common Player:	.25	.20	.10

1	Nolan Ryan	2.50
2	Mark Hutton	.25
3	Shane Andrews	.40
4	Scott Bullett	.40
5	Kurt Miller	.40
6	Carlos Delgado	5.00
7	Chipper Jones	2.00
8	Dmitri Young	1.00
9	Mike Kelly	1.25
10	Javy Lopez	5.00
11	Aaron Sele	5.00
12	Ken Griffey, Jr.	4.00
13	Midre Cummings	.50
14	Salomon Torres	1.00
15	Brien Taylor	1.00
16	Mike Piazza	10.00
17	David McCarty	.75
18	Scott Ruffcorn	1.50
19	Cliff Floyd	8.00
20	Frankie Rodriguez	1.00
21	Paul Shuey	.40
22	Derek Jeter	1.25
23	Derek Wallace	.40
24	Shannon Stewart	.40
25	Jamie Arnold	.40
26	Jason Kendall	1.00
27	Todd Steverson	.75
28	Dan Serafini	.50
29	John Burke	.50
30	Michael Moore	1.00
1	Royce Clayton (Autograph)	40.00

1992 Fleer Excel

Fleer's entry into minor league cards in 1992 is titled Excel. The 250-card set features full-color photos inside a white border with the player's name, team, logo and Excel logo in gold-foil stamping. Backs have large photos, career statistics, team logos and biographical information. Cards are UV coated. Cards were intended to be sold in 14-card packs for a suggested retail price of $1.49 each. The Excel All-Stars are listed at the end of the 250-card checklist. Cards for these 10 players were randomly inserted into the 14-card foil packs.

	MT	NR MT	EX
Complete Set (250):	50.00	38.00	20.00
Common Player:	.10	.08	.04

2	Chipper Jones	1.50
3	Mike Kelly	.75
4	Brian Kowitz	.10
5	Napoleon Robinson	.10
6	Tony Tarasco	1.00
7	Pedro Castellano	.10
8	Doug Glanville	.15
9	Andy Hartung	.15
10	Jay Hassel	.10
11	Ryan Hawblitzel	.10
12	Kevin Roberson	.60
13	Chad Tredaway	.10
14	Jose Vierra	.10
15	Matt Walbeck	.25
16	Tim Belk	.10
17	Jamie Dismuke	.10
18	Chad Fox	.10
19	Micah Franklin	.10
20	Dan Frye	.10
21	Steve Gibralter	.10
22	Demetrish Jenkins	.10
23	Jason Kummerfeidt	.10
24	Bob Loftin	.10
25	Chad Mottola	1.50
26	Bobby Perna	.10
27	Scott Pose	.10
28	Calvin Reese	.25
29	John Roper	.20
30	Jerry Spradlin	.10
31	Roger Bailey	.15
32	Jason Bates	.10
33	John Burke	.25
34	Jason Hutchins	.10
35	Troy Ricker	.10
36	Mark Thompson	.10
37	Lou Lucca	.10
38	John Lynch	.10
39	Todd Pridy	.10
40	Gary Cooper	.10
41	Jim Dougherty	.10
42	Tony Eusebio	.15
43	Chris Hatcher	.10
44	Chris Hill	.10
45	Trent Hubbard	.10
46	Todd Jones	.10
47	Jeff Juden	.20
48	James Mouton	1.00
49	Tom Nevers	.10
50	Jim Waring	.10
51	Chris Abbe	.10
52	Jay Kirkpatrick	.10
53	Raul Mondesi	5.00
54	Vernon Spearman	.10
55	Tavo Alvarez	.15
56	Shane Andrews	.30
57	Yamil Benitez	.10
58	Cliff Floyd	5.00
59	Antonio Grissom	.25
60	Tyrone Horne	.10
61	Mike Lansing	.35
62	Edgar Tovar	.10
63	Ugueth Urbina	.50
64	David Wainhouse	.10
65	Derrick White	.10
66	Gabe White	.75
67	Rondell White	2.00
68	Edgar Alfonzo	.10
69	Jeromy Burnitz	.60
70	Jay Davis	.10
71	Cesar Diaz	.10
72	Todd Douma	.10
73	Brook Fordyce	.20
74	Butch Huskey	.50
75	Bobby Jones	.75
76	Jose Martinez	.10
77	Ricky Otero	.10
78	Jim Popoff	.10
79	Al Shirley	.10
80	Julian Vasquez	.15
81	Quilvio Veras	.10
82	Fernando Vina	.10
83	Ron Blazier	.10
84	Tommy Eason	.10
85	Tyler Green	.25
86	Mike Lieberthal	.10
87	Tom Nuneviller	.10
88	Matt Whisenant	.10
89	Jon Zuber	.10
90	Midre Cummings	.75
91	Jon Farrell	.15
92	Ramon Martinez	.10
93	Antonio Mitchell	.10
94	Keith Thomas	.10
95	Rene Arocha	.40
96	Brian Barber	.35
97	Jamie Cochran	.10
98	Mike Gulan	.25
99	Keith Johns	.10
100	John Kelly	.10
101	Anthony Lewis	.10
102	T.J. Mathews	.10
103	Kevin Meier	.10
104	David Oehrlein	.10
105	Gerry Santos	.10
106	Basil Shabazz	.10
107	Eddie Williams	.10
108	Dmitri Young	.75
109	Jay Gainer	.10
110	Pedro Martinez	.20
111	Dave Staton	.25
112	Tim Worrell	.10
113	Dan Carlson	.10
114	Joel Chimelis	.10
115	Eric Christopherson	.10
116	Adell Davenport	.10
117	Ken Grundt	.10
118	Rick Huisman	.10
119	Andre Keene	.10
120	Kevin McGehee	.10
121	Salomon Torres	.75
122	Damon Buford	.25
123	Stanton Cameron	.10
124	Rick Krivda	.10
125	Alex Ochoa	.40
126	Brad Penington	.10
127	Mark Smith	.40
128	Mel Wearing	.10
129	Cory Bailey	.10
130	Greg Blosser	.25
131	Joe Caruso	.10
132	Jason Friedman	.10
133	Jose Malave	.10
134	Jeff McNeely	.15
135	Luis Ortiz	.10
136	Ed Riley	.10
137	Frank Rodriguez	.60
138	Aaron Sele	3.00
139	Garret Anderson	.20
140	Ron Correia	.10
141	Jim Edmonds	.15
142	John Fritz	.10
143	Brian Grebeck	.10
144	Jeff Kipila	.10
145	Orlando Palmeiro	.10
146	Eduardo Perez	.75
147	John Pricher	.10
148	Chris Pritchett	.10
149	James Baldwin	1.50
150	Rodney Bolton	.25
151	Essex Burton	.10
152	Scott Cepicky	.10
153	Steve Olsen	.10
154	Scott Ruffcorn	1.50
155	Scott Schrenk	.10
156	Larry Thomas	.10
157	Brandon Wilson	.15
158	Paul Byrd	.10
159	Willie Canate	.10
160	Marc Marini	.10
161	Jonathan Nunnally	.10
162	Chad Ogea	.25
163	Herb Perry	.15
164	Manny Ramirez	5.00
165	Omar Ramirez	.20
166	Ken Ramos	.10
167	Tracy Sanders	.10
168	Paul Shuey	.25
169	Kyle Washington	.10
170	Ivan Cruz	.10
171	Lou Frazier	.15
172	Brian Bevil	.10
173	Shane Halter	.10
174	Phil Hiatt	.25
175	Lance Jennings	.10
176	Les Norman	.10
177	Joe Randa	.25
178	Dan Rohrmeier	.10
179	Larry Sutton	.15
180	Joe Vitiello	.25
181	John Byington	.10
182	Edgar Caceres	.10
183	Jeff Cirillo	.20
184	Mike Farrell	.10
185	Kenny Felder	.20
186	Tyrone Hill	.25
187	Brian Hostetler	.10
188	Danan Hughes	.10
189	Scott Karl	.10
190	Joe Kmak	.10
191	Rob Lakachyk	.10
192	Matt Mieske	.40
193	Troy O'Leary	.25
194	Cecil Rodriques	.10
195	Tim Unroe	.10
196	Wes Weger	.10
197	Rich Becker	.10
198	Marty Cordova	.10
199	Steve Dunn	.10
200	Mike Durant	.10
201	Denny Hocking	.10
202	David McCarty	.75
203	Damian Miller	.10
204	Scott Stahoviak	.20
205	Russ Davis	.25
206	Mike Draper	.10
207	Carl Everett	.40
208	Lew Hill	.10
209	Mark Hutton	.25
210	Derek Jeter	1.50
211	Kevin Jordan	.10
212	Lyle Mouton	.10
213	Bobby Munoz	.15
214	Andy Pettitte	.10
215	Brien Taylor	.75
216	Brent Gates	1.00
217	Eric Helfand	.10
218	Curtis Shaw	.10
219	Todd Van Poppel	.25
220	Miah Bradbury	.10
221	Darren Bragg	.10
222	Jim Converse	.10
223	John Cummings	.10
224	Shawn Estes	.10
225	Mike Hampton	.10
226	Derek Lowe	.10
227	Ellerton Maynard	.10
228	Fred McNair	.10
229	Marc Newfield	1.00
230	Desi Relaford	.10
231	Ruben Santana	.25
232	Bubba Smith	.25
233	Brian Turang	.15
234	Benji Gil	.75
235	Jose Oliva	.25
236	Jon Shave	.10
237	Travis Baptist	.10
238	Howard Battle	.35
239	Rob Butler	.20
240	Tim Crabtree	.15
241	Juan DeLaRosa	.10
242	Carlos Delgado	3.00
243	Alex Gonzalez	3.00
244	Steve Karsay	2.50
245	Paul Spoljaric	.50
246	Todd Steverson	.50
247	Nigel Wilson	.75
248	Checklist	.10
249	Checklist	.10
250	Checklist	.10

1992 Fleer Excel All-Stars

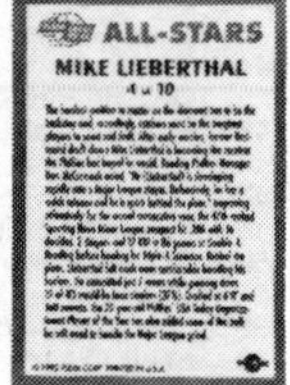

These 10 All-Star cards were randomly inserted in Fleer Excel's 1992-93 foil packs. Cards are UV coated and feature the Excel logo on the front, along with the player's name and All-Star status in stamped in gold foil.

	MT	NR MT	EX
Complete Set (10):	55.00		
Common Player:	2.00		

#	Player	MT
1	Brien Taylor	3.00
2	Chipper Jones	8.00
3	Rondell White	10.00
4	Mike Lieberthal	2.00
5	Bobby Jones	8.00
6	Carlos Delgado	10.00
7	Aaron Sele	12.00
8	Brent Gates	7.50
9	Phil Hiatt	2.50
10	Brandon Wilson	2.00

1992 Fleer Excel League Leaders

These randomly inserted cards feature 20 different Minor League league leaders. "League Leaders" and the player's name are stamnped in gold foil on the front, which also has an Excel logo. The cards were random inserts in 1992-93 Fleer Excel jumbo packs.

	MT	NR MT	EX
Complete Set (20):	25.00	18.50	10.00
Common Player:	.75	.60	.30

#	Player	MT
1	Travis Baptist	.75
2	Bubba Smith	.75
3	Rob Butler	1.25
4	Marty Cordova	1.50
5	John Fritz	.75
6	Quilivio Veras	1.00
7	Cliff Floyd	10.00
8	Denny Hocking	1.00
9	Rich Becker	3.50
10	Jim Popoff	.75
11	John Kelly	.75
12	Tavo Alvarez	1.50
13	Scott Pose	1.00
14	Steve Gibralter	1.00
15	Joe Caruso	1.00
16	Chad Ogea	2.50
17	Troy O'Leary	1.50
18	Russell Davis	3.00
19	John Cummings	1.00
20	Ken Ramos	.75

1992 SkyBox AA

SkyBox Pre-Rookie 1992 baseball cards were released in two 310-card sets; one for Triple A and one for Double A. Each set includes 289 top prospects, plus subsets (1991 statistical leaders, players of the year and minor league stadiums) and checklist cards. Cards were intended to be sold in 15-card packs for a suggested retail price of 95 cents each. SkyBox International also offered 25-card Pre-Rookie team sets which include all players and coaches on the opening day roster of each of the 52 AA and AAA teams, plus a team checklist. Sets were to be available at most of the teams' stadiums. The top prospects which appear in the 15-card packs are also depicted in the team sets, but the team cards use a different numbering system and delete the card back copy except for statistics.

	MT	NR MT	EX
Complete Set (310):	15.00	11.00	6.00
Common Player:	.05	.04	.02

#	Player	MT
1	Rich Batchelor	.05
2	Russ Davis	.25
3	Kiki Hernandez	.15
4	Sterling Hitchcock	.20
5	Darren Hodges	.05
6	Jeff Hoffman	.05
7	Mark Hulton	.20
8	Bobby Munoz	.10
9	Roy Noriega	.05
10	Sherman Obando	.15
11	John Viera	.05
12	Cliff Brannon	.05
13	Chuck Carr	.20
14	Fidel Compres	.05
15	Tripp Cromer	.05
16	John Ericks	.05
17	Gabby Ozuna	.05
18	Don Prybylinski	.05
19	John Sellick	.05
20	John Thomas	.05
21	Tom Urbani	.10
22	Chris Butterfield	.05
23	Todd Douma	.05
24	Brook Fordyce	.05
25	Tim Howard	.05
26	John Johnstone	.05
27	Bobby Jones	.25
28	Rob Katzaroff	.05
29	Gregg Langbehn	.05
30	Curtis Pride	.30
31	Julian Vasquez	.05
32	Joe Vitko	.10
33	Tom Wegmann	.10
34	Mike White	.05
35	Alan Zinter	.15
36	Clemente Alvarez	.05
37	Cesar Bernhardt	.05
38	Wayne Busby	.05
39	Scott Cepicky	.05
40	John Hudek	.40
41	Scott Jaster	.05
42	Bo Kennedy	.05
43	Mike Mongiello	.05
44	Kinnis Pledger	.05
45	Johnny Ruffin	.10
46	Jose Ventura	.05
47	Paul Byrd	.05
48	Colin Charland	.05
49	Miguel Flores	.05
50	Brian Giles	.05
51	Jose Hernandez	.05
52	Nolan Lene	.05
53	David Mlicki	.05
54	Tracy Sanders	.05
55	Mike Soper	.05
56	Kelly Stinnett	.05
57	Joe Turek	.05
58	Kyle Washington	.05
59	Dave Bird	.05
60	Scott Bullett	.05
61	Steve Cooke	.20
62	Alberto De Los Santos	.05
63	Stan Fansier	.05
64	Austin Manahan	.05
65	Daryl Ratliff	.05
66	Mandy Romero	.05
67	Ben Shelton	.05
68	Paul Wagner	.05
69	Mike Zimmerman	.05
70	Phil Dauphin	.20
71	Chris Ebright	.05
72	Mike Grace	.05
73	Ryan Hawbitzel	.05
74	Jessie Hollins	.05
75	Tim Parker	.05
76	Dave Swartzbaugh	.05
77	Steve Trachsel	.50
78	Billy White	.05
79	Bobby Ayala	.05
80	Tim Costa	.10
81	Ty Griffin	.05
82	Cesar Hernandez	.05
83	Trevor Hoffman	.05
84	Brian Lane	.05
85	Scott Pose	.05
86	Johnny Ray	.05
87	John Roper	.15
88	Glenn Sutko	.05
89	Kevin Tatar	.05
90	John Byington	.05
91	Tony Diggs	.05
92	Bo Dodson	.05
93	Craig Faulkner	.05
94	Jim Hunter	.05
95	Oreste Marrero	.05
96	Troy O'Leary	.25
97	Brian Bark	.05
98	Dennis Burlingame	.05
99	Ramon Carabello	.05
100	Mike Kelly	.40
101	Javier Lopez	2.00
102	Don Strange	.05
103	Tony Tarasco	.50
104	Manny Alexander	.05
105	Damon Buford	.05
106	Cesar Devares	.05
107	Rodney Lofton	.05
108	Brent Miller	.05
109	David Miller	.05
110	Daryl Moore	.05
111	John O'Donoghue	.15
112	Erik Schulstrom	.05
113	Mark Smith	.25
114	Mel Wearing	.05
115	Jeff Williams	.05
116	Kip Yaughn	.05
117	Doug Bochller	.05
118	Travis Buckley	.05
119	Reid Cornelius	.05
120	Chris Johnson	.05
121	Tim Laker	.05
122	Chris Martin	.05
123	Mike Mathile	.05
124	Darwin Pennye	.05
125	Doug Platt	.05
126	Kurt Abbott	.25
127	Marcos Amas	.20
128	James Buccheri	.05
129	Kevin Dettola	.05
130	Scott Erwin	.05
131	Johnny Guzman	.10
132	David Jacas	.05
133	Francisco Matos	.05
134	Mike Mohler	.05
135	Craig Paquette	.10
136	Todd Revenig	.05
137	Todd Smith	.05
138	Ricky Strebeck	.05
139	Sam August	.05
140	Tony Eusebio	.05
141	Brian Griffiths	.05
142	Todd Jones	.05
143	Orlando Miller	.05
144	Howard Prager	.05
145	Matt Rambo	.05
146	Lee Sammons	.05
147	Richie Simon	.05
148	Frank Bolick	.05
149	Jim Campanis	.05
150	Jim Converse	.05
151	Bobby Holley	.05
152	Troy Kent	.05
153	Brent Knackert	.05
154	Anthony Manahan	.05
155	Tow Maynard	.05
156	Mike McDonald	.05
157	Marc Newfield	.40
158	Greg Pirki	.20
159	Jesus Tavarez	.10
160	Kerry Woodson	.05
161	Graeme Lloyd	.10
162	Paul Menhart	.05
163	Marcus Moore	.05
164	Greg O'Halloran	.10
165	Mark Ohlms	.05
166	Robert Perez	.10
167	Aaron Small	.05
168	Nigel Wilson	.50
169	Julian Yan	.05
170	Jeff Braley	.05
171	Brian Cornelius	.05
172	Ivan Cruz	.05
173	Lou Frazier	.05
174	Frank Gonzales	.05
175	Tyrone Kingwood	.05
176	Leo Torres	.05
177	Brien Warren	.05
178	Brian Ahern	.05
179	Tony Bridges	.05
180	Paco Burgos	.05
181	Adam Casillas	.05
182	Archie Corbin	.05
183	Phil Hiatt	.25
184	Marcus Lawton	.05
185	Domingo Mota	.05
186	Mark Parnell	.05
187	Ed Pierce	.05
188	Rich Tunison	.05
189	Hugh Walker	.05
190	Skip Wiley	.05
191	Dave Adams	.05
192	Mick Billmeyer	.05
193	Marvin Cobb	.05
194	Jim Edmonds	.10
195	Corey Kapano	.05
196	Jeff Kiplia	.05
197	Joe Kraemer	.05
198	Ray Martinez	.10
199	J.R. Phillips	.75
200	Darryl Scott	.05
201	Paul Swingle	.05
202	Mark Zappelli	.05
203	Greg Blosser	.40
204	Bruce Chick	.05
205	Colin Dixon	.05
206	Gar Finnvold	.05
207	Scott Hatteberg	.10
208	Derek Livernois	.05
209	Jeff McNeely	.10
210	Tony Mosley	.05
211	Bill Norris	.05
212	Ed Riley	.15
213	Ken Ryan	.40
214	Tim Smith	.05
215	Willie Tatum	.05
216	Rex De La Nuez	.05
217	Rich Garces	.05
218	Curtis Leskanic	.05
219	Mica Lewis	.05
220	David McCarty	.50
221	Pat Meares	.15
222	Alan Newman	.05
223	Jay Owens	.05
224	Carlos Pulido	.15
225	Rusty Richards	.05
226	Paul Russo	.20
227	Brad Brink	.05
228	Andy Carter	.05
229	Tyler Green	.10
230	Mike Lieberthal	.05
231	Chris Limbach	.05
232	Ron Lockett	.05
233	Tom Nuneviller	.05
234	Troy Paulsen	.05
235	Todd Pratt	.05
236	Sean Ryan	.05
237	Matt Stevens	.05
238	Sam Taylor	.05
239	Casey Waller	.05
240	Mike Williams	.05
241	Jorge Alvarez	.05
242	Billy Ashley	.40
243	Tim Barker	.05
244	Bill Bene	.05
245	John Deutsch	.05
246	Greg Hansell	.25
247	Matt Howard	.05
248	Ron Maurer	.15
249	Mike Mimbs	.10
250	Chris Morrow	.10
251	Mike Piazza	5.00
252	Dennis Springer	.05
253	Clay Bellinger	.05
254	Dan Carlson	.05
255	Eric Christopherson	.05
256	Adell Davenport	.05
257	Steve Finken	.05
258	Rick Huisman	.05
259	Kevin McGehee	.05
260	Don Rambo	.05
261	Steve Reed	.05
262	Kevin Rogers	.05
263	Salomon Torres	.30
264	Pete Weber	.05
265	Brian Romero	.10
266	Cris Colon	.15
267	Rusty Greer	.25
268	Donald Harris	.10
269	David Hulse	.15
270	Pete Kuld	.05
271	Robb Nen	.20
272	Jose Oliva	.10
273	Steve Rowley	.05
274	Jon Shave	.10
275	Cedric Shaw	.05
276	Dan Smith	.10
277	Matt Whiteside	.10
278	Scott Frederickson	.05
279	Jay Gainer	.05
280	Paul Gonzalez	.05
281	Vince Harris	.05
282	Ray Holbert	.05
283	Dwayne Hosey	.05
284	J.D. Noland	.05
285	Lance Painter	.15
286	Scott Sanders	.10
287	Darrell Sherman	.10
288	Brian Wood	.05
289	Tim Worrell	.10
290	John Jaha	.20
291	Jim Bowie	.05
292	Mark Howie	.05
293	Matt Stairs	.10
294	Larry Carter	.05
295	Pat Mahomes	.20
296	Jeff Mutis	.10
297	Municipal Stadium	.05
298	Knights Castle	.05
299	Engel Stadium	.05
300	Tim McCarver Stadium	.05
301	Beehive Field	.05
302	Tinker Field	.05
303	Checklist Alpha 1	.05
304	Checklist Alpha 2	.05
305	Checklist Alpha 3	.05
306	Checklist Alpha 4	.05
307	Checklist Numeric 1	.05
308	Checklist Numeric 2	.05
309	Checklist Numeric 3	.05
310	Checklist Numeric 4	.05

1992 SkyBox AAA

	MT	NR MT	EX
Complete Set (310):	15.00	11.00	6.00
Common Player:	.05	.04	.02

#	Player	MT
1	Pedro Astacio	.25
2	Bryan Baar	.05
3	Tom Goodwin	.05
4	Jeff Hamilton	.05
5	Pedro Martinez	.20
6	Jarnie McAndrew	.05
7	Mark Mimbs	.05
8	Raul Mondesi	2.00
9	Jose Munoz	.05
10	Henry Rodriguez	.35
11	Eric Young	.15
12	Joe Ausanio	.05
13	Victor Cole	.05
14	Carlos Garcia	.05
15	Bias Minor	.05
16	William Pennyfeather	.05
17	Mark Pelkovsek	.05
18	Jeff Richardson	.05
19	Rosario Rodriguez	.05
20	Tim Wakefield	.10
21	John Wehner	.05
22	Kevin Young	.25
23	Mike Blowers	.05
24	Bret Boone	.25
25	Jim Bowie	.05
26	Dave Brundage	.05
27	Randy Kramer	.05
28	Patrick Lennon	.05

29 Jim Newlin .05
30 Jose Nunez .05
31 Mike Remlinger .05
32 Pat Rice .05
33 Roger Salkeld .20
34 Beau Allred .05
35 Denis Boucher .05
36 Mike Christopher .05
37 Daren Epley .05
38 Tom Kramer .05
39 Jerry DiPoto .05
40 Jeff Mutis .05
41 Jeff Shaw .05
42 Lee Tineley .05
43 Kevin Wickander .05
44 Royal Clayton .05
45 Bobby Dejardin .05
46 Mike Draper .05
47 Mike Humphreys .05
48 Torey Lovulio .05
49 Ed Martel .05
50 Billy Masse .05
51 Hensley Meulens .05
52 Sam Militello .10
53 John Ramos .05
54 David Rosario .05
55 David Silvestri .10
56 J.T. Snow .40
57 Russ Springer .10
58 Jerry Stanford .05
59 Wade Taylor .05
60 Gerald Williams .10
61 Cal Eldred .20
62 Chris George .05
63 Otis Green .05
64 Mike Ignasiak .05
65 John Jaha .20
66 Mark Kiefer .10
67 Matt Mieske .10
68 Angel Miranda .05
69 Dave Nilsson .20
70 Jim Olander .05
71 Jim Tatum .05
72 Jose Valentin .05
73 Don Barbara .05
74 Chris Beasley .05
75 Mike Butcher .05
76 Damion Easley .05
77 Kevin Flora .05
78 Tim Fortugno .05
79 Larry Gonzales .05
80 Todd James .05
81 Tim Salmon 3.00
82 Don Vidmar .05
83 Cliff Young .05
84 Shon Ashley .05
85 Brian Barnes .05
86 Blaine Beatty .05
87 Kent Bottenfield .10
88 Wil Cordero .40
89 Jerry Goff .05
90 Jon Hurst .05
91 Jim Kremers .05
92 Matt Maysey .05
93 Rob Natal .10
94 Matt Stairs .10
95 David Wainhouse .05
96 Alex Arias .05
97 Scott Bryant .10
98 Jim Bullinger .05
99 Pedro Castellano .05
100 Lance Dickson .15
101 John Gardner .05
102 Jeff Hartsock .05
103 Elvin Paulino .05
104 Fernando Ramsey .05
105 Laddie Renfroe .05
106 Kevin Roberson .30
107 John Salles .05
108 Derrick May .10
109 Turk Wendell .10
110 Doug Brocail .10
111 Terry Bross .05
112 Scott Coolbaugh .05
113 Rick Davis .05
114 Jeff Gardner .05
115 Steve Pegues .05
116 Frank Seminara .05
117 Dave Staton .20
118 Will Taylor .05
119 Jim Vatcher .05
120 Guillermo Velasquez .05
121 Dan Walters .05
122 Rene Arocha .40
123 Rod Brewer .05
124 Ozzie Canseco .05
125 Mark Clark .50
126 Joey Fernandez .05
127 Lonnie Maclin .05
128 Mike Milchin .05
129 Stan Royer .10
130 Tracy Woodson .05
131 Bob Buchanan .05
132 Mark Howie .05
133 Tony Menendez .05
134 Gino Minutelli .05
135 Tim Pugh .20
136 Mo Sanford .15
137 Joey Vierra .05
138 Dan Wilson .05
139 Kevin Blankenship .05
140 Todd Burns .05
141 Tom Drees .05
142 Jeff Frye .05
143 Chuck Jackson .05
144 Rob Maurer .05
145 Russ McGinnis .05
146 Dan Peltier .05
147 Wayne Rosenthal .05
148 Bob Sebra .05
149 Sean Berry .20
150 Stu Cole .10
151 Jeff Conine .50
152 Kevin Koslovski .05
153 Kevin Long .05
154 Carlos Maldonado .05
155 Dennis Moeller .05
156 Harvey Pulliam .05
157 Luis Medina .05
158 Steve Shifflett .05
159 Tim Spehr .05
160 Brian Conroy .05
161 Wayne Housie .05
162 Daryl Irvine .05
163 Dave Milstien .05
164 Jeff Plympton .05
165 Paul Quantrill .05
166 Larry Shikles .05
167 Scott Taylor .05
168 Mike Twardoski .05
169 John Valentin .20
170 David Walters .05
171 Eric Wedge .05
172 Bob Zupcic .15
173 Johnny Ard .05
174 Larry Carter .05
175 Steve Decker .10
176 Steve Hosey .15
177 Paul McClellan .05
178 Jim Myers .05
179 Jamie Cooper .05
180 Pat Rapp .05
181 Ted Wood .05
182 Willie Banks .10
183 Bernardo Brito .05
184 J.T. Bruett .15
185 Larry Casian .10
186 Shawn Gilbert .05
187 Greg Johnson .05
188 Terry Jorgensen .05
189 Edgar Naveda .05
190 Derek Parks .20
191 Danny Sheaffer .05
192 Mike Trombley .10
193 George Tsamis .05
194 Rob Waseenaar .05
195 Vinny Castilla .10
196 Pat Gomez .15
197 Ryan Klesko 1.50
198 Keith Mitchell .05
199 Bobby Moore .05
200 David Nied .50
201 Amando Reynoso .10
202 Napoleon Robinson .05
203 Boi Rodriguez .05
204 Randy St. Claire .05
205 Mark Wohlers .10
206 Ricky Gutierrez .10
207 Mike Lehman .05
208 Richie Lewis .05
209 Scott Meadows .10
210 Mike Oquiet .05
211 Arthur Rhodes .15
212 Ken Shamburg .05
213 Todd Stephan .05
214 Anthony Telford .10
215 Jack Voight .05
216 Bob Ayrault .05
217 Toby Borland .05
218 Braulio Castillo .10
219 Darrin Chapin .05
220 Bruce Dostal .05
221 Tim Mauser .10
222 Steve Scarsone .10
223 Rick Schu .05
224 Butch Davis .05
225 Ray Giannelli .05
226 Randy Knorr .10
227 Al Leiter .05
228 Doug Linton .05
229 Domingo Martinez .05
230 Tom Quinlan .05
231 Jerry Schunk .05
232 Ed Sprague .20
233 David Weathers .20
234 Eddie Zosky .05
235 John Briscoe .05
236 Kevin Campbell .05
237 Jeff Carter .05
238 Steve Chitren .05
239 Reggie Harris .05
240 Dann Howitt .05
241 Troy Neel .30
242 Gavin Osteen .05
243 Tim Peek .05
244 Todd Van Poppel .25
245 Ron Witmeyer .05
246 David Zancanaro .05
247 Kevin Baez .05
248 Jeromy Burnitz .40
249 Chris Donnels .10
250 D.J. Dozier .05
251 Terrel Hansen .05
252 Eric Hillman .05
253 Pat Howell .05
254 Lee May .05
255 Pete Schourek .05
256 David Telgheder .10
257 Julio Valera .10
258 Rico Brogna .10
259 Steve Carter .05
260 Steve Cummings .15
261 Greg Gohr .10
262 David Haas .05
263 Shawn Hare .05
264 Riccardo Ingram .05
265 John Kiety .05
266 Kurt Knudsen .05
267 Victor Rosario .10
268 Rich Rowland .15
269 John DeSilva .10
270 Gary Cooper .05
271 Chris Gardner .05
272 Jeff Juden .20
273 Rob Mallicoat .05
274 Andy Mota .10
275 Shane Reynolds .05
276 Mike Simms .05
277 Scooter Tucker .10
278 Brian Williams .05
279 Rod Bolton .10
280 Ron Coomer .05
281 Chris Cron .05
282 Ramon Garcia .05
283 Chris Howard .05
284 Roberto Hernandez .20
285 Derek Lee .05
286 Ever Magallanes .05
287 Norberto Martin .25
288 Greg Perechke .05
289 Ron Stephens .05
290 Derek Bell .25
291 Rich Amaral .10
292 Derek Bell .25
293 Jim Olander .05
294 Gil Heredia .05
295 Rick Reed .05
296 Amando Reynoso .05
297 Charlotte, N.C. .05
298 Ottawa, Ontario .05
299 Pilot Field .05
300 Harold Cooper Stadium .05
301 Bush Stadium .05
302 Silver Stadium .05
303 Checklist Alpha 1 .05
304 Checklist Alpha 2 .05
305 Checklist Alpha 3 .05
306 Checklist Alpha 4 .05
307 Checklist Numeric 1 .05
308 Checklist Numeric 2 .05
309 Checklist Numeric 3 .05
310 Checklist Numeric 4 .05

1992 Upper Deck Minor League Promos

This two-card promo set was distributed at FanFest, the National Sports Collectors Convention and a number of minor league ballgames. Similar in format to Upper Deck's regular minor league issue, the promos feature a star-shaped hologram on back.

	MT	NR MT	EX
Complete Set:	20.00	15.00	8.00

1 Brien Taylor 10.00
350 Frank Rodriguez 10.00

1992 Upper Deck Minor League

	MT	NR MT	EX
Complete Set (330):	75.00	56.00	30.00
Common Player:	.10	.08	.04

1 Draft Pick Checklist .20
2 B.J. Wallace 1.00
3 Jeffrey Hammonds 4.00
4 Chad Mottola 3.00
5 Derek Jeter 3.50
6 Michael Tucker 5.00
7 Derek Wallace .20
8 Chad McConnell .40
9 Rick Greene .50
10 Shannon Stewart .40
11 Benji Grigsby .20
12 Jamie Arnold .30
13 Rick Helling 1.50
14 Jason Kendall .60
15 Eddie Pearson .25
16 Todd Steverson .60
17 John Burke .75
18 Brandon Cromer .25
19 Johnny Damon 1.25
20 Jason Giambi .60
21 John Lynch .20
22 Jared Baker .20
23 Roger Bailey .30
24 Angels Checklist .15
25 Astros Checklist .15
26 Athletics Checklist .10
27 Blue Jays Checklist .10
28 Braves Checklist .15
29 Brewers Checklist .10
30 Cardinals Checklist .10
31 Cubs Checklist .10
32 Dodgers Checklist .15
33 Expos Checklist .25
34 Giants Checklist .10
35 Indians Checklist .30
36 Mariners Checklist .10
37 Mets Checklist .10
38 Orioles Checklist .10
39 Padres Checklist .10
40 Phillies Checklist .10
41 Pirates Checklist .10
42 Rangers Checklist .10
43 Red Sox Checklist .15
44 Reds Checklist .10
45 Royals Checklist .15
46 Tigers Checklist .12
47 Twins Checklist .15
48 White Sox Checklist .10
49 Yankees Checklist .25
50 Diamond Skills Checklist .40
51 Damon Buford .10
52 Mike Nell .10
53 Carlos Delgado 3.00
54 Frank Rodriguez .25
55 Manny Ramirez 4.00
56 Carl Everett .25
57 Brien Taylor .75
58 Kurt Miller .10
59 Alex Ochoa .25
60 Alex Gonzalez 2.00
61 Darrell Sherman .10
62 Dmitri Young .40
63 Cliff Floyd 4.00
64 Ray McDavid .25
65 Rondell White 2.00
66 Chipper Jones 1.25
67 Allen Watson 1.00
68 Tyler Green .10
69 Steve Gibralter .10
70 Calvin Reese .10
71 Scott Burrell .75
72 Julian Vasquez .10
73 Juan Delarosa .10
74 Lance Dickson .10
75 Todd Van Poppel .40
76 Joey Hamilton .25
77 Mark Mimbs .10
78 Austin Manahan .10
79 Mike Milchin .10
80 David Bell .15
81 Terrell Lowery .25
82 Tony Tarasco .90
83 Shon Walker .25
84 Robb Nen .10
85 Turk Wendell .15
86 John Byington .10
87 Derek Reid .10
88 Lee Heath .10
89 Matt Anderson .10
90 Joe Perona .10
91 Tito Navarro .10
92 Scott Erwin .10
93 Jim Pittsley .20
94 Chris Seelbach .12
95 Skeets Thomas .10
96 Kevin Flora .10
97 Scott Pose .20
98 Jason Hardtke .15
99 Joe Ciccarella .10
100 Les Norman .10
101 Joe Calder .10
102 Willie Otanez .10
103 Ray Holbert .10
104 Dan Serafini .40
105 Trevor Hoffman .15
106 Todd Ritchie .20
107 Lance Jennings .10
108 Jon Farrell .20
109 Rick Gorecki .30
110 Kevin Stocker 1.50
111 Joe Caruso .10
112 Tom Nuneviller .10
113 Matt Mieske .40
114 Luis Ortiz .25
115 Marty Cordova .40
116 Rikkert Faneyte .20
117 Rodney Bolton .20
118 Steve Trachsel 1.00
119 Sean Lowe .25
120 Sean Ryan .10
121 Tim Vanegmond .10
122 Craig Paquette .20
123 Andre Keene .15
124 Kevin Roberson 1.00
125 Mark Anthony .10
126 Joe DeBerry .12
127 Tracy Sanders .10
128 Eric Christopherson .10
129 Steve Dreyer .10
130 Jeromy Burnitz .75
131 Mike Lansing .25
132 Russ Davis .50
133 Pedro Castellano .20
134 Troy Percival .20
135 Tyrone Hill .30
136 Rene Arocha .50
137 John DeSilva .10
138 Donnie Wall .10
139 Justin Mashore .15
140 Miguel Flores .10
141 John Finn .10
142 Paul Shuey .25
143 Gabby Martinez .10

144 Ryan Luzinski .25
145 Brent Gates 2.50
146 Manny Ramirez 6.00
147 Mark Hutton .40
148 Derek Lee .10
149 Marc Pisciotta .20
150 Greg Hansell .20
151 Tyler Houston .10
152 Chris Pritchett .10
153 Allen Watson 1.00
154 Steve Karsay 2.00
155 Carl Everett .75
156 Mike Robertson .10
157 Fausto Cruz .10
158 Kiki Hernandez .30
159 Bill Bliss .10
160 Todd Hollandsworth 2.00
161 Justin Thompson .60
162 Ozzie Timmons .75
163 Raul Mondesi 5.00
164 Shawn Estes .15
165 Chipper Jones 2.00
166 Kurt Miller .15
167 Tyler Green .30
168 Jimmy Haynes .30
169 David Doorneweerd .10
170 Bubba Smith .25
171 Scott Lydy .50
172 Aaron Holbert .15
173 Doug Glanville .15
174 Benji Gil 1.75
175 Eddie Williams .25
176 Phil Hiatt 1.00
177 Chris Durkin .15
178 Brian Barber .30
179 John Cummings .15
180 Frank Campos .10
181 Tim Worrell .10
182 Tony Clark .15
183 T.R. Lewis .10
184 Mike Lieberthal .10
185 Keith Mitchell .15
186 Rick Huisman .15
187 Quilvio Veras .25
188 Brian Hancock .10
189 Tarrik Brock .10
190 Herbert Perry .15
191 Dave Staton .40
192 Derek Lowe .15
193 Joel Wolfe .12
194 Lyle Mouton .30
195 Greg Gohr .10
196 Duane Singleton .10
197 Jamie McAndrew .10
198 Brad Pennington .10
199 Pork Chop Pough .10
200 Boo Moore .10
201 Henry Blanco .10
202 Gabe White .50
203 Manny Cora .10
204 Keith Gordon .10
205 John Jackson .10
206 Mike Hostetler .10
207 Jeff McCurry .10
208 Steve Olsen .10
209 Roberto Mejia .50
210 Ramon Caraballo .10
211 Matt Whisenant .10
212 Mike Bovee .10
213 Riccardo Ingram .10
214 Mike Rossiter .20
215 Andres Duncan .10
216 Steve Dunn .15
217 Mike Grace .10
218 Tim Howard .10
219 Todd Jones .15
220 Tyrone Kingwood .10
221 Damon Buford .10
222 Bobby Munoz .25
223 Jim Campanis .10
224 Johnny Ruffin .15
225 Shawn Green .40
226 Calvin Reese .40
227 Kevin McGehee .10
228 J.R. Phillips 2.00
229 Rafael Quirico .10
230 Mike Zimmerman .10
231 Ron Lockett .10
232 Bobby Reed .10
233 John Roper .25
234 John Mabry .10
235 Chris Martin .10
236 Ricky Otero .15
237 Orlando Miller .50
238 Scott Hatteberg .40
239 Toby Borland .25
240 Alan Newman .10
241 Ivan Cruz .25
242 Paul Byrd .20
243 Daryl Henderson .10
244 Adam Hyzdu .60
245 Rich Becker .50
246 Scott Ruffcorn 1.50
247 Tommy Adams .25
248 Jose Martinez .25
249 Darrell Sherman .10
250 Tom Nevers .10
251 Brandon Wilson .25
252 Mike Hampton .25
253 Mo Sanford .25
254 Alex Ochoa .75
255 David McCarty .75
256 Ray McDavid 1.00
257 Roger Salkeld .30
258 Jeff McNeely .20
259 Jim Converse .20
260 Greg Blosser .40
261 Salomon Torres 1.00
262 Tavo Alvarez .25
263 Marc Newfield 2.00
264 Carlos Delgado 6.00
265 Brien Taylor 1.00
266 Frank Rodriguez .75
267 Cliff Floyd 8.00
268 Troy O'Leary .40
269 Butch Huskey .75
270 Michael Carter .25
271 Eduardo Perez 1.00
272 Gary Mota .10
273 Mike Neill .20
274 Dmitri Young 1.00
275 Mike Kelly 1.00
276 Rondell White 5.00
277 Midre Cummings .40
278 Kerwin Moore .40
279 Derrick White .10
280 Howard Battle .50
281 Mark Smith .50
282 Ben Shelton .10
283 Jose Oliva .10
284 Steve Gibralter .10
285 Billy Hall .10
286 Nigel Wilson 1.50
287 Brook Fordyce .10
288 Mike Durrant .10
289 Gary Caraballo .10
290 Shane Andrews .40
291 Aaron Sele 6.00
292 Garret Anderson .20
293 Oscar Munoz .10
294 Bobby Jones 1.00
295 Joe Rossell .10
296 Chad Ogea 1.00
297 Ugueth Urbina 1.00
298 Ryan Hawblitzel .10
299 Dennis Burlingame .10
300 Damon Mashore .20
301 Jeff Jackson .10
302 Glenn Murray .75
303 Darren Burton .15
304 Scott Cepicky .10
305 Phil Dauphin .20
306 Kevin Tatar .15
307 Domingo Jean .40
308 Darren Oliver .10
309 Joe Vitiello .40
310 John Johnstone .10
311 Bo Dodson .20
312 Jon Shave .10
313 Roberto Petagine 1.00
314 Clifton Garrett .10
315 Rob Butler .25
316 Jermaine Swinton .10
317 Alex Gonzalez 3.00
318 Jeff Williams .10
319 James Baldwin 1.50
320 Scott Stahoviak .50
321 John Cotton .10
322 Jim Wawruck .25
324 Brian Hunter 1.00
325 Joe Randa .50
326 Robert Eenhoorn .10
327 Rod Lofton .10
328 Buck McNabb .20
329 Jorge Fabregas .20
330 Brian Koelling .20

1992 Upper Deck Player of the Year

This 26-card insert set features players who are considered as the top minor league player for each major league team. Cards, which are numbered with a PY prefix, have full-bleed photos and gold foil stamping on the fronts.

	MT	NR MT	EX
Complete Set (26):	160.00		
Common Player:	5.00		

1 Garret Anderson 5.00
2 Gary Mota 5.00
3 Scott Lydy 5.00
4 Carlos Delgado 17.00
5 Chipper Jones 14.00
6 Troy O'Leary 5.00
7 Dmitri Young 6.00
8 Ozzie Timmons 6.00
9 Todd Hollandworth 10.00
10 Cliff Floyd 25.00
11 Joe Rossell 5.00
12 Chad Ogea 6.00
13 Tommy Adams 5.00
14 Bobby Jones 10.00
15 Mark Smith 7.00
16 Ray McDavid 7.00
17 Mike Lieberthal 6.00
18 Midre Cummings 6.00
19 Kurt Miller 5.00
20 Aaron Sele 16.00
21 Steve Gibralter 5.00
22 Phil Hiatt 6.00
23 Ivan Cruz 5.00
24 Marty Cordova 6.00
25 Brandon Taylor 6.00
26 Brien Taylor 12.00

1992 Upper Deck Top Prospect Holograms

These nine holograms were random inserts in Upper Deck's 1992 minor league packs. Cards, numbered with a TP prefix, feature nine of the top minor league prospects.

	MT	NR MT	EX
Complete Set (9):	60.00		
Common Player:	6.00		

(1) Midre Cummings 6.00
(2) Cliff Floyd 18.00
(3) Chipper Jones 9.00
(4) Mike Kelly 8.00
(5) David McCarty 7.00
(6) Frank Rodriguez 8.00
(7) Rondell White 12.00
(8) Dmitri Young 7.00
(9) Brien Taylor 6.00

1992 Classic Best Albany Polecats

	MT	NR MT	EX
Complete Set:	25.00		

1 Shane Andrews
2 Jim Ferguson
3 Darrin Paxton
4 Claudio Ozario
5 Matt Allen
6 Rodney Pedraza
7 Jolbert Cabrera
8 Chris Hmielewski
9 Mark LaRosa
10 Robbie Carabba
11 Javier Pages
12 Mark Respondek
13 Jim Wynne
14 Rick Clelland
15 Rick DeHart
16 Vince Fultz
17 Yamil Benitez
18 Matt Conley
19 Alberto Reyes
20 Keith Morrison
21 Urbina Ugueth
22 Cliff Floyd
23 Stan Robertson
24 Gary Hymel
25 Mitch Simons
26 Antonio Grissom
27 Lorenzo Bundy
28 Jeff Kinlaw
29 Gary Lance

1992 Fleer/ProCards Albany Polecats

	MT	NR MT	EX
Complete Set:	27.00		

2297 Rick Clelland
2298 Matt Conley
2299 Rick DeHart
2300 Mark LaRose
2301 Keith Morrison
2302 Darrin Paxton
2303 Rodney Pedraza
2304 Mark Respondek
2305 Alberto Reyes
2306 Ugueth Urbina
2307 Jim Wynne
2308 Matt Allan
2309 Gary Hymel
2310 Javier Pages
2311 Shane Andrews
2312 Jolbert Cabrera
2313 Robb Carabba
2314 Cliff Floyd
2315 Mitch Simons
2316 Antonio Grissom
2317 Chris Hmielewski
2318 Doug O'Neill
2319 Claudio Ozario
2320 Stan Robertson
2321 Lorenzo Bundy
2322 Gary Lance
2323 Checklist

1992 Fleer/ProCards Albany Yankees

	MT	NR MT	EX
Complete Set:	7.00		

2324 Richard Batchelor
2325 Mark Carper
2326 Ken Greer
2327 Sterling Hitchcock
2328 Darren Hodges
2329 Jeff Hoffman
2330 Mark Hutton
2331 Bobby Munoz
2332 Gerald Nielson
2333 Kirt Ojala
2334 Tom Popplewall
2335 Kiki Hernandez
2336 Jeff Livesay
2337 Juan Blackwell
2338 Russell Davis
2339 Sherman Obando
2340 Carlos Rodriguez
2341 Don Sparks
2342 Hector Vargas
2343 Rich Barnwell
2344 Bubba Carpenter
2345 Jay Knoblauh
2346 Rick Strickland
2347 John Viera
2348 Dan Radison
2349 Dave Jorn
2350 Rob Thomson
2351 Checklist

1992 Fleer/ProCards Albuquerque Dukes

	MT	NR MT	EX
Complete Set:	18.00		

710 Pedro Astacio
711 Albert Bustillos
712 Omar Deal
713 Grady Hall
714 Greg Hansell
715 Brian Holton
716 Pedro martinez
717 Mark Mimbs
718 Jim Neidlinger
719 Chris Nichting
720 Dan Opperman
721 Zak Shinall
722 Mike Wilkins
723 Mike Piazza
724 Don Wakamatsu
725 Rafael Bournigal
726 Jeff Hamilton
727 Luis Martinez
728 Jose Munoz
729 Eddie Pye
730 Brian Traxler
731 Billy Ashley
732 Tony Barron
733 Jerry Brooks
734 Tom Goodwin
735 Henry Rodriguez
736 Eric Young
737 Bill Russell
738 Mickey Hatcher
739 Von Joshua
740 Claude Osteen
741 Checklist

1992 Classic Best Appleton Foxes

	MT	NR MT	EX
Complete Set:	6.00		

1 Joe Randa
2 Andres Berumen
3 Andre Newhouse
4 Chad Strickland
5 Roger Landress
6 Danny Miceli
7 Anthony Lee Jr.
8 Shane Halter
9 Brian Bevil
10 Mark Johnson
11 Francisco Baez
12 Paco Burgos
13 Jeff Clarke
14 Les Norman
15 Robert Toth
16 Yobanne DeLeon
17 Shayne Rea
18 Michael Bovee
19 Raul Gonzalez
20 Dan Servello
21 Jeff Smith
22 Kevin Kobetitsch
23 Steve Hinton
24 Juan Indriago
25 Ed Gerald
26 Jason Pruitt
27 Tom Poquette
28 Mike Mason
29 Jeff Stevenson
30 Checklist

1992 Fleer/ProCards Appleton Foxes

	MT	NR MT	EX
Complete Set:	6.00		

974 Fracisco Baez
975 Andres Berumen
976 Brian Bevil
977 Mike Bovee
978 Chris Connolly
979 Brian Harrison
980 Roger Landress
981 Anthony Lee
982 Danny Micelli
983 Jason Pruitt

984 Shayne Rea
985 Robert Toth
986 Carlos Burgos
987 Yobanne de Leon
988 Chad Strickland
989 Troy Babbitt
990 Jeff Clarke
991 Shane Halter
992 Steve Hinton
993 Juan Indriago
994 Mark Johnson
995 Joe Randa
996 Ed Gerald
997 Raul Gonzalez
998 Andre Newhouse
999 Les Norman
1000 Dan Servello
1001 Tom Poquette
1002 Mike Mason
1003 Checklist
1091 Jeff Smith
3105 Sean Delaney

1992 Fleer/ProCards Arkansas Travelers

	MT	NR MT	EX
Complete Set:	6.00		

1120 Paul Anderson
1121 Dave Cassidy
1122 Fidel Compres
1123 Steve Dixon
1124 John Ericks
1125 Steffan Majer
1126 Kevin Meier
1127 Gabriel Ozuna
1128 Lee Plemel
1129 David Richards
1130 Rick Shackle
1131 Dennis Wiseman
1132 Jose Fernandez
1133 Don Prybylinski
1134 Brad Beanblossom
1135 Tripp Cromer
1136 Steve Fanning
1137 David Howell
1138 Jesus Mendez
1139 Mike Ross
1140 John Sellick
1141 Cliff Brannon
1142 Julian Martinez
1143 Skeets Thomas
1144 Joe Pettini
1145 Marty Mason
1146 Checklist

1992 Classic Best Asheville Tourists

	MT	NR MT	EX
Complete Set:	6.00		

1 Gary Mota
2 Jose Flores
3 Henry Centeno
4 Tom Anderson
5 Ed Beuerlein
6 Todd Hobson
7 Kevin Webb
8 Raul Chavez
9 Eric martinez
10 Duane Brown
11 Roy Nieto
12 Jamie Evans
13 Ron Cancini
14 Chris White
15 Eddie Ramos
16 Danny Young
17 Miguel Cabrera
18 Craig Bjornson
19 Bob Abreu
20 Alvin Morman
21 Chris Durkin
22 Mario Linares
23 Chuck Smith
24 Hector Carrasco
25 Mark Loughlin
26 Tim Tolman
27 Bob Robertson
28 Jim Hickey
29 Manny Acta
30 Ron Hanisch

1992 Classic Best Auburn Astros

	MT	NR MT	EX
Complete Set:	6.00		

1 Chris Holt
2 Greg Elliot
3 Chris Thomas
4 Jeffrey Tenbarge
5 Bill Minnich
6 Donovan Mitchell
7 Jeff Rhein
8 Mike Aubel
9 Brian Thompson
10 Bryant Winslow
11 Jose Santana
12 Ernest Martinez
13 Kirk Larson
14 Todd Winston
15 Brett Wyngarden
16 Alan Probst
17 Jamie Walker
18 Doug Mlicki
19 Derrick Bottoms
20 Dwayne Dawson
21 Destry Westbrook
22 Craig Bjornson
23 Wayne Cupit
24 Zak Krislock
25 Juan Holleday
26 Jorge Correa
27 Steve Dillard
28 Clark Crist
29 Bill Kelso

1992 Fleer/ProCards Auburn Astros

	MT	NR MT	EX
Complete Set:	6.00		

1344 Craig Bjornson
1345 Derrick Bottoms
1346 Jorge Correa
1347 Wayne Cupit
1348 Dwayne Dawson
1349 Juan Holleday
1350 Chris Holt
1351 Zak Krislock
1352 Doug Milcki
1353 Jeffrey Tenbarge
1354 Jamie Walker
1355 Destry Westbrook
1356 Alan Probst
1357 Todd Winston
1358 Brett Wyngarden
1360 Kirk Larson
1361 Ernest Martinez
1362 Don Mitchell
1363 Jose Santana
1364 Bryant Winslow
1365 Mike Aubel
1366 Bill Minnich
1367 Jeff Rhein
1368 Chris Thomas
1369 Brian Thompson
1370 Steve Dillard
1371 Bill Kelso
1372 Clark Crist
1373 Team Picture
1374 Checklist

1992 Classic Best Augusta Pirates

	MT	NR MT	EX
Complete Set:	6.00		

1 Jon Farrell
2 Shane Sparks
3 Jim Krevokuch
4 Steve Loaiza
5 Mike Teich
6 Todd Schroeder
7 Jason Christiansen
8 Deon Danner
9 Kevin Rychel
10 Sean Evans
11 Ramon Zapata
12 Mathew Ruebel
13 Antonio Mitchell
14 Mariano De los Santos
15 John Schulte
16 Marty Neff
17 Jeff McCurry
18 Ken Bonifay
19 Jose Sosa
20 Mike Maguire
21 Brian Beck
22 Jeff Leatherman
23 Joe Calder
24 Jeff Conger
25 Scott Little
26 Julio Garcia
27 Rod Leich

1992 Fleer/ProCards Augusta Pirates

	MT	NR MT	EX
Complete Set:	6.00		

229 Glenn Coombs
230 Deon Danner
231 Mariano De Los Santos
232 Dave Doorneweerd
233 Steve Loaiza
234 Jim Martin
235 Jeff McCurry
236 Marc Pisciotta
237 Matt Ruebel
238 Jose Soa
239 Shane Sparks
240 Mike Teich
241 Angelo Encaracion
242 Kevin Maguire
243 Michael Brown
244 Joe Calder
245 Don Garvey
246 Jim Krevokuch
247 Tony Womack
248 Roman Zapata
249 Brian Beck
250 Jeff Conger
251 Jon Farrell
252 Antonio Mitchell
253 Marty Neff
254 John Schulte
255 Scott Little
256 Dave Rajsich
257 Checklist

1992 Cal League Bakersfield Dodgers

	MT	NR MT	EX
Complete Set:	10.00		

1 Todd Hollandsworth
2 Cam Aronetz
3 Henry Blanco
4 Mike Boyzuick
5 Carlos Castillo
6 Juan Castro
7 Nelson Castro
8 Chris Demetral
9 Angel Dotel
10 Ross Farnsworth
11 Scott Freeman
12 Rick Gorecki
13 Jack Johnson
14 Steve Kliafas
15 Al Maldonado
16 Brock McMurray
17 Don Meyers
18 Hector Ortiz
19 Jose Parra
20 Murph Protor
21 Mike Sharp
22 Ira Smith
23 Joe Smith
24 Robert Sweeney
25 Gordon Tipton
26 Eric Vorbeck
27 Mike Walkden
28 Lonnie Webb
29 Todd Williams
30 Tom Beyers
31 Dino Ebel, Goose Gregson
32 Matt Wilson
33 Checklist

1992 Classic Best Baseball City Royals

	MT	NR MT	EX
Complete Set:	6.00		

1 Joe Vitiello
2 Kevin Shaw
3 Pat Dando
4 Dean Tatarian
5 Lance Jennings
6 Damon Pollard
7 Tom Smith
8 Brady Stewart
9 John Gross
10 Jim Chrisman
11 Huascar de Leon
12 Cesar Morillo
13 Andy Stewart
14 Kerwin Moore
15 Butch Cole
16 Anthony Gordon
17 Dario perez
18 Geovany Miranda
19 Gary Caraballo
20 Vladimir Perez
21 Mike Fyhrie
22 Scott Stevens
23 Darren Burton
24 Ron Johnson
25 Rafael Santana
26 Pete Filson
27 Frank Kyte

1992 Fleer/ProCards Baseball City Royals

	MT	NR MT	EX
Complete Set:	6.00		

3837 Jim Chrisman
3838 Mike Fyhrie
3839 John Gross
3840 Doug Harris
3841 Kevin Kobetitsch
3842 Roger Landress
3843 Tony Long
3844 Dario Perez
3845 Damon Pollard
3846 Alex Sanchez
3847 Kevin Shaw
3848 Yobanne De Leon
3849 Andy Stewart
3850 Tony Bridges
3851 Pat Dando
3852 Joe Randa
3853 Brady Stewart
3854 Dean Tatarian
3855 Joe Vitiello
3856 Darren Burton
3857 Butch Cole
3858 Tom Smith
3859 Hugh Walker
3860 Ron Johnson
3861 Rafael Santana
3862 Pete Filson
3863 Checklist

1992 Classic Best Batavia Clippers

	MT	NR MT	EX
Complete Set:	6.00		

1 Jamie Sepeda
2 Michael Murphy
3 Chad Anderson
4 Gary Bennett
5 Lamar Cherry
6 J.J. Cruz
7 Patrick Bojcun
8 Reynaldo De Los Santos
9 Wayne Johnson
10 Alan Burke
11 Shawn Wills
12 Eric Smith
13 Gary Herrmann
14 Glenn Nevill
15 Ron Kratz
16 Laurence Heisler
17 Steve Solomon
18 Mike Gomez
19 Joseph McIntyre
20 Ryan McWilliams
21 Thane Page
22 Mark Tranberg
23 Jon Zuber
24 Dean Hopp
25 Blake Doolan
26 Tom Vilet
27 Tom Irwin
28 Andrew Sallee
29 Ramon Aviles, Floyd Rayford, John Martin

1992 Fleer/ProCards Batavia Clippers

	MT	NR MT	EX
Complete Set:	6.00		

3254 Chad Anderson
3255 Pat Bojcun
3256 Blake Doolan
3257 Laurence Heisler
3258 Gary Herrmann
3259 Tom Irwin
3260 Joe McIntyre
3261 Ryan McWilliams
3262 Glenn Nevill
3263 Thane Page
3264 Jamie Sepeda
3265 Eric Smith
3266 Mark Tranberg
3267 Gary Bennett
3268 J.J. Cruz
3269 Dean Hopp
3270 Alan Burke
3271 Lamar Cherry
3272 Mike Gomez
3273 Ron Kratz
3274 Andy Salles
3275 Jon Zubar
3276 Reynaldo De Los Santos
3277 Wayne Johnson
3278 Mike Murphy
3279 Steven Solomon
3280 Tom Vilet
3281 Shawn Wils
3282 Ramon Aviles
3283 John Martin
3284 Floyd Rayford
3285 Checklist

1992 Classic Best Bellingham Mariners

	MT	NR MT	EX
Complete Set:	6.00		

1 Fred McNair
2 Greg Shockey
3 Derrick Warren
4 Jerry Aschoff
5 Rich Graham
6 Shawn Estes
7 Jamon Deal
8 Ron Cody
9 Tim Harikkala
10 Kelly Hartman
11 Derek Lane
12 Joe Mountain
13 Kevin Stock
14 Ryan Smith
15 Oscar Morales
16 Jackie Nickell
17 Bob Worley
18 James Bonnici
19 Mark Calvi
20 Chris Widger
21 Mike Bond

22 James Clifford
23 Barney Erhard
24 David Lawson
25 Craig Griffey
26 Renaldo Bullock
27 Brian Wallace
28 Mike Hickey
29 Bobby Llanos

1992 Fleer/ProCards Bellingham Mariners

	MT	NR MT	EX
Complete Set:	6.50		

1432 Jerry Aschoff
1433 William Cody
1434 Jamon Deal
1435 Shawn Estes
1436 Richard Graham
1437 Tim Harikkala
1438 Kelly Hartman
1439 Derek Lowe
1440 Joe Mountain
1441 Jackie Nickell
1442 Oscar Rivera
1443 Ryan Smith
1444 Kevin Stock
1445 Bob Worley
1446 James Bonnici
1447 Mark Calui
1448 Chris Widger
1449 Mike Bond
1450 James Clifford
1451 Barney Erhard
1452 Michael Hickey
1453 Bobby Llanos
1454 Brian Wallace
1455 Renaldo Bullock
1456 Craig Griffey
1457 David Lawson
1458 Fred McNair
1459 Greg Shockey
1460 Derrick Warren
1461 Dave Myers
1462 Lem Pilkinton
1463 Bryan Price
1464 Checklist

1992 Classic Best Beloit Brewers

	MT	NR MT	EX
Complete Set:	9.00		

1 Tyrone Hill
2 Scott Vonderleith
3 Terry Christopher
4 Byron Browne
5 Sam Rutter
6 Marshall Boze
7 Scott Talanoa
8 Brian Souza
9 Don Pruitt
10 Mike Couture
11 Chad O'Laughlin
12 Brian Dennison
13 Francisco Mendoza
14 Trini House
15 Tim Albert
16 Mike Stefanski
17 Graciano Enriquez
18 Derek Wachter
19 Bill Dobrolsky
20 Andy Fairman
21 La Rue Baber
22 Gordon Powell Jr.
23 Pat Fetty
24 Rick Zurn
25 Jeff Circillo
26 Mike Huyler
27 Kerry Knox
28 Wayne Krenchicki
29 Steve Foucault
30 Bryan Jaquette

1992 Fleer/ProCards Beloit Brewers

	MT	NR MT	EX
Complete Set:	10.00		

395 Marshall Boze
396 Byron Browne
397 Terry Christopher
398 John Criminger
399 Brian Dennison
400 Pat Fetty
401 Tyrone Hill
402 Kerry Knox
403 Don Pruitt
404 Sam Rutter
405 John Trisler
406 Rick Zurn
407 Bill Dobrolsky
408 Mike Stefanski
409 Jeff Cirillo
410 Andy Fairman
411 Mike Huyler
412 Jason Imperial
413 Francisco Mendoza
414 Gordon Powell
415 Scott Talanoa
416 Tim Albert
417 Larue Baber
418 Mike Couture
419 Graciano Enriquez
420 Trini House
421 Derek Wachter
422 Wayne Krenchicki
423 Steve Foucault
424 Checklist

1992 Classic Best Bend Rockies

	MT	NR MT	EX
Complete Set:	10.00		

1 John Burke
2 Roger Bailey
3 Mark Voisard
4 Ryan Freeburg
5 Carvin Alston
6 Jason Bates
7 Mark Thompson
8 Mike Case
9 Craig Counsell
10 Angel Echevarria
11 Michael Eiffert
12 Chris Henderson
13 Jay Holland
14 James Hovey
15 Jason Hutchins
16 Mike Kotarski
17 Keith Krenke
18 Quinton McCracken
19 Mike Oakland
20 Will Scalzitti
21 Tom Schmidt
22 Tim Scott
23 Mark Strittmatter
24 Gene Glynn
25 Joe Niekro
26 Johnny Zizzo
27 Thomas Probst
28 Scott Schukart

1992 Fleer/ProCards Bend Rockies

	MT	NR MT	EX
Complete Set:	14.00		

1465 Garvin Allston
1466 Roger Bailey
1467 John Burke
1468 Mike Eiffert
1469 Chris Henderson
1470 Jay Holland
1471 Jamie Hovey
1472 Jason Hutchins
1473 Mike Kotarski
1474 Mark Thompson
1475 Mark Voisard
1476 Will Scalzitti
1477 Mark Strittmatter
1478 Jason Bates
1479 Craig Counsell
1480 Quinton McCraken
1481 Mike Garland
1482 Tom Schmidt
1483 Tim Scott
1484 Mike Case
1485 Angel Echevarria
1486 Ryan Freeburg
1487 Keith Krenke
1488 Gene Glynn
1489 Johnny Zizzo
1490 Joe Niekro
1491 Checklist

1992 Fleer/ProCards Billings Mustangs

	MT	NR MT	EX
Complete Set:	9.00		

3346 Jason Angel
3347 Fermin Garcia
3348 Jason Kummerfeldt
3349 Rich Langford
3350 Martin Lister
3351 Bo Loftin
3352 Jeff Murphy
3353 Ricky Pickett
3354 Chris Reed
3355 William Sullivan
3356 Dan Tobin
3357 Bill Dreisbach
3358 Jeff Ramey
3359 Toby Rumfield
3360 Tim Belk
3361 Mike Collins
3362 Derick Graham
3363 Dee Jenkins
3364 Brad Keenan
3365 Matt Martin
3366 Eric Owens
3367 Micah Franklin
3368 Jeff Manship
3369 Mike Meggers
3370 Chad Mottola
3371 Jeff Nagy
3372 Wayne Wilkerson
3373 Donnie Scott
3374 Terry Abbott
3375 Checklist

1992 Fleer/ProCards Binghamton Mets

	MT	NR MT	EX
Complete Set:	8.00		

508 Chris Dorn
509 Todd Dourns
510 John Johnstone
511 Bobby Jones
512 Gregg Langbehn
513 Andy Reich
514 Bryan Rogers
515 Julian Vasquez
516 Joe Vitko
517 Pete Walker
518 Tom Wegmann
519 Andy Oziedkowiec
520 Brook Fordyce
521 Tom Allison
522 Chris Butterfield
523 Joe Dellicarri
524 Jamie Hoffner
525 Doug Saunders
526 Alan Zinter
527 Tim Howard
528 Bert Hunter
529 Rob Katzeroff
530 Curtis Pride
531 Mike White
532 Steve Swisher
533 Ron Gideon
534 Randy Niemann
535 Checklist

1992 Fleer/ProCards Birmingham Barons

	MT	NR MT	EX
Complete Set:	6.00		

2574 Frank Campos
2575 Fred Dabney
2576 Earnie Johnson
2577 Bo Kennedy
2578 Brian Keyser
2579 Frank Merigliano
2580 Mike Mongiello
2581 Jeff Schwarz
2582 Keith Shepherd
2583 Larry Thomas
2584 Jose Ventura
2585 Clemente Alvarez
2586 Al Liebert
2587 James Bishop
2588 Wayne busby
2589 Kevin Castleberry
2590 Scott Cepicky
2591 Lindsay Foster
2592 Kevin Garner
2593 Tom Redington
2594 Robert Harris
2595 Scott Jaster
2596 Scott Tedder
2597 Charlie White
2598 Tony Franklin
2599 Pat Roessler
2600 Don Cooper
2601 Checklist

1992 Classic Best Bluefield Orioles

	MT	NR MT	EX
Complete Set:	6.00		

1 Garrett Stephenson
2 Kyle Veske
3 Mike Thomas
4 Dan Fregoso
5 Mike Porter
6 Ishovany Marquez
7 Francisco Saneaux
8 Jose Serra
9 Feliciano Mercedes
10 Scott Metcalf
11 Duane Thomas
12 Roy Hodge
13 Keith Eaddy
14 Christopher Chatterton
15 Scott Emerson
16 Joe Lantrip
17 Matt Reimer
18 Paul Jones
19 Marco Manrique
20 George Freeberger
21 Armando Benitez
22 Carlos Chavez
23 Mike O'Berry
24 Len Johnson
25 Frank Neville

1992 Fleer/ProCards Bluefield Orioles

	MT	NR MT	EX
Complete Set:	6.00		

2352 Armando Benitez
2353 Chris Chatterton
2354 Carlos Chavez
2355 Scott Emerson
2356 Dan Fergoso
2357 Joe Lantrip
2358 Ihosvany Marquez
2359 Mike Porter
2360 Francisco Saneaux
2361 Garrett Stephenson
2362 George Freeberger
2363 Marco Manrique
2364 Eric Chavez
2365 Paul Jones
2366 Feliciano Mercedes
2367 Scott Metcalf
2368 Matt Riemer
2369 Jose Serra
2370 Keith Eaddy
2371 Roy Hodge
2372 Duane Thomas
2373 Mike Thomas
2374 Kyle Yeske
2375 Mike O'Berry
2376 Charlie Puleo
2377 Checklist

1992 Classic Best Boise Hawks

	MT	NR MT	EX
Complete Set:	6.00		

1 Marquis Riley
2 Max Valennia
3 Joe Hardwick
4 Joel Smith
5 Dave Kessler
6 Dave Partrick
7 Gabriel Jose
8 Michael Pineiro
9 Lyall Barwick
10 Jay Simpson
11 Bill Blanchette
12 John Wylie
13 Mickey Kerns
14 Lino Connell
15 Chris Anderson
16 Javier Martinez
17 Joe Urso
18 John Pricher
19 Anthony Chavez
20 Mike Butler
21 Dallas Rinehart
22 Daron Sutton
23 Bill Dunkel
24 Elgin Bobo
25 Paxton Briley
26 Chris Smith
27 Jeff Schmidt
28 Michael Wolff
29 Bill Simas
30 Larry Hingle

1992 Fleer/ProCards Boise Hawks

	MT	NR MT	EX
Complete Set:	6.00		

3616 Bill Blanchette
3617 Paxton Briley
3618 Mike Butler
3619 Anthony Chavez
3620 Larry Hingel
3621 Dave Patrick
3622 Beban Perez
3623 John Pricher
3624 Dallas Rinehart
3625 Jeff Schmidt
3626 Kyle Sebach
3627 Bill Simas
3628 Daron Sutton
3629 John Wylie
3630 Chris Hunt
3631 Dave Kessler
3632 Mike Pineiro
3633 Joel Smith
3634 Chris Anderson
3635 Elgin Bobo
3636 Lino Connell
3637 Mickey Kerns
3638 Javier Martinez
3639 Mark Simmons
3640 Chris Smith
3641 Lyall Barwick
3642 Bill Dunkel
3643 Joe Hardwick
3644 Marquis Riley
3645 Michael Wolff
3646 Tom Kotchman
3647 Howie Gershberg
3648 Checklist

1992 Classic Best Bristol Tigers

		MT	NR MT	EX
Complete Set:		6.00		
1	Mike Berlin			
2	Jeff Brown			
3	Blas Cedeno			
4	Paul Magrini			
5	Brian Maxcy			
6	Toby McFarland			
7	Trever Miller			
8	Riccardo Munoz			
9	John Rosengren			
10	Henry Santos			
11	Clint Sodowsky			
12	John Grimm			
13	Tim Jones			
14	David Rodriguez			
15	Moises Ayala			
16	Wardell Marine			
17	Kenny Marrero			
18	Matt Evans			
19	Roberto Ortega			
20	Yuri Sanchez			
21	Tim Thomas			
22	Jorge Valeandia			
23	Bart Greene			
24	Johnny Lamar			
25	Darren Milne			
26	John Sutey			
27	Mark Wagner			
28	Jim Van Scoyoc			
29	Mike Quinn			

1992 Fleer/ProCards Bristol Tigers

		MT	NR MT	EX
Complete Set:		6.00		
1399	Mike Berlin			
1400	Jeff Brown			
1401	Blas Cedeno			
1402	John Grimm			
1403	Tim Jones			
1404	Paul Magrini			
1405	Brien Maxcy			
1406	Toby McFarland			
1407	Trever Miller			
1408	Ricky Munoz			
1409	Dave Rodriguez			
1410	Rosey Rosengren			
1411	Henry Santos			
1412	Clint Sodowsky			
1413	Moises Ayala			
1414	Kevin Lidle			
1415	Wardel Marine			
1416	Kenny Marrero			
1417	Matt Evans			
1418	Luis Hernandez			
1419	Art Johnson			
1420	Roberto Ortega			
1421	Yuri Sanchez			
1422	Tim Thomas			
1423	Jorge Velandia			
1424	Bart Greene			
1425	Johnny Lamar			
1426	Darren Milne			
1427	Jorge Moreno			
1428	Roberto Rojas			
1429	John Sutey			
1430	Ken Valdez			
1431	Checklist			

1992 Fleer/ProCards Buffalo Bisons

		MT	NR MT	EX
Complete Set:		6.00		
315	Joe Ausanio			
316	Victor Cole			
317	Mike Dalton			
318	Eddie Dixon			
319	Paul Miller			
320	Blas Minor			
321	Mark Petkovsek			
322	Mike Roesler			
323	Jim Tracy			
324	Tim Wakefield			
325	Pete Beeler			
326	Brian Dorsett			
327	Carlos Garcia			
328	Jeff Richardson			
329	Jose Tolentino			
330	John Wehner			
331	Kevin Young			
332	Dave Clark			
333	Al Martin			
334	Will Pennyfeather			
335	Joe Redfield			
336	Greg Tubbs			
337	Eddie Zambrano			
338	Marc Bombard			
339	Doc Edwards			
340	Spin Williams			
341	Checklist			

1992 Classic Best Burlington Astros

		MT	NR MT	EX
Complete Set:		6.00		
1	David Wallace			
2	Fernando Mercedes			
3	Jeff Miller			
4	Jimmy White			
5	Jermaine Swinton			
6	Jim Waring			
7	Joe Sewell			
8	Raphael Lanfranco			
9	Tyrone Scott			
10	Lance Smith			
11	Dennis Reed			
12	Rod Biehl			
13	Steve Powers			
14	Ed Quijada			
15	Brian Holliday			
16	Brian McGlone			
17	Alberto Montero			
18	Craig Curtis			
19	Dennis Colon			
20	Perry Berry			
21	Pat Murphy			
22	Jim Gonzalez			
23	Al Harley			
24	Rich Schulte			
25	Buck McNabb			
26	Steve Curry			
27	Rick Aponte			
28	Rick Peters			
29	Chris Correnti			

1992 Fleer/ProCards Burlington Astros

		MT	NR MT	EX
Complete Set:		6.00		
536	Rod Biehl			
537	Kevin Gallaher			
538	Brian Holliday			
539	Fernando Mercedes			
540	Jeff Miller			
541	Pat Murphy			
542	Steve Powers			
543	Ed Quijada			
544	Dennis Reed			
545	Heath Rose			
546	Tyrone Scott			
547	Joe Sewell			
548	Jim Waring			
549	Jim Gonzales			
550	Raphael Lanfranco			
551	Lance Smith			
552	Perry Berry			
553	Dennis Colon			
554	Craig Curtis			
555	Al Harley			
556	Brian McGlone			
557	Alberto Montero			
558	Buck McNabb			
559	Rich Schulte			
560	Jermaine Swinton			
561	David Wallace			
562	Jimmy White			
563	Steve Curry			
564	Rick Aponte			
565	Checklist			

1992 Classic Best Burlington Indians

		MT	NR MT	EX
Complete Set:		7.00		
1	John Lewandowski			
2	Jeff Whitaker			
3	Damian Jackson			
4	Germain Mayberry			
5	Craig Sides			
6	Brandon Bluhm			
7	Rodney Koller			
8	Mike Burritt			
9	Jose Cabrera			
10	Leroy Thompson			
11	Jon Zubiri			
12	Chris Maffett			
13	Greg Sinner			
14	Greg Rideau			
15	R.W. Augustine			
16	Roberto Garza			
17	Allen Gallagher			
18	Julian Tavares			
19	Damian Leyva			
20	Michael Moyle			
21	Patricio Claudio			
22	Mitch Meluskey			
23	Huascar Genao			
24	Terry Miller			
25	Chad Townsend			
26	Ronnie Coleman			
27	Brian Holter			
28	Emar Diaz			
29	Eric White			
30	Maximo De La Rosa			

1992 Fleer/ProCards Burlington Indians

		MT	NR MT	EX
Complete Set:		7.00		
1644	Rob Augustine			
1645	Brandon Bluhn			
1646	Mike Burritt			
1647	Jose Cabrera			
1648	Allen Gallagher			
1649	Roberto Garza			
1650	Brian Holter			
1651	Rod Koller			
1652	Damian Leyva			
1653	Chris Maffett			
1654	Greg Rideau			
1655	Craig Sides			
1656	Greg Sinnour			
1657	Julian Tavares			
1658	Jon Zubiri			
1659	John Lewandowski			
1660	Mitch Meluskey			
1661	Michael Moyle			
1662	Einar Diaz			
1663	Huascar Genao			
1664	Damian Jackson			
1665	Chad Townsend			
1666	Jeff Whitaker			
1667	Eric White			
1668	Patricio Claudio			
1669	Ronnie Coleman			
1670	Maximo De La Rosa			
1671	Germaine Mayberry			
1672	Terry Miller			
1673	Leroy Thompson			
1674	Team Picture			
1675	Checklist			

1992 Fleer/ProCards Calgary Connons

		MT	NR MT	EX
Complete Set:		6.00		
3726	Kevin Brown			
3727	Mark Grant			
3728	Jim Newlin			
3729	Mike Remlinger			
3730	Pat Rice			
3731	Ed Vande Berg			
3732	Mike Walker			
3733	Kerry Woodson			
3734	Bill Hasselman			
3735	Chris Howard			
3736	Greg Pirkl			
3737	Rich Amaral			
3738	Kent Anderson			
3739	Mike Blowers			
3740	Bret Boone			
3741	Shane Turner			
3742	Dave Brundage			
3743	John Moses			
3744	Jeff Wetherby			
3745	Keith Bodie			
3746	Ross Grimsley			
3747	Checklist			

1992 Fleer/ProCards Canton-Akron Indians

		MT	NR MT	EX
Complete Set:		6.00		
682	Paul Byrd			
683	Colin Charland			
684	Victor Garcia			
685	Mike Gardella			
686	Brett Gideon			
687	Garland Kiser			
688	David Mlicki			
689	Willie Smith			
690	Wally Trice			
691	Joe Turek			
692	Bill Wertz			
693	Carlos Mota			
694	Kelly Stinnett			
695	Carlo Colombino			
696	Terry Crowley			
697	Miguel Flores			
698	Jose Hernandez			
699	Mike Sarbaugh			
700	Tom Eiterman			
701	Brian Giles			
702	Ken Ramos			
703	Tracy Sanders			
704	Lee Tinsley			
705	Kyle Washington			
706	Brian Graham			
707	Jim Gabella			
708	Ken Rowe			
709	Checklist			

1992 Fleer/ProCards Carolina Mudcats

		MT	NR MT	EX
Complete Set:		6.00		
1172	Dave Bird			
1173	Steve Buckholz			
1174	Jason Bullard			
1175	Stan Fansler			
1176	Lee Hancock			
1177	Bobby Hunter			
1178	Rich Robertson			
1179	Brian Shouse			
1180	Dave Teller			
1181	Paul Wagner			
1182	Ben Webb			
1183	Mike Zimmerman			
1184	Keith Osik			
1185	Mandy Romaro			
1186	Jessie Torres			
1187	Mark Johnson			
1188	Austin Manahan			
1189	Bruce Schreiber			
1190	Ben Shelton			
1191	Scott Bullett			
1192	Alberto De Los Santos			
1193	Tom Green			
1194	Daryl Ratliff			
1195	Don Warner			
1196	Rich Chiles			
1197	Checklist			

1992 Classic Best Cedar Rapids Reds

		MT	NR MT	EX
Complete Set:		6.00		
1	Keith Gordon			
2	Gene Taylor			
3	Leonard Griffen			
4	Johnny Ray			
5	Tom Raffo			
6	Matt Giegling			
7	Mike Ferry			
8	Keith Kessinger			
9	Reggie Leslie			
10	Chris Hook			
11	Larry Luebbers			
12	Jon Fuller			
13	Rodney Steph			
14	Joe DeBerry			
15	Rusty Kilgo			
16	Mike Jones			
17	Steve Gibralter			
18	Kevin Riggs			
19	Chris Vasquez			
20	Willie Greene			
21	Craig Pueschner			
22	Scott Plemmons			
23	Scott Duff			
24	Calvain Culberson			
25	Sean Doty			
26	Brian Koeling			
27	Ryan Edwards			
28	Mark Berry			
29	Mark Jenkins			
30	Tom Iverson			

1992 Fleer/ProCards Cedar Rapids Reds

		MT	NR MT	EX
Complete Set:		6.00		
1061	Calvain Culberson			
1062	Scott Dodd			
1063	Sean Doty			
1064	Scott Duff			
1065	Ryan Edwards			
1066	Mike Ferry			
1067	Leonard Griffen			
1068	Chris Hook			
1069	Rusty Kilgo			
1070	Reggie Leslie			
1071	Larry Luebbers			
1072	Scott Plemmons			
1073	Rodney Steph			
1074	Jon Fuller			
1075	Matt Giegling			
1076	Joe DeBerry			
1077	Mike Jones			
1078	Keith Kessinger			
1079	Brian Koelling			
1080	Tom Ralfo			
1081	Kevin Riggs			
1082	Chris Estep			
1083	Steve Gibraltar			
1084	Keith Gordon			
1085	Bernie Jenkins			
1086	Craig Pueschner			
1087	Chris Pueschner			
1088	Gene Taylor			
1089	Mark Berry			
1090	Checklist			

1992 Classic Best Charleston Rainbows

		MT	NR MT	EX
Complete Set:		6.00		
1	Manny Cora			
2	Adan Ayala			
3	Mark Anthony			
4	Stacy Hamm			
5	J.J. Burns			

6 Greg Mucernio
7 John Roberts
8 Brian D'Amato
9 Macelino De La Cruz
10 Jeff Huber
11 Juan Cruz
12 Charlie Greene
13 Richard Loiselle
14 David Lebak
15 German Carrion
16 Homer Bush
17 Clint Compton
18 John Barnes
19 Saul Soltero
20 Dave Mowry
21 Joey Hamilton
22 Dave Trembley
23 Jack Lamabe
24 Jaime Moreno

1992 Fleer/ProCards Charleston Rainbows

MT NR MT EX
Complete Set: 6.00

111 Greg Anthony
112 Jon Barnes
113 Jerry Burns
114 Eric Ciocca
115 Brian D'Amato
116 Richard Loiselle
117 Michael Grohs
118 Craig Hanson
119 Jeff Huber
120 Saul Soltero
121 Adan Ayala
122 Charlie Greene
123 Tim Hall
124 Homer Bush
125 German Carrion
126 Manny Cora
127 Kyle Moody
128 David Mowry
129 Greg Mucerino
130 Bill Ostermeyer
131 Mark Anthony
132 Stacy Hamm
133 David Lebak
134 John Roberts
135 Dave Trembley
136 Jack Lamabe
137 Jaime Moreno
138 Checklist

1992 Classic Best Charleston Wheelers

MT NR MT EX
Complete Set: 6.00

1 Calvin Reese
2 Charles McClain
3 John Hrusovsky
4 Fermin Garcia
5 Ernie Nieves
6 Richard Zastoupil
7 Roy Hammargren
8 Mike Harrison
9 Rich Langford
10 Eugene Jones
11 Elliott Quinones
12 Kevin Jarvis
13 Armando Morales
14 John Courtright
15 K.C. Gillum
16 Jamie Dismuke
17 Greg Hammond
18 Scott Robinson
19 Carl Stewart
20 Amadoz Arias
21 Bobby Perna
22 Lenny Wentz
23 P.J. Carey
24 Tom Spencer

1992 Fleer/ProCards Charleston Wheelers

MT NR MT EX
Complete Set: 6.00

1 John Courtright
2 Fermin Garcia
3 John Hrusovsky
4 Kevin Jarvis
5 Rich Langford
6 Charles McClain
7 Armando Morales
8 Ernie Nieves
9 Richard Zastoupil
10 Roy Hammargren
11 Greg Hammond
12 Mike Harrison
13 Amador Arias
14 Robert Carlsen
15 Jamie Dismuke
16 Bobby Perna
17 Calvin Reese
18 Lenny Wentz
19 K.C. Gillum
20 Bob Jesperson
21 Eugene Jones
22 Elliott Quinones
23 P.J. Carey
24 Derek Botelho
25 Checklist

1992 Fleer/ProCards Charlotte Knights

MT NR MT EX
Complete Set: 8.00

2764 Troy Bradford
2765 Ryan Hawblitzel
2766 Jessie Hollins
2767 Eric Jaques
2768 Paul Marak
2769 Bill Melvin
2770 Mike Sodders
2771 Dave Swatzbaugh
2772 Steve Trachsel
2773 Travis Willis
2774 Jim Robinson
2775 Matt Walbeck
2776 Rich Casarotti
2777 Rusty Crockett
2778 Chris Ebright
2779 Matt Franco
2780 Mike Grace
2781 Billy White
2782 Phil Dauphin
2783 Richie Grayum
2784 John Jensen
2785 Doug Welch
2786 Marv Foley
2787 Bill Earley
2788 Checklist

1992 Classic Best Charlotte Rangers

MT NR MT EX
Complete Set: 6.00

1 David Lowery
2 Michael Burton
3 Benigno Castillo
4 Roger Luce
5 Frank Turco
6 Craig Newkirk
7 James Hurst
8 Joseph Roebuck
9 Albert Felix
10 Christopher Gies
11 Anthony Bouton
12 Lawrence Hanlon
13 David Rolls
14 Miguel Castellano
15 James Clinton
16 Sid Holland
17 Jim Vleck
18 David Geeve
19 Darren Oliver
20 Barry Goetz
21 Kurt Miller
22 Shelby Shaw
23 Steven Dreyer
24 Michael Arner
25 Terry Burrows
26 Bump Wils
27 Marvin White
28 Doug Sisson
29 Kevin Blaske

1992 Fleer/ProCards Charlotte Rangers

MT NR MT EX
Complete Set: 6.00

2217 Jose Alberro
2218 Tony Bouton
2219 Joe Brownholtz
2220 Steven Dryer
2221 David Geeve
2222 James Hurst
2223 James Hurst
2224 David Perez
2225 Steve Sadecki
2226 Shelby Shaw
2227 Roger Luce
2228 David Rolls
2229 Mike Burton
2230 Miguel Castellanos
2231 James Clinton
2232 Larry Hanlon
2233 David Lowery
2234 Craig Newkirk
2235 Frank Turco
2236 Benigno Castillo
2237 Sid Holland
2238 Timmie Morrow
2239 Joe Roebuck
2240 Bump Wills
2241 Doug Sisson
2242 Marvin White
2243 Checklist

1992 Fleer/ProCards Chattanooga Lookouts

MT NR MT EX
Complete Set: 6.50

3810 Mike Anderson
3811 Bobby Ayala
3812 Matt Grott
3813 Rodney Imes
3814 Rusty Kilgo
3815 Larry Luebbers
3816 David Lynch
3817 Johnny Ray
3818 Scott Robinson
3819 John Roper
3820 Jason Satre
3821 Jerry Spradin
3822 Darron Cox
3823 Glenn Sutko
3824 Tim Costo
3825 Kevin Garner
3826 Willie Greene
3827 Ty Griffin
3828 Frank Kremblas
3829 Ben Colvard
3830 Chris Estep
3831 Scott Pose
3832 Todd Trafton
3833 Ron Oester
3834 Mike Griffin
3835 Tom Nieto
3836 Checklist

1992 Classic Best Clearwater Phillies

MT NR MT EX
Complete Set: 8.00

1 Jeff Jackson
2 Eric Hill
3 Darrell Goedhart
4 Bob Gaddy
5 Steve Bieser
6 Mickey Hyde
7 Jeff Patterson
8 Michael Farmer
9 David Tokheim
10 Kenny Sirak
11 Lee Langley
12 Elliott Gray
13 Bob Wells
14 Joel Adamson
15 Terry Tewell
16 Tony Trevino
17 J.J. Munoz
18 Phillip Geiser
19 Kevin Stocker
20 Duane Mulville
21 Rick Meyer
22 Pat Brady
23 Ronnie Allen
24 Ramon Henderson
25 Darold Knowles
26 Craig Strobel

1992 Fleer/ProCards Clearwater Phillies

MT NR MT EX
Complete Set: 6.00

2045 Joel Adamson
2046 Ronnie Allen
2047 Dan Brown
2048 Andy Carter
2049 Rocky Elli
2050 Robert Gaddy
2051 Joel Gilmore
2052 Todd Goergen
2053 Elliot Gray
2054 Lee Langley
2055 Darrell Lindsey
2056 J.J. Munoz
2057 Mark Randall
2058 Steve Bieser
2059 Duane Mulville
2060 Terry Tewell
2061 Luis Brito
2062 Phil Geisler
2063 Rick Meyer
2064 Ron Ollison
2065 Troy Rusk
2066 Ken Sirak
2067 Corey Thomas
2068 Pat Brady
2069 Mike Farmer
2070 Jeff Jackson
2071 Mark Steffans
2072 David Tokheim
2073 Bill Dancy
2074 Ramon Henderson
2075 Darold Knowles
2076 Checklist

1992 Classic Best Clinton Giants

MT NR MT EX
Complete Set: 6.00

1 Dax Jones
2 Rich Hyde
3 Angel Ortiz
4 Mike Boker
5 Brent Cookson
6 Ken Feist
7 Roberto Delgado
8 Lenny Ayers
9 Ray Jackson
10 Andre Keene
11 Eric Stonecipher
12 Kurt Peltzer
13 Chris Gambs
14 Derek Dana
15 Jarod Juelsgaard
16 Chuck Wanke
17 Doug Vanderweele
18 Albert Rodriguez
19 Charles Alimena
20 Adame Tamarez
21 D.J. Thielen
22 Tim Florez
23 Ken Grundt
24 Marcus Jensen
25 Chris Dotolo
26 Bill Stein
27 Nelson Rood
28 Gary Lucas
29 Bill Carpine
30 Kevin Temperly (General Manager, Lorie Barab, Gady Mayse

1992 Fleer/ProCards Clinton Giants

MT NR MT EX
Complete Set: 6.00

3588 Lenny Ayres
3589 Mike Boker
3590 Chris Gambs
3591 Ken Grundt
3592 Jared Juelsgaard
3593 Jeff Locklear
3594 John Lowery
3595 Mike McLain
3596 Angel Ortiz
3597 Denny Szczechowski
3598 Bill VanLandingham
3599 Chuck Wanke
3600 Dan Calcagno
3601 Derek Dans
3602 Marcus Jensen
3603 C.L. Dotolo
3604 Andre Keene
3605 Tom O'Neill
3606 Adame Tamarez
3607 D.J. Thielen
3608 Ken Feist
3609 Ray Jackson
3610 Dax Jones
3611 Brett McGonnigal
3612 Bill Stein
3613 Nelson Rood
3614 Gary Lucas
3615 Team Picture
3779 Checklist

1992 Fleer/ProCards Colorado Springs Sky Sox

MT NR MT EX
Complete Set: 6.00

742 Brad Armstrong
743 Eric Beil
744 Mike Christopher
745 Terry Clark
746 Jerry DiPoto
747 Bruce Egloff
748 Tom Kramer
749 Jeff Murtis
750 Greg Roscoe
751 Jeff Shaw
752 Willie Smith
753 Alan Cockrell
754 Brian Johnson
755 Jesse Levis
756 Mike Aldrate
757 Alvaro Espinoza
758 Nelson Liriano
759 Tony Perezchicz
760 Dave Rohde
761 Craig Worthington
762 Beau Allred
763 Mark Davidson
764 Wayne Kirby
765 Donnell Nixon
766 Charlie Manuel
767 Luis Isaac
768 Dyar Miller
769 Checklist

1992 Classic Best Columbia Mets

	MT	NR MT	EX
Complete Set:	6.00		

1 Jerome Tolliver
2 hector Ramirez
3 Ottis Smith
4 Mike Patrizi
5 Bradley Schorr
6 Jim Manfred
7 Greg Beals
8 Darian Lindsay
9 Steve Thomas
10 Jason Jacome
11 Todd Fiegel
12 Ricky Otero
13 Robbie Guzik
14 Randy Farmer
15 Ed Perozo
16 danilo Mompres
17 Juan Moreno
18 Craig Bullock
19 Raul Casanova
20 Dwight Robinson
21 Omar Garcia
22 Jim McCready
23 Eric Reichenbach
24 Randy Curtis
25 Quilvio Veras
26 Tim Blackwell
27 jerry Koosman
28 Marlin McPhail
29 David Fricke

1992 Fleer/ProCards Columbia Mets

	MT	NR MT	EX
Complete Set:	6.00		

288 Todd Fiegel
289 Rob Guzik
290 Darian Lindsay
291 Jim Manfred
292 Jim McCready
293 Hector Ramirez
294 Rob Rees
295 Eric Reichenbach
296 Brad Schorr
297 Steve Thomas
298 Greg Beals
299 Raul Casanova
300 Mike Patrizi
301 Craig Bullock
302 Randy Farmer
303 Omar Garcia
304 Denilo Mompres
305 Dwight Robinson
306 Quilvio Veras
307 Randy Curtis
308 Juan Moreno
309 Ricky Otero
310 Ed Perozo
311 Jerome Tolliver
312 Tim Blackwell
313 Marlin McPhail
314 Checklist

1992 Play II Columbia Mets

Play II is owned by Bob McCartha of Continental Cards in Columbia, S.C. The set was released in a box the size of a deck of playing cards. The 42-card sets include several special cards and each box of cards included one of a nine-card set of gold cards. Also included were cards from an exhibition game between local celebrities and former major leaguers to publicize changing the franchise's nickname for 1992. Included was actor Mark Harmon. Gold cards were made for Jose Martinez, Butch Huskey, Chipper Jones, Jose Martinez, Butch Huskey, Bobby Jones, Ricky Otero, Quilvio Veras, Omar Garcia and Jason Jacome.

	MT	NR MT	EX
Complete Set:	4.00		

(1) Tim Blackwell
(2) Jerry Koosman
(3) Marlin McPhail
(4) Steve Thomas
(5) Danilo Mompres
(6) Randy Farmer
(7) Omar Garcia
(8) Greg Beals
(9) Ed Peroso
(10) Juan Moreno
(11) Cesar Diaz
(12) Darian Lindsay
(13) Randy Curtis
(14) Jerome Tolliver
(15) Robbie Guzik
(16) Jim McCready
(17) Eric Reichenbach
(18) Todd Fiegel
(19) Ottis Smith
(20) Brad Schorr
(21) Quilvio Veras
(22) Dwight Robinson
(23) Mike Patrizi
(24) Ricky Otero
(25) Craig Bullock
(26) Jim Manfred
(27) Hector Ramirez
(28) Jason Jacome
(29) Tom Engle
(30) Kooz Krew (Fiegle, Jacome, Guzik, Schorr)
(31) Columbia Cruisers (Curtis, Otero, Veras, Farmer)
(32) David Fricke
(33) "Bomber" and Dave
(34) Eric Margenau
(35) Bill Shanahan
(36) The Bombers
(37) The Spirit
(38) Mark Harmon
(39) Joe Crawford (1991 Update)
(40) Bobby Jones (1991 Update)
(41) Jose Martinez (Flashback)
(42) Butch Huskey (Flashback)

1992 Play II Columbia Mets Inserts

	MT	NR MT	EX
Complete Set:	60.00		

1 Jose Martinez
2 Butch Huskey, Chipper Jones
3 Jose Martinez
4 Butch Huskey
5 Bobby Jones
6 Ricky Otero
7 Quilvio Veras
8 Omar Garcia
9 Jason Jacome

1992 Fleer/ProCards Columbus Clippers

	MT	NR MT	EX
Complete Set:	7.00		

342 Andy Cook
343 Royal Clayton
344 Francisco De La Rose
345 Mike Draper
346 Shawn Hillegas
347 Ed Martel
348 Sam Militello
349 David Rosario
350 Russ Springer
351 Don Stanford
352 Larry Stanford
353 Wade Taylor
354 Bob Wickman
355 Brad Ausmus
356 John Ramos
357 Dave Sax
358 Bobby DeJardin
359 Torey Lovullo
360 Hensley Meulens
361 Dave Silvestri
362 J.T. Snow
363 Mike Humphreys
364 Billy Masse
365 Bernie Williams
366 Gerald Williams
367 Rick Down
368 Coaching Staff
369 Checklist

1992 Police Columbus Clippers

This 25-card set is part of a decade-long series of team sets issued by the Clippers in cooperation with the Columbus Police Department. The cards are numbered in the upper left-hand corner of the front of the card, with player information along the bottom. The back has the previous season's statistics and a anti-drug slogan written by a local fifth or sixth grader.

	MT	NR MT	EX
Complete Set:	6.00		

(1) Ken Schnake, Rich Down
(2) Coaches (Ted Uhlaender, Mike Brown, Hop Cassady, Mike Heifferon (trainer))
(3) Royal Clayton
(4) Francisco del la Rosa
(5) Mike Draper
(6) Ed Martel
(7) Sam Militello
(8) David Rosario
(9) Russ Springer
(10) Don Stanford
(11) Jeff Johnson
(12) Wade Taylor
(13) Bob Wickman
(14) John Ramos
(15) Dave Sax
(16) Bobby DeJardin
(17) Torey Lovullo
(18) Hensley Meulens
(19) Dave Silvestri
(20) J.T. Snow
(21) Mike Humphreys
(22) Bernie Williams
(23) Billy Masse
(24) Gerald Williams
(25) Chief Jackson

1992 Classic Best Columbus RedStixx

	MT	NR MT	EX
Complete Set:	6.00		

1 Pete Rose II
2 Dickie Brown
3 Pat Bryant
4 Wiliam Canate
5 Pat Maxwell
6 Carlos Crawford
7 Sam Hence
8 Mark Sweeney
9 Michael Crosby
10 Marc Marini
11 Kevin Logsdon
12 Paul Meade
13 Mark Charbonnett
14 Gershon Dallas
15 Hernando Harrs
16 Fernando Hernandez
17 Nick Sued
18 Ian Doyle
19 Albie Lopez
20 Andy Baker
21 Alan Walden
22 Rod McCall
23 Robbie Smith
24 Felipe Duran
25 Brian Buzard
26 Joe Fleet
27 Mike Brown
28 Dan Norman
29 Ted Blackwell

1992 Fleer/ProCards Columbus RedStixx

	MT	NR MT	EX
Complete Set:	6.00		

2378 Andy Baker
2379 Sam Baker
2380 Dickie Brown
2381 Carlos Crawford
2382 Ian Doyle
2383 Kenyatta Fleet
2384 Pep Harris
2385 Fernando Hernandez
2386 Joel Johnson
2387 Kevin Logsdon
2388 Albie Lopez
2389 Oscar Resendez
2390 Paul Shuey
2391 Alan Waldin
2392 David Welch
2393 Mike Crosby
2394 Nick Sued
2395 Mark Charbonnet
2396 Felipe Duran
2397 Pat Maxwell
2398 Rod McCall
2399 Paul Meade
2400 Pete Rose
2401 Robbie Smith
2402 Pat Bryant
2403 Willie Canate
2404 Gershon Dallas
2405 Sam Hence
2406 Marc Marini
2407 Mike Brown
2408 Fred Gladding
2409 Checklist

1992 Team Columbus RedStixx

	MT	NR MT	EX
Complete Set:	5.00		

1 Paul Shvey
2 David Welch
3 Nick Sued
4 Mike Crosby
5 Paul Meade
6 Marc Marini
7 Checklist

1992 Fleer/ProCards Denver Zephyrs

	MT	NR MT	EX
Complete Set:	6.00		

2631 Cal Eldred
2632 Chris George
2633 Otis Green
2634 Jim Hunter
2635 Mike Ignasiak
2636 Mark Kiefer
2637 Mark Lee
2638 Angel Miranda
2639 Eric Nolte
2640 Efrain Valdez
2641 Rob Wishnevski
2642 Andy Allanson
2643 Joe Kmak
2644 dave Liddell
2645 Alex Diaz
2646 Sandy Guerrero
2647 John Jaha
2648 Jeff Kunkel
2649 Charlie Montoyo
2650 Williams Suero
2651 Jim Tatum
2652 Jose Valentin
2653 Kenny Jackson
2654 Matt Mieska
2655 Tony Muser
2656 Bill Campbell
2657 Lamar Johnson
2658 Checklist

1992 Team Denver Zephyrs Record Holders

This 20-card set was given out at the last minor league game played in Denver. The cards measure 2-1/2" x 3-1/2", and picture players who hold all-time season records in Denver's long and distinguished minor league history. The photos are black-and-white, sponsored by ReMax Realty. The backs list the records the player holds.

	MT	NR MT	EX
Complete Set:	6.00		

(1) Minnie Mendoza
(2) Mark Freeman
(3) Harry Chappas
(4) Jerry Crider
(5) Ed Donnelly
(6) Norm Siebern
(7) Garland Shifflett
(8) Ryne Duren
(9) Marv Throneberry
(10) Ron Clark
(11) Chris George
(12) Sandy Alomar Sr.
(13) Tony Fossas
(14) Cliff Johnson
(15) Jim Ollom
(16) Roger Freed
(17) Tim Raines
(18) Tim Wallach
(19) Richie Scheinblum
(20) Steve Boros

1992 Classic Best Dunedin Blue Jays

	MT	NR MT	EX
Complete Set:	20.00		

1 Steve Karsay
2 Jeff Ware
3 Scott Brow
4 Eric Brooks
5 Howard Battle
6 Brent Bowers
7 Robert Butler
8 Shawn Green
9 Kris Harmes
10 Tim Hyers
11 Ricardo Jordan
12 Mariano Dotel
13 Scott Grove
14 Raphael Garcia
15 Tim Hodge
16 Tom Singer
17 Giovanni Carrara
18 Rick Steed
19 Ernesto Rodriguez
20 Carlos Delgado
21 Hector Tavarez
22 Kyle Duey
23 Tom Hotchkiss
24 Huck Flener
25 Scott Miller
26 Dennis Holmberg
27 Hector Torres
28 Jon Woddworth
29 Bill Monbouquette
30 Kenny Holmberg

1992 Fleer/ProCards Dunedin Blue Jays

	MT	NR MT	EX
Complete Set:	20.00		

1990 Scott Brow
1991 Kyle Duey
1992 Huck Flener
1993 Joe Ganote
1994 Scott Grove
1995 Tom Hotchkiss
1996 Ricardo Jordan
1997 Steve Karsay
1998 Mike Ogliaruso
1999 Tom Slinger
2000 Rick Steed
2001 Jeff Ware
2002 Eric Brooks
2003 Carlos Delgado
2004 Sharnol Adriana
2005 Howard Battle
2006 Mariano Dotel
2007 Tim Hyers
2008 Ernesto Rodriguez
2009 Brent Bowers
2010 Rob Butler
2011 Shawn Green
2012 Tim Hodge
2013 Dennis Holmberg
2014 Hector Torres
2015 Bill Monboquette
2016 Checklist

1992 Classic Best Durham Bulls

	MT	NR MT	EX
Complete Set:	10.00		

1 Chipper Jones
2 Johnny Cuevas
3 Rick Karcher
4 Scott Ryder
5 Hector Roa
6 Osvaldo Sanchez
7 Lee Heath
8 Kevin Lomon
9 Darren Ritter
10 Grant Brittain
11 Tim Gillis
12 Earl Steinmetz
13 Brad Rippelmeyer
14 Kevin O'Connor
15 Troy Hughes
16 Tyler Houston
17 Mike Hostetler
18 Thomas Leahy
19 Marcos Vasquez
20 Barry Chiles
21 Mike Potts
22 Melvin Nieves
23 Brad Woddall
24 David Williams
25 Leon Roberts
26 Matt West
27 George Threadgill

1992 Fleer/ProCards Durham Bulls

	MT	NR MT	EX
Complete Set:	10.00		

1092 Barry Chiles
1093 Roger Hailey
1094 Mike Hostetler
1095 Tim Leahy
1096 Mike Potts
1097 Darren Ritter
1098 Scott Ryder
1099 Blase Sparma
1100 Earl Steinmetz
1101 David Williams
1102 Brad Woodall
1103 Johnny Cuevas
1104 Tyler Houston
1105 Brad Rippelmeyer
1106 Steve Swail
1107 Tim Gillis
1108 Chipper Jones
1109 Rick Karcher
1110 Hector Roa
1111 Ozzie Sanchez
1112 Lee Heath
1113 Troy Hughes
1114 Brian Kowitz
1115 Leon Roberts
1116 Doug Baker
1117 George Threadgill
1118 Matt West
1119 Checklist

1992 Team Durham Bulls

This 29-card set was issued by the Durham Bulls and sponsored by a local newspaper. The cards are standard size, and have stats and a brief player information on the back. The set is skip-numbered according to the player's uniform number.

	MT	NR MT	EX
Complete Set:	6.50		

(2) Hector Roa
(5) Mike Potts
(7) Leon Roberts
(9) Grant Brittain
(10) Chipper Jones
(11) Brad Woodall
(12) Kevin O'Connor
(13) Jose Olmeda
(14) Kevin Lomon
(15) Brad Ripplemeyer
(17) Ozzie Sanchez
(18) Tim Gillis
(19) Tyler Houston
(20) Marcos Vazquez
(21) Melvin Nieves
(22) Rick Karcher
(23) Earl Steinmetz
(24) Mike Hostetler
(25) Tom Leahy
(26) Scott Ryder
(27) Troy Hughes
(28) Johnny Cuevas
(30) Matt West
(31) Darren Ritter
(32) Roger Hailey
(33) Lee Heath
(34) Barry Chiles
(35) David Williams
---- Team Photo

1992 Fleer/ProCards Edmonton Trappers

	MT	NR MT	EX
Complete Set:	14.00		

3533 Chris Beasley
3534 Mike Butcher
3535 Tim Fortungo
3536 Willie Fraser
3537 Scott Lewis
3538 John Pawlowski
3539 Ray Searage
3540 Don Vidmar
3541 Mick Bilmeyer
3542 Larry Gonzales
3543 Don Barbara
3544 Damion Easley
3545 Kevin Flora
3546 Ramon Martinez
3547 Ken Oberkfell
3548 Ty Van Burkleo
3549 Mark Wasinger
3550 Phil Bradley
3551 Tim Salmon
3552 Reggie Williams
3553 Max Oliveras
3554 Gary Ruby
3555 Lena Sakata
3556 Checklist

1992 Classic Best Elizabethton Twins

	MT	NR MT	EX
Complete Set:	6.00		

1 Shawn Miller
2 Keith Linebarger
3 Craig Saccavino
4 Scott Moten
5 Tim Costic
6 Thomas Horincewich
7 Henry Burrough
8 Kevin Legault
9 Ken Tirpack
10 Jeff Horn
11 Marlon Nava
12 Rafael Pina
13 Blanco Pedro
14 Craig Hawkins
15 Cory Lidle
16 Jose Correa
17 Kenny Norman
18 Ramon Valette
19 Glen Evans
20 Jason Baker
21 Ronald Caridad
22 Joey Miller
23 Ray Smith
24 Rick Tomlin
25 Lanning H. Tucker

1992 Fleer/ProCards Elizabethton Twins

	MT	NR MT	EX
Complete Set:	7.00		

3672 Ron Caridad
3673 Jose Correa
3674 Gus Gandarillas
3675 Kevin Legault
3676 Cory Lidle
3677 Keith Linebarger
3678 Shawn Miller
3679 Scott Moten
3680 Rafael Pina
3681 Craig Saccavino
3682 Jeff Horn
3683 Todd Taylor
3684 Pedro Blanco
3685 Tom Horencewich
3686 Keith Legree
3687 Marlo Nava
3688 Ken Tirpack
3689 Ramon Vallette
3690 Jason Baker
3691 Buth Burrough
3692 Tim Costic
3693 Glenn Evans
3694 Craig Hawkins
3695 Joey Miller
3696 Kenny Norman
3697 Ray Smith
3698 Rick Tomlin
3699 Checklist

1992 Classic Best Elmira Pioneers

	MT	NR MT	EX
Complete Set:	6.00		

1 George Scott
2 Dan Collier
3 Bret Donovan
4 Michael Canton
5 Craig Bush
6 Jason Smith
7 Randy Lawrence
8 John Crimmins
9 Todd Carey
10 Thomas Niles
11 Quinn Feno
12 Cesar Martinez
13 Jose Malave
14 Leif McKinley
15 Gerald Davis
16 Douglas MacNeil
17 Mark Senkowitz
18 Joe Hudson
19 Bill Selby
20 Gettys Glaze
21 Jeff Fanio
22 Andrew Moore
23 Bob Juday
24 Dave Holt
25 Garry Roggenburk
26 James Love

1992 Fleer/ProCards Elmira Pioneers

	MT	NR MT	EX
Complete Set:	6.00		

1374 Craig Bush
1375 Vret Donovan
1376 Jeffrey Faino
1377 Gettys Glaze
1378 Joe Hudson
1379 Randy Lawrence
1380 Doug MacNeil
1381 Cesar Martinez
1382 Leif McKinley
1383 Tom Niles
1384 John Crimmins
1385 Mark Senkowitz
1386 Jason Smith
1387 Michael Canton
1388 Todd Carey
1389 Bob Juday
1390 Jose Malave
1391 Andy Moore
1392 George Scott
1393 Bill Selby
1394 Dan Collier
1395 Gerald Davis
1396 Quinn Feno
1397 Garry Roggenburk
1398 Checklist

1992 Fleer/ProCards El Paso Diablos

	MT	NR MT	EX
Complete Set:	6.00		

3913 Jim Czajkowski
3914 Tim Dell
3915 Mike Farrell
3916 Dave Martinez
3917 Tom McGraw
3918 Rafael Novoa
3919 Dave Richards
3920 Steve Sparks
3921 Jeff Tabaka
3922 Scott Taylor
3923 Brandy Vann
3924 Craig Faulkner
3925 Bob Kappesser
3926 John Byington
3927 Edgar Caceres
3928 Bo Dodson
3929 John Fina
3930 Mike Guerrero
3931 Alan Lewis
3932 Ed Smith
3933 Michael Carter
3934 Vince Castaldo
3935 Tony Diggs
3936 Troy O'Leary
3937 Chris Bando
3938 Rob Derksen
3939 Checklist

1992 Classic Best Erie Sailors

	MT	NR MT	EX
Complete Set:	6.00		

1 Willie Brown
2 Matt Petersen
3 Brad Frazier
4 Freddie Gamble
5 Donald Lemon
6 Tim North
7 Deron Sample
8 Mark Skeels
9 Ryan Whitman
10 Reynol Mendoza
11 Dan Roman
12 Scott Engelhart
13 Scott Samuels
14 Pat Leahy
15 Kenny Kendrena
16 Lou Lucca
17 John Lynch
18 Sean Gousha
19 Doug Pettit
20 Todd Pridy
21 Rick Freehling
22 Ray Cervantes
23 Brad Clem
24 Michael Taylor
25 Luis Cordova
26 Jerry Stafford
27 Matt Donahue
28 Jim Patterson
29 Tony Torres
30 Fredi Gonzalez

1992 Fleer/ProCards Erie Sailors

	MT	NR MT	EX
Complete Set:	6.00		

1611 Matt Donahue
1612 Scott Englehart
1613 Brad Frazier
1614 Kenny Kendrena
1615 Pat Leahy
1616 Donald Lemon
1617 John Lynch
1618 Reynol Mendoza
1619 Jim Patterson
1620 Matt Petersen
1621 Doug Pettit
1622 Dan Roman
1623 Deron Sample
1624 Jerry Stafford
1625 Ryan Whitman
1626 Sean Gousha
1627 Mark Skeels
1628 Mike Taylor
1629 Raymond Cervantes
1630 Freddie Gamble
1631 Lou Lucca
1632 Tim North
1633 Todd Pridy
1634 Tony Torres
1635 Willie Brown
1636 Brad Clem
1637 Luis Cordova
1638 Rick Freehling
1639 Scott Samuels
1640 Fredi Gonzalez
1641 Jose Castro
1642 Marty DeMerritt
1643 Checklist

1992 Classic Best Eugene Emeralds

	MT	NR MT	EX
Complete Set:	6.00		

1 Sherard Clinkscales
2 Ryan Long
3 Jeff Haas
4 Scott Abell
5 Jeff Antoon
6 Dave Bladow
7 Ramy Brooks
8 Bryan Currier
9 John Dickens
10 Aaron Dorlarque
11 Tracey Ealy
12 Chris Eddy
13 Bart Evans
14 Paul Fletcher
15 Tom Heming
16 Jon Lieber
17 Jason Marshall
18 Troy McAllister
19 Darrell McMillin

20 Cesar Morillo
21 Jason Pruitt
22 Chris Sheehan
23 Steve Sisco
24 Larry Sutton
25 Mike Sweeney
26 Brian Teeters
27 John Weglarz

1992 Fleer/ProCards Eugene Emeralds

	MT	NR MT	EX
Complete Set:	6.00		

3017 Dave Bladow
3018 Sherard Clinkscales
3019 Bryan Currier
3020 John Dickens
3021 Aaron Dorlarque
3022 Chris Eddy
3023 Bart Evans
3024 Paul Fletcher
3025 Jeff Haas
3026 Tom Heming
3027 Jon Lieber
3028 Jason Pruitt
3029 Chris Sheehan
3030 John Weglarz
3031 Scott Abell
3032 Ramy Brooks
3033 Mike Sweeney
3034 Jeff Antoon
3035 Ryan Long
3036 Jason Marshall
3037 Troy McAllister
3038 Cesar Morillo
3039 Steve Sisco
3040 Larry Sutton
3041 David Cornell
3042 Tracey Ealy
3043 Darrell McMillin
3044 Brian Teeters
3649 Team Picture
3650 Checklist

1992 Classic Best Everett Giants

	MT	NR MT	EX
Complete Set:	6.00		

1 Mark Saugsrad
2 Petie Roach
3 Tim Luther
4 Marvin Benard
5 Blair Hanneman
6 Ken Henderson
7 Kenny Woods
8 Scott Stroth
9 Benji Simonton
10 Mike McLain
11 Shelby Hart
12 Jeff Myers
13 Butter Jones
14 Clay King
15 Mark Peterson
16 Jim Riley
17 Papo Ramos
18 Jamie Brewington
19 Tom O'Neill
20 Jeff Richey
21 Michael Cavanaugh
22 Dennis Szczechowski
23 Jason Sievers
24 David Baine
25 Bobby Gorham
26 Craig Mayes
27 Charlie Hicks
28 Chad Fonville
29 Andy Heckman
30 Norm Sherry

1992 Fleer/ProCards Everett Giants

	MT	NR MT	EX
Complete Set:	6.00		

1676 David Baine
1677 Jamie Brewington
1678 Bobby Gorham
1679 Blair Hanneman
1680 Andy Heckman
1681 Ken Henderson
1682 Charlie Hicks
1683 Tim Luther
1684 Mike McLain
1685 Jeff Myers
1686 Mark Peterson
1687 Jeff Richey
1688 Jim Riley
1689 Scott Stroth
1690 Dennis Szczechowski
1691 Carlos Valdez
1692 Michael Cavanaugh
1693 Craig Mayes
1694 Jason Sievers
1695 Chad Fonville
1696 Shelby Hart
1697 Clay King
1698 Tom O'Neill
1699 Petie Roach
1700 Mark Saugstad
1701 Kenny Woods
1702 Marvin Bernard
1703 Butter Jones
1704 Papo Ramos
1705 Benji Simonton
1706 Norm Sherry
1707 Checklist

1992 Classic Best Fayetteville Generals

	MT	NR MT	EX
Complete Set:	6.00		

1 Justin Thompson
2 Ben Blomdahl
3 Brian Edmondson
4 John Reid
5 Brian Dubose
6 Tarrick Brock
7 Kevin Miller
8 Bob Lemay
9 greg Haeger
10 James Merriweather
11 Todd Bussa
12 Steve Waite
13 Dan Bautista
14 Rich Kelly
15 Rob Yelton
16 Art Adams
17 Justin Mashore
18 Rob Grable
19 Tom Schwarber
20 Pedro Gonzalez
21 Dave Leonhardt
22 Evan Pratte
23 Dennis Walsh
24 Gerry Groninger
25 Dwight Lowry
26 Sid Monge
27 Bryan Goike
30 Checklist

1992 Fleer/ProCards Fayetteville Generals

	MT	NR MT	EX
Complete Set:	6.50		

2159 Ben Blomdahl
2160 Todd Bussa
2161 Ken Carlyle
2162 Brian Edmondson
2163 Greg Haeger
2164 Rich Kelley
2165 Bob Lemay
2166 John Reid
2167 Tom Schwarber
2168 Justin Thompson
2169 Dennis Walsh
2170 Shannon Withem
2171 Tim McConnell
2172 Kevin Miller
2173 Rob Yelton
2174 Brian Dubose
2175 Dave Leonhardt
2176 James Merriweather
2177 Kevin Morgen
2178 Evan Pratte
2179 Danny Bautista
2180 Tarrik Brock
2181 Carlos Burguillos
2182 Justin Meshore
2183 Brian Sullivan
2184 Gary Groninger
2185 Dwight Lowry
2186 Sid Mongs
2187 Checklist

1992 Classic Best Ft. Lauderdale Yankees

	MT	NR MT	EX
Complete Set:	9.00		

1 Brien Taylor
2 Jovino Carvejal
3 Doug Gogolewski
4 Robert Eenhoorn
5 Andres Rodriguez
6 Jose Pineda
7 Cesar Perez
8 Dan Johnston
9 Tom Carter
10 Michael Figga
11 Luis Gallardo
12 Curtis Ralph
13 Elston Hansen
14 Scott Kamieniecki
15 Scott Romano
16 Larry Walker
17 Pat Morphy
18 Bo Gilliam
19 Brian Faw
20 Brian Turner
21 Tim Demerson
22 Ricky Rhodes
23 Brian Butterfield
24 Mark Shiflett
25 Bob Marino

1992 Fleer/ProCards Ft. Lauderdale Yankees

	MT	NR MT	EX
Complete Set:	9.00		

2602 Dennis Burbank
2603 Tom Carter
2604 Brian Faw
2605 Doug Gogolewski
2606 Jim Haller
2607 Domingo Jean
2608 Dan Johnston
2609 Pat Morphy
2610 Ricky Rhodes
2611 Mariano Rivera
2612 Brien Taylor
2613 Cesar Perez
2614 Mike Figga
2615 John Quintell
2616 Larry Walker
2617 Robert Eenhoorn
2618 Greg Erikson
2619 Luis Gallardo
2620 Mike Hankins
2621 Andres Rodriguez
2622 Scott Romano
2623 Brian Turner
2624 Javino Carvajal
2625 Robert Deller
2626 Carl Everett
2627 Bo Gilliam
2628 Ray Noriega
2629 Brian Butterfield
2630 Bob Mariano
3010 Mark Shiflett
3011 Checklist

1992 Team Fort Lauderdale Yankees

The New York Yankees own their Florida State League affiliate in Fort Lauderdale, and when 1991 #1 draft pick Brien Taylor was assigned to the team, it convinced promotions people in Tampa that a team set was in order. The 33-card set has color borderless photos with stats and a brief bio statement on the back. The cards are unnumbered.

	MT	NR MT	EX
Complete Set:	6.00		

(1) Sam Arena
(2) Dennis Burbank
(3) Brian J. Butterfield
(4) Tom Carter
(5) Jovino Carvajal
(6) Bob Deller
(7) Tim Demerson
(8) Robert Eenhorn
(9) Greg Erick[illegible]
(10) Carl Everett
(11) Brian Faw
(12) Michael Figga
(13) Luis Gallardo
(14) Bo Gilliam
(15) Doug Gogolewski
(16) Jim Haller
(17) Elston Hansen
(18) Kiki Hernandez
(19) Domingo Jean
(20) Dan Johnston
(21) Bob Joseph Mariano
(22) Pat Morphy
(23) Cesar Perez
(24) Jose Pineda
(25) Curtis Ralph
(26) Tom Raynor
(27) Ricky Rhodes
(28) Andres Rodriguez
(29) Scott Romano
(30) Mark Winston Shiflett
(31) Brien Taylor
(32) Brian Turner
(33) Larry Walker

1992 Classic Best Ft. Meyers Miracle

	MT	NR MT	EX
Complete Set:	6.00		

1 Jayson Best
2 Ted Corbin
3 George Evangelista
4 Brian Roberts
5 Apolinar Garcia
6 Pedro Grifol
7 Mike Shirley
8 Brian Raabe
9 Mark Ringkamp
10 Willie Mota
11 Mark Swope
12 Derrell Rumsey
13 Carlos Estevez
14 Tim Nedin
15 David Giberti
16 Tyrone Washington
17 Bart Peterson
18 Mike Misuraca
19 Troy Buckley
20 Nolan Lane
21 Denny Hoppe
22 John Gumpf
23 Greg Wiseman
24 Lance Schuermann
25 Jim Kohl
26 Dan Rohn
27 Dennis Burtt
28 Mark Stoughton

1992 Fleer/ProCards Ft. Myers Miracle

	MT	NR MT	EX
Complete Set:	6.00		

2737 Jayon Best
2738 Apolinar Garcia
2739 Dave Gilberti
2740 Denny Hoppe
2741 Jim Kohl
2742 Mike Misuraca
2743 Tim Persing
2744 Bart Peterson
2745 Mark Ringkamp
2746 Lance Schuermann
2747 Mark Swope
2748 Troy Buckley
2749 Pedro Grifol
2750 Birna Roberts
2751 Ted Corbin
2752 Carlos Estevez
2753 George Evangelista
2754 Willie Mota
2755 Brian Raabe
2756 John Gumpf
2757 Darrell Rumsey
2758 Mike Shirley
2759 Greg Wiseman
2760 Dan Rohn
2761 Bob Zeihen
2762 Dennis Burtt
2763 Checklist

1992 Classic Best Frederick Keys

	MT	NR MT	EX
Complete Set:	6.00		

1 Paul Carey
2 Jim Audley
3 Davide Paveloff
4 Mike Coss
5 Brad Tippitt
6 Brad Tyler
7 Gregg Zaun
8 Stanton Cameron
9 Jason Alstead
10 Jim Wawruck
11 Brad Seitzer
12 Alan Plaster
13 Steve Godin
14 John Polasek
15 James Dedrick
16 Basilio Ortiz
17 Jose Millares
18 Terry Farrar
19 Matt Anderson
20 Brad Pennington
21 Doug McConathy
22 Tommy Taylor
23 Joe Borowski
24 Jimmy Roso
25 Stacy Jones
26 Kevin Ryan
27 Dan Ramirez
28 Oneri Fleita

1992 Fleer/ProCards Frederick Keys

	MT	NR MT	EX
Complete Set:	6.00		

1797 Matt Anderson
1798 Joe Borowski

1799 Jim Dedrick
1800 Terry Farrar
1801 Stacy Jones
1802 Dave Paveloff
1803 Allan Plaster
1804 John Polasek
1805 Kevin Ryan
1806 Tom Taylor
1807 Brad Tippitt
1808 Jimmy Roso
1809 Gregg Zaun
1810 Mike Coss
1811 T.R. Lewis
1812 Doug McConathy
1813 jose Millares
1814 Dan Ramirez
1815 Brad Seitzer
1816 Jason Alstead
1817 Jim Audley
1818 Stanton Cameron
1819 Steven Godin
1820 Basilio Ortiz
1821 Jim Wawruck
1822 Bob Miscik
1823 Oneri Fleita
1824 John O'Donoghue
1825 Checklist

1992 Classic Best Gastonia Rangers

MT NR MT EX
Complete Set: 7.00

1 Benji Gil
2 Steve Sadecki
3 Michael Crespo
4 Bert Gerhart
5 Mark Hampton
6 Jose Alberro
7 Wilson Heredia
8 Joe Brownholtz
9 Jose Texidor
10 Daryl Henderson
11 Darryl Kennedy
12 Mike Edwards
13 Kevin Woodall
14 Bo Magee
15 Kerry Lacy
16 David Gandolph
17 Franklin Parra
18 Paul Matachum
19 Chris Curtis
20 Lanny Williams
21 Steve Burton
22 Mike McCollough
23 Malvin Matos
24 Danny Patterson
25 Walt Williams
26 Stan Cliburn
27 Andy Gruziano

1992 Fleer/ProCards Gastonia Rangers

MT NR MT EX
Complete Set: 8.00

2044 Checklist
2243 Chris Curtis
2244 John Dettmer
2245 Jay Franklin
2246 David Gandolph
2247 Mark Hampton
2248 Daryl Henderson
2249 Wilson Heredia
2250 Kerry Lacy
2251 Bo Magee
2252 Ritchie Moody
2253 Danny Patterson
2254 Heath Vaughn
2255 Mike Crespo
2256 Scot Sealy
2257 Lanny Williams
2258 Steve Burton
2259 Mike Edwards
2260 Benji Gil
2261 Paul Matachun
2262 Mike Smith
2263 John Tornasello
2264 Paul List
2265 Malvin Matos
2266 Kenny Powell
2267 Jose Texidor
2268 Walt Williams
2269 Stan Cliburn
2270 Gary Mielke

1992 Classic Best Geneva Cubs

MT NR MT EX
Complete Set: 7.00

1 Pedro Valdez
2 Jose Trujillo
3 Hector Trinidad
4 Chad Tredaway
5 Paul Stojsavljevic
6 Kennie Steenstra
7 Adan Schulhofer
8 Chris Rodriguez
9 Chris Petersen
10 Geno Morones
11 Dan Madsen
12 Collin Kerley
13 Robin Jennings
14 Jonathan Jarolimek
15 Mike Hubbard
16 Scott Gardner
17 Pat Fairly
18 Todd Edwards
19 Darren Dreyer
20 German Diaz
21 David DeMoss
22 David Dark
23 Chuck Daniel
24 Darren Tillman
25 London Bradley
26 Greg Mahlberg
27 Stan Kyles
28 Brad Bierley
29 Dick Cummings

1992 Fleer/ProCards Geneva Cubs

MT NR MT EX
Complete Set: 8.00

1551 Chuck Daniel
1552 David Dark
1553 Darren Dreyer
1554 Todd Edwards
1555 Scott Gardner
1556 Jonathan Jarolimek
1557 Collin Kerley
1558 Geno Morones
1559 Chris Rodriguez
1560 Adam Schulhofer
1561 Kennie Steenstra
1562 Hector Trinidad
1563 Mike Hubbard
1564 Paul Stojsavljevic
1565 Byron Bradley
1566 German Diaz
1567 Pat Fairly
1568 Chris Petersen
1569 Chad Tredaway
1570 Jose Tuujillo
1571 Dave DeMoss
1572 Robin Jennings
1573 Dan Madsen
1574 Darren Tillman
1575 Pedro Valdez
1576 Brad Bierley
1577 Stan Kyles
1578 Checklist

1992 Classic Best Greensboro Hornets

MT NR MT EX
Complete Set: 6.00

1 Andy Pettitte
2 Keith Garagozza
3 Tim Flannelly
4 Shane Spencer
5 Andrew Croghan
6 Frank Laviano
7 Jorge Posada
8 Sean Smith
9 Ben Short
10 John Thibert
11 Thomas Wilson
12 Steve Phillips
13 Scott Gully
14 Billy Coleman
15 Rick Lantrip
16 Peter Gietzen
17 Bert Inman
18 Steve Anderson
19 Grant Sullivan
20 Lew Hill
21 Tim Cooper
22 Steve Munda
23 Rick Turrentine
24 Mark Hubbard
25 Tate Seefried
26 Trey Hillman
27 Mark Rose
28 Brian Milner
29 Greg Spratt

1992 Fleer/ProCards Greensboro Hornets

MT NR MT EX
Complete Set: 6.00

770 Billy Coleman
771 Andy Croghan
772 Keith Garagozzo
773 Peter Gietzen
774 Scott Gully
775 Bert Inman
776 Steve Munda
777 Andy Petitte
778 Ben Short
779 Sean Smith
780 Grant Sullivan
781 Jose Pineda
782 Jorge Posada
783 Tom Wilson
784 Steve Anderson
785 Tim Cooper
786 Tim Flannelly
787 Elston Hansen
788 Rick Lantrip
789 Tate Seefried
790 Richard Turrentine
791 Tim Demerson
792 Lew Hill
793 Mark Hubbard
794 Steve Phillips
795 Shane Spencer
796 Trey Hillman
797 Brian Milner
798 Mark Rose
799 Checklist

1992 Fleer/ProCards Greenville Braves

MT NR MT EX
Complete Set: 9.00

1147 Brian Bark
1148 Pedro Borbon
1149 Dennis Burlingame
1150 Donnie Elliott
1151 Judd Johnson
1152 Don Strange
1153 Scott Taylor
1154 Marcos Vasquez
1155 Preston Watson
1156 Javy Lopez
1157 Eduardo Perez
1158 Mike Bell
1159 Ed Giovanola
1160 Pat Kelly
1161 Mike Mordecai
1162 Jose Olmeda
1163 Edwin Alicea
1164 Mike Kelly
1165 Melvin Nieves
1166 Tony Tarasco
1167 Aubrey Waggoner
1168 Grady Little
1169 Mark Ross
1170 Bill Slack
1171 Checklist

1992 Fleer/ProCards Gulf Coast Dodgers

MT NR MT EX
Complete Set: 6.00

3557 Jason Bobb
3558 Kenny Cook
3559 Chris Costello
3560 Roberto Durant
3561 Kacy Hendricks
3562 Dan Markham
3563 Jesus Martinez
3564 Jayson Perez
3565 Danny Sarmiento
3566 Kevin Smith
3567 Bill Stephens
3568 Gavin Edmondson
3569 Anthony Rodriguez
3570 Paul Wittig
3571 Dwain Bostic
3572 Miguel Cairo
3573 Eduardo Lantigue
3574 Tyrone Lewis
3575 Brian Richardson
3576 Fausto Urena
3577 Ervan Wingate
3578 Paul Flagg
3579 Eduardo Garcia
3580 Juan Hernaiz
3581 Dwight Maness
3582 Clarence Richmond
3583 John Shoemakere
3584 John Knapp
3586 Doug Simunic
3587 Checklist

1992 Fleer/ProCards Gulf Coast Mets

MT NR MT EX
Complete Set: 6.00

3470 Derek Baker
3471 Bobby Carr
3472 John Harris
3473 Brent Hayward
3474 Jason Isringhausen
3475 James Knott
3476 Juston Krablin
3477 Allen McDill
3478 Mark McGinn
3479 Rafael Roque
3480 Tyril Sherman
3481 R.J. Spang
3482 Ramon Tatis
3483 Chad Epperson
3484 Al Hammell
3485 Heriberto Morales
3486 Thomas Arvelo
3487 Bob Daly
3488 Jose Espinoza
3489 Mike Ferrell
3490 Josh Hagges
3491 Stephen Lackey
3492 Sandy Pichardo
3493 Rafael Guerrero
3494 Jerry Hiraldo
3495 Randy Warner
3496 Ty Young
3497 Junior Roman
3498 Felix Millian
3499 Jeff Edwards
3500 Checklist

1992 Fleer/ProCards Gulf Coast Yankees

MT NR MT EX
Complete Set: 10.00

3780 Charlie Brown
3781 Jeff Calcaterre
3782 Tyron Christopher
3783 Jeff Cindrich
3784 Shane Ferguson
3785 Mike Gordon
3786 Marty Janzen
3787 Kory Kiper
3788 Joe Long
3789 Randall McDermott
3790 Luis Parra
3791 Chad Plonk
3792 Luis Ramrirez
3793 Marcus Gipner
3794 Jaime Torres
3795 Cody Beason-Samuels
3796 Chris Heaps
3797 Derek Jeter
3798 Orangel Lopez
3799 David Renteria
3800 Jason Wuerch
3801 Glenn Dealfield
3802 Ricky Ledee
3803 Brian Lewis
3804 Travion Nelson
3805 Ruben Rivera
3806 Gary Denbo
3807 Rich Arena
3808 Team Picture
3809 Checklist

1992 Fleer/ProCards Hagerstown Suns

MT NR MT EX
Complete Set: 6.00

2549 Jeff Bumgarner
2550 Tim Drummond
2551 David Miller
2552 John O'Donoghue
2553 John Polasek
2554 Chuck Ricci
2555 Erik Schullstrom
2556 Jeff Williams
2557 Brian Wood
2558 Kip Vaughn
2559 Cesar Devares
2560 Manny Alexander
2561 Sam Ferretti
2562 Tim Holland
2563 Brent Miller
2564 Greg Roth
2565 Brad Tyler
2566 Mel Wearing
2567 Damond Buford
2568 Sergio Cairo
2569 Mark Smith
2570 Don Buford
2571 Joe Durham
2572 Moe Drabowsky
2573 Checklist

1992 Classic Best Hamilton Redbirds

MT NR MT EX
Complete Set: 6.00

1 Jeff Tanderys
2 Kirk Bullinger
3 Chad Smith
4 Blaine Milne
5 Jamie Cochran
6 Donnie Bellum
7 Ron French
8 Duff Brumley
9 Antonio Boone
10 Steve Jones
11 Andrew Martin
12 Keith Jones
13 Dennis Milius
14 Al Beavers
15 Tim DeGrasse
16 Ken Britt
17 Trey Ritz
18 Larry Gilligan
19 Tim Mathews
20 Tim Jordan
21 Alan Robinson
22 Darren Doucette
23 Mike Difelice
24 Keith Black

25 Jeff Murphy
26 Mike Gulan
27 Todd Henderson
28 Brad Owens
29 DeLynn Corry
30 Chris Maloney, Scott Melvin

1992 Fleer/ProCards Hamilton Redbirds

	MT	NR MT	EX
Complete Set:	6.00		

1579 Alan Beavers
1580 Antonio Boone
1581 Ken Britt
1582 Paul Brumley
1583 Kirk Bullinger
1584 Jamie Cochran
1585 DeLynn Corry
1586 Tim DeGrasse
1587 Steve Jones
1588 T.J. Mathews
1589 Dennis Milius
1590 David Oehrlein
1591 Chad Smith
1592 Jeff Tanderys
1593 Mike DiFelice
1594 Blaine Milne
1595 Jeff Murphy
1596 Keith Black
1597 Mike Gulan
1598 Darren Doucette
1599 Larry Gilligan
1600 Keith Johns
1601 Andy Martin
1602 Brad Owens
1603 Trey Ritz
1604 Donnie Bellum
1605 Ronnie French
1606 Todd Henderson
1607 Timmy Jordan
1608 Alan Robinson
1609 Field Staff
1610 Checklist

1992 Fleer/ProCards Harrisburg Senators

	MT	NR MT	EX
Complete Set:	6.00		

452 Doug Bochtler
453 Mario Brito
454 Travis Buckley
455 Mark Chapman
456 Chris Johnson
457 Chris Marchok
458 Mike Mathile
459 Chris Myers
460 Doug Piatt
461 Len Picota
462 Chris Pollack
463 Tim Laker
464 Joe Siddall
465 Bryn Kosco
466 Mike Lansing
467 Chris Martin
468 Chad McDonald
469 Derrick White
470 Steve Hecht
471 Rick Hirtensteiner
472 Jerome Nelson
473 Darwin Pennye
474 Jaimie Roseboro
475 Mike Quade
476 Mike Parrott
477 Checklist

1992 Fleer/ProCards Helena Brewers

	MT	NR MT	EX
Complete Set:	6.00		

1708 Jeff Droll
1709 David England
1710 Bobby Jones
1711 Scott Karl
1712 Dan Kyslinger
1713 Chris Petrocella
1714 ROn Rico
1715 Tom Schenbeck
1716 Rafael Torres
1717 Bill Dobrolsky
1718 Brian Hostetler
1719 George Behr
1720 Sean Holub
1721 Mark Kingston
1722 Robert Powers
1723 Scott Richardson
1724 Tim Unroe
1725 Wes Weger
1726 Kenny Felder
1727 Dana Hughes
1728 Shane Lay
1729 Danny Perez
1730 Cecil Rodriques
1731 Jackie Ross
1732 Jarry Dunlop
1733 Mike Caldwell
1734 Checklist

1992 Classic Best High Desert Mavericks

	MT	NR MT	EX
Complete Set:	7.00		

1 Rusty Silcox
2 Steve Gill
3 Brent Bish
4 Bill Meury
5 Pablo Martinez
6 Roberto Arredondo
7 Billy Hall
8 Kelly Lifgren
9 Ray McDavid
10 Linty Ingram
11 Tony Mortensen
12 Ed Zinter
13 Tookie Spann
14 Ted Devore
15 John Kuehl
16 Luis Galindez
17 Sean Mulligan
18 Geoffrey Kellogg
19 Bill Ostermeyer
20 Bryce Florie
21 Ryan Thibault
22 Jose LeBron
23 Rafael Chaves
24 Tom Martin
25 Julio Bruno
26 Lee Henderson
27 Darius Gash
28 Brian McKeon
29 Bryan Little
30 Bruce Tanner

1992 Classic Best Huntington Cubs

	MT	NR MT	EX
Complete Set:	6.00		

1 Brandon Pico
2 Robert Nutting
3 Jason Boehlow
4 Danny Montero
5 Andre Nelson
6 Ricky Perez
7 Roque Colon
8 Kevin Booker
9 Maceo Houston
10 Josh Simmons
11 Scott Barton
12 Micky Reeves
13 Dan Gustavson
14 Matt Lawrence
15 Jose Pacheco
16 Andy Elsbecker
17 Coleman Smith
18 Steven Walker
19 Mitch Root
20 William Latimer
21 Jon Waite
22 Patrick Kendrick
23 Chris Plonk
24 Tim Stutheit
25 Jay Hassel
26 Daryle Gavlick
27 Amaury Telemaco
28 Phillip Hannon
29 Gil Kubski
30 Greg Keuter

1992 Fleer/ProCards Huntington Cubs

	MT	NR MT	EX
Complete Set:	6.00		

3137 Billy Childress
3138 Andy Elsbecker
3139 Mario Garcia
3140 Darlye Gavlick
3141 Dan Gustavson
3142 Jay Hassel
3143 Patrick Kendrick
3144 William Latimer
3145 Matt Lawrence
3146 Luis Matos
3147 Jose Pacheco
3148 Amaury Talemaco
3149 Jon Waite
3150 Scott Barton
3151 Danny Montero
3152 Francisco Morales
3153 Jason Boehlow
3154 Robert Nutting
3155 Richard Perez
3156 Chris Plonk
3157 Mitch Root
3158 Josh Simmons
3159 Tim Stutheit
3160 Kevin Booker
3161 Roque Colon
3162 Maceo Houston
3163 Andre Nelson
3164 Brandon Pico
3165 Mickey Reeves
3166 Coleman Smith
3167 Steven Walker
3168 Checklist

1992 Fleer/ProCards Huntsville Stars

	MT	NR MT	EX
Complete Set:	6.00		

3940 Dana Allison
3941 Jeff Bittiger
3942 Scott Erwin
3943 Johnny Guzman
3944 Chad Kuhn
3945 Dave Latter
3946 Mike Mohler
3947 Gavin Osteen
3948 Bronswell Patrick
3949 Steve Phoenix
3950 Todd Revenig
3951 Rick Strebeck
3952 Dean Borrelli
3953 Jorge Brito
3954 Kurt Abbott
3955 Marcos Armas
3956 Webster Garrison
3957 Craig Paquette
3958 Darryl Vice
3959 Mike Conte
3960 Kevin Dattola
3961 Eric Fox
3962 Dave Jacas
3963 Scott Lydy
3964 Casey Parsons
3965 Bert Bradley
3966 Checklist

1992 Team Huntsville Stars

This set was given away on a special night, continuing a tradition that began in 1985. The 26-card set measures 2-3/8" x 3-1/2", and is unnumbered, listed below in alphabetical order. The cards contain statistical information on the back, and Burger King logos appear on both sides of the card. The format is identical to other team issues in the series from Huntsville. This set may also include a card listing northern Alabama locations of sponsor Burger King.

	MT	NR MT	EX
Complete Set:	4.00		

(1) Kurt Abbott
(2) Dana Allison
(3) Marcos Armas
(4) Dean Borrelli
(5) Bert Bradley
(6) Jorge Brito
(7) Mike Conte
(8) Kevin Dattola
(9) Scott Erwin
(10) Chaon Garland
(11) Webster Garrison
(12) Johnny Guzman
(13) David Jacas
(14) Chad Kuhn
(15) Dave Latter
(16) Scott Lydy
(17) Mike Mohler
(18) Gavin Osteen
(19) Craig Paquette
(20) Casey Parsons
(21) Bronswell Patrick
(22) Steve Phoenix
(23) Todd Revenig
(24) Rick Strebeck
(25) Darryl Vice
(26) Pat Wernig

1992 Fleer/ProCards Idaho Falls Gems

	MT	NR MT	EX
Complete Set:	8.00		

3501 Scott Behrens
3502 Craig Bradshaw
3503 Chris Brock
3504 Burke Cromer
3505 Stewart Ford
3506 Ken Giard
3507 Eric Lairsey
3508 Bill Maitland
3509 Yves Martineau
3510 David Pike
3511 Chris Rusciano
3512 John Simmons
3513 Tony Stoecklin
3514 Terrell Wade
3515 Ben Lavigne
3516 Kevin Schula
3517 Miguel Soto
3518 Kevin Nalls
3519 Rob Newman
3520 Van Torian
3521 Gerald Trevino
3522 Tom Waldrop
3523 Doug Wollenburg
3524 David Bingham
3525 Miguel Correa
3526 Ralph Garr
3527 Andre Johnson
3528 Sherton Saturnino
3529 Michael Warner
3530 Byron Woods
3531 Dave Hilton
3532 Checklist

1992 Fleer/ProCards Indianapolis Indians

	MT	NR MT	EX
Complete Set:	6.00		

1852 Blaine Beatty
1853 Kent Bottenfield
1854 Howard Farmer
1855 Matt Maysey
1856 Dana Ridenour
1857 Bill Risley
1858 Doug Simons
1859 Sergio Valdez
1860 David Wainhouse
1861 Darrin Fletcher
1862 Jim Kremers
1863 Bob Natal
1864 Greg Colbrunn
1865 Will Cordero
1866 Greg Fulton
1867 Jeff Goff
1868 Omer Munoz
1869 F.P. Santangelo
1870 Razor Shines
1871 Shon Ashley
1872 Eric Bullock
1873 Jim Eppard
1874 Quinn Mack
1875 Pat Kelly
1876 Rich Dubee
1877 Gomer Hodge
1878 Checklist

1992 Fleer/ProCards Iowa Cubs

	MT	NR MT	EX
Complete Set:	6.00		

4044 Steve Adkins
4045 Brad Arnsberg
4046 Hector Berrios
4047 John Gardner
4048 Jeff Hartsock
4049 Scott May
4050 Laddie Renfroe
4051 Bob Sebra
4052 Julio Strauss
4053 Mike Knapp
4054 Jorge Pedre
4055 Alex Arias
4056 Billy Bates
4057 Pedro Castellano
4058 Darrin Duffy
4059 Scott Bryant
4060 Tony Chance
4061 Fernando Ramsey
4062 Kevin Roberson
4063 Jeff Schulz
4064 Scott Wade
4065 Brad Mills
4066 Rick Kranitz
4067 Checklist

1992 Fleer/ProCards Jackson Generals

	MT	NR MT	EX
Complete Set:	6.00		

3991 Harold Allen
3992 Jim Bruske
3993 Fred Costello
3994 Brian Griffiths
3995 Dean Hartgraves
3996 Keith Helton
3997 Bob Hurta
3998 Todd Jones
3999 Jim Lewis
4000 Richie Simon
4001 Scott Makarewicz
4002 Jeff Ball
4003 David Hajek
4004 Rusty Harris
4005 Frank Kellner
4006 Lance Madsen
4007 Joe Mikulik
4008 Roberto Petagine
4009 Howard Prager
4010 Willie Ansley
4011 Jeff Baldwin
4012 Ray Montgomery
4013 Lee Sammons
4014 Rick Sweet
4015 Charley Taylor
4016 Don Reynolds
4017 Checklist

1992 Fleer/ProCards Jacksonville Suns

	MT	NR MT	EX
Complete Set:	6.50		

3700 Jeff Borski
3701 Jim Converse
3702 Mark Czarkowski
3703 Fernando Figueroa
3704 Brad Holman
3705 Troy Kent
3706 Scott Pitcher
3707 Kerry Woodson
3708 Clint Zavaras
3709 Jim Campanis
3710 Greg Pirkl
3711 Craig Wilson
3712 Frank Bolick
3713 Mike Bond
3714 Jim Bowie
3715 Bobby Holley
3716 Shane Letterio
3717 Anthony Manahan
3718 Brian Turang
3719 Ellerton Maynard
3720 Mike McDonald
3721 Mark Merchant
3722 Marc Newfield
3723 Jesus Tavarez
3724 Bob Hartsfield
3725 Checklist

1992 Classic Best Jamestown Expos

	MT	NR MT	EX
Complete Set:	6.00		

1 Rodney Henderson
2 Jim Henderson
3 Tom Doyle
4 Steve Falteisek
5 Alex Pacheco
6 Matt Rundels
7 Todd Dreifort
8 Robert Campillo
9 Scott Pisciotta
10 James Ferguson
11 Alfred Kermode
12 Charles Lee
13 Everett Stull
14 Danny Lane
15 Brad Aurila
16 Matt Allen
17 Scott Gentile
18 Curt Schmidt
19 Yamil Benitez
20 Scott Harrison
21 Edgar Tovar
22 Jim Rushworth
23 Matt Raleigh
24 Kevin Northrup
25 David Eggert
26 Q.V. Lowe
27 Jim Fleming
28 Martin Robitaille
29 Lee Slagle

1992 Fleer/ProCards Jamestown Expos

	MT	NR MT	EX
Complete Set:	6.00		

1492 David Eggert
1493 Steven Falteisek
1494 Jim Ferguson
1495 Scott Gentile
1496 Scott Harrison
1497 Rodney Henderson
1498 Al Kermoda
1499 Alex Pacheco
1500 Scott Pisciotta
1501 Jim Rushworth
1502 Curtis Schmidt
1503 Everett Stull
1504 Matt Allen
1505 Robert Campillo
1506 Brad Aurila
1507 Danny Lane
1508 Matt Raleigh
1509 Matt Rundels
1510 Edgar Tovar
1511 Yamil Benitez
1512 Todd Driefort
1513 Charles Lee
1514 Kevin Northrup
1515 Stan Robertson
1516 Q.V. Lowe
1517 Jim Fleming
1518 Martin Robitailk
1519 Checklist

1992 Classic Best Johnson City Cardinals

	MT	NR MT	EX
Complete Set:	6.00		

1 Basil Shabazz
2 Derek Stanley
3 Douglas Goodman
4 Steven Dudek
5 Rongie Dicken
6 Juan Ballara
7 Charles Anderson
8 Jose Vazquez
9 Jesus Uqueto
10 Aldo Pecorilli
11 Santo Mota
12 Antoine Henry
13 Chad Sumner
14 Charles Pittman
15 Jose Lopez
16 Joe Larson
17 Don Slattery
18 Eric Miller
19 Darryl Meek
20 Jeffrey Matulevich
21 James Marchesi
22 Hector Colon
23 Duffy Guyton
24 Joe Carrillo
25 Todd Blake
26 Steve Turco
27 Orlando Thomas
28 Mike Gaddie

1992 Fleer/ProCards Johnson City Cardinals

	MT	NR MT	EX
Complete Set:	6.00		

3106 Todd Blake
3107 Joe Carrillo
3108 Doug Goodman
3109 Duffy Guyton
3110 Joe Larson
3111 Jose Lopez
3112 Jim Marchesi
3113 Jeff Matrange
3114 Jeff Matulevich
3115 Darryl Meek
3116 Eric Miller
3117 Chuck Pittman
3118 Juan Ballera
3119 Aldo Pecorilli
3120 Mark Williams
3121 Charlie Anderson
3122 Rongie Dicken
3123 Steve Dudek
3124 Santo Mota
3125 Don Slattery
3126 John Stutz
3127 Chad Sumner
3128 Jesus Ugueto
3129 Hector Colon
3130 Antoine Henry
3131 Basil Shabazz
3132 Derek Stanley
3133 Jose Vasquez
3134 Steve Turco
3135 Orlando Thomas
3136 Checklist

1992 Classic Best Kane County Cougars

	MT	NR MT	EX
Complete Set:	10.00		

1 B.J. Waszgis
2 Drew Johnson
3 Roy Hodge
4 Don Gilbert
5 Curtis Goodwin
6 Matt Jarvis
7 Mat Sanders
8 T.R. Lewis
9 Kris Gresham
10 Scott McClain
11 Chris Lemp
12 Troy Tallman
13 Alex Ochoa
14 Rick Krivda
15 Keith Schmidt
16 Juan Mercedes
17 Feliciano Mercedes
18 Jimmy Haynes
19 Shawn O'Connell
20 Bobby Chouinard
21 Derek Adams
22 Rick Forney
23 Ihosvany Marquez
24 Steve Firsich
25 Clayton Byrne
26 Joel Youngblood
27 Larry McCall
28 Peter Howell

1992 Fleer/ProCards Kane County Cougars

	MT	NR MT	EX
Complete Set:	10.00		

82 Bobby Chouinard
83 Steve Firsich
84 Rick Forney
85 Jimmy Haynes
86 Matt Jarvis
87 Rick Krivda
88 Chris Lemp
89 Ihosvany Marquez
90 Juan Mercedes
91 Shawn O'Connell
92 Mat Sanders
93 Kris Gresham
94 Troy Tallman
95 B.J. Waszgis
96 Derek Adams
97 Donald Gilbert
98 Drew Johnson
99 T.R. Lewis
100 Scott McClain
101 Feliciano Mercedes
102 Stewart Ruiz
103 Clayton Byrne
104 Curtis Goodwin
105 Roy Hodge
106 Alex Ochoa
107 Keith Schmidt
108 Joel Youngblood
109 Larry McCall
110 Checklist

1992 Team Kane County Cougars

This 30-card set marked the second straight year the Midwest League team issued its own cards. The front of the cards has a high-gloss coating, with player stats and bio information on the back. The cards measure 2-1/2" x 3-1/2", and are skip-numbered according to the player's uniform number.

	MT	NR MT	EX
Complete Set:	6.00		

(2) Curtis Goodwin
(4) Drew Johnson
(6) Estuar Ruiz
(7) Eugenio Delgado
(8) Gregg Castaldo
(9) Chris Lemp
(10) Kris Gresham
(11) Keith Schmidt
(12) Joel Youngblood
(15) B.J. Waszgis
(16) Rick Krivida
(18) Jimmy Haynes
(19) Bobby Chouinard
(20) Derek Adams
(21) Steve Firisch
(22) Brad Brimhall
(23) Alex Ochoa
(24) Scott Klingenbeck
(25) Rich Dauer
(26) Don Gilbert
(31) Clayton Byrne
(32) Juan Mercedes
(34) Billy Owens
(35) Scott McClain
(36) Larry McCall
(37) Matt Jarvis
(39) Mat Sanders
(43) Rick Forney
---- Ozzie the Mascot
---- Peter Howell (trainer)

1992 Classic Best Kenosha Twins

	MT	NR MT	EX
Complete Set:	6.00		

1 Jamie Ogden
2 Jeff Mansur
3 Eddie Guardado
4 David Sartain
5 Glenn Evans
6 Carlos Estevez
7 Tim Moore
8 Todd Blakeman
9 A.J. Johnson
10 Greg Johnson
11 Steve Hazlett
12 Damien Miller
13 Marlo Nava
14 Kerry Taylor
15 Ken Norman
16 Luis Garcia
17 David Garrow
18 Bill Wissler
19 Brent Brede
20 Monte Dufault
21 Bob Carlson
22 Brad Radke
23 Dom Konieczki
24 Michael Fernandez
25 Jim Dwyer
26 Rick Anderson
27 Dan Fox

1992 Fleer/ProCards Kenosha Twins

	MT	NR MT	EX
Complete Set:	6.00		

595 Sandy Diaz
596 Luis Garcia
597 Sean Gavaghan
598 Eddie Guardado
599 Dominic Konieczi
600 Dan Naulty
601 Brad Radke
602 David Sartain
603 Dennis Sweeney
604 Kerry Taylor
605 Scott Watkins
606 Bill Wissler
607 Kyle Caple
608 Damian Miller
609 Marc Claus
610 Monte Dufault
611 Mike Fernandez
612 David Garrow
613 Greg Johnson
614 Andrew Kontorinis
615 Brent Brede
616 Anthony Byrd
617 Steve Hazlett
618 Tim Moore
619 Jamie Ogden
620 Jim Dwyer
621 Rick Anderson
622 Checklist

1992 Classic Best Kingsport Mets

	MT	NR MT	EX
Complete Set:	6.00		

1 Terrell Williams
2 Kenny Bradley
3 Jared Osentowski
4 Travis Shaffer
5 David Swanson
6 Jeff Kiraly
7 Steve Grennan
8 Eric Harris
9 Al Shirley
10 Raul Casanova
11 Steven Steele
12 Allen McDill
13 Erik Hiljus
14 Mark Wipf
15 Tom Pinson
16 Scottie Williams
17 Eddy Beltre
18 Marc Kroon
19 Pedro Belmonte
20 Ervin Collier
21 Jose Flores
22 Andrew Cotner
23 Andre David
24 Jesus Hernaiz
25 Kevin Culpepper
26 Geary Jones

1992 Fleer/ProCards Kingsport Mets

	MT	NR MT	EX
Complete Set:	6.00		

1520 Bill Bellman
1521 Pedro Belmonte
1522 Chris Berg
1523 Ervin Collier
1524 Andrew Cotner
1525 Steve Grennan
1526 Erik Hijus
1527 Marc Kroon
1528 Allen McDill
1529 Tom Pinson
1530 Travis Shaffer
1531 Dave Swanson
1532 Scott Williams
1533 Raul Casanova
1534 Eric Harris
1535 Steve Steele
1536 Eddy Beltre
1537 Kenny Bradley
1538 Joe Flores
1539 Jeff Kiraly
1540 Jim Mrowka
1541 Ozzie Osentowski
1542 Terrell Williams
1543 Don Parker
1544 Al Shirley
1545 Donnie White
1546 Mark Wipf
1547 Andre David

1548 Geary Jones
1549 Jesus Hernaiz
1550 Checklist

1992 Classic Best Kinston Indians

	MT	NR MT	EX
Complete Set:	6.00		

1 Shawn Bryant
2 Ryan Martindale
3 Brian Cofer
4 Omar Ramirez
5 Dickie Brown
6 Ty Kovach
7 Tommy Bates
8 Gary Tatterson
9 Rouglas Odor
10 John Lorms
11 Tim Donahue
12 Raymond Harvey
13 Carl Johnson
14 Chip Winiarski
15 Roberto Rivera
16 John Cotton
17 Alan Embree
18 David Bell
19 Eric Stone
20 Clyde Pough
21 Greg McCarthy
22 Darrell Whitmore
23 Herbert Perry
24 Tom Van Tiger
25 Chad Ogea
26 Dave Keller
27 Rick Horton
28 Rob Swain
29 Dan Doyle

1992 Fleer/ProCards Kinston Indians

	MT	NR MT	EX
Complete Set:	15.00		

2466 Chad Allen
2467 Shawn Bryant
2468 Brian Cofer
2469 Alan Embree
2470 Ty Kovach
2471 Greg McCarthy
2472 Scott Morgan
2473 Chad Ogee
2474 Roberto Rivera
2475 Mark Sweeney
2476 Eric Stone
2477 Chip Winiarski
2478 John Lorms
2479 Ryan Martindale
2480 Tommy Bates
2481 David Bell
2482 John Cotton
2483 Tim Donohue
2484 Ray Harvey
2485 Rouglas Odor
2486 Herbert Perry
2487 Clyde Pough
2488 Manny Ramirez
2489 Omar ramirez
2490 Darrell Whitmore
2491 Dave Keller
2492 Rick Horton
2493 Rob Swain
2494 Checklist

1992 Fleer/ProCards Knoxville Blue Jays

	MT	NR MT	EX
Complete Set:	6.50		

2981 Daren Brown
2982 Tim Brown
2983 Nate Cromwell
2984 Jesse Cross
2985 Daren Kizziah
2986 Graeme Lloyd
2987 Paul Menhart
2988 Marcus Moore
2989 Mike Ogliaruso
2990 Mark Ohims
2991 Aaron Small
2992 Jose Monzon
2993 Greg O'Halloran
2994 Jason Townley
2995 Domingo Cedeno
2996 Derek Henderson
2997 Brad Mengel
2998 Rob Montalvo
2999 Rance Milliniks
3000 David Tollison
3001 Julian Yan
3002 Juan De La Rose
3003 Robert Perez
3004 Shawn Scott
3005 Nigel Wilson
3006 Garth Iorg
3007 Mike McAlpin
3008 Steve Mingori
3009 Checklist

1992 Classic Best Lakeland Tigers

	MT	NR MT	EX
Complete Set:	6.00		

1 Bob Undorf
2 Mike Rendina
3 Eric Albright
4 Dan Ruff
5 Joe Perona
6 Ron Howard
7 Kelley O'Neal
8 Denny McNamara
9 Jose Lima
10 Brian Saltzgaber
11 Jimmy Alder
12 Greg Coppeta
13 Mike Guilfoyle
14 John Kosenski
15 Matt Bauer
16 Felipe Lira
17 Jim Henry
18 Jason Pfaff
19 Sean Bergman
20 Phil Stidham
21 Tom Drell
22 Jim Givens
23 Tom Ealy
24 Warren Sawkiw
25 Ed Rodriguez
26 Rudy Pemberton
27 John Lipon
28 Rich Bombard
29 Dan Raley
30 Steve Carter

1992 Fleer/ProCards Lakeland Tigers

	MT	NR MT	EX
Complete Set:	6.00		

2271 Pat Ahearne
2272 Mike Guilfoyle
2273 John Kosenski
2274 Jose Lima
2275 Felipe Lira
2276 Jason Pfaff
2277 John Reid
2278 Eddy Rodriguez
2279 Phillip Stidham
2280 Bob Undorf
2281 Pedro Gonzalez
2282 Joe Perona
2283 Brian Saltzgaber
2284 Jimmy Alder
2285 Jim Givens
2286 Ron Howard
2287 Kelley O'Neal
2288 Mike Randina
2289 Dan Ruff
2290 Tom Ealy
2291 Denny McNamara
2292 Rudy Pemberton
2293 John Lipon
2294 Rich Bombard
2295 Dan Raley
2296 Checklist

1992 Fleer/ProCards Las Vegas Stars

	MT	NR MT	EX
Complete Set:	6.00		

2789 Doug Brocail
2790 Rick Davis
2791 Jim Deshaies
2792 Jeremy Hernandez
2793 Mark Knudson
2794 Adam Peterson
2795 A.J. Sager
2796 Tim Scott
2797 Rafael Valdez
2798 Mike Basso
2799 Paul Faries
2800 Jeff Gardner
2801 Kevin Higgins
2802 Chris Jelic
2803 Luis Lopez
2804 Phil Stephenson
2805 Guilermo Velasquez
2806 Steve Pegues
2807 Dave Staton
2808 Jim Vatcher
2809 Jim Riggleman
2810 Tony Torchia
2811 Jon Matlack
2812 Checklist

1992 Fleer/ProCards London Tigers

	MT	NR MT	EX
Complete Set:	6.00		

623 Don August
624 Jeff Braley
625 Sherman Corbett
626 Dan Freed
627 Mike Garcia
628 Frank Gonzales
629 Jimmy Henry
630 Mike Lumley
631 Rick Rojas
632 Don Vesling
633 Brian Warren
634 Marty Willis
635 Steve Wolf
636 Mike Gillette
637 Rick Sellers
638 Ivan Cruz
639 Mike DeButch
640 Kirk Mendenhall
641 Bob Reimink
642 Rod Robertson
643 Basilio Cabrera
644 Brian Cornelius
645 Lou Frazier
646 Tyrone Kingwood
647 Greg Sparks
648 Mark DeJohn
649 Bruce Fields
650 Jeff Jones
651 Checklist

1992 Fleer/ProCards Louisville Redbirds

	MT	NR MT	EX
Complete Set:	6.00		

1879 Rene Arocha
1880 Jeff Ballard
1881 Mike Cook
1882 Mark Grater
1883 Mike Hinkle
1884 Blaise Ilsley
1885 Paul Kilgus
1886 Mike Loynd
1887 Tim Sherrill
1888 Tom Urbani
1889 Ed Fulton
1890 Tim Redman
1891 Alex Trevino
1892 Greg Carmona
1893 Bien Figueroa
1894 Stan Royer
1895 Jeff Shireman
1896 Tracy Woodson
1897 Rod Brewer
1898 Ozzie Canseco
1899 Chuck Carr
1900 Curt Ford
1901 Lonnie Maclin
1902 Jack Krol
1903 Mark Riggins
1904 Checklist

1992 Team Louisville Redbirds

As in the previous five seasons, the Redbirds set was released after the end of the regular season. Unlike the past sets, the 1992 issue does not include all players who appeared in a Louisville uniform. Cards 1-22 were of players assigned to the team, 23-28 are players who appeared as part of a rehabilitation assignment, 29 and 30 are special cards of President George Bush (who threw out the first pitch on opening day) and the manager and coach.

	MT	NR MT	EX
Complete Set:	8.00		

(1) Luis Alicea
(2) Rene Arocha
(3) Jeff Ballard
(4) Rod Brewer
(5) Ozzie Canseco
(6) Chuck Carr
(7) Mark Clark
(8) Rheal Cormier
(9) Steve Dixon
(10) Mark Grater
(11) Brian Jordan
(12) Paul Kilgus
(13) Lonnie Maclin
(14) Mike Milchin
(15) Donovan Osborne
(16) Stan Royer
(17) Tim Sherrill
(18) Tom Urbani
(19) Allen Watson
(20) Craig Wilson
(21) Tracy Woodson
(22) Todd Zeile
(23) Andres Galarraga
(24) Pedro Guerrero
(25) Joe Magrane
(26) Jose Oquendo
(27) Geronimo Pena
(28) Bryn Smith
(29) George Bush
(30) Jack Krol, Mark Riggins

1992 Classic Best Lynchburg Red Sox

	MT	NR MT	EX
Complete Set:	16.00		

1 Frank Rodriguez
2 John Eierman
3 Pete Estrada
4 Jose Marin
5 Cory Bailey
6 Jason Friedman
7 Tony Rodriguez
8 Denny Berni
9 Walt McKeel
10 Paul Rappoli
11 Luis Ortiz
12 Tim Graham
13 Erik Plantenberg
14 Andy Rush
15 David Klvac
16 Aaron Sele
17 Kevin Carroll
18 Jim Crowley
19 Boo Moore
20 Joe Caruso
21 Mark Konopki
22 John Malzone
23 Tim VanEgmond
24 Jim Dennison
25 Jim Morrison
26 Buddy Bailey
27 David Duchin

1992 Fleer/ProCards Lynchburg Red Sox

	MT	NR MT	EX
Complete Set:	16.00		

2898 Cory Bailey
2899 Joe Caruso
2900 Jim Dennison
2901 Pete Estrada
2902 Dave Kivac
2903 Mark Konopki
2904 Erik Plantenberg
2905 Frank Rodriguez
2906 Andy Rush
2907 Aaron Sele
2908 Tim Vanegmond
2909 Denny Berni
2910 Kevin Carroll
2911 Walt McKeel
2912 Jim Crowley
2913 Jason Friedman
2914 John Malzone
2915 Jose Marin
2916 Luis Ortiz
2917 Tony Rodriguez
2918 John Eierman
2919 Tim Graham
2920 Boo Moore
2921 Jim Morrison
2922 Paul Rappoli
2923 Checklist

1992 Classic Best Macon Braves

	MT	NR MT	EX
Complete Set:	6.00		

1 Anthony Graffagnino
2 Dirk Blair
3 Lansing Marks
4 David Toth
5 Geroge Virgilio
6 Dario Paulino
7 Steve Swail
8 Vincent Jimenez
9 Joe Ayrault
10 Travis Dunlap
11 Cory Crosnoe
12 John Wilder
13 Blase Sparma
14 Kevin Saulter
15 Jason Butler
16 Michael Josephina
17 Juan Williams
18 Vincent Moore
19 Jason Keeline
20 Carlos Reyes
21 Michael Place
22 Christopher Seelbach
23 Robert Burgess
24 Don Robinson
25 Jason Schmidt
26 Brian Snitker
27 Glenn Hubbard
28 Larry Jaster

1992 Fleer/ProCards Macon Braves

	MT	NR MT	EX
Complete Set:	6.00		

258 Dirk Blair
259 Kurt Burgess
260 Jason Butler

261 Travis Dunlap
262 Scott Francis
263 Jerry Koller
264 Mike Place
265 Carlos Reyes
266 Kevin Saulter
267 Jason Schmidt
268 Chris Seelbach
269 John Wilder
270 Joe Ayrault
271 David Toth
272 Cory Crosnoe
273 Anthony Graffagnino
274 Manny Jimenez
275 Jason Keeline
276 Lance Marks
277 Dominic Therrien
278 George Virgilio
279 Mike Josephino
280 Vince Moore
281 Richard Paulino
282 Don Robinson
283 Juan Williams
284 Brian Snitker
285 Glenn Hubbard
286 Larry Jaster
287 Checklist

1992 Classic Best Madison Muskies

	MT	NR MT	EX
Complete Set:	6.00		

1 Creighton Gubanich
2 Ramon Fermin
3 Jeff Duncan
4 Dane Walker
5 Greg Reid
6 Rob Leary
7 Miguel Jimenez
8 Tom Havens
9 Gary Hust
10 Ricardo Mendez
11 Eric Booker
12 Steve Shoemaker
13 Lee Cusey
14 Luinis Aracena
15 Scott Sheldon
16 George Williams
17 Brad Parker
18 Brad Stowell
19 Ray Sutch
20 Mike Rossiter
21 Tom Myers
22 Robert Pierce
23 Scott Rose
24 Tony Scharff
25 Vincente Francisco
26 Dick Scott
27 Gil Patterson
28 Brian Thorson

1992 Fleer/ProCards Madison Muskies

	MT	NR MT	EX
Complete Set:	6.00		

1226 Lee Cusey
1227 Ramon Fermin
1228 Miguel Jimenez
1229 Keith Millay
1230 Tim Minik
1231 Tom Myers
1232 Rob Pierce
1233 Scott Rosa
1234 Mike Rossiter
1235 Steve Shoemaker
1236 Brad Stowell
1237 Ray Sutch
1238 Creighton Gubanich
1239 George Williams
1240 Jeff Duncan
1241 Vincente Francisco
1242 Tom Havens
1243 Rob Leary
1244 Ricardo Mendez
1245 Brad Parker
1246 Scott Sheldon
1247 Luinis Aracena
1248 Eric Booker
1249 Gary Hust
1250 Greg Reid
1251 Dane Walker
1252 Dickie Scott
1253 Gil Patterson
1254 Checklist

1992 Classic Best Martinsville Phillies

	MT	NR MT	EX
Complete Set:	6.00		

1 Larry Mitchell
2 Michael Crouwel
3 Sean Boldt
4 Charlton Moore
5 Michael Thompson
6 Tony Costa
7 Ben Martinez
8 Joey Jelinek
9 Philip Romero
10 Ricky Bush
11 Jason Urbanek
12 Rob Mitchell
13 Scott Coleman
14 Tim Costa
15 Jeremy Kendall
16 Scott Haws
17 Tim Pugh
18 Brent Bell
19 Mike Shipman
20 David Fisher
21 William Carmona
22 Tony Fiore
23 Sam Edwards
24 Kevin Alger
25 E.J. Brophy
26 Dell Allen
27 Fernando Mejias
28 Steve Nutt
29 Stanley Evans
30 Roly DeArmas

1992 Fleer/ProCards Martinsville Phillies

	MT	NR MT	EX
Complete Set:	6.00		

3045 Kevin Alger
3046 Sean Boldt
3047 Scott Coleman
3048 Tim Costa
3049 Sam Edwards
3050 Tony Fiore
3051 Trevor Humphrey
3052 Fernando Mejias
3053 Larry Mitchell
3054 Rob Mitchell
3055 Steven Nutt
3056 Tim Pugh
3057 E.J. Brophy
3058 Ricky Bush
3059 Mike Crouwell
3060 Scott Haws
3061 Mike Shipman
3062 Dell Allen
3063 Brent Bell
3064 David Fisher
3065 Joey Jelinek
3066 Phillip Romero
3067 Jason Urbanek
3068 William Carmona
3069 Tim Cornish
3070 Stanley Evans
3071 Jeremy Kendall
3072 Ben Martinez
3073 Charlton Moore
3074 Michael Thompson
3075 Roly DeArmas
3076 Checklist

1992 Fleer/ProCards Medicine Hat Blue Jays

	MT	NR MT	EX
Complete Set:	6.00		

3201 Alonso Beltran
3202 Walt Bills
3203 Chad Brown
3204 Pat Crema
3205 Andrew Dolson
3206 Harry Moir
3207 Mike O'Halloran
3208 Randy Phillips
3209 Gabriel Reynoso
3210 Angel Martinez
3211 Pete Polis
3212 Carlos Colmenares
3213 Emanuel Hayes
3214 Matt Johnson
3215 Alexis Luna
3216 Wade Norris
3217 Matt Wilke
3218 Rickey Cradle
3219 Sean Hearn
3220 Jose Herrera
3221 Kadir Villalona
3222 Jim Nettles
3223 Scott Miller
3224 Checklist

1992 Fleer/ProCards Memphis Chicks

	MT	NR MT	EX
Complete Set:	6.00		

2410 Archie Corbin
2411 Steve Curry
2412 Chip Duncan
2413 Greg Harvey
2414 Matt Karchner
2415 Danny Micelli
2416 Mark Parnell
2417 Vladimir Perez
2418 Ed Pierce
2419 Ed Puig
2420 Skip Wiley
2421 Greg David
2422 Carlos Diaz
2423 Lance Jennings
2424 Paco Burgos
2425 Jeff Garber
2426 Phil Hiatt
2427 Domingo Mota
2428 Darryl Robinson
2429 Rich Tunison
2430 Tony Bridges
2431 Tim Leiper
2432 Les Norman
2433 Dan Rohrmeier
2434 Doug Shields
2435 Brian Poldberg
2436 Mike Alvarez
2437 U.L. Washington
2438 Checklist

1992 Fleer/ProCards Midland Angels

	MT	NR MT	EX
Complete Set:	6.00		

4018 Dave Adams
4019 Marvin Cobb
4020 Ken Edenfield
4021 Mark Holzemer
4022 Todd James
4023 Joe Kraemer
4024 Phil Leftwich
4025 Brett Merriman
4026 Steve Peck
4027 Darryl Scott
4028 Paul Swingle
4029 Mark Zappelli
4030 Mick Billmeyeer
4031 Fausto Tejero
4032 Ron Correia
4033 Walt McConnell
4034 Jonathan Romero
4035 Terry Taylor
4036 Tony Brown
4037 Jim Edmonds
4038 Jeff Kipila
4039 Dan Rumsey
4040 Don Long
4041 Nate Oliver
4042 Kernan Ronan
4043 Checklist

1992 Team Midland Angels

This 28-card set was issued by the Midland Angels and sponsored by a local camera shop, One Hour Photo. The cards are 5" x 5-1/2", and have player information on the front of the card, with blank backs (since the cards are printed on photographic stock). The cards are unnumbered. They were given away weekly and included an opportunity for fans receiving the cards to get them autographed by the players. Two of the cards don't have the player's name. Mark Wasinger is pictured in his batting stance, and Fausto Tejero is wearing uniform number 33.

	MT	NR MT	EX
Complete Set:	6.00		

(1) Dave Adams
(2) Garrett Anderson
(3) Tony Brown
(4) Rod Correia
(5) Ken Edenfield
(6) Jim Edmonds
(7) Billy Hathaway
(8) John Jackson
(9) Todd James
(10) Bobby Jones
(11) Corey Kapano
(12) Jeff Kipila
(13) Joe Kraemer
(14) Marcus Lawton
(15) Ray Martinez
(16) Brett Merriman
(17) Nate Oliver
(18) Steve Peck
(19) Troy Percival
(20) Eduardo Perez
(21) J.R. Phillips
(22) Darryl Scott
(23) Paul Swingle
(24) Terry Taylor
(25) Fausto Tejero
(26) Don Vidmar
(27) Mark Wasinger
(28) Mark Zappelli

1992 Classic Best Modesto A's

	MT	NR MT	EX
Complete Set:	8.00		

1 Jason Wood
2 Curtis Shaw
3 Eric Helfand
4 Damond Mashore
5 Chris Hart
6 Steve Wojciechowski
7 Garrett Beard
8 Tanyon Sturtze
9 Eric Booker
10 Ernie Young
11 Chaon Garland
12 Jeff Barnes
13 Steve Callahan
14 Craig Sudbury
15 Brent Gates
16 Brett Hendley
17 Manny Martinez
18 Mike Raczka
19 Carlos Salazar
20 Mike Grimes
21 Jim Dillon
22 Ken Hokuf
23 Jose Martinez
24 Tom Carcione
25 Ted Kubiak
26 Pete Riechart
27 Dave Hollenback

1992 Fleer/ProCards Modesto A's

	MT	NR MT	EX
Complete Set:	8.00		

3891 Steve Callahan
3892 Jim Dillon
3893 Chaon Garland
3894 Mike Grimes
3895 Ken Hokuf
3896 Joe Martinez
3897 Dan Nerat
3898 Curtis Shaw
3899 Craig Sudbury
3900 Steve Wojciechowski
3901 Garrett Beard
3902 Tom Carcione
3903 Eric Helfand
3904 Jeff Barns
3905 Brent Gates
3906 Brett Hendley
3907 Carlos Salazar
3908 Jason Wood
3909 Damon Mashore
3910 Ted Kubiak
3911 Pete Richert
3912 Checklist

1992 Team Modesto Athletics

This 26-card set continued a tradition of black-and-white team sets that dates back to 1977. The cards, given away on a special night by the team, measure 2-3/8" x 3-1/2" and have player stats and bios on the back straight out of the 1992 Oakland A's media guide.

	MT	NR MT	EX
Complete Set:	4.00		

Checklist
(1) Jeff Barns
(2) Garrett Beard
(3) Steve Callahan
(4) Tom Carcione
(5) Jim Dillon
(6) Chaon Garland
(7) Brent Gates
(8) Mike Grimes
(9) Chris Hart
(10) Eric Helfand
(11) Brett Hendley
(12) Ken Hokuf
(13) Chad Kuhn
(14) Joe Martinez
(15) Manny Martinez
(16) Damon Mashore
(17) Carlos Salazar
(18) Curtis Shaw
(19) Craig Sudbury
(20) Steve Wojciechowski
(21) Jason Wood
(22) Ernie Young
(23) Ted Kubiak
(24) Pete Richert
(25) Dave Hollenbeck

A player's name in italic type indicates a rookie card. An (FC) indicates a player's first card for that particular card company.

1992 Classic Best Myrtle Beach Hurricanes

	MT	NR MT	EX
Complete Set:	14.00		

1 Chris Weinke
2 John Tsoukalas
3 Trevor Mallory
4 Rob Adkins
5 Anastacio Garcia
6 Ben Weber
7 Dennis Gary
8 Mike Morland
9 Ronald Reams
10 Chris Stynes
11 Alex Gonzalez
12 Rich Butler
13 Rick Holifield
14 Chris Kotes
15 Joe Lis
16 Stoney Briggs
17 Darin Nolan
18 Tim Lindsay
19 Felipe Crespo
20 Mike Taylor
21 Brent Lutz
22 Gabriel Rosario
23 Paul Spoljaric
24 Albert Montoya
25 Giovanni Carrara
26 Kurt Heble
27 Doug Ault
28 Leroy Stanton
29 Darrin Balsley
30 Dennis Brogna

1992 Fleer/ProCards Myrtle Beach Hurricanes

	MT	NR MT	EX
Complete Set:	15.00		

2188 Travis Baptist
2189 Raphael Garcia
2190 Dennis Gray
2191 Kurt Heble
2192 Chris Kotes
2193 Tim Lindsay
2194 Gregg Martin
2195 Albert Montoya
2196 Ken Robinson
2197 Paul Spoljaric
2198 Ben Weber
2199 Anastacio Garcia
2200 Brent Lutz
2201 Mike Morland
2202 Felipe Crespo
2203 Alex Gonzalez
2204 Joe Lis
2205 Gabriel Rosario
2206 Chris Stynes
2207 John Tsoukalas
2208 Chris Weinke
2209 Stoney Briggs
2210 Rich Butler
2211 Rick Holifield
2212 Ron Reams
2213 Doug Ault
2214 Darren Balsley
2215 Leroy Stanton
2216 Checklist

1992 Fleer/ProCards Nashville Sounds

	MT	NR MT	EX
Complete Set:	6.00		

1826 Brian Fisher
1827 Steve Foster
1828 Milton Hill
1829 Trevor Hoffman
1830 Tony Menendez
1831 Gino Minutelli
1832 Tim Pugh
1833 Joey Vierra
1834 Dan Wilson
1835 Rick Wrona
1836 Jeff Branson
1837 Gary Green
1838 Mark Howie
1839 Brian Lane
1840 Russ Morman
1841 Jeff Small
1842 Todd Trafton
1843 Geronimo Berroa
1844 Jacob Brumfield
1845 Nick Capra
1846 Jeff Stone
1847 Dwight Taylor
1848 Pete Mackanin
1849 Frank Funk
1850 Jim Lett
1851 Checklist

1992 Team Nashville Sounds

This 33-card set is skip-numbered by player uniform number. The cards measure 2-3/8" x 3-1/2". The set, sponsored by Bullpen Chew Bubble Gum, was given away by the team on baseball card night. The backs contain player statistics and biographical information. The cards are unnumbered.

	MT	NR MT	EX
Complete Set:	7.00		

(1) Geronimo Berroa
(2) Scott Bradley
(3) Jeff Branson
(4) Mickey Brantley
(5) Keith Brown
(6) Jacob Brumfield
(7) Nick Capra
(8) Steve Foster
(9) Frank Funk
(10) Gary Green
(11) Milton Hill
(12) Trevor Hoffman
(13) Mark Howie
(14) Brian Lane
(15) Jim Lett
(16) Terry McDaniel
(17) Tony Menendez
(18) Dave Miley
(19) Gino Minutelli
(20) Russ Morman
(21) Ross Powell
(22) Tim Pugh
(23) Mo Sanford
(24) Larry Schmittou
(25) Scott Service
(26) Jeff Small
(27) Dwight Taylor
(28) Todd Trafton
(29) Joey Vierra
(30) Dan Wilson
(31) Rick Wrona
(32) John Young
(33) Team set sponsor card

1992 Fleer/ProCards New Britain Red Sox

	MT	NR MT	EX
Complete Set:	6.00		

425 Brian Conroy
426 Gar Finnvold
427 Don Florence
428 Derek Livernois
429 Tony Mosley
430 Gary Painter
431 Ed Riley
432 Ken Ryan
433 Al Sanders
434 Tim Smith
435 Kevin Uhrhan
436 Joe Demus
437 Scott Hatteberg
438 Scott Bethea
439 Colon Dixon
440 Mike DeKneel
441 Greg Graham
442 Bill Norris
443 Willie Tatum
444 Mike Beams
445 Greg Blosser
446 Bruce Chick
447 Jeff McNeely
448 Paul Thoutsis
449 Jim Pankovits
450 Rick Wise
451 Checklist

1992 Classic Best Niagara Falls Rapids

	MT	NR MT	EX
Complete Set:	6.00		

1 Tony Clark
2 David Robson
3 Scott Pagano
4 Malvin De Jesus
5 Peter Feeley
6 Rick Martinez
7 Kazuharu Yamazaki
8 Rick Navarro
9 Robert Dickerson
10 Yoshitaro Ban
11 Mike Lopez
12 David Mysel
13 Cory Parker
14 Bobby Higginson
15 Casey Mendenhall
16 Shannon Penn
17 Carlos Fermin
18 Scott DuRussel
19 Kevin Crombie
20 John Timko
21 Sean Whiteside
22 Keith Kimsey
23 Brent Killen
24 Curt Bell
25 Dave Verduzco
26 Greg Raffo
27 Larry Parrish
28 Shigeyuki Takahashi
29 Stan Twomey

1992 Fleer/ProCards Niagara Falls Rapids

	MT	NR MT	EX
Complete Set:	6.00		

3314 Yoshitaro Ban
3315 Matt Bauer
3316 Kevin Crombie
3317 Scott DuRussel
3318 Mike Lopez
3319 Doug Martin
3320 Casey Mendenhall
3321 David Mysel
3322 Greg Raffo
3323 Dave Verduzco
3324 Sean Whiteside
3325 Kazu Yamazaki
3326 Curt Bell
3327 David Robson
3328 John Timko
3329 Malvin DeJesus
3330 Peter Feeley
3331 Carlos Fermin
3332 Brent Killen
3333 Rick Martinez
3334 Corey Parker
3335 Shannon Penn
3336 Tony Clark
3337 Robert Dickerson
3338 Robin Higginbotham
3339 Bobby Higginson
3340 Keith Kimsey
3341 Scott Pagano
3342 Larry Parrish
3343 Sran Luketich
3344 Shige Takahashi
3345 Checklist

1992 Fleer/ProCards Oklahoma City 89ers

	MT	NR MT	EX
Complete Set:	6.00		

1905 Gerald Alexander
1906 John Barfield
1907 Kevin Blankenship
1908 Brian Bohanon
1909 Mike Campbell
1910 Don Carman
1911 Narciso Elvira
1912 Steve Fireovid
1913 Barry Manuel
1914 Roger Pavlik
1915 Wayne Rosenthal
1916 Doug Davis
1917 Ray Stephens
1918 Steve Balboni
1919 Mario Diaz
1920 Jeff Frye
1921 Chuck Jackson
1922 Rob Maurer
1923 Keith Miller
1924 Jim Presley
1925 Bob Brower
1926 Monty Fariss
1927 Dan Peltier
1928 Tony Scruggs
1929 Tommy Thompson
1930 Oscar Acosta
1931 Mike Berger
1932 Checklist

1992 Fleer/ProCards Omaha Royals

	MT	NR MT	EX
Complete Set:	6.00		

2952 Brian Ahern
2953 Jose Bautista
2954 Jim Campbell
2955 Dera Clark
2956 Mark Huismann
2957 Reese Lambert
2958 Carlos Maldonado
2959 Josias Manzanillo
2960 Dennis Moeller
2961 Steve Shifflett
2962 Rich Sauveur
2963 Carlos Diaz
2964 Erik Pappas
2965 Tim Spehr
2966 Sean Berry
2967 Stu Cole
2968 Jeff Conine
2969 Luis Medina
2970 Jose Mota
2971 Al Pedrique
2972 Terry Shumpert
2973 Adam Casillas
2974 Leo Garcia
2975 Kevin Koslofski
2976 Kevin Long
2977 Jeff Cox
2978 Bob Herold
2979 Joel Horlen
2980 Checklist

1992 Fleer/ProCards Orlando Sunrays

	MT	NR MT	EX
Complete Set:	7.00		

2840 Rich Garces
2841 Ed Gustafson
2842 Jon Henry
2843 Jason Klonoski
2844 Curtis Leskanic
2845 Marc Lipson
2846 Bob McCreary
2847 Oscar Munoz
2848 Carlos Pulido
2849 Jay Owens
2850 Joe Siwa
2851 Rick Allen
2852 Chris Delarwalle
2853 Cheo Garcia
2854 Dan Masteller
2855 Pat Meares
2856 Paul Russo
2857 Rex De La Nuez
2858 Mica Lewis
2859 Jay Kvansnicka
2860 David McCarty
2861 Ray Ortiz
2862 Phil Roof
2863 Mark Funderburk
2864 Jim Shellenback
2865 Checklist

1992 Classic Best Osceola Astros

	MT	NR MT	EX
Complete Set:	8.00		

1 Tom Nevers
2 Tony Gilmore
3 Chris Hill
4 Kenneth Wheeler Jr.
5 Michael Burns
6 Christopher Hatcher
7 Bryant Winslow
8 Gary Christopherson
9 Brian Hunter
10 Douglas Ketchen
11 Fred Costello
12 Mark Small
13 Mike Groppuso
14 Kevin Scott
15 Layne Lambert
16 Benjamin Gonzales
17 James Dougherty
18 Anthony Gutierrez
19 Donnie Wall
20 Jim Lewis
21 James Mouton
22 Ruben Cruz
23 Roberto Petagine
24 Vince Roman
25 Kevin Lane
26 Sal Butera
27 Mike Freer
28 Jack Billingham
29 Frank Cacciatore

1992 Fleer/ProCards Osceola Astros

	MT	NR MT	EX
Complete Set:	8.00		

2521 Jim Dougherty
2522 Troy Dovey
2523 Ben Gonzales
2524 Anthony Gutierrez
2525 Javier Hernandez
2526 Chris Hill
2527 Doug Ketchen
2528 Kevin Lane
2529 Jim Lewis
2530 Mark Small
2531 Kenny Wheeler
2532 Mike Burns
2533 Tony Gilmore
2534 Kevin Scott
2535 Gary Christopherson
2536 Tim Evans
2537 Mike Groppuso
2538 James Mouton
2539 Tom Nevers
2540 Roberto Petagine
2541 Ruben Cruz
2542 Chris Hatcher
2543 Brian Hunter
2544 Vince Roman
2545 Sal Butera
2546 Frank Cacciatore
2547 Jack Billingham
2548 Checklist

1992 Classic Best Palm Springs Angels

	MT	NR MT	EX
Complete Set:	8.00		

1 Eduardo Perez
2 Robert Saitz
3 Norm Montoya
4 Chris Robinson
5 Victor Silverio
6 Brian Romero
7 John Wylie
8 Bobby Gamez
9 David Holdridge
10 Korey Keling
11 Brian Grebeck
12 Garret Anderson
13 Ken Edenfield
14 Orlando Munoz
15 Luis Raven
16 Shawn Purdy
17 Rod Van Dyke
18 Jorge Fabregas
19 Tom Dodge
20 Mark Dalesandro
21 Emmitt Cohick
22 Mike Musolino
23 Edgar Alfonzo
24 David Colon
25 Cliff Garrett
26 Dan Rumsey
27 Mark Holzemer
28 Mario Mendoza
29 Gene Richards
30 Stewart Cliburn (Checklist)

1992 Fleer/ProCards Palm Springs Angels

	MT	NR MT	EX
Complete Set:	8.00		

830 Bobby Gamez
831 Hilly Hathaway
832 David Holdridge
833 Dominick Johnson
834 Korey Keling
835 Norman Montoya
836 Shawn Purdy
837 Chris Robinson
838 Robbie Saitz
839 Victor Silverio
840 Derek Stroud
841 Rod Van Dyke
842 Tommy Dodge
843 Gorge Fabregas
844 Mike Musolino
845 Edgar Alfonzo
846 Mark Dalesandro
847 Brian Grebeck
848 Orlando Munoz
849 Eduardo Perez
850 Luis Raven
851 Garret Anderson
852 Emmitt Cohick
853 David Colon
854 Clifton Garrett
855 Mario Mendoza
856 Stewart Cliburn
857 Gene Richards
858 Checklist

1992 Fleer/ProCards Pawtucket Red Sox

	MT	NR MT	EX
Complete Set:	7.00		

915 John Cerutti
916 Tom Fischer
917 Peter Hoy
918 Daryl Irvine
919 Kevin Morton
920 Jeff Plympton
921 Paul Quantrill
922 Larry Shikles
923 Scott Taylor
924 David Walters
925 Bob Geren
926 Ruben Rodriguez
927 Eric Wedge
928 Tommy Barrett
929 Mike Brumley
930 Jim Byrd
931 Dave Milstien
932 Mike Twardoski
933 John Valentin
934 Mo Vaughn
935 Wayne Housie
936 Juan Paris
937 John Shelby
938 Van Snider
939 Rico Petrocelli
940 Mark Meleski
941 Dick Pole
942 Checklist

1992 Classic Best Peninsula Pilots

	MT	NR MT	EX
Complete Set:	6.00		

1 Bubba Smith
2 Chuck Wiley
3 Miah Bradbury
4 Lipso Nava
5 Erik O'Donnell
6 Jorge Morales
7 Sean Rees
8 Desi Relaford
9 Scott Pitcher
10 Raul Rodarte
11 Doug Fitzer
12 LaGrande Russell
13 Bill Speakman
14 Ruben Santana
15 Sean Twitty
16 Jeff Darwin
17 John Cummings
18 Willie Wilder
19 Greg Hunter
20 Greg Bicknell
21 Bill Kostich
22 Daniel Sullivan
23 Darren Bragg
24 Brad Holman
25 Todd Youngblood
26 James Terrell
27 Marc Hill
28 Tommy Cruz
29 Paul Lindblad
30 Paul Harker

1992 Fleer/ProCards Peninsula Pilots

	MT	NR MT	EX
Complete Set:	6.00		

2924 Greg Bicknell
2925 John Cummings
2926 Jeff Darwin
2927 Doug Fitzer
2928 Bill Kostich
2929 Erik O'Donnell
2930 Sean Rees
2931 LaGrande Russell
2932 Dan Sullivan
2933 Chuck Wiley
2934 Todd Youngblood
2935 Miah Bradbury
2936 Jorge Morales
2937 Craig Wilson
2938 Greg Hunter
2939 Bob Magallanes
2940 Lipso Nava
2941 Desi Relaford
2942 Raul Rodarte
2943 Ruben Santana
2944 Bubba Smith
2945 Darren Bragg
2946 James Terrell
2947 Willie Wilder
2948 Marc Hill
2949 Tommy Cruz
2950 Paul Lindblad
2951 Checklist

1992 Classic Best Peoria Chiefs

	MT	NR MT	EX
Complete Set:	6.00		

1 Earl Cunningham
2 Darren Tillman
3 Mike Tidwell
4 Bill Bliss
5 Jose Trujillo
6 Joey Terilli
7 Brian Kenny
8 Carl Schramm
9 Todd Stefan
10 German Diaz
11 Tim Moore
12 Ricardo Medina
13 Ed Larregui
14 Willie Gardner
15 Yogi Pacheco
16 Esmili Guerra
17 Tyson Godfrey
18 Adrian Sanchez
19 Terry Adams
20 James Postiff
21 Pedro Valdez
22 Jay Meyer
23 Morris Craig
24 Troy Bradford
25 Jim Wolff
26 Brian McGee
27 Ken Arnold
28 Steve Roadcap
29 Bill McGuire
30 Jim O'Reilly

1992 Team Peoria Chiefs

This 31-card issue features several players chosen in the 1992 amateur draft and assigned near mid-season. The quality of the photography and the graphic design make it one of the most attractive issues of 1992.

	MT	NR MT	EX
Complete Set:	5.00		

(1) Terry Adams
(2) Bill Bliss
(3) Tyson Godfrey
(4) Brian Kenney
(5) Ken Krahenbuhl
(6) Jay Meyer
(7) Adrian Sanchez
(8) Carl Schramm
(9) Kennie Steenstra
(10) Mike Tidwell
(11) Brian McGee
(12) J.P. Postiff
(13) Jim Wolff
(14) Ken Arnold
(15) Joe Biasucci
(16) Brant Brown
(17) Ricardo Medina
(18) Tim Moore
(19) Todd Stefan
(20) Earl Cunningham
(21) Willie Gardner
(22) Ed Larregui
(23) Chris Moock
(24) Joey Terilli
(25) Steve Roadcap
(26) Ray Sadecki
(27) Bill McGuire
(28) Jim O'Reilly
(29) Ken Patterson
(30) Chiefs All-Stars
(31) Derek Wallace

1992 Peoria Midwest League All-Star Team

In addition to the team set, the Chiefs played host to the Midwest League All-Star game, and issued a 54-card set of players participating in the game. The cards are unnumbered.

	MT	NR MT	EX
Complete Set:	7.50		

(1) Mike Badorek
(2) James Baldwin Jr.
(3) Allen Battle
(4) Brian Bevil
(5) Bobby Chouinard
(6) Frank Cimorelli
(7) Jeff Cirillo
(8) Mike Couture
(9) Mike Ferry
(10) Rick Forney
(11) Jon Fuller
(12) Steve Gibralter
(13) Ken Grundt
(14) Gary Hagy
(15) Shane Halter
(16) Jason Hardtke
(17) Heath Haynes
(18) Steve Hazlett
(19) Tyrone Hill
(20) Steve Hinton
(21) Tyrone Horne
(22) Mark Johnson
(23) Andre Keene
(24) Brian Kenny
(25) Brian Koelling
(26) Rick Krivida
(27) Ed Larregui
(28) Buck McNabb
(29) Ricardo Medina
(30) Alex Ochoa
(31) Orlando Palmiero
(32) Jeff Pierce
(33) Chris Pritchett
(34) Joe Randa
(35) Kevin Riggs
(36) Mike Rossiter
(37) Adrian Sanchez
(38) Jerry Santos
(39) Scott Sheldon
(40) Scott Simmons
(41) Mike Stefanski
(42) Jose Stela
(43) Chad Strickland
(44) Scott Talanoa
(45) Joey Terilli
(46) Kerry Valrie
(47) Jim Waring
(48) B.J. Waszgis
(49) Gabe White
(50) Steve Whitehead
(51) Shad Williams
(52) Jim Wolff
(53) Tyrone Woods
(54) Dmitri Young

1992 Fleer/ProCards Phoenix Firebirds

	MT	NR MT	EX
Complete Set:	6.00		

2814 Johnny Ard
2815 Larry Carter
2816 Dave Masters
2817 Paul McClellan
2818 Craig McMurty
2819 Jim Pena
2820 Dan Rambo
2821 Pat Rapp
2822 Steve Reed
2823 Mark Bailey
2824 Steve Decker
2825 Mike Benjamin
2826 Craig Colbert
2827 Erik Johnson
2828 Dan Lewis
2829 Dave Patterson
2830 John Patterson
2831 Andres Santana
2832 Steve Hosey
2833 Mark Leonard
2834 Reed Peters
2835 Gregg Ritchie
2836 Ted Wood
2837 Bill Evers
2838 Todd Oakes
2839 Checklist

1992 Classic Best Pittsfield Mets

	MT	NR MT	EX
Complete Set:	7.00		

1 Bill Pulsipher
2 Demond Smith
3 Tripp Keister
4 Ty Quillin
5 Andy Beckerman
6 Guillermo Garcia
7 Steve Seymour
8 Rafael Hernandez
9 Brett Rossler
10 Edgardo Alfonzo
11 Cesar Diaz
12 Shaun Watson
13 Gregg Stark
14 Mark Fuller
15 Brian Daubach
16 Chris George
17 Cliff Jones
18 Jim Thrift
19 Jeff Morris
20 Howie Freiling
21 Larry Bennese

1992 Fleer/ProCards Pittsfield Mets

	MT	NR MT	EX
Complete Set:	7.00		

3286 Andy Beckerman
3287 Mark Fuller
3288 Chris George
3289 Mark Hokanson
3290 Cliff Jones
3291 Joe Petcka
3292 Jim Popoff
3293 Bill Pulsipher
3294 Steve Seymour
3295 Greg Stark
3296 David Teske
3297 Shaun Watson
3298 Cesar Diaz
3299 Guillermo Garcia
3300 Brett Rossier
3301 Edgardi Alfonzo
3302 Brian Daubach
3303 Jose Flores
3304 Rafael Hernandez
3305 Chris Saunders
3306 Tripp Keister
3307 Ty Quinlin
3308 Demond Smith
3309 John Smith
3310 Jim Thrift
3311 Howie Freiling
3312 Jeff Morris
3313 Checklist

1992 Fleer/ProCards Portland Beavers

	MT	NR MT	EX
Complete Set:	6.00		

2659 Willie Banks
2660 Larry Casian
2661 Mauro Gozzo

2662 Greg Johnson
2663 Orlando Lind
2664 Pat Mahomes
2665 Mike Schwabe
2666 Mike Trombley
2667 George Tsamis
2668 Rob Wassenaar
2669 David West
2670 Derek Parks
2671 Danny Sheaffer
2672 Shawn Gilbert
2673 Chip Hale
2674 Keith Hughes
2675 Terry Jorgensen
2676 Luis Quinones
2677 Bernardo Brito
2678 J.T. Bruett
2679 Jay Kvasnicka
2680 Edgar Naveda
2681 Scott Ullger
2682 Paul Kirsch
2683 Gorman Heimueller
2684 Checklist

1992 Classic Best Princeton Reds

	MT	NR MT	EX
Complete Set:	6.00		

1 Todd Etler
2 Eli Robinson
3 Jeff Ashton
4 Cleveland Ladell
5 Ray Moon
6 Yamil Concepcion
7 Sam Mullins
8 Jim Miller
9 Roger Etheridge
10 Johnny Bess
11 Curtis Lyons
12 Todd Ruyak
13 Chad Fox
14 Will Brunson
15 Denny Fussell
16 James Nix
17 Louis Maberry
18 Brian Silvia
19 Rodney Thomas
20 Rossi Morris
21 Rod Sanders
22 Ramon Hernandez
23 Dan Frye
24 Justin Towle
25 Dan Kopriva
26 Dan Oyas
27 Glen Cullop
28 Darrell "Doc" Rogers
29 Billy Maxwell

1992 Fleer/ProCards Princeton Reds

	MT	NR MT	EX
Complete Set:	6.00		

2685 Glen Cullop
3077 Bill Brunson
3078 Yamil Concepcion
3079 Roger Etheridge
3080 Todd Etler
3081 Chad Fox
3082 Denny Fussell
3083 Curtis Lyons
3084 Louis Maberry
3085 Jim Miller
3086 Sam Mullins
3087 James Nix
3088 Todd Ruyak
3089 Johnny Bess
3090 Brian Silvia
3091 Justin Towle
3092 Jeff Ashton
3093 Dan Frye
3094 Ramon Hernandez
3095 Dan Kopriva
3096 Eli Robinson
3097 Rod Sanders
3098 Cleveland Ladell
3099 Ray Moon
3100 Rossi Morris
3101 Danny Oyas
3102 Rodney Thomas
3103 Doc Rodgers
3104 Checklist

1992 Classic Best Prince Williams Cannons

	MT	NR MT	EX
Complete Set:	6.00		

1 Bruce Prybylinski
2 Andy Fox
3 Ramon Manon
4 Mike Hankins
5 Jalal Leach
6 Richard Hines
7 Andy Albrecht
8 Adin Lohry
9 Matt Dunbar
10 Jeff Motuzas
11 Ramon Jimenez
12 Roger Burnett
13 Tim Rumer
14 Edwin Salcedo
15 Tim Garland
16 Lyle Mouton
17 Rich Polak
18 Shad Smith
19 Jeff Livesey
20 Keith Seiler
21 Ron Frazier
22 Kevin Jordan
23 Todd Malone
24 Jason Robertson
25 Curtis Ralph
26 Mike Hart
27 Dave Schuler
28 Ken Dominguez
29 Adam Wagner

1992 Fleer/ProCards Prince William Cannons

	MT	NR MT	EX
Complete Set:	6.00		

139 Matt Dunbar
140 Rob Frazier
141 Richard Hines
142 Todd Malone
143 Ramon Manon
144 Rich Polak
145 Bruce Prybylinski
146 Rafael Quirico
147 Curtis Ralph
148 Tim Rumer
149 Keith Seiler
150 Shad Smith
151 Adin Lohry
152 Jeff Motuzas
153 Edwin Salcedo
154 Roger Burnett
155 Andy Fox
156 Ramon Jimenez
157 Kevin Jordan
158 Steve Livesay
159 Andrew Albrecht
160 Tim Garland
161 Jalal Leach
162 Lyle Mouton
163 Jason Robertson
164 Mike Hart
165 Ken Dominguez
166 Dave Schuler
167 Checklist

1992 Classic Best Pulaski Braves

	MT	NR MT	EX
Complete Set:	6.00		

1 Theodore Hassan
2 John Avery
3 Jay Noel
4 Kain Sly
5 Mark Chambers
6 Mark St.Claire
7 Thomas Coates
8 Raymond Nunez
9 Marcel Johnson
10 Phil Zimmerman
11 Adrian Garcia
12 Ben Weeks
13 Brad Clontz
14 Aaron Turnier
15 Will Havens
16 Jason Kempfer
17 Kevin Grijak
18 Augie Vivenzio
19 Bryan Spetter
20 Jason Wendt
21 Pedro Swann
22 Billy Paragin
23 Steve Roeder
24 Bill Shafer
25 Mike D'Andrea
26 Nelson Paulino
27 Randy Ingle
28 Douglas Baker
29 Cloyd Boyer

1992 Fleer/ProCards Pulaski Braves

	MT	NR MT	EX
Complete Set:	6.00		

3169 John Avery
3170 Brad Clontz
3171 Mike D'Andrea
3172 Theodore Hassen
3173 Will Havens
3174 Jason Kempfer
3175 Steve Roeder
3176 Bill Shafer
3177 Aaron Turnier
3178 Ben Weeks
3179 Jason Wendt
3180 Adrian Garcia
3181 Billy Paragin
3182 Mark St.Claire
3183 Augue Vivenzio
3184 Marcel Johnson
3185 Raymond Nunez
3186 Nelson Paulino
3187 Bryan Spetter
3188 Phil Zimmerman
3189 Mark Chambers
3190 Thomas Coates
3191 Kevin Grijak
3192 Jay Noel
3193 Kian Sly
3194 Pedro Swann
3195 Randy Ingle
3196 Doug Baker
3197 Cloyd Boyer
3198 Fred Koenig
3199 Team Picture
3200 Checklist

1992 Classic Best Quad City River Bandits

	MT	NR MT	EX
Complete Set:	6.00		

1 Julian Heredia
2 Todd Claus
3 Orlando Palmeiro
4 Mark Ratekin
5 Brandon Markiewicz
6 Chris Turner
7 Shad Williams
8 Eduardo Perez
9 Eric Martinez
10 John Fritz
11 Glenn Mitchell
12 Jose Mussett
13 Ron Watson
14 Chance Gledhill
15 Jose Stela
16 Dennis McCaffery
17 Elgin Bobo
18 P.J. Forbes
19 Mark Mammola
20 Kyle Sebach
21 Mark Sweeney
22 Gary Hagy
23 Tyrone Boykin
24 Mark Brakebill
25 David Staydohar
26 Chris Prichett
27 Mitch Seoane
28 Matt Hyde
29 Joe Georger
30 Dan Pieratt, Checklist

1992 Fleer/ProCards Quad City River Bandits

	MT	NR MT	EX
Complete Set:	6.00		

800 Erik Bennett
801 John Fritz
802 Chance Gledhill
803 Julian Heredia
804 Eric Martinez
805 Glenn Mitchell
806 Jose Musset
807 Beban Perez
808 Mark Ratekin
809 Kyle Sebach
810 Ton Watson
811 Shad Williams
812 Elgin Bobo
813 Jose Stela
814 Chris Turner
815 Mark Brakebill
816 Todd Claus
817 P.J. Forbes
818 Gary Hagy
819 Brandon Markiewicz
820 Chris Pritchett
821 Tyrone Boykin
822 Dennis McCaffery
823 Orlando Palmeiro
824 Dave Staydohar
825 Mark Sweeney
826 Mitch Seoane
827 Joe Georger
828 Matt Hyde
829 Checklist

1992 Fleer/ProCards Reading Phillies

	MT	NR MT	EX
Complete Set:	6.00		

566 Chris Bushing
567 Paul Fletcher
568 Darrell Goedhart
569 Tyler Green
570 Eric Hill
571 Chris Limbach
572 Steve Parris
573 Jeff Patterson
574 Matt Stevens
575 Mike Sullivan
576 Bob Wells
577 Scott Wiegandt
578 Mike Lieberthal
579 Ed Kosado
580 Juan Escobar
581 R.A. Neitzel
582 Troy Paulsen
583 Sean Ryan
584 Tony Trevino
585 Pete Alborano
586 Bruce Dostal
587 Mickey Hyde
588 Ron Lockett
589 Tom Nuneviller
590 Sam Taylor
591 Don McCormack
592 Carlos Arroyo
593 Kelly Heath
594 Checklist

1992 Cal League Reno Silver Sox

	MT	NR MT	EX
Complete Set:	6.50		

34 Scott Lydy
35 Mike Neill
36 Mark Acre
37 Craig Connolly
38 Fausto Cruz
39 Tony DeFranesco
40 Fabio Gomez
41 Hugh Gulledge
42 Scott Henry
43 Todd Ingram
44 Doug Johns
45 Will Love
46 Russ Brock
47 Delfino Mejia
48 Rafael Mercado
49 Islay Molina
50 Tom Meyers
51 Bill Picketts
52 Rob Pierce
53 Enoch Simmons
54 Tim Smith
55 Jim Waggoner
56 Joel Wolfe
57 Joe Misa
58 Greg Smock
59 Gary Jones
60 Scott Budner
61 Jim Slaton
62 Shane Borchert

1992 Fleer/ProCards Richmond Braves

	MT	NR MT	EX
Complete Set:	8.00		

370 Kevin Coffman
371 Pat Gomez
372 Tom McCarthy
373 David Nied
374 Dale Polley
375 Armando Reynoso
376 Napoleon Robinson
377 Randy St. Claire
378 Bill Taylor
379 Francisco Cabrera
380 Brian Deak
381 Joe Szekely
382 Vinny Castilla
383 Ryan Klesko
384 Jeff Manto
385 Boi Rodriguez
386 Keith Smith
387 Keith Mitchell
388 Bobby Moore
389 Sean Ross
390 Andy Tomberlin
391 Chris Chambliss
392 Bruce Dal Canton
393 Sonny Jackson
394 Checklist
3014 Pete Smith
3015 Mark Wohlers
3016 Eddie Williams

1992 Team Richmond Braves

This card set was given out by the Richmond Braves on a promotional night. The cards were in a single sheet, with perforations in between each card to facilitate separation of the cards. In addition, the baseball card shop that sponsored the promotion, Bleacher Bums Sportscards, received several sheets and had them cut into standard baseball card sets. The sets sold by the shop also includes a prototype card of Ryan Klesko.

	MT	NR MT	EX
Complete Set:	7.50		

Ryan Klesko (Prototype)
(1) Jeff Manto
(2) Vinny Castilla
(3) Keith Smith
(4) Ryan Klesko
(5) Chris Chambliss
(6) Mark Wohlers
(7) Armando Reynoso
(8) Andy Tomberlin
(9) Bobby Moore
(10) Keith Mitchell
(11) Ramon Caraballo
(12) Billy Taylor
(13) Brian Deak
(14) Randy St. Claire
(15) Pat Gomez
(16) Joe Szekely
(17) Dale Polley
(18) Pete Smith
(19) Sean Ross
(20) Napoleon Robinson
(21) Francisco Cabrera
(22) David Nied
(23) Sonny Jackson, Bruce Dal Canton
(24) Tom McCarthy
(25) Boi Rodriguez

1992 Bob's Camera Richmond Braves

This 26-card set was issued by the Richmond Braves and sponsored by a local camera shop, Bob's Camera. The cards are 4" x 5", and have player information on the front of the card, with blank backs (since the cards are printed on photographic stock). The set is skip-numbered according to the player's uniform number. The cards were given away weekly and included an opportunity for fans receiving the cards to get them autographed by the players.

	MT	NR MT	EX
Complete Set:	15.00		

(1) Bobby Moore
(4) Andy Tomberlin
(5) Ramon Caraballo
(6) Boi Rodriguez
(7) Nick Esasky
(8) Brian Deak
(10) Chris Chambliss
(12) Sean Ross
(15) Dale Polley
(16) Jeff Manto
(24) Francisco Cabrera
(25) Pete Smith
(27) Armando Reynoso
(29) Keith Mitchell
(30a) Ryan Klesko (batting)
(30b) Ryan Klesko (fielding)
(33) Pat Gomez
(34) Randy St. Claire
(36) Tommy Gregg
(37) David Nied
(42) Mark Wohlers
(43) Billy Taylor
(45) Vinny Castilla
(49) Tom McCarthy
(51) Kevin Coffman
(55) Napoleon Robinson

1992 Richmond Comix amd Cardz Richmond Braves

This 26-card set was issued by the Richmond Braves and sponsored by a local baseball card shop, Richmond Comics and Cardz. The cards are standard size, and have stats and brief player information on the back. The set is skip-numbered according to the player's uniform number. The set was given away in five different segments, with a card good for a sixth set of five cards redeemable at the card shop that sponsored the set.

	MT	NR MT	EX
Complete Set:	9.00		

(1) Bobby Moore
(4) Andy Tomberlin
(6) Boi Rodriguez
(8) Brian Deak
(9) Eddie Williams
(10) Chris Chambliss
(12) Sean Ross
(15) Dale Polley
(16) Jeff Manto
(19) Sonny Jackson
(22) Joe Szekely
(24) Francisco Cabrera
(25) Pete Smith
(27) Armando Reynoso
(29) Keith Mitchell
(30) Ryan Klesko
(33) Pat Gomez
(34) Randy St. Claire
(36) Keith Smith
(37) David Nied
(39) Bruce Dal Canton
(42) Mark Wohlers
(43) Billy Taylor
(45) Vinny Castilla
(49) Tom McCarthy
(55) Napoleon Robinson

1992 Urkrop's Richmond Braves

This 50-card set was sponsored by Ukrop's, a Richmond-area grocery store chain. The cards featured a 1992 Richmond Brave and a former Braves star. They were issued in two-card strips and with cartons of Pepsi.

	MT	NR MT	EX
Complete Set:	10.00		

(1) Armando Reynoso
(2) Steve Bedrosian
(3) Pat Gomez
(4) Zane Smith
(5) Tom McCarthy
(6) Kent Mercker
(7) David Nied
(8) Steve Avery
(9) Dale Polley
(10) Tom Glavine
(11) Napoleon Robinson
(12) John Smoltz
(13) Pete Smith
(14) Tommy Greene
(15) Randy St. Claire
(16) Bob Walk
(17) Billy Taylor
(18) Paul Zuvella
(19) Mark Wohlers
(20) Chico Ruiz
(21) Francisco Cabrera
(22) Mark Lemke
(23) Brian Deak
(24) Dale Murphy
(25) Joe Szekely
(26) Greg Olson
(27) Vinny Castilla
(28) Brook Jacoby
(29) Ryan Klesko
(30) Gerald Perry
(31) Jeff Manto
(32) Jeff Blauser
(33) Boi Rodriguez
(34) Ron Gant
(35) Keith Smith
(36) Deion Sanders
(37) Kevin Coffman
(38) Glenn Hubbard
(39) Keith Mitchell
(40) Rico Rossy
(41) Bobby Moore
(42) Jerry Willard
(43) Sean Ross
(44) Brian Hunter
(45) Andy Tomberlin
(46) David Justice
(47) Ramon Caraballo
(48) Brett Butler
(49) Chris Chambliss
(50) Lonnie Smith

1992 Fleer/ProCards Rochester Red Wings

	MT	NR MT	EX
Complete Set:	6.00		

1933 Tim Layana
1934 Pat Leinen
1935 Jim Lewis
1936 Richie Lewis
1937 Daryl Moore
1938 Mike Oquist
1939 Arthur Rhodes
1940 Todd Stephan
1941 Anthony Telford
1942 Mark Parent
1943 Doug Robbins
1944 Bobby Dickerson
1945 Ricky Gutierrez
1946 Rodney Lofton
1947 Ken Shamburg
1948 Tommy Shields
1949 Paul Carey
1950 Doug Jennings
1951 Scott Meadows
1952 Luis Mercedes
1953 Jack Voight
1954 Ed Yacopino
1955 Jerry Narron
1956 Steve Luebber
1957 Mike Young
1958 Checklist

1992 Classic Best Rockford Expos

	MT	NR MT	EX
Complete Set:	12.00		

1 Chris Falco
2 Scott Dennison
3 Raul Santana
4 Rusty Kilgo
5 Darrin Kotch
6 Mike Hardge
7 Derek Aucoin
8 Ron Gerstein
9 Tyrone Woods
10 Domingo Matos
11 Gabe White
12 Doug O'Neill
13 Kirk Rueter
14 Derek Dehdashtian
15 Carlos Perez
16 Hector Ortega
17 Steve Whitehead
18 Brian Looney
19 William Martinez
20 Mark Grudzielanek
21 Heath Haynes
22 Joe Norris
23 Mike Thomas
24 Tyrone Horne
25 Todd Samples
26 Dusty Freitag
27 Rafael Rijo
28 Rob Leary
29 Herm Starrette
30 Jim Young

1992 Fleer/ProCards Rockford Expos

	MT	NR MT	EX
Complete Set:	12.00		

2106 Derek Aucoin
2107 Vince Fultz
2108 Ron Gerstein
2109 Heath Haynes
2110 Darin Kotch
2111 Brian Looney
2112 Bill Martinez
2113 Joe Norris
2114 Kirk Ruster
2115 Mike Thomas
2116 Gabe White
2117 Steve Whitehead
2118 Derek Dehdashtion
2119 Dusty Freitag
2120 Raul Santana
2121 Scott Dennison
2122 Chris Falco
2123 Mark Grudzielanek
2124 Mike Hardge
2125 Domingo Martos
2126 Hector Ortega
2127 Tyrone Horne
2128 Rafael Rijo
2129 Todd Samples
2130 Tyrone Woods
2131 Rob Leary
3012 Tin Torricelli
3013 Checklist

1992 Classic Best Salem Buccaneers

	MT	NR MT	EX
Complete Set:	6.00		

1 Midre Cummings
2 Ramon Martinez
3 Rich Aude
4 Eric Parkinson
5 Bruce Schreiber
6 Doug Harrah
7 Dave Tellers
8 Pasquale Arace
9 Genaro Campusano
10 Keith Thomas
11 Jason Christiansen
12 Jose Alvarez
13 Bobby Hunter
14 Marcus Hanel
15 John Hope
16 Joe Sondrini
17 Tom Green
18 Rob Bailey
19 Tim Edge
20 Todd Schroeder
21 Dan Jones
22 Troy Mooney
23 Dave Watson
24 Rick White
25 Tony Beasley
26 John Wockenfuss
27 Rick Keeton
28 Bill Zick

1992 Fleer/ProCards Salem Buccaneers

	MT	NR MT	EX
Complete Set:	6.00		

54 Jose Alvarez
55 Jason Christiansen
56 Sean Evans
57 Doug Harrah
58 John Hope
59 Bobby Hunter
60 Dan Jones
61 Troy Mooney
62 Eric Parkinson
63 Kevin Rychel
64 Dave Watson
65 Rick White
66 Tim Edge
67 Marcus Hanel
68 Rich Aude
69 Tony Beasley
70 Ken Bonifay
71 Ramon Martinez
72 Todd Schroeder
73 Joe Sondrini
74 Pasquale Arace
75 Rob Bailey
76 Midre Cummings
77 Joe Ronca
78 Keith Thomas
79 John Wockenfuss
80 Rick Keeton
81 Checklist

1992 Classic Best Salinas Spurs

	MT	NR MT	EX
Complete Set:	6.00		

1 Kiyoshi Arai
2 Greg Fritz
3 Geoff Samuels
4 Dave Trautwein
5 Randy Powers
6 Mark Kubicki
7 Takkayuki Nishijima
8 Mike Lawn
9 Rafael Rivera
10 Hideki Kato
11 Alan Songtag
12 Tommy Helms
13 Don Sheppard
14 Greg McGough
15 Kevin Wong
16 Kevin Tolar
17 Arthur Butcher
18 Hidefumi Hara
19 Tsutomu Yamada
20 Cliff Gonzalez
21 Dave Duplessis
22 Carlos Laboy
23 Mike Bradish
24 Takashi Uchinokura
25 Hide Koga
26 Takayuki Uchinokura
27 Dick Little
28 Kelly Luse
29 Rich Morales
30 Keishi Asano

1992 Fleer/ProCards Salinas Spurs

	MT	NR MT	EX
Complete Set:	6.00		

3748 Bruce Arola
3749 Rick Green
3750 Mike Hooper
3751 Troy Hooper
3752 Geoff Samuels
3753 Alan Sontag
3754 Mark Stephens
3755 Fred Toliver
3756 Dave Trautwein
3757 Tsutoma Yamada
3758 Greg McGough
3759 Rafael Rivera
3760 Andy Skeels
3761 Kiyoshi Arai
3762 Kevin Davis
3763 Dave Duplessis
3764 Hideki Kato
3765 Tokashi Uchinokura
3766 Kevin Wong
3767 Cliff Gonzalez
3768 Hidefumi Hara
3769 Carlos Laboy
3770 Mike Lawn
3771 Takayuki Nishijima
3772 Don Sheppard
3773 Hide Koga
3774 Keishi Asano
3775 Takayuki Kohno
3776 Dick Little
3777 Rich Morales
3778 Checklist

1992 Fleer/ProCards San Antonio Missions

	MT	NR MT	EX
Complete Set:	7.00		

3967 Steve Allen
3968 Ray Calhoun
3969 Balvino Galvez
3970 Mike James
3971 Jamie McAndrew
3972 Michael Mimbs
3973 Dennis Springer
3974 Jody Treadwell
3975 Bill Wengert
3976 Todd Williams
3977 Adam Brown
3978 Lance Rice
3979 Jorge Alvarez
3980 Tim Barker
3981 John Deutsch
3982 Scott Doffek
3983 Matt Howard
3984 Steve Kliafas
3985 Ron Maurer
3986 Garey Ingram
3987 Raul Mondesi
3988 Jerry Royster
3989 Darrell Evans
3990 Checklist

1992 Classic Best San Bernardino Spirit

	MT	NR MT	EX
Complete Set:	6.00		

1 Tommy Adams
2 Ron Pezzoni
3 Pat Garrigan
4 Kyle Duke
5 Matt Kluge
6 Rich Lodding
7 Jeff Borski
8 Tony Kounas
9 Marc Rosenbalm
10 Tommy Robertson
11 Jim Mecir
12 Scott Schanz
13 Craig Bryant
14 Doyle Balthazer
15 George Glinatsis
16 Manny Cervantes
17 Mike Hampton
18 David Adam
19 Julio Fernandez
20 Eddie Diaz
21 Craig Clayton
22 Kevin King
23 Salvy Urso
24 Paul Perkin
25 Paul Brannon
26 David Waldenberger
27 Ivan De Jesus
28 Gary Wheelock
29 Lem Pikington
30 Rory Riddoch

1992 Fleer/ProCards San Bernardino Spirit

	MT	NR MT	EX
Complete Set:	6.00		

228 Ivan DeJesus
943 David Adam
944 Jeff Borski
945 Kyle Duke
946 Geroge Glinatsis
947 Mike Hampton
948 Kevin King
949 Rich Lodding
950 Jim Mecir
951 Paul Perkins
952 Anthony Phillips
953 Scott Schanz
954 Sal Urso
955 Trey Witte
956 Doyle Balthazar
957 Matt Kluge
958 Tony Kounas
959 Alex Sutherland
960 Paul Brannon
961 Craig Bryant
962 Manny Cervantes
963 Craig Clayton
964 Eddy Diaz
965 Pat Garrigan
966 David Henderson
967 Arquimedez Pozo
968 Dave Waldenberger
969 Tommy Adams
970 Ken Pennington
971 Ron Pezzoni
972 Tommy Robertson
973 Sean Twitty
3437 Checklist

1992 Classic Best San Jose Giants

	MT	NR MT	EX
Complete Set:	6.00		

1 Matt Brewer
2 Joe Rosselli
3 Steven Rolen
4 Billy VanLandingham
5 Steve Whitaker
6 Brian McLeod
7 Rikkert Faneyte
8 Adam Hyzdu
9 Barry Miller
10 Andres Duncan
11 Dan Calcagno
12 Dan Flanagan
13 Troy Clemens
14 Don Montgomery
15 Jason McFarlin
16 Greg Brummett
17 Ricky Ward
18 Carl Hanselman
19 Chris Hancock
20 Rod Huffman
21 Pedro Frias
22 Vince Herring
23 Matt Davis
24 Brett McGonnigal
25 Alvaro Benavides
26 Ron Wotus
27 Rick Miller
28 Frank Reberger
29 Brian Costello
30 Mark Wilson

1992 Classic Best Sarasota White Sox

	MT	NR MT	EX
Complete Set:	15.00		

1 Scott Ruffcorn
2 Ken Coleman
3 Rogelio Nunez
4 Brandon Wilson
5 Keith Strange
6 Jason Bere
7 Dean Locklear
8 Kevin Castleberry
9 Mike Eatinger
10 Dean Haase
11 Rolando Caridad
12 Don Perigny
13 Dennis Walker
14 Jerry Wolak
15 Steve Schrenk
16 Randall Hood
17 Shawn Buchanan
18 Frank Campos
19 Kevin Coughlin
20 Mike Robertson
21 Steve Olsen
22 Larry Thomas
23 Monte Mathis
24 Anthony Gordon
25 Stephen Brady
26 Mike Hooper
27 Rick Patterson
28 Kirk Champion
29 Mike Barnett
30 Scott Johnson

1992 Fleer/ProCards Sarasota White Sox

	MT	NR MT	EX
Complete Set:	16.00		

198 Jason Bere
199 Rolando Caridad
200 Tony Gordon
201 Dean Locklear
202 Steve Olsen
203 Don Perigny
204 Robert Person
205 Scott Ruffcorn
206 Johnny Ruffin
207 Steve Schrenk
208 Rogelio Nunez
209 Nilson Robledo
210 Keith Strange
211 Doug Brady
212 Ken Coleman
213 Mike Eatinger
214 Geovaney Miranda
215 Mike Robertson
216 Dennis Walker
217 Brandon Wilson
218 Shawn Buchanan
219 Ray Durham
220 Randall Hood
221 Kinnis Pledger
222 Ron Plemmons
223 Jerry Wolak
224 Rick Patterson
225 Mike Barnett
226 Kirk Champion
227 Checklist

1992 Classic Best Savannah Cardinals

	MT	NR MT	EX
Complete Set:	6.00		

1 Eddie Williams
2 Mike Jolley
3 Kevin Lucero
4 Larry Luchetti
5 Ben Ellsworth
6 Ron Warner
7 Clint Davis
8 John Frascatore
9 Steve Johnson
10 Curtis Underwood
11 DaRond Stovall
12 Jonas Hamlin
13 John Dempsey
14 Gary Taylor
15 Joe Turvey
16 Jason Hisey
17 Rigo Beltran
18 Dan Cholowsky
19 Allan Hammond
20 Tom Frusco
21 Aaron Holbert
22 Derron Spiller
23 Mike Ramsey
24 Ramon Ortiz
25 Pete Fagan

1992 Fleer/ProCards Savannah Cardinals

	MT	NR MT	EX
Complete Set:	6.00		

652 Rigo Beltran
653 Mike Busby
654 Clint Davis
655 John Frascatore
656 Tom Fusco
657 Allan Hammond
658 Jason Hisey
659 Steve Johnson
660 Mike Jolley
661 Greg Knowles
662 Kevin Lucero
663 Larry Lucchetti
664 Derron Spiller
665 Joe Turvey
666 Eddie Williams
667 Dan Cholowsky
668 Ignacio Duran
669 Ben Ellsworth
670 Jonas Hamlin
671 Aaron Holbert
672 Curtis Underwood
673 Ron Warner
674 Brent Bohrofen
675 Eric Mediavilla
676 Darond Stovall
677 Gary Taylor
678 Jose Velez
679 Mike Ramsey
680 Ramon Ortiz
681 Checklist

1992 Fleer/ProCards Scranton-Wilkes Barre Red Barons

	MT	NR MT	EX
Complete Set:	6.00		

2439 Jay Baller
2440 Toby Borland
2441 Darrin Chapin
2442 Pat Combs
2443 Greg Mathews
2444 Tim Mauser
2445 Steve Searcy
2446 Mark Sims
2447 Mickey Weston
2448 Mike Williams
2449 Doug Lindsey
2450 Todd Pratt
2451 Gary Alexander
2452 Greg Legg
2453 Joe Milletta
2454 Vic Rodriguez
2455 Steve Scarsone
2456 Rick Schu
2457 Casey Waller
2458 Braulio Castillo
2459 Wes Chamberlain
2460 Julio Peguero
2461 Cary Williams
2462 Lee Elia
2463 Al LeBoeuf
2464 Jim Wright
2465 Checklist

1992 Team Scranton-Wilkes Barre Red Barons

This 29-card set of the International League team was sponsored by Bullpen Chew Bubble Gum. The cards feature black-bordered color photos with a glossy finish on the front, and full statistics on the back. The cards are unnumbered.

	MT	NR MT	EX
Complete Set:	4.50		

(1) Gary Alexander
(2) Bob Ayrault
(3) Jay Baller
(4) Toby Borland
(5) Brad Brink
(6) Braulio Castillo
(7) Darrin Chapin
(8) Pat Combs
(9) Bruce Dostal
(10) Lee Elia
(11) Jeff Grotewold
(12) Mike Hartley
(13) Al LeBoeuf
(14) Doug Lindsey
(15) Tom Marsh
(16) Greg Mathews
(17) Tim Mauser
(18) Joe Millette
(19) Barney Nugent
(20) Julio Peguero
(21) Steve Scarsone
(22) Rick Schu
(23) Mark Sims
(24) Ray Stephens
(25) Mickey Weston
(26) Cary Williams
(27) Mike Williams
(28) Jim Wright
(29) Team Logo card

1992 Fleer/ProCards Shreveport Captains

	MT	NR MT	EX
Complete Set:	7.00		

3864 Dan Carlson
3865 Rick Huisman
3866 Kevin McGehee
3867 Lou Pote
3868 Dan Rambo
3869 Steve Reed
3870 Kevin Rogers
3871 Rob Taylor
3872 Salomon Torres
3873 Mark Yockey
3874 Eric Christopherson
3875 Ron Crowe
3876 Dan Fernandez
3877 Clay Bellinger
3878 Joel Chimelis
3879 Todd Crosby
3880 Adell Davenport
3881 Mike Easley
3882 Kevin Kasper
3883 Reed Peters
3884 Derek Reed
3885 Reuben Smiley
3886 Pete Weber
3887 Bill Robinson
3888 Steve Cline
3889 Dick Dietz
3890 Checklist

1992 Play II South Atlantic League All-Stars

	MT	NR MT	EX
Complete Set:	30.00		

1 Shane Andrews
2 Joe Ayrault
3 Willie Canate
4 P.J. Carey
5 Giovanni Carrara
6 Dan Cholowsky
7 Manny Cora
8 John Courtright
9 Ian Doyle
10 Cliff Floyd
11 Omar Garcia
12 Benji Gil
13 K.C. Gillum
14 Tucker Hammargren
15 Lew Hill
16 Aaron Holbert
17 John Hrusovsky
18 Rich Kelly
19 Chris Kotes
20 Joe Lis
21 Scott Little
22 Albie Lopez
23 Marc Marini

24 Rod McCall
25 Antonio Mitchell
26 Gary Mota
27 Marty Neff
28 Ernie Nieves
29 Ricky Otero
30 Bobby Perna
31 Andy Pettite
32 Evan Pratte
33 Elliot Quinones
34 Calvin Reese
35 Scott Robinson
36 Matt Ruebel
37 Paul Spaljaric
38 Nick Sued
39 Quilvio Veras
40 Matt Whisenant
41 John Wilder
42 Tom Wilson

1992 Classic Best South Bend White Sox

MT NR MT EX
Complete Set: 6.00

1 Brian Boehringer
2 Don Culberson
3 Robert Ellis
4 Luis Andujar
5 Jeff Pierce
6 Julio Vinas
7 Kerry Valrie
8 Corey Austin
9 Doug Brady
10 Mike Vogel
11 Mike Bertotti
12 Jonathan Jenkins
13 Olmeda Saenz
14 Brian Filosa
15 Glenn DiSarcina
16 Harold Henry
17 Chris Woodfin
18 Alan Levine
19 Ramon Guzman
20 Essex Burton
21 Troy Fryman
22 Henry Manning
23 Hank Tagle
24 Terry Francoma
25 Mark Haley
26 Jaime Garcia
27 Scott Takoa

1992 Fleer/ProCards South Bend White Sox

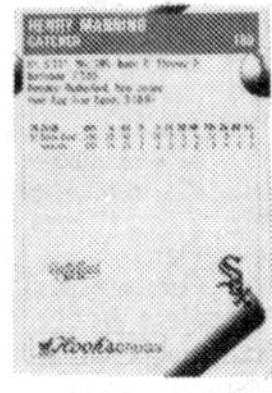

MT NR MT EX
Complete Set: 8.00

168 Luis Andujar
169 James Baldwin
170 Mike Pertotti
171 Brian Boehringer
172 Don Culberson
173 John Herholz
174 Alan Levine
175 Jeff Pierce
176 Hank Tagle
177 Kevin Tolar
178 Chris Woodfin
179 Dean Haase
180 Henry Manning
181 Julio Vines
182 Essex Burton
183 Glenn DiSarcina
184 Brian Filosa
185 Troy Fryman
186 Dave Martorane
187 Olmeda Saenz
188 Corey Austin
189 Harold Henry
190 Rafael Ochoa
191 Charles Poe
192 Kerry Valrie
193 Terry Francona
194 Jaime Garcia
195 Mark Haley
196 Jim Reinebold
197 Checklist

1992 Classic Best Southern Oregon A's

MT NR MT EX
Complete Set: 6.00

1 Troy Penix
2 Bob Bennett
3 Marcel Galligani
4 Steve Lemke
5 Mark Sobolewski
6 Brian Lesher
7 David Cromer
8 Terance Frazier
9 Mark Moore
10 Geoff Loomis
11 Jason White
12 Tim Killeen
13 Jason Geis
14 Craig Gienger
15 Steve Griffin
16 Jeff Post
17 Gary Haught
18 Jim Byerly
19 Tim Bojan
20 James Banks
21 John MacCauley
22 Dan Wengert
23 Herman Johnson
24 Clifton Foster
25 Sean Scott
26 Stan Payne
27 Kurt Endebrock
28 Chris Pittaro
29 Jim Slaton
30 Tony Defrancesco

1992 Fleer/ProCards Southern Oregon A's

MT NR MT EX
Complete Set: 6.00

3404 James Banks
3405 Bob Bennett
3406 Tim Bojan
3407 Jim Byerly
3408 Clifton Foster
3409 Craig Geinger
3410 Steve Griffin
3411 Gary Haught
3412 Richard King
3413 Steve Lemke
3414 John MacCauley
3415 Stan Payne
3416 Jeff Post
3417 Don Wengert
3418 Herman Johnson
3419 Tim Killeen
3420 Mark Moore
3421 Rick Norton
3422 Roberto Ramirez
3423 Terance Frazier
3424 Marcel Galligani
3425 Geoff Loomis
3426 Ricardo Mendez
3427 Troy Penix
3428 Mark Sobolewski
3429 Chris Thomsen
3430 Jason White
3431 D.T. Cromer
3432 Kurt Endebrock
3433 Jason Geis
3434 Brian Lesher
3435 Sean Scott
3436 Checklist

1992 Classic Best Spartanburg Phillies

MT NR MT EX
Complete Set: 6.00

1 Craig Holman
2 Jerome Edwards
3 Johnny Mallee
4 Troy Rusk
5 Jesus Garces
6 Mike Juhl
7 Bryan Manicchia
8 Francisco Tejada
9 Dominic Desantis
10 Ron Blazier
11 John Kupsey
12 Al Bennett
13 Charlie Hurst
14 Mark Randall
15 Lamar Cherry
16 Jeff Bigler
17 Luis Brito
18 David Hayden
19 Mark Steffens
20 Matt Whisenant
21 Pat Ruth
22 Roy Majtyka
23 Tony Scott
24 Buzz Capra
25 Gary Beatty

1992 Fleer/ProCards Spartanburg Phillies

MT NR MT EX
Complete Set: 6.00

1255 Ron Blazier
1256 Rick Bottalico
1257 Greg Brown
1258 Dominic DeSantis
1259 Brad Hassinger
1260 Craig Holman
1261 Charlie Hurst
1262 Mike Juhl
1263 Bryan Manicchia
1264 Matt Whisenant
1265 Tommy Eason
1266 Francisco Tejada
1267 Luis Brito
1268 Jesus Garces
1269 David Hayden
1270 John Kupsey
1271 John Mailee
1272 Troy Rusk
1273 Al Bennett
1274 Jeff Bigler
1275 Lamar Cherry
1276 Jerome Edwards
1277 Pat Ruth
1278 Gene Schaff
1279 Mark Steffens
1280 Roy Majtyka
1281 Buzz Capra
1282 Tony Scott
1283 Checklist

1992 Classic Best Spokane Indians

MT NR MT EX
Complete Set: 6.00

1 Jared Baker
2 Kenneth Grzelaczyk
3 Britton Schreibe
4 Kyle White
5 Bill Robbs
6 Todd Marshall
7 Todd Schmitt
8 Tom Kindler
9 Mike Hermanson
10 Christen Murphy
11 Marcelino Garcia
12 Robert De Leon
13 Kevin Minchk
14 Melvin Rosario
15 Sean Drinkwater
16 Kraig Constantino
17 Manny Gagliano
18 Von Wechsberg
19 Andrian Hollinger
20 Scott Eggleston
21 Arthur Vazquez
22 Tim Ploeger
23 Stacy Hamm
24 Rafael Perez
25 Juan Cruz
26 Marcelino D'la Cruz
27 Ed Romero
28 Fred Cambria
29 Barry Moss
30 Bat Boys

1992 Fleer/ProCards Spokane Indians

MT NR MT EX
Complete Set: 6.00

1284 Jared Baker
1285 Scott Eggleston
1286 Ken Grzelaczyk
1287 Mike Hermanson
1288 Adrian Hollinger
1289 Tom Kindler
1290 Todd Marshall
1291 Chris Murphy
1292 Tim Ploeger
1293 Todd Schmitt
1294 Archie Vazquez
1295 Von Wechsberg
1296 Marcelina Garcia
1297 Melvin Rosario
1298 Kraig Constantino
1299 Marcelino De La Cruz
1300 Robert DeLeon
1301 Sean Drinkwater
1302 Manny Gagliano
1303 Kevin Alinchk
1304 Kyle White
1305 Juan Cruz
1306 Stacy Hamm
1307 Ralph Perez
1308 Bill Robbs
1309 Britton Scheibe
1310 Ed Romero
1311 Fred Cambria
1312 Barry Moos
1313 Checklist

1992 Classic Best Springfield Cardinals

MT NR MT EX
Complete Set: 7.00

1 Dimitri Young
2 Marc Ronan
3 Frank Speek
4 Brian Barber
5 Doug Radziewicz
6 Allen Battle
7 Paul Romanoli
8 Wander Pimentel
9 Mike Badorek
10 Keith Jones
11 Frank Martinez
12 Troy Konemann
13 Chris Vlasis
14 Mark Smith
15 Dennis Sliniger
16 Mark Tranbarger
17 Mike Eicher
18 Darrel Deak
19 John Mabry
20 Kevin Tahan
21 John O'Brien
22 Scott Simmons
23 Frank Cimorelli
24 Gerald Santos
25 Steve Cerio
26 Lorenzo Meza
27 Rick Colbert
28 Roy Silver
29 Mike Evans

1992 Fleer/ProCards Springfield Cardinals

MT NR MT EX
Complete Set: 8.00

859 Mike Badorek
860 Brian Barber
861 Frank Cimorelli
862 Troy Konemann
863 Frank Martinez
864 Paul Romanoli
865 Gerry Santos
866 Scott Simmons
867 Dennis Slininger
868 Mark Smith
869 Frank Speek
870 Mark Tranbarger
871 Steve Cerio
872 Marc Ronan
873 Kevin Tahan
874 Larry Meza
875 John O'Brien
876 Wander Pimentel
877 Doug Radziewicz
878 Ahmed Rodriguez
879 Dmitri Young
880 Allen Battle
881 Mike Eicher
882 Keith Jones
883 John Mabry
884 Chris Vlasis
885 Rick Colbert
886 Roy Silver
887 Checklist

1992 Classic Best St. Catharines Blue Jays

MT NR MT EX
Complete Set: 8.00

1 Todd Steverson
2 Keith Hines
3 Mike Coolbaugh
4 Juan Querecuto
5 Adam Meinershagen
6 Trevor Mallory
7 Roger Doman
8 Ned Darley
9 Lee Daniels
10 Santiago Henry
11 D.J. Boston
12 Lou Benbow
13 Mark Choate
14 Keiver Campbell
15 Rob Adkins
16 Kris Harmes
17 Lonell Roberts
18 Jeff Ladd
19 Gary Miller
20 Scot McCloughan
21 Chris Chandler
22 Brad Cornett
23 Timothy Crabtree
24 Derek Brandow
25 Levon Largusa
26 Aaron Jersild
27 J.J. Cannon
28 Reggie Cleveland
29 Scott Shannon
30 Rolando Pino

1992 Fleer/ProCards St. Catharines Blue Jays

	MT	NR MT	EX
Complete Set:	9.00		

2813 Checklist
3376 Robert Adkins
3377 Derek Brandow
3378 Brad Cornett
3379 Tim Crabtree
3380 Lee Daniels
3381 Ned Darley
3382 Roger Doman
3383 Aaron Jerslid
3384 Levon Largusa
3385 Trevor Mallory
3386 Adam Meinershagen
3387 Gary Miller
3388 Kris Harmes
3389 Jeff Ladd
3390 Juan Querecuto
3391 Louis Benbow
3392 D.J. Boston
3393 Chris Chandler
3394 Mark Choate
3395 Mike Coolbaugh
3396 Santiago Henry
3397 Keiver Campbell
3398 Scot McCloughan
3399 Loneli Roberts
3400 Todd Steverson
3401 J.J. Cannon
3402 Rolando Pino
3403 Team Picture

1992 Classic Best St. Lucie Mets

	MT	NR MT	EX
Complete Set:	7.00		

1 Butch Huskey
2 Bernie Millan
3 Tim Sandy
4 Chris Shanahan
5 Joe Crawford
6 James Harris
7 Mike Freitas
8 Denny Harriger
9 Joe McCann
10 Joe Roa
11 Clyde Keller
12 Rob Carpentier
13 Juan Castillo
14 Jose Martinez
15 Alberto Castillo
16 Mason Rudolph
17 Aaron Ledesma
18 Fernando Vina
19 Gerrod Davis
20 Edwards Fully
21 Tim McClinton
22 Tony Tijerina
23 Jason King
24 Frank Jacobs
25 Chris George
26 John Tamargo
27 Bill Gardner
28 Bill Latham
29 Bob Burton

1992 Fleer/ProCards St. Lucie Mets

	MT	NR MT	EX
Complete Set:	7.00		

1737 Rob Carpentier
1738 Juan Castillo
1739 Joe Crawford
1740 Mike Freitas
1741 Denny Harriger
1742 Jason Jacome
1743 Jose Martinez
1744 Joe McCann
1745 David Proctor
1746 Joe Roa
1747 Chris Shanahan
1748 Alberto Castillo
1749 Mason Rudolph
1750 Tony Tijerina
1751 James Harris
1752 Butch Huskey
1753 Frank Jacobs
1754 Jason King
1755 Aaron Ledesma
1756 Tim McClinton
1757 Bernie Millan
1758 Fernando Vina
1759 Jeff Barry
1760 Jay Davis
1761 Ed Fully
1762 Tim Sandy
1763 John Tamargo
1764 Bill Gardner
1765 Bill Latham
1766 Checklist

1992 Classic Best St. Petersburg Cardinals

	MT	NR MT	EX
Complete Set:	7.00		

1 Allen Watson
2 Dennis Fletcher
3 Andy Beasley
4 Roy Bailey
5 Paul Ellis
6 Juan Andujar
7 Donovan Campbell
8 Franklin Abreu
9 Ron Weber
10 Scott Baker
11 Dave Howell
12 Bryan Eversgerd
13 Kevin Nielsen
14 Joe Aversa
15 Rod Eldridge
16 Jeremy McGarity
17 Anthony Lewis
18 Mateo Ozuna
19 Tremayne Donald
20 John Kelly
21 Odalis Savinon
22 Ezequiel Herrera
23 Ernie Baker
24 Alan Botkin
25 Greg Rudolph
26 Aaron Ledesma
27 Dave Bialas
28 John Stuper
29 Don Doyel

1992 Fleer/ProCards St. Petersburg Cardinals

	MT	NR MT	EX
Complete Set:	6.00		

2017 Roy Bailey
2018 Ernie Baker
2019 Scott Baker
2020 Brian Barber
2021 Alan Botkin
2022 Bryan Eversgard
2023 Dennis Fletcher
2024 John Kelly
2025 Jeremy McGarity
2026 Kevin Nielsen
2027 Troy Salvior
2028 Ron Weber
2029 Andy Beasley
2030 Paul Ellis
2031 Franklin Abrau
2032 Juan Andujar
2033 Andy Bruce
2034 Mike Cantu
2035 Carlos Landinez
2036 Mateo Ozuna
2037 Greg Rudolph
2038 Tremayne Donald
2039 Ezequiel Herrera
2040 Anthony Lewis
2041 Dave Bialas
2042 Checklist

1992 Classic Best Stockton Ports

	MT	NR MT	EX
Complete Set:	6.00		

1 Larry Carter
2 Chuck Bush
3 Bobby Benjamin
4 Ed Smith
5 Michael Baase
6 Tim Carter
7 Duane Singleton
8 Dave Wrona
9 Lincoln Mikkelsen
10 Greg Kobza
11 Charlie Rogers
12 Leon Glenn
13 Bob Lukachyk
14 Michael Hancock
15 Michael Matheny
16 Francisco Gamez
17 Eric Whitford
18 Pat Miller
19 Michael Cater
20 Mark Cole
21 Mike Farrell
22 Kurt Archer
23 Tim Ireland
24 Mark Littell
25 Greg Calhoun

1992 Fleer/ProCards Stockton Ports

	MT	NR MT	EX
Complete Set:	6.00		

26 Kurt Archer
27 Chuck Bush
28 Ramser Correa
29 Mike Farrell
30 Francisco Gamez
31 Michael Hancock
32 Tom McGraw
33 Lincoln Mikkelsen
34 Pat Miller
35 Charlie Rogers
36 Greg Kobza
37 Mike Matheny
38 Tim Carter
39 Mark Cole
40 Leon Glenn
41 Oreste Marrero
42 Julian Salazer
43 Ed Smith
44 Eric Whitford
45 Dave Wrona
46 Mike Basse
47 Mike Carter
48 Michael Harris
49 Mike Lawn
50 Rob Lukachyk
51 Tim Ireland
52 Mark Littell
53 Checklist

1992 Fleer/ProCards Syracuse Chiefs

	MT	NR MT	EX
Complete Set:	7.00		

1959 Pete Blohm
1960 Wayne Edwards
1961 Darren Hall
1962 Pat Hentgen
1963 Al Leiter
1964 Doug Linton
1965 John Shea
1966 Rick Trlicek
1967 Gene Walter
1968 Anthony Ward
1969 David Weathers
1970 Woody Williams
1971 Jose Monzon
1972 Ed Sprague
1973 Bruce Crabbe
1974 Ray Giannelli
1975 Domingo Martinez
1976 Rob Montalvo
1977 Tom Quinlan
1978 Jerry Schunk
1979 Eddie Zosky
1980 Butch Davis
1981 Randy Knorr
1982 Mike Maksudian
1983 Stu Pederson
1984 Ryan Thompson
1985 Turner Ward
1986 Nick Leyva
1987 John Poloni
1988 Rocket Wheeler
1989 Checklist

1992 Team Syracuse Chiefs

The Chiefs gave away a single-sheet photo album on a giveaway night. The sheet folds into a 9-1/2" x 10-1/2" sheet. There are 30 cards on this sheet, each measuring 2-1/8" x 3-1/8" and separated by perforations to facilitate separation of the cards. The cards are unnumbered and have statistics and a facsimile autograph on the back. The cards are listed in the order in which they appear on the sheet.

	MT	NR MT	EX
Complete Set:	7.00		

(1) Nick Leyva
(2) John Poloni
(3) Rocket Wheeler
(4) Pete Blohm
(5) Bruce Crabbe
(6) Butch Davis
(7) Carlos Delgado
(8) Wayne Edwards
(9) Ray Giannelli
(10) Darren Hall
(11) Pat Hentgen
(12) Randy Knorr
(13) Al Leiter
(14) Doug Linton
(15) Mike Maksudian
(16) Domingo Martinez
(17) Stu Pederson
(18) Tom Quinlan
(19) Jerry Schunk
(20) John Shea
(21) Ed Sprague
(22) Ryan Thompson
(23) Mike Timlin
(24) Rick Trlicek
(25) Gene Walter
(26) Anthony Ward
(27) Turner Ward
(28) David Weathers
(29) Eddie Zosky
(30) Scooch (mascot)

1992 Team Syracuse Chiefs Former Stars

In addition to the "perf cards," the Chiefs issued a 10-card set, of former stars, sponsored by Tallmadge Tire and Auto of Syracuse. The cards are 2-3/8" x 3-1/2" and are unnumbered.

	MT	NR MT	EX
Complete Set:	7.00		

(1) Danny Ainge
(2) Derek Bell
(3) Tony Fernandez
(4) Cecil Fielder
(5) Kelly Gruber
(6) Juan Guzman
(7) Tom Henke
(8) Jimmy Key
(9) Fred McGriff
(10) Dave Stieb

1992 Fleer/ProCards Tacoma Tigers

	MT	NR MT	EX
Complete Set:	6.00		

2495 John Briscoe
2496 Steve Chitren
2497 Reggie Harris
2498 Jeff Mussleman
2499 Tim Peek
2500 Mike Reczke
2501 Todd Van Poppel
2502 Bruce Walton
2503 Weston Weber
2504 Bill Wilkinson
2505 Dave Zancanaro
2506 Mike Heath
2507 Henry Mercedes
2508 Scott Brosius
2509 Jeff Carter
2510 Keith Lockhart
2511 Gus Polidor
2512 Jack Smith
2513 Ron Witmeyer
2514 Dan Grunhard
2515 Orsino Hill
2516 Mike Kingery
2517 Troy Neel
2518 Glenn Abbott
2519 Mitchell Page
2520 Checklist

1992 Fleer/ProCards Tidewater Tides

	MT	NR MT	EX
Complete Set:	7.00		

888 Mike Birkbeck
889 Mark Dewey
890 Tom Filer
891 Eric Hillman
892 randy Marshall
893 Brad Moore
894 Dale Plummer
895 Chris Rauth
896 David Telgheder
897 Julio Valera
898 Julian Vasquez
899 Javier Gonzalez
900 Orlando Mercado
901 Mitch Lyden
902 Kevin Baez
903 Tim Bogar
904 Chris Donnels
905 Terrel Hansen
906 Jeff McKnight
907 Steve Springer
908 Jeromy Burnitz
909 D.J. Dozier
910 Pat Howell
911 Lee May
912 Clint Hurdle
913 Bob Apodaca
914 Ron Washington
1736 Checklist

1992 Fleer/ProCards Toledo Mud Hens

	MT	NR MT	EX
Complete Set:	6.00		

1032 William Brennan
1033 Tony Castillo
1034 Steve Cummings
1035 John DeSilva

1036 Greg Gohr
1037 Buddy Groom
1038 David Haas
1039 Jeff Kaiser
1040 John Kiely
1041 Vance Lovelace
1042 Jamie Moyer
1043 Ron Rightnowar
1044 Mike Walker
1045 Pedro Gonzalez
1046 Marty Pevey
1047 Rich Rowland
1048 Karl Allaire
1049 Rico Brogna
1050 Dean DeCillis
1051 Victor Rosario
1052 Greg Smith
1053 Steve Carter
1054 Jody Hurst
1055 Riccardo Ingram
1056 Johnny Paredes
1057 Joe Sparks
1058 Kevin Bradshaw
1059 Ralph Treuel
1060 Checklist

1992 Fleer/ProCards Tucson Toros

	MT	NR MT	EX
Complete Set:	6.00		

478 Willie Blair
479 Ryan Bowen
480 Mike Capel
481 Chris Gardner
482 Jason Grimsley
483 Bobby Hurta
484 Jeff Juden
485 Shane Reynolds
486 Richie Simon
487 Matt Turner
488 Dave Veres
489 Brian Williams
490 Barry Lyons
491 John Massarelli
492 Scooter Tucker
493 Rod Booker
494 Andujar Cedeno
495 Gary Cooper
496 Trent Hubbard
497 Andy Mota
498 Ernest Riles
499 Joe Mikulik
500 Rick Parker
501 Mike Simms
502 Eric Yelding
503 Bob Skinner
504 Dan Angotti
505 Dave Engle
506 Brent Strom
507 Checklist

1992 Fleer/ProCards Tulsa Drillers

	MT	NR MT	EX
Complete Set:	6.00		

2686 Brian Bohanon
2687 Jeff Bronkey
2688 Rob Brown
2689 Don Carman
2690 Bryan Gore
2691 Danilo Leon
2692 Robb Nen
2693 Brian Romaro
2694 Jeff Sellers
2695 Cedric Shaw
2696 Dan Smith
2697 Matt Whiteside
2698 Darren Niethammer
2699 John Russell
2700 Chris Colon
2701 Rusty Greer
2702 Trey McCoy
2703 Jose Oliva
2704 Luke Sable
2705 Jon Shave
2706 Kevin Belcher
2707 David Hulse
2708 Rod Morris
2709 Bobby Jones
2710 Randy Whisler
2711 Jackson Todd
2712 Checklist

1992 Team Tulsa Drillers

The 30 card set is a continuation of a long series of team issues by the Drillers. The cards are standard size, and part of an annual giveaway night.

	MT	NR MT	EX
Complete Set:	6.00		

(1) Mike Arner
(2) Kevin Belcher
(3) Brian Bohanon
(4) Jeff Bronkey
(5) Rob Brown
(6) Don Carman
(7) Cris Colon
(8) Bryan Gore
(9) Rusty Greer
(10) Donald Harris
(11) David Hulse
(12) Bobby Jones
(13) Pete Kuld
(14) Danilo Leon
(15) Kurt Miller
(16) Rod Morris
(17) Darren Niethammer
(18) Jose Oliva
(19) Donna Papangelli
(20) Brian Romer
(21) John Russell
(22) Luke Sable
(23) Jeff Sellers
(24) Jon Shave
(25) Cedric Shaw
(26) Dan Smith
(27) Jackson Todd
(28) Randy Whisler
(29) Matt Whiteside
(30) Kevin Brown (Past Star)

1992 Classic Best Utica Blue Sox

	MT	NR MT	EX
Complete Set:	6.00		

1 Tim Moore
2 Jason Pierson
3 Chris Snopek
4 Jimmy Hurst
5 Carmine Cappuccio
6 Mike Cameron
7 Byron Mathews
8 Jason Ogden
9 Julio Foster
10 Ted Rich
11 Jason Evans
12 Brian Filosa
13 Ricky Bowrosen
14 Robert Machado
15 Julio Vinas
16 Chris Tremie
17 Jason Watkins
18 Doug McGraw
19 Jim McDermont
20 Wayne Lindemann
21 Sean Johnston
22 Steve Gajkowski
23 David Elsbernd
24 Ty Lynch
25 Mike Bertotti
26 John Herrolz

1992 Fleer/ProCards Vancouver Canadians

	MT	NR MT	EX
Complete Set:	6.00		

2713 Rodney Bolton
2714 Jeff Carter
2715 Mike Dunne
2716 Ramon Garcia
2717 Chris Howard
2718 John Hudek
2719 Bo Kennedy
2720 Greg Perschke
2721 Rich Scheid
2722 Jeff Schwarz
2723 Ron Stephens
2724 Steve Wapnick
2725 Matt Merullo
2726 Nelson Santovenia
2727 Ron Coomer
2728 Chris Cron
2729 Drew Denson
2730 Joe Hall
2731 Ever Magallanes
2732 Norberto Martin
2733 Derek Lee
2734 Rick Renick
2735 Roger LaFrancois
2736 Checklist

1992 Classic Best Vero Beach Dodgers

	MT	NR MT	EX
Complete Set:	10.00		

1 Kiki Jones
2 Keoki Farrish
3 Roberto Mejia
4 Alton Pinkney
5 Ken Hamilton
6 Tim Griffin
7 Jay Kirkpatrick
8 Willis Otanez
9 Jason Kerr
10 Sean McKarnie
11 Anthony Collier
12 Vernon Spearman
13 Billy Lott
14 Brian Piotrowicz
15 James Wray
16 Chris Sinacori
17 Ed Stryker
18 Jamie Daspit
19 Steve O'Donnell
20 Dan Gray
21 Mike Brady
22 Javiar De La Hoya
23 Rafael Gutierrez
24 Bill Wengert
25 Steve Mintz
26 Ben Van Ryn
27 Ken Huckaby
28 Dennis Lewallyn
29 Glenn Hoffman
30 Kazushiga Nagashim

1992 Fleer/ProCards Vero Beach Dodgers

	MT	NR MT	EX
Complete Set:	10.00		

2866 Jason Brosnan
2867 Jim Despit
2868 Javier Delahoya
2869 Ken Hamilton
2870 Jason Kerr
2871 Steve Mintz
2872 Brian Piotrowicz
2873 Chris Sinacori
2874 Ed Stryker
2875 Ben Van Ryn
2876 James Weaver
2877 James Wray
2878 Ken Huckaby
2879 Ed Lund
2880 Jonathan Taylor
2881 Mike Boyzuick
2882 Jay Kirkpatrick
2883 Steve Kliafas
2884 Sean McKarnie
2885 Roberto Mejia
2886 Steve O'Donnell
2887 Willis Otanez
2888 Anthony Collier
2889 Freddy Gonzalez
2890 Keoki Farrish
2891 Billy Lott
2892 Vernon Spearman
2893 Glenn Hoffman
2894 Bo Chun
2895 Garrett Teel
2896 Dennis Lewailyn
2897 Checklist

1992 Classic Best Visalia Oaks

	MT	NR MT	EX
Complete Set:	8.00		

1 Scott Stahoviak
2 Rich Becker
3 Dickie Dixon
4 Matt Connolly
5 Marc Morris
6 Dave Bigham
7 Tim Persing
8 Mike Erickson
9 Jeff Thelen
10 Bob Robinson
11 Mark MacArthur
12 Tom Houk
13 Todd Logan
14 Marty Cordova
15 Mike Lewis
16 Matt Brown
17 Ryan Turner
18 David Rivera
19 Steve Dunn
20 Denny Hocking
21 Mike Durant
22 Troy Ricker
23 Todd Ritchie
24 Steve Liddle
25 Brian Allard
26 Joel Safly

1992 Fleer/ProCards Visalia Oaks

	MT	NR MT	EX
Complete Set:	8.00		

1004 Dave Bigham
1005 Carlos Castillo
1006 Matt Connolly
1007 Dickie Dixon
1008 Mike Ericson
1009 Mike Lewis
1010 Jeff Mansur
1011 Bob McCreary
1012 Marc Morris
1013 Tim Persing
1014 Todd Ritchie
1015 Bob Robinson
1016 Jeff Thelen
1017 Matt Brown
1018 Mike Durant
1019 Steve Dunn
1020 Denny Hocking
1021 Tom Houk
1022 Mark MacArthur
1023 David Rivera
1024 Scott Stahoviak
1025 Rich Becker
1026 Marty Cordova
1027 Troy Ricker
1028 Ryan Turner
1029 Steve Liddle
1030 Brian Allard
1031 Checklist

1992 Classic Best Waterloo Diamonds

	MT	NR MT	EX
Complete Set:	6.00		

1 Kevin Farlow
2 Joe Waldron
3 Scott Bream
4 Scotty Pugh
5 Kevin Johnson
6 Bruce Bensching
7 Ryan Ivie
8 Jeff Brown
9 Steve Hoeme
10 Jose Davila
11 Jerrey Thurston
12 Cameron Cairncross
13 Tom Paskievitch
14 Robbie Beckett
15 Tim Goins
16 Derek Vaughn
17 Todd Altaffer
18 Shawn Robertson
19 John Abercrombie Jr.
20 Keith McKoy
21 Jason Hardtkey
22 Shawn Whalen
23 Jeff Pearce
24 Dave Adams
25 Cole Hyson
26 Keith Champion
27 Dean Treanor
28 John Maxwell
29 Jack Grandy
30 Checklist

1992 Fleer/ProCards Waterloo Diamonds

	MT	NR MT	EX
Complete Set:	6.00		

2132 Todd Altaffer
2133 Robbie Beckett
2134 Chris Benhardt
2135 Bruce Bensching
2136 Jeff Brown
2137 Cameron Cairncross
2138 Jose Davila
2139 Ryan Ivie
2140 Tom Martin
2141 Todd Paskievitch
2142 Joe Waldron
2143 Tim Goins
2144 Sean Mulligan
2145 Jerrey Thurston
2146 John Abercrombie
2147 Dave Adams
2148 Scott Bream
2149 Kevin Farlow
2150 Jason Hardtke
2151 Scott Pugh
2152 Keith McKoy
2153 Jeff Pearce
2154 Shawn Robertson
2155 Derek Vaughn
2156 Keith Champion
2157 Dean Treanor
2158 Checklist

1992 Classic Best Watertown Indians

	MT	NR MT	EX
Complete Set:	6.00		

1 Jamie Taylor
2 Paul Gibbs
3 Jason Fronio
4 Scott Sharts
5 Denny Key
6 Mike Jewell
7 Oscar Resendez
8 Ben Blake
9 Charles York
10 Matt Williams
11 Mike Nelson
12 Noe Najera
13 Fred Smith
14 Epi Cardenas
15 Brian Arntzen
16 David Chisum
17 Jonathan Nunnally
18 Pat Bryant
19 Mike Lockhart
20 Brad Kantor
21 Mike Zollars
22 Curtis George
23 Mike Moore
24 Derek Hacopian

25 Kevin DiGiacomo
26 Shawn Pender
27 Greg Ferlenda
28 Ed Stabile
29 Rick Jameyson

1992 Fleer/ProCards Watertown Indians

	MT	NR MT	EX
Complete Set:	6.00		

3225 Ben Blake
3226 Jason Fronio
3227 Paul Gibbs
3228 Mike Jewell
3229 Denny Key
3230 Noe Najera
3231 Mike Neilson
3232 Oscar Resendez
3233 Scott Sharts
3234 Fred Smith
3235 Matt Williams
3236 Charles York
3237 Brian Arntzen
3238 Mike Lockhart
3240 Epi Cardenas
3241 Kevin DiGiacomo
3242 Curtis George
3243 Brad Kantor
3244 Jamie Taylor
3245 Pat Bryant
3246 Dave Chisum
3247 Sam Hence
3248 John Nunnally
3249 Mike Zollars
3250 Shawn Pender
3251 Greg Ferlenda
3252 Derek Hacopian
3253 Checklist

1992 Classic Best Welland Pirates

	MT	NR MT	EX
Complete Set:	6.00		

1 Jacob Austin
2 Miguel Bonilla
3 Aaron Cannaday
4 John Carter
5 John Cranford
6 Angel Colon
7 Ramon Espinosa
8 Frank Garcia-Luna
9 Rico Gholston
10 Riegel Hunt
11 Matt Jones
12 Erskine Kelley
13 Dennis Konuszewski
14 Ted Klamm
15 Michael LaPlante
16 Sean Lawrence
17 Pat Lussier
18 Dave Maize
19 Gil Perez
20 Chance Sanford
21 Craig Shotton
22 Larry Stahlhoefer
23 Chuck Tooch
24 Richard Townsend
25 Marc Wilson
26 Gary Wilson
27 Stanley Wiltz
28 Trent Jewett
29 Julio Garcia

1992 Fleer/ProCards Welland Pirates

	MT	NR MT	EX
Complete Set:	6.00		

1314 Miguel Bonilla
1315 John Carter
1316 Frank Garcia-Luna
1317 Ted Klemm
1318 Michael LaPlante
1319 Sean Lawrence
1320 Mark Mesewicz
1321 Gil Perez
1322 Richard Townsend
1323 Marc Wilkins
1324 Gary Wilson
1325 Aaron Cannaday
1326 Dave Maiza
1327 Larry Stahlhoefer
1328 Angel Colon
1329 John Cranford
1330 Rico Gholston
1331 Matt Jones
1332 Kevin Polcovich
1333 Chance Sanford
1334 Chuck Tooch
1335 Stanley Wiltz
1336 Ramon Esponosa
1337 Riegel Hunt
1338 Erskine Kelley
1339 Pat Lussier
1340 Trent Jewett
1341 Tom Barnard
1342 Julio Garcia
1343 Checklist

1992 Classic Best West Palm Beach Expos

	MT	NR MT	EX
Complete Set:	14.00		

1 Rondell White
2 Ron Krause
3 Tavo Alvarez
4 Rob Fitzpatrick
5 James Austin
6 Steve Keighley
7 Jeff Tuss
8 Kevin McDonald
9 Miguel Batista
10 Scott Campbell
11 Steve Long
12 Ranbir Grewal
13 Shaun Murphy
14 Rafael Diaz
15 Chris Malinoski
16 Bob Baxter
17 Corey Powell
18 Joey Eischen
19 Glenn Murray
20 Billy Brewer
21 Brett Jenkins
22 Randy Wilstead
23 Mike Daniel
24 Felix Moya
25 Mike Weimerskirch
26 Dave Jauss
27 Marc Goldberg
28 Nancy Graham
29 John Picano
30 Chuck Kniffin

1992 Fleer/ProCards West Palm Beach Expos

	MT	NR MT	EX
Complete Set:	14.00		

2077 Tavo Alvarez
2078 Miguel Batista
2079 Bob Baxter
2080 Billy Brewer
2081 Rafel Diaz
2082 Joey Eischen
2083 Kevin Foster
2084 Ranbir Grewel
2085 Steve Long
2086 Kevin McDonald
2087 Felix Moya
2088 Corey Powell
2089 Jeff Tuss
2090 Mike Daniel
2091 Rob Fitzpatrick
2092 Steve Keighley
2093 Scott Campebll
2094 Brett Jenkins
2095 Ron Krause
2096 Chris Malinoski
2097 Randy Wilstead
2098 Jim Austin
2099 Shaun Murphy
2100 Glenn Murphy
2101 Mike Weimerskirch
2102 Rondell White
2103 Dave Jeuss
2104 Chuck Kniffin
2105 Checklist

1992 Fleer/ProCards Wichita Wranglers

	MT	NR MT	EX
Complete Set:	6.00		

3651 Renay Bryand
3652 Mark Ettles
3653 Scott Fredrickson
3654 Steve Hoeme
3655 Mike Linskey
3656 Pedro Martinez
3657 Lance Painter
3658 Royal Thomas
3659 Brian Johnson
3660 Steve Bethea
3661 Jay Gainer
3662 Mark Gieseke
3663 Paul Gonzalez
3664 Ray Holbert
3665 Mat Witkowski
3666 Vince Harris
3667 Dwayne Hosey
3668 Steve Martin
3669 Bruce Bochy
3670 Danny Garcia
3671 Checklist

1992 Classic Best Winston-Salem Spirits

	MT	NR MT	EX
Complete Set:	6.00		

1 Tim Delgado
2 Rafael Soto
3 Jose Vierra
4 Rich Juday
5 Sean Cheetham
6 Paul Torres
7 Scott Taylor
8 Earl Cunningham
9 Jason Doss
10 Mike Little
11 Brad Erdman
12 Rolando Fernandez
13 Andrew Hartung
14 Doug Glanville
15 Ken Krahenbuhl
16 Amilcar Correa
17 Chuck Kirk
18 Rudy Gomez
19 Joe Baisucci
20 Mike Gabbani
21 Pedro Alicano
22 Joe Szczepanski
23 Aaron Taylor
24 Ben Burlingame
25 Tim Budrewicz
26 Bill Hayes
27 Lester Strode
28 Steve Melendez

1992 Fleer/ProCards Winston-Salem Spirits

	MT	NR MT	EX
Complete Set:	6.00		

1198 Pedro Alicano
1199 Tim Budrewicz
1200 Ben Burlingame
1201 Sean Cheetham
1202 Amilcar Correa
1203 Tim Delgado
1204 Jason Doss
1205 Chuck Kirk
1206 Pedro Perez
1207 Joe Szczepanski
1208 Aaron Taylor
1209 Scott Weiss
1210 Brad Erdman
1211 Mike Gabbani
1212 Scott Taylor
1213 Rudy Gomez
1214 Andy Hartung
1215 Rich Juday
1216 Rafael Soto
1217 Jose Vierra
1218 Rolando Fernandez
1219 Doug Glanville
1220 Corey Kapano
1221 Mike Little
1222 Paul Torres
1223 Bill Hayes
1224 Lester Strode
1225 Checklist

1992 Team Winston-Salem Spirts

This 27-card set is skip-numbered by player uniform number. The cards measure 2-3/8" x 3-1/2". The set was given away by the team on baseball card night, and was sponsored by Bullpen Chew Bubble Gum. The backs contain player statistics and biographical information.

	MT	NR MT	EX
Complete Set:	4.00		

() Steve Melendez (trainer)
(1) Rafael Soto
(2) Brad Erdman
(4) Doug Glanville
(6) Corey Kapano
(7) Amilcar Correa
(9) Andrew Hartung
(11) Rudy Gomez
(12) Rolando Fernandez
(18) Pedro Perez
(19) Scott Taylor
(20) Bill Hayes
(21) Sean Cheetham
(23) Rich Juday
(24) Jose Viera
(25) Ozzie Timmons
(27) Mike Gabbani
(28) Scott Weiss
(30) Paul Torres
(32) Lester Strode
(35) Chuck Kirk
(36) Jason Doss
(39) Joe Szczepanski
(41) Tim Budrewicz
(45) Ben Burlingame
(46) Tim Delgado
(47) Aaron Taylor

1992 Classic Best Winter Haven Red Sox

	MT	NR MT	EX
Complete Set:	6.00		

1 Chris Davis
2 Joe Ciccarella
3 Randy Brown
4 David Schmidt
5 William Madril
6 Diogenes Baez
7 Tony Ferreira
8 Gary Villalobos
9 Jim Byrd
10 Terry Powers
11 Doug McNeil
12 Joe Luis
13 Silverio Santa Maria
14 Ron Mahay
15 Joel Bennett
16 Chad Schoenvogel
17 Ryan Maloney
18 Bryan Brown
19 Robert Pickett
20 Dana Levangie
21 Les Wallin
22 Brett Donovan
23 Brian Bright
24 Todd Miller
25 Mark Mitchelson
26 Felix Maldonado
27 Jim Stricek
28 Joe Marchese
29 Steve Braun
30 Lee Stange

1992 Fleer/ProCards Winter Haven Red Sox

	MT	NR MT	EX
Complete Set:	6.00		

1767 Joel Bennett
1768 Joe Ciccarella
1769 Bernie Dzafic
1770 Rob Henkel
1771 Michael Lynch
1772 Ryan Maloney
1773 Todd Miller
1774 Dave Owen
1775 Terry Powers
1776 Steve Renko
1777 Chad Schoenvogel
1778 Brian Young
1779 Alex Delgado
1780 Joe Demus
1781 Dana LaVangie
1782 Emirson Soto
1783 Randy Brown
1784 Felix Colon
1785 Marty Durkin
1786 Tony Ferreira
1787 David Schmidt
1788 Gary Villalobos
1789 Les Wallin
1790 Diogenes Baez
1791 Brian Bright
1792 Bryan Brown
1793 Jose Zambrano
1794 Felix Maldonado
1795 Joe Marchese
1796 Checklist

1992 Classic Best Yakima Bears

	MT	NR MT	EX
Complete Set:	6.00		

1 Doug Bennett
2 John Graves
3 Alton Pinkney
4 Dan Gray
5 Burgess Watts
6 Keith Johnson
7 Patrick Reed
8 Clint Minear
9 Kevin Zahner
10 Robert Legendre
11 Tito Landrum
12 Ken Champman
13 Tory Miran
14 Cliff Anderson
15 Matt Herges
16 Todd Rizzo
17 Todd LaValley
18 Erik Zammarchi
19 Keith Trautman
20 John Callihan
21 Rafael Gutierrez
22 Matt Filson

23 Joe Barbeln
24 Joe Varva
25 Brett Magnusson
26 Barclay Dugger

1992 Fleer/ProCards Yakima Bears

	MT	NR MT	EX
Complete Set:	6.00		

3438 Joe Barbein
3439 Doug Bennett
3440 Brent Colson
3441 John Graves
3442 Rafael Gutierrez
3443 Matt Herges
3444 Todd LaValley
3445 Robert Legendre
3446 Clint Minear
3447 Todd Rizzo
3448 Carlos Thomas
3449 Keith Troutman
3450 Burgess Watts
3451 Chris Abbe
3452 Mike Brown
3453 Dan Gray
3454 Kevin Zahner
3455 Cliff Anderson
3456 John Callihan
3457 Ken Chapman
3458 Keith Johnson
3459 Sandy Martinez
3460 Mike Serbalik
3461 Matt Filson
3462 Tito Landrum
3463 Tory Miran
3464 Michael Moore
3465 Alton Pinkney
3466 Pat Reed
3467 Erik Zammarchi
3468 Joe Vavra
3469 Checklist

1993 Classic Best Foil

Classic Best's 1993 Minor League foil series is 300 cards, plus four insert sets, a puzzle set and autographed cards from eight players. The set includes players from Triple A, Double A and Single A. Autographed Carlos Delgado, Cliff Floyd, Jeffrey Hammonds, Derek Jeter, Mike Kelly, Phil Nevin, Paul Shuey and Dmitri Young cards (1,200 each) were randomly inserted into packs, as were puzzle contest pieces. By completing a nine-card puzzle, 500 collectors could win a plaque of the eight autographed cards featured in the series. The set's insert sets are: Young Guns, Expansion #1 Picks, MVPs and Player and Manager of the Year.

	MT	NR MT	EX
Complete Set (300):	15.00	11.00	6.00

No.	Player	MT
1	Paul Shuey	.10
2	Brad Clontz	.05
3	Phil Dauphin	.10
4	Kevin Flora	.05
5	Doug Glanville	.05
6	Hilly Hathaway	.05
7	Scott Hatteberg	.15
8	Ryan Hawblitzel	.05
9	Bob Henkel	.05
10	Mike Kelly	.20
11	Jose Malave	.10
12	Jeff McNeely	.05
13	Roberto Mejia	.20
14	Kevin Roberson	.20
15	Chad Roper	.10
16	John Roper	.05
17	Pete Rose Jr.	.05
18	Paul Russo	.10
19	John Salles	.05
20	Tracy Sanders	.05
21	Chris Saunders	.10
22	Jason Schmidt	.05
23	Aaron Sele	.75
24	Bob Abreu	.05
25	Don Sparks	.05
26	Scott Stahoviak	.05
27	Matt Stairs	.10
28	Todd Steverson	.20
29	Ozzie Timmons	.20
30	Michael Tucker	.60
31	Jose Viera	.05
32	B.J. Wallace	.15
33	Mark Wohlers	.05
34	Gabe White	.15
35	Rick White	.05
36	Rondell White	.75
37	Gerald Williams	.10
38	Mike Williams	.05
39	Todd Williams	.05
40	Desi Wilson	.10
41	Johnny Ard	.05
42	Jamie Arnold	.15
43	Howard Battle	.10
44	Greg Blosser	.20
45	Rob Butler	.10
46	Dan Carlson	.05
47	Joe Caruso	.05
48	Bobby Chouinard	.10
49	Adell Davenport	.05
50	Juan De La Rosa	.05
51	Alex Gonzalez	.60
52	Steve Hosey	.10
53	Rick Krivda	.10
54	T.R. Lewis	.10
55	Jose Mercedes	.15
56	Melvin Nieves	.20
57	Luis Ortiz	.10
58	Joe Russelli	.05
59	Brian Sackinsky	.05
60	Salomon Torres	.15
61	James Baldwin	.50
62	Travis Baptist	.10
63	Bret Boone	.35
64	Mike Buddie	.05
65	Paul Carey	.05
66	Tim Crabtree	.10
67	Tony Longmire	.15
68	Robert Eenhoorn	.05
69	Paul Ellis	.05
70	Shawn Estes	.20
71	Andy Fox	.05
72	Shawn Green	.15
73	Jimmy Haynes	.05
74	Sterling Hitchcock	.15
75	Mark Hutton	.05
76	Domingo Jean	.20
77	Kevin Jordan	.05
78	Steve Karsay	.75
79	Paul Fletcher	.05
80	Mike Milchin	.05
81	Lyle Mouton	.10
82	Bobby Munoz	.10
83	Alex Ochoa	.20
84	Steve Olsen	.05
85	Billy Owens	.10
86	Eddie Pearson	.05
87	Mike Robertson	.05
88	Johnny Ruffin	.10
89	Mark Smith	.15
90	Brandon Wilson	.05
91	Derek Jeter	.40
92	Edgardo Alfonzo	.05
93	Jeff Alkire	.20
94	Roger Bailey	.05
95	Jeff Barry	.05
96	Terrell Buckley	.25
97	Hector Carrasco	.20
98	Danny Clyburn	.10
99	Darren Burton	.05
100	Scott Eyre	.10
101	Chad Fox	.05
102	Joe Hudson	.05
103	Jason Hutchins	.10
104	Bobby Jones	.25
105	Jason Kendall	.10
106	Rickey Magdaleno	.05
107	Buck McNabb	.05
108	Doug Mlicki	.05
109	Chris Eddy	.10
110	Jon Lieber	.05
111	Ken Powell	.05
112	Todd Pridy	.05
113	Marquis Riley	.05
114	Steve Rodriguez	.15
115	Brian Rupp	.05
116	Yuri Sanchez	.05
117	Al Shirley	.10
118	Paul Spoljaric	.25
119	Amaury Talemaco	.05
120	Shon Walker	.10
121	Tavo Alvarez	.20
122	Shane Andrews	.05
123	Billy Ashley	.35
124	Brian Barber	.10
125	Trey Beamon	.15
126	Scott Bryant	.05
127	Scott Bryant	.05
128	Ozzie Canseco	.05
129	Brian Carpenter	.10
130	Roger Cedeno	.25
131	Randy Curtis	.05
132	Alberto De Los Santos	.05
133	Steve Dixon	.05
134	Joey Eischen	.10
135	Brook Fordyce	.15
136	Rick Gorecki	.05
137	Lee Hancock	.05
138	Todd Hollandsworth	.60
139	Frank Jacobs	.05
140	Mark Johnson	.05
141	Albie Lopez	.10
142	Dan Malendez	.05
143	William Pennyfeather	.05
144	Scott Lydy	.10
145	Chris Snopek	.05
146	Quilvio Veras	.05
147	Jose Vidro	.05
148	Allen Watson	.30
149	Matt Whisenant	.05
150	Craig Wilson	.05
151	Rich Becker	.15
152	Mike Durant	.05
153	Brad Ausmus	.15
154	Robbie Beckett	.10
155	Steve Dunn	.05
156	Paul Byrd	.05
157	Jason Bere	1.00
158	Ben Blomdahl	.05
159	John Brothers	.05
160	Tim Costo	.10
161	Joel Chimelis	.05
162	Kenny Carlyle	.05
163	Garvin Alston	.05
164	Sean Bergman	.05
165	Marshall Boze	.40
166	Terry Burrows	.05
167	Danny Bautista	.10
168	Jason Bates	.15
169	Brent Bowers	.05
170	Rico Brogna	.10
171	Armann Brown	.05
172	Brant Brown	.20
173	Julio Bruno	.10
174	Mike DeJean	.05
175	Nick Delvecchio	.10
176	Bobby Bonds Jr.	.15
177	Miguel Castellano	.05
178	Tommy Adams	.10
179	Alan Burke	.05
180	John Burke	.10
181	Ivan Cruz	.05
182	Johnny Damon	.10
183	Carl Everett	.30
184	Jorge Fabregas	.10
185	John Fantauzzi	.05
186	Mike Farmer	.05
187	Mike Farrell	.05
188	Omar Garcia	.05
189	Brent Gates	.40
190	Jason Giambi	.20
191	K.C. Gullum	.05
192	Chris Gomez	.40
193	Ricky Greene	.10
194	Willie Greene	.15
195	Benji Grigsby	.10
196	Mike Groppuso	.05
197	Johnny Guzman	.10
198	Bob Hamelin	.20
199	Joey Hamilton	.10
200	Chris Haney	.15
201	Donald Harris	.10
202	Andy Hartung	.15
203	Chris Hatcher	.05
204	Rick Helling	.25
205	Edgar Herrera	.05
206	Aaron Holbert	.05
207	Ray Holbert	.05
208	Tyler Houston	.10
209	Brian Hunter	.25
210	Miguel Jiminez	.10
211	Charles Johnson	.35
212	Corey Kapano	.05
213	Tom Knauss	.05
214	Brian Koelling	.10
215	Brian Lane	.05
216	Kevin Legault	.05
217	Mark Lewis	.05
218	Luis Lopez	.10
219	Jose Martinez	.10
220	Mitch Meluskey	.05
221	Casey Mendenhall	.05
222	Danny Mitchell	.05
223	Tony Mitchell	.05
224	Ritchie Moody	.15
225	James Mouton	.30
226	Steve Murphy	.05
227	Mike Neill	.10
228	Tom Nevers	.10
229	Alan Newman	.05
230	Tom Nuneviller	.05
231	Jonathan Nunnally	.15
232	Chad Ogea	.20
233	Ray Ortiz	.05
234	Orlando Palmeiro	.10
235	Craig Paquette	.10
236	Troy Percival	.15
237	Bobby Perna	.05
238	John Pricher	.05
239	Ken Ramos	.05
240	Joe Randa	.15
241	Ron Blazier	.05
242	Terry Bradshaw	.05
243	Jason Hisey	.05
244	Sean Lowe	.10
245	Chad McConnell	.15
246	Jackie Nickell	.10
247	Pat Rapp	.15
248	Calvin Reese	.20
249	Desi Relaford	.05
250	Troy Ricker	.05
251	Todd Ritchie	.15
252	Chris Roberts	.10
253	Scott Sanders	.05
254	Ruben Santana	.05
255	Chris Seelbach	.05
256	Dan Serafini	.10
257	Curtis Shaw	.05
258	Kennie Steenstra	.15
259	Kevin Stocker	.40
260	Tanyon Sturtze	.05
261	Tim Stutheit	.05
262	Jamie Taylor	.10
263	Chad Townsend	.05
264	Steve Trachsel	.60
265	Jose Valentin	.10
266	K.C. Waller	.05
267	Chris Weinke	.10
268	Darrell Whitmore	.25
269	Juan Williams	.05
270	Tim Worrell	.15
271	Tim Belk	.10
272	London Bradley	.05
273	Tilson Brito	.05
274	Felipe Crespo	.10
275	Kenny Felder	.10
276	Billy Hall	.05
277	Terrell Hansen	.05
278	Rod Henderson	.10
279	Bobby Hughes	.05
280	Bobby Hughes	.05
281	Rick Huisman	.05
282	Jack Johnson	.05
283	Gabby Martinez	.10
284	Jose Millares	.05
285	Jason Moler	.20
286	Willie Mota	.10
287	Marty Neff	.05
288	Eric Owens	.05
289	Daryl Ratliff	.15
290	Ozzie Sanchez	.10
291	Dave Silvestri	.15
292	Chris Stynes	.05
293	Aubrey Waggoner	.05
294	Jimmy White	.05
295	Jim Campanis	.05
296	Tony Womack	.10
297	Checklist 1	.05
298	Checklist 2	.05
299	Checklist 3	.05
300	Checklist 3	.05

1993 Classic Best Autographs

In its 1993 foil packs, Classic Best randomly included autographed cards of eight top prospects. Each player signd 1,200 cards.

	MT	NR MT	EX
Complete Set (8):	300.00	225.00	120.00

No.	Player	MT
(1)	Carlos Delgado	50.00
(2)	Cliff Floyd	75.00
(3)	Jeffrey Hammonds	60.00
(4)	Derek Jeter	35.00
(5)	Mike Kelly	30.00
(6)	Phil Nevin	35.00
(7)	Paul Shuey	25.00
(8)	Dmitri Young	30.00

1993 Classic Best Young Guns

These 28 different cards were randomly inserted into Classic Best's 1993 foil packs. The cards are numbered with a YG prefix.

	MT	NR MT	EX
Complete Set (28):	80.00	60.00	32.00

No.	Player	MT
1	Midre Cummings	3.50
2	Carlos Delgado	7.00
3	Cliff Floyd	14.00
4	Jeffrey Hammonds	9.00
5	Tyrone Hill	2.00
6	Butch Huskey	3.00
7	Chipper Jones	4.50
8	Mike Lieberthal	1.25
9	David McCarty	2.00
10	Ray McDavid	3.00
11	Kurt Miller	1.25
12	Raul Mondesi	15.00
13	Chad Mottola	5.00
14	Calvin Murray	2.00
15	Phil Nevin	4.50
16	Marc Newfield	5.00
17	Eduardo Perez	2.00
18	Manny Ramirez	10.00
19	Edgar Renteria	1.25
20	Frank Rodriguez	2.50
21	Scott Ruffcorn	2.50
22	Brien Taylor	1.75
23	Justin Thompson	2.00
24	Mark Thompson	1.50
25	Todd Van Poppel	1.75
26	Joe Vitiello	2.00
27	Derek Wallace	2.00
28	Dmitri Young	2.50

1993 Classic Best Expansion #1 Picks

These two cards, featuring the top picks by the Major League's two new expansion clubs (Colorado Rockies and Floria Marlins), were randomly inserted in 1993 Classic Best foil packs. The cards are numbered with an EP prefix.

	MT	NR MT	EX
Complete Set (2):	4.00		

No.	Player	MT
1	John Burke	2.00
2	Charles Johnson	2.50

1993 Classic Best MVPs

These 10 cards, numbered with an MVP prefix, were randomly inserted into 1993 Classic Best foil packs. The cards fearture MVP-caliber prospects from the minors.

	MT	NR MT	EX
Complete Set (10):	20.00	15.00	8.00
Common Player:	1.00	.70	.40

1	Bubba Smith	1.00
2	Javy Lopez	8.00
3	Marty Cordova	1.00
4	Troy O'Leary	1.50
5	Steve Gibralter	1.50
6	Gary Mota	1.00
7	Larry Sutton	1.00
8	Dan Frye	1.50
9	Russ Davis	4.00
10	Carlos Delgado	7.00

1993 Classic Best Player & Manager of the Year

This two-card set features Carlos Delgado as the player of the year and Marc Hill as the manager of the year. Cards, numbered with a PM prefix, were random inserts in 1993 Classic Best foil packs.

	MT	NR MT	EX
Complete Set (2):	4.00		

1	Carlos Delgado	4.00
2	Marc Hill	.75

1993 Classic Best Gold

The 1993 Classic Best Minor League Baseball Gold Premiere Edition cards feature three color photos of each player and are foil-stamped on both sides. Each card is color-coded using team colors and includes statistics through the 1992 season. The set includes 216 players from Double A, Single A and rookie leagues, plus randomly inserted autographed cards of Barry Bonds and Gary Sheffield. No factory sets or jumbo cases were produced; cards are limited to 6,000 sequentially-numbered 10-box cases.

	MT	NR MT	EX
Complete Set:	25.00	18.50	10.00
Common Player:	.05	.04	.02

1	Barry Bonds	1.00
2	Mark Hutton	.15
3	Lyle Mouton	.15
4	Don Sparks	.05
5	Joe Randa	.10
6	Dave Mlicki	.10
7	Ken Ramos	.05
8	Bill Wertz	.05
9	Jon Shave	.15
10	Dan Smith	.05
11	William Canate	.05
12	Albie Lopez	.10
13	Rod McCall	.05
14	Paul Shuey	.15
15	Ian Doyle	.10
16	Marc Marini	.05
17	Brien Taylor	.30
18	Mike Kelly	.40
19	Andy Nezelek	.05
20	Marcos Armas	.05
21	Chad Ogea	.25
22	Frank Rodriguez	.25
23	Aaron Sele	2.00
24	Tim Vanegmond	.05
25	Phil Hiatt	.20
26	Dan Rohrmeir	.05
27	Greg Blosser	.20
28	Scott Hatteberg	.10
29	Ed Riley	.05
30	Edgar Alfonzo	.05
31	Jorge Fabregas	.10
32	Eduardo Perez	.20
33	John Cummings	.10
34	Bubba Smith	.10
35	Kevin Jordan	.05
36	Tyler Green	.15
37	Heath Haynes	.05
38	Gabe White	.25
39	Doug Glanville	.05
40	Jose Viera	.10
41	Richie Becker	.40
42	Marty Cordova	.20
43	Mike Durant	.05
44	Todd Ritchie	.15
45	Scott Stahoviak	.10
46	Tavo Alvarez	.25
47	Chris Malinoski	.05
48	Rondell White	2.50
49	Tim Worrell	.10
50	Benji Gil	.20
51	Ben Blomdahl	.05
52	Rich Kelley	.05
53	Justin Thompson	.30
54	Scott Pose	.10
55	John Roper	.05
56	Rafael Chaves	.05
57	Billy Hall	.05
58	Ray McDavid	.35
59	Mark Smith	.20
60	Jeff Williams	.05
61	Bobby Jones	.40
62	Stanton Cameron	.05
63	Mike Lumley	.05
64	Troy Buckley	.05
65	James Dougherty	.05
66	Chris Hill	.05
67	Tom Nevers	.05
68	Joe Rosselli	.10
69	Steve Whitaker	.05
70	Butch Huskey	.50
71	Shane Andrews	.60
72	Cliff Floyd	4.00
73	Alex Ochoa	.40
74	Brent Gates	.75
75	Curtis Shaw	.05
76	Midre Cummings	.30
77	Steve Olsen	.05
78	Mike Robertson	.05
79	Scott Ruffcorn	.75
80	Brandon Wilson	.05
81	Darren Burton	.15
82	Kerwin Moore	.10
83	Joe Vitiello	.10
84	Hugh Walker	.15
85	Howard Battle	.20
86	Rob Butler	.10
87	Carlos Delgado	2.00
88	Jeff Ware	.10
89	Mike Hostetler	.10
90	Brian Kowitz	.10
91	Ryan Hawblitzel	.05
92	Juan De La Rosa	.05
93	David McCarty	.25
94	Paul Russo	.25
95	Dan Cholowsky	.30
96	Dmitri Young	.75
97	Paul Ellis	.05
98	Jay Kirkpatrick	.05
99	Jeff Jackson	.05
100	Duane Singleton	.05
101	Kiki Hernandez	.15
102	Raul Hernandez	.05
103	Brian Bevil	.05
104	Mark Johnson	.05
105	Bob Abreu	.05
106	Gary Mota	.10
107	Jose Cabrera	.05
108	Jeff Runion	.05
109	B.J. Wallace	.60
110	Jim Arnold	.05
111	Dwight Maness	.05
112	Fernando DaSilva	.10
113	Chris Burr	.10
114	Dan Serafini	.10
115	Derek Jeter	1.00
116	Lew Hill	.05
117	Andy Pettitte	.15
118	Keith John	.05
119	Sean Lowe	.20
120	T.J. Mathews	.10
121	Ricardo Medina	.05
122	Scott Gentile	.05
123	Everett Stull	.10
124	Manny Ramirez	3.00
125	Archie Corbin	.05
126	Matt Karchner	.05
127	Comingo Mota	.05
128	Alex Gonzalez	1.50
129	Joe Lis	.05
130	Paul Spoljaric	.60
131	Clifton Garrett	.15
132	Marc Hill	.05
133	Jesus Martinez	.05
134	Salomon Torres	.35
135	Tommy Eason	.05
136	Matt Whisenant	.05
137	Jon Zuber	.05
138	Luis Martinez	.10
139	Glenn Murray	.50
140	John Saffer	.05
141	Tommy Adams	.15
142	Manny Cervantes	.05
143	George Glinatsis	.05
144	Chris Dessellier	.05
145	Joe Pomierski	.05
146	John Vanhof	.05
147	Matt Williams	.10
148	Maurice Christmas	.05
149	Damon Hollins	.30
150	Sean Smith	.05
151	Doug Hecker	.25
152	Jamie Sepeda	.05
153	Steve Solomon	.05
154	Jeff Tabaka	.05
155	Greg Elliott	.05
156	Jim Waring	.05
157	Omar Garcia	.05
158	Ricky Otero	.10
159	Jami Brewington	.05
160	Chad Fonville	.10
161	Sean Runyan	.10
162	Jim Givens	.05
163	Dennis McNamara	.05
164	Rudy Pemberton	.05
165	Brian Raabe	.05
166	Jeffrey Hammonds	2.50
167	Chris Hatcher	.05
168	Chris Saunders	.05
169	Aaron Fultz	.05
170	Mike Freitas	.05
171	Tim Adkins	.05
172	Chipper Jones	.75
173	Brandon Cromer	.20
174	Shannon Stewart	.40
175	David Tollison	.05
176	Rob Adkins	.05
177	Todd Steverson	.50
178	Dennis Konuszewski	.05
179	Marty Neff	.05
180	Vernon Spearman	.05
181	Don Wengert	.05
182	Alan Battle	.05
183	Michael Moore	.30
184	Sherard Clinkscales	.10
185	Jamie Dismuke	.05
186	Tucker Hammargren	.05
187	John Hrusovsky	.05
188	Elliott Quinones	.05
189	Calvin Reese	.30
190	Rich Ireland	.05
191	Shawn Estes	.15
192	Greg Shockey	.05
193	Mike Zimmerman	.10
194	Danny Clyburn	.40
195	Jason Kendall	.50
196	Shon Walker	.50
197	Gary Wilson	.05
198	John Dillinger	.15
199	Jim Keefe	.10
200	Eddie Pearson	.10
201	Johnny Damon	.25
202	Jim Pittsley	.05
203	Jason Bere	3.00
204	James Baldwin	1.00
205	John Burke	.25
206	Scot Sealy	.05
207	Ken Carlyle	.15
208	Tim Crabtree	.20
209	Quilvio Veras	.20
210	Edgardo Alfonzo	.05
211	Adell Davenport	.05
212	Dan Frye	.10
213	Derek Lowe	.10
214	Steve Gibralter	.20
215	Troy O'Leary	.20
216	Gary Sheffield	.35
217	Checklist 1-55	.05
218	Checklist 56-110	.05
219	Checklist 111-165	.05
220	Checklist 166-220	.05

1993 Fleer Excel

Fleer's 1993-94 minor league set features players who have never appeared in a Major League game. The set of 300, up from 250 cards the previous year, uses UV coating for card fronts and backs, plus gold-foil stamping on the fronts. There are 297 players included in the regular issue, plus three checklists. Three insert sets were also available: Minor League All-Stars, League Leaders and "First Year Phenoms." Cards from the three insert sets were randomly included in foil packs.

	MT	NR MT	EX
Complete Set (300):	24.00	18.00	9.50
Common Player:	.05	.04	.02

1	Armando Benitez	.10
2	Stanton Cameron	.05
3	Eric Chavez	.05
4	Rick Forney	.25
5	Jim Foster	.10
6	Curtis Goodwin	.10
7	Jimmy Haynes	.15
8	Scott Klingenbeck	.05
9	Rick Krivda	.15
10	T.R. Lewis	.05
11	Brian Link	.05
12	Scott McClain	.05
13	Alex Ochoa	.30
14	Jay Powell	.05
15	Brian Sackinsky	.05
16	Brad Tyler	.05
17	Gregg Zaun	.05
18	Joel Bennett	.25
19	Felix Colon	.10
20	Ryan McGuire	1.00
21	Frank Rodriguez	.30
22	Tim Vanegmond	.05
23	Garret Anderson	.10
24	Jorge Fabregas	.15
25	P.J. Forbes	.20
26	John Fritz	.10
27	Todd Greene	1.00
28	Jose Musset	.05
29	Orlando Palmeiro	.05
30	John Pricher	.05
31	Chris Pritchett	.05
32	Marquis Riley	.05
33	Luis Andujar	.05
34	James Baldwin	.75
35	Brian Boehringer	.05
36	Ron Coomer	.05
37	Ray Durham	.05
38	Robert Ellis	.05
39	Jeff Pierce	.05
40	Olmedo Saenz	.05
41	Brandon Wilson	.20
42	Ian Doyle	.05
43	Jason Fronio	.05
44	Derek Hacopian	.05
45	Daron Kirkreit	.40
46	Mike Neal	.20
47	Chad Ogea	.15
48	Cesar Perez	.05
49	Omar Ramirez	.20
50	J.J. Thobe	.15
51	Casey Whitten	.05
52	Eric Danapilis	.05
53	Brian Edmondson	.05
54	Tony Fuduric	.05
55	Rick Greene	.05
56	Bob Higginson	.05
57	Felipe Lira	.05
58	Joshua Neese	.25
59	Shannon Penn	.15
60	John Rosengren	.05
61	Phil Stidham	.05
62	Justin Thompson	.20
63	Shawn Wooten	.05
64	Brian Bevil	.15
65	Mel Bunch	.05
66	Johnny Damon	.10
67	Chris Eddy	.15
68	Jon Lieber	.10
69	Les Norman	.15
70	Jim Pittsley	.05
71	Kris Ralston	.05
72	Joe Randa	.15
73	Kevin Rawitzer	.05
74	Chris Sheehan	.10
75	Robert Toth	.05
76	Michael Tucker	1.00
77	Brian Banks	.10
78	Marshall Boze	1.00
79	Jeff Cirillo	.15
80	Bo Dodson	.10
81	Bobby Hughes	.05
82	Scott Karl	.05
83	Mike Matheny	.15
84	Kevin Riggs	.05
85	Sid Roberson	.05
86	Charlie Rogers	.05
87	Mike Stefanski	.05
88	Scott Talanoa	.05
89	Derek Wachter	.05
90	Wes Weger	.05
91	Anthony Byrd	.05
92	Marty Cordova	.25
93	Steve Dunn	.10
94	Gus Gandarillos	.05
95	LaTroy Hawkins	.60
96	Oscar Munoz	.05
97	Dan Perkins	.05
98	Ken Serafini	.20
99	Ken Tirpack	.15
100	Russ Davis	.25
101	Nick Delvecchio	.05
102	Robert Eenhoorn	.05
103	Ron Frazier	.15
104	Kraig Hawkins	.05
105	Keith Heberling	.05
106	Derek Jeter	.75
107	Kevin Jordan	.05

108	Ryan Karp	.30
109	Matt Luke	.05
110	Lyle Mouton	.10
111	Andy Pettitte	.05
112	Jorge Posada	.05
113	Ruben Rivera	.15
114	Tate Seefried	.05
115	Brien Taylor	.40
116	Mark Acre	.05
117	Jim Bowie	.20
118	Russ Brock	.05
119	Fausto Cruz	.15
120	Jason Giambi	.40
121	Izzy Molina	.05
122	George Williams	.05
123	Joel Wolfe	.05
124	Ernie Young	.05
125	Tim Davis	.15
126	Jackie Nickell	.05
127	Ruben Santana	.10
128	Makato Suzuki	.40
129	Ron Villone	.15
130	Rich Aurilia	.05
131	John Detmer	.10
132	Scott Eyre	.05
133	Dave Geeve	.05
134	Rick Helling	.50
135	Kerry Lacy	.05
136	Trey McCoy	.05
137	Wes Shook	.05
138	Howard Battle	.15
139	D.J. Boston	.40
140	Rich Butler	.05
141	Brad Cornett	.05
142	Jesse Cross	.05
143	Alex Gonzalez	1.00
144	Kurt Heble	.05
145	Jose Herrera	.05
146	Ryan Jones	.05
147	Robert Perez	.15
148	Jose Silva	.20
149	Shannon Stewart	.15
150	Chris Weinke	.05
151	Jamie Arnold	.10
152	Chris Brock	.05
153	Tony Graffagnino	.05
154	Damon Hollins	.20
155	Mike Hostetler	.05
156	Mike Kelly	.40
157	Andre King	.05
158	Darrell May	.25
159	Vince Moore	.05
160	Don Strange	.15
161	Dominic Therrien	.05
162	Terrell Wade	.40
163	Brant Brown	.05
164	Matt Franco	.05
165	Brooks Kieschnick	2.50
166	Jon Ratliff	.05
167	Kennie Steenstra	.05
168	Amaury Talemaco	.05
169	Ozzie Timmons	.10
170	Hector Trinidad	.05
171	Travis Willis	.05
172	Tim Belk	.05
173	Jamie Dismuke	.05
174	Mike Ferry	.05
175	Chris Hook	.05
176	John Hrusovsky	.05
177	Cleveland Ladell	.05
178	Martin Lister	.05
179	Chad Mottola	.60
180	Eric Owens	.10
181	Scott Sullivan	.05
182	Pat Watkins	.05
183	Jason Bates	.20
184	John Burke	.05
185	Quinton McCracken	.05
186	Neifi Perez	.05
187	Bryan Rekar	.05
188	Mark Thompson	.15
189	Tim Clark	.40
190	Vic Darensbourg	.05
191	Charles Johnson	.75
192	Bryn Kosco	.05
193	Reynol Mendoza	.25
194	Kerwin Moore	.05
195	John Toale	.20
196	Bob Abreu	.05
197	Jim Bruske	.20
198	Jim Dougherty	.05
199	Tony Eusebio	.15
200	Kevin Gallaher	.05
201	Chris Holt	.30
202	Brian Hunter	.25
203	Orlando Miller	.05
204	Donovan Mitchell	.05
205	Alvin Morman	.05
206	James Mouton	1.25
207	Phil Nevin	.75
208	Roberto Petagine	.25
209	Billy Wagner	.35
210	Mike Busch	.05
211	Roger Cedeno	.10
212	Chris Demetral	.05
213	Rick Gorecki	.05
214	Ryan Henderson	.05
215	Todd Hollandsworth	.40
216	Ken Huckaby	.05
217	Rich Linares	.05
218	Ryan Luzinski	.40
219	Doug Newstrom	.05
220	Ben Van Ryn	.10
221	Todd Williams	.05
222	Shane Andrews	.20
223	Reid Cornelius	.05
224	Joey Eischen	.20
225	Heath Haynes	.05
226	Rod Henderson	.15
227	Mark LaRosa	.05
228	Glenn Murray	.20
229	Ugueth Urbina	.20
230	B.J. Wallace	.10
231	Gabe White	.40
232	Edgardo Alfonzo	.05
233	Randy Curtis	.05
234	Omar Garcia	.25
235	Jason Isringhausen	.05
236	Eric Ludwick	.05
237	Bill Pulsipher	.20
238	Chris Roberts	.15
239	Quilivio Veras	.10
240	Pete Walker	.05
241	Mike Welch	.05
242	Preston Wilson	.75
243	Ricky Bottalico	.25
244	Alan Burke	.05
245	Phil Geisler	.30
246	Mike Lieberthal	.10
247	Jason Moler	.20
248	Gene Schall	.20
249	Mark Tranberg	.20
250	Jermaine Allensworth	.40
251	Michael Brown	.30
252	Jason Kendall	.15
253	Jeff McCurry	.05
254	Jeff Alkire	.05
255	Mike Badorek	.05
256	Brian Barber	.10
257	Alan Benes	.40
258	Jeff Berblinger	.05
259	Joe Biasucci	.15
260	Terry Bradshaw	.15
261	Duff Brumley	.20
262	Kirk Bullinger	.15
263	Mike Busby	.05
264	Jamie Cochran	.05
265	Clint Davis	.05
266	Mike Gulan	.05
267	Aaron Holbert	.20
268	John Kelly	.05
269	John Mabry	.05
270	Frankie Martinez	.05
271	T.J. Mathews	.05
272	Aldo Pecorilli	.05
273	Doug Radziewicz	.05
274	Brian Rupp	.05
275	Gerald Witasick	.05
276	Dmitri Young	.30
277	Homer Bush	.05
278	Glenn Dishman	.05
279	Sean Drinkwater	.05
280	Bryce Florie	.05
281	Billy Hall	.05
282	Jason Hardtke	.10
283	Ray Holbert	.15
284	Brian Johnson	.05
285	Ray McDavid	.40
286	Ira Smith	.05
287	Steve Day	.05
288	Kurt Ehmann	.05
289	Chad Fonville	.05
290	Kris Franko	.05
291	Aaron Fultz	.20
292	Marcus Jensen	.20
293	Calvin Murray	.15
294	Jeff Richey	.05
295	Bill VanLandingham	.05
296	Keith Williams	.25
297	Chris Wimmer	.05
298	Checklist	.05
299	Checklist	.05
300	Checklist	.05

1993 Fleer Excel All-Stars

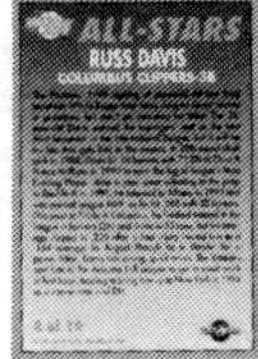

Fleer Excel All-Star cards, random inserts in foil packs, feature 10 Minor League All-Stars. A crown with the player's name and "All-Star" in gold foil on the front indicates the career summary.

		MT	NR MT	EX
Complete Set (10):		18.00		
Common Player:		1.00		
1	Charles Johnson	2.00		
2	Roberto Petagine	1.50		
3	James Mouton	4.00		
4	Russ Davis	2.50		
5	Alex Gonzalez	3.00		
6	Johnny Damon	2.00		
7	Garret Anderson	1.00		
8	Brian Hunter	1.50		
9	D.J. Boston	2.00		
10	Terrell Wade	3.50		

1993 Fleer Excel League Leaders

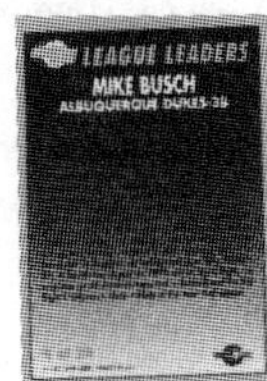

Fleer Excel's League Leader cards feature 10 players who have compiled league-leading statistics. The player's name and "League Leader" are stamped in gold foil on the front; the back has a career summary. Cards, numbered 1 of 10, etc., were random inserts in foil packs.

		MT	NR MT	EX
Complete Set (20):		25.00		
Common Player:		1.00		
1	James Baldwin	3.00		
2	Joel Bennett	1.50		
3	Ricky Bottalico	1.50		
4	Mike Busch	1.00		
5	Duff Brumley	1.50		
6	Jamie Cochran	1.00		
7	John Dettmer	1.50		
8	Joey Eischen	2.00		
9	LaTroy Hawkins	2.00		
10	Derek Jeter	3.00		
11	Ryan Karp	1.50		
12	Rick Krivda	1.50		
13	Trey McCoy	1.00		
14	Jason Moler	1.50		
15	Chad Mottola	3.00		
16	Jose Silva	2.00		
17	Brien Taylor	1.50		
18	Michael Tucker	5.00		
19	Ugueth Urbina	1.50		
20	Ben Van Ryn	1.50		

1993 Fleer Excel 1st Year Phenoms

1st Year Phenoms" is stamped in gold foil on the front of each of the 10 different cards representing players who have made their minor league debuts in a grand fashion. The cards, random inserts in foil backs, are numbered 1 of 10, etc., and feature a summary of the player's minor league accomplishments.

		MT	NR MT	EX
Complete Set (10):		15.00		
Common Player:		1.00		
1	Jim Foster	2.00		
2	Brian Link	2.00		
3	Jeff Berblinger	1.00		
4	Doug Newstrom	1.00		
5	Mike Neal	1.50		
6	Jermaine Allensworth	2.00		
7	Todd Greene	4.00		
8	Keith Williams	1.50		
9	Shawn Wooten	1.00		
10	Joshua Neese	1.50		

Definitions for grading conditions are located in the Introduction of this price guide.

1993 Classic Best Albany Polecats

		MT	NR MT	EX
Complete Set:		6.00		
1	Billy Owens			
2	Myles Barnden			
3	Juan Bautista			
4	Armando Benitez			
5	Calyton Byrne			
6	Christopher Chatterton			
7	Carlos Chavez			
8	Eric Chavez			
9	Howie Clark			
10	Scott Conner			
11	Geno Delgado			
12	Charles Devereux			
13	Keith Eaddy			
14	Scott Emerson			
15	Matt Jarvis			
16	Marco Manrique			
17	Scott Metcalf			
18	Matt Reimer			
19	Jose Serra			
21	Garrett Stephenson			
22	B.J. Waszgis			
23	Kyle Yeske			
24	Mike O'Berry			
25	Charlie Puleo			
26	Larry Shenk			
27	Scott Skadan			
28	Mike Kardamis			
29	Brad Sparesus			
30	Pepper			

1993 Fleer/ProCards Albany Polecats

		MT	NR MT	EX
Complete Set:		5.00		
2017	Armando Benitz			
2018	Chris Chatterton			
2019	Carlos Chavez			
2020	Scott Conner			
2021	Lee Cusey			
2022	Scott Emerson			
2023	Matt Jarvis			
2024	Aaron Lane			
2025	Brian Sackinsky			
2026	Larry Shenk			
2027	Garrett Stephenson			
2028	Marco Manrique			
2029	B.J. Waszgis			
2030	Juan Bautista			
2031	Eric Chavez			
2032	Geno Delgado			
2033	Scott Metcalf			
2034	Billy Owens			
2035	Jose Serra			
2036	Clayton Byrne			
2037	Keith Eaddy			
2038	Roy Hodge			
2039	Keith Schmidt			
2040	Duane Thomas			
2041	Kyle Yeske			
2042	Mike O'Berry			
2043	Charlie Puleo			
2127	Checklist			

1993 Fleer/ProCards Albany-Colonie Yankees

		MT	NR MT	EX
Complete Set:		5.00		
2153	Richard Batchelor			
2154	Mark Carper			
2155	Brian Faw			
2156	Doug Gogolewski			
2157	Jim Haller			
2158	Richard Hines			
2159	Darren Hodges			
2160	Domingo Jean			
2161	Rich Polak			
2162	Tom Popplewell			
2163	Rafael Quirico			
2164	Brien Taylor			
2165	Jeff Livesey			
2166	Jose Pineda			
2167	Bubba Carpenter			
2168	Joe DeBerry			
2169	Robert Eenhoorn			
2170	Andy Fox			
2171	Mike Hankins			
2172	Kevin Jordan			
2173	Rich Barnwell			
2174	Lyle Mouton			
2175	Paul Oster			
2176	Jason Robertson			
2177	Mike Hart			
2178	Jack Butterfield			
2179	Dave Schuler			
2180	Rob Thomson			
2181	Checklist			

1993 Fleer/ProCards Albuquerque Dukes

	MT	NR MT	EX
Complete Set:	7.50		

1451 Steve Allen
1452 Albert Bustillos
1453 Omar Daal
1454 Greg Hansell
1455 Mike James
1456 Jerry Kutzlger
1457 Rod Nichols
1458 Greg Perschke
1459 Dennis Springer
1460 Jody Treadwell
1461 Joey Vierra
1462 Todd Williams
1463 Jerry Brooks
1464 Lance Parrish
1465 Don Wakamatsu
1466 Rafael Burnigal
1467 Mike Busch
1468 Matt Howard
1469 Ron Maurer
1470 Jose Munoz
1471 Eddie Pye
1472 Brian Traxler
1473 Billy Ashley
1474 Tony Barron
1475 Raul Mondesi
1476 Chris Morrow
1477 Henry Rodriguez
1478 Bill Russell
1479 Tom Beyers
1480 Glenn Gregson
1481 Checklist

1993 Classic Best Appleton Foxes

	MT	NR MT	EX
Complete Set:	6.00		

1 Shawn Estes
2 Jerry Aschoff
3 Enrique Atencio
4 Craig Bryant
5 Ron Cody
6 Tim Davis
7 Jamon Deal
8 Charles Gipson
9 Richard Graham
10 Craig Griffey
11 Mike Hickey
12 Raul Ibanez
13 Bill Kostich
14 David Lawson
15 Bobby Llanos
16 Jesus Marquez
17 Jorge Morales
18 Jackie Nickell
19 Erik O'Donnell
20 Robby Robertson
21 Jose Sanchez
22 Alex Sutherland
23 Brian Wallace
24 Trey Witte
25 Rob Worley
26 Carlos Lezcano
27 Orlando Gomez
28 Paul Lindblad
29 Jim Skaalen
30 Allen Wirtala

1993 Fleer/ProCards Appleton Foxes

	MT	NR MT	EX
Complete Set:	6.00		

2451 Jerry Aschoff
2452 Ron Cody
2453 Tim Davis
2454 Jamon Deal
2455 Shawn Estes
2456 Richard Graham
2457 Bill Kostich
2458 Jackie Nickell
2459 Jose Sanchez
2460 Trey Witte
2461 Rob Worley
2462 Raul Ibanez
2463 Jorge Morales
2464 Alex Sutherland
2465 Enrique Atencio
2466 Craig Bryant
2467 Eddy Diaz
2468 Charles Gipson
2469 Mike Hickey
2470 Brian Wallace
2471 Craig Griffey
2472 David Lawson
2473 Bobby Lanos
2474 Jesus Martinez
2475 Robbie Robertson
2476 Carlos Lezcano
2477 Orlando Gomez
2478 Steve Smith
2479 Checklist

1993 Fleer/ProCards Arkansas Travelers

	MT	NR MT	EX
Complete Set:	6.00		

2803 Paul Anderson
2804 Brian Barber
2805 Rigo Beltran
2806 Frank Cimorelli
2807 Doug Creek
2808 Bryan Eversgerd
2809 Luis Faccio
2810 John Kelly
2811 Kerry Knox
2812 Gerald Santos
2813 Rick Shackle
2814 Paul Ellis
2815 Kevin Tahan
2816 Joe Aversa
2817 Darrel Deak
2818 Steve Fanning
2819 Craig Faulkner
2820 Wander Pimentel
2821 Jeff Shireman
2822 Allen Battle
2823 Anthony Lewis
2824 John Mabry
2825 Howard Prager
2826 Odalis Savinon
2827 Joe Pettini
2828 Marty Mason
2829 Checklist

1993 Classic Best Asheville Tourists

	MT	NR MT	EX
Complete Set:	6.00		

1 Richard Hidalgo
2 Randy Albaladejo
3 Marvin Billingsley
4 Eduardo Cedeno
5 Jose Centeno
6 Greg Elliott
7 Sean Fesh
8 Oscar Henriquez
9 Todd Hobson
10 Zak Krislock
11 Shawn Livsey
12 Victor Madrigal
13 James McCutchen
14 Melvin Mora
15 Tyrone Narcisse
16 Alan Probst
17 Mike Rennhack
18 Noel Rodriguez
19 Jose Santana
20 Jeff Tenbarge
21 Victor Valdez
22 Kevin Webb
23 Clifford Williams
24 Danny Young
25 Bobby Ramos
26 Jim Coveney
27 Don Alexander
28 Ron Hanisch

1993 Fleer/ProCards Asheville Tourists

	MT	NR MT	EX
Complete Set:	6.00		

2267 Marvin Billinglsey
2268 Jose Centeno
2269 Sean Fesh
2270 Oscar Henriquez
2271 Zak Krislock
2272 Victor Madrigal
2273 Jim McCutchen
2274 Tyrone Narcisse
2275 Jeff Tenbarge
2276 Victor Valdez
2277 Danny Young
2278 Randy Albaladejo
2279 Alan Probst
2280 Clifford Williams
2281 Ed Cedeno
2282 Greg Elliott
2283 Dan Grapenthien
2284 Melvin Mora
2285 Jose Santana
2286 Jermaine Swinton
2287 Kevin Webb
2288 Richard Hidalgo
2289 Todd Hobson
2290 Shawn Livsey
2291 Mike Rennhack
2292 Noel Rodriguez
2293 Bobby Ramos
2294 Don Alexander
2295 Jim Coveney
2296 Checklist

1993 Fleer/ProCards Auburn Astros

	MT	NR MT	EX
Complete Set:	6.00		

3433 Tom Czanstkowski
3434 Donnie Dault
3435 Mike Diorio
3436 Mike Grzanich
3437 Bill Hartnett
3438 Richard Humphrey
3439 Tim Kester
3440 Arquimedes Lugo
3441 Kendall Rhine
3442 Troy Schulte
3443 Kevin Smith
3444 Josh Spring
3445 Billy Wagner
3446 Brett Callan
3447 Trevor Froschauer
3448 Nate Peterson
3449 Marsalis Basey
3450 Eduardo Cedeno
3451 Carlos Crispin
3452 Tim Forkner
3453 Dan Grapenthien
3454 Steve Verduzco
3455 Klint Klaas
3456 Noel Rodriguez
3457 John Vindivich
3458 Chad White
3459 Ted Wieczorek
3460 Manny Acta
3461 Ted Slowik
3462 Checklist

1993 Classic Best Augusta Pirates

	MT	NR MT	EX
Complete Set:	7.00		

1 Jason Kendall
2 Jake Austin
3 Trey Beamon
4 Miguel Bonilla
5 Danny Clyburn
6 Jay Cranford
7 Ramon Espinosa
8 Rico Gholston
9 G.G. Harris
10 Ted Klamm
11 Michel LaPlante
12 Sean Lawrence
13 Mark Mesewicz
14 Marc Pisciotta
15 Kevin Polcovich
16 Matt Pontbriant
17 John Salamon
18 Manuel Santana
19 Reed Secrist
20 Jose Sosa
21 Larry Stahlhoefer
22 Chuck Tooch
23 Rich Townsend
24 Shon Walker
25 Marc Wilkins
26 Ramon Zapata
27 Wayne Garland
28 Rod Lich

1993 Fleer/ProCards Augusta Pirates

	MT	NR MT	EX
Complete Set:	7.00		

1390 Checklist
1536 Miguel Bonilla
1537 Ted Klamm
1538 Michel LaPlante
1539 Mark Mesewicz
1540 Marc Pisciotta
1541 Matt Pontbriant
1542 John Salamon
1543 Manuel Santana
1544 Jose Sosa
1545 Rich Townsend
1546 Marc Wilkins
1547 Jason Kendall
1548 Larry Stahlhoefer
1549 Jake Austin
1550 Jay Cranford
1551 Rico Gholston
1552 G.G. Harris
1553 Kevin Polcovich
1554 Reed Secrist
1555 Chuck Tooch
1556 Ramon Zapata
1557 Trey Beamon
1558 Danny Clyburn
1559 Ramon Espinosa
1560 Shon Walker
1561 Wayne Garland

1993 Cal League Bakersfield Dodgers

	MT	NR MT	EX
Complete Set:	9.00		

1 Mike Moore
2 Ryan Luzinski
3 Nelson Castro
4 Brent Colson
5 Bubba Costello
6 Gavin Edmondson
7 Matt Filson
8 Jose Garcia
9 Karim Garcia
10 Matt Herges
11 Mike Iglesias
12 Angel Jaime
13 Jason Kenady
14 Jay Kirkpatrick
15 Ty Lewis
16 Ed Lund
17 Jimmy Martin
18 Jesus Martinez
19 Sean McKamie
20 Tory Miran
21 Willie Otanez
22 Frank Smith
23 Carlos Thomas
24 Burgess Watts
25 Eric Weaver
26 Leroy Williams
27 Chad Zerbe
28 Rick Dempsey
29 Guy Conti
30 Dino Ebel
31 Bart Dugger
32 Checklist

1993 Fleer/ProCards Batavia Clippers

	MT	NR MT	EX
Complete Set:	5.00		

3135 Pete Agostinelli
3136 Silvio Censale
3137 Tony Costa
3138 Scott Eggleston
3139 Tony Fiore
3140 Tom Franek
3141 Tom Irwin
3142 Kris Kirkland
3143 Nelson Methenthy
3144 Tim Pugh
3145 Tyrone Swan
3146 Mike Wood
3147 Jeff Gyselman
3148 Dan Held
3149 Neil Murphy
3150 Bruce Petillo
3151 Doug Angeli
3152 Matt Brainard
3153 Shaun McGinn
3154 Jon McMullen
3155 Kevin Sefcik
3156 Brent Bell
3157 Ramon Hernandez
3158 Jeremey Kendall
3159 Joey Madden
3160 Dan McDonald
3161 Charlton Moore
3162 Mike Thompson
3163 Al LeBoeuf
3164 Checklist

1993 Fleer/ProCards Bellingham Mariners

	MT	NR MT	EX
Complete Set:	6.00		

3196 Matt Arana
3197 Tim Bruce
3198 Rafael Carmona
3199 Mike Collett
3200 Dean Crow
3201 Brian Doughty
3202 Ryan Franklin
3203 Tim Harikkala
3204 Matt Mantei
3205 Ivan Montane
3206 Marino Santana
3207 Brian Sosa
3208 Greg Theron
3209 John Thompson
3210 Bob Wolcott
3211 Joe Berube
3212 Johnny Cardenas
3213 Raul Ibanez
3214 Antonio Cabrera
3215 James Clifford
3216 Giomar Guevara
3217 Randy Jorgensen
3218 Jaime Martinez
3219 Roy Miller
3220 Manny Patel
3221 Mike Barger
3222 Chad Dunavan
3223 Keifer Rackley
3224 Nestor Serrano
3225 Marcus Sturdivant
3226 Checklist

1993 Classic Best Beloit Brewers

	MT	NR MT	EX
Complete Set:	7.00		

(1) Cameron Aronetz
(2) Donny Blair
(3) Mike Boyzuick
(4) Kirk Demyan

(5) Jeff Droll
(6) Michael Dumas
(7) Kenny Felder
(8) Steve Foucault
(9) Tom Froning
(10) Brad Gay
(11) Bobby Hughes
(12) Jason Imperial
(13) Bryan Jaquette
(14) Bobby Jones
(15) Wayne Krenchicki
(16) Dan Kyslinger
(17) Bob Mariano
(18) Gabby Martinez
(19) Darryl Meek
(20) Francisco Mendoza
(21) Danny Perez
(22) Scott Richardson
(23) Cecil Rodriques
(24) Jackie Ross
(25) Al Sadler
(26) Tom Schenbeck
(27) Scott Talanoa
(28) Ryan Thibault
(29) Rafael Torres

1993 Fleer/ProCards Beloit Brewers

	MT	NR MT	EX
Complete Set:	6.00		

1700 Cameron Aronetz
1701 Donny Blair
1702 Kirk Demyan
1703 Jeff Droll
1704 Tom Froning
1705 Bobby Jones
1706 Dan Kyslinger
1707 Darryl Meek
1708 Al Sadler
1709 Thomas Sehenbeck
1710 Ryan Thibault
1711 Rafael Torres
1712 Brad Gay
1713 Brian Hostetler
1714 Bobby Hughes
1715 Michael Boyzuick
1716 Michael Dumas
1717 Jason Imperial
1718 Gabby Martinez
1719 Francisco Mendoza
1720 Scott Richardson
1721 Scott Talanoa
1722 Kenny Felder
1723 Danny Perez
1724 Cecil Rodriques
1725 Jackie Ross
1726 Wayne Krenchicki
1727 Steve Foucault
1728 Bob Mariano
1729 Checklist

1993 Fleer/ProCards Bend Rockies

	MT	NR MT	EX
Complete Set:	6.00		

3257 Derrick Calvin
3258 Curt Conley
3259 Mike Eiffert
3260 Jon Goodrich
3261 Chris Henderson
3262 Jason Johnson
3263 Bob Lasbury
3264 Patrick McClinton
3265 Joel Moore
3266 Chris Neier
3267 Bryan Rekar
3268 Phil Schneider
3269 Jeff Sobkoviak
3270 Kevin Wehn
3271 Mike Higgins
3272 Michael Pineiro
3273 Jason Smith
3274 Steve Bernhardt
3275 Greg Boyd
3276 Carlos Cristopher
3277 Nate Holdren
3278 Mario Munoz
3279 Neifi Perez
3280 John Giudice
3281 Terry Jones
3282 Ben Ortman
3283 Howie Bedell
3284 Bill Champion
3285 Bill McGuire
3286 Checklist

1993 Fleer/ProCards Billings Mustangs

	MT	NR MT	EX
Complete Set:	6.00		

3935 Chad Connors
3936 Todd Etler
3937 Denny Fussell
3938 Pete Harvell
3939 Jon Hebel
3940 Curt Lyons
3941 Pete Magre
3942 David McKenzie
3943 Mike Moses
3944 Scott Sullivan
3945 Brad Tweedlie
3946 Steve Wilkerson
3947 Shane Witzel
3948 Paul Bako
3949 Justin Towle
3950 Chad Akers
3951 Jeff Ashton
3952 Steve Eddie
3953 Steve Gann
3954 Doug Durrwachter
3955 Eli Robinson
3956 Chris Sexton
3957 Jason Baker
3958 Ray Moon
3959 Danny Oyas
3960 Rodney Thomas
3961 Pat Watkins
3962 Donnie Scott
3963 Terry Abbott
3964 Checklist

1993 SportPro Billings Mustangs

	MT	NR MT	EX
Complete Set:	8.00		

1 Chad Connors
2 Chris Sexton
3 Ray Moon
4 Justin Towle
5 Todd Etler
6 Curt Lyons
7 Steve Eddie
8 Danny Oyas
9 Pete Harvell
10 Denny Fussell
11 Eli Robinson
12 Pat Watkins
13 Paul Bako
14 Shane Witzel
15 Pete Magre
16 Chad Akers
17 Scott Sullivan
18 Steve Gann
19 Rodney Thomas
20 Michael Moses
21 Jason Baker
22 Jon Hebel
23 Brad Tweedlie
24 Steve Wilkerson
25 David McKenzie
26 Mark Mann
27 Donnie Scott
28 Terry Abbott

1993 Fleer/ProCards Binghamton Mets

	MT	NR MT	EX
Complete Set:	6.00		

2326 Juan Castillo
2327 Chris Dorn
2328 Todd Douma
2329 Denny Harriger
2330 Steve Long
2331 Andy Reich
2332 Joe Roa
2333 Bryan Rogers
2334 Rusty Silcox
2335 Pete Walker
2336 Andy Dziadkowiec
2337 Javier Gonzalez
2338 Alan Zinter
2339 Tom Allison
2340 Butch Huskey
2341 Frank Jacobs
2342 Aaron Ledesma
2343 David Lowery
2344 Quilvio Veras
2345 Chris Butterfield
2346 Jay Davis
2347 Ricky Otero
2348 Tim Sandy
2349 Steve Swisher
2350 Randy Niemann
2351 Checklist

1993 Fleer/ProCards Birmingham Barons

	MT	NR MT	EX
Complete Set:	7.00		

1185 James Baldwin
1186 Frank Campos
1187 Ramon Manon
1188 Frank Merigliano
1189 Mike Mongiello
1190 Steve Olsen
1191 Don Perigny
1192 Jeff Pierce
1193 Scott Ruffcorn
1194 Johnny Ruffin
1195 Clemente Alvarez
1196 Rogelio Nunez
1197 Ron Coomer
1198 Ray Durham
1199 Geovany Miranda
1200 Mike Robertson
1201 Dennis Walker
1202 Brandon Wilson
1203 Kevin Belcher
1204 Sergio Cairo
1205 Kinnis Pledger
1206 Jerry Wolak
1207 Terry Francona
1208 Mike Barnett
1209 Kirk Champion
1210 Mike Rojas
1211 Checklist

1993 Fleer/ProCards Bluefield Orioles

	MT	NR MT	EX
Complete Set:	7.00		

4115 Rick Barrett
4116 Brian Brewer
4117 Cory Brown
4118 Carlos Chavez
4119 Joe Dawley
4120 Ron Kitchen
4121 Calvin Maduro
4122 William Percibel
4123 Mike Porter
4124 Bob Rinderknecht
4125 Mike Trimarco
4126 Shane Ziegler
4127 Hector Castaneda
4128 Jim Foster
4129 Ken Reed
4130 Myles Barnden
4131 Howie Clark
4132 Bryan Link
4133 Lincoln Martin
4134 Matt Riemer
4135 Ron Shankle
4136 Bill Asermely
4137 Kimera Bartee
4138 Brandon Bridgers
4139 Wes Hawkins
4140 Jarvis White
4141 Checklist

1993 Fleer/ProCards Boise Hawks

	MT	NR MT	EX
Complete Set:	7.50		

3904 Bill Blanchette
3905 Willard Brown
3906 Jamie Burke
3907 Geoff Edsell
3908 Brian Fontes
3909 Geoff Grenert
3910 Bryan Harris
3911 Mike Kane
3912 Johnny Lloyd
3913 Matt Myers
3914 John Nedeau
3915 Aaron Puffer
3916 Rodolf Razjigaev
3917 Andy Runzi
3918 Shawn Slade
3919 Brian Cavalli
3920 Will Speakman
3921 Freddie Diaz
3922 John Donati
3923 David Kennedy
3924 Hank King
3925 Julian Vizcaino
3926 Lyall Barwick
3927 Derrin Doty
3928 Todd Greene
3929 Aaron Iatarola
3930 Bobby Kim
3931 Mark Simmons
3932 Zeke Zimmerman
3933 Orv Franchuk

1993 Fleer/ProCards Bowie Baysox

	MT	NR MT	EX
Complete Set:	10.00		

2182 Rafael Chaves
2183 Jim Dedrick
2184 Terry Farrar
2185 Jose Mercedes
2186 Chuck Ricci
2187 Kevin Ryan
2188 Jason Satre
2189 Erik Schullstrom
2190 Tommy Taylor
2191 Jimmy Roso
2192 Gregg Zaun
2193 Edgar Alfonzo
2194 Sam Ferretti
2195 Tim Holland
2196 T.R. Lewis
2197 Brent Miller
2198 Brad Tyler
2199 Stanton Cameron
2200 Jeffrey Hammonds
2201 Kyle Washington
2202 Jim Wawruck
2203 Don Buford
2204 John O'Donoghue
2205 Checklist

1993 Fleer/ProCards Bristol Tigers

	MT	NR MT	EX
Complete Set:	5.00		

3639 Candido Brazoban
3640 Alvin Brown
3641 Tony Fuduric
3642 Yasutara Fursato
3643 Greg Granger
3644 Will Hunt
3645 Ryan Meredith
3646 Shinya Nakagawa
3647 Steve Nowak
3648 Adam Rodriguez
3649 Shawn Wooten
3650 Edward Cordero
3651 Bryan Corey
3652 Luis Garcia
3653 Jason Hamilton
3654 Dalvis Martinez
3655 Kenny Valdez
3656 Chris Wyrick
3657 Frank Catalanotto
3658 Jason Bass
3659 Drew Christmon
3660 Chris Facione
3661 Ismael Guzman
3662 Bobby Jones
3663 Chris Keenan
3664 Lonny Landry
3665 Jose Sanjurjo
3666 Ruben Amaro
3667 Shigeyuki Takahashi
3668 Checklist

1993 Fleer/ProCards Buffalo Bisons

	MT	NR MT	EX
Complete Set:	6.00		

508 Brett Backlund
509 Victor Cole
510 Mike Dalton
511 Daryl Irvine
512 Joel Johnston
513 Tony Menendez
514 Mark Petkovsek
515 Rich Robertson
516 Brian Shouse
517 Roy Smith
518 Jim Tracy
519 Mike Zimmerman
520 Jerry Goff
521 Mandy Romero
522 Mike Bell
523 Gary Cooper
524 Russ Morman
525 Omer Munoz
526 Dave Rohde
527 Jose Sandoval
528 Ben Shelton
529 Scott Bullett
530 William Pennyfeather
531 Andy Tomberlin
532 Glenn Wilson
533 Tom Dettore
534 Checklist

1993 Classic Best Burlington Bees

	MT	NR MT	EX
Complete Set:	6.00		

1 Yamil Benitez
2 Isreal Alcantara
3 Ivan Arteaga
4 Jolbert Cabrera
5 Rick Clelland
6 Fernando DaSilva
7 Thomas Doyle
8 David Eggert
9 Antonio Grissom
10 Chris Hmielewski
11 Jeff Hostetler
12 Gary Hymel
13 Shane McCubbin
14 Doug O'Neill
15 Javier Pages
16 Darrin Paxton
17 Carlos perez
18 Thomas Phelps
19 Acott Pisciotta
20 Corey Powell
21 Al Reyes
22 Matt Rundels
23 James Rushworth
24 Ugueth Urbina
25 Jose Vidro
26 Lorenzo Bundy
27 Pete Dalena
28 Jeff Fischer
29 Alex Ochoa

1993 Fleer/ProCards Burlington Bees

	MT	NR MT	EX
Complete Set:	6.00		

148 Ivan Arteag
149 Rick Clelland
150 Fernando DaSilva
151 Dave Eggert
152 Jeff Hostetler
153 Darrin Paxton
154 Carlos Perez
155 Tom Phelps
156 Scott Pisciotta
157 Alberto Reyes
158 Jim Rushworth
159 Ugueth Urbina
160 Gary Hymel
161 Shane McCubbin
162 Javier Pages
163 Isreal Alcantara
164 Jolbert Cabrera
165 Tom Doyle
166 Chris Hmielewski
167 Matt Rundels
168 Jose Vidro
169 Yamil Benitez
170 Antonio Grissom
171 Doug O'Neill
172 Corey Powell
173 Lorenzo Bundy
174 Jeff Fischer
175 Checklist

1993 Fleer/ProCards Burlington Indians

	MT	NR MT	EX
Complete Set:	6.00		

3287 Dan Brabant
3288 Camp Campbell
3289 Maximo DeLaRosa
3290 Kevin Dinnen
3291 Derrick Hritz
3292 Steve Kline
3293 Damian Leyva
3294 Jason Mackey
3295 Johnny Martinez
3296 Brett Palmer
3297 Cesar Ramos
3298 Brian Wisler
3299 Jon Zubiri
3300 Einar Diar
3301 Todd Johnson
3302 Mike Moyle
3303 Jesus Azuaje
3304 Darnell Batiste
3305 Todd Betts
3306 Mack Chambers
3307 Richard Ramirez
3308 Richie Sexson
3309 Eric White
3310 Ronnie Coleman
3311 Matt Hobbie
3312 Rich Lemons
3313 Alex Ramirez
3314 Leroy Thompson
3315 Norman Williams
3316 Jim Gabella
3317 Checklist

1993 SportPro Butte Copper Kings

	MT	NR MT	EX
Complete Set:	8.00		

1 Dom Gatti
2 Jason Sievers
3 Tiger King
4 Chris Starr
5 Jeff DeRosa
6 Shane McCubbin
7 John Mahalik
8 Matt Huff
9 Steve Cook
10 Kacy Hendricks
11 Ben Week
12 Chris Kelley
13 Marty Watson
14 John Tomasello
15 Rod Holland
16 Jeff Carew
17 Craig Morrill
18 Jason Bobb
19 Reggie Ignash
20 Clint Minear
21 Jon Pitts
22 John Shelby
23 Billy Gardner
24 Tim Conroy

1993 Fleer/ProCards Calgary Cannons

	MT	NR MT	EX
Complete Set:	6.00		

1156 Shawn Barton
1157 Kevin Coffman
1158 Jim Converse
1159 Mark Czarkowski
1160 Eric Gunderson
1161 Brad Holman
1162 Troy Kent
1163 Lance McCullers
1164 Rob Parkins
1165 Dennis Powell
1166 Mike Remlinger
1167 Mike Walker
1168 Brian Deak
1169 Bert Heffernan
1170 Chris Howard
1171 Greg Litton
1172 Anthony Manahan
1173 Greg Pirki
1174 Jack Smith
1175 Brian Turang
1176 Shane Turner
1177 Dann Howitt
1178 Carmelo Martinez
1179 Tow Maynard
1180 Aubrey Waggoner
1181 Keith Bodie
1182 Dave Brundage
1183 Ross Grimsley
1184 Checklist

1993 Fleer/ProCards Canton-Akron Indians

	MT	NR MT	EX
Complete Set:	10.00		

2830 Paul Abbott
2831 Chad Allen
2832 Shawn Bryant
2833 Apolinar Garcia
2834 Mike Gardella
2835 Albie Lopez
2836 Greg McCarthy
2837 Roberto Rivera
2838 Paul Shuey
2839 Mike Soper
2840 Eric Stone
2841 Joe Turek
2842 Ryan Martindale
2843 Carlos Mota
2844 David Bell
2845 Miguel Flores
2846 Luis Lopez
2847 Rouglas Odor
2848 Brian Giles
2849 Manny Ramirez
2850 Omar Ramirez
2851 Tracy Sanders
2852 Brian Graham
2853 Rick Colbert
2854 Ken Rowe
2855 Checklist

1993 Classic Best Capital City Bombers

	MT	NR MT	EX
Complete Set:	6.00		

1 Al Shirley
2 Andy Beckerman
3 Craig Bullock
4 Tom Engle
5 Joe Flores
6 Guillermo Garcia
7 Erik Hiljus
8 Mark Hokanson
9 Jeff Kiraly
10 Marc Kroon
11 Steve Lyons
12 Jacen Martinez
13 Danilo Mompres
14 Juan Moreno
15 Jared Osentowski
16 Mike Patrizi
17 Joe Petcka
18 Eric Reichenbach
19 Dwight Robinson
20 Chris Shanahan
21 Greg Stark
22 Tony Tijerina
23 Donnie White
24 Mark Wipf
25 Ron Washington
26 David Jorn
27 Michael Herbst

1993 Fleer/ProCards Capital City Bombers

	MT	NR MT	EX
Complete Set:	5.00		

451 Andy Beckerman
452 Craig Bullock
453 Tom Engle
454 Erik Hijus
455 Mark Hokanson
456 Marc Kroon
457 Steve Lyons
458 Joe Petcka
459 Eric Reichenbach
460 Chris Shanahan
461 Greg Stark
462 Gullermo Garcia
463 Mike Patrizi
464 Tony Tijernia
465 Jose Flores
466 Jeff Kiraly
467 Jacen Martinez
468 Danilo Mompres
469 Jared Osentowski
470 Dwight Robinson
471 Juan Moreno
472 Al Shirley
473 Demond Smith
474 Don White
475 Mark Wipf
476 Checklist

1993 Fleer/ProCards Carolina League All-Stars

	MT	NR MT	EX
Complete Set:	12.00		

1 Rick Forney
2 Curtis Goodwin
3 Scott McClain
4 Alex Ochoa
5 Joel Bennett
6 Randy Brown
7 Doug Hecker
8 Rob Henkel
9 Bob Juday
10 Jose Malave
11 Rual Gonzalez
12 Brian Harrison
13 Ron Johnson
14 Gary Lance
15 Jon Lieber
16 Jeff Smith
17 Chad Strickland
18 Robert Toth
19 Matt Dunbar
20 greg Erickson
21 Carlton Fleming
22 Ron Frazier
23 Jorge Posada
24 Tate Seefried
25 Juan Andujar
26 Greg Booker
27 John Cotton
28 Dan Devoe
29 Ian Doyle
30 Jason Fronio
31 Dave Keller
32 Pat Maxwell
33 Dan Norman
34 Julian Tavarez
35 Joe Ayrault
36 Dirk Blair
37 Anthony Graffagnino
38 Vince Moore
39 Dominic Therrien
40 Tim Belk
41 John Hrusovsky
42 Motorboat Jones
43 Cleveland Ladell
44 Chad Mottola
45 Ken Bonifay
46 Mike Brown
47 Jason Christiansen
48 Mariano DeLosSantos
49 Angelo Encarnacion
50 Jeff McCurry
51 Tony Womack
52 Checklist

1993 Fleer/ProCards Carolina Mudcats

	MT	NR MT	EX
Complete Set:	7.00		

2044 Blaine Beatty
2045 Jose Cecena
2046 Alex Garza
2047 Lee Hancock
2048 Doug Harrah
2049 John Hope
2050 Bobby Hunter
2051 Dan Jones
2052 Eric Parkinson
2053 Dennis Tafoya
2054 Freddie Toliver
2055 Rick White
2056 Jeff Banister
2057 Tim Edge
2058 Keith Osik
2059 Rich Aude
2060 Tony Beasley
2061 Mark Johnson
2062 Jim Krevokuch
2063 Tim Leiper
2064 Bruce Schreiber
2065 Joe Sondrini
2066 Midre Cummings
2067 Alberto De Los Santos
2068 Tom Green
2069 Daryl Ratliff
2070 Keith Thomas
2071 Joe Lonnett
2072 Spin Williams

1993 Classic Best Cedar Rapids Kernels

	MT	NR MT	EX
Complete Set:	6.00		

1 Clifton Garrett
2 Antonio Castro
3 Tony Chavez
4 Lino Connell
5 Morisse Daniels
6 Miguel Fermin
7 Brian Guzik
8 Joseph Hardwick
9 Larry Hingle
10 Mickey kerns
11 David Kessler
12 Dave Marcon
13 Brandon Markiewicz
14 Dallas Rinehart
15 Jeff Schmidt
16 Kyle Sebach
17 Billy Simas
18 Mark Simmons
19 Chris Smith
20 Jose Stela
21 Robert Tucker
22 Max Valencia
23 Steve White
24 Brian Williard
25 Michael Wolff
26 Mitch Seone
27 Matt Hyde
28 Joe Georger
29 Douglas Baker
30 Ronald Plein

1993 Fleer/ProCards Cedar Rapids Kernels

	MT	NR MT	EX
Complete Set:	5.00		

1730 Tony Chavez
1731 Miguel Fermin
1732 Larry Hingle
1733 Dave Marcon
1734 Jeff Schmidt
1735 Kyle Sebach
1736 Billy Simas
1737 Max Valencia
1738 Rod Van Dyke
1739 Steve White
1740 Brian Williard
1741 Chris Hirsch
1742 David Kessler
1743 Robert Tucker
1744 Antonio Castro
1745 Lino Connell
1746 Brian Guzik
1747 Brandon Markiewicz
1748 Mark Simmons
1749 Chris Smith
1750 Morisse Daniels
1751 Joseph Hardwick
1752 Mickey Kerns
1753 Michael Wolff
1754 Mitch Seoane
1755 Joe Georger
1756 Matt Hyde
1757 Checklist

1993 Classic Best Central Valley Rockies

	MT	NR MT	EX
Complete Set:	6.50		

1 Mark Thompson
2 Juan Acevedo
3 Garvin Alston
4 Roger Bailey
5 John Burke
6 Mike Case
7 Craig Counsell
8 Angel Echevarria
9 Mike Eiffert
10 Mike Ericson
11 Mauricio Gonzalez
12 Mike Grimes
13 Jim Hovey
14 Jason Hutchins
15 Mike Kotarski
16 Keith Krenke
17 Darryl Martin
18 Quinton McCracken
19 Marcus Moore
20 Mike Oakland
21 Will Scalzitti
22 Tom Schmidt
23 Mark Strittmatter
24 Ryan Turner
25 Mark Valsard
26 Paul Zuvella
27 Jack Lamabe
28 Bill Borowski

1993 Fleer/ProCards Central Valley Rockies

		MT	NR MT	EX
Complete Set:		6.00		

2883 Garvin Alston
2884 Roger Bailey
2885 John Burke
2886 Mike Eiffert
2887 Mike Ericson
2888 Mike Grimes
2889 Jim Hovey
2890 Jason Hutchins
2891 Mike Kotarski
2892 Marcu Moore
2893 Mark Thompson
2894 Mark Voisard
2895 Will Scalzitti
2896 Mark Strittmatter
2897 Craig Counsell
2898 Mauricio Gonzalez
2899 Quinton McCracken
2900 Mike Oakland
2901 LaMarr Rogers
2902 Tom Schmidt
2903 Mike Case
2904 Angel Echevarria
2905 Keith Krenke
2906 Darryl Martin
2907 Ryan Turner
2908 Paul Zuvella
2909 P.J. Carey
2910 Jack Lamabe
2911 Checklist

1993 Classic Best Charleston Rainbows

		MT	NR MT	EX
Complete Set:		6.00		

1 Scott Eyre
2 Mike Anderson
3 Jamie Bethke
4 Mark Brandenburg
5 Steve Burton
6 Wayne Eggleston
7 Hanley Frias
8 Jack Kimel
9 Kerry Lacy
10 David Manning
11 Jerry Martin
12 Ramiro Martinez
13 Malvin Matos
14 Guillermo Mercedes
15 Paulino Perez
16 Querbin Reynoso
17 Jeff Runion
18 Scot Sealy
19 Brian Seesz
20 Bob Simonson
21 Heath Vaughn
22 Mike Welch
23 Chad Wiley
24 Kevin Woodall
25 Scott Malone
26 Chris Burr
27 Walt Williams
28 George Threadgill
29 Sponsor
30 Andy Graziano

1993 Fleer/ProCards Charleston Rainbows

		MT	NR MT	EX
Complete Set:		6.00		

1900 Mike Anderson
1901 Mark Brandenburg
1902 Scott Eyre
1903 Jack Kimel
1904 Kerry Lacy
1905 David Manning
1906 Jerry Martin
1907 Ramiro Martinez
1908 Paulino Perez
1909 Querbin Reynoso
1910 Jeff Runion
1911 Heath Vaughn
1912 Chad Wiley
1913 Jamie Bethke
1914 Scot Sealy
1915 Brian Seesz
1916 Chris Burr
1917 Steve Burton
1918 Wayne Eggleston
1919 Hanley Frias
1920 Scott Malone
1921 Guillermo Mercedes
1922 Franklin Parra
1923 Kevin Woodall
1924 Malvin Matos
1925 Bob Simonson
1926 Mike Welch
1927 Walt Williams
1928 Gary Mielke
1929 George Threadgill
1930 Checklist

1993 Fleer/ProCards Charlotte Knights

		MT	NR MT	EX
Complete Set:		6.00		

535 Paul Byrd
536 Jerry DiPoto
537 Jason Grimsley
538 Tom McCarthy
539 Bob Milacki
540 Chad Ogea
541 Zak Shinall
542 Terry Wells
543 Bill Wertz
544 Cliff Young
545 Matt Young
546 Jesse Levis
547 Kelly Stinnett
548 George Canale
549 Sam Horn
550 Jeff Kunkel
551 Mark Lewis
552 Jeff Schaefer
553 Jim Thorne
554 Beau Allred
555 Alan Cockrell
556 Mark Davidson
557 Wayne Kirby
558 Ken Ramos
559 Charlie Manuel
560 Luis Isaac
561 Dyar Miller
562 Checklist

1993 Classic Best Charlotte Rangers

		MT	NR MT	EX
Complete Set:		6.50		

(2) Rich Auralia
(3) Joe Brownholtz
(4) Jim Clinton
(5) Michael Crespo
(6) Chris Curtis
(7) John Dettmer
(8) Mike Edwards
(9) George Evangelista
(10) Dave Gandolph
(11) Dave Geeve
(12) Dave Gilberti
(13) Todd Guggiana
(14) Darryl Henderson
(15) Wilson Heredia
(16) Daryl Kennedy
(17) Bo Magee
(18) Danny Patterson
(19) Steve Sadecki
(20) Lance Schuermann
(21) Mike Smith
(22) Jose Texidor
(23) Tyrone Washington
(24) Lanny Williams
(25) Desi Wilson
(26) Tommy Thompson
(27) Darrin Garner
(28) Greg Kersgelter
(29) Marvin White
(30) Terrell Lowery

1993 Fleer/ProCards Charlotte Rangers

		MT	NR MT	EX
Complete Set:		7.00		

1931 Joe Brownholtz
1932 John Dettmer
1933 Dave Gandolph
1934 Dave Geeve
1935 Dave Giberti
1936 Daryl Henderson
1937 Wilson Heredia
1938 Bo Magee
1939 Danny Patterson
1940 Steve Sadecki
1941 Lance Schuermann
1942 Tyrone Washington
1943 Michael Crespo
1944 Daryl Kennedy
1945 Lanny Williams
1946 Rich Aurilia
1947 Mike Edwards
1948 George Evangelista
1949 Todd Guggiana
1950 Mike Smith
1951 Desi Wilson
1952 Terrell Lowery
1953 Ken Powell
1954 Jose Texidor
1955 Tommy Thompson
1956 Darrin Garner
1957 Marvin White
1958 Checklist

A card number in parentheses () indicates the set is unnumbered.

1993 Fleer/ProCards Chattanooga Lookouts

		MT	NR MT	EX
Complete Set:		6.00		

2352 Mike Anderson
2353 Chris Bushing
2354 John Courtright
2355 Calvain Culberson
2356 Mike Ferry
2357 Victor Garcia
2358 Scott Holcomb
2359 Chris Hook
2360 Rusty Kilgo
2361 Johnny Ray
2362 Scott Robinson
2363 Darron Cox
2364 Jon Fuller
2365 Jamie Dismuke
2366 Keith Kessinger
2367 Brian Koelling
2368 Brian Lane
2369 Calvin Reese
2370 Steve Gibralter
2371 K.C. Gillum
2372 Keith Gordon
2373 Bernie Jenkins
2374 Mark Merchant
2375 Pat Kelly
2376 Grant Jackson
3227 Greg Bobbitt
3228 Chris Bryant
3229 Billy Childress
3230 Geremis Gonzalez
3231 Sean Hennessey
3232 Rodd Kurtz
3233 Mark Lavenia
3234 Orlando Lopez
3235 Danny Ortiz
3236 David Weber
3237 Pat Cline
3238 Tony Khoury
3239 Jacob Serrato
3240 Britt Bonneau
3241 K.J. Ellis
3242 Ariel Martin
3243 Jason Maxwell
3244 Juan Mercedes
3245 Bobby Morris
3246 Brad Sigler
3247 Ronald Smith
3248 Ralph Eusebio
3249 Sean Fric
3250 Artis Johnson
3251 Anthony King
3252 Thomas King
3253 Gabe Whatley
3254 Steve Kolinsky
3255 Phil Hannon
3256 Checklist

1993 Classic Best Clearwater Phillies

		MT	NR MT	EX
Complete Set:		6.00		

1 Jason Moler
2 Jeff Bigler
3 Ron Blazier
4 Ricky Bottallco
5 Greg Brown
6 Dominic Desantis
7 Jerome Edwards
8 David Fisher
9 Phil Geisler
10 Joel Gilmore
11 Mike Gomez
12 Rob Grable
13 David Hayden
14 Craig Holman
15 Dean Hopp
16 Mike Juhl
17 J.J. Munoz
18 Mark Randall
19 Troy Rusk
20 Jamie Sepeda
21 Ken Sirak
22 David Tokheim
23 John Trisler
24 Tom Vilet
25 Jon Zuber
26 Bill Dancy
27 Roly DeArmas
28 Darold Knowles
29 Troy Hoffert

1993 Fleer/ProCards Clearwater Phillies

		MT	NR MT	EX
Complete Set:		6.00		

2675 Ron Blazier
2676 Ricky Bottalico
2677 Greg Brown
2678 Dominic DeSantis
2679 Joel Gilmore
2680 Mike Juhl
2681 J.J. Munoz
2682 Mark Randall
2683 Jamie Sepeda
2684 John Trisler
2685 Dean Hopp
2686 Jason Moler
2687 Troy Rusk
2688 David Fisher
2689 Mike Gomez
2690 Rob Grable
2691 David Hayden
2692 Ken Sirak
2693 Jon Zuber
2694 Jay Edwards
2695 Phil Geisler
2696 Chad McConnell
2697 David Tokheim
2698 Tom Vilet
2699 Bill Dancy
2700 Darold Knowles, Roly DeArmas
2701 Checklist

1993 Classic Best Clinton Giants

		MT	NR MT	EX
Complete Set:		6.00		

1 Jim Rosenbohm
2 Charles Alimena
3 David Baine
4 Marvin Benard
5 Jamie Brewington
6 Marino Castillo
7 Mike Cavanagh
8 Ron Crowe
9 Tracey Ealy
10 Aaron Fultz
11 Chris Gambs
12 Andy Heckman
13 Marcus Jensen
14 Clay King
15 Jeff Locklear
16 Craig Mayes
17 Tom O'Neill
18 Papo Ramos
19 Jeff Richey
20 Petie Roach
21 Mark Saugstad
22 D.J. Thielen
23 Carlos Valdez
24 Kevin Wong
25 Kenny Woods
26 Jack Mull
27 Frank Cacciatore
28 Steve Lienhard
29 Steve Dietzman

1993 Fleer/ProCards Clinton Giants

		MT	NR MT	EX
Complete Set:		6.00		

2480 Jamie Brewington
2481 Marino Castillo
2482 Ron Crowe
2483 Aaron Fultz
2484 Chris Gambs
2485 Andy Heckman
2486 Jeff Locklear
2487 Jeff Myers
2488 Jeff Richey
2489 Jim Rosenbohm
2490 Carlos Valdez
2491 Mike Cavanagh
2492 Marcus Jensen
2493 Craig Mayes
2494 Charles Alimena
2495 Chad Fonville
2496 Tom O'Neill
2497 D.J. Thielen
2498 Kevin Wong
2499 Marvin Benard
2500 Tracey Ealy
2501 Petie Roach
2502 Benji Simonton
2503 Kenny Woods
2504 Jack Mull
2505 Frank Cacciatore
2506 Steve Lienhard
2507 Checklist

1993 Fleer/ProCards Colorado Springs Sky Sox

		MT	NR MT	EX
Complete Set:		6.00		

3080 Steve Allen
3081 Ryan Hawblitzel
3082 Curt Leskanic
3083 Mike Munoz
3084 Lance Painter
3085 Dana Ridenour
3086 Mo Sanford
3087 Mark Thompson
3088 Brad Ausmus
3089 Gilberto Reyes
3090 Jason Bates
3091 Pedro Castellano

3092 Stu Cole
3093 Jay Gainer
3094 Trent Hubbard
3095 Nelson Liriano
3096 Roberto Mejia
3097 Andy Mota
3098 Edwin Alicea
3099 Jim Olander
3100 Sean Ross
3101 Brad Mills
3102 Frank Funk
3103 Bobby Meacham
3104 Checklist

1993 Fleer/ProCards Columbus Clippers

	MT	NR MT	EX
Complete Set:	6.00		

1102 Royal Clayton
1103 Andy Cook
1104 Francisco DeLaRosa
1105 Kenny Greer
1106 Sterling Hitchcock
1107 Mark Hutton
1108 Jeff Johnson
1109 Sam Militello
1110 Bobby Munoz
1111 Kirt Ojala
1112 Don Stanford
1113 Kiki Hernandez
1114 Gordon Sanchez
1115 Russ Davis
1116 Bobby DeJardin
1117 Carlos Rodriguez
1118 Dave Silvestri
1119 Don Sparks
1120 Andy Stankiewicz
1121 Mike Humphreys
1122 Jay Knoblauh
1123 Billy Masse
1124 Hensley Meulens
1125 Gerald Williams
1126 Stump Merrill
1127 Field Staff
1128 Checklist

1993 Police Cracker Jack Columbus Clippers

	MT	NR MT	EX
Complete Set:	7.00		

1 Royal Clayton
2 Andy Cook
3 Francisco de la Rosa
4 Kenny Greer
5 Sterling Hitchcock
6 Kirt Ojala
7 Don Stanford
8 Mark Hutton
9 Sam Militello
10 Bobby Munoz
11 Kiki Hernandez
12 Gordon Sanchez
13 Russ Davis
14 Stump Merrill (Manager)
15 Carlos Rodriguez
16 Dave Silvestri
17 Don Sparks
18 Andy Stankiewicz
19 Hensley Meulens
20 Gerald Wiliams
21 Mike Humphreys
22 Jay Knoblauch
23 Billy Masse
24 Coaching Staff
25 Ken Schnacke (Gen Mgr)

1993 Classic Best Columbus RedStixx

	MT	NR MT	EX
Complete Set:	6.50		

1 Derek Hacopian
2 Brian Arntzen
3 Jim Beauchamp
4 Pat Bryant
5 Jose Cabrera
6 Epi Cardenas
7 John Carter
8 Patricio Claudio
9 Felipe Duran
10 Paul Gibbs
11 Pep Harris
12 Sam Hence
13 Damian Jackson
14 Rod Koller
15 Mitch Meluskey
16 Rafael Mercado
17 Jon Nunnally
18 Cesar Perez
19 Oscar Resendez
20 Scott Sharts
21 Fred Smith
22 Jamie Taylor
23 J.J. Thobe
24 Chad Townsend
25 Andre White
26 Charles York
27 Mike Brown
28 Dan Williams
29 Fred Gladding
30 Ted Blackwell

1993 Fleer/ProCards Columbus RedStixx

	MT	NR MT	EX
Complete Set:	7.50		

588 Jim Beauchamp
589 Jose Cabrera
590 John Carter
591 Paul Gibbs
592 Pep Harris
593 Rod Koller
594 Oscar Resendez
595 Scott Sharts
596 Fred Smith
597 J.J. Thobe
598 Jeff Williams
599 Charles York
600 Brian Arntzen
601 Mitch Meluskey
602 Epi Cardenas
603 Felipe Duran
604 Damian Jackson
605 Rafael Mercado
606 Jonathan Nunnally
607 Jamie Taylor
608 Chad Townsend
609 Pat Bryant
610 Patricio Claudio
611 Derek Hacopian
612 Sam Hence
613 Andre White
614 Mike Brown
615 Fred Gladding
616 Dan Williams
617 Checklist

1993 Fleer/ProCards Danville Braves

	MT	NR MT	EX
Complete Set:	6.00		

3608 Jeff Bock
3609 Craig Bradshaw
3610 Darold Brown
3611 Matt Byrd
3612 Maurice Christmas
3613 Burke Cromer
3614 Will Havens
3615 Ryan Jacobs
3616 Carey Paige
3617 Carl Schutz
3618 Bill Shafer
3619 Esteban Yan
3620 Fernando Benitez
3621 Billy Paragin
3622 Sean Smith
3623 Jose Columna
3624 Chris Cox
3625 Feliberto Selmo
3626 Randall Simon
3627 Kenneth Warner
3628 Mike Wieser
3629 Shawn Brennan
3630 Jason Dailey
3631 Damon Hollins
3632 Andre King
3633 John Reece
3634 Sherton Saturnino
3635 Jason Shelley
3636 Angelo Stutts
3637 Bruce Benedict
3638 Checklist

1993 Classic Best Daytona Cubs

	MT	NR MT	EX
Complete Set:	7.00		

1 Andrew Hartung
2 Terry Adams
3 Adam Brown
4 Ben Burlingame
5 Tim Delgado
6 Lance Dickson
7 Jay Franklin
8 Doug Glanville
9 Rudy Gomez
10 Mike Hubbard
11 Chuck Kirk
12 Ed Larregul
13 Danny Montero
14 Bernardino Nunez
15 Chris Petersen
16 Carl Schramm
17 Daniel Smith
18 Kennie Steenstra
19 Joe Terilli
20 Mike Tidwell
21 Paul Torres
22 Derek Wallace
23 Frederick White
24 Bill Hayes
25 Les Strode
26 Joe Tanner
27 Steve Melendez

1993 Fleer/ProCards Daytona Cubs

	MT	NR MT	EX
Complete Set:	6.00		

850 Terry Adams
851 Ben Burlingame
852 Tim Delgado
853 Lance Dickson
854 Jay Franklin
855 Chuck Kirk
856 Carl Schramm
857 Ken Steenstra
858 Mike Tidwell
859 Derek Wallace
860 Fred White
861 Adam Brown
862 Mike Hubbard
863 Danny Montero
864 Andy Hartung
865 Chris Peterson
866 Dan Smith
867 Tim Stutheit
868 Doug Glavnille
869 Ed Larregui
870 Bernardino Nunez
871 Joe Terilli
872 Paul Torres
873 Bill Hayes
874 Les Strode
875 Checklist

1993 Fleer/ProCards Dunedin Blue Jays

	MT	NR MT	EX
Complete Set:	6.00		

1787 Giovanni Carrara
1788 Dennis Gray
1789 Scott Grove
1790 Kurt Heble
1791 Tom Hotchkiss
1792 Chris Kotes
1793 Al Montoya
1794 Randy Phillips
1795 Tom Singer
1796 Rick Steed
1797 Ben Weber
1798 Eric Brooks
1799 Marc Loeb
1800 Brent Lutz
1801 Tilson Brito
1802 Carlos Cabrera
1803 Felipe Crespo
1804 Matt Johnson
1805 Chris Stynes
1806 Chris Weinke
1807 Rich Butler
1808 Ronald Helsel
1809 Rick Holifield
1810 Todd Steverson
1811 Dennis Holmberg
1812 Bill Monbouquette
1813 Checklist

1993 Classic Best Durham Bulls

	MT	NR MT	EX
Complete Set:	6.50		

1 Vince Moore
2 Joe Ayrault
3 Dirk Blair
4 Kurt Burgess
5 Barry Chiles
6 Brad Clontz
7 Tom Coates
8 Tony Graffanino
9 Manny Jimenez
10 Pat Kelly
11 Jerry Koller
12 Tom Leahy
13 Lance Marks
14 Don Robinson
15 Scott Ryder
16 Ozzie Sanchez
17 Jason Schmidt
18 Chris Seelbach
19 Steve Swall
20 Pedro Swann
21 Dominic Therrien
22 Mike Warner
23 John Wilder
24 Juan Williams
25 Doug Wollenburg
26 Leon Roberts
27 Rick Albert
28 Tack Wilson
29 Matt West
30 Dave Tomchek

1993 Fleer/ProCards Durham Bulls

	MT	NR MT	EX
Complete Set:	6.00		

477 Dirk Blair
478 Kurt Burgess
479 Barry Chiles
480 Brad Clontz
481 Jerry Koller
482 Tom Leahy
483 Kevin Lomon
484 Scott Ryder
485 Jason Schmidt
486 Chris Seelbach
487 John Wilder
488 Joe Ayrault
489 Steve Swail
490 Anthony Graffagnino
491 Manny Jimenez
492 Pat Kelly
493 Lance Marks
494 Dominic Therrien
495 Doug Wollenburg
496 Tom Coates
497 Vince Moore
498 Don Robinson
499 Ozzie Sanchez
500 Pedro Swann
501 Mike Warner
502 Juan Williams
503 Leon Roberts
504 Rick Albert
505 Matt West
506 Tack Wilson
507 Checklist

1993 Fleer/ProCards Edmonton Trappers

	MT	NR MT	EX
Complete Set:	6.00		

1129 Scott Anderson
1130 Jerry Don Gleaton
1131 John Johnstone
1132 Randy Kramer
1133 Jose Martinez
1134 Pat Rapp
1135 Rich Scheid
1136 Matt Turner
1137 Gene Walter
1138 Dave Weathers
1139 Mitch Lyden
1140 Terry McGriff
1141 Bob Natal
1142 Luis DeLosSantos
1143 Chuck Jackson
1144 Al Pedrique
1145 Gus Polidor
1146 Jeff Small
1147 Geronimo Berroa
1148 Nick Capra
1149 Mark Ryal
1150 Darrell Whitmore
1151 Nigel Wilson
1152 Sal Rende
1153 Fernando Arroyo
1154 Adrian Garrett
1155 Checklist

1993 Fleer/ProCards Elizabethton Twins

	MT	NR MT	EX
Complete Set:	6.00		

3408 Shane Bowers
3409 Troy Carrasco
3410 Trevor Cobb
3411 Javier DeJesus
3412 Deron Dowher
3413 Russell Lahoisky
3414 Shawn Miller
3415 Brian O'Brien
3416 David Oiler
3417 Dan Perkins
3418 Jesus Acevedo
3419 Scott Stricklin
3420 Tom Knauss
3421 James Motte
3422 Chad Rupp
3423 Danny Venezia
3424 Ewlegul Wilson
3425 Jason Baker
3426 Pedro Blanco
3427 Armann Brown
3428 Edgar Herrera
3429 Benjamin Jones
3430 Ray Smith
3431 Stu Cliburn
3432 Checklist

1993 Fleer/ProCards Elmira Pioneers

	MT	NR MT	EX
Complete Set:	7.00		

3814 Mitch Bowen
3815 Dan Chergey

3816 Ryan Filbeck
3817 Phil Gomez
3818 Andy Larkin
3819 Sam Minyard
3820 Greg Mix
3821 Clemente Nunez
3822 Paul Thornton
3823 Jon VanZandt
3824 Al Walania
3825 Bryan Ward
3826 Andrew Prater
3827 Mike Sims
3828 Tony Turnbull
3829 Dave Berg
3830 Matt Martinez
3831 Sergio Sanchez
3832 Rich Seminoff
3833 Andru Small
3834 Scott Southard
3835 Ron Brown
3836 Bill McMillon
3837 Rob Moen
3838 Erick Strickland
3839 Lynn Jones
3840 Bernie Flaherty
3841 Jeff Pentland
3842 Checklist

1993 Fleer/ProCards El Paso Diablos

	MT	NR MT	EX
Complete Set:	6.00		

2940 Kurt Archer
2941 Glenn Carter
2942 Tim Dell
2943 Francisco Gamez
2944 Brian Hancock
2945 Dane Johnson
2946 Scott Karl
2947 Mark Kiefer
2948 Kevin Kloek
2949 Dave Richards
2950 Charlie Rogers
2951 Scott Taylor
2952 Bob Kappesser
2953 Mike Matheny
2954 Kevin Castleberry
2955 Jeff Cirillo
2956 Bob Dodson
2957 Al Lewis
2958 Rodney Lofton
2959 Ed Smith
2960 Wes Weger
2961 Mike Basse
2962 Michael Carter
2963 Steve Gill
2964 Rob Lukachyk
2965 Duane Singleton
2966 Tim Ireland
2967 Rob Derksen
2968 Ben Oglivie
2969 Checklist

1993 Fleer/ProCards Erie Sailors

	MT	NR MT	EX
Complete Set:	7.50		

3105 Jeff Davis
3106 Jim Franklin
3107 Bert Gerhart
3108 Pete Hartman
3109 Rob Kell
3110 Devin Kunz
3111 Pasul Lesch
3112 Eric Moody
3113 Joe Morvay
3114 Mark O'Brien
3115 Rodney Seip
3116 Scotty Smith
3117 Greg Willming
3118 Kevin Wozney
3119 Tim Cossins
3120 Jorge Melendez
3121 Wes Shook
3122 Ray Desimone
3123 Eric Dominow
3124 Lonnie Goldberg
3125 Wes Sims
3126 Alfred Triplett
3127 Brian Blair
3128 Mike Hill
3129 Cory Pearson
3130 Marc Sagmoen
3131 Doug Sisson
3132 Jim Benedict
3133 Marc DelPiano
3134 Checklist

1993 Fleer/ProCards Eugene Emeralds

	MT	NR MT	EX
Complete Set:	5.00		

3844 Matthew Aminoff
3845 Neil Atkinson
3846 Rick Bacon
3847 Phil Brassington
3848 Nevin Brewer
3849 Rick Burley
3850 Pat Flury
3851 Phil Grundy
3852 Cody Kosman
3853 Andres Lopez
3854 Kris Ralston
3855 Kevin Rawitzer
3856 Juan Santos
3857 Ryan Towns
3858 Sal Fasano
3859 Mike Sweeney
3860 Jeremy Carr
3861 Lino Diaz
3862 Dwayne Gerald
3863 Braxton Hickman
3864 Carlos Subero
3865 Steve Wojtkowski
3866 Jimmie Byington
3867 Mike Evans
3868 Thomathan Good
3869 Oscar Jimenez
3870 Luke Oglesby
3871 O.J. Rhone
3872 Checklist

1993 Fleer/ProCards Everett Giants

	MT	NR MT	EX
Complete Set:	5.00		

3756 Heath Altman
3757 Clark Anderson
3758 David Baine
3759 Matt Baumann
3760 Steven Bourgeis
3761 Steve Day
3762 Doug Drumm
3763 Kris Franko
3764 Marc Grande
3765 Blair Hanneman
3766 Jeff Martin
3767 Mark Saugstad
3768 Brent Smith
3769 Brook Smith
3770 Scott Barrett
3771 Mike Cecere
3772 Chance Reynolds
3773 Mark Gulseth
3774 Chris Gump
3775 Brett King
3776 Bill Mueller
3777 Gary Phillips
3778 Petie Roach
3779 Mitch Stafford
3780 David Tessicini
3781 Brian Zaletel
3782 Melvin Davis
3783 Brian Lootens
3784 Andy Mason
3785 Keith Williams
3786 Checklist

1993 Classic Best Fayetteville Generals

	MT	NR MT	EX
Complete Set:	6.00		

1 Yuri Sanchez
2 Matt Bauer
3 Curt Bell
4 Mike Berlin
5 Tarrik Brock
6 Todd Bussa
7 Blas Cedeno
8 Kevin Crombie
9 Malvin DeJesus
10 Matt Evans
11 Peter Feeley
12 Keith Kimsey
13 Kevin Lidle
14 Brian Maxcy
15 Trever Miller
16 Jorge Moreno
17 David Mysel
18 Rick Navarro
19 Corey Parker
20 Clarke Rea
21 Roberto Rojas
22 Clint Sodowsky
23 Jorge Velandia
24 Sean Whiteside
25 Mark Wagner
26 Dwight Lowry
27 Brian Allard
28 Doug Teter
29 Jarnzy

1993 Fleer/ProCards Fayetteville Generals

	MT	NR MT	EX
Complete Set:	5.00		

119 Art Adams
120 Matt Bauer
121 Mike Berlin
122 Todd Bussa
123 Blas Cedeno
124 Kevin Crombie
125 Brian Maxcy
126 Trever Miller
127 David Mysel
128 Rick Navarro
129 Clint Sodowsky
130 Sean Whiteside
131 Curt Bell
132 Kevin Lidle
133 Clarke Rea
134 Malvin DeJesus
135 Matt Evans
136 Peter Feeley
137 Corey Parker
138 Yuri Sanchez
139 Jorge Velandia
140 Tarrick Brock
141 Keith Kimsey
142 Jorge Moreno
143 Roberto Rojas
144 Mark Wagner
145 Brian Allard
146 Dwight Lowry
147 Checklist

1993 Fleer/ProCards Florida State League All-Stars

	MT	NR MT	EX
Complete Set:	12.00		

1 Rich Aurilla
2 Todd Guggiana
3 Daryl Henderson
4 Wilson Heredia
5 Daryl Kennedy
6 Terrell Lowery
7 Rich Butler
8 Felipe Crespo
9 Randy Phillips
10 Chris Stynes
11 Ben Weber
12 Chris Weinke
13 Brian Bright
14 Brent Brede
15 Steve Hazlett
16 Damian Miller
17 Brian Edmondson
18 Rich Kelley
19 Phil Stidham
20 Justin Thompson
21 Brian Boehringer
22 Glenn DiSarcina
23 Robert Ellis
24 Milson Robledo
25 Greg Brown
26 Rob Grable
27 Mike Juhl
28 Jason Moler
29 Jon Zuber
30 Tim Delgado
31 Mike Hubbard
32 Bernardino Nunez
33 Ken Steestra
34 Tom Anderson
35 Kevin Lane
36 Buck McNabb
37 Chris White
38 Edgardo Alfonzo
39 Randy Curtis
40 Bernie Millan
41 Chris Roberts
42 Duff Brumley
43 Michael Cantu
44 Clint Davis
45 Jason Hisey
46 Chris Demetral
47 Ken Huckaby
48 Rich Linares
49 Rod Henderson
50 Tyrone Horne
51 Checklist

1993 Classic Best Fort Lauderdale Red Sox

	MT	NR MT	EX
Complete Set:	6.00		

1 Brent Hansen
2 Chad Amos
3 Brian Bright
4 Bryan Brown
5 Todd Carey
6 Chris Davis
7 Tim Davis
8 Alex Delgado
9 Gino Dimare
10 Marty Durkin
11 Tony Ferreira
12 Melvin Gonzalez
13 Pete Hoy
14 Jeff Johnson
15 David Klvac
16 Randy Lawrence
17 Dana Levangie
18 Cesar Martinez
19 Nick Ortiz
20 Ken Osterkamp
21 Hilario Perez
22 Ed Perozo
23 Silverio Santa Maria
24 Ernison Soto
25 Derek Vinyard
26 Jose Zambrano
27 DeMarlo Hale
28 Luis Dorante
29 Lee Stange
30 Jim Love

1993 Fleer/ProCards Ft. Lauderdale Red Sox

	MT	NR MT	EX
Complete Set:	5.00		

1587 Chad Amos
1588 Chris Davis
1589 Melvin Gonzalez
1590 Brent Hansen
1591 Peter Hoy
1592 Jeff Johnson
1593 David Klvac
1594 Randy Lawrence
1595 Cesar Martinez
1596 Ken Osterkamp
1597 Hillario Perez
1598 Silverio Santa Maria
1599 Alex Delgado
1600 Dana Levangie
1601 Emison Soto
1602 Todd Carey
1603 Tim Davis
1604 Marty Durkin
1605 Tony Ferreira
1606 Nick Ortiz
1607 Ed Perozo
1608 Brian Bright
1609 Bryan Brown
1610 Gino DiMare
1611 Derek Vinyard
1612 Jose Zambrano
1613 DeMarlo Hal, DeMarlo Hale)
1614 Luis Dorante
1615 Lee Stange
1616 Checklist

1993 Fleer/ProCards Fort Meyers Miracle

	MT	NR MT	EX
Complete Set:	5.00		

2647 Dave Bigham
2648 Dickie Dixon
2649 Luis Garcia
2650 Jim Krol
2651 Dan Naulty
2652 Brad Radke
2653 Brett Roberts
2654 Craig Saccavino
2655 Dennis Sweeney
2656 Mark Swope
2657 Jeff Thelen
2658 Matt Brown
2659 Damian Miller
2660 Ted Corbin
2661 Mike Fernandez
2662 Dave Garrow
2663 Tom Horincewich
2664 Andrew Kontorinis
2665 Chad Roper
2666 Brent Brede
2667 Butch Burrough
2668 Steve Hazlett
2669 Tim Moore
2670 Ken Norman
2671 Jamie Ogden
2672 Steve Liddle
2673 Jim Shellenback
2674 Checklist

1993 Classic Best Fort Meyers Miracle

	MT	NR MT	EX
Complete Set:	6.00		

1 Chad Roper
2 Dave Bigham
3 Brent Brede
4 Matt Brown
5 Ted Corbin
6 Dickie Dixon
7 Mike Fernandez
8 Luis Garcia
9 David Garrow
10 Steve Hazlett
11 Tom Horincewich
12 Jim Kohl
13 Andrew Kontorinis
14 Damian Miller
15 Tim Moore
16 Willie Mota
17 Dan Naulty
18 Ken Norman
19 James Ogden
20 Brad Radke
21 Brett Roberts
22 Bob Robinson
23 Craig Saccavino

24 Jim Shellenback
25 Dennis Sweeney
26 Jeff Thelen
27 Steve Liddle
28 Joel Safly
29 Kenny Agacinski

1993 Classic Best Fort Wayne Wizards

	MT	NR MT	EX
Complete Set:	6.50		

1 Dan Serafini
2 Armann Brown
3 Anthony Byrd
4 Ron Caridad
5 Marc Claus
6 Jose Correa
7 Tim Costic
8 Gus Gandarillas
9 Sean Gavaghan
10 LaTroy Hawkins
11 Edgar Herrera
12 Jeff Horn
13 Tom Knauss
14 Matt Lawton
15 Kevin Legault
16 Keith Linebarger
17 Rene Lopez
18 Joey Miller
19 Shawn Miller
20 Scott Moten
21 Marlo Nava
22 Todd Taylor
23 Ken Tirpack
24 Ramon Valette
25 Scott Watkins
26 Jim Dwyer
27 Rick Tomlin
28 Dan Fox
29 Eric Margenau
30 Wayne the Wizard

1993 Fleer/ProCards Fort Wayne Wizards

	MT	NR MT	EX
Complete Set:	7.00		

1959 Ron Caridad
1960 Jose Correa
1961 Gus Gandarillas
1962 Sean Gavaghan
1963 LaTroy Hawkins
1964 Kevin Legault
1965 Keith Linebarger
1966 Shawn Miller
1967 Scott Moten
1968 Dan Serafini
1969 Todd Taylor
1970 Scott Watkins
1971 Jeff Horn
1972 Rene Lopez
1973 Marc Claus
1974 Tom Knauss
1975 Marlo Nava
1976 Ken Tirpack
1977 Ramon Valette
1978 Armann Brown
1979 Anthony Byrd
1980 Tim Costic
1981 Edgar Herrera
1982 Matt Lawton
1983 Joe Miller
1984 Jim Dwyer
1985 Rick Tomlin
1986 Checklist

1993 Classic Best Frederick Keys

	MT	NR MT	EX
Complete Set:	7.00		

1 Brian DuBois
2 Jason Alstead
3 Al Benavides
4 Joe Borowski
5 Cesar Devarez
6 Vaughn Eshelman
7 Rick Forney
8 Curtis Goodwin
9 Kris Gresham
10 Jimmy Haynes
11 Stacy Jones
12 Scott Klingenbeck
13 Chris Lemp
14 Scott McClain
15 Doug McConathy
16 Feliciano Mercedes
17 Jose Millares
18 Alex Ochoa
19 Bo Ortiz
20 Dave Paveloff
21 John Polasek
22 Dan Ramirez
23 Brad Seitzer
24 Mark Smith
25 Troy Tallman
26 Pete Mackanin
27 Joe Durham
28 Larry McCall
29 Rudy Higgins
30 Key-ote

1993 Fleer/ProCards Frederick Keys

	MT	NR MT	EX
Complete Set:	6.00		

1016 Al Benadvides (Benavides)
1017 Joe Borowski
1018 Brian DuBois
1019 Vaughn Eshelman
1020 Rick Forney
1021 Jimmy Haynes
1022 Stacy Jones
1023 Scott Klingenbeck
1024 Chris Lemp
1025 Dave Paveloff
1026 John Polasek
1027 Mark Smith
1028 Cesar Devarez
1029 Kris Gresham
1030 Troy Tallman
1031 Gregg Castaldo
1032 Scott McClain
1033 Doug McConathy
1034 Feliciano Mercedes
1035 Jose Millares
1036 Dam Ramirez
1037 Brad Seitzer
1038 Jason Alstead
1039 Curtis Goodwin
1040 Alex Ochoa
1041 Basillio Ortiz
1042 Pete Mackanin
1043 Joe Durham
1044 Larry McCall
1045 Checklist

1993 Fleer/ProCards Geneva Cubs

	MT	NR MT	EX
Complete Set:	5.00		

3165 Tom Ball
3166 Brendan Donnelly
3167 Jim Farrow
3168 Shawn Hill
3169 Greg Hillman
3170 Sean Hogan
3171 Anthony Locey
3172 Jon Ratliff
3173 Greg Twiggs
3174 Wade Walker
3175 Brent Woodall
3176 Ricardo Cruz
3177 Danny Montero
3178 Jared Snyder
3179 J.J. Biernat
3180 Alex Cabrera
3181 Demetrius Dowler
3182 Gabe DuRoss
3183 Karun Jackson
3184 Steve Kulpa
3185 Brent McCabe
3186 Shane McGinnis
3187 Emilio Mendez
3188 Doug Alongi
3189 Kevin Booker
3190 Michael Gibson
3191 Kenneth Jones
3192 James Young
3193 Jerry Weinstein
3194 Alan Dunn
3195 Checklist

1993 Fleer/ProCards Glens Falls Redbirds

	MT	NR MT	EX
Complete Set:	5.00		

3992 Eric Alexandre
3993 Matt Arrandale
3994 Kenny Britt
3995 Chance Cain
3996 Rick Croushore
3997 Craig Grasser
3998 Eddie Kehrli
3999 Joe Larson
4000 Anthony Magnelli
4001 Marc Ottmers
4002 Daniel Pontes
4003 Mike Windham
4004 Greg Almond
4005 Mike Borzello
4006 Mark Williams
4007 Sal Bando Jr.
4008 Jeff Berbinger
4009 Mark Dean
4010 Joey Henson
4011 Joe Jumonville
4012 Victor Llanos
4013 Mike Matvey
4014 Trey Ritz
4015 John Stutz
4016 Mike Taylor
4017 Greg Deares
4018 Ozzie Garcia
4019 Antoine Henry
4020 Steve Santucci
4021 Steve Turco
4022 Checklist

1993 SportPro Great Falls Dodgers

	MT	NR MT	EX
Complete Set:	9.00		

1 Craig Watts
2 Juan Hernaiz
3 Dan Markham
4 Kym Ashworth
5 Brian Clark
6 Mike Biltmier
7 Joshua Rash
8 Juan Rosario
9 Craig Scheffler
10 Eduardo Rios
11 Michael Kinney
12 Brian Rolocut
13 George Perez
14 Ken Sikes
15 Dave Steed
16 Ervan Wingate
17 Dan Sarmiento
18 Keith Troutman
19 Wilton Guerrero
20 Wilfredo Romero
21 Dan Hubbs
22 Daniel Camacho
23 Dwaine Bostic
24 Paul Wittig
25 Jason Kenady
26 Chris Costelly
27 Brian Carpenter
28 Brian Richardson
29 James Breuer

1993 Classic Best Greensboro Hornets

	MT	NR MT	EX
Complete Set:	10.00		

1 Derek Jeter
2 Jeff Antolick
3 Mike Buddle
4 Jeff Cindrich
5 Billy Coleman
6 Andiel Cumberbatch
7 Mike DeJean
8 Nick Delvecchio
9 Eslton Hansen
10 Kraig Hawkins
11 Robert Hinds
12 Bert Inman
13 Ryan Karp
14 Blaise Kozeniewski
15 Joe Long
16 R.D. Long
17 Matt Luke
18 Bruce Pool
19 Scott Romano
20 Sandi Satiago
21 Shane Spencer
22 Ray Suplee
23 Jaime Torres
24 Bill Underwood
25 Kent Wallace
26 Tom Wilson
27 Bill Evers
28 Ken Dominguez

1993 Fleer/ProCards Greensboro Hornets

	MT	NR MT	EX
Complete Set:	11.00		

876 Jeff Antolick
877 Mike Buddie
878 Jeff Cindrich
879 Billy Coleman
880 Mike DeJean
881 Bert Inman
882 Ryan Karp
883 Joe Long
884 Bruce Pool
885 Sandi Santiago
886 Bill Underwood
887 Kent Wallace
888 Jaime Torres
889 Tom Wilson
890 Nick Delvecchio
891 Elston Hansen
892 Robert Hinds
893 Derek Jeter
894 Blaise Kozeniewski
895 R.D. Long
896 Scott Romano
897 Abdiel Cumberbatch
898 Kraig Hawkins
899 Matt Luke
900 Shane Spencer
901 Ray Suplee
902 Jason Wuerch
903 Bill Evers
904 Gary Denbo
905 Mark Rose
906 Checklist

1993 Fleer/ProCards Greenville Braves

	MT	NR MT	EX
Complete Set:	5.50		

341 Brian Boltz
342 Dennis Burlingame
343 Vance Lovelace
344 Dale Polley
345 Mike Potts
346 Carlos Reyes
347 Blase Sparma
348 Don Strange
349 Lee Upshaw
350 Marcos Vasquez
351 Dave Williams
352 Tyler Houston
353 Ed Perez
354 Brad Ripplemeyer
355 Edwin Alicea
356 Tim Gillis
357 Ed Giovanola
358 Jose Olmeda
359 Hector Roa
360 Lee Heath
361 Troy Hughes
362 Brian Kowitz
363 Kevin O'Connor
364 Bruce Kimm
365 Dave Hilton
366 Bill Slack
367 Brian Snitker
368 Checklist

1993 Classic Best Hagerstown Suns

	MT	NR MT	EX
Complete Set:	7.00		

1 Jose Herrera
2 Louis Benbow
3 D.J. Boston
4 Derek Brandow
5 Mike Coolbaugh
6 Brad Cornett
7 Ricky Cradle
8 Ned Darley
9 Andrew Dolson
10 Mariano Dotel
11 Tom Evans
12 Kris Harmes
13 Santiago Henry
14 Keith Hines
15 Aaron Jerslid
16 Jeff Ladd
17 Levon Largusa
18 Trevor Mallory
19 Angel Martinez
20 Scot McCloughan
21 Steve Renko
22 Lonell Roberts
23 Ken Robinson
24 Jose Silva
25 Jim Nettles
26 Leroy Stanton
27 Darren Balsley
28 Dennis Brogna

1993 Fleer/ProCards Hagerstown Suns

	MT	NR MT	EX
Complete Set:	7.50		

1870 Derek Brandow
1871 Brad Cornett
1872 Ned Darley
1873 Andrew Dolson
1874 Roger Doman
1875 Aaron Jersild
1876 Levon Largusa
1877 Trevor Mallory
1878 Steve Renko
1879 Ken Robinson
1880 Jose Silva
1881 Kris Harmes
1882 Jeff Ladd
1883 Angel Martinez
1884 Lou Benbow
1885 D.J. Boston
1886 Mike Coolbaugh
1887 Mariano Dotel
1888 Tom Evans
1889 Santiago Henry
1890 Rick Cradle
1891 Jose Herrera
1892 Keith Hines
1893 Scot McCloughan
1894 Lonell Roberts
1895 Jim Nettles
1896 Darren Balsley
1897 Leroy Stanton
1898 Field Staff
1899 Checklist

1993 Fleer/ProCards Harrisburg Senators

	MT	NR MT	EX
Complete Set:	15.00		

260 Miguel Batista
261 Mario Brito
262 Archie Corbin
263 Reid Cornelius
264 Ralph Diaz
265 Joey Eischen
266 Heath Haynes
267 Chris Johnson
268 Yorkis Perez
269 Kirk Rueter
270 Gabe White
271 Miah Bradbury
272 Rob Fitzpatrick
273 Shane Andrews
274 Cliff Floyd
275 Ron Krause
276 Oreste Marrero
277 Chris Martin
278 Edgar Tovar
279 Glenn Murray
280 Curtis Pride
281 Rondell White
282 Tyrone Woods
283 Greg Fulton
284 Jim Tracy
285 Gomer Hodge
286 Chuck Kniffin
287 Checklist

1993 Fleer/ProCards Helena Brewers

	MT	NR MT	EX
Complete Set:	5.00		

4084 Wagner Ariass
4085 Jim Cole
4086 Jeff Croll
4087 Steve Duda
4088 Chad Kopitzke
4089 Sean Maloney
4090 Matt Murphy
4091 Gary Fhoda
4092 Frankie Rodriguez
4093 Fabian Salmon
4094 Chris Schmitt
4095 Rick Werner
4096 Judd Wilstead
4097 Rob Campillo
4098 Chris Carter
4099 Brad Gay
4100 Eduardo Acosta
4101 Todd Landry
4102 Ed Mackie
4103 Chris McInnes
4104 Mike Olexa
4105 Bobby Powers
4106 Jerry Salzano
4107 Brian Banks
4108 Ruben Cephas
4109 Hayland Hardy
4110 Clayton Hill
4111 Greg Martinez
4112 Harry Dunlop
4113 Mike Caldwell
4114 Checklist

1993 SportPro Helena Brewers

	MT	NR MT	EX
Complete Set:	8.00		

1 Bobby Powers
2 Frank Rodriguez
3 Ruben Cephas
4 Rob Campillo
5 Craig Smith
6 Wagner Arias
7 Clayton Hill
8 Chris Thomas
9 Todd Landry
10 Jerry Salzano
11 Mike Olexa
12 Eduardo Acosta
13 Fabian Salmon
14 Judd Wilstead
15 Matt Murphy
16 Hayland Hardy
17 Sean Maloney
18 Ed Mackie
19 Jim Cole
20 Chris Carter
21 Chad Kopitske
22 Gary Rhoda
23 Chris Schmitt
24 Rick Werner
25 Chris McInnes
26 Roger Caplinger
27 Mike Epstein
28 Mike Caldwell

1993 Classic Best Hickory Crawdads

	MT	NR MT	EX
Complete Set:	6.00		

1 Eddie Pearson
2 Rickey Bennett
3 Mike Bertotti
4 Mark Brincks
5 David Elsbernd
6 Jason Evans
7 Wayne Faircloth
8 David Fitzpatrick
9 Chris Gay
10 Marc Harris
11 Scot Hollrah
12 Toby Lehman
13 Wayne Lindemann
14 Chris Mader
15 Johnny Malaver
16 Mickey McKinion
17 Magglio Ordonez
18 Scott Patton
19 Wilfredo Polidor
20 Jimmy Reyes
21 Eric Richardson
22 Nerio Rodriguez
23 Fred Starks
24 Juan Thomas
25 Chris Tremle
26 Fred Kendall
27 Paul Cassanova
28 Curtis Hasler
29 Mark Salas
30 Joseph Geck

1993 Fleer/ProCards Hickory Crawdads

	MT	NR MT	EX
Complete Set:	5.00		

1269 Ricky Bennett
1270 Mike Bertotti
1271 Mark Brincks
1272 David Elsbernd
1273 David Fitzpatrick
1274 Toby Lehman
1275 Wayne Lindemann
1276 Johnny Malaver
1277 Mickey McKinion
1278 Juan Soto
1279 Fred Starks
1280 Wayne Faircloth
1281 Nerio Rodriguez
1282 Chris Tremie
1283 Jason Evans
1284 Scot Hollrah
1285 Chris Mader
1286 Eddie Pearson
1287 Wilfredo Polidor
1288 Jimmy Reyes
1289 Juan Thomas
1290 Geronimo Aquino
1291 Marc Harris
1292 Magglio Ordonez
1293 Scott Patton
1294 Eric Richardson
1295 Fred Kendall
1296 Curt Hasler
1297 Mark Salas
1298 Checklist

1993 Classic Best High Desert Mavericks

	MT	NR MT	EX
Complete Set:	7.00		

1 Carl Everett
2 Joel Adamson
3 Andres Berumen
4 Tim Clark
5 Sean Gousha
6 Ken Kendrena
7 George Kerfut
8 Bryn Kosco
9 Don Lemon
10 Jim Magill
11 Chris Malinoski
12 Ramon Martinez
13 Kerwin Moore
14 Tim North
15 Barry Parisotto
16 Jim Patterson
17 Robert Person
18 Mark Skeels
19 Randy Snyder
20 Stan Spencer
21 Jerry Stafford
22 Jesus Tavarez
23 John Toale
24 Tony Torres
25 Mike Whitten
26 Fredi Gonzalez
27 Marty DeMerritt
28 Carlos Ponce
29 Mike McGowan

1993 Fleer/ProCards High Desert Mavericks

	MT	NR MT	EX
Complete Set:	7.00		

31 Joel Adamson
32 Andres Berumen
33 Kenny Kendrena
34 George Kerfut
35 Don Lemon
36 Jim Magill
37 Tom McGraw
38 Barry Parisotto
39 Jim Patterson
40 Robert Person
41 Stan Spencer
42 Gerry Stafford
43 Mike Whitten
44 Sean Gousha
45 Mark Skeels
46 Randy Snyder
47 Bryn Kosco
48 Chris Malinoski
49 Ramon Martinez
50 Tim North
51 John Toale
52 Tony Torres
53 Tim Clark
54 Carl Everett
55 Kerwin Moore
56 Jesus Tavarez
57 Fredi Gonzalez
58 Marty DeMerritt
59 Carlos Ponce
60 Checklist

1993 Fleer/ProCards Huntington Cubs

	MT	NR MT	EX
Complete Set:	5.00		

3227 Greg Bobbitt
3228 Chris Bryant
3229 Billy Childress
3230 Geremis Gonzalez
3231 Sean Hennessey
3232 Rodd Kurtz
3233 Mark Lavenia
3234 Orlando Lopez
3235 Danny Ortiz
3236 David Weber
3237 Pat Cline
3238 Tony Khoury
3239 Jacob Serrato
3240 Britt Bonneau
3241 K.J. Ellis
3242 Ariel Martin
3243 Jason Maxwell
3244 Juan Mercedes
3245 Bobby Morris
3246 Brad Sigler
3247 Ronald Smith
3248 Ralph Eusebio
3249 Sean Fric
3250 Artis Johnson
3251 Anthony King
3252 Thomas King
3253 Gabe Whatley
3254 Steve Kolinsky
3255 Phil Hannon
3256 Checklist

1993 Fleer/ProCards Huntsville Stars

	MT	NR MT	EX
Complete Set:	6.00		

2074 Dana Allison
2075 Scott Baker
2076 John Briscoe
2077 Steve Chitren
2078 Miguel Jimenez
2079 Doug Johns
2080 Dave Latter
2081 Gavin Osteen
2082 Curtis Shaw
2083 Roger Smithberg
2084 Tanyon Sturtze
2085 Eric Helfand
2086 George Williams
2087 Jim Bowie
2088 Fabio Gomez
2089 John Kuehl
2090 Francisco Matos
2091 Jim Waggoner
2092 Jason Wood
2093 Kevin Dattola
2094 Chris Hart
2095 Damon Mashore
2096 Enoch Simmons
2097 Casey Parsons
2098 Glenn Abbott
2099 Checklist

1993 Fleer/ProCards Idaho Falls Braves

	MT	NR MT	EX
Complete Set:	5.00		

4023 James Blaine
4024 Alberto Evangelista
4025 Clint Gagnon
4026 Yves Martineau
4027 Earl Nelson
4028 Chris Rusciano
4029 Jason Simmons
4030 Tony Stoecklin
4031 Jason Thomas
4032 Aaron Turnier
4033 Marcus Tyner
4034 David Wells
4035 Casey Burrill
4036 Erik Moreno
4037 Jason Bugg
4038 David Catlett
4039 Mike Eaglin
4040 Charles McBride
4041 Darren Vazquetelles
4042 Cameron Browder
4043 Ralph Denman
4044 Anthony Dileso
4045 Marcel Johnson
4046 Bruce Newman
4047 Eddie Perez
4048 Anthony Ruff
4049 Miguel Valdez
4050 Paul Runge
4051 Steve Givins
4052 Mark Ross
4053 Checklist

1993 SportPro Idaho Falls Braves

	MT	NR MT	EX
Complete Set:	8.00		

1 Alberto Evangelista
2 Eddie Perez
3 Yves Martineau
4 Charles McBride
5 Earl Nelson
6 Erik Moreno
7 Mike Eaglin
8 Anthony Ruff
9 Miguel Valdez
10 Jason Simmons
11 Tony Stoecklin
12 Darren Vazquetelles
13 Marcel Johnson
14 Ralph Denman
15 Chris Rusciano
16 James Blaine
17 Jose Rodriguez
18 Luis Garcia
19 Bruce Newman
20 Cameron Browder
21 Jason Thomas
22 Clint Gagnon
23 Casey Burrill
24 Jason Budd
25 Anthony Dileso
26 David Wells
27 Marcus Tyner
28 Aaron Turnier
29 David Catlett
30 Paul Runge

1993 Fleer/ProCards Indianapolis Indians

	MT	NR MT	EX
Complete Set:	6.00		

1482 Matt Grott
1483 Bo Kennedy
1484 Larry Luebbers
1485 David Lynch
1486 Ross Powell
1487 John Roper
1488 Scott Ruskin
1489 Scott Service
1490 Jerry Spradlin
1491 Troy Afenir
1492 Brian Dorsett
1493 Tom Costo
1494 Gary Green
1495 Willie Greene
1496 Tommy Gregg
1497 Frank Kremblas
1498 Gary Scott
1499 Jacob Brumfield
1500 Steve Carter
1501 Keith Hughes
1502 Greg Tubbs
1503 Marc Bombard
1504 Mike Griffin
1505 Razor Shines
1506 Checklist

1993 Fleer/ProCards Iowa Cubs

MT NR MT EX
Complete Set: 5.00

2128 Shawn Boskie
2129 Jim Bullinger
2130 Michael Dyer
2131 Blaise Ilsley
2132 Heath Slocumb
2133 Steve Trachsel
2134 Ed Vosberg
2135 Turk Wendell
2136 Orlando Mercado
2137 George Pedre
2138 Kent Anderson
2139 Doug Jennings
2140 Dan Lewis
2141 Greg Lonigro
2142 Greg Smith
2143 Craig Worthington
2144 Tony Chance
2145 Fernando Ramsey
2146 Scott Wade
2147 Eddie Zambrano
2148 Marv Foley
2149 Bill Earley
2150 Stan Kylese
2151 Checklist

1993 Fleer/ProCards Jackson Generals

MT NR MT EX
Complete Set: 6.00

2100 James Bruske
2101 Fred Costello
2102 James Dougherty
2103 Benjamin Gonzales
2104 Chris Hill
2105 Bob Hurta
2106 Doug Ketchen
2107 Terry Matthews
2108 Alvin Morman
2109 Mark Small
2110 Tony Gilmore
2111 Scott Makarewicz
2112 Mike Groppuso
2113 Dave Hajek
2114 Frank Kellner
2115 Lance Madsen
2116 Thomas Nevers
2117 Roberto Petagine
2118 Fletcher Thompson
2119 Chris Hatcher
2120 Brian Hunter
2121 Ray Montgomery
2122 Gary Mota
2123 Sal Butera
2124 Dave Hudgens
2125 Charlie Taylor
2126 Checklist

1993 Fleer/ProCards Jacksonville Suns

MT NR MT EX
Complete Set: 7.00

2703 Greg Bicknell
2704 Jeff Darwin
2705 Kevin Foster
2706 George Glinatsis
2707 Reggie Harris
2708 Brett Knackert
2709 Jim Newlin
2710 Paul Perkins
2711 Erik Plantenberg
2712 LaGrande Russell
2713 Scott Schanz
2714 Jim Campanis
2715 Tony Kounas
2716 Eddy Diaz
2717 Lipso Nava
2718 Desi Relaford
2719 Ruben Santana
2720 Bubba Smith
2721 Darren Bragg
2722 Marc Newfeld
2723 Tony Scruggs
2724 Checklist

1993 Fleer/ProCards Jamestown Expos

MT NR MT EX
Complete Set: 6.00

3318 Josh Bullock
3319 Fernando DaSilva
3320 Scott Harrison
3321 Aaron Knieper
3322 Mike Leon
3323 Alex Pacheco
3324 Tommy Phelps
3325 Mark Respondek
3326 Tom Schneider
3327 Dennis Stutts
3328 Neil Weber
3329 Matt Harrell
3330 Bobby Henley
3331 Ramsey Koeyers
3332 Juan Batista
3333 Chris Grubb
3334 Rich Haar
3335 Scott Quade
3336 Matt Raleigh
3337 Jesus Campos
3338 Vince LaChance
3339 Jon Saffer
3340 Angelo Thompson
3341 Joe Tosone
3342 Tim Torricelli
3343 Pat Heiderscheit
3344 Herm Starrette
3345 Checklist

1993 Fleer/ProCards Johnson City Cardinals

MT NR MT EX
Complete Set: 5.00

3668 Jeff Battles
3669 Randy Bledsoe
3670 Domingo Charles
3671 Cory Corrigan
3672 Jim Marchesi
3673 Scott Marquardt
3674 Jamie Sailors
3675 Ron Scott
3676 Duane Stanton
3677 Chris Stewart
3678 Jason Stoppello
3679 Dale Wagner
3680 Jay Witasick
3681 Kevin Herde
3682 George Strus
3683 Joe Wallace
3684 Steve Biermann
3685 Dee Dalton
3686 Rongie Dicken
3687 Pat Donohue
3688 Tom McKinnon
3689 Darek Robinson
3690 Jamie Surratt
3691 Danny Tatrow
3692 Hector Ugueto
3693 Juan Bautista
3694 Chris Christopher
3695 Aaron Gerteisen
3696 Victor Pellot
3697 Robby Strehlow
3698 Checklist

1993 Classic Best Kane County Cougars

MT NR MT EX
Complete Set: 7.00

1 Charles Johnson
2 Hector Carrasco
3 Eddie Christian
4 Chris Clapinski
5 Vic Darensbourg
6 Matt Donahue
7 Brad Frazier
8 Freddie Gamble
9 Jarod Juelsgaard
10 Pat Leahy
11 Lou Lucca
12 John Lynch
13 Reynol Mendoza
14 Matt Petersen
15 Doug Pettit
16 Todd Pridy
17 Mike Redmond
18 Edgar Renteria
19 Dan Robinson
20 Chris Sheff
21 Tony Sylvestri
22 Jim Vicek
23 Matt Whisenant
24 Pookie Wilson
25 Eric Wulf
26 Carlos Tosca
27 Jose Castro
28 Brian Peterson
29 Ozzie Cougar
30 Todd Sorensen

1993 Fleer/ProCards Kane County Cougars

MT NR MT EX
Complete Set: 9.00

907 Hector Carrasco
908 Vic Darensbourg
909 Matt Donahue
910 Brad Frazier
911 Jarod Juelsgaard
912 Pat Leahy
913 Reynol Mendoza
914 Matt Petersen
915 Doug Pettit
916 Jim Vicek
917 Matt Whisenant
918 Charles Johnson
919 Mike Redmond
920 Eric Wulf
921 Chris Clapinski
922 Freddie Gamble
923 Lou Lucca
924 Todd Pridy
925 Edgar Renteria
926 Tony Sylvestri
927 Eddie Christian
928 Dan Robinson
929 Chris Sheff
930 Pookie Wilson
931 Carlos Tosca
932 Jose Castro
933 Brian Peterson
934 Checklist

1993 Fleer/ProCards Kingsport Mets

MT NR MT EX
Complete Set: 8.00

3787 Derek Baker
3788 Bobby Carr
3789 Ervin Collier
3790 Andrew Cotner
3791 Rob Gontkosky
3792 Brian Mast
3793 Juan Moreno
3794 Rafael Roque
3795 Derek Sutton
3796 Ramon Tatis
3797 Tom Wolff
3798 Cesar Diaz
3799 Chad Epperson
3800 Bob Day
3801 Mike Farrell
3802 Mike Johnson
3803 Stephen Lackey
3804 Sandy Pichardo
3805 Freddy Rojas
3806 Preston Wilson
3807 Jason Adams
3808 James Dorsey
3809 Rafael Guerrero
3810 Randy Warner
3811 Ron Gideon
3812 Jesus Hernaiz
3813 Checklist

1993 Classic Best Kinston Indians

MT NR MT EX
Complete Set: 6.00

1 Pete Rose Jr.
2 Juan Andujar
3 Dickie Brown
4 Mark Charbonnet
5 John Cotton
6 Carlos Crawford
7 Mike Crosby
8 Ian Doyle
9 Joe Fleet
10 Jason Fronio
11 Ray Harvey
12 Fernando Hernandez
13 Kevin Logsdon
14 Marc Marini
15 Pat Maxwell
16 Rod McCall
17 Greg McCarthy
18 Paul Meade
19 Tony Mitchell
20 Scott Morgan
21 Cesar Perez
22 Chop Pough
23 Nick Sued
24 Julian Tavarez
25 David Welch
26 Matt Williams
27 Dave Keller
28 Dan Norman
29 Greg Booker
30 Dan DeVoe

1993 Fleer/ProCards Kinston Indians

MT NR MT EX
Complete Set: 6.00

2237 Dickie Brown
2238 Carlos Crawford
2239 Ian Doyle
2240 Joe Fleet
2241 Jason Fronio
2242 Fernando Hernandez
2243 Kevin Logsdon
2244 Greg McCarthy
2245 Scott Morgan
2246 Cesar Perez
2247 Julian Travarez
2248 David Welch
2249 Matt Williams
2250 Mike Crosby
2251 Nick Sued
2252 Juan Andujar
2253 Pat Maxwell
2254 Rod McCall
2255 Paul Meade
2256 Chop Pough
2257 Pete Rose, Jr.
2258 Mark Charbonnet
2259 John Cotton
2260 Ray Harvey
2261 Marc Marini
2262 Tony Mitchell
2263 Dave Keller
2264 Greg Booker
2265 Dan Norman
2266 Checklist

1993 Fleer/ProCards Knoxville Smokies

MT NR MT EX
Complete Set: 16.00

1240 Travis Baptist
1241 Scott Brow
1242 Daren Brown
1243 Tim Crabtree
1244 Nate Cromwell
1245 Kyle Duey
1246 Huck Flener
1247 Joe Ganote
1248 Scott Grove
1249 Steve Karsay
1250 Daren Kizziah
1251 Aaron Small
1252 Carlos Delgado
1253 Anastacio Garcia
1254 Mike Morland
1255 Sharnol Adriana
1256 Howard Battle
1257 Alex Gonzalez
1258 Derek Henderson
1259 Tim Hyers
1260 Joe Lis
1261 Brent Bowers
1262 Shawn Green
1263 Tim Hodge
1264 Ron Reams
1265 Garth Iorg
1266 Mike McAlpin
1267 Steve Mingori
1268 Checklist

1993 Classic Best Lakeland Tigers

MT NR MT EX
Complete Set: 6.00

1 Justin Thompson
2 Pat Ahearne
3 Carlos Burguillos
4 Greg Coppetta
5 Brian DuBose
6 Brian Edmondson
7 Carlos Fermin
8 Pedro Gonzalez
9 Rick Greene
10 Michael Guilfoyle
11 Bob Higginson
12 Brent Killen
13 John Kosenski
14 Johnny LaMar
15 Justin Mashore
16 Tim McConnell
17 Casey Mendenhall
18 Darren Milne
19 Kevin Morgan
20 Kelley O'Neal III
21 Cecil Pettiford
22 Dan Ruff
23 Phil Stidham
24 Timothy Thomas
25 Dennis Walsh
26 Gerry Groninger
27 Kevin Bradshaw
28 Rich Bombard
29 Bryan Golke

1993 Fleer/ProCards Lakeland Tigers

MT NR MT EX
Complete Set: 6.00

1299 Pat Ahearne
1300 Greg Coppeta
1301 Brian Edmondson
1302 Rick Greene
1303 Mike Guilfoyle
1304 Rich Kelley
1305 John Kosenski
1306 Casey Mendenhall
1307 Cecil Pettiford
1308 Greg Raffo
1309 Tom Schwarber
1310 Phil Stidham
1311 Justin Thompson
1312 Dennis Walsh
1313 Pete Gonzalez
1314 Tim McConnell

1315 Rob Yelton
1316 Brian Dubose
1317 Carlos Fermin
1318 Kevin Morgan
1319 Kelley O'Neal
1320 Tim Thomas
1321 Carlos Burguillos
1322 Bob Higginson
1323 John LaMar
1324 Justin Mashore
1325 Dan Ruff
1326 Gerry Groninger
1327 Rich Bombard
1328 Kevin Bradshaw
1329 Checklist

1993 Fleer/ProCards Las Vegas Stars

	MT	NR MT	EX
Complete Set:	5.00		

935 Juan Agosto
936 Denis Boucher
937 Doug Brocail
938 Ricky Davis
939 Mark Ettles
940 Mike Linskey
941 Pedro Martinez
942 Jim Pena
943 Scott Sanders
944 Joe Strong
945 Tim Worrell
946 Ray Young
947 Mike Basso
948 Brian Johnson
949 Billy Bean
950 Steve Bethea
951 Kevin Higgins
952 Luis Lopez
953 Mike Simms
954 Matt Witkowski
956 D.J. Dozier
957 Chris Jelic
958 Steve Pegues
959 Jim Vatcher
960 Russ Nixon
961 Marty Barrett
962 John Cumberland
963 Checklist

1993 Fleer/ProCards Lethbridge Mounties

	MT	NR MT	EX
Complete Set:	6.00		

4142 Dale Ballance
4143 Miguel Bonilla
4144 Rodney Davidson
4145 Elcilio DeLeon
4146 John Dillinger
4147 Merlin Kath
4148 Shawn Ohman
4149 Dan Roman
4150 Ray Solomon
4151 Ben Boka
4152 Jason Marshall
4153 Lee Reiber
4154 John Allen
4155 Gavin Baugh
4156 Matt Jones
4157 Juan Segura
4158 Anthony Bonifazio
4159 Adrian Brown
4160 Willie Brown
4161 Luis Cordova
4162 Corey Lea
4163 Pat Lussier
4164 Phil Wellman
4165 Juan Bustabad
4166 Bill Sizemore
4167 Checklist

1993 SportPro Lethbridge Mounties

	MT	NR MT	EX
Complete Set:	7.00		

1 John Allen
2 Rodney Davidson
3 Ben Boka
4 Adrian Brown
5 Elcilio DeLeon
6 John Dillinger
7 Gavin Baugh
8 Anthony Bonifazio
9 Miguel Bonillia
10 Willie Brown
11 Merlin Kath
12 Jason Marshall
13 Matt Jones
14 Luis Cordova
15 Shawn Ohman
16 Dan Roman
17 Dale Balance
18 Corey Lea
19 Ray Soloman
20 Juan Segura
21 Lee Reiber
22 Pat Lussier
23 Pat Laverty
24 John Bustabad
25 Phillip Wellman
26 Bill Sizemore

1993 Fleer/ProCards London Tigers

	MT	NR MT	EX
Complete Set:	5.00		

2297 Ben Blomdahl
2298 Jeff Braley
2299 Ken Carlyle
2300 Mike Garcia
2301 Henrique Gomez
2302 Jim Henry
2303 Jose Limba
2304 Felipe Lira
2305 Jason Pfaff
2306 Tom Schwarber
2307 Bob Undorf
2308 Brian Warren
2309 Steve Wolf
2310 Joe Perona
2311 Brian Saltzgaber
2312 Rick Sellers
2313 Jimmy Alder
2314 Jim Givens
2315 Kirk Mendenhall
2316 Shannon Penn
2317 Evan Pratte
2318 Mike Rendina
2319 Dan Bautista
2320 Brian Cornelius
2321 Rudy Pemberton
2322 Tom Runnells
2323 Sid Monge
2324 Dan Raley
2325 Checklist

1993 Fleer/ProCards Louisville Redbirds

	MT	NR MT	EX
Complete Set:	6.00		

206 Gary Buckels
207 Fidel Compres
208 Steve Dixon
209 Paul Kilgus
210 Kevin Meier
211 Mike Milchin
212 Gabriel Ozuna
213 Bob Sebra
214 Tom Urbani
215 Allen Watson
216 Dennis Wiseman
217 Ed Fulton
218 Barry Lyons
219 Erik Pappas
220 Tripp Cromer
221 Gien Figueroa
222 Tim Jones
223 Keith Lockhart
224 Stan Royer
225 Jeff Shireman
226 Ozzie Canseco
227 Lonnie Maclin
228 John Morris
229 Van Snider
230 Skeets Thomas
231 Checklist

1993 Classic Best Lynchburg Red Sox

	MT	NR MT	EX
Complete Set:	6.00		

1 Diogenes Baez
2 Scott Bakkum
3 Joel Bennett
4 Randy Brown
5 Tim Carey
6 Felix Colon
7 Bret Donovan
8 John Elerman
9 Jeff Faino
10 Gettys Glaze
11 Doug Hecker
12 Rob Henkel
13 Joe Hudson
14 Bob Juday
15 Ron Mahay
16 Jose Malave
17 Ryan Maloney
18 Jeff Martin
19 Walt McKeel
20 Todd Miller
21 Tommy Niles
22 Steve Rodriguez
23 George Scott III
24 Bill Selby
25 Mark Meleski
26 Joe Marchese
27 Jim Bibby
28 David Duchin

1993 Fleer/ProCards Lynchburg Red Sox

	MT	NR MT	EX
Complete Set:	6.00		

2508 Scott Bakkum
2509 Joel Bennett
2510 Bret Donovan
2511 Jeff Faino
2512 Gettys Glaze
2513 Bob Henkel
2514 Joe Hudson
2515 Ryan Maloney
2516 Todd Miller
2517 Tommy Niles
2518 Tim Carey
2519 Jeff Martin
2520 Walt McKeel
2521 Randy Brown
2522 Felix Colon
2523 Doug Hecker
2524 Bob Juday
2525 Steve Rodriguez
2526 Dave Schmidt
2527 Bill Selby
2528 Diogunes Baez
2529 John Eierman
2530 Ron Mahay
2531 Jose Malave
2532 George Scott III
2533 Mark Meleski
2534 Jim Bibby
2535 Joe Marchese
2536 Checklist

1993 Classic Best Macon Braves

	MT	NR MT	EX
Complete Set:	8.00		

1 Terrell Wade
2 Jamie Arnold
3 Chris Brock
4 Terrell Buckley
5 Jason Butler
6 Mark Chambers
7 Miguel Correa
8 Michael D'Andrea
9 Adrian Garcia
10 Kenneth Giard
11 Kevin Grijak
12 Jason Keeline
13 John Knott
14 Marty Malloy
15 Darrell May
16 Jay Noel
17 Raymond Nunez
18 Nelson Paulino
19 Michael Place
20 Leo Ramirez
21 John Simmons
22 Klan Sly
23 Miguel Soto
24 Tom Thobe
25 David Toth
26 Thomas Waldrop
27 Randy Ingle
28 Joe Szekely
29 Larry Jaster
30 Wailly Johnson

1993 Fleer/ProCards Macon Braves

	MT	NR MT	EX
Complete Set:	8.00		

1391 Jamie Arnold
1392 Chris Brock
1393 Jason Butler
1394 Mike D'Andrea
1395 Ken Giard
1396 Darrell May
1397 Mike Place
1398 Leo Ramirez
1399 John Simmons
1400 Tom Thobe
1401 Terrell Wade
1402 Adrian Garcia
1403 Miguel Soto
1404 David Toth
1405 Terrell Buckley
1406 Kevin Grijak
1407 Jason Keeline
1408 John Knott
1409 Marty Malloy
1410 Raymond Nunez
1411 Nelson Paulino
1412 Mark Chambers
1413 Miguel Correa
1414 Jay Noel
1415 Kian Sly
1416 Tom Waldrop
1417 Randy Ingle
1418 Larry Jaster
1419 Joe Szekely
1420 Checklist

1993 Classic Best Madison Muskies

	MT	NR MT	EX
Complete Set:	6.00		

1 Don Wengert
2 Mark Acre
3 Luinus Aracena
4 James Banks
5 Carlos Bellard
6 Tim Bojan
7 D.T. Cromer
8 Brian Eldridge
9 Cliff Foster
10 David Francisco
11 Vincente Francisco
12 Creighton Gubanich
13 Jose Guillen
14 Gary Haught
15 Stacy Hollins
16 Gary Hust
17 Tim Killeen
18 Rob Leary
19 Brian Lesher
20 Julio Martinez
21 Troy Penix
22 Zack Sawyer
23 Scott Sheldon
24 Greg Smock
25 William Urbina
26 Jason White
27 Gary Jones
28 Gil Patterson

1993 Fleer/ProCards Madison Muskies

	MT	NR MT	EX
Complete Set:	6.00		

1814 James Banks
1815 Carlos Belliard
1816 Tim Bojan
1817 Cliff Foster
1818 Gary Haught
1819 Stacy Hollins
1820 Julio Martinez
1821 Zachary Sawyer
1822 William Urbina
1823 Don Wengert
1824 Creighton Gubanich
1825 Tim Killeen
1826 Brian Eldridge
1827 Vicente Francisco
1828 Jose Guillen
1829 Rob Leary
1830 Troy Penix
1831 Scott Sheldon
1832 Jason White
1833 Luinis Aracena
1834 David Cromer
1835 David Francisco
1836 Gary Hust
1837 Brian Lesher
1838 Gary Jones
1839 Gil Patterson
1840 Checklist

1993 Fleer/ProCards Martinsville Phillies

	MT	NR MT	EX
Complete Set:	5.00		

3463 Scott Barstad
3464 Mark Foster
3465 Todd Genke
3466 Bo Hamilton
3467 Trevor Humphry
3468 Rich Hunter
3469 Bryan Lundberg
3470 Fernando Mejias
3471 Brian O'Connor
3472 Chris Phipps
3473 Jackie Rife
3474 Lance Sanders
3475 Andy Szarko
3476 Robert Estalella
3477 Barry Fitzgerald
3478 Shane Hobbs
3479 Mike Shipman
3480 Dell Allen
3481 Manny Amador
3482 Tim Cornish
3483 Tom McGlawn
3484 Danton Pierre-Louis
3485 Nate Rodriquez
3486 Bryan Wiegandt
3487 Brian Costello
3488 Linardo Diaz

3489 Jeff Key
3490 Derek Stingley
3491 Charles Tinsley
3492 Josh Watts
3493 Checklist

1993 Fleer/ProCards Medicine Hat Blue Jays

	MT	NR MT	EX
Complete Set:	6.00		

3729 Rob Adkins
3730 Brian Grant
3731 Scott Kennedy
3732 Jeff Leystra
3733 Rob Patterson
3734 Scott Jeffery
3735 Mark Sievert
3736 Steve Sinclair
3737 Kielan Smith
3738 Joe Vogelgesang
3739 Hector Martinez
3740 David Morgan
3741 Pete Polis
3742 Carlos Colmenares
3743 Willy Daunic
3744 Freddy Garcia
3745 Ryan Jones
3746 Jeff Patzke
3747 Eddy Vasquez
3748 Ben Candelaria
3749 Lorenzo De La Cruz
3750 Angel Ramirez
3751 Anthony Sanders
3752 Omar Malave
3753 Hal Dyer
3754 Scott Miller
3755 Checklist

1993 SportPro Medicine Hat Blue Jays

	MT	NR MT	EX
Complete Set:	8.00		

1 Carlos Colmenares
2 Steve Sinclair
3 Angel Ramirez
4 Hector Martinez
5 Brian Grant
6 Scott Kennedy
7 Willie Daunic
8 Eddy Vasquez
9 Mike Toney
10 Joe Vogelsgang
11 Rob Adkins
12 Jeff Patzke
13 Ben Candelaria
14 Freddy Garcia
15 Mark Sievert
16 Anthony Sanders
17 Scott Jeffrey
18 Jeff Leystra
19 David Morgan
20 Lorenzo de la Cruz
21 Rob Patterson
22 Mike Wirsta
23 Omar Malave
24 Hal Dyer
25 Scott Miller

1993 Fleer/ProCards Memphis Chicks

	MT	NR MT	EX
Complete Set:	5.00		

369 Brian Givens
370 Matt Karchner
371 Chris Limbach
372 Danny Miceli
373 Vladimir Perez
374 Doug Piatt
375 Eddie Pierce
376 Alex Sanchez
377 Jose Ventura
378 Carlos Diaz
379 Lance Jennings
380 Jeff Garber
381 Mike Guerrero
382 Domingo Mota
383 Joe Randa
384 Joe Vitiello
385 Adam Casillas
386 Butch Cole
387 Scott Jaster
388 Mark Johnson
389 Lee May, Jr.
390 Les Norman
391 Tom Poquette
392 Mike Mason
393 Checklist

1993 Fleer/ProCards Midland Angels

	MT	NR MT	EX
Complete Set:	6.00		

314 Erik Bennett
315 Ken Edenfield
316 John Fritz
317 Bobby Gamez
318 Chance Gledhill
319 Julian Heredia
320 David Holdridge
321 Jose Musset
322 Derek Stroud
323 Shad Williams
324 Jorge Fabregas
325 Fausto Tejero
326 Mark Brakebill
327 Kevin Davis
328 P.J. Forbes
329 Brian Grebeck
330 Chris Pritchett
331 Emmitt Cohick
332 John Jackson
333 Orlando Palmeiro
334 Luis Raven
335 Dan Rumsey
336 Mark Wasinger
337 Don Long
338 Nate Oliver
339 Kernan Ronan
340 Checklist

1993 Fleer/ProCards Midwest League

	MT	NR MT	EX
Complete Set:	12.00		

1 Tim Davis
2 Eddy Diaz
3 Danny Perez
4 Scott Talanoa
5 Anthony Byrd
6 Gus Gandarillas
7 Ken Tirpack
8 Charles Johnson
9 Reynol Mendoza
10 Chris Sheff
11 Mark Acre
12 David Francisco
13 Gary Haught
14 Troy Penis
15 Soctt Sheldon
16 Don Wengert
17 Mel Bunch
18 Steve Sisco
19 Rodney Myers
20 Essex Burton
21 Michael Call
22 Troy Fryman
23 Sean Johnston
24 Robert Machado
25 Byron Mathews
26 Jason Pierson
27 Craig Wilson
28 Steve Worrell
29 Jolbert Cabrera
30 Chris Hmielewski
31 Javier Pages
32 Ugueth Urbina
33 Alberto Reyes
34 Tony Chavez
35 Larry Hingle
36 Chris Smith
37 Michael Wolff
38 Chad Fonville
39 Aaron Fultz
40 Marcus Jensen
41 Jim Rosenbohm
42 Amaury Telemaco
43 Hector Trinidad
44 Pedro Valdez
45 Jeff Ball
46 Tim Evans
47 Chris Holt
48 Joe Biasucci
49 Andy Bruce
50 Kirk Bullinger
51 Keith Johns
52 T.J. Mathews
53 Basil Shabazz
54 Dennis Slininger
55 Homer Bush
56 Checklist

1993 Classic Best Modesto A's

	MT	NR MT	EX
Complete Set:	6.00		

1 Benji Grigsby
2 Jeff Barns
3 Garrett Beard
4 Russell Brock
5 Bobby Chouinard
6 Craig Connolly
7 Fausto Cruz
8 Lauro Felix
9 Ramon Fermin
10 Terance Frazier
11 Jason Giambi
12 Todd Ingram
13 Izzy Molina
14 Tom Myers
15 Rick Norton
16 Allen Plaster
17 Michael Rossiter
18 Scott Shockey
19 Mark Sobolewski
20 Ricky Strebeck
21 Craig Sudbury
22 Dane Walker
23 Steven Wojciechowski
24 Joel Wolfe
25 Ernie Young
26 Ted Kubiak
27 Pete Richert
28 Ric Moreno

1993 Fleer/ProCards Modesto A's

	MT	NR MT	EX
Complete Set:	6.00		

790 Russell Brock
791 Bobby Chouinard
792 Craig Connolly
793 Ramon Fermin
794 Benji Grigsby
795 Todd Ingram
796 Thomas Myers
797 Allen Plaster
798 Michael Rossiter
799 Ricky Stebeck
800 Craig Sudbury
801 Steve Wojciechowski
802 Izzy Molina
803 Rick Norton
804 Jeff Barns
805 Garrett Beard
806 Fausto Cruz
807 Lauro Felix
808 Jason Giambi
809 Scott Shockey
810 Mark Sobolewski
811 Terance Frazier
812 Dane Walker
813 Joel Wolfe
814 Ernie Young
815 Ted Kubiak
816 Pete Richert
817 Checklist

1993 Fleer/ProCards Nashville Sounds

	MT	NR MT	EX
Complete Set:	8.00		
Complete Set:			

563 Jason Bere
564 Jeff Carter
565 Fred Dabney
566 Brian Drahman
567 Ramon Garcia
568 Chris Howard
569 Barry Jones
570 Brian Keyser
571 Larry Thomas
572 Rick Wrona, Esteban Beltre
574 Scott Cepicky
575 Chris Cron
576 Drew Denson
577 Shawn Gilbert
578 Norberto Martin
579 Joe Hall
580 Shawn Jeter
581 Brad Komminsk
582 Scott Tedder
583 Rick Renick
584 Mark Haley
585 Roger LaFrancois
586 Rick Peterson
587 Checklist

1993 Fleer/ProCards Nashville Xpress

	MT	NR MT	EX
Complete Set:	6.00		

394 Jayson Best
395 Eddie Guardado
396 Jason Klonoski
397 Dom Konieczki
398 Jeff Mansur
399 Bob McCreary
400 Mike Misuraca
401 Oscar Munoz
402 Alan Newman
403 Todd Ritchie
404 Bill Wissler
405 Mike Durant
406 Pedro Grifol
407 Steve Dunn
408 Tom Houk
409 Dan Masteller
410 Brian Raabe
411 David Rivera
412 Scott Stahoviak
413 Rich Becker
414 Marty Cordova
415 Rex DeLaNuez
416 Mike McDonald
417 Phil Roof
418 Rick Anderson
419 Mark Funderburk
420 Checklist

1993 Fleer/ProCards New Britain Red Sox

	MT	NR MT	EX
Complete Set:	7.50		

1212 Bernhard Dzafic
1213 Tom Fischer
1214 Peter Hoy
1215 Steve Mintz
1216 Gary Painter
1217 Ed Riley
1218 Frank Rodriguez
1219 John Shea
1220 Tim Smith
1221 Kevin Uhrhan
1222 Tim Vanegmond
1223 Brian Young
1224 Kevin Carroll
1225 Scott Hatteberg
1226 Scott Bethea
1227 Jim Crowley
1228 Collin Dixon
1229 Bill Norris
1230 Tony Rodriguez
1231 Les Wallin
1232 Mike Beams
1233 Boo Moore
1234 Jim Morrison
1235 Paul Rappoli
1236 Paul Thoutsis
1237 Jim Pankovits
1238 Dennis Burtt
1239 Checklist

1993 Fleer/ProCards New Orleans Zephyrs

	MT	NR MT	EX
Complete Set:	6.00		

964 Mike Farrell
965 Jim Hunter
966 Mike Ignasiak
967 Garland Kiser
968 Matt Maysey
969 Jamie McAndrew
970 Eric Nolte
971 Rafael Novoa
972 Steve Sparks
973 Jeff Tabaka
974 Rob Wishnevski
975 Mike Fitzgerald
976 Tom Lampkin
977 John Byington
978 Edgar Caceres
979 John Finn
980 Larry Sheets
981 Jose Valentin
982 Eddie Williams
983 Tony Piggs
984 Matt Mieske
985 Troy O'Leary
986 Chris Bando
987 Bill Campbell
988 Ron Jackson
989 Checklist

1993 Fleer/ProCards Niagara Falls Rapids

	MT	NR MT	EX
Complete Set:	5.00		

3377 Sam Arguto
3378 Eddie Gaillard
3379 Gary Goldsmith
3380 Rod Jackson
3381 Paul Magrini
3382 Toby McFarland
3383 Brian Moehler
3384 Joshua Neese
3385 Corey Reincke
3386 Mike Richardson
3387 David Rodriguez
3388 John Rosengren
3389 Mike Salazar
3390 Henry Santos
3391 Gabe Sollecito
3392 Corey Broome
3393 Del Marine
3394 Ken Marrero
3395 Shawn Brown
3396 Malvin DeJesus
3397 Duane Kinnon
3398 Kirk Ordway
3399 Jorge Velandia
3400 Glen Barker
3401 Eric Danapilis
3402 Robert Dickerson
3403 Tyrone Dixon
3404 Jorge Moreno
3405 Mike Wiseley
3406 Larry Parrish
3407 Checklist

1993 Fleer/ProCards Norfolk Tides

Complete Set: 6.00

2562 Tom Filer
2563 Paul Gibson
2564 Mauro Gozzo
2565 Eric Hillman
2566 Bobby Jones
2567 Gregg Langbehn
2568 Dale Plummer
2569 Dave Telgheder
2570 Brandy Vann
2571 Tom Wegmann
2572 Dann Bilardello
2573 Brook Fordyce
2574 Kevin Baez
2575 Joe Delli Carri
2576 Tito Navarro
2577 Doug Saunders
2578 Steve Springer
2579 Mike Twardoski
2580 Eric Bullock
2581 Jeromy Burnitz
2582 Tim Howard
2583 Bert Hunter
2584 Ryan Thompson
2585 Clint Hurdle
2586 Bob Apodaca
2587 Marlin McPhail
2588 Checklist

1993 Fleer/ProCards Oklahoma City 89ers

MT NR MT EX
Complete Set: 5.00

1617 Allan Anderson
1618 Jeff Bronkey
1619 Rob Brown
1620 Terry Burrows
1621 Steve Fireovid
1622 Mark Lee
1623 Danny Leon
1624 Francisco Oliveras
1625 Roger Pavlik
1626 Mike Schooler
1627 Cedric Shaw
1628 Doug Davis
1629 Ray Stephens
1630 Steve Balboni
1631 Mario Diez
1632 Larry Hanlon
1633 Keith Miller
1634 Luke Sable
1635 Jon Shave
1636 Benny Distefano
1637 Donald Harris
1638 Dan Peltier
1639 Bobby Jones
1640 Mike Berger
1641 Rick Knapp
1642 Checklist

1993 Fleer/ProCards Omaha Royals

MT NR MT EX
Complete Set: 5.00

1671 Brian Ahern
1672 Keith Brown
1673 Enrique Burgos
1674 Jim Campbell
1675 Dera Clark
1676 Chris Haney
1677 Mike Magnante
1678 Rick Reed
1679 Bill Sampen
1680 Steve Shifflett
1681 Mike Knapp
1682 Nelson Santovenia
1683 Kiki Diaz
1684 Bob Hamelin
1685 Russ McGinnis
1686 Jose Mota
1687 Rico Rossy
1688 Terry Shumpert
1689 Shawn Abner
1690 Mike Kingery
1691 Kevin Koslofski
1692 Kevin Long
1693 Kiki Diaz
1694 Karl Rhodes
1695 Dan Rohrmeier
1696 Jeff Cox
1697 Mike Alvarez
1698 Rich Dauer
1699 Checklist

1993 Fleer/ProCards Oneonta Yankees

MT NR MT EX
Complete Set: 6.00

3494 Shawn Alazaus
3495 Chris Cumberland
3496 Al Drumheller
3497 Keith Heberling
3498 Blaise Kozeniewski
3499 Frank Lankford
3500 Jim Musselwhite
3501 Greg Resz
3502 Scott Standish
3503 Jim Thomforde
3504 Joe Wharton
3505 Clint Whitworth
3506 Jaime Torres
3507 Steve Aldridge
3508 Kurt Bierek
3509 Elston Hansen
3510 Rich Josepher
3511 Brian McLamb
3512 Silverio Navas
3513 David Renteria
3514 Mike Schmitz
3515 Abdiel Cumberbatch
3516 Ricky Ledee
3517 Brian Lewis
3518 Ruben Rivera
3519 Ernie Yaroshuk
3520 Ken Dominguez
3521 Steve Chandler
3522 Juan Nieves
3523 Bill Schmidt
3524 Checklist

1993 Fleer/ProCards Orlando Cubs

MT NR MT EX
Complete Set: 6.50

2152 Checklist
2778 Tim Delgado
2779 Chris Johnson
2780 Earnie Johnson
2781 Bill Melvin
2782 John Salles
2783 Dave Stevens
2784 Aaron Taylor
2785 Jimmy Williams
2786 Travis Willis
2787 Brad Erdman
2788 Jack Johnson
2789 Jim Robinson
2790 Chris Ebright
2791 Matt Franco
2792 Mike Grace
2793 Jose Hernandez
2794 Greg Lonigro
2795 Darryl Vice
2796 Phil Dauphin
2797 Richie Grayum
2798 John Jensen
2799 Corey Kapano
2800 Ozzie Timmons
2801 Tommy Jones
2802 Rick Kranitz

1993 Classic Best Osceola Astros

MT NR MT EX
Complete Set: 6.00

1 Buck McNabb
2 Bob Abreu
3 Tom Anderson
4 Perry Berry
5 Duane Brown
6 Mike Burns
7 Raul Chavez
8 Dennis Colon
9 Ruben Cruz
10 Jose Flores
11 Kevin Gallaher
12 Kyle Guerry
13 Al Harley
14 Brian Holliday
15 Kevin Lane
16 Doug Mlicki
17 Roy Nieto
18 Steve Powers
19 Rich Schulte
20 Kevin Scott
21 Joe Sewell
22 Kenny Wheeler
23 Chris White
24 Jimmy White
25 Todd Winston
26 Tim Tolman
27 Bob Robertson
28 Jack Billingham
29 Mike Freer

1993 Fleer/ProCards Osceola Astros

MT NR MT EX
Complete Set: 6.00

618 Tom Anderson
619 Duane Brown
620 Kevin Gallaher
621 Kyle Guerry
622 Brian Holliday
623 Kevin Lane
624 Doug Micki
625 Roy Nieto
626 Steve Powers
627 Joe Sewll
628 Kenny Wheeler
629 Chris White
630 Mike Burns
631 Raul Chavez
632 Kevin Scott
633 Perry Berry
634 Dennis Colon
635 Ruben Cruz
636 Jose Flores
637 Al Harley
638 Bob Abreu
639 Buck McNabb
640 Rich Schulte
641 Jimmy White
642 Todd Winston
643 Tim Tolman
644 Jack Billingham
645 Bob Robertson
646 Checklist

1993 Fleer/ProCards Ottawa Lynx

MT NR MT EX
Complete Set: 6.50

2428 Tavo Alvarez
2429 Tim Fortugno
2430 Gil Heredia
2431 Jonathan Hurst
2432 Mike Mathile
2433 Len Picota
2434 Bill Risley
2435 Doug Simons
2436 Sergio Valdez
2437 Pete Young
2438 Gary Hymel
2439 Joe Siddall
2440 Tim Barker
2441 Vince Castaldo
2442 Todd Haney
2443 Charlie Montoyo
2444 Hector Vargas
2445 Terrel Hansen
2446 Rick Hirtensteiner
2447 F.P. Santangelo
2448 Matt Stairs
2449 Mike Quade
2450 Checklist

1993 Classic Best Palm Springs Angels

MT NR MT EX
Complete Set: 6.00

1 Marquis Riley
2 Chris Anderson
3 Tyrone A. Boykin
4 Tim Burcham
5 Michael Butler
6 Todd Claus
7 Mark Dalesandro
8 Tommy Dodge
9 Gary Hagy
10 Pete Janicki
11 Dominick Johnson
12 Korey Keling
13 Dennis McCaffery
14 Keith Morrison
15 Orlando Munoz
16 Beban Perez
17 John Pricher
18 Mark Ratekin
19 Dallas Rinehart
20 Jay Simpson
21 Joel Smith
22 Jose Stela
23 Mark Sweeney
24 Joseph Urso
25 Pat Warnig
26 Mario Mendoza
27 Gene Richards
28 Howie Gershberg
29 Mike Twomey
30 Stadium

1993 Fleer/ProCards Palm Springs Angels

MT NR MT EX
Complete Set: 6.00

61 Tim Burcham
62 Mike Butler
63 Dominick Johnson
64 Korey Keling
65 Keith Morrison
66 Beban Perez
67 John Pricher
68 Mark Ratekin
69 Dallas Rinehart
70 Jose Trujillo
71 Pat Wernig
72 Mark Dalesandro
73 Jose Stela
74 Chris Anderson
75 Todd Claus
76 Tommy Dodge
77 Gary Hagy
78 Orlando Munoz
79 Joel Smith
80 Joe Urso
81 Tyrone Boykin
82 Dennis McCaffery
83 Marquis Riley
84 Jay Simpson
85 Mark Sweeney
86 Mario Mendoza
87 Howie Gershberg
88 Gene Richards
89 Checklist

1993 Fleer/ProCards Pawtucket Red Sox

MT NR MT EX
Complete Set: 9.00

2399 Cory Bailey
2400 Joe Caruso
2401 Joe Ciccarella
2402 Brian Conroy
2403 Gar Finnvold
2404 Don Florence
2405 Derek Livernois
2406 Jose Melendez
2407 Nate Minchey
2408 Aaron Selse
2409 Scott Taylor
2410 John Flaherty
2411 Ruben Rodriguez
2412 Jim Byrd
2413 Cheo Garcia
2414 John Malzone
2415 Dave Milstein
2416 Luis Ortiz
2417 Jeff Richardson
2418 Greg Sparks
2419 Greg Blosser
2420 Steve Lyons
2421 Jeff McNeely
2422 Sean Ross
2423 Herm Winningham
2424 Buddy Bailey
2425 Luis Aguayo
2426 Rick Wise
2427 Checklist

1993 Classic Best Peoria Chiefs

MT NR MT EX
Complete Set: 6.00

1 Pedro Valdez
2 Bill Bliss
3 London Bradley
4 Chuck Daniel
5 John Deutsch
6 Daryle Gavlick
7 Jay Hassel
8 Robin Jennings
9 Jack Johnson
10 Collin Kerley
11 Anthony Lee
12 Dan Madsen
13 Ricardo Medina
14 Emilio Mendez
15 Geno Morones
16 Richard perez
17 Chris Rodriguez
18 Adam Schulhofer
19 Raphael Soto
20 Tim Stutheit
21 Amaury Telemaco
22 Hector Trinidad
23 Steve Walker
24 Vincent Zarate
25 Scott Krusinski
26 Jim O'Reilly
27 Ralph Rashid

1993 Fleer/ProCards Peoria Chiefs

MT NR MT EX
Complete Set: 5.00

1075 Bill Bliss
1076 Chuck Daniel
1077 Scott Gardner
1078 Daryle Gavlick
1079 Jay Hassel
1080 Collin Kerley
1081 Anthony Lee
1082 Geno Morones
1083 Chris Rodriguez
1084 Adam Schulhofer
1085 Amaury Telemaco
1086 Hector Trinidad
1087 Brad Erdman
1088 Jack Johnson
1089 London Bradley
1090 John Deutsch
1091 Ricardo Medina
1092 Emilio Mendez
1093 Richard Perez
1094 Raphael Soto
1095 Robin Jennings
1096 Dan Madsen
1097 Pedro Valdez
1098 Steve Walker
1099 Vince Zarate
1100 Steve Roadcap
1101 Checklist

1993 Fleer/ProCards Phoenix Firebirds

	MT	NR MT	EX
Complete Set:	7.50		

1507 Terry Bross
1508 Kevin Brown
1509 Dan Carlson
1510 Larry Carter
1511 Brian Fisher
1512 Tim Layana
1513 Kevin McGehee
1514 Jim Myers
1515 Dan Rambo
1516 Rob Taylor
1517 Andy Allanson
1518 Jim McNamara
1519 Clay Bellinger
1520 Joel Chilmelis
1521 Adell Davenport
1522 Paul Faries
1523 Erik Johnson
1524 J.R. Phillips
1525 Mickey Brantley
1526 Rikkert Faneyte
1527 Steve Hosey
1528 Rob Katzaroff
1529 Andy Mota
1530 Reed Peters
1531 Reuben Smiley
1532 Carlos Alfonso
1533 Duane Espy
1534 Joel Horlen
1535 Checklist

1993 Fleer/ProCards Pittsfield Mets

	MT	NR MT	EX
Complete Set:	5.00		

3699 Jeff Cosman
3700 Tom Engle
3701 Steve Grennan
3702 Jason Isringhausen
3703 Scott Jones
3704 Sean Kenny
3705 Eric Ludwick
3706 Allan McDill
3707 Brandon Newell
3708 Travis Shaffer
3709 David Swanson
3710 Jeff Tam
3711 Mike Welch
3712 Terry Childers
3713 Kevin Lewis
3714 David Maize
3715 Josh Haggas
3716 Eric Harris
3717 Rafael Hernandez
3718 Paul Petrulis
3719 Tad Smith
3720 Charlie Sullivan
3721 David Zuniga
3722 Benny Agbayani
3723 Gary Collum
3724 Rodney Mazion
3725 Matt Terrell
3726 Howie Freiling
3727 Jeff Edwards
3728 Checklist

1993 Fleer/ProCards Pocatello Posse

	MT	NR MT	EX
Complete Set:	5.00		

3843 Checklist
4199 Jason Atwood
4200 Louis Birdt
4201 Eugene Caruso
4202 Steve Dempsey
4203 Rafael Diaz
4204 Mark Graham
4205 Cory Lidle
4206 Nick Lymberopoulos
4207 Steve May
4208 Tim Ploeger
4209 Jeff Post
4210 Chris Hunts
4211 Todd Takayoshi
4212 Jeff Boyle
4213 Pedro Caranza
4214 Will Fitzpatrick
4215 Orlando Garcia
4216 D.J. Harris
4217 J.P. Postiff
4218 Julian Salazar
4219 Alonso Mendoza
4220 Jason Pollock
4221 Derek Vaughn
4222 Ernie Rodriguez

1993 SportPro Pocatello Posse

	MT	NR MT	EX
Complete Set:	8.00		

1 Jeff Boyle
2 Alonso Mendoza
3 Gene Caruso
4 Steve Dempsey
5 Rafael Diaz
6 Mark Graham
7 J.P. Postiff
8 Will Fitzpatrick
9 Chris Hunt
10 Cory Lidle
11 Nick Lymberopoulos
12 Orlando Garcia
13 Jason Pollock
14 Ron Matthews
15 Todd Takayoshi
16 Steve May
17 Tim Ploeger
18 Darren Greenlee
19 D.J. Harris
20 Derek Vaughn
21 Jeff Post
22 Julian Salazar
23 Lou Birdt
24 Ernie Rodriguez
25 Adam Sanchez
26 Dan Overman

1993 Fleer/ProCards Portland Beavers

	MT	NR MT	EX
Complete Set:	6.00		

2378 Tom Drees
2379 Rich Garces
2380 Jon Henry
2381 Dave LaPoint
2382 Jim Neidlinger
2383 Carlos Pulido
2384 Mark Sims
2385 Matt Stevens
2386 Derek Parks
2387 Chip Hale
2388 David McCarty
2389 Pat Meares
2390 Paul Russo
2391 Jerry Schunk
2392 Bernardo Brito
2393 Pat Howell
2394 Derek Lee
2395 Ray Ortiz
2396 Scott Ullger
2397 Gorman Heimueller
2398 Checklist

1993 Fleer/ProCards Princeton Reds

	MT	NR MT	EX
Complete Set:	5.00		

4168 Jason Chandler
4169 Roger Etheridge
4170 Luis Fernandez
4171 Joel Franklin
4172 Joe Fuccillo
4173 Danny Hagan
4174 Brad Keenan
4175 Armando Morales
4176 Sam Mullins
4177 Jeff Murphy
4178 Jason Robbins
4179 Trey Rutledge
4180 Jason Sullivan
4181 Randy DeBruhl
4182 Rob Domino
4183 Brian Silvia
4184 Jhonny Carvajal
4185 Yamil Concepcion
4186 Argenis LaBarca
4187 James Lofton
4188 Luis Ordaz
4189 Jeff Ramey
4190 Maximo White
4191 Donald Broach
4192 Cobi Cradle
4193 Jon Dold
4194 Darran Hall
4195 Jackie McCroskey
4196 Sam Osorio
4197 Rod Sanders
4198 Checklist

1993 Classic Best Prince William Cannons

	MT	NR MT	EX
Complete Set:	6.00		

1 Tate Seerfield
2 Roger Burnett
3 Tommy Carter
4 Jovino Carvajal
5 Andy Croghan
6 Bob Deller
7 Matt Dunbar
8 Greg Erickson
9 Tim Flannelly
10 Carlton Fleming
11 Ron Frazier
12 Keith Garagozzo
13 Scott Gully
14 Lew Hill IV
15 Mark Hubbard
16 Eric Knowels
17 Jeff Motuzas
18 Steve Munda
19 Andy Pettitte
20 Jorge Posada
21 Curtis Ralph
22 Keith Seller
23 Grant Sullivan
24 Sean Twitty
25 Jim Wiley
26 Trey Hillman
27 Rich Arena
28 Brian Milner
29 Mark Shiflett
30 Tom Raynor

1993 Fleer/ProCards Prince William Cannons

	MT	NR MT	EX
Complete Set:	6.50		

647 Tom Carter
648 Andy Croghan
649 Matt Dunbar
650 Ron Frazier
651 Keith Garagozzo
652 Scott Gully
653 Steve Munda
654 Curtis Ralph
655 Keith Seiler
656 Grant Sullivan
657 Jim Wiley
658 Scott Epps
659 Jeff Motuzas
660 Jorge Posada
661 Roger Burnett
662 Greg Erickson
663 Tim Flannelly
664 Carlton Fleming
665 Eric Knowles
666 Tate Seefried
667 Jovino Carvajal
668 Bob Deller
669 Lew Hill
670 Mark Hubbard
671 Sean Twitty
672 Trey Hillman
673 Rich Arena
674 Brian Milner
675 Mark Shiflett
676 Checklist

1993 Classic Best Quad City River Bandits

	MT	NR MT	EX
Complete Set:	6.00		

1 Chris Holt
2 Jeff Ball
3 Craig Bjornson
4 Henri Centeno
5 Dwayne Dawson
6 Chris Durkin
7 Jamie Evans
8 Tim Evans
9 Jimmy Gonzalez
10 Anthony Gutierrez
11 Marlo Linares
12 Mark Loughlin
13 Brian McGlone
14 Pat Murphy
15 Ed Ponte
16 Eddy Ramos
17 Rob Rees
18 Jeff Rhein
19 Vince Roman
20 Heath Rose
21 Chuck Smith
22 Damian Torino
23 Jamie Walker
24 Bryant Winslow
25 Steve Dillard
26 Cesar Cedeno
27 Gary Lucas

1993 Fleer/ProCards Quad City River Bandits

	MT	NR MT	EX
Complete Set:	6.50		

90 Craig Bjornson
91 Dwayne Dawson
92 Jamie Evans
93 Anthony Gutierrez
94 Chris Holt
95 Mark Loughlin
96 Jim McCutchen
97 Pat Murphy
98 Ed Ponte
99 Rob Rees
100 Chuck Smith
101 Jamie Walker
102 Jimmy Gonzalez
103 Mario Linares
104 Damian Torino
105 Jeff Ball
106 Ron Cancini
107 Henri Centeno
108 Brian McGlone
109 Eddy Ramos
110 Bryant Winslow
111 Chris Durkin
112 Tim Evans
113 Jeff Rhein
114 Vince Roman
115 Steve Dillard
116 Cesar Cedeno
117 Gary Lucas
118 Checklist

1993 Classic Best Rancho Cucamonga Quakes

	MT	NR MT	EX
Complete Set:	6.00		

1 Julio Bruno
2 Jared Baker
3 Robbie Beckett
4 Brent Bish
5 Scott Bream
6 Jeff Brown
7 Cam Cairncross
8 Clint Champion
9 Sean Drinkwater
10 Anito Encarnacion
11 Luis Galindez
12 Brad Gennero
13 Ken Grzelaczyk
14 Joey Hamilton
15 Jason Hardtke
16 Lee Henderson
17 Jeff Huber
18 Cole Hyson
19 Jason Kerr
20 Tom Martin
21 Sean Mulligan
22 Tom Paskievitch
23 Jeffrey Pearce
24 Scott Pugh
25 Bill Robbs
26 Ira Smith
27 Keith Champion
28 Bruce Tanner
29 Jim Daniel
30 Stadium

1993 Fleer/ProCards Rancho Cucamonga Quakes

	MT	NR MT	EX
Complete Set:	6.00		

818 Jared Baker
819 Robbie Beckett
820 Jeff Brown
821 Cam Cairncross
822 Clint Compton
823 Ron Dale
824 Luis Galindez
825 Ken Grzelaczyk
826 Joey Hamilton
827 Steve Hoeme
828 Jeff Huber
829 Cole Hyson
830 Jason Kerr
831 Tom Martin
832 Tom Paskievitch
833 Andy Rush
834 Anito Encarnacion
835 Lee Henderson
836 Sean Mulligan
837 Brent Bish
838 Julio Bruno
839 Sean Drinkwater
840 Jason Hardtke
841 Scott Pugh
842 Scott Bream
843 Brad Gennaro
844 Jeff Pearce
845 Bill Robbs
846 Ira Smith
847 Keith Champion
848 Bruce Tanner
849 Checklist

1993 Fleer/ProCards Reading Phillies

	MT	NR MT	EX
Complete Set:	6.00		

288 Ron Allen
289 Toby Borland
290 Mike Farmer
291 Robert Gaddy
292 Darrell Goedhart

293 Todd Goergen
294 Eric Hill
295 Mike Sullivan
296 Scott Wiegandt
297 Jose Fernandez
298 Ed Rosado
299 Carlo Colombino
300 John Escobar
301 Keith Kimberlin
302 Mica Lewis
303 Ron Lockett
304 Gene Schall
305 Steve Bieser
306 Pat Brady
307 Mickey Hyde
308 Jeff Jackson
309 Sam Taylor
310 Don McCormack
311 Carlos Arroyo
312 Kelly Heath
313 Checklist

1993 Bleacher Burns Richmond Braves

	MT	NR MT	EX
Complete Set:	16.00		

1 Ryan Klesko
2 Ramon Caraballo
3 Keith Mitchell
4 Napoleon Robinson
5 Melvin Nieves
6 Mike Mordecal
7 Mike Hostetler
8 Mike Kelly
9 Ron Jones
10 Brian Bark
11 Pedro Borbon
12 Tony Tarasco
13 Chipper Jones
14 Shawn Holman
15 Javy Lopez
16 Jose Oliva
17 Barry Jones
18 Donnie Elliott
19 Jerry Willard
20 Mark Wohlers
21 Mike Birkbeck
22 Judd Johnson
23 Bill Taylor
24 Boi Rodriguez
25 Grady Little

1993 Fleer/ProCards Richmond Braves

	MT	NR MT	EX
Complete Set:	8.00		

176 Brian Bark
177 Mike Birkbeck
178 Pedro Borbon
179 Donnie Elliott
180 Shawn Holman
181 Mike Hostetler
182 Judd Johnson
183 Napoleon Robinson
184 Randy St. Claire
185 Bill Taylor
186 Mark Wohlers
187 Javy Lopez
188 Jerry Willard
189 Ramon Caraballo
190 Chipper Jones
191 Ryan Klesko
192 Mike Mordecai
193 Jose Oliva
194 Boi Rodriguez
195 Barry Jones
196 Ron Jones
197 Mike Kelly
198 Keith Mitchell
199 Melvin Nieves
200 Tony Tarasco
201 Grady Little
202 Bruce Dal Canton
203 Glenn Hubbard
204 Jim Snyder
205 Checklist

1993 Benjamin Moore Ricmond Camera Richmond Braves

	MT	NR MT	EX
Complete Set:	30.00		

1 Mike Mordecal
2 Ramon Caraballo
3 Napoleon Robinson
4 Boi Rodriguez
5 Mark Wohlers
6 Mike Birkbeck
7 Jose Oliva
8 Pedro Borbon
9 Shawn Holman
10 Javy Lopez
11 Donnie Elliott
12 Brian Bark
13 Mike Hostetler
14 Mike Kelly
15 Chipper Jones
16 Melvin Nieves
17 Ryan Klesko
18 Keith Mitchell
19 Tony Tarasco
20 Bill Taylor
21 Mike Loynd
22 Judd Johnson
23 Ron Jones
24 Don Strange
25 Grady Little

1993 Pepsi Virginians Richmond Braves

	MT	NR MT	EX
Complete Set:	30.00		

1 Ryan Klesko
2 Javy Lopez
3 Brian Bark
4 Mike Mordecal
5 Pedro Borbon
6 Chipper Jones
7 Jose Oliva
8 Donnie Elliott
9 Mike Birkbeck
10 Don Strange
11 Tony Tarasco
12 Ramon Carabello
13 Mike Loynd
14 Ron Jones
15 Napoleon Robinson
16 Mike Kelly
17 Bill Taylor
18 Keith Mitchell
19 Dennis Burlingame
20 Boi Rodriguez
21 Melvin Nieves
22 Jerry Willard
23 Shawn Holman
24 Judd Johnson
25 Grady Little

1993 Richmond Comix Richmond Braves

	MT	NR MT	EX
Complete Set:	30.00		

1 Grady Little
2 Bruce Dal Canton
3 Glenn Hubbard
4 Jim Snyder
5 Brian Bark
6 Mike Birkbeck
7 Pedro Borbon
8 Ramon Caraballo
9 Donnie Elliott
10 Shawn Hofman
11 Mike Hostetler
12 Judd Johnson
13 Barry Jones
14 Chipper Jones
15 Ron Jones
16 Mike Kelly
17 Ryan Klesko
18 Javy Lopez
19 Jim Lovell
20 Keith Mitchell
21 Mike Mordecal
22 Melvin Nieves
23 Jose Oliva
24 Napoleon Robinson
25 Boi Rodriguez
26 Tony Tarasco
27 Bill Taylor
28 Jerry Willard
29 Mark Wohlers
30 Frank & Jessica Miller

1993 Cal League Riverside Pilots

	MT	NR MT	EX
Complete Set:	9.00		

1 Ron Villone
2 Derek Lowe
3 David Adam
4 James Bonnici
5 Jeff Borski
6 Craig Clayton
7 Tim Furtado
8 Jim Gutierrez
9 Kevin King
10 Tow Maynard
11 Fred McNair
12 Jim Mecir
13 Tony Phillips
14 Arquimedez Pozo
15 Sean Rees
16 Tommy Robertson
17 Raul Rodarte
18 Andy Sheets
19 Greg Shockey
20 Dan Sullivan
21 Dave Waldenberger
22 Chris Widger
23 Willie Wilder
24 Chuck Wiley
25 Todd Youngblood
26 Jim Koehler
27 Craig Griffey
28 Dave Myers
29 Bryan Price
30 Manny Cervantes
31 Robert Nodine

1993 Fleer/ProCards Rochester Red Wings

	MT	NR MT	EX
Complete Set:	12.00		

232 Pat Clements
233 Mike Cook
234 Jamie Moyer
235 John O'Donoghue
236 Mike Oquist
237 Brad Pennington
238 Don Schulze
239 Steve Searcy
240 Todd Stephan
241 Anthony Telford
242 Darrin Campbell
243 Rey Palacios
244 Mark Parent
245 Manny Alexander
246 Paul Carey
247 Scott Coolbaugh
248 Bobby Dickerson
249 Tommy Hinzo
250 Mel Wearing
251 Damon Buford
252 Jeffrey Hammonds
253 Mark Leonard
254 Mark Smith
255 Jack Voigt
256 Ed Yacopino
257 Bob Miscik
258 Steve Luebber
259 Joe Altobelli
421 Checklist

1993 Classic Best Rockford Royals

	MT	NR MT	EX
Complete Set:	9.00		

1 Johnny Damon
2 Jeff Antoon
3 Michael Bovee
4 Ramy Brooks Jr.
5 Melvin Bunch Jr.
6 Rick Burley
7 Sherard Clinkscales
8 Chris Connolly
9 Michael Currier
10 Sean Delaney
11 John Dickens
12 Aaron Dolarque
13 Bart Evans
14 Jeff Haas II
15 Trenton Hauswirth
16 Ryan Long
17 Julio Montilla
18 Cesar Morillo
19 Steve Murphy
20 Roderick Myers
21 Rodney Myers
22 Andre Newhouse
23 Jim Pittsley
24 Chris Sheenan
25 Steve Sisco
26 Larry Sutton
27 John Weglarz
28 Mike Jirschele
29 Tom Burgmeier
30 Jim Thrift

1993 Fleer/ProCards Rockford Royals

	MT	NR MT	EX
Complete Set:	7.00		

704 Mike Bovee
705 Mel Bunch
706 Rick Burley
707 Sherard Clinkscales
708 Chris Connolly
709 Bryan Currier
710 John Dickens
711 Aaron Dorlarque
712 Bart Evans
713 Jeff Haas
714 Rodney Myers
715 Jim Pittsley
716 Chris Sheehen
717 John Weglarz
718 Rae Brooks
719 Sean Delaney
720 Trent Hauswirth
721 Jeff Antoon
722 Ryan Long
723 Julio Montilla
724 Cesar Morillo
725 Steve Sisco
726 Larry Sutton
727 Johnny Damon
728 Steve Murphy
729 Roderick Myers
730 Andre Newhouse
731 Mike Jirschele
732 Tom Burgmeier
733 Jim Thrift
734 Checklist

1993 Classic Best Salem Buccaneers

	MT	NR MT	EX
Complete Set:	6.00		

1 Kenneth Bonifay
2 Michael Brown II
3 Joe Calder
4 Jason Christiansen
5 Jeff Conger
6 Mariano de Los Santos
7 David Doorneweerd
8 Angelo Encardnacion
9 Sean Evans
10 Jon Farrell
11 Don Garvey
12 Marcus Hanel
13 Dennis Konuszewski
14 Esteban Loaiza
15 Jim Martin
16 Tim Marx
17 Jeff McCurry
18 Marty Neff
19 Trace Ragland
20 Matt Ruebel
21 Kevin Rychel
22 Chance Sanford
23 Michael Teich
24 Gary Wilson
25 Tony Womack
26 Scott Little
27 Dave Rajsich
28 Bill Zick
29 Sam Lazzaro
30 Stu Paul

1993 Fleer/ProCards Salem Buccaneers

	MT	NR MT	EX
Complete Set:	5.00		

422 Jason Christiansen
423 Mariano DeLosSantos
424 Dave Doorneweerd
425 Sean Evans
426 Dennis Konuszewski
427 Esteban Loaiza
428 Jim Martin
429 Jeff McCurry
430 Matt Tuebel
431 Kevin Rychel
432 Michael Teich
433 Gary Wilson
434 Angelo Encarnacion
435 Marcus Hanel
436 Tim Marx
437 Ken Bonifay
438 Mike Brown
439 Joe Calder
440 Don Garvey
441 Rich Juday
442 Chance Sanford
443 Tony Womack
444 Jeff Conger
445 Jon Farrell
446 Marty Neff
447 Trace Ragland
448 Scott Little
449 Dave Rajsich
450 Checklist

1993 Fleer/ProCards St. Catharines Blue Jays

	MT	NR MT	EX
Complete Set:	5.00		

3965 Tim Adkins
3966 Alonso Beltran
3967 Chad Brown
3968 Jeff Cheek
3969 Edwin Hurtado
3970 Jay Maldonado
3971 Doug Meiners
3972 Adam Meinershagen
3973 Harry Muir
3974 David Pearlman
3975 Rob Steinert
3976 Dilson Torres
3977 Joe Durso
3978 Juan Querecuto
3979 Brandon Cromer
3980 Emmanuel Hayes
3981 Adam Melhuse
3982 Rob Mummau
3983 Kip Roggendorf
3984 Craig Vaught

3985 Rafael Debrand
3986 Sean Hearn
3987 Patrick Moultrie
3988 Shannon Stewart
3989 J.J. Cannon
3990 Rolando Pino
3991 Checklist

1993 Classic Best St. Lucie Mets

	MT	NR MT	EX
Complete Set:	6.00		

1 Edgardo Alfonzo
2 Jeff Barry
3 Greg Beals
4 Rob Carpentier
5 Alberto Castillo
6 Joe Crawford
7 Randy Curtis
8 Todd Fiegel
9 Mark Fuller
10 Ed Fully
11 Omar Garcia
12 Robbie Guzik
13 Jason Jacome
14 Tripp Keister
15 Jason King
16 Tim McClinton
17 Jim McCready
18 Bernie Millan
19 Pat Miller
20 Chris Roberts
21 Mason Rudolph
22 Chris Saunders
23 Brad Schorr
24 John Smith
25 Ottis Smith
26 John Tamargo
27 Bill Latham
28 Larry Bennese

1993 Fleer/ProCards St. Lucie Mets

	MT	NR MT	EX
Complete Set:	6.00		

2912 Rob Carpentier
2913 Andy Cotner
2914 Joe Crawford
2915 Todd Fiegel
2916 Mark Fuller
2917 Robbie Guzik
2918 Jason Jacome
2919 Jim McCready
2920 Chris Roberts
2921 Brad Schorr
2922 Ottis Smith
2923 Greg Beals
2924 Alberto Castillo
2925 Mason Rudolph
2926 Edgardo Alfonzo
2927 Omar Garcia
2928 Greg Graham
2929 Bernie Millan
2930 Chris Saunders
2931 Jeff Barry
2932 Randy Curtis
2933 Ed Fully
2934 Tim McClinton
2935 Tim Sandy
2936 John Smith
2937 John Tamargo
2938 Bill Latham
2939 Checklist

1993 Classic Best St. Petersburg Cardinals

	MT	NR MT	EX
Complete Set:	6.50		

1 Dmitri Young
2 Mike Badorek
3 Roy Bailey
4 Andy Beasley
5 Alan Botkin
6 Terry Bradshaw
7 Duff Brumley
8 Mike Cantu
9 Steve Cerio
10 Dan Cholowsky
11 John Corona
12 Clint Davis
13 Ed Gerald
14 Jason Hisey
15 Aaron Holbert
16 Keith Jones
17 Sean Lowe
18 Jeremy McGarity
19 Lorenzo Meza
20 Doug Radziewicz
21 Paul Romanoli
22 Marc Ronan
23 Scott Simmons
24 Joe Turvey
25 Jose Vazquez
26 Jose Velez
27 Ron Warner
28 Rich Folkers
29 Terry Kennedy
30 Pete Fagan

1993 Fleer/ProCards St. Petersburg Cardinals

	MT	NR MT	EX
Complete Set:	5.00		

2617 Mike Badorek
2618 Roy Bailey
2619 Alan Botkin
2620 Duff Brumley
2621 John Corona
2622 Clint Davis
2623 Jason Hisey
2624 Sean Lowe
2625 Jeremy McGarity
2626 Paul Romanoli
2627 Scott Simmons
2628 Andy Beasley
2629 Steve Cerio
2630 Marc Ronan
2631 Joe Turvey
2632 Michael Cantu
2633 Dan Cholowsky
2634 Aaron Holbert
2635 Lorenzo Meza
2636 Doug Radziewicz
2637 Ron Warner
2638 Dmitri Young
2639 Terry Bradshaw
2640 Ed Gerald
2641 Keith Jones
2642 Jose Vazquez
2643 Jose Velez
2644 Terry Kennedy
2645 Rich Folkers
2646 Checklist

1993 Fleer/ProCards San Antonio Missions

	MT	NR MT	EX
Complete Set:	7.50		

2996 Bill Bene
2997 Jamie Daspit
2998 Javier Delahoya
2999 Rick Gorecki
3000 Isidro Marquez
3001 Terric McFarlin
3002 Jose Parra
3003 Brian Piotrowicz
3004 Royal Thomas
3005 Ben VanRyn
3006 Joey Vierra
3007 Chris Abbe
3008 Hector Ortiz
3009 Jorge Alvarez
3010 Juan Castro
3011 Garey Ingram
3012 Ron Maurer
3013 Dan Melendez
3014 Murph Proctor
3015 Roger Cedeno
3016 Anthony Collier
3017 Todd Hollandsworth
3018 Billy Loft
3019 Vernon Spearman
3020 Glenn Hoffman
3021 Burt Hooton
3022 Brett Magnusson
3023 Checklist

1993 Classic Best San Bernardino Spirit

	MT	NR MT	EX
Complete Set:	6.00		

1 Rodney Pedraza
2 Steve Anderson
3 Shawn Buchanan
4 Michael Conte
5 Tim Cooper
6 Rick DeHart
7 Tim Demerson
8 Mike Figga
9 Ryan Freeburg
10 Bo Gilliam
11 Adin Lohry
12 Todd Malone
13 Manny Martinez
14 Tim Scott
15 Steve Shoemaker
16 Tim Smith
17 Rick Sutch
18 John Sutherland
19 Makoto Suzuki
20 Brian Turner
21 Gregory J. Mahlberg
22 Steve Livesey
23 Chuck Estrada
24 Chris Phillips
25 The Bug
26 Stadium

1993 Fleer/ProCards San Bernardino Spirit

	MT	NR MT	EX
Complete Set:	7.50		

764 Michael Conte
765 Rick DeHart
766 Todd Malone
767 Rod Pedraza
768 Scott Rose
769 Steve Shoemaker
770 Tom Smith
771 Rick Sutch
772 John Sutherland
773 Mac Suzuki
774 Mike Fiaga
775 Adin Lohry
776 Steve Anderson
777 Tim Cooper
778 Ryan Freeburg
779 Tim Scott
780 Brian Turner
781 Shawn Buchanan
782 Tim Demerson
783 Rick Freehling
784 Sean Gilliam
785 Manny Martinez
786 Greg Mahlberg
787 Chuck Estrada
788 Steve Livesey
789 Checklist

1993 Classic Best San Jose Giants

	MT	NR MT	EX
Complete Set:	6.00		

1 Adam Hyzdu
2 Andrew Albrecht
3 Kevin Bellomo
4 Danny Calcagno
5 Tim Casper
6 Troy Clemons
7 Brent Cookson
8 Ricky Ward
9 Chuck Wanke
10 Brian Dour
11 Kurt Ehmann
12 Charlie Hicks
13 Richard Hyde
14 Brett Jenkins
15 Brian McLeid
16 Doug Mirabelli
17 Don Montgomery
18 Steven Whitaker
19 Kurt Peltzer
20 Mark Peterson
21 Ron Pezzoni
22 Chris Wimmer
23 Eric Stonecipher
24 Doug Vanderweele
25 Bill VanLandingham
26 Dick Dietz
27 Jim Davenport
28 Todd Oakes
29 John Pletsch
30 Ed Bautista

1993 Fleer/ProCards San Jose Giants

	MT	NR MT	EX
Complete Set:	6.00		

1 Brian Dour
2 Charlie Hicks
3 Rich Hyde
4 Brian McLeod
5 Kurt Peltzer
6 Mark Peterson
7 Eric Stonecipher
8 Doug Vanderweele
9 William VanLandingham
10 Chuck Wanke
11 Steve Whitaker
12 Danny Calcagno
13 Troy Clemens
14 Doug Mirabelli
15 Tim Casper
16 Chris Dotolo
17 Kurt Ehmann
18 Brett Jenkins
19 Don Montgomery
20 Ricky Ward
21 Chris Wimmer
22 Drew Albrecht
23 Kevin Bellomo
24 Brent Cookson
25 Adam Hyzdu
26 Ron Pezzoni
27 Dick Dietz
28 Jim Davenport
29 Todd Oakes
1360 Luis Andujar
1361 Brian Boehringer
1362 Tom Fordham
1363 Steve Gajkowski
1364 Robert Ellis
1365 Mike Heathcott
1366 David Keating
1367 Al Levine
1368 Hank Tagle
1369 Kevin Tolar
1370 Chris Woodfin
1371 Nilson Robledo
1372 Chris Tremie
1373 Mike Vogel
1374 Doug Brady
1375 Kevin Coughlin
1376 Glenn DiSarcina
1377 Troy Fryman
1378 Geovany Miranda
1379 Olmedo Saenz
1380 Chris Snopek
1381 Shawn Buchanan
1382 Carmine Cappuccio
1383 Randy Hood
1384 Charles Poe
1385 Kerry Valrie
1386 Dave Huppert
1387 Jon Matlack
1388 Pat Roessler
1389 Checklist

1993 Classic Best Sarasota White Sox

	MT	NR MT	EX
Complete Set:	6.00		

1 Glenn Disarcina
2 Luis Andujar
3 Brian Boehringer
4 Mike Bradish
5 Doug Brady
6 Carmine Cappuccio
7 Ken Coleman
8 Kevin Coughlin
9 Robert Ellis
10 Steve Gajkowski
11 Tony Gordon
12 Mike Heathcott
13 Harold Henry
14 Randy Hood
15 Barry Johnson
16 David Keating
17 Alan Levine
18 Dean Locklear
19 Henry Manning
20 Jason Ogden
21 Charles Poe
22 Nilson Robledo
23 Olmedo Saenz
24 Shane Spry
25 Keith Strange
26 Kevin Tolar
27 Kerry Valrie
28 Dave Huppert
29 Jon Matlack

1993 Fleer/ProCards Sarasota White Sox

	MT	NR MT	EX
Complete Set:	6.00		

1360 Luis Andujar
1361 Brian Boehringer
1362 Tom Fordham
1363 Steve Gajkowski
1364 Robert Ellis
1365 Mike Heathcott
1366 David Keating
1367 Al Levine
1368 Hank Tagle
1369 Kevin Tolar
1370 Chris Woodfin
1371 Nilson Robledo
1372 Chris Tremie
1373 Mike Vogel
1374 Doug Brady
1375 Kevin Coughlin
1376 Glenn DiSarcina
1377 Troy Fryman
1378 Geovany Miranda
1379 Olmedo Saenz
1380 Chris Snopek
1381 Shawn Buchanan
1382 Carmine Cappuccio
1383 Randy Hood
1384 Charles Poe
1385 Kerry Valrie
1386 Dave Huppert
1387 Jon Matlack
1388 Pat Roessler
1389 Checklist

1993 Classic Best Savannah Cardinals

	MT	NR MT	EX
Complete Set:	6.00		

1 Aldo Pecorilli
2 Jeff Alkire
3 Charlie Anderson
4 Keith Black
5 Garrett Blanton
6 Mike Busby
7 Brian Carpenter
8 Joe Carrillo

9 Jamie Cochran
10 Hector Colon
11 Ray Davis
12 Darren Doucette
13 Steve Dudek
14 Ronnie French
15 Doug Goodman
16 Larry Lucchetti
17 Frankie Martinez
18 Joe McEwing
19 Jeff Murphy
20 John O'Brien
21 Brian Rupp
22 Karl Stanley
23 Chad Sumner
24 Mark Tranbarger
25 Jesus Ugueto
26 Chris Maloney
27 Ramon Ortiz
28 Steve Proctor
29 Tommy McCoy

1993 Fleer/ProCards Savannah Cardinals

	MT	NR MT	EX
Complete Set:	6.50		

677 Jeff Alkire
678 Mike Busby
679 Brian Carpenter
680 Joe Carrillo
681 Jamie Cochran
682 Ray Davis
683 Doug Goodman
684 Larry Lucchetti
685 Frankie Martinez
686 Karl Stanley
687 Mike Tranbaerger
688 Jeff Murphy
689 Aldo Pecorilli
690 Charlie Anderson
691 Keith Black
692 Darren Douchette
693 John O'Brien
694 Brian Rupp
695 Chad Sumner
696 Jesus Ugueto
697 Garrett Blanton
698 Hector Colon
699 Steve Dudek
700 Ronnie French
701 Joe McEwing
702 Chris Maloney
703 Checklist

1993 Fleer/ProCards Scranton Wilkes-Barre Red Barron

	MT	NR MT	EX
Complete Set:	7.00		

2537 Kyle Abbott
2538 Cliff Brantley
2539 Brad Brink
2540 Pat Combs
2541 Paul Fletcher
2542 Tyler Green
2543 Tim Mauser
2544 Jeff Patterson
2545 Mike Williams
2546 Mike Lieberthal
2547 Greg Legg
2548 Jeff Manto
2549 Joe Millette
2550 Victor Rodriguez
2551 Sean Ryan
2552 Kevin Stocker
2553 Casey Waller
2554 Steve Bieser
2555 Tony Longmire
2556 Tom Marsh
2557 Cary Williams
2558 George Culver
2559 Dave Cash
2560 Jim Wright
2561 Checklist

1993 Fleer/ProCards Shreveport Captains

	MT	NR MT	EX
Complete Set:	6.00		

2702 Checklist
2752 Brian Griffiths
2753 Chris Hancock
2754 Carl Hanselman
2755 Dave Masters
2756 Jim Myers
2757 Lou Pote
2758 Richie Simon
2759 Shad Smith
2760 Salomon Torres
2761 Mark Yockey
2762 Bert Heffernan
2763 Dan Fernandez
2764 Adell Davenport
2765 Matt Davis
2766 Andres Duncan
2767 Tim Florez
2768 Steve Hecht
2769 Kevin Kasper
2770 Barry Miller
2771 Dax Jones
2772 Rob Katzaroff
2773 Calvin Murray
2774 Pete Weber
2775 Ron Wotus
2776 Steve Cline
2777 Bill Stein

1993 Fleer/ProCards South Atlantic League All-Stars

	MT	NR MT	EX
Complete Set:	14.00		

1 Clayton Byrne
2 Eric Chavez
3 Matt Jarvis
4 Billy Owens
5 B.J. Waszgis
6 Scott Eyre
7 Jack Kimel
8 Kerry Lacy
9 Mike Welch
10 Ted Blackwell
11 Mike Brown
12 Epi Cardenas
13 Derek Hacopian
14 Jonathan Nunnally
15 J.J. Thobe
16 Charles York
17 Roberto Rojas
18 Jeff Antolick
19 Nick Delvecchio
20 Bill Evers
21 Derek Jeter
22 Ryan Karp
23 Ray Suplee
24 D.J. Boston
25 Brad Cornett
26 Kris Harmes
27 Jose Herrera
28 Chris Mader
29 Greg Elliott
30 Richard Hidalgo
31 Melvin Mora
32 Danny Clyburn
33 Jason Kendall
34 Andy Beckerman
35 Guillermo Garcia
36 Miguel Correa
37 Randy Ingle
38 Willy Johnson
39 Marty Malloy
40 Darrell May
41 Raymond Nunez
42 Leo Ramirez
43 Terrell Wade
44 Jeff Alkire
45 Keith Black
46 Mike Busby
47 Jamie Cochran
48 Chris Maloney
49 John O'Brien
50 Aldo Percorilli
51 Brian Rupp
52 Stanley Evans
53 Mike Murphy
54 Mark Tranberg
55 Daniel Kopriva
56 David Tuttle
57 Checklist

1993 Classic Best South Bend White Sox

	MT	NR MT	EX
Complete Set:	6.00		

1 Troy Fryman
2 Ricky Bowrosen
3 Essex Burton
4 Mike Call
5 Mike Cameron
6 Carmine Cappuccio
7 Don Culberson
8 Edgar Devers
9 Greg Fritz
10 Artel Garcia
11 Jimmy Hurst
12 Jon Jenkins
13 Sean Johnston
14 Robert Machado
15 Byron Mathews
16 Tim Moore
17 Jason Pierson
18 Wilfredo Polldor
19 Ted Rich
20 Chris Snopek
21 Hank Tagle
22 Julio Vinas
23 Jason Watkins
24 Craig Wilson
25 Chip Winlarski
26 Steve Worrell
27 Jim Reinebold
28 Jaime Garcia
29 Von Joshua

1993 Fleer/ProCards South Bend White Sox

	MT	NR MT	EX
Complete Set:	6.00		

1421 Micheal Call
1422 Don Culberson
1423 Greg Fritz
1424 Ariel Garcia
1425 Jon Jenkins
1426 Sean Johnston
1427 Jim McDermott
1428 Tim Moore
1429 Jason Pierson
1430 Jason Watkins
1431 Chip Winiarski
1432 Steve Worrell
1433 Robert Machado
1434 Julio Vinas
1435 Mike Vogel
1436 Ricky Bowrosen
1437 Essex Burton
1438 Dan Fraraccio
1439 Troy Fryman
1440 Chris Snopek
1441 Craig Wilson
1442 Mike Cameron
1443 Edgar Devers
1444 Jimmy Hurst
1445 Byron Mathews
1446 Tony Franklin
1447 Jaime Garcia
1448 Von Joshua
1449 Jim Reinebold
1450 Checklist

1993 Fleer/ProCards Southern Oregon A's

	MT	NR MT	EX
Complete Set:	5.00		

4054 Scott Baldwin
4055 Mike Conte
4056 Craig Gierger
4057 Richard King
4058 Steve Lemke
4059 Jason Lowe
4060 John MacCauley
4061 Derek Manning
4062 Chris Michalak
4063 William Urbina
4064 Ryan Whitaker
4065 Steve Zongor
4066 Mark Moore
4067 Willie Morales
4068 Brandy Bergoechea
4069 Steven Cox
4070 Juan Dilone
4071 Marcel Galligani
4072 Geoff Loomis
4073 Pat Sanders
4074 Scott Spiezio
4075 Luini Aracena
4076 Tony Banks
4077 Eric Harris
4078 David Keel
4079 Mathew Reese
4080 Jeff Richardson
4081 Dick Scott
4082 Tony DeFrancesco
4083 Checklist

1993 Classic Best Spartanburg Phillies

	MT	NR MT	EX
Complete Set:	6.00		

1 Mark Tranberg
2 Peter Agostinelli
3 Kevin Alger
4 Chad Anderson
5 Gary Bennett
6 Luis Brito
7 E.J. Brophy
8 Daniel Brown
9 Alan Burke
10 William Carmona
11 Reynaldo Delos Santos
12 Blake Doolan
13 Stanley Evans
14 Scott Haws
15 Ramon hernandez
16 Trevor Humphrey
17 Danny Larson
18 Paul Mitchell
19 Rob Mitchell
20 Mike Murphy
21 Steven Nutt
22 Leonard Romero
23 Pat Ruth
24 Russell Sallee
25 Roy Majtyka
26 Tony Scott
27 Buzz Cappa
28 Clete Sigwart

1993 Fleer/ProCards Spartanburg Phillies

	MT	NR MT	EX
Complete Set:	5.00		

1046 Peter Agostinelli
1047 Kevin Alger
1048 Chad Anderson
1049 Dan Brown
1050 Blake Doolan
1051 Trevor Humphry
1052 Thomas Irwin
1053 Larry Mitchell
1054 Robert Mitchell
1055 Steve Nuitt
1056 Mark Tranberg
1057 Gary Bennett
1058 E.J. Brophy
1059 Scott Haws
1060 Luis Brito
1061 Ramon Hernandez
1062 Brian Lawler
1063 Philip Romero
1064 Andy Sallee
1065 Alan Burke
1066 Reynaldo DeLosSantos
1067 Stanley Evans
1068 Danny Larson
1069 Mike Murphy
1070 Shawn Wills
1071 Roy Majtyka
1072 Buzz Capra
1073 Tony Scott
1074 Checklist

1993 Fleer/ProCards Spokane Indians

	MT	NR MT	EX
Complete Set:	5.00		

3581 Glenn Dishman
3582 Tom Doyle
3583 Dan Drewien
3584 Todd Erdos
3585 Hector Fargas
3586 Brad Kaufman
3587 Gregory Keagle
3588 Alberto Matos
3589 Brian McLain
3590 Derek Mix
3591 Jason Schlutt
3592 Kyle White
3593 Marty Winchester
3594 Bryan Wolff
3595 Leroy McKinnis
3596 Melvin Rosario
3597 Jim Bostock
3598 Jason Thompson
3599 Chris West
3600 Dickie Woodridge
3601 Dan Zanolla
3602 Darrick Duke
3603 Earl Johnson
3604 Chris Prieto
3605 Britton Scheibe
3606 Tim Flannery
3607 Checklist

1993 Classic Best Springfield Cardinals

	MT	NR MT	EX
Complete Set:	6.00		

2 Joe Blasucci
3 Todd Blake
4 Andy Bruce
5 Kirk Bullinger
6 Tim DeGrasse
7 Mike Difellce
8 Mike Eicher
9 Ben Ellsworth
10 John Frascatore
11 Mike Gulan
12 Jonas Hamlin
13 Keith Johns
14 Steve Johnson
15 Tim Jordan
16 Greg Knowles
17 Carlos Landinez
18 T.J. Mathews
19 Eric Miller
20 Dave Oehrlein
21 Greg Rudolph
22 Basil Shabazz
23 Dennis Slininger
24 Chad Smith
25 Derron Spiller
26 DaRond Stovall
27 Gary Taylor
28 Mike Ramsey
29 Eddie Williams
30 Mike Evans

1993 Fleer/ProCards Springfield Cardinals

	MT	NR MT	EX
Complete Set:	6.00		

1841 Todd Blake
1842 Kirk Bullinger

1843 Tim DeGrasse
1844 John Frascatore
1845 Steve Johnson
1846 Greg Knowles
1847 T.J. Mathews
1848 Eric Miller
1849 Dave Oehrlein
1850 Dennis Slininger
1851 Chad Smith
1852 Derron Spiller
1853 Mike DiFelice
1854 Eddie Williams
1855 Joe Biasucci
1856 Andy Bruce
1857 Ben Ellsworth
1858 Mike Gulan
1859 Jonas Hamlin
1860 Keith Johns
1861 Carlos Landinez
1862 Mike Eicher
1863 Tim Jordan
1864 Greg Rudolph
1865 Basil Shabazz
1866 DaRond Stovall
1867 Gary Taylor
1868 Mike Ramsey
1869 Checklist

1993 Classic Best Stockton Ports

	MT	NR MT	EX
Complete Set:	8.00		

1 Tyrone Hill
2 Marshall Boze
3 Bryon Browne
4 Greg Carmona
5 Ramser Correa
6 Mike Coulture
7 John Criminger
8 Tony Diggs
9 Bill Dobrolsky
10 Andy Fairman
11 Pat Fetty
12 Leon Glenn
13 Mark Hampton
14 Bubba Hardwick
15 Michael Harris
16 Brian Hostetler
17 Mike Huyler
18 Brian McKeon
19 Don Pruitt
20 Kevin Riggs
21 Sidney Roberson
22 Todd Samples
23 Mike Stefanski
24 Timothy Unroe
25 Derek Wachter
26 Eric Whitford
27 Lamar Johnson
28 Mick Kelleher
29 Mark Littell
30 Scott Melssner

1993 Fleer/ProCards Stockton Ports

	MT	NR MT	EX
Complete Set:	7.00		

735 Marshall Boze
736 Byron Browne
737 John Criminger
738 Pat Fetty
739 Ron Gerstein
740 Mark Hampton
741 Bubba Hardwick
742 Tyrone Hill
743 Brian McKeon
744 Don Pruitt
745 Sidney Roberson
746 Bill Dobrolsky
747 Brian Hostetler
748 Mike Stefanski
749 Mark Cole
750 Andy Fairman
751 Leon Glenn
752 Mike Huyler
753 Kevin Riggs
754 Tim Unroe
755 Eric Whitford
756 Mike Couture
757 Michael Harris
758 Todd Samples
759 Derek Wachter
760 Lamar Johnson
761 Mick Kelleher
762 Mark Littell
763 Checklist

1993 Fleer/ProCards Syracuse Chiefs

	MT	NR MT	EX
Complete Set:	6.00		

990 Steve Adkins
991 Darrel Akerfelds
992 Pete Blohm
993 Tim Brown
994 Jesse Cross
995 Darren Hall
996 Doug Linton
997 Paul Menhart
998 Mark Ohlms
999 Woody Williams
1000 Jose Monzon
1001 Greg O'Halloran
1002 Domingo Cedeno
1003 Ray Giannelli
1004 Domingo Martinez
1005 Rob Montalvo
1006 Tom Quinlan
1007 Lee Stevens
1008 Julian Yan
1009 Robert Butler
1010 Juan DeLaRosa
1011 Robert Perez
1012 Shawn Scott
1013 Nick Leyva
1014 John Poloni
1015 Rocket Wheeler
1016 Checklist

1993 Fleer/ProCards Tacoma Tigers

	MT	NR MT	EX
Complete Set:	7.00		

3024 Brad Arnsberg
3025 Kevin Campbell
3026 Johnny Guzman
3027 Bronswell Patrick
3028 Tim Peek
3029 Steve Phoenix
3030 Mike Raczka
3031 Lary Shikles
3032 Joe Slusarski
3033 Todd Van Poppel
3034 Dean Borrelli
3035 Henry Mercedes
3036 Doug Robbins
3037 Kurt Abbott
3038 Garrett Beard
3039 Webster Garrison
3040 Brent Gates
3041 Ron Witmeyer
3042 Mike Aldrete
3043 Marcos Armas
3044 Jim Buccheri
3045 Kevin Dattola
3046 Eric Fox
3047 Scott Lydy
3048 Troy Neel
3049 Mitchell Page
3050 Checklist

1993 Fleer/ProCards Toledo Mud Hens

	MT	NR MT	EX
Complete Set:	6.00		

1643 Sean Bergman
1644 Sherm Corbett
1645 John DeSilva
1646 Willie Fraser
1647 Frank Gonzales
1648 Mark Grater
1649 Buddy Groom
1650 John Hudek
1651 Dave Johnson
1652 Kurt Knudsen
1653 Mike Lumley
1654 Ron Rightnowar
1655 Wally Ritchie
1656 Rich Rowland
1657 Rico Brogna
1658 Ivan Cruz
1659 Chris Gomez
1660 Johnny Paredes
1661 Bob Reimink
1662 Rod Robertson
1663 Shawn Hare
1664 Jody Hurst
1665 Riccardo Ingram
1666 Ted Wiliams
1667 Joe Sparks
1668 Bruce Fields
1669 Jeff Jones
1670 Checklist

1993 Fleer/ProCards Triple A All-Star Game

	MT	NR MT	EX
Complete Set:	12.00		

1 Chipper Jones
2 Ryan Klesko
3 Javier Lopez
4 Bill Taylor
5 Kevin Roberson
6 Eddie Zambrano
7 Marc Bombard
8 Brian Dorsett
9 Scott Ruskin
10 Lance Painter
11 David Weathers
12 James Mouton
13 Billy Ashley
14 Stan Johnston
15 Bill Russell
16 Todd Williams
17 Todd Haney
18 Ryan Thompson
19 George Culver
20 Tony Longmire
21 Roy Smith
22 Tripp Cromer
23 Keith Lockhart
24 Allen Watson
25 Steve Pegues
26 Paul Faries
27 J.R. Phillips
28 Tommy Hinzo
29 John O'Donoghue
30 Mark Smith
31 Don Florence
32 Eduardo Perez
33 Darryl Scott
34 Drew Denson
35 Brian Drahman
36 Jerry DiPoto
37 Charlie Manuel
38 Jim Thorne
39 Wally Ritchie
40 Rich Rowland
41 Jeff Cox
42 Rick Reed
43 Karl Rhodes
44 Terry Shumpert
45 Troy O'Leary
46 Bernardo Brito
47 Derek Parks
48 Scott Ullger
49 Billy Masse
50 Kurt Abbott
51 Walt Horn
52 Anthony Manahan
53 Rob Ducey
54 Lee Stevens
55 Checklist

1993 Fleer/ProCards Tucson Toros

	MT	NR MT	EX
Complete Set:	8.00		

3051 Eric Bell
3052 Mike Capel
3053 Eddie Dixon
3054 Dean Hartgraves
3055 Bob Hurta
3056 Todd Jones
3057 Jeff Juden
3058 Shane Reynolds
3059 Dave Veres
3060 Donne Wall
3061 Tony Eusebio
3062 Scooter Tucker
3063 Tommy Barrett
3064 Mike Brumley
3065 Jack Daugherty
3066 Jim Lindeman
3067 Orlando Miller
3068 James Mounton
3069 Phil Nevin
3070 Luis Quinones
3071 Willie Ansley
3072 Braulio Castillo
3073 John Massarelli
3074 Joe Mikulik
3075 Rick Parker
3076 Rick Sweet
3077 Dave Engle
3078 Brent Strom
3079 Checklist

1993 Fleer/ProCards Tulsa Drillers

	MT	NR MT	EX
Complete Set:	7.00		

2725 Jose Alberro
2726 Mike Arner
2727 Steve Dreyer
2728 Chris Gies
2729 Barry Goetz
2730 James Hurst
2731 Kurt Miller
2732 Ritchie Moody
2733 Darren Oliver
2734 Brian Romero
2735 Roger Luce
2736 David Rolls
2737 Miguel Castellano
2738 Jim Clinton
2739 Cris Colon
2740 Benji Gil
2741 Rusty Greer
2742 Ever Magallanes
2743 Trey McCoy
2744 Frank Turco
2745 Benny Castillo
2746 Daren Epley
2747 Paul List
2748 Timmie Morrow
2749 Stan Cilburn
2750 Randy Whisler
2751 Checklist

1993 Fleer/ProCards Utica Blue Sox

	MT	NR MT	EX
Complete Set:	6.00		

3525 Robb Berryman
3526 Craig Bush
3527 Eric Cormier
3528 Danny Johnston
3529 Randy Lawrence
3530 Leif McKinley
3531 Rafael Orellano
3532 Hilario Perez
3533 Chad Renfroe
3534 Jim Tyrrell
3535 Richie Borrero
3536 Mark Senkowitz
3537 John Stratton
3538 Victor Aguado
3539 Juan Debrand
3540 Joe Depastino
3541 Andy Moore
3542 T.J. O'Donnell
3543 Nick Ortiz
3544 Diogenes Baez
3545 Daniel Collier
3546 J.J. Johnson
3547 Ricky Milligan
3548 Dave Holt
3549 Garry Roggenburk
3550 Checklist

1993 Fleer/ProCards Vancouver Canadians

	MT	NR MT	EX
Complete Set:	6.50		

2589 Otis Green
2590 Hilly Hathaway
2591 Mark Holzemer
2592 Phil Leftwich
2593 Jerry Nielsen
2594 Steve Peck
2595 Troy Percival
2596 Darryl Scott
2597 Russ Springer
2598 Paul Swingle
2599 Julian Vasquez
2600 Mark Zappelli
2601 Larry Gonzales
2602 Chris Turner
2603 Rod Correia
2604 Ramon Martinez
2605 Eduardo Perez
2606 Ty Van Burkleo
2607 Jim Walewander
2608 Garret Anderon
2609 Jim Edwards
2610 Jeff Kipila
2611 Jerome Walton
2612 Reggie Williams
2613 Max Oliveras
2614 Gary Ruby
2615 Lenn Sakata
2616 Checklist

1993 Classic Best Vero Beach Dodgers

	MT	NR MT	EX
Complete Set:	6.00		

1 Chris Demetral
2 Jason Brosnan
3 Michael Brown
4 Miguel Cairo
5 Angel Dotel
6 Steve Green
7 Ken Hamilton
8 Ryan Henderson
9 Ken Huckaby
10 Keith Johnson
11 Reggie Johnson
12 Kiki Jones
13 Tito Landrum
14 Eduardo Lantigua
15 Martin Lavigne
16 Richard Licursi
17 Rich Linares
18 Dwight Maness
19 Chris Morrow
20 Javier Puchales
21 Felix Rodriguez
22 Christopher Sinacori
23 Eric Vorbeck
24 Ronnie Walden
25 Brandon Watts
26 Lonnie Webb
27 Brandon White
28 Joe Vavra
29 Garrett Teel
30 Dennis Lewallyn

1993 Fleer/ProCards Vero Beach Dodgers

	MT	NR MT	EX
Complete Set:	6.00		

2206 Jason Brosnan
2207 Edwin Correa

2208 Jamie Daspit
2209 Roberto Duran
2210 Scott Freeman
2211 Ken Hamilton
2212 Ryan Henderson
2213 Kiki Jones
2214 Martin Lavigne
2215 Rich Linares
2216 Kevin Pencavitch
2217 Felix Rodriguez
2218 Chris Sinacori
2219 Ron Walden
2220 Brandon Watts
2221 Brandon White
2222 Mike Brown
2223 Ken Huckaby
2224 Miguel Cairo
2225 Chris Demetral
2226 Angle Dotel
2227 Keith Johnson
2228 Reggie Johnson
2229 Eduardo Lantigua
2230 Steve Green
2231 Tito Landrum
2232 Dwight Maness
2233 Alton Pinkney
2234 Javier Puchales
2235 Eric Vorbeck
2236 Checklist

1993 Classic Best Waterloo Diamonds

	MT	NR MT	EX
Complete Set:	6.00		

1 Bobby Bonds II
2 Greg Anthony
3 Luis Arroyo
4 LaRue Baber
5 Jon Barnes
6 Stoney Briggs
7 Homer Bush
8 German Carrion
9 Raul Casanova
10 Brian D'Amato
11 Roberto DeLeon
12 Keith Dunckel
13 Iggy Duran
14 Todd Erdos
15 John Fantauzzi
16 Charlie Greene
17 Craig Hanson
18 Mike Hermanson
19 Adrian Hollinger
20 Tom Kindler
21 Rich Loiselle
22 Joey Long
23 Kevin Minchk
24 John Roberts
25 Melvin Rosario
26 Todd Schmitt
27 Reggie Stewart
28 Ed Romero
29 Dean Treanor
30 Bill Murray

1993 Fleer/ProCards Waterloo Diamonds

	MT	NR MT	EX
Complete Set:	6.00		

1758 Pepper Anthony
1759 Jon Barnes
1760 Brian D'Amato
1761 Todd Erdos
1762 Craig Hanson
1763 Mike Hermanson
1764 Adrian Hollinger
1765 Tom Kindler
1766 Richard Loiselle
1767 Joey Long
1768 Todd Schmitt
1769 Joe Waldron
1770 Raul Cassanova
1771 Charlie Greene
1772 Homer Bush
1773 Manny Cora
1774 Roberto DeLeon
1775 Iggy Duran
1776 John Fantauzzi
1777 Kevin Minchk
1778 Melvin Rosario
1779 Larue Baber
1780 Bobby Bonds II
1781 Stoney Briggs
1782 John Roberts
1783 Reggie Stewart
1784 Ed Romero
1785 Dean Treanor
1786 Checklist

1993 Fleer/ProCards Watertown Indians

	MT	NR MT	EX
Complete Set:	5.00		

3551 Rob Augstine
3552 Roland De La Maza
3553 Wes Dempsey
3554 German Diaz
3555 Travis Driskill
3556 Robert Garza
3557 Kris Hanson
3558 Mike Mathews
3559 Mike Neilson
3560 Chris Plumlee
3561 Greg Sinner
3562 Casey Whitten
3563 Jeff Williams
3564 Jeff Haag
3565 Robert Lewis
3566 Steven Soliz
3567 Gerad Cawhorn
3568 Blair Hodson
3569 Jason Lyman
3570 Mike Neal
3571 Jon Oram
3572 Rick Prieto
3573 Greg Thomas
3574 Eric Chapman
3575 Bryan Garrett
3576 Chuck Kulle
3577 Pedro Marte
3578 Pat Schulz
3579 Mike Young
3580 Checklist

1993 Fleer/ProCards Welland Pirates

	MT	NR MT	EX
Complete Set:	5.00		

3346 Jason Abramvicius
3347 Brian Beck
3348 Matt Chamberlain
3349 Kenny Fairfax
3350 Jeff Isom
3351 Jeff Lutt
3352 Ramon Morel
3353 Jamison Nuttle
3354 Brian Pelka
3355 Gil Perez
3356 Chris Peters
3357 Jason Phillips
3358 Jeff Pickich
3359 Aaron Cannaday
3360 Sergio Mendez
3361 Joel Williamson
3362 Lou Collier
3363 Pat Gosselin
3364 G.G. Harris
3365 Mitch House
3366 Tom Johnston
3367 Rich Luna
3368 Raul Paez
3369 Maximo Rivera
3370 Stan Wiltz
3371 Jermaine Allensworth
3372 Riegal Hunt
3373 Erskine Kelly
3374 Johnny Mitchell
3375 Pat Reed
3376 Checklist

1993 Classic Best West Palm Beach Expos

	MT	NR MT	EX
Complete Set:	6.50		

1 Matt Allen
2 Derek Aucoin
3 Jim Austin
4 Mike Daniel
5 Scott Gentile
6 Marc Griffin
7 Mark Grudzielanek
8 Mike Hardge
9 Rod Henderson
10 Tyrone Horne
11 Mark LaRosa
12 Brian Looney
13 Austin Manahan
14 Domingo Matos
15 Kevin McDonald
16 Joe Norris
17 Kevin Northrup
18 Claudio Ozoria
19 Terry Powers
20 Raul Santana
21 Curtis Schmidt
22 Mitch Simons
23 Mike Thomas
24 B.J. Wallace
25 Randy Wilstead
26 Rob Leary
27 Rich Dubee
28 Lee Slagle
30 Willie Bananas

1993 Fleer/ProCards West Palm Beach Expos

	MT	NR MT	EX
Complete Set:	6.50		

1330 Derek Aucion
1331 Matt Connolly
1332 Scott Gentile
1333 Rodney Henderson
1334 Mark LaRosa
1335 Brian Looney
1336 Kevin McDonald
1337 Joe Norris
1338 Terry Powers
1339 Curtis Schmidt
1340 Mike Thomas
1341 B.J. Wallace
1342 Matt Allen
1343 Mike Daniel
1344 Tim Hines
1345 Raul Santana
1346 Mark Grudzielanek
1347 Michael Hardge
1348 Austin Manahan
1349 Domingo Matos
1350 Mitch Simons
1351 Randy Wilstead
1352 Jim Austin
1353 Marc Griffin
1354 Tyrone Horne
1355 Kervin Northrup
1356 Claudio Ozoria
1357 Rob Leary
1358 Rich Dubee
1359 Checklist

1993 Classic Best West Virginia Wheelers

	MT	NR MT	EX
Complete Set:	6.00		

1 Chad Fox
2 Johnny Bess
3 John Brothers
4 William Brunson
5 Roger Etheridge
6 Micah Franklin
7 Dan Frye
8 Fermin Garcia
9 Dee Jenkins
10 Bob Jesperson
11 Brad Keenan
12 Dan Kopriva
13 Jason Kummerfeldt
14 Rich Langford
15 Marty Lister
16 Louis Maberry
17 Ricky Magdaleno
18 Matt Martin
19 Mike Meggers
20 Jeff Nagy
21 James Nix
22 Todd Ruyak
23 Dave Tuttle
24 Wayne Wilkerson
25 Tom Nieto
26 Mack Jenkins
27 Tom Iverson

1993 Fleer/ProCards West Virginia Wheelers

	MT	NR MT	EX
Complete Set:	6.00		

2856 John Brothers
2857 William Brunson
2858 Roger Etheridge
2859 Chad Fox
2860 Fermin Garcia
2861 Jason Kummerfeldt
2862 Rich Langford
2863 Marty Lister
2864 Louis Maberry
2865 James Nix
2866 Todd Ruyak
2867 David Tuttle
2868 Johnny Bess
2869 Toby Rumfield
2870 Dan Frye
2871 Dee Jenkins
2872 Brad Keenan
2873 Dan Kopriva
2874 Ricky Magdaleno
2875 Matt Martin
2876 Micah Franklin
2877 Bob Jesperson
2878 Mike Meggers
2879 Jeff Nagy
2880 Wayne Wilkerson
2881 Mack Jenkins
2882 Checklist

1993 Fleer/ProCards Wichita Wranglers

	MT	NR MT	EX
Complete Set:	6.00		

2970 Renay Bryand
2971 Nate Cromwell
2972 Nick Felix
2973 Bryce Florie
2974 Don Heinkel
2975 Steve Hoeme
2976 Geoff Kellogg
2977 Kelly Lifgren
2978 William Wengert
2979 John Abercrombie
2980 Lee Henderson
2981 Jerry Thurston
2982 Mark Gieseke
2983 Paul Gonzalez
2984 Billy Hall
2985 Ray Holbert
2986 Pablo Martinez
2987 Tookie Spann
2988 Darius Gash
2989 Vince Harris
2990 Dwayne Hosey
2991 Ray McDavid
2992 Tracy Sanders
2993 Dave Trembley
2994 Sonny Siebert
2995 Checklist

1993 Classic Best Wilmington Blue Rocks

	MT	NR MT	EX
Complete Set:	10.00		

1 Michael Tucker
2 Francisco Baez
3 Brian Bevil
4 Darren Burton
5 Gary Caraballo
6 Jim Chrisman
7 Pat Dando
8 John Dempsey Jr.
9 Chris Eddy
10 Mike Fyhrie
11 Raul Gonzalez
12 John Gross
13 Shane Halter
14 Brian Harrison
15 Steve Hinton
16 Roger Landress
17 Jon Lieber
18 David Marshall
19 Dario Perez
20 Jeff Smith
21 Tom Smith
22 Andy Stewart
23 Brady Stewart
24 Chad Strickland
25 Robert Toth
26 Hugh Walker
27 Ron Johnson
28 Gary Lance
29 Rafael Santana
30 Marty Yuhas

1993 Fleer/ProCards Wilmington Blue Rocks

	MT	NR MT	EX
Complete Set:	11.00		

1987 Francisco Baez
1988 Brian Bevil
1989 David Bladow
1990 Jim Chrisman
1991 Chris Eddy
1992 John Gross
1993 Brian Harrison
1994 Rogers Landress
1995 Jon Lieber
1996 Dario Perez
1997 Jeff Smith
1998 Robert Toth
1999 John Dempsey
2000 Andy Stewart
2001 Chad Strickland
2002 Gary Caraballo
2003 Pat Dando
2004 Shane Halter
2005 Steve Hinton
2006 Jason Marshall
2007 Brady Stewart
2008 Michael Tucker
2009 Darren Burton
2010 Raul Gonzalez
2011 Tom Smith
2012 Hugh Walker
2013 Ron Johnson
2014 Gary Lance
2015 Rafael Santana
2016 Checklist

1993 Classic Best Winston-Salem Spirits

	MT	NR MT	EX
Complete Set:	8.00		

1 Chad Mottola
2 Jason Angel
3 Amador Arias
4 Tim Belk

5	Troy Buckley	
6	Scott Duff	
7	Greg Hammond	
8	Mike Harrison	
9	John Hrusovsky	
10	Kevin Jarvis	
11	Motor-Boat Jones	
12	Cleveland Laddell	
13	Bo Loftin	
14	Joe McCann	
15	Charles McClain	
16	Eric Owens	
17	Mateo Ozuna	
18	Bobby Perna	
19	Craig Pueschner	
20	Rene Quinones	
21	Kevin Shaw	
22	Rodney Steph	
23	Carl Stewart	
24	Chris Vasquez	
25	Mark Berry	
26	Derek Botelho	
27	Tom Spencer	

1993 Fleer/ProCards Winston-Salem Spirits

	MT	NR MT	EX
Complete Set:			

1562	Jason Angel
1563	Scott Duff
1564	John Hrusovsky
1565	Kevin Jarvis
1566	Bo Loftin
1567	Joe McCann
1568	Charles McClain
1569	Rene Quinones
1570	Kevin Shaw
1571	Rodney Steph
1572	Troy Buckley
1573	Greg Hammond
1574	Mike Harrison
1575	Amador Arias
1576	Tim Belk
1577	Eric Owens
1578	Mateo Ozuna
1579	Bobby Perna
1580	Eugene Jones
1581	Cleveland Ladell
1582	Craig Pueschner
1583	Chris Vasquez
1584	Mark Berry
1585	Derek Botelho
1586	Checklist

1993 Fleer/Pro Cards Yakima Bears

	MT	NR MT	EX
Complete Set:	6.00		

3873	Herb Baxter
3874	Brett Binkley
3875	Nathan Bland
3876	Jake Botts
3877	Kenny Cook
3878	Roberto Duran
3879	Jose Garcia
3880	Franz Groot
3881	Joe Jacobsen
3882	Jayson Perez
3883	Kevin Pincavitch
3884	David Spykstra
3885	Ryan Luzinski
3886	Dilone Uribe
3887	Kevin Zehner
3888	Nathan Dunn
3889	Doug Newstrom
3890	David Post
3891	David Ravitz
3892	Leroy Williams
3893	Bruce Yard
3894	Scott Compton
3895	Rich Haley
3896	John Harris
3897	J.R. Hawkins
3898	Vince Jackson
3899	Chris Latham
3900	Kevin Pitts
3901	John Shoemaker
3902	Luis Tiant
3903	Checklist

1994 Iowa Cubs Yearbook Cards

This nine-card set was inserted into the 1994 Iowa Cubs yearbook sold at Sec Taylor Stadium in Des Moines. Each of the 2-5/8" x 3-5/8" cards is perforated for removal from the sheet. Fronts feature spring training photos of the players surrounded with red and blue borders. Black-and-white backs feature career highlights and stats and the logos of sponsors Norwest banks and Coca-Cola.

	MT	NR MT	EX
Complete Set:	4.00		

(1)	Bill Brennan
(2)	Jim Bullinger
(3)	Darron Cox
(4)	Lance Dickson
(5)	Doug Glanville
(6)	Todd Haney
(7)	Jose Hernandez
(8)	Ozzie Timmons
(9)	Turk Wendell

1994 Action Packed

Action Packed Scouting Report features 72 cards, with a mix of the top prospects from all three levels of the minor leagues. The roster of players includes some of the best prospects in the game, like Chan Ho Park, Brooks Kieschnick, Kirk Presley and Curtis Goodwin, plus Michael Jordan. There is also a subset within the regular issue honoring the 40th anniversary of Roberto Clemente's debut in U.S. professional baseball, plus a checklist card featuring the 125th Anniversary of Baseball Logo in gold foil. All of the cards in the set are done in the detailed embossing, heavy lacquer and gold-foil fashion that is the Action Packed hallmark. The Franchise Gems subsets features a new technology for baseball cards - a "heat and reveal" diamond on the back of the card that reacts to body heat to show either the year of the player's "diamond debut" or the word "winner." The winner cards were redeemable for the diamond-studded versions of the same cards. There were only 100 of each of these (numbered 1/100, 2/100, etc.). Each of the 12 Franchise Gem cards were also be available in 24-karat versions that were randomly inserted (frequency not revealed, but it will obviously be more plentiful than the diamond-studded cards).

	MT	NR MT	EX
Complete Set (72):	30.00	22.00	12.00
Common Player:	.15	.11	.06

1	Alex Rodriguez	3.00
2	Trot Nixon	2.50
3	Chan Ho Park	1.00
4	Brooks Kieschnick	2.00
5	Matt Brunson	.15
6	Wayne Gomes	.25
7	Charles Johnson	.75
8	Kirk Presley	.30
9	Daron Kirkriet	.50
10	Curtis Goodwin	.15
11	Alex Ochoa	.25
12	Midre Cummings	.40
13	Russ Davis	.40
14	Phil Nevin	.60
15	J.R. Phillips	.75
16	Jeff Granger	.50
17	Makato Suzuki	.25
18	Johnny Damon	.15
19	Chad Mottola	1.00
20	Scott Ruffcorn	1.00
21	Brian Barber	.35
22	Frankie Rodriguez	.40
23	Michael Jordan	10.00
24	Michael Tucker	1.00
25	Rondell White	1.00
26	Ugueth Urbina	.35
27	Tyrone Hill	.20
28	Dmitri Young	.40
29	Marshall Boze	.30
30	Marc Newfield	.60
31	James Baldwin	1.50
32	Terrell Wade	1.00
33	Curtis Pride	.60
34	Gabe White	.75
35	Derrek Lee	.30
36	Bill Pulsipher	.20
37	Butch Huskey	.40
38	Nigel Wilson	.50
39	Tim Clark	.25
40	Ozzie Timmons	.15
41	Brien Taylor	.50
42	J.T. Snow	.40
43	Derek Jeter	.75
44	Rick Krivda	.15
45	Kevin Millar	.15
46	Matt Franco	.15
47	Jose Silva	.15
48	Benji Gil	.75
49	Pokey Reese	.15
50	Todd Hollandsworth	.60
51	Robert Ellis	.15
52	Brian Hunter	.40
53	Todd Ritchie	.25
54	Kurt Miller	.15
55	Alex Rodriguez	4.00
56	Chan Ho Park	1.00
57	Brooks Kieschnick	2.00
58	Charles Johnson	.75
59	Alex Ochoa	.50
60	Midre Cummings	.60
61	Phil Nevin	.60
62	Jose Silva	.25
63	James Baldwin	.75
64	Rondell White	1.00
65	Trot Nixon	2.00
66	Todd Hollandsworth	.75
67	Montreal Royals(1954) (Roberto Clemente)	.50
68	Four-Time Batting Champ (Roberto Clemente)	.50
69	NL MVP (1966) (Roberto Clemente)	.50
70	3,000 Hit Club (Roberto Clemente)	.50
71	Hall-of-Fame (1973) (Roberto Clemente)	.50
72	Gold Foil 125th Anniversary LogoChecklist	.50

1994 Action Packed Diamond Franchise Gems

One hundred each of the diamond-studded versions of the Franchise Gems cards were created; randomly-inserted winner cards entitled holders to redeem them for the diamond version. Cards were numbered 1/100, 2/100, etc..

55	Alex Rodriguez	300.00
56	Chan Ho Park	90.00
57	Brooks Kieschnick	175.00
58	Charles Johnson	80.00
59	Alex Ochoa	60.00
60	Midre Cummings	60.00
61	Phil Nevin	75.00
62	Jose Silva	60.00
63	James Baldwin	125.00
64	Rondell White	125.00
65	Trot Nixon	200.00
66	Todd Hollandsworth	100.00

1994 Action Packed Gold Franchise Gems

The 12 24-karat cards in this Action Packed insert set were randomly inserted in packs at a rate less than their diamond- studded counterparts, 100 of which were made and offered as prizes to those who found redeemable "winner" cards in their packs.

55	Alex Rodriguez	90.00
56	Chan Ho Park	30.00
57	Brooks Kieschnick	50.00
58	Charles Johnson	20.00
59	Alex Ochoa	20.00
60	Midre Cummings	25.00
61	Phil Nevin	35.00
62	Jose Silva	20.00
63	James Baldwin	25.00
64	Rondell White	35.00
65	Trot Nixon	60.00
66	Todd Hollandsworth	30.00
72	(Gold Foil 125th Anniversary Logo)Checklist	15.00

1994 Classic Best Minor League Gold

This 200-card set features UV coating on both sides of the cards and foil stamping on the fronts. Virtually every level of minor league baseball is represented in this set. Insert sets highlight first-round draft picks and glow-in-the dark illustrated acetate cards. Also, Classic Best has included one autographed David Justice card in every case of cards.

	MT	NR MT	EX
Complete Set (200):	24.00	18.00	9.50
Common Player:	.05	.04	.02

1	Brien Taylor	.35
2	Jeff D'Amico	.25
3	Trot Nixon	3.00
4	Clayton Byrne	.05
5	Eric Chavez	.05
6	Matt Jarvis	.05
7	Billy Owens	.25
8	Jay Powell	.25
9	Robert Eenhoorn	.05
10	Trey Beamon	.25
11	Todd Williams	.10
12	Tim Davis	.20
13	Brian Barber	.10
14	Jeff Shireman	.05
15	Melvin Mora	.05
16	Phil Nevin	.75
17	Kendall Rhine	.05
18	Billy Wagner	.20
19	Jason Kendall	.25
20	Kelly Wunsch	.25
21	D.J. Boston	.60
22	Shannon Stewart	.15
23	Anthony Manahan	.05
24	Dwight Robinson	.05
25	Alan Benes	.40
26	Dennis Slininger	.05
27	John Burke	.25
28	Jamey Wright	.05
29	Scott Eyre	.05
30	Jack Kimel	.05
31	Kerry Lacy	.05
32	Rich Aurilia	.05
33	Dave Giberti	.05
34	Daryl Henderson	.05
35	Stanley Evans	.05
36	Wayne Gomes	.25
37	Rob Grable	.05
38	Mike Juhl	.05
39	Jason Moler	.25
40	Jon Zuber	.05
41	Chad Fonville	.05
42	Mark Thompson	.05
43	Billy Masse	.05
44	Derek Hacopian	.25
45	J.J. Thobe	.25
46	Charles York	.25
47	Jamie Howard	.10
48	Andre King	.40
49	Tim Delgado	.10
50	Mike Hubbard	.05
51	Bernie Nunez	.05
52	Jon Ratliff	.05
53	Pedro Valdez	.10
54	Rich Butler	.25
55	Felipe Crespo	.05
56	Randy Phillips	.05
57	Todd Steverson	.25
58	Chris Stynes	.05
59	Ben Weber	.05
60	Chris Weinke	.25
61	Rob Lukachyk	.05
62	Brett King	.05
63	Chris Singleton	.05
64	Brian Bright	.05
65	Brent Brede	.05
66	Steve Hazlett	.05
67	Dan Serafini	.25
68	Matt Farner	.10
69	Jeremy Lee	.10
70	Anthony Medrano	.10
71	Josue Estrada	.10
72	Martin Mainville	.05
73	Chris Schwab	.20
74	John Roskos	.05
75	Charles Peterson	.20
76	Kevin Pickford	.05
77	Charles Rice	.05
78	Mike Bell	.10
79	Ed Diaz	.05
80	Torii Hunter	.20
81	Kelcey Mucker	.10
82	Nick Delvecchio	.20
83	Derek Jeter	.75
84	Ryan Karp	.40
85	Matt Luke	.10
86	Ray Suplee	.05
87	Tyler Houston	.10
88	Brad Cornett	.25
89	Kris Harmes	.10
90	Shane Andrews	.30
91	Ugueth Urbina	.40
92	Chris Mader	.10
93	Eddie Pearson	.10
94	Tim Clark	.40
95	Chris Malinoski	.05
96	John Toale	.20
97	Mark Acre	.05
98	Ernie Young	.05
99	Jeff Schmidt	.05
100	Roberto Petagine	.25
101	Eddy Diaz	.05
102	Ruben Santana	.10
103	Ron Villone	.10
104	Nate Dishington	.05
105	Charles Johnson	.50
106	Preston Wilson	.75
107	Paul Shuey	.20
108	Howard Battle	.20
109	Tim Hyers	.20
110	Rick Greene	.20
111	Justin Thompson	.15
112	Frank Rodriguez	.25
113	Jamie Arnold	.10
114	Marty Malloy	.05

115	Darrell May	.25
116	Leo Ramirez	.05
117	Tom Thobe	.05
118	Terrell Wade	1.00
119	Marc Valdes	.20
120	Scott Rolen	.05
121	Les Norman	.05
122	Michael Tucker	1.00
123	Joe Vitiello	.10
124	Chris Roberts	.20
125	Jason Giambi	.20
126	Izzy Molina	.10
127	Scott Shockey	.05
128	John Wasdin	.05
129	Joel Wolfe	.05
130	Brooks Kieschnick	2.00
131	Kennie Steenstra	.75
132	Hector Trinidad	.05
133	Derek Wallace	.05
134	Kevin Lane	.05
135	Buck McNabb	.05
136	James Mouton	1.00
137	Joey Eischen	.25
138	Todd Haney	.05
139	John Pricher	.05
140	Jeff Brown	.05
141	Jason Hardtke	.05
142	Derrek Lee	.25
143	Ira Smith	.05
144	Mike Kelly	.40
145	Mark Smith	.40
146	Sherard Clinkscales	.05
147	Ben VanRyn	.40
148	Tim Cooper	.20
149	Manny Martinez	.20
150	Kurt Ehmann	.05
151	Doug Mirabelli	.05
152	Chris Wimmer	.05
153	Scott Christman	.05
154	Kevin Coughlin	.05
155	Troy Fryman	.05
156	Sean Johnston	.05
157	Jeff Alkire	.25
158	Mike Busby	.10
159	John O'Brien	.10
160	Brian Rupp	.05
161	Steve Soderstrom	.25
162	Craig Wilson	.05
163	Alan Burke	.05
164	Mike Murphy	.10
165	T.J. Mathews	.05
166	Edgardo Alfonzo	.25
167	Randy Curtis	.25
168	Bernie Millan	.05
169	Mike Cantu	.05
170	Clint Davis	.05
171	Jason Kisey	.15
172	Aldo Pecorilli	.20
173	Dmitri Young	.40
174	Marshall Boze	.75
175	Bill Hardwick	.05
176	Kevin Riggs	.05
177	Lee Stevens	.05
178	Webster Garrison	.05
179	Wally Ritchie	.05
180	Cris Colon	.10
181	Rick Helling	.75
182	Trey McCoy	.10
183	Marc Barcelo	.05
184	Chris Demetral	.25
185	Rick Linares	.05
186	Daron Kirkreit	.50
187	Casey Whitten	.25
188	Shon Walker	.05
189	Rod Henderson	.25
190	Tyrone Horne	.05
191	B.J. Wallace	.25
192	Louis Maberry	.05
193	Brian Boehringer	.05
194	Glenn DiSarcina	.05
195	Melvin Bunch	.10
196	Chad Mottola	1.00
197	Ryan Luzinski	.40
198	Tom Wilson	.10
199	Checklist 1	.05
200	Checklist 2	.05

1994 Classic Best Illustrated Acetate

Classic Best's illustrated acetate cards feature illustrations of minor league stars done on acetate by comic artist Neal Adams. The cards, which glow in the dark, are inserted at a rate of four per case of cards and are numbered with an SH prefix.

	MT	NR MT	EX
Complete Set (5):	40.00	30.00	16.00
Common Player:	6.00	4.50	2.50

1	Brien Taylor	6.00
2	Dmitri Young	7.50
3	Derek Jeter	12.00
4	Phil Nevin	12.00
5	Frank Rodriguez	8.00

1994 Classic Best Minor League Gold #1 Picks

Classic Best's #1 Draft Pick insert cards feature 19 top picks. The cards, numbered with an LP prefix, utilize a chromium effect printing process that give the cards a reflective texture effect. They are randomly inserted, 30 cards per case.

	MT	NR MT	EX
Complete Set (19):	70.00	52.00	28.00
Common Player:	3.00	2.25	1.25

1	Alan Benes	4.00
2	Scott Christman	4.00
3	Jeff D'Amico	5.00
4	Wayne Gomes	3.50
5	Torii Hunter	4.00
6	Brooks Kieschnick	12.00
7	Daron Kirkreit	4.00
8	Derrek Lee	5.00
9	Trot Nixon	14.00
10	Charles Peterson	3.00
11	Jay Powell	3.00
12	Jon Ratliff	3.00
13	Chris Schwabb	3.00
14	Steve Soderstrom	4.00
15	Marc Valdes	3.00
16	Billy Wagner	4.00
17	John Wasdin	3.00
18	Jamey Wright	3.00
19	Kelly Wunsch	3.00

1994 Signature Rookies

This 50-card set features top prospects from the minor leagues. The cards are UV coated and have gold foil stamping, plus full color backs and fronts with a full-bleed, borderless design. The cards, sold in packs of seven, were to be sold only through hobby dealers, with no sales to wholesalers or retail outlets. The print run was limited to 1,562 cases, which means there's enough to complete approximately 45,000 complete sets. Each pack has an autographed card, inside, too, so there are also about 9,000 autographed cards per player. In addition to the autographed cards, Signature Rookies has a Hottest Prospects insert set, a five-card Bonus Signature insert set, and a five-card Cliff Floyd insert set.

	MT	NR MT	EX
Complete Set (50):	10.00	7.50	4.00
Common Player:	.10	.08	.04

1a	Russ Davis	.40
1b	Russell Davis (autograph)	10.00
2a	Brant Brown	.20
2b	Brant Brown (autograph)	5.00
3a	Ricky Bottalico	.15
3b	Ricky Bottalico (autograph)	4.00
4a	Brian Bevil	.15
4b	Brian Bevil (autograph)	.15
5a	Garret Anderson	.20
5b	Garret Anderson (autograph)	5.00
6a	Rod Henderson	.15
6b	Rod Henderson (autograph)	5.00
7a	Keith Heberling	.10
7b	Keith Heberling (autograph)	4.00
8a	Scott Hatteberg	.10
8b	Scott Hatteberg (autograph)	4.00
9a	Brook Fordyce	.10
9b	Brook Fordyce (autograph)	4.00
10a	Joey Eischen	.25
10b	Joey Eischen (autograph)	7.00
11a	Orlando Miller	.20
11b	Orlando Miller (autograph)	7.00
12a	Ray McDavid	.35
12b	Ray McDavid (autograph)	10.00
13a	Andre King	.25
13b	Andre King (autograph)	8.00
14a	Todd Hollandsworth	.50
14b	Todd Hollandsworth (autograph)	10.00
15a	Tyrone Hill	.15
15b	Tyrone Hill (autograph)	5.00
16a	Paul Spoljaric	.25
16b	Paul Spoljaric (autograph)	8.00
17a	Todd Ritchie	.10
17b	Todd Ritchie (autograph)	4.00
18a	Herbert Perry	.15
18b	Herbert Perry (autograph)	5.00
19a	Alex Ochoa	.15
19b	Alex Ochoa (autograph)	5.00
20a	Mike Neill	.15
20b	Mike Neill (autograph)	.15
21a	John Burke	.20
21b	John Burke (autograph)	7.00
22a	Alan Benes	.25
22b	Alan Benes (autograph)	8.00
23a	Robbie Beckett	.15
23b	Robbie Beckett (autograph)	5.00
24a	Brian Barber	.15
24b	Brian Barber (autograph)	5.00
25a	Justin Thompson	.20
25b	Justin "J.T." Thompson (autograph)	7.00
26a	Joey Hamilton	.15
26b	Joey Hamilton (autograph)	5.00
27a	Rick Greene	.10
27b	Rick Greene (autograph)	4.00
28a	Wayne Gomes	.15
28b	Wayne Gomes (autograph)	5.00
29a	Matthew "Big Bird" Drews	.20
29b	Matthew "Big Bird" Drews (autograph)	6.00
30a	Jeff D'Amico	.25
30b	Jeff D'Amico (autograph)	8.00
31a	Bryn Kosco	.10
31b	Bryn Kosco (autograph)	4.00
32a	Brooks Kieschnick	1.25
32b	Brooks Kieschnick (autograph)	25.00
33a	Jason Kendall	.25
33b	Jason Kendall (autograph)	7.00
34a	Mike Kelly	.40
34b	Mike Kelly (autograph)	12.00
35a	Derek Jeter	.75
35b	Derek Jeter (autograph)	15.00
36a	Jay Powell	.10
36b	Jay Powell (autograph)	4.00
37a	Phil Nevin	.75
37b	Phil Nevin (autograph)	15.00
38a	Kurt Miller	.10
38b	Kurt Miller (autograph)	4.00
39a	Chad McConnell	.10
39b	Chad McConnell (autograph)	4.00
40a	Sean Lowe	.15
40b	Sean Lowe (autograph)	5.00
41a	Michael Tucker	.75
41b	Michael Tucker (autograph)	15.00
42a	Paul Shuey	.15
42b	Paul Shuey (autograph)	5.00
43a	Dan Smith	.10
43b	Dan Smith (autograph)	4.00
44a	Calvin Reese	.20
44b	Calvin Reese (autograph)	7.50
45a	Kirk Presley	.20
45b	Kirk Presley (autograph)	6.00
46a	Jamey "Jamo" Wright	.15
46b	Jamey "Jamo" Wright (autograph)	5.00
47a	Gabe White	.25
47b	Gabe White (autograph)	8.00
48a	John Wasdin	.10
48b	John Wasdin (autograph)	4.00
49a	Billy Wagner	.15
49b	Billy Wagner (autograph)	5.00
50a	Joe "Vit" Vitiello	.20
50b	Joe "Vit" Vitiello (autograph)	6.00

1994 Signature Rookies Hottest Prospects

Signature Rookies' 12-card Hottest Prospects insert set cards are numbered with an S prefix. There were 5,000 complete sets made.

	MT	NR MT	EX
Complete Set (12):	25.00	18.50	10.00
Common Player:	.50	.40	.20

1a	John Burke	1.00
2a	Russ Davis	1.00
3a	Todd Hollandsworth	2.50
4a	Derek Jeter	4.00
5a	Mike Kelly	2.00
6a	Ray McDavid	1.50
7a	Kurt Miller	.75
8a	Phil Niven	3.50
9a	Alex Ochoa	1.50
10a	Justin "J.T." Thompson	1.50
11a	Michael Tucker	6.00
12a	Gabe White	1.50

1994 Signature Rookies Bonus Signature Set

Signature Rookies packs had Bonus cards randomly inserted in them; there were 1,000 sets of the five-card set made. The cards, are numbered with a P prefix.

	MT	NR MT	EX
Complete Set (5):	100.00	75.00	40.00
Common Player:	20.00	15.00	8.00

1a	Rick Helling	25.00
2a	Charles Johnson	30.00
3a	Chad Mottola	25.00
4a	J.R. Phillips	35.00
5a	Glen Williams	20.00

1994 Signature Rookies Cliff Floyd Set

Montreal Expos' top prospect Cliff Floyd is featured on this five-card Signature Rookies insert set. The cards, numbered with a B prefix, were limited to 10,000 complete sets. Cards were random inserts inside packs.

	MT	NR MT	EX
Complete Set (5):	35.00	26.00	14.00
Common Floyd:	8.00	6.00	3.25

1a	Cliff Floyd	8.00
1b	Cliff Floyd (autograph)	75.00
2a	Cliff Floyd	8.00
2b	Cliff Floyd (autograph)	75.00
3a	Cliff Floyd	8.00
3b	Cliff Floyd (autograph)	75.00
4a	Cliff Floyd	8.00
4b	Cliff Floyd (autograph)	75.00
5a	Cliff Floyd	8.00
5b	Cliff Floyd (autograph)	75.00

1994 Upper Deck

Upper Deck's 1994 minor league cards utilize similar design elements of their major league counterparts. The super-premium set of 270 cards features the top professional players who have yet to appear in a Major League game. Cards have UV coating and foil accents, along with color photography on both sides of the card, including a full-bleed, color photo on the front and a smaller, black-and-white photo in the lower left corner. The player's name is printed in silver foil, as is his Major League team affiliation. The regular player cards (225) have ratings by Baseball America on the back. Subsets include: Major League Evaluations (15), with backs done by noted statistical innovator Bill James; Star Potential (20), showcasing top young players; and Upper Deck All-Stars, one per position, as selected by experts at Upper Deck and Baseball America. Insert sets include: Organizational Players of the Year (28); Trade Cards (2), which can be redeemed by mail for two top picks in the 1993 amateur draft; and Top 10 Prospects (oversized cards), featured on 8-1/2" x 5-1/4" inch cards inserted on each box. These cards are also available as regular-sized cards through an on-pack offer.

	MT	NR MT	EX
Complete Set (270):	25.00	18.00	10.00
Common Player:	.05	.04	.02

1 Alex Gonzalez 1.50
2 Brooks Kieschnick 2.00
3 Michael Tucker 1.00
4 Trot Nixon 3.00
5 Brien Taylor .40
6 Quinton McCracken .15
7 Terrell Wade 1.00
8 Brandon Wilson .25
9 Roberto Petagine .20
10 Chad Mottola 1.00
11 T.R. Lewis .15
12 Herbert Perry .15
13 Bob Abreu .20
14 Jorge Fabregas .10
15 Mike Kelly .40
16 Ryan McGuire .25
17 Alan Zinter .10
18 Troy Hughes .10
19 Brook Fordyce .15
20 Alex Ochoa .20
21 Chris Wimmer .05
22 Jason Hardtke .05
23 Ricardo Hildago .10
24 Greg Zaun .10
25 Roger Cedeno .20
26 Curtis Shaw .20
27 Brian Giles .20
28 Felix Rodriguez .25
29 Motor-Boat Jones .20
30 Dmitri Young .35
31 Justin Mashore .05
32 Curtis Goodwin .10
33 Marquis Riley .10
34 Les Norman .05
35 Billy Hall .05
36 Jamie Arnold .05
37 Mike Farmer .05
38 Brent Bowers .10
39 Chad McConnell .15
40 Mike Robertson .05
41 Brent Cookson .05
42 Dan Cholowsky .15
43 Justin Thompson .20
44 Joe Vitiello .08
45 Todd Steverson .08
46 Brian Bevil .05
47 Paul Shuey .10
48 Scott Eyre .15
49 Rick Greene .05
50 Jose Silva .10
51 Kurt Miller .10
52 Ron Villone .10
53 Darren Bragg .05
54 Mike Lieberthal .05
55 Gabe White .40
56 Vince Moore .05
57 Tony Clark .05
58 Chris Eddy .10
59 Ray Durham .10
60 Todd Hollandsworth .15
61 Andres Berumen .05
62 Quilvio Veras .15
63 Wayne Gomes .15
64 Ryan Karp .08
65 Randy Curtis .08
66 Steve Rodriguez .10
67 Jason Schmidt .08
68 Mark Acre .15
69 B.J. Wallace .10
70 Alvin Morman .15
71 Travis Baptist .15
72 Jim Wawruck .08
73 Marty Cordova .10
74 Jamie Dismuke .10
75 Joe Randa .05
76 Danny Clyburn .10
77 Joey Eischen .10
78 Chris Seelbach .10
79 Izzy Molina .05
80 Chris Roberts .10
81 Rod Henderson .10
82 Kennie Steenstra .10
83 Ugueth Urbina .05
84 Stanton Cameron .10
85 Doug Glanville .10
86 Billy Wagner .40
87 Tate Seefried .05
88 Tyler Houston .15
89 Derek Lowe .25
90 Alan Benes .35
91 Terrell Wade 2.00
92 Rod Henderson (AS) .15
93 Charles Johnson (AS) .75
94 D.J. Boston (AS) .75
95 Ruben Santana (AS) .20
96 Joe Randa (AS) .15
97 Alex Gonzalez (AS) 1.00
98 Tim Clark (AS) .50
99 Randy Curtis (AS) .15
100 Brian Hunter (AS) .20
101 Jose Lima .05
102 Ray Holbert .10
103 Karim Garcia .10
104 Chris Martin .05
105 David Bell .05
106 Tim Clark .15
107 Matt Drews .08
108 Dan Serafini .05
109 Demetrish Jenkins .10
110 Charles Johnson 1.00
111 Jason Moler .40
112 Brett Backlund .10
113 Kevin Jordan .05
114 Jesus Tavarez .05
115 Frank Rodriguez .20
116 Derrek Lee .05
117 Pokey Reese .10
118 Dave Stevens .05
119 Julio Bruno .15
120 D.J. Boston 1.00
121 Jim Dougherty .15
122 Daron Kirkreit .50
123 Kerwin Moore .10
124 Jason Kendall .25
125 Johnny Damon .20
126 Andre King .40
127 Raul Gonzalez .10
128 Eddie Pearson .15
129 Yuri Sanchez .10
130 Russ Davis .60
131 Arquimedez Pozo .10
132 Jon Lieber .05
133 Glenn Murray .10
134 Brant Brown .05
135 Brian Hunter .15
136 Mike Gulan .05
137 Tim Vanegmond .08
138 Billy Vanlandingham .05
139 Robert Ellis .10
140 Calvin Murray .25
141 Kurt Ehmann .05
142 Brian DuBose .10
143 Robert Eenhoorn .10
144 Howard Battle .10
145 Jason Giambi .15
146 James Baldwin (MLE) .75
147 Rick Helling (MLE) .40
148 Ricky Bottalico (MLE) .25
149 Paul Spolijaric (MLE) .50
150 Alex Gonzalez (MLE) 1.00
151 Tavo Alvarez (MLE) .25
152 Joey Eischen (MLE) .15
153 Shane Andrews (MLE) .25
154 James Mouton (MLE) .50
155 Russ Davis (MLE) .50
156 Phil Nevin (MLE) .75
157 Garret Anderson (MLE) .25
158 Gabe White (MLE) .35
159 Brian Hunter (MLE) .10
160 Ray McDavid (MLE) .15
161 Mike Durrant .08
162 Eric Owens .05
163 Rick Gorecki .05
164 Lyle Mouton .05
165 Ray McDavid .25
166 Tony Graffagnino .10
167 Todd Ritchie .05
168 Jose Herrera .05
169 Steve Dunn .05
170 Tavo Alvarez .20
171 Jon Farrell .05
172 Omar Ramirez .15
173 Ruben Santana .10
174 Tracy Sanders .10
175 Shane Andrews .10
176 Rob Henkel .10
177 Joel Wolfe .10
178 Chris Schwab .15
179 Chris Weinke .10
180 Ozzie Timmons .05
181 Jason Bates .15
182 Matt Brunson .20
183 Garret Anderson .10
184 Brian Rupp .05
185 Derek Jeter .25
186 Desi Relaford .05
187 Darren Burton .10
188 David Mysel .05
189 Steve Soderstorm .10
190 Steve Gibralter .15
191 Brian Sackinsky .10
192 Marc Pisciotta .15
193 Gene Schall .10
194 Jimmy Haynes .15
195 Shannon Stewart .10
196 Neifi Perez .10
197 Cris Colon .10
198 Trey Beamon .15
199 Jon Zuber .05
200 John Burke .05
201 Derek Wallace .15
202 Chad Ogea .10
203 Ernie Young .15
204 Jose Malave .20
205 Bill Pulsipher .25
206 Leon Glenn .08
207 Scott Sullivan .10
208 Orlando Miller .10
209 John Wasdin .15
210 Paul Spoljaric .25
211 Charles Peterson .15
212 Ben Van Ryn .10
213 Chris Sexton .10
214 Bobby Bonds Jr. .25
215 James Mouton .75
216 Terrell Lowery .20
217 Oscar Munoz .15
218 Mike Bell .15
219 Preston Wilson 1.00
220 Mark Thompson .15
221 Aaron Holbert .08
222 Tommy Adams .08
223 Ramon D. Martinez .15
224 Tim Davis .10
225 Ricky Bottalico .08
226 Rick Krivda .10
227 Troy Percival .15
228 Mark Sweeney .15
229 Joey Hamilton .20
230 Phil Nevin .75
231 John Ratliff .20
232 Mark Smith .15
233 Tyrone Hill .25
234 Kevin Riggs .10
235 John Dettmer .08
236 Brian Barber .10
237 Hector Trinidad .08
238 Jeff Alkire .10
239 Phil Geisler .25
240 Rick Helling .40
241 Edgardo Alfonzo .20
242 Matt Franco .10
243 Chad Roper .20
244 Basil Shabazz .20
245 James Baldwin .75
246 Scott Hatteberg .10
247 Glenn DiSarcina .10
248 LaTroy Hawkins .40
249 Marshall Boze .50
250 Michael Moore .40
251 Brien Taylor (SP) .50
252 Johnny Damon (SP) .60
253 Curtis Goodwin (SP) .25
254 Jose Silva (SP) .40
255 Terrell Wade (SP) 2.00
256 Dmitri Young (SP) .35
257 Roger Cedeno (SP) .35
258 Alex Ochoa (SP) .35
259 D.J. Boston (SP) 1.00
260 Michael Tucker (SP) 1.25
261 Calvin Murray (SP) .40
262 Frank Rodriguez (SP) .35
263 Michael Moore (SP) .40
264 Ugueth Urbina (SP) .40
265 Chad Mottola (SP) 1.00
266 Todd Hollandsworth (SP) .60
267 Rod Henderson (SP) .35
268 Roberto Petagine (SP) .40
269 Charles Johnson (SP) 1.25
270 Trot Nixon (SP) 5.00
(271) Michael Jordan MJ23 (Silver, Michael Jordan MJ23) 20.00

1994 Upper Deck Player of the Year

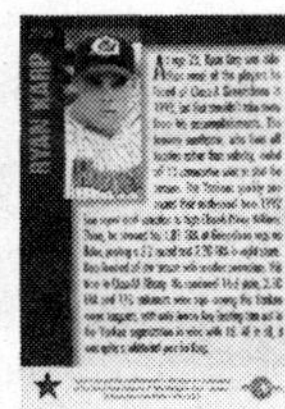

This 28-card insert set features one top prospect from each Major League organization. The cards, numbered with a PY prefix, were random inserts in 1994 Upper Deck Minor League foil packs.

	MT	NR MT	EX
Complete Set (28):	70.00	52.00	28.00
Common Player:	2.50	2.00	1.00

1 Marquis Riley 2.50
2 Roberto Petagine 4.00
3 Ernie Young 3.00
4 Alex Gonzalez 12.00
5 Hiawatha Wade 10.00
6 Marshall Boze 4.00
7 Mike Gulan 3.00
8 Brant Brown 4.00
9 Roger Cedeno 3.50
10 Rod Henderson 3.00
11 Calvin Murray 5.00
12 Omar Ramirez 3.00
13 Ruben Santana 2.50
14 Charles Johnson 7.50
15 Bill Pulsipher 5.00
16 Alex Ochoa 6.00
17 Ray McDavid 4.00
18 Jason Moler 3.00
19 Danny Clyburn 4.00
20 Rick Helling 5.00
21 Frank Rodriquez 5.00
22 Chad Mottola 8.00
23 John Burke 2.50
24 Michael Tucker 10.00
25 Brian DuBose 2.50
26 LaTroy Hawkins 5.00
27 James Baldwin 7.00
28 Ryan Karp 4.00

ALPHABETICAL INDEX

MAJOR LEAGUE

A

1976 A & P Brewers ... 1
1970 Action Cartridge ... 1
1988 Action Packed ... 1
1992 Action Packed Promos ... 1
1992 Action Packed All-Star Gallery Series I ... 1
1992 Action Packed All-Star Gallery Series II ... 2
1992 Action Packed Gold ... 2
1993 Action Packed Tom Seaver Prototypes ... 2
1983 Affiliated Food Rangers ... 2
1990 Agfa Film ... 3
1970 Carl Aldana Orioles ... 3
1990 All American Baseball Team ... 3
1887 Allen & Ginter World's Champions (N28) ... 3
1888 Allen & Ginter World's Champions (N29) ... 3
1910 All Star Base-Ball ... 3
1971 Allstate Insurance ... 4
1987 Allstate Insurance ... 4
1991 Alrak Griffey Gazette ... 4
1993 Alrak Ken Griffey, Jr. ... 4
1908 American Caramel Co. (E91, Set A) ... 4
1909 American Caramel Co. (E91, Set B) ... 4
1910 American Caramel Co. (E91, Set C) ... 5
1910 American Caramel die-cuts (E125) ... 5
1909 - 11 American Caramel Co. (E90-1) ... 5
1910 American Caramel Co. Pirates (E90-2) ... 6
1910 American Caramel Co. Cubs/Sox (E90-3) ... 6
1915 American Caramel (E106) ... 6
1921 American Carmel Series of 80 (E121) ... 6
1922 American Carmel Series of 120 (E121) ... 7
1922 American Carmel Series of 80 (E122) ... 7
1922 American Carmel Series of 240 (E120) ... 8
1927 American Carmel Series of 60 (E126) ... 9
1962 American Tract Society ... 9
1989 Ames 20/20 Club ... 9
1990 Ames All-Stars ... 9
1991 Arena Holograms ... 9
1955 Armour Coins ... 10
1959 Armour Coins ... 10
1960 Armour Coins ... 10
1986 Ault Foods Blue Jays ... 10
1964 Aurovision Records ... 10

B

1914 B18 Blankets ... 11
1916 BF2 Felt Pennants ... 11
1936 - 37 BF3 Felt Pennants ... 12
1949 Baas Cheri-Cola ... 13
1948 Babe Ruth Story ... 13
1986 Baltimore Orioles Team Issue ... 13
1913 Tom Barker Game ... 13
1911 Baseball Bats ... 14
1988 Baseball Immortals ... 14
1987 Baseball Super Stars Discs ... 14
1988 Baseball Super Stars Discs ... 15
1990 Baseball Wit ... 15
1934 Batter-Up ... 15
1959 Bazooka ... 16
1960 Bazooka ... 16
1961 Bazooka ... 17
1962 Bazooka ... 17
1963 Bazooka ... 17
1963 Bazooka All-Time Greats ... 18
1964 Bazooka ... 18
1964 Bazooka Stamps ... 18
1965 Bazooka ... 18
1966 Bazooka ... 19
1967 Bazooka ... 19
1968 Bazooka ... 19
1969 - 70 Bazooka ... 20
1971 Bazooka Unnumbered Set ... 20
1971 Bazooka Numbered Set ... 20
1988 Bazooka ... 20
1989 Bazooka ... 21
1990 Bazooka ... 21
1991 Bazooka ... 21
1992 Bazooka ... 21
1958 Bell Brand Dodgers ... 21
1960 Bell Brand Dodgers ... 22
1961 Bell Brand Dodgers ... 22
1962 Bell Brand Dodgers ... 22
1992 Ben's Bakery Super Hitters Discs ... 22
1993 Ben's Bakery Super Pitchers Discs ... 22
1987 David Berg Hot Dogs Cubs ... 22
1988 David Berg Hot Dogs Cubs ... 23
1951 Berk Ross ... 23
1952 Berk Ross ... 23
1994 Big Apple 1969 Mets Discs ... 24
1986 Big League Chew ... 24
1956 Big League Stars Statues ... 24
1991 Bleachers Frank Thomas ... 24
1992 Bleachers Ken Griffey, Jr. ... 24
1992 Bleachers David Justice ... 24
1933 Blue Bird Babe Ruth ... 25
1987 Boardwalk and Baseball ... 25
1955 - 60 Bill and Bob Braves Postcards ... 25
1987 Bohemian Hearth Bread Padres ... 25
1947 Bond Bread Jackie Robinson ... 25
1984 Borden's Reds Stickers ... 26
1912 Boston Garter ... 26
1913 Boston Garter ... 26
1914 Boston Garter ... 26
1948 Bowman ... 26
1949 Bowman ... 26
1950 Bowman ... 27
1951 Bowman ... 28
1952 Bowman ... 29
1953 Bowman Color ... 30
1953 Bowman Black & White ... 31
1954 Bowman ... 31
1955 Bowman ... 32
1989 Bowman ... 33
1989 Bowman Inserts ... 35
1990 Bowman ... 35
1990 Bowman Inserts ... 36
1991 Bowman ... 36
1992 Bowman ... 39
1993 Bowman ... 41
1903 Breisch Williams Type I (E107) 43
1903 Breisch Williams Type II (E107) ... 43
1909 C.A. Briggs Co. (E97) ... 44
1954 Briggs Meats ... 44
1911 Brunners Bread (D304) ... 44
1977 Burger King Yankees ... 44
1978 Burger King Astros ... 44
1978 Burger King Rangers ... 45
1978 Burger King Tigers ... 45
1978 Burger King Yankees ... 45
1979 Burger King Phillies ... 45
1979 Burger King Yankees ... 45
1980 Burger King Phillies ... 46
1980 Burger King Pitch, Hit & Run ... 46
1982 Burger King Braves ... 46
1982 Burger King Indians ... 46
1986 Burger King ... 47
1987 Burger King ... 47
1933 Butter Cream ... 47
1934 Butterfinger (R310) ... 47

C

1985 CBS Radio Game of the Week 48
1986 CBS Radio Game of the Week 48
1985 Cain's Potato Chips Tigers ... 48
1986 Cain's Potato Chips Tigers ... 48
1987 Cain's Potato Chips Tigers ... 48
1950 Callahan Hall of Fame ... 48
1994 Capital Cards 1969 Mets Postcards ... 49
1989 Cap'n Crunch ... 49
1955 Carling Beer Cleveland Indians ... 49
1956 Carling Beer Cleveland Indians ... 49
1957 Carling Beer Cleveland Indians ... 49

1958 Carling Beer Cleveland Indians 50
1959 Carling Beer Cleveland Indians 50
1961 Carling Beer Cleveland Indians 50
1992 Carl's Jr. Padres 50
1992 Carlson Travel 1982 Brewers .. 50
1964 Challenge the Yankees Game.. 50
1965 Challenge the Yankees Game . 51
1987 Champion Phillies 51
1988 Chef Boyardee 51
1994 Churchs Chicken Hometown Stars 51
1994 Churchs Chicken Show Stoppers 52
1985 CIGNA Phillies 52
1986 CIGNA Phillies 52
1985 Circle K 52
1969 Citgo Coins 52
1987 Classic Major League Baseball Game 52
1987 Classic Travel Edition 53
1988 Classic - Red 53
1988 Classic - Blue 53
1989 Classic 54
1989 Classic Travel Update I 54
1989 Classic Travel Update II 54
1990 Classic Baseball 55
1990 Classic Series II 55
1990 Classic Series III 55
1991 Classic 56
1991 Classic Series II 56
1991 Classic Series III 57
1991 Classic Collector's Edition 57
1992 Classic Series I 58
1992 Classic Series II 58
1992 Classic Collector's Edition 59
1993 Classic 59
1989 Cleveland Indians Team Set ... 60
1961 - 62 Cloverleaf Dairy Minnesota Twins 60
1911 George Close Candy Co. (E94) 60
1988 CMC Don Mattingly 60
1989 CMC Jose Canseco 60
1989 CMC Mickey Mantle 60
1989 CMC Babe Ruth 61
1952 Coca-Cola Playing Tips Test Cards 61
1952 Coca-Cola Playing Tips 61
1981 Coca-Cola 61
1982 Coca-Cola Brigham's Red Sox 61
1982 Coca-Cola Reds 62
1985 Coca-Cola White Sox 62
1986 Coca-Cola White Sox 62
1987 Coca-Cola Tigers 62
1987 Coca-Cola White Sox 63
1988 Coca-Cola Padres 63
1988 Coca-Cola White Sox 63
1989 Coca-Cola Padres 63
1989 Coca-Cola White Sox 63
1990 Coca-Cola Garry Templeton 64
1990 Coca-Cola Padres 64
1990 Coca-Cola Detroit Tigers 64
1990 Coca-Cola White Sox 64
1991 Coca-Cola Tigers 64
1993 Coca-Cola Commanders of the Hill 64
1909 Colgan's Chips (E254) 65
1912 Colgan's Chips Red Borders (E270) 66
1912 Colgan's Chips Tin Tops (E270) 66
1916 Collins-McCarthy (E135) 67
1989 Colla Jose Canseco Postcards 68
1989 Colla Andre Dawson Postcards 68
1989 Colla Mike Greenwell Postcards 68
1989 Colla Don Mattingly Postcards 68
1989 Colla Mark McGwire Postcards 68
1989 Colla Kevin Mitchell Postcards 68
1989 Colla Ozzie Smith Postcards ... 68
1990 Colla Collection Promos 68
1990 Colla Jose Canseco 68
1990 Colla Will Clark 69
1990 Colla Kevin Maas 69
1990 Colla Don Mattingly 69
1990 Colla Will Clark Postcards 69
1991 Colla Collection Promos 69
1991 Colla Roberto Alomar 69
1991 Colla Barry Bonds 69
1991 Colla Joe Carter 69
1991 Colla Dwight Gooden 69
1991 Colla Ken Griffey, Jr. 70
1991 Colla David Justice 70
1991 Colla Ryne Sandberg 70
1991 Colla Darryl Strawberry 70
1991 Colla Ryne Sandberg Postcards 70
1992 Colla Collection Promos 70
1992 Colla All-Stars 70
1992 Colla Steve Avery 70
1992 Colla Jeff Bagwell 71
1992 Colla Barry Bonds 71
1992 Colla Tony Gwynn 71
1992 Colla Mark McGwire 71
1992 Colla Nolan Ryan 71
1992 Colla Frank Thomas 71
1993 Colla All-Stars 71
1993 Colla Mike Piazza Postcards ... 71
1993 Colla Cal Ripken, Jr. Postcards 71
1991 Conlon Collection 72
1992 Conlon Collection 73
1993 Conlon Collection 74
1993 Conlon Color 75
1994 Conlon Collection 75
1991 Country Hearth Mariners 76
1910 Coupon Cigarettes Type 1 (T213) 76
1914 Coupon Cigarettes Type 2 (T213) 77
1919 Coupon Cigarettes Type 3 (T213) 77
1914 Cracker Jack 78
1915 Cracker Jack 78
1982 Cracker Jack 79
1991 Cracker Jack Topps I 79
1991 Cracker Jack Topps II 79
1992 Cracker Jack Donruss I 79
1992 Cracker Jack Donruss II 80
1993 Cracker Jack Anniversary 80
1980 - 83 Cramer Baseball Legends 80
1976 Crane Potato Chips 81
1913 Cravats Felt Pennants 81
1909 Croft's Candy (E92) 81
1909 Croft's Cocoa (E92) 81
1991 Crown/Coke Orioles 82
1992 Crown Orioles Action Standups 83
1911 Cullivan's Fireside Philadelphia A's 83

D

1972 Daily Juice Co. 84
1992 Dairy Queen Team USA 84
1954 Dan-Dee Potato Chips 84
1910 Darby Chocolates (E271) 84
1991 Jimmy Dean 84
1992 Jimmy Dean 85
1992 Jimmy Dean Living Legends ... 85
1993 Jimmy Dean Rookie Cards 85
1933 DeLong 85
1935 Al Demaree Die-cuts 85
1932 Charles Denby Cigars Cubs 86
1991 Denny's Grand Slam 86
1992 Denny's Grand Slam 86
1993 Denny's Grand Slam Holograms 86
1909 Derby Cigars 86
1993 DiamondMarks Promos 86
1993 DiamondMarks 87
1993 DiamondMarks Inserts 87
1934 - 36 Diamond Stars 87
1924 Diaz Cigarettes 88
1992 Diet Pepsi All-Stars 88
1937 Dixie Lids 88
1937 Dixie Lids Premiums 89
1938 Dixie Lids 89
1938 Dixie Lids Premiums 89
1952 Dixie Lids 89
1952 Dixie Lids Premiums 89
1953 Dixie Lids 89
1953 Dixie Lids Premiums 89
1954 Dixie Lids 90
1909 Dockman & Sons Gum (E92) ... 90
1988 Domino's Pizza Tigers 90
1981 Donruss 90
1982 Donruss 92
1983 Donruss 94
1983 Donruss Action All-Stars 97
1983 Donruss Hall of Fame Heroes . 97
1984 Donruss 97
1984 Donruss Action All-Stars 99
1984 Donruss Champions 100
1985 Donruss 100
1985 Donruss Action All-Stars 102
1985 Donruss Box Panels 102

1985 Donruss Diamond Kings Supers 102
1985 Donruss Highlights 103
1985 Donruss Sluggers of The Hall of Fame 103
1986 Donruss 103
1986 Donruss All-Stars 105
1986 Donruss Box Panels 105
1986 Donruss Diamond Kings Supers 106
1986 Donruss Highlights 106
1986 Donruss Pop-Ups 106
1986 Donruss Rookies 106
1987 Donruss 107
1987 Donruss All-Stars 109
1987 Donruss Box Panels 109
1987 Donruss Diamond Kings Supers 109
1987 Donruss Highlights 110
1987 Donruss Opening Day 110
1987 Donruss Pop-Ups 111
1987 Donruss Rookies 111
1988 Donruss 111
1988 Donruss MVP 113
1988 Donruss All-Stars 114
1988 Donruss Baseball's Best 114
1988 Donruss Diamond Kings Supers 115
1988 Donruss Pop-Ups 115
1988 Donruss Rookies 115
1988 Donruss Boston Red Sox Team Book 116
1988 Donruss Chicago Cubs Team Book 116
1988 Donruss New York Mets Team Book 116
1988 Donruss New York Yankees Team Book 116
1988 Donruss Oakland A's Team Book 117
1989 Donruss 117
1989 Donruss MVP 119
1989 Donruss Grand Slammers 119
1989 Donruss All-Stars 119
1989 Donruss Baseball's Best 119
1989 Donruss Pop-Ups 121
1989 Donruss Rookies 121
1989 Donruss Traded 121
1990 Donruss Previews 121
1990 Donruss 121
1990 Donruss MVP 124
1990 Donruss Grand Slammers 124
1990 Donruss A.L. Best 124
1990 Donruss N.L. Best 125
1990 Donruss Diamond Kings Supers 125
1990 Donruss Learning Series 125
1990 Donruss Rookies 126
1991 Donruss Previews 126
1991 Donruss 126
1991 Donruss Highlights 128
1991 Donruss Grand Slammers 129
1991 Donruss Elite 129
1991 Donruss Rookies 129
1992 Donruss Previews 129
1992 Donruss 129
1992 Donruss Bonus Cards 132
1992 Donruss Diamond Kings 132
1992 Donruss Elite 132
1992 Donruss Rookies 132
1992 Donruss Rookie Phenoms 133
1992 Donruss Triple Play 133
1992 Donruss Triple Play Gallery of Stars 134
1992 Donruss McDonald's 134
1992 Donruss Nolan Ryan Career Series 134
1993 Donruss 134
1993 Donruss Long Ball Leaders 137
1993 Donruss MVP's 137
1993 Donruss Spirit of the Game 137
1993 Donruss Diamond Kings 137
1993 Donruss Masters of the Game 137
1993 Donruss Elite 138
1993 Donruss Elite Supers 138
1993 Donruss Elite Dominators 138
1993 Donruss 1992 Blue Jays Commemorative Set 138
1993 Donruss Triple Play 138
1993 Donruss Triple Play Gallery 139
1993 Donruss Triple Play League Leaders 140
1993 Donruss Triple Play Nicknames 140
1993 Donruss Triple Play Action Baseball 140
1994 Donruss Promos 140
1994 Donruss 140
1994 Donruss Decade Dominators 142
1994 Donruss Decade Dominators Supers 142
1994 Donruss Elite 143
1994 Donruss Diamond Kings 143
1994 Donruss Diamond Kings Super 143
1994 Donruss MVPs 143
1994 Donruss Award Winners Supers 143
1994 Donruss Anniversary-1984 144
1994 Donruss Long Ball Leaders 144
1994 Donruss Spirit of the Game 144
1994 Donruss Spirit of the Game Super 144
1994 Donruss Special Edition - Gold 144
1994 Donruss Triple Play Promos 145
1994 Donruss Triple Play 145
1994 Donruss Triple Play Medalists 146
1994 Donruss Triple Play Bomb Squad 146
1994 Donruss Triple Play Nicknames 146
1986 Dorman's Cheese 146
1953 - 55 Dormand Postcards 146
1941 Double Play 147
1950 Drake's 147
1981 Drake's 148
1982 Drake's 148
1983 Drake's 148
1984 Drake's 148
1985 Drake's 149
1986 Drake's 149
1987 Drake's 149
1988 Drake's 149
1989 Dubuque Braves 150
1990 Dubuque Braves Team Photo Set 150
1990 Dubuque Braves 150
1991 Dubuque Braves Team Photo Set 150
1991 Dubuque Braves 151
1888 Duke Talk of the Diamond (N135) 151
1992 Dunkin' Donuts Red Sox 151
1993 Duracell Power Players 151
1914 (D303) 244
1911 (D304) 44
1911 (D359) 486
1911 (D359) 802

E

1910 E98 "Set of 30" 152
1909 E101 "Set of 50" 152
1908 E102 "Set of 25" 152
1966 East Hills Pirates 152
1992 Eclipse Negro League 153
1990 Elite Senior League 153
1954 Esskay Hot Dogs Orioles 153
1955 Esskay Hot Dogs Orioles 153
1949 Eureka Sportstamps 154
1921 Exhibits 154
1922 Exhibits 155
1922 Eastern Exhibit Supply Co. 155
1923 - 24 Exhibits 155
1925 Exhibits 155
1926 Exhibits 156
1927 Exhibits 156
1928 Exhibits 157
1929 "Anonymous" Exhibits 157
1929 - 30 Four-on-One Exhibits 157
1931 - 32 Four-on-One Exhibits 158
1933 Four-on-One Exhibits 158
1934 Four-on-One Exhibits 158
1935 Four-on-One Exhibits 158
1936 Four-on-One Exhibits 158
1937 Four-on-One Exhibits 159
1938 Four-on-One Exhibits 159
1939 - 46 Salutation Exhibits 159
1961 Exhibits - Wrigley Field 159
1948 Baseball's Great Hall of Fame Exhibits 160
1953 Canadian Exhibits 160
1962 Statistic Back Exhibits 160
1963 Statistic Back Exhibits 160
1947 - 66 Exhibits 161
1909 (E92) Croft's Candy 81
1909 (E92) Croft's Cocoa 81
1909 (E92) Dockman & Sons Gum 90
1912 (E270) Red Borders 66
1912 (E270)Tin Tops 66
1903 Type I (E107) 43
1914 Type I (E224) 577
1927 Type I (E210) 808
1903 Type II (E107) 43

1927 Type II (E210) 809
1914 Type II (E224) 577
1909 - 11 (E90-1) 5
1910 (E90-2) 6
1910 (E90-3) 6
1908 (E91, Set A) 4
1909 (E91, Set B) 4
1910 (E91, Set C) 5
1909 (E92) 353
1910 (E93) 550
1911 (E94) 60
1909 (E95) 446
1910 (E96) 446
1909 (E97) 44
1910 (E103) 802
1910 (E104-I) 353
1910 (E104-II) 354
1910 (E104-III) 354
1910 (E105) 329
1915 (E106) 6
1922 (E120) 8
1921 (E121) 6
1922 (E121) 7
1922 (E122) 7
1923 (E123) 263
1910 (E125) 5
1927 (E126) 9
1916 (E135) 67
1888 (E223) 242
1921 (E253) 426
1909 (E254) 65
1910 (E271) 84
1933 (E285) 486
1910 (E286) 275
1912 (E300) 460

F

1904 Fan Craze American League .. 162
1904 Fan Craze National League ... 162
1922 Fans Cigarettes (T231) 163
1988 Fantastic Sam's 163
1987 Farmland Dairies Mets 163
1988 Farmland Dairies Mets 163
1939 Father & Son Shoes Phillies .. 163
1914 Fatima (T222) 163
1913 Fatima Team Cards (T200) 164
1951 Fischer Baking Labels 164
1959 Fleer Ted Williams 164
1960 Fleer 165
1961 - 62 Fleer 165
1963 Fleer 165
1966 Fleer 166
1972 Fleer Famous Feats 166
1973 Fleer Wildest Days and Plays 166
1974 Fleer Baseball Firsts 166
1975 Fleer Pioneers of Baseball 167
1981 Fleer 167
1981 Fleer Star Stickers 169
1982 Fleer 170
1982 Fleer Stamps 172
1983 Fleer 173
1983 Fleer Stamps 175
1983 Fleer Stickers 175
1984 Fleer 176
1984 Fleer Update 178
1984 Fleer Stickers 178
1985 Fleer 179
1985 Fleer Update 181
1985 Fleer Stickers 182
1985 Fleer Limited Edition 182
1986 Fleer 182
1986 Fleer All Stars 184
1986 Fleer Future Hall Of Famers .. 185
1986 Fleer Box Panels 185
1986 Fleer Update 185
1986 Fleer Baseball's Best 185
1986 Fleer League Leaders 186
1986 Fleer Limited Edition 186
1986 Fleer Mini 186
1986 Fleer Star Stickers 187
1986 Fleer Star Stickers Box Panels 187
1987 Fleer 187
1987 Fleer All Stars 189
1987 Fleer Headliners 189
1987 Fleer '86 World Series 190
1987 Fleer Box Panels 190
1987 Fleer Update 190
1987 Fleer Baseball's Award Winners 190
1987 Fleer Baseball All Stars 191
1987 Fleer Baseball's Best 191
1987 Fleer Baseball's Exciting Stars 191
1987 Fleer Baseball's Game Winners 191
1987 Fleer Baseball's Hottest Stars 192
1987 Fleer League Leaders 192
1987 Fleer Limited Edition 192
1987 Fleer Mini 192
1987 Fleer Baseball Record Setters 193
1987 Fleer Star Stickers 193
1987 Fleer Star Sticker Box Panels 194
1988 Fleer 194
1988 Fleer All Stars 196
1988 Fleer Headliners 196
1988 Fleer '87 World Series 196
1988 Fleer Box Panels 196
1988 Fleer Update 197
1988 Fleer Award Winners 197
1988 Fleer Baseball All Stars 197
1988 Fleer Baseball MVP 198
1988 Fleer Baseball's Best 198
1988 Fleer Baseball's Best Box Panel 198
1988 Fleer Baseball's Exciting Stars 198
1988 Fleer Baseball's Hottest Stars 199
1988 Fleer League Leaders 199
1988 Fleer Mini 199
1988 Fleer Record Setters 200
1988 Fleer Star Stickers 200
1988 Fleer Star Stickers Box Panels 200
1988 Fleer Superstars 201
1989 Fleer 201
1989 Fleer All Stars 203
1989 Fleer For The Record 203
1989 Fleer World Series 203
1989 Fleer Box Panels 203
1989 Fleer Update 204
1989 Fleer Baseball All Stars 204
1989 Fleer Baseball MVP 204
1989 Fleer Baseball's Exciting Stars 205
1989 Fleer Heroes of Baseball 205
1989 Fleer League Leaders 205
1989 Fleer Superstars 205
1990 Fleer 206
1990 Fleer All-Stars 208
1990 Fleer League Standouts 208
1990 Fleer World Series 208
1990 Fleer Box Panels 208
1990 Fleer Update 208
1990 Fleer Award Winners 209
1990 Fleer Baseball All Stars 209
1990 Fleer Baseball MVP 209
1990 Fleer League Leaders 210
1990 Fleer Soaring Stars 210
1991 Fleer 210
1991 Fleer All Stars 212
1991 Fleer ProVisions 212
1991 Fleer World Series 213
1991 Fleer Box Panels 213
1991 Fleer Update 213
1991 Fleer Ultra 213
1991 Fleer Ultra Gold 215
1991 Fleer Ultra Update 215
1992 Fleer 215
1992 Fleer All-Stars 217
1992 Fleer Roger Clemens 218
1992 Fleer Lumber Co. 218
1992 Fleer Rookie Sensations 218
1992 Fleer Smoke 'N Heat 218
1992 Fleer Team Leaders 218
1992 Fleer Update 218
1992 Fleer Ultra 219
1992 Fleer Ultra Award Winners 221
1992 Fleer Ultra All-Rookies 221
1992 Fleer Ultra All-Stars 221
1992 Fleer Ultra Tony Gwynn 221
1992 Fleer 7-Eleven 221
1993 Fleer 222
1993 Fleer Golden Moments I 224
1993 Fleer Golden Moments II 224
1993 Fleer Major League Prospects I 224
1993 Fleer Major League Prospects II 224
1993 Fleer All-Stars 224
1993 Fleer ProVisions I 224
1993 Fleer ProVisions II 225
1993 Fleer Tom Glavine Career Highlights 225
1993 Fleer Rookie Sensations I 225
1993 Fleer Rookie Sensations II 225
1993 Fleer AL Team Leaders 225
1993 Fleer NL Team Leaders 225
1993 Fleer Ultra 225
1993 Fleer Ultra All-Rookies 227
1993 Fleer Ultra All-Stars 228

1993 Fleer Ultra Award Winners 228
1993 Fleer Ultra Dennis Eckersley 228
1993 Fleer Ultra Home Run Kings... 228
1993 Fleer Ultra Performers 228
1993 Fleer Ultra Strikeout Kings 228
1993 Fleer Final Edition..... 229
1993 Fleer Flair 230
1993 Fleer Flair Wave of the Future 231
1993 Fleer Atlantic 231
1993 Fleer Fruit of the Loom 231
1994 Fleer 231
1994 Fleer Rookie Sensations 233
1994 Fleer Lumber Co. 234
1994 Fleer Smoke N' Heat 234
1994 Fleer Team Leaders 234
1994 Fleer League Leaders 234
1994 Fleer Award Winners 234
1994 Fleer Major League Prospects 234
1994 Fleer All-Stars 235
1994 Fleer Tim Salmon A.L. Rookie of the Year 235
1994 Fleer Golden Moments 235
1994 Fleer Golden Moments Super 235
1994 Fleer ProVisions 235
1994 Fleer Ultra 236
1994 Fleer Ultra All-Rookie Team .. 237
1994 Fleer Ultra All-Stars 238
1994 Fleer Ultra Award Winners 238
1994 Fleer Ultra Career Achievement Awards 238
1994 Fleer Ultra Firemen 238
1994 Fleer Ultra Hitting Machines .. 238
1994 Fleer Ultra Home Run Kings .. 238
1994 Fleer Ultra On-Base Leaders 239
1994 Fleer Ultra RBI Kings 239
1994 Fleer Ultra League Leaders ... 239
1994 Fleer Ultra Phillies Finest 239
1994 Fleer Ultra Rising Stars 239
1994 Fleer Ultra Second Year Standouts 239
1994 Fleer Ultra Strikeout Kings 240
1994 Fleer Atlantic 240
1962 Ford Detroit Tigers Postcards 240
1887 Four Base Hits 240
1963 French Bauer Milk Caps 240
1987 French/Bray Orioles 240
1988 French/Bray Orioles 241
1989 French/Bray Orioles 241
1992 French's Mustard 241
1928 Fro-joy 241
1985 Fun Food Buttons 241

G

1888 G & B Chewing Gum (E223) .. 242
1983 Gardner's Brewers 242
1984 Gardner's Brewers 243
1985 Gardner's Brewers 243
1989 Gardner's Brewers 243
1986 Gatorade Cubs 243
1987 Gatorade Indians 243
1988 Gatorade Indians 244
1914 General Baking Co. (D303) 244
1985 General Mills Stickers 244
1986 General Mills Booklets 244
1987 General Mills Booklets 245
1953 Glendale Hot Dogs Tigers 245
1969 Globe Imports 245
1887 Gold Coin (Buchner) (N284) .. 245
1934 Gold Medal Flour 246
1961 Golden Press 246
1888 Goodwin Champions (N162) .. 246
1933 Goudey 246
1934 Goudey 247
1934 Goudey Premiums (R309-1) ... 248
1934 Goudey Thum Movies (R342) 248
1935 Goudey 248
1935 Goudey Premiums (R309-2) .. 248
1936 Goudey 248
1936 Goudey "Wide Pen" Premiums (R314) 249
1937 Goudey Baseball Movies (R326) 249
1938 Goudey 249
1939 Goudey Premiums (R303-A) . 250
1939 Goudey Premiums (R303-B) .. 250
1941 Goudey 250
1955 Robert Gould All Stars 250
1981 Granny Goose Potato Chips A's 251
1982 Granny Goose Potato Chips A's 251
1982 Granny Goose Signature Set 251
1983 Granny Goose Potato Chips A's 251
1969 Greiner Tires Pittsburgh Pirates 251
1887 Gypsy Queens 251

H

1888 Joseph Hall Cabinets 252
1911 Helmar Stamps (T332) 252
1888 S.F. Hess (N338-2) 253
1993 Highland Mint Mint-Card 253
1994 Highland Mint Mint-Cards 253
1989 Hills Team MVP's 253
1990 Hills Hit Men 254
1958 Hires Root Beer Test Set 254
1958 Hires Root Beer 254
1992 Holoprisms 254
1989 Holsum Bakeries Superstars Discs 255
1990 Holsum Bakeries Superstars Discs 255
1991 Holsum Bakeries Superstars Discs 255
1959 Home Run Derby 255
1991 Homers Cookies 255
1947 Homogenized Bond Bread 255
1893 Honest (Duke) Cabinets (N142) 256
1975 Hostess 256
1975 Hostess Twinkies 256
1976 Hostess 257
1976 Hostess Twinkies 257
1977 Hostess 258
1977 Hostess Twinkies 258
1978 Hostess 259
1979 Hostess 260
1985 Hostess Braves 260
1987 Hostess Stickers 261
1988 Hostess Potato Chips Expos . 261
1993 Hostess Twinkies 261
1993 Humpty Dumpty 261
1953 Hunter Wieners Cardinals 261
1954 Hunter Wieners Cardinals 262
1955 Hunter Wieners Cardinals 262
1982 Hygrade Expos 262
1887 (H891) 579

I

1976 Icee Drinks Reds 262
1963 I.D.L. Drug Store Pittsburgh Pirates 263
1985 Indians Photo Cards 263
1923 Curtis Ireland Candy (E123) .. 263

J

1984 Jarvis Press Rangers 264
1958 Jay Publishing 5x7 Photos Type 1 264
1962 Jay Publishing 5x7 Photos Type 2 268
1986 Jays Potato Chips 272
1962 Jell-O 272
1963 Jell-O 272
1973 Jewel Food Baseball Photos . 273
1984 Jewel Food Chicago Cubs 274
1986 Jiffy Pop/MSA Promos 274
1986 Jiffy Pop 274
1987 Jiffy Pop 274
1988 Jiffy Pop 274
1973 Johnny Pro Orioles 274
1973 Johnny Pro Phillies 275
1953 Johnston Cookies Braves 275
1954 Johnston Cookies Braves 275
1955 Johnston Cookies Braves 275
1910 Ju-Ju Drums (E286) 275
1990 Jumbo Sunflower Seeds 276
1991 Jumbo Sunflower Seeds 276
1992 Jumbo Sunflower Seeds 276
1893 Just So Tobacco 276

K

1982 K-Mart 276
1987 K-Mart 277
1988 K-Mart 277
1989 K-Mart 277
1990 K-Mart 277
1955 Kahn's Wieners Reds 278
1956 Kahn's Wieners Reds 278
1957 Kahn's Wieners 278
1958 Kahn's Wieners 278
1959 Kahn's Wieners 278

1960 Kahn's Wieners 279
1961 Kahn's Wieners 279
1962 Kahn's Wieners 279
1963 Kahn's Wieners 280
1964 Kahn's Wieners 280
1965 Kahn's Wieners 280
1966 Kahn's Wieners 280
1967 Kahn's Wieners 280
1968 Kahn's Wieners 281
1969 Kahn's Wieners 281
1987 Kahn's Reds 281
1988 Kahn's Mets 282
1988 Kahn's Reds 282
1989 Kahn's Cooperstown Collection 282
1989 Kahn's Mets 282
1989 Kahn's Reds 282
1990 Kahn's Mets 283
1990 Kahn's Reds 283
1991 Kahn's Mets 283
1991 Kahn's Reds 283
1992 Kahn's Mets 283
1992 Kahn's Reds 283
1993 Kahn's Mets 284
1993 Kahn's Reds 284
1887 Kalamazoo Bats (N690) 284
1887 Kalamazoo Bats Cabinets (N690) 284
1887 Kalamazoo Bats Team Cards (N690-1) 285
1986 Kas Potato Chips Cardinals ... 285
1929 Kashin Publications (R316) 285
1986 Kay Bee 285
1987 Kay Bee 285
1988 Kay Bee Superstars of Baseball 286
1988 Kay Bee Team Leaders 286
1989 Kay Bee Superstars 286
1990 Kay Bee Kings of Baseball 286
1968 KDKA Pittsburgh Pirates 287
1993 Keebler Texas Rangers 287
1986 Keller's Butter Phillies 288
1970 Kellogg's 288
1971 Kellogg's 289
1972 Kellogg's 289
1972 Kellogg's All-Time Baseball Greats 290
1973 Kellogg's 290
1974 Kellogg's 290
1975 Kellogg's 290
1976 Kellogg's 291
1977 Kellogg's 291
1978 Kellogg's 291
1979 Kellogg's 292
1980 Kellogg's 292
1981 Kellogg's 293
1982 Kellogg's 293
1983 Kellogg's 293
1991 Kellogg's 3-D 293
1991 Kellogg's Baseball Greats 294
1992 Kellogg's 3-D 294
1969 Kelly's Potato Chips Pins 294
1988 Kenner Starting Lineup 294
1989 Kenner Starting Lineup 295
1989 Kenner Starting Lineup Baseball Greats 295
1990 Kenner Starting Lineup 295
1991 Kenner Starting Lineup 296
1992 Kenner Starting Lineup 296
1993 Kenner Starting Lineup 296
1994 Kenner Starting Lineup 297
1994 Kenner Cooperstown Collection 297
1887 W.S. Kimball Champions (N184) 297
1988 King-B.................................... 297
1989 King-B 297
1990 King-B 298
1993 King-B 298
1994 King-B 298
1986 Kitty Clover Potato Chips Royals 298
1993 Kodak White Sox 298
1987 Kraft 298
1993 Kraft Pop-Up Action 299
1994 Kraft Pop-Ups 299

L

1912 L1 Leathers............................. 299
1960 Lake To Lake Dairy Braves ... 299
1967 Laughlin World Series 300
1972 Laughlin Great Feats 300
1974 Laughlin All-Star Games 300
1974 Laughlin Old-Time Black Stars 301
1974 Laughlin Sportslang 301
1975 Laughlin Batty Baseball 301
1976 Laughlin Diamond Jubilee 301
1976 Laughlin Indianapolis Clowns 301
1978 Laughlin Long Ago Black Stars 302
1980 Laughlin 300/400/500 302
1980 Laughlin Famous Feats 302
1948 Leaf 302
1960 Leaf 303
1985 Leaf-Donruss 303
1986 Leaf 304
1987 Leaf 305
1987 Leaf Candy City Team 306
1988 Leaf 306
1990 Leaf Previews 307
1990 Leaf 307
1991 Leaf Previews 309
1991 Leaf 309
1991 Leaf Gold Rookies 311
1992 Leaf Previews 311
1992 Leaf 311
1992 Leaf Gold Previews 313
1992 Leaf Gold Edition 313
1992 Leaf Gold Rookies 313
1993 Leaf 313
1993 Leaf Fasttrack 315
1993 Leaf Gold All-Stars 315
1993 Leaf Gold Rookies 315
1993 Leaf Heading for the Hall 315
1993 Leaf Frank Thomas 315
1993 Leaf Update Gold All-Stars 316
1993 Leaf Update Gold Rookies 316
1993 Leaf Update Frank Thomas Super 316
1994 Leaf Promos 316
1994 Leaf 316
1994 Leaf Clean-Up Crew 317
1994 Leaf 5th Anniversary 317
1994 Leaf Gamers 317
1994 Gold Leaf Rookies 317
1994 Leaf Gold Stars 317
1994 Leaf Slide Show 317
1994 Leaf Statistical Standouts 318
1991 Lewis Negro League 318
1993 Line Up Venezuelan Baseball 318
1976 Linnett Superstars 319
1985 Lion Photo Chicago Cubs 319
1986 Lite Beer Astros 320
1986 Lite Beer Rangers 320
1886 Lone Jack St. Louis Browns (N370) 320
1886 Lorillard Team Card 320
1988 Louisville Slugger 320
1949 Lummis Peanut Butter Phillies 321
1992 Lyke's Braves Team Photo Set 321
1992 Lyke's Braves 321
1993 Lyke's Braves Team Photo Set 321
1993 Lyke's Braves 321

M

1987 M & M's 322
1960 MacGregor 322
1965 MacGregor 322
1923 Walter Mails Card Game 322
1969 Major League Baseball Photostamps 322
1969 MLBPA Pins 323
1923 Maple Crispette 324
1989 Marathon Cubs 324
1989 Marathon Tigers 324
1990 Marathon Cubs 324
1991 Marathon Cubs 324
1992 Marathon Cubs 325
1993 Marathon Cubs 325
1988 Master Bread Twins 325
1895 Mayo's Cut Plug (N300) 325
1896 Mayo's Die-Cut Game Cards (N301) 325
1900 Mayo's Baseball Comics (T203) 326
1970 McDonald's Brewers 326
1992 McDonald's Cardinals 326
1974 McDonalds Padres Discs 326
1991 McDonald's Cleveland Indians 326
1992 McDonald's Baseball's Best .. 327
1993 MCI Ambassadors 327
1986 Meadow Gold Blank Backs 327
1986 Meadow Gold Statistic Backs 327
1986 Meadow Gold Milk 328
1991 Medford Phillies 328
1992 Medford Phillies 328
1993 Medford Phillies 328
1992 Megacards Babe Ruth 329
1910 Mello-Mint (E105) 329

1993 Metallic Images Cooperstown Collection 329
1931 Metropolitan Studio St. Louis Cardinals 330
1993 Metz Bakeries 330
1993 Milk Bone Super Stars 330
1971 Milk Duds 330
1933 George C. Miller 331
1990 Miller Beer Milwaukee Brewers 331
1991 Miller High Life Brewers 331
1969 Milton Bradley 331
1970 Milton Bradley 332
1972 Milton Bradley 332
1984 Milton Bradley 334
1933 Minneapolis Star Worch Tobacco 334
1983 Minnesota Twins Team Issue 334
1984 Minnesota Twins Team Issue 335
1985 Minnesota Twins Team Issue 335
1986 Minnesota Twins Team Issue 335
1987 Minnesota Twins Team Issue 335
1988 Minnesota Twins Team Issue 335
1991 Mootown Snackers 336
1959 Morrell Meats Dodgers 336
1960 Morrell Meats Dodgers 336
1961 Morrell Meats Dodgers 336
1983 Mother's Cookies Giants 336
1984 Mother's Cookies Astros 336
1984 Mother's Cookies Athletics 337
1984 Mother's Cookies Giants 337
1984 Mother's Cookies Mariners 337
1984 Mother's Cookies Padres 337
1985 Mother's Cookies Astros 338
1985 Mother's Cookies Athletics 338
1985 Mother's Cookies Giants 338
1985 Mother's Cookies Mariners 338
1985 Mother's Cookies Padres 339
1986 Mother's Cookies Astros 339
1986 Mother's Cookies Athletics 339
1986 Mother's Cookies Giants 339
1986 Mother's Cookies Mariners 339
1987 Mother's Cookies Astros 340
1987 Mother's Cookies Athletics 340
1987 Mother's Cookies Dodgers 340
1987 Mother's Cookies Giants 340
1987 Mother's Cookies Mariners 341
1987 Mother's Cookies Rangers 341
1987 Mother's Cookies Mark McGwire 341
1988 Mother's Cookies Astros 341
1988 Mother's Cookies Athletics 341
1988 Mother's Cookies Dodgers 342
1988 Mother's Cookies Giants 342
1988 Mother's Cookies Mariners 342
1988 Mother's Cookies Rangers 342
1988 Mother's Cookies Will Clark ... 342
1988 Mother's Cookies Mark McGwire 343
1989 Mother's Cookies Astros 343
1989 Mother's Cookies Athletics 343
1989 Mother's Cookies Dodgers 343
1989 Mother's Cookies Giants 343
1989 Mother's Cookies Mariners 343
1989 Mother's Cookies Rangers 344
1989 Mother's Cookies Jose Canseco 344
1989 Mother's Cookies Will Clark ... 344
1989 Mother's Cookies Ken Griffey, Jr. 344
1989 Mother's Cookies Mark McGwire 344
1989 Mother's Cookies Rookies of the Year 344
1990 Mother's Cookies Astros 345
1990 Mother's Cookies Athletics 345
1990 Mother's Cookies Dodgers 345
1990 Mother's Cookies Giants 345
1990 Mother's Cookies Mariners 345
1990 Mother's Cookies Rangers 345
1990 Mother's Cookies Jose Canseco 346
1990 Mother's Cookies Will Clark ... 346
1990 Mother's Cookies Mark McGwire 346
1990 Mother's Cookies Nolan Ryan 346
1990 Mother's Cookies Matt Williams 346
1991 Mother's Cookies Astros 346
1991 Mother's Cookies Athletics 346
1991 Mother's Cookies Dodgers 347
1991 Mother's Cookies Giants 347
1991 Mother's Cookies Rangers 347
1991 Mother's Cookies Griffeys 347
1991 Mother's Cookies Nolan Ryan 300 Wins 347
1992 Mother's Cookies Astros 348
1992 Mother's Cookies Athletics 348
1992 Mother's Cookies Dodgers 348
1992 Mother's Cookies Giants 348
1992 Mother's Cookies Mariners 348
1992 Mother's Cookies Padres 349
1992 Mother's Cookies Rangers 349
1992 Mother's Cookies Jeff Bagwell 349
1992 Mother's Cookies Chuck Knoblauch 349
1992 Mother's Cookies Nolan Ryan 7 No-Hitters 349
1993 Mother's Cookies Angels 349
1993 Mother's Cookies Astros 350
1993 Mother's Cookies Athletics 350
1993 Mother's Cookies Dodgers 350
1993 Mother's Cookies Giants 350
1993 Mother's Cookies Mariners 350
1993 Mother's Cookies Padres 351
1993 Mother's Cookies Nolan Ryan Farewell 351
1994 Mother's Cookies Rookies of the Year 351
1994 Mother's Cookies Nolan Ryan Farewell 351
1943 M.P. & Co. (R302-1) 351
1949 M.P. & Co. (R302-2) 352
1992 Mr. Turkey 352
1983 Mr. Z's Milwaukee Brewers 352
1984 Mr. Z's Milwaukee Brewers 352
1916 (M101-4) 543
1915 (M101-5) 543
1919 (M101-6) 544
1926 (M101-7) 544
1911 (M116) 541
1888 (M117) 545

N

1969 Nabisco Team Flakes 352
1992 Nabisco Canadian Tradition ... 352
1993 Nabisco All-Star Autographs .. 353
1994 Nabisco All-Star Legends 353
1909 Nadja Caramels (E92) 353
1910 Nadja Philadelphia Athletics (E104-I) 353
1910 Nadja Pittsburgh Pirates (E104-II) 354
1910 Nadja Carmels (E104-III) 354
1983 Nalley Potato Chips Mariners 354
1921 - 23 National Caramel (E220) . 354
1936 National Chicle Co. "Fine Pens" (R313) 355
1936 National Chicle (R344) 355
1913 The National Game 355
1986 National Photo Royals 356
1952 National Tea Labels 356
1992 Nationwide Insurance Pirates 356
1921 Neilson's Chocolate (V61) 356
1984 Nestle 357
1984 Nestle Dream Team 359
1987 Nestle 359
1988 Nestle 360
1895 Newsboy Cabinets (N566) 360
1969 N.Y. Boy Scouts 360
1954 N.Y. Journal-American 360
1984 N.Y. Mets M.V.P. Club 360
1985 N.Y. Mets Super Fan Club 361
1986 N.Y. Mets Super Fan Club 361
1886 New York Baseball Club (H812) 361
1985 Nike 361
1953 Northland Bread Labels 361
1960 Nu-Card 362
1961 Nu-Card 362
1889 Number 7/Diamond S Cigars (N526) 363
1950 Num Num Cleveland Indians .. 363
1952 Num Num Cleveland Indians .. 363
1887 (Buchner) (N284) 245
1887 (N28) 3
1888 (N29) 3
1888 (N135) 151
1888 (N162) 246
1886 (N167) 363
1887 (N172) 363
1887 (N172) 365
1888 (N173) 381
1888 (N184) 297
1895 (N300) 325
1896 (N301) 325

1888 (N338-2) 253
1886 (N370) 320
1889 (N526) 363
1895 (N566) 360
1887 (N690) 284
1887 (N690-1) 285

O

1886 Old Judge New York Giants (N167) 363
1887 Old Judge (N172) 363
1887 Old Judge (N172) 365
1888 Old Judge Cabinets (N173) 381
1937 O-Pee-Chee 382
1965 O-Pee-Chee 383
1966 O-Pee-Chee 384
1967 O-Pee-Chee 384
1968 O-Pee-Chee 385
1969 O-Pee-Chee 386
1969 O-Pee-Chee Deckle 387
1970 O-Pee-Chee 387
1971 O-Pee-Chee 389
1972 O-Pee-Chee 391
1973 O-Pee-Chee 393
1973 O-Pee-Chee Team Checklists 395
1974 O-Pee-Chee 395
1974 O-Pee-Chee Team Checklists 397
1975 O-Pee-Chee 397
1976 O-Pee-Chee 400
1977 O-Pee-Chee 402
1978 O-Pee-Chee 403
1979 O-Pee-Chee 403
1980 O-Pee-Chee 405
1981 O-Pee-Chee 406
1981 O-Pee-Chee Posters 407
1982 O-Pee-Chee 407
1982 O-Pee-Chee Posters 408
1983 O-Pee-Chee 409
1984 O-Pee-Chee 410
1985 O-Pee-Chee 411
1985 O-Pee-Chee Posters 412
1986 O-Pee-Chee 413
1986 O-Pee-Chee Box Panels 414
1987 O-Pee-Chee 414
1987 O-Pee-Chee Box Panels 415
1988 O-Pee-Chee 415
1988 O-Pee-Chee Box Panels 417
1990 O-Pee-Chee 417
1991 O-Pee-Chee Premier 419
1992 O-Pee-Chee 420
1992 O-Pee-Chee Premier 422
1993 O-Pee-Chee 423
1993 O-Pee-Chee World Champs 424
1993 O-Pee-Chee World Series Heroes 424
1993 O-Pee-Chee Premier 424
1993 O-Pee-Chee Premier Star Performers 425
1993 O-Pee-Chee Premier Top Draft Picks 425
1986 Oh Henry Indians 425
1965 Old London Coins 425
1910 Orange Borders 426
1994 Oscar Mayer Superstar Pop-Ups 426
1921 Oxford Confectionery (E253) 426

P

1910 P2 Sweet Caporal Pins 426
1930 PM8 Our National Game Pins 427
1956 PM15 Yellow Basepath Pins .. 427
1932 PR2 Orbit Gum Pins Numbered 428
1932 PR3 Orbit Gum Pins Unnumbered 428
1930 PR4 Cracker Jack Pins 428
1933 PX3 Double Header Pins 428
1909 PX7 Domino Discs 429
1992 Paccar/Alrak Ken Griffey Jr. 429
1988 Pacific Trading Cards Baseball Legends 429
1988 Pacific Trading Cards "Eight Men Out" 430
1989 Pacific Trading Cards Legends II 430
1990 Pacific Senior League 431
1990 Pacific Legends 431
1991 Pacific Senior League 432
1991 Pacific Nolan Ryan 432
1991 Pacific Nolan Ryan Milestones 433
1991 Pacific Nolan Ryan 7th No-Hitter 433
1991 Pacific Ryan 7th No-Hitter Hologram 433
1992 Pacific Nolan Ryan 433
1992 Pacific Nolan Ryan Gold Inserts 434
1992 Pacific Nolan Ryan Limited 434
1992 Pacific Tom Seaver 434
1992 Pacific Tom Seaver Milestones 435
1993 Pacific Nolan Ryan 27th Season 435
1993 Pacific Nolan Ryan Prism 435
1993 Pacific Nolan Ryan 27th Season Limited 435
1993 Pacific Nolan Ryan 27th Season Gold Ltd. 435
1993 Pacific Spanish 435
1993 Pacific Spanish Gold Foil Stars 437
1993 Pacific Prism Insert 438
1994 Pacific Crown Promos 438
1994 Pacific Crown 438
1994 Pacific Crown Jewels of the Crown 440
1994 Pacific Crown Homerun Leaders 440
1994 Pacific Crown All Latino All-Star Team 440
1958 Packard-Bell 440
1988 Panini Stickers 441
1968 - 69 Partridge Meats Reds 442
1970 - 72 Partridge Meats Reds 442
1963 Pepsi-Cola Colt .45's 442
1977 Pepsi-Cola Baseball Stars 443
1978 Pepsi-Cola Superstars 443
1988 Pepsi-Cola/Kroger Tigers 443
1990 Pepsi-Cola Red Sox 444
1991 Pepsi-Cola Red Sox 444
1985 Performance Printing Rangers 444
1986 Performance Printing Rangers 444
1981 Perma-Graphics All-Star Credit Cards 444
1981 Perma-Graphics Super Star Credit Cards 444
1982 Perma-Graphics Super Star Credit Cards 445
1982 Perma-Graphics All-Star Credit Cards 445
1983 Perma-Graphics Super Star Credit Cards 445
1983 Perma-Graphics All-Star Credit Cards 445
1961 Peters Meats Twins 446
1991 Petro Canada All-Star Fanfest Standups 446
1909 Philadelphia Carmel (E95) 446
1910 Philadelphia Carmel (E96) 446
1994 Phillies Photocards 446
1993 Photo File 500 HR Supercards 447
1951 - 59 Photo-Film Fotos Pirates Postcards 447
1970 Pictures of Champions Orioles 447
1914 Piedmont Art Stamps (T330-2) 447
1992 Pinnacle 448
1992 Pinnacle Rookies 450
1992 Pinnacle Team 2000 450
1992 Pinnacle Slugfest 450
1992 Pinnacle Team Pinnacle 450
1992 Pinnacle Rookie Idols 450
1993 Pinnacle 451
1993 Pinnacle Expansion Opening Day 453
1993 Pinnacle Rookie Team Pinnacle 453
1993 Pinnacle Slugfest 453
1993 Pinnacle Team Pinnacle 453
1993 Pinnacle Team 2001 453
1993 Pinnacle Tribute 454
1993 Pinnacle Cooperstown 454
1993 Pinnacle Home Run Club 454
1993 Pinnacle Joe DiMaggio 454
1994 Pinnacle 454
1994 Pinnacle Artist's Proof 455
1994 Pinnacle Museum Collection 455
1994 Pinnacle New Generation 456
1994 Pinnacle Rookie Team Pinnacle 456
1994 Pinnacle Run Creators 456
1994 Pinnacle Power Surge 456

1994 Pinnacle Tribute 456
1912 Pirate Cigarettes (T215) 457
1939 Play Ball 457
1940 Play Ball 458
1941 Play Ball 459
1976 Playboy Press Who Was Harry Steinfeldt? 459
1910 Plow Boy Tobacco 460
1912 Plow's Candy (E300) 460
1985 Polaroid J.C. Penney Indians 460
1889 Police Gazette Cabinets 460
1970 Police/Fire Safety Senators ... 461
1971 Police/Fire Safety Senators ... 461
1979 Police/Fire Safety Giants 461
1980 Police/Fire Safety Dodgers..... 461
1980 Police/Fire Safety Giants 461
1981 Police/Fire Safety Braves 462
1981 Police/Fire Safety Dodgers 462
1981 Police/Fire Safety Mariners ... 462
1981 Police/Fire Safety Royals 462
1982 Police/Fire Safety Braves 462
1982 Police/Fire Safety Brewers 463
1982 Police/Fire Safety Dodgers 463
1983 Police/Fire Safety Braves 463
1983 Police/Fire Safety Brewers 463
1983 Police/Fire Safety Dodgers 464
1983 Police/Fire Safety Royals 464
1984 Police/Fire Safety Blue Jays 464
1984 Police/Fire Safety Braves 464
1984 Police/Fire Safety Brewers 464
1984 Police/Fire Safety Dodgers 465
1985 Police/Fire Safety Blue Jays .. 465
1985 Police/Fire Safety Braves 465
1985 Police/Fire Safety Brewers 465
1985 Police/Fire Safety Phillies 465
1986 Police/Fire Safety Astros 466
1986 Police/Fire Safety Blue Jays .. 466
1986 Police/Fire Safety Braves 466
1986 Police/Fire Safety Brewers 466
1986 Police/Fire Safety Dodgers 467
1986 Police/Fire Safety Phillies 467
1987 Police/Fire Safety Astros 467
1987 Police/Fire Safety Blue Jays .. 467
1987 Police/Fire Safety Brewers 467
1987 Police/Fire Safety Dodgers 468
1988 Police/Fire Safety Astros 468
1988 Police/Fire Safety Blue Jays .. 468
1988 Police/Fire Safety Brewers 468
1988 Police/Fire Safety Dodgers 469
1988 Police/Fire Safety Tigers 469
1989 Police/Fire Safety Blue Jays .. 469
1989 Police/Fire Safety Brewers 469
1989 Police/Fire Safety Dodgers 469
1989 Police/Fire Safety Tigers 470
1990 Police/Fire Safety Blue Jays .. 470
1990 Police/Fire Safety Brewers 470
1990 Police/Fire Safety Dodgers 470
1991 Police/Fire Safety Brewers 470
1992 Police/Fire Safety Brewers 471
1992 Police/Fire Safety Cardinals .. 471
1992 Police/Fire Safety Dodgers 471
1992 Police/Fire Safety Royals 471
1993 Police/Fire Safety Blue Jays ... 471
1993 Police/Fire Safety Brewers 471
1993 Police/Fire Safety Cardinals .. 472
1993 Police/Fire Safety Dodgers 472
1994 Police/Fire Safety Brewers 472
1994 Police/Fire Safety Dodgers 472
1914 Polo Grounds Game 472
1960 Post Cereal 473
1961 Post Cereal 473
1962 Post Cereal 474
1962 Post Cereal - Canadian 475
1963 Post Cereal 475
1990 Post Cereal 476
1991 Post Cereal 476
1991 Post Cereal - Canadian 477
1992 Post Cereal 477
1992 Post Cereal - Canadian 477
1993 Post Cereal 477
1993 Post Cereal - Canadian 477
1994 Post Cereal 478
1994 Post Cereal - Canadian 478
1986 Provigo Expos 478
1972 Puerto Rican League Stickers 478

Q

1986 Quaker Oats 479

R

1936 R311 Glossy Finish 479
1936 R311 Leather Finish 480
1936 R312 480
1928 R315 480
1932 R337 480
1947 R346 Blue Tint 481
1950 R423 481
1989 Rainier Farms Super Stars Discs 481
1984 Ralston Purina 482
1987 Ralston Purina 482
1987 Ralston Purina Collectors' Sheet 482
1989 Ralston Purina 482
1955 Rawlings Stan Musial 482
1910 Red Cross Cigarettes Type 1 (T215) 482
1912 Red Cross Cigarettes Type 2 (T215) 483
1954 Red Heart Dog Food 483
1982 Red Lobster Cubs 483
1952 Red Man Tobacco 484
1953 Red Man Tobacco 484
1954 Red Man Tobacco 484
1955 Red Man Tobacco 484
1977 Redpath Sugar Expos 485
1886 Red Stocking Cigars 485
1988 Revco 485
1935 Rice-Stix 485
1988 Rite Aid 485
1933 Rittenhouse Candy (E285) 486
1911 Rochester Baking Philadelphia A's (D359) 486
1955 Rodeo Meats Athletics 486
1956 Rodeo Meats Athletics 487
1993 Rolaids Relief Pitcher Set 487
1970 Rold Gold Pretzels 487
1950 Royal Desserts 487
1952 Royal Desserts 487
1928 George Ruth Candy Co. 488
1943 (R302-1) 351
1949 (R302-2) 352
1939 (R303-A) 250
1939 (R303-B) 250
1933 (R308) 576
1934 (R309-1) 248
1935 (R309-2) 248
1934 (R310) 47
1936 (R313) 355
1936 (R314) 249
1929 (R316) 285
1937 (R326) 249
1935 (R332) 491
1934 (R342) 248
1936 (R344) 355

S

1936 S and S Game 488
1909 S74 Silks - White 488
1910 S74 Silks - Colored 489
1912 S81 Silks 489
1962 Salada-Junket Dessert Coins 489
1963 Salada-Junket Dessert Coins 490
1958 San Francisco Call-Bulletin Giants 490
1986 Schnucks Milk Cardinals 491
1935 Schutter-Johnson (R332) 491
1988 Score 491
1988 Score Box Panels 493
1988 Score Traded 493
1988 Score Young Superstar Series I 494
1988 Score Young Superstar Series II 494
1989 Score 494
1989 Score Traded 496
1989 Score Young Superstar Series I 497
1989 Score Young Superstar Series II 497
1989 Score Rising Star 497
1989 Score Superstar 498
1989 Scoremasters 498
1989 Score Yankees 498
1990 Score 499
1990 Score Dream Team 501
1990 Score McDonald's 501
1990 Score Rising Stars 501
1990 Score Superstar 501
1990 Score Traded 502
1990 Score Young Superstars Set I 502
1990 Score Young Superstars Set II 503
1991 Score 503
1991 Score Cooperstown 505
1991 Score Hot Rookies 506
1991 Score Mickey Mantle 506

1991 Score Rising Star 506
1991 Score Superstar 506
1991 Score Rookies 507
1991 Score Traded 507
1992 Score 507
1992 Score Joe DiMaggio 510
1992 Score Factory Inserts 510
1992 Score The Franchise 510
1992 Score Hot Rookies 510
1992 Score Impact Players 510
1992 Score Procter & Gamble 511
1992 Score Rookie & Traded 511
1992 Score Rising Stars 511
1992 Score Superstars 512
1993 Score 512
1993 Score Boys of Summer 514
1993 Score The Franchise 515
1993 Score Gold Dream Team 515
1993 Score Procter & Gamble Rookies 515
1993 Score Select 515
1993 Score Select Aces 516
1993 Score Select Chase Rookies . 516
1993 Score Select Chase Stars 517
1993 Score Select Stat Leaders 517
1993 Score Select Triple Crown 517
1993 Score Select Update 517
1993 Score Select All-Star Rookies 518
1993 Score Select Rookie/Traded Inserts 518
1994 Score 518
1994 Score The Cycle 520
1994 Score Dream Team 520
1994 Score Gold Stars 520
1994 Score Boys of Summer 521
1994 Score Gold Rush 521
1994 Score Cal Ripken, Jr. 521
1994 Score Select Promos 521
1994 Score Select .... "521
1994 Score Select Crown Contenders 522
1994 Score Select Rookie Surge ... 522
1994 Score Select Salute 523
1888 Scrapps Tobacco 523
1949 Sealtest Phillies 523
1983 7-11 Slurpee Coins 523
1984 7-11 Slurpee Coins Eastern Region 523
1984 7-11 Slurpee Coins Central Region 523
1984 7-11 Slurpee Coins Western Region 523
1985 7-11 Twins 524
1985 7-11 Slurpee Coins Eastern Region 524
1985 7-11 Slurpee Coins Southeastern Region 524
1985 7-11 Slurpee Coins Great Lakes Region 524
1985 7-11 Slurpee Coins Southwest/ Central Region 524
1985 7-11 Slurpee Coins Western Region 524
1985 7-11 Slurpee Coins Tigers 524
1986 7-11 Slurpee Coins Eastern Region 525
1986 7-11 Slurpee Coins Mideastern Region 525
1986 7-11 Slurpee Coins Midwestern Region 525
1986 7-11 Slurpee Coins Western Region 525
1987 7-11 Slurpee Coins Eastern Region 525
1987 7-11 Slurpee Coins Mideastern Region 525
1987 7-11 Slurpee Coins Great Lakes Region 525
1987 7-11 Slurpee Coins Western Region 525
1987 7-11 Slurpee Coins Tigers 526
1992 7-11 Slurpee Superstar Action Coins 526
1984 7-Up Cubs 526
1985 7-Up Cubs 526
1992 Silver Star Holograms 526
1984 Smokey Bear Angels 526
1984 Smokey Bear Jackson Mets In Majors 527
1984 Smokey Bear Dodgers 527
1984 Smokey Bear Padres 527
1985 Smokey Bear Angels 527
1986 Smokey Bear Angels 527
1987 Smokey Bear 528
1987 Smokey Bear A's 528
1987 Smokey Bear Angels 528
1987 Smokey Bear Braves 528
1987 Smokey Bear Cardinals 528
1987 Smokey Bear Dodgers 529
1987 Smokey Bear Rangers 529
1988 Smokey Bear Angels 529
1988 Smokey Bear Cardinals 529
1988 Smokey Bear Cubs 530
1988 Smokey Bear Dodgers 530
1988 Smokey Bear Padres 530
1988 Smokey Bear Rangers 530
1988 Smokey Bear Royals 530
1988 Smokey Bear Twins 530
1989 Smokey Bear Angels All-Stars 531
1989 Smokey Bear Cardinals 531
1990 Smokey Bear Angels 531
1991 Smokey Bear Angels 531
1992 Smokey Bear Padres Postcards 531
1957 Sohio Gas Indians/Reds 532
1994 Spectrum 1969 Miracle Mets .. 532
1953 Spic and Span Braves 532
1953 Spic and Span Braves 7x10 Photos 532
1954 Spic and Span Braves 533
1955 Spic and Span Braves Die-cuts 533
1957 Spic and Span Braves 533
1960 Spic and Span Braves 533
1977 - 79 Sportscaster 533
1986 Sportflics 534
1986 Sportflics Decade Greats 535
1986 Sportflics Rookies 535
1987 Sportflics 536
1987 Sportflics Rookie Discs 536
1987 Sportflics Rookie Prospects ... 536
1987 Sportflics Rookies 537
1987 Sportflics Superstar Discs 537
1987 Sportflics Team Preview 537
1988 Sportflics 538
1988 Sportflics Gamewinners 538
1989 Sportflics 539
1990 Sportflics 539
1994 Sportflics 2000 Promos 540
1994 Sportflics 2000 540
1994 Sportflics 2000 Movers 541
1994 Sportflics 2000 Shakers 541
1994 Sportflics Commemoratives..... 541
1906 Sporting Life Team Composites (W601) 541
1911 Sporting Life (M116) 541
1915 The Sporting News (M101-5) 543
1916 The Sporting News (M101-4) 543
1919 Sporting News Supplements (M101-6) 544
1926 Sporting News Supplements (M101-7) 544
1981 Sporting News Conlon Collection 545
1984 Sporting News Conlon Collection 545
1888 Sporting Times (M117) 545
1933 Sport Kings 545
1946 - 49 Sports Exchange (W603) 546
1947 Sports Exchange Baseball Miniatures (W602) 546
1948 Sport Thrills 547
1981 Spot-bilt George Brett 547
1986 Springhill Papers 547
1981 Squirt 547
1982 Squirt 548
1975 SSPC 548
1953 Stahl-Meyer Franks 550
1954 Stahl-Meyer Franks 550
1955 Stahl-Meyer Franks 550
1910 Standard Caramel Co. (E93).. 550
1928 Star Player Candy 551
1983 Star Co. Mike Schmidt 551
1984 Star Co. George Brett 551
1984 Star Co. Steve Carlton 551
1984 Star Co. Steve Garvey 551
1984 Star Co. Darryl Strawberry 551
1984 Star Co. Carl Yastrzemski 551
1985 Star Co. Reggie Jackson 552
1986 Star Co. Wade Boggs 552
1986 Star Co. Jose Canseco 552
1986 Star Co. Rod Carew 552
1986 Star Co. Wally Joyner 552
1986 Star Co. Don Mattingly 552
1986 Star Co. Dale Murphy 552
1986 Star Co. Jim Rice 552
1986 Star Co. Nolan Ryan 553
1986 Star Co. Tom Seaver 553
1987 Star Co. Gary Carter 553
1987 Star Co. Roger Clemens 553
1987 Star Co. Roger Clemens 553
1987 Star Co. Keith Hernandez 553
1987 Star Co. Tim Raines 553

1987 Star Co. Fernando Valenzuela 553
1988 Star Co. "Baseball's Best" 553
1988 Star Co. "Baseball's Best" Limited Edition 554
1988 Star Co. "Best of '87" 554
1988 Star Co. Wade Boggs 554
1988 Star Co. Gary Carter 554
1988 Star Co. Will Clark 554
1988 Star Co. Andre Dawson 554
1988 Star Co. Eric Davis 554
1988 Star Co. Dwight Gooden 554
1988 Star Co. Tony Gwynn 554
1988 Star Co. "Hits 'R Us" 554
1988 Star Co. Bo Jackson 555
1988 Star Co. Don Mattingly 555
1988 Star Co. Mark McGwire 555
1988 Star Co. Mark McGwire #2 555
1988 Star Co. Mark McGwire #3 555
1988 Star Co. Mike Scott 555
1988 Star Co. Kevin Seitzer 555
1988 Star Co. Cory Snyder 555
1988 Star Co. Dave Winfield 555
1988 Star Co. Platinum 556
1989 Star Co. Gold Edition 556
1989 Star Co. Platinum 556
1989 Star Co. Silver Series 556
1990 Star Sophomore Stars 556
1952 Star-Cal Decals - Type I 556
1952 Star-Cal Decals - Type 2 556
1989 Starline Prototypes 556
1990 Starline 557
1988 Starting Lineup Talking Baseball 557
1983 Stuart Expos 557
1984 Stuart Expos 557
1987 Stuart 558
1991 Studio Preview 558
1991 Studio 558
1992 Studio Preview 559
1992 Studio 559
1992 Studio Heritage 560
1993 Studio 560
1993 Studio Heritage 561
1993 Studio Silhouettes 561
1993 Studio Superstars on Canvas 561
1993 Studio Frank Thomas 561
1962 Sugardale Weiners 562
1963 Sugardale Weiners 562
1957 Swift Meats 562

T

1911 Turkey Red (T3) 562
1911 T5 Pinkerton 563
1911 T201 Mecca Double Folders . 564
1912 T202 Hassan Triple Folders .. 564
1909 T204 Ramly 565
1911 T205 Gold Border 566
1909 - 11 T206 White Border 566
1912 T207 Brown Background 568
1914 T216 Kotton 569
1912 T227 Series Of Champions ... 570
1988 T & M Sports Umpires 570
1989 T & M Sports Senior League . 570
1916 Tango Eggs 571
1990 Target Dodgers 571
1984 Tastykake Phillies 574
1985 Tastykake Phillies 574
1986 Tastykake Phillies 575
1987 Tastykake Phillies 575
1988 Tastykake Phillies 575
1989 Tastykake Phillies 575
1990 Tastykake Phillies 576
1933 Tattoo Orbit 576
1933 Tatoo Orbit (R308) 576
1986 Texas Gold Ice Cream Reds . 576
1914 Texas Tommy Type I (E224) . 577
1914 Texas Tommy Type II (E224) 577
1928 Tharp's Ice Cream 577
1985 Thom McAn Discs 577
1983 Thorn Apple Valley Cubs 578
1910 Tip-Top Bread Pittsburgh Pirates 578
1947 Tip Top Bread 578
1952 Tip Top Bread Labels 579
1887 Tobin Lithographs (H891) 579
1994 Tombstone Pizza 579
1948 Topps Magic Photos 579
1951 Topps Red Backs 580
1951 Topps Blue Backs 580
1951 Topps Connie Mack's All-Stars 580
1951 Topps Current All-Stars 580
1951 Topps Teams 580
1952 Topps 581
1953 Topps 582
1954 Topps 583
1955 Topps 584
1955 Topps Doubleheaders 584
1955 Topps Test Stamps 585
1956 Topps 585
1956 Topps Hocus Focus Large 586
1956 Topps Hocus Focus Small 586
1956 Topps Pins 587
1957 Topps 587
1958 Topps 588
1959 Topps 590
1960 Topps 592
1960 Topps Baseball Tattoos 594
1961 Topps 594
1961 Topps Dice Game 596
1961 Topps Magic Rub-Offs 596
1961 Topps Stamps 597
1962 Topps 597
1962 Topps Baseball Bucks 599
1962 Topps Stamps 600
1963 Topps 600
1963 Topps Peel-Offs 603
1964 Topps 603
1964 Topps Coins 605
1964 Topps Giants 605
1964 Topps Photo Tatoos 606
1964 Topps Stand-Ups 606
1965 Topps 606
1965 Topps Embossed 609
1965 Topps Transfers 609
1966 Topps 609
1966 Topps Rub-Offs 611
1967 Topps 612
1967 Topps Pin-Ups 614
1967 Topps Stand-Ups 614
1967 Topps Stickers Pirates 614
1967 Topps Stickers Red Sox 615
1968 Topps 615
1968 Topps Action All-Star Stickers 617
1968 Topps Deckle Edge Test Proofs 617
1968 Topps Discs 617
1968 Topps Game 618
1968 Topps Plaks 618
1968 Topps Posters 618
1968 Topps Punch-outs 618
1968 Topps 3-D 619
1969 Topps 619
1969 Topps Decals 621
1969 Topps Deckle Edge 621
1969 Topps 4-On-1 Mini Stickers ... 622
1969 Topps Stamps 622
1969 Topps Super 622
1969 Topps Team Posters 623
1970 Topps 623
1970 Topps Candy Lids 626
1970 Topps Cloth Stickers 626
1970 Topps Posters 626
1970 Topps Scratch-Offs 626
1970 Topps Story Booklets 626
1970 Topps Super 626
1971 Topps 627
1971 Topps Coins 629
1971 Topps Greatest Moments 630
1971 Topps Super 630
1971 Topps Baseball Tattoos 630
1972 Topps 631
1972 Topps Cloth Stickers 633
1972 Topps Posters 633
1973 Topps 634
1973 Topps Candy Lids 637
1973 Topps Comics 637
1973 Topps 1953 Reprints 637
1973 Topps Pin-Ups 637
1973 Topps Team Checklists 637
1974 Topps 638
1974 Topps Deckle Edge 640
1974 Topps Puzzles 640
1974 Topps Stamps 640
1974 Topps Team Checklists 641
1974 Topps Traded 641
1975 Topps 641
1975 Topps Mini 643
1976 Topps 646
1976 Topps Traded 648
1977 Topps 648
1977 Topps Cloth Stickers 650
1978 Topps 650
1979 Topps 653
1979 Topps Comics 655
1980 Topps 655
1980 Topps Superstar 5x7 Photos .. 657
1981 Topps 658
1981 Topps Traded 660
1981 Topps Home Team 5x7 Photos 660
1981 Topps National 5x7 Photos ... 661
1981 Topps Scratchoffs 661

1981 Topps Stickers 661
1982 Topps 662
1982 Topps Traded 665
1982 Topps Insert Stickers 665
1982 Topps Stickers 666
1983 Topps 667
1983 Topps All-Star Glossy Set of 40 669
1983 Topps Traded 669
1983 Topps Foldouts 670
1983 Topps Stickers 670
1983 Topps Stickers Boxes 671
1984 Topps 671
1984 Topps All-Star Glossy Set of 22 674
1984 Topps All-Star Glossy Set of 40 674
1984 Topps Traded 674
1984 Topps Cereal Series 675
1984 Topps Gallery of Immortals ... 675
1984 Topps Rub Downs 675
1984 Topps Stickers 675
1984 Topps Stickers Boxes 677
1984 Topps Super 677
1985 Topps 677
1985 Topps All-Star Glossy Set of 22 680
1985 Topps All-Star Glossy Set of 40 680
1985 Topps Traded 680
1985 Topps All-Time Record Holders 680
1985 Topps Gallery of Champions . 681
1985 Topps Rub Downs 681
1985 Topps Stickers 681
1985 Topps Super 682
1985 Topps 3-D 683
1986 Topps 683
1986 Topps All-Star Glossy Set of 22 685
1986 Topps All-Star Glossy Set of 60 686
1986 Topps Traded 686
1986 Topps Box Panels 686
1986 Topps Gallery of Champions . 687
1986 Topps Mini League Leaders .. 687
1986 Topps Stickers 687
1986 Topps Super 688
1986 Topps Super Star 688
1986 Topps Tattoos 689
1986 Topps 3-D 689
1987 Topps 689
1987 Topps All-Star Glossy Set of 22 692
1987 Topps All-Star Glossy Set of 60 692
1987 Topps Traded 692
1987 Topps Box Panels 693
1987 Topps Baseball Highlights 693
1987 Topps Coins 693
1987 Topps Gallery of Champions . 693
1987 Topps Glossy Rookies 694
1987 Topps Mini League Leaders .. 694
1987 Topps Stickers 694
1988 Topps 695
1988 Topps All-Star Glossy Set of 22 698
1988 Topps All-Star Glossy Set of 60 698
1988 Topps Traded 698
1988 Topps Box Panels 699
1988 Topps American Baseball 699
1988 Topps Big Baseball 699
1988 Topps Coins 700
1988 Topps Gallery of Champions . 701
1988 Topps Glossy Rookies 701
1988 Topps Mini League Leaders .. 701
1988 Topps Stickercards.................. 701
1988 Topps Stickers 702
1989 Topps 703
1989 Topps All-Star Glossy Set of 22 705
1989 Topps Glossy Rookies Set Of 22 705
1989 Topps All-Star Glossy Set of 60 705
1989 Topps Traded 706
1989 Topps Box Panels 706
1989 Topps Batting Leaders 706
1989 Topps Big Baseball 707
1989 Topps Coins 708
1989 Topps Double Headers All-Stars 708
1989 Topps Major League Debut ... 708
1989 Topps Mini League Leaders .. 709
1989 Topps American Baseball 709
1990 Topps 709
1990 Topps Glossy Rookies 712
1990 Topps All-Star Glossy Set of 22 712
1990 Topps All-Star Glossy Set of 60 712
1990 Topps Traded 712
1990 Topps Box Panels 713
1990 Topps Batting Leaders 713
1990 Topps Big Baseball 713
1990 Topps Major League Debut Promo 714
1990 Topps Major League Debut ... 714
1990 Topps TV All-Stars 715
1990 Topps TV Cardinals Team Set 715
1990 Topps TV Cubs Team Set 716
1990 Topps TV Mets Team Set 716
1990 Topps TV Red Sox Team Set. 716
1990 Topps TV Yankees Team Set 717
1990 Topps Heads Up! 717
1990 Topps Coins 717
1990 Topps Senior League 717
1991 Topps 718
1991 Topps Wax Box Cards 721
1991 Topps All-Star Glossy Set of 22 721
1991 Topps Glossy Rookies 721
1991 Topps Traded 721
1991 Topps Babe Ruth 722
1991 Topps Major League Debut ... 722
1991 Topps Stadium Club 723
1991 Topps Stadium Club Charter Members 724
1991 Topps Stadium Club Members Only 725
1991 Topps East Coast National Reprints.................................. 725
1991 "1953" Topps Archives Promos 725
1991 "1953" Topps Archives 725
1992 Topps Promo Sheet 727
1992 Topps 727
1992 Topps Gold Promo Sheet 730
1992 Topps Gold 730
1992 Topps Gold Winners 730
1992 Topps Traded 730
1992 Topps Traded Gold 730
1992 Topps Kids 730
1992 Topps Triple Header Photo Balls 731
1992 Topps Stadium Club 731
1992 Topps Stadium Club Master Photos 734
1992 Topps Stadium Club Special Edition 734
1992 Topps Stadium Club Members Only 735
1992 Topps Stadium Club First Draft Picks 735
1993 Topps Promo Sheet 735
1993 Topps Promos 735
1993 Topps 735
1993 Topps Gold 738
1993 Topps Black Gold 738
1993 Topps Traded 738
1993 Topps Colorado Rockies Inaugural Year 739
1993 Topps Florida Marlins Inaugural Year 739
1993 Topps Stadium Club 739
1993 Topps Stadium Club Master Photos 741
1993 Topps Stadium Club First Day Production 742
1993 Topps Stadium Club I Inserts 742
1993 Topps Stadium Club II Inserts 742
1993 Topps Stadium Club III Inserts 742
1993 Topps Stadium Club Special . 742
1993 Topps Stadium Club Special Master Photos 743
1993 Topps Stadium Club Members Only 743
1993 Topps Stadium Club Team Sets 743
1993 Topps Stadium Club Ultra Pro 745
1993 Topps Finest Promos 745
1993 Topps Finest 745
1993 Topps Finest Refractors 746
1993 Topps Finest Jumbo All-Stars 746
1993 Topps Full Shot Super 746
1994 Topps Preview 746
1994 Topps 747
1994 Topps Gold 749
1994 Topps Black Gold 749
1994 Topps Finest Promos 749
1994 Topps Finest Series I 750
1994 Topps Finest Refractors Series I 750
1994 Topps Finest Superstars 751

1994 Topps Stadium Club 751
1994 Topps Stadium Club Super Teams 753
1994 Topps Stadium Club Dugout Dirt Series I 753
1994 Topps Stadium Club First Day Production 753
1994 Topps Stadium Club Golden Rainbow 753
1994 Topps Stadium Club Infocards 754
1994 "1954" Topps Archives 754
1994 Topps Gold Archives 755
1987 Toys "R" Us 755
1988 Toys "R" Us Rookies 755
1989 Toys "R" Us Rookies 755
1990 Toys "R" Us Rookies 755
1991 Toys "R" Us Rookies 756
1993 Toys "R" Us Topps Stadium Club 756
1993 Toys "R" Us Master Photos ... 756
1969 Transogram 756
1970 Transogram 757
1970 Transogram Mets 757
1983 True Value White Sox 757
1984 True Value White Sox 757
1986 True Value 758
1911 (T3) 562
1913 (T200) 164
1900 (T203) 326
1911 (T208) 83
1910 Type 1 (T213) 76
1910 Type 1 (T215) 482
1914 Type 2 (T213) 77
1915 (T214) 788
1912 Type 2 (T215) 483
1919 Type 3 (T213) 77
1912 (T215) 457
1914 (T222) 163
1922 (T231) 163
1911 (T332) 252

U

1932 U.S. Caramel 758
1989 Upper Deck Promos 758
1989 Upper Deck 758
1990 Upper Deck 761
1990 Upper Deck Reggie Jackson Heroes 763
1991 Upper Deck 763
1991 Upper Deck Final Edition 766
1991 Upper Deck Hank Aaron Heroes 766
1991 Upper Deck Nolan Ryan Heroes 766
1991 Upper Deck Heroes of Baseball 766
1991 Upper Deck Silver Sluggers .. 767
1991 Upper Deck Comic Ball 2 767
1992 Upper Deck 767
1992 Upper Deck College POY Holograms 769
1992 Upper Deck Ted Williams Heroes 770
1992 Upper Deck Bench/Morgan Heroes 770
1992 Upper Deck Hall of Fame Heroes 770
1992 Upper Deck Home Run Heroes 770
1992 Upper Deck Scouting Report . 770
1992 Upper Deck Ted Williams' Best 770
1992 Upper Deck FanFest 770
1992 Upper Deck MVP Holograms 771
1993 Upper Deck 771
1993 Upper Deck Clutch Performers 774
1993 Upper Deck 5th Anniversary 774
1993 Upper Deck Future Heroes 774
1993 Upper Deck Home Run Heroes 774
1993 Upper Deck Iooss Collection . 774
1993 Upper Deck Willie Mays Heroes 775
1993 Upper Deck On Deck 775
1993 Upper Deck Then And Now 775
1993 Upper Deck "Highlights" 775
1993 Upper Deck Heroes of Baseball Previews 775
1993 Upper Deck All-Time Heroes 775
1993 Upper Deck All-Time Heroes T202 Reprints 776
1993 Upper Deck Iooss Collection Super 776
1993 Upper Deck 5th Anniversary Super 776
1993 Upper Deck Reggie Jackson Heroes Super 777
1993 Upper Deck Triple Crown 777
1993 Upper Deck Diamond Gallery 777
1993 Upper Deck SP 777
1993 Upper Deck SP Platinum Power 778
1993 Upper Deck Fun Packs 778
1993 Upper Deck Fun Packs All-Star Scratch-Offs 779
1993 Upper Deck Fun Packs Mascot Madness 779
1994 Upper Deck Collector's Choice Promo 779
1994 Upper Deck Collector's Choice 780
1994 Collectors Choice Home Run All-Stars 782
1994 Upper Deck Team vs. Team Scratch-Off 782
1994 Upper Deck 782
1994 Upper Deck Electric Diamond 784
1994 Upper Deck Diamond Collection 784
1994 Upper Deck Mickey Mantle's Long Shots 784
1994 Upper Deck Jumbo Checklists 784
1994 Upper Deck Fun Packs 784
1990 U.S. Playing Card All-Stars ... 785
1991 U.S. Playing Card All-Stars ... 786
1992 U.S. Playing Card Aces 786
1992 U.S. Playing Card Team Sets - Braves 786
1992 U.S. Playing Card Team Sets - Cubs 786
1992 U.S. Playing Card Team Sets - Red Sox 787
1992 U.S. Playing Card Team Sets - Tigers 787
1992 U.S. Playing Card Team Sets - Twins 787

V

1989 Very Fine Pirates 787
1915 Victory Tobacco (T214) 788
1913 Voskamp's Coffee Pittsburgh Pirates 788
1921 (V61) 356
1923 (V100) 801
1933 (V353) 806
1934 (V354) 806
1936 (V355) 807

W

1922 W501 788
1928 W502 789
1922 W503 789
1926 W512 789
1926 W513 789
1919 W514 790
1923 W515 790
1920 W516-1 790
1921 W516-2 791
1931 W517 791
1920 W519 - Numbered 791
1920 W519 - Unnumbered 791
1920 W520 791
1921 W521 792
1918 W522 792
1922 W551 792
1907 W555 792
1927 W560 792
1923 W572 793
1922 W573 793
1932 W574 794
1922 W575-1 794
1922 W575-2 795
1938 W711-1 Reds 795
1939 W711-1 Reds 795
1940 W711-2 Harry Hartman Reds 795
1941 W753 St. Louis Browns 795
1941 W754 St. Louis Cardinals 796
1888 WG1 Base Ball Playing Cards 796
1985 Wendy's Tigers 796
1974 Weston Expos 796
1993 Whataburger Nolan Ryan 797
1935 Wheaties - Series 1 797
1936 Wheaties - Series 3 797
1936 Wheaties - Series 4 797

1936 Wheaties - Series 5 797
1937 Wheaties - Series 6 797
1937 Wheaties - Series 7 798
1937 Wheaties - Series 8 798
1937 Wheaties - Series 9 798
1937 Wheaties - Series 14 798
1938 Wheaties - Series 10 798
1938 Wheaties - Series 11 799
1938 Wheaties - Series 15 799
1939 Wheaties - Series 12 799
1939 Wheaties - Series 13 799
1940 Wheaties Champs of the USA 799
1941 Wheaties Champs of the USA 800
1951 Wheaties 800
1952 Wheaties 800
1982 Wheaties Indians 800
1983 Wheaties Indians 800
1984 Wheaties Indians 800
1954 Wilson Franks 801
1923 Willard Chocolate (V100) 801
1911 Williams Baking Philadelphia A's (D359) 802
1910 Williams Caramels (E103) 802
1888 E.R. Williams Card Game 802
1993 Ted Williams Card Co. Premier Edition 802
1993 Ted Williams Co. Etched in Stone 803
1993 Ted Williams Co. Brooks Robinson 803
1993 Ted Williams Co. Locklear Collection 803
1993 Ted Williams Co. Memories ... 803
1994 Ted Williams Card Company . 803
1994 Ted Williams Card Co. Etched in Stone 804
1994 Ted Williams Card Company The 500 Club 804
1994 Ted Williams Card Company Dan Gardiner Collection 804
1994 Ted Williams Co. Locklear Collection 805
1994 Ted Williams Card Company Memories 805
1994 Ted Williams Card Co. LP Cards 805
1994 Ted Williams Co. Mike Schmidt Collection 805
1988 Woolworth 805
1989 Woolworth 805
1990 Woolworth 806
1991 Woolworth 806
1933 World Wide Gum (Canadian Goudey, V353) 806
1934 World Wide Gum (Canadian Goudey, V354) 806
1936 World Wide Gum (Canadian Goudey, V355) 807
1988 Worth Jose Canseco 807
1906 (W601) 541
1947 (W602) 546
1946 - 49 (W603) 546

Y

1928 Yeungling's Ice Cream 807
1959 Yoo-Hoo 808
1993 Yoo-Hoo 808
1994 Yoo-Hoo 808
1927 York Caramels Type I (E210) 808
1927 York Caramels Type II (E210) 809
1888 Yum Yum Tobacco (N403) 809

Z

1982 Zellers Expos 809
1978 Zest Soap 809
1992 Ziploc 809

MINOR LEAGUE

A

1994 Action Packed............... 1075
1994 Action Packed Diamond Franchise Gems............... 1075
1994 Action Packed Gold Franchise Gems 1075
1981 Arby's Nashville Sounds......... 874
1982 Arby's Nashville Sounds......... 880
1960 Armour Meats Denver Bears ... 809
1910 A.W.H. Caramels Virginia League (E222) 809

B

1983 Barry Colla San Jose Bees..... 888
1990 BBC, etc. Salt Lake City Trappers............... 986
1961 Bee Hive Starch Toronto Maple Leafs 809
1993 Benjamin Moore Ricmond Camera Richmond Braves............... 1070
1989 Best Albany Yankees 944
1990 Best Albany Yankees 968
1989 Best All-Decade Albany Yankees............... 944
1989 Best All-Decade Birmingham Barons............... 947
1989 Best All-Decade Cedar Rapids Reds............... 948
1989 Best All-Decade Hagerstown Suns 953
1989 Best All-Decade Springfield Cardinals............... 963
1990 Best Auburn Astros............... 969
1990 Best Beloit Brewers 969
1987 Best Birmingham Barons........ 913
1988 Best Birmingham Barons........ 927
1989 Best Birmingham Barons........ 946
1990 Best Birmingham Baron.......... 970
1990 Best Burlington Braves........... 970
1989 Best Canton-Akron Indians..... 948
1990 Best Canton-Akron Indians..... 971
1989 Best Cedar Rapids Reds........ 948
1990 Best Cedar Rapids Reds........ 972
1990 Best Charleston Rainbows 972
1988 Best Charleston Wheelers...... 928
1989 Best Charleston Wheelers...... 949
1990 Best Charleston Wheelers...... 972
1987 Best Chattanooga Lookouts ... 913
1988 Best Chattanooga Lookouts ... 929
1989 Best Chattanooga Lookouts ... 949
1990 Best Clinton Giants............... 972
1989 Best Columbia Mets 950
1988 Best Columbus Astros............ 929
1989 Best Columbus Mudcats......... 950
1990 Best Columbus Mudcats......... 973
1988 Best El Paso Diablos.............. 930
1988 Best El Paso Diablos Limited Edition 931
1988 Best Eugene Emeralds........... 931
1989 Best Eugene Emeralds........... 952
1990 Best Everett Giants............... 975
1990 Best Gastonia Rangers 975
1990 Best Greensboro Hornets....... 976
1987 Best Greenville Braves........... 916
1988 Best Greenville Braves........... 932
1989 Best Greenville Braves........... 953
1990 Best Greenville Braves........... 976
1989 Best Hagerstown Suns........... 953
1990 Best Hagerstown Suns........... 976
1990 Best Hamilton Redbirds.......... 977
1989 Best Huntsville Stars 953
1990 Best Huntsville Stars 977
1988 Best Jacksonville Expos......... 933
1989 Best Jacksonville Expos......... 954
1990 Best Jacksonville Expos......... 978
1990 Best Kenosha Twins............... 978
1990 Best Kingsport Mets 978
1988 Best Knoxville Blue Jays 933
1989 Best Knoxville Blue Jays 955
1990 Best Knoxville Blue Jays 979
1989 Best Limited-Edition Albany Yankees............... 944
1989 Best Limited-Edition Birmingham Barons 946
1989 Best Limited-Edition Columbus Mudcats 950
1990 Best Madison Muskies............ 980
1989 Best Medford A's 956
1990 Best Medicine Hat Blue Jays.. 980
1987 Best Memphis Chicks............ 918
1988 Best Memphis Chicks............ 934
1989 Best Memphis Chicks............ 956
1990 Best Memphis Chicks............ 980
1990 Best Minor League Baseball... 992
1990 Best New Britain Red Sox 981
1990 Best Orlando Sun Rays 982
1988 Best Orlando Twins 936
1989 Best-ProCards Baseball America Prospects............... 946
1990 Best Pulaski Braves............... 984
1989 Best Quad City Angels 959
1989 Best Reading Phillies............. 960
1990 Best Reading Phillies............. 984
1989 Best Riverside Red Wave....... 960
1990 Best Riverside Red Wave....... 985
1988 Best San Antonio Missions..... 939
1989 Best San Antonio Missions..... 961
1988 Best San Antonio Missions Ltd. Edition 939
1988 Best San Bernadino Spirit 939

1989 Best San Bernadino Spirit 962
1990 Best San Bernadino Spirit 986
1988 Best San Bernadino Spirit Ltd. Edition 939
1989 Best San Jose Giants 962
1990 Best San Jose Giants 987
1990 Best South Bend White Sox ... 987
1990 Best Southern Oregon Athletics 988
1990 Best Spartanburg Phillies 988
1987 Best Springfield Cardinals 923
1988 Best Springfield Cardinals 941
1989 Best Springfield Cardinals 963
1990 Best Springfield Cardinals 988
1989 Best Stockton Ports 963
1990 Best Stockton Ports 988
1990 Best Sumter Braves 989
1989 Best Tulsa Drillers 965
1990 Best Waterloo Diamonds 991
1990 Best Wausau Timbers 991
1990 Best Williamsport Bills 992
1988 Best/ProCards Baseball America AA Prospects 926
1983 BHN Las Vegas Stars 886
1983 BHN Phoenix Giants 888
1911 Big Eater Sacramento Solons 809
1910 Bishop & Co. P.C.L. Teams (E221) 809
1911 Bishop & Co. P.C.L. Type II (E100) 810
1911 Bishop & Co. P.C.L. Type I (E100) 810
1910 Bishop & Co. P.C.L. (E99) 810
1993 Bleacher Burns Richmond Braves 1070
1990 Bob's Camera Richmond Braves 984
1991 Bob's Camera Richmond Braves 1020
1992 Bob's Camera Richmond Braves 1048
1987 Bob's Photo Richmond Braves 921
1988 Bob's Photo Richmond Braves 938
1989 Bob's Photo Richmond Braves 960
1958 Bond Bread Buffalo Bisons 810
1949 Bowman Pacific Coast League 810
1990 Box Scores Appleton Foxes ... 968
1978 Brittling's Memphis Chicks 860
1933 Buffalo Bisons Jigsaw Puzzles 811
1991 Burger King Huntsville Stars .. 1012

C

1988 Cain Elmira Pioneers 930
1988 Cain Elmira Pioneers Test Issue 930
1988 Cal Cards Bakersfield Dodgers 926
1988 Cal Cards California League All-Stars 928
1988 Cal Cards Fresno Suns 931
1988 Cal Cards Modesto A's 935
1988 Cal Cards Palm Springs Angels 936
1988 Cal Cards Reno Silver Sox 938
1988 Cal Cards Riverside Red Wave 938
1988 Cal Cards San Bernadino Spirit 939
1988 Cal Cards San Jose Giants 940
1988 Cal Cards Stockton Ports 941
1988 Cal Cards Visalia Oaks 943
1989 California League All-Stars 948
1990 Cal League All-Stars 971
1989 Cal League Bakersfield Dodgers 946
1990 Cal League Bakersfield Dodgers 969
1991 Cal League Bakersfield Dodgers 1004
1992 Cal League Bakersfield Dodgers 1033
1993 Cal League Bakersfield Dodgers 1057
1991 Cal League Cal League All-Stars 1006
1989 Cal League Modesto A's 957
1990 Cal League Modesto A's 981
1989 Cal League Palm Springs Angels 958
1990 Cal League Palm Springs Angels 983
1989 Cal League Reno Silver Sox .. 960
1990 Cal League Reno Silver Sox .. 984
1991 Cal League Reno Silver Sox 1020
1992 Cal League Reno Silver Sox 1047
1993 Cal League Riverside Pilots . 1070
1989 Cal League Riverside Red Wave 960
1990 Cal League Riverside Red Wave 985
1989 Cal League Salinas Spurs 961
1990 Cal League Salinas Spurs 986
1989 Cal League San Bernadino Spirit 962
1990 Cal League San Bernardino Spirit 986
1989 Cal League San Jose Giants .. 962
1990 Cal League San Jose Giants .. 987
1989 Cal League Stockton Ports 963
1990 Cal League Stockton Ports 988
1989 Cal League Visalia Oaks 966
1990 Cal League Visalia Oaks 991
1989 Candl Coins Fold-Out Set Tidewater Tides 964
1990 Carolina League All-Stars 971
1974 Caruso Albuquerque Dukes ... 847
1975 Caruso Albuquerque Dukes ... 849
1974 Caruso Hawaii Islanders 848
1975 Caruso Hawaii Islanders 850
1976 Caruso Hawaii Islanders 853
1977 Caruso Hawaii Islanders 856
1974 Caruso Phoenix Giants 848
1975 Caruso Phoenix Giants 850
1976 Caruso Phoenix Giants 853
1974 Caruso Sacramento Solons 848
1975 Caruso Sacramento Solons 850
1976 Caruso Sacramento Solons 854
1974 Caruso Salt Lake City Angels 848
1975 Caruso Salt Lake City Gulls 850
1976 Caruso Salt Lake City Gulls 854
1974 Caruso Spokane Indians 848
1975 Caruso Spokane Indians 851
1976 Caruso Spokane Indians 854
1973 Caruso Tacoma Twins 847
1974 Caruso Tacoma Twins 848
1975 Caruso Tucson Toros 851
1976 Caruso Tucson Toros 854
1944 Centennial Flour Seattle Rainers 811
1943 Centennial Flour Seattle Rainiers 811
1945 Centennial Flour Seattle Rainiers 811
1947 Centennial Flour Seattle Rainiers 811
1977 Chong Hawaii Islanders 856
1977 Chong Modesto A's 856
1978 Chong Modesto A's 860
1979 Chong Modesto A's 864
1980 Chong Modesto A's 869
1981 Chong Modesto A's 874
1982 Chong Modesto A's 880
1983 Chong Modesto A's 887
1984 Chong Modesto A's 893
1985 Chong Modesto A's 899
1986 Chong Modesto A's 907
1987 Chong Modesto A's 919
1989 Chong Modesto A's 957
1990 Chong Modesto A's 981
1975 Circle K Foods Phoenix Giants 850
1992 Classic Best 1028
1992 Classic Best Albany Polecats 1032
1993 Classic Best Albany Polecats 1056
1991 Classic Best Appleton Foxes 1003
1992 Classic Best Appleton Foxes 1032
1993 Classic Best Appleton Foxes 1057
1992 Classic Best Asheville Tourists 1033
1993 Classic Best Asheville Tourists 1057
1991 Classic Best Ashville Tourists 1003
1991 Classic Best Auburn Astros .. 1003
1992 Classic Best Auburn Astros .. 1033
1991 Classic Best Augusta Pirates 1003
1992 Classic Best Augusta Pirates 1033
1993 Classic Best Augusta Pirates 1057
1993 Classic Best Autographs 1054
1991 Classic Best Baseball City Royals 1004
1992 Classic Best Baseball City Royals 1033
1991 Classic Best Batavia Clippers 1004
1992 Classic Best Batavia Clippers 1033
1991 Classic Best Bellingham Mariners 1004
1992 Classic Best Bellingham Mariners 1033
1991 Classic Best Beloit Brewers .. 1004

1992 Classic Best Beloit Brewers.. 1034
1993 Classic Best Beloit Brewers.. 1057
1991 Classic Best Bend Bucks...... 1004
1992 Classic Best Bend Rockies... 1034
1992 Classic Best Blue Bonus 1029
1991 Classic Best Bluefield Orioles 1005
1992 Classic Best Bluefield Orioles 1034
1991 Classic Best Boise Hawks.... 1005
1992 Classic Best Boise Hawks.... 1034
1991 Classic Best Bristol Tigers.... 1005
1992 Classic Best Bristol Tigers.... 1035
1991 Classic Best Burlington Astros 1006
1992 Classic Best Burlington Astros 1035
1993 Classic Best Burlington Bees 1058
1992 Classic Best Burlington Indians 1035
1993 Classic Best Capital City Bombers 1059
1993 Classic Best Cedar Rapids Kernels................................ 1059
1991 Classic Best Cedar Rapids Reds 1006
1992 Classic Best Cedar Rapids Reds 1035
1993 Classic Best Central Valley Rockies 1059
1991 Classic Best Charleston Rainbows 1007
1992 Classic Best Charleston Rainbows 1035
1993 Classic Best Charleston Rainbows 1060
1991 Classic Best Charleston Wheelers 1007
1992 Classic Best Charleston Wheelers 1036
1991 Classic Best Charlotte Rangers 1007
1992 Classic Best Charlotte Rangers 1036
1993 Classic Best Charlotte Rangers 1060
1991 Classic Best Clearwater Phillies................................ 1007
1992 Classic Best Clearwater Phillies................................ 1036
1993 Classic Best Clearwater Phillies................................ 1060
1991 Classic Best Clinton Giants .. 1008
1992 Classic Best Clinton Giants .. 1036
1993 Classic Best Clinton Giants .. 1060
1992 Classic Best Columbia Mets. 1037
1991 Classic Best Columbus Indians 1008
1993 Classic Best Columbus RedStixx............................. 1061
1992 Classic Best Columbus Redstixx 1037
1993 Classic Best Daytona Cubs.. 1061
1991 Classic Best Dunedin Blue Jays 1008
1992 Classic Best Dunedin Blue Jays 1037
1991 Classic Best Durham Bulls ... 1009
1992 Classic Best Durham Bulls ... 1038
1993 Classic Best Durham Bulls ... 1061
1992 Classic Best Elizabethton Twins 1038
1991 Classic Best Elmira Pioneers 1009
1992 Classic Best Elmira Pioneers 1038
1991 Classic Best Erie Sailors 1009
1992 Classic Best Erie Sailors 1038
1991 Classic Best Eugene Emeralds............................. 1009
1992 Classic Best Eugene Emeralds............................. 1038
1991 Classic Best Everett Giants .. 1010
1992 Classic Best Everett Giants .. 1039
1993 Classic Best Expansion #1 Picks 1054
1991 Classic Best Fayetteville Generais 1010
1992 Classic Best Fayetteville Generals 1039
1993 Classic Best Fayetteville Generals 1062
1993 Classic Best Foil 1054
1993 Classic Best Fort Lauderdale Red Sox....................................... 1062
1993 Classic Best Fort Meyers Miracle 1062
1993 Classic Best Fort Wayne Wizards.............................. 1063
1991 Classic Best Frederick Keys. 1010
1992 Classic Best Frederick Keys. 1039
1993 Classic Best Frederick Keys. 1063
1991 Classic Best Ft. Lauderdale Yankees.............................. 1010
1992 Classic Best Ft. Lauderdale Yankees.............................. 1039
1992 Classic Best Ft. Meyers Miracle 1039
1991 Classic Best Gastonia Rangers 1010
1992 Classic Best Gastonia Rangers 1040
1991 Classic Best Geneva Cubs... 1011
1992 Classic Best Geneva Cubs... 1040
1993 Classic Best Gold 1055
1991 Classic Best Gold Bonus........ 999
1992 Classic Best Greensboro Hornets 1040
1993 Classic Best Greensboro Hornets 1063
1991 Classic Best Greenville Braves 1011
1993 Classic Best Hagerstown Suns 1063
1991 Classic Best Hamilton Redbirds............................. 1011
1992 Classic Best Hamilton Redbirds............................. 1040
1993 Classic Best Hickory Crawdads............................ 1064
1991 Classic Best High Desert Mavericks............................ 1012
1992 Classic Best High Desert Mavericks............................ 1041
1993 Classic Best High Desert Mavericks............................ 1064
1991 Classic Best Huntington Cubs 1012
1992 Classic Best Huntington Cubs 1041
1991 Classic Best Huntsville Stars 1012
1994 Classic Best Illustrated Acetate............................... 1076
1991 Classic Best Jamestown Expos 1013
1992 Classic Best Jamestown Expos 1042
1991 Classic Best Johnson City Cardinals............................. 1013
1992 Classic Best Johnson City Cardinals............................. 1042
1991 Classic Best Kane County Cougars 1013
1992 Classic Best Kane County Cougars 1042
1993 Classic Best Kane County Cougars 1065
1991 Classic Best Kenosha Twins 1013
1992 Classic Best Kenosha Twins 1042
1991 Classic Best Kingsport Mets. 1014
1992 Classic Best Kingsport Mets. 1042
1991 Classic Best Kinston Indians 1014
1992 Classic Best Kinston Indians 1043
1993 Classic Best Kinston Indians 1065
1991 Classic Best Lakeland Tigers 1014
1992 Classic Best Lakeland Tigers 1043
1993 Classic Best Lakeland Tigers 1065
1991 Classic Best Lynchburg Red Sox 1015
1992 Classic Best Lynchburg Red Sox 1043
1993 Classic Best Lynchburg Red Sox 1066
1991 Classic Best Macon Braves.. 1015
1992 Classic Best Macon Braves.. 1043
1993 Classic Best Macon Braves.. 1066
1991 Classic Best Madison Muskies 1015
1992 Classic Best Madison Muskies 1044
1993 Classic Best Madison Muskies 1066
1991 Classic Best Martinsville Phillies................................ 1015
1992 Classic Best Martinsville Phillies................................ 1044
1991 Classic Best Miami Miracle... 1016
1994 Classic Best Minor League Gold 1075
1994 Classic Best Minor League Gold #1 Picks 1076
1991 Classic Best Minors - Major League Way....................................... 997
1991 Classic Best Modesto A's..... 1016
1992 Classic Best Modesto A's..... 1044
1993 Classic Best Modesto A's..... 1067
1993 Classic Best MVPs 1055
1991 Classic Best Myrtle Beach Hurricanes........................... 1017
1992 Classic Best Myrtle Beach Hurricanes........................... 1045
1991 Classic Best Niagara Falls Rapids 1017

1992 Classic Best Niagara Falls Rapids ... 1045
1991 Classic Best Osceola Astros 1017
1992 Classic Best Osceola Astros 1045
1993 Classic Best Osceola Astros 1068
1992 Classic Best Palm Springs Angels ... 1046
1993 Classic Best Palm Springs Angels ... 1068
1991 Classic Best Peninsula Pilots 1018
1992 Classic Best Peninsula Pilots 1046
1991 Classic Best Peoria Chiefs ... 1018
1992 Classic Best Peoria Chiefs ... 1046
1993 Classic Best Peoria Chiefs ... 1068
1991 Classic Best Pittsfield Mets .. 1019
1992 Classic Best Pittsfield Mets .. 1046
1993 Classic Best Player & Manager of the Year ... 1055
1991 Classic Best Princeton Reds 1019
1992 Classic Best Princeton Reds 1047
1991 Classic Best Prince William Cannons ... 1019
1993 Classic Best Prince William Cannons ... 1069
1992 Classic Best Prince Williams Cannons ... 1047
1991 Classic Best Pulaski Braves. 1019
1992 Classic Best Pulaski Braves. 1047
1991 Classic Best Quad City Angels ... 1020
1992 Classic Best Quad City River Bandits ... 1047
1993 Classic Best Quad City River Bandits ... 1069
1993 Classic Best Rancho Cucamonga Quakes ... 1069
1992 Classic Best Red Bonus ... 1029
1991 Classic Best Rockford Expos 1020
1992 Classic Best Rockford Expos 1048
1993 Classic Best Rockford Royals ... 1070
1991 Classic Best Salem Buccaneers ... 1021
1992 Classic Best Salem Buccaneers ... 1048
1993 Classic Best Salem Buccaneers ... 1070
1991 Classic Best Salinas Spurs... 1021
1992 Classic Best Salinas Spurs... 1048
1991 Classic Best San Bernardino Spirit ... 1022
1992 Classic Best San Bernardino Spirit ... 1049
1993 Classic Best San Bernardino Spirit ... 1071
1991 Classic Best San Jose Giants ... 1022
1992 Classic Best San Jose Giants ... 1049
1993 Classic Best San Jose Giants ... 1071
1991 Classic Best Sarasota White Sox ... 1022
1992 Classic Best Sarasota White Sox ... 1049
1993 Classic Best Sarasota White Sox ... 1071
1991 Classic Best Savannah Cardinals ... 1022
1992 Classic Best Savannah Cardinals ... 1049
1993 Classic Best Savannah Cardinals ... 1071
1991 Classic Best South Bend White Sox ... 1023
1992 Classic Best South Bend White Sox ... 1050
1993 Classic Best South Bend White Sox ... 1072
1991 Classic Best Southern Oregon A's ... 1023
1992 Classic Best Southern Oregon A's ... 1050
1991 Classic Best Spartanburg Phillies ... 1023
1992 Classic Best Spartanburg Phillies ... 1050
1993 Classic Best Spartanburg Phillies ... 1072
1991 Classic Best Spokane Indians ... 1023
1992 Classic Best Spokane Indians ... 1050
1991 Classic Best Springfield Cardinals ... 1023
1992 Classic Best Springfield Cardinals ... 1050
1993 Classic Best Springfield Cardinals ... 1072
1991 Classic Best Stockton Ports . 1024
1992 Classic Best Stockton Ports . 1051
1993 Classic Best Stockton Ports . 1073
1992 Classic Best St. Catharines Blue Jays ... 1050
1991 Classic Best St. Catherines Blue Jays ... 1020
1991 Classic Best St. Lucie Mets .. 1021
1992 Classic Best St. Lucie Mets .. 1051
1993 Classic Best St. Lucie Mets .. 1071
1991 Classic Best St. Petersburg Cardinals ... 1021
1992 Classic Best St. Petersburg Cardinals ... 1051
1993 Classic Best St. Petersburg Cardinals ... 1071
1991 Classic Best Sumter Flyers .. 1024
1991 Classic Best Utica Blue Sox . 1025
1992 Classic Best Utica Blue Sox . 1052
1991 Classic Best Vero Beach Dodgers ... 1025
1992 Classic Best Vero Beach Dodgers ... 1052
1993 Classic Best Vero Beach Dodgers ... 1073
1991 Classic Best Visalia Oaks..... 1026
1992 Classic Best Visalia Oaks..... 1052
1991 Classic Best Waterloo Diamonds ... 1026
1992 Classic Best Waterloo Diamonds ... 1052
1993 Classic Best Waterloo Diamonds ... 1074
1991 Classic Best Watertown Indians ... 1026
1992 Classic Best Watertown Indians ... 1052
1991 Classic Best Welland Pirates 1026
1992 Classic Best Welland Pirates 1053
1991 Classic Best West Palm Beach Expos ... 1026
1992 Classic Best West Palm Beach Expos ... 1053
1993 Classic Best West Palm Beach Expos ... 1074
1993 Classic Best West Virginia Wheelers ... 1074
1993 Classic Best Wilmington Blue Rocks ... 1074
1991 Classic Best Winston-Salem Spirits ... 1027
1992 Classic Best Winston-Salem Spirits ... 1053
1993 Classic Best Winston-Salem Spirits ... 1074
1991 Classic Best Winter Haven Red Sox ... 1027
1992 Classic Best Winter Haven Red Sox ... 1053
1991 Classic Best Yakima Bears .. 1027
1992 Classic Best Yakima Bears .. 1053
1993 Classic Best Young Guns..... 1054
1990 Classic #1 Draft Picks... 997
1991 Classic #1 Draft Picks... 1027
1989 CMC AAA All-Stars... 944
1988 CMC Albuquerque Dukes... 925
1989 CMC Albuquerque Dukes... 945
1990 CMC Albuquerque Dukes... 968
1988 CMC Buffalo Bisons ... 927
1989 CMC Buffalo Bisons ... 947
1988 CMC Calgary Cannons... 928
1989 CMC Calgary Cannons... 948
1988 CMC Colorado Springs Sky Sox ... 929
1989 CMC Colorado Springs Sky Sox ... 949
1988 CMC Columbus Clippers... 929
1989 CMC Columbus Clippers... 950
1988 CMC Denver Zephyrs... 930
1989 CMC Denver Zephyrs... 950
1988 CMC Edmonton Trappers... 930
1989 CMC Edmonton Trappers... 951
1988 CMC Indianapolis Indians... 932
1989 CMC Indianapolis Indians... 954
1988 CMC Iowa Cubs ... 932
1989 CMC Iowa Cubs ... 954
1988 CMC Las Vegas Stars ... 933
1989 CMC Las Vegas Stars ... 955
1988 CMC Louisville Redbirds ... 934
1988 CMC Maine Phillies ... 934
1988 CMC Nashville Sounds... 935
1989 CMC Nashville Sounds... 957
1988 CMC Oklahoma City 89'ers 935
1989 CMC Oklahoma City 89'ers 957
1988 CMC Omaha Royals... 936
1989 CMC Omaha Royals... 957
1988 CMC Pawtucket Red Sox ... 936
1989 CMC Pawtucket Red Sox ... 958
1988 CMC Phoenix Firebirds ... 937

1989 CMC Phoenix Firebirds 959
1988 CMC Portland Beavers........... 937
1989 CMC Portland Beavers........... 959
1988 CMC Richmond Braves.......... 938
1989 CMC Richmond Braves.......... 960
1988 CMC Rochester Red Wings ... 938
1989 CMC Rochester Red Wings ... 961
1989 CMC Scranton-Wilkes Barre Red Barons.................................. 962
1988 CMC Syracuse Chiefs 941
1989 CMC Syracuse Chiefs 964
1988 CMC Tacoma Tigers 941
1989 CMC Tacoma Tigers 964
1988 CMC Tidewater Tides............. 941
1989 CMC Tidewater Tides............. 964
1988 CMC Toledo Mud Hens.......... 942
1989 CMC Toledo Mud Hens.......... 965
1988 CMC Triple A All-Stars 942
1988 CMC Tucson Toros 942
1989 CMC Tucson Toros 965
1988 CMC Vancouver Canadians ... 943
1989 CMC Vancouver Canadians ... 965
1990 CMC (TCMA) Buffalo Bisons.. 970
1990 CMC (TMCA) Calgary Cannons................................ 971
1990 CMC (TCMA) Colorado Springs Sky Sox................................. 973
1990 CMC (TCMA) Columbus Clippers................................. 973
1990 CMC (TCMA) Denver Zephyrs 974
1990 CMC (TCMA) Edmonton Trappers................................ 974
1990 CMC (TCMA) Indianapolis Indians 977
1990 CMC (TCMA) Iowa Cubs........ 978
1990 CMC (TCMA) Las Vegas Stars 979
1990 CMC (TCMA) Louisville Redbirds.............................. 979
1990 CMC (TCMA) Nashville Sounds 981
1990 CMC (TCMA) Oklahoma City 89ers................................... 982
1990 CMC (TCMA) Omaha Royals. 982
1990 CMC (TCMA) Pawtucket Red Sox 983
1990 CMC (TCMA) Phoenix Firebirds............................... 983
1990 CMC (TCMA) Portland Beavers............................... 983
1990 CMC (TCMA) Richmond Braves 984
1990 CMC (TCMA) Rochester Red Wings................................... 985
1990 CMC (TCMA) Scranton-Wilkes Barre Red Barons 987
1990 CMC (TCMA) Syracuse Chiefs 989
1990 CMC (TCMA) Tacoma Tigers. 989
1990 CMC (TCMA) Tidewater Tides 989
1990 CMC (TCMA) Toledo Mud Hens 990
1990 CMC (TCMA) Tucson Toros... 990
1990 CMC (TCMA) Vancouver Canadians............................ 990
1976 Coke Phoenix Giants............. 853
1977 Coke Premium Phoenix Giants 857
1990 Collectors Marketing Corp. Pre-Rookie 993
1910 Contentnea Photo Series (T209) 812
1910 Contentnea 1st Series (T209) 812
1978 Cramer Albuquerque Dukes... 859
1984 Cramer Albuquerque Dukes... 890
1985 Cramer Albuquerque Dukes... 895
1986 Cramer Bellingham Mariners.. 902
1985 Cramer Bend Phillies.............. 895
1986 Cramer Bend Phillies.............. 902
1985 Cramer Calgary Cannons....... 896
1984 Cramer Edmonton Trappers... 891
1985 Cramer Edmonton Trappers... 896
1986 Cramer Eugene Emeralds...... 904
1984 Cramer Everett Giants............ 891
1987 Cramer Everett Giants............ 915
1986 Cramer Everett Giants - Black and White..................................... 904
1986 Cramer Everett Giants - Color 904
1985 Cramer Everett Giants - Series I 897
1985 Cramer Everett Giants - Series II 897
1979 Cramer Hawaii Islanders........ 863
1984 Cramer Hawaii Islanders........ 892
1985 Cramer Hawaii Islanders........ 897
1984 Cramer Las Vegas Stars........ 892
1985 Cramer Las Vegas Stars........ 898
1986 Cramer Medford A's 907
1976 Cramer Phoenix Giants.......... 853
1977 Cramer Phoenix Giants.......... 857
1978 Cramer Phoenix Giants.......... 861
1979 Cramer Phoenix Giants.......... 865
1984 Cramer Phoenix Giants.......... 893
1985 Cramer Phoenix Giants.......... 899
1984 Cramer Portland Beavers....... 893
1985 Cramer Portland Beavers....... 900
1986 Cramer Salem Angels 909
1977 Cramer Salt Lake City Gulls ... 858
1978 Cramer Salt Lake City Gulls ... 861
1984 Cramer Salt Lake City Gulls ... 894
1976 Cramer Seattle Rainiers......... 854
1977 Cramer Spokane Indians........ 858
1978 Cramer Spokane Indians........ 861
1985 Cramer Spokane Indians........ 900
1986 Cramer Spokane Indians........ 910
1985 Cramer Spokane Indians All-Time Greats...................... 900
1979 Cramer 1970s P.C.L. All-Stars 864
1984 Cramer Tacoma Tigers........... 894
1985 Cramer Tacoma Tigers........... 900
1978 Cramer Tacoma Yankees....... 862
1986 Cramer Tri-Cities Triplets 911
1976 Cramer Tucson Toros............. 854
1977 Cramer Tucson Toros............. 858
1978 Cramer Tucson Toros............. 862
1984 Cramer Tucson Toros............. 894
1985 Cramer Tucson Toros............. 901
1984 Cramer Vancouver Canadians 895
1985 Cramer Vancouver Canadians 901
1940 Crowley's Milk........................ 812
1987 Crown Oil Richmond Braves .. 921
1971 Currie Press Richmond Braves 847
1912 (C46) 818

D

1976 Dairy Queen Tacoma Twins... 854
1977 Dairy Queen Tacoma Twins... 858
1986 Daniels Madison Muskies....... 906
1959 Darigold Farms Spokane Indians 813
1960 Darigold Farms Spokane Indians 813
1990 Diamond Appleton Foxes 968
1990 Diamond Cards Kissimmee Dodgers 979
1990 Diamond Cards Princeton Patriots.................................. 984
1990 Diamond Tampa Yankees...... 989
1990 DJ Southern League All-Stars 988
1983 Dog-N-Shake Wichita Aeroes. 890
1986 Donn Jennings Southern League All-Stars 910
1987 Donn Jennings Southern League All-Stars 922
1988 Donn Jennings Southern League All-Stars 940
1989 Donn Jennings Southern League All-Stars 963
1989 Dunkin' Donuts Pawtucket Red Sox... 958
1991 Dunkin' Donuts Pawtucket Red Sox....................................... 1018

E

1982 Ehrler's Dairy Louisville Redbirds................................ 880
1928 Exhibits Pacific Coast League 813
1911 Type I (E100)........................... 811
1911 Type II (E100) 811
1910 (E99) 811
1912 (E136) 817
1910 (E221) 810
1910 (E222) 810

F

1974 Falstaff Beer Omaha Royals .. 848
1992 Fleer Excel............................ 1029
1993 Fleer Excel............................ 1055
1992 Fleer Excel All-Stars 1030
1993 Fleer Excel All-Stars 1056
1992 Fleer Excel League Leaders. 1030
1993 Fleer Excel League Leaders. 1056
1993 Fleer Excel 1st Year Phenoms 1056
1993 Fleer/ProCards Albany-Colonie Yankees 1056
1992 Fleer/ProCards Albany Polecats 1032
1993 Fleer/ProCards Albany Polecats 1056
1992 Fleer/ProCards Albany Yankees 1032

1992 Fleer/ProCards Albuquerque Dukes 1032
1993 Fleer/ProCards Albuquerque Dukes 1057
1992 Fleer/ProCards Appleton Foxes 1032
1993 Fleer/ProCards Appleton Foxes 1057
1992 Fleer/ProCards Arkansas Travelers 1033
1993 Fleer/ProCards Arkansas Travelers 1057
1993 Fleer/ProCards Asheville Tourists 1057
1992 Fleer/ProCards Auburn Astros 1033
1993 Fleer/ProCards Auburn Astros 1057
1992 Fleer/ProCards Augusta Pirates 1033
1993 Fleer/ProCards Augusta Pirates 1057
1992 Fleer/ProCards Baseball City Royals 1033
1992 Fleer/ProCards Batavia Clippers 1033
1993 Fleer/ProCards Batavia Clippers 1057
1992 Fleer/ProCards Bellingham Mariners 1034
1993 Fleer/ProCards Bellingham Mariners 1057
1992 Fleer/ProCards Beloit Brewers 1034
1993 Fleer/ProCards Beloit Brewers 1058
1992 Fleer/ProCards Bend Rockies 1034
1993 Fleer/ProCards Bend Rockies 1058
1992 Fleer/ProCards Billings Mustangs 1034
1993 Fleer/ProCards Billings Mustangs 1058
1992 Fleer/ProCards Binghamton Mets 1034
1993 Fleer/ProCards Binghamton Mets 1058
1992 Fleer/ProCards Birmingham Barons 1034
1993 Fleer/ProCards Birmingham Barons 1058
1992 Fleer/ProCards Bluefield Orioles 1034
1993 Fleer/ProCards Bluefield Orioles 1058
1992 Fleer/ProCards Boise Hawks 1034
1993 Fleer/ProCards Boise Hawks 1058
1993 Fleer/ProCards Bowie Baysox 1058
1992 Fleer/ProCards Bristol Tigers 1035
1993 Fleer/ProCards Bristol Tigers 1058
1992 Fleer/ProCards Buffalo Bisons 1035
1993 Fleer/ProCards Buffalo Bisons 1058
1992 Fleer/ProCards Burlington Astros 1035
1993 Fleer/ProCards Burlington Bees 1059
1992 Fleer/ProCards Burlington Indians 1035
1993 Fleer/ProCards Burlington Indians 1059
1993 Fleer/ProCards Calgary Cannons 1059
1992 Fleer/ProCards Calgary Connons 1035
1992 Fleer/ProCards Canton-Akron Indians 1035
1993 Fleer/ProCards Canton-Akron Indians 1059
1993 Fleer/ProCards Capital City Bombers 1059
1993 Fleer/ProCards Carolina League All-Stars 1059
1992 Fleer/ProCards Carolina Mudcats 1035
1993 Fleer/ProCards Carolina Mudcats 1059
1993 Fleer/ProCards Cedar Rapids Kernels 1059
1992 Fleer/ProCards Cedar Rapids Reds 1035
1993 Fleer/ProCards Central Valley Rockies 1060
1992 Fleer/ProCards Charleston Rainbows 1036
1993 Fleer/ProCards Charleston Rainbows 1060
1992 Fleer/ProCards Charleston Wheelers 1036
1992 Fleer/ProCards Charlotte Knights 1036
1993 Fleer/ProCards Charlotte Knights 1060
1992 Fleer/ProCards Charlotte Rangers 1036
1993 Fleer/ProCards Charlotte Rangers 1060
1992 Fleer/ProCards Chattanooga Lookouts 1036
1993 Fleer/ProCards Chattanooga Lookouts 1060
1992 Fleer/ProCards Clearwater Phillies 1036
1993 Fleer/ProCards Clearwater Phillies 1060
1992 Fleer/ProCards Clinton Giants 1036
1993 Fleer/ProCards Clinton Giants 1060
1992 Fleer/ProCards Colorado Springs Sky Sox 1036
1993 Fleer/ProCards Colorado Springs Sky Sox 1060
1992 Fleer/ProCards Columbia Mets 1037
1992 Fleer/ProCards Columbus Clippers 1037
1993 Fleer/ProCards Columbus Clippers 1061
1993 Fleer/ProCards Columbus RedStixx 1061
1992 Fleer/ProCards Columbus RedStixx 1037
1993 Fleer/ProCards Danville Braves 1061
1993 Fleer/ProCards Daytona Cubs 1061
1992 Fleer/ProCards Denver Zephyrs 1037
1992 Fleer/ProCards Dunedin Blue Jays 1038
1993 Fleer/ProCards Dunedin Blue Jays 1061
1992 Fleer/ProCards Durham Bulls 1038
1993 Fleer/ProCards Durham Bulls 1061
1992 Fleer/ProCards Edmonton Trappers 1038
1993 Fleer/ProCards Edmonton Trappers 1061
1992 Fleer/ProCards Elizabethton Twins 1038
1993 Fleer/ProCards Elizabethton Twins 1061
1992 Fleer/ProCards Elmira Pioneers 1038
1993 Fleer/ProCards Elmira Pioneers 1061
1992 Fleer/ProCards El Paso Diablos 1038
1993 Fleer/ProCards El Paso Diablos 1062
1992 Fleer/ProCards Erie Sailors.. 1038
1993 Fleer/ProCards Erie Sailos ... 1062
1992 Fleer/ProCards Eugene Emeralds 1039
1993 Fleer/ProCards Eugene Emeralds 1062
1992 Fleer/ProCards Everett Giants 1039
1993 Fleer/ProCards Everett Giants 1062
1992 Fleer/ProCards Fayetteville Generals 1039
1993 Fleer/ProCards Fayetteville Generals 1062
1993 Fleer/ProCards Florida State League All-Stars 1062
1993 Fleer/ProCards Fort Meyers Miracle 1062
1993 Fleer/ProCards Fort Wayne Wizards 1063
1992 Fleer/ProCards Frederick Keys 1039
1993 Fleer/ProCards Frederick Keys 1063
1993 Fleer/ProCards Ft. Lauderdale Red Sox 1062
1992 Fleer/ProCards Ft. Lauderdale Yankees 1039
1992 Fleer/ProCards Ft. Meyers Miracle 1039
1992 Fleer/ProCards Gastonia Rangers 1040
1992 Fleer/ProCards Geneva Cubs 1040

1993 Fleer/ProCards Geneva Cubs 1063
1993 Fleer/ProCards Glens Falls Redbirds 1063
1992 Fleer/ProCards Greensboro Hornets 1040
1993 Fleer/ProCards Greensboro Hornets 1063
1992 Fleer/ProCards Greenville Braves 1040
1993 Fleer/ProCards Greenville Braves 1063
1992 Fleer/ProCards Gulf Coast Dodgers 1040
1992 Fleer/ProCards Gulf Coast Mets 1040
1992 Fleer/ProCards Gulf Coast Yankees 1040
1992 Fleer/ProCards Hagerstown Suns 1040
1993 Fleer/ProCards Hagerstown Suns 1063
1992 Fleer/ProCards Hamilton Redbirds 1041
1992 Fleer/ProCards Harrisburg Senators 1041
1993 Fleer/ProCards Harrisburg Senators 1064
1992 Fleer/ProCards Helena Brewers 1041
1993 Fleer/ProCards Helena Brewers 1064
1993 Fleer/ProCards Hickory Crawdads 1064
1993 Fleer/ProCards High Desert Mavericks 1064
1992 Fleer/ProCards Huntington Cubs 1041
1993 Fleer/ProCards Huntington Cubs 1064
1992 Fleer/ProCards Huntsville Stars 1041
1993 Fleer/ProCards Huntsville Stars 1064
1993 Fleer/ProCards Idaho Falls Braves 1064
1992 Fleer/ProCards Idaho Falls Gems 1041
1992 Fleer/ProCards Indianapolis Indians 1041
1993 Fleer/ProCards Indianapolis Indians 1064
1992 Fleer/ProCards Iowa Cubs ... 1041
1993 Fleer/ProCards Iowa Cubs ... 1065
1992 Fleer/ProCards Jackson Generals 1041
1993 Fleer/ProCards Jackson Generals 1065
1992 Fleer/ProCards Jacksonville Suns 1042
1993 Fleer/ProCards Jacksonville Suns 1065
1992 Fleer/ProCards Jamestown Expos 1042
1993 Fleer/ProCards Jamestown Expos 1065
1992 Fleer/ProCards Johnson City Cardinals 1042
1993 Fleer/ProCards Johnson City Cardinals 1065
1992 Fleer/ProCards Kane County Cougars 1042
1993 Fleer/ProCards Kane County Cougars 1065
1992 Fleer/ProCards Kenosha Twins 1042
1992 Fleer/ProCards Kingsport Mets 1042
1993 Fleer/ProCards Kingsport Mets 1065
1992 Fleer/ProCards Kinston Indians 1043
1993 Fleer/ProCards Kinston Indians 1065
1992 Fleer/ProCards Knoxville Blue Jays 1043
1993 Fleer/ProCards Knoxville Smokies 1065
1992 Fleer/ProCards Lakeland Tigers 1043
1993 Fleer/ProCards Lakeland Tigers 1065
1992 Fleer/ProCards Las Vegas Stars 1043
1993 Fleer/ProCards Las Vegas Stars 1066
1993 Fleer/ProCards Lethbridge Mounties 1066
1992 Fleer/ProCards London Tigers 1043
1993 Fleer/ProCards London Tigers 1066
1992 Fleer/ProCards Louisville Redbirds 1043
1993 Fleer/ProCards Louisville Redbirds 1066
1992 Fleer/ProCards Lynchburg Red Sox 1043
1993 Fleer/ProCards Lynchburg Red Sox 1066
1992 Fleer/ProCards Macon Braves 1043
1993 Fleer/ProCards Macon Braves 1066
1992 Fleer/ProCards Madison Muskies 1044
1993 Fleer/ProCards Madison Muskies 1066
1992 Fleer/ProCards Martinsville Phillies 1044
1993 Fleer/ProCards Martinsville Phillies 1066
1992 Fleer/ProCards Medicine Hat Blue Jays 1044
1993 Fleer/ProCards Medicine Hat Blue Jays 1067
1992 Fleer/ProCards Memphis Chicks 1044
1993 Fleer/ProCards Memphis Chicks 1067
1992 Fleer/ProCards Midland Angels 1044
1993 Fleer/ProCards Midland Angels 1067
1993 Fleer/ProCards Midwest League 1067
1992 Fleer/ProCards Modesto A's 1044
1993 Fleer/ProCards Modesto A's 1067
1992 Fleer/ProCards Myrtle Beach Hurricanes 1045
1992 Fleer/ProCards Nashville Sounds 1045
1993 Fleer/ProCards Nashville Sounds 1067
1993 Fleer/ProCards Nashville Xpress 1067
1992 Fleer/ProCards New Britain Red Sox 1045
1993 Fleer/ProCards New Britain Red Sox 1067
1993 Fleer/ProCards New Orleans Zephyrs 1067
1992 Fleer/ProCards Niagara Falls Rapids 1045
1993 Fleer/ProCards Niagara Falls Rapids 1067
1993 Fleer/ProCards Norfolk Tides 1068
1992 Fleer/ProCards Oklahoma City 89ers 1045
1993 Fleer/ProCards Oklahoma City 89ers 1068
1992 Fleer/ProCards Omaha Royals 1045
1993 Fleer/ProCards Omaha Royals 1068
1993 Fleer/ProCards Oneonta Yankees 1068
1993 Fleer/ProCards Orlando Cubs 1068
1992 Fleer/ProCards Orlando Sunrays 1045
1992 Fleer/ProCards Osceola Astros 1045
1993 Fleer/ProCards Osceola Astros 1068
1993 Fleer/ProCards Ottawa Lynx 1068
1992 Fleer/ProCards Palm Springs Angels 1046
1993 Fleer/ProCards Palm Springs Angels 1068
1992 Fleer/ProCards Pawtucket Red Sox 1046
1993 Fleer/ProCards Pawtucket Red Sox 1068
1992 Fleer/ProCards Peninsula Pilots 1046
1993 Fleer/ProCards Peoria Chiefs 1068
1992 Fleer/ProCards Phoenix Firebirds 1046
1993 Fleer/ProCards Phoenix Firebirds 1069
1992 Fleer/ProCards Pittsfield Mets 1046
1993 Fleer/ProCards Pittsfield Mets 1069
1993 Fleer/ProCards Pocatello Posse 1069

1992 Fleer/ProCards Portland Beavers 1046
1993 Fleer/ProCards Portland Beavers 1069
1992 Fleer/ProCards Princeton Reds 1047
1993 Fleer/ProCards Princeton Reds 1069
1992 Fleer/ProCards Prince William Cannons 1047
1993 Fleer/ProCards Prince William Cannons 1069
1992 Fleer/ProCards Pulaski Braves 1047
1992 Fleer/ProCards Quad City River Bandits 1047
1993 Fleer/ProCards Quad City River Bandits 1069
1993 Fleer/ProCards Rancho Cucamonga Quakes 1069
1992 Fleer/ProCards Reading Phillies 1047
1993 Fleer/ProCards Reading Phillies 1069
1992 Fleer/ProCards Richmond Braves 1047
1993 Fleer/ProCards Richmond Braves 1070
1992 Fleer/ProCards Rochester Red Wings 1048
1993 Fleer/ProCards Rochester Red Wings 1070
1992 Fleer/ProCards Rockford Expos 1048
1993 Fleer/ProCards Rockford Royals 1070
1992 Fleer/ProCards Salem Buccaneers 1048
1993 Fleer/ProCards Salem Buccaneers 1070
1992 Fleer/ProCards Salinas Spurs 1048
1992 Fleer/ProCards San Antonio Missions 1049
1993 Fleer/ProCards San Antonio Missions 1071
1992 Fleer/ProCards San Bernardino Spirit 1049
1993 Fleer/ProCards San Bernardino Spirit 1071
1993 Fleer/ProCards San Jose Giants 1071
1992 Fleer/ProCards Sarasota White Sox 1049
1993 Fleer/ProCards Sarasota White Sox 1071
1992 Fleer/ProCards Savannah Cardinals 1049
1993 Fleer/ProCards Savannah Cardinals 1072
1992 Fleer/ProCards Scranton-Wilkes Barre Red Barons 1049
1993 Fleer/ProCards Scranton Wilkes-Barre Red Barron 1072
1992 Fleer/ProCards Shreveport Captains 1049
1993 Fleer/ProCards Shreveport Captains 1072
1993 Fleer/ProCards South Atlantic League All-Stars 1072
1992 Fleer/ProCards South Bend White Sox 1050
1993 Fleer/ProCards South Bend White Sox 1072
1992 Fleer/ProCards Southern Oregon A's 1050
1993 Fleer/ProCards Southern Oregon A's 1072
1992 Fleer/ProCards Spartanburg Phillies 1050
1993 Fleer/ProCards Spartanburg Phillies 1072
1992 Fleer/ProCards Spokane Indians 1050
1993 Fleer/ProCards Spokane Indians 1072
1992 Fleer/ProCards Springfield Cardinals 1050
1993 Fleer/ProCards Springfield Cardinals 1072
1992 Fleer/ProCards Stockton Ports 1051
1993 Fleer/ProCards Stockton Ports 1073
1992 Fleer/ProCards St. Catharines Blue Jays 1051
1993 Fleer/ProCards St. Catharines Blue Jays 1070
1992 Fleer/ProCards St. Lucie Mets 1051
1993 Fleer/ProCards St. Lucie Mets 1071
1992 Fleer/ProCards St. Petersburg Cardinals 1051
1993 Fleer/ProCards St. Petersburg Cardinals 1071
1992 Fleer/ProCards Syracuse Chiefs 1051
1993 Fleer/ProCards Syracuse Chiefs 1073
1992 Fleer/ProCards Tacoma Tigers 1051
1993 Fleer/ProCards Tacoma Tigers 1073
1992 Fleer/ProCards Tidewater Tides 1051
1992 Fleer/ProCards Toledo Mud Hens 1051
1993 Fleer/ProCards Toledo Mud Hens 1073
1993 Fleer/ProCards Triple A All-Star Game 1073
1992 Fleer/ProCards Tucson Toros 1052
1993 Fleer/ProCards Tucson Toros 1073
1992 Fleer/ProCards Tulsa Drillers 1052
1993 Fleer/ProCards Tulsa Drillers 1073
1993 Fleer/ProCards Utica Blue Sox 1073
1992 Fleer/ProCards Vancouver Canadians 1052
1993 Fleer/ProCards Vancouver Canadians 1073
1992 Fleer/ProCards Vero Beach Dodgers 1052
1993 Fleer/ProCards Vero Beach Dodgers 1073
1992 Fleer/ProCards Visalia Oaks 1052
1992 Fleer/ProCards Waterloo Diamonds 1052
1993 Fleer/ProCards Waterloo Diamonds 1074
1992 Fleer/ProCards Watertown Indians 1053
1993 Fleer/ProCards Watertown Indians 1074
1992 Fleer/ProCards Welland Pirates 1053
1993 Fleer/ProCards Welland Pirates 1074
1992 Fleer/ProCards West Palm Beach Expos 1053
1993 Fleer/ProCards West Palm Beach Expos 1074
1993 Fleer/ProCards West Virginia Wheelers 1074
1992 Fleer/ProCards Wichita Wranglers 1053
1993 Fleer/ProCards Wichita Wranglers 1074
1993 Fleer/ProCards Wilmington Blue Rocks 1074
1992 Fleer/ProCards Winston-Salem Spirits 1053
1993 Fleer/ProCards Winston-Salem Spirits 1075
1992 Fleer/ProCards Winter Haven Red Sox 1053
1992 Fleer/ProCards Yakima Bears 1054
1993 Fleer/Pro Cards Yakima Bears 1075
1966 Foremost Milk St. Petersburg Cardinals 813
1984 Forestry Jackson Mets 892
1991 Frank Chong Modesto A's 1016
1982 Fritsch Appleton Foxes 877
1983 Fritsch Appleton Foxes 884
1982 Fritsch Beloit Brewers 877
1983 Fritsch Beloit Brewers 884
1982 Fritsch Burlington Rangers 878
1983 Fritsch Burlington Rangers 884
1983 Fritsch Cedar Rapids Reds 884
1982 Fritsch Clinton Giants 878
1983 Fritsch Clinton Giants 885
1982 Fritsch Danville Suns 878
1982 Fritsch Madison Muskies 880
1983 Fritsch Madison Muskies 886
1983 Fritsch Peoria Suns 887
1982 Fritsch Springfield Cardinals... 882
1983 Fritsch Springfield Cardinals... 888
1983 Fritsch Visalia Oaks 889
1982 Fritsch Waterloo Indians 883
1983 Fritsch Waterloo Indians 889
1982 Fritsch Wausau Timbers 883

1983 Fritsch Wausau Timbers......... 890
1982 Fritsch Wisconsin Rapids Twins 883
1983 Fritsch Wisconsin Rapids Twins 890
1991 Front Row Draft Picks........... 1027

G

1952 Globe Printing Columbus Cardinals................................ 814
1952 Globe Printing Co. Miami Beach Flamingos 814
1951 Globe Printing Fresno Cardinals................................ 813
1952 Globe Printing Oshkosh Giants.................................... 814
1952 Globe Printing San Diego Padres.................................... 814
1951 Globe Printing San Jose Red Sox 813
1952 Globe Printing Ventura Braves 814
1990 Golden Cards Yakima Bears.. 992
1957 Golden State Dairy S.F. Seals Stickers 814
1976 Goof's Pants Tulsa Oilers....... 854
1988 Grand Slam Arkansas Travelers................................ 926
1989 Grand Slam Arkansas Travelers................................ 945
1990 Grand Slam Arkansas Travelers................................ 969
1988 Grand Slam Beloit Brewers 927
1989 Grand Slam Chattanooga Lookouts 949
1990 Grand Slam Chattanooga Lookouts 972
1988 Grand Slam Columbia Mets ... 929
1989 Grand Slam Columbia Mets ... 950
1990 Grand Slam Columbia Mets ... 973
1989 Grand Slam El Paso Diablos.. 951
1990 Grand Slam El Paso Diablos.. 974
1990 Grand Slam Eugene Emeralds 975
1988 Grand Slam Jackson Mets 933
1989 Grand Slam Jackson Mets 954
1990 Grand Slam Jackson Mets 978
1988 Grand Slam Midland Angels... 934
1989 Grand Slam Midland Angels... 956
1990 Grand Slam Midland Angels... 981
1988 Grand Slam Midwest League All-Stars 935
1990 Grand Slam Midwest League All-Stars 981
1988 Grand Slam Quad City Angels 937
1989 Grand Slam Quad City Angels 960
1990 Grand Slam Quad City Angels 984
1990 Grand Slam San Antonio Missions............................... 986
1988 Grand Slam South Atlantic League All-Stars 940
1988 Grand Slam South Bend White Sox... 940
1989 Grand Slam South Bend White Sox... 963
1990 Grand Slam South Bend White Sox... 988
1989 Grand Slam So. Atlantic League All-Stars 962
1988 Grand Slam Texas League All-Stars 942
1989 Grand Slam Texas League All-Stars 964
1990 Grand Slam Texas League All-Stars 989
1989 Grand Slam Tulsa Drillers 965
1988 Grand Slam Wausau Timbers 943
1989 Grand Slam Wausau Timbers 966
1943 Grand Studio Milwaukee Brewers................................ 814

H

1949 Hage's Dairy.......................... 814
1950 Hage's Dairy.......................... 815
1951 Hage's Dairy.......................... 815
1961 Hawaii Islanders 831
1960 Henry House Wieners Seattle Rainiers................................ 816
1947 Hollywood Stars..................... 829
1912 Home Run Kisses (E136)....... 816
1990 1 Hour Photo Midland Angels. 981
1940 Hughes Frozen Confections Sacramento Solons............... 817
1957 Hygrade Meats Seattle Rainiers 817

I

1991 Impel/Line Drive Pre-Rookie AA 1000
1991 Impel/Line Drive Pre-Rookie AAA 999
1912 Imperial Tobacco (C46).......... 817
1994 Iowa Cubs Yearbook Cards.. 1075

J

1980 Jack In The Box San Jose Missions.............................. 871
1971 Jeff Morey Syracuse Chiefs.... 847
1987 Jones Photo Tucson Toros..... 924
1988 Jones Photo Tucson Toros..... 942
1989 Jones Photo Tucson Toros..... 965

K

1962 Kahn's Wieners Atlanta "Crackers" 818
1973 Kansas State Bank Wichita Aeros 847
1983 Kelly Studios Kinston Blue Jays 886
1975 KMO Radio Tacoma Twins..... 851
1952 Knowles Service Stations Stockton Ports.................................... 818
1976 Knowlton's San Antonio Brewers................................ 854
1989 Kodak Gold 200 Peoria Chiefs 959
1991 Kraft Albany-Colonie Yankees 1002
1991 Kraft Syracuse Chiefs........... 1024

L

1952 Laval Dairy Provincial League 818
1988 Legoe Bellingham Mariners.... 926
1989 Legoe Bellingham Mariners.... 946
1990 Legoe Bellingham Mariners.... 969
1988 Legoe Bend Bucks 927
1989 Legoe Bend Bucks 946
1990 Legoe Bend Bucks 970
1947 Los Angeles Angels............... 829

M

1970 Mac's Wichita Aeros.............. 847
1977 McCurdy's Rochester Red Wings 857
1954 MD Super Service Sacramento Solons 818
1991 Merchants Bank Syracuse Chiefs 1024
1963 Milwaukee Sausage Seattle Rainiers................................ 818
1911 Mono Cigarettes (T217).......... 819
1947 Morley Studios Tacoma Tigers 819
1952 Mother's Cookies................... 819
1953 Mother's Cookies................... 819
1977 Mr. Chef's San Jose Missions 858
1978 Mr. Chef's San Jose Missions 861

N

1960 National Bank Washington/Tacoma Giants.................................. 820
1888 (N333) 817
1888 (N388-1) 817

O

1947 Oakland Oaks......................... 829
1911 Obak Cabinets (T4) 822
1909 Obak (T212) 820
1910 Obak (T212) 820
1911 Obak (T212) 821
1955 Old Homestead Franks Des Moines Bruins.................................. 822
1910 Old Mill Cigarettes Series 1 (T210) 822
1910 Old Mill Cigarettes Series 2 (T210) 822
1910 Old Mill Cigarettes Series 3 (T210) 823
1910 Old Mill Cigarettes Series 4 (T210) 823
1910 Old Mill Cigarettes Series 5 (T210) 823
1910 Old Mill Cigarettes Series 6 (T210) 823
1910 Old Mill Cigarettes Series 7 (T210) 824
1910 Old Mill Cigarettes Series 8 (T210) 824

1958 Omaha Cardinals Picture Pak 824
1974 One Day Film Wichita Aeros .. 849

P

1952 Parkhurst 825
1992 Peoria Midwest League All-Star Team 1046
1962 Pepsi-Cola Tulsa Oilers.......... 825
1963 Pepsi-Cola Tulsa Oilers.......... 825
1966 Pepsi-Cola Tulsa Oilers.......... 825
1993 Pepsi Virginians Richmond Braves 1070
1984 Pizza Hut Greenville Braves... 891
1985 Pizza Hut Greenville Braves... 897
1987 Pizza World Peoria Chiefs...... 920
1991 Play II Columbia Mets........... 1008
1992 Play II Columbia Mets........... 1037
1992 Play II Columbia Mets Inserts 1037
1992 Play II South Atlantic League All-Stars 1049
1981 Police Columbus Clippers 873
1982 Police Columbus Clippers 878
1988 Police Columbus Clippers 929
1989 Police Columbus Clippers 950
1990 Police Columbus Clippers 973
1991 Police Columbus Clippers 1008
1992 Police Columbus Clippers 1037
1993 Police Cracker Jack Columbus Clippers.............................. 1061
1979 Police Iowa Oaks.................... 864
1980 Police Iowa Oaks.................... 869
1987 Police Salinas Spurs.............. 922
1980 Police/Fire Safety Columbus Clippers................................ 868
1984 Police/Fire Safety Columbus Clippers................................ 891
1985 Police/Fire Safety Columbus Clippers................................ 896
1987 Police/Fire Safety Columbus Clippers................................ 914
1961 Portland Beavers.................... 831
1987 ProCards Albany-Colonie Yankees 912
1988 ProCards Albany-Colonie Yankees 925
1989 ProCards Albany Yankees 945
1990 ProCards Albany Yankees 968
1991 Procards Albany Yankees 1003
1986 ProCards Albuquerque Dukes 901
1988 ProCards Albuquerque Dukes 925
1989 ProCards Albuquerque Dukes 945
1990 ProCards Albuquerque Dukes 968
1991 ProCards Albuquerque Dukes 1003
1986 ProCards Appleton Foxes 901
1987 ProCards Appleton Foxes 912
1988 ProCards Appleton Foxes 925
1989 ProCards Appleton Foxes 945
1990 ProCards Appleton Foxes 968
1991 ProCards Appleton Foxes 1003
1986 ProCards Arkansas Travelers 901
1987 ProCards Arkansas Travelers 912
1991 ProCards Arkansas Travelers 1003
1987 ProCards Asheville Tourists ... 912
1988 ProCards Asheville Tourists ... 926
1989 ProCards Asheville Tourists ... 945
1990 ProCards Asheville Tourists ... 969
1986 ProCards Ashville Tourists 902
1991 Procards Ashville Tourists 1003
1986 ProCards Auburn Astros......... 902
1987 ProCards Auburn Astros......... 912
1988 ProCards Auburn Astros......... 926
1989 ProCards Auburn Astros......... 945
1989 ProCards (Poster) Auburn Astros.................................... 945
1990 ProCards Auburn Astros......... 969
1991 ProCards Auburn Astros....... 1003
1988 ProCards Augusta Pirates 926
1989 ProCards Augusta Pirates 945
1990 ProCards Augusta Pirates 969
1991 ProCards Augusta Pirates 1003
1990 ProCards A & AA Minor League Stars..................................... 995
1986 ProCards Bakersfield Dodgers 902
1987 ProCards Bakersfield Dodgers 912
1991 ProCards Baseball City Royals 1004
1988 ProCards Batavia Clippers 926
1989 ProCards Batavia Clippers 946
1990 ProCards Batavia Clippers 969
1991 ProCards Batavia Clippers ... 1004
1986 ProCards Beaumont Golden Gators 902
1991 ProCards Bellingham Mariners 1004
1986 ProCards Beloit Brewers 902
1987 ProCards Beloit Brewers 913
1991 ProCards Beloit Brewers 1004
1991 ProCards Bend Bucks 1004
1988 ProCards Billings Mustangs ... 927
1989 ProCards Billings Mustangs ... 946
1990 ProCards Billings Mustangs ... 970
1991 ProCards Billings Mustangs . 1005
1989 ProCards Birmingham Barons 947
1990 ProCards Birmingham Barons 970
1991 ProCards Birmingham Barons 1005
1988 ProCards Boise Hawks........... 927
1989 ProCards Boise Hawks........... 947
1990 ProCards Boise Hawks........... 970
1991 ProCards Boise Hawks......... 1005
1988 ProCards Bristol Tigers 927
1990 ProCards Bristol Tigers 970
1991 ProCards Bristol Tigers 1005
1986 ProCards Buffalo Bisons 902
1988 ProCards Buffalo Bisons 927
1989 ProCards Buffalo Bisons 947
1990 ProCards Buffalo Bisons 970
1991 ProCards Buffalo Bisons 1005
1991 ProCards Burlington Astros .. 1006
1988 ProCards Burlington Braves ... 927
1989 ProCards Burlington Braves ... 947
1990 ProCards Burlington Braves ... 971
1986 ProCards Burlington Expos 902
1987 ProCards Burlington Expos 913
1988 ProCards Burlington Indians... 927
1990 ProCards Burlington Indians... 971
1991 ProCards Burlington Indians. 1006
1986 ProCards Calgary Cannons.... 902
1987 ProCards Calgary Cannons.... 913
1988 ProCards Calgary Cannons.... 928
1989 ProCards Calgary Cannons.... 948
1990 ProCards Calgary Cannons.... 971
1991 ProCards Calgary Cannons.. 1006
1989 ProCards Canton-Akron Indians 948
1990 ProCards Canton-Akron Indians 971
1991 ProCards Canton-Akron Indians 1006
1991 ProCards Carolina League All-Star Game 1006
1991 ProCards Carolina Mudcats . 1006
1987 ProCards Cedar Rapids Reds 913
1988 ProCards Cedar Rapids Reds 928
1989 ProCards Cedar Rapids Reds 948
1990 ProCards Cedar Rapids Reds 972
1991 ProCards Cedar Rapids Reds 1007
1986 ProCards Charleston Rainbows 902
1987 ProCards Charleston Rainbows 913
1988 ProCards Charleston Rainbows 928
1989 ProCards Charleston Rainbows 948
1990 ProCards Charleston Rainbows 972
1991 ProCards Charleston Rainbows 1007
1987 ProCards Charleston Wheelers............................... 913
1989 ProCards Charleston Wheelers............................... 949
1990 ProCards Charleston Wheelers............................... 972
1991 ProCards Charleston Wheelers............................. 1007
1991 ProCards Charlotte Knights.. 1007
1991 ProCards Charlotte Rangers 1007
1986 ProCards Chattanooga Lookouts 903
1991 ProCards Chattanooga Lookouts 1007
1986 ProCards Clearwater Phillies.. 903
1987 ProCards Clearwater Phillies.. 914
1991 ProCards Clearwater Phillies 1007
1986 ProCards Clinton Giants......... 903
1987 ProCards Clinton Giants......... 914
1988 ProCards Clinton Giants......... 929
1989 ProCards Clinton Giants......... 949
1990 ProCards Clinton Giants......... 973
1991 ProCards Clinton Giants....... 1008
1988 ProCards Colorado Springs Sky Sox.. 929
1989 ProCards Colorado Springs Sky Sox.. 949
1990 ProCards Colorado Springs Sky Sox.. 973
1991 ProCards Colorado Springs Sky Sox...................................... 1008
1986 ProCards Columbia Mets 903
1987 ProCards Columbia Mets 914
1986 ProCards Columbus Astros 903

1987 ProCards Columbus Astros 914
1986 ProCards Columbus Clippers . 903
1987 ProCards Columbus Clippers . 914
1988 ProCards Columbus Clippers . 929
1989 ProCards Columbus Clippers . 950
1990 ProCards Columbus Clippers . 973
1991 ProCards Columbus Clippers 1008
1991 ProCards Columbus Indians. 1008
1989 ProCards Columbus Mudcats. 950
1990 ProCards Columbus Mudcats. 973
1987 ProCards Daytona Beach Admirals 914
1986 ProCards Daytona Beach Islanders 903
1987 ProCards Denver Zephyrs 914
1988 ProCards Denver Zephyrs 930
1989 ProCards Denver Zephyrs 950
1990 ProCards Denver Zephyrs 974
1991 ProCards Denver Zephyrs 1008
1987 ProCards Dunedin Blue Jays . 914
1991 ProCards Dunedin Blue Jays 1008
1986 ProCards Durham Bulls 903
1987 ProCards Durham Bulls 914
1991 ProCards Durham Bulls 1009
1991 ProCards Durham Bulls Update 1009
1988 ProCards Eastern League All-Stars 930
1989 ProCards Eastern League All-Stars 951
1989 ProCards Eastern League Diamond Diplomacy 951
1991 ProCards Edmondton Trappers 1009
1986 ProCards Edmonton Trappers 903
1987 ProCards Edmonton Trappers 914
1988 ProCards Edmonton Trappers 930
1989 ProCards Edmonton Trappers 951
1990 ProCards Edmonton Trappers 974
1991 ProCards Elizabethton Twins 1009
1986 ProCards Elmira Pioneers 904
1991 ProCards Elmira Pioneers 1009
1986 ProCards El Paso Diablos 904
1987 ProCards El Paso Diablos 915
1991 ProCards El Paso Diablos 1009
1986 ProCards Erie Cardinals 904
1987 ProCards Erie Cardinals 915
1991 ProCards Erie Sailors 1009
1987 ProCards Eugene Emeralds ... 915
1991 ProCards Eugene Emeralds. 1009
1990 ProCards Everett Giants 975
1991 ProCards Everett Giants 1010
1991 ProCards Fayetteville Generais 1010
1987 ProCards Fayetteville Generals 915
1988 ProCards Fayetteville Generals 931
1989 ProCards Fayetteville Generals 952
1990 ProCards Fayetteville Generals 975
1986 ProCards Florida State League All-Stars 904
1991 ProCards Florida State League All-Stars 1010
1987 ProCards Fort Meyers Royals 915
1991 ProCards Frederick Keys 1010
1988 ProCards Fresno Suns 931
1986 ProCards Ft. Lauderdale Yankees 904
1987 ProCards Ft. Lauderdale Yankees 915
1991 ProCards Ft. Lauderdale Yankees 1010
1986 ProCards Ft. Myers Royals 904
1990 ProCards Future Stars Baseball 996
1987 ProCards Gastonia Rangers .. 915
1988 ProCards Gastonia Rangers .. 931
1989 ProCards Gastonia Rangers .. 952
1990 ProCards Gastonia Rangers .. 975
1991 ProCards Gastonia Rangers 1010
1990 ProCards Gate City Pioneers . 975
1986 ProCards Geneva Cubs 905
1987 ProCards Geneva Cubs 916
1988 ProCards Geneva Cubs 931
1989 ProCards Geneva Cubs 952
1990 ProCards Geneva Cubs 976
1991 ProCards Geneva Cubs 1011
1986 ProCards Glens Falls Tigers .. 905
1987 ProCards Glens Falls Tigers .. 916
1988 ProCards Glens Falls Tigers .. 931
1986 ProCards Greensboro Hornets 905
1987 ProCards Greensboro Hornets 916
1988 ProCards Greensboro Hornets 932
1989 ProCards Greensboro Hornets 952
1990 ProCards Greensboro Hornets 976
1991 ProCards Greensboro Hornets 1011
1986 ProCards Greenville Braves ... 905
1989 ProCards Greenville Braves ... 953
1990 ProCards Greenville Braves ... 976
1991 ProCards Greenville Braves . 1011
1986 ProCards Hagerstown Suns ... 905
1987 ProCards Hagerstown Suns ... 916
1989 ProCards Hagerstown Suns ... 953
1990 ProCards Hagerstown Suns ... 976
1991 ProCards Hagerstown Suns . 1011
1988 ProCards Hamilton Redbirds .. 932
1991 ProCards Hamilton Redbirds 1011
1987 ProCards Harrisburg Senators 916
1988 ProCards Harrisburg Senators 932
1989 ProCards Harrisburg Senators 953
1990 ProCards Harrisburg Senators 977
1991 ProCards Harrisburg Senators 1011
1986 ProCards Hawaii Islanders 905
1987 ProCards Hawaii Islanders 916
1991 ProCards High Desert Mavericks 1012
1990 ProCards Huntington Cubs 977
1991 ProCards Huntington Cubs ... 1012
1991 ProCards Huntsville Stars 1012
1987 ProCards Idaho Falls Braves .. 916
1988 ProCards Idaho Falls Braves .. 932
1989 ProCards Idaho Falls Braves .. 954
1990 ProCards Idaho Falls Braves .. 977
1991 ProCards Idaho Falls Braves 1012
1988 ProCards Indianapolis Indians 932
1989 ProCards Indianapolis Indians 954
1990 ProCards Indianapolis Indians 977
1991 ProCards Indianapolis Indians 1012
1987 ProCards International League All-Stars 916
1986 ProCards Iowa Cubs 905
1988 ProCards Iowa Cubs 932
1989 ProCards Iowa Cubs 954
1990 ProCards Iowa Cubs 978
1991 ProCards Iowa Cubs 1013
1991 ProCards Jackson Generals. 1013
1987 ProCards Jacksonville Expos . 917
1988 ProCards Jacksonville Expos . 933
1989 ProCards Jacksonville Expos . 954
1990 ProCards Jacksonville Expos . 978
1991 ProCards Jacksonville Suns . 1013
1986 ProCards Jamestown Expos .. 906
1987 ProCards Jamestown Expos .. 917
1988 ProCards Jamestown Expos .. 933
1989 ProCards Jamestown Expos .. 954
1991 ProCards Jamestown Expos 1013
1991 ProCards Johnson City Cardinals 1013
1991 ProCards Kane County Cougars 1013
1986 ProCards Kenosha Twins 906
1987 ProCards Kenosha Twins 917
1988 ProCards Kenosha Twins 933
1989 ProCards Kenosha Twins 954
1990 ProCards Kenosha Twins 978
1991 ProCards Kenosha Twins 1014
1991 ProCards Kingsport Mets 1014
1986 ProCards Kinston Eagles 906
1987 ProCards Kinston Indians 917
1991 ProCards Kinston Indians 1014
1991 ProCards Kissimmee Dodgers 1014
1986 ProCards Knoxville Blue Jays 906
1987 ProCards Knoxville Blue Jays 917
1989 ProCards Knoxville Blue Jays 955
1990 ProCards Knoxville Blue Jays 979
1991 ProCards Knoxville Blue Jays 1014
1986 ProCards Lakeland Tigers 906
1987 ProCards Lakeland Tigers 917
1991 ProCards Lakeland Tigers 1014
1986 ProCards Las Vegas Stars 906
1987 ProCards Las Vegas Stars 917
1988 ProCards Las Vegas Stars 933
1989 ProCards Las Vegas Stars 955
1990 ProCards Las Vegas Stars 979
1991 ProCards Las Vegas Stars ... 1014
1986 ProCards Little Falls Mets 906
1987 ProCards Little Falls Mets 918
1989 ProCards London Tigers 955
1990 ProCards London Tigers 979
1991 ProCards London Tigers 1014
1988 ProCards Louisville Redbirds . 934
1989 ProCards Louisville Redbirds . 955
1990 ProCards Louisville Redbirds . 979
1991 ProCards Louisville Redbirds 1015
1986 ProCards Lynchburg Mets 906
1987 ProCards Lynchburg Mets 918
1991 ProCards Lynchburg Red Sox 1015
1991 ProCards Macon Braves 1015
1986 ProCards Macon Pirates 906

1987 ProCards Macon Pirates 918
1986 ProCards Madison Muskies.... 906
1987 ProCards Madison Muskies.... 918
1990 ProCards Madison Muskies.... 980
1991 ProCards Madison Muskies.. 1015
1986 ProCards Maine Guides 907
1987 ProCards Maine Guides 918
1988 ProCards Maine Phillies 934
1990 ProCards Martinsville Phillies. 980
1991 ProCards Martinsville Phillies 1015
1991 ProCards Medicine Hat Blue Jays 1015
1987 ProCards Memphis Chicks..... 918
1989 ProCards Memphis Chicks..... 956
1990 ProCards Memphis Chicks..... 980
1991 ProCards Memphis Chicks... 1016
1986 ProCards Miami Marlins 907
1987 ProCards Miami Marlins 918
1991 ProCards Miami Miracle 1016
1986 ProCards Midland Angels....... 907
1987 ProCards Midland Angels....... 918
1991 ProCards Midland Angels..... 1016
1991 ProCards Midwest League All-Star Game 1016
1986 ProCards Modesto A's........... 907
1987 ProCards Modesto A's........... 919
1990 ProCards Modesto A's........... 981
1991 ProCards Modesto A's.......... 1016
1987 ProCards Myrtle Beach Blue Jays 919
1988 ProCards Myrtle Beach Blue Jays 935
1989 ProCards Myrtle Beach Blue Jays 957
1990 ProCards Myrtle Beach Blue Jays 981
1991 ProCards Myrtle Beach Hurricanes.......................... 1017
1986 ProCards Nashua Pirates....... 907
1988 ProCards Nashville Sounds.... 935
1989 ProCards Nashville Sounds.... 957
1990 ProCards Nashville Sounds.... 981
1991 ProCards Nashville Sounds.. 1017
1987 ProCards Newark Orioles....... 919
1986 ProCards New Britain Red Sox 907
1987 ProCards New Britain Red Sox 919
1988 ProCards New Britain Red Sox 935
1989 ProCards New Britain Red Sox 957
1990 ProCards New Britain Red Sox 982
1991 ProCards New Britain Red So 1017
1991 ProCards Niagara Falls Rapids................................ 1017
1990 ProCards Oklahoma City 89ers 982
1991 ProCards Oklahoma City 89ers 1017
1986 ProCards Oklahoma City 89'ers 908
1987 ProCards Oklahoma City 89'ers 919
1988 ProCards Oklahoma City 89'ers 936
1989 ProCards Oklahoma City 89'ers 957
1986 ProCards Omaha Royals........ 908
1987 ProCards Omaha Royals........ 919
1988 ProCards Omaha Royals........ 936
1989 ProCards Omaha Royals........ 958
1990 ProCards Omaha Royals........ 982
1991 ProCards Omaha Royals...... 1017
1987 ProCards Oneonta Yankees... 919
1988 ProCards Oneonta Yankees... 936
1989 ProCards Oneonta Yankees... 958
1990 ProCards Oneonta Yankees... 982
1991 ProCards Oneonta Yankees. 1017
1990 ProCards Orlando Sun Rays.. 982
1991 ProCards Orlando Sun Rays 1017
1986 ProCards Orlando Twins 908
1987 ProCards Orlando Twins 919
1989 ProCards Orlando Twins 958
1986 ProCards Osceola Astros 908
1987 ProCards Osceola Astros 919
1991 ProCards Osceola Astros 1018
1986 ProCards Palm Springs Angels.................................. 908
1987 ProCards Palm Springs Angels.................................. 920
1988 ProCards Palm Springs Angels.................................. 936
1989 ProCards Palm Springs Angels.................................. 958
1990 ProCards Palm Springs Angels.................................. 983
1991 ProCards Palm Springs Angels................................ 1018
1986 ProCards Pawtucket Red Sox 908
1987 ProCards Pawtucket Red Sox 920
1988 ProCards Pawtucket Red Sox 936
1989 ProCards Pawtucket Red Sox 958
1990 ProCards Pawtucket Red Sox 983
1991 ProCards Pawtucket Red Sox 1018
1991 ProCards Peninsula Pilots.... 1018
1986 ProCards Peninsula White Sox 908
1987 ProCards Peninsula White Sox 920
1986 ProCards Peoria Chiefs.......... 908
1987 ProCards Peoria Chiefs.......... 920
1991 ProCards Peoria Chiefs........ 1018
1986 ProCards Phoenix Firebirds ... 908
1987 ProCards Phoenix Firebirds ... 920
1988 ProCards Phoenix Firebirds ... 937
1989 ProCards Phoenix Firebirds ... 959
1990 ProCards Phoenix Firebirds ... 983
1991 ProCards Phoenix Firebirds . 1018
1986 ProCards Pittsfield Cubs 908
1987 ProCards Pittsfield Cubs 920
1988 ProCards Pittsfield Cubs 937
1991 ProCards Pittsfield Mets....... 1019
1988 ProCards Pocatello Giants 937
1991 ProCards Pocatello Pioneers 1019
1987 ProCards Port Charlotte Rangers 920
1986 ProCards Portland Beavers.... 909
1987 ProCards Portland Beavers.... 921
1988 ProCards Portland Beavers.... 937
1989 ProCards Portland Beavers.... 959
1990 ProCards Portland Beavers.... 984
1991 ProCards Portland Beavers.. 1019
1991 ProCards Princeton Reds..... 1019
1991 ProCards Prince William Cannons.............................. 1019
1986 ProCards Prince William Pirates................................... 909
1987 ProCards Prince William Yankees 921
1988 ProCards Pulaksi Braves........ 937
1989 ProCards Pulaski Braves........ 959
1990 ProCards Pulaski Braves........ 984
1991 ProCards Pulaski Braves...... 1019
1986 ProCards Quad Cities Angels. 909
1987 ProCards Quad City Angels ... 921
1991 ProCards Quad City Angels . 1020
1985 ProCards Reading Phillies...... 900
1986 ProCards Reading Phillies...... 909
1987 ProCards Reading Phillies...... 921
1988 ProCards Reading Phillies...... 937
1989 ProCards Reading Phillies...... 960
1990 ProCards Reading Phillies...... 984
1991 ProCards Reading Phillies.... 1020
1986 ProCards Richmond Braves ... 909
1988 ProCards Richmond Braves ... 938
1989 ProCards Richmond Braves ... 960
1990 ProCards Richmond Braves ... 985
1991 ProCards Richmond Braves. 1020
1988 ProCards Riverside Red Wave 938
1989 ProCards Riverside Red Wave 960
1990 ProCards Riverside Red Wave 985
1986 ProCards Rochester Red Wings 909
1987 ProCards Rochester Red Wings 921
1988 ProCards Rochester Red Wings 938
1989 ProCards Rochester Red Wings 961
1990 ProCards Rochester Red Wings 985
1991 ProCards Rochester Red Wings 1020
1990 ProCards Rockford Expos...... 985
1991 ProCards Rockford Expos.... 1020
1990 ProCards Saint Catharine's Blue Jays...................................... 986
1987 ProCards Salem Angels 921
1987 ProCards Salem Buccaneers . 922
1991 ProCards Salem Buccaneers 1021
1986 ProCards Salem Red Birds 909
1989 ProCards Salinas Spurs 961
1990 ProCards Salinas Spurs 986
1991 ProCards Salinas Spurs 1021
1991 ProCards Salt Lake Trappers 1021
1991 ProCards San Antonio Missions............................. 1021
1990 ProCards San Bernadino Spirit 986
1987 ProCards San Bernadino Spirits................................... 922

1991 ProCards San Bernardino Spirit 1022
1986 ProCards San Jose Bees 909
1987 ProCards San Jose Bees 922
1988 ProCards San Jose Giants 940
1989 ProCards San Jose Giants 962
1990 ProCards San Jose Giants 987
1991 ProCards San Jose Giants 1022
1991 ProCards Sarasota White Sox 1022
1987 ProCards Savannah Cardinals 922
1988 ProCards Savannah Cardinals 940
1989 ProCards Savannah Cardinals 962
1990 ProCards Savannah Cardinals 987
1991 ProCards Savannah Cardinals 1022
1989 ProCards Scanton-Wilkes Barre Red Barons 962
1991 ProCards Scranton Red Barons 1022
1990 ProCards Scranton-Wilkes Barre Red Barons 987
1986 ProCards Shreveport Captains 909
1987 ProCards Shreveport Captains 922
1988 ProCards Shreveport Captains 940
1989 ProCards Shreveport Captains 962
1991 ProCards Shreveport Captains 1022
1991 ProCards South Atlantic League All-Stars 1022
1991 ProCards South Bend White Sox 1023
1990 ProCards Southern Oregon Athletics 988
1988 ProCards Southern Oregon A's 940
1991 ProCards Southern Oregon A's 1023
1987 ProCards Spartanburg Phillies 922
1988 ProCards Spartanburg Phillies 940
1989 ProCards Spartanburg Phillies 963
1990 ProCards Spartanburg Phillies 988
1991 ProCards Spartanburg Phillies 1023
1987 ProCards Spokane Indians 923
1988 ProCards Spokane Indians 940
1991 ProCards Spokane Indians 1023
1991 ProCards Springfield Cardinals 1023
1986 ProCards Stockton Ports 910
1987 ProCards Stockton Ports 923
1988 ProCards Stockton Ports 941
1989 ProCards Stockton Ports 963
1990 ProCards Stockton Ports 989
1991 ProCards Stockton Ports 1024
1988 ProCards St. Catharines Blue Jays 939
1989 ProCards St. Catharines Blue Jays 961
1991 ProCards St. Catharines Blue Jays 1020
1991 ProCards St. Lucie Mets 1021
1987 ProCards St. Petersburg Cardinals 921
1991 ProCards St. Petersburg Cardinals 1021
1986 ProCards St. Petersburg Cards 909
1986 ProCards Sumter Braves 910
1987 ProCards Sumter Braves 923
1988 ProCards Sumter Braves 941
1989 ProCards Sumter Braves 964
1990 ProCards Sumter Braves 989
1991 ProCards Sumter Flyers 1024
1986 ProCards Syracuse Chiefs 910
1987 ProCards Syracuse Chiefs 923
1988 ProCards Syracuse Chiefs 941
1989 ProCards Syracuse Chiefs 964
1990 ProCards Syracuse Chiefs 989
1991 ProCards Syracuse Chiefs 1024
1986 ProCards Tacoma Tigers 910
1987 ProCards Tacoma Tigers 923
1988 ProCards Tacoma Tigers 941
1989 ProCards Tacoma Tigers 964
1990 ProCards Tacoma Tigers 989
1991 ProCards Tacoma Tigers 1024
1986 ProCards Tampa Tarpons 910
1987 ProCards Tampa Tarpons 923
1987 ProCards Tidewater Tides 923
1988 ProCards Tidewater Tides 941
1989 ProCards Tidewater Tides 964
1990 ProCards Tidewater Tides 990
1991 ProCards Tidewater Tides 1024
1986 ProCards Tidewater Tides - Mets Emblem 910
1986 ProCards Tidewater Tides - Tides Emblem 910
1986 ProCards Toledo Mud Hens 911
1987 ProCards Toledo Mud Hens 924
1988 ProCards Toledo Mud Hens 942
1989 ProCards Toledo Mud Hens 965
1990 ProCards Toledo Mud Hens 990
1991 ProCards Toledo Mud Hens. 1025
1991 ProCards Tomorrow's Heroes 1002
1989 ProCards Triple A All-Star Game 965
1991 ProCards Triple A All-Star Game 1025
1988 ProCards Triple-A All-Stars 942
1990 ProCards Triple A All-Stars 990
1986 ProCards Tucson Toros 911
1987 ProCards Tucson Toros 924
1988 ProCards Tucson Toros 942
1989 ProCards Tucson Toros 965
1990 ProCards Tucson Toros 990
1991 ProCards Tucson Toros 1025
1990 ProCards Tulsa Drillers 990
1991 ProCards Tulsa Drillers 1025
1987 ProCards Utica Blue Sox 924
1991 ProCards Utica Blue Sox 1025
1986 ProCards Vancouver Canadians 911
1987 ProCards Vancouver Canadians 924
1988 ProCards Vancouver Canadians 943
1989 ProCards Vancouver Canadians 966
1990 ProCards Vancouver Canadians 991
1991 ProCards Vancouver Canadians 1025
1986 ProCards Ventura Gulls 911
1988 ProCards Vermont Mariners 943
1986 ProCards Vermont Reds 911
1987 ProCards Vermont Reds 924
1986 ProCards Vero Beach Dodgers 911
1987 ProCards Vero Beach Dodgers 924
1991 ProCards Vero Beach Dodgers 1025
1986 ProCards Visalia Oaks 911
1987 ProCards Visalia Oaks 924
1988 ProCards Visalia Oaks 943
1989 ProCards Visalia Oaks 966
1990 ProCards Visalia Oaks 991
1991 ProCards Visalia Oaks 1026
1986 ProCards Waterbury Indians .. 911
1989 ProCards Waterloo Diamonds 966
1990 ProCards Waterloo Diamonds 991
1991 ProCards Waterloo Diamonds 1026
1986 ProCards Waterloo Indians 911
1987 ProCards Waterloo Indians 924
1988 ProCards Waterloo Indians 943
1991 ProCards Watertown Indians 1026
1986 ProCards Watertown Pirates .. 911
1987 ProCards Watertown Pirates .. 924
1986 ProCards Wausau Timbers 912
1987 ProCards Wausau Timbers 925
1990 ProCards Wausau Timbers 991
1991 ProCards Welland Pirates 1026
1986 ProCards West Palm Beach Expos 912
1987 ProCards West Palm Beach Expos 925
1991 ProCards West Palm Beach Expos 1026
1991 Procards Wichita Wranglers. 1026
1987 ProCards Williamsport Bills 925
1988 ProCards Williamsport Bills 944
1989 ProCards Williamsport Bills 967
1990 ProCards Williamsport Bills 992
1991 ProCards Williamsport Bills .. 1027
1986 ProCards Winston-Salem Spirits 912
1987 ProCards Winston-Salem Spirits 925
1991 ProCards Winston-Salem Spirits 1027
1986 ProCards Winter Haven Red Sox 912
1987 ProCards Winter Haven Red Sox 925
1991 ProCards Winter Haven Red Sox 1027
1987 ProCards Wytheville Cubs 925
1988 ProCards Wytheville Cubs 944
1991 ProCards Yakima Bears 1027
1989 Pucko Elmira Pioneers 951
1990 Pucko Elmira Pioneers 974
1990 Pucko Jamestown Expos 978
1988 Pucko Little Falls Mets 933
1989 Pucko Niagara Falls Rapids ... 957
1990 Pucko Niagara Falls Rapids ... 982

1990 Pucko Pittsfield Mets 983
1988 Pucko Rochester Red Wings.. 938
1988 Pucko Utica Blue Sox 943
1989 Pucko Utica Blue Sox 965
1990 Pucko Utica Blue Sox 990
1988 Pucko Watertown Pirates 943
1989 Pucko Welland Pirates 966
1990 Pucko Welland Pirates 991

R

1981 Red Rooster Edmonton Trappers................................ 873
1910 Red Sun Southern Association (T211) 825
1946 Remar Bread Oakland Oaks .. 826
1947 Remar Bread Oakland Oaks .. 826
1948 Remar Bread Oakland Oaks .. 826
1949 Remar Bread Oakland Oaks .. 826
1950 Remar Bread Oakland Oaks .. 826
1978 Richard West Springfield Cardinals............................... 861
1978 Richard West Springfield Redbirds................................ 865
1992 Richmond Comix amd Cardz Richmond Braves................ 1048
1993 Richmond Comix Richmond Braves................................ 1070
1983 Riley's Louisville Redbirds...... 886
1984 Riley's Louisville Redbirds...... 892
1985 Riley's Louisville Redbirds...... 898
1990 Rocks Dugout Wichita Wranglers.............................. 992
1984 Rock's Dugout Wichita Aeros . 895
1988 Rock's Dugout Wichita Pilots.. 944
1989 Rock's Dugout Wichita Wrangers 967
1989 Rock's Dugout Wichita Wrangers Update.................. 967
1989 Rock's Dugout Wichita Wranglers.............................. 966
1991 Rock's-Team Wichita Wranglers.................. 1026, 1027
1966 Royal Crown Cola Columbus Yankees 827

S

1947 Sacramento Solons 829
1961 Sacramento Solons 831
1961 San Diego Padres 831
1950 San Francisco Seals Popcorn 827
1963 Scheible Press Rochester Red Wings 827
1966 Seattle Popcorn Seattle Angels 828
1967 Seattle Popcorn Seattle Angels 828
1968 Seattle Popcorn Seattle Angels 829
1954 Seattle Popcorn Seattle Rainiers 827
1955 Seattle Popcorn Seattle Rainiers 827
1956 Seattle Popcorn Seattle Rainiers 827
1957 Seattle Popcorn Seattle Rainiers 827
1958 Seattle Popcorn Seattle Rainiers 828
1959 Seattle Popcorn Seattle Rainiers 828
1960 Seattle Popcorn Seattle Rainiers 828
1961 Seattle Popcorn Seattle Rainiers 828
1962 Seattle Popcorn Seattle Rainiers 828
1963 Seattle Popcorn Seattle Rainiers 828
1964 Seattle Popcorn Seattle Rainiers 828
1965 Seattle Popcorn Seattle Rainiers 828
1947 Seattle Rainiers 829
1988 SG & CC Tidewater Tides 942
1948 Signal Gasoline Oakland Oaks 829
1947 Signal Gasoline Pacific Coast League 829
1994 Signature Rookies 1076
1994 Signature Rookies Bonus Signature Set 1076
1994 Signature Rookies Cliff Floyd Set 1076
1994 Signature Rookies Hottest Prospects 1076
1992 SkyBox AA........................... 1030
1992 SkyBox AAA 1030
1947 Smith's Oakland Oaks 829
1948 Smith's Oakland Oaks 829
1986 Smokey Bear Fresno Giants .. 904
1986 Smokey Bear Palm Springs Angels 908
1985 Smokey Fresno Giants 897
1948 Sommer & Kaufmann San Francisco Seals 830
1949 Sommer & Kaufmann San Francisco Seals 830
1961 Spokane Indians..................... 831
1990 Sportprint Lynchburg Red Sox 980
1990 Sportprint Prince William Cannons............................... 984
1990 Sportprint Winston-Salem Spirit.................................. 992
1991 Sport Pro Billings Mustangs . 1005
1993 SportPro Billings Mustangs .. 1058
1988 Sport Pro Butte Copper Kings 928
1989 Sport Pro Butte Copper Kings 947
1990 Sport Pro Butte Copper Kings 971
1991 Sport Pro Butte Copper Kings 1006
1991 Sport-Pro Butte Copper Kings 1006
1993 SportPro Butte Copper Kings 1059
1990 Sport Pro Gate City Pioneers . 976
1989 Sport Pro Great Falls Dodgers 952
1990 Sport Pro Great Falls Dodgers 976
1991 Sport Pro Great Falls Dodgers 1011
1993 SportPro Great Falls Dodgers 1063
1991 Sport Pro Gulf Coast Rangers 1011
1989 Sport Pro Helena Brewers...... 953
1990 Sport Pro Helena Brewers...... 977
1991 Sport Pro Helena Brewers.... 1012
1993 SportPro Helena Brewers..... 1064
1991 Sport Pro Idaho Falls Braves 1012
1993 SportPro Idaho Falls Braves. 1064
1993 SportPro Lethbridge Mounties 1066
1991 Sport Pro Medicine Hat Blue Jays 1016
1993 SportPro Medicine Hat Blue Jays 1067
1991 Sport-Pro Pocatello Pioneers 1019
1993 SportPro Pocatello Posse..... 1069
1991 Sport Pro Salt Lake City Trappers............................. 1021
1989 Sport Pro Spokane Indians..... 963
1990 Sport Pro Spokane Indians..... 988
1990 Sportsprint Durham Bulls........ 974
1990 Sportsprint Frederick Keys 975
1990 Sportsprint Kinston Indians..... 979
1989 Star Co. Albany-Colonie Yankees 945
1990 Star Co. Albany Yankees 968
1988 Star Co. Baseball City Royals 926
1989 Star Co. Baseball City Royals 946
1990 Star Co. Baseball City Royals 969
1989 Star Co. Beloit Brewers 946
1990 Star Co. Beloit Brewers 969
1989 Star Co. Bluefield Orioles 947
1990 Star Co. Bluefield Orioles 970
1989 Star Co. Bristol Tigers 947
1990 Star Co. Bristol Tigers 970
1989 Star Co. Burlington Braves..... 947
1990 Star Co. Burlington Braves..... 971
1989 Star Co. Burlington Indians..... 947
1989 Star Co. Canton-Akron Indians 948
1990 Star Co. Canton-Akron Indians 971
1988 Star Co. Carolina League All-Stars 928
1989 Star Co. Cedar Rapids Reds .. 948
1988 Star Co. Charlotte Rangers 928
1989 Star Co. Charlotte Rangers 949
1990 Star Co. Charlotte Rangers 972
1988 Star Co. Clearwater Phillies.... 929
1989 Star Co. Clearwater Phillies.... 949
1990 Star Co. Clearwater Phillies.... 972
1989 Star Co. Columbus Mudcats... 950
1990 Star Co. Columbus Mudcats... 974
1988 Star Co. Dunedin Blue Jays ... 930
1989 Star Co. Dunedin Blue Jays ... 951
1990 Star Co. Dunedin Blue Jays ... 974
1989 Star Co. Durham Bulls............ 951
1988 Star Co. Durham Bulls (Blue) . 930
1988 Star Co. Durham Bulls (Orange)................................ 930
1989 Star Co. Elizabethton Twins ... 951
1990 Star Co. Elizabethton Twins ... 974
1989 Star Co. Erie Orioles.............. 951
1990 Star Co. Erie Sailors 974
1989 Star Co. Everett Giants........... 952
1988 Star Co. Florida State All-Stars 931

1990 Star Co. Florida State League All-Stars 975
1989 Star Co. Fort Lauderdale Yankees.................................. 952
1989 Star Co. Frederick Keys 952
1988 Star Co. Ft. Lauderdale Yankees.................................. 931
1990 Star Co. Ft. Lauderdale Yankees 975
1989 Star Co. Gastonia Rangers 952
1990 Star Co. Gastonia Rangers 975
1990 Star Co. Geneva Cubs 976
1990 Star Co. Greensboro Hornets. 976
1989 Star Co. Greenville Braves..... 953
1990 Star Co. Greenville Braves..... 976
1988 Star Co. Hagerstown Suns..... 932
1989 Star Co. Hagerstown Suns..... 953
1990 Star Co. Hagerstown Suns..... 977
1989 Star Co. Hamilton Redbirds.... 953
1990 Star Co. Hamilton Redbirds.... 977
1989 Star Co. Harrisburg Senators. 953
1990 Star Co. Harrisburg Senators. 977
1989 Star Co. Johnson City Cardinals................................ 954
1990 Star Co. Johnson City Cardinals................................ 978
1989 Star Co. Kenosha Twins......... 955
1990 Star Co. Kenosha Twins......... 978
1989 Star Co. Kingsport Mets 955
1990 Star Co. Kingsport Mets 978
1988 Star Co. Kinston Indians......... 933
1989 Star Co. Kinston Indians......... 955
1989 Star Co. Knoxville Blue Jays .. 955
1990 Star Co. Knoxville Blue Jays .. 979
1988 Star Co. Lakeland Tigers........ 933
1989 Star Co. Lakeland Tigers........ 955
1990 Star Co. Lakeland Tigers........ 979
1988 Star Co. Lynchburg Red Sox.. 934
1989 Star Co. Lynchburg Red Sox.. 956
1989 Star Co. Madison Muskies...... 956
1988 Star Co. Martinsville Phillies... 934
1989 Star Co. Martinsville Phillies... 956
1989 Star Co. Memphis Chicks....... 956
1990 Star Co. Memphis Chicks....... 980
1988 Star Co. Miami Marlins........... 935
1989 Star Co. Miami Miracle........... 956
1989 Star Co. New Britain Red Sox 957
1990 Star Co Miami Miracle I......... 980
1990 Star Co. Miami Miracle II 980
1990 Star Co. New Britain Red Sox 982
1990 Star Co. Orlando Sun Rays.... 982
1988 Star Co. Osceola Astros......... 936
1989 Star Co. Osceola Astros......... 958
1990 Star Co. Osceola Astros......... 983
1989 Star Co. Peninsula Pilots........ 958
1990 Star Co. Peninsula Pilots........ 983
1989 Star Co. Pittsfield Mets........... 959
1988 Star Co. Port Charlotte Rangers 937
1989 Star Co. Princeton Pirates...... 959
1989 Star Co. Prince William Cannons................................ 959
1988 Star Co. Prince William Yankees................................ 937
1989 Star Co. Reading Phillies........ 960
1990 Star Co. Reading Phillies........ 984
1989 Star Co. Saint Lucie Mets....... 961
1990 Star Co. Saint Lucie Mets....... 986
1989 Star Co. Saint Petersburg Cardinals................................ 961
1990 Star Co. Saint Petersburg Cardinals................................ 986
1988 Star Co. Salem Buccaneers ... 939
1989 Star Co. Salem Buccaneers ... 961
1990 Star Co. Salem Buccaneers ... 986
1989 Star Co. San Jose Giants....... 962
1990 Star Co. San Jose Giants....... 987
1989 Star Co. Sarasota White Sox.. 962
1990 Star Co. Sarasota White Sox.. 987
1990 Star Co. Shreveport Captains. 987
1990 Star Co. South Atlantic League All-Stars....................................... 987
1988 Star Co. Spartanburg Phillies. 940
1989 Star Co. Spartanburg Phillies. 963
1990 Star Co. Spartanburg Phillies. 988
1989 Star Co. Stockton Ports.......... 964
1988 Star Co. St. Lucie Mets........... 939
1988 Star Co. St. Petersburg Cardinals................................ 939
1988 Star Co. Tampa Tarpons........ 941
1988 Star Co. Vero Beach Dodgers 943
1989 Star Co. Vero Beach Dodgers 966
1990 Star Co. Vero Beach Dodgers 991
1988 Star Co. Virginia Generals...... 943
1989 Star Co. Waterloo Diamonds.. 966
1989 Star Co. Watertown Indians.... 966
1990 Star Co. Watertown Indians.... 991
1990 Star Co. Wausau Timbers 991
1988 Star Co. West Palm Beach Expos 944
1989 Star Co. West Palm Beach Expos 966
1990 Star Co. West Palm Beach Expos 992
1989 Star Co. Williamsport Bills 967
1990 Star Co. Williamsport Bills 992
1989 Star Co. Winston-Salem Spirit....................................... 967
1988 Star Co. Winston-Salem Spirits 944
1988 Star Co. Winter Haven Red Sox 944
1989 Star Co. Winter Haven Red Sox 967
1990 Star Co. Winter Haven Red Sox 992
1989 Star Co. Wytheville Cubs........ 967
1989 Star Minor League Baseball ... 967
1990 Star Minor League Baseball Wax 997
1984 1st Base Sports Shreveport Captains................................ 894
1975 Stewart Sandwiches Tidewater Tides 851
1946 Sunbeam Bread Sacramento Solons 830
1947 Sunbeam Bread Sacramento Solons 830
1949 Sunbeam Bread Stockton Ports 830
1950 Sunbeam Bread Stockton Ports 830
1975 Sussman Ft. Lauderdale Yankees................................ 849
1976 Sussman Ft. Lauderdale Yankees................................ 853
1977 Sussman Ft. Lauderdale Yankees................................ 856
1975 Sussman West Palm Beach Expos 852
1888 S.F. Hess California League (N388-1)................................ 816
1888 S.F. Hess Newsboys League (N333) 816

T

1961 Tacoma Giants 831
1984 TCMA Albany-Colonie A's...... 890
1983 TCMA Albany-Colonie A's...... 883
1985 TCMA Albany-Colonie Yankees................................ 895
1986 TCMA Albany-Colonie Yankees................................ 901
1979 TCMA Albuquerque Dukes..... 862
1980 TCMA Albuquerque Dukes..... 867
1981 TCMA Albuquerque Dukes..... 872
1982 TCMA Albuquerque Dukes..... 877
1983 TCMA Albuquerque Dukes..... 883
1982 TCMA Alexandria Dukes 877
1983 TCMA Alexandria Dukes 883
1982 TCMA Amarillo Gold Sox........ 877
1980 TCMA Anderson Braves......... 867
1983 TCMA Anderson Braves......... 883
1975 TCMA Anderson Rangers 849
1975 TCMA Appleton Foxes 849
1976 TCMA Appleton Foxes 852
1977 TCMA Appleton Foxes 855
1978 TCMA Appleton Foxes 859
1979 TCMA Appleton Foxes 862
1980 TCMA Appleton Foxes 867
1981 TCMA Appleton Foxes 872
1976 TCMA Arkansas Travelers 852
1977 TCMA Arkansas Travelers 855
1978 TCMA Arkansas Travelers 859
1979 TCMA Arkansas Travelers 862
1980 TCMA Arkansas Travelers 867
1981 TCMA Arkansas Travelers 872
1982 TCMA Arkansas Travelers 877
1983 TCMA Arkansas Travelers 884
1984 TCMA Arkansas Travelers 890
1976 TCMA Asheville Tourists 852
1977 TCMA Asheville Tourists 855
1978 TCMA Asheville Tourists 859
1979 TCMA Asheville Tourists 862
1980 TCMA Asheville Tourists 867
1982 TCMA Auburn Astros.............. 877
1980 TCMA Batavia Trojans 867
1981 TCMA Batavia Trojans 872
1976 TCMA Baton Rouge Cougars. 852
1983 TCMA Beaumont Golden Gators 884
1984 TCMA Beaumont Golden Gators 890
1985 TCMA Beaumont Golden Gators 895
1985 TCMA Beloit Brewers 895

1981 TCMA Birmingham Barons..... 872
1982 TCMA Birmingham Barons..... 877
1983 TCMA Birmingham Barons..... 884
1977 TCMA Bristol Red Sox............ 855
1981 TCMA Bristol Red Sox............ 872
1979 TCMA Buffalo Bisons 863
1980 TCMA Buffalo Bisons 867
1981 TCMA Buffalo Bisons 872
1982 TCMA Buffalo Bisons 878
1983 TCMA Buffalo Bisons 884
1984 TCMA Buffalo Bisons 890
1985 TCMA Buffalo Bisons 895
1975 TCMA Burlington Bees........... 849
1976 TCMA Burlington Bees........... 852
1977 TCMA Burlington Bees........... 855
1978 TCMA Burlington Bees........... 859
1979 TCMA Burlington Bees........... 863
1980 TCMA Burlington Bees........... 867
1981 TCMA Burlington Bees........... 873
1982 TCMA Burlington Rangers...... 878
1983 TCMA Burlington Rangers...... 884
1985 TCMA Burlington Rangers...... 896
1983 TCMA Butte Copper Kings 884
1984 TCMA Butte Copper Kings 890
1974 TCMA Cedar Rapids Astros ... 848
1972 TCMA Cedar Rapids Cardinals................................ 847
1975 TCMA Cedar Rapids Giants... 849
1976 TCMA Cedar Rapids Giants... 852
1977 TCMA Cedar Rapids Giants... 855
1978 TCMA Cedar Rapids Giants... 859
1979 TCMA Cedar Rapids Giants... 863
1980 TCMA Cedar Rapids Reds..... 867
1981 TCMA Cedar Rapids Reds..... 873
1982 TCMA Cedar Rapids Reds..... 878
1983 TCMA Cedar Rapids Reds..... 884
1984 TCMA Cedar Rapids Reds..... 890
1985 TCMA Cedar Rapids Reds..... 896
1986 TCMA Cedar Rapids Reds..... 902
1978 TCMA Charleston Charlies..... 859
1979 TCMA Charleston Charlies..... 863
1980 TCMA Charleston Charlies..... 867
1981 TCMA Charleston Charlies..... 873
1982 TCMA Charleston Charlies..... 878
1983 TCMA Charleston Charlies..... 885
1977 TCMA Charleston Patriots...... 855
1978 TCMA Charleston Pirates....... 859
1981 TCMA Charleston Royals....... 873
1982 TCMA Charleston Royals....... 878
1983 TCMA Charleston Royals....... 885
1984 TCMA Charlotte O's 890
1985 TCMA Charlotte O's 896
1981 TCMA Chattanooga Lookouts 873
1982 TCMA Chattanooga Lookouts 878
1983 TCMA Chattanooga Lookouts 885
1984 TCMA Chattanooga Lookouts 890
1977 TCMA Clinton Dodgers........... 855
1978 TCMA Clinton Dodgers........... 859
1979 TCMA Clinton Dodgers........... 863
1980 TCMA Clinton Giants.............. 868
1981 TCMA Clinton Giants.............. 873
1975 TCMA Clinton Pilots 849
1976 TCMA Clinton Pilots 852
1977 TCMA Cocoa Astros............... 855
1980 TCMA Columbus Astros......... 868
1983 TCMA Columbus Astros......... 885
1977 TCMA Columbus Clippers...... 855
1978 TCMA Columbus Clippers...... 859
1979 TCMA Columbus Clippers...... 863
1980 TCMA Columbus Clippers...... 868
1981 TCMA Columbus Clippers...... 873
1982 TCMA Columbus Clippers...... 878
1983 TCMA Columbus Clippers...... 885
1984 TCMA Columbus Clippers...... 891
1985 TCMA Columbus Clippers...... 896
1987 TCMA Columbus Clippers...... 914
1978 TCMA Daytona Beach Astros. 859
1982 TCMA Daytona Beach Astros. 879
1983 TCMA Daytona Beach Astros. 885
1977 TCMA Daytona Beach Islanders 856
1975 TCMA Dubuque Packers........ 849
1976 TCMA Dubuque Packers........ 852
1978 TCMA Dunedin Blue Jays 860
1981 TCMA Durham Bulls.............. 873
1982 TCMA Durham Bulls.............. 879
1983 TCMA Durham Bulls.............. 885
1984 TCMA Durham Bulls.............. 891
1985 TCMA Durham Bulls.............. 896
1982 TCMA Edmonton Trappers..... 879
1979 TCMA Elmira Pioneers........... 863
1980 TCMA Elmira Pioneers........... 868
1985 TCMA Elmira Pioneers........... 896
1980 TCMA El Paso Diablos........... 868
1981 TCMA El Paso Diablos........... 873
1982 TCMA El Paso Diablos........... 879
1983 TCMA El Paso Diablos........... 885
1984 TCMA El Paso Diablos........... 891
1983 TCMA Erie Cardinals............. 885
1977 TCMA Evansville Triplets 856
1980 TCMA Evansville Triplets 868
1981 TCMA Evansville Triplets 874
1982 TCMA Evansville Triplets 879
1983 TCMA Evansville Triplets 885
1984 TCMA Evansville Triplets 891
1982 TCMA Fort Meyers Royals 879
1985 TCMA Ft. Meyers Royals 897
1980 TCMA Glens Falls White Sox. 868
1981 TCMA Glens Falls White Sox. 874
1982 TCMA Glens Falls White Sox. 879
1983 TCMA Glens Falls White Sox. 885
1983 TCMA Greensboro Hornets.... 885
1984 TCMA Greensboro Hornets.... 891
1985 TCMA Greensboro Hornets.... 897
1978 TCMA Greenwood Braves...... 860
1979 TCMA Hawaii Islanders.......... 863
1980 TCMA Hawaii Islanders.......... 869
1981 TCMA Hawaii Islanders.......... 874
1982 TCMA Hawaii Islanders.......... 879
1977 TCMA Holyoke Millers............ 856
1978 TCMA Holyoke Millers............ 860
1979 TCMA Holyoke Millers............ 863
1980 TCMA Holyoke Millers............ 869
1981 TCMA Holyoke Millers............ 874
1982 TCMA Holyoke Millers............ 879
1982 TCMA Idaho Falls Athletics 879
1983 TCMA Idaho Falls Athletics 886
1975 TCMA International League.... 850
1985 TCMA International League All-Stars 898
1987 TCMA International League All-Stars 917
1982 TCMA Iowa Cubs 880
1983 TCMA Iowa Cubs 886
1984 TCMA Iowa Cubs 892
1985 TCMA Iowa Cubs 898
1975 TCMA Iowa Oaks 850
1979 TCMA Jackson Mets 864
1982 TCMA Jackson Mets 880
1984 TCMA Jackson Mets 892
1986 TCMA Jackson Mets 905
1986 TCMA Jacksonville Expos...... 905
1977 TCMA Jacksonville Suns........ 856
1985 TCMA Kinston Blue Jays........ 898
1980 TCMA Knoxville Blue Jays 869
1982 TCMA Knoxville Blue Jays 880
1983 TCMA Knoxville Blue Jays 886
1978 TCMA Knoxville Knox Sox...... 860
1979 TCMA Knoxville White Sox..... 864
1975 TCMA Lafayette Drillers 850
1984 TCMA Little Falls Mets 892
1985 TCMA Little Falls Mets 898
1977 TCMA Lodi Dodgers............... 856
1978 TCMA Lodi Dodgers............... 860
1979 TCMA Lodi Dodgers............... 864
1977 TCMA Lynchburg Mets........... 856
1982 TCMA Lynchburg Mets........... 880
1983 TCMA Lynchburg Mets........... 886
1985 TCMA Lynchburg Mets........... 898
1975 TCMA Lynchburg Rangers..... 850
1983 TCMA Lynn Pirates 886
1980 TCMA Lynn Sailors................. 869
1981 TCMA Lynn Sailors................. 874
1982 TCMA Lynn Sailors................. 880
1985 TCMA Madison Muskies......... 898
1984 TCMA Maine Guides 893
1985 TCMA Maine Guides 898
1987 TCMA Maine Guides 918
1979 TCMA Memphis Chicks.......... 864
1980 TCMA Memphis Chicks.......... 869
1983 TCMA Memphis Chicks.......... 887
1984 TCMA Memphis Chicks.......... 893
1982 TCMA Miami Marlins 880
1983 TCMA Miami Marlins 887
1981 TCMA Miami Orioles 874
1985 TCMA Midland Angels............ 899
1983 TCMA Midland Cubs 887
1984 TCMA Midland Cubs 893
1983 TCMA Nashua Angels............ 887
1985 TCMA Nashua Pirates............ 899
1977 TCMA Newark Co-Pilots......... 857
1979 TCMA Newark Co-Pilots......... 864
1984 TCMA Newark Orioles............ 893
1985 TCMA Newark Orioles............ 899
1978 TCMA Newark Wayne Co-Pilots 860
1979 TCMA Ogden A's................... 864
1980 TCMA Ogden A's................... 869
1981 TCMA Oklahoma City 89'ers.. 874
1982 TCMA Oklahoma City 89'ers.. 881
1983 TCMA Oklahoma City 89'ers.. 887
1984 TCMA Oklahoma City 89'ers.. 893
1985 TCMA Oklahoma City 89'ers.. 899
1981 TCMA Omaha Royals............. 875
1982 TCMA Omaha Royals............. 881
1983 TCMA Omaha Royals............. 887

1984 TCMA Omaha Royals............. 893
1985 TCMA Omaha Royals............. 899
1986 TCMA Omaha Royals............. 908
1982 TCMA Oneonta Yankees........ 881
1977 TCMA Orlando Twins 857
1978 TCMA Orlando Twins 861
1980 TCMA Orlando Twins 870
1982 TCMA Orlando Twins 881
1983 TCMA Orlando Twins 887
1985 TCMA Orlando Twins 899
1982 TCMA Orlando Twins Southern League Champs..................... 881
1981 TCMA Pawtucket Red Sox 875
1983 TCMA Pawtucket Red Sox 887
1984 TCMA Pawtucket Red Sox 893
1985 TCMA Pawtucket Red Sox 899
1987 TCMA Pawtucket Red Sox 920
1980 TCMA Peninsula Pilots........... 870
1979 TCMA Portland Beavers......... 865
1980 TCMA Portland Beavers......... 870
1981 TCMA Portland Beavers......... 875
1982 TCMA Portland Beavers......... 881
1983 TCMA Portland Beavers......... 888
1984 TCMA Prince William Pirates . 894
1985 TCMA Prince Williams Pirates 900
1980 TCMA Quad Cities Cubs 870
1975 TCMA Quad City Angels 850
1976 TCMA Quad City Angels 853
1977 TCMA Quad City Angels 857
1978 TCMA Quad City Angels 861
1979 TCMA Quad City Cubs 865
1981 TCMA Quad City Cubs 875
1982 TCMA Quad City Cubs 881
1983 TCMA Quad City Cubs 888
1977 TCMA Reading Phillies........... 857
1980 TCMA Reading Phillies........... 870
1981 TCMA Reading Phillies........... 875
1982 TCMA Reading Phillies........... 881
1983 TCMA Reading Phillies........... 888
1981 TCMA Redwood Pioneers 875
1982 TCMA Redwood Pioneers 881
1983 TCMA Redwood Pioneers 888
1978 TCMA Richmond Braves 861
1979 TCMA Richmond Braves 865
1980 TCMA Richmond Braves 870
1981 TCMA Richmond Braves 875
1982 TCMA Richmond Braves 881
1983 TCMA Richmond Braves 888
1984 TCMA Richmond Braves 894
1985 TCMA Richmond Braves 900
1987 TCMA Richmond Braves 921
1978 TCMA Rochester Red Wings . 861
1979 TCMA Rochester Red Wings . 865
1980 TCMA Rochester Red Wings . 870
1981 TCMA Rochester Red Wings . 875
1982 TCMA Rochester Red Wings . 881
1984 TCMA Rochester Red Wings . 894
1985 TCMA Rochester Red Wings . 900
1987 TCMA Rochester Red Wings . 921
1983 TCMA Rochester Redwings ... 888
1977 TCMA Salem Pirates 857
1978 TCMA Salem Pirates 861
1979 TCMA Salt Lake City Gulls 865
1980 TCMA Salt Lake City Gulls 870
1981 TCMA Salt Lake City Gulls 875
1982 TCMA Salt Lake City Gulls 882
1983 TCMA Salt Lake City Gulls 888
1975 TCMA San Antonio Brewers... 851
1979 TCMA Savannah Braves 865
1984 TCMA Savannah Cardinals 894
1975 TCMA Shreveport Captains.... 851
1976 TCMA Shreveport Captains.... 854
1977 TCMA Shreveport Captains.... 858
1981 TCMA Shreveport Captains.... 875
1977 TCMA Spartanburg Phillies 858
1979 TCMA Spokane Indians.......... 865
1980 TCMA Spokane Indians.......... 871
1981 TCMA Spokane Indians.......... 876
1982 TCMA Spokane Indians.......... 882
1985 TCMA Springfield Cardinals ... 900
1986 TCMA Stars Of The Future Post Card Set............................... 910
1977 TCMA St. Petersburg Cardinals.............................. 857
1978 TCMA St. Petersburg Cardinals.............................. 861
1983 TCMA St. Petersburg Cardinals.............................. 888
1978 TCMA Syracuse Chiefs 862
1979 TCMA Syracuse Chiefs 866
1980 TCMA Syracuse Chiefs 871
1981 TCMA Syracuse Chiefs 876
1982 TCMA Syracuse Chiefs 882
1983 TCMA Syracuse Chiefs 888
1984 TCMA Syracuse Chiefs 894
1985 TCMA Syracuse Chiefs 900
1987 TCMA Syracuse Chiefs 923
1980 TCMA Tacoma Tigers 871
1981 TCMA Tacoma Tigers 876
1982 TCMA Tacoma Tigers 882
1983 TCMA Tacoma Tigers 889
1979 TCMA Tacoma Tugs 866
1983 TCMA Tampa Tarpons 889
1978 TCMA Tidewater Tides........... 862
1979 TCMA Tidewater Tides........... 866
1980 TCMA Tidewater Tides........... 871
1981 TCMA Tidewater Tides........... 876
1982 TCMA Tidewater Tides........... 882
1983 TCMA Tidewater Tides........... 889
1984 TCMA Tidewater Tides........... 894
1985 TCMA Tidewater Tides........... 900
1987 TCMA Tidewater Tides........... 923
1985 TCMA Tigers De Mexico 898
1985 TCMA Toldeo Mud Hens 901
1979 TCMA Toledo Mud Hens 866
1980 TCMA Toledo Mud Hens 871
1981 TCMA Toledo Mud Hens 876
1982 TCMA Toledo Mud Hens 882
1983 TCMA Toledo Mud Hens 889
1984 TCMA Toledo Mud Hens 894
1987 TCMA Toledo Mud Hens 924
1983 TCMA Tri-Cities Triplets 889
1979 TCMA Tucson Toros 866
1980 TCMA Tucson Toros 871
1981 TCMA Tucson Toros 876
1982 TCMA Tucson Toros 882
1983 TCMA Tucson Toros 889
1979 TCMA Tulsa Drillers 866
1980 TCMA Tulsa Drillers 871
1981 TCMA Tulsa Drillers 876
1982 TCMA Tulsa Drillers 882
1983 TCMA Tulsa Drillers 889
1980 TCMA Utica Blue Jays............ 871
1985 TCMA Utica Blue Sox............. 901
1979 TCMA Vancouver Canadians . 866
1980 TCMA Vancouver Canadians . 871
1981 TCMA Vancouver Canadians . 876
1982 TCMA Vancouver Canadians . 882
1981 TCMA Vero Beach Dodgers ... 876
1982 TCMA Vero Beach Dodgers ... 883
1983 TCMA Vero Beach Dodgers ... 889
1985 TCMA Vero Beach Dodgers ... 901
1977 TCMA Visalia Oaks 858
1984 TCMA Visalia Oaks 895
1985 TCMA Visalia Oaks 901
1979 TCMA Waterbury A's............. 866
1975 TCMA Waterbury Dodgers 851
1985 TCMA Waterbury Indians 901
1980 TCMA Waterbury Reds 871
1981 TCMA Waterbury Reds 876
1982 TCMA Waterbury Reds 883
1983 TCMA Waterbury Reds 889
1977 TCMA Waterloo Indians 858
1978 TCMA Waterloo Indians 862
1979 TCMA Waterloo Indians 866
1980 TCMA Waterloo Indians 871
1981 TCMA Waterloo Indians 876
1982 TCMA Waterloo Indians 883
1975 TCMA Waterloo Royals 851
1976 TCMA Waterloo Royals 854
1976 TCMA Wausau Mets 854
1977 TCMA Wausau Mets 858
1978 TCMA Wausau Mets 862
1979 TCMA Wausau Timbers 866
1980 TCMA Wausau Timbers 872
1981 TCMA Wausau Timbers 877
1981 TCMA West Haven A's........... 877
1982 TCMA West Haven A's........... 883
1980 TCMA West Haven White Caps 872
1977 TCMA West Haven Yankees .. 858
1979 TCMA West Haven Yankees .. 866
1980 TCMA Wichita Aeros 872
1976 TCMA Williamsport Tomahawks............................ 855
1978 TCMA Wisconsin Rapids Twins 862
1979 TCMA Wisconsin Rapids Twins 866
1980 TCMA Wisconsin Rapids Twins 872
1981 TCMA Wisconsin Rapids Twins 877
1987 Team Albuquerque Dukes...... 912
1976 Team Batavia Trojans 852
1987 Team Bellingham Mariners..... 912
1988 Team Bellingham Mariners..... 926
1985 Team Birmingham Barons...... 895
1991 Team Blue Shield Buffalo Bisons 1005
1987 Team Buffalo Bisons 913
1988 Team Buffalo Bisons 927
1990 Team Buffalo Bisons 970
1988 Team Charlotte Knights.......... 928
1989 Team Charlotte Knights.......... 949
1990 Team Charlotte Knights.......... 972
1980 Team Charlotte O's 867
1981 Team Charlotte O's 873

1987 Team Charlotte O's 913
1982 Team Charlotte O's Heroes Aren't Hard 878
1988 Team Chattanooga Lookout Legends #I 929
1985 Team Chattanooga Lookouts . 896
1989 Team Chattanooga Lookouts . 949
1980 Team Columbus Clippers 868
1986 Team Columbus Clippers 903
1990 Team Columbus Clippers 973
1992 Team Columbus RedStixx 1037
1984 Team Daytona Beach Astros .. 891
1985 Team Daytona Beach Islanders 896
1992 Team Denver Zephyrs Record Holders 1037
1989 Team Durham Bulls 951
1992 Team Durham Bulls 1038
1987 Team Elmira Pioneers - Black 915
1987 Team Elmira Pioneers - Red .. 915
1989 Team Fayetteville Generals 952
1992 Team Fort Lauderdale Yankees 1039
1978 Team Geneva Cubs 860
1988 Team Great Falls Dodgers 931
1985 Team Greenville Braves 897
1990 Team-Hill's Nashville Sounds. 981
1981 Team Holyoke Millers 874
1982 Team Holyoke Millers 879
1985 Team Huntsville Stars 897
1986 Team Huntsville Stars 905
1987 Team Huntsville Stars 916
1988 Team Huntsville Stars 932
1992 Team Huntsville Stars 1041
1984 Team Idaho Falls A's 892
1976 Team Indianapolis Indians 853
1977 Team Indianapolis Indians 856
1978 Team Indianapolis Indians 860
1979 Team Indianapolis Indians 863
1980 Team Indianapolis Indians 869
1981 Team Indianapolis Indians 874
1982 Team Indianapolis Indians 879
1983 Team Indianapolis Indians 886
1984 Team Indianapolis Indians 892
1985 Team Indianapolis Indians 897
1986 Team Indianapolis Indians 905
1987 Team Indianapolis Indians 916
1987 Team Iowa Cubs 917
1953 Team Issue San Francisco Seals 827
1987 Team Jackson Mets 917
1991 Team Kane County Cougars 1013
1992 Team Kane County Cougars 1042
1990 Team-Lithocenter Rockford Expos 985
1989 Team Louisville Cardinals 956
1986 Team Louisville Redbirds 906
1987 Team Louisville Redbirds 918
1988 Team Louisville Redbirds 934
1989 Team Louisville Redbirds 956
1990 Team Louisville Redbirds 980
1991 Team Louisville Redbirds 1015
1992 Team Louisville Redbirds 1043
1991 Team Midland Angels 1016
1992 Team Midland Angels 1044
1992 Team Modesto Athletics 1044
1988 Team Modesto A's 935
1979 Team Nashville Sounds 864
1980 Team Nashville Sounds 869
1983 Team Nashville Sounds 887
1984 Team Nashville Sounds 893
1985 Team Nashville Sounds 899
1986 Team Nashville Sounds 907
1987 Team Nashville Sounds 919
1988 Team Nashville Sounds 935
1989 Team Nashville Sounds 957
1991 Team Nashville Sounds 1017
1992 Team Nashville Sounds 1045
1975 Team Oklahoma City 89'ers ... 850
1976 Team Oklahoma City 89'ers ... 853
1978 Team Oklahoma City 89'ers 861, 864
1980 Team Oklahoma City 89'ers ... 869
1962 Team Omaha Dodgers 824
1980 Team Omaha Royals 870
1985 Team Osceola Astros 899
1988 Team Peoria Chiefs 936
1989 Team Peoria Chiefs 959
1990 Team Peoria Chiefs 983
1991 Team Peoria Chiefs 1018
1992 Team Peoria Chiefs 1046
1986 Team Pittsfield Cubs 909
1987 Team Pittsfield Cubs 920
1988 Team Pittsfield Cubs 937
1988 Team Richmond Braves 938
1989 Team Richmond Braves 960
1990 Team Richmond Braves 985
1992 Team Richmond Braves 1047
1988 Team Rochester Red Wings .. 938
1990 Team Rochester Red Wings .. 985
1988 Team Rockford Expos 939
1989 Team Rockford Expos 961
1989 Team Salem Dodgers 961
1987 Team Salt Lake City Trappers 922
1988 Team Salt Lake City Trappers 939
1987 Team San Antonio Dodgers ... 922
1992 Team Scranton-Wilkes Barre Red Barons 1049
1972 Team Seattle Rainiers 847
1974 Team Seattle Rainiers 848
1973 Team Sherbrooke Pirates 847
1984 Team Spokane Indians 894
1990 Team Sully's Pub Peoria Chiefs 983
1973 Team Syracuse Chiefs 847
1974 Team Syracuse Chiefs 848
1975 Team Syracuse Chiefs 851
1979 Team Syracuse Chiefs 866
1980 Team Syracuse Chiefs 871
1981 Team Syracuse Chiefs 876
1982 Team Syracuse Chiefs 882
1989 Team Syracuse Chiefs 964
1990 Team Syracuse Chiefs 989
1991 Team Syracuse Chiefs 1024
1992 Team Syracuse Chiefs 1051
1992 Team Syracuse Chiefs Former Stars 1051
1972 Team Tacoma Twins 847
1991 Team Tampa Yankees 1024
1990 Team 25th Anniversary Richmond Braves 985
1975 Team Tucson Toros 851
1984 Team Tulsa Drillers 895
1985 Team Tulsa Drillers 901
1986 Team Tulsa Drillers 911
1987 Team Tulsa Drillers 924
1988 Team Tulsa Drillers 942
1991 Team Tulsa Drillers 1025
1992 Team Tulsa Drillers 1052
1982 Team Wichita Aeros 883
1987 Team Wichita Pilots 925
1992 Team Winston-Salem Spirts. 1053
1990 Team-WTAR Tidewater Tides 990
1990 Team (Play II) Columbia Mets 973
1987Texas League All-Stars 923
1987 The Bon Pocatello Giants 920
1978 Tiefel & Associates Denver Bears 859
1986 Time Out Sports Memphis Chicks 907
1966 Toledo Mud Hens 830
1975 Top Trophies Omaha Royals .. 850
1976 Top Trophies Omaha Royals .. 853
1977 Top Trophies Omaha Royals .. 857
1989 Tribune Albuquerque Dukes ... 945
1964 True-Aid Buffalo Bisons 830
1989 Tulsa BB Card Shop Tulsa Drillers 965
1990 Tulsa BB Card Shop Tulsa Drillers 990
1960 Tulsa Oilers 831
1975 7-11 Tulsa Oliers 851
1984 T&J SC Madison Muskies 892
1985 T&J SC Madison Muskies 898
1987 T&J SC Madison Muskies 918
1988 T&J SC Madison Muskies 934
1910 1st Series (T209) 813
1910 Photo Series (T209) 813
1911 (T217) 820

U

1961 Union Oil Pacific Coast League 830
1958 Union Oil Sacramento Solons 831
1960 Union Oil Seattle Rainiers 831
1961 Union Oil Taiyo Whales 831
1986 University City Spokane Indians 910
1979 University Volkswagen Albuquerque Dukes 862
1994 Upper Deck 1076
1992 Upper Deck Minor League 1031
1992 Upper Deck Minor League Promos 1031
1992 Upper Deck Player of the Year 1032
1994 Upper Deck Player of the Year 1077
1992 Upper Deck Top Prospect Holograms 1032
1992 Urkrop's Richmond Braves ... 1048

V

1976 Valley Nat'l Bank Phoenix Giants 853

1977 Valley Nat'l Bank Phoenix Giants.................................... 857
1980 Valley Nat'l Bank Phoenix Giants.................................... 870
1981 Valley Nat'l Bank Phoenix Giants.................................... 875
1982 Valley Nat'l Bank Phoenix Giants.................................... 881
1951 Vancouver Capilanos Popcorn Issue 831
1952 Vancouver Capilanos Popcorn Issue 831
1953 Vancouver Capilanos Popcorn Issue 831
1954 Vancouver Capilanos Popcorn Issue 831

W

1980 WBTV Charlotte O's 867
1986 WBTV Charlotte O's 903
1933 Worch Cigar American Association............................. 832
1950 World Wide Gum 832
1981 WTF Co. Rochester Red Wings 875

Z

1911 Zeenut Pacific Coast League (E136) 832
1912 Zeenut Pacific Coast League (E136) 833
1913 Zeenut Pacific Coast League (E136) 833
1914 Zeenut Pacific Coast League (E136) 834
1915 Zeenut Pacific Coast League (E137) 834
1916 Zeenut Pacific Coast League (E137) 835
1917 Zeenut Pacific Coast League (E137) 835
1918 Zeenut Pacific Coast League (E137) 836
1919 Zeenut Pacific Coast League (E137) 836
1920 Zeenut Pacific Coast League (E137) 837
1921 Zeenut Pacific Coast League (E137) 838
1922 Zeenut Pacific Coast League (E137) 838
1923 Zeenut Pacific Coast League (E137) 839
1924 Zeenut Pacific Coast League (E137) 840
1925 Zeenut Pacific Coast League (E137) 840
1926 Zeenut Pacific Coast League (E137) 841
1927 Zeenut Pacific Coast League (E137) 841
1928 Zeenut Pacific Coast League (E137) 842
1929 Zeenut Pacific Coast League (E137) 843
1930 Zeenut Pacific Coast League (E137) 843
1931 Zeenut Pacific Coast League (E137) 844
1932 Zeenut Pacific Coast League (E137) 844
1937 - 38 Zeenut Pacific Coast League (E137) 846
1933 - 36 Zeenut PCL (black and white) (E137) 845
1933 Zeenut PCL (sepia) (E137)..... 845

CHRONOLOGICAL INDEX

1886 Lone Jack St. Louis Browns (N370) 320
1886 Lorillard Team Card 320
1886 New York Baseball Club (H812) 361
1886 Old Judge New York Giants (N167) 363
1886 Red Stocking Cigars 485
1887 Allen & Ginter World's Champions (N28) 3
1887 Four Base Hits 240
1887 Gold Coin (Buchner) (N284) 245
1887 Gypsy Queens 251
1887 Kalamazoo Bats (N690) 284
1887 Kalamazoo Bats Cabinets (N690) 284
1887 Kalamazoo Bats Team Cards (N690-1) 285
1887 Old Judge (N172) 363
1887 Tobin Lithographs (H891) 579
1887 W.S. Kimball Champions (N184) 297
1888 Allen & Ginter World's Champions (N29) 3
1888 Duke Talk of the Diamond (N135) 151
1888 E.R. Williams Card Game 801
1888 G & B Chewing Gum (E223) 242
1888 Goodwin Champions (N162) 246
1888 Joseph Hall Cabinets 252
1888 Old Judge Cabinets (N173) 381
1888 S.F. Hess (N338-2) 253
1888 S.F. Hess California League (N388-1) 816
1888 S.F. Hess Newsboys League (N333) 816
1888 Scrapps Tobacco 523
1888 Sporting Times (M117) 545
1888 WG1 Base Ball Playing Cards 795
1888 Yum Yum Tobacco (N403) 808
1889 Number 7/Diamond S Cigars (N526) 363
1889 Police Gazette Cabinets 460
1893 Honest (Duke) Cabinets (N142) 256
1893 Just So Tobacco 276
1895 Mayo's Cut Plug (N300) 325
1895 Newsboy Cabinets (N566) 360
1896 Mayo's Die-Cut Game Cards (N301) 325
1900 Mayo's Baseball Comics (T203) 326
1903 Breisch Williams Type I (E107) 43
1903 Breisch Williams Type II (E107) 43
1904 Fan Craze National League 162
1904 Fan Craze American League 162
1906 Sporting Life Team Composites (W601) 541
1907 W555 791
1908 American Caramel Co. (E91, Set A) 4
1908 E102 "Set of 25" 152
1909 - 11 American Caramel Co. (E90-1) 5
1909 - 11 T206 White Border 566
1909 American Caramel Co. (E91, Set B) 4
1909 C.A. Briggs Co. (E97) 44
1909 Colgan's Chips (E254) 65
1909 Croft's Candy (E92) 81
1909 Croft's Cocoa (E92) 81
1909 Derby Cigars 86
1909 Dockman & Sons Gum (E92) 90
1909 E101 "Set of 50" 152
1909 Nadja Caramels (E92) 353
1909 Obak (T212) 820
1909 Philadelphia Carmel (E95) 446
1909 PX7 Domino Discs 429
1909 S74 Silks - White 488
1909 T204 Ramly 565
1910 A.W.H. Caramels Virginia League (E222) 809
1910 All Star Base-Ball 3
1910 American Caramel Co. (E91, Set C) 5
1910 American Caramel Co. Cubs/Sox (E90-3) 6
1910 American Caramel Co. Pirates (E90-2) 6
1910 American Caramel die-cuts (E125) 5
1910 Bishop & Co. P.C.L. (E99) 810
1910 Bishop & Co. P.C.L. Teams (E221) 809
1910 Contentnea 1st Series (T209) 812
1910 Contentnea Photo Series (T209) 812
1910 Coupon Cigarettes Type 1 (T213) 76
1910 Darby Chocolates (E271) 84
1910 E98 "Set of 30" 152
1910 Ju-Ju Drums (E286) 275
1910 Mello-Mint (E105) 329
1910 Nadja Carmels (E104-III) 354
1910 Nadja Philadelphia Athletics (E104-I) 353
1910 Nadja Pittsburgh Pirates (E104-II) 354
1910 Obak (T212) 820
1910 Old Mill Cigarettes Series 1 (T210) 822
1910 Old Mill Cigarettes Series 2 (T210) 822
1910 Old Mill Cigarettes Series 3 (T210) 823
1910 Old Mill Cigarettes Series 4 (T210) 823
1910 Old Mill Cigarettes Series 5 (T210) 823
1910 Old Mill Cigarettes Series 6 (T210) 823
1910 Old Mill Cigarettes Series 7 (T210) 824
1910 Old Mill Cigarettes Series 8 (T210) 824
1910 Orange Borders 426
1910 P2 Sweet Caporal Pins 426
1910 Philadelphia Carmel (E96) 446
1910 Plow Boy Tobacco 460
1910 Red Cross Cigarettes Type 1 (T215) 482
1910 Red Sun Southern Association (T211) 825
1910 S74 Silks - Colored 489
1910 Standard Caramel Co. (E93) 550
1910 Tip-Top Bread Pittsburgh Pirates 578
1910 Williams Caramels (E103) 801
1911 Baseball Bats 14
1911 Big Eater Sacramento Solons 809
1911 Bishop & Co. P.C.L. Type I (E100) 810
1911 Bishop & Co. P.C.L. Type II (E100) 810
1911 Brunners Bread (D304) 44
1911 Cullivan's Fireside Philadelphia A's 83
1911 George Close Candy Co. (E94) 60
1911 Helmar Stamps (T332) 252
1911 Mono Cigarettes (T217) 819
1911 Obak (T212) 821
1911 Obak Cabinets (T4) 822
1911 Rochester Baking Philadelphia A's (D359) 486
1911 Sporting Life (M116) 541
1911 T201 Mecca Double Folders 564
1911 T205 Gold Border 566
1911 T5 Pinkerton 563
1911 Turkey Red (T3) 562
1911 Williams Baking Philadelphia A's (D359) 801
1911 Zeenut Pacific Coast League (E136) 832
1912 Boston Garter 26
1912 Colgan's Chips Red Borders (E270) 66
1912 Colgan's Chips Tin Tops (E270) 66
1912 Home Run Kisses (E136) 816
1912 Imperial Tobacco (C46) 817
1912 L1 Leathers 299
1912 Pirate Cigarettes (T215) 457
1912 Plow's Candy (E300) 460
1912 Red Cross Cigarettes Type 2 (T215) 483
1912 S81 Silks 489
1912 T202 Hassan Triple Folders 564

1912 T207 Brown Background........ 568
1912 T227 Series Of Champions.... 570
1912 Zeenut Pacific Coast League (E136) 833
1913 Boston Garter 26
1913 Cravats Felt Pennants 81
1913 Fatima Team Cards (T200).... 164
1913 The National Game 355
1913 Tom Barker Game 13
1913 Voskamp's Coffee Pittsburgh Pirates 787
1913 Zeenut Pacific Coast League (E136) 833
1914 B18 Blankets 11
1914 Boston Garter 26
1914 Coupon Cigarettes Type 2 (T213) 77
1914 Cracker Jack 78
1914 Fatima (T222) 163
1914 General Baking Co. (D303).... 244
1914 Piedmont Art Stamps (T330-2) 447
1914 Polo Grounds Game 472
1914 T216 Kotton 569
1914 Texas Tommy Type I (E224).. 577
1914 Texas Tommy Type II (E224). 577
1914 Zeenut Pacific Coast League (E136) 834
1915 American Caramel (E106)......... 6
1915 Cracker Jack 78
1915 The Sporting News (M101-5) . 543
1915 Victory Tobacco (T214).......... 787
1915 Zeenut Pacific Coast League (E137) 834
1916 BF2 Felt Pennants 11
1916 Collins-McCarthy (E135) 67
1916 Tango Eggs 571
1916 The Sporting News (M101-4) . 543
1916 Zeenut Pacific Coast League (E137) 835
1917 Zeenut Pacific Coast League (E137) 835
1918 W522 791
1918 Zeenut Pacific Coast League (E137) 836
1919 Coupon Cigarettes Type 3 (T213) 77
1919 Sporting News Supplements (M101-6) 544
1919 W514 789
1919 Zeenut Pacific Coast League (E137) 836
1920 W516-1 789
1920 W519 - Numbered 790
1920 W519 - Unnumbered 790
1920 W520 790
1920 Zeenut Pacific Coast League (E137) 837
1921 - 23 National Caramel (E220) 354
1921 American Carmel Series of 80 (E121) 6
1921 Exhibits 154
1921 Neilson's Chocolate (V61) 356
1921 Oxford Confectionery (E253) 426
1921 W516-2 790
1921 W521 791
1921 Zeenut Pacific Coast League (E137).. 838
1922 American Carmel Series of 120 (E121) 7
1922 American Carmel Series of 240 (E120) 8
1922 American Carmel Series of 80 (E122) 7
1922 Eastern Exhibit Supply Co. 155
1922 Exhibits 155
1922 Fans Cigarettes (T231) 163
1922 W501 787
1922 W503 788
1922 W551 791
1922 W573 792
1922 W575-1 793
1922 W575-2 794
1922 Zeenut Pacific Coast League (E137) 838
1923 - 24 Exhibits 155
1923 Curtis Ireland Candy (E123)... 263
1923 Maple Crispette 324
1923 W515 789
1923 W572 792
1923 Walter Mails Card Game........ 322
1923 Willard Chocolate (V100)........ 800
1923 Zeenut Pacific Coast League (E137) 839
1924 Diaz Cigarettes 88
1924 Zeenut Pacific Coast League (E137) 840
1925 Exhibits 155
1925 Zeenut Pacific Coast League (E137) 840
1926 Exhibits 156
1926 W512 788
1926 W513 788
1926 Zeenut Pacific Coast League (E137) 841
1927 American Carmel Series of 60 (E126) 9
1927 Exhibits 156
1927 W560 791
1927 York Caramels Type I (E210) 807
1927 York Caramels Type II (E210) 808
1927 Zeenut Pacific Coast League (E137) 841
1928 Exhibits 157
1928 Exhibits Pacific Coast League 813
1928 Fro-joy 241
1928 George Ruth Candy Co. 488
1928 R315 480
1928 Star Player Candy 551
1928 Tharp's Ice Cream 577
1928 W502 788
1928 Yeungling's Ice Cream 806
1928 Zeenut Pacific Coast League (E137) 842
1929 - 30 Four-on-One Exhibits 157
1929 "Anonymous" Exhibits 157
1929 Kashin Publications (R316) 285
1929 Zeenut Pacific Coast League (E137) 843
1930 PM8 Our National Game Pins 427
1930 PR4 Cracker Jack Pins........... 428
1930 Zeenut Pacific Coast League (E137) 843
1931 - 32 Four-on-One Exhibits 158
1931 Metropolitan Studio St. Louis Cardinals 330
1931 W517 790
1931 Zeenut Pacific Coast League (E137) 844
1932 Charles Denby Cigars Cubs..... 86
1932 PR2 Orbit Gum Pins Numbered 428
1932 PR3 Orbit Gum Pins Unnumbered 428
1932 R337 480
1932 U.S. Caramel 757
1932 W574 793
1932 Zeenut Pacific Coast League (E137) 844
1933 - 36 Zeenut PCL (black and white) (E137) 845
1933 Blue Bird Babe Ruth 25
1933 Buffalo Bisons Jigsaw Puzzles 811
1933 Butter Cream 47
1933 DeLong 85
1933 Four-on-One Exhibits 158
1933 George C. Miller 331
1933 Goudey 246
1933 Minneapolis Star Worch Tobacco 334
1933 PX3 Double Header Pins........ 428
1933 Rittenhouse Candy (E285)..... 486
1933 Sport Kings 545
1933 Tatoo Orbit (R308) 576
1933 Tattoo Orbit 576
1933 Worch Cigar American Association 832
1933 World Wide Gum (Canadian Goudey, V353) 805
1933 Zeenut PCL (sepia) (E137)..... 845
1934 - 36 Diamond Stars 87
1934 Batter-Up 15
1934 Butterfinger (R310) 47
1934 Four-on-One Exhibits 158
1934 Gold Medal Flour 246
1934 Goudey 247
1934 Goudey Thum Movies (R342) 248
1934 Goudey Premiums (R309-1)... 248
1934 World Wide Gum (Canadian Goudey, V354) 805
1935 Al Demaree Die-cuts 85
1935 Four-on-One Exhibits 158
1935 Goudey 248
1935 Goudey Premiums (R309-2) 248
1935 Rice-Stix 485
1935 Schutter-Johnson (R332) 491
1935 Wheaties - Series 1 796
1936 - 37 BF3 Felt Pennants 12
1936 Four-on-One Exhibits 158

1936 Goudey "Wide Pen" Premiums (R314) 249
1936 Goudey 248
1936 National Chicle (R344) 355
1936 National Chicle Co. "Fine Pens" (R313) 355
1936 R311 Glossy Finish 479
1936 R311 Leather Finish 480
1936 R312 480
1936 S and S Game 488
1936 Wheaties - Series 3 796
1936 Wheaties - Series 4 796
1936 Wheaties - Series 5 796
1936 World Wide Gum (Canadian Goudey, V355) 806
1937 - 38 Zeenut Pacific Coast League (E137) 846
1937 Dixie Lids 88
1937 Dixie Lids Premiums 89
1937 Four-on-One Exhibits 159
1937 Goudey Baseball Movies (R326) 249
1937 O-Pee-Chee 382
1937 Wheaties - Series 14 797
1937 Wheaties - Series 6 796
1937 Wheaties - Series 7 797
1937 Wheaties - Series 8 797
1937 Wheaties - Series 9 797
1938 Dixie Lids 89
1938 Dixie Lids Premiums 89
1938 Four-on-One Exhibits 159
1938 Goudey 249
1938 W711-1 Reds 794
1938 Wheaties - Series 10 797
1938 Wheaties - Series 11 798
1938 Wheaties - Series 15 798
1939 - 46 Salutation Exhibits 159
1939 Father & Son Shoes Phillies 163
1939 Goudey Premiums (R303-A) 250
1939 Goudey Premiums (R303-B) 250
1939 Play Ball 457
1939 W711-1 Reds 794
1939 Wheaties - Series 12 798
1939 Wheaties - Series 13 798
1940 Associated Stations San Francisco Seals 809
1940 Crowley's Milk 812
1940 Hughes Frozen Confections Sacramento Solons 817
1940 Play Ball 458
1940 W711-2 Harry Hartman Reds 794
1940 Wheaties Champs of the USA 798
1941 Double Play 147
1941 Goudey 250
1941 Play Ball 459
1941 W753 St. Louis Browns 794
1941 W754 St. Louis Cardinals 795
1941 Wheaties Champs of the USA 799
1943 Centennial Flour Seattle Rainiers 811
1943 Grand Studio Milwaukee Brewers 814
1943 M.P. & Co. (R302-1) 351
1944 Centennial Flour Seattle Rainers 811
1945 Centennial Flour Seattle Rainiers 811
1946 - 49 Sports Exchange (W603) 546
1946 Remar Bread Oakland Oaks 826
1946 Sunbeam Bread Sacramento Solons 830
1947 - 66 Exhibits 161
1947 Bond Bread Jackie Robinson 25
1947 Centennial Flour Seattle Rainiers 811
1947 Hollywood Stars 829
1947 Homogenized Bond Bread 255
1947 Los Angeles Angels 829
1947 Morley Studios Tacoma Tigers 819
1947 Oakland Oaks 829
1947 R346 Blue Tint 481
1947 Remar Bread Oakland Oaks 826
1947 Sacramento Solons 829
1947 Seattle Rainiers 829
1947 Signal Gasoline Pacific Coast League 829
1947 Smith's Oakland Oaks 829
1947 Sports Exchange Baseball Miniatures (W602) 546
1947 Sunbeam Bread Sacramento Solons 830
1947 Tip Top Bread 578
1948 Babe Ruth Story 13
1948 Baseball's Great Hall of Fame Exhibits 160
1948 Bowman 26
1948 Leaf 302
1948 Remar Bread Oakland Oaks 826
1948 Signal Gasoline Oakland Oaks 829
1948 Smith's Oakland Oaks 829
1948 Sommer & Kaufmann San Francisco Seals 830
1948 Sport Thrills 547
1948 Topps Magic Photos 579
1949 Baas Cheri-Cola 13
1949 Bowman 26
1949 Bowman Pacific Coast League 810
1949 Eureka Sportstamps 154
1949 Hage's Dairy 814
1949 Lummis Peanut Butter Phillies 321
1949 M.P. & Co. (R302-2) 352
1949 Remar Bread Oakland Oaks 826
1949 Sealtest Phillies 523
1949 Sommer & Kaufmann San Francisco Seals 830
1949 Sunbeam Bread Stockton Ports 830
1950 Bowman 27
1950 Callahan Hall of Fame 48
1950 Drake's 147
1950 Hage's Dairy 815
1950 Num Num Cleveland Indians 363
1950 R423 481
1950 Remar Bread Oakland Oaks 826
1950 Royal Desserts 487
1950 San Francisco Seals Popcorn 827
1950 Sunbeam Bread Stockton Ports 830
1950 World Wide Gum 832
1951 - 59 Photo-Film Fotos Pirates Postcards 447
1951 Berk Ross 23
1951 Bowman 28
1951 Fischer Baking Labels 164
1951 Globe Printing Fresno Cardinals 813
1951 Globe Printing San Jose Red Sox 813
1951 Hage's Dairy 815
1951 Topps Blue Backs 580
1951 Topps Connie Mack's All-Stars 580
1951 Topps Current All-Stars 580
1951 Topps Red Backs 580
1951 Topps Teams 580
1951 Vancouver Capilanos Popcorn Issue 831
1951 Wheaties 799
1952 Berk Ross 23
1952 Bowman 29
1952 Coca-Cola Playing Tips 61
1952 Coca-Cola Playing Tips Test Cards 61
1952 Dixie Lids 89
1952 Dixie Lids Premiums 89
1952 Globe Printing Co. Miami Beach Flamingos 814
1952 Globe Printing Columbus Cardinals 814
1952 Globe Printing Oshkosh Giants 814
1952 Globe Printing San Diego Padres 814
1952 Globe Printing Ventura Braves 814
1952 Knowles Service Stations Stockton Ports 818
1952 Laval Dairy Provincial League 818
1952 Mother's Cookies 819
1952 National Tea Labels 356
1952 Num Num Cleveland Indians 363
1952 Parkhurst 825
1952 Red Man Tobacco 484
1952 Royal Desserts 487
1952 Star-Cal Decals - Type 1 556
1952 Star-Cal Decals - Type 2 556
1952 Tip Top Bread Labels 579
1952 Topps 581
1952 Vancouver Capilanos Popcorn Issue 831
1952 Wheaties 799
1953 - 55 Dormand Postcards 146
1953 Bowman Black & White 31
1953 Bowman Color 30
1953 Canadian Exhibits 160
1953 Dixie Lids 89
1953 Dixie Lids Premiums 89
1953 Glendale Hot Dogs Tigers 245

1953 Hunter Wieners Cardinals 261
1953 Johnston Cookies Braves....... 275
1953 Mother's Cookies 819
1953 Northland Bread Labels.......... 361
1953 Red Man Tobacco 484
1953 Spic and Span Braves............ 532
1953 Spic and Span Braves 7x10 Photos 532
1953 Stahl-Meyer Franks 550
1953 Team Issue San Francisco Seals 827
1953 Topps 582
1953 Vancouver Capilanos Popcorn Issue 831
1954 Bowman 31
1954 Briggs Meats 44
1954 Dan-Dee Potato Chips 84
1954 Dixie Lids 90
1954 Esskay Hot Dogs Orioles........ 153
1954 Hunter Wieners Cardinals 262
1954 Johnston Cookies Braves....... 275
1954 MD Super Service Sacramento Solons 818
1954 N.Y. Journal-American 360
1954 Red Heart Dog Food 483
1954 Red Man Tobacco 484
1954 Seattle Popcorn Seattle Rainiers 827
1954 Spic and Span Braves............ 533
1954 Stahl-Meyer Franks 550
1954 Topps 583
1954 Vancouver Capilanos Popcorn Issue 831
1954 Wilson Franks 800
1955 - 60 Bill and Bob Braves Postcards 25
1955 Armour Coins 10
1955 Bowman 32
1955 Carling Beer Cleveland Indians 49
1955 Esskay Hot Dogs Orioles........ 153
1955 Hunter Wieners Cardinals 262
1955 Johnston Cookies Braves....... 275
1955 Kahn's Wieners Reds 278
1955 Old Homestead Franks Des Moines Bruins 822
1955 Rawlings Stan Musial 482
1955 Red Man Tobacco 484
1955 Robert Gould All Stars............ 250
1955 Rodeo Meats Athletics........... 486
1955 Seattle Popcorn Seattle Rainiers 827
1955 Spic and Span Braves Die-cuts 533
1955 Stahl-Meyer Franks 550
1955 Topps 584
1955 Topps Doubleheaders 584
1955 Topps Test Stamps 585
1956 Big League Stars Statues......... 24
1956 Carling Beer Cleveland Indians 49
1956 Kahn's Wieners Reds 278
1956 PM15 Yellow Basepath Pins .. 427
1956 Rodeo Meats Athletics........... 487
1956 Seattle Popcorn Seattle Rainiers 827
1956 Topps 585
1956 Topps Hocus Focus Large 586
1956 Topps Hocus Focus Small...... 586
1956 Topps Pins 587
1957 Carling Beer Cleveland Indians 49
1957 Golden State Dairy S.F. Seals Stickers 814
1957 Hygrade Meats Seattle Rainiers 817
1957 Kahn's Wieners 278
1957 Seattle Popcorn Seattle Rainiers 827
1957 Sohio Gas Indians/Reds........ 532
1957 Spic and Span Braves 533
1957 Swift Meats 562
1957 Topps 587
1958 Bell Brand Dodgers 21
1958 Bond Bread Buffalo Bisons 810
1958 Carling Beer Cleveland Indians 50
1958 Hires Root Beer 254
1958 Hires Root Beer Test Set........ 254
1958 Jay Publishing 5x7 Photos Type 1 264
1958 Kahn's Wieners 278
1958 Omaha Cardinals Picture Pak 824
1958 Packard-Bell 440
1958 San Francisco Call-Bulletin Giants 490
1958 Seattle Popcorn Seattle Rainiers 828
1958 Topps 588
1958 Union Oil Sacramento Solons 831
1959 Armour Coins 10
1959 Bazooka 16
1959 Carling Beer Cleveland Indians 50
1959 Darigold Farms Spokane Indians 813
1959 Fleer Ted Williams 164
1959 Home Run Derby 255
1959 Kahn's Wieners 278
1959 Morrell Meats Dodgers.......... 336
1959 Seattle Popcorn Seattle Rainiers 828
1959 Topps 590
1959 Yoo-Hoo 807
1960 Armour Coins 10
1960 Armour Meats Denver Bears 809
1960 Bazooka 16
1960 Bell Brand Dodgers 22
1960 Darigold Farms Spokane Indians 813
1960 Fleer 165
1960 Henry House Wieners Seattle Rainiers 816
1960 Kahn's Wieners 279
1960 Lake To Lake Dairy Braves 299
1960 Leaf 303
1960 MacGregor 322
1960 Morrell Meats Dodgers.......... 336
1960 National Bank Washington/Tacoma Giants 820
1960 Nu-Card 362
1960 Post Cereal 473
1960 Seattle Popcorn Seattle Rainiers 828
1960 Spic and Span Braves 533
1960 Topps 592
1960 Topps Baseball Tattoos.......... 594
1960 Tulsa Oilers 831
1960 Union Oil Seattle Rainiers 831
1961 - 62 Cloverleaf Dairy Minnesota Twins 60
1961 - 62 Fleer 165
1961 Bazooka 17
1961 Bee Hive Starch Toronto Maple Leafs 809
1961 Bell Brand Dodgers 22
1961 Carling Beer Cleveland Indians 50
1961 Exhibits - Wrigley Field........... 159
1961 Golden Press 246
1961 Hawaii Islanders 831
1961 Kahn's Wieners 279
1961 Morrell Meats Dodgers 336
1961 Nu-Card 362
1961 Peters Meats Twins 446
1961 Portland Beavers 831
1961 Post Cereal 473
1961 Sacramento Solons 831
1961 San Diego Padres 831
1961 Seattle Popcorn Seattle Rainiers 828
1961 Spokane Indians 831
1961 Tacoma Giants 831
1961 Topps 594
1961 Topps Dice Game 596
1961 Topps Magic Rub-Offs............ 596
1961 Topps Stamps 597
1961 Union Oil Pacific Coast League 830
1961 Union Oil Taiyo Whales.......... 831
1962 American Tract Society 9
1962 Bazooka 17
1962 Bell Brand Dodgers 22
1962 Ford Detroit Tigers Postcards 240
1962 Jay Publishing 5x7 Photos Type 2 268
1962 Jell-O 272
1962 Kahn's Wieners 279
1962 Kahn's Wieners Atlanta "Crackers" 818
1962 Pepsi-Cola Tulsa Oilers.......... 825
1962 Post Cereal - Canadian 475
1962 Post Cereal 474
1962 Salada-Junket Dessert Coins 489
1962 Seattle Popcorn Seattle Rainiers 828
1962 Statistic Back Exhibits 160
1962 Sugardale Weiners 562
1962 Team Omaha Dodgers 824
1962 Topps 597
1962 Topps Baseball Bucks 599
1962 Topps Stamps 600

1963 Bazooka 17
1963 Bazooka All-Time Greats.......... 18
1963 Fleer 165
1963 French Bauer Milk Caps......... 240
1963 I.D.L. Drug Store Pittsburgh Pirates 263
1963 Jell-O 272
1963 Kahn's Wieners 280
1963 Milwaukee Sausage Seattle Rainiers 818
1963 Pepsi-Cola Colt .45's 442
1963 Pepsi-Cola Tulsa Oilers 825
1963 Post Cereal 475
1963 Salada-Junket Dessert Coins 490
1963 Scheible Press Rochester Red Wings 827
1963 Seattle Popcorn Seattle Rainiers 828
1963 Statistic Back Exhibits 160
1963 Sugardale Weiners 562
1963 Topps 600
1963 Topps Peel-Offs 603
1964 Aurovision Records 10
1964 Bazooka 18
1964 Bazooka Stamps 18
1964 Challenge the Yankees Game 50
1964 Kahn's Wieners 280
1964 Seattle Popcorn Seattle Rainiers 828
1964 Topps 603
1964 Topps Coins 605
1964 Topps Giants 605
1964 Topps Photo Tatoos 606
1964 Topps Stand-Ups 606
1964 True-Aid Buffalo Bisons.......... 830
1965 Bazooka 18
1965 Challenge the Yankees Game 51
1965 Kahn's Wieners 280
1965 MacGregor 322
1965 Old London Coins 425
1965 O-Pee-Chee 383
1965 Seattle Popcorn Seattle Rainiers 828
1965 Topps 606
1965 Topps Embossed 609
1965 Topps Transfers 609
1966 Bazooka 19
1966 East Hills Pirates 152
1966 Fleer 166
1966 Foremost Milk St. Petersburg Cardinals 813
1966 Kahn's Wieners 280
1966 O-Pee-Chee 384
1966 Pepsi-Cola Tulsa Oilers.......... 825
1966 Royal Crown Cola Columbus Yankees 827
1966 Seattle Popcorn Seattle Angels 828
1966 Toledo Mud Hens 830
1966 Topps 609
1966 Topps Rub-Offs 611
1967 Bazooka 19
1967 Kahn's Wieners 280
1967 Laughlin World Series 300
1967 O-Pee-Chee 384
1967 Seattle Popcorn Seattle Angels 828
1967 Topps 612
1967 Topps Pin-Ups 614
1967 Topps Stand-Ups 614
1967 Topps Stickers Pirates............ 614
1967 Topps Stickers Red Sox......... 615
1968 - 69 Partridge Meats Reds...... 442
1968 Bazooka 19
1968 Kahn's Wieners 281
1968 KDKA Pittsburgh Pirates 287
1968 O-Pee-Chee 385
1968 Seattle Popcorn Seattle Angels 829
1968 Topps 3-D 619
1968 Topps 615
1968 Topps Action All-Star Stickers 617
1968 Topps Deckle Edge Test Proofs 617
1968 Topps Discs 617
1968 Topps Game 618
1968 Topps Plaks 618
1968 Topps Posters 618
1968 Topps Punch-outs 618
1969 - 70 Bazooka 20
1969 Citgo Coins 52
1969 Globe Imports 245
1969 Greiner Tires Pittsburgh Pirates 251
1969 Kahn's Wieners 281
1969 Kelly's Potato Chips Pins........ 294
1969 Major League Baseball Photo-stamps 322
1969 Milton Bradley 331
1969 MLBPA Pins 323
1969 N.Y. Boy Scouts 360
1969 Nabisco Team Flakes 352
1969 O-Pee-Chee 386
1969 O-Pee-Chee Deckle 387
1969 Topps 4-On-1 Mini Stickers 622
1969 Topps 619
1969 Topps Decals 621
1969 Topps Deckle Edge 621
1969 Topps Stamps 622
1969 Topps Super 622
1969 Topps Team Posters 623
1969 Transogram 755
1970 - 72 Partridge Meats Reds...... 442
1970 Action Cartridge 1
1970 Carl Aldana Orioles 3
1970 Kellogg's 288
1970 Mac's Wichita Aeros 847
1970 McDonald's Brewers 326
1970 Milton Bradley 332
1970 O-Pee-Chee 387
1970 Pictures of Champions Orioles 447
1970 Police/Fire Safety Senators 461
1970 Rold Gold Pretzels 487
1970 Topps 623
1970 Topps Candy Lids 626
1970 Topps Cloth Stickers 626
1970 Topps Posters 626
1970 Topps Scratch-Offs 626
1970 Topps Story Booklets 626
1970 Topps Super 626
1970 Transogram 756
1970 Transogram Mets 756
1971 Allstate Insurance 4
1971 Bazooka Numbered Set 20
1971 Bazooka Unnumbered Set 20
1971 Currie Press Richmond Braves 847
1971 Jeff Morey Syracuse Chiefs.... 847
1971 Kellogg's 289
1971 Milk Duds 330
1971 O-Pee-Chee 389
1971 Police/Fire Safety Senators 461
1971 Topps 627
1971 Topps Baseball Tattoos.......... 630
1971 Topps Coins 629
1971 Topps Greatest Moments....... 630
1971 Topps Super 630
1972 Daily Juice Co. 84
1972 Fleer Famous Feats 166
1972 Kellogg's 289
1972 Kellogg's All-Time Baseball Greats 290
1972 Laughlin Great Feats 300
1972 Milton Bradley 332
1972 O-Pee-Chee 391
1972 Puerto Rican League Stickers 478
1972 TCMA Cedar Rapids Cardinals 847
1972 Team Seattle Rainiers 847
1972 Team Tacoma Twins 847
1972 Topps 631
1972 Topps Cloth Stickers 633
1972 Topps Posters 633
1973 Caruso Tacoma Twins 847
1973 Fleer Wildest Days and Plays 166
1973 Jewel Food Baseball Photos .. 273
1973 Johnny Pro Orioles 274
1973 Johnny Pro Phillies 275
1973 Kansas State Bank Wichita Aeros 847
1973 Kellogg's 290
1973 O-Pee-Chee 393
1973 O-Pee-Chee Team Checklists 395
1973 TCMA Cedar Rapids Astros 847
1973 Team Sherbrooke Pirates....... 847
1973 Team Syracuse Chiefs 847
1973 Topps 1953 Reprints 637
1973 Topps 634
1973 Topps Candy Lids 637
1973 Topps Comics 637
1973 Topps Pin-Ups 637
1973 Topps Team Checklists 637
1974 Caruso Albuquerque Dukes 847
1974 Caruso Hawaii Islanders......... 848
1974 Caruso Phoenix Giants........... 848
1974 Caruso Sacramento Solons 848
1974 Caruso Salt Lake City Angels 848
1974 Caruso Spokane Indians 848

1974 Caruso Tacoma Twins 848
1974 Dukes Team 848
1974 Falstaff Beer Omaha Royals 848
1974 Fleer Baseball Firsts 166
1974 Kellogg's 290
1974 Laughlin Old-Time Black Stars 301
1974 Laughlin Sportslang 301
1974 Laughlin All-Star Games.......... 300
1974 McDonalds Padres Discs 326
1974 One Day Film Wichita Aeros 849
1974 O-Pee-Chee 395
1974 O-Pee-Chee Team Checklists 397
1974 TCMA Cedar Rapids Astros 848
1974 TCMA Gastonia Rangers 848
1974 Team Seattle Rainiers 848
1974 Team Syracuse Chiefs 848
1974 Topps 638
1974 Topps Deckle Edge 640
1974 Topps Puzzles 640
1974 Topps Stamps 640
1974 Topps Team Checklists 641
1974 Topps Traded 641
1974 Weston Expos 795
1975 7-11 Tulsa Oliers 851
1975 Caruso Albuquerque Dukes ... 849
1975 Caruso Hawaii Islanders.......... 850
1975 Caruso Phoenix Giants.......... 850
1975 Caruso Sacramento Solons.... 850
1975 Caruso Salt Lake City Gulls.... 850
1975 Caruso Spokane Indians 851
1975 Caruso Tucson Toros 851
1975 Circle K Foods Phoenix Giants 850
1975 Fleer Pioneers of Baseball 167
1975 Hostess 256
1975 Hostess Twinkies 256
1975 Kellogg's 290
1975 KMO Radio Tacoma Twins..... 851
1975 Laughlin Batty Baseball 301
1975 O-Pee-Chee 397
1975 SSPC 548
1975 Stewart Sandwiches Tidewater Tides 851
1975 Sussman Ft. Lauderdale Yankees 849
1975 Sussman West Palm Beach Expos 852
1975 TCMA Anderson Rangers 849
1975 TCMA Appleton Foxes 849
1975 TCMA Burlington Bees 849
1975 TCMA Cedar Rapids Giants ... 849
1975 TCMA Clinton Pilots 849
1975 TCMA Dubuque Packers 849
1975 TCMA International League.... 850
1975 TCMA Iowa Oaks 850
1975 TCMA Lafayette Drillers 850
1975 TCMA Lynchburg Rangers..... 850
1975 TCMA Quad City Angels 850
1975 TCMA San Antonio Brewers 851
1975 TCMA Shreveport Captains 851
1975 TCMA Waterbury Dodgers..... 851
1975 TCMA Waterloo Royals 851
1975 Team Oklahoma City 89'ers ... 850
1975 Team Syracuse Chiefs 851
1975 Team Tucson Toros 851
1975 Top Trophies Omaha Royals.. 850
1975 Topps 641
1975 Topps Mini 643
1976 A & P Brewers 1
1976 Caruso Hawaii Islanders.......... 853
1976 Caruso Phoenix Giants.......... 853
1976 Caruso Sacramento Solons.... 854
1976 Caruso Salt Lake City Gulls.... 854
1976 Caruso Spokane Indians 854
1976 Caruso Tucson Toros 854
1976 Coke Phoenix Giants 853
1976 Cramer Phoenix Giants 853
1976 Cramer Seattle Rainiers 854
1976 Cramer Tucson Toros 854
1976 Crane Potato Chips 81
1976 Dairy Queen Tacoma Twins ... 854
1976 Goof's Pants Tulsa Oilers 854
1976 Hostess 257
1976 Hostess Twinkies 257
1976 Icee Drinks Reds 262
1976 Kellogg's 291
1976 Knowlton's San Antonio Brewers 854
1976 Laughlin Diamond Jubilee 301
1976 Laughlin Indianapolis Clowns. 301
1976 Linnett Superstars 319
1976 O-Pee-Chee 400
1976 Playboy Press Who Was Harry Steinfeldt? 459
1976 Sussman Ft. Lauderdale Yankees 853
1976 TCMA Appleton Foxes 852
1976 TCMA Arkansas Travelers 852
1976 TCMA Asheville Tourists 852
1976 TCMA Baton Rouge Cougars. 852
1976 TCMA Burlington Bees 852
1976 TCMA Cedar Rapids Giants ... 852
1976 TCMA Clinton Pilots 852
1976 TCMA Dubuque Packers 852
1976 TCMA Quad City Angels 853
1976 TCMA Shreveport Captains.... 854
1976 TCMA Waterloo Royals 854
1976 TCMA Wausau Mets 854
1976 TCMA Williamsport Tomahawks 855
1976 Team Batavia Trojans 852
1976 Team Indianapolis Indians.......... 853
1976 Team Oklahoma City 89'ers ... 853
1976 Top Trophies Omaha Royals.. 853
1976 Topps 646
1976 Topps Traded 648
1976 Valley Nat'l Bank Phoenix Giants 853
1977 - 79 Sportscaster 533
1977 Burger King Yankees 44
1977 Caruso Hawaii Islanders.......... 856
1977 Chong Hawaii Islanders.......... 856
1977 Chong Modesto A's 856
1977 Coke Premium Phoenix Giants 857
1977 Cramer Phoenix Giants 857
1977 Cramer Salt Lake City Gulls ... 858
1977 Cramer Spokane Indians 858
1977 Cramer Tucson Toros 858
1977 Dairy Queen Tacoma Twins ... 858
1977 Hostess 258
1977 Hostess Twinkies 258
1977 Kellogg's 291
1977 McCurdy's Rochester Red Wings 857
1977 Mr. Chef's San Jose Missions 858
1977 O-Pee-Chee 402
1977 Pepsi-Cola Baseball Stars 443
1977 Redpath Sugar Expos 485
1977 Sussman Ft. Lauderdale Yankees 856
1977 TCMA Appleton Foxes 855
1977 TCMA Arkansas Travelers 855
1977 TCMA Asheville Tourists 855
1977 TCMA Bristol Red Sox.......... 855
1977 TCMA Burlington Bees 855
1977 TCMA Cedar Rapids Giants ... 855
1977 TCMA Charleston Patriots 855
1977 TCMA Clinton Dodgers.......... 855
1977 TCMA Cocoa Astros 855
1977 TCMA Columbus Clippers 855
1977 TCMA Daytona Beach Islanders 856
1977 TCMA Evansville Triplets 856
1977 TCMA Holyoke Millers 856
1977 TCMA Jacksonville Suns 856
1977 TCMA Lodi Dodgers 856
1977 TCMA Lynchburg Mets 856
1977 TCMA Newark Co-Pilots 857
1977 TCMA Orlando Twins 857
1977 TCMA Quad City Angels 857
1977 TCMA Reading Phillies 857
1977 TCMA Salem Pirates 857
1977 TCMA Shreveport Captains.... 858
1977 TCMA Spartanburg Phillies 858
1977 TCMA St. Petersburg Cardinals 857
1977 TCMA Visalia Oaks 858
1977 TCMA Waterloo Indians 858
1977 TCMA Wausau Mets 858
1977 TCMA West Haven Yankees.. 858
1977 Team Indianapolis Indians.......... 856
1977 Top Trophies Omaha Royals.. 857
1977 Topps 648
1977 Topps Cloth Stickers 650
1977 Valley Nat'l Bank Phoenix Giants 857
1978 Brittling's Memphis Chicks 860
1978 Burger King Astros 44
1978 Burger King Rangers 45
1978 Burger King Tigers 45
1978 Burger King Yankees 45
1978 Chong Modesto A's 860
1978 Cramer Albuquerque Dukes ... 859
1978 Cramer Phoenix Giants 861
1978 Cramer Salt Lake City Gulls ... 861
1978 Cramer Spokane Indians 861
1978 Cramer Tacoma Yankees 862

1978 Cramer Tucson Toros 862
1978 Hostess 259
1978 Kellogg's 291
1978 Laughlin Long Ago Black Stars 302
1978 Mr. Chef's San Jose Missions 861
1978 O-Pee-Chee 403
1978 Pepsi-Cola Superstars............ 443
1978 Richard West Springfield Cardinals 861
1978 Richard West Springfield Redbirds 865
1978 TCMA Appleton Foxes 859
1978 TCMA Arkansas Travelers 859
1978 TCMA Asheville Tourists........ 859
1978 TCMA Burlington Bees 859
1978 TCMA Cedar Rapids Giants .. 859
1978 TCMA Charleston Charlies 859
1978 TCMA Charleston Pirates 859
1978 TCMA Clinton Dodgers 859
1978 TCMA Columbus Clippers 859
1978 TCMA Daytona Beach Astros 859
1978 TCMA Dunedin Blue Jays 860
1978 TCMA Greenwood Braves 860
1978 TCMA Holyoke Millers 860
1978 TCMA Knoxville Knox Sox 860
1978 TCMA Lodi Dodgers 860
1978 TCMA Newark Wayne Co-Pilots 860
1978 TCMA Orlando Twins 861
1978 TCMA Quad City Angels 861
1978 TCMA Richmond Braves 861
1978 TCMA Rochester Red Wings 861
1978 TCMA Salem Pirates 861
1978 TCMA St. Petersburg Cardinals 861
1978 TCMA Syracuse Chiefs 862
1978 TCMA Tidewater Tides 862
1978 TCMA Waterloo Indians 862
1978 TCMA Wausau Mets 862
1978 TCMA Wisconsin Rapids Twins 862
1978 Team Geneva Cubs 860
1978 Team Indianapolis Indians 860
1978 Team Oklahoma City 89'ers .. 861
1978 Team Oklahoma City 89'ers .. 864
1978 Tiefel & Associates Denver Bears 859
1978 Topps 650
1978 Zest Soap 808
1979 Burger King Phillies 45
1979 Burger King Yankees 45
1979 Chong Modesto A's 864
1979 Cramer 1970s P.C.L. All-Stars 864
1979 Cramer Hawaii Islanders 863
1979 Cramer Phoenix Giants 865
1979 Hostess 260
1979 Kellogg's 292
1979 O-Pee-Chee 403
1979 Police Iowa Oaks 864
1979 Police/Fire Safety Giants 461
1979 TCMA Albuquerque Dukes 862
1979 TCMA Appleton Foxes 862
1979 TCMA Arkansas Travelers 862
1979 TCMA Asheville Tourists 862
1979 TCMA Buffalo Bisons 863
1979 TCMA Burlington Bees 863
1979 TCMA Cedar Rapids Giants .. 863
1979 TCMA Charleston Charlies 863
1979 TCMA Clinton Dodgers 863
1979 TCMA Columbus Clippers 863
1979 TCMA Elmira Pioneers 863
1979 TCMA Hawaii Islanders 863
1979 TCMA Holyoke Millers 863
1979 TCMA Jackson Mets 864
1979 TCMA Knoxville White Sox 864
1979 TCMA Lodi Dodgers 864
1979 TCMA Memphis Chicks 864
1979 TCMA Newark Co-Pilots 864
1979 TCMA Ogden A's 864
1979 TCMA Portland Beavers 865
1979 TCMA Quad City Cubs 865
1979 TCMA Richmond Braves 865
1979 TCMA Rochester Red Wings 865
1979 TCMA Salt Lake City Gulls 865
1979 TCMA Savannah Braves 865
1979 TCMA Spokane Indians 865
1979 TCMA Syracuse Chiefs 866
1979 TCMA Tacoma Tugs 866
1979 TCMA Tidewater Tides 866
1979 TCMA Toledo Mud Hens 866
1979 TCMA Tucson Toros 866
1979 TCMA Tulsa Drillers 866
1979 TCMA Vancouver Canadians 866
1979 TCMA Waterbury A's 866
1979 TCMA Waterloo Indians 866
1979 TCMA Wausau Timbers 866
1979 TCMA West Haven Yankees . 866
1979 TCMA Wisconsin Rapids Twins 866
1979 Team Indianapolis Indians 863
1979 Team Nashville Sounds 864
1979 Team Syracuse Chiefs 866
1979 Topps 653
1979 Topps Comics 655
1979 University Volkswagen Albuquerque Dukes 862
1980 - 83 Cramer Baseball Legends. 80
1980 Burger King Phillies 46
1980 Burger King Pitch, Hit & Run ... 46
1980 Chong Modesto A's 869
1980 Jack In The Box San Jose Missions 871
1980 Kellogg's 292
1980 Laughlin 300/400/500 302
1980 Laughlin Famous Feats 302
1980 O-Pee-Chee 405
1980 Police Iowa Oaks 869
1980 Police/Fire Safety Columbus Clippers 868
1980 Police/Fire Safety Dodgers 461
1980 Police/Fire Safety Giants 461
1980 TCMA Albuquerque Dukes 867
1980 TCMA Anderson Braves 867
1980 TCMA Appleton Foxes 867
1980 TCMA Arkansas Travelers 867
1980 TCMA Asheville Tourists 867
1980 TCMA Batavia Trojans 867
1980 TCMA Buffalo Bisons 867
1980 TCMA Burlington Bees 867
1980 TCMA Cedar Rapids Reds 867
1980 TCMA Charleston Charlies 867
1980 TCMA Clinton Giants 868
1980 TCMA Columbus Astros 868
1980 TCMA Columbus Clippers 868
1980 TCMA El Paso Diablos 868
1980 TCMA Elmira Pioneers 868
1980 TCMA Evansville Triplets 868
1980 TCMA Glens Falls White Sox 868
1980 TCMA Glens Falls White Sox 868
1980 TCMA Hawaii Islanders 869
1980 TCMA Holyoke Millers 869
1980 TCMA Knoxville Blue Jays 869
1980 TCMA Lynn Sailors 869
1980 TCMA Memphis Chicks 869
1980 TCMA Ogden A's 869
1980 TCMA Orlando Twins 870
1980 TCMA Peninsula Pilots 870
1980 TCMA Peninsula Pilots 870
1980 TCMA Portland Beavers 870
1980 TCMA Quad Cities Cubs 870
1980 TCMA Reading Phillies 870
1980 TCMA Richmond Braves 870
1980 TCMA Rochester Red Wings 870
1980 TCMA Salt Lake City Gulls 870
1980 TCMA Spokane Indians 871
1980 TCMA Syracuse Chiefs 871
1980 TCMA Tacoma Tigers 871
1980 TCMA Tidewater Tides 871
1980 TCMA Toledo Mud Hens 871
1980 TCMA Tucson Toros 871
1980 TCMA Tulsa Drillers 871
1980 TCMA Utica Blue Jays 871
1980 TCMA Vancouver Canadians 871
1980 TCMA Waterbury Reds 871
1980 TCMA Waterloo Indians 871
1980 TCMA Wausau Timbers 872
1980 TCMA West Haven White Caps 872
1980 TCMA Wichita Aeros 872
1980 TCMA Wisconsin Rapids Twins 872
1980 Team Charlotte O's 867
1980 Team Columbus Clippers 868
1980 Team Indianapolis Indians 869
1980 Team Nashville Sounds 869
1980 Team Oklahoma City 89'ers .. 869
1980 Team Omaha Royals 870
1980 Team Syracuse Chiefs 871
1980 Topps 655
1980 Topps Superstar 5x7 Photos 657
1980 Valley Nat'l Bank Phoenix Giants 870
1980 WBTV Charlotte O's 867
1981 Arby's Nashville Sounds 874
1981 Chong Modesto A's 874
1981 Coca-Cola 61
1981 Donruss 90

1981 Drake's 148
1981 Fleer 167
1981 Fleer Star Stickers 169
1981 Granny Goose Potato Chips A's 251
1981 Kellogg's 293
1981 O-Pee-Chee 406
1981 O-Pee-Chee Posters 407
1981 Perma-Graphics All-Star Credit Cards 444
1981 Perma-Graphics Super Star Credit Cards 444
1981 Police Columbus Clippers 873
1981 Police/Fire Safety Braves 462
1981 Police/Fire Safety Dodgers 462
1981 Police/Fire Safety Mariners ... 462
1981 Police/Fire Safety Royals 462
1981 Red Rooster Edmonton Trappers 873
1981 Sporting News Conlon Collection 545
1981 Spot-bilt George Brett 547
1981 Squirt 547
1981 TCMA Albuquerque Dukes 872
1981 TCMA Appleton Foxes 872
1981 TCMA Arkansas Travelers 872
1981 TCMA Batavia Trojans 872
1981 TCMA Birmingham Barons 872
1981 TCMA Bristol Red Sox 872
1981 TCMA Buffalo Bisons 872
1981 TCMA Burlington Bees 873
1981 TCMA Cedar Rapids Reds 873
1981 TCMA Charleston Charlies 873
1981 TCMA Charleston Royals 873
1981 TCMA Chattanooga Lookouts 873
1981 TCMA Clinton Giants 873
1981 TCMA Columbus Clippers 873
1981 TCMA Durham Bulls 873
1981 TCMA El Paso Diablos 873
1981 TCMA Evansville Triplets 874
1981 TCMA Glens Falls White Sox 874
1981 TCMA Hawaii Islanders 874
1981 TCMA Holyoke Millers 874
1981 TCMA Lynn Sailors 874
1981 TCMA Miami Orioles 874
1981 TCMA Oklahoma City 89'ers 874
1981 TCMA Omaha Royals 875
1981 TCMA Pawtucket Red Sox 875
1981 TCMA Portland Beavers 875
1981 TCMA Quad City Cubs 875
1981 TCMA Reading Phillies 875
1981 TCMA Redwood Pioneers 875
1981 TCMA Richmond Braves 875
1981 TCMA Rochester Red Wings 875
1981 TCMA Salt Lake City Gulls 875
1981 TCMA Shreveport Captains ... 875
1981 TCMA Spokane Indians 876
1981 TCMA Syracuse Chiefs 876
1981 TCMA Tacoma Tigers 876
1981 TCMA Tidewater Tides 876
1981 TCMA Toledo Mud Hens 876
1981 TCMA Tucson Toros 876
1981 TCMA Tulsa Drillers 876
1981 TCMA Vancouver Canadians 876
1981 TCMA Vero Beach Dodgers .. 876
1981 TCMA Waterbury Reds 876
1981 TCMA Waterloo Indians 876
1981 TCMA Wausau Timbers 877
1981 TCMA West Haven A's 877
1981 TCMA Wisconsin Rapids Twins 877
1981 Team Charlotte O's 873
1981 Team Holyoke Millers 874
1981 Team Indianapolis Indians 874
1981 Team Syracuse Chiefs 876
1981 Topps 658
1981 Topps Home Team 5x7 Photos 660
1981 Topps National 5x7 Photos ... 661
1981 Topps Scratchoffs 661
1981 Topps Stickers 661
1981 Topps Traded 660
1981 Valley Nat'l Bank Phoenix Giants 875
1981 WTF Co. Rochester Red Wings 875
1982 Arby's Nashville Sounds 880
1982 Burger King Braves 46
1982 Burger King Indians 46
1982 Chong Modesto A's 880
1982 Coca-Cola Brigham's Red Sox 61
1982 Coca-Cola Reds 62
1982 Cracker Jack 79
1982 Donruss 92
1982 Drake's 148
1982 Ehrler's Dairy Louisville Redbirds 880
1982 Fleer 170
1982 Fleer Stamps 172
1982 Fritsch Appleton Foxes 877
1982 Fritsch Beloit Brewers 877
1982 Fritsch Burlington Rangers 878
1982 Fritsch Clinton Giants 878
1982 Fritsch Danville Suns 878
1982 Fritsch Madison Muskies 880
1982 Fritsch Springfield Cardinals .. 882
1982 Fritsch Waterloo Indians 883
1982 Fritsch Wausau Timbers 883
1982 Fritsch Wisconsin Rapids Twins 883
1982 Granny Goose Potato Chips A's 251
1982 Granny Goose Signature Set 251
1982 Hygrade Expos 262
1982 Kellogg's 293
1982 K-Mart 276
1982 O-Pee-Chee 407
1982 O-Pee-Chee Posters 408
1982 Perma-Graphics All-Star Credit Cards 445
1982 Perma-Graphics Super Star Credit Cards 445
1982 Police Columbus Clippers 878
1982 Police/Fire Safety Braves 462
1982 Police/Fire Safety Brewers 463
1982 Police/Fire Safety Dodgers 463
1982 Red Lobster Cubs 483
1982 Squirt 548
1982 TCMA Albuquerque Dukes 877
1982 TCMA Alexandria Dukes 877
1982 TCMA Amarillo Gold Sox 877
1982 TCMA Arkansas Travelers 877
1982 TCMA Auburn Astros 877
1982 TCMA Birmingham Barons 877
1982 TCMA Buffalo Bisons 878
1982 TCMA Burlington Rangers 878
1982 TCMA Cedar Rapids Reds 878
1982 TCMA Charleston Charlies 878
1982 TCMA Charleston Royals 878
1982 TCMA Chattanooga Lookouts 878
1982 TCMA Columbus Clippers 878
1982 TCMA Daytona Beach Astros 879
1982 TCMA Durham Bulls 879
1982 TCMA Edmonton Trappers 879
1982 TCMA El Paso Diablos 879
1982 TCMA Evansville Triplets 879
1982 TCMA Fort Myers Royals 879
1982 TCMA Glens Falls White Sox 879
1982 TCMA Hawaii Islanders 879
1982 TCMA Holyoke Millers 879
1982 TCMA Idaho Falls Athletics ... 879
1982 TCMA Iowa Cubs 880
1982 TCMA Jackson Mets 880
1982 TCMA Knoxville Blue Jays 880
1982 TCMA Lynchburg Mets 880
1982 TCMA Lynn Sailors 880
1982 TCMA Miami Marlins 880
1982 TCMA Oklahoma City 89'ers 881
1982 TCMA Omaha Royals 881
1982 TCMA Oneonta Yankees 881
1982 TCMA Orlando Twins 881
1982 TCMA Orlando Twins Southern League Champs 881
1982 TCMA Portland Beavers 881
1982 TCMA Quad City Cubs 881
1982 TCMA Reading Phillies 881
1982 TCMA Redwood Pioneers 881
1982 TCMA Richmond Braves 881
1982 TCMA Rochester Red Wings 881
1982 TCMA Salt Lake City Gulls 882
1982 TCMA Spokane Indians 882
1982 TCMA Syracuse Chiefs 882
1982 TCMA Tacoma Tigers 882
1982 TCMA Tidewater Tides 882
1982 TCMA Toledo Mud Hens 882
1982 TCMA Tucson Toros 882
1982 TCMA Tulsa Drillers 882
1982 TCMA Vancouver Canadians 882
1982 TCMA Vero Beach Dodgers .. 883
1982 TCMA Waterbury Reds 883
1982 TCMA Waterloo Indians 883
1982 TCMA West Haven A's 883
1982 Team Charlotte O's Heroes Aren't Hard 878
1982 Team Holyoke Millers 879
1982 Team Indianapolis Indians 879
1982 Team Syracuse Chiefs 882
1982 Team Wichita Aeros 883

1982 Topps 662
1982 Topps Insert Stickers 665
1982 Topps Stickers 666
1982 Topps Traded 665
1982 Valley Nat'l Bank Phoenix Giants 881
1982 Wheaties Indians 799
1982 Zellers Expos 808
1983 7-11 Slurpee Coins 523
1983 Affiliated Food Rangers 2
1983 Barry Colla San Jose Bees 888
1983 BHN Las Vegas Stars 886
1983 BHN Phoenix Giants 888
1983 Chong Modesto A's 887
1983 Dog-N-Shake Wichita Aeroes 890
1983 Donruss 94
1983 Donruss Action All-Stars 97
1983 Donruss Hall of Fame Heroes 97
1983 Drake's 148
1983 Fleer 173
1983 Fleer Stamps 175
1983 Fleer Stickers 175
1983 Fritsch Appleton Foxes 884
1983 Fritsch Beloit Brewers 884
1983 Fritsch Burlington Rangers 884
1983 Fritsch Cedar Rapids Reds ... 884
1983 Fritsch Clinton Giants 885
1983 Fritsch Madison Muskies 886
1983 Fritsch Peoria Suns 887
1983 Fritsch Springfield Cardinals 888
1983 Fritsch Visalia Oaks 889
1983 Fritsch Waterloo Indians 889
1983 Fritsch Wausau Timbers 890
1983 Fritsch Wisconsin Rapids Twins 890
1983 Gardner's Brewers 242
1983 Granny Goose Potato Chips A's 251
1983 Kellogg's 293
1983 Kelly Studios Kinston Blue Jays 886
1983 Minnesota Twins Team Issue 334
1983 Mother's Cookies Giants 336
1983 Mr. Z's Milwaukee Brewers ... 352
1983 Nalley Potato Chips Mariners 354
1983 O-Pee-Chee 409
1983 Perma-Graphics All-Star Credit Cards 445
1983 Perma-Graphics Super Star Credit Cards 445
1983 Police/Fire Safety Braves 463
1983 Police/Fire Safety Brewers 463
1983 Police/Fire Safety Dodgers 464
1983 Police/Fire Safety Royals 464
1983 Riley's Louisville Redbirds 886
1983 Star Co. Mike Schmidt 551
1983 Stuart Expos 557
1983 TCMA Albany-Colonie A's 883
1983 TCMA Albuquerque Dukes 883
1983 TCMA Alexandria Dukes 883
1983 TCMA Anderson Braves 883
1983 TCMA Arkansas Travelers 884
1983 TCMA Beaumont Golden Gators 884
1983 TCMA Birmingham Barons 884
1983 TCMA Buffalo Bisons 884
1983 TCMA Burlington Rangers 884
1983 TCMA Butte Copper Kings 884
1983 TCMA Cedar Rapids Reds 884
1983 TCMA Charleston Charlies 885
1983 TCMA Charleston Royals 885
1983 TCMA Chattanooga Lookouts 885
1983 TCMA Columbus Astros 885
1983 TCMA Columbus Clippers 885
1983 TCMA Daytona Beach Astros 885
1983 TCMA Durham Bulls 885
1983 TCMA El Paso Diablos 885
1983 TCMA Erie Cardinals 885
1983 TCMA Evansville Triplets 885
1983 TCMA Glens Falls White Sox 885
1983 TCMA Greensboro Hornets ... 885
1983 TCMA Idaho Falls Athletics ... 886
1983 TCMA Iowa Cubs 886
1983 TCMA Knoxville Blue Jays 886
1983 TCMA Lynchburg Mets 886
1983 TCMA Lynn Pirates 886
1983 TCMA Memphis Chicks 887
1983 TCMA Miami Marlins 887
1983 TCMA Midland Cubs 887
1983 TCMA Nashua Angels 887
1983 TCMA Oklahoma City 89'ers 887
1983 TCMA Omaha Royals 887
1983 TCMA Orlando Twins 887
1983 TCMA Pawtucket Red Sox 887
1983 TCMA Portland Beavers 888
1983 TCMA Quad City Cubs 888
1983 TCMA Reading Phillies 888
1983 TCMA Redwood Pioneers 888
1983 TCMA Richmond Braves 888
1983 TCMA Rochester Redwings .. 888
1983 TCMA Salt Lake City Gulls 888
1983 TCMA St. Petersburg Cardinals 888
1983 TCMA Syracuse Chiefs 888
1983 TCMA Tacoma Tigers 889
1983 TCMA Tampa Tarpons 889
1983 TCMA Tidewater Tides 889
1983 TCMA Toledo Mud Hens 889
1983 TCMA Tri-Cities Triplets 889
1983 TCMA Tucson Toros 889
1983 TCMA Tulsa Drillers 889
1983 TCMA Vero Beach Dodgers .. 889
1983 TCMA Waterbury Reds 889
1983 Team Indianapolis Indians 886
1983 Team Nashville Sounds 887
1983 Thorn Apple Valley Cubs 578
1983 Topps 667
1983 Topps All-Star Glossy Set of 40 669
1983 Topps Foldouts 670
1983 Topps Stickers 670
1983 Topps Stickers Boxes 671
1983 Topps Traded 669
1983 True Value White Sox 756
1983 Wheaties Indians 799
1984 1st Base Sports Shreveport Captains 894
1984 7-11 Slurpee Coins Central Region 523
1984 7-11 Slurpee Coins Eastern Region 523
1984 7-11 Slurpee Coins Western Region 523
1984 7-Up Cubs 526
1984 Borden's Reds Stickers 26
1984 Chong Modesto A's 893
1984 Cramer Albuquerque Dukes .. 890
1984 Cramer Edmonton Trappers .. 891
1984 Cramer Everett Giants 891
1984 Cramer Hawaii Islanders 892
1984 Cramer Las Vegas Stars 892
1984 Cramer Phoenix Giants 893
1984 Cramer Portland Beavers 893
1984 Cramer Salt Lake City Gulls .. 894
1984 Cramer Tacoma Tigers 894
1984 Cramer Tucson Toros 894
1984 Cramer Vancouver Canadians 895
1984 Donruss 97
1984 Donruss Action All-Stars 99
1984 Donruss Champions 100
1984 Drake's 148
1984 Fleer 176
1984 Fleer Stickers 178
1984 Fleer Update 178
1984 Forestry Jackson Mets 892
1984 Gardner's Brewers 243
1984 Jarvis Press Rangers 264
1984 Jewel Food Chicago Cubs 274
1984 Milton Bradley 334
1984 Minnesota Twins Team Issue 335
1984 Mother's Cookies Astros 336
1984 Mother's Cookies Athletics 337
1984 Mother's Cookies Giants 337
1984 Mother's Cookies Mariners 337
1984 Mother's Cookies Padres 337
1984 Mr. Z's Milwaukee Brewers ... 352
1984 N.Y. Mets M.V.P. Club 360
1984 Nestle 357
1984 Nestle Dream Team 359
1984 O-Pee-Chee 410
1984 Pizza Hut Greenville Braves .. 891
1984 Police/Fire Safety Blue Jays .. 464
1984 Police/Fire Safety Braves 464
1984 Police/Fire Safety Brewers 464
1984 Police/Fire Safety Columbus Clippers 891
1984 Police/Fire Safety Dodgers 465
1984 Ralston Purina 482
1984 Riley's Louisville Redbirds 892
1984 Rock's Dugout Wichita Aeros 895
1984 Smokey Bear Angels 526
1984 Smokey Bear Dodgers 527
1984 Smokey Bear Jackson Mets In Majors 527
1984 Smokey Bear Padres 527
1984 Sporting News Conlon Collection 545
1984 Star Co. Carl Yastrzemski 551

1984 Star Co. Darryl Strawberry 551
1984 Star Co. George Brett 551
1984 Star Co. Steve Carlton 551
1984 Star Co. Steve Garvey 551
1984 Stuart Expos 557
1984 T&J SC Madison Muskies 892
1984 Tastykake Phillies 574
1984 TCMA Albany-Colonie A'S 890
1984 TCMA Arkansas Travelers 890
1984 TCMA Beaumont Golden Gators 890
1984 TCMA Buffalo Bisons 890
1984 TCMA Butte Copper Kings 890
1984 TCMA Cedar Rapids Reds 890
1984 TCMA Charlotte O'S 890
1984 TCMA Chattanooga Lookouts 890
1984 TCMA Columbus Clippers 891
1984 TCMA Durham Bulls 891
1984 TCMA El Paso Diablos 891
1984 TCMA Evansville Triplets 891
1984 TCMA Greensboro Hornets ... 891
1984 TCMA Iowa Cubs 892
1984 TCMA Jackson Mets 892
1984 TCMA Little Falls Mets 892
1984 TCMA Maine Guides 893
1984 TCMA Memphis Chicks 893
1984 TCMA Midland Cubs 893
1984 TCMA Newark Orioles 893
1984 TCMA Oklahoma City 89'ers 893
1984 TCMA Omaha Royals 893
1984 TCMA Pawtucket Red Sox 893
1984 TCMA Prince William Pirates 894
1984 TCMA Richmond Braves 894
1984 TCMA Rochester Red Wings 894
1984 TCMA Savannah Cardinals ... 894
1984 TCMA Syracuse Chiefs 894
1984 TCMA Tidewater Tides 894
1984 TCMA Toledo Mud Hens 894
1984 TCMA Visalia Oaks 895
1984 Team Daytona Beach Astros . 891
1984 Team Idaho Falls A's 892
1984 Team Indianapolis Indians 892
1984 Team Nashville Sounds 893
1984 Team Spokane Indians 894
1984 Team Tulsa Drillers 895
1984 Topps 671
1984 Topps All-Star Glossy Set of 22 674
1984 Topps All-Star Glossy Set of 40 674
1984 Topps Cereal Series 675
1984 Topps Gallery of Immortals ... 675
1984 Topps Rub Downs 675
1984 Topps Stickers 675
1984 Topps Stickers Boxes 677
1984 Topps Super 677
1984 Topps Traded 674
1984 True Value White Sox 756
1984 Wheaties Indians 799
1985 7-11 Slurpee Coins Eastern Region 524
1985 7-11 Slurpee Coins Great Lakes Region 524
1985 7-11 Slurpee Coins Southeastern Region 524
1985 7-11 Slurpee Coins Southwest/ Central Region 524
1985 7-11 Slurpee Coins Tigers...... 524
1985 7-11 Slurpee Coins Western Region 524
1985 7-11 Twins 524
1985 7-Up Cubs 526
1985 Cain's Potato Chips Tigers 48
1985 CBS Radio Game of the Week 48
1985 Chong Modesto A's 899
1985 CIGNA Phillies 52
1985 Circle K 52
1985 Coca-Cola White Sox 62
1985 Cramer Albuquerque Dukes .. 895
1985 Cramer Bend Phillies 895
1985 Cramer Calgary Cannons 896
1985 Cramer Edmonton Trappers 896
1985 Cramer Everett Giants - Series I 897
1985 Cramer Everett Giants - Series II 897
1985 Cramer Hawaii Islanders 897
1985 Cramer Las Vegas Stars 898
1985 Cramer Phoenix Giants 899
1985 Cramer Portland Beavers 900
1985 Cramer Spokane Indians 900
1985 Cramer Spokane Indians All-Time Greats 900
1985 Cramer Tacoma Tigers 900
1985 Cramer Tucson Toros 901
1985 Cramer Vancouver Canadians 901
1985 Donruss 100
1985 Donruss Action All-Stars 102
1985 Donruss Box Panels 102
1985 Donruss Diamond Kings Supers 102
1985 Donruss Highlights 103
1985 Donruss Sluggers of The Hall of Fame 103
1985 Drake's 149
1985 Fleer 179
1985 Fleer Limited Edition 182
1985 Fleer Stickers 182
1985 Fleer Update 181
1985 Fun Food Buttons 241
1985 Gardner's Brewers 243
1985 General Mills Stickers 244
1985 Hostess Braves 260
1985 Indians Photo Cards 263
1985 Leaf-Donruss 303
1985 Lion Photo Chicago Cubs 319
1985 Minnesota Twins Team Issue 335
1985 Mother's Cookies Astros 338
1985 Mother's Cookies Athletics 338
1985 Mother's Cookies Giants 338
1985 Mother's Cookies Mariners 338
1985 Mother's Cookies Padres 339
1985 N.Y. Mets Super Fan Club 361
1985 Nike 361
1985 O-Pee-Chee 411
1985 O-Pee-Chee Posters 412
1985 Performance Printing Rangers 444
1985 Pizza Hut Greenville Braves .. 897
1985 Polaroid J.C. Penney Indians 460
1985 Police/Fire Safety Blue Jays .. 465
1985 Police/Fire Safety Braves 465
1985 Police/Fire Safety Brewers 465
1985 Police/Fire Safety Columbus Clippers 896
1985 Police/Fire Safety Phillies 465
1985 ProCards Reading Phillies 900
1985 Riley's Louisville Redbirds 898
1985 Smokey Bear Angels 527
1985 Smokey Fresno Giants 897
1985 Star Co. Reggie Jackson 552
1985 T&J SC Madison Muskies 898
1985 Tastykake Phillies 574
1985 TCMA Albany-Colonie Yankees 895
1985 TCMA Beaumont Golden Gators 895
1985 TCMA Beloit Brewers 895
1985 TCMA Buffalo Bisons 895
1985 TCMA Burlington Rangers 896
1985 TCMA Cedar Rapids Reds 896
1985 TCMA Charlotte O'S 896
1985 TCMA Columbus Clippers 896
1985 TCMA Durham Bulls 896
1985 TCMA Elmira Pioneers 896
1985 TCMA Ft. Myers Royals 897
1985 TCMA Greensboro Hornets ... 897
1985 TCMA International League All-Stars 898
1985 TCMA Iowa Cubs 898
1985 TCMA Kinston Blue Jays 898
1985 TCMA Little Falls Mets 898
1985 TCMA Lynchburg Mets 898
1985 TCMA Madison Muskies 898
1985 TCMA Maine Guides 898
1985 TCMA Midland Angels 899
1985 TCMA Nashua Pirates 899
1985 TCMA Newark Orioles 899
1985 TCMA Oklahoma City 89'ers . 899
1985 TCMA Omaha Royals 899
1985 TCMA Orlando Twins 899
1985 TCMA Pawtucket Red Sox 899
1985 TCMA Prince Williams Pirates 900
1985 TCMA Richmond Braves 900
1985 TCMA Rochester Red Wings 900
1985 TCMA Springfield Cardinals .. 900
1985 TCMA Syracuse Chiefs 900
1985 TCMA Tidewater Tides 900
1985 TCMA Tigers De Mexico 898
1985 TCMA Toldeo Mud Hens 901
1985 TCMA Utica Blue Sox 901
1985 TCMA Vero Beach Dodgers .. 901
1985 TCMA Visalia Oaks 901
1985 TCMA Waterbury Indians 901
1985 Team Birmingham Barons 895
1985 Team Chattanooga Lookouts 896

1985 Team Daytona Beach Islanders 896
1985 Team Greenville Braves 897
1985 Team Huntsville Stars 897
1985 Team Indianapolis Indians 897
1985 Team Nashville Sounds 899
1985 Team Osceola Astros 899
1985 Team Tulsa Drillers 901
1985 Thom McAn Discs 577
1985 Topps 3-D 683
1985 Topps 677
1985 Topps All-Star Glossy Set of 22 680
1985 Topps All-Star Glossy Set of 40 680
1985 Topps All-Time Record Holders 680
1985 Topps Gallery of Champions . 681
1985 Topps Rub Downs 681
1985 Topps Stickers 681
1985 Topps Super 682
1985 Topps Traded 680
1985 Wendy's Tigers 795
1986 7-11 Slurpee Coins Eastern Region 525
1986 7-11 Slurpee Coins Mideastern Region 525
1986 7-11 Slurpee Coins Midwestern Region 525
1986 7-11 Slurpee Coins Western Region 525
1986 Ault Foods Blue Jays 10
1986 Baltimore Orioles Team Issue 13
1986 Big League Chew 24
1986 Burger King 47
1986 Cain's Potato Chips Tigers 48
1986 CBS Radio Game of the Week 48
1986 Chong Modesto A's 907
1986 CIGNA Phillies 52
1986 Coca-Cola White Sox 62
1986 Cramer Bellingham Mariners . 902
1986 Cramer Bend Phillies 902
1986 Cramer Eugene Emeralds 904
1986 Cramer Everett Giants - Color 904
1986 Cramer Everett Giants - Black and White 904
1986 Cramer Medford A's 907
1986 Cramer Salem Angels 909
1986 Cramer Spokane Indians 910
1986 Cramer Tri-Cities Triplets 911
1986 Daniels Madison Muskies 906
1986 Donn Jennings Southern League All-Stars 910
1986 Donruss 103
1986 Donruss All-Stars 105
1986 Donruss Box Panels 105
1986 Donruss Diamond Kings Supers 106
1986 Donruss Highlights 106
1986 Donruss Pop-Ups 106
1986 Donruss Rookies 106
1986 Dorman's Cheese 146
1986 Drake's 149
1986 Fleer 182
1986 Fleer All Stars 184
1986 Fleer Baseball's Best 185
1986 Fleer Box Panels 185
1986 Fleer Future Hall Of Famers .. 185
1986 Fleer League Leaders 186
1986 Fleer Limited Edition 186
1986 Fleer Mini 186
1986 Fleer Star Stickers 187
1986 Fleer Star Stickers Box Panels 187
1986 Fleer Update 185
1986 Gatorade Cubs 243
1986 General Mills Booklets 244
1986 Jays Potato Chips 272
1986 Jiffy Pop 274
1986 Jiffy Pop/MSA Promos 274
1986 Kas Potato Chips Cardinals 285
1986 Kay Bee 285
1986 Keller's Butter Phillies 288
1986 Kitty Clover Potato Chips Royals 298
1986 Leaf 304
1986 Lite Beer Astros 320
1986 Lite Beer Rangers 320
1986 Meadow Gold Blank Backs 327
1986 Meadow Gold Milk 328
1986 Meadow Gold Statistic Backs 327
1986 Minnesota Twins Team Issue 335
1986 Mother's Cookies Astros 339
1986 Mother's Cookies Athletics 339
1986 Mother's Cookies Giants 339
1986 Mother's Cookies Mariners 339
1986 N.Y. Mets Super Fan Club 361
1986 National Photo Royals 356
1986 Oh Henry Indians 425
1986 O-Pee-Chee 413
1986 O-Pee-Chee Box Panels 414
1986 Performance Printing Rangers 444
1986 Police/Fire Safety Astros 466
1986 Police/Fire Safety Blue Jays .. 466
1986 Police/Fire Safety Braves 466
1986 Police/Fire Safety Brewers 466
1986 Police/Fire Safety Dodgers 467
1986 Police/Fire Safety Phillies 467
1986 ProCards Albuquerque Dukes 901
1986 ProCards Appleton Foxes 901
1986 ProCards Arkansas Travelers 901
1986 ProCards Ashville Tourists 902
1986 ProCards Auburn Astros 902
1986 ProCards Bakersfield Dodgers 902
1986 ProCards Beaumont Golden Gators 902
1986 ProCards Beloit Brewers 902
1986 ProCards Buffalo Bisons 902
1986 ProCards Burlington Expos ... 902
1986 ProCards Calgary Cannons ... 902
1986 ProCards Charleston Rainbows 902
1986 ProCards Chattanooga Lookouts 903
1986 ProCards Clearwater Phillies 903
1986 ProCards Clinton Giants 903
1986 ProCards Columbia Mets 903
1986 ProCards Columbus Astros ... 903
1986 ProCards Columbus Clippers 903
1986 ProCards Daytona Beach Islanders 903
1986 ProCards Durham Bulls 903
1986 ProCards Edmonton Trappers 903
1986 ProCards El Paso Diablos 904
1986 ProCards Elmira Pioneers 904
1986 ProCards Erie Cardinals 904
1986 ProCards Florida State League All-Stars 904
1986 ProCards Ft. Lauderdale Yankees 904
1986 ProCards Ft. Myers Royals ... 904
1986 ProCards Geneva Cubs 905
1986 ProCards Glens Falls Tigers . 905
1986 ProCards Greensboro Hornets 905
1986 ProCards Greenville Braves .. 905
1986 ProCards Hagerstown Suns .. 905
1986 ProCards Hawaii Islanders 905
1986 ProCards Iowa Cubs 905
1986 ProCards Jamestown Expos 906
1986 ProCards Kenosha Twins 906
1986 ProCards Kinston Eagles 906
1986 ProCards Knoxville Blue Jays 906
1986 ProCards Lakeland Tigers 906
1986 ProCards Las Vegas Stars 906
1986 ProCards Little Falls Mets 906
1986 ProCards Lynchburg Mets 906
1986 ProCards Macon Pirates 906
1986 ProCards Madison Muskies ... 906
1986 ProCards Maine Guides 907
1986 ProCards Miami Marlins 907
1986 ProCards Midland Angels 907
1986 ProCards Modesto A's 907
1986 ProCards Nashua Pirates 907
1986 ProCards New Britain Red Sox 907
1986 ProCards Oklahoma City 89'ers 908
1986 ProCards Omaha Royals 908
1986 ProCards Orlando Twins 908
1986 ProCards Osceola Astros 908
1986 ProCards Palm Springs Angels 908
1986 ProCards Pawtucket Red Sox 908
1986 ProCards Peninsula White Sox 908
1986 ProCards Peoria Chiefs 908
1986 ProCards Phoenix Firebirds .. 908
1986 ProCards Pittsfield Cubs 908
1986 ProCards Portland Beavers ... 909
1986 ProCards Prince William Pirates 909

1986 ProCards Quad Cities Angels 909
1986 ProCards Reading Phillies 909
1986 ProCards Richmond Braves .. 909
1986 ProCards Rochester Red Wings 909
1986 ProCards Salem Red Birds ... 909
1986 ProCards San Jose Bees 909
1986 ProCards Shreveport Captains 909
1986 ProCards St. Petersburg Cards 909
1986 ProCards Stockton Ports 910
1986 ProCards Sumter Braves 910
1986 ProCards Syracuse Chiefs 910
1986 ProCards Tacoma Tigers 910
1986 ProCards Tampa Tarpons 910
1986 ProCards Tidewater Tides - Mets Emblem 910
1986 ProCards Tidewater Tides - Tides Emblem 910
1986 ProCards Toledo Mud Hens .. 911
1986 ProCards Tucson Toros 911
1986 ProCards Vancouver Canadians 911
1986 ProCards Ventura Gulls 911
1986 ProCards Vermont Reds 911
1986 ProCards Vero Beach Dodgers 911
1986 ProCards Visalia Oaks 911
1986 ProCards Waterbury Indians 911
1986 ProCards Waterloo Indians ... 911
1986 ProCards Watertown Pirates 911
1986 ProCards Wausau Timbers ... 912
1986 ProCards West Palm Beach Expos 912
1986 ProCards Winston-Salem Spirits 912
1986 ProCards Winter Haven Red Sox 912
1986 Provigo Expos 478
1986 Quaker Oats 479
1986 Schnucks Milk Cardinals 491
1986 Smokey Bear Angels 527
1986 Smokey Bear Fresno Giants 904
1986 Smokey Bear Palm Springs Angels 908
1986 Sportflics 534
1986 Sportflics Decade Greats 535
1986 Sportflics Rookies 535
1986 Springhill Papers 547
1986 Star Co. Dale Murphy 552
1986 Star Co. Don Mattingly 552
1986 Star Co. Jim Rice 552
1986 Star Co. Jose Canseco 552
1986 Star Co. Nolan Ryan 553
1986 Star Co. Rod Carew 552
1986 Star Co. Tom Seaver 553
1986 Star Co. Wade Boggs 552
1986 Star Co. Wally Joyner 552
1986 Tastykake Phillies 575
1986 TCMA Albany-Colonie Yankees 901
1986 TCMA Cedar Rapids Reds 902
1986 TCMA Jackson Mets 905
1986 TCMA Jacksonville Expos 905
1986 TCMA Omaha Royals 908
1986 TCMA Stars Of The Future Post Card Set 910
1986 Team Columbus Clippers 903
1986 Team Huntsville Stars 905
1986 Team Indianapolis Indians 905
1986 Team Louisville Redbirds 906
1986 Team Nashville Sounds 907
1986 Team Pittsfield Cubs 909
1986 Team Tulsa Drillers 911
1986 Texas Gold Ice Cream Reds . 576
1986 Time Out Sports Memphis Chicks 907
1986 Topps 3-D 689
1986 Topps 683
1986 Topps All-Star Glossy Set of 22 685
1986 Topps All-Star Glossy Set of 60 686
1986 Topps Box Panels 686
1986 Topps Gallery of Champions 687
1986 Topps Mini League Leaders .. 687
1986 Topps Stickers 687
1986 Topps Super 688
1986 Topps Super Star 688
1986 Topps Tattoos 689
1986 Topps Traded 686
1986 True Value 757
1986 University City Spokane Indians 910
1986 WBTV Charlotte O's 903
1987 7-11 Slurpee Coins Eastern Region 525
1987 7-11 Slurpee Coins Great Lakes Region 525
1987 7-11 Slurpee Coins Mideastern Region 525
1987 7-11 Slurpee Coins Tigers 526
1987 7-11 Slurpee Coins Western Region 525
1987 Allstate Insurance 4
1987 Baseball Super Stars Discs 14
1987 Best Birmingham Barons 913
1987 Best Chattanooga Lookouts 913
1987 Best Greenville Braves 916
1987 Best Memphis Chicks 918
1987 Best Springfield Cardinals 923
1987 Boardwalk and Baseball 25
1987 Bob's Photo Richmond Braves 921
1987 Bohemian Hearth Bread Padres 25
1987 Burger King 47
1987 Cain's Potato Chips Tigers 48
1987 Champion Phillies 51
1987 Chong Modesto A's 919
1987 Classic Major League Baseball Game 52
1987 Classic Travel Edition 53
1987 Coca-Cola Tigers 62
1987 Coca-Cola White Sox 63
1987 Cramer Everett Giants 915
1987 Crown Oil Richmond Braves 921
1987 David Berg Hot Dogs Cubs 22
1987 Donn Jennings Southern League All-Stars 922
1987 Donruss 107
1987 Donruss All-Stars 109
1987 Donruss Box Panels 109
1987 Donruss Diamond Kings Supers 109
1987 Donruss Highlights 110
1987 Donruss Opening Day 110
1987 Donruss Pop-Ups 111
1987 Donruss Rookies 111
1987 Drake's 149
1987 Farmland Dairies Mets 163
1987 Fleer '86 World Series 190
1987 Fleer 187
1987 Fleer All Stars 189
1987 Fleer Baseball All Stars 191
1987 Fleer Baseball Record Setters 193
1987 Fleer Baseball's Award Winners 190
1987 Fleer Baseball's Best 191
1987 Fleer Baseball's Exciting Stars 191
1987 Fleer Baseball's Game Winners 191
1987 Fleer Baseball's Hottest Stars 192
1987 Fleer Box Panels 190
1987 Fleer Headliners 189
1987 Fleer League Leaders 192
1987 Fleer Limited Edition 192
1987 Fleer Mini 192
1987 Fleer Star Sticker Box Panels 194
1987 Fleer Star Stickers 193
1987 Fleer Update 190
1987 French/Bray Orioles 240
1987 Gatorade Indians 243
1987 General Mills Booklets 245
1987 Hostess Stickers 261
1987 Jiffy Pop 274
1987 Jones Photo Tucson Toros 924
1987 Kahn's Reds 281
1987 Kay Bee 285
1987 K-Mart 277
1987 Kraft 298
1987 Leaf 305
1987 Leaf Candy City Team 306
1987 M & M's 322
1987 Minnesota Twins Team Issue 335
1987 Mother's Cookies Astros 340
1987 Mother's Cookies Athletics 340
1987 Mother's Cookies Dodgers 340
1987 Mother's Cookies Giants 340
1987 Mother's Cookies Mariners 341
1987 Mother's Cookies Mark McGwire 341
1987 Mother's Cookies Rangers 341
1987 Nestle 359
1987 O-Pee-Chee 414
1987 O-Pee-Chee Box Panels 415

1987 Pizza World Peoria Chiefs 920
1987 Police Salinas Spurs 922
1987 Police/Fire Safety Astros 467
1987 Police/Fire Safety Blue Jays .. 467
1987 Police/Fire Safety Brewers 467
1987 Police/Fire Safety Columbus Clippers 914
1987 Police/Fire Safety Dodgers 468
1987 ProCards Albany-Colonie Yankees 912
1987 ProCards Appleton Foxes 912
1987 ProCards Arkansas Travelers 912
1987 ProCards Asheville Tourists .. 912
1987 ProCards Auburn Astros 912
1987 ProCards Bakersfield Dodgers 912
1987 ProCards Beloit Brewers 913
1987 ProCards Burlington Expos ... 913
1987 ProCards Calgary Cannons ... 913
1987 ProCards Cedar Rapids Reds 913
1987 ProCards Charleston Rainbows 913
1987 ProCards Charleston Wheelers 913
1987 ProCards Clearwater Phillies 914
1987 ProCards Clinton Giants 914
1987 ProCards Columbia Mets 914
1987 ProCards Columbus Astros ... 914
1987 ProCards Columbus Clippers 914
1987 ProCards Daytona Beach Admirals 914
1987 ProCards Denver Zephyrs 914
1987 ProCards Dunedin Blue Jays 914
1987 ProCards Durham Bulls 914
1987 ProCards Edmonton Trappers 914
1987 ProCards El Paso Diablos 915
1987 ProCards Erie Cardinals 915
1987 ProCards Eugene Emeralds .. 915
1987 ProCards Fayetteville Generals 915
1987 ProCards Fort Myers Royals 915
1987 ProCards Ft. Lauderdale Yankees 915
1987 ProCards Gastonia Rangers 915
1987 ProCards Geneva Cubs 916
1987 ProCards Glens Falls Tigers . 916
1987 ProCards Greensboro Hornets 916
1987 ProCards Hagerstown Suns 916
1987 ProCards Harrisburg Senators 916
1987 ProCards Hawaii Islanders 916
1987 ProCards Idaho Falls Braves 916
1987 ProCards International League All-Stars 916
1987 ProCards Jacksonville Expos 917
1987 ProCards Jamestown Expos 917
1987 ProCards Kenosha Twins 917
1987 ProCards Kinston Indians 917
1987 ProCards Knoxville Blue Jays 917
1987 ProCards Lakeland Tigers 917
1987 ProCards Las Vegas Stars 917
1987 ProCards Little Falls Mets 918
1987 ProCards Lynchburg Mets 918
1987 ProCards Macon Pirates 918
1987 ProCards Madison Muskies ... 918
1987 ProCards Maine Guides 918
1987 ProCards Memphis Chicks 918
1987 ProCards Miami Marlins 918
1987 ProCards Midland Angels 918
1987 ProCards Modesto A's 919
1987 ProCards Myrtle Beach Blue Jays 919
1987 ProCards New Britain Red Sox 919
1987 ProCards Newark Orioles 919
1987 ProCards Oklahoma City 89'ers 919
1987 ProCards Omaha Royals 919
1987 ProCards Oneonta Yankees .. 919
1987 ProCards Orlando Twins 919
1987 ProCards Osceola Astros 919
1987 ProCards Palm Springs Angels 920
1987 ProCards Pawtucket Red Sox 920
1987 ProCards Peninsula White Sox 920
1987 ProCards Peoria Chiefs 920
1987 ProCards Phoenix Firebirds .. 920
1987 ProCards Pittsfield Cubs 920
1987 ProCards Port Charlotte Rangers 920
1987 ProCards Portland Beavers ... 921
1987 ProCards Prince William Yankees 921
1987 ProCards Quad City Angels .. 921
1987 ProCards Reading Phillies 921
1987 ProCards Rochester Red Wings 921
1987 ProCards Salem Angels 921
1987 ProCards Salem Buccaneers 922
1987 ProCards San Bernadino Spirits 922
1987 ProCards San Jose Bees 922
1987 ProCards Savannah Cardinals 922
1987 ProCards Shreveport Captains 922
1987 ProCards Spartanburg Phillies 922
1987 ProCards Spokane Indians 923
1987 ProCards St. Petersburg Cardinals 921
1987 ProCards Stockton Ports 923
1987 ProCards Sumter Braves 923
1987 ProCards Syracuse Chiefs 923
1987 ProCards Tacoma Tigers 923
1987 ProCards Tampa Tarpons 923
1987 ProCards Tidewater Tides 923
1987 ProCards Toledo Mud Hens .. 924
1987 ProCards Tucson Toros 924
1987 ProCards Utica Blue Sox 924
1987 ProCards Vancouver Canadians 924
1987 ProCards Vermont Reds 924
1987 ProCards Vero Beach Dodgers 924
1987 ProCards Visalia Oaks 924
1987 ProCards Waterloo Indians ... 924
1987 ProCards Watertown Pirates 924
1987 ProCards Wausau Timbers ... 925
1987 ProCards West Palm Beach Expos 925
1987 ProCards Williamsport Bills ... 925
1987 ProCards Winston-Salem Spirits 925
1987 ProCards Winter Haven Red Sox 925
1987 ProCards Wytheville Cubs 925
1987 Ralston Purina 482
1987 Ralston Purina Collectors' Sheet 482
1987 Smokey Bear 528
1987 Smokey Bear A's 528
1987 Smokey Bear Angels 528
1987 Smokey Bear Braves 528
1987 Smokey Bear Cardinals 528
1987 Smokey Bear Dodgers 529
1987 Smokey Bear Rangers 529
1987 Sportflics 536
1987 Sportflics Rookie Discs 536
1987 Sportflics Rookie Prospects ... 536
1987 Sportflics Rookies 537
1987 Sportflics Superstar Discs 537
1987 Sportflics Team Preview 537
1987 Star Co. Fernando Valenzuela 553
1987 Star Co. Gary Carter 553
1987 Star Co. Keith Hernandez 553
1987 Star Co. Roger Clemens 553
1987 Star Co. Roger Clemens Update 553
1987 Star Co. Tim Raines 553
1987 Stuart 558
1987 T&J SC Madison Muskies 918
1987 Tastykake Phillies 575
1987 TCMA Columbus Clippers 914
1987 TCMA International League All-Stars 917
1987 TCMA Maine Guides 918
1987 TCMA Pawtucket Red Sox 920
1987 TCMA Richmond Braves 921
1987 TCMA Rochester Red Wings 921
1987 TCMA Syracuse Chiefs 923
1987 TCMA Tidewater Tides 923
1987 TCMA Toledo Mud Hens 924
1987 Team Albuquerque Dukes 912
1987 Team Bellingham Mariners 912
1987 Team Buffalo Bisons 913
1987 Team Charlotte O's 913
1987 Team Elmira Pioneers - Black 915

1987 Team Elmira Pioneers - Red .. 915
1987 Team Huntsville Stars 916
1987 Team Indianapolis Indians 916
1987 Team Iowa Cubs 917
1987 Team Jackson Mets 917
1987 Team Louisville Redbirds 918
1987 Team Nashville Sounds 919
1987 Team Pittsfield Cubs 920
1987 Team Salt Lake City Trappers 922
1987 Team San Antonio Dodgers .. 922
1987 Team Tulsa Drillers 924
1987 Team Wichita Pilots 925
1987 The Bon Pocatello Giants 920
1987 Topps 689
1987 Topps All-Star Glossy Set of 22 692
1987 Topps All-Star Glossy Set of 60 692
1987 Topps Baseball Highlights 693
1987 Topps Box Panels 693
1987 Topps Coins 693
1987 Topps Gallery of Champions . 693
1987 Topps Glossy Rookies 694
1987 Topps Mini League Leaders .. 694
1987 Topps Stickers 694
1987 Topps Traded 692
1987 Toys “R” Us 754
1987Texas League All-Stars 923
1988 Action Packed 1
1988 Baseball Immortals 14
1988 Baseball Super Stars Discs 15
1988 Bazooka 20
1988 Best Birmingham Barons 927
1988 Best Charleston Wheelers 928
1988 Best Chattanooga Lookouts 929
1988 Best Columbus Astros 929
1988 Best El Paso Diablos 930
1988 Best El Paso Diablos Limited Edition 931
1988 Best Eugene Emeralds 931
1988 Best Greenville Braves 932
1988 Best Jacksonville Expos 933
1988 Best Knoxville Blue Jays 933
1988 Best Memphis Chicks 934
1988 Best Orlando Twins 936
1988 Best San Antonio Missions 939
1988 Best San Antonio Missions Ltd. Edition 939
1988 Best San Bernadino Spirit 939
1988 Best San Bernadino Spirit Ltd. Edition 939
1988 Best Springfield Cardinals 941
1988 Best/ProCards Baseball America AA Prospects 926
1988 Bob's Photo Richmond Braves 938
1988 Cain Elmira Pioneers 930
1988 Cain Elmira Pioneers Test Issue 930
1988 Cal Cards Bakersfield Dodgers 926
1988 Cal Cards California League All-Stars 928
1988 Cal Cards Fresno Suns 931
1988 Cal Cards Modesto A's 935
1988 Cal Cards Palm Springs Angels 936
1988 Cal Cards Reno Silver Sox 938
1988 Cal Cards Riverside Red Wave 938
1988 Cal Cards San Bernadino Spirit 939
1988 Cal Cards San Jose Giants ... 940
1988 Cal Cards Stockton Ports 941
1988 Cal Cards Visalia Oaks 943
1988 Chef Boyardee 51
1988 Classic - Blue 53
1988 Classic - Red 53
1988 CMC Albuquerque Dukes 925
1988 CMC Buffalo Bisons 927
1988 CMC Calgary Cannons 928
1988 CMC Colorado Springs Sky Sox 929
1988 CMC Columbus Clippers 929
1988 CMC Denver Zephyrs 930
1988 CMC Don Mattingly 60
1988 CMC Edmonton Trappers 930
1988 CMC Indianapolis Indians 932
1988 CMC Iowa Cubs 932
1988 CMC Las Vegas Stars 933
1988 CMC Louisville Redbirds 934
1988 CMC Maine Phillies 934
1988 CMC Nashville Sounds 935
1988 CMC Oklahoma City 89'ers ... 935
1988 CMC Omaha Royals 936
1988 CMC Pawtucket Red Sox 936
1988 CMC Phoenix Firebirds 937
1988 CMC Portland Beavers 937
1988 CMC Richmond Braves 938
1988 CMC Rochester Red Wings .. 938
1988 CMC Syracuse Chiefs 941
1988 CMC Tacoma Tigers 941
1988 CMC Tidewater Tides 941
1988 CMC Toledo Mud Hens 942
1988 CMC Triple A All-Stars 942
1988 CMC Tucson Toros 942
1988 CMC Vancouver Canadians 943
1988 Coca-Cola Padres 63
1988 Coca-Cola White Sox 63
1988 David Berg Hot Dogs Cubs 23
1988 Domino's Pizza Tigers 90
1988 Donn Jennings Southern League All-Stars 940
1988 Donruss 111
1988 Donruss All-Stars 114
1988 Donruss Baseball's Best 114
1988 Donruss Boston Red Sox Team Book 116
1988 Donruss Chicago Cubs Team Book 116
1988 Donruss Diamond Kings Supers 115
1988 Donruss MVP 113
1988 Donruss New York Mets Team Book 116
1988 Donruss New York Yankees Team Book 116
1988 Donruss Oakland A's Team Book 117
1988 Donruss Pop-Ups 115
1988 Donruss Rookies 115
1988 Drake's 149
1988 Fantastic Sam's 163
1988 Farmland Dairies Mets 163
1988 Fleer '87 World Series 196
1988 Fleer 194
1988 Fleer All Stars 196
1988 Fleer Award Winners 197
1988 Fleer Baseball All Stars 197
1988 Fleer Baseball MVP 198
1988 Fleer Baseball's Best 198
1988 Fleer Baseball's Best Box Panel 198
1988 Fleer Baseball's Exciting Stars 198
1988 Fleer Baseball's Hottest Stars 199
1988 Fleer Box Panels 196
1988 Fleer Headliners 196
1988 Fleer League Leaders 199
1988 Fleer Mini 199
1988 Fleer Record Setters 200
1988 Fleer Star Stickers 200
1988 Fleer Star Stickers Box Panels 200
1988 Fleer Superstars 201
1988 Fleer Update 197
1988 French/Bray Orioles 241
1988 Gatorade Indians 244
1988 Grand Slam Arkansas Travelers 926
1988 Grand Slam Beloit Brewers ... 927
1988 Grand Slam Columbia Mets .. 929
1988 Grand Slam Jackson Mets 933
1988 Grand Slam Midland Angels .. 934
1988 Grand Slam Midwest League All-Stars 935
1988 Grand Slam Quad City Angels 937
1988 Grand Slam South Atlantic League All-Stars 940
1988 Grand Slam South Bend White Sox 940
1988 Grand Slam Texas League All-Stars 942
1988 Grand Slam Wausau Timbers 943
1988 Hostess Potato Chips Expos 261
1988 Jiffy Pop 274
1988 Jones Photo Tucson Toros 942
1988 Kahn's Mets 282
1988 Kahn's Reds 282
1988 Kay Bee Superstars of Baseball 286
1988 Kay Bee Team Leaders 286
1988 Kenner Starting Lineup 294
1988 King-B 297
1988 K-Mart 277
1988 Leaf 306
1988 Legoe Bellingham Mariners ... 926
1988 Legoe Bend Bucks 927
1988 Louisville Slugger 320
1988 Master Bread Twins 325
1988 Minnesota Twins Team Issue 335

1988 Mother's Cookies Astros 341
1988 Mother's Cookies Athletics 341
1988 Mother's Cookies Dodgers 342
1988 Mother's Cookies Giants 342
1988 Mother's Cookies Mariners 342
1988 Mother's Cookies Mark McGwire 343
1988 Mother's Cookies Rangers 342
1988 Mother's Cookies Will Clark ... 342
1988 Nestle 360
1988 O-Pee-Chee 415
1988 O-Pee-Chee Box Panels 417
1988 Pacific Trading Cards "Eight Men Out" 430
1988 Pacific Trading Cards Baseball Legends 429
1988 Panini Stickers 441
1988 Pepsi-Cola/Kroger Tigers 443
1988 Police Columbus Clippers 929
1988 Police/Fire Safety Astros 468
1988 Police/Fire Safety Blue Jays .. 468
1988 Police/Fire Safety Brewers 468
1988 Police/Fire Safety Dodgers 469
1988 Police/Fire Safety Tigers 469
1988 ProCards Albany-Colonie Yankees 925
1988 ProCards Albuquerque Dukes 925
1988 ProCards Appleton Foxes 925
1988 ProCards Asheville Tourists .. 926
1988 ProCards Auburn Astros 926
1988 ProCards Augusta Pirates 926
1988 ProCards Batavia Clippers 926
1988 ProCards Billings Mustangs .. 927
1988 ProCards Boise Hawks 927
1988 ProCards Bristol Tigers 927
1988 ProCards Buffalo Bisons 927
1988 ProCards Burlington Braves 927
1988 ProCards Burlington Indians 927
1988 ProCards Calgary Cannons 928
1988 ProCards Cedar Rapids Reds 928
1988 ProCards Charleston Rainbows 928
1988 ProCards Clinton Giants 929
1988 ProCards Colorado Springs Sky Sox 929
1988 ProCards Columbus Clippers 929
1988 ProCards Denver Zephyrs 930
1988 ProCards Eastern League All-Stars 930
1988 ProCards Edmonton Trappers 930
1988 ProCards Fayetteville Generals 931
1988 ProCards Fresno Suns 931
1988 ProCards Gastonia Rangers 931
1988 ProCards Geneva Cubs 931
1988 ProCards Glens Falls Tigers . 931
1988 ProCards Greensboro Hornets 932
1988 ProCards Hamilton Redbirds 932
1988 ProCards Harrisburg Senators 932
1988 ProCards Idaho Falls Braves 932
1988 ProCards Indianapolis Indians 932
1988 ProCards Iowa Cubs 932
1988 ProCards Jacksonville Expos 933
1988 ProCards Jamestown Expos 933
1988 ProCards Kenosha Twins 933
1988 ProCards Las Vegas Stars 933
1988 ProCards Louisville Redbirds 934
1988 ProCards Maine Phillies 934
1988 ProCards Myrtle Beach Blue Jays 935
1988 ProCards Nashville Sounds ... 935
1988 ProCards New Britain Red Sox 935
1988 ProCards Oklahoma City 89'ers 936
1988 ProCards Omaha Royals 936
1988 ProCards Oneonta Yankees .. 936
1988 ProCards Palm Springs Angels 936
1988 ProCards Pawtucket Red Sox 936
1988 ProCards Phoenix Firebirds .. 937
1988 ProCards Pittsfield Cubs 937
1988 ProCards Pocatello Giants 937
1988 ProCards Portland Beavers ... 937
1988 ProCards Pulaksi Braves 937
1988 ProCards Reading Phillies 937
1988 ProCards Richmond Braves .. 938
1988 ProCards Riverside Red Wave 938
1988 ProCards Rochester Red Wings 938
1988 ProCards San Jose Giants 940
1988 ProCards Savannah Cardinals 940
1988 ProCards Shreveport Captains 940
1988 ProCards Southern Oregon A's 940
1988 ProCards Spartanburg Phillies 940
1988 ProCards Spokane Indians 940
1988 ProCards St. Catharines Blue Jays 939
1988 ProCards Stockton Ports 941
1988 ProCards Sumter Braves 941
1988 ProCards Syracuse Chiefs 941
1988 ProCards Tacoma Tigers 941
1988 ProCards Tidewater Tides 941
1988 ProCards Toledo Mud Hens .. 942
1988 ProCards Triple-A All-Stars ... 942
1988 ProCards Tucson Toros 942
1988 ProCards Vancouver Canadians 943
1988 ProCards Vermont Mariners 943
1988 ProCards Visalia Oaks 943
1988 ProCards Waterloo Indians ... 943
1988 ProCards Williamsport Bills ... 944
1988 ProCards Wytheville Cubs 944
1988 Pucko Little Falls Mets 933
1988 Pucko Rochester Red Wings 938
1988 Pucko Utica Blue Sox 943
1988 Pucko Watertown Pirates 943
1988 Revco 485
1988 Rite Aid 485
1988 Rock's Dugout Wichita Pilots 944
1988 Score 491
1988 Score Box Panels 493
1988 Score Traded 493
1988 Score Young Superstar Series I 494
1988 Score Young Superstar Series II 494
1988 SG & CC Tidewater Tides 942
1988 Smokey Bear Angels 529
1988 Smokey Bear Cardinals 529
1988 Smokey Bear Cubs 530
1988 Smokey Bear Dodgers 530
1988 Smokey Bear Padres 530
1988 Smokey Bear Rangers 530
1988 Smokey Bear Royals 530
1988 Smokey Bear Twins 530
1988 Sport Pro Butte Copper Kings 928
1988 Sportflics 538
1988 Sportflics Gamewinners 538
1988 Star Co. "Baseball's Best" 553
1988 Star Co. "Baseball's Best" Limited Edition 554
1988 Star Co. "Best of '87" 554
1988 Star Co. "Hits 'R Us" 554
1988 Star Co. Andre Dawson 554
1988 Star Co. Baseball City Royals 926
1988 Star Co. Bo Jackson 555
1988 Star Co. Carolina League All-Stars 928
1988 Star Co. Charlotte Rangers ... 928
1988 Star Co. Clearwater Phillies ... 929
1988 Star Co. Cory Snyder 555
1988 Star Co. Dave Winfield 555
1988 Star Co. Don Mattingly 555
1988 Star Co. Dunedin Blue Jays .. 930
1988 Star Co. Durham Bulls (Blue) 930
1988 Star Co. Durham Bulls (Orange) 930
1988 Star Co. Dwight Gooden 554
1988 Star Co. Eric Davis 554
1988 Star Co. Florida State All-Stars 931
1988 Star Co. Ft. Lauderdale Yankees 931
1988 Star Co. Gary Carter 554
1988 Star Co. Hagerstown Suns 932
1988 Star Co. Kevin Seitzer 555
1988 Star Co. Kinston Indians 933
1988 Star Co. Lakeland Tigers 933

1988 Star Co. Lynchburg Red Sox 934
1988 Star Co. Mark McGwire #2 555
1988 Star Co. Mark McGwire #3 555
1988 Star Co. Mark McGwire 555
1988 Star Co. Martinsville Phillies .. 934
1988 Star Co. Miami Marlins 935
1988 Star Co. Mike Scott 555
1988 Star Co. Osceola Astros 936
1988 Star Co. Platinum 556
1988 Star Co. Port Charlotte Rangers 937
1988 Star Co. Prince William Yankees 937
1988 Star Co. Salem Buccaneers .. 939
1988 Star Co. Spartanburg Phillies 940
1988 Star Co. St. Lucie Mets 939
1988 Star Co. St. Petersburg Cardinals 939
1988 Star Co. Tampa Tarpons 941
1988 Star Co. Tony Gwynn 554
1988 Star Co. Vero Beach Dodgers 943
1988 Star Co. Virginia Generals 943
1988 Star Co. Wade Boggs 554
1988 Star Co. West Palm Beach Expos 944
1988 Star Co. Will Clark 554
1988 Star Co. Winston-Salem Spirits 944
1988 Star Co. Winter Haven Red Sox 944
1988 Starting Lineup Talking Baseball 557
1988 T & M Sports Umpires 570
1988 T&J SC Madison Muskies 934
1988 Tastykake Phillies 575
1988 Team Bellingham Mariners 926
1988 Team Buffalo Bisons 927
1988 Team Charlotte Knights 928
1988 Team Chattanooga Lookout Legends #I 929
1988 Team Great Falls Dodgers 931
1988 Team Huntsville Stars 932
1988 Team Louisville Redbirds 934
1988 Team Modesto A's 935
1988 Team Nashville Sounds 935
1988 Team Peoria Chiefs 936
1988 Team Pittsfield Cubs 937
1988 Team Richmond Braves 938
1988 Team Rochester Red Wings . 938
1988 Team Rockford Expos 939
1988 Team Salt Lake City Trappers 939
1988 Team Tulsa Drillers 942
1988 Topps 695
1988 Topps All-Star Glossy Set of 22 698
1988 Topps All-Star Glossy Set of 60 698
1988 Topps American Baseball 699
1988 Topps Big Baseball 699
1988 Topps Box Panels 699
1988 Topps Coins 700
1988 Topps Gallery of Champions 701
1988 Topps Glossy Rookies 701
1988 Topps Mini League Leaders .. 701
1988 Topps Stickercards 701
1988 Topps Stickers 702
1988 Topps Traded 698
1988 Toys "R" Us Rookies 754
1988 Woolworth 804
1988 Worth Jose Canseco 806
1989 Ames 20/20 Club 9
1989 Bazooka 21
1989 Best Albany Yankees 944
1989 Best All-Decade Albany Yankees 944
1989 Best All-Decade Birmingham Barons 947
1989 Best All-Decade Cedar Rapids Reds 948
1989 Best All-Decade Hagerstown Suns 953
1989 Best All-Decade Springfield Cardinals 963
1989 Best Birmingham Barons 946
1989 Best Canton-Akron Indians 948
1989 Best Cedar Rapids Reds 948
1989 Best Charleston Wheelers 949
1989 Best Chattanooga Lookouts .. 949
1989 Best Columbia Mets 950
1989 Best Columbus Mudcats 950
1989 Best Eugene Emeralds 952
1989 Best Greenville Braves 953
1989 Best Hagerstown Suns 953
1989 Best Huntsville Stars 953
1989 Best Jacksonville Expos 954
1989 Best Knoxville Blue Jays 955
1989 Best Limited-Edition Albany Yankees 944
1989 Best Limited-Edition Columbus Mudcats 950
1989 Best Medford A's 956
1989 Best Memphis Chicks 956
1989 Best Orlando Twins 958
1989 Best Quad City Angels 959
1989 Best Reading Phillies 960
1989 Best Riverside Red Wave 960
1989 Best San Antonio Missions 961
1989 Best San Bernadino Spirit 962
1989 Best San Jose Giants 962
1989 Best Springfield Cardinals 963
1989 Best Stockton Ports 963
1989 Best Tulsa Drillers 965
1989 Best Limited-Edition Birmingham Barons 946
1989 Best-ProCards Baseball America Prospects 946
1989 Bob's Photo Richmond Braves 960
1989 Bowman 33
1989 Bowman Inserts 35
1989 Cal League Bakersfield Dodgers 946
1989 Cal League Modesto A's 957
1989 Cal League Palm Springs Angels 958
1989 Cal League Reno Silver Sox 960
1989 Cal League Riverside Red Wave 960
1989 Cal League Salinas Spurs 961
1989 Cal League San Bernadino Spirit 962
1989 Cal League San Jose Giants . 962
1989 Cal League Stockton Ports 963
1989 Cal League Visalia Oaks 966
1989 California League All-Stars 948
1989 Candl Coins Fold-Out Set Tidewater Tides 964
1989 Cap'n Crunch 49
1989 Chong Modesto A's 957
1989 Classic 54
1989 Classic Travel Update I 54
1989 Classic Travel Update II 54
1989 Cleveland Indians Team Set ... 60
1989 CMC AAA All-Stars 944
1989 CMC Albuquerque Dukes 945
1989 CMC Babe Ruth 61
1989 CMC Buffalo Bisons 947
1989 CMC Calgary Cannons 948
1989 CMC Colorado Springs Sky Sox 949
1989 CMC Columbus Clippers 950
1989 CMC Denver Zephyrs 950
1989 CMC Edmonton Trappers 951
1989 CMC Indianapolis Indians 954
1989 CMC Iowa Cubs 954
1989 CMC Jose Canseco 60
1989 CMC Las Vegas Stars 955
1989 CMC Mickey Mantle 60
1989 CMC Nashville Sounds 957
1989 CMC Oklahoma City 89'ers ... 957
1989 CMC Omaha Royals 957
1989 CMC Pawtucket Red Sox 958
1989 CMC Phoenix Firebirds 959
1989 CMC Portland Beavers 959
1989 CMC Richmond Braves 960
1989 CMC Rochester Red Wings .. 961
1989 CMC Scranton-Wilkes Barre Red Barons 962
1989 CMC Syracuse Chiefs 964
1989 CMC Tacoma Tigers 964
1989 CMC Tidewater Tides 964
1989 CMC Toledo Mud Hens 965
1989 CMC Tucson Toros 965
1989 CMC Vancouver Canadians 965
1989 Coca-Cola Padres 63
1989 Coca-Cola White Sox 63
1989 Colla Andre Dawson Postcards 68
1989 Colla Don Mattingly Postcards 68
1989 Colla Jose Canseco Postcards 68
1989 Colla Kevin Mitchell Postcards 68
1989 Colla Mark McGwire Postcards 68
1989 Colla Mike Greenwell Postcards 68

1989 Colla Ozzie Smith Postcards 68
1989 Donn Jennings Southern League All-Stars 963
1989 Donruss 117
1989 Donruss All-Stars 119
1989 Donruss Baseball's Best 119
1989 Donruss Grand Slammers 119
1989 Donruss MVP 119
1989 Donruss Pop-Ups 121
1989 Donruss Rookies 121
1989 Donruss Traded 121
1989 Dubuque Braves 150
1989 Dunkin' Donuts Pawtucket Red Sox 958
1989 Fleer 201
1989 Fleer All Stars 203
1989 Fleer Baseball All Stars 204
1989 Fleer Baseball MVP 204
1989 Fleer Baseball's Exciting Stars 205
1989 Fleer Box Panels 203
1989 Fleer For The Record 203
1989 Fleer Heroes of Baseball 205
1989 Fleer League Leaders 205
1989 Fleer Superstars 205
1989 Fleer Update 204
1989 Fleer World Series 203
1989 French/Bray Orioles 241
1989 Gardner's Brewers 243
1989 Grand Slam Arkansas Travelers 945
1989 Grand Slam Chattanooga Lookouts 949
1989 Grand Slam Columbia Mets 950
1989 Grand Slam El Paso Diablos 951
1989 Grand Slam Jackson Mets 954
1989 Grand Slam Midland Angels 956
1989 Grand Slam Quad City Angels 960
1989 Grand Slam So. Atlantic League All-Stars 962
1989 Grand Slam South Bend White Sox 963
1989 Grand Slam Texas League All-Stars 964
1989 Grand Slam Tulsa Drillers 965
1989 Grand Slam Wausau Timbers 966
1989 Hills Team MVP's 253
1989 Holsum Bakeries Superstars Discs 255
1989 Jones Photo Tucson Toros 965
1989 Kahn's Cooperstown Collection 282
1989 Kahn's Mets 282
1989 Kahn's Reds 282
1989 Kay Bee Superstars 286
1989 Kenner Starting Lineup 295
1989 Kenner Starting Lineup Baseball Greats 295
1989 King-B 297
1989 K-Mart 277
1989 Kodak Gold 200 Peoria Chiefs 959
1989 Legoe Bellingham Mariners 946
1989 Legoe Bend Bucks 946
1989 Marathon Cubs 324
1989 Marathon Tigers 324
1989 Mother's Cookies Astros 343
1989 Mother's Cookies Athletics 343
1989 Mother's Cookies Dodgers 343
1989 Mother's Cookies Giants 343
1989 Mother's Cookies Jose Canseco 344
1989 Mother's Cookies Ken Griffey, Jr. 344
1989 Mother's Cookies Mariners 343
1989 Mother's Cookies Mark McGwire 344
1989 Mother's Cookies Rangers 344
1989 Mother's Cookies Rookies of the Year 344
1989 Mother's Cookies Will Clark 344
1989 Pacific Trading Cards Legends II 430
1989 Police Columbus Clippers 950
1989 Police/Fire Safety Blue Jays 469
1989 Police/Fire Safety Brewers 469
1989 Police/Fire Safety Dodgers 469
1989 Police/Fire Safety Tigers 470
1989 ProCards (Poster) Auburn Astros 945
1989 ProCards Albany Yankees 945
1989 ProCards Albuquerque Dukes 945
1989 ProCards Appleton Foxes 945
1989 ProCards Asheville Tourists 945
1989 ProCards Auburn Astros 945
1989 ProCards Augusta Pirates 945
1989 ProCards Batavia Clippers 946
1989 ProCards Billings Mustangs 946
1989 ProCards Birmingham Barons 947
1989 ProCards Boise Hawks 947
1989 ProCards Buffalo Bisons 947
1989 ProCards Burlington Braves 947
1989 ProCards Calgary Cannons 948
1989 ProCards Canton-Akron Indians 948
1989 ProCards Cedar Rapids Reds 948
1989 ProCards Charleston Rainbows 948
1989 ProCards Charleston Wheelers 949
1989 ProCards Clinton Giants 949
1989 ProCards Colorado Springs Sky Sox 949
1989 ProCards Columbus Clippers 950
1989 ProCards Columbus Mudcats 950
1989 ProCards Denver Zephyrs 950
1989 ProCards Eastern League All-Stars 951
1989 ProCards Eastern League Diamond Diplomacy 951
1989 ProCards Edmonton Trappers 951
1989 ProCards Fayetteville Generals 952
1989 ProCards Gastonia Rangers 952
1989 ProCards Geneva Cubs 952
1989 ProCards Greensboro Hornets 952
1989 ProCards Greenville Braves 953
1989 ProCards Hagerstown Suns 953
1989 ProCards Harrisburg Senators 953
1989 ProCards Idaho Falls Braves 954
1989 ProCards Indianapolis Indians 954
1989 ProCards Iowa Cubs 954
1989 ProCards Jacksonville Expos 954
1989 ProCards Jamestown Expos 954
1989 ProCards Kenosha Twins 954
1989 ProCards Knoxville Blue Jays 955
1989 ProCards Las Vegas Stars 955
1989 ProCards London Tigers 955
1989 ProCards Louisville Redbirds 955
1989 ProCards Memphis Chicks 956
1989 ProCards Myrtle Beach Blue Jays 957
1989 ProCards Nashville Sounds 957
1989 ProCards New Britain Red Sox 957
1989 ProCards Oklahoma City 89'ers 957
1989 ProCards Omaha Royals 958
1989 ProCards Oneonta Yankees 958
1989 ProCards Orlando Twins 958
1989 ProCards Palm Springs Angels 958
1989 ProCards Pawtucket Red Sox 958
1989 ProCards Phoenix Firebirds 959
1989 ProCards Portland Beavers 959
1989 ProCards Pulaski Braves 959
1989 ProCards Reading Phillies 960
1989 ProCards Richmond Braves 960
1989 ProCards Riverside Red Wave 960
1989 ProCards Rochester Red Wings 961
1989 ProCards Salinas Spurs 961
1989 ProCards San Jose Giants 962
1989 ProCards Savannah Cardinals 962
1989 ProCards Scanton-Wilkes Barre Red Barons 962
1989 ProCards Shreveport Captains 962
1989 ProCards Spartanburg Phillies 963
1989 ProCards St. Catharines Blue Jays 961
1989 ProCards Stockton Ports 963
1989 ProCards Sumter Braves 964
1989 ProCards Syracuse Chiefs 964
1989 ProCards Tacoma Tigers 964

1989 ProCards Tidewater Tides 964
1989 ProCards Toledo Mud Hens .. 965
1989 ProCards Triple A All-Star Game 965
1989 ProCards Tucson Toros 965
1989 ProCards Vancouver Canadians 966
1989 ProCards Visalia Oaks 966
1989 ProCards Waterloo Diamonds 966
1989 ProCards Williamsport Bills ... 967
1989 Pucko Elmira Pioneers 951
1989 Pucko Niagara Falls Rapids .. 957
1989 Pucko Utica Blue Sox 965
1989 Pucko Welland Pirates 966
1989 Rainier Farms Super Stars Discs 481
1989 Ralston Purina 482
1989 Rock's Dugout Wichita Wrangers 967
1989 Rock's Dugout Wichita Wrangers 967
1989 Rock's Dugout Wichita Wrangers Update 967
1989 Rock's Dugout Wichita Wranglers 966
1989 Score 494
1989 Score Rising Star 497
1989 Score Superstar 498
1989 Score Traded 496
1989 Score Yankees 498
1989 Score Young Superstar Series I 497
1989 Score Young Superstar Series II 497
1989 Scoremasters 498
1989 Smokey Bear Angels All-Stars 531
1989 Smokey Bear Cardinals 531
1989 Sport Pro Butte Copper Kings 947
1989 Sport Pro Great Falls Dodgers 952
1989 Sport Pro Helena Brewers 953
1989 Sport Pro Spokane Indians 963
1989 Sportflics 539
1989 Star Beloit Brewers 946
1989 Star Co. Albany-Colonie Yankees 945
1989 Star Co. Baseball City Royals 946
1989 Star Co. Beloit Brewers 946
1989 Star Co. Bluefield Orioles 947
1989 Star Co. Bristol Tigers 947
1989 Star Co. Burlington Braves 947
1989 Star Co. Burlington Indians 947
1989 Star Co. Canton-Akron Indians 948
1989 Star Co. Cedar Rapids Reds 948
1989 Star Co. Charlotte Rangers ... 949
1989 Star Co. Clearwater Phillies ... 949
1989 Star Co. Columbus Mudcats .. 950
1989 Star Co. Dunedin Blue Jays .. 951
1989 Star Co. Durham Bulls 951
1989 Star Co. Elizabethton Twins .. 951
1989 Star Co. Erie Orioles 951
1989 Star Co. Everett Giants 952
1989 Star Co. Fort Lauderdale Yankees 952
1989 Star Co. Frederick Keys 952
1989 Star Co. Gastonia Rangers ... 952
1989 Star Co. Gold Edition 556
1989 Star Co. Greenville Braves 953
1989 Star Co. Hagerstown Suns 953
1989 Star Co. Hamilton Redbirds ... 953
1989 Star Co. Harrisburg Senators 953
1989 Star Co. Johnson City Cardinals 954
1989 Star Co. Kenosha Twins 955
1989 Star Co. Kingsport Mets 955
1989 Star Co. Kinston Indians 955
1989 Star Co. Knoxville Blue Jays . 955
1989 Star Co. Lakeland Tigers 955
1989 Star Co. Lynchburg Red Sox 956
1989 Star Co. Madison Muskies 956
1989 Star Co. Martinsville Phillies .. 956
1989 Star Co. Memphis Chicks 956
1989 Star Co. Miami Miracle 956
1989 Star Co. New Britain Red Sox 957
1989 Star Co. Osceola Astros 958
1989 Star Co. Peninsula Pilots 958
1989 Star Co. Pittsfield Mets 959
1989 Star Co. Platinum 556
1989 Star Co. Prince William Cannons 959
1989 Star Co. Princeton Pirates 959
1989 Star Co. Reading Phillies 960
1989 Star Co. Saint Lucie Mets 961
1989 Star Co. Saint Petersburg Cardinals 961
1989 Star Co. Salem Buccaneers .. 961
1989 Star Co. San Jose Giants 962
1989 Star Co. Sarasota White Sox 962
1989 Star Co. Silver Series 556
1989 Star Co. Spartanburg Phillies 963
1989 Star Co. Stockton Ports 964
1989 Star Co. Vero Beach Dodgers 966
1989 Star Co. Waterloo Diamonds 966
1989 Star Co. Watertown Indians ... 966
1989 Star Co. West Palm Beach Expos 966
1989 Star Co. Williamsport Bills 967
1989 Star Co. Winston-Salem Spirit 967
1989 Star Co. Winter Haven Red Sox 967
1989 Star Co. Wytheville Cubs 967
1989 Star Minor League Baseball .. 967
1989 Starline Prototypes 556
1989 T & M Sports Senior League 570
1989 Tastykake Phillies 575
1989 Team Charlotte Knights 949
1989 Team Chattanooga Lookouts 949
1989 Team Durham Bulls 951
1989 Team Fayetteville Generals ... 952
1989 Team Louisville Cardinals 956
1989 Team Louisville Redbirds 956
1989 Team Nashville Sounds 957
1989 Team Peoria Chiefs 959
1989 Team Richmond Braves 960
1989 Team Rockford Expos 961
1989 Team Salem Dodgers 961
1989 Team Syracuse Chiefs 964
1989 Topps 703
1989 Topps All-Star Glossy Set of 22 705
1989 Topps All-Star Glossy Set of 60 705
1989 Topps American Baseball 709
1989 Topps Batting Leaders 706
1989 Topps Big Baseball 707
1989 Topps Box Panels 706
1989 Topps Coins 708
1989 Topps Double Headers All-Stars 708
1989 Topps Glossy Rookies Set Of 22 . 705
1989 Topps Major League Debut ... 708
1989 Topps Mini League Leaders .. 709
1989 Topps Traded 706
1989 Toys "R" Us Rookies 754
1989 Tribune Albuquerque Dukes .. 945
1989 Tulsa BB Card Shop Tulsa Drillers 965
1989 Upper Deck 757
1989 Upper Deck Promos 757
1989 Very Fine Pirates 786
1989 Woolworth 804
1990 1 Hour Photo Midland Angels 981
1990 Agfa Film 3
1990 All American Baseball Team 3
1990 Ames All-Stars 9
1990 Baseball Wit 15
1990 Bazooka 21
1990 BBC, etc. Salt Lake City Trappers 986
1990 Best Albany Yankees 968
1990 Best Auburn Astros 969
1990 Best Beloit Brewers 969
1990 Best Birmingham Barons 970
1990 Best Burlington Braves 970
1990 Best Canton-Akron Indians 971
1990 Best Cedar Rapids Reds 972
1990 Best Charleston Rainbows 972
1990 Best Charleston Wheelers 972
1990 Best Clinton Giants 972
1990 Best Columbus Mudcats 973
1990 Best Everett Giants 975
1990 Best Gastonia Rangers 975
1990 Best Greensboro Hornets 976
1990 Best Greenville Braves 976
1990 Best Hagerstown Suns 976
1990 Best Hamilton Redbirds 977
1990 Best Huntsville Stars 977
1990 Best Jacksonville Expos 978
1990 Best Kenosha Twins 978
1990 Best Kingsport Mets 978

1990 Best Knoxville Blue Jays 979
1990 Best Madison Muskies 980
1990 Best Medicine Hat Blue Jays . 980
1990 Best Memphis Chicks 980
1990 Best Minor League Baseball .. 992
1990 Best New Britain Red Sox 981
1990 Best Orlando Sun Rays 982
1990 Best Pulaski Braves 984
1990 Best Reading Phillies 984
1990 Best Riverside Red Wave 985
1990 Best San Bernadino Spirit 986
1990 Best San Jose Giants 987
1990 Best South Bend White Sox .. 987
1990 Best Southern Oregon Athletics 988
1990 Best Spartanburg Phillies 988
1990 Best Springfield Cardinals 988
1990 Best Stockton Ports 988
1990 Best Sumter Braves 989
1990 Best Waterloo Diamonds 991
1990 Best Wausau Timbers 991
1990 Best Williamsport Bills 992
1990 Bob's Camera Richmond Braves 984
1990 Bowman 35
1990 Bowman Inserts 36
1990 Box Scores Appleton Foxes 968
1990 Cal League All-Stars 971
1990 Cal League Bakersfield Dodgers 969
1990 Cal League Modesto A's 981
1990 Cal League Palm Springs Angels 983
1990 Cal League Reno Silver Sox . 984
1990 Cal League Riverside Red Wave 985
1990 Cal League Salinas Spurs 986
1990 Cal League San Bernardino Spirit 986
1990 Cal League San Jose Giants . 987
1990 Cal League Stockton Ports 988
1990 Cal League Visalia Oaks 991
1990 Carolina League All-Stars 971
1990 Chong Modesto A's 981
1990 Classic #1 Draft Picks 997
1990 Classic Baseball 55
1990 Classic Series II 55
1990 Classic Series III 55
1990 CMC (TCMA) Buffalo Bisons 970
1990 CMC (TCMA) Colorado Springs Sky Sox 973
1990 CMC (TCMA) Columbus Clippers 973
1990 CMC (TCMA) Denver Zephyrs 974
1990 CMC (TCMA) Edmonton Trappers 974
1990 CMC (TCMA) Indianapolis Indians 977
1990 CMC (TCMA) Iowa Cubs 978
1990 CMC (TCMA) Las Vegas Stars 979
1990 CMC (TCMA) Louisville Redbirds 979
1990 CMC (TCMA) Nashville Sounds 981
1990 CMC (TCMA) Oklahoma City 89ers 982
1990 CMC (TCMA) Omaha Royals 982
1990 CMC (TCMA) Pawtucket Red Sox 983
1990 CMC (TCMA) Phoenix Firebirds 983
1990 CMC (TCMA) Portland Beavers 983
1990 CMC (TCMA) Richmond Braves 984
1990 CMC (TCMA) Rochester Red Wings 985
1990 CMC (TCMA) Scranton-Wilkes Barre Red Barons 987
1990 CMC (TCMA) Syracuse Chiefs 989
1990 CMC (TCMA) Tacoma Tigers 989
1990 CMC (TCMA) Tidewater Tides 989
1990 CMC (TCMA) Toledo Mud Hens 990
1990 CMC (TCMA) Tucson Toros .. 990
1990 CMC (TCMA) Vancouver Canadians 990
1990 CMC (TMCA) Calgary Cannons 971
1990 CMC Albuquerque Dukes 968
1990 Coca-Cola Detroit Tigers 64
1990 Coca-Cola Garry Templeton 64
1990 Coca-Cola Padres 64
1990 Coca-Cola White Sox 64
1990 Colla Collection Promos 68
1990 Colla Don Mattingly 69
1990 Colla Jose Canseco 68
1990 Colla Kevin Maas 69
1990 Colla Will Clark 69
1990 Colla Will Clark Postcards 69
1990 Collectors Marketing Corp. Pre-Rookie 993
1990 Diamond Appleton Foxes 968
1990 Diamond Cards Kissimmee Dodgers 979
1990 Diamond Cards Princeton Patriots 984
1990 Diamond Tampa Yankees 989
1990 DJ Southern League All-Stars 988
1990 Donruss 121
1990 Donruss A.L. Best 124
1990 Donruss Diamond Kings Supers 125
1990 Donruss Grand Slammers 124
1990 Donruss Learning Series 125
1990 Donruss MVP 124
1990 Donruss N.L. Best 125
1990 Donruss Previews 121
1990 Donruss Rookies 126
1990 Dubuque Braves 150
1990 Dubuque Braves Team Photo Set 150
1990 Elite Senior League 153
1990 Fleer 206
1990 Fleer All-Stars 208
1990 Fleer Award Winners 209
1990 Fleer Baseball All Stars 209
1990 Fleer Baseball MVP 209
1990 Fleer Box Panels 208
1990 Fleer League Leaders 210
1990 Fleer League Standouts 208
1990 Fleer Soaring Stars 210
1990 Fleer Update 208
1990 Fleer World Series 208
1990 Golden Cards Yakima Bears . 992
1990 Grand Slam Arkansas Travelers 969
1990 Grand Slam Chattanooga Lookouts 972
1990 Grand Slam Columbia Mets .. 973
1990 Grand Slam El Paso Diablos . 974
1990 Grand Slam Eugene Emeralds 975
1990 Grand Slam Jackson Mets 978
1990 Grand Slam Midland Angels .. 981
1990 Grand Slam Midwest League All-Stars 981
1990 Grand Slam Quad City Angels 984
1990 Grand Slam San Antonio Missions 986
1990 Grand Slam South Bend White Sox 988
1990 Grand Slam Texas League All-Stars 989
1990 Hills Hit Men 254
1990 Holsum Bakeries Superstars Discs 255
1990 Jumbo Sunflower Seeds 276
1990 Kahn's Mets 283
1990 Kahn's Reds 283
1990 Kay Bee Kings of Baseball 286
1990 Kenner Starting Lineup 295
1990 King-B 298
1990 K-Mart 277
1990 Leaf 307
1990 Leaf Previews 307
1990 Legoe Bellingham Mariners ... 969
1990 Legoe Bend Bucks 970
1990 Marathon Cubs 324
1990 Miller Beer Milwaukee Brewers 331
1990 Mother's Cookies Astros 345
1990 Mother's Cookies Athletics 345
1990 Mother's Cookies Dodgers 345
1990 Mother's Cookies Giants 345
1990 Mother's Cookies Jose Canseco 346
1990 Mother's Cookies Mariners 345
1990 Mother's Cookies Mark McGwire 346
1990 Mother's Cookies Matt Williams 346
1990 Mother's Cookies Nolan Ryan 346
1990 Mother's Cookies Rangers 345
1990 Mother's Cookies Will Clark ... 346
1990 O-Pee-Chee 417
1990 Pacific Legends 431
1990 Pacific Senior League 431

1990 Pepsi-Cola Red Sox 444
1990 Police Columbus Clippers 973
1990 Police Columbus Clippers 973
1990 Police/Fire Safety Blue Jays .. 470
1990 Police/Fire Safety Brewers 470
1990 Police/Fire Safety Dodgers 470
1990 Post Cereal 476
1990 ProCards A & AA Minor League Stars 995
1990 ProCards Albany Yankees 968
1990 ProCards Albuquerque Dukes 968
1990 ProCards Appleton Foxes 968
1990 ProCards Asheville Tourists .. 969
1990 ProCards Auburn Astros 969
1990 ProCards Augusta Pirates 969
1990 ProCards Batavia Clippers 969
1990 ProCards Billings Mustangs .. 970
1990 ProCards Birmingham Barons 970
1990 ProCards Boise Hawks 970
1990 ProCards Bristol Tigers 970
1990 ProCards Buffalo Bisons 970
1990 ProCards Burlington Braves .. 971
1990 ProCards Burlington Indians .. 971
1990 ProCards Calgary Cannons ... 971
1990 ProCards Canton-Akron Indians 971
1990 ProCards Cedar Rapids Reds 972
1990 ProCards Charleston Rainbows 972
1990 ProCards Charleston Wheelers 972
1990 ProCards Clinton Giants 973
1990 ProCards Colorado Springs Sky Sox 973
1990 ProCards Columbus Clippers 973
1990 ProCards Columbus Mudcats 973
1990 ProCards Denver Zephyrs 974
1990 ProCards Edmonton Trappers 974
1990 ProCards Everett Giants 975
1990 ProCards Fayetteville Generals 975
1990 ProCards Future Stars AAA Baseball 996
1990 ProCards Gastonia Rangers . 975
1990 ProCards Gate City Pioneers 975
1990 ProCards Geneva Cubs 976
1990 ProCards Greensboro Hornets 976
1990 ProCards Greenville Braves .. 976
1990 ProCards Hagerstown Suns 976
1990 ProCards Harrisburg Senators 977
1990 ProCards Huntington Cubs 977
1990 ProCards Idaho Falls Braves 977
1990 ProCards Indianapolis Indians 977
1990 ProCards Iowa Cubs 978
1990 ProCards Jacksonville Expos 978
1990 ProCards Kenosha Twins 978
1990 ProCards Knoxville Blue Jays 979
1990 ProCards Las Vegas Stars 979
1990 ProCards London Tigers 979
1990 ProCards Louisville Redbirds 979
1990 ProCards Madison Muskies ... 980
1990 ProCards Martinsville Phillies 980
1990 ProCards Memphis Chicks 980
1990 ProCards Modesto A's 981
1990 ProCards Myrtle Beach Blue Jays 981
1990 ProCards Nashville Sounds ... 981
1990 ProCards New Britain Red Sox 982
1990 ProCards Oklahoma City 89ers 982
1990 ProCards Omaha Royals 982
1990 ProCards Oneonta Yankees .. 982
1990 ProCards Orlando Sun Rays 982
1990 ProCards Palm Springs Angels 983
1990 ProCards Pawtucket Red Sox 983
1990 ProCards Phoenix Firebirds .. 983
1990 ProCards Portland Beavers ... 984
1990 ProCards Pulaski Braves 984
1990 ProCards Reading Phillies 984
1990 ProCards Richmond Braves .. 985
1990 ProCards Riverside Red Wave 985
1990 ProCards Rochester Red Wings 985
1990 ProCards Rockford Expos 985
1990 ProCards Saint Catharine's Blue Jays 986
1990 ProCards Salinas Spurs 986
1990 ProCards San Bernadino Spirit 986
1990 ProCards San Jose Giants 987
1990 ProCards Savannah Cardinals 987
1990 ProCards Scranton-Wilkes Barre Red Barons 987
1990 ProCards Southern Oregon Athletics 988
1990 ProCards Spartanburg Phillies 988
1990 ProCards Stockton Ports 989
1990 ProCards Sumter Braves 989
1990 ProCards Syracuse Chiefs 989
1990 ProCards Tacoma Tigers 989
1990 ProCards Tidewater Tides 990
1990 ProCards Toledo Mud Hens .. 990
1990 ProCards Triple A All-Stars ... 990
1990 ProCards Tucson Toros 990
1990 ProCards Tulsa Drillers 990
1990 ProCards Vancouver Canadians 991
1990 ProCards Visalia Oaks 991
1990 ProCards Waterloo Diamonds 991
1990 ProCards Wausau Timbers 991
1990 ProCards Williamsport Bills 992
1990 Pucko Elmira Pioneers 974
1990 Pucko Jamestown Expos 978
1990 Pucko Niagara Falls Rapids .. 982
1990 Pucko Pittsfield Mets 983
1990 Pucko Utica Blue Sox 990
1990 Pucko Welland Pirates 991
1990 Rocks Dugout Wichita Wranglers 992
1990 Score 499
1990 Score Dream Team 501
1990 Score McDonald's 501
1990 Score Rising Stars 501
1990 Score Superstar 501
1990 Score Traded 502
1990 Score Young Superstars Set I 502
1990 Score Young Superstars Set II 503
1990 Smokey Bear Angels 531
1990 Sport Pro Butte Copper Kings 971
1990 Sport Pro Gate City Pioneers 976
1990 Sport Pro Great Falls Dodgers 976
1990 Sport Pro Helena Brewers 977
1990 Sport Pro Spokane Indians 988
1990 Sportflics 539
1990 Sportprint Lynchburg Red Sox 980
1990 Sportprint Prince William Cannons 984
1990 Sportprint Winston-Salem Spirit 992
1990 Sportsprint Durham Bulls 974
1990 Sportsprint Durham Bulls 974
1990 Sportsprint Frederick Keys 975
1990 Sportsprint Kinston Indians 979
1990 Star Co. Albany Yankees 968
1990 Star Co. Baseball City Royals 969
1990 Star Co. Beloit Brewers 969
1990 Star Co. Bluefield Orioles 970
1990 Star Co. Bristol Tigers 970
1990 Star Co. Burlington Braves 971
1990 Star Co. Canton-Akron Indians 971
1990 Star Co. Charlotte Rangers 972
1990 Star Co. Clearwater Phillies.... 972
1990 Star Co. Columbus Mudcats... 974
1990 Star Co. Dunedin Blue Jays ... 974
1990 Star Co. Elizabethton Twin 974
1990 Star Co. Erie Sailors 974
1990 Star Co. Florida State League All-Stars 975
1990 Star Co. Gastonia Rangers 975
1990 Star Co. Geneva Cubs 976
1990 Star Co. Greensboro Hornets 976
1990 Star Co. Greenville Braves..... 976
1990 Star Co. Hagerstown Suns..... 977
1990 Star Co. Hamilton Redbirds.... 977

1990 Star Co. Harrisburg Senators 977
1990 Star Co. Johnson City Cardinals 978
1990 Star Co. Kenosha Twins 978
1990 Star Co. Kingsport Mets 978
1990 Star Co. Knoxville Blue Jays . 979
1990 Star Co. Lakeland Tigers 979
1990 Star Co. Memphis Chicks 980
1990 Star Co. New Britain Red Sox 982
1990 Star Co. Orlando Sun Rays ... 982
1990 Star Co. Osceola Astros 983
1990 Star Co. Peninsula Pilots 983
1990 Star Co. Reading Phillies 984
1990 Star Co. Saint Lucie Mets 986
1990 Star Co. Saint Petersburg Cardinals 986
1990 Star Co. Salem Buccaneers .. 986
1990 Star Co. San Jose Giants 987
1990 Star Co. Sarasota White Sox 987
1990 Star Co. Shreveport Captains 987
1990 Star Co. South Atlantic League All-Stars 987
1990 Star Co. Spartanburg Phillies 988
1990 Star Co. Vero Beach Dodgers 991
1990 Star Co. Watertown Indians 991
1990 Star Co. Wausau Timbers 991
1990 Star Co. West Palm Beach Expos 992
1990 Star Co. Williamsport Bills 992
1990 Star Co. Winter Haven Red Sox 992
1990 Star Ft. Lauderdale Yankees . 975
1990 Star Miami Miracle I 980
1990 Star Miami Miracle II 980
1990 Star Minor League Baseball Wax 997
1990 Star Sophomore Stars 556
1990 Starline 557
1990 Target Dodgers 571
1990 Tastykake Phillies 576
1990 Team (Play II) Columbia Mets 973
1990 Team 25th Anniversary Richmond Braves 985
1990 Team Buffalo Bisons 970
1990 Team Charlotte Knights 972
1990 Team Columbus Clippers 973
1990 Team Louisville Redbirds 980
1990 Team Peoria Chiefs 983
1990 Team Richmond Braves 985
1990 Team Rochester Red Wings . 985
1990 Team Sully's Pub Peoria Chiefs 983
1990 Team Syracuse Chiefs 989
1990 Team-Hill's Nashville Sounds 981
1990 Team-Lithocenter Rockford Expos 985
1990 Team-WTAR Tidewater Tides 990
1990 Topps 709
1990 Topps All-Star Glossy Set of 22 712
1990 Topps All-Star Glossy Set of 60 712
1990 Topps Batting Leaders 713
1990 Topps Big Baseball 713
1990 Topps Box Panels 713
1990 Topps Coins 717
1990 Topps Glossy Rookies 712
1990 Topps Heads Up! 717
1990 Topps Major League Debut ... 714
1990 Topps Major League Debut Promo 714
1990 Topps Senior League 717
1990 Topps Traded 712
1990 Topps TV All-Stars 715
1990 Topps TV Cardinals Team Set 715
1990 Topps TV Cubs Team Set 716
1990 Topps TV Mets Team Set 716
1990 Topps TV Red Sox Team Set 716
1990 Topps TV Yankees Team Set 717
1990 Toys "R" Us Rookies 754
1990 Tulsa BB Card Shop Tulsa Drillers 990
1990 U.S. Playing Card All-Stars ... 784
1990 Upper Deck 760
1990 Upper Deck Reggie Jackson Heroes 762
1990 Woolworth 805
1991 "1953" Topps Archives 725
1991 "1953" Topps Archives Promos 725
1991 Alrak Griffey Gazette 4
1991 Arena Holograms 9
1991 Bazooka 21
1991 Bleachers Frank Thomas 24
1991 Bob's Camera Richmond Braves 1020
1991 Bowman 36
1991 Burger King Huntsville Stars 1012
1991 Cal League Bakersfield Dodgers 1004
1991 Cal League Cal League All-Stars 1006
1991 Cal League Reno Silver Sox 1020
1991 Classic #1 Draft Picks 1027
1991 Classic 56
1991 Classic Best Appleton Foxes 1003
1991 Classic Best Ashville Tourists 1003
1991 Classic Best Auburn Astros 1003
1991 Classic Best Augusta Pirates 1003
1991 Classic Best Baseball City Royals 1004
1991 Classic Best Batavia Clippers 1004
1991 Classic Best Bellingham Mariners 1004
1991 Classic Best Beloit Brewers 1004
1991 Classic Best Bend Bucks 1004
1991 Classic Best Bluefield Orioles 1005
1991 Classic Best Boise Hawks ... 1005
1991 Classic Best Bristol Tigers ... 1005
1991 Classic Best Burlington Astros 1006
1991 Classic Best Cedar Rapids Reds 1006
1991 Classic Best Charleston Rainbows 1007
1991 Classic Best Charleston Wheelers 1007
1991 Classic Best Charlotte Rangers 1007
1991 Classic Best Clearwater Phillies 1007
1991 Classic Best Clinton Giants 1008
1991 Classic Best Columbus Indians 1008
1991 Classic Best Dunedin Blue Jays 1008
1991 Classic Best Durham Bulls .. 1009
1991 Classic Best Elmira Pioneers 1009
1991 Classic Best Erie Sailors 1009
1991 Classic Best Eugene Emeralds 1009
1991 Classic Best Everett Giants 1010
1991 Classic Best Fayetteville Generais 1010
1991 Classic Best Frederick Keys 1010
1991 Classic Best Ft. Lauderdale Yankees 1010
1991 Classic Best Gastonia Rangers 1010
1991 Classic Best Geneva Cubs .. 1011
1991 Classic Best Gold Bonus 999
1991 Classic Best Greenville Braves 1011
1991 Classic Best Hamilton Redbirds 1011
1991 Classic Best High Desert Mavericks 1012
1991 Classic Best Huntington Cubs 1012
1991 Classic Best Huntsville Stars 1012
1991 Classic Best Jamestown Expos 1013
1991 Classic Best Johnson City Cardinals 1013
1991 Classic Best Kane County Cougars 1013
1991 Classic Best Kenosha Twins 1013
1991 Classic Best Kingsport Mets 1014

1991 Classic Best Kinston Indians 1014
1991 Classic Best Lakeland Tigers 1014
1991 Classic Best Lynchburg Red Sox 1015
1991 Classic Best Macon Braves . 1015
1991 Classic Best Madison Muskies 1015
1991 Classic Best Martinsville Phillies 1015
1991 Classic Best Miami Miracle .. 1016
1991 Classic Best Minors - Major League Way 997
1991 Classic Best Modesto A's 1016
1991 Classic Best Myrtle Beach Hurricanes 1017
1991 Classic Best Niagara Falls Rapids 1017
1991 Classic Best Osceola Astros 1017
1991 Classic Best Peninsula Pilots 1018
1991 Classic Best Peoria Chiefs .. 1018
1991 Classic Best Pittsfield Mets 1019
1991 Classic Best Prince William Cannons 1019
1991 Classic Best Princeton Reds 1019
1991 Classic Best Pulaski Braves 1019
1991 Classic Best Quad City Angels 1020
1991 Classic Best Rockford Expos 1020
1991 Classic Best Salem Buccaneers 1021
1991 Classic Best Salinas Spurs 1021
1991 Classic Best San Bernardino Spirit 1022
1991 Classic Best San Jose Giants 1022
1991 Classic Best Sarasota White Sox 1022
1991 Classic Best Savannah Cardinals 1022
1991 Classic Best South Bend White Sox 1023
1991 Classic Best Southern Oregon A's 1023
1991 Classic Best Spartanburg Phillies 1023
1991 Classic Best Spokane Indians 1023
1991 Classic Best Springfield Cardinals 1023
1991 Classic Best St. Catherines Blue Jays 1020
1991 Classic Best St. Lucie Mets 1021
1991 Classic Best St. Petersburg Cardinals 1021
1991 Classic Best Stockton Ports 1024
1991 Classic Best Sumter Flyers . 1024
1991 Classic Best Utica Blue Sox 1025
1991 Classic Best Vero Beach Dodgers 1025
1991 Classic Best Visalia Oaks 1026
1991 Classic Best Waterloo Diamonds 1026
1991 Classic Best Watertown Indians 1026
1991 Classic Best Welland Pirates 1026
1991 Classic Best West Palm Beach Expos 1026
1991 Classic Best Winston-Salem Spirits 1027
1991 Classic Best Winter Haven Red Sox 1027
1991 Classic Best Yakima Bears . 1027
1991 Classic Collector's Edition 57
1991 Classic Series II 56
1991 Classic Series III 57
1991 Coca-Cola Tigers 64
1991 Colla Barry Bonds 69
1991 Colla Collection Promos 69
1991 Colla Darryl Strawberry 70
1991 Colla David Justice 70
1991 Colla Dwight Gooden 69
1991 Colla Joe Carter 69
1991 Colla Ken Griffey, Jr. 70
1991 Colla Roberto Alomar 69
1991 Colla Ryne Sandberg 70
1991 Colla Ryne Sandberg Postcards 70
1991 Conlon Collection 72
1991 Country Hearth Mariners 76
1991 Cracker Jack Topps I 79
1991 Cracker Jack Topps II 79
1991 Crown/Coke Orioles 82
1991 Denny's Grand Slam 86
1991 Donruss 126
1991 Donruss Elite 129
1991 Donruss Grand Slammers 129
1991 Donruss Highlights 128
1991 Donruss Previews 126
1991 Donruss Rookies 129
1991 Dubuque Braves 151
1991 Dubuque Braves Team Photo Set 150
1991 Dunkin' Donuts Pawtucket Red Sox 1018
1991 Fleer 210
1991 Fleer All Stars 212
1991 Fleer Box Panels 213
1991 Fleer ProVisions 212
1991 Fleer Ultra 213
1991 Fleer Ultra Gold 215
1991 Fleer Ultra Update 215
1991 Fleer Update 213
1991 Fleer World Series 213
1991 Frank Chong Modesto A's ... 1016
1991 Front Row Draft Picks 1027
1991 Holsum Bakeries Superstars Discs 255
1991 Homers Cookies 255
1991 Impel/Line Drive Pre-Rookie AA 1000
1991 Impel/Line Drive Pre-Rookie AAA 999
1991 Jimmy Dean 84
1991 Jumbo Sunflower Seeds 276
1991 Kahn's Mets 283
1991 Kahn's Reds 283
1991 Kellogg's 3-D 293
1991 Kellogg's Baseball Greats 294
1991 Kenner Starting Lineup 296
1991 Kraft Albany-Colonie Yankees 1002
1991 Kraft Syracuse Chiefs 1024
1991 Leaf 309
1991 Leaf Gold Rookies 311
1991 Leaf Previews 309
1991 Lewis Negro League 318
1991 Marathon Cubs 324
1991 McDonald's Cleveland Indians 326
1991 Medford Phillies 328
1991 Merchants Bank Syracuse Chiefs 1024
1991 Miller High Life Brewers 331
1991 Mootown Snackers 336
1991 Mother's Cookies Astros 346
1991 Mother's Cookies Athletics 346
1991 Mother's Cookies Dodgers 347
1991 Mother's Cookies Giants 347
1991 Mother's Cookies Griffeys 347
1991 Mother's Cookies Nolan Ryan 300 Wins 347
1991 Mother's Cookies Rangers 347
1991 O-Pee-Chee Premier 419
1991 Pacific Nolan Ryan 432
1991 Pacific Nolan Ryan 7th No-Hitter 433
1991 Pacific Nolan Ryan Milestones 433
1991 Pacific Ryan 7th No-Hitter Hologram 433
1991 Pacific Senior League 432
1991 Pepsi-Cola Red Sox 444
1991 Petro Canada All-Star Fanfest Standups 446
1991 Play II Columbia Mets 1008
1991 Police Columbus Clippers ... 1008
1991 Police/Fire Safety Brewers 470
1991 Post Cereal - Canadian 477
1991 Post Cereal 476
1991 Procards Albany Yankees 1003
1991 ProCards Albuquerque Dukes 1003
1991 ProCards Appleton Foxes ... 1003
1991 ProCards Arkansas Travelers 1003
1991 Procards Ashville Tourists ... 1003
1991 ProCards Auburn Astros 1003
1991 ProCards Augusta Pirates ... 1003
1991 ProCards Baseball City Royals 1004
1991 ProCards Batavia Clippers .. 1004
1991 ProCards Bellingham Mariners 1004
1991 ProCards Beloit Brewers 1004
1991 ProCards Bend Bucks 1004

1991 ProCards Billings Mustangs 1005
1991 ProCards Birmingham Barons 1005
1991 ProCards Bluefield Orioles .. 1005
1991 ProCards Boise Hawks 1005
1991 ProCards Bristol Tigers 1005
1991 ProCards Buffalo Bisons 1005
1991 ProCards Burlington Astros 1006
1991 ProCards Burlington Indians 1006
1991 ProCards Calgary Cannons 1006
1991 ProCards Canton-Akron Indians 1006
1991 ProCards Carolina League All-Star Game 1006
1991 ProCards Carolina Mudcats 1006
1991 ProCards Cedar Rapids Reds 1007
1991 ProCards Charleston Rainbows 1007
1991 ProCards Charleston Wheelers 1007
1991 ProCards Charlotte Knights 1007
1991 ProCards Charlotte Rangers 1007
1991 ProCards Chattanooga Lookouts 1007
1991 ProCards Clearwater Phillies 1007
1991 ProCards Clinton Giants 1008
1991 ProCards Colorado Springs Sky Sox 1008
1991 ProCards Columbus Clippers 1008
1991 ProCards Columbus Indians 1008
1991 ProCards Denver Zephyrs ... 1008
1991 ProCards Dunedin Blue Jays 1008
1991 ProCards Durham Bulls 1009
1991 ProCards Durham Bulls Update 1009
1991 ProCards Edmondton Trappers 1009
1991 ProCards El Paso Diablos ... 1009
1991 ProCards Elizabethton Twins 1009
1991 ProCards Elmira Pioneers ... 1009
1991 ProCards Erie Sailors 1009
1991 ProCards Eugene Emeralds 1009
1991 ProCards Everett Giants 1010
1991 ProCards Fayetteville Generais 1010
1991 ProCards Florida State League All Stars 1010
1991 ProCards Frederick Keys 1010
1991 ProCards Ft. Lauderdale Yankees 1010
1991 ProCards Gastonia Rangers 1010
1991 ProCards Geneva Cubs 1011
1991 ProCards Greensboro Hornets 1011
1991 ProCards Greenville Braves 1011
1991 ProCards Hagerstown Suns 1011
1991 ProCards Hamilton Redbirds 1011
1991 ProCards Harrisburg Senators 1011
1991 ProCards High Desert Mavericks 1012
1991 ProCards Huntington Cubs 1012
1991 ProCards Huntsville Stars ... 1012
1991 ProCards Idaho Falls Braves 1012
1991 ProCards Indianapolis Indians 1012
1991 ProCards Iowa Cubs 1013
1991 ProCards Jackson Generals 1013
1991 ProCards Jacksonville Suns 1013
1991 ProCards Jamestown Expos 1013
1991 ProCards Johnson City Cardinals 1013
1991 ProCards Kane County Cougars 1013
1991 ProCards Kenosha Twins 1014
1991 ProCards Kingsport Mets 1014
1991 ProCards Kinston Indians 1014
1991 ProCards Kissimmee Dodgers 1014
1991 ProCards Knoxville Blue Jays 1014
1991 ProCards Lakeland Tigers ... 1014
1991 ProCards Las Vegas Stars .. 1014
1991 ProCards London Tigers 1014
1991 ProCards Louisville Redbirds 1015
1991 ProCards Lynchburg Red Sox 1015
1991 ProCards Macon Braves 1015
1991 ProCards Madison Muskies 1015
1991 ProCards Martinsville Phillies 1015
1991 ProCards Medicine Hat Blue Jays 1015
1991 ProCards Memphis Chicks .. 1016
1991 ProCards Miami Miracle 1016
1991 ProCards Midland Angels 1016
1991 ProCards Midwest League All-Star Game 1016
1991 ProCards Modesto A's 1016
1991 ProCards Myrtle Beach Hurricanes 1017
1991 ProCards Nashville Sounds 1017
1991 ProCards New Britain Red Sox 1017
1991 ProCards Niagara Falls Rapids 1017
1991 ProCards Oklahoma City 89ers 1017
1991 ProCards Omaha Royals 1017
1991 ProCards Oneonta Yankees 1017
1991 ProCards Orlando Sun Rays 1017
1991 ProCards Osceola Astros 1018
1991 ProCards Palm Springs Angels 1018
1991 ProCards Pawtucket Red Sox 1018
1991 ProCards Peninsula Pilots ... 1018
1991 ProCards Peoria Chiefs 1018
1991 ProCards Phoenix Firebirds 1018
1991 ProCards Pittsfield Mets 1019
1991 ProCards Pocatello Pioneers 1019
1991 ProCards Portland Beavers 1019
1991 ProCards Prince William Cannons 1019
1991 ProCards Princeton Reds 1019
1991 ProCards Pulaski Braves 1019
1991 ProCards Quad City Angels 1020
1991 ProCards Reading Phillies ... 1020
1991 ProCards Richmond Braves 1020
1991 ProCards Rochester Red Wings 1020
1991 ProCards Rockford Expos ... 1020
1991 ProCards Salem Buccaneers 1021
1991 ProCards Salinas Spurs 1021
1991 ProCards Salt Lake Trappers 1021
1991 ProCards San Antonio Missions 1021
1991 ProCards San Bernardino Spirit 1022
1991 ProCards San Jose Giants .. 1022
1991 ProCards Sarasota White Sox 1022
1991 ProCards Savannah Cardinals 1022
1991 ProCards Scranton Red Barons 1022
1991 ProCards Shreveport Captains 1022
1991 ProCards South Atlantic League All-Stars 1022
1991 ProCards South Bend White Sox 1023
1991 ProCards Southern Oregon A's 1023
1991 ProCards Southern Oregon A's 1023
1991 ProCards Spartanburg Phillies 1023
1991 ProCards Spokane Indians .. 1023
1991 ProCards Springfield Cardinals 1023
1991 ProCards St. Catharines Blue Jays 1020

1991 ProCards St. Lucie Mets 1021
1991 ProCards St. Petersburg Cardinals 1021
1991 ProCards Stockton Ports...... 1024
1991 ProCards Sumter Flyers 1024
1991 ProCards Syracuse Chiefs .. 1024
1991 ProCards Tacoma Tigers 1024
1991 ProCards Tidewater Tides ... 1024
1991 ProCards Toledo Mud Hens 1025
1991 ProCards Tomorrow's Heroes 1002
1991 ProCards Triple A All-Star Game 1025
1991 ProCards Tucson Toros 1025
1991 ProCards Tulsa Drillers 1025
1991 ProCards Utica Blue Sox 1025
1991 ProCards Vancouver Canadians 1025
1991 ProCards Vero Beach Dodgers 1025
1991 ProCards Visalia Oaks 1026
1991 ProCards Waterloo Diamonds 1026
1991 ProCards Watertown Indians 1026
1991 ProCards Welland Pirates ... 1026
1991 ProCards West Palm Beach Expos 1026
1991 Procards Wichita Wranglers 1026
1991 ProCards Williamsport Bills 1027
1991 ProCards Winston-Salem Spirits 1027
1991 ProCards Winter Haven Red Sox 1027
1991 ProCards Yakima Bears 1027
1991 Rock's-Team Wichita Wranglers 1026
1991 Rock's-Team Wichita Wranglers 1027
1991 Score 503
1991 Score Cooperstown 505
1991 Score Hot Rookies 506
1991 Score Mickey Mantle 506
1991 Score Rising Star 506
1991 Score Rookies 507
1991 Score Superstar 506
1991 Score Traded 507
1991 Smokey Bear Angels 531
1991 Sport Pro Billings Mustangs 1005
1991 Sport Pro Butte Copper Kings 1006
1991 Sport Pro Great Falls Dodgers 1011
1991 Sport Pro Gulf Coast Rangers 1011
1991 Sport Pro Helena Brewers ... 1012
1991 Sport Pro Idaho Falls Braves 1012
1991 Sport Pro Medicine Hat Blue Jays 1016
1991 Sport Pro Salt Lake City Trappers 1021
1991 Sport-Pro Butte Copper Kings 1006
1991 Sport-Pro Pocatello Pioneers 1019
1991 Studio 558
1991 Studio Preview 558
1991 Team Blue Shield Buffalo Bisons 1005
1991 Team Kane County Cougars 1013
1991 Team Louisville Redbirds 1015
1991 Team Midland Angels 1016
1991 Team Nashville Sounds 1017
1991 Team Peoria Chiefs 1018
1991 Team Syracuse Chiefs 1024
1991 Team Tampa Yankees 1024
1991 Team Tulsa Drillers 1025
1991 Topps 718
1991 Topps All-Star Glossy Set of 22 721
1991 Topps Babe Ruth 722
1991 Topps East Coast National Reprints 725
1991 Topps Glossy Rookies 721
1991 Topps Major League Debut ... 722
1991 Topps Stadium Club 722
1991 Topps Stadium Club Charter Members 724
1991 Topps Stadium Club Members Only 724
1991 Topps Traded 721
1991 Topps Wax Box Cards 721
1991 Toys "R" Us Rookies 755
1991 U.S. Playing Card All-Stars 785
1991 Upper Deck 762
1991 Upper Deck Comic Ball 2 766
1991 Upper Deck Final Edition 765
1991 Upper Deck Hank Aaron Heroes 765
1991 Upper Deck Heroes of Baseball 765
1991 Upper Deck Nolan Ryan Heroes 765
1991 Upper Deck Silver Sluggers .. 766
1991 Woolworth 805
1992 7-11 Slurpee Superstar Action Coins 526
1992 Action Packed All-Star Gallery Series I 1
1992 Action Packed All-Star Gallery Series II 2
1992 Action Packed Gold 2
1992 Action Packed Promos 1
1992 Bazooka 21
1992 Ben's Bakery Super Hitters Discs 22
1992 Bleachers David Justice 24
1992 Bleachers Ken Griffey, Jr. 24
1992 Bob's Camera Richmond Braves 1048
1992 Bowman 39
1992 Cal League Bakersfield Dodgers 1033
1992 Cal League Reno Silver Sox 1047
1992 Carl's Jr. Padres 50
1992 Carlson Travel 1982 Brewers .. 50
1992 Classic Best 1028
1992 Classic Best Albany Polecats 1032
1992 Classic Best Appleton Foxes 1032
1992 Classic Best Asheville Tourists 1033
1992 Classic Best Auburn Astros 1033
1992 Classic Best Augusta Pirates 1033
1992 Classic Best Baseball City Royals 1033
1992 Classic Best Batavia Clippers 1033
1992 Classic Best Bellingham Mariners 1033
1992 Classic Best Beloit Brewers 1034
1992 Classic Best Bend Rockies .. 1034
1992 Classic Best Blue Bonus 1029
1992 Classic Best Bluefield Orioles 1034
1992 Classic Best Boise Hawks ... 1034
1992 Classic Best Bristol Tigers ... 1035
1992 Classic Best Burlington Astros 1035
1992 Classic Best Burlington Indians 1035
1992 Classic Best Cedar Rapids Reds 1035
1992 Classic Best Charleston Rainbows 1035
1992 Classic Best Charleston Wheelers 1036
1992 Classic Best Charlotte Rangers 1036
1992 Classic Best Clearwater Phillies 1036
1992 Classic Best Clinton Giants 1036
1992 Classic Best Columbia Mets 1037
1992 Classic Best Columbus Redstixx 1037
1992 Classic Best Dunedin Blue Jays 1037
1992 Classic Best Elizabethton Twins 1038
1992 Classic Best Elmira Pioneers 1038
1992 Classic Best Erie Sailors 1038
1992 Classic Best Eugene Emeralds 1038
1992 Classic Best Everett Giants 1039
1992 Classic Best Fayetteville Generals 1039
1992 Classic Best Frederick Keys 1039
1992 Classic Best Ft. Lauderdale Yankees 1039
1992 Classic Best Ft. Meyers Miracle 1039

1992 Classic Best Gastonia Rangers 1040
1992 Classic Best Geneva Cubs .. 1040
1992 Classic Best Greensboro Hornets 1040
1992 Classic Best Hamilton Redbirds 1040
1992 Classic Best High Desert Mavericks 1041
1992 Classic Best Huntington Cubs 1041
1992 Classic Best Jamestown Expos 1042
1992 Classic Best Johnson City Cardinals 1042
1992 Classic Best Kane County Cougars 1042
1992 Classic Best Kenosha Twins 1042
1992 Classic Best Kingsport Mets 1042
1992 Classic Best Kinston Indians 1043
1992 Classic Best Lakeland Tigers 1043
1992 Classic Best Lynchburg Red Sox 1043
1992 Classic Best Macon Braves 1043
1992 Classic Best Madison Muskies 1044
1992 Classic Best Martinsville Phillies 1044
1992 Classic Best Modesto A's 1044
1992 Classic Best Myrtle Beach Hurricanes 1045
1992 Classic Best Niagara Falls Rapids 1045
1992 Classic Best Osceola Astros 1045
1992 Classic Best Palm Springs Angels 1046
1992 Classic Best Peninsula Pilots 1046
1992 Classic Best Peoria Chiefs .. 1046
1992 Classic Best Pittsfield Mets 1046
1992 Classic Best Prince Williams Cannons 1047
1992 Classic Best Princeton Reds 1047
1992 Classic Best Pulaski Braves 1047
1992 Classic Best Quad City River Bandits 1047
1992 Classic Best Red Bonus 1029
1992 Classic Best Rockford Expos 1048
1992 Classic Best Salem Buccaneers 1048
1992 Classic Best Salinas Spurs .. 1048
1992 Classic Best San Bernardino Spirit 1049
1992 Classic Best San Jose Giants 1049
1992 Classic Best Sarasota White Sox 1049
1992 Classic Best Savannah Cardinals 1049
1992 Classic Best South Bend White Sox 1050
1992 Classic Best Southern Oregon A's 1050
1992 Classic Best Spartanburg Phillies 1050
1992 Classic Best Spokane Indians 1050
1992 Classic Best Springfield Cardinals 1050
1992 Classic Best St. Catharines Blue Jays 1050
1992 Classic Best St. Lucie Mets 1051
1992 Classic Best St. Petersburg Cardinals 1051
1992 Classic Best Stockton Ports 1051
1992 Classic Best Utica Blue Sox 1052
1992 Classic Best Vero Beach Dodgers 1052
1992 Classic Best Visalia Oaks 1052
1992 Classic Best Waterloo Diamonds 1052
1992 Classic Best Watertown Indians 1052
1992 Classic Best Welland Pirates 1053
1992 Classic Best West Palm Beach Expos 1053
1992 Classic Best Winston-Salem Spirits 1053
1992 Classic Best Winter Haven Red Sox 1053
1992 Classic Best Yakima Bears . 1053
1992 Classic Best/Durham Bulls .. 1038
1992 Classic Collector's Edition 59
1992 Classic Series I 58
1992 Classic Series II 58
1992 Colla All-Stars 70
1992 Colla Barry Bonds 71
1992 Colla Collection Promos 70
1992 Colla Frank Thomas 71
1992 Colla Jeff Bagwell 71
1992 Colla Mark McGwire 71
1992 Colla Nolan Ryan 71
1992 Colla Steve Avery 70
1992 Colla Tony Gwynn 71
1992 Conlon Collection 73
1992 Cracker Jack Donruss I 79
1992 Cracker Jack Donruss II 80
1992 Crown Orioles Action Standups 83
1992 Dairy Queen Team USA 84
1992 Denny's Grand Slam 86
1992 Diet Pepsi All-Stars 88
1992 Donruss 129
1992 Donruss Bonus Cards 132
1992 Donruss Diamond Kings 132
1992 Donruss Elite 132
1992 Donruss McDonald's 134
1992 Donruss Nolan Ryan Career Series 134
1992 Donruss Previews 129
1992 Donruss Rookie Phenoms 133
1992 Donruss Rookies 132
1992 Donruss Triple Play 133
1992 Donruss Triple Play Gallery of Stars 134
1992 Dunkin' Donuts Red Sox 151
1992 Eclipse Negro League 153
1992 Fleer 215
1992 Fleer 7-Eleven 221
1992 Fleer All-Stars 217
1992 Fleer Excel 1029
1992 Fleer Excel All-Stars 1030
1992 Fleer Excel League Leaders 1030
1992 Fleer Lumber Co. 218
1992 Fleer Roger Clemens 218
1992 Fleer Rookie Sensations 218
1992 Fleer Smoke 'N Heat 218
1992 Fleer Team Leaders 218
1992 Fleer Ultra 219
1992 Fleer Ultra All-Rookies 221
1992 Fleer Ultra All-Stars 221
1992 Fleer Ultra Award Winners 221
1992 Fleer Ultra Tony Gwynn 221
1992 Fleer Update 218
1992 Fleer/ProCards Albany Polecats 1032
1992 Fleer/ProCards Albany Yankees 1032
1992 Fleer/ProCards Albuquerque Dukes 1032
1992 Fleer/ProCards Appleton Foxes 1032
1992 Fleer/ProCards Arkansas Travelers 1033
1992 Fleer/ProCards Auburn Astros 1033
1992 Fleer/ProCards Augusta Pirates 1033
1992 Fleer/ProCards Baseball City Royals 1033
1992 Fleer/ProCards Batavia Clippers 1033
1992 Fleer/ProCards Bellingham Mariners 1034
1992 Fleer/ProCards Beloit Brewers 1034
1992 Fleer/ProCards Bend Rockies 1034
1992 Fleer/ProCards Billings Mustangs 1034
1992 Fleer/ProCards Binghamton Mets 1034
1992 Fleer/ProCards Birmingham Barons 1034
1992 Fleer/ProCards Bluefield Orioles 1034
1992 Fleer/ProCards Boise Hawks 1034
1992 Fleer/ProCards Bristol Tigers 1035
1992 Fleer/ProCards Buffalo Bisons 1035

1992 Fleer/ProCards Burlington Astros 1035
1992 Fleer/ProCards Burlington Indians 1035
1992 Fleer/ProCards Calgary Connons 1035
1992 Fleer/ProCards Canton-Akron Indians 1035
1992 Fleer/ProCards Carolina Mudcats 1035
1992 Fleer/ProCards Cedar Rapids Reds 1035
1992 Fleer/ProCards Charleston Rainbows 1036
1992 Fleer/ProCards Charleston Wheelers 1036
1992 Fleer/ProCards Charlotte Knights 1036
1992 Fleer/ProCards Charlotte Rangers 1036
1992 Fleer/ProCards Chattanooga Lookouts 1036
1992 Fleer/ProCards Clearwater Phillies 1036
1992 Fleer/ProCards Clinton Giants 1036
1992 Fleer/ProCards Colorado Springs Sky Sox 1036
1992 Fleer/ProCards Columbia Mets 1037
1992 Fleer/ProCards Columbus Clippers 1037
1992 Fleer/ProCards Columbus Red-stixx 1037
1992 Fleer/ProCards Denver Zephyrs 1037
1992 Fleer/ProCards Dunedin Blue Jays 1038
1992 Fleer/ProCards Durham Bulls 1038
1992 Fleer/ProCards Edmonton Trappers 1038
1992 Fleer/ProCards El Paso Diablos 1038
1992 Fleer/ProCards Elizabethton Twins 1038
1992 Fleer/ProCards Elmira Pioneers 1038
1992 Fleer/ProCards Erie Sailors . 1038
1992 Fleer/ProCards Eugene Emeralds 1039
1992 Fleer/ProCards Everett Giants 1039
1992 Fleer/ProCards Fayetteville Generals 1039
1992 Fleer/ProCards Frederick Keys 1039
1992 Fleer/ProCards Ft. Lauderdale Yankees 1039
1992 Fleer/ProCards Ft. Myers Miracle 1039
1992 Fleer/ProCards Gastonia Rangers 1040
1992 Fleer/ProCards Geneva Cubs 1040
1992 Fleer/ProCards Greensboro Hornets 1040
1992 Fleer/ProCards Greenville Braves 1040
1992 Fleer/ProCards Gulf Coast Dodgers 1040
1992 Fleer/ProCards Gulf Coast Mets 1040
1992 Fleer/ProCards Gulf Coast Yankees 1040
1992 Fleer/ProCards Hagerstown Suns 1040
1992 Fleer/ProCards Hamilton Redbirds 1041
1992 Fleer/ProCards Harrisburg Senators 1041
1992 Fleer/ProCards Helena Brewers 1041
1992 Fleer/ProCards Huntington Cubs 1041
1992 Fleer/ProCards Huntsville Stars 1041
1992 Fleer/ProCards Idaho Falls Gems 1041
1992 Fleer/ProCards Indianapolis Indians 1041
1992 Fleer/ProCards Iowa Cubs .. 1041
1992 Fleer/ProCards Jackson Generals 1041
1992 Fleer/ProCards Jacksonville Suns 1042
1992 Fleer/ProCards Jamestown Expos 1042
1992 Fleer/ProCards Johnson City Cardinals 1042
1992 Fleer/ProCards Kane County Cougars 1042
1992 Fleer/ProCards Kenosha Twins 1042
1992 Fleer/ProCards Kingsport Mets 1042
1992 Fleer/ProCards Kinston Indians 1043
1992 Fleer/ProCards Knoxville Blue Jays 1043
1992 Fleer/ProCards Lakeland Tigers 1043
1992 Fleer/ProCards Las Vegas Stars 1043
1992 Fleer/ProCards London Tigers 1043
1992 Fleer/ProCards Louisville Redbirds 1043
1992 Fleer/ProCards Lynchburg Red Sox 1043
1992 Fleer/ProCards Macon Braves 1043
1992 Fleer/ProCards Madison Muskies 1044
1992 Fleer/ProCards Martinsville Phillies 1044
1992 Fleer/ProCards Medicine Hat Blue Jays 1044
1992 Fleer/ProCards Memphis Chicks 1044
1992 Fleer/ProCards Midland Angels 1044
1992 Fleer/ProCards Modesto A's 1044
1992 Fleer/ProCards Myrtle Beach Hurricanes 1045
1992 Fleer/ProCards Nashville Sounds 1045
1992 Fleer/ProCards New Britain Red Sox 1045
1992 Fleer/ProCards Niagara Falls Rapids 1045
1992 Fleer/ProCards Oklahoma City 89ers 1045
1992 Fleer/ProCards Omaha Royals 1045
1992 Fleer/ProCards Orlando Sunrays 1045
1992 Fleer/ProCards Osceola Astros 1045
1992 Fleer/ProCards Palm Springs Angels 1046
1992 Fleer/ProCards Pawtucket Red Sox 1046
1992 Fleer/ProCards Peninsula Pilots 1046
1992 Fleer/ProCards Phoenix Firebirds 1046
1992 Fleer/ProCards Pittsfield Mets 1046
1992 Fleer/ProCards Portland Beavers 1046
1992 Fleer/ProCards Prince William Cannons 1047
1992 Fleer/ProCards Princeton Reds 1047
1992 Fleer/ProCards Pulaski Braves 1047
1992 Fleer/ProCards Quad City River Bandits 1047
1992 Fleer/ProCards Reading Phillies 1047
1992 Fleer/ProCards Richmond Braves 1047
1992 Fleer/ProCards Rochester Red Wings 1048
1992 Fleer/ProCards Rockford Expos 1048
1992 Fleer/ProCards Salem Buccaneers 1048
1992 Fleer/ProCards Salinas Spurs 1048
1992 Fleer/ProCards San Antonio Missions 1049
1992 Fleer/ProCards San Bernardino Spirit 1049
1992 Fleer/ProCards Sarasota White Sox 1049
1992 Fleer/ProCards Savannah Cardinals 1049
1992 Fleer/ProCards Scranton-Wilkes Barre Red Barons 1049
1992 Fleer/ProCards Shreveport Captains 1049
1992 Fleer/ProCards South Bend White Sox 1050

1992 Fleer/ProCards Southern Oregon A's ... 1050
1992 Fleer/ProCards Spartanburg Phillies ... 1050
1992 Fleer/ProCards Spokane Indians ... 1050
1992 Fleer/ProCards Springfield Cardinals ... 1050
1992 Fleer/ProCards St. Catharines Blue Jays ... 1051
1992 Fleer/ProCards St. Lucie Mets ... 1051
1992 Fleer/ProCards St. Petersburg Cardinals ... 1051
1992 Fleer/ProCards Stockton Ports ... 1051
1992 Fleer/ProCards Syracuse Chiefs ... 1051
1992 Fleer/ProCards Tacoma Tigers ... 1051
1992 Fleer/ProCards Tidewater Tides ... 1051
1992 Fleer/ProCards Toledo Mud Hens ... 1051
1992 Fleer/ProCards Tucson Toros ... 1052
1992 Fleer/ProCards Tulsa Drillers ... 1052
1992 Fleer/ProCards Vancouver Canadians ... 1052
1992 Fleer/ProCards Vero Beach Dodgers ... 1052
1992 Fleer/ProCards Visalia Oaks ... 1052
1992 Fleer/ProCards Waterloo Diamonds ... 1052
1992 Fleer/ProCards Watertown Indians ... 1053
1992 Fleer/ProCards Welland Pirates ... 1053
1992 Fleer/ProCards West Palm Beach Expos ... 1053
1992 Fleer/ProCards Wichita Wranglers ... 1053
1992 Fleer/ProCards Winston-Salem Spirits ... 1053
1992 Fleer/ProCards Winter Haven Red Sox ... 1053
1992 Fleer/ProCards Yakima Bears ... 1054
1992 French's Mustard ... 241
1992 Holoprisms ... 254
1992 Jimmy Dean ... 85
1992 Jimmy Dean Living Legends ... 85
1992 Jumbo Sunflower Seeds ... 276
1992 Kahn's Mets ... 283
1992 Kahn's Reds ... 283
1992 Kellogg's 3-D ... 294
1992 Kenner Starting Lineup ... 296
1992 Leaf ... 311
1992 Leaf Gold Edition ... 313
1992 Leaf Gold Previews ... 313
1992 Leaf Gold Rookies ... 313
1992 Leaf Previews ... 311
1992 Lyke's Braves ... 321
1992 Lyke's Braves Team Photo Set ... 321
1992 Marathon Cubs ... 325
1992 McDonald's Baseball's Best .. 327
1992 McDonald's Cardinals ... 326
1992 Medford Phillies ... 328
1992 Megacards Babe Ruth ... 329
1992 Mother's Cookies Astros ... 348
1992 Mother's Cookies Athletics ... 348
1992 Mother's Cookies Dodgers ... 348
1992 Mother's Cookies Giants ... 348
1992 Mother's Cookies Mariners ... 348
1992 Mother's Cookies Padres ... 349
1992 Mother's Cookies Chuck Knoblauch ... 349
1992 Mother's Cookies Jeff Bagwell ... 349
1992 Mother's Cookies Nolan Ryan ... 7 No-Hitters ... 349
1992 Mother's Cookies Rangers ... 349
1992 Mr. Turkey ... 352
1992 Nabisco Canadian Tradition .. 352
1992 Nationwide Insurance Pirates ... 356
1992 O-Pee-Chee ... 420
1992 O-Pee-Chee Premier ... 422
1992 Paccar/Alrak Ken Griffey Jr. .. 429
1992 Pacific Nolan Ryan ... 433
1992 Pacific Nolan Ryan Gold Inserts ... 434
1992 Pacific Nolan Ryan Limited ... 434
1992 Pacific Tom Seaver ... 434
1992 Pacific Tom Seaver Milestones ... 435
1992 Peoria Midwest League All-Star Team ... 1046
1992 Pinnacle ... 448
1992 Pinnacle Rookie Idols ... 450
1992 Pinnacle Rookies ... 450
1992 Pinnacle Slugfest ... 450
1992 Pinnacle Team 2000 ... 450
1992 Pinnacle Team Pinnacle ... 450
1992 Play II Columbia Mets ... 1037
1992 Play II Columbia Mets Inserts ... 1037
1992 Play II South Atlantic League All-Stars ... 1049
1992 Police Columbus Clippers ... 1037
1992 Police/Fire Safety Brewers ... 471
1992 Police/Fire Safety Cardinals .. 471
1992 Police/Fire Safety Dodgers ... 471
1992 Police/Fire Safety Royals ... 471
1992 Post Cereal - Canadian ... 477
1992 Post Cereal ... 477
1992 Richmond Comix amd Cardz Richmond Braves ... 1048
1992 Score ... 507
1992 Score Factory Inserts ... 510
1992 Score Hot Rookies ... 510
1992 Score Impact Players ... 510
1992 Score Joe DiMaggio ... 510
1992 Score Procter & Gamble ... 511
1992 Score Rising Stars ... 511
1992 Score Rookie & Traded ... 511
1992 Score Superstars ... 512
1992 Score The Franchise ... 510
1992 Silver Star Holograms ... 526
1992 SkyBox AA ... 1030
1992 SkyBox AAA ... 1030
1992 Smokey Bear Padres Postcards ... 531
1992 Studio ... 559
1992 Studio Heritage ... 560
1992 Studio Preview ... 559
1992 Team Columbus RedStixx ... 1037
1992 Team Denver Zephyrs Record Holders ... 1037
1992 Team Durham Bulls ... 1038
1992 Team Fort Lauderdale Yankees ... 1039
1992 Team Huntsville Stars ... 1041
1992 Team Kane County Cougars ... 1042
1992 Team Louisville Redbirds ... 1043
1992 Team Midland Angels ... 1044
1992 Team Modesto Athletics ... 1044
1992 Team Nashville Sounds ... 1045
1992 Team Peoria Chiefs ... 1046
1992 Team Richmond Braves ... 1047
1992 Team Scranton-Wilkes Barre Red Barons ... 1049
1992 Team Syracuse Chiefs ... 1051
1992 Team Syracuse Chiefs Former Stars ... 1051
1992 Team Tulsa Drillers ... 1052
1992 Team Winston-Salem Spirts ... 1053
1992 Topps ... 726
1992 Topps Gold ... 729
1992 Topps Gold Promo Sheet ... 729
1992 Topps Gold Winners ... 729
1992 Topps Kids ... 729
1992 Topps Promo Sheet ... 726
1992 Topps Stadium Club ... 730
1992 Topps Stadium Club First Draft Picks ... 734
1992 Topps Stadium Club Master Photos ... 733
1992 Topps Stadium Club Members Only ... 734
1992 Topps Stadium Club Special Edition ... 733
1992 Topps Traded ... 729
1992 Topps Traded Gold ... 729
1992 Topps Triple Header Photo Balls ... 730
1992 U.S. Playing Card Aces ... 785
1992 U.S. Playing Card Team Sets - Braves ... 785
1992 U.S. Playing Card Team Sets - Cubs ... 785
1992 U.S. Playing Card Team Sets - Red Sox ... 786
1992 U.S. Playing Card Team Sets - Tigers ... 786
1992 U.S. Playing Card Team Sets - Twins ... 786
1992 Upper Deck ... 766
1992 Upper Deck Bench/Morgan Heroes ... 769

1992 Upper Deck College POY Holograms 768
1992 Upper Deck FanFest 769
1992 Upper Deck Hall of Fame Heroes 769
1992 Upper Deck Home Run Heroes 769
1992 Upper Deck Minor League ... 1031
1992 Upper Deck Minor League Promos 1031
1992 Upper Deck MVP Holograms 770
1992 Upper Deck Player of the Year 1032
1992 Upper Deck Scouting Report 769
1992 Upper Deck Ted Williams Heroes 769
1992 Upper Deck Ted Williams' Best 769
1992 Upper Deck Top Prospect Holograms 1032
1992 Urkrop's Richmond Braves 1048
1992 Ziploc 808
1993 Action Packed Tom Seaver Prototypes 2
1993 Alrak Ken Griffey, Jr. 4
1993 Ben's Bakery Super Pitchers Discs 22
1993 Benjamin Moore Ricmond Camera Richmond Braves 1070
1993 Bleacher Burns Richmond Braves 1070
1993 Bowman 41
1993 Cal League Bakersfield Dodgers 1057
1993 Cal League Riverside Pilots 1070
1993 Classic 59
1993 Classic Best Albany Polecats 1056
1993 Classic Best Appleton Foxes 1057
1993 Classic Best Asheville Tourists 1057
1993 Classic Best Augusta Pirates 1057
1993 Classic Best Autographs 1054
1993 Classic Best Beloit Brewers 1057
1993 Classic Best Burlington Bees 1058
1993 Classic Best Capital City Bombers 1059
1993 Classic Best Cedar Rapids Kernels 1059
1993 Classic Best Central Valley Rockies 1059
1993 Classic Best Charleston Rainbows 1060
1993 Classic Best Charlotte Rangers 1060
1993 Classic Best Clearwater Phillies 1060
1993 Classic Best Clinton Giants 1060
1993 Classic Best Columbus RedStixx 1061
1993 Classic Best Daytona Cubs 1061
1993 Classic Best Durham Bulls .. 1061
1993 Classic Best Expansion #1 Picks 1054
1993 Classic Best Fayetteville Generals 1062
1993 Classic Best Foil 1054
1993 Classic Best Fort Lauderdale Red Sox 1062
1993 Classic Best Fort Meyers Miracle 1062
1993 Classic Best Fort Wayne Wizards 1063
1993 Classic Best Frederick Keys 1063
1993 Classic Best Gold 1055
1993 Classic Best Greensboro Hornets 1063
1993 Classic Best Hagerstown Suns 1063
1993 Classic Best Hickory Crawdads 1064
1993 Classic Best High Desert Mavericks 1064
1993 Classic Best Kane County Cougars 1065
1993 Classic Best Kinston Indians 1065
1993 Classic Best Lakeland Tigers 1065
1993 Classic Best Lynchburg Red Sox 1066
1993 Classic Best Macon Braves 1066
1993 Classic Best Madison Muskies 1066
1993 Classic Best Modesto A's 1067
1993 Classic Best MVPs 1055
1993 Classic Best Osceola Astros 1068
1993 Classic Best Palm Springs Angels 1068
1993 Classic Best Peoria Chiefs .. 1068
1993 Classic Best Player & Manager of the Year 1055
1993 Classic Best Prince William Cannons 1069
1993 Classic Best Quad City River Bandits 1069
1993 Classic Best Rancho Cucamonga Quakes 1069
1993 Classic Best Rockford Royals 1070
1993 Classic Best Salem Buccaneers 1070
1993 Classic Best San Bernardino Spirit 1071
1993 Classic Best San Jose Giants 1071
1993 Classic Best Sarasota White Sox 1071
1993 Classic Best Savannah Cardinals 1071
1993 Classic Best South Bend White Sox 1072
1993 Classic Best Spartanburg Phillies 1072
1993 Classic Best Springfield Cardinals 1072
1993 Classic Best St. Lucie Mets 1071
1993 Classic Best St. Petersburg Cardinals 1071
1993 Classic Best Stockton Ports 1073
1993 Classic Best Vero Beach Dodgers 1073
1993 Classic Best Waterloo Diamonds 1074
1993 Classic Best West Palm Beach Expos 1074
1993 Classic Best West Virginia Wheelers 1074
1993 Classic Best Wilmington Blue Rocks 1074
1993 Classic Best Winston-Salem Spirits 1074
1993 Classic Best Young Guns 1054
1993 Coca-Cola Commanders of the Hill 64
1993 Colla All-Stars 71
1993 Colla Cal Ripken, Jr. Postcards 71
1993 Colla Mike Piazza Postcards ... 71
1993 Conlon Collection 74
1993 Conlon Color 75
1993 Cracker Jack Anniversary 80
1993 Denny's Grand Slam Holograms 86
1993 DiamondMarks 87
1993 DiamondMarks Inserts 87
1993 DiamondMarks Promos 86
1993 Donruss 134
1993 Donruss 1992 Blue Jays Commemorative Set 138
1993 Donruss Diamond Kings 137
1993 Donruss Elite 138
1993 Donruss Elite Dominators 138
1993 Donruss Elite Supers 138
1993 Donruss Long Ball Leaders ... 137
1993 Donruss Masters of the Game 137
1993 Donruss MVP's 137
1993 Donruss Spirit of the Game ... 137
1993 Donruss Triple Play 138
1993 Donruss Triple Play Action Baseball 140
1993 Donruss Triple Play Gallery ... 139
1993 Donruss Triple Play League Leaders 140
1993 Donruss Triple Play Nicknames 140
1993 Duracell Power Players 151
1993 Fleer 222
1993 Fleer AL Team Leaders 225
1993 Fleer All-Stars 224
1993 Fleer Atlantic 231

1993 Fleer Excel 1055
1993 Fleer Excel 1st Year Phenoms 1056
1993 Fleer Excel All-Stars 1056
1993 Fleer Excel League Leaders 1056
1993 Fleer Final Edition 229
1993 Fleer Flair 230
1993 Fleer Flair Wave of the Future 231
1993 Fleer Fruit of the Loom 231
1993 Fleer Golden Moments I 224
1993 Fleer Golden Moments II 224
1993 Fleer Major League Prospects I 224
1993 Fleer Major League Prospects II 224
1993 Fleer NL Team Leaders 225
1993 Fleer ProVisions I 224
1993 Fleer ProVisions II 225
1993 Fleer Rookie Sensations I 225
1993 Fleer Rookie Sensations II 225
1993 Fleer Tom Glavine Career Highlights 225
1993 Fleer Ultra 225
1993 Fleer Ultra All-Rookies 227
1993 Fleer Ultra All-Stars 228
1993 Fleer Ultra Award Winners 228
1993 Fleer Ultra Dennis Eckersley 228
1993 Fleer Ultra Home Run Kings .. 228
1993 Fleer Ultra Performers 228
1993 Fleer Ultra Strikeout Kings 228
1993 Fleer/Pro Cards Yakima Bears 1075
1993 Fleer/ProCards Albany Polecats 1056
1993 Fleer/ProCards Albany-Colonie Yankees 1056
1993 Fleer/ProCards Albuquerque Dukes 1057
1993 Fleer/ProCards Appleton Foxes 1057
1993 Fleer/ProCards Arkansas Travelers 1057
1993 Fleer/ProCards Asheville Tourists 1057
1993 Fleer/ProCards Auburn Astros 1057
1993 Fleer/ProCards Augusta Pirates 1057
1993 Fleer/ProCards Batavia Clippers 1057
1993 Fleer/ProCards Bellingham Mariners 1057
1993 Fleer/ProCards Beloit Brewers 1058
1993 Fleer/ProCards Bend Rockies 1058
1993 Fleer/ProCards Billings Mustangs 1058
1993 Fleer/ProCards Binghamton Mets 1058
1993 Fleer/ProCards Birmingham Barons 1058
1993 Fleer/ProCards Bluefield Orioles 1058
1993 Fleer/ProCards Boise Hawks 1058
1993 Fleer/ProCards Bowie Baysox 1058
1993 Fleer/ProCards Bristol Tigers 1058
1993 Fleer/ProCards Buffalo Bisons 1058
1993 Fleer/ProCards Burlington Bees 1059
1993 Fleer/ProCards Burlington Indians 1059
1993 Fleer/ProCards Calgary Cannons 1059
1993 Fleer/ProCards Canton-Akron Indians 1059
1993 Fleer/ProCards Capital City Bombers 1059
1993 Fleer/ProCards Carolina League 1059
1993 Fleer/ProCards Carolina Mudcats 1059
1993 Fleer/ProCards Cedar Rapids Kernels 1059
1993 Fleer/ProCards Central Valley Rockies 1060
1993 Fleer/ProCards Charleston Rainbows 1060
1993 Fleer/ProCards Charlotte Knights 1060
1993 Fleer/ProCards Charlotte Rangers 1060
1993 Fleer/ProCards Chattanooga Lookouts 1060
1993 Fleer/ProCards Clearwater Phillies 1060
1993 Fleer/ProCards Clinton Giants 1060
1993 Fleer/ProCards Colorado Springs Sky Sox 1060
1993 Fleer/ProCards Columbus Clippers 1061
1993 Fleer/ProCards Columbus Redstixx 1061
1993 Fleer/ProCards Danville Braves 1061
1993 Fleer/ProCards Daytona Cubs 1061
1993 Fleer/ProCards Dunedin Blue Jays 1061
1993 Fleer/ProCards Durham Bulls 1061
1993 Fleer/ProCards Edmonton Trappers 1061
1993 Fleer/ProCards El Paso Diablos 1062
1993 Fleer/ProCards Elizabethton Twins 1061
1993 Fleer/ProCards Elmira Pioneers 1061
1993 Fleer/ProCards Erie Sailors 1062
1993 Fleer/ProCards Eugene Emeralds 1062
1993 Fleer/ProCards Everett Giants 1062
1993 Fleer/ProCards Fayetteville Generals 1062
1993 Fleer/ProCards Florida State League All-Stars 1062
1993 Fleer/ProCards Fort Myers Miracle 1062
1993 Fleer/ProCards Fort Wayne Wizards 1063
1993 Fleer/ProCards Frederick Keys 1063
1993 Fleer/ProCards Ft. Lauderdale Red Sox 1062
1993 Fleer/ProCards Geneva Cubs 1063
1993 Fleer/ProCards Glens Falls Redbirds 1063
1993 Fleer/ProCards Greensboro Hornets 1063
1993 Fleer/ProCards Greenville Braves 1063
1993 Fleer/ProCards Hagerstown Suns 1063
1993 Fleer/ProCards Harrisburg Senators 1064
1993 Fleer/ProCards Helena Brewers 1064
1993 Fleer/ProCards Hickory Crawdads 1064
1993 Fleer/ProCards High Desert Mavericks 1064
1993 Fleer/ProCards Huntington Cubs 1064
1993 Fleer/ProCards Huntsville Stars 1064
1993 Fleer/ProCards Idaho Falls Braves 1064
1993 Fleer/ProCards Indianapolis Indians 1064
1993 Fleer/ProCards Iowa Cubs .. 1065
1993 Fleer/ProCards Jackson Generals 1065
1993 Fleer/ProCards Jacksonville Suns 1065
1993 Fleer/ProCards Jamestown Expos 1065
1993 Fleer/ProCards Johnson City Cardinals 1065
1993 Fleer/ProCards Kane County Cougars 1065
1993 Fleer/ProCards Kingsport Mets 1065
1993 Fleer/ProCards Kinston Indians 1065
1993 Fleer/ProCards Knoxville Smokies 1065
1993 Fleer/ProCards Lakeland Tigers 1065
1993 Fleer/ProCards Las Vegas Stars 1066
1993 Fleer/ProCards Lethbridge Mounties 1066
1993 Fleer/ProCards London Tigers 1066
1993 Fleer/ProCards Louisville Redbirds 1066

1993 Fleer/ProCards Lynchburg Red Sox 1066
1993 Fleer/ProCards Macon Braves 1066
1993 Fleer/ProCards Madison Muskies 1066
1993 Fleer/ProCards Martinsville Phillies 1066
1993 Fleer/ProCards Medicine Hat Blue Jays 1067
1993 Fleer/ProCards Memphis Chicks 1067
1993 Fleer/ProCards Midland Angels 1067
1993 Fleer/ProCards Midwest League 1067
1993 Fleer/ProCards Modesto A's 1067
1993 Fleer/ProCards Nashville Sounds 1067
1993 Fleer/ProCards Nashville Xpress 1067
1993 Fleer/ProCards New Britain Red Sox 1067
1993 Fleer/ProCards New Orleans Zephyrs 1067
1993 Fleer/ProCards Niagara Falls Rapids 1067
1993 Fleer/ProCards Norfolk Tides 1068
1993 Fleer/ProCards Oklahoma City 89ers 1068
1993 Fleer/ProCards Omaha Royals 1068
1993 Fleer/ProCards Oneonta Yankees 1068
1993 Fleer/ProCards Orlando Cubs 1068
1993 Fleer/ProCards Osceola Astros 1068
1993 Fleer/ProCards Ottawa Lynx 1068
1993 Fleer/ProCards Palm Springs Angels 1068
1993 Fleer/ProCards Pawtucket Red Sox 1068
1993 Fleer/ProCards Peoria Chiefs 1068
1993 Fleer/ProCards Phoenix Firebirds 1069
1993 Fleer/ProCards Pittsfield Mets 1069
1993 Fleer/ProCards Pocatello Posse 1069
1993 Fleer/ProCards Portland Beavers 1069
1993 Fleer/ProCards Prince William Cannons 1069
1993 Fleer/ProCards Princeton Reds 1069
1993 Fleer/ProCards Quad City River Bandits 1069
1993 Fleer/ProCards Rancho Cucamonga Quakes 1069
1993 Fleer/ProCards Reading Phillies 1069
1993 Fleer/ProCards Richmond Braves 1070
1993 Fleer/ProCards Rochester Red Wings 1070
1993 Fleer/ProCards Rockford Royals 1070
1993 Fleer/ProCards Salem Buccaneers 1070
1993 Fleer/ProCards San Antonio Missions 1071
1993 Fleer/ProCards San Bernardino Spirit 1071
1993 Fleer/ProCards San Jose Giants 1071
1993 Fleer/ProCards Sarasota White Sox 1071
1993 Fleer/ProCards Savannah Cardinals 1072
1993 Fleer/ProCards Scranton Wilkes-Barre Red Barron 1072
1993 Fleer/ProCards Shreveport Captains 1072
1993 Fleer/ProCards South Atlantic League All-Stars 1072
1993 Fleer/ProCards South Bend White Sox 1072
1993 Fleer/ProCards Southern Oregon A's 1072
1993 Fleer/ProCards Spartanburg Phillies 1072
1993 Fleer/ProCards Spokane Indians 1072
1993 Fleer/ProCards Springfield Cardinals 1072
1993 Fleer/ProCards St. Catharines Blue Jays 1070
1993 Fleer/ProCards St. Lucie Mets 1071
1993 Fleer/ProCards St. Petersburg Cardinals 1071
1993 Fleer/ProCards Stockton Ports 1073
1993 Fleer/ProCards Syracuse Chiefs 1073
1993 Fleer/ProCards Tacoma Tigers 1073
1993 Fleer/ProCards Toledo Mud Hens 1073
1993 Fleer/ProCards Triple A All-Star Game 1073
1993 Fleer/ProCards Tucson Toros 1073
1993 Fleer/ProCards Tulsa Drillers 1073
1993 Fleer/ProCards Utica Blue Sox 1073
1993 Fleer/ProCards Vancouver Canadians 1073
1993 Fleer/ProCards Vero Beach Dodgers 1073
1993 Fleer/ProCards Waterloo Diamonds 1074
1993 Fleer/ProCards Watertown Indians 1074
1993 Fleer/ProCards Welland Pirates 1074
1993 Fleer/ProCards West Palm Beach Expos 1074
1993 Fleer/ProCards West Virginia Wheelers 1074
1993 Fleer/ProCards Wichita Wranglers 1074
1993 Fleer/ProCards Wilmington Blue Rocks 1074
1993 Fleer/ProCards Winston-Salem Spirits 1075
1993 Highland Mint Mint-Card 253
1993 Hostess Twinkies 261
1993 Humpty Dumpty 261
1993 Jimmy Dean Rookie Cards 85
1993 Kahn's Mets 284
1993 Kahn's Reds 284
1993 Keebler Texas Rangers 287
1993 Kenner Starting Lineup 296
1993 King-B 298
1993 Kodak White Sox 298
1993 Kraft Pop-Up Action 299
1993 Leaf 313
1993 Leaf Fasttrack 315
1993 Leaf Frank Thomas 315
1993 Leaf Gold All-Stars 315
1993 Leaf Gold Rookies 315
1993 Leaf Heading for the Hall 315
1993 Leaf Update Frank Thomas Super 316
1993 Leaf Update Gold All-Stars 316
1993 Leaf Update Gold Rookies 316
1993 Line Up Venezuelan Baseball 318
1993 Lyke's Braves 321
1993 Lyke's Braves Team Photo Set 321
1993 Marathon Cubs 325
1993 MCI Ambassadors 327
1993 Medford Phillies 328
1993 Metallic Images Cooperstown Collection 329
1993 Metz Bakeries 330
1993 Milk Bone Super Stars 330
1993 Mother's Cookies Angels 349
1993 Mother's Cookies Astros 350
1993 Mother's Cookies Athletics 350
1993 Mother's Cookies Dodgers 350
1993 Mother's Cookies Giants 350
1993 Mother's Cookies Mariners 350
1993 Mother's Cookies Nolan Ryan Farewell 351
1993 Mother's Cookies Padres 351
1993 Nabisco All-Star Autographs 353
1993 O-Pee-Chee 423
1993 O-Pee-Chee Premier 424
1993 O-Pee-Chee Premier Star Performers 425
1993 O-Pee-Chee Premier Top Draft Picks 425
1993 O-Pee-Chee World Champs 424
1993 O-Pee-Chee World Series Heroes 424
1993 Pacific Nolan Ryan 27th Season 435
1993 Pacific Nolan Ryan 27th Season Gold Ltd. 435

1993 Pacific Nolan Ryan .. 27th Season Limited 435
1993 Pacific Nolan Ryan Prism 435
1993 Pacific Prism Insert 438
1993 Pacific Spanish 435
1993 Pacific Spanish Gold Foil Stars 437
1993 Pepsi Virginians Richmond Braves 1070
1993 Photo File 500 HR Supercards 447
1993 Pinnacle 451
1993 Pinnacle Cooperstown 454
1993 Pinnacle Expansion Opening Day 453
1993 Pinnacle Home Run Club 454
1993 Pinnacle Joe DiMaggio 454
1993 Pinnacle Rookie Team Pinnacle 453
1993 Pinnacle Slugfest 453
1993 Pinnacle Team 2001 453
1993 Pinnacle Team Pinnacle 453
1993 Pinnacle Tribute 454
1993 Police Cracker Jack Columbus Clippers 1061
1993 Police/Fire Safety Brewers 471
1993 Police/Fire Safety Cardinals .. 472
1993 Police/Fire Safety Dodgers 472
1993 Police/Fire Safety Blue Jays .. 471
1993 Post Cereal - Canadian 477
1993 Post Cereal 477
1993 Richmond Comix Richmond Braves 1070
1993 Rolaids Relief Pitcher Set 487
1993 Score 512
1993 Score Boys of Summer 514
1993 Score Gold Dream Team 515
1993 Score Procter & Gamble Rookies 515
1993 Score Select 515
1993 Score Select Aces 516
1993 Score Select All-Star Rookies 518
1993 Score Select Chase Rookies 516
1993 Score Select Chase Stars 517
1993 Score Select Rookie/Traded Inserts 518
1993 Score Select Stat Leaders 517
1993 Score Select Triple Crown 517
1993 Score Select Update 517
1993 Score The Franchise 515
1993 SportPro Billings Mustangs 1058
1993 SportPro Butte Copper Kings 1059
1993 SportPro Great Falls Dodgers 1063
1993 SportPro Helena Brewers 1064
1993 SportPro Idaho Falls Braves 1064
1993 SportPro Lethbridge Mounties 1066
1993 SportPro Medicine Hat Blue Jays 1067
1993 SportPro Pocatello Posse..... 1069
1993 Studio 560
1993 Studio Frank Thomas 561
1993 Studio Heritage 561
1993 Studio Silhouettes 561
1993 Studio Superstars on Canvas 561
1993 Ted Williams Card Co. Premier Edition 801
1993 Ted Williams Co. Brooks Robinson 802
1993 Ted Williams Co. Etched in Stone 802
1993 Ted Williams Co. Locklear Collection 802
1993 Ted Williams Co. Memories ... 802
1993 Topps 734
1993 Topps Black Gold 737
1993 Topps Colorado Rockies Inaugural Year 738
1993 Topps Finest 744
1993 Topps Finest Jumbo All-Stars 745
1993 Topps Finest Promos 744
1993 Topps Finest Refractors 745
1993 Topps Full Shot Super 745
1993 Topps Gold 737
1993 Topps Promo Sheet 734
1993 Topps Promos 734
1993 Topps Stadium Club 738
1993 Topps Stadium Club First Day Production 741
1993 Topps Stadium Club I Inserts 741
1993 Topps Stadium Club II Inserts 741
1993 Topps Stadium Club III Inserts 741
1993 Topps Stadium Club Master Photos 740
1993 Topps Stadium Club Members Only 742
1993 Topps Stadium Club Special 741
1993 Topps Stadium Club Special Master Photos 742
1993 Topps Stadium Club Team Sets 742
1993 Topps Stadium Club Ultra Pro 744
1993 Topps Traded 737
1993 Topps Florida Marlins Inaugural Year 738
1993 Toys "R" Us Master Photos ... 755
1993 Toys "R" Us Topps Stadium Club 755
1993 Upper Deck "Highlights" 774
1993 Upper Deck 5th Anniversary 773
1993 Upper Deck 5th Anniversary Super 775
1993 Upper Deck 770
1993 Upper Deck All-Time Heroes . 774
1993 Upper Deck All-Time Heroes T202 Reprints 775
1993 Upper Deck Clutch Performers 773
1993 Upper Deck Diamond Gallery 776
1993 Upper Deck Fun Packs 777
1993 Upper Deck Fun Packs All-Star Scratch-Offs 778
1993 Upper Deck Fun Packs Mascot Madness 778
1993 Upper Deck Future Heroes 773
1993 Upper Deck Heroes of Baseball Previews 774
1993 Upper Deck Home Run Heroes 773
1993 Upper Deck Iooss Collection 773
1993 Upper Deck Iooss Collection Super 775
1993 Upper Deck On Deck 774
1993 Upper Deck Reggie Jackson Heroes Super 776
1993 Upper Deck SP 776
1993 Upper Deck SP Platinum Power 777
1993 Upper Deck Then And Now ... 774
1993 Upper Deck Triple Crown 776
1993 Upper Deck Willie Mays Heroes 774
1993 Whataburger Nolan Ryan 796
1993 Yoo-Hoo 807
1994 "1954" Topps Archives 753
1994 Action Packed 1075
1994 Action Packed Diamond Franchise Gems 1075
1994 Action Packed Gold Franchise Gems 1075
1994 Big Apple 1969 Mets Discs....... 24
1994 Capital Cards 1969 Mets Post-cards 49
1994 Churchs Chicken Hometown Stars 51
1994 Churchs Chicken Show Stoppers 52
1994 Classic Best Illustrated Acetate 1076
1994 Classic Best Minor League Gold #1 Picks 1076
1994 Classic Best Minor League Gold 1075
1994 Collectors Choice Home Run All-Stars 781
1994 Conlon Collection 75
1994 Donruss 140
1994 Donruss Anniversary-1984 144
1994 Donruss Award Winners Supers 143
1994 Donruss Decade Dominators 142
1994 Donruss Decade Dominators Supers 142
1994 Donruss Diamond Kings 143
1994 Donruss Diamond Kings Super 143
1994 Donruss Elite 143
1994 Donruss Long Ball Leaders ... 144
1994 Donruss MVPs 143
1994 Donruss Promos 140

1994 Donruss Special Edition - Gold 144
1994 Donruss Spirit of the Game ... 144
1994 Donruss Spirit of the Game Super 144
1994 Donruss Triple Play 145
1994 Donruss Triple Play Bomb Squad 146
1994 Donruss Triple Play Medalists 146
1994 Donruss Triple Play Nicknames 146
1994 Donruss Triple Play Promos .. 145
1994 Fleer 231
1994 Fleer All-Stars 235
1994 Fleer Atlantic 240
1994 Fleer Award Winners 234
1994 Fleer Golden Moments 235
1994 Fleer Golden Moments Super 235
1994 Fleer League Leaders 234
1994 Fleer Lumber Co. 234
1994 Fleer Major League Prospects 234
1994 Fleer ProVisions 235
1994 Fleer Rookie Sensations 233
1994 Fleer Smoke N' Heat 234
1994 Fleer Team Leaders 234
1994 Fleer Tim Salmon A.L. Rookie of the Year 235
1994 Fleer Ultra 236
1994 Fleer Ultra All-Rookie Team .. 237
1994 Fleer Ultra All-Stars 238
1994 Fleer Ultra Award Winners 238
1994 Fleer Ultra Career Achievement Awards 238
1994 Fleer Ultra Firemen 238
1994 Fleer Ultra Hitting Machines .. 238
1994 Fleer Ultra Home Run Kings .. 238
1994 Fleer Ultra League Leaders ... 239
1994 Fleer Ultra On-Base Leaders . 239
1994 Fleer Ultra Phillies Finest 239
1994 Fleer Ultra RBI Kings 239
1994 Fleer Ultra Rising Stars 239
1994 Fleer Ultra Second Year Standouts 239
1994 Fleer Ultra Strikeout Kings 240
1994 Gold Leaf Rookies 317
1994 Highland Mint Mint-Cards 253
1994 Iowa Cubs Yearbook Cards 1075
1994 Kenner Cooperstown Collection 297
1994 Kenner Starting Lineup 297
1994 King-B 298
1994 Kraft Pop-Ups 299
1994 Leaf 316
1994 Leaf 5th Anniversary 317
1994 Leaf Clean-Up Crew 317
1994 Leaf Gamers 317
1994 Leaf Gold Stars 317
1994 Leaf Promos 316
1994 Leaf Slide Show 317
1994 Leaf Statistical Standouts 318
1994 Mother's Cookies Nolan Ryan Farewell 351
1994 Mother's Cookies Rookies of the Year 351
1994 Nabisco All-Star Legends 353
1994 Oscar Mayer Superstar Pop-Ups 426
1994 Pacific Crown 438
1994 Pacific Crown All Latino All-Star Team 440
1994 Pacific Crown Homerun Leaders 440
1994 Pácific Crown Jewels of the Crown 440
1994 Pacific Crown Promos 438
1994 Phillies Photocards 446
1994 Pinnacle 454
1994 Pinnacle Artist's Proof 455
1994 Pinnacle Museum Collection . 455
1994 Pinnacle New Generation 456
1994 Pinnacle Power Surge 456
1994 Pinnacle Rookie Team Pinnacle 456
1994 Pinnacle Run Creators 456
1994 Pinnacle Tribute 456
1994 Police/Fire Safety Brewers 472
1994 Police/Fire Safety Dodgers 472
1994 Post Cereal - Canadian 478
1994 Post Cereal 478
1994 Score 518
1994 Score Boys of Summer 521
1994 Score Cal Ripken, Jr. 521
1994 Score Dream Team 520
1994 Score Gold Rush 521
1994 Score Gold Stars 520
1994 Score Select 521
1994 Score Select Crown Contenders 522
1994 Score Select Promos 521
1994 Score Select Rookie Surge ... 522
1994 Score Select Salute 523
1994 Score The Cycle 520
1994 Signature Rookies 1076
1994 Signature Rookies Bonus Signature Set 1076
1994 Signature Rookies Cliff Floyd Set 1076
1994 Signature Rookies Hottest Prospects 1076
1994 Spectrum 1969 Miracle Mets 532
1994 Sportflics 2000 540
1994 Sportflics 2000 Movers 541
1994 Sportflics 2000 Promos 540
1994 Sportflics 2000 Shakers 541
1994 Sportflics Commemoratives.... 541
1994 Ted Williams Card Co. Etched in Stone 803
1994 Ted Williams Card Co. LP Cards 804
1994 Ted Williams Card Company . 802
1994 Ted Williams Card Company Dan Gardiner Collection 803
1994 Ted Williams Card Company Memories 804
1994 Ted Williams Card Company The 500 Club 803
1994 Ted Williams Co. Locklear Collection 804
1994 Ted Williams Co. Mike Schmidt Collection 804
1994 Tombstone Pizza 579
1994 Topps 746
1994 Topps Black Gold 748
1994 Topps Finest Promos 748
1994 Topps Finest Refractors Series I 749
1994 Topps Finest Series I 749
1994 Topps Finest Superstars 750
1994 Topps Gold 748
1994 Topps Gold Archives 754
1994 Topps Preview 745
1994 Topps Stadium Club 750
1994 Topps Stadium Club Dugout Dirt Series I 752
1994 Topps Stadium Club First Day Production 752
1994 Topps Stadium Club Golden Rainbow 752
1994 Topps Stadium Club Infocards 753
1994 Topps Stadium Club Super Teams 752
1994 Upper Deck 1076
1994 Upper Deck 781
1994 Upper Deck Collector's Choice 779
1994 Upper Deck Collector's Choice Promo 778
1994 Upper Deck Diamond Collection 783
1994 Upper Deck Electric Diamond 783
1994 Upper Deck Fun Packs 783
1994 Upper Deck Jumbo Checklists 783
1994 Upper Deck Mickey Mantle's Long Shots 783
1994 Upper Deck Player of the Year 1077
1994 Upper Deck Team vs. Team Scratch-Off 781
1994 Yoo-Hoo 807

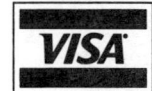

Krause
Publications
CUSTOMER SERVICE AWARD

AN OFFER YOU CAN'T REFUSE

$5.00 PER CARD TIMES 100 IN FIVE WEEKS
$7.00 PER CARD TIMES 100 IN FIVE WEEKS - CANADA
PSA "NO HOLDER SIZE" - SUBMITTED TO •ASA• FREE
THERE IS NO COST TO BECOME A LICENSED • ASA• DEALER, CALL!
YOU CAN PAY THE COMPETITION $500 MORE FOR THE SAME 100 CARDS

YES, THAT'S RIGHT! SUBMIT 100 CARDS AT A COST OF $5.00 PER CARD, RETURNED TO YOU IN 5 WEEKS, OR $7.00 EACH-CANADIAN. THE TOTAL COST IS $500 FOR 100 CARDS PLUS $25 POSTAGE.

FOR THOSE OF YOU WHO HAVE RECEIVED YOUR CARDS BACK FROM PSA WITH A LABEL INFORMING YOU "NO HOLDER SIZE", RESUBMIT YOUR CARD, ALONG WITH THE "PSA LABEL" AND THE "NO HOLDER SIZE LABEL" AND **•ASA• WILL CERTIFY YOUR CARD FREE OF CHARGE** IN AN ACCURATELY SIZED HOLDER MADE JUST FOR YOUR CARD. YOU MUST SEND $6 POSTAGE AND HANDLING, WE WILL DO THE REST. LIMIT 10 PER CLIENT. NO CARDS BIGGER THAN 2-5/8 BY 3-5/8.

ARROWHEAD SAFECASE HOLDERS, - OVER 100,000 SOLD TO DATE, THIS IS THE NUMBER ONE HOLDER FOR VALUABLE SPORTSCARDS. WITH OVER 132 DIFFERENT SIZES TO FIT ALL CARDS IN ANY SPORT. THESE SCREWLESS, SNAP TOGETHER HOLDERS COME 43 TO A BOX AT $100,OR 22 TO A SMALL BOX AT $60 EACH PLUS $6 POSTAGE & HANDLING. IF YOU WANT THE BEST TRY THE **ARROWHEADS.**

•ASA• A COMPANY WHO HAS GRADED AND CERTIFIED OVER 53,000 CARDS TO DATE, VALUED IN EXCESS OF $21 MILLION, HAS THE EXPERTISE TO GRADE YOUR RARE CARDS. THE PRICE IS ONLY $7 PER CARD, A VERY SMALL PRICE TO PAY FOR PEACE OF MIND, WHEN DOCTORED AND COUNTERFEIT CARDS REPRESENT A MAJOR PROBLEM TODAY.

WHETHER YOU HAVE BASEBALL, BASKETBALL, FOOTBALL, HOCKEY, BOXING, GOLF OR NON-SPORT CARDS •ASA• HAS THE EXPERTISE TO GRADE THEM ALL.

•ASA• HAS VERIFIED MANY DIFFERENT COUNTERFEITS FROM 1909 T-206 TO 1951 MANTLES AND ON TO THE MODERN MICHAEL JORDAN STAR RC CARDS. REMEMBER, THERE ARE HUNDREDS OF COUNTERFEITERS OUT THERE TRYING TO SELL YOU COUNTERFEIT CARDS. USE THE EXPERTS WHEN IT COMES TO BUYING CARDS OF $50 O MORE. YOU'LL HAVE PEACE OF MIND.

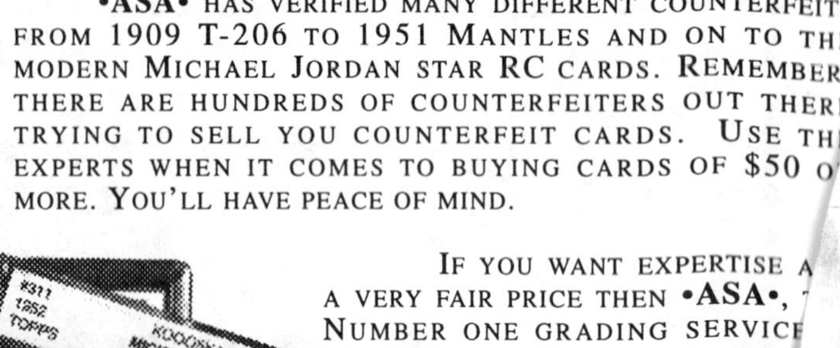

IF YOU WANT EXPERTISE A A VERY FAIR PRICE THEN **•ASA•**, NUMBER ONE GRADING SERVICE THE U.S. AND CANADA, IS THE O CHOICE FOR YOU.

OVER 10% OF ALL CARDS RECEIVE ARE DOCTORED COUNTERFEITED, ESPECIALLY TH VALUED OVER $100. FOR $7 YOU GET THE ASSURANCE THAT YOUR IS GRADED ACCURATELY AS WEL AUTHENTICATED BY THREE EXPER

PACK CARDS SECURELY, VIA REGISTERED INSURED MAIL THE FULL VALUE. INCLUDE $6 FOR 1 TO 10 CARDS, CALL OR FOR A SUBMITTAL FORM.

CAN YOU REALLY AFFORD TO BUY A VALU SPORTSCARD WITHOUT HAVING IT CERTIFI FOR AS LITTLE AS $7 YOU CAN GET INSURANC THAT CARD.

FIVE SERVICES TO MEET YOUR NEE

REGULAR	4-5	WEEK Service	$7.00	Per
PROMPT	2	WEEK Service	$14.00	Per
QUICK	7	DAY Service	$20.00	Per
EXPRESS	4	DAY Service	$30.00	Per
NEXT DAY	48	HOUR Service	$50.00	Per
100 CARDS	5	WEEK Service	$5.00	Per

• ASA • CANADA Inc.
BOX 73038 Woodbine Postal Outlet
Calgary, Alberta T2W 6E0
• (403) - 259-8346 •

DEALER	Quantity		PUBLIC		TOTAL	SERVICE	TIME
$ 6.00	______	X	$ 7.00	=	$ ______	4 Weeks	Regul
$12.00	______	X	$14.00	=	$ ______	14 Day	Prom
$17.00	______	X	$20.00	=	$ ______	7 Days	Quick
$25.00	______	X	$30.00	=	$ ______	4 Days	Expre
$42.00	______	X	$50.00	=	$ ______	48 Hour	Next
			Postage	=	$ 6.00	1 to 10 CARDS	

Total Cards ______ **Total Enclosed** = $ ______

ACCUGRADE, INC.
•ASA•
P.O. BOX 188
NORFOLK, CT 06058
Hours 10 to 6 PM - Monday to Friday
(203) 542-6894

ACCUGRADE AS

SPORTSCARD AUTHENTICATI